AMERICAN MEN & WOMEN OF SCIENCE

CONTENTS

ADVISORY COMMITTEE

PREFACE

American Men and Women of Science is without peer as a chronicle of North American scientific endeavor and achievement. It has recorded the careers of over 280,000 scientists and engineers since the first edition appeared in 1906, and continues to provide current information on the leaders in America's research and academic communities.

The Fifteenth Edition contains the biographies of 130,000 women and men; 7,500 appear for the first time. The names of new entrants were submitted for consideration at the editors' request by current entrants and by persons in charge of academic, government and private research programs. All of those included meet the following criteria:

1. Achievement, by reason of experience and training of a stature in scientific work equivalent to that associated with the doctoral degree, coupled with presently continued activity in such work;

    or

2. Research activity of high quality in science as evidenced by publication in reputable scientific journals; or, for those whose work cannot be published because of governmental or industrial security, research activity of high quality in science as evidenced by the judgment of the individual's peers;

    or

3. Attainment of a position of substantial responsibility requiring scientific training and experience to the extent described for (1) and (2).

This edition profiles living scientists in the physical and biological fields as well as public health scientists, engineers, mathematicians, statisticians, and computer scientists. The information is collected by means of direct communication whenever possible. Forms are sent to all entrants for corroboration and updating, and those whose biographies are appearing for the first time receive verification proofs before publication. The information submitted by entrants is included as completely as possible within the boundaries of editorial and space restrictions. Full entries are repeated for former listees who do not return forms but whose current location can be verified in secondary sources. References to the previous edition are given for those who do not return forms and cannot be located, but who are presumed to be still active in science or engineering. A notation is made when an entrant from the previous edition is known to be deceased. Non-citizens of the Americas are included if working in the United States or Canada for a reasonable duration. Information on former entrants who have entered fields other than science and engineering, or who have been retired for ten years and are no longer professionally active has been omitted.

American Men and Women of Science has experienced many changes in its long history, and this edition is no exception. Following the suggestion of the advisory committee, and based on the recommendation of a user survey, the geographic and discipline indexes have been discontinued in printed form. The Fifteenth Edition will be available for on-line searching, however, through BRS, DIALOG and the Jaques Cattell Press. All elements of an entry, including field of interest, experience and location, can be accessed by the use of key words. Although *American Men and Women of Science* is on a three year publication cycle, the on-line database will be updated at more frequent intervals. Previous users of the directory will be pleased to find that the type size has been enlarged in response to many requests.

The Social and Behavioral Sciences section of *American Men and Women of Science* was last published in 1978. The limited acceptance of this section caused the postponement of subsequent editions. Realizing the importance of maintaining current data on the disciplines, the publishers are considering several possibilities for the future. One is the inclusion of selected, appropriate fields in the *Directory of American Scholars,* also a Bowker/Cattell publication. Another plan under consideration is the systematic addition of social and behavioral scientists to the on-line database for eventual publication in an all-inclusive *American Men and Women of Science.*

The editors take this opportunity to thank the Fifteenth Edition advisory committee for their guidance, encouragement and support. Appreciation is expressed to the many scientific societies who provided their membership lists for the purpose of locating former entrants whose addresses had changed.

Comments and suggestions on any aspect of the Fifteenth Edition are encouraged and should be directed to The Editors, *American Men and Women of Science,* P.O. Box 25001, Tempe, Arizona 85282.

Martha Cargill, *Editor*
Renee Lautenbach, *Managing Editor*
Terence Basom, *General Manager*
JAQUES CATTELL PRESS

August, 1982

ABBREVIATIONS

AAAS—American Association for the Advancement of Science
abnorm—abnormal
abstr—abstract(s)
acad—academic, academy
acct—account, accountant, accounting
acoust—acoustic(s), acoustical
ACTH—adrenocorticotrophic hormone
actg—acting
activ—activities, activity
addn—addition(s), additional
Add—Address
adj—adjunct, adjutant
adjust—adjustment
Adm—Admiral
admin—administration, administrative
adminr—administrator(s)
admis—admission(s)
adv—adviser(s), advisory
advan—advance(d), advancement
advert—advertisement, advertising
AEC—Atomic Energy Commission
aerodyn—aerodynamic(s)
aeronaut—aeronautic(s), aeronautical
aerophys—aerophysical, aerophysics
aesthet—aesthetic(s)
AFB—Air Force Base
affil—affiliate(s), affiliation
agr—agricultural, agriculture
agron—agronomic, agronomical, agronomy
agrost—agrostologic, agrostological, agrostology
agt—agent
AID—Agency for International Development
Ala-Alabama
allergol—allergological, allergology
alt—alternate
Alta—Alberta
Am—America, American
AMA—American Medical Association
anal—analysis, analytic, analytical
analog—analogue
anat—anatomic, anatomical, anatomy
anesthesiol—anesthesiology
angiol—angiology
Ann—Annal(s)
ann—annual
anthrop—anthropological, anthropology
anthropom—anthropometric, anthropometrical, anthropometry
antiq—antiquary, antiquities, antiquity

antiqn—antiquarian
apicult—apicultural, apiculture
APO—Army Post Office
app—appoint, appointed
appl—applied
appln—application
approx—approximate(ly)
Apr—April
apt—apartment(s)
aquacult—aquaculture
arbit—arbitration
arch—archives
archaeol—archaeological, archaeology
archit—architectural, architecture
Arg—Argentina, Argentine
Ariz—Arizona
Ark—Arkansas
artil—artillery
asn—association
assoc(s)—associate(s), associated
asst(s)—assistant(s), assistantship(s)
Assyriol—Assyriology
astrodyn—astrodynamics
astron—astronomical, astronomy
astronaut—astronautical, astronautics
astronr—astronomer
astrophys—astrophysical, astrophysics
attend—attendant, attending
atty—attorney
audiol—audiology
Aug—August
auth—author
AV—audiovisual
Ave—Avenue
avicult—avicultural, aviculture

b—born
bact—bacterial, bacteriologic, bacteriological, bacteriology
BC—British Columbia
bd—board
behav—behavior(al)
Belg—Belgian, Belgium
bibl—biblical
bibliog—bibliographic, bibliographical, bibliography
bibliogr—bibliographer
biochem—biochemical, biochemistry
biog—biographical, biography
biol—biological, biology
biomed—biomedical, biomedicine

biomet—biometric(s), biometrical, biometry
biophys—biophysical, biophysics
bk(s)—book(s)
bldg—building
Blvd—Boulevard
Bor—Borough
bot—botanical, botany
br—branch(es)
Brig—Brigadier
Brit—Britain, British
Bro(s)—Brother(s)
byrol—byrology
Bull—Bulletin
bur—bureau
bus—business
BWI—British West Indies

c—children
Calif—California
Can—Canada, Canadian
cand—candidate
Capt—Captain
cardiol—cardiology
cardiovasc—cardiovascular
cartog—cartographic, cartographical, cartography
cartogr—cartographer
Cath—Catholic
CEngr—Corps of Engineers
cent—central
Cent Am—Central America
cert—certificate(s), certification, certified
chap—chapter
chem—chemical(s), chemistry
chemother—chemotherapy
chmn—chairman
citricult—citriculture
class—classical
climat—climatological, climatology
clin(s)—clinic(s), clinical
cmndg—commanding
Co—Companies, Company
coauth—coauthor
co-dir—co-director
co-ed—co-editor
coeduc—coeducation, coeducational
col(s)—college(s), collegiate, colonel
collab—collaboration, coloborative
collabr—collaborator
Colo—Colorado
com—commerce, commercial

ix

ABBREVIATIONS

Comdr—Commander
commun—communicable, communication(s)
comn(s)—commission(s), commissioned
comnr—commissioner
comp—comparative
compos—composition
comput—computation, computer(s),
    computing
comt(s)—committee(s)
conchol—conchology
conf—conference
cong—congress, congressional
Conn—Connecticut
conserv—conservation, conservatory
consol—consolidated, consolidation
const—constitution, constitutional
construct—construction, constructive
consult(s)—consult, consultant(s)
    consultantship(s), consultation, consulting
contemp—contemporary
contrib—contribute, contributing,
    contribution(s)
contribr—contributor
conv—convention
coop—cooperating, cooperation, cooperative
coord—coordinate(d), coordinating,
    coordination
coordr—coordinator
corp—corporate, corporation(s)
corresp—correspondence, correspondent,
    corresponding
coun—council, counsel, counseling
counr—councilor, counselor
criminol—criminological, criminology
cryog—cryogenic(s)
crystallog—crystallographic, crystallograpi-
    ical, crystallography
crystallogr—crystallographer
Ct—Court
Ctr—Center
cult—cultural, culture
cur—curator
curric—curriculum
cybernet—cybernetic(s)
cytol—cytological, cytology
Czech—Czechoslovakia

DC—District of Columbia
Dec—December
Del—Delaware
deleg—delegate, delegation
delinq—delinquency, delinquent
dem—democrat(s), democratic
demog—demographic, demography
demogr—demographer
demonstr—demonstrator
dendrol—dendrologic, dendrological,
    dendrology
dent—dental, dentistry
dep—deputy
dept—department(al)
dermat—dermatologic, dermatological,
    dermatology
develop—developed, developing, develop-
    ment, developmental
diag—diagnosis, diagnostic
dialectol—dialectological, dialectology
dict—dictionaries, dictionary
Dig—Digest
dipl—diploma, diplomate
dir(s)—director(s), directories, directory
dis—disease(s), disorders

Diss Abstr—Dissertation Abstracts
dist—district
distrib—distributed, distribution, distributive
distribr—distributor(s)
div—division, divisional, divorced
DNA—deoxyribonucleic acid
doc—document(s), documentary,
    documentation
Dom—Dominion
Dr—Drive

e—east
ecol—ecological, ecology
econ(s)—economic(s), economical, economy
economet—econometric(s)
ECT—electroconvulsive or electroshock
    therapy
ed—edition(s), editor(s), editorial
ed bd—editorial board
educ—education, educational
educr—educator(s)
EEG—electroencephalogram, electroenceph-
    alographic, electroencephalography
Egyptol—Egyptology
EKG—electrocardiogram
elec—electric, electrical, electricity
electrochem—electrochemical, electrochem-
    istry
electrophys—electrophysical, electrophysics
elem—elementary
embryol—embryologic, embryological,
    embryology
emer—emeriti, emiritus
employ—employment
encour—encouragement
encycl—encyclopedia
endocrinol—endocrinologic, endocrinology
eng—engineering
Eng—England, English
engr(s)—engineer(s)
enol—enology
Ens—Ensign
entom—entomological, entomology
environ—environment(s), environmental
enzym—enzymology
epidemiol—epidemiologic, epidemiological,
    epidemiology
equip—equipment
ESEA—Elementary & Secondary Education
    Act
espec—especially
estab—established, establishment(s)
ethnog—ethnographic, ethnographical,
    ethnography
ethnogr—ethnographer
ethnol—ethnologic, ethnological, ethnology
Europ—European
eval—evaluation
evangel—evangelical
eve—evening
exam—examination(s), examining
examr—examiner
except—exceptional
exec(s)—executive(s)
exeg—exegeses, exegesis, exegetic, exegetical
exhib(s)—exhibition(s), exhibit(s)
exp—experiment, experimental
exped(s)—expedition(s)
explor—exploration(s), exploratory
expos—exposition
exten—extension

fac—faculty

facil—facilities, facility
Feb—February
fed—federal
fedn—federation
fel(s)—fellow(s), fellowship(s)
fermentol—fermentology
fertil—fertility, fertilitization
Fla—Florida
floricult—floricultural, floriculture
found—foundation
FPO—Fleet Post Office
Fr—French
Ft—Fort

Ga—Georgia
gastroenterol—gastroenterological, gastroen-
    terology
gen—general
geneal—genealogical, genealogy
geod—geodesy, geodetic
geog—geographic, geographical, geography
geogr—geographer
geol—geologic, geological, geology
geom—geometric, geometrical, geometry
geomorphol—geomorphologic,
    geomorphology
geophys—geophysical, geophysics
Ger—German, Germanic, Germany
geriat—geriatric(s)
geront—gerontological, gerontology
glaciol—glaciology
gov—governing, governor(s)
govt—government, governmental
grad—graduate(d)
Gt Brit—Great Britain
guid—guidance
gym—gymnasium
gynec—gynecologic, gynecological,
    gynecology

handbk(s)—handbook(s)
helminth—helminthology
hemat—hematologic, hematological,
    hematology
herpet—herpetologic, herpetological,
    herpetology
Hisp—Hispanic, Hispania
hist—historic, historical, history
histol—histological, histology
HM—Her Majesty
hochsch—hochschule
homeop—homeopathic, homeopathy
hon(s)—honor(s), honorable, honorary
hort—horticultural, horticulture
hosp(s)—hospital(s), hospitalization
hq—headquarters
HumRRO—Human Resources Research
    Office
husb—husbandry
Hwy—Highway
hydraul—hydraulic(s)
hydrodyn—hydrodynamic(s)
hydrol—hydrologic, hydrological, hydrology
hyg—hygiene, hygienic(s)
hypn—hypnosis

ichthyol—ichthyological, ichthyology
Ill—Illinois
illum—illuminating, illumination
illus—illustrate, illustrated, illustration
illusr—illustrator
immunol—immunologic, immunological,
    immunology

Imp—Imperial
improv—improvement
Inc—Incorporated
in-chg—in charge
incl—include(s), including
Ind—Indiana
indust(s)—industrial, industries, industry
inf—infantry
info—information
inorg—inorganic
ins—insurance
inst(s)—institute(s), institution(s)
instnl—institutional(ized)
instr(s)—instruct, instruction, instructor(s)
instrnl—instructional
int—international
intel—intelligence
introd—introduction
invert—invertebrate
invest(s)—investigation(s)
investr—investigator
irrig—irrigation
Ital—Italian

J—Journal
Jan—January
Jct—Junction
jour—journal, journalism
jr—junior
jurisp—jurisprudence
juv—juvenile

Kans—Kansas
Ky—Kentucky

La—Louisiana
lab(s)—laboratories, laboratory
lang—language(s)
laryngol—laryngological, laryngology
lect—lecture(s)
lectr—lecturer(s)
legis—legislation, legislative, legislature
lett—letter(s)
lib—liberal
libr—libraries, library
librn—librarian
lic—license(d)
limnol—limnological, limnology
ling—linguistic(s), linguistical
lit—literary, literature
lithol—lithologic, lithological, lithology
Lt—Lieutenant
Ltd—Limited

m—married
mach—machine(s), machinery
mag—magazine(s)
maj—major
malacol—malacology
mammal—mammalogy
Man—Manitoba
Mar—March
Mariol—Mariology
Mass—Massachusetts
mat—material(s)
mat med—materia medica
math—mathematic(s), mathematical
Md—Maryland
mech—mechanic(s), mechanical
med—medical, medicinal, medicine
Mediter—Mediterranean
Mem—Memorial
mem—member(s), membership(s)

ment—mental(ly)
metab—metabolic, metabolism
metall—metallurgic, metallurgical,
    metallurgy
metallog—metallographic, metallography
metallogr—metallographer
metaphys—metaphysical, metaphysics
meteorol—meteorological, meteorology
metrol—metrological, metrology
metrop—metropolitan
Mex—Mexican, Mexico
mfg—manufacturing
mfr(s)—manufacture(s), manufacturer(s)
mgr—manager
mgt—management
Mich—Michigan
microbiol—microbiological, microbiology
micros—microscopic, microscopical,
    microscopy
mid—middle
mil—military
mineral—mineralogical, mineralogy
Minn—Minnesota
Miss—Mississippi
mkt—market, marketing
Mo—Missouri
mod—modern
monogr—monograph
Mont—Montana
morphol—morphological, morphology
Mt—Mount
mult—multiple
munic—municipal, municipalities
mus—museum(s)
musicol—musicological, musicology
mycol—mycologic, mycology

n—north
NASA—National Aeronautics & Space
    Administration
nat—national, naturalized
NATO—North Atlantic Treaty Organization
navig—navigation(al)
NB—New Brunswick
NC—North Carolina
NDak—North Dakota
NDEA—National Defense Education Act
Nebr—Nebraska
nematol—nematological, nematology
nerv—nervous
Neth—Netherlands
neurol—neurological, neurology
neuropath—neuropathological, neuro-
    pathology
neuropsychiat—neuropsychiatric, neuro-
    psychiatry
neurosurg—neurosurgical, neurosurgery
Nev—Nevada
New Eng—New England
New York—New York City
Nfld—Newfoundland
NH—New Hampshire
NIH—National Institutes of Health
NIMH—National Institute of Mental Health
NJ—New Jersey
NMex—New Mexico
nonres—nonresident
norm—normal
Norweg—Norwegian
Nov—November
NS—Nova Scotia
NSF—National Science Foundation
NSW—New South Wales

numis—numismatic(s)
nutrit—nutrition, nutritional
NY—New York State
NZ—New Zealand

observ—observatories, observatory
obstet—obstetric(s), obstetrical
occas—occasional(ly)
occup—occupation, occupational
oceanog—oceanographic, oceanographical,
    oceanography
oceanogr—oceanographer
Oct—October
odontol—odontology
OEEC—Organization for European
    Economic Cooperation
off—office, official
Okla—Oklahoma
olericult—olericulture
oncol—oncologic, oncology
Ont—Ontario
oper(s)—operation(s), operational,
    operative
ophthal—ophthalmologic, ophthalmological,
    ophthalmology
optom—optometric, optometrical, optometry
ord—ordnance
Ore—Oregon
org—organic
orgn—organization(s), organizational
orient—oriental
ornith—ornithological, ornithology
orthod—orthodontia, orthodontic(s)
orthop—orthopedic(s)
osteop—osteopathic, osteopathy
otol—otological, otology
otolaryngol—otolaryngological, otolaryn-
    gology
otorhinol—otorhinologic, otorhinology

Pa—Pennsylvania
Pac—Pacific
paleobot—paleobotanical, paleobotany
paleont—paleontological, paleontology
Pan-Am—Pan-American
parasitol—parasitology
partic—participant, participating
path—pathologic, pathological, pathology
pedag—pedagogic(s), pedagogical, pedagogy
pediat—pediatric(s)
PEI—Prince Edward Islands
penol—penological, penology
periodont—periodontal, periodontic(s),
    periodontology
petrog—petrographic, petrographical,
    petrography
petrogr—petrographer
petrol—petroleum, petrologic, petrological,
    petrology
pharm—pharmacy
pharmaceut—pharmaceutic(s), pharmaceu-
    tical(s)
pharmacog—pharmacognosy
pharamacol—pharmacologic, pharmaco-
    logical, pharmacology
phenomenol—phenomenologic(al),
    phenomenology
philol—philological, philology
philos—philosophic, philosophical,
    philosophy
photog—photographic, photography
photogeog—photogeographic, photo-
    geography

ABBREVIATIONS

photogr—photographer(s)
photogram—photogrammetric, photogrammetry
photom—photometric, photometrical, photometry
phycol—phycology
phys—physical
physiog—physiographic, physiographical, physiography
physiol—physiological, physiology
Pkwy—Parkway
Pl—Place
polit—political, politics
polytech—polytechnic(al)
pomol—pomological, pomology
pontif—pontifical
pop—population
Port—Portugal, Portuguese
postgrad—postgraduate
PQ—Province of Quebec
PR—Puerto Rico
pract—practice
practr—practitioner
prehist—prehistoric, prehistory
prep—preparation, preparative, preparatory
pres—president
Presby—Presbyterian
preserv—preservation
prev—prevention, preventive
prin—principal
prob(s)—problem(s)
proc—proceedings
proctol—proctologic, proctological, proctology
prod—product(s), production, productive
prof—professional, professor, professorial
Prof Exp—Professional Experience
prog(s)—program(s), programmed, programming
proj—project(s), projection(al), projective
prom—promotion
protozool—protozoology
prov—province, provincial
psychiat—psychiatric, psychiatry
psychoanal—psychoanalysis, psychoanalytic, psychoanalytical
psychol—psychological, psychology
psychomet—psychometric(s)
psychopath—psychopathologic, psychopathology
psychophys—psychophysical, psychophysics
psychophysiol—psychophysiological, psychophysiology
psychosom—psychosomatic(s)
psychother—psychotherapeutic(s), psychotherapy
Pt—Point
pub—public
publ—publication(s), publish(ed), publisher, publishing
pvt—private

Qm—Quartermaster
Qm Gen—Quartermaster General
qual—qualitative, quality
quant—quantitative
quart—quarterly

radiol—radiological, radiology
RAF—Royal Air Force
RAFVR—Royal Air Force Volunteer Reserve

RAMC—Royal Army Medical Corps
RAMCR—Royal Army Medical Corps Reserve
RAOC—Royal Army Ordnance Corps
RASC—Royal Army Service Corps
RASCR—Royal Army Service Corps Reserve
RCAF—Royal Canadian Air Force
RCAFR—Royal Canadian Air Force Reserve
RCAFVR—Royal Canadian Air Force Volunteer Reserve
RCAMC—Royal Canadian Army Medical Corps
RCAMCR—Royal Canadian Army Medical Corps Reserve
RCASC—Royal Canadian Army Service Corps
RCASCR—Royal Canadian Army Service Corps Reserve
RCEME—Royal Canadian Electrical & Mechanical Engineers
RCN—Royal Canadian Navy
RCNR—Royal Canadian Naval Reserve
RCNVR—Royal Canadian Naval Volunteer Reserve
Rd—Road
RD—Rural Delivery
rec—record(s), recording
redevelop—redevelopment
ref—reference(s)
refrig—refrigeration
regist—register(ed), registration
registr—registrar
regt—regiment(al)
rehab—rehabilitation
rel(s)—relation(s), relative
relig—religion, religious
REME—Royal Electrical & Mechanical Engineers
rep—represent, representative
repub—republic
req—requirements
res—research, reserve
rev—review, revised, revision
RFD—Rural Free Delivery
rhet—rhetoric, rhetorical
RI—Rhode Island
Rm—Room
RM—Royal Marines
RN—Royal Navy
RNA—ribonucleic acid
RNR—Royal Naval Reserve
RNVR—Royal Naval Volunteer Reserve
roentgenol—roentgenologic, roentgenological, roentgenology
RR—Railroad, Rural Route
rte—route
Russ—Russian
rwy—railway

s—south
SAfrica—South Africa
SAm—South America, South American
sanit—sanitary, sanitation
Sask—Saskatchewan
SC—South Carolina
Scand—Scandinavia(n)
sch(s)—school(s)
scholar—scholarship
sci—science(s), scientific
SDak—South Dakota
SEATO—Southeast Asia Treaty Organization
sec—secondary
sect—section

secy—secretary
seismog—seismograph, seismographic, seismography
seismogr—seismographer
seismol—seismological, seismology
sem—seminar, seminary
sen—senator, senatorial
Sept—September
ser—serial, series
serol—serologic, serological, serology
serv—service(s), serving
silvicult—silvicultural, silviculture
soc(s)—societies, society
soc sci—social science
sociol—sociologic, sociological, sociology
Span—Spanish
spec—special
specif—specification(s)
spectrog—spectrograph, spectrographic, spectography
spectrogr—spectrographer
spectrophotom—spectrophotometer, spectrophotometric, spectrophotometry
spectros—spectroscopic, spectroscopy
speleol—speleological, speleology
Sq—Square
sr—senior
St—Saint, Street(s)
sta(s)—station(s)
stand—standard(s), standardization
statist—statistical, statistics
Ste—Sainte
steril—sterility
stomatol—stomatology
stratig—stratigraphic, stratigraphy
stratigr—stratigrapher
struct—structural, structure(s)
stud—student(ship)
subcomt—subcommittee
subj—subject
subsid—subsidiary
substa—substation
super—superior
suppl—supplement(s), supplemental, supplementary
supt—superintendent
supv—supervising, supervision
supvr—supervisor
supvry—supervisory
surg—surgery, surgical
surv—survey, surveying
survr—surveyor
Swed—Swedish
Switz—Switzerland
symp—symposia, symposium(s)
syphil—syphilology
syst(s)—system(s), systematic(s), systematical

taxon—taxonomic, taxonomy
tech—technical, technique(s)
technol—technologic(al), technology
tel—telegraph(y), telephone
temp—temporary
Tenn—Tennessee
Terr—Terrace
Tex—Texas
textbk(s)—textbook(s)
text ed—text edition
theol—theological, theology
theoret—theoretic(al)
ther—therapy
therapeut—therapeutic(s)

thermodyn—thermodynamic(s)
topog—topographic, topographical, topography
topogr—topographer
toxicol—toxicologic, toxicological, toxicology
trans—transactions
transl—translated, translation(s)
translr—translator(s)
transp—transport, transportation
treas—treasurer, treasury
treat—treatment
trop—tropical
tuberc—tuberculosis
TV—television
Twp—Township

UAR—United Arab Republic
UK—United Kingdom
UN—United Nations
undergrad—undergraduate
unemploy—unemployment
UNESCO—United Nations Educational Scientific & Cultural Organization
UNICEF—United Nations International Childrens Fund
univ(s)—universities, university
UNRRA—United Nations Relief & Rehabilitation Administration
UNRWA—United Nations Relief & Works Agency
urol—urologic, urological, urology
US—United States

USA—US Army
USAAF—US Army Air Force
USAAFR—US Army Air Force Reserve
USAF—US Air Force
USAFR—US Air Force Reserve
USAR—US Army Reserve
USCG—US Coast Guard
USCGR—US Coast Guard Reserve
USDA—US Department of Agriculture
USMC—US Marine Corps
USMCR—US Marine Corps Reserve
USN—US Navy
USNAF—US Naval Air Force
USNAFR—US Naval Air Force Reserve
USNR—US Naval Reserve
USPHS—US Public Health Service
USPHSR—US Public Health Service Reserve
USSR—Union of Soviet Socialist Republics
USWMC—US Women's Marine Corps
USWMCR—US Women's Marine Corps Reserve

Va—Virginia
var—various
veg—vegetable(s), vegetation
vent—ventilating, ventilation
vert—vertebrate
vet—veteran(s), veterinarian, veterinary
VI—Virgin Islands
vinicult—viniculture
virol—virological, virology
vis—visiting

voc—vocational
vocab—vocabulary
vol(s)—voluntary, volunteer(s), volume(s)
vpres—vice president
vs—versus
Vt—Vermont

w—west
WAC—Women's Army Corps
Wash—Washington
WAVES—Women Accepted for Voluntary Emergency Service
WHO—World Health Organization
WI—West Indies
wid—widow, widowed, widower
Wis—Wisconsin
WRCNS—Women's Royal Canadian Naval Service
WRNS—Women's Royal Naval Service
WVa—West Virginia
Wyo—Wyoming

yearbk(s)—yearbook(s)
YMCA—Young Men's Christian Association
YMHA—Young Men's Hebrew Association
yr(s)—year(s)
YWCA—Young Women's Christian Association
YWHA—Young Women's Hebrew Association

zool—zoological, zoology

AMERICAN MEN & WOMEN OF SCIENCE

Q

QADRI, SYED M HUSSAIN, b Hyderabad, India, Feb 2, 42; m 68; c 1. MEDICAL MICROBIOLOGY. *Educ:* Univ Karachi, BS, 60, MS, 62; Univ Tex, Austin, PhD(microbiol, biochem), 68. *Prof Exp:* Lectr microbiol, Univ Karachi, 62-64, asst prof microbiol, 68-69; microbiol specialist, Harris County Hosp Dist, 69-75; asst prof path, Univ Tex Med Sch, Houston, 75-78; ASSOC PROF PATH, UNIV OKLA, OKLAHOMA CITY, 78-; DIR MICROBIOL, OKLA MEM HOSP & CLIN, 78- *Concurrent Pos:* R A Welch Found fel, Baylor Col Med, 69-74, adj asst prof path, microbiol & immunol, 75-; clin microbiologist, Hermann Hosp, Houston, 75-78. *Mem:* AAAS; Am Soc Microbiol; Am Soc Med Technol; Pakistan Asn Advan Sci. *Res:* Biosynthesis of tripyrrole bacterial pigment, prodigiosin, produced by Serratia marcescens; rapid methods in identification of microorganisms. *Mailing Add:* Dept of Path PO Box 26901 Oklahoma City OK 73190

QASIM, SYED REAZUL, b Allahabad, India, Dec 1, 38; m 67; c 2. SANITARY & ENVIRONMENTAL ENGINEERING. *Educ:* Aligarh Muslim Univ, India, BScEng, 57; WVa Univ, MSCE, 62, PhD(sanit eng), 65. *Prof Exp:* Apprentice eng, Irrig Dept, Govt Utter Pradesh, India, 57-58; sr lectr agr eng, Agr Inst, 58-59, asst dist engr, Municipal Corp, 59-60; res asst, WVa Univ, 62-65; civil engr, Alden E Stilson & Assocs, Consult Engrs, Ohio, 66-68; sr civil engr, Battelle Mem Inst, 68-70; assoc prof civil eng, Polytech Inst Brooklyn, 71-73; assoc prof civil eng, 73-78, PROF CIVIL ENG, UNIV TEX, ARLINGTON, 78- *Mem:* Water Pollution Control Fedn; Am Soc Civil Engrs; Sigma Xi. *Res:* Wastewater treatment and control; water resources management; solid waste management. *Mailing Add:* Dept of Civil Eng Univ of Tex Arlington TX 76019

QAZI, QUTUBUDDIN H, b Pavas, India, June 15, 31; m 62; c 3. PEDIATRICS, GENETICS. *Educ:* Grant Med Col, Bombay, MB, BS, 56; Univ Toronto, MA, 65, PhD(genetics), 70. *Prof Exp:* House physician med & psychiat, J J Group Hosps, Bombay, 57-58; intern, Coney Island Hosp, Brooklyn, 59-60; from jr resident to chief resident pediat, King's County Hosp, Brooklyn, 60-63; fel genetics, Res Inst, Hosp Sick Children, Toronto, 63-68; asst prof, 69-73, ASSOC PROF PEDIAT, STATE UNIV NY DOWNSTATE MED CTR, 73- *Concurrent Pos:* Attend pediat, King's County Hosp, Brooklyn, 69- & State Univ Hosp, 69-; consult pediat, Methodist Hosp, Brooklyn, 74-; consult genetics, St John's Episcopal Hosp, Brooklyn, 73- *Mem:* Soc Pediat Res; fel Am Acad Pediat; Am Soc Human Genetics. *Res:* Microcephaly and mental retardation; congenital adrenal hyperplasia; lead poisoning; dermatoglyphics in congenital malformations. *Mailing Add:* Dept Pediat Downstate Med Ctr State Univ NY 450 Clarkson Ave Brooklyn NY 11203

QUACKENBUSH, CARR LANE W, b Greensboro, NC, May 19, 46; m 69; c 2. CERAMIC TECHNOLOGY, GLASS TECHNOLOGY. *Educ:* Alfred Univ, BS, 68, MS, 69, PhD(ceramics), 73. *Prof Exp:* Prod engr refractories, Norton Co, Worcester, 69-70; asst prof glass & ceramics, Univ Erlangen, WGer, 73-74; mem tech staff glass & ceramics, 74-79, PRIN INVESTR INJECTION MOLDING CERAMICS, GTE LABS, 79- *Mem:* Am Ceramic Soc; Sigma Xi. *Res:* High performance ceramics, including fabrication and characterization of non-silicate refractory glasses; silicon nitride consolidation technology, hot pressing, sintering, thermomechanical properties, oxidation meahanisms and kinetics; silicon nitride shape making technology development; injection molding of turbine engine components, isostatic processing green machinery, process upscale. *Mailing Add:* GTE Labs 40 Sylvan Rd Waltham MA 02154

QUACKENBUSH, FORREST WARD, b Melrose, Wis, Aug 18, 07; m 37; c 2. BIOCHEMISTRY. *Educ:* Univ Wis, BS, 32, PhD(biochem), 37. *Prof Exp:* Asst biochem, Univ Wis, 34 & 36-37; Rockefeller Found fel, Kaiser-Wilhelm Inst & Univ Heidelberg, 38 & Rijk's Univ, Utrecht, 39; res fel, Univ Wis, 39-41, instr biochem, 41-42; prof, 43-74, head dept, 43-65, EMER PROF BIOCHEM, PURDUE UNIV, WEST LAFAYETTE, 74- *Mem:* Am Chem Soc; Am Oil Chemists Soc; Am Soc Biol Chemists; Asn Off Anal Chem. *Res:* Biochemistry and nutrition of lipids; chemistry of carotenoids; biosynthesis of lipids. *Mailing Add:* Dept Biochem Purdue Univ West Lafayette IN 47906

QUADAGNO, DAVID MICHAEL, b Portchester, NY, Jan 15, 41; m 64; c 2. NEUROENDOCRINOLOGY. *Educ:* Pa State Univ, BS, 63; San Francisco State Col, MA, 66; Univ Ill, Urbana, PhD(zool), 69. *Prof Exp:* NIH fel, Med Sch, Univ Calif, Los Angeles, 70-71; assoc prof, 71-77, PROF PHYSIOL, UNIV KANS, 77- *Concurrent Pos:* Grants, NIMH, Univ Kans, 71-74, Laylor Found, 72-73 & Nat Inst Child Health & Human Develop, 78-81. *Mem:* Animal Behav Soc; Soc Neurosci. *Res:* Reproductive neuroendocrinology. *Mailing Add:* Dept of Physiol & Cell Biol Univ of Kans Lawrence KS 66045

QUADE, CHARLES RICHARD, b Glasgow, Mont, June 18, 36; m 58; c 4. MOLECULAR PHYSICS. *Educ:* Univ Okla, BS, 58, MS, 60, PhD(physics), 62. *Prof Exp:* Asst prof physics, Univ Del, 62-65; from asst prof to assoc prof, 65-71, PROF PHYSICS, TEX TECH UNIV, 71- *Concurrent Pos:* Res grants, NSF, Res Corp & Univ Del Res Found, 63-65. *Res:* Internal rotation; microwave spectroscopy; magnetic susceptibilities; crystal field theory. *Mailing Add:* Dept of Physics Tex Tech Univ Lubbock TX 79409

QUADE, DANA EDWARD ANTHONY, b Cardston, Alta, Jan 11, 35; US citizen; m 62; c 3. STATISTICS. *Educ:* Univ Calif, Los Angeles, BA, 55; Univ NC, PhD, 60. *Prof Exp:* Res assoc statist, Univ NC, 60; statistician, Communicable Dis Ctr, USPHS, Ga, 60-61 & Nat Inst Neurol Dis & Blindness, 61-62; from asst prof to assoc prof, 62-70, PROF BIOSTATIST, UNIV NC, CHAPEL HILL, 70- *Mem:* Fel Am Statist Asn; Int Math Statist; Biomet Soc. *Res:* Statistical theory, especially nonparametric. *Mailing Add:* Dept Biostatist Univ NC Sch Pub Health Chapel Hill NC 27514

QUADER, ATHER ABDUL, b Hyderabad, India, Oct 10, 41; m 68; c 2. MECHANICAL ENGINEERING. *Educ:* Osmania Univ, India, BE, 62; Univ Wis, PhD(mech eng), 69. *Prof Exp:* Res asst mech eng, Univ Wis, 63-68; assoc res engr, 68-74, sr res engr, 74-81, STAFF RES ENGR, FUELS & LUBRICANTS DEPT, GEN MOTORS RES LABS, 81- *Honors & Awards:* Horning Mem Award, Soc Automotive Engrs, 74, Arch T Colwell Award, 76. *Mem:* Soc Automotive Engrs; Combustion Inst; AAAS. *Res:* Combustion; internal combustion engines; nitric oxide emissions; spectroscopic studies of engine combustion and pollutant formation; lean misfire limit in engines; stratified charge engines. *Mailing Add:* Fuels & Lubricants Dept Gen Motors Res Labs Tech Ctr Warren MI 48090

QUADREL, RONALD FRANK, analytical chemistry, pharmaceutical chemistry, see previous edition

QUADRI, SYED KALEEMULLAH, b Bidar, India. NEUROENDOCRINOLOGY. *Educ:* Osmania Univ, India, DVM, 60; Kans State Univ, MS, 66; Mich State Univ, MS, 70, PhD(neuroendocrinol), 73. *Prof Exp:* Vet asst surgeon, State Govt India, 60-64; res Gen Animal Primate Res Ctr, assoc, asst scientist neuroendocrinol, 76-77; asst prof physiol, Univ Ore Health Sci Ctr, 75-77; ASSOC PROF PHYSIOL, KANS STATE UNIV, 77- *Mem:* Sigma Xi; Soc Study Reproduction. *Res:* Primate and rodent neuroendocrinology, with special emphasis on prolactin, aging and breast cancer. *Mailing Add:* VMS 228 Kans State Univ Manhattan KS 66506

QUADT, R(AYMOND) A(DOLPH), b Perth Amboy, NJ, Apr 16, 16; m 40; c 1. PHYSICAL METALLURGY. *Educ:* Rutgers Univ, BS, 49; Stevens Inst Technol, MS, 47. *Prof Exp:* Teacher high sch, NJ, 39-42; res metallurgist, Am Smelting & Refining Co, 42-48, mgr aluminum div, 48-50; dir res, Hunter Douglas Aluminum Co, 50-54, vpres res & develop, 54-57, vpres res & develop, Bridgeport Brass Co, 57-60; pres, Reactive Metals, Inc, 60-65; vpres, Pascoe Steel Corp, 65-73; pres, 73-80, CONSULT, PHOENIX CEMENT CO, 80- *Mem:* Am Soc Metals; Am Inst Mining, Metall & Petrol Engrs. *Res:* Physical and process metallurgy of aluminum, titanium, zirconium, columbium and tantalum. *Mailing Add:* 15 E San Miguel Phoenix AZ 85012

QUAGLIANO, JAMES VINCENT, b New York, NY, Nov 9, 15; m 61; c 2. INORGANIC CHEMISTRY. *Educ:* Polytech Inst Brooklyn, BS, 38, MS, 40; Univ Ill, PhD(inorg chem), 46. *Prof Exp:* Instr chem, Villanova Col, 40-43 & Univ Ill, 44-45; asst prof, Univ Md, 46-48; from asst prof to assoc prof, Univ Notre Dame, 48-58; from assoc prof to prof chem, Fla State Univ, 58-75; HUDSON PROF CHEM, AUBURN UNIV, 75- *Mem:* AAAS; Am Chem Soc; Am Inst Chemists; fel Royal Soc Chem; NY Acad Sci. *Res:* Inorganic complex compounds; reduction potentials of some inorganic coordination compounds; infrared absorption of inorganic coordination complexes. *Mailing Add:* Dept of Chem Auburn Univ Auburn AL 36830

1

QUAIFE, MARY LOUISE, b Madison, Wis; m 69. BIOCHEMISTRY. *Educ:* Univ Mich, AB, 38, MS, 39; Univ Ill, PhD(anal chem), 42; Am Bd Clin Chem, dipl, 52; Am Inst Chem, cert, 69. *Prof Exp:* Clin chemist, Univ Hosp, Vanderbilt, 39-40; asst chem, Univ Ill, 41-42, asst physiol, 42-43; sr res chemist, Distillation Prod Industs Div, Eastman Kodak Co, 43-54; res assoc nutrit, Sch Pub Health, Harvard Univ, 56-57, assoc, 57-59; res asst environ health, Sch Pub Health, Univ Mich, 60-61, res assoc obstet & gynec, Med Sch, 61-62; biochemist, Div Toxicol Eval, US Food & Drug Admin, 62-70; BIOCHEMIST, TOXICOL BR, HAZARD EVAL DIV, US ENVIRON PROTECTION AGENCY, 70- *Mem:* Am Chem Soc; Am Soc Biol Chemists; Am Inst Nutrit; fel Am Inst Chemists; Soc Toxicol. *Res:* Toxicological evaluation of pesticides and food additives; analysis and biochemistry of vitamin E; modern analytical techniques. *Mailing Add:* 1506 33rd St NW Washington DC 20007

QUAIL, JOHN WILSON, b Brooklyn, NY, Mar 19, 36; m 59; c 4. INORGANIC CHEMISTRY. *Educ:* Univ BC, BSc, 59, MSc, 61; McMaster Univ, PhD(inorg chem), 63. *Prof Exp:* Fel inorg chem, McMaster Univ, 63-64; asst prof, 64-69, ASSOC PROF CHEM, UNIV SASK, 69- *Concurrent Pos:* Sabbatical leave, Univ Chem Lab, Cambridge Univ, 72-73 & Dept Chem, Univ Alberta, Edmonton, 81-82. *Mem:* Chem Inst Can. *Res:* pulse nuclear magnetic resonance; molybdenum chemistry; crystallography. *Mailing Add:* Dept of Chem & Chem Eng Univ of Sask Saskatoon SK S7N 0W0 Can

QUAILE, JAMES PATRICK, b Philadelphia, Pa, Jan 16, 43; m 68; c 1. MECHANICAL ENGINEERING, ENERGY SCIENCES. *Educ:* NJ Inst Technol, BS, 68; Lehigh Univ, MS, 69, PhD(mech eng), 72. *Prof Exp:* Proj engr transp, Transp Tech Ctr, 72-73; syst engr energy, 74-76, mgr, 76-77, LIAISON SCIENTIST CONSUMER PROD, CORP RES & DEVELOP, GEN ELEC CO, 77- *Mem:* Am Soc Mech Engrs. *Res:* Energy; thermodynamics; heat transfer; fluid dynamics. *Mailing Add:* Corp Res & Develop PO Box 8 Schenectady NY 12301

QUALLS, CLIFFORD RAY, b Duncan, Okla, Oct 31, 36; m 59; c 2. MATHEMATICAL STATISTICS. *Educ:* Calif State Col Long Beach, BA, 61; Univ Calif, Riverside, MA, 64, PhD(math), 67. *Prof Exp:* Mathematician, US Naval Ord Lab, Calif, 56-61; reliability engr, Autonetics Div, NAm Aviation, Inc, 61-64; instr math, Calif State Col Fullerton, 64-67; asst prof, 67-74, assoc prof, 74-80, PROF MATH, UNIV NMEX, 80- *Mem:* Math Asn Am; Inst Math Statist; Inst Elec & Electronics Engrs. *Res:* Crossing problems for stationary stochastic processes; life testing; prediction theory for stochastic processes. *Mailing Add:* Dept of Math & Statist Univ of NMex Albuquerque NM 87106

QUALSET, CALVIN ODELL, b Newman Grove, Nebr, Apr 24, 37; m 57; c 3. GENETICS, PLANT BREEDING. *Educ:* Univ Nebr, BS, 58; Univ Calif, Davis, MS, 60, PhD(genetics), 64. *Prof Exp:* Lab technician agron, Univ Calif, Davis, 60-64; asst prof, Univ Tenn, Knoxville, 64-67; from asst prof to assoc prof, 67-74, chmn dept agron & range sci, 75-81, PROF AGRON, UNIV CALIF, DAVIS, 74-, ASSOC DEAN, COL AGR & ENVIRON SCI, 81- *Concurrent Pos:* Consult, Develop & Resources Corp, 73 & Ford Found, 74; Fulbright sr scholar, 76; mem, Food & Agr Org, UN, 78; ed-in-chief, Crop Sci Soc Am, 80-82. *Mem:* AAAS; Am Genetics Asn; Genetics Soc Am; Genetics Soc Can; fel Am Soc Agron. *Res:* Genetics and evolution of disease resistance in plants; analysis of quantitative genetic variation in plants; breeding for improvement in agronomic and quality characteristics in barley, wheat, oats, triticale and rye. *Mailing Add:* Dept of Agron & Range Sci Univ of Calif Davis CA 95616

QUAM, DAVID LAWRENCE, b Minneapolis, Minn, June 5, 42. AERODYNAMICS, CONTROL SYSTEMS. *Educ:* Univ Minn, BAE, 65; Univ Wash, MSAA, 70, PhD(aerospace & astrodyn), 75. *Prof Exp:* Assoc engr, Lockheed-Calif Co, 65; teaching assoc, Univ Wash, 68-75; ASSOC PROF AEROSPACE ENG, UNIV DAYTON, 75- *Concurrent Pos:* Sr aerodynamicist, Boeing Commercial Airplane Co, 68-69; control systs analyst, Marine Systs Div, Honeywell, 72-75; fac researcher, Fac Res Prog, US Air Force-Am Soc Eng Educ, 77; chmn, Flight Simulation Course, Univ Dayton, 79-80; math modeling consult, Technol, Inc, 79-81; vis prof, Frank J Seiler Res Lab, US Air Force Acad, 80-81. *Mem:* Am Inst Aeronaut & Astronaut; Am Helicopter Soc; Am Soc Eng Educ. *Res:* Perception studies and myoelectric feedback for flight simulation; missile aerodynamics and control; digital control of spacecraft; experimental and theoretical work in unsteady aerodynamics. *Mailing Add:* 37 Seminary Ave Dayton OH 45403

QUAMME, HARVEY ALLEN, b Brownlee, Sask, Apr 23, 40; m 63; c 2. HORTICULTURE. *Educ:* Univ Sask, BSA, 62, MSc, 64; Univ Minn, PhD(hort), 71. *Prof Exp:* From res officer fruit res to res scientist, 63-74, MEM STAFF, RES STA, CAN DEPT AGR, 74- *Honors & Awards:* Gourley Award Res Pomology, Am Soc Hort Sci, 73; Carroll R Miller Award, Nat Peach Coun, 79. *Mem:* Am Soc Hort Sci; Can Soc Hort Sci. *Res:* Evaluation and development of new roots rock varieties of tree fruits and grapes with emphasis on dwarfing precocity, cold hardiness and disease resistance; investigation of mechanisms of winter survival in fruit crops which involve deep supercooling. *Mailing Add:* Can Dept of Agr Res Sta Summerland BC V0H 1Z0 Can

QUANDT, EARL RAYMOND, JR, b Washington, DC, Feb 5, 34; m 56; c 4. CHEMICAL ENGINEERING. *Educ:* Univ Cincinnati, ChE, 56; Univ Pittsburgh, PhD(chem eng), 61. *Prof Exp:* Sr engr, Bettis Atomic Power Lab, Westinghouse Elec Corp, 56-63; res coordr appl mech, US Navy Marine Eng Lab, 63-67, HEAD POWER SYSTS DIV, US NAVY SHIP RES & DEVELOP CTR, 67- *Mem:* Am Inst Chem Engrs. *Res:* Two phase flow; heat transfer; systems dynamics; reliability; marine propulsion. *Mailing Add:* 203 Winchester Rd SW Annapolis MD 21401

QUANE, DENIS JOSEPH, b New York, NY, Oct 28, 35. INORGANIC CHEMISTRY. *Educ:* Manhattan Col, BS, 57; Univ Notre Dame, PhD(inorg chem), 65. *Prof Exp:* Res assoc inorg chem, Georgetown Univ, 64-65; asst prof, 65-69, ASSOC PROF CHEM, EAST TEX STATE UNIV, 69- *Mem:* AAAS; Am Chem Soc; Royal Soc Chem. *Res:* Organogermanium chemistry; comparative chemistry of group IV elements; transition metal peroxides; inorganic kinetics. *Mailing Add:* Dept of Chem E Tex State Univ Commerce TX 75428

QUANSTROM, WALTER ROY, b Gary, Ind, Nov 20, 42; m 63; c 2. ANIMAL BEHAVIOR. *Educ:* Bethany Nazarene Col, BS, 64; Univ Okla, PhD(zool), 68. *Prof Exp:* NASA trainee, Univ Okla, 65-67; asst prof biol, Olivet Nazarene Col, 68-70; assoc prof & chmn dept, Northwest Nazarene Col, 70-74, chmn div natural sci & math, 72-74; staff ecologist, 74-77, dir ecol, 77-79, dir environ & energy conservation, 79-81, MGR, INDUST HYGIENE, TOXICOL & SAFETY, STANDARD OIL CO, IND, 81- *Concurrent Pos:* Mem, Exec Develop Prog, Northwestern Univ, 80. *Mem:* Am Soc Mammalogists. *Res:* Ethoecology of Richardson's ground squirrel, Spermophilus richardsonii. *Mailing Add:* Standard Oil Co MC 3802 200 E Randolph Dr Chicago IL 60601

QUARLES, CARROLL ADAIR, JR, b Abilene, Tex, Nov 24, 38; m 71. ATOMIC PHYSICS. *Educ:* Tex Christian Univ, BA, 60; Princeton Univ, MA, 62, PhD(physics), 64. *Prof Exp:* Res fel physics, Brookhaven Nat Lab, 64-65, asst physicist, 65-67; from asst prof to assoc prof, 67-74, PROF PHYSICS, TEX CHRISTIAN UNIV, 74-, CHMN DEPT, 78- *Concurrent Pos:* Assoc dean, Dept Physics, Tex Christian Univ, 74-78. *Mem:* Fedn Am Scientists; AAAS; Am Phys Soc; Am Asn Physics Teachers. *Res:* Electron and atomic collisions; atomic field bremsstrahlung; inner shell ionization. *Mailing Add:* Dept of Physics Tex Christian Univ Ft Worth TX 76129

QUARLES, GILFORD GODFREY, b Charlottesville, Va, Dec 24, 09; m 34; c 3. PHYSICS. *Educ:* Univ Va, BS, 30, MS, 33, PhD(physics), 34. *Prof Exp:* Instr physics, Univ Va, 31-33; actg prof, Mercer Univ, 34-35 & Univ Ala, 35-41; assoc prof, Furman Univ, 41-43; res assoc, Harvard Univ, 44-45; from assoc prof to prof eng res, Pa State Univ, 45-56; tech & sci consult to commanding gen, Ballistic Missile Agency, US Dept Army, 56-58; chief scientist, Ord Missile Command, Redstone Arsenal, Ala, 58-59; chief sci adv, Corps Engrs, 59-60; dir long-range mil planning, Bendix Corp, 60-61; chief sci adv, Off Chief Engrs, US Army Corps Engrs, 61-75; RETIRED. *Concurrent Pos:* Asst dir, Ord Res Lab, Pa State Univ, 47-52, dir, 52-56. *Mem:* AAAS. *Res:* Photographic latent image; electrooptical Kerr effect; underwater ordnance; sonic and ultrasonic vibrations; ballistic missiles. *Mailing Add:* 1913 Earldale Ct Alexandria VA 22306

QUARLES, JOHN MONROE, b Chattanooga, Tenn, May 24, 42; m 71; c 1. MEDICAL MICROBIOLOGY, ONCOLOGY. *Educ:* Fla State Univ, BS, 63, MS, 65; Mich State Univ, PhD(microbiol), 73; Am Bd Microbiol, cert pub health & med lab microbiol, 75. *Prof Exp:* Res microbiologist, Ctr Dis Control, USPHS, 65-66; head serol-virol lab, Naval Med Sch, Nat Naval Med Ctr, US Navy, 66-69; fel, Univ Tenn & Oak Ridge Nat Lab, 73-74 & Nat Cancer Inst & Oak Ridge Nat Lab, 74-76; ASST PROF MICROBIOL, COL MED, TEX A&M UNIV, 76- *Mem:* Am Soc Microbiol; Tissue Cult Asn; Sigma Xi. *Res:* Transformation of mammalian cells by chemical carcinogens; cellular response of murine leukemia viruses; activation of endogenous tumor virus by chemicals and radiation; dialysis culture of microorganisms and mammalian cells; animal virology; antiviral agents and vaccines; influenza. *Mailing Add:* Dept Microbiol Col Med Tex A&M Univ College Station TX 77843

QUARLES, RICHARD HUDSON, b Baltimore, Md, Sept 23, 39; m 64; c 3. BIOCHEMISTRY, NEUROCHEMISTRY. *Educ:* Swarthmore Col, AB, 61; Harvard Univ, PhD(biochem), 66. *Prof Exp:* From staff fel to sr staff fel biochem, 68-73, res chemist, 73-77, HEAD, SECT MYELIN & BRAIN DEVELOP, NAT INST NEUROL & COMMUNICATIVE DIS & STROKE, 77- *Concurrent Pos:* NSF fel, Inst Animal Physiol, Cambridge, Eng, 66-67, Nat Inst Neurol Dis & Stroke fel, 67-68. *Mem:* AAAS; Am Chem Soc; Am Soc Neurochem; Int Soc Neurochem. *Res:* Metabolism of phospholipids, glycolipids, and glycoproteins; roles of lipids and proteins in membrane structure and function; developing brain; myelination. *Mailing Add:* Lab Neurochem Bldg 10 Rm 3D 17 NIH Bethesda MD 20014

QUARLES, RICHARD WINGFIELD, b Richmond, Va, Mar 21, 11; m 36; c 5. POLYMER CHEMISTRY. *Educ:* Univ Va, BSE, 31, PhD(phys chem), 35. *Prof Exp:* Asst phys chem, Univ Va, 35-37; res chemist, Union Carbide & Carbon Corp, WVa, 37-39; indust fel, Mellon Inst, 39-50, sr fel, 51-55; asst div head, Bakelite Co, 55-56, asst dir develop, Union Carbide Corp, 56, assoc dir develop, Plastics Div, 56-60, mgr patents & licenses, 60-64, dir polymer res & develop, 64-69, mgr patents, 69-76; CONSULT, 76- *Mem:* Am Chem Soc; Am Inst Chem Engrs; Sigma Xi. *Res:* Vinyl resins with special emphasis on their use in surface coatings and adhesives; synthetic resins; adsorption of gases and surface phenomena. *Mailing Add:* 60 Marion Rd W Princeton NJ 08540

QUARLES, VERNON CUTHBERT, b Charlottesville, Va, Aug 18, 17; m 39; c 3. CHEMICAL ENGINEERING. *Educ:* Univ Va, BSE, 39. *Prof Exp:* Chemist, Anal Lab, NJ, 39-40, prod supvr, 40-44, acid supt, Wis, 44-48, hexite supt, NJ, 48-51, dimethyl terephthalate supt, 51-54, asst to prod mgr, Del, 54-59, asst mgr prod, NJ, 59-62, bus anal mgr, Del, 62-67, asst control mgr, 67-68, ASST MGR ACCT & BUS ANAL DIV, EXPLOSIVES DEPT, E I DU PONT DE NEMOURS & CO, DEL, 68- *Mem:* Am Inst Chem Engrs. *Res:* Nitrobenzene; aniline; diphenylamine tetryl; pentaerythital tetranitrate; sodium picrate; dimethyl terephthalate; nitrocellulose; sodium carboxymethl cellulose; ammonia; acrylonitrile; caprolactam; smokeless powder; nitric and sulphuric acids; economic evaluations; operations research and planning. *Mailing Add:* Marshall's Bridge Kennett Square PA 19348

QUARONI, ANDREA, b Milano, Italy, Aug 9, 46; m 75; c 1. DEVELOPMENTAL BIOLOGY. *Educ:* Univ Pavia, Italy, PhD(biochem), 70. *Prof Exp:* Asst volontario biochem, Univ Pavia, Italy, 70-71; asst I biochem, Swiss Fed Inst Technol, Zurich, 72-75; res fel biochem, Harvard Med Sch & Mass Gen Hosp, 75-78; instr, 78-80, ASST PROF BIOCHEM, HARVARD MED SCH, 81- *Concurrent Pos:* asst biochem, Mass Gen Hosp, 78-80. *Mem:* Soc Complex Carbohydrates; Swiss Biochem Soc; Swiss Biochem Soc; Tissue Culture Asn. *Res:* Structure and function of the intestinal epithelium; identification, purification and biosynthesis of surface membrane proteins and glycoproteins and cultured intestinal epithelial cells; structure and composition of the intestinal basement membrane. *Mailing Add:* Gastrointestinal Univ Mass Gen Hosp Boston MA 02114

QUARTARARO, IGNATIUS NICHOLAS, b Brooklyn, NY, July 26, 26; m 52; c 4. DENTISTRY. *Educ:* NY Univ, DDS, 52; Am Bd Endodont, dipl, 59. *Prof Exp:* Asst endodontia, NY Univ, 52-54, from instr to asst prof, 54-68, assoc prof, 68-73. *Concurrent Pos:* Consult, Dept Surg, New York Infirmary Hosp, 61-66; dir endodont, Cath Med Ctr, Brooklyn & Queens. *Mem:* Fel Am Asn Endodont; fel Am Col Dent; Am Acad Oral Med; Sigma Xi; fel Int Col Dentists. *Res:* Temporo-mandibular joint; fluoroscopy of sealing properties of endodontic cements; pathology of the periapical lesion. *Mailing Add:* 520 Franklin Ave Garden City NY 11530

QUARTERMAN, ELSIE, b Valdosta, Ga, Nov 28, 10. BOTANY, ECOLOGY. *Educ:* Ga State Col, AB, 32; Duke Univ, MA, 41, PhD(bot), 49. *Prof Exp:* Pub sch teacher, Ga, 32-43; from instr to assoc prof biol, 43-66, chmn div bact, bot & zool, 60-61, prof biol, 66-76, PROF EMER, VANDERBILT UNIV, 76- *Concurrent Pos:* Mem bd dirs, Tenn Bot Gardens, 71-72. *Mem:* Asn Southeastern Biologists; Bot Soc Am. *Res:* Distribution of the Compositae in south Georgia; composition and structure of plant communities in middle Tennessee; ecology of bryophytes; climax forests of the coastal plain of southeastern United States; autecology of middle Tennessee endemics; conservation of ecosystems. *Mailing Add:* 1313 Belmont Park Ct Nashville TN 37215

QUASS, LA VERNE CARL, b Beloit, Wis, Jan 17, 37; m 59; c 3. INORGANIC CHEMISTRY. *Educ:* Luther Col, BA, 59; Univ Wis-Madison, MS, 64, PhD(chem), 69. *Prof Exp:* Instr chem, Univ Wis-Fox Valley Ctr, 63-66; asst prof chem, Univ Wis-Parkside, 69-76; assoc prof, 76-80, PROF CHEM, GRAND VIEW COL, 80- *Mem:* AAAS; Am Chem Soc; The Chem Soc. *Res:* Organometallic and organosilicon chemistry. *Mailing Add:* Dept of Chem 1200 Grandview Ave Des Moines IA 50316

QUAST, JAY CHARLES, b San Francisco, Calif, Sept 17, 23; m 49. ICHTHYOLOGY. *Educ:* Univ Calif, BA, 48, MA, 50 & 51, PhD(ichthyol), 60. *Prof Exp:* High sch teacher, Calif, 51-53; asst, Univ Calif, Los Angeles, 53-57; res biologist, Scripps Inst, Univ Calif, 58-61; supvry fishery biologist, Nat Marine Fisheries Serv, 61-74, proj scientist, Environ Res Labs, 74-76, nat sci ed, 77-80, RES BIOLOGIST, NAT MARINE FISHERIES SERV, NAT OCEANIC & ATMOSPHERIC ADMIN, 81- *Mem:* Am Fisheries Soc; Am Soc Ichthol & Herpet. *Res:* Fish ecology, taxonomy, variation, osteology and population dynamics; research management. *Mailing Add:* Nat Marine Fisheries Serv (NOAA) Auke Bay Lab Box 155 Auke Bay AK 99821

QUASTEL, D M J, b Cardiff, UK, June 7, 36; Can citizen; m 59; c 2. PHYSIOLOGY. *Educ:* McGill Univ, BS, 55, MD, CM, 59, PhD(physiol), 63. *Prof Exp:* Med Res Coun Can fel, 61-63; Muscular Dystrophy Asn Can fel, 63-65; asst prof physiol, Dalhousie Univ, 65-69; assoc prof, 69-77, PROF PHARMACOL, UNIV BC, 77- *Mem:* Can Physiol Soc. *Res:* mechanisms of synaptic transmission. *Mailing Add:* Dept of Pharmacol Univ of BC Vancouver BC V6T 1W5 Can

QUASTEL, JUDA HIRSCH, b Sheffield, Eng, Oct 2, 99; m 31; c 3. BIOCHEMISTRY. *Educ:* Univ London, BSc, 21, DSc, 26; Cambridge Univ, PhD, 24. *Hon Degrees:* DSc, McGill Univ, 69; PhD, Hebrew Univ Jerusalem, 70. *Prof Exp:* Demonstr & lectr biochem, Cambridge Univ, 23-29, fel, Trinity Col, 24-30; dir res, Cardiff City Ment Hosp, Wales, 29-41 & Metab Unit, Agr Res Coun, Eng, 41-47; prof biochem, McGill Univ, 47-66, dir, McGill Unit Cell Metab, 65-66; PROF NEUROCHEM, FAC MED, UNIV BC, 66- *Concurrent Pos:* Beit Mem fel, 28; Rockefeller traveling fel, 37; Leeuwenhoeck lectr, Royal Soc, 54; Priestman lectr, Univ NB, 56; Kearney Found lectr, Univ Calif, 58; Royal Soc Leverhulme vis prof, India, 66; dir, McGill-Montreal Gen Hosp Res Inst, 47-65; hon consult, Montreal Gen Hosp, 50-; mem, Comt Med & Agr Res Coun, Eng, 33-47, Forestry Comn, 43-47 & Water Pollution Res Bd, 44-47; mem bd gov, Hebrew Univ Jerusalem, 50-; mem neurochem comt, World Fedn Neurol; vis prof, Nat Hosp Nervous Dis, Queen SQ, London, UK, 76; hon pres, Inst Biochem Cong, Toronto, 79. *Honors & Awards:* Meldola Medal, Royal Inst Chem, 27; Award, Can Microbiol Soc, 65; Companion, Order Can, 70; Flavelle Medal, Royal Soc Can, 74; Gairdner Found Award for Med Res, 74. *Mem:* Hon mem Biochem Soc UK; fel Royal Soc Can; Am Soc Biol Chemists; Can Biochem Soc (past pres). *Res:* Enzyme chemistry; biochemistry in relation to mental disorders; biochemistry of microorganisms; soil biochemistry; phyto-biochemistry. *Mailing Add:* 4585 Langara Ave Vancouver BC VR6 1C9 Can

QUASTEL, MICHAEL REUBEN, b Cardiff, Wales, June 30, 33; Can citizen; m 62; c 4. IMMUNOLOGY, RADIOBIOLOGY. *Educ:* McGill Univ, BSc, 53, MD & CM, 57; Univ Ottawa, PhD(immunology), 71. *Prof Exp:* Intern, Charity Hosp La, New Orleans, 57-58; jr res physician, Radiobiol & Nuclear Med Labs, Univ Calif, Los Angeles, 59-61; res assoc, Pasadena Found Med Res, 61-62; asst resident oncol & radiother, Hadassah Hosp, Jerusalem, 62-64; head biol sect, Radiation Protection Div, Dept Nat Health & Welfare, 65-71, asst chief human cytogenetics div & head environ mutagenesis sect, 71-74; ASSOC PROF, SCH MED, BEN GURION UNIV & HEAD, LAB CLIN IMMUNOL, ISOTOPE DEPT, SOROKA MED CTR, BEERSHEBA, ISRAEL, 74- *Concurrent Pos:* Instr, Dept Radiol, Univ Southern Calif, 61-62; res fel physiol, Med Sch, Hebrew Univ, 64-65; sr lectr, Sch Med, Univ Ottawa, 71-74; consult, Ottawa Civic Hosp, Can, 71-74; res & clin fel, Div Nuclear Med, Mass Gen Hosp & Harvard Med Sch, 80-81. *Mem:* Can Soc Immunol; fel Royal Soc Health; Genetics Soc Can; NY Acad Sci; Israel Soc Immunol. *Res:* Medical radiobiology and nuclear medicine; cell biology and tissue culture; human cytogenetics and environmental mutagenesis; clinical immunology. *Mailing Add:* Soroka Med Ctr PO Box 151 Beersheba Israel

QUATE, CALVIN F(ORREST), b Baker, Nev, Dec 7, 23; m 46; c 4. APPLIED PHYSICS, ELECTRICAL ENGINEERING. *Educ:* Univ Utah, BS, 44; Stanford Univ, PhD(elec eng), 50. *Prof Exp:* Tech staff mem, Bell Tel Labs, NJ, 49-58; dir & vpres res, Sandia Corp, NMex, 59-61; PROF APPL PHYSICS & ELEC ENG, STANFORD UNIV, 61- *Mem:* Nat Acad Eng; Nat Acad Sci; Am Phys Soc; Inst Elec & Electronics Engrs; Acoust Soc Am. *Res:* Microwave electronics and solid state devices; physical acoustics. *Mailing Add:* Ginzton Lab Stanford Univ Stanford CA 94305

QUATRANO, RALPH STEPHEN, b Elmira, NY, Aug 3, 41; m 59; c 3. BOTANY. *Educ:* Colgate Univ, AB, 62; Ohio Univ, MS, 64; Yale Univ, PhD(biol), 68. *Prof Exp:* NSF undergrad res partic, Colgate Univ, 61-62; AEC asst bot, plant physiol & biol, Ohio Univ, 62-64; asst, Yale Univ, 64-65, NIH trainee develop biol, 65-67; from asst prof to assoc prof, 68-78, PROF BOT, ORE STATE UNIV, 78- *Mem:* Soc Develop Biol; Bot Soc Am; Am Soc Plant Physiologists. *Res:* Studies in physiology, biochemistry and cytology of plant cell differentiation and embryogenesis in algae and angiosperms. *Mailing Add:* Dept of Bot Ore State Univ Corvallis OR 97331

QUATTRONE, PHILLIP DONALD, b Salamanca, NY, Nov 24, 26; m 50; c 3. PHYSICAL CHEMISTRY, ENGINEERING. *Educ:* Hiram Col, BA, 49; Univ Del, MS, 50. *Prof Exp:* Phys chemist, Eli Lilly & Co, 50-53, Spinco Div, Beckman Labs, 57-58 & Univ Ark Med Sch, 58-59; res phys chemist, Sch Aerospace Med, US Air Force, 59-63; res scientist, 63-70, CHIEF ADVAN LIFE SUPPORT, AMES RES CTR, NASA, 70- *Concurrent Pos:* Chmn crew systs comt, Am Soc Mech Engrs, 75-78. *Honors & Awards:* Exceptional Serv Medal, NASA, 73. *Mem:* Sigma Xi; Am Chem Soc; Am Inst Aeronaut & Astronaut; Soc Automotive Engrs; Am Soc Mech Engrs. *Res:* Advanced life support; electrochemistry; mechanical engineering; control/monitor instrumentation. *Mailing Add:* Ames Res Ctr NASA Moffett Field CA 94035

QUATTRONE, ROBERT, metallurgy, materials science, see previous edition

QUATTROPANI, STEVEN L, b Hartford, Conn, Apr 26, 43; m 66; c 1. ANATOMY, REPRODUCTIVE BIOLOGY. *Educ:* Bates Col, BS, 65; Univ Mass, MA, 69, PhD(zool), 70. *Prof Exp:* Fel reproductive physiol training prog, Worcester Found Exp Biol, Mass, 70-72; res assoc Anat, Obstet & Gynec, Hershey Med Ctr, Col Med, Pa State Univ, 72-73, instr, 73-74, asst prof, 74-75; asst prof, 75-78, ASSOC PROF ANAT, MED COL VA, VA COMMONWEALTH UNIV, 78- *Mem:* Am Asn Anat; Soc Study Reprod. *Res:* Differentiation of reproductive organs. *Mailing Add:* Dept of Anat Med Col of Va Va Commonwealth Univ Richmond VA 23284

QUAY, JOHN FERGUSON, b Galion, Ohio, Feb 29, 32; m 57; c 3. BIOPHYSICS. *Educ:* Ohio State Univ, BS, 57, MS, 58; Ind Univ, PhD(physiol), 68. *Prof Exp:* Phys chemist, sr phys chemist, 68-75, RES SCIENTIST, ELI LILLY & CO RES 75- *Mem:* Am Chem Soc; Biophys Soc; NY Acad Sci; Am Physiol Soc; Sigma Xi. *Res:* Ion transport in the intestinal epithelium; intestinal absorption, permeability and pharmacokinetics of drugs. *Mailing Add:* Eli Lilly & Co Res Labs M909 Indianapolis IN 46207

QUAY, PAUL DOUGLAS, b New York, NY, Oct 10, 49. GEOCHEMISTRY, LIMNOLOGY. *Educ:* City Univ New York, BA, 71; Columbia Univ, PhD(geol), 77. *Prof Exp:* Res assoc geol, Quaternary Res Ctr, 77-80, ASST PROF, DEPT GEOL SCI & OCEANOG, UNIV WASH, 80- *Res:* Determining ocean mixing rates by using radiocarbon distribution; modeling global carbon dioxide and radiocarbon distributions in nature; studying the geochemistry of lakes, rivers and marine systems using naturally occurring radioisotopes; chemical oceanography. *Mailing Add:* Dept Geol Sci AJ-20 Univ Wash Seattle WA 98195

QUAY, PAUL MICHAEL, b Chicago, Ill, Aug 24, 24. NONEQUILIBRIUM THERMODYNAMICS. *Educ:* Loyola Univ, Ill, AB, 50; West Baden Col. lic phil, 52, lic theol, 62; Mass Inst Technol, BS, 55, PhD(statist thermodyn), 58. *Prof Exp:* Res assoc statist mech, Case Inst Technol, 62-63; vis prof physics, Loyola Univ, Ill, 65-67; asst prof, 67-70, ASSOC PROF PHYSICS, ST LOUIS UNIV, 70- *Concurrent Pos:* Physicist, Nat Bur Standards, Colo, 66 & 67; assoc prof spirituality, Dept Theol Studies, St Louis Univ, 75-81; vis assoc prof physics, philos & theol, Loyola Univ, Chicago, 81-82. *Mem:* Am Phys Soc; Philos Sci Asn. *Res:* Statistical and irreversible thermodynamics; generalized master equations; philosophy of physics as mode of human experience; foundations of statistical physics; theory of spiritual development. *Mailing Add:* Dept Physics St Louis Univ St Louis MO 63103

QUAY, THOMAS LAVELLE, b Mt Holly, NJ, Aug 23, 14; m 39; c 1. ANIMAL ECOLOGY. *Educ:* Univ Ark, BS, 38; NC State Col, MS, 40, PhD(zool), 48. *Prof Exp:* Asst, Univ Ark, 35-38; instr zool & entom, 46-48, from asst prof to assoc prof zool, 48-57, PROF ZOOL, NC STATE UNIV, 57- *Mem:* AAAS; Ecol Soc Am; Am Inst Biol Sci; Am Ornithologists Union; Wildlife Soc. *Res:* Ecological succession of birds; habitat associations and niche relationships of animals; animal behavior. *Mailing Add:* Dept of Zool NC State Univ Raleigh NC 27607

QUAY, WILBUR BROOKS, histophysiology, neurobiology, see previous edition

QUAZI, AZIZUL H(AQUE), b Rahimpur, Bangladesh, Jan 1, 35; m 67; c 2. ELECTRICAL ENGINEERING. *Educ:* Univ Dacca, BSEE, 56; Munich Tech Univ, DrEng, 63. *Prof Exp:* Asst engr, Govt Bangladesh & Utah Int Inc, USA, Chittagong H T, Bangladesh, 56-58; res assoc eng, Munich Tech Univ,

64-65; res electronic engr, Info Processing Div, US Navy Underwater Sound Lab, Conn, 65-69, TEAM LEADER, NEW LONDON LAB, US NAVAL UNDERWATER SYST CTR, 69- *Concurrent Pos:* Lectr, Dept Elec Eng, Univ RI, 66-68, Univ Conn, Hartford Grad Ctr, Univ New Haven Ctr. *Mem:* AAAS; Inst Elec & Electronics Engrs; Acoust Soc Am. *Res:* Research and development in the field of statistical theory of communication, especially in detection, localization and classification of underwater targets; semiconductor devices; high frequency; underwater acoustics; advanced systems technology, digital signal processing and underwater communications. *Mailing Add:* New London Lab Ft Trumbull New London CT 06320

QUEBBEMANN, ALOYSIUS JOHN, b Chicago, Ill, Jan 19, 33; m 67; c 5. PHARMACOLOGY. *Educ:* Univ Alaska, BS, 60; NMex Highlands Univ, MS, 64; State Univ NY Buffalo, PhD(pharmacol), 68. *Prof Exp:* USPHS res fel pharmacol, Sch Med, State Univ NY Buffalo, 68-69; Merck Found fac develop award, 69; asst prof, 69-75, ASSOC PROF PHARMACOL, SCH MED, UNIV MINN, MINNEAPOLIS, 75- *Mem:* Am Soc Nephrol. *Res:* Pharmacology of renal transport mechanisms. *Mailing Add:* 77 Valley View Rd Long Lake MN 55356

QUEBEDEAUX, BRUNO, JR, b Arnaudville, La, June 8, 41; m 66; c 4. PLANT PHYSIOLOGY, CROP SCIENCE. *Educ:* La State Univ, BS, 62, MS, 63; Cornell Univ, PhD(veg crops), 68. *Prof Exp:* Prof agr, Chott Maria Agr Col-Tex A&M Univ, Tunisa, Africa, 63-65; res plant physiologist, E I du Pont de Nemours & Co Inc, 68-80; PROG DIR & CHIEF OF PARTY, DEPT STATE, 80- *Mem:* Am Soc Plant Physiologists; Am Soc Hort Sci; Am Soc Agron; Crop Sci Soc Am. *Res:* Growth regulators; mechanisms of action of plant hormones; plant growth and development; mineral nutrition; plant-water relations; oxygen and seed development; photorespiration, translocation and nitrogen fixation. *Mailing Add:* Dept State Nouakchott Mauritania Washington DC 20520

QUEDNAU, FRANZ WOLFGANG, b Dresden, Ger, Apr 27, 30; m 49; c 2. ENTOMOLOGY, TAXONOMIC ENTOMOLOGY. *Educ:* Free Univ, Berlin, BSc, 51, PhD(zool), 53. *Prof Exp:* Res asst entom, Biologische Bundesanstalt, Berlin, 53-60; prof officer, Plant Protection Res Inst, Pretoria, SAfrica, 60-63; RES SCIENTIST II ENTOM, CAN FORESTRY SERV, DEPT ENVIRON, 64- *Concurrent Pos:* Fulbright fel travel grant & Ger Res Coun fel, Dept Biol Control, Univ Calif, Riverside, 58-59. *Mem:* Entom Soc Can. *Res:* Biological control of insect pests; ecology of hymenopterous parasites; toxonomy of trichogramma; taxonomy of aphids. *Mailing Add:* Laurentian Forest Res Ctr PO Box 3800 Ste Foy PQ G1V 4C7 Can

QUEEN, DANIEL, b Boston, Mass, Feb 15, 34; m 57; c 1. ELECTRONIC ENGINEERING, ACOUSTICS. *Prof Exp:* Engr, Magnecord Inc, Ill, 55-57; proj engr, 3M-Revere-Wollensak, 57-62; dir eng, Perma-Power Div, Chamberlain Mfg Co, 63-70; PRES, DANIEL QUEEN ASSOCS, 70- *Concurrent Pos:* Rep, Am Nat Standards Comt, 73- *Mem:* Acoust Soc Am; Inst Elec & Electronics Engr; fel Audio Engr Soc; AAAS; Soc Motion Picture & TV Engr. *Res:* Development of sound reinforcement technology for small meeting and teaching rooms; human factors research data involving simplification of installation and application together with compensation for measured acoustical conditions. *Mailing Add:* 5524 W Gladys Ave Chicago IL 60644

QUEEN, WILLIAM CHARLES, b Brooklyn, NY, May 1, 42; m 64; c 2. INFORMATION PROCESSING. *Educ:* State Univ NY Stony Brook, BES, 63, MS, 66, PhD(appl math), 67. *Prof Exp:* Asst prof appl math, Northwestern Univ, 67-68; res specialist, Elec Boat Div, Gen Dynamics Corp, Conn, 68-70; asst prof appl math, Univ SC, 70-74; assoc prof math, Univ North Fla, 74-80; PRES, CORBEL & CO, JACKSONVILLE, FLA, 80- *Mem:* Am Math Soc; Soc Indust & Appl Math; Asn Comput Mach. *Res:* Data base management, information storage and retrieval; text editing and word processing system design. *Mailing Add:* 4156 Leeward Pt Jacksonville FL 32225

QUEENAN, JOHN T, b Aurora, Ill, May 5, 33; m 57; c 2. OBSTETRICS & GYNECOLOGY. *Educ:* Univ Notre Dame, BS, 54; Cornell Univ, MD, 58; Am Bd Obstet & Gynec, dipl, 66. *Prof Exp:* From clin instr to clin assoc prof obstet & gynec, Med Col, Cornell Univ, 62-72; prof obstet & gynec & chmn dept, Univ Louisville, 72-80; PROF OBSTET & GYNEC & CHMN DEPT, SCH MED, GEORGETOWN UNIV, 80- *Concurrent Pos:* Dir Rh-clin & Lab, New York Hosp, 62-72; from asst attend to sr attend, Greenwich Hosp, Conn, 63-71; obstet & gynec-in-chief, Georgetown Univ Hosp, 80-; chief obstet & gynec, Norton-Children's Hosp, Louisville, 73-80; ed, Contemp Obstet-Gynec. *Mem:* Fel Am Col Obstetricians & Gynecologists; fel Am Col Surgeons; affil Royal Soc Med; fel Am Fertil Soc; NY Acad Sci. *Res:* Treatment of erythroblastosis fetalis by aminiocenteses and in intrauterine transfusions; care of the immunized obstetrical patient and treatment to prevent future immunization; perinatal medicine; management of the high risk pregnancy; perinatal ultrasound; study of intrauterine retardation. *Mailing Add:* Dept Ostet & Gynec Georgetown Univ Univ of Louisville Washington DC 20007

QUEENER, SHERRY FREAM, b Muskogee, Okla, July 8, 43; m 67. BIOCHEMISTRY. *Educ:* Okla Baptist Univ, BS, 65; Univ Ill, Urbana, MS, 68, PhD(biochem), 70. *Prof Exp:* Instr, 71-73, asst prof, 73-78, ASSOC PROF PHARMACOL, SCH MED, IND UNIV, INDIANAPOLIS, 78- *Concurrent Pos:* Am Cancer Soc fel pharmacol, Sch Med, Ind Univ, Indianapolis, 70-71. *Mem:* AAAS; Am Chem Soc; Am Soc Clin Res; NY Acad Sci; Am Soc Biol Chemists. *Res:* Regulation of metabolic pathways; enzyme regulation at the genetic level and as mediated by effector molecules; hormone interaction with adenylate cyclase; adenylate cyclase component structure; diabetes. *Mailing Add:* Dept of Pharmacol Ind Univ Sch of Med Indianapolis IN 46202

QUEENER, STEPHEN WYATT, b Indianapolis, Ind, Jan 31, 43; m 67; c 2. MICROBIOLOGY. *Educ:* Wabash Col, BA, 65; Univ Ill, MS, 68, PhD(biochem), 70. *Prof Exp:* Fel, Univ Ill, 70; sr scientist, 70-74, res scientist, 74-80, RES ASSOC, ELI LILLY & CO, 81- *Concurrent Pos:* Guest lectr, Czechoslovak Acad Sci & Europ Fedn Microbiol Sci, 81. *Mem:* Am Soc Microbiol; Am Chem Soc; Soc Indust Microbiol; Sigma Xi; Mycol Soc. *Res:* Development and application of techniques for efficient mutation and selection, strain breeding, and recombinant DNA manipulations. *Mailing Add:* Eli Lilly & Co 307 E McCarty St Indianapolis IN 46205

QUE HEE, SHANE STEPHEN, b Sydney, Australia, Oct 11, 46. ANALYTICAL CHEMISTRY, ENVIRONMENTAL CHEMISTRY. *Educ:* Univ Queensland, BSc, 68, MSc, 71; Univ Sask, PhD(org chem), 76. *Prof Exp:* Res & teaching fel, McMaster Univ, 76-78; ASST PROF ENVIRON HEALTH, UNIV CINCINNATI, 78- *Mem:* Weed Sci Soc Am; AAAS; Am Chem Soc; Indust Hyg Asn Am; Am Col Toxicol. *Res:* Microanalytical techniques; chemiluminescence; bioluminescence; industrial hygiene; pesticide chemistry; lipid chemistry; photochemistry; analytical chemistry; ecology. *Mailing Add:* Dept of Environ Health Univ of Cincinnati Med Ctr Cincinnati OH 45267

QUELLE, FRED W, JR, lasers, electrooptics, see previous edition

QUENEAU, PAUL E(TIENNE), b Philadelphia, Pa, Mar 20, 11; m 39; c 2. EXTRACTIVE METALLURGY, MINERAL ENGINEERING. *Educ:* Columbia Univ, BA, 31, BSc, 32, EM, 33; Delft Univ Technol, DSc, 71. *Prof Exp:* Metall engr, Int Nickel Co, WVa, 34-37, res engr, Ont, 38-40, dir res, 41 & 46-48, metall engr, Exec Dept, NY, 49-57, vpres, 58-69, tech asst to pres, 60-66, asst to chmn & consult engr, 67-69; vis scientist, Delft Univ Technol, 70-71; PROF ENG, THAYER SCH ENG, DARTMOUTH COL, 71- *Concurrent Pos:* Geographer, Perry River Arctic Exped, 49; chmn adv comt arctic res, US Navy, 57; chmn int symposium extractive metall copper, nickel & cobalt, Am Inst Mining, Metall & Petrol Engrs, 60; mem, Columbia Eng Coun, 65-70; vis comt, Mass Inst Technol, 67-70, dir Eng Found, 66-76, chmn, 73-75; consult engr, 72-; vis prof, Inst Technol, Univ Minn, 74-75. *Honors & Awards:* Egleston Medal, 65; Douglas Gold Medal, 68; Extractive Metall Lect Award, Am Inst Mining, Metall & Petrol Engrs, 77; Inst Mining, Metall & Petrol Engrs Gold Medal, 80. *Mem:* Nat Acad Eng; fel Metall Soc (pres, 69); Nat Soc Prof Engrs; Can Inst Mining & Metall; Am Inst Mining, Metall & Petrol Engrs (vpres, 70). *Res:* Utilization of mineral resources; extractive metallurgy; plant design. *Mailing Add:* Thayer Sch of Eng Dartmouth Col Hanover NH 03755

QUENELLE, ALAN COURTLAND, JR, biochemistry, see previous edition

QUENTIN, GEORGE HEINZ, b Rome, NY, Jan 25, 34; m 60; c 5. CHEMICAL ENGINEERING. *Educ:* Rensselaer Polytech Univ, BChE, 55; Iowa State Univ, MS, 62, PhD(chem eng), 65. *Prof Exp:* Chem engr, Ind Ord Works, E I du Pont de Nemours & Co, Inc, 55-57, process engr, 57-58; technologist, US Indust Chem Div, Nat Distillers & Chem Corp, Ill, 58-60; sr engr cent eng dept, Monsanto Co, Mo, 65-66, eng specialist, 66-69; asst prof chem eng, Univ NMex, 69-73; assoc prof control eng, Univ Tex, 73-77; ENERGY RES PROJ MGR, CLEAN GASEOUS FUELS PROG, ENVIRON PROTECTION RES INST, 77- *Concurrent Pos:* Consult environ control, 81- *Mem:* Am Inst Chem Engrs; Am Chem Soc; Instrument Soc Am. *Res:* Coal gasification research and development for electric power generation; experimental pilot plant studies of process dynamics; control analysis of advanced power plant technology by computer simulation; air pollution control. *Mailing Add:* EPRI 3412 Hillview Ave Palo Alto CA 94303

QUERFELD, CHARLES WILLIAM, b Bloomington, Ill, Mar 29, 33; m 62; c 1. SOLAR PHYSICS. *Educ:* Harvard Univ, BA, 55; Clarkson Col Technol, MS, 69, PhD(physics), 70. *Prof Exp:* Field engr, Darin & Armstrong, 55-56; physicist, US Army Atmospheric Sci Lab, 56-66; res asst physics, Clarkson Col Technol, 66-69; SCIENTIST SOLAR PHYSICS, HIGH ALTITUDE OBSERV, NAT CTR ATMOSPHERIC RES, 70- *Concurrent Pos:* Consult, Atmospheric Sci Lab, White Sands, NMex, 72-73. *Honors & Awards:* Victor K LaMer Award, Am Chem Soc, 70. *Mem:* AAAS; Optical Soc Am; Am Phys Soc; Am Astron Soc. *Res:* Coronal magnetic fields. *Mailing Add:* 1305 Oak Court Boulder CO 80302

QUERRY, MARVIN RICHARD, b Butler, Mo, Nov 7, 35; m 57; c 3. PHYSICS. *Educ:* Univ Kansas City, BS(math) & BS(physics), 61; Kans State Univ, MS, 64, PhD(physics), 68. *Prof Exp:* Asst prof physics, Kans State Univ, 66-67, res assoc, 67-68; from asst prof to assoc prof, 68-75, PROF PHYSICS, UNIV MO-KANSAS CITY, 75- *Concurrent Pos:* Res grants & contracts, Univ Mo, US Dept Interior, US Air Force, US Army, Dept Com & NASA, 69-; lectr med, Univ Mo-Kansas City, 73-; pres, Sci Metrics Inc, 75- *Mem:* AAAS; fel Optical Soc Am; Am Phys Soc; Am Asn Physics Teachers. *Res:* Optical properties and optical constants of water, aqueous solutions and minerals. *Mailing Add:* Dept of Physics Univ of Mo Kansas City MO 64110

QUERTERMUS, CARL JOHN, JR, b Chicago, Ill, June 28, 43; div; c 2. ANIMAL BEHAVIOR, AQUATIC ECOLOGY. *Educ:* Ill State Univ, BS, 65, MS, 67; Mich State Univ, PhD(zool), 72. *Prof Exp:* Instr biol, Ill High Sch, 67-69; asst prof, 72-75, ASSOC PROF BIOL, W GA COL, 76- *Mem:* Animal Behav Soc; Am Soc Zoologists; Am Fisheries Soc. *Res:* Habitat selection and movement patterns of largemouth bass in reservoirs; distribution of fishes in Carroll County, Georgia; prior experience and fish habitat selection. *Mailing Add:* Dept of Biol WGa Col Carrollton GA 30118

QUESADA, ANTONIO F, b San Jose, Costa Rica, Feb 25, 25; nat US; m 54. APPLIED MATHEMATICS. *Educ:* Mass Inst Technol, SB, 47; Harvard Univ, MS, 58, PhD, 64. *Prof Exp:* Instr physics, Univ Costa Rica, 42-44; sr res mathematician, Baird Atomic, Inc, 49-68 & Dynarand, Inc, 68-69; MATHEMATICIAN, AIR FORCE GEOPHYS LAB, 70- *Concurrent Pos:* Consult, Govt Costa Rica, 54-55. *Mem:* Am Math Soc; Soc Indust & Appl Math; Math Asn Am. *Res:* Differential equations; noise theory; magnetodydrodynamics. *Mailing Add:* Box 111 Cambridge MA 02138

QUESENBERRY, CHARLES P, b Dugspur, Va, Apr 13, 31; m 53; c 4. STATISTICS. *Educ:* Va Polytech Inst, 57, MS, 58, PhD(statist), 60. *Prof Exp:* From asst prof to assoc prof math, Mont State Univ, 60-66; assoc prof, 66-69, PROF MATH, NC STATE UNIV, 69- *Concurrent Pos:* NASA grant, 64-66; NSF grant, 77-79. *Mem:* Biomet Soc; fel Am Statist Asn; Inst Math Statist. *Res:* Statistical inference, particularly nonparametric inference; nonparametric discrimination; goodness-of-fit, model discrimination and validity. *Mailing Add:* Dept of Exp Statist NC State Univ Raleigh NC 27650

QUESENBERRY, KENNETH HAYS, b Springfield, Tenn, Feb 28, 47; m 69; c 1. AGRONOMY, PLANT BREEDING. *Educ:* Western Ky Univ, BS, 69; Univ Ky, PhD(crop sci), 75. *Prof Exp:* D F Jones fel cytogenetics, Univ Ky, 72-75; asst prof, 75-80, PROF AGRON, UNIV FLA, 80- *Mem:* Am Soc Agron; Crop Sci Soc Am; Can Genetics Soc. *Res:* Breeding and cytogenetics of tropical forage grasses and legumes; selection of varieties producing greater yield, digestibility and animal performance; investigation of nitrogen fixing capacity of tropical grasses and legumes. *Mailing Add:* Dept of Agron 2183 McCarty Hall Univ of Fla Gainesville FL 32611

QUESNEL, DAVID JOHN, b Plattsburg, NY, Apr 5, 50; m 73. MATERIALS SCIENCE, MECHANICAL METALLURGY. *Educ:* State Univ NY, Stony Brook, BE, 72; Northwestern Univ, MS, 74, PhD(mat sci), 77. *Prof Exp:* ASST PROF MECH, AEROSPACE SCI & MATH SCI, RIVER CAMPUS, UNIV ROCHESTER, 77- *Concurrent Pos:* NSF res initiation grant, 78-79. *Mem:* Sigma Xi; Metall Soc. *Res:* Mechanical metallurgy with emphasis on fatigue of metals; cyclic response of metals to repetitive strain. *Mailing Add:* Dept Mech & Aerospace Sci Univ of Rochester River Campus Rochester NY 14627

QUEST, JOHN ANTHONY, pharmacology, neuropharmacology, see previous edition

QUESTAD, DAVID LEE, b Muskegon, Mich, Aug 22, 52. POLYMER SCIENCE. *Educ:* Pa State Univ, BS, 74; Rutgers Univ, MS, 78, PhD(mech & mat sci), 81. *Prof Exp:* Anal eng, Pratt & Whitney Aircraft, 74-75; asst, Rutgers Univ, 76-78, teaching asst statics & dynamics, 78-79; ASST PROF ENG SCI & MECH, PA STATE UNIV, 81- *Mem:* Am Phys Soc; Soc Plastics Engrs; Sigma Xi; NY Acad Sci. *Res:* Effects of hydrostatic pressure on physical and mechanical properties of polymers, specifically pressure, volume, temperature and dielectric measurements; large scale deformation and thermal aging of polymers. *Mailing Add:* Dept Eng Sci & Mech 227 Hammond Bldg University Park PA 16802

QUEVEDO, WALTER COLE, JR, b Brooklyn, NY, Jan 7, 30; m 55. ANIMAL GENETICS. *Educ:* St Francis Col, BS, 51; Marquette Univ, MS, 53; Brown Univ, PhD(biol), 56. *Prof Exp:* Asst, Marquette Univ, 51-53; teaching assoc, Brown Univ, 53-55; resident res assoc, Argonne Nat Lab, 56-58; sr cancer res scientist, Roswell Park Mem Inst, 58-61; from asst prof to assoc prof, 61-70, PROF BIOL, BROWN UNIV, 70- *Concurrent Pos:* Vis lectr dermat, Harvard Med Sch, 63- *Mem:* AAAS; Radiation Res Soc; Soc Develop Biol; Am Soc Cell Biologists; Soc Exp Biol & Med. *Res:* Mammalian genetics; radiation biology; physiological genetics of coat and skin coloration in mice; regulation of melanin formation in normal and neoplastic pigmented tissues. *Mailing Add:* Div of Biol & Med Brown Univ Providence RI 02912

QUIBELL, CHARLES FOX, b Fresno, Calif, Jan 29, 36; m 70; c 2. PLANT ANATOMY, PLANT SYSTEMATICS. *Educ:* Pomona Col, BA, 58; Univ Calif, Berkeley, PhD(bot), 72. *Prof Exp:* Asst prof, 70-73, assoc prof, 73-81, PROF BIOL, SONOMA STATE UNIV, 81- *Mem:* AAAS; Bot Soc Am; Am Soc Plant Taxonomists; Am Inst Biol Sci; Soc Econ Bot. *Res:* Systematic anatomy of woody saxifrages; comparative wood anatomy of dicotyledonous plants. *Mailing Add:* Dept of Biol Sonoma State Univ Rohnert Park CA 94928

QUICK, JACQUELIN DUNN, b Sidney, Ohio, Jan 24, 42; m 64; c 1. MEDICAL MICROBIOLOGY. *Educ:* Col Wooster, BA, 63; Univ Mo, Columbia, PhD(microbiol), 72. *Prof Exp:* Res asst neurol surg, Ohio State Univ Hosp, 63-64; res asst pediat immunol, Downstate Med Ctr, State Univ NY, 64-68; sr lab tech hemat, Dept Med, Univ Mo Med Ctr, 68-70; microbiologist bact, Alaska Med Labs, 73-74; asst prof, 74-80, ASSOC PROF MED TECHNOL, MT MARTY COL, 80-, HEAD, DIV HEALTH SCI, 78- *Concurrent Pos:* Clin asst prof, Sch Med, Univ SD, 75-; consult, Ctr Community Orgn & Area Develop, Augustana Col, 75- *Mem:* Sigma Xi; Am Soc Microbiol. *Mailing Add:* Dept of Med Technol Mt Marty Col 1100 W Fifth Yankton SD 57078

QUICK, JAMES S, b Devils Lake, NDak, Oct 20, 40; m 68; c 3. PLANT BREEDING, GENETICS. *Educ:* NDak State Univ, BA, 62; Purdue Univ, MS, 65, PhD(plant breeding, genetics), 66. *Prof Exp:* Asst geneticist, Rockefeller Found, 66-69; assoc prof durum wheat breeding, NDak State Univ, 69-76, prof, 76-81; PROF WHEAT BREEDING, COLO STATE UNIV, 81- *Mem:* Crop Sci Soc Am. *Res:* Development of new varieties of wheat, improved breeding methods and genetic, pathological, physiological and agronomic research. *Mailing Add:* Dept of Agron Colo State Univ Ft Collins CO 58102

QUICK, WILLIAM ANDREW, b Senlac, Sask, July 18, 25; m 53; c 3. BOTANY. *Educ:* Univ Sask, BA, 46, BEd, 51, MA, 60, PhD(plant physiol), 63. *Prof Exp:* Asst prof plant physiol, Univ Guelph, 63-67; ASSOC PROF BIOL, UNIV REGINA, 67- *Mem:* AAAS; Am Soc Plant Physiologists; Can Soc Plant Physiologists. *Res:* Nucleic acid Relationships; P-metabolism of high-protein potatoes. *Mailing Add:* Dept of Biol Univ of Regina Regina SK S4S 0A2 Can

QUIE, PAUL GERHARDT, b Dennison, Minn, Feb 3, 25; m 51; c 4. PEDIATRICS. *Educ:* St Olaf Col, BA, 50; Yale Univ, MD, 53; Am Bd Pediat, dipl. *Prof Exp:* Intern, Minneapolis Gen Hosp, 53-54; resident, Hosp, 54, chief resident, 57, from instr to prof pediat, 58-74, Am Legion Mem Heart res prof, 74, PROF PEDIAT & MICROBIOL, UNIV MINN, MINNEAPOLIS, 74-, CONSULT PHYSICIAN, INST CHILD DEVELOP NURSERY SCH, 60- *Concurrent Pos:* Res fels med, Hosp, Univ Minn, Minneapolis, 57-58; USPHS res fel, 60-61 & career develop award, 62-; John & Mary R Markle scholar med sci, 61-; attend physician, Minneapolis Gen Hosp, 59-; guest investr, Rockefeller Inst, 62-64; assoc mem comn streptococcal & staphylococcal dis, Armed Forces Epidemiol Bd, 65- *Mem:* AAAS; Am Fedn Clin Res; Am Soc Microbiol; NY Acad Sci. *Res:* Infectious diseases. *Mailing Add:* Dept of Pediat Univ of Minn Hosp Minneapolis MN 55455

QUIGG, CHRIS, b Bainbridge, Md, Dec 15, 44; m 67; c 2. HIGH ENERGY PHYSICS, THEORETICAL PHYSICS. *Educ:* Yale Univ, BS, 66; Univ Calif, Berkeley, PhD(physics), 70. *Prof Exp:* Res assoc physics, State Univ NY, Stony Brook, 70-71, from asst prof to assoc prof, 71-74; PHYSICIST, FERMI NAT ACCELERATOR LAB, 74-, HEAD THEORET PHYSICS DEPT, 77- *Concurrent Pos:* Sloan Found fel, 74-78; vis scholar, Enrico Fermi Inst, Univ Chicago, 74-78; mem prog adv comt, Stanford Linear Accelerator Ctr, 75-77; mem high energy adv comt, Brookhaven Nat Lab, 78-80 & Lawrence Berkley Lab, 78-81; prof lectr, Univ Chicago, 78-; div assoc ed, Particles & Fields, Phys Review Lett & assoc ed, Reviews Mod Physics, 81-; vis prof, Ecole Normale Superieure, Paris, 81-82. *Mem:* Am Phys Soc; AAAS. *Res:* Phenomenology of elementary particles. *Mailing Add:* Fermi Nat Accelerator Lab PO Box 500 Batavia IL 60510

QUIGG, RICHARD J, b Bethlehem, Pa, Nov 12, 30; m 56; c 3. PHYSICAL METALLURGY. *Educ:* Va Polytech Inst, BS, 52; Lehigh Univ, MS, 54; Case Inst Technol, PhD(phys metall), 59; Baldwin-Wallace Col, JD, 66. *Prof Exp:* Metallurgist, E I du Pont de Nemours & Co, Inc, 52-53; res asst, Lehigh Univ, 53-54; res metallurgist, Rem-Cru Titanium, Inc, 54-56; res asst, Case Inst Technol, 56-59; res metallurgist, TRW Inc, 59-63, res supvr, 63-64, wrought metall mgr, Metals Div, 64-65, res sect mgr, 65-67, mgr mat & processes, 67-68, mgr res & develop, Metals Div, 68-70; exec vpres, Jetshapes, Inc, 70-73, pres, 73-78; sr staff engr, Pratt & Whitney Aircraft, 78-80; VPRES SUPERALLOYS, CANNON-MUSKEGON CORP, 80- *Mem:* Am Inst Mining, Metall & Petrol Engrs; Am Soc Metals; Am Soc Testing & Mat. *Res:* Titanium alloy development; hydrogen embrittlement; superalloy development; phase changes in nickel-base superalloys; law; casting and solidification. *Mailing Add:* Cannon-Muskegon Corp PO Box 506 Muskegon MI 49443

QUIGLEY, FRANK DOUGLAS, b Maysville, Ky, June 5, 28. MATHEMATICS. *Educ:* Harvard Univ, AB, 49; Univ Chicago, PhD(math), 53. *Prof Exp:* From instr to asst prof, Yale Univ, 53-59; assoc prof, 59-64, PROF MATH, TULANE UNIV, 64- *Mem:* Am Math Soc; Math Asn Am. *Res:* Algebraic geometry; commutative Banach algebra; several complex variables. *Mailing Add:* Dept of Math Tulane Univ New Orleans LA 70118

QUIGLEY, GARY JOSEPH, b Syracuse, NY, Aug 1, 42; div. MOLECULAR BIOPHYSICS. *Educ:* State Univ NY Col Environ Sci & Forestry, BS, 64, PhD(chem), 69. *Prof Exp:* FEL & RES ASSOC MOLECULAR BIOPHYS, MASS INST TECHNOL, 69- *Mem:* Am Crystallog Asn; Am Inst Physics. *Res:* Determination of crystal structures of nucleic acids including transfer-RNA, Z-DNA and drug DNA complexes; ion, water and drug interactions with nucleic acids; molecular mechanics to understand nucleic acid structure and structure-function relationships; development of X-ray area detector for X-ray crystallographic data collection for macromolecules. *Mailing Add:* 141 Western Ave Cambridge MA 02139

QUIGLEY, GERARD PAUL, b Boston, Mass, Jan 3, 42; m 66; c 2. LASER CHEMISTRY, LASER PHYSICS. *Educ:* Northeastern Univ, BSEE, 64, MS, 66; Polytech Inst Brooklyn, MS, 70; Cornell Univ, PhD(appl physics), 74. *Prof Exp:* ASST GROUP LEADER LASER PHOTOCHEMISTRY, LOS ALAMOS SCI LAB, 75- *Concurrent Pos:* US Steel fel, Cornell Univ, 74. *Mem:* Am Phys Soc; AAAS; Am Chem Soc. *Res:* Laser photochemistry and isotope separation; physics and kinetics of laser systems; optoacoustic spectroscopy of laser excited systems. *Mailing Add:* Los Alamos Sci Lab Group AP-4/MS-567 Los Alamos NM 87545

QUIGLEY, HENRY CROSKEY, b Bellefonte, Pa, June 15, 28; m 64; c 2. CHEMICAL & NUCLEAR ENGINEERING. *Educ:* Mass Inst Technol, BS, 50. *Prof Exp:* Instrument engr, Eng Dept, Eng Serv Div, 50, field engr, 50-55, reactor engr, Explosives Dept, Atomic Energy Div, 58-63, test engr, Eng Dept, Eng Test Ctr, 63-66, res engr, Electrochem Dept, Res Div, 66-71, bus analyst, Photo Prod Dept, 72-77, bus anal supvr, 77-80, FINANCIAL ANAL MGR, PHOTO PROF DEPT, E I DU PONT DE NEMOURS & CO, INC, 80- *Concurrent Pos:* Mem high temperature fuels comt, AEC, 58-60, mem uranium dioxide exchange sessions, AEC US-Can & US-UK, 58-63; mem subcomt uranium dioxide standards, US Am Standards Inst, 59-63. *Mem:* Am Inst Chem Engrs. *Res:* Chemical process development; instrumentation and automatic control; nuclear fuel development and irradiation; new product development; process scale-up and evaluation; venture planning and business analysis. *Mailing Add:* E I du Pont de Nemours & Co Inc 10th & Market Sts Wilmington DE 19898

QUIGLEY, HERBERT JOSEPH, JR, b Philadelphia, Pa, Mar 6, 37; m 64; c 1. PATHOLOGY, CHEMISTRY. *Educ:* Franklin & Marshall Col, BS, 58; Univ Pa, MD, 62; Am Bd Path, dipl, 68. *Prof Exp:* Resident path, Presby Hosp, New York, 62-66; chief path serv, DePoo Hosp, Key West, Fla, 66-68; from asst prof to assoc prof, 68-72, PROF PATH, CREIGHTON UNIV, 72-; CHIEF PATH SERV, VET ADMIN HOSP, 68- *Concurrent Pos:* NIH acad path career develop trainee, Col Physicians & Surgeons, Columbia Univ, 62-66; chief path serv, Monroe County Gen Hosp & US Naval Hosp, Key West, 66-68; porpoise pathologist & res consult, Off Naval Res Cetacean Lab, Key West, 66-68. *Honors & Awards:* Borden Prize for Med Res, Borden Corp, 62. *Mem:* Fel Col Am Path; fel Am Inst Chem; Am Chem Soc; fel Am Soc Clin Path. *Res:* Blood coagulation; disseminated intravascular coagulation; fibrinolysis; instrumental analytical chemistry. *Mailing Add:* Path Serv Vet Admin Hosp 4101 Woolworth Ave Omaha NE 68105

QUIGLEY, JAMES P, b New York, NY, Mar 18, 42; m 67; c 2. TUMOR CELL BIOLOGY, ENZYMOLOGY. *Educ:* Manhattan Col, New York, BS, 65; Johns Hopkins Univ, PhD(physiol chem), 69. *Prof Exp:* Fel chem biol, Rockefeller Univ, 70-73, asst prof, 73-74; asst prof, 74-77, ASSOC PROF MICROBIOL & IMMUNOL, DOWNSTATE MED CTR, STATE UNIV NY, 78- *Concurrent Pos:* Fel, Leukemia Soc Am, 70-72; scholar, Sinsheimer Found Scholar, 77; vis prof, Sch Path, Oxford Univ, 80-81. *Mem:* Am Asn Cancer Res; Am Soc Cell Biol; Harvey Soc; NY Acad Sci. *Res:* Biochemical examination of normal and malignant cells; role of tumor viruses in malignant transformation; mechanism of tumor cell invasion and metastasis. *Mailing Add:* Downstate Med Ctr Box 44 State Univ NY 450 Clarkson Ave Brooklyn NY 11203

QUIGLEY, ROBERT JAMES, b Cord, Ark, Feb 18, 40; div. VARIABLE STARS. *Educ:* Calif Inst Technol, BS, 61, MS, 62; Univ Calif, Riverside, MA, 64, PhD(physics), 68. *Prof Exp:* Res asst solid state physics, Univ Calif, Riverside, 65-68; asst prof physics, Ill Inst Technol, 68-70; asst prof, 70-74, ASSOC PROF PHYSICS, WESTERN WASH UNIV, 74- *Concurrent Pos:* Vis lectr, Inst Physics, Univ Frankfurt, 69-70; vis scholar astron, Univ Tex & McDonald Observ, 76-77; vis scientist, Sacramento Peak Observ, 80-81. *Mem:* Am Astron Soc; Astron Soc Pac. *Res:* Photoelectric photometry of cataclysmic variable stars. *Mailing Add:* Dept of Physics & Astron Western Wash Univ Bellingham WA 98225

QUIGLEY, ROBERT MURVIN, b Toronto, Ont, Jan 22, 34; m 57; c 3. SOIL MECHANICS, ENGINEERING GEOLOGY. *Educ:* Univ Toronto, BASc, 55, MASc, 56; Mass Inst Technol, PhD(soil mech), 61. *Prof Exp:* From jr to sr engr, Geocon Ltd, Ont & Que, 56-63; from asst prof to assoc prof soil mech, 63-70, PROF SOIL MECH, UNIV WESTERN ONT, 70- *Concurrent Pos:* Consult, Conch Methane Serv, Ltd, Eng, 61-63 & Golder & Assocs Ltd, Can, 63-66; Transcanada lectr, Nat Res Coun, 69; vis sr res fel, Univ Southampton, 71-72; assoc ed, Can Geotech J, 74-80; pres, R M Quigley, Inc, 74-; mem, Natural Sci & Eng Res Coun, Earth Sci Grant Selection Comn, 76-79, chmn, 78-79; ed, Can Geotech J, 80-; vis scientist, Geotech Res Inst, McGill Univ. *Mem:* Can Geotech Soc; Geol Asn Can; Eng Inst Can; Clay Minerals Soc. *Res:* Application of mineralogy, geochemistry to problems in soil and rock mechanics; bacterial oxidation and heave of black shale; coastal erosion and instability; pollutant migration through clays. *Mailing Add:* Fac Eng Univ Western Ont London ON N6A 5B9 Can

QUILL, LAURENCE LARKIN, b Carson City, Nev, Feb 24, 01; m; c 2. INORGANIC CHEMISTRY. *Educ:* Univ Nev, BS, 24, MS, 25; Univ Ill, PhD(inorg chem), 28. *Prof Exp:* High sch teacher, Nev, 24-25; asst chem, Univ Ill, 25-27, res fel, 28-29, instr, 29-30, assoc, 30-31; Nat Res Coun fel, Univ Gottingen, 31-32; assoc chem, Univ Ill, 32-35; from asst prof to prof chem, Ohio State Univ, 35-42; prof & head dept, Univ Ky, 42-45; prof chem, 45-66, head dept, 45-61, dir, Div Math & Phys Sci, 59-62, dir, Inst Water Res, 61-66, EMER PROF CHEM & EMER DIR, INST WATER RES, MICH STATE UNIV, 69- *Concurrent Pos:* Sect ed, Chem Abstr, 39-; chemist, Metall Proj, Univ Chicago, 44-46; chmn water qual control comt, Southeastern Ariz Govts Orgn, 75-78; secy-treas, Coronado Res Conserv & Develop Proj, 75-; secy-treas, Pollution Control Corp County Cochise, 75- *Mem:* AAAS; Am Chem Soc. *Res:* Chemistry of rare earth elements and their compounds; scandium and other less common metals; solubility of rare earth salts; artificial radioactivity of scandium and the rare earths; thermal analysis of rare earth salt mixtures; chelate compounds of the rare earths; borohydride chemistry; corrosion of copper and its alloys. *Mailing Add:* Box 205 Pearce AZ 85625

QUILLEN, DANIEL G, b June 27, 40. MATHEMATICS. *Educ:* Harvard Univ, PhD(math), 69. *Prof Exp:* NORBERT WIENER PROF MATH, MASS INST TECHNOL, 73- *Honors & Awards:* Field Medal, Int Congress Mathematicians, 78. *Mem:* Nat Acad Sci; Am Math Soc. *Mailing Add:* Dept of Math Mass Inst Technol Cambridge MA 02139

QUILLIGAN, JAMES JOSEPH, JR, b Philadelphia, Pa, Oct 18, 12; m 41; c 4. VIROLOGY. *Educ:* Ohio State Univ, BA, 36; Univ Cincinnati, MD, 40. *Prof Exp:* Instr pediat & res assoc epidemiol, Sch Pub Health, Univ Mich, 46-49, asst prof pediat, Univ & asst prof epidemiol, Sch Pub Health, 50; assoc prof pediat, Univ Tex Southwestern Med Sch Dallas, 51-54; assoc prof, 54-59, RES PROF PEDIAT, SCH MED, LOMA LINDA UNIV, 59-, DIR VIRUS LAB, 54- *Concurrent Pos:* Dir Labs, Children's Med Ctr, Dallas, 51-54; res career investr, Nat Inst Allergy & Infectious Dis, 63- *Mem:* Am Acad Microbiol; Soc Pediat Res; Am Acad Pediat; Am Asn Immunol; Infectious Dis Soc Am. *Res:* Influenza; herpes; hepatitis viruses; tumor viruses. *Mailing Add:* Virus Lab Dept of Pediat Loma Linda Univ Med Ctr Loma Linda CA 92354

QUILLIN, CHARLES ROBERT, b Crawfordsville, Ind, Jan 14, 38. CYTOLOGY. *Educ:* Wabash Col, AB, 60; Brown Univ, ScM, 63, PhD(bot), 66. *Prof Exp:* Sr asst, Wabash Col, 60; asst bot, Brown Univ, 60-62, asst biol, 62-65; from instr to asst prof, Colby Col, 65-70, assoc dean students, 67-70; fel, Off Inst Res, Mich State Univ, 70-71; dean students, Marshall Univ, 72-73, asst to vpres student affairs, 73-75; asst prof, 75-78, ASSOC PROF ACAD AFFAIRS, POINT PARK COL, 78-, DEAN STUDENTS, 75-, EXEC ASST VPRES ADMIN, 80- *Concurrent Pos:* NSF vis scientist's prog lectr, 66- *Mem:* Sigma Xi. *Res:* Study of histone as related to deoxyribose nucleic acid, acid cycle in a cell. *Mailing Add:* Off of Dean of Students Point Park Col Pittsburgh PA 15222

QUIMBY, DANIEL JOSEPH, physical organic chemistry, plant chemistry, see previous edition

QUIMBY, FREEMAN HENRY, b Battle Creek, Mich, June 11, 15; m 48; c 3. PHYSIOLOGY. *Educ:* Andrews Univ, BA, 38; Northwestern Univ, MS, 41; Univ Md, PhD(zool), 47. *Prof Exp:* Prof biol & head dept, Columbia Union Col, 41-47; chief investr, US Navy proj, Univ Md, 47-48; head physiol br, Off Naval Res, DC, 48-56, chief scientist, Calif, 56-59; chief res anal, Army Res Off, 59-60; asst dir life sci grants & contracts, Off Life Sci, NASA, 60-62, chief exobiol prog, Off Space Sci & Applns, 62-66; specialist, life sci, Sci Policy Res Div, Cong Res Serv, Lib Cong, 66-76; CONSULT, TRACOR JITCO, 76- *Mem:* AAAS; Am Physiol Soc. *Res:* Nutrition; aviation physiology; microbiology; endocrinology; science and public policy. *Mailing Add:* TRACOR JITCO 1776 E Jefferson St Rockville MD 20852

QUIMPO, RAFAEL GONZALES, b Aklan, Philippines, Mar 23, 39; m 63; c 3. CIVIL ENGINEERING, HYDROLOGY. *Educ:* Feati Univ, Philippines, BS, 59; Seato Grad Sch Eng, Bangkok, ME, 62; Colo State Univ, PhD(civil eng), 66. *Prof Exp:* Civil engr, Am-Asia Eng Assocs, 62-63; res asst, Colo State Univ, 63-66; from asst prof to assoc prof civil eng, 66-75, PROF CIVIL ENG, UNIV PITTSBURGH, 75- *Concurrent Pos:* Res grants, Off Water Resources, US Dept Interior, Univ Pittsburgh, 67-70 & NSF, 70-72, 73-76 & 79-80; consult, Mobay Chem Co, 72; vis prof, Fed Univ Rio de Janeiro, Brazil, 72-73; vis scientist, Philippine Nat Sci Develop Bd, 75-76; NSF int travel grant, 76 & 78; consult, US Army Corps Engrs, 79- *Mem:* AAAS; Am Geophys Union; Am Soc Civil Engrs; Am Soc Eng Educ; Int Asn Hydraul Res. *Res:* Water resources development; applied statistics; stochastic processes; stochastic hydrology; non-conventional energy sources. *Mailing Add:* 940 Benedum Hall Univ of Pittsburgh Pittsburgh PA 15261

QUIN, LOUIS DUBOSE, b Charleston, SC, Mar 5, 28; m 52; c 3. ORGANIC CHEMISTRY. *Educ:* The Citadel, BS, 47; Univ NC, MA, 49, PhD(org chem), 52. *Prof Exp:* Res chemist, Am Cyanamid Co, 49-50; res proj leader, Westvaco Chem Div, Food Mach & Chem Corp, 52-54 & 56; from res assoc to assoc prof, 56-67, chmn dept, 70-76, prof chem, 67-81, JAMES B DUKE PROF CHEM, DUKE UNIV, 81- *Concurrent Pos:* Consult, FMC Corp, 60-; Ford Found fel, Woods Hole Oceanog Inst, 63-64. *Mem:* AAAS; Am Chem Soc; Royal Soc Chem. *Res:* Organo phosphorus and heterocyclic compounds; synthesis, stereochemistry, and spectral properties of cyclic phosphorus compounds; spectra-structure correlations of organophosphorus compounds. *Mailing Add:* Gross Chem Lab Duke Univ Durham NC 27706

QUINAN, JAMES ROGER, b Watervliet, NY, June 27, 21; m 50; c 1. INDUSTRIAL CHEMISTRY. *Educ:* State Univ NY Albany, AB, 42, AM, 48; Rensselaer Polytech Inst, PhD(infrared & Raman spectroscopy), 54. *Prof Exp:* Chemist & foreman, Adirondack Foundries & Steel, 42-45; res assoc biochem, Sterling-Winthrop Res Inst, 48-52; sr chemist, Behr-Manning Div, Norton Co, 54-57, group leader abrasive grain & electrostatics, 57-70, sr res prof, Coated Abrasive Div, 70-75; independent consult, 75-77; tech dir, Albany Mach Div, 77-79, SR PROJ ENG, ENG SYSTS DIV, ALBANY INT CORP, 79- *Mem:* Am Chem Soc; NY Acad Sci. *Res:* Chemical and physical properties of abrasives as related to coated abrasive products; electrostatics as applied to coated abrasives; metallurgical and high temperature materials research. *Mailing Add:* 57 Upper Loudon Rd Loudonville NY 12211

QUINLAN, DENNIS CHARLES, b Detroit, Mich, Jan 29, 43; m 69; c 1. CELL BIOLOGY, BIOCHEMISTRY. *Educ:* Wayne State Univ, BS, 65, MS, 66; Univ Rochester, PhD(microbiol), 73. *Prof Exp:* Sr res assoc cell biol, Worcester Found Exp Biol, 73-76; asst prof, 76-80, ASSOC PROF BIOL, WVA UNIV, 80- *Concurrent Pos:* Prin investr, Am Cancer Soc grant, 77-79 & NIH grant, WVa Univ, 78-81. *Mem:* Am Soc Biol Chemists; Am Soc Zoologists; Develop Biol Soc; Int Soc Differentiation; AAAS. *Res:* Cell cycle regulation in cultured, mammalian cells; membrane dynamics of normal and tumor cells. *Mailing Add:* Dept of Biol WVa Univ Morgantown WV 26506

QUINLAN, JOHN EDWARD, b Milwaukee, Wis, Aug 6, 30; m 57; c 3. PHYSICAL CHEMISTRY. *Educ:* Marquette Univ, BS, 52; Univ Ark, MS, 55; Univ Wis, PhD(chem), 59. *Prof Exp:* From instr to assoc prof, 58-69, dean admis & financial aid, 69-81, ASSOC PROF CHEM, POMONA COL, 69- *Concurrent Pos:* NSF fac fel, 64-65. *Mem:* AAAS. *Res:* Chemical kinetics and mechanisms of gas phase reactions. *Mailing Add:* Sumner Hall Pomona Col Claremont CA 91711

QUINLAN, KENNETH PAUL, b Somerville, Mass, Jan 13, 28; m 64; c 4. INORGANIC CHEMISTRY. *Educ:* Boston Univ, BA, 51; Tufts Univ, MS, 52; Univ Notre Dame, PhD(inorg chem), 59; Northeastern Univ, MS, 81. *Prof Exp:* Res chemist, Corps Engrs, US Army, 52-53, Am Cyanamid Co, 53-54 & Nat Lead Co, Inc, 54-56; PHYS CHEMIST, AIR FORCE CAMBRIDGE RES LABS, 60- *Mem:* AAAS; Am Chem Soc; Electrochem Soc. *Res:* Photosynthesis; solar energy. *Mailing Add:* AF Cambridge Res Labs Hanscom Field Bedford MA 01731

QUINLIVAN, WILLIAM LESLIE G, b Waunfawr, Wales, Dec 20, 21; US citizen; m 50; c 3. OBSTETRICS & GYNECOLOGY. *Educ:* Univ London, MB, BS, 46, MD, 65; FRCS, 65; FRCOG, 66. *Prof Exp:* Asst prof obstet & gynec, Univ Pittsburgh, 62-65; assoc prof, 65-74, PROF OBSTET & GYNEC, UNIV CALIF, IRVINE, 74- *Concurrent Pos:* NIH res fel obstet & gynec, Cancer Res Inst, Univ Calif, San Francisco, 60-62; Health, Res & Serv Found grants, 62-65; NIH res grants, 63-72. *Mem:* Am Physiol Soc; Am Col Obstet & Gynec; Am Fertil Soc. *Res:* Transfer of antibodies between mother and fetus; analysis of proteins and antigens in human seminal plasma; immunological cause of infertility in the human female. *Mailing Add:* Obstet & Gynec Dept Univ of Calif Irvine Orange CA 92668

QUINN, ALFRED O, b Syracuse, NY, Apr 2, 15; m 37; c 4. PHOTOGRAMMETRY. *Educ:* Syracuse Univ, BSCE, 36; Chattanooga Col Law, LLB, 40. *Prof Exp:* Civil engr, Tenn Valley Authority, 36-44; from asst prof to assoc prof photogram, Syracuse Univ, 46-50; chief engr, AeroServ Corp, Pa, 50-65; PRES, QUINN & ASSOCS, 65- *Concurrent Pos:* Consult. *Mem:* Hon mem Am Soc Photogram (vpres, 52, pres, 53); fel Am Soc Civil Engrs; Am Cong Surv & Mapping; Nat Soc Prof Engrs; Sigma Xi. *Res:* Elements of photogrammetry; extension of control; scale checking; sample computations for spatial resection and space orientation. *Mailing Add:* Quinn & Assocs 460 Caredean Dr Horsham PA 19044

QUINN, B(AYARD) E(LMER), b Philadelphia, Pa, May 10, 15; m 45; c 2. MECHANICAL & DESIGN ENGINEERING. *Educ:* Drexel Inst, BS, 37; Cornell Univ, MS, 42, PhD(mech design), 45. *Prof Exp:* Eng draftsman & designer, Radio Corp Am, 35-37; engr, Gen Elec Co, NY, 37-42; asst prof mech, Cornell Univ, 40-46; assoc prof mach dynamics, 46-52, PROF MACH DYNAMICS, PURDUE UNIV, WEST LAFAYETTE, 52- *Concurrent Pos:* Consult, Combination Pump Valve Co, Philadelphia, 44 & 46, Chicago Pneumatic Tool Co, 45, road test vehicle response studies, Am Asn State Hwy Off, 57-59, Boeing Airplane Co, 59, Lawrence Radiation Lab, Univ Calif, 63- & Hall & Myers, 75- *Mem:* Am Soc Mech Engrs; Am Soc Eng Educ. *Res:* Design and analysis of systems having specified dynamic characteristics; vehicle dynamics; machine vibration problems. *Mailing Add:* Sch of Mech Eng Purdue Univ West Lafayette IN 47907

QUINN, BARRY GEORGE, b Rochelle Park, NJ, Dec 2, 34. AQUATIC BIOLOGY. *Educ:* Univ Utah, BS, 57, MA, 58; Univ Colo, PhD(biol), 62. *Prof Exp:* From asst prof to assoc prof, 62-72, PROF BIOL, WESTMINSTER COL, UTAH, 72-, HEAD DEPT, 63- *Concurrent Pos:* NIH fel, Marine Lab, Univ Miami, 63-66; chmn, Div Natural Sci & Math, Westminster Col, 66-71 & 74-77; mem, Eval Panel, NSF Undergrad Instr Sci Equip Prog, 65 & Steering Comt, Utah Conf Higher Educ, 72-74; partic, NSF Summer Inst Comp Anat, Univ Wash, 68. *Mem:* AAAS; Ecol Soc Am; Am Soc Limnol & Oceanog; Sigma Xi. *Res:* Comparative limnology of mountain lakes and streams; limnology of Great Salt Lake; ecology of coral reefs; behavior of marine invertebrates. *Mailing Add:* Dept of Biol Westminster Col Salt Lake City UT 84105

QUINN, CAROLINE ELISABETH, biochemistry, see previous edition

QUINN, CLAYTON BYERLEY, b Los Angeles, Calif, July 22, 43; m 68; c 2. ORGANIC POLYMER CHEMISTRY. *Educ:* Univ Calif, Berkeley, BS, 69; Univ Mich, Ann Arbor, PhD(org chem), 73. *Prof Exp:* Res chemist org & polymer chem, Res & Develop Ctr, NY, 73-77, MEM STAFF, PLASTICS DIV, GEN ELEC CO, IND, 77- *Mem:* Am Chem Soc; The Chem Soc. *Res:* Synthesis of interesting monomers for the preparation of high temperature polymers and the study of flame retardant chemistry. *Mailing Add:* Gen Elec Plastics Div Hwy 69 S Mt Vernon IN 47620

QUINN, COSMAS EDWARD, b Baltimore, Md, Apr 5, 26. BIOLOGY. *Educ:* Manhattan Col, BA, 51; Fordham Univ, MS, 57, PhD(biol), 62. *Prof Exp:* Teacher, Christian Bros Acad, NY, 50-54, St Peter's High Sch, 54-58 & Manhattan Col High Sch, 58-59; from instr to asst prof, 59-68, ASSOC PROF BIOL, MANHATTAN COL, 68- *Mem:* AAAS; Am Soc Zoologists; Sigma Xi. *Res:* Genetics and physiology. *Mailing Add:* Dept of Biol Manhattan Col Bronx NY 10471

QUINN, DAVID LEE, b Steubenville, Ohio, Nov 28, 38; m 59; c 3. NEUROENDOCRINOLOGY, REPRODUCTIVE PHYSIOLOGY. *Educ:* Washington & Jefferson Col, BA, 60; Purdue Univ, MS, 62, PhD(brain & ovulation), 64. *Prof Exp:* NIH fel neuroendocrinol, Sch Med, Duke Univ, 64-66; assoc prof, 66-77, PROF BIOL, MUSKINGUM COL, 77- *Mem:* AAAS; Sigma Xi; Endocrine Soc. *Res:* Comparative analysis of brain mechanisms controlling ovulation and prolactin secretion. *Mailing Add:* Dept of Biol Muskingum Col New Cord OH 43762

QUINN, DENNIS WAYNE, b West Grove, Pa, Apr 20, 47; m 67; c 2. APPLIED MATHEMATICS. *Educ:* Univ Del, BA, 69, MS, 71, PhD(math), 73. *Prof Exp:* Mathematician/programmer, E I du Pont de Nemours, 69-70; from res assoc to appl mathematician, Aerospace Res Lab, 74-75; appl mathematician res, Flight Dynamics Lab, 75-80, MEM STAFF, MATH DEPT, AIR FORCE INST TECHNOL, WRIGHT-PATTERSON AFB, 80- *Concurrent Pos:* Nat Res Coun resident res assoc, Nat Acad Sci, 73-74. *Mem:* Soc Indust Appl Math; Am Math Soc. *Res:* Analysis of the behavior of solutions of singular, elliptic, partial differential equations; numerical solution of partial differential equations, particularly those arising in duct acoustics and in transonic flow. *Mailing Add:* 333 Orchard Dr Dayton OH 45419

QUINN, EDWIN JOHN, b Geneva, Ill, July 20, 27; m 64; c 3. ORGANIC CHEMISTRY, POLYMER CHEMISTRY. *Educ:* St Procopius Col, BSc, 51; Univ Ill, Urbana, MSc, 55; State Univ NY Col Forestry, Syracuse, PhD(org polymer chem), 62. *Prof Exp:* Res asst, US Govt Synthetic Rubber Prog, Univ Ill, Urbana, 53-55; res chemist, Blockson Chem Co div, Olin Mathieson Chem Corp, 55-57 & Naugatuck Chem Div, US Rubber Co, 60-64; RES CHEMIST, ARMSTRONG CORK CO, 64- *Mem:* Am Chem Soc. *Res:* Synthetic polymer chemistry; surfactants; carbohydrates and synthetic polyols; photochemistry; inorganic polymers and polyphosphazenes; polymer flammability and smoke evolution. *Mailing Add:* 1730 Santa Barbara Dr Lancaster PA 17601

QUINN, FRANK HUGH, b Detroit, Mich, Nov 22, 37; m 60; c 3. HYDROLOGY, WATER RESOURCES. *Educ:* Wayne State Univ, BS, 60, MS, 66; Univ Mich, PhD(civil eng), 71. *Prof Exp:* Hydraulic engr, Los Angeles District, US Army Corps Engrs, 60-62, hydraulic engr, Lake Survey District, 62-66, chief, Special Studies Sect, 66-69; phys scientist, Lake Survey Ctr, 69-71, chief, Water Quantity Br, 71-74, HEAD, LAKE HYDROL GROUP, GREAT LAKES ENVIRON RES LAB, NAT OCEANOG & ATMOSPHERIC ADMIN, 74- *Concurrent Pos:* Consult, World Meteorol Orgn, 75-; mem, Int Great Lakes Levels & Flows Adv Bd, 80-, Int Great Lake Info Network Bd, 80- *Mem:* Am Soc Civil Engrs; Int Asn Great Lakes Res; Am Geophys Union; Am Meteorol Soc; AAAS. *Res:* Hydrologic, hydraulic, climatologic and ice research on the Great Lakes; development of mathematical models for simulation, forecasting and water resource applications. *Mailing Add:* 2300 Washtenaw Ave Ann Arbor MI 48104

QUINN, FRANK RUSSELL, b Washington, DC. MEDICINAL CHEMISTRY, INFORMATION SCIENCE. *Educ:* Cath Univ Am, AB, 50; Adelphi Univ, MS, 61; Am Univ, PhD(chem), 75. *Prof Exp:* Res textile chemist, Harris Res Labs, Gillette Corp, 55-58; res asst polymer chem,

Adelphi Univ, 58-60; instr chem, Nassau Col, 60-63; chemist, US Food & Drug Admin, 63-66; asst ed, Chem Abstr Serv, Am Chem Soc, 67; RES CHEMIST MED CHEM, NAT CANCER INST, 68- *Mem:* Am Chem Soc; Am Soc Info Sci; Asn Comput Mach. *Res:* Linear free energy relationships; quantitative structure activity relationships in the design of anticancer agents; computer science; information theory and the design of scientific information systems. *Mailing Add:* Info Tech Br Nat Cancer Inst Blair Bldg Rm 424 Bethesda MD 20205

QUINN, GALEN WARREN, b Tama, SDak, Jan 28, 22; m 36; c 7. ORTHODONTICS. *Educ:* Creighton Univ, DDS, 52; Univ Tenn, MS, 55; Am Bd Orthod, dipl, 69. *Prof Exp:* Teacher rural sch, 40-41; dep supply officer, Vet Admin, 45-47; pvt pract, 52-54; head dept pedodontics, Univ Tenn, 55-58; assoc prof, 58-65, PROF ORTHOD, MED CTR, DUKE UNIV, 65- *Concurrent Pos:* Dean, Sch Dent, Creighton Univ, 61-62. *Mem:* Am Soc Dent for Children; Am Dent Asn; assoc Am Asn Orthod. *Res:* Growth and development of the face and jaw; dental caries; cleft palate rehabilitation and dental care for the handicapped. *Mailing Add:* Div Orthod Box 3806 Duke Univ Med Ctr Durham NC 27710

QUINN, GEORGE F(RANCIS), b Lawrence, Mass, July 29, 20; m 42; c 10. CHEMICAL ENGINEERING. *Educ:* Mass Inst Technol, BS, 41; Columbia Univ, MS, 48. *Prof Exp:* Instr chem eng & dir student res, Columbia Univ, 46-48; indust & prod planning engr, Prod Div, Atomic Energy Comn, Washington, DC, 48-52, chief reactor prod br, 52-54, from asst dir opers to dir, 54-61, asst gen mgr plans & prod, 61-74; CONSULT, 74- *Mem:* Am Inst Chem Engrs. *Res:* Application of chemical engineering principles to atomic energy. *Mailing Add:* PO Box 279 Grantham NH 03753

QUINN, GERTRUDE PATRICIA, b Bronxville, NY, Feb 6, 21. BIOCHEMICAL PHARMACOLOGY. *Educ:* Fordham Univ, BS, 43; Univ Rochester, MS, 48; George Washington Univ, PhD(pharmacol), 56. *Prof Exp:* Asst, Cath Dent, NY Univ, 43-45, 48-49; res pharmacologist, Goldwater Mem Hosp, 49-52 & Lab Chem Pharmacol, Nat Heart Inst, 53-54; instr pharmacol, George Washington Univ, 54-55; res pharmacologist, Lab Chem Pharmacol, Nat Heart Inst, 55-59; RES PHARMACOLOGIST, RES LABS, CIBA-GEIGY CORP, 59- *Mem:* Am Soc Pharmacol & Exp Therapeut. *Res:* Physiological distribution and metabolism of drugs and their mechanism of action. *Mailing Add:* Biochem Dept Res Labs Ciba-Geigy Corp Summit NJ 07901

QUINN, HELEN RHODA, b Melbourne, Australia, May 19, 43; US citizen; m 66; c 2. PHYSICS. *Educ:* Stanford Univ, BS, 63, MS, 64, PhD(physics), 67. *Prof Exp:* Res assoc physics, Stanford Linear Accelerator Ctr, 67-68; guest scientist, Deutsches Elektronen Synchrotron, Hamburg, Ger, 68-70; res fel, Harvard Univ, 71-72, asst prof, 72-76, assoc prof physics, 76-77; STAFF MEM, STANFORD LINEAR ACCELERATOR CTR, 79- *Concurrent Pos:* Alfred P Sloan fel, 74-77; vis assoc prof physics, Stanford Univ, 76-78; vis scientist, Stanford Linear Accelerator Ctr, 77-78, res assoc, 78-79. *Mem:* Am Phys Soc. *Res:* Particle and theoretical physics; gauge field theories and their applications. *Mailing Add:* Stanford Linear Accelerator Ctr PO Box 4349 Stanford CA 94305

QUINN, JAMES AMOS, b Chickasha, Okla, Aug 12, 39. PLANT ECOLOGY, POPULATION ECOLOGY. *Educ:* Panhandle State Col, BS, 61; Colo State Univ, MS, 63, PhD(bot sci), 66. *Prof Exp:* From asst prof to assoc prof, 66-77, PROF BOT, RUTGERS UNIV, 77- *Concurrent Pos:* Travel grants, Rockefeller Found, Int Grassland Cong, 70 & Bot Soc Am, Int Bot Cong, 75; Rutgers Univ Res Coun fac fel, Australia, 72-73; vis scientist, Div Land Resources Mgt, Australia & Univ New England, Australia, 80-81. *Mem:* Soc Range Mgt; Ecol Soc Am; Bot Soc Am; Am Inst Biol Sci; Torrey Bot Club. *Res:* Grassland ecology; population ecology; genetic differentiation within plant species; species interactions; evolutionary biology. *Mailing Add:* Dept Biol Sci Bot Unit Rutgers Univ New Brunswick NJ 08854

QUINN, JAMES GERARD, b Providence, RI, Oct 28, 38; m 65; c 3. BIOCHEMISTRY, ORGANIC CHEMISTRY. *Educ:* Providence Col, BS, 60; Univ RI, MS, 64; Univ Conn, PhD(biochem), 67. *Prof Exp:* USPHS training prog fel steroid biochem, Worcester Found Exp Biol, 67-68; from asst prof to assoc prof, 68-78, PROF CHEM OCEANOG, UNIV RI, 78- *Mem:* AAAS; Am Chem Soc; Am Soc Limnol & Oceanog; Int Asn Geochem & Cosmochem; Geochem Soc. *Res:* Marine organic chemistry; chemistry of organic matter in seawater and sediments; mineral-organic interactions; the effects of organic pollutants on marine systems; geochemistry. *Mailing Add:* Grad Sch of Oceanog Univ of RI Kingston RI 02881

QUINN, JAMES L, III, radiology, nuclear medicine, see previous edition

QUINN, JARUS WILLIAM, optics, see previous edition

QUINN, JOHN A(LBERT), b Springfield, Ill, Sept 3, 32; m 57; c 3. CHEMICAL ENGINEERING. *Educ:* Univ Ill, Urbana, BS, 54; Princeton Univ, PhD(chem eng), 59. *Prof Exp:* Mem fac, Univ Ill, Urbana, 58-70, prof chem eng, 66-70; prof, 71-78, ROBERT D BENT PROF CHEM ENG, UNIV PA, 78-, DEPT CHMN, 80- *Concurrent Pos:* NSF sr fel, 65; vis prof, Imp Col, Univ London, 65-66. *Honors & Awards:* Colburn Award, Am Inst Chem Engrs, 66. *Mem:* Nat Acad Eng; AAAS; Am Inst Chem Engrs; Am Chem Soc. *Res:* Interfacial phenomena; diffusion; transport in biological systems; membrane structure and function. *Mailing Add:* Dept Chem Eng Towne Bldg Univ of Pa Philadelphia PA 19104

QUINN, JOHN JOSEPH, b New York, NY, Sept 25, 33; m 58; c 4. THEORETICAL PHYSICS. *Educ:* St John's Univ, NY, BS, 54; Univ Md, PhD(physics), 58. *Prof Exp:* Res assoc, Univ Md, 58-59; mem tech staff, RCA Labs, 59-64; vis prof, Purdue Univ, 64-65; PROF PHYSICS, BROWN UNIV, 65- *Concurrent Pos:* Vis lectr, Univ Md, 61-62; vis prof, State Univ NY Stony Brook, 68-69. *Mem:* Am Phys Soc. *Res:* Solid state theory. *Mailing Add:* Dept of Physics Brown Univ Providence RI 02912

QUINN, JOHN R, food science, deceased

QUINN, LOYD YOST, b Cutler, Ind, June 16, 17; m 45; c 4. BACTERIOLOGY. *Educ:* Purdue Univ, BS, 41, MS, 47, PhD(bact), 49. *Prof Exp:* From asst prof to assoc prof, 49-63, actg head dept, 57-59, PROF BACT, IOWA STATE UNIV, 63- *Mem:* Tissue Cult Asn; Am Soc Microbiol. *Res:* antibody production by tissue cells grown in continuous culture; computerized feedback control of tissue cell culture conditions; aging in tissue cell cultures; effects of heavy metals on in vivo and tissue cell culture modes of immune response; genetic control of immune responses; computer graphics of protein structures. *Mailing Add:* Dept Microbiol 205 Sci Iowa State Univ Ames IA 50010

QUINN, RICHARD PAUL, b Modesto, Calif, Oct 22, 42; m 64; c 3. IMMUNOCHEMISTRY. *Educ:* Univ San Francisco, BS, 64; Ore State Univ, PhD(biochem), 68. *Prof Exp:* USPHS fel, Biol Div, Oak Ridge Nat Lab, 68-70; res biochemist, 70-75, SR RES BIOCHEMIST, WELLCOME RES LABS, BURROUGHS WELLCOME CO, 75- *Mem:* Reticuloendothelial Soc; Am Chem Soc; NY Acad Sci. *Res:* Immunosuppressive and immunoenhancing agents; immunochemical approaches to drug action; radioimmunoassay development; metabolism of serum proteins. *Mailing Add:* Dept of Exp Ther Wellcome Res Lb 3030 Cornwallis Rd Research Triangle Park NC 27709

QUINN, ROBERT GEORGE, b Beaver Falls, Pa, June 14, 36; m 61; c 5. PLASMA PHYSICS, SPACE SCIENCES. *Educ:* Drexel Inst, BSEE, 59; Cath Univ, MS, 60, PhD(physics), 62. *Prof Exp:* Res assoc, Princeton Univ, 62-63; from asst prof to assoc prof, Dept Space Sci & Appl Physics, Cath Univ, 63-66; assoc prof, Ionosphere Res Lab, 66-71, dean acad instr commonwealth campuses, 71-74, PROF ENG, PA STATE UNIV, 72- *Concurrent Pos:* Res assoc, Goddard Space Flight Ctr, NASA, 65-66. *Mem:* Am Geophys Union; Am Phys Soc; Am Soc Testing & Mat; Int Elec & Electronics Engrs; Am Soc Eng Educ. *Res:* Ionospheric physics; dielectrics. *Mailing Add:* Old Main Bldg Pa State Univ University Park PA 16802

QUINN, ROBERT M(ICHAEL), b Bedford, Ind, July 7, 41; m 61; c 5. ELECTRICAL ENGINEERING, ELECTROPHYSICS. *Educ:* Rensselaer Polytech Inst, BEE, 63, MEE, 65, PhD(elec eng), 68. *Prof Exp:* Staff engr, 68-76, ADV ENGR, IBM CORP, 76- *Res:* Instabilities in magnetoplasmas; integrated circuit device design and process technology. *Mailing Add:* IBM Corp Dept M-77 Bldg 966-1 PO Box 1 Essex Junction VT 05452

QUINN, ROD KING, b Sherman, Tex, Oct 2, 38; m 60; c 2. PHYSICAL INORGANIC CHEMISTRY. *Educ:* Southern Methodist Univ, BS, 61, MS, 63; Univ Tex, PhD(inorg chem), 67. *Prof Exp:* Instr chem, Southern Methodist Univ, 62-63; lab instr anal chem, Univ Tex, 63-64; mem tech staff, 67-78, DIV SUPVR, SANDIA NAT LAB, SANDIA CORP, 78- *Mem:* Am Chem Soc; Electrochem Soc. *Res:* Spectroscopic techniques in solution, molten salt and high temperature chemistry; vacuum techniques and solid state chemistry; electrochemistry; semiconducting materials; thermal batteries; thermochemistry; studies of the discharge and aging mechanisms in lithium organic and inorganic electrochemical power sources; electron microscopic and spectroscopic techniques applied to electrochemical systems. *Mailing Add:* Explor Batteries Div 2523 Sandia Nat Labs Albuquerque NM 87185

QUINN, THOMAS PATRICK, b Freeland, Pa, Mar 20, 30; m 62; c 2. IONOSPHERIC PHYSICS. *Educ:* Pa State Univ, BS, 57, MS, 58, PhD(physics of ionosphere), 64. *Prof Exp:* Instr elec eng, Ionosphere Res Lab, Pa State Univ, 58-64; consult commun, Off Naval Res, 64-77, spec asst systs, Off Asst Secy Navy, 77-79; DEP ASST SECY, DEPT OF DEFENSE, 79- *Concurrent Pos:* Asst prof, Pa State Univ, 64-66; mem, Comn Three, Int Sci Radio Union, 64- *Honors & Awards:* Arthur S Flemming Award, Wash Junior Chamber Com, 67. Mem; Am Geophys Union; Inst Elec & Electronics Engrs. *Res:* Electromagnetic wave propagation; communications theory; radar systems; modulation and detection techniques. *Mailing Add:* Off Under Secy Defense 3E 160 Pentagon Washington DC 20301

QUINN, WILLIAM HEWES, b Syracuse, NY, Sept 28, 18. PHYSICAL OCEANOGRAPHY, METEOROLOGY. *Educ:* Colgate Univ, AB, 40; Univ Mo, AM, 42; Univ Calif, Los Angeles, MS, 50; Ore State Univ, PhD(oceanog), 68. *Prof Exp:* Res assoc oceanog, 67-75, assoc prof & sr researcher, 76-80, EMER ASSOC PROF OCEANOG, ORE STATE UNIV, 81- *Mem:* Am Meteorol Soc; Sigma Xi; Oceanog Soc Japan. *Res:* Large scale air-sea interaction; climate change and its causes; long range ocean and weather forecasting; insolation and weather over tropical oceans. *Mailing Add:* Sch Oceanog Ore State Univ Corvallis OR 97331

QUINNEY, PAUL REED, b Haverhill, Mass, May 11, 24; m 47; c 4. ANALYTICAL CHEMISTRY. *Educ:* Univ NH, BS & MS, 49; Iowa State Col, PhD(chem), 54. *Prof Exp:* Fel chem, Mellon Inst, 54; sr chemist, Brown Co, 54-56 & Koppers Co, 56-58; from asst prof to prof, 58-74, JOHN HUME READE PROF CHEM, BUTLER UNIV, 74-, HEAD DEPT, 72- *Mem:* AAAS; Am Chem Soc; Am Inst Chemists. *Res:* Instrumental analysis. *Mailing Add:* Dept of Chem Butler Univ Indianapolis IN 46208

QUINONES, FERDINAND ANTONIO, b Hormigueros, PR, May 30, 22; m 51; c 7. PLANT BREEDING. *Educ:* Univ PR, BSA, 46; Univ Minn, MS, 48, PhD(plant genetics), 54. *Prof Exp:* Instr hort, Univ PR, 48-50; res asst plant genetics, Univ Minn, 50-54; asst prof, 54-63, ASSOC PROF PLANT GENETICS, NMEX STATE UNIV, 63- *Mem:* Am Soc Agron. *Res:* Plant pathology; agronomy; horticulture; testing and breeding Indian ricegrass, western wheatgrass, tall wheatgrass and black gramagrass. *Mailing Add:* Dept of Agron Box 3Q NMex State Univ Las Cruces NM 88003

QUINONES, MARK A, b New York, NY, Jan 13, 31; m 52; c 2. PREVENTIVE MEDICINE, PUBLIC HEALTH. *Educ:* Southeastern La Univ, BA, 53; La State Univ, MA, 55, PhD(med sociol), 71; Wayne State Univ, MHA, 56; Columbia Univ, MPH, 73. *Prof Exp:* Health educr, Tuberculosis League of Pittsburgh, 56-57; consult, NJ Tuberculosis & Health Asn, 57-62; exec dir, Passaic County Heart Asn, NJ, 62-66; managing dir, Northwest Area Tuberculosis & Respirator Dis Asn, NJ, 66-69; coordr, Develop Dept, 69, adminr, Div Drug Abuse, 69-71, asst prof, 71-75, dir, Div Drug Abuse, 74-80, assoc prof, 76-80, PROF PREV MED & DIR, DIV SOCIAL MED, COL MED & DENT NJ, 80- *Concurrent Pos:* Vis prof, Sch Educ, Fairleigh Dickinson Univ, 71-74; health consult, PR Cong of NJ, 72- *Mem:* Am Pub Health Asn; Asn Teachers Prev Med; Soc Pub Health Educr; Am Sociol Soc. *Res:* Areas concerned with the social aspects of health and medicine, particularly migrant health, criminal offenders, tuberculosis, asthma and allied health. *Mailing Add:* Div Social Med & Drug Abuse Col of Med & Dent of NJ Newark NJ 07103

QUINT, JOSEPH FREEMAN, b Los Angeles, Calif, Jan 6, 46; m 67; c 2. CLINICAL CHEMISTRY. *Educ:* Occidental Col, BA, 67; Univ Calif, Los Angeles, PhD(biol chem), 72. *Prof Exp:* MGR CLIN CHEM, BECKMAN INSTRUMENTS, INC, 73- *Mem:* Am Chem Soc; Am Asn Clin Chemists. *Res:* UV methods and radioimmunoassay for use in the routine clinical laboratory. *Mailing Add:* Beckman Instruments Campus at Jamboree PO Box C19600 Irvine CA 93713

QUINTANA, RONALD PRESTON, b New Orleans, La, Feb 23, 36; m 57; c 2. MEDICINAL CHEMISTRY. *Educ:* Loyola Univ, New Orleans, BS, 56; Univ Wis, MS, 58, PhD(pharmaceut chem), 61. *Prof Exp:* From instr to prof med chem, Col Pharm, 60-71, prof periodont, Col Dent, 72-74, DISTINGUISHED SERV PROF MED CHEM, COL PHARM, UNIV TENN CTR HEALTH SCI, 71-, VCHMN DEPT, 65- *Mem:* Acad Pharm Sci; Am Chem Soc; Am Pharmaceut Asn; The Chem Soc. *Res:* Synthesis of, and surface-chemical studies on, compounds with biological significance. *Mailing Add:* Dept of Med Chem Col of Pharm Univ of Tenn Ctr for Health Sci Memphis TN 38163

QUINTO, ERIC TODD, b Indianapolis, Ind, May 10, 51. RADON TRANSFORMS, COMPUTED TOMOGRAPHY. *Educ:* Ind Univ, AB, 73; Mass Inst Technol, PhD(math), 78. *Prof Exp:* Lectr, 77-78, ASST PROF MATH, TUFTS UNIV, 78- *Concurrent Pos:* Vis scholar, Dept Math, Mass Inst Technol, 78-79. *Mem:* Am Math Soc; Math Asn Am; Asn Women Math. *Res:* Generalized radon transforms, a field of mathematics applicable to partial differential equations and computed tomography; when and how organs (functions) can be recovered from given tomographic data (integrals over surfaces). *Mailing Add:* Dept Math Tufts Univ Medford MA 02155

QUINTON, ARTHUR ROBERT, b Lowestoft, Eng, July 1, 24; m 46; c 3. EXPERIMENTAL NUCLEAR PHYSICS. *Educ:* Univ London, BSc, 44; Univ Western Ont, MSc, 51; Yale Univ, PhD, 54. *Prof Exp:* Res physicist, Mullard Radio Valve Co, 46-48; instr physics, Yale Univ, 54-57, asst prof, 57-63; assoc prof, Univ Fla, 63-66; PROF PHYSICS, UNIV MASS, AMHERST, 66- *Concurrent Pos:* Vis fel, Australian Nat Univ, 61-62, vis prof, 72-73; mem, Publ Comt, Am Asn Physics Teachers, 71-74. *Mem:* Am Phys Soc; Am Asn Physics Teachers. *Res:* Nuclear structure; low energy nuclear physics; fission; heavy ions; x-ray excitation by ion bombardment. *Mailing Add:* 75 Red Gate Lane Amherst MA 01002

QUINTON, DEE ARLINGTON, b Cardston, Alta, May 17, 39; c 6. RANGE NUTRITION, SECONDARY PRODUCTIVITY. *Educ:* Weber State Col, BS, 69; Colo State Univ, PhD(range sci), 72. *Prof Exp:* Res assoc range sci, Colo State Univ, 72-73; asst prof wildlife mgt, Tex Tech Univ, 73-75; RES SCIENTIST RANGE ECOL, AGR CAN, 76- *Mem:* Soc Range Mgt. *Res:* Secondary productivity of range lands; range improvements; range trend studies. *Mailing Add:* Res Sta Agr Can 3015 Ord Rd Kamloops BC V2B 8A9 Can

QUINTON, PAUL MARQUIS, cell physiology, see previous edition

QUINTON-COX, ROBERT, b Pontypool, Wales, Apr 19, 26; m 52; c 2. HISTOLOGY, CYTOLOGY. *Educ:* Emory Univ, PhD(anat), 63. *Prof Exp:* Res asst anat, London Hosp Med Sch, 46-58; res assoc Med Sch, Emory, 58-62; histologist, Yerkes Regional Primate Res Ctr, 63-65; instr anat, Med Sch, Emory Univ, 65-66; asst prof, 66-69, ASSOC PROF ANAT, DENT SCH, UNIV ORE, 69-, ASSOC PROF, MED SCH, 69- *Concurrent Pos:* Consult, Halco Sci Inc, Ga, 59-66. *Mem:* Am Asn Anat; Biol Photog Asn; fel Royal Micros Soc. *Res:* Ultrastructure of aging cells and tissues; neurosecretory mechanisms; structure and function of reteal complexes; electron microscopy autoradiography of teeth and periodontium. *Mailing Add:* Dept of Anat Univ of Ore Dent Sch Portland OR 97201

QUINZI, ANTHONY JOHN, b Chicago Heights, Ill, June 18, 43; m 71; c 3. STATISTICS. *Educ:* Univ Ill, Urbana, BS, 65, MA, 67; Fla State Univ, PhD(statist), 76. *Prof Exp:* Instr math, Danville Jr Col, 67-69; ASST PROF STATIST, TEMPLE UNIV, 76- *Concurrent Pos:* Consult, US Army Mat Systs Anal Activ, 77-78 & Dept Behav Sci, Eastern Pa Psychiat Inst, 78-; prin investr, US Air Force Off Sci Res, 78-79. *Mem:* Am Statist Asn; Inst Math Statist; Math Asn Am; AAAS; Sigma Xi. *Res:* Applied probability modelling; reliability theory; stochastic processes. *Mailing Add:* Dept Statist Temple Univ 1910 Park Mall 290-00 Philadelphia PA 19122

QUIOCHO, FLORANTE A, b Philippines, Oct 26, 37; m 59; c 3. BIOCHEMISTRY. *Educ:* Cent Philippines Univ, BS, 59; Howard Univ, MS, 61; Yale Univ, PhD(biochem), 66. *Prof Exp:* Mem res staff molecular biophys, Yale Univ, 64-66; res fel chem, Harvard Univ, 66-72; from asst prof to assoc prof, 72-81, PROF BIOCHEM, RICE UNIV, 81- *Concurrent Pos:* Mem, Cellular & Mollecular Basis Dis Rev Comt, Nat Inst Gen MedSci, NIH, 78-82; USPHS training fel biochem, Yale Univ, 62-64, res fel, European Molecular Biol Orgn, 80, fel, John Simon Guggenheim Mem Found, 80-81; vis scientist, Lab Molecular Biophysics, Oxford Univ, 80. *Honors & Awards:* Asian chemist award, Am Chem Soc, 61. *Mem:* Am Soc Biol Chemists; Sigma Xi. *Res:* Physical chemistry of biological macromolecules, especially proteins; x-ray crystallographic studies of proteins; mechanisms of enzyme action; chemical behavior of enzymes in the solid state. *Mailing Add:* Dept of Biochem Rice Univ PO Box 1892 Houston TX 77001

QUIRK, JAMES DENIS, chemical physics, theoretical physics, see previous edition

QUIRK, JOHN THOMAS, b Dubuque, Iowa, Jan 21, 33; m 58; c 4. TREE PHYSIOLOGY, FOREST PRODUCTS. *Educ:* Iowa State Univ, BS, 56; Syracuse Univ, MS, 60; Univ Wis, PhD(forestry & forest prod), 67. *Prof Exp:* Res forester, Cent State Forest Exp Sta, USDA, 56-58; RES TECHNOLOGIST, FOREST PROD LAB, USDA, 60- *Mem:* AAAS; Soc Wood Sci & Technol; Soc Am Foresters; Electron Micros Soc Am; Am Inst Biol Sci. *Res:* Anatomy and morphology; structure-function; physiology-structure; structure-strength. *Mailing Add:* US Forest Prod Lab PO Box 5130 Madison WI 53705

QUIRK, RODERIC P, b Detroit, Mich, Mar 26, 41; m; c 3. POLYMER CHEMISTRY. *Educ:* Rensselaer Polytech Inst, BS, 63; Univ Ill, MS, 65, PhD(chem), 67. *Prof Exp:* Anal chemist, Ethyl Corp, 63; res chemist, Minn Mining & Mfg Co, 64; res assoc, Univ Pittsburgh, 67-69; from asst prof to assoc prof chem, Univ Ark, 69-78; SR RES SCIENTIST, MICH MOLECULAR INST, 79- *Concurrent Pos:* Res chemist, Phillips Petrol Co, 74; vis prof, Inst Polymer Sci, Univ Akron, 76-77; adj assoc prof polymer chem, Case Western Reserve Univ, 79-, Cent Mich Univ, 80- *Mem:* Am Chem Soc; Sigma Xi. *Res:* Alkyllithium-initiated polymerization of alkenes and dienes; cationic polymerization of cyclic ethers; solvation of alkyllithium compounds; chemical detection of radical intermediates in organometallic reactions; radical anion chemistry; structure-stability-reactivity relationships for alkoxycarbenium ions. *Mailing Add:* Mich Molecular Inst 1910 W St Andrews Midland MI 48640

QUIRKE, TERENCE THOMAS, JR, b Minneapolis, Minn, Aug 18, 29; m 58; c 1. EXPLORATION GEOLOGY. *Educ:* Univ Ill, BS, 51; Univ Minn, MS, 53, PhD, 58. *Prof Exp:* Asst geol, Univ Minn, 52-53, asst & instr, 55-58; asst prof geol, Univ NDak, 58-60; geologist, Int Nickel Co Can, Ltd, 60-65, res geologist, 65-69, asst mgr, Western Region, Field Explor Dept, 69-71, regional mgr, 71-73, regional geologist, 73-75; district geologist, Eastern US Region, 75-79, supvr sr staff, 79-80, SUPVR GEOL SERV, AM COPPER & NICKEL CO, INC, INCO, LTD, 82- *Mem:* Soc Econ Geologists; Geol Soc Am; Geol Asn Can; Am Inst Mining & Metall. *Res:* Iron, copper and nickel in Canada; uranium, base and precious metal exploration. *Mailing Add:* Am Copper & Nickel Co, Inc 1726 Cole Blvd Suite 110 Golden CO 80401

QUIROS, CARLOS F, b Lima, Peru, Mar 17, 46; m 70; c 2. PLANT GENETICS, PLANT BREEDING. *Educ:* Agrarian Univ, Peru, BSc, 68; Univ NH, MS, 72; Univ Calif, Davis, PhD(genetics), 75. *Prof Exp:* Fel tomato genetics, Univ Calif, Davis, 75-76; res assoc breeding & genetics, Nat Inst Agr Res, Mex, 76-77; fel genetics, Univ Sherbrooke, 77-78; res assoc genetics & breeding, Univ Alta, 78-81; RES SCIENTIST GENETICS & BREEDING, INT PLANT RES INST, 81- *Mem:* Sigma Xi; Am Soc Hort Sci; AAAS. *Res:* Evolution, genetics and breeding of crop plants, specifically solanaceas and legumes; germplasm collection and preservation. *Mailing Add:* Int Plant Res Inst 853 Industrial Rd San Carlos CA 94070

QUIROZ, RODERICK S, b Ajo, Ariz, Nov 6, 23. METEOROLOGY. *Educ:* Univ Calif, Los Angeles, BA, 50; Univ Md, College Park, MS, 70. *Prof Exp:* Res meteorologist, US Air Weather Serv, 59-66; RES METEOROLOGIST, NAT METEOROL CTR, NAT WEATHER SERV, NAT OCEANIC & ATMOSPHERIC ADMIN, 66- *Concurrent Pos:* Mem, US Comt Exten to Standard Atmosphere, 62-; comt chmn, Atmospheric Problems Aerospace Vehicles, 68-72; lectr, Von Karman Inst Fluid Dynamics, Brussels, 70; chmn, Am Meteorol Soc Comt Upper Atmosphere, 73-78. *Honors & Awards:* Meritorious Civilian Serv Awards, US Air Force, 60 & 66. *Mem:* Am Meteorol Soc; Am Geophys Union. *Res:* Structure and circulation of upper atmosphere, emphasizing interaction with the troposhere on long-wave and climatic time-scales; analysis of atmospheric measurements with rockets and satellites. *Mailing Add:* Nat Meteorol Ctr Nat Oceanic Atmospheric Admin 5200 Auth Road Washington DC 20233

QUISENBERRY, DAN RAY, b Lake Co, Ind, Jan 3, 38; m 58; c 1. HEALTH PHYSICS. *Educ:* Univ Ky, AB, 61; Col William & Mary, MS, 66; World Open Univ, PhD(physics), 79. *Prof Exp:* Teacher sci & math, Ft Knox Dependent Schs, 61-66; asst prof sci, Brevard Jr Col, 66-67; asst prof, 68-80, ASSOC PROF PHYSICS, MERCER UNIV, 80-, CHMN DEPT, 81- *Mem:* Am Asn Physics Teachers; Am Phys Soc; Nat Geog Soc. *Res:* Environmental pollution, chiefly environmental effects of tritium; environmental monitoring of nuclear energy facilities. *Mailing Add:* Dept of Physics Mercer Univ Macon GA 31207

QUISENBERRY, KARL SPANGLER, JR, b Washington, DC, Apr 4, 26; m 49; c 3. PHYSICS. *Educ:* Univ Nebr, BS, 49; Univ Minn, MA, 52, PhD(physics), 55. *Prof Exp:* Asst physics, Univ Minn, 49-55, res assoc, 55-57; asst prof, Univ Pittsburgh, 57-60, assoc prof, 60-62; physicist, Knolls Atomic Power Lab, Gen Elec Co, 61-65, mgr advan exp physics, 65-74, spec critical facilities opers & safety, 71-74, mgr exp physics, 74-76, mgr advan develop activity, 76-77; dir nuclear, Schlumberger-Doll Res Ctr, 77-81, DIR HOUSTON ENG, SCHLUMBERGER WELL SERVICES, 81- *Mem:* Am Phys Soc. *Res:* nuclear physics and spectroscopy; neutron and nuclear reactor physics; oil well logging; linear accelerators. *Mailing Add:* 9105 Hilldale St Houston TX 77055

QUISENBERRY, RICHARD KEITH, b Springfield, Ill, July 27, 34; m 57; c 4. SYNTHETIC POLYMERS, FINISHES. *Educ:* Millikin Univ, BA, 56; Univ Utah, PhD(chem), 61. *Prof Exp:* Res chemist, Dacron Res Lab, 60-62, sr res chemist, 62-63, supvr tech plant, 63-64, supvr res, 64-66, sr supvr, Nylon Technol Sect, Del, 66-68, res mgr, Benger Lab, 68-72, tech supt, Va, 72-74, prod supt, 74-75, prin consult, Corp Plans Dept, 75-77, mgr bus planning, Spunbonded Prod, 77-78, prod mgr indust fibers, 78-79, dir, Feedstock Res Div, 79-80, dir pioneering res-fibers, 80-81, DIR RES & DEVELOP, FABRICS & FINISHES DEPT, E I DU PONT DE NEMOURS & CO, INC, DEL, 81- *Mem:* Am Chem Soc; Sigma Xi. *Res:* Synthesis and evaluation of polymeric materials for fibers, plastics, packaging, electronics and finishes. *Mailing Add:* E I du Pont de Nemours & Co Inc Wilmington DE 19898

QUISENBERRY, WALTER BROWN, b Purman, Mo, June 24, 12; m 40; c 3. PREVENTIVE MEDICINE, CANCER. *Educ:* Loma Linda Univ, MD, 41; Westmont Col, BA, 42; Johns Hopkins Univ, MPH, 45; Am Bd Prev Med, dipl, 50. *Prof Exp:* Med intern, Henry Ford Hosp, 40-41; prof chem & sch health physician, Westmont Col, 41-42; venereal dis control officer, Southside Health Dist, Va, 42-44; asst med, Johns Hopkins Hosp, 44-45; dir div venereal dis, Nebr State Dept Health, 45-46; asst prof prev med & pub health, Sch Med, Loma Linda Univ, 46-54, actg head dept, 46-47; chief venereal dis & cancer control, Territorial Dept Health, Hawaii, 47-51, dir div prev med, 51-54; exec dir, Hawaii Cancer Soc, 54-58; dir div prev med, Hawaii State Dept Health, 58-63, dep dir health, 63-66, dir health, 66-74, ASSOC PHYSICIAN, STRAUB CLIN & HOSP, HONOLULU, 75- *Concurrent Pos:* Rockefeller Found fel, Johns Hopkins Univ, 44-45; pvt pract, Long Beach, Calif, 41-42; staff physician, Coleman Med Group, Alhambra, Calif, 46-47; jr attend physician, Los Angeles County Hosp, 46-48; mem teaching staff pub health, Univ Hawaii, 47-75; attend staff, Queens, Kuakini, Kapiolani & Kauikeolani Children's Hosp, Honolulu, 49-; deleg, Nat Cancer Conf, Mich, 56, Int Cancer Cong, Eng, 58, Int Conf Cancer Probs, Japan, 60; partic, Symp Geog Path Gastro-Intestinal Cancer, Denmark, 58; assoc clin prof, Sch Med, Loma Linda Univ, 60-75; lectr, Int Cancer Cong, Moscow, USSR, 62; Univ Sydney lectr oncol, Sydney, Adelaide, Melbourne & Brisbane, Australia & Auckland, NZ, 63; US rep int conf nasopharyngeal cancer, Int Union Against Cancer, Singapore, 64. *Mem:* Fel Am Pub Health Asn; AMA; fel Am Col Prev Med; fel Am Col Physicians; Royal Soc Health. *Res:* Cytologic diagnosis of cancer by the smear technique; ethnic differences in the incidence of cancer; methadone treatment of heroin addiction; epidemiology of cancer of the stomach, breast, liver and lung; epidemiology of venereal diseases; treatment of venereal diseases with antibiotics; twinning; sociocultural factors in cancer. *Mailing Add:* 2128 Kamehameha Ave Honolulu HI 96822

QUISSELL, DAVID OLIN, b Pipestone, Minn, Oct 25, 44; m 72; c 1. REGULATORY BIOLOGY, METABOLIC REGULATION. *Educ:* Augustana Col, BA, 66; Univ Wis, Madison, PhD(biochem), 72. *Prof Exp:* Fel oncol & path, Univ Wis-Madison, 71-73; asst prof biochem, Univ Mo-Columbia, 73-77; asst prof pharmacol, 77-80, ASST PROF BIOCHEM, SCH MED, UNIV COLO, 80- *Concurrent Pos:* Res scholar award, Nat Cystic Fibrosis Found, 79. *Mem:* Am Chem Soc; Am Soc Cell Biol; Soc Complex Carbohydrates; Int Asn Dent Res; Sigma Xi. *Res:* Stimulus-secretion coupling mechanism in exocrine tissue; role of cyclic adenosine monophosphate, cyclic guanosine monophosphate, and calcium in the regulation of secretion; pathogenesis of cystic fibrosis. *Mailing Add:* B-126 Dept Biochem, Biophys & Genetics 4200 E 9th Ave Denver CO 80262

QUIST, ARVIN SIGVARD, b Blair, Nebr, Nov 15, 33; m 57; c 3. PHYSICAL CHEMISTRY. *Educ:* Dana Col, Nebr, BS, 54; Univ Nebr, MS, 57, PhD(chem), 59, Univ Tenn, JD, 75. *Prof Exp:* Asst, Univ Nebr, 54-56; res assoc & instr, Univ Pittsburgh, 59-60; instr chem, Univ Nebr, 60-61; mem res staff, Oak Ridge Nat Lab, 61-76; staff mem, Off Waste Isolation, 76-78, STAFF MEM, GAS CENTRIFUGE ENRICHMENT PLANT, NUCLEAR DIV, UNION CARBIDE CORP, 78- *Mem:* Am Nuclear Soc; Am Bar Asn; AAAS. *Res:* Physical chemistry of aqueous electrolyte solutions and molten salts; electrical conductances and Raman spectroscopy of aqueous solutions and molten salts at high temperatures and pressures; environmental and safety impacts of nuclear facilities. *Mailing Add:* Nuclear Div PO Box Y Oak Ridge TN 37830

QUIST, RAYMOND WILLARD, b Minneapolis, Minn, Nov 26, 34; m 57; c 2. SPEECH PATHOLOGY. *Educ:* Hamline Univ, BA, 52; Univ Minn, Minneapolis, MA, 66, PhD(speech path), 71. *Prof Exp:* Assoc prof speech path, Calif State Col (Pa), 68-71; assoc prof speech path, Madison Col, 71-74; assoc prof, 74-77, PROF SPEECH PATH, IND STATE UNIV, TERRE HAUTE, 77- *Mem:* Am Speech & Hearing Asn; Coun Except Children; Am Asn Univ Professors. *Res:* Behavior modification; stuttering; voice. *Mailing Add:* Speech & Hearing Clin Ind State Univ Terre Haute IN 47809

QUIST, WILLIAM EDWARD, b Seattle, Wash, May 13, 35; m 66; c 2. METALLURGICAL ENGINEERING, MATERIALS SCIENCE. *Educ:* Univ Wash, BS, 57, MS, 63, PhD(metall eng), 74. *Prof Exp:* Engr corrosion, Farwest Corrosion Control, 57; metallurgist, Pacific Car & Foundry Co, 58; RES SPECIALIST AIRCRAFT MAT, BOEING CO, 59- *Concurrent Pos:* Lectr, Univ Wash, 72-73; res assoc, NSF grant, 67-68. *Mem:* Am Soc Metals. *Res:* Phase transformation, fracture, fatigue, and corrosion studies in aluminum, titanium, and nickel base systems as well as the study of strengthening mechanisms, structure and brazing. *Mailing Add:* 18215 NE 27th St Redmond WA 98052

QUISTAD, GARY BENNET, b Riverside, Calif, Jan 17, 47. AGRICULTURAL BIOCHEMISTRY, ORGANIC CHEMISTRY. *Educ:* Univ Calif, Riverside, BS, 69; Univ Calif, Los Angeles, PhD(chem), 72. *Prof Exp:* Sr chemist, 73-80, GROUP LEADER METABOLISM, ZOECON CORP, 80- *Mem:* Am Chem Soc; NY Acad Sci; Sigma Xi; AAAS. *Res:* Pesticide metabolism and environment degradation photochemistry; synthetic chemistry; terpenoid biosynthesis. *Mailing Add:* Zoecon Corp 975 California Ave Palo Alto CA 94304

QUITTNER, HOWARD, b Brooklyn, NY, Feb 1, 22; m 66; c 5. PATHOLOGY. *Educ:* Tulane Univ La, BS, 42, MD, 44; Am Bd Path, dipl, 51. *Prof Exp:* Adj pathologist, Beth Israel Hosp, 51-52; dir labs, Washington Hosp, Pa, 52-64; prof clin path, Sch Med & dir clin labs, Univ Ark, Little Rock, 64-76; prof path, Sch Med, Tulane Univ, 76-78, dir clin labs, Med Ctr, 76-78; PROF PATH, SCH MED, MARSHALL UNIV, 78-; DIR LAB SERV, VET ADMIN MED CTR, HUNTINGTON, 80- *Concurrent Pos:* Levy Found res fel, Beth Israel Hosp, New York, 49-52; adj prof biochem, Tulane Univ, 76-78. *Mem:* Am Soc Path; AMA; Asn Clin Sci (pres, 67). *Res:* Clinical pathology diagnostic techniques. *Mailing Add:* Dept of Path Vet Admin Hosp Huntington WV 25704

QUOCK, RAYMOND MARK, b San Francisco, Calif, June 9, 48; m 75; c 1. NEUROPHARMACOLOGY. *Educ:* Univ San Francisco, BS, 70; Univ Wash, PhD(pharmacol), 74. *Prof Exp:* Lab asst pharmacol, Sch Med, Univ Calif, San Francisco, 63-70; instr, Sch Med, Univ Wash, 74-75; asst prof physiol & pharmacol, Sch Pharm, Univ Pac, 75-79; asst prof, 79-82, ASSOC PROF PHARMACOL, SCH DENT, MARQUETTE UNIV, 82- *Concurrent Pos:* Exam consult, Calif State Bd Pharm; adj asst prof pharmacol & toxicol, Med Col Wis, 80-; res assoc toxicol, Wood Vet Admin Med Ctr, 81- *Mem:* Soc Neurosci; Western Pharmacol Soc; Am Soc Pharmacol & Exp Therapeut; NY Acad Sci. *Res:* Biogenic amine and neuropeptide mechanisms in the central nervous system; neuropsychopharmacology of the hypertensive rat; microwave toxicology. *Mailing Add:* Dept Basic Sci Marquette Univ 604 N 16th St Milwaukee WI 53233

QUON, DAVID SHI HAUNG, b Canton, China, Dec 26, 31; Can citizen; m 60; c 2. MINERALOGY. *Educ:* Sun Yat Sen Univ, BSc, 49; Ohio State Univ, MSc, 59; Univ Mich, PhD(mineral), 65. *Prof Exp:* Geologist, Geotech Develop Co, 54-58; res asst mineral, Univ Mich, 60-64; mem sci staff, Res & Develop Labs, Northern Elec Co, 64-67 & 68-75; asst prof mineral, Lakehead Univ, 67-68; mem sci staff, Res & Develop Labs, Northern Elec Co, Ltd, 68-75; RES SCIENTIST, CANMET ENERGY, MINES & RESOURCES, CAN, 75- *Concurrent Pos:* Nat Res Coun Can res grant, 68-69. *Mem:* Mineral Soc Am; Soc Econ Geologists; Am Ceramic Soc; Mineral Soc Can. *Res:* Mineralogy and geochemistry of carbonates; crystallochemistry; mineralog synthetic ceramic materials; growing single crystals; mineral processing, extraction of aluminum from non-bauxitic minerals and building materials research; solid electrolyte for energy storage. *Mailing Add:* 50 Pellan Crescent Ottawa ON K2K 1J5 Can

QUON, JIMMIE E, environmental engineering, deceased

QURAISHI, MOHAMMED SAYEED, b Jodhpur, Rajasthan, India, June 23, 24; m 53; c 3. PESTICIDE TOXICOLOGY. *Educ:* St John's Col, Agra Univ, BSc, 42; Aligarh Muslim Univ, MSc, 44; Univ Mass, PhD(entom), 48. *Prof Exp:* Sr mem, UN WHO Team to Pakistan, 49-51; entomologist, Malaria Inst Pakistan, 51-55; sr res officer, Pakistan Coun Sci & Indust Res, 55-60; sr sci officer, Pakistan AEC, 60-64; assoc prof entom, Univ Man, 64-66; assoc prof entom, NDak State Univ, 66-70, prof, 70-74; chief sci biol, NY State Sci Serv, 74-75; ENTOMOLOGIST-TOXICOLOGIST CHIEF, PEST CONTROL & CONSULT SECT, NIH, 76- *Concurrent Pos:* Assoc secy, Sci Comn Pakistan, 59-60; sr scientist, Cent Treaty Orgn Inst Nuclear Sci, Tehran, Iran, 60-64; prog mgr, Interdept Contract, Proj Themis, Dept of Defense, 68-74. *Mem:* Entom Soc Am; Am Chem Soc; Soc Environ Toxicol & Chem. *Res:* Chemicals showing transient interference with vital phases of insect development. *Mailing Add:* Bldg 31 B1 C17 NIH Bethesda MD 20205

QURESHI, A H, b Dagi, Pakistan, Oct 28, 32; m 61; c 3. ELECTRICAL ENGINEERING. *Educ:* Univ Peshawar, BEng, 55; Aachen Tech Univ, PhD(elec eng), 61. *Prof Exp:* Guest res collabr, Nuclear Res-Centre, Juelich, Ger, 58-61; asst prof elec eng, Univ Waterloo, 61-64; head dept, Col Eng, Riyadh, Saudi Arabia, 64-65; sessional lectr, Univ Calgary, 65-66; from asst prof to assoc prof, 66-70, PROF ELEC ENG & HEAD DEPT, UNIV WINDSOR, 70- *Res:* Magnetic and solid state materials; high voltage technology. *Mailing Add:* Dept of Elec Eng Univ of Windsor Windsor ON N9B 3P4 Can

QUTUB, MUSA Y, b Jerusalem, Palestine, June 2, 40; US citizen; m 70; c 1. WATER RESOURCES, GEOLOGY. *Educ:* Simpson Col, BA, 64; Colo State Univ, MS, 66; Iowa State Univ, PhD(geol higher educ), 69. *Prof Exp:* Asst dir residence hall, Colo State Univ, 65-66; instr earth sci, Iowa State Univ, 66-69; asst prof, 69-72, assoc prof earth sci, 72-80, PROF GEOG & ENVIRON STUDIES, NORTHEASTERN ILL UNIV, 80- *Concurrent Pos:* NSF & NDEA fels, Northeastern Ill Univ, 69-72; NSF grants, 70-; consult, NSF, 72-, mem aerospace educ comt, 72; Off Environ Educ grant, 73-74; chmn, Six Nat Symposia Environ & Water Resources. *Mem:* AAAS; Int Asn Advan Earth & Environ Sci (pres); Nat Asn Geol Teachers (pres); Nat Sci Teacher Asn. *Res:* Geological education; science learning; ground water and application to city planning in northern Illinois. *Mailing Add:* Dept Geog & Environ Studies Northeastern Ill Univ Chicago IL 60625

QUYNN, RICHARD GRAYSON, b Newport News, Va, Jan 23, 28; m 53; c 2. POLYMER PHYSICS. *Educ:* Col William & Mary, BS, 47; Inst Textile Technol, MS, 49; Princeton Univ, MA, 52, PhD(physics, phys chem), 57. *Prof Exp:* Res physicist, Summit Res Labs, Celanese Corp Am, 53-54; sr res physicist, 57-63, res assoc physics, 63-65; sect head mat sci, Celanese Res Co, Celanese Corp, 65-70; mgr mat sci, Res Ctr, Burlington Industs, 70-72; asst dir mat sci, FRL Div, Albany Int Corp, 72-79; mem tech staff, Jet Propulsion Lab, Calif Inst Technol, 79; sr ed, High Technol Mag, 81; SR SPECIALIST ENGR, BOEING MILITARY AIRPLANE CO, 82- *Mem:* Am Phys Soc; Fiber Soc. *Res:* Infrared spectroscopy; physical structure of fibers and films; high polymer physics. *Mailing Add:* Boeing Military Airplane Co 3801 S Oliver M/S 76-86 Wichita KS 67210

R

RAAB, ALLEN ROBERT, b New York City, NY, Jan 20, 37; m 60; c 3. STRUCTURAL MECHANICS, FINITE ELEMENT ANALYSIS. *Educ:* Columbia Univ, AB, 57, Eng Sch, BS, 58, MS, 59; Cornell Univ, PhD(structural eng), 63. *Prof Exp:* Tech staff mem, Mitre Corp, 71-72; sr engr, Electronic Space Syst Corp, 72-74; proj mgr, 74-77, chief, Structures & Mech Br, 77, Prog Develop Off, 77-80, CHIEF, CONST ENG BR, TRANSP SYST CTR, US DEPT TRANSP, CAMBRIDGE, MASS, 80- *Concurrent Pos:* Consult, Electronic Space Syst Corp, Concord, Mass, 74-; instr, Univ Lowell, 75. *Mem:* Am Soc Civil Engrs. *Res:* Formulation, planning, and direction of urban rail and intercity freight construction, maintenance, and rehabilitation research and development projects involving underground excavation and ground support, track and wayside, elevated track and stations, and construction cost estimation. *Mailing Add:* DTS-741 Transp Syst Ctr US Dept Transp Kendall Square Cambridge MA 02142

RAAB, HARRY F(REDERICK), JR, electrical engineering, see previous edition

RAAB, JACOB LEE, b Elkhart, Ind, Nov 29, 38; m 65; c 3. PHYSIOLOGY. *Educ:* Univ Chicago, BS, 60, MS, 65; Duke Univ, PhD(zool), 71. *Prof Exp:* Instr biol, Franklin & Marshall Col, 66-69; ASST PROF PHYSIOL, RUTGERS UNIV, NEWARK, 71- *Mem:* Am Physiol Soc; AAAS. *Res:* Relationship of the energetics of exercise to variables of temperature, humidity, terrain and the time of day. *Mailing Add:* Dept of Zool & Physiol Rutgers Univ Newark NJ 07102

RAAB, JOSEPH A, b Oshkosh, Wis, Dec 20, 34; m 55; c 6. MATHEMATICS. *Educ:* Wis State Univ, Oshkosh, BS, 57; Univ Ill, MS, 60; Univ Wis, PhD(math), 67. *Prof Exp:* Teacher pub schs, Wis, 57-59; assoc prof math, Wis State Univ, Oshkosh, 60-69; asst vpres acad affairs, 78-79, PROF MATH, METROP STATE COL, 69- *Concurrent Pos:* Chmn dept math, Metrop State Col, 72-75; teacher, Colo State Col, 68; rep, Colo State Col & Univ Consortium, 75-77; coordr acad progs, Consortium State Cols in Colo, 77-78. *Mem:* Math Asn Am. *Res:* Fibonacci sequences; Pascal's triangle higher order continued fractions and associated algorithms; number theory; abstract algebra; analysis. *Mailing Add:* Off Acad Affairs Metrop State Col Denver CO 80204

RAAB, WALLACE ALBERT, b Onawa, Iowa, Nov 4, 21; m 47; c 2. APPLIED MATHEMATICS. *Educ:* Morningside Col, BS, 49; Univ SDak, MA, 49; Iowa State Univ, PhD(math), 58. *Prof Exp:* Mathematician, US Naval Ord Test Sta, Calif, 51-52; sr dynamics engr, Gen Dynamics Corp, 55-58; prof math, Calif State Polytech Col, 57-64; PROF MATH, UNIV SOUTH DAK, 64- & COORD STATIST RES BUR, 80- *Mem:* Math Asn Am; Am Statist Asn; Soc Indust & Appl Math; Sigma Xi. *Res:* Fluid mechanics; differential equations; statistics. *Mailing Add:* Dept of Math Univ of SDak Vermillion SD 57069

RAABE, HERBERT P(AUL), b Halle, Ger, Aug 15, 09; nat US; m 56; c 4. ELECTRICAL ENGINEERING. *Educ:* Berlin Tech Univ, dipl, 36, Dr Ing, 39. *Prof Exp:* From instr to asst prof elec commun technol, Berlin Tech Univ, 36-45; mgr & tech consult, Asn Microfilm, Ger, 45-47; tech consult, Wright Air Develop Ctr, Ohio, 47-56; sr tech specialist, Litton Industs, Inc, 56-66 & Int Bus Mach Corp, NY, 66-68; sr engr, Fed Systs Div, IBM Corp, Gaithersburg, 68-74; CONSULT, 74- *Concurrent Pos:* Res engr, Heinrich Hertz Inst, 37-45; sci consult, Bur Commun Tech, 46-47. *Mem:* Sr mem Inst Elec & Electronics Engrs; Am Inst Aeronaut & Astronaut; hon mem Ger Soc Rocket Technol & Travel. *Res:* Electrical communication technique and radar; information theory; microwave theory and technique; antennas; propagation; electrical countermeasures; infrared technique; military reconnaissance; systems analysis. *Mailing Add:* 10121 Lloyd Rd Potomac MD 20854

RAABE, ROBERT DONALD, b Waukesha, Wis, May 8, 24; m 55; c 2. PLANT PATHOLOGY. *Educ:* Univ Wis, BS, 48, PhD(plant path), 51. *Prof Exp:* Collabr, USDA, Wis & Tex Agr Exp Stas, 51-52; from instr & jr plant pathologist to assoc prof plant path & assoc plant pathologist, Univ Calif, Berkeley, 52-63; plant pathologist, Univ Hawaii, 63-64; assoc prof & assoc plant pathologist, 64-68, PROF PLANT PATH & PLANT PATHOLOGIST, UNIV CALIF, BERKELEY, 68- *Mem:* Am Phytpath Soc; Mycol Soc Am. *Res:* Diseases of ornamentals; Armillaria root rot. *Mailing Add:* Dept of Plant Pathology Univ of Calif Berkeley CA 94720

RAACKE, ILSE DOROTHEA, b Rio de Janeiro, Brazil, Oct 10, 25; US citizen; div; c 2. MOLECULAR ENDOCRINOLOGY, HISTORY OF BIOLOGY. *Educ:* Parana Sch Chem, Brazil, BA, 47; Ore State Col, MA, 49; Univ Calif, Berkeley, PhD(biochem), 54. *Prof Exp:* Teaching asst anal chem, Ore State Col, 48-49; vis res scientist, Univ Upsala, 49-51; asst res biochem, Univ Calif, Berkeley, 52-54, asst res biochemist, 54-56; Am Cancer Soc fel, Chem Lab, Cambridge Univ, 56-57; Am Cancer Soc fel, Virus Lab, Univ Calif, Berkeley, 57-58; USPHS trainee virol, 58-59; assoc res biochemist, Kaiser Found Res Inst, 59-64; assoc prof, 65-69, PROF BIOL, BOSTON UNIV, 69- *Concurrent Pos:* Assoc specialist, Space Sci Lab, Univ Calif, 63-65; res grants, NIH, NSF, Am Cancer Soc, Am Heart Asn & Nat Endowment Humanities; vis scientist, Max Planck Inst Molecular Biol, 71; res assoc hist sci, Univ Calif, Berkeley, 76-78. *Mem:* AAAS; Am Soc Biol Chemists; Am Soc Cell Biol; Endocrine Soc; Hist Sci Soc. *Res:* Protein synthesis, mechanism and regulation; nucleic acid metabolsim; evolution of ribosomes; antibiotics; molecular endocrinology; evolution of genetic information transfer and expression; history of endocrinology and molecular biology. *Mailing Add:* Dept of Biol Boston Univ Boston MA 02215

RAAEN, VERNON F, b Plentywood, Mont, Nov 8, 18; m 49; c 1. ORGANIC CHEMISTRY. *Educ:* Concordia Col, BA, 41; Univ Minn, MS, 50, PhD(chem) 58. *Prof Exp:* Chemist & opers supt, Columbia Powder Co, Olin Mathieson Chem Corp, 42-44; CHEMIST, UNION CARBIDE NUCLEAR CO DIV, OAK RIDGE NAT LAB, 50- *Mem:* AAAS; Am Chem Soc; Sigma Xi. *Res:* Organic reactions studies with the help of radiocarbon and tritium as tracers. *Mailing Add:* 111 Scenic Dr Oak Ridge TN 37830

RAAL, JOHAN DAVID, chemical engineering, see previous edition

RAAM, SHANTHI, b Madras, India, Nov 26, 41. ONCOLOGY. *Educ:* Univ Madras, India, BS, 60, MS, 62; Univ Ga, PhD(immunol & microbiol), 73. *Prof Exp:* RES ASSOC CANCER RES, SCH MED, TUFTS UNIV, 73-; DIR, ONCOL LAB, SAMUEL SHATTUCK HOSP, 77- *Concurrent Pos:* Consult radioimmunoassay, Leary Labs, Boston, Mass, 73-74; consult steroid receptors, New Eng Nuclear, Boston, Mass; researcher estrogen receptor breast cancer, Lemuel Shattuck Hosp, Jamaica Plain, Mass, 75-; prin investr, Am Cancer Soc NY res grants, 79-80 & 80-81; invited speaker consensus comt for steroid receptors in breast cancer, Nat Cancer Inst, 79. *Mem:* Am Asn Cancer Res; AAAS; NY Acad Sci; Am Asn Immunologists. *Res:* Significance of steroid hormone receptors in cancer; search for tumor markers which may prove to be of prognostic and/or diagnostic value in cancer; their purification, characterization and development of clinical assays for the markers; immunoendocrinology. *Mailing Add:* Tufts Cancer Res Unit Oncol Dept L Shattuck Hosp 170 Morton St Jamaica Plain MA 02130

RAAMOT, TONIS, b Tartu, Estonia, Jan 6, 32; US citizen; m 58; c 1. CIVIL ENGINEERING. *Educ:* Columbia Univ, BA, 53, BS, 54, MS, 56; Univ Ill, PhD(civil eng), 62. *Prof Exp:* From asst prof to prof civil eng & asst chmn dept, Newark Col Eng, 62-67; chief civil eng, RCP Div, Raymond Int Inc, NY, 67-69; PARTNER, RAAMOT ASSOCS, CONSULT ENGRS, 69-; PROF CIVIL ENG, NJ INST TECHNOL, 70- *Concurrent Pos:* Soils consult, Raymond Int Inc, 64; NSF res initiation grant, 64-66. *Honors & Awards:* Arthur Wellington Award, Am Soc Civil Engrs, 65. *Mem:* Am Soc Civil Engrs; Nat Soc Prof Engrs; Am Soc Eng Educ; Am Concrete Inst; Am Soc Testing & Mat. *Res:* Soil mechanics; foundation engineering; behavior of deep foundations; pile driving analysis. *Mailing Add:* 2 Pennsylvania Plaza New York NY 10001

RAAPHORST, GIJSBERT PETER, b Holland; Can citizen. BIOPHYSICS, RADIATION BIOLOGY. *Educ:* Univ Waterloo, BSc, 72, MSc, 74, PhD(physics), 76. *Prof Exp:* Res assoc, Colo State Univ, 76-78; ASST RES OFFICER, RADIATION BIOL, ATOMIC ENERGY CAN, 78- *Concurrent Pos:* Res assoc, Med Res Coun Can, 77-78. *Mem:* Radiation Res Soc. *Res:* Radiation biology of mammalian cells and hyperthermic enhancement of radiation effects as manifested in cell survival and cell transformation. *Mailing Add:* Dept of Med Biophys Atomic Energy of Can Pinawa AB R0E 1L0 Can

RAASCH, GILBERT O, b Milwaukee, Wis, May 27, 03; m 25; c 2. GEOLOGY. *Educ:* Univ Wis, BA, 29, PhD(geol), 46. *Prof Exp:* Cur geol mus, Univ Wis, 29-36; surface geologist, Magnolia Petrol Co, 36-37; geologist, Darby Petrol Co, 37-38, petrol explor, 38-40; supvr mus proj, Milwaukee Pub Mus, 40-42; from assoc geologist to geologist, Ill State Geol Surv, 46-53; paleontologist, Can Stratig Surv, 53-56; consult paleont, Shell Oil Co Can, 56-68; CONSULT GEOL, RAASCH & ASSOCS, LTD, 68- *Mem:* Fel Geol Soc Am; Soc Econ Paleontologists & Mineralogists; Can Soc Petrol Geologists; Paleont Asn London. *Res:* Paleozoic paleontology and stratigraphy; Paleozoic biostratigraphy of the Canadian Arctic. *Mailing Add:* Raasch & Assocs Ltd 210 1011 17th Ave SW Calgary AB T2T 0A8 Can

RAASCH, LOU REINHART, b Republican City, Nebr, Apr 27, 44; m 68; c 2. ANALYTICAL CHEMISTRY. *Educ:* Univ Nebr-Lincoln, BS, 65, PhD(chem), 71. *Prof Exp:* Asst prof chem, MacMurray Col, 69-75; ASST PROF CHEM, ETENN STATE UNIV, 75- *Mem:* Am Chem Soc. *Res:* Electrochemistry of coordination compounds; voltammetry involving charge transfers folowed by chemical reactions; non-aqueous solvents for electrochemical investigations. *Mailing Add:* Dept of Chem ETenn State Univ Johnson City TN 37601

RAASCH, MAYNARD STANLEY, b Castlewood, SDak, Feb 27, 15. ORGANIC CHEMISTRY. *Educ:* SDak Sch Mines, BS, 37; Ohio State Univ, MS, 38, PhD(org chem), 41. *Prof Exp:* Lab instr chem, SDak Sch Mines, 35-37; asst gen & org chem, Ohio State Univ, 37-39; RES CHEMIST, EXP STA, E I DU PONT DE NEMOURS & CO, 41- *Mem:* Am Chem Soc. *Res:* Organic fluorine compounds; organic sulfur compounds; synthetic biologically active chemicals. *Mailing Add:* 2300 Inglewood Dr Wilmington DE 19803

RAB, PAUL ALEXIS, b Dayton, Ohio, Mar 2, 44; m 67; c 1. ZOOLOGY. *Educ:* Ohio State Univ, BSc, 66, MSc, 70, PhD(zool), 72. *Prof Exp:* instr, 72-80, PROF BIOL, SINCLAIR COMMUNITY COL, 80- & DEPT CHMN LIFE SCI, 80- *Res:* Social behavior; genetics of behavior. *Mailing Add:* Dept of Biol Sinclair Community Col Dayton OH 45402

RABA, CARL FRANZ, JR, b San Antonio, Tex, Dec 24, 37; c 5. GEOTECHNICAL ENGINEERING, CONSTRUCTION MATERIALS SCIENCE. *Educ:* Tex A&M Univ, BS, 61, ME, 62, PhD(civil eng), 68. *Prof Exp:* Res asst geotech, Tex Transp Inst Tex A&M Univ, 61-62; pres, Raba & Assoc Consult Engrs, Inc, 67-78; pres, 79-80, CHMN, RABA-KISTNER CONSULT, INC, 80- *Concurrent Pos:* Mem comt, Am Soc Test & Mat, 72-; pres Tex Coun Eng Labs, 74-75; chmn, Nat Comt Geotech Eng, Exam, Inst Cert Eng Technicians, 75-78. *Mem:* Sigma Xi; Am Soc Civil Engrs; Am Geophys Union; Am Soc Lubrication Engrs. *Res:* Geotechnical considerations of drilled pier and pile foundation systems, and stabilization aspects of fly ash in pavements and embankments. *Mailing Add:* Raba-Kistner Consults Inc PO Box 32217 San Antonio TX 78216

RABALAIS, FRANCIS CLEO, b Bunkie, La, Aug 16, 37; m 59; c 2. PARASITOLOGY. *Educ:* Univ Southwestern La, BS, 61; La State Univ, MS, 63, PhD(zool), 67. *Prof Exp:* Instr zool, La State Univ, 66-67 & parasitol, Sch Med, Tulane Univ, 67-68; ASSOC PROF BIOL, BOWLING GREEN STATE UNIV, 68-; ASSOC PROF, HEALTH & COMMUNITY SERV, 73- *Concurrent Pos:* Adj assoc prof microbiol, Med Col Ohio; fel, Sch Trop Med, Tulane Univ, 67. *Mem:* Am Soc Trop Med & Hyg; Am Soc Parasitol. *Res:* Biology of trematodes of lower vertebrates; biology of filarial nematodes; host-parasite relationships of filarial nematodes. *Mailing Add:* Dept of Biol Sci Bowling Green State Univ Bowling Green OH 43403

RABALAIS, JOHN WAYNE, b Bunkie, La, Sept 7, 44; m 66. PHYSICAL CHEMISTRY. *Educ:* Univ Southwestern La, BS, 66; La State Univ, PhD(phys chem), 70. *Prof Exp:* NATO fel electron spectros, Univ Uppsala, 70-71; asst prof phys chem, Univ Pittsburgh, 71-75; ASSOC PROF PHYS

CHEM, UNIV HOUSTON, 75- *Mem:* Am Chem Soc; AAAS. *Res:* Ultraviolet and x-ray photoelectron spectroscopy and its applications to surfaces, catalysis, chemisorption, and adsorption; visible and ultraviolet absorption and emission spectroscopy; secondary ion mass spectrometry; applied quantum chemistry. *Mailing Add:* Dept of Chem Univ of Houston Houston TX 77004

RABAN, MORTON, b St Louis, Mo, Oct 18, 40; m 64. ORGANIC CHEMISTRY, NUCLEAR MAGNETIC RESONANCE. *Educ:* Harvard Univ, AB, 62; Princeton Univ, MS, 66, PhD(org chem), 67. *Prof Exp:* Chemist, Res Inst Med & Chem, 62-63; instr chem, Princeton Univ, 66-67; from asst prof to assoc prof, 67-74, fac res fel, 68, PROF CHEM WAYNE STATE UNIV, 74- *Concurrent Pos:* Petrol Res Fund grant, 67-69 & 72-74; Res Corp grant-in-aid, 68-70; NIH res grant, 69-72; NSF res grant, 70-74; Sloan fel, 72-76. *Mem:* AAAS; Am Chem Soc; The Chem Soc. *Res:* Stereochemistry, including optical rotary dispersion-circular dispersion spectroscopy; asymmetric synthesis and determination of absolute configuration; organic chemistry and stereochemistry of sulfur and nitrogen compounds; dynamic nuclear magnetic resonance spectroscopy. *Mailing Add:* Dept of Chem Wayne State Univ Detroit MI 48202

RABB, GEORGE BERNARD, b Charleston, SC, Jan 2, 30; m 53. ZOOLOGY, RESOURCE ADMINISTRATION. *Educ:* Col Charleston, BS, 51; Univ Mich, MA, 52, PhD(zool), 57. *Prof Exp:* Ed asst, Charleston Mus, 49; cur & coordr res, 56-64, assoc dir res & educ, 64-69, dept dir, 69-75, DIR, CHICAGO ZOOL PARK, 76- *Concurrent Pos:* mem, Comt Evolutionary Biol, 69-; herpet ed, Copeia, Am Soc Ichthyol & Herpet, 64-68; res assoc, Field Mus Natural Hist, 65-, Univ Chicago, 60-67; rep, Am Asn Zool Parks & Aquariums, Species Surv Comn, Int Union, Conservation Nature, 78-; adv, Encyclopedia Britannica, Standard Educ Encyclopedia, 63-, Coronet Films, 64- *Mem:* Fel AAAS; Am Soc Ichthyol & Herpet (pres, 78); Animal Behav Soc; Am Soc Mammal; Am Soc Naturalists. *Res:* Vertebrate behavior; evolution; ecology of reptiles; amphibians. *Mailing Add:* Chicago Zool Park Brookfield IL 60513

RABB, ROBERT LAMAR, b Lenoir, NC, Aug 6, 19; m 46; c 2. ENTOMOLOGY, POPULATION BIOLOGY. *Educ:* NC State Univ, BS, 47, MS, 50, PhD(entom), 53. *Prof Exp:* Asst entom, 47-50, asst to exten entomologist, 51-52, from asst prof to assoc prof, 53-63, PROF ENTOM, NC STATE UNIV, 63- *Honors & Awards:* Ciba-Geigy Recognition Award, Entom Soc Am, 73, Founders Mem Award, 77. *Mem:* Entom Soc Am; Ecol Soc Am; AAAS; Am Inst Biol Sci; Int Orgn Biol Control. *Res:* Insect ecology and management of agricultural insect pests. *Mailing Add:* Dept of Entom NC State Univ Raleigh NC 27607

RABE, ALLEN E, b New Holstein, Wis, Nov 12, 31; m 56; c 5. CHEMICAL ENGINEERING. *Educ:* Univ Wis, BS, 54, MS, 55, PhD(chem eng), 58. *Prof Exp:* Develop eng, Linde Co, Union Carbide Corp, 58-60; chem engr, Elec Boat Div, Gen Dynamics Corp, 60-62; SR RES ENGR, E I DU PONT DE NEMOURS & CO, INC, 62- *Mem:* Am Chem Soc; Am Inst Chem Engrs. *Res:* Development of research apparatus for reaction rate constants; measurement of reaction rate constants; analysis and interpretation of kinetic data. *Mailing Add:* Eng Dept E I du Pont de Nemours & Co Inc 1007 Market St Wilmington DE 19898

RABE, AUSMA, b Daugavpils, Latvia, Jan 26, 26; Can citizen. NEUROPSYCHOLOGY. *Educ:* Queen's Univ (Ont), BA, 53, MA, 54; Univ Mich, PhD(physiol psychol), 60. *Prof Exp:* Res scientist, Bur Res Neurol & Psychiat, NJ Neuropsychiat Inst, 60-72; VIS SCIENTIST, NY STATE INST RES MENT RETARDATION, 73- *Concurrent Pos:* Vis prof, Grad Fac, New Sch Social Res, 63- *Mem:* AAAS; Am Psychol Asn; Can Psychol Asn; Soc Neurosci; Int Soc Develop Psychobiol. *Res:* Neural mechanisms of behavior; neuroteratology; behavioral teratology. *Mailing Add:* NY State Inst Res Ment Retard 1050 Forest Hill Rd Staten Island NY 10314

RABE, EDWARD FREDERICK, b Watsontown, Pa, Nov 7, 18; m 43; c 4. PEDIATRIC NEUROLOGY. *Educ:* Bucknell Univ, BS, 39; Yale Univ, MD, 43. *Prof Exp:* Instr pediat, Sch Med, Yale Univ, 47-49; instr, Sch Med, Univ Kans, 49-50, asst prof, 50-51; chief dept, Geisinger Mem Hosp, Danville, Pa, 51-58; asst prof, 61-64, assoc prof, 64-70, PROF PEDIAT, SCH MED, TUFTS UNIV, 70- *Concurrent Pos:* Fel neurol, Mass Gen Hosp, 58-61; dir seizure clin, Pa State Dept Health, 57-58; head sect pediat neurol, New Eng Med Ctr Hosps; pediat neurologist, Boston Floating Hosp; asst pediatrician, Mass Gen Hosp; consult, Paul A Dever State Sch, Mass & New Eng Rehab Inst, Woburn; mem, Task Force II-Minimal Brain Dysfunction, Nat Progs Learning Disabilities in Children, Comt Med & Health Related Servs, 66-69; mem neurol sci res training comt A, Nat Inst Neurol Dis & Stroke, 69-73; mem bd trustees, Easter Seal Res Found, 72-78, chmn, 78-79. *Mem:* Am Acad Pediat; Soc Pediat Res; Am Pediat Soc; Am Acad Neurol. *Res:* Cerebrospinal fluid dynamics; neurological aspects of minimal brain dysfunction; subdural fluid dynamics and treatment of cerebral dysrhythmia; pharmacokinetics of anticonvulsant drugs. *Mailing Add:* Dept Pediat Neurol Tufts-New Eng Med Ctr Hosps Boston MA 02111

RABEL, FREDRIC M, b Mansfield, Ohio, May 29, 38. ANALYTICAL CHEMISTRY. *Educ:* Ohio Univ, BS, 60; Univ Wis-Madison, MS, 62; Univ Pa, PhD(chem), 67. *Prof Exp:* Sr chemist, J T Baker Chem Co, 67-71; sr scientist, H Reeve Angel & Co, Inc, 71-74, TECH SERV MGR, WHATMAN, INC, 74- *Concurrent Pos:* Lectr, Sadtler Res Labs, 70-75 & Ctr Prof Advan, 78- *Mem:* AAAS; Am Chem Soc; Am Soc Testing & Mat. *Res:* Thin layer, column and high performance liquid chromatography, especially applications and materials development; extraction techniques; organometallic syntheses and bonding; development of analytical systems. *Mailing Add:* Whatman Inc 9 Bridewell Pl Clifton NJ 07014

RABEN, IRWIN A(BRAM), b New Orleans, La, Oct 26, 22; m 45; c 4. CHEMICAL ENGINEERING. *Educ:* Tulane Univ, BE, 42; La State Univ, MS, 47. *Prof Exp:* Chem engr, New Orleans Water Purification Plant, La, 42; sr process engr, Cities Serv Refining Corp, 47-55; sr process engr & supvr, Wyatt C Hedrick Corp, 55-58; mgr process develop & design, Southwest Res Inst, 58-60, mgr chem eng res, 60-64; supvr process eng, Bechtel Corp, 64-69, mgr air pollution control eng, 69-73; vpres, Western Opers, Combustion Equip Assocs, Inc, 73-79; PRES, IAR TECHNOL, INC, 79- *Concurrent Pos:* Consult mgt & environ. *Mem:* Am Inst Chem Engrs; Air Pollution Control Asn; Am Chem Soc; Sigma Xi. *Res:* Development and design of chemical processes and equipment; heat transfer; economics; development and design of commercial size flue-gas desulphurization systems for utility boilers; process design of air quality control systems. *Mailing Add:* 130 Sandringham South Moraga CA 94556

RABENSTEIN, ALBERT LOUIS, b East Liverpool, Ohio, May, 20, 31. MATHEMATICS. *Educ:* Washington & Jefferson Col, AB, 52; Univ WVa, MS, 53; Mass Inst Technol, PhD(math), 58. *Prof Exp:* Asst prof math, Allegheny Col, 59-61 & Pa State Univ, 61-64; asst prof, Macalester Col, 64-68, assoc prof, 68-72; assoc prof, 72-75, PROF MATH, WASHINGTON & JEFFERSON COL, 75- *Mem:* Math Asn Am. *Res:* Ordinary differential equations. *Mailing Add:* Dept of Math Washington & Jefferson Col Washington PA 15301

RABENSTEIN, DALLAS LEROY, b Portland, Ore, June 13, 42; m 64; c 2. ANALYTICAL CHEMISTRY. *Educ:* Univ Wash, BS, 64; Univ Wis, PhD(anal chem), 68. *Prof Exp:* Res asst nuclear magnetic resonance, Univ Wis, 65-66, lectr, 67-68; res chemist, Chevron Res Co, 68-69; asst prof, 69-72, assoc prof, 72-79, PROF CHEM, UNIV ALTA, 79- *Concurrent Pos:* Res grants, Nat Res Coun Can, Nat Sci & Eng Res Coun Can & Environ Can. *Mem:* AAAS; Am Chem Soc; Chem Inst Can. *Res:* Nuclear magnetic resonance spectroscopy; solution chemistry of metal-complexes; application of nuclear magnetic resonance to biochemistry; analytical biochemistry. *Mailing Add:* Dept of Chem Univ of Alta Edmonton AB T6G 2G7 Can

RABER, DOUGLAS JOHN, b New York, NY, Nov 13, 42; m 67. CHEMISTRY. *Educ:* Dartmouth Col, AB, 64; Univ Mich, PhD(org chem), 68. *Prof Exp:* NIH fel, Princeton Univ, 68-70; asst prof, 70-75, assoc prof, 75-80, PROF CHEM, UNIV SOUTH FLA, 80- *Mem:* AAAS; Am Chem Soc; The Chem Soc. *Res:* Synthetic organic chemistry, particularly the development of new methods and techniques; synthetic applications of physical organic chemistry. *Mailing Add:* Dept of Chem Univ of South Fla Tampa FL 33620

RABI, ISIDOR ISAAC, b Rymanow, Austria, July 29, 98; US citizen; m 26; c 2. PHYSICS. *Educ:* Cornell Univ, BChem, 19; Columbia Univ, PhD(physics), 27. *Hon Degrees:* DSc, Princeton Univ, 47, Harvard Univ, 56, Williams Col, Mass, 58, Univ Birmingham, 60, Adelphi Col, 62, Clark Univ, 62 & Israel Inst Technol, 63; LLD, Dropsie Col, 56; LHD, Hebrew Union Col, 58, Oklahoma City Univ, 60 & Bates Col, 77; DHL, Yeshiva Univ, 64; ScD, Franklin & Marshall Col, 64 & Univ Coimbra, 66; Dr, Jewish Theol Sem Am, 66. *Prof Exp:* Tutor physics, City Col New York, 24-27; Barnard fel from Columbia Univ to Zurich & Hamburg, 27-28; Int Educ Bd fel, Munich, Hamburg, Zurich, Copenhagen & Leipzig, 28-29; lectr physics, 29-30, from asst prof to prof, 30-50, chmn dept, 45-49, Higgins prof, 51-64, univ prof, 64-67, EMER UNIV PROF PHYSICS, COLUMBIA UNIV, 67- *Concurrent Pos:* Adams fel, 35; chmn vacuum tube develop comt, Nat Defense Res Comt, 42-45; mem staff & assoc dir radiation lab, Mass Inst Technol, 40-45, Karl T Compton lectr, 62; trustee, Assoc Univs, Inc, 46-; pres, 61-62, chmn bd, 62-63; US deleg gen conf, UNESCO, 50, mem US Nat Comt 50-53, 58-; mem & chmn sci adv comt, Off Defense Mobilization, 53-57; US mem sci comt, UN, 54-; Morris Loeb lectr, Harvard Univ, 55-56; vpres, Int Conf Peaceful Uses Atomic Energy, Geneva, 55, 58 & US rep, 64; vis prof, Rockefeller Univ, 57-; assoc mem med testing coun, Europ Molecular Biol Orgn, 65. Mem, Inst Advan Study, 38-39; mem coun, Nat Acad Sci, 46-49; mem gen adv comt, AEC, 46-, chmn comn, 52-56; mem adv coun, Dept Physics, Princeton Univ, 48-51, Dept Hist, 65-68; mem bd gov, Weizmann Inst Sci, 49-; mem adv comt, Inst Math & Mech, NY Univ, 50; mem adv bd, Inst Basic Res Sci, Univ Calif, Berkeley, 56-59; mem, President's Sci Adv Comt, 57-, chmn, 56-57; mem bd consult, Fund for Repub, 57-; sci adv comt, Int Atomic Energy Agency, 58-; sci comt, NATO, 58-; adv coun, NY State Advan Indust Res & Develop, 60-; comt med educ & comt res & fels, Mt Sinai Hosp, 61-62; vis comt bd overseers, Harvard Univ, 61-63; gen adv comt, Arms Control & Disarmament Agency, 62- *Honors & Awards:* Nobel Prize in Physics, 44; Prize, Sigma Xi, 36; Prize, AAAS, 39; Cresson Medal, Franklin Inst, 42; US Medal for Merit, 48; King's Medal, Gt Brit, 48; Comdr, Order Southern Cross, Brazil, 52; Comdr, Legion of Honor, France, 56; Henrietta Szold Award, 56; hon fel, Weizmann Inst Sci, 57; Barnard Medal, 60; Priestley Mem Award, Dickinson Col, 64; Niels Bohr Int Gold Medal, 67; Atoms for Peace Award, 67. *Mem:* Nat Acad Sci; AAAS; fel Am Phys Soc (pres, 50); Am Philos Soc; Brazilian Acad Sci. *Res:* Nuclear physics; quantum mechanics; molecular beams magnetism. *Mailing Add:* 450 Riverside Dr New York NY 10027

RABIDEAU, PETER W, b Johnstown, Pa, Mar 4, 40; m 62; c 4. ORGANIC CHEMISTRY. *Educ:* Loyola Univ, BS, 64; Case Inst Technol, MS, 67; Case Western Reserve Univ, PhD(org chem), 68. *Prof Exp:* Res assoc org chem, Ben May Lab Cancer Res, Univ Chicago, 68-69, instr, 69-70; asst prof, 70-73, assoc prof, 73-77, PROF CHEM, IND UNIV-PURDUE UNIV, INDIANAPOLIS, 77- *Mem:* Am Chem Soc. *Res:* Stereochemistry of cyclic hydrocarbons by nuclear magnetic resonance; metal ammonia reduction of aromatic compounds. *Mailing Add:* 6225 Wedgewood Way Indianapolis IN 46254

RABIDEAU, SHERMAN WEBBER, b Cloquet, Minn, May 9, 20; m 43; c 3. PHYSICAL CHEMISTRY. *Educ:* Univ Minn, BChem, 41; Univ Iowa, MS, 47, PhD(phys chem), 49. *Prof Exp:* Chemist, Firestone Tire & Rubber Co, 41-42; res chemist electrochem, US Naval Res Lab, 42-46; instr chem, Univ Iowa, 47-49; MEM STAFF CHEM RES, LOS ALAMOS NAT LAB, UNIV

CALIF, 49- *Honors & Awards:* Clark Medal, Am Chem Soc. *Mem:* Fel AAAS; fel Am Inst Chemists (dir-at-large, 75-); Am Chem Soc; Sigma Xi. *Res:* Laser induced chemistry; gas phase reaction kinetics; isotope separations. *Mailing Add:* 100 Baranca Rd Los Alamos NM 87544

RABIE, RONALD LEE, b Yakima, Wash, May 2, 46; m 70; c 2. SHOCK WAVE PHYSICS. *Educ:* Cent Wash Univ, BS, 72; Wash State Univ, PhD(shock wave physics), 77. *Prof Exp:* STAFF MEM SHOCK WAVE PHYSICS, LOS ALAMOS NAT LAB, 77- *Concurrent Pos:* Consult, Los Alamos Tech Assoc, 79- *Res:* Reactive flow in heterogeneous materials and vapor phase explosions both theoretical and experimental. *Mailing Add:* Los Alamos Nat Lab WX-7 MS-950 Los Alamos NM 87544

RABIGER, DOROTHY JUNE, b Philadelphia, Pa, May 30, 35. ORGANIC CHEMISTRY. *Educ:* Ursinus Col, BS, 57; Univ Pa, MS, 60, PhD(org chem), 62. *Prof Exp:* Res chemist, Nat Renderers Asn-USDA, 57-58 & Rohm & Haas Co, 62-64; fel org chem & cancer chemother, Ravdin Inst, Hosp Univ Pa, 64-67, res assoc, 67-69; res chemist, Borden Chem Co, 69; instr pharmaceut chem, Sch Pharm, Temple Univ, 69-70, asst prof, 70-74; INDEPENDENT RES CHEMIST, 74- *Concurrent Pos:* Res grant-in-aid, Temple Univ, 70-71. *Mem:* AAAS; Am Chem Soc; Sigma Xi. *Res:* Cancer chemotherapy; effects of substituents and structural modifications on the properties of organic molecules; synthesis of novel organic compounds for biological applications; chemical topology. *Mailing Add:* 517 Boyer Rd Cheltenham PA 19012

RABII, JAMSHID, b Tehran, Iran, July 12, 46; m 68; c 3. ENDOCRINOLOGY, NEUROENDOCRINOLOGY. *Educ:* Univ Calif, Berkeley, BA, 70; Univ Calif, San Francisco, PhD(endocrinol), 75. *Prof Exp:* Res anatomist, Dept Anat & Brain Res, Univ Calif, Los Angeles, 75-76, fel, Mental Health Training Prog, 76-77; ASST PROF PHYSIOL, RUTGERS UNIV, 77- *Concurrent Pos:* Prin investr grants, NIH, 78-79 & Rutgers Univ, 80-83. *Mem:* Endocrine Soc; Am Physiol Soc; Soc Neurosci; Int Soc Neuroendocrinol; Soc Study Reproduction. *Res:* Neuroendocrinology: longterm influences of opiates on various neuroendocrine phenomena; hypothalamic control of anterior pituitary hormone secretion; involvement of biogenic amines in the regulation of anterior pituitary hormone secretion in mammalian and avian species. *Mailing Add:* Dept Biol Sci Nelson Biol Lab Busch Campus Rutgers Univ Piscataway NJ 08854

RABII, SOHRAB, b Ahwaz, Iran, Dec 30, 37; m 66. THEORETICAL SOLID STATE PHYSICS. *Educ:* Univ Southern Calif, BS, 61; Mass Inst Technol, MS, 62, PhD(solid state physics), 66. *Prof Exp:* Res fel solid state physics, Mass Inst Technol, 66-67; sr res physicist, Monsanto Co, Mo, 67-69; from asst prof to assoc prof elec eng, 69-78, PROF ELEC ENG & SCI, MOORE SCH ELEC ENG, UNIV PA, 78-, CHMN DEPT, 77- *Concurrent Pos:* Fel, Max Planck Soc Advan Sci, Repub Ger, 75. *Mem:* Inst Elec & Electronics Engrs; Am Phys Soc. *Res:* Theoretical calculation of energy band structure and electronic properties of crystalline solids and disordered alloys; electronic structure of molecules and localized state in solids; relativistic effects in atoms molecules and solids. *Mailing Add:* Dept Elec Eng & Sci Univ Pa Philadelphia PA 19444

RABIN, ELIJAH ZEPHANIA, b Ottawa, Ont, Jan 30, 37; m 65; c 2. INTERNAL MEDICINE, BIOCHEMISTRY. *Educ:* Queen's Univ, Ont, MD, 61; McGill Univ, PhD(biochem), 71. *Prof Exp:* Assoc med officer, Prudential Assurance Eng, 68-74; asst prof med, Montreal Gen Hosp, McGill Univ, 70-74; ASSOC PROF MED, UNIV OTTAWA, 74- *Concurrent Pos:* Med Res Coun Can scholar, 70-74; chief med dir, Montreal Life Ins Co, 73-74. *Mem:* Can Soc Clin Invest; Am Soc Nephrology; Int Soc Nephrology. *Res:* Ribonuclease activity in renal failure; role of ribonuclease in uremic toxicology; biochemical structure of human urinary ribonuclease. *Mailing Add:* Div Nephrology 1053 Carling Ave Ottawa ON K1Y 4E9 Can

RABIN, ERWIN R, b St Louis, Mo, Oct 22, 30; m 54; c 3. PATHOLOGY, VIROLOGY. *Educ:* Wash Univ, AB, 52, MD, 56. *Prof Exp:* Intern path, Sch Med, Yale Univ, 56-57, resident, 57-59; asst pathologist, Sinai Hosp Baltimore, Inc, 61-62; asst prof path, Baylor Col Med, 62-66, assoc prof, 66-68; assoc prof path, Sch Med, Wash Univ, 68-74; mem staff, Lattimore-Fink Labs, Inc, 74-76; DIR PATH, HURON RD HOSP, 76- *Concurrent Pos:* Life Ins Med Res Fund fel, 57-58 & USPHS trainee, 58-59; from asst to assoc pathologist, Jewish Hosp St Louis, 68-70, actg dir, 71-74. *Mem:* Col Am Pathologists; Am Asn Pathologists; Int Acad Path. *Res:* Ultrastructural changes in in vivo viral infections as related to viral-host interaction and pathogenesis of the disease. *Mailing Add:* Huron Rd Hosp 13951 Terrace Rd Cleveland OH 44112

RABIN, HERBERT, b Milwaukee, Wis, Nov 14, 28; m 62; c 2. QUANTUM OPTICS, SOLID STATE PHYSICS. *Educ:* Univ Wis, BS, 50; Univ Ill, MS, 51; Univ Md, PhD(physics), 59. *Prof Exp:* Physicist, Elec Div, Naval Res Lab, 52-54, Solid State Physics Div, 54-62, head, Radiation Effects Sect, Dielec Br, 62-65, mat sci staff, 65-66, head, Radiation Physics Sect, Optical Mat Br, Optical Physics Div, 66-67, actg head, Appl Optics Br, 67-68, head, Quantum Optics Br, 68-70, assoc dir space & commun sci & technol, Naval Res Lab, 70-79; DEP ASST SECY NAVY, RES, APPL & SPACE TECHNOL, DEPT NAVY, WASHINGTON, DC, 79- *Concurrent Pos:* Vis scientist, Univ Stuttgart, 60-61; consult, Dept Physics, Univ Sao Paulo, 64 & 70; prof lectr, Dept Physics, George Washington Univ, 55-73; mem, Space Panel, Naval Studies Bd, Nat Acad Sci, 78-, Adv Panel NASA, 72-75, corresp mem, Brazilian Acad Sci, 72-; ed, Quantum Electronics: A Treatise, Acad Press, 75. *Honors & Awards:* Navy Meritorious Civilian Serv Award, 69; E O Hulburt Award, 70. *Mem:* AAAS; fel Am Phys Soc; Sigma Xi; Fed Am Scientists; Optical Soc Am. *Res:* Characterization of defect structure in insulating crystals; elucidation of nonlinear optical phenomena; space research and system developments. *Mailing Add:* Off Asst Secy Navy Res Eng & Systs Washington DC 20350

RABIN, MONROE STEPHEN ZANE, b Brooklyn, NY, Dec 12, 39; m 65; c 2. ELEMENTARY PARTICLE PHYSICS. *Educ:* Columbia Col, AB, 61; Rutgers Univ, MS, 64, PhD(physics), 67. *Prof Exp:* Physicist, Univ Calif, Lawrence Berkeley Lab, 67-72; assoc prof, 72-81, PROF PHYSICS, UNIV MASS, 81- *Mem:* Am Phys Soc; NY Acad Sci; Fedn Am Scientists; Sigma Xi. *Res:* Elementary particle physics: lifetimes of charmed particles, electromagnetic interactions, polarization and form factors of hyperons. *Mailing Add:* Dept Physics Univ Mass Amherst MA 01003

RABIN, ROBERT, b Philadelphia, Pa, Aug 22, 28; m 53; c 3. MICROBIOLOGY, RESEARCH ADMINISTRATION. *Educ:* Philadelphia Col Pharm, BS, 50; Pa State Univ, MS, 52, PhD(bact, biochem), 55. *Prof Exp:* Asst, Pa State Univ, 52-55; asst scientist, Commun Dis Ctr, USPHS, 55-56; sr scientist & group leader, Sci Info Dept, Smith Kline & French Labs, 56-61; asst dir res, Albert Einstein Med Ctr, 61-62, assoc mem res labs, 62-69; grants assoc, Grants Assocs Prog, NIH, Md, 69-70; staff assoc, Off Interdisciplinary Res, NSF, 70-71, prog mgr, Div Environ Systs & Resources, 71-74, dep dir, Div Advan Environ Res & Technol, 74-75; dep assoc dir res & develop progs, Div Biomed & Environ Res, US Energy Res & Develop Admin, 75-76; exec asst, Directorate Biol, Behav & Social Sci, 76, dep asst dir, 76-77, sr sci assoc, Off Dir, 77-79, DEP ASST DIR, DIRECTORATE BIOL, BEHAV & SOCIAL SCI, NSF, 79- *Concurrent Pos:* USPHS fel, 62-65. *Mem:* AAAS. *Res:* Fatty acid and glyoxylate metabolism; amino acid biosynthesis; control mechanisms; environmental sciences; research and development administration. *Mailing Add:* US Nat Sci Found Washington DC 20550

RABINER, LAWRENCE RICHARD, b Brooklyn, NY, Sept 28, 43; m 68; c 3. ELECTRICAL ENGINEERING. *Educ:* Mass Inst Technol, BS & MS, 64, PhD(elec eng), 67. *Prof Exp:* MEM TECH STAFF, BELL TEL LABS, 67- *Honors & Awards:* Biennial Award, Acoust Soc Am, 74; Piori Award, Inst Elec & Electronics, Engrs, 80 & Soc Award, 80. *Mem:* Fel Inst Elec & Electronics Engrs; Acoust Soc Am. *Res:* Speech communications including synthesis, perception and analysis; digital filtering and computer applications. *Mailing Add:* Rm 2D-533 Bell Tel Labs Inc Murray Hill NJ 07974

RABINER, SAUL FREDERICK, b New York, NY, Aug 11, 26; m 50; c 3. HEMATOLOGY, INTERNAL MEDICINE. *Educ:* Tulane Univ, BS, 49; State Univ NY, MD, 52; Am Bd Internal Med, dipl, 61, hemat, 72. *Prof Exp:* Intern med, Maimonides Hosp, Brooklyn, NY, 52-53, resident, 53-54; asst instr, State Univ NY & Kings County Hosp, 54-56; resident, Montefiore Hosp, New York, 56-57; instr med, New York Hosp-Cornell Med Ctr, 58-59; asst dir hemat, Michael Reese Hosp, 59-61, assoc dir, 61-64, dir clin hemat, 64-71; asst prof, 71-74, PROF MED, HEALTH SCI CTR, UNIV ORE, PORTLAND, 74-; CHIEF MED, GOOD SAMARITAN HOSP & MED CTR, PORTLAND, 71- *Concurrent Pos:* Fel hemat, New York Hosp-Cornell Med Ctr, 57-58; assoc prof, Pitzker Sch Med, Univ Chicago, 70-71. *Mem:* AAAS; Am Physiol Soc; fel Am Col Physicians; Am Fedn Clin Res; Am Soc Hemat. *Res:* Coagulation of blood; hypercoagulability; fibrinolysis; plasma expanders. *Mailing Add:* Suite 350 2222 NW Lovejoy St Portland OR 97210

RABINOFF, ROBERT ANDREW, b New York, NY, Dec 3, 48; m 73. PHYSICS, ATMOSPHERIC PHYSICS. *Educ:* Columbia Univ, BA, 69; Univ Ariz, MS, 73, PhD(atmospheric physics), 75. *Prof Exp:* Programmer space sci, Goddard Inst Space Studies, NASA, 65-68; programmer plasma physics, Columbia Univ, 68-71; res asst atmospheric physics, Univ Ariz, 71-75; asst prof, 75-79, ASSOC PROF PHYSICS, MAHARISHI INT UNIV, 79- *Mem:* Am Asn Physics Teachers. *Res:* Relationship between physics and consciousness; interaction of consciousness and large-scale physical phenomena, especially weather. *Mailing Add:* Dept of Physics Maharishi Int Univ Fairfield IA 52556

RABINOVICH, SERGIO ROSPIGLIOSI, b Lima, Peru, Apr 4, 28; m 53; c 4. INTERNAL MEDICINE, VIROLOGY. *Educ:* Univ Lima, BM & MD, 54. *Prof Exp:* Intern, Talara Hosp, Peru, 53; asst med resident, Grasslands Hosp, Valhalla, NY, 55-56, chief med resident, 56-57; resident gastroenterol, Henry Ford Hosp, Detroit, 57-58; pvt pract, Peru, 58-59; prof med & head dept, Univ San Agustin, Peru, 60-61; physician-in-chg, Hosp Arzobispo Loayza, Lima, Peru, 63; assoc, Col Med, Univ Iowa, 63, from asst prof to assoc prof med, 65-73; PROF MED & CHMN DIV INFECTIOUS DIS, SCH MED, SOUTHERN ILL UNIV, 73-, CHMN DEPT, 74- *Concurrent Pos:* Consult, Arequipa Gen Hosp, Peru, 60-61; res fel med, Col Med, Univ Iowa, 63-65; res fel, Sch Med, Univ Kans, 64-65. *Mem:* Am Soc Microbiol; AMA. *Res:* Infectious diseases. *Mailing Add:* Dept Med Div Infect Dis Southern Ill Univ Sch Med Springfield IL 62708

RABINOVICI, BENJAMIN, b Vaslui, Rumania, May 17, 22; US citizen; m 53; c 2. SOLID STATE ELECTRONICS. *Educ:* Bucharest Polytech Inst, Dipl Ing, 48; Columbia Univ, MS, 55; Univ Paris, DrSc, 63. *Prof Exp:* Sr engr, CBS Columbia TV Lab, 52-56; staff scientist, IBM Watson Sci Lab, 56-60; sect head res, Radio Corp Am Adv Commun Lab, 60-62, sr staff scientist, 62-64; mgr res, Electronics Data Processing Div, Honeywell, Inc, 64-67; adj prof, 65-67, PROF ELEC ENG, NORTHEASTERN UNIV, 67- *Honors & Awards:* Award, Inst Elec & Electronics Engrs, 62. *Mem:* AAAS; sr mem Inst Elec & Electronics Engrs; Am Phys Soc. *Res:* Magnetic thin film memories; ferromagnetics; optoelectronics; cryogenics; communications. *Mailing Add:* 20 Dean Rd Brookline MA 02146

RABINOVITCH, BENTON SEYMOUR, b Montreal, Que, Feb 19, 19. PHYSICAL CHEMISTRY. *Educ:* McGill Univ, BSc, 39, PhD(phys chem), 42. *Prof Exp:* Res chemist, Chem Warfare Labs, 42; Royal Soc Can fel, Harvard Univ, 46-47, Milton fel, 47-48; from asst prof to assoc prof, 48-57, PROF CHEM, UNIV WASH, 57- *Concurrent Pos:* Guggenheim fel, 61; vis scientist, Nat Res Coun Can, 62; Du Pont lectr, Univ Rochester, 64; mem, various comts, Nat Acad Sci-Nat Res Coun, 65-; vis Sloan prof, Harvard Univ, 66; Reilly lectr, Univ Notre Dame, 68; distinguished vis prof, Univ Ariz, 68 & Israel Inst Technol-Technion, 78; ed, Ann Rev Phys Chem, 75-; Debye lectr, Cornell Univ, 78. vis fel, Trinity Col, Oxford Univ, 71. *Honors & Awards:* Research Prize, Sigma Xi, 81. *Mem:* Fel Am Phys Soc; Am Chem Soc; Royal Soc Chem; fel Am Acad Arts & Sci. *Res:* Chemical kinetics; unimolecular reactions; chemical activation; non-equilibrium systems; energy transfer and relaxation. *Mailing Add:* Dept of Chem BG-10 Univ of Wash Seattle WA 98195

RABINOVITCH, BERNARD, b London, Eng, Nov 4, 22; US citizen; m 51; c 3. BIOPHYSICS, OPHTHALMOLOGY. *Educ:* Univ London, BSc, 44; Cambridge Univ, PhD(phys polymers), 48. *Prof Exp:* Asst prof chem, Ill Inst Technol, 49-55; asst prof biochem, Univ Chicago, 55-60; prin scientist chem, United Technol Ctr, 64-67; prof biochem, Univ Okla, 67-80; MEM FAC, DEPT CHEM, UNIV WASH, 80- *Concurrent Pos:* Eli Lilly fel, Harvard Univ, 48-49; NIH spec fel, Stanford Univ, 65-67; NIH res grant, Univ Okla, 71-74; res consult ophthal, Col Med, Univ Okla, 65-; vis prof chem, Univ Essex, 74. *Mem:* Am Chem Soc; Asn Res Vision & Ophthal; Am Soc Photobiol. *Res:* Biophysics of vision; mechanism of primary visual process; quantum efficiency of photolysis of rhodopsin and model compounds in micellar systems. *Mailing Add:* Dept Chem BG 10 Univ Wash Seattle WA 98195

RABINOVITCH, ELVIRA BORISOVNA, b Kharkov, USSR, Sept 11, 45; US citizen; m 69; c 1. POLYMER ENGINEERING, POLYMER CHEMISTRY. *Educ:* Textile Inst, Moscow, USSR, BS, 68; Case Western Reserve Univ, MS, 80. *Prof Exp:* Qual control engr, Plastic Plant, Lvov, USSR, 68-73; asst develop, 76-77, res & develop engr, 77-80, advan res & develop engr, 80, SR RES & DEVELOP ENGR, BF GOODRICH CHEM GROUP, 80- *Mem:* Soc Plastics Engrs; Soc Plastics Indust. *Res:* Development of polyvinyl chloride compounds; processing, testing and weathering, including exterior application, products-siding, accessories, windows. *Mailing Add:* 3798 Colony Rd South Euclid OH 44118

RABINOVITCH, MICHEL PINKUS, b Sao Paulo, Brazil, Mar 22, 26; m 67; c 2. CELL BIOLOGY, EXPERIMENTAL MEDICINE. *Educ:* Univ Sao Paulo, MD, 49, Livre Docente, 53. *Prof Exp:* Res assoc cellular immunol, Rockefeller Univ, 64-65, asst prof, 65-69; assoc prof, 69-73, PROF CELL BIOL, SCH MED, NY UNIV, 73- *Concurrent Pos:* Rockefeller Found fel, Univ Chicago, Marine Biol Lab & Univ Calif, Berkeley, 53-54. *Mem:* Am Asn Immunol; Am Soc Cell Biol; Harvey Soc. *Res:* Nucleic acids content of tissues; RNA synthesis in amoeba; control of serum ribonuclease by the kidneys; phagocytic recognition by macrophages, tissue culture cells, insect hemocytes, Acanthamoeba; cell adhesion and spreading. *Mailing Add:* Dept of Cell Biol NY Univ Sch of Med New York NY 10016

RABINOVITZ, MARCO, b Braila, Rumania, Dec 12, 23; US citizen; m 57; c 2. BIOCHEMISTRY. *Educ:* Univ Pa, BS, 44; Univ Minn, PhD(biochem), 50. *Prof Exp:* Am Cancer Soc fel, Comt on Growth, Nat Res Coun, Univ Calif, 50-52, res biochemist, Dept Physiol Chem, 52-58; BIOCHEMIST, NAT CANCER INST, 58- *Mem:* AAAS; Am Chem Soc; Am Soc Biol Chem; Soc Exp Biol & Med; Am Asn Cancer Res; Am Soc Cell Biol. *Res:* Protein biosynthebiosynthesis; antimetabolites; biosynthetic control mechanisms; biochemical basis for cancer chemotherapy. *Mailing Add:* Nat Cancer Inst Bldg 37 Rm 6B 05 Bethesda MD 20805

RABINOW, JACOB, b Karkov, Russia, Jan 8, 10; nat US; m 43; c 2. ENGINEERING. *Educ:* City Col New York, BS, 33, EE, 34. *Prof Exp:* Radio technician, Sheffield Radio Co, NY, 34; radio engr, Sterling Radio Co, 34-35 & Halson Radio Mfg Co, 35-37; jr elec engr, Fed Power Comn, 37; eng draftsman, Gibbs & Hill Eng Co, 37-38; mech engr, Nat Bur Standards, 38-53; consult, Diamond Ord Fuze Labs, 53-54; pres, Rabinow Electronics Inc, Control Data Corp, 54-68, vpres, 68-72; CHIEF RES ENGR, NAT ENG LAB, NAT BUR STANDARDS, 72- *Res:* Design of electronic equipment; design and development of ordnance devices such as guided missiles and fuzes; patents on special cameras, watch regulators, headlight dimmers; inventor of magnetic fluid clutch; optical character recognition machines. *Mailing Add:* Nat Bur of Standards Washington DC 20234

RABINOWICZ, ERNEST, b Berlin, Ger, Apr 22, 26; US citizen; m 53; c 3. MECHANICAL ENGINEERING. *Educ:* Cambridge Univ, BA, 47, PhD(phys chem), 50. *Prof Exp:* Mem staff, Div Indust Coop, 50-54, from asst prof to assoc prof mech eng, 54-67, PROF MECH ENG, MASS INST TECHNOL, 67- *Concurrent Pos:* Consult, IBM Corp, 61-75 & Asn Am Railroads, 75-81; vis prof, Israel Inst Technol, 69. *Honors & Awards:* Hodson Award, Am Soc Lubrication Engrs, 57. *Mem:* Am Phys Soc; fel Am Soc Lubrication Engrs; Am Soc Mech Engrs. *Res:* Friction lubrication and wear; surface properties of solids; experimentation and measurement techniques; accelerated testing. *Mailing Add:* Rm 35-010 Mass Inst Technol Cambridge MA 02139

RABINOWITZ, DEBORAH, b Windham, Conn, Sept 9, 47. PLANT ECOLOGY, POPULATION BIOLOGY. *Educ:* New Col, Fla, AB, 70; Univ Chicago, PhD(theoret biol), 75. *Prof Exp:* Asst prof, 75-80, ASSOC PROF BIOL, UNIV MICH, ANN ARBOR, 80- *Mem:* Soc Tropical Biol; AAAS; Ecol Soc Am; Brit Ecol Soc; Soc Int Demographia Plantarum. *Res:* Population ecology; biology of mangroves; biology of rare plants; biology of prairies and grasslands; grass biology. *Mailing Add:* Div of Biol Sci Univ of Mich Ann Arbor MI 48109

RABINOWITZ, ISRAEL NATHAN, b New York, NY, Jan 24, 35; m 59; c 2. BIOCHEMISTRY. *Educ:* City Col New York, BS, 56; Univ Wash, MS, 62; Rutgers Univ, PhD(biochem), 65. *Prof Exp:* Damon Runyon fel, King's Col, London, 65-66; USPHS fel, Stanford Univ, 67-69, res assoc biophys, 69-70, physiol, 71-72, RES ASSOC PHYSIOL, SCH MED, STANFORD UNIV, 72-; CONSULT, VET ADMIN HOSP, PALO ALTO, 74- *Concurrent Pos:* Lectr, Col Notre Dame, Calif, 70- *Mem:* AAAS; Am Crystallog Asn; Biophys Soc; Sigma Xi. *Res:* Biological structure and function; metal complexes; membrane biophysics. *Mailing Add:* 2534 Foothill Rd Santa Barbara CA 93105

RABINOWITZ, JACK GRANT, b New York, NY, July 9, 27; m 51, 72; c 5. RADIOLOGY. *Educ:* Univ Calif, BA, 49; Univ Berne, MD, 55. *Prof Exp:* Instr radiol, State Univ NY Downstate Med Ctr, 60-61; asst radiologist, Mt Sinai Hosp, 62-65; assoc prof radiol, Mt Sinai Sch Med, 65-67; radiologist-in-chief, Brooklyn-Cumberland Med Ctr, 67-70; prof radiol, State Univ NY Downstate Med Ctr, 70-74; prof diag radiol & chmn dept, Univ Tenn, Memphis, 74-78; PROF RADIOL & CHMN DEPT, MT SINAI SCH MED, 78- *Concurrent Pos:* Dir dept radiol, Kings County Hosp Ctr, 70-74; consult, US Vet Admin, Bronx. *Mem:* Fel Am Col Radiol; Radiol Soc NAm; AMA; Asn Univ Radiol. *Mailing Add:* Dept of Radiol Mt Sinai Sch Med New York NY 10029

RABINOWITZ, JAMES ROBERT, b New York, NY, Apr 7, 42. MOLECULAR BIOPHYSICS, ENVIRONMENTAL BIOPHYSICS. *Educ:* Alfred Univ, BA, 62; State Univ NY, Buffalo, PhD(physics), 72. *Prof Exp:* Res assoc, Ctr Theoret Biol, State Univ NY, Buffalo, 70-72, fel, 72-73; assoc res scientist, Inst Environ Med, New York Univ Med Ctr, 73-77; res scientist, New York Inst Technol, 77-80; RES PHYSICIST, HEALTH EFFECTS RES LAB, US ENVIRON PROTECTION AGENCY, 80- *Concurrent Pos:* NATO fel, Uppsala Univ, 69; guest scientist, Northeast Radiol Health Lab, Bur Pub Health, Food & Drug Admin, Dept Health, Educ & Welfare, 73. *Mem:* AAAS; Radiation Res Soc; Bioelectromagnetics Soc; Sigma Xi. *Res:* Interaction of nonionizing radiation and electromagnetic fields with biological systems; the use of molecular interaction theory to predict chemical toxicity. *Mailing Add:* Exp Biol Div MD-74 Health Effects Res Lab US Environ Protection Agency Triangle Park NC 27711

RABINOWITZ, JESSE CHARLES, b New York, NY, Apr 28, 25. BIOCHEMISTRY. *Educ:* Polytech Inst Brooklyn, BS, 45; Univ Wis, MS, 47, PhD(biochem), 49. *Prof Exp:* Nat Heart Inst trainee, Univ Wis, 50-51; USPHS fel, Univ Calif, Berkeley, 51-53; chemist, Nat Inst Arthritis & Metab Dis, Md, 53-57; assoc prof, 57-62, PROF BIOCHEM, UNIV CALIF, BERKELEY, 62-, CHMN DEPT, 78- *Mem:* Nat Acad Sci; Am Soc Biol Chemists; Am Soc Microbiol; Am Chem Soc. *Res:* Enzymology; purine fermentation; folic acid coenzymes; iron-sulfur proteins; protein biosynthesis. *Mailing Add:* Dept of Biochem Univ of Calif Berkeley CA 94720

RABINOWITZ, JOSEPH LOSHAK, b Odessa, Ukraine, Nov 4, 23; US citizen; m 46; c 3. BIOCHEMISTRY. *Educ:* Philadelphia Col Pharm, BS, 44; Univ Pa, MSc, 48, PhD(org chem), 50. *Hon Degrees:* DSc, Univ Bordeaux, France, 79. *Prof Exp:* From res assoc to assoc prof, 53-70, PROF BIOCHEM, SCH DENT MED, UNIV PA, 70-; CHIEF RADIOISOTOPE RES, VET ADMIN HOSP, PHILADELPHIA, 58- *Concurrent Pos:* Fulbright fel, Carlsberg Lab, Copenhagen, Denmark, 58; fel, Eng, 68; prin scientist, Radioisotope Serv, Vet Admin Hosp, Philadelphia, 53-58; ed, Topics Med Chem. *Mem:* Am Chem Soc; Am Soc Biol Chem; Soc Nuclear Med; Soc Exp Biol & Med; Am Nuclear Soc. *Res:* Biochemistry of lipids, thyroid function, obesity and alchoholism; isotope methodology. *Mailing Add:* 127 Juniper Rd Havertown PA 19083

RABINOWITZ, JOSHUA H, b Brooklyn, NY, Aug 21, 52; m 77; c 2. DISCRETE MATHEMATICS, CRYPTOGRAPHY. *Educ:* Yeshiva Col, BA, 72; Columbia Univ, MA, 74, PhD(math), 78. *Prof Exp:* Asst prof math, Univ Ill, 78-81; MEM TECH STAFF, MITRE CORP, 81- *Mem:* Math Asn Am; Am Math Soc. *Res:* Complex variables and complex analytic geometry; discrete mathematics; cryptography; graph theory; combinatorics. *Mailing Add:* Mail Stop E095 Mitre Corp Bedford MA 01730

RABINOWITZ, LAWRENCE, b San Francisco, Calif, Apr 9, 33; m 59; c 3. PHYSIOLOGY. *Educ:* Univ Calif, Berkeley, AB, 56; Univ Calif, San Francisco, PhD(renal physiol), 61. *Prof Exp:* NIH res fel, 61-63; asst prof physiol, Univ NC, Chapel Hill, 63-68; from asst prof to assoc prof, 68-76, PROF HUMAN PHYSIOL, SCH MED, UNIV CALIF, DAVIS, 76- *Mem:* AAAS; Am Physiol Soc; Am Soc Nephrology. *Res:* Renal physiology, particularly the excretion of urea and related organic nonelectrolytes. *Mailing Add:* Dept of Human Physiol Univ of Calif Sch Med Davis CA 95616

RABINOWITZ, MARIO, b Mexico City, Mex, Oct 24, 36. LOW TEMPERATURE PHYSICS, ELECTRICAL ENGINEERING. *Educ:* Univ Wash, BS, 59, MS, 60; Wash State Univ, PhD(physics), 64. *Prof Exp:* Electronics engr, Collins Radio Co, 57; res engr, Nuclear Physics Dept, Boeing Co, 58-61; res asst physics, Wash State Univ, 61-63; sr physicist, Plasma Prog, Westinghouse Res Labs, 63-66; mgr gas discharges & vacuum pump physics, Varian Assocs, 66-67; res physicist, Stanford Linear Accelerator Ctr, 67-74; mgr superconductivity & cryogenics, 74-80, SR SCIENTIST, ELEC POWER RES INST, 80- *Concurrent Pos:* George F Baker scholar, 56-57; assoc prof, San Jose State Univ, 73-76; adj prof, Boston Univ & Case Western Reserve Univ, 75- *Mem:* Am Phys Soc; Am Vacuum Soc; NY Acad Sci; Am Asn Physics Teachers; Am Nuclear Soc. *Res:* Radiation effects; electron and photodesorption of gases; electron emission; gas and metal-vapor arcs and plasmas; electrical discharges in vacuum; electrical explosion of metals; ultrahigh vacuum; superconducting generation, transmission; electric power; cryoresistive transmission; magnetic field trapping. *Mailing Add:* 262 1/2 Arbor Rd Menlo Park CA 94025

RABINOWITZ, MURRAY, b New York, NY, Dec 24, 27; m 66. INTERNAL MEDICINE, BIOCHEMISTRY. *Educ:* NY Univ, BS, 47, MD, 50. *Prof Exp:* Intern, Beth Israel Hosp, New York, 50-51; asst resident med, Montefiore Hosp, 51-52; asst med, Harvard Med Sch, 52-54; asst resident, Mass Gen Hosp, Boston, 54-55; vis investr, Rockefeller Inst, 57-58; dir cardiopulmonary lab, 58-66, from asst prof to prof, 58-73, LOUIS BLOCK PROF MED & BIOCHEM, DIV BIOL SCI, UNIV CHICAGO, 73-, MEM STAFF, FRANKLIN MCLEAN RES INST, PRITZKER SCH MED, 58- *Concurrent Pos:* USPHS res fel, Peter Bent Brigham Hosp, Boston, 52-54; res fel, Harvard Med Sch, 52-54; NSF fel, 56-57; USPHS res fel biochem, Univ Wis, 55-56. *Mem:* Am Heart Asn; Am Fedn Clin. *Res:* Asn Am Physicians; Am Soc Clin Invest; Am Soc Biol Chem. Res: Cardiopulmonary physiology; cardiac metabolism and hypertrophy; biochemistry of nucleic acids and protein synthesis; mitochondrial biogenesis. *Mailing Add:* Dept of Med Univ of Chicago Chicago IL 60637

RABINOWITZ, PHILIP, b Philadelphia, Pa, Aug 14, 26; m 51; c 5. MATHEMATICS. *Educ:* Univ Pa, AB, 46, AM, 48, PhD(math), 51. *Prof Exp:* Mathematician, Nat Bur Standards, 51-55 & 59-60; sr scientist, Weizmann Inst, 55-59, 60-64 & 65-67; vis assoc prof appl math, Brown Univ, 64-65; ASSOC PROF APPL MATH, WEIZMANN INST SCI, 67- *Concurrent Pos:* Vis prof, Hebrew Univ, Jerusalem, 67-68, Latrobe Univ, Australia, 77, Univ Witwatersrand, SAfrica, 78 & Univ New South Wales, Australia, 80; prof, Bar-Illan Univ, Israel, 70-72; assoc ed, Math of Comput, 70- *Honors & Awards:* Info Processing Asn Israel Prize, 68. *Mem:* Fel Japanese Soc Prom Sci. *Res:* Application of electronic digital computers to numerical analysis; numerical integration, theory and practice. *Mailing Add:* Dept of Appl Math Weizmann Inst of Sci Rehovoth Israel

RABINOWITZ, RONALD, b Pittsburgh, Pa, Feb 24, 43; m 67; c 3. PEDIATRIC SURGERY, UROLOGY. *Educ:* Univ Pittsburgh, BS, 64, MD, 68. *Prof Exp:* Intern surg, hosps of Univ Health Ctr Pittsburgh, 68-69, resident, 69-70, resident urol surg, 72-75; resident & clin fel pediat urol surg, Hosp Sick Children, Toronto, 75-76; asst prof, 76-80, ASSOC PROF UROL SURG & PEDIAT, SCH MED, UNIV ROCHESTER, 80-; CHIEF UROL, ROCHESTER GEN HOSP, 76- *Concurrent Pos:* Attend urologist, Rochester Gen Hosp, 76-; attend pediat urologist, Birth Defects Ctr, Univ Rochester & Strong Mem Hosps, 76-; proj surgeon, Artificial Urinary Sphincter Proj, NASA, 78- *Honors & Awards:* Physician's Recognition Award, AMA, 74. *Mem:* Am Urol Asn; Am Acad Pediat; Am Col Surgeons; Soc Pediat Urol. *Res:* Development of an artificial urinary sphincter. *Mailing Add:* Div of Urol Box 656 601 Elmwood Ave Rochester NY 14642

RABINS, MICHAEL J, b New York, NY, Feb 24, 32; m 56; c 3. MECHANICAL ENGINEERING, CONTROL SYSTEMS. *Educ:* Mass Inst Technol, BS, 53; Carnegie Inst Technol, MS, 54; Univ Wis, PhD(mech eng), 59. *Prof Exp:* Design engr, M W Kellogg Co, 53-54; hydraul engr, Repub Aviation Corp, 55; design engr, Atlantic Design Co, 55-56; asst prof mech eng, Univ Wis, 59-60; from asst prof to assoc prof, NY Univ, 60-70; prof syst eng & prog dir, Polytech Inst Brooklyn, 70-75; vis prof, Polytech Inst Grenoble, France, 75; dir, Off Univ Res, Off Secy Transp, Washington, DC, 75-77; CHMN DEPT MECH ENG, WAYNE STATE UNIV, 77- *Concurrent Pos:* NSF sci fac fel, Univ Calif, Berkeley, 67-68. *Mem:* Fel Am Soc Mech Engrs. *Res:* Nonlinear automatic controls; system engineering and design. *Mailing Add:* Dept of Mech Eng 667 Merrick Detroit MI 48202

RABITZ, HERSCHEL ALBERT, b Los Angeles, Calif, Apr 10, 44; m 70. PHYSICAL CHEMISTRY. *Educ:* Univ Calif, Berkeley, BS, 66; Harvard Univ, PhD(chem physics), 70. *Prof Exp:* Asst prof, 71-76, assoc prof, 76-79, PROF CHEM, PRINCETON UNIV, 80- *Concurrent Pos:* Dreyfus Found teacher-scholar, 74; Sloan Found fel, 75. *Mem:* AAAS; Sigma Xi. *Res:* Theoretical chemistry; molecular collisions; time-dependent processes. *Mailing Add:* Frick Chem Lab Princeton Univ Princeton NJ 08540

RABJOHN, NORMAN, b Rochester, NY, May 1, 15; m 43; c 1. ORGANIC CHEMISTRY. *Educ:* Univ Rochester, BS, 37; Univ Ill, MS, 39, PhD(org chem), 42. *Prof Exp:* Chemist, Eastman Kodak Co, NY, 37-38; instr org chem, Univ Ill, 42-44; chemist, Goodyear Tire & Rubber Co, 44-48; assoc prof, 48-52, chmn dept chem, 58-61 & 66-69, PROF CHEM, UNIV MO-COLUMBIA, 52- *Mem:* AAAS; Am Chem Soc. *Res:* Synthesis; pharmaceuticals; hydrocarbons. *Mailing Add:* Dept Chem Univ Mo Columbia MO 65211

RABL, ARI, b Germany, Feb 21, 42. ENERGY CONVERSION. *Educ:* Beloit Col, BSc, 63; Univ Calif, Berkeley, MA, 66, PhD(physics), 69. *Prof Exp:* Res assoc physics, Int Ctr Theoret Physics, Trieste, Italy, 69; res assoc, Weizmann Inst, Israel, 70-71; res assoc, Ohio State Univ, 72-73; asst physicist, Argonne Nat Lab, 74-77, engr, 77-78; prin scientist, Solar Energy Res Inst, Golden, Colo, 78-80. *Concurrent Pos:* Sr res assoc, Univ Chicago, 76-81; vis sr scientist, Princeton Univ, 80-; lectr & consult, 81- *Mem:* Am Soc Mech Engrs; Am Phys Soc; Solar Energy Soc. *Res:* Solar energy conversion; environmental problems; high energy physics. *Mailing Add:* Ctr Energy & Environ Studies Princeton Univ Princeton NJ 08544

RABL, VERONIKA ARIANA, b Michalovce, Czech, Dec 16, 45. TECHNICAL MANAGEMENT, ENERGY UTILIZATION. *Educ:* Weizmann Inst Sci, Israel, MSc, 71; Ohio State Univ, PhD(physics), 74. *Prof Exp:* Jr scientist physics, Weizmann Inst Sci, Israel, 71; res assoc, Syracuse Univ, 74-75; res assoc, Argonne Nat Lab, 75-77, asst scientist energy res, 77-81; PROJ MGR, ELEC POWER RES INST, 81- *Mem:* Sigma Xi. *Res:* Energy storage systems; road management; optimization of energy supply systems; demand forecasting and analysis. *Mailing Add:* Electric Power Res Inst 3412 Hillview Ave Palo Alto CA 94304

RABOLD, GARY PAUL, b Providence, RI, July 10, 39; m 66; c 2. INDUSTRIAL CHEMISTRY. *Educ:* Harvard Univ, AB, 60; Northeastern Univ, PhD(org chem), 65. *Prof Exp:* Fel biophys, Univ Hawaii, 65-67; INDUST CHEMIST PROD DEVELOP, DOW CHEM CO, 67- *Mem:* Am Chem Soc; Soc Automotive Engrs. *Res:* New product development for organic chemicals; solvents and hydraulic fluids. *Mailing Add:* Dow Chem Co 1710 Bldg Midland MI 48640

RABOLT, JOHN FRANCIS, b New York, NY, May 14, 49; m 70. POLYMER PHYSICS, CHEMICAL PHYSICS. *Educ:* State Univ NY Col, Oneonta, BS, 70; Southern Ill Univ, Carbondale, PhD(physics), 74. *Prof Exp:* Fel physics, Univ Mich, 74-75; Nat Res Coun, Nat Acad Sci res assoc, Nat Bur Standards, 75-77; RES STAFF MEM POLYMERS, IBM RES LAB, 78- *Mem:* Am Phys Soc; Soc Appl Spectros. *Res:* Use of Fourier transform infrared and Raman spectroscopy to investigate crystal and molecular structure of long chain molecules, polymers and liquid crystals; integrated optical techniques in conjunction with Raman Spectroscopy to investigate submicron polymer films and polymer surfaces. *Mailing Add:* IBM Res Lab K42-282 5600 Cottle Rd San Jose CA 95193

RABOURN, WARREN JOSEPH, b Indianapolis, Ind, Nov 12, 21; m 46; c 4. INDUSTRIAL ORGANIC CHEMISTRY. *Educ:* Purdue Univ, BS, 49, MS, 50, PhD(biochem), 53. *Prof Exp:* Instr biochem, Univ Pittsburgh, 53-54; asst, Purdue Univ, 54-55, asst prof, 55-57; SR RES CHEMIST, DOW CHEM CO, 57- *Mem:* AAAS; Am Chem Soc; NY Acad Sci. *Res:* Chemistry of carotenoids and natural polyenes; chromatography; organic nitrogen compounds. *Mailing Add:* 1202 E Princeton Lane Deer Park TX 77536

RABOY, SOL, b Ambridge, Pa, Feb 11, 20; m 48; c 7. NUCLEAR PHYSICS. *Educ:* Brooklyn Col, BA, 41; Carnegie Inst Technol, DSc(physics), 50. *Prof Exp:* Instr physics, Carnegie Inst Technol, 49-50, res assoc, 50-51; assoc physicist, Argonne Nat Lab, 51-65; chmn dept, 66-77, PROF PHYSICS, STATE UNIV NY BINGHAMTON, 65- *Mem:* Fel Am Phys Soc. *Res:* Mobility of electrons in insulators; angular distributions of nuclear radiation; spectroscopy of gamma rays; variation of electron mass with velocity; measurements of magnetic moments of excited states of nuclei; measurement of quadrupole moments of nuclei; nuclear structure; muonic x-rays. *Mailing Add:* Dept of Physics State Univ of NY Binghamton NY 13901

RABSON, ALAN S, b New York, NY, July 1, 26; m 50; c 1. PATHOLOGY. *Educ:* Univ Rochester, BA, 48; Long Island Col Med, MD, 50. *Prof Exp:* PATHOLOGIST, NAT CANCER INST, 55- *Mem:* Am Soc Exp Path. *Res:* Oncogenic viruses and viral tumors. *Mailing Add:* Nat Cancer Inst 9000 Rockville Pike Bethesda MD 20014

RABSON, GUSTAVE, b New York, NY, Sept 28, 20; m 58; c 3. MATHEMATICS. *Educ:* Cornell Univ, AB, 41; Univ Mich, MA, 48, PhD(math), 52. *Prof Exp:* Engr, Tank-Automotive Ctr, Univ Mich, 42-44, mathematician, Ballistics Res Lab, 44-45; instr math, Purdue Univ, 49-53; from asst prof to assoc prof, Antioch Col, 53-57; sr mathematician, Am Optical Co, 57-59; res mathematician, Inst Sci & Technol, Univ Mich, 59-66; prof math, Tech Inst Aeronaut, Brazil, 66-67; ASSOC PROF MATH & COMPUT SCI, CLARKSON COL TECHNOL, 67- *Concurrent Pos:* NSF grant, 56; vis scientist, Mass Inst Technol, 78. *Mem:* Am Math Soc; Math Asn Am. *Res:* Topological groups; mathematical statistics; applied mathematics. *Mailing Add:* Dept of Math Clarkson Col of Technol Potsdam NY 13676

RABSON, ROBERT, b Brooklyn, NY, Mar 4, 26; m 50; c 4. PLANT PHYSIOLOGY. *Educ:* Cornell Univ, BS, 51, PhD(plant physiol), 56. *Prof Exp:* Biologist, Oak Ridge Nat Lab, 56-58; from asst prof to assoc prof biol, Univ Houston, 58-64; biochemist, Div Biomed & Environ Res, US AEC, 63-67, asst chief biol br, 67-73, first officer, Food & Agr Orgn-Int Atomic Energy Agency Joint Div, Plant Breeding & Genetics Sect, Int Atomic Energy Agency, Vienna, Austria, 73-76; mem staff div biomed & environ res, Energy Res & Develop Admin, 76-78, DIR, DIV BIOL ENERGY RES, OFF BASIC ENERGY SCI, US DEPT ENERGY, 78- *Mem:* Am Soc Plant Physiol; Crop Sci Soc; AAAS; Am Soc Photobiol; Am Soc Microbiol. *Res:* Genetics and biochemistry of protein synthesis in developing seeds. *Mailing Add:* Off of Basic Energy Sci 17 US Dept of Energy Washington DC 20545

RABSON, THOMAS A(VELYN), b Houston, Tex, July 31, 32; m 57; c 3. ELECTRICAL ENGINEERING, NUCLEAR PHYSICS. *Educ:* Rice Univ, BA, 54, BS, 55, MA, 57, PhD(nuclear physics), 59. *Prof Exp:* From asst prof to assoc prof, 59-70, PROF ELEC ENG, RICE UNIV, 70-, CHMN DEPT, 79- *Concurrent Pos:* NSF sci fac fel, 65-66. *Mem:* Am Phys Soc; Inst Elec & Electronics Engrs; Optical Soc Am. *Res:* Semiconductor physics; lasers; ferroelectrics. *Mailing Add:* Dept of Elec Eng Rice Univ PO Box 1892 Houston TX 77001

RABUNG, JOHN RUSSELL, b Elyria, Ohio, July 22, 43; m 67; c 3. NUMBER THEORY. *Educ:* Univ Akron, BA, 65; Wash State Univ, MA, 67, PhD(number theory), 69. *Prof Exp:* Res mathematician number theory, Math Res Ctr, US Naval Res Lab, 69-70; instr & opers res analyst statist & oper res, US Army Logistics Mgt Ctr, 70-72; asst prof math, Randolph-Macon Col, 72-74; asst prof, 74-81, ASSOC PROF MATH SCI, VA COMMONWEALTH UNIV, 81- *Mem:* Am Math Soc; Math Asn Am. *Res:* Combinatorial problems in number theory, specifically, some aspects of Van der Waerden's theorem on arithmetic progressions. *Mailing Add:* Dept of Math Sci Va Commonwealth Univ Richmond VA 23284

RABUSSAY, DIETMAR PAUL, b Wolfsberg, Austria, Aug 9, 41; m 66; c 2. GENE REGULATION. *Educ:* Tech Univ Graz, Austria, MSc, 67; Univ Munich, PhD(biochem), 71. *Prof Exp:* Wissensch asst molecular biol, Max Planck Inst Biochem, 71-72; fel, Univ Calif, San Diego, 72-75, asst res biologist, 75-79; vis scientist, Max Planck Inst Biochem, 78-79; asst prof microbiol, Fla State Univ, 79-81; SECT HEAD, BETHESDA RES LABS, 81- *Concurrent Pos:* Adj prof, Univ Md, 81- *Mem:* AAAS; Am Soc Microbiol; Europ Molecular Biol Orgn; Am Soc Biol Chemists. *Res:* In vitro protein synthesis; mechanism and regulation of transcription; development of bacterial viruses; DNA enzymology; genetic engineering. *Mailing Add:* Molecular Biol Div Bethesda Res Lab PO Box 6009 Bethesda MD 20877

RABY, BRUCE ALAN, b Seattle, Wash, Aug 22, 30; m 54; c 4. ANALYTICAL CHEMISTRY. *Educ:* Univ Wash, BS, 52; Univ Calif, Berkeley, MS, 54; Iowa State Univ, PhD(anal chem), 63. *Prof Exp:* Proj engr, Wright Air Develop Div, Air Force Systs Command, Wright-Patterson AFB, Ohio, 53-56; res asst anal chem, Inst Atomic Res, Ames Nat Lab, Iowa State Univ, 56-63; scientist, Rocketdyne Div, NAm Aviation, Inc, Calif, 63-64; chemist, Lawrence Radiation Lab, Univ Calif, Berkeley, 64-70; mem staff, Uthe Technol Int, 70-75, admin mgr res & applications, 75-80; CONSULT CHEM & TECHNOL, 80- *Mem:* Am Inst Chemists; Soc Appl Spectros; Am Chem Soc; Am Soc Mass Spectros; Sigma Xi. *Res:* Fluorescence; halogen fluorides as reagents; rocket fuels; magnesium alloys; nuclear reactors; production and separation of trans-lead isotopes; mass spectroscopy. *Mailing Add:* 1547 Arata Ct San Jose CA 95125

RACCAH, PAUL M(ORDECAI), b Tunis, Tunisia, June 24, 33; US citizen; m 54; c 4. MATERIAL SCIENCE, QUANTUM ELECTRONICS. *Educ:* Univ Paris, Exam physics, 56; Univ Lyons, Eng, 59; Univ Rennes, DrIng(phys chem), 62. *Prof Exp:* Group leader optimization, Compagnie de' Automatismes et d'Electronique, Plan Calcul, 62-64; staff mem, Lincoln Lab, Mass Inst Technol, 64-71; prof physics, Belfer Grad Sch, Yeshiva Univ, 71-76; PROF PHYSICS & HEAD DEPT, UNIV ILL, CHICAGO CIRCLE, 76- *Concurrent Pos:* Dir, Maybaum Inst Mat Sci & Quantum Electronics, 71-76. *Mem:* Fel Am Phys Soc. *Res:* Critical phenomena, Raman & Brillouin scattering; neutron diffraction; defects in crystalline solids; modulation spectroscopy; accurate charge density measurements in relation to solid-state theory predictions; laser mechanisms and tunability. *Mailing Add:* 7521 N Albany Chicago IL 60645

RACE, STUART RICE, b Glen Ridge, NJ, Sept 20, 26; m 57; c 4. ENTOMOLOGY. *Educ:* Gettysburg Col, AB, 51; Rutgers Univ, MS, 55, PhD(entom), 57. *Prof Exp:* Asst prof, NMex State Univ, 57-65; assoc prof, 65-70, PROF ENTOM, RUTGERS UNIV, NEW BRUNSWICK, 70- *Mem:* AAAS; Soc Nematol; Entom Soc Am. *Res:* Fruits, vegetables, forage crops, dairy and poultry; corn insect control. *Mailing Add:* Dept Entom & Econ Zool Rutgers Univ New Brunswick NJ 08903

RACETTE, GEORGE WILLIAM, b Schenectady, NY, June 2, 29; m 56; c 4. PHYSICS, SEMICONDUCTORS. *Educ:* Siena Col, NY, BS, 51; Univ Rochester, MS, 54. *Prof Exp:* From jr to sr engr semiconductor devices, Philco Corp Res Div, 53-57, proj scientist infrared & photodevices, 57-64; proj scientist lasers, Philco-Ford Res Div, Ford Sci Lab, 64-66, eng specialist automotive electronics, Philco-Ford Res Div, 66-70; mgr, Whitemarsh Township, 70-74; PHYSICIST SEMICONDUCTOR DETECTORS & PHOTOVOLTAICS, VALLEY FORGE SPACE CTR, GEN ELEC CO, 74- *Mem:* Am Phys Soc. *Res:* Semiconductor materials; infrared; photo detectors; lasers; high intensity light effects; vidicons; solar cells; vacuum deposition. *Mailing Add:* Gen Elec Co Box 8555 Philadelphia PA 19101

RACHELE, HENRY, b Helper, Utah, Aug 8, 29; m 59; c 5. ELECTRICAL ENGINEERING, MATHEMATICS. *Educ:* Utah State Univ, BS, 51; NMex State Univ, PhD(elec eng), 77. *Prof Exp:* Chief, Lower Atmospheric Res Tech Area, 64-69, actg chief, Atmospheric Sci Off, 69, chief, Lower Atmospheric Res Tech Area, 70-72, chief, Meteorol Satellite Tech Area, 72-73, chief, Meteorol Systs Tech Area, 73-74, DEP/TECH DIR, US ARMY ATMOSPHERIC SCI LAB, 74- *Concurrent Pos:* Lectr elec eng, NMex State Univ. *Honors & Awards:* Army Res & Develop Award, Dept Army, 68. *Mem:* Sigma Xi. *Res:* Meteorology; physics; unguided rocket ballistics; sound propagation through atmosphere. *Mailing Add:* US Army Atmospheric Sci Lab White Sands Missile Range NM 88002

RACHFORD, HENRY HERBERT, JR, b El Dorado, Ark, June 14, 25; m 57; c 2. MATHEMATICS, ENGINEERING. *Educ:* Rice Inst, BS, 45, AM, 47; Mass Inst Technol, ScD, 50. *Prof Exp:* Res engr, Humble Oil & Ref Co, 49-56, asst div petrol engr, 56-57, res supvr, 57-64; PROF MATH & COMPUT SCI, RICE UNIV, 64- *Mem:* Am Math Soc; Soc Petrol Eng; Am Inst Mining, Metall & Petrol Eng; Am Inst Chem Eng. *Res:* Numerical techniques, especially for partial differential equations; use of digital computers; solution of engineering problems with mathematical methods. *Mailing Add:* Dept of Math Rice Univ Houston TX 77001

RACHFORD, THOMAS MILTON, b Bellevue, Ky, Mar 14, 42; m 64; c 2. CIVIL ENGINEERING. *Educ:* Univ Ky, BS, 64, MS, 66; Stanford Univ, PhD(civil eng), 72. *Prof Exp:* Asst prof civil eng, Pa State Univ, 69-73; PRIN ENGR, GANNETT FLEMING, CORDDRY & CARPENTER, 74- *Mem:* Water Pollution Control Fedn. *Res:* Civil engineering; hydrology and water resources; sanitary and environmental engineering. *Mailing Add:* Gannett Fleming Corddry & Carpenter PO Box 1963 Harrisburg PA 17105

RACHIE, KENNETH OWEN, b Belview, Minn, Oct 15, 23; m 50; c 3. PLANT GENETICS. *Educ:* Univ Minn, BS, 49, MS, 52, PhD(agron), 54. *Prof Exp:* Asst prof agron, Univ Ariz, 54-55; asst geneticist, Rockefeller Found, Mex, 55-57; geneticist, India, 57-66, NY, 66-68, prof plant breeding, Makerere Univ, Uganda, 68-71, grain legume breeder, Int Inst Trop Agr, Nigeria, 71-75, assoc dir gen res, Int Ctr Trop Agr, Colombia, 75-78, ASSOC DIR AGR SCI, PLANT SCI & LATIN AM, ROCKEFELLER FOUND, NEW YORK, 78- *Concurrent Pos:* Vis geneticist, Univ Calif, Davis, 66-67 & Univ Nebr, 67-68. *Honors & Awards:* Sorghum Producer's Asn Award, 73. *Mem:* Fel AAAS; Am Soc Agron. *Res:* Sorghum and millet breeding in Mexico and India; grain legume breeding in Uganda and Nigeria; research administration in Colombia and New York. *Mailing Add:* Rockefeller Found 1133 Ave of the Americas New York NY 10036 Colombia

RACHINSKY, MICHAEL RICHARD, b Stamford, Conn, Jan 2, 31; m 59; c 2. SCIENCE EDUCATION, BIOCHEMISTRY. *Educ:* Fordham Univ, BS, 52; Purdue Univ, PhD(chem), 60. *Prof Exp:* Res chemist, Res Ctr, Hercules Inc, 59-62; sci & technol consult, Becton, Dickinson & Co, 62-63; independent consult, 63-64 & 73-74; consult & mkt analyst, Hoffman-La Roche Inc, 65-66; instr chem & res asst, Rosemont Col, 67; assoc prof chem, West Chester State Col, 68-71 & Nyack Sr High Sch, 71; curric coordr, Westinghouse Learning Corp, 71-72; assoc prof chem & head natural sci & math div, St Thomas Aquinas Col, 75-77; CONSULT, 77- *Mem:* Am Chem Soc; Sigma Xi. *Res:* Chemistry and chemical marketing; improving curricula in undergraduate science education. *Mailing Add:* 26 Vanech Dr Stamford CT 06905

RACHLIN, JOSEPH WOLFE, b New York, NY, Jan 23, 36; m 60; c 2. AQUATIC BIOLOGY. *Educ:* City Col New York, BS, 57; NY Univ, MS, 62, PhD(aquatic biol), 67. *Prof Exp:* Lab technician chemother, Sloan-Kettering Inst Cancer Res, 57-58; biol sci asst environ med, US Army Med Res Lab, Ky, 58-60; biol sci trainee endocrinol, Sch Med, NY Univ, 60-64, fel radiol health, 64-65, trainee environ health, 65-66; asst prof, from instr to assoc prof, 67-77, PROF BIOL, LEHMAN COL, 77-; ADJ PROF ENVIRON MED,

NY UNIV MED COL, 72- *Concurrent Pos:* Dir, City Univ New York Inst Marine & Atmospheric Sci, 76-77. *Mem:* AAAS; Am Soc Ichthyol & Herpet; Am Soc Limnol & Oceanog; Am Fisheries Soc; Am Soc Zoologists. *Res:* Effects of chemical pollutants on the fresh water and marine environments, particularly the effects of metals; fish cytogenetics. *Mailing Add:* Dept of Biol Sci Lehman Col of City Un of NY Bronx NY 10468

RACHMELER, MARTIN, b New York, NY, Nov 21, 28; m 56; c 3. MICROBIOLOGY, GENETICS. *Educ:* Ind Univ, AB, 50; Western Reserve Univ, PhD(microbiol), 60. *Prof Exp:* Asst geneticist, Univ Calif, Berkeley, 61-62; asst prof, 62-67, ASSOC PROF MICROBIOL, MED SCH, NORTHWESTERN UNIV, CHICAGO, 67-, DIR, RES SERV ADMIN, EVANSTON, 77- *Concurrent Pos:* USPHS fel, Univ Calif, Berkeley, 59-61. *Mem:* AAAS; Am Soc Microbiol; Sigma Xi; Am Inst Biol Sci. *Res:* Biochemistry of human genetic diseases; role of tumor viruses in cell transformation; regulation of cell growth. *Mailing Add:* Res Serv Admin Northwestern Univ Evanston IL 60201

RACIE, FRED ARNOLD, b Columbus, Ohio, Dec 16, 32; m 62. NATURAL SCIENCE. *Educ:* Ohio State Univ, BSc, 60, MSc, 62, PhD(bot), 65. *Prof Exp:* Assoc prof, 65-73, PROF NATURAL SCI, MICH STATE UNIV, 73- *Mem:* Sigma Xi. *Res:* Protein synthesis by fungi; salicylate degradation by fungi. *Mailing Add:* Dept of Natural Sci Univ Col Mich State Univ East Lansing MI 48824

RACINE, MICHEL LOUIS, b Casselman, Ont, Jan 19, 45. ALGEBRA. *Educ:* Univ Ottawa, BSc, 60; Yale Univ, MPhil, 69, PhD(math), 71. *Prof Exp:* Res assoc math, Carleton Univ, 71-72; Nat Res Coun fel, Univ Wis-Madison, 72-73, MacDuffee fel, 73-74; asst prof, 74-78, ASSOC PROF MATH, UNIV OTTAWA, 78- *Concurrent Pos:* Alexander von Humboldt fel, Univ Munster, 80-81. *Mem:* Am Math Soc; Math Asn Am; Can Math Cong. *Res:* Structure of Jordan algebras and related questions. *Mailing Add:* Dept Math Univ Ottawa Ottawa ON K1N 9B4 Can

RACINE, RENE, b Que, Que, Oct 16, 39; m 63; c 2. ASTRONOMY. *Educ:* Laval Univ, BA, 58, BSc, 63; Univ Toronto, MA, 65, PhD(astron), 67. *Prof Exp:* Carnegie fel, Hale Observs, Calif, 67-69; from asst prof to assoc prof astron, Univ Toronto, 69-76; PROF, UNIV MONTREAL, 76- *Concurrent Pos:* Dir, Can-Fran-Haw Tel Corp, 80- *Mem:* AAAS; Am Astron Soc; Can Astron Soc; Royal Astron Soc; Royal Astron Soc. *Res:* Galactic structure; galaxies; open and globular clusters; interstellar matter; optical instrumentation. *Mailing Add:* Dept of Physics Univ of Montreal Montreal PQ H3C 3J7 Can

RACISZEWSKI, ZBIGNIEW, b Uchanie, Poland, Jan 20, 22. POLYMER CHEMISTRY. *Educ:* Univ Sask, MSc, 52; Univ Notre Dame, PhD(chem), 56. *Prof Exp:* Instr food technol, Agr Col Warsaw, Poland, 47-49; sr res chemist, Explor Org Chem Group, Pittsburgh Plate Glass Co, 55-60; res chemist, Consumer Prod Div, Union Carbide Corp, 60-63, Chem Div, WVa, 63-69; assoc ed, 69-74, sr assoc ed, 74-80, SR ED, MACROMOLECULAR SECT, CHEM ABSTR SERV, 80- *Mem:* Am Chem Soc. *Res:* Mechanism of organic reactions; polymer chemistry. *Mailing Add:* Chem Abstr Serv 2540 Olentangy River Rd Columbus OH 43210

RACK, EDWARD PAUL, b Reading, Pa, Dec 13, 31; m 65; c 2. CHEMISTRY, RADIOCHEMISTRY. *Educ:* Pa State Univ, BS, 54; Univ Mich, MS, 58, PhD(chem), 61. *Prof Exp:* Res fel chem, Inst Atomic Res, 61-62; from asst prof to assoc prof, 62-71, PROF CHEM, UNIV NEBR, LINCOLN, 71- *Concurrent Pos:* AEC teaching grant, 65, res contract, 66-; consult, Brookhaven Nat Lab, 71- & Vet Admin Hosp, Omaha, 72- *Mem:* Am Chem Soc. *Res:* Chemical effect of nuclear transformations, particularly involving halogens with solid, liquid and gaseous organic systems; neutron activation analysis of biological samples. *Mailing Add:* Dept of Chem Univ of Nebr Lincoln NE 68508

RACK, HENRY JOHANN, b New York, NY, Nov 1, 42; c 2. MATERIAL SCIENCE, METALLURGY. *Educ:* Mass Inst Technol, SB, 64, SM, 65, ScD(metall), 68. *Prof Exp:* Scientist, Lockheed Ga Co, 68-72; mem tech staff, Sandia Labs, 72-81; prof, NMex Inst Mining & Technol, 75-81; MGR, METALL DEPT, MAT DIV, EXXON ENTERPRISES, 81- *Mem:* Am Soc Metals; Am Inst Mining, Metall & Petrol Engrs; Am Soc Testing & Mat. *Res:* Metal matrix composites; structural materials; fracture; structural reliability; nuclear waste management and transportation; solar materials and applications. *Mailing Add:* Mat Div Exxon Enterprises PO Drawer H Greer SC 29651

RACKER, EFRAIM, b Neu Sandez, Poland, June 28, 13; nat US; m 45. BIOCHEMISTRY. *Educ:* Univ Vienna, MD, 38. *Prof Exp:* Asst biochem, Cardiff City Ment Hosp, SWales, 38-40; res assoc, Univ Minn, 41-42; res fel pneumonia, Harlem Hosp, 42-44; asst prof bact, Col Med, NY Univ, 44-52; assoc prof biochem, Sch Med, Yale Univ, 52-54; chief div nutrit & physiol, New York Pub Health Res Inst, 54-66; chmn dept, 66-70, ALBERT EINSTEIN PROF BIOCHEM & MOLECULAR & CELL BIOL, CORNELL UNIV, 66- *Honors & Awards:* Nat Medal Sci, 77. *Mem:* Nat Acad Sci; Am Soc Biol Chemists; Harvey Soc. *Res:* Mechanism of enzyme action; oxidative phosphorylation; bioenergetics; control mechanism. *Mailing Add:* Sect Biochem Molec & Cell Biol Cornell Univ Ithaca NY 14853

RACKIS, JOSEPH JOHN, b Somersville, Conn, July 29, 22; m 54; c 2. BIOCHEMISTRY, FOOD SCIENCE. *Educ:* Univ Conn, BS, 50; Univ Iowa, PhD(biochem), 55. *Prof Exp:* Chemist, 55-60, PRIN CHEMIST, NORTHERN REGIONAL RES CTR, AGR RES SERV, USDA, 60- *Mem:* Am Chem Soc; Am Soc Biol Chemists; Inst Food Technol; Am Asn Cereal Chem; Phytochem Soc N Am. *Res:* Plant biochemistry; physical organic chemistry of soybean proteins; chromatography; amino acids; plant analysis; lipids; nutritional and physiological evaluation; food and feed uses of soybean products. *Mailing Add:* Northern Regional Res Lab Agr Res Serv USDA Peoria IL 61604

RACKOFF, JEROME S, b Brooklyn, NY, Nov 14, 46; m 71; c 2. VERTEBRATE PALEONTOLOGY. *Educ:* Brooklyn Col, BS, 68; Yale Univ, MPhil, 73, PhD(geobiol), 76. *Prof Exp:* Teacher earth sci, Brooklyn Friends Sch, NY, 69-70; teacher biol, Friends Sem, NY, 70-72; asst prof biol, 75-78, FOUND & GOVT RELS OFFICER, BUCKNELL UNIV, 78- *Mem:* Sigma Xi. *Res:* Functional morphology and evolution of Paleozoic fishes, particularly Crossopterygii and lower tetrapods; the origin of tetrapod limbs and terrestrial locomotion. *Mailing Add:* Found & Govt Rels Off Bucknell Univ Lewisburg PA 17837

RACKOW, HERBERT, b New York, NY, June 17, 17; m 42. ANESTHESIOLOGY. *Educ:* Pa State Univ, BS, 39; Howard Univ, MD, 46. *Prof Exp:* Fel biochem, NY Univ, 48-50; from instr to assoc prof, 52-70, PROF ANESTHESIOL, COL PHYSICIANS & SURGEONS, COLUMBIA UNIV, 70- *Res:* Respiratory physiology. *Mailing Add:* 147-01 Third Ave Whitestone NY 11357

RACUNAS, BERNARD J, b June 12, 43; US citizen. CHEMICAL ENGINEERING. *Educ:* Univ Pittsburgh, BS, 65, MS, 67. *Prof Exp:* Engr, 66-74, sr engr, 74-76, staff engr, 76-78, SECT HEAD, ALCOA LABS, 78- *Mem:* Am Inst Chem Engrs; Am Inst Metall Engrs; Sigma Xi. *Res:* Aluminum smelting; carbon technology; molten salt technology. *Mailing Add:* Alcoa Labs PO Box 772 New Kensington PA 15068

RACUSEN, DAVID, b Chicago, Ill, Feb 26, 25; m 69; c 3. PLANT BIOCHEMISTRY. *Educ:* Hobart Col, BS, 49; Iowa State Col, PhD(plant physiol), 53. *Prof Exp:* Res fel, Calif Inst Technol, 53-54; plant biochemist, Shell Develop Co, 54-58; PROF BIOCHEM, UNIV VT, 58- *Mem:* AAAS; Am Soc Plant Physiologists. *Res:* Protein metabolism of leaves; plant glycoproteins. *Mailing Add:* Dept of Microbiol & Biochem Univ of Vt Burlington VT 05405

RACUSEN, RICHARD HARRY, b Geneva, NY, July 26, 48; m 70. PLANT PHYSIOLOGY. *Educ:* Univ Vt, BS, 70, MS, 72, PhD(cell biol), 75. *Prof Exp:* Res fel cell biol, Unit Vt, 70-75; res fel plant physiol, Yale Univ, 75-78; ASST PROF BOT, UNIV MD, 78- *Mem:* AAAS; Sigma Xi; Am Soc Plant Physiol. *Res:* Ion transport, morphogenesis and plant bioelectric phenomena. *Mailing Add:* Dept Bot Univ Md College Park MD 20742

RAD, FRANZ N, b Zabol, Iran, Sept 25, 43; m 64; c 3. STRUCTURAL ENGINEERING. *Educ:* Univ Tex, Austin, BS, 68, MS, 69, PhD(civil eng), 73. *Prof Exp:* Asst prof, 71-75, assoc prof, 75-79, PROF CIVIL ENG & DEPT HEAD, PORTLAND STATE UNIV, 79- *Concurrent Pos:* Consult, Mackenzie Eng, Inc, 72-; Western Elec Fund Award, Am Soc Eng Educ, 79. *Mem:* Am Soc Civil Engrs; Am Concrete Inst; Am Soc Eng Educ; Nat Soc Prof Engrs; Post Tension Inst. *Res:* Limit states behavior of reinforced concrete members and structures. *Mailing Add:* Dept Civil Eng Portland State Univ Portland OR 97207

RADABAUGH, DENNIS CHARLES, b Detroit, Mich, Sept 27, 42; m 67; c 2. ANIMAL BEHAVIOR. *Educ:* Albion Col, BA, 64; Ohio State Univ, MSc, 67, PhD(animal behav), 70. *Prof Exp:* Vis asst prof, 70-72, asst prof, 72-77, assoc prof, 72-81, PROF ZOOL, OHIO WESLEYAN UNIV, 82- *Mem:* AAAS; Animal Behav Soc; Am Soc Zoologists; Sigma Xi. *Res:* Predator-prey behavioral interactions; effects of parasites on intermediate host behavior; biology of fish. *Mailing Add:* Dept of Zool Ohio Wesleyan Univ Delaware OH 43015

RADABAUGH, ROBERT EUGENE, b West Milton, Ohio, Oct 1, 13; m 64. GEOLOGY. *Educ:* Miami Univ, AB, 35; Univ Mich, MS, 37, PhD(geol), 42. *Prof Exp:* Instr, Miami Univ, 37-38, asst prof, 39-41; geologist, 42-48, chief, Geol & Eng Dept, 48-56, asst to western mgr mines, 56-57, asst mgr explor, 58-66, mgr western explor, NJ Zinc Co, 66-78; RETIRED. *Mem:* Soc Econ Geol; Mining & Metall Soc Am; fel Geol Soc Am; Am Inst Mining, Metall & Petrol Engrs. *Res:* Rogers City limestone; economic geology; metals. *Mailing Add:* 5720 E Ninth St Tucson AZ 85711

RADANOVICS, CHARLES, b Budapest, Hungary, Aug 9, 32; US citizen; m 60; c 3. FOOD SCIENCE. *Educ:* Univ Budapest, BS, 56; Univ Calif, Davis, MS, 63; Mich State Univ, PhD(food sci), 69. *Prof Exp:* Mgr qual control, Model Dairy, Melbourne, Australia, 57-60; sr chemist, Tarax Ale Co, Melbourne, 60-62; proj leader food res, Carnation Co, Calif, 63-65; sect mgr food res, Quaker Oats Co, 69-74; DIR RES & DEVELOP, JOHN SEXTON & CO DIV, BEATRICE FOODS, 74- *Mem:* Inst Food Technol; Am Chem Soc; Res & Develop Assoc (pres, 79). *Res:* Food service; new product development; regulatory activities; formulation of fabricated foods; process innovation; nutrition of foods; teaching food science. *Mailing Add:* John Sexton & Co 1099 Pratt Blvd Elk Grove Village IL 60007

RADBILL, JOHN R(USSELL), b Upland, Pa, Apr 22, 32. NUMERICAL ANALYSIS, FLUID MECHANICS. *Educ:* Mass Inst Technol, BS & MS, 55, MechE, 56, ScD(mech eng), 58. *Prof Exp:* Asst mech eng, Mass Inst Technol, 54-58; develop engr ionic propulsion, Aerojet-Gen Corp, Gen Tire & Rubber Co, 58-61; tech specialist, Space & Info Systs Div, N Am Aviation, Inc, 61-66, sr tech specialist, Ocean Systs Opers, 66, mem tech staff, Autonetics Div, N Am Rockwell Corp, 66-70; MEM TECH STAFF APPL MATH, JET PROPULSION LAB, CALIF INST TECHNOL, 70- *Concurrent Pos:* Instr, Citrus Jr Col, 59-60; consult, Technol Assocs of Southern Calif, Inc, 72- *Mem:* Assoc Am Soc Mech Engrs; Am Inst Aeronaut & Astronaut; Asn Comput Mach. *Res:* Fluid mechanics; numerical analysis; numerical solution of nonlinear partial differential equations; tornado lifted missiles; blood flow in diseased arteries. *Mailing Add:* Jet Propulsion Lab 4800 Oak Grove Dr Pasadena CA 91103

RADBRUCH-HALL, DOROTHY HILL, b Carroll, Iowa, Nov 17, 20; m 72. GEOLOGY. *Educ:* Univ Colo, BA, 48. *Prof Exp:* Chief Wray Proj, Eng Geol Br, US Geol Surv, 48-49; geologist, San Francisco Proj, 49-55, geologist chg reports processing, Alaskan Geol Br, 55-60, chief, Oakland E Proj, Eng Geol

Br, 57-67, chief study Hayward-Calaveras fault zones, 68-70, chief regional slope stability studies, Eng Geol Br, 71-80, proj chief, Nat Landslide Overview Map Proj, 74-80, proj chief, Eng Geol Map of US, 76-81, AMMUITANT, US GEOL SURV, 80- *Concurrent Pos:* US rep, Working Group Eng Geol Mapping, Int Asn Eng Geologists, 68-; partic, NSF Exchange Prog, Czech, 71; ed, Newsletter Geol Soc Am, 62-63 & Newsletter, Asn Eng Geologists, 63. *Mem:* Int Asn Eng Geologists. *Res:* Engineering geology, particularly engineering geology mapping, slope stability, geology related to land-use planning and development. *Mailing Add:* Eng Geol Br US Geol Surv MS 90-A 345 Middlefield Rd Menlo Park CA 94025

RADCLIFFE, ALEC, b Cleethorpes, Eng, Aug 28, 17; nat US; m 46. PHYSICS, SYSTEMS ANALYSIS. *Educ:* Univ London, BSc, 39. *Prof Exp:* Temp exp asst & exp officer, Mine Design Dept, Brit Navy, 40-46; from sci officer to prin sci officer, Nat Gas Turbine Estab, 46-54; PHYSICIST & ASST DIV SUPVR, APPL PHYSICS LAB, JOHNS HOPKINS UNIV, 55- *Mem:* Fel Brit Inst Physics. *Res:* Magnetism; acoustics; combustion; propulsion; fuel injection; unsteady gas dynamics; operations research. *Mailing Add:* 1710 Highland Dr Silver Spring MD 20910

RADCLIFFE, BYRON M, b Weehawken, NJ, Oct 17, 19. ENGINEERING. *Educ:* Purdue Univ, BSME, 48, MSE, 51. *Prof Exp:* Instr eng mech, Purdue Univ, 48-51, from asst prof to assoc prof, Wood Technol Res Lab, 51-56; dir res & develop, Place Construct Co, Inc, 56-58; assoc prof bldg construct, Mich State Univ, 58-66; prof construct sci & chmn dept, 66-81, EMER PROF CONSTRUCTION MANAGEMENT, UNIV NEBR, LINCOLN, 81- *Mem:* Nat Soc Prof Engrs. *Mailing Add:* Dept of Construct Sci Univ of Nebr Lincoln NE 68508

RADCLIFFE, EDWARD B, b Rapid City, Man, Oct 25, 36; US citizen; m 64; c 2. ENTOMOLOGY. *Educ:* Univ Man, BSA, 59; Univ Wis, MS, 61, PhD(entom), 63. *Prof Exp:* Res fel, 63-64, res assoc, 64-65, asst prof, 65-70, assoc prof, 70-76, PROF ENTOM, FISHERIES & WILDLIFE, UNIV MINN, ST PAUL, 76- *Mem:* AAAS; Entom Soc Am; Entom Soc Can; Potato Asn Am. *Res:* Resistance of plants to insect attack; integrated pest management. *Mailing Add:* Dept of Entom Fisheries & Wildlife Univ of Minn St Paul MN 55108

RADCLIFFE, S VICTOR, b England, July 28, 27. MATERIALS ENGINEERING. *Educ:* Univ Liverpool, BEng, 48, PhD(metall), 56. *Prof Exp:* Res metallurgist, Lancashire Steel Corp, 48-53; res assoc metall, Mass Inst Technol, 56-62; res mgr mat, Manlabs, Inc, 62-63; from assoc prof to prof phys metall, Case Western Reserve Univ, 63-74, head div metall & mat sci, 69-74; sr policy analyst, 74-75, fel, Sci & Technol Policy Off, Staff to Sci Adv to Pres, Resources For Future, 76-79; VPRES CORP DEVELOP, NAT FORGE CO, 79- *Concurrent Pos:* Dir study mat sci & eng, Nat Acad Sci, 70-73; consult, UN, 77- *Mem:* Am Inst Mining, Metall & Petrol Engrs; Soc Metals; fel Inst Metall; Am Phys Soc; Am Chem Soc. *Res:* Intercountry study of total requirements for materials in relation to growth of national economies; interpretation of intercountry differences in terms of economic structure, intensity and technology; application to forecasting and public policy. *Mailing Add:* 2101 Connecticut Ave NW Washington DC 20008

RADD, F(REDERICK) J(OHN), b Greenfield, Mass, July 28, 21; m; c 3. METALLURGY. *Educ:* Univ Mo, BS, 43; Mass Inst Technol, ScD(metall), 49. *Prof Exp:* Asst metall, Res Lab, Gen Elec Co, 43; staff mem div indust coop, Mass Inst Technol, 43-45, res metallurgist, Atomic Energy Comn, 49-51; supvr, Boeing Airplane Co, 51-52; staff scientist, 52-77, SR RES ASSOC, CONTINENTAL OIL CO, 78- *Mem:* Am Soc Metals; Nat Asn Corrosion Engrs; Am Chem Soc; Am Inst Mining, Metall & Petrol Engrs. *Res:* Cryogenic and petroleum metallurgy; age hardening of metals; solidification theory; fatigue and corrosion fatigue behavior; high temperature reactions; corrosion processes; hydrogen-metal behaviors; electrochemistry; cemented carbides; coal seam geochemistry. *Mailing Add:* PO Box 1360 Ponca City OK 74602

RADDING, CHARLES MEYER, b Springfield, Mass, June 18, 30; m 54; c 3. BIOCHEMISTRY, GENETICS. *Educ:* Harvard Univ, AB, 52, MD, 56. *Prof Exp:* Intern, Harvard Med Serv, Boston City Hosp, Mass, 56-57; res assoc metab, Nat Heart Inst, 57-59; Am Heart Asn advan res fel biochem, Sch Med, Stanford Univ, 59-62; asst prof human genetics, Univ Mich, 62-65, assoc prof, 65-67; assoc prof, 67-72, PROF MED, MOLECULAR BIOPHYS & BIOCHEM, YALE UNIV, 72- *Concurrent Pos:* prof med, Yale Univ, 72-79, molecular biophysics & biochem, 72-79, human genetics, 79-; prof med, Yale Univ, 72-79, molecular biophysics & biochem, 72-79, human genetics, 79-; vis Miller prof, Univ Calif, Berkeley, 77. *Mem:* Am Soc Biol Chemists. *Res:* Genetic recombination; molecular virology. *Mailing Add:* 333 Cedar St New Haven CT 06510

RADEBAUGH, RAY, b South Bend, Ind, Nov 4, 39; m 62; c 3. CRYOGENICS. *Educ:* Univ Mich, BSE, 62; Purdue Univ, MS, 65, PhD(physics), 66. *Prof Exp:* Res asst physics, Purdue Univ, 62-66; assoc, 66-68, PHYSICIST CRYOG, NAT BUR STANDARDS, 68- *Concurrent Pos:* Vis prof, Univ Tokyo, 72-73. *Honors & Awards:* Nat Bur Stand Superior Performance Award, 68. *Mem:* Am Phys Soc; Sigma Xi. *Res:* Heat transfer, refrigeration, and thermometry at cryogenic temperatures; superconductivity experimental studies of dilution refrigerators, thermal boundary resistance, and thermometers for temperatures below 1K. *Mailing Add:* Cryog Div Nat Bur of Standards Boulder CO 80302

RADEKA, VELJKO, b Zagreb, Yugoslavia, Nov 21, 30; m 58; c 2. INSTRUMENTATION SCIENCE. *Educ:* Univ Zagreb, Dipl Ing, 55, Dr Eng Sci(electronics), 61. *Prof Exp:* Scientist instrumentation, Ruder Boskovic Inst, Zagreb, 55-66; res assoc, 62-64, assoc scientist, 66-69, scientist, 69-73, SR SCIENTIST INSTRUMENTATION, BROOKHAVEN NAT LAB, 73-, DIV HEAD, 72- *Mem:* Fel Inst Elec & Electronics Engrs. *Res:* Scientific instrumentation; nuclear detector signal processing. *Mailing Add:* Instrumentation Div Brookhaven Nat Lab Upton NY 11973

RADEL, STANLEY ROBERT, b New York, NY, July 6, 32; m 54; c 2. THEORETICAL CHEMISTRY. *Educ:* NY Univ, AB, 53, MS, 56, PhD(phys chem), 63. *Prof Exp:* Tutor chem, Queens Col, NY, 57-59, lectr, 59-64; from instr to asst prof, 64-74, ASSOC PROF CHEM, CITY COL NEW YORK, 74- *Mem:* Am Chem Soc; Am Phys Soc. *Res:* Intramolecular forces; molecular dynamics; quantum mechanics and spectroscopy. *Mailing Add:* Dept of Chem City Col of New York New York NY 10031

RADEMACHER, LEO EDWARD, b Brush, Colo, Sept 3, 26; m 53; c 3. ORGANIC CHEMISTRY. *Educ:* Univ Colo, BA, 50, PhD(org chem), 56. *Prof Exp:* Jr chemist, Julius Hyman Co, Colo, 50-52; jr chemist, Shell Chem Co, 52-53; sr chemist, Plastics Div, 55-65, res specialist, Monsanto Polymers & Petrochem Co, 66-77, SR TECHNOL SPECIALIST, MONSANTO PLASTICS & RESINS CO, 77- *Mem:* Am Chem Soc; Soc Plastics Engrs. *Res:* Thermosetting surface coating resins; polymerization and applications of vinyl chloride; graft polymerization; polymer processing; composite systems. *Mailing Add:* 111 Meadowbrook Rd Springfield MA 01128

RADER, CHARLES ALLEN, b Washington, DC, Sept 30, 32; m 56; c 3. SURFACE CHEMISTRY. *Educ:* Univ Md, BS, 55. *Prof Exp:* Chemist, Nat Bur Standards, 55-58; from chemist to sr chemist, Harris Res Labs, Inc, 58-64, res supvr, 64-67; group leader, 67-72, mgr biochem sci dept, 72-76, mgr, Phys Sci Dept, 77-80, DIR, HARRIS RES LABS, GILLETTE RES INST, 80- *Mem:* Am Chem Soc; Am Asn Textile Chemists & Colorists; Am Inst Chemists; Fiber Soc; Tech Mkt Soc Am. *Res:* Surface chemistry; detergents and surfactants; actinic degradation of polymers; cosmetic and personal products; aerosols; chemical and physical properties of skin and hair; textiles; chemical warfare. *Mailing Add:* Gillette Res Inst 1413 Research Blvd Rockville MD 20850

RADER, CHARLES PHILLIP, b Greeneville, Tenn, Apr 9, 35; m 58; c 2. ORGANIC CHEMSITRY, RUBBER CHEMISTRY. *Educ:* Univ Tenn, BS, 57, MS, 60, PhD(chem), 61. *Prof Exp:* Instr chem, Univ Tenn, 59; sr res chemist, Monsanto Co, 61; org chemist, US Army Chem Ctr, 61-63; sr res chemist, 63-69, com develop proj mgr, 69-70, RES GROUP LEADER, MONSANTO CO, 70- *Concurrent Pos:* Asst prof, Univ Md, 62-63. *Mem:* Am Chem Soc; Am Inst Chemists; NY Acad Sci. *Res:* Applications of physical methods to organic chemistry; structure elucidation; conformational analysis; natural products; catalytic hydrogenation; rubber technology and tire technology; polymer chemistry. *Mailing Add:* Monsanto Co 260 Springside Dr Akron OH 44313

RADER, DENNIS, b New York, NY, Sept 12, 40; m 67; c 2. ENGINEERING MECHANICS, GEOPHYSICS. *Educ:* Cooper Union, BCE, 61; Brown Univ, ScM, 63, PhD(eng), 66. *Prof Exp:* Fel eng, Brown Univ, 66-67; from asst prof to assoc prof eng & appl sci, Yale Univ, 67-73; sr res proj engr, Schlumberger Doll Res Ctr, 73-78; mgr sensor develop, NL Petrol Serv/Drilling Systs Technol, 78-80; DIR RES & DEVELOP, TELECO OIL FIELD SERV, 80- *Mem:* Am Soc Mech Engrs; Am Acad Mech; Soc Exp Stress Anal; Acoust Soc Am; Soc Explor Geophysicists. *Res:* Development of advanced technology for oil and gas well measurement while drilling telemetry systems; wave propagation in elastic and inelastic materials; vibrations; fracture of brittle solids; remote sensing. *Mailing Add:* NL Petrol Serv 105 Pondview Dr Meriden CT 06450

RADER, LOUIS T(ELEMACUS), b Frank, Alta, Aug 24, 11; nat US; m 38; c 2. ELECTRICAL ENGINEERING. *Educ:* Univ BC, BSc, 33; Calif Inst Technol, MS, 35, PhD(elec eng), 38. *Prof Exp:* Test engr, Gen Elec Co, NY, 37-38, adv eng prog, Gen Eng Dept, 38-39, sect head, Control Eng Dept, 43-45, div engr, Control Lab Div, 47-49, asst to mgr, 49-50, asst to mgr, Eng Div, 50-51, mgr eng, Control Div, 51-53, gen mgr, Specialty Control Dept, 53-59; dir elec eng dept & consult, Armour Res Found, Ill Inst Technol, 45-47; vpres, US Commercial Group & mem bd dirs, Int Tel & Tel Corp, 59-62; pres, Univac Div, Sperry Rand Corp, 62-64; vpres & gen mgr, Info Systs Div, Gen Elec Co, Charlottesville, 64-68; gen mgr, Indust Process Control Div, 68-69; PROF ELEC ENG & BUS ADMIN, UNIV VA, 69- *Concurrent Pos:* Trustee, Robert A Taft Inst Govt, NY, 63-80. *Mem:* Nat Acad Eng; Am Soc Eng Educ; fel Inst Elec & Electronics Engrs. *Res:* Principles of magnetic design; arc interruption. *Mailing Add:* 1200 Boxwood Circle Waynesboro VA 22980

RADER, ROBERT E, US citizen. CIVIL ENGINEERING. *Educ:* Rose-Hulman Inst Technol, BS, 54; Am Acad Environ Engrs, dipl. *Prof Exp:* Group eng off, Corps Engrs, US Army, 55-57; off & dir firm, George E Synder Assoc, Inc, 57-69; dist off mgr, Black, Crow & Eidsness, Inc, 69-75; PROJ ENGR, WESTON, 75- *Mem:* Am Soc Civil Engrs; Water Pollution Control Fedn; Am Waterworks Asn. *Res:* Municipal water-filtration plants and deep-well supply sources, municipal and industrial wastewater treatment facilities, storm drainage, and municipal streets and interstate highways. *Mailing Add:* Weston Weston Way West Chester PA 19380

RADER, WILLIAM AUSTIN, b Detroit, Mich, Aug 27, 16; m 42; c 4. VETERINARY TOXICOLOGY. *Educ:* Mich State Univ, DVM, 41. *Prof Exp:* Pvt practr vet med, 42-46 & 52-64; pub health off, Mich Dept Health, 46-47; dir res & develop, Vita-Vet Labs, Ind, 64-65; vet toxicologist, Petitions Rev Br, Bur Sci, Food & Drug Admin, US Dept Health, Educ & Welfare, 65-67, vet med off, Div Vet Med Rev, Bur Vet Med, 67-68, chief investr, New Animal Drug Br, New Animal Drugs Div, 68-73; chief toxicologist, Residue Planning & Eval Staff, Animal & Plant Health Inspection Serv, USDA, 73-75; PVT CONSULT ANIMAL & PLANT HEALTH, 75- *Mem:* Am Vet Med Asn; Am Pub Health Asn; fel Am Col Vet Toxicologists; Am Soc Vet Physiologists & Pharmacologists; Soc Toxicologists. *Res:* Toxicological significance of pesticides, herbicides, fungicides, industrial environmental contaminants and chemicals and of oral and injectible drugs under conditions of use. *Mailing Add:* 4638 Bayshore Rd Sarasota FL 33580

RADER, WILLIAM ERNEST, b Ellensburg, Wash, Aug 21, 16; m 38; c 2. PLANT PATHOLOGY. *Educ:* State Col Wash, BS, 39; Utah State Col, MS, 42; Cornell Univ, PhD(plant path), 46. *Prof Exp:* Asst, Utah State Col, 39-42 & Cornell Univ, 44-46; MICROBIOLOGIST, BIOL SCI RES CTR, AGR LAB, SHELL DEVELOP CO, 46- *Mem:* Am Phytopath Soc; Soc Nematol. *Res:* Pesticides and agricultural chemicals; biochemistry of fungicidal action; physiology and biochemistry of plant disease; chemical control of nematodes; biotreatment of industrial wastes. *Mailing Add:* 4901 Dale Rd Modesto CA 95356

RADEWALD, JOHN DALE, b Niles, Mich, Feb 15, 29; m 53; c 2. PLANT PATHOLOGY. *Educ:* Ariz State Univ, BS, 52; Okla State Univ, MS, 56; Univ Calif, PhD(plant path), 61. *Prof Exp:* Res asst plant path, Okla State Univ, 55-56; res asst plant nematol, Univ Calif, 56-60; assoc plant pathologist, Pineapple Res Inst, Hawaii, 60-63; EXTEN NEMATOLOGIST, COOP EXTEN, UNIV CALIF, RIVERSIDE, 64-; LECTR NEMATOL, 74- *Res:* Plant nematology, primarily host-parasite relations; biology and physiology of plant parasitic nematodes. *Mailing Add:* Dept Nematology Univ Calif Riverside CA 92521

RADFORD, ALAN, b Chelmsford, Eng, Mar 31, 40; m 65; c 3. GENETICS. *Educ:* Univ Leeds, BSc, 62; McMaster Univ, MSc, 63, PhD(genetics), 66. *Prof Exp:* Res assoc biol, Stanford Univ, 66-70; asst prof zool, Univ Calif, Los Angeles, 70-71; Sci Res Coun fel, Univ Leeds, 71; lectr bot, Birkbeck Col, Univ London, 72-74; LECTR GENETICS, UNIV LEEDS, 74- *Mem:* Brit Genetical Soc; Europ Environ Mutagenesis Soc; Brit Inst Biol. *Res:* Regulation in the pyrimidine biosynthetic pathway; chromosome breakage; fungal genetics; complementation and mutagenesis at the pyrimidine-3 locus; gene fine structure and function; gene cloning. *Mailing Add:* Dept of Genetics Univ of Leeds Leeds England

RADFORD, ALBERT ERNEST, b Augusta, Ga, Jan 25, 18; m 41; c 3. BOTANY. *Educ:* Furman Univ, BS, 39; Univ NC, PhD(bot), 48. *Prof Exp:* From instr to assoc prof, 47-59, PROF BOT, UNIV NC, CHAPEL HILL, 59- *Res:* Taxonomy of vascular plants; vascular flora of southeastern North America. *Mailing Add:* Dept of Bot Univ of NC Chapel Hill NC 27514

RADFORD, DAVID EUGENE, b Plattsburg, NY, June 4, 43; m 66; c 3. MATHEMATICS. *Educ:* Univ NC, Chapel Hill, BS, 65, MA, 68, PhD(math), 70. *Prof Exp:* Asst prof math, Lawrence Univ, 70-76; ASSOC PROF MATH, UNIV ILL CHICAGO CIRCLE, 76- *Concurrent Pos:* NSF grant, 74-75; vis lectr, Rutgers Univ, 75-76, vis assoc prof, 79-80. *Mem:* Am Math Soc. *Res:* Algebra; Hopf algebras, algebraic groups and co-algebras. *Mailing Add:* Dept of Math PO Box 4348 Chicago IL 60680

RADFORD, EDWARD PARISH, b Springfield, Mass, Feb 21, 22; m 45, 68; c 5. ENVIRONMENTAL MEDICINE, EPIDEMIOLOGY. *Educ:* Harvard Univ, MD, 46. *Prof Exp:* Instr physiol, Med Sch, Harvard Univ, 50-52, assoc sch pub health, 52-55; physiologist, Haskell Lab, E I du Pont de Nemours & Co, 55-59; assoc prof physiol, Sch Pub Health, Harvard Univ, 59-65; prof environ med & dir Kettering Lab, Col Med, Univ Cincinnati, 65-68; prof environ med, Sch Hyg & Pub Health, Johns Hopkins Univ, 68-77; PROF EPIDEMIOL, UNIV PITTSBURGH GRAD SCH PUB HEALTH, 77- *Concurrent Pos:* Teaching fel physiol, Med Sch, Harvard Univ, 49-50; vis prof, Oxford Univ, 75-76; mem comt carbon monoxide, Nat Acad Sci, 76-77; consult med, Westvaco Corp, 77-; mem comt biol effects ionizing radiation, Nat Acad Sci, 70-72, chmn, 77-80; mem air pollution adv bd, State Md, 71-77; fac scholar, Macy Found, 75-76. *Mem:* Am Physiol Soc; Am Pub Health Asn; Radiation Res Soc; Soc Occup & Environ Health. *Res:* Radiation biology; toxicology; occupational medicine; pulmonary physiology; environmental epidemiology. *Mailing Add:* Dept Epidemiol Grad Sch Pub Health Pittsburgh PA 15261

RADFORD, HARRISON E, molecular physics, see previous edition

RADFORD, HERSCHEL DONALD, b Butler, Mo, June 21, 11; m 39; c 2. ORGANIC CHEMISTRY. *Educ:* Park Col, AB, 33; Univ Mo, AM, 44, PhD(chem), 49. *Prof Exp:* Chemist, Res & Develop Dept, Pan-Am Refining Corp, Standard Oil Co, Ind, 41-44, group leader, Chem Res Sect, 44-51, head, Process Develop Sect, 51-57, dir, Process Div, Am Oil Co, 57-60, tech dir, Process Develop Labs, 60-62, asst dir res & develop dept, 62-73, dir process & eng develop, Amoco Oil Co, Standard Oil Co, Ind, 73-76; CONSULT, 76- *Mem:* Am Chem Soc; Am Inst Chem Engrs. *Res:* Alkylation of aromatic and aliphatic hydrocarbons; dealkylation of aromatic hydrocarbons, catalytic hydrogenation of substituted carbonyl and carbinol compounds; organic reactions catalyzed by anhydrous hydrofluoric acid; catalytic reforming; hydrocracking; desulfurization; isomerization; coking; catalytic cracking; synthetic fuels. *Mailing Add:* 1375 Dartmouth Rd Flossmoor IL 60422

RADFORD, KENNETH CHARLES, b Manchester, Eng, July 1, 41; m 65; c 3. METALLURGY. *Educ:* Univ London, BSc, 63; Imp Col, dipl & ARSM, 63, PhD(metall), 67. *Prof Exp:* Sr scientist, 68-78, FEL ENGR, WESTINGHOUSE ELEC CORP, 78- *Mem:* Inst Metall; Am Chem Soc; Am Ceramic Soc. *Res:* Dielectric properties; ceramics; nuclear fuel; electrical properties of ceramics; physical properties of ceramic powders; ceramic fabrication. *Mailing Add:* Res & Develop Ctr Westinghouse Elec Corp Pittsburgh PA 15235

RADFORD, LOREN E, b Randolph, Nebr, Oct 4, 28; m 50; c 1. SOLID STATE PHYSICS. *Educ:* Univ Wash, BS, 50; Univ Va, MS, 60, PhD(physics), 62. *Prof Exp:* From asst prof to assoc prof physics, US Mil Acad, 61-74; PROF PHYSICS & HEAD DIV SCI & MATH, W VA NORTHERN COMMUNITY COL, 74- *Mem:* Am Asn Physics Teachers; Am Phys Soc; Sigma Xi. *Res:* Investigation of crystal defects using technique of electron paramagnetic resonance. *Mailing Add:* Div of Sci & Math WVa Northern Commun Col Wheeling WV 26003

RADFORD, TERENCE, b Sheffield, Eng, Apr 1, 39; m 72. ORGANIC CHEMISTRY. *Educ:* Liverpool Col Technol, ARIC, 62; Sheffield Univ, PhD(org chem), 65. *Prof Exp:* Asst lectr org chem, Sheffield Col Technol, 65-66; res fel, Ohio State Univ, 66-67 & Wayne State Univ, 67-68; res scientist, 68-80, SR RES SCIENTIST MASS SPECTROS, COCA-COLA CO, 80- *Mem:* Royal Soc Chem; Am Chem Soc. *Res:* The application of instrumental techniques, especially combined gas chromatography/mass spectrometry to the identification of natural products. *Mailing Add:* Coca-Cola Co PO Drawer 1734 Atlanta GA 30301

RADFORTH, NORMAN WILLIAM, b Lancashire, Eng, Sept 22, 12; nat Can; m 39; c 2. PALEOBOTANY. *Educ:* Univ Toronto, BA, 36, MA, 37; Univ Glasgow, Scotland, PhD(paleobot), 39. *Prof Exp:* Lectr bot, Univ Toronto, 42-46; prof, McMaster Univ, 46-68, head dept, 46-53, chmn dept biol, 60-66, chmn org & assoc terrain res unit, 61-68, coordr acad develop, 65-66; prof biol & Muskeg Studies, Univ NB, 68-77, head dept biol, 68-70, dir, Muskeg Res Inst, 68-73; CONSULT, RADFORTH & ASSOCS, 77- *Concurrent Pos:* Dir, Royal Bot Gardens, Can, 46-53; mem, Assoc Comt Geotech Res, Nat Res Coun Can, 48-; prog chmn & secy, Int Cong Bot, 59; vpres, Int Orgn Paleont, 59. *Honors & Awards:* Silver Medal, Royal Soc Arts, 58. *Mem:* Royal Soc Can; fel Royal Soc Arts. *Res:* Experimental morphology and embryology of higher plants applying in vitro methods; micropaleobotany and northern peatland interpretation. *Mailing Add:* Radforth & Assocs Limbert Rd RR 3 Parry Sound ON P2A 2W9 Can

RADHAKRISHNAMURTHY, BHANDARU, b Andhra Pradesh, India, July 1, 28; m 53; c 4. BIOCHEMISTRY. *Educ:* Osmania Univ, India, BS, 51, MS, 53, PhD(chem), 58. *Prof Exp:* Res chemist, Sirsilk, Ltd, India, 53-54; lectr chem, Osmania Univ, 55-61; from res assoc to assoc prof, 61-74, PROF MED & BIOCHEM, LA STATE UNIV MED CTR, NEW ORLEANS, 74- *Concurrent Pos:* Fulbright fel med & biochem, Sch Med, La State Univ, New Orleans, 61-62; mem coun atherosclerosis, Am Heart Asn, 71- *Mem:* AAAS; Am Chem Soc; Soc Exp Biol & Med; Am Soc Biol Chem; NY Acad Sci. *Res:* Biochemistry of connective tissue; mucopolysaccharides and glycoproteins. *Mailing Add:* Dept of Med La State Univ Med Ctr New Orleans LA 70112

RADHAKRISHNAN, CHITTUR VENKITASUBHAN, b Mannuthy, India, June 6, 37; m 66; c 2. VETERINARY MICROBIOLOGY. *Educ:* Univ Kerala, India, BVSc, 59; Univ Fla, PhD(vet parasitol), 71. *Prof Exp:* Lectr vet med, Col Vet Med, Univ Kerala, 59-64; sci officer parasitol, Hindustan Antibiotics Res Ctr, 64-68; res asst, Dept Vet Sci, Univ Fla, 68-71, teaching asst parasitol, 71-72; VET, BUR LABS, FLA DEPT AGR, 72- *Concurrent Pos:* Assoc prof pathobiol, Col Vet Med, Pahlaui Univ, Shiraz, Iran, 73-75. *Mem:* Am Oil Chemists' Soc; Am Asn Avian Pathologists; Am Asn Vet Lab Diagnosticians. Am Soc Parasitologists. *Mailing Add:* Bur Labs Box 1031 Fla Dept Agr Dade City FL 33525

RADHAKRISHNAN, EGYARAMAN, b Calcutta, India, Feb 21, 52. CHEMICAL ENGINEERING, ENVIRONMENTAL ENGINEERING. *Educ:* Jadavpur Univ, India, BSChE, 74; Univ Cincinnati, MSChE, 76. *Prof Exp:* Teaching asst chem eng, Univ Cincinnati, 75-77; RESEARCHER ENERGY & ENVIRON TECHNOL, COMBUSTION SYSTS TECHNOL SECT, BATTELLE-COLUMBUS LABS, 77- *Mem:* Assoc mem Am Inst Chem Engrs. *Res:* Combustion, energy conversion and air pollution; foam and other surface phenomena. *Mailing Add:* 599 Beaufort Ct Cincinnati OH 45240

RADIMER, KENNETH JOHN, b Clifton, NJ, Mar 31, 20. INORGANIC CHEMISTRY. *Educ:* Mass Inst Technol, SB, 42, PhD(inorg & anal chem), 47. *Prof Exp:* Res chemist, Nat Res Corp, Mass, 42; asst physics & chem, Mass Inst Technol, 43-44; res chemist chg anal lab, Kellex Corp, NJ & SAM Labs, Carbide & Carbon Chem Corp, 45-46; instr anal chem, Lehigh Univ, 47-48; asst prof inorg & anal chem, Ind Univ, 48-50; res chemist, Gen Chem Div, Allied Chem & Dye Corp, 50-51; sect leader, Vitro Corp Am, 51-54; res chemist, M W Kellog Co div, Pullman, Inc, 54-57 & 59-62 & Minn Mining & Mfg Co, 57-58; chief chemist, CBS Labs, 58-59; mgr metals applns, 62-69, RES ASSOC INDUST CHEMS DIV, FMC CORP, PRINCETON, 69- *Mem:* Fel AAAS; Electrochem Soc; Am Electroplaters Soc; Nat Asn Corrosion Engrs. *Res:* Microrefractometry; fluorine; fluorocarbon analysis; freon synthesis; molten salt electrolysis; reactions of metals with chemicals; chemistry of hydrogen peroxide; electrolytic persulfate processes; production of soda ash, phosphorus and phosphates; corrosion. *Mailing Add:* 12 Martin Pl Little Falls NJ 07424

RADIN, CHARLES LEWIS, b New York, NY, Jan 15, 45; m 69. MATHEMATICAL PHYSICS. *Educ:* City Col New York, BS, 65; Univ Rochester, PhD(physics), 70. *Prof Exp:* Fel math physics, Univ Nijmegen, 70-71; res assoc, Princeton Univ, 71-73; res assoc, Rockefeller Univ, 73-74; instr math, Univ Pa, 74-76; asst prof, 76-80, ASSOC PROF MATH, UNIV TEX, AUSTIN, 80- *Mem:* Am Math Soc; Am Phys Soc; Int Asn Math Physicist. *Res:* Qualitative dynamics of quantum systems, especially many-body systems; automorphisms of operator algebras; classical ground states. *Mailing Add:* Dept of Math Univ of Tex Austin TX 78712

RADIN, JOHN WILLIAM, b New York, NY, Jan 8, 44; m 65; c 2. PLANT PHYSIOLOGY. *Educ:* Univ Calif, Davis, BS, 65, PhD(plant physiol), 70. *Prof Exp:* Assoc agron, Univ Calif, Davis, 70-71; PLANT PHYSIOLOGIST, WESTERN COTTON RES LAB, AGR RES SERV, USDA, 71- *Mem:* Am Soc Plant Physiologists; Crop Sci Soc Am. *Res:* General plant physiology; root physiology; nitrogen metabolism, especially nitrate reduction; hormonal control of growth and development in plants. *Mailing Add:* Western Cotton Res Lab ARS USDA 4135 E Broadway Phoenix AZ 85040

RADIN, NATHAN, b Brooklyn, NY, Jan 22, 19; m 46; c 2. CLINICAL CHEMISTRY. *Educ:* Univ Calif, BA, 41; Columbia Univ, MA, 47; Purdue Univ, PhD(anal chem), 51. *Prof Exp:* Proj engr, Eng Res & Develop Labs, US Army, 51-52; chemist, Lederle Labs, Am Cyanamid Co, 53-54; biochemist, Mt Sinai Hosp, New York, 55-56; instr chem, Rochester Inst Technol, 56-59;

chief biochemist, Rochester Gen Hosp, 58-66; clin chemist, Harrisburg Hosp Inst Path & Res, Pa, 66-67; RES CHEMIST, CTR DIS CONTROL, 67- *Mem:* Am Chem Soc; Am Asn Clin Chem; Sigma Xi. *Res:* Quality control; standards; reference materials; training. *Mailing Add:* Clin Chem Div Ctr Dis Control 1600 Clifton Rd NE Atlanta GA 30333

RADIN, NORMAN SAMUEL, b New York, NY, July 20, 20; m 47; c 2. BIOCHEMISTRY. *Educ:* Columbia Univ, BA, 41, PhD(biochem), 49. *Prof Exp:* Asst res chemist, Off Sci Res & Develop, Pa, 42-45; fel, Univ Calif, 49-50; res scientist, Biochem Inst, Univ Tex, 50-52; res assoc, Med Sch, Northwestern Univ, 52-55, from asst prof to assoc prof, 55-60; RES BIOCHEMIST, MENT HEALTH RES INST, UNIV MICH, ANN ARBOR, 60-, PROF BIOL CHEM IN PSYCHIAT, UNIV MICH, 73- *Concurrent Pos:* Prin scientist, Radioisotope Unit, Vet Admin Hosp, Hines, Ill, 52-54 & Res Hosp, Chicago, 54-57; ed, Anal Biochem. *Mem:* Am Soc Biol Chemists; Am Soc Neurochem; Int Soc Neurochem. *Res:* Brain lipids; lipid methodology; glycolipid metabolism; sphingolipid enzyme inhibitors; Gaucher's disease. *Mailing Add:* 3544 Terhune Rd Ann Arbor MI 48104

RADIN, SHELDEN HENRY, b Hartford, Conn, Dec 24, 36; m 60; c 3. PLASMA PHYSICS. *Educ:* Worcester Polytech Inst, BS, 58; Yale Univ, MS, 59, PhD(physics), 63. *Prof Exp:* From asst prof to assoc prof, 63-74, PROF PHYSICS, LEHIGH UNIV, 74- *Concurrent Pos:* Mem, Exam Comt, Physics Achievement Test, Col Entrance Exam Bd, 70-78, chmn, 72-78. *Mem:* Am Phys Soc; Am Asn Univ Profs; Am Asn Physics Teachers. *Res:* Statistical mechanics of plasmas; kinetic theory of nonequilibrium situations. *Mailing Add:* Dept Physics Bldg 16 Lehigh Univ Bethlehem PA 18015

RADKE, FREDERICK HERBERT, b Jordan, Minn, Jan 19, 23; m 46; c 5. BIOCHEMISTRY. *Educ:* Hamline Univ, BS, 47; Iowa State Col, PhD(chem), 52. *Prof Exp:* Asst chem, Iowa State Col, 47-52; from asst prof to assoc prof, 52-59, PROF BIOCHEM, UNIV MAINE, ORONO, 59-, HEAD DEPT, 58- *Concurrent Pos:* Consult, Vet Admin Hosp, Togus, Maine, 73- *Mem:* AAAS; Am Chem Soc; Sigma Xi; Nutrit Today Soc. *Res:* Protein nutrition; relationships of fats, protein and cholesterol; brain composition as affected by diet. *Mailing Add:* Dept of Biochem Hitchner Hall Univ of Maine Orono ME 04473

RADKE, JERRY KIETH, b Ripon, Wis, Apr 11, 38; m 62; c 3. MICROMETEOROLOGY, SOIL PHYSICS. *Educ:* Univ Wis-Madison, BS, 60, PhD(soil physics), 65; Iowa State Univ, MS, 62. *Prof Exp:* RES SOIL SCIENTIST, SOIL & WATER CONSERV, AGR RES SERV, USDA, 65- *Concurrent Pos:* Asst prof, Dept Soils, Univ Minn, St Paul, 65-74, assoc prof, 74-; sabbatical leave, Dept Soil Sci, Waite Agr Res Inst, Glen Osmond, Australia, 81- *Mem:* Am Soc Agron; Soil Sci Soc Am. *Res:* Micrometeorology and microclimatology of the north central states with special interest on wind turbulence, windbreaks, plant-climate-water-soil interactions, computer implementation and electronic instrumentation. *Mailing Add:* Agr Res Serv USDA N Iowa Ave Morris MN 56267

RADKE, LAWRENCE FREDERICK, b Seattle, Wash, Mar 19, 42. ATMOSPHERIC SCIENCE, CLOUD PHYSICS. *Educ:* Univ Wash, BSc, 64, MSc, 66, PhD(atmospheric sci), 68. *Prof Exp:* Res assoc, 68-70, res asst prof, 70-72, res assoc prof, 72-80, RES PROF ATMOSPHERIC SCI, UNIV WASH, 80- *Mem:* Am Meteorol Soc; AAAS; Sigma Xi. *Res:* Aircraft measurements and instrumental development; meteorology; cloud physics; atmospheric chemistry; air pollution. *Mailing Add:* Dept of Atmospheric Sci Univ of Wash Seattle WA 98195

RADKE, MYRON GLEN, b Sykeston, NDak, Sept 26, 28. MEDICAL PARASITOLOGY, THERAPEUTICS. *Educ:* Jamestown Col, BS, 50; Univ Wyo, MS, 51. *Prof Exp:* Med Serv Corps, US Army, 53-, chief parasitol sect, 3rd Army Area Med Lab, 53-55, parasitologist, Trop Res Med Lab, San Juan, PR, 55-58 & Walter Reed Army Inst Res, 59-62, med chem parasitologist, 64-65, chief, Dept Med Zool, 406th Med Lab, Japan, 65-68, stud detachment, Med Field Serv Sch, Ft Sam Houston, Tex, 68-69, chief div med zool, 9th Med Lab, SVietnam, 69-70, chief parasitol sect, Div Geog Path, Armed Forces Inst Path, Washington, DC, 70-72, chief, US Army Res Unit, Walter Reed Army Inst Res, Brazil, 72-73, comdr, 73-79, ASSOC DIR OPERS, WALTER REED ARMY INST RES, WASHINGTON, DC, 79- *Concurrent Pos:* Vis prof, Fac Health Sci, Univ Brazil, 73- *Mem:* Am Soc Parasitol; Soc Protozool; Am Soc Trop Med & Hyg; Int Soc Trop Dermat; Royal Soc Trop Med & Hyg. *Res:* Ecology and biology of Biomphalaria glabrata; biology and ecology of filariasis; epidemiology, sero-diagnosis and life cycle of Schistosomiasis; biochemistry of parasitic antigens; chemotherapy; anti-schistosome drug screening; epidemiology of paragonimiasis in Japan. *Mailing Add:* Off Assoc Dir Opers Walter Reed Army Inst Res Washington DC 20012

RADKE, RODNEY OWEN, b Ripon, Wis, Feb 5, 42; m 63; c 3. WOOD SCIENCE. *Educ:* Univ Wis-Madison, BS, 63, MS, 65, PhD(soil biochem), 67. *Prof Exp:* Plant physiologist, US Army Biol Res Labs, 67-69; sr res biologist, Agr Div, Monsanto Co, 69-74, res specialist, Monsanto Agr Prods Co, 74-75, SR RES GROUP LEADER, MONSANTO AGR PRODS CO, 81- *Mem:* Am Soc Agron; Weed Sci Soc Am. *Res:* Crop protection chemicals for control of undesirable plants. *Mailing Add:* Monsanto Agr Prods Co 800 N Lindbergh Blvd St Louis MO 63166

RADKE, WILLIAM JOHN, b Mankato, Minn, June 8, 47; m 70. ZOOLOGY, AVIAN BIOLOGY. *Educ:* Mankato State Univ, BS, 70, MA, 72; Univ Ariz, PhD(zool), 75. *Prof Exp:* ASST PROF BIOL, CENT STATE UNIV, OKLA, 75- *Mem:* AAAS; Sigma Xi. *Res:* Hypothalamic-hypophyseal-thyroid axis of the bird; avian air sacs and the relationship to spermatogenesis; avian emetics for stomach contents recovery. *Mailing Add:* Dept of Biol Cent State Univ Edmond OK 73034

RADLOFF, HAROLD DAVID, b Mellen, Wis, Aug 25, 37; m 60; c 2. DAIRY SCIENCE, BIOCHEMISTRY. *Educ:* Univ Wis, BS, 59, MS, 61, PhD(dairy sci, biochem), 64. *Prof Exp:* Res fel dairy sci, Univ Wis, 64-66; asst prof dairy husb, 66-70, assoc prof, 70-77, prof, 77-81, PROF ANIMAL SCI, UNIV WYO, 81-, EXTEN ANIMAL SCIENTIST, 81- *Mem:* Am Dairy Sci Asn; Am Soc Animal Sci. *Res:* Lipid metabolism in ruminants; milk fat synthesis; general dairy cow nutrition. *Mailing Add:* Div of Animal Sci Univ of Wyo Laramie WY 82070

RADLOFF, ROGER JAMES, b Mason City, Iowa, Oct 16, 40; m 68; c 2. VIROLOGY. *Educ:* Iowa State Univ, BS, 62; Calif Inst Technol, PhD(biophys & chem), 68. *Prof Exp:* Fel, Biophys Lab, Univ Wis, 68-72; ASST PROF MICROBIOL, SCH MED, UNIV NMEX, 72- *Concurrent Pos:* NIH fel, 68-70; NSF & NIH res grant, 74- *Mem:* Am Soc Microbiol; AAAS. *Res:* Structure and synthesis of encephalomyocarditis virus. *Mailing Add:* 1408 Mesilla NE Albuquerque NM 87110

RADLOW, JAMES, b New York, NY. APPLIED MATHEMATICS. *Educ:* NY Univ, PhD(math), 57. *Prof Exp:* Assoc prof math, Adelphi Univ, 59-62 & Purdue Univ, 62-65; PROF APPL MATH, UNIV NH, 65- *Res:* Diffraction theory; singular integral equations; Hilbert space; partial differential equations; magnetohydrodynamics. *Mailing Add:* Dept of Math Univ of NH Durham NH 03824

RADNELL, CHRISTOPHER J, b Tallourn, Australia, Sept 24, 53. ATMOSPHERIC CHEMISTRY & PHYSICS. *Educ:* Monash Univ, BSc Hons, 73; Oxford Univ, DPhil(physics), 78. *Prof Exp:* RES ASSOC ISOTOPE GEOCHEM, DEPT GEOSCI, UNIV ARIZ, 79- *Res:* Modelling the carbon 14 in the atmosphere and how it interacts with solar activity and geomagnetic field variations; low level liquid scintillation counting. *Mailing Add:* 232 Geosci Univ Ariz Tucson AZ 85721

RADNITZ, ALAN, b Miami Beach, Fla, Dec 16, 44; m 68; c 2. MATHEMATICS. *Educ:* Univ Calif, Los Angeles, AB, 66, PhD(math), 70. *Prof Exp:* asst prof, 70-75, assoc prof, 75-82, PROF MATH, CALIF STATE POLYTECH UNIV, POMONA, 82- *Mem:* Am Math Soc. *Res:* Differential equations in banach spaces; partial differential equations; functional analysis. *Mailing Add:* Dept of Math Calif State Polytech Univ Pomona CA 91768

RADO, GEORGE TIBOR, b Budapest, Hungary, July 22, 17; nat US; m 64; c 2. SOLID STATE PHYSICS. *Educ:* Mass Inst Technol, SB, 39, SM, 41, PhD(physics), 43. *Prof Exp:* Res assoc, Div Indust Coop, Mass Inst Technol, 42-43 & Radiation Lab, 44-45; physicist, 45-55, HEAD MAGNETISM BR, NAVAL RES LAB, 55- *Concurrent Pos:* Adj prof Univ Md, 62-; mem comm magnetism, Int Union Pure & Appl Physics, 66-75, secy, 69-72, chmn, 72-75. *Honors & Awards:* Pure Sci Award, Naval Res Lab-Sci Res Soc Am; 57; E O Hulburt Sci Award, 65; Distinguished Achievement Sci Award, US Navy, 71. *Mem:* Fel Am Phys Soc. *Res:* Light scattering; microwave propagation; saturation magnetization; magnetic spectra; domain theory; ferrites; Faraday effect; ferromagnetic resonance; magnetocrystalline anisotropy; magnetoelectric effects; ultra-thin magnetic films. *Mailing Add:* Naval Res Lab Washington DC 20375

RADOMSKI, JACK LONDON, b Milwaukee, Wis, Dec 10, 20; m 47, 70; c 4. PHARMACOLOGY. *Educ:* Univ Wis, BS, 42; George Washington Univ, PhD, 50. *Prof Exp:* Chemist, Gen Aniline & Film Corp, 42-44; pharmacologist, Food & Drug Admin, Fed Security Agency, 44-53; from asst prof to assoc prof pharmacol, Sch Med, Univ Miami, 53-59, prof, 59-82; PRES, COVINGTON CEMTOX, 82- *Concurrent Pos:* Consult toxicol. *Mem:* Am Soc Pharmacol & Exp Therapeut; Soc Toxicol; Am Asn Cancer Res; Int Soc Biochem Pharmacol; Acad Toxicol Sci. *Res:* toxicology and metabolism of drugs, chemicals and insecticides; environmental toxicology and carcinogenesis. *Mailing Add:* Rt 6 Box 300A Andalusia AL 36420

RADOMSKI, MARK STEPHEN, theoretical nuclear physics, see previous edition

RADONOVICH, LEWIS JOSEPH, b Curtisville, Pa, July 2, 44; m 66; c 2. STRUCTURAL CHEMISTRY. *Educ:* Thiel Col, BA, 66; Wayne State Univ, PhD(phys chem), 70. *Prof Exp:* Res assoc inorg chem, Cornell Univ, 70-73; asst prof, 73-77, ASSOC PROF CHEM, UNIV NDAK, 77- *Mem:* Am Chem Soc; Am Crystallog Asn. *Res:* Organometallic chemistry, x-ray crystallography and the structural chemistry of compounds of biological interest. *Mailing Add:* Dept of Chem Univ of NDak Grand Forks ND 58202

RADOSEVICH, LEE GEORGE, b Milwaukee, Wis, Nov 5, 38. ENERGY CONVERSION, SOLID STATE PHYSICS. *Educ:* Marquette Univ, BS, 60, MS, 62; Northwestern Univ, Ill, PhD(physics), 68. *Prof Exp:* Physicist, Allis-Chalmers Mfg Co, 62; res assoc physics, Univ Ill, Urbana, 67-69; MEM STAFF PHYSICS, SANDIA LABS, 69- *Mem:* Int Solar Energy Soc; Am Phys Soc. *Res:* Solar thermal power conversion. *Mailing Add:* Sandia Labs PO Box 969 Livermore CA 94550

RADOSEVICH, STEVEN ROBERT, b Yakima, Wash, Apr 30, 46; m 67; c 3. WEED SCIENCE, BOTANY. *Educ:* Wash State Univ, 68; Ore State Univ, MS, 71, PhD(agron), 72. *Prof Exp:* Exten weed scientist, 72-74, asst prof bot, 74-81, ASSOC PROF BOT, UNIV CALIF, DAVIS, 81- *Mem:* Weed Sci Soc Am. *Res:* Developed resistance of weeds to herbicides; ecological and physiological studies relating to management of woody plants. *Mailing Add:* Dept of Bot Univ of Calif Davis CA 95616

RADOSKI, HENRY ROBERT, b Jersey City, NJ, Aug 18, 36; m 59; c 3. SPACE PHYSICS, PLASMA PHYSICS. *Educ:* Col Holy Cross, BS, 58; Mass Inst Technol, PhD(physics), 63. *Prof Exp:* Res asst plasma physics, Res Lab Electronics, Mass Inst Technol, 59-63; res assoc prof geophys, Weston Observ, Boston Col, 63-68; res physicist, Space Physics Lab, Air Force Geophysics Lab, 68-76, PROG MGR, AIR FORCE OFF SCI RES, 76- *Mem:* Am Geophys Union; Am Phys Soc; Am Astron Soc; Fedn Am Scientists; Sigma Xi. *Res:* Magnetospheric physics; solar physics; astronomy. *Mailing Add:* Air Force Off Sci Res AFOSR/NP Bolling AFB Washington DC 20332

RADOVSKY, FRANK JAY, b Fall River, Mass, Jan 5, 29; m 57; c 2. ACAROLOGY, MEDICAL ENTOMOLOGY. *Educ:* Univ Colo, AB, 51; Univ Calif, Berkeley, MS, 59, PhD(parasitol), 64. *Prof Exp:* Actg asst prof entom, Univ Calif, Berkeley, 62-63; asst res parasitologist, Hooper Found, Med Ctr, Univ Calif, San Francisco, 63-69, lectr parasitol, Dept Int Health, 69; asst to dir res, 73-76, actg dir, 76-77, ACAROLOGIST, BISHOP MUS, 70-, CHMN DEPT ENTOM, 72-, ASST DIR, 77- *Concurrent Pos:* Ed & co-ed, J Med Entom, 70-78, exec ed, 78-; secy, Int Cong Acarology, 71-78; mem bd mgt, Wau Ecol Inst, Papua, New Guinea, 72-; mem, Hawaii Animal Species Adv Comn, 72-80; managing ed, Pac Insects, 78-; assoc ed, Annual Review Entom, 78- *Mem:* AAAS; Entom Soc Am; Acarol Soc Am. *Res:* Biology and systematics of acarine parasites; adaptation and evolution of relationships between arthropod parasites and their host; arthropod vectors of disease agents. *Mailing Add:* Dept of Entom Bishop Mus PO Box 19000-A Honolulu HI 96819

RADSPINNER, JOHN ASA, b Vincennes, Ind, May 14, 17; m 42; c 2. PHYSICAL CHEMISTRY. *Educ:* Univ Richmond, BS, 37; Va Polytech Inst, MS, 38; Carnegie Inst Technol, DSc(phys chem), 42. *Prof Exp:* Res chemist, Pan-Am Refining Corp, Div Standard Oil Co Ind, 42-44, supvr operating dept, 44-54, asst dir indust rels, Am Oil Co Div, 54-56, personnel dir, Yorktown Refinery, 56-57; assoc prof, 57-62, actg dean, 69-70, chmn dept chem, 70-72, PROF CHEM, LYCOMING COL, 62- *Mem:* Am Chem Soc; AAAS. *Res:* Thermodynamic properties of solutions. *Mailing Add:* Dept of Chem Lycoming Col Williamsport PA 17701

RADTKE, DOUGLAS DEAN, b New London, Wis, Nov 6, 38; m 62; c 2. PHYSICAL INORGANIC CHEMISTRY. *Educ:* Wis State Univ, Stevens Point, BS, 61; Univ Wis, PhD(phys chem), 66. *Prof Exp:* Asst prof, 66-69, assoc prof, 69-77, PROF CHEM, UNIV WIS-STEVENS POINT, 77- *Mem:* Am Chem Soc. *Res:* Molecular orbital calculations for transition metal complexes; preparation and structure of simple divalent rare earth compounds. *Mailing Add:* Dept of Chem Univ of Wis Stevens Point WI 54481

RADTKE, SCHRADE FRED, b Minneapolis, Minn, Aug 21, 19; m 42; c 2. INORGANIC CHEMISTRY, METALLURGY. *Educ:* Mass Inst Technol, BS, 40, PhD(chem), 49. *Prof Exp:* Teaching fel, Mass Inst Technol, 40-41 & 46-49; tech asst to vpres & gen mgr, NC Shipbldg Co, NC, 41-42; res supvr, Pigments Dept, E I du Pont de Nemours & Co, Del, 49-53; dir, Metall Res Labs, Reynolds Metals Co, Va, 53-58; PRES, INT LEAD ZINC RES ORGN, INC, 58- *Mem:* AAAS; Am Inst Mining, Metall & Petrol Engrs; Inst Elec & Electronics Engrs; Am Chem Soc; NY Acad Sci. *Res:* Rare metals. *Mailing Add:* Int Lead Zinc Res Orgn Inc 292 Madison Ave New York NY 10017

RADWAN, MOHAMED AHMED, b Dakahlia, Egypt, Apr 16, 26; nat US; m 57. PLANT PHYSIOLOGY. *Educ:* Cairo Univ, Egypt, BSc, 46; MS, 50; Univ Calif, PhD(plant physiol), 56. *Prof Exp:* Asst lectr chem, Cairo Univ, 47-52, lectr plant physiol, 56-57; sr lab technician, Univ Calif, 57-58; instr chem, Sacramento City Col, 58-60; plant physiologist, 60-68, PRIN PLANT PHYSIOLOGIST, US FOREST SERV, 68- *Mem:* Am Chem Soc; Am Soc Plant Physiol; Bot Soc Am; Am Soc Agron; Soc Am Foresters. *Res:* Nutrition; fertilization; forest tree physiology. *Mailing Add:* Forestry Sci Lab 3625-93rd Ave SW Olympia WA 98502

RADWANSKA, EWA, b Wilno, Poland, Oct 24, 38; c 1. OBSTETRICS & GYNECOLOGY, ENDOCRINOLOGY. *Educ:* Med Acad, Warsaw, MD, 62, Dr Med Sci, 69; Univ London, MPhil, 75. *Prof Exp:* Resident & instr obstet, gynec & endocrinol, Med Acad, Warsaw, 64-70; fel endocrinol, Univ Col Hosp, London, 70-75; registr, Hillingdon Hosp, London, 75-76; asst prof obstet, gynec & endocrinol, Univ NC, Chapel Hill, 77-79; mem staff, Univ Ark, Little Rock, 79-81; MEM STAFF, DEPT OBSTET & GYNEC, RUSH MED COL, CHICAGO, 81- *Concurrent Pos:* Med officer, City Clin, Warsaw, 64-70, Family Planning Asn, London, 70-76 & Marie Stopes Mem Birth Control Ctr, London, 70-76. *Mem:* Polish Endocrine Soc; Am Med Soc; Royal Col Obstetricians & Gynecologists; Am Fertil Soc; Soc Study Reprod. *Res:* Reproductive endocrinology, particularly induction of ovulation, ovarian failure, luteal deficiency, spontaneous abortions, infertility, progesterone assay, tubal sterilization. *Mailing Add:* Dept of Obstet & Gynec Rush Med Col Chicago IL 60612

RADWIN, GEORGE E, b Far Rockaway, NY, Aug 20, 40; m 62; c 2. MALACOLOGY, INVERTEBRATE ECOLOGY. *Educ:* City Univ New York, BS, 62; Fla State Univ, MS, 64; George Washington Univ, PhD(zool), 68. *Prof Exp:* Smithsonian internship, 66-68; CUR, SAN DIEGO NATURAL HIST MUS, 68- *Concurrent Pos:* Adj prof zool, San Diego State Univ, 74- *Mem:* Soc Syst Zool; Am Malacol Union; Sigma Xi; Coun Syst Malacologists. *Res:* Taxonomy, ecology, and zoogeography of marine gastropod mollusks, especially feeding habits, reproductive biology and evolution; zoogeography. *Mailing Add:* 4341 Rodrigo Dr San Diego CA 92115

RADWIN, HOWARD MARTIN, b New York, NY, Mar 13, 31; m 58; c 3. UROLOGY. *Educ:* Princeton Univ, AB, 52; Columbia Univ, MD, 56. *Prof Exp:* Asst prof urol, Tulane Univ, 64-68; PROF UROL & CHMN DEPT, UNIV TEX HEALTH SCI CTR SAN ANTONIO, 68- *Concurrent Pos:* Nat Cancer Inst fel, Tulane Univ, 61-62; consult, Brooke Army Hosp & Air Force Wilford Hall Hosp, 69- *Mem:* Fel Am Col Surg; Am Urol Asn; Soc Univ Urol. *Res:* Prostate physiology; pyelonephritis; urologic cancer; application of renal physiology to urologic disease. *Mailing Add:* Div Urol Univ Tex Health Sci Ctr San Antonio TX 78284

RADZIALOWSKI, FREDERICK M, b Detroit, Mich, Mar 25, 39; m 60; c 2. PHARMACOLOGY, BIOCHEMISTRY. *Educ:* Wayne State Univ, BS, 60, MS, 64; Purdue Univ, PhD(pharmacol), 68. *Prof Exp:* SR RES INVESTR METAB, G D SEARLE & CO, 68- *Mem:* AAAS; Am Pharmaceut Asn. *Res:* Drug and lipid metabolism; obesity; circadian rhythms. *Mailing Add:* G D Searle & Co PO Box 5110 Chicago IL 60680

RADZIEMSKI, LEON JOSEPH, JR, b Worcester, Mass, June 18, 37; div; c 2. ATOMIC SPECTROSCOPY, LASER SPECTROCHEMISTRY. *Educ:* Col Holy Cross, BS, 58; Purdue Univ, MS, 61, PhD(physics), 64. *Prof Exp:* Lectr physics, US Air Force Inst Technol, 65-67; STAFF MEM, LOS ALAMOS NAT LAB, UNIV CALIF, 67- *Concurrent Pos:* Lectr, Wright State Univ, 75-81; vis mem fac, Univ Fla, 78-79; prin investr, Laser Spectrochem Proj. *Mem:* Optical Soc Am; Am Phys Soc; Soc Applied Spectroscopy; Laser Inst Am. *Res:* Laser spectroscopy; spectrochemical applications of lasers; remote, point, and in situ detection of toxic substances; laser-induced breakdown spectroscopy. *Mailing Add:* 365 Cheryl Ave Los Alamos NM 87544

RADZIKOWSKI, M ST ANTHONY, b Jermyn, Pa, Mar 10, 19. INORGANIC CHEMISTRY. *Educ:* Marywood Col, AB, 39; Univ Notre Dame, MS, 57, PhD(chem), 61. *Prof Exp:* Teacher parochial sch, Pa, 45-55; dean women, 55-58, ASSOC PROF CHEM, MARYWOOD COL, 81-, CHMN CHEM DEPT, 61- *Mem:* Am Chem Soc; Coblentz Soc. *Res:* Complexes of methyl esters of proline and sarcosine; infrared spectra of coordination compounds of amines with metal halides; spectroscopic studies of reactions with organic donor compounds. *Mailing Add:* Dept of Chem Marywood Col 2300 Adams Ave Scranton PA 18509

RAE, MARGARET ENGEL, microbial genetics, see previous edition

RAE, PETER MURDOCH MCPHAIL, b Glasgow, Scotland, Jan 7, 44; US citizen; m 71; c 1. CELL BIOLOGY. *Educ:* Univ Calif, Davis, AB, 65, MA, 66; Univ Chicago, PhD(biol), 70. *Prof Exp:* Lectr biol, Harvard Univ, 70; Max-Planck Inst Biol, Tuebingen, WGer, 71-72, vis scientist, 73; asst prof, 73-79, ASSOC PROF BIOL, YALE UNIV, 79- *Mem:* AAAS: Am Soc Cell Biol. *Res:* Chromosome structure; DNA sequence organization; the role of rare bases in eukaryote DNA; nucleic acid metabolism. *Mailing Add:* 438 Kline Biol Tower Yale Univ New Haven CT 06520

RAE, STEPHEN, b New York, NY, May, 44; m 65. ENVIRONMENTAL PHYSICS. *Educ:* Stevens Inst Technol, BS, 65; Univ Vt, MS, 69, PhD(physics), 73. *Prof Exp:* Eng physicist noise abatement, US Naval Marine Eng Lab, 65-66; anal physicist nuclear reactors, Knolls Atomic Power Lab, 66-67; teaching asst, 69-73, lectr physics, Univ Vt, 75-76; ASST PROF PHYSICS, WELLS COL, 76- *Concurrent Pos:* Pres sci & tech consult serv, N&R Assoc Inc, 75- *Mem:* Am Asn Physics Teachers; Fedn Am Scientists. *Res:* Application and teaching of physics related to environmental problems, currently in the area of energy; theoretical description of atomic collision processes. *Mailing Add:* Dept of Physics Wells Col Aurora NY 13026

RAE, WILLIAM H, JR, b Tacoma, Wash, Nov 16, 27; m 53. AERODYNAMICS. *Educ:* Univ Wash, Seattle, BS, 53, MS, 59. *Prof Exp:* Supvr, Aeronaut Labs, 59-66, asst prof aeronaut & astronaut, 65-67, ASSOC PROF AERONAUT & ASTRONAUT, UNIV WASH, 67-, ASSOC DIR, AERONAUT LABS, 66- *Mem:* Am Inst Aeronaut & Astronaut. *Res:* Aerodynamics of vertical and short take off aircraft and associated wind tunnel testing problems. *Mailing Add:* Dept of Aeronaut Univ of Wash Seattle WA 98105

RAE, WILLIAM J, b Buffalo, NY, Sept 3, 29; m 57; c 4. AERONAUTICAL ENGINEERING, HEAT TRANSFER. *Educ:* Canisius Col, BA, 50; Cornell Univ, PhD(aeronaut eng), 60. *Prof Exp:* Computer, Cornell Aeronaut Lab, Inc, 50-53, jr mathematician, 53-54, jr aerodynamicist, 54-55, res asst, Cornell Univ, 55-59, res aerodynamicist, Cornell Aeronaut Lab, Inc, 59-63, prin aerodynamicist, 63-64, PRIN RES ENGR, ADVAN TECHNOL CTR, CALSPAN CORP, 64- *Concurrent Pos:* Lectr, Medaille Col, 61-67, trustee, 69-76; adj prof, Dept Mech & Aerospace Eng, State Univ NY, Buffalo. *Mem:* Am Inst Aeronaut & Astronaut; Sigma Xi. *Res:* Wing-body interference; viscous acoustics; boundary-layer flow; impact-generated shock-wave propagation in solids; low-density flow, environmental fluid mechanics; turbomachinery; computational fluid dynamics. *Mailing Add:* Advan Technol Ctr Calspan Corp PO Box 400 Cheektowaga NY 14225

RAE-GRANT, QUENTIN A, b Aberdeen, Scotland, Apr 5, 29; US citizen; m 55; c 2. PSYCHIATRY. *Educ:* Aberdeen Univ, MB, ChB, 51; Univ London, dipl psychiat med, 58. *Prof Exp:* Intern med & surg, Aberdeen Univ, 52-53, resident psychiat, 53-54; resident, Maudsley Hosp, London, Eng, 55-58; dir child psychiat, Jewish Hosp, St Louis, Mo, 58-60; instr pediat & psychiat, Univ & psychiatrist, Univ Hosp, Johns Hopkins Univ, 60-61; dir ment health div, St Louis County Health Dept, 62-64; chief social psychiat sect, Community Res & Serv Br, NIMH, 65-66, dir & chief ment health study ctr, Md, 66-68; PROF CHILD PSYCHIAT, UNIV TORONTO, 68-, VCHMN DEPT, 71-; PSYCHIATRIST-IN-CHIEF, HOSP FOR SICK CHILDREN, 68- *Concurrent Pos:* Consult, Sinai Hosp, Baltimore & Rosewood State Hosp, Md, 60-61 & St Louis State Hosp, 62-64; asst prof, Wash Univ, 62-64; lectr, Sch Nursing, St Louis Univ, 62-64; consult pediat, 73- consult, Comn Emotional & Learning Disorders in Children, 68-70, Clarke Inst Psychiat & St Michael's Hosp, Toronto. *Mem:* Am Psychiat Asn; Am Orthopsychiat Asn; Can Psychiat Asn (pres elect, 81-82, pres, 82-83); Royal Col Psychiat. *Res:* Child and adolescent psychiatry; consultation service; new patterns of psychiatric service; evaluation of health care delivery system effectiveness; prevention. *Mailing Add:* Dept of Psychiat Hosp for Sick Children Toronto ON M5G 1X8 Can

RAEL, EPPIE DAVID, b Cochiti, NMex, Jan 17, 43; m 71; c 2. IMMUNOLOGY, MICROBIOLOGY. *Educ:* Univ Albuquerque, BS, 65; NMex Highlands Univ, MS, 70; Univ Ariz, PhD(microbiol), 75. *Prof Exp:* Res asst clin immunol, Med Sch, Univ NMex, 69-71; asst microbiol, Univ Ariz, 71-75; ASST PROF IMMUNOL, UNIV TEX, EL PASO, 75- *Concurrent Pos:* Prin investr, Minority Biomed Support, Nat Cancer Inst, 75-77 & Minority Biomed Support, HEW, 77- *Mem:* Am Soc Microbiol; AAAS; Sigma Xi. *Res:* Brucella cell wall antigens; cellular immune response; rattlesnake venom. *Mailing Add:* Dept of Biol Sci Univ of Tex El Paso TX 79968

RAEMER, HAROLD R, b Chicago, Ill, Apr 26, 24; m 47; c 3. PHYSICS, ELECTRICAL ENGINEERING. *Educ:* Northwestern Univ, BS, 48, MS, 49, PhD(physics), 59. *Prof Exp:* Asst math, Ind Univ, 49-50; asst physics, Northwestern Univ, 50-52; physicist, Res Labs, Bendix Aviation Co, Mich, 52-54, sr physicist, 54-55; sr engr, Cook Res Labs, Ill, 55-57, staff engr, 57-60; asst prof elec eng, Ill Inst Technol, 60; sr eng specialist, Appl Res Labs, Sylvania Electronic Systs, Gen Tel & Electronics Corp, 60-63; assoc prof elec eng, 63-66, chmn dept, 67-77, PROF ELEC ENG, NORTHEASTERN UNIV, 66- *Concurrent Pos:* Vis lectr, Harvard Univ, 62, hon res assoc, 72-73; consult, Sylvania Appl Res Labs, 63-71 & US Naval Res Lab, 69- *Mem:* AAAS; Am Phys Soc; sr mem Inst Elec & Electronics Engrs. *Res:* Electromagnetic radio wave propagation theory; statistical communication theory; plasma physics, particularly wave propagation in plasma. *Mailing Add:* Dept of Elec Eng 360 Huntington Ave Boston MA 02115

RAESE, JOHN THOMAS, b West Chester, Pa, Apr 3, 30; m 53; c 4. AGRONOMY, PLANT PHYSIOLOGY. *Educ:* WVa Univ, BS, 52, MS, 59; Univ Md, PhD(agron), 63. *Prof Exp:* Instr agron, WVa Univ, 58-59; teacher high sch, Md, 62-63; res plant physiologist, Field Lab Tung Invests, La, 63-68, Tung Trees Lab, Fla, 68-71 & Pome Fruit Lab, Wash, 71-73, PLANT PHYSIOLOGIST, AGR RES SERV, USDA, 73- *Mem:* Soc Cryobiol; Am Soc Hort Sci; Sigma Xi. *Res:* Chemical analyses of soils and plant tissues; pasture and forage management; physiological and nutritional studies of the tung tree; plant nutrition, growth regulators, and cold hardiness of pome trees. *Mailing Add:* 1606 N Astor Ct Wenatchee WA 98801

RAESIDE, JAMES INGLIS, b Saskatoon, Sask, May 21, 26; m 54; c 4. PHYSIOLOGY. *Educ:* Glasgow Univ, BSc, 47; Univ Mo, MS, 50, PhD, 54. *Prof Exp:* Sr lectr animal physiol, NZ, 54-57; res fel, McGill Univ, 57-58; PROF PHYSIOL, ONT VET COL, UNIV GUELPH, 58- *Concurrent Pos:* Vis scientist, Karolinska Inst, Sweden, 64-65. *Mem:* Am Soc Animal Sci; Can Biochem Soc; Brit Soc Study Fertil; Soc Study Reprod; AAAS. *Res:* Comparative physiology of reproduction; endocrinology; steroid metabolism; hormone assay; animal production and behavior. *Mailing Add:* Dept of Biomed Sci Ont Vet Col Univ of Guelph Guelph ON N1G 2W1 Can

RAETHER, MANFRED, b Settin, Ger, Jan 22, 27; m 56; c 2. PLASMA PHYSICS. *Educ:* Univ Bonn, Dr rer nat(physics), 58. *Prof Exp:* Asst physics, Univ Bonn, 57-58; res engr, US Army Ballistic Missile Agency, Ala, 58-59; res asst prof, Coord Sci Lab, 59-61, assoc prof, Dept Physics & Coord Sci Lab, 61-67, PROF PHYSICS, UNIV ILL, URBANA, 67-, ASSOC HEAD DEPT, 80- *Mem:* Am Phys Soc. *Res:* Plasma instabilities; plasma turbulence. *Mailing Add:* Dept Physics Univ Ill Urbana IL 61801

RAETZ, CHRISTIAN RUDOLF HUBERT, b Berlin, Ger, Nov 17, 46; US citizen; m 71; c 2. BIOCHEMISTRY, MEDICINE. *Educ:* Yale Univ, BS, 67; Harvard Univ, PhD(biochem) & MD, 73. *Prof Exp:* Intern med, Peter Bent Brigham Hosp, Boston, 73-74; res assoc, NIH, 74-76; asst prof biochem, 76-81, ASSOC PROF BIOCHEM, UNIV WIS-MADISON, 81- *Concurrent Pos:* Nat Found March Dimes Basil O'Connor grant, 76-79; NIH res career develop award, 78; mem study sect physiol chem, NIH, 78- *Honors & Awards:* Harry & Evelyn Steenbock Award, Univ Wis, 76. *Res:* Synthesis and function of biological membranes; metabolism of phospholipids; genetics of bacteria and animal cells grown in tissue culture. *Mailing Add:* Dept of Biochem Univ of Wis Madison WI 53706

RAE-VENTER, BARBARA JOAN, see Huff, Barbara Rae-Venter

RAFAJKO, ROBERT RICHARD, b Chicago, Ill, Sept 3, 31; div; c 5. VIROLOGY. *Educ:* Coe Col, BA, 53; Univ Iowa, MS, 58, PhD(bact), 60. *Prof Exp:* Res assoc biol, Merck Sharp & Dohme, Inc, Pa, 60-61; virologist, Microbiol Assocs, Inc, Md, 61-66; vpres & gen mgr biol res, Med Res Consults Div, NAm Mogul Prod, Inc, 66-69, dir res & develop, Diag Div, 69-71, dir res & develop, NAm Biologicals, Inc, 71-74; PRES, BIOFLUIDS, INC, 75- *Mem:* AAAS; NY Acad Sci; Tissue Cult Asn; Am Soc Microbiol. *Res:* Interferon induction and assay systems; development of live measles virus vaccine; adenovirus strain differences and relatedness to oncogenicty; adeno-associated viruses; adenovirus induced transformation of mammalian cells; cell growth factors. *Mailing Add:* Biofluids Inc 1146 Taft St Rockville MD 20850

RAFANELLI, KENNETH R, b New York, NY, Nov 11, 37; m 61; c 1. THEORETICAL PHYSICS. *Educ:* Stevens Inst Technol, ME, 58, MS, 60, PhD(physics), 64. *Prof Exp:* From asst prof to assoc prof, 64-73, PROF PHYSICS, QUEENS COL, NY, 73- *Concurrent Pos:* Consult, TRW Systs, Calif, 65-68. *Res:* Theoretical research on the elementary particles. *Mailing Add:* Dept of Physics Queens Col Flushing NY 11367

RAFELSON, MAX EMANUEL, JR, b Detroit, Mich, June 17, 21; m 47; c 2. BIOCHEMISTRY. *Educ:* Univ Mich, BS, 43; Univ Southern Calif, PhD(biochem), 51. *Prof Exp:* From asst prof to assoc prof, 53-61, PROF BIOL CHEM, UNIV ILL COL MED, 61-; PROF BIOCHEM, RUSH MED SCH, 70-; VPRES, RUSH-PRESBY-ST LUKE'S MED CTR, 72- *Concurrent Pos:* USPHS res fel, Wenner Grens Inst, Stockholm, Sweden, 51-53; chmn dept biochem, Presby-St Luke's Hosp, 61-70; assoc dean biol & behav sci & serv, Rush Med Sch, 70-72, vpres, mgt info sci, 72-; vis prof, Univ Paris, 61, 77-78. *Mem:* AAAS; Am Chem Soc; Am Soc Biol Chem; Brit Biochem Soc; Nat Acad Clin Biochem. *Res:* Protein chemistry; enzymology; blood; platelets. *Mailing Add:* Dept of Biochem Rush Med Sch Chicago IL 60612

RAFF, ALLAN MAURICE, b Chicago, Ill, May 21, 23; m 47; c 2. PHARMACY. *Educ:* Univ Ill, Chicago, BS, 49, MS, 53; Temple Univ, PhD(phys pharm), 64. *Prof Exp:* Mgr pharmaceut develop, Smith Kline & French Labs, 53-69 & med diag opers, Xerox, 69-70; dir res & develop, Barnes-Hind Pharmaceut Co, 71-72; VPRES PHARMACEUT, RACHELLE LABS, 72- *Mem:* Am Pharmaceut Asn; Am Chem Soc; Am Inst Chem Engr. *Res:* Effects of physical parameters on solid dosage forms. *Mailing Add:* 1500 Lincoln Lane Newport Beach CA 92660

RAFF, LIONEL M, b Mich, Nov 4, 34; m 55; c 2. CHEMICAL PHYSICS, PHYSICAL CHEMISTRY. *Educ:* Univ Okla, BS, 56, MS, 57; Univ Ill, PhD(phys chem), 62. *Prof Exp:* Chemist, Dow Chem Co, 57; NSF fel, Columbia Univ, 63-64; from asst prof to prof phys chem, 64-78, REGENTS PROF CHEM, OKLA STATE UNIV, 78- *Mem:* Am Chem Soc; Am Phys Soc. *Res:* Classical, quasiclassical, and quantum mechanical scattering calculations of inelastic and reactive gas-phase processes; quantum mechanical calculations of potential-energy surfaces; molecular beam investigations of gas-surface interaction phenomena. *Mailing Add:* Dept of Phys Chem Okla State Univ Stillwater OK 74074

RAFF, MARTIN JAY, b Brooklyn, NY, Mar 20, 37; Div; c 4. INFECTIOUS DISEASES. *Educ:* Brandeis Univ, BA, 58; Univ Vt, MS, 60; Univ Tex Med Br Galveston, MD, 65. *Prof Exp:* From asst prof to assoc prof, 71-77, prof med, 80, ASST PROF MICROBIOL, SCH MED, UNIV LOUISVILLE, 77-, CHIEF, DIV INFECTIOUS DIS, 71- *Concurrent Pos:* NIH fel infectious dis, Col Med, Cornell Univ & New York Hosp, 66-67; consult, Vet Admin, Norton Childrens, Hiphlands Baptist, Audulson, Methodist, Suburban, Baptist East, St Mary & Elizabeth Hosps, Louisville, Ky, 71- & Ireland Army Hosp, Ft Knox, Ky, 71-; staff physician, Jewish Hosp, Louisville, Ky & Univ Louisville Hosp, 71- *Mem:* Fel Am Col Physicians; fel Infectious Dis Soc Am; Am Soc Microbiol; AAAS. *Res:* Effects of steroids on the products of bacterial metabolism and on infection in animals; metabolic factors altering humoral and cellular host resistance mechanisms; antibiotic pharmacokinetics and therapeutic efficiency. *Mailing Add:* Dept of Med PO Box 35260 Louisville KY 40232

RAFF, MORTON SPENCER, b Chicago, Ill, Jan 12, 23; m 47; c 2. STATISTICS. *Educ:* Swarthmore Col, BA, 43; Yale Univ, cert, 48; American Univ, MA, 55. *Prof Exp:* Physicist, US Naval Res Lab, 43-44; physicist & mathematician, US Naval Ord Lab, 44-47; res asst hwy traffic, Yale Univ, 48-49; traffic res engr, Eno Found Hwy Traffic Control, 49-50; mathematician, US Bur Pub Roads, 50-55; math statistician, US Bur Lab Statist, 55-67 & 72-78 & Nat Heart & Lung Inst, 67-72. *Concurrent Pos:* Lectr, Johns Hopkins Univ, 56-59, USDA Grad Sch, 61-70 & Georgetown Univ, 67. *Mem:* Am Statist Asn. *Res:* Medical and labor statistics; seasonal adjustment; probability theory applied to traffic behavior; approximations to the binomial distribution. *Mailing Add:* 3803 Montrose Driveway Chevy Chase MD 20015

RAFF, RUDOLF ALBERT, b Shawinigan, Que, Nov 10, 41; US citizen; m 65; c 2. DEVELOPMENTAL BIOLOGY, EVOLUTION. *Educ:* Pa State Univ, BS, 63; Duke Univ, PhD(biochem), 67. *Prof Exp:* Officer, Armed Forces Radiobiol Res Inst, US Navy, 67-69; fel develop biol, Mass Inst Technol, 69-71; assoc prof, 71-80, PROF BIOL, IND UNIV, 80- *Concurrent Pos:* Instr-in-chief embryol, Marine Biol Lab, Woods Hole, Mass, 80-82. *Mem:* Am Soc Cell Biol; Soc Develop Biol; Am Soc Zoologists; Soc Study Evolution. *Res:* Molecular biology of early development; developmental genetics; role of developmental processes in evolution. *Mailing Add:* Dept of Biol Ind Univ Bloomington IN 47405

RAFFAUF, ROBERT FRANCIS, b Buffalo, NY, Jan 8, 16; m 50; c 2. ORGANIC CHEMISTRY. *Educ:* City Col New York, BS, 36; Columbia Univ, MA, 37; Univ Minn, PhD(org chem), 44. *Prof Exp:* Anal chemist, Tex Co, NY, 38-40; asst org chem, Univ Minn, 42-44; sr res chemist, Eaton Labs, Inc, NY, 44-47; asst, Univ Zurich, 47; res asst, Univ Basel, 47-48, fel, 49; res chemist, Nat Drug Co, 50-51; res assoc, Smith Kline & French Labs, 51-53; sr chemist, 53, lit scientist, 54-69; PROF PHARMACOG, COL PHARM, NORTHEASTERN UNIV, 69- *Mem:* AAAS; Am Chem Soc; NY Acad Sci; Swiss Chem Soc. *Res:* Alkaloids. *Mailing Add:* Col of Pharm Northeastern Univ Boston MA 02115

RAFFEL, JACK I, b New York, NY, Apr 1, 30; m 59; c 2. INTEGRATED CIRCUITS. *Educ:* Columbia Univ, AB, 51, BS, 52; Mass Inst Technol, MS, 54. *Prof Exp:* Res asst digital comput lab, 52-54, staff mem, Lincoln Lab, 54-62, GROUP LEADER, LINCOLN LAB, MASS INST TECHNOL, 62- *Mem:* Inst Elec & Electronics Engrs. *Res:* Digital computer research and development; design and fabrication of very large-scale integrated circuits. *Mailing Add:* 23 Eliot Rd Lexington MA 02173

RAFFEL, SIDNEY, b Baltimore, Md, Aug 24, 11; m 38; c 5. MEDICAL BACTERIOLOGY, IMMUNOLOGY. *Educ:* Johns Hopkins Univ, AB, 30, ScD(immunol), 33; Stanford Univ, MD, 43. *Prof Exp:* Asst immunol, Sch Hyg & Pub Health, Johns Hopkins Univ, 33-35; from asst to assoc prof, 35-48, consult physician, Student Health Serv, 42-44, prof bact & exp path, Sch Med, 48-76, chmn dept med microbiol, 53-76, actg dean, 64-65, EMER CHMN DEPT MED MICROBIOL, SCH MED, STANFORD UNIV, 76-, EMER PROF, DEPT DERMAT, 77- 53- *Concurrent Pos:* Guggenheim fel, 49-50; lab dir, Palo Alto Hosp, 45-47; consult, Vet Admin, 47-; chmn study sect allergy & immunol, NIH, 56-59, mem training grant comt, 60- *Mem:* Am Soc Microbiol; Am Soc Exp Path; Am Thoracic Soc; Am Asn Immunol. *Res:* Immunology of tuberculosis; hypersensitivity; cellular immunity. *Mailing Add:* Dept of Dermat Stanford Univ Sch of Med Stanford CA 94305

RAFFELSON, HAROLD, b Sheboygan, Wis, Oct 29, 20; m 48; c 1. PHARMACEUTICAL CHEMISTRY. *Educ:* Univ Wis, BS, 47; Univ Mich, PhD(pharmaceut chem), 51. *Prof Exp:* Org res chemist, Frederick Stearns & Co, 47; res chemist, 51-59, group leader, 59-61, res specialist, 61-73, SR RES SPECIALIST, MONSANTO CO, 73- *Mem:* Am Chem Soc. *Res:* Synthetic antispasmodics; steroid synthesis; organo-phosphorus compounds; process development. *Mailing Add:* 7 Planters Dr Olivette MO 63132

RAFFENETTI, RICHARD CHARLES, b Springfield, Mass, Oct 15, 42. QUANTUM CHEMISTRY. *Educ:* Tufts Univ, BS, 64; Iowa State Univ, PhD(phys chem), 71. *Prof Exp:* Res assoc quantum chem, Battelle Mem Inst, 71-73 & Johns Hopkins Univ, 73-74; vis scientist quantum chem, Inst Comput Applns Sci & Eng, NASA Langley Res Ctr, 74-76; asst chemist quantum chem, Chem Div, 76-79, ASST COMPUT SCIENTIST, APPL MATH DIV,

ARGONNE NAT LAB, 79- *Concurrent Pos:* Consult quantum chem, 81- *Mem:* Am Chem Soc. *Res:* Accurate, self-consistent field and configuration interaction calculations of molecular electronic structure; excited states and potential surfaces. *Mailing Add:* Bldg 221 Argonne Nat Lab Argonne IL 60439

RAFFENSPERGER, EDGAR M, b Gettysburg, Pa, June 13, 26; m 53; c 3. ENTOMOLOGY. *Educ:* Pa State Univ, BS, 51, MS, 52; Univ Wis, PhD(entom), 55. *Prof Exp:* From asst prof to assoc prof entom, Va Polytech Inst, 55-61; assoc prof, 61-77, PROF ENTOM, CORNELL UNIV, 77- *Concurrent Pos:* Vis scientist, Norweg Agr Res Coun, Vollebekk, Norway, 68-69; lectr, Univ Oslo, 69; consult, stored prod insect control. *Mem:* AAAS; Entom Soc Am. *Res:* Taxonomy of Diptera and Mallophaga; insect transmission of fowl diseases; pesticides in agriculture; teaching in general entomology; insect morphology and control; control of stored products insects. *Mailing Add:* Dept of Entom Cornell Univ Ithaca NY 14850

RAFFENSPERGER, EDWARD COWELL, b Dickinson, Pa, July 9, 14; m 49. GASTROENTEROLOGY. *Educ:* Dickinson Col, BS, 36; Univ Pa, MD, 40. *Prof Exp:* Instr gastroenterol, Grad Sch Med, 48-58, assoc, Sch Med, 53-62, from asst prof to assoc prof med, 62-71, PROF MED, SCH MED, UNIV PA, 71- *Concurrent Pos:* Res fel gastroenterol, Grad Hosp, Univ Pa, 46-48; consult, Vet Admin Hosp, Philadelphia & Polyclin Hosp, Harrisburg, 62-, Children's Hosp, Philadelphia, 64- & Lankenau Hosp, 69- *Mem:* Am Gastroenterol Asn; Am Fedn Clin Res. *Res:* Amino acids in nutrition; inflammatory bowel diseases. *Mailing Add:* 290 St James Pl Philadelphia PA 19106

RAFFERTY, FRANK THOMAS, b Greenville, Miss, Jan 28, 25; m; c 7. CHILD PSYCHIATRY. *Educ:* St Mary's Col, Minn, BS, 48; St Louis Univ, MD, 48; Univ Colo, MS, 53. *Prof Exp:* Resident psychiat, Colo Psychopath Hosp, Univ Colo Med Ctr, Denver, 49-50, chief resident, Ment Hyg Clin, 52-53; assoc prof psychiat ment health serv, Div Child Psychiat, Col Med, Univ Utah, 55-58; med dir, Ment Health Serv, Inc, 57-61; dir, Div Child Psychiat, Psychiat Inst, Univ Md, 61-71; PROF PSYCHIAT & DIR, INST JUV RES, ABRAHAM LINCOLN SCH MED, UNIV ILL, 71- *Concurrent Pos:* Fel child psychiat, Univ Colo Med Ctr, Denver, 51-53; mem comn child & adolescent psychiat, Am Psychiat Asn, 69-; Am Psychiat Asn Rep, Nat Consortium Ment Health serv to Children, 71-; mem, Nat Consortium Children Serv, 72. *Mem:* Fel Am Psychiat Asn; fel Am Acad Child Psychiat; Am Col Psychiatrists. *Mailing Add:* Inst Juv Res A Lincoln Sch Med Univ of Ill 907 S Wolcott Ave Chicago IL 60612

RAFFERTY, KEEN ALEXANDER, JR, b Robinson, Ill, Mar 6, 26; m 53; c 2. EMBRYOLOGY, CELL CULTURE. *Educ:* Univ NMex, BS, 50; Univ Ill, MS, 51, PhD(zool), 55. *Prof Exp:* Asst zool, Univ Ill, 50-54; instr microbiol, Yale Univ, 57-58; from asst prof to assoc prof anat, Sch Med, Johns Hopkins Univ, 58-70; head dept, 70-77, PROF, DEPT ANAT, UNIV ILL MED CTR, 70- *Concurrent Pos:* NIH fel microbiol, Yale Univ, 55-57; Fogarty sr fel, 77-78. *Mem:* Am Asn Anat; Am Soc Cell Biol; Soc Develop Biol; Tissue Cult Asn. *Res:* Cellular differentiation and aging of cultured cells. *Mailing Add:* Dept of Anat Univ of Ill Med Ctr Chicago IL 60680

RAFFERTY, NANCY S, b New York, NY, June 11, 30; m 53; c 2. CELL BIOLOGY, ANATOMY. *Educ:* Queens Col (NY), BS, 52; Univ Ill, MS, 53, PhD(zool), 58. *Prof Exp:* Instr anat, Sch Med, Johns Hopkins Univ, 63-66, asst prof, 66-70; from asst prof to assoc prof, 72-76, PROF ANAT, MED & DENT SCH, NORTHWESTERN UNIV, 76- *Concurrent Pos:* NIH res fel, Johns Hopkins Univ, 58-60, fel anat, Sch Med, 60-63; NIH res grants, Johns Hopkins Univ, 65-67 & 68-71 & Northwestern Univ, 68-71, 72-76, 76-80 & 81-86. *Mem:* AAAS; Asn Res Vision & Ophthal; Am Asn Anat; Am Soc Cell Biol. *Res:* Experimental cataract; wound healing; cell population kinetics; electron microscopy of lens; cellular dynamics of the proliferative response in injured frog, mouse and squirrel lens epithelium; etiology of senile cataract; lens aging; mechanism of lens accommodation; cytoskeleton of lens cells. *Mailing Add:* Dept of Anat Northwestern Univ Med & Dent Sch Chicago IL 60611

RAFLA, SAMEER, b Cairo, Egypt, Sept 3, 30; m 65; c 5. RADIATION MEDICINE, ONCOLOGY. *Educ:* Univ Cairo, BS, 47, MB & BCh, 53; London Univ, PhD(radiation med), 70. *Prof Exp:* DIR RADIATION THERAPY, METHODIST HOSP, 69-; DIR RADIOTHERAPY, LUTHERAN MED CTR, 77-; DIR RADIOTHERAPY, MAIMONIDES MED CTR, 79- *Concurrent Pos:* Radiotherapist, Manitoba Cancer Found, 67-69; prin investr, Cancer & Leukemia Group B, State Univ, NY, Downstate, Oncol Prog, Brooklyn Community Hosp, Nat Cancer Inst, Continuing Ed Radiotherapists, Am Cancer Soc Grant; clin prof radiation oncol, Downstate Med Ctr, State Univ NY, 81- *Mem:* Am Radium Soc; Royal Col Radiol; Am Soc Therapeut Radiologists; Soc Surg Oncol; Radiol Soc NAm. *Res:* The effect of radiation on the malignant and normal cell as well as its possible effect on the immune response; the treatment of certain cancers especially head and neck, kidney and lymphoma. *Mailing Add:* Methodist Hosp 506 Sixth St Brooklyn NY 11215

RAFOLS, JOSE ANTONIO, b Guantanamo, Cuba, July 7, 43; US citizen. ANATOMY. *Educ:* St Procopius Col, BS, 65; Univ Kans, PhD(anat), 69. *Prof Exp:* From instr to asst prof, 70-73, ASSOC PROF ANAT, SCH MED, WAYNE STATE UNIV, 73- *Concurrent Pos:* NIH trainee, Cajal Inst, Madrid, Spain, 71. *Mem:* AAAS; Pan-Am Asn Anat. *Res:* Golgi and electron microscopic analysis of the mammalian visual system and basal ganglia. *Mailing Add:* Dept of Anat Wayne State Univ Sch Med Detroit MI 48201

RAFTER, GALE WILLIAM, b Seattle, Wash, Nov 3, 25; m 57; c 3. BIOCHEMISTRY. *Educ:* Univ Wash, BS, 48, PhD(biochem), 53. *Prof Exp:* Asst prof biochem, Sch Hyg & Pub Health, Johns Hopkins Univ, 55-59, asst prof microbiol, Sch Med, 59-65; assoc prof, 65-71, PROF BIOCHEM, SCH MED, WVA UNIV, 71- *Concurrent Pos:* Fel, McCollum-Pratt Inst, Johns Hopkins Univ, 53-55. *Mem:* Am Soc Biol Chem. *Res:* Chemistry of host-parasite relationship. *Mailing Add:* Dept of Biochem WVa Univ Med Ctr Morgantown WV 26506

RAFTER, JOHN ARTHUR, b Ann Arbor, Mich, June 13, 44; m 67; c 1. BIOSTATISTICS. *Educ:* Univ Mich, BS, 66; Mich State Univ, MS, 68, PhD(statist), 71. *Prof Exp:* Asst prof math, Univ Maine, 71-72; consult biostatistician, 73, group leader, 73, asst mgr biomet info, 74-79, MGR STATIST & COMPUT OPERS, JOHNSON & JOHNSON PRODS DIV, 79- *Mem:* Am Statist Asn; Inst Math Statist; Biomet Soc. *Mailing Add:* Johnson & Johnson Prod Res Ctr 501 George New Brunswick NJ 08903

RAFTOPOULOS, DEMETRIOS D, b Argostolion, Greece, May 30, 26; US citizen; m 59; c 1. ENGINEERING MECHANICS, MECHANICAL ENGINEERING. *Educ:* PMC Cols, BSCE, 59; Univ Del, MCE, 63; Pa State Univ, PhD(eng mech), 66. *Prof Exp:* Sr engr, Del State Hwy Dept, 59-61; instr eng, PMC Cols, 61-64; res asst eng mech, Pa State Univ, 64-67; assoc prof mech eng, 67-73, PROF MECH ENG, UNIV TOLEDO, 73- *Concurrent Pos:* Jr investr, Ballistic Res Lab, Aberdeen Proving Ground, Md, 64-67, proj dir, 67-68; prin investr, Naval Res Labs, Washington, DC, 67-69 & Atomic Energy Comn, Md, 68-71; reviewer, Appl Mech Res, 69-; vis prof mech, Nat Tech Univ Athens, 73-74. *Mem:* Am Soc Eng Educ; Am Soc Civil Engrs; Am Soc Mech Engrs; Am Acad Mech; Sigma Xi. *Res:* Elasto-plastic stress waves; analysis of foundation interaction with nuclear power plants during earthquake loading; structure interaction with underwater shock waves; fracture mechanics; bio-mechanics. *Mailing Add:* 2801 W Bancroft St Univ of Toledo Toledo OH 43616

RAFUSE, MARY JANE LOUNSBURY, organic chemistry, see previous edition

RAFUSE, ROBERT P(ENDLETON), b Newton, Mass, Dec 7, 32; div; c 2. ELECTRICAL ENGINEERING. *Educ:* Tufts Col, BSEE, 54; Mass Inst Technol, SM, 57, ScD(elec eng), 60. *Prof Exp:* Teaching asst elec eng, Mass Inst Technol, 54-57, instr, Res Lab Electronics, 57-60, from asst prof to assoc prof, 60-70; pres, Rafuse Assocs, 70-75; mem staff, 75-78, MEM SR STAFF, LINCOLN LAB, MASS INST TECHNOL, 78- *Concurrent Pos:* Adv, NASA, NIH & Dept Defense, 54-66; Consult to many govt & indust orgns; mem, Nat Defense Exec Reserve, 69-, vchmn gov's comn emergency commun, Commonwealth Mass, 70-, mem gov's energy emergency comn, 71; chmn, Nat Acad Sci-Nat Res Coun eval panel for Nat Bur Standards-EMD, 72-78. *Mem:* AAAS; Soc Am Mil Engrs; Inst Elec & Electronics Engrs; Am Defense Preparedness Asn. *Res:* Sensor systems; microwave solid state circuits; space communications; management of energy resources. *Mailing Add:* MIT Lincoln Lab Rm D-430 244 Wood St Lexington MA 02173

RAGAINI, RICHARD CHARLES, b Danbury, Conn, Feb 7, 42; div; c 2. ENVIRONMENTAL CHEMISTRY. *Educ:* Clark Univ, BA, 63; Mass Inst Technol, PhD(nuclear chem), 67. *Prof Exp:* Fel radiochem, Los Alamos Sci Lab, 67-69; res assoc chem, Brookhaven Nat Lab, 69-70; asst prof chem, Wash State Univ, 70-71; chemist, 71-75, sect leader, Radiochem Div, 75-77, dept div leader, 77-81, ACTG DIV LEADER, ENVIRON SCI DIV, LAWRENCE LIVERMORE NAT LAB, 81- *Mem:* Am Phys Soc; Am Chem Soc; Sigma Xi. *Res:* Effects of trace elements and organics in the environment; methods for trace element and organic analysis; trace elements and organics from energy production. *Mailing Add:* L-453 Lawrence Livermore Lab Livermore CA 94550

RAGAN, CHARLES ELLIS, III, b Charleston, SC, Oct 19, 44; div; c 2. NUCLEAR PHYSICS. *Educ:* The Citadel, BS, 66; Duke Univ, PhD(nuclear physics), 71. *Prof Exp:* Res assoc nuclear physics, NC State Univ, 70; physicist, US Air Force Weapons Lab, 70-72; STAFF MEM NUCLEAR PHYSICS, LOS ALAMOS NAT LAB, 72- *Mem:* Am Phys Soc; Sigma Xi. *Res:* Precise equation-of-state measurements of pressures of 10-100 mega-bar using shock waves produced by underground nuclear explosions; nuclear physics experiments using neutrons produced by reactors, Van de Graaff and linear accelerators; nuclear explosions. *Mailing Add:* Los Alamos Nat Lab PO Box 1663 MS-442 Los Alamos NM 87545

RAGAN, DONAL MACKENZIE, b Los Angeles, Calif, Oct 4, 29; m 52; c 2. STRUCTURAL GEOLOGY. *Educ:* Occidental Col, BA, 51; Univ Southern Calif, MS, 54; Univ Wash, PhD(geol), 61; Univ London, DIC, 69. *Prof Exp:* From instr to assoc prof geol, Univ Alaska, 60-67; assoc prof, 67-70, PROF GEOL, ARIZ STATE UNIV, 70- *Concurrent Pos:* NSF res grants, 64-66; fac fel, Imp Col, London, 66-67. *Mem:* AAAS; Int Soc Rock Mech; Am Geophys Union; fel Geol Soc Am; fel Geol Soc London. *Res:* Structural geology; mechanism of rock deformation; regional tectonics. *Mailing Add:* Dept Geol Ariz State Univ Tempe AZ 85287

RAGAN, HARVEY ALBERT, b Boise, Idaho, July 11, 29; m 51; c 3. HEMATOLOGY, RADIOBIOLOGY. *Educ:* Wash State Univ, BS, 56, DVM, 59. *Prof Exp:* Pvt pract, 59-62; scientist radiobiol, Hanford Labs, Gen Elec Co, 62-65; res scientist radiobiol, Pac Northwest Labs, Battelle Mem Inst, 65-66, sr res scientist radiotoxicol, 66-67; NIH spec fel exp hemat, Col Med, Univ Utah, 67-69; sr res scientist hemat, 69-72, staff scientist hemat, 72-77, MGR EXP PATH SECT, PAC NORTHWEST LABS, BATTELLE MEM INST, 77- *Concurrent Pos:* Mem, Nat Coun Radiation Protection, 78-; adj prof, Joint Ctr Grad Studies, 81- *Mem:* Am Soc Vet Clin Path (pres 81-82); Int Soc Exp Hemat; Am Soc Hemat. *Res:* Effects of chemical and physical insults on the hematopoietic system; leukemogenesis; blood cell kinetics; immunology; iron metabolism; clinical pathology. *Mailing Add:* Exp Path Sect Battelle-Northwest Labs Richland WA 99352

RAGAN, JAMES GAY, zoology, marine ecology, see previous edition

RAGAN, ROBERT MALCOLM, b San Antonio, Tex, Dec 19, 32; m 55; c 3. HYDROLOGY. *Educ:* Va Mil Inst, BS, 55; Mass Inst Technol, MS, 59; Cornell Univ, PhD(civil eng), 65. *Prof Exp:* Designer, Whitman Requardt & Assocs, Md, 56-57; res asst sanit eng, Mass Inst Technol, 57-59; from asst prof to assoc prof, Univ Vermont, 59-67; assoc prof, 67-68, head dept, 69-76, PROF CIVIL ENG, UNIV MD, COLLEGE PARK, 69- *Mem:* Am Soc Civil Engrs; Am Geophys Union. *Res:* Watershed hydrology. *Mailing Add:* Dept of Civil Eng Univ of Md College Park MD 20740

RAGENT, BORIS, b Cleveland, Ohio, Mar 2, 24; m 49; c 3. PHYSICS. *Educ:* Marquette Univ, BEE, 44; Univ Calif, Berkeley, PhD(physics), 54. *Prof Exp:* Engr electronics, Victoreen Instrument Co, Cleveland, 46-48; engr & res scientist electronics & physics, Radiation Lab, Univ Calif, Berkeley, 48-53, res scientist physics, Livermore, 53-56; res scientist, Broadview Res Corp, Burlingame, 56-59; staff scientist, Vidya Div, Itek Corp, Palo Alto, 59-66; chief electronic instrument develop br, 66-80, SR STAFF SCIENTIST, SPACE SCI DIV, AMES RES CTR, NASA, 80- *Concurrent Pos:* Lectr, Stanford Univ, 62 & 79. *Mem:* Am Phys Soc; AAAS. *Res:* Nuclear physics; instrumentation; plasma physics; planetary atmospherics. *Mailing Add:* Ames Res Ctr NASA Moffett Field CA 94035

RAGHAVACHARI, KRISHNAN, b Madras, India, Mar 3, 53; m. COMPUTATIONAL CHEMISTRY. *Educ:* Vivekananda Col, India, BSc, 73; Indian Inst Technol, MSc, 75; Carnegie-Mellon Univ, PhD(chem), 80. *Prof Exp:* MEM TECH STAFF CHEM PHYSICS, BELL LABS, MURRAY HILL, NJ, 81- *Mem:* Am Chem Soc. *Res:* Development and application of new molecular orbital methods in quantum chemistry. *Mailing Add:* Bell Labs 600 Mountain Ave Murray Hill NJ 07974

RAGHAVAN, PRAMILA, b Bangalore, India; m 67. NUCLEAR PROPERTIES, HYPERFINE INTERACTIONS. *Educ:* Univ Mysore, India, BSc, 54, MSc, 56; Saha Inst, Univ Calcutta, India, assoc dipl, 58; Mass Inst Technol, PhD(physics), 67. *Prof Exp:* Lectr, Univ Mysore, India, 54-55 & 56-57; res assoc, Tata Inst Fundamental Res, India, 58-61; commonwealth scholar, Nuclear Physics Lab, Oxford Univ, 61-62; res asst, Mass Inst Technol, 62-67; guest prof, Univ Munchen, WGer, 67-69; asst, Technol Univ Munich, WGer, 70-72; fel, 72-80, RES ASSOC PHYSICS, RUTGERS UNIV, 80- *Concurrent Pos:* Consult, Bell Labs, NJ, 72- *Mem:* Am Phys Soc. *Res:* Nuclear structure; nulear moments using radioactivity and nuclear reactions; interaction of nuclei with its environment; hyperfine interactions; applications to solid state physics, atomic physics and material science. *Mailing Add:* Dept Physics & Astron Rutgers Univ Busch Campus Piscataway NJ 08854

RAGHAVAN, RAJAGOPAL, b Tiruchirappalli, India, July 26, 43. PETROLEUM ENGINEERING. *Educ:* Birla Inst Technol, Mesra, India, BSc, 66; Univ Birmingham, dipl, 67; Stanford Univ, PhD(petrol & mech eng), 70. *Prof Exp:* Res assoc petrol eng, Stanford Univ, 70-71, asst prof, 71-72; sr res engr, Amoco Prod Co, 72-75; assoc prof, 75-80, PROF PETROL ENG, UNIV TULSA, 80- *Concurrent Pos:* Tech ed, Soc Petrol Engrs, 78-79, 80-82. *Mem:* Soc Petrol Engrs; assoc fel, Brit Inst Petrol; NY Acad Sci; Soc Petrol Engrs; AAAS. *Res:* Unsteady state fluid flow and heat transfer in porous media, including well test analysis, stability of liquid interfaces, compaction and subsidence, geothermal energy and application of computers. *Mailing Add:* Dept of Petrol Eng Univ of Tulsa Tulsa OK 74104

RAGHAVAN, RAMASWAMY SRINIVASA, b Tanjore, India, Mar 31, 37; m 67. SOLID STATE PHYSICS, NUCLEAR ASTROPHYSICS. *Educ:* Univ Madras, India, MA, 57, MSc, 58; Purdue Univ, PhD(physics), 65. *Prof Exp:* Res asst, Tata Inst Fundamental Res, 59-62 & Purdue Univ, 62-65; fel, Bartol Res Found, 65-66; vis prof, Univ Bonn, Ger, 66-67; res assoc, Tech Univ, Munich, 67-72; MEM STAFF PHYSICS, BELL LABS, NJ, 72- *Concurrent Pos:* Assoc grad fac, Rutgers Univ, 74- *Mem:* Am Phys Soc. *Res:* Nuclear structure; nuclear interactions with matter; solid state physics; nuclear electronics and detector hardware; neutrino physics; detection of solar neutrinos; application of nuclear accelerators to geochronology and cosmochronology. *Mailing Add:* Bell Labs Murray Hill NJ 07974

RAGHAVAN, SRINIVASA, b Madras, India, July 1, 40; nat US; m 77; c 2. BIOCHEMISTRY. *Educ:* Univ Madras, India, BSc, 60, MSc, 63; Indian Inst Sci, PhD(biochem), 70. *Prof Exp:* Res fel, Mass Gen Hosp, Boston, 70-73; res assoc, 73-74, sr res fel, 74-77, sr res assoc, 77-78, asst biochemist, 78-82, ASSOC BIOCHEMIST, E K SHRIVER CTR, MASS, 82- *Concurrent Pos:* Asst biochemist, neurol res, Mass Gen Hosp, 79- *Mem:* Am Soc Neurochem. *Res:* Inherited neurological diseases of glycorphingolipid metabolism resulting from genetic deficiency of specific lysosomal hydrolases; animal models to understand the function of glycolipids in cell development differentiation myclination and demyelination in the nervous system. *Mailing Add:* E K Shriver Ctr Mental Retardation Inc 200 Trapelo Rd Waltham MA 02254

RAGHAVAN, THIRUKKANNAMANGAI E S, b Madras, India, Aug 5, 40; m 67; c 2. MATHEMATICS. *Educ:* Loyola Col, Madras, India, BSc, 60; Presidency Col, Madras, India, MSc, 62; Indian Statist Inst, Calcutta, PhD(statist, math), 66. *Prof Exp:* Lectr math, Univ Essex, 66-69; asst prof, 69-72, assoc prof, 72-79, PROF MATH, UNIV ILL, CHICAGO CIRCLE, 79- *Res:* Positive operations; non cooperative games; stochastic and differential games; matrix theory; statistical decision theory; mathematical economics; applied statistics. *Mailing Add:* Dept of Math Univ of Ill at Chicago Cir Chicago IL 60680

RAGHAVAN, VALAYAMGHAT, b Edavanakad, Cochin, India, Mar 19, 31; m 62; c 1. PLANT MORPHOGENESIS. *Educ:* Univ Madras, BS, 50; Benares Hindu Univ, MS, 52; Princeton Univ, PhD(biol), 61. *Prof Exp:* Res assoc biol, Harvard Univ, 61-63; reader bot, Univ Malaya, 63-70, guest investr biol, Rockefeller Univ, 66-67; vis prof, Dartmouth Col, 69-70; asst prof, 70-73, assoc prof, 73-77, PROF BOT, OHIO STATE UNIV, 77- *Mem:* Bot Soc Am; Int Soc Plant Morphologists. *Res:* Developmental physiology of lower plants; photomorphogenesis and biochemical cytology of spore germination; experimental plant embryogenesis. *Mailing Add:* Dept Bot Ohio State Univ Columbus OH 43210

RAGHEB, HUSSEIN S, b Cairo, Egypt, Jan 30, 24; m 56; c 1. MICROBIOLOGY, BIOCHEMISTRY. *Educ:* Cairo Univ, BS, 44, MS, 50; Mich State Univ, PhD(fermentation), 56. *Prof Exp:* Res asst microbiol, Mich State Univ, 53-56, res assoc, 57; fel food tech, Iowa State Univ, 56; asst prof biochem & microbiol, Ferris State Col, 57-61; ASST PROF BIOCHEM, PURDUE UNIV, LAFAYETTE, 61- *Mem:* Am Soc Microbiol; Asn Official Anal Chemists. *Res:* Microbial chemistry; mode of action, methods of assay and characterization of antibiotics. *Mailing Add:* Dept of Biochem Purdue Univ West Lafayette IN 47907

RAGHU, SIVARAMAN, b Tanjore, India, July 19, 43; m 69; c 2. SYNTHETIC ORGANIC CHEMISTRY. *Educ:* Delhi Univ, BS, 62, MS, 64; Mich State Univ, PhD(chem), 72. *Prof Exp:* Lectr chem, Delhi Univ, India, 64-67; asst chem, Mich State Univ, 67-72; res assoc chem, Brandeis Univ, 72-74; res chemist, 74-77, sr res chemist, 77-78, proj leader, 78-81, MGR, AM CYANAMID CO, 81- *Mem:* Am Chem Soc. *Res:* Organic synthesis and reaction mechanisms; organometallic chemistry; homogeneous catalysis; asymmetric synthesis. *Mailing Add:* Am Cyanamid Co 1937 W Main St Stamford CT 06904

RAGHUVIR, NUGGEHALLI NARAYANA, b Bangalore, India, July 12, 30; m 57; c 1. ENTOMOLOGY. *Educ:* Univ Poona, India, BSc, 50; Karnatak Univ, MSc, 55; Utah State Univ, PhD(entom), 62. *Prof Exp:* Malaria supvr, Pub Health Dept, Poona, 50-51; res asst entom, Cent Food Tech Res Inst, Mysore, 56-58; instr zool, Duke Univ, 62-63; from instr to asst prof, 63-74, ASSOC PROF BIOL, UNIV BRIDGEPORT, 74- *Concurrent Pos:* Acad Year Exten res award, 64-65; consult entom, 78- *Mem:* Entom Soc Am; Sigma Xi. *Res:* Basic and applied aspects of insect physiology; general entomology, agricultural entomology and animal physiology. *Mailing Add:* Dept Biol Univ Bridgeport Bridgeport CT 06601

RAGINS, HERZL, b Tel Aviv, Israel, July 27, 29; US citizen; m 59; c 3. SURGERY. *Educ:* Univ Ill, BS, 47, MS & MD, 51; Univ Chicago, PhD(surg, gastric physiol), 56. *Prof Exp:* Instr surg, Univ Chicago, 59-60; instr, 60-62, from asst prof to assoc prof, 62-75, CLIN PROF SURG, ALBERT EINSTEIN COL MED, 75-; ATTEND SURG, BRONX MUNIC HOSP CTR, 68- *Concurrent Pos:* Am Cancer Soc fel, 57-58. *Mem:* Am Col Surg; Am Physiol Soc; Soc Surg Alimentary Tract; Am Gastroenterol Asn. *Res:* Gastric physiology; histochemistry of gastric mucosa; histamine metabolism; mast cells and parietal cell turn over in gastric mucosa; radiation effects on gastric mucosa; effect of intrajejunal amino acids on pancreatic secretion. *Mailing Add:* Dept of Surg Albert Einstein Col of Med Bronx NY 10461

RAGINS, NAOMI, b Chicago, Ill; m 55. PSYCHIATRY. *Educ:* Univ Chicago, BS, 47, MD, 51; Am Bd Psychiat & Neurol, dipl, 59, cert child psychiat, 61. *Prof Exp:* Asst prof psychiat, 57-63, clin asst prof, 63-71, CLIN ASSOC PROF CHILD PSYCHIAT, SCH MED, UNIV PITTSBURGH, 71- *Concurrent Pos:* Fac psychoanal, Pittsburgh Psychoanal Inst, 67-, supv child analyst, 71-, training & supv analyst, 77-; teaching consult, Children's Hosp, Pittsburgh, 72-; consult, Child Develop Prog, Head Start, Pittsburgh Child Guid Ctr, 73-76. *Mem:* Am Psychoanal Asn; Am Psychiat Asn; Am Acad Child Psychiat; Asn Child Psychoanal. *Res:* Ego development in infancy. *Mailing Add:* Univ Pittsburgh 121 University Pl Pittsburgh PA 15213

RAGLAND, JAMES BENJAMIN, b Louisburg, NC, Apr 18, 27; m 53; c 3. BIOCHEMISTRY. *Educ:* Univ NC, BA, 48, MA, 50; Univ Tex, PhD(zool, genetics), 55. *Prof Exp:* Res scientist, Biochem Inst, Univ Tex, 54-55; fel biochem & nutrit, Exp Sta, Agr & Mech Col, Tex, 55-57; asst prof biochem, Col Med, Baylor Univ, 57-65; assoc prof biochem, 65-76, assoc prof med & gastroenterol, 76-81, PROF BIOCHEM & MED GASTROENTEROL, UNIV TENN, MEMPHIS, 81-, DIR CORE LAB, CLIN RES CTR, 65- *Concurrent Pos:* Biochemist, Methodist Hosp, Houston, Tex, 57-60; head div biochem & pharmacol, Houston State Psychiat Inst, 60-65; clin assoc prof biochem, Univ Tenn, 76- *Mem:* Genetics Soc Am; Am Chem Soc; Am Soc Microbiol; Brit Biochem Soc. *Res:* Biochemistry behavior; clinical chemistry; biochemical genetics. *Mailing Add:* Clin Res Ctr Univ of Tenn Memphis TN 38163

RAGLAND, JOHN LEONARD, b Beaver Dam, Ky, Oct 30, 31; m 56; c 3. SOIL CHEMISTRY, PLANT NUTRITION. *Educ:* Univ Ky, BS, 55, MS, 56; NC State Univ, PhD(soil sci), 59. *Prof Exp:* Asst prof soil technol, Pa State Univ, 59-61; from asst prof to assoc prof, 61-66, chmn dept agron, 66-69, PROF AGRON, UNIV KY, 66-, ASSOC DEAN EXTEN & ASSOC DIR COOP EXTEN SERV, 69- *Concurrent Pos:* Chmn state comt rural community develop, USDA, 70- *Honors & Awards:* Thomas Poe Cooper Award Distinguished Agr Res, Univ Ky, 67. *Mem:* Soil Sci Soc Am; Am Soc Agron; Int Soc Soil Sci. *Res:* Interaction of plant nutrient availability with the microclimatic; cation exchange equilibria in soils. *Mailing Add:* Dept of Agron Univ of Ky Lexington KY 40506

RAGLAND, PAUL C, b Lubbock, Tex, June 28, 36; m 58; c 2. GEOCHEMISTRY, PETROLOGY. *Educ:* Tex Tech Col, BS, 58; Rice Univ, MA, 61, PhD(geol), 62. *Prof Exp:* From asst prof to prof geol, Univ NC, Chapel Hill, 62-78; chmn natural sci area, 80-82, PROF GEOL & CHMN DEPT, FLA STATE UNIV, 78- *Concurrent Pos:* Consult, Sinclair Res, 65, US Naval Ord Labs, 68-69, Va Div Mineral Resources, 70-71, Dames & Moore, 73-77, E I du Pont de Nemours, 75-77, Ebasco, Inc, 75- & NUS Corp, 78; Adv Res Projs Agency Mat Res Ctr grant, 66-74; vis prof, Duke Univ, 68 & 75, Mineral Mus, Oslo, Norway, 69-70 & Univ Ky, 75; assoc dean res admin, Univ NC, 71, assoc chmn dept geol, 75; Dept Energy grant, 76-78 & NSF grant, 79-81. *Mem:* Fel Geol Soc Am; Geochem Soc. *Res:* Application of analytical chemical data to petrogenesis of igneous and metamorphic rocks; geochemical prospecting; trace elements in chemical weathering and diagenesis. *Mailing Add:* Dept Geol Fla State Univ Tallahassee FL 32303

RAGLAND, WILLIAM LAUMAN, III, b Richmond, Va, Aug 24, 34; m 61; c 3. PATHOLOGY, BIOCHEMISTRY. *Educ:* Col William & Mary, BS, 56; Univ Ga, DVM, 60; Wash State Univ, PhD(vet path & biochem), 66. *Prof Exp:* Res asst path, Tulane Univ, 60-61, instr, 61-62; Nat Cancer Inst spec res fel, McArdle Lab, Univ Wis, 66-68, asst prof path & vet sci, 68-70; assoc prof, 70-76, PROF, DEPTS AVIAN MED, PATH & MED MICROBIOL, COL VET MED, UNIV GA, 76- *Concurrent Pos:* Pres, Ragland Res Inc, Athens, Ga, 80- *Mem:* AAAS; Soc Toxicol; Int Acad Path; Am Asn Pathologists; Am Asn Cancer Res. *Res:* Avian thymic antigens; immunoregulation and immunomodulation of chickens; immunoassay of xenobiotic residues. *Mailing Add:* Poultry Dis Res Ctr 953 College Station Rd Athens GA 30605

RAGLE, JOHN LINN, b Colorado Springs, Colo, Feb 4, 33; m 69. PHYSICAL CHEMISTRY. *Educ:* Univ Calif, BS, 54; Wash State Univ, PhD(chem), 57. *Prof Exp:* Asst prof chem, Univ Mass, 57-60; fel, Cornell Univ, 60-62; mem res staff, Northrop Space Labs, 62-64; assoc prof, 64-69, PROF CHEM, UNIV MASS, AMHERST, 70- *Concurrent Pos:* Vis assoc prof chem, Univ BC, Vancouver, 69-70; preistrager, Alexander von Humboldt stiftung award, 75. *Mem:* Am Phys Soc. *Res:* Chemistry and physics of molecular structure. *Mailing Add:* Dept of Chem Univ of Mass Amherst MA 01003

RAGLE, RICHARD HARRISON, b Boston, Mass, June 11, 23; m 49; c 3. GEOLOGY. *Educ:* Middlebury Col, BA, 52; Dartmouth Col, MA, 58. *Prof Exp:* Geologist, Cold Regions Res & Eng Lab, US Army Corps Engrs, Greenland & Antarctic, 54-60; res scientist, Arctic Inst NAm, 60-64, staff scientist, 64-74; sr geologist, Dames & Moore, 74-77; mem staff, Naval Arctic Res Lab, 77-79; sr hyrogeologist, Northern Tech Serv, 80-81; CONSULT, 79- *Concurrent Pos:* Field sci leader, Icefield Ranges Res Proj, St Elias Mt, Yukon Terr, Can, 63-70, dir, 70-74. *Honors & Awards:* Exceptional Civilian Serv Medal, US Dept Army, 60. *Mem:* Fel Arctic Inst NAm; fel Geol Soc Am; Glaciol Soc. *Res:* Glaciology, glacio-meteorology and climatology; ice and snow stratigraphy and metamorphism; glacial geology and geomorphology in regions lying near the nival line. *Mailing Add:* 2419 Telequana Dr Anchorage AK 99503

RAGONE, STEPHEN EDWARD, geochemistry, water chemistry, see previous edition

RAGOTZKIE, ROBERT AUSTIN, b Albany, NY, Sept 13, 24; m 49; c 3. METEOROLOGY, OCEANOGRAPHY. *Educ:* Rutgers Univ, BS, 48, MS, 50; Univ Wis-Madison, PhD(zool & meteorol), 53. *Prof Exp:* Proj assoc meteorol, Univ Wis-Madison, 53; coord marine biol lab & asst prof biol, Univ Ga, 54-57, dir marine inst & assoc prof biol, 57-59; from asst prof to assoc prof, 59-65, chmn dept meteorol, 64-67, dir marine studies ctr, 67-69, dir sea grant prog, 68-80, PROF METEOROL, UNIV WIS-MADISON, 65-, PROF ENVIRON SCI, 71-, DIR, SEA GRANT INST, 80- *Mem:* Fel AAAS; Am Soc Limnol & Oceanog; Am Meteorol Soc; Am Geophys Union; Int Asn Gt Lakes Res. *Res:* Physical limnology of Great Lakes, thermal structure and currents; Great Lakes as systems. *Mailing Add:* Sea Grant Inst Univ Wis-Madison Madison WI 53706

RAGOZIN, DAVID LAWRENCE, b Brooklyn, NY, Apr 20, 41; m 70. MATHEMATICAL ANALYSIS, NUMERICAL ANALYSIS. *Educ:* Reed Col, BA, 62; Harvard Univ, AM, 63, PhD(math), 67. *Prof Exp:* Instr math, Mass Inst Technol, 67-69; asst prof, 69-75, ASSOC PROF MATH, UNIV WASH, 75- *Concurrent Pos:* NSF grant, Mass Inst Technol, 68-69, res assoc & NSF grant, 70-71; NSF grant, Univ Wash, 71-77. *Mem:* Am Math Soc; Math Asn Am. *Res:* Harmonic analysis on Lie groups and homogeneous spaces; applications of differential geometry; numerical analysis. *Mailing Add:* Dept of Math Univ of Wash GN-50 Seattle WA 98195

RAGSDALE, DAVID WILLARD, b Boise, Idaho, Nov 8, 52; m 73; c 1. INTEGRATED PEST MANAGEMENT. *Educ:* Pt Loma Col, BA, 74; La State Univ, MS, 77, PhD(entom), 80. *Prof Exp:* Res assoc, La State Univ, 79-81; ASST PROF ENTOM, UNIV MINN, 81- *Mem:* Entom Soc Am; Am Phytopath Soc; Sigma Xi; AAAS. *Res:* Insects as vectors of plant disease agents; integrated pest management of field crops; use of serology in determining predator-prey relationships. *Mailing Add:* Dept Entom 219 Hodson Hall Univ Minn 1980 Folwell Ave St Paul MN 55108

RAGSDALE, HARVEY LARIMORE, b Atlanta, Ga, Mar 6, 40. ECOLOGY, BOTANY. *Educ:* Emory Univ, AB, 62; Univ Tenn, MS, 64, PhD(bot), 68. *Prof Exp:* Asst prof, 68-72, ASSOC PROF BIOL, EMORY UNIV, 72- *Concurrent Pos:* Consult, Allied Gen Nuclear Serv, 70-78 & Environ Div, Tex Instruments, Inc, 78; co-prin investr grants, US Energy Res & Develop Admin, 70-76 & NSF, 76-78; prin investr grants, US Dept Energy, 76-79. *Mem:* Am Inst Biol Sci; AAAS; Ecol Soc Am; Sigma Xi. *Res:* Ecological chemical element cycling; ecosystem modeling and simulation; radiation effects and cycling; deciduous forest community studies; solar energy from woody biomass fuel species. *Mailing Add:* Dept of Biol Emory Univ Atlanta GA 30322

RAGSDALE, NANCY NEALY, b Griffin, Ga, Feb 5, 38; m 59; c 2. PESTICIDE CHEMISTRY, CELL PHYSIOLOGY. *Educ:* Cent Conn State Col, BS, 62; Univ Md, MS, 66, PhD(bot), 74. *Prof Exp:* Res asst, Univ Md, 66-74, res assoc fungal physiol, Dept Bot, 74-78; pesticide assessment specialist, Sci & Educ Admin-Chem Res, 78-80, COORDR, COOP STATE RES SERV, USDA, 80- *Mem:* AAAS; Am Phytopath Soc; Am Chem Soc; Soc Environ Toxicol Chem; Sigma Xi. *Res:* Mode of action of pesticides and coordination of cooperative state research service effort to collect data on agricultural pesticide use and exposure hazards. *Mailing Add:* Sci & Educ Admin-Chem Res USDA Washington DC 20250

RAGSDALE, RONALD O, b Boise, Idaho, Dec 10, 32; m 56; c 3. INORGANIC CHEMISTRY. *Educ:* Brigham Young Univ, BS, 57; Univ Ill, MS, 59, PhD(chem), 60. *Prof Exp:* Res chemist, Gen Chem Div, Allied Chem Corp, 60-63; from asst prof to assoc prof, 63-72, PROF CHEM, UNIV UTAH, 72- *Mem:* Am Chem Soc; Royal Soc Chem. *Res:* Metal ion complexes; Lewis acid-base interactions; nuclear magnetic resonance. *Mailing Add:* Dept of Chem Univ of Utah Salt Lake City UT 84112

RAGSDELL, KENNETH MARTIN, b Jacksonville, Ill, Sept 3, 42; m 62; c 3. MECHANICAL ENGINEERING. *Educ:* Univ Mo-Rolla, BS, 66, MS, 67; Univ Tex, Austin, PhD(mech eng), 72. *Prof Exp:* Instr eng, Okla State Univ, 67-68; mech engr, IBM Corp, 68-70; instr eng, Univ Tex, Austin, 70-72; asst prof mech eng, 72-76, ASSOC PROF MECH ENG, PURDUE UNIV, WEST LAFAYETTE, 76- *Concurrent Pos:* Consult, various corps; pres, CAD Serv, Inc. *Res:* Computational aspects of design; optimization theory dynamics; computer aided design; engineering computation; optimization theory; design of dynamic mechanical systems. *Mailing Add:* Sch of Mech Eng Purdue Univ West Lafayette IN 47907

RAHA, CHITTA RANJAN, b Faridpur, EBengal, Apr 1, 26; m 54; c 3. ORGANIC CHEMISTRY, BIOCHEMISTRY. *Educ:* Univ Calcutta, BSc, 45, MSc, 47, DPhil(chem), 54. *Prof Exp:* Pool officer, Govt India, 61-65; asst prof oncol, Chicago Med Sch, 65-68; ASSOC PROF BIOCHEM, UNIV NEBR MED CTR, OMAHA, 68- *Concurrent Pos:* Int Agency Res Cancer travel fel, Wenner-Gren Inst, Univ Stockholm, 70. *Mem:* AAAS; Am Asn Cancer Res; Am Chem Soc; The Chem Soc. *Res:* Organic chemistry as applied to cancer research. *Mailing Add:* 7432 Spring St Omaha NE 68105

RAHAL, LEO JAMES, b Detroit, Mich, July 22, 39; m 71; c 2. NUCLEAR ENGINEERING, PLASMA PHYSICS. *Educ:* Univ Detroit, BS, 62, MS, 64; Univ NMex, PhD(physics), 78. *Prof Exp:* Physicist, LTV Aerospace, 68-73, Kirtland Weapons Lab, 73-76, Los Alamos Nat Lab, 76-77, Los Alamos tech assoc, 77-81; PHYSICIST, DIKEWOOD CORP, 81- *Res:* Plasma physics microinstability analysis: in the area of high density plasmas; nuclear waste management including waste disposal and air dispersion; nuclear reactor safety-hydrogen buildup in reactors and consequences. *Mailing Add:* 9417 Regal Ridge NE Albuquerque NM 87111

RAHE, JAMES EDWARD, b Muncie, Ind, Mar 12, 39; m 66; c 3. PLANT PATHOLOGY. *Educ:* Purdue Univ, BS, 61, PhD(biochem), 69. *Prof Exp:* Asst prof, 69-77, ASSOC PROF BIOL SCI, SIMON FRASER UNIV, 77- *Mem:* Am Phytopath Soc; Phytochem Soc NAm; Sigma Xi. *Res:* Biochemistry and physiology of host-parasite interaction; biological and integrated control of plant disease. *Mailing Add:* Dept of Biol Sci Simon Fraser Univ Burnaby BC V5A 1S6 Can

RAHE, MAURICE HAMPTON, b Tucumcari, NMex, Jan 17, 44; m 73; c 1. MATHEMATICS. *Educ:* Pomona Col, BA, 65; Stanford Univ, MS, 70, PhD(math), 76. *Prof Exp:* Lectr & fel, Univ Toronto, 76-78; ASST PROF MATH, TEX A&M UNIV, 78- *Concurrent Pos:* Vis asst prof, Rice Univ, 81. *Mem:* Am Math Soc; Inst Elec & Electronics Engrs. *Res:* Ergodic theory; information theory; probability. *Mailing Add:* Dept Math Tex A&M Univ College Station TX 77843

RAHE, RICHARD HENRY, b Seattle, Wash, May 28, 36; m 60; c 2. PSYCHIATRY. *Educ:* Univ Wash, MD, 61. *Prof Exp:* Intern med, Bellevue Hosp, New York, 61-62; from resident to chief resident psychiat, Univ Wash, 62-65; res psychiatrist, US Navy Neuropsychiat Res Univ, 65-68; head stress med div, 70-74, COMNDG OFFICER, US NAVAL HEALTH RES CTR, 70- *Concurrent Pos:* NIH spec fel, Karolinska Inst, Sweden, 68-69; adj prof psychiat, Neuropsychiat Inst; PROF PSYCHIAT, UNIV CALIF, LOS ANGELES, 75- Karolinska Inst, Sweden, 68-69; assoc prof psychiat, Univ Calif, San Diego & Univ Calif, Los Angeles, 70-74. *Honors & Awards:* McDonnell Prize, Univ Wash, 61. *Mem:* Fel Am Psychiat Asn; Am Psychosom Soc; NY Acad Sci; World Psychiat Asn. *Res:* Life changes and illness onset; psychosocial aspects of coronary heart diseases; sports medicine in the middle-aged athlete; biochemical correlates of stress. *Mailing Add:* Naval Health Res Ctr San Diego CA 92152

RAHEEL, MASTURA, b Lahore, Pakistan, Mar 1, 38; m 59; c 2. TEXTILE SCIENCE, ORGANIC CHEMISTRY. *Educ:* Punjab Univ, Pakistan, BSc, 57, MSc, 59; Okla State Univ, MS, 62; Univ Minn, St Paul, PhD(textile sci), 71. *Prof Exp:* Asst prof & head textiles & clothing, Col Home Econ, Lahore, 60-77; lectr, Univ Minn, St Paul, 77-78; ASST PROF TEXTILE SCI, UNIV ILL, URBANA, 78- *Mem:* Am Asn Textile Chemists & Colorists; Am Home Econ Asn; Am Col Prof Textiles & Clothing; Sigma Xi. *Res:* Physical metrology of consumer textile products; chemical finishing of textiles. *Mailing Add:* Dept Textiles & Interior Design Univ Ill 905 S Goodwin Urbana IL 61801

RAHIJA, RICHARD JAMES, b Kansas City, Kans, Dec 7, 49; m 77. BIOMATERIAL SCIENCE. *Educ:* Kans State Univ, BS, 72, DVM, 74. *Prof Exp:* Staff vet clin practice, Panama Animal Hosp & Brentwood Animal Hosp, 74-77; clin res vet pharmacol, Pitman-Moore, Inc, 77-79; SR SCIENTIST EXP SURG BIOMAT, ETHICON RES FOUND, 79- *Mem:* Soc Biomat; Am Vet Med Asn; Am Asn Indust Vet. *Res:* Mechanical property characterization of surgical devices fabricated from absorbable and nonabsorbable biomaterials. *Mailing Add:* Ethicon Res Found US Highway 22 Somerville NJ 08876

RAHIMTOOLA, SHAHBUDIN HOOSEINALLY, b Bombay, India, Oct 17, 31; Brit citizen; m 67; c 2. CARDIOLOGY, INTERNAL MEDICINE. *Educ:* Univ Karachi, MB & BS, 56; MRCPE, 63; FRCP, 72. *Prof Exp:* Sr house officer, Barrowmore Chest Hosp, Chester, Eng, 56-57 & Whittington Hosp, London, 58-59; house physician, Cardiac Unit, London Chest Hosp, 59-60; Locum med registr, Whittington Hosp, London, 60; registr cardiac unit, Wessex Reg Hosp Bd, Chest Hosp, Southampton, Eng, 60-63; co-dir, Cardiac Lab, Mayo Clin, Rochester, Minn, 65-66; sr registr cardiopulmonary dis, Dept Med, Queen Elizabeth Hosp, Birmingham, Eng, 66-67; res asst & hon sr registr, Dept Med, Royal Postgrad Med Sch & Hammersmith Hosp, London, 67-68; assoc prof med, Abraham Lincoln Sch Med, Col Med, Univ Ill, 69-72; prof med, Health Sci Ctr, Univ Ore, 72-80, dir res, 73-78; PROF MED & CHIEF SECT CARDIOL, UNIV SOUTHERN CALIF, 80- *Concurrent Pos:* Co-dir, Dept Adult Cardiol, Cook County Hosp, Chicago, 69-70, dir, 70-72; consult cardiol, Madigan Gen Army Hosp, Ft Lewis, Wash, 72-; NIH grant, 72-77, 78-; Ore Heart Asn & Med Res Found Ore grants, 73-77; rep for Ore, Coun Clin Cardiol, Am Heart Asn, 75-77, mem exec comt, 77-, mem long range planning comt & mem nominating comt, 78-; consult, Nat Coop Study Valvular Heart Dis, 76-77; mem planning comt, Vet Admin, Washington, DC, 76-77, mem exec comt, 77-; mem circulatory systs devices panel, Food & Drug Admin, HEW, 76-80, chmn dept, 77-80; vis scientist, Cardiovasc Res Inst & vis prof med, Sch Med, Univ Calif, San Francisco, 78-79; grants, Coun Clin Cardiol, Am Heart Asn & Coun Circulation; mem adv panel cardiovascular drugs, US Pharmacopia, Nat Forumlary, 81-; ed, Newsletter, Coun Clin Cardiol, An Heart Asn, 79-, Clin Cardiol, Am Med Asn, 80. *Mem:* Fel Am Col Cardiol; fel Am Col Chest Physicians; fel Am Col Physicians; Asn Univ Cardiologists. *Res:* Left ventricular performance in various disease states; coronary artery disease; valvular heart disease; cardiac electrophysiology. *Mailing Add:* Univ Southern Calif 2025 Zonal Ave Los Angeles CA 90033

RAHLAMANN, DONALD FREDERICK, b San Francisco, Calif, July 21, 23; m 49; c 3. GRAVITATIONAL PHYSIOLOGY. *Educ:* Univ Calif, Davis, BS, 55, MS, 56, PhD(animal physiol), 62. *Prof Exp:* Jr specialist, Dept Animal Husbandry, Univ Calif, Davis, 49-50, asst specialist reproductive physiology, 50-62; jr res physiologist, Dept Physiol & Anat, 62-63, asst res physiologist space physiol, 63-81, ASSOC RES PHYSIOLOGIST, ENVIRON PHYSIOL LAB, UNIV CALIF, BERKELEY, 81- *Concurrent Pos:* Consult, Lawrence Hall Sci, Univ Calif, Berkeley, 66-67; Int Govt Personnel Act, Ames Res Ctr, NASA, Moffett Field, Calif, 75-76; participant, Joint US-USSR Cosmos 1129 Flight Exp, 78-79. *Mem:* Am Physiol Soc; Sigma Xi; AAAS; Am Asn Lab Animal Sci. *Res:* Animal experimentation in metabolism related to environmental changes; physiology of non-human primates; development of equipment and instrumentation for measurement of physiological response. *Mailing Add:* Environ Physiol Lab Bldg T2251 Univ Calif Berkeley CA 94720

RAHM, DAVID CHARLES, b Ironwood, Mich, Dec 1, 27; m 51; c 2. PHYSICS. *Educ:* Univ Chicago, SB, 49; Univ Mich, MS, 51, PhD(physics), 56. *Prof Exp:* From asst physicist to assoc physicist, 55-62, physicist, 62-82, SR PHYSICIST, BROOKHAVEN NAT LAB, 82- *Concurrent Pos:* Physicist, Nuclear Res Ctr, Saclay, France, 60-61; vis scientist, Europ Orgn Nuclear Res, Geneva, 68-69 & 75-80. *Mem:* Fel Am Phys Soc. *Res:* Particle physics; particle detectors; particle beams; superconducting magnets; accelerators. *Mailing Add:* Physics Dept Bldg 510 Brookhaven Nat Lab Upton NY 11973

RAHMAN, ANEESUR, b Hyderabad, India, Aug 24, 27; m 56; c 1. THEORETICAL PHYSICS. *Educ:* Osmania Univ, India, BSc, 46; Cambridge Univ, MA, 48, MA, 49; Louvain, DSc(physics), 53. *Prof Exp:* Lectr physics, Osmania Univ, India, 49-57; res scientist, Tata Inst Fundamental Res, India, 57-59; assoc physicist, 60-77, SR PHYSICIST, ARGONNE NAT LAB, 77- *Honors & Awards:* Langmuir Award Chem Physics, Am Phys Soc, 77. *Res:* Computer simulation of liquids and solids; neutron inelastic scattering; structure and dynamical correlations in water and ice; theory of liquids; motion of ions in superionic conductors. *Mailing Add:* Argonne Nat Lab Argonne IL 60439

RAHMAN, MATIUR, b Dumuni Chowki, India, Sept 1, 40; m 66; c 2. FLUID MECHANICS. *Educ:* Gauhati Univ, BSc, 62, MSc, 64; Univ London, DIC, 69, MPhil, 69; Windsor Univ, Can, PhD(fluid mech), 73. *Prof Exp:* Lectr math, Jorhat Eng Col, India, 64-66; res fel fluid mech, Imp Col, Univ London, 66-69; res fel, Windsor Univ, 69-73, teaching asst math, 69-73; fel heat transfer, Univ Moncton, 73-75, res prof fluid mech & math, 74-76; res assoc, Dept Appl Math, Univ Man, 76-77; ASST RES OFFICER, HYDRAUL LAB, DIV MECH ENG, NAT RES COUN CAN, 77- *Concurrent Pos:* Mem Convocation Comt, Univ London, 69-; rev papers, Chem Eng Sci, 74- & Am Inst Chem Engr, 75-; asst ed, Int J Math & Math Sci, 78- *Mem:* Tensor Soc; Can Soc Mech Eng; Eng Inst Can. *Res:* Chemical flow reactors; thermal stratification in large bodies of water; pneumatic structure of inflatable shell; boundary-layer consideration in chemical flow problems; tidal flow in estuaries; application of array processor in hybrid model; wave forces on structures; resonance in harbor. *Mailing Add:* 43 Woodmount Circle Nepean ON K2E 5P9 Can

RAHMAN, TALAT SHAHNAZ, b Calcutta, India, Feb 5, 48; Pakistan citizen. SOLID STATE PHYSICS. *Educ:* Univ Karachi, BSc, 68, MSc, 69; Univ Rochester, PhD(physics), 77. *Prof Exp:* Res asst physics, Univ Rochester, 71-76, teaching asst, 73 & 76-77; RES PHYSICIST, UNIV CALIF, IRVINE, 77- *Mem:* Am Phys Soc; Asn Women Sci. *Res:* Surface physics and optical properties of solids. *Mailing Add:* Dept of Physics Univ of Calif Irvine CA 92717

RAHMAN, YUEH ERH, b Canton, China, June 10, 30; m 56; c 1. MEDICINE, HEALTH SCIENCES. *Educ:* Univ Louvain, MD, 56. *Prof Exp:* Med officer, Belgian Leprosy Ctr, India, 57-58; asst res officer, Indian Cancer Res Ctr, 58-59; res assoc biochem cytol, Univ Louvain, 59-60; res assoc, Biol Div, 60-63, asst biologist, 63-72, biologist, 72-81, SR BIOLOGIST, BIOL DIV, ARGONNE NAT LAB, 81- *Concurrent Pos:* Vis scientist, Dept Biochem, Univ Utrecht, 68-69; adj assoc prof, Dept Biol Sci, Northern Ill Univ, 71-; mem rev group, Exp Therapeut Study Sect, NIH, 79-83. *Mem:* Am Soc Cell Biol; Radiation Res Soc; NY Acad Sci; AAAS; Asn Women Sci. *Res:* Cellular biochemistry; cell membranes; radiation and lysosomes; chemotherapy by use of liposome encapsulation of drugs, such as chelating agents and anti-tumor drugs. *Mailing Add:* Argonne Nat Lab 9700 S Cass Ave Argonne IL 60439

RAHN, HERMANN, b East Lansing, Mich, July 5, 12; m 39; c 2. PHYSIOLOGY. *Educ:* Cornell Univ, AB, 33; Univ Rochester, PhD, 38. *Hon Degrees:* Dr, Univ Paris, 64; LLD, Yonsei Univ, Korea, 65; DSc, Univ Rochester, 73, Dr, Univ Bern, Switz, 81. *Prof Exp:* Nat Res Coun fel, Harvard Univ, 38-39; instr physiol, Univ Wyo, 39-41; from asst to assoc prof physiol & vchmn dept, Sch Med, Univ Rochester, 41-56; prof & chmn dept, 56-73, DISTINGUISHED PROF PHYSIOL, SCH MED, STATE UNIV NY BUFFALO, 73- *Concurrent Pos:* Mem adv comt physiol sci, Off Naval Res, 57-60, physiol study sect, 58-62, prog-proj comt, 63-67, bd sci counsr, Nat Heart Inst, 65-68, cardiopulmonary adv comt, 68-71, res career award comn, Nat Inst Gen Med Sci, 68-72, adv comt biol sci, Air Force Off Sci Res, 58-64 & working comt, Space Sci Bd, Nat Acad Sci-Nat Res Coun, 62-65; vis prof, San Marcus Univ, Lima, Peru, 55 & Dartmouth Med Sch, 62; mem coun, Int Union Physiol Sci, 65-, vpres & mem exec comt, 71-; vpres & mem exec comt, US Nat Comn, 66-; mem environ biol adv panel, Am Inst Biol Sci, 67-71; mem nat adv bd, R/V Alpha Helix, 68-71; chmn, Comn Underwater Physiol & Med, Nat Res Coun, 72-74. *Mem:* Sr mem Inst Med-Nat Acad Sci; Am Physiol Soc (pres, 63-64); Am Soc Zoologists; Am Acad Arts & Sci. *Res:* Pulmonary physiology; physiology of gas exchange; environmental physiology. *Mailing Add:* Dept of Physiol State Univ of NY Sch Med Buffalo NY 14214

RAHN, JOAN ELMA, b Cleveland, Ohio, Feb 5, 29. PLANT MORPHOLOGY. *Educ:* Western Reserve Univ, BS, 50; Columbia Univ, AM, 52, PhD, 56. *Prof Exp:* From asst prof to assoc prof biol, Thiel Col, 56-59; instr bot, Ohio State Univ, 59-60; instr biol, Int Sch Am, 60-61; asst prof, Lake Forest Col, 61-67; SCI RES & WRITING, 67- *Mem:* AAAS; Bot Soc Am; Am Inst Biol Sci. *Mailing Add:* 1656 Hickory St Highland Park IL 60035

RAHN, KENNETH ALBERT, b Hackensack, NJ, Aug 10, 40; m 71; c 2. ATMOSPHERIC CHEMISTRY. *Educ:* Mass Inst Technol, BS, 62; Univ Mich, PhD(meteorol), 71. *Prof Exp:* Sci/math teacher, Classical High Sch, Barrington College, 63-68; res assoc atmospheric chem, Inst Nuclear Sci, Univ Ghent, 71-73; res assoc, Grad Sch Oceanog, Univ RI, 73-75; vis scientist, Max Planck Inst Chem, 75-76; RES ASSOC ATMOSPHERIC CHEM, GRAD SCH OCEANOG, UNIV RI, 76- *Mem:* Am Chem Soc; AAAS; Am Meteorol Soc; Gesellschaft Fur Agrosolforschung. *Res:* Aerosols; arctic air chemistry; long-range transport. *Mailing Add:* Grad Sch of Oceanog Univ of RI Kingston RI 02881

RAHN, PERRY H, b Allentown, Pa, Oct 27, 36; m 62; c 4. HYDROLOGY, GEOMORPHOLOGY. *Educ:* Lafayette Col, BS & BA, 59; Pa State Univ, PhD(geol), 65. *Prof Exp:* Civil engr, Calif Dept Water Resources, 59-61; asst prof geol, Univ Conn, 65-68; asst prof, 68-71, assoc prof, 71-78, PROF GEOL, SDAK SCH MINES & TECHNOL, 78- *Mem:* Fel Geol Soc Am; Int Asn Hydrogeol; Nat Water Well Asn; Am Quaternary Asn; Sigma Xi. *Res:* Engineering geology; hydrology of glacial and limestone terranes; uranium tailing pond contamination; engineering geology. *Mailing Add:* Dept of Geol & Geol Eng SDak Sch of Mines & Technol Rapid City SD 57701

RAHN, RONALD OTTO, b Bridgeport, Conn, Feb 7, 35; m 63; c 2. BIOPHYSICAL CHEMISTRY. *Educ:* Univ Conn, BA, 57; Brandeis Univ, PhD(chem), 63. *Prof Exp:* Res staff biophys, Bell Tel Labs, 63-65; RES STAFF BIOPHYS, BIOL DIV, OAK RIDGE NAT LAB, 65- *Concurrent Pos:* Prof, Biomed Sch, Univ Tenn. *Mem:* AAAS; Am Soc Photobiol. *Res:* Luminescence and photochemistry of nucleic acids; quantitation of DNA damage; binding of small molecules to DNA. *Mailing Add:* Biol Div Oak Ridge Nat Lab Oak Ridge TN 37830

RAHWAN, RALF GEORGE, b Egypt; Feb 28, 41; US citizen. PHARMACOLOGY, TOXICOLOGY. *Educ:* Cairo Univ, BS, 61; Butler Univ, MS, 70; Purdue Univ, PhD(pharmacol), 72. *Prof Exp:* Retail pharmacist, 61-64; head sci doc & training dept, Hoechst Orient Pharmaceut Co, 64-67; assoc pharmacologist, Human Health Res & Develop Labs, Dow Chem Co, 67-70; asst prof pharmacol, 72-75, ASSOC PROF PHARMACOL, COL PHARM, OHIO STATE UNIV, 75- *Mem:* Am Soc Pharmacol & Exp Therapeut; Soc Toxicol; Sigma Xi. *Res:* Endocrine pharmacology and toxicology. *Mailing Add:* Div of Pharmacol Ohio State Univ Col of Pharm Columbus OH 43210

RAI, CHARANJIT, b Barabanki, India, July 19, 29. CHEMICAL ENGINEERING, CHEMISTRY. *Educ:* Univ Agra, BSc, 48; Lucknow Univ, MSc, 50; Indian Inst Sci, Bangalore, dipl, 52, PhD(chem), 59; Univ Ill, MS, 56; Ill Inst Technol, PhD(chem eng), 60. *Prof Exp:* Res asst chem eng, Univ Ill, 54-56; instr, Ill Inst Technol, 56-58; sr res scientist, Pure Oil Co, 59-65; sr res supvr, Richardson Co, Ill, 65-66; dept head prod & process res, Cities Serv Oil Co, 66-76; prof, US Energy Res & Develop Agency, Morgantown Energy Res, 77-80; MEM FAC, DEPT CHEM & NATURAL GAS ENG, TEX A&I UNIV, 80- *Concurrent Pos:* Prof chem eng & chmn dept, Indian Inst Technol, Kanpur, 63-64. *Mem:* AAAS; Am Inst Chem Engrs; Am Chem Soc; Indian Inst Chem Engrs. *Res:* Mass transfer; thermodynamics; oxidation of hydrocarbons; petrochemicals; fuels and lubricants. *Mailing Add:* Dept Chem & Natural Gas Eng Tex A&I Univ Kingsville TX 78363

RAI, DHANPAT, b June 12, 43; US citizen; m 72; c 1. SOIL CHEMISTRY, SOIL MINERALOGY. *Educ:* Panjab Agr Univ, BSc, 63, MSc, 65; Ore State Univ, PhD(soil sci), 70. *Prof Exp:* Res assoc soil sci, Ore State Univ, 70-71; fel, Colo State Univ, 72-73; res asst prof, NMex State Univ, 74-75; SR RES SCIENTIST SOIL SCI, BATTELLE MEM INST, 75- *Mem:* Am Soc Agron; Soil Sci Soc Am; Int Soc Soil Sci; Res Soc NAm. *Res:* Soil chemistry; environmental chemistry of actinides; geochemistry. *Mailing Add:* Battelle Mem Inst PO Box 999 Richland WA 99352

RAI, IQBAL SINGH, b Majali Kalan, India, Jan 29, 36; m 62; c 2. STRUCTURAL ENGINEERING, ENGINEERING MECHANICS. *Educ:* Punjab Univ, India, BA, 56, BSc, 60; Univ Roorkee, ME, 66; Ohio State Univ, PhD(civil eng), 75. *Prof Exp:* From lectr to assoc prof struct eng, Guru Nanak Eng Col Ludhiana, India, 60-71; res assoc civil eng, Ohio State Univ, 71-77; SR RES ENGR, GOODYEAR TIRE & RUBBER CO, 77- *Concurrent Pos:* Consult, Nankana Sahib Educ Trust, Ludhiana, India, 63-71 & Columbus Aircraft Div, Rockwell Int, 76-77. *Mem:* Am Soc Civil Engrs; Soc Exp Stress Anal. *Res:* Finite element analysis; mechanics of structures; structural analysis and design. *Mailing Add:* Res Div 142 Goodyear Blvd Akron OH 44316

RAI, KANTI R, b Jodhpur, India, May 10, 32; m 68; c 2. HEMATOLOGY, ONCOLOGY. *Educ:* Med Col, Univ Rajasthan, MB & BS, 55; Am Bd Pediat, dipl, 61. *Prof Exp:* Head exp med, Inst Nuclear Med, Delhi, India, 62-66; assoc scientist, Brookhaven Nat Lab, 66-70; assoc prof med, 72-80, PROF MED, SCH MED, STATE UNIV NY STONY BROOK, 80-; CHIEF, DIV HEMAT-ONCOL, LONG ISLAND JEWISH-HILLSIDE MED CTR, 81- *Concurrent Pos:* Leukemia res scholar, Nat Leukemia Asn, 66-67 & 75-77; attending physician hemat-oncol, Long Island Jewish-Hillside Med Ctr, 70-80. *Mem:* Am Soc Hemat; Am Soc Clin Oncol; Am Asn Cancer Res; Soc Nuclear Med; Soc Exp Biol & Med. *Res:* Natural history and biology of leukemias; cell kinetics in leukemias; new therapeutic approaches in the malignancies of blood. *Mailing Add:* Long Island Jewish-Hillside Med Ctr New Hyde Park NY 11042

RAI, KARAMJIT SINGH, b Moranwali, Punjab, India, Mar 24, 31; m 56; c 5. CYTOGENETICS, GENETIC CONTROL. *Educ:* Punjab Univ, India, BSc, 53, MSc, 55; Univ Chicago, PhD(bot), 60. *Prof Exp:* Lectr bot, Khalsa Col, Amritsar, 55-56; head dept bot, Deshbandhu Col, Delhi, 56-58; Charles Hutchinson fel & Coulter res fel, Univ Chicago, 58-60; assoc, Chicago Natural Hist Mus, Ill, 60; res assoc, Radiation Lab & dept biol, 60-62, sr staff mem radiation lab, 62-77, from asst prof to assoc prof, 62-70, dir mosquito biol training prog, 69-75, PROF BIOL, UNIV NOTRE DAME, 70-, SR. *Concurrent Pos:* Consult, Ill Inst Technol, 64-68; Int Atomic Energy Agency, Vienna, 66 & 69 & WHO, Geneva, 66-75; adv, Govt Ceylon, 66 & Govt Brazil, 69; mem Int Atomic Energy Agency panels, 68 & 70; vis prof, Univ Pernambuco, Brazil, 69 & Guru Nanak Dev Univ, India, 73-74; co-prin investr, Mosquito Biol Unit, Mombasa, Nairobi, Kenya, 71-76; mem, Rockfeller Found, Conf Genetics Dis Vectors, Bellagio, Italy, 81. *Mem:* AAAS; Genetics Soc Am; Entom Soc Am; Am Mosquito Control Asn; Am Inst Biol Sci. *Res:* Cytogenetics and radiation genetics of mosquitoes and plants; synthetic genomes and insect population control; genetics of speciation in Aedes mosquitoes; mechanics of mutagen-induced chromosomal aberrations; genetic control of cell division; genetic manipulations of mosquitoes. *Mailing Add:* Dept Biol Univ Notre Dame Notre Dame IN 46556

RAIBLE, RAYMOND W, instrumentation, deceased

RAIBLE, ROBERT H(ENRY), b Cincinnati, Ohio, Aug 27, 35; m 58; c 1. ELECTRICAL ENGINEERING. *Educ:* Univ Cincinnati, EE, 58; Purdue Univ, PhD(elec eng), 64. *Prof Exp:* Proj engr, Cincinnati Milling Mach, 57-58; instr, Purdue Univ, 59-64; from asst prof to assoc prof, 64-76; PROF ELEC ENG, UNIV CINCINNATI, 77- *Concurrent Pos:* Consult, Spati Industs; Metcut Assoc. *Mem:* Inst Elec & Electronics Engrs. *Res:* Analysis and design of automatic control systems; theory and application of adaptive and learning systems. *Mailing Add:* Dept of Elec Eng Univ of Cincinnati Cincinnati OH 45221

RAICH, HENRY, b Philadelphia, Pa, June 11, 19; m 43; c 2. PHYSICAL CHEMISTRY. *Educ:* Rensselaer Polytech Inst, BS, 40 & 44, PhD, 49. *Prof Exp:* Chemist, Am Smelting & Refining Co, 40-43 & Los Alamos Sci Lab, 44-46; fel, Mellon Inst, 49-52; chemist, Nuodex Prod Co, Inc, 52-54; RES ASSOC LUBRICANTS, MOBIL OIL CORP, 54- *Mem:* Am Chem Soc; Am Soc Lubrication Engrs; Am Soc Testing & Mat; Nat Lubricating Grease Inst. *Res:* Lubricants; colloids; rheology; metal soaps. *Mailing Add:* Dept of Res Paulsboro Lab Mobil Oil Corp Paulsboro NJ 08066

RAICH, JOHN CARL, b Badgastein, Austria, May 9, 37; US citizen; m 63; c 2. SOLID STATE PHYSICS. *Educ:* Iowa State Univ, BS, 59, PhD(physics), 63. *Prof Exp:* Res assoc physics, Iowa State Univ, 64 & Purdue Univ, 64-66; from asst prof to assoc prof, 66-72, prof & chmn physics, 72-78, ASSOC DEAN, COL NAT SCI, COLO STATE UNIV, 78- *Concurrent Pos:* Consult, Los Alamos Sci Lab, 71-; NATO sr fel sci, NSF, 75, Humboldt fel, 77. *Mem:* Am Phys Soc. *Res:* Molecular crystals. *Mailing Add:* Dept Physics Colo State Univ Ft Collins CO 80521

RAICH, WILLIAM JUDD, b Keokuk, Iowa, May 1, 27; m 49; c 6. POLYMER CHEMISTRY. *Educ:* Mass Inst Technol, BS, 49; Univ Nebr, MS, 54, PhD(org chem), 57. *Prof Exp:* Chemist, Merck & Co, NJ, 49-51; teaching asst org chem, Univ Nebr, 51-54; chemist, 55-63, sr res chemist, 63-65, group leader polymer chem, 65-69, sect leader, 69-72, RES SPECIALIST, DOW CHEM CO, 72- *Mem:* Am Chem Soc. *Res:* Polymer synthesis, emulsion process, polymer property measurements; thiophene chemistry; polymerization process development. *Mailing Add:* 205 W Collins St Midland MI 48640

RAICHEL, DANIEL R(ICHTER), b Paterson, NJ, Aug 22, 35; m 67; c 2. ENGINEERING SCIENCE, THEORETICAL PHYSICS. *Educ:* Rensselaer Polytech Inst, BME, 57; Mass Inst Technol, SM, 58; Columbia Univ, MechEngr, 67; NY Univ, EngScD, 70. *Prof Exp:* Asst proj engr, Curtiss-Wright Corp, 61-62; instr wind tunnel lab, Case Inst Technol, 62-63; eng consult, Polytech Design Corp, 63-64; asst res scientist aeronaut & astronaut, NY Univ, 64-65; instr mech eng, Newark Col Eng, 65-67; independent consult, 67-68; consult advan develop eng, Electro-Nucleonics, Inc, 69-71; pres & chief scientist med & lab instrumentation, Dathar Corp, 71-75; prin, Ingenieurs Int, 75-79; PRIN, RAICHEL TECHNOL GROUP & RAMAR CONSULT, 79- *Concurrent Pos:* Adj prof mech eng, NJ Inst Technol, 78- *Mem:* Am Soc Mech Engrs; Am Phys Soc; Acoust Soc Am; Audio Eng Soc; Sigma Xi. *Res:* Acoustics; design and development of high fidelity speakers; energy conservation and conversion studies; molecular physics. *Mailing Add:* 532 Spencer Dr Wyckoff NJ 07481

RAICHLE, MARCUS EDWARD, b Hoquaim, Wash, Mar 15, 37; m 64; c 4. NEUROLOGY. *Educ:* Univ Wash, BS, 60, MD, 64. *Prof Exp:* Instr neurol, New York Hosp-Cornell Med Ctr, 68-69; consult neurol, Sch Aerospace Med, US Air Force, 69-71; asst prof, 71-75, assoc prof, 75-78, PROF NEUROL & RADIATION SCI, SCH MED, WASHINGTON UNIV, 78- *Concurrent Pos:* NIH teacher-investr award, Nat Inst Neurol & Commun Dis & Stroke, 71-; mem, Neurol A Study Sect, NIH, 75 & Cardiovasc D Res Study Comt, Am Heart Asn, 75- *Mem:* Am Neurol Asn; Am Acad Neurol; Am Physiol Soc; Soc Neurosci; AMA. *Res:* In vivo measurement of brain hemodynamics, metabolism and exchange processes using trace kinetic techniques and positron-emitting, cyclotron-produced radioisotopes. *Mailing Add:* Div Radiation Sci Mallinckrodt Inst Washington Univ St Louis MO 63110

RAIDER, STANLEY IRWIN, b New York, NY, July 21, 34; m 60; c 1. CHEMISTRY. *Educ:* Brooklyn Polytech Inst, BChE, 57; State Univ NY Syracuse, MS, 62; State Univ NY Stony Brook, PhD(chem), 67. *Prof Exp:* Chem engr, US Naval Powder Plant, 56 & Hooker Chem Co, 58-59; chemist, East Fishkill Facility, IBM Components Div, Hopewell Junction, NY, 67-75, CHEMIST, T J WATSON RES CTR, IBM CORP, 75- *Mem:* AAAS; Electrochem Soc; Am Vacuum Soc. *Res:* Surface and interface chemistry; failure mechanisms in thin dielectric films; spectroscopy; superconductive materials; superconducting tunnel junctions. *Mailing Add:* T J Watson Res Ctr IBM Corp Yorktown Heights NY 10598

RAIFORD, MORGAN B, b Franklin, Va, Oct 28, 12; m 49; c 3. OPHTHALMOLOGY. *Educ:* Guilford Col, BS, 33; Va Commonwealth Univ, MD, 37; Univ Pa, MSc, 49, DSc(med), 54; Am Bd Ophthal, dipl, 65. *Prof Exp:* FOUNDER & MED DIR, ATLANTA EYE CLIN, 63- *Concurrent Pos:* Mem bd, Atlanta Hosp, 67- & bd mem, Am Acad Prev Med, 73- *Honors & Awards:* Physicians Recognition Award, AMA, 73-79. *Mem:* AMA; Pan Am Asn Ophthal; Am Acad Ophthal & Otolaryngol; fel Am Col Nuclear Med. *Mailing Add:* Atlanta Eye Clin 705 Juniper St NE Atlanta GA 30308

RAIKOW, RADMILA BORUVKA, b Prague, Czech, Mar 20, 39; US citizen; m 66; c 2. CARCINOGENESIS, IMMUNOLOGY. *Educ:* NY Univ, BA, 60; Brooklyn Col, MA, 65; Univ Calif, Berkeley, PhD(genetics), 70. *Prof Exp:* Res assoc genetics, Univ Hawaii, 70-71; fel biochem, Univ Pittsburgh, 71-72; fel cancer biol, 75-78, RES ASSOC CANCER RES, ALLEGHENY-SINGER RES CORP, PITTSBURGH, 78- *Mem:* AAAS; Sigma Xi; Am Asn Cancer Res. *Res:* Biological modifyers in cancer etiology; chemical-viral co-carcinogenesis; involvement of immune functions in cancer etiology. *Mailing Add:* Allegheny-Singer Res Corp 320 E North Ave Pittsburgh PA 15212

RAIKOW, ROBERT JAY, b Detroit, Mich, May 28, 39; m 66; c 2. ANATOMY, ORNITHOLOGY, SYSTEMATICS. *Educ:* Wayne State Univ, BS, 61, MS, 64; Univ Calif, Berkeley, PhD(zool), 69. *Prof Exp:* Actg asst prof zool, Univ Calif, Berkeley, 69-70; NIH fel, Univ Hawaii, 70-71; 71-77, asst prof biol, 71-77, ASSOC PROF BIOL SCI, UNIV PITTSBURGH, 77- *Concurrent Pos:* Rev ed, Wilson Bulletin, 74-; prin investr NSF res grants, 74- *Mem:* AAAS; Soc Syst Zool; Am Soc Zool; fel Am Ornith Union; Am Asn Anat. *Res:* Avian anatomy and systematics; vertebrate functional anatomy. *Mailing Add:* Dept Biol Sci Univ Pittsburgh Pittsburgh PA 15260

RAIMI, RALPH ALEXIS, b Detroit, Mich, July 25, 24; m 47; c 2. MATHEMATICAL ANALYSIS. *Educ:* Univ Mich, BS, 47, MS, 48, PhD(math), 54. *Prof Exp:* Instr math, Univ Rochester, 52-55; Lloyd fel, Univ Mich, 55-56; from asst prof to assoc prof, 56-66, assoc dean grad studies, Col Arts & Sci, 67-75, PROF MATH, UNIV ROCHESTER, 66- *Mem:* Am Math Soc; Math Asn Am. *Res:* Functional analysis; topological linear spaces; invariant measures and means. *Mailing Add:* Dept of Math Univ of Rochester Rochester NY 14627

RAIMONDI, ALBERT ANTHONY, b Plymouth, Mass, Mar 29, 25. MECHANICAL ENGINEERING. *Educ:* Tufts Col, BS, 45; Univ Pittsburgh, MS, 63, PhD(mech eng), 68. *Prof Exp:* Fel res engr, Mech Dept, Res Labs, Westinghouse Elec Corp, 46-68, mgr lubrication mech, 68-78, MGR TRIBOLOGY & EXP STRUCT MECH, WESTINGHOUSE RES & DEVELOP CTR, 78- *Concurrent Pos:* Ed, Soc Lubrication Engrs, 71. *Honors & Awards:* Hunt Mem Award, Soc Lubrication Engrs, 59, Nat Award, 68. *Mem:* Am Soc Mech Engrs; fel Soc Lubrication Engrs. *Res:* Tribology; constitutive relations; experimental mechanics; photoelasticity; bearing and seal design and application. *Mailing Add:* 140 LaVale Dr Monroeville PA 15146

RAIMONDI, ANTHONY JOHN, b Chicago, Ill, July 16, 28; m 54; c 3. NEUROSURGERY, NEUROANATOMY. *Educ:* Univ Ill, BA & BS, 50; Univ Rome, MD, 54. *Prof Exp:* Instr neurosurg, Univ Chicago, 61-62; instr, Northwestern Univ, 62-64; clin asst prof, Univ Chicago, 64-66; clin assoc prof, 66-67; assoc prof neurl surg, Univ Ill Col Med, 67-69; PROF NEUROSURG & CHMN DIV, SCH MED, NORTHWESTERN UNIV, CHICAGO, 69-, PROF ANAT, 74- *Concurrent Pos:* Attend neurosurg, Children's Mem Hosp, 62-63, chmn div neurol surg, 69-; prof, Cook County Grad Sch Med, 63-70, chmn dept, Cook County Hosp, 63-70; mem fac adv bd, Chicago Med Sch Quart, 64-66; chmn neurosurg, Vet Res Hosp, Chicago, 72-; attend neurosurgeon, Passavant Mem Hosp, 69- & Northwestern Mem Hosp, 74-; attend physician neurosurg, Surg Serv, Vet Admin Hosp; consult-lectr, Great Lakes Naval Hosp; chmn med adv comt, Am Spina Bifida Asn; Epilepsy Fund Am & Asn Brain Tumor Res. *Mem:* Am Col Surg; Am Asn Neurol Surg; Am Asn Neuropath; Int Soc Pediat Neurosurg (secy); Am Asn Surg of Trauma. *Res:* Ultrastructural characteristics of normal edematous, neoplastic and toxic glia; cerebral angiography in the newborn and infant; pediatric neurosurgery; pediatric neuroradiology. *Mailing Add:* 330 E Chicago Ave Chicago IL 60611

RAIMONDI, DONALD LOUIS, b San Francisco, Calif, Oct 16, 41; m 61; c 3. CHEMISTRY. *Educ:* San Jose State Col, BS, 63; Univ Calif, Berkeley, PhD(chem), 66. *Prof Exp:* MEM STAFF, IBM CORP, 63- *Res:* Computer automation of laboratory instruments. *Mailing Add:* 6440 Mojave Dr San Jose CA 95120

RAIMONDI, PIETRO, b Acqui, Italy, Feb 18, 29; m 56; c 6. CHEMICAL ENGINEERING. *Educ:* Univ Notre Dame, BS, 52, MS, 53; Carnegie Inst Technol, PhD(chem eng), 57. *Prof Exp:* From proj chem engr to sr res engr, 57-70, SECT SUPVR, GULF RES & DEVELOP CO, 70- *Mem:* Am Inst Chem Engrs; Am Inst Mining, Metall & Petrol Engrs. *Res:* Single and multiphase flow and diffusion and mixing of fluids in porous media; oil reservoir mechanics; synthetic fuel by in-situ method. *Mailing Add:* Gulf Res & Develop Co PO Drawer 2038 Pittsburgh PA 15230

RAIN, DON W(ARREN), b Chicago, Ill, July 6, 37; m 59; c 2. COMPUTER SCIENCE, ENGINEERING. *Educ:* Purdue Univ, BS, 58; Univ Conn, MS, 61; Univ Ill, PhD(elec eng), 64. *Prof Exp:* SR ENGR, IBM CORP, 64- *Res:* Computer system performance evaluation and throughput studies; simulation; high level language system architecture; computer application methodology development. *Mailing Add:* Dept H18 Bldg 705 IBM Corp Poughkeepsie NY 12601

RAINBOLT, MARY LOUISE, b Cleveland, Okla, June 21, 25. BIOLOGY. *Educ:* Okla Baptist Univ, BS, 46; Okla State Univ, MS, 48; Univ Okla, PhD, 63. *Prof Exp:* Prof biol, Southwestern State Col, Okla, 48-65; prof, 64-81, HITCHCOCK PROF BIOL, ILL COL, 81-, HEAD DEPT, 64- *Mem:* Am Soc Zool. *Res:* Physiology; endocrinology. *Mailing Add:* Ill Col Jacksonville IL 62650

RAINBOW, ANDREW JAMES, b Essex, Eng, Dec 18, 43; Can citizen; m 72; c 2. MEDICAL BIOPHYSICS, RADIOBIOLOGY. *Educ:* Univ Manchester, BS, 65; Univ London, MS, 67; McMaster Univ, PhD(biol), 70. *Prof Exp:* Fel biol, McMaster Univ, 70-71; radiol hosp physicist & assoc scientist, Royal Victoria Hosp, Montreal, 71-72; asst prof, 72-78, ASSOC PROF RADIOL, McMASTER UNIV, 78- ASSOC MEM BIOL, 73- *Concurrent Pos:* Lectr radiol, McGill Univ, 71-72; lectr radiography, Dawson Col, 71-72; radiol physicist, Hamilton & Dist Hosps, 72-80; instr radiation physics & radiobiol, Mohawk Col, Ont, 72-; dir, Regional Radiol Sci Prog, Chedoke-McMaster Hosp, 80- *Mem:* Fel Can Col Physicists Med; Can Asn Physicists; Radiation Res Soc; Am Soc Photobiol. *Res:* Radiobiology of the virus-cell interaction DNA repair and cancer; diagnostic radiological physics. *Mailing Add:* Dept of Radiol McMaster Univ Med Ctr Hamilton ON L8S 4L8 Can

RAINE, CEDRIC STUART, b Eastbourne, Eng, May 11, 40; m 63. NEUROPATHOLOGY. *Educ:* Univ Durham, BSc, 62; Univ Newcastle, PhD(med), 67, DSc(med), 75. *Prof Exp:* Sci officer neuropath, Demyelinating Dis Unit, Med Res Coun, Eng, 64-68; from asst prof to assoc prof path, 69-78, PROF PATH, ALBERT EINSTEIN COL MED, 78-, PROF NEUROSCI, 80- *Concurrent Pos:* NIH interdisciplinary fel, Albert Einstein Col Med, 68-69; NIH career develop award, 72-77. *Honors & Awards:* Weil Award, Am Asn Neuropath, 69 & 75. *Mem:* AAAS; Assoc Am Asn Neuropath; Soc Neurosci; NY Acad Sci. *Res:* Demyelinating conditions; nervous system development; ultrastructure; viral infections of nervous tissue; multiple sclerosis; invitro studies of organized nervous tissue; myelin pathology; neuroimmunology. *Mailing Add:* Dept of Path Albert Einstein Col of Med Bronx NY 10461

RAINER, JOHN DAVID, b Brooklyn, NY, July 13, 21; m 44; c 2. PSYCHIATRY, MEDICAL GENETICS. *Educ:* Columbia Univ, AB, 41, MA, 44, MD, 51. *Hon Degrees:* LittD, Gallaudet Col, 68. *Prof Exp:* Assoc res scientist, 56-65, actg chief psychiat res, 65-68, CHIEF PSYCHIAT RES, NY STATE PSYCHIAT INST, 68- *Concurrent Pos:* From asst to assoc clin prof, Columbia Univ, 59-72, prof clin psychiat, 72- *Mem:* Asn Res Nerv Ment Dis; Am Soc Human Genetics; fel Am Psychiat Asn; Am Psychoanal Asn; Am Psychopath Asn. *Res:* Application of human genetics to psychiatry on molecular, cellular, chemical, psychological and social levels; psychiatric treatment of the deaf. *Mailing Add:* NY State Psychiat Inst 722 W 168th St New York NY 10032

RAINER, NORMAN BARRY, b New York, NY, May 14, 29. APPLIED CHEMISTRY. *Educ:* Univ Chicago, MS, 50; Univ Del, PhD(phys org chem), 56. *Prof Exp:* Res chemist polymers, Textile Fibers Div, E I du Pont de Nemours & Co, Inc, 56-61; res mgr polymers, Fibers Div, Allied Chem Corp, 61-68; SR SCIENTIST CATALYSIS & NATURAL PRODS, RES & DEVELOP, PHILIP MORRIS CORP, 68- *Mem:* Am Chem Soc. *Res:* Catalysis; fast organic reactions; inorganic chemistry; pyrolysis of cellulose. *Mailing Add:* Philip Morris USA Res Ctr PO Box 26583 Richmond VA 23261

RAINES, JEREMY KEITH, b Washington, DC, Nov 25, 47. ELECTROMAGNETIC ENGINEERING. *Educ:* Mass Inst Technol, BS, 69, PhD(electromagnetics), 74; Harvard Univ, MS, 70. *Prof Exp:* Instr elec eng, Mass Inst Technol, 69-73; CONSULT ANTENNAS, 73- *Concurrent Pos:* Elec engr commun, Naval Electronics Systs Command, 70; elec engr opers res, Naval Ship Res & Develop Ctr, Carderock, 71; elec engr electronics, Naval Electronics Lab Ctr, San Diego, 72; lectr antennas, George Washington Univ, 75- *Mem:* Asn Fed Commun Consult Engrs; Am Phys Soc; Fedn Am Scientists; Inst Elec & Electronics Engrs; Soc Am Mil Engrs. *Res:* Mathematical modeling of antennas and antenna arrays; analysis and design of communication and data transmission networks; radio wave propagation; electromagnetic theory; biological hazards of electromagnetic fields. *Mailing Add:* 13420 Cleveland Dr Rockville MD 20850

RAINES, THADDEUS JOSEPH, b Jersey City, NJ, Apr 17, 18; m 54; c 2. PHYSICAL CHEMISTRY. *Educ:* St Peter's Col, BS, 39; Columbia Univ, MA, 45, PhD(chem), 49; NY Univ, MBA, 63. *Prof Exp:* Asst prof, Boston Col, 49-52; group leader, Reaction Motors Div, Thiokol Chem Corp, 52-53, head propellant eval & anal dept, 54-59, supvr mkt anal, 59-61; sr mkt analyst & staff consult res & develop planning, Air Reduction Co, 61-66; mgr prog develop, Am Gas Asn, Inc, 66-70; chmn dept, 70-73, PROF CHEM & BUS ADMIN, JERSEY CITY STATE COL, 70- *Mem:* Am Chem Soc; Sigma Xi; Chem Mkt Res Asn; Am Asn Univ Professors. *Res:* Physical chemistry of high polymer solutions; light scattering; physicochemical research on rocket propellants; research and development planning; commercial and technical intelligence; marketing research; chemicals from coal; business aspects of chemistry. *Mailing Add:* Dept of Chem Jersey City State Col Jersey City NJ 07305

RAINEY, JOHN MARION, JR, b Atlanta, Ga, June 20, 42; m 69. PSYCHIATRY, BIOCHEMISTRY. *Educ:* Vanderbilt Univ, BA, 63, MD, 69, PhD(biochem), 72. *Prof Exp:* Intern path, Vanderbilt Univ Hosp, 70-71, from resident to chief resident psychiat, 71-74; ASST PROF PSYCHIAT, WAYNE STATE UNIV & DIR RES, LAFAYETTE CLIN, 74- *Honors & Awards:* William C Menninger Award, Cent Neuropsychiat Asn, 74. *Mem:* Soc Biol Psychiat; Sigma Xi; Am Psychiat Asn; AMA. *Res:* Biological psychiatry and biochemistry; neurophysiology and psychobiology of sudden death in psychiatric disorders; cardiovascular effects of psychotropic drugs; anxiety disorders. *Mailing Add:* Lafayette Clin 951 E Lafayette Detroit MI 48207

RAINEY, MARY LOUISE, b Flagler, Colo, Jan 20, 43; m 67. ANALYTICAL CHEMISTRY. *Educ:* Knox Col, BA, 64; Univ Md, PhD(anal chem), 74. *Prof Exp:* Teacher math, Cordozo High Sch, Washington, DC, 67-69; master teacher, Urban Teacher Corps, Washington, DC, 68-69; teacher math, Walt Whitman High Sch, Bethesda, Md, 69-71; res specialist, Anal Labs, 74-79, GROUP LEADER, DESIGNED LATEXES & RESINS DIV, DOW CHEM CO, 79- *Mem:* Sigma Xi; Asn Women Sci; Am Chem Soc. *Res:* High performance liquid chromatography, gas chromatography. *Mailing Add:* Anal Lab Dow Chem Midland MI 48640

RAINEY, ROBERT HAMRIC, b Charleston, Miss, Mar 23, 18; m 47; c 3. RADIOCHEMISTRY. *Educ:* Memphis State Univ, BS, 42. *Prof Exp:* Chemist, Oak Ridge Gaseous Diffusion Plant, 45-51; group leader process develop, Oak Ridge Nat Lab, 51-78; OAK RIDGE ASSOC UNIVS, 78- *Mem:* Am Nuclear Soc; Sigma Xi. *Res:* Nuclear reactor fuel recovery process development, separation and isolation of thorium, uranium, plutonium, protactinium, and americium by solvent extraction and ion exchange; environmental impact studies of nuclear reactors and nuclear fuel reprocessing facilities. *Mailing Add:* 518 Rockingham Dr Knoxville TN 37919

RAINEY, WILLIAM THOMAS, JR, b Salisbury, NC, Sept 1, 19; m 50; c 4. ORGANIC CHEMISTRY. *Educ:* Davidson Col, BS, 39; Univ NC, PhD(chem), 49. *Prof Exp:* Instr chem, Davidson Col, 41-42; chemist, US Naval Res Labs, 42-44; prof, Clemson Univ, 49-59; CHEMIST, UNION CARBIDE CORP, 59- *Mem:* Am Chem Soc; Am Soc Mass Spectrometry. *Res:* Textile finishing process; use of radioisotopes as tracers; organic reaction mechanisms; mass spectrometry. *Mailing Add:* 112 Dana Dr Oak Ridge TN 37830

RAINIS, ALBERT EDWARD, b Chicago, Ill, May 15, 41; m 63; c 2. RADIATION PHYSICS. *Educ:* DePaul Univ, BS, 63, MS, 65; Univ Notre Dame, PhD(nuclear physics), 71, Central Mich Univ, MBA, 81. *Prof Exp:* Asst prof physics, Tri-State Col, 70-72 & WVa Univ, 72-75; PHYSICIST, BALLISTICS RES LAB, 75- *Concurrent Pos:* Geothermal consult, WVa Univ, 75- *Mem:* Am Phys Soc; Sigma Xi. *Res:* Nuclear radiation transport; geothermal phenomena; shielding calculations. *Mailing Add:* Armament Res & Develop Command Ballistic Res Lab Aberdeen Proving Grounds MD 21005

RAINIS, ANDREW, b Riga, Latvia, June 6, 40; Australian citizen; m 68; c 2. SURFACE CHEMISTRY, COAL PREPARATION. *Educ:* Univ New South Wales, Australia, BSc, 65, PhD(phys chem), 69. *Prof Exp:* Res assoc phys chem, Columbia Univ, 69-70 & Col Environ Sci & Forestry, State Univ NY, Syracuse, 70-75; proj mgr, Otisca Indust Ltd, 75-80; SR RES CHEMIST, CHEVRON RES CO, 80- *Mem:* Am Chem Soc; AAAS. *Res:* Mineral beneficiation; fossil fuel recovery and upgrading. *Mailing Add:* Chevron Res Co 576 Standard Ave Richmond CA 94802

RAINS, DONALD W, b Fairfield, Iowa, Dec 16, 37; m 59; c 3. PLANT NUTRITION, SOIL SCIENCE. *Educ:* Univ Calif, Davis, BS, 61, MS, 63, PhD(soil sci), 66. *Prof Exp:* NSF fel, 65-66; asst soil scientist, 66-70, assoc prof agron & range sci, 74-77, ASST AGRONOMIST, UNIV CALIF, DAVIS, 70- PROF AGRON, 77- *Concurrent Pos:* Consult, 65; lectr soil sci, 68-74; dir Plant Growth Lab. *Mem:* AAAS; Am Soc Plant Physiol; Am Soc Agron; Crop Sci Soc Am. *Res:* Ion transport and translocation in plants; plant nutrition and salinity; mineral cycling; heavy metal nutrition in soil-plant ecosystems; plant cell culture. *Mailing Add:* Dept of Agron & Range Sci Univ of Calif Davis CA 95616

RAINS, ROGER KERANEN, b Ann Arbor, Mich, May 11, 40; m 67; c 2. PROCESS RESEARCH, APPLIED MATHEMATICS. *Educ:* Univ Mich, BSE, 63, MSE, 64, MS, 65, PhD(chem eng), 68. *Prof Exp:* Sr res engr, Technol Dept, Monsanto Indust Chem Co, 68-72, res group leader, 72-78, SR RES GROUP LEADER, MONSANTO CO, 78- *Mem:* Am Chem Soc. *Res:* Process research and development, primarily separation processes and chemical reaction engineering; process research and development; rubber chemicals. *Mailing Add:* 3453 Timberwood Trail Richfield OH 44286

RAINS, THEODORE CONRAD, b Pleasureville, Ky, Jan 10, 25; m 47; c 3. ANALYTICAL CHEMISTRY. *Educ:* Eastern Ky Univ, BS, 50. *Prof Exp:* Teacher pub sch, Ky, 50-51; chemist, Ky Synthetic Rubber Co, 51-52 & Union Carbide Nuclear Co, 52-65; RES CHEMIST, NAT BUR STANDARDS, 65- *Concurrent Pos:* Vis prof, Univ Md, College Park, 75; column ed, J Appl Spectros, 75- *Honors & Awards:* Cert Recognition, Ez & E3, Am Soc Testing & Mat, 68. *Mem:* Am Chem Soc; Soc Appl Spectros (pres, 82). *Res:* Solvent extraction with applications for analytical chemistry; atomic absorption; emission and fluorescence spectrometry. *Mailing Add:* Anal Chem Div Nat Bur Standards Washington DC 20234

RAINWATER, JAMES CARLTON, b New York, NY, Jan 9, 46; m 74. STATISTICAL MECHANICS, KINETIC THEORY. *Educ:* Univ Colo, BA, 67, PhD(physics), 74. *Prof Exp:* Lectr physics, Univ Colo, Denver, 74; res fel chem, Univ BC, 75-76; res fel, 76-78, PHYSICIST, NAT BUR STANDARDS, BOULDER, COLO, 78- *Concurrent Pos:* Vis physicist, Nat Bur Standards, Washington, DC, 79. *Mem:* Am Asn Physics Teachers. *Res:* Classical and quantum statistical mechanics; kinetic theory; phase transitions in mixtures; fluctuations in non-equilibrium fluids; liquid helium three. *Mailing Add:* Nat Bur of Standards Boulder CO 80303

RAINWATER, LEO JAMES, b Council, Idaho, Dec 9, 17; m 42; c 3. PHYSICS. *Educ:* Calif Inst Technol, BS, 39; Columbia Univ, MA, 41, PhD(physics), 46. *Prof Exp:* Asst, 39-41, res scientist, Off Sci Res & Develop, Manhattan Dist, 41-46 & AEC, 46, from instr to assoc prof, 46-52, dir Nevis Cyclotron Labs, 51-54 & 57-61, PROF PHYSICS, COLUMBIA UNIV, 52- *Concurrent Pos:* Res scientist, Off Naval Res & AEC, 47-; mem, Adv Comt, NSF, 57-60, Adv Panel Physics & Electronuclear Div, Oak Ridge Nat Lab, 61-65 & Phys Rev Panel, Argonne Nat Lab, 69-71. *Honors & Awards:* Ernest

Orlando Lawrence Mem Award, 63; Nobel Prize Physics, 75. *Mem:* Nat Acad Sci; fel AAAS; fel Inst Elec & Electronics Eng; fel NY Acad Sci; fel Am Phys Soc. *Res:* Neutron cross sections; meson physics; nuclear size from u-meson x-rays; nuclear models. *Mailing Add:* Dept of Physics Columbia Univ New York NY 10027

RAIRDEN, JOHN RUEL, b Denver, Colo, Apr 9, 30; m 50; c 2. METALLURGICAL ENGINEERING. *Educ:* Colo Sch Mines, MetE, 51; Rensselaer Polytech Inst, MMetE, 58. *Prof Exp:* Trainee engr, 51-53, specialist, Res Lab, 53-57, METALL ENGR, RES & DEVELOP CTR, GEN ELEC CO, 57- *Mem:* Electrochem Soc. *Res:* Anodizing and surface treatment of metals; vacuum deposition and sputtering of thin films; oxidation and corrosion resistant coatings for high temperature alloys. *Mailing Add:* Gen Elec Res & Develop Ctr PO Box 8 Schenectady NY 12301

RAISBECK, BARBARA, b Arlington, Mass, Feb 7, 28; m 48; c 5. DEVELOPMENTAL BIOLOGY, INSECT PHYSIOLOGY. *Educ:* Boston Univ, BS, 51; Brandeis Univ, PhD(biol), 69. *Prof Exp:* Res assoc biol, Tufts Univ, 69-71; Nat Res Coun vis scientist, Pioneering Res Labs, US Army Natick Labs, 71-73; instr, 70-71, asst prof, 73-74, res assoc biol, Northeastern Univ, 75-76; mem fac, Middlesex Community Col, 78-79; SCIENCE WRITER, 79- *Concurrent Pos:* Consult, Arthur D Little, 74-76. *Res:* Insect development; tissue culture; insect behavior; human anatomy and physiology. *Mailing Add:* 40 Bloomfield St Lexington MA 02173

RAISBECK, GORDON, b New York, NY, May 4, 25; m 48; c 5. MATHEMATICS: ELECTRICAL ENGINEERING. *Educ:* Stanford Univ, BA, 44; Mass Inst Technol, PhD(math), 49. *Prof Exp:* Asst, Stanford Univ, 43-44; instr math, Mass Inst Technol, 46-47 & 48-49; mem tech staff, Bell Tel Labs, Inc, 49-54, dir transmission line res, 54-61; sr staff mem systs eng, 61-64, dir systs eng, 65-72, dir phys sensor systs res, 72-75, VPRES, ARTHUR D LITTLE, INC, 73- *Concurrent Pos:* Inst Defense Anal, 59-60. *Mem:* Fel Inst Elec & Electronics Eng; Math Asn Am; fel Acoust Soc Am; Opers Res Soc Am. *Res:* Information theory; communication technology and system analysis; transmission lines; underwater acoustics; research and development planning; air traffic control. *Mailing Add:* 40 Bloomfield St Lexington MA 02173

RAISEN, ELLIOTT, b New York, NY, Apr 24, 28; m 50; c 3. INORGANIC CHEMISTRY, PHYSICAL CHEMISTRY. *Educ:* City Col New York, BS, 50; Univ Cincinnati, MS, 52, PhD(inorg chem), 60. *Prof Exp:* Asst, Univ Cincinnati, 50-52; res chemist, Bell Aircraft Corp, NY, 54-56; res chemist, IIT Res Inst, 56-62, sr scientist, 62-72, mgr phys chem sect, 72-76; dir chem res div, Toth Aluminum Corp, New Orleans, 76-77; PRES, E&S ENTERPRISES, INC, 77-; PRES, CARDIO-RESPIRATORY HOME CARE INC, 79- *Mem:* Am Chem Soc; Am Inst Aeronaut & Astronaut; Am Ornance Asn; Sigma Xi; NY Acad Sci. *Res:* Inorganic complexes; phosphate and high temperature chemistry; high temperature reactions; visible and infrared radiation from chemical reactions; water treatment; oxygen production. *Mailing Add:* 4721 Taft Park Metairie LA 70002

RAISZ, LAWRENCE GIDEON, b New York, NY, Nov 13, 25; m 48; c 5. INTERNAL MEDICINE, ENDOCRINOLOGY. *Educ:* Harvard Med Sch, MD, 47. *Prof Exp:* Instr physiol, Col Med, NY Univ-Bellevue Med Ctr, 48-50; resident med, Vet Admin Hosp, Boston, 52-54; instr, Sch Med, Boston Univ, 54-56; asst prof, Col Med, State Univ NY Upstate Med Ctr, 56-61; assoc prof pharmacol & med, Sch Med & Dent, Univ Rochester, 61-66, assoc prof med, 66-68, prof pharmacol & toxicol, 66-74; PROF MED & HEAD DIV ENDOCRINOL & METAB, SCH MED, UNIV CONN HEALTH CTR, FARMINGTON, 74- *Concurrent Pos:* USPHS spec fel, Strangeways Res Lab, Cambridge, Eng, 60-61, Nat Inst Dent Res, NIH, 71-72; asst chief radioisotopes, Vet Admin Hosp, Syracuse Univ, 56-57, clin investr, 57-61; physician, Strong Mem Hosp, 68-74. *Mem:* AMA; Am Fedn Clin Res; Am Soc Pharmacol & Exp Therapeut; Am Soc Clin Invest; Asn Am Physicians. *Res:* Parathyroid and calcium metabolism; clinical pharmacology; endocrinology and metabolism. *Mailing Add:* Div Endocrinol & Metab Sch Med Univ of Conn Health Ctr Farmington CT 06032

RAITT, RALPH JAMES, JR, b Santa Ana, Calif, Feb 9, 29; m 53; c 2. VERTEBRATE ZOOLOGY. *Educ:* Stanford Univ, AB, 50; Univ Calif, Berkeley, PhD(zool), 59. *Prof Exp:* Technician, Mus Vert Zool, Univ Calif, Berkeley, 53-55, teaching asst zool, 56-58; from instr to assoc prof, 58-68, PROF BIOL, NMEX STATE UNIV, 68- *Concurrent Pos:* Guggenheim Mem fel, 67; ed, The Condor, 69-71. *Mem:* Soc Study Evolution; Soc Syst Zool; Animal Behav Soc; Cooper Ornith Soc; Am Ornith Union. *Res:* Ecology, behavior, evolution and systematics of birds, especially those of southwestern United States and Latin America. *Mailing Add:* Dept of Biol NMex State Univ Las Cruces NM 88003

RAIZADA, MOHAN K, b Fatehpur, India, Oct 21, 48; m 79. CELLULAR ENDOCRINOLOGY, CELLULAR BIOLOGY. *Educ:* Univ Lucknow, India, BS, 64, MSc, 66; Univ Kanpur, PhD(biol sci), 72. *Prof Exp:* Fel biochem, Med Col Wis, 73-74; assoc cell biol, Lady Davis Inst, Montreal, 74-76; res assoc, 76-78, asst prof, 79-80, ASSOC PROF PHYSIOL & BIOCHEM, UNIV FLA, 81- *Mem:* Endocrine Soc; Tissue Culture Asn; Am Soc Cell Biol; Am Physiol Soc; AAAS. *Res:* Regulation of insulin receptors in cells cultured from nondiabetic and diabetic animals and humans; role of the central nervous system angiotensin-effector system in the development and maintenance of hypertension. *Mailing Add:* Dept Physiol Box J274 Col Med Univ Fla Gainsville FL 32610

RAIZEN, CAROL EILEEN, b Oklahoma City, Okla, May 10, 38. MICROBIAL GENETICS. *Educ:* Univ Okla, BS, 60, MS, 63; Univ Wis, PhD(bact), 67. *Prof Exp:* Fel microbiol, Sch Med, Univ Colo, 66-67; asst res prof, Univ Pittsburgh, 67-69; from asst prof to assoc prof biol, Duquesne Univ, 72-77; exec secy, Microbial Chem Study Sect, Div Res Grants, 77-79, Microbiol Physiol Study Sect, 79-80, Microbial Genetics Study Sect, 78-81, EXEC SECY, SPEC STUDY SECTIONS, NIH, 81- *Concurrent Pos:* Asst prof adult nursing educ, Ohio Univ, 70-74; instr, Pa State Univ Continuing Educ, 74-77. *Mem:* AAAS; Am Soc Microbiol; Am Inst Biol Sci. *Res:* Microbial genetics, particularly bacterial pili-structure, function and biosynthesis; pili bacteriophages; cyanophyte genetics and cyanophages. *Mailing Add:* 2233 Chestertown Dr Vienna VA 22180

RAIZEN, SENTA AMON, b Vienna, Austria, Oct 28, 24; US citizen; m 48; c 3. PHYSICAL CHEMISTRY, RESEARCH ADMINISTRATION. *Educ:* Guilford Col, BS, 44; Bryn Mawr Col, MA, 45. *Prof Exp:* Res chemist, Sun Oil Co, Pa, 45-48; staff asst chem, Nat Acad Sci-Nat Res Coun, 60-62; prof asst sci educ & admin, NSF, 62-65, asst prog dir, 65-68, assoc prog dir, 68-69, spec tech asst, 69-71; sr prog planner, Nat Inst Educ, 71-72; sr researcher, Domestic Prog Ctr, Rand Corp, 72-74; assoc dir, Nat Inst Educ, 74-78; independent consult, 78-80; STUDY DIR, NAT ACAD SCI, 80- *Concurrent Pos:* Abstractor, Chem Abstr, 46-60; consult, US Off Educ. *Mem:* Fel AAAS; Am Chem Soc; Am Educ Res Asn. *Res:* Critical data compilations; strategies for educational and other domestic sector research, dissemination and utilization of research and development; federal education policy and support of research; evaluation of research and development programs. *Mailing Add:* 5513 N 31st St Arlington VA 22207

RAIZMAN, PAULA, b Vilnius, Lithuania, Jan 30, 11; US citizen; m 42; c 2. ORGANIC CHEMISTRY. *Educ:* Vilnius State Univ, MS, 35; Univ Paris, PhD(org chem), 54. *Prof Exp:* Asst chemist, Col of France, 36-39 & Med Fac, Paris, 38-42; res assoc org chem, French Nat Sci Res Ctr, 46-54; res chemist, Columbia Univ, 54-57; asst ed, Chem Abstr, 57-60; LIT CHEMIST, CENT RES DEPT, MONSANTO CO, 60- *Mem:* AAAS; NY Acad Sci; Am Chem Soc. *Res:* Inorganic analysis of radioactive minerals; hypoglycemic activity of insulin; synthesis of various organic compounds; medicinals, heterocycles. *Mailing Add:* Cent Res Dept Monsanto Co 800 N Lindbergh Blvd St Louis MO 63166

RAJ, BALDEV, b DI Kahn, Pakistan, Jan 8, 35; m 62; c 3. BOTANY. *Educ:* Panjab Univ, BSc, 57, MSc, 59; Univ Delhi, PhD(bot), 65. *Prof Exp:* Asst prof bot, Univ Delhi, 64-68; fel biol, Univ SC, 68-69; from asst prof to assoc prof, 69-76, PROF BIOL, JACKSON STATE UNIV, 76- *Res:* Embryology of vascular plants; isolation of plant protoplasts. *Mailing Add:* Dept of Biol Jackson State Univ Jackson MS 39217

RAJ, HARKISAN D, b Sehwan, Pakistan, Jan 1, 26; m 56; c 2. MICROBIAL PHYSIOLOGY, METABOLISM. *Educ:* Univ Bombay, BS hon, 47; Univ Poona, India, MS, 52, PhD(biochem & microbiol), 55. *Prof Exp:* Bacteriologist Pub Health Serv, India, 48-56; res fel biochem & nutrit, Tex A&M Univ, 56-57; instr microbiol, Ore State Univ, 57-58; asst prof, Univ Wash, 59-62; PROF MICROBIOL, CALIF STATE UNIV, LONG BEACH, 62- *Concurrent Pos:* Res grant, NIH, NSF & private corp, 60-; speciality expert, Food & Agr Orgn, UN, Rome, Italy, 67-; mem adv bd, Advan Med Sci, Inc, Lawndale, Calif, 72-77. *Mem:* Electron Micros Soc Am; Am Soc Microbiol; Can Soc Microbiol; Sigma Xi. *Res:* Studies concerning metabolism, physiology and ultrastructure of microorganisms to correlate structures with functions and numerical taxonomy; author of new species of bacteria, Microcyclus flavus and Cyclobacterium marinus; author or co author of over 50 publications. *Mailing Add:* Dept Microbiol Calif State Univ Long Beach CA 90840

RAJ, PRADEEP, b Meerut, India, Dec 15, 49; m 80; c 1. AEROSPACE ENGINEERING. *Educ:* Indian Inst Sci, BE, 71, ME, 73; Ga Inst Technol, PhD(aerospace eng), 76. *Prof Exp:* Asst prof, Iowa State Univ, 76-78; asst prof mech & aerospace eng, Univ Mo-Rolla, 78-79; SR AERODYNAMICS ENGR, LOCKMEED-CALIF CO, BURBANK, 79- *Mem:* Am Inst Aeronaut & Astronaut; Am Helicopter Soc. *Res:* Applied computational aerodynamics; simulation of inviscid and viscous transonic flow problems. *Mailing Add:* Dept 75-52 Bldg 63-3 Lockmeed-Calif Co Burbank CA 91520

RAJA, RAJENDRAN, b Gurvvayur, India, July 14, 48. HIGH ENERGY PHYSICS. *Educ:* Univ Cambridge, Eng, BA, 70, PhD(bubble chamber physics), 75. *Prof Exp:* Res assoc, 74-78, PHYSICIST, FERMI NAT ACCELERATOR LAB, 78- *Mem:* Am Inst Phys Soc. *Res:* Charm search in 217 GeV/c pion interactions; Psi production from decay of Chi particles; tests of GLUON fusion models. *Mailing Add:* Dept of Physics Fermi Lab PO Box 500 Batavia IL 60510

RAJAGOPAL, ATTIPAT KRISHNASWAMY, b Mysore City, India, June 3, 37; m 64; c 2. THEORETICAL PHYSICS. *Educ:* Lingaraj Col, India, BSc, 57; Indian Inst Sci, Bangalore, MSc, 60; Harvard Univ, PhD(appl physics), 65. *Prof Exp:* Res fel, Harvard Univ, 64-65; asst prof physics, Univ Calif, Riverside, 65-68; fel & reader theoret physics, Tata Inst Fundamental Res, India, 68-70; assoc prof, 70-72, PROF PHYSICS, LA STATE UNIV, BATON ROUGE, 72- *Concurrent Pos:* Prof, Ctr Theoret Studies, Indian Inst Sci, Bangalore, India, 74-75; consult, Oak Ridge Nat Lab & Naval Res Lab, Washington, DC, 80-81. *Mem:* Fel Am Phys Soc. *Res:* Quantum mechanics of two, three and many particle systems; solid state physics; mathematical physics. *Mailing Add:* Dept of Physics & Astron La State Univ Baton Rouge LA 70803

RAJAGOPAL, P K, b India, June 18, 36; m; c 1. FISH BIOLOGY. *Educ:* Annamalai Univ, Madras, BS, 57, MS, 58; Utah State Univ, PhD(fish biol), 75. *Prof Exp:* Sr res scholar, Zool Res Lab, Univ Madras, 58-62; res fel zool, Univ Col Rhodesia & Nyasaland, 62-65; sr res officer, Ghana Acad Sci, 66-71, instr gen biol for lab technicians, Inst Aquatic Biol, 66-70; res technologist, US-IBP Desert Biome Prog, Utah Coop Fishery Unit, Utah State Univ, 71-72, res asst, Utah Coop Fishery Unit, 72-75, instr fish biol, Utah State Univ, 74-75; BIOLOGIST, STATE FISHERY EXP STA, 75- *Mem:* Am Fisheries Soc; Am Inst Fishery Res Biologists; Am Inst Biol Sci; Freshwater Biol Asn UK. *Res:* General and aquatic biology; ecology and ecological physiology; fishery science; effects of pollution on aquatic animals; respiratory metabolism. *Mailing Add:* 1540 N 1600 E Logan UT 84321

RAJAGOPALAN, K V, b Mysore, India, Apr 11, 30; m 58; c 3. BIOCHEMISTRY. *Educ:* Presidency Col, Madras, BSc, 51; Univ Madras, MSc, 54, PhD(biochem), 57. *Prof Exp:* Asst res officer, Indian Coun Med Res, Madras, 58-59; fel biochem, Med Sch, 59-66, from asst prof to assoc prof, 67-77, PROF BIOCHEM, MED SCH, DUKE UNIV, 77- *Res:* Enzymology; metalloenzymes. *Mailing Add:* Dept of Biochem Duke Univ Med Sch Durham NC 27710

RAJAGOPALAN, PARTHASARATHI, b Mannargudi, India, Mar 13, 30; m 51; c 2. ORGANIC CHEMISTRY, MEDICINAL CHEMISTRY. *Educ:* Univ Madras, BS, 49; Univ Delhi, MS, 51; NY Univ, PhD(org chem), 60. *Prof Exp:* USPHS fel, Sch Med, NY Univ, 59-60; inst fel, Rockefeller Inst, 60-61; sr res scientist med chem, Ciba Res Ctr, Ciba India Ltd, Bombay, 62-67; sr res scientist, Endo Labs Inc, 67-73, res assoc, 73-80; MEM STAFF, EXP STA, E I DU PONT DE NEMOURS & CO, INC, 80- *Concurrent Pos:* Adj assoc prof, Queens Col, City Univ New York, 72- *Mem:* Am Chem Soc. *Res:* Heterocyclic chemistry; new, 1,3-dipolar cycloaddition reactions. *Mailing Add:* Bldg 335 Rm 108 Exp Sta E I du Pont de Nemours & Co Inc Wilmington DE 19898

RAJAN, THIRUCHANDURAI VISWANATHAN, b Tanjore, India, Oct 1, 45; m 77; c 3. SOMATIC CELL GENETICS, IMMUNOGENETICS. *Educ:* All India Inst Med Sci, MB & BS, 69; Albert Einstein Col Med, PhD(cell biol), 74. *Prof Exp:* Asst prof path, 75-80, asst prof genetics, 78-80, ASSOC PROF PATH & GENETICS, ALBERT EINSTEIN COL MED, 80- *Concurrent Pos:* Attending pathologist, Bronx Municipal Hosp Ctr, 75- *Res:* Expression and function of transplantation antigens on surface of mouse leokemic cells by isolation mutants in their expression and evaluating the physiological consequences of such mutations. *Mailing Add:* Dept Path Albert Einstein Col Med Bronx NY 10461

RAJAN, VARAGUR SRINIVASA VAIKUNTA, b Tamilnadu, India, Nov 2, 41; Can citizen; m 76; c 2. CHEMICAL ENGINEERING, ENGINEERING PHYSICS. *Educ:* Univ Delhi, BChE, 63; Indian Inst Technol, Kharagpur, MTech, 65; Univ NB, Fredericton, PhD(chem eng), 70. *Prof Exp:* Assoc lectr chem eng, Indian Inst Technol, Delhi, 65-66; Nat Res Coun Can fel, Univ NB, Fredericton, 70-72, res assoc & lectr, 72-74; PROF ENGR NUCLEAR RES, ATOMIC ENERGY CAN LTD, 74- *Mem:* Chem Inst Can; Can Soc Chem Eng; Am Inst Chem Engrs. *Res:* Transport phenomena; two-phase flow; rheology; chemical physics and instrumentation. *Mailing Add:* PO Box 88 Pinawa MB R0E 1L0 Can

RAJANNA, BETTAIYA, b Bangalore, India; m 67; c 2. TOXICOLOGY, ENVIRONMENT POLLUTION. *Educ:* Mysore Univ, India, BS, 59 & 63; Miss State Univ, MS, 70, PhD(physiol), 72. *Prof Exp:* Res asst hort, Hort Dept, Mysore State, India, 63-64, asst dir, 64-67; res asst plant sci, Agron Dept, Miss State Univ, 67-72, fel ecol, Dept Zool, 73-75; assoc prof biol, 75-77, PROF & CHMN, DIV NATURAL & APPL SCI, SELMA UNIV, 77- *Concurrent Pos:* Panelist, Sci Educ, NSF, 77-81; prin investr, MBS, Res Prog, NIH, 79-, consult, 80; consult, NIH, 80- *Mem:* Am Soc Agron; Am Soc Crop Sci; Am Soc Plant Physiologists; Indian Soc Seed Technologists; Sigma Xi. *Res:* Interaction of heavy metals, cadmium, lead and mercury, with catecholamines uptake by rat brain and heart; biochemical changes due to aging in plant seeds; pollution ecology: effects of air pollutants on plants; seed physiology. *Mailing Add:* Div Natural & Appl Sci Selma Univ Selma AL 36701

RAJARATNAM, N(ALLAMUTHU), b Mukuperi, India, Dec 18, 34; m 61; c 1. HYDRAULIC ENGINEERING, FLUID MECHANICS. *Educ:* Univ Madras, BE, 57, MSc, 58; Indian Inst Sci, Bangalore, PhD(hydraul), 61. *Prof Exp:* Jr res engr, Irrig Res Sta, Madras, India, 58-59; sr sci officer hydraul, Indian Inst Sci, 60-63; Nat Res Coun Can fel, 63-65; session lectr, 65-66, from asst prof to assoc prof, 66-71, PROF HYDRAUL, UNIV ALTA, 71- *Concurrent Pos:* Nat Res Coun Can res grants, 65- *Mem:* Am Soc Civil Engrs; Eng Inst Can; Am Water Resources Asn; Int Asn Hydraul Res. *Res:* Open channel flow; hydraulics of energy dissipations; turbulent boundary layers, jets and wakes; non-Newtonian flow; rivers; thermal and oil pollution problems. *Mailing Add:* Dept of Civil Eng Univ of Alta Fac of Eng Edmonton AB T6G 2G7 Can

RAJCHMAN, JAN A(LEKSANDER), b London, Eng, Aug 10, 11; nat US; m 44; c 2. ELECTRONICS. *Educ:* Swiss Fed Inst Technol, EE, 35, DrSc, 38. *Prof Exp:* Student engr, Radio Corp Am Mfg Co, NJ, 35, mem tech staff, Labs, Radio Corp Am, 36-58, assoc dir, Res Syst Lab, 58-61, dir, Comput Res Lab, 61-67, staff vpres data processing res, RCA Labs, 67-69, staff vpres info sci, 69-76; Mackay Prof, Univ Calif, Berkeley, 77; CONSULT, 77- *Concurrent Pos:* Mem adv comt elec eng, Newark Col Eng; mem user-grantee comt, NSF, 69-76; mem adv comt, Adv Res Proj Agency, 75. *Honors & Awards:* Levy Medal, Franklin Inst, 47; Liebman Award, Inst Elec & Electronics Engrs, 60, Edison Medal, 74; Harold Pender Award, Univ Pa, 77. *Mem:* Nat Acad Eng; fel Am Phys Soc; fel Inst Elec & Electronics Engrs; Franklin Inst; fel AAAS. *Res:* Electron optics and electronics; secondary emission electron multipliers; electron accelerators; electronic computing circuits and tubes; magnetic memories; transfluxors; magnetic switching circuits; solid state display devices; high speed and optical computers; optical holographic memories; large scale display devices. *Mailing Add:* 268 Edgerstoune Rd Princeton NJ 08540

RAJENDRAN, NARAYANAN, b Madras, India, June 27, 48; m 75; c 1. ENVIRONMENTAL SCIENCE. *Educ:* Univ Madras, BS, 69; State Univ NY Buffalo, MS, 74, PhD(eng sci), 77. *Prof Exp:* RES ENG AIR POLLUTION, IIT RES INST, 77- *Mem:* Air Pollution Control Asn. *Res:* Aerosol science; air pollution control; fluid dynamics; air pollution control devices. *Mailing Add:* 702 N 16th Ave Melrose Park IL 60160

RAJHATHY, TIBOR, b Pozsony, Hungary, Mar 27, 20; m 58; c 2. PLANT GENETICS & CYTOLOGY. *Educ:* Univ Tech & Econ Sci, Hungary, DSc(agr), 47. *Prof Exp:* Res assoc, Genetics Inst, Hungary, 39-43; asst prof, Univ Agr Sci Hungary, 47-49; head genetics dept, Hungarian Acad Sci, 49-56; cytogeneticist, Genetics & Plant Breeding Res Inst, 56-67, chief cytogenetics sect, Res Br, 67-73, sect head Cytogenetics Sect, 73-76; DIR OTTAWA RES STA & CENT EXP FARM, CAN DEPT AGR, 76- *Concurrent Pos:* Consult, Minister Agr, 52-56. *Mem:* Genetics Soc Can; Hungarian Soc Agr Sci; fel Royal Soc Can. *Res:* Cytogenetics and radiation genetics of grasses and cereals; auto and allopolyploids; evolution of species. *Mailing Add:* Bldg 55 Cent Exp Farm Can Dept of Agr Ottawa ON K1A 0C6 Can

RAJNAK, KATHERYN EDMONDS, b Kalamazoo, Mich, Apr 30, 37; m 61. ATOMIC PHYSICS. *Educ:* Kalamazoo Col, BA, 59; Univ Calif, Berkeley, PhD(chem), 63. *Prof Exp:* Fel chem, Lawrence Radiation Lab, 62-65; asst prof physics, Kalamazoo Col, 67-70; physicist, 74-75, CONSULT, LAWRENCE LIVERMORE LAB, 75- *Concurrent Pos:* Consult, Argonne Nat Lab, 66-; adj lectr physics, Kalamazoo Col, 76-; vis prof, Univ Paris, IV, 79 & 80 & Univ Paris, Orsay, 79 & 81. *Mem:* Am Phys Soc; Am Asn Physics Teachers. *Res:* Theory and analysis of lanthanide and actinide spectra. *Mailing Add:* Kalamazoo Col Kalamazoo MI 49007

RAJNAK, STANLEY L, b Richmond, Calif, Apr 23, 36; m 61. MATHEMATICS. *Educ:* Univ Calif, Berkeley, AB, 60, PhD(math), 66. *Prof Exp:* From asst prof to assoc prof, 65-77, PROF MATH, KALAMAZOO COL, 77- *Mem:* Am Math Soc; Math Asn Am. *Res:* Analysis; linear topological spaces; distribution theory. *Mailing Add:* Dept of Math Kalamazoo Col Kalamazoo MI 49007

RAJU, IVATURY SANYASI, b Kakinada,India, Aug 9, 44; m 71; c 1. ENGINEERING, AERONAUTICS. *Educ:* Andhra Univ, India, BE, 65; Indian Inst Sci, ME, 67, PhD(aeronaut eng), 73. *Prof Exp:* Sr eng, Vikram Sarabhai Space Ctr, Trivandrum, 71-75; res assoc, Nat Res Coun, 75-77, res assoc, 77-79, ASST RES PROF, JOINT INST FLIGHT SCI, GEORGE WASHINGTON UNIV, LANGLEY RES CTR, NASA, 79- *Concurrent Pos:* Leverhulme overseas fel, Univ Liverpool, Eng, 73-74. *Res:* Static; dynamic and stability analysis of aerospace structures; fracture mechanics; finite element methods; laminated composite structures. *Mailing Add:* MS 188E NASA Langley Res Ctr Hampton VA 23665

RAJU, MUDUNDI RAMAKRISHNA, b Bhimavaram, India, July 15, 31. RADIATION BIOPHYSICS, RADIOTHERAPY. *Educ:* Univ Madras, BSc, 52, MA, 54; Andhra Univ, India, MSc, 55, DSc(nuclear physics), 60. *Prof Exp:* Lectr nuclear instruments, Andhra Univ, India, 57-61; fel biophys, Mass Gen Hosp, Mass Inst Technol & Harvard Univ, 61-63; Donner fel, Donner Lab, Univ Calif, Berkeley, 63-64, biophysicist, 64-65; from asst prof to assoc prof biophys, Univ Tex, Dallas, 65-71; staff mem biophys, 71-79, FEL, LOS ALAMOS NAT LAB, 80- *Concurrent Pos:* Vis scientist, Hammersmith Hosp, London, 67-68; guest scientist, Lawrence Radiation Lab, Univ Calif, 65- *Mem:* Radiation Res Soc. *Res:* Physics and radiobiology of new radiations, pi mesons, heavy charged particles and neutrons, and their potential applications in radiation therapy. *Mailing Add:* Los Alamos Nat Lab Los Alamos NM 87544

RAJU, NAMBOORI BHASKARA, b Pothumarru, India, Jan 1, 43; m 64; c 3. FUNGAL GENETICS, FUNGAL CYTOLOGY. *Educ:* Banaras Hindu Univ, BSc, 65, MSc, 67; Univ Guelph, PhD(genetics), 72. *Prof Exp:* Scientist, Coun Sci & Indust Res, India, 73-74; RES ASSOC, CYTOGENETICS, STANFORD UNIV, 74- *Mem:* Genetics Soc Am; Mycological Soc Am. *Res:* Cytology of fungi, especially Neurospora and Coprinus: meiotic and mitotic processes, including ascus or basidial development, behavior of chromosomes, nucleolus and spindle pole bodies; cytogentic behavior of Neurospora mutants that affect ascus and ascospore differentiation and chromosome rearrangements that involve the nucleolus organizer region. *Mailing Add:* Dept Biol Sci Stanford Univ Stanford CA 94305

RAJU, PALANICHAMY PILLAI, b Theni, India, June 15, 37; US citizen; m 62; c 3. ENGINEERING MECHANICS, STRUCTURAL ENGINEERING. *Educ:* Madras Univ, BE, 60, MSc, 61; Univ Del, PhD(eng mech), 68. *Prof Exp:* Design engr, Larson & Toubro, 61-64; res fel aerospace, Univ Del, 64-68; lead engr, Westinghouse Nuclear Energy Systs, 68-76; CONSULT ENGR, TELEDYNE ENG SERV, TELEDYNE INC, 76- *Concurrent Pos:* Mem pressure vessel res comts & nuclear code comts, Am Soc Mech Engrs. *Mem:* Am Soc Mech Engrs; Am Soc Civil Engrs; Sigma Xi. *Res:* Shell theory of composite materials known for their anisotropic properties, both mechanical and thermal; safety and reliability of nuclear power plant components and piping systems; new analysis techniques; vibration and 3D analysis; fracture mechanics evaluation. *Mailing Add:* Teledyne Eng Serv 303 Bear Hill Rd Waltham MA 02154

RAJU, SATYANARAYANA G V, b Undi, India, Jan 8, 34; m 55; c 2. ENGINEERING, ELECTRICAL ENGINEERING. *Educ:* Andhra Univ, BS, 55; Banaras Univ, MS, 57; Indian Inst Technol, MTech, 59; Polytech Inst Brooklyn, PhD(elec eng), 65. *Prof Exp:* Res asst electronics, Phys Res Labs, Polytech Inst Brooklyn, 59-61, fel, 61-65; asst prof elec eng, Clarkson Col Technol, 65-67; from asst prof to assoc prof, 67-72, PROF ELEC ENG, OHIO UNIV, 72-, CHMN DEPT, 73- *Mem:* Sr mem Inst Elec & Electronics Engrs; Sigma Xi. *Res:* Control systems; design of control systems; adaptive control; system identification; pattern recognition; stability theory; air traffic control. *Mailing Add:* Dept of Elec Eng Ohio Univ Athens OH 45701

RAKA, EUGENE CD, b Detroit, Mich, Aug 24, 24; m 66. PHYSICS. *Educ:* Univ Mich, BS, 49, PhD(physics), 54. *Prof Exp:* Res asst, Eng Res Inst, Univ Mich, 50-53; assoc physicist, 53-63, PHYSICIST, BROOKHAVEN NAT LAB, 63- *Mem:* Am Phys Soc. *Res:* High energy accelerator design, instrumentation and operation. *Mailing Add:* Bldg 911 Brookhaven Nat Lab Upton NY 11973

RAKE, ADRIAN VAUGHAN, b New York, NY, Mar 27, 34; m 61; c 3. BIOCHEMISTRY, BEHAVIORAL BIOLOGY. *Educ:* Swarthmore Col, BA, 56; Univ Pa, PhD(microbiol), 64; Pa State Univ, BS, 75. *Prof Exp:* NIH res fel biochem, Univ BC, 64-66; fel, Carnegie Inst, 66-68; asst prof biophys, Pa State Univ, 68-75; ASSOC PROF BIOL, WRIGHT STATE UNIV, 76- *Mem:* AAAS; NY Acad Sci; Genetics Soc Am; Sigma Xi; Biophys Soc. *Res:* Reassociation and hybridization of ribonucleic acids and deoxyribonucleic acids; neural biochemical changes associated with the learning behavior of animals. *Mailing Add:* Dept of Biol Wright State Univ Dayton OH 45435

RAKER, CHARLES W, b Daylesford, Pa, July 19, 20; m 55; c 2. VETERINARY SURGERY. *Educ:* Univ Pa, DVM, 42. *Prof Exp:* Gen pract, 45-50; asst prof vet med, 50-53, asst prof surg, 54-55, assoc prof surg & chmn dept vet surg, 56-57, prof surg, 57-67, chief sect, 62-76, LAWRENCE BAKER SHEPPARD PROF SURG, SCH VET MED, UNIV PA, 67-, PROF COMP SURG, DIV GRAD MED, 58- *Concurrent Pos:* Dir clins Bolton Farm, Sch Vet Med, Univ Pa, 50-52 & New Bolton Ctr, 52-53, in charge large animal clin, 54-63, assoc chief staff & head surg serv, 64-, chmn dept surg, Sch Vet Med, S7-58, interim chief sect, 58-62. *Mem:* Am Asn Equine Practrs; Am Vet Med Asn; Am Asn Vet Clinicians; fel Am Col Vet Surg (pres, 75-76). *Res:* Orthopedic surgery; histology and histopathology in normal and diseased flexor tendons; surgical diseases of the equine upper respiratory tract. *Mailing Add:* Univ of Pa Sch of Vet Med New Bolton Ctr RD 1 Kennett Square PA 19348

RAKES, ALLEN HUFF, b Floyd, Va, Aug 19, 33; m 58; c 2. DAIRY NUTRITION. *Educ:* Va Polytech Inst, BS, 56, MS, 57; Cornell Univ, PhD(animal nutrit), 60. *Prof Exp:* Asst prof dairy sci, WVa Univ, 60-63; from asst prof to assoc prof, 63-73, PROF ANIMAL SCI, NC STATE UNIV, 73- *Mem:* Am Dairy Sci Asn; Am Soc Animal Sci. *Res:* Energy utilization of ruminants; voluntary feed intake control mechanisms. *Mailing Add:* Dept of Animal Sci NC State Univ Raleigh NC 27650

RAKES, JERRY MAX, b Bentonville, Ark, Dec 7, 32; m 49; c 3. ANIMAL SCIENCE. *Educ:* Univ Ark, BS, 54, MS, 55; Iowa State Univ, PhD(physiol), 58. *Prof Exp:* Asst prof dairy physiol, Iowa State Univ, 56-58; assoc prof, 58-63, PROF DAIRY GENETICS, UNIV ARK, FAYETTEVILLE, 63- *Mem:* Am Soc Animal Sci; Am Dairy Sci Asn. *Res:* Dairy physiology and biochemistry; dairy cattle genetics. *Mailing Add:* Dept of Animal Sci Univ of Ark Fayetteville AR 72701

RAKESTRAW, JAMES WILLIAM, b Reidsville, NC, July 20, 36; m 61; c 2. ELECTRONIC SYSTEMS. *Educ:* Va Polytech Inst, BS, 59; Johns Hopkins Univ, PhD(physics), 64. *Prof Exp:* Engr, Philco Corp, 55-58; mem tech staff, Bell Tel Labs, 59-60; res asst physics, Johns Hopkins Univ, 61-64; mem staff, Westinghouse Defense & Space Ctr, 64-65, group leader systs anal, 65-66; mem tech staff systs anal group, Lincoln Lab, Mass Inst Technol, 68-72; mem tech staff, Electronics Systs Div, MRI, 72-77; mgr aerospace syst group & systs anal group, Comput Sci Corp, 77-78, sr prin engr, 77-80; CONSULTING SYSTEMS SCIENTIST, PLANNING RES CORP, 80- *Mem:* Inst Elec & Electronics Engrs; Commun Soc; Am Phys Soc. *Res:* Systems analysis; communications systems; digital computer applications and simulation; space systems; radar systems. *Mailing Add:* Planning Res Corp Old Springhouse Rd McLean VA 22102

RAKESTRAW, ROY MARTIN, b Redding, Calif, Jan 31, 42; m 62; c 2. MATHEMATICS, COMPUTER SCIENCES. *Educ:* Okla State Univ, BS, 65, MS, 66, PhD(math), 69. *Prof Exp:* asst prof math, Univ Mo-Rolla, 69-76; ASSOC PROF MATH, WHEATON COL, 76- *Mem:* Math Asn Am; Am Math Soc; Am Sci Affil. *Res:* Convex sets; functional analysis. *Mailing Add:* Dept of Math Wheaton Col Wheaton IL 65401

RAKHIT, GOPA, b India; US citizen; m 77. BIOCHEMISTRY, PHARMACOLOGY. *Educ:* Univ Calcutta, BSc, 65, MSc, 67; Univ Utah, PhD(chem physics), 76. *Prof Exp:* Vis fel, Nat Heart, Lung & Blood Inst, 76-78; STAFF FEL, BUR DRUGS, FOOD & DRUG ADMIN, 78- *Mem:* Biophys Soc; Am Chem Soc; AAAS. *Res:* Spectroscopic studies of enzyme-substrate, protein-ligand, and drug-biomolecular interaction; structure-function relation in proteins, nucleic acids and membranes; effects of radiation and the role of free radicals in drug-toxicty. *Mailing Add:* Div Drug Biol Food & Drug Admin 200 Ct St SW Washington DC 20204

RAKHIT, SUMANAS, b Banaras, India, Oct 17, 30; m 59; c 1. ORGANIC CHEMISTRY. *Educ:* Banaras Hindu Univ, MPharm, 53, PhD(pharmaceut), 57. *Prof Exp:* Coun Sci & Indust Res India sr res fel org chem, Cent Drug Res Inst, Univ Lucknow, 57-59; res assoc, Laval Univ, 59-60, Nat Res Coun Can fel, 60-62; staff scientist, Worcester Found Exp Biol, 62-65; SR RES CHEMIST, AYERST RES LABS, 65- *Concurrent Pos:* Mem grants selection comt chem sect, Nat Sci & Eng Res Coun, Can, 81- *Mem:* Am Chem Soc; Chem Inst Can. *Res:* Structural determination; synthesis of steroids and other natural products; phospholipids; biosynthesis of steroids; synthesis of pharmacologically active compounds; antibiotics. *Mailing Add:* Ayerst Res Labs PO Box 6115 Montreal PQ H3C 3J1 Can

RAKIC, PASKO, b Ruma, Yugoslavia, May 15, 33; m 69. NEUROSCIENCES, DEVELOPMENTAL BIOLOGY. *Educ:* Univ Belgrade, MD, 59, ScD(neuroembryol), 69. *Prof Exp:* Instr path physiol, Med Sch, Univ Belgrade, 59-61, resident neurosurg, Neurosurg Hosp, 61-62; NIH res fel neuropath, Harvard Med Sch, 62-66; res assoc develop biol, Inst Biol Res, Belgrade, 67-68; from asst prof to assoc prof neuropath, Harvard Med Sch, 69-77; prof neurosci, 77-78, DORYS MCCONNELL DUBERG PROF NEUROSCI, YALE MED SCH, 78-, CHMN SECT NEUROANAT, 77- *Mem:* Int Brain Res Orgn; Am Asn Anat; Am Asn Neuropath; Soc Neurosci. *Res:* Normal and pathological brain development; studies of patterns of cell proliferation, displacement, migration and connectivity in normal and mutant mammals. *Mailing Add:* Dept of Neuroanat Yale Med Sch New Haven CT 06510

RAKITA, LOUIS, b Montreal, Que, US citizen; m 45; c 1. CARDIOVASCULAR DISEASES, INTERNAL MEDICINE. *Educ:* Sir George Williams Univ, BA, 42; McGill Univ, MD, CM, 49; Am Bd Internal Med, dipl, 56; Royal Col Physicians & Surgeons, Can, cert, 56. *Prof Exp:* Intern, Montreal Gen Hosp, 49-50; resident med, Jewish Gen Hosp, Montreal, 50-51; fel, Alton Ochsner Med Found, 51-52; chief resident, Cleveland City Hosp, 52-53; from instr to assoc prof, 54-71, PROF MED, CASE WESTERN RESERVE UNIV, 71-; DIR CARDIOL, CLEVELAND METROP GEN HOSP, 66- *Concurrent Pos:* Am Heart Asn fel, Inst Med Res, Cedars Lebanon Hosp, Los Angeles, 53-54; Am Heart Asn Fel, Cleveland City Hosp, 54-55, advan fel, 59-61; USPHS sr res fel, Cleveland City Hosp, 61-62; USPHS res career develop award, Cleveland Metrop Gen Hosp, 62-69; asst vis physician, Cleveland City Hosp, 54-57, vis physician, 57-; vis cardiologist, Sunny Acres Hosp, 73- *Mem:* AAAS; Am Fedn Clin Res; Am Heart Asn; fel Am Col Physicians; fel Am Col Cardiol. *Res:* Electrophysiology and biochemistry of cardiac hypertrophy. *Mailing Add:* Cleveland Metrop Gen Hosp Cleveland OH 44100

RAKITA, PHILIP ERWIN, b Cleveland, Ohio, Sept 4, 44; m 67; c 2. ORGANOMETALLIC CHEMISTRY. *Educ:* Case Inst, BSc, 66; Mass Inst Technol, PhD(chem), 70. *Prof Exp:* Asst prof inorg chem, Univ NC, Chapel Hill, 70-75; grants officer, Indust Environ Res Lab, US Environ Protection Agency, 75-76; sr Fulbright prof, Moscow State Univ, USSR, 76; prof inorg chem, Univ Minn, 76-77; sr res chemist, Ferro Corp, 77-78, int prod mgr, 79-80; TECH MGR, M&T CHEM INC, 81- *Mem:* Am Chem Soc. *Res:* Organometallic chemistry; PVC stabilization. *Mailing Add:* M&T Chem Inc PO Box 1104 Rahway NJ 07090

RAKOFF, HENRY, b Brooklyn, NY, Nov 13, 24; div; c 3. ORGANIC CHEMISTRY. *Educ:* City Col New York, BS, 44; Purdue Univ, MS, 48, PhD(chem), 50. *Prof Exp:* Asst chem, Purdue Univ, 46-48; petrol chemist, Natural Resources Res Inst, Univ Wyo, 50-52; sr res chemist, Velsicol Corp, Ill, 52-53; from asst prof to assoc prof chem, Tex A&M Univ, 53-66; prof, Parsons Col, 66-73, chmn dept, 67-73; res assoc, Univ Mo-Columbia, 73-74; RES CHEMIST, NORTHERN REGIONAL RES CTR, AGR RES SERV, USDA, 74- *Mem:* AAAS; Am Chem Soc; Am Oil Chemists Soc. *Res:* Synthesis of pharmacologically active compounds; chemistry of fatty acids and glycerides. *Mailing Add:* Northern Regional Lab USDA 1815 N University St Peoria IL 61604

RAKOFF, VIVIAN MORRIS, b Capetown, SAfrica, Apr 28, 28; Can citizen; m 59; c 3. PSYCHIATRY. *Educ:* Univ Capetown, BA, 47, MA, 49; Univ London, MB, BS, 57; McGill Univ, DPsych, 63; FRCP(C), 64. *Prof Exp:* Psychologist, Tavistock Clin, 50-51; house officer surg, St Charles Hosp, 57; house officer med, Victoria Hosp, 58; registr, Groote Schuur Hosp, 58-61; resident psychiat, McGill Univ, 61-63; assoc dir res, Jewish Gen Hosp, 63-67, asst prof & dir res, 67-68; from assoc prof to prof psychiat, 68-74, dir postgrad educ, 68-71, PROF PSYCHIAT EDUC, UNIV TORONTO, 74- *Concurrent Pos:* Prof & chmn dept psychiat, Univ Toronto, 80; dir & psychiatrist in chief, Clarke Inst Psychiat. *Mem:* Am Psychiat Asn; Can Psychiat Asn; Am Col Psychiatrists. *Res:* Patterns of mutual perception within the family; neurophysiological substrates of addictive behavior; adolescence and the family. *Mailing Add:* 250 College St Toronto ON M5T 1R8 Can

RAKOSKY, JOSEPH, JR, b Harrisburg, Pa, Apr 17, 21; m 44; c 4. FOOD SCIENCE, SANITATION. *Educ:* Univ Md, BS, 49, MS, 50; Pa State Univ, PhD(bact), 53. *Prof Exp:* Dairy technician, Univ Md, 49-50; asst bact, Pa State Univ, 50-51; sr microbiologist & group leader, Baxter Labs, Inc, 53-55; res microbiologist & group leader, Glidden Co, 55-58; res microbiologist, Cent Soya Co, Inc, Chicago, leader, 58-64, asst div prod mgr, 64-65, tech serv mgr, 65-70, dir tech mkt 70-76; sr consult, Bernard Wolnak & Assoc, 76-77; FOOD INDUSTRY CONSULT, J RAKOSKY SERV, INC, 78- *Mem:* AAAS; Am Chem Soc; Am Soc Microbiol; Inst Food Technol; Am Pub Health Asn. *Res:* Soy products, manufacture and use; regulatory matters, government liaison, technical literature and manuals, technical sales training; nutrition; marketing feasibility studies and surveys; plant sanitation. *Mailing Add:* 5836 Crain St Morton Grove IL 60053

RAKOWSKI, ROBERT F, b Rahway, NJ, Oct 8, 41; m 64; c 3. MEMBRANE BIOPHYSICS, IONIC CHANNELS & PUMPS. *Educ:* Cornell Univ, BChE, 64, MEng, 66; Univ Rochester, PhD(physiol), 72. *Prof Exp:* ASST PROF PHYSIOL, WASHINGTON UNIV, 75- *Mem:* Am Soc Zoologists; Biophys Soc; Soc Gen Physiologists. *Res:* Mechanism of voltage-dependent ion conductance changes in excitable cells; voltage-clamp studies of sodium pump activity in cells. *Mailing Add:* Dept Physiol & Biophysics Washington Univ 660 S Euclid St Louis MO 63110

RAKOWSKY, FREDERICK WILLIAM, b Cleveland, Ohio, Aug 24, 28; m 53; c 2. PHYSICAL CHEMISTRY. *Educ:* Baldwin-Wallace Col, BS, 50; Ohio State Univ, MS, 51, PhD(chem), 54. *Prof Exp:* Asst, Ohio State Univ, 50-54; RES ASSOC AMOCO OIL CO, 54- *Mem:* Am Chem Soc; Am Soc Testing & Mat. *Res:* Corrosion in hydrocarbon and water systems; hydrocarbon oxidation; air pollution. *Mailing Add:* Amoco Res Ctr PO Box 400 Naperville IL 60566

RAKSHYS, JOSEPH W, JR, polymer chemistry, see previous edition

RAKTOE, B LEO, b Dist Surinan, Aug 2, 32; m 53; c 2. STATISTICS, EXPERIMENTAL DESIGN. *Educ:* State Col Trop Agr, dipl, Neth, 52; Cornell Univ, MS, 62, PhD(biomet, econ statist, agr econ), 64. *Prof Exp:* Agr officer, Agr Exp Sta, Ministry of Agr, Surinam, 53-60; asst prof biol statist, Cornell Univ, 64-65; agr statistician, Food & Agr Orgn, UN, Uruguay, 65-67; assoc prof, 67-70, PROF STATIST, UNIV GUELPH, 70- *Concurrent Pos:* Vis assoc prof, Cornell Univ, 69, vis prof, 71-72; agr statistician, Asian Statist Inst of UN, Tokyo, Japan, 73-74; vis prof, Univ Hawaii, 76-78, Univ Ill, Chicago Circle, 77, Stanford Univ, 77 & Univ Calif, Davis, 78-79. *Mem:* Fel Am Statist Asn; fel AAAS; fel Royal Statist Soc; Int Statist Inst; fel Inst Math Statist. *Res:* Lattice designs; mixed factorials; fractional replicates and their applications in the biological and physical sciences. *Mailing Add:* Dept of Math & Statist Univ of Guelph Guelph ON N1G 2W1 Can

RAKUSAN, KAREL JOSEF, b Slany, Czech, Jan 28, 35; Can citizen; m 61. PHYSIOLOGY. *Educ:* Charles Univ, Prague, MD, 60; Czech Acad Sci, PhD(physiol), 64. *Prof Exp:* Asst prof pathophysiol, Charles Univ, Prague, 60-64, assoc prof, 67-68; vis scientist, 68-69, assoc prof, 69-74, PROF PHYSIOL, UNIV OTTAWA, 74- *Concurrent Pos:* Mem, Int Study Group Res Cardiac Metab; NIH fel cardiol, Wayne State Univ, 65-66; Med Res Coun grant, Univ Ottawa, 69- *Honors & Awards:* Award, Czech Acad Sci, 66. *Mem:* Am Physiol Soc; Can Physiol Soc; Europ Soc Clin Invest. *Res:* Microcirculatory aspects of the oxygen supply; experimental cardiomegaly; oxygen in the heart muscle; developmental physiology. *Mailing Add:* Dept Physiol Univ Ottawa Ottawa ON K1N 9A9 Can

RALEIGH, CECIL BARING, b Little Rock, Ark, Aug 11, 34; m 76; c 4. GEOPHYSICS. *Educ:* Pomona Col, BA, 56, MA, 59; Univ Calif, Los Angeles, PhD(geol), 63. *Prof Exp:* Res fel geophys, Inst Advan Studies, Australian Nat Univ, 63-65, fel, 65-66; res geophysicist, Nat Ctr Earthquake Res, US Geol Surv, 66-73, br chief earthquake tectonics; DIR, LAMONT-DOHERTY GEOL OBSERV & CHMN, DEPT GEOL SCI, COLUMBIA UNIV, 81- *Honors & Awards:* Interdisciplinary Award, Intersoc Comt Rock Mech, 69 & 74; Meritorious Serv Award, Dept Interior, 75. *Mem:* Fel Geol Soc Am; fel Am Geophys Union. *Res:* Experimental deformation of rocks at high pressure and temperature; studies of earthquakes triggered by fluid injection; plastic deformation of rock forming minerals. *Mailing Add:* Lamont-Doherty Geol Observ Palisades NY 10964

RALEIGH, DOUGLAS OVERHOLT, b New York, NY, Aug 19, 29; m 60, 76; c 1. ELECTROCHEMISTRY. *Educ:* Rensselaer Polytech Inst, BS, 51; Columbia Univ, MA, 55, PhD(chem), 60. *Prof Exp:* Res chemist, Sylvania Elec Prod Corp, NY, 51-52; sr chemist, Atomics Int Div, 58-62, MEM TECH STAFF, SCI CTR, ROCKWELL INT, 62- *Concurrent Pos:* Invited lectr, Gordon Conf Electrochem, 68, Solid State, 73, Electrochem, 74 & high temperature chem, 78; vis assoc prof, Univ Utah, 69; invited tutorial lectr, NATO Advan Study Insts, Belgirate, Italy, 72 & Ajaccio, Corsica, 75, mem sci comt, 75; mem steering & prog comts, NBS Workshop on Electrocatalysis, 75-; US-Japan Joint Sem, Defects & Diffusion in Solids, Tokyo, 76. *Mem:* Electrochem Soc. *Res:* Electrochemical processes in molten salts and solid ionic conductors. *Mailing Add:* Sci Ctr Rockwell Int 1049 Camino Dos Rios Thousand Oaks CA 91360

RALEIGH, JAMES ARTHUR, b Vancouver, BC, Feb 21, 38; m 62; c 4. ORGANIC CHEMISTRY, RADIATION BIOCHEMISTRY. *Educ:* Univ BC, BSc, 60, MSc, 62; Mass Inst Technol, PhD(org chem), 67. *Prof Exp:* Fel, Univ Sussex, 66-68; res off med biophys, Whiteshell Nuclear Res Estab, Atomic Energy Can Ltd, 68-78; SR RADIATION CHEM & RADIOBIOL, CROSS CANCER INST, 78-; ASSOC CLIN PROF, UNIV ALBERTA, CAN, 78- *Mem:* Am Chem Soc; Radiation Res Soc; Chem Inst Can; Royal Soc Chem; AAAS. *Res:* Radiation chemistry of biologically important compounds; biochemistry of nitroaromatic compounds, radiobiology of blood cells. *Mailing Add:* Radiobiol Cross Cancer Inst 11560 University Ave Edmonton AB T6G 1Z2 Can

RALEIGH, ROBERT FRANKLIN, b Ogden, Utah, Sept 19, 26; m 46; c 5. FISH BIOLOGY. *Educ:* Utah State Univ, BSc, 54, MSc, 60; Univ Idaho, PhD(fishery sci), 69. *Prof Exp:* Res biologist, US Bur Com Fisheries, 55-70; res biologist, US Bur Sport Fisheries & Wildlife, 70-72, unit leader, Va Coop Fishery Unit, 72-75, aquatic ecologist, off biol serv, Western Energy & Land Use Team, 75-77, AQUATIC ECOLOGIST, US FISH & WILDLIFE SERV, ECOL SERV, PROJ IMPACT EVAL, 77- *Honors & Awards:* Wildlife Soc Award Outstanding Publ in Fishery Ecol & Mgt, 64; Am Fisheries Soc Publ Award, 72. *Mem:* Am Fisheries Soc; Sigma Xi. *Res:* Management, behavior and ecology of fishes. *Mailing Add:* Ecol Serv Proj Impact Eval 2625 Redwing Rd Ft Collins CO 80526

RALEY, CHARLES FRANCIS, JR, b Baltimore, Md, May 8, 23; m 47; c 3. ORGANIC CHEMISTRY. *Educ:* Univ Notre Dame, BS, 43, MS, 47; Univ Del, PhD(org chem), 50. *Prof Exp:* Org chemist, Southwest Res San Antonio, Univ Tex, 50-56; org chemist, Dow Chem USA, 57-64, sr res chemist, 63-73, sr res specialist, Dow Chem Co, 73-75, assoc scientist, 75-82; RETIRED. *Mem:* Am Chem Soc; Sigma Xi. *Res:* Self-extinguishing plastics; thermal halogenations; high temperature reactions; free radical chemistry; halomethylation. *Mailing Add:* 830 N Saginaw Rd Midland MI 48640

RALEY, FRANK AUSTIN, b Calumet, Mich, Feb 23, 17; m 40; c 2. INDUSTRIAL & MECHANICAL ENGINEERING. *Educ:* Mich Technol Inst, BS, 38 & 39; Univ Minn, MS, 57; Purdue Univ, PhD, 72. *Prof Exp:* Trainee sales eng, Chase Brass & Copper Co, Wis, 39-40, engr, Waterbury Mfg Div, 40-41; electrician plant maintenance, Bethlehem Pac Coast Steel Co, 47-48; mem sales staff, Noma, Inc, 48-49; instr elec eng, Univ Minn, Duluth, 50-52, instr mech eng, 52-60; assoc prof, 60-61, chmn dept, 61-78, PROF INDUST ENG & MGT, NDAK STATE UNIV, 61- *Concurrent Pos:* Partner, Cosmo Eng Co, Minn, 54-55 & Eng & Mgt Consult, Inc, 72-78. *Mem:* Am Soc Eng Educ; sr mem Am Inst Indust Engrs; Am Soc Mech Engrs; sr mem Soc Mfg Engrs; Am Mfg Asn. *Res:* Statistical quality control; manufacturing methods and processes. *Mailing Add.* Dept of Indust Eng NDak State Univ Fargo ND 58102

RALEY, JOHN HOWARD, b Salt Lake City, Utah, Sept 28, 16; m 41; c 2. PHYSICAL ORGANIC CHEMISTRY. *Educ:* Univ Utah, AB, 37, AM, 39; Univ Rochester, PhD(chem), 42. *Prof Exp:* Chemist, Shell Develop Co, Calif, 42-51, refinery technologist, Shell Oil Co, Tex, 51-52, res supvr, Shell Develop Co, Calif, 52-68, dir phys sci, 68-69, res supvr, 69-72; CHEMIST, LAWRENCE LIVERMORE NAT LAB, UNIV CALIF, 75- *Concurrent Pos:* Chmn, Gordon Res Conf Hydrocarbon Chem, 63. *Mem:* Am Chem Soc. *Res:* Exploratory research petroleum and petrochemical processes products; hydrocarbon chemistry; oxidation; chemistry of reactive intermediates; metal complexes; homogeneous, heterogeneous catalysis; oil shale; shale oil. *Mailing Add:* 1040 Homestead Ave Walnut Creek CA 94598

RALL, DAVID PLATT, b Aurora, Ill, Aug 3, 26; m 54; c 2. PHARMACOLOGY. *Educ:* NCent Col (Ill), BA, 46; Northwestern Univ, MD & PhD(pharmacol), 51. *Prof Exp:* Res assoc pharmacol, Northwestern Univ, 51-52; intern, 2nd Med Div, Bellevue Hosp, Cornell Univ, 52-53; pharmacologist, Lab Chem Pharmacol, Nat Cancer Inst, 53-55, clin pharmacol & exp ther serv, 55-58, head, 58-63, chief lab chem pharmacol, 63-71, assoc sci dir exp therapeut, 65-71, DIR, NAT INST ENVIRON HEALTH SCI, 71-, DIR, NAT TOXICOL PROG, 78- *Concurrent Pos:* Adj prof, Univ NC, Chapel Hill, 72- *Mem:* Soc Toxicol; Am Soc Pharmacol & Exp Therapeut; Inst Med; Am Asn Cancer Res; Soc Occup & Environ Health. *Res:* Bacterial pyrogens; toxicology; drug distribution; cancer chemotherapy. *Mailing Add:* Nat Inst of Environ Health Sci PO Box 12233 Research Triangle Park NC 27709

RALL, ELIZABETH PRETZER, b Cleveland, Ohio, Apr 10, 22; m 49; c 4. STRATIGRAPHY. *Educ:* Brown Univ, AB, 43; Columbia Univ, MA, 46; Univ Ill, PhD(geol), 56. *Prof Exp:* Res asst & asst geologist, State Geol Surv, Ill, 45-47; instr geol, Univ Ill, 47-49; pvt res, 56-63, consult geologist, Tex, 63-68; consult, Pennzoil Petrol, 68-72 & Wainoco Oil, Calgary, 72-73; in-house consult, Kerr-McGee Corp, 73-78; sr geologist, Mich-Wis Pipeline Co, 78-81; AREA GEOLOGIST, OXY PETROL, INC, HOUSTON, 81- *Concurrent Pos:* Instr, Mt Royal Jr Col, 68-69. *Mem:* Sigma Xi; Geol Soc Am; Asn Women Geoscientists. *Res:* Jurassic and Cretaceous stratigraphy of the Gulf Coast. *Mailing Add:* 12619 Taylorcrest Houston TX 77024

RALL, JACK ALAN, b Detroit, Mich, Apr 12, 44; m 67; c 2. MEDICAL PHYSIOLOGY. *Educ:* Olivet Col, Mich, BA, 66; Univ Iowa, PhD(physiol), 72. *Prof Exp:* Fel, Univ Calif, Los Angeles, 72-74; asst prof physiol, 74-79, ASSOC PROF PHYSIOL, OHIO STATE UNIV, 79- *Concurrent Pos:* Fel, Muscular Dystrophy Asns Am, 72. *Mem:* Am Physiol Soc; Biophys Soc. *Res:* Elucidation of the mechanism of muscle contraction with emphasis on the energetics of the contractile process. *Mailing Add:* Dept of Physiol 1645 Neil Ave Ohio State Univ Columbus OH 43210

RALL, JOSEPH EDWARD, b Naperville, Ill, Feb 3, 20; m 44, 78; c 2. PHYSIOLOGY. *Educ:* NCent Col, BA, 40; Northwestern Univ, MS, 44, MD, 45; Univ Minn, PhD(med), 52. *Hon Degrees:* DSc, NCent Col, 66; Dr, Free Univ Brussels, 75. *Prof Exp:* Asst pharmacol, Northwestern Univ, 41-44; asst prof med, Med Col, Cornell Univ, 50-55; chief clin endocrinol br, 55-62, DIR INTRAMURAL RES, NAT INST ARTHRITIS, METAB & DIGESTIVE DIS, 62-, ACTG DEP DIR SCI, NIH, 81- *Concurrent Pos:* Asst mem, Sloan-Kettering Inst, 50-51, assoc mem, 51-55; from asst attend physician to assoc attend physician, Med Serv, Mem Hosp, New York, 50-55; consult, Brookhaven Nat Lab, 50-; mem, Nat Res Coun, 60- *Honors & Awards:* Van Meter Prize, Am Thyroid Asn, 50, Distinguished Serv Award, 67; Fleming Award, 59; Outstanding Achievement Award, Univ Minn & Mayo Found, 64; Superior Serv Award, US Dept Health, Educ & Welfare, 69, Distinguished Serv Award, 68. *Mem:* Nat Acad Sci; Endocrine Soc; Asn Am Physicians; Fr Soc Biol; Am Thyroid Asn. *Res:* Endocrinology. *Mailing Add:* Bldg 10 Rm 9N222 NIH Bethesda MD 20205

RALL, LLOYD L(OUIS), b Galesville, Wis, Dec 7, 16; m 52; c 4. ENGINEERING. *Educ:* Univ Wis, BSCE, 40. *Prof Exp:* Dept Engr forward area, US Army Strategic Air Force, Corps Engrs, US Army, 44-45, chief construct div, Far East Air Forces, Tokyo, 45-47, engr mem, Mil Surv Mission to Turkey, 47, Off Joint Chief Staff, Pentagon, 47-49, exec officer, Res & Develop Off, Chief Engrs, 49-51, asst dist engr, Seattle Dist, Wash, 52-54, dep engr, Commun Zone, France, 54-56, commanding officer, 540th combat engr group, 56-57, prof mil sci & tactics, Mo Sch Mines & Metall, 57-60, dep dir topog, Off Chief Engrs, 60-64, dir, Geod Intel & Mapping Res & Develop Agency, Ft Belvoir, Va, 64-66, dep asst dir, Defense Intel Agency Mapping, Charting & Geod, 66-69, asst dir, Defense Intel Agency Mapping & Charting, 69-72; DIR WASHINGTON OFF, OPTICAL SYSTS DIV, ITEK CORP, 77- *Concurrent Pos:* Mem, Nat Tech Adv Comt, Antarctica Mapping, 60-64. *Mem:* Am Soc Photogram; Am Cong Surv & Mapping; Am Inst Aerospace & Astronaut; Nat Space Club. *Res:* Mapping, charting and geodesy; geographic intelligence data. *Mailing Add:* 301 Cloverway Alexandria VA 22314

RALL, LOUIS BAKER, b Kansas City, Mo, Aug 1, 30; m 52; c 2. NUMERICAL ANALYSIS. *Educ:* Col Puget Sound, BS, 49; Ore State Col, MS, 54, PhD(math), 56. *Prof Exp:* Asst, Ore State Col, 53-56; mathematician, Shell Develop Co, 56-57; assoc prof math, Lamar State Col Technol, 57-60; from assoc prof to prof, Va Polytech Inst & State Univ, 60-62; from asst dir to assoc dir, 65-73, RES MEM, MATH RES CTR, UNIV WIS-MADISON, 62-, PROF MATH, UNIV, 69- *Concurrent Pos:* Vis prof, Innsbruck Univ, 70, Oxford Univ, 72-73 & Univ Copenhagen & Tech Univ Denmark, 80. *Mem:* Soc Indust & Appl Math; Am Math Soc; Math Asn Am; Inst Math & Its Appln. *Res:* Functional and numerical analysis; integral equations; machine computing; interval analysis; development of the theory of interval analysis and its applications to scientific computation. *Mailing Add:* Math Res Ctr Univ of Wis Madison WI 53706

RALL, RAYMOND WALLACE, b Hanover, Ill, Mar 23, 26; m 49; c 4. EXPLORATION GEOLOGY. *Educ:* Univ Ill, BS, 50, MS, 51. *Prof Exp:* Res asst, Ill State Geol Surv, 50-51; geologist & stratigrapher, Pure Oil Co, 51-59; sr geologist, Tenneco Oil Co, 59-67, sr geologist, Tenneco Oil & Minerals Ltd, 67-74, GEOL SPECIALIST, TENNECO OIL CO, 74- *Mem:* Soc Econ Paleont & Mineral; Am Asn Petrol Geologists. *Res:* Paleozoic stratigraphy of Texas, upper midwest United States, Williston Basin, northern Canada, east coast United States and Canada. *Mailing Add:* 12619 Taylorcrest Houston TX 77024

RALL, STANLEY CARLTON, JR, b Seattle, Wash, May 18, 43; m 69. BIOCHEMISTRY. *Educ:* Whitman Col, AB, 65; Univ Calif, Berkeley, PhD(biochem), 70. *Prof Exp:* Res asst biochem, Univ Calif, Berkeley, 65-70, fel, 71-74; FEL BIOCHEM, LOS ALAMOS NAT LAB, 75- *Concurrent Pos:* Fel, Am Cancer Soc, 71-73, Dernham Jr fel, 73. *Res:* Radiobiology of cells and chromatin; histone and chromatin structure. *Mailing Add:* Biochem Dept PO Box 1663 Univ Calif Los Alamos Nat Lab Los Alamos NM 87544

RALL, THEODORE WILLIAM, b Chicago, Ill, Apr 7, 28; m 49. PHARMACOLOGY. *Educ:* Univ Chicago, SB, 48, PhD(biochem), 52. *Prof Exp:* From res assoc to prof, Case Western Reserve Univ, 54-73, dir dept pharmacol, Sch Med, 73-75; PROF PHARMACOL, SCH MED, UNIV VA, 75- *Mem:* Am Soc Pharmacol & Exp Therapeut; Am Soc Biol Chemists; Soc Neurosci. *Res:* Hormonal regulatory mechanisms; neuropharmacology. *Mailing Add:* Dept of Pharmacol Univ VA Sch Med Charlottesville VA 22903

RALL, WALDO, b Los Angeles, Calif, Mar 20, 24; wid; c 2. PHYSICS, RESEARCH ADMINISTRATION. *Educ:* Wash Univ, BA, 44; Ind Univ, MS, 48, PhD, 50. *Prof Exp:* Asst cyclotron lab, Wash Univ, 43-44; asst metall lab, Univ Chicago, 44; jr scientist, Clinton Lab, Tenn, 44-45; jr scientist, Los Alamos, NMex, 45-46; nuclear studies, 46-47; asst physics, Ind Univ, 47-49; from instr to asst prof, Yale Univ, 49-56; from asst div chief to div chief, 56-75, mgr anal & planning, 75-80, DIR CONTRACT RES, RES LAB, US STEEL CORP, 80- *Mem:* AAAS; fel Am Phys Soc; Am Soc Metals; Sigma Xi. *Res:* Nuclear, instrumental, vacuum and metal physics; research planning and budgeting; marketing of research. *Mailing Add:* Res Lab US Steel Corp Monroeville PA 15146

RALL, WILFRID, b Los Angeles, Calif, Aug 29, 22; m 46; c 2. BIOPHYSICS, NEUROPHYSIOLOGY. *Educ:* Yale Univ, BS, 43; Univ Chicago, MS, 48; Univ NZ, PhD(physiol), 53. *Prof Exp:* Jr physicist, Manhattan Proj, Chicago, 43-46; lectr biophys, Med Sch, Otago, NZ, 49-51, sr lectr physiol, 51-56; head biophys div, Naval Med Res Inst, Nat Naval Med Ctr, 56-57; res biophysicist, 57-67, SR RES PHYSICIST, MATH RES BR, NAT INST ARTHRITIS, DIABETES, DIGESTIVE & KIDNEY DIS, 67- *Concurrent Pos:* Rockefeller Found fel, Univ Col London. 54, Rockefeller Inst, 54-55; mem neurocommun & biophys panel, Int Brain Res Orgn, 60-, rep, Cent Coun, 68-73; mem Nat Res Coun nat comt, 72-76; comt brain sci, Nat Res Coun, 68-73. *Mem:* Soc Neurosci; Biophys Soc; Brit Physiol Soc; Am Physiol Soc. *Res:* Theoretical and experimental neurophysiology; dendritic branching; synaptic structure, function and integration; intracellular and extracellular potentials; computation with mathematical models. *Mailing Add:* Math Res Br NIADDK Room 4B-54 Bldg 31 NIH Bethesda MD 20205

RALLEY, THOMAS G, b Chicago, Ill, July 10, 39; m 61; c 2. MATHEMATICS. *Educ:* Ill Inst Technol, BS, 61; Univ Ill, MS, 63, PhD(math), 66. *Prof Exp:* Asst prof, 67-73, ASSOC PROF MATH, OHIO STATE UNIV, 73- *Mem:* Am Math Soc. *Res:* Representations of finite groups and associative algebras. *Mailing Add:* Dept of Math Ohio State Univ Columbus OH 43210

RALLS, JACK WARNER, b Los Angeles, Calif, Feb 1, 20; m 46; c 4. CHEMISTRY. *Educ:* Univ Calif, Los Angeles, BA, 43, MA, 44; Northwestern Univ, PhD(chem), 49. *Prof Exp:* Proj assoc, Univ Wis, 49-51; res chemist, G D Searle & Co, Ill, 51-55; res chemist, Calif Res Corp, 55-58; res chemist, Nat Canners Asn, 58-67, res mgr, Western Res Lab, 67-73, mgr res serv, 73-77. *Concurrent Pos:* Lectr exten div, Univ Calif, Berkeley, 58-71; collabr, Western Utilization Res & Develop Div, USDA, 58-64, res coordr, 64-67, res mgr, 67-73; sr res scientist, Eng Exp Sta, Ga Inst Technol, 77-78; gen mgr, Temp Tech Assocs, Kensington, 78-80; dir, Org Labs, Univ SC, 80-81. *Mem:* Am Chem Soc; Inst Food Technol. *Res:* Food processing; organic chemistry of thermally processed foods; flavor chemistry of fruits and vegetables; canned food technology; environmental chemistry. *Mailing Add:* 6 Highgate Rd Kensington CA 94707

RALLS, KATHERINE SMITH, b Oakland, Calif, Mar 21, 39; div; c 3. ETHOLOGY. *Educ:* Stanford Univ, AB, 60; Radcliffe Col, MA, 62; Harvard Univ, PhD(biol), 65. *Prof Exp:* Fel animal behav, Univ Calif, Berkeley, 65-67; guest investr, Rockefeller Univ, 68-70; asst prof, Sarah Lawrence Col, 70-73; fel Radcliffe Inst, 73-74; fel, 73-75, RES ZOOLOGIST, SMITHSONIAN INST, 76- *Concurrent Pos:* Adj asst prof animal behav, Rockefeller Univ, 70-76; Am Asn Univ Women, 75-76; mem psychobiol adv comt, NSF, 81- *Mem:* Am Soc Mammal; Animal Behav Soc; Asn Women Sci. *Res:* Mammalian social behavior; chemical communication; sexual dimorphism in mammals; inbreeding. *Mailing Add:* DZR Nat Zoo Smithsonian Inst Washington DC 20008

RALLS, KENNETH M(ICHAEL), b Salt Lake City, Utah, Feb 14, 38; m 78; c 4. MATERIALS SCIENCE, PHYSICAL METALLURGY. *Educ:* Stanford Univ, BS, 60; Mass Inst Technol, SM, 62, ScD(phys metall), 64. *Prof Exp:* Res assoc metall, Mass Inst Technol, 64-65; fel, Inorg Mat Res Div, Lawrence Radiation Lab, Calif, 65-67; from asst prof to assoc prof, 67-76, PROF MECH ENG, UNIV TEX, AUSTIN, 76- *Mem:* Am Inst Mining, Metall & Petrol Engrs (Metall Soc); Am Soc Metals; Am Phys Soc; fel Am Inst Chemists; Metal Soc Gr Brit. *Res:* Physical metallurgy of high magnetic field superconductive materials; fabrication and preparation of multifilamentary superconducting composites. *Mailing Add:* Dept of Mech Eng Univ of Tex Austin TX 78712

RALPH, C(LEMENT) JOHN, b Oakland, Calif, Sept, 3, 40; m 73; c 2. AVIAN ECOLOGY. *Educ:* Univ Calif, Berkeley, AB, 63; Calif State Univ, San Jose, MS, 69; Johns Hopkins Univ, ScD(pathobiol), 74. *Prof Exp:* Dir, Point Reyes Bird Observ, 66-69; asst prof ecol/behav, Dickinson Col, 73-76; RES ECOLOGIST, INST PAC ISLAND FORESTRY, US FOREST SERV, 76- *Concurrent Pos:* Comnr, Animal Species Adv Comn, Hawaii, 80-; ed, Elepaio. *Honors & Awards:* Tucker Award, Cooper Ornith Soc, 67; Wilson Award, Wilson Ornith Soc, 73. *Mem:* Am Ornithologists Union; Cooper Ornith Soc; Ecol Soc Am; Animal Behav Soc; Wilson Ornith Soc. *Res:* Life history and ecological relationships of native Hawaiian and Pacific forest birds, especially rare and endangered species. *Mailing Add:* Inst Pac Islands Forestry Rm 323 1151 Punchbowl St Honolulu HI 96822

RALPH, CHARLES LELAND, b Flint, Mich, Aug 16, 29; m 80; c 2. PHYSIOLOGY. *Educ:* Southeast Mo State Col, BS, 52; Northwestern Univ, MS, 53, PhD(biol), 55. *Prof Exp:* Spec prof personnel corps, US Army Chem Ctr, Md, 55-57; physiologist, USDA, 57-59; from asst prof to prof biol, Univ Pittsburgh, 59-74, chmn dept, 72-74; PROF ZOOL & ENTOM & CHMN DEPT, COLO STATE UNIV, 74- *Mem:* Fel AAAS; Am Soc Zool; Am Physiol Soc; Am Asn Anat; Am Inst Biol Sci. *Res:* Comparative physiology; neuroendocrinology; physiology of the pineal body; vertebrate color change. *Mailing Add:* Dept Zool & Entom Colo State Univ Ft Collins CO 80523

RALSTON, ANTHONY, b New York, NY, Dec 24, 30; m 58; c 4. COMPUTER SCIENCE. *Educ:* Mass Inst Technol, SB, 52, PhD(math), 56. *Prof Exp:* Mem tech staff, Bell Tel Labs, Inc, 56-59; lectr math, Univ Leeds, 59-60; mgr tech comput, Am Cyanamid Co, 60-61; from assoc prof to prof math, Stevens Inst Technol, 60-65, dir comput ctr, 60-65, dir comput serv, 65-70, chmn dept, 67-80, PROF COMPUT SCI, STATE UNIV NY BUFFALO, 65- *Mem:* Asn Comput Mach (vpres, 70-72, pres, 72-74); Soc Indust & Appl Math; Am Fedn Info Processing Socs (pres, 75-76); Math Asn Am. *Res:* Discrete mathematics; education in computer science. *Mailing Add:* Dept Comput Sci State Univ NY Buffalo 4226 Ridge Lea Rd Amherst NY 14226

RALSTON, CHARLES WILLIAM, b Chicago, Ill, Mar 3, 21; m 48; c 4. FOREST SOILS. *Educ:* Colo State Univ, BSF, 42; Duke Univ, MF, 47, PhD(forest soils), 49. *Prof Exp:* Asst prof, Univ Fla, 49-54; from asst prof to assoc prof, 54-64, dean, Sch Forestry, 69-76, PROF FOREST SOILS, DUKE UNIV, 64- *Concurrent Pos:* Consult, Weyerhaeuser Timber Co, St Regis Paper Co, Armstrong Cork Co, Anglo-Can P&P Co & Container Corp Am; mem task force on educ in agr & renewable nat resources, Nat Acad Sci, 74- *Mem:* Soil Sci Soc Am; Am Soc Agron; Soc Am Foresters. *Res:* Forest site evaluation; mineral nutrition of trees; wetland management; accumulation of dry matter and nutrients in forest stands; soil compaction; water quality; effects of intense forestry practices on soil and water quality. *Mailing Add:* Sch of Forestry & Environ Studies Duke Univ Durham NC 27706

RALSTON, DOUGLAS EDMUND, b Cherokee, Iowa, July 9, 32; m 53; c 2. BIOCHEMISTRY. *Educ:* Wayne State Col. BS. 55, MS, 57; SDak State Univ, MA, 59; Univ Minn, Minneapolis, PhD(biochem), 69. *Prof Exp:* Asst prof chem, Wayne State Col, 59-60; ASSOC PROF BIOCHEM, MANKATO STATE UNIV, 62- *Concurrent Pos:* Chmn, Nat Educ Asn Higher Educ Coun, 78-80. *Res:* Membrane transport. *Mailing Add:* Dept of Biochem Mankato State Univ Box 40 Mankato MN 56001

RALSTON, ELIZABETH WALL, b Urbana, Ill, June 26, 45; m 69. ALGEBRA. *Educ:* Stanford Univ, BS, 66; Yale Univ, PhD(math), 70. *Prof Exp:* Instr math, Fordham Univ, 70-71; asst prof, Calif State Col, Dominguez Hills, 71-73; adj asst prof, Univ Calif, Los Angeles, 73-75; asst prof math, Fordham Univ, 75-77; MEM TECHNOL STAFF, AEROSPACE CORP, 77- *Mem:* Am Math Soc; Math Asn Am. *Res:* Finite group theory. *Mailing Add:* 10347 Tennessee Ave Los Angeles CA 90064

RALSTON, HENRY JAMES, b San Francisco, Calif, Feb 10, 06; m 34; c 3. PHYSIOLOGY. *Educ:* Univ Calif, AB, 29, PhD(zool), 34. *Prof Exp:* Lectr zool, Univ Calif, 34-35; instr physiol, San Francisco Jr Col, 35-39; instr, Col Dent, Univ Calif, 39-44, res assoc, 42-44; asst prof, Sch Med, Univ Tex, 44-45; from asst prof to assoc prof, 45-53, PROF PHYSIOL, UNIV OF THE PAC, 53-; RES PHYSIOLOGIST, SCH MED, UNIV CALIF, SAN FRANCISCO, 55- *Mem:* AAAS; Soc Exp Biol & Med; Am Physiol Soc. *Res:* Effects of x-rays on protozoa; dynamics of circulation; physiology of human muscle; energy expenditure in locomotion. *Mailing Add:* Biomech Lab 471 Univ of Calif Hosp San Francisco CA 94143

RALSTON, HENRY JAMES, III, b Berkeley, Calif, Mar 12, 35; m 60; c 2. NEUROANATOMY, ELECTRON MICROSCOPY. *Educ:* Univ Calif, Berkeley, AB, 56; Univ Calif, San Francisco, MD, 59. *Prof Exp:* Intern med, Mt Sinai Hosp, New York, 59-60; resident, Univ Calif, San Francisco, 60-61; asst prof anat, Sch Med, Stanford Univ, 65-69; assoc prof anat, Univ Wis-Madison, 69-73; PROF ANAT & CHMN DEPT, UNIV CALIF, SAN FRANCISCO, 73- *Concurrent Pos:* Nat Inst Neurol Dis & Blindness spec fel neuroanat, Univ Col, Univ London, 63-65; prin investr, Nat Inst Neurol & Communicative Dis & Stroke res grants, 65-82; mem neurol A study sect, NIH, 77-81. *Honors & Awards:* Borden Award, 59. *Mem:* AAAS; Am Soc Cell Biol; Am Asn Anat; Soc Neurosci; Int Asn Study Pain. *Res:* Fine structural organization of mammalian nervous system. *Mailing Add:* Dept Anat Univ Calif San Francisco CA 94143

RALSTON, JAMES VICKROY, JR, b Elyria, Ohio, June 26, 43; m 69. MATHEMATICS. *Educ:* Harvard Univ, BA, 64; Stanford Univ, PhD(math), 69. *Prof Exp:* Vis mem, Courant Inst Math Sci, 68-70; asst prof math, NY Univ, 70-71; from asst prof to assoc prof, 71-77, PROF MATH, UNIV CALIF, LOS ANGELES, 77- *Concurrent Pos:* Fel, Alfred Sloan Found, 74-76. *Mem:* Am Math Soc. *Res:* Hyperbolic partial differential equations; scattering theory. *Mailing Add:* Dept Math Univ Calif Los Angeles CA 90024

RALSTON, ROBERT D, b Petersburg, NDak, July 7, 24; m 48; c 4. PLANT ECOLOGY. *Educ:* Mayville State Col, BS, 50; Univ Utah, MS, 60; Univ Sask, PhD(plant ecol), 68. *Prof Exp:* Teacher high sch, NDak, Nev & Minn, 50-59; PROF BIOL, MAYVILLE STATE COL, 60- *Mem:* Ecol Soc Am. *Res:* Ecological research on native grasslands of northern Great Plains; phytosociological data and environmental factors correlated; part affects and fire recovery of woodlands in Little Missouri Badlands. *Mailing Add:* Dept of Sci Mayville State Col Mayville ND 58257

RAM, BUDH, b Delhi, India, Jan 12, 35; m 64; c 2. PHYSICS. *Educ:* Univ Delhi, BS, 55, MS, 57; Univ Colo, PhD(physics), 63. *Prof Exp:* Lectr physics, Univ Delhi, 57-58, lectr, Panjab Univ, India, 58-59; teaching asst, Univ Colo, 59-62; res fel, Battersea Col Technol, Univ London, 63-64; res assoc, Univ NC, 64-66; from asst prof to assoc prof, 66-77, PROF PHYSICS, NMEX STATE UNIV, 77- *Mem:* Am Phys Soc. *Res:* Elementary particles; theoretical physics. *Mailing Add:* Dept of Physics NMex State Univ Las Cruces NM 88001

RAM, GERSON LOUIS, b Bloomfield, NJ, Oct 18, 19; m 46; c 1. BIOCHEMISTRY. *Educ:* Upsala Col, BA, 41; Rutgers Univ, dipl sanit eng, 43, MS, 47; Johns Hopkins Univ, ScD(parasitol, biochem), 53. *Prof Exp:* Asst chem, Upsala Col, 40-41; chemist, Crucible Steel Corp, 41-42; from instr to assoc prof, 47-65, PROF CHEM, NJ INST TECHNOL, 65- *Mem:* AAAS; fel Am Inst Chem; fel Royal Soc Health. *Res:* Biochemistry of malaria; colloid chemistry of the red cell. *Mailing Add:* Dept of Chem NJ Inst Technol Newark NJ 07102

RAM, J SRI, b India, Apr 5, 28; m 50; c 2. BIOCHEMISTRY, IMMUNOLOGY. *Educ:* Andhra Univ, India, BSc, 48; Univ Bombay, PhD(biochem), 52. *Prof Exp:* Res assoc, Columbia Univ, 54-55; res assoc immunochem, Univ Pittsburgh, 55-59, asst prof biochem, 59-61; asst prof biol chem, Univ Mich, 61-65; res biochemist, Nat Inst Arthritis, Metab & Digestive Dis, 65-74; exec secy, Pathobiol Chem Study Sect, Div Res Grants, GRANTS, NIH, 74-76; actg chief, 76-80, CHIEF, AIRWAYS DIS BR, DIV OF LUNG DIS, NAT HEART, LUNG & BLOOD INST, NIH, 80- *Concurrent Pos:* Lady Tata scholar biochem, Indian Inst Sci, Bangalore, 52-53 & Fordham Univ, 53-54; 53-54; Fulbright vis prof, India, 71. *Mem:* Am Soc Exp Path; Am Soc Biol Chem; Am Asn Immunol; Soc Exp Biol & Med. *Res:* Immunochemistry; research administration; mechanism of enzyme action; antigen-antibody interactions; protein modification; antigenicity of hormones and drugs; immunology and biochemistry of disease; aging; science policy; science and research administration. *Mailing Add:* Rm 6A-11 Westwood Bldg Nat Heart Lung & Blood Inst NIH Bethesda MD 20025

RAM, JEFFREY L, b Newark, NJ, Sept 25, 45; m 77; c 2. INVERTEBRATE NEUROPHYSIOLOGY, ENDOCRINOLOGY. *Educ:* Univ Pa, BA, 67; Calif Inst Technol, PhD(biochem), 74. *Prof Exp:* Fel neurosci, Univ Calif, Santa Cruz, 73-77; asst prof, 77-82, ASSOC PROF NEUROPHYSIOL, WAYNE STATE UNIV, 82- *Concurrent Pos:* Stipendiary fel, Marine Biol Lab, Woods Hole Oceanog Inst, 75. *Mem:* AAAS; Am Physiol Soc; Am Soc Neurosci. *Res:* Comparative aspects of gastropod egg hormones; modulatory effects of serotonin; activation of neurons by peptides; biophysics membranes. *Mailing Add:* Dept Physiol Sch Med Wayne State Univ Detroit MI 48201

RAM, MADHIRA DASARADHI, b Visakhapatnam, India, Apr 6, 35; US citizen; m 67; c 4. SURGERY, EXPERIMENTAL PATHOLOGY. *Educ:* Andhra Univ, India, BSc, 52, MB, BS, 57, MS, 61; FRCS & FRCS(E), 65; Case Western Reserve Univ, PhD(path), 75. *Prof Exp:* Asst prof surg, Med Col, Andhra Univ, India, 61-64; instr surg, Royal Postgrad Med Sch, Univ London, 67-69; asst clin prof surg, Case Western Reserve Univ, 72-77, asst clin prof exp path, 75-77; ASSOC PROF SURG, UNIV KY, 77- *Concurrent Pos:* Dir surg, Huron Rd Hosp, Cleveland, Ohio, 71-77; chief surg serv, Vet Admin Med Ctr Surgeon, Albert Chandler Med Ctr, Lexington. *Mem:* Fel Am Col Surgeons; fel Royal Soc Med; Asn Acad Surgeons; Am Fedn Clin Res; Soc Surg Alimentary Tract. *Res:* Immunology of AKR mouse leukemia; antibiotic excretion in human bile. *Mailing Add:* Dept Surg 800 Rose St Lexington KY 40506

RAM, MICHAEL, b Alexandria, Egypt, Dec 18, 36; m 59; c 3. THEORETICAL PHYSICS, EXPERIMENTAL PHYSICS. *Educ:* Israel Inst Technol, BSc, 60, MSc, 62; Columbia Univ, PhD(physics), 65. *Prof Exp:* Res assoc physics, Johns Hopkins Univ, 65-67; asst prof, 67-72, ASSOC PROF PHYSICS, STATE UNIV NY BUFFALO, 72- *Concurrent Pos:* Chmn dept, State Univ NY, 74-77. DEPT, 74- *Mem:* Am Phys Soc. *Res:* Field theory; ice physics; atmospheric physics; elementary particles. *Mailing Add:* Dept of Physics State Univ NY Buffalo NY 14260

RAM, MICHAEL JAY, b Newark, NJ, Dec 18, 40; m 64; c 3. MEDICAL DEVICES, PATENT LAW. *Educ:* Lafayette Col, BS, 62; Newark Col Eng, MS, 63, DSc(chem eng), 66; Seton Hall Univ, JD, 72. *Prof Exp:* Sr res engr, Celanese Res Co, Summit, 67-73; patent atty, Brooks, Haidt, Haffner, 73-74; div patent coun, 74-77, corp coordr res & develop, 77-81, DIR TECH LIAISON, C R BARD INC, 81- *Mem:* Am Chem Soc; Am Inst Chem Engrs; Am Bar Asn. *Res:* Synthetic fibers; plastics; medical products; patent law; medical devices and the patent protection of products. *Mailing Add:* 11 Mohawk Rd Short Hills NJ 07078

RAMACHANDRAN, JANAKIRAMAN, b Bombay, India, June 12, 35; m 67; c 1. ENDOCRINOLOGY, BIOCHEMISTRY. *Educ:* Univ Madras, MA, 56; DePaul Univ, MS, 59; Univ Calif, Berkeley, PhD(biochem), 62. *Prof Exp:* Jr res biochemist, Hormone Res Lab, Univ Calif, Berkeley, 62-63, asst res biochemist, 63-68; lectr, Sch Med, 64-68, from asst prof to assoc prof, 68-78, PROF BIOCHEM, MED CTR, UNIV CALIF, SAN FRANCISCO, 78- *Concurrent Pos:* Weizmann Mem fel biophys, Weizmann Inst, 65-66. *Mem:* AAAS; NY Acad Sci; Endocrine Soc; Tissue Cult Asn; Am Soc Biol Chemists. *Res:* Study of the mode of action of polypeptide hormones. *Mailing Add:* 1088 HSW Univ of Calif Med Ctr San Francisco CA 94143

RAMACHANDRAN, PALLASSANA N, b Palghat, India; US citizen; m 66; c 1. PHYSICAL CHEMISTRY, SURFACE CHEMISTRY. *Educ:* Univ Bombay, BSc, 56; Temple Univ, MA, 62, PhD(phys chem), 65. *Prof Exp:* Fel chem, Textile Res Inst, NJ, 65-67; sr res chemist, 67-80, RES ASSOC, COLGATE-PALMOLIVE RES CTR, 80- *Mem:* Am Chem Soc; Am Oil Chemists Soc; Fiber Soc. *Res:* Development and processing of household products. *Mailing Add:* Colgate-Palmolive Res Ctr 909 River Rd Piscataway NJ 08854

RAMACHANDRAN, SUBRAMANIA, b Madras, India, Jan 8, 38; m 68; c 1. ORGANIC CHEMISTRY, BIOCHEMISTRY. *Educ:* Annamalai Univ, Madras, 57, Hons, 59, MSc, 60; Ohio State Univ, MS, 64, PhD(biochem), 68. *Prof Exp:* Asst chem, Ohio State Univ, 61-68, fel physiol chem, 68-69; from asst mgr to mgr, Biochem Dept, 69-72, vpres res & develop, 72-74, MGR RES & DEVELOP, APPL SCI LABS, INC, 74- *Mem:* Am Oil Chem Soc. *Res:* Synthesis of lipids, including steroids; metabolism of lipids; chromatographic separation of organic compounds; analytical methods in clinical chemistry and pharmacology. *Mailing Add:* Res & Develop Labs Appl Sci Labs 135 N Gill St State College PA 16801

RAMACHANDRAN, VENKATANARAYANA D, b Mysore City, India, May 3, 34; m 60; c 1. ELECTRICAL ENGINEERING. *Educ:* Cent Col, Bangalore, BSc, 53; Indian Inst Sci, Bangalore, BE, 56, ME, 58, PhD(elec eng), 65. *Prof Exp:* Sr res asst elec eng, Indian Inst Sci, Bangalore, 58-59, lectr, 59-65; asst prof, NS Tech Col, 66-69; assoc prof, 69-71, PROF ELEC ENG, CONCORDIA UNIV, 71- *Mem:* Inst Elec & Electronics Engrs. *Res:* Circuit theory; active, lumped and multivariable networks. *Mailing Add:* Dept of Elec Eng Concordia Univ Montreal PQ H3G 1M8 Can

RAMAGE, COLIN STOKES, b Napier, NZ, Mar 3, 21; nat US. METEOROLOGY. *Educ:* Victoria Univ, NZ, BSc, 40, DSc, 61. *Prof Exp:* Meteorologist, Meteorol Serv. NZ, 41, sci officer, 46-53; dep dir, Royal Observ, Hong Kong, 54, actg dir, 55-56, assoc meteorologist, 56; assoc prof, 57, PROF METEOROL, UNIV HAWAII, 58-, CHMN DEPT, 71- *Concurrent Pos:* Meteorol & oceanog, 60-62, geosci, 64-69, assoc dir, Hawaii Inst Geophys, 64-71; Commonwealth Fund fel, 53-54; consult, US Air Force, 56-61, US Navy, 69-71; sci dir, Indian Ocean Exped, 62-73. *Mem:* fel Am Meteorol Soc; Am Geophys Union. *Res:* Meteorology of the tropics, south and southeast Asia; monsoons. *Mailing Add:* Dept of Meteorol Univ of Hawaii Honolulu HI 96822

RAMAKER, DAVID ELLIS, b Sheboygan, Wis, Aug 11, 43; m 66; c 3. SURFACE CHEMISTRY, SOLID STATE PHYSICS. *Educ:* Univ Wis-Milwaukee, BS, 65; Univ Iowa, MS, 68, PhD(phys chem), 71. *Prof Exp:* Res physics, Sandia Labs, 70-72; res assoc & assoc instr, Univ Utah, 72-74; vis asst prof, Calvin Col, 74-75; asst prof, 75-78, ASSOC PROF PHYS CHEM, GEORGE WASHINGTON UNIV, 78- *Concurrent Pos:* Consult res chem, Naval Res Lab, 76- *Mem:* Am Chem Soc; Am Vacuum Soc. *Res:* Theoretical studies of surfaces and chemisorption; auger spectroscopy; electron and photon stimulated desorption. *Mailing Add:* Dept of Chem George Washington Univ Washington DC 20052

RAMAKRISHNAN, VENKATASWAMY, b Coimbatore, India, Feb 27, 29; m 62; c 2. STRUCTURAL ENGINEERING. *Educ:* Govt Col Technol, Coimbatore, India, BE, 52; PSG Col Technol, Coimbatore, dipl soc sci, 53; Univ London, PhD(civil eng), 60, Imp Col, dipl hydraul power, 56 & concrete technol, 57. *Prof Exp:* Jr engr, Madras Pub Works Dept, India, 52; asst lectr civil eng, PSG Col Technol, Coimbatore, 52-53, lectr, 53-60, asst prof, 60-61, prof & head dept, 61-69; PROF CIVIL ENG & DIR CONCRETE TECHNOL RES, SDAK SCH MINES & TECHNOL, 69- *Concurrent Pos:* Visitor, Bldg Res Inst, Prague Tech Univ, 67, Asian Inst Technol, Bangkok, SDak Sch Mines & Technol, Univs Colo, Ill, Chicago Circle & Mo-Columbia, 69, Norwegian Inst Tech, Swedish Cement & Concrete Res Inst, Univ West Indies & Inst Technol, Stockholm; coordr, Advan Summer Schs Struct Eng for Eng Col Teachers, India, 68 & 69; partic, Sem Recent Trends in Struct Design, 61, Ind Cong Appl of Math in Eng, Weimar, Ger, 67 & Int Conf Struct, Solid Mech & Eng Design in Civil Eng Mar, Southampton, Eng, 69; organizing secy & ed proc, Int Conf Shear, Torsion & Bond in Reinforced & Prestressed Concrete, 69; mem comt mech properties of concrete, Hwy Res Bd, Nat Acad Sci-Nat Res Coun; archit & struct eng consult; founding dir & guide prof, World Open Univ, 74-, vpres, 79- *Mem:* Am Concrete Inst; Am Soc Civil Engrs; Nat Soc Prof Engrs; Am Soc Eng Educ; Sigma Xi. *Res:* Concrete technology, particularly ultimate behavior and strength of reinforced concrete; materials technology; structural engineering and mechanics. *Mailing Add:* 1809 Sheridan Lake Rd Rapid City SD 57701

RAMAKUMAR, RAMACHANDRA GUPTA, b Coimbatore, India, Oct 17, 36; m 63; c 2. ELECTRICAL ENGINEERING, ENERGY. *Educ:* Univ Madras, India, BE, 56; Indian Inst Technol, Kharagpur, India, MTech, 57; Cornell Univ, PhD(elec eng), 62. *Prof Exp:* From asst lectr to lectr elec eng, Coimbatore Inst Technol, India, 57-62, asst prof, 62-67; vis assoc prof, 67-70, assoc prof, 70-76, PROF ELEC ENG, OKLA STATE UNIV, 76- *Concurrent Pos:* Consult, Jet Propulsion Lab, Calif, 78-79, Nat Sci Found, Washington, DC, 80, Florida Solar Energy Ctr, 81 & Kuwait Univ, 82. *Honors & Awards:* Outstanding Eng Achievement Award, Okla Soc Prof Engrs, 72. *Mem:* Inst Elec & Electronics Engrs; Int Solar Energy Soc; Am Soc Eng Educr; Sigma Xi. *Res:* Alternate energy sources development and application in developing countries for rural development; energy storage; energy conversion and power engineering; solar and wind energy systems. *Mailing Add:* Sch of Elec Eng Okla State Univ Stillwater OK 74078

RAMALEY, JAMES FRANCIS, b Columbus, Ohio, Oct 10, 41; m 67; c 2. MATHEMATICS. *Educ:* Ohio State Univ, BSc, 62; Univ Calif, Berkeley, MA, 64; Univ NMex, PhD(math), 67. *Prof Exp:* Reader math, Univ Calif, 63-64; res asst, Univ NMex, 64-65; lectr, Carnegie Inst Technol, 65-66; asst prof math, Bowling Green State Univ, 66-70; asst prof, Univ Pittsburgh, 70-73; systs analyst, On-Line Systs, Inc, 73-74; mgr info systs, 74-76, BUDGET DIR CIRCULATION, ZIFF-DAVIS PUBL CO, 76- *Concurrent Pos:* Vis mem math res inst, Swiss Fed Inst Technol, 69; adj prof math, Univ Pittsburgh, 73-76. *Mem:* Am Math Soc; Math Asn Am; Opers Res Soc Am; Asn Comput Mach. *Res:* Category theory; logic; systems software; applications software. *Mailing Add:* Ziff-Davis Publ Co One Park Ave New York NY 10016

RAMALEY, JUDITH AITKEN, b Vincennes, Ind, Jan 11, 41; m 66; c 2. ENDOCRINOLOGY, REPRODUCTIVE BIOLOGY. *Educ:* Swarthmore Col, BA, 63; Univ Calif, Los Angeles, PhD(anat), 66. *Prof Exp:* Asst prof anat & physiol, Ind Univ, Bloomington, 69-72; from asst prof to assoc prof, 72-78, PROF PHYSIOL & BIOPHYS, UNIV NEBR MED CTR, OMAHA, 78-, ASST VPRES ACAD AFFAIRS, 81- *Concurrent Pos:* NIH fel, Ctr Neurol Sci, Ind Univ, Bloomington, 67-68, NIH fel chem, 68; mem, NSF, Regulatory Biol Panel, 78-81; mem, Biochem Endocrinol Study Sect, NIH, 81- *Mem:* Am Physiol Soc; Am Asn Anat; Soc Neurosci; Endocrine Soc; Soc Study Reproduction. *Res:* Physiology of puberty; control of male and female fertility. *Mailing Add:* Dept of Physiol & Biophys Univ of Nebr Med Ctr Omaha NE 68105

RAMALEY, LOUIS, b El Paso, Tex, Oct 7, 37; m 64; c 2. ANALYTICAL CHEMISTRY. *Educ:* Univ Colo, BA, 59; Princeton Univ, MA. 61, PhD(electrochem), 64. *Prof Exp:* Assoc, Univ Ill, 63-64; asst prof chem, Univ Ariz, 64-70; ASSOC PROF CHEM, DALHOUSIE UNIV, 70- *Mem:* AAAS; Am Chem Soc; Electrochem Soc; Chem Inst Can. *Res:* Chemical instrumentation; electrochemistry; electroanalytical and surface chemistry; spectroscopy. *Mailing Add:* Dept of Chem Dalhousie Univ Halifax NS B3H 3J5 Can

RAMALEY, ROBERT FOLK, b Colorado Springs, Colo, Dec 15, 35; m 66; c 2. BIOCHEMISTRY, MICROBIOLOGY. *Educ:* Ohio State Univ, BS, 59, MS, 62; Univ Minn, PhD, 64. *Prof Exp:* Asst prof microbiol, Ind Univ, Bloomington, 66-72; assoc prof, 72-78, PROF BIOCHEM, UNIV NEBR MED CTR, OMAHA, 78- *Concurrent Pos:* USPHS fel, 64-66. *Mem:* Am Soc Microbiol; Am Soc Biol Chem. *Res:* Physiology of sporulation; control of intermediate metabolism and enzyme intermediates; thermophilic microorganism and medical microbiology. *Mailing Add:* Dept of Biochem Univ of Nebr Med Ctr Omaha NE 68105

RAMALHO, RUBENS S, b Rio de Janeiro, Brazil, Oct 24, 24; US citizen; m 51; c 2. CHEMICAL ENGINEERING. *Educ:* Univ Brazil, BS, 46; Vanderbilt Univ, MS, 49, PhD(phys chem, chem eng), 54. *Prof Exp:* Asst prof chem eng, Vanderbilt Univ, 52-55; process engr, Arthur G McKee & Co, Ohio, 55-57; assoc prof chem eng, Univ Mo-Rolla, 57-61 & Univ Rochester, 61-65; PROF CHEM ENG, LAVAL UNIV, 65- *Concurrent Pos:* Fulbright lectr, Univ Guayaquil, 59-60, hon prof, 64. *Mem:* Am Inst Chem Engrs; Am Chem Soc; Chem Inst Can. *Res:* Thermodynamics and applied mathematics to chemical engineering problems; water pollution control engineering. *Mailing Add:* Dept of Chem Eng Laval Univ Quebec PQ G1K 7P4 Can

RAMAMOORTHY, CHITTOOR V, b Henzada, Burma, May 5, 26; US citizen; m 57; c 3. COMPUTER SCIENCES, ELECTRICAL ENGINEERING. *Educ:* Univ Madras, BS, 46 & 49; Univ Calif, Berkeley, MS, 51, MechEng, 53; Harvard Univ, AM & PhD(appl math & comput theory), 64. *Prof Exp:* Res engr, Honeywell Inc, 56-57, sr engr, Electronic Data Processing Div, 58-60, staff engr, 61-65, sr staff scientist, 65-67; prof elec eng, Univ Tex, Austin, 67-72, prof comput sci, 68-72; PROF ELEC ENG & COMPUT SCI, UNIV CALIF, BERKELEY, 72- *Concurrent Pos:* Res fel appl math, Harvard Univ, 66-67. *Mem:* Asn Comput Mach; fel Inst Elec & Electronics Engrs. *Res:* Computer theory, design, use and applications information sciences. *Mailing Add:* Dept of Elec Eng & Comput Sci Univ of Calif Berkeley CA 94720

RAMAN, ARAVAMUDHAN, b Madras, India, Oct 13, 37; m 65; c 3. CORROSION, PHYSICAL METALLURGY. *Educ:* St Joseph's Col, India, MA, 58; Indian Inst Sci, Bangalore, BEng, 60; Tech Univ Stuttgart, Dr rer Nat(phys metall), 64. *Prof Exp:* Assoc lectr metall, Indian Inst Technol, Bombay, 61; res assoc phys metall, Univ Ill, Urbana, 64-65; fel mat sci, Univ Tex, Austin, 65-66; PROF MAT SCI, LA STATE UNIV, BATON ROUGE, 66- *Concurrent Pos:* NASA res grant, 66-68; Sea res grant, 78-81. *Mem:* Am Soc Metals; Sigma Xi; Nat Asn Corrosion Engrs. *Res:* X-ray metallography; x-ray crystallography; crystal and alloy chemistry of metallic phases; low temperature physical properties of alloys; structural imperfections and stacking faults in alloys; corrosion science and engineering; metallic coatings. *Mailing Add:* 6919 N Rothmer Dr Baton Rouge LA 70808

RAMAN, SUBRAMANIAN, b North Parur, India, Apr 2, 38; US citizen; m 67; c 3. NUCLEAR PHYSICS. *Educ:* Univ Madras, BE, 59; Rensselaer Polytech Inst, MEE, 61; Pa State Univ, University Park, PhD(physics), 66. *Prof Exp:* res staff mem, 66-80, SR RES STAFF MEM, OAK RIDGE NAT LAB, 66- *Mem:* fel Am Phys Soc. *Res:* Nuclear spectroscopy and reactions; data compilations; heavy ion applications. *Mailing Add:* Oak Ridge Nat Lab Oak Ridge TN 37830

RAMAN, VARADARAJA VENKATA, b Calcutta, India; m 62; c 2. THEORETICAL PHYSICS, HISTORY OF SCIENCE. *Educ:* St Xavier's Col, India, BS, 52; Univ Calcutta, MS, 54; Univ Paris, PhD(theoret physics), 58. *Prof Exp:* Res assoc physics, Saha Inst Nuclear Physics, India, 59-60; assoc prof, Univ PR, Mayaguez, 60-63; chmn dept, Inst Telecommun, Columbia, 63-64; UNESCO expert appl math, Nat Polytech Sch, Univ Algiers, 64-66; assoc prof, 66-77, PROF PHYSICS, ROCHESTER INST TECHNOL, 77- *Mem:* Am Asn Physics Teachers; Hist Sci Soc. *Res:* Historical aspects of physics. *Mailing Add:* Dept of Sci & Humanities Rochester Inst of Technol Rochester NY 14623

RAMANAN, V R V, b Madras, India, July 5, 52. FERROMAGNETISM, AMORPHOUS MATERIALS. *Educ:* Univ Delhi, BSc, 71, MSc, 73, Carnegie-Mellon Univ, MS, 75, PhD(physics), 79. *Prof Exp:* STAFF PHYSICIST, MAT LAB, ALLIED CORP, 79- *Mem:* Inst Elec & Electronics Engrs; Am Phys Soc; Mat Res Soc. *Res:* Ferromagnetic behavior, thermal and magnetic stabilities; structure-property relationships in metallic glasses; design and optimization of new metallic glasses for specific applications. *Mailing Add:* Allied Corp PO Box 1021R Morristown NJ 07960

RAMANATHAN, GANAPATHIAGRAHARAM V, b Madras, India; m 74; c 1. APPLIED MATHEMATICS, STATISTICAL MECHANICS. *Educ:* Madras Univ, BE, 57; Princeton Univ, PhD(aerospace), 66. *Prof Exp:* Asst lectr mech eng, Govt Col Technol, Coimbatore, 57-58; sci officer nuclear eng, Atomic Energy Estab, Bombay, 59-60; assoc res scientist math, Courant Inst Math Sci, NY Univ, 65-66; Nat Acad Sci res assoc plasma physics, Goddard Space Flight Ctr, 66-68; assoc res scientist math, Courant Inst Math Sci, NY Univ, 68-69, asst prof, 69-70; ASSOC PROF MATH, UNIV ILL, CHICAGO, 70- *Res:* Singular and secular perturbation theories. *Mailing Add:* Dept of Math Univ of Ill Box 4348 Chicago IL 60680

RAMANATHAN, M, US citizen. ENVIRONMENTAL ENGINEERING. *Educ:* Madras Univ, BE, 58, MSc, 59; Case Inst Technol, MS, 63; Okla State Univ, PhD(environ sci), 66; Am Acad Environ Engrs, dipl. *Prof Exp:* Mem, Coun Sci & Indust Res, India, 59-60; mem staff, John G Reutter Assoc, 69-71, Weston, 71-79, Environ Quality Syst, Inc, Rockville, Md, 79-80; ENGR, WESTON, 80- *Concurrent Pos:* Mem, Water Pollution Control Fedn. *Mem:* Sigma Xi; Am Soc Civil Engrs. *Res:* Wastewater treatment process development and design; conceptual process design; water quality; field surveys, including sampling, analysis and pilot-plant evaluations; and design installation. *Mailing Add:* Weston Weston Way West Chester PA 19380

RAMANATHAN, VEERABHADRAN, b Madras, India, Nov 24, 44; m 73; c 2. ATMOSPHERIC SCIENCE. *Educ:* Annamalai Univ, India, BE, Hons, 65; Indian Inst Sci, Bangalore, India, MSc, 70; State Univ NY, Stony Brook, PhD(atmospheric sci), 74. *Prof Exp:* Nat Acad Sci-Nat Res Coun fel atmospheric sci, NASA Langley Res Ctr, 74-75; vis scientist, 75-76; vis scientist climate, 76-77, STAFF SCIENTIST, NAT CTR ATMOSPHERIC RES, 77-, LEADER CLOUD CLIMATE INTERACTIONS GROUP, 81- *Concurrent Pos:* Mem panel, Comt Impacts Stratospheric Change, AMPS, Nat Acad Sci, 78-, mem, Comt Solar-Terrestrial Res Panel, Geophys Res Bd, 78-; assoc ed, J Atmospheric Sci, 79-82; mem sci team, Earth Radiation Budget Satellite Exp, NASA, 79-84. *Honors & Awards:* NASA Spec Achievement Award, 75-76. *Mem:* Am Meteorol Soc; AAAS; Am Geophys Union. *Res:* Climate, especially theory, modeling and cloud feedback mechanisms; stratospheric research, especially radiative-dynamic interactions, troposphere-stratosphere interactions, ozone-climate effects; atmospheric radiation, especially greenhouse effects of atmospheric trace gases such as ozone, carbon-dioxide, and chlorofluoromethanes. *Mailing Add:* Climate Sensitivity Group Box 3000 Boulder CO 80307

RAMANI, RAJA VENKAT, b Madras, India, Aug 4, 38; US citizen; m 72; c 2. MINING, COMPUTER SCIENCE. *Educ:* Ranchi Univ, India, BS, 62; Indian Sch Mines, Dhanbad, AISM, 62; Pa State Univ, University Park, MS, 68, PhD(mining), 70. *Prof Exp:* Safety officer, vent officer & prod mgr, Bengal Coal Co, Andrew Yule, India, 62-66; from asst prof to assoc prof, 70-78, PROF MINING ENG, PA STATE UNIV, UNIVERSITY PARK, 78-, CHMN MINERAL ENG MGT, 74- *Concurrent Pos:* Proj dir develop mine vent similator, US Bur Mines, 73-77, proj dir appln total systs simulator to surface coal mining, 75-78; proj dir, Premining Planning Manual Eastern Surface Coal Mining, Environ Protection Agency, 75-78; chmn, Comt Underground Mine Disaster Survival & Rescue, Nat Acad Sci, 79-81; vis prof, Mo Sch Mines, Rolla, 80; proj dir, Integration Surface Mining & Lane Use Planning, US Off Surface Mining, 79-82. *Mem:* Am Inst Mining, Metall & Petrol Engrs; Inst Mgt Sci; Am Soc Eng Educ; Mine Ventilation Soc SAfrica. *Res:* Surface mining and underground mining methods; ventilation; health and safety; computer-oriented planning and control; management; resource management; technical management. *Mailing Add:* Pa State Univ 126A Mineral Sci Bldg University Park PA 16802

RAMANUJAM, V M SADAGOPA, b July 2, 46; m 74; c 1. ORGANIC CHEMISTRY, ENVIRONMENTAL CHEMISTRY. *Educ:* Univ Madras, India, BSc, 66, MSc, 68, PhD(org chem), 73. *Prof Exp:* Instr chem, Vivekananda Col, Madras, India, 68-72; develop chemist, Res Div, Greaves Foseco, Ltd, Calcutta, India, 73; Robert A Welch Found fel, 74-78, ASST PROF, DEPT PREV MED & COMMUNITY HEALTH, ENVIRON HEALTH LAB, UNIV TEX MED BR, GALVESTON, 79- *Concurrent Pos:* Consult, Nat Acad Sci, 79-; sci advr, US Environ Protection Agency, 80-81. *Mem:* Sigma Xi; Am Chem Soc. *Res:* Physico-chemical characterization of toxins from Gymnodinium breve Davis; structure-activity relationship studies on drugs; carcinogens and mutagens; development of analytical methods for drugs, toxins and environmental pollutants; mutagenicity studies on atomatic hydrocarbons and amines; oxidation reaction mechanisms. *Mailing Add:* Environ Health Lab Univ Tex Med Br Galveston TX 77550

RAMANUJAN, MELAPALAYAM SRINIVASAN, b Coimbatore, India, July 16, 31; m 65. MATHEMATICS. *Educ:* Annamalai Univ, Madras, BS, 51, MA, 52, MSc, 53, DSc(math). 58. *Prof Exp:* Res assoc math, Ramanujan Inst Math, 57-58; lectr, Aligarh Muslim Univ, India, 58-59; from instr to assoc prof, 59-72, PROF MATH, UNIV MICH, ANN ARBOR, 72- *Concurrent Pos:* Reader, Ramanujan Inst Math, 61-63; Humboldt fel, Univ Frankfurt, 69-70. *Honors & Awards:* Narasinga Rao Gold Medal, Indian Math Soc, 53. *Mem:* Am Math Soc; Math Asn Am; Indian Math Soc (secy, 62-63). *Res:* Summability; moment problems; topological vector spaces; duality theory; abstract sequence spaces. *Mailing Add:* Dept of Math Univ of Mich Ann Arbor MI 48104

RAMASWAMI, DEVABHAKTUNI, b Pedapudi, India, Apr 4, 33. CHEMICAL ENGINEERING. *Educ:* Andhra, India, BSc, 53, MSc, 54, DSc, 58; Univ Wis, PhD(chem eng), 61. *Prof Exp:* Res scholar chem eng, Andhra, India, 54-56; Indian Inst Technol, Kharagpur, 56-57; asst prof, Benares Hindu Univ, 57-58; res asst, Univ Wis, 58-61; res engr, Int Bus Mach Corp, 61-62; res assoc, 62, CHEM ENGR, ARGONNE NAT LAB, 62- *Mem:* mem Am Inst Chem Engrs. *Res:* Nuclear reactor core; development; engineering; author or coauthor of over 84 publications. *Mailing Add:* Eng Div D207 9700 S Cass Ave Argonne IL 60439

RAMASWAMI, VAIDYANATHAN, b Kerala, India, Feb 24, 50; m 77; c 2. OPERATIONS RESEARCH, STATISTICS. *Educ:* Univ Madras, BSc, 69, MSc, 71; Purdue Univ, MS, 76, PhD(opers res), 78. *Prof Exp:* Lectr statist, Loyola Col, Madras, India, 71-74; ASST PROF MATH, DREXEL UNIV, 78- *Concurrent Pos:* Statist consult, Madras, Ctr Soc Med & Community Health, Jawaharlal Nehru Univ, New Delhi, India, 72-74. *Mem:* Opers Res Soc Am. *Res:* Stochastic processes; computational probability; queueing theory; mathematical programming; discrete optimization. *Mailing Add:* Dept of Math Drexel Univ Philadelphia PA 19104

RAMASWAMY, H N, b Honnavally, India, Oct 30, 37; m 66; c 2. INORGANIC CHEMISTRY, ANALYTICAL CHEMISTRY. *Educ:* Univ Mysore, BSc, 58; Karnatak Univ, India, MSc, 61; Tulane Univ, PhD(inorg chem), 67. *Prof Exp:* Teacher, Govt High Sch, India, 58-59; lectr chem, A P S Col, Bangalore, 61-63; lectr, Tulane Univ, 63-67; res assoc, Southern Regional Res Lab, USDA, La, 67-69; sr chemist, Thiokol Chem Corp, Ga, 69-70; HEAD ANAL LABS, AZS CHEMICAL CO, 70- *Concurrent Pos:* Int Inst Educ NY youth leadership opportunity award, 66-67; NSF fel, 67-69. *Mem:* Am Chem Soc; Sigma Xi; Am Asn Textile Chemists & Colorists. *Res:* Spectroscopy; infrared chemical analysis; pyrolysis and gas-liquid chromatography; textile chemicals and polymers; liquid chromatography, amines, alkyd resins, hydrogenation, distillation product and process development. *Mailing Add:* AZS Chem Co 762 Marietta Blvd NW Atlanta GA 30318

RAMASWAMY, KIZHANATHAM V, b Jalarpet, India, July 17, 35; m 65; c 1. INDUSTRIAL ENGINEERING. *Educ:* Univ Madras, BE, 57; Tex Tech Univ, MS, 59, PhD(indust eng), 71. *Prof Exp:* Trainee nuclear eng, Bhaba Atomic Res Ctr, Bombay, India, 58-59; design engr, 59-61, fabrication engr, 61-64, plant engr, Radiochem Plant, 64-66, asst plant supt, 66-67; asst prof prod mgt, 71-80, ASST PROF GEN BUS, TEX SOUTHERN UNIV, 80- *Mem:* Am Inst Indust Engrs; Soc Mfg Engrs; Indian Inst Eng. *Res:* Manufacturing science; operations research; engineering analysis and design. *Mailing Add:* Sch of Bus Tex Southern Univ Houston TX 77004

RAMATY, REUVEN, b Timisoara, Rumania, Feb 25, 37; m 61; c 2. ASTROPHYSICS. *Educ:* Tel-Aviv Univ, BSc, 61; Univ Calif, Los Angeles, PhD(space sci), 66. *Prof Exp:* Asst res geophysicist, Inst Geophys & Planetary Physics, Univ Calif, Los Angeles, 66-67; Nat Res Coun resident res assoc astrophys, 67-69, PHYSICIST, GODDARD SPACE FLIGHT CTR, NASA, 69- *Concurrent Pos:* Vis scientist, Stanford Univ, 72; vis prof physics, Washington Univ, 78; Alexander von Humboldt Found US sr scientist award, Fed Repub Ger, 75; Sr US Scientist Award, Alexander von Humboldt Found, Fed Repub Ger, 75; Fairchild Scientist, Calif Inst Technol, 79. *Honors & Awards:* Lindsay Award, Goddard Space Flight Ctr, NASA, 80. *Mem:* Am Astron Soc; Int Astron Union. *Res:* High energy astrophysics; solar physics; gamma-ray line astronomy. *Mailing Add:* Goddard Space Flight Ctr NASA Code 660 Greenbelt MD 20771

RAMAYYA, AKUNURI V, b Bezwada, India, Aug 15, 38; m 65; c 1. EXPERIMENTAL NUCLEAR PHYSICS. *Educ:* Andhra Univ. India, BSc, 57, MSc, 58; Ind Univ, PhD(physics), 64. *Prof Exp:* Asst physics, Ind Univ, Bloomington, 60-64; res assoc, 64-70, asst prof, 70-75, assoc prof, 75-80, PROF NUCLEAR PHYSICS, VANDERBILT UNIV, 80- *Concurrent Pos:* Alexander von Humboldt fel, 81-82. *Mem:* Sigma Xi; Am Phys Soc. *Res:* Heavy ion nuclear physics. *Mailing Add:* Dept of Physics Vanderbilt Univ Nashville TN 37235

RAMAZZOTTO, LOUIS JOHN, b New York, NY, Dec 18, 40; m 66; c 2. PHYSIOLOGY. *Educ:* Fairleigh Dickinson Univ, BS, 62; Fordham Univ, MS, 64, PhD(physiol), 66. *Prof Exp:* Lab instr biol, Fairleigh Dickinson Univ, 62-63; lectr, St Peters Col (NJ), 63-64; lectr physiol, Hunter Col, 64-66; asst prof, Marymount Col (NY), 66-67; from asst prof to assoc prof, 67-74, PROF PHYSIOL, SCH DENT & GRAND SCH, FAIRLEIGH DICKINSON UNIV, 74-, CHMN DEPT, 67- *Mem:* AAAS; NY Acad Sci; Am Phys Soc; Fed Am Soc Exp Biol; Int Asn Dent Res. *Res:* Effects of nitrous oxide and other inhalation anesthetics on blood and reproductive system. *Mailing Add:* Fairleigh Dickinson Univ Sch of Dent Hackensack NJ 07601

RAMBAUT, PAUL CHRISTOPHER, b Southampton, Eng, May 23, 40; US citizen. PUBLIC HEALTH, PHYSIOLOGY. *Educ:* McGill Univ, BSc, 62, MSc, 64; Mass Inst Technol, ScD, 66; Harvard Univ, MPH, 68. *Prof Exp:* Instr nutrit, Mass Inst Technol, 66; biochemist, Miami Valley Labs, Procter & Gamble Co, 66-67; biochemist, Johnson Space Ctr, NASA, 68-75; from asst to assoc dir, Bur of Foods, Food & Drug Admin, 75-76; chief, Med Res Br, Johnson Space Ctr, 76-79, MGR BIOMED RES, HQ, NASA, 79- *Honors & Awards:* Underwood Prescott Award, Mass Inst of Technol, 74. *Mem:* Am Chem Soc; Sigma Xi; Aerospace Med Asn; Am Physiol Soc; Am Inst Nutrit. *Res:* Characterization of neurotransmitter substances; sulfur amino acid metabolism; dietary control of cholesterol metabolism; energy and calcium metabolism studies. *Mailing Add:* NASA HQ Washington DC 20546

RAMBERG, STEVEN ERIC, b Boston, Mass, Jan 4, 48; m 67; c 2. MECHANICAL ENGINEERING, FLUID MECHANICS. *Educ:* Univ Lowell, BS, 70, MS, 72; Cath Univ Am, PhD(mech eng), 78. *Prof Exp:* RES ENGR FLUID MECH, NAVAL RES LAB, 72- *Honors & Awards:* Moisseif Award, Am Soc Civil Engrs, 79. *Mem:* Am Soc Mech Engrs; Sigma Xi. *Res:* Flow-induced vibrations; bluff body wakes; ocean wave forces; cable dynamics; wind-wave growth; stratified flows. *Mailing Add:* Naval Res Lab Washington DC 20375

RAMBOSEK, G(EORGE) M(ORRIS), b Eureka, Mont, July 26, 20; m 45; c 5. CHEMICAL ENGINEERING. *Educ:* Mont State Col, BS, 42; Ohio State Univ, MS, 49, PhD(chem eng), 50. *Prof Exp:* Mfg engr, Phillips Petrol Co, 42-46; asst chem eng, Ohio State Univ, 46-47, instr, 47-50; res chem engr, Stanolind Oil & Gas Co, Standard Oil Co, Ind, 50-52; res chem engr, 52-64, res specialist, 64-67, sr res specialist, 67-70, mem staff patent liasion, New Bus Ventures Div, 70-81, MGR, INTELLECTUAL PROP, TECHNOL ENTERPRISES DIV, 3M CO, 81- *Res:* Pressure-volume-temperature-composition data; hydrocarbon synthesis; polymer processing; product development; structural and medical adhesives; dental restorative materials; oil resistant beater additives; synthetic surfacing materials; urethane catalysis; new product development. *Mailing Add:* 3M Ctr Bldg 201-15 3M Co St Paul MN 55144

RAMDAS, ANANT KRISHNA, b Poona, India, May 19, 30; m 56. SOLID STATE PHYSICS, OPTICS. *Educ:* Univ Poona, BSc, 50, MSc, 53, PhD(physics), 56. *Prof Exp:* Res assoc physics, 56-60, from asst prof to assoc prof, 60-67, PROF PHYSICS, PURDUE UNIV, LAFAYETTE, 67- *Concurrent Pos:* Alexander von Humboldt US sr scientist, 77-78. *Mem:* Fel Am Phys Soc; fel Indian Acad Sci. *Res:* Spectroscopy; application of spectroscopic techniques to solid state physics; electronic and vibrational spectra of solids studied by absorption and emission spectra in the visible and the infrared and by laser Raman spectroscopy. *Mailing Add:* Dept of Physics Purdue Univ West Lafayette IN 47907

RAMER, LUTHER GRIMM, b Pawpaw, Ill, May 24, 08; m 35; c 1. ACOUSTICS. *Educ:* Univ Ill, BS, 30, MS, 34. *Prof Exp:* Engr, Bell Tel Labs, 30-32; res engr, Univ Ill, 34-36; res physicist, Riverbank Acoust Labs, Armour Res Found, 36-47, lab supvr acoust, 47-54; res engr, Mech Div, Gen Mills, Inc, 54-60; mgr acoust lab, Wood Conversion Co, 60-62; sr res engr, Trane Co, 62-74; ACOUSTICAL CONSULT, 74- *Mem:* Acoust Soc Am. *Res:* Developmental research in architectural acoustics and acoustical materials; acoustics related to sounds of air conditioning equipment. *Mailing Add:* Rt 10 Box 373 Ft Myers FL 33908

RAMETTE, RICHARD WALES, b Stafford Springs, Conn, Oct 9, 27; m 49; c 5. ANALYTICAL CHEMISTRY, PHYSICAL CHEMISTRY. *Educ:* Wesleyan Univ, BA, 50; Univ Minn. PhD(chem), 54. *Prof Exp:* From asst prof to assoc prof chem, 54-65, chmn dept, 60-72, dir off sci activ, 69-72, PROF CHEM, CARLETON COL, 65- *Concurrent Pos:* Vis scholar, St Olaf Col, 62-63; resident res assoc, Argonne Nat Lab, 66-67; sci adv, US Food & Drug Admin, 69-80; vis prof, Univ Fla, 75-76; chmn, Am Chem Soc, Div of Chem Educ, 77. *Honors & Awards:* Col Chem Teachers Award, Mfr Chemists Asn, 66. *Res:* Aqueous equilibria; solution thermodynamics. *Mailing Add:* Dept Chem Carleton Col Northfield MN 55057

RAMEY, BOBBIE JOE, organic chemistry, see previous edition

RAMEY, CHESTER EUGENE, b Santa Maria, Calif, Jan 15, 43; m 64; c 3. ORGANIC CHEMISTRY. *Educ:* Univ Calif, Berkeley, BS, 64; Univ Ore, PhD(org chem), 68. *Prof Exp:* Sr res chemist, Plastics & Additives Div, Ciba-Geigy Corp, 68-76; GROUP LEADER SYNTHESIS, CORP RES, FERRO CORP, 76- *Mem:* Am Chem Soc. *Res:* Polymer additives; antioxidants; ultra violet stabilizers; heat stabilizers; stabilization and degradation of polymers. *Mailing Add:* Corp Res Ferro Corp 7040 Krick Rd Bedford OH 44146

RAMEY, DANIEL BRUCE, b Shelby, Mich, Dec 11, 49; m 75; c 1. CLUSTER ANALYSIS. *Educ:* Mich State Univ, BA, 71, MS, 73; Yale Univ, MPhil, 79, PhD(statist, 82. *Prof Exp:* Analyst, Gerber Prod Co, 74-77; res asst, Yale Univ, 79-81; SCIENTIST, LOCKHEED-EMSCO, 81- *Concurrent Pos:* Lectr, South Conn State Co, 80 & Univ Houston, 81- *Mem:* Am Statist Asn; Inst Math Statist; Royal Statist Soc. *Res:* Cluster analysis techniques and computing algorithms; application of statistical techniques to remote sensor data. *Mailing Add:* #531 17700 El Camino Real Houston TX 77058

RAMEY, ESTELLE R, b Detroit, Mich, Aug 23, 17; m 41; c 2. PHYSIOLOGY, ENDOCRINOLOGY. *Educ:* Columbia Univ, MA, 40; Univ Chicago, PhD(physiol), 50. *Prof Exp:* Tutor chem, Queens Col (NY), 38-41; lectr, Univ Tenn, 42-47; instr physiol, Univ Chicago, 51-54, asst prof, 54-58; from asst prof to assoc prof, 56-66, PROF PHYSIOL, SCH MED, GEORGETOWN UNIV, 66-, PROF BIOPHYS, 80- *Concurrent Pos:* USPHS fel, Univ Chicago, 50-51. *Mem:* Am Physiol Soc; Am Chem Soc; Endocrine Soc; Am Diabetes Asn; Am Acad Neurol. *Res:* Endocrinology metabolism chiefly in the field of adrenal function and insulin action. *Mailing Add:* Dept of Physiol Georgetown Univ Sch of Med Washington DC 20007

RAMEY, H(ENRY) J(ACKSON), JR, b Pittsburgh, Pa, Nov 30, 25; m 48; c 4. CHEMICAL ENGINEERING. *Educ:* Purdue Univ, BS, 49, PhD(chem eng), 52. *Prof Exp:* Asst chem eng, Unit Opers Lab, Purdue Univ, 49; asst radiant heat transfer from gases, 51-52; sr res technologist, petrol prod res, Magnolia Petrol Co, Socony Mobil Oil Co, Inc, 52-55, proj engr, Gen Petrol Corp, 55-60; staff reservoir engr, Mobil Oil Co Div, 60-63; prof petrol eng, Tex A&M Univ, 63-66; PROF PETROL ENG, STANFORD UNIV, 66- *Concurrent Pos:* Consult, Chinese Petrol Corp, Taiwan, 62-63. *Honors & Awards:* Ferguson Medal, Am Inst Mining, Metall & Petrol Engrs, 59. *Mem:* Am Inst Chem Engrs; Am Inst Mining, Metall & Petrol Engrs. *Res:* Heat transfer, thermodynamics; fluid flow; petroleum production. *Mailing Add:* Dept of Petrol Eng Stanford Univ Stanford CA 94305

RAMEY, HARMON HOBSON, JR, b Russell, Ark, Dec 4, 30; m 54; c 2. PLANT GENETICS. *Educ:* Univ Ark, BSA, 51, MS, 52; NC State Col, PhD(plant breeding, genetics), 59. *Prof Exp:* Asst, Univ Ark, 51-52; asst cotton geneticist, Delta Br Exp Sta, Miss State Univ, 55-57; asst, NC State Col, 57-59; asst cotton geneticist, Delta Br Exp Sta, Miss State Univ, 59-61; geneticist & fiber scientist, Nat Cotton Coun Am, Tenn, 61-70; RES GENETICIST, SCI & EDUC ADMIN, USDA, 70- *Mem:* Am Soc Qual Control; Am Soc Testing & Mat; Fiber Soc; Am Soc Agron; Genetics Soc Am. *Res:* Evolution and differentiation within a genus; quantitative genetics; breeding methodology; fiber technology. *Mailing Add:* Cotton Qual Labs Univ of Tenn-Agr Campus Knoxville TN 37916

RAMEY, MADISON LOUIE, b Gladewater, Tex, Sept 3, 19; m 48; c 4. AEROSPACE ENGINEERING & TECHNOLOGY. *Educ:* Univ Tex, CE, 41. *Prof Exp:* Engr, 41-45, proj stress engr, 45-55, chief struct res engr, 55-59, mgr struct, 59-68, mgr eng technol, 68-69, DIV VPRES ENG TECHNOL, MCDONNELL AIRCRAFT CO, MCDONNELL DOUGLAS CORP, 69- *Mem:* Assoc fel Am Inst Aeronaut & Astronaut. *Res:* Aircraft structures; technology integration; engineering management. *Mailing Add:* McDonnell Aircraft Co Dept 230 Bldg 1 PO Box 516 St Louis MO 63166

RAMEY, MELVIN RICHARD, b Pittsburgh, Pa, Sept 13, 38; m 64; c 2. CIVIL ENGINEERING, BIOMECHANICS. *Educ:* Pa State Univ, BS, 60; Carnegie-Mellon Univ, MS, 65, PhD(civil eng), 67. *Prof Exp:* Bridge design engr, Pa State Dept Hwys, 60-63; res asst, Carnegie-Mellon Univ, 63-67; from asst prof to assoc prof, 67-73, PROF CIVIL ENG, UNIV CALIF, DAVIS, 73- *Concurrent Pos:* Consult, Calif State Div Hwys, 68-69, Murray & McCormick Consult Engrs, 69 & Fireman's Fund Am Ins Co, 70; struct design consult, 67- *Mem:* Am Soc Civil Engrs; Forest Prod Res Soc. *Res:* Structural design and analysis; materials behavior and testing; biomechanics with applications to human movement and sports. *Mailing Add:* Dept of Civil Eng Univ of Calif Davis CA 95616

RAMEY, ROBERT LEE, b Middletown, Ohio, June 26, 22; m 46; c 2. ENGINEERING PHYSICS. *Educ:* Duke Univ, BSEE, 45; Univ Cincinnati, MS, 47; NC State Col, PhD(elec eng, physics), 54. *Prof Exp:* Asst elec eng, Univ Cincinnati, 46-48; instr, NC State Col, 49-54; res lab dir, Wright Mach Div, Sperry-Rand Corp, 54-56; assoc prof elec eng, 56-62, PROF ELEC ENG, UNIV VA, 62- *Concurrent Pos:* Ed, Encycl Sci & Technol, 59; NASA res grant, 62-70. *Mem:* Am Phys Soc; Inst Elec & Electronics Engrs. *Res:* Physical electronics, including vacuum, gaseous and solid state. *Mailing Add:* Dept of Elec Eng Univ of Va Charlottesville VA 22903

RAMEY, ROY RICHARD, b Kansas City, Mo, July 11, 47; m 70; c 2. CERAMIC ENGINEERING. *Educ:* Univ Mo, Rolla, BS, 70, MS, 72, PhD(ceramic eng), 74. *Prof Exp:* Res engr, Inland Steel Co, 74-79; MGR, A P GREEN REFRACTORIES CO, 80- *Mem:* Am Ceramic Soc; Nat Inst Ceramic Engrs. *Res:* Refractory-slag interactions; thermo-mechanical properties of refractories. *Mailing Add:* A P Green Refractories Co Green Blvd Mexico MO 65265

RAMFJORD, SIGURD, b Kolvereid, Norway, June 6, 11; nat US; m 56; c 1. DENTISTRY, PERIODONTOLOGY. *Educ:* Univ Mich, MS, 48, PhD, 51. *Hon Degrees:* DMD, Univ Geneva, 78, Dr Odontol, Gothenburg Univ, 80 & Oslo Univ, 81. *Prof Exp:* Pvt pract, Oslo, Norway, 34-46; PROF DENT, SCH DENT, UNIV MICH, ANN ARBOR, 58- *Concurrent Pos:* Consult, Vet Admin Hosp, Ann Arbor & WHO, India; emer nat consult, US Air Force. *Honors & Awards:* Basic Res Award, Int Asn Dent Res, 68; William J Gies Found Award, 71. *Mem:* Am Dent Asn; Am Acad Periodont; Am Acad Oral Path; NY Acad Sci; Int Asn Dent Res. *Res:* Periodontics; occlusion; electromyography; radioisotopes. *Mailing Add:* Univ of Mich Sch of Dent Ann Arbor MI 48104

RAMIG, ROBERT E, b McGrew, Nebr, June 22, 22; m 43; c 3. SOIL CONSERVATION, SOIL FERTILITY. *Educ:* Univ Nebr, BSc, 43, PhD(soils), 60; Wash State Univ, MSc, 48. *Prof Exp:* Asst agronomist, Exp Sta, Univ Nebr, 48-51; coop agent, Exp Sta, Univ Nebr & USDA, 51-57; soil scientist, Agr Res Serv, 57-71, DIR, COLUMBIA PLATEAU CONSERV RES CTR, AGR RES SERV, USDA, 71- *Mem:* Am Soc Agron; Soil Sci Soc Am; Soil Conserv Soc Am; AAAS. *Res:* Soil and moisture conservation using balanced fertility to give maximum production per unit of water. *Mailing Add:* Agr Res Serv USDA PO Box 370 Pendleton OR 97801

RAMILINGAM, SUBBIAH, b Udumalpet, India, June 15, 35; m 67. MECHANICAL ENGINEERING, MATERIALS ENGINEERING. *Educ:* Indian Inst Technol, Khapagpur, India, BTech Hons, 56; Univ Ill, Urbana, MS, 61, PhD(mech eng), 67. *Prof Exp:* Instr, Univ Ill, Urbana, 61-67; asst prof, 67-68; from asst prof to prof mech eng, State Univ NY, Buffalo, 68-77; PROF MECH ENG, GA INST TECHNOL, 77- *Concurrent Pos:* Vis prof, Monash Univ, Australia, 75-76. *Mem:* Am Inst Mining, Metall & Petrol Engrs; Am Soc Metals; Soc Mfg Engrs; Japan Soc Precision Engrs; Am Soc Mech Engrs. *Res:* Machining theory; theory of tool wear; tribology; deformation processing; alloy design for processing; thin film science and technology; materials conservation through thin film technology; electron microscopy of metals; magnetron melting and plasma processing. *Mailing Add:* Sch of Mech Eng Ga Inst of Technol Atlanta GA 30332

RAMIREZ, DONALD EDWARD, b New Orleans, La, May 21, 43; m 64; c 3. MATHEMATICS. *Educ:* Tulane Univ, BS, 63, PhD(math), 69. *Prof Exp:* Off Naval Res fel & res assoc, Univ Wash, 66-67; asst prof, 67-71, ASSOC PROF MATH, UNIV VA, 71- *Mem:* Am Math Soc. *Res:* Abstract harmonic analysis. *Mailing Add:* Dept of Math Univ of Va Charlottesville VA 22903

RAMIREZ, FAUSTO, b Zulueta, Cuba, June 15, 23; nat US; m 47; c 2. ORGANIC CHEMISTRY. *Educ:* Univ Mich, BS, 46, MS, 47, PhD(org chem), 49. *Prof Exp:* McConnell fel, Univ Va, 49-50; from instr to asst prof chem, Columbia Univ, 50-58; assoc prof, Ill Inst Technol, 58-59; PROF CHEM, STATE UNIV NY STONY BROOK, 59- *Concurrent Pos:* Lectr, Gordon Res Conf Org Reactions Processes, 59, Org Reactions, 62 & Heterocyclics, 66; Sloan fel, 61-63; symp organophosphorus compounds, Int Union Pure & Appl Chem, Ger, 64; colloquium phosphorus chem, Nat Ctr Sci Res, Toulouse, France, 65; NSF fel, 65-66; distinguished res fel, Res Found, State Univ NY, 67; plenary lectr, Int Colloquium Phosphorus, Paris, 69; frontier-in-chem lectr, Case Western Reserve Univ, 70; lectr, Conf Org Reaction Mech, Univ Calif, Santa Cruz, 70; plenary lectr, All Union Conf Organophosphorous Chem, Moscow, 72, Int Colloquium Phosphorus, Gdansk, Poland & Int Conf on Oligonucleatide Synthesis, Poznan, Poland, 74, Dymaczewo, Poland, 76, Int Conf on Phosphorus, Halle, East Ger, 79 & Int Conf on Phosphorus Chem, Durham, NC, 81; Alexander von Humboldt Found award, Munich Tech Univ, 73-74. *Honors & Awards:* Silver Medal, City of Paris, 69; A Cresy-Morrison Award, NY Acad Sci, 68. *Mem:* Am Chem Soc; fel NY Acad Sci. *Res:* Theoretical and practical aspects of the chemistry of phosphorus and sulfur compounds; organic synthesis; molecular biology. *Mailing Add:* Dept of Chem State Univ of NY Stony Brook NY 11794

RAMIREZ, GUILLERMO, b Bogota, Colombia, Sept 19, 34; US citizen; m 57; c 2. ONCOLOGY. *Educ:* Nat Col St Bartholomew, BS, 51; Nat Univ Colombia, MD, 58. *Prof Exp:* ASSOC PROF HUMAN ONCOL, SCH MED, UNIV WIS-MADISON, 71- *Concurrent Pos:* Consult, Vet Admin Hosps, 68-; prin investr, Cent Oncol Group, 72- *Mem:* Am Asn Cancer Res; Am Soc Clin Oncol; Int Asn Study Lung Cancer; NY Acad Sci; Am Asn Study Neoplastic Dis. *Res:* Clinical-pharmacological studies; phase I, II and III drug studies. *Mailing Add:* Univ Wis Hosp 600 Highland Ave Madison WI 53792

RAMIREZ, J ROBERTO, b Ponce, PR, Feb 17, 41; US citizen; m 72; c 1. BIO-ORGANIC CHEMISTRY. *Educ:* Univ Notre Dame, BSc, 63; Univ PR, MSc, 66; Univ Karlsruhe, Ger, Dr rer nat, 70. *Prof Exp:* Fel, Swiss Fed Inst Technol, 71-72; CHMN & ASSOC PROF CHEM, UNIV PR, RIO PIEDRAS CAMPUS, 75- *Mem:* Soc Chemists PR (secy, 73-74, pres-elect, 74-75, pres, 75-); Am Chem Soc. *Res:* Biosynthesis of acyclic carotenes; synthesis of carotenoids and model compounds. *Mailing Add:* Univ PR Sta Box 22161 San Juan PR 00931

RAMIREZ, JESUS EMILIO, geophysics, deceased

RAMIREZ, SAMUEL AMADOR, b El Paso, Tex, Apr 28, 36; m 57; c 2. GENETICS, DEVELOPMENTAL BIOLOGY. *Educ:* Univ Tex, El Paso, BA, 58; Tex Tech Univ, MS, 66; Ind Univ, Bloomington, PhD(genetics-develop biol), 74. *Prof Exp:* Teaching assoc biol, Univ Tex, El Paso, 56-58; noncom officer-in-chg med technol, US Army Med Corps, 58-61; biol teacher, Bel Air High Sch, 61-66; instr biol sci, Univ Tex, El Paso, 66-69; assoc instr cell biol, Ind Univ, Bloomington, 69-70; USPHS fel pharmacol, Baylor Col Med, 73-75; ASST PROF GENETICS, UNIV TEX, SAN ANTONIO, 75- *Concurrent Pos:* Prin investr, Bur Land Mgt, S Tex Study, 76-78; consult, HEW Minority Biomed Support Prog, 76- & Eagle Pass High Sch Migrant Workers' Children Comn, 78-; mem adv bd & co-investr, Minority Biomed Support Prog-United Cols San Antonio, 77-; reviewer, NSF, Div Sci Educ Resources Improv, 78-; fel, Nat Chicano Coun, Higher Educ, 78-79. *Mem:* Genetics Soc Am; Am Genetic Asn; Am Soc Cell Biol; AAAS; Sigma Xi. *Res:* Developmental and histopathological studies of marine organisms in the Gulf of Mexico; cytogenetic studies of marine organisms, karyologic analysis and the study of position effect as it relates to the ribosomal ribonucleic acid cistrons. *Mailing Add:* 11915 Mesquite Mesa San Antonio TX 78249

RAMIREZ, W FRED, JR, b New Orleans, La, Feb 19, 41; m 63; c 3. CHEMICAL ENGINEERING. *Educ:* Tulane Univ, BS, 62, MS, 64, PhD(chem eng), 65. *Prof Exp:* From asst prof to assoc prof, 65-75, chmn dept, 71-79, Croft res prof, 80, PROF CHEM ENG, UNIV COLO, BOULDER, 75- *Concurrent Pos:* Fulbright res fel, France, 76. *Honors & Awards:* Dow Award, Am Soc Eng Educ, 74; Levey Award, Tulane Univ, 74; Western Elec Award, Am Soc Eng Educ, 80. *Mem:* Am Inst Chem Engrs; Am Soc Eng Educ; Soc Petrol Engrs. *Res:* Optimal control of chemical processes; enhanced oil recovery; membrane transport. *Mailing Add:* Dept of Chem Eng Univ of Colo Boulder CO 80309

RAMIREZ-RONDA, CARLOS HECTOR, b Mayaguez, PR, Jan 24, 43; US citizen; m 63; c 2. INFECTIOUS DISEASES. *Educ:* Northwestern Univ, Chicago, BSM, 64, MD, 67. *Prof Exp:* Res fel infectious dis, Southwestern Med Sch, Univ Tex, 73-75; asst prof med, Sch Med, Univ Puerto Rico, 75-78; assoc prof med, 78-82, DIR INFECTIOUS DIS, SCH MED, VET ADMIN HOSP, 78-, PROF MED, 82-; ASSOC CHIEF STAFF RES & DEVELOP, VET ADMIN MED CTR, SAN JUAN, 75-, CHIEF, INFECTIOUS DISEASE RES LAB, 76- *Concurrent Pos:* Vis prof, Autonomous Univ, Mex, 78, 79 & 80; mem bacteriol & mycol study sect, NIH, 81-85; consult infectious dis, San Juan City Hosp, 76-; investr, Am Heart Asn & PR Heart Asn, 77-; assoc ed, Puerto Rico Med Asn J, 78-; prog dir infectious dis, Univ Hosp, San Juan, 78- *Mem:* Infectious Dis Soc; Am Fedn Clin Res; Am Soc Microbiol; Am Col Physicians. *Res:* Pathogenesis of bacterial diseases especially adherence and bacterial endocarditis; clinical microbiology; microbiol susceptibility and resistance; antibiotic pharmacology; seroepidemiology. *Mailing Add:* Vet Admin Med Ctr PO Box 4867(151) San Juan PR 00936

RAMKE, THOMAS FRANKLIN, b Bancker, La, Jan 1, 17; m 41; c 4. FORESTRY. *Educ:* La State Univ, BS, 40. *Prof Exp:* Forester, La Dept Conserv, 40-41; asst dist forester, 41-42; forester, Tenn Valley Auth, 42-61; asst dist forester, 48-49; chief forestry field br, 61-66; forest mgt br, Norris, 66-67; tributary area rep, 67-74; dist mgt, Off Tributary Area Develop, 74-79; RETIRED. *Mem:* AAAS; Soc Am Foresters; Commun Develop Soc. *Res:* Factors related to the application of forest and watershed management and skillful use of forest reserves; elements related to improving community structure for effective citizen participation; community planning, evaluation and development. *Mailing Add:* 4107 Fulton Rd Knoxville TN 37918

RAMLER, EDWARD OTTO, b Washington, DC, Sept 25, 16; m 42; c 3. ORGANIC CHEMISTRY. *Educ:* Cath Univ Am, BS, 38; Pa State Col, MS, 40, PhD(org chem), 42. *Prof Exp:* Asst chem, Pa State Col, 39-41, instr, 41-42; res chemist, Plastics Dept, E I du Pont de Nemours & Co, Inc, 46-46, tech investr, Textile Fibers Dept, 46-53, supvr patent div, 53-60, patent adminr, Int Dept, 60-70, mgr patents, Trademarks & Contracts Sect, 70-80; RETIRED. *Mem:* Am Chem Soc. *Res:* Organic chemistry of fluorine; synthesis of vinyl type monomers and polymers; plastics technology; reactions catalyzed by hydrogen fluoride. *Mailing Add:* 513 Woodside Ave Woodside Hills Wilmington DE 19809

RAMLER, W(ARREN) J(OSEPH), b Joliet, Ill, Jan 1, 21; m; c 3. ELECTRICAL ENGINEERING. *Educ:* Ill Inst Technol, BS, 43, MS, 51. *Prof Exp:* Student engr, Westinghouse Elec Corp, 43; instr elec eng, Carnigie Inst Technol, 43-44 & 46; asst elec eng, Tenn Eastman Corp, 44-46; assoc elec eng, Argonne Nat Lab, 46-49, asst group leader, Cyclotron Proj, 49-56, group leader, 56-59, sr scientist, 59, group leader low energy accelerators, 59-73; gen mgr, 73-81, SR VPRES, RADIATION POLYMER CO, PPG INDUSTS,

INC, 81- *Concurrent Pos:* Consult, Argonne Nat Lab, 73- *Mem:* Inst Elec & Electronics Engrs; Am Phys Soc; NY Acad Sci; Am Mgt Asn. *Res:* Development, design and construction of radiation generating equipment for industrial use and laboratory research; Dc and cyclic accelerators, linacs, and ultraviolet processors. *Mailing Add:* 15 Buckingham Dr Prestbury Aurora IL 60504

RAMLOW, GERHARD G, b Berlin, Ger, Jan 4, 40; m 64; c 2. POLYMER CHEMISTRY, ORGANIC CHEMISTRY. *Educ:* Free Univ, Berlin, Dipl, 65, Dr rer nat, 67. *Prof Exp:* Chemist fibers, BASF AG Ludwigshafen, Ger, 68-71, sr res chemist polyols, Wyandotte, Mich, 71-73, mgr res & develop expandable PS, Jamesburg, NJ, 73-77, mgr res & develop, 77-79, DIR, URETHANE CHEM RES & DEVELOP & TECH SERV, BASF WYANDOTTE CORP, WYANDOTTE, MICH, 79- *Mem:* Am Chem Soc. *Res:* Polyurethanes, especially raw materials, application; polymer dispersions in non aqueous media, reinforced polymers. *Mailing Add:* BASF Wyandotte Corp 1419 Biddle Wyandotte MI 48192

RAMM, DIETOLF, b Berlin, Ger, June 17, 42; US citizen; m 66. COMPUTER SCIENCE. *Educ:* Cornell Univ, BA, 64; Duke Univ, PhD(physics), 69. *Prof Exp:* Assoc community health sci, Med Ctr, Duke Univ, 69-70, asst prof community health sci, univ, 70-71, asst prof info sci in psychiat, 70-76 & comput sci, 71-76, ASSOC MED RES PROF PSYCHIAT, MED CTR, DUKE UNIV, 76-, DIR GERIAT COMPUT CTR, CTR STUDY AGING & HUMAN DEVELOP, 69- *Concurrent Pos:* Lectr comput sci, Duke Univ, 76- *Mem:* AAAS; Asn Comput Mach; Geront Soc; Am Phys Soc. *Res:* Medical applications for computing; micro-computers in the laboratory; human-machine interface problems; interactive computing; computers in psychiatry and the study of aging. *Mailing Add:* Box 3003 Duke Univ Med Ctr Durham NC 27710

RAMMELKAMP, CHARLES HENRY, internal medicine, deceased

RAMMER, IRWYN ALDEN, b Stockton, Calif, Aug 15, 28; m 56; c 3. AGRICULTURE, ENTOMOLOGY. *Educ:* Univ Calif, BS, 51, MS, 52, PhD(entom), 60. *Prof Exp:* Res asst entom, Univ Calif, 56-59; SR RES BIOLOGIST, AGR CHEM GROUP, FMC CORP, 59- *Mem:* Entom Soc Am. *Res:* Pesticides for control of agricultural pests. *Mailing Add:* Develop Dept Agr Chem Group FMC Corp 855 Parr Blvd Richmond CA 94804

RAMMING, DAVID WILBUR, b Oklahoma City, Okla, Oct 31, 46; m 75; c 3. PLANT BREEDING. *Educ:* Okla State Univ, BA, 68, MA, 72; Rutgers Univ, PhD(hort), 76. *Prof Exp:* Teaching asst crop sci, Okla State Univ, 68-69, asst hort, 71-72; asst fruit breeding, Rutgers Univ, 72-75; RES LEADER FRUIT BREEDING, WESTERN REGION, SCI & EDUC ADMIN, AGR RES, USDA, 75- *Mem:* Am Soc Hort Sci; Am Pomol Soc. *Res:* Fruit breeding, development of improved stone fruit and grape varieties, cytological analysis of Prunus chromosomes and pollen tube incompatibility; embryo culture of prunus and vitis. *Mailing Add:* PO Box 8143 Fresno CA 93747

RAM-MOHAN, L RAMDAS, b Poona, India, July 21, 44; US citizen. SOLID STATE PHYSICS. *Educ:* Univ Delhi, BSc, 64; Purdue Univ, MS, 67, PhD(physics), 71. *Prof Exp:* Instr physics, Purdue Univ, 75-78; asst prof, 78-80, ASSOC PROF, WORCESTER POLYTECH INST, 80- *Mem:* Am Phys Soc. *Res:* Theory of electromagnetic properties of metals; optical properties of semiconductors; phase transitions in nuclear matter; many-body theory; quantum field theory. *Mailing Add:* Dept Physics Worcester Polytech Inst Worcester MA 01609

RAMO, SIMON, b Salt Lake City, Utah, May 7, 13; m 37; c 2. ELECTRICAL ENGINEERING, PHYSICS. *Educ:* Univ Utah, BS, 33; Calif Inst Technol, PhD(elec eng, physics), 36. *Hon Degrees:* DEng, Case Inst Technol, 60, Univ Mich, 66 & Polytech Inst New York, 71; DSc, Univ Utah, 61, Union Col, 63, Worcester Polytech Inst, 68, Univ Akron, 69 & Cleveland State Univ, 76; LLD, Carnegie-Mellon Univ, 70 & Univ Southern Calif, 72. *Prof Exp:* Res engr, Gen Elec Co, NY, 36-46; vpres & dir opers, Hughes Aircraft Co, 46-53; exec vpres, Ramo-Wooldridge Corp, 53-58; sci dir, US Intercontinental Guided Missile Prog, 54-58; exec vpres, 58-61, vchmn bd, 61-78, chmn exec comt, 69-78, DIR, TRW INC, 54-, CHMN BD, TRW-FUJITSU CO, 80- *Concurrent Pos:* Pres & dir, Bunker Ramo Corp, 64-66; dir, Union Bank & Times Mirror Co; mem, White House Energy Res & Develop Coun, 73-75, adv comt sci & foreign affairs, US Dept State, 73-75 & bd dirs, Los Angeles World Affairs Coun; trustee, Calif Inst Technol; chmn, President's Comt Sci & Technol, 76-77, co-chmn, Transition Task Force Sci & Technol, 80-81; mem, Secy's Adv Coun, Dept Commerce, 76-77 & roster consult to adminr, ERDA, 76-77; vis prof mgt sci, Calif Inst Technol, 78-; fac fel, John F Kennedy Sch Govt, Harvard Univ, 80-; mem bd adv sci & technol, Repub China, 81-; Regent's lectr, Univ Calif, Los Angeles, 81-82. *Honors & Awards:* Nat Medal Sci, Franklin Inst, 79. *Mem:* Nat Acad Sci; Nat Acad Eng; fel Am Inst Aeronaut & Astronaut; fel Am Phys Soc; fel Inst Elec & Electronics Engrs. *Res:* Electronics; microwaves; guided missiles. *Mailing Add:* TRW Inc One Space Park Redondo Beach CA 90278

RAMOHALLI, NANJUDA RAO KUMAR, b Karnataka, India, Nov 12, 45; m 77. COMBUSTION, ACOUSTICS. *Educ:* Univ Col Eng, BE, 67; Indian Inst Sci, ME, 68; Mass Inst Technol, PhD(propulsion), 71. *Prof Exp:* Res fel propulsion, Guggenheim Jet Propulsion Ctr, 71-74, sr res fel, 74-75, sr sect mem tech staff advan technol, 75-79, GROUP LEADER & GROUP SUPVR THERMODYN & CHEM, JET PROPULSION LAB, CALIF INST TECHNOL, 79-, RES ENGR, 81- *Concurrent Pos:* Vis scientist, Indian Inst Sci, Indian Space Res Orgn, 78; mgr, Sunfuels, Jet Propulsion Lab, Calif Inst Technol, 80-81. *Mem:* Assoc fel Am Inst Aeronaut & Astronaut; Combustion Inst; Sigma Xi. *Res:* Combustion involving solids and gases; theory of hybrid combustion; composite solid propellant combustion including nitramines; novel perforated porous plate analogue for heterogeneous combustion; acoustic diagnostics of burners; graphite compostes and their hazards alleviation through gasification. *Mailing Add:* 125-159 Jet Propulsion Lab Pasadena CA 91109

RAMON, SERAFIN, b Feb 3, 34; US citizen; m 58; c 2. CYTOGENETICS. *Educ:* Panhandle Agr & Mech Col, BS, 57; Univ N Mex MS, 62; Univ Kans, PhD(bot), 67. *Prof Exp:* From instr to asst prof biol, Panhandle Agr & Mech Col, 59-65; assoc prof biol, 67-71, head dept, 69-73, head dept sci, 73-75, PROF BIOL, PANHANDLE STATE UNIV, 71-, HEAD DEPT, 77- *Mem:* AAAS; Genetics Soc Am; Bot Soc Am; Am Genetic Asn. *Res:* Plant morphology and root anatomy; cytogenetic and biosystematics of selected Compositae. *Mailing Add:* Dept of Biol Panhandle State Univ Goodwell OK 73939

RAMOND, PIERRE MICHEL, b Neuilly-Seine, France, Jan 31, 43; US citizen; m 67; c 3. ELEMENTARY PARTICLE PHYSICS. *Educ:* Newark Col Eng, BSE, 65; Syracuse Univ, PhD(physics), 69. *Prof Exp:* Res assoc physics, Fermi Lab, 69-71; instr, Yale Univ, 71-73, asst prof, 73-76; Millikan fel, Calif Inst Technol, 75-80; PROF PHYSICS, UNIV FLA, 80- *Concurrent Pos:* Trustee, Aspen Ctr Physics, Univ Fla, 80- *Res:* Grand unified theories; unification of gravity with elementary particles via supersymetry. *Mailing Add:* Dept Physics Univ Fla Gainesville FL 32611

RAMON-MOLINER, ENRIQUE, b Murcia, Spain, July 11, 27; Can citizen; m 57; c 4. NEUROANATOMY. *Educ:* Inst Cajal, Madrid, MD, 56; McGill Univ, PhD, 59. *Prof Exp:* Asst res prof anat, Univ Md, 59-63; from asst prof to assoc prof physiol, Laval Univ, 63-68; assoc prof, 68-74, PROF ANAT, SCH MED, UNIV SHERBROOKE, 74- *Concurrent Pos:* Assoc, Med Res Coun Can, 63-81. *Mem:* Am Asn Anat; Can Asn Anat; Can Physiol Soc; Int Brain Res Orgn; Soc Neurosci. *Res:* Histology and cytology of the central nervous system; structure of the cerebral cortex; morphological varieties and classification of nerve cells; correlation between dendritic morphology and function of nerve cells; ultrastructure of the central nervous system; neurohistochemistry; corticothalamic connections. *Mailing Add:* Dept of Anat Univ of Sherbrooke Sch Med Sherbrooke PQ J1K 2R1 Can

RAMOS, HAROLD SMITH, b Atlanta, Ga, July 20, 28; m 54; c 3. MEDICINE. *Educ:* Johns Hopkins Univ, AB, 48; Med Col Ga, MD, 54. *Prof Exp:* From asst prof to assoc prof, 63-75, PROF MED, SCH MED, EMORY UNIV, 75-, ASST DEAN SCH MED, 72-; CHIEF MED & DIR MED EDUC, CRAWFORD W LONG MEM HOSP, 63- *Concurrent Pos:* Fel hemat & renal dis, Walter Reed Army Inst Res, Washington, DC, 58-59. *Mem:* AMA; Am Col Physicians; NY Acad Sci. *Res:* Medical education; cardiology. *Mailing Add:* 35 Linden Ave NE Atlanta GA 30308

RAMOS, JUAN IGNACIO, b Bernardos, Spain, Jan 28, 53. MECHANICAL ENGINEERING. *Educ:* Madrid Polytech Univ, BAEng, 75; Princeton Univ, MA, 79, PhD(mech eng), 80. *Prof Exp:* Res engr, Int Air Safety Asn, Spain, 76-77; ASST PROF MECH ENG, CARNEGIE-MELLON UNIV, 80- *Concurrent Pos:* Consult, PPG Industs, 82-; prin investr, NASA Lewis Res Ctr, 80-, NSF, 81- *Honors & Awards:* Ralph R Teetor Award, Soc Automotive Eng, 81. *Mem:* Soc Indust & Appl Math; Am Inst Aeronaut & Astronaut; Sigma Xi; Soc Automotive Engrs; Soc Eng Sci. *Res:* Numerical modeling of internal combustion engines and gas turbines (combustion and fluid mechanics); numerical analysis finite elements; heat transfer and ignition, thermal sciences; applied mathematics, wave propagation. *Mailing Add:* Dept Mech Eng Carnegie-Mellon Univ Pittsburgh PA 15213

RAMOS, LILLIAN, b Ponce, PR; US citizen. CHEMISTRY, SCIENCE EDUCATION. *Educ:* Cath Univ PR, BS, 54; Fordham Univ, MSEd, 60, PhD, 71. *Prof Exp:* Prof chem, biol, phys sci & math, 55-70, prof educ, 70-78, dir grad studies educ, 71-77, PROF SCH ADMIN, CATH UNIV PR, 70- *Mem:* Am Chem Soc; Col Chem PR. *Res:* School administration. *Mailing Add:* Dept of Educ Cath Univ of Puerto Rico Ponce PR 00731

RAMOSKA, WILLIAM ALLEN, b Akron, Ohio, Jan 24, 49; m 71. INSECT PATHOLOGY. *Educ:* Ohio State Univ, BS, 71, MS, 73, PhD(entom), 75. *Prof Exp:* Field researcher, Dow Chem Int, 72; res assoc entom, Ohio State Univ, 73-75; insect pathologist, Lee County Mosquito Abatement Dist, Ft Myers, Fla, 76-77; ASST PROF ENTOM, KANS STATE UNIV, 77- *Concurrent Pos:* Consult, Chem-Lawn Corp, 71-72, Extermital Termite Serv, 71- & WHO, 78- *Mem:* Am Mosquito Control Asn; Soc Invert Path; Tissue Cult Asn; Entom Soc Am. *Res:* Virus infective to Autographa Californica, Trichoplusia ni, Heliothis virescens; nature of research is to determine invasive entities of the virus in vivo as well as in vitro; basic and applied investigations into use of various fungal and bacterial pathogens against insects; epizootology; microbial control of insects. *Mailing Add:* Dept Entom Kans State Univ Manhattan KS 66506

RAMP, FLOYD LESTER, b Newman, Ill, Mar 6, 23; m 48; c 4. ORGANIC CHEMISTRY. *Educ:* Univ Ill, BS, 44; Univ Minn, PhD, 50. *Prof Exp:* Du Pont fel, Mass Inst Technol, 51; res chemist, 51-62, sr res assoc, 62-69, RES FEL CHEM, RES CTR, B F GOODRICH CO, BRECKSVILLE, 69- *Mem:* Am Chem Soc. *Res:* Chemical reactions of high polymers; electrochemistry. *Mailing Add:* BF Goodrich Res & Develop Ctr 9921 Brecksville Rd Brecksville OH 44141

RAMP, WARREN KIBBY, b New York, NY, Aug 19, 39; m 63; c 2. PHYSIOLOGY, BIOCHEMISTRY. *Educ:* State Univ NY Col Oneonta, BS, 63; Colo State Univ, MS, 64; Univ Ky, PhD(physiol, biophys), 67. *Prof Exp:* assoc prof oral biol & pharmacol, Univ NC, Chapel Hill, 70-79; ASSOC PROF ORAL BIOL, PHARMACOL & TOXICOL, UNIV LA, 79- *Concurrent Pos:* Nat Inst Dent Res fel, Univ Rochester, 67-70. *Mem:* Am Physiol Soc; Soc Exp Biol & Med; Am Soc Bone & Mineral Res; AAAS. *Res:* Calcium metabolism; bone metabolism; effects of humoral and nutritional factors on calcium homeostasis and connective tissues. *Mailing Add:* Dept Biol Pharmacol & Toxicol Univ La South Third St Louisville KY 40208

RAMPACEK, CARL, b Omaha, Nebr, Aug 7, 13; m 39; c 2. METALLURGY, MINERAL RESOURCES. *Educ:* Creighton Univ, BS, 35, MS, 37. *Prof Exp:* Chemist, Phillips Petrol Co, Okla, 39-41; mineral technologist, US Bur Mines, Ala, 41-43, phys chemist, 43-45, metallurgist, Ariz, 45-51, chief, Process

Develop & Res Br, Metall Div, 51-54, supvry metallurgist, Southwest Exp Sta, 54-60, res dir, Tuscaloosa Metall Res Ctr, 60-63, asst dir admin, 63-67, res dir, Col Park Metall Res Ctr, 67-69, asst dir metall, US Bur Mines, 69-75; DIR, MINERAL RESOURCES INST, UNIV ALA, 76- *Honors & Awards:* Henry Krumb Lectr Metall, Am Inst Mining & Metall Engrs, 77; Robert Earll McConnell Award, Am Inst Mining, Metall & Petrol Engrs, 78. *Mem:* Am Chem Soc; Am Inst Mining, Metall & Petrol Engrs; AAAS; Fedn Mat Soc (vpres-pres elect, 78). *Res:* Metallurgical research. *Mailing Add:* Mineral Resources Inst PO Drawer AY University AL 35486

RAMPINO, MICHAEL ROBERT, b Brooklyn, NY, Feb 8, 48. CLIMATE CHANGE, COASTAL SEDIMENTOLOGY. *Educ:* Hunter Col, BA, 68; Columbia Univ, PhD(geol), 78. *Prof Exp:* Instr geol, Hunter Col, 72-74 & Rutgers Univ, 76-78; Nat Acad Sci res assoc, 78-80, RES ASSOC CLIMATOL, GODDARD INST SPACE STUDIES, NASA, 80- *Concurrent Pos:* Adj instr geol, Lehman Col, NY, 74-77; instr, Earth Sci Dept, Fairleigh-Dickinson Univ, 78-79; vis lectr, Dartmouth Col, 80; lectr geol, Columbia Univ, 79-; adj instr, Sch Visual Arts, 80-; adj asst prof, Barnard Col, 82- *Mem:* AAAS; Am Geophys Union; Geol Soc Am; Soc Economic Paleontologists & Mineralogists; NY Acad Sci. *Mailing Add:* Goddard Inst Space Studies NASA 2880 Broadway New York NY 10025

RAMPONE, ALFRED JOSEPH, b Kelowna, BC, May 21, 25; nat US; m 57; c 4. PHYSIOLOGY. *Educ:* Univ BC, BA, 47, MA, 50; Northwestern Univ, PhD, 54. *Prof Exp:* Res assoc physiol, Sch Med, Northwestern Univ, 54-55; instr, St Louis Univ, 55; from instr to assoc prof, 55-71, actg chmn, Dept Physiol, 79-81, PROF PHYSIOL, MED SCH, UNIV ORE, 71- *Mem:* Am Physiol Soc; Soc Exp Biol & Med. *Res:* Intestinal transport of lipids; energy metabolism. *Mailing Add:* Dept of Physiol Sch Med Ore Health Sci Univ Portland OR 97201

RAMPP, DONALD L, b Meramac, Okla, Feb 10, 35; m; c 2. SPEECH PATHOLOGY. *Educ:* Northeastern State Col, BAEd, 57; Ohio State Univ, MA, 58; Univ Okla, PhD(speech path), 67. *Prof Exp:* Speech pathologist, Pub Sch, Okla, 57-58; asst prof speech path, Northeastern State Col, 58-62; chief speech path & audiol, Child Develop Ctr, Med Units, Univ Tenn, 66-69; assoc prof speech path & coordr med serv, Memphis State Univ, 69-74; PROF & HEAD DEPT AUDIOL & SPEECH PATH, LA STATE UNIV MED CTR, NEW ORLEANS, 74- & PROF DEPT OTOLARYNGOL & BIOCOMMUN, SCH MED, 74- *Concurrent Pos:* Speech pathologist, Med Ctr, Univ Okla, 66-68; supvr speech, lang & hearing, Collaborative Perinatal Res Proj, Med Units, Univ Tenn, Memphis, 69-, prof, 71-; consult, Vet Admin Hosp, Memphis, Tenn, 70- *Mem:* Am Cleft Palate Asn; Am Speech & Hearing Asn. *Res:* Auditory processing of verbal stimuli and its relationship to learning disabilities in children; voice quality characteristics of cleft palate persons. *Mailing Add:* Dept of Audiol & Speech Path 100 Derbigny St New Orleans LA 70112

RAMRAS, MARK BERNARD, b Brooklyn, NY, May 18, 41. MATHEMATICS. *Educ:* Cornell Univ, BA, 62; Brandeis Univ, MA, 64, PhD(math), 67. *Prof Exp:* Asst prof math, Harvard Univ, 67-70 & Boston Col, 70-74; assoc prof math, Univ Mass, Boston, 74-75; ASSOC PROF MATH, NORTHEASTERN UNIV, 75- *Mem:* Am Math Soc; Math Asn Am. *Res:* Ring theory; homological algebra. *Mailing Add:* Dept of Math Northeastern Univ Boston MA 02115

RAMSAY, ARLAN (BRUCE), b Dodge City, Kans, July 1, 37; m 58; c 2. GROUPOIDS, REPRESENTATION THEORY. *Educ:* Univ Kans, BA, 58; Harvard Univ, AM, 59, PhD(math), 62. *Prof Exp:* Instr math, Mass Inst Technol, 62-64; vis asst prof, Brandeis Univ, 64-65; asst prof, Univ Rochester, 65-68; assoc prof, 68-72, PROF MATH, UNIV COLO, BOULDER, 72- *Mem:* Am Math Soc. *Res:* Locally compact groups; representation theory; groupoids in analysis; orthmodular lattices. *Mailing Add:* Dept Math Box 426 Univ Colo Boulder CO 80309

RAMSAY, DAVID JOHN, b Hornchurch, Essex, Eng, Apr 20, 39; m 65; c 3. MEDICAL PHYSIOLOGY. *Educ:* Oxford Univ, BA, 60, MA & DPhil(renal physiol), 63, BM, BCh, 66. *Prof Exp:* Demonstr physiol, Oxford Univ, 63-66, med tutor, Corpus Christi Col & Univ lectr, 66-75; vis prof, 75, assoc prof, 75-78, PROF PHYSIOL, SCH MED, UNIV CALIF, SAN FRANCISCO, 78- *Mem:* Am Physiol Soc; Endocrine Soc; Soc Neurosci; Am Soc Nephrol; Brit Physiol Soc. *Res:* The control of fluid intake and output; the role of the renin-angiotensin system and the etiology of edema in congestive cardiac failure. *Mailing Add:* Dept of Physiol Sch of Med Univ of Calif San Francisco CA 94143

RAMSAY, DONALD ALLAN, b London, Eng, July 11, 22; Can citizen; m 46; c 4. MOLECULAR SPECTROSCOPY. *Educ:* Cambridge Univ, BA, 43, MA & PhD, 47, ScD, 76. *Hon Degrees:* DSc, Univ Reims, 69. *Prof Exp:* Jr res officer, 47-49, asst res officer, 50-54, assoc res officer, 55-60, sr res officer, 61-67, PRIN RES OFFICER, NAT RES COUN CAN, 68- *Concurrent Pos:* Guest lectr, Univ Ottawa, 55-67; vis prof, Univ Minn, 64, Univ Orsay, 66, 75, Univ Stockholm, 67, 71, 74, Univ Sao Paulo, 72, 78 & Univ Western Australia & Australian Nat Univ, 76; regents lectr, Univ Calif, Irvine, 70. *Honors & Awards:* Queen Elizabeth II Silver Jubilee Medal, 77. *Mem:* Fel Am Phys Soc; fel Chem Inst Can; Royal Soc Can (vpres acad sci, 75-76, hon treas, 76-79); fel Royal Soc; Can Asn Physicists. *Res:* Molecular spectroscopy, especially the spectra of free radicals. *Mailing Add:* Herzberg Inst of Astrophys Nat Res Coun 100 Sussex Dr Ottawa ON K1A 0R6 Can

RAMSAY, FREDERICK J, anatomy, see previous edition

RAMSAY, JOHN BARADA, b Phoenix, Ariz, Dec 28, 29; m 53; c 4. DETONATION PHYSICS, PHYSICAL CHEMISTRY. *Educ:* Univ Tex, El Paso, BS, 50; Univ Wis, PhD(anal chem), 55. *Prof Exp:* Staff mem anal chem, Los Alamos Sci Lab, 54-57, staff mem detonation physics, 57-70; assoc prof anal chem, Univ Petrol & Minerals, Saudi Arabia, 70-73; STAFF MEM DETONATION PHYSICS, LOS ALAMOS NAT LAB, 73- *Concurrent Pos:* Lectr, Univ NMex, Los Alamos Campus, 80- *Mem:* AAAS; Sigma Xi. *Res:* Explosive initiation and related phenomena; saline deposits of arid areas. *Mailing Add:* Los Alamos Nat Lab PO Box 1663 M-3 MS-960 Los Alamos NM 87545

RAMSAY, JOHN MARTIN, b Bethlehem, Pa, Apr 9, 30; m 54; c 2. ANIMAL BREEDING. *Educ:* Berea Col, BS, 52; Iowa State Univ, MS, 64, PhD(animal breeding), 66. *Prof Exp:* Instr agr, Warren Wilson Jr Col, 52-55; assoc dir rural life, John C Campbell Folk Sch, 66-67, dir, 67-73; asst prof recreation exten, 74-76, DIR RECREATION & ASST PROF ANIMAL SCI, DEPT ANIMAL SCI, BEREA COL, 76- *Mem:* Am Dairy Sci Asn. *Res:* Use of identical twins in dairy breeding research; genetic interpretation of heterogeneous variance of milk production; economic feasibility of crossing and upgrading a Jersey herd to Holsteins. *Mailing Add:* Dept of Animal Sci Berea Col Box 1548 Berea KY 40404

RAMSAY, MAYNARD JACK, b Buffalo, NY, Nov 22, 14; m 41; c 5. ENTOMOLOGY. *Educ:* Univ Buffalo, AB, 36, AM, 38; Cornell Univ, PhD, 42. *Prof Exp:* Asst zool, Univ Buffalo, 36-38; asst insect morphol & insect physiol, Cornell Univ, 39-40, biol, 40-42; hort inspector, Bur Plant Indust, State Dept Agr & Mkts, NY, 42-43; plant quarantine inspector, Plant Quarantine Div, Agr Res Serv, USDA, 43-50, port entomologist, Plant Importations Br, 50-56, training off, 56-66, head post-entry quarantine sect, 66-67, AGRICULTURIST, ANIMAL & PLANT HEALTH INSPECTION SERV, PLANT PROTECTION & QUARANTINE PROGS, PLANT QUARANTINE DIV, AGR RES SERV, USDA, 67-, STAFF OFFICER NAT PROG PLANNING STAFF, 75- *Concurrent Pos:* Head publ coop econ insect rep weekly, Nat Econ Insect Surv, 73- *Honors & Awards:* Superior Serv Award, USDA, 56. *Mem:* Entom Soc Am. *Res:* Coleoptera of Allegany State Park, NY; Mexican bean beetle control; Dutch elm disease control; international plant quarantine; survey methods for economic insects; losses due to pests. *Mailing Add:* 3806 Viser Ct Bowie MD 20715

RAMSAY, OGDEN BERTRAND, b Baltimore, Md, Sept 24, 32; m 62; c 1. ORGANIC CHEMISTRY, HISTORY OF CHEMISTRY. *Educ:* Washington & Lee Univ, BS, 55; Univ Pa, PhD(org chem), 60. *Prof Exp:* Fel org chem, Ga Inst Technol, 59-61; asst prof chem, Univ of the Pacific, 61-63; res fel org chem, Northwestern Univ, 63-64, instr chem, 64-65; from asst prof to assoc prof, 65-74, actg head dept, 80-82, PROF CHEM, EASTERN MICH UNIV, 74- *Concurrent Pos:* NSF sci fac fel, Dept Chem, Univ Wis-Madison, 68-69. *Mem:* AAAS; Am Chem Soc; Royal Soc Chem; Sigma Xi; Hist Sci Soc. *Res:* Physical organic chemistry; mechanisms of hydrolysis of phosphate esters; photo-induced nucleophilic aromatic substitution; mechanisms of photochemical reactions; history and literature of chemistry. *Mailing Add:* Dept of Chem Eastern Mich Univ Ypsilanti MI 48197

RAMSAY, WILLIAM CHARLES, b Jamaica, NY, Nov 6, 30; m 66. RESOURCE MANAGEMENT. *Educ:* Univ Colo, BA, 52; Univ Calif, Los Angeles, MA, 57, PhD(physics), 62. *Prof Exp:* NSF fel, Univ Calif, San Diego, 62-63, res assoc physics, 63-64; asst prof, Univ Calif, Santa Barbara, 64-67; sr staff scientist, Systs Assocs, Inc, 67-72; sr environ economist, Atomic Energy Comn, 72-75; tech adv, Nuclear Regulatory Comn, 75-76; FEL, RESOURCES FOR THE FUTURE, 76- *Mem:* Am Phys Soc; Am Astron Soc. *Res:* Energy strategies; environmental management. *Mailing Add:* Resources for the Future 8707 Cranbrook Ct Bethesda MD 20034

RAMSDALE, DAN JERRY, b El Paso, Tex, Dec 12, 42; m 69; c 2. UNDERWATER ACOUSTICS, SIGNAL PROCESSING. *Educ:* Univ Tex, El Paso, BS, 64; Kans State Univ, PhD(physics), 69. *Prof Exp:* Res dir, Gus Mfg, Inc, Globe Universal Sci, Inc, 69-74; res physicist, Acoust div, US Naval Res Lab, 74-77, res physicist, 77-81, SUPVR RES PHYSICIST & HEAD, ARRAY EFFECTS BR, OCEAN ACOUST DIV, NAVAL OCEAN RES & DEVELOP ACTIV, 81- *Concurrent Pos:* Adj prof, El Paso Community Col, 71-74; adj prof physics, Univ New Orleans, 81- *Mem:* Acoust Soc Am; Sigma Xi; Am Geophys Union; Inst Elec & Electronics Engrs; Am Inst Physics. *Res:* Atmospheric acoustics, infrasonics, acoustic echo-sounding and the acoustic grenade sounding technique; electroacoustics and electrostatic transducer design; theoretical atomic physics, Auger and x-ray transition rates; seismic waves; underwater acoustics, especially low frequency propagation studies and fluctuations; the use of acoustic arrays as measurement tools. *Mailing Add:* Naval Ocean Res & Develop Activ Ocean Acoust Div NSTL Station MS 39529

RAMSDELL, DONALD CHARLES, b Yuba City, Calif, Dec 28, 38; m 60; c 2. PLANT PATHOLOGY. *Educ:* Univ Calif, Davis, BS, 60, MS, 70, PhD(plant path), 71. *Prof Exp:* Res asst plant path, Univ Calif, Davis, 68-71; asst prof, 72-75, assoc prof, 75-78, PROF PLANT PATH, DEPT BOT & PLANT PATH, MICH STATE UNIV, 78- *Concurrent Pos:* Mem, Int Coun Study Virus & Virus-Like Dis of Grapevine, 75- *Honors & Awards:* Lee M Hutchins Award, Am Phytopath Soc. *Mem:* Am Phytopath Soc; Brit Asn Appl Biol; Int Soc Hort Sci. *Res:* Etiology, epidemiology and control of viral and fungal diseases of small fruits crops. *Mailing Add:* Dept of Bot & Plant Path 166 PB Bldg Mich State Univ East Lansing MI 48824

RAMSDELL, ROBERT COLE, b Trenton, NJ, July 8, 20; m 46; c 1. GEOLOGY. *Educ:* Lehigh Univ, BA, 43; Rutgers Univ, MS, 48; Princeton Univ, MA, 50. *Prof Exp:* With State Bur Mineral Res, NJ, 48-50; from instr to asst prof geol, Williams Col, 50-61; asst prof, Rutgers Univ, 61-66; ASSOC PROF, GEOSCI DIV, MONTCLAIR STATE COL, 66- *Mem:* AAAS; Geol Soc Am; Paleont Soc; Soc Econ Paleont & Mineral; Nat Asn Geol Teachers. *Res:* Paleontology and stratigraphy of Atlantic coastal plain; Silurian and Devonian Appalach(ian paleontology and stratigraphy. *Mailing Add:* Dept of Geosci Montclair State Col Upper Montclair NJ 07043

RAMSDEN, HUGH EDWIN, b Amesbury, Mass, May 30, 21; m 46; c 3. ORGANIC CHEMISTRY. *Educ:* Mass Inst Technol, SB, 43, PhD(org chem), 46. *Prof Exp:* Res chemist, E I du Pont de Nemours & Co, NJ, 46-48; res chemist, Metal & Thermit Corp, 49-52, res supvr & head dept org chem,

52-59; res chemist, Esso Res & Eng Co, 59-61, res assoc, 61-70, Esso Agr Prod Lab Div, 66-70; res assoc, R T Vanderbilt Co, 70-71; mem staff, Rhodia Inc, 71-79; SCIENTIST, J T BAKER CHEM CO, 79- *Mem:* Am Chem Soc; AAAS; NY Acad Sci. *Res:* Sugars; organoalkali reagents; fluorine chemistry; condensation polymers; plasticizers; coordination compounds; rubber; reaction of rubbers with organometallic compounds; organic synthesis; vinyl grignards; gasoline additives; pesticides synthesis; terpenes, perfume and flavor, fine chemicals. *Mailing Add:* J T Baker Chem Co 222 Red Sch Lane Phillipsburg NJ 08865

RAMSEUR, GEORGE SHUFORD, b Burke Co, NC, July 19, 26; m 53; c 3. BOTANY. *Educ:* Elon Col, AB, 48; Univ NC, MEd, 53, PhD(bot), 59. *Prof Exp:* Teacher high sch, NC, 49-54; from instr to assoc prof, 58-73, PROF BOT, UNIV OF THE SOUTH, 73- *Mem:* AAAS; Bot Soc Am; Am Soc Plant Taxon. *Res:* Taxonomy of vascular plants; southern Appalachian flora. *Mailing Add:* Dept of Biol Univ of the South Box 1218 Sewanee TN 37375

RAMSEY, ALAN T, b Madison, Wis, May 23, 38; m 60; c 2. PLASMA SPECTROSCOPY. *Educ:* Princeton Univ, AB, 60; Univ Wis, MS, 62, PhD(physics), 64. *Prof Exp:* Physicist, Lawrence Radiation Lab, Univ Calif, 64-67; asst prof physics, Brandeis Univ, 67-73; proj scientist, Am Sci & Eng, 74-76; res scientist, Mass Inst Technol, 76-78; RES SCIENTIST, PRINCETON PLASMA PHYSICS LAB, 79- *Res:* Optical pumping and atomic beam research on atomic and nuclear structure; x-ray astronomy; plasma diagnostics; spectroscopic instrumentation; medical instrumentation and research. *Mailing Add:* Princeton Plasma Physics Lab PO Box 451 Princeton NJ 08540

RAMSEY, ARTHUR ALBERT, b Schenectady, NY, Apr 11, 40; m 62; c 3. PESTICIDE CHEMISTRY. *Educ:* Albany Col Pharm, BS, 62; Univ Kans, PhD(med chem), 68. *Prof Exp:* Sr res chemist, Agr Chem Div, 68-77, MGR, COMPOUND ACQUISITION, AGR CHEM GROUP, FMC CORP, 77- *Mem:* Am Chem Soc. *Res:* Potential fungicides, herbicides, insecticides, and nematicides; physiological chemistry of plants, fungi and insects. *Mailing Add:* Agr Chem Group FMC Corp Box 8 Princeton NJ 08540

RAMSEY, BRIAN GAINES, b Union, SC, Mar 17, 37; m 76; c 3. PHYSICAL ORGANIC CHEMISTRY, MOLECULAR SPECTROSCOPY. *Educ:* Univ SC, BSc, 56; Univ Wis, MSc, 58; Fla State Univ, PhD(chem), 62. *Prof Exp:* Fel, Pa State Univ, 62-64; asst prof, Univ Akron, 64-69; assoc prof chem, San Francisco State Univ, 69-80; MEM FAC, DEPT CHEM, ROLLINS COL, 80- *Concurrent Pos:* Sr Fulbright res fel, Ger, 72-73. *Mem:* Am Chem Soc. *Res:* Spectroscopic investigations of reactive intermediates in organic chemistry; electronic transitions in organometallics; chemistry of organoboranes. *Mailing Add:* Dept Chem Rollins Col Winter Park FL 32789

RAMSEY, CLOVIS BOYD, b Sneedville, Tenn, Aug 1, 34; m 58; c 2. ANIMAL SCIENCE. *Educ:* Univ Tenn, BS, 56; Univ Ky, MS, 57, PhD(meats), 60. *Prof Exp:* Asst prof meat sci, Univ Tenn, 60-68; PROF MEAT SCI, TEX TECH UNIV, 68- *Mem:* Am Meat Sci Asn; Am Soc Animal Sci; Inst Food Technol; Sigma Xi. *Res:* Physical, chemical and organoleptic properties of beef, lamb and pork; live-animal carcass evaluation; meat processing methods; factors affecting meat quality and quantity. *Mailing Add:* Dept of Animal Sci Tex Tech Univ Lubbock TX 79409

RAMSEY, DERO SAUNDERS, b Starkville, Miss, June 17, 28; m 50; c 2. DAIRY SCIENCE. *Educ:* Miss State Univ, BS, 50, MS, 53; Univ Wis, PhD(dairy husb), 57. *Prof Exp:* From asst prof to assoc prof, 56-68, PROF DAIRY SCI, MISS STATE UNIV, 68- *Mem:* AAAS; Am Dairy Sci Asn; Am Soc Animal Sci. *Res:* Physiology and nutrition of dairy cattle. *Mailing Add:* Dept of Dairy Sci Miss State Univ Drawer DD Mississippi State MS 39762

RAMSEY, ELIZABETH MAPELSDEN, b New York, NY, Feb 17, 06; m 34. PLACENTOLOGY, PATHOLOGY. *Educ:* Mills Col, BA, 28; Yale Univ, MD, 32; Med Col Pa, DSc, 65. *Prof Exp:* Asst path, Yale Univ, 33-34; guest investr, Carnegie Inst Dept Embryol, 34-49, res assoc, 49-51, staff mem placentology & path, 51-71; Mamie A Jessup vis prof obstet & gynec, Sch Med, Univ Va, 71-76; RES ASSOC, DEPT EMBRYOL, CARNEGIE INST, 75- *Concurrent Pos:* Assoc, George Washington Univ, 34-41, prof lectr, 41-55; asst info off, Off Med Info, Nat Res Coun, 42-45; prof lectr obstet & gynec, Med Sch, Georgetown Univ, 81- *Mem:* AAAS; perinatal Res Soc; Soc Gynec Invest; Am Col Obstet & Gynec; Am Gynecol Soc. *Res:* Vasculature of pregnant endometrium; radioangiography of placenta in rhesus monkey; placental circulation; placentation; myometrial activity in pregnancy. *Mailing Add:* 3420 Que St NW Washington DC 20007

RAMSEY, FRED LAWRENCE, b Ames, Iowa, Mar 3, 39; m 66. MATHEMATICAL STATISTICS. *Educ:* Univ Ore, BA, 61; Iowa State Univ, MS, 63, PhD(statist), 64. *Prof Exp:* Asst prof statist, Iowa State Univ, 64; NIH fel, Johns Hopkins Univ, 65-66; asst prof, 66-72, ASSOC PROF STATIST, ORE STATE UNIV, 72- *Mem:* Inst Math Statist. *Res:* Time series analysis; non-parametric statistics. *Mailing Add:* Dept of Statist Ore State Univ Corvallis OR 97331

RAMSEY, GWYNN W, b Drexel, NC, Nov 13, 31; m 52; c 3. PLANT SYSTEMATICS. *Educ:* Appalachian State Teachers Col, BS, 55, MA, 58; Univ Tenn, PhD(bot), 65. *Prof Exp:* Teacher high sch, NC, 55-58; instr biol & bot, Lees-McRae Col, 58-61; chmn dept, 68-71, PROF BIOL, LYNCHBURG COL, 65-, CUR HERBARIUM, 66- *Mem:* Bot Soc Am; Am Soc Plant Taxon. *Res:* Biosystematics of the genus Cimicifuga; Virginia flora. *Mailing Add:* Dept of Biol Lynchburg Col Lynchburg VA 24501

RAMSEY, HAL HARRISON, b Abilene, Tex, Aug 13, 26; m 48; c 2. BACTERIOLOGY. *Educ:* Univ Tex, AB, 48, MA, 50, PhD(bact), 53. *Prof Exp:* From asst prof to assoc prof bact, Sch Med, Univ Okla, 52-58; REGIONAL DIR GRANTS, RES CORP, 58- *Mem:* AAAS; Am Soc Microbiol; NY Acad Sci; Brit Soc Gen Microbiol. *Res:* Bacterial physiology; antibiotic resistance to staphylococcus. *Mailing Add:* Res Corp Grants Progs 1290 Bayshore Hwy Burlingame CA 94010

RAMSEY, HAROLD ARCH, b Ft Scott, Kans, Sept 16, 27; m 51; c 3. ANIMAL NUTRITION. *Educ:* Kans State Univ, BS, 50; NC State Univ, MS, 53, PhD(animal nutrit), 55. *Prof Exp:* From asst prof to assoc prof animal nutrit, NC State Univ, 55-62; vis assoc prof dairy sci, Univ Ill, 62-63; assoc & prof animal nutrit, 63-65, prof animal nutrit, 65-69, head dairy husb sect, 65-70, prof animal sci, 69-81, PROF NUTRIT, NC STATE UNIV, 81- *Mem:* Am Dairy Sci Asn; Am Inst Nutrit. *Res:* Nutritional requirements of ruminants; nutritional value of enzyme-modified plant protein. *Mailing Add:* Dept of Animal Sci NC State Univ Raleigh NC 27607

RAMSEY, JAMES CARROLL, cell biology, molecular biology, see previous edition

RAMSEY, JAMES MARVIN, b Wilmington, Ohio, May 21, 24; m 58; c 3. ENVIRONMENTAL PHYSIOLOGY. *Educ:* Wilmington Col, BS, 48; Miami Univ, MS, 51. *Prof Exp:* Instr biol sci, Cedarville Col, 48-52; res assoc skin allergy & toxicol, Col Med, Univ Cincinnati, 52-53; instr physiol, Miami Univ, 55-60; assoc prof, 64-80, PROF BIOL SCI, UNIV DAYTON, 80- *Concurrent Pos:* NSF instnl res grants, 66-68 & 71-; NIH res grant, 68-71. *Mem:* AAAS; Sigma Xi; Air Pollution Control Asn. *Res:* Carbon monoxide toxicology; environmental physiology; the relation of carbon monoxide inhalation to tissue hypoxia; the relation of non-specific stress to asthmatic bronchoconstriction. *Mailing Add:* Respiratory Lab Dept of Biol Univ Dayton 300 College Park Ave Dayton OH 45409

RAMSEY, JED JUNIOR, b Dighton, Kans, Oct 17, 25; m 48; c 4. ZOOLOGY. *Educ:* Kans State Univ, BS, 49; Kans State Teachers Col, MS, 62; Okla State Univ, PhD(zool), 66. *Prof Exp:* Teacher high schs, Kans, 50-63; assoc prof, 65-72, PROF BIOL, LAMAR UNIV, 72- *Mem:* AAAS; Am Ornith Union; Nat Asn Biol Teachers. *Res:* Metabolic changes in Chimney Swifts at lowered environmental temperatures; ecology and behavior of ciconiiform birds; avifauna of the Beaumont unit of the Big Thicket. *Mailing Add:* Lamar Univ Box 10037 Lamar Station Beaumont TX 77710

RAMSEY, JERRY DWAIN, b Tulia, Tex, Nov 6, 33; m 56; c 4. INDUSTRIAL & BIOMEDICAL ENGINEERING. *Educ:* Tex A&M Univ, BS, 55, MS, 60; Tex Tech Univ, PhD(indust eng & biotech), 67. *Prof Exp:* Indust eng trainee, Square D Co, Wis, 53, Mich, 54; engr, Great Western Drilling Co, Tex, 55; indust engr, Collins Radio Co, Tex, 57-58; instr indust eng, Tex A&M Univ, 58-60, asst prof, 60-61; tech staff mem, Sandia Corp, NMex, 61-65; from asst prof to assoc prof, 67-75, PROF INDUST ENG, TEX TECH UNIV, 75-, ASSOC V PRES, 77- *Concurrent Pos:* Mem, President's Comt Employment of Handicapped; consult, Occup Safety & Health Admin, Washington, DC, 72 & US Consumer Prod Safety Comn, 76; chmn, Nat Standards Adv Comt Heat Stress, 73-74. *Mem:* Nat Soc Prof Engrs; Am Inst Indust Engrs; Human Factors Soc; Nat Safety Coun; Am Indust Hyg Asn. *Res:* Biotechnology and human performance; ergonomics; human factors engineering; product safety; occupational safety and health; management systems and optimization techniques; effects of environmental stressors on human performance. *Mailing Add:* Dept of Indust Eng Tex Tech Univ Lubbock TX 79409

RAMSEY, JERRY WARREN, b Springfield, Ill, June 30, 32; m 52; c 3. RESEARCH ADMINISTRATION, SYNTHETIC FUELS. *Educ:* Ill Col, AB, 56; Agr & Mech Col, Tex, MS, 58. *Prof Exp:* Instr gen chem, Tex Western Col, 58-59; instr, Pa State Univ, 59-61, instr org chem, 61-62; chemist, Anthracite Res Ctr, US Bur Mines, 62-64, res chemist, 64-65, Laramie Petrol Res Ctr, Wyo, 65-67, chemist, Off of Dir Petrol Res, 67-70, staff chemist & asst to chief, Div Shale Oil, 70-75, br chief oil shale conversion, Div Oil, Gas & Shale Technol, 75-80, ASST DIR, DIV OIL SHALE, US DEPT ENERGY, 80- *Concurrent Pos:* Consult, El Paso Natural Gas Co, 58-59; chemist, Anthracite Res Ctr, US Bur Mines, 60-62; instr, Pottsville Hosp Sch Nursing, Pa, 61-62; mem task force for prototype oil shale leasing prog, US Dept of the Interior, 72-73; chmn oil shale task group synthetic fuels commercialization prog, Off Mgt & Budget, 75. *Honors & Awards:* Cert of Commendation for Outstanding Serv, US Dept of the Interior, 73. *Mem:* Am Chem Soc. *Res:* All areas of oil shale and shale oil research management. *Mailing Add:* US Dept Energy Washington DC 20545

RAMSEY, JOHN CHARLES, b Yakima, Wash, June 19, 33. TOXICOLOGY. *Educ:* Univ Puget Sound, BS, 55; Ore State Univ, PhD(plant biochem), 64; Am Bd Toxicol, dipl. *Prof Exp:* Res chemist pesticide residues, Dept Agr-Chemicals, 64-71, RES TOXICOLOGIST INDUST & AGR CHEM, DEPT TOXICOL, DOW CHEM CO, 71- *Mem:* Am Chem Soc; AAAS; Soc Toxicol; Sigma Xi. *Res:* Pharmacokinetics and toxicology of agricultural and industrial chemicals; mathematical modeling of chemicals in biological systems. *Mailing Add:* Toxicol 1803 Bldg Dow Chem Co Midland MI 48640

RAMSEY, JOHN S, b Tsingtao, China, June 23, 39; US citizen. FISH BIOLOGY. *Educ:* Cornell Univ, BS, 60; Tulane Univ, PhD(ichthyol), 65. *Prof Exp:* Assoc investr, Inst Marine Biol & asst prof biol, Univ PR, 65-67; UNIT LEADER ALA COOP FISHERY RES UNIT, US FISH & WILDLIFE SERV & RES ASSOC PROF ZOOL & FISHERIES, AUBURN UNIV, 67- *Mem:* Am Fisheries Soc; Am Soc Ichthyol & Herpet; Soc Syst Zool. *Res:* Systematics and ecology of fishes, especially eastern North America. *Mailing Add:* Ala Coop Fishery Unit Auburn Univ Auburn AL 36830

RAMSEY, LAWRENCE WILLIAM, b Louisville, Ky, Mar 14, 45; m 70. STELLAR SPECTROSCOPY, SPECTROSCOPIC INSTRUMENTATION. *Educ:* Univ Mo, St Louis, BA, 68; Kans State Univ, MS, 72; Ind Univ, PhD(astron), 76. *Prof Exp:* Simulation systs design engr, 66-70, res asst solar physics, Kitt Peak Nat Observ, 72-73; ASST PROF ASTRON, PA STATE UNIV, 76- *Mem:* Am Astron Soc; Optical Soc Am; Int Astron Union; Astron Soc Pac. *Res:* Cool star atmospheres; solar-like phenomenon on other stars; stellar spectroscopy and astronomical instrumentation. *Mailing Add:* Pa State Univ 525 Davey Lab University Park PA 16802

RAMSEY, LLOYD HAMILTON, b Lexington, Ky, June 10, 21; wid; c 4. MEDICAL ADMINISTRATION, INTERNAL MEDICINE. *Educ:* Univ Ky, BS, 42; Wash Univ, MD, 50; Am Bd Internal Med, dipl, 59. *Prof Exp:* Intern med, Duke Univ, 50-51; asst resident, Peter Bent Brigham Hosp, Boston, 51-52, asst, 52-53; instr, 54-55, asst prof, 55-63, investr, Howard Hughes Med Inst, 55-65, assoc prof, 63-78, PROF MED, SCH MED, VANDERBILT UNIV, 78-, ASSOC DEAN, 75- *Concurrent Pos:* Fel, Harvard Med Sch, 52-53; res fel, Sch Med, Vanderbilt Univ, 53-54; chief resident physician, Univ Hosp, Vanderbilt Univ, 54-55; consult, Mid Tenn State Tuberc Hosp, Nashville, 55-65. *Mem:* AAAS; fel Am Col Physicians; Am Clin & Climat Asn. *Res:* Pulmonary physiology, especially gas diffusion and relationships of external respiration to blood flow. *Mailing Add:* Vanderbilt Univ Med Sch 21st & Garland Ave Nashville TN 37232

RAMSEY, MAYNARD, III, b Birmingham, Ala, Aug 28, 43; m 69; c 2. BIOMEDICAL ENGINEERING. *Educ:* Emory Univ, BA, 65; Duke Univ, MD, 69, PhD(biomed eng), 75. *Prof Exp:* Dir res, Appl Med Res Corp, 75-79; VPRES RES & DEVELOP, CRITIKON, 79- *Mem:* Inst Elec & Electronics Engrs; Asn Advan Med Instrumentation. *Res:* Principles and mechanism of indirect and direct measurement of blood pressure; body surface electrocardiography and its implementation for clinical use. *Mailing Add:* Critikon Inc PO Box 22800 Tampa FL 33622

RAMSEY, NORMAN FOSTER, JR, b Washington, DC, Aug 27, 15; m 40; c 4. PHYSICS. *Educ:* Columbia Univ, AB, 35, PhD(physics), 40; Cambridge Univ, MA, 41, DSc, 54. *Hon Degrees:* MA Harvard Univ, 47; DSc, Case Western Reserve Univ, 68, Middlebury Col, 69 & Oxford Univ, 73. *Prof Exp:* Assoc physics, Univ Ill, 40-42; assoc prof, Columbia Univ, 42-47; from assoc prof to prof, 47-66, dir nuclear lab, 48-50 & 52, HIGGINS PROF PHYSICS, HARVARD UNIV, 66- *Concurrent Pos:* Consult, Off Sci Res & Develop & Nat Defense Res Comt, 40-45; consult US Secy War, 42-45; res assoc, Radiation Lab, Mass Inst Technol, 40-42; group leader & assoc div head, Atomic Energy Proj Lab, Los Alamos Sci Lab, Univ Calif, 43-45; head physics dept, Brookhaven Nat Lab, 46-47; mem sci adv bd, US Dept Air Force, 49-56 & US Dept Defense, 54-58; trustee, Brookhaven Nat Lab, 52-56, Carnegie Endowment Int Peace, 63- & Rockefeller Univ, 76-; Guggenheim fel, 54-55; sci adv, NATO, 58-59; mem gen adv comt, AEC, 60-72; chmn high energy physics panel, Sci Adv Bd, Off of the President, 63; dir, Varian Assocs, 63-66, sr fel, Harvard Soc Fels, 69-; pres, Univs Res Asn, 66-81 & chmn physics sect, AAAS, 77-78; Eastman prof, Oxford Univ, 73-74; chmn bd govrs, Am Inst Physics, 80- *Honors & Awards:* Lawrence Award & Medal, 60; Davisson-Germer Prize, Am Phys Soc, 74. *Mem:* Nat Acad Sci; AAAS; fel Am Phys Soc (pres, 78-79); Am Philos Soc. *Res:* Nuclear moments; molecular beams; high energy particles; nuclear interactions in molecules; deuteron quadrupole moment; molecular structure; diamagnetism; thermodynamics; proton-proton scattering; high energy accelerators; atomic masers; electron scattering; neutrons. *Mailing Add:* Lyman Physics Lab Harvard Univ Cambridge MA 02138

RAMSEY, O C, JR, b Mars Hill, NC, July 28, 35; m 66. MATHEMATICS. *Educ:* Univ Wash, BS, 61; Wash State Univ, MA, 65, PhD(math), 67. *Prof Exp:* Trainee, Pac Mutual Life Ins Co, 61; programmer, Syst Develop Corp, Calif, 61-63; asst prof math, Univ Iowa, 67-70; mem fac, Calif Polytech State Univ, San Luis Obispo, 70-73; MEM TECH STAFF, LOGICON INC, 73- *Mem:* Am Math Soc. *Res:* General topology, particularly uniform spaces. *Mailing Add:* 16120 Mt Hicks St Fountain Valley CA 92708

RAMSEY, PAUL ROGER, b Lake Charles, La, July 27, 45; m 67; c 2. POPULATION BIOLOGY, GENETICS. *Educ:* Tex Tech Univ, BS, 67, MS, 69; Univ Ga, PhD(zool & ecol), 74. *Prof Exp:* Asst prof biol, Presby Col, 73-75; ASSOC PROF ZOOL, LA TECH UNIV, 75- *Concurrent Pos:* Adj asst prof biol, Fla Inst Technol, 78- *Mem:* Am Soc Mammalogists; Entom Soc Am; Soc Study Evolution. *Res:* Genetics of pesticide resistance; ecological genetics and allozyme variation of insects and small mammals. *Mailing Add:* Dept of Zool La Tech Univ Ruston LA 71272

RAMSEY, PAUL W, b Wilkinsburg, Pa, Feb 17, 19; m 42; c 3. METALLURGY. *Educ:* Carnegie Inst Technol, BS, 40; Univ Wis, MS, 56. *Prof Exp:* Sr investr, NJ Zinc Co, Pa, 40-51; proj engr, 51-56, supvr, 56-65, mgr welding, 65-81, MGR WELDING & METALL RES & DEVELOP, A O SMITH CORP, 81- *Honors & Awards:* Nat Award, Am Welding Soc, 71; S W Miller Mem Award, Am Welding Soc, 80. *Mem:* Am Welding Soc (vpres, 72-75, pres, 75-76); Am Inst Mining, Metall & Petrol Eng; fel Am Soc Metals; Soc Automotive Engrs; Soc Metall Engrs. *Res:* Welding metallurgy, mechanical testing; welding controls; power sources; physical metallurgy. *Mailing Add:* Welding & Metall Res & Develop Lab A O Smith Corp 3533 N 27th St Milwaukee WI 53201

RAMSEY, RICHARD HAROLD, b San Francisco, Calif, Nov 21, 36; m 60; c 2. PHYTOPATHOLOGY, MYCOLOGY. *Educ:* Univ Calif, Davis, 58, PhD(phytopath), 66. *Prof Exp:* From asst prof to assoc prof, 62-75, PROF BIOL, ROCKY MT COL, 75- *Res:* Genetics of Pleospora herbarum. *Mailing Add:* 3237 Aljema Ave Billings MT 59102

RAMSEY, ROBERT BRUCE, b Moline, Ill, Jan 4, 44; m 67; c 2. TUMOR MARKER BIOLOGY, NEUROCHEMISTRY. *Educ:* Augustana Col, BA, 66; St Louis Univ, PhD(biochem), 71. *Prof Exp:* Asst prof neurol, Sch Med, St Louis Univ, 72-78, assoc prof, 78-79; ONCOL SPECIALIST & MGR CLIN INVEST, SHERWOOD MED, 79- *Concurrent Pos:* NIH fel, Inst Neurol, Univ London, 71-73; assoc clin prof neurol, Sch Med, St Louis Univ, 79- *Mem:* AAAS; Am Chem Soc; Brit Biochem Soc; Am Soc Biol Chemists; Int Soc Oncol Develop Biol Med. *Res:* Clinical application of tumor marker measurement. *Mailing Add:* Sherwood Med 1831 Olive St Louis MO 63103

RAMSEY, WILLIAM JAMES, b Los Angeles, Calif, Apr 20, 28; m 53; c 2. INORGANIC CHEMISTRY. *Educ:* Calif Inst Technol, BS, 49, PhD(chem), 53. *Prof Exp:* Res chemist, Calif Res & Develop Co, 53; CHEMIST, LAWRENCE LIVERMORE LAB, UNIV CALIF, 53- *Concurrent Pos:* Consult chemist, 78- *Mem:* Sigma Xi; fel AAAS; Am Chem Soc. *Res:* Reaction kinetics; high temperature processes; intermetallic compounds; technology assessment. *Mailing Add:* Lawrence Livermore Lab PO Box 808 L-362 Livermore CA 94550

RAMSEY, WILLIAM SCOTT, b South Bend, Ind, May 26, 39; m 67; c 2. MICROBIOLOGY. *Educ:* Ind Univ, AB, 61; Univ Minn, MS, 67, PhD(microbiol), 69; Syracuse Univ, MBA, 79. *Prof Exp:* Res assoc biol, Yale Univ, 69-72; microbiologist, 72-81, MGR MKT DEVELOP-BIOTECHNOL, CORNING GLASS WORKS, 81- *Mem:* Am Chem Soc; Am Soc Microbiol; Am Soc Cell Biol. *Res:* Development of methods and instruments for clinical microbiology; mechanisms of leucocyte chemotaxis; biotechnology market development. *Mailing Add:* Corning Glass Works Res & Develop Lab Corning NY 14830

RAMSHAW, JOHN DAVID, b Salt Lake City, Utah, Mar 20, 44; m 68; c 2. STATISTICAL MECHANICS, DIELECTRIC THEORY. *Educ:* Col Idaho, BS, 65; Mass Inst Technol, PhD(chem physics), 70. *Prof Exp:* Res assoc & assoc instr, Univ Utah, 71-72; staff scientist physics & eng, Appl Theory Inc, 72-73; assoc scientist, Aerojet Nuclear Co, 73-75; staff mem chem physics, 75-80, STAFF MEM THEORET DIV, LOS ALAMOS NAT LAB, 80- *Concurrent Pos:* Air Force Off Sci Res-Nat Res Coun res award chem physics, Univ Md, 70-71. *Mem:* Am Phys Soc. *Res:* Equilibrium and nonequilibrium staistical mechanics, especially theory of dielectrics and theory of liquids; analytical and numerical fluid dynamics, especially fluid flow with chemical reactions and combustion. *Mailing Add:* Los Alamos Nat Lab PO Box 1663 Los Alamos NM 87545

RAMSLEY, ALVIN OLSEN, b North Bergen, NJ, Feb 6, 20; m 49; c 2. PHYSICAL CHEMISTRY. *Educ:* Houghton Col, BS, 43; Columbia Univ, MA, 48. *Prof Exp:* Chemist, Gen Elec Co, 48-50; chemist, Gen Test Labs, 50-53, RES CHEMIST, NATICK LABS, US ARMY QM, 53-, CHIEF COUNTERSURVEILLANCE SECT, NATICK RES & DEVELOP COMMAND, 74- *Mem:* Am Chem Soc; Optical Soc Am; Inter-Soc Color Coun; Sigma Xi. *Res:* Physical chemistry of excited states as related to chemical structure, absorption spectra, and luminescence; photodegradation of dyes; materials research for visual and non-visual counter-surveillance measures; vision, color measurement and colorant formulation. *Mailing Add:* Attn: DRDNA-VTC Res & Develop Command Natick MA 01760

RAMSPOTT, LAWRENCE DEWEY, b Jacksonville, Fla, Dec 9, 34; m 60; c 2. GEOLOGY. *Educ:* Principia Col, BS, 56; Pa State Univ, PhD(geol), 62. *Prof Exp:* Asst prof geol, Univ Ga, 62-67; sr geologist, 67-70, group leader geol & geophys, 70-74, sect leader geol, 74-75, sect leader appl geophys, 75-76, PROJ LEADER WASTE ISOLATION, LAWRENCE LIVERMORE NAT LAB, 76- *Concurrent Pos:* NSF grant, 63-66. *Mem:* AAAS; Geol Soc Am; Am Soc Testing & Mat. *Res:* Petrology, mineralogy and structural geology; applied geology and geophysics; relation between site geology and containment of radioactivity and seismic coupling from an underground nuclear explosion. *Mailing Add:* Lawrence Livermore Nat Lab PO Box 808 Livermore CA 94550

RAMSTAD, PAUL ELLERTSON, b Minneapolis, Minn, Jan 30, 18; m 41; c 4. FOOD SCIENCE. *Educ:* Univ Minn, BS, 39, PhD(agr biochem), 42. *Prof Exp:* Coop agent, USDA, 39-42; res chemist, Gen Mills, Inc, Minn, 42-46, head cereal res sect, 47-48; assoc prof biochem, Sch Nutrit, Cornell Univ, 48-53; asst dir res, Oscar Mayer & Co, Wis, 53-55; tech dir dept qual control, Gen Mills, Inc, 55-65; vpres res & develop, Am Maize-Prod Co, 65-68, pres, Corn Processing Processing Div, 69-75, pres, Co, 76-78; CONSULT, 78- *Concurrent Pos:* Ed, Cereal Sci Today, 57-62; sci ed, Cereal Chem, 78- *Mem:* AAAS; Am Chem Soc; Am Asn Cereal Chemists (pres, 64-65); Inst Food Technol. *Res:* Research administration; cereal chemistry and technology; grain storage; starches; syrups; vegetable gums; packaged foods; nutrition. *Mailing Add:* PO Box 841 Ithaca NY 14850

RAMUS, JOSEPH, b Detroit, Mich, May 7, 40; m 63, 81; c 2. BOTANY. *Educ:* Univ Calif, Berkeley, AB, 63, PhD(bot), 68. *Prof Exp:* From asst prof to assoc prof biol, Yale Univ, 68-78; ASSOC PROF BOTANY, DUKE UNIV, 78-, ASST DIR, MARINE LAB, 81- *Mem:* Am Soc Limnol & Oceanog; Phycol Soc Am; Am Soc Plant Physiol. *Res:* Algal ecological physiology. *Mailing Add:* Marine Lab Duke Univ Beaufort NC 28516

RAMWELL, PETER WILLIAM, b Bradford, UK, Apr 3, 30; US citizen. PHARMACOLOGY, PHYSIOLOGY. *Educ:* Univ Sheffield, BS, 51; Univ Leeds, PhD(anesthesiol), 58. *Prof Exp:* Mem sci staff, Med Res Coun, Univ Leeds, 55-58; sr lectr pharmacol, Univ Bradford, 58-60; mem sci staff, Med Res Coun, Univ Birmingham & Oxford Univ, 60-64; sr scientist, Worcester Found Exp Biol, Mass, 64-69; prin scientist, Dept Pharmacol & Toxicol, Alza Corp, Palo Alto, 69-74; PROF PHYSIOL & BIOPHYS, SCH MED, GEORGETOWN UNIV, 74- *Concurrent Pos:* Indust consult, UK & US, 60-69; dir, NIMH Postdoctoral Training Prog, 67-69; actg assoc prof physiol, Stanford Univ, 69-74. *Mem:* Am Physiol Soc; Physiol Soc; Am Pharmacol Soc; Brit Pharmacol Soc. *Res:* Prostaglandins and cell biology. *Mailing Add:* Dept of Physiol & Biophys Georgetown Univ Sch of Med Washington DC 20007

RANA, MOHAMMED WAHEEDUZ-ZAMAN, b Lahore, WPakistan, May 28, 34; US citizen; m 65; c 4. HUMAN ANATOMY. *Educ:* Olivet Col, BA, 64; Wayne State Univ MS, 66, PhD(anat), 68. *Prof Exp:* From instr to asst prof, 68-78, ASSOC PROF ANAT, SCH MED, ST LOUIS UNIV, 78- *Mem:* Am Asn Anat; Southern Soc Anat; Soc Exp Biol & Med. *Res:* Effect of chemotherapy on human tumors in vitro. *Mailing Add:* Dept Anat St Louis Sch Med St Louis MO 63104

RANADE, MADHAV (ARUN) BHASKAR, b Indore City, India, Sept 27, 42; m 68; c 1. CHEMICAL ENGINEERING, PARTICLE TECHNOLOGY. *Educ:* Nagpur Univ, BTech, 64; Ill Inst Technol, MS, 68, PhD(chem eng), 74. *Prof Exp:* Res engr chem eng, Chicago Bridge & Iron Co,

68-70; res engr particle technol, IIT Res Inst, 72-77; sr engr, 77-78, SECT HEAD PARTICLE TECHNOL, RES TRIANGLE INST, 78-, MGR, ENVIRON TECHNOL DEPT, 80- *Concurrent Pos:* Adj assoc prof, dept environ eng, Univ NC, 80- *Mem:* Fine Particle Soc; Am Inst Chem Engrs; Am Chem Soc; Sigma Xi; Air Pollution Control Asn. *Res:* Fine particles technology; aerosol science; air pollution measurement and control; particle size measurement; powder technology. *Mailing Add:* Res Triangle Inst PO Box 12194 Research Triangle Park NC 27709

RANADE, VINAYAK VASUDEO, b Wani, India, Feb 5, 38; m 64; c 1. MEDICINAL CHEMISTRY. *Educ:* Univ Bombay, BSc, 58, MSc, 61, PhD(org chem), 65. *Prof Exp:* Res assoc med chem, Col Pharm, Univ Mich, Ann Arbor, 65-75, univ fel, 65-68; SR PHARMACOLOGIST, ABBOTT LABS, 75- *Honors & Awards:* GC Prize for Nuclear Med & Radio Pharmacol, Tel-Aviv Univ, Israel, 74. *Mem:* Am Chem Soc; Am Pharmaceut Asn; Acad Pharmaceut Sci; fel Am Inst Chemists; Sigma Xi. *Res:* Synthetic medicinal chemistry and synthesis of radio pharmaceuticals; drug metabolism, biotransformation. *Mailing Add:* Dept of Drug Metab Abbott Labs D-463 AP-9 North Chicago IL 60064

RANADIVE, NARENDRANATH SANTURAM, b Bombay, India, Sept 9, 30; m 60; c 2. IMMUNOLOGY, EXPERIMENTAL PATHOLOGY. *Educ:* Univ Bombay, BSc, 52, MSc, 57; McGill Univ, PhD(biochem), 65. *Prof Exp:* Res asst biophys, Indian Cancer Res Ctr, Bombay, India, 58-59; analyst, Glaxo Labs, Bombay, 59-60; asst prof, 69-74, ASSOC PROF PATH, DEPT PATH & INST IMMUNOL, UNIV TORONTO, 74- *Concurrent Pos:* Fel, Scripps Clin & Res Found, Calif, 66-69; Med Res Coun Can scholar, 69-72. *Mem:* Am Asn Pathologists; Am Asn Immunol; Can Soc Immunol. *Res:* Cellular mechanism in anaphylaxis; immunologic tissue injury; chemical mediators in neutrophil lysosomes; mechanism of the release of lysosomal constituents. *Mailing Add:* Dept Path Univ Toronto Toronto ON M5S 1A8 Can

RANALLI, ANTHONY WILLIAM, b Portchester, NY, Jan 13, 30; m 64; c 3. FOOD TECHNOLOGY. *Educ:* Syracuse Univ, BS, 52, MS, 53, PhD(microbiol), 59. *Prof Exp:* Res supvr, Continental Baking Co, 59-63; tech dir refined syrups & sugars div, CPC Int, Inc, 63-70; asst to pres, 70-73, dir qual control, Peperidge Farms, Inc, 70-77; mem staff, Quaker Oats Co, Chicago, 77-80; MEM STAFF, PEPPERIDGE FARMS INC, 80- *Mem:* Am Chem Soc; Inst Food Technol; fel Am Inst Chem. *Res:* Chemistry; plant sanitation; product development; quality control. *Mailing Add:* Pepperidge Farms Inc PO Box 5500 Norwalk CT 06856

RANCK, JOHN PHILIP, b Needmore, Pa, Aug 20, 36; m 61; c 2. COMPUTER INTERFACING, ARMS CONTROL. *Educ:* Elizabethtown Col, BS, 58; Princeton Univ, MA, 60, PhD(chem), 62. *Prof Exp:* Instr chem, Upsala Col, 62-63; from asst prof to assoc prof, 63-69, PROF CHEM, ELIZABETHTOWN COL, 69- *Concurrent Pos:* Schering Found award for grad teaching asst, Princeton Univ, 62; Sigma Xi fel, 62; NSF partic, Univ Calif, Berkeley, 64, NSF fac fel, H C Orsted Inst, Copenhagen Univ, 70-71. *Mem:* AAAS; Am Chem Soc; Am Asn Physics Teachers. *Res:* Molecular orbital theory; molecular spectroscopy; equilibria of transition metal ions with asymmetric ligands; computers in chemistry; computer interfacing; mathematical modeling and arms control. *Mailing Add:* Dept of Chem Elizabethtown Col Elizabethtown PA 17022

RANCK, RALPH OLIVER, b Carney's Point, NJ, July 17, 23; m 59; c 1. ORGANIC CHEMISTRY. *Educ:* Bucknell Univ, BS, 44; Purdue Univ, MS, 51; Iowa State Univ, PhD(chem), 57. *Prof Exp:* Chemist, E I du Pont de Nemours & Co, 44-49, 51; teaching asst, Purdue Univ, 49-51; asst, Iowa State Univ, 51-57; res chemist, 57-65, STAFF SCIENTIST, E I DU PONT DE NEMOURS & CO, INC, 65-, DIVISION CHEMIST, 81- *Mem:* Am Chem Soc; fel Am Inst Chemists. *Res:* Polymerization; polymer characterization and coatings; development of coatings for food packaging films; product and process development. *Mailing Add:* 9213 Venetian Way Richmond VA 23229

RAND, ARTHUR GORHAM, JR, b Boston, Mass, Sept 29, 35; m 60; c 3. FOOD SCIENCE. *Educ:* Univ NH, BS, 58; Univ Wis, MS, 61, PhD(dairy & food indust, biochem), 64. *Prof Exp:* Res asst dairy & food indust, Univ Wis, 58-63; instr animal & dairy sci, 63-65, from asst prof to assoc prof animal sci & food & resource chem, 65-75, PROF FOOD SCI & NUTRIT, UNIV RI, 75-, CHMN DEPT, 81- *Concurrent Pos:* Vis prof, Univ New South Wales, 71. *Mem:* AAAS; Am Chem Soc; Inst Food Technologists; Am Dairy Sci Asn; NY Acad Sci. *Res:* Food enzyme technology; immobilized enzyme applications to food processing and food analysis; seafood quality. *Mailing Add:* Dept of Food Sci & Technol Univ of RI Woodward Hall Kingston RI 02881

RAND, AUSTIN STANLEY, b Seneca Falls, NY, Sept 19, 32; m 61; c 3. EVOLUTIONARY BIOLOGY. *Educ:* De Pauw Univ, BA, 55; Harvard Univ, PhD(biol), 61. *Prof Exp:* Asst mammal, Field Mus Natural Hist, Chicago, 57; res asst herpet, Mus Comp Zool, Cambridge Univ, 61-62; zoologist, Secy Agr, Sao Paulo, 62-64; BIOLOGIST HERPET, SMITHSONIAN TROP RES INST, 64-70, 71- *Concurrent Pos:* Adj assoc prof, Univ Pa, 70-75. *Mem:* Am Soc Naturalists; Soc Study Evolution; Am Soc Ichthyologists & Herpetologists; Soc Study Amphibians & Reptiles; Herpetologists League. *Res:* Studies of behavior and ecology of reptiles and amphibians, particularly social behavior and communication as adaptations to resource partitioning in lizards and frogs in tropical environments. *Mailing Add:* Smithsonian Trop Res Inst PO Box 2072 Balboa Repub Panama

RAND, JAMES LELAND, b Ft Worth, Tex, Dec 23, 35; m 74; c 6. AEROSPACE ENGINEERING, MECHANICAL ENGINEERING. *Educ:* Univ Md, College Park, BS, 61, MS, 63, PhD(mech eng), 67. *Prof Exp:* Instr eng, Univ Md, College Park, 61-62; res engr, Naval Ord Lab, 62-68; from asst prof to prof struct mech, Tex A&M Univ, 68-78; MGR DYNAMIC ANAL, SOUTHWEST RES INST, 78- *Concurrent Pos:* Dir, Balloon Eng Lab, 77-78; vis mem, Grad Fac, Tex A&M Univ, 78- *Honors & Awards:* Award, US Navy, 66. *Mem:* Am Inst Aeronaut & Astronaut; Am Soc Mech Engrs; Am Acad Mech; Am Soc Eng Educ. *Res:* Stress wave propagation; internal ballistics; hypervelocity impact effects shock wave propagation; structural mechanics; dynamic plasticity; scientific balloon design-analysis. *Mailing Add:* Southwest Res Inst PO Drawer 28510 San Antonio TX 78284

RAND, LEON, b Boston, Mass, Oct 8, 30; m 59; c 3. ORGANIC CHEMISTRY. *Educ:* Northeastern Univ, BS, 53; Univ Tex, MA, 56, PhD(chem), 58. *Prof Exp:* Fel, Purdue Univ, 58-59; from asst prof to assoc prof chem, Univ Detroit, 59-68; prof chem, Youngstown State Univ, 68-81, dean grad studies & res, 73-81; PROF CHEM & VCHANCELLOR ACAD AFFAIRS, PEMBROKE STATE UNIV, 81- *Mem:* Am Chem Soc; Am Inst Chemists. *Res:* Steric effects and use of potassium fluoride in organic chemistry; anodic oxidation reactions; urethane chemistry; carbonium ion processes; halide catalysis. *Mailing Add:* Pembroke State Univ Pembroke NC 28372

RAND, MYRON J, b Portsmouth, NH, Aug 11, 21; m 46. THIN FILMS, INTEGRATED CIRCUIT PROCESSING. *Educ:* Univ NH, BS, 41, MS, 43; Columbia Univ, PhD(chem), 50. *Prof Exp:* Chemist, Manhattan Proj, Columbia Univ, 44-46; dir pub off, Nat Acad Sci, 49-53; investr, Res Div, NJ Zinc Co, Pa, 53-59; MEM TECH STAFF, BELL LABS, INC, 59- *Mem:* Electrochem Soc. *Res:* Vapor deposition and thin film technology; surface chemistry; solid state device and integrated circuit processing; photolithography. *Mailing Add:* Bell Labs Inc 555 Union Blvd Allentown PA 18103

RAND, PATRICIA JUNE, b St Paul, Minn, June 6, 26. PLANT ECOLOGY. *Educ:* Univ Minn, Minneapolis, BS, 47, MS, 53; Duke Univ, PhD(bot), 65. *Prof Exp:* Teaching asst, res asst & instr bot, Univ Minn, Minneapolis, 47-53; instr biol, Hamline Univ, 53-58; teaching asst bot, Duke Univ, 58-60; from instr to asst prof, Univ Ark, Fayetteville, 62-66; asst prof, Univ Nebr, Lincoln, 66-73; SR SCI ADV ECOL, ATLANTIC RICHFIELD CO, 73- *Concurrent Pos:* Seed technologist, Northrup, King & Co, 51-52; collabr, US Nat Park Serv, 59-70; adj prof, Univ Nebr, Lincoln, 73-76. *Mem:* Fel AAAS; Ecol Soc Am; Bot Soc Am; Am Inst Biol Sci. *Res:* Reclamation of disturbed areas; land use management; physiological ecology of woody plants. *Mailing Add:* Health Safety & Environ Protection Atlantic Richfield Co 515 S Flower St Los Angeles CA 90071

RAND, PETER W, b Boston, Mass, Oct 26, 29; m 53; c 2. CARDIOVASCULAR PHYSIOLOGY, HEMATOLOGY. *Educ:* Harvard Univ, AB, 51, MD, 55. *Prof Exp:* Intern, 55-56, resident internal med, 56-57 & 59-60, DIR RES DEPT, MAINE MED CTR, 65- *Concurrent Pos:* Fel cardiol, Maine Med Ctr, 60-61; USPHS fel, 61-63, NIH grant, 63. *Mem:* Am Fedn Clin Res; Am Physiol Soc; Am Heart Asn; Soc Rheol; Microcirc Soc. *Res:* Blood rheology and viscosity; oxygen transport; hemodynamics. *Mailing Add:* Maine Med Ctr 22 Bramhall St Portland ME 04102

RAND, PHILLIP GORDON, b Meredith, NH, Nov 5, 34; m 55; c 3. BIOCHEMISTRY. *Educ:* John Brown Univ, BA, 56; Univ Wyo, MS, 58; Purdue Univ, PhD(biochem), 63. *Prof Exp:* Res biochemist, 63-71, sr res biochemist & sect head, 71-73, prod develop mgr, 73-77, PRIN RES SCIENTIST, AMES CO DIV, MILES LABS INC, 77- *Mem:* Am Chem Soc; Am Oil Chem Soc. *Res:* Nutritional effects of fats; cholesterol metabolism; clinical diagnosis of disease. *Mailing Add:* Ames Co Div Miles Labs Inc Elkhart IN 46514

RAND, RICHARD PETER, b Can, Jan 31, 37; c 3. MEMBRANE BIOLOGY, ELECTROPHYSIOLOGY. *Educ:* Carleton Univ, BSc, 59; Univ Western Ont, MSc, 61, PhD(biophysics), 65. *Prof Exp:* Fel, Med Res Coun Can, Nat Ctr Sci Res, Paris, 64-66; asst prof, 66-68, assoc prof, 68-73, PROF BIOL SCI, BROCK UNIV, 73- *Concurrent Pos:* Chmn, Brock Univ, 73-; assoc mem, Dept Biol, McMaster Univ, & Dept Physics, Guelph Univ, 76-; mem, Grant Selection Comt, Natural Sci & Eng Res Coun Can, 78-80. *Mem:* Biophys Soc. *Res:* Measurements of the forces of interaction between model and biological cell membranes and mechanisms of membrane fusion; developmental aspects of the electrical properties of nerve cells in culture. *Mailing Add:* Biol Sci Brock Univ Glenridge Campus St Catharines ON L25 3A1 Can

RAND, ROBERT COLLOM, b Pittsburgh, Pa, Aug 24, 17; m 42; c 3. MATHEMATICS. *Educ:* Duke Univ, AB, 39, AM, 40; Univ Md, PhD(math), 43. *Prof Exp:* Asst, Univ Md, 40-43; stress analyst, Eng & Res Corp, 42-44; instr math, US Naval Acad, 46-48; SR MATHEMATICIAN, APPL PHYSICS LAB, JOHNS HOPKINS UNIV, 48- *Mem:* Math Asn Am. *Res:* Shock waves in non-steady flow; supersonic aerodynamics and shock waves; rectilinear motion of a gas subsequent to an internal explosion; dynamics of guided missiles; radar countermeasures; reliability; transportation systems. *Mailing Add:* Fulton MD 20759

RAND, SALVATORE JOHN, b Brooklyn, NY, Dec 1, 33; m 56; c 5. ANALYTICAL CHEMISTRY, PHYSICAL CHEMISTRY. *Educ:* Fordham Univ, BS, 56; Rensselaer Polytech Inst, PhD(phys chem), 60. *Prof Exp:* Sr res chemist, Colgate-Palmolive Co, 60-62; res scientist, Res Labs, United Technols, 62-67; res chemist, 67-80, SR RES CHEMIST, RES & TECH DEPT, TEXACO INC, 80- *Concurrent Pos:* Mem adj fac, Grad Sch Chem, St Joseph Col, Conn, 64-67. *Mem:* AAAS; Am Chem Soc; Am Phys Soc. *Res:* Photochemistry; spectroscopy; kinetics of gas and liquid phase reactions; lasers; radiochemistry; lubrication chemistry; hydrocarbon analysis; gas and liquid chromatography. *Mailing Add:* Res & Tech Dept Texaco Inc PO Box 509 Beacon NY 12508

RAND, WILLIAM B, b Salt Lake City, Utah, Jan 17, 02; m 27, 70; c 1. GEOLOGY. *Educ:* Univ Calif, Berkeley, AB, 26, PhD(geol sci), 33. *Prof Exp:* Geologist, Shell Oil Co, 26-31, trainee petrol mfg, Martinez Refinery, 31, mgr, Distilling Dept, 31-32, sr & area geologist, 33-45; area geologist, Union

Oil Co, Calif, 46-50; pres, Submarex Corp, Submar, Marex, Mardril & Rexmar, 51-66; proj mgr deep sea drilling, Scripps Inst Oceanog, Univ Calif, San Diego, 66-67; mem comt ocean eng, Nat Acad Eng, 66-70, Marine Bd, 70-75; PRES, SUBMAREX CORP, 75- *Mem:* Fel Geol Soc Am; Nat Acad Engrs; Am Asn Petrol Geologists. *Res:* Earth and geological sciences; development and exploitation of methods and equipment for oceanographic exploration; core drilling in deep Atlantic and Pacific ocean basins for scientific information; marine geology and petroleum exploration; ocean engineering. *Mailing Add:* Submarex Corp 34 Avon Rd Kensington CA 94707

RAND, WILLIAM MEDDEN, b Seneca Falls, NY, June 26, 38; m 67. BIOSTATISTICS. *Educ:* Ind Univ, BA, 59; Brandeis Univ, MA, 61; Univ Calif, Los Angeles, PhD(biostatist), 69. *Prof Exp:* Engr, Jet Propulsion Labs, 62-64; res assoc med, Univ Southern Calif, 65-68; from asst prof to assoc prof biostatist, Mass Inst Technol, 69-77, lectr, 77- *Mem:* Biomet Soc; Am Statist Asn; Inst Math Statist. *Res:* Mathematical and statistical biology and ecology. *Mailing Add:* Dept of Nutrit & Food Sci Mass Inst of Technol Rm 56-301 Cambridge MA 02139

RANDA, JAMES P, b Chicago, Ill. GAUGE THEORIES, HIGH ENERGY PHENOMENOLOGY. *Educ:* Ill Benedictine Col, BSc, 69; Univ Ill, Urbana, MSc, 70, PhD(physics), 74. *Prof Exp:* Vis asst prof, Dept Physics, Tex A&M Univ, 74-75; res fel, Dept Theoret Physics, Univ Manchester, 75-78; vis asst prof, 78-80, ASST PROF, DEPT PHYSICS, UNIV COLO, BOULDER, 80- *Mem:* Am Phys Soc. *Res:* Mechanisms for symmetry breaking and mass generation in gauge theories for elementary particles; theoretical study of the behavior of quarks, gluons, and photons in very high energy collisions. *Mailing Add:* Dept Physics Univ Colo Campus Box 390 Boulder CO 80309

RANDALL, BARBARA FEUCHT, b Buffalo, NY, Jan 7, 25; m 49; c 4. PHYSIOLOGY. *Educ:* State Univ NY, BS, 45; Univ Iowa, MS, 48, PhD, 51. *Prof Exp:* Asst physiol, Univ Iowa, 47-52; res assoc phys med, Ohio State Univ, 53-55; instr med, Med Ctr, Univ Mo, 55-62; lectr phys med, Med Sch, Northwestern Univ, 64-69; ASST PROF PHYSIOL, IND UNIV, BLOOMINGTON, 69- *Mem:* Am Phys Ther Asn. *Mailing Add:* Physiol Sect Med Sci Prog Ind Univ Myers Hall Bloomington IN 47405

RANDALL, CHARLES ADDISON, JR, b Daytona Beach, Fla, Sept 12, 15; m 41; c 2. COSMIC RAY PHYSICS. *Educ:* Kalamazoo Col, AB, 36; Cornell Univ, MA, 39; Univ Mich, PhD(physics), 51. *Prof Exp:* Instr physics, Allen Acad, Tex, 39-40; instr, Wayland Jr Col & Acad, 40-42; res physicist, Fairbanks Morse & Co, 42-45; asst, Univ Mich, 46-50; from asst prof to assoc prof, 50-60, PROF PHYSICS, OHIO UNIV, 60- *Concurrent Pos:* Off Europ Econ Coop sr sci fel, NSF Europ Orgn Nuclear Res Lab, 60-61; res partic, Oak Ridge Nat Lab, 52; instr, Goodyear Atomic Corp, 54; consult, Los Alamos Sci Lab, 56-; consult nuclear emulsion inst, Univ Chicago, 56; on sabbatical leave, Sandia Corp, NMex & Atomic Energy Res Estab, Eng, 68-69; mem int comt of the forum on physics & soc, Am Phys Soc, 75- *Mem:* AAAS; Am Geophys Union; fel Am Phys Soc; Am Asn Physics Teachers. *Res:* Cosmic rays; fundamental particles. *Mailing Add:* 62 Avon Pl Athens OH 45701

RANDALL, CHARLES CHANDLER, b Cedar Rapids, Iowa, Mar 27, 13; m 41; c 2. MICROBIOLOGY. *Educ:* Univ Ky, BS, 36; Vanderbilt Univ, MD, 40; Am Bd Path, dipl. *Prof Exp:* NIH fel, Vanderbilt Univ, 48-49, instr path, Sch Med, 49-51, asst prof path & bact, 51-52, assoc prof bact, 52-55, prof microbiol & actg head dept, 55-57; prof & chmn dept, 57-78, EMER PROF MICROBIOL, SCH MED, UNIV MISS, 78- *Mem:* AAAS; Am Soc Microbiol; Am Asn Path & Bact; Am Soc Exp Path; NY Acad Sci. *Res:* Virology. *Mailing Add:* Dept Microbiol Univ Miss Med Ctr Jackson MS 39216

RANDALL, CHARLES HAMILTON, b New York, NY, Feb 21, 28; m 53; c 3. MATHEMATICS, PHYSICS. *Educ:* Polytech Inst Brooklyn, BS, 51; Univ Pittsburgh, MS, 57; Rensselaer Polytech Inst, PhD(math), 66. *Prof Exp:* Nuclear engr, Atomic Power Div, Westinghouse Elec Corp, 53-56; nuclear specialist, Nuclear Div, Martin Co, 56-58; reactor physicist, Knolls Atomic Power Lab, Gen Elec Co, NY, 58-67; PROF MATH, UNIV MASS, AMHERST, 67- *Mem:* Am Math Soc; Am Phys Soc. *Res:* Stochastic theory; statistical inference; empirical logic; reactor physics; heterogeneous materials; mathematical foundations of quantum theory. *Mailing Add:* Dept of Math & Statist Univ of Mass Amherst MA 01003

RANDALL, CHARLES MCWILLIAMS, b Visalia, Calif, May 3, 38; m 60. ATMOSPHERIC PHYSICS. *Educ:* Union Col, Nebr, BA, 60; Mich State Univ, MS, 62, PhD(physics), 64. *Prof Exp:* Asst prof physics, Mich State Univ, 64-65; mem tech staff, 65-78, SR SCIENTIST, CHEM & PHYSICS LAB, AEROSPACE CORP, 78- *Mem:* Am Meteorol Soc; Optical Soc Am; Sigma Xi. *Res:* Infrared properties of the atmosphere; solar energy resource assessment. *Mailing Add:* 4925 Calle de Arboles Torrance CA 90505

RANDALL, CLIFFORD W(ENDELL), b Somerset, Ky, May 1, 36; m 59; c 2. POLLUTION CONTROL, ENVIRONMENTAL HEALTH ENGINEERING. *Educ:* Univ Ky, BSCE, 59, MSCE, 63; Univ Tex, Austin, PhD(environ health eng), 66. *Prof Exp:* Asst prof civil eng, Univ Tex, Arlington, 65-68; asst prof sanit eng, 68-69, assoc prof, 69-72, prof sanit eng, 72-81, CHARLES P LUNSFORD PROF CIVIL ENG, VA POLYTECH INST & STATE UNIV, 81- *Concurrent Pos:* Res specialist, Aerobiol Lab, Southwest Med Sch, Univ Tex, 66-68; res dir, San Antonio River Auth, 67; consult pollution control, United Piece Dye Works, Inc, 69, Blue Ridge Winkler, 76-, Hester Industs, 78-, Holly Farms Inc, 79- & Celanese Inc, 81-; consult waste treatment & munitions, Hercules, Inc, & Radford Army Ammunitions Plant, Va, 70-74; consult munic, Wiley & Wilson, Inc, Lynchburg, 70-71 & Harwood Beebe, Inc, Spartanburg, SC; consult indust, E I du Pont de Nemours & Co, Inc, Martinsville, 70, 72 & 78, Waynesboro, Va, 77-; consult, Mead Corp, Lynchburg, 70-71, & Belding Corticelli Fiber Glass Fabrics Co, Bedford, Va, 71-73; res & training grant consult, Environ Protection Agency, 70-71; chmn watershed monitoring subcomt & dir, Occoquan Watershed Water Qual Monitoring Prog, State Water Control Bd Va, 71-; affiliated consult, George A Jeffreys & Co, Inc, Salem, Va, 72-78; consult indust waste treatment, Am Cyanamid, 72-78, Va Bd Cert Water & Wastewater Works Operators, Va-NC Chowan River Basin Tech Panel. *Mem:* Water Pollution Control Fedn; Am Soc Civil Engrs; Am Water Works Asn; Int Asn Water Pollution Res; Asn Environ Eng Professors (secy-treas, 79-80). *Res:* Mechanisms of sludge dewatering; munitions wastes treatment; reservoir eutrophication; sanitary microbiology and stormwater runoff pollution control, industrial waste treatment, and trihalomethane contamination of water. *Mailing Add:* Dept of Civil Eng Va Polytech Inst & State Univ Blacksburg VA 24061

RANDALL, DAVID CLARK, b St Louis, Mo, Apr 23, 45; m 68; c 1. PHYSIOLOGY. *Educ:* Taylor Univ, AB, 67; Univ Wash, PhD(physiol & biophys), 71. *Prof Exp:* Asst prof behav biol, Sch Med, Johns Hopkins Univ, 72-75; asst prof, 75-78, ASSOC PROF PHYSIOL, SCH MED, UNIV KY, 78- *Mem:* Am Physiol Soc; Fedn Am Soc Exp Biol; Am Sci Affil; Soc Exp Biol & Med; Pavlovian Soc NAm. *Res:* Nervous control of the heart during periods of behavioral and environmental stress in unanesthetized non-human primates and dogs. *Mailing Add:* Dept of Physiol & Biophys Univ Ky Sch of Med Lexington KY 40506

RANDALL, DAVID JOHN, b London, Eng, Sept 15, 38; Can citizen; m 62; c 5. ZOOLOGY, PHYSIOLOGY. *Educ:* Univ Southampton, BSc, 60, PhD(physiol), 63. *Prof Exp:* From asst prof to assoc prof zool, 63-73, PROF ZOOL, UNIV BC, 73- *Concurrent Pos:* Vis lectr, Bristol Univ, 68-69; Guggenheim Found fel, 68-69; vis scientist, Marine Labs, Univ Tex, 70 & Zool Sta, Naples, 73; chmn animal biol comt, Nat Res Coun, Can, 74; NATO vis scientist, Acadia Univ, 75 & Marine Lab, Univ Tex, 77; chief scientist, Alpha Helix Amazon Exped, 76; mem adv bd, J Comp Physiol, 77- *Mem:* Can Soc Zoologists; Soc Exp Biologists; Am Phys Soc. *Res:* Respiration and circulation in fish and amphibia with an emphasis on oxygen and carbon dioxide transfer and hydrogen ion regulation across the gills of fish. *Mailing Add:* Dept of Zool Univ of BC Vancouver BC V6T 1W5 Can

RANDALL, EILEEN LOUISE, b Dayton, Ohio, Aug 9, 26. MEDICAL MCIROBIOLOGY. *Educ:* Ohio State Univ, BSc, 48; Am Soc Clin Path, cert med technologist, 49; Jefferson Med Col, MSc, 52, PhD(microbiol), 60; Am Bd Med Microbiol, dipl, 70. *Prof Exp:* Res med technologist, Pa Hosp, Philadelphia, 49; asst microbiol, Jefferson Med Col, 49-55, asst prof microbiol, 53-63, asst prof path, 68-69, assoc prof microbiol & path, 69-73; ASSOC PROF CLIN PATH, MED SCH, NORTHWESTERN UNIV, EVANSTON, 73- *Concurrent Pos:* Asst microbiol, Thomas Jefferson Univ Hosp, 49-55, microbiologist, 55-73; clin microbiologist, Evanston Hosp, 73- *Mem:* Fel Am Acad Microbiol; Am Soc Clin Pathologists; Med Mycol Soc of the Americas; Am Soc Microbiol; Am Soc Trop Med & Hyg. *Res:* Infectious diseases, especially diagnosis and control of hosptial acquired infections; microbiology of perinatal infections; diagnosis of fungous infections and parasitic diseases; automation in microbiology; bacteremia. *Mailing Add:* Dept Path & Lab of Med Evanston Hosp Evanston IL 60201

RANDALL, ERIC A, b Silver Springs, NY, June 12, 46; m 71; c 1. BRYOLOGY. *Educ:* State Univ NY Oswego, BS, 68; Pa State Univ, PhD(bot), 73. *Prof Exp:* Asst prof, 73-77, ASSOC PROF BIOL, STATE UNIV NY BUFFALO, 77- *Mem:* Am Bryol & Lichenological Soc; Am Soc Plant Taxon; Ecol Soc Am; Int Asn Plant Taxon; Nordic Bryol Soc. *Res:* Bryological and phytogeographic studies of Atlantic northern United States and Canada; determination of the impact of a nuclear reprocessing facility on a northern deciduous forest ecosystem. *Mailing Add:* 362 N Sci Dept of Biol State Univ Col 1300 Elmwood Ave Buffalo NY 14222

RANDALL, FRANCIS JAMES, b Williston, NDak, Feb 17, 42. POLYMER CHEMISTRY. *Educ:* Dickinson State Col, NDak, BA, 63; Univ Sask, MS, 68; Univ NDak, PhD(chem), 70. *Prof Exp:* CHEMIST PROD DEVELOP, S C JOHNSON & SON, INC, 69- *Mem:* Am Chem Soc; AAAS; NY Acad Sci. *Res:* Polymer coatings. *Mailing Add:* 1525 Howe St Racine WI 53403

RANDALL, GYLES WADE, b Rochester, Minn, Jan 3, 42; m 66. SOIL SCIENCE. *Educ:* Univ Minn, St Paul, BS, 63, MS, 68; Univ Wis-Madison, PhD(soils), 72. *Prof Exp:* Res asst soils, Univ Minn, 64-65, res fel, 65-69; res asst, Univ Wis, 69-72; asst prof, 72-76, assoc prof, 76-80, PROF SOILS, FAC SOIL SCI, SOUTHERN EXP STA, UNIV MINN, 80- *Mem:* Am Soc Agron; Soil Sci Soc Am; Soil Conserv Soc Am. *Res:* Tillage, soil fertility and plant nutrition with emphasis on nutrient accumulation and movement. *Mailing Add:* Southern Exp Sta Univ of Minn Waseca MN 56093

RANDALL, HENRY THOMAS, b New York, NY, Aug 29, 14; m 40; c 3. SURGERY. *Educ:* Princeton Univ, AB, 37; Columbia Univ, MD, 41, ScD(surg), 50. *Hon Degrees:* MA, Brown Univ, 68. *Prof Exp:* Instr surg, Col Physicians & Surgeons, Columbia Univ, 50, asst prof, 51; assoc prof, Med Col, Cornell Univ, 51-52, prof, Sloan-Kettering Div, 52-55, prof, Med Col, 55-67; prof med sci, 67-79, chmn, Sect Surg, Div Biol & Med Sci, 71-79, EMER PROF MED SCI, BROWN UNIV, 79- *Concurrent Pos:* Asst attend surgeon, Presby Hosp & asst vis surgeon, Delafield Hosp, 50-51; clin dir, Mem Hosp, 51-61, chmn dept surg, 51-66, attend surgeon, 51-67, med dir & vpres med affairs, 61-65; vis surgeon, James Ewing Hosp, 51-67; surgeon-in-chg, Div Surg Res, RI Hosp, 67-75, surgeon-in-chief, 70-79, consult surgeon, 79. *Mem:* Soc Univ Surg (pres, 58-59); Am Soc Clin Surg; Am Surg Asn; fel Am Col Surg; Int Surg Soc. *Res:* Metabolic response to surgery, especially electrolyte and water balance; renal and gastrointestinal tract physiology; surgical and nutritional problems of patients with cancer; nutrition of surgical patients. *Mailing Add:* RI Hosp 593 Eddy St Providence RI 02903

RANDALL, HOWARD M, b Rockville Ctr, NY, May 5, 36; m 62; c 1. PHYSIOLOGY. *Educ:* Univ RI, BS, 58; Univ Rochester, PhD(physiol), 65. *Prof Exp:* Instr, 65-68, asst prof, 68-71, ASSOC PROF PHYSIOL, SCH MED, LA STATE UNIV MED CTR, NEW ORLEANS, 71- *Concurrent*

Pos: La Heart Asn grant, 66-67; NIH grant, 68-; asst dean student affairs & records, Sch Med, La State Univ. *Mem:* AAAS; Am Physiol Soc; Biophys Soc. *Res:* Relationships between physiological functions and metabolism in the kidney. *Mailing Add:* Off of Student Affairs 1542 Tulane Ave New Orleans LA 70112

RANDALL, I(SAAC) ERIC, b New York, NY, Nov 6, 33; m 67; c 2. CHEMICAL ENGINEERING, NUCLEAR ENGINEERING. *Educ:* City Col New York, BChE, 56; Purdue Univ, MSChE, 57; Univ Southern Calif, MBA, 75. *Prof Exp:* Engr, Atomics Int Div, NAm Aviation Inc, 58-59; sr engr, Indust Prod Div, Int Tel & Tel Corp, 59-61; consult, Arthur D Little, Inc, 61-64; proj engr, Atomics Int Div, NAm Aviation, Inc, 64-70; proj nuclear engr & asst to mgr int opers, Bechtel Corp, Norwalk, 70-75; PROJ MGR, C F BRAUN & CO, 75- *Concurrent Pos:* Instr eng ext, Univ Calif, Los Angeles, 63- *Mem:* Am Inst Chem Engrs; Am Nuclear Soc. *Res:* Heat transfer; fluid dynamics; nuclear and electrical power generation systems; coal gasification. *Mailing Add:* C F Braun & Co 1000 S Fremont Alhambra CA 91802

RANDALL, JAMES CARLTON, JR, b Florence, SC, May 26, 37; m 60; c 4. PHYSICAL CHEMISTRY. *Educ:* Univ SC, BS, 59; Emory Univ, MS, 61; Duke Univ, PhD(phys chem), 64. *Prof Exp:* Res chemist, Chemstrand Res Ctr, Inc, Monsanto Co, 64-68; RES ASSOC, PHILLIPS PETROL CO, 68- *Mem:* Am Chem Soc. *Res:* Nuclear magnetic resonance of polymers; structure and properties of polymers. *Mailing Add:* 209 RB-6 Phillips Res Ctr Phillips Petrol Co Bartlesville OK 74003

RANDALL, JAMES EDWIN, b Bloomington, Ind, July 23, 24; m 49; c 4. BIOPHYSICS, PHYSIOLOGY. *Educ:* Purdue Univ, BSEE, 47; State Univ Iowa, 52; Ohio State Univ, PhD(biophys), 55. *Prof Exp:* Electronics eng, Collins Radio Co, Cedar Rapids, 47-49; from asst prof to assoc prof physiol, Univ Mo, 55-63; prof, Northwestern Univ, 63-68; PROF PHYSIOL, IND UNIV, BLOOMINGTON, 68- *Concurrent Pos:* Consult, Nat Health & Lung Prog Proj Comt, 70-74. *Mem:* AAAS; Am Physiol Soc; Biophys Soc; Inst Elec & Electronics Eng. *Res:* Physiological variables as statistical signals; physiological simulations with microcomputers; physiological time series; laboratory digital computation. *Mailing Add:* Dept of Anat & Physiol Ind Univ Bloomington IN 47401

RANDALL, JOHN DEL, b Whittier, Calif, Nov 19, 32; m 53; c 4. NUCLEAR ENGINEERING. *Educ:* Univ Calif, BS, 55, MS, 56; Tex A&M Univ, PhD(nuclear eng), 65. *Prof Exp:* Physicist, Lawrence Radiation Lab, Calif, 55-56; nuclear engr, Nucleonics Div, Aerojet Gen Corp, Gen Tire & Rubber Co, 56-58; asst prof nuclear eng, 58-63, assoc head, Nuclear Sci Ctr, 63-65, PROF NUCLEAR ENG & DIR, NUCLEAR SCI CTR, TEX A&M UNIV, 65- *Concurrent Pos:* Vis lectr, Am Inst Biol Sci, 65- *Mem:* Fel Am Nuclear Soc; Health Phys Soc. *Res:* Neutron activation analysis; utilization of radioactive and non-radioactive tracers; industrial applications of nuclear energy; forensic neutron activation analysis. *Mailing Add:* Nuclear Sci Ctr Tex A&M Univ College Station TX 77843

RANDALL, JOHN DOUGLAS, b Corning, NY, July 23, 42; m 69; c 2. APPLIED MATHEMATICS, SOFTWARE SYSTEMS. *Educ:* Cornell Univ, BMchE, 65, PhD(fluid dynamics), 72; Clarkson Col, MSME, 67. *Prof Exp:* Instr thermodynamics, Clarkson Col, 66-67; sr engr, Appl Physics Lab, Johns Hopkins Univ, 73-80; MODELING ANALYST, US NUCLEAR REGULATORY COMN, 80- *Mem:* AAAS; Am Soc Mech Engrs; Soc Indust & Appl Math; Am Inst Aeronaut & Astronaut. *Res:* Development and coordination of research projects to provide information for regulation of radioactive waste disposal. *Mailing Add:* 6329 Tamar Dr Columbia MD 21045

RANDALL, JOHN ERNEST, b Los Angeles, Calif, May 22, 24; m 51; c 2. MARINE BIOLOGY. *Educ:* Univ Calif, Los Angeles, BA, 50; Univ Hawaii, PhD(marine zool), 55. *Prof Exp:* Asst zool, Univ Calif, Los Angeles, 50; asst, Univ Hawaii, 50-53; Bishop Mus fel, Yale Univ, 55-56; res asst prof ichthyol, Marine Lab, Univ Miami, 57-61; prof biol & dir inst marine biol, Univ PR, 61-65; MARINE ZOOLOGIST & SR ICHTHYOLOGIST, BERNICE P BISHOP MUS, 65- *Concurrent Pos:* Dir, Oceanic Inst, Waimanalo, 65-66; marine biologist, Inst Marine Biol, Univ Hawaii, 67-69; mem subcomt conserv ecosysts, Int Biol Prog; Great Barrier Reef Comt. *Mem:* Am Soc Ichthyol & Herpet. *Res:* Tropical marine ichthyology and biology. *Mailing Add:* Div of Ichthyol Box 19000-A Bernice P Bishop Mus Honolulu HI 96819

RANDALL, JOHN FRANK, b Walnut, NC, Aug 2, 18; m 50; c 1. BIOLOGY. *Educ:* Univ NC, AB, 41; Univ Mich, MS, 50; Univ SC, PhD(biol), 57. *Prof Exp:* Instr biol, Alpena Community Col, 52-55; from assoc prof to prof zool, 57-77, PROF BIOL, APPALACHIAN STATE UNIV, 77- *Mem:* AAAS; Ecol Soc Am. *Res:* Vertebrate ecology; ornithology; ichthyology. *Mailing Add:* Dept of Biol Appalachian State Univ Boone NC 28608

RANDALL, JOHN J, JR, b Newport, RI, Jan 24, 32; m 54; c 3. PHYSICAL CHEMISTRY, INORGANIC CHEMISTRY. *Educ:* Providence Col, BS, 53; Univ Conn, MS, 56, PhD(inorg chem), 59. *Prof Exp:* Res chemist, 58-63, head electrochem res dept, 63-71, sr process engr, 71-77, HEAD ADVAN DEVELOP ENG GROUP, SPRAGUE ELEC CO, 77- *Res:* Anodization of valve metals, especially aluminum, tantalum, niobium and titanium; thermal oxidation of metals; radiotracer study of anodic oxide film composition; etching of aluminum; alternating and direct current properties of anodic aluminum oxide. *Mailing Add:* Sprague Elec Co North Adams MA 01247

RANDALL, JOSEPH LINDSAY, b Clanton, Ala, Dec 7, 32; m 54; c 4. LASERS, COMMUNICATIONS. *Educ:* Univ Ala, BS, 54, MS, 56, PhD(physics), 60. *Prof Exp:* Res physicist, Lockheed Aircraft, 60-61 & Redstone Arsenal, 61-62; res physicist, Astrionics Lab, 62-67, BR CHIEF, TECHNOL DIV, ASTRIONICS LAB, MARSHALL SPACE FLIGHT CTR, NASA, 67- *Honors & Awards:* NASA Exceptional Sci Achievement Medal. *Mem:* Am Phys Soc; Optical Soc Am. *Res:* Laser communication systems for space application; atmospheric effects on optical communication. *Mailing Add:* 2212 Shades Crest Rd SE Huntsville AL 35801

RANDALL, LAWRENCE KESSLER, JR, b Rochester, NY, Oct 21, 38; m 63; c 1. LARGE TELESCOPE DESIGN. *Educ:* Univ Ariz, BS, 62, MS, 73. *Prof Exp:* Res assoc, Solar Div, Kitt Peak Nat Observ, 62-65, sr engr, 65-68, eng mgr 4-M telescopes, 68-71; sr scientist, Europ Orgn Nuclear Res, 72-73; dir eng, Kitt Peak Nat Observ, 73-77; prog mgr radio astron, Div Astron Sci, NSF, sect head, Astron Ctr, 81-82; DEP DIR, CTR ASTROPHYSICS & SPACE SCI, UNIV CALIF, SAN DIEGO, 82- *Concurrent Pos:* Consult, La State Univ, 67-71, Europ Southern Observ, 70-73, Univ Hawaii, 75-79, NASA, 75-81, & Univ Calif, 76-80; sci leader, US Antarctic Res Prog, South Pole, 78-79; staff, Pres Comn Nat Agenda 80's, 80-81. *Mem:* Am Astron Soc; Am Soc Mech Engrs; Soc Photo-Optical Instrumentation Engrs; Am Soc Tool & Mfg Engrs. *Mailing Add:* Ctr Astrophys & Space Sci C-011 Univ Calif San Diego La Jolla CA 92093

RANDALL, LINDA LEA, b Montclair, NJ, Aug 7, 46; m 70. MEMBRANE BIOLOGY. *Educ:* Colo State Univ, BS, 68; Univ Wis, Madison, PhD(molecular biol), 71. *Prof Exp:* Fel, Inst Pasteur, France, 71-73; res assoc molecular biol, Univ Uppsala, 73-75, asst prof, 75-81; ASSOC PROF BIOCHEM, WASH STATE UNIV, 81- *Mem:* Am Soc Microbiol; AAAS; Am Soc Biol Chemists. *Res:* Molecular mechanism of export of protein through biological membranes using proteins in envelope of E coli. *Mailing Add:* Biochem & Biophysics Prog Wash State Univ Pullman WA 99164

RANDALL, P(RYOR) N(EIL), b Chrisman, Ill, Oct 22, 20; m 47; c 2. CIVIL ENGINEERING. *Educ:* Univ Ill, PhD(civil eng), 48. *Prof Exp:* Res engr & supvr, Standard Oil Co Ind, 48-61; mem tech staff, TRW Systs Group, 61-72; SR MAT ENGR, OFF NUCLEAR RES, US NUCLEAR REGULATORY COMN, 72- *Mem:* Am Soc Mech Engrs; Am Soc Testing & Mat. *Res:* Creep and fatigue of metals; brittle fracture. *Mailing Add:* Nuclear Regulatory Comn 1717 H St NW Washington DC 20555

RANDALL, PETER, b Philadelphia, Pa, Mar 29, 23; m 48; c 4. PLASTIC SURGERY. *Educ:* Princeton Univ, AB, 44; Johns Hopkins Univ, MD, 46; Am Bd Plastic Surg, dipl, 55. *Prof Exp:* Intern, Union Mem Hosp, Baltimore, Md, 46-47; resident, US Naval Hosp, Philadelphia, 47-48; asst instr surg, Sch Med & resident, Hosp, Univ Pa, 49-50; asst instr surg, Sch Med, Wash Univ, 50-53; instr, Sch Med, 53-56, assoc, Hosp, 53-59, assoc, Sch Med, 56-59, from asst prof to assoc prof, 59-70, chief div, 80, PROF PLASTIC SURG, SCH MED & HOSP, UNIV PA, 70- *Concurrent Pos:* Resident, Barnes & St Louis Children's Hosp, 52-53; from asst surgeon to sr surgeon, Children's Hosp, Philadelphia, 53-, chief Div Plastic Surg, 62-81; attend plastic surgeon, Vet Admin Hosp, 54-; chief dept plastic surg, Lankenau Hosp, 71; bd mem, Am Bd Plastic Surg, 71. *Mem:* Am Soc Plastic & Reconstruct Surg (secy, 66-69, vpres, 75-76, pres, 77-78); Am Asn Plastic Surg; Am Col Surg; Am Cleft Palate Asn (pres, 66-67); Plastic Surg Res Coun (pres, 64-65). *Res:* Cleft lip and palate; wound healing and tissue transplantation. *Mailing Add:* Dept Surg Hosp Univ Pa Philadelphia PA 19104

RANDALL, RAYMOND VICTOR, b Washington, DC, Aug 1, 20; m 46; c 3. MEDICINE, ENDOCRINOLOGY & METABOLISM. *Educ:* Harvard Univ, AB, 42, MD, 45; Univ Minn, MS, 51. *Prof Exp:* House officer med, Mass Gen Hosp, 45-46; instr, 54-59, from asst prof to assoc prof, 59-70, head sect internal med & endocrinol, 63-74, PROF MED, MAYO GRAD SCH MED, UNIV MINN, 70- *Concurrent Pos:* Clin & res fel, Mass Gen Hosp, 51-52; teaching fel pediat, Harvard Med Sch, 51, teaching fel med, 52; resident physician, House of the Good Samaritan, Boston, 51; asst to staff, Mayo Clin, 52; consult, St Mary's Hosp & Rochester Methodist Hosp, 53-; consult, Mayo Clin, 53-74, sr consult 74- *Mem:* Endocrine Soc; Am Fedn Clin Res; Int Endocrine Soc; Int Soc Neuroendocrinol; Int Soc Psychoneuroendocrinol. *Res:* Endocrine and metabolic diseases. *Mailing Add:* Mayo Clin Rochester MN 55905

RANDALL, ROGERS ELLIS, SR, b Browntown, La, Feb 2, 25; m 50; c 2. INORGANIC CHEMISTRY, SCIENCE EDUCATION. *Educ:* Dillard Univ, BA, 50; Univ Mich, MA, 51; Miami Univ, MA, 61; Ohio State Univ, PhD(sci ed), 74. *Prof Exp:* Asst prof phys sci & physics, Southern Univ, 51-57; asst prof chem & phys sci & head dept chem, Roosevelt Sch, 58-71; ASSOC PROF CHEM & PHYSICS & CHMN DIV SCI & MATH, CALUMET COL, 71- *Mem:* Nat Inst Sci; Am Asn Physics Teachers; Nat Sci Teachers Asn; Am Inst Chem. *Res:* Physical sciences; general chemistry; physics. *Mailing Add:* 2395 W 20th Pl Gary IN 46404

RANDALL, ROYAL WILLIAM, JR, b Holyoke, Mass, Oct 17, 22; m 49. MATHEMATICS. *Educ:* Rice Inst, BA, 44, MA, 49, PhD(math), 54. *Prof Exp:* Instr physics, Sch Dent, Univ Tex, 49-52; instr math, Purdue Univ, 54-56; analyst, Opers Eval Group, Mass Inst Technol, 56-64; sci analyst, Inst Defense Anal, 64-66; proj mgr, Planning Res Corp, 66-69; proj mgr, Tetra Tech Inc, 69-74; consult, Auerbach Assocs, 74-79; PROJ MGR, TETRA TECH, 79- *Mem:* Am Math Soc; Opers Res Soc Am. *Res:* Military operations analysis. *Mailing Add:* 1516 34th St NW Washington DC 20007

RANDALL, WALTER CLARK, b Akeley, Pa, Dec 12, 16; m 43; c 4. PHYSIOLOGY. *Educ:* Taylor Univ, AB, 38; Purdue Univ, MS, 40, PhD(physiol), 42. *Prof Exp:* Asst biol, Purdue Univ, 38-42; from instr to assoc prof, Sch Med, St Louis Univ, 43-54; chmn physiol dept, 54-75, PROF PHYSIOL, STRITCH SCH MED, LOYOLA UNIV CHICAGO, 54- *Concurrent Pos:* Fel physiol, Sch Med, Western Reserve Univ, 42-43; mem prog-proj comt, Nat Heart & Lung Inst, 63-67 & 68-72; chmn, Nat Bd Med Examr, 68; mem field mus, Smithsonian Inst. *Honors & Awards:* Stritch Medal Award, 71; Wiggers Award, Am Physiol Soc, 79. *Mem:* Hon fel Am Col Cardiol; Am Asn Higher Educ; Am Inst Biol Sci; Am Physiol Soc (pres-elect, 81-82, pres, 82-83); Soc Exp Biol & Med. *Res:* Sweating; temperature regulation; circulation and autonomic nervous system; nervous control of the heart. *Mailing Add:* Stritch Sch of Med Loyola Univ Med Ctr Maywood IL 60153

RANDALL, WILLIAM CARL, b Hampton, Iowa, Jan 27, 41. PHYSICAL CHEMISTRY. *Educ:* Iowa State Univ, BS, 63; Univ Wis, PhD(phys chem), 67. *Prof Exp:* Res fel, 67-80, SR RES FEL, MERCK SHARP & DOHME RES LABS, WEST POINT, 80- *Mem:* AAAS; Am Chem Soc. *Res:* Kinetics of reactions in solution and the application of physical chemistry to medicinal chemistry. *Mailing Add:* 26-410 Merck Sharp & Dohme Res Labs West Point PA 19486

RANDAZZO, ANTHONY FRANK, b Staten Island, NY, Sept 20, 41; m 65; c 2. GEOLOGY, RESEARCH ADMINISTRATION. *Educ:* City Col New York, BS, 63; Univ NC, Chapel Hill, MS, 65, PhD(geol), 68. *Prof Exp:* From asst prof to assoc prof, 67-77, asst dir, 77-80, PROF GEOL, UNIV FLA, 77-, ASSOC DEAN SPONSORED RES, 80- *Mem:* Fel Geol Soc Am; Soc Econ Paleont & Mineral; Sigma Xi; Am Asn Petrol Geologists. *Res:* Structure of the Carolina Slate Belt; petrography and geohydrology of limestones of Florida, Georgia and Alabama; reduction of paperwork in contract and grant administration. *Mailing Add:* Div Sponsored Res Univ of Fla Gainesville FL 32611

RANDELS, JAMES BENNETT, b Detroit, Mich, June 13, 31; m 56; c 2. COMPUTER SCIENCE. *Educ:* Univ Calif, Los Angeles, BA, 53; Ohio State Univ, MA, 58, PhD(math), 65. *Prof Exp:* Res engr, Univ Calif, Los Angeles, 54; instr math, Univ Dayton, 56-57; res assoc, Numerical Comput Lab, Ohio State Univ, 57-58; mem tech staff comput & data reduction, Space Tech Labs, Inc, 58-60, head spec proj group, 60-61; res assoc, Comput Ctr, Ohio State Univ, 61-63, chief systs programmer, 63-65, asst prof math, 65-66, asst prof comput sci, 66-70, chmn comput coord comt, 70-73, asst dir learning resources comput ctr, 70-72, asst dir univ systs, 72-75, assoc prof comput & info sci, 70-80, assoc dir comput systs programming, Univ Systs, 75-80; assoc prof, Denison Univ, 80-81; SR PROGRAMMER ANALYST, COMPUT CTR & SR COMPUT SPECIALIST, UNIV SYSTS, OHIO STATE UNIV, 82- *Mem:* Asn Comput Mach; Math Asn Am. *Res:* Digital computer programming; computer operating systems; simulation of systems. *Mailing Add:* 999 Greenridge Rd Worthington OH 43085

RANDEN, NEIL ALLEN, b Lemmon, SDak, June 15, 43; m 66; c 1. ORGANIC CHEMISTRY, COSMETIC CHEMISTRY. *Educ:* SDak Sch Mines & Technol, BS, 65, MS, 66; Univ Iowa, PhD(org chem), 70. *Prof Exp:* Sr res chemist, Ashland Chem Co, Dublin, 70-74; RES SPECIALIST, 3M CO, 74- *Res:* Synthesis of organic materials for use in cosmetic preparations. *Mailing Add:* 2913 Marine Circle Stillwater MN 55082

RANDERATH, KURT, b Dusseldorf, Ger, Aug 2, 29; m 62. BIOCHEMISTRY. *Educ:* Univ Heidelberg, DrMed, 55, dipl, 58. *Prof Exp:* Asst org chem, Darmstadt Tech, 59-62; from res assoc to asst prof, Harvard Med Sch, 64-71; assoc prof, 71-74, PROF PHARMACOL, BAYLOR COL MED, 74- *Concurrent Pos:* Res fel biol chem, Harvard Med Sch, 63-64; Nat Cancer Inst res career develop award, 69; Am Cancer Soc fac res award, 72. *Mem:* AAAS; Am Soc Biol Chem; Am Asn Cancer Res; Am Chem Soc. *Res:* Analysis of nucleic acids and derivatives; drug effects on nucleic acids; separation methods, particularly thin-layer chromatography; chemical carccinogenesis. *Mailing Add:* Dept of Pharmacol Baylor Col of Med Houston TX 77030

RANDERSON, DARRYL, b Houston, Tex, July 8, 37; m 61; c 2. METEOROLOGY. *Educ:* Tex A&M Univ, BS, 60, MS, 62, PhD(meteorol), 68. *Prof Exp:* Instr meteorol, Tex A&M Univ, 62-65; res scientist air pollution, Tex A&M Res Found, 67-68, res assoc, 68-69; RES METEOROLOGIST, NAT WEATHER SERV NUCLEAR SUPPORT OFF, 69- *Concurrent Pos:* Res asst, Tex A&M Univ, 61-65; traineeship, NIH, 65-67; vis meteorol, Univ Nev, Las Vegas, 70- *Honors & Awards:* NASA Group Achievement Award, Johnson Space Ctr, Houston, Tex, 74; Nat Oceanic & Atmospheric Admin Spec Achievement Award, Nat Weather Serv, Las Vegas, Nev, 75. *Mem:* Am Meteorol Soc. *Res:* Numerical modeling; thunderstorms; weather forecasting; satellite meteorology; air pollution meteorology; radar meteorology. *Mailing Add:* Nat Weather Serv PO Box 14985 Las Vegas NV 89114

RANDERSON, SHERMAN, b Little Chute, Wis, Nov 20, 35. GENETICS. *Educ:* St Norbert Col, BS, 57; Univ Detroit, MS, 59; Univ Mich, MS, 63, PhD(genetics), 65. *Prof Exp:* Asst prof biol, Stout State Univ, 65-66; asst prof, 66-74, ASSOC PROF BIOL, UNIV WIS-OSHKOSH, 74- *Mem:* Genetics Soc Am; AAAS; Am Genetics Asn; NY Acad Sci. *Res:* Genetic control of enzyme structure; human biochemical genetics; hereditary metabolic disorders; problems in the teaching of genetics. *Mailing Add:* Dept of Biol Univ of Wis Oshkosh WI 54901

RANDHAVA, SARABJIT SINGH, chemical engineering, see previous edition

RANDHAWA, JAGIR SINGH, b Vahila, India, Nov 1, 22; US citizen; m 54; c 2. PHYSICS. *Educ:* Univ Punjab, WPakistan, BS, 45, MS, 46; Univ Colo, Boulder, MS, 59; NMex State Univ, PhD(physics), 64. *Prof Exp:* Lectr physics, Eudc Dept, Univ Punjab, India, 50-57; teaching asst, Univ Colo, Boulder, 57-59; res assoc, NMex State Univ, 59-64; RES PHYSICIST, ATMOSPHERIC SCI LAB, WHITE SANDS MISSILE RANGE, 64- *Concurrent Pos:* Spec Act Award, US Army, 67-72. *Honors & Awards:* Cert, NSF, 67; Sustained Super Perform Award, Atmospher Sci Lab, US Army, 75. *Mem:* Am Phys Soc; Am Geophys Union; Am Meteorol Soc; Am Inst Aeronaut & Astronaut. *Res:* Physics of upper atmosphere; aeronomy; meteorology; photochemistry of ozone. *Mailing Add:* 2095 Payne Ct Las Cruces NM 88001

RANDIC, MIRJANA, b Ogulin, Yugoslavia, Oct 12, 34; m 60; c 1. NEUROPHYSIOLOGY. *Educ:* Univ Zagreb, MD, 59, PhD(pathophysiol), 62. *Prof Exp:* From asst to assoc prof neurophysiol, Rudjer Boskovic Inst, Yugoslavia, 59-70; asst prof, McGill Univ, 64-65; assoc prof neuropharmacol, Dept Biochem & Pharmacol, Sch Med, Tufts Univ, 72-75; assoc prof, 75-77,

PROF PHARMACOL, DEPT VET ANAT PHARMACOL & PHYSIOL, IOWA STATE UNIV, 77- *Mem:* Int Asn Study Pain; Brit Physiol Soc; Brit Pharmacol Soc; Int Brain Res Orgn; Soc Neurosci. *Res:* Chemical synaptic transmission; the physiological role of peptides, especially substance P, endorphins and somatostatin in nociceptive pathways. *Mailing Add:* Dept Vet Anat Pharmacol & Physiol Iowa State Univ Ames IA 50011

RANDINITIS, EDWARD J, b Scranton, Pa, Apr 7, 40; m 72. BIOPHARMACEUTICS. *Educ:* Wayne State Univ, Detroit, BS, 62, MS, 64, PhD(pharm), 69. *Prof Exp:* Asst pharm, Wayne State Univ, 62-69; res pharmacist, 69-72, res scientist, 72-76, RES ASSOC PHARM, PARKE-DAVIS & CO, WARNER-LAMBERT, 76- *Mem:* Am Pharmaceut Asn; Acad Pharmaceut Sci; Sigma Xi. *Res:* Assessment of pharmaceutical formulations regarding bioavailability; assay of biological fluids for drugs and metabolites; development of assay for such. *Mailing Add:* Parke-Davis Co Jos Campau at the River Detroit MI 48232

RANDLE, ROBERT JAMES, b Detroit, Mich, July 19, 23; m 50; c 2. PHYSIOLOGICAL OPTICS. *Educ:* Stanford Univ, AB, 51; Calif State Univ, San Jose, MA, 56; Univ Calif, Berkeley, MS, 73. *Prof Exp:* Res psychologist, Aero-Med Lab, Wright Air Develop Centre, US Air Force, 56-59; eng psychologist, Human Factors Off, Pac Missile Range, Calif, 59-61; sr engr, Philco Western Develop Lab, Calif, 61-62; RES SCIENTIST, BIOTECH DIV, AMES RES CTR, NASA, 62- *Res:* Application of experimental techniques of psychology to the definition and solution of problems in vision and optics in the operations of aerospace vehicles and systems. *Mailing Add:* Ames Res Ctr NASA Moffett Field CA 94035

RANDLES, CHESTER, b Painesville, Ohio, Sept 14, 18; m 41; c 3. MICROBIOLOGY. *Educ:* Kent State Univ, BS, 42; Ohio State Univ, PhD(bact), 47. *Prof Exp:* Asst bact, Ohio State Univ, 42-44; asst prof, Rutgers Univ, 47-49; from asst prof to assoc prof, 49-71, PROF MICROBIOL, OHIO STATE UNIV, 71- *Mem:* AAAS; Am Soc Microbiol. *Res:* Organic and inorganic aspects of bacterial physiology, including respiratory mechanisms, nutrition and polysaccharide production; relation of physiology to virulence and to viral duplication; sulfur bacteria. *Mailing Add:* Dept of Microbiol Ohio State Univ Columbus OH 43210

RANDLES, RONALD HERMAN, b Canton, Ohio, Sept 4, 42; m 68; c 2. STATISTICS. *Educ:* Col Wooster, BA, 64; Fla State Univ, MS, 66, PhD(statist), 69. *Prof Exp:* From asst prof to assoc prof, Univ Iowa, 69-78, prof statist, 78-81; PROF STATIST, UNIV FLA, 81- *Concurrent Pos:* Assoc ed, Am Statistician, 74-76. *Mem:* Fel Am Statist Asn; Inst Math Statist. *Res:* Selection procedures and nonparametrics. *Mailing Add:* Dept of Statist Univ Fla Gainesville FL 32611

RANDLETT, HERBERT ELDRIDGE, JR, b Centralia, Wash, July 17, 17; m 46; c 2. COMPUTER SYSTEMS, CHEMICAL ENGINEERING. *Educ:* Univ Calif, BS, 39. *Prof Exp:* Mgr exp lab, Shell Oil Co, 54-64, systs mgr mfg, 64-74, staff systs rep, Rep Opers, 47-79; RETIRED. *Res:* Computer systems applications. *Mailing Add:* 1324 Chardonnay Houston TX 77077

RANDOL, BURTON, b New York, NY, Sept 16, 37; m 64. MATHEMATICS. *Educ:* Rice Univ, BA, 59; Princeton Univ, PhD(math), 62. *Prof Exp:* Instr math, Princeton Univ, 62-63; lectr, Yale Univ, 63-64, asst prof, 64-69; assoc prof, 69-74, PROF MATH, GRAD CTR, CITY UNIV NEW YORK, 75- *Mem:* Am Math Soc. *Res:* Analysis. *Mailing Add:* Dept of Math City Univ of New York Grad Ctr New York NY 10036

RANDOLPH, ALAN DEAN, b Muskogee, Okla, Mar 25, 34; m 57; c 3. CHEMICAL ENGINEERING. *Educ:* Univ Colo, BSChE, 56; Iowa State Univ, MSChE, 59, PhD(crystallization), 62. *Prof Exp:* Asst technologist, Shell Chem Corp, 56-58; res proj engr, Am Potash & Chem Corp, Calif, 62-65, head crystallization sect, Res Dept, 65; assoc prof chem eng, Univ Fla, 65-68; assoc prof, 68-70, PROF CHEM ENG, UNIV ARIZ, 70- *Concurrent Pos:* NSF res grant crystallization, 66-; consult, Dow Chem Co, 68-70 & Kerr-McGee Corp, 69-; mem, Consult Comt Nuclear Waste Immobilization, Atlantic Richfield Hanford Co, 71-79; consult, Los Alamos Sci Lab, 78-81, US Borax, 78- & E I du Pont de Nemours & Co Inc, 78-; vis prof, Univ Col, London, 81. *Mem:* Am Inst Chem Engrs; Am Chem Soc; Am Soc Eng Educ. *Res:* Mathematical simulation, description and control of particulate systems, especially crystallization processes, theoretical and experimental study of nucleation-growth rate kinetics and residence-time distributions of particulate systems. *Mailing Add:* 2131 Rainbow Vista Dr Tucson AZ 85712

RANDOLPH, JAMES COLLIER, b Knox City, Tex, Mar 26, 44; m 68. ECOLOGY. *Educ:* Univ Tex, Austin, BA, 66, MA, 68; Carleton Univ, PhD(biol), 71. *Prof Exp:* Res scientist, Ecol Sci Div, Oak Ridge Nat Lab, 72-74; asst prof, 74-77, ASSOC PROF BIOL, SCH PUB & ENVIRON AFFAIRS, DIR, SPEA ENVIRON PROGS & ENVIRON SYSTS APPLN CTR, IND UNIV, BLOOMINGTON, 77- *Mem:* AAAS; Am Inst Biol Sci; Ecol Soc Am; Am Soc Mammal. *Res:* Physiological ecology and applied ecology. *Mailing Add:* Dept Zool Ind Univ Bloomington IN 47401

RANDOLPH, JAMES E, b Los Angeles, Calif, Jan 19, 40; m 68; c 1. SOFTWARE MANAGEMENT, COMPUTER AIDED DESIGN. *Educ:* Calif State Univ Los Angeles, BS, 64; Univ Southern Calif, MS, 67. *Prof Exp:* Systs engr, Viking Mars Studies, 70-72, leader, Mission Planning Team, 72-75, mission engr, Voyager, 75-77, mgr, Starprobe Mission Study, 78-82, MGR, FAR OUTER PLANETS STUDY, JET PROPULSION LAB, CALIF INST TECHNOL, 80- *Mem:* Am Inst Aeronaut & Astronaut; Am Astron Soc. *Res:* Application of advanced mission and systems engineering techniques to the design, implementation, and management of interplanetary missions to optimize the return of scientific data. *Mailing Add:* Jet Propulsion Lab Calif Inst Technol MS 156-220 4800 Oak Grove Dr Pasadena CA 91109

RANDOLPH, JOHN, environmental engineering, energy systems, see previous edition

RANDOLPH, JOHN FITZ, b Newton, Iowa, May 2, 04; m 32, 71; c 2. MATHEMATICS. *Educ:* WTex State Teachers Col, BS, 26; Univ Mich, MA, 28; Cornell Univ, PhD(math), 34. *Prof Exp:* Teacher high sch, Tex, 26-27; instr math, Syracuse Univ, 28-29, instr math & astron & dir observ, 29-31; instr math, Cornell Univ, 31-36, asst prof, 38-43; mem, Inst Adv Study, 36-38; prof math, Oberlin Col, 43-48; prof math, Univ Rochester, 48-69, chmn dept, 48-59; PROF MATH, ROCHESTER INST TECHNOL, 69- *Concurrent Pos:* Vis prof, Am Univ, Beirut, 55-56 & 62-63. *Mem:* Am Math Soc; Math Asn Am. *Res:* Measure theory; topology; genetics; analysis; metric properties of point-sets; numerical analysis. *Mailing Add:* Dept of Math Rochester Inst of Technol Rochester NY 14623

RANDOLPH, JUDSON GRAVES, b Macon, Ga, July 19, 27; m 52; c 5. SURGERY. *Educ:* Vanderbilt Univ, BA, 50, MD, 53. *Prof Exp:* Teaching fel, Harvard Med Sch, 60-61; asst surgeon, Children's Hosp Med Ctr, Boston, 61-63; assoc prof, 64-68, PROF SURG, SCH MED, GEORGE WASHINGTON UNIV, 68-, PROF CHILD HEALTH & DEVELOP, 71-; SURGEON-IN-CHIEF, CHILDREN'S HOSP, WASHINGTON, DC, 64- *Concurrent Pos:* Instr, Harvard Med Sch, 62-63; consult, Nat Naval Med Ctr, Bethesda, 64- & Walter Reed Army Med Ctr, DC, 65-; mem staff, NIH, 65- *Mem:* Am Col Surg; Am Acad Pediat; Am Asn Thoracic Surg; Am Pediat Surg Asn; Soc Univ Surg. *Res:* Burns in children; surgical metabolism in infants; jejunoileal bypass in adolescents; esophageal surgery in infants and children. *Mailing Add:* Childrens Hosp Nat Med Ctr 111 Michigan Ave NW Washington DC 20010

RANDOLPH, KENNETH NORRIS, b Oxford, Miss, Dec 27, 38; m 61; c 3. AQUACULTURE, ZOOLOGY. *Educ:* Delta State Univ, BS, 60; Memphis State Univ, MS, 69; Univ Okla, PhD(zool), 75. *Prof Exp:* Crop reporter, Agr Stability & Conserv Serv, Miss Dept Agr, 60-61; lab technician, US Army Recruiting Serv, US Army, 61-63; inspector, Seafood Inspection & Cert Unit, US Dept Com, 64-67; ASST PROF, DEPT FISHERIES, AUBURN UNIV, 76- *Concurrent Pos:* Consult, US Agency Int Develop Mission-Jamaica, Kingston, 77-79; vis lectr, Jamaica Sch Agr, Kingston, 77-; proj mgr inland fisheries, Ministry Agr, Jamaica, 78- *Mem:* Am Fisheries Soc; World Maricult Soc; Catfish Farmers Am. *Res:* Applied research in the field of aquaculture, especially in the areas of fish behavior, fish nutrition and fish physiology. *Mailing Add:* Dept of Fisheries & Allied Aquacult Auburn Univ Auburn AL 36830

RANDOLPH, LYNWOOD PARKER, b Richmond, Va, May 21, 38; m 60; c 4. ELECTRICAL ENGINEERING, COMPUTER SCIENCES. *Educ:* Va State Univ, BS, 59; Howard Univ, MS, 64, PhD(physics), 72. *Prof Exp:* Physicist, Harry Diamond Labs, 64-68, res physicist, 68-75; prog mgr, 75-80, MGR, NAT AERONAUT & SPACE ADMIN, 80- *Concurrent Pos:* Lectr, Univ DC, 72-80; adj prof, Univ DC & Howard Univ, 80- *Mem:* Am Inst Aeronaut & Astronaut; Am Phys Soc. *Res:* Solar cells and other devices which convert sunlight into electrical energy; lasers to be used in the future to transmit power or propel spacecraft into space. *Mailing Add:* 3000 Fairhill Ct Suitland MD 20746

RANDOLPH, MALCOLM LOGAN, b West Palm Beach, Fla, Oct 11, 20; m 49; c 2. BIOPHYSICS, RADIOBIOLOGY. *Educ:* Univ Va, BA, 43, MS, 46, PhD(physics), 47. *Prof Exp:* Instr, Univ Va, 41-44, res assoc, Manhattan Dist & Off Sci Res & Develop, 42-46; from instr to asst prof physics, Tulane Univ, 47-53; biophysicist, Biol Div, 52-77, BIOPHYSICIST HEALTH & SAFETY RES OAK RIDGE NAT LAB, 77- *Mem:* AAAS; Am Phys Soc; Biophys Soc; Health Physics Soc; Radiation Res Soc. *Res:* Technology assessments; radiological physics; radiobiology; electron spin resonance; ultra centrifugation; molecular biology. *Mailing Add:* Health & Safety Res Div Oak Ridge Nat Lab PO Box X Oak Ridge TN 37830

RANDOLPH, PAUL HERBERT, b Jamestown, NY, Jan 14, 25; m 48; c 6. OPERATIONS RESEARCH. *Educ:* Univ Minn, BA, 48, MA, 49, PhD(statist), 55. *Prof Exp:* Instr math, Bethany Lutheran Col, 49-50; instr bus admin, Univ Minn, 50-53; asst prof indust eng, Ill Inst Technol, 54-57; assoc prof math & statist, Purdue Univ, 57-66; from assoc prof to prof math, NMex State Univ, 66-74; prof eng, Iowa State Univ, 74-76; opers res analyst, Dept Energy, 76-77; vpres energy econ, Chase Manhattan Bank, 77-79; sr assoc engr, Mobil Res & Develop Corp, 79-81; PROF & CHMN, INFO SYSTS & QUANTITATIVE SCI, COL BUS ADMIN, TEX TECH UNIV, 81- *Concurrent Pos:* Guest prof, Univ Heidelberg, 64-65; sci adv, Norsk Regnesentral, 65-66; consult, Braddock, Dunn & McDonald, 66-69; consult, White Sands Missile Range, 69-73; vis prof, Mid East Tech Univ, Turkey, 70-71; vis prof, Inst Math, Univ Oslo, 73-74. *Mem:* Opers Res Soc Am; Inst Mgt Sci; Am Inst Indust Engrs. *Res:* Optimization techniques. *Mailing Add:* Quan Sci Col Bus Tex Tech Univ Lubbock TX 79409

RANDOLPH, PHILIP L, b Casper, Wyo, Feb 25, 31; m 52; c 2. PHYSICS, RESEARCH ADMINISTRATION. *Educ:* Univ Wash, BS, 52, PhD(physics), 58. *Prof Exp:* Physicist, Lawrence Radiation Lab, Univ Calif, Livermore, 58-61, dep tech dir, Proj Gnome, 61-62, tech dir, Salmon Event, Proj Dribble, 62-63 & 64-66, assoc div leader, 66-68; mgr nuclear group, El Paso Natural Gas Co, 68-74, dir res, 74-77; assoc dir, 77-79, DIR CONVENTIONAL SUPPLY RES, INST GAS TECHNOL, 79- *Mem:* Am Phys Soc; Am Nuclear Soc; Soc Petrol Engrs. *Res:* Nuclear explosive test execution; use of nuclear explosives to stimulate natural gas production and produce underground storage for natural gas; massive hydraulic fracturing of tight natural gas reservoirs; improving quantitative understanding of natural gas well completions and reservoir rock properties; producing natural gas from aquifers and coal seams; underground gas storage. *Mailing Add:* Inst Gas Technol 3424 S State St Chicago IL 60616

RANDOLPH, POLLEY ANN, see McClure, Polley Ann

RANDT, CLARK THORP, b Lakewood, Ohio, Nov 18, 17; m 44; c 3. NEUROLOGY. *Educ:* Colgate Univ, AB, 40; Western Reserve Univ, MD, 43. *Prof Exp:* Intern & asst resident internal med, Univ Hosps Cleveland, 43-45; demonstr med, Sch Med, Western Reserve Univ, 45; asst resident & resident neurol, Neurol Inst, Columbia-Presby Med Ctr, 47-50; from sr instr to assoc prof, Sch Med, Western Reserve Univ, 50-56; dir div neurol, Univ Hosps Cleveland, 56-59; dir off life sci, NASA, 60-61; PROF NEUROL & CHMN DEPT, SCH MED & DIR, NY UNIV-BELLEVUE NEUROL SERV, NY UNIV, 62- *Concurrent Pos:* Sr consult, NY Vet Admin Hosp; mem comt bioastronaut, Armed Forces-Nat Res Coun, mem panel manned space flight, NASA; mem, NASA-US Dept Defense Aeronaut & Astronaut Coord Bd. *Mem:* Soc Exp Biol & Med; Am Neurol Asn; Aerospace Med Asn (vpres, 60); fel Am Acad Neurol. *Res:* Physiology of sensory systems; neurophysiological effects of anesthetic agents; memory; applications of computer technology; brain and behavior in early life; nutritional deprivation; mental retardation. *Mailing Add:* Dept of Neurol NY Univ Sch of Med 550 First Ave New York NY 10016

RANEY, EDWARD COWDEN, b Pittsburgh, Pa, May 23, 09. ICHTHYOLOGY. *Educ:* Slippery Rock State Col, BS, 31; Cornell Univ, MS, 35, PhD(vert zool), 38. *Prof Exp:* Teacher high sch, Pa, 32-35; teacher biol, Oneonta Teachers Col, 35-36; asst zool, 36-39, from instr to prof, 39-71, EMER PROF ZOOL, CORNELL UNIV, 71-; PRES, ICHTHYOL ASSOCS, INC, 66-, DIR, 71- *Concurrent Pos:* Coordr, Atlantic Coast Coop Striped Bass Prog, US Fish & Wildlife Serv, 53-57. *Mem:* Fel AAAS; Am Soc Zool; Am Soc Ichthyol & Herpet (secy, 48, pres, 55); Soc Study Evolution; Soc Syst Zool. *Res:* Taxonomy; ecology behavior; life histories of Eastern North American fresh and salt water fishes; growth, movements, food and habits of toads, frogs and snakes. *Mailing Add:* Ichthyol Assocs 301 Forest Dr Ithaca NY 14850

RANEY, GEORGE NEAL, b Portland, Ore, Oct 14, 22; m 52; c 2. MATHEMATICS. *Educ:* Queens Col, NY, BS, 43; Columbia Univ, PhD(math), 53. *Prof Exp:* Instr math, Mass Inst Technol, 43-44; lectr, Columbia Univ, 46-50, instr, 50-53; instr, Brooklyn Col, 53-55; from asst prof to assoc prof, Pa State Univ, 55-61; vis assoc prof, Wesleyan Univ, 61-63; assoc prof, 63-66, PROF MATH, UNIV CONN, 66- *Mem:* Am Math Soc; Math Asn Am; Asn Symbolic Logic. *Res:* Lattice theory; combinatorial analysis; automata theory; continued fractions. *Mailing Add:* Dept Math Univ Conn Storrs CT 06268

RANEY, HARLEY GENE, b Ardmore, Okla, Feb 25, 40; m 63; c 4. ENTOMOLOGY. *Educ:* Okla State Univ, BS, 67, MS, 69, PhD(entom), 70. *Prof Exp:* asst prof entom, 70-77, assoc exten prof, 77-79, EXTEN PROF, WEST KY EXP STA, UNIV KY, 79- *Concurrent Pos:* Sigma Xi grant-in-aid, Okla State Univ, 70-71. *Honors & Awards:* Award, NSF, 69. *Mem:* Entom Soc Am; Entom Soc Can. *Res:* Biology, ecology and biological control; pest management in corn, soybeans, tobacco and sorghum; state pest management coordination. *Mailing Add:* Dept of Entom Univ of Ky Lexington KY 40506

RANEY, J(OHN) P(HILIP), b Kendallville, Ind, Jan 20, 31. MECHANICAL ENGINEERING. *Educ:* Purdue Univ, BS, 54, MS, 57, PhD(mech eng), 59. *Prof Exp:* Instr mech eng, Purdue Univ, 57-59; assoc prof, Univ Va, 59-63; head, Anal Dynamics Sect, 63-78, head, Nastran Mgt Off, 70-73, head, Noise Technol Br, 78-81, HEAD, NOISE PREDICTION BR, LANGLEY RES CTR, NASA, 81- *Mem:* Am Soc Mech Engrs. *Res:* Mechanical vibrations and dynamics; aircraft noise. *Mailing Add:* Noise Technol Br MS 461 Langley Res Ctr NASA Hampton VA 23665

RANEY, RICHARD BEVERLY, b Raleigh, NC, July 21, 06; m 38; c 2. ORTHOPEDIC SURGERY. *Educ:* Univ NC, BA, 26; Harvard Univ, MD, 30. *Prof Exp:* Instr surg, Med Sch, Univ Rochester, 33-34; from instr to asst prof orthop surg, Sch Med, Duke Univ, 34-52; prof orthop surg & chmn div, Sch Med, Univ NC, Chapel Hill, 52-67, clin prof, 67-77; RETIRED. *Concurrent Pos:* Orthop surgeon, NC Mem Hosp, 52-67; writer & consult, 77- *Mem:* Am Orthop Asn; Orthop Res Soc; Am Med Asn; Am Col Surg; Am Acad Orthop Surg. *Res:* Orthopedic surgical education. *Mailing Add:* Box 2467 Chapel Hill NC 27514

RANEY, RUSSELL KEITH, b Auburn, NY, Dec 26, 37; m; c. REMOTE SENSING. *Educ:* Harvard Univ, BS, 60; Purdue Univ, MS, 62; Univ Mich, Ann Arbor, PhD(comput, info & control eng), 68. *Prof Exp:* Asst engr, Zenith Radio Corp, Ill, 60; engr, Systs Div, Bendix Corp, Mich, 62-63; res engr, Willow Run Labs, Univ Mich, Ann Arbor, 62-74, res engr, Environ Res Inst Mich, 74-76; RES SCIENTIST, DEPT ENERGY, MINES & RESOURCES, FED GOVT CAN, 76- *Concurrent Pos:* Consult, NASA, 74- *Mem:* Can Remote Sensing Soc; Inst Elec & Electronics Engrs. *Res:* Application of radar remote sensing systems to environmental surveillance, synthetic aperture radar research; dissemination and utilization of scientific knowledge; oceanic reflectivity; systems development; planetary radar. *Mailing Add:* Can Ctr Remote Sensing 2464 Sheffield Rd Ottawa ON K1A 0E4 Can

RANEY, WILLIAM PERIN, b Neenah, Wis, June 27, 27; m 53; c 4. PHYSICS, ACOUSTICS. *Educ:* Harvard Univ, AB, 50; Brown Univ, ScM, 53, PhD(physics), 55. *Prof Exp:* Res assoc physics, Brown Univ, 54-55; res fel acoustics, Harvard Univ, 55-56, asst prof appl physics, 56-60; assoc prof elec eng, Univ Minn, 60-62; exec secy, Comt Undersea Warfare, Nat Acad Sci-Nat Res Coun, 62-64; spec asst to asst secy navy for res & develop, 64-72; DEP & CHIEF SCIENTIST, OFF NAVAL RES, 72- *Concurrent Pos:* Mem tech staff, Bell Tel Labs, 59-60. *Mem:* AAAS; Acoust Soc Am; Am Phys Soc. *Res:* Physical acoustics; sound propagation in inhomogeneous media; finite amplitude effects; propagation at hypersonic frequencies; linear systems analysis. *Mailing Add:* Off Sci & Technol Applications NASA Code E Rm 268 Washington DC 20546

RANFTL, ROBERT M(ATTHEW), b Milwaukee, Wis, May 31, 25; m 46. TECHNOLOGICAL PRODUCTIVITY, RESEARCH & DEVELOPMENT MANAGEMENT. *Educ:* Univ Mich, BSEE, 46. *Prof Exp:* Prod engr, Russell Elec Co, 46-47; head, Eng Dept, Radio Inst Chicago, 47-50; sr proj engr, Webster Chicago Corp, 50-51; prod design engr, 51-53, head equip design group, 53-54, head electronic equip sect, 54-55, mgr, Prod Eng Dept, 55-58, mgr reliability & qual control, 58-59, mgr admin, 59-61, mgr, Prod Effectiveness Lab, 61-77; corp dir configuration mgt, data mgt &

design rev, 64-74, CORP DIR ENG & DESIGN MGT, HUGHES AIRCRAFT CO, 74-, ASST DIR PROD INTEGRITY, 77- *Concurrent Pos:* Teacher res & develop mgt & prod, Hughes Aircraft Co, 75-; consult, res & develop mgt & prod, 78- *Mem:* AAAS; Am Inst Aeronaut & Astronaut; sr mem Inst Elec & Electronics Eng; NY Acad Sci. *Res:* means of improving productivity in technology-based organizations. *Mailing Add:* Hughes Aircraft Co Centinela Ave & Teale St Culver City CA 90230

RANGANAYAKI, RAMBABU POTHIREDDY, b Secunderabad, India, Jan 15, 42; m 68; c 2. GEOPHYSICS. *Educ:* Osmania Univ, India, MSc, 64; Univ Hawaii, Honolulu, MS, 72; Mass Inst Technol, PhD(geophys), 78. *Prof Exp:* Sr sci asst geomagnetism, Nat Geophys Res Inst, India, 64-69, scientist, 69-70; res asst geophys, Mass Inst Technol, 72-78; res assoc geophys, Carnegie Inst Washington, 78-80; RES GEOPHYSICIST, MOBIL RES & DEVELOP CORP, 81- *Mem:* Am Geophys Union; Soc Explor Geophysicists; Sigma Xi. *Res:* Magnetotelluric depth sounding; geomagnetic depth sounding; data analysis and interpretation; model development; paleomagnetism; induced polarization; general physics. *Mailing Add:* Res Fuels Lab Mobil Res & Develop Corp PO Box 900 Dallas TX 75221

RANGER, KEITH BRIAN, b Salisbury, Eng, Aug 11, 35; m 59; c 2. APPLIED MATHEMATICS. *Educ:* Univ London, BSc, 56, PhD, 59. *Prof Exp:* Asst lectr math, Bedford Col, London, 58-61; lectr, 61-63, from asst prof to assoc prof, 63-70, PROF MATH, UNIV TORONTO, 70- *Mem:* Am Math Soc; Soc Indust & Appl Math; Can Math Cong. *Res:* Axially symmetric potentials; slow motion of a viscous fluid; magnetohydrodynamics. *Mailing Add:* Dept of Math Univ of Toronto Toronto ON M5S 2R8 Can

RANGO, ALBERT, b Cleveland, Ohio, Nov 7, 42; m 66; c 1. WATERSHED MANAGEMENT, REMOTE SENSING. *Educ:* Pa State Univ, BS, 65, MS, 66; Colo State Univ, PhD(watershed mgt), 69. *Prof Exp:* Asst prof meteorol, Pa State Univ, University Park, 69-72; sr hydrologist, 72-80, HEAD, HYDROLOGICAL SCI BR, NASA, 80- *Concurrent Pos:* Consult, Environ Serv Oper, E G & G, 68-69; vis instr, State Univ NY Col Buffalo, 70. *Honors & Awards:* Except Serv Medal, NASA, 74. *Mem:* Am Meteorol Soc; Am Geophys Union; Am Water Resources Asn. *Res:* Weather modification effects; fluvial geomorphology; snow hydrology; bioclimatology; watershed modelling; watershed physiography; floodplain mapping; soil moisture; meteorology; snowmelt-runoff modeling. *Mailing Add:* Code 913 Goddard Space Flight Ctr Greenbelt MD 20771

RANHAND, JON M, b New York, NY, Feb 11, 39; m 63; c 2. MICROBIAL PHYSIOLOGY. *Educ:* City Col New York, BS, 61; Johns Hopkins Univ, MS, 64; Univ Cincinnati, PhD(microbiol), 68. *Prof Exp:* Fel, 68-69, staff fel, Lab Microbiol, NIH, 69-73; SR SCIENTIST, USPHS, 73- *Mem:* Am Soc Microbiol. *Res:* Bacterial physiology with respect to competence development and transformation. *Mailing Add:* Nat Inst Allergy & Infectious Dis Bldg 7 Rm 237 Nat Inst of Health Bethesda MD 20014

RANHOTRA, GURBACHAN SINGH, b Abbotabad, India, Aug 8, 35; m 60; c 2. NUTRITIONAL BIOCHEMISTRY. *Educ:* Agra Univ, BVSc, 58, MVSc, 60; Univ Minn, St Paul, PhD(nutrit), 64. *Prof Exp:* Fel nutrit biochem, Univ Ill, Urbana, 64-65; assoc prof nutrit, Punjab Agr Univ, 65-68; assoc mem biochem, Univ Okla, 68-69; group leader, 69-80, DIR NUTRIT, AM INST BAKING, 81- *Concurrent Pos:* Adj prof foods & nutrit, Kans State Univ; assoc ed, Cereal Chem. *Mem:* Am Inst Nutrit; Am Asn Cereal Chem; Inst Food Technologists. *Res:* Lipids; minerals; cereal-based foods. *Mailing Add:* Nutrit Res Am Inst of Baking 1213 Bakers Way Manhattan KS 66502

RANIERI, RICHARD LEO, b Chicago Heights, Ill, Oct 30, 43; m 71. ORGANIC CHEMISTRY, NATURAL PRODUCTS CHEMISTRY. *Educ:* Univ Ill, BS, 65; Univ Toledo, PhD(chem), 73. *Prof Exp:* Fel, Dept Med Chem & Pharmacog, Purdue Univ, 73-76; res chem, Wash Res Ctr, W R Grace & Co, 76-80; MEM STAFF, SODYECO DIV, MARTIN MARIETTA CO, 80- *Mem:* Am Soc Pharmacog; UNIV, 73- *Mem:* Am Chem Soc. *Res:* Structure elucidation by spectroscopy; tetrahydrolsoquinoline synthesis; chromatography; organophosphorus chemistry. *Mailing Add:* Sodyeco Div Martin Marietta Co PO Box 33429 Charlotte NC 28233

RANISESKI, JOHN WALTER, photochemistry, physical organic chemistry, see previous edition

RANISH, JOSEPH MICHAEL, materials science, physical chemistry, see previous edition

RANK, DAVID HERR, physics, deceased

RANK, GERALD HENRY, b Man, Sept 30, 40; m 68; c 2. GENETICS. *Educ:* Univ Man, BScAg, 63, MSc, 64; Univ BC, PhD(genetics), 70. *Prof Exp:* ASSOC PROF BIOL, UNIV SASK, 70- *Mem:* Can Soc Genetics; Am Soc Genetics. *Res:* Genetic and biochemical analysis of membrane molecular interactions; pleiotropic cross resistance and collateral sensitivity in yeast. *Mailing Add:* Dept of Biol Univ of Sask Saskatoon SK S7N 0W0 Can

RANKEL, LILLIAN ANN, b New York, NY. INORGANIC CHEMISTRY, CATALYSIS. *Educ:* Molloy Col, BS, 66; Fordham Univ, MS, 68; Princeton Univ, PhD(inorg chem), 77. *Prof Exp:* Assoc mem technol staff chem, Bell Labs, Murray Hill, NJ, 68-73; res asst, Princeton Univ, 73-77; SR RES CHEMIST CATALYSIS, MOBIL RES & DEVELOP CORP, 77- *Mem:* Am Chem Soc. *Res:* Catalytic hydroprocessing of crude oils; upgrading and processing shale oils. *Mailing Add:* Mobil Res & Develop Corp PO Box 1025 Princeton NJ 08540

RANKEN, WILLIAM ALLISON, b Amityville, NY, Jan 18, 28; m 51; c 3. ENERGY CONVERSION. *Educ:* Yale Univ, BS, 49; Rice Univ, MS, 56, PhD(physics), 58. *Prof Exp:* Res asst weapons develop, Los Alamos Sci Lab, 50-52, staff mem, 52-54; res physicist, Union Carbide Nuclear Co, NY, 57-58;

staff mem Advan Propulsion Group, 58-62, from asst group leader to group leader, 62-73, group leader, Advan Heat Transfer Group, 73-77, ALT GROUP LEADER, REACTOR & ADVAN HEAT TRANSFER TECHNOL GROUP, LOS ALAMOS SCI LAB, 77- *Mem:* AAAS; Am Phys Soc. *Res:* Heat pipe technology; thermionic conversion; radiation damage; low energy nuclear physics; nuclear reactor development. *Mailing Add:* Los Alamos Sci Lab Energy Div PO Box 1663 Los Alamos NM 87545

RANKIN, ALEXANDER DONALD, b Troy, NY, July 5, 16; m 43; c 3. VETERINARY MEDICINE. *Educ:* Cornell Univ, DVM, 39, MS, 40. *Prof Exp:* Asst vet physiol, Cornell Univ, 39-42, 46-47, actg prof, 53-54; assoc prof physiol, Colo State Univ, 47-48; prof & head dept, 48-55; from asst clin res dir to assoc clin res dir, Squibb Inst Med Res Div, Olin Mathieson Chem Corp, 56-64, dir agr sci sect, 64-66, dir animal health res, 66-67; exec dir animal sci res, Merck Sharp & Dohme Res Labs, 67-73; exec dir res & develop, Lambert Kay Div, Carter-Wallace, Inc, 73-75; CONSULT INDUST VET MED, 75- *Concurrent Pos:* Mem animal health comt, Nat Res Coun, 69-73, Inter-Soc Comt Drugs & Chem, 69-74, Indust Vet Asn del, Am Vet Med Asn, 69-75, bd dirs, Agr Res Inst, Nat Acad Sci-Nat Res Coun, 71-74, chmn feed adjuvants comt, 72; pvt vet pract, 75- *Mem:* Am Soc Vet Physiol & Pharmacol (pres, 62-63); Am Soc Animal Sci; Am Vet Med Asn; Am Asn Vet Nutritionists (pres, 75-76); Indust Vet Asn (pres, 60-61). *Res:* Ruminant physiology; role of antibiotic feed additives in meat production; endocrinological aspects of animal reproduction; application of pharmaceutical developments to the veterinary field; medical and health sciences. *Mailing Add:* 11731 Heathcliff Dr Santa Ana CA 92705

RANKIN, DAVID, b Calgary, Alta, July 2, 17; m 39; c 3. PHYSICS, GEOPHYSICS. *Educ:* Univ BC, BA, 48, MA, 49; Univ Alta, PhD(physics), 60. *Prof Exp:* Jr geophysicist, Western Geophys, 53-57; asst prof physics, Assumption Univ, 59-61; assoc prof, Victoria Univ, Ont, 61-64; assoc prof, 64-74, PROF PHYSICS, UNIV ALTA, 74- *Mem:* Soc Explor Geophys; Am Geophys Union; Can Asn Physicists. *Res:* Electromagnetic phenomenon in their interaction between naturally occurring sources and the earth. *Mailing Add:* Dept of Physics Univ of Alta Edmonton AB T6G 2E1 Can

RANKIN, DOUGLAS WHITING, b Wilmington, Del, Sept 9, 31; m 56; c 2. TECTONICS, VOLCANOLOGY. *Educ:* Colgate Univ, BA, 53; Harvard Univ, MA, 55, PhD, 61. *Prof Exp:* Field asst, US Geol Surv, Colo, 54; asst prof geol, Vanderbilt Univ, 58-61; geologist & teacher, AID, Washington, DC, 61-62; geologist, 62-78, SUPVRY GEOLOGIST, US GEOL SURV, 78- *Concurrent Pos:* Staff scientist, Lunar Sample Off, NASA, 72; coordr, Charleston Invests, SC, 76-78; chief, Br Eastern Regional Geol, 78- *Mem:* AAAS; fel Geol Soc Am; Mineral Soc Am; Am Geophys Union. *Res:* Paleovolcanology and tectonics of the Appalachian orogenic belt; geology of the Absaroka volcanic field in Wyoming; intraplate earthquakes. *Mailing Add:* US Geol Surv Stop 926-A Nat Ctr Reston VA 22092

RANKIN, JAMES EDWIN, electrodynamics, computer science, see previous edition

RANKIN, JOANNA MARIE, b Denver, Colo. RADIO ASTRONOMY. *Educ:* Southern Methodist Univ, BS, 65; Tulane Univ, MS, 66; Univ Iowa, PhD(astrophys), 70. *Prof Exp:* Res assoc radio astronomy, Univ Iowa, 70-74; asst prof astron, Cornell Univ, 74-78, sr res assoc hist, 78-80; ASSOC PROF PHYSICS, UNIV VT, 80- *Concurrent Pos:* Vis scientist, Arecibo Observ, PR, 69-78; Am Philos Soc res grant, Radiophys Div, Commonwealth Sci Indust Res Orgn, Sydney, Australia, 72; actg head, Arecibo Observ Comput Dept, 75. *Mem:* AAAS; Int Union Radio Sci; Int Astron Union; Am Astron Soc. *Res:* Observational properties of pulsars and the interstellar medium; history and philosophy of contemporary physical science. *Mailing Add:* Dept Physics Cook Bldg A405 Univ Vt Burlington VT 05405

RANKIN, JOEL SENDER, b Brockton, Mass, Sept 13, 31. OBSTETRICS & GYNECOLOGY. *Educ:* Yale Univ, BA, 53; Boston Univ, MD, 57; Am Bd Obstet & Gynec, dipl, 65. *Prof Exp:* Intern med, Beth Israel Hosp, Boston, 57-58; resident surg, Mass Mem Hosp, 58-59; resident obstet & gynec, Boston City Hosp, 59-62; officer in chg, Castle AFB Hosp, Calif, 62-64; asst clin prof obstet & gynec, Western Reserve Univ, 66-69; ASSOC PROF OBSTET & GYNEC, SCH MED, BOSTON UNIV, 69-; DIR OBSTET & GYNEC, FRAMINGHAM UNION HOSP, 75- *Concurrent Pos:* USPHS fel endocrinol, Jefferson Med Col, 64-66; asst dir obstet & gynec, Mt Sinai Hosp Cleveland, Ohio; asst obstetrician & gynecologist, Cleveland Metrop Gen Hosp, dir endocrine-sterility clin, 66-69, asst vis obstetrician & gynecologist, 67-69; dir gynec-infertility clin, Boston City Hosp, Mass, 69-75, assoc vis surg, 69-; assoc vis gynecologist, Univ Hosp, Boston, 69- *Mem:* Am Col Obstet & Gynec; Am Fertil Soc. *Mailing Add:* Framingham Union Hosp Framingham MA 01701

RANKIN, JOHN, b Glasgow, Scotland, Jan 29, 23; m 54; c 3. INTERNAL MEDICINE, PHYSIOLOGY. *Educ:* Glasgow Univ, MB, ChB, 46; Univ Wis, MD, 47; FRCPS, 49; FRCP, 64. *Prof Exp:* Asst lectr med, Materia Medica, Univ Glasgow, 49-52; from instr to Rennebohm prof, 53-70, PROF MED & CHMN DEPT PREV MED, UNIV WIS-MADISON, 70-, DIR PULMONARY FUNCTION LAB, 53-, DIR PULMONARY RES & TRAINING PROG, 64-, CHMN FAC DIV BIOL SCI, 67- *Concurrent Pos:* Registr, Stobhill Hosp, Glasgow, 49-53; fel physiol, Univ Pa, 55-57; mem comt chest dis, Second Nat Conf Cardiovasc Dis, 63-64; consult, Appellate Div, Social Security Serv, 63- & Vet Admin Coop Study Pulmonary Physiol, 63-; mem res training comt, Nat Heart Inst, 64- *Mem:* Am Soc Clin Invest; Am Physiol Soc; Am Fedn Clin Res; Am Thoracic Soc. *Res:* Occupational diseases of the lung, including the epidemiology, pathology and immunology of farmers lung; normal and abnormal pulmonary physiology; exercise physiology; diffusion and gas exchange. *Mailing Add:* Dept of Prev Med Univ of Wis Med Ctr Madison WI 53706

RANKIN, JOHN CARTER, b Knoxville, Tenn, Dec 21, 19; m 43; c 3. CEREAL CHEMISTRY. *Educ:* Bradley Univ, BS, 42, MS, 55. *Prof Exp:* Chemist carbohydrate & starch chem, 46-58, res chemist, 58-67, PROJ LEADER CEREAL CHEM, NORTHERN REGIONAL RES LAB, AGR RES SERV, USDA, 67- *Honors & Awards:* Distinguished Serv Award, USDA, 55 & 64. *Mem:* Am Chem Soc; Am Asn Cereal Chem; AAAS; Sigma Xi. *Res:* Reactions of carbohydrates; structure of starch and dextrans; starch and flour derivatives; utilization of cereal grains and fractions therefrom in films, paper, and textiles. *Mailing Add:* 1734 East Maple Ridge Dr Peoria IL 61614

RANKIN, JOHN HORSLEY GREY, b Gosforth, Eng, May 1, 37; US citizen; m 64; c 2. PHYSIOLOGY, OBSTETRICS & GYNECOLOGY. *Educ:* Univ Melbourne, BSc, 59; Univ Tenn, Knoxville, MS, 63; Univ Ore, PhD(physiol), 68. *Prof Exp:* Teacher biol, Hobart High Sch, Tasmania, 64-65; from instr to asst prof physiol, Univ Colo Med Ctr, Denver, 68-71; asst prof, 71-74, assoc prof, 74-77, PROF PHYSIOL & OBSTET & GYNEC, DIV FETAL-PERINATAL MED, UNIV WIS-MADISON, 77- *Mem:* Perinatal Res Soc; Soc Gynec Invest; Am Physiol Soc; Int Soc Oxygen Transport to Tissue; Soc Exp Biol & Med. *Res:* Fetal physiology and physiology of the placenta. *Mailing Add:* Div Fetal-Perinatal Med Madison Gen Hosp 202 S Park St Madison WI 53715

RANKIN, JOHN STEWART, JR, b Manchester, NH, Sept 27, 11; m 41; c 1. MARINE BIOLOGY. *Educ:* Wesleyan Univ, AB, 33, MA, 34; Duke Univ, PhD(parasitol), 36. *Prof Exp:* Asst, Wesleyan Univ, 32-34 & Duke Univ, 34-36; teaching fel biol, Amherst Col, 36-38, instr, 38-41; asst prof zool, Univ Wash, 41-43; from asst prof to prof, 43-76, dir marine res lab, 57-71, EMER PROF ZOOL, UNIV CONN, 76- *Concurrent Pos:* Jr instr, Marine Biol Lab Woods Hole, 36-38, sr instr, 39-41, naturalist, 47-57, mem corp, 38-, trustee, 50-55, emer trustee, 78-; prog dir environ biol, NSF, 64-65, consult, 65-66. *Mem:* AAAS; fel Am Soc Zoologists; Am Soc Parasitol; Am Micros Soc; Ecol Soc Am. *Res:* Ecology of benthic marine invertebrates. *Mailing Add:* Box 97 Ashford CT 06278

RANKIN, JOSEPH EUGENE, b Washington, DC, Jan 13, 20; m 43; c 3. PSYCHIATRY. *Educ:* Cath Univ Am, BS, 42; George Washington Univ, MD, 46; Washington Psychoanal Inst, grad, 66. *Prof Exp:* Intern, US Naval Hosp, Oakland, Calif, 47; intern, US Naval Hosp, Bethesda, Md, 47, resident neurol, 48; resident psychiat, St Elizabeth's Hosp, Washington, DC, 50-52; mem staff, Child Guid Clin, Cath Univ Am, 52-56; PROF PSYCHIAT, SCH MED, GEORGE WASHINGTON UNIV, 56- *Concurrent Pos:* Mem psychother dept, St Elizabeth's Hosp, Washington, DC, 52-56, consult, 57-62; consult, DC Gen Hosp, 57-61 & Crownsville State Hosp, Md, 62-81; pvt pract psychiat & psychoanal, 72-; mem bd dirs, Psychiat Inst Washington, DC & Psychiat Inst Found. *Mem:* Fel Am Psychiat Asn; Am Psychoanal Asn. *Res:* Psychoanalysis; adolescence. *Mailing Add:* 25 Shaw St Annapolis MD 21401

RANKIN, SIDNEY, b Baltimore, Md, Dec 18, 31; m 60; c 1. CHEMICAL ENGINEERING. *Educ:* Johns Hopkins Univ, BE, 53; Univ Del, MChE, 55, PhD(chem eng), 61. *Prof Exp:* Sr process engr, Kordite Co, NY, 57-60; chem engr, Monsanto Chem Co, Mass, 60-62; process develop & design engr, Silicone Prod Dept, Gen Elec Co, NY, 62-70; process supt, Borden Chem Co, Mass, 71-74; dir res & eng, Dacor Inc, 74-75; sr staff engr, GAF Corp, 75-77; SR RES ENGR, CELANESE RES CO, SUMMIT, NJ, 77- *Mem:* Am Inst Chem Engrs. *Res:* Product and process development, especially aspects of commercial development and process design for chemicals, polymers, specialties and agricultural products. *Mailing Add:* 137 Tulip St Summit NJ 07901

RANNELS, DONALD EUGENE, JR, b Lancaster, Pa, Apr 5, 46; m 67; c 1. PHYSIOLOGY. *Educ:* Pa State Univ, BS, 68, PhD(physiol), 72. *Prof Exp:* Res assoc, 71-73, from instr to asst prof physiol, 73-78, ASSOC PROF PHYSIOL, HERSHEY MED CTR, PA STATE UNIV, 78- *Mem:* Am Diabetes Asn; Am Thoracic Soc; Am Physiol Soc; Am Heart Asn. *Res:* Hormonal and substrate control of protein turnover in heart, skeletal muscle and lung; effects of oxygen deprivation on myocardial metabolism; control of protein metabolism in pulmonary aviolar macrophages; compartmentation of intracellular amino acids. *Mailing Add:* Dept of Physiol Hershey Med Ctr Pa State Univ 500 Univ Dr Hershey PA 17033

RANNEY, BROOKS, b Daytona Beach, Fla, Jan 31, 15; m 30; c 3. OBSTETRICS & GYNECOLOGY. *Educ:* Oberlin Col, AB, 36; Northwestern Univ, BM, 40, MD, 41, MS, 48. *Prof Exp:* Lab instr physiol, Med Sch, Northwestern Univ, 47-48; clin asst prof, 48-51, clin prof, 51-76, PROF OBSTET & GYNEC, 76-, CHMN DEPT, SCH MED, UNIV S DAK, YANKTON CLIN, 51- *Mem:* Am Col Obstet & Gynec; Am Col Surg; Cent Asn Obstet & Gynec (pres, 74-75). *Res:* Obstetric analgesia and anesthesia; congenital incompetence of the cervix; paracervical block analgesia for primigravidas; diagnosis and treatment of enterocele; family planning and sex education; external cephalic version; prenatal care studies; clinical studies of endometriosis; advantages of local anesthesia for cesarean section. *Mailing Add:* Yankton Clin 400 Park Ave Yankton SD 57078

RANNEY, CARLETON DAVID, b Jackson, Minn, Jan 23, 28; m 49; c 2. PLANT PATHOLOGY. *Educ:* Agr & Mech Col, Tex, BS, 54, MS, 55, PhD(plant path), 59. *Prof Exp:* Asst plant path, Agr & Mech Col, Tex, 54-55; agent, Field Crops Res Br, 55-57, plant pathologist, Crops Res Div, Cotton & Cordage Fibers Res Br, Tex, 57-58, plant pathologist, Delta Exp Sta, Miss, 58-70, leader cotton path invest, Plant Indust Sta, Md, 70-72, asst area dir, Agr Res Serv, Ala-N Miss Area, 72-78, AREA DIR, DELTA STATES AREA, SCI & EDUC, AGR RES SERV, USDA, 78- *Concurrent Pos:* Adj prof, Dept Agron, Miss State Univ, 74- *Mem:* Am Phytopath Soc; Cotton Dis Coun (secy, 59-60); Am Soc Agron; Crop Sci Soc Am; Sigma Xi. *Res:* Chemical control of plant diseases; physiology of disease resistance; nature of host parasite relationships. *Mailing Add:* Area Dir Off PO Box 225 Stoneville MS 38776

RANNEY, DAVID FRANCIS, b Chicago, Ill, Feb 14, 43. IMMUNOBIOLOGY, ONCOLOGY. *Educ:* Oberlin Col, BA, 65; Case Western Reserve Univ, MD, 69. *Prof Exp:* From intern to resident surg, Stanford Univ Hosp, 69-71; res assoc immunol, Nat Inst Dent Res, 71-73; res assoc immunol, Dept Surg, 73-75, asst prof microbiol-immunol & surg, Med Sch, Northwestern Univ, 75-78; ASST PROF PATH, MED SCH, UNIV TEX HEALTH SCI CTR, DALLAS, 78- *Concurrent Pos:* Consult, Natural Prod Sect, Drug Res & Develop Br, NIH, 75- *Res:* Regulation of the immune response by natural products from normal and malignant tissues and by synthetic drugs; regulation of lymphoid neoplasias and autoimmunity by natural products; surgery. *Mailing Add:* 3539 Courtdale Dallas TX 75234

RANNEY, HELEN M, b Summer Hill, NY, Apr 12, 20. INTERNAL MEDICINE, HEMATOLOGY. *Educ:* Bernard Col, AB, 41; Columbia Univ, MD, 47. *Prof Exp:* Asst prof clin med, Columbia Univ, 58-60; from assoc prof to prof med, Albert Einstein Col Med, Yeshiva Univ, 60-70; prof, State Univ NY Buffalo, 70-73; CHMN DEPT MED, UNIV CALIF, SAN DIEGO, 73- *Honors & Awards:* Joseph Mather Smith Prize, Columbia Univ, 55. *Mem:* Nat Acad Sci; Am Soc Clin Invest; Asn Am Physicians. *Mailing Add:* Dept of Med T006 Univ Calif San Diego La Jolla CA 92093

RANNEY, J BUCKMINSTER, b Brattleboro, Vt, Dec 26, 19; m 80. COMMUNICATIONS SCIENCE, AUDIOLOGY. *Educ:* NY Univ, BA, 46, MA, 47; Ohio State Univ, PhD(speech), 57. *Prof Exp:* From asst prof to assoc prof speech, Ohio Northern Univ, 48-57; clin dir commun sci, Auburn Univ, 57-69; exec secy, CDRC, 69-75, chief, Sci Eval Br, 75-78, DEP DIR COMMUNICATIVE DISORDERS PROG, NAT INST NEUROL & COMMUN DISORDERS & STROKE ADMIN, NIH, 78- *Concurrent Pos:* Nat Inst Neurol & Commun Disorders & Stroke Spec fel, Johns Hopkins Univ Hosp, 62-63; audiol consult, State Ala Maternal & Child Health, 64-69; chief audio & speech path, Vet Admin Hosp, San Juan, PR, 66-67; assoc ed, Deafness, Speech, Hearing Abstr, 68; actg dir, HEW/NIH/Nat Inst Neurol & Commun Disorders & Stroke/Extramural Activ Prog, 78. *Mem:* Fel Am Speech & Hearing Asn; AAAS; Alexander Graham Bell Asn. *Res:* Deafness; language pathology and speech pathology. *Mailing Add:* Commun Dis Prog 7550 Wisconsin Ave Bethesda MD 20205

RANNEY, MAURICE WILLIAM, b Buffalo, NY, Jan 13, 34; m 53; c 4. PHYSICAL CHEMISTRY, ORGANIC CHEMISTRY. *Educ:* Niagara Univ, BS, 57, MS, 59; Fordham Univ, PhD(org chem), 67. *Prof Exp:* Chemist, Union Carbide Corp, NY, 57-58; proj leader anal res, Res & Develop Dept, Chem Div, 59-60, coatings technol, 60-62 & polymeric oil additives, 62-67, group leader, Silicones Technol, Int, 68-74, TECHNOL MGR, UNION CARBIDE CORP, 74- *Mem:* AAAS; Sigma Xi. *Res:* Silicones industry; coatings and adhesives; reinforced plastics; elastomers; cellular plastics; flame retardant research. *Mailing Add:* Union Carbide Corp PO Box 65 Tarrytown NY 10591

RANNEY, RICHARD RAYMOND, b Atlanta, Ga, July 11, 39; m 69; c 4. DENTISTRY, PERIODONTOLOGY. *Educ:* Univ Iowa, DDS, 63; Univ Rochester, MS, 69; Eastman Dent Ctr, cert, 69. *Prof Exp:* Dent intern, USPHS Hosp, San Francisco, 63-64, chief dent officer, USPHS Outpatient Clin, 64-66; teacher res training grant dent sci & periodont, Nat Inst Dent Res, Univ Rochester & Eastman Dent Ctr, 66-69; asst prof periodont, Dent Sch, Univ Ore, 69-72; assoc prof, 72-76, chmn dept, 74-77, ASST DEAN RES & GRAD AFFAIRS, VA COMMONWEALTH UNIV, 77-, PROF PERIODONT & DIR, CLIN RES CTR PERIODONT DIS, 78- *Concurrent Pos:* Prin investr grants, Nat Inst Dent Res, 71-; consult, McGuire Vet Admin Hosp, 76- & Ctr Res Oral Biol, Univ Wash, 81-; mem bd sci counr, Nat Inst Dent Res, 81- *Honors & Awards:* Balint Orban Prize, Am Acad Periodont, 69. *Mem:* Int Asn Dent Res; Am Acad Periodent; Am Asn Dent Schs; AAAS; NY Acad Sci. *Res:* Etiology of periodontal disease; microbiology; immunology. *Mailing Add:* Va Commonwealth Univ Box 566 Med Col Va Sta Richmond VA 23298

RANOV, THEODOR, b Campina, Romania, Oct 15, 10; nat US; m 41; c 3. ENGINEERING MECHANICS. *Educ:* Tech Univ, Berlin, Dipl Ing, 35, Dr Ing, 37. *Prof Exp:* Instr math & mech, Tech Col Wellington, NZ, 46-48; from asst prof to prof, 49-75, EMER PROF ENG, STATE UNIV NY, BUFFALO, 76- *Concurrent Pos:* Consult, Buffalo Forge Co. *Mem:* Fel Am Soc Mech Engrs; Soc Lubrication Engrs; Am Soc Eng Educ; Sigma Xi; Am Inst Aeronaut & Astronaut. *Res:* Fluid mechanics; lubrication; turbomachinery; diffusion flow. *Mailing Add:* 414 53rd St West Palm Beach FL 33407

RANSFORD, GEORGE HENRY, b Detroit, Mich, Oct 26, 41; m 66; c 2. ORGANIC CHEMISTRY. *Educ:* Albion Col, BA, 63; Wayne State Univ, PhD(org chem), 70. *Prof Exp:* Res chemist, Ash Stevens, Inc, 64-65, sr res chemist, 70-76; RES CHEMIST, ETHYL CORP, 76- *Mem:* Am Chem Soc; Sigma Xi. *Res:* Organic synthesis; nucleoside, nucleotide, cardiac glycoside synthesis; halogen chemicals; process research; carbohydrate chemistry; phase transfer catalysis; heterocycles; condensed aromatics; phenols. *Mailing Add:* Ethyl Corp 1600 W Eight Mile Rd Ferndale MI 48220

RANSIL, BERNARD JEROME, b Pittsburgh, Pa, Nov 15, 29. MOLECULAR STRUCTURE, MEDICAL RESEARCH. *Educ:* Duquesne Univ, BS, 51; Cath Univ Am, PhD(phys chem), 55; Univ Chicago, MD, 64. *Prof Exp:* Res assoc physics, Lab Molecular Struct & Spectra, Univ Chicago, 56-64; intern, Harbor Gen Hosp, Univ Calif, Los Angeles, 64-65; res assoc, 66-67, assoc, 67-71, PRIN ASSOC MED, HARVARD MED SCH, 71- *Concurrent Pos:* Nat Res Coun-NSF fel, Nat Bur Standards, 55-56; Guggenheim fel, 65-66; consult, Nat Bur Stand, 56-58; from asst vis physician to assoc vis physician, Boston City Hosp, 67-73; asst physician, Beth Israel Hosp, 74- *Mem:* AAAS; Am Inst Chem; AMA; Sigma Xi; NY Acad Sci. *Res:* AB initio calculation of properties and structures of diatomic molecules; statistical comparison of computed and experimental molecular properties; charge density and chemical bonding; biomedical data analysis and inference; medical information systems. *Mailing Add:* Dept of Med Beth Israel Hosp Boston MA 02215

RANSLEBEN, GUIDO E(RNST), JR, b Comfort, Tex, Oct 19, 25; m 51; c 4. AERONAUTICAL ENGINEERING. *Educ:* Tex A&M Col, BS, 50. *Prof Exp:* Traffic analyst, US Air Force Security Serv, 50-51; draftsman, Douglas Aircraft Corp, 51; engr, Reynolds Andricks Consult Eng, 51-52; res engr, Southwest Res Inst, 52-56; aircraft eng supvr, Mfg Div, Howard Aero, Inc, 56-58, SR RES ENGR, SOUTHWEST RES INST, 58- *Mem:* Am Inst Aeronaut & Astronaut. *Res:* Vibrations; dynamics; aeroelasticity; hydro-elasticity; wind tunnel and towing tank testing; instrumentation. *Mailing Add:* Southwest Res Inst 6220 Culebra Rd San Antonio TX 78284

RANSLEY, DEREK LEONARD, b Bristol, Eng, July 22, 35; m 57; c 2. ORGANIC CHEMISTRY. *Educ:* Univ Wales, BSc, 56; Yale Univ, MS, 59, PhD(reaction mechanisms), 62. *Prof Exp:* Scientist, Nat Coal Board, Eng, 56-58; res chemist, 62-78, MGR PROCESS IMPROVEMENT DIV, CHEVRON RES CO, RICHMOND, 78- *Res:* Reaction kinetics and mechanisms; alkylation of aromatics; aromatics processing; general products and processes. *Mailing Add:* 576 Hauth Lane Walnut Creek CA 94596

RANSOHOFF, JOSEPH, b Cincinnati, Ohio, July 1, 15; m 37; c 2. NEUROSURGERY. *Educ:* Harvard Univ, BS, 38; Univ Chicago, MD, 41; Am Bd Neurol Surg, dipl, 51. *Prof Exp:* Instr surg, Med Sch, Univ Cincinnati, 43-44; asst neurol surg, Col Physicians & Surgeons, Columbia Univ, 49-50, instr neurol surg & assoc neurol surgeon, 50-52, asst prof clin neurol surg, 54-58, assoc prof, 59-61; PROF NEUROSURG & CHMN DEPT, MED CTR, NY UNIV, 61-; DIR NEUROSURG, BELLEVUE HOSP CTR, 61- *Concurrent Pos:* From asst attend neurol surgeon to attend neurol surgeon, Neurol Inst, Presby Hosp, New York, 49-61, chief clin neurosurg, Vanderbilt Clin, 53-55; consult, St John's Riverside & Yonkers Gen Hosps, 61-; consult, St Francis Hosp, Port Jervis; chief consult, Manhattan Vet Admin Hosp. *Mem:* Am Acad Neurol; Cong Rehab Med; AMA; Am Acad Neurol Surg; Soc Neurol Surg (pres). *Res:* Surgery of intracranial tumors, vascular malformations and aneurysms; epilepsy and hydrocephalus. *Mailing Add:* Dept of Neurosurg NY Univ Med Ctr New York NY 10016

RANSOM, BRUCE DAVIS, b Binghamton, NY, Apr 15, 51; m 78. PHYSICAL CHEMISTRY. *Educ:* State Univ NY, Binghamton, BA, 73, PhD(chem), 78. *Prof Exp:* ASSOC CHEM, RENSSELAER POLYTECH INST, 78- *Mem:* Am Chem Soc. *Res:* Excited electronic states of large polyotomic molecules; excited states of butadiene and pyridazine; naphthalene type heterocyles. *Mailing Add:* Dept of Chem Rensselaer Polytech Inst Troy NY 12181

RANSOM, J(OHN) T(HOMPSON), b Philadelphia, Pa, Aug 4, 20; m 45; c 3. PHYSICAL METALLURGY. *Educ:* Lehigh Univ, BS, 42; Carnegie Inst Technol, DSc(metall), 50. *Prof Exp:* Instr metall, Carnegie Inst Technol, 46-48; res engr, 48-55, res supvr, 55-62, res mgr, 62-63, res sect mgr, 63-66, sr eng assoc, 66-81, DU PONT RES FEL, E I DU PONT DE NEMOURS & CO, INC, 81- *Mem:* Am Soc Metals. *Res:* Materials engineering and fabrication. *Mailing Add:* Eng Technol Lab Exp Sta E I du Pont de Nemours & Co Inc Wilmington DE 19898

RANSOM, PRESTON LEE, b Peoria, Ill, Jan 2, 36; m 62; c 2. ELECTRICAL ENGINEERING. *Educ:* Univ Ill, Urbana, BS, 62, MS, 65, PhD(elec eng), 69. *Prof Exp:* Technician electronics, Res Div, Caterpillar Tractor Co, Peoria, 59-60; student technician, Antenna Lab, Univ Ill, 60-62; elec engr microwave antennas, Raytheon Co, Bedford, 62-63; res asst, Antenna Lab, 63-67, instr, 67-69, res assoc, 69-70, asst prof, 70-72, ASSOC PROF ELEC ENG, UNIV ILL, 72- *Concurrent Pos:* Paul V Galvin teaching fel, Univ Ill, 67-68; prin investr, NSF Grant, 71-72 & 73-74; hon res fel, Univ Col London, 76; mem adv comt, USSR & Eastern Europe, Nat Acad Sci, 76- *Mem:* Inst Elec & Electronics Engrs; Optical Soc Am; Am Soc Eng Educ. *Res:* Coherent optical processing; holography; diffraction theory; frequency independent antennas. *Mailing Add:* 457 Elec Eng Br Univ of Ill Urbana IL 61801

RANT, WILLIAM HOWARD, b Dothan, Ala, May 24, 45. MATHEMATICS. *Educ:* Univ Ala, BS, 66, MA, 68, PhD(math), 70. *Prof Exp:* Asst prof, Jacksonville State Univ, 70-74; ASST PROF MATH, LINCOLN UNIV, MO, 74- *Mem:* Math Asn Am. *Res:* Ring theory with emphasis on perfect rings and theory of modules. *Mailing Add:* Lincoln Univ Jefferson City MO 65101

RANTA, LAWRENCE EDWARD, b Toronto, Ont, Apr 30, 10; m 41; c 5. HEALTH SERVICES ADMINISTRATION. *Educ:* Univ Toronto, MD, 36, DPH, 39; FRCPS(C). *Prof Exp:* Res physician, Riverdale Isolation Hosp, Toronto, Ont, 36-37; res physician & surgeon, St Michael's Hosp, 37-38; asst prof bact & prev med & lectr, Dept Nursing & Health, Univ BC, 39-47, from assoc prof to prof bact & prev med, 47-52, asst dean, Fac Med, 50-52, prof pub health & head dept, 52; from asst med dir to assoc med dir, 52-66, dir med servs, 66-69, med dir, Vancouver Gen Hosp, 69-75; dir res & coun serv, BC Health Asn, 75-80; CONSULT HEALTH CARE SERV, 80- *Concurrent Pos:* Asst, Connaught Med Res Labs, Toronto, Ont, 39-46, res assoc, 46-51; from asst prof to assoc prof, Dept Nursing & Health, Univ BC, 47-51, lectr, Fac Med, 64- *Mem:* Am Pub Health Asn; Am Col Hosp Adminr; Can Pub Health Asn; Can Col Health Serv Exec. *Res:* Toxigenic properties of hemolytic streptococci; survival of salmonella typhi; serological properties of cholera vibrio; legislative control of communicable diseases; salmonella typing and antigenicity; preparation of cholera vaccine in fluid media; institutional medical care. *Mailing Add:* 4182 W 8th Ave Vancouver BC V6R 1Z6 Can

RANZ, WILLIAM E(DWIN), b Blue Ash, Ohio, June 3, 22; m 52; c 4. CHEMICAL ENGINEERING. *Educ:* Univ Cincinnati, ChE, 47; Univ Wis, PhD(chem eng), 50. *Prof Exp:* Res assoc, Univ Ill, 50-51, asst prof chem eng, 51-53; from assoc prof to prof eng res, Pa State Univ, 53-58; PROF CHEM ENG, UNIV MINN, MINNEAPOLIS, 58- *Concurrent Pos:* NSF fel, Cambridge Univ, 52-53. *Mem:* Am Chem Soc; Am Inst Chem Engrs. *Res:* Aerosols; sprays; heat and mass transfer; fluid mechanics. *Mailing Add:* Dept of Chem Eng Univ of Minn Minneapolis MN 55455

RANZONI, FRANCIS VERNE, b Los Angeles, Calif, Nov 29, 16; m; c 2. MYCOLOGY. *Educ:* Univ Calif, PhD(mycol), 50. *Prof Exp:* Asst prof biol, Eastern Wash Col, 50-53; asst res botanist, Univ Calif, 53-55; from asst prof bot to assoc prof plant sci, 55-62, chmn, Dept Plant Sci, 60-63, chmn, Dept Biol, 65-68, prof, 62-82, EMER PROF BIOL, VASSAR COL, 82- *Concurrent Pos:* NSF sci fac fel, 64-65. *Mem:* Bot Soc Am; Mycol Soc Am; Ecol Soc Am; NY Acad Sci. *Res:* Fungi imperfecti; ascomycetes; plant physiology. *Mailing Add:* Dept of Biol Vassar Col Poughkeepsie NY 12601

RAO, AKKINAPALLY V, b Hyderabad, India, Apr 6, 36; m 67; c 2. FOOD SCIENCE. *Educ:* Osmania Univ, BSc, 56; Univ Minn, MSc, 61; Ore State Univ, MSc, 63, PhD(food sci), 66. *Prof Exp:* Agr exten officer, Govt Andhra-Pradesn, India, 56-58; res asst agr chem, Ore State Univ, 63-64; asst prof food sci, Univ Toronto, 66-70, assoc mem, Inst Environ Studies, 72-80. *Concurrent Pos:* Exec mem, Can Inst Food Sci & Technol, 73-75. *Mem:* Can Inst Food Sci & Technol. *Res:* Behavioural and toxicological effects of food additives; toxicological and metabolic aspects of trace metals; nutritional quality of processed foods; vegetable proteins toxicology, nutrition and chemical characterization. *Mailing Add:* 66 Portico Dr Scarborough ON M1G 3R6 Can

RAO, ANANDA G, b Quilon, India, Dec 27, 30; US citizen; m 62; c 3. BIOCHEMISTRY. *Educ:* Univ Kerala, BSc, 52, MSc, 54; Univ Tex Southwestern Med Sch Dallas, 62-66, PhD(biochem), 66. *Prof Exp:* Lectr chem, Sree Sankara Col, Kalady, India, 54-55; res scholar, Univ Kerala, 55-58; asst res off biochem, Indian Coun Med Res, 58-59; res asst, Wellcome Res Lab, Vellore, 59-62; Welch Found fel, Univ Tex Southwestern Med Sch, Dallas, 62-67; res assoc, Tex A&M Univ, 67-69, res scientist, 69-71; RES BIOCHEMIST, VET ADMIN MED CTR, MARTINEZ, 71- *Concurrent Pos:* NIH res grant, 70-73; Vet Admin res grant, 71- *Mem:* NY Acad Sci; AAAS; Am Chem Soc; Am Oil Chem Soc; Am Inst Nutrit. *Res:* Lipid metabolism; biochemical regulation; hematology, erythropoiesis; role of drugs and diet fat on lipid composition; structure and function of erythrocytes; biological effects of zero gravity; alcoholic fatty liver damage; dietary control of alcoholic liver damage. *Mailing Add:* Vet Admin Med Ctr Martinez CA 94553

RAO, B SESHAGIRI, b Masulipatam, India, Apr 18, 36; m 63; c 3. SPECTROSCOPY, OPTICS. *Educ:* Andhra Univ, BSc, 53; Banaras Hindu Univ, MSc, 56; Pa State Univ, PhD(physics), 63. *Prof Exp:* Instr physics, Pa State Univ, 64; sr scientist, Warner & Swasey Co, 64-65; asst prof, Duquesne Univ, 65-66; from asst prof to assoc prof physics, 66-78, PROF PHYSICS, UNIV NDAK, 78- *Mem:* Am Phys Soc; Optical Soc Am. *Res:* Line positions and line strengths of vibration-rotation lines in the simple molecules using infrared spectroscopy; optical properties of matter. *Mailing Add:* Dept of Physics Univ of NDak Grand Forks ND 58202

RAO, BALAKRISHNA RAGHAVENDRA, b Udipi, India, Sept 15, 36; m 65; c 2. INSECT PHYSIOLOGY. *Educ:* Banaras Hindu Univ, BScAg, 57; Karnatak Univ, India, MScAgr, 59; Ohio State Univ, PhD(entom), 64. *Prof Exp:* Lectr agr entom, Col Agr, Dharwar, India, 59-60; res assoc, Johns Hopkins Univ, 64-65 & Univ Conn, 65-67; assoc prof entom, 67-71, prof entom, 71-80, PROF BIOL, EAST STROUDSBURG STATE COL, 80- *Concurrent Pos:* Res fel, Marine Biol Lab, Woods Hole, Mass, 64-67. *Mem:* AAAS; Entom Soc Am. *Res:* Reproductive physiology of cockroaches. *Mailing Add:* Dept of Biol East Stroudsburg State Col East Stroudsburg PA 18301

RAO, CHALAMALASETTY VENKATESWARA, b Bantumelli, India, Dec 26, 41; m 71; c 2. REPRODUCTIVE ENDOCRINOLOGY. *Educ:* Sri Venkateswara Univ, BVSc, 64; Wash State Univ, MS, 66, PhD(animal sci), 69. *Prof Exp:* Res asst animal sci, Wash State Univ, 66-69; res fel biochem & assoc urol, Albert Einstein Col Med, 69-70; res fel reproductive endocrinol, Med Col, Cornell Univ, 70-72; from asst prof to assoc prof obstet & gynec, 72-79, fac assoc biochem, 72-76, PROF OBSTET & GYNECOL, SCH MED, UNIV LOUISVILLE, 79- *Mem:* Am Soc Biol Chemists; Endocrine Soc; Soc Study Reproduction; Am Fertil Soc; AAAS. *Res:* Mechanism of action of prostaglandins and gonadotropins in Corpus Luteum; identification of receptors for these agents in luteal cell organelles and molecular mechanisms involved beyond receptor binding. *Mailing Add:* Dept of Obstet & Gynec Univ of Louisville Sch of Med Louisville KY 40202

RAO, CHARAGUNDLA SEETA RAMACHANDRA, fossil energy, combustion, see previous edition

RAO, DESIRAJU BHAVANARAYANA, b Visakhapatnam, India, Dec 8, 36; US citizen; m 65; c 2. OCEANOGRAPHY. *Educ:* Andhra Univ, India, BSc, 56, MSc, 59; Univ Chicago, MS, 62, PhD(geophys), 65. *Prof Exp:* Fel, Nat Ctr Atmospheric Res, Boulder, 65-67; res scientist oceanog, Marine Sci Br, Dept Energy, Mines & Resources, Ottawa, 67-68; asst prof meteorol, Dept Atmospheric Sci, Colo State Univ, 68-71; vis assoc prof oceanog, Dept Physics, Univ Wis-Milwaukee, 71-72, assoc prof, Dept Energetics, 72-74, prof, 74-75; head phys limnol & meteorol, Great Lakes Environ Res Lab, Nat Oceanic & Atmospheric Admin, Ann Arbor, 75-80; WITH OCEANS-ICE BR, ATMOSPHERIC SCI LAB, GODDARD SPACE FLIGHT CTR, 80- *Concurrent Pos:* Consult, Can Ctr Inland Waters, Burlington, Ont, 71 & Marine Environ Data Serv, Dept Environ, Ottawa, 74; adj prof limnol & meteorol, Univ Mich, 77- *Mem:* Sigma Xi; Am Meteorol Soc; Int Water Resources Asn; Am Soc Limnol & Oceanog. *Res:* Oscillations and circulations in lakes; numerical modeling of lake and atmospheric phenomena; waves on continental shelves. *Mailing Add:* Code 912 Oceans-Ice Br Atmospheric Sci Lab Goddard Space Flight Ctr Greenbelt MD 20770

RAO, DEVULAPALLI V G L N, b Pithapuram, India, July 6, 33; m 62; c 3. SOLID STATE PHYSICS, LASERS. *Educ:* Andhra Univ, India, BSc(Hons), 53, MSc, 54, DSc, 58. *Prof Exp:* Lectr physics, Andhra Univ, India, 57-59; res assoc, Duke Univ, 59-61; lectr, Andhra Univ, 61-63; sr scientist, Solid State Physics Lab, Govt of India, Delhi, 63-66; res physicist, Maser Optics

Inc, 66-68; mgr, Spacerays Inc, 68; assoc prof, 68-75, chmn dept, 78-81, PROF PHYSICS, UNIV MASS, BOSTON, 75- *Concurrent Pos:* Res fel eng & appl physics, Harvard Univ, 67-68; dir, Laser Nucleonics Inc, 68-75; NSF res grant, Univ Mass, Boston, 70-74. *Mem:* Am Phys Soc. *Res:* Nonlinear optics of liquid crystals. *Mailing Add:* Dept of Physics Univ of Mass Boston MA 02125

RAO, GANDIKOTA V, b Vizianagram, India, July 15, 34; m 65; c 2. METEOROLOGY. *Educ:* Andhra Univ, BS, 54, MSc, 55; Indian Inst Technol, Kharagpur, MTech, 58; Univ Chicago, MS, 61, PhD(meteorol), 65. *Prof Exp:* Res assoc meteorol, Univ Chicago, 65; Environ Sci Serv Admin fel & asst prof, Nat Hurricane Res Labs, Univ Miami, 65-68; Nat Res Coun Can fel, Can Meteorol Serv, 68-70 & Univ Waterloo, 70-71; NSF fel & asst prof, 71-74, assoc prof, 74-79, PROF METEOROL, ST LOUIS UNIV, 79-, DIR METEOROL & ASSOC CHMN, 80- *Mem:* Am Meteorol Soc; Sigma Xi; Am Geophys Union; Royal Meteorol Soc; India Meteorol Soc. *Res:* Mesometeorology; tropical meteorology; attacking meteorological problems with sound dynamical and numerical techniques; analyzing structure of the atmosphere over the Indian Ocean during a southwest monsoon season. *Mailing Add:* Box 8099 Laclede Sta St Louis MO 63156

RAO, GHANTA NAGESWARA, b Gudavalli, India, July 8, 39; c 2. BIOCHEMISTRY, VETERINARY SCIENCE. *Educ:* Sri Venkateswara Univ, India, BVSc, 60; Univ Wis-Madison, MS, 63, PhD(vet sci, biochem), 65; Educ Comn for Vet Grads, cert, 67; Am Col Lab Animal Med, dipl; Am Bd Toxicol, dipl. *Prof Exp:* Vet surgeon, Govt Andhra Pradesh, India, 60; proj asst vet sci, Univ Wis-Madison, 61-65; sr scientist, Endocrine Labs, Madison, Inc, 65-70, assoc dir, 70-74, vpres & mgr, 74-77; DIR TOXICOL, RALTECH SCI SERV, INC, 78- *Mem:* Am Soc Microbiol; fel Am Inst Chemists; Am Vet Med Asn; Am Asn Lab Animal Sci; AAAS. *Res:* Clinical pathology and anatomic pathology of experimental animals including monkeys; laboratory animal medicine and science; preclinical safety evaluation of environmental chemicals, drugs and devices; teratology, immunology, reproductive physiology and endocrinology. *Mailing Add:* Raltech Sci Serv Inc 3301 Kinsman Blvd Madison WI 53704

RAO, GIRIMAJI J SATHYANARAYANA, b Bethamangala, India, Feb 13, 34; m 64; c 2. ENZYMOLOGY, GENETICS. *Educ:* Univ Mysore, BSc, 53; Indian Inst Sci, MSc, 59, PhD(biochem), 64. *Prof Exp:* Lectr chem, Univ Mysore, 53-55; asst prof pediat, 71-76, ASSOC PROF PEDIAT, MED SCH, NORTHWESTERN UNIV, CHICAGO, 76-; RES ASSOC BIOCHEM GENETICS, CHILDREN'S MEM HOSP, 69-; ASST PROF PATH, BROWN UNIV, 80-; ASST DIR CLIN CHEM, RI HOSP, 80- *Concurrent Pos:* W B Lawson fel, NY State Dept Health, Albany, 64-67; S M & O M Rosen fel, Albert Einstein Col Med, 67-69; Robert & Mary Wood innovative res fel in cystic fibrosis, 72; trainer in biochem, Prog in Human Biochem Genetics, Children's Mem Hosp, 70- *Mem:* AAAS; Soc Pediat Res; Am Chem Soc; Am Soc Human Genetics. *Res:* Enzymology of cystic fibrosis; control mechanisms in cultured cells; chemical modification of enzymes and proteins. *Mailing Add:* Biochem APC 1158 RI Hosp 593 Eddy St Providence RI 02902

RAO, GOPAL SUBBA, b India, Aug 12, 38; US citizen; m 72; c 1. PERIODONTAL DISEASES, ORAL BIOLOGY. *Educ:* Madras Univ, India, BSc, 58; Howard Univ, MS, 65; Univ Mich, Ann Arbor, PhD(pharmaceut chem), 69. *Prof Exp:* Chemist forensic chem, Lab Chem & examiner to the Govt Mysore, Public Health Inst, Bangalore, 58-61; instr biomed chem, Col Pharm, Howard Univ, 62-65; res asst, Dept Pharmaceut, Col Pharm, Univ Mich, Ann Arbor, 65-69; NIH fel, Lab Chem, Nat Heart, Lung & Blood Inst, NIH, 69-72, NIH fel, Lab Chem Pharmacol, 72-74; CHIEF, LAB PHARMACOL, RES INST, AM DENT ASN HEALTH FOUND, CHICAGO, 74-, DIR & CHIEF RES SCIENTIST, DIV BIOCHEM, 78- *Concurrent Pos:* Prin investr grants & contracts, NIH & Am Fund Dent Health, 74-; Sigma Xi lectr, Med Ctr, Univ Mississippi, 82. *Mem:* Am Soc Pharmacol & Exp Therapeut; Soc Toxicol; Am Chem Soc; Am Pharmaceut Asn; Am & Int Asn Dent Res. *Res:* Biochemical etiology of periodontal diseases; development of new diagnostic methods and novel drugs and procedures useful in the treatment of oral diseases; salivary nitrite and carcinogenic nitrosamine formation; occupational hazards in dental practice. *Mailing Add:* Res Inst Am Dent Asn Health Found 211 E Chicago Ave Chicago IL 60611

RAO, JAGANMOHAN BOPPANA LAKSHMI, b Raghavapuram, India, Aug 6, 36; US citizen; m 60; c 3. ATENNAS, RADAR SYSTEMS. *Educ:* Andhra Univ, India, BSc, 56; Madras Inst Technol, DMIT, 59; Univ Wash, MS, 63, PhD(elec eng), 66. *Prof Exp:* Asst res engr antennas, Univ Mich, 66-68; staff engr microwave antennas, Northrop Corp, 68-70; asst prof elec eng, Savannah State Col, 70-71; res assoc, NASA, 71-73; ELECTRONICS ENGR RADAR, NAVAL RES LAB, 74- *Concurrent Pos:* Asst prof elec eng, Howard Univ, 73. *Honors & Awards:* Spec Recognition Award, Inst Elec & Electronics Engrs, 69. *Mem:* Sr mem, Inst Elec & Electronics Engrs. *Res:* Antennas; electromagnetic theory; radar systems and radar signal processing. *Mailing Add:* Radar Div Code 5372 Naval Res Lab Washington DC 20375

RAO, JAMMALAMADAKA S, b Munipalle, India, Dec 7, 43; m 72; c 1. DIRECTIONAL DATA ANALYSIS. *Educ:* Indian Statist Inst, Calcutta, BA, 64, MA, 65, PhD(statist), 69. *Prof Exp:* Res scholar statist, Indian Statist Inst, 65-69; vis asst prof probability & statist, Ind Univ, 69-70; assoc prof, 70-76; asst prof, 76-80, assoc prof, 80-82, PROF PROBABILITY & STATIST, UNIV CALIF, SANTA BARBARA, 82- *Concurrent Pos:* Vis prof, Univ Wis-Madison, 75-76 & Univ Leeds, 76; dir, Statist Consult Ctr, Univ Calif, Santa Barbara, 80- *Mem:* Am Statist Asn; Inst Math Statist; Royal Statist Soc; Int Statist Inst. *Res:* Nonparametric statistical methods; inference based on sample spacings; large sample theory; efficiencies of test procedures; statistics of directional data. *Mailing Add:* Dept Math Univ Calif Santa Barbara CA 93106

RAO, JONNAGADDA NALINI KANTH, b Eluru, India, May 16, 37; m 65; c 2. STATISTICS. *Educ:* Andhra Univ, India, BA, 54; Univ Bombay, MA, 58; Iowa State Univ, PhD(statist), 61. *Prof Exp:* Asst prof statist, Iowa State Univ, 61-63; assoc prof, Grad Res Ctr Southwest, 64-65; assoc prof, Tex A&M Univ, 65-69; prof, Univ Man, 69-73; PROF STATIST, CARLETON UNIV, 73- *Concurrent Pos:* Consult, Statist Can, 73-; mem grants comt, Nat Res Coun Can, 74-77 & Natural Sci & Eng Res Coun Can, 78-81. *Mem:* Fel Inst Math Statist; Int Statist Inst; fel Am Statist Asn; Can Statist Asn; Biomet Soc. *Res:* Sample survey theory and practice; linear models and variance components; chisquare tests; optimization. *Mailing Add:* Dept Math & Statist Carleton Univ Ottawa ON K1S 5B6 Can

RAO, K V N, b Visakhapatnam, India, June 22, 33; US citizen; m 67. PHYSICS, ELECTRICAL ENGINEERING. *Educ:* Andhra Univ, India, BSc, 52; Indian Inst Sci, dipl, 55; Univ Ill, Urbana, PhD(elec eng), 62. *Prof Exp:* From res asst to res assoc elec eng, Univ Ill, Urbana, 55-63; res physicist, Air Force Cambridge Res Labs, 63-76; RES PHYSICIST, ROME AIR DEVELOP CTR / ELECTROMAGNETIC SCI DIV, HANSCOM AFB, 76- *Concurrent Pos:* Adj prof, Northeastern Univ, 65-69; adv, Rensselaer Polytech Inst, 70- *Mem:* Inst Elec & Electronics Eng; Am Inst Physics. *Res:* Reentry plasma physics; gaseous electronics; microwave interaction with gyrotropic media; propagation in ionosphere; basic atomic and molecular physics; laser interaction with solid dielectrics radar systems, EM transmission. *Mailing Add:* Radio Frequency Intrusion Systs Hanscom AFB Bedford MA 01731

RAO, KANDARPA NARAHARI, b Kovvur, India, Sept 5, 21; m 52; c 1. PHYSICS, ASTROPHYSICS. *Educ:* Andhra Univ, India, BSc, 41, MSc, 42; Univ Chicago, PhD, 49. *Prof Exp:* With Govt Meteorol Serv, India, 42-46; with sci off, Nat Phys Lab, 50-52; res assoc physics, Duke Univ, 52-53; res assoc & asst prof, Univ Tenn, 53-54; res assoc, 54-60, lectr, 59-60, assoc prof, 60-63, PROF PHYSICS, OHIO STATE UNIV, 63- *Concurrent Pos:* Consult, Nat Oceanic & Atmospheric Admin, 73- *Mem:* Am Astron Soc; Optical Soc Am; Am Phys Soc. *Res:* Structures of molecules, especially their electronic spectra in the ultraviolet and high resolution absorption and emission spectra in the infrared. *Mailing Add:* Dept of Physics Ohio State Univ Columbus OH 43210

RAO, KANNEGANTI NAGESWARA, b Nandivelugu, India, May 25, 34; US citizen. MATHEMATICS. *Educ:* Andhra Univ, India, BA, Hons, 55, MA, 56; Sri Venkateswara Univ, India, MPhil, 60; Univ Delhi, PhD(math), 68. *Prof Exp:* Tutor math, Sri Venkateswara Col, India, 55-57, res scholar, 57-60; lectr, V S R Col, 61; lectr & chmn dept, S V Col, Univ Delhi, 61-69, bursar, 61-65; from asst prof to assoc prof, 69-77, PROF MATH, NDAK STATE UNIV, 77- *Concurrent Pos:* Vis prof, Univ Calcutta, 80- *Mem:* Am Math Soc; Australian Math Soc; Indian Math Soc. *Res:* Algebra; number theory; combinatorics. *Mailing Add:* Dept Math NDak State Univ Fargo ND 58105

RAO, KROTHAPALLI RANGA, b Amartaluru, India, Sept 24, 41; m 65; c 2. COMPARATIVE PHYSIOLOGY, COMPARATIVE ENDOCRINOLOGY. *Educ:* Andhra Univ, India, BS, 58, MS, 61, PhD(zool), 67. *Prof Exp:* Demonstr biol, Andhra Christian Col, 58-59; demonstr zool, Andhra Univ, India, 61-62, res fel, 62-65; res assoc biol, Tulane Univ, 66-72; from asst prof to assoc prof, 72-78, PROF BIOL, UNIV WEST FLA, 78- *Mem:* Am Soc Zool. *Res:* Biology of reproduction in molluscs; control of color changes and molting in crustaceans; pollution physiology of marine animals; isolation and characterization of the crustacean neurohormones. *Mailing Add:* Fac Biol Univ WFla Pensacola FL 32504

RAO, MALEMPATI MADHUSUDANA, b June 6, 29; Indian citizen. MATHEMATICS. *Educ:* Andhra Univ, India, BA, 49; Univ Madras, MA, 52, MSc, 55; Univ Minn, PhD, 59. *Prof Exp:* Lectr math, Univ Col Andhra Univ, India, 52-53; res mathematician, Carnegie-Mellon Univ, 59-60, from asst prof to prof, 60-72; PROF MATH, UNIV CALIF, RIVERSIDE, 72- *Concurrent Pos:* NSF grants, 60-62, 63-65 & 66-79. *Mem:* Am Math Soc; Inst Math Statist; AAAS; Int Statist Inst. *Res:* Probability; function spaces; related areas in analysis. *Mailing Add:* Dept of Math Univ of Calif Riverside CA 92521

RAO, MAMIDANNA S, b Kaikalur, India, June 21, 31. BIOSTATISTICS. *Educ:* Univ Madras, BSc, 51; Univ Punjab, MA, 60; Univ Pittsburgh Sch Pub Health, MSHyg, 68, ScD(biostatist), 70. *Prof Exp:* Statistician biostat, Venereal Dis Training Ctr, 55-64 & Indian Coun Med Res, 64-67; biostatistician, St Francis Gen Hosp, Community Mental Health Ctr, 69-70; asst prof biostatist, Univ Tex Med Br, 70-71; asst dir biostatist, Montefiore Hosp & Med Ctr, 71-72; statistician biostatist, Pan Am Health Orgn, WHO, 72-76; ASSOC PROF BIOSTATIST, COL MED, HOWARD UNIV, 76- *Mem:* Sigma Xi; Am Pub Health Asn; fel Royal Soc Trop Med & Hyg; Am Statist Asn; Biomet Soc. *Res:* Teaching of biostatistics; consultation and research; design of experiments; sample surveys; computer applications. *Mailing Add:* Howard Univ Col of Med 520 W St NW Rm 2400 Washington DC 20059

RAO, MENTREDDI ANANDHA, b Dornakal, India, July 4, 37; US citizen; m 70; c 1. FOOD ENGINEERING. *Educ:* Osmania Univ, India, BChE, 58; Univ Cincinnati, MS, 63; Ohio State Univ, PhD(chem eng), 69. *Prof Exp:* Res assoc chem eng, US Air Force, Dayton, Ohio, 63-65; proj engr, Am Standards, Inc, 69-71; prof & head food eng, Univ Campinas, Brazil, 71-73; asst prof, 73-78, ASSOC PROF FOOD SCI, CORNELL UNIV, 78- *Concurrent Pos:* Fulbright res scholar, Brazil, 80-81. *Mem:* Inst Food Technologists; Am Soc Agr Engrs; Am Inst Chem Engrs; Soc Rheology; Am Soc Heating, Refrig & Air Conditioning. *Res:* Energy use and conservation for foods; rheology of fluid foods; heat transfer in food processing. *Mailing Add:* Dept of Food Sci Cornell Univ Geneva NY 14456

RAO, MRINALINI CHATTA, b Bangalore, India. MEMBRANE TRANSPORT, HORMONE ACTION. *Educ:* Univ Delhi, BSC, 69, MSC, 71; Univ Mich, MS, 74, PhD(cell & molecular biol), 77. *Prof Exp:* Fel, 77-80, ASST PROF & RES ASSOC, UNIV CHICAGO, 80- *Concurrent Pos:* Teaching asst fel, Univ Mich, 74. *Mem:* Am Soc Cell Biologists. *Res:* Molecular mechanisms involved in agonist (hormone) and mediator dependent regulation of cell function; regulation of ion transport in epithelial cells. *Mailing Add:* Dept Med Univ Chicago Box 400 950 E 59th St Chicago IL 60637

RAO, NUTAKKI GOURI SANKARA, b Tenali, India, Dec 2, 33; m 60; c 3. TOXICOLOGY. *Educ:* Univ Saugar, BSc, 55, MSc, 57, BPharm, 58; St Louis Col Pharm, MS, 62; NDak State Univ, PhD(pharmaceut chem), 66; dipl, Am Bd Forensic Toxicol. *Prof Exp:* Chemist, Ciba Pharmaceut Ltd, 58-59; asst prof toxicol, 66-70, asst state toxicologist, 66-73, chmn dept toxicol, 73-76, assoc prof, 70-76, PROF TOXICOL, NDAK STATE UNIV, 76-, STATE TOXICOLOGIST, 73- *Mem:* Am Acad Clin Toxicologists; Am Acad Forensic Sci; Int Asn Forensic Toxicologists; Sigma Xi. *Res:* Detection and quantitation of drugs and metabolites from biological tissues; analytical and clinical toxicology. *Mailing Add:* State Toxicol Lab PO Box 5195 State Univ Sta Fargo ND 58105

RAO, P KRISHNA, b Kapileswarapuram, India, Mar 26, 30; m 54; c 2. METEOROLOGY, OCEANOGRAPHY. *Educ:* Andhra Univ, India, BS, 50, MS, 52; Fla State Univ, MS, 57; NY Univ, PhD(meteorol, oceanog), 68. *Prof Exp:* Asst res scientist, NY Univ, 56-60; meteorologist, Can Meteorol Serv, 60-61; DIR, APPLN LAB, NAT EARTH SATELLITE SERV, NAT OCEANIC & ATMOSPHERIC ADMIN, 61- *Concurrent Pos:* Dept Commerce sci & technol fel & mem Rann Prog, NSF, 71-72; expert meteorol satellites, World Meteorol Orgn, Geneva, 74-76. *Mem:* Am Meteorol Soc; fel Royal Meteorol Soc; fel NY Acad Sci. *Res:* Satellite meteorology and oceanography. *Mailing Add:* Nat Environ Satellite Ctr Suitland MD 20233

RAO, PALAKURTHI SURESH CHANDRA, b Warangal, India, Feb 15, 47. SOIL PHYSICS, SOIL CHEMISTRY. *Educ:* Andhra Pradesh Agr Univ, Hyderabad, India, BSc, 67; Colo State Univ, MS, 69; Univ Hawaii, PhD(soil sci), 74. *Prof Exp:* Res assoc, 75-77, asst res scientist, 77-79, ASST PROF SOIL SCI, UNIV FLA, 79- *Concurrent Pos:* Mem, Comt Water in Unsaturated Zone, Am Geophys Union; assoc ed, J Environ Quality, 80-83. *Mem:* Am Soc Agron; Soil Sci Soc Am; Int Soil Sci Soc; Am Geophys Union. *Res:* Environmental quality; computer modeling of soil-water- plant systems. *Mailing Add:* 2169 McCarty Hall Univ Fla Gainesville FL 32611

RAO, PAPINENI SEETHAPATHI, b Vetapalam, India, Apr 19, 37; m 67; c 3. REPRODUCTIVE PHYSIOLOGY, CARDIOVASCULAR PHYSIOLOGY. *Educ:* Andhra Vet Col, India, BVSc, 59; Univ Mo- Columbia, MS, 61, PhD(reproductive physiol), 65. *Prof Exp:* Vet asst surgeon, Dept Vet Med, Andhra, India, 59-60; res asst, Univ Mo-Columbia, 62-65, res assoc, 65-66; from instr to assoc prof gynec, obstet & physiol, Sch Med, St Louis Univ, 66-69; ASSOC PROF PHYSIOL, UNIV SOUTH FLA, 69- *Mem:* AAAS; NY Acad Sci; Soc Study Reproduction; Am Physiol Soc. *Res:* Clinical veterinary medicine; conception and contraception; endotoxic shock; toxemia of pregnancy. *Mailing Add:* Dept Obstet/Gynec Box 18 Univ SFla Col Med Tampa FL 33612

RAO, PEJAVER VISHWAMBER, b Udipi, India, June 11, 35; m 62; c 2. MATHEMATICAL STATISTICS. *Educ:* Univ Madras, BA, 54; Univ Bombay, MA, 56; Univ Ga, PhD(statist), 63. *Prof Exp:* Lectr statist, Col Sci, Univ Nagpur, 56-60; asst statistician, Univ Ga, 62-64, asst prof math, 63-64; from asst prof to assoc prof, 64-72, PROF STATIST, UNIV FLA, 72- *Mem:* Inst Math Statist; Biomet Soc. *Res:* Theory and methods of mathematical statistics; design of experiments and nonparametric statistics. *Mailing Add:* Dept Statist 530 Nuclear Sci Bldg Univ of Fla Gainesville FL 32611

RAO, PEMMARAJU NARASIMHA, b Rajahmundry, India, Dec 20, 28; m 53; c 3. ORGANIC CHEMISTRY. *Educ:* Andhra Univ, India, BSc, 48, MSc, 50; Univ Calcutta, DPhil(chem), 54. *Prof Exp:* Fulbright travel grant & fel steroid chem, Sch Med, Univ Rochester, 54-55; res assoc org chem, Indian Inst Sci, Bangalore, 55-56; jr sci officer, Nat Chem Lab, Poona, 56-58; res assoc steroid chem, 58-61, chief org chem sect, 61-65, chmn dept org chem, 65-67, asst found scientist, 67-73, found scientist organic chem, 73-77, DIR, DEPT ORGANIC & BIOL CHEM, SOUTHWEST FOUND RES & EDUC, 78- *Concurrent Pos:* Res prof, St Mary's Univ, Tex, 60-; adj assoc prof biochem, Univ Tex Health Sci Ctr San Antonio, 74-77, adj assoc prof, Div Earth & Phys Sci, 76- *Mem:* Am Chem Soc; Royal Soc Chem; Indian Chem Soc. *Res:* Organic synthesis; natural products chemistry, particularly steroids and diterpenes; synthesis of polycyclic hydrocarbons; steroid radioimmunoassays. *Mailing Add:* Southwest Found for Res & Educ PO Box 28147 San Antonio TX 78284

RAO, PEMMARAJU VENUGOPALA, b Tirupatipuram, India, Sept 1, 32; m 58; c 2. NUCLEAR PHYSICS, ATOMIC PHYSICS. *Educ:* Andhra Univ, India, BSc, 53, MSc, 54; Univ Ore, PhD(physics), 64. *Prof Exp:* Demonstr physics, Andhra Univ, India, 55-57, lectr, 58-59; res assoc, Univ Ore, 64-66; res assoc, Ga Inst Technol, 66-67; asst prof, 67-71, ASSOC PROF PHYSICS, EMORY UNIV, 71- *Concurrent Pos:* Ed, Vijnana Patrika, 70-76. *Mem:* AAAS; Sigma Xi; Am Phys Soc; Am Asn Physics Teachers. *Res:* Nuclear spectroscopy; fast neutron reactions, atomic fluorescence yields and inner shell ionization. *Mailing Add:* Dept of Physics Emory Univ Atlanta GA 30322

RAO, PEMMASANI DHARMA, b Burripalem, Andhra Pradesh, Apr 15, 33; m; c 3. MINERAL ENGINEERING. *Educ:* Andhra Univ, India, BSc, 52, MSc, 54; Pa State Univ, MS, 59, PhD(mineral prep), 61. *Prof Exp:* Jr sci asst petrol, Ore Dressing Div, Nat Metall Lab, Jamshedpur, India, 55-57; asst mineral prep, Pa State Univ, 58-61; tech adv coal & mineral processing, McNally-Bird Eng Co Ltd, India, 62-66; from asst prof to assoc prof coal technol, 66-76, PROF COAL TECHNOL, UNIV ALASKA, FAIRBANKS, 76- *Mem:* Am Inst Mining, Metall & Petrol Engrs. *Res:* Coal petrology; coal characterization and utilization; ore microscopy; mineral processing. *Mailing Add:* Mineral Indust Res Lab Univ Alaska Fairbanks AK 99701

RAO, PODURI S R S, b Kakinada, India, Dec 13, 34; m 70; c 1. MATHEMATICS, STATISTICS. *Educ:* Andhra Univ, India, BA, 55; Karnatak Univ, India, MA, 57; Harvard Univ, PhD(statist), 65. *Prof Exp:* Demonstr & lectr statist, Univ Bombay, 57-60; asst prof, Univ Rochester, 64-66; sr math statistician, Info Res Assocs Inc, 66-67; assoc prof statist, 67-73, PROF STATIST, UNIV ROCHESTER, 74- *Concurrent Pos:* Fulbright travel grant, 60; J N Tata endowment; elect mem, Int Statist Inst. *Mem:* Am Statist Asn; Inst Math Statist. *Res:* Sampling; linear models; mullivariate analysis. *Mailing Add:* Dept of Statist Univ of Rochester Rochester NY 14627

RAO, POTU NARASIMHA, b Muppalla, India, July 1, 30; m 57; c 3. CELL BIOLOGY, CYTOGENETICS. *Educ:* Andhra Univ, India, BSc, 52; Univ Ky, PhD(cytogenetics), 63. *Prof Exp:* Instr cellular physiol, Univ Ky, 64-66, asst prof 66-68; asst prof cell biol, Sch Med, Univ Colo, Denver, 68-71; assoc prof, 71-77, PROF CELL BIOL, UNIV TEX M D ANDERSON HOSP & TUMOR INST, 77- *Mem:* AAAS; Am Asn Cancer Res; Am Soc Cell Biol. *Res:* Biochemical processes related to the regulation of DNA synthesis and mitosis in mammalian cells in culture. *Mailing Add:* Dept of Develop Therapeut M D Anderson Hosp & Tumor Inst Houston TX 77025

RAO, PRAKASH, b Bangalore, India, Oct 16, 41. MATERIALS SCIENCE, ENGINEERING. *Educ:* Univ Delhi, BS, 61; Univ Bombay, BS, 63; Indian Inst Sci, BEng, 65; Univ Calif, Berkeley, MS, 66, PhD(mat sci & eng), 69. *Prof Exp:* Res asst inorg mat res div, Lawrence Radiation Lab, Univ Calif, Berkeley, 65-69; mem tech staff, Ingersoll-Rand Res, Inc, 70-71; instr mat sci & eng & res assoc, Cornell Univ, 71-72; staff mats scientist, 72-77, actg mgr, Chem & Structural Anal Br, 77-78, MGR, TECH RELATIONS, ENERGY SCI & ENG, CORP RES & DEVELOP, GEN ELEC CO, 78- *Mem:* Am Inst Mining, Metall & Petrol Engrs; Am Soc Metals; Electron Micros Soc Am. *Res:* High voltage transmission electron microscopy and electron diffraction techniques for the study of irradiation effects in metals and alloys; metallurgy. *Mailing Add:* Corp Res & Develop Gen Elec Co PO Box 8 Schenectady NY 12301

RAO, R(AMACHANDRA) A, b Kanakapura, India. HYDROLOGY, WATER RESOURCES. *Educ:* Univ Mysore, BE, 60; Univ Minn, MSCE, 64; Univ Ill, PhD(civil eng), 68. *Prof Exp:* Lectr civil eng, Univ Mysore, 60-62; instr lang, Univ Minn, 62-63, res asst hydraul, 63-64; res asst hydrol, Univ Ill, 64-68; asst prof civil eng, 68-76, assoc prof, 76-79, PROF CIVIL ENG, PURDUE UNIV, WEST LAFAYETTE, 79- *Concurrent Pos:* Consult to several orgns, 68- & Engrs Collab, 70-71. *Mem:* AAAS; Am Geophys Union; Am Soc Civil Engrs; Int Asn Hydraul Res; Int Asn Sci Hydrol. *Res:* Urban and stochastic hydrology. *Mailing Add:* Sch Civil Eng Purdue Univ West Lafayette IN 47907

RAO, R(ANGAIYA) A(SWATHANARAYANA), b Bangalore, India, Feb 27, 34; m 67. ELECTRONICS. *Educ:* Univ Mysore, BSc, 53; Indian Inst Sci, Bangalore, dipl elec commun eng, 57; Univ Calif, Berkeley, MS, 61, PhD(elec eng), 66. *Prof Exp:* Sir Dorabji Tata scholar, Indian Inst Sci, Bangalore, 56-57; jr sci officer microwave tubes. Cent Electronic Eng Res Inst, Pilani, India, 57-59; grad res engr, Electronics Res Lab, Univ Calif, Berkeley, 59-66; mem tech staff, Fairchild Semiconductor Res & Develop Lab, Calif, 66-68; asst prof solid state electronics, 68-77, ASSOC PROF ELEC ENG, CALIF STATE UNIV, SAN JOSE, 77- *Mem:* Inst Elec & Electronics Engrs. *Res:* Electron beams and guns; microwave tubes; solid state devices; microwaves. *Mailing Add:* Dept of Elec Eng Calif State Univ San Jose CA 95192

RAO, RAMACHANDRA M R, b Bangalore City, India, Oct 30, 31. FOOD SCIENCE & TECHNOLOGY. *Educ:* Univ Mysore, BSc, 59; Univ Houston, BS, 62; La State Univ, Baton Rouge, MS, 63, PhD(food sci), 66. *Prof Exp:* Chemist, Savage Labs, Houston, 60-62; dir res, AME Enterprises, NJ, 66-67; asst prof food sci, 67-70, assoc prof, Food Preservation, 70-80, PROF FOOD SCI, LA STATE UNIV, BATON ROUGE, 80- *Concurrent Pos:* Allen Prod grant, La State Univ, Baton Rouge, 67-68; fel, Int Atomic Energy Agency, SVietnam & adv, Vienna, Austria, 70. *Honors & Awards:* US AEC Award, 66. *Mem:* Assoc Am Inst Chem Eng; Inst Food Technol; Can Inst Food Sci & Technol. *Res:* Food processing and preservation; water and air pollution; waste utilization and disposal; fermentation technology. *Mailing Add:* Dept of Food Sci La State Univ Baton Rouge LA 70803

RAO, SALEM S, b Bangalore, India, Apr 12, 34; Can citizen; m 64; c 2. MICROBIOLOGY, BACTERIOLOGY. *Educ:* Univ Mysore, PhD(zool), 64; Royal Soc London, FRSH, 65. *Prof Exp:* Res microbiologist, Rensselaer Polytech Inst, 61-64; res scientist, Ont Res Found, 64-65; scientist bacteriol, Ont Dept Health, 65-73; RES SCIENTIST, NAT WATER RES INST, CAN, 73- *Mem:* Am Soc Limnologists & Oceanographers; Int Asn Great Lakes Res; Sigma Xi; Am Soc Testing & Mat. *Res:* Limnology of aquatic ecosystems; cold water bacteriology; assimilation under low temperatures; bacterial nutrient relationships under different temperatures; acid rain bacteriology (biodegradation and bioassimilation). *Mailing Add:* Microbiol Lab Nat Water Res Inst Burlington ON L7R 4A6 Can

RAO, SAMOHINEEVEESU TRIVIKRAMA, b India, July 2, 44; US citizen; m 74; c 1. AIR POLLUTION METEOROLOGY. *Educ:* Andhra Univ, India, BSc, 62, MSc, 65; State Univ NY at Albany, PhD(atmospheric sci), 73. *Prof Exp:* Lectr physics, Govt Arts Col, Nizamabad, India, 65-66; sr sci asst meteorol, Inst Tropical Meteorol, Govt India, 66-69; res fel, State Univ NY at Albany, 69-72, res assoc atmospheric sci, 73-74; RES SCIENTIST AIR POLLUTION & METEOROL & CHIEF ATMOSPHERIC MODELING SECT & MATH MODELING SECT, NY STATE DEPT ENVIRON CONSERV, 74- *Concurrent Pos:* Prin investr, Funded Res Proj, US Environ Protection Agency, 75-; Consult, State Univ NY at Albany, 75-76, M B Assoc, San Francisco, 77-78; adj prof, State Univ NY at Albany, 78-; panel mem, Nat Coop Highway Res Prog, Nag Acad Sci, 78-; mem, Tech Coun Meteorol, Air Pollution Control Asn, 79- *Mem:* Am Meteorol Soc; Air Pollution Control Asn. *Res:* Mathematical modeling of transport and diffusion of pollutants in the atmosphere; develop and validate air pollution dispersion models. *Mailing Add:* 30 Hunt Wood Dr Clifton Park NY 12065

RAO, SHANKARANARAYANA RAMOHALLINANJUNDA, b Hiriyur, India, July 11, 23; m 58. CIVIL ENGINEERING, SOIL MECHANICS. *Educ:* Univ Mysore, BE, 46; Univ Roorkee, ME, 58; Univ Conn, MS, 61; Rutgers Univ, PhD(soil mech), 64. *Prof Exp:* Supvr irrig-works, Mysore Pub Works Dept, 46-50; tech asst, River Valley Projs, 50-57; asst engr, Mysore Eng Res Sta, 58-59; assoc prof, 64-65, PROF CIVIL ENG, PRAIRIE VIEW A&M UNIV, 65- *Concurrent Pos:* Mem Transp Res Bd, Nat Acad Sci-Nat Res Coun. *Mem:* Am Soc Civil Engrs; Am Soc Eng Educ; Am Soc Testing & Mat; Concrete Inst; Sigma Xi. *Res:* Field study of restriction of evaporation from open water surfaces; problem of canal lining; phenomena of frost action in highways; permeability of soils; structural strength of brick masonry prisms; correlation of data from field for remote sensing of wheat canopy. *Mailing Add:* Dept of Civil Eng PB 2345 Prairie View A&M Univ Prairie View TX 77445

RAO, SREEDHAR P, b Jan 2, 43; India citizen. PEDIATRICS, HEMATOLOGY. *Educ:* Kakatiya Med Col, Warangal, India, MBBS, 66; Am Bd Pediat, cert pediat hemat-oncol, 76. *Prof Exp:* Internship med-surg, Bergen Pines County Hosp, Paramus, NJ, 67-68; resident pediat, 68-71, fel pediat-hemat-oncol, 71-73, fel pediat-oncol, 73-74, instr pediat, 74-75, asst prof pediat, 75-81, ASSOC PROF CLIN PEDIAT, STATE UNIV NY DOWNSTATE MED CTR, 81- *Concurrent Pos:* Attend physician pediat, Kings County Hosp, 73-; consult pediat-hemat-oncol, Methodist Hosp Brooklyn, 77- *Mem:* Assoc fel Am Acad Pediat; Am Soc Hemat; Am Soc Pediat Hemat-Oncol. *Res:* Sickle cell disease in children; infections; osteomyelitis versus bone infarction in sickle cell disease; leukemia in children; testicular involvement; early diagnosis. *Mailing Add:* Dept Pediat Box 49 450 Clarkson Ave Brooklyn NY 11203

RAO, SURYANARAYANA K, b Hyderabad, India, Feb 20, 39; m; c 2. TOXICOLOGY. *Educ:* Osmania Univ, India, DVM, 61; Magadh Univ, India, MS, 63, PhD(toxicol), 68. *Prof Exp:* Res fel toxicol, Magadh Univ, India, 64-67; asst res officer, Nutrit Res Labs, Hyderabad, 67-68; fel physiol, Case Western Reserve Univ, 68-69; res assoc pharmacol, Mich State Univ, 69-71; res investr, Dept Path-Toxicol, Searle Labs, 71-72, sr res investr toxicol, 72-77; res specialist, 77-80, RES LEADER TERATOLOGY & REPRODUCTION, DEPT TOXICOL, DOW CHEM CO, 80- *Mem:* Soc Toxicol; Teratology Soc. *Res:* Carbon tetrachloride hepatotoxicity in the rat; aflatoxin induced hepatotoxicity in the Rhesus monkey; physical examination procedures, teratology, reproduction and mutagenicity testing, monitoring cardiovascular parameters and data recording methodology employed in safety studies. *Mailing Add:* Dept Toxicol Bldg 1803 Dow Chem Co Midland MI 48640

RAO, THAMMAVARAPU R N, b Andhra, India, June 5, 33; m 55; c 3. COMPUTER SCIENCE, ELECTRICAL ENGINEERING. *Educ:* Andhra Univ, India, BSc, 52; Indian Inst Sci, Bangalore, DIISc, 55; Univ Mich, MSE, 61, PhD(elec eng), 64. *Prof Exp:* Asst res engr, info systs, Univ Mich, 61-63; mem tech staff, Bell Tel Labs, NJ, 64-66; from asst prof to assoc prof elec eng, Univ Md, College Park, 66-80; PROF COMPUT SCI & ELEC ENG, SOUTHERN METHODIST UNIV, 80- *Mem:* Inst Elec & Electronics Engrs; Asn Comput Mach. *Res:* Computer architecture, arithmetic, number systems, coding theory and arithmetic error codes; fault-tolerant computing. *Mailing Add:* Dept Comput Sci Southern Methodist Univ Dallas TX 75275

RAO, V UDAYA S, b Visakhapatnam, India, Aug 4, 38; m 66; c 1. CATALYSIS, SOLID STATE CHEMISTRY. *Educ:* Andhra Univ, BS, 58; Tata Inst Fundamental Res, PhD(physics), 67. *Prof Exp:* Res fel, Tata Inst Fundamental Res, India, 59-68; res assoc, 69-71, asst prof superconductivity of intermetallics, Univ Pittsburgh, 71-78; RES CHEMIST, US DEPT ENERGY, 78- *Mem:* Am Chem Soc. *Res:* Indirect liquefaction of coal using zeolite catalysts. *Mailing Add:* Process Sci Div Pittsburgh Energy Technol Ctr DOE PO Box 10940 Pittsburgh PA 15236

RAO, VALLURU BHAVANARAYANA, b Tenali, India, June 27, 34; m 56; c 1. MATHEMATICAL STATISTICS, OPERATIONS RESEARCH. *Educ:* Andhra, India, BSc, 54, MSc, 56; Univ Ill, Urbana, MS, 65; Wash Univ, DSc(appl math & comput sci), 67. *Prof Exp:* Sr res investr, directorate econ & statist, Ministry Food & Agr, India, 57-62; asst prof math, 67-73, chmn dept math & co-chmn, Dept Comput Sci, 77-79, ASSOC PROF MATH, UNIV BRIDGEPORT, 73- *Concurrent Pos:* Res grant, Univ Bridgeport, 68-69; fac res grant, 69-70; consult, Glendinning Co, Conn, 67-69, Marena Systs, 79 & Honeywell Info Systs, 81. *Mem:* Math Asn Am; Am Asn Univ Prof; Opers Res Soc Am; fel AAAS. *Res:* Integer, dynamic and stochastic programming. *Mailing Add:* 10 James St Fairfield CT 06430

RAO, VELDANDA VENUGOPAL, b Padkal, India, Sept 8, 30; m 53; c 4. PURE MATHEMATICS. *Educ:* Loyola Col, Madras, India, 51; Univ Madras, MA, 52; Univ Bombay, PhD(math), 57. *Prof Exp:* Lectr math, Univ Baroda, 58-59; reader, Univ Poona, 59-64; vis asst prof, Univ Ariz, 64-65; vis assoc prof, Univ Hawaii, 65-66; assoc prof, Univ Calgary, 66-68; assoc prof, 68-74, PROF MATH, UNIV REGINA, 74- *Concurrent Pos:* NSF res grant, 65-66. *Honors & Awards:* Narasinga Rao Gold Medal, Indian Math Soc, 58. *Mem:* Am Math Soc; Indian Math Soc; Can Math Cong. *Res:* Analytical theory of numbers. *Mailing Add:* Dept of Math Univ of Regina Regina SK S4S 0A2 Can

RAO, YALAMANCHILI A K, b Godavarru, India, Sept 15, 43; m 70; c 2. ALLERGY, IMMUNOLOGY. *Educ:* Guntur Med Col, India, MD, 69; Columbia Univ, MS, 71. *Prof Exp:* Resident pediat, 71-73, fel allergy & immunol, 73-75, resident internal med, 75-77, EDUC DIR ALLERGY & IMMUNOL, LONG ISLAND COL HOSP, 77- *Concurrent Pos:* Asst clin prof, Downstate Med Ctr, Brooklyn. *Mem:* Am Acad Allergy; fel Am Col Allergists; assoc Am Col Physicians; fel Am Acad Pediat. *Res:* Immunotherapy in cancer; cancer immunology; chronic lung disease. *Mailing Add:* 159 Clinton St Brooklyn NY 11201

RAO, YALAMANCHILI KRISHNA, b India, May 09, 41; m 69; c 3. METALLURGICAL ENGINEERING, PHYSICAL CHEMISTRY. *Educ:* Banaras Hindu Univ, BS, 62; Univ Pa, PhD(metall), 65. *Prof Exp:* Res engr, Inland Steel Co, 65-67; res metallurgist, Corning Glass Works, 67-68; from asst prof to assoc prof extractive metall, Columbia Univ, 68-76; assoc prof, 76-80, PROF, UNIV WASH, 80- *Mem:* Am Inst Mining, Metall & Petrol Engrs; Am Chem Soc. *Res:* Physical chemistry of metal extraction; reaction kinetics and mass transfer; thermodynamics of metallurgical systems. *Mailing Add:* 323 Roberts FB-10 Univ of Wash Seattle WA 98195

RAO, YEDAVALLI SHYAMSUNDER, b Rajahmundry, India, Nov 15, 30; m 52; c 4. ORGANIC CHEMISTRY. *Educ:* Andhra Univ, India, BSc, 50; Osmania Univ, India, MSc, 54; Ill Inst Technol, PhD(org chem), 63. *Prof Exp:* USPHS fel, Ill Inst Technol, 62-63; res chemist, Richardson Co, Melrose Park, 63-65 & CPC Int Co, Argo, 68-70; assoc prof chem, 70-77, PROF CHEM, KENNEDY-KING COL, 77- *Concurrent Pos:* USPHS fel, Ill Inst Technol, 67-68, asst prof, Eve Div, 67- *Mem:* Am Chem Soc; Royal Soc Chem. *Res:* Heterocycles; fluorine chemistry; amino acids. *Mailing Add:* Dept of Chem Kennedy-King Col Chicago IL 60621

RAOUF, ABDUL, b Jullundur, India, Jan 15, 29; Can citizen; m 62. INDUSTRIAL ENGINEERING. *Educ:* WPakistan Univ Eng & Technol, EE, 50; Univ Toledo, MSIE, 66; Univ Windsor, PhD, 70. *Prof Exp:* Eng positions of various responsibility, Ministry of Defense, Govt Pakistan, 51-61; indust engr, Can Acme Screw & Gear Co, 62-64; teaching fel, Univ Toledo, 65-66; from asst prof to assoc prof human factors eng, 66-76, head dept, 76-81, PROF INDUST ENG, 76- *Concurrent Pos:* Nat Res Coun Can grants, 66-68. *Mem:* Sr mem Am Inst Indust Engrs; sr mem Am Soc Qual Control; Am Soc Eng Educ; Eng Inst Can. *Res:* Human performance, including prediction, reliability and optimization in man machine systems. *Mailing Add:* Dept of Indust Eng Univ of Windsor Windsor ON N9B 3P4 Can

RAPACZ, JAN, b Lubien, Poland, Jan 21, 28; US citizen; m 69; c 2. IMMUNOGENETICS. *Educ:* Jagiellonian Univ, BS, 53, MS, 55, PhD(immunogenetics), 59. *Prof Exp:* Res assoc, Jagiellonian Univ, 58-61; fel, Univ Wis-Madison, 61-63; head, Polish Zootech Inst, Krakow, 63-65; vis prof immunogenetics, Univ Wis-Madison, 65-68; dir, Polish Zootech Inst, 68-70; vis prof, 70-71, assoc prof, 72-78, PROF IMMUNOGENETICS, UNIV WIS-MADISON, 78- *Mem:* Am Genetic Asn; Am Heart Asn. *Res:* Serum protein and blood group polymorphisms; immunogenetics of immunoglobulins; active and passive immunity; lipoprotein immunogenetics and atherogenesis. *Mailing Add:* Dept of Genetics Univ of Wis Madison WI 53706

RAPAKA, RAO SAMBASIVA, b Rapaka, India, June 16, 43; US citizen; m 71. PHARMACEUTICAL CHEMISTRY. *Educ:* Andhra Univ, India, BS, 63, MS, 64; Univ Calif, San Francisco, MS, 68, PhD(pharmaceut chem), 70. *Prof Exp:* Res chemist, Univ Calif, San Francisco, 70, asst res biochemist, 71-75; res assoc radiation biol, Albert Einstein Med Ctr, Philadelphia, 75-76; res assoc, Lab Molecular Biophys, Med Ctr, Univ Ala, Birmingham, 76-78; MEM STAFF, BIOPHARMACEUT LAB, FOOD & DRUG ADMIN, 78- *Mem:* Am Chem Soc. *Res:* Synthesis of polymeric peptides as models for enzymes, and as models for collagen; studies on collagen chemistry, biochemistry and radiobiology; synthesis of peptides as models for elastin and mechanisms of arterial wall calcification; gas chromatographic, HPLC, studies on thyroidal amino acids; studies on bioequivalency of drugs. *Mailing Add:* Biopharmaceut Lab 200 C St SW Washington DC 20204

RAPAPORT, ELLIOT, b Los Angeles, Calif, Nov 22, 24; m 43; c 3. INTERNAL MEDICINE. *Educ:* Univ Calif, AB, 44, MD, 46. *Prof Exp:* Intern, San Francisco Gen Hosp, 46-47; asst resident med, Univ Hosp, Univ Calif, 47-50; instr, Albany Med Col, 55-56, asst prof, 56-57; dir cardiopulmonary lab, Mt Zion Hosp, San Francisco, Calif, 57-60; assoc prof, 60-66, assoc dean, 70-73, PROF MED, SCH MED, UNIV CALIF, SAN FRANCISCO, 66-, WILLIAM WATT KERR PROF CLIN MED, 76- DIR CARDIOPULMONARY UNIT, SAN FRANCISCO GEN HOSP, 60- *Concurrent Pos:* Res fel, Med Sch, Univ Calif, 50-51 & Harvard Med Sch, 53-55; dir res, Vet Admin Hosp, Albany, NY, 55-57; consult, USPHS Hosp, San Francisco, 58- & Letterman Army Hosp, 59-; coordr regional med progs, Area I, Calif, 67-73. *Mem:* Am Heart Asn (pres, 74-75); Am Fedn Clin Res; Am Soc Clin Invest; Am Physiol Soc; Asn Am Physicians. *Res:* Cardiovascular physiology, particularly blood flows and regional volumes. *Mailing Add:* Dept of Med Univ of Calif Med Ctr San Francisco CA 94143

RAPAPORT, FELIX THEODOSIUS, b Munich, Ger, Sept 27, 29; m 69. SURGERY, TRANSPLANTATION IMMUNOLOGY. *Educ:* NY Univ, AB, 51, MD, 54. *Prof Exp:* Asst med, Med Ctr, NY Univ, 58-60, from instr to prof surg, 60-77, dir transplantation & immunol div, 65-77; PROF SURG, DEP CHMN DEPT, DIR TRANSPLANTATION DIV & ATTEND SURGEON SURG SERV, STATE UNIV NY STONY BROOK, 77- *Concurrent Pos:* Res fel med & surg, Sch Med, NY Univ, 54-55, res fel path, 56; USPHS res career develop award, 61-62; City of New York Health Res Coun career scientist award, 63-72; intern, Mt Sinai Hosp, New York, 55-56; asst resident & chief resident, Med Ctr, NY Univ, 58-62; mem adv comt collab res in transplantation & immunol, Nat Inst Allergy & Infectious Dis, 64-68; chmn arthritis & metab dis prog proj adv comt, Div Res Grants, NIH, Md, 68-72; consult, Vet Admin Hosp, Manhattan, 64-77; assoc attend surg, NY Univ Hosp, 69-77; vis surgeon, NY Univ Surg Div, Bellevue Hosp, New York, 70-77; mem sci adv bd, Nat Kidney Found, 72-; mem Am Inst Biol Sci adv bd to Off Naval Res, 74-76; mem merit rev bd immunol, Vet Admin, 74-78; mem, Sci Adv Bd, Am Cancer Soc, 75-77; mem, Surg Study Sect B, Div of Res Grants, NIH, Md, 75-76 & Surg Study Sect A, 76-; ed-in-chief, Transplantation Proc, 76-; consult surgeon, Vet Admin Hosp, Northport, NY, 77-; attend surg & dir, Transplantation Serv, Univ Hosp, State Univ NY, Stonybrook, 79- *Honors & Awards:* Comdr, Order of Sci Merit of France, 68; Chevalier, Nat Order of Merit of France, 70; Gold Medal, City Paris, 79. *Mem:* AAAS; Transplantation Soc (secy, 66-74, vpres, 74-76, pres elect, 76-78, pres, 78-); Am Burn Asn; Am Asn Immunol; Soc Univ Surg. *Res:* Transplantation biology and medicine; trauma; burns. *Mailing Add:* Dept of Surg State Univ NY Stony Brook NY 11794

RAPAPORT, IRVING, b New York, NY, May 21, 25; m 52; c 4. MINING GEOLOGY. *Educ:* Univ Minn, BS, 49. *Prof Exp:* Explor geologist, AEC, Colo, 49-50, proj chief explor, Utah & NMex, 50-52; mgr, Hanosh Mines Corp, 52; OWNER, FOUR CORNERS EXPLOR CO, 53- *Concurrent Pos:* Consult, Chilean Nitrate Corp, 52-53, J H Whitney & Co, Kerr McGee Corp, Santa Fe Railway Corp, Spencer Chem Corp & others, 53- *Honors & Awards:* Small Mining Co Award, Mining World, 59. *Mem:* Am Inst Mining, Metall & Petrol Engrs; fel Geol Soc Am. *Res:* Exploration and development of uranium ore bodies. *Mailing Add:* Four Corners Explor Co PO Box 116 Grants NM 87020

RAPAPORT, JACOBO, b Santiago, Chile, Nov 30, 30; m 58; c 2. EXPERIMENTAL NUCLEAR PHYSICS. *Educ:* Univ Chile, Engr, 56; Univ Fla, MSc, 57; Mass Inst Technol, PhD(physics), 63. *Prof Exp:* Instr physics, Univ Chile, 57-60, prof, 63-65, dir inst physics, 64; asst prof, Mass Inst Technol, 65-69; assoc prof, 69-73, prof, 73-81, DISTINGUISHED PROF PHYSICS, OHIO UNIV, 81- *Mem:* Fel Am Phys Soc. *Res:* Experimental information on nuclear spectroscopy obtained by means of low energy nuclear reactions; nuclear reaction studies induced with high energy neutrons; charge exchange (pion, muon); reactions at intermediate energies. *Mailing Add:* Dept of Physics Ohio Univ Athens OH 45701

RAPAPORT, SAMUEL I, b Los Angeles, Calif, Nov 19, 21; m 51; c 4. INTERNAL MEDICINE, HEMATOLOGY. *Educ:* Univ Southern Calif, MD, 45. *Prof Exp:* Instr physiol, Univ Southern Calif, 48-49, vis asst prof, 49-55; chief hemat sect, Vet Admin Hosp, Long Beach, Calif, 55-57; assoc prof med, Med Ctr, Univ Calif, Los Angeles, 57-58; from assoc prof to prof, Sch Med, Univ Southern Calif, 58-74; PROF MED, UNIV CALIF, SAN DIEGO, 74-, CO-HEAD HEMAT/ONCOL DIV, DEPT MED, 78-, PROF PATH & DIR, HEMAT LAB, MED CTR, 80- *Concurrent Pos:* Chief hemat sect, Vet Admin Hosp, Long Beach, 50-53, consult, 59-68; Fulbright res scholar, Univ Oslo, Norway, 53-54; head hemat sect, Med Serv, Los Angeles County Hosp-Univ Med Ctr, 66-74; chief med serv, San Diego Vet Admin Hosp, 74-78. *Mem:* Am Soc Hemat (pres, 77); Soc Exp Biol & Med; fel Am Col Physicians; Am Asn Physicians; Int Soc Hemat. *Res:* Coagulation; hemostasis and thrombosis. *Mailing Add:* Univ Hosp H811K 225 Dickinson San Diego CA 92103

RAPER, CARLENE ALLEN, b Plattsburgh, NY, Jan 9, 25; m 49; c 2. MYCOLOGY, DEVELOPMENTAL GENETICS. *Educ:* Univ Chicago, BS, 46, MS, 48; Harvard Univ, PhD(biol), 77. *Prof Exp:* Res scientist radiation biol, Argonne Nat Labs, Chicago, 47-53; res scientist fungal genetics develop, 61-74, lectr & res assoc, Dept Biol, Harvard Univ, 74-78; lectr microbiol, Bridgewater State Col, Mass, 78; ASST PROF BIOL & GENETICS DEVELOP BIOL, DEPT BIOL SCI, WELLESLEY COL, MASS, 78- *Concurrent Pos:* Coop investr, US-Israel Binat Sci Orgn, 74-77; res grants, Campbell Inst Agr Res, 74-78, Maria Moores Cabot Fount, Harvard Univ, 75-77, Netherlans Orgn Advan Pure Res, 77 & Res Corp, 77-81; res fel, Univ Groningen, Netherlands, 77; assoc ed, Exp Mycology, 79-; co-vice-chmn, Gordon Conf Fungal Metabolism, 82, co-chmn, 84. *Honors & Awards:* NSF fac award, 82. *Mem:* Genetics Soc Am; Mycol Soc Am; AAAS; NY Acad Sci; Sigma Xi. *Res:* Genetic regulation of morphogenesis in the sexual cycle of higher fungi; comparative biology, sexuality and breeding of edible fungi, especially Agaricus species. *Mailing Add:* Dept Biol Sci Wellesley Col Wellesley MA 02181

RAPER, KENNETH BRYAN, b Welcome, NC, July 11, 08; m 36; c 1. MYCOLOGY. *Educ:* Univ NC, AB, 29; George Washington Univ, AM, 31; Harvard Univ, AM, 35, PhD(biol), 36. *Hon Degrees:* DSc, Univ NC, 61. *Prof Exp:* Jr mycologist, Div Soil Microbiol, Bur Chem & Soils, USDA, 29-34, jr mycologist, Bur Plant Indust, 34-36, asst mycologist, 36-40, microbiologist, Fermentation Div, North Regional Res Lab, Bur Agr Chem & Eng, 40-41, sr microbiologist, 41-42, sr microbiologist, Bur Agr & Indust Chem, 42-47, prin microbiologist, 47-53; PROF BACT & BOT, UNIV WIS-MADISON, 53- *Concurrent Pos:* Trustee, Biosci Info Serv, 67-70, vpres, 69- *Honors & Awards:* Award of Merit, Bot Soc Am, 61; Charles Thom Award, Soc Indust Microbiol, 67; Distinguished Mycologist Award, Mycol Soc Am, 81. *Mem:* Nat Acad Sci; AAAS; Bot Soc Am; Mycol Soc Am (pres, 51); Soc Indust Microbiol (pres, 53). *Res:* Morphology and physiology of the Acrasiae; development of improved penicillin-producing molds; taxonomy of Aspergillus and Penicillium. *Mailing Add:* Dept of Bact Univ of Wis Madison WI 53706

RAPHAEL, HAROLD JAMES, b North Bergen, NJ, Apr 15, 18; m 43; c 4. WOOD SCIENCE & TECHNOLOGY. *Educ:* Mich State Univ, BS, 42; Ore State Col, MS, 50; Mich State Univ, PhD(wood tech), 54. *Prof Exp:* Asst forest prod, Mich State Univ, 50-51, from instr to asst prof, 53-56, from asst prof to prof packaging, 56-70; res assoc, Avon Prod, Inc, 70-73; DIR, DEPT PACKAGING SCI, ROCHESTER INST TECHNOL, 73- *Concurrent Pos:* Mem, Packaging Inst, USA. *Mem:* Soc Packaging & Handling Engrs; Tech Asn Pulp & Paper Indust; Am Soc Testing & Mat. *Res:* Structure of paper and paperboard; structural design of packages; packaging graphics; disposability and reuse of packaging materials; cosmetic packaging; new packaging materials and techniques; package evaluation. *Mailing Add:* Rochester Inst of Technol One Lomb Mem Dr Rochester NY 14623

RAPHAEL, LOUISE ARAKELIAN, b New York, NY, Oct 24, 37; m 66; c 2. MATHEMATICAL ANALYSIS. *Educ:* St Johns Univ, BS, 59; Cath Univ Am, MA, 62, PhD(math), 67. *Prof Exp:* Asst prof math, Howard Univ, 66-70; ASSOC PROF MATH, CLARK COL, 71- *Concurrent Pos:* NSF res grant, 75-76; vis assoc prof math, Mass Inst Technol, 77-78. *Mem:* Am Math Soc; Math Asn Am; AAAS; Sigma Xi; Nat Coun Teachers Math. *Res:* Summability theory. *Mailing Add:* Dept of Math Clark Col Atlanta GA 30345

RAPHAEL, ROBERT B, b Los Angeles, Calif, Oct 28, 29; m 66. THEORETICAL PHYSICS. *Educ:* Rensselaer Polytech Inst, BS, 50; Harvard Univ, MS, 51, PhD(physics), 54. *Prof Exp:* Res asst physics, Lawrence Radiation Lab, Univ Calif, 54-56; mem, Inst Advan Study, 56-57; res asst, Univ Pa, 57-58; asst prof, St Michael's Col, Vt, 58-59; vis lectr, Cath Univ Am, 65-66, from asst prof to assoc prof, 66-70; assoc prof, Emory Univ, 70-73; assoc prof math & physics, Oglethorpe Univ, 73-80; MEM FAC, ST JOHN'S COL, MD, 80- *Res:* Phenomenological nucleon scattering theory; nuclear structure philosophy of science; epistemology. *Mailing Add:* St John's Col 60 College Ave Annapolis MD 21401

RAPHAEL, THOMAS, b Somerville, Mass, June 9, 22; m 48; c 4. APPLIED CHEMISTRY, PHOTOGRAPHIC CHEMISTRY. *Educ:* Harvard Univ, AB, 44; Univ Chicago, PhSc, 45. *Prof Exp:* Div res mgr, Dewey & Almy Chem Co, W R Grace & Co, 46-56; group leader, Arthur D Little, Inc, 56-66; asst mgr, Tech Control Ctr, 66-69, mgr spec projs, 69-74, sr tech mgr, Appl Technol Div, 74-81, SR MGR MAT DEVELOP, TECH PHOTO DIV, POLAROID CORP, 81. *Mem:* Electrochem Soc; Am Chem Soc; Soc Plastics Indust; Soc Plastics Eng; Tech Asn Pulp & Paper Indust. *Res:* Process and product development in photographic products, plastics, rubber, paper and textiles. *Mailing Add:* Polaroid Corp 28 Osborne St Cambridge MA 02139

RAPIN, ISABELLE (MRS HAROLD OAKLANDER), b Lausanne, Switz, Dec 4, 27; US citizen; m 59; c 4. NEUROLOGY, PEDIATRIC NEUROLOGY. *Educ:* Univ Lausanne, Swiss Fed physician dipl, 52, Dr(med), 55. *Prof Exp:* Intern pediat, NY Univ-Bellevue Med Ctr, 53-54; asst resident neurol, Columbia-Presby Med Ctr, 54-57; instr neurol, 58-61, from assoc to assoc prof neurol & pediat, 61-72, dir pediat neurol training prog, 70-74, PROF NEUROL & PEDIAT, ALBERT EINSTEIN COL MED, 72- *Concurrent Pos:* Fel pediat neurol & asst neurologist, Columbia-Presby Med Ctr, 57-58; asst vis physician, Bronx Munic Hosp Ctr, 58-63, assoc vis physician, 63-, vis neurologist, 69-; prin investr, Nat Inst Neurol Dis & Blindness res grant, 59-74; prin investr, Children's Bur, USPHS grant, 68-74; adj vis physician, Montefiore Hosp, 64-; assoc vis pediatrician, Lincoln Hosp, 64-74; vis physician, Hosp, Albert Einstein Col Med, 66-, vis neurologist, 69- *Mem:* AAAS; Int Neuropsychol Soc; Am Neurol Asn (vpres, 81-); Child Neurol Soc; Int Child Neurol Asn (secy gen, 79-82). *Res:* Deaf and nonverbal children; brain damage in children; degenerative diseases of the nervous system in children. *Mailing Add:* Rm 341 Kennedy Ctr Albert Einstein Col of Med Bronx NY 10461

RAPISARDA, CARMEL, b Rome, Italy, Feb 1, 32; US citizen; m 67; c 1. PHYSICAL CHEMISTRY. *Educ:* Univ Karalis, PhD(phys chem), 56. *Prof Exp:* Assoc chemist cosmetics & dietics, J Muller Co, Switzerland, 57-58; res chemist polymers, Battelle Mem Inst, Geneva, 58-63; res chemist textile fibers, 64-76, SR RES CHEMIST BIOCHEM, E I DU PONT DE NEMOURS & CO, INC, 76- *Res:* New galvanic cells; catalysts; radiochemicals; polyesters; textile compounds flammability; antioxidants; radiochemicals; metabolism of biochemicals. *Mailing Add:* Dept Biochem 324/337 Exp Sta E I Du Pont de Nemours & Co Inc Wilmington DE 19898

RAPISARDI, SALVATORE C, b New York, NY, July 8, 41; m 79. NEUROSCIENCE, ANATOMY. *Educ:* Duke Univ, BA, 63; Temple Univ, MA, 66; Univ Calif, Riverside, PhD(physiol psychol), 71. *Prof Exp:* Fel anat, Dept Neurol & Anat, Sch Med, Stanford Univ, 72-74; instr, Univ Calif, Berkeley, 77; fel, Med Sch, Univ Calif, San Francisco, 74-77; ASST PROF ANAT, COL MED, HOWARD UNIV, 77- *Concurrent Pos:* prin investr, Nat Eye Inst, 79-82 & Biomed Interdisplinary Proj, NIH, 79- *Mem:* Am Soc Neurosci; AAAS; Am Asn Anatomists; European Soc Neurosci. *Res:* Synaptology of the dorsal lateral geniculate in cat and monkey by analysis of series of consecutive thin sections; reconstruction of neural processes form consecutive thin sections. *Mailing Add:* Dept Anat Col Med Howard Univ 520 W Street NW Washington DC 20001

RAPKIN, MYRON COLMAN, b Rochester, NY, Nov 24, 38; m 66; c 2. CLINICAL CHEMISTRY, PAPER CHEMISTRY. *Educ:* Rochester Inst Technol, BS, 63. *Prof Exp:* Clin chemist, Genessee Hosp, 65-66; med lab technologist, Wilson Mem Hosp, 66-68; develop chemist emulsions & color photog, Gen Aniline & Film, 68-70; SR ASSOC RES SCIENTIST PROD RES & DEVELOP, AMES CO DIV, MILES LAB, 70- *Mem:* Am Chem Soc; Tech Asn Pulp & Paper Indust. *Res:* Diagnostic systems; confirmatory tests; clinical and urinalysis control systems; performance and proficiency testing. *Mailing Add:* 3425 Wood St Elkhart IN 46514

RAPOPORT, ABRAHAM, b Toronto, Ont, Aug 18, 26; m 52; c 4. MEDICINE. *Educ:* Univ Toronto, MD, 49, MA, 52; FRCP(C), 54. *Prof Exp:* Dir dept biochem, 57-71, dir metab renal unit, 59-73, PHYSICIAN IN CHIEF, TORONTO WESTERN HOSP, 73-; PROF MED, UNIV TORONTO, 71- *Concurrent Pos:* Asst prof med & path chem, Univ Toronto, 65-71. *Mem:* Fel Am Col Physicians. *Res:* Renal and metabolic diseases; hypertension. *Mailing Add:* Toronto Western Hosp 399 Bathurst St Toronto ON M5T 2S8 Can

RAPOPORT, HENRY, b Brooklyn, NY, Nov 16, 18; m 44; c 3. ORGANIC CHEMISTRY. *Educ:* Mass Inst Technol, SB, 40, PhD(org chem), 43. *Prof Exp:* Chemist Heyden Chem Corp, NJ, 43-45; Nat Res Coun fel, NIH, 46; from instr to assoc prof, 46-57, PROF CHEM, UNIV CALIF, BERKELEY, 57- *Honors & Awards:* Res Achievement Award, Acad Pharmaceut Sci, 72. *Mem:* Am Chem Soc. *Res:* Alkaloids; heterocyclic compounds; natural products; pigments; biosynthesis. *Mailing Add:* Dept of Chem Univ of Calif Berkeley CA 94720

RAPOPORT, JUDITH LIVANT, b New York, NY, July 12, 33; m 61; c 2. CHILD PSYCHIATRY. *Educ:* Swarthmore Col, BA, 55; Harvard Univ, MD, 59; Am Bd Psychiat & Neurol, dipl & cert child psychiat, 69. *Prof Exp:* Intern, Mt Sinai Hosp, 59-60; resident psychiat, Mass Ment Health Ctr, Boston, 60-61 & St Elizabeth's Hosp, Washington, DC, 61-62; NIMH health fel, Psychol Inst, Uppsala & Karolinska Hosp, Stockholm,

Sweden, 62-64; NIMH fel child psychiat, Children's Hosp, Washington, DC, 64-66; spec fel, Lab Psychol, NIMH, 66-67; clin assoc prof pediat & psychiat, Med Sch, Georgetown Univ, 67-77; MEM STAFF, NIMH, 77- *Concurrent Pos:* Prin investr, USPHS grant biol factors in hyperactivity, 72-76. *Mem:* Fel Am Psychiat Asn; Am Col Neuropsychopharmacol; Psychiat Res Soc; fel Am Acad Child Psychiat. *Res:* Biological child psychiatry; pediatric psychopharmacology; learning disabilities. *Mailing Add:* Unit on Childhood Mental Illness Nat Inst of Mental Health Bethesda MD 20014

RAPOPORT, LORENCE, b Springfield, Mass, Oct 8, 19; m 46; c 3. ORGANIC POLYMER CHEMISTRY. *Educ:* Harvard Univ, AB, 41; Duke Univ, PhD(org chem), 44. *Prof Exp:* Asst, Boston Woven Hose & Rubber Co, 41; lab instr, Duke Univ, 41-44; B F Goodrich fel, Ohio State Univ, 44-45; Upjohn fel, 45-46; res chemist, Am Cyanamid Co, 46-54, group leader, 54-63; dir, Res Sect, 64-67, dir, Res & Develop Sect, 67-70, dir new prod res & develop, 70-75, MGR PROD & PROCESS DEVELOP, OLIN CORP, 75- *Concurrent Pos:* Res assoc, Off Sci Res & Develop, Ohio State Univ, 45; vis scientist, Cath Univ Louvain, 60-61. *Mem:* Am Chem Soc. *Res:* Synthesis of detergents; carcinogenic hydrocarbons; acrylonitrile and derivatives; nitrogen compounds; s-triazines; cellophane; cellulose derivatives; polymers; coatings; plastic films. *Mailing Add:* Film Div Olin Corp PO Box 200 Pisgah Forest NC 28768

RAPOPORT, STANLEY I, b New York, NY, Nov 24, 32; m 61; c 2. MEDICINE, PHYSIOLOGY. *Educ:* Princeton Univ, AB, 54; Harvard Med Sch, MD, 59. *Prof Exp:* Intern med, Bellevue Hosp, New York, 59-60; res scientist neurophysiol, NIMH, 60-62, res scientist physiol, 64-78; CHIEF LAB NEUROSCI, GERONT RES CTR, NAT INST ON AGING, BALTIMORE, MD, 78- *Concurrent Pos:* NSF fel biophys, Physiol Inst, Uppsala, Sweden, 62-64; prof lectr, Georgetown Univ Sch Med, 71- *Mem:* AAAS; Biophys Soc; Soc Neurosci; Soc Gen Physiol; Am Physiol Soc. *Res:* Physiology of blood brain barrier; aging of nervous system membrane phenomena; excitation-contraction coupling in muscle. *Mailing Add:* 3010 44th Pl NW Washington DC 20016

RAPOZA, NORBERT PACHECO, b New Bedford, Mass, Oct 23, 29; m 54; c 2. MICROBIOLOGY. *Educ:* Oberlin Col, BA, 53; Ohio State Univ, MS, 55, PhD(bact), 60. *Prof Exp:* Asst virol, Univ Pittsburgh, 59-60, res assoc, 60-65, asst prof, 65-69; sr res investr, 67-71, group leader virol, 71-78, RES SCIENTIST, G D SEARLE & CO, 78- *Mem:* AAAS; Am Soc Microbiol; NY Acad Sci. *Res:* Virology; cell biology; microbiology. *Mailing Add:* Div Biol Res Dept Biol G D Searle & Co Box 5110 Chicago IL 60680

RAPP, DONALD, b Brooklyn, NY, Sept 27, 34; m 56; c 2. SOLAR ENERGY, NATURAL RESOURCES. *Educ:* Cooper Union, BS, 55; Princeton Univ, MS, 56; Univ Calif, Berkeley, PhD(phys chem), 60. *Prof Exp:* Staff scientist, Lockheed Palo Alto Res Labs, 59-65; assoc prof chem, Polytech Inst Brooklyn, 65-69; assoc prof chem, Univ Tex, Dallas, 69-73, prof solar energy, 73-79; SR RES SCIENTIST & DIV TECHNOLOGIST, JET PROPULSION LAB, CALIF INST TECHNOL, 79- *Concurrent Pos:* Consult, Solar Energy Proj, Am Technol Univ, 74-79. *Res:* Molecular collisions; solar energy conversion; natural resource management. *Mailing Add:* Jet Propulsion Lab Calif Inst Technol 4800 Oak Grove Dr Pasadena CA 91030

RAPP, DOROTHY GLAVES, b Sheffield, Eng, Auug 14, 43; m 78. EXPERIMENTAL CANCER METASTASIS. *Educ:* Univ London, BSc, 65; Univ Nottingham, PhD(tumor immunol), 69. *Prof Exp:* Res officer, Cancer Res Campaign, Univ Nottingham, 69-72; CANCER RES SCIENTIST, NY STATE DEPT HEALTH, ROSWELL PARK MEM INST, 72- *Mem:* AAAS; NY Acad Sci. *Res:* Characterization of host and tumor related factors which determine the fate of cancer cells during the post-intravasation phases of metastasis. *Mailing Add:* Dept Esp Path Roswell Park Mem Inst 666 Elm St Buffalo NY 14263

RAPP, EGON, irrigation engineering, see previous edition

RAPP, FRED, b Fulda, Ger, Mar 13, 29; nat US; m 74; c 3. VIROLOGY. *Educ:* Brooklyn Col, BS, 51; Union Univ, NY, MS, 56; Univ Southern Calif, PhD(med microbiol), 58; Am Bd Med Microbiol, dipl. *Prof Exp:* Jr bacteriologist, Div Labs & Res, NY State Dept Health, 52-53, bacteriologist, 53-55; instr med microbiol, Sch Med, Univ Southern Calif, 56-59; virologist, Philip D Wilson Res Found, 59-62; asst prof microbiol & immunol, Med Col, Cornell Univ, 61-62; from assoc prof to prof virol & epidemiol, Baylor Col Med, 62-69; PROF MICROBIOL & CHMN DEPT, COL MED, PA STATE UNIV, 69-, ASSOC PROVOST & DEAN HEALTH AFFAIRS, 73-, DIR SPECIALIZED CANCER RES CTR, 73- *Concurrent Pos:* Consult supvry microbiologist, Hosp Spec Surg, New York, 59-62; res career prof virol, Am Cancer Soc, 66-69, prof, 77-; sr mem grad sch & mem res ref reagents comt, Nat Inst Allergy & Infectious Dis, NIH, 67-71, chmn, Atlantic Coast Tumor Virol Group, 71; mem virol study sect, 72-76, mem virol task force, 76-; assoc ed, Immunology, 71-73; assoc ed, Cancer Res & sect ed oncol, Intervirology, 72-; mem, Nat Bladder Cancer Proj, 73-76; mem, Gordon Res Conf Cancer, 75; mem deleg viral oncol, US-USSR Joint Comt Health Coop & US-France & mem adv bd, Cancer Info Dissemination & Anal Ctr, 76-; consult virus cancer prog, Nat Cancer Inst. study sect, 71-75 & consult virus cancer prog; mem viral oncol, US-USSR Joint Comt Health Cooperation; Am Asn Univ Prof. *Mem:* AAAS; Am Soc Microbiol; Am Asn Immunol; Am Asn Cancer Res; Soc Exp Biol & Mem: Sigma Xi; Soc Gen Microbiol; Am Asn Univ Prof. *Res:* Replication of viruses; transformation of mammalian cells by viruses; viral genetics and immunology; tumor viruses; herpesviruses; measles virus. *Mailing Add:* 2 Laurel Ridge Rd Hershey PA 17033

RAPP, GEORGE ROBERT, JR, b Toledo, Ohio, Sept 19, 30; m 56; c 2. GEOLOGY. *Educ:* Univ Minn, BA, 52; Pa State Univ, PhD(geochem), 60. *Prof Exp:* Asst prof mineral, SDak Sch Mines & Technol, 58-61; assoc prof & curator mineral, 61-65; assoc prof mineral, Univ Minn, Minneapolis, 65-75, assoc chmn dept, 69-72; Fulbright sr scholar, Fulbright-Hays Prog, 72-73; DEAN, COL LETTERS & SCI, UNIV MINN, DULUTH, 75-, PROF

GEOL & ARCHAEOL, 76- *Concurrent Pos:* NSF fel, 63-64; assoc dir, Minn Messenia Exped, 69-; chmn, Coun Educ Geol Sci, 69-73; archaeom dir, Tel Michal Excavation, 77-80. *Mem:* Geol Soc Am; Mineral Soc Am; Nat Asn Geol Teachers (pres, 69-70); Archaeol Inst Am; Asn Field Archaeol (pres, 79-81). *Res:* Archaeological geochemistry; archaeological geology; trace element fingerprinting of metals. *Mailing Add:* Col of Letters & Sci Univ of Minn 108 Math-Geol Bldg Duluth MN 55812

RAPP, HERBERT JOSEPH, microbiology, deceased

RAPP, JOHN P, b New York, NY, Dec 22, 34; m 65. PATHOLOGY. *Educ:* Cornell Univ, DVM & MS, 59; Univ Pa, PhD(path), 64. *Prof Exp:* Res assoc physiol, Penrose Res Lab, Zool Soc Philadelphia, 62-76; assoc prof, 76-80, PROF, DEPT MED, MED COL OHIO, 80- *Concurrent Pos:* NIH fels, Univ Pa, 62-63 & Univ Utah, 64-65. *Res:* Biomedical research in experimental hypertension and function of renal juxtaglomerular apparatus; quantitative methods in steroid biochemistry; biochemical genetics of blood pressure regulation. *Mailing Add:* Dept of Med CS 10008 Toledo OH 43699

RAPP, PAUL ERNEST, b Chicago, Ill, Sept 2, 49. THEORETICAL NEUROPHYSIOLOGY. *Educ:* Univ Ill, Urbana-Champaign, BS(physiol) & BS(physics), 72; Cambridge Univ, Eng, PhD(math), 75. *Prof Exp:* Fel math, Cains Col, Cambridge Univ, 75-79; ASST PROF PHYSIOL, MED COL, PA, 79- *Concurrent Pos:* Vis fac, Dept Math, Rutgers Univ, 78. *Mem:* Am Math Soc; Biophys Soc; Soc Math Biol. *Res:* Mathematical investigations of biochemical and biophysical control systems; large dimension nonlinear differential equations; theoretical neurobiology. *Mailing Add:* Dept Physiol Med Col Pa 3300 Henry Ave Philadelphia PA 19129

RAPP, R ROBERT, meteorology, see previous edition

RAPP, RICHARD HENRY, b Danbury, Conn, Aug 26, 37; m 65; c 2. GEODESY. *Educ:* Rensselaer Polytech Inst, BS, 59; Ohio State Univ, MSc, 61, PhD(geod sci), 64. *Prof Exp:* Res assoc, 61-65, asst supvr, 65-66, instr geod, 63-64, from asst prof to assoc prof, 64-71, PROF GEOD SCI, OHIO STATE UNIV, 71-, RES SUPVR, RES CTR, 66- *Concurrent Pos:* Assoc ed, J Geophys Res, 77-79. *Mem:* Fel Am Geophys Union; Am Cong Surv & Mapping. *Res:* Gravimetric, geometric and satellite geodesy; applications of digital computers to geodesy. *Mailing Add:* Dept of Geod Sci Ohio State Univ 1958 Neil Ave Columbus OH 43210

RAPP, ROBERT, b Toronto, Ont, Oct 10, 29; m 66. PEDODONTICS, HISTOLOGY. *Educ:* Univ Toronto, DDS, 53; Univ Mich, MS, 56; FRCD(C), 66. *Prof Exp:* Intern, Hosp for Sick Children, 53-54; res assoc, Univ Mich, 56-57; from asst to assoc hist, Univ Toronto, 59-62; asst prof pedodontics, Univ Mich, 62-65; assoc prof, 65-68, dir, Dent Asst Utilization Prof, 67-71, PROF PEDODONTICS, UNIV PITTSBURGH, 68-, CHMN DEPT, 65- *Concurrent Pos:* Res grants, 62-67, 68-; WHO fel, Eng, Scand & USSR, 71-; consult, Pan Am Health Orgn, Brazil & Mexico; mem, Am Asn Dent Schs. *Mem:* Am Acad Pedodont; Int Asn Dent Res; Am Asn Dent Res; fel Am Col Dentists; fel Int Col Dentists. *Res:* Histology and histochemistry of innervation of dental tissues; circulation in dental pulp; pathology; evaluation of audio-visual teaching procedures. *Mailing Add:* Dept of Pedodontics Sch of Dent Univ of Pittsburgh Pittsburgh PA 15261

RAPP, ROBERT, b Reading, Pa, Apr 22, 21; m 45. RADIOLOGY. *Educ:* Ursinus Col, BS, 42; Temple Univ, MD, 46; Am Bd Radiol, dipl. *Prof Exp:* From instr to asst prof, 53-70, assoc prof, 70-80, EMER ASSOC PROF RADIOL, UNIV MICH, ANN ARBOR, 80- *Mem:* Am Col Radiol; Radiol Soc NAm. *Res:* Clinical radiology; teaching. *Mailing Add:* 1460 Cedar Bend Dr Ann Arbor MI 48105

RAPP, ROBERT ANTHONY, b Lafayette, Ind, Feb 21, 34; m 60; c 4. METALLURGY. *Educ:* Purdue Univ, BS, 56; Carnegie Inst Technol, MS, 59, PhD(metall eng), 60. *Prof Exp:* Fulbright fel, Max Planck Inst Phys Chem, 59-60; from asst prof to assoc prof, 63-69, PROF METALL ENG, OHIO STATE UNIV, 69- *Concurrent Pos:* Guggenheim fel, Univ Grenoble, 72-73. *Honors & Awards:* Stoughton Young Teacher Award, Am Soc Metals, 67, Howe Gold Medal, 73. *Mem:* Fel Am Inst Mining, Metall & Petrol Engrs; fel Am Soc Metals; Electrochem Soc; Nat Asn Corrosion Engrs. *Res:* Oxidation of metals and alloys; thermodynamics; electrochemistry, point defects in compounds. *Mailing Add:* 1379 Southport Dr Columbus OH 43220

RAPP, ROBERT DIETRICH, b Reading, Pa, Dec 21, 30; m 53; c 2. ORGANIC CHEMISTRY. *Educ:* Tufts Univ, BS, 55; Lehigh Univ, PhD(org chem), 67. *Prof Exp:* Chemist, Glidden Co, 55-57 & Polymer Corp, 57; biochemist, Reading Hosp, 57-64; asst chem, Lehigh Univ, 64-65, res asst, 65-66; instr, Lafayette Col, 66-67; asst prof, 67-70, assoc prof, 70-79, PROF CHEM, ALBRIGHT COL, 79- *Concurrent Pos:* Sigma Xi res grant, 67. *Mem:* AAAS; Am Chem Soc; An Soc Pharmacog; NY Acad Sci. *Res:* Synthesis of the macrolide antibiotics; peracid oxidation of enol ethers; synthesis of antimalarial compounds; structure and synthesis of pyrrolizidine alkaloids. *Mailing Add:* Dept Chem Albright Col Reading PA 19604

RAPP, WALDEAN G, b Oakley, Kans, Mar 30, 36; m 57; c 3. BIOCHEMISTRY, ORGANIC CHEMISTRY. *Educ:* Univ Ottawa, BS, 59; Univ Ark, MS, 61, PhD(chem), 63. *Prof Exp:* Res chemist, Chem Res Dept, Food Div, Anderson, Clayton & Co, 63-67; chief chemist, Hubinger Co, Iowa, 67-70; TECH DIR, CARGILL, INC, CORN STARCH & SYRUP, 70- *Mem:* Am Chem Soc; Am Asn Cereal Chem; Am Soc Brewing Chemists; Am Oil Chem Soc; Inst Food Technol. *Res:* Hormonal effects on the acid soluble nucleotides of liver; flavor studies of various food and food products, including sensory evaluation of foods; basic food science; corn wet-milling. *Mailing Add:* Cargill Inc Corn Starch & Syrup PO Box 1467 Cedar Rapids IA 52401

RAPP, WILLIAM FREDERICK, JR, b Newark, NJ, Mar 24, 18; m 44; c 3. ENTOMOLOGY, ARACHNOLOGY. *Educ:* Rutgers Univ, BS, 44; Univ Ill, MS, 45. *Prof Exp:* Asst entom, Univ Ill, 44-47; instr biol & chem, Doane Col, 47-49, asst prof, 49-51; chief chemist, Crete Mills, 51 & Feed Serv Corp, 51-52; aquatic biologist, 68-71, ENTOMOLOGIST, STATE DEPT HEALTH, NEBR, 52- *Concurrent Pos:* Pres, Archem Corp, 49-52; res assoc zool, Doane Col, 75- *Mem:* Wilson Ornith Soc; Cooper Ornith Soc; Am Entom Soc; Am Arachnol Soc; Am Ornith Union. *Res:* Siphonaptera, ticks and insects of public health importance in Nebraska; systematic studies of Araneae; Isopods(Oniscoidea) systematics and distribution; Opiliones North American species; spiders of North America. *Mailing Add:* Nebr State Health Dept 1003 O St Lincoln NE 68501

RAPP, WILLIAM RODGER, b Dover, NJ, May 18, 36; m 66. PATHOLOGY. *Educ:* Kans State Univ, BS, 64, DVM, 66, MS, 70. *Prof Exp:* Res assoc neuropath, Kans State Univ, 66-67, instr path, 67-72; dir path, Bio Dynamics Inc, East Millstone, NJ, 72-76; CONSULT PATHOLOGIST, 76- *Mem:* Am Vet Med Asn; Am Asn Vet Lab Diagnosticians; Soc Toxicol Pathologist. *Res:* Comparative pathology; veterinary pathology; experimental toxicology and neoplasia epidemiology. *Mailing Add:* 214 Ann St Millstone NJ 08876

RAPPAPORT, ARON M, b Sereth, Austria, June 7, 04; m 50; c 2. PHYSIOLOGY, SURGERY. *Educ:* Ger Univ Prague, Czech, MD, 29; Univ Paris, dipl, 34; Univ Toronto, PhD(physiol), 52. *Prof Exp:* Resident surg, Friedrichshain Hosp, Berlin, Ger, 29-33; clin asst surg, Cochin Hosp, Paris, France, 33-34; head surg, Jewish Community Hosp, Botoshani, Rumania, 35-41; surgeon, Hosp Love-of-Men, Bucharest, 42-48; res assoc, Banting & Best Dept Med Res, 48, lectr, 52, from assoc prof to prof, 55-73, EMER PROF PHYSIOL, FAC MED, UNIV TORONTO, 73- *Concurrent Pos:* Clin asst, Toronto Gen Hosp, 52; sr res scientist, Dept Med, Sunnybrook Med Ctr, Univ Toronto, 78- *Mem:* Microcirc Soc; Can Physiol Soc; Am Asn Study Liver Dis; Europ Microcirc Soc; Can Microcirc Soc. *Res:* Structure, function and experimental surgery and pathology of liver; hepatic microcirculation and radiology; pancreas and cardiovascular system. *Mailing Add:* Div of Gastroenterol 2075 Bayview Ave Toronto ON M4N 3M5 Can

RAPPAPORT, DAVID, b Kiev, Russia, June 13, 07; m 33; c 2. MATHEMATICS EDUCATION. *Educ:* Univ Chicago, BS, 28; Northwestern Univ, MA, 54, EdD(educ), 57. *Prof Exp:* Teacher, Pub Schs, Ill, 37-40; teacher, High Sch, 40-56; PROF MATH EDUC, NORTHEASTERN ILL UNIV, 57- *Concurrent Pos:* Math consult, Am Educ Publs, 71-72. *Res:* Problems of teaching elementary school mathematics. *Mailing Add:* 2747 Coyle Ave Chicago IL 60645

RAPPAPORT, GEORGE, b Jaszbereny, Hungary, May 27, 23; US citizen; m 46; c 3. INSTRUMENTATION, PHYSICAL CHEMISTRY. *Educ:* Univ Miami, BS, 44; Ohio State Univ, MS, 50, PhD(phys chem), 66. *Prof Exp:* Chemist, Mat Lab, Wright-Patterson AFB, 46-53; sr chemist, 53-57, sr exp chemist, 57-61, SECT HEAD MAT CHARACTERIZATION & SPECIFICATION, INLAND DIV, GEN MOTORS CORP, 61- *Concurrent Pos:* Lectr, Xavier Univ, 65 & Eng Found Dayton, 69. *Honors & Awards:* Cleery Award, Mat Lab, Wright-Patterson AFB, 54. *Mem:* Soc Appl Spectros; Am Chem Soc; Coblentz Soc. *Res:* Application of infrared spectroscopic and other instrumental methods of analysis to the characterization and quantitation of materials. *Mailing Add:* 4455 Hoffman Dr Dayton OH 45415

RAPPAPORT, HARRY P, b Los Angeles, Calif, Oct 9, 27. BIOLOGY. *Educ:* Calif Inst Technol, BS, 51; Yale Univ, PhD(physics), 56. *Prof Exp:* USPHS fel, Yale Univ, 56-58, asst prof biophys, 59-65; assoc prof biol, 65-71, PROF BIOL, TEMPLE UNIV, 71- *Mem:* Am Chem Soc; Am Soc Biol Chem. *Res:* Ligand-protein interactions; bacterial secretion of proteins. *Mailing Add:* Dept of Biol Temple Univ Col Lib Arts Philadelphia PA 19122

RAPPAPORT, IRVING, b New York, NY, Sept 4, 23; m 48; c 3. IMMUNOLOGY. *Educ:* Cornell Univ, AB, 48; Calif Inst Technol, PhD(immunol, biochem), 53. *Prof Exp:* Res botanist, Univ Calif, Los Angeles, 53-61; asst prof microbiol, Univ Chicago, 61-64; actg chmn dept, 66-67, PROF MICROBIOL, NEW YORK MED COL, 64- *Mem:* Fel AAAS; Am Asn Immunol; Reticuloendothelial Soc; Genetics Soc Am; Am Soc Microbiol. *Res:* Antigenic structure of viruses; antibody synthesis in vitro. *Mailing Add:* Dept of Microbiol New York Med Col Valhalla NY 10595

RAPPAPORT, LAWRENCE, b New York, NY, May 28, 28; m 53; c 3. PLANT PHYSIOLOGY, HORTICULTURE. *Educ:* Univ Idaho, BS, 50; Mich State Univ, MS, 51, PhD(hort), 56. *Prof Exp:* Lectr veg crops, 56-68, from jr olericulturist to assoc olericulturist, 56-68, actg dir, Plant Growth Lab, 74-76, dir, 78-79, OLERICULTURIST & PROF VEG CROPS, UNIV CALIF, DAVIS, 68- *Concurrent Pos:* Res fel, Calif Inst Technol, 58; Fulbright & Guggenheim fels, Hebrew Univ & Univ Tokyo, 63-64; NIH spec vis prof & fel org chem, Univ Bristol, 70-71. *Mem:* Am Soc Hort Sci; Am Soc Plant Physiol; Scand Soc Plant Physiol; Japanese Soc Plant Physiol; Soc Exp Biol. *Res:* Growth and development; plant growth regulators; gibberellins; plant cell culture; somatic cell biology; plant regeneration; hormonal regulation; mode of action of plant hormones. *Mailing Add:* Dept Veg Crops/Plant Growth Lab Univ Calif Davis CA 95616

RAPPAPORT, MAURICE, b New York, NY, Feb 9, 26; c 6. PSYCHIATRY, NEUROPSYCHOLOGY. *Educ:* Stanford Univ, MD, 62; Ohio State Univ, PhD(psychol), 64. *Prof Exp:* Chief res, Agnews State Hosp, 62-72; RESEARCHER PSYCHIAT, UNIV CALIF, 72- *Mem:* AAAS; Am Med Asn; Human Factors Soc; Am Psychiat Asn. *Res:* Neuropsychiatry; psychopharmacology. *Mailing Add:* 1120 McKendrie St San Jose CA 95126

RAPPAPORT, PAUL, solar energy, solid state physics, deceased

RAPPAPORT, RAYMOND, JR, b North Bergen, NJ, May 21, 22; m 48; c 3. EMBRYOLOGY. *Educ:* Bethany Col, WVa, BS, 48; Univ Mich, MS, 48; Yale Univ, PhD, 52. *Prof Exp:* Lab instr gen biol, Yale Univ, 51-52; from asst prof to assoc prof biol, 52-61, PROF BIOL, UNION COL, NY, 61- *Concurrent Pos:* Trustee, Mt Desert Island Biol Lab, 54-70, dir 56-59. *Mem:* AAAS; Am Soc Zool; Am Micros Soc; Am Soc Cell Biol; Soc Develop Biol. *Res:* Animal cell division; role of water in growth and differentiation. *Mailing Add:* Dept Biol Sci Union College Schenectady NY 12308

RAPPAPORT, STEPHEN MORRIS, b San Antonio, Tex, Jan 6, 48; m 70. INDUSTRIAL HYGIENE. *Educ:* Univ Ill, BS, 69; Univ NC, Chapel Hill, MSPH, 73, PhD(indust hyg), 74; Am Bd Indust Hyg, cert, 75. *Prof Exp:* Anal chemist, Hazleton Labs, Inc, 69-71; staff mem indust hyg, Los Alamos Sci Lab, Univ Calif, 74-76; asst prof, 76-82, ASSOC PROF INDUST HYG, SCH PUB HEALTH, UNIV CALIF, BERKELEY, 82- *Mem:* Am Indust Hyg Asn; Am Acad Indust Hyg; Am Conf Gov Indust Hygienists; Am Chem Soc. *Mailing Add:* Sch of Pub Health Univ Calif Berkeley CA 94720

RAPPAPORT, STEPHEN S, b New York, NY, Sept 26, 38; m 66; c 2. COMMUNICATIONS & SYSTEMS ENGINEERING. *Educ:* Cooper Union, BEE, 60; Univ Southern Calif, MSEE, 62; NY Univ, PhD(eng sci), 65. *Prof Exp:* Mem tech staff, Hughes Aircraft Co, 60-62; instr elec eng, NY Univ, 64-65; mem tech staff, Bell Tel Labs, 65-68; asst prof, 68-71, chmn undergrad prog, Col Eng & Appl Sci, 78, ASSOC PROF ENG, STATE UNIV NY STONY BROOK, 71-, DIR GRAD PROG, 78- *Concurrent Pos:* Indust consult, 69-; assoc ed, Commun Soc Mag, Inst Elec & Electronics Engrs, 74-; NSF grant commun tech, 76- *Mem:* AAAS; sr mem Inst Elec & Electronics Engrs. *Res:* Communications systems and theory; analytical modelling and simulation; network architecture, multiple access techniques, and communications traffic; data, voice, and computer communications. *Mailing Add:* Dept of Elec Eng State Univ NY Stony Brook NY 11794

RAPPERPORT, EUGENE J, b St Louis, Mo, Mar 13, 30; m 50; c 3. METALLURGY, MECHANICAL ENGINEERING. *Educ:* Mass Inst Technol, BS, 52, ScD(metall), 55. *Prof Exp:* Group leader metall, Nuclear Metals, Inc, 51-63; metallurgist, Ledgemont Labs, Kennecott Copper Corp, 63-73; prof, New Col, 73-74; CONSULT, E RAPPERPORT & ASSOCS, 74- *Mem:* Am Inst Mining, Metall & Petrol Engrs; Am Welding Soc; Am Soc Metals; Am Sci Testing & Mat; AAAS. *Res:* Diffusion; x-ray physics; refractory metal technology; phase equilibrium and electron microprobe studies; deformation of metals; chemical thermodynamics and kinetics; computer applications; mass spectrometry; nuclear fusion engineering; magnetohydrodynamics engineering; magnet design and construction. *Mailing Add:* E Rapperport & Assoc Old County Rd Lincoln MA 01773

RAPPORT, DAVID JOSEPH, b Omaha, Nebr, Feb 16, 39; m 65. ECOLOGY, THEORETICAL BIOLOGY. *Educ:* Univ Mich, BBA, 60, MA, 66, PhD(econ), 67. *Prof Exp:* Res assoc econ, Univ Mich, 67-68; fisheries res bd fel, Univ Toronto, 68-69, fel ecol, 69-70; vis asst prof & Can Coun Killam sr res fel, Simon Fraser Univ, 70-74; environmentalist, Statist Can, 74-81; prof, 77-80, TITULAR PROF ZOOL, UNIV TORONTO, 80- *Concurrent Pos:* Sci adv, Statist Can, 82- *Mem:* Inst Ecol; Soc Am Naturalists. *Res:* Evolution; application of economic models to biology; behavior of ecosystems under stress; framework for environmental statistics; state of environment reporting. *Mailing Add:* Dept of Zool Univ of Toronto Toronto ON M5S 2R8 Can

RAPPORT, ELLEN WYNNE, b Paterson, NJ, Apr 28, 42; Can citizen; m 65; c 1. DEVELOPMENTAL GENETICS. *Educ:* Univ Mich, BSc, 63, MSc, 67, PhD(zool), 69. *Prof Exp:* Fel cytogenetics, York Univ, 69-70; fel genetics, Simon Fraser Univ, 70-74; asst prof, 74-79, ASSOC PROF GENETICS, UNIV TORONTO, 79- *Mem:* AAAS; Genetics Soc Am; Genetics Soc Can. *Res:* Developmental homeostasis in fruit flies. *Mailing Add:* Univ of Toronto 25 Harbord St Toronto ON M5S 1A1 Can

RAPPORT, MAURICE M, b New York, NY, Sept 23, 19; m 42; c 2. BIOCHEMISTRY. *Educ:* City Col New York, BS, 40; Calif Inst Technol, PhD(org chem), 46. *Prof Exp:* Technician, Rockefeller Inst, 40-41; asst, Off Sci Res & Develop, Calif Inst Technol, 42-45; mem res staff, Cleveland Clin Found, 46-48; res assoc, Col Physicians & Surgeons, Columbia Univ, 48-51; assoc res scientist immunol, Div Labs & Res, State Dept Health, NY, 51-58; prof biochem, Albert Einstein Col Med, 58-61, Am Cancer Soc prof, 62-67; PROF BIOCHEM, COL PHYSICIANS & SURGEONS, COLUMBIA UNIV, 67-; CHIEF DIV NEUROSCI, NY STATE PSYCHIAT INST, 68- *Concurrent Pos:* Fulbright scholar, 1st Superiore Sanita, Italy, 52; head immunol sect, Sloan-Kettering Inst, 54-58. *Mem:* Am Chem Soc; Am Soc Biol Chem; Soc Exp Biol & Med; Am Soc Neurochem; Fedn Am Soc Exp Biol. *Res:* Serotonin; lipid haptens; immunofluorescence of brain proteins; plasmalogens; lipid-protein interactions; immunoneurology. *Mailing Add:* NY State Psychiat Inst 722 W 168th St New York NY 10032

RARD, JOSEPH ANTOINE, b St Louis, Mo, Sept 29, 45; m 71; c 1. PHYSICAL CHEMISTRY. *Educ:* Southern Ill Univ, Edwardsville, BA, 67; Iowa State Univ, PhD(phys chem), 73. *Prof Exp:* Fel, Ames Lab, Dept Energy, 73-76; vis res asst prof geol, Univ Ill, Urbana-Champaign, 77-78; CHEMIST THERMODYN & TRANSP PROPERTIES, LAWRENCE LIVERMORE NAT LAB, UNIV CALIF, 79- *Mem:* Sigma Xi. *Res:* Experimental determination of the thermodynamic and transport properties of aqueous solutions, especially brine salts, rare earth electrolytes and transition metal electrolytes. *Mailing Add:* Lawrence Livermore Lab PO Box 808 Livermore CA 94550

RARICK, GEORGE LAWRENCE, b Stockton, Kans, Aug 30, 11; m 30; c 3. PHYSICAL EDUCATION. *Educ:* Ft Hays Kans State Col, AB & BS, 33, MS, 35; Univ Iowa, PhD, 37. *Prof Exp:* Teacher high sch, Kans, 33-35; dir men's phys educ, Univ Wichita, 37-41; from asst prof to assoc prof educ, Boston Univ, 41-50; prof phys educ, Univ Wis-Madison, 50-68; prof, 68-79, EMER PROF EDUC, UNIV CALIF, BERKELEY, 79- *Concurrent Pos:*

Lectr, Harvard-Boston exten serv, 46-50; vis distinguished prof, Univ Southern Ill, 57-58; consult, US Off Educ & Jospeh P Kennedy, Jr Found; Alliance scholar, Am Alliance Health, Phys Educ, Res & Develop, 79-80, distinguished scholar, 80. *Honors & Awards:* Hon Award, Am Asn Health, Phys Educ & Recreation, 64. *Mem:* AAAS; Am Asn Health, Phys Educ & Recreation (vpres); Brit Soc Study Human Biol; Am Acad Phys Educ & Rehab. *Res:* Development of strength and neuromuscular skills in children; motor performance of mentally retarded children; bone and soft tissue development in Mongolism; factors affecting handwriting legibility. *Mailing Add:* Dept of Phys Educ Univ of Calif Berkeley CA 94720

RARIDON, RICHARD JAY, b Newton, Iowa, Oct 25, 31; m 56; c 2. PHYSICAL CHEMISTRY. *Educ:* Grinnell Col, BA, 53; Vanderbilt Univ, MA, 55, PhD(chem), 59. *Prof Exp:* Assoc prof physics, Memphis State Univ, 58-62; res chemist, 62-71, COMPUT SPECIALIST, OAK RIDGE NAT LAB, 72- *Concurrent Pos:* Res specialist, Coop Sci Educ Ctr, 71-72. *Mem:* Fel AAAS; Sigma Xi; Asn Acad Sci (secy-treas, 71-75, pres, 77). *Res:* Temperature dependence of chemical equilibria; physical properties of solutions; water desalination; environmental education; environmental modeling. *Mailing Add:* 111 Columbia Dr Oak Ridge TN 37830

RARITA, WILLIAM ROLAND, b Bordeaux, France, Mar 21, 07; nat US; m 49; c 1. ELEMENTARY PARTICLE PHYSICS. *Educ:* City Col NY, BS, 27, EE, 29; Columbia Univ, MA, 30, PhD(physics), 37. *Prof Exp:* Tutor, City Col NY, 28-30; tutor & instr physics, Brooklyn Col, 30-41, from asst prof to prof, 41-62; res physicist, Space Sci Lab, 62-63, VIS SCIENTIST, LAWRENCE BERKELEY LAB, UNIV CALIF, 63- *Concurrent Pos:* Sr scientist, Manhattan Proj, 44-46; consult, Res Inst Advan Study, 56-62. *Mem:* Fel Am Phys Soc. *Res:* Photoelectric effect; beta activity; deuteron and triton; high energy nucleon-nucleon interaction; Regge poles. *Mailing Add:* 752 Grizzly Peak Blvd Berkeley CA 94708

RASAIAH, JAYENDRAN C, b Colombo, Ceylon, Apr 1, 34. PHYSICAL CHEMISTRY. *Educ:* Univ Ceylon, BSc, 57; Univ Pittsburgh, PhD(chem), 65. *Prof Exp:* Off Saline Water fel, State Univ NY Stony Brook, 65-68, instr chem, 68-69; from asst prof to assoc prof, 69-78, PROF CHEM, UNIV MAINE, ORONO, 78- *Concurrent Pos:* Sr vis fel, Sci Res Coun, Oxford Univ & London Univ, 75-76; vis fel, Dept Appl Math, Australian Nat Univ, Carberra; vis prof, Dept Chem, Univ New South Wales, Australia, 80. *Mem:* Am Chem Soc; Am Phys Soc; Royal Soc Chem. *Res:* Statistical mechanics of electrolyte solutions; perturbation theories of polar and non-polar fluids; experimental determination of activity coefficients in heavy water; computer simulation studies of fluids and solutions; non linear effects in polar fluids. *Mailing Add:* Dept of Chem Univ of Maine Orono ME 04473

RASBAND, S NEIL, b Ogden, Utah, June 21, 39; m 63; c 3. PHYSICS. *Educ:* Univ Utah, BA, 64, PhD(physics), 69. *Prof Exp:* AEC fel, Princeton Univ, 69-70; res assoc physics, La State Univ, Baton Rouge, 70-71, vis asst prof, 71-72; asst prof, 72-74, ASSOC PROF PHYSICS, BRIGHAM YOUNG UNIV, 74- *Mem:* Am Phys Soc; Am Astron Soc. *Res:* Plasma physics; magnetic confinement fusion. *Mailing Add:* Dept of Physics Brigham Young Univ Provo UT 84601

RASCATI, RALPH JOSEPH, b New Haven, Conn, Dec 29, 47; m 76. GENE EXPRESSION REGULATION. *Educ:* Rensselaer Polytech Inst, BS, 69; Univ Mass, Amherst, PhD(biochem), 75. *Prof Exp:* Investr, Oak Ridge Nat Lab, 75-77, res assoc, 77-79; ASST PROF MICROBIOL, ILL STATE UNIV, 79- *Mem:* Am Soc Microbiol; AAAS; Tissue Cult Asn; Sigma Xi. *Res:* Regulation of gene expression in eukaryotic cells in culture; interactions between endogenous murine retroviruses and chemical carcinogens. *Mailing Add:* Dept Biol Sci Ill State Univ Normal IL 61761

RASCH, ARTHUR ALLYN, b Rochester, NY, May 31, 26; m 49; c 3. PHOTOGRAPHIC CHEMISTRY, VACUUM TECHNOLOGY. *Educ:* Oberlin Col, BA, 47. *Prof Exp:* Res chemist, Res Labs, 47-59, RES ASSOC, EASTMAN KODAK CO, 59- *Mem:* Am Chem Soc; Soc Photog Sci & Eng; Electrochem Soc; Am Vacuum Soc. *Res:* Chemistry of photographic systems and processing methods; characterization of thin films prepared by deposition in vacuum; vacuum systems design. *Mailing Add:* Res Labs Eastman Kodak Co Rochester NY 14650

RASCH, CARL HENRY, chemistry, deceased

RASCH, ELLEN M, b Chicago Heights, Ill, Jan 31, 27; m 50; c 1. CELL BIOLOGY, CYTOCHEMISTRY. *Educ:* Univ Chicago, PhB, 45, BS, 47, MS, 48, PhD(bot), 50. *Prof Exp:* Asst histologist, Am Meat Inst Found, Chicago, Ill, 50-51; USPHS fel zool, Univ Chicago, 51-53, from res asst to res assoc, 53-59; instr civil defense, Milwaukee Civil Defense Dept, 60-62; res assoc prof biol, 62-65, assoc prof, 65-68, prof biol, Marquette Univ, 68-78; PROF BIOPHYS, QUILLEN-DISHNER COL MED, EAST TENN STATE UNIV, 78- *Concurrent Pos:* Nat Inst Gen Med Sci Res Career Develop Award, 67-72. *Mem:* Fel AAAS; Am Soc Zool; Royal Micros Soc; Am Soc Cell Biol; Histochem Soc (secy, 75-79). *Res:* Quantitative cytophotometry; nucleoprotein synthesis in dipteran polytene chromosomes; evolutionary biology of unisexual fish. *Mailing Add:* Dept Biophys East Tenn State Univ Johnson City TN 37601

RASCH, ROBERT, b Chicago, Ill, Nov 19, 26; m 50, c 1. PHYSIOLOGY. *Educ:* Univ Chicago, PhB, 46, PhD(physiol), 59; Northwestern Univ, MD, 51. *Prof Exp:* Instr, 59-61, from asst prof to assoc prof physiol, Med Col Wis, 61-77; PROF & CHMN PHYSIOL, QUILLEN-DISHNER COL MED, 77- *Mem:* Am Soc Cell Biol; NY Acad Sci. *Res:* Chromosome structure and nucleocytoplasmic interaction; compensatory physiological mechanisms, chromosome structure and nucleocytoplasmic interaction. *Mailing Add:* Dept Physiol Quillen-Dishner Med Col Box 19780A Johnson City TN 39614

RASCHE, JOHN FREDERICK, b Bonne Terre, Mo, Apr 14, 36; m 58; c 3. CHEMICAL ENGINEERING. *Educ:* Univ Mo-Rolla, BS, 58. *Prof Exp:* Assoc develop chem engr, 58-61, develop engr, 61-65, sr develop engr, 65-75, group leader process res & develop, 75-79, PROCESS ENGR MGR, A E STALEY MFG CO, 79- *Mem:* Am Inst Chem Engrs. *Res:* Catalysis of carbohydrates using soluble and immobilized enzymes; purification and separation processes applied to corn and soybean processing. *Mailing Add:* A E Staley Mfg Co 22nd & Eldorado Sts Decatur IL 62521

RASCOE, BAILEY, JR, geology, see previous edition

RASE, DANIEL E(DWARD), b Youngstown, Ohio, June 23, 24; m 49; c 2. PHASE EQUILIBRIA, MICROSCOPY. *Educ:* Alfred Univ, BS, 50, MS, 51; Pa State Univ, PhD(ceramics), 55. *Prof Exp:* From asst prof to assoc prof res, 54-64, ASSOC PROF CERAMIC SCI, STATE UNIV NY COL CERAMICS, ALFRED UNIV, 64- *Concurrent Pos:* Vpres, Alfred Atlas Gravel & Sand Corp, 75- *Mem:* AAAS; Am Ceramic Soc; Am Soc Eng Educ; Sigma Xi. *Res:* Phase equilibria of oxide systems, especially titanates; mineral synthesis; dielectrics; teaching methods. *Mailing Add:* State Univ NY Col of Ceramics Alfred Univ Alfred NY 14802

RASE, HOWARD F, b Buffalo, NY, Oct 18, 21; m 54; c 2. CHEMICAL ENGINEERING. *Educ:* Univ Tex, BS, 42; Univ Wis, MS, 50, PhD(chem eng), 52. *Prof Exp:* Chem engr res & develop, Dow Chem Co, 42-44; process engr, Eastern State Petrol Co, 44; process engr & proj engr, Foster Wheeler Corp, 44-49; from asst prof to prof, 52-74, chmn dept, 63-68, W A CUNNINGHAM PROF CHEM ENG, UNIV TEX, AUSTIN, 74- *Concurrent Pos:* Fulbright lectr, Tech Univ Denmark, 57; consult catalysis & reactor design. *Mem:* Am Chem Soc; fel Am Inst Chem Engrs. *Res:* Applied kinetics and reactor design; homogeneous and heterogeneous catalysis; catalyst development; process design techniques. *Mailing Add:* Dept of Chem Eng Univ of Tex Austin TX 78712

RASEKH, JAMSHID G, b Tehran, Iran, Oct 2, 35; US citizen. FOOD SCIENCE. *Educ:* Univ Tehran, MSE, 60; Univ Md, MS, 64, PhD(food sci), 68. *Prof Exp:* Res asst food sci, Univ Md, 61-68; proj leader & res food technologist food sci, Dept Interior, 67-71; RES FOOD TECHNOLOGIST FOOD SCI & BIOCHEM, NAT OCEANIC ATMOSPHERIC ADMIN, DEPT COM, COLLEGE PARK, MD, 71-, MEM STAFF, NAT MARINE FISHERIES SERV, 77- *Mem:* Sigma Xi; Inst Food Technologists; Am Asn Cereal Chemists; Asn Off Anal Chemists. *Res:* Protein research for human food; utilization of the under-utilized species of fish to make a better source of human food such as meat. *Mailing Add:* 11102 Conti Pl Silver Spring MD 20902

RASEMAN, CHAD J(OSEPH), b Detroit, Mich, Aug 29, 18; m 45; c 5. CHEMICAL & NUCLEAR ENGINEERING. *Educ:* Wayne State Univ, BS, 41; Univ Mich, MS, 44; Cornell Univ, PhD(chem eng), 51. *Hon Degrees:* EngD, Wayne State Univ, 58. *Prof Exp:* Chief chem engr, R P Scherer Corp, 41-44 & Boyle-Midway, Inc, 46-47; head, Oak Ridge Chem Eng Div, Kellex Corp, 47-48; fel, Brookhaven Nat Lab, 48-51, group leader, Nuclear Eng Dept, 51-58, asst div head, 58-65, tech asst to dept chmn, Dept Appl Sci, 65-70, group leader rotating fluidized bed reactor, Space Nuclear Propulsion Proj, 70-73; VPRES, SOLAR SUNSTILL, INC, 67- *Concurrent Pos:* Asst, Cornell Univ, 48-49; chief eval sect, Div Reactor Develop, US AEC, 60-62; dir, Nat Agr Plastics Asn, 72-76. *Mem:* AAAS; Am Chem Soc; fel Am Inst Chem; Am Nuclear Soc; Int Solar Energy Soc. *Res:* Design, evaluation and testing of the fluidized bed concept for space nuclear propulsion and unique chemical reactions; co-inventor of solar distillation units and special coatings that control condensation and light transmission. *Mailing Add:* Solar Sunstill Inc Setauket NY 11785

RASERA, ROBERT LOUIS, b New York, NY, July 25, 39; m 61; c 2. SOLID STATE PHYSICS, NUCLEAR PHYSICS. *Educ:* Wheaton Col, BS, 60; Purdue Univ, PhD(physics), 65. *Prof Exp:* Res assoc, Purdue Univ, 65; guest prof, Inst Radiation & Nuclear Physics, Univ Bonn, 65-66; asst prof, Univ Pa, 66-71; assoc prof, 71-81, PROF PHYSICS, UNIV MD, BALTIMORE COUNTY, 81- *Mem:* Am Phys Soc; Am Asn Physics Teachers; Sigma Xi. *Res:* Perturbed angular correlations of nuclear radiations; hyperfine fields in solids. *Mailing Add:* Dept of Physics Univ of Md Baltimore County Baltimore MD 21228

RASEY, JANET SUE, b Fremont, Mich, June 13, 42. CANCER, RADIOBIOLOGY. *Educ:* Univ Mich, BS, 64; Ore State Univ, MS, 65; Univ Ore, PhD(biol), 70. *Prof Exp:* NIH fel, Cell & Radiation Biol Lab, Allegheny Gen Hosp, Pittsburgh, 70-72; ASSOC PROF TUMOR RADIATION & CELL BIOL, DEPT RADIATION ONCOL, MED SCH, UNIV WASH, 72- *Mem:* Cell Kinetics Soc; Radiation Res Soc; Am Soc Therapeut Radiologists. *Res:* Tumor radiation response cell cycle kinetics; mechanisms of variations in tumor repopulation rate following radiation or drug treatment; neutron radiation biology. *Mailing Add:* Div Radiation Oncol Univ of Wash Med Sch Seattle WA 98195

RASH, JAY JUSTEN, b Iowa Falls, Iowa, Dec 26, 41; m 61; c 3. METABOLISM. *Educ:* Northwest Mo State Univ, BS, 66; Univ Mo-Columbia, MS, 67, PhD(anal biochem), 71. *Prof Exp:* Res scientist metab, Cent Res Labs, 72-81, DIR REGULATORY AFFAIRS, PFIZER, INC, 81- *Mem:* Am Chem Soc; Sigma Xi. *Res:* Development of analytical methods in tissues and biological fluids for drugs, metabolites and important biological compounds; the determination of the metabolic pathways of xenobiotics in biological systems. *Mailing Add:* Pfizer Inc 1107 S Hwy 291 Lee's Summit MO 64063

RASH, JOHN EDWARD, b Dallas, Tex, Feb 16, 43; m 65. NEUROBIOLOGY. *Educ:* Univ Tex, BA, 65, MA, 67, PhD(zool), 69. *Prof Exp:* Teaching asst biol, Univ Tex, 66-67; fel surg & cancer res, Sch Med, Johns Hopkins Univ, 69-70; asst investr, Dept Embryol, Carnegie Inst Wash, 70-72; res assoc, Univ Colo, 72-74; asst prof, 74-77, assoc prof pharmacol &

exp therapeut, Sch Med, Univ Md, 77-79; ASSOC PROF ANAT, COLO STATE UNIV, 79- *Concurrent Pos:* Muscular Dystrophy Asn grant-in-aid, 75; prin investr, NIH grants; instr, Marine Biol Lab, Woods Hole, Mass. *Mem:* AAAS; Am Soc Cell Biol; Soc Neurosci. *Res:* Myogenesis; membrane differentiation; electron microscopy; freeze-fracture of mammalian neuromuscular junctions. *Mailing Add:* Dept Anatomy Colo State Univ Ft Collins CO 80521

RASHEED, KHALID, b Karnal, India, Aug 2, 35; m 68; c 1. CHEMISTRY. *Educ:* Forman Christian Col, Pakistan, BS, 55; Univ Karachi, Pakistan, MS, 57; Univ Heidelberg, PhD(org chem), 64. *Prof Exp:* Petrol res grant & fel, Dept Chem, Univ Mich, Ann Arbor, 64-65; sr res off org chem, Cent Res Labs, Pakistan Coun Sci & Indust Res, 65-68; NIH res assoc, Dept Chem, Mich State Univ, 68-70; sr res chemist, 70-75, SECT HEAD ORG CHEM, RES & DEVELOP CTR, ANSUL CO, 75- *Concurrent Pos:* Sr lectr, Dept Chem, Univ Karachi, Pakistan, 67-68. *Mem:* Am Chem Soc. *Res:* Organic synthesis and reaction mechanisms; organosulfur chemistry; synthesis of biologically active heterocyclic compounds and correlation of biological activity with molecular structure. *Mailing Add:* Dept Chem Res Res & Develop Ctr Ansul Co PO Drawer 1165 Weslaco TX 78596

RASHKIN, JAY ARTHUR, b New York, NY, Sept 21, 33; div; c 2. PHYSICAL CHEMISTRY. *Educ:* NY Univ, BA, 55; Princeton Univ, MA, 57, PhD(phys chem), 61. *Prof Exp:* Res chemist, E I du Pont de Nemours & Co, 59-62; mem tech staff, Space Tech Labs, 62-64; res specialist, Monsanto Co, 64-66; sr res chemist, Cities Serv Oil Co, 66-76; RES ASSOC, HALCON CATALYST INDUST, 77- *Mem:* Am Chem Soc; NY Acad Sci; fel Am Inst Chem; Catalysis Soc; Am Phys Soc. *Res:* Heterogeneous catalysis; differential thermal analysis and x-ray structure studies of catalysts; catalytic oxidation of hydrocarbons; catalytic processes in petroleum refining and petrochemicals; surface chemistry and physics; electron spectroscopy for chemical analysis; surface analysis; chemisorption; temperature programmed desorption. *Mailing Add:* Halcon Catalyst Indust 59 Industrial Ave Little Ferry NJ 07643

RASHKIND, WILLIAM JACOBSON, b Paterson, NJ, Feb 12, 22; m 49; c 3. PEDIATRICS. *Educ:* Univ Louisville, AB & MD, 46. *Prof Exp:* Asst prof physiol, 50-53, asst prof pediat, 57-65, assoc prof, 65-71, PROF PEDIAT, SCH MED, UNIV PA, 71- *Concurrent Pos:* Assoc cardiologist & dir cardiovasc labs, Children's Hosp, Philadelphia. *Mem:* Am Physiol Soc; Am Acad Pediat. *Res:* Pediatric cardiology; congenital heart disease; hemodynamics. *Mailing Add:* Children's Hosp of Philadelphia 34th St & Civic Ctr Blvd Philadelphia PA 19104

RASILEWICZ, CASIMIR E, bacteriology, see previous edition

RASK, NORMAN, b Duanesburg, NY, June 26, 33; m 55; c 4. AGRICULTURAL ECONOMICS. *Educ:* Cornell Univ, BS, 55, MS, 60; Univ Wis, PhD(agr econ), 64. *Prof Exp:* Exten assoc agr econ, Cornell Univ, 59-60; asst prof, Univ Wis, 64-65; from asst prof to assoc prof, 65-73, PROF AGR ECON, OHIO STATE UNIV, 73- *Concurrent Pos:* Consult, World Bank, Food & Agr Orgn & US Agency Int Develop. *Res:* Energy policy; energy from biomass; economics of farm size, and world food population problems. *Mailing Add:* 2120 Fyffe Rd Columbus OH 43210

RASKA, KAREL FRANTISEK, JR, b Prague, Czech, May 26, 39; US citizen; m 60; c 2. PATHOLOGY, MICROBIOLOGY. *Educ:* Charles Univ, MD, 62; Czech Acad Sci, PhD(biochem), 65. *Prof Exp:* Commonwealth Fund res fel pharmacol, Sch Med, Yale Univ, 65-66; res assoc, Inst Microbiol, Rutgers Univ, New Brunswick, 66-67; scientist, Inst Org Chem & Biochem, Czech Acad Sci, 67-68; from asst prof to assoc prof microbiol, 71-78, assoc prof path, 73-76, PROF PATH, COL MED & DENT NJ, RUTGERS MED SCH, 76-, PROF MICROBIOL, 78- *Concurrent Pos:* Pathologist, Middlesex Gen Hosp, 77- *Honors & Awards:* Prize, Czech Acad Sci, 65. *Mem:* AAAS; Am Soc Microbiol; Am Asn Pathologists; Am Asn Immunologists; Am Asn Cancer Res. *Res:* Molecular biology of animal viruses; cell transformation by oncogenic viruses; cancer chemotherapy; immunopathology. *Mailing Add:* Dept of Microbiol Rutgers Med Sch Piscataway NJ 08854

RASKAS, HESCHEL JOSHUA, b St Louis, Mo, June 11, 41; m 62; c 4. BIOCHEMISTRY. *Educ:* Mass Inst Technol, BS, 62; Harvard Univ, PhD(biochem, molecular biol), 67. *Prof Exp:* Res fel, Inst Molecular Virol, 67-69, asst prof molecular virol & path, Sch Med, Inst Molecular Virol & Dept Path, St Louis Univ, 69-73; assoc prof, 73-77, dir, Ctr Basic Cancer Res, 77-80, PROF PATH & MICROBIOL, SCH MED, WASH UNIV, 77- *Concurrent Pos:* Assoc ed virol, 75-78. *Mem:* AAAS; Am Soc Microbiol. *Res:* Regulation of oncogenic viral gene expression in eukaryotic cells. *Mailing Add:* Dept of Path Wash Univ Sch of Med St Louis MO 63110

RASKI, DEWEY JOHN, b Kenilworth, Utah, Dec 12, 17; m 43; c 3. NEMATOLOGY. *Educ:* Univ Calif, BS, 41, PhD(nematol), 48. *Prof Exp:* Instr & jr nematologist, 48-50, from lectr & asst nematologist to lectr & assoc nematologist, 50-60, PROF NEMATOL & NEMATOLOGIST, UNIV CALIF, DAVIS, 60- *Mem:* Am Phytopath Soc; Am Soc Nematol; Soc Europ Nematol. *Res:* Plant parasitic nematodes; virus-nematode vector relationships; biology, control and systematics. *Mailing Add:* Dept of Nematol Univ of Calif Davis CA 95616

RASKIN, BETTY LOU, b Baltimore, Md, Apr 9, 24. PLASTICS CHEMISTRY, PSYCHOLOGY. *Educ:* Goucher Col, AB, 44; Johns Hopkins Univ, MA, 47, PhD, 68. *Prof Exp:* Lab asst Manhattan Proj, Johns Hopkins Univ, 44-45, res chemist, Inst Coop Res, 45-50, res staff asst, 51-54, res assoc & head plastics res & develop, Radiation Lab, 54-64; asst prof psychol, 67-69, ASSOC PROF PSYCHOL, TOWSON STATE COL, 69-; CONSULT FOAMED PLASTICS, 64- *Mem:* Fel AAAS; fel Am Inst Chemists; Am Psychol Asn; Fine Particle Soc. *Res:* Foamed plastic; reinforced plastics; foamed plastic particles and smokes; consumer psychology. *Mailing Add:* Dept of Psychol Towson State Col Baltimore MD 21204

RASKIN, HOWARD F, b Baltimore, Md, Apr 28, 26; m 57; c 2. MEDICINE. *Educ:* Johns Hopkins Univ, AB, 48; Univ Md, MD, 49. *Prof Exp:* USPHS fel, Sch Med, Univ Chicago, 54-56, asst prof med, 56-63; ASSOC PROF MED, SCH MED, UNIV MD, BALTIMORE CITY, 63- *Concurrent Pos:* Chief, Div Gastroenterol, Md Gen Hosp, 81- *Mem:* Am Soc Cytol; Am Gastroenterol Asn; Am Fedn Clin Res. *Res:* Gastroenterology; cancer diagnosis by exfoliative cytology; primary investigation of barium-burger gastric motility test; four-day gall bladder dye retention study. *Mailing Add:* Chief Div Gastroenterol Md Gen Hosp 827 Linden Ave Baltimore MD 21201

RASKIN, JOAN, b Baltimore, Md, Aug 11, 30. MEDICINE, DERMATOLOGY. *Educ:* Goucher Col, BA, 51; Univ Md, MD, 55; Am Bd Dermat, dipl, 61. *Prof Exp:* Intern, Hosp, Univ Md, 55-56, asst resident med, 56-57, resident dermat, 57-58; assoc med, Sch Med, 60-63, lectr, Sch Phys Ther, 61-66, asst prof, Sch Med, 63-66, ASSOC PROF MED, DIV DERMAT, SCH MED, UNIV MD, BALTIMORE CITY, 66- *Concurrent Pos:* Fel, Hosp, Univ Md, 58-59; fel, Hosps, Univ Minn, 59-60; NIH grants, 61-65; Bressler Fund grant, 62-66; mem courtesy staff, South Baltimore Gen Hosp, 61-71, sr staff, 72-, head, Div Dermat, 80-; mem courtesy staff, Sinai Hosp, 61-64, active staff, 64-; mem staff, Mercy Hosp, 74-; dermatologist, Md Sch for Blind, 74-; active staff, Union Mem Hosp, 75- *Mem:* Am Acad Dermat; AMA; Am Med Women's Asn; Am Soc Microbiol; Soc Invest Dermat. *Res:* Dermatologic areas of autoimmune diseases and virology. *Mailing Add:* 3737 Clarks Lane Baltimore MD 21215

RASKIN, NEIL HUGH, b New York, NY, Jan 16, 35. NEUROLOGY, NEUROCHEMISTRY. *Educ:* Dartmouth Col, AB, 56; Harvard Med Sch, MD, 59. *Prof Exp:* Resident neurol, Columbia Univ Col Physicians & Surgeons, 61-64, res fel cerebral metab, 64-65; chief of serv neurol, US Naval Hosp, Philadelphia, 65-66; res assoc cerebral metab, NIH, 66-68; from asst prof to assoc prof, 68-79, PROF NEUROL & VCHMN DEPT, UNIV CALIF, SAN FRANCISCO, 79- *Concurrent Pos:* NIH res career develop awardee, 68-73; res grant, Nat Inst for Alcohol Abuse & Alcoholism, 68-73; mem, Res Group on Migraine & Headache, World Fedn of Neurol, 76-; dir neurol outpatient & consult serv, Sch Med, Univ Calif, San Francisco, 77- *Mem:* Am Neurol Asn; Am Soc Neurochem; Asn Res Nerv & Ment Dis; Int Asn Study Pain; Am Acad Neurol. *Res:* Biochemical effects of alcohol upon the nervous system; mechanisms of migraine; metabolic neurologic disorders. *Mailing Add:* Dept of Neurol Univ Calif Sch Med San Francisco CA 94143

RASKOVA, JANA D, b Prague, Czech, Oct 18, 40; US citizen; m 60; c 2. PATHOLOGY. *Educ:* Charles Univ, Prague, MD, 63. *Prof Exp:* Res fel pharmacol, Sch Med, Yale Univ, 65-66; vis investr immunol, Inst Microbiol, Rutgers Univ, 66-67; fel genetics, Inst Exp Biol & Genetics, Czech Acad Sci, Prague, 67-68; res assoc immunol, Inst Microbiol, Rutgers Univ, 69-70, asst prof path, 70-78, ASSOC PROF PATH, COL MED & DENT NJ, RUTGERS MED SCH, 78- *Mem:* AAAS; Am Asn Pathologists; Am Soc Cell Biol; Int Acad Path; Am Soc Clin Invest. *Res:* Immunopathology and pathology of chronic renal failure. *Mailing Add:* Dept of Path Col Med & Dent NJ Rutgers Med Sch Piscataway NJ 08854

RASMUSEN, BENJAMIN ARTHUR, b Somonauk, Ill, Nov 29, 26; m 57; c 3. ANIMAL GENETICS. *Educ:* Univ Ill, BS, 49; Cornell Univ, MS, 51, DVM, 55; Univ Calif, Davis, PhD(genetics), 58. *Prof Exp:* Asst animal genetics, Dept Poultry Husb, Cornell Univ, 49-54; asst specialist, Univ Calif, Davis, 55-58; assoc prof, 58-65, PROF ANIMAL GENETICS, UNIV ILL, URBANA, 65- *Concurrent Pos:* Sabbatical, Animal Breeding Res Orgn, Edinburgh, Scotland, 65-66 & Inst Animal Physiol, Cambridge, Eng, 72-73. *Mem:* AAAS; Int Soc Animal Blood Group Res (pres, 76-84); Am Genetic Asn; Am Soc Human Genetics; Am Soc Animal Sci. *Res:* Blood groups in pigs and sheep. *Mailing Add:* 110 Animal Genetics Lab Univ Ill 1301 W Lorado Taft Dr Urbana IL 61801

RASMUSSEN, AARON FREDERICK, JR, b St Anthony, Idaho, May 27, 15; m 41; c 3. MEDICAL MICROBIOLOGY, IMMUNOLOGY. *Educ:* Univ Idaho, BS, 37; Univ Wis, MS, 40, PhD(med bact), 41, MD, 44; Am Bd Path, dipl; Am Bd Med Microbiol, dipl. *Prof Exp:* From asst to instr med bact, Univ Wis, 37-43; chief chemother res sect, Dept Virus & Rickettsial Dis, US Army Med Ctr, 47-48; assoc prof med microbiol & prev med, Med Sch, Univ Wis, 48-51, prof, 51-52; prof infectious dis & chief div virol, Med Ctr, 52-62, chmn dept med microbiol & immunol, 62-70, PROF MED MICROBIOL & IMMUNOL, SCH MED, UNIV CALIF, LOS ANGELES, 62-, ASSOC DEAN SCH MED, 69- *Mem:* Am Soc Microbiol; Am Soc Clin Invest; Soc Exp Biol & Med; AMA; Am Asn Immunol. *Res:* Viruses; nonspecific resistance to infection. *Mailing Add:* Off of Dean Univ of Calif Sch of Med Los Angeles CA 90024

RASMUSSEN, ARLETTE IRENE, b Thief River Falls, Minn. NUTRITION. *Educ:* Northwestern Univ, Ba, 56; Univ Wis, MS, 58, PhD(human nutrit & biochem), 61. *Prof Exp:* Res asst, Univ Wis, 56-61; asst prof, 61-65, ASSOC PROF NUTRIT, UNIV DEL, 65- *Concurrent Pos:* Sr fel, Dept Med, Hematol Div, Sch Med, Univ Wash, 70-71; co-chair, Northeast Res Prog, Steering Comt Nutrit & Food Safety, US Dept Agr & State Agr Exp Sta, 77-82; exec bd mem, Nat Nutrit Consortium 77-80; actg chair, Dept Food Sci & Human Nutrit, Univ Del, 78-79; nutritionist, Coop State Res Serv, US Dept Agr, 79-80. *Mem:* Am Inst Nutrit; Am Dietetic Asn; Soc Nutrit Educ; Sigma Xi; AAAS. *Res:* Protein evaluation; amino acid utilization; vitamin B-6; mineral nutrition; human nutrition and metabolism; nutrient interactions. *Mailing Add:* Dept Food Sci & Human Nutrit Col Humam Resources Univ Del Newark DE 19711

RASMUSSEN, CHRIS ROYCE, b Trenton, Nebr, Feb 19, 31; m 52; c 4. MEDICINAL CHEMISTRY. *Educ:* Ft Hays Kans State Col, AB, 54; Univ Kans, PhD(org & pharmaceut chem), 62. *Prof Exp:* Res assoc, Ind Univ, 62-63; res scientist, 64-70, group leader, 70-76, RES FEL, McNEIL LABS, INC, 76- *Mem:* Am Chem Soc. *Res:* Hypoglycemic agents; central nervous system drugs, specifically muscle relaxants, anticonvulsants, anti-anxiety agents, cardiovascular-anti-anginal, antihypertensive and antiarrhythmic drugs; gastro-intestinal-antisecretory agents; anti-irritable bowel. *Mailing Add:* McNeil Pharmaceut Welsh & McKean Rds Spring House PA 19477

RASMUSSEN, DAVID IRVIN, b Ogden, Utah, Dec 11, 34; m 54; c 4. EVOLUTIONARY BIOLOGY, GENETICS. *Educ:* Univ Utah, BS, 56, MS, 58; Univ Mich, PhD(zool), 62. *Prof Exp:* NIH fel genetics, Univ Calif, Berkeley, 62-63; from asst prof to assoc prof zool, 63-75, PROF ZOOL, ARIZ STATE UNIV, 75- *Concurrent Pos:* Prin investr fac res grant, Ariz State Univ, 63-64, 66-67 & 75-76 & NIH res grants, 64-72. *Mem:* Am Soc Mammal; Soc Study Evolution; Am Soc Nat. *Res:* Genetic polymorphisms in natural populations of small mammals and ants. *Mailing Add:* Dept of Zool Ariz State Univ Tempe AZ 85281

RASMUSSEN, DON HENRY, b Wild Rose, Wis, Sept 20, 44; m 66; c 3. CHEMICAL METALLURGY, MATERIALS SCIENCE. *Educ:* Univ Wis-Madison, BA, 67, MS, 71, PhD(mat sci), 74. *Prof Exp:* Res assoc, Cryobiol Res Inst of Am Found, Madison, 67-75; res assoc metall, Dept Metals & Minerals Eng, Univ Wis-Madison, 75-78; asst prof, 78-80, PROF CHEM ENG, CLARKSON COL TECHNOL, 80- *Mem:* Am Chem Soc; Am Inst Mining, Metall & Petrol Engrs; Am Inst Chem Engrs; Sigma Xi. *Res:* Surface properties of liquid metals; phase transformations; nucleation in the liquid to solid transformation; thermodynamics; properties of metastable states. *Mailing Add:* Dept of Chem Eng Clarkson Col of Technol Potsdam NY 13676

RASMUSSEN, GORDON KEITH, b Minn, Aug 6, 29; m 74; c 1. PLANT PHYSIOLOGY. *Educ:* Moorhead State Teachers Col, BS, 50; Miami Univ, MS, 52; Purdue Univ, PhD(plant physiol), 56. *Prof Exp:* PLANT PHYSIOLOGIST, SCI & EDUC ADMIN-AGR RES, USDA, 55-, RES LEADER, 77- *Mem:* Am Soc Hort Sci; Am Soc Plant Physiol. *Res:* Plant chemistry; mineral nutrition of citrus; respiration and enzyme action in green plants. *Mailing Add:* Sci & Educ Admin-Agr Res USDA 2120 Camden Rd Orlando FL 32803

RASMUSSEN, HARRY PAUL, b Tremonton, Utah, July 18, 39; m 58; c 4. PLANT PHYSIOLOGY, PLANT NUTRITION. *Educ:* Utah State Univ, BS, 61; Mich State Univ, MS, 62, PhD(hort), 65. *Prof Exp:* Asst prof plant physiol, Conn Agr Exp Sta, 65-66; from asst prof to assoc prof hort, Mich State Univ, 66-73, prof, 73-80; CHMN DEPT HORT & LANDSCAPE ARCHIT, WASH STATE UNIV, 80- *Honors & Awards:* Alex Laurie Award, 75. *Mem:* Am Soc Hort Sci. *Res:* Leaf and fruit abscission; botanical histochemistry; electron microprobe x-ray analysis and scanning electron microscopy of plant tissues and cells. *Mailing Add:* Dept Hort & Landscape Archit Wash State Univ Pullman WA 99163

RASMUSSEN, HOWARD, b Harrisburg, Pa, Mar 1, 25; m 50; c 4. MEDICINE, CELL BIOLOGY. *Educ:* Gettysburg Col, AB, 48; Rockefeller Inst, PhD, 59; Gettysburg Col, DSc, 66. *Hon Degrees:* MA, Univ Pa, 71. *Prof Exp:* Asst prof physiol, Rockefeller Inst & assoc physician, Hosp, 59-61; assoc prof biochem, Univ Wis, 61-64, prof, 64-65; chmn dept biochem, Med Sch, Univ Pa, 65-71, prof pediat, biochem & biophys, 65-77; PROF MED & CELL BIOL, SCH MED, YALE UNIV, 77- *Concurrent Pos:* NSF sr fel, Cambridge Univ, 71-72; mem endocrine study sect, NIH, 63-65, mem cardiovasc study sect, 73-74; mem fel panel, NSF, 69; sr physician, Children's Hosp Philadelphia, 70-77; trustee, Gettysburg Col, 71-77; mem, Gen Med B Study Sect, 74-77; assoc endocrinologist, Children's Hosp, 75-; consult metab bone dis, Hosp Lariboisiere, Paris. *Honors & Awards:* Andre Lichwitz Prize, France, 71. *Mem:* AAAS; Endocrine Soc; Soc Gen Physiol; Am Soc Cell Biol; Am Soc Biol Chem. *Res:* Biochemistry and physiology of ion transport and of peptide and steroid hormone action; cellular basis of oxygen-2 toxicity. *Mailing Add:* Dept of Internal Med 333 Cedar St New Haven CT 06510

RASMUSSEN, JAMES L, b Stevens Point, Wis, May 9, 36; m 59; c 2. METEOROLOGY. *Educ:* St Olaf Col, BA, 58; Univ Utah, BS, 59; Colo State Univ, MS, 63, PhD(atmospheric sci), 68. *Prof Exp:* From instr to assoc prof atmospheric sci, Colo State Univ, 63-72; meteorol sci adv, Global Atmospheric Res Prog, Atlantic Trop Exp, Oceanic & Atmospheric Admin, 72-74, dir, US Gate Proj Off, 74-76; MGR, GLOBAL WEATHER EXP, WORLD METEOROL ORGN, GENEVA, SWITZ, 76- *Honors & Awards:* Dept Commerce Gold Medal, 75. *Mem:* AAAS; Am Meteorol Soc; Am Water Resources Asn; Am Geophys Union. *Res:* Atmospheric water resources; hydrometeorology; dynamics of weather systems; hydrology. *Mailing Add:* 68 Chemiben Ami Argand Versoix 1290 Switzerland

RASMUSSEN, JEWELL J, b Palo Alto, Calif, Jan 30, 40. CERAMICS. *Educ:* Univ Utah, BS, 64; Mass Inst Technol, PhD(ceramics), 69. *Prof Exp:* Res asst ceramics, Mass Inst Technol, 65-68; sr res scientist, Pac Northwest Lab, Battelle Mem Inst, 68-76; MGR APPL RES, MONT ENERGY & MONT HOUSING & DEVELOP RES & DEVELOP INST, 76- *Concurrent Pos:* Tech consult, Manlabs, Inc, 65-67; adj assoc prof, Mont Col Mineral Sci & Technol, 77- *Mem:* Am Ceramic Soc. *Res:* Growth; properties of molten oxides; materials development and characterization; fuel cell power systems; materials development for industrial products. *Mailing Add:* Mont Energy Res & Develop Inst PO Box 3809 Butte MT 59701

RASMUSSEN, JOHN OSCAR, JR, b St Petersburg, Fla, Aug 8, 26; m 50; c 4. NUCLEAR CHEMISTRY. *Educ:* Calif Inst Technol, BS, 48; Univ Calif, Berkeley, PhD(chem), 52. *Hon Degrees:* AM, Yale Univ, 69. *Prof Exp:* From instr to prof chem, Univ Calif, Berkeley, 52-69; prof chem, Yale Univ, 69-73; PROF CHEM, UNIV CALIF, BERKELEY, 73- *Concurrent Pos:* Vis prof, Nobel Inst Physics, Stockholm, Sweden, 53; NSF sr fel, Niels Bohr Inst, Copenhagen, Denmark, 61-62; vis prof, Fadan Univ, Shanghai, 79. *Honors & Awards:* E O Lawrence Award, 67; Am Chem Soc Award for Nuclear Applns in Chem, 76. *Mem:* Am Chem Soc; fel Am Phys Soc; fel AAAS; Fedn Am Scientists. *Res:* Nuclear structure theory and experiment; heavy ion nuclear reactions, especially pion production. *Mailing Add:* Bldg 70A Lawrence Berkeley Lab Berkeley CA 94720

RASMUSSEN, LOIS E LITTLE, b Summit, NJ, Nov 11, 38; m 61; c 2. ANIMAL PHEROMONE, NEUROCHEMISTRY. *Educ:* Stanford Univ, BA, 60; Washington Univ, PhD(neurochem), 64. *Prof Exp:* NIH fel, Dept Psychiatry, Med Sch, Washington Univ, 61-64; NIH staff fel, Sect Chem Neuropath, Nat Inst Neurol Dis & Blindness, NIH, 64-66; proj biochemist, Dow Corning Corp, 66-68; adj scientist, Dept Zool, Washington State Univ, 70-77; SR SCIENTIST, ORE GRAD CTR, 77- *Concurrent Pos:* Lectr, Saginaw Valley Col, 60-69; instr, invertebrate & vertebrate embryol & fresh water ecol, Saginaw Valley Col, 68-69; res assoc & consult, Dept Zool, Wash State Univ, 75-77. *Mem:* Am Fisheries Soc; Am Soc Mammologists; AAAS; Am Soc Neurochem; Soc Protection Old Fishes. *Res:* Elephant pheromone study; comparative study of temporal gland secretions in Asian and African elephants; role of urea in lactate dehydrogenase in nervous system associated fluids of primitive fishers. *Mailing Add:* Ore Grad Ctr 19600 Walker Rd Beaverton OR 97006

RASMUSSEN, LOWELL W, b Redmond, Utah, Mar 21, 10; m 38; c 2. AGRONOMY. *Educ:* Utah State Univ, BS, 40, MS, 41; Iowa State Univ, PhD(plant physiol), 47. *Prof Exp:* Field supvr, Exp Sta, Utah State Col, 37-41; asst county supvr, Farm Security Admin, 41; jr agronomist, Soil Conserv Serv, USDA, 41-42; county agr agent, Exten Serv, Univ Utah, 42-45; from asst prof & asst agronomist to prof & agronomist, 47-56, from asst dir res to assoc dir res, 56-75, EMER ASSOC DIR RES, COL AGR, WASH STATE UNIV, 75- *Concurrent Pos:* Ford Found adv, Ministry Agr, Saudi Arabia, 65-67. *Mem:* AAAS; Weed Sci Soc Am; Am Soc Plant Physiol. *Res:* Weed control; action of growth regulator herbicides; techniques in weed research; research administration. *Mailing Add:* SE 910 Glen Echo Rd Pullman WA 99163

RASMUSSEN, MAURICE L, b Coon Rapids, Iowa, June 2, 35; m 61; c 2. AERONAUTICS, ASTRONAUTICS. *Educ:* Ore State Univ, BS, 57, MS, 59; Stanford Univ, PhD(aeronaut, astronaut), 64. *Prof Exp:* Res engr, Ames Res Ctr, NASA, 58-59; res asst aeronaut & astronaut, Stanford Univ, 59-64, lectr & res assoc, gas dynamics, 64-65, actg asst prof, 64-67; assoc prof, 67-70, PROF GAS DYNAMICS, UNIV OKLA, 70- *Mem:* Am Inst Aeronaut & Astronaut; Am Phys Soc; Am Soc Eng Educ. *Res:* Gas dynamics; rarefied plasma dynamics; nonlinear oscillations; hypersonic ballistics. *Mailing Add:* Sch of Aerospace & Mech Eng Univ of Okla Norman OK 73019

RASMUSSEN, NORMAN CARL, b Harrisburg, Pa, Nov 12, 27; m 54; c 2. NUCLEAR ENGINEERING. *Educ:* Gettysburg Col, BA, 50; Mass Inst Technol, PhD(physics), 56. *Prof Exp:* From instr to assoc prof, 56-65, PROF NUCLEAR ENG, MASS INST TECHNOL, 65-, HEAD DEPT, 75- *Concurrent Pos:* Consult, Am Nuclear Insurers, 58-, Nuclear Regulatory Comn, 72-, Burns & Roe, Inc & Cabot, Corp, 73-, EG&G Idaho, Inc, 76- & Nuclear Utility Serv Corp, 77-; mem, Defense Sci Bd, 74-77, Presidential Adv Group on Contributions of Technol to Econ Strength, 75 & bd trustees, Northeast Utilities, 77- *Honors & Awards:* Distinguished Achievement Award, Health Physics Soc, 76; Distinguished Serv Award, US Nuclear Regulatory Comn, 76; Assessments Nuclear Power Reactor Safety Spec Award, Am Nuclear Soc, 76. *Mem:* Nat Acad Eng; fel Am Nuclear Soc; AAAS; Inst Nuclear Mat Mgt. *Res:* Early research in activation analysis; low-level counting techniques and gamma-ray spectroscopy; nuclear safety and environmental impact of nuclear power; reliability analysis and risk assessment. *Mailing Add:* Mass Inst Technol 77 Massachusetts Ave Rm 24-102 Cambridge MA 02139

RASMUSSEN, OSCAR GUSTAV, b Chicago, Ill, Jan 24, 32; m 53; c 3. NUTRITION, BIOCHEMISTRY. *Educ:* Univ Ill, BS, 54, MS, 58, PhD(nutrit, biochem), 65. *Prof Exp:* Assoc nutrit & biochem, Am Meat Inst Found, 57-64; nutritionist, Armour & Co, 64-66; dir res, Triple T Feeds, 66-71; asst to pres, 71-72, EXEC VPRES, MILLER PHARMACAL, WEST CHICAGO, ILL, 72- *Mem:* Animal Nutrit Res Coun; Am Soc Animal Sci. *Res:* Preventative medicine in human nutrition; trace mineral deficiency in grains; water quality for animal and human consumption. *Mailing Add:* 64 Waxwing Ave Naperville IL 60540

RASMUSSEN, PAUL, b Chicago, Ill, Jan 27, 39; m 60; c 3. PHYSICAL INORGANIC CHEMISTRY. *Educ:* St Olaf Col, BA, 60; Mich State Univ, PhD, 64. *Prof Exp:* Asst prof, 64-70, assoc prof, 70-75, PROF CHEM, UNIV MICH, ANN ARBOR, 75-, ASSOC DEAN RES & FACIL, 74- *Mem:* Am Chem Soc. *Res:* Investigation of electronic structure in coordination compounds by physical and chemical methods; transition metal chemistry. *Mailing Add:* Dept Chem Univ Mich Ann Arbor MI 48109

RASMUSSEN, PETER, b Perth Amboy, NJ, Oct 13, 27; m 52; c 3. PATHOLOGY. *Educ:* Temple Univ, MD, 52. *Prof Exp:* Asst prof path, Univ Kans Med Ctr, 59-61; from asst prof to assoc prof, 61-73, PROF PATH, SCH MED, UNIV MD, BALTIMORE CITY, 73- *Concurrent Pos:* Nat Heart Inst fel, 58- *Mem:* AAAS; Int Acad Pathologists; NY Acad Sci. *Res:* Pathogenesis of fatty change in myocardium and kidney of mammals; nature of the greater amount of essential hypertension in American Negroes as compared with Caucasian populations. *Mailing Add:* Dept of Path Univ of Md Sch of Med Baltimore MD 21201

RASMUSSEN, REINHOLD ALBERT, b Brockton, Mass, Nov 4, 36; m 61. PLANT PHYSIOLOGY, CHEMICAL ENGINEERING. *Educ:* Univ Mass, BS, 58, MEd, 60; Wash Univ, PhD(bot), 64. *Prof Exp:* Plant biochemist, Agr Div, Monsanto Co, 62-63; clin biochemist, Walter Reed Army Med Ctr, 64-67; res proj chemist & head plant sci sect, Biomed Res Lab, Dow-Corning Corp, 67-69; assoc plant physiologist, Air Pollution Res Sect, Col Eng, 69-74, prof, 74-75, sect head, Ar Resources Sect, Chem Eng Br, Wash State Univ, 75-77; PROF ENVIRON TECHNOL, ORE GRAD CTR, 77- *Concurrent Pos:* Consult, US Army Tropic Test Ctr, 64-67 & Nat Ctr Atmospheric Res, 67-; lectr, Saginaw Valley Col, 67-; consult, Vapor Phase Org Air Pollutants from Hydrocarbons, Nat Acad Sci-Nat Res Coun, 72, consult, Panel Ammonia; consult, Air Pollution Physics & Chem Adv Comt, Environ Protection Agency, 72-75; mem, Intersoc Comt D-5 Hydrocarbon Anal; affil prof, Inst Environ Studies, Univ Wash, 75- *Mem:* Am Chem Soc; Am

Meteorol Soc. *Res:* Role of naturally occurring organic volatiles in the atmosphere, especially their chemical identification, photochemistry and biological interactions with the environment and man. *Mailing Add:* Ore Grad Ctr 19600 NW Walker Rd Beaverton OR 97005

RASMUSSEN, RICHARD ORMSBY, b Twin Falls, Idaho, Oct 23, 29; m 52; c 3. ENGINEERING, AGRICULTURE. *Educ:* Univ Calif, Berkeley, BS, 52. *Prof Exp:* Electronic eng, Collins Radio Co, 52-55; from spec asst to pres & prog mgr, Summers Gyroscope Co, 55-59; dir eng, Controls & Guid Div, Whittaker Corp, 59-69; PRES & BD CHMN, SPACE VECTOR CORP, 69- *Concurrent Pos:* Comt mem, White Sands Missile Range Rocket Scheduling Comt, 72-; dir, Am Asn Small Res Co, 73-; chmn eng adv coun, Calif State Univ Northridge, 76-; mem int affairs comt, Los Angeles Chamber of Com, 76-77; deleg, White House Conf on Small Bus, 80. *Mem:* Am Inst Aeronaut & Astronaut; Am Asn Small Res Co; Irrig Asn; Int Drip Irrig Asn. *Res:* Gyroscopes, platforms, and missile systems; hydropulse water irrigation systems. *Mailing Add:* Space Vector Corp 19631 Prairie St Northridge CA 91324

RASMUSSEN, ROBERT A, b St Peter, Minn, Aug 31, 33; m 61; c 4. PHYCOLOGY. *Educ:* Col St Thomas, BS, 56; Univ Minn, Minneapolis, MS, 62; Univ Canterbury, PhD(zool), 65. *Prof Exp:* Res assoc, Friday Harbor Marine Labs, Univ Wash, 65-66; from asst prof to assoc prof bot, 66-77, PROF BOT, HUMBOLDT STATE UNIV, 77- *Concurrent Pos:* Mem Environ Consults, Pac Marine Eng, Inc, 72- *Mem:* Int Phycol Soc; Phycol Soc Am; Brit Phycol Soc. *Res:* Morphology of crustose coralline seaweed; seaweed autoecology. *Mailing Add:* Dept of Biol Humboldt State Univ Arcata CA 95521

RASMUSSEN, RUSSELL LEE, b Allen, Nebr; m 65; c 2. INORGANIC CHEMISTRY, BIO-ORGANIC CHEMISTRY. *Educ:* Univ Nebr, BS, 60, PhD(inorg biochem), 70. *Prof Exp:* Asst prof chem, Stout State Univ, 66-67; from asst prof to assoc prof, 69-74, PROF CHEM, WAYNE STATE COL, 74-, HEAD DEPT PHYS SCI, 72- *Mem:* AAAS; Am Chem Soc; Am Inst Biol Sci. *Res:* Model enzyme systems; coordination compounds; thiol esters of amino acids; pyridoxal containing enzymes; relationship of verbal ability and scientific achievement; the two cultures. *Mailing Add:* Dept of Chem Wayne State Col Wayne NE 68787

RASMUSSEN, THEODORE BROWN, b Provo, Utah, Apr 28, 10; m 47; c 4. NEUROLOGY, NEUROSURGERY. *Educ:* Univ Minn, BS & MB, 34, MD, 35, MS, 39; FRCS(C). *Hon Degrees:* DrMed, Edinburgh Univ, 80. *Prof Exp:* Lectr neurol & neurosurg, McGill Univ, 46-47; prof neurol surg, Univ Chicago, 47-54; neurosurgeon, Montreal Neurol Inst, 54-80; prof, 54-80, EMER PROF NEUROL & NEUROSURG, MCGILL UNIV, 80- *Concurrent Pos:* Assoc neurosurgeon, Montreal Neurol Inst, 46-47, dir, 60-72, sr neurosurg consult, 72-; mem, Int Brain Res Orgn. *Mem:* AAAS; Neurosurg Soc Am; Am Asn Neurol Surg; Soc Neurol Surg; AMA. *Res:* Cerebral circulation; localization of cortical function; effects of radiation on cerebral tissue; focal epilepsy. *Mailing Add:* 3801 University St Montreal PQ H3A 2B4 Can

RASMUSSEN, V PHILIP, JR, b Logan, Utah, Apr 3, 50; m 74; c 4. SOILS & SOIL SCIENCE. *Educ:* Utah State Univ, BS, 74, MS, 76; Utah State Univ, PhD(agron), 79. *Prof Exp:* Res assoc soil physics, Utah State Univ, 74-76, crop modelling, Kans State Univ, 76-78; asst prof, Ricks Col, 78-81; ASSOC PROF SOIL PHYSICS, UTAH STATE UNIV, 81- *Concurrent Pos:* Consult, Campbell Sci, Inc, 76-81; Omnidata Int, 80-; lectr, Prof Farmers Inst, Data Processing Mgt Asn & Farmers Home Admin, USDA. *Mem:* Sigma Xi; Am Soc Agron; Soil Sci Soc Am; Int Soc Soil Sci. *Res:* On farm microcomputers; plant growth modelling. *Mailing Add:* UMC 48 Utah State Univ Logan UT 84322

RASMUSSEN, WILLIAM OTTO, b Burley, Idaho, Jan 29, 42; m 64; c 2. MODELING, COMPUTER SIMULATION. *Educ:* Univ Idaho, BS, 64, MS, 66; Univ Ariz, PhD(watershed mgt), 73. *Prof Exp:* Explor geophysicist, Heinrichs Geoexplor Co, 68-70; ASST RES PROF COMPUT MAPPING & REMOTE SENSING, UNIV ARIZ, 73- *Concurrent Pos:* Dir remote sensing & comput mapping, Univ Ariz, 73-, remote sensing exten specialist, 75- *Res:* Simulation of electromagnetic radiation-environment interaction; scene synthesis; simulation of natural resource systems; digital image processing; atmospheric optics; ecosystem modeling; prediction of imaging sensor spectral irradiance from a scene; simulation and prediction of strip mine resources, mass balance, and reclamation; development of geographic data analysis and display systems; visibility analysis in vegetated scenes; computer software design and development. *Mailing Add:* 4817 E Montecito St Tucson AZ 85711

RASMUSSON, DONALD C, b Ephraim, Utah, May 28, 31; m 50; c 5. PLANT GENETICS, PLANT BREEDING. *Educ:* Utah State Univ, BS, 53, MS, 56; Univ Calif, PhD(genetics), 58. *Prof Exp:* Res assoc, 58-72, PROF PLANT GENETICS, UNIV MINN, ST PAUL, 72- *Mem:* Fel Am Soc Agron; Crop Sci Soc Am. *Res:* Plant breeding and genetics. *Mailing Add:* Rm 311 Agron Bldg Univ of Minn St Paul MN 55108

RASMUSSON, DOUGLAS DEAN, b Denver, Colo, Aug 4, 46; Can citizen. NEUROPHYSIOLOGY, SOMATOSENSORY SYSTEM. *Educ:* Colo Col, BA, 68; Dalhousie Univ, MA, 70, PhD(physiol), 75. *Prof Exp:* Fel neurophysiol, Univ Toronto, 75-77; ASST PROF PHYSIOL & BIOPHYSICS, DALHOUSIE UNIV, 77- *Mem:* Can Physiol Soc; Soc Neurosci; Can Asn Neuroscientists. *Res:* Organization and function of somatosensory cortex; plasticity due to changes in peripheral nervous system. *Mailing Add:* Dept Physiol & Biophysics Dalhousie Univ Halifax NS B3H 4H7 Can

RASMUSSON, EUGENE MARTIN, b Lindsborg, Kans, Feb 27, 29; m 60; c 3. METEOROLOGY. *Educ:* Kans State Univ, BS, 50; St Louis Univ, MS, 63; Mass Inst Technol, PhD(meteorol), 66. *Prof Exp:* Design engr, Kans State Hwy Comn, 50-51; engr, Pac Tel Co, 55-56; meteorologist & hydrologist, US Weather Bur, 56-60; meteorologist forecaster, 60-63; RES METEOROLOGIST, NAT OCEANIC & ATMOSPHERIC ADMIN, ROCKVILLE, MD, 63- *Concurrent Pos:* Mem steering comt, Int Field Year for Great Lakes, 67-71; US co-chmn lake meteorol panel, 69-79. *Mem:* AAAS; Am Geophys Union; Am Meteorol Soc. *Res:* Atmospheric general circulation; large scale water balance; air-sea interactions; tropical meteorology; climate variability. *Mailing Add:* 10005 Autumnwood Way Potomac MD 20854

RASMUSSON, GARY HENRY, b Clark, SDak, Aug 2, 36; m 58; c 4. MEDICINAL CHEMISTRY. *Educ:* St Olaf Col, BA, 58; Univ Ill, Urbana, PhD(org chem), 62. *Prof Exp:* NSF res fel, Stanford Univ, 62-63; NIH res fel, 63-64; sr chemist, 64-72, res fel, 72-77, SR RES FEL, MERCK SHARP & DOHME RES LABS, RAHWAY, 77- *Mem:* Am Chem Soc. *Res:* Synthetic organic chemistry in the areas of heterocycles, terpenes, steroids and pharmaceutically active compounds. *Mailing Add:* 155 Park Place Watchung NJ 07060

RASNAKE, MONROE, b Buchanan County, Va, Feb 8, 42; c 2. SOIL CHEMISTRY, SOIL FERTILITY. *Educ:* Berea Col, BS, 65; Va Polytech Inst, MS, 67; Univ Ky, PhD(soil chem), 73. *Prof Exp:* High sch teacher math sci & biol, Grundy, Va, 67-70; grad asst res lab instr, Univ Ky, 70-73; asst prof, Southern Piedmont Res & Continuing Educ Ctr, Va, 73-77; supvry mgt agronomist, Dept Army, Blackstone, Va, 77-78; EXTEN AGRON SPECIALIST, UNIV KY, 78- *Concurrent Pos:* Asst prof, Va Polytech Inst & State Univ. *Mem:* Soil Sci Soc Am; Am Soc Agron; Sigma Xi; Am Forage & Grasslands Soc. *Res:* Fire-cured tobacco information; effect of soil fertility level on ozone injury of tobacco; effect of agricultural drainage on water quality; effect of tobacco nutrition on occurrence of insect pests; soil erosion as related to soybean production practices; no-till corn fertilization; effect of soil pH and lime on crop rotations. *Mailing Add:* Western Ky Substa PO Box 469 Princeton KY 42445

RASOR, NED S(HAURER), b Dayton, Ohio, Jan 2, 27; m 47; c 2. ENERGY CONVERSION, CARDIOVASCULAR DEVICES. *Educ:* Ohio State Univ, BS, 48; Univ Ill, MS, 51; Case Inst Technol, PhD(physics), 54. *Prof Exp:* Res engr, N Am Aviation, Inc, 48-50, sr res engr, 51-52, sr res specialist, Atomics Int Div, 54-56, proj engr, 56-59, group leader, 59-60, dir energy conversion dept, 60-62; dir res, Thermo Electron Corp, Mass, 62-63, vpres, 63-65; consult, 65-72; PRES, RASOR ASSOCS, INC, 71- *Mem:* Am Phys Soc; assoc fel Am Inst Aeronaut & Astronaut; sr mem Inst Elec & Electronics Engrs. *Res:* Surface physics; gaseous discharge; thermionic energy conversion; thermal properties; high temperature materials; nuclear space power; bioengineering. *Mailing Add:* 253 Humboldt Ct Sunnyvale CA 94086

RASSIN, DAVID KEITH, b Liverpool, Eng, Dec 1, 42; m 65; c 2. NEUROCHEMISTRY. *Educ:* Columbia Univ, AB, 65; City Univ New York, PhD(pharmacol), 74. *Prof Exp:* Res fel neurol, Columbia Univ, 66, res asst, 66-67; asst res scientist, NY State Inst Basic Res Ment Retardation, 67-70, res scientist, 70-74, sr res scientist human develop & nutrit, 74-77, res scientist IV, 77-79, res scientist V, 79-80; ASSOC PROF, UNIV TEX MED BR, GALVESTON, 80- *Concurrent Pos:* Adj asst prof Mt Sinai Sch Med, 76-80 & adj assoc prof, Col Staten Island, City Univ New York, 79-80. *Mem:* Int Soc Neurochem; Am Soc Neurochem; Am Soc Clin Nutrit; Soc Pediat Res; Am Soc Exp Pharmacol & Therapeut. *Res:* Neurochemistry of amino acids, especially sulfur containing amino acids, as they relate to inborn errors of metabolism and nutrition in children. *Mailing Add:* Dept Pediat Univ Tex Med Br Galveston TX 77550

RASSWEILER, MERRILL (PAUL), b Chicago Heights, Ill, Feb 28, 10; m 33. PHYSICS. *Educ:* Beloit Col, BS, 30; Univ Ill, MS, 32, PhD(physics), 37. *Prof Exp:* From instr to assoc prof physics & math, Northern Mont Col, 37-48; from asst prof to prof phys sci & math, 48-74, head div, Sci & Math, 57-74, EMER PROF SCI, BUS & MATH, UNIV MINN, MINNEAPOLIS, 74- *Concurrent Pos:* Lectr, 43-45; vis prof, Univ PR, 46-47. *Mem:* Nat Asn Physics Teachers. *Res:* Band spectra of caesium hydride. *Mailing Add:* 9813 Loma Blanca Dr Sun City AZ 85351

RAST, HOWARD EUGENE, JR, b Mexia, Tex, June 8, 34; m 58; c 2. SOLID STATE SCIENCE, FIBER OPTICS. *Educ:* Univ Tex, BA, 56; Univ Ore, PhD(phys chem), 64, Univ Southern Calif, MS, 77. *Prof Exp:* Res chemist, Calif Ink Co, Div Tenneco Inc, 58-60; res asst chem, Univ Ore, 60-64; phys chemist, US Naval Weapons Ctr, 64-70; res chemist, 70-80, SUPVRY SCIENTIST, NAVAL OCEAN SYSTS CTR, 80- *Mem:* Am Phys Soc. *Res:* Spectra and optical properties of materials; lattice dynamics; display technology; military optical counter-measures; electro-optics and optical technology; fiber optics. *Mailing Add:* Code 9225 Naval Ocean Systs Ctr San Diego CA 92152

RAST, WALTER, JR, b San Antonio, Tex, Jan 14, 44; m 71; c 1. AQUATIC CHEMISTRY, LIMNOLOGY. *Educ:* Univ Tex, Austin, BA, 70; Univ Tex, Dallas, MS(molecular biol), 74, PhD(environ sci), 78. *Prof Exp:* Res asst, Genetics Res Found, Univ Tex, Austin, 69-70; hydrol field asst stream flow and quality monitoring, Water Resources Div, US Geol Surv, 70-71; res asst, Molecular Biol Inst, Univ Tex, Dallas, 71-74, res asst aquatic chem, Environ Sci Prog, 74-75, teaching asst, Environ Sci Prog, 75-77; limnologist, Great Lakes Water Qual, Great Lakes Regional Off, US/Can Int Joint Comn, Windsor, Ont, 77-79, ENVIRON ADVR, US SECT, INT JOINT COMN, WASHINGTON, DC, 79- *Concurrent Pos:* Assoc, Enviroqual Consult & Labs, Inc, 74-77; adj asst prof, Biol Dept, Wayne State Univ, 79-82. *Mem:* AAAS; Am Soc Limnol & Oceanog; Am Water Works Asn; Soc Environ Toxicol Chem; Water Pollution Control Fedn. *Res:* Nutrient load-lake response relationships and trophic status indices in natural waters; environmental chemistry of toxic and hazardous substances;

environmental modelling of effects of eutrophication and toxic and hazardous substances on water quality and biota; watershed land use activities--lake water quality relationships. *Mailing Add:* Int Joint Comn 1717 H St NW Washington DC 20440

RASTALL, PETER, b Washingborough, Eng, Nov 18, 31. THEORETICAL PHYSICS. *Educ:* Univ Manchester, BSc, 52, PhD(theoret physics), 55. *Prof Exp:* With aerodyn dept, Rolls Royce, Ltd, 55-57; lectr physics, 57-58, from instr to assoc prof, 58-71, PROF PHYSICS, UNIV BC, 71- *Res:* Field theory interpretation of quantum mechanics. *Mailing Add:* Dept of Physics Univ of BC Vancouver BC V6T 1W5 Can

RASTETTER, WILLIAM HARRY, b Coco Solo, Panama, Apr 13, 48; US citizen. ORGANIC CHEMISTRY. *Educ:* Mass Inst Technol, SB, 71; Harvard Univ, MA, 72, PhD(chem), 75. *Prof Exp:* asst prof chem, 75-79, Firmenich asst prof natural prod chem, 79-81, ASSOC PROF CHEM, MASS INST TECHNOL, 81- *Concurrent Pos:* Alfred P Sloan fel, 80-82. *Mem:* Am Chem Soc; The Chem Soc. *Res:* Natural product synthesis and mechanistic studies applied to structure/reactivity and structure/activity correlations of biologically related compounds. *Mailing Add:* Dept Of Chem Bldg 18-Rm 207 Mass Inst Technol Cambridge MA 02139

RASTOGI, PRABHAT KUMAR, b Chapra, India, June 7, 44; m 69; c 2. MATERIAL SCIENCE, METALLURGY. *Educ:* Indian Inst Technol, Kanpur, India, BTech, 65; State Univ NY Stony Brook, MS, 67; Calif Inst Technol, PhD(mat sci), 70. *Prof Exp:* Res engr, 70-75, sr res engr, 75-79, STAFF RES ENGR MAGNETISM & PHYS METALL, INLAND STEEL CO, IND, 79- *Mem:* Am Soc Metals. *Res:* Metal physics; magnetism; physical metallurgy; development of new and improved products for electromagnetic applications. *Mailing Add:* Inland Steel Co 3001 E Columbus Dr East Chicago IN 46312

RASTOGI, SURESH CHANDRA, b Sambhal, India, July 7, 37; US citizen; m 66; c 4. MATHEMATICAL STATISTICS, BIOSTATISTICS. *Educ:* Univ Lucknow, BSc, 57, MSc, 60; Univ Iowa, PhD(statist), 65. *Prof Exp:* Lectr statist, Univ Lucknow, 60-62; statistician, Univ Md, Baltimore City, 66-67; asst prof statist, Univ Md, College Park, 67-72; mgr statist, Hq, US Postal Serv, 72-73; MATH STATISTICIAN, BUR BIOLOGICS, FOOD & DRUG ADMIN, DEPT HEALTH, EDUC & WELFARE, 73- *Concurrent Pos:* Consult div biologics stand, NIH, 67-70. *Mem:* Am Statist Asn; Biomet Soc; Int Asn Survey Statist. *Res:* Multivariate statistical methods; regression and analysis of variance; sample survey techniques as used in applied fields; bioassay. *Mailing Add:* Bur Biologics Food & Drug Admin 8800 Rockville Pike Bethesda MD 20205

RASWEILER, JOHN JACOB, IV, b Newport, RI, June 4, 43; m 64; c 1. REPRODUCTIVE PHYSIOLOGY, ANATOMY. *Educ:* Colgate Univ, BA, 65; Cornell Univ, PhD(physiol), 70. *Prof Exp:* Vis asst prof morphol, Div Health, Univ Valle, Colombia, 70-72; asst prof anat, Col Physicians & Surgeons, Columbia Univ, 72-78; ASST PROF ANAT, MED COL, CORNELL UNIV, 78- *Concurrent Pos:* Pop Coun fel, Univ Valle, Colombia, 70-72; NIH grant, Int Ctr Med Res & Training, Tulane Univ, 71-72; vis scientist, Int Ctr Med Res & Training, Tulane Univ, 72-74. *Mem:* AAAS; Soc Study Reproduction; Am Asn Anatomists; Am Soc Mammal. *Res:* Reproductive physiology; development of bats as laboratory models. *Mailing Add:* Dept of Anat Med Col Cornell Univ New York NY 10021

RATCHES, JAMES ARTHUR, b Hartford, Conn, May 12, 42; m 73. ELECTRO-OPTICS, SYSTEMS ANALYSIS. *Educ:* Trinity Col, Conn, BA, 64; Worcester Polytechnic Inst, MS, 66, PhD(physics), 69. *Prof Exp:* Res physicist, Night Vision & Electro-Optics Lab, 69-81, ACTG DIR, VISIONICS DIV, DEPT ARMY, 81- *Res:* Development of target acquisition models for thermal imaging devices; analysis and design evaluation of electro-optical sensors; atmospheric propagation effects on electro-optical devices. *Mailing Add:* Night Vision & Electro-Optics Lab Ft Belvoir VA 22060

RATCHFORD, JOSEPH THOMAS, b Kinstree, SC, Sept 30, 35; m 60; c 4. SOLID STATE PHYSICS. *Educ:* Davidson Col, BS, 57; Univ Va, MA, 59, PhD(physics), 61. *Prof Exp:* Staff mem, Sandia Corp, 59; asst prof physics, Washington & Lee Univ, 61-64; proj scientist, Solid State Sci Div, Air Force Off Sci Res, Arlington, 64-70; sci consult, Comt Sci & Technol, US House Rep, 70-77; ASSOC EXEC OFFICER, AAAS, WASHINGTON, DC, 77- *Concurrent Pos:* Res physicist, US Naval Ord Lab, 63-64; Am Polit Sci Asn cong fel, 68-69; res scholar, Int Inst Appl Systs Anal, Laxenburg, Austria, 76; chmn, Res Coord Panel, Gas Res Inst, Chicago, Ill, 76-79, mem, 76-; chmn, Adv Panel to US Congressional Off Technol Assessment, Solar Energy, Energy Conserv & Energy Biol Processes, 78-80. *Mem:* Fel AAAS; Am Phys Soc; Sigma Xi. *Res:* Science and government; materials sciences; energy technology and policy; international science cooperation and policy. *Mailing Add:* AAAS 1776 Massachusetts NW Washington DC 20036

RATCHFORD, ROBERT JAMES, b Firesteel, SDak, Nov 16, 24. PHYSICAL CHEMISTRY. *Educ:* Spring Hill Col, BS, 53; Cath Univ, PhD(chem), 58. *Prof Exp:* Res asst, Max Planck Inst Phys Chem & Karlsruhe Tech Univ, 62-63; asst prof chem, Loyola Univ, La, 64-80, dean arts & sci, 75-80; RETIRED. *Mem:* Am Chem Soc; Electrochem Soc. *Res:* Solution electrochemistry; electrochemistry of solid state electrolytes. *Mailing Add:* 500 S Jefferson Davis Pkwy New Orleans LA 70119

RATCHFORD, WILLIAM PAUL, b Scranton, Pa, May 5, 15; m 41; c 4. PHYSICAL CHEMISTRY, ORGANIC CHEMISTRY. *Educ:* Univ Scranton, BS, 37; Cath Univ, PhD(chem), 41. *Prof Exp:* Res chemist, Eastern Regional Res Lab, Bur Agr Chem & Eng, USDA, 41-50, tech asst to dir, Eastern Regional Res Ctr, Agr Res Serv, 50-55, asst to dir, 55-59, asst dir 59-70; lectr chem, St Joseph's Col, Pa, 63-80 & Beaver Col, Pa, 78-79; LECTR CHEM, GWYNEDD-MERCY COL, 76- *Mem:* AAAS; Am Chem Soc. *Res:* Physical-organic chemistry of lactic acid derivatives; chemical education. *Mailing Add:* Gwynedd-Mercy Col Gwynedd PA 19437

RATCLIFF, BLAIR NORMAN, b Grinnell, Iowa, Sept 26, 44; m 76. ELEMENTARY PARTICLE PHYSICS. *Educ:* Grinnell Col, BA, 66; Stanford Univ, MS, 68, PhD(physics), 71. *Prof Exp:* Res assoc, Rutherford High Energy Lab, 71-74; res assoc, 75-79, STAFF PHYSICIST, STANFORD LINEAR ACCELERATOR CTR, 74- *Concurrent Pos:* Vis scientist, European Orgn Nuclear Res, 71-74. *Mem:* Am Phys Soc; AAAS. *Res:* Experimental high energy physics; meson spectroscopy; strange baryon spectroscopy; hadrom production mechanisms; lepton pair production. *Mailing Add:* Stanford Linear Acclerator Ctr Stanford CA 94305

RATCLIFF, KEITH FREDERICK, b Drexel Hill, Pa, Nov 15, 38; div; c 2. NUCLEAR PHYSICS, THEORETICAL PHYSICS. *Educ:* Northwestern Univ, Evanston, BA, 60; Univ Pittsburgh, PhD(physics), 65. *Prof Exp:* Res assoc physics, Univ Rochester, 65-67 & Mass Inst Technol, 67-68, instr, 68-69; asst prof, 69-78, ASSOC PROF PHYSICS, STATE UNIV NY ALBANY, 78- *Concurrent Pos:* Vis assoc prof, State Univ NY Stony Brook, 72-73. *Mem:* AAAS; Am Phys Soc; Am Asn Physics Teachers. *Res:* Theoretical investigations of nuclear structure and nuclear reactions; neutron star evolution; cosmic dust problems; many-body theory. *Mailing Add:* Dept of Physics State Univ of NY Albany NY 12222

RATCLIFF, MILTON, JR, b Memphis, Tenn, Apr 19, 44; m 73. ANALYTICAL CHEMISTRY, ORGANIC CHEMISTRY. *Educ:* Southwestern at Memphis, BS, 66; Case Western Reserve Univ, PhD(org chem), 70. *Prof Exp:* Fel geochem, Indiana Univ, 70-72; proj leader chem, Jet Propulsion Lab, Calif Inst Technol, 72-74; sr chemist geochem, US Geol Surv, 74-76; mgr anal res & residue methods anal chem, Zoecon Corp-Subsid Hooker Chem Co, 76-80; PROJ LEADER COMPUT SCI, NELSON ANAL INC, 80- *Mem:* Am Chem Soc; Asn Comput Mach. *Res:* Gas chromatography; mass spectrometry; trace analysis; chemical applications of data processing; instrument interfacing; capillary column development. *Mailing Add:* Nelson Anal Inc 20370 Town Center Lane # 130 Cupertino CA 95014

RATCLIFFE, CHARLES THOMAS, b Malad, Idaho, Nov 18, 38; m 64; c 2. INORGANIC CHEMISTRY. *Educ:* Univ Idaho, BS, 61, MS, 63, PhD(inorg chem), 67. *Prof Exp:* Sci Res Coun fel chem, Glasgow Univ, 67-68; res chemist, Corp Res Ctr, Allied Chem Corp, 68-72, sr res chemist, 72-76, res group leader, 76-80; WITH EXXON RES ENG CO, 80- *Concurrent Pos:* Sci Res Coun fel, Great Britain, 67-68. *Mem:* Sigma Xi; Am Chem Soc; fel NY Acad Sci. *Res:* Catalysis reactions with coal, sulfur; coal chemistry; heterogeneous sulfur containing catalysts; reduction reactions; fluorocarbon synthesis. *Mailing Add:* Exxon Res Eng Co PO Box 45 Linden NJ 07036

RATCLIFFE, NICHOLAS MORLEY, b Bryn Mawr, Pa, Feb 4, 38; m 60; c 1. GEOLOGY. *Educ:* Williams Col, BA, 60; Pa State Univ, PhD(geol), 65. *Prof Exp:* Assoc prof geol, City Col New York, 65-74, prof earth & planetary sci, 74-80; WITH US GEOL SURVEY, 80- *Mem:* Geol Soc Am. *Res:* Structural geology and petrology; igneous and metamorphic petrology. *Mailing Add:* US Geol Surv National Ctr MS 925 Reston VA 22092

RATEAVER, BARGYLA, b Ft Dauphin, Madagascar, Aug 3, 16; US citizen; c 1. CONSERVATION, SOIL FERTILITY. *Educ:* Univ Calif, Berkeley, AB, 43, MSLS, 59; Univ Mich, Ann Arbor, MS, 50, PhD(bot), 51. *Prof Exp:* Specialist, food technol, Univ Calif, Davis, 51-52; private plant propagator, 55-56; tech abstractor, G C Rocket Co, 59-60; librarian, D Victor Co, 61; regional rep sci & technol books, J S Stacey, 63; automation analyst, Space & Info Systs, NAm Aviation, 64; instr, Manpower Develop Training Prog, 65-67; librarian, Marin County Sch Syst, Calif, 67-68; instr org gardening & farming, Jr Cols, Univ Calif & Calif State Univs, 70-78; ED & PUBL CONSERV GARDENING & FARMING SERIES, THE RATEAVERS, 73- *Concurrent Pos:* Longworth Gardens grant, 55; Am Acad Arts & Sci grant, 57; assoc prof, Calif State Univ, Sacramento, 72-73; instr, Calif State Univ, Long Beach, 75. *Mem:* Int Fedn Org Agr Movements. *Res:* Madagascar plants; tropical agriculture; world literature on tropical plants; biological agriculture and horticulture; science education in conservation; soil fertility of field crops, tree and vegetable crops; utilization of weeds; fertilizer comparisons. *Mailing Add:* Pauma Valley CA 92061

RATH, BHAKTA BHUSAN, b Banki, India, Oct 28, 34; m 63; c 1. METALLURGY. *Educ:* Utkal, India, BSc, 55; Mich Technol Univ, MS, 58; Ill Inst Technol, PhD(metall), 62. *Prof Exp:* Res assoc metall, Ill Inst Technol, 60-61; asst prof & res metallurgist, Washington State Univ, 61-65; res scientist, E C Bain Lab Fundamental Res, US Steel Corp, 65-71; mem res staff, McDonnell Douglas Res Labs, St Louis, 72-76; BR HEAD MAT SCI DIV, US NAVAL RES LAB, 77- *Concurrent Pos:* Adj fac mem, Carnegie-Mellon Univ. *Mem:* AAAS; Am Soc Metals; Am Inst Mining, Metall & Petrol Engrs; Brit Inst Metals; Phys Soc Japan. *Res:* Recovery, recrystallization and grain growth in metals; teaching physics of metals; x-ray diffraction; theory of solids; crystallography; deformation and recrystallization textures; micro-calorimetry; surface physics. *Mailing Add:* Mat Sci Div US Naval Res Lab Code 6320 Washington DC 20375

RATH, CHARLES E, b Philippines, Aug 14, 19; m 41; c 4. HEMATOLOGY. *Educ:* Col Wooster, AB, 40; Western Reserve Univ, MD, 43; Am Bd Internal Med, dipl, 51. *Prof Exp:* From instr to assoc prof med, 49-61, dir hemat & blood bank, 49-61, PROF MED, UNIV & DIR LABS, UNIV HOSP, GEORGETOWN UNIV, 61- *Concurrent Pos:* Consult, NIH Clin Ctr, 53- & Bethesda Naval Hosp, 54- *Mem:* Am Soc Hemat; AMA; Am Fedn Clin Res; fel Am Col Physicians; Int Soc Hemat. *Res:* Iron metabolism. *Mailing Add:* Georgetown Univ Hosp Washington DC 20007

RATH, MAURICE MONROE, b Newark, NJ, Oct 2, 14; m 40; c 2. PHARMACOLOGY, PHYSIOLOGY. *Educ:* Ind Univ, AB, 36, MD, 43; NY Univ, MS, 41; Univ Md, PhD(pharmacol), 42. *Prof Exp:* Sr asst surgeon, USPHS, 43-46; pvt pract, 46-63; mem staff, Food & Drug Admin, 63-65; dir med res, Wallace Pharmaceut, 65-68, med dir, Wallace Pharmaceut Div, Carter Wallace Inc, 69-70; chief restoration ctr, Vet Admin Hosp, East

Orange, NJ, 70-73; chief rehab ward, Vet Admin Hosp, Tampa, 73-75; MEM STAFF, NURSING HOME & GERIAT RES, MED DEPT, VET ADMIN MED CTR, BAY PINES, FLA, 75- *Concurrent Pos:* Assoc clin prof, Col Med & Dent NJ, 71-73; assoc prof comprehensive med, Col Med, Univ SFla, 73- *Mem:* Fel AAAS; Am Chem Soc; AMA; fel Am Col Cardiol; fel Am Col Angiol. *Res:* Relation of hypertension to urologic disease; physiology & pharmacology of nitrates and nitrites; biometric study of age-cancer relationship; geriatric research; age-hypertension relationship; nutritional requirements of older age groups; internal medicine; clinical pharmacology; drugs; rehabilitation medicine. *Mailing Add:* 100 Pierce St Clearwater FL 33516

RATH, NARRAYAN CHANDRA, b Khantapara, India, Oct 21, 46; m 76; c 2. CONNECTIVE TISSUE BIOLOGY, ENDOCRINOLOGY. *Educ:* Univ Delhi, MSc, 69, PhD(zool), 74. *Prof Exp:* Lectr zool, Berhampur Univ, India, 74-75; full researcher reproduction, Hosp Bictre, Nat Ctr Sci Res, France, 75-77; vis fel connective tissue, NIH, Bethesda, 77-79; RES ASST PROF BIOPHYSICS, STATE UNIV NY, BUFFALO, 79- *Mem:* AAAS; NY Acad Sci. *Res:* Induction and development of cartilage bone and bone marrow by bone matrix implant and their physiological regulations; connective tissue biology. *Mailing Add:* 380 Campus Dr Apt 2 Amherst NY 14226

RATHBUN, EDWIN ROY, JR, b Kansas City, Mo, Apr 6, 22; m 49; c 5. PHYSICS, ELECTRONICS ENGINEERING. *Educ:* Iowa State Col, BS, 48, MS, 50. *Prof Exp:* Asst electronics engr physics instr, Argonne Nat Lab, 54-56; staff engr nuclear physics, Cook Elec Co, Skokie, Ill, 56-64; consult engr nuclear weapons effects, Gen Elec Co, Philadelphia, 65-68, specialist consult engr nucleonics electromagnetics, Syracuse, NY, 68-69; chief electromagnetic pulse branch, Naval Ord Lab, 69-74; PROJ ENGR NUCLEAR VULNERABILITY & HARDENING, NAVAL SURFACE WEAPONS CTR, 74- *Mem:* Inst Elec & Electronics Engrs. *Res:* Nuclear electromagnetic pulse; nuclear vulnerability of naval systems; effects of nuclear weapons; nuclear hardening of military systems; nuclear radiation effects. *Mailing Add:* Naval Surface Weapons Ctr Code F-32 White Oak MD 20910

RATHBUN, TED ALLAN, b Ellsworth, Kans, Apr 11, 42; m 64; c 1. PHYSICAL ANTHROPOLOGY. *Educ:* Univ Kans, BA, 64, MA, 66, PhD(anthrop), 71. *Prof Exp:* Instr eng, Ahwaz Agr Col, Peace Corps, 66-68; instr anthrop, Univ SC, 70-71, asst prof, 71-75, ASSOC PROF ANTHROP, UNIV SC, 75- *Concurrent Pos:* Res assoc, Inst Archaeol, Univ SC, 71-; Comt Res & Prod Scholar grant, 71 & 78; consulting phys anthropologist, Off State Med Examr, Med Univ SC, 72-; Field Res Projs grant, Field Mus Natural Hist & Univ SC, 72-73. *Mem:* Am Anthrop Asn; Am Asn Phys Anthrop; fel Archaeol Inst Am; Am Acad Forensic Sci; Paleopath Asn. *Res:* Osteology; Bronze and Iron Ages in Southwest Asia; social structure and fertility; physical anthropology of groups in Southwest Asia; forensic anthropology; paleopathology; non-metric variation; colonial South Carolina; paleonutrition. *Mailing Add:* Dept of Anthrop Univ of SC Columbia SC 29208

RATHBUN, WILLIAM B, b Wisconsin Dells, Wis, June 20, 32; m 54; c 2. BIOCHEMISTRY. *Educ:* Univ Wis, BS, 54, MS, 55; Univ Minn, Minneapolis, PhD(biochem), 63. *Prof Exp:* Res assoc, 64-67, asst prof, 67-73, ASSOC PROF OPHTHAL BIOCHEM, UNIV MINN, MINNEAPOLIS, 73- *Concurrent Pos:* NIH fel ophthal biochem, Univ Minn, Minneapolis, 63-64, grants, 69-71, 73-76, 77-81 & 82-87. *Mem:* Am Res Vision & Ophthal; Am Chem Soc; Sigma Xi; Int Soc Eye Res; Asn Eye Res. *Res:* Lens enzymes; biochemistry of cataracts; biosynthesis and metabolism of glutathione. *Mailing Add:* Dept of Ophthal Univ of Minn Minneapolis MN 55455

RATHBURN, CARLISLE BAXTER, JR, b Fulton, NY, Apr 23, 24; m 51; c 2. PUBLIC HEALTH ENTOMOLOGY, MOSQUITO BIOLOGY & CONTROL. *Educ:* Syracuse Univ, AB, 46; Univ Fla, BSA, 50, MAg, 51; Cornell Univ, PhD(entom), 64. *Prof Exp:* Res asst entom, Cornell Univ, 53-57; entomologist, Entom Res Ctr, 57-64, ENTOMOLOGIST, FLA STATE DEPT HEALTH & REHAB SERV, W FLA ARTHROPOD RES LAB, 64- *Concurrent Pos:* Prin investr, USPHS res grant, 60-66; ed, J Florida Anti-Mosquito Asn, 79- *Mem:* Sigma Xi; Entom Soc Am; Am Mosquito Control Asn. *Res:* Author or coauthor of 64 scientific papers in seven journals on the biology and control of mosquitoes and related subjects. *Mailing Add:* Fla State Dept of Health & Rehab Serv WFla Arthropod Res Lab PO Box 2326 Panama City FL 32401

RATHCKE, BEVERLY JEAN, b Wadena, Minn, July 12, 45. ECOLOGY. *Educ:* Gustavus Adolphus Col, BA, 67; Imperial Col, Univ London, MSc, 68; Univ Ill, Urbana-Champaign, PhD(ecol), 73. *Prof Exp:* Student ecol, Cornell Univ, 73-75; res assoc ecol, Brown Univ, 75-78; ASST PROF BIOL SCI, UNIV MICH, 78- *Concurrent Pos:* Ed jour, Ecol Soc Am, 75-82; NATO fel, 79. *Mem:* Ecol Soc Am; Brit Ecol Soc. *Res:* Animal-plant interactions and community ecology. *Mailing Add:* Div Biol Sciof Univ Mich Ann Arbor MI 48109

RATHER, JAMES B, JR, b Bryan, Tex, Feb 2, 11; m 35; c 3. CHEMICAL ENGINEERING. *Educ:* Lehigh Univ, ChE, 32. *Prof Exp:* Asst chief chemist, Magnolia Petrol Co, 35-37, supvr eng, Tech Serv Div, Socony Mobil Oil Co, 38-41, asst mgr div, 43-56, admin dir, 56-60, mgr toxicol & pollution, Res Dept, Mobil Oil Corp, 60-67, corp asst air & water conserv coord, 67-72; PRES, SCH HOUSE ENTERPRISES LTD, 72- *Concurrent Pos:* Mem, Ny State Action for Clean Air Comt. *Mem:* Air Pollution Control Asn; Am Nat Standards Insts; Am Soc Testing & Mat (vpres, 64, pres, 66); Am Chem Soc. *Res:* Petroleum technology; air and water pollution control; standardization; toxicology. *Mailing Add:* PO Box 178 Birch Harbor ME 04613

RATHER, LELLAND JOSEPH, b College Station, Tex, Dec 22, 13; m 40, 59; c 3. PATHOLOGY. *Educ:* Johns Hopkins Univ, AB, 34, MD, 39; Univ Chicago, MS, 36. *Prof Exp:* House officer pediat, Children's Hosp, Philadelphia, 39-40; house officer surg, Duke Hosp, NC, 40-41; asst resident path, Henry Ford Hosp, Detroit, 41-42; asst resident, Stanford Hosp, Calif, 46; from instr to assoc prof, 46-57, PROF PATH, SCH MED, STANFORD UNIV, 57- *Mem:* Fel Soc Exp Biol & Med; Am Asn Path & Bact. *Res:* Renal athrocytosis; cardiac hypertrophy; cirrhosis and testicular atrophy; nuclear size, experimental hypertension. *Mailing Add:* Stanford Univ Sch of Med Palo Alto CA 94305

RATHJEN, WARREN FRANCIS, b New York, NY, Mar 4, 29; m 62; c 2. FISHERIES, DEVELOPMENTAL BIOLOGY. *Educ:* Univ Miami, BS, 53. *Prof Exp:* Aquatic biologist, NY State Conserv Dept, 54-56; FISHERIES ADMINR, NAT MARINE FISHERIES SERV, US DEPT COMMERCE, 56- *Concurrent Pos:* Lectr, Salem State Col, 78-79. *Mem:* fel Am Inst Fishery Res Biologists; Am Soc Ichthyol & Herpet; Am Fisheries Soc; Gulf & Carribbean Fisheries Inst. *Res:* Fisheries exploration and development in Atlantic and Pacific oceans; species of potential commercial interest; cephalopod utilization. *Mailing Add:* Nat Marine Fisheries Serv Box 1109 Gloucester MA 01930

RATHKE, JEROME WILLIAM, b Humboldt, Iowa, July 10, 47; m 68; c 2. CATALYSIS. *Educ:* Iowa State Univ, BS, 69; Ind Univ, PhD(inorg chem), 73. *Prof Exp:* Fel chem, Cornell Univ, 73-75; CHEMIST, ARGONNE NAT LAB, 75- *Mem:* Am Chem Soc. *Res:* Catalysis; Organometallic chemistry; coal conversion chemistry. *Mailing Add:* Chem Eng Div Argonne Nat Lab Argonne IL 60439

RATHKE, MICHAEL WILLIAM, b Humboldt, Iowa, Aug 13, 41; m 65; c 1. ORGANIC CHEMISTRY. *Educ:* Iowa State Univ, BS, 63; Purdue Univ, PhD(chem), 67. *Prof Exp:* NSF fel, Purdue Univ, 67-68; from asst prof to assoc prof, 68-78, PROF CHEM, MICH STATE UNIV, 78- *Mem:* Am Chem Soc. *Res:* Synthetic organic chemistry; organometallic chemistry, particularly boron organic chemistry. *Mailing Add:* Dept of Chem Mich State Univ East Lansing MI 48824

RATHMANN, CARL ERICH, b Chicago, Ill, June 27, 45; m 68; c 3. THERMODYNAMICS. *Educ:* Northwestern Univ, BS, 68, MS, 70, PhD(mech eng), 75. *Prof Exp:* Engr, Res Div, Gen Am Transp Corp, 65-75; vis asst prof mech eng, Northwestern Univ, 76-77; staff mem, Mo Res Corp, 77-78; asst prof physics, Westmont Col, 79; ASSOC PROF MECH ENG, CALIF STATE POLYTECH UNIV, 79- *Concurrent Pos:* Instr mech eng, Univ Calif, Santa Barbara, 79; consult, Gen Dynamics Corp, 80-; adj assoc prof, Harvey Mudd Col, 81- *Mem:* Sigma Xi; Am Soc Mech Engrs; Am Phys Soc; AAAS; Am Soc Eng Educ. *Res:* Numerical simulation of plasma phenomena including development of methods for simulation long-time-scale wave-particle (resonance) interactions; investigation of spectral decomposition techniques appropriate to plasma parameters. *Mailing Add:* Dept Mech Eng Calif State Polytech Univ 3801 W Temple Pomona CA 91768

RATHMANN, FRANZ HEINRICH, b Gotha, Fla, Apr 8, 04; m 49; c 2. CHEMISTRY, ASTRONOMY. *Educ:* Univ Minn, BA, 24, MA, 27; Univ Gottingen, PhD(org chem), 41. *Prof Exp:* Asst, Univ Minn, 25-27; asst prof chem, Millikin Univ, 29-31; sr sci worker, Inst Chem Physics, Leningrad, Russia, 31-35 & Inst Food-Pharm Res, Leningrad-Moscow, 35-37; res assoc phys chem, Univ Minn, 47-51; assoc prof chem, Univ Omaha, 51-55; from assoc prof to prof, 55-74, EMER PROF CHEM, NDAK STATE UNIV, 74- *Concurrent Pos:* Rockefeller Found fel, Univ Minn, 42; NSF res grants, 59-60; grad prof org chem, Univ Saigon, 62-63; adj prof astron, Moorhead State Univ, Minn, 74- *Mem:* AAAS; Am Chem Soc; Asn Acad Sci (pres, 73-76). *Res:* Hydroximic and hydroxamic acids; mechanism and kinetics of tautomerization reactions; mass spectra and purines; vitamins B-1 and E; isoxazoles. *Mailing Add:* Dept of Chem Ladd Hall 210 NDak State Univ Fargo ND 58102

RATHNAM, PREMILA, b India, Jan 7, 36. BIOCHEMISTRY, ENDOCRINOLOGY. *Educ:* Univ Madras, BSc, 55; Univ Wis, MS, 62; Seton Hall Univ, PhD(biochem), 66. *Prof Exp:* Res asst biochem & home econ, Univ Wis, 61-62; res asst chem, Seton Hall Univ, 62-66; fel endocrinol in med, 66-69, instr biochem in med, 69-71, asst prof biochem in med & endocrinol in obstet & gynec, 71-78, ASSOC PROF BIOCHEM IN MED & ENDOCRINOL IN OBSTET & GYNEC, MED COL, CORNELL UNIV, 78- *Concurrent Pos:* Lalor Found fel, Med Col, Cornell Univ, 66-68; USPHS trainee, 66-69; Int Cong Biochem travel awards, 70 & 73 & Endocrine Soc travel award, 80. *Mem:* NY Acad Sci; Am Chem Soc; Endocrine Soc. *Res:* Isolation, characterization and structure function relationships of human anterior pituitary hormones and its receeptors. *Mailing Add:* Div of Endocrinol Cornell Univ Med Col New York NY 10021

RATLIFF, CHARLES RAY, b Robertsdale, Ala, July 28, 26; m 52; c 3. BIOCHEMISTRY, MICROBIOLOGY. *Educ:* Samford Univ, BS, 54; Birmingham-South Col, MS, 60; Univ Ala, PhD, 65. *Prof Exp:* Supvr lab, Peoples Hosp, Jasper, Ala, 54-57 & Birmingham Baptist Hosps, 57-64; dir clin biochem, Baptist Med Ctr, 64-68; chief sect biochem, Scott & White Clin, 68-74; vpres & sci dir, Damon Corp, Med Serv Div, Needham Heights, Mass, 74-75; exec vpres, Med Ref Lab, Int Clin Labs, Inc, ICL of Ga, Columbus, 75-76; sci dir & vpres lab opers, Corp Off, 76-79; PROF PATH, COL MED, EAST TENN STATE UNIV, 79- *Concurrent Pos:* Instr, Walker Col, 56-; consult, Peoples Hosp, Jasper, 60-, Holy Family Hosp, Birmingham, 64-, Longview Gen Hosp, Graysville, 64- & Sci Develop, Walker Col, 64-; asst prof, Univ Ala, 66-; consult, Santa Fe Hosp, Temple, Tex, 68-, Bioregional Ref Lab, San Antonio, 70-, Vet Ctr Hosp, Temple, 71- & Data Med Assocs, Dallas, 71; mem Digestive Dis Found; assoc lab dir, Doctors Hosp, Columbus, Ga, 75-76. *Mem:* Am Inst Biol Sci; fel Am Inst Chem; fel Am Col Gastroenterol; Am Chem Soc; Am Asn Clin Chem. *Res:* Responses in infectious diseases, proteins and enzymes; instrumentation and automation; analytical biochemistry; enzymology; clinical applications. *Mailing Add:* Dept Path East Tenn State Univ Johnson City TN 37614

RATLIFF, FLOYD, b La Junta, Colo, May 1, 19; m 42; c 1. NEUROPHYSIOLOGY. *Educ:* Colo Col, AB, 47; Brown Univ, MSc, 49, PhD(psychol), 50. *Hon Degrees:* DSc, Colo Col, 75. *Prof Exp:* Nat Res Coun fel, Johns Hopkins Univ, 50-51; instr psychol, Harvard Univ, 51-52, asst prof, 52-54; from assoc to assoc prof, 54-66, PROF BIOPHYS, ROCKEFELLER UNIV, 66- *Honors & Awards:* Warren Medal, Soc Exp Psychol, 66; Tillyer Award, Optical Soc Am, 76. *Mem:* Nat Acad Sci; Optical Soc Am; fel Am Acad Arts & Sci; Am Psychol Asn; Am Philos Soc. *Res:* Neurophysiology of vision. *Mailing Add:* Rockefeller Univ 1230 York Ave New York NY 10021

RATLIFF, FRANCIS TENNEY, b Bogalusa, La, Oct 6, 19; m 44; c 1. PAPER TECHNOLOGY. *Educ:* La State Univ, BS, 40; Lawrence Col, MS, 42, PhD(paper chem), 48. *Prof Exp:* Res chemist, Standard Oil Develop Co, La, 42-45 & Johns-Manville Co, 48-51; paper technologist, Personal Prod Co, 51-54, tech dir, Paper Div, 54-57; asst res dir, Rhinelander Paper Co, 57-60, res dir, Rhinelander Div, St Regis Paper Co, 60-71, prod develop mgr, 71-73, asst tech dir, 73-74, RES DIR, RHINELANDER DIV, ST REGIS PAPER CO, 74-, ASST TECH DIR, 77- *Mem:* Tech Asn Pulp & Paper Indust; Am Soc Qual Control; Can Pulp & Paper Asn; Brit Paper & Bd Makers' Asn. *Res:* Physical properties of wood pulps; roofing papers; creped tissues; glassine, greaseproof, reprographic and packaging papers. *Mailing Add:* Rhinelander Div St Regis Paper Co Rhinelander WI 54501

RATLIFF, LARRY E, b Mar 7, 44; m 62; c 1. GEOLOGY, GEOPHYSICS. *Educ:* Morehead State Univ, BS, 66; Univ Tenn, MS, 68, PhD(geol), 74. *Prof Exp:* Instr geol, Murray State Univ, 69-70; explor geologist, Texaco Inc, 73-78; EXPLOR GEOLOGIST GEOL & GEOPHYS, CEJA CORP, 78- *Mem:* Am Asn Petrol Geologists; Soc Econ Paleontologists & Mineralogists; Geol Soc Am. *Res:* Recognition and definition of ancient environments by use of geological and geophysical techniques. *Mailing Add:* 4340 East 72nd Pl Tulsa OK 74113

RATLIFF, LOUIS JACKSON, JR, b Cedar Rapids, Iowa, Sept 1, 31. MATHEMATICS. *Educ:* Univ Iowa, BA, 53, MA, 58, PhD(math), 61. *Prof Exp:* Lectr math, Ind Univ, 61-63; lectr, 63-64, from asst prof to assoc prof, 64-69, PROF MATH, UNIV CALIF, RIVERSIDE, 69- *Concurrent Pos:* NSF grants, 64-68, 70-72 & res grant, 72-82. *Mem:* Am Math Soc. *Res:* Commutative algebra; local ring theory. *Mailing Add:* Dept of Math Univ of Calif Riverside CA 92521

RATLIFF, PRISCILLA N, b Uniontown, Pa, Dec 26, 40; m 69; c 1. CHEMICAL INFORMATION SCIENCE. *Educ:* Maryville Col, BS, 62; Vanderbilt Univ, MS, 64. *Prof Exp:* Asst ed, Chem Abstr Serv, 64-67; info scientist, Battelle Columbus Labs, 67-73; tech writer, Warren-Teed Pharmaceut, Inc, 73-76; res chemist, 76-78, SUPVR TECH INFO CTR, ASHLAND CHEM CO, 78- *Mem:* Am Chem Soc; Am Soc Info Sci; Spec Libr Asn. *Res:* Computerized and manual information retrieval systems. *Mailing Add:* Ashland Chem Co PO Box 2219 Columbus OH 43216

RATLIFF, ROBERT L, b Shawnee, Okla, Dec 1, 31; m 59; c 2. BIOCHEMISTRY. *Educ:* Univ Santa Clara, BS, 56; St Louis Univ, PhD(biochem), 60. *Prof Exp:* Am Cancer Soc fel enzymol, Univ Wis, 60-63; STAFF MEM BIOMED RES GROUP ENZYMOL, LOS ALAMOS NAT LAB, 63- *Mem:* Fedn Am Soc Exp Biol; AAAS; Am Soc Biol Chem. *Res:* Steroid--metabolism of bile acids; enzymes--purification of enzymes nucleoside diphosphokinases; nucleic acids; enzymatic synthesis of DNA and RNA. *Mailing Add:* Los Alamos Nat Lab MS-886 Los Alamos NM 87545

RATNER, ALBERT, b Brooklyn, NY, Sept 10, 37; m 67; c 2. ENDOCRINOLOGY, PHYSIOLOGY. *Educ:* Brooklyn Col, BS, 59; Mich State Univ, 62, PhD(physiol), 65. *Prof Exp:* ASSOC PROF PHYSIOL, SCH MED, UNIV NMEX, 67- *Concurrent Pos:* NIH fel physiol, Univ Tex Southwestern Med Sch Dallas, 65-67; NSF grant, 68-75. *Mem:* Int Soc Res Reproduction; Am Physiol Soc; Fedn Am Soc Exp Biol; Int Neuroendocrine Soc; Endocrine Soc. *Res:* Neuroendocrine control of anterior pituitary function. *Mailing Add:* Dept of Physiol Univ of NMex Sch of Med Albuquerque NM 87131

RATNER, BUDDY DENNIS, b Brooklyn, NY, Jan 19, 47; m 68; c 1. POLYMER CHEMISTRY, BIOMEDICAL ENGINEERING. *Educ:* Brooklyn Col, BS, 67; Polytech Inst Brooklyn, PhD(polymer chem), 72. *Prof Exp:* Res assoc, 72-75, res asst prof, 75-79, RES ASSOC PROF CHEM ENG, UNIV WASH, 79- *Concurrent Pos:* NIH prin investr; asst ed, J Biomed Mats Res; consult. *Mem:* Am Chem Soc; AAAS; Soc Biomat; Adhesion Soc. *Res:* Interaction of biological systems with synthetic polymeric materials; materials for blood-contact and ophthalmologic applications; surface analysis of materials. *Mailing Add:* Dept Chem Eng BF-10 Univ Wash Seattle WA 98195

RATNER, LAWRENCE THEODORE, b Philadelphia, Pa, Feb 16, 23; m 47. MATHEMATICS. *Educ:* Univ Calif, Los Angeles, AB, 44, MA, 45, PhD(math), 49. *Prof Exp:* Asst math, Univ Calif, Los Angeles, 44-45 & 47-49; asst prof, 49-54, ASSOC PROF MATH, VANDERBILT UNIV, 54- *Mem:* Am Math Soc; Math Asn Am. *Res:* Analysis in abstract spaces; topology; probability. *Mailing Add:* Dept Math Box 43 Sta B Vanderbilt Univ Nashville TN 37240

RATNER, LAZARUS GERSHON, b Chicago, Ill, Sept 14, 23; m 53; c 3. HIGH ENERGY PHYSICS, ACCELERATOR PHYSICS. *Educ:* Univ Calif, Berkeley, AB, 48, MA, 50. *Prof Exp:* Asst physicist accelerator physics, Lawrence Berkeley Lab, Univ Calif, 50-60; physicist accelerator & high energy physics, Argonne Nat Lab, 60-81; PHYSICIST ACCELERATOR, BROOKHAVEN NAT LAB, 81- *Concurrent Pos:* Vis scientist, Ctr Europ Nuclear Res, Geneva, Switz, 71-72. *Mem:* AAAS; Sigma Xi. *Res:* Strong interaction physics; polarization phenomena in high energy scattering; acceleration of polarized beams; design of high energy accelerators. *Mailing Add:* 911-B Brookhaven Nat Lab Upton NY 11973

RATNER, MARK A, b Cleveland, Ohio, Dec 8, 42; m 69. PHYSICAL CHEMISTRY. *Educ:* Harvard Univ, AB, 64; Northwestern Univ, Evanston, PhD(chem), 69. *Prof Exp:* Amanuensis chem, Arhaus Univ, Denmark, 69-70; asst, Munich Tech Univ, 70; from asst prof to assoc prof, NY Univ, 70-75; assoc prof, 75-80, PROF CHEM, NORTHWESTERN UNIV, 80- *Concurrent Pos:* A P Sloan fel. *Mem:* AAAS; Am Phys Soc; NY Acad Sci; The Chem Soc; Am Chem Soc. *Res:* Theoretical chemistry; nonadiabatic problems; hydrogen bonding; kinetics; spectra; green functions; electron transfer. *Mailing Add:* Dept of Chem Northwestern Univ Evanston IL 60201

RATNER, MICHAEL IRA, b New York, NY, June 30, 49; m 75; c 1. RADIO ASTRONOMY. *Educ:* Yale Col, BS, 71; Univ Colo, PhD(astro-geophysics), 76. *Prof Exp:* RES ASSOC RADIO ASTRON, DEPT EARTH & PLANETARY SCI, MASS INST TECHNOL, 76- *Res:* Computerized analyses of interferometric observations of radio signals from spacecraft and natural radio sources; observational tests of gravitation theory; continental drift; motions and natures of radio sources. *Mailing Add:* 54-627 Mass Inst Technol Cambridge MA 02139

RATNER, ROBERT (STEPHEN), b Newark, NJ, Apr 13, 41; m 64; c 1. TRANSPORTATION, SYSTEMS ENGINEERING. *Educ:* Mass Inst Technol, BS; Stanford Univ, MS, 65, PhD(elec eng), 68. *Prof Exp:* Res engr & sr res engr, Stanford Res Inst, 68-71; assoc mgr transp eng & control, 71-76, dir, Transp & Indust Systs Ctr, 76-81, VPRES, SYSTS CONSULT DIV, SRI INT, 82- *Mem:* Opers Res Soc Am. *Res:* Air transportation and railroad operations and management consulting; air traffic Control; transportation systems. *Mailing Add:* SRI Int Menlo Park CA 94025

RATNER, SARAH, b New York, NY, June 9, 03. BIOCHEMISTRY. *Educ:* Cornell Univ, AB, 24; Columbia Univ, MA, 27, PhD(biochem), 37. *Hon Degrees:* DSc, Univ NC, 81. *Prof Exp:* Asst biochem, Col Physicians & Surgeons, Columbia Univ, 30-31, 32-34, Macy res fel, 37-39, instr, 39-43, assoc, 43-46, asst prof, 46; asst prof pharmacol, Col Med, NY Univ, 46-53, assoc prof, 53-54; assoc mem, Div Nutrit & Physiol, 54-57, MEM, DEPT BIOCHEM, PUB HEALTH RES INST CITY NEW YORK, INC, 57- *Concurrent Pos:* Ed, J Biol Chem, 59- & Anal Biochem, 74-; res prof, Col Med, NY Univ; Fogarty scholar-in-residence, NIH, 78-79. *Honors & Awards:* Schoenheimer lectr, 56; Neuberg Medal, 59; Garvan Medal, Am Chem Soc, 61; L & B Freedman Found Award, NY Acad Sci, 75. *Mem:* Nat Acad Sci; Am Acad Arts & Sci; Am Soc Biol Chem; fel Harvey Soc; fel NY Acad Sci. *Res:* Metabolism and chemistry of amino acids; application of isotopes to intermediary metabolism; enzymatic mechanisms of arginine biosynthesis and urea formation and other nitrogen transferring reactions; regulation and structure-function relationships in arginine biosynthesis. *Mailing Add:* Dept of Biochem NYC Pub Health Res Inst Inc 455 First Ave New York NY 10016

RATNEY, RONALD STEVEN, b Brooklyn, NY, June 1, 32; m 57; c 3. INDUSTRIAL HYGIENE. *Educ:* Calif Inst Technol, BS, 54; Yale Univ, PhD(chem), 59; Harvard Sch Pub Health, MS, 72. *Prof Exp:* Chemist, Trubek Labs, 58-60; from asst prof to assoc prof chem, Hood Col, 60-67; assoc prof chem, Bentley Col, 67-71; chemist, Mass Div Occup Hyg, 72-75; INDUST HYGIENIST, OCCUP SAFETY & HEALTH ADMIN, 75- *Mem:* Am Chem Soc; Sigma Xi; Am Indust Hyg Soc; Am Conf Govt Indust Hygienists; NY Acad Sci. *Res:* Toxicology. *Mailing Add:* 167 Old Billerica Rd Bedford MA 01730

RATNOFF, OSCAR DAVIS, b New York, NY, Aug 23, 16; m 45; c 2. INTERNAL MEDICINE. *Educ:* Columbia Univ, AB, 36, MD, 39. *Prof Exp:* Intern, Med Serv, Johns Hopkins Hosp, 39-40; asst resident med, Montefiore Hosp, New York, 42; asst med, Col Physicians & Surgeons, Columbia Univ, 42-46; instr, Johns Hopkins Univ, 48-50; asst prof, Sch Med, 50-56, assoc prof, 56-61, asst vis physician, 52-57, assoc vis physician, 57-67, PROF MED, SCH MED, CASE WESTERN RESERVE UNIV, 61-, VIS PHYSICIAN, UNIV HOSPS, 67- *Concurrent Pos:* Austin teaching fel physiol, Harvard Med Sch, 40-41; fel, Sch Med, Johns Hopkins Univ, 46-48; resident, Res Serv Chronic Dis, Goldwater Mem Hosp, 42; assoc, Mt Sinai Hosp, Cleveland, Ohio, 50-52; career investr, Am Heart Asn, 60- *Mem:* Nat Acad Sci; Am Soc Hemat; Am Col Physicians; Cent Soc Clin Res; Asn Am Physicians. *Res:* Hemostatic mechanisms. *Mailing Add:* 2916 Sedgewick Rd Shaker Heights OH 44120

RATTAN, KULDIP SINGH, b India, Apr 25, 48; m 76; c 1. ELECTRICAL ENGINEERING, HARDWARE SYSTEMS. *Educ:* Punjab Eng Col, India, BSc, 69; Univ Ky, MS, 72, PhD(elec eng), 75. *Prof Exp:* Fel bio-eng, Univ Ky, 76, res assoc, 77-78; asst prof, 79-82, ASSOC PROF ELEC ENG, WRIGHT STATE UNIV, 82- *Concurrent Pos:* Res assoc & SCEE fel, SCEEE Fac Res Prog, US Air Force, 80; prin investr, US Air Force Off Sci Res, 81- *Mem:* Inst Elec & Electronics Engrs; Am Inst Aeronaut & Astronaut. *Res:* Design and analysis of digital control systems; develop a computer aided method for redesign of existing continuous control systems; robotics and computer control; computer aided design; model reduction. *Mailing Add:* Dept Eng Wright State Univ Dayton OH 45435

RATTAZZI, MARIO CRISTIANO, b Naples, Italy, Oct 1, 35; m 62; c 1. HUMAN GENETICS, BIOCHEMICAL GENETICS. *Educ:* Univ Naples, MD, 61. *Prof Exp:* Res asst prof human genetics, Univ Leiden, Neth, 62-69; from res asst prof to assoc prof, 69-80, PROF PEDIAT, STATE UNIV NY BUFFALO, 80- *Concurrent Pos:* Adv, WHO, 63; res career develop award, Nat Inst Gen Med Sci, 73. *Mem:* Am Soc Human Genetics; AAAS; NY Acad Sci; Soc Pediat Res; Soc Inherited Metab Dis. *Res:* Human lysosomal storage diseases; biochemical genetic diagnostic and therapeutic aspects. *Mailing Add:* Div of Human Genetics Dept of Pediat Childrens Hosp Buffalo NY 14222

RATTE, CHARLES A, b Brattleboro, Vt, Mar 3, 27; m 55; c 2. GEOLOGY. *Educ:* Middlebury Col, BA, 53; Dartmouth Col, MA, 55; Univ Ariz, PhD(geol), 63. *Prof Exp:* Teaching asst geol, Dartmouth Col, 53-55 & Univ Ariz, 55-56; geologist, US Steel Corp, 56-61; instr geol, Univ Ariz, 61-63; prof geol & chmn dept, Windham Col, 63-76, chmn div sci, 64-66; VT STATE GEOLOGIST, 76- *Mem:* Am Geol Inst; Geol Soc Am. *Res:* Groundwater investigations; igneous, metamorphic and glacial terrains. *Mailing Add:* 10 Independence Green Montpelier VT 05602

RATTENBORG, CHRISTEN C, b Denmark, Sept 26, 18; US citizen; m 44; c 4. ANESTHESIOLOGY. *Educ:* Aarhus Univ, BA, 40; Copenhagen Univ, MD, 47; Danish Bd Anesthesiol, dipl, 62; Am Bd Anesthesiol, dipl, 64. *Prof Exp:* Intern, Amtssygehuset, Skive, Denmark, 47-48; resident anesthesiol, NY Presby Hosp, 56-57; from asst prof to assoc prof, 59-71, PROF ANESTHESIOL, SCH MED, UNIV CHICAGO, 71- *Mem:* AMA; fel Am Col Chest Physicians. *Res:* Respiratory mechanics. *Mailing Add:* Dept of Anesthesiol Univ of Chicago Sch of Med Chicago IL 60637

RATTI, JOGINDAR SINGH, b Rajoya, India, Jan 1, 35; m 62; c 2. ANALYTICAL MATHEMATICS. *Educ:* Univ Bombay, BSc, 55, MSc, 58; Wayne State Univ, PhD(math), 66. *Prof Exp:* Lectr math, Khalsa Col, India, 58-60 & Nat Col, Bombay, India, 60-61; instr, Nev Southern Univ, 63-65 & Wayne State Univ, 65-66; asst prof, Oakland Univ, 66-67; assoc prof, 67-69, chmn dept, 69-77, PROF MATH, UNIV S FLA, 69- *Mem:* Am Math Soc; Math Asn Am. *Res:* Graph theory; summability; univalent functions; polynomials; graphs of semigroups and semirings. *Mailing Add:* Dept of Math Univ of SFla Tampa FL 33620

RATTNER, BARNETT ALVIN, b Washington, DC, Oct 4, 50; m 78. REPRODUCTIVE PHYSIOLOGY, ENVIRONMENTAL TOXICOLOGY. *Educ:* Univ Md, BS, 72, MS, 74, PhD(reprod physiol), 77. *Prof Exp:* Teaching asst zool, Univ Md, 72-76, instr, 76-77; Nat Res Coun res assoc, Naval Med Res Inst, Nat Naval Med Ctr, Bethesda, Md, 77-78; RES PHYSIOLOGIST, PHYSIOL SECT, PATUXENT WILDLIFE RES CTR, 78- *Mem:* Am Physiol Soc; Am Soc Zoologists; Soc Study Reprod; Soc Exp Biol & Med. *Res:* Environmental and nutritional effects on endocrine and reproductive function; embryonic implantation; hypobaric and hyperbaric physiology; toxicology. *Mailing Add:* Physiol Sect US Fish & Wildlife Serv Laurel MD 20708

RATTNER, JEROME BERNARD, b Cincinnati, Ohio, Aug 12, 45; m 73; c 1. ANATOMY. *Educ:* Miami Univ, BS, 67; Univ Tex, MS, 69; Washington Univ, PhD(biol), 73. *Prof Exp:* Fel cell biol, Univ Calif, Irvine, 73-75; NATO fel biol, Nat Ctr Sci Res, France, 75-76; res asst, Univ Calif, Irvine, 76-81; ASST PROF ANAT, UNIV CALGARY, 81- *Mem:* Am Soc Cell Biol. *Res:* Organization of chromatin and chromosomes in eukaryotic cells. *Mailing Add:* Univ Calgary 3330 Hosp Dr NW Calgary AB T2N 4N1 Can

RATTO, PETER ANGELO, b San Francisco, Calif, Jan 31, 30; m 66. PHARMACEUTICAL CHEMISTRY. *Educ:* Univ Calif, BS, 51, MS, 56, PhD(pharmaceut chem), 59. *Prof Exp:* Asst prof pharm & pharmaceut chem, Loyola Univ, 58-63; sr res scientist, Bristol Labs, 63-71; res pharmacist, Norwich-Eaton Pharmaceut Co, 71-80; MEM FAC SCH PHARM, SOUTHWESTERN OKLA STATE UNIV, 80- *Mem:* Am Pharmaceut Asn; Am Chem Soc. *Res:* Synthesis of organic medicinal agents; physical chemical evaluation and preparation of pharmaceutical dosage formulations. *Mailing Add:* Sch Pharm Southwestern Okla State Univ Weatherford OK 73096

RATTRAY, BASIL ANDREW, b Iron Hill, Que, Nov 16, 27; m 55. MATHEMATICS. *Educ:* McGill Univ, BSc, 48, MSc, 49; Princeton Univ, PhD(math), 54. *Prof Exp:* Lectr math, Univ NB, 52-54; asst prof, 54-59, ASSOC PROF MATH, McGILL UNIV, 59- *Mem:* Am Math Soc; Can Math Cong. *Res:* Topology. *Mailing Add:* Dept of Math McGill Univ Montreal PQ H3A 2T5 Can

RATTRAY, MAURICE, JR, b Seattle, Wash, Sept 16, 22; m 51; c 3. HYDRODYNAMICS, PHYSICAL OCEANOGRAPHY. *Educ:* Calif Inst Technol, BS, 44, MS, 47, PhD(physics), 51. *Prof Exp:* From asst prof to assoc prof, 50-62, chmn dept, 68-78, PROF OCEANOG, UNIV WASH, 62- *Concurrent Pos:* Rossby fel, Woods Hole Oceanog Inst, 66-67; mem adv panel earth sci, NSF, 66-68; mem exec comt, Joint Oceanog Insts Deep Earth Studies, 68-78, chmn, 69 & 76-78; consult, US Naval Oceanog Off, 68-74; consult sci adv comt, US Coast Guard, 69-72; mem ocean sci comt & Aidjex rev panel, Nat Acad Sci, 71-74; mem environ pollutant movement & transformation adv comt, Environ Protection Agency, 76-78. *Mem:* Am Soc Limnol & Oceanog (vpres, 63-64, pres-elect, 64-65, pres, 65-66); Am Geophys Union. *Res:* Oceanographic models; dynamics of estuarine and oceanic current systems. *Mailing Add:* Dept of Oceanog Univ of Wash WB-10 Seattle WA 98195

RATTS, KENNETH WAYNE, b Martinsville, Ill, July 7, 32; m 59; c 3. ORGANIC CHEMISTRY. *Educ:* Univ Eastern Ill, BS, 54; Ohio State Univ, PhD, 59. *Prof Exp:* Asst chem, Ohio State Univ, 54-55, asst org chem, 55-57, asst instr, 57-59; res chemist, 59-62, sr res specialist, 63-65, sr group leader, 66, sci fel, 66-75, mgr res, 75-78, res dir process technol, 78-80, DIR CHEM RES, MONSANTO CO, 80- *Mem:* Am Chem Soc; Sigma Xi; NY Acad Sci. *Res:* 5-halobenzo (a) biphenylenes and transformations; agricultural chemicals; ylid and phosphorus chemistry; sulfur chemistry. *Mailing Add:* Monsanto Co T480 800 N Lindbergh Blvd St Louis MO 63166

RATTY, FRANK JOHN, JR, b San Diego, Calif, June 26, 23; wid; c 1. GENETICS. *Educ:* San Diego State Col, BA, 48; Univ Utah, MS, 49, PhD(genetics), 52. *Prof Exp:* Instr biol, Univ Utah, 52-53; res geneticist poultry husb, Univ Calif, 53-54; from instr to assoc prof zool, 55-62, PROF BIOL, SAN DIEGO STATE UNIV, 62- *Mem:* AAAS; Genetics Soc Am. *Res:* Mutation; cytogenetics. *Mailing Add:* Dept Biol San Diego State Univ San Diego CA 92182

RATZ, H(ERBERT) C(HARLES), b Hamilton, Ont, July 23, 27; m 55; c 3. ELECTRICAL ENGINEERING. *Educ:* Univ Toronto, BASc, 50; Mass Inst Technol, SM, 52; Univ Sask, PhD(elec eng), 63. *Prof Exp:* Res engr, Ferranti-Electronics, Ltd, Ont, 52-55, proj engr, 56-57; design engr, Fischer & Porter (Can) Ltd, 57-59; asst prof elec eng, Univ Sask, 60-63; assoc prof, 63-66, assoc dean, 68-71, PROF ELEC ENG, UNIV WATERLOO, 66- *Concurrent Pos:* Nat Res Coun Can res grants, 62-72; consult, Ferranti-Electronics, Ltd, 64-66, Can Westinghouse Co, 65 & Naval Res Estab, 67-71; vis prof, NS Tech Col, 71. *Mem:* sr mem Inst Elec & Electronics Engrs. *Res:* Information processing systems; signal analysis and communications; computer communications networks. *Mailing Add:* 288 Lourdes Crescent Waterloo ON N2L 1P5 Can

RATZLAFF, KERMIT O, b Hillsboro, Kans, Dec 26, 21; m 44; c 5. PHYSIOLOGY, ZOOLOGY. *Educ:* Univ Calif, Los Angeles, AB, 49, MA, 51, PhD(zool), 62. *Prof Exp:* Res technician, White Mem Hosp, Los Angeles, Calif, 52-56; teaching asst zool, Univ Calif, Los Angeles, 56-58; res physiologist, Sch Med, Univ Calif, 59-62; asst prof physiol & zool, 62-74, ASSOC PROF BIOL SCI, SOUTHERN ILL UNIV, EDWARDSVILLE, 74- *Concurrent Pos:* Instr, Biola Col, 50-54; consult, Vet Admin Ctr, Los Angeles, 60-62 & Vet Admin Hosp, Long Beach, 62. *Mem:* AAAS; Am Sci Affil. *Res:* Mechanisms of functioning of sense organs, particularly regeneration of visual pigments; problems related to ocular metabolism. *Mailing Add:* Dept of Biol Sci Southern Ill Univ Edwardsville IL 62025

RATZLAFF, MARC HENRY, b Bakersfield, Calif, Feb 21, 42; m 63; c 2. ANATOMY, VETERINARY MEDICINE. *Educ:* Univ Calif, Davis, AB, 64, MA, 66, PhD(anat), 69; Mich State Univ, DVM, 74. *Prof Exp:* Asst prof anat, Mich State Univ, 69-74; pvt vet pract, Eagle, Idaho, 74-75; ASSOC PROF ANAT, WASH STATE UNIV, 76- *Mem:* Am Asn Vet Anatomists; Am Vet Med Asn. *Res:* Equine locomotion; biomechanics. *Mailing Add:* Dept of Vet Anat Pharm & Physiol Wash State Univ Pullman WA 99164

RATZLAFF, WILLIS, b Fairview, Okla, June 1, 26; m 49; c 4. LIMNOLOGY. *Educ:* Kans State Teachers Col, BS, 50, MS, 51; Univ Kans, PhD, 72. *Prof Exp:* Teacher high schs, Kans, 51-53; supv prin pub sch, Ohio, 53-56; teacher high sch, Kans, 56-58; supt Princeton schs, Kans, 59-61; assoc prof, 63-72, PROF LIFE SCI, MILLERSVILLE STATE COL, 72- *Concurrent Pos:* Consult, Sci Teachers Inst, Kans State Teachers Col, 59. *Mem:* AAAS; Am Soc Limnol & Oceanog; Ecol Soc Am; Am Fisheries Soc; Am Inst Biol Sci. *Res:* Ecology of small and ephemeral bodies of water; zooplankton population dynamics; ecological effects of electric power generation on the lower Susquehanna River. *Mailing Add:* Dept of Biol Millersville State Col Millersville PA 17551

RAU, A RAVI PRAKASH, b Calcutta, India, Aug 9, 45; m 69; c 2. ATOMIC PHYSICS. *Educ:* Univ Delhi, BSc, 64, MSc, 66; Univ Chicago, PhD(atomic physics), 70. *Prof Exp:* Res assoc physics, Univ Chicago, 70; assoc res scientist physics, NY Univ, 70-72; vis fel theoret physics, Tata Inst Fundamental Res, Bombay, India, 72-73; from asst prof to assoc prof, 74-81, PROF PHYSICS, LA STATE UNIV, BATON ROUGE, 81- *Concurrent Pos:* Conf fel, III Int Conf Atomic Physics, Boulder, Colo, 72; vis assoc prof, Yale Univ, 78-79; Alfred P Sloan Found fel. *Mem:* Sigma Xi. *Res:* Two-electron phenomena, structure and properties of atoms in intense magnetic fields, such as those on pulsars; development and application of general variational principles in atomic physics and in other areas of physics. *Mailing Add:* Dept of Physics La State Univ Baton Rouge LA 70803

RAU, BANTWAL RAMAKRISHNA, b Lucknow, India, Feb 13, 51; m 75; c 1. COMPUTER SCIENCE, COMPUTER ENGINEERING. *Educ:* Indian Inst Technol, Madras, BTech, 72; Stanford Univ, MS, 73, PhD(elec eng), 77. *Prof Exp:* Mem tech staff comput design, Palyn Assocs, Inc, 73-74; res asst elec eng, Stanford Univ, 75-77; ASST PROF ELEC ENG, UNIV ILL, URBANA-CHAMPAIGN, 77- *Concurrent Pos:* Assoc consult, Palyn Assocs, Inc, 78- *Mem:* Inst Elec & Electronics Engrs; Asn Comput Mach. *Res:* Computer architecture; computer performance evaluation; applied queueing theory. *Mailing Add:* Dept of Elec Eng Coord Sci Lab Univ of Ill Urbana IL 61801

RAU, CHARLES ALFRED, JR, b Philadelphia, Pa, Jan 28, 42; m 65; c 3. MATERIALS SCIENCE, ENGINEERING MECHANICS. *Educ:* Lafayette Col, BS, 63; Stanford Univ, MS, 65, PhD(mat sci), 67. *Prof Exp:* Res asst metal fracture, Stanford Univ, 64-67; sr res assoc mech behav, Advan Mat Res & Develop Lab, Pratt & Whitney Aircraft Div, United Aircraft Corp, 67-70, supvr life prediction methods group, Mat Eng & Res Lab, 70-74; gen mgr, 74-76, vpres & prin engr, 76-80, EXEC VPRES, FAILURE ANAL ASSOC, 80- *Concurrent Pos:* Lectr metall, Univ Conn, 67-68; lectr fracture mech, Univ Calif, Los Angeles, 78-; hon fel, Stanford Univ. *Mem:* Am Inst Mining, Metall & Petrol Engrs; Am Soc Metals; Soc Exp Stress Anal; Am Nuclear Soc; Am Soc Testing Mat. *Res:* Deformation and fracture of materials, including both theoretical and experimental studies of the application of fracture mechanics to lifetime prediction and mechanical reliability. *Mailing Add:* Failure Anal Assoc 750 Welch Rd Palo Alto CA 94304

RAU, ERIC, b Weissenfels, Ger, Sept 25, 28; US citizen; m 55; c 2. INDUSTRIAL CHEMISTRY, WASTE MANAGEMENT. *Educ:* NY Univ, BA, 51, PhD(phys chem), 55. *Prof Exp:* Chemist, US Naval Air Rocket Test Sta, 50-52; from engr to sr engr, Bettis Atomic Power Lab, Westinghouse Elec Corp, 52-60; res chemist, Cent Res FMC Corp, Princeton, NJ, 60-63, supvr, Inorg Chem Div, 63-65, mgr, Phys Chem Sect, Inorg Res & Develop Dept, 65-74, asst dir process develop, Indust Chem Div, Res & Develop Dept, 74-78; dir res & develop, 78-81, DIR TECHNOL, CONVERSION SYSTS, INC, 81-, VPRES, 81- *Mem:* Am Chem Soc; Electrochem Soc; fel Am Inst Chemists. *Res:* Phosphorus; alkali salts; corrosion; high temperature reactions; coal; electrochemistry; waste management and ultimate disposal; pozzalanic reactions; alkaline earth salts. *Mailing Add:* 115 Gibraltar Horsham PA 19044

RAU, GREGORY HUDSON, b Tacoma, Wash, Dec 14, 48. BIOGEOCHEMISTRY. *Educ:* Western Wash State Col, BA, 71; Univ Wash, MS, 74, PhD(ecol), 79. *Prof Exp:* Res asst, Western Wash State Col, 71; res asst, Univ Wash, 73-78; res assoc, Ore State Univ, 79; fel scholar, Univ Calif, Los Angeles, 79-81; fel, Scripps Inst Oceanog, 81; NAT RES COUN RES ASSOC, AMES RES CTR, NASA, 81- *Concurrent Pos:* Consult, Coop Fisheries Unit, Univ Wash, 72 & Southern Calif Coastal Water Res Proj, 81; technician, Global Geochem Corp, 80-81. *Mem:* Am Soc Limnol & Oceanog; Am Geophys Union; AAAS; Int Soc Limnol; Ecol Soc Am. *Res:* Carbon and nitrogen flow and cycling in past and present environments; microbial, plant, animal and human biology, ecology, and nutrition; interpretation of preceding based on stable isotope natural abundances. *Mailing Add:* Ames Res Ctr NASA Mail Stop 239-12 Moffett Field CA 94035

RAU, JON LLEWELLYN, b Fargo, NDak, June 11, 31; m 62; c 2. GEOLOGY. *Educ:* Univ North Dakota, BS, 53; Univ Cincinnati, MS, 55; Yale Univ, PhD(geol), 59. *Prof Exp:* From instr to asst prof geol, Univ NDak, 57-59; geologist, US Geol Surv, 59-62; from asst prof to assoc prof geol, Kent State Univ, 62-70; ASSOC PROF GEOL, UNIV BC, 70- *Concurrent Pos:* Asst dean, Col Arts & Sci, Kent State Univ, 65-66. *Mem:* AAAS; Geol Asn Can; Geol Soc Am; Am Asn Petrol Geol. *Res:* Hydrogeology of western Canada especially Gulf Islands; Rocky Mountain Trench and Chilcotin of British Columbia; environmental geology of British Columbia; trace element geochemistry; Pleistocene geology of British Columbia. *Mailing Add:* Dept of Geol Sci Univ of BC Vancouver BC V6T 1W5 Can

RAU, MANFRED ERNST, b May 30, 42; m 69; c 1. PARASITOLOGY, ECOLOGY. *Educ:* Univ Western Ont, BSc, 65; Univ BC, PhD(parasitol), 70. *Prof Exp:* Fel, 69-70, res assoc, 70-75, asst prof, 75-79, ASSOC PROF, INST PARASITOL, MCGILL UNIV, 79- *Mem:* Can Soc Zool; Am Soc Parasitologists; Am Soc Zoologists. *Res:* Ecology of parasite transmission; developmemt of strategies for the management of parasites in free-living animal populations; immunology of parasitic infections. *Mailing Add:* Inst Parasitol MacDonald Campus McGill Univ MacDonald Col PO PQ H9X 1C0 Can

RAU, R RONALD, b Tacoma, Wash, Sept 1, 20; m 44; c 2. PHYSICS, ACCELERATORS. *Educ:* Col Puget Sound, BS, 41; Calif Inst Technol, MS, 43, PhD(physics), 48. *Prof Exp:* Physicist, Calif Inst Technol, 43-45; from instr to asst prof physics, Princeton Univ, 47-56; from assoc physicist to sr physicist, 56-70, chmn dept physics, 66-70, assoc dir high energy physics, 70-81, SR PHYSICIST, BROOKHAVEN NAT LAB, 81- *Concurrent Pos:* Fulbright fel, France, 54-55; mem policy comt, Stanford Linear Accelerator Ctr, 67-73; mem prog comt, Los Alamos Meson Physics Fac, 70-74; chmn high energy adv comt, Brookhaven Nat Lab, 70-81; mem high energy physics adv panel, AEC, 70-74; adj prof, Univ Wyo, 70-; mem bd trustees, Univ Puget Sound, 78- *Mem:* Am Phys Soc; AAAS; NY Acad Sci. *Res:* Cloud chamber studies of cosmic rays at high altitudes and of heavy mesons; experimental high energy particle physics; bubble chambers; strong interactions; resonance production; particle accelerators; superconducting magnets. *Mailing Add:* Brookhaven Nat Lab Upton NY 11973

RAU, RICHARD RAYMOND, b Philadelphia, Pa, Apr 17, 28; m 54; c 4. PHYSICS, COMPONENT ENGINEERING. *Educ:* Muhlenberg Col, BS, 49; Yale Univ, MS, 50; Univ Pa, PhD(solid state physics), 55. *Prof Exp:* Sr engr semiconductor develop, Sperry Rand Corp, 56-59; dir eng, Nat Semiconductor Corp, 59-67; mgr eng digital integrated circuit, Transitron Electronic Corp, 67-70; mgr prod procurement electronic components, Raytheon Co, 71-72; mgr eng hybrid circuits, Control Prod Div, Bell & Howell Co, 72-78; SR ENGR COMPONENTS & CIRCUITS, PERKIN-ELMER CO, DANBURY, 78- *Concurrent Pos:* Asst instr, Univ Bridgeport, 59; lectr, Univ Conn, 65-67. *Mem:* Am Phys Soc; Inst Elec & Electronics Engrs; Res Soc Am. *Res:* Silicon devices. *Mailing Add:* 17 Longview Heights Rd Newtown CT 06470

RAU, WELDON WILLIS, b Tacoma, Wash, Jan 20, 21; m 44; c 1. MICROPALEONTOLOGY, BIOSTRATIGRAPHY. *Educ:* Col Puget Sound, BS, 43; Univ Iowa, MS, 46, PhD(paleont), 50. *Prof Exp:* Asst geol, Univ Iowa, 43-47; from instr to asst prof, Col Puget Sound, 47-50; geologist stratig micropaleont, Geol Div, US Geol Surv, 50-60; GEOLOGIST, DIV GEOL & EARTH RESOURCES, WASH STATE DEPT NATURAL RESOURCES, 60- *Concurrent Pos:* Geol consult, US Geol Surv, 60- *Mem:* Paleont Soc; Geol Soc Am; Soc Econ Paleont & Mineral; Am Asn Petrol Geol. *Res:* Tertiary Foraminifera of the Pacific Northwest and Southeast Alaska; stratigraphic micropaleontology of West Coast Tertiary rocks. *Mailing Add:* Div of Geol & Earth Resources Wash State Dept Natural Resources Olympia WA 98501

RAUB, HARRY LYMAN, III, b Lancaster, Pa, Oct 22, 19; m 47; c 2. PHYSICS. *Educ:* Franklin & Marshall Col, 41; Cornell Univ, PhD(exp physics), 47. *Prof Exp:* Asst, Cornell Univ, 41-47; res assoc, 47; from asst prof to assoc prof, 47-56, PROF PHYSICS, MUHLENBERG COL, 56- *Mem:* Am Phys Soc; Am Asn Physics Teachers. *Res:* Elastic losses in high polymers; study of sound velocities with acoustic interferometer; x-ray diffraction. *Mailing Add:* Dept of Physics Muhlenberg Col Allentown PA 18104

RAUB, WILLIAM F, b Alden Station, Pa, Nov 25, 39; m 64; c 3. PHYSIOLOGY, COMPUTER SCIENCE. *Educ:* Wilkes Col, AB, 61; Univ Pa, PhD(physiol), 65. *Prof Exp:* Pa Plan fel, Univ Pa, 65-66; health sci admnr, Div Res Facil & Resources, 66-69, chief, Biotechnol Resources Br, Div Res Resources, 69-75, assoc dir extramural & collab progs, Nat Eye Inst, 75-78, ASSOC DIR EXTRAMURAL RES, NIH, BETHESDA, MD, 78- *Mem:* AAAS. *Res:* Automated information-handling in biology and medicine and respiratory physiology. *Mailing Add:* 11408 Rolling House Rockville MD 20852

RAUCH, DONALD J(OHN), b St Peters, Mo, Oct 20, 35; m 58; c 2. ELECTRICAL ENGINEERING. *Educ:* Washington Univ, St Louis, BS, 57; Mich State Univ, MS, 60, PhD(elec eng), 63. *Prof Exp:* Radar engr, Emerson Elec Mfg Co, 57-58; sr lectr elec eng, SDak State Col, 58-59; systs res assoc, Planning Res Corp, 63-67; sr engr guid & control systs, Litton Industs, 67-71; vpres & dir, Sysdyne, Inc, 71-76, pres, 76-78; PRES, EVOLVING TECHNOL CO, 79- *Concurrent Pos:* Sr lectr, Univ Southern Calif, 65-; chmn session on state space synthesis, Asilomar Conf Circuits & Systs, 70; mem tech prog comt, Joint Nat Conf Major Systs, 71; chmn, Los Angeles Prof Group Circuit Theory. *Res:* Radar cross sections, extended diffraction scattering model for electromagnetic waves to include plasma or multilayered media; adaptive control processes; development of techniques for synthesizing physical systems from a time domain model. *Mailing Add:* 3725 Talbot St Suite F San Diego CA 92106

RAUCH, EMIL BRUNO, b Friedland, Czech, Mar 19, 19; nat US; m 60; c 2. ORGANIC CHEMISTRY. *Educ:* Univ Heidelberg, PhD, 53. *Prof Exp:* Res assoc org chem, Wash Univ, 53-55; res chemist, Indust Photo Div, GAF Corp, 55-64, res assoc, 64-67, mgr color res & develop, 67-74, dir res & develop, 74-77, sr scientist, 77-80; SR SCIENTIST, ANITEC IMAGE CORP, 80- *Mem:* Am Chem Soc; Soc Ger Chem; Soc Photog Sci & Engr. *Mailing Add:* Anitec Image Corp PO Box 4444 Binghamton NY 13902

RAUCH, FRED D, b Rainier, Ore, Jan 17, 31; m 58; c 2. HORTICULTURE, PLANT PHYSIOLOGY. *Educ:* Ore State Univ, BS, 56, MS, 63; Iowa State Univ, PhD(hort, plant physiol), 67. *Prof Exp:* Exp farm technician, Ore State Univ, 58-60, asst hort, Mid-Columbia Exp Sta, Hood River, 60-63; instr, Iowa State Univ, 63-67; asst prof, Miss State Univ, 67-70; asst specialist, 70-74, assoc specialist, 74-80, SPECIALIST, DEPT HORT, UNIV HAWAII, 80- *Mem:* Int Plant Propagators Soc; Am Soc Hort Sci. *Res:* Stock-scion relationships; plant nutrition; growth regulators; herbicides. *Mailing Add:* Dept Hort 3190 Maile Way Univ Hawaii Honolulu HI 96822

RAUCH, GARY CLARK, b Dayton, Ohio, Oct 14, 42; m 67; c 2. PHYSICAL METALLURGY. *Educ:* Mass Inst Technol, BS, 64, PhD(metall), 68; Univ Ill, Urbana, MS, 65. *Prof Exp:* Scientist, Fundamental Res Lab, US Steel Corp, Pa, 68-71; SR ENGR, MAGNETICS DEPT, WESTINGHOUSE RES & DEVELOP CTR, 72- *Mem:* Am Soc Metals; Metall Soc of Am Inst Mining, Metall & Petrol Engrs. *Res:* Phase transformations and precipitation in iron-base alloys; mechanical properties of martensite; physical metallurgy of ferromagnetic materials; core loss phenomena in transformer steels; magnetic domains; phase transformations and precipitation in iron-base alloys. *Mailing Add:* Magnetics Dept Westinghouse Res & Develop Ctr Pittsburgh PA 15235

RAUCH, HAROLD, b New York, NY, Oct 13, 25; m 52; c 3. ZOOLOGY. *Educ:* Queens Col (NY), BS, 44; Univ Ill, MS, 47; Brown Univ, PhD(biol), 50. *Prof Exp:* From instr to assoc prof, 50-60, PROF ZOOL, UNIV MASS, AMHERST, 60-, CHMN DEPT, 71-74. *Mem:* Genetics Soc Am; Am Soc Zool. *Res:* Mammalian physiological genetics; nervous system, pigmentation and copper metabolism in the mouse. *Mailing Add:* Dept of Zool Univ of Mass Amherst MA 01002

RAUCH, HARRY ERNEST, mathematics, see previous edition

RAUCH, HELENE COBEN, b Los Angeles, Calif. IMMUNOLOGY, MICROBIOLOGY. *Educ:* Univ Calif, Los Angeles, BA, 51, PhD(microbiol), 58. *Prof Exp:* Bacteriologist, Los Angeles County Dept Pub Health, 51-52; part-time asst, Univ Calif, Los Angeles, 53-57; res assoc, Dept Allergy & Immunol, Palo Alto Med Res Found, 57-60; res assoc, Div Infectious Dis, Sch Med, Stanford Univ, 60-61, prin investr, Nat Inst Neurol Dis & Stroke Grant & res assoc, Dept Med Microbiol, 64-75; ASSOC PROF IMMUNOL, WAYNE STATE UNIV, 75- *Concurrent Pos:* Nat Multiple Sclerosis Soc fel, Sch Med, Stanford Univ, 61-64. *Mem:* AAAS; Am Soc Microbiol; Sigma Xi; Am Asn Immunologists; Tissue Cult Asn. *Res:* Auto-allergic diseases, especially experimental allergic encephalomyelitis; immunopathology; cellular hypersensitivity; multiple sclerosis. *Mailing Add:* Dept of Immunol & Microbiol Wayne State Univ Detroit MI 48202

RAUCH, HENRY WILLIAM, b Amsterdam, NY, Oct 23, 42; m 71; c 1. HYDROGEOLOGY, GEOCHEMISTRY. *Educ:* Alfred Univ, BA, 65; Pa State Univ, PhD(geochem), 72. *Prof Exp:* ASSOC PROF GEOL, WVA UNIV, 70- *Honors & Awards:* Cert Merit, Nat Speleol Soc, 74. *Mem:* Am Geophys Union; Geol Soc Am; Am Water Resources Asn; Nat Water Well Asn; fel Nat Speleol Soc. *Res:* Ground water hydrology and aqueous geochemistry; karst hydrogeology; ground water pollution; ground water exploration; effects of coal mining on ground water; hydrogeologic methods for natural gas exploration. *Mailing Add:* 419 White Hall WVa Univ Morgantown WV 26506

RAUCH, HERBERT EMIL, b St Louis, Mo, Oct 6, 35; m 61; c 4. SIGNAL PROCESSING, OPTIMAL CONTROL. *Educ:* Calif Inst Technol, BS, 57; Stanford Univ, MS, 58, PhD(elec eng), 62. *Prof Exp:* Mem tech staff, Hughes Aircraft Co, 58-62; STAFF SCIENTIST & SR MEM RES LAB, LOCKHEED PALO ALTO RES LAB, 62- *Concurrent Pos:* Assoc prof, San Jose State Univ, 68-70; orgn chmn working group, Math Control Comt, Int Fedn Automatic Control, 78-; ed, J Astronaut Sci, 80- *Mem:* Sr mem Inst Elec & Electronics Engrs; assoc fel Am Inst Aeronaut & Astronaut; Soc Indust & Appl Math; sr mem Am Astronaut Soc (vpres, 80-82); AAAS. *Res:* Optimal estimation and control; optimization; astrodynamics; guidance; low thrust interplanetary transfers; stochastic optimization. *Mailing Add:* 401 Dracena Lane Los Altos CA 94022

RAUCH, JEFFREY BARON, b New York, NY, Nov 29, 45; div. MATHEMATICAL PHYSICS. *Educ:* Harvard Univ, AB, 67; NY Univ, PhD(math), 71. *Prof Exp:* Instr math, NY Univ, 68-71; asst prof, 71-76, ASSOC PROF MATH, UNIV MICH, ANN ARBOR, 76- *Mem:* Am Math Soc. *Res:* Hyperbolic partial differential equations. *Mailing Add:* Dept of Math Angell Hall Univ of Mich Ann Arbor MI 48104

RAUCH, JOSEFINE CONSTANTIA, b Austria; Can citizen. COMPARATIVE PHYSIOLOGY, ZOOLOGY. *Educ:* Univ Sask, BA, 62; Univ Alta, MSc, 68, PhD(zool), 72. *Prof Exp:* Asst prof, 71-75, ASSOC PROF ZOOL, UNIV MAN, 75- *Concurrent Pos:* Grants, Univ Man, 71, Nat Res Coun Can, 71-73 & 74-77, Northern Studies, 74 & 75 & Nat Sci Eng Res Coun, 77-78 & 80-83; res assoc, Inst Arctic Biol, Univ Alaska, 78-79. *Mem:* Am Soc Mammal; Am Soc Zoologists; Can Soc Zool. *Res:* Thermoregulation; problems of dealing with homeothermia, hypothermia and hibernation. *Mailing Add:* Dept of Zool Univ Man Winnipeg MB R3T 2N2 Can

RAUCH, LAWRENCE L(EE), b Los Angeles, Calif, May 1, 19; m 61; c 2. APPLIED MATHEMATICS, COMMUNICATIONS ENGINEERING. *Educ:* Univ Southern Calif, AB, 41; Princeton Univ, MA, 48, PhD(math), 49. *Prof Exp:* Asst, Uranium Separation Proj, Princeton Univ, 42, & anti-aircraft fire control, 42-43, instr math, 42-49, instr pre-radar sch, 43-44, res supvr radio telemetering systs for aircraft, 44-46, supvr air blast telemetering, Oper Crossroads, Bikini, 46, supvr nonlinear differential equations proj, US Off Naval Res, 47-49; from asst prof to prof aeronaut eng, Univ Mich, Ann Arbor, 49-79, chmn nuclear eng prog, 51-52, instrumentation prog, 52-63 & mgt sci prog, 58-59, chmn comput, info & control eng, 71-76, assoc chmn dept elec & comput eng, 72-76; VIS PROF, CALIF INST TECHNOL, 77- *Concurrent Pos:* Consult, 45-; mem res adv comt commun, instrumentation & data processing, NASA, 63-70. *Honors & Awards:* Army & Navy Award, Off Sci Res & Develop, 47; Spec Award, Inst Elec & Electronics Engrs, 57; Annual Award, Nat Telemetering Conf, 60; Eckman Award, Instrument Soc Am, 66. *Mem:* AAAS; Am Math Soc; fel Inst Elec & Electronics Engrs; Am Inst Aeronaut & Astronaut. *Res:* Radio telemetry and communication theory; mathematical models and physical realizations of communication operations. *Mailing Add:* 759 N Citrus Ave Los Angeles CA 90038

RAUCH, STEWART EMMART, JR, b Bethlehem, Pa, Aug 29, 21; m 47; c 4. ORGANIC CHEMISTRY. *Educ:* Moravian Col, BSc, 42; Lehigh Univ, MS, 47. *Prof Exp:* Instr meteorol, Univ Va, 42-43; from asst prof to assoc prof chem, Moravian Col, 47-62; RES ENGR, BETHLEHEM STEEL CORP, 62- *Mem:* AAAS. *Res:* Antimalarials; developments commercially marketed; photoelectric colorimeter; portable potentiometer; portable wheatstone bridge; self-contained portable gas chromatograph; electronic clinical thermometer; chemical instrumentation; internal ballistics. *Mailing Add:* RD 4 Bethlehem PA 18015

RAUCHER, STANLEY, b St Paul, Minn, Nov 4, 48. SYNTHETIC ORGANIC CHEMISTRY. *Educ:* Univ Minn, BA, 70, PhD(chem), 73. *Prof Exp:* Asst prof, 75-81, ASSOC PROF CHEM, UNIV WASH, 81- *Mem:* Am Chem Soc. *Res:* Synthesis of natural products. *Mailing Add:* Dept Chem Univ Wash Seattle WA 98195

RAUCHFUSS, THOMAS BIGLEY, b Baltimore, Md, Sept 11, 49; m 77; c 1. INORGANIC CHEMISTRY, CATALYSIS. *Educ:* Univ Puget Sound, BS, 71; Wash State Univ, PhD(inorg chem), 75. *Prof Exp:* RES FEL CHEM, AUSTRALIAN NAT UNIV, 75- *Mem:* Am Chem Soc. *Res:* Preparative inorganic; homogeneous catalysis; organometallic; ligand design and synthesis; organic synthesis with metal ions; phosphorus and sulfur chemistry. *Mailing Add:* Noyes Lab 505 S Mathews Ave Urbana IL 61801

RAUCHWERGER, JOEL M, hematology, anatomy, see previous edition

RAUCKHORST, WILLIAM H, b Covington, Ky, Sept 9, 40; m 64; c 3. LOW TEMPERATURE PHYSICS. *Educ:* Thomas More Col, BA, 62; Univ Cincinnati, PhD(physics), 67. *Prof Exp:* Asst prof physics & chmn dept, Bellarmine Col, Ky, 67-71, assoc prof physics & chmn div natural sci, 71-72; planner phys sci prog, Sangamon State Univ, 72-73, coordr, 73-75, assoc prof phys sci, 72-76; prog mgr, Fac Develop Prog, US Dept Energy, Washington, DC, 76-78; PRIN COORDR COL/UNIV, RES PARTICIPATION PROGS, ARGONNE NAT LAB, 78- *Mem:* Am Phys Soc; Am Asn Physics Teachers. *Res:* Specific heat studies; superconductivity. *Mailing Add:* Argonne Nat Lab Argonne IL 60439

RAUD, HEINZ RANDAR, b Tallinn, Estonia, Dec 10, 41; Can citizen; m 66. ENDOCRINOLOGY, BIOCHEMISTRY. *Educ:* McGill Univ, BSc, 63, MSc, 65, PhD(biochem), 68; Univ Western Ont, MD, 77. *Prof Exp:* NIH trainee, Univ Calif, Los Angeles-Harbor Gen Hosp, Torrance, 67-70; ASST PROF OBSTET & GYNEC & PATH CHEM, UNIV WESTERN ONT, 70- *Concurrent Pos:* Med Res Coun Can res grant, Univ Western Ont, 70-; consult, John Wyeth & Bros, Ltd, 71-; pvt practice, 77- *Mem:* Endocrine Soc; Can Med Asn; Can Biochem Soc. *Res:* Reproductive endocrinology; control of the hypothalmic-pituitary-ovarian axis; hormonal control of pregnancy; endocrine methodology. *Mailing Add:* Dept of Obstet & Gynec Univ of Western Ont London ON M3J 2K3 Can

RAUDORF, THOMAS WALTER, b Berlin, Ger, May 6, 43; Can citizen; m 75; c 1. PHYSICS, NUCLEAR INSTRUMENTATION. *Educ:* Concordia Univ, BSc, 64; McGill Univ, MSc, 67, PhD(physics), 71. *Prof Exp:* Staff physicist, Simtec Industs Ltd, 71-73 & Electronic Assocs Can Ltd, 73-75; STAFF PHYSICIST, EG&G ORTEC INC, 75- *Mem:* Can Asn Physicist; Am Phys Soc; Inst Elec & Electronics Engrs. *Res:* Rectifying and ohmic contacts on semiconductors; charge carrier transport in semiconductors; semiconductor surface physics. *Mailing Add:* EG&G Ortec Inc 100 Midland Rd Oak Ridge TN 37830

RAUH, ROBERT DAVID, JR, b Medford, Mass, Nov 15, 43; m 69; c 1. ELECTROCHEMISTRY, PHOTOCHEMISTRY. *Educ:* Bowdoin Col, AB, 65; Wesleyan Univ, MA, 68; Princeton Univ, PhD(chem), 72. *Prof Exp:* Fel chem, Brandeis Univ, 72-74; sr scientist, 74-76, prin scientist, 76-79, DIR RES, EIC LAB, INC, 79- *Mem:* Am Chem Soc; Electrochem Soc; Sigma Xi. *Res:* Chemical aspects of energy conversion; high energy density batteries; photochemical storage of solar energy; photovoltaic devices. *Mailing Add:* EIC Lab Inc 55 Chapel St Newton MA 02158

RAUHUT, MICHAEL MCKAY, b New York, NY, Dec 4, 30; m 57; c 3. ORGANIC CHEMISTRY, PHOSPHORUS CHEMISTRY. *Educ:* Univ Nev, BS, 52; Univ NC, PhD(chem), 55. *Prof Exp:* Chemist, Cent Res Div, Conn, 55-62, sr res chemist, 62, group leader, 63-70, res mgr, Chem Res Div, 70-81, MGR VENTURE TECHNOLOGY RES, AM CYANAMID CO, BOUND BROOK, 81- *Honors & Awards:* IR-100 Award, Indust Res, Inc, 70. *Mem:* Am Chem Soc. *Res:* Physical organic chemistry; mechanisms of aromatic nucleophilic substitution and organophosphorus reactions; mechanisms of chemiluminescent reactions. *Mailing Add:* 1266 Sherlin Dr Bridgewater NJ 08807

RAUK, ARVI, b Estonia, Sept 30, 42; Can citizen; m 68; c 2. CHEMISTRY. *Educ:* Queen's Univ, Ont, BSc, 65, PhD(chem), 68. *Prof Exp:* Nat Res Coun Can fel, Princeton Univ, 68-70; asst prof chem, 70-77, assoc prof, 77-80, PROF CHEM, UNIV CALGARY, 80- *Mem:* Am Chem Soc; Am Phys Soc. *Res:* Theoretical and experimental studies of optical activity of organic and organometallic systems. *Mailing Add:* Dept of Chem Univ of Calgary Calgary AB T2N 1N4 Can

RAULINS, NANCY REBECCA, b Dickson, Tenn, Oct 17, 16. ORGANIC CHEMISTRY. *Educ:* Tulane Univ, BA, 36, MS, 38; Univ Wyo, PhD(chem), 53. *Prof Exp:* Teacher high sch, La, 38-39, sci & math, All Saints Col, 39-41; teacher physics & chem, Spartanburg Jr Col, 41-42; chemist, Chickasaw Ord Works, 42-43; head dept chem, Lambuth Col, 43-46; from instr to prof, 48-79, EMER PROF CHEM, UNIV WYO, 80- *Mem:* Am Chem Soc. *Res:* Physical and chemical analytical methods in organic research; mechanism of reactions; hydrogen bonding in heterocyclic systems. *Mailing Add:* Dept of Chem Univ of Wyo Laramie WY 82071

RAULSTON, JAMES CHESTER, b Enid, Okla, Nov 24, 40. HORTICULTURE. *Educ:* Okla State Univ, BS, 62; Univ MD, MS, 66, PhD(hort), 69. *Prof Exp:* Instr plant sci, Inst Appl Agr, Univ Md, 65-66; asst prof ornamental hort, Agr Res & Educ Ctr, Univ Fla, 69-72; assoc prof ornamental hort, Tex A&M Univ, 72-75; ASSOC PROF ORNAMENTAL HORT, NC STATE UNIV, 75- *Mem:* Am Soc Hort Sci; Int Soc Hort Sci. *Res:* Research in production and utilization of perennial landscape plants, including production, marketing and establishment of woody plants; production and use of native plants; physiology of landscape plants. *Mailing Add:* Dept of Hort Sci NC State Univ Raleigh NC 27650

RAUN, ARTHUR PHILLIP, b Upland, Nebr, Apr, 28, 34; m 58; c 2. ANIMAL NUTRITION. *Educ:* Univ Nebr, BS, 55; Iowa State Univ, MS, 56, PhD(animal nutrit), 58. *Prof Exp:* Asst prof chem & physiol, US Air Force Acad, 59-62; sr res chemist, 62-68, res scientist, 69-70, head animal sci field res, 71-72, HEAD ANIMAL NUTRIT RES, LILLY RES LABS, ELI LILLY & CO, 72- *Mem:* Am Soc Animal Sci. *Res:* Ruminant nutrition, specifically action of anabolic compounds in ruminants; ruminant bloat and rumen microbial metabolism. *Mailing Add:* Box 708 Greenfield IN 46140

RAUN, EARLE SPANGLER, b Sioux City, Iowa, Aug 28, 24; m 46; c 3. ENTOMOLOGY. *Educ:* Iowa State Col, BS, 46, MS, 50, PhD, 54. *Prof Exp:* Entomologist, Bur Entom & Plant Quarantine, USDA, Fla, 46-48; exten entomologist, Iowa State Univ, 48-60; res entomologist corn borer invests, Entom Res Div, Agr Res Serv, USDA, 61-66; prof entom, Univ Nebr, Lincoln, 66-74, assoc dir, Nebr Coop Exten Serv, 70-74, chmn dept entom, 66-70; ENTOMOLOGIST, PEST MGT CONSULTS, INC, 74-, PRES, 80- *Concurrent Pos:* consult, Alliance Independent Crop, 78-80. *Mem:* Entom Soc Am. *Res:* Integration of insect population techniques for grower use in corn, alfalfa, soybeans, and grain sorghum. *Mailing Add:* 3036 Prairie Rd Lincoln NE 68506

RAUN, GERALD GEORGE, vertebrate ecology, see previous edition

RAUN, NED S, b Upland, Nebr, Feb 10, 25; m 46; c 6. ANIMAL NUTRITION, BIOCHEMISTRY. *Educ:* Univ Nebr, BS, 48; Iowa State Univ, PhD(nutrit), 61. *Prof Exp:* Animal scientist, Rockefeller Found, 61-64; assoc prof animal nutrit, Okla State Univ, 64-65; animal scientist, Rockefeller Found, 65-77; dir animal sci, Int Ctr Trop Agr, Cali, Colombia, 69-76; chief livestock div, AID, Dept State, 76-78; dir, 78-80, VPRES PROD PROGS, WINROCK INT, 80- *Mem:* Am Soc Animal Sci; Fedn Am Soc Exp Biol; Am Inst Nutrit; Latin Am Asn Animal Prod. *Res:* Ruminant nutrition; pasture and forage utilization. *Mailing Add:* Winrock Int Rte 3 Morrilton AR 72110

RAUNIO, ELMER KAUNO, b Columbia City, Ore, Dec 29, 18. ORGANIC CHEMISTRY. *Educ:* Univ Wyo, BA, 40; NDak State Col, MS, 42; Univ Mich, PhD(chem), 50. *Prof Exp:* Chemist, Hercules Powder Co, 42-45; from asst prof to assoc prof, 49-60, chmn dept, 62-68, assoc dean col, 68-70, actg dean col, 70-71, PROF CHEM, UNIV IDAHO, 60-, DEAN COL LETTERS & SCI, 71- *Mem:* AAAS; Am Chem Soc. *Res:* Stereochemistry of Michael condensations. *Mailing Add:* Dept of Chem Univ of Idaho Moscow ID 83843

RAUP, DAVID MALCOLM, b Boston, Mass, Apr 24, 33; m 56; c 1. INVERTEBRATE PALEONTOLOGY. *Educ:* Univ Chicago, SB, 53; Harvard Univ, AM, 55, PhD(geol), 57. *Prof Exp:* Instr invertebrate paleont, Calif Inst Technol, 56-57; from asst prof to assoc prof geol, Johns Hopkins Univ, 57-65; from assoc prof to prof geol, Univ Rochester, 66-78, chmn dept, 69-71; res assoc geophys sci, 78-80, LECTR EVOLUTIONARY BIOL, UNIV CHICAGO, 79-, PROF GEOPHYS SCI, 80-, PROF CONCEPTUAL FOUNDATIONS SCI, 81- *Concurrent Pos:* Grants, Am Asn Petrol Geol, 57, Am Philos Soc, 59, NSF, 61-64, 65-69, 75-79 & Am Chem Soc, 65-71; resident mem staff, Morgan State Col, 58; guest prof, Univ Tübingen, 65 & 72; vis prof, Univ Chicago, 77 & 78; cur & chmn, Dept Geol, Field Mus Natural History, 78-80, dean sci, 80- *Honors & Awards:* Best Paper Award, Soc Econ Paleont & Mineral, 66; Schuchert Award, Paleont Soc, 73. *Mem:* Nat Acad Sci; fel Geol Soc Am; Soc Study Evolution; Paleont Soc (pres, 76-77); AAAS. *Res:* Skeletal mineralogy and crystallography; theoretical morphology; paleoecology; computer applications. *Mailing Add:* Dept of Geol Field Mus of Natural History Chicago IL 60605

RAUP, HUGH MILLER, b Springfield, Ohio, Feb 4, 01; m 25; c 2. BOTANY. *Educ:* Wittenberg Col, AB, 23; Univ Pittsburgh, AM, 25, PhD, 28. *Prof Exp:* From instr to asst prof biol, Wittenburg Col, 23-32; asst, Arnold Arboretum, 32-34, res assoc, 34-38, asst prof plant ecol, 38-45, assoc prof plant geog, 45-49, prof bot, 49-60, prof forestry, 60-67, EMER PROF FORESTRY, HARVARD UNIV, 67-, DIR HARVARD FOREST, 46- Harvard Univ, 29-30; fel, Nat Res Coun, 30-32; mem bot surv expeds, Mackenzie River Basin, 26-30, 32, 35, 39, Alcan Hwy, 43, 44, Southwestern Yukon, 48 & Northeast Greenland, 56-58, 60, 64; vis prof, Johns Hopkins Univ, 67-70. *Mem:* AAAS; Ecol Soc Am; Soc Am Foresters; Asn Am Geog; Arctic Inst N Am. *Res:* Plant ecology and geography. *Mailing Add:* PO Box 325 Petersham MA 01366

RAUP, OMER BEAVER, b Washington, DC, July 14, 30; m 60; c 2. GEOLOGY, GEOCHEMISTRY. *Educ:* Am Univ, BS, 52; Univ Colo, PhD(geol), 62. *Prof Exp:* Geologist, 53-72, chief, Chem Resources Br, 72-76, RES GEOLOGIST, US GEOL SURVEY, 76- *Mem:* Am Asn Petrol Geologists; Geol Soc Am. *Res:* Geology of plateau uranium deposits; quadrangle and reconnaissance mapping of Washington and Oregon; clay mineralogy of redbeds; geology and mineralogy of marine evaporites. *Mailing Add:* Geol Survey Denver Fed Ctr Denver CO 80225

RAUP, ROBERT BRUCE, JR, b New York, NY, Nov 4, 29; m 55; c 3. GEOLOGY. *Educ:* Columbia Univ, BA, 51; Univ Mich, MA, 52. *Prof Exp:* Geologist, Geol Div, 52-70, asst chief geologist environ geol, 70-74, GEOLOGIST, GEOL DIV, US GEOL SURVEY, 74- *Mem:* Geol Soc Am. *Res:* Geology of uranium in Precambrian rocks of central Arizona; geology and mineral deposits of southern Arizona; environmental geologic aspects of coal and oil shale, northwestern Colorado. *Mailing Add:* 6570 S Crestbrook Dr Morrison CO 80465

RAUSCH, DAVID JOHN, b Aurora, Ill, Oct 24, 40; m 62; c 5. ORGANIC CHEMISTRY, BIOCHEMISTRY. *Educ:* ST Procopius Col, BS, 62; Iowa State Univ, PhD(org chem), 66. *Prof Exp:* Res assoc chem, Univ Wis, 65-66; from asst prof to assoc prof, 66-71, PROF CHEM, ILL BENEDICTINE COL, 71-, CHMN DEPT, 77- *Concurrent Pos:* Consult, Continental Can Co, 66-67, Argonne Nat Lab, 67-78 & Res Corp, 70-72. *Mem:* AAAS; Am Chem Soc; Royal Soc Chem. *Res:* Organic reaction mechanisms, including beta-elimination reactions of free radical substitution reactions and pyrolysis reactions; photochemistry of aromatic compounds; nuclear magnetic resonance and spectral interpretation; stereochemistry and conformational analysis; anticoagulant surfaces. *Mailing Add:* Dept of Chem Ill Benedictine Col Lisle IL 60532

RAUSCH, DAVID LEON, b Marysville, Ohio, Apr 3, 37; m 61; c 3. AGRICULTURAL ENGINEERING. *Educ:* Ohio State Univ, BAgrE, 60, MS, 61. *Prof Exp:* AGR ENGR RESERVOIRS, AGR RES, USDA, 65- *Mem:* Am Soc Agr Engrs. *Res:* Control of reservoir sedimentation and eutrophication and how they are effected by the recently developed Automatic Bottom-Withdrawal Spillway. *Mailing Add:* Agr Res Serv USDA 207 Business Loop 70 E Columbia MO 65201

RAUSCH, DOUGLAS ALFRED, b Ft Wayne, Ind, July 26, 28; m 53; c 3. ORGANIC CHEMISTRY. *Educ:* Univ Ind, BS, 50; Univ Colo, PhD(chem), 54. *Prof Exp:* Asst, Univ Colo, 50-53; res chemist, E I du Pont de Nemours & Co, 53-54; res mgr, 56-79, DIR PROD STEWARDSHIP, DOW CHEM CO, 79- *Mem:* AAAS; Am Chem Soc; Sigma Xi. *Res:* Fluorine and inorganic chemistry. *Mailing Add:* 4518 James Dr Midland MI 48640

RAUSCH, DOYLE W, b Dover, Ohio, May 3, 31; m 64; c 2. METALLURGY, PHYSICAL CHEMISTRY. *Educ:* Ohio State Univ, BMetE, 61, PhD(metall eng), 65. *Prof Exp:* Asst to plant mgr, US Ceramic Tile Co, 51-56, res asst, 58; tech asst process metall, Battelle Mem Inst, 59-60; res fel metall eng, Ohio State Univ Res Found, 60-64; asst prof, Ill Inst Technol, 65-68; assoc div chief, Mat Processing Div, Battelle Mem Inst, 68-73; asst dir res, 73-76, DIR RES, NAT-STANDARD CO, 76- *Mem:* Am Soc Metals; Am Inst Mining, Metall & Petrol Engrs; Am Soc Testing & Mat; Nat Asn Corrosion Engrs; Electrochem Soc. *Res:* Teflon processing; thermochemical and metallurgical process development; characterization and consolidation of metal and nonmetal powders; gas-metal reactions; corrosion; metallic surfac characterization; mechanical deformation of metals. *Mailing Add:* Nat-Standard Co Niles MI 49120

RAUSCH, GERALD, b New Hampton, Iowa, Mar 18; 38; m 60; c 1. ORGANIC CHEMISTRY. *Educ:* Univ Iowa, MS, 62, PhD(org chem), 63. *Prof Exp:* Res chemist, Chem Div, Union Carbide Corp, 63-65; from asst prof to assoc prof, 65-69, PROF ORG & ANAL CHEM, UNIV WIS-LA CROSSE, 69- *Mem:* Am Chem Soc. *Res:* Organic synthesis; N-acyl lactam chemistry; amines and amine derivatives; analytic separations, alcohols. *Mailing Add:* Dept of Chem Univ of Wis La Crosse WI 54601

RAUSCH, JAMES PETER, b Ravenna, Ohio, Aug 17, 38; m 65; c 3. MARINE ZOOLOGY, PHYSIOLOGY. *Educ:* Kent State Univ, BA, 64, MA, 66, PhD(physiol), 71. *Prof Exp:* Instr physiol, Kent State Univ, 68-69; asst prof biol, 69-76, ASSOC PROF BIOL, ALFRED UNIV, 76- *Mem:* Int Oceanog Found. *Res:* Taxonomy of marine invertebrates; physiology of marine and freshwater invertebrates; respiratory physiology. *Mailing Add:* Dept of Biol Alfred Univ Alfred NY 14802

RAUSCH, MARVIN D, b Topeka, Kans, June 27, 30; m 53; c 1. ORGANOMETALLIC CHEMISTRY, ORGANIC CHEMISTRY. *Educ:* Univ Kans, BS, 52, PhD, 55. *Prof Exp:* NSF fel, Univ Munich, 57-59; sr res chemist, Monsanto Co, 59-63; assoc prof, 63-68, PROF CHEM, UNIV MASS, AMHERST, 68- *Concurrent Pos:* Alexander von Humboldt fel & vis prof, Univ Munich, 69-70 & 77. *Mem:* Royal Soc Chem; Am Chem Soc. *Res:* Organic derivatives of transition metals; metallocene chemistry; organometallic photochemistry; metalation reactions; reactions of activated acetylenic systems. *Mailing Add:* Dept of Chem Univ of Mass Amherst MA 01003

RAUSCH, ROBERT LLOYD, b Marion, Ohio, July 20, 21; m 53; c 1. VETERINARY PARASITOLOGY. *Educ:* Ohio State Univ, BA, 42, DVM, 45; Mich State Col, MS, 46; Univ Wis, PhD(parasitol), 49. *Prof Exp:* Asst, Ohio State Univ, 43-45 & Mich State Col, 45-46; from asst to instr, Univ Wis, 46-49; parasitologist, USPHS, Alaska, 49-51, chief, Infectious Dis Sect, Arctic Health Res Ctr, 51-74; prof parasitol, Western Col Vet Med, Univ Sask, 75-78; PROF PATHOBIOL & ANIMAL MED, UNIV WASH, 78- *Mem:* AAAS; Am Soc Parasitol; Micros Soc Am; Wildlife Soc; Am Soc Mammal. *Res:* Host-parasite ecology and epizootiology of helminths and diseases in wildlife; diseases of wildlife in relation to public health. *Mailing Add:* Div of Animal Med SB 42 Sch of Med Univ of Wash Seattle WA 98195

RAUSCHER, ELIZABETH ANN, cosmology, quantum physics, see previous edition

RAUSCHER, FRANK JOSEPH, JR, b Hellertown, Pa, May 24, 31; m 55; c 5. MICROBIOLOGY. *Educ:* Moravian Col, BS, 53; Rutgers Univ, PhD(virol), 57. *Prof Exp:* Res asst virol, Rutgers Univ, 55-57, res assoc, 57-58, asst prof, 58-59; microbiologist, Lab Viral Oncol, Nat Cancer Inst, 59-64, head, Viral Oncol Sect, 64-66, chmn spec virus cancer prog, 64-70, chief, Viral Leukemia & Lymphoma Br, 66-67, assoc sci dir viral oncol, 67-70, sci dir etiol, 70-72, dir inst, 72-76; vpres, 76-80, SR VPRES RES, AM CANCER SOC, 80- *Concurrent Pos:* Vis instr, Trinity Col, 59-; hon investr, Rutgers Univ, 62-67; mem fel adv bd, Nat Acad Sci, 70; sci coun, Int Agency Res Cancer, 72-74; mem expert adv panel on cancer, WHO, 72-77; mem bd dirs, Whittaker Corp, Los Angeles, 77- *Honors & Awards:* Selman A Waksman Hon Lectureship Award, Nat Acad Sci, 67; Arthur S Fleming Award, 68; Superior Serv Award, Dept Health Educ & Welfare, 72, Distinguished Serv Award, 75; Man of Sci Award, ARCS Found, 75; Charles R Drew Mem Cancer Award, Howard Univ, 77; David A Karnovsky Mem Award, Am Soc Clin Oncologists, 77; Papanicolaou Award, Papanicolaou Cancer Res Inst, 78; Selman A Waksman Award, Rutgers Univ, 78; Janeway Award, Am Radium Soc, 78. *Mem:* Am Asn Cancer Res; Am Asn Immunologists; Am Acad Microbiol; World Soc Leukemia & Related Dis; hon mem Am Soc Clin Oncol. *Res:* Comparative host responses to the necrotizing and to the tumorigenic viruses; known tumor-virus-host model systems to the search for etiologic agents in human neoplasms. *Mailing Add:* Am Cancer Soc 777 Third Ave New York NY 10017

RAUSCHER, GRANT K, b Sherrill, NY, Jan 5, 22; m 43; c 4. PHYSICAL CHEMISTRY. *Educ:* Colgate Univ, BA, 43; Rensselaer Polytech Inst, PhD(phys chem), 49. *Prof Exp:* Sr chemist, Air Reduction Co, 49-54; group leader chem res, Behr-Manning Div, Norton Co, NY, 55-58; group leader paper res, Int Paper Co, 58-66; tech dir, Eaton-Dikeman Div, 67-74, RES ASSOC, KNOWLTON BROS, INC, 74- *Honors & Awards:* Bolton-Emerson Award, 65. *Mem:* Am Chem Soc; Tech Asn Pulp & Paper Indust. *Mailing Add:* Knowlton Bros Inc 105 W 45th St Chattanooga TN 37410

RAUSCHER, HERBERT EDSON, b Troy, NY, Aug 4, 33; m 58; c 2. GLASS CHEMISTRY, PHYSICAL CHEMISTRY. *Educ:* Rensselaer Polytech Inst, BS, 55; Columbia Univ, MA, 57, PhD(chem), 60. *Prof Exp:* Res assoc, 60-71, mgr, Advan Mat Res Dept, 71-75, SR RES ASSOC, CORNING GLASS WORKS, 75- *Concurrent Pos:* Mem panel, Nat Mat Adv Bd. *Mem:* Am Chem Soc; Am Ceramic Soc; Brit Soc Glass Technol. *Res:* Radiochemistry; hot atom chemistry; ion exchange and diffusion in glass; glass composition research; composite materials. *Mailing Add:* 4060 Grove St Painted Post NY 14870

RAUSCHKOLB, ROY SIMPSON, b St Louis, Mo, Apr 18, 33; m 53; c 3. SOIL FERTILITY. *Educ:* Ariz State Univ, BA, 61; Univ Ariz, MS, 63, PhD(agr chem, soils), 68. *Prof Exp:* Cotton specialist, Agr Exten, Univ Ariz, 65-66, supt exp sta & adminr exp farms opers, Col Agr, 66-67, soil specialist, Agr Exten 67-69; soil specialist, Agr Exten & res assoc, Exp Sta, 69-77, asst dir, 77-81, ASSOC DEAN, COL AGR & DIR, COOP EXTEN RESOURCE SCI & ENG, UNIV CALIF, DAVIS, 81- *Concurrent Pos:* Consult, United Nations Food & Agr Orgn, 71, 74; mem intergovt personnel act assignment staff, US Environ Protection Agency, R S Kerr Lab, 76-77. *Mem:* Soil Sci Soc Am; Am Soc Agron. *Res:* Soil-plant relationships; plant nutrition; soil and plant tissue testing; soil pollution; soil incorporation and recycling of plant residues and animal wastes; reactions and movement of plant nutrients in soils. *Mailing Add:* Coop Exten Bldg Univ of Calif Davis CA 95616

RAUSEN, AARON REUBEN, b Jersey City, NJ, June 30, 30; m 68; c 3. PEDIATRICS, HEMATOLOGY. *Educ:* Dartmouth Col, 47-50; State Univ NY Downstate Med Ctr, MD, 54. *Prof Exp:* USPHS fel pediat hemat, Children's Hosp, Boston & Harvard Med Sch, 59-61; assoc prof, 66-72, PROF PEDIAT, MT SINAI SCH MED, 72-; DIR PEDIAT, BETH ISRAEL MED CTR, 73- *Concurrent Pos:* Chief pediat, Greenpoint Hosp, 62-64 & City Hosp Ctr, Elmhurst, 64-73; from asst attend pediatrician to attend pediatrician, Mt Sinai Hosp, 63-; mem acute leukemia study group B, NIH, 64-; consult, USPHS Hosp, 71-, Beekman-Downtown Hosp, 74- & Hackensack Hosp, 78-; vis physician, Rockefeller Univ Hosp, 78- *Mem:* Am Asn Cancer Res; Am Pediat Soc; Am Soc Hemat; Am Acad Pediat, Am Soc Clin Oncol. *Res:* Disorders of blood in children and cancer in childhood; oncology. *Mailing Add:* Dept of Pediat Beth Israel Med Ctr New York NY 10003

RAUSER, WILFRIED ERNEST, b Arlesheim, Switz, Oct 11, 36; Can citizen; m 61; c 2. PLANT PHYSIOLOGY, PLANT BIOCHEMISTRY. *Educ:* Univ Toronto, BSA, 59, MSA, 61; Univ Ill, Urbana, PhD(agron), 65. *Prof Exp:* Res officer agron, Exp Farm, Can Dept Agr, Sask, 61-62, res scientist plant physiol, Res Sta, Man, 65-66; asst prof plant physiol, 67-72, assoc prof, 72-82, PROF BOT & GENETICS, UNIV GUELPH, 82- *Concurrent Pos:* Fel, Div Biosci, Nat Res Coun Can, 66-67. *Mem:* Am Soc Plant Physiol; Can Soc Plant Physiol. *Res:* Physiological effects of excess metal ions on plants; mechanisms of metal ion toxicity and tolerance; plant metallothioneins. *Mailing Add:* Dept Bot & Genetics Univ Guelph Guelph ON N1G 2W1 Can

RAUT, KAMALAKAR BALKRISHNA, b Bombay, India, Aug 10, 20; m 45; c 5. ORGANIC CHEMISTRY. *Educ:* Univ Bombay, BSc, 41, BA, 42, MSc, 46; Univ Okla, PhD(chem, pharmaceut chem), 59; Univ Ga, certs, 65, 66 & 67. *Prof Exp:* Res chemist, India Pharmaceut Labs, 46-55; asst, Univ Okla, 55-59; vis instr org chem, ETex State Univ, 59-60; sci officer, Cent Drug Res Inst, Govt India, Lucknow, 60-61; asst prof, Indian Inst Technol, Kanpur, 62-64; PROF CHEM, SAVANNAH STATE COL, 64- *Concurrent Pos:* Abstractor, Chem Abstr Serv, 59-; counr, Am Chem Soc, 71-73 & cong sci counr, 73- *Mem:* Am Chem Soc; Indian Sci Cong Asn. *Res:* Synthetic dyes; natural products; flavons; chalcones; chromones; synthetic medicinal products; reaction mechanisms; computer programming; chemical education; use of computers in chemical education. *Mailing Add:* Dept of Chem Savannah State Col Savannah GA 31404

RAUTAHARJU, PENTTI M, b Tuusniemi, Finland, Dec 23, 32; m 57; c 3. PHYSIOLOGY, BIOPHYSICS. *Educ:* Univ Helsinki, MD, 59; Univ Minn, PhD(biophys), 63. *Hon Degrees:* DrMed, Univ Kuopio, 78. *Prof Exp:* Res assoc electrophysiol, Int Inst Occup Health, 55-58; res fel electrocardiography, Univ Minn, 58-61, res assoc biophys, 61-62; asst prof physiol, 62-64, assoc prof, 64-66, PROF PHYSIOL & BIOPHYS, DALHOUSIE UNIV, 66- *Concurrent Pos:* Med Res Coun Can res scholar, 63-66; Med Res Coun Can res assoc, 66- *Mem:* Fel Am Col Cardiol; fel Coun Epidemiol. *Res:* Cardiovascular biophysics and bioengineering; medical computing; electrocardiography; vector-cardiography; noninvasive cardiac function testing. *Mailing Add:* Med Biophys & Bioeng Res Lab Dalhousie Univ Halifax NS B3H 3J5 Can

RAUTENBERG, THEODORE HERMAN, b Cleveland, Ohio, May 14, 30; m 54. PHYSICS. *Educ:* Amherst Col, BA, 52. *Prof Exp:* Physicist, Light Prod Physics Br, 53-72, physicist, Plasma Physics Br, 72-74, physicist, Electronic Power Systs Br, 74-81, PHYSICIST, ENG PHYSICS BR, RES & DEVELOP CTR, GEN ELEC CO, 81- *Mem:* Am Phys Soc; Optical Soc Am; Inst Elec & Electronics Engrs; Audio Eng Soc. *Res:* Fundamental studies of chemical and gas discharge light sources; experimental optical spectroscopy and photometry; electrooptical devices, application to light control systems; electroacoustics, design of sound reinforcement systems. *Mailing Add:* Res & Develop Ctr Gen Elec Co PO Box 8 Schenectady NY 12301

RAUTENSTRAUCH, CARL PETER, b New York, NY, Sept 19, 36; m 59; c 2. APPLIED MATHEMATICS. *Educ:* Univ Fla, BS, 58; Univ Ala, MA, 60; Auburn Univ, PhD(math), 67. *Prof Exp:* Instr math, Auburn Univ, 63-66; asst prof, Univ Tex, Arlington, 67-68; asst prof, 68-72, ASSOC PROF MATH, UNIV CENTRAL FLA, 72- *Mem:* Am Math Soc; Soc Indust & Appl Math. *Res:* Special functions; complex analysis; differential equations. *Mailing Add:* Dept Math Univ Cent Fla Box 25000 Orlando FL 32816

RAUTENSTRAUS, R(OLAND) C(URT), b Gothenburg, Nebr, Feb 27, 24; m 46; c 1. CIVIL ENGINEERING. *Educ:* Univ Colo, BS, 46, MS, 49. *Hon Degrees:* DL, Univ NMex, 76. *Prof Exp:* Instr civil eng, 47-50, from asst prof to assoc prof, 50-57, head, Dept Civil Eng, 59-64, assoc dean fac, 64-68, vpres educ & student rels, 68-70, vpres univ rels, 70-73, exec vpres, 73-74, PROF CIVIL & ENVIRON ENG, UNIV COLO, BOULDER, 57-, PRES, 74- *Concurrent Pos:* Consult, Travelers Ins Co, 58-59; mem educ panel, Esso Refining Humble Oil Co, 60; mem bd dirs, Northwest Eng Co, 69-; mem, Gov's Energy Task Force, 73-74; mem, Regional Adv Bd, Inst Int Educ, 75- *Honors & Awards:* Lincoln Gold Medal, Am Welding Soc; Robert L Stearns Award; Norlen Medal. *Mem:* Am Soc Photogram; Am Soc Eng Educ; Am Soc Civil Engrs. *Res:* Altimetry; photogrammetry; highway engineering. *Mailing Add:* Univ Colo Regent Hall Box 16 Boulder CO 80302

RAUTH, ANDREW MICHAEL, b Rochester, NY, Oct 8, 35; m 68; c 2. BIOPHYSICS. *Educ:* Brown Univ, BSc, 58; Yale Univ, PhD(biophys), 62. *Prof Exp:* Nat Cancer Inst grant, Ont Cancer Inst, Toronto, 62-65; asst prof biophys, 65-74, assoc prof, 74-79, PROF BIOPHYS, UNIV TORONTO, 79-; PHYSICIST, ONT CANCER INST, TORONTO, 65- *Mem:* Radiation Res Soc; Biophys Soc; Can Soc Cell Biol; Am Soc Cell Biol. *Res:* Radiation biology; study of repair systems in mammalian cells in vitro and in vivo; somati cell genetics; mutational processes in mammalian cells in vitro; radiobiology of solid tumors. *Mailing Add:* Dept Med Biophys Physics Div Ont Cancer Inst Toronto ON M4X 1K9 Can

RAVAL, DILIP N, b Bombay, India, June 3, 33; US citizen; m 61. PHYSICAL BIOCHEMISTRY. *Educ:* Univ Bombay, BS, 53, MS, 55; Univ Ore, PhD(chem), 62. *Prof Exp:* NIH fel, Univ Ore, 61-62; fel virus res, Univ Calif, Berkeley, 62-64; res scientist, Palo Alto Med Res Inst, 64-66; mgr res, Varian Assocs, 66-68; dir clin labs, Med Ctr, Univ Calif, San Francisco, 68-70; dir res, 70-72, gen mgr, Sci & Technol Div, 72-73, VPRES, RES & DEVELOP DIV, ALCON LABS, 73- *Mem:* Acad Clin Lab Physicians & Sci. *Res:* Enzyme kinetics protein structure; medical instrument development; pharmaceutical drug development. *Mailing Add:* Alcon Lab Inc 6201 S Freeway Ft Worth TX 76134

RAVARIS, CHARLES LEWIS, b Detroit, Mich, Aug 21, 26; m 55; c 3. PSYCHIATRY. *Educ:* Boston Univ, AB, 49; McGill Univ, PhD(physiol), 54; Univ BC, MD, 58; Am Bd Psychiat, cert, 70. *Prof Exp:* Assoc med dir clin drug res, Squibb Inst Med Res, New Brunswick, NJ, 59-62; asst prof, Col Med, Univ Vt, 65-70, assoc prof psychiat, 70-78; PROF PSYCHIAT & VCHMN DEPT, EAST CAROLINA UNIV, 78- *Concurrent Pos:* Consult, Squibb Inst Med Res, 65- & State Dept Ment Health, Vt, 65-; attend psychiatrist, Med Ctr Hosp, Burlington, Vt, 65-; consult psychiatrist, Cent Vt Med Ctr Hosp, Montpelier & Copley Hosp, Morrisville, 72- *Mem:* AAAS; AMA; Am Psychiat Asn; Can Psychiat Asn. *Res:* Neuropharmacology; psychopharmacology; biochemical factors in mental disease. *Mailing Add:* Dept Psychiat East Carolina Univ Sch Med Greenville NC 27834

RAVE, TERENCE WILLIAM, b Mendota, Ill, Aug 23, 38; m 65; c 3. SYNTHETIC POLYOLEFIN PULPS, PAPER CHEMISTRY. *Educ:* Bradley Univ, BS, 60; Univ Wis, PhD(org chem), 65. *Prof Exp:* Res chemist, Procter & Gamble Co, 65-67; res chemist, 67-73, sr res chemist, 73-76, RES SCIENTIST, HERCULES, INC, 76- *Mem:* Am Chem Soc. *Res:* Organic nitrogen and phosphorous chemistry; paper chemistry; polymer synthesis and modification, synthetic polyolefin pulps; preparation, modification and applications of synthetic polyolefin pulps; paper wet and dry strength resins. *Mailing Add:* Res Ctr Hercules Inc Wilmington DE 19899

RAVECHE, HAROLD JOSEPH, b New York, NY, Mar 18, 43. CHEMICAL PHYSICS. *Educ:* Hofstra Univ, BA, 63; Univ Calif, San Diego, PhD(chem physics), 68. *Prof Exp:* Nat Res Coun-Nat Acad Sci assoc statist physics, 68-70, res chemist, 70-78, CHIEF, THERMOPHYSICS DIV, NAT BUR STANDARDS, 78- *Mem:* Soc Indust & Appl Math; Am Phys Soc. *Res:* Statistical mechanics of equilibrium and non-equilibrium phenomena in dense fluids. *Mailing Add:* Rm A311 Physics Bldg Nat Bur of Standards Washington DC 20234

RAVEED, DAN, b Baltimore, Md, Aug 12, 21; m 46; c 2. PLANT PHYSIOLOGY, BIOCHEMISTRY. *Educ:* Univ Calif, Berkeley, BS, 56; Univ Calif, Davis, PhD(plant physiol), 65. *Prof Exp:* Lab head soil & water relations, Water Authority, Israel, 54-55; lab technician, Univ Calif, Davis, 56-59, res chemist, 59-61, teaching asst plant physiol, 61-64, fel ion uptake, 67-68; assoc biochemist, Negative Inst, Beer Sheva, Israel, 64-67; staff scientist, 68-72, HEAD ELECTRON MICROS LAB, PHOTOBIOL BR, C F KETTERING RES LAB, 72- *Mem:* AAAS; Am Soc Cell Biologists; Japanese Soc Plant Physiol; Scand Soc Plant Physiol; Electron Micros Soc Am. *Res:* Biochemical ultrastructure of functional enzyme complexes from membranes of chloroplasts, bacterial chromatophores, retinas; immuno-electron microscopy; membrane response to stress, pollutants and inhibitors; physiology of photosynthesis; ion uptake by plants. *Mailing Add:* Photobiol Br 150 E South College St Yellow Springs OH 45387

RAVEL, JOANNE MACOW, b Austin, Tex, July 28, 24; m 46; c 2. BIOCHEMISTRY. *Educ:* Univ Tex, BS, 44, MA, 46, PhD(chem), 54. *Prof Exp:* Res scientist, Clayton Found Biochem Inst, 44-53, Hite fel, 54-56, res scientist, 56-70, assoc prof chem, Univ Tex, Austin, 72-74, ASST DIR, CLAYTON FOUND BIOCHEM INST, 70-, PROF CHEM, UNIV TEX, AUSTIN, 74- *Mem:* Am Soc Biol Chem; Am Chem Soc. *Res:* Cell-free protein synthesis; biological control mechanisms. *Mailing Add:* Clayton Found Biochem Inst Univ Tex Austin TX 78712

RAVELING, DENNIS GRAFF, b Devils Lake, NDak, Feb 28, 39; m 62. WILDLIFE BIOLOGY. *Educ:* Southern Ill Univ, BA, 60; Univ Minn, MA, 63; Southern Ill Univ, PhD(zool, physiol), 67. *Prof Exp:* Res biologist, Ont Dept Lands & Forests, 67; res scientist, Can Wildlife Serv, 67-70; from asst prof to assoc prof, 71-80, PROF WILDLIFE BIOL, UNIV CALIF, DAVIS, 80-, CHMN DEPT, 80- *Mem:* Fel AAAS; Wildlife Soc; Am Ornith Union; Wilson Ornith Soc; Am Soc Naturalists. *Res:* Taxonomy; zoogeography; physiology; behavior; population dynamics and management of birds. *Mailing Add:* Div Wildlife and Fisheries Biol Univ of Calif Davis CA 95616

RAVEN, FRANCIS HARVEY, b Erie, Pa, July 29, 28; m 52; c 7. MECHANICAL ENGINEERING. *Educ:* Gannon Col, BS, 48; Pa State Univ, BS, 50, MS, 51; Cornell Univ, PhD(mech eng), 58. *Prof Exp:* Anal design engr, Hamilton Standard Div, United Aircraft Corp, 50-54; instr mech eng, Cornell Univ, 54-58; from asst prof to assoc prof, 58-68, PROF MECH ENG, UNIV NOTRE DAME, 68- *Mem:* Assoc Am Soc Mech Engrs; Am Soc Eng Educ. *Res:* Kinematics and automatic control systems. *Mailing Add:* Dept of Aerospace & Mech Eng Univ of Notre Dame Notre Dame IN 46556

RAVEN, PETER HAMILTON, b Shanghai, China, June 13, 36; US citizen; m 58, 68; c 3. BOTANY, POPULATION BIOLOGY. *Educ:* Univ Calif, Berkeley, AB, 57; Univ Calif, Los Angeles, PhD(bot), 60. *Prof Exp:* NSF fel, Brit Mus Nat Hist, 60-61; botanist, Rancho Santa Ana Bot Garden, 61-62; from asst prof to assoc prof biol sci, Stanford Univ, 62-71; ENGELMANN PROF BOT, WASH UNIV, 71-; DIR, MO BOT GARDEN, 71- *Concurrent Pos:* NSF grants, 61-; Guggenheim fel & sr res fel, Dept Sci Indust Res, NZ, 69-70. *Mem:* Nat Acad Sci; Am Acad Arts & Sci; Soc Study Evolution (vpres, 68, 72, pres, 78); Am Soc Naturalists (pres, 83); Am Soc Plant Taxon (pres, 72). *Res:* Taxonomy, especially Onagraceae; general botany; biogeography; ethnobotany; taxonomic theory; biosystematics; cytogenetics; geography; ethnobotany; taxonomic theory; biosystematics; cytogenetics; pollination systems. *Mailing Add:* Mo Botanical Garden PO Box 299 St Louis MO 63133

RAVENEL, DOUGLAS CONNER, b Alexandria, Va, Feb 17, 47; m 71; c 2. MATHEMATICS. *Educ:* Oberlin Col, BA, 69; Brandeis Univ, MA, 69, PhD(math), 72. *Prof Exp:* Instr math, Mass Inst Technol, 71-73; asst prof, Columbia Univ, 73-76; mem staff, Inst Advan Study, 74-75; asst prof, 76-78, assoc prof, 78-81, PROF MATH, UNIV WASH, 81- *Concurrent Pos:* Alfred P Sloan Found res fel, 77-79. *Mem:* Am Math Soc. *Res:* Algebraic topology; complex cobordism theory; homotopy theory. *Mailing Add:* Dept of Math Univ of Wash Seattle WA 98195

RAVENHALL, DAVID GEOFFREY, b Birmingham, Eng, Mar 4, 27; US citizen; m 52; c 2. THEORETICAL PHYSICS. *Educ:* Univ Birmingham, BSc, 47, PhD(electrodynamics), 50. *Prof Exp:* Dept Sci & Indust Res sr fel theoret physics, Univ Birmingham, 50-51; res physicist, Carnegie Inst Technol, 51-52; mem, Inst Adv Study, 52-53; res assoc theoret physics, Stanford Univ, 53-57; from asst prof to assoc prof, 57-63, PROF THEORET PHYSICS, UNIV ILL, URBANA, 63- *Concurrent Pos:* NSF sr fel, 63-64. *Mem:* Am Phys Soc. *Res:* Theoretical nuclear physics at intermediate energies; particle physics. *Mailing Add:* Dept of Physics Univ of Ill Urbana IL 61801

RAVENHOLT, REIMERT THOROLF, b Milltown, Wis, Mar 9, 25; m 48, 81; c 4. EPIDEMIOLOGY, PUBLIC HEALTH. *Educ:* Univ Minn, BS, 48, MB, 51, MD, 52; Univ Calif, Berkeley, MPH, 56; Am Bd Prev Med, dipl & cert pub health, 60. *Prof Exp:* Intern, USPHS Hosp, San Francisco, 51-52; mem staff, Epidemic Intel Serv, Nat Commun Dis Ctr, USPHS, Ga, 52-54; dir epidemiol & commun dis div, Seattle-King County Dept Pub Health, 54-61; epidemiol consult, Europ Area, USPHS, Am Embassy, Paris, France, 61-63; assoc prof prev med, Sch Med, Univ Wash, 63-66; chief pop br, Health Serv, Off Tech Coop & Res, Develop Support Bur, 66-67, dir pop serv, Off War on Hunger, 67-69, dir, Off Pop, Tech Assistance Bur, 69-72, dir, Off Pop, Pop & Humanitarian Assistance, 72-77, dir, Off Pop, 77-79; DIR, WORLD HEALTH SURVEYS, CTRS FOR DIS CONTROL, ROCKVILLE, MD, 80- *Concurrent Pos:* Originator & mem prog steering comn, World Fertility Surv, 71- *Honors & Awards:* John J Sippy Mem Award, Am Pub Health Asn, 61; Sesquicentennial Award, Univ Mich, 67; Distinguished Honor Award, AID, 72; Hugh Moore Mem Award, 74; Carl Schultz Award, Am Pub Health Asn, 79. *Mem:* AAAS; fel Am Pub Health Asn; Int Epidemiol Asn. *Res:* Population; preventive medicine; infectious diseases; immunization; diseases of smoking and ionizing radiation; malignant cellular evolution; mortality and fertility patterns; contraceptive development; population dynamics. *Mailing Add:* World Health Surs Ctrs Dis Control 5600 Fisher's Lane Rockville MD 20857

RAVENTOS, ANTOLIN, IV, b Wilmette, Ill, June 3, 25; m 76. RADIOLOGY. *Educ:* Univ Chicago, SB, 45, MD, 47; Univ Pa, MSc, 55. *Prof Exp:* From asst instr to prof radiol, Sch Med, Univ Pa, 51-70; chmn dept, 70-80, PROF RADIOL, SCH MED, UNIV CALIF, DAVIS, 70- *Concurrent Pos:* Spec consult, Nat Cancer Inst, Surgeon Gen Army, 61-62 & Armed Forces Radiobiol Res Inst, 64-67; consociate mem, Nat Coun Radiation Protection & Measurements; pres, Am Registry Radiol Technol, 66. *Mem:* Am Med Writers Asn; Am Radium Soc (pres, 72); Radiol Soc NAm; Radiation Res Soc; Am Soc Cancer Educ. *Res:* Radiation therapy; radioactive isotopes in medicine; radiobiology. *Mailing Add:* Radiotherapy Vet Admin Med Ctr Univ Calif Sch Med 150 Muir Rd Martinez CA 94553

RAVERA, ROBERT JOHN, transportation research, see previous edition

RAVICZ, ARTHUR EUGENE, b New Rochelle, NY, Oct 28, 30; m 57; c 3. CHEMICAL ENGINEERING. *Educ:* Univ Colo, BS, 52; Univ Tex, MS, 55; Univ Mich, PhD(chem eng), 59. *Prof Exp:* Res engr, Calif Res Corp, 52 & 58-63, sr res engr, 63-67, sr eng assoc, 67-81, SUPERVISING PROCESS ENGR, CHEVRON RES CO, 81- *Concurrent Pos:* Instr, Exten Div, Univ Calif, 63-64, lectr, Univ Calif, Davis, 70. *Mem:* Am Inst Chem Engrs. *Res:* Distillation; applications of automatic computers in chemical engineering; petroleum and petrochemical process design. *Mailing Add:* Chevron Res Co 576 Standard Ave Richmond CA 94802

RAVILLE, MILTON E(DWARD), b Malone, NY, July 12, 21; m 43; c 6. ENGINEERING. *Educ:* Norwich Univ, BS, 43; Kans State Univ, MS, 47; Univ Wis, PhD(mech), 55. *Prof Exp:* Instr appl mech, Kans State Univ, 47-50, from asst prof to assoc prof, 50-56, prof & head dept, 56-62; PROF & DIR SCH ENG SCI & MECH, GA INST TECHNOL, 62- *Concurrent Pos:* Res engr, Forest Prod Lab, Wis, 54-55 & Gen Dynamics, 63. *Mem:* Am Soc Eng Educ; Nat Soc Prof Engrs; Soc Eng Sci; Am Acad Mech. *Res:* Stress analysis and vibrations of solid bodies; analysis of sandwich structures. *Mailing Add:* Sch Eng Sci & Mech Ga Inst of Technol Atlanta GA 30332

RAVIN, ARNOLD WARREN, genetics, deceased

RAVIN, LOUIS JOSEPH, b Glen Lyon, Pa, May 26, 25; m 47; c 2. PHARMACY. *Educ:* Temple Univ, BS, 52, MS, 54; Univ Wis, PhD, 57. *Prof Exp:* Instr chem, Sch Pharm, Temple Univ, 52-54; sr pharmacist, 57-66, group leader, Infectious Disease Dept, 66-72, ASST DIR, PHARMACEUT CHEM SECT, SMITH, KLINE & FRENCH LABS, 72- *Concurrent Pos:* Adj prof, Sch Pharm, Temple Univ. *Mem:* Am Chem Soc; Am Pharmaceut Asn; Am Acad Pharmaceut Sci; NY Acad Sci. *Res:* Phase behavior of pharmaceutical systems; kinetics of drug breakdown in pharmaceutical systems. *Mailing Add:* Smith, Kline & French Labs 1500 Spring Garden St Philadelphia PA 19101

RAVINDRA, RAVI, b Patiala, India, Jan 14, 39; m 65. GEOPHYSICS, COSMOLOGY. *Educ:* Indian Inst Technol, Kharagpur, BSc, 59, MTech, 61; Univ Toronto, MSc, 62, PhD(physics), 65; Dalhousie Univ, MA, 68. *Prof Exp:* From asst prof to assoc prof physics & philos, Dalhousie Univ, 66-73; vis scholar, Dept Relig, Columbia Univ, 73-74; assoc prof, 75-79, PROF PHYSICS & RELIG, DALHOUSIE UNIV, 79- *Concurrent Pos:* Res grants, Nat Res Coun Can, 66-72, Geol Surv Can, 66- & Dom Observ Can, 66-; Can Coun fel philos & Killam res fel, 68-69; vis fel philos sci, Princeton Univ, 68-69; Can Coun res grant, 72-77; cross-disciplinary fel, Soc Relig Higher Educ, 73-74; Can Coun fel, 73-74; Can Coun Leave fel, 77-78; Indo-Can Inst sr fel, 77-78; Soc Sci & Humanities Res Coun Can res grant, 77-78; dir, Threshhold Award, 78-80. *Res:* Relativistic cosmology; elastic wave propagation; philosophy of religion, particularly spiritual traditions; history of science. *Mailing Add:* Dept Physics Dalhousie Univ Halifax NS B3H 3J5 Can

RAVINDRAN, NAIR NARAYANAN, b Vechoor, India, Nov 25, 34; m 66; c 1. ORGANIC CHEMISTRY. *Educ:* Univ Kerala, India, BS, 58, MS, 60; Purdue Univ, PhD(chem), 72. *Prof Exp:* Sci officer radiochem, Bhabha Atomic Res Ctr, Bombay, 58-67; res assoc org chem, Purdue Univ, 72-74; res chemist, 74-80, SR RES CHEMIST, EASTMAN KODAK CO, 80- *Mem:* Am Chem Soc. *Res:* Design and synthesis of photographically useful organic compounds to meet the needs of future photographic products of the company; design and building of color photographic film products. *Mailing Add:* Res Labs Kodak Park Bldg 59 Eastman Kodak Co Rochester NY 14650

RAVIOLO, VICTOR G(INO), b New York, NY, June 20, 14; m 31; c 4. ENGINEERING. *Educ:* Wayne State Univ, 32-36. *Prof Exp:* Mem staff, Van Ranst Co, Mich, 37-40, Ford Motor Co, 40-42 & Consol Vultee Aircraft Corp, Calif, 42-45; exec engr, Ford Motor Co, 45-57, spec asst to vpres res & eng, 57-59, exec dir eng staff, Ford Motor Co & dir eng, Ford of England, 57-63; consult, 63-66; group vpres automotive prod, Am Motors Corp, 66-68; CONSULT, 68- *Concurrent Pos:* Wakefield Mem lectr, 63; mem internal combustion engine indust adv comt, Munitions Bd; mem ad hoc tank & automotive engine fuel study group, US Res & Develop Bd; mem compressor comt, Nat Adv Comt Aeronaut; mem fuel & engine res adv comt, War Prod Bd; mem bd dirs, Coord Res Coun, 58-60. *Honors & Awards:* L R Buckendale, Soc Automotive Engrs. *Mem:* AAAS; Soc Automotive Engrs; Soc Exp Stress Anal; Sigma Xi; fel Brit Inst Mech Engrs. *Res:* Engines; aerodynamics; automotive products. *Mailing Add:* 1456 NE Ocean Blvd Stuart FL 33494

RAVITCH, MARK MITCHELL, b New York, NY, Sept 12, 10; m 32. SURGERY. *Educ:* Univ Okla, AB, 30; Johns Hopkins Univ, MD, 34; Am Bd Surg, dipl, 43, cert thoracic surg, 50, pediat surg, 75. *Prof Exp:* House officer surg, Johns Hopkins Hosp, 34-35; house officer pediat, Harriet Lane Home, 35-36; from asst to assoc prof surg, Johns Hopkins Univ, 36-52; clin prof, Columbia Univ, 52-56; assoc prof, Johns Hopkins Univ, 56-65, prof, 65-66; prof surg & pediat surg & head div pediat surg, Univ Chicago, 66-69; PROF SURG, UNIV PITTSBURGH, 69-; SURGEON-IN-CHIEF, MONTEFIORE HOSP, 69- *Concurrent Pos:* Hunterian fel, Johns Hopkins Univ, 36-37, Halsted fel, 37-38; asst resident surgeon, Johns Hopkins Hosp, 38-42, researcher, 42-43, surgeon, 47-52 & 56-66, dir blood bank, 39-52; hon assoc consult surgeon, Guy's Hosp, London, 49-; dir dept surg, Mt Sinai Hosp, New York, 52-56; surgeon-in-chief, Baltimore City Hosps, 56-66. *Honors & Awards:* Ladd Medal, Royal Col Phys Surg, Glasgow & Royal Australasian Col Surg, Melbourne, 72. *Mem:* Soc Vascular Surg; Soc Univ Surg; Am Surg Asn; Am Asn Thoracic Surg; Am Col Surg. *Res:* Blood transfusion; bowel surgery; pediatric and thoracic surgery. *Mailing Add:* Montefiore Hosp 3459 Fifth Ave Pittsburgh PA 15213

RAVITSKY, CHARLES, b New York, NY, May 25, 17; m 40; c 2. APPLIED PHYSICS, OPTICS. *Educ:* City Col NY, BS, 38, MS, 39. *Prof Exp:* Teacher high sch, NY, 38; from jr physicist to prin physicist, Nat Bur Stand, 41-53; prin physicist, Diamond Ord Fuze Labs, 53-54, chief systs res sect, 54-58, res supvr, 58-62; chief physics br, US Army Res & Develop Group, Europe, 62-67; sr prog mgr, 67-72, asst to dir tactical technol, Defense Advan Res Projs Agency, Off Secy Defense, 72-75; consult, Battelle Columbus Labs, 75-77; physicist, Cerberonics, Inc, 77-78; STAFF ENGR, SWL INC, 78- *Concurrent Pos:* Assoc physics, George Washington Univ, 43-50, lectr, 50-54; asst chmn electronic scientist panel, Bd Civil Serv Exam, Nat Bur Stands, 50-55, chmn, 55-59, mem bd, 55-61; mem, US Deleg, NATO Panel IV Optics & Infrared, 71-75. *Honors & Awards:* US Naval Ord Develop award, 45; awards, Diamond Ord Fuze Labs, 55, US Army Sci Conf, 62 & Harry Diamond Labs, 65; Outstanding Performance, Defense Advan Res Proj Agency, 75. *Mem:* Am Phys Soc; Optical Soc Am; Soc Photo-Optical Instrumentation Engrs. *Res:* Administration of research and development programs; communications research and development; surveillance; military systems utilizing infrared or visible radiation; development of submersible vehicles; remote sensors; anti-submarine warfare; intrusion detection sensors; airborne reconnaissance systems. *Mailing Add:* 1505 Drexel St Takoma Park MD 20912

RAVIV, JOSEF, b Slonim, Poland, Mar 11, 34; US citizen; m 56; c 3. APPLIED MATHEMATICS, COMPUTER SCIENCE. *Educ:* Stanford Univ, BS, 55, MS, 60; Univ Calif, Berkeley, MA, 63, PhD(elec eng), 64. *Prof Exp:* Res staff mem, T J Watson Res Ctr, 64-72, MGR, IBM ISRAEL SCI CTR, HAIFA, 72- *Concurrent Pos:* Lectr, Univ Conn, 65-; assoc prof, Technion, Israel, 71- *Mem:* Inst Elec & Electronics Engrs. *Res:* Decision making; pattern recognition; data compaction; recognition of continuous speech. *Mailing Add:* IBM Israel Sci Ctr Comput Sci Bldg Technion City Haifa 32000 Israel

RAW, CECIL JOHN GOUGH, b Ixopo, SAfrica, Oct 20, 29; US citizen; m 56; c 4. PHYSICAL CHEMISTRY. *Educ:* Univ Natal, BSc, 51, MSc, 52, PhD(phys chem), 56. *Prof Exp:* Lectr chem, Univ Natal, 54-57, sr lectr, 58-59; res assoc, Univ Minn, 59-60; from asst prof to assoc prof, 60-66, PROF CHEM, ST LOUIS UNIV, 66- *Concurrent Pos:* African Explosives & Chem Industs res fel, 57-59; summer vis asst prof, Univ Minn, 60 & Univ Md, 62. *Mem:* Am Chem Soc; Am Asn Univ Professors; Sigma Xi. *Res:* Transport phenomena; microcomputers in chemistry; molecular dynamics; oscillating chemical reactions. *Mailing Add:* Dept of Chem St Louis Univ St Louis MO 63103

RAWAL, KANTI M, b Karachi, Pakistan, Sept 25, 40; m 72; c 2. CROP IMPROVEMENT, SCIENTIFIC INFORMATION SYSTEMS. *Educ:* Gujarat Univ, India, BSc, 61, MSc, 64; Univ Ill, PhD(genetics), 69. *Prof Exp:* Fel biochem & genetics, Univ Ill, 69-70; asst prof genetics, Univ Ibadan, Nigeria, 70-72; geneticist plant genetics, Int Inst Trop Agr, Nigeria, 72-75; chief scientist theory orgn, Lab Info Sci & Genetic Resources, Univ Colo, Boulder, 75-78, plant breeding, 78-80; PLANT BREEDER, DEL MONTE CORP, R J REYNOLDS INDUST, 80- *Concurrent Pos:* Mem, Int Wheat Descriptor Comt, Food & Agr Orgn, Rome, 75-80, Int Sorghum Germplasm Comt, 76-80 & Tech Adv Comt Wheat, Sorghum, Peas, Beans & Tomatoes, Sea Sci & Educ Admin, Agr Res, USDA, 78-80. *Mem:* fel Linnean Soc; Am Genetic Asn; Am Soc Agron; Crop Sci Soc Am; Soc Economic Bot. *Res:* Plant breeding of tomatoes, dry legumes, cucumbers; germplasm resources exploration, utilization and management; population biology of native plants; computerized information management for agriculture; statistics; biosystematics; crop evolution and tropical agricultural ecosystems. *Mailing Add:* Corp Agr Res Del Monte Corp PO Box 36 San Leandro CA 94577

RAWALAY, SURJAN SINGH, b Langai Chhanni, India, Mar 4, 33, m 53, c 3. ORGANIC CHEMISTRY, BIOCHEMISTRY. *Educ:* Govt Agr Col, Ludhiana, India, BSc, 56; Ohio State Univ, MSc, 59, PhD(chem), 62. *Prof Exp:* Fel biochem, Univ Calif, Los Angelex, 62-63; asst prof, Punjab Agr Univ, India, 63-64; res chemist, Univ BC, 64-65 & Agr & Tech Col NC, 65-66; asst prof chem, WLiberty State Col, 66-71; PROF CHEM, VOORHEES COL, 71- *Mem:* Am Chem Soc. *Res:* Permanganate oxidation of organic compounds; mechanisms of some biochemical reactions; synthesis of unusual benzamides. *Mailing Add:* Dept of Chem Voorhees Col Denmark SC 29042

RAWAT, ARUN KUMAR, b Uttar Pradesh, India, Sept 19, 45; m 74. BIOCHEMISTRY. *Educ:* Univ Lucknow, BSc, 62, MSc, 64; Univ Copenhagen, DSc(biochem), 69. *Prof Exp:* NIH fel, 69-70; instr med, City Univ New York, 70; asst prof psychiat, State Univ NY Downstate Med Ctr, 70-72; assoc prof psychiat & biochem, Med Col Ohio, 73-78; PROF PHARMACOL, UNIV TOLEDO, 78- *Concurrent Pos:* Dir div neurochem, Dept Psychiat, State Univ NY Downstate Med Ctr, 70-72; dir, Alcohol Res Ctr, 73- *Mem:* Am Soc Biol Chemists; Am Soc Neurochem; Am Soc Clin Res. *Res:* Neurochemistry of alcoholism; effects of alcohol on fetus; mechanisms of addiction; effect of alcohol on protein synthesis in brain. *Mailing Add:* Alcohol Res Ctr Univ Toledo CS No 10002 Toledo OH 43699

RAWDON, ALBERT HENRY, JR, b Worcester, Mass, Apr 26, 23; m 48; c 2. MECHANICAL ENGINEERING, AIR POLLUTION CONTROL. *Educ:* Worcester Polytech Inst, BS, 47, MS, 61. *Prof Exp:* Mech engr res & develop, US Envelope Co, 47-48; mech engr appln design, Riley Stoker Corp, 48-53, mech engr design, 53-59; staff engr res & develop, Arthur D Little, Inc, 59-64; asst dept mgr develop, 65-70, res & develop mgr, 70-73, dir res & develop, 73-79, STAFF CONSULT, RILEY STOKER CORP, 79- *Concurrent Pos:* Lectr, Inst Fuels, Australia, 74- *Mem:* Am Soc Mech Engrs; Combustion Inst; Air Pollution Control Asn. *Res:* Oxides of nitrogen formation and control from utility steam generators; boiler appertances, burners, separators, exchangers. *Mailing Add:* Riley Stoker Corp Res & Develop 9 Neponset St Worcester MA 01613

RAWITCH, ALLEN BARRY, b Chicago, Ill, Dec 29, 40; m 62; c 2. BIOCHEMISTRY, SPECTROSCOPY. *Educ:* Univ Calif, Los Angeles, BS, 63, PhD(biochem), 67. *Prof Exp:* Res chemist, Wadsworth Vet Admin Hosp, Los Angeles, 62-63; res assoc biochem, Univ Ill, Urbana, 67-69; from asst prof to assoc prof chem, Kent State Univ, 73-75; assoc prof, 75-82, PROF BIOCHEM, MED SCH, UNIV KANS, 82- *Concurrent Pos:* Fel, Univ Ill, Urbana, 67-69; scientist, Mid Am Cancer Ctr Prog. *Honors & Awards:* Res Career Develop Award, NIH, 72. *Mem:* AAAS; Am Chem Soc; Am Soc Biol Chemists; Sigma Xi; Am Thyroid Asn. *Res:* Physical and chemical properties of proteins; application of ultra-centrifugation and fluorescence spectroscopy to study macromolecules; structure of thyroid proteins; thyroid hormone biosynthesis, fluorescence polarization applied to the study of protein conformation and interacting protein systems; blood clotting factors--conformation and activation. *Mailing Add:* Dept of Biochem Med Ctr Univ of Kans Kansas City KS 66103

RAWITSCHER, GEORGE HEINRICH, b Freiburg, Ger, Feb 27, 28; US citizen; m 57; c 2. THEORETICAL NUCLEAR PHYSICS. *Educ:* Univ Sao Paulo, Brazil, AB, 49; Stanford Univ, PhD(physics), 56. *Prof Exp:* Instr physics, Brazil Ctr of Invest Physics, 50-52; asst, Stanford Univ, 53-56; instr, Univ Rochester, 56-58; instr, Yale Univ, 58-61, asst prof, 61-64; assoc prof, 66-72, PROF PHYSICS, UNIV CONN, 72- *Concurrent Pos:* Alexander V Humboldt Stiftung fel, Max Planck Inst Nuclear Physics, 64-66; Brazilian Army Res, 50-71. *Mem:* Am Phys Soc. *Res:* Elementary particle and nuclear physics; mu mesons; scattering and reaction theory in nuclear physics. *Mailing Add:* Dept of Physics Univ of Conn Storrs CT 06268

RAWLING, FRANK L(ESLIE), JR, b Lowell, Mass, Dec 2, 35; m 66; c 2. CHEMICAL ENGINEERING. *Educ:* Lowell Tech Inst, BS, 59; Univ Maine, MS, 61; Iowa State Univ, PhD(chem eng), 64. *Prof Exp:* Res asst chem eng, Iowa State Univ, 61-64; res engr, 64-68, sr res engr, Textile Fibers Dept, 68-80, PROJ ENGR, ENG DEPT, E I DU PONT DE NEMOURS & CO, INC, 81- *Mem:* Am Inst Chem Engrs; Newcomen Soc. *Res:* Polymer processing, especially with regard to man-made fibers; fluid-solid systems; mixing technology, process design. *Mailing Add:* 32 Carriage Lane Newark DE 19711

RAWLINGS, CHARLES ADRIAN, b Paducah, Ky, Nov 11, 36. BIOMEDICAL ENGINEERING. *Educ:* Univ Ill, BSEE, 59; Southern Ill Univ, MS, 65, PhD(eng & physiol), 74. *Prof Exp:* Engr, Sperry Utah Eng Labs, div Sperry Rand Corp, 59-61; field eng training rep, Autonetics Div, NAm Aviation, 61-65, mem tech staff clin eng, 66-69, sr logistics field engr, Space & Info Syst, 65; lectr, 64-65 & 66-74, asst prof, 74-77, ASSOC PROF ENG, DEPT ELEC SCI & SYST ENG & PROG DIR ENG BIOPHYSICS/BIOMED ENG, SOUTHERN ILL UNIV, CARBONDALE, 77- *Concurrent Pos:* Mem, Bd Examrs Cert Biomed Equip Technicians, 73-75, chmn, 75-79, chmn cert comn, 79-81; qualified instr, Defense Civil Preparedness Agency, 70. *Mem:* Fel Royal Soc Health; sr mem Instrument Soc Am; Inst Elec & Electronics Engrs; Asn Advan Med Instrumentation (pres, 81-82); Am Soc Hosp Eng. *Res:* Medical instrumentation, especially that related to cardiovascular system; rehabilitation engineering; systems analysis of intensive coronary care. *Mailing Add:* Engineering Southern Ill Univ Carbondale IL 62901

RAWLINGS, CLARENCE ALVIN, b Olney, Ill, Apr 18, 43; m 67; c 2. VETERINARY SURGERY, CARDIOPULMONARY PHYSIOLOGY. *Educ:* Univ Ill, BS, 65, DVM, 67; Colo State Univ, MS, 69; Univ Wis, PhD(vet med), 74; Am Col Vet Surgeons, dipl. *Prof Exp:* Staff vet, Humane Soc Mo, St Louis, 67-68; Nat Defense Educ Act fel surg, Col Vet Med, Colo State Univ, 68-69; chief & asst chief exp surg, US Air Force Sch of Aerospace Med, Brooks AFB, Tex, 69-72; fel physiol, Univ Wis, 72-74; ASSOC PROF SURG, UNIV GA, 72- *Mem:* Am Vet Med Asn; Acad Vet Cardiol; Am Soc Vet Anesthesiol; Am Soc Vet Physiologist & Pharmacologists; Am Heart Asn. *Res:* Understanding cardiopulmonary function in clinical conditions; heartworm disease, anesthesia, shock, cardiac tamponade, and congenital heart disease; prospective clinical studies involve soft tissue surgery. *Mailing Add:* Dept of Small Animal Med Univ of Ga Col of Vet Med Athens GA 30602

RAWLINGS, GARY DON, b Houston, Tex, Feb 6, 48; m 69. ENVIRONMENTAL SCIENCE, PHYSICS. *Educ:* Southwest Tex State Univ, BS, 70, MS, 71; Tex A&M Univ, PhD(environ sci, eng), 74. *Prof Exp:* Res asst & grant, Tex Exp Sta, Tex A&M Univ, 73-74; CONTRACT MGR & ENG SPECIALIST ENVIRON RES & DEVELOP, DAYTON LAB, MONSANTO RES CORP, 74- *Mem:* Air Pollution Control Asn; Am Inst Chem Engrs; Sigma Xi. *Res:* Solution to environmentally related problems; detection systems; analytical techniques; control technology alternatives. *Mailing Add:* Monsanto Res Corp Sta B Box 8 Dayton OH 45407

RAWLINGS, JOHN OREN, b Archer, Nebr, July 26, 32; m 52; c 3. BIOMETRICS. *Educ:* Univ Nebr, BS, 53, MS, 57; NC State Col, PhD, 60. *Prof Exp:* Geneticist, Agr Res Serv, USDA, 59-60; asst statist, 60-61, from asst prof to assoc prof, 61-68, PROF STATIST, INST STATIST, NC STATE UNIV, 68-, PROF GENETICS, 76- *Concurrent Pos:* Vis res fel appl statist, Univ Reading, 67-68; assoc ed, Biometrics, Biomet Soc, 75. *Mem:* Am Soc Agron; Crop Sci Soc Am; Biomet Soc; Am Statist Asn; AAAS. *Res:* Statistical concepts in genetics; design and analysis of experiments. *Mailing Add:* Dept Statist NC State Univ Raleigh NC 27650

RAWLINS, NOLAN OMRI, b McRae, Ga, Nov 30, 38; m 64; c 3. AGRICULTURAL ECONOMICS. *Educ:* Univ Ga, BSA, 61, MS, 63; Tex A&M Univ, PhD(agr econ), 68. *Prof Exp:* Asst prof econ & sociol, Middle Ga Col, 67-68; from asst prof to assoc prof, 68-81, PROF AGR, MIDDLE TENN STATE UNIV, 81- *Mailing Add:* Dept Agr Middle Tenn State Univ Murfreesboro TN 37130

RAWLINS, STEPHEN LAST, b Lewiston, Utah, May 29, 32; m 52; c 7. SOILS, PHYSICS. *Educ:* Brigham Young Univ, BS, 54; Washington State Univ, MS, 56, PhD(soils), 61. *Prof Exp:* Soil physicist, Conn Agr Exp Sta, 60-64; res soil scientist, Soil & Water Conserv Res Div, 64-71, SUPVRY SOIL SCIENTIST, US SALINITY LAB, SCI & EDUC ADMIN, USDA, 71- *Concurrent Pos:* Adj prof, Univ Calif, Riverside, 71- *Mem:* Am Soc Agron; Am Soc Plant Physiol. *Res:* Physics of water movement in soils and plants; instrument for measurement of energy status of water in soils and plants; modeling soil-plant-water system. *Mailing Add:* US Salinity Lab Sci & Educ Admin USDA 4500 Glenwood Dr Riverside CA 92501

RAWLINS, WILLIAM ARTHUR, b Geneva, NY, Dec 5, 08; m 32; c 2. ECONOMIC ENTOMOLOGY. *Educ:* Cornell Univ, BS, 30, PhD(entom), 36. *Prof Exp:* From asst to prof, 30-71, EMER PROF ENTOM, CORNELL UNIV, 71- *Concurrent Pos:* Mem, Food & Agr Orgn, UN Mission, Poland, 47; Uttar Pradesh Agr Univ, India, 51-52; vis prof, Rockefeller Found & Indian Agr Res Inst, 66; mem, Plant Protection Eval Team, Ford Found, India, 69-70. *Mem:* Fel AAAS; Entom Soc Am; Ecol Soc Am; Am Inst Biol Sci; NY Acad Sci. *Res:* Biology and control of potato and vegetable insects. *Mailing Add:* 115 James St Ithaca NY 14850

RAWLINS, WILSON TERRY, b Edinburg, Tex, Nov 8, 49; m 75; c 1. PHYSICAL CHEMISTRY, CHEMICAL KINETICS. *Educ:* Univ Tex, Austin, BS & BA, 72; Univ Pittsburgh, PhD(chem), 77. *Prof Exp:* PRIN SCIENTIST CHEM, PHYS SCI INC, 77- *Mem:* Am Geophys Union; Combustion Inst; Soc Photo-Optical Instrumentation Engrs. *Res:* Gas phase kinetics, photochemistry and spectroscopy; chemistry of planetary atmospheres; combustion chemistry. *Mailing Add:* Phys Sci Inc 30 Commerce Way Woburn MA 01801

RAWLINSON, DAVID JOHN, b Manchester, Eng, May 14, 35. ORGANIC CHEMISTRY. *Educ:* Oxford Univ, BA, 57, PhD(chem), 59. *Prof Exp:* Res assoc, Univ Ore, 59-61; tech officer, Plant Protection Ltd, Eng, 61-63; chemist, Agr Chem Div, Shell Develop Co, US, 63-65; fel, Ill Inst Technol, 65-66; fel & lectr, Univ Wis, Milwaukee, 66-68; from asst prof to assoc prof, 68-77, PROF CHEM, WESTERN ILL UNIV, 77- *Mem:* Am Chem Soc; Royal Soc Chem. *Res:* Free radical chemistry; chemistry of peroxides. *Mailing Add:* Dept of Chem Western Ill Univ Macomb IL 61455

RAWLINSON, JOHN ALAN, b Liverpool, Eng, Nov 30, 40; Can citizen; m 67; c 3. MEDICAL PHYSICS. *Educ:* Univ London, BSc Hons, 63; Univ Toronto, MSc, 70. *Prof Exp:* Clin physicist, Ont Cancer Inst, 65-68, sr clin physicist, 70-77; head physicist, Inst Radiother, Brazil, 77-78; PHYSICIST-IN-CHG HIGH ENERGY SECT, ONT CANCER INST, 78- *Concurrent Pos:* Mem tech comt, 62, Can Nat Comt, Int Electrotech Comn, 76- *Mem:* Can Asn Physicists; Am Asn Physicists in Med; Brazilian Asn Med Physics. *Res:* Improvement in the radiation characteristics of equipment used in radiation therapy; improvements in treatment techniques in radiation therapy. *Mailing Add:* 8 Dunhill Toronto ON M1C 1Y4 Can

RAWLS, HENRY RALPH, b Chattahoochee, Fla, Nov 19, 35; m 78. PHYSICAL CHEMISTRY, DENTAL RESEARCH. *Educ:* La State Univ, BS, 57; Fla State Univ, PhD(phys chem), 64. *Prof Exp:* Res chemist, Unilever Res Lab, Unilever NV, Holland, 64-67; res chemist, Gulf S Res Inst, 68-73, sr res chemist, 73-76; asst prof, 76-80, ASSOC PROF BIOMAT, SCH DENT, LA STATE UNIV, 80- *Concurrent Pos:* Vis scientist, Forsyth Dent Ctr, Boston, 78 & Mat Tech Lab, Groningen, Holland, 80; consult, Gulf Res Inst, 76- & Johnson & Johnson, 79; adj assoc prof biomed eng, Tulane Univ, 80-; prin investr, NIH res grants, 77-82. *Mem:* Am Soc Photobiol; Soc Biomat; Am Chem Soc; Int Asn Dental Res. *Res:* Photochemistry; photophysics; applications of physical and polymer chemistry to biomedical problems; cariology; development of restorative, preventive and prosthetic materials for dentistry. *Mailing Add:* La State Univ Sch Dent 1100 Florida Ave New Orleans LA 70119

RAWLS, HUGH CECIL, malacology, see previous edition

RAWLS, JOHN MARVIN, b Springfield, Tenn, Nov 25, 20; m 42; c 3. DEVELOPMENTAL PHYSIOLOGY, GENETICS. *Educ:* George Peabody Col, BS, 52, MA, 53; Univ Fla, PhD(zool), 61. *Prof Exp:* Instr biol, Austin Peay State Col, 53-57, assoc prof, 61-62; assoc prof, Lamar State Col Technol, 62-64; assoc prof, Univ South Ala, 64-68, chmn dept, 64-71, prof biol, 68-80; MEM FAC, BIOL DEPT, UNIV KY, 80- *Mem:* AAAS. *Res:* Curriculum development; physiology of development, with emphasis on the physiology of fertilization of the ova. *Mailing Add:* Biol Dept Univ Ky Lexington KY 40506

RAWLS, WILLIAM EDGAR, b Akron, Ohio, June 7, 33; m 57; c 4. VIROLOGY, EPIDEMIOLOGY. *Educ:* Ariz State Univ, BA, 55; Univ Tenn, Memphis, MD, 58; Univ Minn, Rochester, MS, 64. *Prof Exp:* Asst staff, Mayo Clin, 64; from trainee to prof virol & epidemiol, Baylor Col Med, 64-73; PROF PATH, McMASTER UNIV, 74- *Concurrent Pos:* Resident fel, Mayo Found, 61-64; NIH spec fel med, Baylor Col Med, 65-67, res career develop award, 67-72. *Mem:* AAAS; Am Soc Microbiol; Reticuloendothelial Soc; Am Asn Immunol. *Res:* Infectious diseases; chronic virus infection; viral oncology with specific research on the role of herpesvirus type 2 and carcinoma of the cervix. *Mailing Add:* Dept Path McMaster Univ Hamilton ON L8N 3Z5 Can

RAWLS, WILLIAM SHELTON, b Mayfield, Ky, Apr 4, 20; m 49; c 3. PHYSICS. *Educ:* Murray State Col, BS, 41; Tulane Univ, MS, 43; Iowa State Univ, PhD, 59. *Prof Exp:* Res engr, Airborne Instruments Lab, Inc, 43-44; develop engr, Nat Carbon Co, Union Carbide Corp, 44-45; from instr to assoc prof, 49-59, PROF PHYSICS, ARIZ STATE UNIV, 59- *Mem:* Am Phys Soc; Am Asn Physics Teachers. *Res:* Low energy nuclear physics; cosmic rays; physics education. *Mailing Add:* Dept of Physics Ariz State Univ Tempe AZ 85281

RAWNSLEY, HOWARD MELODY, b Long Branch, NJ, Nov 20, 25; m 67; c 2. PATHOLOGY. *Educ:* Haverford Col, AB, 49; Univ Pa, MD, 52; Am Bd Path, cert anat path, 57, clin path, 58. *Prof Exp:* From assoc to assoc prof clin path, Sch Med, Univ Pa, 57-69, prof path, 69-75, from asst dir to dir, William Pepper Lab, 60-75, assoc dir clin res ctr, Univ Hosp, 62-70; vchmn dept, 75-79, PROF PATH, DARTMOUTH MED SCH, 75-, CHMN DEPT, 79- *Mem:* AAAS; AMA; Am Asn Clin Chem; Col Am Path; Am Soc Clin Path. *Res:* Clinical chemistry; liver disease; serum proteins; interpretation of laboratory information. *Mailing Add:* Dept Path Dartmouth Med Sch Hanover NH 03755

RAWSON, ARNOLD JOSEPH, b New York, NY, Nov 26, 14; m 40; c 3. PATHOLOGY. *Educ:* Harvard Univ, BS, 36; Columbia Univ, MD, 40; Univ Pa, DSc(med), 49. *Prof Exp:* Instr path, Univ Pa, 48-50; dir dept, Norfolk Gen Hosp, Va, 50-57; asst prof, 58-64, assoc prof, 64-68, actg chmn dept, 78-80, PROF PATH, SCH MED, UNIV PA, 68- *Concurrent Pos:* Consult, US Naval Hosp, Portsmouth, Va, 51-57. *Mem:* Am Soc Exp Pathologists; Am Asn Pathologists & Bacteriologists; Col Am Pathologists; Int Acad Path. *Res:* Lymphocyte structure and function in autoimmune disease. *Mailing Add:* Dept of Path Univ of Pa Sch of Med Philadelphia PA 19104

RAWSON, EDWARD BYRD, b Philadelphia, Pa, Aug 15, 27; m 48; c 3. MICROPROCESSOR SYSTEMS, FORTH LANGUAGE. *Educ:* Swarthmore Col, AB, 48; Yale Univ, MS, 49, PhD(physics), 53. *Prof Exp:* Staff mem, Lincoln Lab, Mass Inst Technol, 52-58; staff physicist, Sci Eng Inst, United Aircraft Corp, 58-66, gen mgr, 66-68; vpres, Searle Medidata, Inc, 68-74; PRES, RAWSON ENG, 74- *Concurrent Pos:* Res assoc, Mt Washington Observ, 81- *Mem:* AAAS; Sigma Xi; sr mem Inst Elec & Electronics Engrs. *Res:* Design and construction of microprocessor systems and applications software; reusable software modules for executive and operating systems, data manipulation, real time control and data communication. *Mailing Add:* Moccasin Hill Lincoln MA 01773

RAWSON, ERIC GORDON, b Saskatoon, Sask, Mar 4, 37; m 66; c 3. OPTICS. *Educ:* Univ Sask, BA, 59, MA, 60; Univ Toronto, PhD(physics), 66. *Prof Exp:* Mem tech staff optics, Bell Tel Labs, 66-73; mem res staff optics, 73-80, MGR I&TT AREA, OPTICS, XEROX PALO ALTO RES CTR, 80- *Mem:* Fel Optical Soc Am; Inst Elec & Electronics Engrs; Soc Photo Instrumentation Engrs. *Res:* Fiber-optical waveguides and systems; optics of display systems; light scattering; 3-dimensional displays. *Mailing Add:* Xerox Palo Alto Res Ctr 3333 Coyote Hill Rd Palo Alto CA 94304

RAWSON, JAMES RULON YOUNG, b Boston, Mass, July 28, 43; m 70; c 2. PLANT MOLECULAR BIOLOGY. *Educ:* Cornell Univ, BS, 65; Northwestern Univ, PhD(biol), 69. *Prof Exp:* NIH fel, Univ Chicago, 69-71, trainee biophys, 71-72; asst prof, 72-78, ASSOC PROF BOT & BIOCHEM, UNIV GA, 78- *Concurrent Pos:* NSF res grants, 73-75, 75-77, 77-79, 79-81, 80-82 & 82-85; Res Corp grant, 75-76; USDA grant, 80-82. *Mem:* Cell Biol Soc; Am Soc Biol Chemists. *Res:* Molecular genetics of photosynthesis. *Mailing Add:* Dept Bot Univ Ga Athens GA 30602

RAWSON, RICHARD RAY, b Loma Linda, Calif, Dec 31, 28; m 52; c 6. GEOLOGY. *Educ:* Brigham Young Univ, BS, 56, MS, 57; Univ Wis, PhD(geol), 66. *Prof Exp:* Res geologist, Continental Oil Co, 57-63; asst prof geol, Emory Univ, 66-67; from asst prof to assoc prof geol, Northern Ariz Univ, 67-80; SR GEOLOGIST, MARATHON OIL CO, 80- *Mem:* Am Asn Petrol Geol; Soc Econ Paleont & Mineral. *Res:* Depositional environments carbonate sediments; stratigraphy; sedimentation; basin analysis; petroleum exploration. *Mailing Add:* Marathon Oil Co Box 120 Casper WY 82601

RAWSON, ROBERT ORRIN, b East St Louis, Ill, Apr 25, 17; c 3. PHYSIOLOGY. *Educ:* Univ Ill, Urbana, BS, 40; Loyola Univ, Ill, PhD(physiol), 60. *Prof Exp:* Res metallurgist, Am Zinc Co, Ill, 40-44; radio & TV broadcasting, St Louis & Chicago, 44-56; instr biol, Univ Ill, Chicago Circle, 56-58; instr physiol, 61-68, asst prof epidemiol, 68-75, SR RES ASSOC & LECTR, SCH MED, YALE UNIV, 75- *Concurrent Pos:* Fel physiol, Loyola Univ, Ill, 60-61; from asst fel physiol to fel, John B Pierce Found, Conn, 61- *Mem:* Am Physiol Soc. *Res:* Physiology of temperature regulation; nervous control of circulation; physiology and pharmacology of the autonomic nervous system. *Mailing Add:* John B Pierce Found of Conn 290 Congress Ave New Haven CT 06519

RAWSON, RULON WELLS, b Idaho Falls, Idaho, Sept 28, 08; m 40; c 3. MEDICINE. *Educ:* Northwestern Univ, MB, 37, MD, 38. *Prof Exp:* Univ cancer comt fel, Harvard Med Sch, 38-41, Am Col Physicians fel thyroid physiol, Harvard Med Sch & Mass Gen Hosp, 41-42; Walcott fel, Harvard Univ, 42-45; assoc med, Mass Gen Hosp, 45-46; asst prof, Harvard Med Sch, 46-48; assoc prof, Med Col, Cornell Univ, 48-51, prof, Sloan-Kettering Div, 51-54, prof, Med Col, 54-67; prof med, dean med & vpres, Col Med & Dent NJ, 67-72; dir extramural prog, Univ Tex Syst Cancer Ctr, Houston, 72-75, assoc dir prog plannning, 75-77; dir, Bonneville Ctr Res, 77-80; RETIRED. *Concurrent Pos:* Mem, Sloan-Kettering Inst Cancer Res, 48-67; attend physician, Dept Med, Mem Hosp, 48-67, exec officer, 48-58, chmn dept med, Mem Ctr, 58-67; Am Cancer Soc Comt on Personnel for Res, 58-63; mem adv comt sr clin traineeships, Dept Health, Educ & Welfare, 63-65. *Honors & Awards:* Meritorious Serv Award, Goiter Asn, 59; Centennial Award, Northwestern Univ, 59. *Mem:* AAAS; Am Physiol Soc; Endocrine Soc (vpres, 57-58, pres, 66-67); Am Soc Clin Invest; Harvey Soc (secy, 55-57). *Res:* Thyroid physiology and diseases; neoplastic diseases; radioisotopes in biology. *Mailing Add:* Bonneville Ctr Res 520 Wakara Way Salt Lake City UT 84108

RAY, AJIT KUMAR, b Calcutta, India, Feb 1, 25; m 56; c 2. APPLIED MATHEMATICS, FLUID DYNAMICS. *Educ:* Univ Calcutta, BSc, 44, MSc, 47; Univ Göttingen, DSc(math, natural sci), 55. *Prof Exp:* Prof appl math, Asutosh Col, Univ Calcutta, 48-56; reader aeronaut sci, Indian Inst Sci, Bangalore Univ, 56-60; assoc res officer, Nat Aeronaut Estab Nat Res Coun Can, 61-64; math adv & res scientist, Dept Transport, Govt Can, 64-65; asst prof appl math, Clarkson Tech, 65-66; assoc prof, 66-75, PROF APPL MATH & DIR RES, UNIV OTTAWA, 75- *Concurrent Pos:* Reviewer, Appl Mech Rev, 66-; vis prof, Ctr Advan Study Appl Math, Univ Calcutta, 70 & 76; sect chmn boundary layer theory, Third Canadian Appl Mech Cong, Calgary, Can, 71; sessional chmn, Euromech Colloquium-27, Poland, 72; vis res prof, Indian Inst Sci, Bangalore & Indian Inst Technol, Kanpur, Jadavpore Univ, India, 76; consult, 80- *Mem:* Fel AAAS; Am Math Soc; assoc fel Am Inst Aeronaut & Astronaut; fel Inst Math & Appln UK; fel Royal Aeronaut Soc. *Res:* Non-linear partial differential equations in fluid dynamics and aerodynamics; numerical mathematics class, functional analysis and discrete mathematics. *Mailing Add:* Dept Math Univ Ottawa Ottawa ON K1N 9B4 Can

RAY, ALDEN E(ARL), b Centralia, Ill, Feb 14, 31; m 52; c 4. PHYSICAL METALLURGY. *Educ:* Southern Ill Univ, BA, 53; Iowa State Univ, PhD(metall), 59. *Prof Exp:* Jr chemist, Ames Lab, Iowa State Univ, 53-56, res asst, 56-59; res metallurgist, Res & Eng Div, Monsanto Chem Co, 59-61; sr res metallurgist, 61-74, assoc prof, 61-71, dir grad prog mat sci, 71-74, PROF, RES INST, UNIV DAYTON, 71-, SUPVR, METALS & CERAMICS DIV, 74- *Mem:* Fel Am Soc Metals; Am Welding Soc; Sigma Xi. *Res:* Structure-property relationships of intermetallic phases, especially of rare earth transition metal alloys; magnetic properties; phase stability; phase diagrams. *Mailing Add:* Res Inst Univ of Dayton Dayton OH 45469

RAY, ALLEN COBBLE, b Jacksonville, Tex, Nov 17, 41; m 73. VETERINARY TOXICOLOGY, ANALYTICAL TOXICOLOGY. *Educ:* Univ Tex, Austin, BS, 64, PhD(chem), 71. *Prof Exp:* Teaching asst chem, Univ Tex, Austin, 64-67; res scientist, Clayton Found, Biochem Inst, Univ Tex, 67-71, res assoc, 72-73; VET TOXICOLOGIST, TEX VET MED DIAG LAB, TEX A&M UNIV, 73- *Concurrent Pos:* Vis mem, Dept Vet Physiol & Pharmacol, Tex A&M Univ, 78- *Mem:* Am Chem Soc; Am Asn Vet Lab Diag. *Res:* Development of analytical and diagnostic methods in veterinary and human toxicology; chemistry modes of action and metabolism of naturally occurring and environmental toxins. *Mailing Add:* Tex Vet Med Diag Lab PO Drawer 3040 College Station TX 77843

RAY, BRONSON SANDS, b New Albany, Ind, Jan 4, 04; m 33; c 2. SURGERY. *Educ:* Franklin Col, BS, 24; Northwestern Univ, MD, 28. *Hon Degrees:* DSc, Franklin Col, 50. *Prof Exp:* Gen intern, Wesley Mem Hosp, Chicago, 28-29; asst resident med, Passavant Mem Hosp, 29-30; instr surg, Harvard Med Sch, 31-32; asst, 32-35, instr surg, 35-36, assoc, 36-39, from asst prof to assoc prof, 39-45, from assoc prof to prof clin surg, 45-70, prof, 70-76, EMER PROF SURG, MED COL, CORNELL UNIV, 76- *Concurrent Pos:* Surg house officer, Peter Bent Brigham Hosp, 31-32; surg house officer, NY Hosp, 32-35, resident surg, 35-36, from asst attend surgeon to attend surgeon in charge neurosurg, 36-71, hon staff, 76, proj dir, AV Educ Prog Neurosurg, 71-75; assoc attend surgeon, St Luke's Hosp, 42-43, emer, 81; attend neurosurgeon, Mem Hosp, 44-76; consult neurosurg, Roosevelt Hosp, 46-76, emer, 81; attend; neurosurgeon, Greenwich Hosp, Conn, 48-65; mem, Am Bd Neurol Surg, 48. *Honors & Awards:* Harvey Cushing Award, 81; Medal of Honor, World Fedn Neurosurg Soc, 81. *Mem:* Soc Univ Surg; Soc Neurol Surg (secy); Soc Clin Surg; Harvey Cushing Soc; Am Neurol Asn. *Res:* Surgery of the nervous system. *Mailing Add:* New York Hosp-Cornell Med Ctr 525 E 68th St New York NY 10021

RAY, CARLETON, zoology, see previous edition

RAY, CHARLES, JR, b Baltimore, Md, Dec 6, 11; m 37; c 1. GENETICS. *Educ:* Lafayette Col, AB, 37; Univ Va, PhD(genetics), 41. *Prof Exp:* Geneticist, Plant Res Dept, Cent Fibre Corp, 41-52; from asst prof to prof, 52-80, EMER PROF BIOL, EMORY UNIV, 80- *Concurrent Pos:* Mem, Marine Biol Lab, Woods Hole Oceanog Inst. *Mem:* AAAS; Genetics Soc Am; Am Genetic Asn. *Res:* Population genetics; computer simulation. *Mailing Add:* Dept of Biol Emory Univ Atlanta GA 30322

RAY, CLARENCE THORPE, b Hutto, Tex, July 17, 16; m 42; c 1. INTERNAL MEDICINE. *Educ:* Univ Tex, BA, 37, MD, 41; Am Bd Internal Med & Am Bd Cardiovasc Dis, dipl. *Prof Exp:* Intern, Scott & White Hosp, Temple, Tex, 41-42; resident, Parkland Hosp, Dallas, 42-44, dir outpatient dispensary, 43-44; from instr to assoc prof med, Sch Med, Tulane Univ, 45-58, dir heart sta, 47-58; prof med & chmn dept, Sch Med & physician & chief med serv, Hosp, Univ Mo-Columbia, 58-67; dir educ & res, Alton Ochsner Med Found, 67-75; PROF MED & CHMN DEPT, SCH MED, TULANE UNIV, 75- *Concurrent Pos:* Instr, Southwestern Med Found, Inc, 43-44; from asst vis physician to sr vis physician, Charity Hosp, 45-58; consult, Vet Admin, 53-58; USPHS, 55-58 & Vet Admin Hosps, New Orleans & Alexandria, La, 57-58; head sect cardiol, Dept Med, Ochsner Clin, New Orleans, La, 68-75, trustee & vpres, Alton Ochsner Med Found, 70-75. *Mem:* Am Soc Clin Invest; AMA; fel Am Col Physicians. *Res:* Cardiovascular disease. *Mailing Add:* Dept of Med Sch Med Tulane Univ New Orleans LA 70118

RAY, CLAYTON EDWARD, b New Castle, Ind, Feb 6, 33; m 53; c 4. VERTEBRATE PALEONTOLOGY. *Educ:* Harvard Univ, BA, 55, MA, 58, PhD(geol), 62. *Prof Exp:* Asst cur vert paleont, State Mus & asst prof biol, Univ Fla, 59-63; assoc cur later cenozoic mammals, 64-68, CUR QUATERNARY & MARINE MAMMALS, NAT MUS NATURAL HIST, SMITHSONIAN INST, 69- *Mem:* Am Soc Mammal; Soc Vert Paleont. *Res:* Systematics, morphology, distribution and evolution of Cenozoic mammals including living ones; emphasis on pinnipeds. *Mailing Add:* Nat Mus of Natural Hist Smithsonian Inst Washington DC 20560

RAY, DALE ALLEN, plant genetics, deceased

RAY, DALE C(ARNEY), b Highland Park, Mich, Aug 31, 33; m 53; c 4. ELECTRICAL ENGINEERING, SOLID STATE PHYSICS. *Educ:* Univ Mich, BSE, 56, MSE, 57, PhD(cryomagnetics), 62. *Prof Exp:* Res asst comput design & technol, Eng Res Inst, Univ Mich, 56-57, instr elec eng, Univ, 57-62, admin dir solid state devices lab, 60-61, asst prof elec eng, Univ, 62-66; assoc prof, 66-77, assoc dean, Div Grad Studies & Res, 69-77, PROF ELEC ENG, GA INST TECHNOL, 77- *Concurrent Pos:* Consult, Off Res Admin, Univ Mich, 57-; Power Equip Div, Lear Siegler, Inc, 62-63, Sensor Dynamics, Inc, 63-64 & Lockheed-Ga Co, 67-; Ford Found fel, 62-63; prin engr, Raytheon Corp, 63-64. *Mem:* AAAS; Am Phys Soc; Inst Elec & Electronics Engrs; Am Asn Physics Teachers; Am Soc Eng Educ. *Res:* Cryomagnetics; magnetic measurements and application; heat transfer; non-electromechanical energy conversion; microwave integrated circuit technology and studies in sociotechnology. *Mailing Add:* Dept of Elec Eng Ga Inst of Technol Atlanta GA 30332

RAY, DAN S, b Memphis, Tenn, Dec 27, 37; c 2. MOLECULAR BIOLOGY, BIOPHYSICS. *Educ:* Memphis State Univ, BS, 59; Western Reserve Univ, MS, 61; Stanford Univ, PhD(biophysics), 65. *Prof Exp:* US Pub Health Serv fel, biochem virol, Max-Planck Inst Biochem, 65-66; from asst prof to assoc prof, 66-73, PROF MOLECULAR BIOL, UNIV CALIF, LOS ANGELES, 73- *Concurrent Pos:* US Pub Health Serv res grants, 67-70 & 72-86, Am Cancer Soc grant, 78-80, WHO grant, 80-82; found scientist, Int Genertic Eng, Inc, 81. *Mem:* AAAS; Biophys Soc; Am Soc Microbiol. *Res:* Structure and replication of desoxyribonucleic acid; genetic control of desoxyribonucleic acid replication; molecular cloning of desoxyribonucleic acid; transposable genetic elements; desoxyribonucleic acid sequence analysis; replication mechanisms of small viruses; genetic and biochemical analysis of tryponasomes. *Mailing Add:* Dept of Biol & Molecular Biol Inst Univ of Calif Los Angeles CA 90024

RAY, DAVID SCOTT, b New Haven, Conn, Oct 5, 30; m 56; c 4. MATHEMATICS. *Educ:* Washington & Jefferson Col, AB, 52; Univ Mich, MA, 56; Univ Tenn, PhD(math), 64. *Prof Exp:* Teaching fel math, Univ Mich, 56-58; instr, Univ Tenn, 58-64; assoc prof, 64-70, PROF MATH & CHMN DEPT, BUCKNELL UNIV, 70- *Mem:* Am Math Soc; Math Asn Am. *Res:* Topology, especially problems associated with the imbedding of Peano continua in Euclidean spaces. *Mailing Add:* Dept of Math Bucknell Univ Lewisburg PA 17837

RAY, EARL ELMER, b Burnsville, NC, Aug 5, 29; m 55; c 1. MEAT SCIENCE. *Educ:* NC State Col, BS, 52, MS, 54; Ore State Col, PhD(genetics), 58. *Prof Exp:* Asst, NC State Col, 52-54; animal husbandman sheep breeding, Agr Res Serv, USDA, NMex, 59-61; asst prof, 61-72, assoc prof, 72-74, PROF ANIMAL SCI NMEX STATE UNIV, 74- *Res:* Improvement of beef tenderness by postmortem treatments; palatability characteristics of hot-boned, prerigor meat. *Mailing Add:* Dept of Animal Range & Wildlife Sci NMex State Univ Las Cruces NM 80001

RAY, FREDERICK KALB, b Zanesville, Ohio, Mar 23, 44; m 71; c 2. FOOD SCIENCE & TECHNOLOGY. *Educ:* Ohio State Univ, BScAg, 67, MS, 74; Purdue Univ, PhD(animal sci), 78. *Prof Exp:* Prod supvr meat packing, Dinner Bell Foods, Defiance, Ohio, 70-72; EXTEN ANIMAL FOODS SPECIALIST MEAT & DAIRY PROD, DEPT ANIMAL SCI, OKLA STATE UNIV, 78- *Mem:* Am Soc Animal Sci; Inst Food Technologists; Am Meat Sci Asn. *Res:* Emulsion technology; factors effecting emulsion stability; evaluation of meat emulsions using scanning electron microscopy to observe the structure of fat and protein. *Mailing Add:* Dept of Animal Sci 004 A H Bldg Stillwater OK 74074

RAY, HEMEN, b Calcutta, India, Dec 26, 42; US citizen. STRUCTURAL MECHANICS, COMPOSITE MATERIALS. *Educ:* Calcutta Univ, BE, 65; Univ Wis-Madison, MS(mech eng), 68, MS(eng mech), 75, PhD(eng mech), 79. *Prof Exp:* Methods engr, Mach Mfg Corp, Calcutta, 65-66; teaching asst mech eng, Univ Wis-Madison, 67-68; mfg develop engr, Standard Pressed Steel Co, 69-70; lectr & teaching asst eng mech, Univ Wis-Madison, 72-79; assoc res scientist struct dynamics, Lockheed Missiles & Space Co, 79-80; ASST PROF SOLID MECH, RUTGERS UNIV, 80- *Mem:* Soc Exp Stress Anal; Sigma Xi. *Res:* Dynamic response in shells due to thermal loadings; design with composites; delamination in composites. *Mailing Add:* Mech Eng Dept Rutgers Univ PO Box 909 Piscataway NJ 08854

RAY, HOWARD EUGENE, b Iola, Kans, Aug 15, 26; m 46; c 3. COMMUNICATION SCIENCE, SOIL FERTILITY. *Educ:* Kans State Univ, BS, 49, MS, 50; Univ Minn, PhD(soils), 56. *Prof Exp:* Instr soils, Kans State Univ, 49-50; instr high sch, Kans, 50-51; exten soils specialist, Univ Ariz, 51-54; asst soils, Univ Minn, 54-56; asst soils chemist, Everglades Exp Sta, Fla, 56-58; agronomist, Agr Ext Serv, Univ Ariz, 58-66; dep team leader, Ford Found IADP Prog, 67-73; prog leader, Acad Educ Develop, Basic Village Educ Proj, Guatemala, 73-76; RURAL DEVELOP ADV & DIR, ASIAN PROGS, ACAD FOR EDUC DEVELOP, 76- *Mem:* Am Soc Agron; Soil Sci Soc Am; Soc Int Develop; Indian Soil Sci Soc. *Res:* Plant nutrition; nitrogen movement and transformations in soil; cotton production; intensive agricultural development; use of communication technology in development programs. *Mailing Add:* 2526 E Blanton Dr Tucson AZ 85716

RAY, JAMES ALTON, b Hicksville, Ohio, Sept 29, 32; m 60; c 2. VETERINARY PATHOLOGY, VETERINARY MICROBIOLOGY. *Educ:* Ohio State Univ, DVM, 57; Mich State Univ, MS, 61, PhD(path), 66. *Prof Exp:* Instr microbiol & pub health & leader microbiol diag lab, Mich State Univ, 57-59, co-dir tuberculosis res, 59-66; res assoc, Upjohn Co, 66-72; sect head, 72, mgr, 72-73, DIR, ETHICON RES FOUND, SOMERVILLE, NJ, 74- *Mem:* Am Vet Med Asn; Am Asn Lab Animal Med; AAAS; NY Acad Sci; Soc Biomat. *Res:* Industrial pathology; toxicology; experimental surgery; histology; histochemistry product development and research. *Mailing Add:* Ethicon Res Found Somerville NJ 08876

RAY, JAMES DAVIS, JR, b Starkville, Miss, May 5, 18; m 46; c 4. BOTANY. *Educ:* Miss State Univ, BS, 39, MS, 47; Univ Ill, PhD, 51. *Prof Exp:* Asst bot, Miss State Univ, 34-41, from instr to assoc prof, 46-59, cur herbarium, 55-59; from assoc prof to prof, 59-73, chmn dept, 62-71, interim chmn dept, 71-73, actg dean, 73-74, DEAN, COL NATURAL SCI, UNIV SOUTH FLA, 75- *Mem:* Bot Soc Am; Am Soc Plant Taxon; Int Soc Plant Taxon. *Res:* Flora of Mississippi and Florida; scrub vegetation; lysimachia; taxonomy of flowering plants. *Mailing Add:* Univ SFla Tampa FL 33620

RAY, JAMES P, b New York, NY, Jan 16, 44; m 63. CORAL REEF ECOLOGY, CRUSTACEAN SYSTEMATICS. *Educ:* Univ Miami, BS, 66; Tex A&M Univ, MS, 70, PhD(biol oceanog), 74. *Prof Exp:* Sr staff scientist marine biol, 74-82, MGR ENVIRON SCI SUPPORT, CORP ENVIRON AFFAIRS, SHELL OIL CO, 82- *Concurrent Pos:* Contrib author, Petrol in the Marine Environ, Nat Acad Sci, 81; panel mem, Fate & Effects of Drilling Muds in the Marine Environ, Nat Acad Sci, 81-83. *Mem:* Int Soc Petrol Indust Biologists (pres, 81-82). *Res:* Petroleum industry research on fate and effects of drilling fluids and petroleum hydrocarbons in marine environment. *Mailing Add:* Environ Affairs Dept Shell Oil Co PO Box 4320 Houston TX 77210

RAY, JESSE PAUL, b Central Lake, Mich, Nov 8, 16; m 39; c 1. ANALYTICAL CHEMISTRY. *Educ:* Asbury Col, AB, 39; Univ Syracuse, PhD(anal chem), 47. *Prof Exp:* Teacher high sch, Ill, 39-42; chief chemist, Chem & Metall Lab, Remington Arms Co, Inc, 42-44; asst chem, Univ Syracuse, 44-45; res engr, Battelle Mem Inst, 46-47; assoc prof, 47-51, PROF CHEM, ASBURY COL, 51- *Concurrent Pos:* Consult chemist, 47- *Mem:* Fel Am Chem Soc. *Res:* Physical chemistry of metals; determination of metal phase diagrams; development of analytical methods of steel analysis; instrumentation. *Mailing Add:* Dept Chem Asbury Col Wilmore KY 40390

RAY, JOHN DELBERT, b Murphysboro, Ill, Aug 21, 30; m 56; c 3. MECHANICAL ENGINEERING. *Educ:* Univ Ill, BS, 56, MS, 57; Univ Okla, PhD(mech eng), 68. *Prof Exp:* Engr, McDonnell Aircraft Corp, 57-62; res dir, Res Inst, Univ Okla, 62-68; from asst prof to assoc prof mech eng, 68-77, PROF MECH ENG & ACTG CHMN DEPT & DIR GRAD STUDIES & RES, COL ENG, MEMPHIS STATE UNIV, 77- *Mem:* Am Soc Mech Engrs; Am Soc Testing & Mat. *Res:* Vibrations; structural dynamics; design; high temperature metal erosion and fatigue; composite material. *Mailing Add:* Dept Mech Eng Col Eng Memphis State Univ Memphis TN 38152

RAY, JOHN ROBERT, b Beckley, WVa, Jan 27, 39; m 65; c 2. PHYSICS. *Educ:* Rose-Hulman Inst Technol, BS, 61; Univ Ohio, PhD(physics), 64. *Prof Exp:* Asst prof physics, Auburn Univ, 64-65; res assoc, Coord Sci Lab, Univ Ill, 65-66; from asst prof to assoc prof, 66-77, PROF PHYSICS, CLEMSON UNIV, 77- *Concurrent Pos:* Fel, Marshall Space Flight Ctr, Huntsville, Ala, 81. *Mem:* Int Soc Gravitation & Gen Relativity; Am Phys Soc. *Res:* Relativity; field theory; theoretical physics. *Mailing Add:* Dept of Physics & Astron Clemson Univ Clemson SC 29631

RAY, LEE EDMISTEN, biochemistry, see previous edition

RAY, MAURICE L, b West Fork, Ark, Nov 14, 20; m 42; c 3. ANIMAL HUSBANDRY. *Educ:* Univ Ark, BS, 42, MS, 48; Univ Ill, PhD, 53. *Prof Exp:* From asst prof to assoc prof, 53-60, PROF ANIMAL SCI, UNIV ARK, FAYETTEVILLE, 60- *Mem:* Am Soc Animal Sci. *Res:* Beef Cattle; ruminant nutrition; production. *Mailing Add:* Dept of Animal Sci Col of Agr & Econ Univ of Ark Fayetteville AR 72701

RAY, OAKLEY S, b Altoona, Pa, Feb 6, 31; m 53; c 4. PSYCHOPHARMACOLOGY. *Educ:* Cornell Univ, BA, 52; Univ Pittsburgh, MEd, 54, PhD(psychol), 58. *Prof Exp:* Assoc prof psychol pharmacol, Univ Pittsburgh, 60-70; PROF PSYCHOL, VANDERBILT UNIV, 70-, ASSOC PROF PHARMACOL, MED CTR, 70-; CHIEF MENT HEALTH UNIT PATIENT CARE, VET ADMIN CTR, NASHVILLE, 73- *Concurrent Pos:* Fel, Neuropharmacol Res Labs, NIMH, Pittsburgh, 58-60; chief psychol serv, Vet Admin Med Ctr, Nashville, 70-; chief, Psychol Res Lab, Vet Admin Med Ctr, Nashville, 70-; mem, Grad Neurobiol Res Training Progs, NIMH, 74-78. *Mem:* Fel Am Col Neuropsychopharmacol; fel Am Psychol Asn; Am Soc Pharmacol & Exp Therapeut. *Res:* Research centers around the genetic and developmental determinants of brain function in animals, and on the effects of CNS drugs on behavior during development and at maturity. *Mailing Add:* Vet Admin Med Ctr 1310 24th Ave S Nashville TN 37203

RAY, PAUL DEAN, b Monmouth, Ill, Dec 7, 34; m 57; c 4. BIOCHEMISTRY. *Educ:* Monmouth Col, Ill, AB, 56; St Louis Univ, PhD(biochem), 62. *Prof Exp:* Am Cancer Soc fel, Enzyme Inst, Univ Wis-Madison, 62-65; univ fel, 65-67; from asst prof to assoc prof, 67-73, PROF BIOCHEM, SCH MED, UNIV N DAK, 73- *Concurrent Pos:* Estab investr, Am Heart Asn, 67-72; mem Great Plains regional res rev & adv comn, 74-78; mem study sect arthritis metab & digestive dis, NIH, 69-73. *Mem:* AAAS; Am Chem Soc; Am Soc Biol Chem. *Res:* Carbohydrate metabolism, gluconeogenesis, and metabolic regulation; endocrinology. *Mailing Add:* Dept of Biochem Univ of NDak Sch of Med Grand Forks ND 58202

RAY, PAUL H, microbiology, biochemistry, see previous edition

RAY, PETER MARTIN, b San Jose, Calif, Dec 17, 31; m 54; c 1. PLANT PHYSIOLOGY. *Educ:* Univ Calif, AB, 51; Harvard Univ, PhD(biol), 55. *Prof Exp:* Jr fel, Soc Fels, Harvard Univ, 55-58; from asst prof to prof bot, Univ Mich, Ann Arbor, 58-65; prof biol, Univ Calif, Santa Cruz, 66-68; PROF BIOL SCI, STANFORD UNIV, 68- *Honors & Awards:* Charles Albert Schull Award, Am Soc Plant Physiol, 71. *Mem:* Bot Soc Am; Am Soc Plant Physiol. *Res:* Physiology and biochemistry of plant growth and development; plant hormones. *Mailing Add:* Dept of Biol Sci Stanford Univ Stanford CA 94305

RAY, PETER SAWIN, b Iowa City, Iowa, July 26, 44; m 70; c 1. METEOROLOGY. *Educ:* Iowa State Univ, BS, 66; Fla State Univ, MS, 70, PhD(meteorol), 73. *Prof Exp:* Res meteorologist, 73-80, CHIEF, METEOROL RES GROUP, NAT SEVERE STORMS LAB, NAT OCEANIC & ATMOSPHERIC ADMIN, 80- *Concurrent Pos:* Nat Res Coun fel, Nat Severe Storms Lab, 73-74; adj asst prof, Depts Meteorol & Elec Eng, Univ Okla, 74- *Mem:* Am Meteorol Soc; Am Geophys Union; Am Inst Physics. *Res:* Scattering physics of radiation and hydrometeors; using models and observations, the study of the morphology and dynamics of severe storms. *Mailing Add:* Nat Severe Storms Lab Nat Oceanic & Atmospheric Admin 1313 Halley Circle Norman OK 73069

RAY, PRASANTA K, b Calcutta, India, Sept 29, 41; m 68; c 2. IMMUNOTHERAPY OF CANCER. *Educ:* Univ Calcutta, BS, 62, MS, 64, PhD(biochem), 68. *Hon Degrees:* Univ Calcutta, DSc, 74. *Prof Exp:* Sr scientist res & teaching tumor immunol, Biomed Group, Bhabha Atomic Res Ctr, 73-76; dir admin & res cancer, Chittaranjan Nat Res Ctr, India, 76-77; asst prof, 78-80, DIR ADMIN & RES TUMOR IMMUNOL, ALMA DEA MORANI LAB SURG IMMUNOBIOL, MED COL PA & HOSP, 78-, ASSOC PROF TRANSPLANTATION & TUMOR IMMUNOL, DEPT SURG & MICROBIOL, 81- *Concurrent Pos:* Prin investr, Med Col Pa & Hosp, 78-; chief, Comt Nutrit & Immunol, Int Fedn Biosocial Develop & Human Health, NY, 80- *Mem:* NY Acad Sci; Int Soc Detection & Prevention Cancer; Am Asn Immunologists; Am Asn Apheresis; Indian Immunol Soc. *Res:* Investigations to remove blocking factors extracorporeally or ex vivo from both animal and human tumor-bearing hosts to study its therapeutic benefit. *Mailing Add:* Alma Dea Morani Lab Surg Immunobiol Med Col Pa & Hosp 3300 Henry Ave Philadelphia PA 19129

RAY, RICHARD G, b North Adams, Mass, July 15, 20; m 47; c 2. GEOLOGY. *Educ:* Williams Col, BA, 42; Brown Univ, ScM, 43; Johns Hopkins Univ, PhD, 50. *Prof Exp:* Geologist, US Geol Surv, 43-61; prog dir geol, NSF, 61-75; RETIRED. *Concurrent Pos:* Mem Bd Mineral & Energy Resources, Nat Acad Sci, 76-, consult, 81- *Mem:* AAAS; Geol Soc Am; Soc Econ Paleont & Mineral. *Res:* Areal mapping and detailed study of ore deposits of Alaska; aerial photographs and applications of photogrammetric techniques in geologic research. *Mailing Add:* 11409 Farmland Dr Rockville MD 20852

RAY, RICHARD SCHELL, b Antwerp, Ohio, May 21, 28; m 54; c 3. VETERINARY PHARMACOLOGY. *Educ:* Ohio State Univ, BA, 50, DVM, 55, MSc, 58, PhD(physiol, pharmacol), 63. *Prof Exp:* From instr to assoc prof, 55-73, PROF VET CLIN SCI & DIR, PRE & POST RACE TESTING LABS, OHIO STATE UNIV, 73- *Concurrent Pos:* Grants, NY Racing Asn & Jockey Club, 65-66, Harness Racing Inst, 66-67 & Thoroughbred Racing Fund, 68- *Mem:* Am Asn Equine Practitioners; Am Soc Vet Physiol & Pharmacol; World Asn Physiologists, Pharmacologists, Biochemists; Asn Drug Detection Labs; fel Am Col Vet Pharmacol & Therapeut. *Res:* Intermediate metabolism and diseases related to metabolism; detection of illegally used drugs; serum transaminase changes related to disease; research and development of drug detection methods in biological fluids; general physiology. *Mailing Add:* Vet Teaching Hosp Ohio State Univ 1935 Coffey Rd Columbus OH 43210

RAY, ROBERT ALLEN, b Scottsbluff, Nebr, Dec 19, 39; m 60; c 4. CLINICAL CHEMISTRY. *Educ:* Univ Nebr, BS, 61, MS, 63, PhD(biochem), 66. *Prof Exp:* Res chemist, 66-74, eng mgr, 74-78, PROG MGR, BECKMAN INSTRUMENTS, 81- *Mem:* AAAS; Am Chem Soc; Am Asn Clin Chemists. *Res:* Chemical and biomedical instrumentation for the assay of enzymes or their substrates. *Mailing Add:* 18946 Gordon Lane Yorba Linda CA 92686

RAY, ROBERT DURANT, b Cleveland, Ohio, Sept 21, 14; m 53; c 5. ORTHOPEDIC SURGERY. *Educ:* Univ Calif, BA, 36, MA, 38, PhD(anat), 48; Harvard Univ, MD, 43. *Hon Degrees:* MedDrSci, Royal Univ Umea, 72. *Prof Exp:* Asst anat, Med Sch, Univ Calif, 37-38; intern surg, Peter Bent Brigham Hosp, Boston, 43; asst orthop surg, Harvard Med Sch, 44-45; instr anat, Med Sch, Univ Calif, 47-48; asst prof orthop surg, Sch Med, Wash Univ, 48-51, assoc prof & head dept, 54-56; PROF ORTHOP SURG & HEAD DEPT, COL MED, UNIV ILL, CHICAGO, 56- *Concurrent Pos:* Mem staff, Ravens Wood Hosp, 71- *Mem:* Am Orthop Res Soc (pres, 59); Am Asn Anat; Am Orthop Asn; Am Col Surg; Am Acad Orthop Surg. *Res:* Bone growth, maturation and metabolism; influence of intrinsic and extrinsic factors on these processes including endocrines and radiation; kinetics of bone-seeking radioactive isotopes. *Mailing Add:* Dept of Orthop Surg Univ of Ill Col of Med Chicago IL 60612

RAY, ROSE MARIE, b Hayward, Calif, Mar 30, 43; m 73; c 3. MATHEMATICAL STATISTICS. *Educ:* Univ Calif, Berkeley, BA, 65, PhD(statist), 72. *Prof Exp:* From actg instr to actg asst prof statist, Univ Calif, Berkeley, 71-72; asst prof math, Northwestern Univ, 72-74; asst prof statist, Univ Fla, 74-76; statist consult, 76; PERSONNEL RES STATISTICIAN, PAC GAS & ELEC, SAN FRANCISCO, 78- *Concurrent Pos:* Consult mkt res, Montgomery Wards Co, Chicago, 74; consult, Biostatist Unit, J Hillis Miller Health Ctr, Univ Fla, 74-76; sr statistician, Sci Comput Serv, Univ Calif, San Francisco, 76-; sr biostatistician, Contraceptive Drug Study, Kaiser Found Hosp, Walnut Creek, Calif, 76-; lectr, Dept Statist, Univ Calif, Berkeley, 77- *Mem:* Inst Math Statist; Am Statist Asn; AAAS; Sigma Xi; Biomet Soc. *Res:* Development and application of special stochastic models for research in medicine, biology, marketing, manpower planning and cost analysis; research in the theory of C-alpha tests. *Mailing Add:* Personnel Res 245 Market St Rm 932 San Francisco CA 94106

RAY, SAMMY MEHEDY, b Mulberry, Kans, Feb 25, 19; m 43; c 4. MARINE BIOLOGY. *Educ:* La State Univ, BS, 42; Rice Inst, MA, 52, PhD(biol), 54. *Prof Exp:* Fishery res biologist, US Fish & Wildlife Serv, 54-59; asst prof oceanog & meteorol, 59-63, assoc prof oceanog, 63-69, PROF BIOL, OCEANOG, MARINE SCI & WILDLIFE FISHERIES SCI, TEX A&M UNIV, 69-, DIR, MARINE LAB, 63-, HEAD DEPT MARINE SCI, 74-, DIR SCH MARINE TECHNOL, 77- *Mem:* AAAS; Nat Shellfisheries Asn; Am Soc Limnol & Oceanog; Phycol Soc Am; Am Inst Fishery Res Biol. *Res:* Oyster biology; marine microbiology, phytoplankton and pollution. *Mailing Add:* Dept of Wildlife & Fish Sci Tex A&M Univ College Station TX 77840

RAY, SIBA PRASAD, b Dinhata, India, Jan 4, 44; m 77. MATERIALS SCIENCE, METALLURGY. *Educ:* Univ Calcutta, BE, 64; Columbia Univ, MS, 70, DEngSc, 74. *Prof Exp:* Sci officer metall, Bhabha Atomic Res Ctr, India, 65-69; scientist, 77-78, SR SCIENTIST MAT SCI, ALCOA LABS, 78- *Concurrent Pos:* Res assoc, Pa State Univ, 74-77. *Mem:* Am Ceramic Soc; Sigma Xi. *Res:* High temperature materials; conducting ceramics; aluminum smelting process development; refractory electrodes; oxygen sensors; solid state chemistry. *Mailing Add:* Alcoa Tech Ctr Alcoa Center PA 15069

RAY, SYLVIAN RICHARD, b Pineville, La, Aug 26, 31; m 59; c 2. COMPUTER SCIENCE, ELECTRICAL ENGINEERING. *Educ:* Southwestern La Inst, BS, 51; Univ Ill, MS, 57, PhD(elec eng), 60. *Prof Exp:* Elec scientist, Naval Res Lab, 51-54; res assoc elec eng, 60-61, from asst prof to assoc prof, 61-76, PROF ELEC ENG, UNIV ILL, URBANA, 76- *Mem:* Sigma Xi. *Res:* Digital computer circuit design; properties of magnetic materials; image processing. *Mailing Add:* Dept Comput Sci Univ Ill Urbana IL 61801

RAY, VERNE A, b Portsmouth, NH, July 28, 29; m 52; c 2. MICROBIOLOGY, BIOCHEMISTRY. *Educ:* Univ NH, BS, 51, MS, 55; Univ Tex, PhD(bact), 59. *Prof Exp:* Sr res scientist, Chas Pfizer & Co, 59-67, proj leader, 67-72, mgr, 72-75, ASST DIR, DEPT DRUG SAFETY EVAL, CENT RES, PFIZER INC, 75- *Mem:* Am Soc Microbiol. *Res:* Molecular biology of virus infectious process; factors controlling induced mutation frequency in microorganisms; elaboration products of microorganisms and methods of increasing yield. *Mailing Add:* Med Res Lab Pfizer Inc Eastern Pt Rd Groton CT 06340

RAY, W(ILLIS) HARMON, b Washington, DC, Apr 4, 40; m 62; c 3. CHEMICAL ENGINEERING. *Educ:* Rice Univ, BA, 62, BSChE, 63; Univ Minn, PhD(chem eng), 66. *Prof Exp:* Asst prof chem eng, Univ Waterloo, 66-69, assoc prof, 69-70; from assoc prof to prof, State Univ NY Buffalo, 70-76; PROF CHEM ENG, UNIV WIS-MADISON, 76-, CHMN DEPT, 81- *Honors & Awards:* Eckman Award, Am Automatic Control Coun, 69; A K Doolittle Award, Am Chem Soc, 81. *Mem:* Am Inst Chem Engrs; Am Chem Soc; Am Soc Eng Educ; Soc Indust & Appl Math; Chem Inst Can. *Res:* Process optimization; optimal control; supervisory adaptive control of chemical processes; chemical reactor design, especially polymerization reactors; modeling, optimization and control of metallurgical processes. *Mailing Add:* Dept of Chem Eng Univ of Wis Madison WI 53706

RAY, WILLIAM J, b Birmingham, Ala, Sept 3, 45; m 72; c 2. CLINICAL PSYCHOLOGY, PSYCHOPHYSIOLOGY. *Educ:* Eckerd Col, St Petersburg, Fla, BA, 67; Vanderbilt Univ, MA, 69, PhD(clin psychol), 71. *Prof Exp:* Fel med psychol, Langley Porter Neuropsychiat Inst, 71-72; MEM FAC PSYCHOL, PA STATE UNIV, 72- *Res:* Psychophysiological assessment-brain/behavior relationships; biofeedback; behavioral medicine; interdependence of mental, emotional and physiological/motor activities. *Mailing Add:* Dept of Psychol Pa State Univ University Park PA 16802

RAY, WILLIAM JACKSON, JR, b Bradenton, Fla, Mar 19, 32; m 54; c 2. ORGANIC CHEMISTRY. *Educ:* Bethany-Nazarene Col, BS, 49; Purdue Univ, PhD(org chem), 57. *Prof Exp:* Res assoc biochem, Brookhaven Nat Lab, 57-59; asst prof, Rockefeller Inst, 59-61; from asst prof to assoc prof, 61-70, PROF BIOCHEM, PURDUE UNIV, LAFAYETTE, 70- *Mem:* Am Chem Soc; Am Soc Biol Chem. *Res:* Mechanism of enzyme action. *Mailing Add:* Dept of Biol Sci Purdue Univ Lafayette IN 47907

RAYBORN, GRAYSON HANKS, b Columbia, Miss, May 26, 39; m 65. ATOMIC PHYSICS. *Educ:* Rensselaer Polytech Inst, BS, 61; Univ Fla, PhD(physics), 69. *Prof Exp:* Asst engr, Sperry Rand Corp, 61-62; res asst physics, Univ Fla, 68-69; asst prof physics, Old Dominion Univ, 69-70; asst prof, 70-75, assoc prof, 75-79, PROF PHYSICS, UNIV SOUTHERN MISS, 79- *Concurrent Pos:* Consult, Langley Res Ctr, NASA, 71. *Mem:* Am Asn Physics Teachers; Am Phys Soc; Fed Am Sci. *Res:* Photoionization and dissociative photoionization; deconvolution and inverse digital filtering; free electron magnetometer; development of novel apparatus for use by undergraduate physics majors. *Mailing Add:* 2012 Eddy St Hattiesburg MS 39401

RAYBURN, DONALD ROY, b Calgary, Alta, Mar 24, 46; m 81; c 1. ASTROPHYSICS, COMPUTATIONAL HYDRODYNAMICS. *Educ:* Univ Calgary, BSc, 68; Queen's Univ, Kingston, PhD(physics), 71. *Prof Exp:* Res fel, Inst Theoret Astron, Univ Cambridge, 71-72; res fel astrophys, Calif Inst Technol, 72-73; asst prof physics, Univ Waterloo, 73-81; ASSOC SCIENTIST, APPLIED RES CORP, 81- *Concurrent Pos:* Nat Res Coun Can fel, 71-73. *Mem:* Can Astron Soc; Royal Astron Soc; Am Astron Soc. *Res:* Simulation of hydrodynamical processes in astronomical objects; atmospheric dynamics. *Mailing Add:* 2308 13 N Berkshire Rd Charlottesville VA 22901

RAYBURN, LOUIS ALFRED, b Columbus, Ga, Dec 10, 21; m 48; c 4. PHYSICS. *Educ:* Univ Ky, BS, 48, MS, 50, PhD(physics), 54. *Prof Exp:* Instr physics, Univ Ky, 48-50; assoc physicist, Oak Ridge Nat Lab, 50-52; res asst physics, Univ Ky, 52-54; asst physicist, Argonne Nat Lab, 54-59; prof physics & head dept physics & astron, Univ Ga, 59-64; head univ participation officer, Oak Ridge Assoc Univs, 64-70; PROF PHYSICS & CHMN DEPT, UNIV TEX, ARLINGTON, 70- *Mem:* AAAS; Am Phys Soc. *Res:* Low energy nuclear physics. *Mailing Add:* Dept of Physics Univ of Tex Arlington TX 76019

RAYBURN, MARLON CECIL, JR, b Clay, Ky, Sept 29, 31; m 62; c 3. TOPOLOGY. *Educ:* Evansville Col, BA, 52; Auburn Univ, MS, 56; Univ Ky, PhD(math), 69. *Prof Exp:* Instr math & physics, Earlham Col, 59-62; asst prof math, State Univ NY Col Geneseo, 65-68; asst prof, 69-74, ASSOC PROF MATH, UNIV MAN, 74- *Mem:* Can Math Cong; Am Math Soc; Math Asn Am. *Res:* General topology; compactifications and realcompactifications; uniformities; proximities; applications to analysis; sigma algebras. *Mailing Add:* 18 Fordham Winnipeg MB R3T 3B7 Can

RAYBURN, WILLIAM REED, b St Louis, Mo, Apr 7, 40; m 67; c 2. BOTANY & MICROBIOLOGY. *Educ:* Wash Univ, BA, 63; Ind Univ, Bloomington, MA, 67, PhD(bot, microbiol), 71. *Prof Exp:* Instr, 67-69, asst prof bot & gen biol, 69-78, ASSOC PROF BACTERIOL, PUB HEALTH & BOT, WASH STATE UNIV, 78- *Mem:* Bot Soc Am; Phycol Soc Am; Brit Phycol Soc; Int Phycol Soc; Am Soc Microbiol. *Res:* Sexuality of algae; emission of volatile sulfur compounds by microorganisms; microbial extracellular polysaccharides. *Mailing Add:* Dept of Bot Wash State Univ Pullman WA 99164

RAYCHAUDHURI, ANILBARAN, b Tipperah, India; m 64; c 3. IMMUNOLOGY. *Educ:* Univ Calcutta, BSc, 51; Univ Rangoon, MS, 58; Univ Cincinnati, PhD(biol sci), 63. *Prof Exp:* Res chemist geront, Vet Admin Hosp, Baltimore, Md, 65-67; res assoc, Georgetown Univ, 67-70; sr scientist, Merrell-Nat Lab, Cincinnati, 70-78; SR SCIENTIST IMMUNOL, CIBA-GEIGY CORP, ARDSLEY, NY, 78- *Concurrent Pos:* Vis fel, NIH, Bethesda, Md, 63-65; consult, Vet Admin Hosp, Baltimore, 64-65. *Mem:* NY Acad Sci; AAAS; Sigma Xi. *Res:* Immunology in general and cell-mediated immunity in particular; application of chemotherapy to rheumatoid arthritis involving a unique type of compound designated as disease modifying antirheumatic drugs. *Mailing Add:* Ciba-Geigy Corp Metab Dis Dept 444 Saw Mill River Rd Ardsley NY 10502

RAY-CHAUDHURI, DILIP K, b Dacca, E Pakistan, Sept 4, 29; m 61; c 2. POLYMER CHEMISTRY, ORGANIC CHEMISTRY. *Educ:* Univ Dacca, BSc, 48, MSc, 49; Univ Calcutta, PhD(chem), 56. *Prof Exp:* Jr res asst chem jute cellulose, Tech Res Lab, India, 56-58; fel, Cellulose Res Inst, State Univ NY Col Forestry, Syracuse, 58-61; res assoc, Ont Res Found Can, 61-64; proj supvr org chem res, 64-67; sect leader, 67-72, mgr cent res, 72-77, dir corp res, 77-81, DIV VPRES & DIR CORP RES, NAT STARCH & CHEM CORP, 81- *Mem:* AAAS; Am Chem Soc; NY Acad Sci; Sigma Xi. *Res:* Polyelectrolytes; adhesives; wet strength additives; polyurethanes and polyesters. *Mailing Add:* Nat Starch & Chem Corp 10 Finderne Ave Bridgewater NJ 08876

RAY-CHAUDHURI, DWIJENDRA KUMAR, b Narayangang, Bangladesh, Nov 1, 33; m 62; c 2. APPLIED MATHEMATICS, PURE MATHEMATICS. *Educ:* Presidency Col, Calcutta, BSc, 53; Calcutta Univ, MSc, 55; Univ NC, Chapel Hill, PhD(math statist), 59. *Prof Exp:* Res assoc, Case Inst Technol, 59-60; asst prof math statist, Univ NC, Chapel Hill, 60-61; reader, Indian Statist Inst, 61-62; mem res staff math, T J Watson Res Ctr, IBM Corp, NY, 62-64; consult statist & math, Cornell Med Ctr & Sloan-Kettering Inst, 64-65; vis assoc prof math, Math Res Ctr, Univ Wis-Madison, 65-66; PROF MATH, OHIO STATE UNIV, 66-, CHMN DEPT, 80- *Concurrent Pos:* Invited speaker, Int Math Cong, 70. *Mem:* Am Math Soc. *Res:* Combinatorial mathematics; finite geometry; graph and information theory; error-correcting codes; statistical design experiments. *Mailing Add:* Dept of Math Ohio State Univ Columbus OH 43210

RAYCHAUDHURI, KAMAL KUMAR, b Dinapore, India, Nov 11, 47; m 74; c 1. EXPERIMENTAL HIGH ENERGY PHYSICS. *Educ:* Univ Calcutta, India, BSc, 67, MSc, 69; Univ Pa, PhD(physics), 77, MSE, 78. *Prof Exp:* Assoc, Saha Inst Nuclear physics, Calcutta, India, 71; res fel physics, Univ Pa, 77-78; res assoc, 78-79, ASST PROF PHYSICS, UNIV MASS, AMHERST, 80- *Mem:* Am Phys Soc. *Res:* Experimental high energy physics: hyperon studies and studies of new particles using high speed electronic detectors. *Mailing Add:* Dept Physics Univ Mass Amherst MA 01002

RAYCHOWDHURY, PRATIP NATH, b Calcutta, India, Jan 1, 32. APPLIED MATHEMATICS, MATHEMATICAL PHYSICS. *Educ:* Univ Calcutta, BS, 51; Univ Col, BA, 55; Brigham Young Univ, MS, 58; George Washington Univ, PhD(math physics), 66. *Prof Exp:* Asst prof physics, Rutgers Univ, 64-65; asst prof math, Royal Mil Col Can, 65-67; assoc prof lectr eng, George Washington Univ, 67; sr staff scientist, 67-68; assoc prof physics, NY Inst Tech, 68-69; assoc prof, 69-74, PROF MATH SCI, VA COMMONWEALTH UNIV, 74- *Mem:* Am Math Soc; Soc Indust & Appl Math; Am Phys Soc; Int Asn Math Physics. *Res:* Excited states of many-body systems; shock waves and high velocity plasma; group theory and application in physics. *Mailing Add:* Dept of Math Sci Va Commonwealth Univ Richmond VA 23284

RAYFIELD, GEORGE W, b San Francisco, Calif, Feb 17, 36; m 59; c 1. PHYSICS. *Educ:* Stanford Univ, BS, 58; Univ Calif, Berkeley, MS & PhD(physics), 64. *Prof Exp:* Res asst eng sci, Univ Calif, Berkeley, 60-61, physics, 61-64; asst prof, Univ Pa, 64-68; ASSOC PROF PHYSICS, UNIV ORE, 68- *Mem:* Am Phys Soc. *Res:* Solid state physics; liquid helium; ionic probes in liquid helium; microwave tubes; electron beams. *Mailing Add:* Dept of Physics Univ of Ore Eugene OR 97403

RAYFORD, PHILLIP LEON, b Roanoke, Va, July 25, 27; m 52. PHYSIOLOGY, ENDOCRINOLOGY. *Educ:* NC A&T State Univ, BS, 49; Univ Md, College Park, MS, 69, PhD(reproductive endocrinol), 73. *Prof Exp:* Supvy biologist endocrinol, Nat Cancer Inst, 55-62, supvy biologist, NIHMR, 62-64, supvy biologist radioimmunoassay, Nat Cancer Inst, 64-70, supvy biology, NICHO, 70-73; from asst prof to assoc prof biochem, Div Human Cell Biol & Genetics, Univ Tex Med Br Galveston, 73-77, prof & dir, Biochem Lab, Dept Surg, 77-80; PROF & CHMN DEPT PHYSIOL, UNIV ARK SCH MED, LITTLE ROCK, 80- *Mem:* Endocrinol Soc; Am Physiol Soc; Am Gastroenterol Asn; Soc Exp Biol & Med; NY Acad Sci. *Res:* Metabolism and catabolism of gastrointestinal and pancreatic hormones in man and dogs; research and development of radioimmunoassay systems for measuring hormones of gastrointestinal, pancreatic and pituitary origin. *Mailing Add:* Dept Physiol & Biophys 4301 W Markham Slot 505 Little Rock AR 72205

RAYLE, DAVID LEE, b Pasadena, Calif, Oct 22, 42; m 67; c 2. PLANT PHYSIOLOGY. *Educ:* Univ Calif, Santa Barbara, BA, 64, PhD(biol), 67. *Prof Exp:* NSF fel & res assoc bot, Mich State Univ-Atomic Energy Comn Plant Res Lab, Mich State Univ, 67-68; res assoc, Univ Wash, 68-70; from asst prof to assoc prof, 70-75, chmn dept, 74-80, PROF BOT, SAN DIEGO STATE UNIV, 80- *Mem:* Am Soc Plant Physiol. *Res:* Mechanism of action of plant growth hormones; physical properties of plant cell walls; plant growth and development. *Mailing Add:* Dept of Bot San Diego State Univ San Diego CA 92182

RAYLE, RICHARD EUGENE, b Freesoil, Mich, Apr 5, 39; m 63; c 1. GENETICS. *Educ:* Mich State Univ, BS, 62; Univ Ill, Urbana, PhD(genetics), 67. *Prof Exp:* NIH trainee, Univ Calif, Davis, 67-69; res assoc zool, Univ NC, Chapel Hill, 69-70, vis asst prof, 70; ASST PROF ZOOL, MIAMI UNIV, 70- *Mem:* AAAS; Genetics Soc Am. *Res:* Structural and functional organization of Eukaryotic genetic systems. *Mailing Add:* Dept of Zool Miami Univ Oxford OH 45056

RAYMAN, MOHAMAD KHALIL, b Guyana, SAm, Feb 23, 38; Can citizen; m 59; c 2. FOOD MICROBIOLOGY. *Educ:* McGill Univ, BSc, 66, PhD(microbiol), 70. *Prof Exp:* Fel, Med Res Coun Can, Univ Toronto, 70-73; RES SCIENTIST, HEALTH & WELFARE, CAN, 73- *Mem:* Can Soc Microbiol; Am Soc Microbiol. *Res:* Methodology related to isolation and identification of food poisoning organisms; mechanism of succinate transport into membrane vesicles of Escherichia coli; mechanism of thermal injury in Salmonella; testing replacement for nitrite in food preservation. *Mailing Add:* Health Protection Br Tunney's Pasture Sir FG Banting Bldg Ottawa ON K1A 0L2 Can

RAYMON, LOUIS, b New Brunswick, NJ, Oct 17, 39; m 62; c 3. MATHEMATICS. *Educ:* Yeshiva Col, BA, 60; Yeshiva Univ, MA, 61, PhD(math), 66. *Prof Exp:* from asst prof to assoc prof, 66-77, PROF MATH, TEMPLE UNIV, 77- *Mem:* Am Math Soc. *Res:* Classical problems in real and complex analysis, especially approximation theory. *Mailing Add:* Dept of Math Temple Univ Col Liberal Arts Philadelphia PA 19122

RAYMOND, ARTHUR E(MMONS), b Boston, Mass, Mar 24, 99; m 21; c 1. AERONAUTICAL ENGINEERING. *Educ:* Harvard Univ, BS, 20; Mass Inst Technol, MS, 21. *Hon Degrees:* DSc, Polytech Inst Brooklyn, 47. *Prof Exp:* Engr, Douglas Aircraft Co, 25-34, vpres eng, 34-60; CONSULT, RAND CORP, 60- *Concurrent Pos:* Mem, Nat Adv Comt Aeronaut, 46-56, consult, NASA, 62-68; trustee, Aerospace Corp, 60-71 & Res Anal Corp, 65-71. *Mem:* Nat Acad Sci; Nat Acad Eng; Soc Automotive Engrs; hon fel Am Inst Aeronaut & Astronaut. *Res:* Aeronautics; astronautics. *Mailing Add:* 73 Oakmont Dr Los Angeles CA 90049

RAYMOND, CHARLES FOREST, b St Louis, Mo, Oct 31, 39; m 65. GEOPHYSICS. *Educ:* Univ Calif, Berkeley, BA, 61; Calif Inst Technol, PhD(geophys), 69. *Prof Exp:* Asst prof, 69-73, ASSOC PROF GEOPHYS, UNIV WASH, 73- *Mem:* Am Geophys Union; Glaciol Soc. *Res:* Rheology of earth materials; flow and structure of glaciers. *Mailing Add:* Geophysics Prog Univ of Wash Seattle WA 98105

RAYMOND, DAVID JAMES, b Hammond, Ind, Oct 24, 43. PHYSICS, METEOROLOGY. *Educ:* Rensselaer Polytech Inst, BS, 65; Stanford Univ, PhD(physics), 70. *Prof Exp:* Asst prof meteorol, Univ Hawaii, 70-73; res assoc, 73-75, asst prof, 75-79, ASSOC PROF PHYSICS, NMEX INST MINING & TECHNOL, 79- *Mem:* Am Phys Soc; Am Meteorol Soc. *Res:* Mesoscale meteorology; turbulence in geophysical flows. *Mailing Add:* Dept of Physics NMex Inst Mining & Technol Socorro NM 87801

RAYMOND, FRANK LEROY, b Medford, Ore, Nov 12, 24; m 45; c 3. RESOURCE MANAGEMENT. *Educ:* Ore State Col, BS, 49; Harvard Univ, AM, 52, PhD(biol), 54. *Prof Exp:* Asst mycol, Harvard Univ, 49-54; forest pathologist, Southern Res Sta, Can Dept Agr, Ont, 54-64; BIOMATHEMATICIAN, SOUTH RES STA ONT, MINISTRY NATURAL RESOURCES, 64- *Mem:* The Biomet Soc; Statist Sci Asn Can; Can Inst Forestry. *Mailing Add:* Southern Res Sta Ont Ministry Nat Resources RR2 Maple ON L0J 1E0 Can

RAYMOND, GERALD PATRICK, b Bagdad, Iraq, June 25, 33; Can citizen; m 59; c 2. CIVIL ENGINEERING. *Educ:* Univ London, BSc, 56, PhD(soil mech), 65, DSc(eng), 73; Princeton Univ, MSE, 57. *Prof Exp:* Eng asst, Howard Humphries & Sons, 51-54 & Kennedy & Donkin, 54-56; engr, Procter & Redfern, 57-58; dep city engr, North Bay, Ont, 58-59; lectr civil eng, Univ Sydney, 59-61; from asst prof to assoc prof, 61-72, chmn grad studies, 75-77, PROF CIVIL ENG, QUEEN'S UNIV, ONT, 72- *Concurrent Pos:* Current mem comts soil & rock properties, mech of earth masses & layered systs & track struct syst design, Transp Res Bd, Nat Res Coun; current exec mem geotech res comt, Nat Res Coun Can; consult, Cent Technol, Inc, Bechtel Can Ltd & Terrafix-Toronto. *Honors & Awards:* Walmsley Mem Prize, 56. *Mem:* Am Soc Civil Engrs; Am Rwy Eng Asn; Can Peat Soc; Can Geotech Soc. *Res:* Consolidation of clays and settlement of foundations on clays; bearing capacity of peat; stresses and deformations under dynamic and static load systems in railroad track structure and support. *Mailing Add:* Ellis Hall Queen's Univ Kingston ON K7L 3N6 Can

RAYMOND, HOWARD LAWRENCE, b Seattle, Wash, Aug 2, 29; m 70; c 2. FISHERIES. *Educ:* Univ Wash, BS, 53. *Prof Exp:* Fishery biologist res, Bur Com Fisheries, 54-57; design engr statist, Boeing Co, 57-60; SUPVRY FISHERY BIOLOGIST RES, NAT MARINE FISHERIES SERV, 60- *Concurrent Pos:* Consult, Tech Adv Comt, Columbia Basin Fisheries, 75- *Mem:* Am Fisheries Soc; Am Inst Fisheries Res Biologists. *Res:* Development of methodology for protecting migrating anadromous fish in dammed and impounded rivers. *Mailing Add:* Northwest & Alaska Fisheries Ctr 2725 Montlake Blvd E Seattle WA 98102

RAYMOND, JOHN CHARLES, b Edgerton, Wis, Nov 28, 48; m 75; c 1. ASTROPHYSICS. *Educ:* Univ Wis, Madison, BA, 70, PhD(physics), 76. *Prof Exp:* RES FEL ASTROPHYS, HARVARD COL OBSERV, 76- *Mem:* Am Astron Soc. *Res:* Ultraviolet astronomy; solar physics; interstellar medium. *Mailing Add:* Ctr for Astrophys 60 Garden St Cambridge MA 02138

RAYMOND, JOSEPH L(AWRENCE), b Niagara Falls, NY, Aug 30, 22; m 45; c 2. AERONAUTICAL ENGINEERING. *Educ:* Univ Mich, BSE, 44, MSE, 49. *Prof Exp:* Mathematician, Douglas Aircraft Co, Inc, Calif, 46-47; asst aeronaut eng, Univ Mich, 47-50; develop engr, Proj Hermes, Gen Elec Co, 50-52; engr, Hughes Tool Co & Hughes Aircraft Co, 52-54 & Rand Corp, 54-66; SR STAFF ENGR, HUGHES AIRCRAFT CO, CANOGA PARK, 66- *Mem:* Am Inst Aeronaut & Astronaut. *Res:* Aerodynamics and radar preliminary design; ballistic missile defense; preliminary design of missiles; laser gasdynamics. *Mailing Add:* 571 Lucero Ave Pacific Palisades CA 90272

RAYMOND, KENNETH NORMAN, b Astoria, Ore, Jan 7, 42; m 65; c 1. INORGANIC CHEMISTRY, CRYSTALLOGRAPHY. *Educ:* Reed Col, BA, 64; Northwestern Univ, Evanston, PhD(chem), 68. *Prof Exp:* from asst prof to assoc prof, 68-78, PROF INORG CHEM, UNIV CALIF, BERKELEY, 78- *Concurrent Pos:* Vis prof, Stanford Univ, Australian Nat Univ, Univ Sydney & Univ Strasbourg; Miller prof, Univ Calif, 77-78; Guggenheim fel, 80-81. *Mem:* Am Chem Soc; Am Crystallog Asn; Sigma Xi. *Res:* Chemistry of transition metal coordination compounds. *Mailing Add:* Dept of Chem Univ Calif Berkeley CA 94720

RAYMOND, LOREN ARTHUR, b Sebastopol, Calif, Nov 23, 43; m 65; c 1. STRUCTURAL GEOLOGY, PETROLOGY. *Educ:* San Jose State Col, BS, 67, MS, 69; Univ Calif, Davis, PhD(geol), 73. *Prof Exp:* Instr, Appalachian State Univ, 72-73; asst prof geol, 73-76 & 77-78; asst prof geol, S Ore State Col, 76-77; ASSOC PROF GEOL APPALACHIAN STATE UNIV, 78- *Mem:* Geol Soc Am; Am Geophys Union. *Res:* Understanding the deformational and metamorphic processes in subduction zones as revealed by the Franciscan Complex of California. *Mailing Add:* Dept of Geol Appalachian State Univ Boone NC 28608

RAYMOND, LOUIS, b Natrona, Pa, Nov 18, 34; m 57; c 4. METALLURGY. *Educ:* Carnegie Inst Technol, BS, 56, MS, 58; Univ Calif, Berkeley, PhD(metall), 63. *Prof Exp:* Methods engr mat process, Pittsburgh Plate Glass Co, 55; res engr stainless steel, Allegheny Ludlum Steel Co, 56-58; mech metall, Inst Eng Res, Univ Calif, Berkeley, 58-63; sr res engr strength mech, Aeronautic Div, Ford Motor Co, 63-65; MEM TECH STAFF, AEROSPACE CORP, 65-, HEAD METALL RES, 67-, STAFF SCIENTIST, 77-; PROF, CALIF STATE UNIV, LONG BEACH, 79- *Concurrent Pos:* Mem fac, Calif State Univ, Long Beach, 63-; spec consult, UNESCO-UN Develop Prog Proj, Higher Mining Eng Sch, Oviedo, Spain; lectr exten course, Univ Calif, Los Angeles; consult failure anal, Dept of Transp, US Coast Guard, 75-77; consult struct integrity offshore platforms, US Geol Surv, Dept Interior, 76; consult life prediction anal, Dept Transp, Fed Railroad Admin, 77-; mem fracture toughness testing comt, Nat Mat Adv Bd-Nat Acad Sci, 75-76, mem fracture toughness requirements in design comt, 77- *Honors & Awards:* Am Soc Testing & Mat Award, 63-64; Space Processing Invention Award, NASA, 78. *Mem:* Am Inst Mining, Metall & Petrol Engrs; fel Inst Advan Eng; Sigma Xi; Am Soc Testing & Mat; AAAS. *Res:* Mechanical metallurgy; thermal mechanical processing; strengthening mechanisms; fracture toughness; hydrogen embrittlement; corrosion-fatigue; space processing; failure analysis. *Mailing Add:* 915 Celtis Pl Newport Beach CA 92660

RAYMOND, MAURICE A, b New Bedford, Mass, Jan 8, 38; m 63; c 2. ORGANIC CHEMISTRY, POLYMER CHEMISTRY. *Educ:* Providence Col, BS, 58; Univ Fla, PhD(org chem), 62. *Prof Exp:* Sr res chemist, 62-64, group supvr, 64-67, sect mgr, 67-70, tech mgr, 70-77, mkt mgr rigid urethanes, 77-78, BUS MGR CHEM SPECIALTIES, OLIN CORP, NEW HAVEN, 78- *Mem:* Am Chem Soc; Sigma Xi; Soc Cosmetics Chemists; Soc Plastics Eng. *Res:* Cyclopolymerization; fluoraromatics; nitrenes and carbenes; plasticizers; functional fluids; thermally stable elastomers; homogeneous catalysis; urethane foam machinery and chemical systems. *Mailing Add:* 74 Eden Rd Stamford CT 06907

RAYMOND, MICHAEL GRINDLEY, b Dayton, Ohio, Sept 20, 39; m 71. PHYSICS, COMPUTER SCIENCE. *Educ:* Mass Inst Technol, SB, 61; Univ Chicago, SM, 63, PhD(physics), 71. *Prof Exp:* Fel solid state physics, Geophys Lab, Carnegie Inst Wash, 71-74; comput scientist war games, Anagram Corp, 75-76; oper res analyst mil personnel, US Army Mil Personnel Ctr, 76-78; PHYSICIST & COMPUT SCIENTIST SOLAR ENERGY RES, INTERTECHNOL/SOLAR CORP, 78- *Res:* Solar energy; chemical bonding in crystals; photovoltaics. *Mailing Add:* InterTechnol/Solar Corp 100 Main St Warrenton VA 22186

RAYMOND, SAMUEL, b Chester, Pa, Feb 7, 20; m 51; c 2. MEDICINE, CHEMISTRY. *Educ:* Swarthmore Col, BA, 41; Univ Pa, MA & PhD(chem), 45; Columbia Univ, MD, 57. *Prof Exp:* Asst instr, Univ Pa, 41-45; asst, Col Physicians & Surgeons, Columbia Univ, 47-48, instr, 49-52; asst prof, 58-72, ASSOC PROF CLIN PATH, UNIV PA, 72- *Concurrent Pos:* Dir, Am Bd Clin Chem, 71-76; mem lab adv bd, Pa State Dept Health. *Mem:* AAAS; Am Chem Soc; AMA; Am Asn Clin Chem; Asn Comput Mach. *Res:* Electrophoresis; medical applications of computers. *Mailing Add:* 4312 Osage Ave Philadelphia PA 19104

RAYMONDA, JOHN WARREN, b Wickenburg, Ariz, May 2, 39; m 63; c 2. PHYSICAL CHEMISTRY. *Educ:* Cornell Univ, BA, 61; Univ Wash, Seattle, PhD(chem), 66. *Prof Exp:* Res assoc molecular beam spectros, Harvard Univ, 66-68; asst prof phys chem, Univ Ariz, 68-72; prin chemist, Aerodyn Res Dept, Calspan Corp, 72-76; RES CHEMIST, HIGH ENERGY LASER TECHNOL DEPT, BELL AEROSPACE TEXTRON, 76- *Res:* Electronic spectroscopy of sigma bonded systems; molecular beam spectroscopy of high temperature species; primary events in photochemical processes; chemical

lasers, laser induced chemical reactions, high temperature thermodynamics, laser radar; chemical laser modeling and development, laser diagnostics using nonlinear optics. *Mailing Add:* High Energy Laser Technol Dept PO Box 1 Buffalo NY 14240

RAYMOND-SAVAGE, ANNE, b Scituate, RI, Apr 10, 39; div; c 4. MARINE BIOLOGY. *Educ:* Univ RI, BS, 59, MA, 69; Ore State Univ, PhD(sci educ), 71. *Prof Exp:* Teacher sci, Coventry Schs, RI, 59-61 & West Warwick Schs, 64-66; instr sci educ, Univ RI, 67-69; ASSOC PROF SCI EDUC & MARINE BIOL, OLD DOMINION UNIV, NORFOLK, VA, 71-, DIR, CTR INSTRNL DEVELOP, 78- *Concurrent Pos:* Consult, WHRO-TV, Norfolk, Va, 73- & Corp Pub Broadcasting, Dept Defense. *Mem:* AAAS; Asn Educrs Teaching Sci; Nat Sci Teachers Asn. *Res:* Marine biology education models; coral reef ecology. *Mailing Add:* Curric & Instr Sch of Educ Old Dominion Univ Norfolk VA 23508

RAYMUND, MAHLON, b Columbus, Ohio, June 10, 32; m 56; c 3. FRACTURE, FINITE ELEMENTS. *Educ:* Univ Chicago, AB, 51, SB, 54, SM, 60, PhD(physics), 63. *Prof Exp:* Res assoc hyperfragments, Enrico Fermi Inst, Univ Chicago, 63-64; Kaonproton scattering, 65-68; SR SCIENTIST NEUTRON CROSS SECT DATA & REACTOR COMPUT, NUCLEAR ENERGY SYSTS, WESTINGHOUSE ELEC CORP, 68- *Concurrent Pos:* Dept Sci & Indust Res sr vis fel, Univ Col, Univ London, 64-65; res collabr, Nat Neutron Cross Sect Ctr, Brookhaven Nat Lab, 70-71. *Mem:* Am Phys Soc; Am Nuclear Soc. *Res:* Finite element methods for fracture and seismic analysis; computer applications. *Mailing Add:* 1148 Clemson Dr Monroeville PA 15146

RAYNAL, DUDLEY JONES, b Greenville, SC, Jan 1, 47; m 71; c 2. PLANT ECOLOGY. *Educ:* Clemson Univ, SC, BS, 69; Univ Ill, Urbana, PhD(bot), 74. *Prof Exp:* Vis lectr bot, Univ Ill, Urbana, 74; asst prof, 74-78, ASSOC PROF BOT, STATE UNIV NY, COL ENVIRON SCI & FORESTRY, SYRACUSE, NY, 78- *Mem:* Ecol Soc Am; Bot Soc Am; Brit Ecol Soc; AAAS; Sigma Xi. *Res:* Plant population and community ecology; plant succession plant life history studies; role of man-induced disturbance on terrestrial ecosystems. *Mailing Add:* Dept of Environ & Forest Biol Col of Environ Sci & Forestry Syracuse NY 13210

RAYNE, JOHN A, b Sydney, Australia, Mar 22, 27; m 54; c 3. PHYSICS. *Educ:* Univ Sydney, BSc, 48, BE, 50; Univ Chicago, MS, 51, PhD, 54. *Prof Exp:* Sci officer, Commonwealth Sci & Indust Res Orgn, Australia, 54-56; res engr, Westinghouse Elec Co, Pa, 56-61, adv engr, 61-64; assoc prof, 64-65, PROF PHYSICS, CARNEGIE-MELLON UNIV, 65- *Mem:* Am Phys Soc. *Res:* Cryogenics; physics of metals; alloy theory. *Mailing Add:* Dept of Physics Carnegie-Mellon Univ Pittsburgh PA 15213

RAYNER-CANHAM, GEOFFREY WILLIAM, b London, Eng, 1944; Can citizen. INORGANIC CHEMISTRY, SCIENCE EDUCATION. *Educ:* Univ London, BSc, 66, DIC, 69, PhD(inorg chem), 69. *Prof Exp:* Fel, Simon Fraser Univ, 69-71, York Univ, 71-72 & Simon Fraser Univ, 72-73; vis asst prof inorg chem, Univ Victoria, 73-74; vis asst prof, Bishop's Univ, 74-75; asst prof, 75-80, ASSOC PROF INORG CHEM, MEM UNIV, NFLD, 80- *Concurrent Pos:* Vis assoc prof, Colo Sch Mines, 81-82. *Honors & Awards:* Polysar Award, Chem Inst Can, 80. *Mem:* Chem Inst Can; Royal Soc Chem; Royal Soc Arts & Technol & Com. *Res:* Synthesis and spectroscopic study of biologically relevant complexes of niobium; development of chemistry in late 18th and early 19th century. *Mailing Add:* Dept Chem Sir Wilfred Grenfell Col Mem Univ Nfld Corner Brook NF A2H 6T9 Can

RAYNES, BERTRAM C(HESTER), b Jersey City, NY, Mar 12, 24; m 44. CHEMICAL ENGINEERING. *Educ:* Pa State Univ, BS, 44; Union Univ, NY, MS, 49. *Prof Exp:* Asst res lab, Gen Elec Co, 44-50; develop engr, Brush Beryllium Co, 50-51; head process eng, Horizons, Inc, 51-62; vpres appl res, Rand Develop Corp, 62-70; head environ eng, Trygve Hoff & Assocs Consult Engrs, 70-72; CONSULT CHEM ENG, 72- *Mem:* Am Chem Soc; Am Inst Chem Engrs; Water Pollution Control Fedn. *Res:* Process research and development; fused salt electrolysis of refractory metals; high temperature ceramics; water pollution control; nonbiologic waste water treatment; land use management; environmental controls. *Mailing Add:* PO Box LL Jackson WY 83001

RAYNOLDS, STUART, b Chicago, Ill, Oct 29, 27; m 61; c 3. ORGANIC CHEMISTRY, POLYMER CHEMISTRY. *Educ:* Cornell Univ, AB, 50; Univ Pittsburgh, MS, 55, PhD(org chem), 59. *Prof Exp:* Asst assayer, US Bur Mint, DC, 50-51; jr fel, Mellon Inst, 51-55; chemist, Jackson Labs, 59-65, res supvr, 65-69, res assoc, 69-72, RES FEL, E I DU PONT DE NEMOURS & CO, INC, 72- *Mem:* AAAS; Am Chem Soc. *Res:* Tar base and textile chemistry; polymers; colloid chemistry. *Mailing Add:* 2716 Silverside Rd Wilmington DE 19810

RAYNOR, SUSANNE, b Philadelphia, Pa, May 18, 48; m 72. THEORETICAL CHEMISTRY. *Educ:* Duke UUniv, BS, 70; Georgetown Univ, PhD(chem), 76. *Prof Exp:* Res assoc chem, Univ Toronto, 76-78; res assoc, Harvard Univ, 78-82; RES ASST PROF CHEM, RUTGERS UNIV, NEWARK, 82- *Concurrent Pos:* Lectr, Univ Toronto, New College, 78. *Mem:* Am Phys Soc. *Res:* Theoretical studies of the dynamics and kinetics of molecular energy transfer and reaction; abinitro and semiempirical quantum mechanics. *Mailing Add:* Olson Chem Lab Rutgers Univ Newark NJ 02138

RAYPORT, MARK, b Kharkov, Russia, Sept 6, 22; US citizen; m 51; c 3. NEUROSURGERY. *Educ:* Earlham Col, BA, 43; McGill Univ, MD, CM, 48, PhD(neurophysiol), 58. *Prof Exp:* Neurosurg resident, Montreal Neurol Inst, 54-57; asst prof neurosurg, Albert Einstein Col Med, 58-61, assoc prof, 61-68, asst prof physiol, 58-68; asst chief surg, Neurol Inst, Mt Zion Hosp & Med Ctr, San Francisco, 68-69; PROF NEUROL SURG & CO-CHMN NEUROSCI, MED COL OHIO, 69- *Concurrent Pos:* Duggan fel neuropath, Montreal Neurol Inst, 53, res fel, 55-56 & 58; res fel, USPHS, 55-56 & 58;

NIMH Interdisciplinary Prog spec sr fel, 58-61; career scientist award, Health Res Coun NY, 62-68; vis prof, Univ Paris, 67-68. *Mem:* AAAS; Asn Res Nerv & Ment Dis; Am Acad Neurol Surg; Am Electroencephalog Soc; Soc Neurosci. *Res:* Basic approaches to clinical problems; neurosurgical treatment of epilepsy and pain; neurophysiology of mammalian and human cortex; interdisciplinary studies of brain and behavior. *Mailing Add:* Dept of Neurosci Med Col of Ohio Toledo OH 43699

RAYSIDE, JOHN STUART, b Quebec, Que, Can, Aug 24, 42; m 67; c 2. INSTRUMENTATION. *Educ:* Carleton Univ, Ottawa, BS, 67; Univ Minn, MS, 69, PhD(physics), 73. *Prof Exp:* Res assoc optical spectroscopy, Dept Chem, Univ Tenn, 72-76; DEVELOP ENGR, UNION CARBIDE NUCLEAR DIV, 76- *Concurrent Pos:* Consult, NIH, 73-74. *Mem:* Optical Soc Am; Am Asn Physics Teachers. *Res:* Raman spectroscopy; optics; computer interfacing; instrumentation in general. *Mailing Add:* Union Carbide Nuclear Div PO Box Y Bldg 9202 MS 3 Oak Ridge TN 37830

RAYUDU, GARIMELLA V S, b Andhra Pradesh, India, Oct 1, 36; m 65; c 4. NUCLEAR CHEMISTRY, NUCLEAR MEDICINE. *Educ:* Andhra Univ, India, BSc, 56, MSc, 57; McGill Univ, PhD(nuclear chem), 61; Am Bd Radiol, cert, 77; Am Bd Nuclear Med, cert, 79. *Prof Exp:* Res asst health physics, Atomic Energy Estab, Bombay, India, 57-58; res assoc, Carnegie Inst Technol, 61-65; sr res assoc nuclear activation anal, Univ Toronto, 65-67; asst prof radiochem & nuclear chem, Loyola Univ, La, 67-68; ASST PROF NUCLEAR MED, RUSH MED SCH, 68-; ASSOC PROF, RUSH UNIV, 76- *Concurrent Pos:* US AEC grant nuclear & cosmochem, Carnegie Inst Technol, 61-65; Food & Drug Directorate Can pub health grant, Univ Toronto, 65-67; sr scientist, Rush-Presby St Luke's Med Ctr, 68- *Mem:* AAAS; Am Chem Soc; The Chem Soc; Am Asn Physicists in Med; Soc Nuclear Med. *Res:* Organ imaging radiopharmaceuticals; trace elements in liver, lung, pancreas, muscle and kidney; radiochemistry; cosmochemistry; instrumental analytical chemistry. *Mailing Add:* 1008 Clinton Oak Park IL 60304

RAZAK, CHARLES KENNETH, b Collyer, Kans, Sept 15, 18; m 40; c 2. FORENSIC ENGINEERING, ENGINEERING. *Educ:* Univ Kans, BS, 39, MS, 42. *Prof Exp:* From instr to asst prof aeronaut eng, Univ Kans, 29-43; 39-43; assoc prof & head dept, Wichita Univ, 43-48, prof, 48-64, dir dept eng, 48-51, actg dean col bus admin, 51-53, dean sch eng & dir eng res, 53-64; prof eng & dir indust exten serv, Kans State Univ, 64-70; ENG & MGT CONSULT, 70- *Concurrent Pos:* Mem bd dirs, KARD-TV, Wichita, Kans, Kans Invest Co & Midland Metal Craft, Inc; pres, Pane, Inc, Aerial Distributors, Inc, 64 & Managers, Inc, 66- *Mem:* Am Soc Eng Educ; Soc Hist Technol; hon mem Soc Advan Mgt; Nat Soc Prof Engrs; Soc Mfg Engrs. *Res:* Low speed aerodynamics; aircraft design. *Mailing Add:* 1305 E Waterman St Wichita KS 67211

RAZDAN, MOHAN KISHEN, b Srinagar, India. COMBUSTION, FLUID MECHANICS. *Educ:* Regional Eng Col, India, BE, 71; Indian Inst Technol, Kanpur, MTech, 74; Pa State Univ, MS, 76, PhD(mech eng), 79. *Prof Exp:* Res asst, Pa State Univ, 77-79, asst prof mech eng, 79-80; RES ENGR, EXXON RES & ENG CO, 80- *Mem:* Combustion Inst; assoc mem Am Soc Mech Engrs; Am Inst Aeronaut & Astronaut; Sigma Xi. *Res:* Effects of fluid mechanics on combustion processes and heat transfer in turbulent reacting flows with an emphasis on reduction of pollutants. *Mailing Add:* 111 Windy Willow Way Somerville NJ 08876

RAZDAN, RAJ KUMAR, b Simla, India, Dec 19, 29; m 56; c 2. ORGANIC CHEMISTRY, MEDICINAL CHEMISTRY. *Educ:* Univ Delhi, BSc, 48; Indian Inst Sci, Bangalore, Dipl, 51; Univ Glasgow, PhD(chem), 54. *Prof Exp:* Jr sci officer, Nat Chem Lab, India, 54-56; sci officer, Glaxo Labs Ltd, Eng, 56-58, joint works mgr fine chem prod, India, 58-63; res assoc org chem, Univ Mich, 63-64; sr staff scientist, Arthur D Little, Inc, Mass, 64-70; vpres res, 70-80, PRES, SISA INST RES & SISA, INC, 81-, DIR TOXICOL, SISA, INC, 81- *Concurrent Pos:* Consult, Nat Inst Drug Abuse, Nat Cancer Inst & Sarabhai Industs, India. *Mem:* Am Chem Soc; assoc, Royal Inst Chem; fel Royal Soc Chem. *Res:* Cannabinoids; terpenes; steroids; central nervous system active drugs; molecular rearrangements; morphine chemistry; narcotic antagonists; lysergic acid chemistry. *Mailing Add:* SISA Inc 763D Concorde Ave Cambridge MA 02138

RAZGAITIS, RICHARD A, b Chicago, Ill, Jan 13, 44; m 67; c 4. MECHANICAL ENGINEERING, THERMAL & FLUID SCIENCES. *Educ:* Univ Ill, BS, 65; Univ Fla, MS, 69; Southern Methodist Univ, PhD(mech eng), 74. *Prof Exp:* Mem Apollo launch team, Cape Kennedy Space Ctr, McDonnell-Douglas Corp, 65-69; asst prof, Univ Portland, 69-72; asst prof eng, Ohio State Univ, 74-81; PRIN RES SCIENTIST, BATTELLE MEM INST, 81- *Concurrent Pos:* Dresser fel, Southern Methodist Univ, 72-74; Dupont asst prof, Ohio State Univ, 75-76. *Mem:* Am Soc Mech Engrs; Am Soc Eng Educ. *Res:* Swirl flow heat transfer; aerosol mechanics; cyclonic separation techniques of particulates and steam. *Mailing Add:* 2070 W Lane Ave Columbus OH 43221

RAZINSKY, ELIAS (HIRSH), b New York, NY, June 23, 42; m 67; c 1. MECHANICAL ENGINEERING. *Educ:* Union Col, NY, BS, 64; Pa State Univ, MS, 66, PhD(mech eng), 69. *Prof Exp:* ASSOC SR RES ENGR, RES LABS, GEN MOTORS CORP, 69- *Mem:* Am Soc Mech Engrs. *Res:* Gas turbine technology; internal fluid mechanics. *Mailing Add:* Gen Motors Res Labs 12 Mile & Mound Rds Warren MI 48090

RAZNIAK, STEPHEN L, b Detroit, Mich, May 23, 34; m 65. ORGANIC CHEMISTRY. *Educ:* Wayne State Univ, BS, 55; Washington State Univ, PhD(chem), 59. *Prof Exp:* NSF fel org chem, Brown Univ, 59-60, instr, 60-61; from asst prof to assoc prof, 61-64, PROF ORG CHEM, EAST TEX STATE UNIV, 64-, HEAD DEPT, 74- *Mem:* Am Chem Soc; Royal Soc Chem. *Res:* Organic sulfur chemistry; Grignard reactions. *Mailing Add:* Dept of Chem East Tex State Univ Commerce TX 75428

RAZOUK, RASHAD ELIAS, b Dumiat, Egypt, Aug 22, 11; m 46; c 2. CHEMISTRY. *Educ:* Cairo Univ, BSc, 33, MSc, 36, PhD(chem), 39. *Prof Exp:* Asst prof chem, Cairo Univ, 39-47, assoc prof, 47-50; prof & chmn dept, Ain Shams Univ, Cairo, 50-56, vdean, 54-60; prof, Am Univ Cairo, 66-68; prof, 68-78, EMER PROF CHEM, CALIF STATE UNIV, LOS ANGELES, 79- *Concurrent Pos:* Actg dir, Div Colloid & Surface Chem, Nat Res Ctr, Cairo, 50-68. *Mem:* Am Inst Chem; Am Chem Soc; The Chem Soc. *Res:* Surface chemistry; adsorption on carbons and active solids; solid reactions; surface tension and contact angles; wetting and wettability. *Mailing Add:* Dept of Chem Calif State Univ Los Angeles CA 90032

RAZZELL, WILFRED EDWIN, b St Boniface, Man, May 10, 31; m 51; c 3. MICROBIOLOGY, BIOCHEMISTRY. *Educ:* Univ BC, BA, 52; Univ Ill, Urbana, PhD(bact, chem), 57. *Prof Exp:* Res asst chem, BC Res Coun, Vancouver, 56-57, res assoc, 57-59, res scientist, 59-61; sect head enzym, Syntex Inst Molecular Biol, Palo Alto, 61-64, actg dir, 62-64; assoc prof microbiol, Univ BC, 64-66; prof & head dept, Univ Alta, 66-69; res assoc, MacMillan-Bloedel Res Ltd, BC, 70-71; DIR VANCOUVER LAB, FISHERIES RES BD, CAN DEPT ENVIRON, 71- *Concurrent Pos:* Grants, Jane Coffin Childs Mem Fund med res, 59-61 & 64-66; USPHS, 62-63; Nat Res Coun Can, 64-70; Med Res Coun Can, 66-70. *Mem:* Am Soc Microbiol; Am Soc Biol Chem; Can Soc Microbiol; Can Biochem Soc. *Res:* Structure and enzymology of nucleic acids; activities of autotrophic bacteria in mineral leaching; nucleic acid degradative enzymes in cells; environmental distribution of microorganisms; water quality assessments; applied research into marine products refrigeration and processing. *Mailing Add:* 4153 W 14th Vancouver BC V6R 2X6 Can

REA, DAVID KENERSON, b Pittsburgh, Pa, June 2, 42; m 67; c 2. GEOLOGICAL OCEANOGRAPHY. *Educ:* Princeton Univ, AB, 64; Univ Ariz, MS, 67; Ore State Univ, PhD(oceanog), 74. *Prof Exp:* Asst prof oceanog, Sch Oceanog, Ore State Univ, 74-75; asst prof, 75-80, ASSOC PROF OCEANOG, DEPT ATMOSPHERIC & OCEANIC SCI, UNIV MICH, 80- *Mem:* Geol Soc Am; Am Geophys Union; AAAS; Sigma Xi. *Res:* Structure and tectonics of ocean basins and rises; marine and lacustrine sediments and sedimentation. *Mailing Add:* Dept of Atmospheric & Oceanic Sci Univ of Mich Ann Arbor MI 48109

REA, DAVID RICHARD, b Indianapolis, Ind, May 4, 40; m 64; c 4. CHEMICAL ENGINEERING. *Educ:* Purdue Univ, BS, 62; Princeton Univ, MA, 64, PhD(chem eng), 67. *Prof Exp:* TECH SUPT, PLASTIC PRODS & RESINS DEPT, E I DU PONT DE NEMOURS & CO, INC, 66- *Mem:* Am Inst Chem Engrs. *Res:* Rheology as applied to plastics; process development of fluorocarbon chemistry products; low-density polyethylene; nylon intermediates work; engineering thermoplastics. *Mailing Add:* E I du Pont de Nemours & Co Inc Sabine River Labs PO Box 1089 Orange TX 77630

REA, DONALD GEORGE, b Portage La Prairie, Man, Sept 21, 29; nat US. PLANETARY SCIENCES. *Educ:* Univ Man, BSc, 50, MSc, 51; Mass Inst Technol, PhD(chem), 54. *Prof Exp:* Nat Res Coun Can fel, Oxford Univ, 54-55; res chemist, Calif Res Corp, 55-61; assoc res chemist, Space Sci Lab, Univ Calif, Berkeley, 61-68; dep dir planetary progs, Off Space Sci & Appln, NASA Hq, 68-70; asst lab dir sci, Jet Propulsion Lab, 70-76, dep asst lab dir, 76-80, ASST LAB DIR, TECHNOL & SPACE PROGS DEVELOP, CALIF INST TECHNOL, 80- *Concurrent Pos:* Res fel, John F Kennedy Sch Govt, Harvard Univ, 79-80. *Mem:* Am Chem Soc; Am Phys Soc; Optical Soc Am; Am Astron Soc; Am Geophys Union. *Res:* Molecular spectroscopy of planetary atmospheres; remote sensing of planetary surfaces. *Mailing Add:* 1605 Pegfair Estates Dr Pasadena CA 91103

REA, KENNETH HAROLD, b Red Oak, Iowa, Aug 20, 46; m 67; c 4. PLANT SYNECOLOGY, COMPUTER SCIENCE. *Educ:* NMex State Univ, BS, 69, MS, 72; Utah State Univ, PhD(ecol), 76. *Prof Exp:* STAFF MEM ECOL, LOS ALAMOS NAT LAB, 76- *Mem:* AAAS; Soc Range Mgt. *Res:* Plant demography; impacts of geothermal energy development. *Mailing Add:* PO Box 1663 MS 490 Los Alamos Nat Lab Los Alamos NM 87545

READ, ALBERT JAMES, b Albany, NY, June 8, 26; m 53; c 1. PHYSICS. *Educ:* State Univ NY Col Educ, Albany, BA, 47, MA, 54. *Prof Exp:* Instr physics, Rensselaer Polytech Inst, 47-50; asst prof, Morrisville Agr & Tech Inst, 52-57; assoc prof, 57-71, PROF PHYSICS, STATE UNIV NY COL ONEONTA, 71- *Mem:* Int Solar Energy Soc; Am Asn Physics Teachers; Nat Sci Teachers Asn; Hist Sci Soc; Soc Hist Technol. *Mailing Add:* Dept of Physics State Univ of NY Col at Oneonta Oneonta NY 13820

READ, CHARLES H, b Amherst, NS, July 22, 18; m 42; c 5. PEDIATRICS, ENDOCRINOLOGY. *Educ:* Acadia Univ, BSc, 39; McGill Univ, MD & CM, 43. *Prof Exp:* Rutherford Caverhill fel, Fac Med, McGill Univ, 47-49; Commonwealth Fund fel, Harvard Med Sch & Mass Gen Hosp, Boston, 49-51; asst prof pediat, Fac Med, Univ Man, 51-52, assoc prof, 52-54; asst prof, 54-55, assoc prof, 55-59, PROF PEDIAT, COL MED, UNIV IOWA, 59- *Mem:* NY Acad Sci; Soc Pediat Res; Endocrine Soc; Am Diabetes Asn; Am Acad Pediat. *Mailing Add:* Dept of Pediat Univ Hosps Iowa City IA 52240

READ, DAVID HADLEY, b Seattle, Wash, May 20, 21; m 51, 63; c 5. PHYSICAL ORGANIC CHEMISTRY. *Educ:* Seattle Univ, BS, 42; Univ Ill, MS, 44; Univ Notre Dame, PhD(org chem), 49. *Prof Exp:* Asst prof chem, Univ Seattle, 48-51; res chemist, Am-Marietta Co, 51-54; assoc prof, 54-65, PROF CHEM, SEATTLE UNIV, 65- *Mem:* AAAS; Am Chem Soc; The Chem Soc. *Res:* Vinyl polymerization; electronic effects in rigid systems; clinical separations by high-performance liquid chromatography. *Mailing Add:* Dept of Chem Seattle Univ Seattle WA 98122

READ, DAVID THOMAS, b Seattle, Wash, Sept 17, 47; m 72; c 3. FRACTURE MECHANICS, PHYSICAL METALLURGY. *Educ:* Univ Santa Clara, BS, 69; Univ Ill, MS, 71, PhD(physics), 75. *Prof Exp:* PHYSICIST MECH PROPERTIES, US NAT BUR OF STANDARDS, 75-

Concurrent Pos: Nat Res Coun fel, Nat Bur Standards, 75-76. *Mem:* Am Phys Soc. *Res:* Low-temperature mechanical properties of metals; fracture mechanics; measurements of the J contour integrad. *Mailing Add:* Nat Bur of Standards Boulder CO 80302

READ, DONALD EARLE, b Calgary, Alta, July 17, 24; m 47; c 1. SCIENCE POLICY. *Educ:* Mt Allison Univ, BSc, 45; McGill Univ, PhD(org chem), 49. *Prof Exp:* Res chemist, Cent Res Lab, Can Industs Ltd, 49-56, res coordr, Chem Div, Que, 56-67; process specialist, Sandwell & Co Ltd, 67-72; sr policy adv, 72-75, PROJ DIR, MINISTRY OF STATE FOR SCI & TECHNOL, 75- *Mem:* Can Pulp & Paper Asn; Chem Inst Can. *Res:* Forestry, pulp and paper, chlorohydrocarbons; environment. *Mailing Add:* Ministry State Sci & Technol 270 Albert St Ottawa ON K1A 1A1 Can

READ, FLOYD M, b Ray City, Ga, Oct 4, 24; m 43; c 1. PHYSICS. *Educ:* Univ Fla, BSEd, 52, MEd, 56; NY Univ, PhD, 69. *Prof Exp:* Asst prof phys sci, 57-60, from asst prof to assoc prof physics, 60-75, PROF PHYSICS, E CAROLINA UNIV, 75- *Mem:* Nat Sci Teachers Asn; Am Asn Physics Teachers; Nat Asn Res Sci Teaching; Sigma Xi. *Res:* Solar radiometry; teaching of physics. *Mailing Add:* Dept Physics E Carolina Univ Greenville NC 27834

READ, GEORGE WESLEY, b Los Angeles, Calif, June 24, 34; div; c 3. PHARMACOLOGY, AUTACOIDS. *Educ:* Stanford Univ, BA, 59, MS, 62; Univ Hawaii, PhD, 69. *Prof Exp:* Instr gen sci, Univ Hawaii, Hilo, 63-64; res asst, 64-68, asst prof, 68-74, ASSOC PROF PHARMACOL, UNIV HAWAII, MANOA, 74- *Concurrent Pos:* Vis scientist, Univ Tex, Dallas, 75, Univ Wash, 78 & NIH, 78. *Mem:* Am Soc Pharmacol & Exp Therapeut; AAAS; Sigma Xi; Am Asn Univ Prof. *Res:* Pharmacology of histamine release, excitation-secretion coupling; computer-assisted instruction. *Mailing Add:* Dept Pharmacol Univ Hawaii Sch Med Honolulu HI 96822

READ, JOHN FREDERICK, b Reading, Eng, Apr 11, 40; m 63; c 2. PHYSICAL CHEMISTRY. *Educ:* Univ Nottingham, BSc, 61, PhD(phys chem), 64. *Prof Exp:* Fel chem, Northwestern Univ, 64-65; teaching fel, Hope Col, 65-66; from asst prof to assoc prof, Mt Allison Univ, 66-74, asst dean, Col Arts & Sci, 66-74; asst prof, 74-78, ASSOC PROF GEOL SCI, VA POLYTECH INST & STATE UNIV, 78- *Mem:* Chem Inst Can. *Res:* Heterogeneous catalysis of simple gas phase reactions by rare-earth compounds. *Mailing Add:* Dept of Geol Sci Va Polytech Inst & State Univ Blacksburg VA 24061

READ, JOHN HAMILTON, b Joliette, Que, Feb 20, 24; m 48; c 3. PEDIATRICS, PREVENTIVE MEDICINE. *Educ:* McGill Univ, BSc, 48, MD, CM, 50; Univ Toronto, DPH, 52. *Prof Exp:* Med officer, Simcoe Co, Ont, 52-54; resident pediat, Univ Mich, 54-56, instr, 56-58; asst prof pediat & prev med, Univ BC, 58-62; prof prev med & head dept & asst prof pediat, Queen's Univ, Ont, 62-68, PROF & HEAD DIV COMMUN HEALTH SCI & PROF PEDIAT, FAC MED, UNIV CALGARY, 68- *Mem:* Am Pub Health Asn. *Res:* Preventive pediatrics. *Mailing Add:* Div of Community Health Sci Fac of Med Univ of Calgary Calgary AB T2N 1N4 Can

READ, MERRILL STAFFORD, b Baltimore, Md, June 3, 28; m 53; c 2. BIOCHEMISTRY, NUTRITION. *Educ:* Northwestern Univ, BS, 49; Ohio State Univ, MS, 51, PhD(biochem), 56. *Prof Exp:* Asst biochem, Ohio State Univ, 49-52; chief irradiated food br, Med Res & Nutrit Lab, Fitzsimons Army Hosp, Denver, 54-59; tech coordr, Radiation Preservation of Food Prog, Off Surgeon Gen, US Army, 59; vis prof biochem & nutrit, Va Polytech Inst & State Univ, 59-60; dir nutrit res, Nat Dairy Coun, 60-65, exec asst to pres, 64-66; nutrit prog admnr, Nat Inst Child Health & Human Develop, 66, dir growth & develop br, 66-76, actg dep dir, Ctr Res Mothers & Children, 74-76; adv nutrit res, Div Family Health/Nutrit Unit, Pan Am Health Orgn, 76-79; CHIEF CLIN NUTRIT & EARLY DEVELOP BR, NAT INST CHILD HEALTH & HUMAN DEVELOP, 80- *Concurrent Pos:* Mem adv comt food irradiation, Am Inst Biol Sci-AEC, 60-62; mem comn III, Int Union Nutrit Sci, 67-; vis scientist, Mass Inst Technol, 70; mem nat adv coun, NY State Col Human Ecol, Cornell Univ, 71-76; mem subcomt malnutrit, brain develop & behav, Nat Acad Sci-Nat Res Coun, 75-; mem, Gov Coun, Am Pub Health Asn, 81- *Mem:* AAAS; Am Med Asn; Am Inst Nutrit; Am Soc Clin Nutrit; Am Pub Health Asn. *Res:* Child growth and development; mental development; vitamin metabolism; nutritional surveillance. *Mailing Add:* 7505 Democracy Blvd Apt A417 Bethesda MD 20034

READ, PAUL EUGENE, b Canandaigua, NY, July 13, 37; div; c 3. HORTICULTURE. *Educ:* Cornell Univ, BS, 59, MS, 64; Univ Del, PhD(Biol sci), 67. *Prof Exp:* County 4-H Club agent, Fulton County Exten Serv Asn, NY, 59-62; teaching asst hort, Cornell Univ, 62-64; res assoc, Univ Del, 64-67; from asst prof to assoc prof, 67-78, PROF HORT, UNIV MINN, ST PAUL, 78- *Mem:* Am Soc Hort Sci; Int Asn Plant Tissue Cult; Am Soc Plant Physiol; Am Hort Soc; Bot Soc Am. *Res:* Plant tissue culture; plant propagation; chemical plant growth regulation; nutrition of horticultural plants; irrigation crop research. *Mailing Add:* Dept of Hort Sci Univ of Minn St Paul MN 55108

READ, PHILIP LLOYD, b Flint, Mich, Jan 9, 32; m 56; c 3. PHYSICS, INSTRUMENTATION *Educ:* Oberlin Col, AB, 53; Univ Mich, MS, 54, PhD(physics), 60. *Prof Exp:* Physicist, Res Lab, Gen Elec Co, NY, 60-67, mgr x-ray components eng, X-Ray Dept, Wis, 67-70, mgr cardio-surg systs sect, Med Systs Div, 70-75; vpres & gen mgr, Prod Systs Div, 75-81, SR VPRES & CHIEF OPER OFFICER, COMPUTERVISION CORP, BEDFORD, 81- *Mem:* AAAS; NY Acad Sci; Am Asn Physicists in Med; Am Heart Asn. *Res:* Ionic conduction in solids; circuit theory; thermionic emission; ultrahigh vacuum; electrical transport properties of insulator surfaces; biophysics; computer graphics; Computer-Aided Design/Computer-Aided Manufacturing. *Mailing Add:* 80 Witherell Dr Sudbury MA 01776

READ, RALSTON BAKER, JR, bacteriology, see previous edition

READ, RAYMOND CHARLES, b London, Eng, Jan 26, 24; nat US; m 46; c 3. SURGERY. *Educ:* Cambridge Univ, MA, 44, MB, BCh, 47; Univ Minn, MB, 46, MD, 51, MS, 57, PhD, 58. *Prof Exp:* Intern & resident surg, Kings Col, Univ London, Harvard Univ & Univ Hosps, Univ Minn, 46-51; Harvey Cushing res fel, Harvard Med Sch, 51-53; Life Ins Med res fel, Med Sch, Univ Minn, Minneapolis, 56-58, asst prof surg, 58-61; assoc prof surg, Wayne State Univ, 61-66; PROF SURG, UNIV ARK, LITTLE ROCK, 66-; CHIEF SURG SERV & STAFF SURGEON, VET ADMIN HOSP, 66- *Concurrent Pos:* Staff surgeon, Vet Admin Hosp, Minneapolis, 58-61; mem sr staff, Detroit Gen Hosp, 61-66. *Mem:* AAAS; Soc Exp Biol & Med; AMA. *Res:* Fundamental and surgical cardiovascular physiology. *Mailing Add:* Dept of Surg Univ of Ark Little Rock AR 72201

READ, RICHARD BRADLEY, physics, radio astronomy, see previous edition

READ, ROBERT E, b Stoke on Trent, Eng, Jan 30, 33; US citizen; m 55; c 2. ORGANIC CHEMISTRY. *Educ:* Haverford Col, BS, 55; Univ Del, MS, 57, PhD(org chem), 60. *Prof Exp:* Chemist, Chem Dyes & Pigments Dept, 60-80, MEM STAFF, CENTRAL RES & DEVELOP DEPT, E I DU PONT DE NEMOURS & CO, INC, 81- *Mem:* Am Chem Soc; Am Asn Textile Chemists & Colorists; Sigma Xi. *Res:* Urethanes, organic carbodiimides and isocyanate related chemistry; polymer chemistry; development of chemical finishing agents for textiles. *Mailing Add:* Planning & Develop Div Cent Res & Develop E I du Pont de Nemours & Co Inc Wilmington DE 19898

READ, ROBERT G, b Kingston, NY, Apr 2, 18; m 47; c 6. METEOROLOGY, OCEANOGRAPHY. *Educ:* US Naval Postgrad Sch, BSc, 53, MSc, 61. *Prof Exp:* Instr meteorol & oceanog, US Naval Postgrad Sch, 59-61; from asst prof to assoc prof, 61-74, PROF METEOROL, SAN JOSE STATE UNIV, 74- *Concurrent Pos:* Assoc dir, NSF Summer Inst Earth Sci, 64 & Partic in-serv inst oceanog, Moss Landing Marine Labs & instnl grant marine influences on potential evaporation in coastal Calif, 68-69; investr, Sea Trout Prog, Moss Landing Marine Labs, Calif, 70-71; estab environ measurement network on Barro Colorado Island, CZ, Smithsonian Inst Trop Res, 71; joint researcher with Mid Am Res Unit, NIH. *Mem:* AAAS; Am Meteorol Soc; Am Geophys Union. *Res:* Problems in evaporation in the tropics and in the marine coastal atmosphere; marine meteorology and the energy transport across the air-ocean interface; general synoptic meteorology. *Mailing Add:* Dept of Meteorol San Jose State Univ San Jose CA 95192

READ, ROBERT H, b Jacksonville, Ill, Feb 15, 28; m 50; c 3. METALLURGY, PHYSICS. *Educ:* Ill Col, AB, 52; Pa State Univ, MS, 53, PhD(metall), 55. *Prof Exp:* Res metallurgist, Armour Res Found, Ill Inst Technol, 56-57, supvr powder metals res, 57-58, supvr phys metall, 59-62; dir res, Atlas Steels Co, Rio Algom Mines Ltd, Ont, 62-64; mgr technol, 64-69, vpres res & metall, Co, 69-72, mgr corp planning, 72-73; sr vpres technol & sales, Teledyne Vasco, 73-76, exec vpres, 76-80, PRES, TELEDYNE PORTLAND FORGE, 80- *Mem:* Am Iron & Steel Inst; Am Soc Metals; Am Inst Mining, Metall & Petrol Engrs; Can Inst Mining & Metall. *Mailing Add:* Teledyne Portland Forge Portland IN 47371

READ, ROBERT RICHARD, b Columbus, Ohio, Oct 5, 29; m 63; c 3. MATHEMATICAL STATISTICS. *Educ:* Ohio State Univ, BS, 51; Univ Calif, PhD(math statist), 57. *Prof Exp:* Asst res statistician, Univ Calif, 57-60; vis asst prof statist, Univ Chicago, 60-61; assoc prof, 61-71, PROF PROBABILITY & STATIST, NAVAL POSTGRAD SCH, 71- *Concurrent Pos:* Lectr, Univ Calif, 58-59; consult, Maritime Cargo Transportation Conf, Nat Acad Sci-Nat Res Coun, Lockheed Calif Co & ARRO Res Corp. *Mem:* Inst Math Statist. *Res:* Probability; statistics; operations research. *Mailing Add:* Dept of Opers Res Naval Postgrad Sch Monterey CA 93940

READ, ROBERT WILLIAM, b Woodbury, NJ, Dec 13, 31. TAXONOMIC BOTANY. *Educ:* Univ Miami, BSc, 58; Cornell Univ, MSc, 61; Univ West Indies, PhD(bot), 68. *Prof Exp:* Botanist, Fairchild Trop Bot Garden, Fla, 60-65; Nat Res Coun vis res assoc, 67-68, chief, Ceylon Flora Proj, 69-70; head Index Nomenum Genericorum Proj, 70-72, CUR DEPT BOT, NAT MUS NATURAL HIST, SMITHSONIAN INST, 73- *Concurrent Pos:* Vis prof lectr, George Washington Univ, 80-81. *Mem:* Int Asn Plant Taxon; Am Soc Plant Taxon; Asn Trop Biol; Am Inst Biol Sci; Bot Soc Am. *Res:* Monographic studies of tropical monocotyledons, particularly American Palmae, Bromeliaceae, and Cycadaceae, supplemented by ecological, anatomical, cytological, palynological, and biosystematic research. *Mailing Add:* Dept Bot Nat Mus Natural Hist Smithsonian Inst Washington DC 20560

READ, RONALD CEDRIC, b London, Eng, Dec 19, 24; m 49; c 2. MATHEMATICS, COMPUTER SCIENCE. *Educ:* Cambridge Univ, BA, 48, MA, 53; Univ London, PhD(math), 58. *Prof Exp:* Lectr math, Univ West Indies, 50-60, sr lectr, 60-66, reader, 66-67, prof, 67-70; PROF MATH, UNIV WATERLOO, 70- *Concurrent Pos:* US Air Force Off Sci Res grant, Univ West Indies, 65-68; Nat Res Coun Can grant, Univ Waterloo, 71-; ed, J Asn Comput Mach, 71-75. *Mem:* Asn Comput Mach. *Res:* Enumerative graph theory; applications of computers to graph theoretical and combinatorial problems. *Mailing Add:* Dept of Combinatorics & Optimization Univ of Waterloo Waterloo ON N2L 3G1 Can

READ, THOMAS THORNTON, b Philadelphia, Pa, Jan 24, 43; m 67; c 1. MATHEMATICAL ANALYSIS. *Educ:* Oberlin Col, BA, 65; Yale Univ, MA, 65, PhD(math), 69. *Prof Exp:* From asst prof to assoc prof, 67-76, PROF MATH, WESTERN WASH UNIV, 76- *Concurrent Pos:* Vis lectr, Chalmers Univ Technol, Gothenburg, Sweden, 73-74; vis prof, Univ Groningen, Neth, 78-80. *Mem:* Am Math Soc. *Res:* Linear differential equations, especially spectral theory. *Mailing Add:* Dept of Math Western Wash Univ Bellingham WA 98225

READ, VIRGINIA HALL, b Louisville, Miss, Oct 15, 37; m 60; c 3. BIOCHEMISTRY, ENDOCRINOLOGY. *Educ:* Univ Miss, BS, 59, PhD(biochem), 64. *Prof Exp:* Instr biochem, Sch Med, Univ Miss, 65-66, asst prof, 66-68; asst prof, 70-74, ASSOC PROF BIOCHEM, SCH MED, UNIV MISS, 74-, ASSOC PROF CLIN LAB SCI, 79- *Concurrent Pos:* NIH spec fel endocrinol, Sch Med, Univ Ala, Birmingham, 68-70; Miss Heart Asn fel, 65-67. *Mem:* Sigma Xi; Am Chem Soc; Endocrine Soc; Am Soc Nephrology. *Res:* Control of aldosterone secretion; mechanism of aldosterone action and its relationship to diseases; relationship of adrenal steroids and thyroid hormones to electrolyte and water metabolism; radioimmunoassay of hormones. *Mailing Add:* Dept Clin Lab Sci Univ of Miss Med Sch Jackson MS 39216

READ, WILLARD OLIVER, physiology, deceased

READ, WILLIAM GEORGE, b Stratton, Colo, Apr 13, 21; m 48. NUCLEAR PHYSICS. *Educ:* Kans State Teachers Col, Ft Hays, BS, 43, MS, 48; Univ Kans, PhD(physics), 56. *Prof Exp:* Instr physics, Kans State Teachers Col, Ft Hays, 47-48; from asst prof to prof, 49-59, head dept, 59-70, vpres acad affairs & dean of fac, 70-78, PROF, MURRAY STATE UNIV, 78- *Mem:* AAAS; Am Phys Soc; Nat Asn Physics Teachers. *Res:* Experimental nuclear physics and physical properties of soils; electronics. *Mailing Add:* Dept Physics & Astron Murray State Univ Murray KY 42071

READDY, ARTHUR F, JR, b Jersey City, NJ, Mar 4, 28; m 60; c 3. PHYSICAL CHEMISTRY, MATERIALS ENGINEERING. *Educ:* St Peters Col, BS, 49; Stevens Inst Technol, MS, 57. *Prof Exp:* Res chemist, Onyx Oil & Chem Co, 49-51, Theobald Industs, 51-53 & Colgate-Palmolive Co, 53-56; head chem sect, Appl Sci Br, Naval Supply Res & Develop Facility, 56-66; SCIENTIST, ARMAMENT RES & DEVELOP COMMAND, US DEPT DEFENSE, DOVER, 66- *Concurrent Pos:* Vis prof, Jersey City State Col, 59-61. *Res:* Surface chemistry and physics; radiations effects and applications; composite materials; chemical-biological-nuclear warfare; protection-decontamination of equipment; electrical, electronic and other properties of materials. *Mailing Add:* 9 Lenox Ave Cranford NJ 07016

READE, MAXWELL OSSIAN, b Philadelphia, Pa, Apr 11, 16; m 43; c 3. MATHEMATICS. *Educ:* Brooklyn Col, BS, 36; Harvard Univ, MA, 37; Rice Inst, PhD(math), 40. *Prof Exp:* Instr math, Ohio State Univ, 40-42 & Purdue Univ, 42-44 & 46; from asst prof to assoc prof, 46-59, PROF MATH, UNIV MICH, ANN ARBOR, 59- *Mem:* AAAS; assoc Am Math Soc; assoc Math Asn Am; assoc London Math Soc. *Res:* Theory of functions of one complex variable. *Mailing Add:* Dept of Math 3220 Angell Hall Univ of Mich Ann Arbor MI 48109

READE, RICHARD FRANCIS, b New York, NY, Mar 12, 32. PHYSICAL CHEMISTRY, INORGANIC CHEMISTRY. *Educ:* Fordham Univ, BS, 54; Iowa State Univ, PhD(phys chem), 59. *Prof Exp:* Res asst radiochem, Iowa State Univ, 54-59; res assoc, AEC, 59-60; RES CHEMIST, CORNING GLASS WORKS, 61- *Mem:* Am Chem Soc; Am Ceramic Soc; Electrochem Soc. *Res:* Glass and glass ceramics; luminescence; radiation effects; solid state. *Mailing Add:* Corning Glass Works Sullivan Park Corning NY 14830

READER, GEORGE GORDON, b Brooklyn, NY, Feb 8, 19; m 42; c 4. MEDICINE, PUBLIC HEALTH. *Educ:* Cornell Univ, BA, 40, MD, 43. *Prof Exp:* Intern med, NY Hosp, 44, res fel, 46-47, asst res physician, 47-49; from instr to prof med, 49-72, LIVINGSTON FARRAND PROF PUB HEALTH & CHMN DEPT, MED COL, CORNELL UNIV, 72- *Concurrent Pos:* Chmn human ecol study sect, NIH, 61-65; ed, Milbank Mem Fund Quart, Health & Soc, 72-76. *Mem:* Fel Am Pub Health Asn; fel Am Col Physicians; fel Am Col Prev Med; fel Am Sociol Asn. *Res:* Medical education and medical care; medical sociology. *Mailing Add:* New York Hosp Cornell Med Ctr 1300 York Ave New York NY 10021

READER, JOSEPH, physics, see previous edition

READER, WAYNE TRUMAN, b Danville, Pa, May 3, 39; m 61; c 5. ACOUSTICS. *Educ:* Univ Md BS, 63; Cath Univ Am, MS, 68, PhD(appl physics), 70. *Prof Exp:* Proj scientist, Struct Acoust Br, 63-73, br head, Target Acoustic Br, 73-77, RES SCIENTIST, SHIP ACOUST DEPT, D W TAYLOR NAVAL SHIP RES & DEVELOP CTR, 77- *Concurrent Pos:* Res assoc, Cath Univ Am, 70-71, instr, 71-72, lectr, 78- *Mem:* Sigma Xi; Acoust Soc Am. *Res:* Determining and characterizing the mechanisms by which submerged structures radiate and scatter sound; devising and developing techniques for reducing the radiated and scattered fields. *Mailing Add:* Naval Ship Res & Develop Code 1905 2 Bethesda MD 20084

READEY, DENNIS W(ILLIAM), b Aurora, Ill, Aug 6, 37; m 58; c 2. METALLURGY, CERAMICS. *Educ:* Univ Notre Dame, BS, 59; Mass Inst Technol, ScD(ceramics), 62. *Prof Exp:* Group leader phys ceramics, Argonne Nat Lab, 64-67; mgr mat processing lab, Res Div, Raytheon Co, 67-74; ceramist mat sci prog, Div Res, US Energy Res & Develop Admin, 74-77; assoc prof, 77-79, PROF CERAMIC ENG, OHIO STATE UNIV, 79- *Mem:* Am Ceramic Soc; AAAS; Am Inst Mining & Metall Engrs. *Res:* Ceramics processing; optical materials; electrical and electronic properties; ceramics corrosion; transport properties. *Mailing Add:* Dept of Ceramic Eng Ohio State Univ 2041 College Rd Columbus OH 43210

READHEAD, CAROL WINIFRED, b Johannesburg, SAfrica, Sept 9, 47; m 69; c 2. BIOLOGY. *Educ:* Univ Witwatersrand, BSc hons, 70; Cambridge Univ, PhD(biol), 77. *Prof Exp:* Res asst biochem, Cambridge Univ, 70-72; fel biol, 77-79, SR RES FEL, CALIF INST TECHNOL, 80- *Concurrent Pos:* Asst prof, Univ Southern Calif, 79-80. *Res:* Recombinant DNA research on immunoglobulin genes; tumor antigens that occur on ultraviolet induced mouse fibrosarcomas and the relationships of these antigens to fetal antigens; mammalian oocyte maturation. *Mailing Add:* Dept of Biol Calif Inst of Technol Pasadena CA 91107

READING, ANTHONY JOHN, b Sydney, Australia, Sept 10, 33; c 2. PSYCHIATRY. *Educ:* Univ Sydney, MB & BS, 57; Johns Hopkins Univ, MPH, 61, ScD(animal behav), 64; Am Bd Psychiat & Neurol, cert, 71. *Prof Exp:* Jr resident med officer, Sydney Hosp, Australia, 57-58, sr resident med officer, 58-59; pvt pract, 59-60; instr pathobiol & ment hyg, Sch Med, Johns Hopkins Univ, 62-65, asst prof pathobiol, 64-65, asst resident psychiat, 65-68, lectr pathobiol, 66-71, instr med, 68-69, asst prof psychiat, 68-73, assoc prof psychiat, 73-75, asst prof med, 69-75, assoc dir, Psychiat Liaison Serv, Johns Hopkins Hosp, 74-75, dir comprehensive alcoholism prog, 72-75; PROF & CHAIRPERSON PSYCHIAT, UNIV S FLA, TAMPA, 75- *Concurrent Pos:* physician-in-charge, Alcoholism Clin, John Hopkins Hosp, 69-75, physician-in-charge, Psychosomatic Clin, 74-75. *Mem:* AAAS; Am Psychiat Asn; Am Psychosom Soc. *Res:* Psychosocial aspects of illness; psychobiology. *Mailing Add:* Dept Psychiat 12901 N 30th St Tampa FL 33612

READING, JAMES CARDON, b Ogden, Utah, Dec 7, 37; m 64; c 4. BIOSTATISTICS, MATHEMATICAL STATISTICS. *Educ:* Stanford Univ, BS, 60, MS, 66, PhD(statist), 70. *Prof Exp:* Comput programmer & math analyst, Lockheed Missiles & Space Co, 62-67; instr, 70-72, asst prof biostatist & adj asst prof math, 72-76, ASSOC PROF BIOSTATIST & ADJ ASSOC PROF MATH, 76-, CHMN DIV BIOSTATIST, 77- *Mem:* Inst Math Statist; Am Statist Asn; Biomet Soc; Soc Clin Trials. *Res:* Methodological aspects of the analysis of clinical trials including design, conduct and statistical methods; classification problems. *Mailing Add:* 1298 E Billbrook Way Bountiful UT 84010

READING, JOHN FRANK, b West Bromwich, Eng, Oct 19, 39; m 63; c 4. THEORETICAL PHYSICS. *Educ:* Christ Church Col, Oxford Univ, BA, 60, MA, 64; Univ Birmingham, dipl math physics, 61, PhD(physics), 64. *Prof Exp:* Instr theoret physics, Mass Inst Technol, 64-66; sr res assoc, Univ Wash, 66-68; Harwell fel, Atomic Energy Res Estab, Harwell, Eng, 68-69; assoc prof, Northeastern Univ, 69-71; assoc prof, 71-81, PROF THEORET PHYSICS, TEX A&M UNIV, 71- *Res:* Scattering theory in atomic, nuclear and solid state physics. *Mailing Add:* Dept Physics Tex A&M Univ College Station TX 77843

READING, ROGERS W, b Toledo, Ohio, Apr 2, 34; m 61; c 1. PHYSIOLOGICAL OPTICS, OPTOMETRY. *Educ:* Ind Univ, BS, MO, 57, PhD(physiol optics), 68. *Prof Exp:* From instr to asst prof, 64-74, ASSOC PROF OPTOM, IND UNIV, BLOOMINGTON, 74- *Concurrent Pos:* Asst investr, Extrahoropteral Stereopsis in Tracking Performance, US Army grant, 64-68; prin investr, Some Time Factors in Stereopsis, NASA grant, 68-70; vpres, Nat Bd Examr Optom; prin investr fusional stimuli & corresp pts, Nat Eye Inst, NIH, 81- *Mem:* Am Acad Optom; AAAS; Am Optom Asn. *Res:* Binocular vision; photometry; psychophysics. *Mailing Add:* Sch of Optom Ind Univ Bloomington IN 47405

READNOUR, JERRY MICHAEL, b Muncie, Ind, Oct 19, 40; m 62; c 2. PHYSICAL INORGANIC CHEMISTRY. *Educ:* Ball State Teachers Col, BS, 62; Purdue Univ, PhD(chem), 69. *Prof Exp:* Asst prof, 68-74, assoc prof, 74-78, PROF CHEM, SOUTHEAST MO STATE UNIV, 78- *Concurrent Pos:* Mem, Gen Chem Exam Subcomts, Am Chem Soc, 79- *Mem:* Am Chem Soc. *Res:* Thermodynamic properties of aqueous solutions; stability constants. *Mailing Add:* Dept of Chem Southeast Mo State Univ Cape Girardeau MO 63701

READY, JOHN FETSCH, b St Paul, Minn, July 13, 32; m 53; c 6. LASERS. *Educ:* Col St Thomas, BS, 54; Univ Minn, MS, 56. *Prof Exp:* From res scientist to sr res scientist, 58-66, sr prin res scientist, Honeywell Corp Res Ctr & Mat Sci Ctr, 66-78, staff scientist, 78-79, GROUP LEADER, HONEYWELL CORP TECHNOL CTR, 79- *Mem:* Am Phys Soc; Inst Elec & Electronics Eng; Laser Inst Am. *Res:* Nuclear radiation damage; infrared materials and components; lasers, particularly effects of laser radiation and laser applications. *Mailing Add:* Honeywell Corp Technol Ctr 10701 Lyndale Ave S Bloomington MN 55420

REAGAN, DARYL DAVID, b Longview, Wash, Apr 29, 25; m 59; c 2. PHYSICS. *Educ:* Stanford Univ, MS, 49, PhD(physics), 55. *Prof Exp:* Sr physicist plasma physics, Lawrence Livermore Lab, 55-63; res assoc, Oxford Univ, 58-59; PHYSICIST ACCELERATOR PHYSICS, STANFORD UNIV, 63- *Mem:* Am Phys Soc. *Res:* Photonuclear physics; shock hydrodynamics; plasma physics; accelerator physics; magnetic measurements; synchrotron radiation. *Mailing Add:* Stanford Linear Accelerator Ctr PO Box 4349 Stanford CA 94305

REAGAN, JAMES OLIVER, b Lampasas, Tex, Nov 13, 45. MEAT SCIENCES. *Educ:* Tex A&M Univ, BS, 68, MS, 70, PhD(animal sci), 74. *Prof Exp:* Instr animal sci, Tex A&M Univ, 72-73; asst prof, Ore State Univ, 73-74; asst prof, 74-78, ASSOC PROF FOOD SCI & ANIMAL SCI, UNIV GA, 78- *Mem:* Am Meat Sci Asn; Am Soc Animal Sci; Inst Food Technologists; Sigma Xi. *Res:* Quantitative and qualitative evaluation of meat animals, methods of extending the caselife of fresh meats; factors effecting the yield and palatability attributes of commercially cured and country cured hams. *Mailing Add:* Dept of Food Sci Univ of Ga Athens GA 30601

REAGAN, JAMES W, b Oakmont, Pa, Aug 6, 18; m 44; c 5. PATHOLOGY. *Educ:* Univ Pittsburgh, BS, 42, MD, 43. *Prof Exp:* From demonstr to assoc prof, 46-58, PROF PATH & REPRODUCTIVE BIOL, CASE WESTERN RESERVE UNIV, 58- *Concurrent Pos:* Fel, Univ Hosps Cleveland, 46-49, assoc pathologist, 49-, pathologist in chg cytol lab, 49-70, pathologist in charge surg path, 57; assoc dir tutorials clin cytol, Univ Chicago, 74- & Int Acad Cytol, 74- *Honors & Awards:* Goldblatt Award, Int Acad Cytol, 64; Papanicolaou Award, Am Soc Cytol, 69; Ward Burdick Award, Am Soc Clin Path, 73. *Mem:* Am Soc Cytol (pres, 64); Am Soc Clin Path; fel Col Am Path; assoc fel Am Col Obstet & Gynec; Int Acad Cytol. *Mailing Add:* Case Western Reserve Univ 2085 Adelbert Rd Cleveland OH 44106

REAGAN, THOMAS EUGENE, b Tylertown, Miss, Jan 12, 47; m 68; c 1. ENTOMOLOGY. *Educ:* La State Univ, Baton Rouge, BS, 70, MS, 72; NC State Univ, PhD(entom, ecol, statist), 75. *Prof Exp:* asst prof & exten specialist entom, NC State Univ, 75-77; ASST PROF ENTOM, LA STATE UNIV, 77- *Mem:* Sigma Xi; Entom Soc Am. *Res:* Applied research on insects of tobacco; research on integrated and interdisciplinary aspects of tobacco pest management including modeling; pest management of sugarcane insects. *Mailing Add:* Dept of Entom La State Univ 402 Life Sci Bldg Baton Rouge LA 70803

REAGAN, WILLIAM JOSEPH, b Salem, Mass, Nov 16, 43; m 65; c 3. INORGANIC CHEMISTRY. *Educ:* Boston Col, BS, 65; Mich State Univ, PhD(inorg chem), 70. *Prof Exp:* Res asst, Mich State Univ, 66-69; res assoc, Univ Southern Calif, 70; sr res chemist, Mobil Res & Develop Corp, 70-78; GROUP LEADER CATALYST RES, ENGLEHARD MINERALS & CHEM CORP, 78-, RES ASSOC, CATALYST RES, ENGELHARD CORP, 81- *Mem:* Am Chem Soc. *Res:* Synthesis and characterization of molybdenum and tungsten compounds and fluorocarbon phosphine transition element compounds; transition metals in catalysis; solid state chemistry of heterogeneous catalysts. *Mailing Add:* Minerals & Chem Div Engelhard Corp Edison NJ 08817

REAGOR, JOHN CHARLES, b Llano, Tex, Mar 25, 38; m 61; c 2. TOXICOLOGY, BIOCHEMISTRY. *Educ:* Tex A&M Univ, BS, 60, MS, 63, PhD(biochem, nutrit), 66. *Prof Exp:* Asst prof biochem, 65-71, VIS MEM, DEPT VET PHYSIOL & PHARMACOL, UNIV & HEAD DEPT TOXICOL, TEX VET MED DIAG LAB, TEX A&M UNIV, 69- *Mem:* Asn Off Anal Chemists; Am Col Vet Toxicologists; Am Asn Vet Lab Diagnosticians. *Res:* Development of analytical methods and techniques for forensic analyses of biological materials; study of poisonous plants including diagnostic methods. *Mailing Add:* PO Drawer 3040 College Station TX 77840

REAL, LESLIE ALLAN, b Philadelphia, Pa, June 22, 50. ECOLOGY, POPULATION BIOLOGY. *Educ:* Ind Univ, BA, 72; Univ Mich, MS, 75, PhD(zool), 77. *Prof Exp:* Fel biol, Univ Miami, 77-78; ASST PROF ZOOL & BIOMATH, NC STATE UNIV, 78- *Concurrent Pos:* Rosenstiel fel, Univ Miami, 77; prof develop award, NC State Univ, 78. *Mem:* Soc Study Evolution; Ecol Soc Am; AAAS. *Res:* Theoretical population biology; pollination ecology; animal behavior; ecological genetics. *Mailing Add:* Dept of Zool NC State Univ Raleigh NC 27650

REALS, WILLIAM JOSEPH, b Hot Springs, SDak, June 22, 20; m 44; c 5. PATHOLOGY. *Educ:* Creighton Univ, BS, 44, MD, 45, MS, 49. *Prof Exp:* Instr path, Sch Med, Creighton Univ, 49-50; PATHOLOGIST & DIR LABS, ST JOSEPH'S HOSP & PROF PATH & DEAN, SCH MED, UNIV KANS, 50- *Concurrent Pos:* Asst pathologist, Creighton Mem-St Joseph's Hosp, Omaha, Nebr, 49-50; consult, Wichita Vet Admin Hosp, 50-; lectr, Med Ctr, Univ Kans, 55-72; consult, Surgeon Gen, US Air Force, DC, 59-77 & Civil Air Surgeon, Fed Aviation Agency, 60-75. *Mem:* Am Soc Clin Path; Asn Mil Surg US; Aerospace Med Asn; Col Am Path (pres, 71-73). *Res:* Oncology; hormone chemistry, especially thyroid diseases; forensic pathology related to aircraft accidents. *Mailing Add:* Dept Path St Joseph's Med Ctr Wichita KS 67218

REAM, BERNARD CLAUDE, b Johnstown, Pa, Jan 30, 39; m 67; c 1. ORGANIC CHEMISTRY. *Educ:* Seton Hall Univ, BS, 61; Ohio State Univ, MS, 63, PhD(org chem), 65. *Prof Exp:* PROJ SCIENTIST, UNION CARBIDE CORP, 66- *Mem:* Am Chem Soc. *Res:* Metal-catalyzed synthesis of organic compounds; ethylene oxide/ethylene glycol process chemistry. *Mailing Add:* 1807 Rolling Hills Rd Charleston WV 25314

REAMER, DONALD CHARLES, b Washington, DC, Sept 8, 46; m 79; c 1. ANALYTICAL CHEMISTRY. *Educ:* Am Univ, BS, 72; Univ Md, MS, 75, PhD(environ chem), 78. *Prof Exp:* Fel, Univ Md, 79-80; RES ASSOC, USDA, 80- *Mem:* Soc Appl Spectros. *Res:* Development of analytical techniques for the determination of essential trace elements in biological material using stable isotope dilution, gas chromatography, mass spectrometry and atomic absorption. *Mailing Add:* Human Nutrit Bldg 307 Rm 215 USDA Beltsville MD 20705

REAMES, DONALD VERNON, b West Palm Beach, Fla, Dec 30, 36. ASTROPHYSICS, PHYSICS. *Educ:* Univ Calif, Berkeley, AB, 58, PhD(physics), 64. *Prof Exp:* ASTROPHYSICIST COSMIC RAYS, NASA, GODDARD SPACE FLIGHT CTR, 64- *Mem:* Am Phys Soc; Inst Elec & Electronics Engrs Comput Soc. *Res:* Cosmic rays, solar physics; interplanetary particles and fields; particle detectors; nuclear physics; microprocessor controlled experiments. *Mailing Add:* NASA Goddard Space Flight Ctr Code 661 Greenbelt MD 20771

REAMS, MAX WARREN, b Virgil, Kans, Mar 10, 38; m 61; c 3. GEOMORPHOLOGY, SEDIMENTARY PETROLOGY. *Educ:* Univ Kans, BA & BS, 61, MS, 63; Washington Univ, PhD(geol), 68. *Prof Exp:* From asst prof to assoc prof, 67-77, PROF GEOL, OLIVET NAZARENE COL, 77- CHMN DEPT EARTH & SPACE SCI, 69-, CHMN DIV NATURAL SCI, 75- *Mem:* Geol Soc Am; Am Quaternary Asn; Clay Minerals Soc; Sigma Xi. *Res:* Geology and geochemistry of caves and cave sediment; weathering of carbonate rocks; experimental models of solution features in karst regions; trace elements in speleothems and cave minerals. *Mailing Add:* Dept of Earth & Space Sci Olivet Nazarene Col Kankakee IL 60901

REAMS, WILLIE MATHEWS, JR, b Richmond, Va, Feb 23, 30; m 56; c 3. DEVELOPMENTAL BIOLOGY. *Educ:* Univ Richmond, BS, 51; Johns Hopkins Univ, PhD(embryol), 56. *Prof Exp:* Jr instr biol, Johns Hopkins Univ, 52-55; instr anat, Med Col Va, 52-60; asst prof zool, La State Univ, 60-64; assoc prof, 64-70, PROF BIOL, UNIV RICHMOND, 70-; RES ASST CLIN PROF DERMAT, MED COL VA, 66- *Mem:* AAAS; Am Soc Zoologists; Soc Develop Biol; Am Asn Anatomists; Soc Invest Dermat. *Res:* Experimental pigment cell differentiation in mice. *Mailing Add:* Dept of Biol Univ of Richmond Richmond VA 23173

REAP, JAMES JOHN, b Hazelton, Pa, Jan 22, 48; m 70; c 2. ORGANIC CHEMISTRY. *Educ:* Villanova Univ, BS, 69; Univ Pittsburgh, PhD(org chem), 75. *Prof Exp:* Teacher physics & chem, Gloucester Cath Sr High Sch, 69-70; RES CHEMIST BIOCHEM DEPT, E I DU PONT DE NEMOURS & CO, INC, 75- *Res:* Synthesis of novel biologically active organic chemicals. *Mailing Add:* 2505 Bona Rd Wilmington DE 19810

REARDON, ANNA JOYCE, b East St Louis, Ill, Jan 22, 10. PHYSICS. *Educ:* Col St Teresa, BA, 30; St Louis Univ, MS, 33, PhD(physics), 37. *Prof Exp:* High sch instr, Minn, 30-31 & Mo, 32-35; instr physics & Math, Ursuline Col, La, 36-37, Mt St Scholastica Col, 37-39, Col St Teresa, 39-40 & Loretto Heights Col, 40-41; from instr to assoc prof & head dept, 41-65, PROF PHYSICS, UNIV NC, GREENSBORO, 65- *Concurrent Pos:* Chmn, NC Comt High Sch Physics, 67-, instr spec course in physics for x-ray technician students. *Mem:* AAAS; Am Phys Soc; Photog Soc Am; Am Asn Physics Teachers. *Res:* Theoretical photography. *Mailing Add:* 1105 Dover Rd Greensboro NC 27408

REARDON, EDWARD JOSEPH, JR, b Southbridge, Mass, Apr 24, 43; m 78. RADIATION CURED COATINGS, PHOTORESISTS. *Educ:* Brown Univ, ScB, 65; Seton Hall Univ, MS, 67, PhD(org chem), 69. *Prof Exp:* NIH fel, Ind Univ, Bloomington, 69-70; assoc, Univ NC, Chapel Hill, 70-72; vis asst prof org chem, Bucknell Univ, 72-73; sr res assoc, Photohorizons Div, Horizons Res, 74-75; sr chemist, 76-77, group leader, 78-79, RES MGR, DYNACHEM CORP, SUBSIDIARY THIOKOL CORP, 79- *Mem:* Am Chem Soc; Soc Photographic Scientists & Engrs. *Res:* Applied research and development of radiation sensitive coatings, primarily resists for fabrication of electronic circuits; synthesis of polymers and sensitizers; formulation, applications, manufacturing, and quality control methodologies. *Mailing Add:* 21795 Meadowview Lane El Toro CA 92630

REARDON, FREDERICK H(ENRY), b Philadelphia, Pa, Oct 22, 32; m 56; c 3. MECHANICAL ENGINEERING, ENVIRONMENTAL ENGINEERING. *Educ:* Univ Pa, BS, 54, MS, 56; Princeton Univ, PhD(aeronaut eng), 61. *Prof Exp:* Instr mech eng, Univ Pa, 54-56; res engr, Princeton Univ, 56-61; supvr, Liquid Rocket Opers, Aerojet-Gen Corp, Sacramento, 61-64, tech specialist, 64-65, sr res engr, 65-66; asst prof mech eng, 66-68, assoc prof eng, 68-73, chmn dept, 76-81, PROF ENG, CALIF STATE UNIV, SACRAMENTO, 73-, ASSOC DEAN, 81- *Concurrent Pos:* Mem working group combustion, Joint Army-Navy-NASA-Air Force, 64-; consult, Liquid Rocket Oper, Aerojet-Gen Corp, 66-, US Air Force, 76- & Chem Systs Div, United Technol Corp, 80- *Mem:* Sigma Xi; Am Soc Mech Engrs; Am Inst Aeronaut & Astronaut; Combustion Inst; Am Soc Eng Educ. *Res:* Combustion and flow processes in engines, furnaces and waste recovery systems; automobile economy and emissions control; impact of scientific technology on society; development of educational simulations and games. *Mailing Add:* 5619 Haskell Ave Carmichael CA 95608

REARDON, JOHN DEVEREAUX, b Dover, NH, Dec 17, 29; m 60; c 2. MICROBIOLOGY. *Educ:* Univ NH, BS, 53, MA, 59. *Prof Exp:* Bacteriologist, US Army Biol Labs, 55-59; dir admin, Booz Allen Appl Res Inc, Md, 59-70; exec vpres, Woodard Res Corp, 70-72; spec asst to adminr, 72-74, DEP DIR, DIV EMERGENCY MED SERV, HEALTH SERV & MENT HEALTH ADMIN, 74- *Mem:* Am Soc Microbiol; Am Mgt Asn; Am Burn Asn; Inst Mgt Sci. *Res:* Infectious diseases; public health economics; operations research; medical systems; medical administration. *Mailing Add:* 12306 Captain Smith Ct Potomac MD 20854

REARDON, JOHN JOSEPH, b Westerly, RI, July 27, 21; m 47; c 2. ECOLOGY. BIOLOGY. *Educ:* Univ Mich, BS, 48, MA, 49; Univ Ore, PhD(biol), 50. *Prof Exp:* Asst prof biol & head dept, Col Charleston, 49-52; asst prof, Los Angeles State Col, 54-58; assoc prof & chmn dept, San Fernando Valley State Col, 58-62; assoc prof, Eastern Ore Col, 62-64; asst prof zool, Univ Toronto, 64-65; chmn dept, 65-74, PROF BIOL, SOUTHEASTERN MASS UNIV, 65- *Concurrent Pos:* Team leader, Westinghouse Ocean Res Lab Starfish Reef Exped, Micronesia, 68. *Mem:* AAAS; Ecol Soc Am; Am Soc Mammal; Am Inst Biol Sci. *Res:* Biology of mammals; ecology of dune inhabiting organisms; radioisotope pollution of environment; ecology of reef environments; ecology and behavior of Birgus latro, the coconut crab. *Mailing Add:* Dept of Biol Old Westport Rd Southeastern Mass Univ North Dartmouth MA 02747

REARDON, JOSEPH DANIEL, b Buffalo, NY, Aug 24, 44; m 68. PHYSICAL CHEMISTRY. *Educ:* Univ Rochester, BS, 66; Univ Conn, PhD(phys chem), 70. *Prof Exp:* Res & develop engr, GTE Sylvania Inc, 70-73; assoc dir res, Quantum, Inc, 73-77; SUPVR MATS ENG, METCO INC, 77- *Mem:* Am Soc Metals; Am Chem Soc. *Res:* development of composite powders for plasma and vacuum plasma flame spray applications especially for sprayed abradable coatings; mass spectrometry and high vacuum technology; processing parameters for high performance plastics; development of synthetic membranes. *Mailing Add:* Metco Inc 5 Tower Pl Hauppauge NY 11788

REARDON, JOSEPH EDWARD, b Albany, NY, Jan 25, 38; m 60; c 3. ORGANIC CHEMISTRY, POLYMER CHEMISTRY. *Educ:* Canisius Col, BS, 61; Univ Notre Dame, PhD(org chem), 67. *Prof Exp:* Chemist, Carborundum Co, 61-63; res chemist, Plastics Dept, E I Du Pont de Nemours & Co, Inc, 66-67, res chemist, Electrochem Dept, 67-72, res chemist, Plastics Dept, 72-80; WITH THIOKOL DYNACHEM CO, 80- *Mem:* Am Chem Soc. *Res:* Dispersion chemistry and polymer synthesis. *Mailing Add:* Thiodol Dynachem Co PO Box 12047 Santa Ana CA 92711

REARDON, JOSEPH PATRICK, b Pittston, Pa, Sept 26, 40; m 69; c 2. PHYSICAL CHEMISTRY, MATERIALS SCIENCE. *Educ:* Spring Hill Col, BS, 65; Am Univ, MS, 69, PhD(chem), 75. *Prof Exp:* Instr chem, Georgetown Prep Sch, 65-67; res chemist, Naval Res Lab, 71-79; mgr mat develop, Pure Carbon Co, 79-80; MGR MAT DEVELOP, TRIBON BEARING CO, 80- *Mem:* Am Chem Soc. *Res:* Low surface energy polymers; adhesives; carbon fibers and graphite intercalation chemistry; electrets and piezoelectric polymers; electrically conductive organic polymers. *Mailing Add:* Tribon Bearing Co 5581 W 164th St Cleveland OH 44142

REARDON, PAUL JOSEPH, b Haverhill, Mass, Dec 13, 30; m 52; c 7. PLASMA PHYSICS, ACCELERATOR PHYSICS. *Educ:* Boston Col, AB, 52; Rutgers Univ, MS, 60. *Prof Exp:* Physicist, Johns-Manville Res Ctr, 54-56; head synchrontron operating div accelerator physics, Princeton Univ, 56-64; accelerator physicist high energy physics sect, Div Res, US AEC, 64-66; res physicist accelerator physics & proj mgr Bates linear accelerator, Lab Nuclear Sci, Mass Inst Technol, 66-69; sr physicist & assoc lab dir accelerator physics, Fermi Nat Accelerator Lab, 68-75, head booster synchrontron sect, 68-70, dir bus admin, 69-72, head energy doubler sect, 72-74, assoc lab dir & head accelerator div, 72-75; proj mgr, Tokamak Fusion Test Reactor, 75-78, ASSOC DIR & HEAD DEPT TECHNOL, PLASMA PHYSICS LAB, PRINCETON UNIV, 78- *Concurrent Pos:* Consult, Nuclear Physics Accelerator, NSF, 73-76; consult several technol adv panels to Off Fusion Energy, US Dept Energy, 75-; mem, Positron Policy Comt, Univ Calif & Stanford Univ, 76-80; mem, Lawrence Berkeley Lab Accelerator & Fusion Res Review Comt, 77-79; mem high energy physics adv sub panel new facil, 77; mem, Fermilab Review Comt, 78- *Mem:* Am Phys Soc. *Res:* Design, construction, management, operation and research; exploration of large particle accelerators and fusion research devices. *Mailing Add:* Princeton Plasma Physics Lab Forrestal Campus Princeton Univ Princeton NJ 08540

REARDON, WILLIAM ALBERT, physics, operations research, see previous edition

REARICK, DAVID F, b Danville, Ill, Aug 5, 32; div. MATHEMATICS. *Educ:* Univ Fla, BS, 54; Adelphi Univ, MS, 56; Calif Inst Technol, PhD(math), 60. *Prof Exp:* Instr math, Univ BC, 60-61; asst prof, 61-66, ASSOC PROF MATH, UNIV COLO, BOULDER, 66- *Mem:* Am Math Soc; Math Asn Am. *Res:* Analytic number theory; arithmetic functions. *Mailing Add:* Dept Math Univ Colo Boulder CO 80309

REAS, WILLIAM HARRY, chemistry, see previous edition

REASENBERG, JULIAN ROBERT, b Spring Glen, NY, Oct 4, 16; m 40; c 3. SYNTHETIC ORGANIC CHEMISTRY, MINERALOGY. *Educ:* Polytech Inst Brooklyn, BS, 36, MS, 38, PhD(org chem), 41. *Prof Exp:* Res chemist, Novocol Chem Co, NY, 40-41; chief chemist, Oradent Chem Co & G-M Chem Co, 41-44; res dir, Mizzy, Inc, 44-60; pres, Ortho Chem Corp, 60-62; PRES, ROEHR CHEM INC, NEW YORK, 63- *Mem:* AAAS; Am Chem Soc; Am Inst Chemists; Mineralog Asn Can; Mineral Soc Am. *Res:* Synthesis and evaluation of local anesthetics; dental impression materials; catalytic hydrogenation; sterilizing through cellophane. *Mailing Add:* 277 Rugby Rd Brooklyn NY 11226

REASENBERG, ROBERT DAVID, b New York, NY, Apr 27, 42; m 65; c 1. PHYSICS, ASTRONOMY. *Educ:* Polytech Inst Brooklyn, BS, 63; Brown Univ, PhD(physics), 70. *Prof Exp:* Res assoc, 69-71, res staff mem, 71-79, PRIN RES SCIENTIST, MASS INST TECHNOL, 81- *Concurrent Pos:* Consult, Lincoln Lab, Mass Inst Technol, 70-76, C S Draper Lab, Inc, 78-80 & NASA; assoc mem, Viking Radio Sci Team, Mariner-Venus-Mercury Radio Sci Team, Mariner-9 Celestial Mech Team & Pioneer Venus Science Steering Group. *Honors & Awards:* Newcomb Cleveland Award, AAAS, 77. *Mem:* Am Phys Soc; AAAS; Am Astron Soc; Am Geophys Union; Sigma Xi. *Res:* Gravity research, especially tests of theories of gravitation, determination of solar-system constants and planetary ephermerides, and determination of the structure, gravitational potential and rotational motion of planets. *Mailing Add:* 16 Garfield St Lexington MA 02173

REASER, DONALD FREDERICK, b Wichita Falls, Tex, Sept 30, 31. GEOLOGY, TECTONICS. *Educ:* Southern Methodist Univ, BS, 53, MS, 58; Univ Tex, Austin, PhD(geol), 74. *Prof Exp:* Geol asst, De Golyer & MacNaughton, Dallas, 56-57; instr introductory & struct geol, Arlington State Col, 61-64; petrol geologist, Humble Oil & Refining Co, 65-66; asst prof, W Tex State Univ, 67-68; ASSOC PROF STRUCT GEOL & TECTONICS, UNIV TEX, ARLINGTON, 68- *Concurrent Pos:* Grant-in-aid res, Sigma Xi, 60; field trip consult, Shell Develop Co, 64-; res asst, Bur Economic Geol, Austin, 67-68; consult geologist, Cor Labs, Dallas, 74-79; instr, Inst Energy Develop, Ft Worth, 78-79; Tex Elec Serv Co, 81- *Mem:* Am Asn Petrol Geologists; Geol Soc Am; Soc Economic Paleontologists & Mineralogists; Sigma Xi. *Res:* Structure and regional tectonics of west Texas and northern Mexico; stratigraphy and structure of upper Cretaceous rocks in north-central Texas; petroleum possibilities of subsurface Mesozoic rocks in northeast Texas. *Mailing Add:* Dept Geol PO Box 19049 Univ Tex Arlington TX 76019

REASONER, JOHN W, b Winona, Mo, Feb 28, 40; m 61; c 3. PHOTOCHEMISTRY. *Educ:* Southeast Mo State Col, BS, 61; Iowa State Univ, PhD(org chem), 65. *Prof Exp:* PROF CHEM, WESTERN KY UNIV, 65- *Mem:* Am Chem Soc; Royal Soc Chem; Sigma Xi. *Res:* Photochemistry of unsaturated nitrocompounds. *Mailing Add:* Dept of Chem Western Ky Univ Bowling Green KY 42101

REAVES, CARL ALVIN, agricultural engineering, see previous edition

REAVES, GIBSON, b Chicago, Ill, Dec 26, 23; m 55; c 1. ASTRONOMY. *Educ:* Univ Calif, Los Angeles, BA, 47; Univ Calif, Berkeley, PhD(astron), 52. *Prof Exp:* Asst astron, Univ Calif, 47-49; from instr to assoc prof, 52-65, chmn dept, 69-74, PROF ASTRON, UNIV SOUTHERN CALIF, 65- *Mem:* Am Astron Soc; Royal Astron Soc; Int Astron Union. *Res:* Extragalactic problems. *Mailing Add:* Dept of Astron Univ of Southern Calif Los Angeles CA 90007

REAVES, HARRY LEE, b Clarksburg, WVa, Feb 25, 27. PHYSICS, MATHEMATICS. *Educ:* WVa Univ, AB & MS, 49; Va Polytech Inst, PhD, 63. *Prof Exp:* Asst prof physics, Clemson Col, 49-52; asst prof physics & math, Hampden-Sydney Col, 52-56; asst prof physics, Va Polytech Inst, 56-63; physicist, Humble Res Lab, Houston, 63-64; physicist, Houston Res Lab, Shell Oil Co, 64-71; ASST PROF PHYSICS & MATH, SAN JACINTO COL, 71- *Mem:* Am Asn Physics Teachers; Sigma Xi; Am Phys Soc. *Res:* Nuclear magnetic resonance and solid state physics. *Mailing Add:* San Jacinto Col Pasadena TX 77505

REAVEY-CANTWELL, NELSON HENRY, b Buffalo, NY, May 8, 26. MEDICINE. *Educ:* Canisius Col, BS, 44; Fordham Univ, MS, 48, PhD(phys org chem), 52; Columbia Univ, MD, 59; Henry George Sch, dipl, 58. *Prof Exp:* From asst to instr chem, Fordham Univ, 47-52; from instr to asst prof, Yale Univ, 52-55; intern, Bellevue Hosp & Mem Ctr Cancer & Allied Dis, 59-60; resident internal med, Vet Admin Hosp, Manhattan, NY, 60-61; asst dir med res, Merck Inst, 61-68; asst prof, 68-71, ASSOC PROF CLIN MED, THOMAS JEFFERSON UNIV, 71- *Concurrent Pos:* Fel, Harvard Univ, 49; attend physician, Curtis Clin, Thomas Jefferson Univ Hosp, 68-; dir div res, William H Rorer, Inc, 68-69, vpres res, 69-78, vpres med & sci affairs, Rorer Int, 78- *Mem:* Am Soc Clin Pharmacol & Therapeut; Am Soc Internal Med; fel Am Col Clin Pharmacol; Am Fedn Clin Res; fel Royal Soc Med. *Res:* Internal medicine; endocrinology and immunology; kinetics and mechanisms of metabolic reactions; steroid and electrolyte metabolism. *Mailing Add:* William H Rorer Inc Virginia Dr Ft Washington PA 19034

REAVIS, JAMES GENE, b Lanton, Mo, July 24, 29; m 53; c 4. NUCLEAR CHEMISTRY. *Educ:* Southwest Mo State Col, BS, 50; Univ Wis, PhD(chem), 55. *Prof Exp:* CHEMIST, LOS ALAMOS NAT LAB, 54- *Mem:* Am Chem Soc; Am Nuclear Soc. *Res:* High temperature chemistry of systems containing plutonium and uranium metals, hydrides, halides, carbides and nitrides; design of plutonium laboratories and equipment. *Mailing Add:* 2530 35th St Los Alamos NM 87544

REAY, JOHN R, b Pocatello, Idaho, Oct 27, 34; m 58; c 3. MATHEMATICS. *Educ:* Pac Lutheran Univ, BA, 56; Univ Idaho, MS, 58; Univ Wash, PhD(math), 63. *Prof Exp:* Assoc prof, 63-68, PROF MATH, WESTERN WASHINGTON UNIV, 68- *Mem:* Am Math Soc; Math Asn Am. *Res:* Convexity and geometry. *Mailing Add:* Dept of Math Western Wash Univ Bellingham WA 98225

REAZIN, GEORGE HARVEY, JR, b Chicago, Ill, Feb 3, 28; m 50; c 3. PLANT PHYSIOLOGY, BIOCHEMISTRY. *Educ:* Northwestern Univ, BS, 49; Univ Mich, MS, 51, PhD(plant physiol), 55. *Prof Exp:* Res assoc, Brookhaven Nat Lab, 54-56; res scientist, 56-62, head biochem sect, 62-71, HEAD CHEM SECT, JOSEPH E SEAGRAM & SONS, INC, LOUISVILLE, KY, 71- *Honors & Awards:* Guymon Mem Lectr, Am Soc Enologists, 81. *Mem:* Bot Soc Am; Am Chem Soc; Am Soc Plant Physiologists. *Res:* Chemistry of flavors and biochemistry of their formation. *Mailing Add:* 1544 Cliftwood Dr Clarksville IN 47130

REBA, RICHARD CHARNEY, b Milwaukee, Wis, July 1, 32; m 54; c 2. MEDICINE, NUCLEAR MEDICINE. *Educ:* Univ Md, MD, 57; Am Bd Internal Med, dipl, 64; Am Bd Nuclear Med, dipl, 72. *Prof Exp:* Asst resident med, Univ Hosp, Baltimore, Md, 59-61; fel nuclear med, Johns Hopkins Univ, 61-62; sr investr, Walter Reed Army Inst Res, 62-65, actg chief dept isotope metab, 64, chief, 64-65, chief med serv, 85th Evacuation Hosp, Vietnam, 65-66; from asst prof to assoc prof radiol & radiol sci, Sch Hyg & Pub Health, Johns Hopkins Univ, 66-70, asst prof internal med, 67-70, assoc radiol sci, 70-78; chmn dept nuclear med, Wash Hosp Ctr, 70-76; PROF RADIOL, SCH MED, GEORGE WASHINGTON UNIV, 71-, PROF MED, SCH MED, 76-, DIR DIV NUCLEAR MED, MED CTR, 78- *Concurrent Pos:* Asst chief gen med, Sect Four, Walter Reed Army Gen Hosp, 64-65; chief clin nuclear med sect, Johns Hopkins Med Insts, 68-70; clin prof med, Sch Med, Georgetown Univ, 71-; mem coun thrombosis, Am Heart Asn. *Mem:* AAAS; Soc Nuclear Med; fel Am Col Nuclear Physicians (pres, 77-); Am Col Physicians; Am Fedn Clin Res. *Res:* Diagnostic and research applications of radioisotopes in clinical medicine. *Mailing Add:* George Washington Univ Med Ctr 901 23rd St NW Washington DC 20037

REBACH, STEVE, b New York, NY, Nov 15, 42; m 68. BIOLOGICAL RHYTHMS, MIGRATION. *Educ:* City Col New York, BS, 63; Univ RI, PhD(oceanog), 70. *Prof Exp:* Instr oceanog, Grad Sch Oceanog, Univ RI, 69-70; asst prof biol, St Mary's Col Md, 70-72; asst prof, 72-81, ASSOC PROF BIOL, UNIV MD, EASTERN SHORE, 81- *Concurrent Pos:* USDA res grants mariculture, behavior & ecology; chmn grad prog marine, estuarine & environ sci, Univ Md, 81-; prin investr, Crab Ecol & Maricult Proj, Am Inst Biol Sci. *Mem:* AAAS; Animal Behav Soc; Am Inst Biol Sci; Sigma Xi. *Res:* Biological rhythms, particularly in relation to marine organisms, navigation, orientation, and migration; mariculture of crustacea. *Mailing Add:* Dept of Biol Univ of Md Eastern Shore Princess Anne MD 21853

REBBI, CLAUDIO, b Trieste, Italy, Mar 1, 43; m 67; c 2. THEORETICAL PHYSICS. *Educ:* Univ Torino, Italy, Laurea, 65, PhD(nuclear physics), 67. *Prof Exp:* Prof, Univ Trieste, 70-72; res assoc, Europ Orgn Nuclear Res, 72-74; vis assoc prof, Mass Inst Technol, 74-77; PHYSICIST, BROOKHAVEN NAT LAB, 77- *Concurrent Pos:* Fel, Calif Inst Technol, 68-69. *Res:* Elementary particle theory; quantum field theory. *Mailing Add:* Brookhaven Nat Lab Upton NY 11973

REBEK, JULIUS, JR, b Beregszasz, Hungary, Apr 11, 44; US citizen. ORGANIC CHEMISTRY. *Educ:* Univ Kans, BA, 66; Mass Inst Technol, PhD(chem), 70. *Prof Exp:* Am Chem Soc-Petrol Res Fund fel, 70-73, Eli Lilly res fel, 72-74, asst prof chem, Univ Calif, Los Angeles, 70-76; assoc prof, 76-80, PROF CHEM, UNIV PITTSBURGH, 80- *Concurrent Pos:* A P Sloan fel, 76-78, Alexander von Humboldt fel, 81. *Mem:* Am Chem Soc. *Res:* Epoxidation reactions; organic reaction mechanisms; heterocyclic chemistry; synthesis of natural products and catalysis. *Mailing Add:* Dept Chem Univ Pittsburgh Pittsburgh PA 15260

REBEL, WILLIAM J, b Troy, NY, Mar 15, 34. POLYMER CHEMISTRY. *Educ:* State Univ NY Albany, BS, 57, MS, 59; Univ Alta, PhD(org chem), 63. *Prof Exp:* Fel org chem, Univ Rochester, 63-64; chemist, Chem Div, Union Carbide Corp, 64-66; chemist, Polymer Technol Div, 66-74, TECH ASSOC, MFG TECHNOL DIV, EASTMAN KODAK CO, 74- *Mem:* Am Chem Soc; NY Acad Sci. *Res:* Decomposition of iodonium salts; characterization and synthesis of cellulose esters; synthesis of addition polymers; preparation of new polymers; dispersion of pigments and radiation curing of monomer/polymer systems. *Mailing Add:* 770 Van Voorsis Ave Rochester NY 14617

REBENFELD, LUDWIG, b Czech, July 10, 28; nat US; m 56. ORGANIC CHEMISTRY. *Educ:* Lowell Tech Inst, BS, 51; Princeton Univ, MA, 53, PhD(org chem), 55. *Hon Degrees:* DSc, Philadelphia Col, 79. *Prof Exp:* Asst instr chem, Lowell Tech Inst, 49-51; sr chemist, 54-55, group leader, 55-60, assoc res dir, 60-65, vpres educ & res, 66-70, PRES, TEXTILE RES INST, 71- *Concurrent Pos:* Vis lectr, Princeton Univ, 65-; chmn bd, Philadelphia Col Textiles & Sci. *Honors & Awards:* Smith Medal, Am Soc Textile & Mat, 74; Inst Medal, Textile Inst Eng, 76. *Mem:* Fiber Soc (secy-treas); Am Chem Soc; Am Asn Textile Chemists & Colorists; fel Brit Textile Inst. *Res:* Chemistry of cellulose and cellulose derivatives; chemical and physical properties of textile fibers; cotton fiber technology; keratin fiber deformation processes; structure and properties of synthetic polymers. *Mailing Add:* Textile Res Inst PO Box 625 Princeton NJ 08540

REBER, ELWOOD FRANK, b Reading, Pa, June 24, 19; m 42; c 3. NUTRITION, BIOCHEMISTRY. *Educ:* Berea Col, AB, 44; Cornell Univ, MNS, 48; Okla State Univ, MS, 50, PhD(chem), 51. *Prof Exp:* Food inspector, Kroger Grocery & Baking Co, 44-45; lab asst biochem, Okla State Univ, 48-49, asst microbiol assays, 49-51; res chemist, Swift & Co, 51-52; from asst prof to prof vet physiol & pharmacol, Univ Ill, 52-64; prof foods & nutrit & head dept, Univ Mass, Amherst, 64-68 & Purdue Univ, La Fayette, 68-74; prof nutrit & dean col nutrit, textiles & human develop, 74-78, PROF NUTRITION & FOOD SCI, TEX WOMAN'S UNIV, 78- *Concurrent Pos:* Fulbright res fel, Col Agr & Vet Med, Copenhagen, Denmark, 61-62. *Mem:* Am Chem Soc; Am Home Econ Asn; Inst Food Technologists; Am Inst Nutrit. *Res:* Human nutrition and foods; food science; wholesomeness of irradiated foods; nutrition and disease; metabolic disorders. *Mailing Add:* Col of Nutrit Textiles & Human Develop Tex Woman's Univ Denton TX 76201

REBER, JERRY D, b Lebanon, Pa, May 25, 39; m 63; c 2. NUCLEAR PHYSICS. *Educ:* Franklin & Marshall Col, AB, 61; Univ Ky, MS, 64, PhD(nuclear physics), 67. *Prof Exp:* NSF fel, Univ Ky, 65; res assoc & asst prof physics, Univ Va, 68-69; assoc prof, 69-79, PROF PHYSICS, STATE UNIV NY COL GENESEO, 80-, CHMN DEPT, 69- *Mem:* Am Phys Soc. *Res:* Neutron scattering studies of calcium, potassium, vanadium and holmium; isobaric spin impurities of fluorine; ion induced x-ray fluorescence; neutron-proton scattering; ion beam lithography. *Mailing Add:* Dept Physics State Univ NY Geneseo NY 14454

REBERS, PAUL ARMAND, b Minneapolis, Minn, Jan 24, 23; m 52; c 3. IMMUNOCHEMISTRY. *Educ:* Univ Minn, Minneapolis, BS, 43, MS, 46; Univ Minn, St Paul, PhD(agr biochem), 53. *Prof Exp:* Process engr, Rohm & Haas, 46-49; res chemist, Nat Animal Disease Lab, 61-; mem grad fac, 66-, ASSOC PROF BIOCHEM, IOWA STATE UNIV, 70- *Mem:* AAAS; Am Chem Soc; Am Soc Microbiol; Am Asn Immunol; Soc Exp Biol & Med. *Res:* Purification, isolation and structure of carbohydrate antigens; colorimetric analysis of sugars; immunology of fowl cholera. *Mailing Add:* Nat Animal Dis Ctr PO Box 70 Ames IA 50010

REBERT, CHARLES J, b Ann Arbor, Mich, Dec 27, 18; m 47; c 2. CHEMICAL ENGINEERING. *Educ:* Univ Detroit, BChE, 43; Univ Mich, MSE & ChE, 48; Ohio State Univ, PhD(chem eng), 55. *Prof Exp:* Instr chem eng, Univ Detroit, 47-50 & Ohio State Univ, 50-55; ASSOC PROF CHEM ENG, UNIV SOUTHERN CALIF, 55- *Concurrent Pos:* Consult, Shell Chem Co, 56 & NAm Aviation, Inc. *Res:* Thermodynamics; physical properties of liquid and vapor mixtures. *Mailing Add:* Dept of Chem Eng Sch of Eng Univ of Southern Calif Los Angeles CA 90007

REBERT, RICHARD ROSS, b Washington, DC, May 16, 20; m 46; c 3. NEUROPHARMACOLOGY, PSYCHOPHARMACOLOGY. *Educ:* George Washington Univ, BA, 41 & 47, MA, 48; Vanderbilt Univ, PhD(anat), 52. *Prof Exp:* Assoc zool & comp anat, George Washington Univ, 47-48, assoc gen zool, 49; instr anat, La State Univ, 51-53; chief sci info div, Mead Johnson & Co, 53-54; med res rep, Merck Sharp & Dohme Res Labs, Pa, 54-68, clin assoc, 68-76; res assoc pharmacol, Col Med, Univ South Ala, 75, instr, 75-80; CONSULT, DRUG & CHEM INDUST, 80- *Mem:* Am Asn Anatomists; NY Acad Sci; Microcirc Soc; Sigma Xi. *Res:* Brain metabolism of amino acids; clinical pharmacology. *Mailing Add:* 7133 Lakeview Dr E Mobile AL 36609

REBHUHN, DEBORAH, b Heidenheim, Ger, Oct 23, 46; US citizen. APPLIED MATHEMATICS. *Educ:* Cornell Univ, AB, 68; Univ Ill, MS, 70, PhD(math), 74. *Prof Exp:* Teaching asst math, Univ Ill, 68-73; asst prof math, Vassar Col, NY, 73-80; MEM TECH STAFF, BELL LABS, 80- *Mem:* Am Math Soc; Math Asn Am; Asn Women Math. *Res:* Qualitative properties of control systems, particularly the study of properties of control systems that are stable under sufficiently small perturbations. *Mailing Add:* Bell Labs 6 Corporate Pl Piscataway NJ 08854

REBHUN, LIONEL ISRAEL, b Bronx, NY, Apr 19, 26; m 49; c 2. ZOOLOGY, CELL BIOLOGY. *Educ:* City Col New York, BS, 49; Univ Chicago, MS, 51, PhD(zool), 55. *Prof Exp:* From instr to asst prof anat, Col Med, Univ Ill, 55-58; from asst prof to assoc prof biol, Princeton Univ, 58-69; prof, 69-77, COMMONWEALTH PROF BIOL, UNIV VA, 77- *Concurrent Pos:* Lalor fel, 56; Guggenheim fel, 62. *Mem:* Am Soc Cell Biologists; Biophys Soc; Electron Micros Soc Am; Soc Develop Biol; Soc Gen Physiologists. *Res:* Control of cell division; cellular motility, cell ultrastructure; cryobiology. *Mailing Add:* Dept of Biol Univ of Va Charlottesville VA 22903

REBICK, CHARLES, b Halifax, NS, Oct 21, 44; m 71; c 2. PHYSICAL CHEMISTRY. *Educ:* Univ Toronto, BSc, 67; Mass Inst Technol, PhD(phys chem), 71. *Prof Exp:* Fel phys chem, Hebrew Univ, Jerusalem, 72 & Theoret Chem Inst, Univ Wis-Madison, 73; RES CHEMIST, EXXON RES ENG CO, EXXON CORP, 73- *Honors & Awards:* Sigma Xi Award, 71. *Mem:* Am Chem Soc. *Res:* Kinetics and mechanisms of free radical reactions, especially thermal reactions of hydrocarbons. *Mailing Add:* Exxon Res & Eng Co PO Box 45 Linden NJ 07036

REBMAN, KENNETH RALPH, b Mishawaka, Ind, Oct 4, 40; m 64. MATHEMATICS. *Educ:* Oberlin Col, AB, 62; Univ Mich, Ann Arbor, MA, 64, PhD(math), 69. *Prof Exp:* Asst prof, 69-72, ASSOC PROF MATH, CALIF STATE UNIV HAYWARD, 72- *Mem:* Am Math Soc; Math Asn Am; Soc Indust & Appl Math. *Res:* Mathematical optimization; combinatorics. *Mailing Add:* Dept of Math Calif State Univ Hayward CA 94542

REBOUL, THEO TODD, III, b New Orleans, La, Oct 3, 22; m 52; c 2. SOLID STATE PHYSICS. *Educ:* Tulane Univ, BS, 44, MS, 48; Univ Pa, PhD(physics), 53. *Prof Exp:* Instr, Gen & Intermediate Physics Labs, Tulane Univ, 46-48; instr gen physics, Univ Pa, 48-50 & Drexel Inst, 51-53; physicist, Photo Prod Dept, E I du Pont de Nemours & Co, 53-59; sr engr, Radio Corp Am, 59-63, staff engr, 63-69; staff tech adv, 69-74, CHMN EDUC AID COMT, RCA CORP, 74- *Concurrent Pos:* Mem, Overseas Schs Adv Coun, US State Dept. *Mem:* Am Phys Soc; Am Inst Aeronaut & Astronaut; Inst Elec & Electronics Engrs; Sigma Xi. *Res:* Photographic properties; plasma physics; electro-optics; imaging sensors; administration. *Mailing Add:* 132 Ramblewood Rd Moorestown NJ 08057

REBSTOCK, MILDRED CATHERINE, organic chemistry, see previous edition

REBSTOCK, THEODORE LYNN, b Elkhart, Ind, June 24, 25; m 57; c 2. PLANT BIOCHEMISTRY. *Educ:* NCent Col, BA, 49; Mich State Univ, MS, 51, PhD(chem), 56. *Prof Exp:* From asst to asst prof agr chem, Mich State Univ, 49-59; assoc prof, 59-66, PROF CHEM, WESTMAR COL, 66-, CHMN DEPT, 63-, DIR, NATURAL SCI DIV, 80- *Mem:* AAAS; Am Inst Chemists; Am Chem Soc. *Res:* Mechanism of action and synthesis and isolation of plant growth reg regulators. *Mailing Add:* Dept of Chem Westmar Col LeMars IA 51031

REBUCK, ERNEST C(HARLES), b Klingerstown, Pa, Sept 24, 44; m 69. HYDROLOGY, AGRICULTURAL ENGINEERING. *Educ:* Pa State Univ, BSAE, 66, MS, 67; Univ Ariz, PhD(hydrol), 72. *Prof Exp:* Asst prof agr eng, Univ Md, 71-74; hydrogeologist, 74-78, CHIEF, WATER SUPPLY DIV, MD DEPT NATURAL RESOURCES, 78- *Mem:* Am Soc Civil Engrs; Am Soc Agr Engrs; Soil Conserv Soc Am; Am Geophys Union; Sigma Xi. *Res:* Groundwater hydraulics; groundwater modeling; surface water resources. *Mailing Add:* Water Resources Admin Tawes State Off Bldg Annapolis MD 21401

REBUCK, JOHN WALTER, b Minneapolis, Minn, Nov 24, 14; m 43. HEMATOLOGY. *Educ:* Creighton Univ, AB, 35; Univ Minn, MA, 40, MB, MD, 43, PhD(hemat), 47. *Prof Exp:* Asst hemat, Univ Minn, 38-42; intern, Henry Ford Hosp, 43; hematopathologist, Army Inst Path, 46; pathologist, 47-76, SR HEMATOPATHOLOGIST, LABS, HENRY FORD HOSP, 76-, CHIEF, DIV LAB HEMAT, 71- *Concurrent Pos:* Ed, R E S, 65-74; prof, Wayne State Univ, 70- & Univ Mich, 71- *Mem:* Am Soc Hemat (secy, 58-61); Am Soc Clin Path; Reticuloendothelial Soc (pres, 58-60); Am Asn Pathologists & Bacteriologists; fel Int Soc Hemat. *Res:* Electron microscopy of blood cells; functions of leukocytes; cytology of inflammatory exudate; ultrastructure of sickle cells; hematopathology. *Mailing Add:* Div of Lab Hemat Henry Ford Hosp 2799 W Grand Blvd Detroit MI 48202

RECANT, LILLIAN, b New York, NY, Mar 7, 22; m 55. MEDICINE. *Educ:* Hunter Col, BA, 41; Columbia Univ, MD, 46. *Prof Exp:* Intern med, Col Physicians & Surgeons, Columbia Univ & Presby Hosp, 46-48; asst med & endocrinol, Peter Bent Brigham Hosp, 48-49; asst resident, Col Physicians & Surgeons, Columbia Univ & Presby Hosp, 49-50, Commonwealth fel biochem, 50-51; Commonwealth fel biochem, Sch Med, Washington Univ, 51-53, from asst prof to assoc prof med & prev med, 53-66; PROF MED, SCH MED, GEORGETOWN UNIV, 66-; CHIEF DIABETES RES LAB, VET ADMIN HOSP, 66- *Mem:* Am Soc Clin Invest; Endocrine Soc; Asn Am Physicians; Asn Teachers Prev Med; Soc Exp Biol & Med. *Res:* Metabolism and endocrinology; nephrosis; diabetes and liver diseases. *Mailing Add:* Vet Admin Hosp 50 Irving St NW Washington DC 20422

RECH, RICHARD HOWARD, b Irvington, NJ, Mar 20, 28; m 52; c 3. NEUROPHARMACOLOGY, PSYCHOPHARMACOLOGY. *Educ:* Rutgers Univ, BSc, 52; Univ Mich, MSc, 55, PhD(pharmacol), 60. *Prof Exp:* Pharmacist, Univ Hosp, Univ Mich, 55-56, asst pharmacol, Univ, 57-58; from instr to assoc prof, Dartmouth Med Sch, 61-71; PROF PHARMACOL, MICH STATE UNIV, 71-, PROF TOXICOL, 77- *Concurrent Pos:* USPHS fel, Univ Utah, 59-61. *Mem:* AAAS; Am Soc Pharmacol & Exp Therapeut; Am Col Neuropsychopharmacol. *Res:* Pharmacology. *Mailing Add:* Dept of Pharmacol Mich State Univ East Lansing MI 48824

RECHARD, OTTIS WILLIAM, b Laramie, Wyo, Nov 13, 24; m 43; c 4. COMPUTER SCIENCE, MATHEMATICS. *Educ:* Univ Wyo, BA, 43; Univ Wis, MA, 46, PhD(math), 48. *Prof Exp:* Asst, Alumni Res Found, Univ Wis, 45-48, instr math, 48; from instr to asst prof, Ohio State Univ, 48-51; staff mem, Los Alamos Sci Lab, Univ Calif, 51-56; assoc prof math, Wash State Univ, 56-61, dir comput ctr, 56-68, prof comput sci & math, 61-76, chmn dept comput sci, 63-76, dir systs & comput, 68-70; dir comput serv, 76-79, PROF MATH & COMPUT SCI, UNIV DENVER, 76- *Concurrent Pos:* Consult, Los Alamos Sci Lab, Univ Calif, 56-59, vis staff mem, 74-75; consult, Atomic Energy Div, Phillips Petrol Co, 59-; consult, NSF, 63-64 & 65-; dir comput sci prog, 64-65. *Mem:* AAAS; Am Math Soc; Soc Indust & Appl Math; Math Asn Am; Asn Comput Mach. *Res:* Electronic computers; computer architecture and operating systems; design and analysis of algorithms. *Mailing Add:* Univ of Denver Denver CO 80208

RECHARD, PAUL A(LBERT), b Laramie, Wyo, June 4, 27; m 51; c 2. HYDROLOGY ENGINEERING, CIVIL ENGINEERING. *Educ:* Univ Wyo, BS, 48, MS, 49, CE, 55. *Prof Exp:* Civil engr, US Bur Reclamation, 48-49, hydraul engr, 49-54, asst proj hydrologist, 53-54; dir water resources & interstate streams comnr, Wyo Natural Resource Bd, 54-58; prin hydraul engr, Upper Colo River Comn, 58-64; water resources res engr, 64-66, asst dir, Natural Resources Res Inst, 66-71, dir, Water Resources Res Inst, 66-81, PROF CIVIL ENG, UNIV WYO, 64-; PRES, WESTERN WATER CONSULTS, INC, 80- *Concurrent Pos:* Off Water Resources Res grants, 66-; grants, Environ Protection Agency, 73-81. *Mem:* Int Comn Irrig & Drainage; AAAS; Am Geophys Union; Am Soc Civil Engrs; Am Water Resources Asn. *Res:* Hydrologic research dealing with precipitation-runoff relationships; consumptive use by agricultural and municipal and users; water planning criteria; hydrologic aspects of surface mining. *Mailing Add:* Water Resources Res Inst Univ of Wyo Box 3067 Laramie WY 82071

RECHCIGL, MILOSLAV, JR, b Mlada Boleslav, Czech, July 30, 30; nat US; m 53; c 2. NUTRITIONAL BIOCHEMISTRY, ANIMAL NUTRITION. *Educ:* Cornell Univ, BS, 54, MNS, 55, PhD, 58. *Prof Exp:* Asst, Cornell Univ, 52-57, asst, Grad Sch Nutrit, 57-58, res assoc biochem & nutrit, 58; USPHS fel, Lab Biochem, Nat Cancer Inst, 58-60, chemist, Enzyme & Metab Sect, 60-61, res biochemist, Tumor-Host Rels Sect, 62-64, sr investr, 64-68, sr investr, Biosynthesis sect, 68, assoc USPHS grants, 68-69; spec asst nutrit & health, Off Dir, Regional Med Progs Serv, Health Serv & Ment Health Admin, 69-70; chief, Res & Inst Grants Div, 70-73, asst dir, Off Res & Inst Grants, 73-74, actg dir, 74-75, dir interregional res staff, 75-80, NUTRIT ADV, AID, US DEPT OF STATE, WASHINGTON, DC, 70- *Concurrent Pos:* Nat Acad Sci travel grant, 62; mem educ comn, Nat Cancer Inst Assembly of Scientists, 62-63, chmn commun & mem comn & mem coun, 63-65; deleg, White House Conf Food, Nutrit & Health, 69; consult, Off Secy, USDA, 69-70, US Dept Treasury, 73-, Off Technol Assessment, 77- & Food & Drug Admin, 79-; exec secy nutrit prog adv comt, Health Serv & Ment Health Admin, 69-70; co-ed, J Interdisciplinary Cycle Res, 69-74; exec secy, Res & Inst Grants Coun, Res Adv Comn & Rep, Consult Group Gen Res, US Dept State, 71-; AID rep to USC/FAR Comt, 72- *Mem:* Am Chem Soc; Am Soc Biol Chem; Am Inst Nutrit; Soc Int Develop; Czech Soc Arts & Sci (pres, 74-78). *Res:* Amino acid nutrition; vitamin A and protein relationship; tumor-host relationship; regulatory mechanisms of enzyme activity; enzyme degradation and turnover; catalase; biblography history and historiography of science; research management; science administration; international development. *Mailing Add:* 1703 Mark Lane Rockville MD 20852

RECHNITZ, GARRY ARTHUR, b Berlin, Ger, Jan 1, 36; US citizen; m 58. ANALYTICAL BIOCHEMISTRY. *Educ:* Univ Mich, BS, 58; Univ Ill, MS, 59, PhD(chem), 61. *Prof Exp:* Asst prof chem, Univ Pa, 61-66; from asst prof to prof, State Univ NY Buffalo, 66-77, assoc provost natural sci & math, 67-69; UNIDEL PROF CHEM, UNIV DEL, 78- *Concurrent Pos:* Sloan Found res fel, 66-68. *Honors & Awards:* Val Slyke Award, 78. *Mem:* AAAS; Am Chem Soc. *Res:* Membrane electrodes; ion selectivity in liquid and crystal membranes; clinical instrumentation. *Mailing Add:* Dept of Chem Univ of Del Newark DE 19711

RECHT, HOWARD LEONARD, b Pittsburgh, Pa, July 16, 27; m 52; c 4. WATER CHEMISTRY, ELECTROCHEMISTRY. *Educ:* Carnegie Inst Technol, BS, 48; Cornell Univ, PhD(phys chem), 54. *Prof Exp:* Res chemist, Res & Develop Div, Consol Coal Co, Pa, 54-59; sr chemist, Atomics Int Div, NAm Aviation, Inc, Calif, 59-60, res specialist, 60-61; head electrochem, Astropower, Inc, Douglas Aircraft Corp, 61-62; supvr electrochem, 62-70, proj engr water technol, Atomics Int Div, NAm Rockwell Corp, 70-77, MEM TECH STAFF, ENERGY SYSTS GROUP, ROCKWELL INT CORP, 77- *Mem:* AAAS; Am Chem Soc; Am Phys Soc; Electrochem Soc. *Res:* Electrochemical energy conversion, including high temperature fuel cells, radiation effects on batteries; sodium vapor-graphite interaction; corrosion, water and wastewater treatment; phosphate removal; nuclear waste disposal. *Mailing Add:* Energy Systs Group 8900 Desoto Ave Canoga Park CA 91304

RECHT, RODNEY F(RANK), b Denver, Colo, Feb 5, 27; m 50; c 3. IMPACT DYNAMICS, MECHANICS OF MATERIALS. *Educ:* Univ Denver, BSEE, 49, MSME, 60. *Prof Exp:* Engr, Hanford Atomic Prod Oper, Gen Elec Co, 49-54; engr, Universal Elec Western Co, 54-55 & Colo Interstate Gas Co, 55-56; res engr, 56-64, from asst prof to assoc prof mech eng, 62-76, actg head mech sci div, 62-64, head div, 64-66, SR RES ENGR, DENVER RES INST, UNIV DENVER, 64- *Mem:* Am Soc Mech Engrs; Am Soc Eng Educ; Soc Exp Stress Anal. *Res:* High rate deformation and fracture; dynamic behavior of materials; dynamics of machining process; stress waves in solids; impulsive loading and ballistic impact dynamics. *Mailing Add:* Labs for Appl Mech Univ of Denver Denver Res Inst Denver CO 80208

RECHTIEN, RICHARD DOUGLAS, b St Louis, Mo, Sept 10, 33; m 53; c 2. GEOPHYSICS. *Educ:* Wash Univ, BS, 58, MA, 59, PhD(geophys), 64. *Prof Exp:* Engr, McDonnell Aircraft Corp, Mo, 59-62; fluid dynamicist, Marshall Space Flight Ctr, NASA, 62-66; asst prof, 66-70, ASSOC PROF GEOPHYS, UNIV MO-ROLLA, 70- *Mem:* Soc Explor Geophys; Acoust Soc Am. *Res:* Noise generation in turbulent flow; rocket acoustics; random noise theory; nonlineal wave propagation; geomagnetism; magnetohydrodynamics of the earth's core; interplanetary magnetic fields. *Mailing Add:* Dept of Geophys Univ of Mo Rolla MO 65401

RECHTIN, EBERHARDT, b Orange, NJ, Jan 16, 26; m 51; c 5. ELECTRICAL ENGINEERING. *Educ:* Calif Inst Technol, BS, 46, PhD, 50. *Prof Exp:* Res engr, Jet Propulsion Lab, Calif Inst Technol, 49-52, group supvr secure commun, 52-54, sect chief commun res, 54-57, dir chief guid res, 57-59, dir chief telecommun, 59-60, dir NASA deep space instrumentation prog, 60-63, asst dir tracking & data acquisition, 63-67; dir, Advan Res Projs Agency, US Dept Defense, 67-70, prin dep dir, Defense Res & Eng, 70-72, asst secy defense, Telecommun, 72-73, chief 72-73; chief engr, Hewlett-Packard, 73-77; PRES, AEROSPACE CORP, 77- *Concurrent Pos:* Mem, US Air Force Sci Adv Bd, Defense Comput Inst, Sci & Technol Adv Panel, US Air Force, Aeronaut Systs Div, Adv Group; chmn, Naval Studies Bd, Nat Res Coun. *Honors & Awards:* NASA Medal for Except Sci 65; Aerospace Commun Award, Am Inst Aeronaut & Astronaut, 69; Dept Defense Distinguished Pub Serv Award, 73; Alexander Bell Award, 77. *Mem:* Nat Acad Eng; fel Am Inst Aeronaut & Astronaut; fel Inst Elec & Electronics Engrs; Int Acad Astronaut. *Res:* Information and communication theory; space and secure communication; international cooperative space research. *Mailing Add:* Aerospace Corp PO Box 92957 Los Angeles CA 90009

RECHTIN, MICHAEL DAVID, b Ft Smith, Ark, Feb 1, 44; m 66; c 3. MATERIALS SCIENCE, PHYSICS. *Educ:* Univ Ill, Urbana, BS, 66; Mass Inst Technol, PhD(metall & mat sci), 70. *Prof Exp:* Res assoc metall & mat sci, Mass Inst Technol, 70-73; staff scientist solid state sci, Res Lab, Tex Instruments Inc, 73-75; ASSOC SCIENTIST MAT SCI, ARGONNE NAT LAB, 75- *Concurrent Pos:* IBM fel, Mass Inst Technol, 70-71. *Mem:* Am Ceramic Soc; Am Phys Soc; AAAS. *Res:* Electron microscopy of defect structures in silicon and ion bombarded glasses and insulators; structure and computer models of amorphous materials, infrared optical properties of glasses; electronic and catalytic properties of insulators and magnetic and structural phase transformations in insulators. *Mailing Add:* Argonne Nat Lab Mat Sci Div 9700 S Cass Ave Argonne IL 60439

RECK, GENE PAUL, b Chicago, Ill, Sept 12, 37; c 2. PHYSICAL CHEMISTRY. *Educ:* Univ Ill, Urbana, BS, 59; Univ Minn, PhD(phys chem), 63. *Prof Exp:* Instr phys chem, Univ Minn, 63-64; res assoc, Brown Univ, 64-65; from asst prof to assoc prof, 65-75, PROF PHYS CHEM, WAYNE STATE UNIV, 75- *Concurrent Pos:* Eastman Kodak sci award, Univ Minn, 62. *Mem:* Am Phys Soc; Am Chem Soc. *Res:* Spectral line shapes and their relationship to intermolecular forces; atomic and molecular scattering; laser driven chemistry. *Mailing Add:* Dept of Chem Wayne State Univ Detroit MI 48202

RECK, RUTH ANNETTE, b Rolla, Mo; div; c 2. ATMOSPHERIC PHYSICS, ATMOSPHERIC CHEMISTRY. *Educ:* Mankato State Univ, BA, 54; Univ Minn, PhD(phys chem), 64. *Prof Exp:* Instr physics & chem, Wis State Univ, River Falls, 59-61; res assoc chem, Brown Univ, 64-65; assoc sr res physicist, 65-70, assoc sr res chemist, 71-74, sr res chemist, 74-76, sr scientist, 76-79, STAFF RES SCIENTIST, GEN MOTORS RES LABS, 79- *Concurrent Pos:* Consult, Environ Movement & Transformation Adv Comt, Environ Protection Agency, 75-76, mem, 76-81, mem, Adv Bd, 77-; mem, Climate Modeling Group VIII Exchange with USSR, 76; US rep CO2 Workshop, Int Inst Appl Systs Anal, Austria, 78 & Workshop Extended Clouds, World Meterol Orgn, Oxford Univ, 78; US rep, Int Asn Meterol & Atmospheric Physics, 81. *Mem:* AAAS; Am Chem Soc; Am Phys Soc; Sigma Xi; Am Geophys Union. *Res:* Statistics of climate change, atmospheric radiative transfer and related thermal effects from trace gases and particles; statistical properties of magnetic materials; transport-limited rate processes in random systems. *Mailing Add:* 7165 Old Mill Rd Birmingham MI 48010

RECKEL, RUDOLPH P, b New York, NY, Feb 14, 34; m 57; c 3. IMMUNOLOGY, BIOCHEMISTRY. *Educ:* Brooklyn Col, BS, 56; Georgetown Univ, MS, 62; Rutgers Univ, PhD(biochem), 68. *Prof Exp:* Biochemist, Pioneer Blood Antigen Lab, USDA, Md, 59-62; biochemist, Ortho Res Inst Med Sci, 63-75, dir div clin immunol, Ortho Res Found, 70-75, immunochemist & dir div immunol, 75-80; DIR DIV CLIN IMMUNOL, ORTHO DIAG SYSTS INC, 81- *Concurrent Pos:* Mem, Nat Comt Clin Lab Standards, 68-; mem work party, Int Comt Standardization Hematol, Standardization Anti-Human Globulin Reagents, 74- *Mem:* Am Chem Soc; NY Acad Sci; fel Am Inst Chemists; Am Asn Blood Banks. *Res:* Immunopathology of immune complexes in connective tissue diseases and cancer, especially detection methods, analysisand diagnostic algorithms. *Mailing Add:* Div of Immunol Ortho Res Inst of Med Sci Raritan NJ 08869

RECKHOW, KENNETH HOWLAND, b San Francisco, Calif, Feb 7, 48; m 75; c 1. WATER QUALITY MODELING, APPLIED STATISTICS. *Educ:* Cornell Univ, SB, 71; Harvard Univ, SM, 72, PhD(environ systs), 77. *Prof Exp:* Asst prof water resources, Dept Resource Develop, Mich State Univ, 77-80; ASST PROF WATER RESOURCE SYSTS, SCH FORESTRY & ENVIRON STUDIES, DEPT CIVIL ENG, DUKE UNIV, 80- *Concurrent Pos:* Assoc ed, J Water Resources Res, 80-84; consult, US Army Corps Engrs & US Environ Protection Agency, 79-; prin investr, Nat Oceanic & Atmospheric Admin, 79- *Mem:* Am Geophys Union; Am Water Resources Asn; Am Statist Asn; Soc Risk Anal. *Res:* Mathematical and statistical methods employed in water quality management, including techniques for mathematical model confirmation, risk analysis, uncertainty analysis and statistical descriptions of space-time variability. *Mailing Add:* Sch Forestry & Environ Studies Duke Univ Durham NC 27706

RECKHOW, WARREN ADDISON, b Brooklyn, NY, Mar 29, 21; m 45; c 4. ORGANIC CHEMISTRY, INFORMATION SCIENCE. *Educ:* Drew Univ, BA, 43; Univ Rochester, PhD(chem), 50. *Prof Exp:* Chemist, 46-47, res chemist, 50-55, RES ASSOC, RES LAB, EASTMAN KODAK CO, 55- *Concurrent Pos:* Lectr, Univ Rochester, 51-52. *Mem:* Am Chem Soc. *Res:* Fries rearrangement reactions; synthetic curariform compounds; color photographic chemistry; the use of microform in scientific information. *Mailing Add:* 54 Coronado Dr Rochester NY 14617

RECKNAGEL, RICHARD OTTO, b Springfield, Mo, Jan 11, 16; m 43; c 2. PHYSIOLOGY, TOXICOLOGY. *Educ:* Wayne State Univ, BS, 38; Univ Pa, PhD(zool), 49. *Prof Exp:* Nat Res Coun fel, McArdle Lab Cancer Res, Univ Wis-Madison, 49-51; PROF PHYSIOL, SCH MED, CASE WESTERN RESERVE UNIV, 74-, DIR DEPT, 77- *Mem:* Am Soc Biol Chem; Am Physiol Soc; Am Asn Study Liver Dis. *Res:* Toxic liver injury. *Mailing Add:* Dept of Physiol Case Western Reserve Univ Cleveland OH 44106

RECKTENWALD, GERALD WILLIAM, b Lexington, Ky, June 28, 29; m 55; c 2. PHYSICAL CHEMISTRY, RESEARCH ADMINISTRATION. *Educ:* Univ Ky, BS, 49, MS, 50; Ind Univ, PhD(phys chem), 55. *Prof Exp:* Asst chem, Ind Univ, 52-54; radiochemist, Dow Chem Co, Mich, 54-55; chemist, Major Appliance Lab, Gen Elec Co, 55-65; mgr res & develop rigid foams, Olin Mathieson Chem Corp, 65-69, plant mgr plastics div, Cellular Prod Dept, Olin Corp, 69-72; proj mgr, 72-74, mgr new ventures, 74-78, DIR COM DEVELOP, AIR PROD & CHEM, INC, 78- *Concurrent Pos:* Lectr, Ind Univ, 57-58, Univ Louisville, 58 & Nazareth Col, Ky, 59-60. *Mem:* Am Chem Soc; Soc Plastics Indust; Soc Plastic Engrs. *Res:* Polyurethane foams and hermetic systems; surface active agents; wire enamels; radiochemistry; chemical instrumentation; barrier properties of plastics; medical instrumentation. *Mailing Add:* 314 N 28th St Allentown PA 18104

RECORD, FRANK ALASTER, b Livermore Falls, Maine, July 10, 17; m 46; c 3. AIR POLLUTION, METEOROLOGY. *Educ:* Colby Col, AB, 38; Mass Inst Technol, SM, 43, ScD(meteorol), 49. *Prof Exp:* Res meteorologist, Mass Inst Technol, 49-65; prin scientist atmospheric diffusion, air pollution studies & air qual mgt, 65-74, mgr environ planning & anal dept, 74-78, sr staff scientist, 78-80, CONSULT, GCA/TECHNOL DEPT, 80- *Mem:* AAAS; Am Meteorol Soc; Air Pollution Control Asn; Am Geophys Union; Royal Meteorol Soc. *Res:* Environmental management for control of atmospheric pollution. *Mailing Add:* GCA/Technol Div 213 Burlington Rd Bedford MA 01730

RECORD, M THOMAS, JR, b Exeter, NH, Dec 18, 42; c 2. BIOPHYSICAL CHEMISTRY. *Educ:* Yale Univ, BA, 64; Univ Calif, San Diego, PhD(chem), 67. *Prof Exp:* NSF fel biochem, Stanford Univ, 68-70; asst prof, 70-76, assoc prof, 76-80, PROF CHEM, UNIV WIS-MADISON, 80- *Concurrent Pos:* NSF & NIH grants. *Mem:* AAAS; Am Chem Soc; Biophys Soc. *Res:* Physical chemistry of nucleic acids and viruses; interactions of nucleic acids with ions and biological polyelectrolytes. *Mailing Add:* Dept of Chem Univ of Wis Madison WI 53706

RECSEI, ANDREW A, b Kula, Yugoslavia, July 22, 02; nat US; m 42; c 3. ORGANIC CHEMISTRY. *Educ:* Univ Vienna, Austria, BA, 22; Univ Brno, Czech, MA, 24, PhD, 26. *Prof Exp:* Res chemist, Dr Honsig Chem Lab, 26-30; plant mgr, Pharmador Pty Ltd, SAfrica, 31-39; pres, Recsei Labs, Calif, 40-42; res assoc, Univ Calif, Los Angeles, 42-43; res chemist, Calif Inst Technol, 43-44 & Printing Arts Res Lab, 44-46; PRES, RECSEI LABS, 46- *Concurrent Pos:* Instr, Univ Calif, Santa Barbara, 54-56, assoc, 56-65. *Mem:* Am Chem Soc. *Res:* Antihistamines; allergy; nutrition; antimitotic compounds and anti-tumor agents. *Mailing Add:* 633 Tabor Lane Santa Barbara CA 93108

RECSEI, PAUL ANDOR, b Santa Barbara, Calif, Feb 24, 45. BIOCHEMISTRY. *Educ:* Harvard Univ, BS, 67; Univ Calif, PhD(biochem), 72. *Prof Exp:* Fel biochem, Univ Calif, 73-75; V PRES PHARMACEUT, RECSEI LABS, 75- *Res:* Development and design of pharmaceuticals. *Mailing Add:* Recsei Labs 330 S Kellogg Ave Goleta CA 93017

RECTOR, CHARLES WILLSON, b Sioux City, Iowa, Apr 29, 26; m 54; c 2. SOLID STATE PHYSICS. *Educ:* Univ Chicago, PhB, 46, SB, 49; Franklin & Marshall Col, MS, 59; Johns Hopkins Univ, PhD(physics), 66. *Prof Exp:* Design engr, Tube Div, Radio Corp Am, 54-59, mem tech staff, RCA Labs, 60-62; assoc prof, 66-75, PROF PHYSICS, US NAVAL ACAD, 75- *Concurrent Pos:* Instr, Elizabethtown Col, 57-59; res assoc physics, Johns Hopkins Univ, 66. *Mem:* Am Asn Physics Teachers; Am Phys Soc. *Res:* Photoconductivity; semiconductor smokes; rare earth ions in crystals; electron paramagnetic resonance; optical spectroscopy. *Mailing Add:* Dept of Physics US Naval Acad Annapolis MD 21402

RECTOR, FLOYD CLINTON, JR, b Slaton, Tex, Jan 28, 29; m 50; c 3. NEPHROLOGY. *Educ:* Tex Tech Univ, BS, 50; Univ Tex Southwestern Med Sch, MD, 54. *Prof Exp:* Intern, Parkland Mem Hosp, Dallas, 55, resident, 56; instr internal med, Univ Tex Southwestern Med Sch, 58-59, asst prof, 59-63, assoc prof nephrol, 63-66, prof & dir div, 66-73; SR SCIENTIST, CARDIOVASC RES INST & PROF MED & PHYSIOL & DIR DIV NEPHROLOGY, UNIV CALIF, SAN FRANCISCO, 77- *Concurrent Pos:* Mem & chmn, Cardiovasc Study Sect, NIH, 65-69, mem, Nephrol & Urol Fel & Training Grants Comt, 71-76, chmn, 72-73; chmn, Fel & Res Grants Comt, Nat Kidney Found, 68-71, chmn, Sci Adv Bd, 71-73. *Mem:* Am Soc Clin Invest; Am Asn Physicians; Am Physiol Soc; Am Soc Nephrol (secy-treas, 73-76, pres, 76-77); Biophys Soc. *Res:* Mechanisms of ion and water transport by renal tubules. *Mailing Add:* Div Nephrol Room 1065 HSE Univ of Calif San Francisco CA 94143

REDALIEU, ELLIOT, b Bronx, NY, Dec 12, 39; m 62; c 3. DRUG METABOLISM, MEDICINAL CHEMISTRY. *Educ:* Fordham Univ, BS, 61; Univ Mich, MS, 63, PhD(pharmaceut chem), 66. *Prof Exp:* Teaching asst pharmaceut anal, Univ Mich, 61-62; fel, Stanford Res Inst, 66-68; res biochemist, Pharmaceut Div, Geigy Chem Corp, 68-71; sr scientist, 71-80, sr scientist II, 75-80, MGR, BIOAVAILABILITY & PHARMACOKINETICS, PHARMACEUT DIV, CIBA-GEIGY CORP, 80- *Mem:* AAAS; Am Chem Soc. *Res:* Metabolism of drugs; organic synthesis; analgesics; cardiovascular compounds; radiotracer techniques; gas chromatography; liquid chromatography; bioavailability; pharmacokinetics. *Mailing Add:* 32 Hickory Lane Garnerville NY 10923

REDBURN, DIANNA AMMONS, b Many, La, Oct 21, 43; m 65. NEUROBIOLOGY. *Educ:* Centenary Col, BS, 64; Univ Kans, PhD(neurobiol), 72. *Prof Exp:* Fel psychobiol, Univ Calif, Irvine, 72-74; asst prof, 74-80, ASSOC PROF NEUROBIOL, MED SCH UNIV TEX, HOUSTON, 80- *Mem:* AAAS; Soc Neurosci; Neurochem Soc; Soc Cell Biol; Asn Women in Sci. *Res:* The nature of chemical transmission in neuronal tissue; mechanisms of neurotransmitter release, identification of functional neurotransmitters, modulation of chemical transmission by intrinsic and extrinsic factors; development of in vitro techniques for biochemical analysis of neurotransmitter systems; neurochemistry of the retina. *Mailing Add:* Dept of Neurobiol & Anat Univ of Tex Med Sch Houston TX 77025

REDDAN, JOHN R, b Trenton, NJ, Apr 18, 39; m 62; c 4. CELL PHYSIOLOGY. *Educ:* St Michaels Col, BA, 61; Univ Vt, PhD(zool), 66. *Prof Exp:* NIH fel cell biol, 65-67, from asst prof to assoc prof, 67-78, PROF BIOL, OAKLAND UNIV, 78- *Mem:* AAAS; Am Soc Cell Biol; Asn Res Vision & Ophthal; Am Soc Zool. *Res:* Metabolic and cytological, light and electron microscopic changes which precede and accompany the initiation of cell division in normal, injured and cultured mammalian lenses epitherial cells. *Mailing Add:* Dept of Biol Sci Oakland Univ Rochester MI 48063

REDDAN, WILLIAM GERALD, b St Louis, Mo, Aug 29, 27; m 52; c 3. PHYSIOLOGY. *Educ:* Univ Mo-Columbia, BS, 51; Univ Wis-Madison, MS, 55, PhD(biodynamics), 65. *Prof Exp:* Teacher, Spring Green Pub Schs, 55-60; res asst physiol, 60-62, proj assoc pulmonary physiol, 62-64, instr, 64-65, asst prof environ physiol, 65-72, ASSOC PROF PREV MED, MED SCH, UNIV WIS-MADISON, 72-, ASSOC PROF ANAT, 77- *Mem:* Am Physiol Soc. *Res:* Gas exchange in the lung; pulmonary physiology applied to occupational and environmental lung disease; physical education. *Mailing Add:* Dept of Prev Med Univ Wis Med Sch 504 N Walnut St Madison WI 53706

REDDELL, DONALD LEE, b Tulia, Tex, Sept 28, 37; m 57; c 3. AGRICULTURAL ENGINEERING, HYDROLOGY. *Educ:* Tex Technol Col, BS, 60; Colo State Univ, MS, 67, PhD(agr eng), 69. *Prof Exp:* Jr engr, High Plains Underground Water Conserv Dist, Tex, 60-62, agr engr, 62-64, engr, 64-65; from asst prof to assoc prof agr eng, 69-77, PROF AGR ENG, TEX A&M UNIV, 77- *Mem:* Am Soc Agr Engrs; Am Geophys Union. *Res:* Pollution problems of large cattle feeding operations; groundwater hydrology, hydraulics and quality; heat transfer in groundwater aquifers; mathematical modeling of hydrological systems; irrigation and drainage; pollution problems in agriculture. *Mailing Add:* Dept of Agr Eng Tex A&M Univ College Station TX 77843

REDDEN, DAVID RAY, b McKinney, Tex, Dec 22, 21; m 48; c 5. MEDICAL PHYSIOLOGY, ANIMAL PHYSIOLOGY. *Educ:* NTex State Col, BS, 46, MS, 49; Baylor Univ, PhD(physiol, biochem), 60. *Prof Exp:* Instr biol, Texarkana Jr Col, 49-51, East Tex State Col, 51-53, pub sch, Tex, 53-54 & NTex State Univ, 55-57; instr physiol, Col Dent, Baylor Univ, 57-60; from asst prof to assoc prof, 60-66, PROF BIOL, NTEX STATE UNIV, 66- *Concurrent Pos:* Prof med physiol, Tex Col Osteop Med, 72- *Mem:* AAAS; Soc Exp Biol & Med. *Res:* Cardiovascular physiology; space related muscle and bone physiology; capillary dynamics; hypothermia. *Mailing Add:* Dept Biol Sci NTex State Univ Denton TX 76203

REDDEN, JACK A, b Rossville, Ill, Sept 24, 26; m 51; c 2. GEOLOGY. *Educ:* Dartmouth Col, AB, 48; Harvard Univ, MA, 50, PhD, 55. *Prof Exp:* Geologist, US Geol Surv, 48-58; assoc prof geol, Va Polytech Inst & State Univ, 58-64; assoc prof geol & dir, Wright State Univ, 64-68, assoc dean sci & eng, 68-69; DIR ENG & MINING EXP STA, S DAK SCH MINES & TECHNOL, 69- *Mem:* Geol Soc Am; Mineral Soc Am. *Res:* Petrology; structure and ore deposits. *Mailing Add:* Eng & Mining Exp Sta SDak Sch of Mines & Technol Rapid City SD 57701

REDDEN, PATRICIA ANN, b New York, NY, Sept 10, 41. PHYSICAL CHEMISTRY, EDUCATION. *Educ:* Cabrini Col, BS, 62; Fordham Univ, PhD(phys chem), 68. *Prof Exp:* Asst prof anal chem, 68-74, assoc prof chem, 74-80, PROF CHEM, ST PETER'S COL, NJ, 80-, CHMN DEPT, 77- *Mem:* Am Chem Soc; Am Asn Univ Professors; Sigma Xi; NY Acad Sci. *Res:* Food analysis; lab safety. *Mailing Add:* Dept of Chem St Peter's Col Jersey City NJ 07306

REDDICK-MITCHUM, RHODA ANNE, b Waynesboro, Ga, Nov 2, 37; m 70. MEDICAL MICROBIOLOGY. *Educ:* Ga Col, AB, 58; Emory Univ, cert med technol, 59; Med Col Ga, MS, 65, PhD(med microbiol), 68; Am Bd Med Microbiol, dipl, 73. *Prof Exp:* Med technologist, Emory Univ Hosp, 59-61 & Eugene Talmadge Hosp, Med Col Ga, 62-64; fel med microbiol, Ctr Dis Control, USPHS, Atlanta, Ga, 68-70; dir, Div Diag Microbiol, Bur Labs, 70-75, DIR, DIV LAB IMPROV, SC DEPT HEALTH & ENVIRON CONTROL, 75- *Mem:* Am Soc Microbiol; Am Pub Health Asn; fel Am Acad Microbiol; Am Veneral Dis Asn; NY Acad Sci. *Res:* Development of new diagnostic procedures in medical microbiology and evaluation of products available to diagnostic microbiology laboratories. *Mailing Add:* SC Dept Health & Environ Control Bur Labs PO box 2202 Columbia SC 29201

REDDING, FOSTER KINYON, b Owatonna, Minn, July 22, 29; m 60; c 4. NEUROLOGY, NEUROPHYSIOLOGY. *Educ:* Univ Pa, MD, 54; McGill Univ, PhD(neurophysiol), 64. *Prof Exp:* Physician & surgeon, Palen Clin, Minneapolis, 55-56; asst prof neurol, Sch Med, Univ Ill, 64-67; neurologist & neurophysiologist, Henry Ford Hosp, Detroit, 67-73, chief neurol, 72-73; PROF NEUROL, SCH MED, WAYNE STATE UNIV, 73- *Concurrent Pos:* USPHS res grant, Sch Med, Univ Ill, 66-69. *Mem:* Am Acad Neurol; Am Electroencephalog Soc; Am Epilepsy Soc. *Res:* Relationship of rhinencephalon with brain stem reticular formation. *Mailing Add:* Dept of Neurol Wayne State Univ Detroit MI 48201

REDDING, JOSEPH STAFFORD, b Macon, Ga, May 29, 21; m 49; c 5. ANESTHESIOLOGY. *Educ:* Univ NC, Chapel Hill, BA, 43; Univ Md, Baltimore City, MD, 48. *Prof Exp:* Resident anesthesiol, Univ NC, 56-58; from instr to assoc prof anesthesiol, Johns Hopkins Univ, 58-70; prof anesthesiol, Univ Nebr Med Ctr, Omaha, 70-74; PROF ANESTHESIOL & HEAD, DIV RESPIRATORY/CRITICAL CARE, MED UNIV SC, 74- *Concurrent Pos:* Nat Heart Inst res grant, Baltimore City Hosps, 60-69, from asst chief to chief anesthesiol, Baltimore City Hosps, 58-70; assoc prof, Univ Md, 63-67, prof, 67-70. *Mem:* Am Soc Anesthesiol; Int Anesthesia Res Soc; Soc Critical Care Med; fel Am Col Physicians; Royal Soc Med. *Res:* Cardiopulmonary resuscitation; physiology of sudden death; life support measures; critical care medicine. *Mailing Add:* Dept of Anesthesiol Med Univ of SC Charleston SC 29425

REDDING, RICHARD WILLIAM, b Toledo, Ohio, Mar 18, 23; m 46; c 3. VETERINARY PHYSIOLOGY, PHARMACOLOGY. *Educ:* Ohio State Univ, DVM, 46, MSc, 50, PhD(vet physiol & pharmacol), 57. *Prof Exp:* Instr vet surg, Ohio State Univ, 48-50; asst prof, Univ Calif, 50-51 & Univ Ga, 51-53; from instr to assoc prof vet physiol & pharmacol, Ohio State Univ, 53-63, prof, Col Vet Med & Grad Sch, 63-68; PROF SMALL ANIMAL SURG & MED & PHYSIOL & PHARMACOL, AUBURN UNIV, 68- *Concurrent Pos:* Consult, Martin Co, 63 & US Navy Radiol Defense Labs, 66- *Mem:* AAAS; Am Vet Med Asn; Am Soc Vet Physiol & Pharmacol; Am Asn Vet Neurol (secy-treas, 72-). *Res:* Techniques, application and use of electroencephalograph in canine diagnosis; surgical control of behavior in the canine species. *Mailing Add:* Dept of Physiol Auburn Univ Auburn AL 36830

REDDING, ROGERS WALKER, b Louisville, Ky, July 15, 42; m 66; c 2. PHYSICAL CHEMISTRY, PHYSICS. *Educ:* Ga Inst Technol, BS, 65; Vanderbilt Univ, PhD(chem), 69. *Prof Exp:* Nat Acad Sci fel, Nat Bur Standards, Washington, DC, 69-70; asst prof, 70-73, assoc prof, 73-79, PROF PHYSICS, NORTH TEX STATE UNIV, 79-, CHMN DEPT, 80- *Mem:* AAAS; Am Phys Soc; Am Asn Physics Teachers. *Res:* Theoretical molecular physics; molecular spectroscopy. *Mailing Add:* Dept of Physics N Tex State Univ Denton TX 76203

REDDISH, PAUL SIGMAN, b Durham, NC, June 8, 10; m 36. BIOLOGY. *Educ:* Duke Univ, AB, 33, AM, 35. *Prof Exp:* Head sci dept, NC High Sch, 35-43; instr eng physics, NC State Col, 43-44, asst, Off Sci Res & Develop, 44; assoc cult dept, Carolina Biol Supply Co, 44-45; from asst prof to prof, Elon Col, 45-76, chmn dept, 73-75; RETIRED. *Concurrent Pos:* Consult microbiol, 76- *Mem:* AAAS; Nat Asn Biol Teachers; Am Inst Biol Sci; Am Micros Soc. *Res:* Ecology of protozoa; physiology; bacteriology. *Mailing Add:* 614 E Haggard Ave Elon College NC 27244

REDDISH, ROBERT LEE, b Odum, Ga, Apr 6, 19; m 46; c 3. ANIMAL SCIENCE. *Educ:* Univ Ga, BSA, 47; Cornell Univ, MS, 49; Agr & Mech Col Tex, PhD(animal husb), 56. *Prof Exp:* Asst, Cornell Univ, 47-49; asst prof, Tex Col Arts & Indust, 49-53; asst, Agr & Mech Col Tes, 53-54; PROF ANIMAL SCI & MEAT SPECIALIST, EXTEN SERV, UNIV FLA, 54- *Concurrent Pos:* Conuslt, Dominican Repub, 60. *Mem:* Am Soc Animal Sci. *Res:* Biochemistry; animal nutrition and veterinary physiology. *Mailing Add:* 402 Rolfs Hall Univ of Fla Gainesville FL 32601

REDDOCH, ALLAN HARVEY, b Montreal, Que, Jan 19, 31; m 70. CHEMICAL PHYSICS. *Educ:* Queen's Univ, Ont, BSc, 53, MSc, 55; Univ Calif, Berkeley, PhD(phys chem), 60. *Prof Exp:* Fel chem, 59-61, from asst res officer to assoc res officer, Div Chem, 61-74, SR RES OFFICER, DIV CHEM, NAT RES COUN CAN, 74- *Concurrent Pos:* Lectr, Univ Ottawa, 61-65. *Mem:* Am Chem Soc; Am Phys Soc; Chem Inst Can; Royal Soc Chem. *Res:* Electron spin resonance of organic radicals in solution; organic charge-transfer crystals; hydrogen-bonded ferroelectrics. *Mailing Add:* Div of Chem Nat Res Coun Can Ottawa ON K1A 0R6 Can

REDDY, BANDARU SIVARAMA, b Nellore, India, Dec 30, 32; m 62; c 3. BIOCHEMISTRY, NUTRITION. *Educ:* Madras Univ, BVSc, 55; Univ NH, MS, 60; Mich State Univ, PhD(biochem), 63; Nat Registry Clin Chem, cert. *Prof Exp:* Vet surg & med, Andhra Pradesh Govt, India, 55-58; res assoc biochem, Lobund Lab, Univ Notre Dame, 63-65, res scientist, 65-68, assoc res prof, 68-72; HEAD DEPT NUTRIT BIOCHEM, AM HEALTH FOUND, 71-, ASSOC CHIEF, DIV NUTRIT, 79-; RES PROF MICROBIOL, NEW YORK MED COL, 76- *Concurrent Pos:* NIH res grants, 65; nat corresp, Pub Affairs Comt, Fedn Am Socs Exp Biol. *Mem:* Am Inst Nutrit; Am Asn Pathologists; Asn Gnotobiotics; Soc Exp Biol & Med; Am Asn Cancer Res. *Res:* Effect of intestinal microflora on the nutritional biochemistry of host; role of bile acids and microflora on the etiology of colon cancer; chemical carcinogenesis; nutrition and cancer; nutritional toxicology; mechanism of carcinogenesis. *Mailing Add:* Am Health Found Hammond House Rd Valhalla NY 10595

REDDY, CHURKU MOHAN, b Kothapalli, India, Aug 3, 42; c 2. PEDIATRIC ENDOCRINOLOGY. *Educ:* Osmania Univ, India, MB, BS, 66; Am Bd Pediat, dipl, 75. *Prof Exp:* Med officer, Primary Health Ctr, India, 68-70; asst instr pediat, State Univ NY, Downstate Med Ctr, 71-75; asst prof, 75-77, ASSOC PROF PEDIAT, MEHARRY MED COL, 77-, DIR DIV ENDOCRINOL & METAB, 75- *Concurrent Pos:* Fel pediat endocrinol & metab, State Univ NY, Downstate Med Ctr, Kings County Hosp Ctr, 73-75. *Mem:* Fel Am Acad Pediat; AMA. *Res:* Clinical research. *Mailing Add:* Dept of Pediat Meharry Med Col Nashville TN 37208

REDDY, DABBALA RAJAGOPAL, b Katoor, India, June 13, 37; m 66. COMPUTER SCIENCE. *Educ:* Univ Madras, BE, 58; Univ New South Wales, MTech, 61; Stanford Univ, MS, 64, PhD(comput sci), 66. *Prof Exp:* Appl sci rep, Int Bus Mach Corp, 61-63; from instr to asst prof comput sci, Stanford Univ, 66-69; assoc prof, 69-78, PROF COMPUT SCI, CARNEGIE-MELLON UNIV, 73- *Concurrent Pos:* Consult, Litton Indust, Inc, 67-69, Stanford Res Inst, 71 & Xerox Corp, 71-; dir, Robotics Inst, Carnegie-Mellon Univ, Pittsburgh, Pa, 80. *Mem:* Asn Comput Mach; Asn Comput Ling; Acoust Soc Am; Inst Elec & Electronics Engrs. *Res:* Speech and visual input to computers; graphics; man machine communication; artificial intelligence. *Mailing Add:* Dept of Comput Sci Carnegie-Mellon Univ Pittsburgh PA 15213

REDDY, GADE SUBBARAMI, b Aluru, India, May 20, 35; m 56; c 4. PHYSICAL CHEMISTRY. *Educ:* Andhra Univ, India, BSc, 54; Benares Hindu Univ, MSc, 56; Emory Univ, PhD(phys chem), 60. *Prof Exp:* Govt India sr res scholar phys chem, Benares Hindu Univ, 56-57; res assoc spectros, Emory Univ, 60-62; res chemist, Eastern Lab, 62-66, RES CHEMIST, CENT RES DEPT, EXP STA, E I DU PONT DE NEMOURS & CO, INC, 66- *Mem:* Am Chem Soc. *Res:* Nuclear magnetic resonance spectroscopy; nuclear magnetic resonance in liquid crystals; kinetics and reaction mechanisms by nuclear magnetic resonance. *Mailing Add:* Cent Res Dept Exp Sta E I du Pont de Nemours & Co Inc Wilmington DE 19898

REDDY, GUNDA, b Cheekodu, India. ENTOMOLOGY. *Educ:* Osmania Univ, India, BSc, 60, MSc, 62, PhD(zool, entom), 68. *Prof Exp:* Fel pesticide & residues, Dept Entom, Univ Ky, 69-70; res assoc metab ammonia & calcium, Dept Biol, Rice Univ, 70-71; vis scholar insect hormones, Dept Biol, Marquette Univ, 71-73; res assoc pesticide metab, Dept Biol, Univ Ill, 73-76; res assoc insect hormones, Marquette Univ, 76-78; RES ASSOC PCB METAB & PATH, DEPT PATH, UNIV WIS-MADISON, 78- *Mem:* Entom Soc Am; Soc Toxicol; Am Chem Soc; Indian Sci Cong; Am Col Toxicol. *Res:* Action and metabolism of pesticides; insect endocrine interactions; ecological and health effect of pollutants. *Mailing Add:* Dept of Path Vet Admin Hosp Madison WI 53705

REDDY, JANARDAN K, b India, Oct 7, 38; m 62; c 2. PATHOLOGY. *Educ:* Osmania Univ, India, MB, BS, 61; All India Inst Med Sci, MD, 65. *Prof Exp:* From asst prof to assoc prof path & oncol, Univ Kans Med Ctr, Kansas City, 70-76; PROF PATH, NORTHWESTERN UNIV MED SCH, CHICAGO, 76- *Mem:* AAAS; Am Asn Pathologists; Soc Exp Biol & Med; Histochem Soc; Am Soc Cell Biol. *Res:* Experimental chemcial carcinogenesis; effect of drugs and carcinogens on the structure and function of liver and pancreas; role of hypolipidemic drugs on the induction of peroxisome proliferation in liver cells. *Mailing Add:* Dept of Path 303 E Chicago Ave Chicago IL 60611

REDDY, JUNUTHULA N, b Warangal, India, Aug 12, 45; m 68; c 2. MECHANICAL ENGINEERING, APPLIED MECHANICS. *Educ:* Osmania Univ, India, BE, 68; Okla State Univ, MS, 70; Univ Ala, Huntsville, PhD(appl mech), 73. *Prof Exp:* Res assoc mech, Univ Ala, 70-73; fel, Univ Tex, Austin, 73-74; res assoc aeromech, Lockheed Missiles & Space Co, 74-75; from asst prof to assoc prof mech eng, Univ Okla, 75-80; PROF, VA POLYTECH INST, 80- *Concurrent Pos:* Consult, Univ Engrs, Norman, Okla, 76-77 & Univ Technologists, 77-; res grants, NSF, Off Naval Res & pvt co. *Honors & Awards:* Teetor Award Res & Teaching, Soc Automotive Engrs, 76. *Mem:* Am Acad Mech; Soc Indust & Appl Math; Am Soc Mech Engrs; Soc Eng Sci; Am Soc Eng Educ. *Res:* Analysis of structural components; computational fluid mechanics; theory and application of the finite element method in solid and fluid mechanics; variational methods. *Mailing Add:* Dept Eng Sci Va Polytech Inst 220 Norris Blacksburg VA 24061

REDDY, KAPULURU CHANDRASEKHARA, b Nellore, India, Aug 20, 42; m 67; c 1. APPLIED MATHEMATICS, FLUID MECHANICS. *Educ:* V R Col, India, BA, 59; Sri Venkateswara Univ, India, MSc, 61; Indian Inst Technol, Kharagpur, MTech, 62, PhD(appl math), 65. *Prof Exp:* Assoc lectr math, Indian Inst Technol, Kharagpur, 64-65; instr aerospace eng, Univ Md, College Park, 65-66; from asst prof to assoc prof math, 66-75, PROF MATH, SPACE INST, UNIV TENN, TULLAHOMA, 75- *Concurrent Pos:* Staff engr, Lockheed Electronics Co, Houston, 69 & 70; consult, US Army Res Off, Durham, 73 & Lockheed Ga Co, Marietta, Ga, 76; res engr, AROC, Inc, Arnold Eng Develop Ctr, 77-78. *Mem:* Am Inst Aeronaut & Astronaut; Sigma Xi; Soc Indust & Appl Math. *Res:* Computational fluid mechanics; transonic flow problems; numerical analysis; boundary layers. *Mailing Add:* Space Inst Univ of Tenn Tullahoma TN 37388

REDDY, NARENDER PABBATHI, b Karimnagar, India, May 5, 47; m 76; c 1. BIOMEDICAL ENGINEERING, MECHANICAL ENGINEERING. *Educ:* Osmania Univ, India, BE, 69; Univ Miss, MS, 71; Tex A&M Univ, PhD(bioeng), 74. *Prof Exp:* Res asst, Tex A&M Univ, 71-74, res assoc bioeng, 74-75; res assoc rehab eng, Baylor Col Med, 75-76; res physiologist, Univ Calif, San Francisco, 77-78; sr res scientist, Biomech Res Unit, Helen Hays Hosp, NY, 78-81; ASSOC PROF, INST BIOMED ENG RES, UNIV AKRON, 81- *Concurrent Pos:* Res fel, Cardiovasc Res Inst, Univ Calif, San Francisco, 77-78. *Mem:* Biomed Eng Soc; Am Soc Mech Engrs; Int Soc Biomech; Int Soc Lymphology. *Res:* Biomechanical engineering; computer modeling; physiology and bioengineering of lymphatic system; soft tissue mechanics; rehabilitation engineering; orthopedic biomechanics. *Mailing Add:* Inst Biomed Eng Res Univ Akron Akron OH 44325

REDDY, PARVATHAREDDY BALARAMI, b Nellore, India, Dec 1, 42; US citizen; m 67; c 2. CONTROL SYSTEMS, ELECTRICAL ENGINEERING. *Educ:* Sri Venkateswara Univ, BE hons, 65; Indian Inst Technol, MTech, 67; Rutgers Univ, PhD(elec eng controls), 73. *Prof Exp:* Res & teaching asst elec eng, Rutgers Univ, 69-73; sr systs analyst control & navig, Dynamics Res Corp, 73-78; mem tech staff navig & guid, Litton Guid & Control Systs, 78-80; RES SCIENTIST, TELEDYNE SYSTS CO, 80- *Mem:* Inst Elec & Electronics Engrs. *Res:* Guidance, navigation, statistical modeling; modeling and simulation with general modeling interest; strapdown systems using ring laser gyros. *Mailing Add:* Teledyne Systs Co 19601 Nordhoff St Northridge CA 91324

REDDY, REGINALD JAMES, b Staten Island, NY, July 16, 34. MOLECULAR SPECTROSCOPY. *Educ:* St Bonaventure Univ, BA, 57; Holy Name Col, STM, 61; Univ SC, PhD(physics), 77. *Prof Exp:* Instr physics & math, Archbishop Walsh High Sch, 61-65; teaching asst, Univ SC, 68-73; ASST PROF PHYSICS, SIENA COL, NY, 73- *Mem:* Am Asn Physics Teachers; Nat Sci Teachers Asn; Sigma Xi. *Res:* Flash photolysis studies of various polycyclic hydrocarbons including triplet-triplet transitions, quenching of the triplet states by various impurities, energy transfer between triplets. *Mailing Add:* Dept of Physics Siena Col Loudonville NY 12211

REDDY, SATTI PADDI, b Jan 8, 31; Can citizen; m 55; c 3. PHYSICS, MOLECULAR SPECTROSCOPY. *Educ:* Andhra Univ, India, BSc, 54, MSc, 55, DSc(molecular spectros), 59. *Prof Exp:* Lectr physics, Andhra Univ, India, 59-61; res assoc, Univ Toronto, 61-63; res fel, 63-64, from asst prof to assoc prof, 64-72, PROF PHYSICS, MEM UNIV NFLD, 72- *Concurrent Pos:* Sr res fel, Andhra Univ, India, 60-61; vis prof physics, Ohio State Univ, 77-78. *Mem:* Fel Brit Inst Physics; Can Asn Physicists; Am Phys Soc. *Res:* Molecular physics; infrared, laser and optical spectroscopy. *Mailing Add:* Dept of Physics Mem Univ Nfld St John's NF A1B 3X7 Can

REDDY, SUDHAKAR M, b Gadwal, India, Jan 5, 38; m 63. ELECTRICAL ENGINEERING. *Educ:* Osmania Univ, India, BS, 58 & 62; Indian Inst Sci, MS, 63; Univ Iowa, PhD(elec eng), 68. *Prof Exp:* Asst prof elec eng, 68-77, PROF INFO ENG, UNIV IOWA, 77- *Concurrent Pos:* NSF grant, 69-71. *Mem:* Inst Elec & Electronics Engrs. *Res:* Coding theory; digital systems. *Mailing Add:* Div of Info Eng Univ of Iowa Iowa City IA 52242

REDDY, THOMAS BRADLEY, b Amesbury, Mass, Sept 11, 33; div; c 3. ELECTROCHEMISTRY. *Educ:* Yale Univ, BS, 55; Univ Minn, PhD(phys chem), 60. *Prof Exp:* Res assoc chem, Univ Ill, 59-61; mem tech staff electrochem, Bell Tel Labs, 61-65; proj leader, Am Cyanamid Co, 65-74, prin res chemist, Stamford Res Labs, 74-79; dir-battery-technol, Stonehart Assocs, Inc, Madison, Conn, 79-80; DIR TECHNOL, POWER CONVERSION,

INC, MT VERNON, NY, 80- *Mem:* Am Chem Soc; Electrochem Soc. *Res:* Lithium battery systems; organic electrochemistry; fused salts; electrodeposition; corrosion; electrochromic display devices; non-aqueous solvents. *Mailing Add:* David's Lane Pound Ridge New York NY 10576

REDDY, VENKAT N, b Hyderabad, India, Nov 4, 22; nat US; m 55; c 2. BIOCHEMISTRY. *Educ:* Madras Univ, BSc, 45; Fordham Univ, MS, 49, PhD(biochem), 52. *Prof Exp:* Asst chem, Fordham Univ, 48-50, sr asst biochem, 50-52; res asst obstet & gynec, Columbia Univ, 52-54, res assoc, 54-56, res fel, Banting & Best Inst, Can, 56; asst prof ophthalmic biochem, Kresge Eye Inst, 57-61, assoc prof ophthal, 61-77, PROF OPHTHAL, WAYNE STATE UNIV, 77- PROF BIOL SCI, OAKLAND UNIV, 68-, DIR INST BIOL SCI, 75- *Concurrent Pos:* Mem visual sci study sect, NIH, 66-70, consult, Cataract Workshop, 73; asst dir inst biol sci, Oakland Univ, 68-75; Nat Acad Sci-Nat Res Coun Comt Vision, 71-; consult, Nat Adv Eye Coun Vision Res Prog Planning Comt, 74; bd sci counr, Nat Eye Inst, 78-82. *Honors & Awards:* Fight for Sight Citation, Nat Coun Combat Blindness, 68; Friedenwald Award, Asn Res Vision & Ophthal, 79. *Mem:* AAAS; Am Soc Biol Chemists; NY Acad Sci; Asn Res Vision & Ophthal; Brit Biochem Soc. *Res:* Transport mechanisms; aqueous humor dynamics; metabolism of ocular tissues; cataract. *Mailing Add:* Inst of Biol Sci Oakland Univ Rochester MI 48063

REDDY, WILLIAM JOHN, b Boston, Mass, Aug 10, 26; m 55; c 4. BIOCHEMISTRY, ENDOCRINOLOGY. *Educ:* Harvard Univ, AB, 49, MS, 57, ScD(biochem), 60. *Prof Exp:* Chemist, Endocrine Lab, Peter Bent Brigham Hosp, Boston, 49-60; res assoc med, Harvard Med Sch, 60-61, res assoc biol chem, 61-64, assoc, 64-68; dir chem dept, St Vincent Hosp, Worcester, Mass, 68-70; PROF MED, SCH MED, UNIV ALA, BIRMINGHAM, 70- *Concurrent Pos:* Nat Inst Arthritis & Metab Dis res grants, 61-73; Boston Med Soc grant, 66-67; Am Heart Asn grant, 67-71; dir endocrine lab, Peter Bent Brigham Hosp, 55-62, consult, Dept Psychiat, 55-68, assoc staff med, 60-68; dir, Baker Res Lab, New Eng Deaconess Hosp, 64-68; mem bd dirs, St Vincent Res Found, Worcester, 67-73; mem exec comt, Ala Diabetes Asn, 71- *Mem:* AAAS; Am Chem Soc; Am Soc Biol Chem; Am Physiol Soc; fel Am Inst Chem. *Res:* Mechanism of action of hormones. *Mailing Add:* Univ of Ala Sch of Med 1919 Seventh Ave S Birmingham AL 35233

REDDY, WILLIAM L, b Albany, NY, Dec 15, 38; div; c 1. TOPOLOGY. *Educ:* Siena Col, BS, 60; Syracuse Univ, MA, 62, PhD(math), 64. *Prof Exp:* Asst prof math, Webster Col, 64-65 & State Univ NY Albany, 67-68; from asst prof to assoc prof, 68-75, chmn dept, 74 & 77-80, assoc dir, Grad Summer Sch, 76-79, PROF MATH, WESLEYAN UNIV, 75-, ACTG CHMN, COMPUT CTR, 80- *Concurrent Pos:* Mem, Inst Advan Study, 69. *Mem:* AAAS; Math Asn Am; Am Math Soc. *Res:* Branched coverings; topological dynamics. *Mailing Add:* Dept of Math Wesleyan Univ Middletown CT 06457

REDEI, GYORGY PAL, b Vienna, Austria, June 14, 21; m 53; c 1. GENETICS, PLANT PHYSIOLOGY. *Educ:* Magyarovar Acad Agr, Hungary, dipl, 48; Univ Agr Sci, Hungary, dipl, 49; Hungarian Acad Sci, CSc, 55. *Prof Exp:* Res asst, Nat Inst Plant Breeding, Magyarovar, Hungary, 48, Inst Genetics, Hungarian Acad Sci, 49 & Agr Exp Sta, Kisvarda, 50; res adminr, Ministry Agr, Budapest, 51; res assoc, Inst Genetics, Hungarian Acad Sci, 52-56; from asst prof to assoc prof, 57-69, PROF GENETICS, UNIV MO-COLUMBIA, 69- *Concurrent Pos:* Grants, NSF, 59, 61, 63, 65 & 69, NIH, 63 & 64, Atomic Energy Comn, 66, 67 & 68, NATO, 75 & 79 & Environ Protection Agency, 79 & 80. *Mem:* Genetics Soc Am. *Res:* Physiological genetics of Arabidopsis; thiamine auxotrophy; regulation of gene activity by metabolites and antimetabolites; genetics of organelles; mutation. *Mailing Add:* Dept of Agron Univ of Mo Columbua MO 65201

REDEKER, ALLAN GRANT, b Lincoln, Nebr, Sept 10, 24; m 50; c 3. MEDICINE. *Educ:* Northwestern Univ, BS, 49, MD, 52. *Prof Exp:* From instr to assoc prof, 58-69, PROF MED, UNIV SOUTHERN CALIF, 69- *Concurrent Pos:* Schweppe Found res fel, Sch Med, Univ Southern Calif, 54-56; Bank of Am-Giannini Found res fel, 56-57; Bank of Am-Giannini Found traveling res fel, Minn, London & Malmo Clins, Sweden, 57; Lederle med fac award, 59-62; USPHS career develop award, 62-69; mem attend staff, Los Angeles County Hosp, 55- & Rancho Los Amigos Hosp. *Mem:* Am Fedn Clin Res; Am Soc Clin Invest; Am Asn Study Liver Dis (pres, 71); Int Soc Study Liver; Asn Am Physicians. *Res:* Hepatic physiology and diseases of the liver; bilirubin and pyrrole pigment metabolism. *Mailing Add:* Liver Unit Ranch Los Amigos Hosp 7601 E Imperial Downey CA 90242

REDENTE, EDWARD FRANCIS, b Derby, Conn, Feb 18, 51; m 73; c 1. MINED LAND RECLAMATION, PLANT ECOLOGY. *Educ:* Western Mich Univ, BA, 72; Colo State Univ, MS, 74, PhD(range ecol), 80. *Prof Exp:* Environ engr, Utah Int Inc, 74-76; res assoc, 76-79, instr, 79-80, ASST PROF MINED LAND RECLAMATION, RANGE SCI DEPT, COLO STATE UNIV, 80- *Concurrent Pos:* Consult, Thorne Ecol Inst, 76-77, Colo State Dept Natural Resources, 80-81; prin investr, Oil Shale Reclamation Proj, US Dept Energy, 80- *Mem:* Am Soc Range Mgt; Soil Conserv Soc Am; Sigma Xi. *Res:* Primary and secondary successional processes that occur on arid and semiarid land disturbed by energy development; determine effects of revegetation practices on rate and direction of plant succession and interaction between succession and soil microbial processes. *Mailing Add:* Dept Range Sci Colo State Univ Ft Collins CO 80523

REDER, FRIEDRICH H, b Garsten, Austria, Dec 9, 19; US citizen; m 52; c 1. PHYSICS. *Educ:* Graz Univ, MS, 47, PhD(physics), 49. *Prof Exp:* Asst physics, Graz Univ, 48-52; physicist, Frequency Control Div, US Army Electronics Labs, 53-62, sr scientist, Inst Explor Res, 62-71, chief antennas & geophys res area, Electronics Technol & Devices Lab, 71-73, chief commun res technol area, Commun/ADP Lab, 73-78; res physicist, Ctr Commun Systs, Commun Res & Develop Command, 78-80; CONSULT, OMEGA RADIO NAVIGATION, 80- *Concurrent Pos:* UNESCO fel plasma physics, Radiation Lab Electronics, Mass Inst Technol, 50-51; US Indust fel, 51; mem laser comt, US Dept Defense, 61-62. *Honors & Awards:* Res & Develop Ann Achievement Award, Army Materiel Command, 70. *Res:* Atomic frequency, time control and propagation of very low frequency electromagnetic waves. *Mailing Add:* 480 Marvin Dr Long Branch NJ 07740

REDETZKI, HELMUT M, b Memel, Lithuania, Sept 23, 21; nat US; m 57. PHARMACOLOGY. *Educ:* Univ Hamburg, MD, 48; Am Bd Med Toxicol, dipl, 75. *Prof Exp:* Intern, Med Sch, Univ Hamburg, 47-48, res assoc biochem, 48-51, res assoc virol, Poliomyelitis Res Inst, 51-52; resident internal med, St George Hosp, Hamburg, Ger, 52-56; instr pharmacol, Univ Tex Med Br Galveston, 59-60, asst prof, 60-61; assoc prof, Sch Med, La State Univ, New Orleans, 61-66, prof 66-68; PROF PHARMACOL & HEAD DEPT, SCH MED, LA STATE UNIV, SHREVEPORT, 68- *Concurrent Pos:* McLaughlin Found fel, Tissue Metab Res Lab, Univ Tex Med Br Galveston, 56-59. *Honors & Awards:* Dehnecke Medal & Award, Univ Hamburg, 55; H M Hub Cotton Faculty Excellence Award, 75. *Mem:* fel Am Acad Clin Toxicol; Soc Exp Biol & Med; Am Heart Asn; fel Am Col Physicians; Am Soc Clin Pharmacol & Therapeut. *Res:* Alcohol metabolism; cancer chemotherapy; drug-enzyme interactions. *Mailing Add:* Dept of Pharmacol & Therapeut La State Univ Sch of Med Shreveport LA 71130

REDFEARN, PAUL LESLIE, JR, b Sanford, Fla, Oct 5, 26; m 49; c 2. BRYOLOGY. *Educ:* Fla Southern Col, BS, 48; Univ Tenn, MS, 49; Fla State Univ, PhD, 57. *Prof Exp:* Instr bot, Univ Fla, 50-51; PROF LIFE SCI, SOUTHWEST MO STATE UNIV, 57- *Concurrent Pos:* Res assoc, Mo Bot Garden, 74. *Mem:* Fel AAAS; Am Bryol & Lichenological Soc (pres, 71-73); Ecol Soc Am; Am Soc Plant Taxonomists. *Res:* Taxonomy and ecology of bryophytes. *Mailing Add:* Dept of Life Sci Southwest Mo State Univ Springfield MO 65802

REDFERN, ROBERT EARL, b Blackburn, Ark, July 29, 29; m 55; c 4. ENTOMOLOGY. *Educ:* Univ Ark, BS, 59, MS, 61. *Prof Exp:* Entomologist, Fruit & Veg Res Br, Ind, 60-62, entomologist-in-charge, Pesticide Chem Res Br, Tex, 63-68, Md, 68-72, chief biol eval chem lab, 72-74, RES ENTOMOLOGIST, BIOL EVAL CHEM LAB, AGR ENVIRON QUAL INST, USDA, 74- *Mem:* Entom Soc Am. *Res:* Insects affecting deciduous fruits; primary screening of juvenile and molting hormones. *Mailing Add:* Sci & Educ Admin Beltsville Agr Res Ctr-East Beltsville MD 20705

REDFIELD, ALFRED CLARENCE, b Philadelphia, Pa, Nov 15, 90; m 22; c 3. OCEANOGRAPHY, PHYSIOLOGY. *Educ:* Harvard Univ, BS, 14, PhD(zool), 17. *Hon Degrees:* PhD, Univ Oslo, 56; DSc, Lehigh Univ, 65; Mem Univ Nfld, 67 & Univ Alaska, 71. *Prof Exp:* Asst prof physiol, Univ Toronto, 19-20; from asst prof to prof, 21-57, dir biol labs, 34-35, chmn dept biol, 35-38, EMER PROF PHYSIOL, HARVARD UNIV, 57- *Concurrent Pos:* Sr biologist, Woods Hole Oceanog Inst, 30-38, trustee, 36-64, res assoc, 38-40, assoc marine biol, 40-42, sr biologist, 42-53, assoc dir, 42-56, sr oceanogr, 53-56, emer sr oceanogr, 56- Managing ed, Biol Bull, 30-42; trustee, Marine Biol Lab, Woods Hole, 30-53; lectr, Comn Relief Belg Educ Found, 31; trustee, Bermuda Biol Sta, 44-, pres, 62-66; chmn, Nat Resources Coun, 46-48, hon mem, 48- Consult, Bur Ships, US Dept Navy, 42-43, US Weather Bur, 54-55, Beach Erosion Bd, 55, Creole Petrol Corp, 55 & Univ Minn, 56. *Honors & Awards:* Agassiz Medal, Nat Acad Sci, 56. *Mem:* Nat Acad Sci; Am Acad Arts & Sci; Am Physiol Soc (secy, 29-30); Ecol Soc Am (vpres, 45, pres, 46); Am Soc Limnol & Oceanog (pres, 56). *Res:* Ecology; tides; salt marshes. *Mailing Add:* PO Box 106 Woods Hole MA 02543

REDFIELD, ALFRED GUILLOU, b Boston, Mass, Mar 11, 29; m 60; c 3. PHYSICAL BIOCHEMISTRY. *Educ:* Harvard Univ, BA, 50; Univ Ill, MA, 52, PhD(physics), 53. *Prof Exp:* NSF fel, Harvard Univ, 53-54; univ fel appl sci, 54-55; physicist, Watson Lab, IBM Corp, 55-71; PROF PHYSICS & BIOCHEM, BRANDEIS UNIV, 72-, PROF OF ROSENSTIEL BASIC MED SCI RES CTR, 77- *Concurrent Pos:* Assoc, Columbia Univ, 55-61, adj asst prof, 61-63, adj prof, 63-71; vis physicist, Atomic Energy Comn, Saclay, France, 60-61; Miller Miller vis prof, Univ Ill, Urbana, 61; mem corp, Woods Hole Oceanog Inst, 64-; vis physicist, Univ Calif, Berkeley, 70-71, NSF sr fel, 71-72; Little vis prof, Mass Inst Technol, 72; staff mem, Rosensteil Ctr Basic Med Res, Brandeis Univ, 72- *Mem:* Fel Am Phys Soc; Am Soc Biol Chemists; Am Chem Soc. *Res:* Nuclear magnetic resonance and relaxation; protein catalysis and electronic structure; superconductivity. *Mailing Add:* Dept of Physics Brandeis Univ Waltham MA 02154

REDFIELD, DAVID, b New York, NY, Sept 20, 25; m 50; c 2. OPTOELECTRONIC MATERIALS, SOLAR ENERGY. *Educ:* Univ Calif, Los Angeles, AB, 48; Univ Md, MS, 53; Univ Pa, PhD(physics), 56. *Prof Exp:* Electronic scientist, Nat Bur Standards, 49-52; sr res physicist, Union Carbide Corp, 55-64; assoc prof elec eng, Columbia Univ, 64-67; RES PHYSICIST, RCA CORP, 67- *Mem:* AAAS; fel Am Phys Soc; sr mem Inst Elec & Electronics Engrs; Fedn Am Scientists. *Res:* Optical and electronic properties of solids; effects of surfaces, defects; optical and transport properties of disordered semiconductors; solar energy. *Mailing Add:* RCA Labs Princeton NJ 08540

REDFIELD, JOHN A(LDEN), b Orange, NJ, Mar 18, 33; m 54; c 3. NUCLEAR ENGINEERING. *Educ:* Univ Cincinnati, BS, 55; Univ Pittsburgh, MS, 60, PhD(chem eng), 63. *Prof Exp:* Assoc engr, 57-59, from engr to sr engr, 59-66, fel engr, 66-69, adv engr, 69-71, mgr thermal-hydraulic develop, 71-73, mgr A4W reactor eng, 73-75, mgr LWBR technol, 75-77, mgr reactor technol, 77-78, mgr advan water breeder, 78, MGR LIGHT WATER BREEDER REACTOR, BETTIS ATOMIC POWER LAB, WESTINGHOUSE ELEC CORP, 78- *Mem:* Am Inst Chem Engrs; Am Nuclear Soc; Inst Elec & Electronics Engrs. *Res:* Heat transfer; fluid flow; systems analysis; reactor plant kinetics; dynamics of physical systems. *Mailing Add:* Bettis Atomic Power Lab PO Box 79 Westinghouse Elec Corp West Mifflin PA 15122

REDFIELD, WILLIAM DAVID, b Portland, Ore, July 26, 15; m 41, 67; c 2. MICROBIOLOGY, ORGANIC GEOCHEMISTRY. *Educ:* Univ Calif, Los Angeles, AB, 39, MA, 40; Scripps Inst Oceanog, PhD(microbiol), 45. *Prof Exp:* Asst bact, Univ Calif, Los Angeles, 39-40; bacteriologist, Hunt Foods, Calif, 41-43; res asst microbiol, Scripps Inst Oceanog, Univ Calif, San Diego, 43-45, res assoc, 45-47; res microbiologist, 47-59, sr res biochemist, 59-66, SR RES ASSOC, CHEVRON OIL FIELD RES CO, 66- *Mem:* AAAS; Soc Gen Microbiol; Am Soc Microbiol; Soc Indust Microbiol; Geochem Soc; fel Am Acad Microbiol. *Res:* Geomicrobiology; petroleum microbiology; organic geochemistry. *Mailing Add:* Chevron Oil Field Res Co PO Box 446 La Habra CA 90631

REDFORD, JOHN W B, b Victoria, BC, Aug 7, 28. REHABILITATION MEDICINE. *Educ:* Univ BC, BA, 49; Univ Toronto, MD, 53; Mayo Clin & Mayo Found, MS, 58; Am Bd Phys Med & Rehab, dipl, 62. *Prof Exp:* From instr to asst prof phys med & rehab, Sch Med, Univ Wash, 58-63; prof & chmn dept, Med Col Va, 63-67; prof rehab med & dir sch, Univ Alta, 67-72, chmn dept phys med & rehab, Univ Hosp, 67-74; PROF REHAB MED & CHMN DEPT, UNIV KANS MED CTR, KANSAS CITY, 74- *Mem:* Can Asn Phys Med & Rehab; AMA; Am Acad Phys Med & Rehab; Am Cong Rehab Med. *Mailing Add:* A Bldg Univ of Kans Med Ctr Rainbow Blvd at 39th St Kansas City KS 66103

REDGATE, EDWARD STEWART, b Yonkers, NY, Mar 13, 25; m 54; c 3. NEUROPHYSIOLOGY, NEUROENDOCRINOLOGY. *Educ:* Bethany Col, BS, 49; Univ Minn, MS, 52, PhD(physiol), 54. *Prof Exp:* Asst, Univ Minn, 49-54; instr, Western Reserve Univ, 57-59, asst prof physiol, 59-62; ASSOC PROF PHYSIOL, SCH MED, UNIV PITTSBURGH, 62- *Concurrent Pos:* Fel neurophysiol, Univ Minn, 55-56; USPHS fel, Western Reserve Univ, 56-57. *Mem:* Am Physiol Soc; Endocrine Soc. *Res:* Brain stem regulations; cardiovascular, respiratory and autonomic nervous systems; viscera; norephinephrine; aldosterone; physiology of the hypothalamus; neural control of adrenocorticotropic hormone release; x-irradiation and electroencephalographic analysis. *Mailing Add:* Dept of Physiol Univ of Pittsburgh Sch of Med Pittsburgh PA 15261

REDHEAD, PAUL AVELING, b Brighton, Eng, May 25, 24; m 48; c 2. SURFACE PHYSICS, VACUUM PHYSICS. *Educ:* Cambridge Univ, BA, 44, MA, 49, PhD, 69. *Prof Exp:* Sci officer electronics, Brit Admiralty, 44-47; from res officer to prin res officer, 47-71, dir prog planning & anal, 70-72, dir gen planning, 72-73, DIR, DIV PHYSICS, NAT RES COUN CAN, 73-, GROUP DIR, PHYS & CHEM SCI LABS, 74-, CHMN, COMT DIRS, 81- *Concurrent Pos:* Ed, J Vacuum Sci & Technol, 69-74. *Honors & Awards:* Welch Award, Am Vacuum Soc, 75. *Mem:* Fel Am Phys Soc; Can Asn Physicists; fel Inst Elec & Electronics Engrs; hon mem Am Vacuum Soc (pres, 68); fel Royal Soc Can. *Res:* Electron physics; surface science; mass spectrometry. *Mailing Add:* 1958 Norway Crescent Ottawa ON K1H 5N7 Can

REDHEFFER, RAYMOND MOOS, b Chicago, Ill, Apr 17, 21; m 51; c 1. MATHEMATICS. *Educ:* Mass Inst Technol, SB, 43, SM, 46, PhD(math), 48. *Prof Exp:* Mem staff, Radiation Lab, Mass Inst Technol, 42-46, res assoc, Lab Electronics, 46-48; instr math, Harvard Univ, 48-50; from instr to assoc prof, 50-60, PROF MATH, UNIV CALIF, LOS ANGELES, 60- *Concurrent Pos:* Pierce fel, Harvard Univ, 48-50; NSF sr fel, Univ Gottingen, 56-57; Fulbright fel, Univ Vienna, 56-57; Fulbright res fel, Univ Hamburg, 61-62, guest prof, 66; guest lectr, Tech Univ Berlin, 62; guest prof, Univ Karlsruhe, 72; Humboldt Found sr US scientist award, 76. *Mem:* AAAS; Math Asn Am; Am Math Soc; sr mem Inst Elec & Electronics Engrs. *Res:* Differential and integral inequalities. *Mailing Add:* Dept of Math Univ of Calif Los Angeles CA 90024

REDI, MARTHA HARPER, b Bryn Mawr, Pa; m 63; c 1. PHYSICS, BIOPHYSICS. *Educ:* Mass Inst Technol, BS, 64; Rutgers Univ, MS, 66, PhD(physics), 69. *Prof Exp:* Fel physics, Rutgers Univ, 69-70; fel quantum chem, 76-77, VIS RES FEL PHYSICS, PRINCETON UNIV, 77- *Concurrent Pos:* NIH vis res fel, 77- *Mem:* Am Phys Soc; AAAS. *Res:* Biophysics of electron transfer; hemoglobin action; superconductivity; magnetic interactions. *Mailing Add:* Dept of Physics Princeton Univ Princeton NJ 08544

REDI, OLAV, b Tallinn, Estonia, May 29, 38; US citizen; m 63; c 1. EXPERIMENTAL ATOMIC PHYSICS. *Educ:* Rensselaer Polytech Inst, BS, 60; Mass Inst Technol, PhD(physics), 65. *Prof Exp:* Res assoc physics, Princeton Univ, 64-66, from instr to asst prof, 66-71; MEM FAC PHYSICS, NY UNIV, 71- *Mem:* Am Phys Soc. *Res:* Nuclear moments and isotope shifts; atomic level-crossing spectroscopy; optical and atomic beam hyperfine structure studies. *Mailing Add:* 6 Berrien Ave Princeton Junction NJ 08550

REDICK, THOMAS FERGUSON, b Youngstown, Ohio, Oct 20, 21; m 52. PHYSIOLOGY. *Educ:* Miami Univ, BA, 48; Univ Pittsburgh, MS, 52, PhD, 55. *Prof Exp:* Asst zool, Univ Pittsburgh, 50-52; jr fel, Mellon Inst, 52-54; from instr to asst prof physiol, Sch Med, Univ Pittsburgh, assoc prof, State Univ NY, 63-66; PROF PHYSIOL & BIOL, FROSTBURG STATE COL, 66- *Concurrent Pos:* Dept Health, Educ & Welfare fel neuropharmacol, Leech Farm Vet Hosp, Pittsburgh, 62-63; vis investr, Radiobiol Lab, US Bur Fisheries, NC, 70-72; mem staff marine sci, Univ La Laguna, Spain, 71-72, res prof, 72- res fel, NASA Langley Field, 77. *Mem:* Soc Syst Zool. *Res:* Mollusks; cardiovascular research; neuropharmacology in tunicates. *Mailing Add:* Beall's Lane Frostburg MD 21532

REDIKER, ROBERT HARMON, b Brooklyn, NY, June 7, 24; m 80; c 2. ELECTROOPTIC DEVICES, SEMICONDUCTOR LASERS. *Educ:* Mass Inst Technol, BS, 47, PhD(physics), 50. *Prof Exp:* Asst physics, Mass Inst Technol, 48-50, res assoc, 50-51, mem staff, Lincoln Lab, 51-52; res assoc, Ind Univ, 52-53; mem staff, 53-57, asst group leader, 57-59, group leader appl physics, 59-66, prof, 66-76, assoc head, Optics Div, 70-72, head, 72-80, ADJ PROF DEPT ELEC ENG, MASS INST TECHNOL, 76-, SR STAFF,

LINCOLN LAB, 80- *Concurrent Pos:* Mem Nat Acad Sci evaluation panel for Nat Bur Standards. *Honors & Awards:* David Sarnoff Award, Inst Elec & Electronics Engrs, 69. *Mem:* Fel Am Phys Soc; Optical Soc Am; fel Inst Elec & Electronics Engrs. *Res:* Solid state devices; optics; guided-wave optics; semiconductor lasers and light emitters; semiconductor devices. *Mailing Add:* Lincoln Lab Mass Inst Technol PO Box 73 Lexington MA 02173

REDIN, ROBERT DANIEL, b Rockford, Ill, Jan 18, 28. SOLID STATE PHYSICS. *Educ:* Iowa State Univ, BS, 52, MS, 55, PhD(physics), 57. *Prof Exp:* Asst physics, Iowa State Univ, 54-57; physicist, Electronics Lab, US Dept Navy, 57-62; PROF PHYSICS, SDAK SCH MINES & TECHNOL, 62- *Mem:* Am Asn Physics Teachers; Am Soc Eng Educ; Sigma Xi. *Res:* Thermal conductivity in solids; semiconductors; transport properties of solids; quantum size effect in thin films. *Mailing Add:* SDak Sch of Mines & Technol Rapid City SD 57701

REDINBO, GEORGE ROBERT, b Lafayette, Ind, July 11, 39; m 61; c 3. ELECTRICAL ENGINEERING. *Educ:* Purdue Univ, BS, 62, MS, 66, PhD(elec eng), 70. *Prof Exp:* Instr elec eng, Purdue Univ, 65-70; asst prof, Univ Wis-Madison, 70-76; ASSOC PROF ELEC & SYSTS ENG, RENSSELAER POLYTECH INST, 76- *Concurrent Pos:* Trustee, Nat Electronics, Inc, 72-; NASA-Am Soc Eng Educ fel, Goddard Space Flight Ctr, 72; NSF fel, Univ Wis, 72-73. *Mem:* Inst Elec & Electronics Engrs; Soc Indust & Appl Math; Am Soc Eng Educ. *Res:* Algebraic coding theory; communication theory; generalized transforms; digital filtering in communications systems. *Mailing Add:* Dept of Elec & Systs Eng Rensselaer Polytech Inst Troy NY 12181

REDINGER, RICHARD NORMAN, b Essex Co, Ont, Feb 18, 38; m 65; c 4. GASTROENTEROLOGY. *Educ:* Univ Western Ont, BA, 60, MD, 62; FRCP(C), 68 & 75. *Prof Exp:* Res assoc med, Sch Med, Boston Univ, 68-71; mem med staff, Univ Hosp, 72-78, dir gastrointestinal lab, 73-78; chief gastrointestinal res, Univ Hosp, 78-81, assoc prof dept med, Boston Univ Med Ctr, 78-81, assoc vis physician & assoc mem, Evans Mem, 78-81; PROF MED, DEPT MED, UNIV LOUISVILLE, 81-, CHIEF DIGESTIVE DIS & NUTRIT, 81-, ASSOC PROF DEPT BIOCHEM, 81- *Concurrent Pos:* Consult gastrointestinal dis, Westminster Hosp, 71-; asst prof med, Univ Western Ont, 71, assoc prof, 75-78; Nat Inst Health res grant, 78-81. *Mem:* Can Med Asn; Can Soc Clin Invest; Am Fedn Clin Res; Am Gastroenterol Asn. *Res:* Hepato biliary research in human and nonhuman primate; effects of phenobarbital and cholesterol lowering agents on biliary lipid composition and gallstone formation and/or dissolution. *Mailing Add:* ACB-3rd Floor 530 S Jackson St Dept Med Louisville KY 40202

REDINGTON, RICHARD LEE, b Minneapolis, Minn, May 16, 33; m 57; c 1. PHYSICAL CHEMISTRY. *Educ:* Univ Minn, BA, 55; Univ Wash, PhD(phys chem), 61. *Prof Exp:* Res fel, Mellon Inst, 61-64; asst prof chem, Utah State Univ, 64-67; from asst prof to assoc prof, 67-73, PROF CHEM, TEX TECH UNIV, 73- *Mem:* Am Chem Soc; Optical Soc Am; Am Phys Soc. *Res:* Infrared spectroscopy; molecular structure. *Mailing Add:* Dept of Chem Tex Tech Univ Lubbock TX 79412

REDINGTON, ROWLAND WELLS, b Otego, NY, Sept 26, 24; m 47; c 2. SOLID STATE PHYSICS. *Educ:* Stevens Inst Technol, ME, 45; Cornell Univ, PhD(exp physics), 51. *Prof Exp:* Teaching asst, Cornell Univ, 46-51; physicist, 51-66, prog mgr, 66-76, BR MGR, GEN ELEC RES & DEVELOP CTR, 76- *Concurrent Pos:* Adj prof, Rensselaer Polytech Inst, 64-66. *Mem:* Am Phys Soc; Inst Elec & Electronics Engrs. *Res:* Electronic imaging devices; photoconductivity; photoemission; stereographic display; computed tomography. *Mailing Add:* Gen Elec Res & Develop Ctr PO Box 8 Schenectady NY 12301

REDISCH, WALTER, b Prague, Czech, Sept 26, 98; nat US; m 35; c 2. PHYSIOLOGY. *Educ:* Ger Univ, Prague, 22; Am Bd Internal Med, dipl, 42. *Prof Exp:* Res fel, 38-39, from asst to asst prof med, 40-52, assoc prof clin med, 53-78, RES PROF PHYSIOL, SCH MED, NY UNIV, 78- *Concurrent Pos:* Assoc attend physician, Hosp, NY Univ, 53-; vis physician & res assoc, Res Serv, Goldwater Mem Hosp; vis res prof, New York Med Col, 69-; assoc vis physician, Bellevue Hosp; chief circulation res unit, NY Med Col; consult, Vet Admin Hosp, New York. *Mem:* Geront Soc; Am Physiol Soc; Harvey Soc; AMA; Am Heart Asn. *Res:* Circulation. *Mailing Add:* 10 East End Ave New York NY 10021

REDISH, EDWARD FREDERICK, b New York, NY, Apr 1, 42; m 67; c 2. THEORETICAL NUCLEAR PHYSICS. *Educ:* Princeton Univ, AB63; Mass Inst Technol, PhD(physics), 68. *Prof Exp:* Fel, Ctr Theoret Physics, 68-70, asst prof, 70-74, ASSOC PROF PHYSICS, UNIV MD, COLLEGE PARK, 74- *Concurrent Pos:* Vis scientist, Saclay Nuclear Res Ctr, France, 73-74; Nat Acad Sci-Nat Res Coun sr resident res assoc, Goddard Space Flight Ctr, 77-78. *Mem:* AAAS; Sigma Xi; Am Phys Soc. *Res:* Many body theory of nuclear reactions; three body aspects of nuclear scattering problems; off-energy-shell effects in direct nuclear reactions. *Mailing Add:* Dept of Physics & Astron Univ of Md College Park MD 20742

REDISH, KENNETH ADAIR, b London, Eng, May 6, 26; m 50; c 7. COMPUTER SCIENCE. *Educ:* Univ London, BSc, 53. *Prof Exp:* Asst lectr math, Woolwich Polytech Inst Eng, 53-55; lectr, Battersea Col Adv Technol, 55-59; lectr comput, Univ Birmingham, 60-62, sr lectr, 62-67, dir comput serv, 64-67; ASSOC PROF APPL MATH, McMASTER UNIV, 67- *Mem:* Asn Comput Mach; fel Brit Comput Soc. *Res:* Numerical analysis. *Mailing Add:* Dept of Appl Math McMaster Univ Hamilton Can

REDLICH, DOROTHY VON, organic chemistry, biochemistry, see previous edition

REDLICH, FREDRICK CARL, b Vienna, Austria, June 2, 10; nat US; m 37, 55; c 2. PSYCHIATRY. *Educ:* Univ Vienna, MD, 35. *Prof Exp:* Intern, Allgem Krankenhaus, Vienna, 35-36; resident, Univ Psychiat Clin, Univ Vienna, 36-38; asst physician, State Hosp, Iowa, 38-40; resident, Neurol Unit, Boston City Hosp, 40-42; from instr to assoc prof psychiat, Sch Med, Yale Univ, 42-59, exec officer, 47-50, prof psychiat & chmn dept, 50-67, assoc provost med affairs & dean, 67-72, prof psychiat, Sch Med, 72-77, dir, Behav Sci Study Ctr, 73-77; ASSOC CHIEF OF STAFF FOR EDUC, VET ADMIN MED CTR, BRENTWOOD, 77-; PROF PSYCHIAT, UNIV CALIF, LOS ANGELES, 77- *Concurrent Pos:* Teaching fel, Harvard Med Sch, 41-42; dir, Conn Ment Health Ctr, 64-67; consult, NIMH & Off Surgeon Gen, US Army. *Mem:* Inst Med-Nat Acad Sci; Am Psychosom Soc; fel Am Psychiat Asn; Am Orthopsychiat Asn; AAAS. *Res:* Personality theory; social structure and mental disorder; scientific methodology in psychiatry. *Mailing Add:* Vet Admin Med Ctr Brentwood Wilshire & Sarvtelle Blvds Los Angeles CA 90073

REDLICH, MARTIN GEORGE, b Vienna, Austria, Dec 1, 28; US citizen. PHYSICS. *Educ:* Univ Calif, Berkeley, AB, 48; Princeton Univ, PhD(physics), 54. *Prof Exp:* Res asst physics, Princeton Univ, 54; proj assoc, Univ Wis-Madison, 54-56; res assoc, Washington Univ, 56-57; res, Mass Inst Technol, 57-59; res, 61-62, MEM NUCLEAR THEORY GROUP, LAWRENCE BERKELEY LAB, UNIV CALIF, 62- *Concurrent Pos:* NSF fel, 57-58. *Mem:* Am Phys Soc. *Res:* Theory of the structure of the nucleus. *Mailing Add:* Bldg 70A Lawrence Berkeley Lab Univ Calif Berkeley CA 94720

REDLICH, ROBERT WALTER, b Lima, Peru, Sept 20, 28; US citizen; m 60; c 2. ELECTRONIC ENGINEERING, ELECTROMAGNETISM. *Educ:* Rensselaer Polytech Inst, BS, 50, PhD(physics), 60; Mass Inst Technol, MS, 51. *Prof Exp:* Develop engr gyroscopes, Gen Elec Co, 51-52; res & develop engr inertial navig, US Army Ballistic Missiles Agency, 54-56; from asst to assoc prof elec eng, Clarkson Tech Univ, 60-65; sr res fel, Univ Sydney, 65-68; from assoc prof to prof, Ohio Univ, 68-75; CHIEF ENGR, GORMAN-REDLICH MFG CO, 74- *Concurrent Pos:* Consult, 79- *Res:* Electromagnetic theory, especially radiation from aerials and moving charges; electronics. *Mailing Add:* 9 Grand Park Blvd Athens OH 45701

REDLINGER, LEONARD MAURICE, b Keota, Iowa, Dec 4, 22; m 49; c 6. ENTOMOLOGY. *Educ:* Iowa Wesleyan Col, BS, 46; Kans State Col, MS, 47. *Prof Exp:* Lab instr zool & cur insect collection, Iowa Wesleyan Col, 43-46; entomologist, Mosquito Control Proj, Bur Entom & Plant Quarantine, USDA, Alaska, 47, Stored-Prod Insects Sect, 48-54 & Mkt Res Div, Agr Mkt Serv, 54-56; entomologist, Pfeffer & Son Warehouse Co, Tex, 56-60; sta leader, Stored-Prod Insects Br, Mkt Qual Res Div, 60-65, leader, Peanut & Southern Corn Insects Invests, 65-73, RES ENTOMOLOGIST, STORED-PROD INSECTS RES & DEVELOP LAB, CHEM CONTROL RES UNIT, USDA, 73- *Mem:* Entom Soc Am; Am Peanut Res & Educ Asn; Sigma Xi. *Res:* Applied and developmental research to improve existing and to devise new chemical methods of controlling or preventing insect infestations of post harvest agricultural commodities in the marketing channels. *Mailing Add:* 734 Beechwood Dr Savannah GA 31406

REDMAN, CHARLES EDWIN, b Pawtucket, RI, Aug 1, 31; m 53; c 4. BIOLOGY, STATISTICS. *Educ:* Univ Mass, BS, 54, MS, 56; Univ Minn, PhD(statist), 60. *Prof Exp:* Sr biometrician, 60-62, dept head statist, 62-64, asst head, 64-65, head statist & rec, 65-69, asst dir sci serv, 69-72, dir sci info, 72-80, DIR MED INFO SYSTS, ELI LILLY & CO, 80- *Mem:* Am Statist Asn; Biomet Soc; Drug Info Asn; Pharmaceut Mfrs Asn; Sigma Xi. *Res:* Population genetics and associated statistical design problems; design, analysis and interpretation of screening and physiology studies. *Mailing Add:* Eli Lilly & Co Dept M-756 307 E McCarty St Indianapolis IN 46206

REDMAN, COLVIN MANUEL, b Dominican Repub, Jan 26, 35; US citizen; m 65; c 3. BIOCHEMISTRY. *Educ:* McGill Univ, BS, 57; Univ Wis-Madison, PhD(physiol chem), 62. *Prof Exp:* Fel biochem, Univ Wis-Madison, 62-63 & Rockefeller Univ, 63-65; staff fel, Addiction Res Ctr, NIMH, Ky, 65-66, res biochemist, 67; assoc investr, 70-76, SR INVESTR, NY BLOOD CTR, 76- *Mem:* Am Soc Biol Chem; Am Soc Cell Biol; Harvey Soc; Am Chem Soc. *Res:* Role of the endoplasmic reticulum in protein synthesis and secretion; membrane structure and function. *Mailing Add:* NY Blood Ctr 310 E 67th St New York NY 10021

REDMAN, DONALD ROGER, b Eaton, Ohio, Jan 21, 36; m 61; c 3. VETERINARY MEDICINE, VETERINARY SURGERY. *Educ:* Ohio State Univ, BS, 58, DVM, 62, MS, 66, PhD(prev med), 73. *Prof Exp:* Clin instr, 62-73, asst prof, 72-76, ASSOC PROF PREV MED, OHIO AGR RES & DEVELOP CTR, 76- *Mem:* Am Vet Med Asn; Int Embryo Transfer Soc; Am Asn Swine Practitioners. *Res:* Developmental and immune response of porcine fetus exposed to viral agents; reproductive efficiency of domestic animals; embryo transfer techniques; enteric diseases of neonatal calves. *Mailing Add:* Dept of Vet Sci Ohio Agr Res & Develop Ctr Wooster OH 44691

REDMAN, KENNETH, b Melbourne, Wash, July 20, 06; m 32; c 2. PHARMACOGNOSY. *Educ:* Univ Wash, BS, 30; Univ Wis, PhD(pharmacog), 41. *Prof Exp:* Instr pharm, NDak Agr Col, 30-38, instr pharmacog, 38-39; asst, Univ Wis, 41; asst prof pharm, Univ Toledo, 41-42; prof mat med, NDak Agr Col, 42-47; prof pharm, Univ Ga, 47-49; dean sch pharm, Col Ozarks, 49-51; prof & head dept, 51-73, EMER PROF PHARMACOG, SDAK STATE UNIV, 73- *Honors & Awards:* Am Heart Asn Medal, 72. *Mem:* Am Pharmaceut Asn. *Res:* History of pharmacy; field trials with insecticides; plant chemistry. *Mailing Add:* Rte 3 Box 30 Brookings SD 57006

REDMAN, ROBERT SHELTON, b Fargo, NDak, Aug 1, 35; m 58. DENTISTRY, PATHOLOGY. *Educ:* SDak State Univ, *Educ:* Univ Minn, Minneapolis, BS & DDS, 59, MSD, 63; Univ Wash, PhD(exp path), 69; Am Bd Oral Path, cert, 73. *Prof Exp:* Clin asst prof oral path, Sch Dent, Univ Minn, Minneapolis, 63-64; instr oral biol, Sch Dent, Univ Wash, 68-69; assoc prof oral biol, Sch Dent, Univ Minn, Minneapolis, 69-75; asst oral pathologist, Vet Admin Hosp, Denver, Colo, 75-78; STAFF ORAL PATHOLOGIST & CHIEF, ORAL PATH RES LAB, VET ADMIN MED CTR, WASHINGTON, DC, 78- *Concurrent Pos:* Am Cancer Soc Clin fels, 62-64; Nat Inst Dent Res trainee path, Univ Wash, 64-68, Nat Inst Dent Res career develop award oral biol, 68-69; Nat Inst Dent Res career develop award, Sch Dent, Univ Minn, Minneapolis, 71-75; consult, Children's Orthop Hosp, Seattle, Wash, 66-69; assoc prof oral biol, Sch Dent, Univ Colo Med Ctr, Denver, 75-78; Vet Admin Res Career Prog Clin Investr, Vet Admin Hosp, Denver, Colo, 76-78. *Mem:* Am Dent Asn; Am Acad Oral Path; Int Asn Dent Res. *Res:* Salivary gland growth and development; morphogenesis of salivary gland neoplasms; etiology of tongue diseases; etiology of dental cares. *Mailing Add:* Dent Serv Vet Admin Med Ctr 50 Irving St NW Washington DC 20422

REDMAN, RUSSELL ORMOND, b Victoria, BC, June 16, 51; m 79. MOLECULAR RADIO ASTRONOMY, GALACTIC STRUCTURE. *Educ:* Univ Victoria, BSc, 74; Calif Inst Technol, PhD(astron), 82. *Prof Exp:* RES ASSOC, JET PROPULSION LAB, CALIF INST TECHNOL, 81- *Res:* Spectroscopy of interstellar molecules; dynamics of the interstellar medium. *Mailing Add:* Jet Propulsion Lab TR 1166 4800 Oak Grove Dr Pasadena CA 91109

REDMAN, WILLIAM CHARLES, b Washington, DC, June 19, 23; m 48; c 3. REACTOR PHYSICS, MAGNETOHYDRODYNAMICS. *Educ:* Georgetown Univ, BS, 43; Yale Univ, MS, 47, PhD(physics), 49. *Prof Exp:* Jr physicist, Dept Terrestrial Magnetism, Carnegie Inst & Nat Bur Standards, 43; asst instr physics, Yale Univ, 43-44; jr physicist, Manhattan Dist, Argonne Nat Lab, Univ Chicago, 44-46; asst instr physics, Yale Univ, 47-48; assoc physicist, Argonne Nat Lab, 49-54; pres, Fournier Inst Technol, 54-55; assoc physicist, 55-59, sr physicist, 59-63, assoc dir appl physics div, 63-72, sr physicist, 72-74, DEP DIR ENERGY CONVERSION PROGS, ARGONNE NAT LAB, 74- *Concurrent Pos:* Lectr, Fournier Inst Technol, 52-54. *Mem:* Fel Am Phys Soc; fel Am Nuclear Soc. *Res:* Physics of neutrons and nuclear reactors; instrumentation; environmental planning and impact, and energy conversion systems. *Mailing Add:* Argonne Nat Lab 9700 S Cass Ave Argonne IL 60439

REDMANN, ROBERT EMANUEL, b Jamestown, NDak, Nov 24, 41; m 63; c 4. PLANT ECOLOGY. *Educ:* Univ NDak, BA, 64; Univ Ill, Urbana, MS & PhD(bot), 68. *Prof Exp:* Asst prof, 68-72, assoc prof, 72-78, PROF PLANT ECOL, UNIV SASK, 78- *Mem:* AAAS; Sigma Xi; Ecol Soc Am. *Res:* Grassland ecosystem structure and function; plant carbon dioxide exchange; plant water relations; salt tolerance in plants; environmental impact studies. *Mailing Add:* Dept Plant Ecol Univ Sask Saskatoon SK S7H 0W0 Can

REDMON, JOHN KING, b Lexington, Ky, Nov 4, 20; m 67; c 5. ELECTRICAL ENGINEERING. *Educ:* Newark Col Eng, BS, 42; Stevens Inst Technol, MS, 49; Worcester Polytech Inst, MS, 70. *Prof Exp:* Sales engr, Westinghouse Elec Corp, 45-51, consult & appln engr, 53-60; from asst prof to assoc prof elec eng, Newark Col Eng, 60-70; PROF ELEC ENG, GRAD SCH, LEHIGH UNIV, 70-; educ adminr, Pa Power & Light Co, 70-81; CONSULT EDUC, REDMON ASSOCS, 81- *Concurrent Pos:* Consult, Pub Serv Elec & Gas Co, 61-66; adj prof, Northampton County Area Community Col, 75- *Mem:* Inst Elec & Electronics Engrs; Am Soc Eng Educ; Nat Soc Prof Engrs. *Res:* Application of power equipment to industrial use; electrical distribution and lightning protection; power systems and circuit analysis. *Mailing Add:* Redmon Assocs 915 S 14th St Allentown PA 18103

REDMON, MICHAEL JAMES, b Long Beach, Calif, Oct 3, 41; m 75. PHYSICAL CHEMISTRY, ATOMIC PHYSICS. *Educ:* Fla State Univ, BS, 63; Rollins Col, MS, 68; Univ Fla, PhD(chem), 73. *Prof Exp:* Res engr physics, Orlando Div, Martin Co, 63-67; asst prof, Valdosta State Col, 67-73; res assoc chem, Univ Tex, Austin, 74-77; res scientist chem physics, Columbus Labs, Battelle Mem Inst, 77-80; WITH CHEM DYNAMICS CORP, 80- *Concurrent Pos:* Res asst, Univ Fla, 68-74; Robert Welch Found fel, 75. *Mem:* Am Phys Soc; Am Chem Soc. *Res:* Atomic and molecular collisions; quantum chemistry; chemical physics. *Mailing Add:* Chem Dynamics Corp 1550 West Henderson Rd N140 Columbus OH 43220

REDMOND, BILLY LEE, b Franklin, Tenn, May 25, 42. ENTOMOLOGY, ELECTRON MICROSCOPY. *Educ:* Univ Tenn, Martin, BS, 64; Univ Ill, Urbana, MS, 67; Cornell Univ, PhD(zool), 71. *Prof Exp:* Lab instr zool, Univ Tenn, Martin, 64-65; NIH fel entom & zool, Ohio State Univ, 71-72; asst prof gen biol & anat, Otterbein Col, 72-73; asst prof, 73-80, ASSOC PROF BIOL, STATE UNIV NY NEW PALTZ, 80-, DIR, ELECTRON MICROSCOPY LAB, 77- *Concurrent Pos:* Ed, NAm Registry Electron Microscopy Courses, 80- *Mem:* Electron Micros Soc Am; Entom Soc Am; Acarological Soc Am. *Res:* Developmental morphology and fine structure of tissues, especially those of the arthropods; electron microscopy. *Mailing Add:* Dept of Biol State Univ NY New Paltz NY 12561

REDMOND, DONALD EUGENE, JR, b San Antonio, Tex, June 17, 39. BIOLOGICAL PSYCHIATRY, NEUROPHARMACOLOGY. *Educ:* Southern Methodist Univ, BA, 61; Baylor Col Med, MD, 68; Am Bd Psychiat & Neurol, cert, 77. *Prof Exp:* Intern, Ben Taub Hosp, 68-69; resident res, Ill State Psychiat Inst, 69-72; clin assoc, NIMH, 72-74; asst prof, 74-78, ASSOC PROF PSYCHIAT, SCH MED, YALE UNIV, 78- *Concurrent Pos:* Falk fel, Am Psychiat Asn, 70-71; mem fac biol sci training grant, NIH, 74-; Guggenheim Found grant, 77-81; NIMH grant, 78-81 & Nat Inst Drug Abuse grant, 79-84. *Mem:* Am Psychiat Asn; Am Psychosom Med Soc; Soc Neurosci; Am Soc Primatologists. *Res:* Biology of depression, anxiety, opioid drugs. *Mailing Add:* 34 Park St New Haven CT 06508

REDMOND, DONALD MICHAEL, b San Francisco, Calif, Feb 5, 48; m 77. MATHEMATICS, NUMBER THEORY. *Educ:* Univ Santa Clara, BS, 70; Univ Ill, MS, 73, PhD(math), 76. *Prof Exp:* ASST PROF MATH, SOUTHERN ILL UNIV, 77- *Mem:* Am Math Soc; Math Asn Am. *Res:* Analytic number theory, particularly the properties of Dirichlet series satisfy functional equation involving gamma factors. *Mailing Add:* Dept of Math Southern Ill Univ Carbondale IL 62901

REDMOND, DOUGLAS ROLLEN, b Upper Musquodoboit, NS, Aug 30, 18; m 43; c 3. FORESTRY. *Educ:* Univ NB, BScF, 49; Yale Univ, MF, 50, PhD(forest path), 54. *Prof Exp:* Prov forest pathologist, NS, 50-51; officer chg forest path invests, Sci Serv, Can Dept Agr, 51-57; chief forest res div, Forestry Br, Dept Northern Affairs & Nat Resources, 57-60; dir forest res br, Dept Forestry, 60-65, sci adv, 65-69, dir forestry rels, Dept Fisheries & Forestry, 69-71; dir forestry rels, Dept Environ, 71-75, dir, Nat Forestry Insts, 75-79; CONSULT FORESTRY, 79- *Concurrent Pos:* Hon lectr, Univ NB, 51-57; mem permanent comt, Int Union Forest Res Orgn, 61-71, vpres, 71-72. *Honors & Awards:* Fernow Award, Am Forestry Asn, 75. *Mem:* Can Inst Forestry (pres, 78-82); Commonwealth Forestry Asn. *Res:* Forest ecology. *Mailing Add:* 643 Tillbury Ave Ottawa ON K2A 0Z9 Can

REDMOND, JAMES RONALD, b Ohio, July 14, 28; m 49; c 2. COMPARATIVE PHYSIOLOGY. *Educ:* Univ Cincinnati, BS, 49; Univ Calif, Los Angeles, PhD(zool), 54. *Prof Exp:* Asst prof biol, Univ Fla, 56-62; assoc prof, 62-67, PROF ZOOL, IOWA STATE UNIV, 67- *Mem:* AAAS; Am Soc Zoologists; Am Physiol Soc. *Res:* Blood pigments; circulatory and respiratory physiology of invertebrates. *Mailing Add:* Dept Zool Iowa State Univ Ames IA 50011

REDMOND, JOHN LYNN, b Maple Creek, Sask, Sept 19, 30; m 62; c 2. PETROLEUM GEOLOGY. *Educ:* Univ Tulsa, BS, 53; Stanford Univ, MS, 62; Univ Ore, PhD(geol), 66. *Prof Exp:* Geologist, Marathon Oil Co, US, Can & Libya, 53-60; lectr, Univ Ore, 65; geologist, Tex Petrol Co, Colombia, 66-72; staff geologist Latin Am, Texaco, Inc, 72-75; VPRES GEOL, TREND EXPLOR LTD, 75- *Mem:* Am Asn Petrol Geol; Can Soc Petrol Geologists. *Res:* Structural geology; structural petrology; worldwide evaluation of geologic basins for their hydrocarbon potential. *Mailing Add:* Trend Explor Ltd 600 Capitol Life Ctr Denver CO 80203

REDMOND, JOHN PETER, b Camden, NJ, Aug 1, 25; m 50; c 4. PLASTICS CHEMISTRY. *Educ:* Cath Univ Am, BS, 50, MS, 55; Pa State Univ, PhD(fuel tech), 59. *Prof Exp:* Phys chemist, Chem Div, US Naval Res Lab, 51-55; asst, Pa State Univ, 55-59; sr chemist, Appl Physics Lab, Johns Hopkins Univ, 59-65; sr scientist, Gen Tech Corp, 65-66; res dir & vpres, Commonwealth Sci Corp, 66-69; RES ASSOC, RES DIV, AMP INC, 69- *Mem:* Am Chem Soc. *Res:* Chemical kinetics; heterogeneous catalysis; vapor deposition; mass spectrometry; plastics, injection and transfer molding; rheology studies; resin selection and compounding for electronic industry. *Mailing Add:* Res Div AMP Inc Box 3608 Harrisburg PA 17105

REDMOND, NINFA INDACOCHEA, pharmacology, toxicology, see previous edition

REDMOND, PETER JOHN, b Southampton, Eng, July 1, 29; US citizen; m 54; c 4. PHYSICS. *Educ:* Cooper Union, BEE, 51; Univ Birmingham, PhD(physics), 54. *Prof Exp:* Instr physics, Columbia Univ, 54-57; res physicist, Univ Calif, Berkeley, 57-59, assoc prof, Univ Calif, Santa Barbara, 59-63; mem tech staff physics, Defense Res Corp, 63-72, MEM TECH STAFF PHYSICS, GEN RES CORP, 72- *Concurrent Pos:* Fulbright scholar, 51-53; consult, Rand corp, 56-62 & Gen Elec Co, Tempo, Calif, 60-63. *Mem:* Am Phys Soc. *Res:* Atomic and molecular scattering; lasers; quantum field theory; nuclear physics; electromagnetic scattering theory. *Mailing Add:* 1809 Anapaca St Santa Barbara CA 93101

REDMOND, ROBERT F(RANCIS), b Indianapolis, Ind, July 15, 27; m 52; c 5. NUCLEAR ENGINEERING, ENERGY CONVERSION. *Educ:* Purdue Univ, BS, 50; Univ Tenn, MS, 55; Ohio State Univ, PhD(nuclear physics), 61. *Prof Exp:* Engr, Oak Ridge Nat Lab, 50-53; fel, Anal Physics Div, Battelle Mem Inst, 53-70; prof nuclear eng & chmn dept, 70-77, ASSOC DEAN, COL ENG, OHIO STATE UNIV, 77-, DIR ENG EXP STA, 77- *Concurrent Pos:* Mem bd trustees, Argonne Univs Asn, 72-80; mem, Ohio Power Siting Comn, 78- *Mem:* Am Nuclear Soc; Am Soc Eng Educ; Nat Soc Prof Engrs. *Res:* Nuclear and reactor physics and engineering; research engineering. *Mailing Add:* Col of Eng 2070 Neil Ave Ohio State Univ Columbus OH 43210

REDMORE, DEREK, b Horncastle, Eng, Aug 8, 38; m 65. ORGANIC CHEMISTRY. *Educ:* Univ Nottingham, BSc, 59, PhD(org chem), 62. *Prof Exp:* Res assoc chem, Wash Univ, 62-65; res chemist, 65-67, SECT LEADER ORG CHEM, TRETOLITE DIV, PETROLITE CORP, 67- *Mem:* Am Chem Soc; Royal Soc Chem. *Res:* Organic, organophosphorus, alicyclic and heterocyclic chemistry. *Mailing Add:* 300 Park Rd St Louis MO 63119

REDMOUNT, MELVIN B(ERNARD), b Lakewood, Pa, Oct 11, 26; m 52; c 3. CHEMICAL ENGINEERING, ECONOMICS. *Educ:* Pa State Univ, BChE, 48; Polytech Inst Brooklyn, MChE, 52. *Prof Exp:* Chem engr, Develop Dept, Tidewater Oil Co, 51-53; group leader & res chem engr, Columbia Univ, 53-57; resident supvr develop, Speer Carbon Co, 57-64, resident mgr develop, 64-66, mgr new prod com develop, 66-70, mgr planning, Airco Speer Carbon-Graphite Div, 70-74, DIR PLANNING, AIRCO SPEER CARBON-GRAPHITE DIV, AIRCO, INC, 74- *Mem:* Am Chem Soc; Am Inst Mining, Metall & Petrol Engrs. *Res:* Carbon; graphite; high temperature materials; continuous fermentation; minerals processing; economics analyses. *Mailing Add:* Airco Speer Div Airco Inc Theresia St St Marys PA 15857

REDNER, SIDNEY, b Hamilton, Can, Nov 10, 51; m 77. PHYSICS. *Educ:* Univ Calif, Berkeley, AB, 72; Mass Inst Technol, PhD(physics), 77. *Prof Exp:* Res assoc physics, Boston Univ, 77; fel, Univ Toronto, 77-78; vis asst prof, 78-79, ASST PROF PHYSICS, BOSTON UNIV, 79- *Mem:* Am Phys Soc. *Res:* Phase transitions and critical phenomena; percolation theory; polymers; computer simulations. *Mailing Add:* Dept of Physics Boston Univ Boston MA 02215

REDO, SAVERIO FRANK, b Brooklyn, NY, Dec 28, 20; m 48; c 2. SURGERY. *Educ:* Queens Col, NY, BS, 42; Cornell Univ, MD, 50; Am Bd Surg & Am Bd Thoracic Surg, dipl. *Prof Exp:* From intern to resident surg, 50-57, asst attend surgeon, 59-60, ASSOC ATTEND SURGEON & DIR DEPT PEDIAT SURG, NY HOSP, 60-; PROF SURG, MED COL, CORNELL UNIV, 73- *Concurrent Pos:* Ledyard fel, NY Hosp, 57-59; asst prof surg, Med Col, Cornell Univ, 59-61, clin assoc prof, 61- *Mem:* Soc Univ Surg; fel Am Col Surg; Am Acad Pediat; Am Fedn Clin Res; Am Surg Asn. *Res:* Etiology and methods of surgical management of peptic esophagitis and esophageal pathology; cardiovascular research, including development of an artificial heart and procedures for myocardial revascularization. *Mailing Add:* Dept of Surg Cornell Univ Med Col New York NY 10021

REDONDO, ANTONIO, b Guatemala City, Guatemala, Dec 10, 48; Span citizen; m 71; c 2. SURFACE SCIENCE. *Educ:* Utah State Univ, BSc, 71; Calif Inst Technol, MSc, 72, PhD(appl physics), 77. *Prof Exp:* Asst prof physics & surface sci, Univ Los Andes, Merida, Venezuela, 77-80; vis assoc, 80-81, RES ASSOC CHEM, CALIF INST TECHNOL, 81- *Mem:* Am Phys Soc; Am Chem Soc; Am Vacuum Soc. *Res:* Applications of quantum mechanics to the study of surfaces, interfaces and solids. *Mailing Add:* A A Noyes Lab 127-72 Calif Inst Technol Pasadena CA 91106

REDSHAW, PEGGY ANN, b Beardstown, Ill, Sept 4, 48. MICROBIAL GENETICS. *Educ:* Quincy Col, BS, 70; Ill State Univ, PhD(biol sci), 74. *Prof Exp:* Fel microbiol, Sch Med, St Louis Univ, 74-77; asst prof biol, Wilson Col, 77-80; MEM FAC, DEPT BIOL, AUSTIN COL, 80- *Concurrent Pos:* Primary researcher, Cottrell Col Sci grant, Res Corp, 78- *Mem:* Am Soc Microbiol; Genetics Soc Am; AAAS. *Res:* Genetics of streptomyces; response of developing microorganisms to chemical mutagens. *Mailing Add:* Dept Biol Austin Col Sherman TX 75090

REDWINE, LOWELL E, b Denison, Tex, Sept 1, 11; m 37; c 3. GEOLOGY. *Educ:* Univ Calif, Los Angeles, AB, 35, MA, 37, PhD(geol), 72. *Prof Exp:* Res fel oceanog, Scripps Inst, Univ Calif, 37-38; core analyst, Superior Oil Co, 38-43; geologist, Honolulu Oil Corp, 43-49, dist geologist, Calif Coastal Dist, 49-59, Great Basin Dist, 59-61; consult geologist, 61-64; geologist, Richfield Res Ctr, Atlantic Richfield Co, 64-66; res assoc explor geol, Res Ctr, Union Oil Co, Brea, 66-76, CONSULT GEOLOGIST, 76- *Mem:* AAAS; Am Asn Petrol Geol; Geol Soc Am. *Res:* Petroleum and structural geology; stratigraphy; sedimentology. *Mailing Add:* 2728 Loreto Ave Costa Mesa CA 92626

REDWINE, RICHARD H(ORACE), b Winston-Salem, NC, Feb 5, 38; m 61; c 2. CERAMICS ENGINEERING, MATERIALS SCIENCE. *Educ:* NC State Univ, BS, 59, MS, 60, PhD(ceramic eng), 63. *Prof Exp:* Res scientist, 63-72, sect chief, Physics & Chem Sect, Glass & Ceramic Res Dept, 67-69, sect chief, Glass Sci Dept, 70-72, dir glass & ceramic res dept, 72-73, eng dept mgr, Kimble Div, 73-74, prod supt borosilicate glass melting, 75-76, TECH DIR, KIMBLE DIV, OWENS-ILL TECH CTR, OWENS-ILL, INC, TOLEDO, 76- *Mem:* Am Ceramic Soc; Nat Inst Ceramic Engrs; Am Soc Testing & Mat; Brit Soc Glass Technol. *Res:* Physical properties of glass, glass-ceramic and ceramic materials with specific interest in microstructure versus property relationships; electrical properties of glass and glass-ceramic materials; borosilicate glasses; physical properties, melting and forming. *Mailing Add:* Owens-Ill Inc One Seagate Toledo OH 43666

REDWINE, ROBERT PAGE, b Raleigh, NC, Dec 3, 47. NUCLEAR PHYSICS, PARTICLE PHYSICS. *Educ:* Cornell Univ, BA, 69; Northwestern Univ, PhD(physics), 73. *Prof Exp:* Res assoc physics, Los Alamos Sci Lab, 73-74 & Univ Bern, 74-75; res assoc, Los Alamos Sci Lab, 75-77, staff scientist, 77-79; ASST PROF PHYSICS, MASS INST TECHNOL, 79- *Mem:* Am Phys Soc. *Res:* Intermediate energy nuclear and particle physics especially pion-nucleus interactions and weak interaction physics. *Mailing Add:* Dept Physics Mass Inst Technol Cambridge MA 02139

REDWOOD, R(ICHARD) G(EORGE), b Dorset, Eng, May 1, 36; Can citizen; m 68; c 2. CIVIL ENGINEERING, STRUCTURAL ENGINEERING. *Educ:* Bristol Univ, BSc, 57, PhD(civil eng), 64; Univ Toronto, MASc, 60. *Prof Exp:* Asst engr, Shawinigan Eng Co, 57-58 & W S Atkins & Assoc, 58-59; lectr civil eng, Bristol Univ, 64-65; from asst prof to assoc prof, 65-73, PROF CIVIL ENG, MCGILL UNIV, 74- *Mem:* Can Soc Civil Eng; fel Brit Inst Struct Eng; Brit Inst Civil Eng. *Res:* Structural engineering; behaviour and design of metal structures; numerical analysis. *Mailing Add:* Dept of Civil Eng 817 Sherbrooke St W Montreal PQ H3A 2K6 Can

REDWOOD, WILLIAM RAYMOND, b Glamorgan, Gt Brit, July 27, 42; m 70. BIOCHEMISTRY, BIOPHYSICS. *Educ:* Cambridge Univ, BA, 64, MA & PhD(membrane biophys), 67. *Prof Exp:* NIH res assoc biochem, Univ Va, 68-70; asst prof biochem, Col Med NJ, 70-75, assoc prof, 75-80, assoc prof med, 77-80; MEM FAC, SCH MED, JOHNS HOPKINS UNIV, 80- *Concurrent Pos:* NIH proj grant, Col Med NJ, 72- *Mem:* Am Physiol Soc; Am Soc Biol Sci; Biophys Soc; Fedn Am Socs Exp Biol. *Res:* Membrane biophysics; investigation of lipid-protein interactions; structure and function of biological membranes; diffusion; membrane changes in neoplasia. *Mailing Add:* Sch Med Johns Hopkins Univ 601 N Broadway Baltimore MD 21205

REE, ALEXIUS TAIKYUE, b Korea, Jan 26, 02; m 32; c 4. PHYSICAL CHEMISTRY. *Educ:* Kyoto Imp Univ, Japan, BS, 27, ScD(chem), 31. *Hon Degrees:* DSc, Seoul Nat Univ, 64, Sogang Univ, Seoul, 76, Korea Univ, Seoul, 79. *Prof Exp:* Instr chem, Kyoto Imp Univ, 31-36, from asst prof to prof, 36-45; prof chem & dean col lib arts & sci, Seoul Nat Univ, 45-48; res prof, 49-65, prof, 66-70, EMER PROF CHEM, UNIV UTAH, 70- *Concurrent Pos:* Distinguished prof, Korea Advan Inst Sci, Seoul, 73- *Honors & Awards:* First Order Civil Merit, Govt Repub Korea; Award, Korean Nat Acad, 60. *Mem:* Am Chem Soc; Am Phys Soc; Korean Chem Soc (pres, 46-48); Korean Nat Acad. *Res:* Chemical kinetics; catalysis; rheology; quantum chemistry; theory of liquids. *Mailing Add:* Dept of Chem Univ of Utah Salt Lake City UT 84112

REE, BUREN RUSSEL, b Bentley, Alta, Feb 15, 43; m 66; c 1. ORGANIC CHEMISTRY. *Educ:* Univ Alta, BSc, 64; Univ Ill, MS, 66, PhD(chem), 69. *Prof Exp:* Sr res chemist, 69-73, RES SPECIALIST, 3M CO, 73- *Mem:* Am Chem Soc. *Res:* Molecular weight modification in vinyl polymers. *Mailing Add:* 236-2D-06 3M Ctr 3M Co St Paul MN 55101

REE, FRANCIS H, b Kyoto, Japan, Sept 6, 36; US citizen. THEORETICAL PHYSICS. *Educ:* Univ Utah, BA, 57, PhD(physics), 60. *Prof Exp:* RES PHYSICIST, LAWRENCE LIVERMORE LAB, UNIV CALIF, 60- *Mem:* Am Phys Soc; Biophys Soc. *Res:* Classical statistical mechanics, thermodynamics; theoretical studies on thermodynamic and statistical mechanical properties of gases, liquids and solids; high pressure physics; quantum chemistry. *Mailing Add:* Lawrence Livermore Lab Univ of Calif Livermore CA 94551

REE, WILLIAM O(SCAR), b South Milwaukee, Wis, Mar 13, 13; m 48; c 1. CIVIL ENGINEERING. *Educ:* Univ Wis, BS, 35. *Prof Exp:* Draftsman, Bucyrus Erie Co, Wis, 29-31; draftsman, Soil Conserv Serv, USDA, 35-37, jr engr, SC, 37-38, proj supvr, 38-41, proj supvr, Okla, 41-54, proj supvr, Agr Res Serv, 54-64, res invest leader, 64-75; HYDRAUL ENG CONSULT, 75- *Mem:* Am Soc Agr Engrs; Am Soc Civil Engrs; Int Asn Hydraul Res. *Res:* Hydraulics; hydraulics of conservation structures, hydrology and sedimentology. *Mailing Add:* Box 96 Stillwater OK 74076

REEBER, ROBERT RICHARD, b Flushing, NY, Jan 22, 37; m 72; c 3. MATERIALS ENGINEERING, MINERAL PHYSICS. *Educ:* NY Univ, BE, 58, MS, 60; Ohio State Univ, PhD(indust mineral), 68. *Prof Exp:* Mat engr transistors, Radio Corp Am, Somerville, Mass, 59-60; mat engr ceramics, Aerospace Res Labs, 60-63, vis res assoc phase transformations, 63-69; asst prof mat sci, Mich State Univ, 69-70; asst prof metall eng, Arya-Mehr Indust Univ, 70-71; res assoc crystallog, T H Aachen, 72-73; sr res asst mineral, Cambridge Univ, 73-74; prog mgr geochem eng, Dept Energy, 76-81; MAT ENGR, ARMY RES OFF, 81- *Concurrent Pos:* Adj asst prof, Mich State Univ, 71-73; sr res Fulbright, Inst Crystallog, T H Aachen, Ger, 72; vis sr researcher, Electron Micros Inst, Fritz Haber Inst Max Planck Soc, Berlin, 75; vis researcher, Inorganic Mat Div, Nat Bur Standards, 78- *Mem:* Fel AAAS; fel Am Inst Chemists; Mineral Soc Am; Am Ceramic Soc; Am Soc Metals. *Res:* Crystalchemistry; thermalexpansion; phase transformations in solids; materials engineering; materials policy and planning; geothermal engineering. *Mailing Add:* Army Res Off PO Box 12211 Research Triangle Park NC 27709

REEBURGH, WILLIAM SCOTT, b Port Arthur, Tex, Feb 25, 40; m 63; c 3. CHEMICAL OCEANOGRAPHY. *Educ:* Univ Okla, BS, 61; Johns Hopkins Univ, MA, 64, PhD(oceanog), 67. *Prof Exp:* Res asst, Chesapeake Bay Inst, Johns Hopkins Univ, 61-68; asst prof, 68-72, assoc prof, 72-77, PROF MARINE SCI, INST MARINE SCI, UNIV ALASKA, 77- *Mem:* Am Chem Soc; Geochem Soc; Am Soc Limnol & Oceanog. *Res:* Physical and chemical properties of sea water; gases in natural waters; composition of interstitial waters, fluvial geochemistry, microbial ecology. *Mailing Add:* Inst Marine Sci Univ Alaska Fairbanks AK 99701

REECE, FLOYD N(ORMAN), b Earlton, Kans, May 19, 26; m 51; c 3. AGRICULTURAL ENGINEERING. *Educ:* Kans State Univ, BS, 52, MS, 59. *Prof Exp:* Exten engr, Kans State Univ, 56-62, asst prof agr eng, 62-66; res engr, USDA, 66-73, RES LEADER, USDA, 73- *Mem:* Am Soc Agr Engrs; Poultry Sci Asn. *Res:* Environmental engineering research with specific application to control of environment in poultry research and production facilities; research and development of use of solar energy in livestock production. *Mailing Add:* 716 Cypress Starkville MS 39759

REECE, JOE WILSON, b Elkin, NC, Mar 1, 35; m 55; c 2. MECHANICAL ENGINEERING, APPLIED MATHEMATICS. *Educ:* NC State Univ, BSNE, 57, MS, 61; Univ Fla, PhD(eng mech), 63. *Prof Exp:* Instr eng mech, NC State Univ, 58-61; from asst prof to assoc prof, 64-76, PROF MECH ENG, AUBURN UNIV, 76- *Concurrent Pos:* Dep dir, Div Oper Reactors, US Nuclear Regulatory Comn, 76-78; consult combustion eng, US Army, E I du Pont de Nemours & Co & US Nuclear Regulatory Comn. *Mem:* Soc Eng Educ; Am Soc Mech Engrs. *Res:* Inviscid unsteady flow; steam generator mechanics; reactor hydraulics. *Mailing Add:* Dept of Mech Eng Auburn Univ Auburn AL 36830

REECK, GERALD RUSSELL, b Tacoma, Wash, Dec 28, 45; m 67; c 2. BIOCHEMISTRY. *Educ:* Seattle Pac Col, Wash, BA, 67; Univ Wash, PhD(biochem), 71. *Prof Exp:* Res assoc develop biochem, Lab Nutrit & Endocrinol, Nat Inst Arthritis, Metab & Digestive Dis, NIH, Bethesda, Md, 71-74; asst prof, 74-78, ASSOC PROF BIOCHEM, KANS STATE UNIV, MANHATTAN, KANS, 78- *Res:* Structure and function of chromatin proteins, especially the nonhistone chromatin proteins; trypsin inhibitors. *Mailing Add:* Dept of Biochem Kans State Univ Manhattan KS 66506

REED, A THOMAS, b Anderson, Ind, Apr 10, 46. INORGANIC CHEMISTRY. *Educ:* Ball State Univ, Ind, BS, 69. *Prof Exp:* Asst city chemist, Anderson Munic Water Works, Anderson, Ind, 65-69; NSF grant chem, Univ Nebr, Lincoln, 75-76; MEM STAFF, DEPT CHEM, MIAMI UNIV, OXFORD, 76- *Mem:* Am Chem Soc; Am Crystallog Asn; Sigma Xi. *Res:* Crystal and molecular structure of metal-dicarboxylate including the synthesis of compounds, growth of single crystals and x-ray determination. *Mailing Add:* Dept of Chem Miami Univ Oxford OH 45056

REED, ADRIAN FARAGHER, b Terre Haute, Ind, Dec 22, 06; m 35. MEDICINE, ANATOMY. *Educ:* DePauw Univ, BA, 28; Cornell Univ, MA, 31, PhD(neuroanat), 33; Tulane Univ, MD, 43. *Prof Exp:* Asst neuroanat & gross anat, Med Col, Cornell Univ, 29-30, instr, 30-33; from instr to prof gross anat, Sch Med, Tulane Univ, 33-56; house physician, McLeod Infirmary, 56-60; assoc prof internal med, Sch Med, Tulane Univ, 60-62, prof, 62-68, clin prof, 68-77; head dept anat, 68-77, PROF ANAT, SCH MED, LA STATE UNIV, SHREVEPORT, 77- *Concurrent Pos:* Vis prof, Bowman Gray Sch Med, 45. *Mem:* Am Asn Anatomists; AMA. *Res:* Neuroanatomy; neurophysiology; autonomic nervous system; cerebrovascular system; migraine. *Mailing Add:* Dept of Anat La State Univ Sch of Med Shreveport LA 71130

REED, ALLAN HUBERT, b Youngstown, Ohio, Jan 4, 41; m 66; c 2. ELECTROCHEMISTRY, PHYSICAL CHEMISTRY. *Educ:* Thiel Col, AB, 63; Case Western Reserve Univ, MS, 64, PhD(phys chem), 68. *Prof Exp:* Res asst phys chem, Case Western Reserve Univ, 66-68; res chemist, Columbus Labs, Battelle Mem Inst, 68-73; eng scientist res div, AMP, Inc, 73-81; MGR RES, ELECTROCHEM, 81- *Mem:* Electrochem Soc; Am Chem Soc; Am Electroplaters Soc. *Res:* Electrode processes; batteries, electrodeposition of precious metals; electroforming; high-rate electrochemical processes; electrochemical synthesis; internal reflection spectroscopy. *Mailing Add:* 19 Centennial Dr Poland OH 44514

REED, BRUCE LORING, b Jackman, Maine, July 31, 34; m 60; c 4. GEOLOGY. *Educ:* Univ Maine, BA, 56; Wash State Univ, MS, 58; Harvard Univ, PhD(geol), 66. *Prof Exp:* GEOLOGIST, ALASKAN BR, US GEOL SURV, 62- *Mem:* Geol Soc Am; Asn Explor Geochem; Arctic Inst NAm; Soc Econ Geol; Am Geophys Union. *Res:* Geology of Alaska; economic geology and the structural control of ore deposits; tin commodity specialist; exploration geochemistry; mechanics of igneous intrusion; geochronology, chemistry and generation of batholiths in the circum-Pacific region. *Mailing Add:* US Geol Surv Alaska Pac Univ Gould Hall Univ Dr Anchorage AK 99504

REED, CHARLES ALLEN, b Portland, Ore, June 6, 12; m 51; c 3. ANTHROPOLOGY, ZOOLOGY. *Educ:* Univ Ore, BS, 37; Univ Calif, PhD(zool), 43. *Prof Exp:* Instr zool, Univ Ore, 36-37; asst, Univ Calif, 37-42, asst anat, Med Sch, 43; instr biol, Reed Col, 43-46; from instr to asst prof zool, Univ Ariz, 46-49; from asst prof to assoc prof, Col Pharm, Univ Ill, 49-61; assoc prof biol, Yale Univ & cur mammal & herpet, Peabody Mus, 61-66; prof anthrop & biol sci, Univ Ill, Chicago Circle, 66-67; actg head dept, 67-70, prof, 67-80, EMER PROF ANTHROP, UNIV ILL, CHICAGO CIRCLE, 80- *Concurrent Pos:* Mem, Univ Ore Archaeol Exped, Catlow Caves, 37, John Day Archaeol Exped, 46 & Univ Chicago Oriental Inst Prehist Proj, Iraq, 54-55, Iran, 60 & Turkey, 70; dir, Yale Prehist Exped, Nubia, 62-65; res assoc vert anat, Field Mus, 66- *Mem:* AAAS; Am Asn Phys Anthropologists; Am Anthrop Asn; Am Soc Zoologists; Soc Vert Paleont. *Res:* Origins of agriculture, human evolution; evolutionary anatomy; prehistory of Near East. *Mailing Add:* Dept of Anthrop Univ of Ill at Chicago Circle Chicago IL 60680

REED, CHARLES E(LI), b Findlay, Ohio, Aug 11, 13. CHEMISTRY, CHEMICAL ENGINEERING. *Educ:* Case Inst Technol, BS, 34; Mass Inst Technol, ScD(chem eng), 37. *Prof Exp:* Asst prof chem eng, Mass Inst Technol, 37-42; res assoc res lab, 42-45, eng mgr, Chem Div, 45-52, gen mgr, Silicone Prod Dept, 52-59 & Metall Prod Dept, 59-62, vpres & gen mgr, Chem & Metall Div, 62-68, vpres & group exec, Components & Mat Group, 68-71, SR V PRES CORP TECHNOL, GEN ELEC CO, 71- *Mem:* Nat Acad Eng; AAAS; Am Chem Soc; fel Am Inst Chem Engrs; Am Inst Chemists. *Res:* Colloid chemistry; high polymers; distillation. *Mailing Add:* Gen Elec Co 3135 Easton Turnpike Fairfield CT 06431

REED, CHARLES E, b Boulder, Colo, Mar 13, 22. INTERNAL MEDICINE, ALLERGY. *Educ:* Columbia Univ, MD, 45. *Prof Exp:* Intern, Sch Med, Univ Colo, 45-46; resident med, Roosevelt Hosp, 48-51; clin instr med, Med Sch, Univ Ore, 51-58, clin asst prof, 58-61; from asst prof to prof med, Univ Wis-Madison, 61-78; PROF MED MAYO GRAD SCH MED, UNIV MINN-ROCHESTER, 78- *Concurrent Pos:* Pvt pract, Ore, 51-61. *Mem:* Am Acad Allergy (pres, 76); Am Col Physicians; Am Asn Immunol; Am Fedn Clin Res; Cent Soc Clin Res. *Res:* Bronchial asthma; nonasthmatic allergic diseases of the lung. *Mailing Add:* Mayo Grad Sch Med Univ Minn Rochester MN 55901

REED, CHRISTOPHER ALAN, b Auckland, NZ, Feb 25, 47; m 70. INORGANIC CHEMISTRY. *Educ:* Auckland Univ, NZ, BSc, 68, MSc hon, 69, PhD(chem), 71. *Prof Exp:* Res assoc chem, Stanford Univ, 71-73; asst prof, 73-79, ASSOC PROF CHEM, UNIV SOUTHERN CALIF, LOS ANGELES, 79- *Mem:* Am Chem Soc; NZ Inst Chem. *Res:* Bioinorganic chemistry of the transition metals particularly the structure and the reactivity of hemes, oxygen carriers and cytochromes; organo-transition metal chemistry and homogeneous catalysis. *Mailing Add:* Dept Chem Univ Southern Calif Los Angeles CA 90007

REED, CLYDE F, b High Point, NC, Apr 30, 18; m 49; c 1. BOTANY. *Educ:* Loyola Col, Md, AB, 38; Johns Hopkins Univ, MA, 40; Harvard Univ, PhD(biol), 42. *Prof Exp:* Food chemist & bacteriologist, Canning Co Md, 42-47; prof biol, Morehead Univ, 47-50 & Baltimore Jr Col, 50-61; asst prof bot, Howard Univ, 61-63; res assoc, Agr Res Serv, USDA, Md, 64-65; prof biol, Coppin State Col, 65-79; RETIRED. *Concurrent Pos:* Prof biol, Gallaudet Col, 62-64; res botanist & plant explorer, USDA; fel bot, Smithsonian Inst. *Mem:* Bot Soc Am; Am Fern Soc; Am Soc Ichthyol & Herpet; Am Bryol & Lichenol Soc; Am Soc Plant Taxon. *Res:* Weeds of the world; agronomics; economic botany; herpetology; flora of Kentucky, Maryland, Delaware and the Virginias; serpentine floras; contributions of reed herbarium. *Mailing Add:* 10105 Harford Rd Baltimore MD 21234

REED, COKE S, b Austin, Tex, Mar 8, 40; m 61; c 1. MATHEMATICS. *Educ:* Univ Tex, BS, 62, MA, 65, PhD(math), 66. *Prof Exp:* Asst prof math, Ga Inst Tech, 66-67; asst prof, 67-75, assoc prof, 75-81, PROF MATH, AUBURN UNIV, 81- *Mem:* Am Math Soc. *Res:* Real variables; topological dynamics. *Mailing Add:* Dept of Math Auburn Univ Auburn AL 36830

REED, DALE HARDY, b Houston, Tex, Aug 5, 30; m 54; c 4. EXPLORATION GEOPHYSICS, ELECTRICAL ENGINEERING. *Educ:* Rice Univ, BA, 52, BSEE, 53. *Prof Exp:* Res engr, 53-72, res dir, 64-72, RES ASSOC, ATLANTIC RICHFIELD CO, 72- *Mem:* Soc Explor Geophys. *Res:* Borehole logging; reflection seismic; magnetics; geochemistry; planning and evaluation; marine seismic systems. *Mailing Add:* 10415 Coleridge Dallas TX 75218

REED, DAVID KENT, b Wichita Falls, Tex, Mar 6, 32; m 57; c 3. ENTOMOLOGY, INSECT PATHOLOGY. *Educ:* Purdue Univ, BS, 56; Tex A&M Univ, MS, 60; Univ Calif, Riverside, PhD, 71. *Prof Exp:* Field rep, Swift & Co, Tex, 60-61; entomologist, US Dept Agr, Fla, 61-65, Tex, 66-68, entomologist, USDA, Calif, 69-76, supvr, Citrus Insects Proj, Boyden Lab, 74-76, RES & LOCATION LEADER, FRUIT & VEG INSECTS RES LAB, USDA, VINCENNES, 76- *Mem:* Entom Soc Am; Soc Invert Path. *Res:* Biology and control of citrus insects and mites in Florida; biological control, biology and ecology of brown soft scale in Texas; citrus insects research in California; fruit and vegetable insect research in Vincennes. *Mailing Add:* USDA PO Box 944 Vincennes IN 47591

REED, DAVID WILLIAM, b Opelousas, La, Dec 7, 52; m 74; c 1. HORTICULTURE, FLORICULTURE. *Educ:* Univ Southwestern La, BS, 74; Cornell Univ, MS, 77, PhD(hort), 79. *Prof Exp:* ASST PROF HORT, TEX A&M UNIV, 78- *Mem:* Am Soc Hort Sci. *Res:* Penetration of foliar-applied compounds into the leafs of plants; structure, development and function of the plant cuticle of leaves; mineral nutrition of plants. *Mailing Add:* Dept of Hort Sci Tex A&M Univ College Station TX 77843

REED, DENNIS KEITH, b Maple, Tex, Oct 3, 33; m 52; c 1. MATHEMATICS. *Educ:* Univ Tex, BS, 59, PhD(math), 65. *Prof Exp:* Asst prof, 65-71, assoc prof, 71-81, PROF MATH, UNIV UTAH, 81- *Mem:* Math Asn Am; Nat Coun Teachers Math. *Res:* Topology, mapping and decomposition spaces; probability, gambling theory. *Mailing Add:* Dept Math Univ Utah Salt Lake City UT 84112

REED, DONAL J, b Riverdale, Calif, Apr 24, 24; m 45; c 5. PHARMACOLOGY. *Educ:* Col Idaho, BA, 48; Univ Calif, PhD(physiol), 59. *Prof Exp:* Asst physiol, Univ Calif, 56-57 & 58-59; instr, 62-65, asst prof, 65-68, assoc prof, 68-76, PROF PHARMACOL, COL MED, UNIV UTAH, 76-, ACTG CHMN DEPT, 80- *Concurrent Pos:* NIH res fel pharmacol, Col Med, Univ Utah, 59-62. *Mem:* AAAS; Am Soc Pharmacol & Exp Therapeut; Am Physiol Soc. *Res:* Mechanism and kinetics of distribution of electrolytes and other substances among the blood, cerebrospinal fluid and the brain; neuropharmacology; pharmaco-kinetics; adrenal steroids. *Mailing Add:* Dept of Pharmacol Univ of Utah Col of Med Salt Lake City UT 84132

REED, DONALD EUGENE, b Dover, Del, Feb 21, 38; m 62; c 3. BIOCHEMISTRY. *Educ:* Univ Del, BS, 60; Yale Univ, PhD(biochem), 65. *Prof Exp:* SR RES BIOCHEMIST, ICI US, INC, 67- *Mem:* Am Chem Soc; NY Acad Sci. *Res:* Metabolic fate of specific drugs in dog, rat and monkey, using radioisotopes to label compounds and various chromatographic techniques to resolve, purify and identify metabolites. *Mailing Add:* Biol Med Res New Murphy & Concord Pike Wilmington DE 19897

REED, DONALD JAMES, b Montrose, Kans, Sept 26, 30; m 49; c 6. BIOCHEMISTRY, ENVIRONMENTAL HEALTH. *Educ:* Col Idaho, BS, 53; Ore State Univ, MS, 55, PhD(chem), 57. *Prof Exp:* Asst, Ore State Univ, 53-55; assoc biochemist cereal invests, Western Regional Res Lab, Agr Res Serv, USDA, Calif, 57-58; asst prof chem, Mont State Univ, 58-62; from asst prof to assoc prof, 62-72, PROF BIOCHEM, ORE STATE UNIV, 72-, DIR ENVIRON HEALTH SCI CTR, 81- *Concurrent Pos:* USPHS spec res fel, NIH, 69-70, mem toxicol study sect, 71-75; Eleanor Roosevelt Am Cancer Soc Int Cancer fel, Karolinska Inst, Stockholm, 76-77; environ sci review panel health res, Environ Protection Agency, 81; environ health sci review comt, Nat Inst Environ Health Sci, 82-85. *Mem:* Am Soc Biol Chem; Am Soc Pharmacol & Exp Therapeut; Soc Toxicol; Am Asn Cancer Res. *Res:* Biological oxidations; biochemical toxicology; biochemical anticancer drugs; glutathione protective mechanisms. *Mailing Add:* Dept of Biochem & Biophys Ore State Univ Corvallis OR 97331

REED, DWAYNE (MILTON), epidemiology, see previous edition

REED, EDITH IRENE, b Rhinelander, Wis, Jan 31, 28; m 51; c 2. ATMOSPHERIC PHYSICS. *Educ:* Univ Wis, BPh, 48. *Prof Exp:* Physicist, Naval Res Lab, 48-59; PHYSICIST ATMOSPHERIC RES, NASA, GODDARD SPACE FLIGHT CTR, 59- *Mem:* Am Geophys Union. *Res:* Physics and chemistry of the stratosphere; airglow in the mesosphere and thermosphere; atmospheric studies by balloon borne sensors, ozone. *Mailing Add:* Goddard Space Flight Ctr Greenbelt MD 20771

REED, EDWARD BRANDT, b Longmont, Colo, Jan 11, 20; m 46; c 2. LIMNOLOGY, ECOLOGY. *Educ:* Colo State Univ, BS, 53, MS, 55; Univ Sask, PhD(biol), 59. *Prof Exp:* Fisheries biologist, Sask Dept Natural Resources, 56-59; from asst prof to prof zool, 59-74, MEM AFFIL FAC ZOOL & ENTOM, COLO STATE UNIV, PRES ECOL CONSULTS, INC, 74- *Concurrent Pos:* Dir, NSF Summer Inst, 60-64; environ consult, Nat Park Serv, 67 & Western Solo Resource Study, 70-71; Environ Protection Agency res grant, 70-71. *Mem:* Fel AAAS; Int Asn Theoret & Appl Limnol; Am Soc Limnol & Oceanog; Am Quaternary Asn; Ecol Soc Am. *Res:* Application of limnological principles to problems associated with water resource use; abatement of ecological problems associated with disturbed lands and resource development. *Mailing Add:* Colo State Univ Dept of Zool & Entom Fort Collins CO 80521

REED, ELIZABETH WAGNER, b Baguio, Philippines, Aug 27, 12; m 40, 46; c 3. HUMAN GENETICS. *Educ:* Ohio State Univ, AB, 33, MA, 34, PhD(plant physiol), 36. *Prof Exp:* Prof biol, Atlantic Christian Col, 38-40; res assoc, Res Found, Ohio State Univ, 43-44; instr plant sci, Vassar Col, 44-45; asst prof bot, Ohio Wesleyan Univ, 45-46; res assoc, Dight Inst Human Genetics, 40-66, asst prof curriculum res staff, Math & Sci Teaching Ctr, 66-69, LECTR, HUMAN GENETICS, CONTINUING EDUC WOMEN, UNIV MINN, MINNEAPOLIS, 69-, ASST PROF WOMEN'S STUDIES DEPT, 76-, LECTR, MINN HUMAN GENETICS LEAGUE, 69- *Mem:* Fel AAAS. *Res:* Effects of chemical dusts on transpiration; production and testing of penicillin; population studies on Drosophila; inheritance of mental retardation; school curricula; biology of women; early women in science. *Mailing Add:* 1588 Vincent St St Paul MN 55108

REED, ELLEN ELIZABETH, b Covina, Calif, Sept 16, 40. MATHEMATICS. *Educ:* Gonzaga Univ, BA, 62; Univ Colo, Boulder, MA, 64, PhD(math), 66. *Prof Exp:* From asst prof to assoc prof math, Univ Mass, Amherst, 66-77; MEM STAFF, DEPT MATH, ST MARY'S COL, 77- *Concurrent Pos:* Lectr, Smith Col, 72. *Mem:* Am Math Soc. *Res:* Uniform spaces and generalizations; extensions and compactifications of topological spaces and convergence spaces. *Mailing Add:* Dept of Math St Mary's Col Notre Dame IN 46556

REED, EUGENE D, b Vienna, Austria; nat US. ELECTRICAL ENGINEERING. *Educ:* Univ London, BSEE, 42; Columbia Univ, PhD(elec eng), 53. *Prof Exp:* With Bell Labs, 47-75, EXEC DIR, BELL LABS, 66-, VPRES, SANDIA NAT LABS, 75- *Mem:* Nat Acad Eng; fel Inst Elec & Electronics Engrs. *Mailing Add:* Sandia Labs Albuquerque NM 87185

REED, F(LOOD) EVERETT, JR, b North Stonington, Conn, Aug 23, 14; m 39; c 4. MECHANICAL & MARINE ENGINEERING. *Educ:* Webb Inst Naval Archit, BS, 36; Mass Inst Technol, MS, 51. *Prof Exp:* From asst marine engr to sr marine engr, US Maritime Comn, 39-46; asst prof mech eng, Mass Inst Technol, 46-49; mech engr, Arthur D Little, Inc, 49-51, leader, Appl Mech Group, 51-55, sr mech engr & head appl mech, Tech Opers, Inc, 55-59; partner, Conesco Consults, 59-61, tech vpres, Conesco, Inc & FLow Corp, 62; PRES & TREAS, LITTLETON RES & ENG CORP, 62- *Mem:* Am Soc Lubrication Engrs; Am Soc Mech Engrs; Soc Exp Stress Anal; Soc Naval Archit & Marine Engrs; Acoust Soc Am. *Res:* Vibration; stress analysis; applied mechanics; hydrodynamics; ship structure vibration; mechanical vibration; applied mechanics. *Mailing Add:* Littleton Res & Eng Corp 95 Russell St Littleton MA 01460

REED, FRED DEWITT, JR, b Port Arthur, Tex, Apr 25, 37; m 58. MEDICINAL CHEMISTRY. *Educ:* Univ Tex, PhD(med chem), 70. *Prof Exp:* Tex pharmacol res fel med chem, Col Pharm, Univ Tex, 68-69; Phillip Morris res fel, Univ Va, 69-70; Ger sci asst, Org Chem Inst, Univ Heidelberg, 70-72; asst prof med chem, Col Pharm, Idaho State Univ, 73-77, assoc prof, 77-79; CONSULT BIOMED, 79- *Mem:* Am Chem Soc; Am Pharmaceut Asn. *Res:* Design and synthesis of potentially active medicinal agents; natural products. *Mailing Add:* Route 4 Box 855 Flagstaff AZ 86001

REED, GARY LEE, b Ottumwa, Iowa, Jan 23, 42; m 63; c 2. ENTOMOLOGY, HOST PLANT RESISTANCE. *Educ:* Iowa State Univ, BS, 65, MS, 70, PhD(entom), 74. *Prof Exp:* Res technician, 65-68, entomologist, 68-70, res entomologist, 70-76, RES ENTOMOLOGIST, AGR RES SERV, USDA, 76- *Concurrent Pos:* Chmn, Nat Muskmelon Res Workers Group, 78- *Mem:* Entom Soc Am; Sigma Xi; Am Soc Hort Sci. *Res:* Development of vegetable and fruit germ plasma resistant to insect and to insect vectored diseases; biological and ecological relationships between host plant, phytophagous insect and insect vectored disease. *Mailing Add:* Fruit & Vegetable Insects Res USDA-NCR PO Box 944 Vincennes IN 47591

REED, GEORGE BENSON, pathology, pediatrics, see previous edition

REED, GEORGE ELLIOTT, b New York, NY, Aug 4, 23; m 44; c 2. CARDIOVASCULAR SURGERY, SURGERY. *Educ:* Cornell Univ, DVM, 44; NY Univ, MD, 51; Am Bd Surg & Am Bd Thoracic Surg, dipl. *Prof Exp:* Asst prof, 59-64, assoc prof, 64-69, prof surg, Sch Med, NY Univ, 69-78, PROF, NY MED COL, 78- *Concurrent Pos:* Consult cardiovasc surg, Vet Admin, 65-, Riverside Res Inst, Lenox Hill Hosp, Kingston Hosp & NY State Dept Health. *Mem:* AAAS; Soc Thoracic Surg; Am Col Surg; Am Asn Thoracic Surg; Am Trauma Soc. *Res:* Congestive heart failure; development of new techniques in cardiovascular surgery; anaerobic energy production in the myocardium; development of an artificial heart; myocardial preservation. *Mailing Add:* Dept Cardiothoracic Surg Westchester County Med Ctr Valhalla NY 10595

REED, GEORGE FARRELL, b Oswego, NY, Oct 25, 22; m 47; c 4. OTOLARYNGOLOGY, MEDICAL EDUCATION. *Educ:* Colgate Univ, AB, 44; Syracuse Univ, MD, 46. *Prof Exp:* Asst clin prof, Mass Eye & Ear Infirmary, 52-60; prof otolaryngol & chmn dept, State Univ NY Upstate Med Ctr & chief otolaryngol, State Univ Hosp, 65-76, dean grad & continuing med educ, Univ Med Ctr, 74-76, EXEC V PRES UNIV NY UPSTATE MED CTR & DEAN COL MED, 76- *Concurrent Pos:* Asst, Am Bd Otolaryngol, 52-56, vpres, 72, pres, 76; sr fac mem, Home Study Courses, Am Acad Ophthal & Otolaryngol, 53-60, consult, 60-, secy continuing educ, 70-; consult, Mass Health Ctr, Boston, 53-65; consult to surgeon gen, Otolaryngol Training Grant Comt, USPHS, 56-60; consult, Norwood Hosp, Mass, 63-65; consult, Crouse Irving, Syracuse Psychiat, St Joseph's Vet Admin Hosps & VanDuyn Home & Hosp, Syracuse, NY, 65-; chmn med bd, State Univ Hosp, 68-72; mem sci info prog activities comt, Nat Inst Neurol Dis & Stroke, 70-, chmn, 72. *Honors & Awards:* Award of Merit, Am Acad Ophthal & Otolaryngol, 61. *Mem:* AMA; Am Acad Ophthal & Otolaryngol; fel Am Laryngol, Rhinol & Otol Soc; fel Am Col Surg; fel Am Acad Facial Plastic & Reconstruct Surg. *Res:* Clinical and basic research, especially oncology related to the head and neck. *Mailing Add:* Office of the Dean State Univ of NY Upstate Med Ctr Syracuse NY 13210

REED, GEORGE HENRY, b Muncie, Ind, Aug 29, 42. BIOPHYSICS, BIOCHEMISTRY. *Educ:* Purdue Univ, BS, 64; Univ Wis, PhD(chem), 68. *Prof Exp:* Lectr chem, Univ Wis, 67-68; asst prof biophys, 71-76, ASSOC PROF BIOCHEM & BIOPHYS, UNIV PA, 76- *Concurrent Pos:* NIH fel, Univ Pa, 69-71 & USPHS career develop award, 72-77. *Mem:* Am Chem Soc; Am Soc Biol Chemists; Sigma Xi. *Res:* Spectroscopic investigation of enzyme-substrate complexes; applications of electron paramagnetic resonance and nuclear magnetic resonance spectroscopy in biological chemistry; interactions of inorganic cations in biological processes. *Mailing Add:* Dept of Biochem & Biophys Univ of Pa Philadelphia PA 19104

REED, GEORGE W, JR, b Washington, DC, Sept 25, 20; m 45; c 4. NUCLEAR CHEMISTRY, GEOCHEMISTRY. *Educ:* Howard Univ, BS, 42, MS, 44; Univ Chicago, PhD(chem), 52. *Prof Exp:* Asst chemist, SAM Labs, Columbia Univ & Metall Labs, Univ Chicago, 44-47; assoc chemist, 52-68, SR SCIENTIST, ARGONNE NAT LAB, 68- *Concurrent Pos:* Sr res assoc, Univ Chicago, 74. *Mem:* Am Chem Soc; Am Geophys Union; Sigma Xi. Geochem Soc; Meteoritical Soc. *Res:* Lunar and meteoritic science; radiochemistry; geocosmochemistry. *Mailing Add:* Argonne Nat Lab Box 299 Argonne IL 60439

REED, GERALD, b Berlin, Ger, Mar 14, 13; nat US; m 38; c 1. CHEMISTRY. *Educ:* Prague Univ, PhD(chem), 37. *Prof Exp:* Oderberger Chem Works fel inst tech, Prague Univ, 37; res assoc, Dent Col, Univ Chicago, 38-41; res chemist, Upjohn Co, 41-44; head res dept, Libby, McNeill & Libby, 44-47; mem tech sales, Rohm and Haas Co, 47-56; dir res, Red Star Yeast & Prod Co, Universal Foods Corp, 56-66, vpres res, 66-78; VPRES CORP DEVELOP, AMBER LABS, 78- *Mem:* Am Chem Soc; Am Soc Enol; Am Soc Bakery Eng; Am Asn Cereal Chemists; fel Inst Food Technol. *Res:* Polarography; spectroscopy; fat soluble vitamins; infant nutrition; enzyme technology; industrial microbiology. *Mailing Add:* Amber Labs 6101 N Teutonia Ave Milwaukee WI 53209

REED, HOMER VERNON, b Beulah, Mo, Sept 4, 18; m 47; c 3. ORAL SURGERY, DENTISTRY. *Educ:* Univ Tenn, DDS, 42. *Prof Exp:* Fel anesthesia, exodontia & oral surg, Col Dent, 42-44, from instr to asst prof oper dent, Crown & Bridge Div, 49-59, PROF OPER DENT, PARTIAL DENTURE DIV, COL DENT, UNIV TENN, MEMPHIS, 59-, ASST CHIEF DEPT CROWN & BRIDGE, 68- *Concurrent Pos:* Intern, John Gaston Hosp, Univ Tenn, 42-44 & Shelby County Hosp & Penal Farm, 42-44; consult, Vet Admin & Kennedy Vet Hosp, Memphis, 60- *Mem:* Fel Am Col Dent; fel Int Col Dentists; Am Asn Crown & Bridge Prosthodontics; Fedn Dent Int; Prosthodontic Fedn Orgn. *Res:* Crown, bridge and partial denture prosthetics. *Mailing Add:* Univ of Tenn Col of Dent 847 Monroe Memphis TN 38103

REED, HORACE BEECHER, JR, b Etowah, Tenn, July 8, 23; m 64. MEDICAL ENTOMOLOGY, INSECT ECOLOGY. *Educ:* Univ Tenn, AB, 46, MS, 48, PhD(entom), 53; Univ Mich, MA, 52. *Prof Exp:* Instr zool, Univ Maine, 48-49; asst, Univ Tenn, 52-53, asst entom, 54, asst, bact, 57; head sci dept high sch, Ga, 59; prof biol & head dept, Shorter Col, Ga, 59-63; asst prof, 64-67, ASSOC PROF BIOL, MID TENN STATE UNIV, 67- *Res:* Ecology of medically important arthropods. *Mailing Add:* Dept of Biol Mid Tenn State Univ Murfreesboro TN 37132

REED, JACK WILSON, b Corning, Iowa, Sept 24, 23; m 44; c 1. METEOROLOGY. *Educ:* Univ NMex, BS, 48. *Prof Exp:* meteorologist, 48-51, METEOROLOGIST, SANDIA NAT LABS, 53- *Concurrent Pos:* Chmn working group, Atmospheric Blast Effects, Am Nat Standards Inst, 52-54. *Mem:* AAAS; Am Meteorol Soc; Am Geophys Union; Am Nuclear Soc; Int Solar Energy Soc. *Res:* Atmospheric propagation of explosion effluents; wind power chromatology; meteorological statistics. *Mailing Add:* 1128 Monroe SE Albuquerque NM 87108

REED, JAMES ROBERT, JR, b Wayland, NY, Apr 29, 40; m 65; c 2. FISH BIOLOGY, AQUATIC ECOLOGY. *Educ:* Harvard Univ, AB, 62; Cornell Univ, MS, 64; Tulane Univ, PhD(biol), 66. *Prof Exp:* Fel environ sci, Oak Ridge Nat Lab, 66-68; asst prof, Va Commonwealth Univ, 68-73, assoc prof biol, 73-77; PRES, JAMES R REED & ASSOCS, INC, 77- *Mem:* Am Soc Ichthyologists & Herpetologists; Am Fisheries Soc; Ecol Soc Am; Am Coun Independent Labs; Am Soc Testing & Mat. *Res:* Ecology of fishes with respect to effects of pollution; aquaculture; fish behavior; environmental monitoring. *Mailing Add:* James R Reed & Assocs Inc 813 Forrest Dr Newport News VA 23606

REED, JAMES STALFORD, b Jamestown, NY, June 7, 38; m 61; c 1. CERAMICS. *Educ:* Pa State Univ, BS, 60; Alfred Univ, PhD(ceramic sci), 65. *Prof Exp:* Res engr, Harbison-Walker Refractories Co, 60-62; from asst prof to assoc prof ceramic eng, 66-78, PROF CERAMIC ENG, NY STATE COL CERAMICS, ALFRED UNIV, 78- *Mem:* Am Ceramic Soc; Nat Inst Ceramic Engrs. *Res:* Mechanics of fabrication processes; mechanical properties of ceramics; firing whiteware ceramics. *Mailing Add:* Dept of Ceramic Eng Alfred Univ Alfred NY 14802

REED, JOHN C(LIFFORD), mechanical engineering, deceased

REED, JOHN CALVIN, JR, b Erie, Pa, July 24, 30; m 60; c 2. GEOLOGY. *Educ:* Johns Hopkins Univ, PhD, 54. *Prof Exp:* Geologist, 54-55, 57-74, chief, Off Environ Geol, 74-79, GEOLOGIST, US GEOL SURV, 79- *Concurrent Pos:* Chief, Eastern States Br, US Geol Surv, Md, 65-69; mem, Adv Comn Basic Res, Nat Res Coun-US Army, 73-; mem, Comt Stratigraphic Names, US Geol Surv, 74-; assoc ed, Map & Chart Series, Geol Soc Am. *Honors & Awards:* Antarctic Serv Award, US Dept Interior, 72 & Meritorious Serv Award, 73. *Mem:* Fel Geol Soc Am; AAAS. *Res:* Geology of crystalline rocks of central and southern Appalachians, western Wyoming, New Mexico and Colorado; geology of central Alaska Range; Appalachian structure and tectonics; geochronology; Precambrian crystalline rocks of Wyoming, Colorado and New Mexico. *Mailing Add:* US Geol Surv Fed Ctr MS 913 Box 25046 Denver CO 80225

REED, JOHN FRANCIS, b Chicago, Ill, June 1, 23; m 46, 78; c 4. PHYSICAL CHEMISTRY. *Educ:* Ill Inst Technol, BS, 49; Univ Wash, PhD(chem), 53. *Prof Exp:* Asst prof, 53-58, ASSOC PROF CHEM, LOYOLA UNIV CHICAGO, 58- *Concurrent Pos:* Lectr, Mundelen Col, 57-61; consult, Inst Gas Technol, 54-56 & 62-67, Booz-Allen, 58-61 & Inst Mining & Chem, 62. *Honors & Awards:* W M Blaines Robinson Mem lectr, Southern Univ, 70. *Mem:* Am Chem Soc; Am Phys Soc. *Res:* Chemical kinetics; properties of gases; thermochemistry. *Mailing Add:* Dept Chem Loyola Univ 6525 N Sheridan Rd Chicago IL 60626

REED, JOHN FREDERICK, b Rockport, Maine, Nov 18, 11; m 34, 69; c 3. BOTANY. *Educ:* Dartmouth Col, AB, 33; Duke Univ, MA, 35, PhD(bot), 36. *Prof Exp:* Asst bot, Duke Univ, 33-34; instr natural sci, Amarillo Col, 36-38; from instr to assoc prof biol, Baldwin-Wallace Col, 38-46, dean men, 42-46; from asst prof to prof bot, Univ Wyo, 46-56; prof, Univ NH, 56-62, dean grad sch, 56-60 & col lib arts, 58-60, vpres, 61, actg pres, 61-62; prof bot & pres, Ft Lewis Col, 62-69; sect head ecol & syst biol, Div Biol & Med Sci, NSF, 69-70; prof ecosyts anal & chmn dept, 70-75, dean acad affairs, 75-77, PROF ENVIRON SCI, UNIV WIS-GREEN BAY, 75- *Concurrent Pos:* Technician Pedo Bot Mission to Ruanda-Urundi, Africa, Econ Coop Admin, 51-52; mem environ biol panel, NSF, 56-59; mem coun, Nat Inst Dent Res, 59-63; comn plans & objectives higher educ, Am Coun Educ, 63-66; comt radioactive waste mgt, Nat Res Coun, 70-74; chmn, US Nat Comt Int Biol Prog, 72-74; mem, US Nat Comt Man & the Biosphere, 73-75; mem, US Nat Comn, UNESCO, 73-78. *Mem:* Fel AAAS; Brit Ecol Soc; Am Soc Range Mgt; Ecol Soc Am (secy, 53-57, pres, 63); fel Explorers Club. *Res:* Plant ecology; forest ecology of the Rocky Mountains. *Mailing Add:* 2745 N Nicolet Dr Green Bay WI 54301

REED, JOHN J R, b Eunice, La, Oct 2, 32; m 65. ANALYTICAL CHEMISTRY. *Educ:* Southwestern La Univ, BS, 57; Tulane Univ, PhD(chem), 63. *Prof Exp:* SR RES CHEMIST, EXXON RES & ENG CO, 61- *Mem:* Am Chem Soc; Sigma Xi; Asn Comput Mach. *Res:* Infrared spectroscopy; nuclear magnetic resonance; liquid chromatography; computer science. *Mailing Add:* Exxon Res & Eng Co PO Box 4255 Baytown TX 77520

REED, JOSEPH, b Bradenton, Fla, Jan 18, 44; m 66. ORGANOMETALLIC CHEMISTRY. *Educ:* Lincoln Univ, AB, 66; Temple Univ, MA, 71; Brown Univ, PhD(chem), 74. *Prof Exp:* Chemist, E I du Pont de Nemours & Co, Inc, 66-70 & Rohm and Haas, 70; chemist, Bell Labs, 74-77; CHEMIST, EXXON RES & ENG CO, 77- *Concurrent Pos:* Adj prof chem, Lincoln Univ, 79- *Mem:* Am Chem Soc; Nat Orgn Prof Advan Black Chemist & Chem Engrs; NY Acad Sci. *Res:* Chemistry and homogeneous catalytic approach to hydrodesulfurization with organometallic complexes. *Mailing Add:* Exxon Res & Eng Co PO Box 45 Linden NJ 07036

REED, JUTA KUTTIS, b Can citizen. BIOCHEMISTRY. *Educ:* Queen's Univ, BA, 66; Univ Western Ont, MSc, 67; Univ Wis, PhD(biochem), 72. *Prof Exp:* Res fel, Calif Inst Technol, 73-75; asst prof, 75-81, ASSOC PROF CHEM, ERINDALE COL, UNIV TORONTO, 81- *Mem:* Am Chem Soc; Can Biochem Soc. *Res:* Functional and molecular properties of chemically and electrically excitable membranes. *Mailing Add:* Dept of Chem Erindale Col Univ of Toronto Mississauga ON L5L 1C6 Can

REED, KENNETH JOSEPH, b Rochester, NY, Oct 5, 48; m 66; c 2. PHYSICAL CHEMISTRY. *Educ:* Rochester Inst Technol, BS, 71; Stanford Univ, PhD(phys chem), 75. *Prof Exp:* Res chemist calculational quantum mech, 71, RES CHEMIST ELEC SPECTROS DYES, EASTMAN KODAK CO, 75- *Mem:* Am Phys Soc. *Res:* Electron protodetachment and photo electron spectroscopy of molecular gases and solids; photographic science. *Mailing Add:* Eastman Kodak Res Labs Bldg 59 Rochester NY 14650

REED, KENNETH PAUL, b Covington, Ky, Aug 30, 37; m 66; c 1. ANALYTICAL CHEMISTRY, INDUSTRIAL HYGIENE. *Educ:* Thomas More Col, AB, 57; Xavier Univ, MS, 59; La State Univ, PhD(chem), 68. *Prof Exp:* From instr to prof chem, Thomas More Col, 59-78, chmn dept, 68-72, dir freshman studies prog, 72-75, dir develop, 75-78; staff consult, Actus Environ Serv, Florence, 78-80, gen mgr, 80; PRES, NORTHERN KY ENVIRON SERV, 80- *Concurrent Pos:* NSF Sci Fac Fel, 66-67. *Mem:* Am Chem Soc; Am Indust Hyg Asn; Am Conf Govt Indust Hygienists; Sigma Xi; Am Asn Higher Educ. *Res:* Analytical separations; fractional entrainment sublimation; metal chelates; organic synthesis of chelating agents; sampling methods for industrial toxicology; environmental chemistry. *Mailing Add:* Rte 5 Ryland Lakes Covington KY 41015

REED, LESTER JAMES, b New Orleans, La, Jan 3, 25; m 48; c 4. ENZYMOLOGY. *Educ:* Tulane Univ, BS, 43; Univ Ill, PhD(chem), 46. *Hon Degrees:* DSc, Tulane Univ, 77. *Prof Exp:* Asst, Nat Defense Res Comt, Univ Ill, 44-46; res assoc biochem, Med Col, Cornell Univ, 46-48; from asst to assoc prof, 48-58, PROF CHEM, UNIV TEX, AUSTIN, 58-, DIR CLAYTON FOUND BIOCHEM INST, 63- *Honors & Awards:* Lilly Award, Am Chem Soc, 58. *Mem:* Nat Acad Sci; AAAS; Am Chem Soc; Am Soc Biol Chemists; Am Acad Arts & Sci. *Res:* Chemistry and function of lipoic acid; enzyme chemistry; structure, function and regulation of multienzyme complexes. *Mailing Add:* Dept of Chem Univ of Tex Austin TX 78712

REED, LESTER W, b Elgin, Iowa, Sept 4, 17; m 41; c 3. SOIL CHEMISTRY, MINERALOGY. *Educ:* Okla Agr & Mech Col, BS, 41, MS, 47; Univ Mo, PhD, 53. *Prof Exp:* From asst prof to assoc prof, 47-57, PROF AGRON, OKLA STATE UNIV, 57- *Mem:* Fel AAAS; Am Soc Agron; Soil Sci Soc Am; Crop Sci Soc Am; Clay Minerals Soc. *Res:* Clay mineralogy; phosphoric chemistry of soils; soil testing; water chemistry and pollution; amino acid composition of plants; laboratory instrumentation. *Mailing Add:* Dept of Agron Okla State Univ Stillwater OK 74074

REED, MARION GUY, b Osceola, Iowa, June 26, 31; m 51; c 2. SOIL CHEMISTRY. *Educ:* Iowa State Univ, BS, 57, PhD(soil chem), 63. *Prof Exp:* Res assoc soils, Iowa State Univ, 57-62; res chemist, Chevron Res Co, Calif, 62-69, sr res chemist, 69-73, SR RES ASSOC, CHEVRON OIL FIELD RES CO, 73- *Mem:* Am Soc Agron; Soil Sci Soc Am; Clay Minerals Soc; Soc Petrol Eng; Am Inst Mining, Metall & Petrol Engrs. *Res:* Physical chemistry of clays and clay-fluid interactions as related to petroleum, uranium and geothermal energy production; kinetics and mechanism of potassium release from micaceous minerals. *Mailing Add:* Chevron Oil Field Res Co PO Box 446 LaHabra CA 90631

REED, MARY FRANCES, b Lynn, Mass, Aug 31, 41. PHYSICS, HEALTH PHYSICS. *Educ:* Univ Calif, Berkeley, BS, 64, PhD(nuclear chem), 68; Am Bd Radiol, cert nuclear med physics, 72. *Prof Exp:* Lab technician, Dow Chem Co, 61-62; asst prof chem, Centre Col Ky, 68-69; res chemist, Univ Ky, 69-71, vis asst prof chem, 71-72, res assoc radiation med, 72-73, asst prof nuclear med, Med Ctr, 73-78; health physicist, Radiol Health Sect, 78-80, CHIEF, NUCLEAR POWER PLANT PLANNING, CALIF OFF EMERGENCY SERV, 80- *Mem:* AAAS; Am Chem Soc; Am Phys Soc; Health Physics Soc; Soc Nuclear Med. *Res:* Nuclear chemistry and physics and its application to the medical radiation and radiopharmaceutical fields, particularly in the diagnosis, localization and treatment of cancer; radioactive material regulation and licensing within the state of California. *Mailing Add:* Calif Off Emergency Serv PO Box 9577 Sacramento CA 95823

REED, MELVIN LEROY, b Kalamazoo, Mich, Oct 28, 29; m; c 2. INTERNAL MEDICINE, ONCOLOGY. *Educ:* Kalamazoo Col, AB, 51; Univ Mich, MD, 55. *Prof Exp:* Intern med, City Mem Hosp, Winston-Salem, NC, 55-56; resident, Henry Ford Hosp, Detroit, 58-60, assoc physician med oncol, 62-63; ASSOC PROF ONCOL, SCH MED, WAYNE STATE UNIV, 63- *Concurrent Pos:* Nat Cancer Inst fel clin cancer res, Henry Ford Hosp, Detroit, 60-62; assoc dir, Darling Mem Ctr, Mich Cancer Found, 63-75; dir, Southeastern Mich Regional Cancer Prog, 71-76. *Mem:* Am Fedn Clin Res; Am Soc Clin Oncol; fel Am Col Physicians; Am Asn Cancer Res. *Res:* Experimental drugs and methods in therapy of human malignant diseases. *Mailing Add:* Dept of Oncol Wayne State Univ Sch of Med Detroit MI 48201

REED, MICHAEL CHARLES, b Kalamazoo, Mich, May 7, 42. MATHEMATICAL PHYSICS. *Educ:* Yale Univ, BS, 63; Stanford Univ, MS, 66, PhD(math), 69. *Prof Exp:* From instr to asst prof math, Princeton Univ, 68-74; PROF MATH, DUKE UNIV, 74- *Concurrent Pos:* Ed, Duke J Math, 74- *Mem:* Am Math Soc. *Res:* Problems in nonlinear harmonic analysis and partial differential equations, especially scattering theory and propagation of singularities. *Mailing Add:* Dept of Math Duke Univ Durham NC 27706

REED, NORMAN D, b Lyons, Kans, July 6, 35; m 62; c 4. IMMUNOLOGY. *Educ:* Kans State Univ, BS, 59, MS, 62; Montana State Univ, PhD(microbiol), 66. *Prof Exp:* Bacteriologist, Kans State Bd Health, 61-62; res virologist, Mont Vet Res Lab, 62-63; asst prof microbiol, Univ Nebr, Lincoln, 66-70; from asst prof to assoc prof, 70-76, PROF MICROBIOL, MONT STATE UNIV, 76-, HEAD DEPT, 77- *Concurrent Pos:* Sigma Xi res award, Kans State Univ, 62; consult, Dorsey Labs, Nebr, 66-68; career develop award, USPHS, NIAID, Dept HEW, 72-77. *Mem:* Fel AAAS; Am Soc Microbiol; fel Am Acad Microbiol; Am Asn Pathologists; Am Asn Immunol. *Res:* Immunological tolerance; functions of thymus gland; generation and regulation of immune responses; immunoparasitology. *Mailing Add:* Dept of Microbiol Mont State Univ Bozeman MT 59715

REED, P(HILIP) W(ARREN), b Wellsville, NY, Mar 16, 26; m 53; c 2. PETROLEUM ENGINEERING. *Educ:* Pa State Univ, BS, 48, MS, 55. *Prof Exp:* Petrol engr, Phillips Petrol Co, 48-49; asst petrol engr, Pa State Univ, 52-55; sr res engr, Res & Develop Dept, Continental Oil Co, 55-80; SR ENG SCIENTIST, RES & DEVELOP DEPT, CONOCO INC, 80- *Mem:* Instrument Soc Am; Am Inst Mining, Metall & Petrol Engrs. *Res:* Methods of operation of petroleum reservoirs leading to increased recovery; new metering techniques for fluids produced from wells. *Mailing Add:* Res & Develop Dept Conoco Inc Ponca City OK 74603

REED, PETER WILLIAM, b White Plains, NY, July 1, 39. BIOCHEMISTRY, PHARMACOLOGY. *Educ:* Syracuse Univ, BA, 61; State Univ NY Upstate Med Ctr, PhD(pharmacol), 68. *Prof Exp:* Asst res prof, Inst Enzyme Res, Univ Wis-Madison, 70-73; from asst prof to assoc prof physiol, Med Ctr, Univ Mass, 73-75; ASSOC PROF PHARMACOL, MED SCH, VANDERBILT UNIV, 75- *Concurrent Pos:* NIH fel, Inst Enzyme Res, Univ Wis-Madison, 68-70; estab investr, Am Heart Asn, 72-77. *Mem:* Am Soc Biol Chemists; Am Chem Soc; NY Acad Sci; Am Soc Pharmacol & Exp Therapeut; Biophys Soc. *Res:* Leukocyte metabolism; mitochondria and antibiotics; calcium and magnesium in metabolism; toxic antibiotic effects on cells. *Mailing Add:* Dept of Pharmacol Vanderbilt Univ Med Sch Nashville TN 37232

REED, R(OBERT) M(ARION LAFOLLETTE), b Bend, Ore, Sept 13, 06; m 32; c 3. CHEMICAL ENGINEERING. *Educ:* Univ Wash, BS, 29, MS, 30, PhD(chem), 35. *Prof Exp:* Res chemist, Procter & Gamble Co, 30-37; chemist, Swann & Co, 37-38; chemist, Gas Processes Div, Girdler Corp, 38-40, tech dir, 40-43, chief process engr, 43-45, chief chem engr, 45-49, tech dir, 49-55, proj mgr, 55-57, tech adv, 57-60, tech dir, 60-69, CONSULT, GAS PROCESSES DIV, C&I/GIRDLER, INC, 70- *Mem:* Am Chem Soc; Am Inst Chem Engrs; Sigma Xi. *Res:* Essential oils and soap perfumes; detergents; gas purification; hydrogen and hydrogen synthetic sulfide manufacture; heavy water production; ammonia manufacturing, storage and transportation; nitric acid and ammonium nitrate production; urea production. *Mailing Add:* 4800 N 68th St No 331 Scottsdale AZ 85251

REED, RANDALL R, b Davis, WVa, Sept 1, 21; m 48; c 2. ANIMAL PHYSIOLOGY. *Educ:* WVa Univ, BSc, 49, MSc, 52; Ohio State Univ, PhD, 60. *Prof Exp:* County agr agent, WVa Univ, 49-50, res asst animal sci, 50-51; res assoc animal sci, Rutgers Univ, 52-55, asst prof, 55-57; res asst animal

physiol, 57-59, state exten meat specialist, 59-60, assoc prof, 60-65, PROF ANIMAL SCI, 65-, DIST SUPVR COOP EXTEN SERV, 65- *Mem:* Am Soc Animal Sci; Am Meat Sci Asn. *Res:* Animal reproductive physiology and parasitology; meat and carcass evaluation studies; beef industry education. *Mailing Add:* 4218 Fairoaks Dr Columbus OH 43214

REED, RAYMOND EDGAR, b Kankakee, Ill, May 11, 22; m 46; c 2. ANIMAL PATHOLOGY. *Educ:* Wash State Univ, BS, 50, DVM, 51; Am Col Vet Path, dipl. *Prof Exp:* From asst prof to assoc prof, 52-59, actg head dept, 64-65, head dept, 65-77, PROF VET SCI, UNIV ARIZ, 59- *Mem:* Am Vet Med Asn; Am Col Vet Path. *Res:* Pathology of animal diseases. *Mailing Add:* Dept of Vet Sci Univ of Ariz Tucson AZ 85721

REED, RICHARD EUGENE, SR, physical metallurgy, deceased

REED, RICHARD JAY, b Gilmer, Tex, July 23, 28; m 53; c 3. MEDICINE, PATHOLOGY. *Educ:* Tulane Univ, MD, 52; Am Bd Path, dipl, 61. *Prof Exp:* Gen pract, Tex, 53-55; from instr to prof, 57-75, CLIN PROF PATH, SCH MED, TULANE UNIV, 75- *Concurrent Pos:* Fel, Tulane Univ, 57-60; fel surg path, Barnes Hosp, St Louis, Mo, 60-61; fel, Warren Found Path Lab, Tulsa, Okla, 70-71; consult, USPHS Hosp, New Orleans, 62-; consult, Ochsner Found Hosp, 65-; physician, Charity Hosp, New Orleans, 71-; surg path, Touro Infirmary & partner, Dermatopath Lab, New Orleans, 75- *Mem:* Fel Col Am Path; Am Acad Dermat; AMA. *Res:* Dermatopathology; orthopedic and surgical pathology. *Mailing Add:* Rm 603 234 Loyola Ave New Orleans LA 70112

REED, RICHARD JOHN, b Braintree, Mass, June 18, 22; m 50; c 3. METEOROLOGY. *Educ:* Calif Inst Technol, BS, 45; Mass Inst Technol, ScD(meteorol), 49. *Prof Exp:* Mem staff, Mass Inst Technol, 49-54; from asst prof to assoc prof, 54-63, PROF METEOROL, UNIV WASH, 63- *Concurrent Pos:* Ed, J Appl Meteorol, 66-68. *Honors & Awards:* Meisinger Award, Am Meteorol Soc, 64, 2nd Half Century Award, 72. *Mem:* Nat Acad Sci; Am Meteorol Soc (pres, 72); Am Geophys Union. *Res:* Weather analysis and forecasting; stratospheric and tropical meteorology. *Mailing Add:* Dept of Atmospheric Sci Univ of Wash Seattle WA 98195

REED, RICHARD P, b Hammond, Ind, May 17, 34; m 57; c 3. PHYSICAL METALLURGY. *Educ:* Purdue Univ, BS, 56; Univ Colo, MS, 58; Colo Sch Mines, MS, 62; Univ Denver, PhD(metall), 66. *Prof Exp:* supvry metallurgist, 57-79, CHIEF, FRACTURE & DEFORMATION DIV, NAT BUREAU STANDARDS, 79- *Concurrent Pos:* Ed, Advances Cryog Eng & Cryogenic Series. *Honors & Awards:* Silver Medal, Nat Bureau Standards. *Mem:* Am Phys Soc; Am Inst Mining, Metall & Petrol Engrs; Am Soc Testing & Mat. *Res:* Deformation, fracture and phase transformations. *Mailing Add:* Nat Bur of Standards Boulder CO 80302

REED, RICHARD SMYTHE, b Evansville, Ind, Sept 20, 24; m 67; c 6. CHEMICAL ENGINEERING. *Educ:* Purdue Univ, BS, 45; MS, 49. *Prof Exp:* Process engr plant design, C F Braun & Co, 50-52; petrol engr syst planning, US Dept Defense, 52-54; process develop chem, Standard-Vacuum Oil Co, 54-58; dir proj process develop, Columbian Carbon Co, 59-67; staff consult process eval, Bechtel Corp, 67-68; dir res & develop aquacult, Inmont Corp, 68-70; PRES PROCESS DEVELOP, REED PROCESS CO INC, 71- *Concurrent Pos:* Pres, Catalox Corp, 75- *Mem:* Am Inst Chem Engrs; Asn Consult Chemists & Chem Engrs. *Res:* Chemical process development; coal gasification and liquefaction; fluidized bed combustion; methanol; sulfur dioxide absorption and conversion in molten salts; fluoride recovery in phosphoric acid manufacture; carbon fibers; pyrogenic pigments. *Mailing Add:* 715 White Bridge Rd Millington NJ 07946

REED, ROBERT MARSHALL, b Berea, Ohio, June 29, 41; m 66. PLANT ECOLOGY. *Educ:* Duke Univ, BA, 63; Wash State Univ, PhD(plant ecol), 69. *Prof Exp:* Asst prof biol, Univ Ottawa, 69-77; res assoc, 77-80, STAFF RES MEM, OAK RIDGE NAT LAB, 80- *Mem:* Ecol Soc Am; Am Inst Biol Sci; Soil Conserv Soc Am. *Res:* Synecology, with emphasis on forest communities and relationship of vegetation to soil; environmetal assessment of energy technologies. *Mailing Add:* Environ Sci Div Oak Ridge Nat Lab Oak Ridge TN 37830

REED, ROBERT WILLARD, b Fountain Hill, Pa, Jan 31, 41; m 63. LOW TEMPERATURE PHYSICS, ACOUSTICS. *Educ:* Lafayette Col, BS, 63; Pa State Univ, PhD(physics), 68. *Prof Exp:* Instr, 68-70, ASST PROF PHYSICS, PA STATE UNIV, 70- *Mem:* Acoust Soc Am; Am Phys Soc; AAAS. *Res:* Low temperature physics; ultrasonics and hypersonics; fermi surface studies; propagation of sound in liquid helium; superconductivity; nondestructive testing and evaluation; underwater sound propagation. *Mailing Add:* 104 Davey Bldg Dept of Physics Col of Sci Pa State Univ University Park PA 16802

REED, ROBERTA GABLE, b Baltimore, Md, Sept 18, 45; m 67. BIOCHEMISTRY. *Educ:* Lebanon Valley Col, Pa, BS, 67; Wesleyan Univ, MA, 69, PhD(org chem), 71. *Prof Exp:* Res asst chem, Res Triangle Inst, NC, 71-72; instr chem, State Univ NY Col Oneonta, 72-73; ASSOC RES BIOCHEMIST, MARY IMOGENE BASSETT HOSP, COOPERSTOWN, NY, 73- *Res:* Dynamic and structural relationships in binding of ions and small organic molecules to proteins. *Mailing Add:* Mary Imogene Bassett Hosp Cooperstown NY 13326

REED, ROGER J, fish biology, deceased

REED, RUDDELL, JR, industrial engineering, see previous edition

REED, RUSSELL, JR, b Glendale, Calif, Dec 25, 22; m 56; c 3. PROPELLANT CHEMISTRY, ORGANIC CHEMISTRY. *Educ:* Univ Calif, Los Angeles, BS, 44, PhD(org chem), 50. *Prof Exp:* Res chemist, US Naval Ord, China Lake Test Sta, 51-58; head org & polymer res sect, Hughes Tool Co, Culver City, Calif, 58-59; head, Dept Chem, Rocket Power Inc,

Mesa, Ariz, 59-64; head propellant res sect, Thiokol Corp, Brigham City, Utah, 64-72; head appl res & processing div, 72-76, SR RES SCIENTIST, US NAVAL WEAPONS CTR, 76- *Mem:* Am Chem Soc; Am Inst Aeronaut & Astronaut. *Res:* Propellant chemistry combustion; pyrotechnic and explosive chemistry; processing of energetic materials; polymer chemistry. *Mailing Add:* US Naval Weapons Ctr China Lake CA 93555

REED, RUTH ELIZABETH, b Ames, Iowa, Dec 14, 46; m 72. BIOCHEMISTRY. *Educ:* Winthrop Col, BA, 68; Va Polytech Inst & State Univ, PhD(biochem), 74. *Prof Exp:* Fel biochem, Dept Physiol Chem, Sch Med, Johns Hopkins Univ, 74-76; asst prof, 76-80, ASSOC PROF CHEM, JUNIATA COL, 80- *Concurrent Pos:* Nat Heart, Lung & Blood Inst res fel, Johns Hopkins Univ, 75-76; Fulbright award, Univ Gottingen, 68-69; Fulbright inter-univ exchange, Polytech de Lille, France, 81. *Mem:* Sigma Xi; Am Chem Soc. *Res:* Regulation of carbon and nitrogen metabolism in photosynthetic tissue of higher plants. *Mailing Add:* Dept of Chem Juniata Col Huntingdon PA 16652

REED, SHERMAN KENNEDY, b Chicago, Ill, Apr 11, 19; m 43; c 3. CHEMISTRY. *Educ:* Univ Ill, BS, 40, Cornell Univ, PhD(chem), 49. *Prof Exp:* Asst chem, Cornell Univ, 40-43; Nat Defense Res Comt, 43; res scientist, SAM Labs, Columbia Univ, 43-46; from instr to asst prof chem, Bucknell Univ, 46-50; group leader, Res & Develop Dept, Westvaco Chem Div, 50-53, asst dir res, Niagara Chem Div, 53-57, dir res & develop, Chem & Plastics Div, 57-60, dir cent res dept, 60-72, vpres technol, Chem Group, 72-74, VPRES, FMC CORP, 74- *Concurrent Pos:* Consult, Smith Kline Corp, 47-50; dir, Franklin Inst, Birkett Mills, Avicon, Inc & Indust Res Inst; chmn, Franklin Res Ctr. *Mem:* Am Chem Soc. *Res:* Fluorine phosphorus and agricultural chemistry; plastics. *Mailing Add:* FMC Corp 2000 Market St Philadelphia PA 19103

REED, STUART ARTHUR, b Erie, Pa, Jan 29, 30; m 53; c 4. ZOOLOGY, PHYSIOLOGY. *Educ:* Kent State Univ, BS, 51, MS, 53; Mich State Univ, PhD(zool), 62. *Prof Exp:* Instr physiol, Mich State Univ, 57-58, zool, 59-60, biol, 61-63, asst prof, 63-69; assoc prof, 69-73, PROF ZOOL, UNIV HAWAII, 73- *Concurrent Pos:* NSF sci fac fel, 66-67. *Mem:* AAAS; Nat Asn Biol Teachers; Am Soc Zoologists; Sigma Xi; Am Inst Biol Sci. *Res:* Invertebrate zoology; curriculum developmental in marine biology. *Mailing Add:* Dept of Zool Univ of Hawaii 2538 The Mall Honolulu HI 96822

REED, TERRY EUGENE, b Mechanicsburg, Pa, Oct 7, 45; m 73; c 1. MEDICAL GENETICS. *Educ:* Juniata Col, BS, 67; Ind Univ, PhD(med genetics), 71. *Prof Exp:* Fel, 71-72, instr med genetics, 72-76, asst prof med genetics, Sch Med, Ind Univ, 76-81, ASSOC PROF MED GENETICS, SCH MED, IND UNIV, 81- *Concurrent Pos:* Dir, Genetic Serv, Indianapolis Comprehensive Sickle Cell Ctr, 73-77; fel, Dept Epidemiology, Sch Pub Health, Univ Pittsburgh, 81-82. *Mem:* Am Soc Human Genetics; Int Dermatoglyphics Asn; Am Dermatoglyphics Asn. *Res:* Multivariate analysis and family studies of dermatoglyphics in man to better understand their inheritance and develop their usefulness in syndrome diagnosis and twin zygosity determinations; human genetic linkage investigations. *Mailing Add:* Dept of Med Genetics Sch Med Ind Univ Indianapolis IN 46223

REED, THEODORE H(AROLD), b Washington, DC, July 25, 22; m 80; c 2. VETERINARY MEDICINE. *Educ:* Kans State Col, DVM, 45. *Prof Exp:* Instr vet path, Kans State Col, 45-46; asst state vet, Ore, 46-48; vet, Portland Zoo, 49-55; vet, 55-56, actg dir, 56-58, DIR, NAT ZOOL PARK, 58- *Concurrent Pos:* Pvt pract, Idaho & Ore, 49-55; mem, Mayor's Zoo Comn, Portland Zoo, 51-55. *Honors & Awards:* Arthur S Flemming Award, 72. *Mem:* Fel Am Asn Zool Parks & Aquariums (pres, 63-64). *Res:* Zoo administration and zoo veterinary medicine. *Mailing Add:* Nat Zool Park Washington DC 20008

REED, THOMAS BINNINGTON, b Chicago, Ill, Jan 2, 26; m 47; c 4. ENERGY CONVERSION. *Educ:* Northwestern Univ, BS, 47; Univ Minn, PhD(phys chem), 52. *Prof Exp:* Chemist, Oil Explor & Develop Lab, Shell Oil Co, 47-48; res chemist, Linde Air Prod Co, Union Carbide & Carbon Corp, 52-59; mem staff, Solid State Div, Lincoln Lab, Mass Inst Technol, 59-77; sr staff, Biochem Conversion Br, 77-80, PRIN SCIENTIST, THERMOCHEM & ELECTROCHEM RES BR, NAT SOLAR ENERGY RES INST, 80- *Concurrent Pos:* Sci Res Coun sr fel inorg chem, Oxford Univ, 65-66; mem high temperature chem comt, NSF; grant, Methanol as a Synthetic Fuel, J B Hawley Found, 74-; mem renewable resources comt, NSF, 75- *Mem:* AAAS. *Res:* X-ray crystallography; thermal plasmas; solid state chemistry; high temperature processes; heat mirrors for solar insulation; synthetic fuel manufacture and use, biomass conversion processes. *Mailing Add:* Solar Energy Res Inst 1536 Cole Blvd Golden CO 80401

REED, THOMAS EDWARD, JR, b Gadsen, Ala, Nov 12, 23; m 49; c 2. HUMAN GENETICS, BEHAVIORAL GENETICS. *Educ:* Univ Calif, AB, 48; Univ London, PhD(zool), 52. *Prof Exp:* Jr geneticist, Univ Mich, 52-56, asst prof, 56-57, res assoc, 57-60; assoc prof zool & pediat, 60-69, PROF ZOOL & ANTHROP, UNIV TORONTO, 69- *Concurrent Pos:* Vis assoc prof, Sch Pub Health, Univ Calif, Berkeley, 65-66. *Mem:* AAAS; Am Soc Human Genetics; Genetics Soc Am; Am Asn Phys Anthrop; Behavior Genetics Asn. *Res:* Human population and behavioral genetics; genetics of responses to alcohol. *Mailing Add:* Dept of Zool Univ of Toronto Toronto ON M5S 2R8 Can

REED, THOMAS FREEMAN, b Webster Co, Iowa, Jan 9, 37; m 58; c 2. POLYMER CHEMISTRY, RUBBER CHEMISTRY. *Educ:* Univ Iowa, BS, 59; Univ Akron, MS, 65, PhD(polymer sci), 70. *Prof Exp:* Prod engr, B F Goodrich Co, 59-65, res chemist, 65-66; res chemist, Univ Akron, 66-68; mem tech staff polymer sci, Bell Tel Labs, 70-73; res scientist, 73-78, sect head tire cord adhesives, 78-80, MGR RUBBER RES, GEN TIRE & RUBBER CO, 80- *Mem:* Am Chem Soc; Sigma Xi; Adhesion Soc. *Res:* Light scattering of polymers in solution; diffusion of polymers in solution; physical properties of polymers; rubber dynamic properties; rubber to cord adhesives. *Mailing Add:* Res Div Gen Tire & Rubber Co 2990 Gilchrist Rd Akron OH 44305

REED, WALTER T, b Rochester, NY, May 3, 42; m 78. ENTOMOLOGY. *Educ:* Franklin & Marshall Col, AB, 64; Rutgers Univ, PhD(entom), 68. *Prof Exp:* Entomologist, 68-75, field rep, 75-76, MGR PESTICIDE DEVELOP DEPT, SHELL DEVELOP CO, 76- *Mem:* Entom Soc Am; Sigma Xi. *Res:* Biochemical aspects of insecticide research, including mode of action, detoxication and resistance; plus field performance and environmental effects of newly developed pesticides. *Mailing Add:* Shell Develop Co Box 4248 Modesto CA 95352

REED, WARREN DOUGLAS, b Boulder, Colo, June 4, 38. BIOCHEMISTRY, TOXICOLOGY. *Educ:* Univ Calif, Riverside, BA, 61, PhD(toxicol & biochem), 68. *Prof Exp:* NIH staff fel, Geront Res Ctr, NIH, Md, 68-71; fel physiol chem, Sch Med, Johns Hopkins Univ, 72-74; mem staff, Dept Pediat Res, 74-81, ASSOC PROF PEDIAT RES, SCH MED, UNIV MD, BALTIMORE CITY, 81- *Mem:* Am Chem Soc; Entom Soc Am. *Res:* Enzyme control and mechanisms. *Mailing Add:* Dept of Pediat Res HHT 655 W Baltimore St Baltimore MD 21201

REED, WILLIAM ALFRED, b Rochester, NY, Jan 5, 36; m 58; c 2. EXPERIMENTAL SOLID STATE PHYSICS. *Educ:* Oberlin Col, BA, 57; Northwestern Univ, PhD(physics), 62. *Prof Exp:* Mem tech staff, Metal Physics Dept, 61-71, MEM TECH STAFF, CONDENSED STATE RES DEPT, BELL LABS, 71- *Mem:* Am Phys Soc. *Res:* Galvanomagnetic effects; Fermi surface studies; resistive behavior of superconductors; compton scattering of x-rays. *Mailing Add:* Condensed State Res Dept Bell Labs Rm 1A 118 Murray Hill NJ 07974

REED, WILLIAM EDWARD, b Columbia, La, July 15, 14; m 42; c 3. SOIL CHEMISTRY. *Educ:* Southern Univ, BS, 37; Iowa State Univ, MS, 41; Cornell Univ, PhD(soil sci), 46. *Prof Exp:* Asst agr engr, Soil Conserv Serv, USDA, 36-37; county agent, La State Univ, 37-40; instr soil sci & chem, Southern Univ, 42-47; agr res specialist, US Dept State, Liberia, 47-49; dean, Sch Agr, Agr & Tech Col NC, 48-57; chief field staff, Int Coop Admin contract, Int Develop Serv, Inc, Ghana, 57-59, Int Coop Admin rep, Lome, 61, opers off, Ibadan, 61, asst dir, Lagos, 61-68, dep dir mission to Ethiopia, 68-72, officer-in-residence, USAID, 72-74, spec asst to chancellor int progs, 74-76, assoc dean res & spec projs, 78, DIR, INT PROGS & SPEC PROJS, NC A&T STATE UNIV, 78- *Concurrent Pos:* Mem US deleg, Soviet Union, 55; mem US deleg, UN Conf Sci & Technol, 63. *Mem:* AAAS; Am Chem Soc; Am Soc Agron; Am Foreign Serv Asn; Soil Sci Soc Am. *Res:* Soil genesis, fertility and morphology; agronomy. *Mailing Add:* 2711 McConnell Rd Greensboro NC 27401

REED, WILLIAM ROBERT, b Graham, Tex, Oct 21, 22; m 46; c 4. PHYSICAL INORGANIC CHEMISTRY. *Educ:* Univ Okla, BS, 48, MS, 50; Mich State Univ, PhD, 54. *Prof Exp:* From asst ed to sr assoc ed, 54-69, SR ED, CHEM ABSTRACTS SERV, 69- *Mem:* Am Chem Soc. *Res:* Scientific literature; literature storage and retrieval. *Mailing Add:* 1612 Penworth Dr Columbus OH 43229

REED, WILMER H, III, b Mexico, Mo, Sept 24, 25; m 49; c 3. AEROSPACE ENGINEERING. *Educ:* Auburn Univ, BS, 48; Univ Va, MS, 53. *Prof Exp:* Aerospace engr struct & dynamics, 48-65, asst head aeroelasticity br, 65-73, head aeroelasticity br, 73-80, CHIEF SCIENTIST, LOADS & AEROELASTICITY DIV, LANGLEY RES CTR, NASA, 80- *Honors & Awards:* Spec Achievement Award, NASA Langley Res Ctr, 69 & 78. *Mem:* Assoc fel Am Inst Aeronaut & Astronaut. *Res:* Research and development activities in the NASA Langley Transonic Dynamics Tunnel; development of aircraft and launch vehicles; author of numerous publications. *Mailing Add:* NASA Langley Res Ctr Mail Stop 340 Hampton VA 23665

REEDER, CHARLES EDGAR, b Fairfield, Iowa, July 20, 27; m 56; c 3. PHYSICAL CHEMISTRY, ORGANIC CHEMISTRY. *Educ:* Wheaton Col, BS, 51; Iowa State Col, PhD(chem), 55. *Prof Exp:* Draftsman, Louden Mach Co, 45-47; asst, Parsons Col, 48, Wheaton Col, 49-50 & Iowa State Col, 51-55; instr chem, Bates Col, 55-57; asst prof, 57-64, ASSOC PROF CHEM, BAYLOR UNIV, 64- *Mem:* Am Chem Soc. *Res:* Reaction mechanisms; catalysis; molecular structure; coordination compounds; chemistry teaching methods and effectiveness. *Mailing Add:* 717 Falcon Dr Waco TX 76710

REEDER, CLYDE, b Huntingdon, Pa, Mar 2, 24; m 46; c 3. CHEMICAL ENGINEERING. *Educ:* Juniata Col, BS, 48; Ohio State Univ, PhD(chem eng), 51. *Prof Exp:* Res engr, Org Chem Dept, Jackson Lab, E I du Pont de Nemours & Co, 51-60, sr res engr, Elastomer Chem Dept, Exp Sta, 60-63; mgr process develop, Agr Chem, Atlanta Res Ctr, Armour Agr Chem Co, 63-68, lab mgr, USS Agrichem, Inc, 68-69; TECHNOLOGIST, MOBAY CHEM CO, 69- *Mem:* Am Chem Soc; Am Inst Chem Engrs. *Res:* Fluorinated elastomers; process development; kinetics; economic analyses of chemical processes; elastomer chemical and engineering technology; urethanes; agricultural chemicals. *Mailing Add:* Dept of Eng Mobay Chem Co Pkwy W Pittsburgh PA 15205

REEDER, DON DAVID, b Dubuque, Iowa, Aug 18, 35; m 58; c 2. HIGH ENERGY PHYSICS. *Educ:* Univ Ill, BS, 58; Univ Wis, MS, 62, PhD(physics), 66. *Prof Exp:* From asst prof to assoc prof, 66-72, PROF PHYSICS, UNIV WIS MADISON, 72 *Concurrent Pos:* Fel, NATO, 74. *Mem:* Am Phys Soc. *Res:* Experimental elementary particle physics. *Mailing Add:* Dept of Physics Sterling Hall Univ of Wis Madison WI 53706

REEDER, JOHN HAMILTON, b Baltimore, Md, Jan 25, 44; m 74. MATHEMATICS. *Educ:* Stevens Inst Technol, BS, 66; Northwestern Univ, MS, 67, PhD(math), 72. *Prof Exp:* Vis asst prof math, Ore State Univ, 71-72; vis scholar, Univ Victoria, 72-73; ASST PROF MATH, UNIV MO-COLUMBIA, 73- *Mem:* Am Math Soc. *Res:* Water waves; kinetic theory of fluids; Wiener-Hopf operators. *Mailing Add:* Dept of Math Univ of Mo Columbia MO 65201

REEDER, JOHN RAYMOND, b Grand Ledge, Mich, July 29, 14; m 41. BOTANY. *Educ:* Mich State Col, BS, 39; Northwestern Univ, MS, 40; Harvard Univ, MA, 46, PhD(syst bot), 47. *Prof Exp:* Hon prof, Univ Venezuela, 66-; ed, Brittonia, 67-71. *Concurrent Pos:* Vis scholar, Univ Ariz, 76- Concurrent. *Mem:* Am Soc Nat; Int Asn Plant Taxon; Torrey Bot Club; Sigma Xi; fel Linnean Soc London. *Res:* Taxonomy of vascular plants; taxonomy and phylogeny of Gramineae. *Mailing Add:* Herbarium Rm 113 Agr Sci Bldg Univ of Ariz Tucson AZ 85721

REEDER, PAUL LORENZ, b Dayton, Ohio, Sept 28, 36; c 3. NUCLEAR CHEMISTRY, FISSION PRODUCTS. *Educ:* Col Wooster, Ohio, AB, 58; Univ Calif, Berkeley, PhD(nuclear chem), 63. *Prof Exp:* Fel nuclear chem, Brookhaven Nat Lab, Upton, NY, 63-65; asst prof chem, Washington Univ, St Louis, 65-70; SR RES SCIENTIST NUCLEAR CHEM, PAC NORTHWEST LABS, BATTELLE MEM INST, RICHLAND, WASH, 70- *Concurrent Pos:* NATO fel, Orsay, France, 68. *Mem:* Am Phys Soc; Am Chem Soc. *Res:* Fission yields; nuclear decay properties of short-lived isotopes; on-line mass spectrometry; ion sources for negative ions. *Mailing Add:* Pac Northwest Labs Battelle Mem Inst Battelle Blvd Richland WA 99352

REEDER, RAY ROBERT, b Cleveland, Ohio, July 18, 43; m 65; c 1. PHYSICAL CHEMISTRY, INORGANIC CHEMISTRY. *Educ:* Case Inst Technol, BS, 65; Brown Univ, PhD(chem), 70. *Prof Exp:* From instr to assoc prof chem, 69-76, interim dean fac, 76-77, dir, Ctr Community Educ, 76-78, ASSOC PROF CHEM, ELIZABETHTOWN COL, 78-, DEPT CHMN, 81- *Mem:* Am Chem Soc. *Res:* Inorganic systems through use of physical techniques; computer applications in undergraduate chemical education; computer simulation and graphics. *Mailing Add:* Dept Chem Elizabethtown Col Elizabethtown PA 17022

REEDER, RONALD HOWARD, b Denver, Colo, Sept 7, 39; m 54. MOLECULAR BIOLOGY. *Educ:* Columbia Union Col, Md, BS, 61; Mass Inst Technol, PhD(biol), 65. *Prof Exp:* Staff mem, dept embryol, Carnegie Inst Washington, 69-78; MEM & SECT CHIEF, HUTCHINSON CANCER RES CTR, 78- *Concurrent Pos:* Mem, NIH Cell Biol Study Sect, 75-77; ed, J Cell Biol, 77- & J Biol Chem, 79- *Mem:* Am Soc Cell Biol; Am Soc Biol Chemists. *Res:* Study of the primary structure of the ribosomal genes and the proteins which bind to them. *Mailing Add:* Hutchinson Cancer Res Ctr 1124 Columbia St Seattle WA 98104

REEDER, WILLIAM GLASE, b Los Angeles, Calif, Feb 4, 29; m 51; c 4. ANIMAL ECOLOGY, VERTEBRATE PALEONTOLOGY. *Educ:* Univ Calif, Los Angeles, BA, 50; Univ Mich, MS, 53, PhD(zool), 57. *Prof Exp:* Instr zool, Univ Calif, Los Angeles, 55-56; from instr to prof zool, Univ Wis-Madison, 56-78; PROF ZOOL, UNIV TEX, AUSTIN, 78-; DIR TEX MEM MUS, 78- *Mem:* AAAS; Am Soc Mammal; Am Soc Archnology. *Res:* Vertebrate ecology, especially of North American deserts, the Arctic and tropics, especially Galapagos Islands; problems of thermoregulation; paleoecology, especially of rodents; human ecology; biogeography and ecology of arachnids. *Mailing Add:* Tex Mem Mus Univ of Tex Austin TX 78705

REED-HILL, ROBERT E(LLIS), b Detroit, Mich, Nov 19, 13; m 38; c 2. METALLURGY. *Educ:* Univ Mich, BS, 36, MS, 38; Yale Univ, DEng, 56. *Prof Exp:* From instr to assoc prof eng, US Coast Guard Acad, 39-60; assoc prof metall, 60-64, PROF METALL, DEPT MAT SCI & ENG, UNIV FLA, 64- *Mem:* Am Inst Mining, Metall & Petrol Engrs; fel Am Soc Metals; Brit Inst Metals; Am Soc Testing & Mat. *Res:* Mechanical metallurgy; deformation twinning; dynamic strain aging; slow strain-rate embrittlement. *Mailing Add:* Dept of Mats Sci & Eng Univ of Fla Gainesville FL 32611

REEDS, LLOYD GEORGE, b Lindsay, Ont, July 11, 17; m 49; c 3. AGRICULTURAL GEOGRAPHY. *Educ:* Univ Toronto, BA, 40, MA, 42, PhD(geog), 56. *Prof Exp:* Soil survr, Ont Agr Col, 42-43; lectr geog, Univ Toronto, 45-48; PROF GEOG, McMASTER UNIV, 48- *Mem:* Asn Am Geog; Can Asn Geog (pres, 61-62). *Res:* Agricultural land-use problems in Southern Ontario. *Mailing Add:* Dept of Geog McMaster Univ Hamilton ON L8S 4L8 Can

REEDY, JOHN JOSEPH, b Buffalo, NY, May 14, 27; m 52; c 4. BIOLOGY. *Educ:* Niagara Univ, BSNS, 48; Notre Dame Univ, MS, 50, PhD(zool), 52; Bridgewater State Col, MEd, 60. *Prof Exp:* Instr, Univ Detroit, 52-53; from asst prof to prof zool, Stonehill Col, 53-60; PROF ZOOL, NIAGARA UNIV, 60- *Mem:* AAAS; Soc Syst Zool; Am Genetics Soc; Soc Study Evolution; Sigma Xi. *Res:* Human genetics; radiobiology; Drosophila genetics dealing with Epistosis. *Mailing Add:* Dept of Biol Niagara Univ Niagara NY 14109

REEDY, MICHAEL K, b Seattle, Wash, June 19, 34; m 60; c 3. CELL BIOLOGY. *Educ:* Univ Wash, BA, 58, MD, 62. *Prof Exp:* Intern path, Univ Hosp, Seattle, Wash, 62-63; NIH res fel, 63-66; asst prof physiol, Med Ctr, Univ Calif, Los Angeles, 66-68, assoc prof, 68-69; ASSOC PROF ANAT, SCH MED, DUKE UNIV, 69- *Concurrent Pos:* NIH res career develop award, 67-69 & 72-75; Alexander von Humboldt US Sr Scientist Award & Guggenheim fel, 78. *Honors & Awards:* Newcomb S Cleveland Prize, AAAS, 67. *Mem:* AAAS; Am Soc Cell Biol; Biophys Soc. *Res:* Ultrastructure of myofibrils; mechanisms of contractility; preparative methods for biological electron microscopy. *Mailing Add:* Dept Anat Sch Med Duke Univ Durham NC 27710

REEDY, ROBERT CHALLENGER, b Summit, NJ, Mar 5, 42; m 69; c 2. NUCLEAR CHEMISTRY, COSMOCHEMISTRY. *Educ:* Colgate Univ, BA, 64; Columbia Univ, PhD(chem physics), 69. *Prof Exp:* Stud dir comput ctr, Colgate Univ, 62-64; res assoc nuclear chem, Columbia Univ, 64-69; res chemist, Univ Calif, San Diego, 69-72; STAFF MEM, LOS ALAMOS NAT LAB, 72- *Concurrent Pos:* Consult, NASA, 74-76. *Mem:* AAAS; Am Phys Soc; Meteoritical Soc. *Res:* Nuclear interactions and nuclear reactions in the moon and other extraterrestrial matter; chemistry of planets from orbit by gamma-ray spectroscopy. *Mailing Add:* Group CNC-11 Mail Stop 514 Los Alamos Nat Lab Los Alamos NM 87545

REEGEN, SIDNEY LLOYD, b New York, NY, July 30, 23; m 48; c 2. POLYMER CHEMISTRY. *Educ:* City Col New York, BS, 44; Polytech Inst Brooklyn, MS, 49, PhD(chem), 51. *Prof Exp:* Res chemist polymer chem, Indust Rayon Corp, 52-58, Res Labs, Gen Motors Corp, 58-62 & Res Labs, Wyandotte Chem Corp, Mich, 62-69; RES PROF POLYMER SCI & ENG, UNIV DETROIT, 69-, ASSOC DIR, POLYMER INST, 69- *Mem:* AAAS; Am Chem Soc; NY Acad Sci. *Res:* Polymerization kinetics; polycondensation reactions; fibers; adhesion; polyurethanes; high temperature polymers; irradiation and cross-linking of polyethylene. *Mailing Add:* Polymer Sci Grad Sch Univ Detroit 4001 W McNichols Rd Detroit MI 48221

REEKE, GEORGE NORMAN, JR, b Green Bay, Wis, Oct 16, 43; m 69. CRYSTALLOGRAPHY. *Educ:* Calif Inst Technol, BS, 64; Harvard Univ, MA, 66, PhD(chem), 69. *Prof Exp:* Res asst chem, Harvard Univ, 69-70; asst prof biochem, 70-76, ASSOC PROF DEVELOP & MOLECULAR BIOL, ROCKEFELLER UNIV, 76- *Concurrent Pos:* Res fel, Alfred P Sloan Found, 75-77. *Mem:* AAAS; Am Soc Biol Chemists; Am Crystallog Asn. *Res:* Protein crystallography. *Mailing Add:* Rockefeller Univ New York NY 10021

REEKER, LARRY HENRY, b Spokane, Wash, Feb 2, 43; m 64; c 3. COMPUTER SCIENCE, COMPUTATIONAL LINGUISTICS. *Educ:* Yale Univ, BA, 64; Carnegie-Mellon Univ, PhD(comput sci), 74. *Prof Exp:* Asst prof comput & info sci & ling, Ohio State Univ, 68-73; asst prof comput sci, Univ Ore, 73-75; assoc prof, Univ Ariz, 75-78; READER & HEAD COMPUT SCI, UNIV QUEENSLAND, 78- *Concurrent Pos:* Consult, Tech/Ops Corp, 67-68; vis lectr comput sci, Univ Pittsburgh, 68; asst dir, Ling Inst, Ling Soc Am, 70; ed consult, Barnes & Noble Inc, 70-71; ed, SIGACT News, Asn Comput Mach, 70-78; vis res scientist, Chemical Abstracts Serv, 82. *Mem:* Asn Comput Mach; Asn Comput Ling; Ling Soc Am; Europ Asn Theoret Comput Sci; Australian Comput Soc. *Res:* Computer modeling of language acquisition; formal language theory and related theory of computing; programming languages. *Mailing Add:* 16 Belsize St Kenmore Brisbane Queensland 4069 Australia

REEL, JERRY ROYCE, b Washington, Ind, May 4, 38; m 65; c 1. ENDOCRINOLOGY. *Educ:* Ind State Univ, BA, 60; Univ Ill, MS, 63, PhD(physiol), 66. *Prof Exp:* USPHS fel, Oak Ridge Nat Lab, 66, Am Cancer Soc fel, 66-68; res scientist, 68, endocrinologist biochemist, 68-70, sect dir endocrinol, 70-75, sr res scientist, Parke Davis & Co, 75-78; sect mgr endocrinol, 78-80, DIR LIFE SCI & TOXICOL DIV RES TRIANGLE INST, 80- *Concurrent Pos:* Adj assoc prof, Wayne State Univ Sch Med, 74- *Mem:* Am Chem Soc; Soc Biol Reproduction; Endocrine Soc; Am Physiol Soc; Tissue Cult Asn. *Res:* Reproduction; teratology; cell culture; hormone and drug binding; hormone and drug action; hypothalamic releasing factors and their antagonists; reproductive toxicology. *Mailing Add:* Res Triangle Inst PO Box 12194 Res Triangle Park NC 27709

REEMTSMA, KEITH, b Madera, Calif, Dec 5, 25; c 2. SURGERY. *Educ:* Idaho State Univ, BS, 48; Univ Pa, MD, 49; Columbia Univ, MedScD, 58; Am Bd Surg, dipl, 58; Am Bd Thoracic Surg, dipl, 60. *Prof Exp:* From intern to resident, Presby Hosp, New York, 50-57; asst, Col Physicians & Surgeons, Columbia Univ, 57; asst prof, Sch Med, Tulane Univ, 57-62, assoc prof surg, 62-66; prof & head dept, Sch Med, Univ Utah, 66-71; PROF SURG & CHMN DEPT, COL PHYSICIANS & SURGEONS, COLUMBIA UNIV, 71-; DIR SURG SERV, PRESBY HOSP, 71- *Concurrent Pos:* Mem study sect A, Surg, NIH, 65- *Mem:* Soc Clin Surg; Am Surg Asn; Soc Univ Surgeons; Am Col Surgeons; Am Fedn Clin Res. *Res:* Transplantation; cardiovascular surgery. *Mailing Add:* Dept Surg Columbia-Presby Med Ctr New York NY 10032

REENSTRA, ARTHUR LEONARD, b Clifton, NJ, Mar 5, 36; m 59; c 3. ELECTRICAL ENGINEERING, SOLID STATE ELECTRONICS. *Educ:* Bucknell Univ, BS, 59; Carnegie Inst Technol, MS, 60; Purdue Univ, PhD(elec eng), 67. *Prof Exp:* Res engr, Res Labs, US Rubber Co, 60-62; instr elec eng, Purdue Univ, 62-64; mem tech staff, Res & Develop Dept, Mat & Electronic Controls Group, Tex Instruments, Inc, 67-76; dir prod develop, Beede Elec Instrument Co, 76-77, dir eng, 77-78, vpres, 79-80; DIR ENG, PACKAGING & WEIGHT DIV, FRANKLIN ELEC CO, 80- *Mem:* Soc Automotive Engrs; Inst Elec & Electronics Engrs. *Res:* Positive temperature coefficient thermistor; thermistoic networks; control sensors and actuators. *Mailing Add:* Franklin Elec Co Packaging & Weight Div PO Box 666 Levittown PA 19058

REES, ALLAN W, b Piqua, Ohio, Dec 23, 33; m 59; c 2. PHYSICAL BIOCHEMISTRY. *Educ:* Univ Cincinnati, ChE, 56, MS, 63, PhD(biochem), 67. *Prof Exp:* Res chemist, Cincinnati Milling Mach Co, 56-62; asst prof biochem, Univ Tex Health Sci Ctr, 69-77, ASST PROF, UNIV TEX DIV EARTH SCI, SAN ANTONIO, 77- *Concurrent Pos:* Nat Cancer Inst res fel, 67-68. *Mem:* AAAS; Fedn Am Socs Exp Biol; Am Chem Soc; Biophys Soc. *Res:* Structure and conformation of DNA and nucleoproteins; centrifugal and hydrodynamic techniques. *Mailing Add:* Univ Tex Div of Earth Sci San Antonio TX 78285

REES, ALUN HYWEL, b Pontypridd, Wales, Aug 30, 28; m 51; c 2. ORGANIC CHEMISTRY. *Educ:* Cambridge Univ, BA, 49, MA, 53, PhD(chem), 68; Univ London, PhD(org chem), 58; Oxford Univ, MA, 65. *Prof Exp:* Res chemist, Roche Prod Ltd, Eng, 49-53; lectr chem, Univ Ibadan, 53-62, sr lectr, 62-64; res fel, Oxford Univ, 64-66; assoc prof, 66-74, PROF CHEM, TRENT UNIV, 74- *Concurrent Pos:* Fulbright scholar & res fel, Harvard Univ, 59 & 63; vis prof pharmaceut chem, Univ Ife, Nigeria, 74-75; vis prof org appl chem, Univ Port, Harcourt, Nigeria, 81. *Mem:* Chem Inst Can; Am Chem Soc; Royal Soc Chem. *Res:* Heterocyclic, medicinal and natural product chemistry. *Mailing Add:* Dept of Chem Trent Univ Peterborough ON K9J 7B8 Can

REES, CHARLES SPARKS, b Dallas, Tex, Nov 21, 40; m 62; c 2. MATHEMATICS. *Educ:* La State Univ, BS, 62; Univ Kans, MA, 63, PhD(math), 67. *Prof Exp:* Asst prof math, Univ Tenn, Knoxville, 67-70; from asst prof to assoc prof math, 70-77, PROF MATH, UNIV NEW ORLEANS, 77- *Mem:* Am Math Soc; Math Asn Am. *Res:* Integration and summability of Fourier series. *Mailing Add:* Dept of Math Univ of New Orleans New Orleans LA 70122

REES, EARL DOUGLAS, b Cleveland, Ohio, May 1, 28; m; c 4. ONCOLOGY, METABOLISM. *Educ:* Harvard Univ, AB, 50; Yale Univ, MD, 54. *Prof Exp:* Intern, Hosps, Ohio State Univ, 55-56; mem biophys sect, Armed Forces Inst Path, 56-57, chief biochem sect, 57-58; instr, Ben May Lab, Univ Chicago, 58-60; asst prof med, 60-65, assoc prof Med & pharmacol, 65-70, PROF MED & PHARMACOL, MED CTR, UNIV KY, 70-, DIR CLIN RES LAB, 66- *Concurrent Pos:* Nat Found fel, Yale Univ, 54-55; Res Found res award, Med Ctr, Univ Ky, 71. *Mem:* AAAS; Am Asn Clin Chemists; Am Physiol Soc; Soc Exp Biol & Med; Am Fedn Clin Res. *Res:* Endocrine and cytogenetic aspects of carcinogenesis; protein and biophysical chemistry; clinical lipid metabolism and pharmacology; clinical endocrinology. *Mailing Add:* Dept of Med Univ of Ky Med Ctr Lexington KY 40506

REES, EBERHARD F M, b Trossingen, Ger, Apr 28, 08; US citizen; m 47. AEROSPACE TECHNOLOGY. *Educ:* Stuttgart Tech Univ, BS; Dresden Inst Technol, MS, 34. *Hon Degrees:* DSc, Rollins Col, 59, Univ Ala, Huntsville, 72. *Prof Exp:* Tech asst, Meier & Weichelt Foundry & Steel Mill, Leipzig, 34-40; plant mgr, Guided Missile Ctr, Peenemuende, Ger, 40-45; aerodyn develop engr, Ord Res & Develop, Ft Bliss, 45-50; dep chief, Guided Missile Develop Div, Huntsville, Ala, 50-56, dep dir, Army Ballistic Missile Agency, 56-60, dep dir, G C Marshall Space Flight Ctr, NASA, 60-70, dir, 70-73; RETIRED. *Honors & Awards:* Except Civil Serv Award, Secy of the Army, 59; Distinguished Civil Serv Award, Dept Defense, 60; Medal Outstanding Leadership, NASA, 66, Distinguished Serv Medal, 68 & 69. *Mem:* Nat Acad Eng; fel Am Astronaut Soc; hon mem Hermann Oberth Soc; fel Am Inst Aeronaut & Astronaut. *Res:* Rocketry; space flight technology. *Mailing Add:* 3917 Panorama Dr SE Huntsville AL 35801

REES, HORACE BENNER, JR, b Big Lake, Tex, July 25, 26; m 54; c 1. VIROLOGY. *Educ:* Univ Tex, BA, 49, MA, 50; George Washington Univ, PhD, 66. *Prof Exp:* Asst immunologist, Tex State Dept Health, 50-52; asst dir, Regional Lab, San Antonio City Health Dept, 52; dir, Abilene-Taylor County Health Unit Lab, 53; asst dir, Wene's Poultry Labs, Pleasantville, NJ, 54; microbiologist, Viral & Rickettsial Div, US Army Biol Ctr, Ft Detrick, Md, 54-66; CHIEF ECOL & TECHNOL BR, LIFE SCI LAB DIV, DESERT TEST CTR, 66- *Mem:* Am Soc Microbiol; Tissue Cult Asn; NY Acad Sci. *Res:* Rickettsiae; medical bacteriology. *Mailing Add:* Life Sci Lab Div Baker Lab Dugway UT 84022

REES, JOHN DAVID, b Los Angeles, Calif, Mar 16, 32. BIOGEOGRAPHY, CULTURAL GEOGRAPHY. *Educ:* Univ Calif, Los Angeles, BA, 55, MA, 61, PhD(geog), 71. *Prof Exp:* Asst prof, 65-66 & 68-77, ASSOC PROF GEOG, CALIF STATE UNIV, LOS ANGELES, 77- *Mem:* AAAS; Asn Am Geogr; Soc Econ Botanists. *Res:* Peasant utilization of biotic resources in middle America; rural economy; neotropical biogeography and conservation; regional geography of middle America. *Mailing Add:* Dept of Geog Calif State Univ Los Angeles CA 90032

REES, JOHN ROBERT, b Peru, Ind, Feb 17, 30; m 56; c 2. HIGH ENERGY PHYSICS. *Educ:* Ind Univ, AB, 51, MS, 54, PhD(physics), 57. *Prof Exp:* Res fel physics, Harvard Univ, 56-65; staff mem, Stanford Linear Accelerator Ctr, 65-67; chief advan accelerators br, High Energy Physics Prog Div Res, US Atomic Energy Comn, DC, 67-69; adj prof, 69-80, ASSOC DIR, STANFORD LINEAR ACCELERATOR CTR, 80- *Concurrent Pos:* Guest, Dept Physics, Mass Inst Technol, 56-65; instr, Northeastern Univ, 59-60. *Mem:* Am Phys Soc. *Res:* Particle accelerators. *Mailing Add:* Stanford Linear Accelerator Ctr PO Box 4349 Stanford CA 94305

REES, JOHN TONKS, b Kingston, Pa, Feb 6, 44. AQUATIC BIOLOGY, INVERTEBRATE ZOOLOGY. *Educ:* Wesleyan Univ, BA, 66; Univ PR, MS, 69; Univ Calif, Berkeley, PhD(zool), 75. *Prof Exp:* FEL, LAWRENCE BERKELEY LAB, UNIV CALIF, 75- *Res:* Ecology and systematics of hydrozoan; systems design for laboratory freshwater ecosystems; invertebrate culture; field limnology. *Mailing Add:* Lawrence Berkeley Lab Bldg 70 Rm 222 Univ Calif Berkeley CA 94720

REES, MANFRED HUGH, b Ger, June 29, 26; nat US; m 49; c 2. AERONOMY. *Educ:* WVa Univ, BSEE, 48, Univ Colo, MS, 56, PhD(physics), 58. *Prof Exp:* Engr, Nat Adv Comt Aeronaut, 48-49; proj engr, Sperry Gyroscope Co, 51-53; instr physics, Univ Colo, 53-58; asst prof geophys, Geophys Inst, Univ Alaska, 58-60; sr res fel appl math, Queen's Univ, Belfast, 60-61; res physicist, Univ Colo, 61-65; assoc prof physics & head dept, Univ Alaska, 65-66; mem staff, Lab Atmospheric & Space Physics, Univ Colo, Boulder, 66-75, lectr astro-geophys, 70-75; PROF GEOPHYS, UNIV ALASKA, 75- *Concurrent Pos:* Physicist, Nat Bur Standards, 56-58. *Mem:* AAAS; Optical Soc Am; Am Geophys Union. *Res:* Upper atmosphere physics; aurora and airglow; zodiacal light; spectroscopy; atomic and molecular collision processes; solar-terrestrial relations. *Mailing Add:* Geophys Inst Univ of Alaska Fairbanks AK 99701

REES, MINA SPIEGEL, b Cleveland, Ohio, Aug 2, 02; m 55. MATHEMATICS. *Educ:* Hunter Col, AB, 23; Columbia Univ, AM, 25; Univ Chicago, PhD(math), 31. *Hon Degrees:* Eighteen from US cols & univ. *Prof Exp:* From instr to prof math, Hunter Col, 26-61, dean fac, 53-61; dean grad studies, 61-68, provost, Grad Div, 68-69, pres, 69-72, EMER PROF MATH, CITY UNIV NEW YORK, 72-, EMER PRES GRAD SCH, 72- *Concurrent Pos:* Tech aide & exec asst to chief appl math panel, Nat Defense Res Comt, Off Sci Res & Develop, 43-46; head math br, Off Naval Res, 46-49, dir math sci div, 49-52, dep sci dir, 52-53; mem math div, Nat Res Coun, 53-56, mem exec comt, 54-56, comt surv math in US, 54-57; chmn adv comt math, Nat Bur Standards, 54-57, mem, 54-58; adv panel math, NSF, 55-58; Nat Sci Bd, 64-70; subcomt prof, Sci & Tech Manpower, Nat Manpower Adv Comt. *Honors & Awards:* King's Medal for Serv, Eng, 48. *Mem:* Fel AAAS (vpres & chmn sect A, 54, pres, 71, chmn bd, 72); Am Math Soc; Math Asn Am; Soc Indust & Appl Math; Inst Math Statist. *Res:* Linear algebras; numerical analysis. *Mailing Add:* 301 E 66th St New York NY 10021

REES, PAUL KLEIN, b Center Point, Tex, June 10, 02; m 35; c 2. MATHEMATICS. *Educ:* Southwestern Univ, Tex, AB, 23; Univ Tex, MA, 25; Rice Inst, PhD(math), 33. *Prof Exp:* Teacher high sch, Tex, 23-26; instr math, Tex Tech Col, 26-28; asst prof, Univ Miss, 28-30; instr math, Tex Tech Col, 34-35; asst prof, NMex Col, 35-39; from asst prof to assoc prof, Southern Methodist Univ, 39-43; prof, Southwestern La Inst, 43-46; from assoc prof to prof, 46-67, actg head dept, 47-48, EMER PROF MATH, LA STATE UNIV, BATON ROUGE, 67- *Mem:* Am Math Soc; Math Asn Am. *Res:* Fuchsian groups; automorphic functions; algebra; trigonometry; analytic geometry; mathematics of finance; calculus. *Mailing Add:* 345 Centenary Dr Baton Rouge LA 70808

REES, RICHARD WILHELM A, b Bruchsal, Ger, Oct 2, 31; US citizen; m 68; c 2. CHEMISTRY, MEDICINAL CHEMISTRY. *Educ:* Univ Basel, PhD(chem), 59. *Prof Exp:* Fel chem, Univ Calif, Los Angeles, 60-62; sr res chemist, 62-72, mgr, 72-77, ASSOC DIR RES CHEM, DIV AM HOME PROD, WYETH LABS, 77- *Mem:* Am Chem Soc. *Res:* Synthesis of chemotherapeutically active compounds. *Mailing Add:* Wyeth Labs Inc Box 8299 Philadelphia PA 19101

REES, ROBERTS M, b Akron, Ohio, Mar 15, 20; m 45; c 2. MEDICINE. *Educ:* Temple Univ, MD, 45. *Prof Exp:* Pvt pract, Akron, Ohio & Beverly Hills, Calif, 52-58; med dir, Pfizer Labs, 60-64, dir clin res, Chas Pfizer & Co, Inc, 61-64; dir clin res, Winthrop Prod Inc, 64-66; dir clin res, Winthrop Labs, Sterling Drug Inc, 66-68, vpres, 67-73, dir med res div, Sterling-Winthrop Res Inst, 68-73, corp med officer, Sterling Drug Inc, 70-73; PRES, CLIN RESOURCES INC, 78- *Concurrent Pos:* Spec consult to Exec Off of President, Spec Action Off Drug Abuse Prev, 71-72. *Mem:* AMA; Am Soc Clin Pharmacol & Therapeut. *Mailing Add:* 7 Tobacco Rd Weston CT 06883

REES, THOMAS CHARLES, b Pottsville, Pa, June 6, 39; m 65; c 2. ORGANIC CHEMISTRY. *Educ:* Mt St Mary's Col, Md, BS, 61; Pa State Univ, PhD(org chem), 66. *Prof Exp:* Fel radiation chem div, Max Planck Inst Coal Res, 65-66; sr chemist, 67-72, group leader pigment dispersions, 72-76, group leader plastics additives, 76-81, MGR, POLYMER ADDITIVES LAB, SHERWIN-WILLIAMS CO, CHICAGO, 81- *Mem:* Soc Plastics Engrs; Am Chem Soc. *Res:* Ultraviolet and heat stabilization of polymers; organometallic chemistry, including Grignard and lithium reagents and transition metal organometallics; photochemistry and color properties of pigments; flame retardants. *Mailing Add:* 516 Circle Dr Park Forest South IL 60466

REES, WILLIAM JAMES, b Kansas City, Mo, July 13, 22; m 50; c 5. MEDICINE, DERMATOLOGY. *Educ:* Rockhurst Col, AB, 42; St Louis Univ, MD, 46; Univ Minn, MPH, 50. *Prof Exp:* Pvt pract, Mo, 50-52; scientist admin med, Sci Liaison & Adv Group, DC, 52-57; Europ rep, Upjohn Co, 57-58; scientist admin med, Sci Liaison & Adv Group, Ger, 58-61; clin investr, Abbott Labs, Ill, 61-63; resident dermat, Med Ctr, Univ Calif, San Francisco, 63-65; assoc exec dir life sci res & chmn biomed res, Stanford Res Inst, 65-69, dir life sci activities, Europ Off, Switz, 69-71, asst dir, DC Off, 71-72; DIR CLIN RES, INT MED AFFAIRS, G D SEARLE & CO, 72- *Concurrent Pos:* Consult, Div Occup Health, Calif Dept Pub Health, 63-68; clin instr dermat, Med Ctr, Univ Calif, San Francisco, 65-69, asst clin prof, 69-71; colonel, Med Corps, US Army Reserve, 72- *Mem:* Am Acad Clin Toxicol; assoc Am Acad Dermat; Am Pub Health Asn; Asn Mil Surgeons US; Royal Soc Health. *Res:* Dermatology, especially occupational and tropical aspects. *Mailing Add:* Int Med Affairs G D Searle & Co Box 1045 Skokie IL 60076

REES, WILLIAM WENDELL, b Albany, NY, Dec 21, 33; m 80; c 3. ORGANIC CHEMISTRY. *Educ:* Amherst Col, BA, 55; Mass Inst Technol, PhD(chem), 58. *Prof Exp:* Asst, Amherst Col, 53-55 & Mass Inst Technol, 55-57; res chemist, 58-60, photog scientist, 60-65, admin asst, Gen Mgt Staff, 65-67, lab head, Res Labs, 67-69, sr lab head, 69-72, asst div dir, 72-77, DIV DIR, RES LABS, EASTMAN KODAK CO, 77- *Mem:* Soc Photog Sci & Eng; Am Chem Soc. *Res:* Physical organic chemistry; kinetics and mechanisms of organic reactions; photographic process; research administration. *Mailing Add:* Eastman Kodak Co Res Lab 1669 Lake Ave Rochester NY 14650

REESE, ANDY CLARE, b Wann, Okla, June 22, 42; m 65. IMMUNOLOGY. *Educ:* Univ Okla, BS, 64; Univ Mo, PhD(biochem), 71. *Prof Exp:* Assoc chemist, Skelly Oil Co, 64-66; Res assoc med, Sch Med, Case Western Reserve Univ, 70-72, fel microbiol, 72-74; asst res prof path, Mt Sinai Sch Med, 74-75; asst prof, 75-81, ASSOC PROF IMMUNOL, MED COL GA, 81- *Mem:* Am Asn Immunologists; Reticuloendothelial Soc; Am Soc Microbiol; Shock Soc; NY Acad Sci. *Res:* Physiological activities and mechanism of action of fibronectin, particularly in its interaction with macrophages; role of macrophage factors in control of the immune response. *Mailing Add:* Cell & Molecular Biol Med Col Ga Augusta GA 30912

REESE, BRUCE ALAN, b Provo, Utah, Aug 3, 23; m 45; c 3. AEROSPACE ENGINEERING, PROPULSION. *Educ:* Univ NMex, BS, 44; Purdue Univ, MS, 48, PhD(mech eng), 53. *Prof Exp:* From asst prof to prof mech eng, 53-73, dir, Jet Propulsion Ctr, 65-73, HEAD, SCH AERONAUT & ASTRONAUT, PURDUE UNIV, 73- *Concurrent Pos:* Dep dir, Nike Zeus Res & Develop, US, Army, 61-62 & tech dir, Nike X Proj Off, US Army, 62-63; consult, Sci Adv Panel, US Army, 67-; mem Sci Adv Bd, US Air Force, 69-76, Adv Group Foreign Tech Div, 70-74 & Div Adv Group Aeronaut Systs Div, 73-76; chmn, Tank & Automotive Command Sci Adv Group, 70-74; mem, Missile Command Adv Comt, 72- & Navel Res Adv Comt, 78-; adv, Assembly Engrs, Nat Res Coun, 77; consult, Aerospace Govt Agencys & Industs, 53- *Honors & Awards:* Civilian Serv Medals, US Army, 71 & 74. *Mem:* Am Inst Aeronaut & Astronaut; Am Soc Mech Eng; Sigma Xi. *Res:* Heat transfer; gas dynamics; hybrid fueled rockets; laser diffusers; slurry fuel combustion. *Mailing Add:* Sch of Aeronaut & Astronaut Purdue Univ West Lafayette IN 47907

REESE, CECIL EVERETT, b Benson, Utah, July 3, 21; m 46; c 5. POLYMER CHEMISTRY. *Educ:* Univ Utah, BS, 45, MS, 47, PhD(chem), 49. *Prof Exp:* Asst prof chem, Kans State Col, 49-50; res chemist, 50-59, res assoc, 59-67, RES FEL, E I DU PONT DE NEMOURS & CO, INC, 67- *Res:* Specific heats of organic liquids; diffusion and membrane permeability; visco-elastic properties of hair and other fibers; mechanical behavior of polyacrylonitrile fibers in the presence of an external plasticizer. *Mailing Add:* E I du Pont de Nemours & Co Inc Kinston NC 28501

REESE, ELWYN THOMAS, b Scranton, Pa, Jan 16, 12; m 40; c 2. MYCOLOGY. *Educ:* Pa State Col, BS, 33, MS, 38, PhD(mycol), 46. *Prof Exp:* Teacher high sch, Pa, 34-39; mycologist, Knaust Bros Mushroom Co, NY, 42-43; bacteriologist, Phila Qm Corps Depot, 44-45; mycologist, J T Baker Chem Co, 46-48; mycologist lab, Qm Res & Develop Ctr, Mass, 48-72, MYCOLOGIST FOOD SCI LAB, US ARMY NATICK LABS, 72- *Concurrent Pos:* Secy Army fel, 64-65. *Mem:* Mycol Soc Am; Am Chem Soc. *Res:* Decomposition of cellulose by microorganisms; physiology of fungi. *Mailing Add:* SATL US Army Natick Labs Natick MA 01760

REESE, ERNST S, b Madison, Wis, Jan 26, 31; m 61. ANIMAL BEHAVIOR, ECOLOGY. *Educ:* Princeton Univ, AB, 53; Univ Calif, Los Angeles, PhD(zool), 60. *Prof Exp:* Assoc prof, 60-71, PROF ZOOL, UNIV HAWAII, 71-, NSF RES GRANT, 63- *Concurrent Pos:* NSF fel, Univ Groningen, 61-62; mem adv sci comt, Charles Darwin Found for Galapagos Isles, 66- *Mem:* AAAS; Ecol Soc Am; Animal Behav Soc (pres-elect). *Res:* Ecology and behavior of marine animals, especially crustacea and fish; emphasis on comparative developmental aspects and ecological significance behavior. *Mailing Add:* Dept of Zool Univ of Hawaii Honolulu HI 96822

REESE, FLOYD ERNEST, b Ransomville, NY, Nov 8, 17; m 43; c 3. BIOCHEMISTRY, ORGANIC CHEMISTRY. *Educ:* Greenville Col, BS, 41; Purdue Univ, MS, 44, PhD(biochem), 47. *Prof Exp:* Res chemist biochem, Upjohn Co, Mich, 47-48; from assoc prof to prof chem, Houghton Col, 48-56; from asst prof to assoc prof, 56-65, head dept, 63-67, PROF CHEM, CALIF STATE UNIV, CHICO, 65- *Mem:* Am Chem Soc. *Res:* Metabolism of amino acids and guanidino acids; gamma irradiation of proteins. *Mailing Add:* 908 Wagstaff Paradise CA 95969

REESE, HAMIT DARWIN, b Somerset, Colo, Dec 28, 17; m 40; c 4. BIOCHEMISTRY. *Educ:* Brigham Young Univ, AB, 40; Iowa State Col, PhD(biophys chem), 47. *Prof Exp:* Instr chem, Iowa State Col, 44-46, asst, 46-47; assoc prof, 47-74, PROF CHEM, ORE STATE UNIV, 74- *Concurrent Pos:* Sci adv, Int Coop Admin contract, Kasetsart Univ, Bangkok, 57-58; dir chem dept, TV Teacher Training Prog, 67-; assoc dir, NSF-Col Sci Improv Prog Teacher Training for Community Col Sci Teachers, 69-71. *Mem:* Am Chem Soc; Sigma Xi. *Res:* Industrial fermentations; evaluation of enzyme preparations; analytical methods for biological organic and inorganic chemicals; microbiological preparation of biochemical compounds; training methods for chemistry teachers. *Mailing Add:* Dept of Chem Ore State Univ Corvallis OR 97330

REESE, LYMON C(LIFTON), b Murfreesboro, Ark, Apr 27, 17; m 48; c 3. CIVIL ENGINEERING. *Educ:* Univ Tex, BS, 49, MS, 50; Univ Calif, PhD, 55. *Prof Exp:* Rodman, Int Boundary Comn, 39-41; layout engr, E I du Pont de Nemours & Co, 41-42; field engr, Assoc Contractors & Engrs, 45; draftsman, Phillips Petrol Co, 46-48; res scientist, Univ Tex, 48-50; asst prof civil eng, Miss State Col, 50-51, 53-55; from asst prof to assoc prof, 55-64, chmn dept, 65-72, T U Taylor prof & assoc dean res, 72-79, PROF CIVIL ENG, UNIV TEX, AUSTIN, 64-, RASHID CHAIR, 81- *Concurrent Pos:* Consult, var companies & govt agencies, 55-; Karl Terzaghi lectr, 76. *Honors & Awards:* Middlebrooks Award, Am Soc Civil Engrs, 58. *Mem:* Nat Acad Eng; Am Soc Eng Educ; Am Soc Civil Engrs. *Res:* Soil mechanics; interaction between soils and structures; analysis and design of foundations for offshore structures; behavior of laterally loaded piles. *Mailing Add:* Dept of Civil Eng Univ of Tex Austin TX 78712

REESE, MILLARD GRIFFIN, JR, b Dinwiddie, Va, Aug 14, 31; m 58. ORGANIC CHEMISTRY. *Educ:* Randolph-Macon Col, BS, 52; Univ Va, MS, 55, PhD(org chem), 57. *Prof Exp:* RES CHEMIST, DACRON RES LAB, E I DU PONT DE NEMOURS & CO, INC, 57- *Res:* Unsaturated diketones, reactions; reaction mechanisms and derivatives; condensation polymerization; properties of high polymers; textile fibers. *Mailing Add:* Dacron Res Lab E I du Pont de Nemours & Co Inc Kinston NC 28501

REESE, NATHAN ALLAN, b Mooreland, Okla, Feb 16, 37; m 58; c 2. BIOCHEMISTRY, ANIMAL NUTRITION. *Educ:* Okla State Univ, BS, 60; Univ Wis-Madison, MS, 62, PhD(animal sci, biochem), 65. *Prof Exp:* Nutritionist, Anderson, Clayton & Co, Inc, 65-66, Anderson, Clayton & Co, SA, Mex, 66-68 & Anderson, Clayton & Co, Inc, 68-73; INDEPENDENT CONSULT NUTRIT, 73- *Mem:* Am Soc Animal Sci; Am Dairy Sci Asn; Coun Agr Sci & Technol. *Res:* Applied beef cattle nutrition; utilization of non-protein nitrogen; total protein; energy-protein relationships. *Mailing Add:* Box 1007 Hooker OK 73945

REESE, ROBERT LEWIS, horticulture, weed science, see previous edition

REESE, ROBERT TRAFTON, b Norfolk, Va, Apr 11, 42; m 71. IMMUNOLOGY. *Educ:* Va Polytech Inst, BS, 64; Yale Univ, PhD(microbiol), 73. *Prof Exp:* Fel immunol, Johns Hopkins Univ, 70-74; res assoc, Rockefeller Univ, 74, asst prof immunol, 74-80; MEM FAC, DEPT BIOL, JOHNS HOPKINS UNIV, 80- *Mem:* Sigma Xi. *Res:* Regulation of the immune response; immunology of malaria. *Mailing Add:* Dept Biol Johns Hopkins Univ Baltimore MD 21218

REESE, THOMAS SARGENT, b Cleveland, Ohio, May 20, 35; m 75; c 2. CELL BIOLOGY, NEUROSCIENCE. *Educ:* Harvard Univ, BA, 57; Columbia Univ, MD, 62. *Prof Exp:* Res asst, Psycho-Acoust Lab, Harvard Univ, 57-58; intern, Boston City Hosp, 62-63; res assoc, NIH, 63-65; res fel anat, Harvard Med Sch, 65-66; res med officer, NIH, 66-70; HEAD, SECT FUNCTIONAL NEUROANAT, LAB NEUROPATH & NEUROANAT SCI, NAT INST NEUROL & COMMUN DISORDERS & STROKE, 70- *Concurrent Pos:* Instr neurobiol, Marine Biol Labs, Woods Hole, Mass, 74- *Honors & Awards:* C Judson Herrick Award; Superior Serv AWard, USPHS; Mathilde Solowey Award. *Mem:* Am Asn Anatomists; Am Soc Cell Biol; Soc Neurosci; Biophys Soc. *Res:* Membrane structure and function in neural cells, particularly synapses. *Mailing Add:* Bldg 36 Rm 3B-24 NIH Bethesda MD 20205

REESE, WELDON HAROLD, b Stonewall Co, Tex, May 5, 27; m 48; c 2. POLLUTION BIOLOGY, PHYCOLOGY. *Educ:* Tex Tech Col, BS, 52, MS, 61; Ore State Univ, PhD(pollution biol, phycol), 66. *Prof Exp:* Teacher sec schs, 52-61; NSF fel pollution res, 61-62; res asst, Ore State Univ, 62-63, fel pollution res & res asst, 63-64; assoc prof, 66-77, PROF BIOL, WAYLAND COL, 77-, HEAD DEPT BIOL & CHMN DIV SCI, 66- *Concurrent Pos:* Lectr, Jamaica, 67-68; Terra-Rite Corp res grant, 67-; res grant, Tex Agr Exp Sta, 68-; mem int comn inter-col educ, Southern Asn Baptist Col & Schs, 68- *Mem:* AAAS; Am Soc Limnol & Oceanog; Phycol Soc Am. *Res:* Effects of community imbalance in lentic and lotic environments caused by organic enrichment and other pollutants; periphyton community. *Mailing Add:* Dept of Biol Wayland Col Plainview TX 79072

REESE, WILLIAM, b Kansas City, Mo, Feb 24, 37; m 58; c 1. THERMAL PHYSICS. *Educ:* Reed Col, BA, 58; Univ Ill, MS, 60, PhD(physics), 62. *Prof Exp:* Res assoc physics, Univ Ill, 62-63; from asst prof to assoc prof, 63-73, PROF PHYSICS, US NAVAL POSTGRAD SCH, 73- *Mem:* Am Phys Soc. *Res:* Low temperature physics; thermal properties of polymers; second order phase transitions; military systems analysis. *Mailing Add:* Dept of Physics US Naval Postgrad Sch Monterey CA 93940

REESE, WILLIAM DEAN, b Baltimore, Md, Sept 10, 28; m 50; c 4. BIOLOGY. *Educ:* Univ Md, BS, 53; Fla State Univ, MS, 55, PhD(bot), 57. *Prof Exp:* Asst bot, Fla State Univ, 53-55; from asst prof to assoc prof, 57-66, chmn dept, 74-77, PROF BIOL, UNIV SOUTHWESTERN LA, 66-, HEAD DEPT, 81- *Concurrent Pos:* Ed, The Bryologist, 70-74. *Mem:* AAAS; Soc Bot Mex; Am Bryol & Lichenological Soc (vpres, 77-79, pres, 79-81); Int Asn Plant Taxon; Brit Bryol Soc. *Res:* Taxonomy, distribution and ecology of Musci. *Mailing Add:* Dept of Biol Univ of Southwestern La Lafayette LA 70504

REESE, WILLIAM GEORGE, b Lewiston, Utah, Apr 2, 17; m 42; c 3. PSYCHIATRY. *Educ:* Univ Idaho, BS & MS, 38; Washington Univ, MD, 42. *Prof Exp:* Intern internal med, Barnes Hosp, St Louis, 42-43; resident psychiat, Johns Hopkins Hosp, 46-48, instr psychiatrist, 48-51; PROF PSYCHIAT & CHMN DEPT, COL MED, UNIV ARK MED SCI, LITTLE ROCK, 51- *Concurrent Pos:* Commonwealth fel, Johns Hopkins Univ, 46-48; dir prof educ, Vet Admin Hosp, Perry Point, Md, 48-51, consult, North Little Rock. *Mem:* AMA; fel Am Psychiat Asn; Pavlovian Soc; fel Am Col Psychiat. *Res:* Basic psychophysiology. *Mailing Add:* Dept Psychiat Univ Ark Med Sci 4301 W Markham Little Rock AR 72201

REESMAN, ARTHUR LEE, b Eldorado, Ill, Feb 20, 33; m 63; c 3. GEOLOGY. *Educ:* Eureka Col, BS, 55; Univ Mo-Columbia, AM, 61, PhD(geol), 66. *Prof Exp:* Asst geol, Univ Mo-Columbia, 59-62; asst prof, Univ NDak, 62-63 & Western Mich Univ, 66-67; asst prof, 68-70, ASSOC PROF GEOL, VANDERBILT UNIV, 70- *Mem:* AAAS; Mineral Soc Am; Clay Minerals Soc; Geochem Soc. *Res:* Chemical weathering of rocks and minerals; genesis of clay minerals. *Mailing Add:* Dept of Geol Vanderbilt Univ Nashville TN 37235

REESOR, JOHN ELGIN, b Saskatoon, Sask, June 2, 20; m 54; c 3. GEOLOGY. *Educ:* Univ BC, BASc, 49; Princeton Univ, PhD(geol), 52. *Prof Exp:* GEOLOGIST, CAN GEOL SURV, 52- *Mem:* Geol Soc Am. *Mailing Add:* Geol Surv of Can 601 Booth St Ottawa ON K1A 0E8 Can

REETHOF, GERHARD, b Teplice, Czech, July 1, 22; US citizen; m 56; c 3. MECHANICAL ENGINEERING, ACOUSTICS. *Educ:* Mass Inst Technol, SB, 47, SM, 49, ScD(mech eng). 54. *Prof Exp:* Proj engr, Sperry Gyroscope Co, NY, 49-50; asst prof fluid power & mech eng, Dynamic Anal & Controls Lab, Mass Inst Technol, 50-55; chief res, Vickers Inc, Mich, 55-58; mgr acoustics eng, Flight Propulsion Div, Gen Elec Co, Ohio, 58-67; ALCOA PROF MECH ENG, PA STATE UNIV, 67- *Concurrent Pos:* Fulbright prof, Finland Inst Technol, Helsinki, 53-54; consult, Electronics Div, Gen Dynamics Corp, 67-70, US Nuclear Regulatory Comn, 68- & Army Mat Command, 71-; expert witness, Du Pont Atomic Energy Div, 75- *Mem:* Am Soc Mech Engrs; Acoust Soc Am; Inst Noise Control; Am Soc Eng Educ; Am Inst Aeronaut & Astronaut. *Res:* Acoustics and noise control; jet noise; fan noise; propagation and attenuation of complex acoustic waves in ducts; valve noise; transportation noise; probabilistic methods in design and reliability. *Mailing Add:* 213 Eng Unit E Pa State Univ University Park PA 16802

REETZ, HAROLD FRANK, JR, b Watseka, Ill, Mar 10, 48; m 73; c 2. CROP PRODUCTION, COMPUTER SIMULATION. *Educ:* Univ Ill, BS, 70; Purdue Univ, MS, 72, PhD(agron, crop physiol), 76. *Prof Exp:* EXTEN RES AGRONOMIST GRAIN CROP PROD, DEPT AGRON, PURDUE UNIV, 74- *Concurrent Pos:* Consult, Control Data Corp & Int Harvester, 78- *Mem:* Am Soc Agron; Crop Sci Soc Am; Coun Agr Scientists & Technologists. *Res:* Computer simulation of crop production; physiological reactions and production impact of environmental stresses; cultural practices in grain crop production; computer applications in agribusiness and farming. *Mailing Add:* Dept of Agron Purdue Univ West Lafayette IN 47907

REEVE, AUBREY C, b Staines, Eng, June 23, 37; m 59; c 3. ENVIRONMENTAL CONTROL, CHEMICAL ENGINEERING. *Educ:* Univ Birmingham, BSc, 58, PhD(gasification of hydrocarbons), 61. *Prof Exp:* Res fel movement of particles, McGill Univ & Pulp & Paper Res Inst Can,

61-63; sr chem engr, Res Div, Carrier Corp, 63-73, mgr systs develop, 73-74, proj control coordr, 74-75; res engr, 75-78, SR RES ENGR, AMOCO CHEM CORP, 78- *Mem:* Assoc mem Am Inst Chem Engrs. *Res:* By-product aromatics during gasification of hydrocarbons; motion of particles through force fields; removal of odors; air pollution control; gas absorption in packed columns; process development. *Mailing Add:* Amoco Chem Corp PO Box 400 Naperville IL 60540

REEVE, EDWARD WILKINS, b Westmont, NJ, July 31, 13; m 40; c 3. ORGANIC CHEMISTRY. *Educ:* Drexel Inst Technol, BS, 36; Univ Wis, PhD(org chem), 40. *Prof Exp:* Instr org chem, Univ Md, 40-41; tech aide, Off Sci Res & Develop, 41-46; assoc prof, 46-51, PROF CHEM, UNIV MD, COLLEGE PARK, 51- *Mem:* AAAS; Am Chem Soc. *Res:* Mechanism of reactions; catalytic hydrogenation; epoxides; synthesis of alpha-methoxyarylacetic acids; reactions of trichloromethylcarbinols; acidities of alcohols. *Mailing Add:* 4708 Harvard Rd College Park MD 20740

REEVE, ELDROW, b Hurricane, Utah, Feb 4, 17; m 41; c 2. PLANT PHYSIOLOGY, SOILS. *Educ:* Utah State Univ, BS, 39, MS, 41; Rutgers Univ, PhD(plant physiol), 44. *Prof Exp:* Asst plant physiol & bot, Utah State Univ, 39-41; soil chemist, Grocery Store Prod Co, Pa, 44-45; div mgr agr res, 45-60, assoc dir, 60-66, VPRES VEG RES, INST AGR RES, CAMPBELL SOUP CO, 66- *Mem:* AAAS; Sigma Xi; Am Inst Biol Sci; Am Soc Agron; Soil Sci Soc Am. *Res:* Soil fertility; plant nutrition, cultural practices-vegetable production. *Mailing Add:* Campbell Soup Co Campbell Pl Camden NJ 08101

REEVE, ERNEST BASIL, b Liverpool, Eng, May 5, 12; m 53; c 4. PHYSIOLOGY. *Educ:* Oxford Univ, BA, 35, BM, BCh, 38. *Prof Exp:* Clin asst & mem staff, Clin Res Unit, Guys Hosp, London, 40-52; mem permanent staff, Med Res Coun, London, 46-52; vis prof physiol, Columbia Univ, 53; assoc prof, 53-63, PROF MED, SCH MED, UNIV COLO, DENVER, 63- *Mem:* Am Physiol Soc; Brit Physiol Soc. *Res:* Metabolism of plasma proteins, especially clotting proteins; regulation of body water, sodium, calcium and phosphate; systems analysis of physiological functions. *Mailing Add:* Div of Lab Med Univ of Colo Med Ctr Denver CO 80262

REEVE, MARIAN E, b Placerville, Calif, Aug 28, 20; m 41; c 4. PLANT ANATOMY. *Educ:* Univ Calif, Berkeley, AB, 40, PhD(bot), 49. *Prof Exp:* prof biol, Merritt Col, 55-81; RETIRED. *Mem:* AAAS; Bot Soc Am; Nat Asn Biol Teachers. *Res:* Identification and preservation of the diverse plant habitats of northern California. *Mailing Add:* 4325 Mountain View Ave Oakland CA 94605

REEVE, PETER, b London, Eng, Jan, 3, 34; m 62; c 2. IMMUNOLOGY, MICROBIOLOGY. *Educ:* London Univ, BSc, 55, PhD(anat), 61. *Prof Exp:* Virologist, Med Res Coun, 58-67; asst prof microbiol, San Francisco Med Sch, 63-64; Wellcome lectr virol, Royal Postgrad Med Sch, 67-72; lectr bact, Univ Col Hosp Med Sch, London, 72-75; lab mgr, Sandoz Res Inst, Vienna, 75-79; sr scientist, Nat Inst Biol Standards, London, 79-81; SCIENTIFIC MGR, SMITH KLINE & FRENCH LABS, 81- *Mem:* Inst Biol; Royal Col Path; Soc Gen Microbiol. *Res:* Mechanisms of viral pathoglinicity; chlamydial infections; influenza, parainfluenza and polioviruses. *Mailing Add:* PO Box 7929 Philadelphia PA 19101

REEVE, RONALD C(ROPPER), b Hinckley, Utah, Mar 27, 20; m 40; c 3. AGRICULTURAL ENGINEERING. *Educ:* Utah State Univ, BS, 43; Iowa State Univ, MS, 49. *Prof Exp:* Engr, Boeing Aircraft Co, Wash, 43-45; irrig & drainage engr, Salinity Lab, USDA, 46-55, tech staff specialist, Salinity Lab & Western Soil & Water Mgt Br, Soil & Water Conserv Res Div, Agr Res Serv, 55-57, agr engr, Salinity Lab, 57-64, res invests leader, 64-74, staff scientist water mgt, Nat Prog Staff, Soil, Water & Air Sci, 73-77; TECH DIR, ADVAN DRAINAGE SYSTS, INC, 77- *Concurrent Pos:* Consult, Abaca invests, div cotton & other fiber crops & dis, Bur Plant Indust, Soils & Agr Eng, Costa Rica, 51; drainage res proj consult, PR Agr Exp Sta & Univ PR, 55 & 56; consult, Col Agr Eng, Punjab Agr Univ, 66, Int Eng Co, Inc, Ankara, Turkey, 66 & Food & Agr Orgn, UN, Mexico City, 68; adj prof agr eng, Ohio State Univ, 70-74. *Mem:* Fel Am Soc Agr Engrs; Am Soc Civil Engrs; Int Comn Irrig & Drainage. *Res:* Water management, especially irrigation, drainage and salinity control. *Mailing Add:* Advan Drainage Systs Inc 3300 Riverside Dr Columbus OH 43221

REEVES, ANDREW LOUIS, b Budapest, Hungary, Oct 13, 24; nat US; m 51; c 3. TOXICOLOGY. *Educ:* Univ Munich, dipl, 51-53; Wayne State Univ, PhD(physiol chem), 59. *Prof Exp:* Res assoc indust med & hyg, 55-63, from asst prof to assoc prof, 63-72, PROF OCCUP & ENVIRON HEALTH, SCH MED, WAYNE STATE UNIV, 72- *Concurrent Pos:* Sr sci fel, Univ Milan, 73; mem permanent comn, Int Asn Occup Health; vis prof, Univ Wurzburg, 80-81. *Mem:* AAAS; Am Chem Soc; Am Indust Hyg Asn; NY Acad Sci. *Res:* Biochemical aspects of industrial toxicology; mechanism of action of air pollutants; etiology of pulmonary carcinogenesis; toxicology of arsenic, asbestos, barium, beryllium. *Mailing Add:* Dept of Occup & Environ Health Wayne State Univ Sch of Med Detroit MI 48226

REEVES, BARRY L(UCAS), b St Louis, Mo, Jan 11, 35; m 54; c 3. MECHANICAL ENGINEERING, PHYSICS. *Educ:* Washington Univ, St Louis, BS, 56, MS, 58, DSc(eng, physics), 60. *Prof Exp:* Res assoc, McDonnell Aircraft Corp, Mo, 59-60; Air Force Off Sci Res fel, Aeronaut Dept, Calif Inst Technol, 60-64; sr staff scientist, 64-72, SR CONSULT SCIENTIST, AVCO SPACE SYSTS DIV, AVCO CORP, 72- *Concurrent Pos:* Consult, Space Gen Corp, 62-63 & Nat Eng & Sci Co, 63-64. *Res:* Hypersonic wakes and boundary layers; laminar and turbulent separated flows; massive turbulent ablation; shock wave-boundary layer interactions. *Mailing Add:* 10 Hillcrest Pkwy Winchester MA 01890

REEVES, CORWIN C, JR, b Cincinnati, Ohio, May 19, 30; div; c 6. GEOLOGY. *Educ:* Univ Okla, BS, 55, MS, 57; Tex Tech Univ, PhD(geol), 70. *Prof Exp:* Geologist, Texaco, Inc, 56-57; from instr to assoc prof, 57-72, PROF GEOL, TEX TECH UNIV, 72- *Mem:* Am Inst Prof Geol; Am Asn Petrol Geologists; Geol Soc Am; Am Quaternary Asn. *Res:* Aerial photography uses in geomorphic studies; remote sensing methods for mineral evaluations; uranium mineralization in calcrete, lacustrine. *Mailing Add:* Dept of Geosci Tex Tech Univ Lubbock TX 79409

REEVES, DALE LESLIE, b Norton, Kans, Mar 24, 36; m 57; c 3. PLANT BREEDING, AGRONOMY. *Educ:* Kans State Univ, BS, 58, MS, 63; Colo State Univ, PhD(plant genetics), 69. *Prof Exp:* Asst county agent, Kans State Univ, 62-63; instr field crops, Colo State Univ, 63-70; asst prof, 70-74, assoc prof, 74-80, PROF PLANT BREEDING, SOUTH DAK STATE UNIV, 80- *Mem:* Am Soc Agron; Crop Sci Soc Am. *Res:* Oat improvement; improving yield, straw strength and rust resistance in oats; increasing protein levels by breeding. *Mailing Add:* Dept of Plant Sci S Dak State Univ Brookings SD 57007

REEVES, EDMOND MORDEN, b London, Ont, Jan 14, 34; m 56; c 2. SPACEFLIGHT INSTRUMENTATION, SOLAR PHYSICS. *Educ:* Western Ontario Univ, BSc, 56, MSc, 57, PhD(physics), 59. *Prof Exp:* Nat Res Coun Can overseas fel, Imp Col, Univ London, 59-61; res physicist & lectr astron, Harvard Univ, 61-78, sr res assoc, Harvard Col Observ, 68-78, assoc, 78-80, sect head, Nat Ctr Atmospheric Res, High Altitude Observ, 78-82; CHIEF, INST DEVELOP BR, SPACELAB FLIGHT DIV, OFF SPACE SCI & APPLICATIONS, NASA, 82- *Concurrent Pos:* Mem solar physics panel, Astron Missions Bd, NASA, 68-71, consult, 68-77 & 79-81, mem space shuttle opers mgt working group, 72-76; physicist, Smithsonian Astrophys Observ, 73-78. *Honors & Awards:* Except Sci Achievement Medal, NASA, 74. *Mem:* Int Astron Union; Am Astron Soc; fel Optical Soc Am; Int Acad Astronautics. *Res:* Vacuum ultraviolet spectroscopy of the sun from rockets and satellites; related problems in laboratory astrophysics using laboratory plasmas from the far ultraviolet to the visible. *Mailing Add:* NASA Hq Code SM-8 300 Maryland Ave SW Washington DC 20546

REEVES, FONTAINE BRENT, JR, b Eufaula, Ala, May 16, 39; m 64; c 2. MYCOLOGY. *Educ:* Tulane Univ, BS, 61, MS, 63; Univ Ill, PhD(bot), 66. *Prof Exp:* From asst prof to assoc prof bot, 66-79, PROF PLANT PATH, COLO STATE UNIV, 79- *Mem:* AAAS; Mycol Soc Am; Bot Soc Am. *Res:* Cytology and evolution of fungi; ultrastructure of fungi; mycorrhizae. *Mailing Add:* Dept of Bot & Plant Path Colo State Univ Ft Collins CO 80523

REEVES, HARRY JOSEPH, b New York, NY, Nov 11, 31. PHYSICAL SCIENCE. *Educ:* Fla State Univ, BS, 64. *Prof Exp:* Mathematician, 68-74, PHYSICAL SCIENTIST, US ARMY BALLISTIC RES LAB, 74- *Res:* Develop and evaluate the effectiveness of materials and techniques designed to reduce the hazards associated with the transport, storage and use of ammunition stores in a combat environment. *Mailing Add:* Ballistic Res Lab USDA-ARRADCOM DRDAR-BLV Aberdeen Proving Ground MD 21005

REEVES, HENRY COURTLAND, b Camden, NJ, Nov 25, 33; m 52; c 2. BIOCHEMISTRY, BACTERIAL PHYSIOLOGY. *Educ:* Franklin & Marshall Col, BS, 55; Vanderbilt Univ, MA, 56, PhD(biochem), 59. *Prof Exp:* USPHS fels bact physiol, Walter Reed Army Inst Res, Washington, DC, 60-61 & biochem, Albert Einstein Med Ctr, 61-63, USPHS res career develop awardee, 62-69; vis investr, Max Planck Inst Cell Chem, 65-66; mem fac biochem, Albert Einstein Med Ctr, 66-69; chmn dept bot & microbiol, 72-77, PROF MICROBIOL, ARIZ STATE UNIV, 69- *Concurrent Pos:* Vis investr Biochem Inst, Freiburg, Ger, 75-76; dir Div Physiol, Cell & Molecular Biol, NSF, 77-79. *Mem:* Sigma Xi; AAAS; Am Soc Biol Chem; Am Chem Soc; Am Soc Microbiol. *Res:* Enzymology; intermediary metabolism; bacterial genetics. *Mailing Add:* Dept of Bot & Microbiol Ariz State Univ Tempe AZ 85281

REEVES, HOMER EUGENE, b Atoka, Okla, Dec 4, 28; m 60; c 3. AGRONOMY. *Educ:* Okla State Univ, BS, 55, MS, 57; Kans State Univ, PhD, 71. *Prof Exp:* Asst, Okla State Univ, 55-57; from asst prof to assoc prof agron, 57-73, PROF AGRON & BIOL SCI, PANHANDLE STATE UNIV, 73- *Concurrent Pos:* Asst, Kans State Univ, 65-67, vis asst prof, 70-72. *Mem:* Am Soc Agron. *Res:* Crop ecology; crop and soil management; weed control; forage crops; plant identification; seed technology; plant growth and development; water management. *Mailing Add:* Dept Agron Panhandle State Univ Box 338 Goodwell OK 73939

REEVES, JAMES BLANCHETTE, b Beaumont, Tex, Jan 24, 24; m 47; c 2. MEDICAL MICROBIOLOGY. *Educ:* La State Univ, BS, 48, MS, 49; Univ Tex, PhD, 64. *Prof Exp:* Lab dir, State Health Dept, Tex, 50-55; from asst prof to assoc prof biol sci, Univ Tex, 55-61, prof & head dept, 61-70, coordr health related progs, 70-75; asst dean, 75-77, PROF MICROBIOL, TEX COL OSTEOP MED, 77- *Concurrent Pos:* USPHS res grant, 58-59; Res Corp grant, 62-63. *Mem:* AAAS; Am Soc Microbiol. *Res:* Sanitary bacteriology; composting of sewage sludge; growth initiation and inhibition; public health bacteriology; proteases from pseudomonas aeruginosa burn strains. *Mailing Add:* 5433 Northcrest Rd Ft Worth TX 76107

REEVES, JERRY JOHN, b Watsonville, Calif, Oct 5, 43; m 66; c 1. ENDOCRINOLOGY, REPRODUCTIVE PHYSIOLOGY. *Educ:* Ore State Univ, BS, 65, MS, 67; Univ Nebr, Lincoln, PhD(reprod physiol & animal sci), 69. *Prof Exp:* Res asst animal sci, Univ Nebr, Lincoln, 67-69; instr med & NIH fel, Med Sch, Tulane Univ, La & endocrine & polypeptide lab, Vet Admin Hosp, New Orleans, La, 69-70; asst prof, 70-75, ASSOC PROF ANIMAL SCI, WASH STATE UNIV, 75- *Concurrent Pos:* NIH grant, Wash State Univ, 70- *Mem:* Am Soc Animal Sci; Soc Study Reproduction; Endocrine Soc. *Res:* Neuroendocrinology concerning hypothalamic control of reproduction, growth and lactation. *Mailing Add:* Dept of Animal Sci Clark Hall Wash State Univ Pullman WA 99163

REEVES, JOHN PAUL, b Bryn Mawr, Pa, June 16, 42; m 67; c 3. BIOCHEMISTRY, PHYSIOLOGY. *Educ:* Juniata Col, BS, 64; Mass Inst Technol, PhD(biol), 69. *Prof Exp:* Asst prof biol, Allen Univ, 69-70; NIH fel, Rutgers Univ, 70-72; guest worker biochem, Roche Inst Molecular Biol, 72-73; from asst prof to assoc prof physiol, Univ Tex Health Sci Ctr, Dallas, 73-81; ASSOC RESEARCHER, ROCHE INST MOLECULAR BIOL, NJ, 81- *Concurrent Pos:* NIH grantee, 74- & NSF, 78- *Mem:* AAAS; Biophys Soc; Am Physiol Soc. *Res:* Permeability properties and transport activities of biological membranes. *Mailing Add:* Dept Biochem Roche Inst Molecular Biol Nutley NJ 07110

REEVES, JOHN T, b Hazard, Ky, Nov 17, 28; c 2. CARDIOLOGY. *Educ:* Mass Inst Technol, BS, 50; Univ Pa, MD, 54. *Prof Exp:* USPHS res fel cardiol, Univ Colo, 57-58, Colo Heart Asn res fel, 58-59, Am Heart Asn advan res fel, 59-61; from asst prof to prof med, Univ Ky, 61-72; PROF MED, UNIV COLO MED CTR, DENVER, 72- *Mem:* Am Physiol Soc; Soc Exp Biol Med; Am Col Chest Physicians; Am Thoracic Soc. *Mailing Add:* Box B-133 Univ Colo Med Ctr Denver CO 80262

REEVES, LEONARD WALLACE, b Bristol, Eng, Feb 8, 30; m 54. PHYSICAL CHEMISTRY. *Educ:* Bristol Univ, BSc, 51, PhD(phys chem), 54, DSc, 65. *Prof Exp:* Res asst, Univ Calif, 54-56; fel, Nat Res Coun Can, 56-57; fel, Mellon Inst, 57-58; from asst prof to prof chem, Univ BC, 58-69; chmn dept, 69-71; PROF CHEM, UNIV WATERLOO, 69- *Concurrent Pos:* Vis prof, Univ Sao Paulo, 67-; Noranda lectr, 69. *Mem:* AAAS; Am Chem Soc; fel Chem Inst Can; Am Phys Soc; Int Soc Magnetic Resonance. *Res:* Metal ions in aqueous and ordered environments; lyotropic liquid crystals and membranes; chemical exchange and reaction mechanisms; pulsed and continuous wave nuclear magnetic resonance; molecular structure and intermolecular forces. *Mailing Add:* Rm 131 Dept of Chem Univ of Waterloo Waterloo ON N2L 3G1 Can

REEVES, MELVIN MITCHELL, cardiovascular surgery, see previous edition

REEVES, PERRY CLAYTON, b Brady, Tex, Nov 9, 42; m 64; c 2. CHEMISTRY. *Educ:* Abilene Christian Col, BS, 65; Univ Tex, Austin, PhD(chem), 69. *Prof Exp:* From asst prof to prof chem, Southern Methodist Univ, 69-80; PROF CHEM, ABILENE CHRISTIAN UNIV, 80-, DEAN, COL NATURAL & APPL SCI, 81- *Mem:* Am Chem Soc; Royal Soc Chem. *Res:* Organic synthesis via organometallic compounds. *Mailing Add:* Dept Chem Abilene Christian Univ Abilene TX 79699

REEVES, RAYMOND, b St Louis, Mo, June 29, 43; div; c 2. NUCLEIC ACID BIOCHEMISTRY, BIOCHEMISTRY OF GENE REGULATION. *Educ:* Univ Calif, Berkeley, BA, 66, PhD, 71. *Prof Exp:* Fel, Oxford Univ, Eng, 71-72; fel, Med Res Coun Lab Molecular Biol, Cambridge, 72-73; asst prof, Univ BC, 73-78; ASSOC PROF BIOCHEM, BIOPHYS, MOLECULAR GENETICS & CELL BIOL, WASHINGTON STATE UNIV, 79- *Mem:* Am Soc Biol Chemists; Can Biochem Soc; Am Soc Cell Biol; Int Soc Develop Biol; Tissue Cult Asn. *Res:* Biochemistry of eukaryotic gene regulation; control of messenger RNA transcription and translation during cellular differentiation; chromatin structure and function. *Mailing Add:* Biochem/Biophys Prog Washington State Univ Pullman WA 99164

REEVES, RICHARD EDWIN, b Lincoln, Nebr, Oct 28, 12; m. ORGANIC CHEMISTRY. *Educ:* Doane Col, BA, 33; Yale Univ, PhD(chem), 36. *Prof Exp:* Nat Tuberc Asn res fel, Yale Univ, 36-37; Wood mem fel, 40-41; fel chem, Rockefeller Inst, 37-38; res chemist, Boyce Thompson Inst Plant Res, 38-40; from assoc chemist to chemist, Southern Regional Res Lab, Bur Agr & Indust Chem, USDA, 41-53, Southern Utilization Res Br, Agr Res Serv, 53-54; res assoc, 54-57, assoc prof, 57-63, PROF BIOCHEM, SCH MED, LA STATE UNIV, NEW ORLEANS, 63-, PROF TROP MED & MED PARASITOL, 74- *Mem:* Am Chem Soc; Am Soc Trop Med & Hyg; Am Soc Biol Chem. *Res:* Bacterial lipids and carbohydrates; cellulose chemistry; fine structure of glycosides; nutrition and biochemistry of Entamoeba Histolytica. *Mailing Add:* La State Univ Sch of Med New Orleans LA 70112

REEVES, ROBERT BLAKE, b Philadelphia, Pa, July 26, 30; m 67; c 2. PHYSIOLOGY. *Educ:* Swarthmore Col, AB, 52; Harvard Univ, PhD(physiol), 59. *Prof Exp:* Res assoc physiol, Univ Pa, 59-60; res assoc biophys, Sch Med, State Univ NY Buffalo, 60-61; asst prof physiol, Cornell Univ, 61-66; assoc prof, 66-76, PROF PHYSIOL, STATE UNIV NY BUFFALO, 76- *Concurrent Pos:* Jr fel, Soc Fels, Harvard Univ, 57-60. *Mem:* Am Physiol Soc; Am Ornith Union; Soc Gen Physiol; Am Soc Cell Biol; Biophys Soc. *Res:* Renal and cardiovascular physiology; cardiac metabolism; acid-base balance; oxygen transport. *Mailing Add:* Dept of Physiol State Univ NY Sch of Med Buffalo NY 14214

REEVES, ROBERT DONALD, b Lubbock, Tex, Jan 14, 42; m 67; c 2. NUTRITION, BIOCHEMISTRY. *Educ:* Tex Tech Univ, BA, 64, MS, 65; Iowa State Univ, PhD(nutrit), 71. *Prof Exp:* Res assoc nutrit, Agr Exp Sta, Iowa State Univ, 65-71; res & teaching nephrology med, Vet Admin Hosp, Little Rock, Ark, 71-77; from instr to asst prof med & biochem, Med Sci, Univ Ark, Little Rock, 74-77; ASSOC PROF NUTRIT, DEPT FOODS & NUTRIT, KANS STATE UNIV, 77- *Concurrent Pos:* Scientist nutrit, Agr Exp Sta, Kans State Univ, 77- *Mem:* Am Inst Nutrit; Am Fedn Clin Res; Am Dietetic Asn; Sigma Xi. *Res:* Clinical nutrition and nutritional aspects of metabolic disease; nutritional factors influencing somatomedin activity; lipid metabolism in renal failure. *Mailing Add:* Dept of Foods & Nutrit Kans State Univ Manhattan KS 66506

REEVES, ROBERT GRIER (LEFEVRE), b York, Pa, May 30, 20; m 42; c 2. ECONOMIC GEOLOGY, GEOPHYSICS. *Educ:* Univ Nev, BS, 49; Stanford Univ, MS, 50, PhD(econ geol, geochem), 65. *Prof Exp:* Geophysicist, US Geol Surv, 49-50; geologist, 50-69; sr Fulbright lectr, Univ Adelaide, 69; prof geol, Colo Sch Mines, 69-73; phys scientist, US Geol Surv, 73-78; PROF & CHMN FAC EARTH SCI, UNIV TEX, PERMIAN BASIN, 78-, DEAN, COL SCI & ENG, 79- *Concurrent Pos:* Co-leader, Int Field Inst Brazil, 66; vis geologist, Boston Col & Boston Univ, 67; mem, Coun Educ Geol Sci, Am Geol Inst, 68-74; ed-in-chief, Manual of Remote Sensing, Am Soc Photogram, 70-75. *Mem:* Fel Geol Soc Am; fel AAAS; fel Geol Soc Brazil; Am Inst Mining, Metall & Petrol Engrs; Soc Econ Geologists. *Res:* Remote sensing applied to geology and mineral resource exploration; economic geology of iron ore and non-ferrous metals; application of electromagnetic remote sensor and geophysical data to geology and mineral exploration; economic geology and geochemistry of iron and manganese. *Mailing Add:* Univ of Tex of Permian Basin Odessa TX 79762

REEVES, ROBERT LLOYD, b Oxnard, Calif, June 16, 23; m 48; c 4. DENTISTRY. *Educ:* Univ Southern Calif, DDS, 45; Am Bd Periodont, dipl, 55. *Prof Exp:* From instr to prof periodont, 46-66, asst dean preclin affairs, 66-69, assoc dean, Sch Dent, 69-76, HEAD DEPT PERIODONT, UNIV SOUTHERN CALIF, 52-66. *Mem:* Fel Am Col Dent; Am Acad Periodont (vpres, 78-); Am Bd Periodont (exec secy-treas, 72-). *Res:* Periodontology. *Mailing Add:* Univ of Southern Calif Sch of Dent 925 W 34th St Los Angeles CA 90007

REEVES, ROBERT R, b Albany, NY, June 16, 30; m 55; c 3. PHYSICAL CHEMISTRY, CHEMICAL ENGINEERING. *Educ:* Rensselaer Polytech Inst, BChe, 51, MChe, 52, PhD(chem eng), 54. *Prof Exp:* Res assoc chem, 54-71, assoc prof, 71-76, PROF CHEM, RENSSELAER POLYTECH INST, 76- *Concurrent Pos:* Prog mgr, US Dept Energy, 77, consult, 78- *Mem:* Sigma Xi; Am Chem Soc. *Res:* Photochemistry; atmospheric phenomena and reaction kinetics; laser studies. *Mailing Add:* Dept of Chem Rensselaer Polytech Inst Troy NY 12181

REEVES, ROBERT WILLIAM, b Morristown, NJ, Aug 12, 39; m 64; c 2. TROPICAL METEOROLOGY. *Educ:* NY Univ, BS, 61, MS, 65; Univ Wash, PhD(meterol), 80. *Prof Exp:* Res meteorologist, Nat Hurricane Res Lab, 65-69; METEOROLOGIST, CTR ENVIRON ASSESSMENT SERV, 69- *Concurrent Pos:* Coordr aircraft opers, Barbados Oceanog & Meteorol Exp, 69; Rawinsonda data qual expert, Workshop Global Atmospheric Res Prog, Atlantic Tropical Exp, 77. *Mem:* Am Meteorol Soc. *Res:* Investigation of the dynamics of the disturbed and undisturbed tradewind atmosphere; implementation of existing coastal ocean circulation modeling to aid in marine environmental assessment. *Mailing Add:* 5400 Waneta Rd Bethesda MD 20816

REEVES, ROGER MARCEL, b Rochester, NY, Feb 7, 34; m 63. ENTOMOLOGY. *Educ:* State Univ NY Col Forestry, Syracuse Univ, BS, 57, PhD(entom), 65; Cornell Univ, MS, 61. *Prof Exp:* Asst prof, 64-74, ASSOC PROF ENTOM & FORESTRY, UNIV NH, 74- *Mem:* Entom Soc Am; Acarological Soc Am; Am Entom Soc. *Res:* Taxonomy and ecology of Acari, particularly the Oribatei found on trees and in forest soils and litter; Carabidae, spiders. *Mailing Add:* Dept of Entom Univ of NH Durham NH 03824

REEVES, ROY FRANKLIN, b Warrensburg, Mo, July 8, 22; m 51; c 5. MATHEMATICS. *Educ:* Univ Colo, BS, 47; Iowa State Col, PhD(math), 51. *Prof Exp:* Instr math, Univ Colo, 47-48; instr elec eng, Iowa State Col, 48-50, instr math, 50-51; prof math, Ohio State Univ, 51-81, dir, Computer Ctr, 55-81; PROF MATH SCI, OTTERBEIN COL, 81- *Mem:* Am Mgt Asn; NY Acad Sci; AAAS; Am Math Soc; Math Asn Am. *Res:* Numerical analysis and computing; computer science. *Mailing Add:* 1640 Sussex Ct Columbus OH 43220

REEVES, T JOSEPH, b Waco, Tex, Apr 22, 23; m; c 3. CARDIOVASCULAR PHYSIOLOGY, MEDICINE. *Educ:* Baylor Univ, BS, 43, MD, 46. *Prof Exp:* Intern med, Parkland Hosp, Dallas, Tex, 46-47, resident, 49-51; pvt pract, Beaumont, Tex, 52-54; from asst prof to prof med, Sch Med, Univ Ala, Birmingham, 54-73, dir cardiovasc div, 58-66, assoc prof physiol & biophys, 58-73, dir cardiovasc res & training prog, 66-73, chmn dept med, 70-73; DIR CARDIOVASC LAB, ST ELIZABETH HOSP, 73-; CLIN PROF MED, UNIV TEX, HOUSTON, 81- *Concurrent Pos:* Fel heart dis, Univ Ala, 51-52; Nat Heart Inst spec fel, Queen Elizabeth Hosp, Birmingham, Eng, 57-58; chief med serv, Vet Admin Hosp, Birmingham, Ala, 54-55, consult, 56-73; mem exec comt, Coun Circulation, Am Heart Asn, 63-66; mem nat adv comt, Heart Dis Control Prog & chmn prog proj comt, Nat Heart Inst, 65-67; chmn adv comt cardiol, Nat Heart & Lung Inst, 74-77. *Mem:* Am Soc Clin Invest; Am Physiol Soc; Am Fedn Clin Res. *Res:* Myocardial contraction; physiology of muscular exercise; cardiac diagnosis. *Mailing Add:* Cardiovasc Lab St Elizabeth Hosp Beaumont TX 77706

REEVES, W PRESTON, b Handley, Tex, Sept 22, 35; m 60; c 1. ORGANIC CHEMISTRY. *Educ:* Tex Christian Univ, BS, 57, MA, 59; Univ Tex, Austin, PhD(chem), 66. *Prof Exp:* Instr chem, Arlington State Col, 61-62; asst prof, 65-69, assoc prof, 69-77, PROF CHEM, TEX LUTHERAN COL, 77- *Mem:* Am Chem Soc. *Res:* Thermal reactions of strained rings; allene chemistry; phase transfer catalysis. *Mailing Add:* Dept of Chem Tex Lutheran Col Seguin TX 78155

REEVES, WILLIAM CARLISLE, b San Francisco, Calif, Mar 27, 43; m 66; c 2. EPIDEMIOLOGY, INFECTIOUS DISEASES. *Educ:* Univ Calif, Berkeley, AB, 65; Univ Calif, San Francisco, MD, 69; Univ Wash, MS, 75. *Prof Exp:* Intern pediat, Charity Hosp, New Orleans, La, 69-70; staff assoc epidemiol, Mid Am Res Unit, Nat Inst Allergy & Infectious Dis, NIH, Balboa, CZ, 70-73; sr fel med & epidemiol, Univ Wash, 73-75; asst prof epidemiol, 75-77; CHIEF VIROL UNIT, GORGAS MEM LAB, 77- *Concurrent Pos:* Adj asst prof, Univ Wash, 77-; consult, Gorgas Hosp, 77- & Pan-Am Health Orgn, 78- *Mem:* Infectious Dis Soc Am; Am Soc Trop Med & Hyg; Soc Epidemiol Res; Soc Exp Biol & Med; Am Soc Microbiol. *Res:* Epidemiology; virology; immunology. *Mailing Add:* Gorgas Mem Lab Apt 6991 Panama 5 Panama

REEVES, WILLIAM CARLISLE, b Riverside, Calif, Dec 2, 16; m 40; c 3. EPIDEMIOLOGY. *Educ:* Univ Calif, BS, 38, PhD(entom), 43, MPH, 48. *Prof Exp:* Lab asst, Entom Div, 38-42, entomologist, Hooper Found, 41-42, asst epidemiol, Entom Div, 42-46, asst, Med Sch, 45-48, res asst, 46-49, lectr, Sch Pub Health, 47-54, assoc prof pub health, 49-54, from actg dean to dean, Sch Pub Health, 67-71, PROF EPIDEMIOL, SCH PUB HEALTH, UNIV CALIF, BERKELEY, 54- *Concurrent Pos:* Consult, Commun Dis Ctr, USPHS & State Dept Health, Calif. *Mem:* AAAS; Am Soc Trop Med & Hyg; Entom Soc Am; Am Pub Health Asn; Am Mosquito Control Asn. *Res:* Epidemiology of the arthropod-borne virus encephalitides; mosquito biology and systematics; avian malaria epidemiology. *Mailing Add:* Sch of Pub Health Univ of Calif Berkeley CA 94720

REEVES, WILLIAM JOHN, JR, b Eugene, Ore, July 26, 32; m 57. MEDICINE, BIOCHEMISTRY. *Educ:* Univ Ore, BS, 55, MS & MD, 58; Univ Calif, San Francisco, PhD(biochem), 67. *Prof Exp:* USPHS traineeship, Univ Calif Med Ctr, San Francisco, 61-62, Am Cancer Soc scholar, 62-65, clin instr med, Sch Med, 65-67, Am Cancer Soc Dernham fel & asst prof in residence, 67-69, res assoc oncol & attend physician, Cancer Res Inst, Med Ctr, 65-69; ASST PROF MED & ASST INTERNIST, UNIV TEX M D ANDERSON HOSP & TUMOR INST, HOUSTON, 69- *Concurrent Pos:* Consult end results studies, Nat Cancer Inst, 67-; lectr, Sch Med, Univ Calif, San Francisco, 68-69. *Mem:* AAAS; Tissue Cult Asn; Am Asn Cancer Res; Int Soc Cell Biol; NY Acad Sci. *Res:* Biochemistry of cancer; cancer chemotherapy; medical oncology; tissue culture. *Mailing Add:* 8100 Greenbriar Houston TX 77054

REEVES, WILSON ALVIN, b Mittie, La, July 14, 19; m 42; c 4. TEXTILE CHEMISTRY. *Educ:* Southwestern La Inst, BS, 41; Tulane Univ, La, MS, 50; Clemson Univ, DSc, 69. *Prof Exp:* Chemist, Southern Regional Res Lab, Agr Res Serv, US Dept Agr, 42-74; CONSULTANT, 74- *Honors & Awards:* Superior Serv Award, US Dept Agr, 54 & 60, Distinguished Serv Award, 64 & 68; John Scott Award, 65; Olney Medal, 66; Honor Award, Am Inst Chem, 70, 76, 78. *Mem:* Am Chem Soc; Sigma Xi; Am Asn Textile Chem & Colorists; Fiber Soc. *Res:* Organic, polymer and cellulose chemistry; fire retardant textiles. *Mailing Add:* 651 Chippenham Dr Baton Rouge LA 70808

REFFES, HOWARD ALLEN, b New York, NY, Sept 18, 28. ANALYTICAL CHEMISTRY. *Educ:* Queens Col, NY, BS, 50; Stevens Inst Technol, MS, 56. *Prof Exp:* Res anal chemist, Colgate-Palmolive Co, 52-57; sr chemist & head anal develop, Wallace & Tiernan, Inc, 57-61; mgr qual control, Flavor Div, Int Flavors & Fragrances, Inc, NJ, 61-68, plant mgr, 68-73; indust mgr, North Am Dairy Industs, 73-81; VPRES & GEN MGR, FOOD DIV, GOODHOST FOODS, LTD, 81- *Concurrent Pos:* Instr, New York Community Col, 56-68. *Mem:* AAAS; Am Chem Soc; Inst Food Technol; Am Soc Qual Control; fel Am Inst Chem. *Res:* Methods development for food additives and residues, pharmaceuticals, plasticizers and fatty acids; analytical research in condensed phosphates; polymeric anhydrides; analytical instrumentation; quality control of flavors; flavor manufacturing. *Mailing Add:* Goodhost Food Ltd 20 Huddersfield Rd Rexdale ON M4T 1A5 Can

REFFNER, JOHN A, b Akron, Ohio, Jan 5, 35; m 57; c 2. PHYSICAL CHEMISTRY, CRYSTALLOGRAPHY. *Educ:* Univ Akron, BS, 56; Ill Inst Technol, MS, 60; Univ Conn, PhD(polymer sci), 75. *Prof Exp:* Mat engr, B F Goodrich Co, 55-57; dir res, W C McCrone Assoc, 58-66; asst dir, Inst Mat Sci, Univ Conn, 66-77; PRIN RES MICROSCOPIST, AM CYANAMID RES LABS, 77- *Concurrent Pos:* Sci consult, Conn State Police, 74- *Mem:* Am Chem Soc; Elec Micro Soc Am; Northeastern Asn Forensic Sci; Am Soc Testing & Mat. *Res:* Chemical microscopy; optical and x-ray crystallography; ultramicro analysis; polymer science; forensic science; failure analysis; electron optics. *Mailing Add:* Am Cyanamid Res Lab Stamford CT 06904

REFOJO, MIGUEL FERNANDEZ, b Santiago, Spain, July 6, 28; US citizen; m 59; c 2. BIOMATERIALS, OPHTHALMOLOGY. *Educ:* Univ Santiago, Lic Sc, 53, DSc(org chem), 56. *Prof Exp:* Fel, Yale Univ, 56-59; res chemist, Tech Dept, Du Pont Can, Ont, 59-63; res assoc, Mass Eye & Ear Infirmary, Boston, 63-64; res assoc, 64-70, assoc, 70-71, SR SCIENTIST, EYE RES INST RETINA FOUND, 71-, HEAD POLYMER CHEM UNIT, 71- *Concurrent Pos:* Dir, Corneal Sci, Inc, Boston, 72-79; prin assoc ophthal, Harvard Med Sch, 75- *Mem:* AAAS; Am Chem Soc; Asn Res Vision & Ophthal; Sigma Xi; Soc Biomat. *Res:* Ophthalmology; synthetic polymers in medicine and surgery; hydrogels; contact lenses; drug delivery. *Mailing Add:* Eye Res Inst of Retina Found 20 Staniford St Boston MA 02114

REFT, CHESTER STANLEY, b Pittsburgh, Pa, Sept 29, 44; m 68; c 3. MEDICAL PHYSICS, RADIATION DOSIMETRY. *Educ:* Carnegie-Melon Univ, BS, 66; Univ Pittsburgh, PhD(physics), 73. *Prof Exp:* Res physicist, US Army-Harry Diamond Lab, 72-75; res assoc, Old Dominion Univ, 75-77, asst prof physics, 77-78, res assoc, 78-79, asst prof, 79-80; RES ASSOC, UNIV CHICAGO, 80- *Mem:* Am Phys Soc; Am Asn Physicists Med. *Res:* Improving the dosimetry of electron, photon and neutron teletheupy units for radiation therapy. *Mailing Add:* 246 Indiana St Park Forest IL 60466

REGAL, PHILIP JOE, b Los Angeles, Calif, Dec 2, 39. BEHAVIORAL BIOLOGY, EVOLUTION. *Educ:* San Diego State Col, BA, 62; Univ Calif, Los Angeles, MA, 66, PhD(zool), 68. *Prof Exp:* Trainee, NIMH Brain Res Inst-Univ Calif, Los Angeles-Univ Calif, San Diego-Scripps Inst Oceanog, 68-70; ASSOC PROF ECOL & BEHAV BIOL & CUR HERPET, MUS NATURAL HIST, UNIV MINN, MINNEAPOLIS, 70- *Concurrent Pos:* Mem US directorate UNESCO Man in Biosphere Prog. *Mem:* AAAS; Animal Behav Soc; Am Soc Ichthyologists & Herpetologists; Soc Study Amphibians & Reptiles; Ecol Soc Am. *Res:* Behavioral and physiological adaptations; behavioral temperature regulation; evolutionary processes; evolutionary trends in vertebrates, particularly amphibians and reptiles, evolutionary ecology of plants. *Mailing Add:* Mus of Natural Hist Univ of Minn Minneapolis MN 55455

REGAN, FRANCIS, b Vigo Co, Ind, Jan 10, 03. MATHEMATICS. *Educ:* Ind State Univ, AB, 22; LaSalle Exten Univ, LLB, 26; Ind Univ, AM, 30; Univ Mich, PhD(math), 32. *Prof Exp:* Teacher high sch, Ind, 23-25; prof commerce & asst prof math, Columbus Col, 25-29; asst prof math, Colo State Univ, 29-30; from instr to prof, 32-71, dir dept, 50-71, EMER PROF MATH, ST LOUIS UNIV, 71- *Concurrent Pos:* Ed-in-chief, Pi Mu Epsilon Nat J, 57-63. *Honors & Awards:* C C MacDuffee Award, 70; Nancy McNeir Ring Award, 71. *Mem:* Am Math Soc; Math Asn Am; Inst Math Statist; Sigma Xi. *Res:* Infinite series; foundations of probability; mathematical analysis and statistics. *Mailing Add:* RR 12 Box 39 West Terre Haute IN 47885

REGAN, GERALD THOMAS, b Omaha, Nebr, Apr 19, 31. ECOLOGY. *Educ:* St Louis Univ, AB, 55, PhL, 57, MS, 62; Univ Kans, PhD(zool), 72. *Prof Exp:* Instr biol, Creighton Univ, 68-71; asst prof, 72-77, ASSOC PROF BIOL, SPRING HILL COL, 77- *Mem:* Ecol Soc Am; Am Soc Ichthyologists & Herpetologists; Soc Study Amphibians & Reptiles; Am Soc Zool. *Res:* Evolution; ecological biogeography; herpetology. *Mailing Add:* Dept of Biol Spring Hill Col Mobile AL 36608

REGAN, JAMES DALE, b Lancaster, Ohio, May 23, 31; m 55; c 2. HUMAN GENETICS. *Educ:* Univ Ohio, BS, 53; Univ Miami, Fla, MS, 59; Univ Hawaii, PhD(genetics), 64. *Prof Exp:* Asst prof biol, Chaminade Col Honolulu, 62-64; Nat Cancer Inst fel, 64-66, BIOLOGIST, OAK RIDGE NAT LAB, 66- *Concurrent Pos:* Am Cancer Soc Hawaii Div res grant, 62-64; vis lectr, Univ Tenn, 66- *Mem:* AAAS; Tissue Cult Asn; Am Asn Cancer Res; Biophys Soc; Am Soc Human Genetics. *Res:* Genetics of human cells in vitro; repair of DNA and repair-deficient diseases; DNA repair and carcinogenesis; nutritional requirements and chemotherapy of leukemia cells. *Mailing Add:* Biol Div Oak Ridge Nat Lab Oak Ridge TN 37830

REGAN, ROBERT DAVID, b Newton, Mass, Aug 28, 39. GEOPHYSICS. *Educ:* Boston Col, BS, 62, MS, 65; Mich State Univ, PhD(geophysics), 73. *Prof Exp:* Physicist microwave, A S Thomas, Inc, Westwood, Mass, 63-65; geophysicist, US Geol Surv, Flagstaff, Ariz, 65-71, Silver Spring, Md, 71-74, staff geophysicist, Reston, Va, 74-80; WITH PHOENIX CORP, 80- *Mem:* Am Geophys Union; Soc Explor Geophysicists. *Res:* Analysis of global potential fields; satellite magnetometer; global gravimetry. *Mailing Add:* Phoenix Corp 1700 Old Meadow Rd McLean VA 22102

REGAN, THOMAS HARTIN, b Pittsburgh, Pa, June 7, 25; m 51; c 6. ORGANIC CHEMISTRY. *Educ:* Duquesne Univ, 49, MS, 51; Mass Inst Technol, PhD(org chem), 55. *Prof Exp:* Res chemist, Explosives Dept, E I du Pont de Nemours & Co, 55-64; sr res chemist, 64-66, RES ASSOC, EASTMAN KODAK CO, ROCHESTER, 66- *Mem:* Am Chem Soc. *Res:* Kinetics of ester aminolysis and nitrous acid oxidation; synthetic organic chemistry; nuclear magnetic resonance; application to structure determination of organic molecules. *Mailing Add:* Eastman Kodak Co Res Labs 1669 Lake Ave Rochester NY 14650

REGAN, THOMAS M(ICHAEL), b New Orleans, La, Nov 28, 41; m 64; c 2. CHEMICAL ENGINEERING, BIOENGINEERING. *Educ:* Tulane Univ, BS, 63, PhD, 67. *Prof Exp:* From asst prof to assoc prof, 66-76, PROF CHEM ENG, UNIV MD, COLLEGE PARK, 76- *Mem:* Am Inst Chem Engrs; Am Chem Soc. *Res:* Optimization of artificial kidney systems; membrane test cell design; testing of blood-gas exchangers; ionic and membrane diffusion. *Mailing Add:* Dept of Chem Eng Univ of Md College Park MD 20740

REGAN, TIMOTHY JOSEPH, b Boston, Mass, July 24, 24; m; c 4. INTERNAL MEDICINE, CARDIOLOGY. *Educ:* Boston Col, AB, 48; Boston Univ, MD, 52; Am Bd Internal Med, dipl, 60. *Prof Exp:* Rotating intern, City Detroit Receiving Hosp, 56-57; instr med, Sch Med, Wayne State Univ, 57-59, asst prof, 59-60; from asst prof to assoc prof, 60-66, PROF MED, COL MED & DENT NJ, 66-, DIR DIV CARDIOVASC DIS, 65- *Concurrent Pos:* Jr assoc med, City Detroit Receiving Hosp, 57-60; assoc in med, Children's Hosp, Detroit, 59-60; assoc dir, T J White Cardiopulmonary Inst, B S Pollak Hosp, Jersey City, 60-65, dir, 65-71, attend physician, Hosp, 60-71; estab investr, Am Heart Asn, 61-66; attend physician, Vet Admin Hosp, East Orange, NJ & Martland Hosp, Newark, 65-; chmn subcomt diag procedures in heart dis, NJ Regional Med Prog, 69-; mem cardiovasc study sect, Nat Adv Coun & Comts, NIH, 69- *Mem:* Am Fedn Clin Res; Am Physiol Soc; Am Heart Asn; Am Soc Clin Invest; Am Diabetes Asn. *Res:* Myocardial metabolism in disease. *Mailing Add:* Dept of Med Col of Med & Dent of NJ Newark NJ 07103

REGELSON, WILLIAM, b New York, NY, July 12, 25; m 48; c 6. MEDICINE. *Educ:* Univ NC, AB, 48; State Univ NY, MD, 52. *Prof Exp:* Intern med, Maimonides Hosp, Brooklyn, NY, 52-53; from asst resident to sr resident, Mem Ctr Cancer & Appl Dis, New York, 53-55; spec fel cancer res, Roswell Park Mem Inst, 55-56; sr cancer res internist, 56-57, assoc cancer res internist, 57-59, assoc chief med, 59-67; asst res prof med, State Univ NY Buffalo, 65-67; chief div med oncol, 67-76, PROF MED, MED COL VA, 67- *Concurrent Pos:* Consult, Monsanto Chem Co, 59, A H Robins Co, Inc, 69-71, Hercules, Inc, 71-74 & Merrell-Nat Labs, 71-76. *Mem:* Reticuloendothelial Soc; Am Heart Asn; Am Asn Cancer Res; Am Fedn Clin Res; Am Soc Clin Oncol. *Res:* Effect of polyelectrolytes on cell growth and differentiation and on enzyme and viral function; effects of various chemotherapeutic and immunotherapeutic agents on cancer in man and animal; production and prevention of tumor growth; aging. *Mailing Add:* Dept of Med Med Col of Va Richmond VA 23219

REGEN, DAVID MARVIN, b Nashville, Tenn, Mar 18, 34, m 58; c 3. PHYSIOLOGY, BIOCHEMISTRY. *Educ:* Davidson Col, BS, 56; Vanderbilt Univ, PhD(physiol), 62. *Prof Exp:* Instr physiol, Vanderbilt Univ, 62-63; guest investr, Max Planck Inst Cell Chem, 63-64; asst prof, 64-69, assoc prof, 69-76, PROF PHYSIOL, VANDERBILT UNIV, 76- *Concurrent Pos:* Howard Hughes Med Inst fel, 63-64, investr, 64-71; NIH res grant, 65- *Mem:* AAAS; Am Physiol Soc; NY Acad Sci. *Res:* Mechanism and kinetics of glucose transport; regulatory effects of insulin, diabetes, anoxia and work on glucose utilization in muscle; control of hepatic cholesterol synthesis; monocarboxylate transport; regulation of glucose transport in lymphocytes; brain glucose metabolism; brain ketone-body metabolism; cardiac dynamics. *Mailing Add:* Dept of Physiol Vanderbilt Univ Nashville TN 37232

REGENBRECHT, D(OUGLAS) E(DWARD), b Bryan, Tex, June 8, 24; m 58; c 3. MECHANICAL ENGINEERING. *Educ:* Tex A&M Univ, BSME, 48; Purdue Univ, MSME, 51, PhD(mech eng), 62. *Prof Exp:* Instr mech eng, Purdue Univ, 50-57; asst prof, Univ Tulsa, 57-63, assoc prof & head dept, 63-67; sr mem tech staff, 67-77, STAFF SCIENTIST, BALL BROS RES CORP, 77- *Concurrent Pos:* Consult, Space & Info Systs Div, N Am Aviation, Inc, Tulsa, 62-66. *Mem:* Am Soc Mech Engrs; Am Soc Eng Educ; Am Inst Aeronaut & Astronaut; Soc Packaging & Handling Engrs. *Res:* Fluid mechanics; convective and radiative heat transfer; thermal energy conversion systems. *Mailing Add:* Ball Bros Res Corp Boulder Indust Park Boulder CO 80302

REGENER, VICTOR H, b Berlin, Ger, Aug 25, 13; nat US; m 41; c 2. PHYSICS. *Educ:* Univ Stuttgart, DrIng, 38. *Prof Exp:* Res fel, Padova Univ, 38-40; res fel, Univ Chicago, 40-42, instr physics, 42-46; from assoc prof to prof physics, Univ NMex, 46-57, chmn dept, 46-57 & 62-79, res prof, 57-76; OWNER, VHR SYSTS, 79- *Concurrent Pos:* Assoc cur, Mus Sci & Indust, Univ Chicago, 45-46; hon prof, Univ Mayor de San Andres, La Paz, Bolivia. *Mem:* Fel Am Phys Soc; Am Astron Soc; Am Geophys Union; fel NY Acad Sci. *Res:* Atmospheric ozone; cosmic radiation; zodiacal light; balloon and satellite experiments; optical studies of pulsars and x-ray emitting binary systems; electronics. *Mailing Add:* VHR Systs 7200 Jefferson NE Albuquerque NM 87109

REGENSTEIN, JOE MAC, b Brooklyn, NY, Sept 22, 43; m 66; c 2. FOOD SCIENCE. *Educ:* Cornell Univ, BA, 65, MS, 66; Brandeis Univ, PhD(biophys), 72. *Prof Exp:* Fel muscle, Children's Cancer Res Ctr, Boston, 73 & Brandeis Univ, 73-74; asst prof poultry sci, 74-80, asst prof food sci, 75-80, ASSOC PROF POULTRY SCI & FOOD SCI, CORNELL UNIV, 80- *Concurrent Pos:* Sabbatical leave, Torry Res Sta, Aberdeen, Scotland, 80-81. *Mem:* Am Chem Soc; Poultry Sci Asn; Inst Food Technologists; AAAS. *Res:* Functional properties of muscle proteins, especially water retention properties and emulsification; frozen storage changes in gadoid fish; shelf-life extension of fresh poultry and fish; new product development from minced fish and poultry; kosher foods. *Mailing Add:* Dept Poultry & Avian Sci 112 Rice Hall Cornell Univ Ithaca NY 14853

REGER, BONNIE JANE, b Fargo, NDak, Sept 29, 40. PLANT PHYSIOLOGY. *Educ:* NDak State Univ, BS, 62; Univ Md, MS, 65; PhD(plant physiol), 68. *Prof Exp:* Fel biochem, Oak Ridge Nat Lab, 68-71; plant physiologist, Southern Weed Sci Lab, Agr Res Serv, Stoneville, Miss, 71-76; PLANT PHYSIOLOGIST, RUSSELL RES CTR, SCI & EDUC ADMIN, USDA, 76- *Concurrent Pos:* USPHS fel, 69-70; NATO travel grant, Spetsai, Greece, 69-; adv, Nat Res Coun-Agr Res Postdoctoral Res Associateship Prog, 73-76; consult, Substitute Chem Prog, Environ Protection Agency. *Mem:* Am Soc Plant Physiologists; Am Chem Soc; AAAS; Weed Sci Soc Am; Sigma Xi. *Res:* Photosynthesis especially regulation of RuBP carboxylase synthesis, cell separation of C4 plants and enzymatic characterization, chloroplast biogenesis; intergeneric crosses especially methods for overcoming rejection of incompatible pollen. *Mailing Add:* Sci & Educ Admin USDA PO Box 5677 Athens GA 30604

REGER, DANIEL LEWIS, b Mineral Wells, Tex, Sept 16, 45; m 68; c 2. ORGANOMETALLIC CHEMISTRY. *Educ:* Dickinson Col, BS, 67; Mass Inst Technol, PhD(chem), 72. *Prof Exp:* Asst prof, 72-77, ASSOC PROF CHEM, UNIV SC, 77- *Mem:* Am Chem Soc; Sigma Xi. *Res:* Transition metal organometallic synthesis; organic synthesis via organometallics; homogeneous catalysis. *Mailing Add:* Dept of Chem Univ of SC Columbia SC 29208

REGER, JAMES FREDERICK, b Norway, Iowa, Oct 27, 24; m 46; c 3. CYTOLOGY. *Educ:* Univ Iowa, PhD(zool), 54. *Prof Exp:* Asst, Univ Iowa, 50-54; asst prof zool, Ariz State Univ, 54-55; from res assoc to asst prof anat, Sch Med, Univ Colo, 55-65; assoc prof, 65-70, PROF ANAT, MED UNITS, UNIV TENN, MEMPHIS, 70- *Concurrent Pos:* USPHS career develop award, 59-65. *Mem:* AAAS; Am Soc Zoologists; Soc Protozool; Am Asn Anatomists; Am Soc Cell Biol. *Res:* Cytology of spinal ganglion cells; electron microscopy of euglena, myoneural junction, the synapse, kidney, muscle, oocytes; spermatozoa. *Mailing Add:* Dept of Anat Univ of Tenn Med Units Memphis TN 38163

REGER, RICHARD DAVID, b Chico, Calif, May 10, 39; m 68; c 2. GLACIAL GEOLOGY, QUATERNARY GEOLOGY. *Educ:* Univ Alaska, Fairbanks, BS, 63, MS, 64; Ariz State Univ, PhD(geol), 75. *Prof Exp:* Instr geol, Ariz State Univ, 72-73; sr geologist, R & M Consult, Inc, 73-75; GEOLOGIST III, ALASKA DIV GEOL & GEOPHYS SURV, 75- *Res:* Mapping surficial deposits, especially glacial deposits, throughout Alaska for a comprehensive environmental evaluation. *Mailing Add:* Box 80317 College Station AK 72053

REGEZI, JOSEPH ALBERTS, b Grand Rapids, Mich, May 14, 43; m 64; c 2. ORAL PATHOLOGY. *Educ:* Univ Mich, DDS, 68, MS, 71. *Prof Exp:* Chmn dept path, David Grant Med Ctr, US Air Force, 71-73; asst prof oral path, 73-77, ASST PROF DENT, DEPT HOSP DENT, UNIV MICH HOSP, 73-, ASSOC PROF ORAL PATH, SCH DENT, UNIV MICH, ANN ARBOR, 77- ASST PROF PATH, MED SCH, 76- *Mem:* Fel Am Acad Oral Path; Int Asn Dent Res. *Res:* Light and electron microscopic studies of head and neck neoplasms, especially salivary gland and odontogenic tumors, in regard to their classification, diagnosis, and histogenesis. *Mailing Add:* Dept of Oral Path Univ of Mich Sch of Dent Ann Arbor MI 48109

REGIER, HENRY ABRAHAM, b Brainerd, Alta, Mar 5, 30; m 56; c 3. ECOLOGY, FISHERIES. *Educ:* Queen's Univ, BA, 54; Cornell Univ, MS, 59, PhD(fishery biol), 62. *Prof Exp:* Teacher sci, Stamford Collegiate Inst, Ont, 55-57; res scientist, Ont Dept Lands & Forests, 61-63; res assoc biomet, Cornell Univ, 63-64, asst prof conserv & asst leader, NY Coop Fish Unit, 64-66; from asst prof to assoc prof, 66-73, PROF ZOOL, UNIV TORONTO, 73- *Concurrent Pos:* Chief resource eval br fisheries, Food & Agr Orgn, UN, Rome, 70-71; trustee, Inst Ecol, 73-75; res plan consult, Fisheries Res Bd Can, 73-76; comnr, Great Lakes Fishery Comn, 79- *Mem:* Int Union Theoret & Appl Limnol; Int Asn Gt Lakes Res (dir, 74-77); Am Fisheries Soc (pres, 78-79); Int Asn Ecol (dir, 74-78); Am Inst Fishery Res Biol. *Res:* Ecology of aquatic ecosystems, particularly large-scale responses of fish communities to major cultural stresses; screening and assessing ecological models and methods for interdisciplinary application. *Mailing Add:* Inst Environ Studies Univ of Toronto Toronto ON M5S 1A4 Can

REGIER, LLOYD WESLEY, b Hillsboro, Kans, Sept 19, 28; m 53; c 4. FOOD SCIENCE, FISHERIES. *Educ:* Univ Calif, Berkeley, BS, 50; Univ Calif, Davis, PhD(agr chem), 61. *Prof Exp:* Food technologist, Procter & Gamble Co, Ohio, 56-59; chemist, Western Res Labs, Nat Canners Asn, Calif, 59-63; assoc prof environ chem, Univ NC, Chapel Hill, 63-68; group leader process & prod res, 68-71, res scientist, Fish Utilization Prog, 71-75, PROG MGR & RES SCIENTIST FISH UTILIZATION, HALIFAX LAB, FISHERIES & MARINE SCI, FISHERIES RES BD CAN, 75- *Mem:* Am Chem Soc; Inst Food Technol; Int Asn Milk, Food & Environ Sanit; Can Inst Food Sci & Technol. *Res:* Fishery science; processing of and products from underutilized fish species; preservation by refrigeration; drying, chemicals or solvent extraction; byproduct characterization. *Mailing Add:* Fisheries & Oceans Technol Br Box 550 Halifax NS B3J 2S7 Can

REGISTER, ULMA DOYLE, b West Monroe, La, Feb 4, 20; m 42; c 3. BIOCHEMISTRY, NUTRITION. *Educ:* Madison Col, BS, 42; Vanderbilt Univ, MS, 44; Univ Wis, PhD(biochem), 50. *Prof Exp:* Fel, Sch Med, Tulane Univ, 50-51; from instr to assoc prof biochem, 51-67, chmn grad prog nutrit, 69, chmn dept dietetics, 72, PROF NUTRIT & CHMN DEPT, LOMA LINDA UNIV, 67- *Concurrent Pos:* Commonwealth Fund fel, Karolinska Inst, Sweden, 63-64. *Mem:* Am Inst Nutrit; Soc Exp Biol & Med; Am Dietetic Asn; Am Pub Health Asn; Am Soc Clin Nutrit. *Res:* Vitamin metabolism; protein nutrition; diet and alcohol. *Mailing Add:* Dept of Nutrit Sch of Health Loma Linda Univ Loma Linda CA 92354

REGNA, PETER P, b Hoboken, NJ, May 26, 09; m; c 2. ORGANIC BIOCHEMISTRY. *Educ:* Polytech Inst NY, BS, 32, MS, 37, PhD(phys org chem), 42. *Prof Exp:* Res group leader, Chas Pfizer & Co, Inc, 45-50, tech asst to dir res, 50-54, coordr cancer prog, 54-57, spec projs officer, 57-62; dir res planning, Squibb Inst Med Res, NJ, 62-68; sr partner, 68-72, MANAGING DIR, HARRINGTON RES CO, 72- *Mem:* AAAS; Am Chem Soc; Am Mgt Asn; fel Am Inst Chemists; fel NY Acad Sci. *Res:* Kinetic reactions; carbohydrate chemistry; synthetic vitamins; structure antibiotics; chemotherapeutic agents; development of pharmaceuticals; antineoplastic substances. *Mailing Add:* Harrington Res Co PO Box 295 Harrington Park NJ 07640

REGNER, JOHN LAVERNE, b Columbus, Ohio, Oct 24, 46; m 68; c 1. NUCLEAR PHYSICS, SYSTEMS ANALYSIS. *Educ:* Ohio State Univ, BS, 69, MS, 69, PhD(physics), 76. *Prof Exp:* Systs analyst missile systs, NAm Rockwell, 69-73; res assoc nuclear physics, Ohio State Univ, 73-76, assoc, Van de Graaff Lab, 76-77; SYSTS ANALYST DEFENSE SYSTS, INST DEFENSE ANAL, 77- *Mem:* Am Phys Soc. *Res:* Nuclear physics utilizing polarized particles; nuclear spectroscopy; communication systems for command and control. *Mailing Add:* Inst for Defense Anal 400 Army-Navy Dr Arlington VA 22202

REGNERY, DAVID COOK, b La Grange, Ill, June 26, 18; m 45; c 3. BIOLOGY. *Educ:* Stanford Univ, AB, 41; Calif Inst Technol, PhD(genetics), 47. *Prof Exp:* From instr to assoc prof, 47-53, PROF BIOL, STANFORD UNIV, 53- *Res:* Genetics of Drosophila, Neurospora and Chlamydomonas; leucineless mutants of Neurospora crassa. *Mailing Add:* Dept of Biol Stanford Univ Stanford CA 94305

REGNIER, FREDERICK EUGENE, b Fairbury, Nebr, July 7, 38; m 60. BIOCHEMISTRY. *Educ:* Nebr State Teachers Col, Peru, BS, 60; Okla State Univ, PhD(chem), 65. *Prof Exp:* Fel, Okla State Univ, 65-66 & Univ Chicago, 66-68; from asst prof to assoc prof, 68-76, PROF BIOCHEM, PURDUE UNIV, LAFAYETTE, 76- *Mem:* Am Chem Soc; Am Soc Biol Chemists. *Res:* Pheromones; hormones; instrumental analysis. *Mailing Add:* Dept of Biochem Purdue Univ Lafayette IN 47907

REGULSKI, THOMAS WALTER, b Detroit, Mich, Dec 13, 43; m 63; c 3. POLYMER CHEMISTRY. *Educ:* Wayne State Univ, BS, 67; Univ Nebr, PhD(org chem), 71. *Prof Exp:* Assoc, Univ Toronto, 71-73; SR RES CHEMIST, DOW CHEM CO, 73- *Mem:* Am Chem Soc. *Res:* Area of polymer synthesis for industrial and biomedical applications. *Mailing Add:* 1416 Airfield Lane Midland MI 48640

REH, THOMAS ANDREW, b Chicago, Ill, Feb 17, 55; m 81. DEVELOPMENTAL NEUROBIOLOGY. *Educ:* Univ Ill, Champaign, BS(biochem) & BS(physiol), 77; Univ Wis-Madison, PhD(neurosci), 81. *Prof Exp:* VIS FEL, NEUROSCI, PRINCETON UNIV, 81- *Concurrent Pos:* Reviewer ad hoc grant, NSF, 82- *Honors & Awards:* Jerzy Rose Award, Univ Wis-Madison, 82. *Mem:* Soc Neurosci. *Res:* Elucidating the anatomical, electrophysiological and biochemical mechanisms by which neural specificity is generated during the development of the vertebrate central nervous system. *Mailing Add:* Dept Biol Guyot Hall Princeton Univ Princeton NJ 08021

REHAK, MATTHEW JOSEPH, b Baltimore, Md, Apr 24, 29; m 53; c 3. CLINICAL CHEMISTRY. *Educ:* Loyola Col, AB, 50; Univ Md, MS, 55, PhD(biochem, pharmacol), 58. *Prof Exp:* Chemist, Off Chief Med Exam, Md, 50-51, asst, 53-54; asst pharmacol, Med Sch, Univ Md, 54-57; state toxicologist, Conn State Health Dept, 57-60; CLIN CHEMIST, ST AGNES HOSP, 60- *Concurrent Pos:* Consult clin chem, Dept of State, Washington, DC, 68-73. *Mem:* Am Asn Clin Chem (chmn capital sect, 71-72); Clin Radioassay Soc; Am Chem Soc; Nat Acad Clin Biochem. *Res:* New analytical methods for drugs and metabolites; detection and determination of drug effects on enzyme systems. *Mailing Add:* St Agnes Hosp 1000 Caton Ave Baltimore MD 21229

REHAK, PAVEL, b Prague, Czech, Dec 5, 45; m 77. HIGH ENERGY PHYSICS, ELECTRODYNAMICS. *Educ:* Charles Univ, Prague, RNDr(nuclear physics), 69; State Univ Col Pisa, PhD(elem particle physics), 72. *Prof Exp:* Res physicist particle physics, Kernforschungscentrum, Karlsruhe, WGer, 72-73; res assoc, Yale Univ, 73-76; RES PHYSICIST PARTICLE PHYSICS, BROOKHAVEN NAT LAB, 76- *Res:* Experiments in elementary particle physics; detector and particle detection system development; electrodynamics in strong magnetic field. *Mailing Add:* Dept of Physics Brookhaven Nat Lab Upton NY 11973

REHBERG, CHESSIE ELMER, b Cairo, Ga, Aug 15, 11; m 42; c 3. ORGANIC CHEMISTRY. *Educ:* Ga State Col for Men, BS, 33; Emory Univ, MS, 37; Univ Tex, PhD(org chem), 41. *Prof Exp:* Teacher high sch, Ga, 34-36; asst & instr, Emory Univ, 36-38; instr math & physics, Emory Jr Col, Valdosta, 38; instr chem, Univ Tex. 38-41; org res chemist, Sharples Chems, Inc, Mich, 41-42; org res chemist, Eastern Regional Lab, Bur Agr & Indust Chem, USDA, 42-51, tech analyst & patents, Eastern Utilization Res Br, 51-56; group leader, Patent Dept, Dow Chem USA, 56-68, sr patent agent, 68-75; RETIRED. *Mem:* Am Chem Soc; Sci Res Soc Am. *Res:* Synthetic resins and plasticizers; esters of lactic and acrylic acids; phenacyl carbinamines; alkylene oxides; polyglycols; polyurethanes. *Mailing Add:* PO Box 208 Penrose NC 28766

REHDER, KAI, b Hohenwestedt, WGer, Dec 17, 28; m 58; c 4. ANESTHESIOLOGY, PHYSIOLOGY. *Educ:* Univ Freiburg, MD, 53. *Prof Exp:* Intern pediat, Univ Hosp, Freiburg, 53-54; resident pharmacol, 56-57; resident oncol, Jeanes Hosp, Philadelphia, Pa, 54-55; resident internal med, Mayo Grad Sch Med, Univ Minn & Mayo Clin, 57-58, resident anesthesiol, 58-60, res asst physiol, 60-61; docent anesthesiol, Univ Würzburg, 62, head dept, Univ Hosp, 62-65; asst prof anesthesiol, Mayo Grad Sch Med, Univ Minn & consult, Mayo Clin & Mayo Found, 66-77, PROF PHYSIOL & ANESTHESIOL, MAYO CLIN, UNIV MINN, 77-, PROF MAYO GRAD SCH, 76- *Mem:* Ger-Austrian-Swiss Soc Anesthesia & Resuscitation. *Res:* Pulmonary physiology; metabolism of volatile anesthetics; neuroanesthesia. *Mailing Add:* Dept of Anesthesiol Mayo Clin 200 First St SW Rochester MN 55901

REHFELD, CARL ERNEST, b Warner, SDak, July 1, 18; m 51; c 4. VETERINARY PATHOLOGY. *Educ:* SDak State Univ, BS, 44; Kans State Univ, DVM, 47; Univ Minn, MS, 55. *Prof Exp:* Asst prof vet sci, SDak State Univ, 47-48; asst prof vet path, Kans State Univ, 48-50; instr, Univ Minn, 50-55; head clin sect, Radiobiol Lab, Col Med, Univ Utah, 55-61; assoc vet, Div Biol & Med Res, Argonne Nat Lab, 61-71; supvry vet med officer, Animal & Plant Health Inspection Serv, USDA, 71-78; CONSULT, VET TOXICOL, 80- *Mem:* Am Col Lab Animal Med; Am Vet Med Asn; Am Col Vet Toxicol; Conf Res Workers Animal Dis. *Res:* Pathology and toxicology of domestic animals; laboratory animal medicine; clinical and pathological effects of ionizing radiation in dogs and other mammals; hematology in radiation research; definition of sub-populations in animal colonies; pathology of domestic meat animals. *Mailing Add:* 33976 Weld County Rd 53 Gill CO 80624

REHFIELD, DAVID MICHAEL, b Mason City, Iowa, Aug 19, 42. BETA-RAY SPECTROSCOPY. *Educ:* Seattle Univ, BSc, 64; Univ Ariz, MSc, 67; McGill Univ, PhD(physics), 77. *Prof Exp:* Fel, II Physikalishes Inst Justus Liebig Univ, Ger, 77-79; res assoc, Foster Radiation Lab, McGill Univ, 79-81; instr, Vanier Col, Montreal, 81-82; asst prof, Swarthmore Col, 81-82; ASST PROF PHYSICS, LAFAYETTE COL, 82- *Concurrent Pos:* Vis scientist, Brookhaven Nat Lab, 80-; res collabr, Nat Res Coun Can, 81- *Mem:* Sigma Xi; Am Asn Physics Teachers. *Res:* Nuclear physics, with emphasis on beta-ray spectroscopy, involving solid-state detectors and the development of superconducting-solenoid beta-ray spectrometers, and data-analysis programs. *Mailing Add:* Dept Physics Swarthmore Col Swarthmore PA 19081

REHFIELD, LAWRENCE WILMER, b Miami, Fla, Feb 1, 38. AEROSPACE ENGINEERING. *Educ:* Ga Inst Technol, BAeroE, 61; Mass Inst Technol, MS, 62; Stanford Univ, PhD(aeronaut, astronaut), 65. *Prof Exp:* Res asst aeronaut & astronaut, Stanford Univ, 63-65; asst prof aeronaut & astronaut & fel eng, Mass Inst Technol, 65-67; from asst prof to assoc prof aerospace eng, 67-77, PROF AEROSPACE ENG, GA INST TECHNOL, 77- *Mem:* Am Inst Aeronaut & Astronaut; Soc Exp Stress Anal; Am Inst Ultrasonics in Med. *Res:* Structural mechanics as applied to vehicle technology; stability of shell structures. *Mailing Add:* Sch of Aerospace Eng Ga Inst of Technol Atlanta GA 30332

REHFUSS, MARY, b Albany, NY, Sept 16, 27. ORGANIC CHEMISTRY. *Educ:* Col St Rose, BS, 49; St Louis Univ, PhD(org chem), 58. *Prof Exp:* Instr, 49-50, 53-54, from asst prof to assoc prof, 58-65, PROF CHEM, COL ST ROSE, 65- *Mem:* Sigma Xi; Am Chem Soc. *Res:* Kinetics of molecular rearrangements; applications of chemistry to conservation of art objects. *Mailing Add:* Dept Chem Col St Rose Albany NY 12203

REHKUGLER, GERALD E(DWIN), b Lyons, NY, Apr 11, 35; c 3. AGRICULTURAL & FOOD ENGINEERING. *Educ:* Cornell Univ, BS, 57, MS, 58; Iowa State Univ, PhD, 66. *Prof Exp:* From asst prof to assoc prof, 58-77, PROF AGR ENG, CORNELL UNIV, 77- *Concurrent Pos:* NSF sci fac fel, 64; vis prof, Mich State Univ, 74. *Honors & Awards:* Paper Awards, Am Soc Agr Engrs, 65, 74, 77. *Mem:* Am Soc Agr Engrs; Inst Food Technologists. *Res:* Design and development of machinery for handling, harvesting and processing of food and agricultural products; dynamics of agricultural vehicles; computer control and simulation in agricultural and food processing machinery. *Mailing Add:* Dept of Agr Eng Cornell Univ 228 Riley-Robb Hall Ithaca NY 14853

REHM, GEORGE W, b St Clairsville, Ohio, Oct 1, 41; m 64; c 3. SOIL FERTILITY, AGRONOMY. *Educ:* Ohio State Univ, BS, 63; Univ Minn, MS, 65, PhD(soil sci), 69. *Prof Exp:* Teaching asst soil sci, Univ Minn, 63-69; dist exten agronomist, 69-80, EXTEN SOILS SPECIALIST, UINV NEBR, 80- *Mem:* Am Soc Agron; Soil Sci Soc Am; Am Forage & Grassland Coun. *Res:* Soil fertility, particularly nitrogen-sulfur interactions; plant nutrition; soil-plant relationships; plant nutrition research with corn and forage crops. *Mailing Add:* Northeast Exp Sta Univ of Nebr Concord NE 68728

REHM, RONALD GEORGE, b Chicago, Ill, Nov 6, 38; m 59; c 5. APPLIED MATHEMATICS, FLUID DYNAMICS. *Educ:* Purdue Univ, BS, 60; Mass Inst Technol, PhD(appl math), 65. *Prof Exp:* Prin engr appl math & fluid dynamics, Cornell Aeronaut Lab, Buffalo, NY, 65-75; MATHEMATICIAN APPL MATH & FLUID DYNAMICS, NAT BUR STANDS, 75- *Mem:* Am Phys Soc; Soc Indust Appl Math. *Res:* Waves in stratified fluids; buoyancy-induced fluid flows; fluid flows induced by laser heating of materials; fire-induced fluid flows. *Mailing Add:* Nat Bur of Stands Admin Bldg A 302 Gaithersburg MD 20234

REHM, THOMAS R(OGER), b Los Angeles, Calif, Nov 11, 29; m 57; c 1. CHEMICAL ENGINEERING. *Educ:* Univ Wash, BSChE, 52, PhD(chem eng), 60. *Prof Exp:* From asst prof to assoc prof chem eng, Univ Denver, 60-66; from asst prof to assoc prof, 66-76, PROF CHEM ENG, UNIV ARIZ, 76- *Concurrent Pos:* Res engr, Denver Res Inst, 60-66; consult, Walvoord, Inc, Colo, 61, Thermo-Tech, Inc, 62-65, Monsanto Co, 73 & Criterion Anal, 77-78; dir property develop, Rehm & Condon, Inc, 65-; abstr nuclear tech, Chem Abstracts, 65-76. *Mem:* Am Inst Chem Engrs. *Res:* Boiling heat transfer; suspended solid-liquid mass transfer; turbulent fluid dynamics. *Mailing Add:* Dept of Chem Eng Univ of Ariz Tucson AZ 85721

REHN, JOHN WILLIAM HOLMAN, b Philadelphia, Pa, June 14, 15; m 40. ENTOMOLOGY. *Educ:* Cornell Univ, BS, 38, PhD(entom), 50. *Prof Exp:* Asst entom, Acad Natural Scis, Philadelphia, 37, 39-40; asst parasitol, Cornell Univ, 40-42; chief med entomologist, Douglas Aircraft Co, 42-43; sanitarian, Tompkins County Health Dept, NY, 47-48; invert biologist, Pa Stream Surv, 48; chief of party, Columbia Univ Anopheles Res Prog, PR, 48-50; entomologist, USPHS, 50; prof biol, Marlboro Col, 50-51; dir entom div, First US Army Med Lab, 51-55; spec asst appl biol, Eastern Div Naval Facilities Eng Command, NY, 55-65; INDEPENDENT CONSULT, 65- *Concurrent Pos:* Res assoc, Dept Insects, Acad Natural Scis, Philadelphia, 39-70; lectr, Sch Pub Health, Columbia Univ, 56-70. *Mem:* AAAS; Am Entom Soc. *Res:* Medical and systematic entomology; applied biology. *Mailing Add:* 105 Squire Hill Rd Upper Montclair NJ 07043

REHN, LYNN EDUARD, b Detroit, Mich, Sept 12, 45; m 75. PHYSICS, MATERIALS SCIENCE. *Educ:* Albion Col, BA, 67; Univ Ill, Urbana, MS, 69, PhD(physics), 73. *Prof Exp:* Scientist solid state, Kernforschungsanlage, Julich, WGer, 73-76; asst physicist, 76-80, PHYSICIST MAT SCI, ARGONNE NAT LAB, 80- *Mem:* Am Phys Soc; Sigma Xi. *Res:* Defects in metals; ultrasonics; Auger electron spectroscopy; internal friction; radiation damage. *Mailing Add:* Mat Sci Div Argonne Nat Lab Argonne IL 60439

REHN, VICTOR LEONARD, b Ophiem, Ill, Aug 14, 27; m 54; c 3. EXPERIMENTAL SOLID STATE PHYSICS. *Educ:* Univ Calif, Berkeley, AB, 53; Univ Pittsburgh, PhD(physics), 62. *Prof Exp:* Physicist, Westinghouse Res Labs, 53-55; res physicist, Armour Res Found, Ill Inst Technol, 60-62; res assoc, Inst Study Metals, Univ Chicago, 62-65; res physicist, US Naval Ord Test Sta, 66-67, head electron struct solids, 67-80, HEAD SEMICONDUCTOR & SURFACE SCI, PHYSICS DIV, MICHELSON LAB, NAVAL WEAPONS CTR, 80-, SPOKESMAN, MICHELSON LABS SYNCHROTRON RADIATION PROJ, 72- *Concurrent Pos:* Vis sr res assoc, Stanford Synchrotron Radiation Lab; guest scientist, Lawrence Berkeley Labs, 77-79. *Honors & Awards:* L T E Thompson Award, 81. *Mem:* AAAS; Am Phys Soc; Am Vacuum Soc; Sigma Xi. *Res:* Electroreflectance studies of electronic energy-band structures of semiconductors, insulators and metals; ultraviolet and soft x-ray properties of semiconductors and insulators using synchrotron radiation; surface science of molecular and semiconducting materials. *Mailing Add:* Michelson Labs Code 3813 Naval Weapons Ctr China Lake CA 93555

REHR, JOHN JACOB, b Carlisle, Pa, May 6, 45; m 66; c 2. SOLID STATE PHYSICS. *Educ:* Univ Mich, BSE, 67; Cornell Univ, PhD(theoret physics), 72. *Prof Exp:* Scholar physics, Univ Calif, San Diego, 73-75; asst prof, 75-80, ASSOC PROF PHYSICS, UNIV WASH, 80- *Concurrent Pos:* NATO fel, King's Col, London, Eng, 72-73; Humboldt fel, Max Planck Inst Solid State, Stuttgart, W Ger, 78. *Mem:* Am Phys Soc. *Res:* condensed matter; critical phenomena. *Mailing Add:* Dept of Physics FM-15 Univ of Wash Seattle WA 98195

REHWALDT, CHARLES A, b Kewanee, Ill, Sept 7, 25; m 52; c 3. GENETICS, PLANT PHYSIOLOGY. *Educ:* Mankato State Univ, BA, 51; Univ Minn, MS, 53; State Univ NY Col Forestry, Syracuse, Univ, PhD(genetics), 65. *Prof Exp:* Teacher high sch, Minn, 55-57; instr biol, Austin Community Col, 57-62; head dept, 68-78, PROF BIOL, ST CLOUD STATE UNIV, 65- *Concurrent Pos:* Lectr, NSF Summer Insts, 67, 68. *Mem:* Genetics Soc Am; Am Soc Human Genetics; Sigma Xi. *Res:* Genetics and physiology of seed dormancy. *Mailing Add:* Dept of Biol Sci St Cloud State Univ St Cloud MN 56301

REHWOLDT, ROBERT E, b New York, NY, Oct 13, 35; m 65; c 3. ANALYTICAL CHEMISTRY. *Educ:* Queen's Col, BS, 57; Lehigh Univ, MS, 59, PhD(anal chem), 62. *Prof Exp:* Instr chem, Vassar Col, 62-64, asst prof, 62-64; from assoc prof to prof chem, Marist Col, 68-80, chmn natural sci, 75, dir environ sci major prog, 72-80; prog mgr, Nat Sci Found, 78-80; SR STAFF OFFICER, NAT RES COUN-NAT ACAD SCI, 80- *Concurrent Pos:* Adv environ affairs, City of Poughkeepsie & County of Duchess; vis scientist, SGAE, Austria. *Mem:* Am Chem Soc; Am Fisheries Soc. *Res:* Molecular complexes; chelating agents; spectrophotometry; heavy metal toxicity toward aquatic life; effects of heavy metals on aquatic communities. *Mailing Add:* Nat Res Coun Nat Acad Sci Washington DC 20418

REIBEL, KURT, b Vienna, Austria, May 23, 26; nat US; m 54; c 3. PHYSICS. *Educ:* Temple Univ, BA, 54; Univ Pa, MS, 56, PhD(physics), 59. *Prof Exp:* Jr res assoc physics, Brookhaven Nat Lab, 57-59; res assoc, Univ Pa, 59-61; from asst prof to assoc prof, 61-70, PROF PHYSICS, OHIO STATE UNIV, 70- *Mem:* AAAS; Am Phys Soc; Fedn Am Sci. *Res:* High energy physics; particle detectors; instrumentation; polarized targets. *Mailing Add:* Dept of Physics Ohio State Univ Columbus OH 43210

REICE, SETH ROBERT, b Brooklyn, NY, June 30, 47; m 71. STREAM ECOLOGY, DECOMPOSITION. *Educ:* Univ Rochester, BA, 69; Mich State Univ, PhD(zool), 73. *Prof Exp:* asst prof, 73-79, ASSOC PROF ZOOL, UNIV NC, CHAPEL HILL, 79- *Concurrent Pos:* Vis prof zool, Hebrew Univ, Jerusalem, 81. *Mem:* Ecol Soc Am; Am Inst Biol Sci; Sigma Xi; Int Limnol Asn; Am Soc Limnol Oceanog. *Res:* Regulation of benthic community structure and litter decomposition in woodland streams; roles of substrate type, disturbance and predation. *Mailing Add:* Dept Zool 202 Wilson Hall 046A Univ NC Chapel Hill NC 27514

REICH, BRIAN M, b Pretoria, SAfrica, May 16, 27; m 52; c 3. CIVIL ENGINEERING, HYDROLOGY. *Educ:* Univ Witwatersrand, BSc, 51; Iowa State Univ, MS, 59; Colo State Univ, PhD(civil eng), 62. *Prof Exp:* Conserv officer, Dept Conserv, SRhodesia, 51-53; engr, Dept Agr Tech Serv, SAfrica, 53-62; invests leader hydrol res, Natal Region, SAfrica, 62-64; asst prof civil eng, Colo State Univ, 64-66; from assoc prof to prof, Pa State Univ, 66-74; flood plain engr, City Tucson, 75-77; flood plain mgr, Pima Co, 78-80; FLOOD PLAIN ENGR, CITY TUCSON, 80- *Concurrent Pos:* Mem, US working group floods & their comput, Int Hydrol Decade; eng consult. *Mem:* Fel Am Soc Civil Engrs; Am Soc Agr Engrs; Am Geophys Union; Am Water Resources Asn. *Res:* Rainstorms; floods from rural area; urban hydrology; planning of open space in suburban watersheds; personal programmable calculators. *Mailing Add:* Eng Div 250 W Alameda Tucson AZ 85701

REICH, CHARLES, b Minneapolis, Minn, Aug 2, 42; m 63; c 3. RESEARCH ADMINISTRATION, ORGANIC CHEMISTRY. *Educ:* Univ Minn, Minneapolis, BS, 64; Univ Wis-Madison, PhD(org chem), 68. *Prof Exp:* NIH fel, Mass Inst Technol, 68; res specialist, Org Chem Res Lab, 68-74, tech mgr, 74-78, TECH DIR, BLDG SERVS & CLEANING PRODS DIV, 3M CO, 78- *Mem:* Am Chem Soc. *Res:* Organometallic synthesis; polymer chemistry; catalyst synthesis. *Mailing Add:* 3M Ctr 3M Co St Paul MN 55101

REICH, CHARLES WILLIAM, b Oklahoma City, Okla, Sept 12, 30; m 52; c 3. NUCLEAR PHYSICS. *Educ:* Univ Okla, BS, 52; Rice Inst, MA, 54, PhD(physics), 56. *Prof Exp:* Group leader, Radioactivity & Decay Schemes Group, Atomic Energy Div, Phillips Petrol Co, 59-66; group leader, Idaho Nuclear Corp, 66-71; group leader, Radioactivity & Decay Schemes Group, Aerojet Nuclear Co, 71-74, sect chief, 74-76; SECT CHIEF, NUCLEAR STRUCT SECT, EG & G IDAHO, INC, 76- *Concurrent Pos:* Guest scientist, Niels Bohr Inst, Copenhagen, Denmark, 64-65; chmn, Decay-Date Subcomt, Cross Sect Eval Working Group 73-; US Coordr & rep, Int Atomic Energy Agency Coord Res Prog, Measurement Actinide Decay Data, 77-; prin scientist, EG&G Idaho, Inc, 81-; prin investr, Dept Energy res progs, 60-, mem, Transplutonium Prog Comt, 78-; adj prof, Utah State Univ, 68-; physics curriculum coordr, Idaho Nat Eng Lab Educ Prog, Univ Idaho, 79- *Mem:* AAAS; fel Am Phys Soc; Sigma Xi; NY Acad Sci. *Res:* Experimental investigation and analysis of nuclear energy level structure; compilation and evaluation of nuclear data. *Mailing Add:* Idaho Nat Eng Lab PO Box 1625 Idaho Falls ID 83415

REICH, CLAUDE VIRGIL, b Reading, Pa, May 18, 21; m 48; c 1. MEDICAL MICROBIOLOGY, LEPROLOGY. *Educ:* Pa State Univ, BS, 53, PhD(bact), 58; Univ Wis, MS, 54. *Prof Exp:* Instr vet sci, Pa State Univ, 54-58; instr bact, Col Med, Univ Ill, 58-59; assoc bacteriologist, 59-62, LAB DIR & MICROBIOLOGIST, LEONARD WOOD MEM LAB, JOHNS HOPKINS UNIV, CEBU, PHILIPPINES, 62-, CHIEF LAB BR, PHILIPPINES DIV, 63-, ASST PROF PATHOBIOL, SCH HYG, 59-, CHIEF OPERS, PHILIPPINES DIV, 73- *Concurrent Pos:* Mem leprosy expert panel, WHO, 68- *Mem:* Am Soc Microbiol; Conf Res Workers Animal Dis; Int Leprosy Asn. *Res:* Immunologic and nutritional aspects of bacteria related to infectious infertility; factors associated with non-cultivable states of mycobacteria; clinical chemistry and bacteriology of leprosy; animal transmission of mycobacterial diseases; leprosy immunology. *Mailing Add:* Leonard Wood Mem Lab Sch of Hyg Johns Hopkins Univ Baltimore MD 21205

REICH, DANIEL, b New York, NY, June 25, 41; m 65; c 1. MATHEMATICS. *Educ:* Cornell Univ, AB, 62; Princeton Univ, MA, 64, PhD, 66. *Prof Exp:* Instr math, Johns Hopkins Univ, 66-68, asst prof, 68-70; ASST PROF MATH, TEMPLE UNIV, 70- *Mem:* Am Math Soc. *Res:* Number theory; algebraic geometry. *Mailing Add:* Dept of Math Temple Univ Philadelphia PA 19122

REICH, DONALD ARTHUR, b Quincy, Ill, Dec 14, 29; m 51; c 1. ORGANIC CHEMISTRY. *Educ:* Millikin Univ, BA, 52; Univ Mo, PhD(chem), 56. *Prof Exp:* Supvr org chem, Chem Div, Pittsburgh Plate Glass Co, Ohio, 56-81, SR SUPVR ORG RES, PPG INDUSTS, INC, 67- *Mem:* Am Chem Soc; Am Soc Testing Mats. *Res:* Application research; process and product development. *Mailing Add:* Org Res Chem Div Barberton Tech Ctr PPG Ind PO Box 31 Barberton OH 44203

REICH, EDGAR, b Vienna, Austria, June 7, 27; nat US; m 49; c 2. MATHEMATICS. *Educ:* Polytech Inst Brooklyn, BEE, 47; Mass Inst Technol, MS, 49; Univ Calif, Los Angeles, PhD(math), 54. *Prof Exp:* Asst servomech lab, Mass Inst Technol, 47-49; mathematician, Rand Corp, 49-56; from asst prof to assoc prof, 56-61, PROF MATH, UNIV MINN, MINNEAPOLIS, 61- *Concurrent Pos:* NSF fel, 54-55; mem, Inst Advan Study, 54-55; consult, Rand Corp, 56-66; Guggenheim fel & Fulbright res grant, Math Inst, Aarhus Univ, 60-61; vis prof, Israel Inst Technol, 65-66; mem, Math Res Inst, Zurich, Switz, 71-72 & 78-79; vis prof, Swiss Fed Inst Technol, Zurich, 82-83. *Mem:* Am Math Soc; Math Asn Am; foreign mem Finnish Acad Sci & Letters. *Res:* Complex analysis. *Mailing Add:* Sch of Math Inst of Technol Univ of Minn Minneapolis MN 55455

REICH, GEORGE ARTHUR, b Los Angeles, Calif, Jan 18, 33; m 57; c 7. MEDICINE, EPIDEMIOLOGY. *Educ:* Univ Fla, BS, 56; Univ Iowa, MD, 62; Univ NC, MPH, 69. *Prof Exp:* Intern, Hosp, USPHS, Norfolk, Va, 62-63, staff physician, Outpatient Clin, Miami, Fla, 63-64, chief med serv, 64-65, field epidemiologist, Commun Study on Pesticides, Bur State Serv, 65-66, asst chief commun studies, Pesticides Prog, Nat Commun Dis Ctr, 66-69; chief epidemiologist, Div Commun Studies, Food & Drug Admin, 69-70; dir health maintenance orgn serv, 71-73, dir, PSRO Prog, 73-74, dir div qual & standards, 74, REGIONAL HEALTH ADMINR, REGION IV, USPHS, 74- *Mem:* AMA. *Res:* Delivery of health care. *Mailing Add:* Dept Health Educ & Welfare 101 Marietta Tower Atlanta GA 30323

REICH, HANS JURGEN, b Danzig, Ger, May 6, 43; Can citizen; m 69. ORGANIC CHEMISTRY. *Educ:* Univ Alta, BSc, 64; Univ Calif, Los Angeles, PhD(org chem), 68. *Prof Exp:* Nat Res Coun Can fel, Calif Inst Technol, 68-69 & Harvard Univ, 69-70; from asst prof to assoc prof, 70-79, PROF CHEM, UNIV WIS-MADISION, 79- *Concurrent Pos:* Res grants, Petrol Res Found, 70, 73, 76 & 81, Res Corp, 72, NSF, 74, 77 & 81 & NIH, 78 & 81; Sloan Found fel, 75. *Mem:* Am Chem Soc; The Chem Soc. *Res:* Organic and organometalloid chemistry; synthetic applications, stereochemistry and mechanism in organosulfur, -selenium, -iodine and -silicon chemistry; synthesis of theoretically interesting molecules; nuclear magnetic resonance spectroscopy. *Mailing Add:* Dept Chem Univ Wis Madison WI 53706

REICH, HASKELL, AARON, b San Francisco, Calif, Jan 1, 26; m 45; c 2. APPLIED PHYSICS. *Educ:* City Col New York, BS, 49; Columbia Univ, PhD, 56. *Prof Exp:* RES PHYSICIST, THOMAS J WATSON RES CTR, IBM CORP, 55- *Mem:* Am Phys Soc. *Res:* Liquid and solid helium; computer assisted design systems; graphic display systems; visual displays; nuclear resonance; tunneling in thin superconducting films. *Mailing Add:* Thomas J Watson Res Ctr IBM Corp PO Box 218 Yorktown Heights NY 10598

REICH, HERBERT JOSEPH, b Staten Island, NY, Oct 25, 00; m 26; c 2. ELECTRONICS, ELECTRICAL ENGINEERING. *Educ:* Cornell Univ, ME, 24, PhD(physics), 28. *Prof Exp:* Instr mach design, Cornell Univ, 24-25, instr physics, 25-29; from asst prof to prof elec eng, Univ Ill, 29-46; prof elec eng, 46-64, prof eng & appl sci, 64-69, EMER PROF ENG & APPL SCI, YALE UNIV, 69- *Concurrent Pos:* Spec res assoc, Radio Res Lab, Harvard Univ, 44-46; mem adv group electron tubes, Off Asst Secy Defense, Res & Develop, 51-59; US deleg tech comt electron tubes, Int Electrotech Comn, 60-71, chmn subcomt microwave tubes, 65-72; prof physics & math, Deep Springs Col, Calif, 76-79. *Mem:* AAAS; fel Am Phys Soc; fel Inst Elec & Electronics Engrs. *Res:* Electron devices and electron-device circuits; microwave devices and microwave-device circuits electronics. *Mailing Add:* 8 Park St Groveland MA 01834

REICH, IEVA LAZDINS, b Riga, Latvia, June 30, 42; US citizen; m 69. ORGANIC CHEMISTRY. *Educ:* Univ Wash, BS, 64; Univ Calif, Los Angeles, PhD(org chem), 69. *Prof Exp:* NIH fel, Harvard Univ, 69-70; RES ASSOC ORG CHEM, UNIV WIS-MADISON, 70- *Concurrent Pos:* Consult, Miles Labs, Madison, 74-79; lectr gen chem, Univ Wis-Madison, 81- *Mem:* Am Chem Soc. *Res:* Chlorolium ions; solvolysis of vinyl halides; synthesis of polychlorinated biphenyl arene oxides; synthetic methods involving organo-selenium compounds. *Mailing Add:* Dept of Chem Univ of Wis Madison WI 53706

REICH, ISMAR M(EYER), b New York, NY, Aug 13, 24; m 56; c 3. CHEMICAL ENGINEERING, FOOD TECHNOLOGY. *Educ:* City Col New York, BChE, 45; Polytech Inst Brooklyn, MChE, 55. *Prof Exp:* Chem engr, Fleischmann Labs, Standard Brands, Inc, 45-48, head pilot plant dept, 48-53, head process develop div, 53-60, dir res, Coffee Instants, Inc, 60-65, dir mfg & res, 65-66, vpres mfg, 66-69; vpres, 69-80, gen mgr, Sol Cafe Div, 76-80, TECH DIR, CHOCK FULL O'NUTS CORP, JAMAICA, NY, 80- *Mem:* AAAS; Am Chem Soc; Am Inst Chem Engrs; NY Acad Sci; fel Am Inst Chem. *Res:* Food technology; extraction; dehydration; instrumentation; agglomeration. *Mailing Add:* 2136 Holland Way Merrick NY 11566

REICH, LEO, b Brooklyn, NY, June 23, 24; m 54; c 1. POLYMER CHEMISTRY. *Educ:* Polytech Inst Brooklyn, MS, 49; Stevens Inst Technol, PhD(chem), 59. *Prof Exp:* Sr develop chemist, Nepera Chem Co, Inc, 49-57; instr chem eng, Stevens Inst Technol, 57-59; sr res chemist, Air Reduction Co, Inc, 59-61; polymer res chemist, Picatinny Arsenal, Dover, 61-74; AFFIL PROF, STEVENS INST TECHNOL, 72- *Mem:* Am Chem Soc. *Res:* Reaction kinetics; electric discharge phenomena; photochemistry; thermal and thermooxidative degradation of polymers. *Mailing Add:* 3 Wessman Dr West Orange NJ 07052

REICH, MARVIN FRED, b Brooklyn, NY, Dec 30, 47. MEDICINAL CHEMISTRY. *Educ:* Polytech Inst, Brooklyn, BS, 68; NY Univ, MS, 72; Univ Ill, PhD(org chem), 78. *Prof Exp:* Chemist, Lederle Labs Div, Am Cyanamid Co, 69-73; teaching asst org chem, Univ Ill, 73-75, res asst, 75-78; staff fel, NIH, 78-79; res chemist, Bound Brook Res Labs, 79-80, SR RES CHEMIST, LEDERLE LAB DIV, AM CYANAMID CORP, 80- *Mem:* Am Chem Soc. *Res:* Medicinal and organic chemistry; design, synthesis and characterization of new pharmaceutical agents; anti-inflammatory drugs. *Mailing Add:* Med Res Div Lederle Labs Am Cyanamid Co Pearl River NY 10965

REICH, MELVIN, b New York, NY, July 17, 32; m 63; c 2. MICROBIOLOGY, BIOCHEMISTRY. *Educ:* City Col New York, BS, 53; Rutgers Univ, PhD(biochem, physiol), 60. *Prof Exp:* Asst biochem, Rutgers Univ, 55-60; asst res prof pharmacol, 60-64; asst prof microbiol, 64-68, assoc prof, 68-79, PROF MICROBIOL, SCH MED, GEORGE WASHINGTON UNIV, 79- *Mem:* AAAS; Am Soc Microbiol; Sigma Xi; Am Asn Univ Professors. *Res:* Bacterial physiology; mycobacteria; antimicrobials. *Mailing Add:* Dept Microbiol Sch Med George Washington Univ Washington DC 20037

REICH, MURRAY H, b Brooklyn, NY, May 29, 22; m 50; c 3. POLYMER CHEMISTRY. *Educ:* City Col New York, BS, 43; Univ Akron, MS, 54; Trenton State Col, MED, 74. *Prof Exp:* Process engr elastomers, US Govt Labs, 47-52, group leader, 52-55, chief engr, 55-56; res chemist, FMC Corp, 56-62; res chemist, 62-64, lab mgr res & develop lab, 64-70, 74-76, tech dir, 76-77, DEVELOP CHEMIST, PRINCETON CHEM RES, INC, 70-, TECH DIR & CONSULT, 77- *Concurrent Pos:* Preretirement counr, gerontologist & dir, Premac Assocs; adj prof, gerontology. *Mem:* Am Chem Soc. *Res:* Emulsion and solution polymerization of dienes; rubber and epoxy development; polyacetal and polyolefin research and degradable plastics. *Mailing Add:* 184 Loomis Ct Princeton NJ 08540

REICH, NATHANIEL EDWIN, b New York, NY, May 19, 07; m 43; c 2. MEDICINE. *Educ:* NY Univ, BS, 27; Univ Chicago, MD, 32; Am Bd Internal Med, dipl, 42. *Prof Exp:* Instr phys diag, 38-42, assoc prof, 52-74, prof, 74-77, EMER PROF CLIN MED, COL MED, STATE UNIV NY DOWNSTATE MED CTR, 77- *Concurrent Pos:* Asst attend physician, NY Postgrad Med Sch, Columbia Univ, 38-40; attend physician, Kings County Hosp, 47- & State Univ NY Downstate Med Ctr; impartial specialist, State Dept Labor, NY, 52-58; attend cardiologist, Kingsbrook Jewish Med Ctr, 52-; consult, Unity Hosp, 54-, Kings Hwy & Long Beach Mem Hosps, 54-, Catholic Diocese Brooklyn & Queen's, 55- & Flatbush Gen Hosp, 60-; vis prof, Fac Med, San Carlos Univ, 68, Medico, Afghanistan, 70 & Indonesia, 72; consult, US Dept Health, Educ & Welfare & US RR Retirement Bd. *Honors & Awards:* Am Col Angiol Res Awards, 57 & 58. *Mem:* Fel Royal Soc Med; fel Am Col Physicians; fel Am Col Chest Physicians; fel Am Col Cardiol; fel Am Col Angiol. *Mailing Add:* 135 Eastern Pkwy Brooklyn NY 11238

REICH, SIMEON, b Cracow, Poland, Aug 12, 48; Israeli citizen; m 74; c 2. NONLINEAR EVOLUTION EQUATIONS. *Educ:* Israel Inst Technol, BSc, 70, DSc, 73. *Prof Exp:* Lectr math, Tel Aviv Univ, 73-75; Dickson instr, Univ Chicago, 75-77; asst prof, 77-79, ASSOC PROF MATH, UNIV SOUTHERN CALIF, 79- *Concurrent Pos:* Vis scientist, Argonne Nat Lab, 78; consult, Math Res Ctr, Madison, Wis, 78 & 80; vis assoc prof, Univ Calif, Berkeley, 81. *Mem:* Am Math Soc; Math Asn Am; Soc Indust & Appl Math; Sigma Xi. *Res:* Nonlinear functional analysis: fixed point theory, asymptomatic behavior of nonlinear semigroups, constructive solvability of nonlinear equations, and properties of accretive and monotone operators in Banach spaces. *Mailing Add:* Dept Math Univ Southern Calif Los Angeles CA 90007

REICH, VERNON HENRY, b Rushville, Ill Apr 30, 39; m 66. AGRONOMY. *Educ:* Univ Ill, BS, 61, MS, 65; Iowa State Univ, PhD(agron, plant breeding), 68. *Prof Exp:* Res assoc agron, Iowa State Univ, 65-68; asst prof agron, 68-76, ASSOC PROF PLANT & SOIL SCI, UNIV TENN KNOXVILLE, 76- *Mem:* Am Soc Agron; Crop Sci Soc Am; Genetics Soc Am; Am Genetic Asn. *Res:* Plant breeding and genetics. *Mailing Add:* 349 Buford Ellington Plant Sci Dept Plant & Soil Sci Univ Tenn Knoxville TN 37916

REICHARD, DOUGLAS WARREN, organic chemistry, see previous edition

REICHARD, H(AROLD) F(ORREST), b Easton, Pa, Apr 15, 20; m 44; c 3. CHEMICAL ENGINEERING. *Educ:* Lafayette Col, BS, 41. *Prof Exp:* Develop chem engr, E I du Pont de Nemours & Co, 41-44 & 46-48; supvr chem eng res, prod contracts, US Atomic Energy Comn, 48-51; proj & group leader & supvr lab & pilot res, Vitro Corp, 51-56; asst dir res & develop, Mining & Mat Dept, Mining & Metals Div, Union Carbide Corp, 56-68, prod mgr spec alloys, 68-71, gen mgr alloys prod, 71-81; MGR PROD SPEC METALS, ELKEM METALS CO, 81- *Mem:* Fel Am Inst Chemists; Am Inst Mining, Metall & Petrol Engrs; Am Inst Chem Engrs. *Res:* Unit operations of distilling, drying, grinding, crystallizing and extracting; process development in dyestuffs, vitamins, fine chemicals, resin polymerization, organic chlorination, uranium chemistry and physical metallurgy; hydrometallurgy, ion exchange, adsorption, industrial minerals processing and applications; electrolytic process metallurgy. *Mailing Add:* Elkem Metals Co PO Box 266 Pittsburgh PA 15230

REICHARD, SHERWOOD MARSHALL, b Easton, Pa, June 24, 28; m 54; c 3. RADIOBIOLOGY, PHYSIOLOGY. *Educ:* Lafayette Col, BA, 48; NY Univ, MS, 50, PhD(endocrine physiol), 55. *Prof Exp:* Res collabr, Dept Biol, Brookhaven Nat Lab, 53-55, res assoc, 55; Muscular Dystrophy Asn Am Lilienthal Mem fel, McCollum-Pratt Inst, Johns Hopkins Univ, 57-58, advan res fel, Am Heart Asn, 58-60; asst prof physiol, Fla State Univ, 60-64; assoc prof, 64-69, dir, Div Radiobiol, 69-76, PROF RADIOL & PHYSIOL, MED COL GA, 69 , REGENTS PROF, 79- *Concurrent Pos:* Vis investr, Dept Radiobiol, Armed Forces Inst Path, 58-60; consult, Off Tech Utilization, NASA. *Honors & Awards:* Founders Day Award, NY Univ, 56; Zool Medal, Int Cong Zool, 63; Fred Conrad Koch Travel Award, Endocrine Soc, 65. *Mem:* Fel AAAS; Am Physiol Soc; Am Soc Zoologists; Radiation Res Soc; Endocrine Soc. *Res:* Physiology of reticuloendothelial system; endocrine inter-relations; protection against traumatic shock and x-irradiation; radiation effects; vitamin E and electron transport; hormones and enzymes and terminal respiration. *Mailing Add:* Div Radiobiol Med Col Ga Augusta GA 30912

REICHARDT, JOHN WILLIAM, b Imperial, Nebr, Nov 18, 40. PHYSICS, DEVICE ENGINEERING. *Educ:* Univ Denver, BS, 62; Univ Wichita, MS, 64; Univ Va, PhD(physics), 67. *Prof Exp:* Staff scientist res & develop, Sandia Labs, 67-73; staff scientist, 73-75, PROD MGR NEUTRON GENERATORS, KAMAN INSTRUMENTATION CORP, 75- *Res:* Neutron production and instrumentation for borehole geophysics; neutron activation analysis; small accelerator design; vacuum tube design; vacuum technology; materials and process technology; physics and chemistry of solid surface. *Mailing Add:* Kaman Instrumentation Corp 1500 Garden of the Gods Rd Colorado Springs CO 80907

REICHART, CHARLES VALERIAN, b Zanesville, Ohio, Feb 8, 10. ENTOMOLOGY. *Educ:* St Thomas Aquinas C, BA, 35; Ohio State Univ, MSc, 45, PhD(entom), 47. *Hon Degrees:* MA, Providence Col, 58. *Prof Exp:* Instr, Aquinas Col High Sch, Ohio, 39-43; instr biol, Providence Col, 43-44; instr zool, Ohio State Univ, 44-47; assoc prof biol, 47-48, head dept natural sci, 48-55, chmn dept biol, 55-71, prof, 48-78, EMER PROF BIOL, PROVIDENCE COL, 78- *Mem:* AAAS; Entom Soc Am; Entom Soc Can. *Res:* Notonectid taxonomy; genus anisops. *Mailing Add:* Martin Hall Dept of Biol Providence Col Providence RI 02918

REICHBERG, SAMUEL BRINGEISSEN, b Santiago, Chile, Aug 30, 46; m 72; c 2. CLINICAL LABORATORY MEDICINE, CELL BIOLOGY. *Educ:* Univ Chile, LicMed, 70, MD, 71; Yale Univ, MPhil, 73, PhD(biochem), 75. *Prof Exp:* Fel human genetics, Med Sch, Yale Univ, 72-74, med, 74-76, residency lab med, 76-78; ASST PROF PATH, NY MED COL, 78- *Concurrent Pos:* Dir, Clin Lab Dept, Brookdale Hosp, 83-; fac, Med Sch, NY Univ, Downstate, 82- *Mem:* AAAS; NY Acad Sci. *Res:* Regulation of cell plasma membrane transport activity; correlation between transport effects and chemical changes in membrane composition produced by the hormones insulin and glucocorticoids and by growth regulatory compounds. *Mailing Add:* 54 Caterson Terrace Hartsdale NY 10530

REICHE, LUDWIG P(ERCY), b Ger, Dec 26, 19; m 51; c 3. COMMUNICATIONS. *Educ:* NY Univ, BEE, 48. *Prof Exp:* Proj engr, Victor Div, Radio Corp Am, Calif, 50-52; staff engr, Int Telemeter Corp, 52-53; sr proj engr, Hoffman Labs, 53-54; sr res engr, Radio Systs Lab, Stanford Res Inst, 54-60; mgr microwave commun, Melabs, 60-64; mem staff, 64-72, SR PROJ ENGR, HUGHES AIRCRAFT CO, 72- *Concurrent Pos:* Coordr, Indonesian Pub Tel Enterprise, 75-77. *Mem:* Inst Elec & Electronics Engrs. *Mailing Add:* 843 Via Campobello Santa Barbara CA 93111

REICHEL, WILLIAM LOUIS, b Philadelphia, Pa, July 10, 27; m 53; c 2. ENVIRONMENTAL CHEMISTRY. *Educ:* Philadelphia Col Pharm, BSc, 52. *Prof Exp:* Org chemist, Philadelphia Naval Shipyard, 52-59; res chemist, 59-66, CHIEF CHEMIST, BUR SPORT FISHERIES & WILDLIFE, US FISH & WILDLIFE SERV, 66- *Mem:* Am Chem Soc. *Res:* Development of procedures for isolation, identification and quantitative measurement of pesticide residues in animal tissues and their environment. *Mailing Add:* 9145 Winding Way Ellicott City MD 21043

REICHELDERFER, CHARLES FRANKLIN, b Wadena, Minn, Mar 19, 37; m 76. INVERTEBRATE PATHOLOGY, ENTOMOLOGY. *Educ:* St Cloud State Col, BS, 60; Univ Calif, Riverside, PhD(entom), 68. *Prof Exp:* Asst prof, 68-76, ASSOC PROF ENTOM, UNIV MD, COLLEGE PARK, 76- *Mem:* AAAS; Am Inst Biol Sci; Entom Soc Am; Soc Invertebrate Path. *Res:* Genetics and host relationships of insect viruses; immunological characterization of insect viruses; distribution and abundance of insect viruses in nature. *Mailing Add:* Dept Entom 3317 Symons Hall Univ of Md College Park MD 20740

REICHELDERFER, FRANCIS WILTON, b Harlan, Ind, Aug 6, 95; m 20; c 1. METEOROLOGY. *Educ:* Northwestern Univ, AB, 17. *Hon Degrees:* DSc, Northwestern Univ, 39. *Prof Exp:* Meteorologist, US Dept Navy, 18-32, exec officer & other positions, 28-38; chief, US Weather Bur, 38-63; CONSULT, 63- *Concurrent Pos:* Pres, N & Cent Am meteorol regions, World Meteorol Orgn, 39-47, 59-63, pres orgn, 51-55; vchmn, Nat Adv Comt Aeronaut, 41-59; vpres, Int Meteorol Asn, Int Union Geod & Geophys, 48-51; consult, Int Meteorol Progs; mem US-Japan Coop Sci Prog, US Dept State; mem missions, World Meteorol Orgn & US State Dept, Thailand & Japan. *Honors & Awards:* Awards for int meteorol activities, Japanese Govt, 62; World Meteorol Orgn, 64; citations from Chile, Cuba, Peru & others; Losey Award, Am Inst Aeronaut & Astronaut; ABBE Award Award, Am Meteorol Soc, 64, Distinguished Service Pub Meteorol Services, 73-74. *Mem:* Nat Acad Sci; AAAS; Am Meteorol Soc; hon mem Am Inst Aerospace & Aeronaut; Am Geophys Union. *Res:* Atmospheric sciences; international meteorological programs. *Mailing Add:* Tilden Gardens 201E Conn Ave at Tilden NW Washington DC 20008

REICHELDERFER, THOMAS ELMER, b Newark, NJ, Aug 21, 16; m 43; c 3. PEDIATRICS, PUBLIC HEALTH. *Educ:* Rutgers Univ, BS, 39; Johns Hopkins Univ, MD, 50, MPH, 56. *Prof Exp:* From asst to instr pediat, Johns Hopkins Univ, 51-54, instr pediat & pub health admin, 54-56; asst prof pediat, Univ Minn, 56-57; chief gen study unit, Lab Infectious Dis, Nat Inst Allergy & Infectious Dis, 57-58; chief med officer, DC Gen Hosp, 58-72; ASSOC PROF PEDIAT, JOHNS HOPKINS UNIV, 73- *Concurrent Pos:* Asst resident, Johns Hopkins Hosp, Baltimore, Md, 51-52, resident pediatrician, 52-54; consult, Nat Naval Med Ctr, 53-54; pediatrician, Johns Hopkins Hosp, Baltimore, Md, 54-56 & 73-; clin prof pediat, Howard Univ, 58-72; assoc clin prof, George Washington & Georgetown Univs, 58-72. *Mem:* AAAS; AMA; fel Am Acad Pediat. *Res:* Infectious diseases; newborn infants. *Mailing Add:* 2029 Chesapeake Rd Tydings on the Bay Annapolis MD 21401

REICHELT, WALTER HERBERT, b New York, NY, July 27, 25; m 48; c 3. NUCLEAR PHYSICS, PLASMA PHYSICS. *Educ:* Univ NC, BS, 54; Johns Hopkins Univ, PhD(physics), 60. *Prof Exp:* STAFF MEM PHYSICS, LOS ALAMOS SCI LAB, 60- *Mem:* Am Phys Soc. *Res:* Low temperature cesium plasmas; direct energy conversion. *Mailing Add:* Los Alamos Sci Lab Los Alamos NM 87544

REICHENBACH, GEORGE SHERIDAN, b Waterbury, Conn, May 25, 29; m 56; c 3. MECHANICAL ENGINEERING. *Educ:* Yale Univ, BME, 51; Mass Inst Technol, MS, 52, ScD, 56. *Prof Exp:* From asst prof to assoc prof mech eng, Mass Inst Technol, 56-66; asst dir res, 66-69, dir res & develop, 69-74, vpres & gen mgr org prod, Grinding Wheel Div, 74-79, vpres & gen mgr, Mat Div, 79-81, VPRES BONDED ABRASIVES, NORTON CO, 81- *Honors & Awards:* Alfred Noble Prize, Joint Eng Socs, 60; Yale Eng Award, 61. *Mem:* Am Soc Mech Engrs. *Res:* Materials, lubrication and metal processing. *Mailing Add:* Norton Co One New Bond St Worcester MA 01606

REICHENBACH, ROY EARL, aeronautical engineering, engineering mechanics, see previous edition

REICHENBACHER, PAUL H, b Aurora, Ill, Feb 4, 40; m 63; c 4. REINFORCED PLASTICS, ORGANIC CHEMISTRY. *Educ:* St Mary's Col, BA, 62; Pa State Univ, PhD(chem), 67. *Prof Exp:* Res chemist, Corp Res Ctr, 67-72, group leader, 72-77, DIR TECHNOL, NORPLEX DIV, UOP INC, SIGNAL CO, 77- *Concurrent Pos:* Adj prof, Ill Benedictine Col, 69-70 & Concordia Teachers Col, 70-71; dir, Alumni Bd, St Mary's Col, 78-, pres, 80- *Mem:* Am Chem Soc; Inst Interconnecting & Packaging Electronic Circuits; Sigma Xi; Int Electronic Packaging Soc. *Res:* Reinforced thermoset laminates; electronic interconnects; composite materials; electrical properties of materials; polymerization reactions; specialty organic chemicals; physical organic chemistry. *Mailing Add:* Norplex Div UOP Inc 1300 Norplex Dr LaCrosse WI 54601

REICHENTHAL, JULES, b New York, NY, June 30, 27; m 61; c 2. MEDICINAL CHEMISTRY. *Educ:* NY Univ, AB, 48; Georgetown Univ, MS, 53; Polytech Inst Brooklyn, PhD(org chem), 66. *Prof Exp:* Chemist, Nat Heart Inst, 50-52; chemist, Goldwater Mem Hosp, 53-55; biochemist, Lederle Lab Div, Am Cyanamid Co, 55-62, chemist, 65-66; sr res chemist, Schwarz Biores Div, Becton, Dickinson & Co, 67-69; sr res chemist, Endo Labs, Garden City, 69-76, SR RES CHEMIST DEPT BIOCHEM, PHARMACEUT DIV-PROCESS DEVELOP, E I DU PONT DE NEMOURS & CO, INC, WILMINGTON, 76- *Mem:* Am Chem Soc. *Res:* Synthesis of heterocyclic compounds of biological interest. *Mailing Add:* E I du Pont de Nemours & Co Inc Exp Sta B335/210 Wilmington DE 19898

REICHERT, JOHN DOUGLAS, b Cameron, Tex, Nov 29, 38; m 61; c 2. THEORETICAL PHYSICS, OPTICAL PHYSICS. *Educ:* Univ Tex, Austin, BS & BA, 61; Calif Inst Technol, PhD(theoret physics), 65. *Prof Exp:* Fel theoret physics, Relativity Ctr, Univ Tex, Austin, 65-66; res assoc, Univ Southern Calif, 66-67, asst prof physics, 67-71; ASSOC PROF ELEC ENG, TEX TECH UNIV, 71- *Concurrent Pos:* Adj prof, Optical Sci Ctr, Univ Ariz, 71- *Mem:* Optical Soc Am; Am Phys Soc. *Res:* Laser beam propagation; optical resonators; diffraction and scattering theory; nonlinear interactions of light with matter; Fourier optics; quantum theory. *Mailing Add:* Dept of Elec Eng Tex Tech Univ Lubbock TX 79409

REICHERT, JONATHAN F, b Cincinnati, Ohio, Aug 29, 31; m 53; c 3. EXPERIMENTAL SOLID STATE PHYSICS, MAGNETIC RESONANCE. *Educ:* Case Western Reserve Univ, BS, 53; Wash Univ, PhD(physics), 62. *Prof Exp:* Fel physics, Harvard Univ, 63-65; asst prof, Case Western Reserve Univ, 65-70; ASSOC PROF PHSYICS, STATE UNIV NY BUFFALO, 70- *Concurrent Pos:* Air Force res grant, 66-69; NY State Res Found grant, 72; NSF grant ions in liquid helium, 74-76; NY Res Found grant, 75-76; NSF grant, 76-78; chmn fac senate, State Univ NY Buffalo, 76-78; vis assoc prof, Princeton Univ, 78-79; ions in liquid helium grants, NSF, 78-81. *Mem:* Am Phys Soc. *Res:* Mossbauer spectroscopy and liquid helium; nuclear and electronic magnetic resonance and solid state physics of defects. *Mailing Add:* Dept of Physics Hochstetter Hall State Univ of NY Buffalo NY 14214

REICHERT, LEO E, JR, b New York, NY, Jan 9, 32; m 57; c 4. BIOCHEMISTRY, ENDOCRINOLOGY. *Educ:* Manhattan Col, BS, 55; Loyola Univ Chicago, MS, 57, PhD(biochem), 60. *Prof Exp:* From instr to assoc prof biochem, Emory Univ, 60-71, prof, 71-79; PROF & CHMN, ALBANY MED COL, 79- *Concurrent Pos:* Secy gonadotropin subcomt, Nat Pituitary Agency, 68-, mem med adv bd, Agency, 71-74; mem reproductive biol study sect, NIH, 71-75. *Honors & Awards:* Ayerst Award, Endocrine Soc, 71. *Mem:* AAAS; Am Soc Biol Chemists; Endocrine Soc. *Res:* Biochemistry and physiology of gonadotropin hormones and their receptors; relationship of structure to function. *Mailing Add:* Dept Biochem Albany Med Col Albany NY 12208

REICHERT, THOMAS ANDREW, b Youngstown, Ohio, Mar 13, 42; m 74; c 3. ONCOLOGY, PATTERN RECOGNITION. *Educ:* Western Reserve Univ, AB, 62; Univ Calif, Berkeley, PhD(phys chem), 68; Univ Miami, MD, 78. *Prof Exp:* Asst prof elec eng, Carnegie-Mellon Univ, 70-74, assoc prof & chmn, Biotechnol Prog, 74-78; intern, Duke Hosp, 78-79, resident, 78-80, fel oncol, 80-81, ASSOC MED, DUKE UNIV, 81- *Concurrent Pos:* NSF grant under Dr S A Friedberg, Carnegie-Mellon Univ, 68-69, NIH trainee, Biotechnol Prog, 69-70; NSF grant, 71-; Nat Inst Gen Med Sci res grant, 71-; Nat Heart & Lung Inst res grant, 74-; lectr, Chatham Col, 69-70; consult, Nat Cancer Inst, Dept Defense & AEC; partner anal firm, Entropy Ltd, 73- *Mem:* Inst Elec & Electronics Engrs; Am Col Physicians. *Res:* Information stored in biological molecules; physiological and medical pattern recognition; visual psychophysics; elucidation of biosignals. *Mailing Add:* Div Hemat & Oncol Med Ctr Duke Univ Box 3290 Durham NC 27710

REICHERTZ, PAUL PETER, b Aurora, Ill, Aug 16, 15; m 44; c 3. PHYSICS. *Educ:* NCent Col, Ill, BA, 37; Brown Univ, ScM, 39, PhD(physics), 43. *Prof Exp:* Lab asst, Brown Univ, 37-40, res investr, Off Sci Res & Develop, 42-43; instr, Georgetown Univ, 40-41; res physicist, Magnolia Petrol Co, Socony Mobil Oil Co, Inc, 43-46, res assoc, 46-51, asst supvr prod res, 51-56, asst mgr & supvr, 56-61, mgr, 61-64, pres, Mobil Oil Venezuela, 64-65, mgr mgt serv & comput systs, Mobil Oil Corp, 65-80 ; RETIRED. *Mem:* Am Phys Soc; AAAS; Am Inst Mining, Metall & Petrol Eng; Opers Res Soc Am; Inst Mgt Sci. *Res:* X-ray and electron diffraction; flow of fluids through porous media; petroleum production; data processing; information science. *Mailing Add:* 20 Greenleaf Ave Darien CT 06820

REICHES, NANCY A, b Cleveland, Ohio, Jan 26, 49. EPIDEMIOLOGY, BIOSTATISTICS. *Educ:* Univ Colo, Boulder, BA, 71, MA, 72; Ohio State Univ, PhD(prev med), 77. *Prof Exp:* Lectr commun theory, Univ Nev, Las Vegas, 72-73; res asst biostatist, Biomet, 73-76, res assoc epidemiol, Comprehensive Cancer Ctr, 76-77, SR RES ASSOC EPIDEMIOL & BIOSTATIST, COMPREHENSIVE CANCER CTR, OHIO STATE UNIV, 77- *Concurrent Pos:* Consult, Battelle Mem Inst, Columbus, Ohio, 77- *Mem:* Am Pub Health Asn; Soc Epidemiol Res; Am Soc Prev Oncol. *Res:* Cancer epidemiology; environmental epidemiology; biostatistical methods; biomedical computing. *Mailing Add:* Dept of Prev Med 410 W 10th Ave Columbus OH 43210

REICHGOTT, MICHAEL JOEL, b Newark, NJ, July 26, 40; m 62; c 3. MEDICINE, CLINICAL PHARMACOLOGY. *Educ:* Gettysburg Col, AB, 61; Albert Einstein Col Med, MD, 65; Univ Calif, San Francisco, PhD(pharmacol), 73. *Prof Exp:* Trainee clin pharmacol, Med Ctr, Univ Calif, San Francisco, 69-72; assoc med, 72-73; asst prof med, 73-81, dir, Outpatient Clins, 75-78, dir, Dept Pract, 78-80, assoc chief staff ambulatory care, Med Ctr, 80-81, PROF MED, HOSP, UNIV PA, 73-, CHIEF, SECT GEN MED, MED CTR, 81- *Mem:* Fel Am Col Physicians; AAAS; Am Soc Pharmacol & Exp Therapeut; Am Fedn Clin Res; Soc Res & Educ Primary Care Internal Med. *Res:* Clinical pharmacology of antihypertensive agents; compliance; health services delivery involving non-physician health care providers; ambulatory care; hypertension. *Mailing Add:* Dept Med Hosp Univ Pa Philadelphia PA 19104

REICHL, ERIC H, b 1913; m; c 2. PETROLEUM CHEMISTRY. *Educ:* Vienna Tech Univ, MS, 33. *Prof Exp:* Mem staff, Babcock & Wilcox Co, 38; mem staff res plant design construct opers, Winkler-Koch Eng, 38-44; mem staff, Stanolind Oil & Gas of Ind, 44-46; mem staff, Calif Res Corp, 46-48; Consol Coal Co res mgr, 48-54, dir res, 54-62, vpres, 62-76, PRES, CONOCO COAL DEVELOP CO, CONTINENTAL OIL CO, 76- *Concurrent Pos:* Dir, Bituminous Coal Res Inc. *Mem:* Nat Acad Eng; Am Inst Civil Engrs. *Res:* Process research on synthetic liquid fuels. *Mailing Add:* Conoco Coal Develop Co High Ridge Park Stamford CT 06904

REICHLE, ALFRED DOUGLAS, b Port Arthur, Tex, Dec 19, 20; m 43; c 2. PETROLEUM REFINING, CATALYSIS. *Educ:* Rice Univ, BS, 42, MS, 43; Univ Wis, PhD(chem eng), 48. *Prof Exp:* Chemist petrol refining, Shell Develop Co, 43-57; staff asst process develop, Phillips Petrol Co, 57-59; engr, 59-60, sr res engr, 60-62, eng assoc, 62-63, sect head, 63-67, sr eng assoc, 67-71, ENG ADV PETROL REFINING, EXXON RES & DEVELOP CO, 71- *Mem:* Am Inst Chem Engrs. *Res:* Petroleum process development; catalytic refining processes; catalyst development. *Mailing Add:* Exxon Res & Develop Labs PO Box 2226 Baton Rouge LA 70821

REICHLE, DAVID EDWARD, b Cincinnati, Ohio, Oct 19, 38; m 61; c 3. ECOLOGY. *Educ:* Muskingum Col, BS, 60; Northwestern Univ, MS, 61, PhD(biol sci), 64. *Prof Exp:* AEC fel, Oak Ridge Nat Lab, 64-66; ecologist, 66-72, ASSOC DIR, ENVIRON SCI DIV, OAK RIDGE NAT LAB, 72- *Concurrent Pos:* Consult, ecosyst anal panel, NSF; mem environ studies & toxicol & environ health bds, Nat Acad Sci, US SCOPE Comt & directorate, US MAB Prog; prof grad prog ecol, Univ Tenn; Danforth Assoc. *Mem:* Fel AAAS; Ecol Soc Am; Am Inst Biol Sci; Health Physics Soc; Soc Environ Geochem & Health. *Res:* Environmental geochemistry and health; terrestrial invertebrate ecology, bioenergetics, structure and function of arthropod communities; radioecology, movement of radioisotopes through food chains, effects of ionizing radiation upon natural arthropod communities; mineral cycling; ecosystem analysis. *Mailing Add:* Environ Sci Div B 1505 Oak Ridge Nat Lab Box X Oak Ridge TN 37830

REICHLE, FREDERICK ADOLPH, b Neshaminy, Pa, Apr 20, 35. SURGERY. *Educ:* Temple Univ, BA, 57, MS, 61 & 66, MD, 61. *Prof Exp:* Intern med, Abington Mem Hosp, 61-62; resident, 62-66, from instr to assoc prof, 66-76, PROF SURG, HEALTH SCI CTR, TEMPLE UNIV, 76-, CHIEF SECT PERIPHERAL VASCULAR SURG, 74-; CHMN & PROF SURG, PRESBYTERIAN-UNIV PA MED CTR, 80- *Concurrent Pos:* Fel vascular surg, Health Sci Ctr, Temple Univ, 66-67; asst attend surgeon, Episcopal & St Christopher's Hosps, 66-; mem coun thrombosis, Am Heart Asn, 71-; mem, Nat Kidney Found, 72; consult, Vet Admin Hosp, Wilkes-Barre. *Mem:* Fel Am Col Surgeons; Am Surg Asn; Soc Surg Alimentary Tract; AAAS; Int Soc Thrombosis & Haemostasis. *Res:* Vascular surgery; liver metabolism; amino acid metabolism; cancer; thrombosis. *Mailing Add:* 51 North 39th St Philadelphia PA 19104

REICHLE, WALTER THOMAS, b Cleveland, Ohio, Aug 2, 28; m 53; c 3. CHEMISTRY. *Educ:* Newark Col Eng, BS, 53; Ohio State Univ, PhD(chem), 58. *Prof Exp:* Res chemist, Res Labs, Plastics Div, 58-69, SR RES SCIENTIST, CHEM & PLASTICS, RES & DEVELOP LAB, UNION CARBIDE CORP, 69- *Concurrent Pos:* Vis fel, Princeton Univ, 73-74. *Mem:* Am Chem Soc; Sci Res Soc Am; NY Acad Sci. *Res:* Organo-metallic and inorganic chemistry; catalytic agents; homogeneous and heterogeneous catalysis. *Mailing Add:* Res & Develop Lab Union Carbide Corp PO Box 670 Bound Brook NJ 08805

REICHLER, ROBERT JAY, b Bronx, NY, Nov 22, 37; c 2. CHILD PSYCHIATRY. *Educ:* Univ Chicago, BA, 57; Albert Einstein Col Med, MD, 61; Am Bd Psychiat & Neurol, dipl, 71. *Prof Exp:* Instr psychiat, Strong Mem Hosp, Univ Rochester, 64-65; clin asst prof, Med Col Charleston, 68-69; asst prof, Sch Med, Univ NC, Chapel Hill, 69-72, assoc prof child psychiat & co-dir, Div TEACCH, 72-76; PROF PSYCHIAT & HEAD, DIV CHILD PSYCHOL, SCH MED, UNIV WASH, 76-; DIR, DEPT BEHAV SCI, CHILDREN'S ORTHOP HOSP & MED CTR, 76- *Concurrent Pos:* NIMH fel psychiat, Strong Mem Hosp, Univ Rochester, 62-65; NIMH fel child psychiat, NC Mem Hosp, Univ NC, 65-67; from asst surgeon to sr surgeon, USPHS, 67-69; mem child & family develop res rev comt, Off Child Develop, Dept Health, Educ & Welfare, 72-74; mem prof adv bd, Nat Soc Autistic Children, 72-, chmn, 77-; mem intervention comt, NC Coun Develop

Disabilities, 72-75; consult, Div Neuropharm, Food & Drug Admin, 76- & Off Sci Eval, Bur Drugs, Food & Drug Admin & Div Neuropharmacol; adj prof pediat, Sch Med, Univ Wash, 77-; actg head inpatient psychiat treat div, Children's Orthop Hosp & Med Ctr, 78- *Honors & Awards:* Gold Achievement Award, Am Psychiat Asn, 72. *Mem:* AAAS; Am Orthopsychiat Asn; Soc Res Child Develop; Am Psychiat Asn; Am Acad Child Psychiat. *Res:* Psychotic and communication disordered children; parent and professional estimates of current and future abilities; psychophysiological parameters in childhood psychosis; nosology for child psychopathology; developmental psychopharmacology; anxiety disorders; high risk children. *Mailing Add:* Div Child Psychiat Coach House Rm 831 2309 NE 48th St Seattle WA 98105

REICHLIN, MORRIS, b Toledo, Ohio, Feb 2, 34; m 58; c 2. MEDICINE. *Educ:* Washington Univ, AB, 55, MD, 59. *Prof Exp:* Fel biochem, Brandeis Univ, 61-63 & Univ Rome, 63-64; instr med, Col Med, Univ Vt, 64-65; from asst prof to assoc prof med & biochem, State Univ NY Buffalo, 65-71, prof, 71-80; MEM & HEAD, ARTHRITIS & IMMUNOL LAB, OKLA MED RES FOUND, PROF & CHIEF, IMMUNOL SECT, COL MED, OKLA HEALTH SCI CTR, 80- *Mem:* Am Soc Biol Chemists; Am Asn Immunologists. *Res:* Immunochemistry of hemoglobin and cytochrome C. *Mailing Add:* Okla Med Res Found 825 NE 13th St Oklahoma City OK 73104

REICHLIN, SEYMOUR, b New York, NY, May 31, 24; m 51; c 3. INTERNAL MEDICINE, PHYSIOLOGY. *Educ:* Antioch Col, AB, 45; Washington Univ, MD, 48; Univ London, PhD, 54. *Prof Exp:* Commonwealth Fund fel, 52-54; instr med & psychiat, Sch Med, Washington Univ, 54-56, asst prof, 56-61; assoc prof med, Sch Med & Dent, Univ Rochester, 62-66, prof, 66-69; prof med & chmn dept med & pediat specialties, Sch Med, Univ Conn, 69-71, prof physiol & head dept, 71-72; PROF MED, SCH MED, TUFTS UNIV, 72- *Concurrent Pos:* Palmer Fund fel, 54-56; mem endocrinol study sect, USPHS, 66-70. *Honors & Awards:* Eli Lilly Award, Endocrine Soc, 72. *Mem:* Endocrine Soc (pres, 75-76); Am Physiol Soc; Am Psychosom Soc; Asn Res Nerv & Ment Disease (pres, 77); Asn Am Physicians. *Res:* Endocrinology; neuroendocrinology; thyroid and pituitary physiology. *Mailing Add:* New England Med Ctr 171 Harrison Ave Boston MA 02111

REICHMAN, OMER JAMES, b Tampa, Fla, Jan 4, 47; m 68. ECOLOGY. *Educ:* Tex Tech Univ, BA, 68, MS, 70; Northern Ariz Univ, PhD(biol), 74. *Prof Exp:* Instr biol, Northern Ariz Univ, 72-74; res asst prof biol, Univ Utah, 74-75; RES ECOLOGIST BIOL & ASST DIR, MUS NORTHERN ARIZ, 75- *Concurrent Pos:* Fel, Univ Utah, 74-75. *Mem:* Ecol Soc Am; Am Soc Mammal; Soc Study Evolution; Am Soc Nat. *Res:* Plant and animal interactions; resource distribution particularly seeds; pocket gopher ecology; resource utilization by rodents. *Mailing Add:* Div Biol Kans State Univ Manhattan KS 66506

REICHMAN, SANDOR, b Nov 24, 41; US citizen; m 66; c 2. PHYSICAL CHEMISTRY. *Educ:* City Col NY, BS, 63; NY Univ, PhD(phys chem), 67. *Prof Exp:* Fel infrared spectros, Univ Minn, 66-68; asst prof, 68-72, assoc prof, 72-76, PROF PHYS CHEM, CALIF STATE UNIV, NORTHRIDGE, 76- *Mem:* Am Phys Soc. *Res:* Infrared spectroscopy; molecular dynamics; high resolution infrared spectroscopy; anharmonicity calculations. *Mailing Add:* Dept of Chem Calif State Univ Northridge CA 91324

REICHMANIS, ELSA, b Melbourne, Australia, Dec 9, 53; US citizen; m 79. ORGANIC CHEMISTRY. *Educ:* Syracuse Univ, BS, 72, PhD(org chem), 75. *Prof Exp:* Intern org chem, Syracuse Univ, 75-76, Chaim Weizmann fel sci res, 76-78; MEM TECH STAFF ORG CHEM, BELL LABS, 78- *Mem:* Am Chem Soc; AAAS. *Res:* Heteroaromatic chemistry; synthesis; photochemistry; photodegradation of polymers and their application to integrated circuit technology. *Mailing Add:* Bell Labs 600 Mountain Ave Murray Hill NJ 07974

REICHMANIS, MARIA, experimental biophysics, see previous edition

REICHMANN, KEITH WILFORD, pharmacy, see previous edition

REICHMANN, MANFRED ELIEZER, b Trencin, Czech, Apr 16, 25; m 57; c 3. BIOCHEMISTRY. *Educ:* Hebrew Univ, Israel, MSc, 49, PhD, 51. *Prof Exp:* USPHS fel, Harvard Univ, 51-53; Nat Res Coun Can fel, 53-55; res officer, Plant Virus Inst, Res Br, Can Dept Agr, 55-64; prof bot, 64-71, PROF MICROBIOL, UNIV ILL, URBANA, 71- *Concurrent Pos:* Prof biochem, Univ BC, 62-64; assoc mem, Ctr Adv Studies, Univ Ill, 77-78; Scholar, Am Cancer Soc, 77-78. *Mem:* Am Soc Biol Chemists; Am Soc Microbiol; AAAS. *Res:* Physiochemical studies of viruses; chemical composition of viral proteins and nucleic acids; defective interfering particles; mechanism of autointerference; Vesicular Stomatitis virus. *Mailing Add:* Dept Microbiol 131 Burrill Hall Univ Ill Urbana IL 61801

REICHSMAN, FRANZ KARL, b Vienna, Austria, Sept 26, 13; nat US; m 45; c 5. PSYCHOSOMATIC MEDICINE. *Educ:* Univ Vienna, MD, 38; Am Bd Internal Med, dipl. *Prof Exp:* Res asst, Johns Hopkins Hosp, 39-40; intern med, Sinai Hosp, Baltimore, 40-41, asst path, 41-42, asst resident med, 42-43; asst prof, Univ Tex Southwestern Med Sch Dallas, 46-49, clin asst prof, 49-52; from instr to assoc prof med & psychiat, Sch Med, Univ Rochester, 52-64; PROF MED & PSYCHIAT, STATE UNIV NY DOWNSTATE MED CTR, 64- *Concurrent Pos:* Dazian Found fel, Bowman Gray Sch Med, 43-44 & Univ Tex Southwestern Med Sch Dallas, 44-45; Commonwealth Fund fel, Sch Med, Univ Rochester, 52-54; chief chest serv, Vet Admin Hosp, McKinney, Tex, 47-50, asst chief med serv, 50-52; career investr, USPHS, 56-61; vis physician, Kings County Hosp, 64-; assoc physician & assoc psychiatrist, Strong Mem Hosp; vis prof, Oxford Univ, 71-72. *Mem:* Royal Soc Med; Am Psychiat Asn; Group Advan Psychiat; Am Psychosom Soc (pres elect, 80-81). *Res:* Dynamics of congestive heart failure; arterial hypertension; adaptation to hemodialysis; emotions and gastric function. *Mailing Add:* Dept of Med State Univ NY Downstate Med Ctr Brooklyn NY 11203

REICOSKY, DONALD CHARLES, b Canton, Ohio, Aug 12, 41; m 65. AGRONOMY, SOIL PHYSICS. *Educ:* Ohio State Univ, BS, 63, MS, 65; Univ Ill, Urbana, PhD(soil physics, agron), 69. *Prof Exp:* SOIL SCIENTIST, AGR RES SERV, USDA, 69- *Concurrent Pos:* Wright fel & Hatch assistantship, Ohio State Univ. *Mem:* Am Soc Agron; Soil Sci Soc Am. *Res:* Soil-plant-water relations as affected by root activity and water uptake. *Mailing Add:* N Iowa Ave W Florence Station Morris MN 29501

REID, ALLEN FRANCIS, b Deer River, Minn, July 31, 17; m 43; c 2. BIOPHYSICS. *Educ:* Univ Minn, BCh, 40; Columbia Univ, AM, 42, PhD(chem), 43; Southwest Sch Med, Univ Tex, MD, 59. *Prof Exp:* Asst chem, Columbia Univ, 40-42, res scientist in chg radioactivity labs, 42-46; indust consult, Sun Oil Co, Pa, 46-47; from assoc prof to prof biophys, Southwest Med Sch, Univ Tex, 47-60, chmn dept, 47-60; prof biol & chmn dept, Univ Dallas, 60-68; dir, Clin Biochem, Brooklyn-Cumberland Med Ctr, 68-74; PROF BIOL & CHMN DEPT, STATE UNIV NY COL GENESEO, 74- *Concurrent Pos:* Prof & chmn dept biophys & phys chem, Grad Res Inst, Baylor Univ, 47-50, biophysicist, Univ Hosp, 47-50; consult, Oak Ridge Inst Nuclear Studies, 50-52; biophysicist, Parkland Mem Hosp, Dallas, 50-58; consult, US Vet Admin, 50-67; clin prof path, State Univ NY Downstate Med Ctr, 68-74; dir path, Brooklyn-Cumberland Med Ctr, 70-74. *Mem:* Fel AAAS; fel Am Inst Chemists; Am Chem Soc; Am Phys Soc; Am Physiol Soc. *Res:* Energy recovery; tracer work in chemical and biological systems; radioactivity; methods of fractionation; reaction and biologic mechanisms; desalinization. *Mailing Add:* 4736 Reservoir Rd Geneseo NY 14454

REID, ARCHIBALD, b Janesville, Wis, Nov 23, 30; m 57. PLANT ECOLOGY. *Educ:* Wis State Univ, Platteville, BS, 57; Univ Wis, MS, 59, PhD(bot), 62. *Prof Exp:* Asst prof bot, Univ Wyo, 61-66; assoc prof landscape archit & regional planning, Univ Pa, 66-68; assoc prof, 68-72, PROF BIOL, STATE UNIV NY COL GENESEO, 72- *Mem:* AAAS; Ecol Soc Am. *Res:* Growth inhibitors produced by vascular plants; ecology as the base for landscape architecture and regional planning; structure of plant communities; environmental measurements. *Mailing Add:* Dept of Biol State Univ of NY Col Geneseo NY 14454

REID, BOBBY LEROY, b San Benito, Tex, Aug 28, 29; m 50; c 3. BIOCHEMISTRY, NUTRITION. *Educ:* Agr & Mech Col, Tex, BS, 50, MS, 52, PhD, 55. *Prof Exp:* Asst prof, Agr & Mech Col, Tex, 55-59; dir prod res, Feed Div, Pillsbury Co, 59-60; PROF POULTRY SCI, UNIV ARIZ, 60-, HEAD DEPT & POULTRY SCIENTIST, AGR EXP STA, 74- *Concurrent Pos:* Biochemist, Nutrit Surv Haiti, Williams-Waterman Found, 58; spec consult, Nutrit Surv Turkish Armed Forces, Interdept Comt Nutrit for Nat Defense, 57. *Mem:* Soc Exp Biol & Med; Poultry Sci Asn; Animal Nutrit Res Coun. *Res:* Poultry nutrition research on unidentified factors, antibiotics, vitamin A, caloric-protein relationships, fat metabolism and B vitamins. *Mailing Add:* Dept of Poultry Sci Univ of Ariz Tucson AZ 85721

REID, BRIAN DOUGLAS, nuclear medicine, see previous edition

REID, BRIAN ROBERT, b Gillingham, Eng, Nov 14, 38; m 61; c 2. BIOCHEMISTRY. *Educ:* Cambridge Univ, BA, 60; Univ Calif, Berkeley, PhD(biochem), 65. *Prof Exp:* Jane Coffin Childs Mem fel biochem, Dartmouth Med Sch, 64-66; from asst prof to assoc prof, 71-75, PROF BIOCHEM, UNIV CALIF, RIVERSIDE, 75- *Concurrent Pos:* Guggenheim Found fel, Med Res Coun Lab Molecular Biol, Cambridge Univ, 72-73. *Mem:* Am Soc Biol Chemists. *Res:* Protein biosynthesis; nucleic acids; structure and function of transfer RNA. *Mailing Add:* Dept of Biochem Univ of Calif Riverside CA 92502

REID, CHARLES DAVID, b Toronto, Ont, Apr 28, 99. PHYSICS. *Educ:* Univ Alta, BSc, 23, MSc, 24; Harvard Uiv, AM, 28, PhD, 30. *Prof Exp:* Instr physics, Harvard Univ, 26-30; physicist, Develop Dept, Eastman Kodak Co, 30-51, qual control dept, Hawk Eye Works, 51-54, Lincoln Plant, 54-65; sci writing, 64-75; RETIRED. *Res:* Energy distribution in ultrasonic beams; velocity of sound of ultrasonic frequencies; motion picture projectors; optical testing; photographic exposure meters; emissivity measurements in infrared; history of testing of photographic lenses up to 1900. *Mailing Add:* 1570 East Ave Rochester NY 14610

REID, CHARLES FEDER, b New York, NY, Feb 28, 33; m 66; c 2. VETERINARY RADIOLOGY. *Educ:* Cornell Univ, DVM, 56, MS, 60; Univ Pa, MA, 71. *Prof Exp:* Radiologist & head radioisotope lab, Animal Med Ctr, New York, 61-63; assoc prof radiol, 70-76, assoc prof radiol sci, 73-78, PROF RADIOL, SCH VET MED, UNIV PA, 76- ASSOC PROF RADIOL SCI, 78- *Concurrent Pos:* Res consult radiol, Hosp Spec Surg & Margaret M Caspary Clin, New York, NY, 63-75. *Mem:* Am Vet Med Asn; Radiol Soc NAm; Am Asn Equine Practrs; Am Vet Radiol Soc; Am Col Vet Radiol. *Res:* Thyroid function studies in the horse; use of high kilovoltage x-ray diagnostics procedures in large animals; radiation therapy in large animals. *Mailing Add:* Sch of Vet Med Univ of Pa New Bolton Ctr RD 1 Kennett Square PA 19348

REID, CHARLES PHILLIP PATRICK, b Columbia, Mo, Jan 8, 40; m 61; c 2. FOREST ECOLOGY, PHYSIOLOGY. *Educ:* Univ Mo, BSF, 61; Duke Univ, MF, 66, PhD(forest ecol), 68. *Prof Exp:* Nat Acad Sci-Nat Res Coun assoc herbicide res, Plant Sci Lab, Ft Detrick, Dept Army, 67-69; from asst prof to assoc prof, 69-76, PROF TREE PHYSIOL, COLO STATE UNIV, 76- *Mem:* AAAS; Soc Am Foresters; Am Soc Plant Physiol; Ecol Soc Am. *Res:* Mycorrhizae of forest trees; plant-microbiol interactions; root exudation; ecosystem nutrient cycling; plant-water relations; iron nutrition of plants. *Mailing Add:* Dept Forest & Wood Sci Colo State Univ Fort Collins CO 80523

REID, CYRIL, b Luton, Eng, Dec 26, 17. CHEMICAL PHYSICS. *Educ:* Univ London, BSc, 38, Imp Col, dipl & PhD, 40. *Prof Exp:* Head res dept, Brit Periclase Co, 41-44; sr sci officer, AEC Can, 44-46; Commonwealth Fund fel, 46-48; from asst prof to assoc prof, 48-55, PROF CHEM, UNIV BC, 55- *Concurrent Pos:* Nat Res Coun fel, 48-50; vis assoc prof, Univ Chicago, 52-53;

Rockefeller Found fel, Cambridge Univ, 57-58. *Mem:* Am Phys Soc; fel Inst Chem Can; The Chem Soc. *Res:* Radiation chemistry; molecular structure and spectra; energetics of biological reactions. *Mailing Add:* Dept of Chem Univ of BC Vancouver BC V6T 1W5 Can

REID, DAVID MAYNE, b Belfast, Northern Ireland, Dec 7, 40; m 67. PLANT PHYSIOLOGY. *Educ:* Queen's Univ, Belfast, BSc, 64, PhD(plant physiol), 67. *Prof Exp:* Asst lectr bot, Queen's Univ, Belfast, 67-68; from asst prof to assoc prof, 68-76, PROF BOT, UNIV CALGARY, 76- *Mem:* Brit Photobiol Soc; Can Soc Plant Physiol; Am Soc Plant Physiol; Sigma Xi; Soc Exp Biol. *Res:* Sites of synthesis of hormones in plants; interactions of hormones and phytochrome; root-shoot relations. *Mailing Add:* Dept of Biol Univ of Calgary Calgary AB T2N 1N4 Can

REID, DONALD EUGENE, b Brookville, Pa, July 18, 30; m 52; c 3. ORGANIC CHEMISTRY. *Educ:* Franklin & Marshall Col, BS, 52; Ohio State Univ, PhD(org chem), 57. *Prof Exp:* Res chemist, 57-73, SR RES CHEMIST, HERCULES INC, WILMINGTON, 73- *Mem:* Am Chem Soc; Sci Res Soc Am. *Res:* Fatty and resin acids; coatings; polyolefins; rubber; polymer stabilization; polypropylene film. *Mailing Add:* 25 Mars Rd North Star Newark DE 19711

REID, DONALD HOUSE, environmental physiology, see previous edition

REID, DONALD J, b Whitney, Tex, Jan 29, 38; m 61; c 2. AGRONOMY, FIELD CROPS. *Educ:* Calif State Polytech Inst, BS, 59; Cornell Univ, MS, 61, PhD(agron). 64. *Prof Exp:* Tech rep, Agr Chem Div, Shell Chem Co, 64-66; asst prof crop & soil sci, Mich State Univ, 66-75; ASSOC PROF & EXTEN AGRONOMIST-CROPS, SDAK STATE UNIV, 75- *Mem:* Am Soc Agron; Crop Sci Soc Am. *Res:* Information dissemination on small grains and row crops in the eastern half of South Dakota. *Mailing Add:* Dept of Plant Sci SDak State Univ Brookings SD 57006

REID, EVANS BURTON, b Brock Twp, Ont, Mar 29, 13; nat US; m 42, 63; c 1. ORGANIC CHEMISTRY. *Educ:* McGill Univ, BSc, 37, PhD(org chem), 40. *Prof Exp:* Asst eng, McGill Univ, 37-38; demonstr chem, 38-40; res chemist, Dom Tar & Chem Co, Que, 40-41; instr chem, Middlebury Col, 41-43, asst prof, 43-46; asst prof, Johns Hopkins Univ, 46-54; actg dean fac, 67-68, dir, NSF Summer Inst sci, 58-60, 61-67, 68-73, Merrill prof & chmn dept chem, 54-78, EMER PROF, COLBY COL, 78- *Concurrent Pos:* Consult, Tainton Prod, Md, 51-54; vis prof, Univ Baghdad, 60-61; consult, Comt Educ & Personnel, NSF, 63-65; corporator, Maine Med Care Develop, Inc, 68-; chmn, Maine Sect Am Chem Soc, 56, 62, 71. *Mem:* Am Chem Soc; Royal Soc Chem. *Res:* Chemistry of tetronic acids; Michael condensation; cyclobutane acids; plant growth hormones; chemistry of neurospora; dimeric ketenes and cyclobutanediones; sesquiterpenes; organic alicyclics; natural products. *Mailing Add:* Dept of Chem Colby Col Keyes Sci Bldg Waterville ME 04901

REID, F JOSEPH, b Lancaster, Ohio, Mar 19, 30; m 54; c 6. SOLID STATE PHYSICS. *Educ:* Ohio State Univ, BS, 52, MS, 57. *Prof Exp:* Prin physicist, Phys Chem Div, Battelle Mem Inst, Ohio, 56-59, proj leader, 59-62, assoc chief, 62-67; group mgr, 67-69, dept mgr, 69-72, res mgr, 72-78, DIR GTE LABS, INC, GEN TEL & ELECTRONICS CORP, 78- *Mem:* Electrochem Soc; Am Phys Soc; Am Ceramic Soc. *Res:* Electronic and semiconductor materials. *Mailing Add:* GTE Labs Inc 40 Sylvan Rd Waltham MA 02154

REID, GEORGE KELL, b Fitzgerald, Ga, Mar 23, 18; m 49; c 2. AQUATIC ECOLOGY. *Educ:* Presby Col, BS, 40; Univ Fla, MS, 49, PhD(zool), 52. *Prof Exp:* Instr biol sci, Univ Fla, 49-52; asst prof biol, Col William & Mary, 52-53; asst prof wildlife mgt, Agr & Mech Col, Univ Tex, 53-56; asst prof zool, Rutgers Univ, 56-60; PROF BIOL, ECKERD COL, 60- *Mem:* Ecol Soc Am; Am Soc Ichthyologists & Herpetologists; Am Soc Limnol & OceaOceanog; Am Soc Zool; fel AAAS. *Res:* Ichthyology; limnology; ecology of mangrove communities; intertidal zones, lakes and streams. *Mailing Add:* Dept of Biol Eckerd Col 5401 34th St St Petersburg FL 33733

REID, GEORGE W(ILLARD), b Indianapolis, Ind, Dec 18, 17; m 45; c 4. CIVIL & SANITARY ENGINEERING. *Educ:* Purdue Univ, BSCE, 42; Harvard Univ, SM, 43. *Hon Degrees:* CE, Purdue Univ, 50. *Prof Exp:* Instr civil eng, Purdue Univ, 42; asst prof, Univ Fla, 43-44; sanit engr, Ind State Health Dept, 44-45; indust hyg engr, Bell Aircraft Co, 45; sanit engr, USPHS, 45-46; assoc prof civil eng, Ga Inst Technol, 46-50; from assoc prof to prof, 50-72, REGENTS PROF CIVIL ENG, UNIV OKLA, 72-, DIR, 59- *Concurrent Pos:* Consult, USPHS, 50-; US Air Force, 56-, US Navy & US Army; mem, Interstate Water Comn, Okla, 58-; mem, Sen Select Comt Water Resources, 59-60; WHO traveling fel, 60; gov confs water res & long range planning, Okla, 65- *Honors & Awards:* Rudolf Herring Prize, Am Soc Civil Engrs, 74. *Mem:* Am Soc Civil Engrs; Sigma Xi; Am Pub Health Asn. *Res:* Water resources; radiation; radioisotope applications to sanitary engineering; environmental sanitation; biokinetics; systems research. *Mailing Add:* 808 Brittany Court Norman OK 73069

REID, H(ARRY) F(RANCIS), JR, b Coshocton, Ohio, Sept 15, 17; m 60; c 2. METALLURGY. *Educ:* Geneva Col, BS, 39; Ohio State Univ, MS, 48. *Prof Exp:* Chemist, Ceramic Color & Chem Mfg Co, Pa, 39-42; res engr, Battelle Mem Inst, 42-51; mgr tech serv div, McKay Co, 51-68, asst to vpres mkt, 68-73, asst vpres tech serv, 73-81, TECH STAFF ENGR, TELEDYNE-McKAY, 81- *Mem:* Am Cryog Soc; Nat Asn Corrosion Engrs; Am Welding Soc; Am Soc Metals; Tech Asn Pulp & Paper Indust. *Res:* Development of coating for ferrous and nonferrous arc welding electrodes. *Mailing Add:* Am Welding Soc 550 LeJeune Rd Miami FL 33126

REID, HAY BRUCE, JR, b Hyannis, Mass, Sept 15, 39. PLANT PHYSIOLOGY, BOTANY. *Educ:* Drew Univ, AB, 61; Univ Mass, Amherst, MA, 63; Univ Calif, Los Angeles, PhD(bot), 66. *Prof Exp:* Scholar, Univ Calif, Los Angeles, 66-67; asst prof bot, Rutgers Univ, New Brunswick, 67-73; ASSOC PROF BIOL, KEAN COL, NJ, 73- *Mem:* Am Asn Plant Physiologists. *Res:* Photoperiodism; physiology of flowering. *Mailing Add:* Dept of Biol Kean Col Union NJ 07083

REID, IAN ANDREW, b Hobart, Australia, Aug 31, 43; m 71; c 2. PHYSIOLOGY. *Educ:* Univ Melbourne, BAgSc, 65; Monash Univ, PhD(renal physiol), 69. *Prof Exp:* Sr teaching fel physiol, Monash Univ, 69-70; fel physiol, 70-72, lectr & asst res physiologist, 72-73, adj asst prof, 73-77, ASSOC PROF PHYSIOL, UNIV CALIF, SAN FRANCISCO, 77- *Concurrent Pos:* NIH res career develop award, 75; consult, Hypertension Task Force, Nat Heart & Lung Inst, 76-77. *Mem:* Am Physiol Soc; Endocrine Soc; AAAS; Am Fedn Clin Res; Soc Exp Biol Med. *Res:* Regulation of fluid and electrolyte balance and blood pressure with emphasis on the role of the renin-angiotensin system. *Mailing Add:* Dept of Physiol S-762 Univ of Calif San Francisco CA 94143

REID, JACK RICHARD, b Youngstown, Ohio, Oct 31, 47; m 69; c 2. ORGANIC CHEMISTRY, MEDICINAL CHEMISTRY. *Educ:* Lebanon Valley Col, Pa, BS, 69; Lehigh Univ, MS, 72, PhD(chem), 73. *Prof Exp:* Air pollution chemist anal chem, US Army Environ Hyg Agency, 70-72; SR RES CHEMIST ORG CHEM, LORILLARD DIV, LOEWS THEATRE, INC, 75- *Concurrent Pos:* Res assoc med chem, Univ Kans, 73-75. *Mem:* Am Chem Soc; Sigma Xi. *Res:* Natural products, terpenes, alkaloids; heterocyclic chemistry; phosphorous chemistry; flavor chemistry. *Mailing Add:* Lorillard Res Ctr Loews Theatre Box 21688 Greensboro NC 27420

REID, JAMES CUTLER, b Akron, Ohio, Apr 17, 18. ORGANIC CHEMISTRY. *Educ:* Univ Pa, BS, 39; Pa State Col, MS, 40; Univ Calif, PhD(org chem), 44. *Prof Exp:* Instr chem, Bowling Green State Univ, 40-42; asst, Univ Calif, 42-44, res assoc, 44-45, mem sci staff, Radiation Lab, 45-49; SR CHEMIST, PHYSIOL LAB, NAT CANCER INST, 49- *Mem:* AAAS; Am Chem Soc; Am Soc Biol Chem. *Res:* Metabolism of compounds labeled with carbon 14 with special reference to cancer; tracer and other metabolic studies with special reference to tumor-host relationships. *Mailing Add:* Physiol Lab Nat Cancer Inst NIH Bethesda MD 20014

REID, JAMES DOLAN, b Augusta, Ga, June 24, 30; m 59; c 3. MATHEMATICS. *Educ:* Fordham Univ, BS, 52, MA, 53; Univ Wash, PhD(math), 60. *Prof Exp:* Instr math, Univ Wash, 59-60; asst prof, Syracuse Univ, 60-61 & Amherst Col, 62-63; from asst prof to assoc prof, Syracuse Univ, 63-69; assoc prof, 69-71, PROF MATH, WESLEYAN UNIV, 71- *Concurrent Pos:* Off Naval Res res fel, Yale Univ, 61-62. *Mem:* Soc Indust & Appl Math; Am Math Soc; Math Asn Am. *Res:* Algebra. *Mailing Add:* Dept of Math Wesleyan Univ Middletown CT 06457

REID, JOHN DAVID, b Portland, Ore, Feb 19, 09; m 31; c 2. TEXTILE CHEMISTRY. *Educ:* State Col Wash, BS, 30; George Wash Univ, MA, 32; American Univ, PhD(chem), 37. *Prof Exp:* Jr chemist, Color & Farm Waste Div, Bur Chem & Soils, USDA, 30-37, asst chemist, Agr By-prods Lab, Iowa State Col, 37-40, assoc chemist, Southern Regional Res Lab, Bur Agr & Indust Chem, 40-42, chemist, 42-44, sr chemist, 44-45, in charge, Finishing Unit, Cotton Chem Processing Sect, Southern Utilization Res Br, 54-58, head chem finishing invests, Cotton Chem Lab, Southern Utilization Res & Develop Div, 58-75; CONSULT TEXTILE CHEM, 75- *Mem:* Am Chem Soc; Am Inst Chem. *Res:* Chemical modification of cotton fibers; creative problem solving; creative thinking and efficiency in research. *Mailing Add:* 4519 Banks St New Orleans LA 70119

REID, JOHN REYNOLDS, JR, b Melrose, Mass, Jan 4, 33; m 56; c 4. GLACIOLOGY, GEOLOGY. *Educ:* Tufts Univ, BS, 55; Univ Mich, MS, 57, PhD(geol), 61. *Prof Exp:* Asst prof geol, Mt Union Col, 59-60; lectr, Univ Mich, 60-61; from asst prof to assoc prof, 61-71, assoc dean, Col Arts & Sci, 67-78, PROF GEOL, UNIV NDAK, 71- *Concurrent Pos:* Res geologist, Great Lakes Res Div, Inst Sci Technol, 60-61; NSF res grant, 65-67; fel, Quaternary Res Ctr, Univ Wash, 69-70; assoc dir, NDak Regional Environ Assessment Prog, 75-77, Interim Dir, 77-78. *Mem:* AAAS; fel Geol Soc Am; Glaciol Soc; Nat Asn Geol Teachers; Am Quaternary Asn. *Res:* Glacial geology; geomorphology of North Dakota and Alaska; glacial deposits; regimen of Alaska glaciers; structural glaciology of Antarctic firn folds; environmental geology of potential impact areas; shoreline erosion processes. *Mailing Add:* Dept of Geol Univ of NDak Grand Forks ND 58202

REID, JOHN THOMAS, b Cumberland, Md, Mar 14, 19; m 45; c 5. ANIMAL NUTRITION. *Educ:* Univ Md, BS, 41; Mich State Col, MS, 43, PhD(nutrit), 45. *Prof Exp:* Asst nutrit, Mich State Col, 41-44, asst res prof dairy sci, 44-45; assoc prof & dir dairy res sta, Rutgers Univ, 45-47; assoc prof dairy cattle nutrit, Cornell Univ, 48-51, prof animal sci & animal nutrit, 51-76, head, Dept Animal Sci, 71-76, Liberty Hyde Bailey prof, 77-80. *Concurrent Pos:* Traveling fel, Cornell Univ, 55-56; Guggenheim fel, 55-56; consult, USDA, 57-; consult, Food & Agr Orgn, 64-74; consult, Food & Agr Orgn, WHO, 75; mem comn ruminants as food producers, energy use in agr & food from animals, Coun Agr Sci & Technol, 74, 77, 78. *Honors & Awards:* Nutrit Award, Am Dairy Sci Asn, 50, Borden Award, 57; NY Farmer's Award, 63; Northrup-King honoree, 64; Am Grassland Coun Merit Award, 65; Morrison Award, Am Soc Animal Sci, 67. *Mem:* Am Soc Animal Sci; Am Dairy Sci Asn; Am Inst Nutrit; Brit Nutrit Soc. *Res:* Body composition of mammals; energy metabolism of homeotherms. *Mailing Add:* 415 Cornell Ithaca NY 14850

REID, JOSEPH LEE, b Franklin, Tex, Feb 7, 23; m 53; c 2. OCEANOGRAPHY. *Educ:* Univ Tex, BA, 42; Univ Calif, MS, 50. *Prof Exp:* Res oceanographer & lectr, 50-74, PROF OCEANOG & DIR MARINE LIFE RES GROUP, SCRIPPS INST OCEANOG, UNIV CALIF, SAN DIEGO, 74- *Mem:* Fel Am Geophys Union; Am Soc Limnol & Oceanog; Oceanog Soc Japan; AAAS. *Res:* Ocean circulation; distribution of temperature, salinity, oxygen, phosphate and marine life; wind-driven and thermohaline circulation; exchange between oceans; Antarctic Ocean circulation; California current; descriptive physical oceanography; world ocean. *Mailing Add:* Scripps Inst of Oceanog Univ of Calif La Jolla CA 92093

REID, KARL NEVELLE, JR, b Fayetteville, Ark, Oct 10, 34; m 56; c 2. MECHANICAL ENGINEERING. *Educ:* Okla State Univ, BS, 56, MS, 58; Mass Inst Technol, ScD(mech eng), 64. *Prof Exp:* Asst mech eng, Mass Inst Technol, 58-60, instr, 60-64, lab coordr, 61-62; from instr to assoc prof mech & aero-eng, 64-70, dir ctr systs sci, 68-72, PROF MECH & AERO-ENG, OKLA STATE UNIV, 70-, HEAD SCH, 72- *Concurrent Pos:* Tech consult, Scovill Mfg, Westinghouse Elec Co; educ consult to NSF & USAID; chmn components comt, Am Automatic Control Coun, 72-; US mem tech comt components, Int Fedn Automatic Control; assoc ed, Transactions/J Dynamic Systs, Measurements & Control, 71-73, ed, 74-76, sr tech ed, 76- *Mem:* Am Soc Mech Engrs; Am Soc Eng Educ; Fluid Power Soc; Nat Soc Prof Engrs. *Res:* Systems dynamics; analysis and design of fluid control systems; automatic control systems; fluidics; biomedical engineering. *Mailing Add:* Sch of Mech & Aerospace Eng Okla State Univ Stillwater OK 74074

REID, KENNETH BROOKS, b Jacksonville, Fla, Mar 2, 43; m 66; c 2. MATHEMATICS. *Educ:* Univ Calif, Berkeley, BA, 64; Univ Ill, Urbana, MA, 66, PhD(math), 68. *Prof Exp:* From asst prof to assoc prof, 68-80, PROF MATH, LA STATE UNIV, BATON ROUGE, 80- *Concurrent Pos:* Vis assoc prof, Univ Waterloo, Can, 74-75; vis fel, Inst Advan Studies, Australian Nat Univ, 75; vis prof, Johns Hopkins Univ, 82; W K Kellogg Nat fel, 81-84; vis lectr, Math Asn Am, 75- *Mem:* Am Math Soc; Math Asn Am; Soc Indust & Appl Math; Australian Math Soc; Econometrics Soc. *Res:* Combinatorial theory, particularly graph theory; enumeration of various discrete structures; existence problems concerning structure in graphs and directed graphs, particularly tournaments; extremal problems in graphs and directed graphs; combinatorics of permutation groups. *Mailing Add:* Dept of Math La State Univ Baton Rouge LA 70803

REID, KENNETH IAN GOWER, industrial chemistry, petroleum, see previous edition

REID, LOIS JEAN, b Portsmouth, Va, Sept 23, 37. MATHEMATICS. *Educ:* Col William & Mary, BS, 59; Duke Univ, MA, 61, PhD(math), 67. *Prof Exp:* Part-time instr math, Duke Univ, 60-61; from instr to asst prof, Mary Wash Col, Univ Va, 63-66; asst prof, Univ NC, Greensboro, 67-70; assoc prof, Longwood Col, 70-74; MATHEMATICIAN, NAVAL SURFACE WEAPONS CTR, DAHLGREN LAB, 74- *Mem:* Math Asn Am. *Res:* Algebra and number theory, particularly symmetric q-polynomials, their generalizations and applications. *Mailing Add:* Re-Entry Anal Br DK 55 Naval Surface Weapons Ctr Dahlgren VA 22448

REID, LOLA CYNTHIA MCADAMS, b Charlotte, NC, May 25, 45; m 82. BIOCHEMISTRY. *Educ:* Univ NC, BA, 68, PhD(neuroendocriol), 74. *Prof Exp:* Technician physiol ecol, Univ NC, Chapel Hill, 68, teaching asst, 73; fel cancer biol, Univ Calif, San Diego, 74-77; ASST PROF DIFFERENTIATION, ALBERT EINSTEIN COL MED, 77- *Concurrent Pos:* Res fel, Bar Harbor, Maine, 75, Pasteur Inst, 76; Career Develop Award Sinsheimer, 77; prin investr, var res proj, 77-; consult, var co, 76- *Mem:* Am Asn Cancer Res; AAAS; Am Soc Zoologists. *Res:* Regulation of differentiation in normal and neoplastic cells especially by the synergistic interactions of hormones and exgracellular matrix. *Mailing Add:* Albert Einstein Col Med 601 Chanin Cancer Ctr Bronx NY 10461

REID, PARLANE JOHN, b Long Beach, Calif, Apr 14, 37; m 59; c 2. BIOCHEMISTRY, MICROBIAL GENETICS. *Educ:* Univ Calif, Santa Barbara, BA, 60, MA, 61, PhD(biol), 66. *Prof Exp:* Res assoc genetics, Univ Calif, Santa Barbara, 60-61; instr biol, Calif State Polytech Col, 61-62; fel biochem, Sch Med, Stanford Univ, 66-68; ASST PROF BIOCHEM, SCH MED, UNIV CONN, 68- *Res:* Mechanisms of RNA and protein synthesis in microbes and bacteriophage. *Mailing Add:* 84 Helm Dr Farmington CT 06032

REID, PHILIP DEAN, b Ypsilanti, Mich, Mar 6, 37; m 62; c 1. PLANT PHYSIOLOGY. *Educ:* Eastern Mich Univ, BA, 62; Univ Mo, MS, 64; Univ Mass, PhD(bot), 70. *Prof Exp:* Res biol, Uniroyal Corp, 64-66; res fel, Univ Calif, Riverside, 70-71; asst prof, 71-78, ASSOC PROF BIOL SCI, SMITH COL, 78-, ASST TO PRES CAMPUS PLANNING. *Mem:* AAAS; Am Soc Plant Physiol; Am Inst Biol Sci. *Res:* Hormonal control of plant metabolism and development. *Mailing Add:* Dept of Biol Sci Smith Col Northampton MA 01060

REID, PRESTON HARDING, b Akron, Colo, Nov 15, 23; m 48; c 1. SOIL CHEMISTRY, SOIL FERTILITY. *Educ:* Colo State Univ, BS, 49; NC State Univ, MS, 51, PhD(soils), 56. *Prof Exp:* Res asst prof soils, NC State Univ, 56-60, assoc prof, 60-66, prof soil sci, 66-69, dir soil test div, NC Dept Agr, 65-69; DIR, TIDEWATER RES & CONTINUING EDUC CTR, VA POLYTECH INST & STATE UNIV, 69- *Concurrent Pos:* Soils adv to Peru, 61-63; ed, Peanut Science, J of Am Peanut Res & Educ Asn, 74-75; exten specialist, soybeans, Va Polytech Inst & State Univ, 75- *Mem:* Am Soc Agron; Soil Sci Soc Am; Am Soybean Asn. *Res:* Soil Testing. *Mailing Add:* Tidewater Res & Continuing Educ Ctr Holland Station Suffolk VA 23437

REID, RICHARD J(AMES), b Burlington, Iowa, Oct 29, 32; m 52; c 5. ELECTRICAL ENGINEERING. *Educ:* Iowa State Univ, BS, 55, MS, 56; Mich State Univ, PhD, 59. *Prof Exp:* Instr elec eng, Iowa State Univ, 55-56; from instr to assoc prof, 56-70, PROF COMPUT SCI, MICH STATE UNIV, 70- *Mem:* Inst Elec & Electronics Engrs; Asn Comput Mach. *Res:* Artificial intelligence. *Mailing Add:* Dept of Comput Sci Mich State Univ East Lansing MI 48824

REID, ROBERT C(LARK), b Denver, Colo, June 11, 24; m 50; c 2. CHEMICAL ENGINEERING. *Educ:* Purdue Univ, BS, 50, MS, 51; Mass Inst Technol, ScD(chem eng), 54. *Prof Exp:* From asst prof to assoc prof, 54-64, prof chem eng, 64-81, CHEVRON PROF, MASS INST TECHNOL, 81- *Concurrent Pos:* Am Soc Eng Educ lectr chem eng, 77; Olaf A Hougen prof, Univ Wis-Madison, 80-81. *Honors & Awards:* Warren K Lewis Award, Am Inst Chem Engrs, 76. *Mem:* Nat Acad Eng; Am Inst Chem Engrs. *Res:* Thermodynamics; cryogenics; liquefied natural gas and petroleum gas; safety; critical point extraction; migration of chemicals from polymer food wraps to food; superheated liquid explosions; botanical engineering. *Mailing Add:* Dept of Chem Eng 66-540 Mass Inst Technol Cambridge MA 02139

REID, ROBERT LELON, b Detroit, Mich, May 20, 42; m 62; c 3. SOLAR ENERGY, HEAT TRANSFER. *Educ:* Univ Mich, BSE, 63; Southern Methodist Univ, MSE, 66, PhD(mech eng), 69. *Prof Exp:* Res engr, Atlantic Richfield Corp, 64-65; staff engr, Linde Div, Union Carbide Corp, 66-68; prof, Exxon Prod Res Corp, 72 & 73, NASA, 70 & 76; assoc prof mech eng, Univ Tenn, Knoxville, 69-75, Cleveland State Univ, 75-77; prof mech eng & asst dir, Energy, Environ & Resources Ctr, Univ Tenn, Knoxville, 77-82; CHMN MECH AND INDUST ENG DEPT, UNIV TEX, EL PASO, 82- *Concurrent Pos:* Prin investr contracts, Exxon Corp, 72-73, Union Carbide, 74-, NASA, 77-78, NSF, 77-79, Tenn Valley Authority, 79-; consult, Oak Ridge Nat Lab, 80-81; assoc ed, J Solar Energy Eng, Am Soc Mech Engrs, 81- *Honors & Awards:* Centennial Medallion, Am Soc Mech Engrs. *Mem:* Am Soc Mech Engrs; Am Soc Heating, Refrigerating & Air Conditioning Engrs; Int Solar Energy Soc. *Res:* Solar energy; energy conservation; heat transfer; author or coauthor of over 50 publications. *Mailing Add:* Mech & Indust Eng Dept Univ Tex El Paso TX 79968

REID, ROBERT OSBORNE, b Milford, Conn, Aug 24, 21; m 47; c 6. OCEANOGRAPHY. *Educ:* Univ Southern Calif, BE, 46; Univ Calif, MS, 48. *Prof Exp:* Asst, Scripps Inst, Univ Calif, 46-47, oceanogr, 48-51; meteorologist, US Naval Electronics Lab, Calif, 47-48; from assoc prof to prof phys oceanog, 51-74, PROF CIVIL ENG & OCEANOG, TEX A&M UNIV, 74- *Concurrent Pos:* Ed, J Phys Oceanog, 70- *Mem:* Fel Am Meteorol Soc; Am Soc Limnol & Oceanog; Am Geophys Union; Int Asn Hydraul Res. *Res:* Physical oceanography, especially problems in ocean waves; storm tides and circulation. *Mailing Add:* Dept of Oceanog Tex A&M Univ College Station TX 77843

REID, RODERICK VINCENT, JR, b Charlotte, NC, Oct 17, 32; m 59; c 3. THEORETICAL PHYSICS. *Educ:* Univ Denver, AB, 58, MS, 59; Cornell Univ, PhD(physics), 68. *Prof Exp:* Physicist, Mass Inst Technol, 67-69; asst prof, 69-74, ASSOC PROF PHYSICS, UNIV CALIF, DAVIS, 74- *Mem:* Am Inst Physics. *Res:* Nuclear theory. *Mailing Add:* Dept of Physics Univ of Calif Davis CA 95616

REID, ROLLAND RAMSAY, b Wilbur, Wash, Nov 12, 26; m 47, 75; c 3. GEOLOGY. *Educ:* Univ Wash, PhD(geol), 59. *Prof Exp:* Instr geol, Mont Sch Mines, 53-55; asst prof, 55-60, assoc prof geol & head dept geol & geog, 60-65, actg dean, 63-65, actg head dept geol & geog, 59-60, dean, Col Mines, 65-74, PROF GEOL, UNIV IDAHO, 65- *Concurrent Pos:* NSF fac fel, 58-59; dep asst secy, Energy & Minerals, US Dept Interior, 75-76. *Mem:* Geol Soc Am; Soc Econ Geologists. *Res:* Metamorphic and structural petrology; structural geology. *Mailing Add:* Col of Mines Univ of Idaho Moscow ID 83843

REID, RUSSELL MARTIN, b St Louis, Mo, July 30, 41; m 64; c 2. PHYSICAL ANTHROPOLOGY, BIOLOGICAL ANTHROPOLOGY. *Educ:* Univ Ill, BS, 63, PhD(anthrop), 71. *Prof Exp:* Asst prof anthrop, Univ Tex, Austin, 69-76; asst prof, 76-78, ASSOC PROF ANTHROP & CHMN, DEPT ANTHROP, UNIV HOUSTON, 78- *Concurrent Pos:* NSF-Univ Sci Develop Prog grant, Univ Tex, Austin Field Res, Ceylon, 69-73, Haiti, 78. *Mem:* Am Anthrop Asn; Am Asn Phys Anthrop; Brit Soc Study Human Biol; Soc Study Social Biol. *Res:* Human population genetics, especially the role of social organization on genetic structure of populations, particularly consanguinity and inbreeding in human populations; dietary behavior and nutrition. *Mailing Add:* Dept of Anthrop Univ of Houston Houston TX 77004

REID, SIDNEY GEORGE, b Glamis, Scotland, Sept 21, 23; Can citizen; m 51; c 2. ORGANIC CHEMISTRY. *Educ:* Univ St Andrews, BSc, 44, PhD(chem), 49. *Prof Exp:* Fel, Univ Edinburgh, 48-51; res fel lignin chem, 51, asst dept dir, 57-63, DIR DEPT APPL CHEM, ONT RES FOUND, 63- *Mem:* Fel Chem Inst Can; Can Pulp & Paper Asn; Tech Asn Pulp & Paper Inst. *Res:* Wood, cellulose and lignin chemistry; paper additives; utilization of pulp and paper wastes and industrial wastes. *Mailing Add:* Ont Res Found Sheridan Park Mississauga ON L5K 1B3 Can

REID, STANLEY LYLE, b Royal Oak, Mich, June 8, 30; m 54; c 2. ORGANIC CHEMISTRY. *Educ:* Univ Mich, PhD(chem), 57. *Prof Exp:* CHEMIST, MONSANTO CO, 57- *Mem:* Am Chem Soc. *Res:* Natural products; organic synthesis; oxidation. *Mailing Add:* Monsanto Co T3F 800 N Lindbergh Ave St Louis MO 63167

REID, TED WARREN, b Cayuga, Ind, Sept 26, 39; m 61; c 2. BIOCHEMISTRY. *Educ:* Occidental Col, BS, 61; Univ Ariz, MS, 63; Univ Calif, Los Angeles, PhD(chem), 67. *Prof Exp:* Asst prof molecular biophys & biochem, 70-75, ASSOC PROF MOLECULAR BIOPHYS & BIOCHEM, OPHTHAL & VISUAL SCI, MED SCH, YALE UNIV, 75- *Concurrent Pos:* Res to Prevent Blindness res prof, 74. *Mem:* Am Chem Soc; Asn Res Vision & Ophthal. *Res:* Biochemistry of the retina and cell growth factors. *Mailing Add:* Dept of Ophthal & Visual Sci Yale Univ Sch of Med New Haven CT 06510

REID, THOMAS S, b Trenton, NJ, Dec 20, 11; m 42; c 2. ORGANIC CHEMISTRY. *Educ:* Rutgers Univ, BS, 36, MS, 38; Univ Minn, PhD(biochem), 42. *Prof Exp:* Res chemist, Eastern Regional Res Lab, USDA, Pa, 42-44; res chemist, 44-51, sect leader, Org Sect, 51-55, assoc dir, Cent Res Dept, 55-60, coordr, Div Res, 60-62, mgr biochem res, 62-64, dir biochem res, 64-71, dir biosci res lab, 71-77, CONSULT, MINN MINING & MFG CO, 77- *Mem:* AAAS; Am Chem Soc; Am Ceramic Soc. *Res:* Biochemistry, polymer and fluorine chemistry; medicinal and health sciences. *Mailing Add:* Cent Res Labs Minn Mining & Mfg Co 3M Ctr St Paul MN 55101

REID, WILLARD MALCOLM, b Ft Morgan, Colo, Oct 9, 10; m 37; c 5. PARASITOLOGY, POULTRY SCIENCE. *Educ:* Monmouth Col, BS, 32; Kans State Univ, MS, 37, PhD, 41. *Hon Degrees:* DSc, Monmouth Col, 59. *Prof Exp:* Instr biol & head dept, Assiut Col, Egypt, 33-35; prof & head dept, Monmouth Col, 38-51; head poultry unit, US State Dept, Egypt, 52-55; from assoc prof to prof, 55-78, EMER PROF AVIAN PARASITOL, UNIV GA, 78- *Concurrent Pos:* Consult, Eli Lilly & Co, Greenfield, Ind, 68- & Mathtech Poultry Proj, Egypt, 78- *Mem:* Fel AAAS; Am Soc Parasitologists; Am Soc Zoologists; Am Asn Avian Pathologists; Poultry Sci Asn. *Res:* Parasitic diseases of poultry and their control using pharmaceutical drugs and biological control measures. *Mailing Add:* Dept of Poultry Sci Univ of Ga Athens GA 30602

REID, WILLIAM BRADLEY, b Indianapolis, Ind, Aug 2, 20; m 45; c 2. PHARMACEUTICALS. *Educ:* Butler Univ, BS, 42; Ind Univ, MA, 44, PhD(org chem), 46. *Prof Exp:* Res chemist, 46-52, SECT HEAD, UPJOHN CO, 52- *Concurrent Pos:* Mgr, Facilities Planning & Environ Regulatory Afffairs, 74- *Mem:* Am Chem Soc; Am Soc Test Mat. *Res:* Synthetic organic chemistry; bacteriology; administration. *Mailing Add:* Upjohn Co 301 Henrietta St Kalamazoo MI 49001

REID, WILLIAM HARPER, b Bridgeport, Conn, Nov 16, 33. POPULATION ECOLOGY. *Educ:* Univ Mo, BS, 59; Univ Colo, PhD(biol), 74. *Prof Exp:* Design engr cryog, Beech Aircraft Corp, 59-61; develop engr liquid rockets, Aerojet-Gen Corp, 61-62; group engr spacecraft systs, Beech Aircraft Corp, 62-66; chief struct aircrew systs, Stanley Aviation Corp, 66-67; sr engr spacecraft thermodyn, Martin-Marietta Corp, 67-68; asst prof, 75-81, ASSOC PROF, DEPT BIOL SCI, UNIV TEX, EL PASO, 81- *Mem:* AAAS; Ecol Soc Am; Sigma Xi; Asn Trop Studies. *Res:* Ecology, adaptation and evolution of sympatric populations; field studies and computer simulation of single and multiple species sets; Chihuahuan desert ecology; dune field community structure and successional processes; pollination biology of xerophytes; biogeography. *Mailing Add:* Dept of Biol Sci Univ of Tex El Paso TX 79968

REID, WILLIAM HILL, b Oakland, Calif, Sept 10, 26; m 62; c 1. APPLIED MATHEMATICS. *Educ:* Cambridge Univ, PhD(math), 55; Brown Univ, AM ad eundem, 61. *Hon Degrees:* ScD, Cambridge Univ, 67. *Prof Exp:* NSF fel math, Yerkes Observ, Univ Chicago, 57, res assoc astron, 58; from asst prof to assoc prof appl math, Brown Univ, 58-63; assoc prof appl math, 63-65, prof geophys sci, 76-80, PROF APPL MATH, UNIV CHICAGO, 65- *Concurrent Pos:* Lectr, Johns Hopkins Univ, 55-56; Fulbright res grant math, Australian Nat Univ, 64-65; consult, Gen Motors Corp, 60-75. *Mem:* Am Phys Soc; Am Astron Soc; Am Math Soc; Soc Indust & Appl Math. *Res:* Fluid mechanics; hydrodynamic stability; asymptotic analysis; applications to astrophysics and geophysics. *Mailing Add:* Dept Math Univ Chicago Chicago IL 60637

REID, WILLIAM JAMES, b Abbeville, SC, Nov 2, 27; m 64; c 3. PHYSICS. *Educ:* Erskine Col, AB, 49; Duke Univ, MA, 58; Clemson Univ, PhD(physics), 67. *Prof Exp:* Instr chem, Erskine Col, 49-51, field rep, 51-52, asst prof physics & math, 56-62, assoc prof physics, 66-68; pres fac senate, 71-72 & 76-77, PROF PHYSICS & HEAD DEPT, JACKSONVILLE STATE UNIV, 68- *Mem:* Am Phys Soc; Sigma Xi. *Res:* Superconductivity in thin films; pedagogy of physics; physics lecture demonstrations. *Mailing Add:* Dept of Physics Jacksonville State Univ Jacksonville AL 36265

REID, WILLIAM JOHN, b Dublin, Ireland, Jan 29, 45; Can citizen; m 69; c 2. POLYMER CHEMISTRY, PHYSICAL CHEMISTRY. *Educ:* Univ Dublin, BS, 67; Univ BC, MS, 70, PhD(chem), 72. *Prof Exp:* Res assoc polymer chem, Ecoplastics, Univ Toronto, 72-73; res chemist, Res Lab, Uniroyal Ltd, 73-76, res chemist, Uniroyal Inc, 76-78; TECHNOL MGR, PLASTICS & ADDITIVES DIV, CIBA-GEIGY CORP, 78- *Mem:* Am Chem Soc. *Res:* Stabilization and degradation mechanisms in polymers; relationship of properties of polymers to molecular structure and morphology. *Mailing Add:* Ciba-Geigy Corp Plastics & Additives Div Ardsley NY 10502

REID, WILLIAM SHAW, b Slate Springs, Miss, Feb 24, 38; m 60; c 2. AGRONOMY, SOILS. *Educ:* Miss State Univ, BS, 59, MS, 61, PhD(agron, soils), 65. *Prof Exp:* Proj officer radiation biol, Air Force Weapons Lab, Kirtland AFB, NM, 63-66; asst prof, 66-72, ASSOC PROF SOIL SCI, CORNELL UNIV, 72-, DEPT AGRON EXT LEADER, 75- *Mem:* Am Soc Agron; Soil Sci Soc Am. *Res:* Interactions of fertilizers and climate on the uptake of plant nutrients and plant growth with respect to efficient agricultural production. *Mailing Add:* Dept of Agron Cornell Univ Ithaca NY 14853

REID, WILLIAM T(HOMAS), b Racine, Wis, Feb 14, 07; m 30; c 3. ENERGY CONVERSION. *Educ:* Univ Wash, BS, 29. *Prof Exp:* Jr fuel engr, US Bur Mines, Pa, 29-34, from asst fuel engr to assoc fuel engr, 34-42, fuel engr, 42-43, supv engr, 43-46; asst supvr combustion res, Battelle Mem Inst, 46-47, supvr combustion res, 47-50, supvr graphic arts res, 50-53, asst tech dir, 53-65, sr fel mech eng, 65-72; RETIRED. *Concurrent Pos:* Energy conversion consult, 72- *Honors & Awards:* Melchett Medal, Brit Inst Fuel, 69. *Mem:* Am Soc Mech Engrs (vpres, 71-73); Brit Inst Fuel. *Res:* Fuel-cell technology; energy sources for electric automobiles; corrosion and deposits in boiler furnaces; coal-ash technology. *Mailing Add:* 2470 Dorset Rd Columbus OH 43221

REIDENBERG, MARCUS MILTON, b Philadelphia, Pa, Jan 3, 34; m 57; c 3. PHARMACOLOGY, MEDICINE. *Educ:* Temple Univ, MD, 58. *Prof Exp:* From instr to asst prof pharmacol, Temple Univ, 62-72, assoc prof pharmacol & med, 72-76, chief sect clin pharmacol, 72-74; assoc prof med, 76-80, PROF PHARMACOL & HEAD DIV, MED COL, CORNELL UNIV, 76-, PROF MED, 80- *Concurrent Pos:* NIH fel, Temple Univ, 59-60, NIH res career develop award, 71-74. *Honors & Awards:* Rawls Palmer Award, Am Soc Clin Pharmacol & Therapeut, 81. *Mem:* Am Soc Pharmacol & Exp Therapeut; Am Col Physicians; Am Soc Clin Invest; Am Soc Clin Pharmacol & Therapeut; Am Fedn Clin Res. *Res:* Clinical pharmacology; drug metabolism; adverse drug reactions. *Mailing Add:* Cornell Univ Med Col 1300 York Ave New York NY 10021

REIDER, MALCOLM JOHN, b Reading, Pa, Feb 16, 14; m 37; c 4. ORGANIC CHEMISTRY, FORENSIC CHEMISTRY. *Educ:* Albright Col, BS, 36; Columbia Univ, PhD(org chem), 41. *Prof Exp:* Res chemist, Am Cyanamid Co, Conn, 40-41; chief chemist, Geo W Bollman & Co, 41-42, res dir, 42-52; pres, Pagoda Industs, Inc, 51-56; PRES, M J REIDER ASSOCS INC, 56- *Concurrent Pos:* Indust consult & consult chemist, 52-56; pres, Nat Stand Test Labs, Inc, 58- *Mem:* AAAS; Am Chem Soc; Am Acad Forensic Sci; Am Soc Qual Control; Am Asn Textile Chem & Colorists. *Res:* Synthetic tanning agents; deodorizing of tung oil; surface active agents; studies in the pyridine series; technology of long vegetable fibers; air, land and water pollution and control; legal chemistry, arson and fire investigations. *Mailing Add:* M J Reider Assocs Inc 107 Angelica St Reading PA 19602

REIDER, PAUL JOSEPH, b New York, NY, June 7, 51; m 74. SYNTHETIC ORGANIC CHEMISTRY. *Educ:* Washington Square Col, AB, 72; Univ Vt, PhD(org chem), 78. *Prof Exp:* NIH fel, Colo State Univ, 78-80; SR RES CHEMIST, MERCK, SHARP & DOHME RES LABS, 80- *Mem:* Am Chem Soc. *Res:* Synthesis of complex organic molecules of pharmacological interest; development of viable processes for such synthesis. *Mailing Add:* Merck, Sharp & Dohme Res Labs PO Box 2000 Rahway NJ 07065

REIDER, RICHARD GARY, b Denver, Colo, Feb 7, 41. PHYSICAL GEOGRAPHY. *Educ:* Univ Northern Colo, BA, 63, MA, 65; Univ Nebr, PhD(geog), 71. *Prof Exp:* Instr geog, Ind Univ, Pa, 65-66; instr, Univ Nebr, Lincoln, 66-69; asst prof, 69-77, ASSOC PROF GEOG, UNIV WYO, 77- *Concurrent Pos:* NSF grant & Sigma Xi grant, 74-77; soils consult, Dept of Anthrop, Univ Wyo & Smithsonian Inst, 75-82; ed, Great Plains-Rocky Mountain Geog J, 76-80. *Mem:* Am Quaternary Asn; Sigma Xi; Asn Am Geographers. *Res:* Geomorphology and soils geography. *Mailing Add:* Dept of Geog Univ of Wyo Laramie WY 82071

REIDIES, ARNO H, b Tilsit, Ger, July 31, 25; US citizen; m 53; c 3. INORGANIC CHEMISTRY. *Educ:* Univ Freiburg, Dipl, 54. *Prof Exp:* Res chemist, 54-58, chief res chemist, 58-64, res mgr, 64-68, DIR RES, CARUS CHEM CO, INC, 68- *Mem:* Am Chem Soc; Electrochem Soc; Ger Chem Soc. *Res:* Chemistry of manganese, specifically manganates and permanganates, quinones and hydroquinones; environmental odor control research. *Mailing Add:* Carus Chem Co Eighth St LaSalle IL 61301

REIDINGER, RUSSELL FREDERICK, JR, b Reading, Pa, June 19, 45; m 73; c 3. FISH & WILDLIFE SCIENCES. *Educ:* Albright Col, BS, 67; Univ Ariz, PhD(zool), 72. *Prof Exp:* Asst prof biol, Augustana Col, 71-74; res physiologist, Philippines, 74-78, ASST MEM, MONELL CHEM SENSES CTR & WILDLIFE BIOLOGIST, DENVER WILDLIFE RES CTR, US FISH & WILDLIFE SERV, PHILADELPHIA, 78- *Concurrent Pos:* Vis prof, Dept Zool, Univ Philippines, 75-78; consult, Bangladesh Agr Res Coun, US Agency Int Develop, 77, Ministry Agr Develop & Agrarian Reform, Nicaragua, 81. *Mem:* Am Soc Mammalogists; Am Mus Natural Hist; Asn Chemoreception Sci. *Mailing Add:* Monell Chem Senses Ctr 3500 Market St Philadelphia PA 19104

REIDLINGER, ANTHONY A, b Islip, NY, Nov 30, 26; m 59. ORGANIC CHEMISTRY. *Educ:* Hofstra Univ, BA, 49; NY Univ, MS, 51, PhD(org chem), 55. *Prof Exp:* Assoc eng scientist, Res Div, Col Eng, NY Univ, 55-57; assoc prof org chem, Grad Sch, St John's Univ, NY, 56-60; assoc prof, 60-64, PROF ORG CHEM, LONG ISLAND UNIV, 64-, CHMN DEPT CHEM, 66- *Concurrent Pos:* Consult, Evans Chemetics, 59-60. *Mem:* Am Chem Soc; Electrochem Soc. *Res:* Polarography of organic compounds; nitro derivatives of naphthalene. *Mailing Add:* Dept of Chem Long Island Univ Brooklyn NY 11201

REIDY, JAMES JOSEPH, b Tulsa, Okla, June 12, 36; m 62; c 3. PHYSICS. *Educ:* Univ Notre Dame, BS, 58, PhD(nuclear physics), 63. *Prof Exp:* Instr physics, Univ Notre Dame, 62-63; res assoc, Univ Mich, 63-65, asst prof, 65-71; vis prof, Franklin & Marshall Col, 71-72; ASSOC PROF PHYSICS, UNIV MISS, 72- *Concurrent Pos:* Vis prof, Tech Univ, Munich, Germany, 74-77. *Mem:* Am Asn Physicists Med; Am Phys Soc; Am Asn Physics Teachers. *Res:* Physics of negative muon and pion capture by atoms; interaction of negative pions at near rest with nuclei; chemical effects in negative pion and muon atomic capture; material analysis using muonic x-ray spectra; determination of nuclear decay schemes. *Mailing Add:* Dept of Physics & Astron Univ of Miss University MS 38677

REIERSON, JAMES (DUTTON), b Seward, Nebr, Oct 14, 41. NUCLEAR PHYSICS, OPERATIONS RESEARCH. *Educ:* Univ Nebr, Lincoln, BS, 63; Iowa State Univ, PhD(physics), 69. *Prof Exp:* Systs analyst, Anal Serv, Inc, 69-73; lectr physics, Univ South Pac, 73-75; comput scientist, Comput Sci Corp, 76-78; SYST ANALYST, MITRE CORP, 78- *Concurrent Pos:* Mem, Inst Phys, George Mason Univ, 79. *Mem:* Am Phys Soc; Am Nuclear Soc. *Mailing Add:* 3311 N George Mason Dr Arlington VA 22207

REIF, ARNOLD E, b Vienna, Austria, July 15, 24; US citizen; m 50, 79; c 3. IMMUNOLOGY. *Educ:* Cambridge Univ, BA, 45, MA, 49; Univ London, BSc, 46; Carnegie Inst Technol, MS, 49, DSc(phys chem), 50. *Prof Exp:* From jr sci officer to sci officer, Dept Sci & Indust Res, Gt Brit, 44-47; res fel, Carnegie-Mellon Univ, 47-50; fel oncol, McArdle Mem Lab Cancer Res, Sch Med, Univ Wis, 50-53; res assoc, Lovelace Found, NMex, 53-57; asst prof surg & biochem, 57-69, assoc prof surg, Sch Med, Tufts Univ, 69-75; RES PROF PATH, SCH MED, BOSTON UNIV, 75- *Concurrent Pos:* Res pathologist, Mallory Inst Path, Boston City Hosp, 73- *Mem:* Am Asn Immunol; Am Asn Cancer Res; Transplantation Soc; NY Acad Sci; Brit Soc Immunol. *Res:* Cancer research; immunology; health education. *Mailing Add:* Boston City Hosp Boston MA 02118

REIF, CHARLES BRADDOCK, b Washington, DC, July 31, 12; m 47. ZOOLOGY. *Educ:* Univ Minn, BA, 35, MA, 38, PhD(zool), 41. *Prof Exp:* Asst zool, Univ Minn, 35-41; cur educ, Mus Natural Hist, Minn, 41-42; from asst to assoc prof zool, 42-54, PROF ZOOL, WILKES COL, 54- *Concurrent Pos:* With US Forest Serv, 36 & 38. *Mem:* Am Soc Limnol & Oceanog; Phycol Soc Am. *Res:* Limnology; biology. *Mailing Add:* Dept of Biol Wilkes Col Wilkes-Barre PA 18766

REIF, DONALD JOHN, b Oshkosh, Wis, Feb 6, 31; m 52; c 2. NUCLEAR CHEMISTRY. *Educ:* Univ Wis, BS, 53; Mass Inst Technol, PhD(org chem), 57. *Prof Exp:* Asst, Mass Inst Technol, 53-57; res chemist, 57-65, sr res chemist, Old Hickory, Tenn, 65-77, STAFF CHEMIST, SAVANNAH RIVER LAB, RES & DEVELOP LABS, E I DU PONT DE NEMOURS & CO, INC, AIKEN, SC, 77- *Res:* Spent nuclear fuel reprocessing. *Mailing Add:* 722 Ravenel Rd Augusta GA 30909

REIF, FREDERICK, b Vienna, Austria, Apr 24, 27; nat US; m 69. PHYSICS. *Educ:* Columbia Univ, AB, 48; Harvard Univ, AM, 49, PhD(physics), 53. *Prof Exp:* From instr to asst prof physics, Univ Chicago, 53-60; assoc prof, 60-64, Miller prof, 64-65, PROF PHYSICS, UNIV CALIF, BERKELEY, 64- *Concurrent Pos:* Alfred P Sloan fel, Univ Chicago, 55-59. *Mem:* AAAS; Am Phys Soc; Am Educ Res Asn. *Res:* Nuclear magnetic resonance; solid state and low temperature physics; superconductivity; superfluidity of liquid helium; educational research and development. *Mailing Add:* Dept of Physics Univ of Calif Berkeley CA 94720

REIF, JOHN H, b Madison, Wis, Aug 4, 51. COMBINATORIAL ALGORITHUMS, PARALLEL ALGORITHUMS. *Educ:* Harvard Univ, PhD(comput sci), 74. *Prof Exp:* ASST PROF COMPUT SCI, HARVARD UNIV, 79-83. *Res:* Games, robotics, combinatorics, graphs and program optimization; algorithms for real time synchronization of parallel distributed computer systems, using probabilistic methods; parallel algorithms for sorting, searching, addition. *Mailing Add:* Aiken Comput Lab Harvard Univ Cambridge MA 02138

REIF, THOMAS HENRY, b Dayton,Ohio, Dec 24, 50. BIOMECHANICAL ENGINEERING, FLUID MECHANICS. *Educ:* Ohio State Univ, BSME, 73, MS, 74, PhD(mech eng), 77; Chicago Med Sch, MD, 83. *Prof Exp:* asst prof mech eng, US Naval Acad, 76-79; CONSULT, 83- *Concurrent Pos:* Consult, Gibson Consol Industries, 74-, researcher, Naval Acad Res Coun, 77-, consult, Med Inc, 78- *Mem:* Am Soc Mech Engrs; Naval Architects & Marine Engrs; Sigma Xi; Am Inst Aeronaut & Astronaut; Am Soc Eng Educ. *Res:* Analytical, numerical and experimental fluid mechanics and heat transfer; bio-medical engineering. *Mailing Add:* 5215 Greencroft Dr US Naval Acad Dayton OH 45426

REIF, VAN DALE, b Burlington, Iowa, Feb 18, 47; m 81. PHARMACEUTICAL CHEMISTRY. *Educ:* Univ Iowa, BS, 70; Univ Mich, MS, 71, PhD(pharmaceut chem), 75. *Prof Exp:* Sr sci assoc pharmaceut anal, Drug Res & Testing Lab, US Pharmacopeia, 75-78; UNIT SUPVR, ANAL RES & DEVELOP SUBDIV, WYETH LABS, 78- *Mem:* Am Chem Soc; Am Pharmaceut Asn; Acad Pharmaceut Sci. *Res:* Pharmaceutical analysis, drug metabolism, analytical chemistry, chromatography. *Mailing Add:* Wyeth Labs PO Box 8299 Philadelphia PA 19101

REIFENBERG, GERALD H, b Brooklyn, NY, Jan 18, 31; m 60; c 2. ORGANOMETALLIC CHEMISTRY. *Educ:* City Col New York, BS, 55; NY Univ, PhD(chem), 62. *Prof Exp:* Anal chemist, Refining Unincorp, 55-57; chemist, NY Naval Shipyard, 57-58; teaching fel org chem, NY Univ, 58-59; chemist, Gen Chem Div, Allied Chem Corp, 61-62; res chemist, M & T Chem, Inc, NJ, 63-68, supvr specialty chem, 68-69; scientist, Am Cyanamid Co, 69-71; dir res, Magic Marker Corp, 71-73; RES CHEMIST, PENNWALT CORP, 73- *Concurrent Pos:* Instr, Rutgers Univ, 64-65 & Newark Col Eng, 65-67. *Mem:* Am Chem Soc; Sigma Xi. *Res:* Organometallic chemistry, especially organotins; radioisotopes in tracer work; organofluorine and organophosphorus chemistry. *Mailing Add:* Pennwalt Corp 900 First Ave King of Prussia PA 19406

REIFENRATH, WILLIAM GERALD, b Crofton, Nebr, Mar 2, 47; m 79. DERMATOLOGY. *Educ:* Univ Nebr-Lincoln, BS, 69, MS, 72, PhD(med chem), 75. *Prof Exp:* RES CHEMIST, DIV CUTANEOUS HAZARDS, LETTERMAN ARMY INST RES, 76- *Mem:* Am Chem Soc. *Res:* Interaction of chemicals with skin; animal and in vitro models and analytical procedures for studying mechanisms of percutaneous penetration. *Mailing Add:* Div Cutaneous Hazards Letterman Army Inst Res San Francisco CA 94129

REIFF, GLENN AUSTIN, b Newton, Kans, Nov 18, 23; m 47; c 2. ELECTRONIC ENGINEERING. *Educ:* US Naval Acad, BS, 45; US Naval Postgrad Sch, BS, 52, MS, 53. *Prof Exp:* Officer, US Navy, 42-61; prog mgr & engr, NASA, 62-70; engr, US Dept Transp, 71-78; PROF IN RESIDENCE ENG TECH, UNIV SOUTHERN COLO, 78- *Honors & Awards:* Except Serv Award, NASA, 71. *Mem:* Sr mem Inst Elec & Electronics Engrs; Data Processing Mgt Asn. *Mailing Add:* 59Villa Dr Pueblo CO 81001

REIFF, HARRY ELMER, b Allentown, Pa, Apr 19, 24; m 47; c 3. ORGANIC CHEMISTRY. *Educ:* Lehigh Univ, BSChE, 49, MS, 50; Univ Minn, PhD(org chem), 55. *Prof Exp:* Asst, Lehigh Univ, 49-50; jr chemist, Merck & Co, Inc, 50-52, asst, Univ Minn, 52-54, sr chemist, 55-58, group leader, 58-60, asst sect head, 60-62, head org chem sect, 62-67, dir chem support & lab animal sci, Res & Develop Div, 67-72, dir phys sci mfg & planning, 72-78, dir tech planning, 78-81, DIR TECH ASSURANCE, SMITH KLINE & FRENCH LABS, 81- *Mem:* Fel AAAS; Am Chem Soc; Am Inst Chem Eng; fel Am Inst Chem; NY Acad Sci. *Res:* Physical sciences research and development involving pharmaceuticals and drugs, particularly synthetic organic chemistry. *Mailing Add:* Smith Kline & French Labs 1500 Spring St Philadelphia PA 19101

REIFF, PATRICIA HOFER, b Oklahoma City, Okla, Mar 14, 50; m 76. MAGNETOSPHERIC PHYSICS. *Educ:* Okla State Univ, BS, 71; Rice Univ, MS, 74, PhD(space physics, astron), 75. *Prof Exp:* Res assoc magnetospheric physics, Rice Univ, 75; Nat Acad Sci-Nat Res Coun resident res assoc magnetospheric physics, Marshall Space Flight Ctr, NASA, 75-76; asst prof magnetospheric physics, 76-81, ASSOC RES SCIENTIST, CTR FOR SPACEPHYSICS, RICE UNIV, 81-, ASST CHMN, DEPT SPACE PHYSICS & ASTRON, 79- *Concurrent Pos:* US deleg, Int Union Goed &

Geophys, 75 & 81; fac assoc, Nat Res Coun-Nat Acad Sci, 79, mem comt solar-terrestrial res, 79- *Mem:* Am Geophys Union; AAAS; Sigma Xi; Audubon Soc. *Res:* Study of solar wind, magnetosphere and ionosphere interactions, theoretically and using on atmosphere explorer satellites -C and -D; low-energy electron experiment data and Apollo 14 charged particle data; co-investigator on high altitude plasma instrument on dynamic explorer spacecraft; computer simulation of magnetospheric convertion. *Mailing Add:* Dept of Space Physics & Astron Rice Univ Houston TX 77001

REIFF, WILLIAM MICHAEL, b Binghamton, NY, Mar 9, 42; m 67; c 2. INORGANIC CHEMISTRY. *Educ:* State Univ NY Binghamton, AB, 64; Syracuse Univ, PhD(chem), 68. *Prof Exp:* NSF fel & fac assoc chem & physics, Univ Tex, Austin, 68-70; ASST PROF CHEM, NORTHEASTERN UNIV, 70- *Concurrent Pos:* Vis scientist, Francis Bitter Nat Magnetic Lab, Mich Inst Technol, 72- *Mem:* Am Chem Soc. *Res:* Physical inorganic chemistry; magnetically perturbed Mossbauer spectroscopy; magnetochemistry, electronic structure of coordination compounds and solid state materials. *Mailing Add:* Dept of Chem Northeastern Univ Boston MA 02115

REIFFEN, BARNEY, b Brooklyn, NY, Oct 5, 27; m 50; c 2. ELECTRICAL ENGINEERING. *Educ:* Cooper Union, BS, 49; Polytech Inst Brooklyn, MS, 53; Mass Inst Technol, PhD(elec eng), 60. *Prof Exp:* Engr, Harvey-Wells Electronics, Inc, 51-53 & Balco Res Labs, 53-55; staff mem, 55-61, group leader, 61-73, DIV HEAD, LINCOLN LAB, MASS INST TECHNOL, 73- *Concurrent Pos:* Prin assoc med, Beth Israel Hosp, Harvard Med Sch, 69-73. *Mem:* Sr mem Inst Elec & Electronics Engrs. *Res:* Satellite communications systems; information systems. *Mailing Add:* 26 Peacock Farm Rd Lexington MA 02173

REIFFENSTEIN, RHODERIC JOHN, b Montreal, Que, Nov 1, 38; m 61; c 4. PHARMACOLOGY. *Educ:* McGill Univ, BSc, 59; Univ Man, PhD(pharmacol), 65. *Prof Exp:* Teaching fel pharmacol, Univ Man, 59-64; asst prof, 64-72, ASSOC PROF PHARMACOL, UNIV ALTA, 72- *Concurrent Pos:* Med Res Coun Can vis scientist, Sch Pharm, Univ London, 71-72; vis prof, Anaesthesia Res, McGill Univ, 79-80. *Mem:* NY Acad Sci; European Soc Neurochem; Brit Pharmacol Soc; Pharmacol Soc Can; Soc Neurosci. *Res:* Mode of action of cocaine in potentiation of noradrenaline effects; allosteric interactions between drug receptors; cellular mechanism of focal cortical epilepsy; toxicity of sedative/hypnotic and ethanol combinations; alpha 2 adrenoreceptors in locus coeruleus; behavioral and single cell actions of amphetamine-hallucinogens; computer assisted instruction of pharmacology. *Mailing Add:* Dept of Pharmacol Univ of Alta Edmonton AB T6G 2H7 Can

REIF-LEHRER, LIANE, b Vienna, Austria, Nov 14, 34; US citizen; m 60; c 2. MOLECULAR BIOLOGY. *Educ:* Barnard Col, Columbia Univ, BA, 56; Univ Calif, Berkeley, PhD(phys org chem), 60. *Prof Exp:* Staff scientist, Res & Adv Develop Div, Avco Corp, Mass, 60-62; res fel molecular biol, 63-66, instr opthal res, 66-71, asst prof biochem opthal, 71-77, ASSOC PROF BIOCHEM OPTHAL, HARVARD MED SCH, 77-, DIR OFF ACAD CAREERS, HARVARD UNIV 81-; SR SCIENTIST, EYE RES INST, 75- *Concurrent Pos:* NIH fel, 64-66, res grant, 68-; prof, Boston Biomed Res Inst, Harvard Univ, 72- *Mem:* Asn Res Vision & Opthal; NY Acad Sci; AAAS; Am Soc Biol Chemists. *Res:* Mechanism of disproportionation of ethylbenzene under Friedel-Crafts conditions; control mechanisms in animal cells; biochemical controls in the normal and diseased retina; effects of ingestion of excess monosodium glutamate on humans. *Mailing Add:* Eye Res Inst 20 Staniford St Boston MA 02114

REIFLER, CLIFFORD BRUCE, b Chicago, Ill, Dec 28, 31; m 54; c 3. PSYCHIATRY, MEDICAL ADMINISTRATION. *Educ:* Univ Chicago, AB, 51; Northwestern Univ, Evanston, BS, 53; Yale Univ, MD, 57; Univ NC, Chapel Hill, MPH, 67. *Prof Exp:* USPHS fel & resident psychiat, Strong Mem Hosp, Rochester, NY, 58-61; from instr to assoc prof psychiat, Sch Med, Univ NC, Chapel Hill, 63-70, from asst prof to assoc prof ment health, Sch Pub Health, 68-70; PROF HEALTH SERV, PSYCHIAT, PREV MED & COMMUNITY HEALTH & DIR UNIV HEALTH SERV, UNIV ROCHESTER, 70- *Concurrent Pos:* Assoc physician-in-chg psychiat, Student Health Serv, Univ NC, Chapel Hill, 63-67, sr psychiatrist, 67-70; consult psychiat, Rochester Inst Technol, 76-; interim vpres student affairs, Univ Rochester, 80-81; mem vis comt, Harvard Univ Health Serv, 78- *Honors & Awards:* Edward Hitchcock Award, Am Col Health Asn, 81. *Mem:* Am Occup Med Asn; fel Am Pub Health Asn; fel Am Psychiat Asn; fel Am Col Health Asn (pres, 75-77); Am Acad Med Dirs. *Res:* Psychiatric epidemiology; health care delivery systems. *Mailing Add:* Univ Health Serv Box 617 Univ of Rochester Rochester NY 14642

REIFSCHNEIDER, WALTER, b Vienna, Austria, July 29, 26; nat US; m 59; c 1. ORGANIC CHEMISTRY. *Educ:* Univ Vienna, PhD(chem), 53. *Prof Exp:* Res assoc chem, Univ Ill, 53-57; res chemist, 57-61, group leader, 61-70, assoc scientist, 70-81, RES SCIENTIST, DOW CHEM CO, 81- *Mem:* AAAS; Am Chem Soc; Sci Res Soc Am. *Res:* General organic synthesis; heterocycles; sulfur compounds; pesticide chemistry; natural products. *Mailing Add:* 3538 Bayberry Dr Walnut Creek CA 94598

REIFSNIDER, KENNETH LEONARD, b Baltimore, Md, Feb 19, 40; m 63; c 2. MATERIAL SCIENCE, MECHANICS. *Educ:* Western Md Col, BA, 63; Johns Hopkins Univ, BES, 64, MSE, 65, PhD(metall), 68. *Prof Exp:* From asst prof to assoc prof eng mech, 68-75, PROF ENG MECH, VA POLYTECH INST & STATE UNIV, 75-, CHMN MAT ENG SCI PROG, 71- *Concurrent Pos:* NATO mat sci consult, 69 & 78; sabbatical leave, Univ Calif, Livermore, 81. *Mem:* Am Inst Mining, Metall & Petrol Engrs; Am Soc Metals; Am Soc Testing & Mat. *Res:* Composite materials; nondestructive testing and evaluation; mechanics of inhomogeneous deformation including fatigue and fracture; continuum theories of material defects. *Mailing Add:* 5 Woodland Hills Dr Blacksburg VA 24060

REIFSNYDER, WILLIAM EDWARD, b Ridgway, Pa, Mar 29, 24; m 54; c 3. FOREST METEOROLOGY. *Educ:* NY Univ, BS, 44; Univ Calif, MF, 49; Yale Univ, PhD(forest meteorol), 54. *Prof Exp:* Meteorologist, Calif Forest & Range Exp Sta, 51-54; from asst prof to assoc prof, 55-65, PROF FOREST METEOROL, YALE UNIV, 65-, PUB HEALTH, 67- *Concurrent Pos:* Mem & chmn adv comt climate, US Weather Bur, Nat Acad Sci-Nat Res Coun, 57-63, mem sci task force atmospheric sci, 61, panel educ, Comt Atmospheric Sci, 62-64, chmn adv comt biometeorol; vis scientist, Soc Am Foresters-NSF, 61-; vis prof, Univ Munich, 68; consult forest meteorol, World Meteorol Orgn, 73, chmn working group on the applications of meterology to forestry, 75-80; vis scientist, Swed Univ Agr Sci, 81. *Mem:* Fel AAAS; Soc Am Foresters; Am Meteorol Soc; Int Soc Biometeorol. *Res:* Energy budgets; air pollution meteorology. *Mailing Add:* 360 Prospect St New Haven CT 06511

REIHER, HAROLD FREDERICK, b Detroit, Mich, July 8, 27; m 53; c 3. ACOUSTICS. *Educ:* Univ Mich, BS, 50. *Prof Exp:* Lab asst, Eng Res Inst, Univ Mich, 49-51, res assoc, 51-56, assoc res engr, 56-57; res engr, 57-64, VPRES, GEIGER & HAMME, INC, 64- *Mem:* Inst Elec & Electronics Engrs; Am Soc Test & Mat. *Res:* Architectural acoustics; measurement and control of sound and vibration; evaluation of acoustical properties and performance of materials, structures and equipment; electronic instrumentation. *Mailing Add:* 1835 Knight Rd Ann Arbor MI 48103

REILING, GILBERT HENRY, b St Paul, Minn, Sept 19, 28; m 51; c 8. ENGINEERING PHYSICS. *Educ:* Col St Thomas, BS, 51; Univ NDak, MS, 52; Univ Mo, PhD(physics), 57. *Prof Exp:* Instr physics, Univ Mo, 53; physicist, 57-61, MGR ENG, LIGHTING RES & TECH SERV, GEN ELEC CO, 61- *Concurrent Pos:* lectr, Siena Col, 58-; John Carroll, 60- *Mem:* Am Phys Soc; Inst Elec & Electronics Eng. *Res:* Optical properties of solid state materials; fundamental processes in low pressure arcs. *Mailing Add:* Lighting Res & Tech Serv O 1301 Gen Elec Co Nela Park Cleveland OH 44112

REILING, THEODORE PAUL, b St Paul, Minn, Nov 16, 29; m 57. PLANT PATHOLOGY, HORTICULTURE. *Educ:* Univ Minn, BS, 51, PhD(plant path), 57; Iowa State Univ, MS, 53. *Prof Exp:* Asst hort, Iowa State Univ, 51-53; asst plant path, Univ Minn, 53-57; asst plant pathologist & breeder, 56-57, SR PLANT BREEDER, GREEN GIANT CO, 57- *Mem:* Am Phytopath Soc. *Res:* Virus and root rot in vegetable crops and ornamentals; resistance to root rot and virus movement. *Mailing Add:* Agr Res Dept Green Giant Co LeSueur MN 56058

REILLEY, CHARLES NORWOOD, b Charlotte, NC, Mar 2, 25. ANALYTICAL CHEMISTRY. *Educ:* Univ NC, BS, 47; Princeton Univ, MA, 51, PhD(chem), 52. *Prof Exp:* Instr chem, Queen's Col, NC, 47-49; from instr to prof, 52-63, KENAN PROF CHEM, UNIV N C, CHAPEL HILL, 63- *Concurrent Pos:* Ed, J Electroanal Chem, 59-; ed, Adv Anal Chem & Instrumentation, 60- *Honors & Awards:* Fisher Award, Am Chem Soc, 65, Hertz Medal, 68, Stone Award, 71; MCA Award, Mfg Chemists Asn, 75. *Mem:* Nat Acad Sci; Am Chem Soc. *Res:* Electroanalytical chemistry; transient electrode processes; theory and applications of metal chelates; nuclear magnetic resonance; computerized instrumentation. *Mailing Add:* Dept of Chem Univ of NC Chapel Hill NC 27514

REILLY, ALFRED EMMANUEL, b Jersey City, NJ, Aug 9, 28; m 65. GEOPHYSICS, SOLAR PHYSICS. *Educ:* Boston Col, AB, 52. *Prof Exp:* Physicist, Nat Bur Standards, Washington, DC, 52; teaching asst physics, Boston Col, 52-53; physicist, Air Force Cambridge Res Ctr, Mass, 53-55 & Aberdeen Proving Ground, Md, 55-57; PHYSICIST, AIR FORCE GEOPHYS LAB, 57- *Mem:* Am Geophys Union. *Res:* Solar and geophysical physics and inter-relationships, especially ionospheric, auroral and magnetospheric. *Mailing Add:* Space Physics Div Air Force Geophys Lab Hanscom AFB MA 01731

REILLY, BERNARD EDWARD, b Meadville, Pa, June 9, 35; m 70. PLASMID BIOLOGY, VIROLOGY. *Educ:* Westminster Col, BS, 58; Case Western Reserv Univ, PhD(microbiol), 65. *Prof Exp:* Res fel microbiol, Univ Minn, Minneapolis, 62-65; res assoc microbiol, Scripps Clin & Res Found, 65-68; asst prof biol, NMex State Univ, 68-69; vis prof genetics, 69-71, asst prof, 72-75, ASSOC PROF MICROBIOL, SCH DENT, UNIV MINN, MINNEAPOLIS, 75- *Mem:* Bacteriophage and microbial genetics, viral and post transcriptional function modification of proteins. *Res:* viral assemlidy. *Mailing Add:* Sch of Dent 18-246A Health Sci Univ of Minn Minneapolis MN 55455

REILLY, CHARLES AUSTIN, b Summerside, PEI, May 18, 16; nat US; m 42. CHEMICAL PHYSICS. *Educ:* Dalhousie Univ, BSc, 39, MSc, 40; Harvard Univ, AM, 46, PhD(chem physics), 50. *Prof Exp:* Asst res physicist, Nat Res Coun Can, 40-43; asst prof chem, DAlhousie Univ, 48-51; physicist, Belleaire, 51-80, SR STAFF PHYSICIST, SHELL DEVELOP CO, HOUSTON, 80- *Mem:* Fel Am Phys Soc; Am Chem Soc; fel Am Inst Chemists. *Res:* Molecular beams; nuclear magnetic resonance; field emission spectroscopy. *Mailing Add:* 2622 Country Club Blvd Sugar Land TX 77478

REILLY, CHARLES BERNARD, b New York, NY, Dec 7, 29; m 55; c 6. ORGANIC CHEMISTRY, POLYMER CHEMISTRY. *Educ:* Queen's Col, NY, BS, 53; Univ Cincinnati, MS, 55, PhD(chem), 57. *Prof Exp:* Res & develop chemist, Gen Elec Co, 57-65, sr chemist, 65-66, mgr process develop, 66-69; group leader, 69-80, SR CHEMIST RUBBER COMPOUNDINGS, URETHANE APPLNS, GOODYEAR TIRE & RUBBER CO, 80- *Mem:* Am Chem Soc. *Res:* Polymer chemistry specializing in thermoset resins as epoxies and urethanes; organic synthesis of polymer intermediates; physical properties of polymers. *Mailing Add:* Urethane Applns Goodyear Tire & Rubber Co 1144 E Market Akron OH 44305

REILLY, CHARLES DUFF, b Denver, Colo, Oct 24, 24; m 47; c 2. PHYSICS. *Educ:* Univ Wyo, BS, 50, MS, 53. *Prof Exp:* Res engr, 53-57, res proj engr, 57-62, res assoc, 62-73, RES FEL, ENG PHYSICS LAB, E I DU PONT DE NEMOURS & CO, 73- *Mem:* Optical Soc Am; Inter-Soc Color Coun; Sigma Xi. *Res:* Physical optics; color theory and measurement. *Mailing Add:* E357/251 E I du Pont de Nemours & Co Wilmington DE 19898

REILLY, CHRISTOPHER ALOYSIUS, JR, b Tucson, Ariz, Aug 8, 42; m 68; c 3. VIROLOGY. *Educ:* Loyola Univ, Los Angeles, BS, 64; Univ Ariz, MS, 66, PhD(microbiol), 68. *Prof Exp:* Fel virol, 68-69, asst microbiologist, 69-73, MICROBIOLOGIST, ARGONNE NAT LAB, 73-, DEP PROG MGR, SYNFUELS ENVIRON RES PROG, 80- *Concurrent Pos:* Adj assoc prof biol sci, Northern Ill Univ, 75- *Mem:* Am Soc Microbiol; Am Asn Cancer Res; Sci Exp Biol & Med; AAAS; Sigma Xi. *Res:* Characterization of the health effects associated with coal-derived synthetic fuels, with particular emphasis on carcinogenesis and chemical toxicology. *Mailing Add:* Carcinogenesis Bldg 202 Argonne Nat Lab 9700 S Cass Ave Argonne IL 60439

REILLY, EDWARD LEO, b Dunbar, Pa, Oct 25, 24; m 50; c 11. ORGANIC CHEMISTRY. *Educ:* St Vincent Col, BS, 48; Univ Notre Dame, PhD(chem), 52. *Prof Exp:* Sr res chemist, Explosives Dept, Eastern Lab, 52-59, sect head, 60-66, spec assignment, Cent Res Dept, 66-67, res assoc, Eastern Lab, 67-72, RES ASSOC EXP STA, E I DU PONT DE NEMOURS & CO, INC, 72- *Mem:* Am Chem Soc. *Res:* Organosilicon and nitric oxide chemistry; homogeneous and heterogeneous catalytic oxidations. *Mailing Add:* 315 A Pennock Bridge Rd West Grove PA 19390

REILLY, EDWIN DAVID, JR, b Troy, NY, Apr 27, 32; m 54; c 6. COMPUTER SCIENCE, PHYSICS. *Educ:* Rensselaer Polytech Inst, BS, 54, MS, 58, PhD(physics), 69. *Prof Exp:* Mathematician, Knolls Atomic Power Lab, Gen Elec Co, 56-61, mgr digital anal & comp, 61-65; dir comput ctr, 65-70, chmn dept, 67-73, ASSOC PROF COMPUT SCI, STATE UNIV NY ALBANY, 67- *Concurrent Pos:* Supvr, Town of Niskayuna, NY, 70-79; pres, Cybernetic Info Systs, 80- *Mem:* AAAS; Asn Comput Mach; Am Phys Soc; Inst Elec & Electronic Engrs; Sigma Xi. *Res:* Application of computers to the humanities; computer organization; cryptography; scattering of electromagnetic waves from nonspherical targets. *Mailing Add:* Dept of Comput Sci Rm ES-315 State Univ NY Albany NY 12222

REILLY, EMMETT B, b Los Angeles, Calif, Aug 19, 20; m 55; c 6. PATHOLOGY, HEMATOLOGY. *Educ:* Loyola Univ, Calif, BS, 42; Univ Southern Calif, MD, 46; Am Bd Path, dipl, 52, cert clin path, 56, cert hemat, 63, cert radioisotopic path, 74. *Prof Exp:* Chief clin path, Vet Admin Hosp, Long Beach, 50-57; chief pathologist, Orange County Hosp, 57-65; CHIEF PATHOLOGIST, DANIEL FREEMAN HOSP, 65- *Concurrent Pos:* Consult, Vet Admin Hosp, Long Beach, Calif, 57-; clin prof, Univ Southern Calif, 65- *Mem:* Fel Am Soc Clin Pathologists; NY Acad Sci; fel Col Am Pathologists. *Res:* Coagulation of blood; neoplasia. *Mailing Add:* Dept Path Daniel Freeman Hosp 333 N Prairie Ave Inglewood CA 90306

REILLY, EUGENE PATRICK, b New York, NY, Mar 12, 39; m 69; c 2. ORGANIC CHEMISTRY. *Educ:* St Peter's Col, NJ, BS, 63; Fordham Univ, PhD(org chem), 68. *Prof Exp:* Res chemist plastics, acrylics & acetals, E I duPont de Nemours Co, Inc, Wilmington, 67-71; develop chemist polyesters, Plastics Dept, Gen Elec Co, Pittsfield, Mass, 71-73; res scientist terpen chem, Union Camp Corp, Princeton, 73-76; SR RES SCIENTIST RESOURCE RECOVERY, AM CAN CO, 76- *Mem:* Am Inst Chem Engrs; Tech Asn Pulp & Paper Indust. *Res:* Plastics especially acrylics, acetals, polyesters, thermosets; laboratory to plant scale; upgrading of natural products especially terpenes and talloils to useful products; resource recovery, utilization of natural organic waste materials from paper making processes. *Mailing Add:* 243 Glenn Ave Lawrenceville NJ 08648

REILLY, FRANK DANIEL, b Fairborn, Ohio, Aug 20, 49; m 69; c 1. HUMAN ANATOMY, MEDICAL PHYSIOLOGY. *Educ:* Ohio State Univ, BS, 71; Univ Cincinnati, PhD(anat), 75. *Prof Exp:* Asst prof anat, Col Med, Univ Cincinnati, 75-78; ASSOC PROF ANAT, SCH MED, WVA UNIV, 78- *Mem:* Am Asn Anatomists; Microvascular Soc; Sigma Xi. *Res:* Hematology and microvascular physiology; morphology and pharmacology. *Mailing Add:* Dept of Anat WVa Univ Morgantown WV 26506

REILLY, GEORGE JOSEPH, b Camden, NJ, Aug 26, 38; m 65; c 2. PHYSICAL ORGANIC CHEMISTRY. *Educ:* Drexel Inst Tech, BS, 62; Univ Mass, MS, 65, PhD(chem), 67. *Prof Exp:* Res chemist plastics, E I duPont de Nemours Co, Inc, 67-70; MUS SCIENTIST CONSERV COORDR, HENRY FRANCIS DUPONT WINTERTHUR MUS, 70- *Concurrent Pos:* Adj assoc prof, Univ Del, 73-; res & publ comt, Nat Conserv Adv Coun, Washington, DC, 76- *Mem:* Am Chem Soc; Am Inst Conserv. *Res:* Authentication of art objects by physical and chemical means; mechanisms of degradation in early and modern art materials. *Mailing Add:* Henry Francis DuPont Winterthur Mus Winterthur DE 19735

REILLY, HILDA CHRISTINE, b New Brunswick, NJ, Feb 25, 20. MICROBIOLOGY. *Educ:* Rutgers Univ, BSc, 41, PhD(microbiol), 46. *Prof Exp:* Lab technician chem, E R Squibb & Sons, NJ, 41-42; chemist, White Labs, Inc, 42-43; asst, Rutgers Univ, 46-47; asst prof microbiol, Sloan-Kettering Div, Med Col, Cornell Univ, 52-56, assoc prof, 56-71; mem faculty, Dept Bact, 71-75, ASSOC PROF BIOL SCI, DOUGLASS COL, RUTGERS UNIV, 75- *Concurrent Pos:* Asst, Sloan-Kettering Inst, 47-49, assoc, 49-60, assoc mem, 60-71, head microbiol sect, 56-71. *Mem:* AAAS; Am Soc Microbiol; Harvey Soc; Am Asn Cancer Res; fel Am Acad Microbiol; fel NY Acad Sci. *Res:* Production, isolation and mode of action of antibiotics; microbial physiology; experimental cancer chemotherapy. *Mailing Add:* Dept of Biol Rutgers Univ New Brunswick NJ 08903

REILLY, HUGH THOMAS, b New York, NY, Apr 19, 25. PHYSICAL CHEMISTRY, CHEMICAL ENGINEERING. *Educ:* St Peter's Col, NJ, BS, 50; Polytech Inst NY, MS, 53. *Prof Exp:* Res & teaching fel, Polytech Inst Brooklyn, 50-51; proj engr, Thiokol Chem Corp, Elkton, Md, 57-59, mgr space propulsion systs, 59-60, mgr new prod develop, 60-63; tech adv & proj engr, Land Warfare Lab, 63-74, chief lethal group, Edgewood Arsenal, 74-76, team leader pipeline gas prog, 76-78, chief, Dept Energy Support Off & Supvry Chem Engr, 78-81, CHIEF, ENVIRON TECH DIV CHEM SYSTS LAB, US ARMY ARMAMENT RES & DEVELOP COMMAND, 81-

Mem: Fel Am Inst Aeronaut & Astronaut; Am Chem Soc; fel Am Inst Chemists. *Res:* Atmospheric sensing; chemical process; chemical detection; pollution; cloud physics, coal process. *Mailing Add:* US Army Chem Systs Lab Attn: DRDAR-CLT Aberdeen Proving Ground MD 21010

REILLY, JAMES PATRICK, b Mt Vernon, NY, Aug 29, 50. PHYSICAL CHEMISTRY. *Educ:* Princeton Univ, AB, 72; Cambridge Univ, CPGS, 73; Univ Calif, Berkeley, PhD(chem), 77. *Prof Exp:* Guest researcher, Max Planck Inst, Garching, 77-79; ASST PROF CHEM, IND UNIV, 79- *Concurrent Pos:* Alfred P Sloan fel, Alfred P Sloan Found, 82. *Mem:* Sigma Xi. *Res:* Probing optical transitions in transient species and excited molecular states; investigation of the chemistry of excited molecules; the interaction of radiation and matter. *Mailing Add:* Dept Chem Ind Univ Bloomington IN 47405

REILLY, JAMES WILLIAM, b Jersey City, NJ, Oct 18, 35; m 56; c 3. CHEMICAL ENGINEERING, PHYSICAL CHEMISTRY. *Educ:* Seton Hall Col, BS, 56; Stevens Inst Technol, MS, 59, ScD(chem eng), 65. *Prof Exp:* Develop engr, Turbomotor Div, Curtiss-Wright Corp, 56-57; sr res engr, Tex-US Chem Co, 57-60; proj engr, Plastics Div, Koppers Co, 60; teaching asst, Mass Inst Technol, 60-61; asst prof chem & chem eng, Newark Col Eng, 61-65; sr develop engr, 65-74, prin engr, 74-81, MGR PROJ ENG, BLOOMFIELD DIV, ENG DEVELOP CTR, LUMMUS CO, COMBUSTION ENG, INC, 81- *Mem:* Am Inst Chem Engrs; Sigma Xi. *Res:* Engineering process research and development for proprietary processes in catalyst, hydrogenation and process design. *Mailing Add:* Eng Develop Ctr Combustion Eng Co 1515 Broad St Bloomfield NJ 07003

REILLY, JOSEPH F, b Waucoma, Iowa, May 14, 15; m 48; c 5. PHARMACOLOGY, TOXICOLOGY. *Educ:* Univ Ill, BA, 37; Harvard Univ, MA, 39; Univ Chicago, PhD(pharmacol), 47. *Prof Exp:* Chemist, Chem Res Dept, Armour Labs, Ill, 39-43; res assoc, Anti-Malarial Prog & asst pharmacol, Univ Chicago, 43-47; pharmacologist, US Army Chem Ctr, Md, 47-48; res fel, Med Sch, Cornell Univ, 48-49, from instr to asst prof pharmacol, 49-54, asst prof pharmacol & psychiat, 54-62; chief pharmacodyn sect, Div Pharmacol, Bur Sci, 63-70, CHIEF DRUG BIOANAL BR, DIV DRUG BIOL, BUR DRUGS, US FOOD & DRUG ADMIN, DC, 70- *Concurrent Pos:* Chief pharmacologist, Payne Whitney Clin, NY Hosp-Cornell Med Ctr, 54-62; consult, Coun Drugs, AMA, 58 & 65; collabr, US Pharmacopoeia Standards, 70-72; actg dep dir, Div Drug Biol, Bur Drugs, US Food & Drug Admin, Washington, DC, 78-80. *Mem:* Am Soc Pharmacol & Exp Therapeut; Soc Toxicol; Soc Exp Biol & Med; Harvey Soc; Sigma Xi. *Res:* Anti-malarials; plasma enzymes; diethylstilbestrol-enzymes; acetylstrophanthidin-fluoroacetate-heart; experimental arrythmias; catecholamines-psychiatric patients; reserpine; glutathione reductase-carbon tetrachloride; shellfish toxin; desmethylimipramine toxicity; age, sex, ulcers; age-catecholamines; organochlorine and monosodium glutamate effects. *Mailing Add:* Div of Drug Biol Bur of Drugs HFD410 US Food & Drug Admin Washington DC 20204

REILLY, KEVIN DENIS, b Omaha, Nebr, Sept 12, 37; m 61; c 3. COMPUTER SCIENCE. *Educ:* Creighton Univ, BS, 59; Univ Nebr, Lincoln, MS, 62; Univ Chicago, PhD(math biol), 66. *Prof Exp:* Res scientist, Univ Calif, Los Angeles, 66-70, lectr comp sci, 69-70; ASSOC PROF COMPUT & INFO SCI, UNIV ALA, BIRMINGHAM, 70- *Concurrent Pos:* Sr lectr, Sch Bus, Univ Southern Calif, 69-70. *Mem:* AAAS; Am Soc Info Sci; Asn Comput Mach. *Res:* Digital modeling and simulation, discret-event programming systems; information storage and retrieval, file structures; artificial intelligence; programming systems; mathematical biology; biological and library applications; physiology; biophysics. *Mailing Add:* Dept of Comput & Info Sci Univ of Ala Birmingham AL 35294

REILLY, MARGUERITE, b Troy, NY, Mar 20, 19. PROTOZOOLOGY, MICROBIOLOGY. *Educ:* Col St Rose, BA, 53, MS, 60; St John's Univ, NY, PhD(zool), 63. *Prof Exp:* Teacher high schs, Albany & Syracuse Diocese, 51-60; PROF BIOL, COL ST ROSE, 63-, CHAIRPERSON DEPT, 66- & NATURAL SCI DIV, 77- *Mem:* Soc Protozoologists; Am Inst Biol Sci. *Res:* Nutrition of Protozoa and the effect of radiation on Protozoa grown under varying conditions. *Mailing Add:* Dept of Biol Col of St Rose 432 Western Ave Albany NY 12203

REILLY, MICHAEL HUNT, b Rochester, NY, Dec 23, 39; m 65; c 2. THEORETICAL PHYSICS. *Educ:* Univ Rochester, BS, 61, PhD(solid state physics), 67. *Prof Exp:* RES PHYSICIST MATH PHYSICS, NAVAL RES LAB, 66- *Concurrent Pos:* Nat Acad Sci-Nat Res Coun fel, Naval Res Lab, 66-68. *Mem:* Am Phys Soc; Am Geophys Union. *Res:* Space science; communications science; fluid dynamics. *Mailing Add:* Space Sci Code 4180.2 Naval Res Lab Washington DC 20375

REILLY, NORMAN RAYMUND, b Glasgow, Scotland, Jan 30, 40; m 66; c 3. SEMIGROUUPS, ORDERED ALGEBRAIC SYSTEMS. *Educ:* Univ Glasgow, BSc Hons, 61, PhD(math), 65. *Prof Exp:* Asst lectr math, Univ Glasgow, 64-65; vis asst prof math, Newcomb Col, Tulane Univ, New Orleans, 65-66; asst prof, 66-69, assoc prof, 69-74, chmn, 76-78, actg assoc vpres, 78-79, PROF MATH, SIMON FRASER UNIV, 74- *Concurrent Pos:* Vis prof math, Monash Univ, Melbourne, Australia, 71. *Mem:* Can Math Soc; Am Math Soc; Soc Actuaries. *Res:* Algebra especially in the structure, representations and varieties of algebras. *Mailing Add:* Dept Math Simon Fraser Univ Burnaby BC V5A 1S6 Can

REILLY, PARK MCKNIGHT, b Welland, Ont, May 14, 20; m 45; c 4. STATISTICS, CHEMICAL ENGINEERING. *Educ:* Univ Toronto, BASc, 43; Univ London, PhD(statist) & dipl, Imp Col, 62. *Prof Exp:* Jr chem engr, Welland Chem Works, 41-45; lectr chem eng, Ajax Div, Univ Toronto, 45-47; prin chem engr, Polysar Ltd, 47-67; PROF CHEM ENG, UNIV WATERLOO, 67- *Concurrent Pos:* Adj prof, Univ Waterloo, 64-67; consult several chem industs, 67- *Mem:* Fel Can Soc Chem Eng; fel Royal Statist Soc. *Res:* Application of statistical methods to chemical engineering research and plant operation; design of experiments; model discrimination. *Mailing Add:* Dept of Chem Eng Univ of Waterloo Waterloo ON N2L 3G1 Can

REILLY, PETER JOHN, b Newark, NJ, Dec 26, 38; m 65, 76; c 2. CHEMICAL ENGINEERING. *Educ:* Princeton Univ, AB, 60; Univ Pa, PhD(chem eng), 64. *Prof Exp:* Res engr, Org Chem Dept, Jackson Lab, E I du Pont de Nemours & Co, Inc, 64-68; asst prof chem eng, Univ Nebr, Lincoln, 68-74; assoc prof, 74-79, PROF CHEM ENG, IOWA STATE UNIV, 79- *Mem:* Am Chem Soc; Am Inst Chem Engrs. *Res:* Biochemical engineering; immobilized enzyme kinetics; agricultural residue utilization. *Mailing Add:* Dept of Chem Eng Iowa State Univ Ames IA 50011

REILLY, RICHARD J, b La Crosse, Wis, Jan 15, 30; m 54; c 1. HEAT TRANSFER. *Educ:* Univ Minn, BS, 51. *Prof Exp:* Jr res engr, Rosemount Res Facility, Univ Minn, 51; res engr, Aeronaut Res Div, Gen Mills, Inc, 51-54; res engr, Northrop Aircraft Inc, 54-57; sr develop engr, Aeronaut Div, Honeywell Inc, Minn, 57-60, sr res scientist fluid mech, Mil Prod Res, 60-63, prin res scientist, 63-64, supvr res, 64-65, res sect head, Systs & Res Ctr, 65-67; fluid sci res mgr, 67-69; exec vpres, Cytec Corp, 69-74; PRES, GALILEO CO, 74-; dir, BMT, Inc, 76-79; PRES, CAYANA CORP, 78- *Concurrent Pos:* Pvt consult, 59-64; consult lectr, Adv Group Aerospace Res & Develop, NATO, 66-70. *Honors & Awards:* US Air Force Systs Command Award, 63. *Mem:* Assoc fel Am Inst Aeronaut & Astronaut. *Res:* Aerodynamics; compressible flow; boundary layer flows; supersonic inlets; fluidics; alternate energy sources. *Mailing Add:* 1759 Venus Ave St Paul MN 55112

REILLY, WILLIAM LEO, organic chemistry, analytical chemistry, see previous edition

REILY, WILLIAM SINGER, b Chicago, Ill, June 13, 24; m 51; c 6. ORGANIC CHEMISTRY. *Educ:* Roosevelt Univ, BS, 48; De Paul Univ, MS, 50. *Prof Exp:* Develop chemist, Bauer & Black Lab, Kendall Co, 52-53; res chemist, Baxter Labs, Inc, 53-54; develop chemist, G D Searle & Co, 54-57; proj engr, Amphenol Electronics Co, 57-58; develop chemist, Du Kane Corp, 58-67; PROJ LEADER, US GYPSUM, 67- *Mem:* Am Chem Soc. *Res:* Applied and industrial chemistry; process and product development; trouble shooting and environmental testing. *Mailing Add:* 884 Horne Terr Des Plaines IL 60016

REIM, ROBERT E, b Abrams, Wis. ELECTROCHEMISTRY. *Educ:* Univ Wis, OshKosh, BS, 71, Milwaukee, MS, 74. *Prof Exp:* SR RES CHEMIST, DOW CHEM CO, 74- *Mem:* Am Chem Soc; Soc Appl Spectros. *Res:* Development and application of analytical techniques including electroanalytical chemistry, spectroscopy and chromatography. *Mailing Add:* 2506 Lucky Ct Midland MI 48640

REIMANN, BERNHARD ERWIN FERDINAND, b Berlin, Ger, May 30, 22; m 49; c 1. ELECTRON MICROSCOPY. *Educ:* Free Univ Berlin, Dr rer nat, 59. *Prof Exp:* Asst, Bot Inst, Marburg, 58-60; asst res biologist, Scripps Inst, Univ Calif, San Diego, 61-67, supvr electron microscope facil, 64-67; CHIEF ELECTRON MICROS, WILLIAM BEAUMONT ARMY MED CTR, US ARMY, 67- *Concurrent Pos:* NSF grant, 65-67 & 68-69; assoc prof, NMex State Univ, 67-; assoc, Grad Fac, Univ Tex, El Paso, 68-71; assoc clin prof pathol, Tex Tech Med Sch. *Mem:* Fel AAAS; Phycol Soc Am; Electron Micros Soc Am; Int Phycol Soc; Asn Mil Surgeons US. *Res:* Cytology and ultrastructure of mineral deposition in biological systems; histopathology diagnostic at ultrastructure level. *Mailing Add:* 8312 Turquoise El Paso TX 79904

REIMANN, ERWIN M, b Parkston, SD, July 26, 42; m 61; c 2. BIOCHEMISTRY. *Educ:* Augustana Col, SDak, BA, 64; Univ Wis-Madison, PhD(biochem), 68. *Prof Exp:* Fel biochem, Univ Calif, Davis, 68-70; asst prof, 70-75, ASSOC PROF BIOCHEM, MED COL OHIO, TOLEDO, 75- *Concurrent Pos:* Vis asst prof physiol, Vanderbilt Univ, Nashville, 74. *Mem:* Sigma Xi; Am Chem Soc; AAAS. *Res:* The role of cyclic adenosine monophosphate and protein kinases in cellular function, especially their roles in glycogen metabolism and in gastric secretion. *Mailing Add:* Dept of Biochem Med Col of Ohio Toledo OH 43614

REIMANN, HANS, b Vienna, Austria, Dec 28, 30; nat US; m 57; c 1. ORGANIC CHEMISTRY. *Educ:* Univ Calif, Los Angeles, BS, 51, PhD(chem), 57. *Prof Exp:* From chemist to sr chemist, 57-68, unit head, 68-71, asst to dir, Chem & Microbiol Develop, 71-73, coordr, Corp Prod Develop, 73-74, mgr prod planning & control, 74-77, assoc dir,Tech Regulatory Doc & Actives Control, 78-80, DIR, REGULATORY AFFAIRS-TECH, SCHERING CORP, 80- *Mem:* Am Chem Soc; Am Soc Microbiol. *Res:* Natural products; steroids; antibiotics. *Mailing Add:* Schering Corp 60 Orange St Bloomfield NJ 07003

REIMANN, HOBART ANSTETH, b Bufffalo, NY, Oct 31, 97; m 26, 50; c 2. MEDICINE. *Educ:* Univ Buffalo, MD, 21. *Hon Degrees:* DSc, Thomas Jefferson Univ, 77. *Prof Exp:* Asst, Rockefeller Inst Hosp, New York, 23-26; Nat Res Coun fel path, Prague Tech Univ, 26; assoc prof med, Peking Union Med Col, China, 27-30; from assoc prof to prof, Med Sch, Univ Minn, 30-36; prof, Jefferson Med Col, 36-52; prof, Am Univ Beirut, 52-54; Univ Calif Indonesia proj vis prof, Univ Indonesia, 54-55; vis prof, Med Col, Univ Shiraz, 57-59; prof med, Hahnemann Med Col, 60-79. *Concurrent Pos:* Med officer, UNRRA, China, 45; field dir, AMA Proj Vietnam, 67; Care-Medico consult, Kabul, Afghanistan, 68 & Honduras, 70; lectr, Bogota, Leticia, 70; vis prof med, Jefferson Med Col, 79. *Honors & Awards:* Charles V Chapin Medal, 51; Order of Cedars of Lebanon, 54; Shaffrey Medal, 74. *Mem:* Am Soc Clin Invest; Soc Exp Biol & Med; Am Soc Exp Path; Am Soc Trop Med & Hyg; Asn Am Physicians. *Res:* Internal medicine; viral pneumonia and dysentery; periodic disease. *Mailing Add:* 125 Old Gulph Rd Wynnewood PA 19096

REIMANN, JESSICA ELIZABETH, biochemistry, see previous edition

REIMER, CHARLES BLAISDELL, b San Francisco, Calif, Dec 6, 21; m 48; c 5. IMMUNOLOGY. *Educ:* Mass Inst Technol, BS, 49, MS, 49, Johns Hopkins Univ, PhD(biochem), 57. *Prof Exp:* Asst biol, Mass Inst Technol, 49-50; assoc med, Univ Rochester, 50-52; assoc biophys, Johns Hopkins Univ,

52-58; sr phys chemist, Physico-chem Res Div, Eli Lilly & Co, 58-65, sr scientist, Biol Res Div, 65-67; chief biophys separations unit, Biol Reagents Sect, 67-74, CHIEF IMMUNOL PROD BR, BUR LABS, CTR DIS CONTROL, US DEPT HEALTH, EDUC & WELFARE, 74- *Concurrent Pos:* Chmn standardization comt, Am Asn Immunologists, 73-77; chmn various imunnobiol standardization subcomt, Int Union Immunol Socs, 74-; spec consult immunol, WHO, 71, 73, 76 & 81; mem expert group diagnostic kits, Int Fedn Clin Chemists, 76-79; Ctr Dis Control rep, Adv Comt Invitro Diagnostic Prod, Food & Drug Admin, 75-; fel, Am Acad Microbiol, 77-; adj prof & assoc prof, Dept Parasitol, Univ NC, Chapel Hill, 79-; chmn, Alpha-Fetoprotein Subcomt & mem, Diagnostic Immunol Comt, Nat Comt Clin Lab Standards, 79-; mem, Serology Comt, Arthritis Found, 80- *Mem:* AAAS; Am Asn Immunologists; Am Soc Microbiol; Conf Pub Health Lab Dirs; Int Asn Biol Standardization. *Res:* Immunochemical and immunobiological standardization of diagnostic reagents, vaccines and biologicals; biophysical separations technology; quantitation of human serum proteins. *Mailing Add:* Chief Immunol Prod Br Bur Labs Ctr Dis Control Atlanta GA 30333

REIMER, DENNIS D, b Corn, Okla, May 20, 40; m 61; c 2. MATHEMATICS, COMPUTER SCIENCE. *Educ:* Southwestern Okla State Univ, BSEd, 62; Okla State Univ, MS, 64; NTex State Univ, EdD(math), 69. *Prof Exp:* Instr, 63-65, PROF MATH, SOUTHWESTERN OKLA STATE UNIV, 67- *Mem:* Nat Coun Teachers Math; Math Asn Am. *Mailing Add:* Dept of Math Southwestern Okla State Univ Weatherford OK 73096

REIMER, DIEDRICH, b Altona, Man, May 6, 25; US citizen; m 51; c 3. GENETICS, ANIMAL SCIENCE. *Educ:* Univ Man, BScA, 50; Univ Minn, MS, 55, PhD(genetics, animal sci), 59. *Prof Exp:* Vet agr instr, US Dept Vet Affairs, 50-53; from instr to assoc prof, Univ Minn, 55-64; assoc prof animal sci, 64-74, ANIMAL SCIENTIST, HAWAII INST TROP AGR & HUMAN RESOURCES, UNIV HAWAII, 74- *Mem:* AAAS; Am Genetic Asn; Am Soc Animal Sci. *Res:* Improvement of beef cattle, swine and sheep through breeding methods; swine nutrition and livestock management. *Mailing Add:* Hawaii Agr Exp Sta 461 W Lanikaula St Hilo HI 96720

REIMERS, THOMAS JOHN, b West Point, Nebr. ENDOCRINOLOGY, REPRODUCTIVE PHYSIOLOGY. *Educ:* Univ Nebr, BS, 67; Univ Ill, MS, 69, PhD(animal sci), 74. *Prof Exp:* Res asst animal sci, Univ Ill, 67-69 & 71-74; fel physiol, Colo State Univ, 74-75, res assoc, 75-78; ASST PROF ENDOCRINOL, COL VET MED, CORNELL UNIV, 78- *Mem:* Soc Study Reproduction; Am Soc Animal Sci; AAAS. *Res:* Reproduction physiology in domestic animals; clinical endocrinology in large and small domestic animals. *Mailing Add:* Diagnostic Lab Cornell Univ PO Box 786 Ithaca NY 14850

REIMOLD, ROBERT J, b Greenville, Pa, Nov 15, 41; m 63; c 1. ECOLOGY. *Educ:* Thiel Col, BA, 63; Univ Del, MA, 65, PhD(biol sci), 68. *Prof Exp:* Teaching asst biol, Thiel Col, 62-63; res asst salt marsh ecol, Marine Labs, Univ Del, 63-68; res assoc, Marine Inst, Univ Ga, 68-69, asst prof zool & marine inst, 69-74, ecologist, Marine Resources Ext Ctr, 75-77; DIR, COASTAL RESOURCES DIV, GA DEPT NATURAL RESOURCES, 77- *Concurrent Pos:* Univ Ga Marine Inst res fel, 68-69; vis prof, W I Lab, Fairleigh Dickinson Univ; ed comt, Estuarine Res Fedn, 74-; sci consult, Encycl Britannica Corp, 74- *Mem:* AAAS; Am Soc Limnol & Oceanog; Ecol Soc Am; Estuarine & Brackish Water Scis Soc; Brit Ecol Soc. *Res:* Quantification of similarities and differences of floral productivity and faunal species diversity in global salt marshes using remote sensors and chemical and mathematical techniques. *Mailing Add:* Coastal Resources Div 1200 Glynn Ave Brunswick GA 31520

REIMSCHUSSEL, ERNEST F, b Poischwitz, Ger, July 21, 17; US citizen; m 40; c 5. HORTICULTURE. *Educ:* Brigham Young Univ, BA, 40, MS, 51. *Prof Exp:* Gardner, Brigham Young Univ, 41-42, asst land archit, 42-47, instr, 47-54, asst hort, 47-54, from instr to assoc prof 54-72, chmn dept, 58-66, assoc prof agron & hort, 72-82. *Res:* Ornamental woody plants; landscape architecture; trees. *Mailing Add:* Dept of Agron & Hort Brigham Young Univ Provo UT 84601

REIN, ALAN JAMES, b New York, NY, Nov 1, 48; m 80. PHYSICAL CHEMISTRY, SPECTROSCOPY. *Educ:* Rutgers Univ, BA, 70, MS, 73, PhD(phys chem), 74. *Prof Exp:* Sr res chemist phys & anal chem, Merck Sharp & Dohme Res Labs, 73-77, res fel phys chem, 77-79; adv scientist appl sci, 79-80, SR SCIENTIST & TECH MGR, IBM INSTRUMENTS, INC, 80- *Mem:* Sigma Xi; Soc Appl Spectros; Am Chem Soc. *Res:* Vibrational spectroscopy of inorganic, organometallic and biochemical species; laser raman spectroscopy; Fourier transform infrared spectroscopy. *Mailing Add:* IBM Instruments Inc Po Box 332 Danbury CT 06810

REIN, CHARLES RICHARD, b Gretna, La, Nov 17, 40; m 67; c 3. MECHANICAL ENGINEERING, OCEAN ENGINEERING. *Educ:* Mass Inst Technol, BS, 62; Tulane Univ, MS, 65, PhD(mech eng), 68. *Prof Exp:* Mech engr inertial guid, Instrument Lab, Mass Inst Technol, 62-63; RES MECH ENGR, OCEAN SYSTS, NAVAL COASTAL SYSTS CTR, 68- *Honors & Awards:* Super Performance Award, Naval Coastal Systs Ctr, 76. *Mem:* Am Soc Mech Engrs. *Res:* Towed submerged bodies and ocean sampling. *Mailing Add:* 103 Carolyn Ave Panama City FL 32407

REIN, JAMES EARL, b Chicago, Ill, Mar 24, 23; m 48; c 2. ANALYTICAL CHEMISTRY. *Educ:* Univ Ill, BS, 44, PhD(chem), 49. *Prof Exp:* Res chemist, Los Alamos Sci Lab, 49-53; group leader anal & radiochem methods develop, Atomic Energy Div, Phillips Petrol Co, 53-66; sect leader anal chem develop, Idaho Nuclear Corp, 66-69; MEM STAFF, LOS ALAMOS NAT LAB, UNIV CALIF, 69- *Mem:* Am Chem Soc. *Res:* Analytical methods development; radiochemistry; remote handling techniques for highly radioactive samples; analytical chemistry of the transuranic elements; statistics and quality control. *Mailing Add:* Los Alamos Nat Lab Univ of Calif MS 740 Los Alamos NM 87545

REIN, RICHARD HUGH, metallurgy, see previous edition

REIN, ROBERT, b Ada, Yugoslavia, June 1, 28; m 70. QUANTUM CHEMISTRY, BIOPHYSICS. *Educ:* Hebrew Univ, Israel, MSc, 55, PhD(phys chem), 60. *Prof Exp:* Res asst, Weizmann Inst, 56-60; sr res scientist, Quantum Chem Group, Univ Uppsala, 63-65; asst prof theoret biol, 65-66, assoc res prof theoret biol & biophys, 66-68, RES PROF BIOPHYS SCI, SCH PHARM, STATE UNIV NY BUFFALO, 68-; PRIN CANCER RES SCIENTIST, ROSWELL PARK MEM INST, STATE UNIV NY BUFFALO, 67-, RES PROF & CHMN, BIOMET DEPT, 80- *Mem:* AAAS; Am Chem Soc; Biophys Soc; Int Soc Quantum Biol. *Res:* Molecular orbital theory of organic and biomolecules; quantum theory of intermolecular interactions and their application to molecular recognition in biology; electronic and physicochemical aspects of biopolymers. *Mailing Add:* Roswell Park Mem Inst 666 Elm St Buffalo NY 14263

REIN, ROBERT G, JR, b Detroit, Mich, Jan 16, 40; m 67; c 2. CHEMICAL ENGINEERING, RHEOLOGY. *Educ:* Mass Inst Technol, SB, 61; Univ Okla, PhD(eng), 67. *Prof Exp:* Res assoc, Res Inst, Univ Okla, 67-75; sr engr, Univ Engrs, Norman, Okla, 75-76; SR RES ASSOC, QUATERNARY RES CTR, UNIV WASH, 76- *Concurrent Pos:* Adj asst prof, Univ Okla, 71-75. *Mem:* Am Chem Soc; Am Inst Chem Engrs; Soc Rheol. *Res:* Rheological properties of fluids and solids; properties of frozen soil; behavior of freezing and thawing ground; high pressure phenomena; properties of lubricants at high pressures; fire research. *Mailing Add:* Quaternary Res Ctr Univ of Wash Seattle WA 98195

REINBERG, ALAN R, b New York, NY, Oct 19, 31; m 54; c 4. SOLID STATE PHYSICS. *Educ:* Univ Chicago, BA, 52; Ill Inst Technol, BS, 57, MS, 59, PhD(physics), 61. *Prof Exp:* Res physicist, Res Inst, Ill Inst Technol, 60-63; sr physicist, Lear Siegler Inc, 63-64; mem tech staff physics, Tex Instruments Inc, 64-80; WITH PERKIN ELMER CORP, 80- *Mem:* Am Phys Soc. *Res:* Properties of point defects by magnetic resonance; optical properties; plasma chemistry. *Mailing Add:* Perkin Elmer Corp Norwalk CT 06856

REINBERGS, ERNESTS, b Latvia, Mar 1, 20; nat Can; m 44; c 2. PLANT BREEDING. *Educ:* Univ Toronto, MSA, 54; Univ Man, PhD(cytogenetics, plant breeding), 57. *Prof Exp:* Lectr field husb, 54-57, asst prof, 57-61, assoc prof crop sci, 61-69, PROF CROP SCI, ONT AGR COL, UNIV GUELPH, 69- *Mem:* Can Soc Agron; Genetics Soc Can; Agr Inst Can. *Res:* Barley, oat and triticale breeding; double haploids and breeding methods in barley; irradiation breeding; cytogenetics; disease resistance. *Mailing Add:* Dept Crop Sci Ont Agr Col Univ Guelph Guelph ON N1G 2W1 Can

REINBOLD, GEORGE W, b Williamsport, Pa, Apr 10, 19; m 42; c 3. BACTERIOLOGY, DAIRY INDUSTRY. *Educ:* Pa State Univ, BS, 42; Univ Ill, MS, 47, PhD(dairy mfg), 49. *Prof Exp:* Proj dir bact, Kraft Foods Co, Nat Dairy Prod Corp, 49-53, prod technician dairy indust, 53-58; prod mgr, Tolibia Cheese Mfg Corp, 58-59; exten specialist, Iowa State Univ, 59-60, from assoc prof to prof dairy bact, 60-74; VPRES RES & DEVELOP, LEPRINO FOODS, 74- *Honors & Awards:* Pfizer Cheese Res Award, 70; Dairy Res Inc Award, 77. *Mem:* Am Dairy Sci Asn; Am Soc Microbiol; Int Asn Milk, Food & Environ Sanitarians. *Res:* Dairy microbiology, especially indicator organisms, sanitation and cheese microbiology and manufacture. *Mailing Add:* Leprino Foods Denver CO 80211

REINBOLD, PAUL EARL, b Vincennes, Ind, Oct 21, 43; m 65; c 1. ANALYTICAL CHEMISTRY, INORGANIC CHEMISTRY. *Educ:* Olivet Nazarene Col, AB, 65; Purdue Univ, Lafayette, MS, 68; Tex A&M Univ, PhD(anal chem), 70. *Prof Exp:* Anal chemist, Armour Pharmaceut Co, Ill, 64-65; Robert A Welch-Tex A&M Res Coun fel, Tex A&M Univ, 69-70; from asst prof to assoc prof, 70-76, PROF CHEM & HEAD DEPT, BETHANY NAZARENE COL, 76- *Mem:* Am Chem Soc. *Res:* Optically active inorganic coordination complexes; kinetics and mechanisms of inorganic exchange reactions; kinetics of electrode deposition processes from metal ion complexes; microcomputers in chemical education. *Mailing Add:* Dept of Chem Bethany Nazarene Col Bethany OK 73008

REINCKE, URSULA, b Rostock, Ger, Feb 13, 31. RADIOBIOLOGY, CELL BIOLOGY. *Educ:* Univ Freiburg, MD, 61, PRIVAT DOZENT, 67. *Prof Exp:* Res assoc radiobiol, Dept Radiation Ther, Univ Freiburg, 63-67; res collabr hemat, Brookhaven Nat Lab, Upton, NY, 68-73, asst scientist, 73-75, scientist, 75-78; ASSOC PROF RADIATION THER, HARVARD MED SCH, 79- *Concurrent Pos:* Fel, Damon Runyon Mem Cancer Fund, 68-70; res assoc res prof physiol, Mt Sinai Sch Med, 70-; scholar, Leukemia Soc Am, 72-77. *Mem:* Europ Soc Radiation Biol; Int Soc Hemat; Soc Biol & Med; Cell Kinetics Soc. *Res:* Cytocidal effects of isotopes; limit of division capacity of mammalian cells. *Mailing Add:* Dept of Radiation Ther 50 Binney St Boston MA 02115

REINDERS, VICTOR A, b Mallard, Iowa, Dec 27, 06; m 42. CHEMISTRY. *Educ:* Carroll Col, Wis, BA, 29; Univ Wis, MA, 30, PhD(inorg chem), 35. *Prof Exp:* Instr, 30-33, from instr to prof, 35-72, EMER PROF CHEM, EXTEN DIV, UNIV WIS-MILWAUKEE, 72- *Res:* Chemistry of rhenium in its lower valence state. *Mailing Add:* 416 McCall St Waukesha WI 53186

REINECCIUS, GARY (AUBREY), b Webster, Wis, Jan 12, 44; m 64; c 2. FOOD SCIENCE. *Educ:* Univ Minn, BS, 64, MS, 67; Pa State Univ, PhD(food sci), 70. *Prof Exp:* Assoc prof, 70-80, PROF FOOD SCI, UNIV MINN, ST PAUL, 80- *Mem:* Am Chem Soc; Inst Food Technol. *Res:* Chemistry of food flavor, including biogenesis and chemical composition of flavor. *Mailing Add:* Dept of Food Sci Univ of Minn St Paul MN 55101

REINECKE, JOHN PHILIP, b Washington, DC, May 15, 35; m 65; c 2. ENTOMOLOGY, PHYSIOLOGY. *Educ:* Washburn Univ, BA, 65; NDak State Univ, MS, 68, PhD, 79. *Prof Exp:* Tissue culturist & res photographer, Northwestern Univ, 56-61; entomologist, 65-74, RES ENTOMOLOGIST, METAB & RADIATION RES LAB, USDA, 74- *Mem:* AAAS; Entom Soc Am; Am Soc Zoologists. *Res:* Invertebrate tissue culture, electron microscopy; insect physiology and internal morphology; neuroendocrinology; insect behavior; insect nutrition. *Mailing Add:* Metab & Radiation Res Lab PO Box 5674 State Univ Sta Fargo ND 58105

REINECKE, MANFRED GORDON, b Milwaukee, Wis, May 19, 35; m 57; c 3. ORGANIC CHEMISTRY. *Educ:* Univ Wis, BS, 56; Univ Calif, Berkeley, PhD(org chem), 60. *Prof Exp:* Asst org chem, Univ Calif, Berkeley, 56-57, instr, 59-60; asst prof, Univ Calif, Riverside, 60-64; from asst prof to assoc prof, 64-74, PROF ORG CHEM, TEX CHRISTIAN UNIV, 74- *Concurrent Pos:* NSF fac fel, Univ Tubingen, 71-72; Nat Acad Sci exchange scientist, Acad Wissenschaften, Ger Dem Repub, 79. *Mem:* AAAS; Am Chem Soc; The Chem Soc. *Res:* Chemistry of behavior; natural products; heterocyclic sulfur and nitrogen compounds; mass spectroscopy. *Mailing Add:* Dept Chem Tex Christian Univ Ft Worth TX 76129

REINECKE, ROBERT DALE, b Ft Scott, Kans, Mar 26, 29; m 52; c 1. OPHTHALMOLOGY. *Educ:* Ill Col Optom, OD, 51; Univ Kans, AB, 55, MD, 59. *Prof Exp:* From asst instr to asst prof, Harvard Univ, 64-69, sci dir, Vision Info Ctr, 67-70; PROF OPHTHAL & CHMN DEPT, ALBANY MED COL, 70- *Concurrent Pos:* Teaching fel ophthal, Harvard Med Sch, 63-64; grant, Albany Med Col, 72-; instr eye anat, Simmons Col, 62-68; chief instr Infirmary, 63-67, dir ocular motility clin, 67-69, asst instr, Infirmary, 63-69; asst instr, Mass Gen Hosp, 63-69; mem bd dirs, Conrad Berens Int Eye Film Libr, 70-; mem visual sci study sect, NIH, 71-75; chmn med adv comt, Comn Blind & Visually Handicapped, 71-76; mem comt vision, Nat Acad Sci-Nat Res Coun, 77-80; chmn panel ophthal devices, Food & Drug Admin, 74-78. *Mem:* AAAS; AMA; Am Acad Ophthal & Otolaryngol; Asn Res Vision & Ophthal (secy-treas, 71-76). *Res:* Eye movement; visual acuity; stereopsis. *Mailing Add:* Dept of Ophthal Albany Med Col Albany NY 12208

REINECKE, THOMAS LEONARD, b Park Falls, Wis, Sept 14, 45. ELECTRONIC PROPERTIES OF SOLIDS, PHASE TRANSITIONS. *Educ:* Ripon Col, Wis, BA, 68; Oxford Univ, PhD(physics), 72. *Prof Exp:* Res assoc & lectr, Dept Physics, Brown Univ, Providence, RI, 72-74; res assoc, 74-76, res physicist, 76-80, HEAD, THEORY SECT SEMICONDUCTORS BR, NAVAL RES LAB, 80- *Concurrent Pos:* Guest scientist, Electron Micros Inst, Fritz Harbor Inst, Max Planck Soc, 79. *Mem:* Am Phys Soc. *Res:* Solid state theory including interacting electronic systems, phase trasitions, surfaces and interfaces; various systems including semiconductors, and magnetic and ferroelectric materials. *Mailing Add:* Code 6877 Naval Res Lab Washington DC 20375

REINECKE, WILLIAM GERALD, b Indianapolis, Ind, July 21, 35; m 59; c 2. AERODYNAMICS. *Educ:* Purdue Univ, BS, 57; Princeton Univ, MA & PhD(aeronaut eng), 61. *Prof Exp:* Sr staff scientist, Res & Develop Div, 64-65, group leader exp aerodyn, Ballistic Range Group, Res & Technol Labs, 65-66, sect chief, Exp Fluid Physics Sect, 66-71, sr consult scientist, Technol Directorate, 71-77, mgr ballistics lab, Avco Systs Div, 77-78, DIR BALLISTICS & ORDNANCE TECHNOL, AVCO CORP, 78- *Concurrent Pos:* Mem, Aeroballistic Range Asn. *Mem:* Assoc fel Am Inst Aeronaut & Astronaut; Am Defence Preparedness Asn. *Res:* Aerodynamics, especially high speed flows, high speed erosion and internal and terminal ballistics. *Mailing Add:* Avco Systs Div 201 Lowell St Wilmington MA 01915

REINEKE, CHARLES EVERETT, b Edgerton, Mo, Aug 1, 38; m 61; c 2. ORGANIC CHEMISTRY. *Educ:* William Jewell Col, BA, 60; Southern Ill Univ, MA, 62; Kans State Univ, PhD(org chem), 66. *Prof Exp:* Res chemist, Dow Chem Co, 66-67, Halogens Res Lab, 67-69, proj leader, 69-71, sr res chemist, 71-72, RES SPECIALIST, DOW CHEM CO, MI, 72- *Mem:* Am Chem Soc; Sigma Xi. *Res:* Fire retardancy; chemistry of halogen compounds; carbonium ion and halonium ion chemistry; organic synthesis; small ring chemistry. *Mailing Add:* Cent Res Plastics Lab Bldg 1702 Dow Chem Co Midland MI 48640

REINEMUND, JOHN ADAM, b Muscatine, Iowa, Jan 14, 19; m 43. GEOLOGY. *Educ:* Augustana Col, BA, 40. *Hon Degrees:* DHuL, Augustana Col, 67. *Prof Exp:* Geologist, Strategic Mineral Invests, 42-44, geologist, Oceanog Res, Off Sci Res & Develop, 44-45, geologist, Mineral Fuel Invests, 46-49, geologist, Coal Surv, Econ Coop Admin, Korea, 49-50, asst chief, Eastern Field Invest Sect, Fuels Br, 51-53, regional supvr, Midcontinent Region, 53-56, geol adv, AID, Geol Surv, Pakistan, 56-64, chief, Br Foreign Geol, DC, 64-69, CHIEF, OFF INT GEOL, US GEOL SURV, 69- *Concurrent Pos:* Bd mem, Int Geol Corr Prog, 73-79. *Mem:* Geol Soc Am; Am Asn Petrol Geol; Am Geophys Union; Int Union Geol Sci (treas, 79-). *Res:* Structural geology; sedimentary petrology; geology of fuels; origin of mineral and fuel resources in relation to sedimentary and tectonic processes. *Mailing Add:* Off Int Geol US Geol Surv Nat Ctr Reston VA 22092

REINER, ALBEY M, b Brooklyn, NY, Aug 11, 41; m 65; c 2. MICROBIOLOGY, GENETICS. *Educ:* Princeton Univ, BS, 62; Oxford Univ, cert math statist, 63; Univ Wis-Madison, MS, 64; Harvard Univ, PhD(molecular biol), 69. *Prof Exp:* Rothschild Found fel, Hebrew Univ, Israel, 68-69; NIH fel, Univ Calif, Berkeley, 69-70; asst prof, 71-77, ASSOC PROF MICROBIOL, UNIV MASS, AMHERST, 77- *Res:* Microbial genetics. *Mailing Add:* Dept Microbiol Univ Mass Amherst MA 01003

REINER, CHARLES BRAILOVE, b Ellenville, NY, Dec 3, 20; m 51; c 3. PATHOLOGY, PEDIATRICS. *Educ:* Temple Univ, AB, 42, MD, 45, MSc, 53; Am Bd Pediat, dipl, 54; Am Bd Path, dipl, 66. *Prof Exp:* Fel histochem, Univ Chicago, 51-52, physician-in-chg, Pediat Outpatient Clin, Univ Hosp, Temple Univ, 52-55; asst prof path, Col Med, State Univ NY Downstate Med Ctr, 56-59; asst prof, 59-69, ASSOC PROF PATH & PEDIAT, COL MED, OHIO STATE UNIV, 69-; CHIEF DIV ANAT PATH, DEPT LAB MED, CHILDREN'S HOSP, COLUMBUS, 72- *Concurrent Pos:* Assoc pathologist, Children's Hosp, Columbus, 59-72; pathologist, Inst Perinatal Studies, 60-64. *Mem:* AMA. *Res:* Pediatric pathology; perinatal problems, especially hyaline membrane syndrome; heparin in human tissues; laboratory aspects of blood coagulation; sudden infant death syndrome. *Mailing Add:* Children's Hosp Columbus OH 43205

REINER, IRMA MOSES, b Newburgh, NY, Mar 3, 22; m 48; c 2. MATHEMATICS. *Educ:* Cornell Univ, AB, 42, AM, 44, PhD(algebra, geom, physics), 46. *Prof Exp:* Instr math, Temple Univ, 46-48, Univ Ill, Urbana, 48-49 & Danville Community Col, Ill, 49-50; instr 56-57, ASST PROF MATH, UNIV ILL, URBANA, 57-62, 63-66, 67- *Mem:* Am Math Soc; Math Asn Am. *Res:* Theory of numbers. *Mailing Add:* Dept Math Univ Ill Urbana IL 61801

REINER, IRVING, b Brooklyn, NY, Feb 8, 24; m 48; c 2. MATHEMATICS. *Educ:* Brooklyn Col, BA, 44; Cornell Univ, MA, 45, PhD(math), 47. *Prof Exp:* Asst math, Cornell Univ, 44-47; mem, Inst Advan Study, 47-48; from asst prof to assoc prof, 48-58, PROF MATH, UNIV ILL, URBANA, 58- *Concurrent Pos:* Mem, Inst Advan Study, 54-56; mem staff numerical anal res, Univ Calif, Los Angeles, 56 & 57; Guggenheim fel, Univ Paris, 62-63; NSF contract, Univ London, 66; ed, Proceedings Am Math Soc, 66-70, Proceedings Symp Rep Theory Finite Groups, 70 & Ill J Math, 78-; mem, Ctr Adv Study, Univ Ill, 75-76; assoc ed, Contemp Mat, Am Math Soc, 80-. *Honors & Awards:* Distinguished Alumnus Award, Brooklyn Col, 63. *Mem:* Am Math Soc; Math Asn Am. *Res:* Group representations; algebraic K-theory; matrix theory; algebraic number theory. *Mailing Add:* Dept of Math Univ of Ill Urbana IL 61801

REINER, JOHN MAXIMILIAN, b Boston, Mass, Apr 19, 12; m 34, 63; c 1. MATHEMATICAL BIOLOGY. *Educ:* Univ Chicago, BSc, 38, MSc, 39; Univ Minn, PhD(physiol), 46. *Prof Exp:* Asst math biophys, Univ Chicago, 36-39; instr physics, City Col New York, 40-41; instr, Univ Minn, 43, res assoc physiol, 43-44, instr, 44-46; Nat Res Coun fel, Wash Univ, 46, Am Cancer Soc fel, 47; res assoc, Med Sch, Tufts Col, 48-49, asst prof, 49-50; asst prof biochem, Col Physicians & Surgeons, Columbia Univ & sr enzyme chemist, Inst Cancer Res, 50-54; res dir, Simon Baruch Res Labs, Saratoga Spa, 54-57; biochemist, Radioisotope Labs, Vet Admin Hosp, Albany, NY, 57-58; assoc prof microbiol, Sch Med, Emory Univ, 58-68; PROF BIOCHEM & RES PROF PATH, ALBANY MED COL, 68- *Concurrent Pos:* Assoc, Albany Med Co, 54-57. *Mem:* Soc Develop Biol; Soc Math Biol; Soc Indust & Appl Math; Am Math Soc; Marine Biol Lab. *Res:* Molecular biology of growth, differentiation and senescence; enzyme kinetics; transport processes; population dynamics; neural models of behavior; philosophy of science. *Mailing Add:* Dept Biochem Albany Med Col Albany NY 12208

REINER, LEOPOLD, b Leipzig, Ger, Jan 22, 11; nat US; m 46. MEDICINE. *Educ:* Univ Vienna, MD, 36; Am Bd Path, dipl, 50. *Prof Exp:* Intern, Rothschild Hosp, Vienna, Austria, 36-38; from resident path to asst pathologist, W Jersey Hosp, Camden, NJ, 41-46; instr path, Harvard Med Sch, 50-53, clin assoc, 53-56; vis assoc prof, 56-72, prof, 72-79, EMER PROF PATH, ALBERT EINSTEIN COL MED, 79-; PATHOLOGIST & DIR LABS, BRONX-LEBANON HOSP CTR, 56- *Concurrent Pos:* From resident path to actg pathologist, Beth Israel Hosp, Boston, 46-56. *Mem:* Histochem Soc; Am Asn Path; NY Acad Med; Int Acad Path; Am Soc Clin Path. *Res:* Pathology, especially cardiovascular pathology; coronary arterial and mesenteric arterial circulation; cardiac hypertrophy. *Mailing Add:* Bronx-Lebanon Hosp Ctr 1276 Fulton Ave Bronx NY 10456

REINER-DEUTSCH, WILLIAM, microbiology, deceased

REINERS, WILLIAM A, b Chicago, Ill, June 10, 37; m 62; c 2. ECOLOGY. *Educ:* Knox Col, BA, 59; Rutgers Univ, MS, 62, PhD(bot), 64. *Prof Exp:* Instr bot, Univ Minn, 64-65, asst prof, 65-67; asst prof, 67-70, assoc prof, 70-76, PROF BIOL, DARTMOUTH COL, 76- *Honors & Awards:* Henry J Oasting lectr, Duke Univ. *Mem:* AAAS; Ecol Soc Am (treas, 81-); Brit Ecol Soc. *Res:* Energy flow and nutrient cycling in forest ecosystems; structure and function of successional ecosystems; biogeochemistry. *Mailing Add:* Dept of Biol Sci Dartmouth Col Hanover NH 03755

REINERT, JAMES ARNOLD, b Enid, Okla, Jan 26, 44; m 63; c 3. ENTOMOLOGY. *Educ:* Okla State Univ, BS, 66; Clemson Univ, MS, 68, PhD(entom), 70. *Prof Exp:* Res asst entom, Clemson Univ, 66-70; entomologist, State Bd Agr, Univ Md, College Park, 70; from asst prof to assoc prof, 70-79, PROF ENTOM, AGR RES CTR, UNIV FLA, 79- *Mem:* Entom Soc Am; Int Turfgrass Soc. *Res:* Urban entomology in turfgrass and ornamental plant insects and mites; host resistance; biology, behavior and control by chemical or biological agents of insect and mite pests. *Mailing Add:* Agr Res Ctr Univ of Fla Inst Food & Agr Sci 3205 SW 70th Ave Ft Lauderdale FL 33314

REINERT, JOHN FRANCIS, entomology, see previous edition

REINERT, RICHARD ALLYN, b Elkhorn, Wis, June 3, 35; m 59; c 3. PLANT PATHOLOGY, HORTICULTURE. *Educ:* Univ Wis, BS, 58, PhD(plant path, hort), 62. *Prof Exp:* Asst prof plant path, Univ Ky, 62-67; res plant pathologist, R A Taft Sanit Eng Ctr, USDA-USPHS, Ohio, 67-69, Nat Environ Res Ctr, Plant Sci Res Div, USDA-Environ Protection Agency, 69-73; adj assoc prof, Univ NC, 69-73, assoc prof, Sci & Admin-Agr Res, 73-77, PROF PLANT PATH, SOUTHERN REGION, AGRICULTURAL RES SERV, USDA & NC STATE UNIV, 77- *Mem:* AAAS; Am Phytopath Soc; Am Soc Hort Sci. *Res:* Plant virology and tissue culture; physiology of growth and development; effects of air pollutants on cultivated plants and diseases of horticulture and ornamental crops. *Mailing Add:* Dept of Plant Path NC State Univ Raleigh NC 27607

REINERTSEN, DAVID LOUIS, b Chicago, Ill, Mar 9, 27; m 58; c 2. GEOLOGY. *Educ:* Augustana Col, Ill, AB, 50; Univ Mo, AM, 53. *Prof Exp:* Asst geol, Univ Mo, 51-55; field geologist, Mo Geol Surv & Water Resources, 53; from asst geologist coal sect to assoc geologist educ exten sect, 55-69, GEOLOGIST & ACTG HEAD, EDUC EXTEN SECT, ILL STATE GEOL SURV, 69- *Mem:* Geol Soc Am; Nat Asn Geol Teachers. *Res:* Educational extension services; stratigraphy; geomorphology. *Mailing Add:* Ill State Geol Surv 100 Natural Resources Bldg Urbana IL 61801

REINES, FREDERICK, b Paterson, NJ, Mar 16, 18; m 40; c 2. ELEMENTARY PARTICLE PHYSICS, COSMIC RAY PHYSICS. *Educ:* Stevens Inst Technol, ME, 39, MS, 41; NY Univ, PhD(theoret physics), 44. *Hon Degrees:* DSc, Univ Witwatersrand, 66. *Prof Exp:* Mem staff, Los Alamos Sci Lab, 44-46, group leader, 46-59, dir bomb test exp, 49-51; prof physics & head dept, Case Inst Technol, 59-66; dean phys sci, 66-74, PROF PHYSICS, UNIV CALIF, IRVINE, 66- *Concurrent Pos:* Lectr, Exten Div, Univ Calif, 49; consult, Armed Forces spec weapons proj, 49-53 & Rand Corp, 50; centennial lectr, Univ Md, 56; fels, Guggenheim Found, 58-59 & Sloan Found, 59-63; mem, NASA Electrophys Adv Comt, 63-64 & Fulbright Physics Screening Comt, 64-66; consult, Inst Defense Anal, 65-; trustee, Argonne Univ Assocs, 66. *Honors & Awards:* J Robert Oppenheimer Mem Prize, 81. *Mem:* Nat Acad Sci; fel Am Phys Soc; fel Am Acad Arts & Sci; Am Soc Physics Teachers; AAAS. *Res:* Nuclear fission; physics of nuclear weapons and effects; scintillation detectors; free neutrino; cosmic rays. *Mailing Add:* Dept of Physics Univ of Calif Irvine CA 92717

REINESS, (CECIL) GARY, b Pittsburgh, Pa, Aug 20, 45; m 68; c 1. NEUROBIOLOGY. *Educ:* Johns Hopkins Univ, BA, 67; Columbia Univ, MPhil, 74, PhD(biol), 75. *Prof Exp:* Fel, Dept Neurobiol, Harvard Med Sch, 75-76; scholar, Dept Physiol, Univ Calif, San Francisco, 76-81; ASST PROF BIOL, DEPT BIOL, POMONA COL, 81- *Mem:* Soc Neursci; AAAS; Am Chem Soc. *Res:* Development of neuromuscular junction, particularly regarding the regulation and properties of acetylcholine receptors and acetylcholinesterase; development of sympathetic nervous system and its regulation by nerve growth factor. *Mailing Add:* Dept Biol Pomona Col Claremont CA 91711

REINFURT, DONALD WILLIAM, b Wilkes-Barre, Pa, Aug 30, 38; m 65; c 2. APPLIED STATISTICS. *Educ:* State Univ NY Albany, BS, 60; State Univ NY Buffalo, MA, 63; NC State Univ, PhD(statist), 70. *Prof Exp:* staff assoc, 68-80, ASSOC DIR, ANAL STUDIES, HWY SAFETY RES CTR, UNIV NC, 68- *Concurrent Pos:* Adj assoc prof, Biostatist Dept, Univ NC, 78- *Mem:* Sigma Xi; Am Asn Automotive Med; Am Statist Asn. *Res:* Application of statistical methods, particularly categorical data analysis, to traffic safety problems. *Mailing Add:* 403 Highview Dr Chapel Hill NC 27514

REINGOLD, EDWARD MARTIN, b Chicago, Ill, Nov 12, 45; m 68; c 3. ANALYSIS ALGORITHMS, DATA STRUCTURES. *Educ:* Ill Inst Technol, BS, 67; Cornell Univ, MS, 69, PhD(comput sci), 71. *Prof Exp:* From asst prof to assoc prof, 70-81, PROF COMPUT SCI, UNIV ILL, URBANA-CHAMPAIGN, 81- *Mem:* Asn Comput Mach; Soc Indust & Appl Math; Am Math Soc; Math Asn Am. *Res:* Design and analylsis of algorithms and data structures for non-numerical problems such as sorting, searching, graph and tree manipulation and exhaustive search. *Mailing Add:* Dept of Comput Sci Univ Ill 1304 W Springfield Ave Urbana IL 61801

REINGOLD, HAIM, b Lodz, Poland, Mar 16, 10; nat US; m 66; c 3. MATHEMATICS. *Educ:* Univ Cincinnati, AB, 33, AM, 34, PhD(math), 38. *Prof Exp:* Instr math, Univ Cincinnati, 35-36; prof & head dept, Our Lady Cincinnati Col, 38-42; supvr instr, Signal Corps Training Schs, 42-43, from asst prof to assoc prof, 43-56, PROF MATH, ILL INST TECHNOL, 56-, DIR EVE DIV, 46-, CHMN DEPT MATH, 54- *Concurrent Pos:* Actg chmn dept math, Ill Inst Technol, 51-54; prof math, Ind Univ Northwest, 75- *Mem:* AAAS; Am Math Soc; Am Soc Eng Educ; Math Asn Am. *Res:* Invariants of a system of linear homogeneous differential equations of the second order; generalized determinants of Vandermonde; basic mathematics for engineers and scientists. *Mailing Add:* 1329 E 55th St Chicago IL 60615

REINGOLD, IRVING, b Newark, NJ, Nov 13, 21; m 48; c 2. ELECTRONIC ENGINEERING. *Educ:* Newark Col Eng, BS, 42. *Prof Exp:* Elec mfg engr, Westinghouse Elec Co, NJ, 43-45; proj engr, Air Force Watson Labs, NJ, 45-51; proj engr, Chief Switching Devices Sect, Microwave Tubes Br, Electronics Technol & Devices Lab, NJ, 51-60, dep br chief, 60-66, br chief, Pickup, Display & Storage Devices Br, 66-75, dir, Beam Plasma & Display Div, 75-81, DEP DIR, ELECTRONICS TECHNOL & DEVICES LAB, US ARMY ELECTRONICS RES & DEVELOP COMMAND, 81- *Concurrent Pos:* Mem adv group on electron devices, US Dept Defense. *Honors & Awards:* Tech Leadership Award, US Army Electronic Res & Develop Lab, 62; Soc Info Francis Rice Darne Mem Award, 78. *Mem:* Fel Inst Elec & Electronics Engrs; fel Soc Info Display. *Res:* Research and development in the fields of microwave tubes and devices, pulsers and display devices; microelectronics; integrated circuits; solid state microwave devices. *Mailing Add:* 409 Runyon Ave Deal Park Deal NJ 07723

REINHARD, EDWARD HUMPHREY, b St Louis, Mo, Dec 9, 13; m 40, 76; c 4. MEDICINE. *Educ:* Washington Univ, AB, 35, MD, 39. *Prof Exp:* From instr to prof, 43-80, EMER PROF MED, SCH MED, WASHINGTON UNIV, 81- *Mem:* Am Soc Hemat; fel Am Col Physicians; Asn Am Physicians; Int Soc Hemat. *Res:* Hematology; therapy of malignant diseases; treatment of leukemia; anemia associated with malignant diseases. *Mailing Add:* Suite 4102 Queeny Tower Barnes Hosp Plaza St Louis MO 63110

REINHARD, JOHN FREDERICK, b New York, NY, Aug 26, 08; m 50; c 3. PHARMACOLOGY. *Educ:* NY Univ, BS, 33, MS, 34, PhD(pharmacol), 41. *Prof Exp:* Instr bact, Col Med, NY Univ, 35-38, instr pharmacol, Col Med & Col Dent, 38-42; pharmacologist, Wellcome Res Labs, Burroughs Wellcome & Co, Inc, NY, 42-47; chief pharmacologist, Pyridium Corp, 47-49; dir pharmacol res, Nepera Chem Co, Inc, 49-52; dir pharmacol res, Warner-Chilcott Labs Div, Warner-Hudnut, Inc, 52-55; dir biol res, Baxter Labs, Inc, Ill, 55-56; head pharmacol labs, Wallace & Tiernan, Inc, 56-63; chmn dept pharmacol, Col Pharm & Grad Sch Pharmaceut Sci, Northeastern Univ, 63-71, prof pharmacol, Col Pharm & Allied Health Prof, 63-75; prof, 75-78, EMER PROF PHARMACOL, MASS COL PHARM, 78- *Mem:* AAAS; Am Soc Pharmacol & Exp Therapeut; Soc Exp Biol & Med; fel NY Acad Med; NY Acad Sci. *Res:* Pharmacology of the central nervous system; psychopharmacologic, analgesic and sedative-hypnotic drugs; antihistaminics; antispasmodics. *Mailing Add:* Dept Pharmacol Mass Col Pharm Boston MA 02115

REINHARD, KARL R, b Coplay, Pa, Jan 13, 16; m 45; c 3. VETERINARY MEDICINE. *Educ:* Muhlenberg Col, BS, 36; Pa State Univ, MS, 40; Cornell Univ, DVM, 49, PhD(microbiol), 50. *Prof Exp:* Asst animal path res, Pa State Univ, 39-41; prof bact, Univ Ky, 50-51; chief leptospirosis res, Rocky Mountain Lab, USPHS, 51-54, chief infectious dis prog, Arctic Health Res Ctr, Alaska, 54-60, exec secy, Gen Med Study Sect, Div Res Grants, NIH, 60-63, asst to chief, 63-66, chief eval staff, Bur Dis Prev & Environ Control, 66-67, chief prog eval, Div Indian Health, 67-68; prof microbiol & dean col vet med, Okla State Univ, 68-69; chief health status surveillance, Health Prog Systs Ctr, Indian Health Serv, USPHS, 69-79; ASSOC, DEPT FAMILY & COMMUNITY MED, UNIV ARIZ, 70- *Concurrent Pos:* Consult, WHO, 73, 75, 76, 77, 80 & 81. *Mem:* Am Soc Circumpolar Health; Am Pub Health Asn; US-Mex Border Pub Health Asn; Arctic Inst NAm. *Res:* Microbiology; experimental pathogenesis of infectious diseases; semiotics of health documentation; taxonomy of health problems; ecology of disease; research administration; health programs planning and evaluation; lay reporting of disease; group health statistics from automated health records systems. *Mailing Add:* 4911 Hidden Valley Rd Tucson AZ 85715

REINHARDT, CHARLES FRANCIS, b Spring Grove, Ind, Nov 25, 33; m 56; c 4. OCCUPATIONAL MEDICINE, TOXICOLOGY. *Educ:* Wabash Col, BA, 55; Ind Univ, MD, 59; Ohio State Univ, MSc, 64; Am Bd Prev Med, dipl & cert occup med, 67; Am Bd Toxicol, dipl & cert gen toxicol, 80. *Prof Exp:* Plant physician, Chambers Works, 64-66, physiologist, 66-69, chief physiol sect, 69-70, res mgr environ sci, 70-71, asst dir, 71-74, assoc dir, 74-76, DIR, HASKELL LAB FOR TOXICOL & INDUST MED, E I DU PONT DE NEMOURS & CO, INC, 76- *Mem:* AMA; Am Indust Hyg Asn; Am Occup Med Asn; Am Acad Occup Med; Soc Toxicol. *Mailing Add:* Haskell Lab E I du Pont de Nemours & Co Inc Newark DE 19711

REINHARDT, DONALD JOSEPH, b New York, NY, Dec 6, 38. MICROBIOLOGY, MYCOLOGY. *Educ:* Manhattan Col, BS, 60; Columbia Univ, MA, 62, PhD(microbiol), 66; Am Bd Microbiol, dipl. *Prof Exp:* Teaching asst mycol, Columbia Univ, 61-66; res fel med microbiol, Ctr Dis Control, USPHS, Ga, 66-69; ASSOC PROF MICROBIOL, GA STATE UNIV, 69- *Mem:* Bot Soc Am; Mycol Soc Am; Am Soc Microbiol. *Res:* Cell development and physiology of Amebae, fungi, bacteria and algae; clinical medical microbiology; chemical and medical microbiology; epidemiology and infection control in hospitals. *Mailing Add:* Dept of Biol Ga State Univ Atlanta GA 30303

REINHARDT, HOWARD EARL, b Nezperce, Idaho, Mar 16, 27; m 56; c 3. MATHEMATICAL STATISTICS. *Educ:* Univ Idaho, BS, 49; State Col Wash, MA, 51; Univ Mich, PhD(math), 59. *Prof Exp:* Instr math, State Col Wash, 52-53; from asst prof to assoc prof, 57-66, chmn dept, 66-73, PROF MATH, UNIV MONT, 66- *Mem:* Inst Math Statist; Math Asn Am. *Res:* Statistical inference, particularly parametric and non-parametric hypothesis testing techniques. *Mailing Add:* Dept of Math Univ of Mont Missoula MT 59812

REINHARDT, JUERGEN, b Eutingen-Baden, WGer, Oct 27, 46; US citizen; m 68; c 2. GEOLOGY, SEDIMENTOLOGY. *Educ:* Brown Univ, AB, 68; Johns Hopkins Univ, PhD(geol), 73. *Prof Exp:* Geologist, Md Geol Surv, 73-75; GEOLOGIST, US GEOL SURV, 75- *Concurrent Pos:* Lectr sedimentology, Johns Hopkins Univ, 73-74. *Mem:* Geol Soc Am; Int Soc Sedimentologists; Soc Econ Sedimentologists & Mineralogists; Am Asn Petrol Geologists. *Res:* Comparative sedimentology of sedimentary basins; carbonate-clastic rock transitions; Cenozoic tectonics; cretaceous stratigraphy; penecontemporaneous deformation structures. *Mailing Add:* US Geol Surv 928 Nat Ctr Reston VA 22092

REINHARDT, RICHARD ALAN, b Berkeley, Calif, Oct 18, 22. INORGANIC CHEMISTRY. *Educ:* Univ Calif, BS, 43, PhD(chem), 47. *Prof Exp:* Asst chem, Univ Calif, 43-44; jr scientist, Univ Chicago, 44-45; jr scientist, Los Alamos Sci Lab, 45-46; asst chem, Univ Calif, 46; instr chem, Cornell Univ, 47-51; res chemist, Wright Air Develop Ctr, Wright-Patterson AFB, 51-53; from asst prof to assoc prof, 54-67, PROF CHEM, NAVAL POSTGRAD SCH, 67- *Mem:* Am Chem Soc. *Res:* Kinetics of inorganic redox reactions; transition-metal complexes; thermodynamics of internal explosions. *Mailing Add:* Dept of Physics & Chem Naval Postgrad Sch Monterey CA 93940

REINHARDT, ROBERT MILTON, b New Orleans, La; m 51; c 2. ORGANIC CHEMISTRY. *Educ:* Tulane Univ, BS, 47. *Prof Exp:* Chemist, Chem Properties Sect, Cotton Fiber Div, 47-54, chemist, Chem Finishing Invests, Cotton Chem Lab, 54-61, chemist, Wash-Wear Invests, Cotton Finishes Lab, 61-76, SR RES CHEMIST, COTTON TEXTILE CHEM LAB, SOUTHERN REGIONAL RES CTR, USDA, 76- *Mem:* Am Chem Soc; Sigma Xi; Am Asn Textile Chemists & Colorists. *Res:* Chemical modification and finishing of cotton and cellulose derivatives; chemistry of crosslinking agents for cellulose; properties of chemically modified cottons; free radical modification of cellulose. *Mailing Add:* Southern Regional Res Ctr USDA PO Box 19687 New Orleans LA 70179

REINHARDT, WALTER ALBERT, b Barstow, Calif, Oct 17, 31; m 55; c 2. APPLIED PHYSICS, AERONAUTICS. *Educ:* San Jose State Col, BA, 53; Stanford Univ, MS, 61, PhD(aeronaut, astronaut), 69. *Prof Exp:* Engr, Ames Res Lab, Nat Adv Comt Aeronaut, 56-58, mathematician, 58-60, res scientist appl physics, 60-69, res scientist aeronaut, 69-80, ASST CHIEF, APPL COMPUT AERODYNAMICS BR, AMES RES CTR, NASA, 80- *Mem:* Assoc fel Am Inst Aeronaut & Astronaut; Am Phys Soc; Combustion Inst. *Res:* Fluid flow simulations with advanced computers of chemically reacting gas mixtures about hypersonic bodies during planetary entry; mixtures of dense fluids; cryogenic fluids in weightless environment; turbulent fluids; air about transonic and supersonic aircraft. *Mailing Add:* Appl Comput Aerodynamics Br 202A-1 Ames Res Ctr NASA Moffett Field CA 94035

REINHARDT, WILLIAM NELSON, b Bartlesville, Okla, May 12, 39; m 59; c 2. MATHEMATICS. *Educ:* Col Wooster, BA, 61; Univ Calif, Berkeley, PhD(math), 67. *Prof Exp:* Asst prof, 67-73, ASSOC PROF MATH, UNIV COLO, BOULDER, 73- *Concurrent Pos:* NSF grants, 67- *Mem:* Am Math Soc; Math Asn Am. *Res:* Set theory and foundations of mathematics; logic; model theory. *Mailing Add:* Dept of Math Univ of Colo Boulder CO 80309

REINHARDT, WILLIAM OSCAR, b Colorado Springs, Colo, Apr 18, 12; m 40; c 2. MEDICAL ADMINISTRATION. *Educ:* Univ Calif, AB, 34, MD, 38. *Prof Exp:* Intern surg, Univ Hosp & mem fac anat, Sch Med, 38-56, prof anat, 52-82, chmn dept, 56-63, dean, 63-66, assoc dean, 69-82, actg dean, 77-78, EMER PROF ANAT, SCH MED, UNIV CALIF, SAN FRANCISCO, 81- *Concurrent Pos:* Nat Heart Inst res fel, 54-55; Gregg traveling fel med educ, 61; vis prof, Bristol Univ, 54-55, Univ Indonesia, 55-56, Kyoto Univ, 61 & Nat Defense Med Ctr, Taiwan, 66-67. *Mem:* AAAS; AMA; Soc Exp Biol & Med; Am Physiol Soc; Am Asn Anatomists. *Res:* Anatomy and physiology of lymphatic system. *Mailing Add:* Univ of Calif Sch of Med San Francisco CA 94143

REINHARDT, WILLIAM PARKER, b San Francisco, Calif, May 22, 42. CHEMICAL PHYSICS. *Educ:* Univ Calif, Berkeley, BS, 64; Harvard Univ, AM, 66, PhD(chem physics), 68. *Prof Exp:* From instr to assoc prof chem, Harvard Univ, 67-74; chmn dept, 77-80, PROF CHEM, UNIV COLO, BOULDER, 74- . *Concurrent Pos:* Vis fel, Joint Inst Lab Astrophys, 72, fel, 74-; Sloan Found fel, 72, Dreyfus Found teacher scholar, 72-77; Guggenheim Mem fel, 78; fac fel, Coun Res & Creative Work, Univ Colo, 78. *Mem:* Am Chem Soc; AAAS; fel Am Phys Soc. *Res:* Atomic and molecular structure; scattering processes; many-body theory as applied to chemical problems; classicial and semiclassical theories of highly excited electronic and vibrational states; atoms in intense fields. *Mailing Add:* Dept Chem Univ Colo Box 215 Boulder CO 80309

REINHART, BRUCE LLOYD, b Wernersville, Pa, Oct 20, 30; m 55; c 3. GEOMETRY, TOPOLOGY. *Educ:* Lehigh Univ, BA, 52; Princeton Univ, MA, 54, PhD(math), 56. *Prof Exp:* Instr math, Princeton Univ, 55-56 & Univ Chicago, 56-58; res assoc, Univ Mich, 58-59; from asst prof to assoc prof, 59-65, PROF MATH, UNIV MD, COLLEGE PARK, 65- *Concurrent Pos:* Mathematician, Res Inst Advan Study, 59-64; NATO fel, Univ Strasbourg, France, 61-62; Fulbright sr res fel, Univ Pisa, Italy, 65-66. *Mem:* AAAS; Am Math Soc; Math Asn Am; Math Soc France. *Res:* Foliated manifolds, especially metric foliations and vector fields; topology of surfaces. *Mailing Add:* Dept Math Univ Md College Park MD 20742

REINHART, GREGORY DUNCAN, b Chicago, Ill, Nov 1, 51; m 76. BIOCHEMISTRY. *Educ:* Univ Ill, BS, 73; Univ Wis, Madison, PhD(biochem), 79. *Prof Exp:* Res fel, 79-80, res assoc, 80-81, ASSOC CONSULT BIOCHEM, MAYO CLIN & FOUND, 81-; INSTR BIOCHEM, MAYO MED SCH, 81- *Mem:* Biophys Soc; NY Acad Sci; Sigma Xi; AAAS. *Res:* Regulation· of enzyme activity; biophysical properties of enzymes; regulation of carbohydrate metabolism. *Mailing Add:* Dept Cell Biol Biochem Sect Mayo Found Rochester MN 55905

REINHART, JOHN BELVIN, b Merrill, Wis, Dec 22, 17; m 49; c 6. PSYCHIATRY, PEDIATRICS. *Educ:* Duke Univ, AB, 39; Wake Forest Col, MD, 43. *Prof Exp:* Instr pediat, Bowman Gray Sch Med, Wake Forest Col, 50-52; dir dept psychiat, Children's Hosp, 56-74; from asst prof to assoc prof, 56-69, PROF PEDIAT & CHILD PSYCHIAT, SCH MED, UNIV PITTSBURGH, 69-; DIR DIV BEHAV SCI, CHILDREN'S HOSP, PITTSBURGH, 74- *Mem:* Am Psychiat Asn; Am Acad Pediat; Am Acad Child Psychiat; Am Pediat Soc. *Res:* Child abuse and neglect; consultation-liaison to psychiatry; failure to thrive; psychosomatic disease in children; brief pediatric-child psychiatry liaison. *Mailing Add:* Sch Med Univ Pittsburgh 4200 Fifth Ave Pittsburgh PA 15260

REINHART, RICHARD D, b Austin, Minn, Nov 12, 29; m 80; c 4. CHEMICAL ENGINEERING. *Educ:* Univ Minn, BS & BChE, 53. *Prof Exp:* Jr develop engr, Union Carbide Nuclear Co, 53-54, assoc engr, 56-57, sect leader prog planning, 57-59; res engr, 59-63, staff asst prog rev, 63-65, group leader food res, 65-66, dept head spec develop, 66-70, dept head non-cereal breakfast prod develop, 70-80, DEPT HEAD NEW VENTURES DEVELOP, GEN MILLS, INC, 80- *Mem:* Inst Food Technol. *Res:* Gaseous diffusion barrier theory and mechanics; cascade theory and economics; engineering economics; food research and process development; research planning and project evaluation; management; new product development. *Mailing Add:* Gen Mills Inc 9000 Plymouth Ave N Minneapolis MN 55427

REINHART, ROY HERBERT, b Cincinnati, Ohio, Sept 11, 19; m 41; c 3. GEOLOGY, VERTEBRATE PALEONTOLOGY. *Educ:* Miami Univ, AB, 41; Univ Chicago, MS, 49; Univ Calif, Berkeley, PhD(paleont), 52. *Prof Exp:* Asst geol, WTex State Univ, 50-51; from asst prof to assoc prof, 51-62, actg chmn dept, 64-65, PROF GEOL, MIAMI UNIV, 62- *Concurrent Pos:* Fel, Miami Univ, 59; res assoc, Univ Fla, 61-66. *Mem:* Soc Vert Paleont. *Res:* Fossil marine mammals, especially orders Sirenia and Desmostylia of world; correlation of Cenozoic stratigraphy of world. *Mailing Add:* Dept of Geol Miami Univ Oxford OH 45056

REINHART, STANLEY E, JR, b Cincinnati, Ohio, Apr 25, 28; m 52; c 5. ELECTRICAL ENGINEERING. *Educ:* US Mil Acad, BS, 50; Ga Inst Technol, MS, 64, PhD(electromagnetic theory), 66. *Prof Exp:* US Army, 46-, from instr to assoc prof elec eng, 53-77, PROF ELEC ENG & ACTG HEAD DEPT, US MIL ACAD, 77- *Mem:* Inst Elec & Electronics Engrs; Am Soc Eng Educ. *Res:* Electromagnetic theory; near fields of antennas; numerical calculation of fields; undergraduate electrical engineering curricula. *Mailing Add:* Dept of Elec Eng US Mil Acad West Point NY 10996

REINHEIMER, JOHN DAVID, b Springfield, Ohio, Dec 23, 20; m 44; c 5. ORGANIC CHEMISTRY. *Educ:* Kenyon Col, AB, 42; Johns Hopkins Univ, AM, 44, PhD(chem), 48. *Prof Exp:* From instr to assoc prof, 48-58, PROF CHEM, COL WOOSTER, 58- *Concurrent Pos:* Von Humboldt fel, 63. *Mem:* Am Chem Soc. *Res:* Qualitative and physical organic chemistry; kinetics of organic reactions; kinetics of the aromatic nucleophilic substitution reaction; nuclear magnetic resonance studies. *Mailing Add:* Dept of Chem Col of Wooster Wooster OH 44691

REINHEIMER, JULIAN, b Philadelphia, Pa, Oct 19, 25; m 56; c 1. PHYSICS. *Educ:* Pa State Col, BS, 49; Univ Minn, MS, 50; NY Univ, PhD(physics), 68. *Prof Exp:* Physicist, Minn Mining & Mfg Co, 50-52; proj engr, Fisher Sci Co, 52-53; res physicist, Inst Coop Res, Univ Pa, 53-58; from staff scientist to sect head, Repub Aviation Corp, 58-64; sect mgr, 64-68, assoc dept head, 68-72, assoc prog dir, 72-76, SYSTS DIR, AEROSPACE CORP, EL SEGUNDO, 76- *Mem:* Am Phys Soc; Optical Soc Am; Am Asn Physics Teachers. *Res:* Optics; astrophysics; mathematical physics; solid state physics, radiation effects. *Mailing Add:* 4112 Quinlin Dr Palos Verdes Peninsula CA 90274

REINHOLD, VERNON NYE, b Beverly, Mass, May 13, 31; m 53; c 5. ANALYTICAL BIOCHEMISTRY. *Educ:* Univ NH, BS, 59, MS, 61; Univ Vt, PhD(biochem), 65. *Prof Exp:* AEC fel protein chem, Brookhaven Nat Lab, NY, 65-67; Helen Hay Whitney fel, Mass Inst Technol & Harvard Med Sch, 67-71, jr res assoc chem, Mass Inst Technol, 71-76; LECTR DEPT BIOL CHEM, HARVARD MED SCH, 76- *Mem:* AAAS; Soc Complex Carbohydrates; Am Chem Soc. *Res:* Gas chromatography-mass spectrometry; computer assisted analysis of biochemical components; glycoprotein structure and carbohydrate sequence analysis via gas liquid chromatography-mass spectrometry; protein and organic chemistry. *Mailing Add:* Dept of Biol Chem LHRRB 45 Shattuck St Boston MA 02115

REINIG, WILLIAM CHARLES, b New York, NY, June 5, 24; m 49; c 2. HEALTH PHYSICS. *Educ:* Polytech Inst Brooklyn, BME, 45; Am Bd Health Physics, dipl; Am Bd Indust Hyg, dipl. *Prof Exp:* Med engr, Hanford Works, Gen Elec Co, 46-48; assoc health physicist, Brookhaven Nat Lab, 48-51; area supvr health physics, 51-61, chief tech supvr, 61-65, sr res supvr environ effects, 65-76, res mgr environ anal & planning, 76-78, SUPT HEALTH PROTECTION DEPT, SAVANNAH RIVER PLANT, E I DU PONT DE NEMOURS & CO, INC, 78- *Concurrent Pos:* Chmn, Am Bd Health Physics, 74-; chmn comt tritium measurement, Nat Coun Radiation Protection & Measurements. *Mem:* Health Physics Soc (secy, 64-66, pres, 80-81). *Res:* Environmental radiation and radioactivity; radiological health. *Mailing Add:* Savannah River Plant E I du Pont de Nemours & Co Inc Aiken SC 29808

REININGER, EDWARD JOSEPH, b Chicago, Ill, Dec 30, 29; c 2. PHYSIOLOGY. *Educ:* Univ Ill, BS, 50, MS, 52; Ohio State Univ, PhD(physiol), 57. *Prof Exp:* From asst to instr physiol, Ohio State Univ, 52-58; lectr, McGill Univ, 58-60, asst prof, 60-71; assoc prof, Sch Med, Ind Univ, Terre Haute, 71-74; prof physiol, Sch Med, Southern Ill Univ, Springfield, 74-76; prof & chmn dept physiol & pharm, 77-78, PROF PHYSIOL, SCH MED, UNIV CENT CARIBE, 78- *Concurrent Pos:* Grants, Que Heart Found, 59-65 & Med Res Coun Can, 66-70; summer res prog, Minority Hypertension, Univ Fla, 81. *Mem:* Am Physiol Soc; Am Thoracic Soc; Can Physiol Soc. *Res:* Cardiovascular effects of cardiac pacing and feeding; sighing in man and spontaneous gasps and post-gasp apnea in dogs; mechanism that prevents atelectasis; measurement of cardiac output; minicomputer programming for teaching and research. *Mailing Add:* Dept of Physiol & Pharm Box 935 Cayey PR 00633

REINISCH, RONALD FABIAN, b New York, NY, Mar 21, 31; m 62; c 2. CHEMISTRY. *Educ:* Univ Mich, BSChem, 53; Harvard Univ, MA, 55; Tulane Univ, PhD(org chem), 59. *Prof Exp:* Sr chemist, US Vitamin Corp, 59; res assoc, Plastics Lab, Sch Appl Sci, Princeton Univ, 59-63; res scientist, Ames Res Ctr, NASA, 63-65, group leader photochem, 65-77; sr scientist, Solar Energy Res Inst, 77-78; consult, 78-79; TECH DIR, SOLARADO INC, 79- *Concurrent Pos:* Consult, Calif State Energy Comn, 75-77; vis scholar, Dept Aeronaut & Astronaut, Stanford Univ, 75-77. *Honors & Awards:* Cert Recognition, NASA, 73. *Mem:* Int Solar Energy Soc; AAAS; fel Am Inst Chem; Am Chem Soc; NY Acad Sci. *Res:* Photochemistry of macromolecules; materials science; synthesis of photostable polymers; air pollution; chemical kinetics; computer modeling of atmospheres; application of photochemistry to materials and environmental problems; design of solar collectors. *Mailing Add:* 5662 S Hanover Way Englewood CO 80111

REINKE, DAVID ALBERT, b Manitowoc, Wis, May 15, 33; m 56; c 2. PHARMACOLOGY, PHYSIOLOGY. *Educ:* Univ Wis, BS, 55; Univ Mich, MBA, 60, PhD(pharmacol), 64. *Prof Exp:* Res chemist, Dow Corning Corp, 55-58; ASSOC PROF PHARMACOL & TOXICOL, MICH STATE UNIV, 64- *Mem:* Am Soc Pharmacol & Exp Therapeut. *Res:* Prostaglandins and other autacoids. *Mailing Add:* Dept of Pharmacol Mich State Univ East Lansing MI 48824

REINKE, WILLIAM ANDREW, b Cleveland, Ohio, Aug 10, 28; m 60; c 4. BIOSTATISTICS. *Educ:* Kenyon Col, BA, 49; Univ Pa, MBA, 50; Case Western Reserve Univ, PhD(statist), 61. *Prof Exp:* Staff asst to controller, Warner & Swasey Co, 50-55; syst analyst, US Steel Corp, 55-56; statistician, Union Carbide Corp, 56-59; instr statist, Case Western Reserve Univ, 59-61; sr res mathematician, Corning Glass Works, 61-63; asst prof biostatist, Univ Md, 63-64; asst dean, 74-76, assoc dean, 76-77, PROF INT HEALTH, SCH HYG, JOHNS HOPKINS UNIV, 64- *Concurrent Pos:* Assoc ed, Opers Res, 71-74; treas, Univ Assoc for Int Health Inc, 73-; mem comt tech consult, Nat Ctr Health Statist, 73; mem, Nursing Res & Educ Adv Comt, 74-78. *Mem:* Opers Res Soc Am; Inst Mgt Sci; fel Am Pub Health Asn; Am Statist Asn. *Res:* Health planning methodology; health practice research in relation to health services delivery. *Mailing Add:* Dept of Int Health Johns Hopkins Univ Sch Hyg 615 N Wolfe St Baltimore MD 21205

REINKING, NORMAN HERBERT, b Beverly, Kans, Dec 2, 23; m 45; c 2. ORGANIC POLYMER CHEMISTRY. *Educ:* Kans State Univ, BS, 46; Rutgers Univ, MS, 54. *Prof Exp:* Res chemist, Res Dept, 46-56, group leader, 56-57, res & develop dept, 57-63, asst dir res & develop, Chem & Plastics Div, 63-78, ASSOC DIR RES & DEVELOP, COATINGS MAT DIV, UNION CARBIDE CORP, 78- *Mem:* AAAS; Am Chem Soc; Sigma Xi. *Res:* Polyolefins; phenoxy polymers; epoxy resins; polyesters; phenolics; plastics product development and fabrication processes; coatings and adhesives. *Mailing Add:* PO Box 670 Bldg 95 Union Carbide Corp Bound Brook NJ 08805

REINKING, ROBERT LOUIS, b Colorado Springs, Colo, May 25, 41; m 63; c 2. GEOLOGY. *Educ:* Colo Col, BS, 63; Univ Ill, Urbana, MS, 65, PhD(geol), 67. *Prof Exp:* Geol field asst, US Geol Surv, 63; asst prof geol, Tex Tech Univ, 67-70, dir geol field camp, 70; asst prof, 70-74, ASSOC PROF GEOL, HOPE COL, 74-, RES CORP GRANT, 71- *Concurrent Pos:* Univ grant, Tex Tech Univ, 68-69. *Mem:* AAAS; Geol Soc Am; Geochem Soc; Mineral Soc Am. *Res:* Mineral deposits; mineralogical and geochemical effects of hydrothermal alteration; geochemical prospecting. *Mailing Add:* Dept of Geol Hope Col Holland MI 49423

REINMUTH, OSCAR MCNAUGHTON, b Lincoln, Nebr, Oct 23, 27; m 51; c 3. NEUROLOGY, INTERNAL MEDICINE. *Educ:* Univ Tex, AB, 48; Duke Univ, MD, 52. *Prof Exp:* Intern, Duke Hosp, 52-53; asst resident, New Haven Med Ctr, 53-55; asst resident to chief resident, Boston City Hosp, 55-57; assoc prof neurol, Sch Med, Univ Miami, 58-65, prof, 65-77; PROF & CHMN DEPT NEUROL, SCH MED, UNIV PITTSBURGH, 77- *Concurrent Pos:* NIH trainee, Med Sch, Yale Univ, 54-55; lectr neurol, Sargent Col, Boston Univ, 55-56; teaching fel, Harvard Med Sch, 56-57; NIH spec trainee, Nat Hosp, Queen's Square, London, 57-58; consult, Nat Inst Neurol Dis & Stroke, 68-; consult adv comt, Sect Head Injury & Stroke, NIH, 73-; mem coun stroke, Am Heart Asn. *Mem:* Am Acad Neurol (vpres, 71-75); Am Neurol Asn (vpres, 78-79); fel Am Col Physicians; fel Am Heart Asn; Soc Neurosci. *Res:* Cerebral circulation and metabolism in humans and experimental animals; cerebral vascular disease. *Mailing Add:* Univ Pittsburgh Sch Med Dept Neurol 322 Scaife Hall Pittsburgh PA 15261

REINMUTH, WILLIAM HENRY, b Baltimore, Md, Sept 1, 32; m 64; c 1. ANALYTICAL CHEMISTRY. *Educ:* Univ Chicago, AB, 52, MS, 54; Mass Inst Technol, PhD(chem), 57. *Prof Exp:* From instr to assoc prof, 57-64, PROF CHEM, COLUMBIA UNIV, 64- *Concurrent Pos:* Sloan Found fel, 62-66; Guggenheim fel, 66-67. *Mem:* Am Chem Soc; Electrochem Soc. *Res:* Electroanalytical chemistry. *Mailing Add:* Dept of Chem Columbia Univ New York NY 10027

REINSBOROUGH, VINCENT CONRAD, b Buctouche, NB, May 14, 35; m 77; c 2. PHYSICAL CHEMISTRY. *Educ:* Univ Toronto, BA, 58, MA, 59, STB, 64; Univ Tasmania, PhD(chem), 69. *Prof Exp:* Teacher high sch, Ont, 59-61; lectr chem, Univ St Michael's Col, 61-65; Nat Res Coun Can fel, Univ Toronto, 69-70; asst prof, 70-75, ASSOC PROF CHEM, MT ALLISON UNIV, 75- *Mem:* Chem Inst Can; Royal Soc Chem; Electrochem Soc. *Res:* Molten salts; solubilization, kinetics and catalysis in micellar solutions. *Mailing Add:* Dept of Chem Mt Allison Univ Sackville NB E0A 3L0 Can

REINSCHMIDT, KENNETH F(RANK), b Cincinnati, Ohio, Mar 26, 38; m 67. CIVIL ENGINEERING, ENERGY ECONOMICS. *Educ:* Mass Inst Technol, SB, 60, SM, 62, PhD(civil eng), 65. *Prof Exp:* From asst prof to assoc prof civil eng, Mass Inst Technol, 65-73, sr res assoc, 73-75; consult engr, 75-80, VPRES & SR CONSULT ENGR, STONE & WEBSTER ENG CORP, 80- *Mem:* AAAS; Am Soc Civil Engrs; Opers Res Soc Am; Inst Mgt Sci. *Res:* Historical development of building science; economic analysis of energy systems; computer modeling of energy-related industries; applications of mathematical programming to the optimization of engineering and construction systems; computer-aided design; large-scale organizational design; computer graphics. *Mailing Add:* 20 Tahattawan Rd Littleton MA 01460

REINSTEIN, JEROME ALAN, physical pharmacy, cosmetic chemistry, see previous edition

REINSTEIN, LAWRENCE ELLIOT, b New York, NY, Apr 18, 45; m 68; c 3. MEDICAL PHYSICS. *Educ:* Brooklyn Col, BS, 66; Yale Univ, MS, 68; Boston Univ, PhD(physics), 75. *Prof Exp:* Fel med physics, Mem Sloan-Kettering Cancer Inst, 75-76; PHYSICIST RADIATION ONCOL, RI HOSP, PROVIDENCE, 76- *Concurrent Pos:* Asst prof bio-med, Brown Univ, 76- *Mem:* Am Phys Soc; Am Asn Physicists Med. *Res:* Electron beam radiation as used in treatment of cancer; 3- dimensional treatment planning. *Mailing Add:* Dept of Radiation Oncol RI Hosp Providence RI 02902

REINTJES, JOHN FRANCIS, JR, b Boston, Mass, Dec 7, 45; m 71; c 1. LASERS, QUANTUM OPTICS. *Educ:* Mass Inst Technol, BS, 66; Harvard Univ, PhD(appl physics), 72. *Prof Exp:* Appointee nonlinear optics res, IBM Watson Res Ctr, 71-73; res physicist, Naval Res Lab, 73-80; MEM FAC, MASS INST TECHNOL, 80- *Mem:* Am Phys Soc; Inst Elec & Electronics Engrs. *Res:* Investigation of techniques for extending lasers to x-ray wavelengths; study of uses of nonlinear optics for control and shaping of ultra short laser pulses. *Mailing Add:* Mass Inst Technol 77 Mass Ave Cambridge MA 02139

REINTJES, JOHN WILLIAM, b Minneapolis, Minn, Nov 1, 20; m 50; c 4. ZOOLOGY, CHEMISTRY. *Educ:* St John's Univ, Minn, 47; Univ Hawaii, MS, 52. *Prof Exp:* Fishery biologist, US Fish & Wildlife Serv, Hawaii, 49-51, Delaware, 52-55 & Maine, 55-56, FISHERY BIOLOGIST, BEAUFORD LAB, NAT MARINE FISHERIES SERV, 56- *Mem:* Am Fisheries Soc; Am Inst Fishery Res Biologists. *Res:* Fishery biology; distribution and abundance of marine clupeid fishes; ichthyology, and biological oceanography. *Mailing Add:* Nat Marine Fisheries Serv Beauford Lab Beaufort NC 28516

REINTJES, MARTEN, b Meeden, Netherlands, Mar 13, 32; US citizen; m 57; c 2. ORGANIC CHEMISTRY. *Educ:* Univ Calif, Riverside, BA, 59, PhD(chem), 66. *Prof Exp:* Analyst, Chemische Fabriek Flebo, Netherlands, 49-52; asst chemist, Orange County Sanit Dist, Calif, 55-57; res chemist, Sunkist Growers, Inc, 59-62 & Arapahoe Chem Div, Syntex Corp, Colo, 65-68; from res chemist to res group leader, 68-73, sect leader, 73-77, SECT SUPVR, OLYMPIC RES DIV, ITT RAYONIER, INC, 78- *Mem:* Soc Petrol Engrs; Am Inst Mining, Metall & Petrol Engrs; Am Forestry Asn; Am Chem Soc. *Res:* Organic synthesis and natural products; process development; organo-boron, boron-hydride and carborane chemistry; silvichemicals. *Mailing Add:* Olympic Res Div ITT Rayonier Inc Shelton WA 98584

REIS, ARTHUR HENRY, JR, b Chicago, Ill, Nov 6, 46; m 70; c 2. INORGANIC CHEMISTRY. *Educ:* Cornell Col, Iowa, BA, 68; Harvard Univ, MA, 69, PhD(chem), 72. *Prof Exp:* Teaching fel org chem, Harvard Univ, 72; space systs analyst satellite tracking, US Air Force, Ent AFB, Colo, 72-73; space oper officer satellite tracking, US Air Force, Thule AFB, Greenland, 73-74; post-doctoral appointee, Argonne Nat Lab, Argonne, Ill, 74-75, res assoc inorg chem, 75-76, asst chemist, 76-79; ASSOC PROF CHEM, BRANDEIS UNIV, 79- *Concurrent Pos:* Consult, Picker X-Ray Corp, 71-72; assoc proj dir, Undergrad Res Particip Proj, NSF-GTE Corp, 81. *Mem:* Am Chem Soc; Am Crystallog Asn; Coun Chem Res. *Res:* Synthesis and structural characterization by x-ray and neutron diffraction of one-dimensional transition metal conductors, pulsed neutron diffraction and exafs studies of metal complexes in zeolites. *Mailing Add:* Dept Chem Brandeis Univ Waltham MA 02254

REIS, DONALD J, b New York, NY, Sept 9, 31. NEUROLOGY, NEUROPHYSIOLOGY. *Educ:* Cornell Univ, AB, 53, MD, 56. *Prof Exp:* Res anatomist, Univ Calif, Los Angeles, 54-55; intern med, New York Hosp, 56-57; resident neurol, Boston City Hosp, 57-59; res assoc neurophysiol, NIMH, 60-62; from asst prof to assoc prof neurol, 63-71, PROF NEUROL, MED COL, CORNELL UNIV, 71-, DIR LAB NEUROBIOL. *Concurrent Pos:* Teaching fel, Harvard Med Sch, 57-59; United Cerebral Palsy Found fel brain res, Nat Hosp, London, Eng, 59-60; Nat Inst Neurol Dis & Blindness spec fel, Nobel Neurophysiol Inst, Karolinska Inst, Sweden, 62-63; Nat Inst Neurol Dis & Blindness career develop res award, 66-; USPHS career develop award; mem, Karolinska Inst, Sweden, 59-60; vis scientist, Chiba Univ Med Sch, Japan, 63; vis scientist, Lab Clin Sci, NIMH, 70. *Mem:* Am Acad Neurol; Am Physiol Soc; Am Soc Pharmacol & Exp Therapeut; Am Soc Clin Invest; Am Soc Neurochem. *Res:* Central neural autonomic regulation; central nervous regulation of cardiovascular function; neural mechanisms of emotive behavior; central neurotransmitters; brain monoamines and behavior. *Mailing Add:* Lab of Neurobiol Dept of Neurol Cornell Univ Med Col New York NY 10021

REIS, IRVIN L, b Lincoln, Nebr, Oct 5, 26; m 51; c 2. MECHANICAL & INDUSTRIAL ENGINEERING. *Educ:* Univ Nebr, BSME, 49, MSME, 50; Univ Ill, PhD(indust eng), 57. *Prof Exp:* Job analyst, Univ Nebr, 49, supvr insts, 50-53; lectr indust eng, Univ Ill, 53-57; res engr, Lincoln Steel Corp, 57; assoc prof mech eng, Univ Nebr, 57-59; prof indust eng & head dept, Kans State Univ, 59-62; prof, Univ Ark, 62-64; vis prof mech eng, Univ Tex, 64-66; prof mech eng & head dept, Mont State Univ, 66-70; prof mech eng, Lamar Univ, 70-80, dept head, 77-80; MEM FAC, INDUST ENG DEPT, MONT STATE UNIV, 80- *Concurrent Pos:* Indust training consult, 50-62; consult, City of Lincoln, Nebr, 58-59 & Bayer & McElrath, Mich, 64-; prof indust eng & head dept, Mont State Univ, 66-67; partner, Mgt Insts Unlimited, 75- *Mem:* Am Soc Eng Educ; Am Inst Indust Engrs; Am Soc Mech Engrs. *Res:* Probabilistic models; conveyer theory; economics. *Mailing Add:* Indust Eng Dept Mont State Univ Bozeman MT 59715

REIS, PAUL G(EORGE), b St Cloud, Minn, May 3, 25; m 53; c 6. CHEMICAL ENGINEERING. *Educ:* Northwestern Univ, BS, 45, MS, 49; Univ Wis, PhD(chem eng), 54. *Prof Exp:* Chem engr, process develop, E I du Pont de Nemours & Co, 45 & 47-48; asst, Univ Wis, 49-52; CHEM ENGR PROCESS DEVELOP, PIGMENTS DEPT, E I DU PONT DE NEMOURS & CO, INC, 54- *Mem:* Am Inst Chem Engrs; Am Chem Soc. *Res:* Chemical equilibrium and kinetics. *Mailing Add:* 4 Toby Ct Newport DE 19804

REIS, WALTER JOSEPH, b Würzburg, Ger, Aug 5, 18; nat US; m 43; c 3. PSYCHIATRY, CLINICAL PSYCHOLOGY. *Educ:* Univ Gonzaga, BPh, 47; City Col New York, BS, 47; Western Reserve Univ, PhD(psychol), 51; Emory Univ, MD, 55; Am Bd Psychiat & Neurol, dipl, 62; Pittsburgh Psychanal Inst, cert, 67. *Prof Exp:* Intern, USPHS Hosp, Norfolk, Va, 55-56; fel, Western Psychiat Inst, Pa, 56-59; clin instr psychiat, Univ Pittsburgh, 59-63, clin asst prof, 63-69; PSYCHIATRIST & PSYCHOANALYST, PSYCHIAT ASSOCS, 69-, CLIN ASSOC PROF PSYCHIAT, SCH MED, UNIV PITTSBURGH, 74- *Concurrent Pos:* Mem fac, Pittsburgh Psychoanal Inst, 67-, pvt practr psychiat, 59-; consult, Dixmont State Hosp, Sewickley, Pa, 68-73; training analyst, Pittsburgh Psychoanal Inst, Pa, 72- *Mem:* Fel Am Psychiat Asn; Am Psychol Asn; Soc Pe rsonality Assessment. *Res:* Psychotherapy; psychoanalysis. *Mailing Add:* 230 N Craig St Pittsburgh PA 15213

REISA, JAMES JOSEPH, JR, b Oak Park, Ill, Dec 13, 41; div. ENVIRONMENTAL BIOLOGY, SCIENCE POLICY. *Educ:* Loyola Univ, Chicago, BS, 66; Northwestern Univ, Evanston, Ill, MS, 68, PhD(biol sci), 71. *Prof Exp:* US Environ Protection Agency res fel, Dept Biol Sci, Northwestern Univ, 71-72; staff biologist, Argonne Nat Lab, Argonne, Ill, 72-74; staff mem, Coun Environ Qual, Exec Off President, Washington, DC, 74-75, coordr environ monitoring prog, 75-77, sr staff mem, 77-78; DIR ENVIRON RES DIV, OFF TOXIC SUBSTANCES, US ENVIRON PROTECTION AGENCY, 78- ENVIRON QUAL, EXEC OFF PRESIDENT, WASHINGTON, DC, 75- *Concurrent Pos:* Vis lectr biol, Mundelein Col, Chicago, 70-71, vis asst prof biol, 71-72; chmn Fed Interagency Task Force Air Qual Indicators, 75-77; chmn, President's Task Force Environ Data & Monitoring, 77-78; chmn, Toxics Res Comt, US Environ Protection Agency, 79-81. *Mem:* Ecol Soc Am; AAAS; Am Soc Limnol & Oceanog; Am Inst Biol Sci; Sigma Xi. *Res:* Assessment of environmental fate and effects of toxic chemicals; science policy and regulatory decision making. *Mailing Add:* Off Explor Res RD-675 US Environ Protection Agency Washington DC 20460

REISBERG, BORIS ELLIOTT, b New York, NY, Dec 12, 35. MEDICINE, INFECTIOUS DISEASES. *Educ:* Brown Univ, AB, 57; State Univ NY, MD, 61; Am Bd Internal Med, dipl, 68, cert infectious dis, 74. *Prof Exp:* Instr internal med, New Eng Ctr Hosp, Tufts Univ, 64-66; NIH fel, 66-67; assoc, 68-69, ASST PROF INTERNAL MED, NORTHWESTERN UNIV, CHICAGO, 69- *Mailing Add:* Northwestern Mem Hosp 250 E Superior St Chicago IL 60611

REISBERG, JOSEPH, b New York, NY, May 10, 21; m 53. CHEMISTRY. *Educ:* City Col New York, BS, 43. *Prof Exp:* Res chemist, SAM Lab, Columbia Univ, 43-44, Los Alamos Sci Lab, Univ Calif, 44-47 & Colgate-Palmolive-Peet Corp, NJ, 47-48; res chemist, explor & prod res lab, 49-66, res assoc, 66-70, Shell Lab, Rijswijk, Holland, 70-71, sr res assoc, 71-74, SR STAFF RES CHEMIST, SHELL DEVELOP CO, TEX, 74- *Mem:* AAAS; Am Chem Soc; Am Inst Mining, Metall & Petrol Engrs; NY Acad Sci. *Res:* Surface and colloid chemistry; unconventional methods for petroleum recovery. *Mailing Add:* Shell Develop Co PO Box 481 Houston TX 77001

REISBIG, RONALD LUTHER, b Kalamazoo, Mich, Jan 31, 38; m 58; c 2. MECHANICAL ENGINEERING, THERMODYNAMICS. *Educ:* Mich State Univ, BSME, 60, PhD(mech eng), 66; Univ Wash, MSME, 63. *Prof Exp:* Res engr, Boeing Co, 60-63; asst heat transfer, Mich State Univ, 63-64; asst prof eng, Western Mich Univ, 65-66; asst prof mech eng, Wayne State Univ, 66-69; assoc prof, Univ Mo-Rolla, 69-75; prof & dean, Victoria Campus, Univ Houston, 75-77; DEAN ENG, WESTERN NEW ENG COL, 77- *Concurrent Pos:* Consult, Nat Waterlift Co, Mich, 65-66; Westinghouse scholar, Mich State Univ, 59-60. *Mem:* Am Soc Mech Engrs; Am Soc Eng Educ; Instrument Soc Am; Sigma Xi. *Res:* Thermal science; interferometric holography; solar energy. *Mailing Add:* 1215 Wilbraham Rd Springfield MA 01119

REISCH, BRUCE IRVING, b New York, NY, July 23, 55. PLANT BREEDING, GENETICS & TISSUE CULTURE. *Educ:* Cornell Univ, BS, 76; Univ Wis, Madison, MS, 78, PhD(plant breeding), 80. *Prof Exp:* ASST PROF VITICULT, NY STATE AGR EXP STA, CORNELL UNIV, 80- *Mem:* Int Asn Plant Tissue Culture; Am Soc Enol; Crop Sci Soc Am; Am Soc Hort Sci; Sigma Xi. *Res:* Application of new technology to plant breeding, including gene transformation, tissue culture, grape genetics and grape breeding. *Mailing Add:* Cornell Univ NY State Agr Exp Sta Geneva NY 14456

REISCH, KENNETH WILLIAM, b Southington, Conn, Oct 7, 29; m 52; c 4. HORTICULTURE. *Educ:* Univ Conn, BSc, 52; Ohio State Univ, MSc, 53, PhD(hort), 56. *Prof Exp:* From instr to assoc prof, 53-66, PROF HORT, OHIO STATE UNIV, 66-, ASSOC DEAN COL AGR & HOME ECON, 72- *Mem:* Am Soc Hort Sci; Sigma Xi. *Res:* Physiological and taxonomical studies with woody ornamental plants, especially growth, reproduction and nutrition. *Mailing Add:* Agr Admin Ohio State Univ 2120 Fyffe Rd Columbus OH 43210

REISCHMAN, PLACIDUS GEORGE, b South Bend, Wash, Sept 15, 26. ZOOLOGY. *Educ:* St Martin's Col, BA, 50; Cath Univ Am, MSc, 57, PhD, 60. *Prof Exp:* Instr, 55-56, PROF BIOL, ST MARTIN'S COL, 59- *Mem:* AAAS. *Res:* Marine invertebrate zoology; parasitic Crustacea; Rhizocephala. *Mailing Add:* Dept of Biol St Martin's Col Olympia WA 98503

REISEL, ROBERT BENEDICT, b Chicago, Ill, Apr 27, 25; m 61; c 3. MATHEMATICS. *Educ:* DePaul Univ, BS, 49; Univ Chicago, MS, 51; Northwestern Univ, PhD(math), 54. *Prof Exp:* From instr to asst prof, 54-63, ASSOC PROF MATH, LOYOLA UNIV CHICAGO, 63- *Mem:* Am Math Soc; Math Asn Am. *Res:* Associative algebras. *Mailing Add:* 5052 N Nordica Ave Chicago IL 60656

REISENAUER, ANDREW E, b Colton, Wash, July 16, 25; m 51; c 10. HYDROLOGY. *Educ:* Wash State Univ, BS, 51. *Prof Exp:* Sanitarian, Gen Elec Co, 51-55, scientist, 55-64; RES HYDROLOGIST, PAC NORTHWEST LABS, BATTELLE MEM INST, 65- *Honors & Awards:* Robert E Horton Award, 63. *Mem:* Am Geophys Union. *Res:* Radioactive waste disposal; saturated and partially saturated flow of groundwater; mathematical and computer solution to groundwater flow problems; transport of wastes in groundwater; data base management; computer technology. *Mailing Add:* Sigma Xi Bldg 3000 Area Battelle Pac Northwest Labs Richland WA 99352

REISENAUER, HUBERT MICHAEL, b Portland, Ore, Mar 11, 20; m 45; c 2. SOIL SCIENCE. *Educ:* Univ Idaho, BS, 41; NC State Univ, PhD(agr), 49. *Prof Exp:* Prof soils, Wash State Univ, 49-62; PROF SOIL SCIENCE & SOIL SCIENTIST, UNIV CALIF, DAVIS, 62- *Mem:* AAAS; Am Soc Agron; Soil Sci Soc Am; Int Soil Sci Soc. *Res:* Plant nutrition; micronutrients; soil fertility and soil-plant interrelationships. *Mailing Add:* Land Air & Water Resources Univ of Calif Davis CA 95616

REISER, CASTLE O, b Berthoud, Colo, Dec 21, 12; m 35; c 2. CHEMICAL & NUCLEAR ENGINEERING. *Educ:* Colo Agr & Mech Col, BS, 34; Colo Sch Mines, PE, 38; Univ Wis, PhD(chem eng), 45. *Prof Exp:* Res engr, Pilot Plant, Standard Oil Develop Co, 38-41; instr & res assoc chem eng, Univ Wis, 41-45; asst prof, Univ Colo, 45-46; assoc prof, Okla Agr & Mech Col, 46-47; prof & head dept, Univ Idaho, 47-53; pilot plant supvr, Chem Res Ctr, Food Mach & Chem Corp, 53-55; sr res engr, Atomics Int Div, N Am Aviation, Inc, 55-56; prof chem eng & chmn dept, Univ Seattle, 56-58; prof eng & chmn dept, 58-78, EMER PROF, DEPT CHEM ENG, ARIZ STATE UNIV, 80- *Concurrent Pos:* Consult, Water Planning for Israel, 67-68. *Mem:* Am Chem Soc; fel Am Inst Chem Engrs; Am Soc Eng Educ; Am Nuclear Soc. *Res:* Industrial wastes; nitrogen fixation; process design; evaporation control; pollution abatement; environmental control; nuclear fuel cycle. *Mailing Add:* 4224 E Mitchell Dr Phoenix AZ 85018

REISER, MORTON FRANCIS, b Cincinnati, Ohio, Aug 22, 19; m 45; c 3. PSYCHIATRY. *Educ:* Univ Cincinnati, BS, 40, MD, 43. *Prof Exp:* Instr psychiat & internal med, Med Sch, Cincinnati Gen Hosp, 49-50, asst prof, 50-52; res psychiatrist, Neuropsychiat Div, Walter Reed Army Inst Res, 54-55; dir res psychiat, Albert Einstein Col Med, 55-65, from assoc prof to prof, 55-69; PROF PSYCHIAT & CHMN DEPT, COL MED, YALE UNIV, 69- *Concurrent Pos:* Fel psychiat, Cincinnati Gen Hosp, 47-50; vis psychiatrist, Bronx Munic Hosp, 54-69; mem small grants comt, NIMH, 56-58, mem career investr comt, 59-63; consult, Walter Reed Army Inst Res, Washington, DC, 57-58; prof lectr, State Univ NY Downstate Med Ctr, 59-65; chief div psychiat, Montefiore Hosp & Med Ctr, 65-69; mem fac, Western New Eng Inst Psychoanal, 69-; mem, Jerusalem Ment Health Ctr, 72-; mem, Comn Present Condition & Future Acad Psychiat, Josiah Macy Jr Found, 77; mem exec coun, Acad Behav Med Res, 78. *Mem:* Am Psychosom Soc (secy-treas, 56-59, pres, 60); Am Soc Clin Invest; fel Am Psychiat Asn; fel Am Col Psychiatrists; Int Col Psychosom Med (pres, 75-77). *Res:* Psychoanalysis and psychophysiology; psychosomatic medicine. *Mailing Add:* Dept of Psychiat Yale Univ Sch of Med New Haven CT 06510

REISER, RAYMOND, b Philadelphia, Pa, July 28, 06; m 39; c 2. BIOCHEMISTRY. *Educ:* Western Reserve Univ, BA, 29; Ohio State Univ, PhD(agr chem), 36. *Prof Exp:* Hanes fel med, Duke Univ, 36-40; from asst chemist to assoc chemist, Div Chem Exp Sta, 40-48, from assoc prof to prof, 48-65, distinguished prof, 65-76, EMER PROF BIOCHEM & NUTRIT, TEX A&M UNIV, 76- *Concurrent Pos:* NIH res career award, 62, mem, Nutrit Study Sect, 63-67. *Honors & Awards:* Glycerine Producer's Asn Award, 52; Southwest Regional Award, Am Chem Soc, 64; Can Award, Am Oil Chem Soc, 63; Dr Norman E Borlaug Award, 73; Alton Bailey Medal, Am Oil Chemists' Soc, 76. *Mem:* AAAS; Am Chem Soc; Am Oil Chem Soc (vpres, 66, pres, 67); Am Soc Biol Chemists; Am Inst Nutrit. *Res:* Fat absorption; glyceride and essential fatty acid metabolism; lipid analysis; fats in nutrition. *Mailing Add:* Dept of Biochem & Biophys Tex A&M Univ College Station TX 77843

REISER, SHELDON, b New York, NY, Oct 13, 30; m 55; c 2. BIOCHEMISTRY, ANIMAL NUTRITION. *Educ:* City Col New York, BS, 53; Univ Wis, MS, 57, PhD(biochem), 60. *Prof Exp:* Assoc prof biochem & med, Med Ctr, Ind Univ, Indianapolis, 60-73; LAB CHIEF, NUTRIT INST, USDA, 73-, RES BIOCHEMIST, 77- *Concurrent Pos:* Mem staff, Vet Admin Hosp, Indianapolis, 60-73. *Mem:* Am Inst Nutrit; Am Chem Soc; Biophys Soc; Am Soc Biol Chem. *Res:* The effects of the type and amount of dietary carbohydrate consumed by animals and humans and carbohydrate and lipid metabolism, intestinal absorption and digestion, and hormone responses. *Mailing Add:* Carbohydrate Nutrit Lab USDA ARS Beltsville MD 20705

REISERT, PATRICIA, b New York, NY, July 2, 37; m 62; c 2. MICROBIOLOGY, BOTANY. *Educ:* Manhattanville Col, BA, 59; Brown Univ, MA, 61, PhD(bot), 65. *Prof Exp:* Instr biol, St Joseph's Col, Pa, 65-66, asst prof, 66-68; asst prof, Villanova Univ, 69-71 & Worcester Polytech Inst, 74-75; asst prof, 75-80, ASSOC PROF NATURAL SCI, ASSUMPTION COL, 80- *Concurrent Pos:* Fac res fel, St Joseph's Col, Pa, 67; affil asst prof life sci, Worcester Polytech Inst, 75-; sabbatical leave, Med Sch Pharmacol, Univ Mass, 81-82; NSF fac develop fel, 81-82. *Mem:* AAAS, Bot Soc Am; Am Inst Biol Sci; Mycol Soc Am. *Res:* Cell surface phenomena in plants; biology of Epstein Burr Virus. *Mailing Add:* 83 Spring St Shrewsbury MA 01545

REISFELD, RALPH ALFRED, b Suttgart, Ger, Apr 23, 26; US citizen; m 56; c 2. IMMUNOCHEMISTRY, BIOCHEMISTRY. *Educ:* Rutgers Univ, BS, 52; Ohio State Univ, PhD, 57. *Prof Exp:* Biochemist, Endocrinol Br, Nat Cancer Inst, 57-59; sr chemist, Merck & Co, 59-63; biochemist, Immunol Lab, Nat Inst Allergy & Infectious Dis, Md, 63-70; mem dept exp path, 70-74, MEM DEPT MOLECULAR IMMUNOL, SCRIPPS CLIN & RES FOUND, 74- *Concurrent Pos:* Adj prof, Univ Calif, San Diego, 72. *Mem:* AAAS; Am Chem Soc; Soc Exp Biol & Med; Am Asn Immunol. *Res:* Isolation and biological characterization of transplantation antigens from inbred guinea pigs; isolation and biochemical characterization of human lencocytc-a, b, c and human leucocyte-DR antigens; expression and biosynthesis of cell surface antigens on human and murine lymphoid cells; biosynthesis and structure of human melanoma associated antigens. *Mailing Add:* Dept of Molecular Immunol Scripps Clin 476 Prospect St La Jolla CA 92037

REISH, DONALD JAMES, b Corvallis, Ore, June 15, 24; m 52; c 3. MARINE ZOOLOGY. *Educ:* Univ Ore, BS, 46; Ore State Col, MA, 49; Univ Southern Calif, PhD(zool), 52. *Prof Exp:* Res asst, Hancock Found, Univ Southern Calif, 53, res assoc, 53-58; from asst prof to assoc prof, 58-66, PROF BIOL, CALIF STATE UNIV, LONG BEACH, 66- *Concurrent Pos:* Mem staff, Arctic Res Lab, 53 & Eniwetok Marine Biol Lab, 57-58; mem Pac expeds, Hancock Found, Univ Southern Calif, 49 & 53, res assoc, Univ, 73- *Mem:* AAAS; Soc Syst Zool; Ecol Soc Am; Water Pollution Control Fedn; Marine Biol Asn UK. *Res:* Systematics and biology of polychaetous annelids; marine ecology and pollution. *Mailing Add:* Dept of Biol Calif State Univ Long Beach CA 90840

REISING, RICHARD F, b St Louis, Mo, Nov 18, 34; m 59; c 4. PHYSICAL INORGANIC CHEMISTRY. *Educ:* Princeton Univ, BA, 56; Wash Univ, PhD(chem), 63. *Prof Exp:* Mem staff, Argonne Nat Lab, 63-65; res scientist, McDonnell Aircraft Corp, Mo, 65-67; assoc sr res chemist, 76-81, sr res scientist, 76-81, STAFF RES SCIENTIST, GEN MOTORS RES LABS, 81- *Mem:* Electrochem Soc; Nat Asn Corrosion Engrs; Am Vacuum Soc. *Res:* Electrochemical and strength-of-material studies of the effects of aqueous corrosion of automotive metals of construction; high temperature corrosion studies of superalloys; applied nuclear technology. *Mailing Add:* Gen Motors Res Lab Phys Chem Dpt 12 Mile & Mound Rds Warren MI 48090

REISINGER, JOSEPH G, b New York, NY, Dec 22, 29. PHYSICS. *Educ:* Hofstra Univ, BS, 55; NY Univ, MS, 59, PhD(physics), 64. *Prof Exp:* Instr physics, Queens Col, 56-57; health physicist, Mem Ctr Cancer, 57-58; instr physics, Queens Col, 59-60; res asst environ radiation, NY Univ, 60-64; asst prof, 64-80, PROF PHYSICS, HOFSTRA UNIV, 80- *Res:* Charge distribution in irradiated materials; environmental radiation. *Mailing Add:* Dept of Physics Hofstra Univ Hempstead NY 11550

REISINGER, ROBERT, b Miami, Fla, Sept 1, 21. VIROLOGY, IMMUNOLOGY. *Educ:* Ala Polytech Inst, DVM, 44; Univ Wis, MS, 57; Am Bd Vet Pub Health, dipl, 65. *Prof Exp:* Pvt pract, Md, 44-45; vet, DC & Mex & vet in chg animal shipments to Greece & Poland, UNRRA, 45-46, vet consult, China, 46-47; vet consult, Food & Agr Orgn, Ethiopia, 48-49; pvt pract, Fla & Md, 49; vet consult, Econ Coop Admin, Formosa, 49-50; asst chief vet affairs div, Pub Health & Welfare Sect, Gen Hq, Supreme Command Allied Powers, Japan, 50-51; chief vet & livestock sect, UN Korean Reconstruct Agency, 51-54; pvt pract, Fla, 54-55; res asst vet sci, Univ Wis, 55-57; sr res vet, Animal Dis & Parasite Res Div, Agr Res Serv, USDA, 57-60, asst chief emergency dis staff, Animal Dis Eradication Div, 60-62, asst to dir animal inspection & quarantine div, 62-65, chief staff vet, Animal Health Div, 65-66; DEP SCI CHMN SPEC VIRUS-LEUKEMIA PROG, NAT CANCER INST, 66- *Concurrent Pos:* Mem subcomt livestock damage, Adv Comt Civil Defense, Nat Acad Sci-Nat Res Coun, 60-63, mem study group animal dis in Africa, 64-65, mem subcomt health stand int shipment of lab animals, Inst Lab Animal Resources, 65- *Honors & Awards:* Presidential Commendation, Repub Korea, 52, Medal Indust Merit, 54. *Mem:* Conf Res Workers Animal Dis; Am Vet Med Asn; US Livestock Sanit Asn; hon mem Japanese Vet Med Asn. *Res:* Interactions of microbial agents and various stressors in pathogenesis and epidemiology of disease; rinderpest; shipping fever; malignant lymphoma; calf diarrhea in the bovine; swine and fowl cholera. *Mailing Add:* 3801 Dustin Rd Burtonsville MD 20730

REISKIN, ALLAN B, b New York, NY, Apr 24, 36; m 62; c 2. RADIOLOGICAL SCIENCES, ONCOLOGY. *Educ:* City Col New York, BA, 63; Univ Pa, DDS, 63; Oxford Univ, DPhil, 66. *Prof Exp:* Am Cancer Soc Brit-Am fel, 63-66; from asst biologist to assoc biologist, Argonne Nat Lab, 68-70; PROF ORAL RADIOL, UNIV CONN, 70- *Concurrent Pos:* Res assoc, Zoller Dent Clin & asst prof path, Univ Chicago, 68-70; consult clin assoc prof, Loyola Univ Chicago, 70; consult, Am Dent Asn. *Mem:* Am Asn Cancer Res; Radiol Soc NAm; Am Acad Dent Radiol; Radiation Res Soc; Int Asn Dent Res. *Res:* Diagnostic imaging; carcinogenesis; radiation safety. *Mailing Add:* Univ of Conn Health Ctr Farmington CT 06032

REISKIND, JONATHAN, b Staten Island, NY, May 27, 40; m 66; c 2. EVOLUTIONARY BIOLOGY, ARACHNOLOGY. *Educ:* Amherst Col, AB, 62; Harvard Univ, MA, 65, PhD(biol), 68. *Prof Exp:* Asst prof, 67-72, ASSOC PROF ZOOL, UNIV FLA, 72- *Concurrent Pos:* Res assoc, Fla State Collection Arthropods, 68- *Mem:* AAAS; Soc Study Evolution; Am Arachnol Soc (pres, 81-83); Asn Trop Biol; Soc Syst Zool. *Res:* Systematics and biology of spiders; mimicry in spiders; spider-plant associations; ethology of arachnids; tropical biology; ecology. *Mailing Add:* Dept Zool Univ Fla Gainesville FL 32611

REISLER, DONALD LAURENCE, b Brooklyn, NY, May 28, 41; m 64; c 1. INFORMATION SCIENCE, PHYSICS. *Educ:* Rutgers Univ, AB, 63; Yale Univ, MS, 65, PhD(physics), 67. *Prof Exp:* Staff analyst, Res Anal Corp, 67-70 & Lambda Corp, Va, 70-73; PRES, DBS CORP, 73- *Mem:* Inst Elec & Electronics Engrs; NY Acad Sci. *Res:* Design and installation of information systems; mathematical formulation and solution of organizational problems and decisions. *Mailing Add:* 360 Glyndon St NE Vienna VA 22180

REISLER, HANNA, b Tel-Aviv, Israel, July 12, 43; m 66; c 1. CHEMICAL KINETICS, PHOTOCHEMISTRY. *Educ:* Hebrew Univ, BSc, 64, MSc, 66; Weizmann Inst Sci, PhD(phys chem), 72. *Prof Exp:* Fel chem, Johns Hopkins Univ, 72-74; sr scientist, Soreg Nuclear Res Ctr, 74-77; res scientist elec eng, 77-79, RES ASST PROF ELEC ENG & CHEM, UNIV SOUTHERN CALIF, 79- *Mem:* Am Phys Soc. *Res:* Kinetics and dynamics of elementary processes in the gas phase; laser kinetic spectroscopy of free radicals; multi photon ionization and dissociation; unimolecular reactions of molecules and ions. *Mailing Add:* Dept Elec Eng SSC 405 Univ Southern Calif Los Angeles CA 90007

REISMAN, ABRAHAM JOSEPH, b Springfield, Mass, Dec 28, 25; m 49; c 2. POLYMER CHEMISTRY. *Educ:* Univ Mass, BS, 59, MS, 73. *Prof Exp:* SR RES CHEMIST, MONSANTO CO, INDIAN ORCHARD, 59- *Mem:* Am Chem Soc. *Res:* Development and design of stable addition polymer. *Mailing Add:* Monsanto 730 Worcester St Indian Orchard MA 01151

REISMAN, ARNOLD, b New York, NY, June 12, 27; m 48; c 4. PHYSICAL CHEMISTRY, INORGANIC CHEMISTRY. *Educ:* Brooklyn Col, MA, 53; Polytech Inst Brooklyn, PhD(chem), 58. *Prof Exp:* Control chemist, City New York, 49-51; res staff mem, US Govt, 51-53; MEM RES STAFF, T J WATSON RES CTR, IBM CORP, 53- *Concurrent Pos:* Assoc ed, J Electronics Materials; Solid State Sci Panel, Nat Res Coun. *Mem:* Am Chem Soc; Electrochem Soc; fel Am Inst Chemists; Am Inst Mining, Metall & Petrol Engrs. *Res:* Materials science of semiconductors and solid-gas reaction phenomena; epitaxial growth via chemical transport reactions; high pressure reactions; plasma enhanced reactions; radiation induced insulator defects. *Mailing Add:* Explor Semiconductor Technol Dept IBM Corp PO Box 218 Yorktown Heights NY 10598

REISMAN, ARNOLD, b Lodz, Poland, Aug 2, 34; nat US; m 54; c 4. OPERATIONS RESEARCH, INDUSTRIAL ENGINEERING. *Educ:* Univ Calif, Los Angeles, BS, 55, MS, 57, PhD(eng), 63. *Prof Exp:* Asst mech engr, Los Angeles Dept Water & Power, 55-57; from asst prof to assoc prof eng, Calif State Col Los Angeles, 57-66; vis prof eng & bus admin, Univ Wis-Milwaukee, 66-68; PROF OPERS RES, CASE WESTERN RESERVE UNIV, 68- *Concurrent Pos:* Consult, 57-; NSF fac fel, 62-63; assoc res engr, Western Mgt Sci Inst, Univ Calif, Los Angeles, 64-65; vpres, Univ Assocs, Inc, 69-74; mem, Coun AAAS & prog coordr, AAAS-Inst Mgt Sci, 73-75; vis prof, Hebrew Univ of Jerusalem, 74-75; mem, Japan-Am Inst Mgt Sci, Honolulu & mem, Inst Planning Comt & Bd Trustees, 75-; mem, Rev Bd, Lake Erie Regional Transp Authority, 75-76. *Honors & Awards:* Engr of Year Award, var eng socs, 73. *Mem:* Opers Res Soc Am; Inst Mgt Sci; fel AAAS; sr mem, Am Inst Indust Engrs; NY Acad Sci. *Res:* Engineering economy; systems analysis applications to operations management problems in health care delivery, industry and educational institutions; basic research in manpower planning and decision analysis; authored books in engineering economy, systems analysis, materials management, health care planning. *Mailing Add:* Dept of Opers Res Case Western Reserve Univ Cleveland OH 44106

REISMAN, ELIAS, b New York, NY, Mar 12, 26; m 48; c 3. EXPERIMENTAL PHYSICS. *Educ:* Cornell Univ, AB, 50, PhD(exp physics), 57. *Prof Exp:* Asst mass spectros, Cornell Univ, 50-55; sr physicist, Radiation Lab, Univ Calif, 57-60; SR SCIENTIST, AERONUTRONIC DIV, PHILCO-FORD CORP, 60- *Mem:* Am Phys Soc; Sigma Xi; Optical Soc Am. *Res:* Atmospherics; propagation and scattering; quantum electronics and laser applications. *Mailing Add:* Aeronutronic Res Lab Philco-Ford Corp Ford Rd Newport Beach CA 92660

REISMAN, HAROLD BERNARD, b Brooklyn, NY, Oct 29, 35; m 60; c 2. BIOCHEMICAL ENGINEERING. *Educ:* Columbia Univ, BS, 56, PhD(chem eng), 65; Cornell Univ, MS, 59. *Prof Exp:* Chem engr, Merck & Co, 61-64, sr chem eng, Merck Sharp & Dohme Res Labs, Rahway, 64-67, sect mgr biochem eng, 67-73; dir, Bioeng Lab, 73-75, plant mgr, 75-76, DIR MFG, FOOD INGREDIENTS DIV, STAUFFER CHEM CO, 76- *Mem:* Am Inst Chem Engrs; Am Chem Soc; Am Technion Soc; Inst Food Technologists; Coun Agr Sci & Technol. *Res:* Biochemical engineering, especially fermentation technology; natural product isolation and purification; design of fermentors and auxiliaries; pilot plant operations; process development. *Mailing Add:* 15 October Dr Weston CT 06883

REISMAN, HOWARD MAURICE, b Syracuse, NY, May 23, 37; m 64; c 3. ICHTHYOLOGY. *Educ:* Syracuse Univ, BA, 59, MA, 61; Univ Calif, Santa Barbara, PhD(biol), 67. *Prof Exp:* NIH fel, Cornell Univ, 67-69; asst prof biol, 69-73, assoc prof, 75-80, PROF BIOL & MARINE SCI, SOUTHAMPTON COL, LONG ISLAND UNIV, 80- *Mem:* AAAS; Am Soc Ichthyol & Herpet; Ecol Soc Am; Animal Behav Soc; Am Inst Biol Sci. *Res:* Animal behavior; general marine biology. *Mailing Add:* Div Natural Sci Southampton Col Southampton NY 11968

REISMAN, OTTO, b Vienna, Austria, July 29, 28; US citizen; m 58; c 2. NUCLEAR ENGINEERING, PHYSICS. *Educ:* City Col New York, BS, 58; NY Univ, MS, 60, PhD(nuclear eng), 73. *Prof Exp:* Jr engr physics, Weston Elec Instruments, 57-58; proj engr elec eng, Bendix Aviation, 58-61; instr physics, St Peter's Col, 61-62; ASST PROF PHYSICS, NJ INST TECHNOL, 62- *Mem:* Sigma Xi; Am Nuclear Soc. *Res:* Nuclear reactor heat transfer. *Mailing Add:* Dept Physics NJ Inst Technol 323 High St Newark NJ 07102

REISMAN, STANLEY S, b New York, NY, June 11, 41; c 2. ELECTRICAL ENGINEERING, BIOENGINEERING. *Educ:* Polytech Inst NY, BS, 62, PhD(bioeng), 74; Mass Inst Technol, MS, 63. *Prof Exp:* Mem tech staff, Bell Tel Labs Inc, 63-68; from instr to asst prof elec eng, 68-68, ASSOC PROF ELEC ENG, NJ INST TECHNOL, 78- *Concurrent Pos:* Lectr elec eng, City Col New York, 68. *Mem:* Inst Elec & Electronics Engrs; Am Soc Eng Educ. *Res:* Mathematical and computer simulation of physiologic systems; biomedical instrumentation. *Mailing Add:* NJ Inst of Technol 323 High St Newark NJ 07102

REISMANN, HERBERT, b Vienna, Austria, Jan 26, 26; US citizen; m 53; c 2. SOLID MECHANICS, AERONAUTICAL ENGINEERING. *Educ:* Ill Inst Technol, BS, 47, MS, 49; Univ Colo, PhD(eng mech), 62. *Prof Exp:* Instr mech, Ill Inst Technol, 47-50; proj struct engr, Gen Dynamics Corp, 51-53; prin systs engr, Repub Aviation Corp, 54-56; sect chief solid mech, Martin-Marietta Corp, 57-64; PROF ENG, STATE UNIV NY BUFFALO, 64- *Concurrent Pos:* Grants shell dynamics, US Air Force Off Sci Res & Army Res Off, 65-; consult, Bell Aerosysts Co, 65- *Mem:* AAAS; assoc fel Am Inst Aeronaut & Astronaut; Am Soc Mech Engrs; Int Asn Bridge & Struct Engrs. *Res:* Elasticity theory, particularly the dynamics of plates and shells; aeroelasticity; elastokinetics; dynamics of elastic bodies; geophysics. *Mailing Add:* 71 Chaumont Dr Williamsville NY 14221

REISNER, GERALD SEYMOUR, b Brooklyn, NY, Apr 10, 26; m 49; c 4. MICROBIOLOGY. *Educ:* State Univ NY Col Educ Albany, AB, 49, MA, 51; Cornell Univ, MS, 55, PhD(plant physiol), 56. *Prof Exp:* Teacher high sch, NY, 49-52; plant physiologist, Plant, Soil & Nutrit Lab, Soil & Water Conserv Res Div, Agr Res Serv, USDA, 52-56; mem fac biol, Goddard Col, 56-58; asst prof, 58-65, assoc prof microbiol, 63-70, PROF BIOL, ALLEGHENY COL, 70-, CHMN DEPT, 81- *Concurrent Pos:* Nat Acad Sci res assoc, USDA, 64-65; NIH fel, Ctr Biol of Natural Systs, Washington Univ, 71-72; bacteriologist, Bd Health, City Meadville, Pa, 58- *Mem:* Sigma Xi; Am Soc Microbiol; NY Acad Sci; Am Asn Univ Professors. *Res:* The application of asymbiotic nitrogen fixing bacteria to the growth of crop plants; effects of cations on bacterial enzymes. *Mailing Add:* Dept of Biol Allegheny Col Meadville PA 16335

REISNER, RONALD M, b Buffalo, NY, May 2, 29; m 72; c 2. DERMATOLOGY. *Educ:* Univ Calif, Los Angeles, BA, 52, MD, 56; Am Bd Dermat, dipl, 61. *Prof Exp:* From asst resident to resident dermat, Harbor Gen Hosp, 59, res trainee, 60, chief div dermat, 62-73; from asst prof to assoc prof dermat, 62-73, coordr dermat, Complex Affil Insts, 73-77, PROF & CHIEF DIV, SCH MED, UNIV CALIF, LOS ANGELES, 73-; DIR, COMBINED UNIV CALIF-VET ADMIN WADSWORTH MED CTR DERMAT PROG, 77- *Concurrent Pos:* Consult, US Air Force Ballistics

Missile Div Med Facility, 62-72; consult, Us Naval Regional Hosp, San Diego Calif, 76-; chief dermat serv, Vet Admin Wadsworth Med Ctr, Los Angeles, 77-; exec comt, Pac Dermat Asn, 78-; mem bd dirs, Soc Invest Dermat, 74-79. *Mem:* Fel Am Acad Dermat; Soc Invest Dermat; Am Dermat Asn; Am Asn Prof Dermat (secy-treas, 74-77); Int Soc Trop Dermat; fel Pan-Am Med Asn. *Res:* Pathogenesis of acne. *Mailing Add:* Div Dermat Sch Med Univ Calif Los Angeles CA 90024

REISS, ALICE MARGARET, b St Joseph, Mo, Jan 1, 28. IMMUNOLOGY. *Educ:* Univ Kans, BA, 49; Rutgers Univ, MS, 59, PhD(microbiol), 63. *Prof Exp:* Med technician, Clin Lab, Univ Kans Med Ctr, 50-53; res asst immunohemat, 53-55, asst scientist, 55-57, assoc scientist, 57-59, sr scientist, Div Diag Clin Path, 62-65, dir div immunol develop, 69-70, from asst dir to assoc dir res diag, Ortho Res Found, 70-74, ASSOC DIR RES DIAG, ORTHO DIAG INC, 74- *Concurrent Pos:* Res fel, Ortho Res Found, Ortho Pharmaceut Corp, 65-68. *Res:* Clinical immunology; transplantation and immunology. *Mailing Add:* Ortho Diag Inc Raritan NJ 08869

REISS, ERIC, b Vienna, Austria, Feb 29, 24; nat US; m 50; c 1. MEDICINE. *Educ:* Randolph Macon Col, BS, 43; Med Col Va, MD, 48. *Prof Exp:* Med house officer, Philadelphia Gen Hosp, 48-50; asst resident med, Barnes Hosp, Washington Univ, 54-55, instr med, Sch Sch Med, 56-58, asst prof med & prev med, 58-62, assoc prof, 62-64, dir, Irene Walter Johnson Inst Rehab, 58-64; prof med, Chicago Med Sch, 64-70; prof, Univ Chicago, 70-72; vchmn dept, 72-78, PROF MED & ACTING CHMN DEPT, SCH MED, UNIV MIAMI, 78- *Concurrent Pos:* Am Cancer Soc scholar, Metab Div, Dept Med, Sch Med, Washington Univ, 55-60; chmn dept med, Michael Reese Hosp & Med Ctr, 64-71. *Mem:* Am Soc Clin Invest; Asn Am Physicians; Am Soc Nephrology; Soc Exp Biol & Med; Endocrine Soc. *Res:* Burns; parathyroid physiology. *Mailing Add:* Dept of Med Univ of Miami PO Box 016760 Miami FL 33101

REISS, HOWARD, b New York, NY, Apr 5, 22; m 45; c 2. PHYSICAL CHEMISTRY. *Educ:* NY Univ, AB, 43; Columbia Univ, PhD(phys chem), 49. *Prof Exp:* Chemist, Tenn Eastman Corp, Tenn, 44-45; instr chem, Boston Univ, 49-51; chemist, Celanese Corp Am, 51-52 & Bell Tel Labs, Inc, 52-60; from assoc dir to dir res dept, Atomics Int Div, NAm Aviation, Inc, 6 0-62, pres & dir sci ctr, Thousand Oaks, 62-68; PROF CHEM, UNIV CALIF, LOS ANGELES, 68- *Concurrent Pos:* Corp rep, Am Inst Physics, 63-66; mem, Physics Res Eval Group, Air Force Off Sci Res, 66-, Reactor Chem Eval Comt, Oak Ridge Nat Lab, 66-68, Mat Res Coun, Advan Res Proj Agency, 68- & Adv Comt Math & Phys Sci, NSF, 70-74; Guggenheim fel, 78-79; ed, J Statist Physics, 68-78; mem comn socio-tech systs, Nat Res Coun; ed, Progress in Solid State Chem, 63-70 & J Statist Physics, 68-78. *Honors & Awards:* Tolman Medal, Am Chem Soc, 73; Herbert Newby McCoy Award, 74; Colloid & Surface Chem Prize, Am Chem Soc, 80. *Mem:* Nat Acad Sci; Am Phys Soc; Sigma Xi; NY Acad Sci; Am Chem Soc. *Res:* Semiconductors; statistical mechanics; solid state chemistry; thermodynamics; nucleation theory; information theory; electrochemistry. *Mailing Add:* Dept of Chem Univ of Calif Los Angeles CA 90024

REISS, HOWARD ROBERT, b Brooklyn, NY, July 29, 29; div; c 2. QUANTUM PHYSICS, ELECTRODYNAMICS. *Educ:* Polytech Inst Brooklyn, BAE, 50, MAE, 51; Univ Md, PhD(physics), 58. *Prof Exp:* Asst, Polytech Inst Brooklyn, 51; physicist, David W Taylor Model Basin, Bur Ships, US Dept Navy, 51-55, Naval Ord Lab, 55-58, chief nuclear physics div, 58-69; mem fac, Dept Physics, 78-81, RES PROF, ARIZ RES LAB, UNIV ARIZ, 81-; PROF PHYSICS, AM UNIV, 69- *Concurrent Pos:* Vis prof physics, Univ Ariz, 75-81. *Mem:* Fel Am Phys Soc; AAAS. *Res:* Development of theoretical methods for very intense electromagnetic fields, and applications to interaction of intense fields with matter. *Mailing Add:* Dept of Physics Univ of Ariz Tucson AZ 85721

REISS, KEITH WESTCOTT, b Washington DC, July 22, 45; m 66; c 1. MICROWAVE PHYSICS, ENGINEERING PHYSICS. *Educ:* Univ Va, BS, 66; Wake Forest Univ, MA, 68; Duke Univ, PhD(physics), 71. *Prof Exp:* Chmn natural sci & math div & dept head phys sci, Truett-McConnell Col, 71-73; PHYSICIST US NAVY SUPPORT, VITRO LABS DIV, AUTOMATION INDUST, 73- *Mem:* Am Phys Soc; Sigma Xi. *Res:* Development and analysis of US Navy surface-to-surface missile systems. *Mailing Add:* Sperry Div 6521 Arlington Blvd 208 Falls Church VA 22042

REISS, OSCAR KULLY, b Bad-Duerkheim, Ger, May 6, 21; nat US; m 44; c 3. BIOCHEMISTRY. *Educ:* Univ Chicago, BS, 50, PhD(biochem), 54. *Prof Exp:* Instr physiol chem, Sch Med, Johns Hopkins Univ, 57-58, asst prof, 58-59; asst prof, 59-67, ASSOC PROF BIOCHEM, SCH MED, UNIV COLO, DENVER, 67- *Mem:* Am Soc Biol Chemists; Am Chem Soc; Brit Biochem Soc. *Res:* Intermediary and lipid metabolism of lung and other tissues; structure and function of membranes; effects of organothiophosphates on pulmonary enzyme systems. *Mailing Add:* Webb-Waring Lung Inst Univ of Colo Sch of Med Denver CO 80262

REISS, WILLIAM DEAN, b Breese, Ill, July 24, 37; m 61; c 2. AGRONOMY. *Educ:* Southern Ill Univ, BS, 60, MS, 61; Univ Ill, PhD(crop prod), 67. *Prof Exp.* Res asst crop prod, Southern Ill Univ, 60-61; asst, Univ Ill, 61-65; exten agronomist, 65 71, RES AGRONOMIST, PURDUE UNIV, WEST LAFAYETTE, 74- *Concurrent Pos:* Mem, Bd Dirs, Asn Off Seed Certifying Agencies, 67- *Mem:* Am Soc Agron. *Res:* Influence of density of stand, row width, planting date and plant nutrients on behavior of corn, sorghum and soybeans; factors affecting seed quality of soybeans and small grains; seed certification. *Mailing Add:* Dept of Agron Purdue Univ West Lafayette IN 47907

REISSE, ROBERT ALAN, b Philadelphia, Pa, Apr 9, 46; m 73. PHYSICS. *Educ:* Wesleyan Univ, BA, 67; Univ Md, MS, 70, PhD(physics), 76. *Prof Exp:* Res assoc, Physics Dept, Univ Md, 76-77; mem tech staff physics, Sperry Res Ctr, Sperry Rand Corp, 77-81; RES ASST PROF & MEM STAFF, ARIZ RES LABS & SANTA CATALINA LAB EXP RELATIVITY BY ASTROMETRY, UNIV ARIZ, 81- *Mem:* Am Phys Soc; Optical Soc Am. *Res:* Optical information processing; quantum electronics; experimental general relativity; solar astrophysics. *Mailing Add:* 1781 N Fountain Park Dr Tucson AZ 85715

REISSIG, JOSE LUIS, b Buenos Aires, Arg, June 21, 26; div; c 3. GENETICS, MOLECULAR BIOLOGY. *Educ:* Univ Mich, BS, 48; Calif Inst Technol, PhD(genetics), 52. *Prof Exp:* Researcher microbial genetics, Juan Noe Inst Biol, Univ Chile, 53; vis res assoc, Cornell Univ, 55; Melville Trust fel, Inst Animal Genetics, Univ Edinburgh, 55-58; Rask Orsted fel, Inst Genetics, Univ Copenhagen, 59-60; guest investr, Dept Microbial Physiol, Pasteur Inst, Paris, 60; prof genetics, Sch Sci, Univ Buenos Aires, 61-66; RES PROF, C W POST COL, LI UNIV, 67- *Concurrent Pos:* Arg Asn Advan Sci fel, Inst Biochem Res, Campomar Found, Buenos Aires, 52-55; res fel, Calif Inst Technol, 66, vis assoc, 75. *Mem:* Am Soc Microbiol; Am Soc Cell Biol. *Res:* Role of ribosomes in complementation; biochemistry and genetics of growth control; the microbial surface. *Mailing Add:* Dept of Biol C W Post Col Greenvale NY 11548

REISSIG, MAGDALENA, b Buenos Aires, Arg, Sept 1, 23. ELECTRON MICROSCOPY, VIROLOGY. *Educ:* Univ Buenos Aires, Arg, MD, 50. *Prof Exp:* Res asst cell ultrastruct, Inst Biol Sci, Uruguay, 50-53; res asst prev med, Sch Med, Yale Univ, 53-56, res assoc, 56-58; res assoc microbiol, Albert Einstein Med Ctr, 58-61; asst prof, 61-68, ASSOC PROF PATHOBIOL, JOHNS HOPKINS UNIV, 68- *Mem:* Electron Micros Soc Am; Am Asn Immunologists; Am Soc Cell Biol. *Res:* Cytology; cytopathology of virus infections; ultrastructure of parasitic helminths, particularly schistosomes and cestodes. *Mailing Add:* Dept of Path Johns Hopkins Univ Sch of Hyg & Pub Health Baltimore MD 21205

REISSMANN, KURT RUDOLPH, b Schoenebeck, Ger, Feb 25, 12; nat US; m 51; c 2. MEDICINE, PHYSIOLOGY. *Educ:* Univ Berlin, MD, 36. *Prof Exp:* Head physiol div, Helmholtz Inst, 44-46; scientist, Sch Aviation Med, US Air Force, 47-50; assoc prof med & chief exp med, Med Sch, Univ Kans, 51-57; vis prof, Univ Philippines, 57-58; PROF MED & CHIEF SECT EXP MED, MED SCH, UNIV KANS, 59- *Concurrent Pos:* Consult, Vet Admin Hosps. *Mem:* Am Physiol Soc; fel Am Col Physicians; Am Soc Hemat; Asn Am Physicians; Int Soc Exp Hemat. *Res:* Regulation of erythropoiesis and leukopoiesis; erythropoietin, hematopoietic stem cells; abnormal hemoglobin; iron metabolism. *Mailing Add:* Dept of Med Univ of Kans Med Ctr Kansas City KS 66103

REISSMANN, THOMAS LINCOLN, b Wilmington, Del, Feb 12, 20; m 51; c 2. ANALYTICAL CHEMISTRY. *Educ:* Pa State Univ, BS, 42, MS, 47, PhD(chem), 49. *Prof Exp:* Chemist, Atlas Powder Co, 42 & 45-46; asst chief chemist, Ky Ord Works, 42-45; asst chem, Pa State Col, 46-49; res chemist, 49-58, dept mgr collagen res, 58-69, absorbable suture res & develop, 70-72, dept mgr chem, 73-80, ASST TO CORP DIR, QUAL ASSURANCE, ETHICON INC, 80- *Mem:* AAAS; Am Chem Soc; Am Soc Qual Control; NY Acad Sci. *Res:* Collagen chemistry; fibers and films; medical products; chemical quality of drugs; application of computerized systems to the quality assurance function. *Mailing Add:* Ethicon Inc Route 22 Somerville NJ 08876

REISSNER, ERIC, b Aachen, Ger, Jan 5, 13; US citizen; m 38; c 2. APPLIED MECHANICS, APPLIED MATHEMATICS. *Educ:* Tech Univ, Berlin, Dipl Ing, 35, Dr Ing (civil eng), 36; Mass Inst Technol, PhD(math), 38. *Hon Degrees:* Dr Ing(mech eng), Hannover Tech Univ, 64. *Prof Exp:* From instr to prof math, Mass Inst Technol, 39-69; PROF APPL MECH, UNIV CALIF, SAN DIEGO, 70- *Concurrent Pos:* Guggenheim fel, 62; NSF sr fel, 67. *Honors & Awards:* Theodore von Karman Medal, Am Soc Civil Eng, 64; Timoshenko Medal, Am Soc Mech Eng, 73. *Mem:* Am Math Soc; Soc Indust Appl Math; Am Soc Mech Eng; Am Inst Aeronaut & Astronaut; Nat Acad Eng. *Res:* Theory of elasticity, especially application of variational methods and behavior of beams, plates and shells. *Mailing Add:* Dept Appl Mech B010 Univ Calif San Diego La Jolla CA 92093

REIST, ELMER JOSEPH, b Can, Aug 29, 30; nat US; m 54; c 2. ORGANIC CHEMISTRY. *Educ:* Univ Alta, BSc, 52; Univ Calif, PhD(org chem), 55. *Prof Exp:* Fel, Nat Res Coun Can, 55-56; asst dir, 56-80, ASSOC DIR BIOORG CHEM, STANFORD RES INST INT, 80- *Mem:* Am Chem Soc. *Res:* Carbohydrates; synthesis; nitrogen mustards; neuraminic acid; enzyme chemistry; nitrosamines; chemical carcinogenesis; nucleic acids; antiviral agents. *Mailing Add:* Life Sci Div Stanford Res Inst Int Menlo Park CA 94025

REIST, PARKER CRAMER, b Williamsport, Pa, Mar 3, 33; m 55; c 2. INDUSTRIAL HYGIENE. *Educ:* Pa State Univ, BS, 55; Mass Inst Technol, SM, 57; Harvard Univ, SMHyg, 63, ScD(radiol health), 66. *Prof Exp:* Lectr indust hyg, Harvard Univ, 65-66, from asst prof to assoc prof, 66-72; PROF AIR & INDUST HYG & DIR PROG AREA, SCH PUB HEALTH, UNIV NC, CHAPEL HILL, 72- *Concurrent Pos:* Chmn, Triangle Univs Consortium Air Pollution, 73-; mem, NC State Bd Refrigeration Examrs, 75- *Mem:* Am Bd Indust Hyg; Am Indust Hyg Asn. *Res:* Industrial hygiene; respiratory protection; air pollution control; aerosol technology and particle behavior; radiation protection; disposal of radioactive gaseous and particle wastes. *Mailing Add:* Sch of Pub Hyg Univ of NC Chapel Hill NC 27511

REISTAD, GORDON MACKENZE, b Philipsburg, Mont, Oct 21, 44; m 65; c 2. ENGINEERING. *Educ:* Mont State Univ, BS, 66; Univ Wis-Madison, MS, 67, PhD(mech eng), 70. *Prof Exp:* Instr mech eng, Univ Wis-Madison, 69-70; from asst prof to assoc prof, 70-81, PROF MECH ENG, ORE STATE UNIV, 81- *Concurrent Pos:* Consult, Battelle Northwest, Lawrence Livermore Labs, Elec Power Res Inst, Nat Bur Standards, Int Dist Heating Asn & others. *Mem:* Am Soc Mech Engrs; Geothermal Resources Coun; Am Soc Heating, & Air-Conditioning Engrs. *Res:* Energy systems evaluation and design; second law of thermodynamics; geothermal energy systems analysis and design. *Mailing Add:* 4370 NW Queens Ave Corvallis OR 97330

REISTER, DAVID B(RYAN), b Los Angeles, Calif, Feb 22, 42; m 63; c 2. ENGINEERING SCIENCE, SYSTEMS ANALYSIS. *Educ:* Univ Calif, Berkeley, BS, 64, MS, 66, PhD(eng sci), 69. *Prof Exp:* Lectr eng sci, State Univ NY Buffalo, 68-69, asst prof, 69-74; SCIENTIST, INST ENERGY ANAL, 74- *Concurrent Pos:* NSF grant, 71-73. *Mem:* AAAS; Am Nuclear Soc; Int Asn Energy Economists; Sigma Xi; Opers Res Soc Am. *Res:* Energy demand models; net energy analysis; non-technical aspects of nuclear power. *Mailing Add:* PO Box 117 Oak Ridge TN 37830

REISWIG, ROBERT D(AVID), b Wichita, Kans, July 14, 29; m 51; c 2. METALLURGY. *Educ:* Univ Kans, BS, 51; Univ Wis, MS, 53, PhD, 56. *Prof Exp:* Res engr, Battelle Mem Inst, 51-52; STAFF MEM, LOS ALAMOS SCI LAB, 55- *Mem:* Am Inst Mining, Metall & Petrol Engrs; Am Soc Metals. *Res:* Titanium casting; pyrophoric alloys; transformations; phase equilibria; thermal conductivity; temperature measurement; microstructures; carbons and graphites; carbide-carbon composites; corrosion. *Mailing Add:* Los Alamos Sci Lab MS-734 Los Alamos NM 87545

REIT, BARRY, b New York, NY, Oct 27, 42. ENDOCRINOLOGY, PHYSIOLOGY. *Educ:* Mich State Univ, BS, 64; Univ Tenn, Knoxville, MS, 68; Univ Ky, PhD(animal physiol), 71. *Prof Exp:* Vis scientist metab endocrinol, Div Biol Standards, Nat Inst Med Res, London, Eng, 71-72, mem sci staff, 72-74; res assoc orthop surg, Children's Hosp Med Ctr, 74-78; INSTR MED, HARVARD MED SCH, 78- *Concurrent Pos:* Asst biol, Mass Gen Hosp, 78- *Mem:* Soc Endocrinol; Brit Bone & Tooth Soc; Sigma Xi; Am Soc Bone & Mineral Res; AAAS. *Res:* Calcium physiology; endocrine influences on calcified tissue and mineral metabolism measured by bioassay and intravenous administration of parathyroid hormone; mechanism of action of parathyroid hormone; metabolic endocrinology. *Mailing Add:* Dept Endocrinol Lab Renal Biophys 1 Scarsdale Rd Tuckahoe NY 10707

REIT, ERNEST MARVIN I, b New York, NY, July 3, 32; m 56; c 4. PHARMACOLOGY. *Educ:* Cornell Univ, BS, 53, DVM, 57; Yale Univ, PhD(pharmacol), 64. *Prof Exp:* Asst prof, 66-69, ASSOC PROF PHARMACOL, COL MED, UNIV VT, 69- *Concurrent Pos:* Spec fel, Nat Inst Med Res, Mill Hill, Eng, 64-65; USPHS career develop award, 67-72. *Mem:* AAAS; Am Soc Pharmacol & Exp Therapeut; Brit Pharmacol Soc. *Res:* Neuropharmacology, especially chemical mediation and modulation of the transmission of nerve impulses. *Mailing Add:* Dept of Pharmacol Univ of Vt Col of Med Burlington VT 05401

REITAN, PAUL HARTMAN, b Kanawha, Iowa, Aug 18, 28; m 62; c 2. GEOCHEMISTRY, PETROLOGY. *Educ:* Univ Chicago, AB, 53; Univ Oslo, PhD(geol), 59. *Prof Exp:* Geologist, US Geol Surv, 53-56; state geologist, Geol Surv Norway, 56-60; asst prof mineral, Stanford Univ, 60-66; assoc prof, 66-69, assoc provost, Fac Natural Sci & Math, 70-75, dir, Natural Sci & Math Res Inst, 70-80, actg provost, 75-76, provost, 76-78, dean, Fac Natural Sci & Math, 78-80, PROF GEOL, STATE UNIV NY, BUFFALO, 69- *Mem:* AAAS; fel Geol Soc Am; fel Mineral Soc Am; Geochem Soc; Int Asn Geochem & Cosmochem. *Res:* Metamorphic petrology and recrystallization; fractionation of elements between coexisting minerals; temperatures of metamorphism; cycling of elements in earth's crust; genesis of pegmatites and magma in crust. *Mailing Add:* Dept of Geol Sci State Univ of NY Buffalo NY 14226

REITAN, PHILLIP JENNINGS, b Grove City, Minn, July 14, 29; m 53; c 5. ZOOLOGY. *Educ:* Concordia Col, Moorhead, Minn, BA, 52; Univ Wis, MS, 54, PhD(zool), 58. *Prof Exp:* Teacher pub sch, NDak, 49-50; from instr to assoc prof biol, Wagner Col, 57-62; assoc prof, 62-67, PROF BIOL, LUTHER COL, IOWA, 67-, CHMN DEPT, 62- *Concurrent Pos:* Co-prin investr, NIH res grant, 58-63; NSF sci fac fel, Harvard Univ, 65-66. *Mem:* AAAS; Am Soc Zoologists; Am Inst Biol Sci; Nat Asn Biol Teachers. *Res:* Drosophila development, especially the relationship between inherited abnormalities and normal embryology; relationship between dehydration and radiation effects in Drosophila embryology; function of avian amnion in development. *Mailing Add:* Dept of Biol Luther Col Decorah IA 52101

REITAN, RALPH MELDAHL, b Beresford, SDak, Aug 29, 22; div; c 5. NEUROPSYCHOLOGY. *Educ:* Univ Chicago, PhD(psychol), 50. *Prof Exp:* Lectr psychol, South Bend Exten Ctr, Ind Univ, Indianapolis, 48-51, from asst prof to assoc prof surg, Sch Med, 51-60, prof psychol & dir sect neuropsychol, 60-70; prof psychol & neurol surg, Univ Wash, 70-77; PROF PSYCHOL, UNIV ARIZ, 77- *Concurrent Pos:* Instr, Univ Chicago, 49-51; consult, Space Med Adv Group, NASA, 64-65, Off Assoc Dir, Nat Inst Neurol Dis & Blindness, 66- & Vet Admin Hosp, Seattle, 71- *Honors & Awards:* Gordon Barrows Mem Award, 65. *Mem:* Geront Soc; Am Psychol Asn; Am Neurol Asn; Am Aacd Neurol. *Res:* Brain localization of abilities, neuropsychology; brain-behavior relationships. *Mailing Add:* Dept of Psychol Univ of Ariz Tucson AZ 85721

REITER, ELMAR RUDOLF, b Wels, Austria, Feb 22, 28; m 54; c 3. METEOROLOGY. *Educ:* Univ Innsbruck, PhD(meteorol, geophys), 53. *Prof Exp:* Res asst meteorol, Univ Chicago, 52-53, res assoc & instr, 54-56; instr, NATO Officer's Sch, Germ 53-54; res assoc meteorol & geophys, Univ Innsbruck, 56-59, asst prof, 59-61; assoc prof, 61-65, head dept, 68-74, PROF ATMOSPHERIC SCI, COLO STATE UNIV, 65- *Concurrent Pos:* Res fel, Deutscher Wetterdienst, Repub Ger, 59; lectr, SEATO Grad Sch, Bangkok, 63; consult, Ger Lufthansa Airlines, 59-61, Meteorol Res Inc, Calif, 63-65, Univ Melbourne, 63, Litton Industs, Minn, 64, Boeing Aircraft Co, Seattle, 65, NASA-Marshall Space Flight Ctr, Huntsville & US Army Missile Commmand, 65- & Nat Comt Clear Turbulence, 66, Inst Defense Analysis, 73-75 & Nat Acad Sci, 73-75. *Honors & Awards:* Advan Sci Award, Govt Upper Austria, 62; Silver Anniversary Medal Distinguished Serv, Univ Innsbruck, 70; Robert M Losey Award, Am Inst Aeronaut & Astronaut, 67. *Mem:* Fel Am Meteorol Soc; Am Geophys Union; Am Inst Aeronaut & Astronaut; Royal Meteorol Soc; Meteorol Soc Japan. *Res:* General circulation of the atmosphere; aviation meteorology, especially clear-air turbulence; climatology, air pollution, atmospheric variability. *Mailing Add:* Dept Atmospheric Sci Colorado State Univ Ft Collins CO 80521

REITER, HAROLD BRAUN, b Jackson, Tenn, Oct 14, 42; m 66. MATHEMATICS. *Educ:* La State Univ, Baton Rouge, BS, 64; Clemson Univ, MS, 65, PhD(math), 69. *Prof Exp:* Asst prof math, Univ Hawaii, 69-72; ASSOC PROF MATH, UNIV NC, CHARLOTTE, 72- *Mem:* Am Math Soc; Math Asn Am. *Res:* Comparison of topologies; function algebras; convexity; game theory. *Mailing Add:* Dept of Math Univ of NC Charlotte NC 28223

REITER, MARSHALL ALLAN, b Pittsburgh, Pa, Sept 11, 42; m 64; c 3. GEOPHYSICS. *Educ:* Univ Pittsburgh, BS, 65; Va Polytech Inst, PhD(geophysics), 70. *Prof Exp:* From asst prof to assoc prof geophysics, NMex Inst Mining & Technol, 70-75; geophysicist, 75-79, SR GEOPHYSICIST, NMEX BUR MINES & MINERAL RESOURCES, 79- *Concurrent Pos:* Adj assoc prof geophysics, NMex Inst Mining & Technol, 75-80, adj prof, 80- *Mem:* Am Geophys Union; fel Geol Soc Am; Soc Explor Geophysicists; Sigma Xi. *Res:* Geothermal studies; define the geographic variation of terrestrial heat flux in the Southwestern United States with borehole temperature measurements, locate geothermal areas, thermal conditions in the crust and upper mantle. *Mailing Add:* Bur Mines & Mineral Resources Campus Station NM 87801

REITER, RAYMOND, b Toronto, Ont, June 12, 39. COMPUTER SCIENCE. *Educ:* Univ Toronto, BA, MA, 63; Univ Mich, Ann Arbor, PhD(comput sci), 67. *Prof Exp:* Nat Res Coun Can fel, Univ London, 68-69; asst prof, 69-74, ASSOC PROF COMPUT SCI, UNIV BC, 74- *Mem:* Asn Comput Mach; Asn Symbolic Logic. *Res:* Artificial intelligence; mechanical theorem proving; theory of computation. *Mailing Add:* Dept of Comput Sci Univ of BC Vancouver BC V6T 1W5 Can

REITER, RUSSEL JOSEPH, b St Cloud, Minn, Sept 22, 36; m 62; c 2. NEUROENDOCRINOLOGY, NEUROANATOMY. *Educ:* St John's Univ, Minn, BA, 59; Bowman Gray Sch Med, MS, 61, PhD(anat), 64. *Prof Exp:* Exp endocrinologist, Edgewood Arsenal, Md, 66; asst prof anat, Med Ctr, Univ Rochester, 66-69, assoc prof, 69-71; assoc prof, 71-73, PROF ANAT, MED SCH, UNIV TEX, SAN ANTONIO, 73- *Concurrent Pos:* NIH career develop award, 69-74. *Mem:* Int Soc Chronobiol; Am Asn Anatomists; Int Fertil Asn; Pan-Am Asn Anatomists; Int Soc Neuroendocrinol. *Res:* Neuroendocrinology, especially the pineal gland and reproductive physiology; brain chemistry and behavior. *Mailing Add:* Dept of Anat Univ of Tex Med Sch San Antonio TX 78229

REITER, WILLIAM FREDERICK, JR, b Egg Harbor City, NJ, July 20, 38; m 72; c 2. MECHANICAL ENGINEERING. *Educ:* Rutgers Univ, BS, 61; Auburn Univ, MS, 66; NC State Univ, PhD(mech eng), 73. *Prof Exp:* Instr mech eng, Auburn Univ, 66-69; asst prof, 73-77, ASSOC PROF MECH ENG, NC STATE UNIV, 78- *Mem:* Am Soc Mech Engrs; Soc Automotive Engrs. *Res:* Dynamics of rotating machinery; vibration and sound radiation from structures; sound and vibration signal processing. *Mailing Add:* Dept of Mech & Aerospace Eng NC State Univ Box 5246 Raleigh NC 27650

REITH, EDWARD JOHN, b Mackenzell, Ger, Apr 22, 25; nat US; m 46; c 4. ANATOMY. *Educ:* St John's Univ, NY, BS, 49, MS, 53; NY Univ, PhD(anat), 57. *Prof Exp:* From instr to assoc prof anat, Sch Med, NY Univ, 56-64; prof, New York Med Col, 64-72; prof anat, Col Med, Univ Fla, 72-78; PROF & CHMN ANAT SCI, TEMPLE UNIV SCH DENT, 78- *Concurrent Pos:* USPHS grants, 61- *Mem:* Am Asn Anatomists; NY Acad Sci; Int Asn Dent Res. *Res:* Microscopic anatomy, ultrastructure, histochemistry and autoradiography of tooth development. *Mailing Add:* Temple Univ Sch Dent 3223 N Broad St Philadelphia PA 19140

REITMAN, LARRY N, synthetic organic chemistry, see previous edition

REITMAN, MORTON, b Atlantic City, NJ, Feb 18, 19; m 45; c 2. MEDICAL MICROBIOLOY, IMMUNOLOGY. *Educ:* Transylvania Col, BA, 41; Univ Ky, MS, 50; George Washington Univ, PhD(microbiol), 55. *Prof Exp:* Res bacteriologist, US Army Biol Ctr, Ft Detrick, Md, 48-57, br chief tech info, 57-60, spec asst to dir med res, 60-63, prin investr vaccines, 63-71; scientist adminr, 71-73, exec secy spec study sect, Div Res Grants, 73-77, EXEC SECY, ALLERGY & IMMUNOL STUDY SECT, NIH, 77- *Mem:* Am Soc Microbiol; Am Acad Microbiologists; Sigma Xi. *Res:* Microbiological safety and laboratory techniques; vaccines; radiation inactivation of viruses; science administration. *Mailing Add:* Div of Res Grants Nat Insts of Health Bethesda MD 20014

REITMEYER, WILLIAM L, b Deer Lodge, Mont, Apr 15, 28; m 62; c 5. ASTRONOMY, AEROSPACE ENGINEERING. *Educ:* St Louis Univ, BS, 52; Marquette Univ, MS, 60; Univ Ariz, PhD(astron, aerospace eng), 64. *Prof Exp:* From instr to asst prof eng, Marquette Univ, 54-65; assoc prof mech eng, NMex State Univ, 65-66, assoc prof earth sci, 66-69; staff assoc astron, NSF, 69-70; chmn dept, 70-74, PROF ASTRON, NMEX STATE UNIV, 70- *Concurrent Pos:* Grants, NSF, 63-65 & NASA, 65-66. *Mem:* AAAS; Am Astron Soc; Royal Astron Soc. *Res:* Photoelectric photometry and associated astrophysical problems of interstellar medium and galaxies. *Mailing Add:* Dept of Astron NMex State Univ Las Cruces NM 88003

REITNOUR, CLARENCE MELVIN, b Spring City, Pa, Oct 17, 33; m 69. ANIMAL NUTRITION. *Educ:* Pa State Univ, BS, 59; Univ Ky, MS, 62, PhD, 68. *Prof Exp:* Res asst, Univ Ky, 60-62; res asst, Univ Md, 62-64; exten specialist, Univ Ky, 64-66, res asst, 66-68; assoc prof, 68-80, PROF, UNIV DEL, 80-, EQUINE SPECIALIST, 68- *Mem:* Am Soc Animal Sci. *Res:* Equine nitrogen metabolism. *Mailing Add:* Dept of Animal Sci & Agr Biochem Univ of Del Newark DE 19711

REITSEMA, ROBERT HAROLD, b Grand Rapids, Mich, Jun 25, 20; m; c 4. GEOCHEMISTRY. *Educ:* Calvin Col, AB, 42; Univ Ill, PhD(org chem), 45. *Prof Exp:* Res chemist, Upjohn Co, 46-48; chief chemist, A M Todd Co, 48-57; sr res chemist, 57-60, sr planning assoc, 60-62, mgr, Chem Develop Div, Ohio, 62-69, RES ASSOC, DENVER RES CTR, MARATHON OIL CO, 69- *Concurrent Pos:* Adj prof, Findlay Col, 63-69, chmn natural sci div,

68-69. *Mem:* Am Chem Soc; European Asn Org Geochem; Sigma Xi; Geochem Soc. *Res:* Synthetic pharmaceuticals; essential oils; terpenes; petrochemical processes; plant design; organic geochemistry; origin and migration of natural gases and petroleum. *Mailing Add:* Denver Res Ctr Marathon Oil PO Box 269 Littleton CO 80120

REITZ, HERMAN J, b Belle Plaine, Kans, July 5, 16; m 45; c 2. HORTICULTURE. *Educ:* Kans State Col, BS, 39; Ohio State Univ, MS, 40, PhD(hort), 49. *Prof Exp:* From assoc horticulturist to horticulturist, 46-56, horticulturist chg, 57-65, DIR, FLA AGR RES & EDUC CTR, 65- *Mem:* Fel AAAS; Int Soc Citricult (pres, 73-77); Int Soc Hort Sci; fel Am Soc Hort Sci. *Res:* Mineral nutrition of citrus; citrus growing, harvesting and processing. *Mailing Add:* Agr Res & Educ Ctr PO Box 1088 Lake Alfred FL 33850

REITZ, JOHN MARSTELLER, organic chemistry, chemical engineering, see previous edition

REITZ, JOHN RICHARD, b Lakewood, Ohio, Feb 7, 23; m 47; c 4. THEORETICAL PHYSICS. *Educ:* Case Inst Technol, BS, 43; Univ Chicago, MS, 47, PhD(physics), 49. *Prof Exp:* Res assoc acoust, Underwater Sound Lab, Harvard Univ, 43-45; mem staff theoret physics, Los Alamos Sci Lab, Univ Calif, 49-52; sci liaison officer physics, Off Naval Res, London, 52-54; from asst prof to prof, Case Inst Technol, 54-65; MGR PHYSICS DEPT, SCI LAB, FORD MOTOR CO, 65- *Mem:* Fel Am Phys Soc. *Res:* Cohesion of solids; imperfection in alkalihalide crystals; electronic structure and transport properties of solids; plasma physics; high speed ground transportation; electricity and magnetism. *Mailing Add:* 3066 Overridge Dr Ann Arbor MI 48104

REITZ, LOUIS POWERS, b Belle Plaine, Kans, June 3, 07; m 33; c 2. PLANT BREEDING. *Educ:* Kans State Col, BS, 30; Univ Nebr, MS, 37; Univ Minn, PhD, 55. *Prof Exp:* Asst agronomist, Mont State Col, 30-35; agent grass breeding & ecol, Div Forage Crops & Dis, Bur Plant Indust, USDA, 35-38; from assoc prof to prof crop improv, Kans State Col, 39-47; agronomist, Div Cereal Crops & Dis, Bur Plant Indust, Soils & Agr Eng, USDA, 47-54; Cereal Crops Res Br, Agr Res Serv, 54-72; Nat Prog Staff, 72-75; RETIRED. *Mem:* AAAS; Am Soc Agron. *Res:* Plant breeding and ecology; cereal grain improvement. *Mailing Add:* 10654 Boswell Blvd Sun City AZ 85373

REITZ, RICHARD HENRY, b Minneapolis, Minn, Sept 1, 40; m 63; c 1. BIOCHEMISTRY, TOXICOLOGY. *Educ:* DePauw Univ, BS, 62; Northwestern Univ, Evanston, PhD(biochem), 66, Am Bd Toxicol, dipl. *Prof Exp:* Res biochemist drug develop, Human Health Res & Develop, 66-74, sr res biochemist fermentation, Cent Res Lab, 74-78, RES SPECIALIST, TOXICOL RES LAB, DOW CHEMICAL, 78- *Mem:* Am Chem Soc; Am Soc Microbiol; AAAS. *Res:* Chemical carcinogenesis and mutagenesis; microbiological production of chemicals; asthma and hypersensitivity; psychopharmacology. *Mailing Add:* Toxicol Res Lab 1803 Bldg Dow Chem Co Midland MI 48640

REITZ, ROBERT ALAN, b Lakewood, Ohio, Sept 8, 26; m 48; c 4. PHYSICS. *Educ:* Case Inst Technol, BS, 49; Univ Ill, MS, 51, PhD(physics), 55. *Prof Exp:* Asst physics, Univ Ill, 49-51 & 52-54; from asst prof to assoc prof, 54-65, chmn dept, 57-71, PROF PHYSICS, CARLETON COL, 65- *Concurrent Pos:* NSF fac fel, Ger, 63-64; vis scholar, Stanford Univ, 71-72 & Univ Calif, San Diego, 79-80. *Mem:* Am Phys Soc; Am Asn Physics Teachers; Sigma Xi. *Res:* Solid state physics. *Mailing Add:* Dept of Physics Carleton Col Northfield MN 55057

REITZ, ROBERT REX, b Oklahoma City, Okla, Dec 18, 43; m 67; c 2. ORGANIC CHEMISTRY. *Educ:* Austin Col, BA, 66; Kans State Univ, PhD(chem), 71. *Prof Exp:* Assoc org chem, Ohio State Univ, 72-73; RES CHEMIST, ELASTOMER CHEM DEPT, E I DU PONT DE NEMOURS & CO, INC, 73- *Mem:* Am Chem Soc. *Res:* Research and development of new synthetic rubber and rubber chemicals. *Mailing Add:* Beaumont Works PO Box 3269 Beaumont TX 77704

REITZ, RONALD CHARLES, b Dallas, Tex, Feb 27, 39; m 65; c 2. BIOCHEMISTRY. *Educ:* Tex A&M Univ, BS, 61; Tulane Univ, PhD(biochem), 66. *Prof Exp:* USPHS fel, Univ Mich, Ann Arbor, 66-69; asst prof biochem, Univ NC, Chapel Hill, 69-75; assoc prof, 75-80, PROF BIOCHEM, UNIV NEV, RENO, 80- *Concurrent Pos:* Vis scientist, Unilever Res Lab, Frythe, Welwyn, Eng, 68; sci consult, NC Ctr Alcohol Studies, 74-76. *Mem:* Am Soc Biol Chemists; Am Soc Pharmacol & Exp Ther; AAAS; Am Oil Chemists Soc; Western Pharmacol Soc. *Res:* Lipid metabolism; effects of chronic alcoholism on membrane lipids, liver glycogen, and on membrane function; membrane lipids of tumor tissue; sex pheromone synthesis in houseflies. *Mailing Add:* Dept of Biochem Univ of Nev Reno NV 89577

REIVICH, MARTIN, b Philadelphia, Pa, Mar 2, 33; m 60; c 2. NEUROLOGY. *Educ:* Univ Pa, BS, 54, MD, 58. *Prof Exp:* Intern med, King County Hosp, Seattle, Wash, 58-59; resident neurol, Hosp Univ Pa, 59-61; clin clerk, Nat Hosp, London, Eng, 61-62; instr, 62-65, instr pharmacol, 63-64, asst prof neurol, 66-68, assoc prof, 68-72, dir cerebrovascular res lab, 66-73, PROF NEUROL, SCH MED, UNIV PA, 72-, DIR CEREBROVASCULAR RES CTR, 73- *Concurrent Pos:* NIH res fel, 60-61, training grant, 63; Fulbright fel, 61-62; USPHS career res develop award, 66-75; res assoc physiol, NIMH, 64-65; mem coun cerebrovascular dis, Am Heart Asn, 67-; mem, Int Study Group Cerebral Circulation, 68-; mem neurol A study sect, NIH, 71-75; consult, Vet Admin Hosp, Philadelphia, 68- & US Naval Air Develop Ctr, 70-72; co-dir stroke ctr, Philadelphia Gen Hosp, 71-72; mem task force stroke, Nat Heart, Blood Vessel, Lung & Blood Prog. *Mem:* Am Neurol Asn; Am Physiol Soc; Soc Neurosci; Am Acad Neurol; Asn Res Nerv & Ment Dis. *Res:* Cerebral circulation and metabolism; cerebrovascular disease. *Mailing Add:* Dept of Neurol Hosp of Univ of Pa Philadelphia PA 19104

REJALI, ABBAS MOSTAFAVI, b Aug 19, 21; US citizen; m 54; c 1. RADIOLOGY, NUCLEAR MEDICINE. *Educ:* State Univ NY Downstate Med Ctr, MD, 51; Am Bd Radiol, dipl, 55. *Prof Exp:* Intern med, Grasslands Hosp, Valhalla, NY, 51-52; resident radiol, Univ Hosps, Cleveland, 52-55, teaching fel radiation ther & actg dir radiation ther, 56-57; assoc chief radiol, Roswell Park Mem Inst, 59-61; assoc prof radiol & nuclear med, 63-68, asst prof radiol, 68-76, ASSOC PROF RADIOL, CASE WESTERN RESERVE UNIV, 76-, DIR DEPT NUCLEAR MED, 74- *Concurrent Pos:* Atomic Energy Proj fel, Case Western Reserve Univ, 55-57; sect assoc radiation biol, 56-57; US rep, Int Atomic Energy Agency, 68 & 70; consult radiologist, Highland View Hosp, Metrop Gen Hosp & Huron Rd Hosp. *Mem:* Radiol Soc NAm; fel Am Col Nuclear Med; Soc Nuclear Med; Am Col Radiol. *Res:* Diagnostic use of radioisotope tracer; development of radioisotopic instrumentation. *Mailing Add:* Dept of Radiol Case Western Reserve Univ Cleveland OH 44106

REJTO, PETER A, b Budapest, Hungary, Apr 28, 34; US citizen; m 60; c 1. MATHEMATICS. *Educ:* NY Univ, PhD(math), 59. *Prof Exp:* Asst prof, NY Univ, 60-64 & Math Res Ctr, Univ Wis, 64-65; asst prof, 65-77, PROF MATH, SCH MATH, UNIV MINN, MINNEAPOLIS, 77- *Mem:* Am Math Asn; Am Math Soc; Soc Indust & Appl Math. *Res:* Spectral theory of operators in Hilbert space. *Mailing Add:* 1539 E River Terrace Minneapolis MN 55455

REKASIUS, ZENONAS V, b Lithuania, Jan 1, 28; m 60; c 3. ELECTRICAL ENGINEERING. *Educ:* Wayne State Univ, BS, 54, MS, 56; Purdue Univ, PhD(elec eng), 60. *Prof Exp:* From asst prof to assoc prof elec eng, Purdue Univ, 60-64; assoc prof, 64-68, PROF ELEC ENG, TECHNOL INST, NORTHWESTERN UNIV, 68- *Mem:* Inst Elec & Electronics Engrs. *Res:* Control systems; stability; optimization. *Mailing Add:* Dept of Elec Eng Northwestern Univ Technol Inst Evanston IL 60201

REKERS, ROBERT GEORGE, b Rochester, NY, Feb 1, 20; m 51; c 3. ANALYTICAL CHEMISTRY. *Educ:* Univ Rochester, BSc, 42; Univ Colo, PhD(chem), 51. *Prof Exp:* Asst foundry chemist, Gen Rwy Signal Co, 41; anal chemist & group leader, Eastman Kodak Co, 42-47; asst phys chem, Univ Colo, 47-51; spectroscopist, US Naval Ord Test Sta, Calif, 51-55; asst prof, 55-61, asst chmn dept, 69-75, ASSOC PROF CHEM, TEX TECH UNIV, 61- *Mem:* AAAS; Am Chem Soc; Colbentz Soc. *Res:* Spectroscopy of flames; instrumental methods of analysis. *Mailing Add:* Dept of Chem Tex Tech Univ Lubbock TX 79409

REKLAITIS, GINTARAS VICTOR, b Posen, Poland, Oct 20, 42; US citizen; m 66; c 2. COMPUTER AIDED DESIGN, APPLIED MATHEMATICS. *Educ:* Ill Inst Technol, BS, 65; Stanford Univ, MS, 68, PhD(chem eng), 69. *Prof Exp:* NSF fel, Inst Opers Res, Zurich, Switz, 69-70; asst prof, 70-76, assoc prof, 76-80, PROF CHEM ENG, PURDUE UNIV, WEST LAFAYETTE, 80- *Concurrent Pos:* Fulbright sr lectr, Lithuania, 80. *Mem:* Am Chem Soc; Math Prog Soc; Opers Res Soc Am; Am Inst Chem Engrs. *Res:* Optimization theory; process simulation; computer aided design; modelling and analysis of coal conversion processes; analysis and design of batch processes. *Mailing Add:* Sch Chem Eng Purdue Univ West Lafayette IN 47907

REKOFF, M(ICHAEL) G(EORGE), JR, b Galveston, Tex, July 27, 29; m 51; c 3. ELECTRICAL ENGINEERING. *Educ:* Agr & Mech Col, Tex, BSEE, 51, MSEE, 55; Univ Wis, PhD(elec eng), 61. *Prof Exp:* Instr elec eng, Agr & Mech Col, Tex, 54-56 & Univ Wis, 56-59; from asst prof to assoc prof, Tex A&M Univ, 59-69; mem tech staff, TRW Systs Group, 69-70; staff engr, Telelyn Brown Eng, 70-76; dir elec res & develop, Onan Corp, 76-79; EMER PROF, UNIV TENN CHATTANOOGA, 79- *Mem:* Inst Elec & Electronics Engrs; Instrument Soc Am; Soc Mfg Engrs. *Res:* Servo-mechanisms; computing; machines; systems engineering. *Mailing Add:* Sch Eng Chattanooga TN 37402

RELLER, HERBERT HENRY, b Rochester, NY, July 22, 25; m 49; c 3. BIOCHEMISTRY, DERMATOLOGY. *Educ:* Evansville Col, AB, 48; Univ Ind, PhD(biochem), 52. *Prof Exp:* RES BIOCHEMIST, PROCTER & GAMBLE CO, 52- *Concurrent Pos:* Vis res prof, Dept Dermat, Med Sch, Univ Ore, 67-68. *Mem:* Am Chem Soc; Am Acad Dermat; Soc Invest Dermat. *Res:* Biology and chemistry of the skin; clinical skin studies; percutaneous absorption; physiology of epidermis and appendages, sweat glands, sebaceous glands; sebaceous and epidermal lipids; hydration characteristics of stratum corneum; topically applied drugs. *Mailing Add:* 5935 Farlook Dr Cincinnati OH 45239

RELMAN, ARNOLD SEYMOUR, b New York, NY, June 17, 23; m 53; c 3. MEDICINE. *Educ:* Cornell Univ, AB, 43; Columbia Univ, MD, 46; Am Bd Internal Med, dipl, 52, 74. *Prof Exp:* House officer med, New Haven Hosp & asst internal med, Sch Med, Yale Univ, 46-49; asst prof med, Sch Med, Boston Univ, 50-56, assoc prof, 56-61, prof, 61, Sch Med & vis physician & head renal sect, Mass Mem Hosp, 61-68; Frank Wister Thomas prof med & chmn dept, Sch Med, Univ Pa, 68-77; dir med serv, Hosp Univ Pa, 68-77; PROF MED, HARVARD MED SCH, 77- *Concurrent Pos:* Nat Res Coun fel med sci, Evans Mem Dept Clin Res, Mass Mem Hosps, 49-50; Nat Inst Arthritis & Metab Dis res career award, 61-67; consult, Boston Vet Admin Hosp, 55-68; spec consult, NIH, 59-62; ed-in-chief, J Clin Invest, Am Soc Clin Invest, 62-67; mem bd, Am Bd Internal Med, 65-69; chief, Boston Univ Med Serv, Boston City Hosp, 67-78; ed, New Eng J Med; attend physician, Brigham & Women's Hosp, Boston; mem, Inst Med, Nat Acad Sci, 77-; vis mem, Merton Col, Univ Oxford, 75-76. *Mem:* Am Acad Arts & Sci; Am Col Physicians; Am Physiol Soc; Am Fedn Clin Res (vpres, 59-60, pres, 60-61); Am Soc Clin Invest (pres, 68-69). *Res:* Kidney physiology and disease; acid-base and electrolyte physiology; internal medicine and medical education. *Mailing Add:* 10 Shattuck St Boston MA 02115

RELYEA, DOUGLAS IRVING, b Rochester, NY, Sept 20, 30; m 57; c 4. ORGANIC CHEMISTRY. *Educ:* Clarkson Tech, BS, 51; Cornell Univ, MS, 53; Univ SC, PhD(chem), 54. *Prof Exp:* Proj assoc org chem, Univ Wis, 54-56; res scientist, Gen Labs, US Rubber Co, 56-57 & Res Ctr, 57-64, sr res scientist, 64-70; res assoc corp res & develop, Oxford Mgt & Res Ctr, 72-80, RES ASSOC CROP PROTECTION CHEM RES, NAUGATUCK RES CTR, UNIROYAL, INC, 80- *Mem:* Am Chem Soc; Royal Soc Chem. *Res:* Free radical reactions; chemistry of sulfur compounds, aromatic substitution; chemistry of nitrogen compounds; biological activity of organic compounds; chemical structure retrieval. *Mailing Add:* Naugatuck Res Ctr Uniroyal Inc Naugatuck CT 06770

RELYEA, JOHN FRANKLIN, b Stuttgart, Ark, Oct 25, 47; m 74; c 1. SOIL SCIENCE. *Educ:* Univ Ark, BS, 69, MS, 72, PhD(agron), 78. *Prof Exp:* RES SCIENTIST ENVIRON CHEM, BATTELLE PAC NORTHWEST LABS, 77- *Mem:* AAAS; Am Soc Agron. *Res:* Soil chemistry and soil physics; environmental chemistry; radionuclide chemistry in geologic media. *Mailing Add:* Waste Geol Media Interaction Sect PO Box 999 Richland WA 99352

RELYEA, KENNETH GEORGE, b New York, NY, Oct 24, 41; m 62; c 1. ICHTHYOLOGY, ECOLOGY. *Educ:* Fla State Univ, BA, 62, MS, 65; Tulane Univ, PhD(ichthyol), 67. *Prof Exp:* Asst prof, 67-72, ASSOC PROF BIOL, JACKSONVILLE UNIV, 72- *Mem:* AAAS; Am Soc Ichthyol & Herpet; Ecol Soc Am. *Res:* Systematics, ecology and behavior of Ictalurid catfishes and killifishes. *Mailing Add:* Dept Biol Jacksonville Univ Jacksonville FL 32211

REMAR, JOSEPH FRANCIS, b Bridgeport, Pa, Oct 2, 38; m 67; c 1. ORGANIC CHEMISTRY. *Educ:* Villanova Univ, BS, 60; Pa State Univ, PhD(chem), 66. *Prof Exp:* SR RES CHEMIST, ARMSTRONG CORK CO, 66- *Mem:* Am Chem Soc. *Res:* Urethane foams and coatings. *Mailing Add:* 127 Wellington Rd Lancaster PA 17603

REMBAUM, ALAN, b Ciechanow, Poland, Jan 8, 16; US citizen; m 54; c 1. AGRICULTURAL & FOOD CHEMISTRY. *Educ:* Univ Lyon, France, Lic sci, 41, Univ Syracuse, PhD(chem), 56. *Prof Exp:* Asst prof polymer chem, Akron Univ, 56-59; res assoc, Princeton Univ, 59-61; sr res assoc, 61-70, SUPVR TECH GROUP, JET PROPULSION LAB, CALIF INST TECHNOL, 70-, RES SCIENTIST, 81- *Concurrent Pos:* Lectr, Calif Inst Technol, 64-72. *Mem:* Am Chem Soc; Sigma Xi. *Res:* Synthesis and electronic transfer properties of polymers, polyelectrolytes and charge transfer complexes; colloidal properties of polymeric spherical particles and their applications in immunology and clinical medicine; author or coauthor of over 120 publications. *Mailing Add:* Jet Propulsion Lab Calif Inst Technol 4800 Oak Grove Dr Pasadena CA 91109

REMEDIOS, E(DWARD) C(HARLES), b Vengurla, India, Nov 17, 41. CHEMICAL ENGINEERING. *Educ:* Univ Edinburgh, BSc, 65, PhD(chem eng), 69; Univ Calif, Berkeley, MBA, 79. *Prof Exp:* Res engr, Chevron Res Co, 69-73; sr resource engr, 73-78, supv resource engr, 78-80, COORDR, PAC GAS & ELEC CO, 80- *Mem:* Pac Coast Gas Asn. *Res:* Development, design and economic evaluation of gas supply projects from alternate energy sources. *Mailing Add:* Pac Gas & Elec Co 245 Market St San Francisco CA 94106

REMENYIK, CARL JOHN, b Budapest, Hungary, May 5, 27; US citizen; m 68; c 1. FLUID MECHANICS. *Educ:* Swiss Fed Inst Technol, Dipl, 51; Johns Hopkins Univ, PhD(aeronaut), 62. *Prof Exp:* Asst fluid dynamics, Swiss Fed Inst Technol, 51-52, asst mach tools, 52-53; sr aeronaut engr, Convair Div, Gen Dynamics, Tex, 57; eng specialist, Martin-Marietta, Md, 61-64; asst prof fluid mech, 64-66, assoc prof fluid mech, 66-80, PROF DEPT ENG SCI & MECH, UNIV TENN, KNOXVILLE, 80- *Concurrent Pos:* Consult, Reactor Div, Oak Ridge Nat Labs, 64- & molecular anat prog, 72- *Mem:* Am Phys Soc. *Res:* Aerodynamically generated sound in boundary layers; heat transfer in hypersonic boundary layers; mechanics of biological fluids; centrifugation; dynamics of oscillating liquids and bubbles; magnetohydrodynamic vortex flow. *Mailing Add:* Dept of Eng Sci & Mech Univ of Tenn Knoxville TN 37916

REMER, DONALD SHERWOOD, b Detroit, Mich, Feb 16, 43; m 69. ENGINEERING ECONOMICS, CHEMICAL ENGINEERING. *Educ:* Univ Mich, Ann Arbor, BS, 65; Calif Inst Technol, MS, 66, PhD(chem eng, bus econ), 70. *Prof Exp:* Tech contact engr chem raw mat, Exxon Chem Co, USA, 70-71, div coordr, 72, startup engr new ethylene unit, 72-73, sr proj engr, 72-73, econ & forecast coordr, 73-75, task force mgr, 74-75; assoc prof, 75-80, PROF ENG, HARVEY MUDD COL ENG & SCI, CLAREMONT, 80-, DIR ENERGY INST, 81- *Concurrent Pos:* Sr eng consult, Caltech's Jet Propulsion Lab, 75-80, mem tech staff, 80-; Westinghouse Found grant eng econ & Shelby Cullum Found grant eng mgt, Harvey Mudd Col, 78-; case study ed, The Eng Economist; mem adv coun, Nat Energy Found, 81- *Mem:* Am Inst Chem Engrs; Am Soc Eng Mgt; Am Soc Eng Educ; Int Asn Energy Economists. *Res:* Life cycle cost economic analysis; engineering management and engineering economic analysis and optimization of capital projects; energy management and planning; air and water pollution abatement; oil shale, solar energy and cogeneration. *Mailing Add:* Dept of Eng Harvey Mudd Col of Eng & Sci Claremont CA 91711

REMERS, WILLIAM ALAN, b Cincinnati, Ohio, Oct 14, 32; m 61; c 2. ORGANIC CHEMISTRY, MEDICINAL CHEMISTRY. *Educ:* Mass Inst Technol, BS, 54; Univ Ill, PhD, 58. *Prof Exp:* USPHS res fel org chem, Oxford Univ, 58-59; org chemist, Lederle Labs, Am Cyanamid Co, NY, 59-70; assoc prof, 70-72, prof med chem, Sch Pharm & Pharmaceut Sci, Purdue Univ, 72-76, assoc head dept, 74-76; PROF MED CHEM, COL PHARM, UNIV ARIZ, 76-, HEAD DEPT, 80- *Concurrent Pos:* Res grants, Nat Cancer Inst, 71- & Bristol Labs, 75- *Mem:* The Chem Soc; Acad Pharmaceut Sci; Am Chem Soc; Am Pharmaceut Asn; Am Soc Microbiol. *Res:* Antibiotics; heterocycles; synthetic methods; cancer chemotherapeutic agents; cardiotonics. *Mailing Add:* Col of Pharm Univ of Ariz Tucson AZ 85721

REMES, NATHANIEL L, organic chemistry, deceased

REMICK, FORREST J(EROME), b Lock Haven, Pa, Mar 16, 31; m 53; c 2. NUCLEAR ENGINEERING, MECHANICAL ENGINEERING. *Educ:* Pa State Univ, BS, 55, MS, 58, PhD, 63. *Prof Exp:* Design engr, Bell Tel Labs, Inc, 55; nuclear engr, Nuclear Reactor Facil, Pa State Univ, 56-59, dir, 59-65, assoc prof, 63-67, actg dir, Ctr Air Environ Studies, 76-78, dir, Inst Sci & Eng & asst to vpres res & grad studies, 67-79, prof nuclear eng, 67-81, asst vpres res & grad studies & dir inter-col res progs, 79-81; DIR, OFF POLICY EVAL, US NUCLEAR REGULATORY COMN, 81- *Concurrent Pos:* Dir, Curtiss-Wright Nuclear Res Lab, 60-65; mem res reactor subcomt, Nat Acad Sci-Nat Res Coun, 63-65; mem, Atomic Safety & Licensing Bd Panel, 72-; consult, US Nuclear Regulatory Comn, US Air Force & Dept of Energy. *Mem:* Fel Am Nuclear Soc; Am Soc Mech Engrs; Am Soc Eng Educ. *Res:* Reactor design and operation; heat transfer and fluid flow in reactor systems. *Mailing Add:* US Nuclear Regulatory Comn 1717 H St NW Washington DC 20555

REMINE, WILLIAM HERVEY, b Richmond, Va, Oct 11, 18; m 43; c 4. SURGERY. *Educ:* Univ Richmond, BS, 40; Med Col Va, MD, 43; Univ Minn, MS, 52; Am Bd Surg, dipl. *Hon Degrees:* DSc, Univ Richmond, 65. *Prof Exp:* From asst prof to assoc prof, 59-69, PROF SURG, MAYO GRAD SCH MED, UNIV MINN, 69-, HEAD SECT SURG, MAYO FOUND, 52- *Concurrent Pos:* Consult, Surgeon Gen, 53- *Mem:* Fel Am Col Surgeons; Asn Mil Surgeons US; Soc Surg Alimentary Tract; hon fel Venezuelan Soc Surg; hon fel Colombian Col Surg. *Res:* Surgery of the gastrointestinal tract; head and neck surgery. *Mailing Add:* 200 First St SW Rochester MN 55901

REMINGTON, C(HARLES) R(OY), JR, b Webster Groves, Mo, July 15, 24; m 46; c 2. MECHANICAL ENGINEERING. *Educ:* Mo Sch Mines, BSME, 49, MSME, 50. *Prof Exp:* From instr to assoc prof, 50-61, PROF MECH ENG, UNIV MO, ROLLA, 61- *Concurrent Pos:* Asst dir indust res ctr, Univ Mo, 65-66. *Mem:* Am Soc Eng Educ; Soc Automotive Engrs; Am Soc Mech Engrs; Nat Soc Prof Engrs. *Res:* Heat transfer by conduction in solids, liquids and gases; thermal contact resistance; automotive emission studies and control. *Mailing Add:* Dept Mech Eng Univ Mo Rolla MO 65401

REMINGTON, CHARLES LEE, b Reedville, Va, Jan 19, 22; m 46; c 3. EVOLUTIONARY GENETICS, ENTOMOLOGY. *Educ:* Principia Col, BS, 43; Harvard Univ, AM, 47, PhD(biol), 48. *Prof Exp:* From instr to asst prof zool, Yale Univ, 48-56, res assoc, Peabody Mus, 53-56, assoc cur entom, 56-74, ASSOC PROF BIOL, YALE UNIV, 56-, FEL, PIERSON COL, 50-, CUR ENTOM, PEABODY MUS, 74-, ASSOC PROF FOREST ENTOM, 79- *Concurrent Pos:* Ed, Jour Lepidopterists Soc, 47-64; entom ed, Conn Geol & Natural Hist Surv, 51-76; secy, Rocky Mountain Biol Lab, 55-59, trustee, 62-63; dir, Zero Pop Growth, 68-71, vpres, 69-71; dir, Coun Pop & Environ, 69-76, prog chmn, First Nat Cong; dir, Equil Fund, 70-76, pres, 73-75; res fel entom, CSIRO, Australia, 76; res fel zool, Campinas Univ, Brazil, 81; res assoc entom, Univ Calif, Berkeley, 81; mem, Survival Serv Comn, Int Union Conserv Nature & Natural Resources, 79- *Mem:* Soc Study Evolution; Am Soc Naturalists; Ecol Soc Am; Soc Syst Zool; Lepidopterists Soc (pres, 71). *Res:* Animal interspecific hybridization; island biology; genetics and biology of mimicry; systematics and caryology of Lepidoptera, Thysanura and Microcoryphia; biomed ethics. *Mailing Add:* Dept of Biol Yale Univ New Haven CT 06511

REMINGTON, JACK SAMUEL, b Chicago, Ill, Jan 19, 31; m 55; c 2. INTERNAL MEDICINE. *Educ:* Univ Ill, BS, 54, MD, 56; Am Bd Internal Med, dipl, 65. *Prof Exp:* Intern, Univ Calif Serv, San Francisco County Hosp, 56; res assoc, Nat Inst Allergy & Infectious Dis, 57-59; asst resident med, Med Ctr, Univ Calif, San Francisco, 59-60; Nat Inst Allergy & Infectious Dis sr res fel infectious dis, Harvard Med Sch & Thorndike Mem Lab, 60-62; from instr to assoc prof, 62-74, PROF MED, SCH MED, STANFORD UNIV, 74-; CHMN, DEPT IMMUNOL & INFECTIOUS DIS, RES INST & CHIEF CONSULT INFECTIOUS DIS, MED CLIN, PALO ALTO MED FOUND, 62- *Concurrent Pos:* Scientist under US-Soviet Health Exchange, 66, 69; consult, Vet Admin Hosp, Palo Alto, 62-; spec consult, Proctor Found, Med Ctr, Univ Calif, San Francisco, 66-; infectious dis consult, WHO, 67-, Pan-Am Health Orgn, 67- & Dept Army, Ft Ord, Calif, 71-; mem bd, Gorgas Mem Inst, 72-78. *Mem:* Am Asn Immunol; Am Soc Microbiol; Infectious Dis Soc Am. *Res:* Congenital infection; acquired toxoplasmosis; compromised host and infection; immunoglobulins in body secretions; defense mechanisms of the host; role of cellular immunity in resistance to infections with intracellular organisms; tumor immunology. *Mailing Add:* Res Inst Palo Alto Med Found 860 Bryant St Palo Alto CA 94301

REMINGTON, JOHN ALVAH, molecular, cell biology, see previous edition

REMINGTON, LLOYD DEAN, b Jackson, Mich, Dec 29, 19; m 44; c 4. ANALYTICAL CHEMISTRY. *Educ:* Univ Mich, BS, 42; Univ Fl, MEd, 54, PhD(anal chem), 66; Cornell Univ, MST, 62. *Prof Exp:* Chemist, Buick Motors Div, Gen Motors Corp, 42-45; teacher jr high schs & jr cols, Pinellas County, Fla, 46-66; asst prof, 65-67, assoc prof, 67-80, PROF CHEM, UNIV NC, ASHEVILLE, 80- *Concurrent Pos:* Ford Found Univ Chicago Proj sci adv, EPakistan Exten Ctr, 69-71. *Honors & Awards:* Am Chem Soc Award, 61. *Mem:* Am Chem Soc; fel Am Inst Chemists; AAAS. *Res:* Chemistry curriculum at secondary school and college level; science curriculum at elementary and junior high school level; codirector program in England on comparison of British and North American practices in teaching science. *Mailing Add:* Dept of Chem Univ of NC Asheville NC 28804

REMINGTON, RICHARD DELLERAINE, b Nampa, Idaho, Aug 2, 31; m 52; c 2. BIOSTATISTICS. *Educ:* Mon State Univ, BA, 52, MA, 54; Univ Mich, MPH, 57, PhD(biostatist), 58. *Prof Exp:* Instr math, Mont State Univ, 55-56; from asst prof to prof biostatist, Univ Mich, Ann Arbor, 58-69; prof biomet & assoc dean, Sch Pub Health, Univ Tex, Houston, 69-74; DEAN SCH PUB HEALTH, UNIV MICH, ANN ARBOR, 74- *Concurrent Pos:* USPHS spec res fel, Dept Med, Statist & Epidemiol, London Sch Hyg & Trop Med, Eng, 66-67; vis prof, Univ Calif, Berkeley, 72; vpres res, Am Heart Asn, 74-75 & 78-80; consult, USPHS, US Vet Admin & Nat Res Coun, Mich State

Dept Health. *Mem:* Fel Am Statist Asn; Am Pub Health Asn; Biomet Soc; Asn Schs Pub Health (pres, 75-77); Am Epitomiological Soc. *Res:* Medical and health applications of statistical and mathematical models. *Mailing Add:* Sch of Pub Health Univ of Mich Ann Arbor MI 48109

REMINGTON, WILLIAM ROSCOE, b Danville, Ohio, Nov 10, 18; m 42; c 6. ORGANIC CHEMISTRY. *Educ:* Univ Chicago, SB, 40, PhD(org chem), 44. *Prof Exp:* Asst, Nat Defense Res Comt Proj, Univ Chicago, 42-44, group leader, 44-45; res chemist, Jackson Lab, E I du Pont de Nemours & Co, 45-51, group leader, 51, div head, 51-71; prof, Nat Polytech Sch, Quito, Ecuador, 71-73; div head, 73-76, RES ASSOC, JACKSON LAB, E I DU PONT DE NEMOURS & CO, 76- *Mem:* Am Chem Soc. *Res:* Dyes; dyeing mechanisms; polymer permeability; organic synthesis. *Mailing Add:* E I du Pont de Nemours & Co Box 525 Wilmington DE 19899

REMLER, EDWARD A, b Vienna, Austria, Dec 26, 34; US citizen; m 61; c 2. PHYSICS. *Educ:* Mass Inst Technol, BS, 55; Columbia Univ, MS, 60; Univ NC, PhD(physics), 63. *Prof Exp:* Res assoc physics, Univ NC, 63-64; instr, Princeton Univ, 64-66; fel, Lawrence Livermore Lab, Univ Calif, 66-67; from asst prof to assoc prof, 67-77, PROF PHYSICS, COL WILLIAM & MARY, 77- *Mem:* Am Phys Soc. *Res:* Quantum mechanics; particle physics. *Mailing Add:* Dept of Physics Col of William & Mary Williamsburg VA 23185

REMLEY, FRANK MORRIS, b Berwick, Pa, Apr 2, 20; m 52; c 3. CROP BREEDING, PLANT BREEDING. *Educ:* Cornell Univ, BS, 56. *Prof Exp:* Geneticist, 60-66, mgr tech serv, Seed Dept, 66-68, mgr res & develop, 68-72, asst vpres res & develop, 72-75, CORP MGR SEED RES & DEVELOP, CARGILL INC, 75- *Mem:* Am Soc Agron. *Mailing Add:* Cargill Inc Seed Div PO Box 9300 Dept 16 Minneapolis MN 55440

REMLEY, MARLIN EUGENE, b Walcott, Ark, Apr 25, 21; m 43; c 3. PHYSICS. *Educ:* Southeast Mo State Col, AB, 41; Univ Ill, MS, 48, PhD(physics), 52. *Prof Exp:* Instr physics & math, Southeast Mo State Col, 46-47; asst physics, Univ Ill, 47-52; res engr exp physics, NAm Aviation, Inc, 52-55, supvr exp physics, Atomics Int Div, 55-56, group leader reactor kinetics, 56-58, actg chief reactor develop, 58, dir spec projs, 59-60, reactor physics & instrumentation, 60-61, dir health safety & radiation serv, 61-67, DIR HEALTH SAFETY & RADIATION SERV, ENERGY SYSTS GROUP, ROCKWELL INT, 67- *Mem:* Am Phys Soc; fel Am Nuclear Soc; Atomic Indust Forum. *Res:* Nuclear and reactor physics; nuclear scattering; scintillation counters; reactor design and development; reactor dynamics and safety; radiological safety; nuclear materials management and safeguards; author or coauthor of over 50 publications. *Mailing Add:* Rockwell Int Corp Energy Systs Group 8900 De Soto Ave Canoga Park CA 91304

REMMEL, RANDALL JAMES, b Peoria, Ill, Aug 23, 49. INORGANIC CHEMISTRY. *Educ:* Ill State Univ, BS, 71; Ohio State Univ, PhD(inorg chem), 75. *Prof Exp:* Res assoc, Mat Lab, Polymer Br, US Air Force, 75-76; ASST PROF CHEM, UNIV ALA, BIRMINGHAM, 76- *Mem:* Am Chem Soc. *Res:* Synthesis and characterization of metallacarboranes, metallaboranes and boron-boron bonded polyhedcal boraves; nuclear magnetic resonance relaxation studies of boranes; borane derivatives and their anions. *Mailing Add:* Dept Chem Univ Ala Birmingham AL 35294

REMMEL, RONALD SYLVESTER, b West Bend, Wis, July 18, 43; m 72. NEUROPHYSIOLOGY, NEUROANATOMY. *Educ:* Calif Inst Technol, BS, 65; Princeton Univ, PhD(physics), 71. *Prof Exp:* Res assoc physics, Princeton Univ, 71-72; fel physiol, Univ Calif, Berkeley, 72-74; fel ophthal, Med Sch, Johns Hopkins Univ, 74-75; asst prof, 75-81, ASSOC PROF PHYSIOL, UNIV ARK FOR MED SCI, 81- *Concurrent Pos:* NIH fel, 72-75; fel, Fight for Sight Inc, NY, 75; NIH gen res grant, Univ Ark for Med Sci, 75-76; prin invest, Nat Eye Inst res grant, 76-79; grants, NIMH, 79-81 & NSF, 80- *Mem:* Soc Neurosci; Asn Res Vision & Ophthal; Am Physiol Soc; AAAS; Sigma Xi. *Res:* Study of cat brainstem neurons involved in the control of eye movements; vestibular reflexes and spinal motor mechanisms through use of electrophysiological techniques. *Mailing Add:* Dept Physiol & Biophys 4301 W Markham St Little Rock AR 72205

REMMENGA, ELMER EDWIN, b Douglas, Nebr, Jan 9, 27; m 53; c 5. STATISTICS. *Educ:* Univ Nebr, BS, 50; Purdue Univ, MS, 53, PhD, 55. *Prof Exp:* Asst statistician, Exp Sta, Purdue Univ, 50-55; from asst prof to assoc prof math, 55-62, sta statistician, 55-64, chief comput ctr, 57-62, PROF APPL STATIST, COLO STATE UNIV, 62- *Concurrent Pos:* Math consult, Bur Mines Res Ctr, Colo, 58-; vis biometrician, Waite Agr Res Inst, Univ Adelaide, 61-62; vis prof, Univ Colo, 62-65; statist consult, Nat Water Qual Lab, Environ Protection Agency, Minn, 70-; vis prof, Swiss Fed Forestry Res Inst. *Mem:* Biomet Soc; Am Statist Asn; Inst Math Statist. *Res:* Application of statistical methods to biological sciences; design sampling; computing. *Mailing Add:* Dept Statist Colo State Univ Ft Collins CO 80521

REMOLE, ARNULF, b Melhus, Norway, July 1, 28; Can citizen; m 65; c 1. PHYSIOLOGICAL OPTICS, OPTOMETRY. *Educ:* Univ Man, BFA, 58; Ont Col Optom, OD, 62; Ind Univ, Bloomington, MS, 67, PhD(physiol optics), 69. *Prof Exp:* Instr optom, Sch Optom, Ont Col Optom, 62-66; teaching assoc physiol optics, Ind Univ, Bloomington, 68-69; asst prof, 69-74, assoc prof, 74-81, PROF OPTOM, UNIV WATERLOO, 81- *Mem:* Fel Am Acad Optom; Can Asn Optom, Optical Soc Am. *Res:* Psychophysics of vision; border effects; visual pattern responses arising from temporal modulations of the stimulus; binocular vision; visual performance evaluation; optics of the eye; optometrical instrumentation; aniseikonia. *Mailing Add:* Sch of Optom Univ of Waterloo Waterloo ON N2L 3G1 Can

REMONDINI, DAVID JOSEPH, b Deming, NMex, Dec 27, 31; m 52; c 6. GENETICS. *Educ:* Univ Calif, Santa Barbara, BA, 55; Univ Utah, MS, 64; Utah State Univ, PhD(zool-genetics), 67. *Prof Exp:* Teacher pub schs, Calif, 55-62; asst prof biol, Gonzaga Univ, 67-74; assoc prof biol sci, Mich Technol Univ, 74-77; EXEC SECY GENETICS STUDY SECT, DIV RES GRANTS, NIH, HEW, 77- *Concurrent Pos:* Jesuit Res Coun res grant, Gonzaga Univ,

67-71, dir summer sessions & spec progs, 71-73; consult genetics, Sacred Heart Med Ctr, Spokane, 73-74. *Mem:* AAAS; Genetics Soc Am; Am Soc Human Genetics; Genetics Soc Can. *Res:* Human cytogenetics; Drosophila genetics; temperature sensitivity; maternal effects. *Mailing Add:* Div Res Grants SRB NIH Bethesda MD 20014

REMPEL, ARTHUR GUSTAV, b Russia, Jan 5, 10; nat US; m 34; c 3. ZOOLOGY. *Educ:* Oberlin Col, AB, 34; Univ Calif, PhD(zool), 38. *Prof Exp:* Actg cur, Mus Zool & Anthrop, Oberlin Col, 31-34; custodian, Dept Zool, Univ Calif, 34-35, asst, 35-38; from instr to prof, 38-75, cur, Mus Natural Hist, 38-46 & 53-71, EMER PROF BIOL, WHITMAN COL, 75- *Mem:* Fel AAAS. *Res:* Embryology. *Mailing Add:* 635 University St Walla Walla WA 99362

REMPEL, GARRY LLEWELLYN, b Regina, Sask, Aug 20, 44. INORGANIC CHEMISTRY, CATALYSIS. *Educ:* Univ BC, BSc, 65, PhD(phys inorg chem), 68. *Prof Exp:* Nat Res Coun Can fel, Imp Col, Univ London, 68-69; asst prof, 69-73, assoc prof, 73-80, PROF CHEM ENG, UNIV WATERLOO, 80- *Concurrent Pos:* Consult, Polysar Ltd, 81- & Chinook Chem, 81- *Mem:* Royal Soc Chem; fel Chem Inst Can; Am Chem Soc. *Res:* Coordination chemistry and homogeneous catalysis; organometallic chemistry; physical chemistry of hydrometallurgical processes; polymer supported and entrapped metal catalysts; catalyts for waste water treatment. *Mailing Add:* Dept of Chem Eng Univ of Waterloo Waterloo ON N2L 3G1 Can

REMPEL, HERMAN G, b Ukraine, Apr 8, 02; nat US; m 33; c 3. CHEMISTRY. *Educ:* Bethel Col, Kans, BA, 27. *Prof Exp:* Chemist, Inyo Chem Co, 27-29; chief chemist, Twining Labs, Calif, 29-71; AGR CONSULT, RESOURCES INT, 71- *Mem:* Am Chem Soc; Nat Soc Prof Engrs; Int Food Technologists. *Res:* Agricultural chemistry; insecticides; toxicology; chemical engineering. *Mailing Add:* Resources Int 402 Rowell Bldg Fresno CA 93721

REMPEL, WILLIAM EWERT, b Man, Can, July 6, 21; nat US; m 48; c 2. ANIMAL BREEDING. *Educ:* Univ Man, BSA, 44, MSc, 46; Univ Minn, PhD(animal breeding), 52. *Prof Exp:* Instr animal husb, Univ Man, 46-47; agr rep, Man Dept Agr, 47-48; asst, 48-49, from instr to assoc prof, 50-64, PROF ANIMAL HUSB, UNIV MINN, ST PAUL, 64- *Concurrent Pos:* Dir genetics ctr, Univ Minn, 65-67. *Mem:* Fel AAAS; Am Soc Animal Sci; Genetics Soc Am. *Res:* Genetics. *Mailing Add:* Dept of Animal Sci Univ of Minn St Paul MN 55108

REMPFER, GERTRUDE FLEMING, b Seattle, Wash, Jan 30, 12; m 42; c 4. PHYSICS. *Educ:* Univ Wash, BS, 34, PhD(physics), 39. *Prof Exp:* Instr physics, Mt Holyoke Col, 39-40 & Russell Sage Col, 40-42; physicist, Naval Res Lab, 42-43 & SAM Lab, Columbia Univ, 44; proj engr, Farrand Optical Co, 45-51; assoc prof eng, Antioch Col, 51-52; assoc prof physics, Fisk Univ, 53-57; assoc prof, Pac Univ, 57-59; assoc prof, 59-68, prof, 68-77, EMER PROF PHYSICS, PORTLAND STATE UNIV, 77- *Concurrent Pos:* Consult, AMP, Inc, 51-57; Tektronix, 60-70 & Elektros, 70-75; NSF grant, 79-82; pres, E-scope, 75- *Mem:* Am Phys Soc; Am Asn Physics Teachers; Electron Micros Soc Am; Sigma Xi. *Res:* Electron physics; electron and ion optics; electron microscopy. *Mailing Add:* Dept of Physics Portland State Univ PO Box 751 Portland OR 97207

REMPFER, ROBERT WEIR, b Parkston, SDak, Apr 14, 14; m 42; c 4. MATHEMATICS. *Educ:* Univ SDak, BA, 33; Northwestern Univ, MA, 34, PhD(math), 37. *Prof Exp:* Instr math, Rensselaer Polytech Inst, 37-44; physicist, SAM Labs, Columbia Univ, 44-45 & Farrand Optical Co, 45-50; prof math, Antioch Col, 50-53; assoc prof, Fisk Univ, 53-57; assoc prof, 57-58, PROF MATH, PORTLAND STATE UNIV, 58- *Concurrent Pos:* Chmn dept math, Portland State Univ, 58-67. *Mem:* Am Math Soc. *Res:* Gaseous diffusion; electron optical design; interference optics; probability; information theory; geometry. *Mailing Add:* Dept of Math Portland State Univ Portland OR 97207

REMSBERG, ELLIS EDWARD, b Buckeystown, Md, Oct 24, 43; m 67; c 2. ATMOSPHERIC PHYSICS. *Educ:* Va Polytech Inst, BS, 66; Univ Wis-Madison, MS, 68, PhD(meteorol), 71. *Prof Exp:* Jr res asst, Nat Radio Astron Observ, 62-65; geophysicist, US Coast & Geod Surv, 66; res asst chem, Univ Minn, 69-70; lectr meteorol, Univ Wis-Madison, 71; res asst prof chem, Col William & Mary, 71-72; res asst prof & NASA res grant geophys, Old Dominion Univ, 72-73; aerospace technologist, 73-80, SR RES SCIENTIST, LANGLEY RES CTR, NASA, 80- *Mem:* Am Geophys Union; Am Meteorol Soc. *Res:* Air chemistry; radiative energy budgets; satellite meteorology; processes in the stratosphere; laser applications. *Mailing Add:* 124 Sleepy Hollow Lane Yorktown VA 23692

REMSBERG, LOUIS PHILIP, JR, b Rupert, Idaho, Sept 14, 33; m 57; c 3. NUCLEAR CHEMISTRY. *Educ:* Univ Idaho, BS, 55, MS, 56; Columbia Univ, PhD(phys chem), 61. *Prof Exp:* Actg instr chem, Univ Idaho, 55-56; CHEMIST, BROOKHAVEN NAT LAB, 61- *Mem:* Am Chem Soc. *Res:* Nuclear reactions and properties *Mailing Add:* Brookhaven Nat Lab Upton NY 11973

REMSEN, CHARLES C, III, b Newark, NJ, May 16, 37; m 60, 76; c 4. MICROBIOLOGY, LIMNOLOGY. *Educ:* Nat Agr Col, BS, 60; Syracuse Univ, MS, 63, PhD(microbiol), 65. *Prof Exp:* NIH fel, 65-67; asst scientist biol, Woods Hole Oceanog Inst, 67-71, assoc scientist, 71-75; MEM FAC, DEPT ZOOL, UNIV WIS-MILWAUKEE, 75-, ASSOC PROF ZOOL & SR SCIENTIST, CTR GREAT LAKES STUDIES, 75-, COORDR, ZOOL/ MICROBIOL, 76- *Concurrent Pos:* Spec serv appointment, Grad Sch, Boston Univ; NSF rep, 2nd US-Japan Conf Microbiol. *Mem:* Int Asn Great Lakes Res; Am Soc Limnol Oceanog; Electron Micros Soc Am. *Res:* Aquatic microbiology, microbial ecology and ultrastructure. *Mailing Add:* Ctr for Great Lakes Studies Univ of Wis Milwaukee WI 53201

REMSEN, JOYCE F, b Trenton, NJ, May 18, 36; m 67. RADIOBIOLOGY, CHEMICAL CARCINOGENSIS. *Educ:* Douglass Col, BA, 57; Cornell Univ, MS, 60; Rutgers Univ, PhD(biochem), 69. *Prof Exp:* Info scientist, E R Squibb & Son, 60-64; fel, Princeton Univ, 69-71; instr, 71-75, ASST PROF BIOCHEM, UNIV FLA, 75- *Mem:* Am Soc Biol Chemists; Radiation Res Soc; Am Soc Photobiol; NY Acad Sci; AAAS. *Res:* DNA damage and repair following exposure to radiation or chemical carcinogens; role of lipoproteins in the transport of hydrophobic compounds. *Mailing Add:* Dept Biochem & Molecular Biol Univ Fla J Hillis Miller Health Ctr J-245 Gainesville FL 32610

REMSON, IRWIN, b New York, NY, Jan 23, 23; m 48; c 2. HYDROLOGY, ENVIRONMENTAL GEOLOGY. *Educ:* Columbia Univ, AB, 46, AM, 49, PhD, 54. *Prof Exp:* Asst geol, Columbia Univ, 47-49; geologist, US Geol Surv, 49-60; assoc prof civil eng, Drexel Inst, 60-65, prof & chief marshal fac, 65-68; PROF GEOL, STANFORD UNIV, 68-, CHMN DEPT APPL EARTH SCI, 75- *Concurrent Pos:* Lectr, Drexel Inst, 54-60; Lindback Found Award, 66. *Mem:* Geol Soc Am; Am Geophys Union; Soil Sci Soc Am. *Res:* Ground water geology; soil moisture movement; ground water recharge. *Mailing Add:* Dept of Geol Stanford Univ Stanford CA 94305

REMY, CHARLES NICHOLAS, b Hudson, NY, May 31, 24; m 52; c 4. BIOCHEMISTRY. *Educ:* Syracuse Univ, PhD(biochem), 52. *Prof Exp:* Am Cancer Soc fel, Sch Med, Univ Pa, 52-53 & Div Biochem, Mass Inst Technol, 53-54; instr biochem, State Univ NY Upstate Med Ctr, 54-60, asst prof, 60-62; assoc prof, 62-68, PROF BIOCHEM, BOWMAN GRAY SCH MED, 68- *Concurrent Pos:* Biochemist, Med Res Div, Vet Admin Hosp, Syracuse, NY, 54-56, prin scientist, 56-62. *Mem:* AAAS; Am Soc Biol Chemists; Am Chem Soc; Soc Exp Biol & Med; Am Soc Microbiol. *Res:* Biomethylation of nucleic acids; biosynthesis of ribosomes; biological regulation of nucleic acids and protein synthesis and transport. *Mailing Add:* Dept Biochem Bowman Gray Sch Med Winston-Salem NC 27103

REMY, DAVID CARROLL, b Waco, Tex, July 17, 29; m 63; c 2. MEDICINAL CHEMISTRY. *Educ:* Univ Calif, Los Angeles, BS, 51, MS, 52; Univ Wis, PhD, 58. *Prof Exp:* Res chemist, Elastomer Chem Dept, E I du Pont de Nemours & Co, 58-60; fel oncol, McArdle Mem Lab, Med Sch, Univ Wis, 60-62; sr res fel, 62-80, SR INVESTIGATOR, MERCK, SHARP & DOHME RES LABS, 80- *Mem:* Am Chem Soc. *Res:* Medicinal chemistry; CNS drugs. *Mailing Add:* Merck Sharp & Dohme Res Labs West Point PA 19486

REN, PETER, b Macau, Mar 12, 48; Hong Kong citizen; m 78. BIOCHEMISTRY. *Educ:* Adelphia Univ, BA, 71; Univ RI, PhD(biochem), 76. *Prof Exp:* Res asst, Univ RI, 71-76; res assoc biochem, Sch Med, Univ Md, 76-78; RES BIOCHEM, COLGATE-PALMOLIVE CO, 78- *Mem:* Am Chem Soc; AAAS. *Res:* Mechanism of action of vitamin K; anticoagulant drugs; clotting proteins synthesis; basement membrane metabolism; collagen metabolism; oral hygiene; bacterial adhesion; caries formation; inflammations; chemotaxis. *Mailing Add:* Colgate-Palmolive Res Ctr 909 River Rd Piscatawy NJ 08854

RENARD, KENNETH G, b Sturgeon Bay, Wis, May 5, 34; m 56; c 3. HYDRAULIC ENGINEERING. *Educ:* Univ Wis, BS, 57, MS, 59; Univ Ariz, PhD(civil eng), 72. *Prof Exp:* Hydraul engr, Agr Res Serv, USDA, Wis, 57-59, res hydraul engr, Ariz, 59-64, res hydraul engr, Southwest Watershed Res Ctr, 64-68, DIR, SOUTHWEST WATERSHED RES CTR, AGR RES SERV, USDA, 68- *Concurrent Pos:* Adj prof, Univ Ariz. *Mem:* Soil Conserv Soc Am (pres, 79); Am Soc Civil Engrs; AAAS; Am Soc Agr Engrs; Am Geophys Union. *Res:* Watershed hydrology relating land practices to water yields and peak rates of discharge; sediment transport phenomenon in ephemeral stream beds. *Mailing Add:* Southwest Watershed Res Ctr 442 E Seventh Tucson AZ 85705

RENARD, ROBERT JOSEPH, b Green Bay, Wis, Dec 22, 23; m 47; c 4. METEOROLOGY. *Educ:* Univ Chicago, MS, 52; Fla State Univ, PhD(meteorol), 70. *Prof Exp:* Asst meteorol, Univ Chicago, 51-52; from asst prof to assoc prof, 52-70, PROF METEOROL, US NAVAL POSTGRAD SCH, 70-, CHMN DEPT, 80- *Mem:* Am Meteorol Soc; Am Geophys Union; Nat Weather Asn; Am Polar Soc. *Res:* Synoptic, polar and satellite meteorology; emphasis on maine fog visibility and Antactic. *Mailing Add:* Dept of Meteorol Naval Postgrad Sch Monterey CA 93940

RENAU, JACQUES, b Beirut, Lebanon, Mar 15, 25; nat US; div; c 2. THEORETICAL PHYSICS. *Educ:* Univ Chicago, BS, 54, MS, 55; Cornell Univ, PhD(physics), 59. *Prof Exp:* Asst, Univ Chicago, 52-55 & Cornell Univ, 55-59; res physicist, Cornell Aeronaut Lab, Inc, 59-63; mem tech staff, Bell Tel Labs, 63-67; MEM TECH STAFF, AEROSPACE CORP, 67-, MGR, PLASMA & ELECTROMAGNETICS SECT, RADAR & MICROWAVE DEPT, 81-, PROJ ENGR, SPACE DEFENSE SURVEILLANCE, COMMAND & CONTROL SUBDIV, 81- *Res:* Radar, laser, space defense command and control analysis; system engineering studies; satellite communication studies. *Mailing Add:* Aerospace Corp PO Bx 92957 Los Angeles CA 90009

RENAUD, SERGE, b Cartelegue, France, Nov 21, 27; Can citizen; m 55; c 1. EXPERIMENTAL PATHOLOGY. *Educ:* Univ Bordeaux, BA, 47; Univ Montreal, VMD, 57, PhD(exp med), 60. *Prof Exp:* Res assoc, Montreal Heart Inst, 60-63, chief lab exp path, 63-73; DIR, UNIV 63, NIH & MED RES, FRANCE, 73- *Concurrent Pos:* Med Res Coun Can & Que Heart Found grants, 61-; vis prof, Boston Univ, 71-72; prof path, Univ Montreal, 72-73. *Mem:* Soc Exp Biol & Med; Am Heart Asn; Nutrit Soc Can; Am Soc Exp Path; Int Acad Path. *Res:* Influence of nutrition, stress, hormones on the pathogenesis of thrombosis and atherosclerosis. *Mailing Add:* Unit 63 Nat Inst Health & Med Res 69500 Bron France

RENAULT, JACQUES ROLAND, b Alameda, Calif, July 26, 33; m 56; c 2. GEOCHEMISTRY, PETROLOGY. *Educ:* Stanford Univ, BS, 57; NMex Inst Mining & Technol, MS, 59; Univ Toronto, PhD(geol), 64. *Prof Exp:* Explor geologist, Bear Creek Mining Co, 59-60, Southwest Potash Corp, 61, F R Joubin & Assoc, 62-63; geologist, 64-80, SR GEOLOGIST, STATE BUR MINES & MINERAL RESOURCES, NMEX INST MINING & TECHNOL, 80- *Concurrent Pos:* Grant, Geol Surv Can, 62-63, NMex Energy Inst, 76, 78; exec bd, NMex Energy Inst, NMex State Univ, 78-80; adj prof, geosci dept, NMex Tech. *Mem:* AAAS; Geol Soc Am; Mineral Soc Am; Am Geophys Union; Sigma Xi. *Res:* Mineral physics, especially X-ray diffraction and thermoluminescence; igneous petrology; ore genesis; x-ray flourescence spectroscopy. *Mailing Add:* NMex Bur Mines & Mineral Res NMex Tech Campus Sta Socorro NM 87801

RENCHER, ALVIN C, b St Johns, Ariz, Dec 21, 34; m 62; c 3. STATISTICS. *Educ:* Brigham Young Univ, BS, 59, MA, 62; Va Polytech Inst, PhD(statist), 68. *Prof Exp:* Statistician, Hercules Inc, 62-63; PROF STATIST, BRIGHAM YOUNG UNIV, 63-, CHMN DEPT, 80- *Concurrent Pos:* NSF fac fel, 67-68; epidemiol consult, Kennecott Copper Corp, 70-71. *Mem:* Am Statist Asn. *Res:* Best subset regression; discriminant analysis. *Mailing Add:* 222 TMCB Brigham Young Univ Provo UT 84602

RENCRICCA, NICHOLAS JOHN, b New York, NY, Mar 22, 41. HEMATOLOGY, MALARIOLOGY. *Educ:* St Francis Col, NY, BS, 62; St John's Univ, NY, MS, 64; Boston Col, PhD(physiol), 67. *Prof Exp:* Teaching asst physiol, anat & zool, St John's Univ, NY, 62-64; NIH-Nat Heart Inst res fel hematol, Sch Med, Tufts Univ, 67-70; assoc prof, 70-77, PROF BIOL SCI, UNIV LOWELL, 77- *Concurrent Pos:* Res assoc, Dept Army & Univ Lowell, 73-75; ref ed, J Hematol, 75; NSF fel, Boston Univ, 78-80. *Mem:* AAAS; Am Soc Hemat; Int Soc Exp Hemat; NY Acad Sci; Soc Exp Biol & Med. *Res:* Adult and neonatal control of hemopoiesis; stem cell proliferation and differentiation; erythropoiesis and cell-mediated immune mechanisms in rodent malaria. *Mailing Add:* Univ of Lowell Dept of Biol Sci Lowell MA 01854

RENDA, FRANCIS JOSEPH, b Brooklyn, NY, June 16, 39; m 63; c 2. SOLID STATE PHYSICS. *Educ:* Brooklyn Col, BS, 62; Syracuse Univ, MS, 65, PhD(physics), 69. *Prof Exp:* MEM TECH STAFF PHYSICS, SANTA BARBARA RES CTR, HUGHES AIRCRAFT CO, 69- *Mem:* Am Inst Physics. *Res:* Photoconductivity. *Mailing Add:* 270 Savona Ave Goleta CA 93017

RENDELL, DAVID H, b St John's, Nfld, July 28, 35; m 61; c 3. THEORETICAL PHYSICS. *Educ:* Dalhousie Univ, BSc, 56, MSc, 57; Univ BC, PhD(physics), 62. *Prof Exp:* Asst prof, 59-60 & 61-66, assoc prof, 66-77, asst dean sci, 71-74, PROF PHYSICS, MEM UNIV NFLD, 77-, ASSOC DEAN SCI, 74- *Mem:* Am Asn Physics Teachers; Can Asn Physicists. *Res:* Atomic and molecular physics; quantum mechanics. *Mailing Add:* Off Dean Sci Mem Univ of Nfld St John's NF A1B 3X7 Can

RENDIG, VICTOR VERNON, b Wis, July 4, 19; m 44; c 2. SOIL FERTILITY, PLANT PHYSIOLOGY. *Educ:* Univ Wis, BS, 42, PhD(soil sci, biochem), 49. *Prof Exp:* From jr soil chemist to assoc prof, 49-63, PROF SOILS & PLANT NUTRITION, UNIV CALIF, DAVIS, 63- *Mem:* Soil Sci Soc Am; Am Soc Agron; Am Soc Plant Physiologists; Am Inst Biol Sci; Am Chem Soc. *Res:* Effects of soil fertility and plant nutrition on plant composition and metabolism and on nutritive value of forages and cereal grains. *Mailing Add:* Dept of Land Air & Water Res Univ of Calif Davis CA 95616

RENDINA, GEORGE, b New York, NY, July 1, 23; m 48; c 4. BIOCHEMISTRY. *Educ:* NY Univ, AB, 49; Univ Kans, MA, 53, PhD, 55. *Prof Exp:* Instr biochem, Univ Kans, 54-55; Nat Found Infantile Paralysis fel, Univ Mich, 55-56, sr biochemist, 57; sr fel, E B Ford Inst Med Res, 57-58; instr physiol chem, Sch Med, Johns Hopkins Univ, 58-61; res biochemist, Training Sch, 62-63, chief biochemist, 64-66, dir, Isotope Lab, Cent Wis Colony, 66-67; ASSOC PROF CHEM, BOWLING GREEN STATE UNIV, 67- *Concurrent Pos:* Adj assoc prof, Med Col Ohio, 70-; grants, NSF & NIH. *Mem:* AAAS; Am Chem Soc. *Res:* Neurochemistry; protein synthesis; kinetics; enzymology. *Mailing Add:* Dept of Chem Bowling Green State Univ Bowling Green OH 43402

RENDTORFF, ROBERT CARLISLE, b Carlisle, Pa, Mar 22, 15; m 37; c 1. TROPICAL MEDICINE. *Educ:* Univ Ill, AB, 37, MS, 39; Johns Hopkins Univ, ScD(protozool), 44, MD, 49. *Prof Exp:* Instr epidemiol, Virol Lab, Mich, 42-44; med entomologist, Ministry Sanit & Social Assistance, Venezuela, 46; sr asst scientist, USPHS, 48, from asst surgeon to surgeon, 49-55; from asst prof to assoc prof, Col Med, 55-66, prof community med, 66-79, EMER PROF, UNIV TENN, MEMPHIS, 79- *Concurrent Pos:* Ed, Tenn Med Alumnus; consult epidemiologist infection control, 79- *Res:* Medical parasitology; epidemiology of human protozoan diseases, venereal diseases and respiratory viruses. *Mailing Add:* 276 Buena Vista Pl Memphis TN 38112

RENEAU, DANIEL DUGAN, JR, b Woodville, Miss, June 11, 40; m 61; c 1. CHEMICAL ENGINEERING. *Educ:* La Polytech Inst, BS, 63, MS, 64; Clemson Univ, PhD(chem eng), 66. *Prof Exp:* Res engr, Commercial Solvents Corp, 62-63; actg instr chem eng, La Polytech Inst, 63-64; res engr, Esso Res & Eng Co, 66-67; from asst prof to assoc prof chem eng, 67-77, prof biomed eng & head dept, 77-80, VPRES ACAD AFFAIRS, LA TECH UNIV, 80-- *Concurrent Pos:* Res engr, Humble Oil & Refining Co, 64; NIH fel, 66. *Mem:* Am Chem Soc; Am Inst Chem Engrs. *Res:* Chemical and biomedical engineering, especially mathematical modeling, dynamic system behavior, transport phenomena, mass transport and oxygen diffusion in brain; iron metabolism; oxygen transport in placenta. *Mailing Add:* Dept of Chem Eng La Tech Univ Ruston LA 71270

RENEAU, JOHN, b Beloit, Wis, May 1, 27; m 55; c 3. AUDIOLOGY, SPEECH PATHOLOGY. *Educ:* Univ Wis, BS, 51; Univ Denver, MS, 58, PhD(audiol, speech path), 60. *Prof Exp:* Dir speech & hearing, State Home & Training Sch, Denver, Colo, 56-60; DIR SPEECH & HEARING, CENT WIS COLONY, 64- *Concurrent Pos:* Fel med audiol, Med Sch, Univ Iowa, 60-63; NIH spec fel neurophysiol, Inst Med Physics, Utrecht, Neth, 63-64; lectr, Univ Wis-Madison, 71-; mem comt hearing, bioacoust & biomech, Nat Acad Sci, 71; mem sensory study sect, Social & Rehab Serv, Dept Health, Educ & Welfare, 71- *Honors & Awards:* Rosemary Dybwad Int Award, 67. *Mem:* Fel Am Speech & Hearing Asn. *Res:* Study of sensory electroneurophysiology using averaged evoked responses; research audiology. *Mailing Add:* Cent Wis Colony 317 Knutson Dr Madison WI 53704

RENEAU, RAYMOND B, JR, b Burkesville, Ky, Sept 11, 41. SOIL CHEMISTRY. *Educ:* Berea Col, BS, 64; Univ Ky, MS, 66; Univ Fla, PhD(soil chem), 69. *Prof Exp:* Asst prof agron, Tex Tech Univ, 70-71; asst prof soil pollution, 71-78, ASSOC PROF SOIL POLLUTION, VA POLYTECH INST & STATE UNIV, 78- *Concurrent Pos:* Consult, Jamaica Sch Agr, 70- *Mem:* AAAS; Am Soc Agron. *Res:* Movement of septic pollutants through natural soil systems and the potential contamination of ground and surface waters. *Mailing Add:* Dept of Agron Va Polytech Inst & State Univ Blacksburg VA 24061

RENEKE, JAMES ALLEN, b Jacksonville, Fla, Sept 21, 37; m 61; c 4. MATHEMATICAL ANALYSIS. *Educ:* Univ Fla, BA, 58, MA, 60; Univ NC, Chapel Hill, PhD(math), 64. *Prof Exp:* Assoc prof math, Newberry Col, 64-66; asst prof, 66-71, ASSOC PROF MATH, CLEMSON UNIV, 71- *Concurrent Pos:* Vis assoc prof, Univ Houston, 72-73. *Mem:* Am Math Soc. *Res:* Mathematical system theory, in particular, system problems of realization, identification and control. *Mailing Add:* Dept of Math Sci Clemson Univ Clemson SC 29631

RENEKER, DARRELL HYSON, b Birmingham, Iowa, Dec 5, 29; m 53; c 2. PHYSICS. *Educ:* Iowa State Univ, BS, 51; Univ Chicago, MS, 55, PhD, 59. *Prof Exp:* Mem tech staff, Bell Tel Labs, Inc, 51-53; physicist, Polychems Dept, Exp Sta, E I du Pont de Nemours & Co, 59-63, eng mat lab, 63-64, cent res dept, 64-69; chief polymer crystal physics sect, 73, dep chief polymer sci & standards div, 75-80, DEP DIR, CTR MAT SCI, NAT BUR STANDARDS, 80- *Mem:* Am Phys Soc. *Res:* Ultra- sonic waves in metals; electronic properties of metals; physical properties of polymers and molecular solids. *Mailing Add:* Ctr Mat Sci Nat Bur Standards Washington DC 20234

RENFREW, EDGAR EARL, b Colfax, Wash, Apr 8, 15; m 43; c 2. INDUSTRIAL ORGANIC CHEMISTRY. *Educ:* Univ Idaho, BS, 36; Univ Minn, PhD(org chem), 44. *Prof Exp:* Chemist, Bunker Hill & Sullivan Mining Co, Idaho, 36-38; asst, Univ Minn, 39-43; res chemist, Gen Aniline & Film Corp, Pa, 44-58; mgr dyestuffs res, Koppers Co, Inc, 58-62; res chemist, Minn Mining & Mfg Co, 62-66; dir res & develop, Am Aniline Prod, Inc, 66-72; vpres res & develop, Am Color & Chem Co, 72-80; RETIRED. *Concurrent Pos:* Consult, 80- *Mem:* Am Chem Soc; Am Asn Textile Chemists & Colorists. *Res:* Dyestuffs and intermediates; aromatic intermediates. *Mailing Add:* Am Color & Chem Co PO Box 88 Lock Haven PA 17745

RENFREW, MALCOLM MACKENZIE, b Spokane, Wash, Oct 12, 10; m 38. PHYSICAL CHEMISTRY. *Educ:* Univ Idaho, BS, 32, MS, 34; Univ Minn, PhD(phys chem), 38. *Prof Exp:* Asst physics, Univ Idaho, 32-33, chem, 33-35; asst chem, Univ Minn, 35-37; res chemist, E I du Pont de Nemours & Co, 38-44, res suprv, 44-49; dir chem res, Gen Mills Inc, 49-54; dir res & develop, Spencer Kellog & Sons, Inc, 54-58; prof chem & head div phys sci, Univ Idaho, 59-67; staff assoc, Adv Coun Col Chem, Stanford Univ, 67-68; head dept, 68-73, prof chem, 68-76, EMER PROF, UNIV IDAHO, 76- *Concurrent Pos:* Consult, Mat Adv Bd, Nat Acad Sci-Nat Res Coun, 62-67; dir, Col Chem Consult Serv; exec vpres, Idaho Res Found, 77-78, patent mgr, 78-, safety ed, J Chem Educ, 77- *Mem:* AAAS; Am Chem Soc; Am Inst Chemists; Am Inst Chem Engrs. *Res:* Polymer chemistry; organic coatings and plastics. *Mailing Add:* Dept Chem Univ Idaho Moscow ID 83843

RENFRO, WILLIAM CHARLES, b Hillsboro, Tex, Jan 16, 30; m 55; c 4. BIOLOGICAL OCEANOGRAPHY. *Educ:* Univ Tex, BA, 51, MA, 58; Ore State Univ, PhD(oceanog), 67. *Prof Exp:* Marine biologist, Tex Game & Fish Comn, 58-59; fishery res biologist, US Bur Com Fisheries, 59-64; asst prof oceanog, Ore State Univ, 67-71; chief radiobiol group, Int Atomic Energy Agency, Lab Marine Radioactivity, Monaco, 71-73; chief environ progs, 73-80, DIR ENVIRON PROGS, NORTHEAST UTILITIES CO, 80- *Mem:* AAAS; Am Nuclear Soc; Am Soc Limnol & Oceanog. *Res:* Marine and aquatic radioecology; estuarine ecology; marine pollution; radiochemistry; shrimp life history and ecology; fish physiology. *Mailing Add:* Environ Progs NE Utilities Co PO Box 270 Hartford CT 06101

RENFROE, CARL A(NDREW), JR, b Ashland, Ky, Aug 14, 35; m 66. CHEMICAL & SYSTEMS ENGINEERING. *Educ:* Va Polytech Inst, BS, 58, MS, 60, PhD(chem eng), 65. *Prof Exp:* Sr lab technician, Battelle Mem Inst, 53-56; asst chem eng, Va Polytech Inst, 62-63, asst prof, 63-67, dir instnl res, 66-67; SR PROCESS ENGR, ETHYL CORP, 67- *Mem:* Am Inst Chem Engrs. *Res:* Drug and food chemicals; coal and minerals economics; process economics; chemical process kinetics, dynamics and control; computer applications in process modeling; nuclear chemical engineering. *Mailing Add:* Ethyl Corp PO Box 341 Baton Rouge LA 70821

RENFROE, HARRIS BURT, b Meridian, Miss, Nov 22, 36; m 64; c 2. ORGANIC CHEMISTRY, PHARMACEUTICAL CHEMISTRY. *Educ:* Miss State Univ, BS, 58; Univ Ill, PhD(org chem), 61. *Prof Exp:* NIH fel org chem, Zurich, 61-62; chemist, Lederle Labs, Am Cyanamid Co, 63-65; res chemist, Geigy Res Labs, 65-69, proj leader, 69-71, group leader, Dept Org Chem, 72-81, DIR CHEM RES, CIBA-GEIGY CORP, 81- *Mem:* Am Chem Soc; Sigma Xi. *Res:* Synthesis of pharmacologically active compounds; exploratory organic synthesis. *Mailing Add:* Ciba-Geigy Corp Ardsley NY 10502

RENGAN, KRISHNASWAMY, b Varalotti, India, Aug 9, 37; m 69; c 2. NUCLEAR CHEMISTRY, ANALYTICAL CHEMISTRY. *Educ:* Univ Kerala, BSc, 57; Univ Mich, PhD(chem), 66. *Prof Exp:* Sci off radiochem div, Bhabha Atomic Res Ctr, Bombay, 58-70; assoc prof, 70-80, PROF CHEM, EASTERN MICH UNIV, 80- *Mem:* Am Phys Soc; Am Chem Soc; AAAS; Health Phys Soc; Sigma Xi. *Res:* Decay scheme studies; radiochemical separations; application of activation analysis to environmental problems. *Mailing Add:* Dept of Chem Eastern Mich Univ Ypsilanti MI 48197

RENGSTORFF, GEORGE W(ILLARD) P(EPPER), b Seattle, Wash, Oct 27, 20; m 42; c 2. METALLURGY. *Educ:* Univ Wash, BS, 42; Mass Inst Technol, SM, 48, ScD, 50. *Prof Exp:* Res engr, Process Metall Div, Battelle Mem Inst, 49-51, asst chief, Phys Metall Div, 51-55, asst chief, Metals Sci Group, 60-61, res assoc, Process Metall Div, 61-66, tech adv, 66-69; assoc prof, 69-75, PROF MAT SCI, UNIV TOLEDO, 75- *Mem:* AAAS; Am Soc Metals; Am Inst Mining, Metall & Petrol Engrs; Soc Die Casting Engrs; Am Soc Eng Educ. *Res:* Chemical metallurgy; refractory metals; high purity metals. *Mailing Add:* Dept of Chem Eng Univ of Toledo Toledo OH 43606

RENICH, PAUL WILLIAM, b La Junta, Colo, May 5, 19; m 43; c 3. PHYSICAL CHEMISTRY. *Educ:* Bethel Col Kans, AB, 42; Univ Kans, MA, 44, PhD(phys chem), 49. *Prof Exp:* Prof chem, Kans Wesleyan Univ, 48-74, dean, 51-69, pres, 69-73; INSTR, HASKELL INDIAN JR COL, 74- *Concurrent Pos:* Ford Found fel, Mass Inst Technol, 54-55; assoc, NCent Asn Cols, 59-60, consult-examr, 60- *Mem:* Am Chem Soc; AAAS. *Res:* Physical chemistry, including electrodeposition and physiochemical properties. *Mailing Add:* 2133 Carolina Lawrence KS 66044

RENIS, HAROLD E, b Highland Park, Ill, Jan 1, 30; m 51; c 3. VIROLOGY, BIOCHEMISTRY. *Educ:* Elmhurst Col, BS, 51; Bradley Univ, MS, 54; Purdue Univ, PhD(biochem), 56. *Prof Exp:* Asst instr chem, Bradley Univ, 52-53; res asst biochem, Purdue Univ, 53-56, Nat Heart Inst fel microbiol, 56-59; RES ASSOC VIROL, UPJOHN CO, 59- *Mem:* AAAS; Am Chem Soc; Am Microbiol Soc; Tissue Cult Asn; Soc Exp Biol Med. *Res:* Tissue culture; viruses; nucleic acid antagonists; virus chemotherapy; animal virology; intermediary metabolism. *Mailing Add:* 6631 Trotwood Kalamazoo MI 49002

RENKEN, JAMES HOWARD, b El Paso, Tex, July 1, 35; m 78; c 3. COMPUTATIONAL PHYSICS. *Educ:* Ohio State Univ, BSc & MSc, 58; Calif Inst Technol, PhD(physics), 63. *Prof Exp:* Staff mem Theory & Anal Div, 64-67, supvr Theoret Div, 67-80, SUPVR HOSTILE ENVIRON DIV, SANDIA NAT LABS, 80- *Mem:* Am Phys Soc; Am Nuclear Soc. *Res:* Transport theory; interaction of radiation with matter; mathematical physics. *Mailing Add:* Sandia Nat Labs Div 4365 KAFB E Albuquerque NM 87185

RENKEY, EDMUND JOSEPH, JR, b Pittsburgh, Pa, May 19, 40. SEISMIC RESTRAINT APPLICATIONS, DIAPHRAGM COMPRESSOR DEVELOPMENT. *Educ:* Pa State Univ, BS, 63, MBA, 66. *Prof Exp:* Assoc engr, Wright Aero Div, Curtiss-Wright Corp, 63-65; sr contract adminr, Marvel-Schebler Div, Borg Warner Corp, 67-71; proposal adminr power generation, Babcock & Wilcox Co, 71-72; sr procurement specialist, 72-74, sect mgr, 74-78, sr engr, 78-81, PRIN ENGR, WESTINGHOUSE HANFORD CO, WESTINGHOUSE ELEC CO, 81- *Concurrent Pos:* Adj prof, Cent Wash Univ, 76 & 78. *Mem:* Am Soc Mech Engrs. *Mailing Add:* Westinghouse Hanford Co PO Box 1970 Richland WA 99352

RENKIN, EUGENE MARSHALL, b Boston, Mass, Oct 21, 26; m 55, 67; c 4. PHYSIOLOGY, PHARMACOLOGY. *Educ:* Tufts Col, BS, 48; Harvard Univ, PhD(med sci), 51. *Prof Exp:* Assoc biologist, Brookhaven Nat Lab, 51-55; sr asst scientist, Nat Heart Inst, 55-57; from asst prof to prof physiol & chmn dept, Sch Med, George Washington Univ, 57-63; prof pharmacol & head div, Sch Med, Duke Univ, 63-69, prof physiol, 69-74; PROF HUMAN PHYSIOL & CHMN DEPT, SCH MED, UNIV CALIF, DAVIS, 74- *Concurrent Pos:* NSF sr fel, 60-61; Bowditch lectr, Am Physiol Soc, 63. *Mem:* AAAS; Am Physiol Soc; Am Heart Asn; Microcirculatory Soc (pres, 75). *Res:* Peripheral circulation; capillary and membrane permeability; lymph circulation. *Mailing Add:* Dept of Human Physiol Univ of Calif Sch of Med Davis CA 95616

RENLUND, ROBERT N, phycology, see previous edition

RENN, DONALD WALTER, b East Rutherford, NJ, Mar 23, 32; m 55; c 3. NATURAL PRODUCTS CHEMISTRY, IMMUNOCHEMISTRY. *Educ:* Franklin & Marshall Col, BS, 53; Mich State Univ, PhD(org chem), 57. *Prof Exp:* Res chemist, John L Smith Mem Cancer Res, Pfizer, Inc, 57-65, asst dept head chem, 61-65, group leader immunochem cancer & viral chem, 62-65; sr chemist, 65-68, res scientist, 68-69, sr scientist, Marine Colloids Div, 69-79, corp res fel, 79-81, SR RES FEL, FMC CORP, ROCKLAND, 81- *Concurrent Pos:* Dir biomed res, Marine Colloids, 71-75, mgr, Biotechnol Ventures, 76- *Mem:* Am Chem Soc; Sigma Xi; AAAS; fel Am Inst Chemists. *Res:* Marine natural product chemistry; immunochemical and electrophoretic methods for disease detection; isolation and characterization of antibotics and anti-tumor agents from natural product sources; immunochemistry of cancer; viral and polysaccharide chemistry; microbial products, organic synthesis; biotechnology. *Mailing Add:* Brewster Point Glen Cove ME 04846

RENNAT, HARRY O(LAF), b Estonia, Aug 6, 22; nat US; m 51; c 3. MECHANICAL ENGINEERING. *Educ:* Univ Wis, BS, 53, MS, 54, PhD(mech eng), 56. *Prof Exp:* Res asst, Bjorksten Res Labs, Univ Wis, 51-56; ASSOC PROF MECH ENG, COLO STATE UNIV, 56- *Mem:* Am Soc Mech Engrs. *Res:* Heat transfer; materials science. *Mailing Add:* Dept of Mech Eng Col of Eng Colo State Univ Ft Collins CO 80521

RENNE, DAVID SMITH, b Harvey, Ill, Nov 27, 43; m 66; c 2. METEOROLOGY. *Educ:* Kalamazoo Col, BA, 66; Colo State Univ, MS, 69, PhD(earth resources), 75. *Prof Exp:* Meteorologist, US Weather Bur, Lansing, 66; res asst atmospheric sci, Colo State Univ, 66-71; meteorologist air pollution, Environ Qual Bd, San Juan, PR, 71-72; res asst earth resources, Colo State Univ, 72-74; RES SCIENTIST METEOROL, PAC NORTHWEST LABS, BATTELLE MEM INST, 75- *Concurrent Pos:* Consult air pollution, Marlatt & Assoc, Ft Collins, Colo, 72-75 & Inst Ecol-Urban Secondary Impacts Workshop, 74; consult hydrol, City of Ft Collins Planning Dept, 73-74. *Mem:* Am Meteorol Soc; Sigma Xi; Air Pollution Control Asn. *Res:* Research and project management in wind characteristics for wind energy utilization; long range transport and wet and dry deposition of pollutants. *Mailing Add:* 5105 W Irving Pasco WA 99301

RENNEKE, DAVID RICHARD, b Gaylord, Minn, June 29, 40; m 63; c 3. PHYSICS, COMPUTER SCIENCE. *Educ:* Gustavus Adolphus Col, BS, 62; Iowa State Univ, MS, 64; Univ Kans, PhD(physics), 70. *Prof Exp:* Asst prof, 68-77, ASSOC PROF PHYSICS, AUGUSTANA COL ILL, 77- *Concurrent Pos:* Consult comput graphics, John Deere Tech Ctr, Moline, 77- *Mem:* Am Asn Physics Teachers; Sigma Xi. *Res:* Computer applications in education; mathematical modeling of physical systems; holography; optical reflection from solids; photoconductivity in ionic crystals; atomic imperfections in solids; cryogenic gas storage systems; computer graphics. *Mailing Add:* Dept of Physics Augustana Col Rock Island IL 61201

RENNELS, EDWARD GERALD, b Charleston, Ill, May 7, 20; m 42; c 2. REPRODUCTIVE BIOLOGY, ENDOCRINOLOGY. *Educ:* Eastern Ill State Teachers Col, BEd, 47; Harvard Univ, MA, 48, PhD(biol), 50. *Prof Exp:* Instr zool, Eastern Ill State Teachers Col, 47; asst histol, Harvard Univ, 48; from instr to prof anat, Med Br, Univ Tex, 50-66; chmn dept, 66-80, PROF ANAT, UNIV TEX HEALTH SCI CTR, SAN ANTONIO, 66- *Mem:* Am Soc Zoologists; Endocrine Soc; Am Asn Anatomists; Soc Exp Biol & Med; Soc Study Reproduction. *Res:* Histochemistry of rat ovary; cytophysiology of pituitary gland and pituitary cell clones; ultrastructure of luteal cells. *Mailing Add:* 104 Bent Oak San Antonio TX 78231

RENNELS, MARSHALL L, b Marshall, Mo, Sept 2, 39; m 71. NEUROANATOMY. *Educ:* Eastern Ill Univ, BS, 61; Univ Tex Med Br Galveston, MA, 64, PhD(neuroendocrinol, neurocytol), 66. *Prof Exp:* Asst prof anat, 66-71, asst prof neurol, 69-71, assoc prof anat, 71-79, PROF ANAT & ASSOC PROF NEUROL, SCH MED, UNIV MD, BALTIMORE, 79- *Mem:* AAAS; Electron Micros Soc Am; Am Asn Anatomists; Soc Neurosci; Int Soc Cerebral Blood Flow & Metab. *Res:* Ultrastructural and histochemical investigations of the cerebrovascular system and its innervation by autonomic and central neurons; related studies examine the characteristics of the cerebral microcirculatory system and its relationships to the cerebral parenchyma. *Mailing Add:* Dept Anat Sch Med Univ Md Baltimore MD 21201

RENNER, DARWIN S(PRATHARD), b Powell, Ohio, Oct 15, 10; m 44; c 3. ELECTRICAL ENGINEERING. *Educ:* Ohio State Univ, BEE, 32, MSc, 33. *Prof Exp:* Comput, Geophys Serv, Tex, 35-37, res engr, 37-42, supt electronics div, 42-45, sr engr, 45-47; vpres, 47-50, PRES, GEOTRONIC LABS, INC, 50- *Mem:* Am Phys Soc; Soc Explor Geophys; Inst Elec & Electronics Engrs; Am Geophys Union. *Res:* Automatic amplifiers; servomechanisms; filter systems; magnetic detectors; test sets-fault locators; mixing systems; noise meters; interference eliminators; cameras; recording oscillographs; inductive and capacitive components; computers. *Mailing Add:* 1314 Cedar Hill Ave Dallas TX 75208

RENNER, GERARD W, b Boston, Mass, Dec 23, 21. PHYSICS, ELECTRONICS. *Educ:* Harvard Univ, AB, 43. *Prof Exp:* Spec res assoc, Underwater Sound Lab, Harvard Univ, 43-45, spec res assoc, Systs Res Lab, 45; sect head transducers, Submarine Signal Co, 46-49; dept mgr, Submarine Signal Div, Raytheon Corp, 49-62; res assoc & consult, Parke Math Labs, Inc, 62; dept mgr acoust systs, Hazeltine Corp, 62-67; pres-treas, Appl Res Assocs, Inc, Uphams Corner, 67-77; dir advan develop, MASSA Corp, 77-78, mgr eng, 78; dir advanced acoustic technol, Hazelting Corp, 78-81; PRES, APPL RES ASSOC, INC, 81- *Concurrent Pos:* Group leader, Lowell Technol Inst Res Found, 67-69; consult, Advan Technol Systs, Inc, Arlington, Va, 69- *Mem:* Acoust Soc Am; Am Phys Soc; Inst Elec & Electronics Engrs; NY Acad Sci. *Res:* Acoustics; magnetostriction, piezoelectric, ceramic transducer; underwater sound; ultrasonics; telecommunications; biomedical engineering. *Mailing Add:* 51 Bellevue St Dorchester MA 02125

RENNER, JOHN WILSON, b De Smet, SDak, July 25, 24; m 48; c 2. SCIENCE EDUCATION, PHYSICS. *Educ:* Univ SDak, BA, 46, MA, 48; Univ Iowa, PhD(sci educ), 55. *Prof Exp:* Teacher high sch, SDak, 46-47; instr physics, Univ SDak, 47-52; instr physics & math, Minn State Teachers Col, 48-49; supvr & teacher phys sci, Univ High Sch, Iowa, 52-55; asst prof sci educ, Univ Ill, 55-56; dir radiol defense sch, Fed Civil Defense Admin, 56-58; asst prof physics & sci educ & actg head dept physics, Creighton Univ, 58-59; assoc exec secy, Nat Sci Teachers Asn, 59-62; PROF SCI EDUC, UNIV OKLA, 62- *Concurrent Pos:* Consult, Educator's Progress Serv, Wis; dir teacher serv, Frontiers Sci Found Okla, 62-68; coordr, Okla Trial Ctr, Sci Curric Improv Study, Lawrence Hall Sci, Univ Calif, Berkeley, 65-73. *Mem:* Nat Asn Res Sci Teaching (pres, 79-80); Nat Educ Asn; Nat Sci Teacher's Asn; Sigma Xi; Am Asn Physics Teachers. *Res:* author of over 125 articles and publications. *Mailing Add:* Col Educ Univ Okla Norman OK 73069

RENNER, RUTH, b Lewistown, Mont, Nov 17, 25. NUTRITION. *Educ:* Univ Alta, BSc, 48, MSc, 50; Cornell Univ, PhD(animal nutrit), 60. *Prof Exp:* Res asst soils, Univ Alta, 50-52, res asst poultry, 52-55; res assoc nutrit & poultry, Cornell Univ, 55-58, asst, 58-60; from asst prof to assoc prof, 60-70, PROF NUTRIT, SCH HOUSEHOLD ECON, UNIV ALTA, 70- *Honors & Awards:* Borden Award, Nutrit Soc Can, 70. *Mem:* Am Inst Nutrit; Poultry Sci Asn; Nutrit Soc Can. *Res:* Nutritive value of proteins; energy and fat metabolism. *Mailing Add:* Sch Household Econ Univ of Alta Edmonton AB T6G 1M8 Can

RENNER, TERRENCE ALAN, b Evergreen Park, Ill, Dec 1, 47. PHYSICAL CHEMISTRY. *Educ:* DePaul Univ, Chicago, BS, 69; Yale Univ, PhD(phys chem), 72. *Prof Exp:* ASST CHEMIST PHYS CHEM, CHEM ENG DIV, ARGONNE NAT LAB, ARGONNE, ILL, 73- *Concurrent Pos:* Fel, Argonne Nat Lab, Argonne, Ill, 72-73. *Res:* Transport properties of reacting gas mixtures; thermal conductivity; nucleation of superheated liquids; tritium and hydrogen transport in sodium-cooled fast breeder reactors; tritium permeation through reactor construction materials; sodium cold trap optimization. *Mailing Add:* Chem Eng Div Argonne Nat Lab 9700 S Cass Ave Argonne IL 60439

RENNERT, JOSEPH, b Mannheim, Ger, July 26, 19; nat US; m 47; c 2. PHOTOCHEMISTRY. *Educ:* City Col New York, BS, 48; Syracuse Univ, MS, 52, PhD(chem), 53. *Prof Exp:* Asst anal chem, Syracuse Univ, 48-50 & phys chem, 50-52; res chemist, Ozalid div, Gen Aniline & Film Corp, 52-54 & Chas Bruning Co, 54-55; proj engr, Balco Res Labs, 55-56; from res scientist to sr res scientist, Inst Math Scis, NY Univ, 56-62; from asst prof to assoc prof, 62-73, PROF CHEM, CITY COL NEW YORK, 73- *Concurrent Pos:* Lectr, City Col New York, 56-; consult, Itek Corp, 60-62. *Mem:* AAAS; Am Chem Soc; fel Am Inst Chemists; NY Acad Sci; Am Soc Photobiol. *Res:* Photochemistry; mechanisms of photo-cyclo-addition, photo- scission, photo-redox and photosensitized reactions; photochemical and photophysical imaging and information storage systems; solid state photochemistry; photobiology. *Mailing Add:* 525 Fordham Pl Paramus NJ 07652

RENNERT, OWEN M, b New York, NY, Aug 8, 38; m 63; c 3. PEDIATRICS, BIOCHEMISTRY. *Educ:* Univ Chicago, BS & BA, 57, MD, 61, MS, 63; Am Bd Pediat, dipl, 67. *Prof Exp:* Res & clin assoc neurol, Nat Inst Neurol Dis & Blindness, Md, 64-66; instr pediat & chief resident, Univ Chicago, 66-67, asst prof pediat, 67-68; assoc prof, 68-71, prof pediat & biochem, Col Med, Univ Fla, 71-78, head inst div genetics, endocrinol & metab, 70-77; PROF PEDIAT & BIOCHEM, 77-, HEAD DEPT PEDIAT, COL MED, UNIV OKLA, 77- *Concurrent Pos:* Mem bd med examr, Ill, 61, Fla, 70 & Nat Bd Med Examr, 62; mem adv comt inborn errors of metab, Bd Health, Fla; NIH & Nat Cystic Fibrosis Fedn fels, 71-76; Fla Heart Asn fel, 72-73. *Mem:* AAAS; fel Am Acad Pediat; Soc Pediat Res; dipl mem Pan-Am Med Asn. *Res:* Inborn errors of metabolism; human genetics. *Mailing Add:* Dept of Pediat PO Box 16901 Oklahoma City OK 73190

RENNHARD, HANS HEINRICH, b Aarau, Switz, Sept 26, 28; nat US; m 55; c 2. ORGANIC CHEMISTRY, METABOLISM OF FOOD ADDITIVES. *Educ:* Swiss Fed Inst Technol, dipl, 52, DSc, 55. *Prof Exp:* Fel, Mass Inst Technol, 55-57; from res chemist to sr res chemist, 57-73, sr res investr, 74-79, PRIN RES INVESTR, PFIZER, INC, 80- *Mem:* Swiss Chem Soc; Am Chem Soc. *Res:* Antibiotics; tetracyclines; flavor enhancers; pharmacology of food additives; carbohydrate chemistry and metabolism; radiobiology; analytical methods development. *Mailing Add:* Cent Res Pfizer Inc Groton CT 06340

RENNICK, BARBARA RUTH, b Ashtabula, Ohio, Oct 23, 19. PHYSIOLOGY. *Educ:* Wayne State Univ, BSc, 42, MSc, 44; Univ Mich, MD, 50. *Prof Exp:* Pharmacologist, Ciba Pharmaceut Prod, 44-46; instr physiol, State Univ NY Upstate Med Ctr, 50-54, asst prof, 54-61; assoc prof, Mt Holyoke Col, 61-64; PROF PHARMACOL, MED SCH, STATE UNIV NY BUFFALO, 65- *Concurrent Pos:* USPHS spec fel, Oxford Univ, 54-55; Wellcome Found traveling fel, 58. *Mem:* AAAS; Am Physiol Soc; Am Soc Pharmacol & Exp Therapeut; Am Soc Nephrology. *Res:* Renal tubular function; membrane transport; autonomic pharmacology; newborn physiology. *Mailing Add:* Dept of Pharmacol & Ther State Univ NY Med Sch Buffalo NY 14214

RENNIE, DONALD ANDREWS, b Medicine Hat, Alta, Apr 21, 22; m 48; c 3. SOIL CHEMISTRY. *Educ:* Univ Sask, BSA, 49; Univ Wis, PhD(soils), 52. *Prof Exp:* From asst prof to assoc prof, 52-64, head dept, 65-81, PROF SOIL SCI, UNIV SASK, 65- *Concurrent Pos:* Dir, Sask Inst Pedology, 65-81; head soils irrig & crop prod sect, Int Atomic Energy Agency, Vienna, Austria, 68-70. *Honors & Awards:* Award, Am Chem Soc, 67; Centennial Medal, Can, 67. *Mem:* Fel Can Soc Soil Sci (secy-treas, 56-58, pres, 76-77); fel Agr Inst Can (vpres, 59-60); fel Soil Sci Soc Am; fel Am Soc Agron. *Res:* Soil chemistry and fertility. *Mailing Add:* Dept of Soil Sci Univ of Sask Saskatoon SK S7N 0W0 Can

RENNIE, DONALD WESLEY, b Seattle, Wash, Apr 2, 25; m 47; c 3. PHYSIOLOGY. *Educ:* Univ Wash, BS, 47; Univ Ore, MS & MD, 52. *Prof Exp:* Instr physiol, Univ Wis, 53; asst prof, 59-62, assoc prof, 62-66, PROF PHYSIOL, SCH MED, STATE UNIV NY BUFFALO, 66-, CHMN DEPT, 72- *Concurrent Pos:* Res fel, Harvard Med Sch, 56-58. *Mem:* AAAS; Am Physiol Soc; Am Fedn Clin Res; Undersea Med Soc. *Res:* Hemodynamics; heart; environmental physiology; metabolism; kidneys. *Mailing Add:* Dept of Physiol State Univ of NY Sch of Med Buffalo NY 14214

RENNIE, JAMES CLARENCE, b Ont, Sept 14, 26; m 50; c 1. ANIMAL BREEDING. *Educ:* Univ Toronto, BS, 47; Iowa State Col, MS, 50, PhD, 52. *Prof Exp:* Asst agr rep, Dept Agr, Ont, 47-49; tech off, Cent Exp Farm, Ottawa, 49; assoc prof animal husb, Ont Agr Col, Univ Guelph, 52-56, chmn dept, 65-71, prof, 56-74; exec dir educ & res, 74-78, ASST DEP MINISTER EDUC, RES & SPEC SERV, ONT MINISTRY AGR & FOOD, 78- *Concurrent Pos:* Coordr exten, Dept Animal & Poultry Sci, Ont Agr Col, Univ Guelph, 71-73, actg dean res, 73-74. *Mailing Add:* Ont Ministry of Agr & Food Legis Bldg Queen's Park Toronto ON M7A 1A3 Can

RENNIE, PAUL STEVEN, b Toronto, Ont, Feb 9, 46; m 68; c 1. BIOCHEMISTRY, ENDOCRINOLOGY. *Educ:* Univ Western Ont, BSc, 69; Univ Alta, PhD(biochem), 73. *Prof Exp:* Res assoc, Univ Alta, 75-76, asst prof med, 76-79, assoc prof, 79; RES SCIENTIST, CANCER CONTROL AGENCY BC, 79-; ASSOC PROF SURG, UNIV BC, 80- *Concurrent Pos:* Med Res Coun res fel, Imperial Cancer Res Fund, 73-75; res scholar & grant, Nat Cancer Inst Can, 76-79. *Mem:* Endocrine Soc; Can Soc Clin Invest. *Res:* Biochemical control of growth in androgen responsive organs and neoplasms. *Mailing Add:* Cancer Control Agency BC 2656 Heather St Vancouver BC V5Z 3J3 Can

RENNIE, PETER JOHN, b Worthing, Eng, Dec 8, 18; m 46. SOIL SCIENCE. *Educ:* Univ London, BSc, 39; Oxford Univ, 1 DPhil(soil chem), 56. *Prof Exp:* Res chemist, Brit Ministry Agr, 43-46; sci secy to postwar comt for Europe, Brit Foreign Off, 46-47; res officer forest soils, Oxford Univ, 47-58; res scientist, Can Dept Forestry & Rural Develop, Ont, 58-71; mem staff, 71-74, COORDR, DEPT FISHERIES & FORESTRY CAN, 74- *Mem:* Soil Sci Soc Am; Can Soc Soil Sci; The Chem Soc; Brit Soc Chem Indust; Can Bot Asn. *Res:* Long-term relationships between tree growth and soil properties; forest productivity; land utilization; analytical chemistry and coordination compounds. *Mailing Add:* Dept Fisheries & Forestry Can W Mem Bldg Wellington & Lyon Ottawa ON K1A 0H3 Can

RENNIE, ROBERT JOHN, b Prince Albert, Sask, Sept 12, 49; m 70; c 2. SOIL MICROBIOLOGY. *Educ:* Univ Sask, BSA Hons, 71; Laval Univ MSc, 72; Univ Minn, PhD(soil microbiol), 75. *Prof Exp:* Res assoc dinitrogen fixation, Agr Res Coun, nit Nitrogen Fixation, UK, 75-76; assoc officer, Food & Agr Orgn, Int Atomic Energy Agency, Div Atomic Energy Food & Agr, UN, 76-78; RES SCIENTIST DINITROGEN FIXATION, AGR CAN, 78- *Concurrent Pos:* Nat Res Coun Can fel, Agr Res Coun Unit Nitrogen Fixation, UK, 75-76; mem Can comt nitrogen fixation, Agr Can, 78- *Mem:* Am Soc Microbiol; Am Soc Agron; Agr Inst Can; Can Soc Microbiologists. *Res:* Dinitrogen fixing bacteria associated with legumes and non-legumes such as spring wheat and temperate prairie grasses; isotope techniques and immunofluorescent procedures are applied throughout. *Mailing Add:* 6 29 Brock Place Lethbridge AB T1K 4C7 Can

RENNIE, THOMAS HOWARD, b Coral Gables, Fla, Nov 26, 43; m 68; c 1. AQUATIC ECOLOGY, INVERTEBRATE ZOOLOGY. *Educ:* Univ Miami, BS, 65; Tex A&M Univ, MS, 67, PhD(aquatic biol), 75. *Prof Exp:* Instr zool, Ohio State Univ, 72-73; asst prof biol, Augustana Col, Rock Island, Ill, 74-79; MEM STAFF, US ARMY CORPS ENGRS, SAVANNAH, GA, 79- *Mem:* Am Soc Limnol & Oceanog; Ecol Soc Am; Sigma Xi. *Res:* Freshwater and marine invertebrate ecology, mainly of zooplankton and benthos; copepod taxonomy and physiology; secondary productivity; thermal entrainment and effluent effects on plankton. *Mailing Add:* US Army Corps Engrs PO Box 889 Savannah GA 31402

RENNILSON, JUSTIN J, b Berkeley, Calif, Dec 10, 26; m 54; c 3. PHOTOMETRY, SPECTRORADIOMETRY. *Educ:* Univ Calif, AB, 50; Tech Univ, Berlin, 55. *Prof Exp:* Assoc engr, Visibility Lab, Univ Calif, San Diego, 55-61; sr scientist, Jet Propulsion Lab, Calif Inst Technol, 61-69, sr res fel, 69-74; VPRES RES & ENG, GAMMA SCI, INC, 74- *Concurrent Pos:* Instr, San Diego State Col, 56-58; co-investr, NASA Surveyor TV Exp, 63-68; consult, Cohu Electronics Co, 68-74 & Photo Res Co, 71-74; co-investr, NASA Apollo Geol Exp 11-17. *Mem:* Optical Soc Am; Sigma Xi; Am Soc Testing & Mat. *Res:* Photometry, colorimetry; optical instrument design; spectroradiometric standards; specroradiometry; retroreflection. *Mailing Add:* 4141 S Tropico Dr La Mesa CA 92041

RENO, FREDERICK EDMUND, b Reno, Nev, July 20, 39; m 64; c 2. TOXICOLOGY, TERATOLOGY. *Educ:* Univ San Francisco, BS, 61; Univ Nev, Reno, MS, 63; Utah State Univ, PhD(toxicol), 67. *Prof Exp:* Lab instr human anat & physiol, Univ Nev, 63-64; res assoc emergency med servs, State of Nev, 64; assoc res coordr toxicol, Hazleton Labs, 67-68, proj mgr toxicol, 68-72, dir toxicol dept, 72-80, dir sci develop, 80-81, VPRES, HAZLETON LABS AM, INC, 82- *Mem:* AAAS; Soc Toxicol; Am Col Vet Toxicol; Europ Soc Toxicol. *Res:* Toxicological and teratological evaluation of new drugs, agricultural chemicals, food additives, cosmetics and industrial chemicals; reproductive physiology. *Mailing Add:* Hazelton Raltech Inc PO Box 7545 Madison WI 53707

RENO, HARLEY W, b Oakland, Calif, Feb 13, 39; m 68. HAZARDOUS WASTES MANAGEMENT, ENVIRONMENTAL MANAGEMENT. *Educ:* Okla State Univ, BS, 61, MS, 63, PhD, 67. *Prof Exp:* Asst biol fishes, Okla State Univ, 62-67; from asst prof to assoc prof biol, Baylor Univ, 67-74; vis prof, Pan Am Univ, 74-75; tech coordr & supvr ecol sci, Williams Bros Environ Serv, Williams Bros Eng Co, Resource Sci Corp, 75-78; environ mgr, Nuclear Waste Prog, 78-81, SR PROJ ENGR & CONSULT, EG&G IDAHO, INC, 81-; PROF ENVIRON SCI, IDAHO NAT ENG LAB, UNIV IDAHO, 80- *Concurrent Pos:* Fel, Univ Okla, 74; adj prof environ sci, Univ Tulsa, 76-78. *Honors & Awards:* Stoye Award, Am Soc Ichthyol & Herpet, 64. *Mem:* AAAS; Am Soc Zoologists; Am Soc Study Evolution; Sigma Xi; Ecol Soc Am. *Res:* Environmental transport of radioactive isotopes; hydrocarbon transport systems; surface coal mining; biological morphomechanics and systems evolution. *Mailing Add:* Waste Progs Div Box 1625 EG&G Idaho Inc Idaho Falls ID 83415

RENO, MARTIN A, b Erie Co, Pa, July 14, 36; m 55; c 3. CHEMICAL PHYSICS. *Educ:* Edinboro State Col, BS, 55; Harvard Univ, EdM, 58; Rensselaer Polytech Inst, MS, 60; Western Reserve Univ, PhD(chem), 66. *Prof Exp:* Teacher, High Sch, Ohio, 58-66; asst dean natural & social sci, 70-72, PROF PHYSICS, HEIDELBERG COL, 66-, DIR COMPUT CTR, 75- *Concurrent Pos:* Dir col sci improv prog, Heidelberg Col, 69-73. *Mem:* Am Chem Soc; Am Asn Physics Teachers; Nat Sci Teachers Asn. *Res:* Low temperature calorimetry; thermodynamic properties of fluorine containing gases; x-ray structure determination of biologically important molecules. *Mailing Add:* Dept of Physics Heidelberg Col Tiffin OH 44883

RENO, ROBERT CHARLES, b New York, NY, Feb 26, 43; m 65; c 2. SOLID STATE PHYSICS, NUCLEAR SPECTROSCOPY. *Educ:* Manhattan Col, BS, 65; Brandeis Univ, MA, 67, PhD(physics), 71. *Prof Exp:* Nat Res Coun res assoc physics, Nat Bur Standards, 71-73; asst prof, 73-78, ASSOC PROF PHYSICS, UNIV MD, BALTIMORE COUNTY, 78- *Concurrent Pos:* Consult, Nat Bur Standards, 74-; prin investr, Petrol Res Fund grant, 77- *Mem:* Am Phys Soc. *Res:* Hyperfine interactions in solids; perturbed angular correlations; Mossbauer spectroscopy; physics of metals and alloys; positron annihilation. *Mailing Add:* Dept of Physics Univ of Md Baltimore County Baltimore MD 21228

RENOLD, ALBERT ERNST, experimental medicine, biochemistry, see previous edition

RENOLL, ELMO SMITH, b Glen Rock, Pa, Jan 25, 22; m 45; c 2. AGRICULTURAL ENGINEERING. *Educ:* Auburn Univ, BS, 47; Iowa State Univ, MS, 49. *Prof Exp:* Engr agr eng, USDA, 45-49; from asst prof to assoc prof, 49-72, PROF AGR ENG, AUBURN UNIV, 72- *Honors & Awards:* Outstanding Serv Cert, Am Soc Agr Engrs, 64. *Mem:* Sr mem Am Soc Agr Engrs; Am Soc Eng Educr; AAAS. *Res:* Agricultural power and machinery; machinery use and selection; programming, modeling and simulation; hay and forage machinery utilization; alcohol and other alternative fuel utilization. *Mailing Add:* Dept of Agr Eng Auburn Univ Auburn AL 36830

RENOLL, MARY WILHELMINE, b St Petersburg, Pa, June 26, 06. CHEMISTRY. *Educ:* Grove City Col, AB, 27; Ohio State Univ, MS, 30. *Prof Exp:* Chemist, Midgley Found, Ohio State Univ, 30-38; res chemist, Monsanto Chem Co, Ohio, 39-44; res assoc chem, Res Found, Ohio State Univ, 45-57, from asst supvr to assoc supvr, 58-67, res assoc, 68, independent researcher chem, food sci & nutrit, 69-73, res assoc, Res Found, 73-76; RETIRED. *Mem:* AAAS; Am Chem Soc; fel Am Inst Chemists; NY Acad Sci. *Res:* Organic fluorine compounds; nucleoproteins; organic and rubber chemistry; nucleic acids. *Mailing Add:* 886 W Tenth Ave Columbus OH 43212

RENSCHLER, CLIFFORD LYLE, b Evansville, Ind, Sept 20, 55; m 78. ENERGY TRANSFER. *Educ:* Univ Evansville, BS, 77; Univ Ill, PhD(chem), 81. *Prof Exp:* MEM TECH STAFF, SANDIA NAT LABS, 81- *Mem:* Am Chem Soc; Sigma Xi. *Res:* Energy transfer kinetics between molecules dispersen in thin polymer films; time-resolved fluorescence spectroscopy; plastic scintillator development. *Mailing Add:* Orgn 5811 Sandia Nat Labs Albuquerque NM 87185

RENSE, WILLIAM A, b Massillon, Ohio, Mar 11, 14; m 42; c 3. SPACE PHYSICS. *Educ:* Case Western Reserve Univ, BS, 35; Ohio State Univ, MS, 37, PhD(physics), 39. *Prof Exp:* Instr physics, La State Univ, 39-40; asst prof, Univ Miami, 40; vis asst prof, Rutgers Univ, 41-42; from asst prof to assoc prof, La State Univ, 43-49; assoc prof, 49-56, co-dir lab atmospheric & space physics, 56-78, prof physics, 56-80, EMER PROF, UNIV COLO, BOULDER, 80- *Mem:* Am Geophys Union; Am Phys Soc; Sigma Xi; Am Astron Soc. *Res:* Vacuum spectroscopy; solar ultraviolet and stellar spectroscopy; upper air physics; space science, rocket and satellite experiments. *Mailing Add:* PO Box 95 Allenspark CO 80510

RENSINK, MARVIN EDWARD, b Mason City, Iowa, Jan 29, 39. MAGNETIC FUSION ENERGY. *Educ:* St Johns Univ, BS, 60; Univ Calif, Los Angeles, MS, 62, PhD(physics), 67. *Prof Exp:* Physicist, Hughes Aircraft Co, 60-63; res asst, Univ Calif, Los Angeles, 65-67; PHYSICIST, LAWRENCE LIVERMORE NAT LAB, 67- *Mem:* Am Phys Soc. *Res:* Theoretical studies of plasma confinement in magnetic mirror devices. *Mailing Add:* Lawrence Livermore Nat Lab L-630 Livermore CA 94550

RENTHAL, ROBERT DAVID, b Chicago, Ill, Oct 29, 45. PROTEIN CHEMISTRY. *Educ:* Princeton Univ, BA, 67; Columbia Univ, PhD(biochem), 72. *Prof Exp:* NIH fel molecular biophys, Yale Univ, 72-74; Nat Res Coun assoc life sci, Ames Res Ctr, NASA, 74-75; asst prof, 75-80, ASSOC PROF BIOCHEM, UNIV TEX, SAN ANTONIO, 80-, CHMN, DEPT BIOCHEM, UNIV TEX HEALTH SCI CTR, 77- *Mem:* AAAS; Am Chem Soc; Biophys Soc; Am Soc Cell Biol; NY Acad Sci. *Res:* Structure and function of membrane proteins; mechanisms of energy transduction by photoreceptor membranes; rhodopsin and bacteriorhodopsin. *Mailing Add:* Div of Earth & Phys Sci Univ of Tex San Antonio TX 78285

RENTMEESTER, KENNETH R, b Green Bay, Wis, Apr 26, 31; m 67; c 1. ORGANIC CHEMISTRY. *Educ:* St Norbert Col, BS, 52; Northwestern Univ, MS, 61. *Prof Exp:* Res assoc, 50-80, CHEMIST, RES CTR, AM CAN CO, 52-, SR RES ASSOC, 80- *Mem:* AAAS; Am Chem Soc. *Res:* Protective organic coatings for glass, metal and plastic packages; high strength adhesive bonding systems; coil and sheet applied precoatings for deep prawn food containers with formulation and application. *Mailing Add:* Tech Ctr Am Can Co 433 N Northwest Hwy Barrington IL 60010

RENTON, JOHN JOHNSTON, b Pittsburgh, Pa, Nov 25, 34; m 61; c 2. GEOCHEMISTRY. *Educ:* Waynesburg Col, BS, 56; WVa Univ, MS, 59, PhD(geol), 65. *Prof Exp:* Mem staff solid state physics, Res & Develop Off, US Air Force, 60-63; from asst to assoc prof, 65-75, PROF GEOL GEOCHEM, WVA UNIV, 75-, COOP GEOCHEMIST, WVA GEOL & ECON SURV, 65- *Concurrent Pos:* NSF grant exp diagenesis, WVa Univ, 65-67. *Mem:* AAAS; Geol Soc Am; Am Asn Petrol Geol. *Res:* Geochemistry of coal; acid mine drainage. *Mailing Add:* Dept of Geol WVa Univ Morgantown WV 26506

RENTON, KENNETH WILLIAM, b Galashiels, Scotland, Apr 6, 44; Can citizen; m 66; c 2. PHARMACOLOGY. *Educ:* Sir George Williams Univ, BSc, 72; McGill Univ, PhD(pharmacol), 75. *Prof Exp:* Fel pharmacol, Univ Minn, 75-77; ASST PROF PHARMACOL, DALHOUSIE UNIV, 77- *Concurrent Pos:* Can Med Res Coun fel, 75-77, scholar, 77- *Mem:* Can Fedn Biol Sci. *Res:* Drug biotransformation by cytochrome P-450, drug metabolism in the fetus and newborn. *Mailing Add:* Dept Pharmacol Dalhousie Univ Halifax NS B3H 3J5 Can

RENTZ, DAVID CHARLES, b San Francisco, Calif, May 14, 42; m 63. SYSTEMATIC ENTOMOLOGY. *Educ:* Univ Calif, Berkeley, BS, 65, MS, 66, PhD(entom), 70. *Prof Exp:* Asst cur entom, Acad Natural Sci Philadelphia, 70-75; asst cur, Calif Acad Sci, 75-77; PRIN RES SCIENTIST, DIV ENTOM, COMMONWEALTH SCI & INDUST RES ORGN, 77- *Concurrent Pos:* Res assoc, Calif Acad Sci, 69-75. *Mem:* AAAS; Am Entom Soc (vpres, 71); Am Inst Biol Sci; Asn Trop Biol; Soc Syst Zool; Entom Soc Am (pres, 73-74). *Res:* Classification and behavior of katydids of the subfamily Decticinae; origin and evolution of the Orthoptera of the Channel Islands, California; taxonomy and ecology of Australian orthoptera. *Mailing Add:* Div of Entom CSIRO PO Box 1700 Canberra City ACT 2601 Australia

RENTZEPIS, PETER M, b Kalamata, Greece, Dec 11, 34; US citizen; m 60; c 1. CHEMICAL PHYSICS. *Educ:* Denison Univ, BS, 58; Syracuse Univ, MS, 60; Cambridge Univ, PhD(phys chem), 63. *Prof Exp:* Mem tech staff phys chem, Gen Elec Res Labs, 60-61; mem tech staff phys chem, 63-73, HEAD, PHYS CHEM DEPT, BELL LABS, 73- *Concurrent Pos:* Adj prof, Univ Pa, 69-; exec mem comt phys chem div, Am Chem Soc; prof, Yale Univ, 81. *Honors & Awards:* Langmuir Prize in Chem Physics, Am Phys Soc, 73; Peter Debye Award, Am Chem Soc, 79; A Cressy Morrison Award, NY Acad Sci, 78. *Mem:* Nat Acad Sci; fel Am Phys Soc; fel NY Acad Sci; The Chem Soc. *Res:* Lasers; photochemistry; kinetics; picosecond spectroscopy. *Mailing Add:* Bell Labs Murray Hill NJ 07971

RENUART, ADHEMAR WILLIAM, b Miami, Fla, Aug 10, 31; m 52; c 9. PEDIATRIC NEUROLOGY, NEUROCHEMISTRY. *Educ:* Duke Univ, BS, 52, MD, 56. *Prof Exp:* Assoc, Duke Univ, 61-71, from asst prof to assoc prof pediat, Med Ctr, 72-76, assoc clin prof peds, 72-76; ASSOC CLIN PROF NEUROL, UNIV NC MED CTR, CHAPEL HILL, 76- *Concurrent Pos:* Dir res, Murdoch Ctr, 61-76. *Mailing Add:* 1830 Hillandale Rd Durham NC 27705

RENWICK, J ALAN A, b Dundee, Scotland, May 7, 36. INSECT BEHAVIOR. *Educ:* Dundee Tech Col, HNC, 60; City Col New York, MA, 64; Univ Gottingen, DF, 70. *Prof Exp:* Lab asst, Scottish Hort Res Inst, 58-60; res asst, 60-66, asst chemist, 66-73, ASSOC CHEMIST, BOYCE THOMPSON INST, CORNELL UNIV, 73- *Mem:* Am Chem Soc; Entom Soc Am. *Res:* Chemical factors affecting oviposition behavior of phytophagous insects; positive stimuli (recognition of suitable host plants) and negative stimuli that ensure spacing of populations. *Mailing Add:* Boyce Thompson Inst Cornell Univ Ithaca NY 14853

RENZEMA, THEODORE SAMUEL, b Grand Rapids, Mich, July 12, 12; m 39 & 68; c 1. EXPERIMENTAL SOLID STATE PHYSICS. *Educ:* Hope Col, AB, 34; Rutgers Univ, MS, 37; Purdue Univ, PhD(physics), 48. *Prof Exp:* Asst physics, Rutgers Univ, 34-37; asst physics, Purdue Univ, 37-42, instr, 42-47, Off Res & Inventions & Off Naval Res indust res fel, 46-48; assoc prof physics, Clarkson Col Technol, 48-50, prof & chmn dept, 50-65; vis prof, 65-66, chmn dept, 73-74, PROF PHYSICS, STATE UNIV NY ALBANY, 66- *Concurrent Pos:* Res assoc, Dudley Observ, 65-66. *Mem:* Am Phys Soc; Am Crystallog Asn; Am Asn Physics Teachers; Microbeam Anal Soc. *Res:* Electron diffraction investigations of thin films of metals; semiconductor surfaces; corrosion; x-ray crystallography; electron microprobe analysis; x-ray spectroscopy. *Mailing Add:* 3 Toll Lane Albany NY 12203

RENZETTI, ATTILIO D, JR, b New York, NY, Nov 11, 20; m 47; c 4. PULMONARY DISEASES, PHYSIOLOGY. *Educ:* Columbia Univ, AB, 41, MD, 44. *Prof Exp:* Asst prof indust med, Postgrad Med Sch, NY Univ, 49-51; asst prof med, Sch Med, Univ Utah, 52-53; asst prof, Col Med, State Univ NY Upstate Med Ctr, Syracuse Univ, 53-59, assoc prof, 59-60; assoc prof, Johns Hopkins Univ & Univ Md, 60-61; assoc prof, 61-67, PROF MED, COL MED, UNIV UTAH, 67-, CHMN PULMONARY DIS DIV, 61- *Concurrent Pos:* Fel cardio-pulmonary physiol, Bellevue Hosp Chest Serv, 49-51; Nat Heart & Lung Inst grants, Univ Utah, 61-; mem subspecialty bd pulmonary dis, Am Bd Internal Med, 65-72, chmn, 70-72; mem epidemiol & biomet adv comt, Nat Heart & Lung Inst, 70-73, mem comt spec ctr res, 71; consult, Vet Admin Hosp, Salt Lake City, Utah, 70- *Mem:* Am Lung Asn; Am Fedn Clin Res; Am Thoracic Soc (pres-elect, 74-75, pres, 75-76); fel Am Col Physicians; NY Acad Sci. *Res:* Pulmonary function in disease; applied respiratory physiology. *Mailing Add:* Pulmonary Div Univ of Utah Med Ctr Salt Lake City UT 84132

RENZETTI, NICHOLAS A, b New York, NY, Sept 30, 14; m 45; c 4. PHYSICS. *Educ:* Columbia Univ, AB, 35, AM, 36, PhD(physics), 40. *Prof Exp:* Asst physics, Columbia Univ, 37-40, res assoc, 40; physicist, Bur Ord, US Navy, 40-44, sci res administr, Naval Ord Test Sta, Calif, 44-54; sr physicist, Air Pollution Found, Calif, 54-59; sect chief telecommun, 59-63, mgr, Tracking & Data Systs for Planetary Projs, 64, TECH MGR, ENG, JET PROPULSION LAB, CALIF INST TECHNOL, 64- *Concurrent Pos:* Consult, US Naval Ord Test Sta, Pasadena, Calif, 54-62, Gen Motors Corp, Mich, 56-61 & Air Pollution Found, 59-61. *Res:* Tracking and communications with regard to ballistic and space vehicles; air pollution; underwater technology. *Mailing Add:* 1321 Virginia Rd San Marino CA 91108

RENZI, ALFRED ARTHUR, b Rochester, NY, July 20, 25; m 54; c 5. PHYSIOLOGY, ENDOCRINOLOGY. *Educ:* Fordham Univ, BS, 47; Syracuse Univ, MS, 49, PhD(zool), 52. *Prof Exp:* Asst endocrinol, Syracuse Univ, 47-51; from assoc endocrinologist to sr endocrinologist, Ciba Pharmaceut Co, NJ, 52-60, assoc dir physiol, 60-62, head endocrine-pharmacol sect, 62-67; head pharmacol dept, Dow Human Health Res & Develop Labs, Ind, 67-71, assoc scientist, Dow Chem Co, 71-80, ASSOC SCIENTIST, MED DEPT, MERRELL DOW PHARMACEUT, INC, 80- *Mem:* Am Physiol Soc; Am Soc Pharmacol & Exp Therapeut; Endocrine Soc. *Res:* Steroid hypertension; water metabolism; kidney function; adrenal cortex; inflammation; reproduction; atherosclerosis; lipid metabolism. *Mailing Add:* Med Dept Merrell Dow Pharmaceut Inc Indianapolis IN 46268

REPA, BRIAN STEPHEN, b Detroit, Mich, Apr 5, 42; m 70; c 2. BIOENGINEERING. *Educ:* Univ Mich, Dearborn Campus, BS, 65, Ann Arbor, MS, 66, PhD(bioeng), 72. *Prof Exp:* Co-op & res engr elec eng, Eng & Res Ctr, Ford Motor Co, 62-65; res asst math-mach systs, Univ Mich, 68-70, lab instr analog comput, 70-71; sr proj engr impaired driver countermeasures, 72-73, proj mgr driver physiol, 73-74, SR RES ENGR DRIVER-VEHICLE PERFORMANCE, GEN MOTORS RES LABS, 74- *Concurrent Pos:* Mem road user characteristics comt, Transp Res Bd, 74-, mem simulation & measurement of driving comt, 75-; mem passenger car safety comt, Soc Automotive Engrs, 75- *Mem:* Soc Automotive Engrs. *Res:* Mathematical modeling of the driver-vehicle system; effects of vehicle characteristics on driver-vehicle performance; perceptual cues used by drivers in controlling their vehicles. *Mailing Add:* Gen Motors Res Labs Mound & 12 Mile Rd Warren MI 48090

REPAK, ARTHUR JACK, b New York, NY, Mar 19, 40; m 66; c 2. PROTOZOOLOGY. *Educ:* Univ Mich, Ann Arbor, BS, 61; LI Univ, MS, 64; NY Univ, PhD(biol), 67. *Prof Exp:* Res asst biochem, Rockefeller Inst, 61-62; jr bacteriologist, Dept Water Supply, New York City, 62-63; teaching fel biol, NY Univ, 63-65; lectr, City Col New York, 65-67; clin lab intern, Malcolm Grow Air Force Hosp, Washington, DC, 67-68; dir clin lab, 2845th Air Force Hosp, Rome, NY, 68-70; assoc prof, 70-80, PROF BIOL, QUINNIPIAC COL, 80- *Concurrent Pos:* Consult, Ecol Consults, 70-; Yale-Lilly fel, 77-78; vis fac fel, Yale Univ, 78-82, res assoc, 71-82. *Mem:* Am Micros Soc; Am Soc Microbiol; Sigma Xi; Soc Protozoologists; NY Acad Sci. *Res:* Taxonomy and morphology of heterotrichous ciliates; encystment and excystment of protozoa; nutritional studies of marine heterotrechons ciliates; numerical taxonomy of protozoa; isolation and purification of marine ultraphytoplankton. *Mailing Add:* Dept Biol Sci Quinnipiac Col Box 158 Hamden CT 06518

REPASKE, ROY, b Cleveland, Ohio, Mar 17, 25; m 50; c 3. MOLECULAR BIOLOGY, MICROBIAL BIOCHEMISTRY. *Educ:* Western Reserve Univ, BS, 48; Univ Mich, MS, 50; Univ Wis, PhD(bact, biochem), 54. *Prof Exp:* Res assoc bact metab, Univ Wis, 53; from instr to assoc prof bact, Ind Univ, 54-59; chemist, Lab Microbiol, 59-74, chemist, Off Sci Dir, 74-80, CHEMIST, LAB MOLECULAR MICROBIOL, NAT INST ALLERGY & INFECT DIS, 80- *Concurrent Pos:* Consult, NASA, 62-65. *Mem:* Fel AAAS; Am Soc Microbiol; Am Soc Biol Chem; Brit Soc Gen Microbiol; Brit Biochem Soc. *Res:* Molecular bioogy of retroviruses, recombinant DNA; DNA sequencing. *Mailing Add:* Inst Allergy & Infectious Dis Nat Inst Health Bethesda MD 20014

REPENNING, CHARLES ALBERT, b Chicago, Ill, Aug 4, 22; m 49; c 4. PALEONTOLOGY, MAMMALOGY. *Educ:* Univ NMex, BS, 49; Univ Calif, Berkeley, MA, 64. *Prof Exp:* GEOLOGIST, US GEOL SURV, 49- *Res:* Cenozoic stratigraphy of the western United States; mammalian biostratigraphy, paleontology and zoology; geochronology; marine mammal and rodent evolution, adaptation and classification. *Mailing Add:* 2440 Villa Nulva Way Mountain View CA 94040

REPETSKI, JOHN EDWARD, b Wheeling, WVa, Dec 31, 47; m 73. PALEONTOLOGY, STRATIGRAPHY. *Educ:* Indiana Univ of Pa, BS, 69; Univ Mo-Columbia, MA, 73, PhD(geol), 75. *Prof Exp:* Instr geol, Univ Mo-Columbia, 74; res assoc, 75-76, GEOLOGIST PALEONT, US GEOL SURV, 76- *Mem:* Geol Soc Am; Soc Econ Paleontologists & Mineralogists; Brit Palaeont Asn; Pander Soc. *Res:* Paleobiology, biostratigraphy and ultrastructure studies of Cambrian and Ordovician conodonts, vertebrates and other phosphatic microfossils. *Mailing Add:* US Geol Surv E-501 US Nat Mus Washington DC 20560

REPINE, JOHN E, b Rock Island, Ill, Dec, 26, 44; m 69; c 3. LUNG & PHAGOCYTE RESEARCH. *Educ:* Univ Wis-Madison, BS, 67; Univ Minn, Minneapolis, MD, 71. *Prof Exp:* From instr to assoc prof internal med, Univ Minn, 74-79; ASSOC PROF MED, SCH MED, UNIV COLO, 79-, ASSOC PROF PEDIAT, 81-; ASST DIR & DIV EXP MED, WEBB-WARING LUNG INST, 79- *Concurrent Pos:* Mem res comt & site vis, Am Lung Asn, NIH; Young Plumonary investr for NIH grant, Heart & Lung Inst, 74-75; Basil O'Connor starter res award, Nat Found March of Dimes, 75-77; estab investr award, Am Heart Asn, 76-81; co-chmn steering comt, Apsen Lung Conf, 80, chmn, 81. *Mem:* AAAS; Am Asn Immunologists; Am Fedn Clin Res; Am Heart Asn; Am Thoracic Soc. *Res:* Role of phagocytes in lung injury and host defense. *Mailing Add:* Webb-Waring Lung Inst Box C321 E Ninth Ave Denver CO 80262

REPKA, BENJAMIN C, JR, b Buffalo, NY, July 5, 27; m 53; c 4. POLYPROPLENE, POLYETHYLENE. *Educ:* Canisius Col, BS, 49, MS, 52; Purdue Univ, PhD(phys org chem), 57. *Prof Exp:* Chemist, Carborundum Co, 50-53; res chemist polymers, Hercules, Inc, 56-71, sr res chemist, Polymers Res Div, 71-73, res scientist, 73-78, RES ASSOC, DEVELOP DEPT, HERCULES RES CTR, HERCULES, INC, 78- *Mem:* Am Chem Soc; Sigma Xi; Soc Automotive Eng. *Res:* Polyolefins; organometallics; heterogeneous catalysis; polymerization processes. *Mailing Add:* Develop Dept Hercules Res Ctr Wilmington DE 19899

REPKO, WAYNE WILLIAM, b Detroit, Mich, Mar 21, 40; m 66; c 3. ELEMENTARY PARTICLE PHYSICS. *Educ:* Wayne State Univ, BS, 63, PhD(theoret physics), 67. *Prof Exp:* Res assoc theoret physics, Wayne State Univ, 67-68 & Johns Hopkins Univ, 68-70; from asst prof to assoc prof, 70-79, PROF THEORET PHYSICS, MICH STATE UNIV, 79- *Concurrent Pos:* Vis assoc prof, Johns Hopkins Univ, 76- *Mem:* Am Phys Soc. *Res:* Quantum field theory; quantum electrodynamics; elementary particle physics. *Mailing Add:* Dept of Physics Mich State Univ East Lansing MI 48824

REPLOGLE, CLYDE R, b Detroit, Mich, Nov 13, 35; div; c 1. BIOENGINEERING, PHYSIOLOGY. *Educ:* Mich State Univ, BS, 58, MS, 60, PhD(physiol), 67. *Prof Exp:* Instr physiol, US Air Force Inst Technol, 62-64, asst prof bioeng & physiol, 64-68, chief environ physiol br, 68-72, adj prof bioeng, 68-77; chief manned systs effectiveness div, 77-79, CHIEF ENVIRON MED DIV, AEROSPACE MED RES LAB, 72-, ASST CHIEF SPECIAL PROJ, HUMAN ENG DIV, 79- *Concurrent Pos:* Assoc prof biomed sci, Wright State Univ, 79- *Mem:* Inst Elec & Electronics Engrs. *Res:* Chemical warfare defense analysis; man-machine system, human operator and manned weapon system performance; hemodynamics; vestibular function; biosystems analysis; muscle control modeling; environmental medicine. *Mailing Add:* Human Eng div Aerospace Med Res Lab Wright-Patterson AFB OH 45433

REPLOGLE, JOHN A(SHER), b Charleston, Ill, Jan 13, 34; m 57; c 2. HYDRAULICS, AGRICULTURAL ENGINEERING. *Educ:* Univ Ill, BS, 56, MS, 58, PhD(civil eng), 64. *Prof Exp:* Agr engr, Soil Conserv Serv, USDA, 56; res asst agr eng, Univ Ill, 56-58, instr, 58-63; res agr engr, 63-66, res hydraul engr, 66-75, RES LEADER, WATER CONSERV LAB, AGR RES

SERV, USDA, 75- *Honors & Awards:* James R Croes Medal, Am Soc Civil Engrs, 77. *Mem:* AAAS; Am Soc Agr Engrs; Am Soc Civil Engrs. *Res:* Agricultural land drainage, irrigation and hydrology; fluid mechanics; hydraulic structures; water resources planning and development; flow measurement; basic physical science. *Mailing Add:* US Water Conserv Lab 4331 E Broadway Phoenix AZ 85040

REPLOGLE, LANNY LEE, b San Bernardino, Calif, Oct 30, 34; m 58; c 2. ORGANIC CHEMISTRY. *Educ:* Univ Calif, Berkeley, BS, 56; Univ Wash, PhD(org chem), 60. *Prof Exp:* Res instr chem, Univ Wash, 60-61; from asst prof to assoc prof, 61-69, PROF CHEM, CALIF STATE UNIV, SAN JOSE, 69- *Concurrent Pos:* NSF grants, San Jose State Col, 62-69; Nat Res Coun sr res associateship, Ames Res Ctr, NASA, 70-71; consult, Paul Masson Vineyards. *Mem:* Am Chem Soc. *Res:* Chemistry of azulene and its derivatives; nonbenzenoid aromatics; hetercyclic analogs of nonbenzenoid aromatic hydrocarbons; wine chemistry. *Mailing Add:* Dept of Chem Calif State Univ San Jose CA 95114

REPLOGLE, ROBERT LEE, b Ottumwa, Iowa, Sept 30, 31; m 58; c 2. CARDIOVASCULAR SURGERY, THORACIC SURGERY. *Educ:* Cornell Col, BS, 56; Harvard Med Sch, MD, 60. *Hon Degrees:* DSc, Cornell Col, 72. *Prof Exp:* Asst resident surg, Peter Bent Brigham Hosp, Boston, Mass, 61-63; res fels, Children's Hosp Med Ctr, Boston & Harvard Med Sch, 63-64; sr resident, Children's Hosp Med Ctr, Boston, 64-65; asst resident, Mass Gen Hosp, Boston, 65-66; sr resident, Children's Hosp Med Ctr, 66, asst, 66-67; asst prof surg, 67-70, assoc prof surg & chief pediat surg, 70-74, PROF SURG & CHIEF CARDIAC SURG, PRITZKER SCH MED, UNIV CHICAGO, 74- *Concurrent Pos:* Asst surg, Harvard Med Sch, 66-67; dir cardiac surg, Michael Reese Hosp & Med Ctr, 77- *Mem:* Soc Univ Surg; Am Asn Thoracic Surg; Int Soc Surg. *Res:* Cardiovascular physiology; rheology. *Mailing Add:* Dept Surg Pritzker Sch Med Univ Chicago Chicago IL 60637

REPORTER, MINOCHER C, b Bombay, India, Feb 8, 28; US citizen; m 52; c 4. DEVELOPMENTAL BIOLOGY, BIOCHEMISTRY. *Educ:* Johns Hopkins Univ, AB, 52; Mass Inst Technol, PhD(food technol), 59. *Prof Exp:* Res asst, Develop Dept, A D Witten Co, Mass, 59; res asst nutrit, Mass Inst Technol, 59; res fel, Geront Br, Nat Heart Inst, 59-62; asst investr develop biol, Carnegie Inst Dept Embryol, 62-65; staff scientist, 65-68, INVESTR, CHARLES F KETTERING RES LAB, 68- *Concurrent Pos:* Adj assoc prof, Antioch Col, 68- *Mem:* AAAS; Am Soc Microbiol; Am Soc Biol Chemists; Am Soc Cell Biol; Am Soc Plant Physiol. *Res:* Nitrogen fixation and control of energy supply; differentiation and cellular development; cell physiology; nitrogen fixation in culture. *Mailing Add:* Charles F Kettering Res Lab 150 E South College St Yellow Springs OH 45387

REPPER, CHARLES JOHN, b Philadelphia, Pa, Nov 1, 34. SOLID STATE PHYSICS. *Educ:* St Joseph's Col, Pa, BS, 56; Drexel Inst Technol, MS, 65. *Prof Exp:* Physicist, Res Lab & Appl Res Lab, 56-64, RES SCIENTIST & PROJ ENGR, PHYS ELECTRONICS DEPT, PHILCO CORP, 66- *Mem:* Am Phys Soc. *Res:* Photoconductivity; electroluminescent gallium arsenide P-N junctions; thin film metal-oxide structures; solid state photo detectors; metallurgy and measurements of the electrical and optical properties of semiconductors. *Mailing Add:* 7324 N 20th St Philadelphia PA 19138

REPPERGER, DANIEL WILLIAM, b Charlestown, SC, Nov 24, 42; m 68; c 2. ELECTRICAL ENGINEERING, MATHEMATICS. *Educ:* Rensselaer Polytech Inst, BSEE, 67, MSEE, 68; Purdue Univ, PhD(elec eng), 73. *Prof Exp:* Res asst elec eng, Rensselaer Polytech Inst, 67-68; teaching instr, Purdue Univ, 68-71, David Ross res fel, 71-73; Nat Res Coun appointment eng control theory, Aerospace Med Res Lab, 73-74; systs analyst elec eng, Systs Res Lab, 74-75, SYSTS ANALYST ELEC ENG, AEROSPACE MED RES LAB, WRIGHT PATTERSON AFB, 75- *Concurrent Pos:* Reviewer tech papers, IEEE Trans Automatic Control, 72-, IEEE Trans Systs, Man & Cybernet, 74- & Human Factors, 75- *Mem:* Inst Elec & Electronics Engrs; Nat Soc Prof Engrs; AAAS. *Res:* Modern control systems theory; modeling; identification; man-machine systems; numerical algorithms; applications and theoretical aspects of optimal control and estimation theory; human factors engineering. *Mailing Add:* Bldg 33 Aerospace Med Res Lab Wright Patterson AFB Dayton OH 45433

REPPOND, KERMIT DALE, b Farmerville, La, Oct 31, 45. ORGANIC CHEMISTRY, PHYSICAL CHEMISTRY. *Educ:* Northeast La Univ, BS, 67; Univ Ark, PhD(chem), 74. *Prof Exp:* CHEMIST, KODIAK LAB, NAT MARINE FISHERY SERV, 76- *Res:* Development of methods to enhance utilization of various seafood for human consumption. *Mailing Add:* Kodiak Utilization Lab Box 1638 Kodiak AK 99615

REPPY, JOHN DAVID, b Lakewood, NJ, Feb 16, 31; m 59; c 3. PHYSICS. *Educ:* Univ Conn, BA, 54, MS, 56; Yale Univ, PhD(physics), 61. *Prof Exp:* NSF fel physics, Oxford Univ, 61-62; asst prof, Yale Univ, 62-66; assoc prof, 66-69, PROF PHYSICS, CORNELL UNIV, 69- *Concurrent Pos:* Guggenheim fel, 72-73; Fulbright-Hays fel, 78; Guggenheim fel & Sci Res Coun sr res fel, 79-80. *Honors & Awards:* Fritz London Award. *Mem:* Fel Am Phys Soc. *Res:* Macroscopic quantum properties of superconductors and superfluid helium; cooperative phenomena. *Mailing Add:* Dept of Physics Cornell Univ Ithaca NY 14853

REQUARTH, WILLIAM H, b Charlotte, NC, Jan 23, 13; m 48; c 4. SURGERY. *Educ:* James Milliken Univ, BS, 34; Univ Ill, MD, 39, MSc, 40; Am Bd Surg, dipl, 47. *Prof Exp:* Intern, St Luke's Hosp, Chicago, 38-39; residency surg, Cook County Hosp, 39-46; asst prof, 47-66, PROF SURG, UNIV ILL COL MED, 66- *Concurrent Pos:* Mem attend staff, Macon County Hosp, St Mary's Hosp, Decatur, Ill & Ill Res Hosp. *Mem:* Am Soc Surg of Hand; Am Asn Surg of Trauma; fel Am Col Surgeons; AMA; Soc Surg Alimentary Tract. *Res:* General surgery; surgery of the hand. *Mailing Add:* 1 Memorial Dr Decatur IL 62526

REQUE, PAUL GERHARD, b New York, NY, May 28, 07; m 36; c 2. MEDICINE. *Educ:* Duke Univ, MD, 34. *Prof Exp:* Assoc dermat & instr internal med, Sch Med, Duke Univ, 40-46; ASSOC PROF DERMAT, SCH MED, UNIV ALA, BIRMINGHAM, 46-; ASSOC DIR DERMAT & SYPHIL, LLOYD NOLAND FOUND HOSP, 47- *Concurrent Pos:* Lectr, Univ NC, 40-42; consult, Vet Admin Hosp, 46-52. *Mem:* Soc Invest Dermat; Am Acad Dermat. *Res:* Borate absorption through the dermis and mucous membranes; chromatography; drug idiosyncrasy; antibody-antigen reactions; systemic sclerosis. *Mailing Add:* 800 Montclair Rd Birmingham AL 35213

RERICK, MARK NEWTON, b Syracuse, NY, Jan 31, 34; m 56; c 5. ORGANIC CHEMISTRY, SYSTEMS ANALYSIS. *Educ:* Le Moyne Col, BS, 55; Univ Notre Dame, PhD(chem), 58. *Prof Exp:* Res assoc, Univ Notre Dame, 58-59; res fel, Calif Inst Technol, 59-60; from asst prof to assoc prof, 60-68, PROF ORG CHEM, PROVIDENCE COL, 69- *Mem:* AAAS; Am Chem Soc. *Res:* Reductions of organic compounds with complex and mixed metal hydrides; conformational analysis of mobile cyclohexane systems; systems analysis of complex systems. *Mailing Add:* Dept of Chem Providence Col Providence RI 02918

RESCH, GEORGE MICHAEL, b Baltimore, Md, Mar 26, 40; m 64; c 1. PHYSICS, ASTRONOMY. *Educ:* Univ Md, BS, 63; Fla State Univ, MS, 65, PhD(physics), 74. *Prof Exp:* Res asst physics, Fla State Univ, 63-68; res assoc astron, Clark Lake Radio Observ, 68-71; res asst astron, Univ Md, 71-74; MEM TECH STAFF, JET PROPULSION LAB, 74- *Mem:* Am Inst Physics; Am Astron Soc; Am Geophys Union. *Res:* Instrumentation development and measurement systems with application to geodesy and astronomy. *Mailing Add:* Jet Propulsion Lab 4800 Oak Grove Dr Pasadena CA 91103

RESCH, HELMUTH, b Vienna, Austria, May 22, 33; m 60; c 2. FOREST PRODUCTS. *Educ:* Agr Univ, Vienna, dipl eng, 56; Utah State Univ, MS, 57, PhD(wood technol), 60. *Prof Exp:* Res asst, Utah State Univ, 56-57, US Forest Serv, 57 & J Neils Lumber Co, 58; asst, Agr Univ, Vienna, 58-60; asst & assoc prof wood technol, Univ Calif, Berkeley, 62-70; PROF & HEAD DEPT FOREST PROD DEPT, SCH FORESTRY, ORE STATE UNIV, 70- *Mem:* Soc Wood Sci & Technol (pres, 80-81); Forest Prod Res Soc; Am Wood Preservers Asn. *Res:* Physical properties of wood, processing of timber into lumber, plywood and other manufactured products. *Mailing Add:* Dept of Forest Prod Sch of Forestry Ore State Univ Corvallis OR 97331

RESCH, JOSEPH ANTHONY, b Milwaukee, Wis, Apr 29, 14; m 39; c 3. NEUROLOGY. *Educ:* Univ Wis, BS, 36, MD, 38; Am Bd Psychiat & Neurol, dipl. *Prof Exp:* Rockefeller fel neurol, Univ Minn, 46-48; pvt pract, 48-62; assoc prof, 62-65, asst vpres health sci affairs, 70-77, PROF NEUROL, UNIV MINN, MINNEAPOLIS, 65-, HEAD DEPT, 77- *Mem:* Fel Am Acad Neurol; Am Asn Neuropath; Am Electroencephalog Soc; Am Neurol Asn. *Res:* Cerebrovascular disease; geographic pathology. *Mailing Add:* Dept of Neurol Univ of Minn Minneapolis MN 55455

RESCHER, NICHOLAS, b Hagen, Ger, July 15, 28; nat US. PHILOSOPHY OF SCIENCE, SYMBOLIC LOGIC. *Educ:* Queens Col NY, BS, 49; Princeton Univ, PhD(philos), 51. *Hon Degrees:* LHD, Loyola Univ, 70. *Prof Exp:* Instr philos, Princeton Univ, 51-52; res mathematician, Rand Corp, 54-57; assoc prof philos, Lehigh Univ, 57-61; prof, 61-71, UNIV PROF PHILOS, UNIV PITTSBURGH, 71-, DIR, INST INT DE PHILOS, 70- *Concurrent Pos:* Ford Found fel, 59; NSF res award, 69-70; Guggenheim fel, 70-71; ed-in-chief, Am Philos Quart; secy gen, Int Union Hist & Philos Sci, 69-75; mem staff, Corpus Christi Col, Oxford, 78- *Mem:* Am Philos Asn; Philos Sci Soc. *Res:* Philosophy of science. *Mailing Add:* Dept of Philos Univ of Pittsburgh Pittsburgh PA 15213

RESCIGNO, ALDO, b Milan, Italy, Aug 27, 24; m 50; c 1. MATHEMATICAL BIOLOGY. *Educ:* Univ Milan, Laurea in Physics, 48. *Prof Exp:* Res asst med physics, Tumor Ctr, Italy, 49-52; asst phys chem, Bracco Indust Chim, 52-55; tech dir nuclear instrumentation, Metalnova SpA, 55-59 & DISI, 59-61; res asst biophys, Donner Lab, Univ Calif, Berkeley, 61-62; lectr med physics, 62-63, asst prof, 63-64; fel phys biochem, Australian Nat Univ, 65-69; assoc prof physiol, Univ Minn, Minneapolis, 69-75; mathematician, Lab Theoret Biol, Nat Cancer Inst, NIH, 75-77; prof physiol, Univ Minn, Minneapolis, 77-79; prof biomath, Univ Witwatersrand, Johannesburg, 80-81; RES PRIN, SCH MED, YALE UNIV, NEW HAVEN, 82- *Concurrent Pos:* Vis prof, LADSEB, Ctr Nuclear Res, Padova, Italy, 75. *Honors & Awards:* Killam Scholar, Univ Calgary, 79. *Mem:* Soc Gen Systs Res; Brit Inst Physics; Soc Math Biol. *Res:* mathematical models of biological system; theory of compartments; drug and tracer kinetics; general system theory; deterministic population dynamics. *Mailing Add:* 615 Seventh St SE Minneapolis MN 55414

RESCIGNO, THOMAS NICOLA, b New York, NY, Sept 10, 47; div. CHEMICAL PHYSICS. *Educ:* Columbia Col, BA, 69; Harvard Univ, MA, 71, PhD(chem physics), 73. *Prof Exp:* Res fel, Calif Inst Technol, 73-75; staff scientist, 75-79, GROUP LEADER, LAWRENCE LIVERMORE NAT LAB, 79- *Mem:* Am Phys Soc. *Res:* Theoretical atomic and molecular physics-low energy electron scattering; atomic and molecular photoabsorption; electronic structure of atoms and molecules; manybody theory. *Mailing Add:* Lawrence Livermore Nat Lab PO Box 5508 Livermore CA 94550

RESCONICH, EMIL CARL, b Portage, Pa, Oct 17, 23. PLANT VIROLOGY. *Educ:* St Francis Col, Pa, BA, 54; Univ Notre Dame, PhD(biol), 59. *Prof Exp:* NSF fel, Univ Calif, Berkeley, 59-60; asst prof biol, Col Steubenville, 60-62; assoc prof, 62-72, chmn dept, 62-72, PROF BIOL, ST FRANCIS COL, PA, 72- *Mem:* Am Soc Plant Physiol; Bot Soc Am; Am Phytopath Soc. *Res:* Physiology of plant virus infection; cell physiology; plant virology. *Mailing Add:* Dept Biol St Francis Col Loretto PA 15940

RESCONICH, SAMUEL, b Portage, Pa, July 31,33. ORGANIC CHEMISTRY. *Educ:* St Francis Col, Pa, BS, 54; Purdue Univ, PhD(org chem), 61. *Prof Exp:* Teaching asst gen chem, Purdue Univ, 54-56, Westinghouse Elec fel, 56-59, Naval ord res fel org chem, 59-60; from asst prof to assoc prof, 60-70, PROF CHEM, ST FRANCIS COL, PA, 70- *Mem:* Am Chem Soc; Sigma Xi; Am Asn Univ Professors. *Res:* Organometallic compounds; organic synthesis of fluorine containing compounds. *Mailing Add:* Sullivan Hall Dept Chem St Francis Col Loretto PA 15940

RESHKIN, MARK, b East Orange, NJ, May 31, 33; m 61; c 1. GEOMORPHOLOGY. *Educ:* Rutgers Univ, AB, 55; Ind Univ, MA, 58, PhD(geol), 63. *Prof Exp:* Instr geol, Univ Maine, 63-64; from asst prof to assoc prof geol, 64-71, chmn dept, 68-71, dir, Div Pub & Environ Affairs, 72-75, assoc prof pub & environ affairs, 71-77, PROF PUB & ENVIRON AFFAIRS, IND UNIV NORTHWEST, 71-, PROF GEOL, 77- *Mem:* AAAS; Geol Soc Am; Glaciol Soc; Am Quaternary Asn; Am Pub Admin. *Res:* Geomorphology of northern Rocky Mountains; geomorphology and glacial geology of northern Indiana; environmental geology of northwest Indiana; environmental management. *Mailing Add:* Dept of Environ Geol Ind Univ Northwest Gary IN 46408

RESHOTKO, ELI, b New York, NY, Nov 18, 30; m 53; c 3. AEROSPACE SCIENCES. *Educ:* Cooper Union, BME, 50; Cornell Univ, MME, 51; Calif Inst Technol, PhD(aeronaut, physics), 60. *Prof Exp:* Aeronaut res scientist, Lewis Lab, Nat Adv Comt Aeronaut, 51-55, head fluid mech sect, 56-57, head high temperature plasma sect, Lewis Res Ctr, NASA, 60-61, chief plasma physics br, 61-64; assoc prof eng, 64-66, head div fluid thermal & aerospace sci, 70-76, chmn dept mech & aerospace eng, 76-79, PROF ENG, CASE WESTERN RESERVE UNIV, 66- *Concurrent Pos:* Mem res adv comt fluid mech, NASA, 61-64; mem plasma physics panel, Physics Study Comt, Nat Acad Sci, 64; Susman vis prof, Israel Inst Technol, 69-70; chmn, US Boundary Layer Transition Study Group, 70-; consult, BoH, Beranek & Newman, Gould Corp, Arvin/Colspan, Dynamics Technol Inc, Lockheed Calif Co & NSF; US mem, Fluid Dynamics Panel, Adv Group Aerospace Res & Develop, NATO, 81- *Honors & Awards:* Fluid & Plasmadynamics Award, Am Inst Aeronaut & Astronaut, 80. *Mem:* Fel Am Acad Mech; fel AAAS; fel Am Soc Mech Engrs; fel Am Inst Aeronaut & Astronaut; fel Am Phys Soc. *Res:* Boundary layer theory and transition; aerodynamic heating; hydrodynamic stability; magnetohydrodynamics; advanced propulsion and power generation. *Mailing Add:* Sch of Eng Case Western Reserve Univ Cleveland OH 44106

RESING, HENRY ANTON, b Chicago, Ill, May 23, 33; m 56; c 7. PHYSICAL CHEMISTRY. *Educ:* DePaul Univ, BS, 55; Univ Chicago, MS, 57, PhD(chem), 59. *Prof Exp:* Phys chemist, Solid State Div, 59-69, Sect Head, Surface & Solid Kinetics Sect, 69-76, Sect Head, Electroactive Solids Sect, 76-80, SR SCIENTIST, CHEM DIV, US NAVAL RES LAB, 80- *Concurrent Pos:* Nat Acad Sci-Nat Res Coun fel, 59-61; vis scientist, Mass Inst Technol, 71-72; vis lectr, Inst Earth Sci, Louvain Univ, 71. *Mem:* Am Chem Soc. *Res:* Self diffusion in molecular crystals and motion of molecules adsorbed on solid surfaces by means of nuclear magnetic resonance; properties of conducting polymers and graphites; surface and polymer analysis. *Mailing Add:* Chem Div US Naval Res Lab Code 6173 Washington DC 20375

RESKO, JOHN A, b Patton, Pa, Oct 28, 32; m 62; c 2. REPRODUCTIVE PHYSIOLOGY. *Educ:* St Charles Sem, AB, 56; Marquette Univ, MS, 60; Univ Ill, PhD(physiol), 63. *Prof Exp:* USPHS fel steroid biochem, Col Med, Univ Utah, 63-64; asst scientist, 64-77, from asst prof to assoc prof, 65-77, PROF PHYSIOL, UNIV ORE HEALTH SCI CTR, 77-, CHMN DEPT, 81-; SCIENTIST REPRODUCTIVE PHYSIOL, ORE REGIONAL PRIMATE RES CTR, 71- *Mem:* AAAS; Soc Study Reproduction; Am Physiol Soc; Endocrine Soc. *Res:* Fetal endocrinology; influence of hormones on behavior; ovarian steroid biosynthesis. *Mailing Add:* Dept Physiol Oregon Health Sci Univ Portland OR 97201

RESLER, E(DWIN) L(OUIS), JR, b Pittsburgh, Pa, Nov 20, 25; m 48; c 5. AERONAUTICAL ENGINEERING. *Educ:* Univ Notre Dame, BS, 47; Cornell Univ, PhD(aeronaut eng), 51. *Prof Exp:* Res assoc, Grad Sch Aeronaut Eng, Cornell Univ, 48-51, asst prof, 51-52; assoc prof aero, Inst Fluid Dynamics & Appl Math, Univ Md, 52-56; assoc prof aerospace & elec eng & appl physics, 56-68, PROF AEROSPACE & ELEC ENG & APPL PHYSICS, CORNELL UNIV, 58-, DIR GRAD SCH AEROSPACE ENG, 63-, JOSEPH NEWTON PEW, JR PROF ENG, 68- *Mem:* Am Phys Soc; Am Inst Aeronaut & Astronaut; Int Acad Astronaut. *Res:* Gas dynamics; aerodynamics; shock waves; magnetohydrodynamics. *Mailing Add:* 162 Turkey Hill Rd Ithaca NY 14850

RESNEKOV, LEON, b Cape Town, SAfrica, Mar 20, 28; m 55; c 2. MEDICINE. *Educ:* Univ Cape Town, MB, ChB, 51, MD, 65; FRCP, 72. *Prof Exp:* Intern med & surg, Groote Schuur Hosp, Univ Cape Town, 52; registr med, Kings Col Hosp, London, 54-59, registr cardiol, 59-61, sr registr, Inst Cardiol, Nat Heart Hosp, London, 61-67; assoc prof, 67-71, PROF MED, UNIV CHICAGO, 71-, DIR MYOCARDIAL INFARCTION RES UNIT, 67-, JOINT DIR SECT CARDIOL, 71- *Mem:* Fel Royal Soc Med; Brit Cardiac Soc; fel Am Col Cardiol. *Res:* Hemodynamics and cardiac physiology in humans and experimental animals; high energy electrical current on cardiac function; electrical control of cardiac rhythm disturbances. *Mailing Add:* Dept of Med Univ of Chicago Chicago IL 60637

RESNICK, CHARLES A, b New York, NY, July 28, 39; m 63; c 3. PHARMACOLOGY, TOXICOLOGY. *Educ:* Brooklyn Col Pharm, BS, 62; Univ Pittsburgh, PhD(pharmacol), 70. *Prof Exp:* PHARMACOLOGIST, FOOD & DRUG ADMIN, 70- *Mem:* NY Acad Sci; Am Heart Asn. *Res:* Beta adrenoceptor blocking agents; cardiovascular applications and oncogenic potential. *Mailing Add:* Food & Drug Admin 5600 Fishers Lane Rockville MD 20857

RESNICK, H(YMAN), b Cambridge, Mass, Dec 21, 24; m 59; c 3. CHEMICAL ENGINEERING. *Educ:* Northeastern Univ, BS, 47; Mass Inst Technol, SM, 49, ScD(chem eng), 52. *Prof Exp:* Engr, Div Indust Coop, Mass Inst Technol, 49-50, asst, 50-52; res engr, Chevron Res Co, Standard Oil Co Calif, 52-56, group supvr, 56-60, supv res engr, 60-62, sr supv res engr, Chevron Oil Field Res Co, La Habra, 62-64, sect supvr, 64-68, mgr, 68-73, MGR, COMP & SYSTS DIV, CHEVRON RES CO, RICHMOND, 74- *Mem:* Am Chem Soc; Am Inst Chem Engrs. *Res:* Design of petroleum process and plants; oil field research; systems engineering; computer technology. *Mailing Add:* Chevron Res Co 576 Standard Ave Richmond CA 94802

RESNICK, HAROLD, b Brooklyn, NY, Oct 23, 20. BIOCHEMISTRY. *Educ:* City Col New York, BS, 48; Brooklyn Col, MA, 55; Univ Iowa, PhD(biochem), 59. *Prof Exp:* Jr bacteriologist, State Dept Health, NY, 49-53; bacteriologist, State Univ NY, 53-55; asst, Univ Iowa, 55-57; instr biochem, Sch Med, Univ Ark, Little Rock, 59-61, asst prof, 61-67; assoc prof, 67-74, PROF BIOCHEM, MED CTR, WVA UNIV, 74- *Concurrent Pos:* Chief biochem br, Appalachian Lab Occup Respiratory Dis, Dept Health, Educ & Welfare, Morgantown, WVa. *Mem:* AAAS; Am Chem Soc; NY Acad Sci. *Res:* Protein chemistry; enzymes. *Mailing Add:* Dept of Biochem WVa Univ Med Ctr Morgantown WV 26506

RESNICK, JOEL B, b Brooklyn, NY, Jan 24, 35; m 57; c 6. SYSTEMS ENGINEERING. *Educ:* City Col New York, BS, 57; Mass Inst Technol, MS, 62. *Prof Exp:* Staff engr, Lincoln Lab, Mass Inst Technol, 57-65, group leader, 65-70; systs engr & analyst, US Arms Control & Disarmament Agency, 70-71; dir strategic forces div, Off Asst Secy Defense for systs anal, planning, anal & eval, 71-78, dir, Prog Assessment Off, Intel Community Staff, 78-80; SR ANALYST & DIR PROGRAM ALPHA, SCIENCE APPLICATIONS INC, 80- *Res:* Analysis of national security issues related to strategic defensive and offensive systems, theatre nuclear forces and space systems. *Mailing Add:* 10604 Trotters Trail Potomac MD 20854

RESNICK, LAZER, b Montreal, Que, June 25, 38; m 64; c 3. PARTICLE PHYSICS, THEORETICAL PHYSICS. *Educ:* McGill Univ, BSc, 59; Cornell Univ, PhD(theoret physics), 65. *Prof Exp:* Res assoc physics, Brookhaven Nat Lab, 64-65; Nat Res Coun Can fel, Niels Bohr Inst, Copenhagen Denmark, 65-66 & Tel-Aviv Univ, 66-67; asst prof, 67-71, ASSOC PROF PHYSICS, CARLETON UNIV, 71- *Mem:* Am Phys Soc; Can Asn Physicists. *Res:* High energy and elementary particle physics; quantum mechanics. *Mailing Add:* Dept of Physics Carleton Univ Ottawa ON K1S 5B6 Can

RESNICK, MICHAEL AARON, biophysics, genetics, see previous edition

RESNICK, OSCAR, b Bayonne, NJ, Apr 27, 24; m 49; c 2. PHYSIOLOGY, PHARMACOLOGY. *Educ:* Clark Univ, AB, 44; Harvard Univ, MA, 45; Boston Univ, PhD(biol), 55. *Prof Exp:* Instr biol, St Petersburg Jr Col, 46-47; instr physiol, Univ Minn, 49-50; ed asst, Biol Abstr, 50-51; res scientist, Nat Drug Co, Pa, 51-53; SR SCIENTIST, WORCESTER FOUND EXP BIOL, 53- *Concurrent Pos:* Lectr physiol, Grad Sch Dent, Boston Univ, 62-; lectr psychol, Clark Univ, 65-; res consult, Abraham Ribicoff Res Ctr, Norwich Hosp, Conn; mem, Psychodelic Res & Study Group. *Mem:* AAAS; fel Am Col Neuropsychopharmacol. *Res:* Metabolism of biogenic amines in man; clinical psychopharmacology. *Mailing Add:* Worcester Found for Exp Biol 222 Maple Ave Shrewsbury MA 01545

RESNICK, PAUL R, b New York, NY, Apr 7, 34; m 66; c 1. FLUORINE CHEMISTRY. *Educ:* Swarthmore Col, BA, 55; Cornell Univ, PhD(org chem), 61. *Prof Exp:* Fel, Univ Calif, Berkeley, 60-62; from chemist to sr res chemist, 62-74, RES ASSOC, E I DU PONT DE NEMOURS & CO, INC, 74- *Mem:* Am Chem Soc. *Mailing Add:* Plastics Dept Exp Sta E I du Pont de Nemours & Co Wilmington DE 19898

RESNICK, ROBERT, b Baltimore, Md, Jan 11, 23; m 45; c 3. PHYSICS. *Educ:* Johns Hopkins Univ, AB, 43, PhD(physics), 49. *Prof Exp:* Physicist, Nat Adv Comt Aeronaut, 44-46; from asst prof to assoc prof physics, Univ Pittsburgh, 49-56; from assoc prof to prof physics, 56-75, EDWARD P HAMILTON DISTINGUISHED PROF SCI, RENSSELAER POLYTECH INST, 75- *Concurrent Pos:* Mem, Comn Col Physics, 60-68; hon res fel, Harvard Univ, 64-65; adv ed, John Wiley & Sons, Inc, 67-; Fulbright prof, Peru, 71. *Honors & Awards:* Exxon Found Award, 53; Oersted Medal, Am Asn Physics Teachers, 75. *Mem:* Am Phys Soc; Am Soc Eng Educ; Am Asn Physics Teachers; AAAS; Sigma Xi. *Res:* Aerodynamics; nuclear and atmospheric physics; instructional materials; educational research and development; relativity and quantum physics; history of physics. *Mailing Add:* Dept Physics Rowland Lab Rensselaer Polytech Inst Troy NY 12181

RESNICK, SIDNEY I, b New York, NY, Oct 27, 45; m 69; c 1. MATHEMATICS. *Educ:* Queens Col, NY, BA, 66; Purdue Univ, Lafayette, MS, 68, PhD(math statist), 70. *Prof Exp:* Lectr probability & statist, Israel Inst Technol, 69-72; asst prof statist, Stanford Univ, 72-77; assoc prof, 78-80, PROF STATIST, COLO STATE UNIV, 81- *Concurrent Pos:* Vis prof, Erasmus Univ, 81-82. *Mem:* Fel Inst Math Statist. *Res:* Probability and stochastic processes; extreme value theory; regular variation; weak convergence; stochastic models. *Mailing Add:* Dept of Statist Colo State Univ Ft Collins CO 80523

RESNICK, SOL DONALD, b Milwaukee, Wis, June 15, 18. HYDROLOGY. *Educ:* Univ Wis, BS, 41 & 42, MS, 49. *Prof Exp:* Asst hydrol engr, Tenn Valley Authority, 42-43; instr math, Carson-Newman Col, 43-44; asst prof hydrol, Colo State Univ, 49-52; irrig specialist, Int Coop Admin, 52-57; assoc prof, Water Resources Res Ctr, 66-72, PROF HYDROL & HYDROLOGIST, UNIV ARIZ, 57-, DIR, WATER RESOURCES RES CTR, 72- *Mem:* Am Soc Agr Eng; Am Soc Civil Engr. *Res:* Irrigation. *Mailing Add:* Water Resources Res Ctr Univ of Ariz Tucson AZ 85721

RESNIK, FRANK EDWARD, b Pleasant Unity, Pa, Oct 14, 28; m 52; c 3. ANALYTICAL CHEMISTRY. *Educ:* St Vincent Col, BS, 52; Univ Richmond, MS, 55. *Prof Exp:* Res chemist, Philip Morris USA, 52-54, group leader, 54-56, from asst supvr to sr supvr, 56-60, tech asst to mgr res, 60-62, mgr, Anal Serv Div, 62-67, dir com develop, 67-71, dir develop, 71-72, dir, Res Ctr Opers, 72-75, vpres opers coord, 76-78, vpres opers, 78-80, VPRES & EXEC VPRES, TOBACCO TECHNOL GROUP, PHILIP MORRIS INC, 80- *Mem:* AAAS; Am Chem Soc. *Res:* Mass spectrometry; infrared, near-infrared and ultraviolet spectrometry; polarography; chromatography; paper, column and gas chromatography; ion exchange; analytical chemistry; instrumental and colorinetric methods development; microtechniques in spectroscopy and chromatography. *Mailing Add:* Philip Morris Inc 100 Park Ave New York NY 10017

RESNIK, HARVEY LEWIS PAUL, b Buffalo, NY, Apr 6, 30; m 64; c 3. PSYCHIATRY, PSYCHOANALYSIS. *Educ:* Univ Buffalo, BA, 51; Columbia Univ, MD, 55; Univ Pa, certs med hypnosis & marriage counseling, 62; Del Valley Group Psychother Inst, cert group ther, 62; Philadelphia Psychoanal Inst, cert psychoanal, 67; Am Bd Psychiat & Neurol, dipl. *Prof Exp:* Intern, Philadelphia Gen Hosp, 55, resident, 56; resident, Jackson Mem Hosp, Miami, 59-61; consult, Ment Health Asn Southeastern Pa, 65-67; assoc prof psychiat & assoc chmn dept, Sch Med, State Univ NY Buffalo, 67-68, prof psychiat & dep chmn dept, 68-69; chief ctr studies suicide prev, NIMH, 69-72, chief sect crisis intervention, Suicide & Ment Health Emergencies, 72-74; MED DIR, HUMAN BEHAV FOUND, 74- *Concurrent Pos:* Fel, Hosp Univ Pa, 62; fel, Reproductive Biol Res Found, St Louis, 71; clin prof, Sch Med, George Washington Univ, 69-; prof lectr, Sch Med, Johns Hopkins Univ, 69-; ed, Bull Sociol, Am Psychiat Asn, 69-74; prof, Fed City Col, 71-72; consult, WHO, Am Red Cross, Nat Cancer Inst, Nat Naval Med Ctr, Dept Defense & Pub Defender's Off; clin prof, Sch Med, Uniformed Serv Univ Health Sci, 77-79; med dir, Forensic Psychiat Asn, Ltd, 77- *Honors & Awards:* Charles W Burr Res Prize, Philadelphia Gen Hosp, 56; Gold Medal, Am Psychiat Asn, 72. *Mem:* AAAS; AMA; fel Am Psychiat Asn; fel Am Col Psychiat; Group Advan Psychiat. *Res:* Crisis intervention; emergency mental health services; suicide, including prevention programs, diagnosis and management of suicidal and depressed individuals; treatment of sexual dysfunctions and criminal sexual offenders. *Mailing Add:* Bethesda Med Bldg 8218 Wisconsin Ave Suite 201 Bethesda MD 20814

RESNIK, ROBERT ALAN, b New York, NY, Nov 11, 24; m 52. BIOCHEMISTRY. *Educ:* Purdue Univ, BS, 48, MS, 50, PhD(biophys, physiol), 52. *Prof Exp:* NIH fel, Northwestern Univ Ill, 52-53; chief biochemist, Ophthalmic Chem Sect, Nat Inst Neurol Dis & Blindness, NIH, 53-63, chemist, Lab Phys Biol, Nat Inst Arthritis & Metab Dis, 63-68, chief eval scientist biophys sci, Div Res Grants, NIH, 68-70, chief, Res Anal & Eval Br, 70-71, prog planning off, Nat Eye Inst, 71-73, chief reports & eval br, Nat Heart & Lung Inst, 73-78; CONSULT, 78- *Mem:* AAAS; Am Chem Soc; Am Soc Biol Chemists. Res; Interactions of metals with proteins; protein chemistry; nucleic acids and proteins; science administration. *Mailing Add:* 5508 Hoover St Bethesda MD 20817

RESNIK, ROBERT KENNETH, b Pleasant Unity, Pa, May 19, 36; m 64. INORGANIC CHEMISTRY. *Educ:* St Vincent Col, BS, 58; Univ Pittsburgh, PhD(inorg chem), 64. *Prof Exp:* Res chemist, Exxon Res & Eng Co, 64-65; sr inorg chemist, 65-66, SCIENTIST, RES LABS, J T BAKER CHEM CO, 66- *Mem:* Am Chem Soc. *Res:* Coordination and inorganic compounds; agriculture chemicals; industrial inorganic chemicals; properties of antacid chemicals. *Mailing Add:* Dept Inorg Chem Res Labs J T Baker Chem Co N Broad St Phillipsburg NJ 08865

RESNIKOFF, GEORGE JOSEPH, b New York, NY, Mar 25, 15; m 43; c 1. MATHEMATICAL STATISTICS. *Educ:* Univ Chicago, SB, 50; Stanford Univ, MS, 52, PhD, 55. *Prof Exp:* Res assoc statist, Stanford Univ, 52-57; from assoc prof to prof indust eng, Ill Inst Technol, 57-64; dean grad studies, 72-80, PROF MATH & STATIST & CHMN, DEPT STATIST, CALIF STATE UNIV, HAYWARD, 64- *Concurrent Pos:* Chmn, Dept Indust Eng, Ill Inst Technol, 58-64; lectr, Univ Chicago, 60-64; vis scholar, Univ Calif, Berkeley, 62-63; NSF fel, 62-63. *Mem:* Fel AAAS; fel Inst Math Statist (treas, 64-72, exec secy, 73-78); fel Am Statist Asn. *Res:* Applications of mathematics and statistics to industrial problems. *Mailing Add:* Dept of Statist Calif State Univ Hayward CA 94542

RESNIKOFF, HOWARD L, b New York, NY, May 13, 37; m 59; c 3. MATHEMATICS. *Educ:* Mass Inst Technol, BS, 57; Univ Calif, Berkeley, PhD(math), 63. *Prof Exp:* Mathematician, Electrodata Div, Burroughs Corp, 57-58; res scientist, Res Labs, Lockheed Missiles & Space Co, 62-64; mem, Inst Advan Study, 64-66; asst prof math, Rice Univ, 66-68, actg dir comput ctr, 71, assoc prof math, 68-73, prof, 73-75; chmn math, Univ Calif, Irvine, 75-78, prof math, 75-80; dir div info sci & technol, NSF, 78-80; MEM FAC, HARVARD UNIV, 80- *Concurrent Pos:* NSF fel, Univ Munich, 62-63; partner, R&D Consult Co, Calif, 64- & R&D Press, Calif, 72-77; Alexander von Humboldt Found, US sr scientist award, Univ Muenster, 74-75. *Res:* Automorphic function theory; theory of Jordan algebras; linguistic structure of written language; information retrieval; library automation; history of mathematics. *Mailing Add:* 1350 Massachusetts Ave Room 880 Cambridge MA 02138

RESO, ANTHONY, b London, Eng, Aug 10, 31; nat US. STRATIGRAPHY, PETROLEUM GEOLOGY. *Educ:* Columbia Univ, AB, 54, MA, 55; Rice Univ, PhD(geol), 60. *Prof Exp:* Instr geol, Queens Col, NY, 54; asst, Columbia Univ, 54-55; geologist, Atlantic Refining Co, 55-56; asst, Univ Cincinnati, 56-57; asst prof geol, Amherst Col, 59-62; STAFF RES GEOLOGIST, TENNECO OIL CO, 62- *Concurrent Pos:* Res consult, 60-61; Geol Soc Am grant & Am Asn Petrol Geologists grant, 58-59; NSF fel, 59; cur invert paleont, Pratt Mus, Amherst, Mass, 59-62; lectr, Univ Houston, 62-65; mem, Bd Advs, Gulf Univ Res Corp, 67-75, chmn, 68-69; vis prof geol, Rice Univ, Houston, 80. *Mem:* Fel Geol Soc Am; fel AAAS; Am Asn Petrol Geologists; Paleont Soc; Soc Econ Paleontologists & Mineralogists. *Res:* Earth history and subdivision of the geological time scale; invertebrate paleontology; world cretaceous stratigraphy; petroleum geology; distribution of economic resources and international trade. *Mailing Add:* Tenneco Oil Co PO Box 2511 Houston TX 77001

RESSLER, CHARLOTTE, b West New York, NJ, July 21, 24. ORGANIC CHEMISTRY, BIOCHEMISTRY. *Educ:* NY Univ, BA, 44; Columbia Univ, MA, 46, PhD(org chem), 49. *Prof Exp:* Res assoc biochem, Med Col, Cornell Univ, 49-54, from asst prof to assoc prof, 55-74; PROF PHARMACOL, UNIV CONN HEALTH CTR, FARMINGTON, 74- *Concurrent Pos:* Am Heart Asn estab investr, Med Col, Cornell Univ, 57-59; assoc mem, Inst Muscle Dis, Inc, 59-63, mem, 63-, head div protein chem, 59-74; mem med chem study sect, NIH, 72-75. *Mem:* AAAS; Am Chem Soc; Am Soc Biol Chemists. *Res:* Peptide hormones; amino acid metabolism; natural and synthetic neurothyrogens; enzyme characterization; amide reactions; organic rearrangements. *Mailing Add:* Dept of Pharmacol Univ of Conn Health Ctr Farmington CT 06032

RESSLER, NEIL WILLIAM, b Columbus, Ohio, June 1, 39; m 81; c 3. ENGINEERING, LASERS. *Educ:* Gen Motors Inst, BSME, 62; Univ Mich, MS, 63, PhD(physics), 67. *Prof Exp:* Res scientist, Sci Res Staff, 67-71, prin eng chassis, 71-73, supvr, 73-76, dept mgr, 76-78, exec engr, 78-81, CHIEF ENGR, CLIMATE CONTROL DIV, FORD MOTOR CO, 81- *Mem:* Soc Automotive Engrs. *Res:* Research development and production engineering of automotive climate control systems and heat exchangers. *Mailing Add:* 3612 Frederick Dr Ann Arbor MI 48105

RESSLER, NEWTON, b Detroit, Mich, Sept 19, 23; m 53; c 2. BIOCHEMISTRY. *Educ:* Univ Mich, BS, 47; Univ Chicago, MS, 49; Wayne State Univ, PhD(biochem), 53. *Prof Exp:* Res biochemist, Wayne County Gen Hosp, 53-65; asst prof biochem, Univ Mich, 65-68; assoc prof, 68-76, PROF BIOCHEM PATH, UNIV ILL MED CTR, 76- *Mem:* Am Chem Soc; Am Asn Clin Chemists; Biophys Soc; Sigma Xi. *Res:* Nature and control of enzymes; multiple enzyme forms and energy transduction. *Mailing Add:* 30 Red Haw Northbrook IL 60062

REST, DAVID, b Chicago, Ill, Mar 27, 17; m 39; c 2. CHEMICAL ENGINEERING. *Educ:* Armour Inst Technol, BS, 37; Univ Calif, MS, 60. *Prof Exp:* Supt chem prod, G D Searle & Co, 38-47; chief res engr, Armed Forces Qm Food & Container Inst, 47-55, chief nuclear effects br, 55-58, dir food radiation preserv div, 58-62; FOOD PROCESSING CONSULT, ARTHUR D LITTLE, INC, 62- *Mem:* Am Chem Soc; Health Physics Soc; Inst Food Technol. *Res:* Radiation processing of biological materials; low pressure sublimation of water in food stuffs; process control of food production facilities; chemical and nuclear engineering design; technical and economic evaluation of international food processing enterprises. *Mailing Add:* 178 Arnold Rd Newton Centre MA 02159

REST, RICHARD FRANKLIN, b Chicago, Ill. MICROBIOLOGY. *Educ:* Univ Mass, Amherst, BS, 70; Univ Kans, PhD(microbiol), 74. *Prof Exp:* Fel neutrophil functions, Dept Bact & Immunol, Sch Med, Univ NC, Chapel Hill, 74-77, ASST PROF PHAGOCYTE BACT INTERACTIONS, DEPT MICROBIOL, SCH MED, HEALTH SCI CTR, UNIV ARIZ, 77- *Concurrent Pos:* NIH fel, Dept Bact & Immunol, Sch Med, Univ NC, 75-77; Nat Inst Allergy & Infectious Dis grant, Dept Microbiol, Col Med, Ariz Health Sci Ctr, 78-81 & 81-84; NIH & Nat Inst Alergy & Infectious Diseases grant, 79-82; Nat Inst Alergy & Infectious Diseases career develop award, 80-85. *Mem:* Am Soc Microbiol; AAAS; Reticuloendothelial Soc. *Res:* How human neutrophils, monocytes and macrophages engulf and kill Neisseria gonorrhoeae; biochemical and enzymatic analysis of human leukocyte phagolysosomes. *Mailing Add:* Dept Molecular Med & Microbiol Univ Ariz Health Sci Ctr Tucson AZ 85724

RESTAINO, ALFRED JOSEPH, b Brooklyn, NY, Feb 18, 31; m 53; c 5. PHYSICAL CHEMISTRY, POLYMER CHEMISTRY. *Educ:* St Francis Col, NY, BS, 52; Polytech Inst Brooklyn, MS, 54, PhD(chem), 55. *Prof Exp:* AEC fel, 54-56; supvr radiation res, Martin Co, 56-58; mgr radiation chem sect, 58-68, mgr polymer chem, 68-71, asst dir chem, Res Dept, 71-74, DIR, CORP RES DEPT, ICI AMERICAS, INC, 75- *Concurrent Pos:* Asst prof, St Francis Col, NY, 55-56; adj prof, Drexel Inst Technol, 57; mem Gov Sci Adv Coun, Del, 70-72; mem sci adv comt, AEC, 70-73; prof grad exten, Univ Del, 71-74. *Mem:* Am Chem Soc; NY Acad Sci; AAAS. *Res:* Organic chemistry; thermoset polymers, water soluble polymers, thermoplastics and photochemistry; novel reactions for synthesis of specialty products including agricultural chemicals; reaction injection molding. *Mailing Add:* Corp Res Dept ICI AMERICAS Wilmington DE 19899

RESTAINO, FREDERICK A, b Brooklyn, NY, Dec 9, 34; m 58; c 3. PHYSICAL PHARMACY. *Educ:* St John's Univ, NY, BS, 56; Rutgers Univ, MS, 58; Purdue Univ, PhD(phys pharm), 62. *Prof Exp:* From asst instr to instr org chem, Rutgers Univ, 56-58; unit head aerosol res, 62-65, unit head sterile prod, 65-70, unit head fluids-topicals, 69-70, UNIT HEAD TABLET & CAPSULES & SR RES FEL, RES LABS, MERCK SHARP & DOHME, 70- *Mem:* Am Pharmaceut Asn. *Res:* Solubilization; aerosol research; sterile products research and development; fluids-topical development; tablet and capsule research and development; solid dosage form development. *Mailing Add:* Merck Sharp & Dohme Res Labs West Point PA 19486

RESTEMEYER, WILLIAM EDWARD, b Cincinnati, Ohio, Apr 28, 16; m 43; c 2. APPLIED MATHEMATICS, ELECTRICAL ENGINEERING. *Educ:* Univ Cincinnati, EE, 38, MA, 39. *Hon Degrees:* DSc, Capitol Inst Technol, 76. *Prof Exp:* Officer, Naval Res Lab, 45; from instr to assoc prof math, Univ Cincinnati, 40-61, admin aide, Dept Math, 68-75, PROF ELEC & COMPUT ENG & MATH SCI, UNIV CINCINNATI, 61-, ASST DEPT HEAD, 76- *Concurrent Pos:* Consult, Avco-Crosley, Kettering Lab, Fed Security Agency, Gen Elec Corp, Argonne Nat Lab, Math Asn Am, NSF, NATO US Off Educ, Nat Aero & Space Admin & Cincinnati Milacron Corp, 44-; accrediation bd, Eng & Technol, NY State Dept Educ; vis scientist, Ohio Acad Sci. *Mem:* Am Soc Eng Educ; Math Asn Am; sr mem Inst Elec & Electronics Engrs; Int Math Union. *Res:* Signal and systems analysis. *Mailing Add:* Col Eng Univ Cincinnati Cincinnati OH 45221

RESTER, ALFRED CARL, JR, b New Orleans, La, July 11, 40; m 64; c 2. NUCLEAR PHYSICS. *Educ:* Miss Col, BS, 62; Univ NMex, MS, 65; Vanderbilt Univ, PhD(physics), 69. *Prof Exp:* Fel, Delft Univ Technol, 69-70; scientist, 70-71; scientist, Oak Ridge Nat Lab, 71-72; guest prof physics, Inst Radiation & Nuclear Physics, Univ Bonn, 72-75; asst prof physics, Emory Univ, 75-76; assoc prof, Tenn Technol Univ, 76-77; vis assoc prof physics, 78-81, ASSOC RES SCIENTIST, SPACE ASTRON LAB, UNIV FLA, 81- *Mem:* Am Phys Soc; Sigma Xi. *Res:* Heavy ion reactions; nuclear structure; studies of medium mass nuclei; on-line isotope separators; computer analysis of nuclear data; nuclear astrophysics and astronomy. *Mailing Add:* Space Astron Lab Univ Fla 1810 NW 6th St Gainesville FL 32601

RESTER, DAVID HAMPTON, b Bogalusa, La, June 14, 34; m 58. NUCLEAR PHYSICS. *Educ:* Tulane Univ, BS, 56; Rice Univ, MA, 58, PhD(physics), 60. *Prof Exp:* Asst prof physics, Tulane Univ, 60-63; sr scientist, Ling-Tempco-Vought Inc Res Ctr, 63-71; sr scientist, Advan Technol Ctr, Inc, 71-73, supvr electrophys, 73-79; MGR ANAL METHODS, MEAD OFF SYSTS, 79- *Mem:* Am Phys Soc; Soc Info Display. *Res:* Low energy studies of nuclear structure by method of internal conversion electron spectroscopy; study of electron scattering at intermediate energies observing bremsstrahlung production and scattered electrons. *Mailing Add:* 1307 Glenville Dr Mead Off Systs Richardson TX 75081

RESTORFF, JAMES BRIAN, b Wytheville, Va, June 22, 49; m 73; c 1. SOLID STATE PHYSICS. *Educ:* Univ Md, BS, 71, MS, 75, PhD(physics), 76. *Prof Exp:* RES PHYSICIST, NAVAL SURFACE WEAPONS CTR, 76- *Mem:* Am Phys Soc. *Res:* Semiconductor for electronic device use. *Mailing Add:* Naval Surface Weapons Ctr Code R45 White Oak Silver Spring MD 20910

RESTREPO, RODRIGO ALVARO, b Medellin, Colombia, Nov 6, 30. MATHEMATICS. *Educ:* Lehigh Univ, BA, 51; Calif Inst Technol, PhD(math), 55. *Prof Exp:* Res fel, Calif Inst Technol, 55-56; lectr, Univ BC, 56-58; vis asst prof, Stanford Univ, 58-59; from asst prof to assoc prof, 59-70, PROF MATH, UNIV BC, 70- *Concurrent Pos:* Vis prof, Interam Statist Training Ctr, Chile, 63-64 & COPPE, Fed Univ Rio de Janeiro, 70-71, 72 & 74. *Mem:* Am Math Soc; Math Asn Am; Can Math Cong. *Res:* Game theory; linear programming. *Mailing Add:* Dept Math Univ BC Vancouver BC V6T 1W5 Can

RESWICK, JAMES BIGELOW, b Ellwood City, Pa, Apr 16, 22; m 73; c 3. BIOMEDICAL ENGINEERING. *Educ:* Mass Inst Technol, SB, 43, SM, 48, ScD(mech eng), 54. *Hon Degrees:* DEng, Rose Polytech Inst, 68. *Prof Exp:* Instr mach design, Mass Inst Technol, 46-50, from asst prof to assoc prof mech eng, 50-59; prof mech eng & dir eng design, Case Inst Technol, 59-70; PROF BIOMED ENG & ORTHOPAED, UNIV SOUTHERN CALIF, 70-; ASSOC DIR, NAT INST HANDICAPPED RES, US DEPT EDUC, WASHINGTON, DC, 81- *Concurrent Pos:* NSF sr fel, Imp Col, Univ London, 57-58; mem prosthetics res & develop comt, Nat Acad Sci, 60 & Inst Med, 72; dir, Rehab Eng Ctr, Rancho Los Amigos, 70-80. *Honors & Awards:* Isabel & Leonard Goldenson Award, United Cerebral Palsy Asn, 74. *Mem:* Inst Med-Nat Acad Sci; Nat Acad Eng; assoc Am Acad Orthop Surgeons; Biomed Eng Soc; fel Inst Elec & Electronics Engrs. *Res:* Engineering design education; automatic control theory and application; dynamics; product design and development; biomedical engineering; administration of rehabilitation engineering. *Mailing Add:* 1003 Dead Run Dr McLean VA 22101

RETALLACK, GREGORY JOHN, b Hobart, Australia, Nov 8, 51; M 81. PALEOPEDOLOGY, TERRESTRIAL PALEOECOLOGY. *Educ:* Macquarie Univ, Australia, BA, 73; Univ New Eng, BSc Hons, 74, PhD(geol), 78. *Prof Exp:* Vis asst prof geol, Northern Ill Univ, 77-78; vis scholar biol, Ind Univ, 78-79 & proj co-dir, 79-81; ASST PROF GEOL, UNIV ORE, EUGENE, 81- *Honors & Awards:* Stillwell Medal, Geol Soc Australia. *Mem:* Sigma Xi; Geol Soc Am; Geol Soc Australia; Bot Soc Am; AAAS. *Res:* Paleopedological and paleoecological research into Gondwanan Triassic fossil plants; cretaceous dispersal and rise to dominance of angiosperms; tertiary development of grasslands; evolution of soils through geological time. *Mailing Add:* Dept Geol Univ Ore Eugene OR 97403

RETALLICK, WILLIAM BENNETT, b Yonkers, NY, Jan 16, 25; m 49; c 1. CHEMICAL ENGINEERING. *Educ:* Univ Mich, BSE, 48; Univ Ill, MS, 52, PhD(chem eng), 53. *Prof Exp:* Process engr, Phillips Petrol Co, 48-50 & Consol Coal Co, 53-64; res engr, Houdry Process & Chem Co, 64-71, sr chem engr, 71-74; vpres res & develop, Oxy-Catalyst, Inc, 74-80; CONSULT CHEM ENGR, 80- *Mem:* Am Chem Soc; Am Inst Chem Engrs; Sigma Xi. *Res:* Pilot scale research in coal; exploratory research on chemicals and catalysts; catalysts and catalytic processes; catalytic combustion. *Mailing Add:* 1432 Johnny's Way West Chester PA 19380

RETCOFSKY, HERBERT L, b Brownsville, Pa, Apr 1, 35; m 61; c 7. SPECTROSCOPY, COAL SCIENCE. *Educ:* Calif State Col, Pa, BS, 57; Univ Pittsburgh, MS, 65. *Prof Exp:* Res physicist phys chem, 58-76, chief molecular spectros Br Anal Chem Coal, 76-79, MGR ANAL CHEM DIV, PITTSBURGH ENERGY TECHNOL CTR, US DEPT ENERGY, 79- *Concurrent Pos:* US assoc ed, FUEL, 81- *Mem:* Am Chem Soc; Soc Appl Spectros. *Res:* Applications of spectral techniques in coal research. *Mailing Add:* Pittsburgh Energy Technol Ctr PO Box 10940 Pittsburgh PA 15236

RETELLE, JOHN POWERS, JR, b Flushing, NY, Jan 1, 46; m 75; c 2. AEROSPACE ENGINEERING. *Educ:* US Air Force Acad, BS, 67; Univ Colo, MS, 69; Golden Gate Univ, MBA, 71. *Prof Exp:* Flight test engr aerospace eng, Air Force Flight Test Ctr, Edwards AFB, Calif, 69-72 & French Flight Test Ctr, Istres, France, 72-73; from instr to asst prof aeronaut, 73-75, ASSOC PROF AERONAUT, US AIR FORCE ACAD, 79- *Concurrent Pos:* Flight test engr, NASA Dryden Flight Res Ctr, Edwards, 75- *Mem:* Am Inst Aeronaut & Astronaut; mem rep Subsonic Aerodyn Testing Asn. *Res:* Wind tunnel experimentation on dynamic stall and unsteady flow separation using laser Doppler techniques and numerical simulation. *Mailing Add:* Dept of Aeronaut US Air Force Academy CO 80840

RETHERFORD, JAMES RONALD, b Panama City, Fla, Oct 1, 37; m 61. MATHEMATICS. *Educ:* Fla State Univ, BS, 59, MS, 60, PhD(math), 63. *Prof Exp:* Asst prof math, Univ Chattanooga, 60-61; instr, Fla State Univ, 64; from asst prof to assoc prof, 64-70, PROF MATH, LA STATE UNIV, BATON ROUGE, 70- *Mem:* Am Math Soc; Math Asn Am. *Res:* Series and operators determined by series in Banach spaces. *Mailing Add:* Dept of Math La State Univ Baton Rouge LA 70803

RETNAKARAN, ARTHUR, b Trichy, India, Aug 28, 34; m 60; c 2. INSECT PHYSIOLOGY. *Educ:* Univ Madras, MA, 55; Univ Wis, MS, 64, PhD(entom), 67. *Prof Exp:* Lectr zool, Voorhees Col, Vellore, India, 55-58, prof, 58-62; fel, Univ Wis, 67-68; RES SCIENTIST, INSECT PATH RES INST, 68- *Concurrent Pos:* vis prof, Univ Louis Pasteur, Strasbourg, France, 74-75; Fulbright scholar, 62-67. *Mem:* Entom Soc Am; Entom Soc Can; NY Acad Sci. *Res:* Use of juvenile hormone analogs and moult inhibitors in controlling forest insect pests; tyrosine metabolism in insects; insect reproductive physiology; benzoyl ureas for insect control; antijuvenile hormones. *Mailing Add:* Forest Pest Mgt Inst PO Box 490 Sault Ste Marie ON P6A 5M7 Can

RETSEMA, JAMES ALLAN, b Muskegon, Mich, Feb 27, 42; m 69; c 2. BIOCHEMISTRY, MICROBIOLOGY. *Educ:* Mich State Univ, BS, 64; Univ Iowa, MS, 67, PhD(biochem), 69. *Prof Exp:* Res asst biochem, Univ Iowa, 64-69; MEM STAFF BIOCHEM & MICROBIOL, CENT RES, PFIZER, INC, 69- *Mem:* Am Soc Microbiol. *Res:* Antibiotics and their spectrum of activity, mode of action, mechanism of destruction, ability to enter the cell and structural activity relationships. *Mailing Add:* Cent Res Pfizer Inc Groton CT 06340

RETSKY, MICHAEL WALTER, electron optics, electron microscopy, see previous edition

RETTALIATA, JOHN THEODORE, b Baltimore, Md, Aug 18, 11; m 70; c 2. MECHANICAL ENGINEERING. *Educ:* Johns Hopkins Univ, BE, 32, DEng, 36. *Hon Degrees:* DEng, Mich Col Mining & Technol, 56 & Rose Polytech Inst, 70; DSc, Valparaiso Univ, 59; LLD, DePaul Univ, 62, 62 & Chicago-Kent Col Law, 69; LHD, Loyola Univ, 70. *Prof Exp:* Instr & head dept, Baltimore Col Ctr, Md, 34-35; lab technician, USDA, 35; head calculation div, Allis-Chalmers Co, Wis, 36-44, mgr res & gas turbine develop div, 44-45; prof mech eng & head dept, Ill Inst Technol, 45-48, dean eng, 48-52, vpres, 50-52, pres, Inst, IIT Res Inst & Inst Gas Technol, 52-73; CHMN BD, BANCO DI ROMA, CHICAGO, 73- *Concurrent Pos:* Mem bd vis, Air Univ, 55-58, chmn, 57-58; mem, Nat Aeronaut Space Coun, 59. *Honors & Awards:* Jr Award, Am Soc Mech Engrs, 41, Spec Award, 51. *Mem:* Fel AAAS; fel Am Soc Mech Engrs. *Res:* Super-Saturated steam; gas turbine engineering; jet engineering; science administration. *Mailing Add:* Banco Di Roma 230 W Monroe St Chicago IL 60606

RETTENMEYER, CARL WILLIAM, b Meriden, Conn, Feb 10, 31; m 54; c 2. ENTOMOLOGY, ECOLOGY. *Educ:* Swarthmore Col, BA, 53; Univ Kans, PhD(entom), 62. *Prof Exp:* From asst prof to assoc prof, entom, Kans State Univ, 60-71; PROF BIOL, UNIV CONN, 71-, HEAD SYST & EVOLUTIONARY BIOL, 80- *Concurrent Pos:* NSF res grants, 62- & Orgn Trop Studies, 65, 67 & 69. *Mem:* Fel AAAS; Entom Soc Am; Ecol Soc Am; Asn Trop Biol; Animal Behav Soc. *Res:* Ecology and behavior of army ants and associated arthropods; taxonomy of Dorylinae; insect behavior; mimiery and mutualism; biological photography; Neotropical insects. *Mailing Add:* Biol Sci Group Life Sci Bldg Univ of Conn Storrs CT 06268

RETZ, KONRAD CHARLES, b Oelwein, Iowa, Feb 19, 52. NEUROPHARMACOLOGY, NEUROCHEMISTRY. *Educ:* Augustana Col, Ill, BA, 74; Univ Iowa, PhD(pharmacol), 79. *Prof Exp:* Dept Pharmacol & Exp Therapeut, 79-81, FEL, DEPT NEUROSCI, SCH MED, JOHNS HOPKINS UNIV, BALTIMORE, 81- *Mem:* AAAS; Am Chem Soc; Soc Neurosci. *Res:* Mechanisms of analgesia; mode of action of excitatory amino acid neurotransmitters; regulation of energy metabolism in the central nervous system and calcium involvement in neurotransmission. *Mailing Add:* Dept Neurosci Sch Med Johns Hopkins Univ 725 N Wolfe St Baltimore MD 21205

RETZER, KENNETH ALBERT, b Jacksonville, Ill, Nov 6, 33; m 53; c 3. MATHEMATICS EDUCATION. *Educ:* Ill Col, AB, 54; Univ Ill, EdM, 57, PhD(math educ), 67. *Prof Exp:* Instr, High Sch, Ill, 54-58, asst supt, 55-58; from asst prof to assoc prof, 59-74, asst head dept, 68-70, PROF MATH, ILL STATE UNIV, 74- *Concurrent Pos:* Partic, NSF Acad Year Inst Math, Univ Ill, 58-59. *Mem:* AAAS; Math Asn Am. *Res:* Effects of teaching logic on verbalization and on transfer of discovered mathematical generalizations; strategies for teaching mathematics. *Mailing Add:* Dept of Math Ill State Univ Normal IL 61761

RETZLAFF, ERNEST (WALTER), b Helena, Mont, Feb 19, 18. NEUROPHYSIOLOGY, MEDICAL PHYSIOLOGY. *Educ:* Ore State Col, BS, 45, MS, 49; Univ Mich, PhD(physiol), 53, MPH, 72. *Prof Exp:* Instr physiol, Univ Mich, 53-54; res assoc & asst prof psychiat, Med Sch, Univ Ill, 54-55; asst prof, Columbus Psychiat Inst, Ohio State Univ, 56-66; pvt res consult neurol sci, 66-67; prof biomed sci & coordr spec proj, Boise State Col, 67-68; dir commun & training, Detroit-Wayne County Health Dept, 68-69; prof physiol & anat, Col Osteop Med, 69-71; PROF BIOMECH, MICH STATE UNIV, 72- *Concurrent Pos:* Consult, Western Int Mountain States Regional Med Prog, 67-68; res consult neurol sci. *Mem:* AAAS; Biophys Soc; Geront Soc; Am Asn Anatomists; NY Acad Sci. *Res:* Nervous system structure-function relationships; central nervous system integrative mechanisms; neurohistology and sensory-motor reflex responses; effect of controlled exercises on aging process; apparatus design; cryography-vacuum technology; medical education; neurohistology. *Mailing Add:* 31515 Lahser Rd Birmingham MI 48010

RETZLOFF, DAVID GEORGE, b Pittsburgh, Pa, Feb 19, 39; m 71; c 1. CATALYSIS, MODELING. *Educ:* Univ Pittsburgh, BS, 63, MS, 65, PhD(chem eng), 67. *Prof Exp:* Mem staff, Lab Chem, Technol & Tech High Sch, Delft, Neth, 67-68; res assoc, Univ Colo, 68-69; asst prof chem eng, Kans State Univ, 69-73; res engr, Exxon Res & Eng Co, 73-75; ASST PROF CHEM ENG, UNIV MO, COLUMBIA, 75- *Mem:* Am Inst Physics; Am Math Soc; Am Chem Soc; AAAS. *Res:* Development of catalysts to perform specific chemical transformations; mathematical analysis of models for chemical reactors. *Mailing Add:* Dept Chem Eng Rm 1030 Univ Mo Columbia MO 65211

RETZLOFF, JAMES B, b Hammond, Ind, July 2, 24; m 48; c 4. MECHANICAL & AUTOMOTIVE ENGINEERING. *Educ:* Purdue Univ, BSME, 49, MSME, 51. *Prof Exp:* Proj engr, 51-59, asst res supvr, 59-66, res supvr, 66-69, RES ASSOC, ETHYL CORP RES LABS, 69- *Mem:* Am Soc Testing & Mat; Soc Automotive Engrs; Am Soc Lubrication Engrs. *Res:* Development and evaluation of automotive fuel and lubricant additives; development of engine test procedure for evaluation of such products. *Mailing Add:* Ethyl Corp Res Labs 1600 W Eight Mile Rd Ferndale MI 48220

REUBEN, JOHN PHILIP, b Seattle, Wash, Mar 12, 30; m 55; c 3. BIOPHYSICS. *Educ:* Grinnell Col, BA, 54; Univ Rochester, MS, 56; Univ Fla, PhD(physiol), 59. *Prof Exp:* Res assoc, 59-60, NSF fel, 60-62, asst prof, 60-67, assoc prof, 67-78, PROF NEUROL, COL PHYSICIANS & SURGEONS, COLUMBIA UNIV, 78- *Mem:* Biophys Soc; Am Physiol Soc. *Res:* Neurophysiology; neuropharmacology; muscle; molecular studies of synaptic and electrically excitable membranes. *Mailing Add:* Dept of Neurol Columbia Univ Col Physicians & Surg New York NY 10032

REUBEN, RICHARD N, b New York, NY, June 21, 20; m 49; c 3. MEDICINE. *Educ:* Columbia Univ, AB, 40, MD, 43. *Prof Exp:* Assoc prof pediat neurol, 54-70, ASSOC PROF CLIN NEUROL, SCH MED, NY UNIV, 70- *Res:* Neurological disorders of childhood. *Mailing Add:* Dept of Neurol NY Univ Sch of Med New York NY 10016

REUBER, MELVIN D, b Blakeman, Kans, Nov 10, 30. PATHOLOGY, MEDICINE. *Educ:* Univ Kans, AB, 52, MD, 58. *Prof Exp:* Intern path, Sch Med, Univ Md, 58-59, resident, 59-61; res fel, Beth Israel Hosp & Harvard Med Sch, 61-62, asst pathologist & asst instr, 62-63; med officer, Lab Path, Nat Cancer Inst, 63-65; from asst prof to assoc prof path, Sch Med, Univ Md, Baltimore City, 65-74; consult human & exp path, 75-76; pathologist, Frederick Cancer Res Ctr, Md, 76-81; CONSULT HUMAN & EXP PATH, 81- *Concurrent Pos:* Med officer, Lab Biol, Nat Cancer Inst, 65-69 & etiol, 69-71. *Mem:* Am Soc Exp Path; Am Asn Cancer Res; Am Asn Path & Bact; Soc Toxicol; Int Acad Path. *Res:* Hepatic carcinogenesis; toxicology. *Mailing Add:* 11014 Swansfield Rd Columbia MD 21044

REUCROFT, PHILIP J, b Leeds, Eng, Mar 29, 35; m 61; c 3. MATERIALS SCIENCE, POLYMER PHYSICS. *Educ:* Univ London, BSc, 56, PhD(phys chem) & dipl, Imp Col, 59. *Prof Exp:* Fel phys chem, Nat Res Coun Can, 59-61; res chemist, Franklin Inst Res Labs, Pa, 61-63, sr res chemist, 63-65, sr staff chemist, 65-66, actg lab mgr, 66-67, lab mgr, 67-69; assoc prof, 69-75, PROF MAT SCI, UNIV KY, 75- *Concurrent Pos:* Consult, Franklin Inst Res Labs, Pa, 69-; Ashland Oil Found prof, Univ Ky, 70-74, Inst for Mining & Minerals Res fel, 78-; mem, Adv Comt, Am Carbon Soc, 79-85. *Mem:* Am Soc Metals; Am Chem Soc; The Chem Soc; Am Phys Soc. *Res:* Solid-gas interactions; adsorption; intermolecular forces; thermodynamics; solid state properties of polymers and molecular solids; conductivity; photoconductivity; molecular diffusion; crystallinity and crystal growth; coal science; heterogeneous catalysts. *Mailing Add:* Dept Metall Eng & Mat Sci Univ Ky Lexington KY 40506

REUCROFT, STEPHEN, b Leeds, Eng, May 17, 43; m 70. PARTICLE PHYSICS. *Educ:* Univ Liverpool, BSc, 65, PhD(physics), 69. *Prof Exp:* Demonstr, Univ Liverpool, 65-69; res fel, Europ Orgn Nuclear Res, Switz, 69-71; res assoc, Vanderbilt Univ, 71-73; asst prof res, Vanderbilt Univ, 73-78; STAFF PHYSICIST, EUROP ORGN NUCLEAR RES, GENEVA, SWITZ, 79- *Concurrent Pos:* Vis scientist, Europ Orgn Nuclear Res, 71-78, sci assoc, 78; vis physicist, Fermilab, Chicago, 75- & Brookhaven Nat Lab, 76-; staff scientist, Max-Planck Inst, Munich, 77; adj assoc prof, Vanderbilt Univ, 79- *Mem:* Fel Inst Physics Eng; Am Phys Soc. *Res:* Fundamental structure and basic interactions of sub-nuclear particles. *Mailing Add:* Eng & Physics Div Conseil Europ Resch Nucleaire 1211 Geneva 23 Switzerland

REUDINK, DOUGLAS O, b West Point, Nebr, May 6, 39; m 61. MATHEMATICS, PHYSICS. *Educ:* Linfield Col, BA, 61; Ore State Univ, PhD(math), 65. *Prof Exp:* Mem tech staff, 65-72, head, Satellite Systs Res Dept, 72-79, DIR, RADIO RES LAB, BELL LABS, 79- *Mem:* Am Inst Aeronaut & Astronaut; fel Inst Elec & Electronics Engrs. *Res:* Communications; satellite systems; mobile radio; integral transforms; wave propagation. *Mailing Add:* Bell Labs Holmdel NJ 07733

REULAND, DONALD JOHN, b Philadelphia, Pa, May 25, 37; m 60; c 2. NUCLEAR CHEMISTRY. *Educ:* St Joseph's Col, Pa, BS, 59; Carnegie Inst Technol, MS, 61, PhD(nuclear-inorg chem), 63. *Prof Exp:* teaching asst chem, Carnegie Inst Technol, 59-61, proj chemist, 61-63; res chemist, Thomas A Edison Res Lab, 63-64; asst prof inorg-nuclear chem, 64-68, assoc prof chem, 68-75, PROF CHEM, IND STATE UNIV, TERRE HAUTE, 75- *Concurrent Pos:* Res chemist, Ames Nat Lab, 67. *Mem:* Midwestern Asn Forensic Scientists. *Res:* Determining the mechanisms of nuclear reactions; nuclear spectroscopy; forensic chemistry. *Mailing Add:* Dept of Chem Ind State Univ Terre Haute IN 47809

REULAND, ROBERT JOHN, b Philadelphia, Pa, Feb 9, 35; m 59; c 2. RADIOCHEMISTRY. *Educ:* St Joseph's Col, Philadelphia, BS, 56; Iowa State Univ, MS, 59, PhD(inorg chem), 63. *Prof Exp:* Instr chem, St Joseph's Col, Philadelphia, 59-60; mem tech staff mat res, Tex Instruments Inc, Dallas, 63-64; PROF CHEM, LORAS COL, IOWA, 64- *Mem:* Sigma Xi. *Res:* Preparation and structure determination of metal tungsten bronzes. *Mailing Add:* Dept of Chem Loras Col Dubuque IA 52001

REUNING, RICHARD HENRY, b Wellsville, NY, Jan 3, 41; m 63; c 2. PHARMACOLOGY. *Educ:* State Univ NY Buffalo, BS, 63, PhD(pharmaceut), 68. *Prof Exp:* USPHS fel pharmacol, Univ Mo-Kansas City, 68-69; from asst prof to assoc prof, 70-80, PROF PHARMAEUT, COL PHARM, OHIO STATE UNIV, 80- *Honors & Awards:* Lyman Award, Am Asn Cols Pharm, 75. *Mem:* AAAS; Acad Pharmaceut Sci; Am Asn Cols Pharm; Am Soc Pharmacol Exp Therapeut. *Res:* Biological drug transport; biopharmaceutics of digitalis glycosides; pharmacokinetics; assay, metabolism and pharmacokinetics of narcotic antagonists; alterations of membrane permeability. *Mailing Add:* Col of Pharm Ohio State Univ Columbus OH 43210

REUSCH, WILLIAM HENRY, b Carbondale, Ill, Dec 2, 31; m 56; c 3. SYNTHETIC ORGANIC CHEMISTRY. *Educ:* Univ Mich, BS, 53; Columbia Univ, PhD(chem), 57. *Prof Exp:* NSF fel, Imp Col, Univ London, 57-58; from asst prof to assoc prof, 58-68, PROF CHEM, MICH STATE UNIV, 68- *Concurrent Pos:* NIH spec fel, Stanford Univ, 65-66. *Mem:* Am Chem Soc; Royal Soc Chem. *Res:* Natural products and their rational synthesis; cyclopropanols and cyclopropanediols as synthetic intermidiates; reactions of epoxides and epoxy ketones. *Mailing Add:* Dept Chem Mich State Univ East Lansing MI 48823

REUSS, ROBERT L, b New York, NY, May 31, 42; m 66. GEOLOGY. *Educ:* Ohio Wesleyan Univ, AB, 64; Univ Mich, Ann Arbor, MS, 67, PhD(geol), 70. *Prof Exp:* Asst prof, 69-75, ASSOC PROF GEOL, TUFTS UNIV, 75- *Mem:* Mineral Soc Am; Geol Soc Am; Soc Econ Geologists. *Res:* Igneous and metamorphic petrology; relationship and timing of igneous events, metamorphic reactions and structural deformation. *Mailing Add:* Dept of Geol Tufts Univ Medford MA 02155

REUSS, RONALD MERL, b Buffalo, NY, Jan 29, 33; m 54, 79; c 4. HUMAN BIOLOGY, SCIENCE EDUCATION. *Educ:* State Univ NY, Albany, BA, 54, MA, 55; State Univ NY, Buffalo, DEd, 70. *Prof Exp:* Sci teacher gen sci & biol, Kenmore Pub Schs, 55-64; ASSOC PROF BIOL, STATE UNIV COL BUFFALO, 64-, INSTR ANAT & PHYSIOL & PRE-HEALTH ADV, 78- *Concurrent Pos:* Sci consult, Carson City Schs, 68 & S-K Sci Co, Tonawanda, NY, 70-82; mem res staff, Lung Tumor Antigens, Roswell Park Inst, NY, 79. *Mem:* Nat Sci Teachers Asn; AAAS. *Res:* Individualized instruction in anatomy and physiology and muscle physiology. *Mailing Add:* State Univ Col Buffalo 1300 Elmwood Ave Buffalo NY 14222

REUSSER, FRITZ, b Steffisburg, Switz, Dec 19, 28; US citizen; m 53; c 2. MOLECULAR BIOLOGY, MICROBIOLOGY. *Educ:* Swiss Fed Inst Technol, Dipl, 53, DSc(microbiol), 55. *Prof Exp:* Res asst microbiol, Swiss Fed Inst Technol, 53-55; Nat Res Coun Can fel, Univ Sask, 55-57; res assoc, Res Labs, 57-71, SR SCIENTIST, RES DIV, UPJOHN CO, KALAMAZOO, 71- *Mem:* Am Chem Soc; Am Soc Microbiol. *Res:* Fermentation; genetic engineering; antibiotics; mode of action. *Mailing Add:* 6548 Trotwood Portage MI 49081

REUSSNER, GEORGE HENRY, b Bethlehem, Pa, Dec 18, 18; m 50; c 2. DENTAL RESEARCH, NUTRITION. *Educ:* Lehigh Univ, BA, 40; Purdue Univ, MS, 50. *Prof Exp:* Chemist, Bethlehem Steel Corp, 40-42 & 46-48; assoc chemist, Gen Foods Corp, 49-54, proj leader biochem, 54-60, from chemist to sr chemist, Tech Ctr, 61-70, res specialist, 70-75, sr res specialist, 75-81, PRIN SCIENTIST, CENT RES, GEN FOODS TECH CTR, 81- *Mem:* Am Chem Soc; Am Asn Lab Animal Sci; Am Inst Nutrit; Soc Environ Geochem & Health; Int Asn Dental Res. *Res:* Mineral nutrition; dental health and diet; cereal nutrition. *Mailing Add:* Corp Res Gen Foods Tech Ctr White Plains NY 10625

REUSZER, HERBERT WILLIAM, b Jamestown, Mo, Aug 4, 03; m 35; c 2. SOIL MICROBIOLOGY. *Educ:* Univ Mo, BS, 25; Rutgers Univ, MS, 30, PhD(soil microbiol), 32. *Prof Exp:* Res specialist agron, NJ Exp Sta, 26-29, asst soil microbiol, 29-32, instr, 32-33; assoc bacteriologist, Exp Sta, Colo State Col, 33-40; coop agent, Soil Conserv Serv, USDA & Exp Sta, Univ Ala, 40-47; assoc microbiologist, Exp Sta, 47-70, EMER PROF AGRON, PURDUE UNIV, 70- *Concurrent Pos:* Asst marine bact, Oceanog Inst Woods Hole, 30-31, jr marine bacteriologist, 32-33. *Mem:* Fel AAAS; Am Soc Microbiol; Soil Sci Soc Am; Am Soc Agron; Brit Biochem Soc. *Res:* Soil microbiology; origin and nature of soil organic matter; decomposition of cellulose; nonsymbiotic nitrogen fixation; relation of microorganisms to soil physical properties and liberation of plant nutrients in the soil; microbial decomposition of organotoxicants; axenic growth of plants. *Mailing Add:* 1222 N Salisbury St West Lafayette IN 47906

REUTER, GERALD LOUIS, b Providence, RI, Mar 16, 34; m 57; c 3. VETERINARY PHARMACY, AGRICULTURAL PHARMACY. *Educ:* RI Col Pharm, BS, 56. *Prof Exp:* Pharmaceut chemist, Hess & Clark Div, Richardson Merrell, Inc, 60-68; sect head vet formulations pharmaceut develop, 68-79, RES ASSOC PHARMACEUT RES & DEVELOP, AYERST LABS, 79- *Mem:* Acad Pharmaceut Sci; Am Pharmaceut Asn; Inst Food Technol; Int Pharmaceut Fedn. *Res:* Veterinary pharmaceutical products, including animal health products and feed medication products; insecticide products research and development; aerosol technology; plant pathogen and piscicide formulations: liquid and parenteral formulation, research and development. *Mailing Add:* 23 Crescent Dr Plattsburgh NY 12901

REUTER, JOHANNES HELMUT, b Cologne, Ger, Oct 18, 30; m 59; c 3. ORGANIC GEOCHEMISTRY. *Educ:* Univ Cologne, BS, 57; Univ Würzburg, 60, Dr rer nat(geochem), 61. *Prof Exp:* Res fel geochem, Calif Inst Technol, 61-63; assoc res scientist, Nuclear Res Ctr, Ger, 63-67; ASSOC PROF GEOCHEM, GA INST TECHNOL, 68- *Mem:* Geochem Soc; Int Asn Geochem & Cosmochem. *Res:* Early diagenesis of organic matter in sediments; role of organic matter in mass transport continent-ocean; interaction clay-water-organics; estuarine and near-shore marine environmental quality. *Mailing Add:* Sch of Geophys Sci Ga Inst of Technol Atlanta GA 30332

REUTER, ROBERT A, b Dunkirk, NY, Aug 3, 28; m 56; c 3. MATERIAL SCIENCE, PHYSICAL CHEMISTRY. *Educ:* St Bonaventure Univ, BS, 49; Univ Utah, MS, 52. *Prof Exp:* Exp chemist, Am Locomotive Co, 49-50; engr, Nat Carbon Co, 53-57; group leader nuclear fuel develop, Carbon Prod Div, Union Carbide Corp, 57-63, proj engr, High Temperature Coatings, Tenn, 63-71, proj engr, High Temperature Coatings, Ohio, 71-73; PRES, DYLON INDUSTS INC, 73- *Mem:* Am Nuclear Soc; Am Ceramic Soc; Am Soc Lubrication Engrs. *Res:* Uranium carbide nuclear fuels; chemical vapor deposition coatings; high temperature materials processing; polycrystalline graphite production; refractory cements; solid state lubricants. *Mailing Add:* Dylon Industs Inc 120 1st Ave Berea OH 44017

REUTER, ROBERT CARL, JR, b Pittsburgh, Pa, Apr 30, 39; m 61; c 3. THEORETICAL & APPLIED MECHANICS. *Educ:* Univ Ill, BS, 64, MS, 65, PhD(appl mech), 67. *Prof Exp:* Mem tech staff struct mech, Martin Marietta Corp, 67-68; mem tech staff, 68-79, SUPVR APPL MECH DIV III, SANDIA NAT LABS, 79- *Mem:* Am Acad Mech. *Res:* Development and application of the mechanics of composite materials and fluid/structure interaction; development of analytical technology for evaluation and design of wind and solar energy structural components and systems; nonlinear mechanics. *Mailing Add:* Appl Mech Div 5523 PO Box 5800 Albuquerque NM 87185

REUTER, STEWART R, b Detroit, Mich, Feb 14, 34; m 66. RADIOLOGY. *Educ:* Ohio Wesleyan Univ, AB, 55; Case Western Reserve Univ, MD, 59; Am Bd Radiol, dipl, 64. *Prof Exp:* Intern med, Hosp, Univ Calif, 59-60, res asst, 60-63; instr radiol, Stanford Univ, 63-64; Picker res fel, 64-66; from asst prof to assoc prof, Univ Mich, 66-69; assoc prof, Univ Calif, San Diego, 69-72; prof radiol, Univ Mich, Ann Arbor, 72-75; prof radiol & vchmn radiol, Univ Calif, Davis, 76-80 & prof radiol, Univ Calif, San Francisco, 76-80; chief radiol, Martinez Vet Admin Hosp, 76-80; PROF RADIOL & CHMN DEPT, UNIV TEX HEALTH SCI CTR, SAN ANTONIO, 80- *Res:* Angiography, particularly visceral circulation and development of techniques to improve visceral angiography; therapeutic anglography. *Mailing Add:* 1718 Donerail San Antonio TX 78248

REUTER, WILHAD, b Flensburg, Ger, Jan 2, 30; m 53; c 2. ANALYTICAL CHEMISTRY. *Educ:* Univ Mainz, BS, 54, MS, 56, PhD, 58. *Prof Exp:* Anal chemist, O Hommel Co, 58 & Keystone Carbon Co, 59; anal chemist, Int Bus Mach Corp, NY, 60-70, ANAL CHEMIST, IBM RES CTR, 70- *Mem:* Am Chem Soc. *Res:* Instrumental analytical chemistry. *Mailing Add:* IBM Res Ctr PO Box 218 Yorktown Heights NY 10598

REUTER, WILLIAM L(EE), b Hartford, SDak, July 21, 34; m 59; c 2. ELECTRICAL ENGINEERING. *Educ:* SDak Sch Mines & Technol, BS, 56, MS, 58; Iowa State Univ, PhD(elec eng), 67. *Prof Exp:* From instr to assoc prof elec eng, SDak Sch Mines & Technol, 56-72; mgr res & develop, Dunham Assocs, Inc, 72-79; Pres, Rapidata, Inc, 73-79; CHIEF ENGR, PETE LIEN & SONS, INC, 79- *Concurrent Pos:* VPres, Res Specialists Inc, 69-80, bd dir, 80- *Mem:* Inst Elec & Electronics Engrs; Sigma Xi; Nat Soc Prof Engrs. *Res:* Systems; network theory; numerical methods; computer programming; process control; signal processing. *Mailing Add:* 3402 Fairhaven Rapid City SD 57701

REUTHER, THEODORE CARL, JR, b Wheeling, WVa, Apr 16, 33; m 55; c 2. METALLURGICAL ENGINEERING, NUCLEAR MATERIALS. *Educ:* Carnegie Inst Technol, BS, 56, MS, 58; Cath Univ Am, DrEngr, 65. *Prof Exp:* Res metallurgist, US Naval Res Lab, 59-68; METALL ENGR, OFF FUSION ENERGY, US DEPT ENERGY, 68- *Mem:* Metall Soc; Am Soc Metals. *Res:* Diffusion; crystal growth and defects; refractory metals and alloys; creep; nuclear metallurgy; grain boundary energy and structure; irradiation effects; fusion reactor materials development. *Mailing Add:* US Dept of Energy Off of Fusion Energy Washington DC 20545

REUTHER, WALTER, b Manganoui, NZ, Sept 21, 11; nat US; m 35; c 2. HORTICULTURE. *Educ:* Univ Fla, BS, 33; Cornell Univ, PhD(hort), 40. *Prof Exp:* Instr res, Univ Fla, 33-36; asst horticulturist, Citrus Exp Sta, Univ Fla, 36-37; asst, Cornell Univ, 37-40, asst prof pomol, 40; from assoc horticulturist to prin horticulturist, USDA, 40-55; sr horticulturist in-chg, US Date Garden, Calif, 41-46; head dept hort, Univ Fla, 55-56; chmn dept, 56-66, prof, 56-77, EMER PROF HORT, UNIV CALIF, RIVERSIDE, 77- *Concurrent Pos:* Mem adv comt citrus & subtrop fruit res, USDA, 62-63 & hort crops res, 63-69; mem eval comt sr fels, Nat Acad Sci, 64-; mem comt trop studies; consult to var govts & pvt industs, 63- *Mem:* AAAS; fel Am Soc Hort Sci (vpres, 61-62, pres, 62-63); Am Soc Plant Physiol; Am Pomol Soc (vpres, 65-66). *Res:* Mineral nutrition of tree fruits; relation of leaf analysis to nutritional status of citrus; water relations and irrigation of tree fruits; toxicity of copper in citrus orchard soils; influence of climate on citrus. *Mailing Add:* Dept of Bot & Plant Sci Univ of Calif Riverside CA 92502

REUTZEL, LAWRENCE FREDERICK, b O'Neill, Nebr, Aug 12, 43; m 68; c 2. BIOMETRICS, COMPUTER SCIENCE. *Educ:* Univ Nebr, BS, 64, MS, 66; Purdue Univ, PhD(pop genetics), 69. *Prof Exp:* STATISTICIAN BIOMET & COMPUT SCI, RALSTON PURINA CO, ST LOUIS, MO, 69- *Mem:* Biomet Soc; Am Soc Animal Sci. *Res:* Design and development of computerized systems for acquisition and statistical analysis of research data and of systems for laboratory information management. *Mailing Add:* Ralston Purina Co Checkerboard Sq St Louis MO 63188

REUVENY, ZIVA, b Israel. BIOCHEMISTRY, PLANT PHYSIOLOGY. *Educ:* Hebrew Univ, Jerusalem, BSc, 69; Mich State Univ, PhD(biochem), 75. *Prof Exp:* Res asst plant biochem, Plant Res Lab, Mich State Univ, 70-75; fel regulation gene expression, Biol Div, Oak Ridge Nat Lab, 75-77; vis scientist plant cell cult, W Alton Jones Cell Sci Ctr, 77; res assoc microbiol nitrogen pathway, Dept Biol, Mass Inst Technol, 77-79; Asst prof, Dept Appl Microbiol, Hebrew Univ, Isreal, 79-80; MGR PLANT CELL CULTURE, BIOASSAY STSTS CORP, 80- *Mem:* Am Soc Plant Physiologists; AAAS; Am Soc Microbiologists. *Res:* Regulations of enzymes of metabolic pathways in higher plants; the sulfate assimilation and nitrate assimilation pathways; plant tissue culture; molecular biology of plant cells; production of secondary metabolites by cultured plant cells. *Mailing Add:* Bioassay Systs Corp 225 Wildwood Ave Woburn MA 01801

REUWER, JOSEPH FRANCIS, JR, b Harrisburg, Pa, May 31, 31; m 58; c 2. PHYSICAL ORGANIC CHEMISTRY, POLYMER CHEMISTRY. *Educ:* Lehigh Univ, BS, 53; Mass Inst Technol, SM, 57; Univ NH, PhD(org chem), 62. *Prof Exp:* Res chemist, 62-65, res supvr, 65-69, SR SCIENTIST, ARMSTRONG CORK CO, 69- *Concurrent Pos:* Adj prof, Franklin & Marshall Col, 64-66. *Mem:* Am Chem Soc; Royal Soc Chem. *Res:* Reaction mechanisms; chemical kinetics; surface chemistry; free radical polymerization; plasma chemistry; ceramics. *Mailing Add:* 144 N School Lane Lancaster PA 17603

REVAY, ANDREW W, JR, b New Kensington, Pa, Oct 8, 33; m 57; c 2. ELECTROMAGNETICS, ENGINEERING EDUCATION. *Educ:* Univ Pittsburgh, BS, 55, MS, 56, PhD(elec eng), 63. *Prof Exp:* Asst prof elec eng, Univ Pittsburgh, 59-64, assoc res prof, 64-67; assoc prof elec eng, 67-69, head dept, 71-80, head dept mech eng, 72-78, assoc dean res, 77-80, PROF ELEC ENG, FLA INST TECHNOL, 69-, DEAN SCI & ENG, 80- *Concurrent Pos:* Consult adv bd hardened elec power systs, Nat Acad Sci, 63-70 & Harris Corp, 68-; prin investr res contracts. *Mem:* Inst Elec & Electronics Engrs; Am Soc Eng Educ; Am Soc Mech Engrs; Sigma Xi. *Res:* Methods of semiconductor device analysis and design; semiconductor electronic circuity, electromagnetic field theory and application. *Mailing Add:* Dept of Elec Eng Fla Inst of Technol Melbourne FL 32901

REVEAL, JAMES L, b Reno, Nev, Mar 29, 41; m 61, 78; c 3. PLANT TAXONOMY. *Educ:* Utah State Univ, BS, 63, MS, 65; Brigham Young Univ, PhD(bot), 69. *Prof Exp:* Asst prof, 69-74, assoc prof, 74-81, PROF BOT, UNIV MD, COLLEGE PARK, 81- *Concurrent Pos:* Res assoc, Smithsonian Inst, 70-; secy-gen, Int Cong Syst & Evolutionary Biol, 73- *Mem:* AAAS; Am Inst Biol Sci; Bot Soc Am; Am Soc Plant Taxon; Int Asn Plant Taxon. *Res:* Floristic studies in intermountain West, vascular plants of North America, northern Mexico and state of Maryland; monographical studies in Eriogonum and related genera. *Mailing Add:* Dept Bot Univ Md College Park MD 20742

REVEL, JEAN PAUL, b Strasbourg, France, Dec 7, 30; nat US; m 57; c 3. CELL BIOLOGY. *Educ:* Univ Strasbourg, France, BS, 49; Harvard Univ, PhD, 57. *Prof Exp:* Whitney fel anat, Med Col, Cornell Univ, 57-58, res assoc, 58-59; instr, Harvard Med Sch, 61, assoc, 61-63, from asst prof to prof, 63-71; prof biol, 71-78, ALBERT BILLING RUDDOCK PROF BIOL, CALIF INST TECHNOL, 78- *Concurrent Pos:* Mem, Molecular Biol Study Sect, NIH, 70-74; mem, Develop Biol Panel, NSF, 76-80; mem bd sci adv, Nat Inst Aging. *Mem:* AAAS; Am Asn Anat; Am Soc Cell Biol (pres, 72); Soc Develop Biol; Soc Gen Physiol. *Res:* Correlation between structure and function; ultrastructural cytochemistry. *Mailing Add:* Div of BIol 156-29 Calif Inst of Technol Pasadena CA 91109

REVELANTE, NOELIA, b Rovinj, Croatia, Yugoslavia, Jan 17, 42; m 74; c 1. BIOLOGICAL OCEANOGRAPHY. *Educ:* Univ Zagreb, Yugoslavia, BSc, 66, MSc, 70, PhD, 74. *Prof Exp:* From res asst to sr assoc res scientist, Ctr Marine Res, Inst Rudjer Boskovic, Yugoslavia, 66-75; sr res scientist, Australian Inst Marine Sci, 76-78; ASSOC RES PROF, UNIV MAINE, 78- *Concurrent Pos:* Int Comn Sci Explor Mediter Sea. *Mem:* AAAS; Am Soc Limnol & Oceanog; Int Asn Trop Biol; Int Phycol Soc. *Res:* Phytoplankton ecology and taxonomy; primary and secondary aquatic production. *Mailing Add:* Dept Oceanog Univ Maine Orano ME 04469

REVELL, JAMES D(EWEY), b Toledo, Ohio, Feb 17, 29; m 55; c 2. AIRCRAFT NOISE CONTROL, AERODYNAMICS. *Educ:* Univ Calif, Los Angeles, BS, 52, MS, 58, PhD(eng), 66. *Prof Exp:* Thermodynamicist, Northrup Aircraft, Inc, Calif, 52-54, aerodynamicist, 54-57; sr tech specialist, N Am Aviation, Inc, 57-60; sr specialist dynamics & loads, Norair Div, Northrup Corp, 60-62, mem tech mgt, 62-65; res develop scientist, 65-75, RES & DEVELOP SCIENTIST ACOUST, LOCKHEED AIRCRAFT CORP, CALIF, 75- *Mem:* Assoc fel Am Inst Aeronaut & Astronaut; Acoust Soc Am. *Res:* Fluid mechanics; unsteady aerodynamics; acoustics of moving fluids; aerodynamic noise and jet noise theory; turbulence; boundary layer theory; gas dynamics; scattering refraction; aeroelasticity; noise transmission through structures. *Mailing Add:* Flight Sci Div Dept 74-31/243/2 Lockheed Calif Co Burbank CA 91503

REVELLE, CHARLES S, b Rochester, NY, Mar 26, 38; m 62; c 2. ENVIRONMENTAL & SYSTEMS ENGINEERING. *Educ:* Cornell Univ, BChE, 61, PhD(civil eng), 67. *Prof Exp:* Res assoc, Ctr Environ Qual Mgt, Cornell Univ, 67, asst prof environ systs eng, 67-70; assoc prof, 70-75, PROF GEOG & ENVIRON ENG, JOHNS HOPKINS UNIV, 75- *Concurrent Pos:* Vis asst prof, Johns Hopkins Univ, 68-69. *Mem:* Regional Sci Asn; Inst Mgt Sci; Opers Res Soc Am; Am Geophys Union; AAAS. *Res:* Applications of systems analysis and operations research to environmental problems such as water quality and water quantity management, public health systems; modelling of public systems, especially location systems such as ambulance and fire systems. *Mailing Add:* Ames Hall Johns Hopkins Univ Baltimore MD 21218

REVELLE, DOUGLAS ORSON, b Rochester, NY, Dec 9, 45; m 67; c 1. ATMOSPHERIC PHYSICS, SOLAR SYSTEM PHYSICS. *Educ:* Univ Mich, BS, 68, MS, 70, PhD(atmospheric sci), 74. *Prof Exp:* Teaching fel atmospheric sci, Univ Mich, 68-72, res asst, , 71-74; fel, Nat Res Coun Can, 74-75, res assoc, 75-76; ASST PROF PHYSICS, NORTHERN ARIZ UNIV, 78- *Concurrent Pos:* Fel, Carnegie Inst Washington, 77-78, vis scientist, 79; vis scientist, Herzberg Inst Astrophys, Nat Res Coun Can, 77 & 81; Nat Acad Sci exchange scientist, Czech, 80. *Mem:* Acoust Soc Am; Am Geophys Union; Am Meteorol Soc; Int Astron Union. *Res:* Radiation gas dynamics; meteors, fireballs, meteorites and comets; planetary atmospheres; geophysical fluid dynamics; short-lived atmospheric phenomena; linear and non-linear acoustics; meteorology of mountainous terrain; air pollution meteorology. *Mailing Add:* Dept of Physics Northern Ariz Univ Flagstaff AZ 86011

REVELLE, ROGER (RANDALL DOUGAN), b Seattle, Wash, Mar 7, 09; m 31; c 4. OCEANOGRAPHY, SCIENCE POLICY. *Educ:* Pomona Col, AB, 29; Univ Calif, PhD, 36. *Hon Degrees:* ScD, Pomona Col, 57, Carleton Col, 66, Univ Mass, 68, Dartmouth Col, 68, Bucknell Col, 68, Colby Col, 71 & State Univ Utah, 76; AM, Harvard Univ, 64; LHD, Williams Col, 69; LLD, Carnegie-Mellon Univ, 71. *Prof Exp:* Teaching asst, Pomona Col, 29-30; teaching asst, Univ Calif, Berkeley, 30-31, res asst, Scripps Inst Oceanog, 31-36, from instr to prof, Univ Calif, 36-48, assoc dir, Scripps Inst, 48-50, actg dir, 50-51, dir, 51-64, dir, La Jolla Campus & dean, Sch Sci & Eng, 58-61, univ dean of res, 63-64; Richard Saltonstall prof pop policy, Harvard Univ, 64-76, prof pop policy, 76-78, dir, Ctr Pop Studies, 64-76, fel, Adams House, 70-78; EMER UNIV DEAN RES, UNIV CALIF, SAN DIEGO, 64-, EMER DIR, SCRIPPS INST OCEANOG, 64-, PROF SCI & PUB POLICY, 76- *Concurrent Pos:* Head geophys br, Off Naval Res, 46-48; chmn, Comt Biol Effects Radiation in Oceanog & Fisheries, Nat Acad Sci, 54-60; mem, NAm UNESCO Int Adv Comt Marine Sci, 55-60, mem, US Nat Comn, UNESCO, 58-64 & 67-71, vchmn, 61-64, chmn comt natural & social sci, 61-64, mem US deleg, UNESCO Gen Conf, 60, 64 & 80; pres sci comt oceanic res, Int Coun Sci Unions, 57-60; pres, Int Oceanog Cong, 59; chmn comt math, phys & eng sci, NSF, 59-60; mem, Naval Res Adv Comt, 59-72; mem US deleg, Intergovt Oceanog Comn, 60-64; trustee, Scripps Clin & Res Found, 60-66 & Woods Hole Oceanog Inst, 72-; sci adv, Secy Interior, 61-63; mem, Fed Coun Sci & Technol, 61-63; chmn, Comt Natural Resources, Comt Water Resources Res & Panel Nuclear Power & Saline Water Conversion; chmn, White House-Dept Interior Panel Land & Water Develop in Indus Plain, WPakistan; mem res adv comt, AID, 63-72; mem coun, Nat Acad Sci, 62-65 & 73-76, mem governing bd, Nat Res Coun, 73-76; chmn sect geophys, 63-66, chmn comt int biol prog, 65-68, chmn bd sci & technol for develop, 68-72, mem, Comn Int Relations, 73-; mem comt oceanog, ad hoc comt adv to subcomt sci, US House of Rep, Bd Natural Resources; mem finance comt, Murray Fund Comt; chmn, Panel of US-Japan Comt Sci Coop, 63-65; mem panel res, Univs & Fed Govt, panel int sci affairs, panel pollution & panel on world pop & food supplies, President's Sci Adv Comt; mem, President's Comt Nat Medal of Sci, 63-66; pres, Int Asn Phys Sci of Oceans, 63-66; mem educ comn, Govt of India, 64-66. *Honors & Awards:* Agassiz Medal, Nat Acad Sci; Order of Sitara-i-Imtiaz, Govt of Pakistan; Albatross Medal, Swedish Royal Soc Sci & Letters; Bowie Medal, Am Geophys Union. *Mem:* Nat Acad Sci; Geol Soc Am; Am Geophys Union (vpres oceanog sect, 50-53, pres, 56-59); Am Meteorol Soc; Am Soc Limnol & Oceanog. *Res:* Physical oceanography; geology of the sea floor; natural resource analysis; population studies. *Mailing Add:* Univ of Calif La Jolla CA 92093

REVESZ, AKOS GEORGE, b Balassagyarmat, Hungary, July 25, 27; US citizen; m 56 & 75; c 1. SOLID STATE CHEMISTRY. *Educ:* Budapest Tech Univ, Dipl Ing, 50, Dr Ing, 68. *Prof Exp:* Res asst x-ray crystallog, Phys Chem Inst, Budapest Tech Univ, 49; staff mem thermodyn iron metall, Iron & Metal Res Inst, Budapest, 50; staff mem semiconductors, Tungsram Co, 51-54, dept head, 55-56; staff mem anodic oxide films & solid state capacitors, Philips Co, Neth, 57-59 & growth & properties thin films, RCA Labs, 60-69; mem tech staff, 69-72, dept head, 72-74, sr staff scientist, 74-81, SR SCIENTIST, COMSAT LABS, 81- *Honors & Awards:* Achievement Award, RCA Labs, 64. *Mem:* Fel Am Inst Chemists. *Res:* Semiconductor and solid state devices; oxidation of semiconductors; insulator-semiconductor interfaces; properties of thin oxide films; noncrystalline solids. *Mailing Add:* 7910 Park Overlook Dr Bethesda MD 20817

REVESZ, GEORGE, b Budapest, Hungary, July 29, 23; nat US; m 48; c 2. RADIOLOGY, ELECTRICAL ENGINEERING. *Educ:* Swiss Fed Inst Technol, MS, 48; Univ Pa, PhD, 64. *Prof Exp:* Develop engr, Salford Labs, Gen Elec Co, Eng, 49-52; mem staff res, Brit Rayon Res Asn, 52-54; sr proj engr, Robertshaw-Fulton Controls Co, 54-57, sect head, 57-59, tech dir, 59-61; res sect mgr, Philco Corp, Pa, 61-62, mgr instrumentation, Microelectronics Div, 62-68; assoc prof, 66-76, PROF RADIOL, SCH MED, TEMPLE UNIV, 76- *Mem:* Sr mem Inst Elec & Electronics Engrs; sr mem Instrument Soc Am; Am Asn Physicists in Med; Optical Soc Am; Am Thermographic Soc. *Res:* Measuring and improving diagnostic accuracy in medicine; computer analysis of medical images; clinical thermography. *Mailing Add:* Dept of Radiol Temple Univ Sch of Med Philadelphia PA 19140

REVETTA, FRANK ALEXANDER, b Monongahela, Pa, June 18, 28; m 61; c 2. GEOPHYSICS. *Educ:* Univ Pittsburgh, BS, 53; Ind Univ, MA, 57; Univ Rochester, PhD(geophys), 70. *Prof Exp:* Geophysicist, Geophys Serv Inc, 57-58; teacher earth sci, Elizabeth-Forward High Sch, 59-62; instr geol, 62-77, ASSOC PROF GEOL, STATE UNIV NY COL POTSDAM, 77- *Mem:* Am Geophys Union; Geol Soc Am; Nat Asn Geol Teachers. *Res:* Gravity and magnetic surveys; seismology. *Mailing Add:* Dept of Geol Sci State Univ of NY Col Potsdam NY 13676

REVOILE, SALLY GATES, b Pittsburgh, Pa. AUDIOLOGY. *Educ:* Univ Md, BA, 62, MA, 65, PhD(hearing sci), 70. *Prof Exp:* Res audiologist, Vet Admin Hosp, Washington, DC, 62-76; ASST PROF AUDIOL RES, DEPT HEARING RES, GALLAUDET COL, 76- *Mem:* Am Speech & Hearing Asn; Acoust Soc Am. *Res:* Use of hearing aids by the hearing impaired. *Mailing Add:* Dept of Hearing Res SCRL/MTB Gallaudet Col Washington DC 20002

REVOIR, WILLIAM H(ENRY), JR, b New Britain, Conn, July 26, 24; m 50; c 1. CHEMICAL ENGINEERING. *Educ:* Mass Inst Technol, BS, 48; Northeastern Univ, MS, 54. *Prof Exp:* Res assoc fluidized solids, Mass Inst Technol, 48-49; chem engr, Arthur D Little, Inc, 49-51; chief engr, Respirator Res & Develop Lab, Am Optical Corp, Mass, 51-58, mgr, 58-74; dir, Respirator Res & Develop Sect, Los Alamos Sci Lab, 74-75; vpres res & develop, Welsh Div, Textron Inc, 75-76; DIR RES, DEVELOP & ENG, SAFETY PROD DIV, NORTON CO, CRANSTON, 76- *Concurrent Pos:* Chmn respirator comt, Am Conf Gov Indust Hyg & Am Indust Hyg Asn, 66-70; secy respiratory protection comt, Am Nat Standards Inst, 70-, gas canister & cartridge identification comt, 71-; gen chmn, Am Indust Hyg Conf, 73. *Honors & Awards:* Charles R Williams Mem Award, 68. *Mem:* AAAS; Air Pollution Control Asn; Am Chem Soc; Am Indust Hyg Asn; Am Inst Chemists. *Res:* Aerosol particulate filtration; vapor-gas adsorption; toxicology. *Mailing Add:* 36 Laurel Hill Rd East Greenwich RI 02818

REVZIN, ALVIN MORTON, b Chicago, Ill, Nov 8, 26; m 56. PHARMACOLOGY, NEUROPHYSIOLOGY. *Educ:* Univ Chicago, SB, 47, SM, 48; Univ Colo, PhD(physiol), 57. *Prof Exp:* Instr physiol, Med Col SC, 48-49; asst, Col Dent, NY Univ, 49-50; asst, Child Res Coun, Denver, Colo, 51-55; med res assoc, Galesburg State Res Hosp, 57-60; pharmacologist, Nat Heart Inst, 60-63; PHARMACOLOGIST, CIVIL AEROMED INST, FED AVIATION ADMIN, 63- *Concurrent Pos:* Adj asst prof pharmacol, Univ Okla, 63-71, adj assoc prof pharmacol & psychiat, 71- *Mem:* Am Soc Pharmacol & Exp Therapeut; Soc Neurosci; Bioelectromagnetics Soc. *Res:* Neuropharmacology of psychotomimetic compounds; neurotoxicity of pesticides and environmental pollutants; comparative neurology of the avian brain; bioeffects of nonionizing electromagnetic radiation. *Mailing Add:* Civil Aeromed Inst AAC-114 Fed Aviation Admin PO Box 25082 Oklahoma City OK 73125

REW, ROBERT SHERRARD, b Pendleton, Ore, Aug 14, 43; m 74; c 1. BIOLOGICAL CHEMISTRY, PHARMACOLOGY. *Educ:* Whitman Col, BS, 66; Wash State Univ, MS, 68; Johns Hopkins Univ, ScD(cell biol), 74. *Prof Exp:* Res assoc biochem, Notre Dame Univ, 72-76; RES SCIENTIST, ANIMAL PARASITOL INST, USDA, MD, 76- *Mem:* Am Soc Parasitologists; Controlled Release Soc. *Res:* Mode of action of anthelmintics; biochemistry of carbohydrate metabolism in parasitic helminths; new antiparasitic drug delivery systems; ultrastructure of parasitic helminths; parasitology. *Mailing Add:* Animal Parasitol Inst BARC-East Beltsville MD 20705

REWCASTLE, NEILL BARRY, b Sunderland, Eng, Dec 12, 31; Can citizen; m 58; c 4. NEUROPATHOLOGY. *Educ:* St Andrews Univ, MB, ChB, 55; Univ Toronto, MA, 62; Royal Col Physicians & Surgeons, Can, cert, 62, FRCP(C), 68. *Prof Exp:* Lectr path, 64-68, actg head div neuropath, Banting Inst, 65-69, assoc prof, 69-70, PROF NEUROPATH, BANTING INST, UNIV TORONTO, 70-, HEAD DIV, 69-; PATHOLOGIST, TORONTO GEN HOSP, 64- *Concurrent Pos:* Res fel path, Med Res Coun Can, 60-64; Med Res Coun Can & Muscular Dystrophy Asn Can res fels, 64-70. *Mem:* Am Asn Neuropath; Can Asn Path; Can Asn Neuropath (secy, 65-69, pres, 77-79); Can Med Asn. *Res:* Human nervous system diseases; skeletal muscle diseases; electron microscopy. *Mailing Add:* Div of Neuropath Banting Inst Univ of Toronto 100 College St Toronto ON M5S 2R8 Can

REWOLDT, GREGORY, b Ann Arbor, Mich, Apr 21, 48. PLASMA PHYSICS. *Educ:* Calif Inst Technol, BS, 70; Mass Inst Technol, PhD(physics), 74. *Prof Exp:* Physicist, Res Lab Electronics, Mass Inst Technol, 74-75; RES PHYSICIST, PLASMA PHYSICS LAB, PRINCETON UNIV, 75- *Concurrent Pos:* Lectr, Dept Astrophys Sci, Princeton Univ, 79- *Mem:* Am Phys Soc. *Res:* Theoretical plasma physics, especially drift and trapped particle instabilities. *Mailing Add:* Plasma Physics Lab Princeton Univ PO Box 451 Princeton NJ 08544

REX, ROBERT WALTER, b New York, NY; m 52. EXPLORATION GEOLOGY. *Educ:* Univ Costa Rica, BS, 46; Harvard Univ, AB, 51; Stanford Univ, MS, 53; Univ Calif, PhD(oceanog), 58. *Prof Exp:* Geologist, US Geol Surv, 51-53; oceanogr, US Navy Electronics Lab, 53; geologist, Scripps Inst Oceanog, Univ Calif, San Diego, 54-57; sr res assoc geochem, Chevron Oil Field Res Co, Standard Oil Co Calif, 58-67; prof geol sci, Univ Calif, Riverside, 67-72; vpres explor, Pac Energy Corp, Marina Del Rey, Calif, 72-73; PRES, REPUB GEOTHERMAL INC, SANTE FE SPRINGS, 73- *Concurrent Pos:* Dir geothermal resources prog, Univ Calif, Riverside, 68-72; res geologist, Inst Geophys & Planetary Physics, 67-72, asst dir, 71-72; chmn, Geothermal Adv Bd, Univ Calif, 70-72; consult, Jet Propulsion Lab, Calif Inst Technol, 63-65; consult, US Bur Reclamation; res affil, Inst Geophys, Univ Hawaii, 69-; mem, Tech Adv Comt, Calif Geothermal Resources Bd, 71-; consult, Los Alamos Sci Lab, 71- & Oak Ridge Nat Lab, 72-; mem, President's Panel, Off Sci & Technol, 71-73 & Nat Adv Panel, Hawaii Geothermal Proj, 73- *Mem:* Geol Soc Am; Am Geophys Union; AAAS; Geochem Soc; Geothermal Resources Coun. *Res:* Exploration and resource assessment of geothermal resources; oil and gas exploration; economic geology; mineral-water interactions; mineralogy of deep sea sediments and atmospheric dust; x-ray powder diffraction; geochemistry of geothermal systems; clays and clay minerals; exploration systems, strategy, economics and technology. *Mailing Add:* Repub Geothermal Inc 11823 E Slauson Ave Sante Fe Springs CA 90670

REXER, JOACHIM, b New York, NY, Nov 30, 28; m 62; c 2. METALLURGY. *Educ:* Brooklyn Col, BA, 52; Iowa State Univ, MS, 59, PhD(metall), 62. *Prof Exp:* Jr chemist, Ames Labs, Iowa State Univ, 52-54 & 57, asst metall, 57-62; metallurgist, 62-71, SR RES SCIENTIST, PARMA TECH CTR, CARBON PRODS DIV, UNION CARBIDE CORP, 71- *Mem:* Am Soc Metals. *Res:* High temperature reaction kinetics; chemical vapor deposition; free space reactions; vacuum and pressure technology, powder metallurgy; high temperature processing in hydrogen atmospheres. *Mailing Add:* 9269 Highland Dr Cleveland OH 44141

REXFORD, DEAN R, b Orleans, Vt, Oct 1, 15; m 43; c 3. FLUORINE CHEMISTRY. *Educ:* Norwich Univ, BS, 37; Swiss Fed Inst Tech, Dr Tech, 43. *Prof Exp:* Chemist dyestuffs, Ciba Co, Inc, NY, 37-39; Rockefeller Res Asn fel, Princeton Univ, 45-46, instr chem, 46-50, asst prof, Frick Chem Lab, 50-53; from res chemist to sr patent chemist, E I Du Pont de Nemours & Co, Inc, 56-74, patent assoc, 74-80; PATENT CONSULT, UNIV DEL & INDUST, 80- *Mem:* Am Chem Soc; Am Inst Chemists. *Mailing Add:* 2323 W 16th St Wilmington DE 19806

REXFORD, EVEOLEEN NAOMI, b Corning, NY, May 7, 11. PSYCHIATRY, PSYCHOANALYSIS. *Educ:* Keuka Col, BS, 30; Cornell Univ, MS, 31; Univ Buffalo, MD, 35; Boston Psychoanal Inst, cert, 48. *Prof Exp:* Mem staff psychiat, Cent Islip State Hosp, NY, 38-42, Judge Baker Guid Ctr, 43-48 & James Jackson Putnam Children's Ctr, 43-49; dir, Thom Clin Children, Boston, 49-65; prof child psychiat & dir dept, 65-73, div prof, 73-76, EMER PROF PSYCHIAT & CHILD PSYCHIAT, SCH MED, BOSTON UNIV, 76- *Concurrent Pos:* Commonwealth fel child psychiat, Judge Baker Guid Ctr, Boston, 42-43; consult psychiat, Wellesley Col, 43-44; lectr, Harvard Med Sch, 60; ed, J Am Acad Child Psychiat, 65-75; pres, Am Asn Psychiat Serv Children, 66-68; Commonwealth grant-in-aid med, Sch Med, Boston Univ, 72-73. *Mem:* Am Acad Child Psychiat; Am Psychoanal Asn; Am Psychiat Asn; Soc Prof Child Psychiat. *Res:* History of attitudes toward children in the United States and other western countries; discrepancies between plans and implementation; planning child psychiatric services; antisocial behavior. *Mailing Add:* 143 Mount Auburn St Cambridge MA 02138

REXROAD, CAIRD EUGENE, JR, b Fairmont, WVa, Jan 6, 47; m 68; c 2. REPRODUCTIVE PHYSIOLOGY. *Educ:* WVa Univ, BS, 68; Univ Wis-Madison, MS, 72, PhD(reproductive physiol & endocrinol), 74. *Prof Exp:* RES PHYSIOLOGIST DAIRY CATTLE, REPRODUCTION LAB, ANIMAL SCI INST, BELTSVILLE AGR RES CTR, MD, 74- *Mem:* Am Soc Animal Sci; Soc Study Reproduction. *Res:* Endocrine regulation of sperm transport and uterine motility; direct effect of steroids on follicle growth and atresia. *Mailing Add:* Bldg 200 Beltsville Agr Res Ctr-E Beltsville MD 20705

REXROAD, CARL BUCKNER, b Columbus, Ohio, Apr 2, 25; m 51; c 1. GEOLOGY. *Educ:* Univ Mo, BA, 49, MS, 50; Univ Iowa, PhD(geol), 55. *Prof Exp:* Instr geol, La Tech Univ, 50-53; asst prof, Tex Tech Univ, 55-58; assoc prof, Univ Houston, 58-61; PALEONTOLOGIST, IND GEOL SURV, 61- *Concurrent Pos:* Adj prof, Ind Univ, 79- *Mem:* Geol Soc Am; Soc Econ Paleontologists & Mineralogists; Am Asn Petrol Geol; Pander Soc. *Res:* Mississippian and Silurian conodonts and related stratigraphy. *Mailing Add:* Ind Geol Surv 611 N Walnut Grove Bloomington IN 47405

REY, CHARLES ALBERT, b Oklahoma City, Okla, Apr 8, 34; m 60; c 2. PHYSICS, APPLIED PHYSICS. *Educ:* Univ Chicago, AB, 56, BS, 57, MS, 59, PhD(physics), 64. *Prof Exp:* Res assoc physics, Enrico Fermi Inst Nuclear Studies, 63-64; physicist, Lawrence Radiation Lab, Univ Calif, 64-70; asst prof physics, Univ Notre Dame, 70-74; DIR RES, INTERAND CORP, 77- *Mem:* AAAS; Am Phys Soc. *Res:* Acoustics; materials processing; communications engineering; high energy physics; elementary particle structure; particle detectors; electronics. *Mailing Add:* 1473 Farington Ct Naperville IL 60540

REY, WILLIAM K(ENNETH), b New York, NY, Aug 11, 25; m 46; c 2. AEROSPACE ENGINEERING. *Educ:* Univ Ala, BSAE, 46, MSCE, 49. *Prof Exp:* Asst & instr math, 46-47, from instr to asst prof eng mech, 47-52, from assoc prof to prof aeronaut eng, 52-60, PROF AEROSPACE ENG, UNIV ALA, 60-, ASST DEAN ENG, 76- *Concurrent Pos:* Proj dir res projs, NASA. *Mem:* Am Soc Eng Educ; assoc fel Am Inst Aeronaut & Astronaut; Nat Soc Prof Engrs. *Res:* Properties of materials under various environments, especially fatigue behavior at elevated temperatures; analytical and experimental determination of stress distributions in aircraft and missile components. *Mailing Add:* Col of Eng PO Box 1968 University AL 35486

REYBURN, ALAN KIM, b Tulsa, Okla, Aug 22, 40; m 66; c 2. CHEMICAL ENGINEERING. *Educ:* Mass Inst Technol, SB, 62; Okla State Univ, MS, 64, PhD(chem eng), 68. *Prof Exp:* Res scientist, Sinclair Oil Corp, Okla, 66-69; chem engr, John Zink Co, 69-71; proj coordr, Incineration Systs, Williams Bros Waste Control, Inc, 72-73; MGR, POLLUTION CONTROL & PROCESS ENG DEPT, CREST ENG, INC, 74- *Mem:* Am Inst Chem Engrs; Air Pollution Control Asn. *Res:* Research and process development in oil shale retorting; design engineering for liquid and gaseous chemicals incinerators; design and project management of air pollution control systems; management of process and pollution control design engineering. *Mailing Add:* Crest Eng Inc PO Box 1859 Tulsa OK 74101

REYER, RANDALL WILLIAM, b Chicago, Ill, Jan 23, 17; m 43; c 2. DEVELOPMENTAL BIOLOGY. *Educ:* Cornell Univ, BA, 39, MA, 42; Yale Univ, PhD(zool), 47. *Prof Exp:* Lab asst biol, Yale Univ, 42-46, instr zool, 47-50; instr biol, Wesleyan Univ, 46-47; asst prof anat, Sch Med, Univ Pittsburgh, 50-57; assoc prof, 57-67, actg chmn dept, 77-78, PROF ANAT, SCH MED, WVA UNIV, 67- *Mem:* Am Soc Zoologists; Soc Develop Biol; Am Asn Anat; Asn Res Vision & Ophthal; Int Soc Develop Biol. *Res:* Embryonic development and regeneration of the crystalline lens and neural retina in Amphibia; embryology; microscopic anatomy. *Mailing Add:* Dept of Anat WVa Univ Sch of Med Morgantown WV 26506

REYES, ANDRES ARENAS, b Bongabon, Philippines, Feb 26, 31; Can citizen; m 58; c 3. PLANT PATHOLOGY, AGRICULTURAL MICROBIOLOGY. *Educ:* Araneta Univ, Philippines, BSA, 54; Wash State Univ, Pullman, MSA, 58; Univ Wis-Madison, PhD(plant path), 61. *Prof Exp:* Instr plant path, Araneta Univ, Philippines, 54-55; plant quarantine officer, Bur Plant Indust, Philippines, 55-57; plant pathologist, Philippine Packing Corp, Bukidnon, 61-63; res scientist plant path, Nat Inst Sci & Technol, Philippines, 63-65; RES SCIENTIST PLANT PATH, AGR CAN, 67- *Concurrent Pos:* Res asst, Univ Wis-Madison, 57-61; lectr, Araneta Univ, Philippines, 64-65 & Adamson Univ, Philippines, 64-65; fel, Tex A&M Univ, 65-67. *Honors & Awards:* Spec Citation Plant Protection, Philippine Soc Advan Sci, 64. *Mem:* Am Phytopath Soc; Am Soc Hort Sci; Can Phytopath Soc; Agr Inst Can. *Res:* Biological control of soilborne diseases of vegetable crops. *Mailing Add:* Plant Path Sect Agr Can Vineland Station ON L0R 2E0 Can

REYES, PHILIP, b Tulare, Calif, Sept 5, 36; m 62; c 3. BIOCHEMISTRY. *Educ:* Univ Calif, Davis, 58, MS, 59, PhD(biochem), 63. *Prof Exp:* Res fel, McArdle Lab Cancer Res, Univ Wis-Madison, 63-65; USPHS fel enzymol, Scripps Clin & Res Found, 65-67; res assoc, Children's Cancer Res Found, 67-70; asst prof biochem, 70-75, ASSOC PROF BIOCHEM, SCH MED, UNIV NMEX, 75- *Mem:* AAAS; Am Asn Cancer Res; Am Soc Pharmacol & Exp Therapeut; Am Chem Soc; Am Soc Biol Chemists. *Res:* Molecular basis for the mechanism of action of fluorinated pyrimidines and folic acid analogs; nucleotide synthesis and metabolism; cancer chemotherapy; biochemistry of malaria parasites. *Mailing Add:* Dept Biochem Univ NMex Sch of Med Albuquerque NM 87131

REYES, ZOILA, b Bucaramanga, Colombia, July 18, 20. ORGANIC CHEMISTRY. *Educ:* Univ WVa, AB & MS, 45; Johns Hopkins Univ, PhD(org chem), 48. *Prof Exp:* Res chemist, Gen Aniline & Film Corp, 48; SR ORG CHEMIST, SRI INT, 56- *Mem:* AAAS; Am Chem Soc; Sigma Xi; NY Acad Sci. *Res:* Proteins; amino acids; fatty acids and derivatives; heterocyclic compounds; photochemistry; photopolymers; polymer technology; microencapsulation; chemical and radiation induced graft copolymerization. *Mailing Add:* SRI Int 333 Ravenswood Ave Menlo Park CA 94025

REYHNER, THEODORE ALISON, b Paterson, NJ, Nov 17, 40; m 68. FLUID MECHANICS. *Educ:* Stanford Univ, BS, 62, MS, 63, PhD(eng mech), 67. *Prof Exp:* sr specialist engr, 60-80, PRIN ENGR, BOEING COMMERCIAL AIRPLANE CO, SEATTLE, 80- *Mem:* Assoc fel Am Inst Aeronaut & Astronaut. *Res:* Boundary layer and shock wave-boundary layer interactions computations; three-dimensional transonic potential flow; computational fluid mechanics; numerical analysis. *Mailing Add:* 2435 S 304th St Federal Way WA 98003

REYHNER, THEODORE O, b Paterson, NJ, Apr 19, 15; m 40; c 2. ENGINEERING. *Educ:* Newark Col Eng, BS, 37; Columbia Univ, AM, 38; NY Univ, PhD(educ admin), 50; Stanford Univ, MS, 63. *Prof Exp:* Struct draftsman, Robins Conveying Belt Co, NY, 37-38; instr math & physics, Newark Col Eng, 40-42; instr physics, Cooper Union, 42-43; instr civil eng, Lehigh Univ, 43-44; engr timber mech div, Forest Prods Lab, US Forest Serv, Wis, 44-46; assoc prof civil eng, Univ NDak, 46-47; assoc prof archit, Sch Archit & Allied Arts, Univ Ore, 47-49; assoc prof civil eng, Univ Denver, 49-53 & Mich Col Mining & Technol, 53-56; actg head dept eng, 57-58, head civil eng, 67-74 & 78, PROF CIVIL ENG, CALIF STATE UNIV, CHICO, 56-, CHMN DIV ENG, 78- *Concurrent Pos:* NSF sci fac fel, 62-63. *Mem:* Fel Am Soc Civil Engrs; Am Soc Eng Educ; Am Concrete Inst. *Res:* Reinforced concrete; structural engineering; statistical education. *Mailing Add:* Dept of Civil Eng Calif State Univ Chico CA 95929

REYMANN, GREGORY ANDRE, physics, engineering, see previous edition

REYNARD, ALAN MARK, b Boston, Mass, Oct 11, 32; m 61; c 2. PHARMACOLOGY. *Educ:* George Washington Univ, BS, 53; Univ Minn, PhD(biochem), 60. *Prof Exp:* Fel biochem, Univ Wash, 60-62; fel pharmacol, Yale Univ, 62-64; asst prof, 64-68, ASSOC PROF PHARMACOL, SCH MED, STATE UNIV NY BUFFALO, 68- *Res:* Antibiotics; antibiotic-resistance in bacteria complement. *Mailing Add:* Dept Pharmacol 12 Farber Hall State Univ of NY Sch of Med Buffalo NY 14214

REYNARD, KENNARD ANTHONY, b Philadelphia, Pa, Jan 13, 39; m 66; c 1. POLYMER CHEMISTRY, INORGANIC CHEMISTRY. *Educ:* St Louis Univ, BS, 60, MS, 64, PhD(chem), 67. *Prof Exp:* Proj engr, US Air Force, Fla, 66-69; group leader polymer chem, Horizons Res Inc, 69-72, head chem dept, 72-74, mgr contract res & develop, 74-76; tech mgr, 76-79, TECH DIR FLUIDS, EMULSIONS & COMPOUNDS, SWS SILICONES CORP, 79- *Honors & Awards:* IR-100 Award, Indust Res Mag, 71. *Mem:* Am Chem Soc. *Res:* Synthesis of monomers and polymers; characterization of polyphosphazenes, inorganic chemistry, polysiloxanes; phosphorus-nitrogen compounds, boron-nitrogen compounds, organo-silicon compounds, organometallic chemistry; waste utilization, electrostatics, inks and toners; research and development in chemistry and physics as related to materials and processes. *Mailing Add:* SWS Silicones Corp Sutton Rd Adrian MI 49221

REYNES, ENRIQUE G, b Manila, Philippines; US citizen. CHEMICAL ENGINEERING, CHEMISTRY. *Educ:* Univ Philippines, BS, 52; Northwestern Univ, MS, 59, PhD(chem eng), 64; Case Western Reserve Univ, MS, 68. *Prof Exp:* Instr, Univ Philippines, 52-58; engr, B F Goodrich Chem Co, 59-60; assoc develop scientist, 64-65, develop scientist, 65-78, SR RES & DEVELOP ASSOC, AVON LAKE TECH CTR, B F GOODRICH CHEM CO, 78- *Res:* Polymerization of olefins; elastomer polymerization; rubber additives. *Mailing Add:* Avon Lake Tech Ctr B F Goodrich Chem Co Avon Lake OH 44012

REYNHOUT, JAMES KENNETH, b Mysore City, India, July 6, 42; US citizen; m 63; c 4. DEVELOPMENTAL BIOLOGY. *Educ:* Barrington Col, BS, 64; Brown Univ, MS, 68, PhD(develop biol), 71. *Prof Exp:* Res assoc biol, Purdue Univ, 70-73; asst prof biol, Holy Cross Col, 73-75; res scientist, Mich Cancer Found, 76-78; ASST PROF BIOL, OAKLAND UNIV, 78- *Mem:* Soc Develop Biol; Am Soc Zoologists; AAAS; Sigma Xi. *Res:* Developmental regulation, especially endocrine mechanisms stimulating meiosis; chromosomal interaction in hybrids; chromosomal proteins in developmental regulation. *Mailing Add:* Dept of Biol Sci Oakland Univ Rochester MI 48063

REYNIK, ROBERT JOHN, b Bayonne, NJ, Dec 25, 32; m 56; c 6. MATERIALS SCIENCE, RESEARCH ADMINISTRATION. *Educ:* Univ Detroit, BS, 56; Univ Cincinnati, MS, 60, PhD(theoret phys chem), 63. *Prof Exp:* Mem tech staff, Bell Tel Labs, Inc, NY, 57-58; res fel appl sci & elec eng, Univ Cincinnati, 58-59, instr math & elec eng, 59-61; head physics dept, Ohio Col Appl Sci, 61-62; lectr math, Xavier Univ, Ohio, 62-63; fel metall eng, Univ Pa, 63-64; from asst prof to assoc prof, Drexel Univ, 64-70; assoc prog dir eng mat, Div Eng, 70-71, actg prog dir, Div Mat Res, 71-72, dir eng mat prog, 72-74, DIR METALL PROG, NAT SCI FOUND, 74- *Concurrent Pos:* Indust consult, 65-; res grants, NSF, 65-72 & Am Iron & Steel Inst, 67-71; NIH dent training grant, 67-72; chmn, Metall Soc & Am Inst Mining, Metall & Petrol Engrs, chmn Publ Comt, mem first deleg, People's Rep China, 78 & mem Prog Comt, 80-83; mem Planning Group & prog dir, Electo, Metall & Corrosion Work Group, US-USSR Sci & Technol Int Agreement, 73-; deleg to nat comn on mat policy, Univ Forum, Mass Inst Technol, 72; mem var comt, Ultra High Pressure, Nat Acad Sci, 71 & Sci Base Mil Processing, 78; mem, Int Coun Alloy Phase Diagrams, 78-; mem comt sci base for mat processing, Nat Acad Sci, 78. *Mem:* Am Inst Mining, Metall & Petrol Engrs; Metall Soc; Sigma Xi. *Res:* High temperature, high pressure transport properties of liquid metals; biomaterials; electronic and magnetic behavior of materials; nondestructive evaluation and materials characterization. *Mailing Add:* Div Mat Res Nat Sci Found Washington DC 20550

REYNOLDS, ALBERT KEITH, b St Thomas, Ont, June 2, 14. PHARMACOLOGY. *Educ:* Univ Western Ont, PhD(pharmacol), 51. *Prof Exp:* Instr biochem, Univ Western Ont, 39-40, res assoc pharmacol, 41-49; from asst prof to assoc prof, 49-75, PROF PHARMACOL, DALHOUSIE UNIV, 75- *Mem:* AAAS; Am Pharmaceut Asn; Can Pharmacol Soc. *Res:* Cardiovascular research. *Mailing Add:* Dept Pharmacol Dalhousie Univ Halifax NS B3H 3J5 Can

REYNOLDS, BRIAN EDGAR, b Drogheda, Ireland, Mar 5, 36; m 60; c 2. MEDICINAL CHEMISTRY, ORGANIC CHEMISTRY. *Educ:* Queen's Univ, Belfast, 59, PhD(org chem), 62. *Prof Exp:* Res fel chem, Univ Rochester, 62-64; RES SCIENTIST, MED CHEM, McNEIL LABS, INC, 64- *Mem:* Am Chem Soc; Royal Soc Chem. *Res:* Synthesis and biosynthesis of natural products; synthesis of organic chemicals for possible use as pharmaceuticals. *Mailing Add:* 1644 Arran Way Dresher PA 19025

REYNOLDS, BRUCE G, b Ft Myers, Fla, Jan 16, 37; m 61; c 2. NUCLEAR PHYSICS. *Educ:* Fla State Univ, BS, 61, PhD(physics), 66. *Prof Exp:* Asst prof physics, Fla State Univ, 66-68; asst prof physics & elec eng, Ohio Univ, 68-71; physicist & staff engr, Martin Marietta Corp, 71-74; physicist, Argonne Nat Lab, 74-80; mem tech staff, Bell Tel Labs, 80-81; PRIN ENGR, STROMBERG CARLSON, 81- *Mem:* Am Phys Soc; Am Nuclear Soc; Inst Elec & Electronics Engrs. *Res:* Experimental high energy particle physics; hardware/software design of data analysis systems; electrooptical instrumentation and systems engineering; operations research and economic planning; electromagnetic pulse phenomena and electromagnetic compatibility; analysis of telecommunication systems; hydrology and water resource analysis. *Mailing Add:* 34 Village Grove Mount Dora FL 32757

REYNOLDS, CHARLES ALBERT, b Colorado Springs, Colo, Apr 1, 23; m 53; c 6. CHEMISTRY. *Educ:* Stanford Univ, AB, 44, MA, 46, PhD(anal chem), 47. *Prof Exp:* Asst instr chem, Stanford Univ, 44-47; from asst prof to assoc prof, 47-59, assoc chmn dept, 61-67, PROF CHEM, UNIV KANS, 60- *Concurrent Pos:* Mem opers res group, US Army Chem Corps, 51-53; tech dir, Edgewood Arsenal, 67-69. *Mem:* Am Chem Soc. *Res:* Organic functional group analysis; complex ion reactions in non-aqueous solvents; thermochemical methods of analysis. *Mailing Add:* Dept of Chem Univ of Kans Lawrence KS 66044

REYNOLDS, CHARLES C, b Webb City, Mo, July 17, 27; m 48; c 3. METALLURGY, CERAMICS. *Educ:* Mass Inst Technol, SB, 47, SM, 54, PhD(metall), 64. *Prof Exp:* Asst prof metall, Mass Inst Technol, 54-57; asst prof, Thayer Sch, Dartmouth Col, 57-60, asst dean, 57-59; fel, Mass Inst Technol, 60-62; assoc prof mech eng, 62-67, prof, 67-81, GEORGE F FULLER PROF MECH ENG, WORCESTER POLYTECH INST, 81- *Mailing Add:* Dept of Mech Eng Worcester Polytech Inst Worcester MA 01609

REYNOLDS, CHARLES WILLIAM, b Ala, Nov 30, 17; m 55; c 1. HORTICULTURE. *Educ:* Univ Ala, AB, 41; Ala Polytech Inst, BS, 47, MS, 49; Univ Md, PhD(hort), 54. *Prof Exp:* Instr hort, Ala Polytech Inst, 49-52, assoc prof, 52-53; from asst prof to assoc prof veg crops, 54-65, PROF HORT, UNIV MD, COLLEGE PARK, 65- *Mem:* Am Soc Hort Sci; Am Soc Agron. *Res:* Mineral nutrition of cucumbers; effects of supplemental irrigation on yield and quality of vegetable corps; cultural studies with cauliflower. *Mailing Add:* Dept of Hort Univ of Md College Park MD 20740

REYNOLDS, CLAUDE LEWIS, JR, b Roanoke, Va, Dec 16, 48; m 70. EXPERIMENTAL SOLID STATE PHYSICS, LOW TEMPERATURE PHYSICS. *Educ:* Va Mil Inst, BS, 70; Univ Va, MS, 72, PhD(mat sci), 74. *Prof Exp:* Sr scientist, Dept Mat Sci, Univ Va, 74-75; res assoc physics, Univ Ill, Urbana, 75-77; sr proj engr, Union Carbide Corp, 77-80; MEM TECH STAFF, BELL LABS, 80- *Mem:* Am Phys Soc; Am Asn Physics Teachers; Sigma Xi. *Res:* Growth and properties of aluminum gallium arsenide, liquid phase epitaxy, semiconductor injection lasers; properties of materials at low temperatures; amorphous materials; cryogenic techniques; thermal boundary resistance; amalgams. *Mailing Add:* Bell Labs 2525 N 12th St Reading PA 19604

REYNOLDS, DAVID GEORGE, b South Chicago Heights, Ill, Nov 25, 33; div; c 2. PHYSIOLOGY. *Educ:* Knox Col, Ill, BS, 55; Univ Ill, Urbana, MS, 57; Univ Iowa, PhD(physiol), 63. *Prof Exp:* Med Serv Corps, US Army, 57-, chief basic sci br, US Army Med Field Serv Sch, Tex, 58-60 & 63-65, actg chief dept gastroenterol, Walter Reed Army Inst Res, 65-68, asst chief, 68-72, dep dir div surg, 72-74, dir div surg, 74-77; assoc prof, 77-81, PROF SURG, UNIV IOWA, 81-, DIR, SURG LABS & RES, HOSPS & CLINS, 77- *Concurrent Pos:* Spec lectr, Sch Hosp Admin, Baylor Univ, 63-65. *Mem:* Am Physiol Soc; Soc Exp Biol & Med; Asn Acad Surg; Am Fedn Clin Res; NY Acad Sci. *Res:* Gastrointestinal physiology and pharmacology; microvascular architecture; sphlanchnic blood flow; shock. *Mailing Add:* Dept of Surg Univ Iowa Hosps & Clins Iowa City IA 52242

REYNOLDS, DAVID STEPHEN, b Cincinnati, Ohio, Nov 12, 32; m 58; c 4. APPLIED STATISTICS, APPLIED MATHEMATICS. *Educ:* Univ Cincinnati, Mech Engr, 54; Fla State Univ, MS, 65, PhD(statist), 69. *Prof Exp:* Dept mgr mfg, 54-60, statist engr, 60-62, statist serv group leader, 63-73, DATA SERV MGR PROD DEVELOP, PROCTER & GAMBLE CO, 73- *Mem:* Am Statist Asn; Inst Math Statist. *Mailing Add:* 9636 Leebrook Dr Cincinnati OH 45231

REYNOLDS, DON RUPERT, b Shreveport, La, Aug 22, 38. MYCOLOGY. *Educ:* Tex A&M Univ, BS, 60; La State Univ, MS, 62; Univ Tex, Austin, PhD(bot), 70. *Prof Exp:* Mycologist, Univ Philippines, 63-67; CUR & HEAD BOT, NATURAL HIST MUS, LOS ANGELES, 75- *Concurrent Pos:* Adj prof, Univ Southern Calif, 75. *Mem:* Mycol Soc Am. *Res:* Systematics, ultrastructure, ecology and developmental morphology of tropical fungi, especially the ascomycetes. *Mailing Add:* Natural Hist Mus 900 Expos Blvd Los Angeles CA 90007

REYNOLDS, DONALD KELLY, b Portland, Ore, Dec 9, 19; m 45; c 3. ELECTRICAL ENGINEERING. *Educ:* Stanford Univ, BA, 41, MA, 42; Harvard Univ, PhD(eng sci, appl physics), 48. *Prof Exp:* Res engr, Radio Res Lab, Harvard Univ, 42-45; sr res engr, Stanford Res Inst, 48-53; assoc prof elec eng, Tech Inst Aeronaut, Brazil, 53-56; prof & head dept, Seattle Univ, 56-59; PROF ELEC ENG, UNIV WASH, 59- *Concurrent Pos:* Sci attache, US Dept State, Am Embassy, Brazil, 72-74. *Mem:* Fel Inst Elec & Electronics Engrs. *Res:* Electronic circuits; antennas; applied electromagnetic theory. *Mailing Add:* Dept of Elec Eng Univ of Wash Seattle WA 98195

REYNOLDS, E(DWARD) E(VANS), metallurgical engineering, mechanical engineering, see previous edition

REYNOLDS, EDWARD STORRS, JR, b East Orange, NJ, Dec 3, 28; m 50; c 4. EXPERIMENTAL PATHOLOGY. *Educ:* Williams Col, AB, 50; Wash Univ, MD, 54. *Prof Exp:* Asst path, Peter Bent Brigham Hosp, 56-59; pathologist, Armed Forces Inst Path, 59-61; from instr to assoc prof path, Harvard Med Sch, 62-76; PROF PATH & CHMN DEPT, UNIV TEX MED BR, 76- *Concurrent Pos:* Teaching fel path, Harvard Med Sch, 55-59 & 61-62; Nat Res Coun fel, 57-59; from asst path to sr assoc path, Peter Bent Brigham Hosp, 61-76; USPHS career develop award, 66-76. *Mem:* AAAS; Biophys Soc; Am Soc Cell Biol; Am Asn Path; Soc Toxicol. *Res:* Biochemical and biophysical cytology; electron microscopy; biochemistry; cell injury; metabolism of injured cells; toxicology; membrane permeability; electrolyte transport. *Mailing Add:* Dept Path Univ Tex Med Br Galveston TX 77550

REYNOLDS, ELBERT BRUNNER, JR, b Bryan, Tex, Sept 17, 24; m 64; c 2. MECHANICAL ENGINEERING. *Educ:* Tex A&M Univ, BS, 47; Pa State Univ, MS, 48; Univ Wis, PhD(mech eng), 57. *Prof Exp:* From instr to asst prof mech eng, Pa State Univ, 48-53; serv engr, E I du Pont de Nemours & Co, 57-61; assoc prof mech eng, Univ Va, 61-64; ASSOC PROF MECH ENG, TEX TECH UNIV, 64- *Concurrent Pos:* Consult, US Naval Weapons Lab, Va, 63-64; NSF grant, 65-67. *Mem:* Am Soc Mech Engrs; Soc Automotive Engrs. *Res:* Thermodynamics; heat transfer; compressible fluid flow; optical instruments for study of heat transfer and compressbile fluid flow; direct energy conversion. *Mailing Add:* Dept of Mech Eng Tex Tech Univ Lubbock TX 79409

REYNOLDS, ERNEST WEST, JR, b Bristow, Okla, May 11, 20. CARDIOLOGY. *Educ:* Univ Okla, BS, 42, MD, 46, MS, 52. *Prof Exp:* Res assoc cardiol, Med Sch, Univ Mich, Ann Arbor, 54-56, from asst prof to prof internal med & cardiol, 56-72; PROF CLIN CARDIOL & DIR, SCH MED, UNIV WIS-MADISON, 72- *Concurrent Pos:* Chmn cardiovasc & pulmonary A study sect, NIH, 72-73; fel coun clin cardiol, Am Heart Asn. *Res:* Electrophysiology and electrocardiography. *Mailing Add:* Dept of Cardiol Sch of Med Univ Wis-Madison 420 N Charter Madison WI 53706

REYNOLDS, FRANCIS JOSEPH, b Minersville, Pa, Jan 23, 35. ORGANIC CHEMISTRY. *Educ:* Pa State Univ, BS, 56; Univ Pa, PhD(org chem), 63. *Prof Exp:* Assoc prof, 61-64, chmn dept, 68-74, PROF CHEM, WEST CHESTER STATE COL, 64- *Mem:* Am Chem Soc. *Res:* Dipole moment measurements on organic compounds; synthesis of small ring compounds; conformational studies on small ring systems. *Mailing Add:* Dept of Chem West Chester State Col West Chester PA 19380

REYNOLDS, FRED C, b Texarkana, Tex, Feb 19, 08; m 45; c 3. ORTHOPEDIC SURGERY. *Educ:* Wash Univ, AB, 31, MD, 34; Am Bd Orthop Surg, dipl, 46. *Prof Exp:* Assoc prof clin orthop surg, 53-56, PROF ORTHOP SURG, SCH MED, WASH UNIV, 56- *Concurrent Pos:* Pres, Am Bd Orthop Surg, 62-63. *Mem:* Clin Orthop Soc; Am Orthop Asn; Am Acad Orthop Surg (pres, 65); Am Col Surgeons; Orthop Res Soc. *Res:* Bone healing and growth. *Mailing Add:* 224 S Woods Mill Rd Chesterfield MO 63017

REYNOLDS, GARTH FREDRIC, b Springfield, Ohio, Sept 6, 29; m 60; c 2. PHYSICAL CHEMISTRY. *Educ:* Wittenberg Univ, BA, 53; Univ Cincinnati, PhD(phys chem), 59. *Prof Exp:* Mem res staff phys chem, Bell Labs, Inc, 59-61; asst prof chem, Colo Sch Mines, 61-65; assoc prof, 65-68; assoc prof, 68-77, PROF CHEM, MICH TECHNOL UNIV, 77- *Concurrent Pos:* NSF grant, Colo Sch Mines, 64-65; vis investr, Duke Univ, 74-75. *Mem:* Am Chem Soc; Sigma Xi. *Res:* Solid State Chemistry; molecular structure; magnetic resonance; kinetics; mechanism. *Mailing Add:* Dept Chem & Chem Eng Mich Technol Univ Houghton MI 49931

REYNOLDS, GEORGE ARTHUR, b West Palm Beach, Fla, June 30, 24; m 50; c 1. ORGANIC CHEMISTRY. *Educ:* Univ Fla, BS, 45; Duke Univ, PhD(org chem), 51. *Prof Exp:* Res assoc, 50-69, SR RES ASSOC, EASTMAN KODAK CO, 69- *Res:* Synthetic organic research in the field of heterocycles. *Mailing Add:* Eastman Kodak Co Res Labs 1669 Lake Ave Rochester NY 14650

REYNOLDS, GEORGE THOMAS, b Trenton, NJ, May 27, 17; m 44; c 4. BIOPHYSICS, HIGH ENERGY PHYSICS. *Educ:* Rutgers Univ, BS, 39; Princeton Univ, MA, 42, PhD(physics), 43. *Prof Exp:* Res physicist, Nat Defense Res Comt, 41-44, from asst prof to assoc prof, 46-58, dir, Ctr Environ Studies, 71-77, PROF PHYSICS, PRINCETON UNIV, 58- *Concurrent Pos:* Guggenheim fel, 55-56; consult radiation detection, blast effects & oceanog, 58-; fel, Churchill Found, Cambridge Univ, 73-74; mem bd trustees, Rutgers Univ, 75- *Mem:* Fel Am Phys Soc; Am Geophys Union; Biophys Soc. *Res:* Mass spectroscopy; fluid dynamics; cosmic ray; high energy nuclear physics; image intensification; bioluminescence; x-ray diffraction of biological structures. *Mailing Add:* Dept of Physics Princeton Univ Princeton NJ 08540

REYNOLDS, GEORGE WILLIAM, JR, b South Glens Falls, NY, Aug 18, 28; m 80; c 3. MATERIALS PHYSICS, CHEMICAL PHYSICS. *Educ:* Col Educ, Albany, BS, 53, MS, 58; Ohio State Univ, PhD(physics), 66. *Prof Exp:* Teacher, Del Acad & Cent Sch, 53-56; teacher & chmn sci dept, Fulton High Sch, 56-59; asst prof sci educ, Col Educ, Albany, 59-61; instr physics, Ohio State Univ, 62-63; from asst prof to assoc prof sci educ, 63-65, assoc prof sci, 65-70, ASSOC PROF PHYSICS, STATE UNIV NY, ALBANY, 70- *Concurrent Pos:* Lectr, Naval Res Off Sch, 61-63 & 69-72; consult, Naval Res Lab, 79- *Mem:* Am Asn Physics Teachers; Nat Sci Teachers Asn; Am Meteorol Soc; Mat Res Soc; Am Phys Soc. *Res:* Chemical kinetics; ion beam-solid interactions and analysis; design and development of instrumentation; ion beam metallurgy. *Mailing Add:* Dept Physics State Univ NY Albany NY 12222

REYNOLDS, GLENN MYRON, b Alexandria, Minn, Jan 30, 36; m 58; c 3. NUCLEAR PHYSICS. *Educ:* Univ Minn, BPhysics, 61, MS, 63, PhD(physics), 66. *Prof Exp:* Res assoc nuclear physics, Cyclotron Lab, Univ Mich, 66-68; staff assoc, Gulf Gen Atomic, Inc, 68-70; STAFF SCIENTIST NUCLEAR PHYSICS, SCI APPLNS, INC, 70- *Mem:* Am Phys Soc; Am Soc Nondestructive Testing; Am Nuclear Soc. *Res:* Charged particle reactions; gamma ray spectroscopy; fission; neutron spectroscopy; nondestructive testing; radiation effects; infrared detectors. *Mailing Add:* Sci Applns Inc PO Box 2351 La Jolla CA 92037

REYNOLDS, HARLAN KENDALL, b Olympia, Wash, Aug 2, 26; m 50; c 3. EXPERIMENTAL ATOMIC PHYSICS. *Educ:* Denison Univ, BA, 49; Calif Inst Technol, MS, 51, PhD(physics), 53. *Prof Exp:* From asst prof to prof physics, Univ Houston, 53-68, chmn dept, 60-65, adv basic sci, Univ Prog in Ecuador, 65-66; DEAN DIV ARTS & SCI, STATE UNIV NY COL CORTLAND, 68- *Concurrent Pos:* Consult, Thermonuclear Div, Oak Ridge Nat Lab. *Mem:* AAAS; Am Phys Soc; Am Asn Physics Teachers; Philos Sci Asn. *Res:* Stopping and charge exchange cross sections; sputtering; plasma physics; history and philosophy of science. *Mailing Add:* Div of Arts & Sci State Univ of NY Col, Cortland Cortland NY 13045

REYNOLDS, HAROLD TRUMAN, b Manteca, Calif, Oct 28, 18; m 46; c 4. ENTOMOLOGY. *Educ:* Univ Calif, BS, 41, PhD, 49. *Prof Exp:* From asst entomologist to assoc entomologist, 48-62, chmn dept, 69-74, PROF ENTOM & ENTOMOLOGIST, UNIV CALIF, RIVERSIDE, 62-, HEAD, DIV BIOL CONTROL, 78- *Mem:* AAAS; Entom Soc Am. *Res:* Biology, ecology and pest management of pests affecting field crops, particularly cotton; selective insecticides. *Mailing Add:* Dept Entom Univ Calif Riverside CA 92502

REYNOLDS, HARRY AARON, JR, b Lumberton, NJ, Feb 6, 28; m 59; c 2. VETERINARY PATHOLOGY. *Educ:* Gettysburg Col, AB, 52; Univ Pa, VMD, 56; Univ Ill, Urbana, MS, 63, PhD(vet med sci), 66. *Prof Exp:* Instr vet path, Univ Pa, 56-59; USPHS fel, 60-63, instr, 63-66, ASSOC PROF VET PATH, UNIV ILL, URBANA, 66- *Honors & Awards:* Norden Award, Norden Labs, 70. *Mem:* AAAS; Am Vet Med Asn; Int Acad Path; NY Acad Sci. *Res:* Viral cytopathology; small animal reproduction and diseases of reproductive organs; neoplastic diseases. *Mailing Add:* 36B Vet Med Bldg Univ Ill Urbana IL 61820

REYNOLDS, HARRY LINCOLN, physics, see previous edition

REYNOLDS, HERBERT MCGAUGHEY, b Bryan, Tex, Aug 28, 42; m 67; c 2. PHYSICAL ANTHROPOLOGY, ANTHROPOMETRICS. *Educ:* Southern Methodist Univ, BA, 64, MA, 71, PhD(phys antrhop), 74. *Prof Exp:* Anthropologist, Protection & Survival Lab, Civil Aeromed Inst, Fed Aviation Admin, 69-73, res anthrop, 73; res investr, Univ Mich, 73-74, asst res scientist phys anthrop, Dept Biomed, Hwy Safety Res Inst, 74-77; asst prof, 77-79, ASSOC PROF DEPT BIOMECH & DEPT ANTHROP, MICH STATE UNIV, 79- *Concurrent Pos:* Consult, Biomed Sci Dept, Res Labs, Gen Motors Corp, 75-76, Franklin Inst, Philadelphia, 77-78 & Haworth Inc, 79- *Mem:* Soc Study Human Biol; Human Biol Coun; Am Soc Biomechanics; Am Asn Phys Anthropologist. *Res:* Three-dimensional systems anthropometry; biomechanics; kinematics; human morphology; osteology; mathematical modeling of the human body; human factors. *Mailing Add:* Dept of Biomech Mich State Univ East Lansing MI 48824

REYNOLDS, JACK, b Norman, Okla, Jan 11, 29; m 64; c 2. ELECTRICAL & NUCLEAR ENGINEERING. *Educ:* Univ Okla, BSEE, 56, ME, 58; Univ Lund, PhD(physics), 64. *Prof Exp:* Engr, Radio Corp Am, 56; adv studies scientist, Lockheed Missile Systs Div, 58; instr elec eng, Univ Okla, 56-58, instr & engr comput proj, 59-61, res assoc, Res Inst, 61; consult, Standard Elec A/B, Denmark, 62-63; asst prof elec eng, Univ Okla & res assoc, Res Inst, 64-67, proj dir, 65-67; MEM TECH STAFF, EQUIP RES & DEVELOP LAB, TEX INSTRUMENTS INC, 67- *Concurrent Pos:* NSF res grant, 65-67; vis indust prof, Southern Methodist Univ. *Mem:* Inst Elec & Electronics Engrs. *Res:* Solid state nuclear particle detectors; measurement of beta spectra; investigation of nonlinear effects in semiconductor devices; microwave integrated circuits; solid state microwave devices and components. *Mailing Add:* 13215 Roaring Springs Lane Dallas TX 75240

REYNOLDS, JACK, b Houston, Tex, Sept 27, 22; m 52; c 1. RADIOLOGY. *Educ:* Wesleyan Univ, AB, 48; Columbia Univ, MD, 52; Am Bd Radiol, dipl, 57. *Prof Exp:* Resident physician med, St Luke's Hosp, New York, 52-54, resident physician radiol, 54-57; clin instr, 57-59, from asst prof to assoc prof, 59-67, PROF RADIOL, UNIV TEX HEALTH SCI CTR DALLAS, 67-, VCHMN DEPT, 68- *Concurrent Pos:* Consult, Vet Admin Hosp, Dallas, 60- & Presby Hosp, 66- *Mem:* Fel Am Col Radiol. *Res:* Diagnostic radiology. *Mailing Add:* Dept of Radiol Univ Tex Health Sci Ctr Dallas TX 75235

REYNOLDS, JACQUELINE ANN, b Los Angeles, Calif, Oct 19, 30; c 4. BIOCHEMISTRY. *Educ:* Pac Univ, BS, 51; Univ Wash, PhD(phys chem), 63. *Prof Exp:* Res asst prof microbiol, Wash Univ, 66-69; asst prof, 69-74, assoc prof biochem, 74-80, PROF PHYSIOL, DUKE UNIV, 80- *Mem:* Am Soc Biol Chemists; Biophys Soc; NY Acad Sci. *Res:* Lipid-proteins interactions; structure of serum lipoproteins and biological membranes; physical chemistry of amphiphiles. *Mailing Add:* Dept Physiol Duke Univ Med Ctr Durham NC 27701

REYNOLDS, JAMES BLAIR, b Ypsilanti, Mich, Nov 9, 39; m 60; c 6. FISHERY SCIENCE. *Educ:* Utah State Univ, BS, 61; Iowa State Univ, MS, 63, PhD(fishery biol), 66. *Prof Exp:* Fishery biologist, Great Lakes Fishery Lab, US Fish & Wildlife Serv, 66-72; asst leader, Mo Coop Fishery Unit, US Fish & Wildlife Serv & asst prof, Sch Forestry, Fisheries & Wildlife, Univ Mo-Columbia, 72-78; LEADER & ASSOC PROF, ALASKA COOP FISH RES UNIT, UNIV ALASKA, FAIRBANKS, 78- *Mem:* Am Fisheries Soc; NAm Benthological Soc; Am Inst Fishery Res Biol. *Res:* Fishery mensuration and dynamics, including effects of exploitation; aquatic habitat alteration; biometrics and sampling methodology. *Mailing Add:* Coop Fish Res Unit Univ Alaska 901 Koyukuk Ave S Fairbanks AK 99701

REYNOLDS, JAMES HAROLD, b Ogden, Utah, Feb 18, 45; m 67; c 5. ENVIRONMENTAL ENGINEERING. *Educ:* Utah State Univ, BS, 70, MS, 72, PhD(environ eng), 74. *Prof Exp:* Res engr, Utah Water Res Lab, 73-74; asst prof environ eng, Utah State Univ, 74-80, head div, 78-80; PRIN ENGR, JAMES M MONTGOMERY CONSULT ENGRS INC, 80- *Concurrent Pos:* Consult engr & vpres, Middlebrooks & Assoc, 72-; pres, Intermountain Consults & Planners, 78- *Mem:* Water Pollution Control Fedn; Asn Environ Eng Profs; Govt Refuse Collection & Disposal Asn. *Res:* Water and wastewater treatment; biological kinetics; physical chemical waste treatment lagoons; small wastewater treatment systems toxicity. *Mailing Add:* James M Montgomery Consult Engrs 624 N 300 W Salt Lake City UT 84103

REYNOLDS, JEFFERSON WAYNE, b Elizabethton, Tenn, Sept 11, 26; m 54; c 2. PHYSICAL CHEMISTRY. *Educ:* ETenn State Col, BS, 50; Ohio State Univ, MS, 54. *Prof Exp:* Res chemist, 51-52 & 54-63, SR RES CHEMIST, TENN EASTMAN CO, EASTMAN KODAK CO, 63- *Mem:* Am Chem Soc; fel Am Inst Chemists. *Res:* Surface chemistry--surface area and pore structure; transition elements--preparation of heterogeneous catalysts; aliphatic chemistry--evaluation of catalysts in hydrogenations, oxidations, condensations; measurement of design data; thermodynamics. *Mailing Add:* Tenn Eastman Co PO Box 115 Kingsport TN 37662

REYNOLDS, JOHN C, b Ill, June 1, 35; m 60; c 2. COMPUTER SCIENCES. *Educ:* Purdue Univ, BS, 56; Harvard Univ, AM, 57, PhD(physics), 61. *Prof Exp:* From asst physicist to assoc physicist, appl math div, Argonne Nat Lab, 61-70; PROF COMPUT & INFO SCI, SYRACUSE UNIV, 70- *Concurrent Pos:* Actg asst prof, Stanford Univ, 65-66; prof lectr comt info sci, Univ Chicago, 68; mem working group 2.3 prog methodology, Int Fedn Info Processing, 69-; sr res assoc, Queen Mary Col, Univ London, 70-71; vis res fel, Univ Edinburgh, 76-77; mem working group, Int Fedn Info Processing, 77- *Honors & Awards:* Annual Prog Systs & Lang Paper Award, Asn Comput Mach, 71. *Mem:* Asn Comput Mach. *Res:* Design of computer programming languages; mathematical semantics; programming methodology. *Mailing Add:* Comput & info Sci 313 Link Hall Syracuse Univ Syracuse NY 13210

REYNOLDS, JOHN DICK, b Darby, Pa, June 6, 21; m 48. PLANT EMBRYOLOGY. *Educ:* Temple Univ, BS, 49, MEduc, 51; Univ SC, PhD(biol), 66. *Prof Exp:* Instr biol, Hampden-Sidney Col, 50-51; asst prof, Coker Col, 51-62; instr, Univ SC, 62-65; asst prof, Univ Southern Miss, 65-67; ASSOC PROF BIOL, VA COMMONWEALTH UNIV, 67- *Concurrent Pos:* Instr, Univ SC, Lancaster Campus, 59-62. *Mem:* AAAS; Am Inst Biol Sci; Bot Soc Am; Int Soc Plant Morphol; Phytochem Soc. *Res:* Uses of infrared spectrophotometry in plant taxonomy; studies in cytoplasmic male sterility; callose distribution and function in the plant kingdom. *Mailing Add:* Dept of Biol Va Commonwealth Univ 816 Park Ave Richmond VA 23284

REYNOLDS, JOHN HAMILTON, b Cambridge, Mass, Apr 3, 23; m 75; c 5. PHYSICS. *Educ:* Harvard Univ, AB, 43; Univ Chicago, SM, 48, PhD(physics), 50. *Prof Exp:* Asst, Electro-Acoustic Lab, Harvard Univ, 41-43; assoc physicist, Argonne Nat Lab, 50; from asst prof to assoc prof, 50-61, PROF PHYSICS, UNIV CALIF, BERKELEY, 61- *Concurrent Pos:* Guggenheim fel, Bristol Univ, 56; NSF sr fel, Univ Sao Paulo, 63; Fulbright-Hays res award, Univ Coimbra, Portugal, 71; NSF US-Australia Cooperative Sci awardee, Univ Western Australia, 78. *Honors & Awards:* John Price Wetherill Medal, Franklin Inst, 65; J Lawrence Smith Medal, Nat Acad Sci, 67; Leonard Medal, Meteoritical Soc, 73. *Mem:* Nat Acad Sci; AAAS; fel Am Phys Soc; Geochem Soc; Meteoritical Soc. *Res:* Mass spectrometry; meteoritics; lunar studies; origin and chronology of solar system. *Mailing Add:* Dept Physics Univ Calif Berkeley CA 94720

REYNOLDS, JOHN HORACE, b Darby, Pa, Aug 7, 37; m 63; c 2. AGRONOMY, PLANT PHYSIOLOGY. *Educ:* Univ Md, BS, 59; Univ Wis, MS, 61, PhD(forage crop physiol), 62. *Prof Exp:* Res asst agron, Univ Wis, 59-62; asst prof, 62-69, assoc prof agron, 69-78, PROF PLANT & SOIL SCI, UNIV TENN, KNOXVILLE, 78- *Mem:* Am Soc Agron; Soil Conserv Soc Am; Crop Sci Soc Am. *Res:* Forage crop physiology; forage quality analysis. *Mailing Add:* Dept of Plant & Soil Sci Univ of Tenn Knoxville TN 37996

REYNOLDS, JOHN HUGHES, IV, b Rome, Ga, Sept 25, 40; m 63; c 1. PHYSICAL CHEMISTRY. *Educ:* Shorter Col, Ga, BA, 62; Clemson Univ, MS, 65, PhD(chem), 68. *Prof Exp:* SR RES CHEMIST, R J REYNOLDS INDUSTS, 68- *Concurrent Pos:* Res group leader, R J Reynolds Industs, 76, mgr biobehav res, 80. *Mem:* Sigma Xi; Asn Chemoreception Sci. *Res:* Biobehavioral aspects of tobacco product use. *Mailing Add:* Res Dept R J Reynolds Tobacco Co Winston-Salem NC 27102

REYNOLDS, JOHN KEITH, b London, Ont, Sept 29, 19; m 45; c 3. WILDLIFE MANAGEMENT. *Educ:* Univ Western Ont, BSc, 49, MSc, 50, PhD, 52. *Prof Exp:* Wildlife biologist, Ont Dept Lands & Forests, 52-54, from asst dist forester to dist forester, 54-63, supvr fisheries, 63-64, chief exec off, Prime Minister's Dept, 64-69, secy cabinet, Off of the Prime Minister, 69-71, dep minister, Prime Minister's Dept, 71-72, dep prov secy resources develop, 72-74, dep minister, Ministry Natural Resources, 74-81; CHMN, TORONTO REGION CONSERV AUTHORITY, 81- *Concurrent Pos:* Mem adv comt sci policy, comt coordrs Can coun resource & environ ministers, Can forestry adv coun, fac adv bd, Fac Forestry, Univ Toronto & adv coun, Sch Admin Studies, York Univ; mem bd trustees, Can Nat Sportsmen's Fund; pres, J K Reynolds Consult Inc. *Mem:* Wildlife Soc; Can Can Soc Environ Biologists. *Res:* Life history studies on Canadian birds and mammals; management of fur-bearers and big game; administration of natural resources. *Mailing Add:* 43 Bridlewood Blvd Scarborough ON M1T 1P6 Can

REYNOLDS, JOHN TERRENCE, b Savannah, Ga, Oct 26, 37; m 59; c 4. FLUID MECHANICS, NUCLEAR PHYSICS. *Educ:* Rice Univ, BA, 60; Duke Univ, PhD(physics), 64. *Prof Exp:* PHYSICIST, KNOLLS ATOMIC POWER LAB, GEN ELEC CO, 64- *Mem:* Am Phys Soc. *Res:* Turbulent fluid flow; neutron cross sections. *Mailing Add:* Knolls Atomic Power Lab Schenectady NY 12301

REYNOLDS, JOHN THEODORE, b Boston, Mass, Apr 27, 25; m 48; c 1. BACTERIOLOGY. *Educ:* Boston Col, BS, 51; Univ Mass, MS, 55, PhD(bact), 62. *Prof Exp:* Instr biol, Springfield Col, 52-54; instr bact, Smith Col, 54-56; from asst prof to prof bact, 56-74, PROF MICROBIOL, CLARK UNIV, 74- *Concurrent Pos:* NIH fel marine microbiol, Univ Miami, 63-64; res assoc, Inst Indust & Agr Microbiol, Univ Mass, 65-; Fulbright lectr, Univ Saigon, 66-67; adj prof, Univ Mass, Amherst, 69- *Res:* Aquatic bacteriology; microbiological cellulolytic activity; microbial physiology. *Mailing Add:* Dept of Biol Clark Univ Worcester MA 01610

REYNOLDS, JOHN WESTON, b Portland, Ore, Aug 5, 30; m 54. PEDIATRICS. *Educ:* Reed Col, BA, 51; Univ Ore, MD, 56. *Prof Exp:* From intern to resident, Med Sch, Univ Minn, Minneapolis, 56-59, from instr to prof pediat, 61-77; PROF DEPT PEDIAT, HEALTH SCI CTR, UNIV ORE, 77- *Concurrent Pos:* NIH spec res fel, Med Sch, Univ Minn, Minneapolis, 59-61; NIH career develop award, 64-74. *Mem:* AAAS; Soc Pediat Res; Endocrine Soc; Am Pediat Soc. *Res:* Pediatric endocrinology; metabolism and nutrition; steroid metabolism in infants and children; neonatal medicine. *Mailing Add:* Dept of Pediat Univ of Ore Health Sci Ctr Portland OR 97201

REYNOLDS, JOHN Z, b Kansas City, Kans, July 31, 40; m 63; c 2. TECHNICAL MANAGEMENT. *Educ:* Kans State Univ, BS, 62; Univ Mich, MS & MPh 64, PhD(environ health), 66. *Prof Exp:* Consult, Resource Develop, James Calvert Consult Engr, 67; engr, Indust Conserv, Commonwealth Assoc Inc, 67-69; DIR STAFF, ENVIRON/CORP PLANNING, CONSUMERS POWER CO, 69- *Concurrent Pos:* Tech adv, Edison Elec Inst, 70-80; mem, Lake Michigan Cooling Water Studies Panel, 73-75, Non-Radiation Environ Effects Comt, Nat Standards Inst, 75, Michigan Sea Grant External Adv Comt, 76; instr, Jackson Community Col, 77; proj mgr, Electric Power Res Inst, 78-79. *Mem:* AAAS. *Res:* Environmental effects of pumped storage hydroelectric development, cooling systems and water resource development. *Mailing Add:* Consumers Power Co 212 W Michigan Ave Jackson MI 49201

REYNOLDS, JOSEPH, b New York, NY, May 19, 35; m 73; c 2. CHEMICAL ENGINEERING, AIR POLLUTION CONTROL EQUIPMENT. *Educ:* Cath Univ Am, BA, 57; Rensselaer Polytech Inst, PhD(chem eng), 64. *Prof Exp:* From asst prof to assoc prof, 64-77, PROF CHEM ENG & CHMN DEPT, MANHATTAN COL, 77- *Concurrent Pos:* Consult, Argonne Nat Lab & private indust; chmn, Nat Conf Energy & Environ. *Mem:* Am Inst Chem Engrs; Air Pollution Control Asn; Am Soc Eng Educ. *Res:* Modelling of air pollution control equipment; electrostatic precipitators; filter bag houses; modelling and design of heat recovery equipment. *Mailing Add:* Manhattan Col Manhattan Col Pkwy Riverdale NY 10471

REYNOLDS, JOSEPH MELVIN, b Woodlawn, Tenn, June 16, 24; m 50; c 3. PHYSICS. *Educ:* Vanderbilt Univ, BA, 46; Yale Univ, MS, 47, PhD(physics), 50. *Prof Exp:* Instr physics, Conn Col, 46-47; from asst prof to prof, 50-62, head, Dept Physics & Astron, 62-65, vpres grad studies & res, 65-68, vpres instr & res, 68-81, actg vpres acad affairs, 66-68, BOYD PROF PHYSICS, LA STATE UNIV, BATON ROUGE, 82-, VPRES ACAD AFFAIRS, 81- *Concurrent Pos:* Guggenheim fel, Kamerlingh Onnes Lab, Univ Leiden, 58-59; mem nat sci bd, Nat Sci Found, 66-78; mem navig studies bd, Nat Acad Sci, 74-, chmn, Panel Advan Navig Systs, 78- *Mem:* Am Phys Soc; AAAS; Sigma Xi; Am Inst Aeronaut & Astronaut. *Res:* Low temperature physics; liquid helium; superconductivity in pure metals and alloys; gravitational radiation; magnetic properties of metals; transport effects and nuclear magnetic resonance in metals; gravitational physics. *Mailing Add:* Box 16070 La State Univ Baton Rouge LA 70893

REYNOLDS, JOSHUA PAUL, b High Falls, NC, Oct 17, 06; m 37; c 2. ZOOLOGY. *Educ:* Guilford Col, BS, 28; Univ NC, MS, 29; Johns Hopkins Univ, PhD(zool), 34. *Prof Exp:* Instr biol, Guilford Col, 29-31; actg asst prof zool, Univ NC, 32-33; from asst prof to prof biol, Birmingham-Southern Col, 34-49; prof zool, Fla State Univ, 49-64, from asst dean to dean col arts & sci, 51-64; prof biol & dean fac, 64-71, vchancellor acad affairs, 71, ADJ

PROF BIOL, UNIV NC, WILMINGTON, 71- *Concurrent Pos:* Gen Educ Bd grants, Univ Pa, 40-41 & 48-49. *Mem:* Fel AAAS; Am Soc Zoologists; Genetics Soc Am. *Res:* Genetics and cytology of Sciara; human genetics; chromosome behavior. *Mailing Add:* 1813 Azalea Dr Wilmington NC 28403

REYNOLDS, LARRY OWEN, b Norfolk, Va, Dec, 11, 40. ELECTROMAGNETICS, RADIATIVE TRANSPORT. *Educ:* Univ Wash, BSEE, 69, MSEE, 70, PhD(elec eng), 75. *Prof Exp:* Res asst electromagnetics, Ctr Bioeng, 69-70, res assoc, 70-75, sr NIH fel, 75-76, fac res assoc, Dept Elec Eng, 76-79, RES ASST PROF, DEPT NUCLEAR ENG, UNIV WASH, 79-, ADJ RES ASST PROF, CTR BIOENG, 81- *Concurrent Pos:* Consult scientist, Puget Sound Blood Ctr, Seattle, 76-77; Math Sci NW, Bellevue, 78-; prin investr, Dept Elec Eng, Univ Wash, 76-79, Dept Nuclear Eng, 78-81, Ctr Bioeng, 81-83. *Mem:* Sigma Xi; Optical Soc Am; Soc Biomat. *Res:* Elecromagnetic wave propagation with applications in the area of inverse and direct remote calculational techniques for characterizing dense scattering media such as found in the ocean, atmosphere and biological tissue; inverse and direct remote calculational techniques for characterizing dense scattering media such as found in the ocean, atmosphere and biological tissue. *Mailing Add:* Dept Nuclear Eng Univ Wash Seattle WA 98195

REYNOLDS, LESLIE BOUSH, JR, b Lakeland, Fla, Aug 16, 23; m 47; c 2. PHYSIOLOGY, CLINICAL MEDICINE. *Educ:* Randolph-Macon Col, BS, 49; Ga Inst Technol, MS, 51; Univ SC, PhD(physiol), 61; Northwestern Univ, MD, 66. *Prof Exp:* Engr textile fibers dept, Dacron Res Div, E I du Pont de Nemours & Co, 51-54, group leader anal res & process control, 54-58; asst physiol, Med Col SC, 58-61; asst prof, Med Sch, Northwestern Univ, Chicago, 61-64, res assoc med, 64-67; actg chmn dept physiol, Univ Tenn Med Units, Memphis, 68-69, assoc prof physiol & med, 67-76; staff mem, Al-Med Pract Corp, Dresden, Tenn, 76-77; PROF PHYSIOL & FAMILY PRACT, QUILLEN-DISHNER COL MED, EAST TENN STATE UNIV, JOHNSON CITY, 77-, ASST DEAN & DIR MED EDUC, 77- *Concurrent Pos:* Dir, Memphis Emphysema Clin, 70-72; pres, Asseverator Enterprises, Inc. *Mem:* Aerospace Med Asn; Am Physiol Soc; Am Chem Soc; Am Thoracic Soc; Am Col Chest Physicians. *Res:* Lung mechanics and reflexes; medical education; chest disease. *Mailing Add:* Dept of Physiol Col of Med Johnson City TN 37601

REYNOLDS, MARION RUDOLPH, JR, b Salem, Va, Nov 1, 45; m 67; c 2. MATHEMATICAL STATISTICS. *Educ:* Va Polytech Inst & State Univ, BS, 68; Stanford Univ, MS, 71, PhD(oper res), 72. *Prof Exp:* Statistician, Hercules, Inc, 68; asst prof, 72-81, ASSOC PROF STATIST & FORESTRY, VA POLYTECH INST & STATE UNIV, 81- *Mem:* Am Statist Asn; Inst Math Statist; Opers Res Soc Am. *Res:* Sequential analysis; nonparametric statistics; quality control; validation of simulation models; regression with heteroscedastic errors; applications of statistics and operations research to forestry. *Mailing Add:* Dept Statist Va Polytech Inst Blacksburg VA 24061

REYNOLDS, MARJORIE LAVERS, b Collingwood, Ont, Jan 10, 31; m 63; c 2. NUTRITION. *Educ:* Univ Toronto, BA, 53; Univ Minn, MS, 57; Univ Wis, PhD(nutrit, biochem), 64. *Prof Exp:* Res dietitian, Mayo Clinic, 57-59 & Cleveland Metrop Gen Hosp, 59-60; res asst nutrit, Univ Wis, 60-63; res assoc, Univ Tenn, 63-66; instr nutrit, Ft Sanders Hosp Sch Nursing, 67-76, reneal dietitian, Ft Sanders Kidney Ctr, 78-79. *Mem:* Am Dietetic Asn. *Res:* Human nutrition; obesity; gastric secretion. *Mailing Add:* 7112 Stockton Dr Knoxville TN 37919

REYNOLDS, NANCY MILLER, see Goorey, Nancy Reynolds

REYNOLDS, ORLAND BRUCE, b Mountain Home, Idaho, Feb 15, 22; m 54; c 1. BIOCHEMISTRY. *Educ:* Idaho State Col, BS, 44; Boston Univ, AM, 55, PhD(biochem), 60. *Prof Exp:* Fel biol, Harvard Univ, 60-61; instr, Sch Med, Boston Univ, 61-62; asst prof, Middlebury Col, 62-68; asst prof, 68-71, ASSOC PROF BIOL, NORTHERN MICH UNIV, 71- *Mem:* AAAS; Am Chem Soc. *Res:* Comparative physiology; vision. *Mailing Add:* Dept of Biol Northern Mich Univ Marquette MI 49855

REYNOLDS, ORR ESREY, b Baltimore, Md, Mar 3, 20; m 42, 71; c 2. PHYSIOLOGY. *Educ:* Univ Md, BS, 41, MS, 43, PhD(physiol), 46. *Prof Exp:* Asst physiologist, NIH, Md, 43-44; physiologist, Marine Corps Air Sta, Va, 44-45; physiologist, Aviation Br, Res Div, Bur Med, US Dept Navy, 45-46, dir biol sci div, Off Naval Res, 47-57; dir off sci, US Dept Defense, 57-62; dir biosci prog, NASA, 62-70; educ officer, 70-72, EXEC SECY-TREAS, AM PHYSIOL SOC, BETHESDA, MD, 72- *Concurrent Pos:* Exec dir surv physiol, Am Physiol Soc, 52-53, exec secy-treas, Soc, 72-; lectr, Univ Md, 47-51. *Mem:* AAAS; Am Physiol Soc; Aerospace Med Asn; Am Soc Zoologists; Am Inst Biol Sci. *Res:* Respiratory physiology; physiology of pain perception. *Mailing Add:* 6828 Granby St Kenwood Park Bethesda MD 20034

REYNOLDS, PAUL JOSEPH, b Milan, Ind, Apr 28, 30; m 53. ANIMAL NUTRITION, BIOCHEMISTRY. *Educ:* Purdue Univ, BS, 52, MS, 54; Cornell Univ, PhD(animal nutrit), 67. *Prof Exp:* RES ANIMAL SCIENTIST, RUMINANT NUTRIT LAB, NUTRIT INST, SCI & EDUC ADMIN-AGR RES, USDA, 56-58, 62- *Mem:* Am Soc Animal Sci; Am Dairy Sci Asn; Am Chem Soc. *Res:* Ruminant nutrition and intermediary metabolism; effects of agricultural chemicals on livestock; chemical defleecing of sheep. *Mailing Add:* Bldg 200 USDA Beltsville MD 20705

REYNOLDS, PETER HERBERT, b Toronto, Ont, Sept 28, 40; m 67; c 2. GEOCHRONOLOGY, GEOPHYSICS. *Educ:* Univ Toronto, BSc, 63; Univ BC, PhD(geochronology), 67. *Prof Exp:* Nat Res Coun Can fel, Australian Nat Univ, 68-69; asst prof physics, 69-76, ASSOC PROF PHYSICS & GEOL, DALHOUSIE UNIV, 76- *Mem:* Can Geophys Union; Geol Asn Can. *Res:* Potassium-argon geochronology; oxygen isotope abundance patterns. *Mailing Add:* 36 Inverness Ave Halifax NS B3P 1X7 Can

REYNOLDS, PETER JAMES, b New York, NY, Nov 19, 49. STATISTICAL PHYSICS, PHASE TRANSITIONS. *Educ:* Univ Calif, Berkeley, AB, 71; Mass Inst Technol, PhD(physics), 79. *Prof Exp:* RES ASSOC-INSTR PHYSICS, BOSTON UNIV, 79-, ASST RES PROF, 79- *Concurrent Pos:* Vis scientist, Nat Res Comput Chem, Lawrence Berkeley Labs, 80-81. *Mem:* Am Phys Soc; Sigma Xi; NY Acad Sci. *Res:* Phase transitions in disordered systems, particularly the critical properties of generalized percolation models near their connectivity threshold, and of polymeric systems, especially by renormalization group and Monte Carlo simulation techniques; quantum Monte Carlo studies of molecules. *Mailing Add:* Dept of Physics 111 Cummington St Boston MA 02215

REYNOLDS, RAY THOMAS, b Lexington, Ky, Sept 2, 33; m 62; c 2. PLANETARY SCIENCES. *Educ:* Univ Ky, BS, 54, MS, 60. *Prof Exp:* Proj scientist, Am Geog Soc, Thule, Greenland, 60-61; res scientist, Theoret Studies Br, Space Div, 62-70, chief, 70-79, RES SCIENTIST, THEORET & PLANETARY STUDIES BR, SPACE SCI DIV, AMES RES CTR, NASA, 79- *Honors & Awards:* Newcomb Cleveland Award, AAAS, 79. *Mem:* AAAS; Am Astron Soc; Am Geophys Union; Meteoritical Soc; Am Inst Aeronaut & Astronaut. *Res:* Theoretical studies of the origin, evolution and present state of the solar system with emphasis upon the composition, structure and thermal history of the planets and their satellites. *Mailing Add:* Theoret Studies Br Space Sci Div NASA Ames Res Ctr Moffett Field CA 94035

REYNOLDS, RICHARD ALAN, b Los Angeles, Calif, Dec 14, 38; m 63; c 2. MATERIALS SCIENCE, SOLID STATE PHYSICS. *Educ:* Stanford Univ, BSc, 60, MSc, 63, PhD(mat sci), 66; Univ Sheffield, MSc, 61. *Prof Exp:* Mem tech staff mat physics, Cent Res Labs, Tex Instruments, Inc, 65-77; DEP DIR, DEFENSE SCI OFF, DEFENCE ADVAN RES PROJ AGENCY, 75- *Mem:* Inst Elec & Electronics Engrs Electrochem Soc; Infrared Info Asn; Sigma Xi. *Res:* Electron transport in semiconductors; photoconductive processes in infrared detector materials; materials preparation; processing of semiconductors; compound semiconductors; display technology; high temperature mechanical properties of metals. *Mailing Add:* Mat Sci Off 1400 Wilson Blvd Arlington VA 22209

REYNOLDS, RICHARD CLYDE, b Saugerties, NY, Sept 2, 29; m 54; c 3. MEDICAL EDUCATION. *Educ:* Rutgers Univ, New Brunswick, BS, 49; Johns Hopkins Univ, MD, 53. *Prof Exp:* From intern to resident med, Johns Hopkins Hosp, 53-55, resident, 57-58, fel med, 58-59; pvt pract, 59-68; assoc prof med, 68-71, asst dean community health, 71-73, prof community health & family med & chmn dept, Col Med, Univ Fla, 71-78; DEAN & PROF MED, RUTGERS MED SCH, 78- *Mem:* Am Col Physicians; AMA; Am Acad Family Physicians. *Res:* Rural health; problems of health care delivery; evaluation of medical education. *Mailing Add:* Col of Med & Dent NJ Univ Heights Piscataway NJ 08854

REYNOLDS, RICHARD JOHNSON, b Salt Lake City, Utah, June 6, 25; m 50; c 3. ORGANIC CHEMISTRY. *Educ:* Univ Utah, AB, 48, PhD(chem), 51. *Prof Exp:* Chemist, Jackson Lab, E I du Pont de Nemours & Co, 51-55; chemist, Emeryville Res Ctr, Shell Develop Co, 55-58, supvr, 58-61, tech asst, Pres Off, 61-63, supvr plastics, Plastics & Resins Div, Shell Chem Co, 63-65, dept head elastomer res, Emeryville Res Ctr, 65, dir plastics & resins res, 65-67, mgr purchasing chem & process mat, Shell Oil Co, 69-70 & Shell Int Petrol Co, Ltd, London, 70-72, mgr vinyl chloride, Shell Chem Co, 72-74, mgr chem intermediates, 74-81. *Mem:* Am Chem Soc. *Res:* Polymer chemistry; elastomers, plastics, resins and related chemicals. *Mailing Add:* 862 Augusta Dr Houston TX 77057

REYNOLDS, ROBERT COLTART, JR, b Scranton, Pa, Oct 4, 27; m 50; c 3. PETROLOGY, GEOCHEMISTRY. *Educ:* Lafayette Col, BA, 51; Wash Univ, PhD(geol), 55. *Prof Exp:* Sr res engr, Res Ctr, Pan-Am Petrol Corp, 55-60; from asst prof to assoc prof, 60-69, PROF GEOL, DARTMOUTH COL, 69- *Concurrent Pos:* Instr, Benedictine Heights Col, 56-60; expert, US Army Cold Regions Res & Eng Lab, 64-; consult, Oak Ridge Nat Lab, 66. *Mem:* Geochem Soc; fel Geol Soc Am; fel Mineral Soc Am; Clay Minerals Soc. *Res:* Rates and types of chemical weathering and aqueous transport in extreme environments; clay mineralogy and ion exchange processes on clays; computer modeling of the chemistry of aquatic systems. *Mailing Add:* Dept of Earth Sci Dartmouth Col Hanover NH 03755

REYNOLDS, ROBERT DAVID, b Mansfield, Ohio, June 25, 43; m 64; c 2. NUTIRITION, BIOLOGICAL CHEMISTRY. *Educ:* Ohio State Univ, Columbus, BS, 65; Univ Wis-Madison, PhD(cancer res), 71. *Prof Exp:* Res fel cancer res, Biochem Inst, Univ Freiburg, WGer, 71-72; asst mem cancer res, Fred Hutchinson Cancer Res Ctr, Seattle, 72-73; res assoc vitamin D metabol, Dept Biochem, Univ Wis, 73-75; RES CHEMIST VITAMIN B6 NUTRIT, VITAMIN & MINERAL NUTRIT LAB, NUTRIT INST, USDA, 75- *Concurrent Pos:* Fel, Damon Runyon Mem Fund for Cancer Res, 71-72; adj prof, Dept Foods, Nutrition & Inst Admin, Univ Md, 80- *Mem:* AAAS; Am Inst Nutrit; Am Asn Cancer Res. *Res:* Regulation of metabolism of specific mammalian proteins by vitamin cofactors during various stages of vitamin nutrition; nutritional requirements of vitamin B-6. *Mailing Add:* Vitamin & Mineral Nutrit Lab Nutrit Inst Agr Res Serv USDA Beltsville MD 20705

REYNOLDS, ROBERT EUGENE, b Dallas, Tex, Nov 25, 34; m 56, 70; c 3. PHYSICS. *Educ:* Univ Tex, BA(math) & BS(physics), 56, MA, 58, PhD(physics), 61. *Prof Exp:* From asst prof to assoc prof, 63-79, PROF PHYSICS, REED COL, 79- *Mem:* Am Phys Soc; Am Asn Physics Teachers. *Res:* Theoretical physics. *Mailing Add:* Dept of Physics Reed Col Portland OR 97202

REYNOLDS, ROBERT N, b Troy, NY, Feb 26, 22; m 51; c 3. ANESTHESIOLOGY. *Educ:* Yale Univ, BS, 44; Albany Med Col, MD, 46. *Prof Exp:* Instr surg anesthesia, 52-54, from asst prof to assoc prof anesthesia, 54-66, PROF ANESTHESIA, SCH MED, TUFTS UNIV, 66- *Concurrent Pos:* Asst anesthesiol, New Eng Med Ctr Hosp, Boston, Mass, 51-53, asst anesthetist, 54-55, anesthetist, 55-67, sr anesthetist, 67-; consult pediat anesthesiol, US Naval Hosp, Chelsea, Mass, 68- *Mem:* AMA; Am Soc Anesthesiol; Am Acad Pediat; Am Soc Pharmacol & Exp Therapeut; Asn Univ Anesthetists. *Res:* Respiratory physiology in infants; pediatric anesthesia. *Mailing Add:* New Eng Med Ctr Hosps 171 Harrison Ave Boston MA 02111

REYNOLDS, ROBERT WARE, b Kingsport, Tenn, Sept 21, 42; m 65; c 2. SOLID STATE PHYSICS. *Educ:* Davidson Col, BS, 64; Vanderbilt Univ, PhD(physics), 69. *Prof Exp:* Res scientist, Advan Technol Ctr, Inc, 69-76; MEM TECH STAFF, GEN RES CORP, 76- *Mem:* Am Phys Soc; Sigma Xi. *Res:* Military systems analysis; high energy laser effects and propagation modeling; electron paramagnetic resonance spectroscopy; infrared detection. *Mailing Add:* Gen Res Corp 307 Wynn Dr Huntsville AL 35805

REYNOLDS, ROBERT WILLIAMS, b Buffalo, NY, Feb 9, 27; m 51; c 2. PHYSIOLOGY, PSYCHOLOGY. *Educ:* Cornell Univ, AB, 49; Univ Buffalo, MA, 50, PhD(psychol), 57. *Prof Exp:* Res chemist, E I du Pont de Nemours & Co, 52-53; asst psychol, Univ Buffalo, 54-55; from instr to assoc prof psychol, 56-72, chmn dept, 73-76, PROF PSYCHOL, UNIV CALIF, SANTA BARBARA, 72- *Concurrent Pos:* Fel, Dept Physiol & Biophys, Univ Wash, 61-62. *Mem:* AAAS; Am Physiol Soc; Psychonomic Soc. *Res:* Influence of drugs on the nervous system and motivated behavior; nervous system and problems of learning and consciousness; physiological basis of motivations, emotions and attention. *Mailing Add:* Dept of Psychol Univ of Calif Santa Barbara CA 93106

REYNOLDS, ROGER SMITH, b Las Vegas, Nev, Oct 28, 43; m 65; c 2. NUCLEAR ENGINEERING. *Educ:* Univ Nev, Reno, BS, 65; Kans State Univ, MS, 69, PhD(nuclear eng), 71. *Prof Exp:* Res asst struct shielding res, Kans State Univ, 67-69, exp supvr, 69-70, proj dir, 70-71; ASST PROF NUCLEAR ENG, MISS STATE UNIV, 71- *Mem:* Am Nuclear Soc. *Res:* Radiation detection and measurement; neutron activation analysis; dosimetry; shielding. *Mailing Add:* Dept of Nuclear Eng Miss State Univ Mississippi State MS 39762

REYNOLDS, ROLLAND, b Pomona, Calif, Feb 18, 25; m 46; c 1. PATHOLOGY. *Educ:* Southern Methodist Univ, BA, 49; Univ Tex, MD, 56; Am Bd Path, cert path anat & clin path. *Prof Exp:* Intern, Dallas Vet Admin Hosp, 56; fel path, 57-61, from asst prof to assoc prof, 61-70, PROF PATH, UNIV TEX HEALTH SCI CTR DALLAS, 70- *Concurrent Pos:* Resident, Parkland Mem Hosp, 57-61, pathologist & jr attend staff, 61-; dir labs chest div, Woodlawn Hosp, 62-74. *Mem:* Am Thoracic Soc; Am Soc Microbiol; Am Soc Cell Biol; Am Soc Clin Path; Electron Micros Soc. *Res:* Experimental pathology of nucleus and nucleolus in experimental carcinogenesis and inhibition of nucleic acid synthesis; experimental pulmonary disease. *Mailing Add:* Dept of Path Univ Tex Health Sci Ctr Dallas TX 75235

REYNOLDS, RONALD J, b Chicago Heights, Ill, May 17, 43; m 66; c 2. SPACE PHYSICS, ASTRONOMY. *Educ:* Univ Ill-Champaign, BS, 65; Univ Wis-Madison, MS, 67, PhD(physics), 71. *Prof Exp:* Res assoc, Nat Acad Sci-Nat Res Coun, Goddard Space Ctr, NASA, 71-73; res assoc & lectr physics, 73-76, asst scientist, 76-81, ASSOC SCIENTIST, DEPT PHYSICS, UNIV WIS-MADISON, 81- *Mem:* Am Astron Soc; Am Inst Physics; Int Astron Union. *Res:* Detection and spectroscopic analysis of faint emission lines from the interstellar medium and the earth's upper atmosphere. *Mailing Add:* Dept of Physics Univ of Wis Madison WI 53706

REYNOLDS, ROSALIE DEAN (SIBERT), b Jacksonville, Ill, Mar 8, 26; m 48. ORGANIC CHEMISTRY. *Educ:* Ill Col, AB, 47; Univ Wyo, MS, 50, PhD(org chem), 53. *Prof Exp:* Instr chem, Univ Wyo, 52; res assoc, Univ Colo, 53-54; lectr & res assoc, Univ Southern Calif, 54-55; asst prof, Univ Wyo, 55-60; from assoc prof to prof chem, Northern Ill Univ, 60-81. *Concurrent Pos:* Consult, Acad Press, 73- *Mem:* Am Chem Soc; Royal Soc Chem. *Res:* Theoretical and synthetic organic chemistry. *Mailing Add:* 1852 Perry Ct Sycamore IL 60178

REYNOLDS, STEPHEN EDWARD, b Decatur, Ill, Dec 11, 16; m 38; c 1. MECHANICAL ENGINEERING. *Educ:* Univ NMex, BS, 39. *Hon Degrees:* HDL, NMex State Univ, 77. *Prof Exp:* From apprentice engr to process engr, Phillips Petrol Co, Okla, 39-42; asst prof mech eng, Univ NMex, 42-43 & 46; proj supvr, Thunderstorm Res Prog, NMex Inst Mining & Technol, 46-55; STATE ENGR, N MEX, 55- *Concurrent Pos:* Consult, President's Adv Comt Weather Modification, 54-57; mem adv panel weather modification, NSF, 60-63; mem, President's Water Pollution Control Adv Bd, 67-70 & NMex Water Qual Control Comn, 67-; mem comt water qual policy, Nat Acad Sci, 73-; mem comt water resources, Natural Resources Coun, 75- *Mem:* AAAS; Am Phys Soc; Am Meteorol Soc; Sigma Xi. *Res:* Atmospheric electricity; cloud physics; properties of water; water resources development and management. *Mailing Add:* 614 E Alameda Santa Fe NM 87501

REYNOLDS, TELFER BARKLEY, b Regina, Sask, July 30, 21; nat US; m 55; c 2. INTERNAL MEDICINE. *Educ:* Univ Calif, Los Angeles, AB, 41; Univ Southern Calif, MD, 45; Am Bd Internal Med, dipl, 53. *Prof Exp:* Chief resident physician, Los Angeles County Gen Hosp, 50-51; Giannini res fel med, Hammersmith Hosp, London, Eng, 52; res fel, 53, from asst prof to assoc prof, 53-60, PROF MED, SCH MED, UNIV SOUTHERN CALIF, 60- *Mem:* Am Soc Clin Invest; Asn Am Physicians; fel Am Col Physicians. *Res:* Liver and kidney diseases; calcium and phosphate metabolism. *Mailing Add:* Dept of Internal Med Sch of Med Univ of Southern Calif Los Angeles CA 90033

REYNOLDS, THOMAS DE WITT, b Detroit, Mich, July 25, 29; m 51; c 3. PSYCHIATRY. *Educ:* Univ Chicago, BA, 47, MD, 55. *Prof Exp:* Intern med, George Washington Univ Hosp, 55-56; resident psychiat, 56-57 & 59-61, asst dir behav studies, 61-70, supvry med officer psychiat res, W A White Serv, 70-71, chief, 71-72, CLIN DIR, W A WHITE SERV, ST ELIZABETHS

HOSP, WASHINGTON, DC, 72- *Concurrent Pos:* Assoc prof, George Washington Univ, 67- *Res:* Mathematical approaches to behavioral time series; stability characteristics of such time series in schizophrenic and other types of psychiatric patients. *Mailing Add:* W A White Serv St Elizabeths Hosp Washington DC 20032

REYNOLDS, THOMAS GROVER, III, b Richmond, Va, Aug 31, 42; m 62; c 2. MATERIALS SCIENCE, INORGANIC CHEMISTRY. *Educ:* Univ Va, BS, 64, MS, 67; Brown Univ, PhD(mat sci), 74. *Prof Exp:* Mem tech staff mat & new prod, Tex Instrument, 66-73; MGR CORP RES & ENG MAT & NEW PROD, FERROXCUBE DIV, AMPEREX ELECTRONIC CORP, 73- *Mem:* Fel Am Ceramic Soc; Sigma Xi. *Res:* Oxide chemistry; ceramics; single crystal growth; electrical and magnetic properties of materials; ferrites; piezoelectrics. *Mailing Add:* Ferroxcube Div 5083 Kings Hwy Saugerties NY 12477

REYNOLDS, TOM DAVIDSON, b Gatesville, Tex, Apr 2, 29; m 54; c 2. ENVIRONMENTAL ENGINEERING. *Educ:* Tex A&M Univ, BSCE, 50; Univ Tex, MSSE, 61, PhD(civil eng), 63. *Prof Exp:* Proj engr, Lockwood, Andrews & Newnan, Consult Engrs, 50-51 & 53-59; asst prof civil eng, Univ Tex, 64-65; from asst prof to assoc prof, 65-77, PROF CIVIL ENG, TEX A&M UNIV, 77- *Mem:* Am Soc Civil Engrs; Am Water Works Asn; Water Pollution Control Fedn. *Res:* Investigations concerning water and waste treatment, particularly industrial waste treatment using biological processes. *Mailing Add:* Dept of Civil Eng Tex A&M Univ College Station TX 77840

REYNOLDS, VERNON H, b Oak Park, Ill, Dec 31, 26; m; c 2. SURGERY, ONCOLOGY. *Educ:* Vanderbilt Univ, BA, 52, MD, 55. *Prof Exp:* Res assoc microbiol & surg, 60-61, asst prof, 62-69, ASSOC PROF SURG, SCH MED, VANDERBILT UNIV, 69- *Concurrent Pos:* Intern & resident surg, Peter Bent Brigham Hosp, Boston, 55-62; NIH fel exp path, 57-58; Arthur Tracy Cabot teaching fel surg, Harvard Med Sch, 61-62; Am Cancer Soc adv clin fel, 62-65; Markle scholar med sci, 62- *Mem:* Am Col Surgeons. *Res:* Carbohydrate chemistry; tumor metabolism; cancer chemotherapy. *Mailing Add:* Dept of Surg Vanderbilt Univ Med Sch Nashville TN 37232

REYNOLDS, WARREN DUDLEY, analytical chemistry, see previous edition

REYNOLDS, WARREN LIND, b Gull Lake, Sask, Nov 29, 20; m 46; c 3. INORGANIC CHEMISTRY. *Educ:* Univ BC, BA, 49, MA, 50; Univ Minn, PhD, 55. *Prof Exp:* Asst, 52-54, lectr anal chem, 54-55, lectr inorg chem, 55-56, from asst prof to assoc prof, 56-67, PROF INORG CHEM, UNIV MINN, MINNEAPOLIS, 67- *Concurrent Pos:* Fulbright-Hays res award, 72-73. *Mem:* Am Chem Soc; Am Phys Soc; Royal Soc Chem. *Res:* Kinetics of electron-transfer and substitution reactions; solvation numbers, labilities and contact shifts of metal ions in non-aqueous solvents; bonding in inorganic species. *Mailing Add:* Dept of Chem Univ of Minn Minneapolis MN 55455

REYNOLDS, WILLIAM CRAIG, b Berkeley, Calif, Mar 16, 33; m 53; c 3. MECHANICAL ENGINEERING. *Educ:* Stanford Univ, BS, 54, MS, 55, PhD(mech eng), 57. *Prof Exp:* Aeronaut res scientist, Ames Lab, Nat Adv Comt Aeronaut, 54; from asst prof to assoc prof, 57-66, PROF MECH ENG, STANFORD UNIV, 66-, CHMN DEPT, 72- *Concurrent Pos:* Nuclear engr, Aerojet-Gen Nucleonics Div, Gen Tire & Rubber Co, 57; NSF sr fel, Nat Phys Lab, UK, 64-65; vis prof, Pa State Univ, 72. *Honors & Awards:* G Edwin Burks Award, Am Soc Eng Educ, 72. *Mem:* Am Soc Mech Engrs; Am Phys Soc. *Res:* Fluid mechanics; heat transfer; thermodynamics; applied mathematics. *Mailing Add:* Dept of Mech Eng Stanford Univ Stanford CA 94305

REYNOLDS, WILLIAM FRANCIS, b Boston, Mass, Jan 31, 30; m 62; c 2. ALGEBRA. *Educ:* Col of the Holy Cross, AB, 50; Harvard Univ, AM, 51, PhD(math), 54. *Prof Exp:* Res fel math, Harvard Univ, 54-55; C L E Moore instr, Mass Inst Technol, 55-57; from asst prof to prof, 57-70, WALKER PROF MATH, TUFTS UNIV, 70- *Concurrent Pos:* Instr, Col of the Holy Cross, 54-55. *Mem:* AAAS; Am Math Soc; Math Asn Am. *Res:* Representation theory of finite groups, especially modular and projective representations with applications to structure of groups. *Mailing Add:* 3 Preble Gardens Rd Belmont MA 02178

REYNOLDS, WILLIAM ROGER, b Chicago, Ill, Dec 27, 29; m 56; c 5. ZEOLITE PETROLOGY. *Educ:* Univ Wis, BS, 58; Fla State Univ, MS, 62, PhD(geol), 66. *Prof Exp:* Sr geologist, Pan Am Petrol Corp, 66-68; asst prof, 68-73, ASSOC PROF GEOL, UNIV MISS, 73- *Mem:* Soc Econ Paleontologists & Mineralogists; Nat Asn Geol Teachers; Sigma Xi; Mineral Soc Am; Clay Minerals Soc. *Res:* Stratigraphy; clay mineralogy; sedimentation. *Mailing Add:* Dept Geol & Geol Eng Univ Miss University MS 38677

REYNOLDS, WILLIAM WALLACE, biology, see previous edition

REYNOLDS, WILLIAM WALTER, b Pasadena, Calif, Jan 29, 25; m 53; c 3. PHYSICAL CHEMISTRY. *Educ:* Univ Calif, BS, 48. *Prof Exp:* Res chemist, Shell Oil Co, 48-55, group leader, 55-60, asst chief res chemist, 60-63, spec analyst, 63-65, mgr prod planning, Petrochem Div, Shell Chem Co, 65-67, mgr mkt res, 67-68, mgr econ coord, Chem Econ Dept, 68-75, mgr chem prod econ, 75-79, mgr chem stategic studies, 79-81, ECONOMICS CONSULT, PROD ECON DEPT, SHELL OIL CO, 81- *Mem:* Am Chem Soc; Chem Mkt Res Asn. *Res:* Petroleum solvents; surface coatings technology; polymer solutions; antioxidants; high temperature fluids; wear of internal combustion engines; petroleum derived additives; petrochemicals; market planning and decision theory; micro-economics; organizational effectiveness. *Mailing Add:* Prod Econ Dept Shell Oil Co One Shell Plaza Houston TX 77002

REYNOLDS, WYNETKA ANN KING, b Coffeyville, Kans, Nov 3, 37; m 58; c 2. EMBRYOLOGY. *Educ:* Kans State Teachers Col, BS, 58; Univ Iowa, MS, 60, PhD(zool), 62. *Prof Exp:* Asst prof biol, Ball State Univ, 62-65; from asst prof to prof anat, Univ Ill Med Ctr, 65-79, res prof obstet & gynec, 73-79, assoc vchancellor res & dean, Grad Col, 77-79; PROF ANAT, OBSTET & GYNEC & PROVOST, OHIO STATE UNIV, 79- *Concurrent Pos:* Mem biol bd, Grad Record Exam, Am Inst Biol Sci; mem comt nutrit mother & presch children, Nat Acad Sci; mem, Primate Adv Bd, Res Resources, NIH. *Honors & Awards:* Prize Award, Cent Asn Obstet & Gynec, 68. *Mem:* Am Asn Anat; Am Soc Zoologists; Soc Develop Biol; Soc Gynec Invest; Endocrine Soc. *Res:* Transplantation of endocrine pancreas; calcium metabolism in pregnancy; toxicity of methylmercury for fetus and neonate; nutrition during development of fetus. *Mailing Add:* Off Acad Affairs Ohio State Univ 203 Admin 190 N Oval Mall Columbus OH 43210

REYNOLDS-WARNHOFF, PATRICIA, b Washington, DC, Feb 26, 33; m 56; c 3. ORGANIC CHEMISTRY. *Educ:* Trinity Col, DC, AB, 54; Mass Inst Technol, SM, 59; Univ Southern Calif, PhD(org chem), 62. *Prof Exp:* Res asst org chem, Nat Heart Inst, 55-57; res assoc org biochem, 62-63, instr, 63-64, sessional lectr org chem, 64-65, ASST PROF ORG CHEM, UNIV WESTERN ONT, 65- *Res:* Natural product structure determination; mechanisms of epoxide rearrangements; rearrangements of alpha-haloketones; hydride transfer reactions. *Mailing Add:* Dept of Chem Univ of Western Ont London ON N6A 5B8 Can

REYNOSO, GUSTAVO D, b Gomez Palacio, Mex, Sept 18, 32; US citizen; m 59; c 4. MEDICINE, PATHOLOGY. *Educ:* Ateneo Fuente Univ, Mex, BS, 50; Univ Nuevo Leon, MD, 58. *Prof Exp:* Resident path, St Luke's Hosp, Milwaukee, Wis & Marquette Univ, 61; M K Kellogg Found grant, prof path, Sch Med & dir clin labs, Univ Hosp, Univ Nuevo Leon, 61-65; asst clin prof path, Sch Med, Marquette Univ, 65-68; chief cancer res pathologist, Roswell Park Mem Inst, 68-72; CHIEF PATH, WILSON MEM HOSP, 72- *Concurrent Pos:* Assoc pathologist, St Luke's Hosp, Milwaukee, 65-68; asst prof exp path, State Univ NY Buffalo, 68-72; mem immunol subcomt, Nat Colorectal Cancer Prog, 71- *Mem:* AAAS; Am Soc Clin Pathologists; Col Am Pathologists; Asn Clin Scientists; Am Asn Clin Chemists. *Res:* Cancer immunology; biochemical diagnosis of cancer; hormonal interactions in cancer patient. *Mailing Add:* Dept of Path Wilson Mem Hosp Johnson City NY 13790

REZAK, MICHAEL, b Feldafing, Ger, Sept 10, 48; US citizen. NEUROANATOMY, NEUROPHYSIOLOGY. *Educ:* Univ Wis, BA, 70; Bradley Univ, MA, 72; Univ Ill, PhD(anat-neuroanat), 76. *Prof Exp:* Assoc anat, 76-77, ASST PROF, DEPT ANAT, MED CTR, UNIV ILL, 77- *Mem:* Soc Neurosci; Asn Res Vision & Ophthal; AAAS; Am Soc Primatologists; Am Psychol Asn. *Res:* Neuroanatomical and neurophysiological organization of the mammalian central nervous system. *Mailing Add:* Dept of Anat Univ of Ill Med Ctr Chicago IL 60612

REZAK, RICHARD, b Syracuse, NY, Apr 26, 20; m 65; c 1. GEOLOGICAL OCEANOGRAPHY. *Educ:* Syracuse Univ, AB, 47, PhD(geol), 57; Wash Univ, AM, 49. *Prof Exp:* Instr geol, St Lawrence Univ, 49-51; geologist, US Geol Surv, 52-58; res geologist, Shell Develop Co, 58-63, res assoc, 63-67; assoc prof, 67-71, PROF OCEANOG, TEX A&M UNIV, 71- *Mem:* Fel Geol Soc Am; Soc Econ Paleont & Mineral; Int Phycol Soc; fel AAAS. *Res:* Systematics and environmental significance of fossil algae; contributions of algae to carbonate sediments; carbonate sedimentology and diagenesis, especially cementation; seismic stratigraphy and salt tectonics. *Mailing Add:* Dept of Oceanog Tex A&M Univ College Station TX 77843

REZANKA, IVAN, b Prachatice, Czech, Sept 30, 31; m 59; c 2. PHYSICS. *Educ:* Charles Univ, Prague, MS, 54; Czech Acad Sci, PhD(physics), 62. *Prof Exp:* Res asst aerodynamics, Res & Testing Inst Aerodynamics, Czech, 54-55; from physicist to sr physicist, Nuclear Res Inst, 55-68; res assoc nuclear physics, Res Inst Physics, Stockholm, 68-69; res assoc & lectr, Heavy Ion Accelerator Lab, Yale Univ, 69-74, asst dir, 71-74; scientist, 74-81, SR SCIENTIST, XEROX CORP, 81- *Concurrent Pos:* Consult, Doll Res, Inc, 74- *Honors & Awards:* Czech Acad Sci Award, 62, Prize, 68. *Mem:* Am Phys Soc. *Res:* Nuclear physics; gamma ray and beta ray spectroscopy; computer hardware and software; activation analysis; medical physics; applied physics, fluid dynamics, continuum mechanics, acoustics; xerography; electrography; ink jet physics. *Mailing Add:* Xerox Corp Rochester NY 14644

REZNICEK, ANTON ALBERT, b Plochingen, WGer, June, 11, 50; Can citizen; m 78. PLANT TAXONOMY, PHYTOGEOGRAPHY. *Educ:* Univ Guelph, BSc, 71; Univ Toronto, MSc, 73, PhD(bot), 78. *Prof Exp:* ASST CURATOR, UNIV MICH, ANN ARBOR, 78- *Mem:* Am Soc Plant Taxonomists; Int Asn Plant Taxon; Bot Soc Am; Can Bot Asn. *Res:* Taxonomy of New World Carex (Cyperaceae); geography of the North American flora; plant migrations and persistance of relict flora in northeastern North America; floristics of the Great Lakes region. *Mailing Add:* N Univ Bldg Univ Mich Herbarium Ann Arbor MI 48109

REZNIK, BRUCE ARIE, b New York, NY, Feb 3, 53. ANALYSIS, COMBINATORICS. *Educ:* Calif Inst Technol, BS, 73; Stanford Univ, PhD(math), 76. *Prof Exp:* Asst prof math, Duke Univ, 76-78; NSF fel, Univ Calif, Berkeley, 78-79; ASST PROF MATH, UNIV ILL, URBANA-CHAMPAIGN, 79- *Mem:* Am Math Soc; Math Asn Am; Asn Women Math; Soc Values Higher Educ. *Res:* Analysis, algebra and number theory which are susceptible to combinatorial methods including polynomials, lattice points and inequalities. *Mailing Add:* Math Dept Univ Ill 1409 W Green St Urbana IL 61801

REZNIKOFF, WILLIAM STANTON, b New York, NY, Apr 29, 41; m 67; c 3. MOLECULAR GENETICS. *Educ:* Williams Col, Mass, BA, 63; Johns Hopkins Univ, PhD(biol), 67. *Prof Exp:* Fel bact genetics, Harvard Med Sch, 68-70; from asst prof to assoc prof biochem genetics, 70-78, PROF BIOCHEM, COL AGR & LIFE SCI, UNIV WIS-MADISON, 78-

Concurrent Pos: Nat Inst Gen Med Sci career develop award, 72-77; Harry & Evelyn Steenbock career develop award, Univ Wis, 74-78; mem, Adv Subcomt Genetic Biol, 76-79; mem, Rev Comt Cellular & Molecular Basis Dis, Nat Inst Gen Med Sci, 80-82; consult, Biogen SA, 81. *Mem:* Am Soc Microbiol; Am Soc Biol Chemists. *Res:* Analysis of the structure and function of genetic regulatory regions, promoters, operators, associated with genes in Escherichia coli and its viruses. *Mailing Add:* Dept of Biochem Univ of Wis 420 Henry Mall Madison WI 53706

RHAMY, ROBERT KEITH, b Indianapolis, Ind, Nov 26, 27; m 51; c 4. UROLOGY, PHYSIOLOGY. *Educ:* Ind Univ, BS, 49, MS, 50, MD, 52; Am Bd Urol, dipl, 62. *Prof Exp:* Res assoc physiol, Ind Univ, 48-49, intern, 52-53, asst resident, 55-56, resident urol, 56-59, from instr to assoc prof, 59-64; PROF UROL & HEAD DEPT, SCH MED, VANDERBILT UNIV, 64-, CHIEF UROL SURG, UNIV HOSP, 64- *Concurrent Pos:* Chief urol, Nashville Gen Hosp, 64-; consult, US Vet Admin Hosp, 64-, Jr League Home Crippled Children, 65- & USPHS, 65-; prog consult, Nat Found, 65-; mem, Int Cong Nephrology, Nat Dialysis Comt & Nat Kidney Found. *Mem:* Am Urol Asn; Soc Pediat Urol; Am Acad Pediat; Am Soc Nephrology; Am Fertil Soc. *Res:* Renal hypertension; pediatric urology; ureteral physiology; chemical carcinogenesis. *Mailing Add:* Dept of Urol Vanderbilt Univ Sch of Med Nashville TN 37203

RHEE, CHOON JAI, b Pyungyang, Korea, Sept 13, 35; m 64. TOPOLOGY. *Educ:* Univ of the South, BA, 60; Univ Ga, MA, 62, PhD(math), 65. *Prof Exp:* Asst prof math, Randolph-Macon Woman's Col, 65-66; asst prof, 66-71, ASSOC PROF MATH, WAYNE STATE UNIV, 71- *Mem:* Am Math Soc; Math Asn Am; Sigma Xi. *Res:* Homotopy functors; point set topology. *Mailing Add:* Dept of Math Wayne State Univ Detroit MI 48202

RHEE, G-YULL, b Kyunggi-Do, Korea, Feb, 10, 39; US citizen; m 68; c 2. PHYSIOLOGICAL ECOLOGY OF ALGAE. *Educ:* Seoul Nat Univ, BS, 61; Northeastern Univ, Boston, MS, 67; Cornell Univ, Ithaca, NY, PhD(aquatic microbiol), 71. *Prof Exp:* From res scientist I to res scientist IV, 71-80, RES SCIENTIST V, CTR FOR LABS & RES, NY DEPT HEALTH, ALBANY, 80- *Concurrent Pos:* Adj assoc prof, Cornell Univ, Ithaca, NY, 80- *Mem:* Am Soc Limnol & Oceanog; Phycol Asn Am; Am Soc Microbiol; AAAS. *Res:* Effects of environmental factors in algae physiology and ecology. *Mailing Add:* Ctr for Labs & Res NY Dept Health Albany NY 12201

RHEE, HAEWUN, b Seoul, Korea, Sept 12, 37; m 65; c 2. MATHEMATICS. *Educ:* Johns Hopkins Univ, AB, 60; Univ Mass, Amherst, PhD(math), 68. *Prof Exp:* Instr math, Ohio Wesleyan Univ, 64-65; asst prof, Am Int Col, 67-68; assoc prof, 68-72, PROF MATH, STATE UNIV NY COL ONEONTA, 72- *Mem:* Am Math Soc. *Res:* Partial differential equations. *Mailing Add:* Dept of Math State Univ of NY Col Oneonta NY 13820

RHEE, JAY JEA-YONG, b Seoul, Korea, Oct 3, 37; US citizen; m 63; c 2. CHEMICAL PHYSICS, PHYSICAL CHEMISTRY. *Educ:* Univ La Verne, BA, 62; Univ NMex, MS, 66, PhD(chem), 67. *Prof Exp:* From asst prof to assoc prof, 68-77, PROF CHEM, UNIV LA VERNE, 77- *Concurrent Pos:* Vis assoc prof chem, Univ Calif, Davis, 75; consult, Synthane-Taylore Corp, La Verne, Calif; resident dir, Korea Telecommun Co, Ltd, Bell Tel, Antwerp, Belgium, 79-81. *Mem:* Am Chem Soc; Am Inst Physics; Korean Chem Soc. *Res:* Multiphoton spectroscopy and ODMR applications; laser applications on isotope separations; quantum theory; molecular spectroscopy. *Mailing Add:* Dept Chem 1950 Third St La Verne CA 91750

RHEE, JOHN WILLIAMS, space physics, astrophysics, deceased

RHEE, MOON-JHONG, b Shinanchoo, Korea, Feb 19, 35; m 66; c 4. PLASMA PHYSICS. *Educ:* Seoul Nat Univ, BS, 58, MS, 60; Cath Univ Am, PhD(appl physics), 70. *Prof Exp:* Instr physics, Seoul Nat Univ, 64-66; res fel appl physics, Cath Univ Am, 66-70; asst prof, 70-74, ASSOC PROF ELEC ENG, UNIV MD, 75- *Concurrent Pos:* Vis prof, Seoul Nat Univ, 77-78; consult, Naval Surface Weapons Ctr, 80- *Mem:* Am Phys Soc; Korean Phys Soc; Inst Elec & Electronics Engrs. *Res:* Collective ion acceleration; generation and measurement of charged particles in plasma focus and in laser produced plasma; microwave generation; pulsed power system; picosecond optoelectronic switching. *Mailing Add:* Lab Plasma & Fusion Energy Studies Univ Md College Park MD 20742

RHEE, SEONG KWAN, b Mokpo, Korea, Aug 18, 36; US citizen; m 63; c 4. MATERIALS SCIENCE, METALLURGY. *Educ:* Chosun Univ, BS, 59; Univ Cincinnati, MS, 62, PhD(mat sci), 66. *Prof Exp:* Mem tech staff, Sci Res Inst, Korean Ministry Nat Defense, 59-60; DIR, CORP MAT DEVELOP CTR, BENDIX CORP, 81- *Mem:* Metall Soc; Am Soc Mech Engrs; fel Am Ceramic Soc; fel Am Inst Chemist; Nat Inst Ceramic Engrs. *Res:* Surface energy of solids; oxidation of metals; alloying behavior of metals; composite materials; tribology; abrasive ceramics; grain growth in metals and ceramics; hard coatings. *Mailing Add:* Corp Mat Develop Ctr 20800 Civic Ctr Dr Southfield MI 48076

RHEES, RAYMOND CHARLES, b Ogden, Utah, Jan 29, 14; m 38; c 5. INORGANIC CHEMISTRY, ANALYTICAL CHEMISTRY. *Educ:* Utah State Univ, BS, 40, MS, 44; Iowa State Univ, PhD(light scattering), 51. *Prof Exp:* Chemist, Kalunite Inc, 42-44; instr chem, Utah State Univ, 44-45 & Iowa State Univ, 45-51; sr chemist, Union Carbide Nuclear Corp, 51-52, sect head atomic energy, 52-53, dept head, 53-56; sect head anal chem, Am Potash & Chem Corp, 56-60, sect head boron hydrides, 60-63, sect head tech serv, 63-68; dir res & develop, 68-70, VPRES RES, PAC ENG & PROD CO NEV, 70- *Mem:* Am Chem Soc; Water Pollution Control Fedn; Electrochem Soc; Air Pollution Control Asn. *Res:* Light scattering; analytical and uranium chemistry; fine particle properties; boron hydrides; chlorates and perchlorates; borates; chemical specialties; electrolytic processes in pollution control. *Mailing Add:* Pac Eng & Prod Co of Nev PO Box 797 Henderson NV 89015

RHEES, REUBEN WARD, b Ogden, Utah, Apr 1, 41; m 63; c 5. NEUROENDOCRINOLOGY. *Educ:* Univ Utah, BS, 67; Colo State Univ, PhD(physiol), 71. *Prof Exp:* Res asst physiol, Colo State Univ, 67-70, teaching asst physiol, 70-71; fel anat, Univ Utah Med Sch, 71-72; asst prof physiol, Weber State Col, 72-73; asst prof, 73-77, ASSOC PROF ZOOL, BRIGHAM YOUNG UNIV, 77- *Mem:* Am Physiol Soc. *Res:* Neuroendocrine mechanisms by which hormones exert regulatory and behavioral effects on the central nervous system; interrelationships between the endocrine and nervous systems. *Mailing Add:* Dept of Zool Brigham Young Univ Provo UT 84602

RHEIN, ROBERT ALDEN, b San Francisco, Calif, Aug 18, 33; m 56; c 5. INORGANIC CHEMISTRY, POLYMER CHEMISTRY. *Educ:* Univ Calif, BS, 55; Univ Pittsburgh, MS, 58; Univ Wash, PhD(chem), 62. *Prof Exp:* Assoc engr, Westinghouse Elec Corp, 55-58; eng designer, Boeing Airplane Co, 58-60; SR ENGR CHEM, JET PROPULSION LAB, CALIF INST TECHNOL, 62- *Mem:* Am Chem Soc. *Res:* Ultrasonics in liquid systems; inorganic fluorine chemistry; powdered metals combustion; propellant chemistry. *Mailing Add:* 424 Kendall Ave Ridgecrest CA 93555

RHEINBOLDT, WERNER CARL, b Berlin, Ger, Sept 18, 27; US citizen; m 59. NUMERICAL ANALYSIS. *Educ:* Heidelberg Univ, dipl, 52; Univ Freiburg, PhD(math), 55. *Prof Exp:* Mathematician aerodyn, Eng Bur Blume, Ger, 55-56; fel appl math, Inst Fluid Dynamics & Appl Math, Univ Md; 56-57; mathematician numerical anal, Comput Lab, Nat Bur Standards, 57-59; asst prof & dir comput ctr, Syracuse Univ, 59-62; dir comput sci ctr, Univ Md, College Park, 62-65, res assoc prof, Inst Fluid Dynamics & Appl Math, 62-63, res prof, 63-72, res prof comput sci ctr, 68-72, prof, Dept Math, 72-78, dir appl math prog, 74-78; ANDREW W MELLON PROF MATH, UNIV PITTSBURGH, 78- *Concurrent Pos:* Asn Comput Mach rep, Nat Acad Sci-Nat Res Coun, 65-67; ed, J Numerical Anal, Soc Indust & Appl Math, 65-, managing ed, 70-73; consult ed, Acad Press, 67-; vis prof, Soc Math Data Processing, Bonn, Ger, 69; consult, Div Comput Res, NSF, 72-75 & 81-; chmn, Comt Appl Math, Nat Res Coun, 79-, mem, Adv Comt, Army Res Off, 74-78, exec comt, 81- *Mem:* Am Math Soc; Soc Indust & Appl Math (vpres, 76, pres, 77-78); Math Asn Am. *Res:* Numerical and functional analysis; computer applications. *Mailing Add:* Dept of Math & Statist Univ of Pittsburgh Pittsburgh PA 15260

RHEINGOLD, ARNOLD L, b Chicago, Ill, Oct 6, 40; m 66; c 2. ORGANOMETALLIC CHEMISTRY. *Educ:* Case Western Reserve Univ, AB, 62, MS, 63; Univ Md, PhD(inorg chem), 69. *Prof Exp:* Proj mgr organometall chem, Glidden-Durkee Div, SCM Corp, 63-65; res fel, Va Polytech Inst, 69-70; asst prof chem, State Univ NY Col Plattsburgh, 70-75, assoc prof, 75-81; VIS PROF, UNIV DEL, 81- *Mem:* AAAS; Am Chem Soc. *Res:* Physical organometallic chemistry; synthesis and characterization of main group compounds; preparative electrochemistry; main-group homoatomic ring and chain structures; crystallography. *Mailing Add:* Dept Chem Univ Del Newark DE 19711

RHEINLANDER, HAROLD F, b Ashland, Maine, June 10, 19; m 42. SURGERY. *Educ:* Univ Maine, BA, 41; Harvard Med Sch, MD, 44; Am Bd Surg, dipl, 52; Am Bd Thoracic Surg, dipl, 62. *Prof Exp:* Asst surg, Harvard Univ, 45-46, John Milton fel, 48-49; from instr to assoc prof, 49-66, PROF SURG, SCH MED, TUFTS UNIV, 66-, VCHMN, DEPT SURG, 79- *Concurrent Pos:* Intern, Peter Bent Brigham Hosp, 44-45; resident, 45-46; resident, Childrens Hosp, Boston, 48-49; resident, New Eng Ctr Hosp, 49-51, asst surg, 50-52, asst surgeon, 52-58, surgeon & chief thoracic serv, 58-; consult, Boston Vet Admin Hosp, 66- *Mem:* Am Heart Asn; Am Col Surg; Am Soc Artificial Internal Organs; Am Col Chest Physicians; Soc Vasc Surg. *Mailing Add:* Dept of Surg Sch of Med Tufts Univ 136 Harrison Ave Boston MA 02111

RHEINS, MELVIN S, b Cincinnati, Ohio, May 13, 20; m 48; c 2. MICROBIOLOGY, IMMUNOLOGY. *Educ:* Miami Univ, BA & MA, 46; Ohio State Univ, PhD(microbiol), 49. *Prof Exp:* From instr to assoc prof pathogenic microbiol, 49-59, actg chmn dept microbiol, 64-65, chmn, 65-67, PROF MICROBIOL, OHIO STATE UNIV, 59- *Concurrent Pos:* Spec consult, USPHS, 61-63. *Mem:* Fel Am Acad Microbiol; Am Soc Microbiol; NY Acad Sci. *Res:* Pathogenesis and immunology of pulmonary diseases, collagen diseases and ocular infection, diseases and malignancies. *Mailing Add:* Dept of Microbiol Ohio State Univ 484 W 12th Ave Columbus OH 43210

RHEINSTEIN, JOHN, b Gardelegen, Ger, May 23, 30; US citizen; m 56; c 3. PHYSICS. *Educ:* Dartmouth Col, AB, 51; Univ Chicago, MS, 57; Munich Tech Univ, PhD(physics), 61. *Prof Exp:* Lectr physics, Munich Br, Univ Md, 58-60; staff mem systs anal, 61-66, assoc group leader, 66-69, from asst site mgr to assoc site mgr, 69-73, GROUP LEADER, LINCOLN LAB, MASS INST TECHNOL, 73- *Mem:* Am Phys Soc; Inst Elec & Electronics Engr. *Res:* Medical physics; electromagnetic theory; reentry physics; systems analysis. *Mailing Add:* Lincoln Lab Mass Inst of Technol Box 73 Lexington MA 02173

RHEINWALD, JAMES GEORGE, b Chicago, Ill, June 25, 48; m 68; c 1. CYTOLOGY, MICROBIOLOGY. *Educ:* Univ Ill, Urbana, BS & MS, 70; Mass Inst Technol, PhD(cell biol), 75. *Prof Exp:* Res assoc cell biol, Mass Inst Technol, 76-78; ASST SCIENTIST TUMOR BIOL, SIDNEY FARBER CANCER INST, 78-; ASST PROF PHYSIOL, HARVARD MED SCH, 78- *Mem:* Tissue Culture Asn; Am Soc Cell Biol. *Res:* Growth control and differentiated function in human epithelial tissues and cultured cells; identification and study of tissue- and tumor-specific keratins; cancer-related phenotypes expressed in cell culture. *Mailing Add:* Sidney Farber Cancer Inst Dana 840C 44 Binney St Boston MA 02115

RHIM, JOHNG SIK, b Korea, July 24, 30; US citizen; m 62; c 5. VIROLOGY, MEDICAL SCIENCES. *Educ:* Seoul Nat Univ, BS, 53, MD, 57. *Prof Exp:* Res fel poliovirus, Children's Hosp Res Found, Cincinnati, Ohio, 58-60; res fel reovirus, Baylor Col Med, 60-61; res fel Japanese B encephalitis, Grad Sch Pub Health, Univ Pittsburgh, 61-62; res assoc infant diarrhea, Sch Med, La State Univ, Costa Rica, 62-64; vis scientist arbovirus, Nat Inst Allergy & Infectious Dis, 64-66; proj dir career res, Microbiol Asn Inc, 66-78; virologist, 78-80, SR RES SCIENTIST CANCER RES, NAT CANCER INST, 80- *Concurrent Pos:* mem bd dir, Winchester Sch, Silver Spring, Md. *Mem:* AAAS; Am Asn Cancer Res; Am Asn Immunologists; Soc Exp Biol & Med; Am Soc Microbiol. *Res:* In vitro chemical and viral cocarcinogenesis; immunoprevention of cancer; mechamism of carcinogenesis. *Mailing Add:* Bldg 37 1A03 Nat Cancer Inst NIH 9000 Rockville Pike Bethesda MD 20205

RHIM, WON-KYU, b Seoul, Korea, Oct 20, 37; US citizen; m 64; c 4. PHYSICS, PHYSICAL CHEMISTRY. *Educ:* Seoul Nat Univ, Korea, BS, 61, MS, 63; Univ NC, Chapel Hill, PhD(physics), 70. *Prof Exp:* Res assoc chem phys, Mass Inst Technol, 69-71; res fel chem phys, Dept Chem Eng, 71-73, MEM TECH STAFF PHYSICS, JET PROPULSION LAB, CALIF INST TECHNOL, 73- *Mem:* Am Phys Soc. *Res:* Solid state nuclear spin dynamics and spin thermodynamics; study of magnetic interactions in solids; instrumentation for magnetic resonance experiments. *Mailing Add:* 1800 San Pasqual St Pasadena CA 91106

RHINES, DON SCOTT, experimental high energy physics, see previous edition

RHINES, FREDERICK N(IMS), b Toledo, Ohio, July 25, 07; m 41, 79; c 2. METALLURGY. *Educ:* Univ Mich, BSE, 29; Univ Berlin, cert lang, 32; Yale Univ, PhD(metall), 33. *Prof Exp:* Metallurgist, Res Labs, Aluminum Co Am, Ohio, 29-31; asst metall, Yale Univ, 33-34; from instr to prof, Carnegie Inst Technol, 34-59, mem staff, Metals Res Lab, 34-59, metall supvr, Eve Sch, 39-59; metall supvr, Aluminum Co Am prof light metals, 45-59; prof metall & mat eng & head metall res lab, Eng Indust Exp Sta, 59-73, chmn dept metall & mat eng, 63-73, distinguished serv prof, 73-78, EMER DISTINGUISHED SERV PROF MAT SCI & ENG, UNIV FLA, 78- *Concurrent Pos:* AID-Univ Houston lectr grad educ metall eng, Univ Brazil, 66; assoc in estab of grad educ metall, Mil Inst Engenhari, Brazil, 69; Zay Jeffries lectr, Cleveland Am Soc Metals, 71. *Honors & Awards:* Mathewson Medal, Am Inst Mining, Metall & Petrol Engrs, 39 & 42; Howe Howe Medal, Am Soc Metals, 57 & 60, Albert Easton White Award, 71; Award, Am Soc Testing & Mat, 62; Sorby Medal, Int Metallog Soc, 79; Willis Rodney Whitney Award, Nat Asn Corrosion Engrs. *Mem:* Fel Am Soc Metals; fel Am Soc Testing & Mat; fel Am Inst Mining, Metall & Petrol Engrs; Brit Inst Metals; Brit Iron & Steel Inst. *Res:* copper oxide, indium-tin and indium-zinc; internal oxidation of alloys of copper, silver and tin; diffusion in alloys of copper and aluminum; powder metallurgy; mechanism of sintering; gas-metal equilibria; oriented overgrowths in metals; freezing of metals; grain boundary creep; plasticity of metals; quantitative metallography. *Mailing Add:* 1540 NW 37th Terr Gainesville FL 32605

RHINES, PETER BROOMELL, b Hartford, Conn, July, 23, 42; m 68. FLUID DYNAMICS. *Educ:* Mass Inst Technol, BSc & MSc, 64; Cambridge Univ, UK, PhD(appl math & theoret physics), 67. *Prof Exp:* Fel oceanog, Dept Meterol, Mass Inst Technol, 67-68, asst prof, 68-71; res scientist, Cambridge Univ, UK, 71-72; assoc scientist, 72-74, SR SCIENTIST OCEANOG, WOODS HOLE OCEANOG INST, 74- *Concurrent Pos:* Vis prof, Nat Ctr Atmospheric Res, 69 & 72, Univ BC, 75, Univ Colo, 76, Calif Inst Tech & Princeton Univ, 78; fel, Christ's Col, Cambridge, UK, 79-80; Guggenheim fel, Dept Appl Math & Theoret Physics, Cambridge Univ, 79-80; Green scholar, Inst Geophys & Planetary Physics, Univ Calif, San Diego, 81. *Mem:* Nat Acad Sci. *Res:* Circulation of the oceans, waves, eddies and currents; climate and transport of natural and artificial trace chemicals in the seas. *Mailing Add:* Woods Hole Oceanog Inst Woods Hole MA 02543

RHINESMITH, HERBERT SILAS, b Westtown, NY, Oct 25, 07; m 39; c 2. ORGANIC CHEMISTRY. *Educ:* Wesleyan Univ, AB, 29, AM, 30; Harvard Univ, AM, 31, PhD(chem), 33. *Prof Exp:* Teaching fel chem, Wesleyan Univ, 34-36, instr, 36-38; from instr to prof, 38-74, EMER PROF CHEM, ALLEGHENY COL, 74- *Concurrent Pos:* Mem staff, Keystone Ord Works; res assoc, Calif Inst Technol, 55-57. *Mem:* AAAS; Am Chem Soc; fel Am Inst Chemists; NY Acad Sci. *Res:* Action of Grignard reagent on acetylenic esters; epoxidations with peracetic acid; beta, gamma-oxido esters; amino acid; protein chemistry; normal and abnormal hemoglobins; chemistry of serotonin, especially quantitative determinations. *Mailing Add:* 1656 Hibiscus Dr Sanibel FL 33957

RHO, JINNQUE, b Korea, Sept 15, 38; US citizen; m 70; c 1. MICROBIOLOGY. *Educ:* Seoul Nat Univ, BS, 61, Clark Univ, MS, 69; Univ Mass, PhD(microbiol), 72. *Prof Exp:* Teaching asst microbiol, Dept Biol, Clark Univ, 66-68; res asst, Inst Agr & Indust Microbiol, Univ Mass, 68-71, teaching asst soil microbiol, 71-72, fel, Dept Environ Sci Sci, 72-74, sr res assoc agr microbiol, Mass Agr Exp Sta, 74-77, asst prof aquatic microbiol, Dept Environ, 77-79; asst prof, 79-82, ELIPHALET REMINGTON PROF APPL & ENVIRON MICROBIOL, BIOL DEPT, UNIV BRIDGEPORT, 82- *Concurrent Pos:* Consult, New Eng Res Inc, Mass, 72-73; co-prin investr nitrogen transformation by heterotrphs, Mass Agr Exp Sta, 74-77; affil asst prof, Dept Biol, Clark Univ, 77-79. *Mem:* Am Soc Microbiol; Am Soc Limnol & Oceanog; Sigma Xi. *Res:* Nitrogen transformation in soil and waters; ecology and biochemistry of heterotrophic nitrifying microorganisms; exploitation of aquatic weeds and algae for biomass production in wastewater lagoons; development of aquatic weeds and algae as biofuel feed stocks. *Mailing Add:* Dept Biol Dana Hall Univ Bridgeport Bridgeport CT 06603

RHO, JOON H, b Pyongbuk, Korea, Jan 19, 22; m 47; c 5. BIOCHEMISTRY. *Educ:* Seoul Nat Univ, BS, 50; Duke Univ, MS, 56, PhD(biochem), 58. *Prof Exp:* Asst prof biol, Sung Kyun Kwan Univ, Korea, 53-56, from assoc prof to prof, 57-59; Nat Acad Sci fel, Calif Inst Technol, 59-62, sr scientist, Jet Propulsion Lab, 62-66, tech staff mem, 67-73, sr biologist, Calif Inst Technol, 73-75; ASSOC PROF MED & PHARM, SCHS MED & PHARM, UNIV SOUTHERN CALIF, 75- *Concurrent Pos:* Prin investr, Apollo Sample Anal for Porphyrin Compounds, 71. *Mem:* Am Chem Soc; AAAS; Int Soc Study Origin of Life. *Res:* Neurogenic hypertension; chemical carcinogenesis, metabolism of antihypertentive drugs; fluorometric analyses of biological and biomedicinal compounds. *Mailing Add:* 1555 Hillcrest Ave Pasadena CA 91106

RHOADES, BILLY EUGENE, b Lima, Ohio, Sept 27, 28; m 49; c 2. MATHEMATICS. *Educ:* Ohio Northern Univ, AB, 51; Rutgers Univ, MS, 53; Lehigh Univ, PhD, 58. *Prof Exp:* Asst math, Rutgers Univ, 52-53; from instr to prof, Lafayette Col, 53-65; assoc prof, 65-69, PROF MATH, IND UNIV, BLOOMINGTON, 69- *Mem:* Am Math Soc; Math Asn Am. *Res:* Transformations in sequence spaces; fixed point theorems. *Mailing Add:* 4400 Sheffield Dr Bloomington IN 47401

RHOADES, EVERETT RONALD, b Lawton, Okla, Oct 24, 31; m 53; c 5. INTERNAL MEDICINE, MICROBIOLOGY. *Educ:* Univ Okla, MD, 56. *Prof Exp:* Intern, Gorgas Hosp, CZ, 56-57; resident med, Med Ctr, Univ Okla, 57-60, clin asst, 60-61; chief infectious dis, Wilford Hall, US Air Force Hosp, 61-66; from asst prof med & microbiol to prof med, Med Ctr, Univ Okla, 66-82, chief infectious dis, 68-82; DIR, INDIAN HEALTH SERV, 82- *Concurrent Pos:* Consult, Med Ctr, Univ Okla, 63-66, Surgeon Gen, 65-66 & Eastern & Western Okla Tuberc Sanatarium, 66-75; chief infectious dis, Vet Admin Hosp, Oklahoma City, 66-; mem adv coun, Nat Inst Allergy & Infectious Dis; mem health comt, Asn Am Indian Affairs; Markle scholar acad med, 67-72. *Mem:* Am Soc Microbiol; Am Fedn Clin Res; Am Col Physicians; Asn Am Indian Physicians (pres, 75); Infectious Dis Soc Am. *Res:* Various aspects of cryptococcosis, including the effect of antifungal compounds on organisms and humans; host-parasite factors in lower respiratory infections. *Mailing Add:* 921 NE 13th St Oklahoma City OK 73104

RHOADES, HARLAN LEON, b Tuscola, Ill, Mar 7, 28; m 53; c 2. PLANT NEMATOLOGY. *Educ:* Univ Ill, BS, 52, MS, 57, PhD(plant path), 59. *Prof Exp:* Soil conservationist, Agr Res Serv, USDA, 52-55; asst plant nematologist, 59-67, assoc prof & assoc nematologist, 67-73, PROF NEMATOL & NEMATOLOGIST, UNIV FLA, 73- *Mem:* Soc Nematol. *Res:* Control of plant nematodes attacking vegetables. *Mailing Add:* Agr Res & Educ Ctr Univ of Fla PO Box 909 Sanford FL 32771

RHOADES, JAMES DAVID, soil science, clay mineralogy, see previous edition

RHOADES, JAMES LAWRENCE, b Mishawaka, Ind, Apr 24, 33; m 58; c 4. ENZYMOLOGY, PROTEIN CHEMISTRY. *Educ:* Purdue Univ, BS, 55, MS, 57, PhD(chem), 61. *Prof Exp:* From asst prof to assoc prof chem, Northwestern State Col, La, 60-70; prof chem, 70-80, WILLIAM E REID PROF CHEM, BERRY COL, 80-, CHMN DEPT, 70- *Concurrent Pos:* Vis assoc prof chem, Purdue Univ, 65, 67 & 69; res assoc, Univ Tenn, Memphis, 63, 75. *Mem:* Am Chem Soc. *Res:* Chemistry and mechanism of action of enzymes, especially the plant phenolase complex; biosynthesis of coenzyme A; B-protein assay for cancer. *Mailing Add:* Dept Chem Berry Col Mt Berry GA 30149

RHOADES, MARCUS MORTON, b Graham, Mo, July 24, 03; m 31; c 2. GENETICS. *Educ:* Univ Mich, BS, 27, MS, 28; Cornell Univ, PhD(genetics), 32. *Prof Exp:* Researcher genetics, Cornell Univ, 28-29; plant breeding, 30-35; agent, USDA, 35-37, geneticist, Arlington Exp Farm, 37-40; from assoc prof to prof bot, Columbia Univ, 40-48; prof, Univ Ill, 48-58; prof & chmn dept, 58-68, distinguished prof, 68-74, EMER PROF BOT, IND UNIV, BLOOMINGTON, 74- *Concurrent Pos:* Managing ed, Genetics, 40-47; vis prof, Univ Sao Paulo, 47-48, NC State Col, 53 & Cornell Univ, 56; Jesup lectr, Columbia Univ, 58; mem vis comt biol, Brookhaven Nat Lab, 62-65; mem div comt biol & med, NSF, 63-66; mem genetics study sect, NIH, 63-66; mem exec comt, Div Biol & Agr, Nat Res Coun, 63-66; hon fel, Australian Nat Univ, 65-66; mem selection comt, Guggenheim Mem Found, 65-76. *Honors & Awards:* Thomas Hunt Morgan Medal, Genetics Soc Am. *Mem:* Nat Acad Sci; Am Soc Naturalists; Genetics Soc Am (vpres, 42, pres, 43); Bot Soc Am; Am Genetic Asn (pres, 50-53). *Res:* Cytogenetics of maize. *Mailing Add:* Dept Biol Ind Univ Bloomington IN 47401

RHOADES, RICHARD G, b Northampton, Mass, Aug 15, 38; m 67; c 3. CHEMICAL ENGINEERING, MATHEMATICS. *Educ:* Rensselaer Polytech Inst, BChE, 60, PhD(chem eng, math), 64; Mass Inst Technol, MS, 77. *Prof Exp:* Res chem engr, Propulsion Lab, US Army Missile Command, 63-66, prog mgr air breathing propulsion, 66-72, dir, Army Rocket Propulsion Technol & Mgt Ctr, 68-70, chief, Adv Res Projs Div, 69, group leader ballistic missile defense propulsion, 70-73, dir propulsion directorate, US Army Missile Res & Develop Command, 73-81, ASSOC DIR TECHNOL, US ARMY MISSILE COMMAND, 81- *Concurrent Pos:* Adj asst prof, Univ Ala, Huntsville, 65-69. *Mem:* Assoc mem Am Inst Chem Engrs. *Res:* Fluid dynamics of packed beds; gas generation and pressurization for missiles; analytical techniques and methodology for propulsion system selection and technology planning; air breathing propulsion system analysis, design and experimentation. *Mailing Add:* Army Missile Lab US Army Missile Command Redstone Arsenal AL 35898

RHOADES, RODNEY A, b Greenville, Ohio, Jan 5, 39; m 61; c 1. PHYSIOLOGY. *Educ:* Miami Univ, BS, 61, MS, 63; Ohio State Univ, PhD(physiol), 66. *Prof Exp:* NASA fel, Ohio State Univ, 64-66; asst prof appl physiol, Pa State Univ, 66-72, assoc prof biol, 72-77; assoc prof, 77-81, PROF PHYSIOL & CHMN DEPT, SCH MED, IND UNIV, 81- *Concurrent Pos:* NIH career develop award, 75-80. *Mem:* AAAS; Am Physiol Soc; Biophys Soc; Am Thoracic Soc; Soc Exp Biol & Med. *Res:* Lung metabolism. *Mailing Add:* Dept of Physiol Ind Univ Indianapolis IN 16202

RHOADS, ALLEN R, b Reading, Pa, Dec 19, 41; m 69. ENZYMOLOGY. *Educ:* Kutztown State Col, BS, 66; Univ Md, PhD(biochem), 71. *Prof Exp:* Fel biochem & pharmacol, 71-72, asst prof, 72-77, ASSOC PROF BIOCHEM, COL MED, HOWARD UNIV, 77- *Concurrent Pos:* Prin investr regulation cyclic 3 & nucleotide phosphodiesterases, USPHS grant, 78-; investr, Cancer Ctr, Howard Univ, 79- *Mem:* Am Chem Soc; AAAS; NY Acad Sci. *Res:* Regulation of cyclic nucleotide metabolism and calcium flux in normal and neoplastic tissues. *Mailing Add:* Dept Biochem Col Med Howard Univ 520 West ST NW Washington DC 20059

RHOADS, DONALD CAVE, b Rockford, Ill, Feb 14, 38; m 59; c 2. PALEOECOLOGY. *Educ:* Cornell Col, BA, 60; Univ Iowa, MS, 63; Univ Chicago, PhD(paleo zool), 65. *Prof Exp:* Assoc prof, 65-75, PROF GEOL, YALE UNIV, 75- *Concurrent Pos:* assoc ed, Am J Sci & J Marine Res. *Res:* Organism-sediment relationships in marine environment; biogenic sedimentary structures in marine sediments; environmental events recorded in skeletal structures of marine invertebrates; biogenic processes on the seafloor. *Mailing Add:* Dept of Geol & Geophys Yale Univ New Haven CT 06520

RHOADS, FREDERICK MILTON, b New Site, Miss, Jan 12, 36; m 53; c 2. SOIL CHEMISTRY, SOIL PHYSICS. *Educ:* Miss State Univ, BS, 58, PhD(soil chem), 66; Tex A&M Univ, MS, 63. *Prof Exp:* Soil scientist, Soil Conserv Serv, USDA, 58-61; asst soil chemist, 66-72, assoc soil chemist, 72-78, PROF SOIL SCI, AGR RES & EDUC CTR, UNIV FLA, 78- *Mem:* Soil Sci Soc Am. *Res:* Plant nutrition of field crops; irrigation of field crops; soil fertility and testing; soil-water. *Mailing Add:* Agr Res & Educ Ctr Univ of Fla Quincy FL 32351

RHOADS, GEORGE GRANT, b Philadelphia, Pa, Feb 11, 40; m 65; c 2. EPIDEMIOLOGY, INTERNAL MEDICINE. *Educ:* Haverford Col, BA, 61; Harvard Univ, MD, 65; Univ Hawaii, MPH, 70. *Prof Exp:* Intern, Univ Pa Hosp, 65-66, resident, 66-68; lt commander, Heart Dis Control Prog, USPHS, 68-70; asst dir, Honolulu Heart Study, 70-71 & 72-74; assoc prof, 74-79, chmn, Dept Pub Health Sci, 78-81, PROF PUB HEALTH, UNIV HAWAII, 79- *Mem:* AAAS; Soc Epidemiol Res; Int Epidemiol Asn; Am Pub Health Asn; Am Epidemiol Soc. *Res:* Epidemiology of chronic disease; coronary heart disease and stroke in Japanese migrants and their descendants. *Mailing Add:* Sch of Pub Health Univ of Hawaii Honolulu HI 96822

RHOADS, JOHN MCFARLANE, b Vineland, NJ, Jan 7, 19; m 44; c 4. PSYCHIATRY. *Educ:* Va Polytech Inst, BS, 40; Temple Univ, MD, 43, MSc, 52; Am Bd Psychiat & Neurol, dipl, 50. *Prof Exp:* Instr psychiat, Sch Med, Temple Univ, 49-53, assoc, 53-55, asst prof, 55-56; assoc prof, 56-62, PROF PSYCHIAT, SCH MED, DUKE UNIV, 62- *Concurrent Pos:* Consult, US Vet Admin Hosp, Philadelphia, 53-56 & Durham, 57-; lectr, Sch Theol, Temple Univ, 53-56; instr, Wash Psychoanal Inst, 58- *Mem:* AMA; Am Psychiat Asn; Am Psychoanal Asn. *Res:* Psychotherapy and psychoanalysis; relationships between psychiatry and religion. *Mailing Add:* Dept of Psychiat Duke Univ Sch Med Durham NC 27710

RHOADS, JONATHAN EVANS, b Philadelphia, Pa, May 9, 07; m 36; c 6. SURGERY. *Educ:* Haverford Col, BA, 28; Johns Hopkins Univ, MD, 32; Univ Pa, DSc(med), 40. *Hon Degrees:* LLD, Univ Pa, 60, MA, 71; DSc, Haverford Col, 62, Swarthmore Col, 69, Med Col Pa, 74 & Hahnemann Med Col, 78; DLitt, Jefferson Univ, 79, Duke Univ, 79 & Georgetown Univ, 81. *Prof Exp:* Intern, Hosp Univ Pa, 32-34, asst chief resident, 34; asst instr surg, Sch Med, 34-35, instr, 35-39, assoc, 39-47, assoc prof, 47-49, J William White prof surg res, 49-50, prof surg, Grad Sch Med, 50-64, prof surg, Sch Med, 51-57, provost, Univ, 56-59, from actg dir to dir, Harrison Dept Surg Res, 44-72, John Rhea Barton prof surg, 59-72, PROF SURG, SCH MED, UNIV PA, 72- *Concurrent Pos:* Mem, Franklin Inst, Pa; mem adv coun, Nat Inst Gen Med Sci, 63-67; vpres sci affairs, Inst Med Res, 64-76; mem, US Senate Panel Consults on Conquest of Cancer, 70; mem & chmn, Nat Cancer Adv Bd, 72- *Honors & Awards:* Sheen Award, Am Med Asn, 80. *Mem:* Am Philos Soc (secy, 63-66, pres, 76-); Int Fedn Surg Cols (vpres, 72-78, pres, 78-81); Soc Clin Surg (pres, 58-60); Am Surg Asn (pres, 72-73); Am Col Surgeons (pres, 71-72). *Res:* Nutrition of surgical patients; physiological factors regulating the level of prothrombin; factors affecting adhesion formation; clinical aspects of cancer. *Mailing Add:* Dept of Surg Sch Med Univ of Pa Philadelphia PA 19104

RHOADS, PAUL SPOTTSWOOD, b Terre Haute, Ind, Mar 12, 98; m 25; c 4. MEDICINE. *Educ:* Univ Chicago, BS, 22; Rush Med Col, MD, 24. *Prof Exp:* Asst med, Rush Med Col, 26-28, from instr to asst prof, 28-35; from asst prof to prof, 35-66, EMER PROF MED, MED SCH, NORTHWESTERN UNIV, 66-; DIR MED EDUC, REID MEM HOSP, 72- *Concurrent Pos:* Physician, Scarlet Fever Comt, McCormick Inst, Univ Chicago, 26-35; chmn med, Chicago Wesley Mem Hosp, 46-66; chief ed, Arch Internal Med, AMA, 51-62. *Mem:* Cent Soc Clin Res; Soc Exp Biol & Med; Am Asn Path & Bact; Am Col Physicians. *Res:* Infectious diseases; infection chemotherapy; antibiotic therapy. *Mailing Add:* Reid Mem Hosp 1401 Chester Blvd Richmond IN 47374

RHOADS, SARA JANE, b Kansas City, Mo, June 1, 20. ORGANIC CHEMISTRY. *Educ:* Univ Chicago, BS, 41; Columbia Univ, PhD(chem), 49. *Prof Exp:* Instr chem, Hollins Col, 44-45; from instr to assoc prof, 48-58, PROF CHEM, UNIV WYO, 58- *Concurrent Pos:* NSF sr fel, Swiss Fed Inst Technol, 56-57; vis prof, Univ Wash, 65. *Honors & Awards:* Garvan Medal, Am Chem Soc, 82. *Mem:* Am Chem Soc; The Chem Soc. *Res:* Mechanisms of organic reactions; thermal rearrangements and decompositions. *Mailing Add:* Dept of Chem Univ of Wyo Laramie WY 82071

RHOADS, WILLIAM DENHAM, b Livingston, Mont, Dec 8, 34; m 59; c 3. ANALYTICAL CHEMISTRY, METABOLISM. *Educ:* Col of the Pac, BS, 59, MS, 60, PhD(chem), 68. *Prof Exp:* Res assoc anal chem, Allergan Pharmaceut, Calif, 64-66; res asst, Diamond Walnut Growers, Calif, 66-68; sr anal chemist, Abbott Labs, Ill, 68-70; pres & dir res, 71-75, DIR RHOADS SCI CO, ANAL DEVELOP CORP, 76- *Mem:* Am Chem Soc. *Res:* Development of analytical procedures for the pharmaceutical, veterinary, agricultural chemical and food and beverage industries, specializing in gas and high speed liquid chromatography. *Mailing Add:* Rhoads Sci Co 4620 Edison Ave B Colorado Springs CO 80915

RHODA, RICHARD NOBLE, b Philadelphia, Pa, Oct 29, 18; m 45; c 2. CHEMISTRY. *Educ:* Univ Pittsburgh, BS, 39; Lehigh Univ, MS, 40, PhD(chem), 44. *Prof Exp:* Asst chem, Lehigh Univ, 40-43; asst prof & head dept, Albright Col, 43-44; from instr to asst prof, Lehigh Univ, 46-53; admin asst to the mgr, Int Nickel Co, 53-69, asst to the mgr, Paul D Merica Res Lab, 69-74, mgr admin serv, 74-76, PRIN SCIENTIST, INT NICKEL CO, 76- *Mem:* Am Chem Soc; Am Inst Mining, Metall & Petrol Eng; Am Soc Metals; Am Electroplaters Soc. *Res:* Ion exchange resin mechanisms; adsorption from solutions; specific gravity of pigments; inorganic preparations; platinum group chemistry; electroless plating; brazing alloys. *Mailing Add:* Int Nickel Co Sterling Forest Suffern NY 10901

RHODE, EDWARD A, JR, b Amsterdam, NY, July 25, 26; m 55; c 5. VETERINARY MEDICINE, PHYSIOLOGY. *Educ:* Cornell Univ, DVM, 47. *Prof Exp:* Instr vet med, Kans State Col, 48-51; from asst prof to assoc prof vet med, 51-64, actg dean, Sch Vet Med, 77-78, PROF VET MED, UNIV CALIF, DAVIS, 64-, ASSOC DEAN INSTR, SCH VET MED, 71- *Concurrent Pos:* USPHS spec fel, 59-60 & 66-67; mem basic sci coun, Am Heart Asn. *Mem:* AAAS; Am Vet Med Asn; Am Physiol Soc; Am Soc Vet Physiol & Pharmacol; Am Col Vet Internal Med. *Res:* Comparative mammalian cardiovascular physiology; veterinary cardiology; clinical medicine. *Mailing Add:* 1114 W Eighth St Davis CA 95616

RHODE, SOLON LAFAYETTE, III, b Reading, Pa, Dec 28, 38; m 65; c 2. VIROLOGY, CELL BIOLOGY. *Educ:* Princeton Univ, AB, 60; Thomas Jefferson Univ, MD, 64, PhD(exp path), 68. *Prof Exp:* Fel exp path, Jefferson Med Col, 68-69; med officer, US Navy, 69-70; assoc investr, 70-80, DIR, INST MED RES, BENNINGTON, VT, 80- *Res:* Virology of parvoviruses and DNA viruses; DNA replication and repair; molecular genetics; cancer. *Mailing Add:* Inst for Med Res 110 Hospital Dr Bennington VT 05201

RHODE, WILLIAM STANLEY, b Chicago, Ill, Nov 4, 41; c 4. NEUROPHYSIOLOGY. *Educ:* Univ Wis, Madison, BS, 63, MS, 64, PhD(elec eng), 70. *Prof Exp:* Fel neurophysiol, 69-70, asst dir, Comput Facil Lab, 70-72, DIR, COMPUT FACIL LAB & ASST PROF NEUROPHYSIOL, UNIV WIS, 72- *Honors & Awards:* Samuel Talbot Award, Inst Elec & Electronic Engrs, 70. *Mem:* Sigma Xi. *Res:* Investigation of cochlear mechanics and auditory neurophysiology; use of computers and instrumentation in neurophysiology. *Mailing Add:* 283 Med Sci Bldg Univ of Wis Madison WI 53706

RHODEN, RICHARD ALLAN, b Coatesville, Pa, May 8, 30; m 69; c 1. MAMMALIAN TOXICOLOGY. *Educ:* Lincoln Univ, AB, 51; Drexel Univ, MS, 67, PhD(environ toxicol), 71. *Prof Exp:* Chemist mil procurement, Defense Personnel Support Ctr, 51-56; chemist coatings develop, Naval Air Eng Ctr, 56-62, chemist aerospace safety & health, 62-66, res chemist, Naval Air Develop Ctr, 66-72; environ scientist environ health, Environ Protection Agency, 72-75; RES PHARMACOLOGIST OCCUP HEALTH, CTR DIS CONTROL, NAT INST OCCUP SAFETY & HEALTH, 75- *Concurrent Pos:* Lectr, Philadelphia Col Art, 71-72; lectr biol sci, Fed City Col, 73-74; fed exec, Develop Prog, 78-80. *Mem:* Am Chem Soc; Soc Occup & Environ Health; NY Acad Sci; Am Indust Hyg Asn; fel Am Inst Chemists. *Res:* Inhalation toxicology; occupational and environmental health effects. *Mailing Add:* Ctrs Dis Control 5600 Fishers Lane 8A 53 Rockville MD 20857

RHODES, ANDREW JAMES, b Inverness, Scotland, Sept 19, 11; Can citizen. MEDICAL MICROBIOLOGY, PUBLIC HEALTH. *Educ:* Univ Edinburgh, MB, ChB, 34, MD, 41; FRCP(E), 41; FRCP(C), 53; FFCM, 77. *Prof Exp:* House surgeon & asst bacteriologist, Royal infirmary Edinburgh, 34-35; lectr bact, Univ Edinburgh, 35-41; pathologist, Emergency Med Serv, Shropshire, 41-45; lectr, Dept Bact & Immunol, London Sch Hyg & Trop Med, 45-47; prof virus infections, Sch Hyg, 47-56, PROF MICROBIOL, SCH HYG & FAC MED, UNIV TORONTO, 56- *Concurrent Pos:* Bacteriologist, Shropshire County Coun, 41-45; res assoc, Connaught Med Res Labs, Univ Toronto, 47-53; dir & virologist, Res Inst, Hosp for Sick Children, Toronto, 53-56, active consult, 56-; chmn sect animal viruses, Int Cong Microbiol, Italy, 53; assoc prof pediat, Univ Toronto, 53-56, head dept microbiol, 56-70, dir sch hyg, 56-70; mem exp panel virus dis, WHO, Switz, 53-78, rapporteur, Exp Comt Poliomyelitis, Italy, 54, mem sci group human virus vaccines, Switz, 65; Can del, Int Conf Health Educ, USA, 62; Can rep, Int Comt Virus Nomenclature, 64-78; from assoc med dir to med dir, Lab Br, Ont Ministry Health, 70-75; consult, Ministry Health, 75-80; chmn, Rabies Adv Comt, Ont Ministry Natural Resources, 79-82. *Mem:* Am Epidemiol Soc; Am Soc Microbiol; Can Asn Med Bact; Can Pub Health Asn; Fel Royal Soc Can. *Res:* Virology; public health; microbiology. *Mailing Add:* 79 Rochester Ave Toronto ON M4N 1N7 Can

RHODES, ASHBY MARSHALL, b Hinton, WVa, July 5, 23. PLANT BREEDING. *Educ:* WVa Univ, BS, 48; Mich State Col, PhD(farm crops), 51. *Prof Exp:* From instr to asst prof, 51-65, assoc prof, 65,79, PROF VEG CROPS, UNIV ILL, URBANA, 79- *Mem:* Am Soc Hort Sci; Am Genetic Asn; Soc Syst Zool. *Res:* Breeding of sweet corn, cucurbits and horse radish; taxonomy; economic botany. *Mailing Add:* Veg Crops Bldg Univ of Ill Urbana IL 61801

RHODES, BUCK AUSTIN, b LaUnion, NMex, Aug 30, 35; c 1. RADIOLOGY, PHARMACOLOGY. *Educ:* NMex State Univ, BS, 58; Johns Hopkins Univ, PhD(radiol sci), 68. *Prof Exp:* From asst prof radiol sci to assoc prof radiol & environ health, Sch Med, Hyg & Pub Health, Johns Hopkins Univ, 66-75; prof pharmacol & radiol, Univ Kans Med Ctr, 75-76; prof pharm & radiol, Univ NMex, 76-91; VPRES SCI AFFAIRS, NUC-MED, INC, ALBUQUERQUE, NMEX, 81- *Mem:* Am Bd Sci Nuclear Med;

Soc Nuclear Med. *Res:* Development of new radiopharmaceuticals and diagnostic tests for peripheral vascular diseases; immuno diagnostics and therapy. *Mailing Add:* Nuc MED, Inc 3240 Juan Tabo Blvd NE Albuquerque NM 87111

RHODES, CHARLES KIRKHAM, b NY, June 30, 39; m 64; c 3. ATOMIC PHYSICS, LASERS. *Educ:* Cornell Univ, BEE, 63; Mass Inst Technol, MEE, 65, PhD(physics), 69. *Prof Exp:* Staff specialist, Control Data Corp, NY, 69-70; physicist, Lawrence Livermore Lab, Univ Calif, 70-75; sr physicist, Molecular Physics Ctr, SRI Int, 75-77; PROF PHYSICS, UNIV ILL-CHICAGO CIRCLE, 78- *Concurrent Pos:* Lectr appl sci, Univ Calif, Davis, 71-75; mem, Adv Group Electron Devices; comt mem, Joint Coun Quantum Electronics; adj prof elec eng, Stanford Univ. *Mem:* Fel Am Phys Soc; sr mem Inst Elec & Electronics Engrs. *Res:* Atomic and molecular energy transfer, chemical processes and kinetics, coherent pulse propagation, saturation spectroscopy; nonlinear optics; collisional broadening of spectral lines, and high pressure electron-beam excited ultraviolet and visible lasers. *Mailing Add:* Dept of Physics PO Box 4348 Chicago IL 60680

RHODES, DALLAS D, b El Dorado, Kans, Aug 8, 47; m 81. GEOMORPHOLOGY. *Educ:* Univ Mo-Columbia, BS, 69; Syracuse Univ, MA & PhD(geol), 73. *Prof Exp:* Asst prof geol, Univ Vt, 73-77; asst prof, 77-81, ASSOC PROF GEOL & DIR, FAIRCHILD AERIAL PHOTOG COLLECTION, WHITTIER COL, 81- *Concurrent Pos:* Consult geologist, NY State Geol Surv, 75-76 & Jet Propulsion Lab, 80- *Mem:* Am Geophys Union; Geol Soc Am; Sigma Xi; Soc Econ Paleontologists & Mineralogists. *Res:* Detailing relationships of fluvial hydraulic geometry to the river's sedimentology, channel shape, and channel pattern; analysis of hydralic geometry in terms of a most probable state; planetary geomorphology with emphasis on Mars. *Mailing Add:* Dept of Geol Whittier Col Whittier CA 90608

RHODES, DAVID R, b Wichita, Kans, Oct 22, 36; m 54; c 4. ANALYTICAL CHEMISTRY, ELECTROCHEMISTRY. *Educ:* Friends Univ, BA, 57; Univ Ill, MS, 59, PhD(chem), 61. *Prof Exp:* Res chemist, 61-71, sr res chemist, 71-74, SR RES ASSOC, CHEVRON RES CO, 74- *Mem:* Am Chem Soc; Electrochem Soc. *Res:* Electroanalytical chemistry; pollution analysis; trace analysis; corrosion; fuel cells. *Mailing Add:* Chevron Res Co 576 Standard Ave Richmond CA 94802

RHODES, DONALD R(OBERT), b Detroit, Mich, Dec 31, 23. ELECTRICAL ENGINEERING. *Educ:* Ohio State Univ, BEE, 45, MSc, 48, PhD(elec eng), 53. *Prof Exp:* Res assoc elec, Ohio State Univ, 44-54; res engr, Cornell Aeronaut Lab, Inc, 54-57; head basic res dept, Radiation, Inc, 57-61, sr scientist, 61-66; PROF ELEC ENG, NC STATE UNIV, 66- *Concurrent Pos:* Instr, Ohio State Univ, 48-52; mem comn B, Int Sci Radio Union. *Honors & Awards:* John T Bolljahn Award, Inst Elec & Electronics Engrs, 63; Benjamin G Lamme Medal, Ohio State Univ, 75. *Mem:* Fel AAAS; fel Inst Elec & Electronics Engrs. *Res:* Antenna synthesis. *Mailing Add:* Dept Elec Eng NC State Univ Raleigh NC 27650

RHODES, DONALD WALTER, applied chemistry, see previous edition

RHODES, E(DWARD), b Elland, Eng, Jan 31, 38; m 62; c 3. CHEMICAL ENGINEERING. *Educ:* Univ Manchester, BScTech, 60, MScTech, 61, PhD(chem eng), 64. *Prof Exp:* Asst lectr chem eng, Univ Manchester, 62-64; from asst prof to assoc prof, 64-74, PROF CHEM ENG, UNIV WATERLOO, 74-, CHMN DEPT, 76- *Mem:* Brit Inst Chem Engrs; Am Inst Chem Engrs; Can Soc Chem Eng. *Res:* Multiphase flow; mass transfer; boiling; condensation. *Mailing Add:* Dept of Chem Eng Univ of Waterloo Waterloo ON N2L 3G1 Can

RHODES, EDWARD JOSEPH, JR, b San Diego, Calif, June 1, 46; m 72; c 1. SOLAR ASTRONOMY, SPACE PHYSICS. *Educ:* Univ Calif, Los Angeles, BS, 68, MA, 71, PhD(astron), 77. *Prof Exp:* Fel researcher, Univ Calif, Los Angeles, 75-77, asst res astronomer, 78-79; ASST PROF ASTRON, UNIV SOUTHERN CALIF, 79- *Concurrent Pos:* Scientist, Jet Propulsion Lab, 70-77, sr scientist, 78-; res fel, Dept Physics, Calif Inst Technol, 77-78; adj asst prof astron, Univ Southern Calif, 78-79; mem, Adv Solar Observ Sci Study Team, NASA, 81-, Solar Beacon Sci Study Team, 81-, Solar Cycle & Dynamics Sci Working Group, 78-79 & Star Probe Imaging Comt, 79-80. *Mem:* Am Astron Soc; Am Geophys Union. *Res:* Observational and theoretical research into the internal structure of the sun using the tool of solar oscillations; spatial behavior of the solar wind. *Mailing Add:* Dept Astron Sci B-3 Univ Southern Calif Los Angeles CA 90007

RHODES, FRANK HAROLD TREVOR, b Warwickshire, Eng, Oct 29, 26; m 52; c 4. GEOLOGY, PALEONTOLOGY. *Educ:* Univ Birmingham, BSc, 48, PhD, 50, DSc, 63. *Prof Exp:* Fel & Fulbright scholar, Univ Ill, 50-51; lectr geol, Univ Durham, 51-54; asst prof, Univ Ill, 54-55, assoc prof, 55-56, dir, Wyo Field Sta, 56; prof geol & head dept, Univ Wales, Swansea, 56-68, dean fac sci, 67-68; prof geol & mineral, Univ Mich, Ann Arbor, 68-77, res assoc, Mus Paleont & dean, Col Lit Sci & Arts, 71-74, vpres acad affairs, 74-77; PRES, CORNELL UNIV, 77-, PROF GEOL & MINERAL, 77- *Concurrent Pos:* External examinerships, Univ Bristol, 58-61, Univ Belfast, 60-62, Oxford Univ & Univ Reading, 63-65, vis prof, Univ Ill, 59; Gurley lectr, Cornell Univ, 60; dir first int field studies conf, Nat Sci Found-Am Geol Inst, 61; ed geol ser, Commonwealth & Int Libr, 62-; mem, Bd Geol Surv Gt Brit, 63-65; mem Australian vchancellor's comt vis, Australian Univs, 64; Brit Coun lectr univs & geol surveys, India, Pakistan, Thailand, Turkey & Iran, 64; NSF sr scientist fel, Ohio State Univ, 65-66; mem geol & geophys comt & subcomt postgrad awards, Nat Environ Res Coun, 65-68; Bownocker lectr, Ohio State Univ, 66; mem curric panel, Coun Educ Geol Sci, 70-71, chmn panel, 71; mem bd trustees, Carnegie Found Advan Teaching, 78- *Honors & Awards:* Daniel Pidgeon Fund Award, Geol Soc London, 53; Lyell Fund Award, 57; Bigsby Medal, 67. *Mem:* Geol Soc London; Brit Palaeont Asn (vpres, 63-68); Brit Asn Advan Sci; Geol Soc Am; Paleont Soc. *Res:* Stratigraphy; micropaleontology, especially conodonts; evolution; extinction; biogeochemistry; paleoecology; higher education; science and public policy. *Mailing Add:* Off of the President Cornell Univ Ithaca NY 14853

RHODES, GEORGE WYATT, lasers, see previous edition

RHODES, IAN BURTON, b Melbourne, Australia, May 29, 41; m 64; c 2. ELECTRICAL ENGINEERING, APPLIED MATHEMATICS. *Educ:* Melbourne, BE, 63, MEngSc, 65; Stanford Univ, PhD(elec eng), 68. *Prof Exp:* Res engr, Stanford Res Inst, 67; asst prof elec eng, Mass Inst Technol, 68-70; assoc prof eng & appl sci, Washington Univ, 70-76, prof, 76-80; PROF ELEC & COMPUT ENG, UNIV CALIF, SANTA BARBARA, 80- *Mem:* Soc Indust & Appl Math; Inst Elec & Electronics Engrs. *Res:* Decision and control sciences; system theory; control theory; estimation theory; optimization theory. *Mailing Add:* Dept Elec & Comput Eng Univ Calif Santa Barbara CA 93106

RHODES, JACOB LESTER, b Linville, Va, Jan 13, 22; m 60; c 4. NUCLEAR PHYSICS. *Educ:* Lebanon Valley Col, BS, 43; Univ Pa, PhD, 58. *Prof Exp:* Asst res physicist, Johns Hopkins Univ, 43-46; asst instr physics, Univ Pa, 46-49, asst res physicist, 49-52; asst prof & chmn dept, Roanoke Col, 52-56; assoc prof, 57-65, PROF PHYSICS, LEBANON VALLEY COL, 65- *Mem:* Am Phys Soc; Am Asn Physics Teachers; Sigma Xi. *Res:* Low energy nuclear physics, electronics; x-ray diffraction. *Mailing Add:* Dept of Physics Lebanon Valley Col Annville PA 17003

RHODES, JAMES B, b Kansas City, Mo, July 22, 28; m 60; c 3. GASTROENTEROLOGY, BIOCHEMISTRY. *Educ:* Univ Kans, AB, 54, MD, 58. *Prof Exp:* Intern med & surg, Univ Chicago Hosps, 58-59, resident med, 60-62; asst med, 64-66; asst prof med & physiol, 66-70, assoc prof med & physiol, 70-79, PROF MED, UNIV KANS MED CTR, KANSAS CITY, 79- *Concurrent Pos:* Fel biochem, Ben May Lab Cancer Res, Univ Chicago, 59-60, trainee gastroenterol, Univ Hosps, 62-64; fel, Chicago Med Sch, 64-66, res assoc biochem, 64-66. *Mem:* AAAS; Am Physiol Soc; AMA; Am Gastroenterol Asn; Am Soc Gastrointestinal Endoscopy. *Res:* Clinical gastroenterology; digestive biochemistry; digestion and absorption of the intestinal epithelial cell; physiology. *Mailing Add:* Dept Med Univ Kans Med Ctr Kansas City KS 66103

RHODES, JOHN LEWIS, b Columbus, Ohio, July 16, 37. MATHEMATICS. *Educ:* Mass Inst Technol, BS, 60, PhD(math), 62. *Prof Exp:* NSF fel, Paris, France, 62-63; from asst prof to assoc prof, 63-70, PROF MATH, UNIV CALIF, BERKELEY, 70- *Concurrent Pos:* Vpres, Krohn-Rhodes Res Inst, 64-68; US Air Force res grant, Univ Calif, Berkeley, 65-68; mem, Inst Advan Study, 66; Alfred P Sloan fel, 67. *Res:* Algebraic theory of finite state machines and finite semigroups; finite physics from an algebraic viewpoint; neural nets; context free languages. *Mailing Add:* Dept of Math Univ of Calif Berkeley CA 94720

RHODES, JOHN MARSHELL, b Oakland, Calif, Mar 26, 26; m 67; c 2. NEUROPSYCHOLOGY. *Educ:* Univ Calif, Los Angeles, BA, 53; Los Angeles State Col, MA, 55; Univ Southern Calif, PhD, 59. *Prof Exp:* Instr, Whittier Col, 58-59; holder of USA table comp zool, Sta Zool, Naples, 59-60; USPHS fel neurophysiol, Fac Med, Univ Aix Marseille, 60-62; asst res anatomist & assoc mem brain res inst, Space Biol Lab, Univ Calif, Los Angeles, 62-65; assoc prof psychol, 65-71, PROF PSYCHOL & NEUROL, UNIV NMEX, 71- *Mem:* Am Psychol Asn; Am Physiol Soc; Am EEG Soc. *Res:* Acute and chronic animal experiments with implanted electrodes; clinical electroencephalographic studies with neurological disorders in humans; multiple physiological recording and its computer application; clinical neuropsychology. *Mailing Add:* Dept of Psychol Univ of NMex Albuquerque NM 87106

RHODES, LANDON HARRISON, b Alton, Ill, Mar 15, 47; m 70. PLANT PATHOLOGY. *Educ:* Univ Ill, BS, 70, MS, 75, PhD(plant path), 77. *Prof Exp:* ASST PROF PLANT PATH, OHIO STATE UNIV, 76- *Mem:* Am Phytopath Soc; Mycol Soc Am. *Res:* Ecology and physiology of vesicular-arbuscular mycorrhizae; utilization of mycorrhizae in agricultural systems. *Mailing Add:* Dept of Plant Path Ohio State Univ Columbus OH 43210

RHODES, MITCHELL LEE, b Chicago, Ill, Feb 12, 40; m 63; c 3. PULMONARY DISEASES. *Educ:* Univ Ill, Urbana, BS, 61, Chicago, MD, 65. *Prof Exp:* USPHS trainee pulmonary dis, Univ Chicago, 68-70, instr med, 70; clin instr med, Univ Calif, San Francisco, 71-72; from asst prof to assoc prof med, Col Med, Univ Iowa, 72-76; assoc prof, 76-81, PROF MED, COL MED, IND UNIV, 81- *Concurrent Pos:* Chief pulmonary dis, USPHS Hosp, San Francisco, 70-72; NIH pulmonary acad awardee, Nat Heart & Lung Inst, 74- *Honors & Awards:* Cecile Lehman Mayer Res Award Pulmonary Dis, Am Col Chest Physicians, 74. *Mem:* Am Thoracic Soc; Am Fedn Clin Res; Am Col Chest Physicians. *Res:* Use of computer assidted instruction in medical education; correlation of ultrastructural and metabolic changes in lung tissue; studies of adaptive responses of pulmonary cells to oxidative injury. *Mailing Add:* Ind Univ Sch of Med 1100 W Michigan St Indianapolis IN 46202

RHODES, RICHARD KENT, b Portsmouth, Va, Sept 4, 48; m 73; c 1. CONNECTIVE TISSUE BIOCHEMISTRY, DEVELOPMENTAL BIOLOGY. *Educ:* Davidson Col, BS, 70; Emory Univ, PhD(develop biol), 74. *Prof Exp:* Res assoc, 75-78, instr, 79-81, RES ASST PROF BIOCHEM, UNIV ALA, BIRMINGHAM, 81- *Concurrent Pos:* Investr, Inst Dent Res, Univ Ala, Birmingham, 79- *Mem:* AAAS. *Res:* Biochemical characterization of genetically distinct collagens, their interaction with cells of connective tissue matrix and the role of extracellular matrix in developmental processes. *Mailing Add:* Inst Dent Res Univ Ala Birmingham AL 35294

RHODES, ROBERT ALLEN, b Harrisonburg, Va, May 10, 41; m 63; c 3. PHARMACEUTICAL CHEMISTRY. *Educ:* Bridgewater Col, BA, 63; Univ Md, Baltimore, PhD(pharmaceut chem), 68. *Prof Exp:* Asst biochem, Ahmadu Bello Univ, Nigeria, 68-70; asst prof, 70-77, ASSOC PROF CHEM, MID GA COL, 70- *Concurrent Pos:* Fel, Oak Ridge Assoc Univs, 76. *Mem:* AAAS; Am Chem Soc; Sigma Xi. *Res:* Indole and heterocyclic synthesis. *Mailing Add:* 224 Brookwood Dr Dublin GA 31021

RHODES, ROBERT CARL, b Detroit, Mich, Nov 14, 36; m 65; c 1. ORGANIC CHEMISTRY, ANALYTICAL CHEMISTRY. *Educ:* Univ Calif, Riverside, BA, 58; NMex Highlands Univ, MS, 59; Univ Wash, PhD(org chem), 63. *Prof Exp:* Res chemist, 63-70 & sr res chemist, Wilmington plant, 70-77, SUPVR ANAL CHEMISTS LAB, BIOCHEM DEPT, E I DU PONT DE NEMOURS & CO, INC, LA PORTE, TX, 77- *Mem:* Am Chem Soc; Sigma Xi. *Res:* Behavior and movement of organic chemicals in soil. *Mailing Add:* Biochem Dept E I du Pont de Nemours & Co Inc La Porte TX 77571

RHODES, ROBERT SHAW, b Orangeburg, SC, Mar 3, 36; m 64; c 2. HEMATOLOGY, OCCUPATIONAL MEDICINE. *Educ:* SC State Col, BS, 58; Meharry Med Col, MD, 62. *Prof Exp:* Intern, Hubbard Hosp, Nashville, 62-63; med officer & aviation pathologist, Armed Forces Inst Path Aerospace Br, 67-70; fel hemat, Dept Internal Med, Vanderbilt Univ, 70-72; resident path, Meharry Med Col, 63-67, dir hemat & clin labs, 72-75, assoc prof internal med & path, 72-78; assoc med dir, 78-82, DIR HEALTH SERV, HYDROMATIC DIV, GEN MOTORS, 82- *Concurrent Pos:* Consult Aerospace Pathologists, Nat Transp Safety Bd, 67-70; assoc investr clin studies, Vanderbilt Univ Clin Res Ctr, 70-72; proj dir, Nat Heart & Lung Inst Contract, Clin Trials Vaso-occlusive Crisis Treatment, Meharry Med Col, 71-73; mem ad hoc sickle cell contracts rev comt, Nat Heart & Lung Inst, 74-76; consult, Nat Asn Sickle Cell Dis, Nat Educ Proj Sickle Cell Dis, 75- *Mem:* Am Soc Clin Path; Am Asn Blood Banks; Am Soc Hemat; AAAS. *Res:* Miscellaneous studies on the natural history of sickle cell disease and the sickling process. *Mailing Add:* 3428 Oak Dr Ypsilanti MI 48197

RHODES, RONDELL H, b Abbeville, SC, May 25, 18. DEVELOPMENTAL BIOLOGY, HISTOLOGY. *Educ:* Benedict Col, BS, 40; Univ Mich, MS, 50; NY Univ, PhD(biol), 60. *Prof Exp:* Instr biol, Lincoln Univ, Mo, 47-49; asst prof, Tuskegee Inst, 50-55; assoc prof, 61-68, actg chmn dept, 66-67, chmn dept biol sci, 67-70, 73-76 & 74-82, PROF BIOL, FAIRLEIGH DICKINSON UNIV, 68- *Mem:* AAAS; Nat Asn Biol Teachers; Am Soc Zool. *Res:* Histochemical studies involving ribonucleic acid and alkaline phosphatase in developing pituitary glands of the amphibia. *Mailing Add:* Dept of Biol Sci Fairleigh Dickinson Univ Teaneck NJ 07666

RHODES, RUSSELL G, b St Louis, Mo, Aug 28, 39; m 61; c 1. PHYCOLOGY. *Educ:* Univ Mo-Kansas City, BS, 61; Univ Tenn, MS, 63, PhD(bot), 66. *Prof Exp:* Res assoc bot, Univ Tenn, 66; assoc prof bot, Kent State Univ, 66-77; PROF LIFE SCI & HEAD DEPT, SOUTHWEST MO STATE UNIV, 77- *Concurrent Pos:* Mem, Ohio Biol Surv, 67. *Mem:* Phycol Soc Am; Brit Phycol Soc; Int Phycol Soc. *Res:* Morphogenesis of brown algae; cultivation of acidophilic algae; isolation and cultivation of Chyrsophytan algae. *Mailing Add:* Dept Biol SW Missouri State Univ Springfield MO 65804

RHODES, WILLIAM CLIFFORD, b Birmingham, Ala, Aug 8, 32; m 57; c 3. THEORETICAL CHEMISTRY, CHEMICAL DYNAMICS. *Educ:* Howard Col, AB, 54; Johns Hopkins Univ, PhD(biochem), 58. *Prof Exp:* Am Cancer Soc fel chem, 58-59, from instr to assoc prof, 59-70, exec dir, Inst Molecular Physics, 75-79, dir, 79-80, PROF CHEM, FLA STATE UNIV, 70- *Concurrent Pos:* Am Cancer Soc fel, 60-61; NSF sr fel, 64-65; NIH career develop award, 65-70. *Res:* Biophysics; quantum chemistry; dynamic aspects of molecular excitation and relaxation processes; selective excitation by laser and conventional light; energy channeling in molecular systems. *Mailing Add:* Dept of Chem Fla State Univ Tallahassee FL 32306

RHODES, WILLIAM GALE, b Eden, NC, Apr 13, 43; m 65; c 2. ORGANIC CHEMISTRY, BIOCHEMISTRY. *Educ:* NC State Univ, BS, 65; Univ NC, PhD(chem), 71. *Prof Exp:* Res assoc chem, Univ NC, 70-71; asst prof chem, Northeast Mo State Col, 71-72; asst prof chem, Maryville Col, Tenn, 72-73, chmn dept, 73-77; ASST PROF CHEM, WHITMAN COL, WALLA WALLA, 77- *Concurrent Pos:* Cottrell Col Sci grant, Res Corp, 74-75. *Mem:* Am Chem Soc. *Res:* Molecular evolution; studies on the origin of conjugated proteins and of catalytic and ion-transporting proteins. *Mailing Add:* Dept of Chem Whitman Col Walla Walla WA 99362

RHODES, WILLIAM HARKER, b Titusville, NJ, Apr 26, 25; m 58; c 5. VETERINARY MEDICINE. *Educ:* NY Univ, BA, 51; Univ Pa, VMD, 55, MMedSci, 58. *Prof Exp:* Instr, 55-58, assoc, 58-59, from asst prof to assoc prof, 59-70, PROF RADIOL, SCH VET MED, UNIV PA, 70-, CHIEF SECT, 64- *Concurrent Pos:* Chmn organizing comt, Am Bd Vet Radiol; ed, Jour Am Vet Radiol Soc. *Mem:* Am Vet Med Asn; Am Vet Radiol Soc (past pres); Educ Vet Radio Sci (past pres). *Res:* Veterinary clinical radiology; degenerative joint disease and radiology of the canine thorax. *Mailing Add:* Sch of Vet Med Univ of Pa 39th & Woodland Philadelphia PA 19174

RHODES, WILLIAM HOLMAN, b Oneonta, NY, Sept 13, 35; m 57; c 2. CERAMICS, METALLURGY. *Educ:* Alfred Univ, BS, 57; Mass Inst Technol, ScD(ceramics), 65. *Prof Exp:* Trainee, Gen Elec Co, 57-58, engr, 60-62; group leader ceramics, Mat Sci Dept, Avco Systs Div, 65-73; MEM TECH STAFF, GTE LABS, INC, 73- *Concurrent Pos:* Prof lectureship, Northeastern Univ, 71- *Mem:* Fel Am Ceramic Soc. *Res:* Physical ceramics, especially mechanical and optical properties, kinetics of densification by sintering and pressure sintering and basic diffusion studies; fabrication of ceramics, composites and metals from powders. *Mailing Add:* GTE Labs Inc 40 Sylvan Rd Waltham MA 02154

RHODES, WILLIAM TERRILL, b Palo Alto, Calif, Apr 14, 43; m 64; c 2. ELECTRICAL ENGINEERING, OPTICS. *Educ:* Stanford Univ, BS, 66, MSEE, 68, PhD(elec eng), 72. *Prof Exp:* Res asst electronics labs, Stanford Univ, 69-71; from asst prof to assoc prof, 71-80, PROF ELEC ENG, GA INST TECHNOL, 81- *Concurrent Pos:* Consult, Resalab, Inc, 70-73 & Naval Res Lab, 74-; Humboldt res fel, Univ Erlangen, Nurnberg, 76. *Mem:* Fel Soc Photo-Optical Instrumentation Engrs; fel Optical Soc Am; Inst Elec & Electronics Engrs. *Res:* Synthetic aperture optics; image formation; hybrid optical-digital signal processing; numerical and algebraic optical processing; noncoherent optical processing; acousto-optic signal processing. *Mailing Add:* Sch of Elec Eng Ga Inst of Technol Atlanta GA 30332

RHODES, YORKE EDWARD, b Elizabeth, NJ, Mar 25, 36; m 57; c 3. PHYSICAL ORGANIC CHEMISTRY, SPACE CHEMISTRY. *Educ:* Univ Del, BS, 57, MS, 59; Univ Ill, PhD(org chem), 64. *Prof Exp:* NIH fel org chem, Yale Univ, 64-65; asst prof, 65-71, ASSOC PROF ORG CHEM, NY UNIV, 71- *Concurrent Pos:* Guest prof, Freiburg Univ, 72-73; guest prof, Tech Univ Munich, 77-78; Alexander von Humboldt US sr scientist award, 78- *Mem:* Am Chem Soc; The Chem Soc. *Res:* Small ring chemistry; carbonium ion rearrangements; neighboring group participation, especially by cyclopropane; solvolysis mechanisms; nonaqueous solvents; stereochemistry and reaction mechanisms; synthesis and reactions of strained polycyclic systems; organic chemistry of the interstellar media, including proposal and synthesis of new compounds. *Mailing Add:* Dept of Chem NY Univ 4 Washington Pl New York NY 10003

RHODIN, JOHANNES A G, b Lund, Sweden, Sept 30, 22; m 80; c 2. CELL BIOLOGY, ELECTRON MICROSCOPY. *Educ:* Karolinska Inst, Stockholm, MD, 50, PhD(anat), 54. *Prof Exp:* Instr anat, Karolinska Inst, 50-54, asst prof, 54-57; assoc prof, Sch Med, New York Univ, 58-60, prof, 60-64; prof & chmn, Dept Anat, New York Med Col, 64-74, Univ Mich, Ann Arbor, 74-77 & Med Sch, Karolinska Inst, 77-79; PROF & CHMN, DEPT ANAT, UNIV SOUTH FLA, 79- *Concurrent Pos:* Landis Res Award, Microcirulatory Soc, 70. *Mem:* Am Soc Cell Biol; Am Asn Anatomists; Microcirculatory Soc; Europ Soc Microcirculation; Europ Artery Club. *Res:* Functional and ultrastructural changes that precede and occur during the development of hypertension in the spontaneously hypertensive rat, using a combination of intravital microscopy and electron microscopy. *Mailing Add:* Dept Anat Col Med Univ South Fla 12901 N 30th St Tampa FL 33612

RHODIN, THOR NATHANIEL, JR, b Buenos Aires, Arg, Dec 9, 20; US citizen; m 48; c 4. CHEMICAL PHYSICS. *Educ:* Haverford Col, BS, 42; Princeton Univ, AM, 45, PhD(chem physics), 46. *Prof Exp:* Res assoc, Manhattan Proj, Princeton Univ, 42-47; mem staff, Inst Study Metals, Univ Chicago, 47-51; res assoc, Eng Res Lab, E I du Pont de Nemours & Co, 51-58; assoc prof appl physics, 58-68, PROF APPL PHYSICS & MEM FAC, SCH APPL & ENG PHYSICS, CORNELL UNIV, 68- *Concurrent Pos:* NSF fel, Cambridge Univ, 64-65; vis prof, Mass Inst Technol, Univ Munich & Univ Tokyo; adv ed, Surface Sci J. *Mem:* Fel Am Phys Soc. *Res:* Physics and chemistry of metal and semiconductor surfaces and interfaces; synchronae radiation spectroscopy; cluster chemistry. *Mailing Add:* Sch of Appl & Eng Physics Clark Hall G217 Cornell Univ Ithaca NY 14850

RHODINE, CHARLES NORMAN, b Denver, Colo, Jan 10, 31; m 57; c 3. ELECTRICAL & BIOLOGICAL ENGINEERING. *Educ:* Univ Wyo, BS, 57, MS, 59; Purdue Univ, PhD, 73. *Prof Exp:* Assoc prof, 59-80, PROF ELEC ENG, UNIV WYO, 80- *Concurrent Pos:* NSF fel, Purdue Univ, 67-69. *Mem:* Inst Elec & Electronics Engrs; Nat Soc Prof Engrs; Sigma Xi. *Res:* Communications and information theory, its application to biological systems; development of computer-aided teaching equipment. *Mailing Add:* Dept of Elec Eng Univ of Wyo Laramie WY 82070

RHOTEN, WILLIAM BLOCHER, b Orange, NJ, Feb 11, 43; m 69; c 2. ANATOMY, PHYSIOLOGY. *Educ:* Colo State Univ, BS, 65; Univ Ill, Urbana, MS, 68; Pa State Univ, PhD(anat), 71. *Prof Exp:* Res fel path, Sch Med, Washington Univ, 71-73; instr med, Div Endocrinol & Metab, Sch Med, Univ Ala, 73-74; asst prof anat, Sch Basic Med Sci, Col Med, Univ Ill, Urbana, 74-80; asst prof, 80-82, ASSOC PROF ANAT, NJ MED SCH, UNIV MED & DENT NJ, 82- *Concurrent Pos:* Solocited reviewer, Reg Biol, Anat Record Sci, Div Int Prog, Vet Admin East Res Develop Off, NSF, 82- *Mem:* Am Asn Anat; Am Diabetes Asn; AAAS; NY Acad Sci; Sigma Xi. *Res:* Cell biology; developmental biology; experimental diabetes; diabetes mellitus; structure-function relationships in the endocrine pancreas; peptide secretion; myoinositol metabolism; binding proteins. *Mailing Add:* Dept Anat NJ Med Sch Univ Med & Dent NJ 100 Bergen St Newark NJ 07103

RHOTON, ALBERT LOREN, JR, b Parvin, Ky, Nov 18, 32; m 57; c 4. NEUROSURGERY. *Educ:* Ohio State Univ, BS, 54; Wash Univ, MD, 59. *Prof Exp:* Fel neurol surg, Sch Med, Wash Univ, 63-65, NIH spec fel neuroanat, 65-66; from instr to asst prof neurol surg, Mayo Found, Univ Minn, 66-72; prof neurol surg & chief div, 72-79, R D KEENE FAMILY PROF NEUROL SURG & CHMN DEPT, UNIV FLA, 79- *Concurrent Pos:* Consult, Gainesville Vet Admin Hosp; NIH travel award, 65; Krayenbuhl lectr & hon guest, Swiss Soc Neurol Surg, 75 & Japanese Neurosurg Soc, 77; vis fac mem & lectr, Harvard Univ, Duke Univ, Johns Hopkins Univ, Univ Pa, Univ Chicago & Univ Calif, San Francisco & Los Angeles. *Honors & Awards:* Billings Bronze Medal Sci Exhibit, AMA, 69; Jones Award Outstanding Med Exhibit, Am Asn Med Illustrators, 69. *Mem:* Am Asn Neurol Surg; Am Col Surgeons; Cong Neurol Surg (vpres, 73-74, pres, 78); Neurosurg Soc Am; Soc Neurol Surg (treas, 76-79). *Res:* Microneurosurgery; microsurgical anatomy; neuroanatomy of the cranial nerves; microsurgery of cerebrovascular disease. *Mailing Add:* Box J265 Univ of Fla Med Ctr Gainesville FL 32610

RHUM, DAVID, polymer chemistry, organic chemistry, see previous edition

RHYKERD, CHARLES LOREN, b Cameron, Ill, Apr 7, 29; m 54; c 3. PLANT PHYSIOLOGY. *Educ:* Univ Ill, BS, 51, MS, 52; Purdue Univ, PhD(agron), 57. *Prof Exp:* Asst agron, Univ Ill, 51-52; technician, Producers Seed Co, Ill, 53-54; asst instr agron, Ohio State Univ, 54-55; asst, Purdue Univ, 55-56, instr, 56-57; soil scientist, US Regional Pasture Res Lab, Pa, 57-60; from asst prof to assoc prof, 60-66, PROF AGRON, PURDUE UNIV, WEST LAFAYETTE, 66- *Concurrent Pos:* AID consult, Brazil, 65; vis prof, Univ Calif, Davis, 67-68; co-dir, Nat Corn & Sorghum Proj, Brazil, AID contract with Brazilian Ministry of Agr & Purdue Univ, 73-75; mem, Am Forage & Grassland Coun. *Mem:* Am Soc Agron; Crop Sci Soc Am. *Res:* Physiology of forage crops; soil fertility. *Mailing Add:* Dept of Agron Purdue Univ West Lafayette IN 47907

RHYNE, A LEONARD, b Charlotte, NC, Dec 19, 34; m 56; c 4. MATHEMATICAL STATISTICS. *Educ:* Univ NC, AB, 57; NC State Univ, PhD(math statist), 64. *Prof Exp:* Prof math, Elon Col, 60-62; ASSOC PROF BIOSTATIST, BOWMAN GRAY SCH MED, 62-, DIR COMPUT CTR, 65- *Mem:* Inst Math Statist; Biomet Soc; Am Statist Asn. *Res:* Applications of computer science and statistical methods in various areas of medical research. *Mailing Add:* Comput Ctr Bowman Gray Sch of Med Winston-Salem NC 27103

RHYNE, JAMES JENNINGS, b Oklahoma City, Okla, Nov 14, 38; m 61; c 2. SOLID STATE PHYSICS. *Educ:* Univ Okla, BS, 59; Univ Ill, Urbana, MS, 61; Iowa State Univ, PhD(physics), 65. *Prof Exp:* Res asst physics, Iowa State Univ, 63-65; res physicist, Solid State Div, US Naval Ord Lab, 65-75; PHYSICIST, REACTOR DIV, NAT BUR STANDARDS, 75- *Concurrent Pos:* Nat Acad Sci-Nat Res Coun associateship, US Naval Ord Lab, 65-66; adj prof, Am Univ, 75- co-ed, Proc Conf Magnetism & Magnetic Mat, 70-75. *Mem:* Fel Am Phys Soc. *Res:* Magnetic and transport properties of rare-earth metals and compounds; neutron scattering in magnetic materials. *Mailing Add:* Reactor Div Nat Bur of Standards Washington DC 20234

RHYNE, THOMAS CROWELL, b Lincolnton, NC, Nov 8, 42; m 65; c 1. PHYSICAL INORGANIC CHEMISTRY. *Educ:* Appalachian State Univ, BS, 65, MA, 67; Va Polytech Inst & State Univ, PhD(chem), 71. *Prof Exp:* Res assoc chem, Aerospace Res Labs, Wright-Patterson AFB, Ohio, 71-72; asst prof, 72-80, ASSOC PROF CHEM & ASST DEAN, GRAD SCH, APPALACHIAN STATE UNIV, 80- *Concurrent Pos:* Nat Acad Sci-Nat Res Coun fel, 71-72. *Mem:* Am Chem Soc; Am Soc Mass Spectrometry. *Res:* Positive and negative ion chemical ionization mass spectrometry; gas chromatography; mass spectrometry; chemical ionization techniques applied to inorganic systems. *Mailing Add:* Dept of Chem Appalachian State Univ Boone NC 28608

RHYNE, V(ERNON) THOMAS, b Gulfport, Miss, Feb 18, 42; m 61. ELECTRICAL ENGINEERING, COMPUTER SCIENCE. *Educ:* Miss State Univ, BS, 62; Univ Va, MEE, 64; Ga Inst Technol, PhD(elec eng), 67. *Prof Exp:* Aerospace technologist data systs, Langley Res Ctr, NASA, 62-65; instr elec eng, Ga Inst Technol, 65-67; from asst prof to assoc prof, 67-77, PROF ELEC ENG, TEX A&M UNIV, 77- *Concurrent Pos:* Consult, Tex Instruments Inc, Dallas, 68-69, Pinnel-Anderson-Wilshire, Inc, 70-, Elec Power Res Inst, 78- & NASA, 78-; pres, Tex Digital Systs, Inc, Bryan, 72- *Mem:* Inst Elec & Electronics Engrs; Asn Comput Mach. *Res:* Digital systems design in various applications areas, especially satellite navigation systems and electric power distribution automation; computer design; arithmetic processes; computer software. *Mailing Add:* Dept of Elec Eng Tex A&M Univ College Station TX 77840

RHYNER, CHARLES R, b Wausau, Wis, Mar 25, 40; m 63; c 4. SOLID STATE PHYSICS. *Educ:* Univ Wis, BS, 62, MS, 64, PhD(physics), 68. *Prof Exp:* Asst prof physics, Univ Wis, Kenosha, 67-68; physicist, US Naval Radiol Defense Lab, Calif, 68; asst prof, 68-72, ASSOC PROF PHYSICS, UNIV WIS-GREEN BAY, 72- *Mem:* Am Phys Soc; Sigma Xi; Am Asn Physics Teachers. *Res:* Thermoluminescence; color centers in alkali halides; radiation dosimetry; solid waste management. *Mailing Add:* Col of Environ Sci Univ of Wis Green Bay WI 54305

RHYNSBURGER, ROBERT WHITMAN, b Kalamazoo, Mich, Dec 5, 25. ASTRONOMY. *Educ:* George Washington Univ, BA, 50; Georgetown Univ, MA, 55. *Prof Exp:* Astronomer, US Naval Observ, 52-80; RETIRED. *Honors & Awards:* Supt's Award, US Naval Observ, 75. *Res:* Meridian astrometry; proper motions; astronomical history. *Mailing Add:* 1428 Wellington Court Cape Coral FL 33904

RIAZ, M(AHMOUD), b Paris, France, Feb 27, 25; nat US; m 64; c 1. ELECTRICAL ENGINEERING. *Educ:* Univ Paris, LLB, 44; Univ Cairo, Egypt, BSc, 46; Rensselaer Polytech Inst, MEE, 47; Mass Inst Technol, ScD, 55. *Prof Exp:* Asst elec eng, Mass Inst Technol, 52-54, from instr to asst prof, 54-59; assoc prof, 59-78, PROF ELEC ENG, UNIV MINN, MINNEAPOLIS, 78- *Concurrent Pos:* Consult, Suntee Systs Inc. *Honors & Awards:* Levy Medal, Franklin Inst, 72. *Mem:* Inst Elec & Electronics Engrs; Tensor Soc; Brit Inst Elec Eng; Int Solar Energy Soc. *Res:* Energy conversion and control; electromechanical systems; power systems; solar energy systems. *Mailing Add:* Dept of Elec Eng Univ of Minn Minneapolis MN 55455

RIBAK, CHARLES ERIC, b Albany, NY, July 19, 50; m 77; c 1. NEUROSCIENCE, NEUROANATOMY. *Educ:* State Univ NY, Albany, BS, 71; Boston Univ, PhD(neuroanat), 76. *Prof Exp:* Assoc res scientist neurosci, City Hope Nat Med Ctr, 75-78; ASST PROF ANAT, UNIV CALIF, IRVINE, 78- *Mem:* Am Asn Anatomists; Soc Neurosci; NY Acad Sci; AAAS. *Res:* Analysis of neurons in normal and epileptic cerebral cortex with the electron microscope; neurocytology of gama-aminobutyric acid neurons with immunocytochemistry; electron microscopic studies of local circuit neurons in the hippocampus and neocortex. *Mailing Add:* Dept Anat Univ Calif Irvine CA 92717

RIBAN, DAVID MICHAEL, b Chicago, Ill, May 10, 36; m 63; c 3. SCIENCE EDUCATION. *Educ:* Northern Ill Univ, BSEd, 57; Univ Mich, MA, 60; Purdue Univ, MS, 67, PhD(physics educ), 69. *Prof Exp:* Teacher physics, Luther High Sch South, Chicago, 57-60 & Leyden Sch, Northlake, Ill, 60-67; teaching asst physics, Purdue Univ, 68-69; assoc prof, 70-73, PROF PHYSICS, INDIANA UNIV PA, 74- *Concurrent Pos:* Dir, Intermediate Sci Curric Study Training Prog, Installed User Prog, NSF, 72-73 & Teacher Training Prog, 75-76, dir, Proj Physics Training Prog, 74-75 & 75-76. *Mem:* Nat Asn Res Sci Teaching; Am Asn Physics Teachers; AAAS; Nat Sci Teachers Asn; Nat Educ Asn. *Res:* Science curriculum implementation; learning theory; effects of field work in science in promoting learning; history of the development of scientific ideas. *Mailing Add:* Dept of Physics Indiana Univ of Pa Indiana PA 15701

RIBAS, JORGE LUIS, b Guayaquil, Ecuador, Jan 19, 42; US citizen; m 67; c 2. NEUROPATHOLOGY, INFECTIOUS DISEASE PATHOLOGY. *Educ:* Southwest Mo State Univ, BS, 68; Univ Mo-Columbia, DVM, 71. *Prof Exp:* Res vet neurobiol, Walter Reed Army Inst Res, Washington, DC, 72-75; res vet, Armed Forces Radiobiol Res Inst, Bethesda, 75-77; from asst prof to assoc prof anat, Sch Med, Uniformed Serv Univ Health Sci, 76-81; NAT CANCER INST FEL, COMPARATIVE PATH, SCH MED, UNIV ALA, BIRMINGHAM, 81- *Concurrent Pos:* USPHS fel, Sch Med, Univ Rochester, NY, 71-72; guest worker neuropath, Armed Forces Inst Path, Washington, DC, 73-75; guest worker neurochem, NIMH, Bethesda, 75-76; vis scientist, Armed Forces Inst Pathol, Washington, DC, 81. *Mem:* Soc Neurosci; Am Asn Anatomists; Electron Micros Soc; Am Asn Neuropathologists. *Res:* Morphology and function of brain perinventricular regions and comparative neuroendocrinology. *Mailing Add:* 655 Scottwood Dr Auburn AL 36830

RIBBE, PAUL HUBERT, b Bristol, Conn, Apr 2, 35; m 58; c 3. MINERALOGY. *Educ:* Wheaton Col, Ill, BS, 56; Univ Wis, MS, 58; Cambridge Univ, PhD(crystallog), 63. *Prof Exp:* Mineralogist, Corning Glass Works, 58-60; NSF fel, Univ Chicago, 63-64; asst prof geol, Univ Calif, Los Angeles, 64-66; assoc prof, 66-72, PROF MINERAL, VA POLYTECH INST & STATE UNIV, 72- *Concurrent Pos:* Ed, Reviews Mineral. *Mem:* Microbeam Anal Soc; fel Mineral Soc Am; Mineral Asn Can; Asn Earth Sci Ed. *Res:* Crystal structure analysis and chemistry of rock-forming minerals, particularly feldspars and orthosilicates. *Mailing Add:* Dept of Geol Sci Va Polytech Inst & State Univ Blacksburg VA 24061

RIBBENS, WILLIAM B(ENNETT), b Grand Rapids, Mich, May 26, 37; m 72. ELECTRICAL ENGINEERING. *Educ:* Univ Mich, Ann Arbor, BSEE, 60, MS, 61, PhD(elec eng), 65. *Prof Exp:* Design engr, Lear Inc, Mich, 60; res asst, 60-63, res engr, Cooley Elec Lab, 63-65, assoc res engr, 65-67, proj dir, 67-69, ASSOC PROF ELEC & COMPUT ENG, UNIV MICH, ANN ARBOR, 69- *Concurrent Pos:* Consult to various industs. *Mem:* Inst Elec & Electronics Engrs; Optical Soc Am. *Res:* Coherent optical data processing and optical metrology; instrumentation. *Mailing Add:* Dept of Elec & Comput Eng Univ of Mich Ann Arbor MI 48109

RIBBONS, DOUGLAS WILLIAM, b London, Eng, Aug 28, 36; m 61; c 2. BIOCHEMISTRY, MICROBIOLOGY. *Educ:* Univ Wales, BSc, 57, PhD(microbial metab), 60, DSc(microbial metab), 72. *Prof Exp:* Asst lectr, univ Glasgow, 60-63; lectr, Univ Hull, 63-64; sr scientist, Shell Res Ltd, 64-68; assoc prof, 69-71, RES PROF BIOCHEM & MICROBIOL, SCH MED, UNIV MIAMI, 71-, VCHMN DEPT BIOCHEM, 72- *Concurrent Pos:* Fel, Howard Hughes Med Inst, 68-72, dir labs microbial & biochem res, 68-72; NSF res grant, NIH res grants. *Mem:* Am Soc Biol Chemists; Brit Biochem Soc; Brit Soc Gen Microbiol; Am Soc Microbiol; Am Chem Soc. *Res:* Microbial growth and metabolism of hydrocarbons and aromatic compounds; oxygenases. *Mailing Add:* Dept of Biochem Sch Med Univ of Miami Miami FL 33124

RIBE, FRED LINDEN, b Laredo, Tex, Aug 14, 24; m 46; c 4. PHYSICS. *Educ:* Univ Tex, BS, 44; Univ Chicago, SM, 50, PhD(physics), 51. *Prof Exp:* Engr, Eng Res Assocs, Inc, 46-47; asst, Inst Nuclear Studies, Univ Chicago, 47-50; mem staff, Los Alamos Sci Lab, Univ Calif, 51-74, div leader, Controlled Thermonuclear Res Div, 74-77; PROF NUCLEAR ENG, UNIV WASH, SEATTLE, 77- *Concurrent Pos:* Vis prof, Univ Iowa, 56; Guggenheim fel, Inst Plasma Physics, Munich, Ger, 63-64; adj prof physics, Univ Tex, Austin, 74- *Mem:* Fel Am Phys Soc; Am Nuclear Soc. *Res:* Nuclear reactions; fast neutron research; atomic collisions; plasma physics. *Mailing Add:* 6079 Wellesley Way NE Seattle WA 98115

RIBE, M(ARSHALL) L(OUIS), b San Antonio, Tex, June 17, 19; m 43; c 2. ELECTRICAL ENGINEERING. *Educ:* Univ Tex, BSEE, 39, BSME, 40; Rutgers Univ, MSEE, 50. *Prof Exp:* Chief radio relay br, Signal Corps Eng Labs, US Dept Army, Ft Monmouth, NJ, 51-56; mgr systs eng projs, Int Div, Radio Corp Am, 56-59, mgr common systs progs, Commun Lab, 59-64, mgr ground equip prog, Commun Systs Div, 64-66, mgr eastern region, Defense Electronic Prod, 67-69, MGR, EASTERN FIELD OFF OPERS, GOVT SYSTS DIV, RCA CORP, 69- *Mem:* Sr mem Inst Elec & Electronics Engrs. *Res:* Management of electronic systems marketing, design and development. *Mailing Add:* Eastern Field Off Opers RCA Gov Syst Div 90 Monmouth St Red Bank NJ 07701

RIBELIN, WILLIAM EUGENE, b Oxnard, Calif, Oct 1, 24; m 49; c 1. VETERINARY PATHOLOGY. *Educ:* Iowa State Col, DVM, 49; Wash State Col, MSc, 52; Univ Wis, PhD, 56. *Prof Exp:* Instr vet path, Wash State Col, 49-52; res vet, USDA, Holland, 52-54; prof vet path, Auburn Univ, 56-58; head path invests, Western Regional Lab, USDA, 58-61; sr scientist, Environ Health Lab, Am Cyanamid Co, 61-68; dir res, Animal Resource Ctr & prof vet path & med path, Univ Wis-Madison, 68-78; SR PATHOLOGIST, MONSANTO CO, 78- *Mem:* Am Vet Asn; Am Asn Pathologists; Soc Toxicol; Conf Res Workers Animal Dis; Am Col Vet Path. *Res:* Comparative and toxicologic pathology. *Mailing Add:* Monsanto Environ Health Lab 800 N Lindbergh St St Louis MO 63166

RIBENBOIM, PAULO, b Recife, Brazil, Mar 13, 28; m 51; c 2. MATHEMATICS. *Educ:* Univ Brazil, BS, 48; Univ Sao Paulo, PhD, 57. *Hon Degrees:* Dr, Univ Caen, France. *Prof Exp:* Asst, Cent Brazil Phys Res, 49-50; prof math, Army Tech Sch, Brazil, 52-53; res chief, Inst Pure & Appl Math, 57-59; vis assoc prof, Univ Ill, 59-62; PROF MATH, QUEEN'S UNIV, ONT, 62- *Concurrent Pos:* Vis prof, Northeastern Univ, 65 & Univ Paris, 69-70. *Mem:* Fel Royal Soc Can; Am Math Soc; assoc Brazilian Acad Sci; Can Math Soc; Math Soc France. *Res:* Algebra; theory of ideals; commutative algebra; algebraic number theory; Fermat's last theorem. *Mailing Add:* Dept of Math Queen's Univ Kingston ON K7L 3NG Can

RIBES, LUIS, b Madrid, Spain, Sept 12, 40; m 64; c 2. ALGEBRA. *Educ:* Univ Madrid, Licenciado, 62; Univ Rochester, MA, 65, PhD(math), 67; Univ Madrid, DrCiencias, 69. *Prof Exp:* Asst prof math, Univ Ill, Urbana, 67-68; res assoc & asst prof math, Queen's Univ, 68-70; res assoc prof, 72-79, PROF MATH, CARLETON UNIV, 79- *Mem:* Am Math Soc; Can Math Cong; Spanish Math Soc. *Res:* Cohomology of groups, discrete and profinite; structure of free profinite and free products of profinite groups; combinational group theory. *Mailing Add:* Dept Math Carleton Univ Ottawa ON K1S 5B6 Can

RIBI, EDGAR, b Zurich, Switz, Sept 5, 20; nat US; m 51; c 2. BIOPHYSICS. *Educ:* Univ Berne, PhD(chem, physics, mineral), 48. *Prof Exp:* Asst teacher chem, Univ Berne, 46-48; res assoc phys chem, Upsala Col, 49-50, res assoc biochem, 51; fel, NIH, 52, biophysicist, Rocky Mountain Lab, Nat Inst Allergy & Infectious Dis, 52-57, HEAD MOLECULAR BIOL SECT, ROCKY MOUNTAIN LAB, NAT INST ALLERGY & INFECTIOUS DIS, 57- *Concurrent Pos:* NIH lectr, 62; mem tuberc panel, US-Japan Coop Med Serv Prog, 65- *Honors & Awards:* Product & Eng Master Design Award, 62; US Dept Health, Educ & Welfare Superior Serv Award, 67. *Mem:* AAAS; Am Thoracic Soc; Int Cong Microbiol; Am Venereal Dis Asn. *Res:* Structure and biological function of Enterobacteriaceae, mycobacteria and tumor cells; development of vaccines against tuberculosis and identification of mycobacterial adjuvants useful for immunotherapy of cancer. *Mailing Add:* 311 S Eighth Hamilton MT 59840

RIBLE, JOHN MAURICE, soil science, deceased

RIBLET, GORDON POTTER, b Boston, Mass, Dec 12, 43; m 72; c 1. ELECTRICAL ENGINEERING, PHYSICS. *Educ:* Yale Univ, BS, 65; Univ Pa, MS, 66, PhD(physics), 70. *Prof Exp:* Res scientist physics, Univ Cologne, 70-72; RES SCIENTIST ENG, MICROWAVE DEVELOP LABS, INC, 72- *Concurrent Pos:* Dir, Parametric Indust, 76-; pres, Fab-Braze Corp, 77- *Mem:* Am Phys Soc; Inst Elec & Electronics Engrs. *Res:* Solid state physics, especially effect of magnetic impurities on superconductivity; microwave technology, especially circuit properties of multiport networks. *Mailing Add:* 11 Michigan Dr Natick MA 01760

RIBLET, LESLIE ALFRED, b Wayne County, Ohio, Aug 10, 41; m 65; c 1. PHARMACOLOGY, PHYSIOLOGY. *Educ:* Ashland Col, BS, 63; Univ Mo-Kansas City, BS, 66, MS, 68; Univ Iowa, PhD(pharmacol), 71. *Prof Exp:* Sr scientist, Mead Johnson Res Ctr, 71-74; sr investr, 74-76, sr res assoc pharmacol, 76-79, SECT MGR, MEAD JOHNSON PHARMACEUT DIV, 79- *Mem:* Soc Neurosci; Sigma Xi; AAAS; Soc Exp Biol Med; NY Acad Sci. *Res:* Central nervous system pharmacology with emphasis on quantitative electroencephalogram correlates of behavioral and neurochemical indices of brain function. *Mailing Add:* Dept of Biol Res Mead Johnson Pharmaceut Div Evansville IN 47721

RIBLET, ROY JOHNSON, b Charlotte, NC, Dec 24, 42; m 64; c 3. IMMUNOLOGY, GENETICS. *Educ:* Calif Inst Technol, BS, 64; Stanford Univ, PhD(genetics), 71. *Prof Exp:* Fel immunol, Salk Inst, 71-74; res assoc immunogenetics, 74-75, asst mem, 75-78, ASSOC MEM IMMUNOGENETICS, INST CANCER RES, 78- *Concurrent Pos:* Fel, Damon Runyon Mem Fund Cancer Res, Inc, 71-73; spec fel, Leukemia Soc Am, 73-75; NIH res grant, 77-84. *Mem:* Genetics Soc Am; AAAS; Am Asn Immunologists. *Res:* Genetic control of the immune response; mouse antibody genetics; mitogen response genetics; antibody structure and function. *Mailing Add:* Inst for Cancer Res 7701 Burholme Ave Philadelphia PA 19111

RIBNER, HERBERT SPENCER, b Seattle, Wash, Apr 9, 13; m 49; c 2. ACOUSTICS: AERODYNAMICS. *Educ:* Calif Inst Technol, BS, 35; Washington Univ, MS, 37, PhD(physics), 39. *Prof Exp:* From physicist to dir lab, Brown Geophys Co, Tex, 39-40; from physicist to head stability anal sect, Langley Lab, Nat Adv Comt Aeronaut, Va, 40-49, from consult to head boundary layer sects, Lewis Lab, Ohio, 49-54; res assoc, Inst Aerospace Studies, Univ Toronto, 55-56, from asst prof to prof, 56-59; PROF AEROSPACE STUDIES, INST AEROSPACE STUDIES, UNIV TORONTO, 59- *Concurrent Pos:* Vis prof, Univ Southampton, 60-61; consult, De Havilland Aircraft; chmn sonic boom panel, Int Civil Aviation Orgn, 70-71; consult, Ministry Transport, Can, 70-73 & Gen Elec Co, Cincinnati, 73-75; staff scientist aeroacoustics, NASA Langley Res Ctr, 75-76. *Honors & Awards:* Aeroacoustics Award, 76; Dryden lectr, Am Inst Aeronaut & Astronaut, 81. *Mem:* Fel Am Inst Aeronaut & Astronaut; fel Royal Soc Can; fel Am Phys Soc; fel Acoust Soc Am; fel Can Aeronaut & Space Inst. *Res:* X-rays; cosmic rays; development of gravity meter; aerodynamics; aeroacoustics; jet noise; sonic boom; acoustics of thunder. *Mailing Add:* Inst Aerospace Studies Univ Toronto 4925 Dufferin St Downsview ON M3H 5T6 Can

RICARDI, LEON J, b Brockton, Mass, Mar 21, 24; m 47; c 3. ELECTRICAL ENGINEERING. *Educ:* Northeastern Univ, BS, 49, MS, 52, PhD(elec eng), 69. *Prof Exp:* Proj engr, James L Waters, Inc, 49-50, Andrew Alford Consult Eng, 50-51 & Gabriel Labs, 51-54; staff mem microwave antenna & component design, Mass Inst Technol, 54-57, asst group leader, Lincoln Lab, 57-59, group leader radio frequency components & propagation, 59-80, GROUP LEADER ANTENNAS, LINCOLN LAB, MASS INST TECHNOL, 80- *Concurrent Pos:* Lectr & teacher, Northeastern Univ, 69- *Mem:* Fel Inst Elec & Electronics Engrs. *Res:* Design and development of microwave components and antennas for use in ground, air and space communications systems and radars; investigation of electromagnetic wave propagation phenomena; communications systems analysis. *Mailing Add:* 12 Priscilla Circle Wellesley Hills MA 02181

RICCA, PAUL JOSEPH, b Brooklyn, NY, Apr 25, 39; m 61; c 2. ANALYTICAL CHEMISTRY. *Educ:* Syracuse Univ, AB, 61; Purdue Univ, PhD(anal chem), 66. *Prof Exp:* Asst, Purdue Univ, 61-65; adv planning analyst, LTV Aerospace Corp, Dallas, 67-68; eng specialist, 68-71, dir labs &

vpres, Anderson Labs, Inc, Ft Worth, 71-75; PRES, RICCA CHEM CO, 75- *Mem:* AAAS; Am Chem Soc; Am Ord Asn. *Res:* Electrochemical kinetics and reaction mechanisms; formulation and development of new missile system concepts; production of prepared chemical reagents and testing solutions. *Mailing Add:* 1512 Oak Glen Court Arlington TX 76012

RICCA, PETER M, engineering, see previous edition

RICCA, VINCENT THOMAS, b New York, NY, Dec 19, 35; m 57; c 3. HYDROLOGY, HYDRAULIC ENGINEERING. *Educ:* City Col New York, BS, 62; Purdue Univ, Lafayette, MSCE, 64, PhD(water resources eng), 66. *Prof Exp:* Teaching assoc civil eng, Purdue Univ, Lafayette, 62-63; from asst prof to assoc prof, 63-73, PROF CIVIL ENG, OHIO STATE UNIV, 73- *Concurrent Pos:* Hydrol & hydraul eng consult, 66- *Honors & Awards:* Raymond Q Armington Award, Ohio State Univ, 68. *Mem:* Am Soc Civil Engrs; Am Soc Eng Educ; Am Water Resources Asn; Am Geophys Union. *Res:* Small watershed hydrology; flood plain management; streamflow simulation computer modeling; groundwater studies; stream surface profiles; acid mine drainage models. *Mailing Add:* Dept of Civil Eng Ohio State Univ Columbus OH 43210

RICCI, BENJAMIN, b Cranston, RI, Apr 5, 23; m 44; c 3. APPLIED PHYSIOLOGY. *Educ:* Springfield Col, BPE, 49, MS, 50, PhD(appl physiol), 58. *Prof Exp:* Chmn dept, 71-73, PROF EXERCISE SCI, UNIV MASS, AMHERST, 66- *Concurrent Pos:* Fulbright fel, Inst Work Physiol, Oslo, Norway, 71 & Inst Human Physics, Rome, Italy, 78. *Res:* Adaptation of biochemical, biomechanical, heat regulatory, cardiopulmonary and neuromuscular systems to stress imposed by work or exercise. *Mailing Add:* Dept Exercise Sci Univ Mass Amherst MA 01003

RICCI, ENZO, b Buenos Aires, Arg, Nov 8, 25; m 57; c 3. APPLIED PHYSICS, ATOMIC PHYSICS. *Educ:* Univ Buenos Aires, Lic chem sci, 52, PhD(chem), 54; Univ Tenn, MS, 71. *Prof Exp:* Staff mem nuclear chem res, Arg Atomic Energy Comn, 53-61, head activation anal group nuclear chem res & develop, 61-62; staff mem nuclear chem & physics res & develop, Oak Ridge Nat Lab, 62-80; MGR RES & DEVELOP ENRICHMENT SAFEGUARDS, NUCLEAR DIV, UNION CARBIDE CORP, 80- *Concurrent Pos:* Lab asst, Univ Buenos Aires, 50-57, lab demonstr, 58-59, prof, 61-62; Int Atomic Energy Agency fel, Chalk River Nuclear Labs, Can, 59-61. *Mem:* Fel Am Nuclear Soc; Am Chem Soc; Arg Chem Asn. *Res:* Nuclear methods of analysis; nuclear reaction cross sections; fusion plasma-wall interactions; x-ray and electron spectroscopy. *Mailing Add:* Union Carbide Corp Nuclear Div PO Box P Oak Ridge TN 37831

RICCI, JOHN ETTORE, b New York, NY, Jan 1, 07; m. PHYSICAL CHEMISTRY. *Educ:* NY Univ, BS, 26, MS, 28, PhD(chem), 31. *Prof Exp:* From instr to prof, 31-77, EMER PROF CHEM, NY UNIV, 77- *Concurrent Pos:* Consult, Oak Ridge Nat Lab, 53- *Mem:* Am Chem Soc. *Res:* Phase rule; aqueous solubilities; solid solutions; non-aqueous solvents; ionization constants; hydrogen ion concentration; fused salts. *Mailing Add:* Dept Chem NY Univ Washington Sq New York NY 10003

RICCI, JOHN SILVIO, JR, b Springfield, Mass, Aug 17, 40. PHYSICAL CHEMISTRY, INORGANIC CHEMISTRY. *Educ:* Am Int Col, AB, 62; Columbia Univ, MA, 63; State Univ NY, Stony Brook, PhD(chem), 69. *Prof Exp:* Fel chem, Northwestern Univ, 69-70; prof, Windham Col, 70-77; PROF CHEM, WILLIAMS COL, 77- *Concurrent Pos:* Res collabr, Brookhaven Nat Lab, 71- *Mem:* Am Chem Soc; Am Crystallog Asn. *Res:* Molecular structure determination of transition metal complexes; organo-phosphorus and organo-sulfur compounds. *Mailing Add:* Dept of Chem Williams Col Williamstown MA 01267

RICCI, ROBERT WILLIAM, physical organic chemistry, see previous edition

RICCIUTI, FLORENCE CHRISTINE, b New Haven, Conn, Aug 29, 44. HUMAN GENETICS. *Educ:* Albertus Magnus Col, BA, 66; Yale Univ, PhD(biol), 73. *Prof Exp:* Asst res med genetics, Yale Univ Med Sch, 66-68, fel, Dept Human Genetics, 72-75; ASST PROF BIOL & CHMN DEPT BIOL, ALBERTUS MAGNUS COL, 75- *Mem:* Sigma Xi. *Res:* Human gene mapping using somatic cell genetics and studying differentiation and X chromosome inactivation in embryonic and adult tissues. *Mailing Add:* Dept of Biol 700 Prospect St Albertus Magnus Col New Haven CT 06511

RICCOBONO, PAUL XAVIER, b New York, NY, Jan 5, 39; m 59. ORGANIC CHEMISTRY, POLYMER CHEMISTRY. *Educ:* Brooklyn Col, BS, 59; NY Univ, MS, 63, PhD(org chem), 64. *Prof Exp:* Res chemist, Nat Biscuit Co, 59-60 & E I du Pont de Nemours & Co, Inc, 64-67; sr res chemist, Airco, 67-68; group leader, Cent Res Labs, J P Stevens & Co, Inc, 68-71, mgr, Cent Anal Dept, 71-73, mgr, 73-77, dir, Mat Res & Eval Dept, 77-81; DIR RES, CONGOLEUM CORP, 81- *Concurrent Pos:* Assoc res dir, Indust Res Inst. *Mem:* Instrument Soc Am; Am Chem Soc; Am Soc Testing & Mat. *Res:* Resolution of optically active cyclooctatetraene derivatives; photochemistry of maleic anhydride derivatives; preparation and properties of graft copolymers; toxic chemicals legislation; textile chemistry; advanced materials characterization and analysis techniques; utilization of cold plasma and radiation for materials performance modification. *Mailing Add:* Congoleum Corp Sloan Ave Trenton NJ 08619

RICE, ANDREW CYRUS, food bacteriology, see previous edition

RICE, BARBARA SLYDER, b Chambersburg, Pa, Dec 19, 37; m 63; c 3. MATHEMATICS. *Educ:* Clark Univ, AB, 59; Univ Va, MA, 61, PhD(math), 65. *Prof Exp:* Res asst math, Univ Va, 61-63; adj prof, Fla Inst Technol, 63-73; ASST PROF MATH, ALA AGR & MECH UNIV, 75- *Mem:* Am Math Soc; Math Asn Am; Sigma Xi; Nat Asn Mathematicians. *Res:* Development of more effective teaching processes for use with mathematically inexperienced students. *Mailing Add:* 308 Flemington Rd SE Huntsville AL 35802

RICE, BERNARD, b Milwaukee, Wis, Dec 5, 14. PHYSICAL CHEMISTRY. *Educ:* George Washington Univ, BS, 37; Univ Chicago, PhD(chem), 48. *Prof Exp:* Chemist, Nat Bur Standards, 38-42; from asst prof to assoc prof, 49-61, PROF CHEM, ST LOUIS UNIV, 61- *Mem:* Am Chem Soc. *Res:* Molecular structure; spectroscopy; theoretical chemistry. *Mailing Add:* Dept of Chem St Louis Univ St Louis MO 63103

RICE, CHARLES EDWARD, b Seminole, Okla, Feb 13, 32; m 56; c 2. ENGINEERING, AGRICULTURE. *Educ:* Okla State Univ, BS, 60, MS, 61; Univ Minn, Minneapolis, PhD(agr eng), 72. *Prof Exp:* Res engr, Agr Res Serv, USDA, 61-66; asst prof, 66-74, ASSOC PROF AGR ENG, OKLA STATE UNIV, 74-; RES HYDRAULIC ENGR, AGR RES SERV, USDA, 78- *Mem:* Am Soc Agr Engrs. *Res:* Open channel hydraulics; hydraulics of conservation structures; overland flow. *Mailing Add:* Rte 5 Box 366 Okla State Univ Stillwater OK 74074

RICE, CHARLES MERTON, b Whitmore Lake, Mich, Jan 26, 25; m 47; c 8. NUCLEAR ENGINEERING. *Educ:* Albion Col, AB, 48; Univ Mo-Rolla, MS, 49. *Prof Exp:* Assoc prof physics, Oglethorpe Univ, 49-51; physicist, Atomic Energy Comn, 51-54; proj supvr, Ford Instrument Co, 54-55; head atomic power eng group, Sargent & Lundy, 55-56; mgr reactor eng dept, Advanced Technol Lab, 56-59; prog mgr, Aerojet Gen Corp, 59-69; pres, Idaho Nuclear Corp, 69-70 & Aerojet Nuclear Co, 70-72; pres & chmn bd, Energy Inc, 72-81; PRES, RICE INC, 78- *Concurrent Pos:* Prin, LRS Consult, 81- *Mem:* Fel Am Nuclear Soc; Atomic Indust Forum. *Res:* Gas cooled reactor technology and nuclear rocket propulsion. *Mailing Add:* Rice Inc 355 W 14th St Idaho Falls ID 83402

RICE, DALE WARREN, b Grand Haven, Mich, Jan 21, 30. MARINE MAMMALOGY. *Educ:* Ind Univ, AB, 52; Univ Fla, MS, 55. *Prof Exp:* Wildlife res biologist, US Fish & Wildlife Serv, 55-58; WILDLIFE RES BIOLOGIST, NAT MARINE FISHERIES SERV, 58- *Concurrent Pos:* Mem whale specialist group, Survival Serv Comn, Int Union Conserv Nature & Natural Resources, 67- *Mem:* Am Soc Mammalogists; Wildlife Soc; Soc Syst Zool; Am Inst Biol Sci; Am Ornithologist Union. *Res:* Life history, ecology and population dynamics of marine mammals, especially baleen whales and sperm whales. *Mailing Add:* Nat Marine Fisheries Serv 7600 Sand Point Way Bldg 32 Seattle WA 98115

RICE, DALE WILSON, b Jamestown, NY, Nov 21, 32; m 60; c 2. PHYSICAL CHEMISTRY. *Educ:* Mass Inst Technol, SB, 54, PhD(polymer chem), 61. *Prof Exp:* Res assoc, Corning Glass Works, 61-75; eng consult, Centorr Assocs, Inc, 75-78, tech dir, 78-81; PRES, DELTA LABS, 81- *Mem:* AAAS; Am Chem Soc; Am Ceramic Soc; Am Asn Crystal Growth. *Res:* High temperature technology; engineering design; high temperature and vacuum technology. *Mailing Add:* Delta Q Labs PO Box 64 West Nottingham NH 03291

RICE, DAVID E, b Northfield, Minn, Dec 8, 33; m 65; c 3. ORGANIC CHEMISTRY, POLYMER CHEMISTRY. *Educ:* St Olaf Col, BA, 55; Univ Minn, PhD(org chem), 59. *Prof Exp:* res specialist, 59-80, STAFF SCIENTIST, 3M CO, 80- *Mem:* AAAS; Am Chem Soc; Sigma Xi. *Res:* Fluorocarbon polymers; organic synthesis. *Mailing Add:* 3M Co 3M Ctr St Paul MN 55144

RICE, DENNIS KEITH, b Newell, WVa, Dec 12, 39; m 70; c 3. LASER PHYSICS, STRATEGIC PLANNING. *Educ:* Cleveland State Univ, BEE, 64; Univ Southern Calif, MSEE, 66, PhD(elec eng), 70. *Prof Exp:* Prin engr, Laser Technol Labs, 71-74, dir eng, 74, mgr, Laser Lab, 74-76, prog mgr, 76-78, mgr laser-optical eng, Northrop Corp Res & Technol Ctr, 78-80, ASST TO GEN MGR TECHNOL & PLANNING, NORTHROP ELECTRO-MECH DIV, 80- *Res:* Optics; thin films; spectroscopy; solid state physics; atmospheric physics. *Mailing Add:* Northrop Electro-Mech Div 500 E Orangethorpe Ave Anaheim CA 92801

RICE, DOROTHY PECHMAN, b Brooklyn, NY, June 11, 22; m 43; c 3. HEALTH STATISTICS. *Educ:* Univ Wis, BA, 41. *Prof Exp:* Pub health analyst health serv res, Div Hosp & Med Facil, USPHS, 60-62; social sci analyst, Div Res & Statist, Social Security Admin, 62-64; pub health analyst econ, Div Community Health Serv, USPHS, 64-65; chief, Health Ins Res Br, Social Security Admin, 65-72, dep asst comnr res & statist, 72-76; DIR HEALTH STATIST, NAT CTR HEALTH STATIST, 76- *Honors & Awards:* Jack C Massey Award, 78; Award for Excellence, Am Pub Health Asn, 78. *Mem:* Inst of Med; fel Am Statist Asn; fel Am Pub Health Asn; Am Econ Asn. *Res:* Primary responsibility at the federal level to provide national statistics in matters relating to health, including births, deaths, illness, disability, health services, marriages and divorces. *Mailing Add:* 8410 Barron St Takoma Park MD 20912

RICE, E(LBERT) F(LOYD), b Jerome, Idaho, Apr 7, 23; m 44; c 4. CIVIL & HYDRAULIC ENGINEERING. *Educ:* Univ Idaho, BS, 48; Ore State Col, MS, 49, PhD, 55. *Prof Exp:* Instr gen eng, Ore State Col, 47-52; from asst prof to assoc prof civil eng, UNIV ALASKA, 65- *Concurrent Pos:* Consult, 52-; NSF fac fel, city & regional planning, Mass Inst Technol, 58-59. *Mem:* Fel AAAS; fel Am Soc Civil Engrs; Am Soc Eng Educ; Int Glaciological Soc; Nat Soc Prof Engrs. *Res:* Arctic engineering; regional planning. *Mailing Add:* Dept of Civil Eng Univ of Alaska Fairbanks AK 99701

RICE, ELMER HAROLD, b Alhambra, Calif, Feb 1, 23; m 46; c 2. BIOCHEMISTRY. *Educ:* Whittier Col, AB, 47; Univ Southern Calif, PhD(biochem), 58. *Prof Exp:* Asst biochem, Univ Southern California, 49-50; jr res biochemist, Med Ctr, Univ Calif, 57-59; from asst prof to assoc prof chem, 59-71, PROF CHEM, CALIF STATE POLYTECH UNIV, POMONA, 71- *Mem:* AAAS; Am Soc Microbiol; Am Chem Soc. *Res:* Liptropic factors related to cholesterol metabolism; carbohydrate containing proteins; bacterial antigens; steroid compounds related to bile acids. *Mailing Add:* Dept of Chem Calif State Polytech Univ Pomona CA 91768

RICE, ELROY LEON, b Edmond, Okla, Jan 31, 17; m 45; c 2. BOTANY. *Educ:* Cent State Col, Okla, BA, 38; Univ Okla, MS, 42; Univ Chicago, PhD(bot), 47. *Prof Exp:* From asst prof to assoc prof, 48-62, PROF PLANT SCI, UNIV OKLA, 62-, DAVID ROSS BOYD PROF BOT, 67- *Mem:* AAAS; Ecol Soc Am; Am Soc Plant Physiol; Am Inst Biol Sci; Brit Ecol Soc. *Res:* Growth and development of range grasses; plant inhibitors, especially allelopathy; old-field succession. *Mailing Add:* Dept of Bot & Microbiol Univ of Okla Norman OK 73069

RICE, EUGENE WORTHINGTON, b Martinsburg, WVa, Aug 12, 20; m 46; c 2. CLINICAL BIOCHEMISTRY, BIOANALYTICAL CHEMISTRY. *Educ:* WVa Univ, BS, 42; George Washington Univ, MS, 48, PhD(biochem), 50. *Prof Exp:* Anal chemist, Celanese Corp Am, Md, 42; res biochemist, Warwich Cancer Clin, George Washington Univ, 50-51; asst prof biochem, Sch Med, Creighton Univ, 51-53; head biochem dept, Jewish Hosp, Cincinnati, Ohio, 53-54; asst prof biochem in path, Sch Med, Univ Pittsburgh & head biochem dept, Presby Univ Hosp, 55-62; adj assoc prof biochem, Pa State Univ & head biochem dept, W H Singer Mem Res Inst, Allegheny Gen Hosp, Pa, 62-68; chief appln chemist, Perkin-Elmer Corp, 69; head biochem dept, Allentown Hosp Asn, 69-77; BUR MED DEVICES, FOOD & DRUG ADMIN, 78- *Mem:* Fel Am Asn Clin Chem; Soc Exp Biol & Med; Am Chem Soc; Can Soc Clin Chemists. *Res:* Bioanalytical chemistry; medical technology and clinical chemistry education. *Mailing Add:* Food & Drug Admin 8757 Georgia Ave Silver Spring MD 20910

RICE, FRANK J, b Putnam, Conn, Oct 10, 24; m 52; c 7. GENETICS, BIOSTATISTICS. *Educ:* Colo State Univ, BS, 50; Univ Wyo, MS, 51; Univ Mo, PhD(genetics), 56. *Prof Exp:* Mgr beef cattle ranch, San Carlos Apache Tribal Enterprises, Ariz, 53-54; geneticist, USDA, Mont, 56-61; from asst prof to assoc prof biol, 61-79, chmn dept, 70-76, PROF BIOL, FAIRFIELD UNIV, 79- *Mem:* Fel AAAS; Am Soc Animal Sci; Nat Coun Family Rels. *Res:* Genetics; physiology of reproduction. *Mailing Add:* Dept of Biol Fairfield Univ Fairfield CT 06430

RICE, FREDERICK ANDERS HUDSON, b Bismarck, NDak, Feb 19, 17; m 49. ORGANIC CHEMISTRY. *Educ:* Dalhousie Univ, BA, 37, MSc, 45; Ohio State Univ, PhD(org chem), 48. *Prof Exp:* Res assoc bact, Johns Hopkins Univ, 48-50, asst prof microbiol, 51-54; res chemist, US Naval Powder Factory, 54-55, assoc head chem div, 55-56, head fundamental process div, 56-60; chief res, Off Qm Gen, 59-62; phys scientist, res div, Army Materiel Command, 62-63; PROF CHEM, AM UNIV, 63- *Concurrent Pos:* Sr Fulbright award, Univ London, 52-53. *Honors & Awards:* Hillebrand Prize, Washington Chem Soc, 72. *Mem:* AAAS; Am Chem Soc; NY Acad Sci; Royal Soc Chem; Soc Exp Biol & Med. *Res:* Carbohydrate chemistry; chemistry of microorganisms; biochemistry of blood cell regulation; physics and chemistry of propellants; ultrasonics. *Mailing Add:* 8005 Carita Ct Bethesda MD 20034

RICE, GREGG EDWARD, b New York, NY, Dec 21, 43; m 69; c 2. PLANT PHYSIOLOGY, MARINE BIOLOGY. *Educ:* Princeton Univ, AB, 66; Univ Rochester, MS, 69, PhD(biol), 72. *Prof Exp:* Res assoc biol oceanog, Lamont-Doherty Geol Observ, Columbia Univ, 72-75; ASST PROF BIOL, FAIRLEIGH DICKINSON UNIV, 75- *Concurrent Pos:* Adj lectr, Teachers Col, Columbia Univ, 73-78. *Mem:* NY Acad Sci. *Res:* Photosynthesis and photobiology; algal physiology with emphasis on marine organisms. *Mailing Add:* Dept of Biol Fairleigh Dickinson Univ Teaneck NJ 07666

RICE, JACK MORRIS, b Salina, Kans, Aug 30, 48; m 75; c 2. GEOLOGY. *Educ:* Dartmouth Col, AB, 70; Univ Wash, MS, 72, PhD(geol), 75. *Prof Exp:* Gibbs instr, Yale Univ, 75-77; ASST PROF GEOL, UNIV ORE, 77- *Mem:* Geol Soc Am; Mineral Soc Am; Am Geophys Union. *Res:* Field, analytical and theoretical studies bearing on the mineralogy and petrology of metamorphic rocks; thermodynamics of rock-forming silicate minerals. *Mailing Add:* Dept of Geol Univ of Ore Eugene OR 97403

RICE, JAMES K, b Pittsburgh, Pa, Mar 12, 23; m 46; c 2. WATER CHEMISTRY. *Educ:* Carnegie Inst Technol, BS, 46, MS, 47. *Prof Exp:* Res engr, Cyrus W Rice & Co, 47-52, sr engr, 52-59, pres, 59-67, pres & gen mgr, Rice Div, NUS Corp, 67-73, sr vpres, 73-76; CONSULT ENGR, 76- *Concurrent Pos:* Mem, Coal Slurry Adv Panel, Off Technol Assessment, US Cong, 76-78. *Honors & Awards:* Award of Merit, Am Soc Testing & Mat, 70. *Mem:* Fel Am Soc Testing & Mat; fel Am Inst Chemists; Am Chem Soc; Nat Asn Corrosion Engrs; fel Am Soc Mech Engrs. *Res:* Monitoring of microchemical contaminants in the aquatic environment and in industrial water and waste water; water technology of thermal power systems. *Mailing Add:* 17415 Batchellor's Forest Olney MD 20832

RICE, JAMES KINSEY, b Harvey, Ill, June 5, 41; m 63; c 2. CHEMICAL PHYSICS, LASERS. *Educ:* Ind Univ, Bloomington, BA, 63; Calif Inst Technol, PhD(chem), 68. *Prof Exp:* Res fel chem, Calif Inst Technol, 68-69; STAFF MEM CHEM PHYSICS, SANDIA LABS, 69- *Mem:* AAAS; Am Chem Soc; Am Phys Soc; Am Soc Mass Spectrom. *Res:* Chemical lasers; reaction dynamics; electron beam pumped gas laser. *Mailing Add:* Orgn 5216 Sandia Labs Albuquerque NM 87115

RICE, JAMES THOMAS, b Birmingham, Ala, Feb 7, 33; m 54; c 4. WOOD TECHNOLOGY. *Educ:* Auburn Univ, BS, 54; NC State Univ, MS, 60, PhD(wood technol), 64. *Prof Exp:* From instr to asst prof wood technol, NC State Univ, 59-65; assoc prof, Univ Ga, 65-69; mgr wood adhesives develop, Central Resin Develop Lab, Ga-Pac Corp, 69-70; ASSOC PROF FOREST RESOURCES, UNIV GA, 70- *Concurrent Pos:* Tech coordr, Adhesive & Sealant Coun, 66-69 & 72-78. *Mem:* Am Soc Testing & Mat; Forest Prod Res Soc. *Res:* Adhesives and adhesive bonded products, especially those with wood as an adherent. *Mailing Add:* Sch of Forest Resources Univ of Ga Athens GA 30602

RICE, JERRY MERCER, b Washington, DC, Oct 3, 40; m 69, 78; c 1. EXPERIMENTAL PATHOLOGY, BIOCHEMISTRY. *Educ:* Wesleyan Univ, BA, 62; Harvard Univ, PhD(biochem), 66. *Prof Exp:* Res scientist, Biol Br, 66-69, head perinatal carcinogenesis sect, Lab Exp Path, 73-80, SR SCIENTIST, LAB EXP PATH, DIV CANCER CAUSE & PREV, NAT CANCER INST, 69-, CHIEF, LAB COMPARATIVE CARCINOGENESIS, 81- *Mem:* Sigma Xi; Am Chem Soc; Teratology Soc; Am Asn Cancer Res; NY Acad Sci. *Res:* Chemical carcinogenesis, especially transplacental carcinogenesis. *Mailing Add:* Lab Comparative Carcinogenesis Nat Cancer Inst Ft Detrick Frederick MD 21701

RICE, JIMMY MARSHALL, mathematics, deceased

RICE, JOHN RISCHARD, b Tulsa, Okla, June 6, 34; m 54; c 2. APPLIED MATHEMATICS, COMPUTER SCIENCE. *Educ:* Okla State Univ, BS, 54, MS, 56; Calif Inst Technol, PhD(math), 59. *Prof Exp:* Nat Res Coun-Nat Bur Stand res fel math, Nat Bur Stand, 59-60; sr res mathematician, Gen Motors Res Labs, 60-64; PROF MATH & COMPUT SCI, PURDUE UNIV, WEST LAFAYETTE, 64- *Concurrent Pos:* Chmn, COSERS Panel on Numerical Computation, 74-78; ed-in-chief, Asn Comput Mach Trans Math Software, 74-; chmn, Signum, 77-79; George E Forsythe Mem lectr, 75; Int Fed Info Processing Working Group 2.5. *Mem:* Am Math Soc; Soc Indust & Appl Math; Asn Comput Mach. *Res:* Approximation theory; numerical analysis; mathematical software; author or coauthor of various publications. *Mailing Add:* Div Math Sci 428 Purdue Univ West Lafayette IN 47907

RICE, JOHN T(HOMAS), b New London, Conn, Feb 4, 31. MECHANICAL ENGINEERING. *Educ:* Univ Conn, BSE, 52; Newark Col Eng, MSME, 54; Columbia Univ, EngScD(mech of solids), 62. *Prof Exp:* Engr propeller div, Curtiss-Wright Corp, 52-54, proj engr, Wright Aeronaut Div, 54-57; supvr struct mech, Elec Boat Div, Gen Dynamics Corp, 62-64; PROF MECH ENG, PRATT INST, 64- *Mem:* Am Soc Mech Engrs; Am Soc Eng Educ. *Res:* Dynamics; vibrations; mechanical design; systems engineering. *Mailing Add:* Dept of Mech Eng Pratt Inst Brooklyn NY 11205

RICE, KENNER CRALLE, b Rocky Mount, Va, May 14, 40. SYNTHETIC ORGANIC CHEMISTRY, MEDICINAL CHEMISTRY. *Educ:* Va Mil Inst, BS, 61; Ga Inst Technol, PhD(org chem), 66. *Prof Exp:* Capt, Walter Reed Army Inst Res, Washington, DC, 66-68; NIH fel, Ga Inst Technol, 68-69; sr scientist, Process Res, Ciba Pharmaceut Co, Ciba-Geigy Corp, 69-72; NIH sr staff fel, 72-76, RES CHEMIST, NAT INST ARTHRITIS, METAB & DIGESTIVE DIS, 77- *Mem:* Am Chem Soc. *Res:* The chemistry of analgesics, their antagonists and other drugs which act on the central nervous system. Stereochemistry of drugs in relation to their mechanism of action and receptor interactions. Isolation, structural elucidation and synthesis of natural products, especially alkaloids. *Mailing Add:* Bldg 4 Room 133 NIH Bethesda MD 20014

RICE, LESLIE IRENE, b Greensburg, Pa; m 46; c 2. BIOCHEMISTRY. *Educ:* Whittier Col, BS, 47; Univ Southern Calif, MS, 49, PhD, 53. *Prof Exp:* USPHS fel physiol chem, Sch Med, Univ Calif, Los Angeles, 54-55; res assoc pharmacol, 56-61, RES ASSOC BIOCHEM, SCH MED, UNIV SOUTHERN CALIF, 61- *Mem:* AAAS; Reticuloendothelial Soc. *Res:* Mucopolysaccharide metabolism; sulfated lipids. *Mailing Add:* Dept of Biochem Sch of Med Univ of Southern Calif Los Angeles CA 90007

RICE, MARION MCBURNEY, b Syracuse, NY, Feb 20, 23; m 52; c 2. BACTERIOLOGY, BOTANY. *Educ:* DePauw Univ, AB, 48, MA, 49; Univ Wis, PhD(bact), 53. *Prof Exp:* With Eli Lilly & Co, 41-44, asst, 45; asst, Ind Univ, 48; asst, Eli Lilly & Co, 49; asst bact, Univ Wis, 49-50; bacteriologist, Stuart Circle Hosp, Richmond, Va, 53-54; instr biol, Richmond Prof Inst, Col William & Mary, 55-58; asst prof bot & bact, Rockford Col, 58-60; instr biol, Beloit Col, 60; asst prof bot & bact, Rockford Col, 63-66; ASSOC PROF BOT, UNIV WIS, ROCK COUNTY CAMPUS, 66- *Concurrent Pos:* Asst bact, Univ Wis, 59. *Mem:* Am Soc Microbiol. *Res:* Antibiotics; cytology of streptomyces; phytogeography; botulism. *Mailing Add:* Dept of Bot & Zool Univ of Wis Rock County Campus Janesville WI 53545

RICE, MARY ESTHER, b Washington, DC, Aug 3, 26. INVERTEBRATE ZOOLOGY. *Educ:* Drew Univ, AB, 47; Oberlin Col, MA, 49; Univ Wash, PhD(zool), 66. *Prof Exp:* Instr zool, Drew Univ, 49-50; res assoc radiation biol, Col Physicians & Surgeons, Columbia Univ, 50-53; res biologist, NIH, 53-61; teaching asst, Univ Wash, 61-66; assoc cur invert zool, 66-74, CUR INVERTEBRATE ZOOL, MUS NATURAL HIST, SMITHSONIAN INST, 74- *Mem:* Fel AAAS; Am Inst Biol Sci; Am Soc Zoologists (pres, 79). *Res:* Development, reproductive biology and systematics of marine worms of the phylum Sipuncula. *Mailing Add:* Dept of Invertebrate Zool Smithsonian Mus Natural Hist Washington DC 20560

RICE, MICHAEL JOHN, b Cowes, UK, Dec 25, 40; m 65; c 3. CONDENSED MATTER PHYSICS, THEORETICAL PHYSICS. *Educ:* Univ London, BSc, 62, PhD(theoret physics), 66. *Prof Exp:* Asst prof physics, Imp Col, Univ London, 65-68; staff physicist, Gen Elec Res & Develop Lab, 68-71; staff mem, Brown Boveri Res Ctr, Switz, 71-74; SR SCIENTIST, XEROX WEBSTER RES CTR, XEROX CORP, 74- *Concurrent Pos:* Vis asst prof physics, State Univ NY, Stony Brook, 68; Nordita prof physics, Nordisk Inst Theoret Atomic Physics, Denmark, 78-79; consult, Optical Spectros Prog, Xerox-Ohio State Univ, 78- *Mem:* Fel Am Phys Soc; Am Chem Soc; fel Inst Physics; fel Phys Soc UK; fel Swiss Phys Soc. *Res:* Microscopic theory of quantum fluids, metals and alloys, semiconductors, ionic conductors and organic radical-ion solids. *Mailing Add:* Xerox Webster Res Ctr Bldg W 114 Webster NY 14580

RICE, NANCY REED, b Chicago, Ill, July 20, 40. ONCOGENIC RETROVIRUSES. *Educ:* Stanford Univ, BA, 61; Harvard Univ, MA, 63, PhD(biol), 69. *Prof Exp:* Fel molecular biol, 68-71, staff mem molecular biol, Carnegie Inst Wash Dept Terrestrial Magnetism, 72-76; staff, 76-80, SR SCIENTIST, FREDERICK CANCER RES FAC, 80- *Concurrent Pos:* Mem aging rev comt, Nat Inst Aging, 74-78; mem develop biol panel, NSF, 75. *Res:* Molecular biology of RNA tumor viruses. *Mailing Add:* Frederick Cancer Res Ctr Frederick MD 21701

RICE, NOLAN ERNEST, b Covington, Ky, July 2, 08; m 32; c 3. ZOOLOGY. *Educ:* Univ Ky, AB, 31; Duke Univ, AM, 33, PhD(protozool), 34. *Prof Exp:* Asst zool, Duke Univ, 31-33; prof biol, Brenau Col, 34-35; instr zool, Univ Tenn, 35-37; prof biol, Middle Ga Col, 37-43; head culture dept, Carolina Biol Supply Co, 43-50; prof biol, 50-78, EMER PROF BIOL, UNIV RICHMOND, 78- *Mem:* Am Soc Zool; Soc Protozool; Sigma Xi; Asn Southeastern Biologists. *Res:* Nutrition and locomotion of amebas; culture of protozoa; toxins of jellyfishes. *Mailing Add:* 8200 Larcom La Richmond VA 23229

RICE, NORMAN MOLESWORTH, b Ottawa, Ont, Oct 13, 39; m 62; c 2. MATHEMATICS. *Educ:* Queen's Univ, Ont, BS, 62; Calif Inst Technol, PhD(math), 66. *Prof Exp:* ASSOC PROF MATH, QUEEN'S UNIV, ONT, 65- *Mem:* Am Math Soc; Math Asn Am; Can Math Cong. *Res:* Functional analysis; vector lattices. *Mailing Add:* Dept of Math Queen's Univ Kingston ON K7L 3N6 Can

RICE, ORVILLE MILLARD, b Toledo, Ill, Aug 28, 18; m 43; c 4. MATHEMATICS. *Educ:* Eastern Ill State Teachers Col, BEd, 42; Univ Ill, MS, 50. *Prof Exp:* High sch teacher, Ill, 45-49; teacher, Jr Col Flat River, 52-56; ASSOC PROF MATH, UNIV WIS-STEVENS POINT, 56- *Mem:* Math Asn Am; Nat Coun Teachers Math. *Res:* Physics; abstract and linear algebra; calculus. *Mailing Add:* Dept of Math Univ of Wis Stevens Point WI 54481

RICE, PAUL LAVERNE, b Bancroft, Nebr, Dec 28, 06; m 39; c 3. MEDICAL ENTOMOLOGY. *Educ:* Univ Idaho, BS, 31, MS, 32; Ohio State Univ, PhD(entom), 37. *Hon Degrees:* DSc, Alma Col, Mich, 67. *Prof Exp:* Instr entom & asst entomologist, Univ Idaho, 31-33; asst entomologist, Univ Del, 36-37; prof biol, Alma Col, 37-42; assoc entomologist & actg head dept, Univ Del, 42-45; prof biol, head dept & dean fac, Alma Col, 45-50; prof biol, Whittier Col, 50-58; assoc dir, Malaria Eradication training ctr, AID, Jamaica, 58-62; mem staff grants prog, NIH, 62-64; various pos, Vector-Borne Dis Training, Ctr Dis Control, USPHS, 64-70; consult, 70-72; contractor various assignments, Vector Borne Dis Training, USPHS Ctr Dis Control, 72- *Concurrent Pos:* In chg malaria team, USPHS, Int Coop Admin, Ethiopia, 55-57. *Res:* Mosquito borne diseases. *Mailing Add:* 2373 Burnt Creek Rd Decatur GA 30033

RICE, PETER (FRANKLIN), b Toronto, Ont, May 18, 39; m 64; c 2. FOREST PATHOLOGY. *Educ:* Univ Toronto, BScF, 62, MScF, 64, PhD(forest path), 68. *Prof Exp:* Lectr forest path, Univ Toronto, 66-68; PATHOLOGIST, ROYAL BOT GARDENS, 68- *Mem:* Can Phytopath Soc; Am Phytopath Soc; Can Inst Forestry. *Res:* Diseases of ornamental plants, especially woody plants. *Mailing Add:* Royal Bot Gardens PO Box 399 Hamilton ON L8N 3H8 Can

RICE, PETER MILTON, b Montclair, NJ, Oct 14, 37; m 62; c 2. APPLIED MATHEMATICS. *Educ:* St John's Col, MD, AB, 59; Fla State Univ, PhD(math), 63. *Prof Exp:* Asst prof, 63-69, asst to dean, 77-82, ASSOC PROF MATH, UNIV GA, 69- *Concurrent Pos:* Alexander von Humbolt res fel & Sarah Moss res fel, Univ Bonn, 66-67; Alexander von Humboldt res fel, Inst Math Econ, Univ Bielefeld & Inst Higher Educ, Vienna, 75-76. *Mem:* Pub Choice Soc. *Res:* Application of mathematics to modeling in the social sciences. *Mailing Add:* Dept of Math Univ of Ga Athens GA 30601

RICE, PHILIP A, b Ann Arbor, Mich, Aug 3, 36; m 59; c 3. CHEMICAL ENGINEERING. *Educ:* Univ Mich, BSE, 59, MSE, 60, PhD(chem eng), 63. *Prof Exp:* NATO fel, Inst Phys Chem, Univ Gottingen, 62-63; chem engr, Anal Serv, Inc, Va, 63-65; from asst prof to assoc prof, 65-77, PROF CHEM ENG, SYRACUSE UNIV, 77- *Concurrent Pos:* Res assoc prof, Upstate Med Ctr, State Univ NY, 70- *Mem:* Am Inst Chem Engrs; Am Chem Soc. *Res:* Transfer processes in the human placenta; thermal energy storage; water reservation processes. *Mailing Add:* 1026 Ackerman Ave Syracuse NY 13210

RICE, PHILIP JOSEPH, JR, b Middletown, Conn, Feb 28, 17; m 56; c 2. ELECTRONIC PHYSICS. *Educ:* Brown Univ, AB, 40; Case Inst Technol, MS, 42; Yale Univ, MS, 46, PhD(physics), 48. *Prof Exp:* Mem staff radiation lab, Mass Inst Technol, 42-45; tech staff, Bell Tel Labs, Inc, 48-52; head vacuum tube lab, 52-56, mgr electron devices lab, 56-66, prog mgr eng sci & indust develop, 66-71, gen mgr technol innovation, 71-76, DIR ELECTRONICS LAB, SRI INT, 76- *Concurrent Pos:* Mem bd dirs, Western Electronics Educ Fund. *Honors & Awards:* Vladimir K Zworykin TV Prize, Inst Elec & Electronics Engrs, 63. *Mem:* Am Phys Soc; Sigma Xi; sr mem Inst Elec & Electronics Engrs. *Res:* Electron accelerators and optics; microwave vacuum tubes; electrostatic printing tubes; videodiscs. *Mailing Add:* Stanford Res Inst 333 Ravenswood Ave Menlo Park CA 94025

RICE, PHILIP KEARNEY, b Pittsburgh, Pa, July 15, 09; m 33; c 3. ENGINEERING. *Educ:* Carnegie Inst Technol, BS, 32. *Prof Exp:* With Linde Co Div, Union Carbide Corp, 33-35, res & develop engr, Res Lab, NY, 35-50, mgr works dept, 50-58, mgr, Union Carbide Develop Co Div, 58-64, eng specialist eng dept, Chem & Plastics Oper Div, 64-76; RETIRED. *Mem:* Am Soc Mech Engrs. *Res:* Application of thermodynamics, heat transfer and fluid dynamics; strength of materials; equipment for production and distribution of liquefied gases from the air; petrochemical process engineering. *Mailing Add:* 1207 Williamsburg Way Charleston WV 25314

RICE, RANDALL GLENN, b Smithfield, Utah, Nov 13, 18; m 46. INFORMATION SCIENCE. *Educ:* Pomona Col, BA, 40; Stanford Univ, PhD(biochem), 44. *Prof Exp:* Asst biochem, Stanford Univ, 40-42, Off Sci Res & Develop Contract, 43-44; Corn Prod Co fel, Cornell Univ, 45-46, instr chem, 46-48; chemist, USDA, 48-54; from asst ed to assoc ed, Chem Abstr, 54-59, head biochem, Indexing Dept, 59-62; chief mat sci div, Dept Defense Doc Ctr, Cameron Sta, Va, 63-64; dep chief & ed officer, Study Support Br, Hq US Air Force, Pentagon, 65-68, chief, Study Support Br, 68-71, chief tech info serv br, 71-78; RETIRED. *Mem:* AAAS; Am Chem Soc. *Res:* Flavor chemistry of citrus products; chemistry of natural products; isolation and identification of natural constituents; chemical literature; classification and indexing vocabularies for military science. *Mailing Add:* Apt 1509 1600 S Joyce St Riverhouse Arlington VA 22202

RICE, RICHARD G(REENE), chemical engineering, see previous edition

RICE, RICHARD W, b Ainsworth, Nebr, Aug 10, 31; m 52; c 2. ANIMAL NUTRITION, BIOCHEMISTRY. *Educ:* Univ Nebr, BS, 53, MS, 58; Mich State Univ, PhD(animal nutrit), 60. *Prof Exp:* From asst prof to prof animal sci, Univ Wyo, 60-75; PROF ANIMAL SCI & HEAD DEPT, UNIV ARIZ, 75- *Mem:* Soc Range Mgt; Am Soc Animal Sci; Am Dairy Sci Asn. *Res:* Ruminant nutrition; forage evaluation; factors affecting feed intake; fat metabolism in the ruminant; applied animal ecology. *Mailing Add:* Dept of Animal Sci Univ of Ariz Tucson AZ 85721

RICE, RIP G, b New York, NY, Apr 19, 24; m 48; c 1. CHEMISTRY, ENVIRONMENTAL SCIENCES. *Educ:* George Washington Univ, BS, 47; Univ Md, PhD, 57. *Prof Exp:* Anal chemist, Nat Bur Standards, DC, 47-50; chemist, US Naval Res Lab, 50-55; org chemist, US Naval Ord Lab, Md, 55-57; res chemist, Gen Dynamics/Convair, Tex, 57-59, staff scientist, Sci Res Lab, 59-60, tech dir adv prod dept, Calif, 60-62; sr chemist, W R Grace & Co, 62-63, res supvr, 63-64, mgr inorg chem res, 64-67, dir contract opers, 67-72; mgt consult-resident rep, 72-77; corp mgr gov relations, 77-81, DIR, ENVIRON SYSTS, ADV SYSTS DIV, JACOBS ENG GROUP, 81- *Concurrent Pos:* Tech adv, Int Ozone Asn, 74- *Honors & Awards:* Founders Award, Int Oxone Asn, 79. *Mem:* Am Chem Soc; Water Pollution Control Fedn; Int Ozone Asn (pres-elect, 79-81, pres, 82-84); Am Water Works Asn; Am Soc Chem Engrs. *Res:* Ozone technology; inorganic, polymer, organic chemistry. *Mailing Add:* 1331 Patuxent Dr Ashton MD 20861

RICE, ROBERT ARNOT, b San Francisco, Calif, Apr 4, 11; m 36. SCIENCE EDUCATION. *Educ:* Univ Calif, BA, 34, MA, 47. *Prof Exp:* Teacher, Geyserville Union High Sch, Calif, 35-40, prin, 40-41; teacher, Berkeley High Sch, 41-61, chmn dept sci, 49-61; supvr sci & math, Berkeley Unified Sch Dist, 61-64, consult, 64-70, dir on target sch, 71-73, work experience coordr, 73-75; DIR NORTHERN CALIF, WESTERN NEVADA JR SCI & HUMANITIES SYMPOSIUM, 70- *Concurrent Pos:* Mem, Int Sci Fair Coun, Sci Serv, Inc, 59-67; liaison with Northern Calif Indust Educ Coun; mem US group, OEEC Sem, Ireland, 60; ed, Sci Teacher, Nat Sci Teachers Asn, 60-61; coordr children's area, US Sci Exhibit, Century 21 Expos, Seattle, 61; resource consult, Calif Farm Bur Fedn, 66; dir, Int Sci Fair, San Francisco, 67; coordr pub progs, Lawrence Hall Sci, Univ Calif, Berkeley, 69-75. *Honors & Awards:* Armed Forces Chem Asn Award, 56. *Mem:* Nat Sci Teachers Asn (pres, 60-61). *Mailing Add:* Lawrence Hall of Sci Univ of Calif Berkeley CA 94720

RICE, ROBERT BRUCE, b Bartlesville, Okla, Jan 11, 20; m 40; c 2. GEOPHYSICS, MATHEMATICS. *Educ:* Col Wooster, BA, 41. *Prof Exp:* Asst math, Ohio State Univ, 41-45; process & design engr gasoline dept, Phillips Petrol Co, 45-46, master mathematician res dept, 46-47, sr physicist, 47-50, geophys mathematician, 51-56; sr res mathematician, Marathon Oil Co, 56-60, mgr physics & math dept, Denver Res Ctr, 60-78; CONSULT EXPLORATION GEOPHYS, 78- *Concurrent Pos:* Instr exten div, Okla State Univ, 48-49 & Univ Colo, 58-60. *Mem:* European Asn Explor Geophys; Am Inst Prof Geologists; Soc Explor Geophys; Sigma Xi; Math Asn Am. *Res:* Geophysical exploration for oil and gas, particularly the acquisition, processing and interpretation of seismic data. *Mailing Add:* PO Box 3170 Estes Park CO 80517

RICE, ROBERT HAFLING, b Birmingham, Ala, Dec 31, 44. TOXICOLOGY, CELL BIOLOGY. *Educ:* Mass Inst Technol, SB, 67; Univ Calif, Berkeley, PhD(molecular biol), 72. *Prof Exp:* Fel, Univ Calif, Davis, 72-73, 73-75, Mass Inst Technol, 75-79; ASST PROF TOXICOL, HARVARD SCH PUB HEALTH, 79- *Mem:* AAAS. *Res:* Biochemical aspects of differentiation and toxicology of cultivated epithelial cells, with emphasis on mechanisms of cross-linked envelope formation and chronic effects of exposure to xenobiotics in the environment. *Mailing Add:* Lab Toxicol Harvard Sch Pub Health 665 Huntington Ave Boston MA 02115

RICE, ROBERT VERNON, b Barre, Mass, Aug 13, 24; div; c 2. BIOCHEMISTRY. *Educ:* Northeastern Univ, BS, 50; Univ Wis, MS, 52, PhD(biochem), 55. *Prof Exp:* Asst biochem, Univ Wis, 51-54; fel chem physics, Mellon Inst Sci, 54-57, sr fel independent res, 57-67, prof biol sci & chmn dept, Mellon Inst Sci, 71-77, PROF BIOCHEM, CARNEGIE-MELLON UNIV, 67- *Concurrent Pos:* Vis prof, Med Ctr, Univ Calif, San Francisco, 63. *Mem:* AAAS; Am Soc Biol Chem; Am Soc Cell Biol; Biophys Soc. *Res:* Electron microscopy of muscle; physical biochemistry of macromolecules; cell biology. *Mailing Add:* Dept Biol Sci Mellon Inst Sci Carnegie-Mellon Univ Pittsburgh PA 15213

RICE, ROY WARREN, b Seattle, Wash, Aug 31, 34; m 64; c 2. CERAMICS, PHYSICS. *Educ:* Univ Wash, BS, 57, MS, 62. *Prof Exp:* Res engr, Boeing Co, 57-68; sect head, 68-74, HEAD CERAMICS BR, NAVAL RES LAB, 74- *Mem:* Am Phys Soc; fel Am Ceramic Soc; Am Chem Soc; Am Soc Metals; AAAS. *Res:* Ceramics, especially the relationships between processing-microstructure and mechanical properties. *Mailing Add:* Code 6360 US Naval Res Lab Washington DC 20375

RICE, STANLEY ALAN, b Los Angeles, Calif, Mar 4, 47. POLLUTION BIOLOGY, BIOASSAYS. *Educ:* Calif State Univ, Long Beach, BS, 73, MS, 75; Univ SFla, PhD(invertebrate zool), 78. *Prof Exp:* Res asst, Calif State Univ, Long Beach, 73-75, Univ SFla, 75-78; fel, Harbor Br Found, 78-80; STAFF SCIENTIST, MOTE MARINE LAB, 80- *Mem:* Am Soc Zoologists; Am Micros Soc; Sigma Xi. *Res:* Invertebrate life histories; polychaete reproduction and development; population genetics; culture of marine invertebrates; pollution biology. *Mailing Add:* Mote Marine Lab 1600 City Island Park Sarasota FL 33577

RICE, STANLEY DONALD, b Vallejo, Calif, Jan 20, 45; m 66; c 1. POLLUTION BIOLOGY, COMPARATIVE PHYSIOLOGY. *Educ:* Chico State Col, BA, 66, MA, 68; Kent State Univ, PhD(physiol), 71. *Prof Exp:* RES PHYSIOLOGIST, AUKE BAY FISHERIES LAB, NAT MARINE FISHERIES SERV, 71- *Concurrent Pos:* Invited contribr, Petrol Marine Environ, Nat Acad Sci. *Mem:* Am Soc Zoologists; Sigma Xi; AAAS. *Res:* Acute toxicity of oil; uptake, depuration, and metabolism of oil; effects on physiology of oil to a variety of Alaskan marine organisms; author of 25 scientific publications. *Mailing Add:* PO Box 155 Auke Bay Fisheries Lab Auke Bay AK 99821

RICE, STEPHEN LANDON, b Oakland, Calif, Nov 23, 41; m 65; c 2. MECHANICAL ENGINEERING. *Educ:* Univ Calif, Berkeley, BS, 64, MEng, 69, PhD(mech eng), 72. *Prof Exp:* Design engr, Lawrence Berkeley Lab, 64-69; asst prof, 72-77, assoc prof, 77-82, PROF MECH ENG, UNIV CONN, 82- *Concurrent Pos:* Dir, Automation, Robotics, Mfg Lab, Univ Conn, 80- & Design Proj Prog, 73-; prin investr, AFOSR Wear Proj, Univ Conn, 76-80, Dept Energy Wear Proj, 81- & CAD/CAM Kinematics Proj, Control Data, 80-; ed, DELOS Lab Compendium, Am Soc Eng Educ, 76- *Honors & Awards:* Teetor Award, Soc Automotive Engrs, 75. *Mem:* Am Soc Eng Educ; Am Soc Mech Engrs; Am Soc Lubrication Engrs; Soc Mfg Engrs. *Res:* Wear of materials, including role of mechanical parameters in formation of characteristic subsurface zones in sliding and repetitive impulsive loading in metals, polymers, composites and dental restoratives; computer based education; evaluation of educational effectiveness; robotics, automation and manufacturing. *Mailing Add:* Univ Conn U-139 Storrs CT 06268

RICE, STEPHEN O(SWALD), b Shedd, Ore, Nov 29, 07; m 31; c 3. COMMUNICATION ENGINEERING. *Educ:* Ore State Col, BS, 29. *Hon Degrees:* DSc, Ore State Univ, 61. *Prof Exp:* Mem tech staff, Bell Tel Labs, Inc, 30-72; RETIRED. *Concurrent Pos:* McKay vis lectr, Harvard Univ, 58. *Honors & Awards:* Mervin J Kelly Award, Inst Elec & Electronics Engrs, 65. *Mem:* Nat Acad Eng; Inst Elec & Electronics Engrs. *Res:* Propagation of electromagnetic waves in transmission lines and wave guides; theory of random noise. *Mailing Add:* 8110 El Paseo Grande La Jolla CA 92037

RICE, STUART ALAN, b New York, NY, Jan 6, 32; m 52; c 2. PHYSICAL CHEMISTRY. *Educ:* Brooklyn Col, BS, 52; Harvard Univ, AM, 54, PhD(chem), 55. *Prof Exp:* Jr fel, Soc Fels, Harvard Univ, 55-57; from asst prof to prof, Univ Chicago, 57-60, dir, James Franck Inst, 62-68, chmn dept, 71-77, Louis Block prof, 69-77, FRANK P HIXON DISTINGUISHED SERV PROF CHEM, UNIV CHICAGO & JAMES FRANCK INST, 77-, MEM COMT MATH BIOL, 68-, DEAN, DIV PHYS SCI, 80- *Concurrent Pos:* Alfred P Sloane fel, 58-62; Guggenheim fel, 60-61; NSF sr fel & vis prof, Free Univ Brussels, 65-66; mem bd dirs, Bull Atomic Sci, 65-; co-ed Advan Chem Physics, 66-; mem adv bd inst statist mech & thermodyn, Univ, Tex, 67-; vis prof, H C Orsted Inst, Copenhagen Univ, 70-71. King lectr, Johns Hopkins Univ, 63; Falk-Plaut lectr, Columbia Univ, 64; Reilly lectr, Univ Notre Dame, 64; Farkas lectr, Hebrew Univ Jerusalem, 65; Venable lectr, Univ NC, 68; G K Rollefson lectr, Univ Calif, Berkeley, 68; Louderman lectr, Wash Univ, 68; W A Noyes lectr, Univ Tex, 75, A D Little lectr, Northeastern Univ, 76; Foster lectr, Univ Buffalo, 76; Liversidge lectr, Univ Sydney, 78; F T Gucker lectr, Univ Indiana, 76; A R Gordon distinguished lectr, Univ Toronto, 78. *Honors & Awards:* A Cressy Morrison Prize, NY Acad Sci, 55; Award Pure Chem, Am Chem Soc, 62, L H Baekeland Award, 71; Marlowe Medal, Faraday Soc, 63; Medal of Free Univ Brussels, 66; Llewellyn John & Harriet Manchester Quantrell Award, 70; Sci Achievement Award Medal, City Univ NY, 78. *Mem:* Nat Acad Sci; AAAS; Am Chem Soc; Am Phys Soc; The Chem Soc. *Res:* Statistical theory of matter; transport phenomena in dense media; electronic structure of liquids, solids and molecular crystals; statistical mechanics of simple systems; theory of phase transitions; photochemistry; properties of water. *Mailing Add:* James Franck Inst 5640 Ellis Ave Chicago IL 60637

RICE, THEODORE ROOSEVELT, b Ky, Jan 19, 19; m 41; c 3. MARINE ECOLOGY. *Educ:* Berea Col, AB, 41; Harvard Univ, MA & PhD(zool), 49. *Prof Exp:* From fishery res biologist to dir radiobiol lab, Bur Com Fisheries, US Fish & Wildlife Serv, 49-69, dir, Atlantic Estuarine Fisheries Ctr, 69-76, DIR BEAUFORT LAB, NAT MARINE FISHERIES SERV, 76- *Concurrent Pos:* Adj prof zool, NC State Univ, 63- *Honors & Awards:* Nat Oceanic & Atmospheric Admin Award, 72. *Mem:* Am Soc Limnol & Oceanog; Atlantic Estuarine Res Soc; Am Nuclear Soc; Am Fisheries Soc. *Res:* Estuarine productivity; pollution. *Mailing Add:* Beaufort Lab Nat Marine Fisheries Serv Beaufort NC 28516

RICE, THOMAS KENNETH, b Evergreen Park, Ill, Sept 18, 41; m 67; c 1. IMMUNOBIOLOGY, MICROBIOLOGY. *Educ:* Iona Col, BS, 63; Univ Okla, MNS, 68, PhD(microbiol), 71. *Prof Exp:* Off Naval Res grant, Purdue Univ, Lafayette, 71-72; SR IMMUNOLOGIST, RIKER LABS, 3M CO, 72- *Mem:* AAAS; Am Soc Microbiol; Brit Soc Gen Microbiol; Sigma Xi. *Res:* Development of anti-allergics and immunosuppressants. *Mailing Add:* Riker Labs 3M Ctr St Paul MN 55101

RICE, THOMAS MAURICE, b Dundalk, Ireland, Jan 26, 39; nat US; m 66; c 3. THEORETICAL SOLID-STATE PHYSICS. *Educ:* Univ Col Dublin, Ireland, BSc, 59, MSc, 60; Univ Cambridge, Eng, PhD(physics), 64. *Prof Exp:* Asst lectr physics, Univ Birmingham, 63-64; res assoc physics, Univ Calif, San Diego, 64-66; mem tech staff physics, Bell Labs, 66-75, res head theoret physics dept, 75-78, head surface physics dept, 78-81; PROF, FED TECH INST, ZURICH, SWITZ, 81- *Concurrent Pos:* Vis lectr physics, Fed Tech Inst, Zurich, Switzerland, 70-71; prof physics, Simon Fraser Univ, Burnaby, BC, 74-75. *Mem:* Fel Am Phys Soc. *Mailing Add:* Theoretische Phyik ETH-Honggerberg 8093 Zurich 07974 Switzerland

RICE, W(ILLIAM) B(OTHWELL), b Montreal, Que, June 10, 18; m 44; c 3. MECHANICAL ENGINEERING. *Educ:* McGill Univ, BEng, 44, MEng, 56; Sir George Williams Univ, BSc, 50; Univ Montreal, DASc, 59. *Prof Exp:* Asst prof mech eng, McGill Univ, 47-50; assoc prof, 50-62, PROF MECH ENG, QUEEN'S UNIV, KINGSTON, ONT, 62- *Concurrent Pos:* Distinguished vis prof, Arizona State Univ, 82-83. *Mem:* Fel Am Soc Mech Engrs; fel Eng Inst Can; Soc Mfg Engrs; Int Inst Prod Eng Res; Can Soc Mech Eng (pres, 80-81). *Res:* Manufacturing processes, particularly the effect of friction on mechanics of cutting, extrusion and rolling; manufacturing systems. *Mailing Add:* Dept of Mech Eng Queen's Univ Kingston ON K7L 3N6 Can

RICE, WALTER WILBURN, b Harrogate, Tenn, Apr 30 18; m 43; c 1. ANALYTICAL CHEMISTRY. *Educ:* Lincoln Mem Univ, BS, 42. *Prof Exp:* CHEMIST & LAB SUPVR, DOE, UNION CARBIDE NUCLEAR CO, 46- *Mem:* AAAS; Am Chem Soc; Am Vacuum Soc; Am Soc Mass Spectrometry. *Res:* Mass spectrometry; vacuum technology; gamma ray scintillation. *Mailing Add:* 121 W Maiden Lane Oak Ridge TN 37830

RICE, WARREN, b Okla, Oct 11, 25; m; c 3. ENGINEERING. *Educ:* Agr & Mech Col, Tex, PhD(mech eng), 58. *Prof Exp:* Instr mech eng, Tex Tech Col, 49-50; from instr to assoc prof, Agr & Mech Col, Tex, 50-58; chmn dept mech eng, 67-74, PROF ENG, ARIZ STATE UNIV, 58- *Concurrent Pos:* NSF grants, 56-57; indust res grants, 58-66 & 67-74. *Mem:* Am Soc Mech Engrs. *Res:* Engineering science; fluid mechanics; heat transfer, particularly boundary layer study and devices influenced by boundary layer phenomena. *Mailing Add:* 2042 E Balboa Dr Tempe AZ 85282

RICE, WENDELL ALFRED, b Saskatoon, Sask, Apr 24, 39; m 62; c 3. SYMBIOTIC DINITROGEN FIXATION. *Educ:* Univ Sask, BSA, 63, MSc, 66, PhD(soil microbiol), 70. *Prof Exp:* RES SCIENTIST SOIL MICROBIOL, RES STA, CAN DEPT AGR, 70- *Mem:* Can Soc Soil Sci; Int Soc Soil Sci; Can Soc Microbiologists. *Res:* Effect of environmental factors on Rhizobium growth and survival, nodulation, and nitrogen fixation; microbial transformations of soil nitrogen. *Mailing Add:* Soil Sect Res Sta Can Dept of Agr Beaverlodge AB T0H 0C0 Can

RICE, WILLIAM ABBOTT, b Delaware, Ohio, Dec 8, 12; m 46; c 2. PHYSICAL GEOLOGY. *Educ:* Ohio Wesleyan Univ, BA, 34; Yale Univ, PhD(geol), 40. *Prof Exp:* Instr geol, Yale Univ, 36-38; instr, Utah State Col, 38-40; geol trainee, Shell Oil Co, 40-41; asst prof geol, Univ NC, 41-42; chemist, Tenn Valley Authority, 42-47; from asst prof to prof geol, 47-75, EMER PROF GEOL, MT UNION COL, 76- *Concurrent Pos:* Instr, Ohio State Univ, 47, 49, 51, 55, 59 & 63-65; geologist, Exp Sta, 47; vis assoc prof, Univ Ill, 59-60. *Mem:* AAAS; Geol Soc Am. *Res:* Chemical industrial microscopy; huronian geology, geography, philosophy and implications of science. *Mailing Add:* 2241 S Seneca Alliance OH 44601

RICE, WILLIAM JAMES, b Whallonsburgh, NY, Aug 6, 27. CHEMICAL ENGINEERING, SOLAR ENERGY. *Educ:* Worcester Polytech Inst, BS, 47, MS, 48; Princeton Univ, PhD(chem eng), 64. *Prof Exp:* Instr chem eng, Cath Univ Am, 48-53; from asst prof to assoc prof, 57-69, PROF CHEM ENG, VILLANOVA UNIV, 69- *Concurrent Pos:* Vis res prof, Inst Energy Conversion, Univ Del, 77-78. *Mem:* Am Inst Chem Engrs; Int Solar Energy Soc; Am Soc Eng Educ. *Res:* Fluid dynamics; transport properties; thermal energy storage using phase change materials; heat transfer; fluid calorimetry. *Mailing Add:* Dept of Chem Eng Villanova Univ Villanova PA 19085

RICE-WRAY, EDRIS, b Newark, NJ, Jan 21, 04; m 29; c 2. PREVENTIVE MEDICINE. *Educ:* Vassar Col, BA, 27; Northwestern Univ, MD, 32; Univ Mich, MPH, 50; Am Bd Prev Med, dipl. *Prof Exp:* Pvt pract, Ill, 35-48; dir pub health dist, Govt of PR, 48-49; dir pub health training ctr, 50-57; med officer, WHO, 57-58; co-founder & dir, Mex Asn Family Welfare, 59-62; founder & dir, Asn for Maternal Health, Mex, 63-75; prof, 75-76, ASST PROF POP STUDIES, UNIV OF THE AMERICAS, 76- *Concurrent Pos:* Co-founder, Inst Family Rels, PR, 50; asst prof, Sch Pub Health, Univ PR, 50-56; vol med dir, PR Asn for Well-Being of Family, 51-56. *Honors & Awards:* Univ Mich 150th Anniversary Award, 67; Margaret Sanger Award, Planned Parenthood-World Pop, 78. *Mem:* AMA; Am Pub Health Asn; Pop Asn Am; NY Acad Sci; fel Am Col Prev Med. *Res:* Clinical studies with oral and injectable contraceptives; population and family planning. *Mailing Add:* Apartado 13 Univ of the Americas Santa Catarina Martir Puebla Mexico

RICH, ALEXANDER, b Hartford, Conn, Nov 15, 24; m 52; c 4. MOLECULAR BIOPHYSICS, MOLECULAR BIOLOGY. *Educ:* Harvard Univ, AB, 47; Harvard Med Sch, MD, 49. *Prof Exp:* Res fel chem, Calif Inst Technol, 49-54; chief sect phys chem, NIH, 54-58; from assoc prof to prof, 58-74, WILLIAM THOMPSON SEDGWICK PROF BIOPHYS, MASS INST TECHNOL, 74- *Concurrent Pos:* Vis scientist, Cavendish Lab, Cambridge, Eng, 55-56; mem postdoctoral fel bd, NIH, 55-58; mem career award comt, 64-67; Guggenheim Found fel, 63; mem vis comt biol dept, Yale Univ, 63; mem exobiol comt, Space Sci Bd, Nat Acad Sci, 64-65, mem US nat comt, Int Orgn Pure & Appl Biophys, 65-67, chmn, Comt USSR & Eastern Europe Exchange Prog, 73-76, mem adv bd, Acad Forum, 75-; mem vis comt biol dept, Weizmann Inst Sci, 65-66; mem corp, Marine Biol Lab, Woods Hole, 65-77; mem lunar & planetary missions bd, NASA, 68-71, mem biol team, Viking Mars Mission, 69-, mem life sci comt, 70-75; mem biol adv comt, Oak Ridge Nat Lab, 72-76; mem int res & exchanges bd, Am Coun Learned Socs, 73-76; mem sci adv bd, Stanford Synchroton Radiation Proj, 76-; mem, Nat Sci Bd, 76-; mem, US-USSR Joint Comn Sci & Technol, Dept State & sr consult, Off Sci & Technol Policy, Exec Off President, Washington, DC, 77-81; mem, US Nat Comt Int Union Pure & Appl Biophysics, Nat Acad Sci, 79- *Honors & Awards:* Theodore von Karmen Award for Viking Mars Mission, 76. *Mem:* Nat Acad Sci; Am Chem Soc; Biophys Soc; Am Crystallog Asn; fel Am Acad Arts & Sci. *Res:* Molecular structure of biological systems; x-ray crystallography; protein chemistry; nucleic acid chemistry; polymer molecular structure; information transfer in biological systems; mechanism of protein synthesis; origin of life; author or coauthor of over 300 publications. *Mailing Add:* Dept of Biol Mass Inst of Technol Cambridge MA 02139

RICH, ARTHUR, b New York, NY, Aug 30, 37; m 59; c 3. ATOMIC PHYSICS. *Educ:* Brooklyn Col, BS, 59; Columbia Univ, MA, 61; Univ Mich, PhD(physics), 65. *Prof Exp:* Res assoc, 65-66, from asst prof to assoc prof, 66-75, PROF PHYSICS, UNIV MICH, ANN ARBOR, 75- *Mem:* Fel Am Phys Soc. *Res:* Basic principles of atomic physics. *Mailing Add:* Dept of Physics Univ of Mich Ann Arbor MI 48104

RICH, ARTHUR GILBERT, b Brooklyn, NY, Mar 21, 36; m 64; c 2. PHYSICAL PHARMACY, PHARMACEUTICAL CHEMISTRY. *Educ:* Columbia Univ, BS, 57; Univ Iowa, MS, 59, PhD, 62. *Prof Exp:* Res chemist, Julius Schmid, Inc, 62-63, proj leader pharmaceut res & develop, 63-65; sr res scientist, Johnson & Johnson, New Brunswick, 65-69; group leader, Ortho Pharmaceut Corp, 69-72; SECT MGT, AVON PRODS, INC, SUFFERN, NY, 72- *Concurrent Pos:* Union Carbide res fel, State Univ Iowa, 57-62; lectr, Ctr Prof Advan, 76-77. *Mem:* AAAS; Acad Pharmaceut Sci; Soc Cosmetic Chemists; NY Acad Sci; fel Royal Soc Health. *Res:* Design and development of suitable pharmaceutical and cosmetic vehicles for maximum topical effect of drug and cosmetic agents. *Mailing Add:* Avon Prod Inc Division St Suffern NY 10977

RICH, AVERY EDMUND, b Charleston, Maine, Apr 9, 15; m 38; c 2. PLANT PATHOLOGY. *Educ:* Univ Maine, BS, 37, MS, 39. *Prof Exp:* Asst supvr, Farm Security Admin, Maine, 39-40; instr high sch, Maine, 40-41; 4-H Club agent, Univ NH, 41-43; asst agronomist, Exp Sta, RI State Col, 43-47, exten agronomist, 46-47; asst plant pathologist, Exp Sta, State Col Wash, 47-51, from instr to asst prof, 47-51; assoc prof, 51-58, PROF BOT, UNIV NH, 58-, PLANT PATHOLOGIST, 51-, ASSOC DEAN LIFE SCI & AGR, 72- *Res:* Potato diseases; fungicides; virus diseases; phytopathology. *Mailing Add:* Life Sci & Agr Taylor Hall Univ of NH Durham NH 03824

RICH, CHARLES CLAYTON, b Cincinnati, Ohio, Dec 8, 22; m 66; c 2. GEOLOGY. *Educ:* Wittenberg Univ, AB, 45; Harvard Univ, MA, 50, PhD(geol), 60. *Prof Exp:* Lectr geol, Victoria Univ, NZ, 52-54; from instr to assoc prof geol, 58-68, dir univ honors prog, 65-69, PROF GEOL, BOWLING GREEN STATE UNIV, 68- *Mem:* Geol Soc Am; Nat Asn Geol Teachers; Am Quaternary Asn. *Res:* Glacial and Pleistocene geology. *Mailing Add:* Dept of Geol Bowling Green State Univ Bowling Green OH 43403

RICH, CLAYTON, b New York, NY, May 21, 24; div; c 1. MEDICINE, ENDOCRINOLOGY. *Educ:* Cornell Univ, MD, 48. *Prof Exp:* Extern path, NY Hosp, Cornell Univ, 48, asst physician, 49-50; intern med, Albany Hosp & Med Col, Union Univ, NY, 48-49, asst resident & asst med, 50-51; asst, Rockefeller Inst & asst physician, Hosp, 53-58, asst prof, Inst & assoc physician, Hosp, 58-60; from asst prof to prof med, Sch Med, Univ Wash, 60-71, assoc dean, 68-71; chief staff, Stanford Univ Hosp, 71-77, dean, Sch Med & vpres med affairs, 71-80, PROF MED, STANFORD UNIV, 80- *Concurrent Pos:* Chief radioisotope serv, Vet Admin Hosp, 60-70, assoc chief of staff, 62-71, chief of staff, 68-70; attend physician, Univ & King County Hosps, Seattle, 62-71. *Mem:* Am Soc Clin Invest; Endocrine Soc; Am Col Physicians; Am Soc Bone & Mineral Res; Asn Am Physicians. *Res:* Academic administration. *Mailing Add:* Off of the Dean Rm M123 Stanford Univ Sch of Med Stanford CA 94305

RICH, DANIEL HULBERT, b Fairmont, Minn, Dec 12, 42; m 64; c 2. BIO-ORGANIC CHEMISTRY. *Educ:* Univ Minn, BS, 64; Cornell Univ, PhD(org chem), 68. *Prof Exp:* Res assoc org chem, Cornell Univ, 68; res chemist, Dow Chem Co, 68-69; fel org chem, Stanford Univ, 69-70; asst prof, 70-75, assoc prof, 75-81, PROF PHARMACEUT CHEM UNIV, WIS-MADISON, 81- *Concurrent Pos:* NIH fel, 68; mem Bioorg Natural Prod Study Sect, NIH, 81-; consult, 80- *Honors & Awards:* H I Romnes Award, 80. *Mem:* AAAS; Am Chem Soc; Am Pharmaceut Asn. *Res:* Synthesis of peptides and hormones; inhibition of peptide receptors and proteases; characterization, synthesis, and mechanisms of action of peptide natural products. *Mailing Add:* Dept of Pharmaceut Chem Univ of Wis Madison WI 53706

RICH, EARL ROBERT, b Marquette, Mich, Aug 30, 25. ECOLOGY. *Educ:* Univ Chicago, SB, 49, PhD(zool), 54. *Prof Exp:* NSF fel statist, Univ Calif, 54-55, lectr, 55-56, instr biostatist, 56-57; from asst prof to assoc prof zool, 57-70, assoc dean col arts & sci, 68-70, PROF BIOL, UNIV MIAMI, 70- *Concurrent Pos:* Pres, Rio Palenque Res Corp, 72- *Mem:* Ecol Soc Am; AAAS; Am Soc Zool; Biomet Soc. *Res:* Population dynamics and ecology; biological effects of irradiation; man's impact on environment; inshore marine biology. *Mailing Add:* Dept Biol Univ Miami PO Box 249118 Coral Gables FL 33124

RICH, ELLIOT, b Brigham City, Utah, May 27, 19; m 43; c 6. CIVIL ENGINEERING. *Educ:* Utah State Univ, BS, 43; Univ Utah, MS, 51; Univ Colo, PhD(civil eng), 68. *Prof Exp:* Hydraul engr, US Bur Reclamation, 46-47; instr, Weber Col, 47-50, head eng dept, 50-56; assoc prof, 56-67, head dept civil eng, 67-75, PROF CIVIL ENG, UTAH STATE UNIV, 67-, ASSOC DEAN, COL ENG, 75- *Concurrent Pos:* Consult, AEC, 59. *Mem:* Am Soc Eng Educ; Am Soc Civil Engrs (pres, 77-78). *Res:* Structures. *Mailing Add:* Col of Eng Utah State Univ Logan UT 84322

RICH, ERNEST I, geology, see previous edition

RICH, JOHN CHARLES, b Wichita, Kans, Oct 12, 37; m 63; c 3. ASTROPHYSICS, LASERS. *Educ:* Harvard Univ, AB, 59, AM, 60, PhD(astron), 67. *Prof Exp:* Physicist, 60-74, div chief, 74-77, COMDR, AIR FORCE WEAPONS LAB, 77- *Concurrent Pos:* Instr, Univ Va, 69-70. *Mem:* Am Astron Soc; Am Geophys Union; Int Aeronaut & Astronaut; Sigma Xi. *Res:* Atomic and molecular physics; radiative processes; stellar atmospheres. *Mailing Add:* 1727 Chacoma Pl SW Albuquerque NM 87104

RICH, JOSEPH ANTHONY, b Hazardville, Conn, July 23, 16; m 45; c 2. PLASMA PHYSICS. *Educ:* Harvard Univ, BSc, 38; Brown Univ, MSc, 39; Yale Univ, PhD(physics), 50. *Prof Exp:* Physicist, Cent Res Lab, Monsanto Chem Co, 43-45; sr physicist, 45-47; physicist, Knolls Atomic Power Lab, 49-52 & Electron Physics Dept, Res & Develop Ctr, 52-60, PHYSICIST, GEN PHYSICS LAB, RES & DEVELOP CTR, GEN ELEC CO, 60- *Mem:* Am Phys Soc; Math Asn Am; sr mem Inst Elec & Electronics Engrs. *Res:* Microwave electronics; nuclear physics. *Mailing Add:* Res & Develop Ctr Gen Elec Co PO Box 8 Schenectady NY 12301

RICH, KENNETH EUGENE, b Alton, Ill, Nov 19, 43; m 68; c 2. BIOPHYSICS, INSTRUMENTATION. *Educ:* Rose-Hulman Inst Technol, BS, 66; Univ Rochester, PhD(biophys), 71. *Prof Exp:* Res assoc biophys & instrumentation, Dept Biochem, Case Western Reserve Univ, 71-75; staff fel comput instrumentation & molecular biol, Nat Inst Neurologic Commun Dis & Stroke, 76-78; scientist comput instrumentation, Technico Instrument Corp, 78-81; SR COMPUT APPL SCIENTIST, CAPINTEC INC, 81- *Concurrent Pos:* USPHS fel, Case Western Reserve Univ, 71-75. *Mem:* Biophys Soc; Am Chem Soc; Sigma Xi; AAAS. *Res:* Computer instrumentation of laboratory instruments and procedures biological in nature. *Mailing Add:* Capintec Inc 6 Arrow Rd Ramsey NJ 07644

RICH, LEONARD G, b New York, NY, Mar 28, 25; m 55; c 1. PHYSICS, ELECTRICAL ENGINEERING. *Educ:* St Lawrence Univ, BS, 45. *Prof Exp:* Res physicist, Crystal Res Labs, Inc, 46-47; pres, Norbert Photo Prod Co, 47-49; asst chief engr electronics, McMurdo Silver Co, 49-50, chief engr, 50-51; proj engr, New London Instrument Co, Inc, 51-53; proj leader res & develop, Anderson Labs, Inc, 53-56; sr proj engr, Roth Lab, 56-65; SCI DIR, GERBER SCI INC, 65-, VPRES RES PROD, 80- *Mem:* Inst Elec & Electronics Engrs. *Res:* Electronic physics; ultrasonic delay lines; magnetic memory for signal-to-noise improvement through video integration; signal generators and test instruments for industry; computer-controlled digital and analog graphic output devices; robotic scanners; digital adaptive servos. *Mailing Add:* Gerber Sci Inc PO Box 305 Hartford CT 06101

RICH, LINVIL G(ENE), b Pana, Ill, Mar 10, 21; m 44; c 2. ENVIRONMENTAL ENGINEERING. *Educ:* Va Polytech Inst, BS, 47, MS, 48, PhD(biochem), 51; Environ Eng Intersoc, dipl. *Prof Exp:* From instr to assoc prof sanit eng, Va Polytech Inst, 48-55; from assoc prof to prof, Ill Inst Technol, 56-61; dean eng, 61-72, PROF ENVIRON SYSTS ENG, CLEMSON UNIV, 72- *Concurrent Pos:* Consult, Environ Protection Agency. *Mem:* Fel Am Soc Civil Engrs; Am Soc Eng Educ; Am Acad Environ Engrs; Asn Environ Eng Prof. *Res:* Environmental engineering. *Mailing Add:* Col of Eng Clemson Univ Clemson SC 29631

RICH, MARK, b Chicago, Ill, Feb 1, 32; m 58; c 3. GEOLOGY. *Educ:* Univ Calif, Los Angeles, AB, 54; Univ Southern Calif, MA, 56; Univ Ill, PhD(geol), 59. *Prof Exp:* Asst geol, Univ Ill, 57-59; asst prof, Univ NDak, 59-63; assoc prof, 63-70, PROF GEOL, UNIV GA, 70- *Mem:* Geol Soc Am; Paleont Soc; Soc Econ Paleont & Mineral; Am Asn Petrol Geol; Brit Palaeont Asn. *Res:* Sedimentary petrology; stratigraphy; micropaleontology; structural geology. *Mailing Add:* Dept of Geol Univ of Ga Athens GA 30601

RICH, MARVIN A, b New York, NY, Apr 21, 31; m 66. MICROBIOLOGY, VIROLOGY. *Educ:* Brooklyn Col, BS, 52; Rutgers Univ, MS, 54, PhD(microbiol), 57. *Prof Exp:* Res asst biochem, Inst Appl Biol, 52-53; res asst microbiol, Med Ctr, Columbia Univ, 53; res assoc biophys, Sloan-Kettering Inst Cancer Res, 57-59, asst mem, 59-61, assoc, 61-62; asst mem, Albert Einstein Med Ctr, 61-62, assoc mem & dir lab cancer res, 62-65, mem & chmn dept cell biol, 65-72; chmn biol dept, 72-73, dir div biol sci, 73-74, EXEC VPRES & SCI DIR, MICH CANCER FOUND, 75- *Concurrent Pos:* Res collabr, Brookhaven Nat Lab, 61-62; USPHS career develop award, 64-72; consult, spec virus cancer prog, Nat Cancer Inst, 66-; mem leukosis team, WHO, 71-; mem bd gov, Nat Found Encephalitis Res. *Mem:* AAAS; Am Chem Soc; Am Asn Immunol; Am Asn Cancer Res; Am Soc Cell Biol. *Res:* Relationship between viruses and cancer, especially the characterization of virus-induced neoplasias in animal systems as models for leukemia and mammary carcinoma in man. *Mailing Add:* Mich Cancer Found 110 E Warren Ave Detroit MI 48201

RICH, MICHAEL, b Chicago, Ill, July 23, 40; m 63; c 4. MATHEMATICS. *Educ:* Roosevelt Univ, BS, 62; Ill Inst Technol, MS, 65, PhD(math), 69. *Prof Exp:* Asst prof math, Ind Univ, 67-69; asst prof, 69-73, assoc prof, 73-80, PROF MATH, TEMPLE UNIV, 80- *Concurrent Pos:* Vis assoc prof, Ben Gurion Univ Negev, 74-75. *Mem:* Am Math Soc. *Res:* Ring theory; nonassociative algebras; software systems. *Mailing Add:* Dept Math Temple Univ Philadelphia PA 19122

RICH, PATRICIA VICKERS, b Exeter, Calif, July 11, 44; m 66; c 1. VERTEBRATE PALEONTOLOGY, BIOGEOGRAPHY. *Educ:* Univ Calif, Berkeley, AB, 66; Columbia Univ, MA, 69, PhD(geol), 73. *Prof Exp:* Asst geol, Columbia Univ, 67-68; asst prof geosci geol, Dept Geosci, Tex Tech Univ & assoc cur vert paleont, Mus, 73-76; LECTR DEPT EARTH SCI, MONASH UNIV, 76- *Concurrent Pos:* Fulbright fel, Australian Am Educ Found, Australia, 73-74; hon res assoc, Nat Mus Victoria, 78-; Nat Geog Soc grants, 78, 80; Australian Res grants comn grantee, 78-82; Australian China Coun grantee, 80-81; Australian Acad Sci Chinese exchange scientist, 79; Australian Nat Parks Wildlife grantee, 81. *Mem:* Am Ornith Union; Geol Soc Australia; Royal Australian Ornith Union; Soc Vert Paleontologists; Sigma Xi. *Res:* Description and evaluation of Cenozoic fossil birds from Australia and Norfolk Island; Peleogene birds from Indonesia, Europe and South America; Neogene avifaunas from east and south Africa; development of bird bone key for archaeological use; investigation into phylogenetic usefulness of the avian quadrate; development of a machine translation system for chinese scientific literature; avian systematics. *Mailing Add:* Dept of Earth Sci Monash Univ Clayton Victoria 3168 Australia

RICH, PETER HAMILTON, b Wellfleet, Mass, Nov 7, 39; div; c 1. LIMNOLOGY. *Educ:* Hunter Col, AB, 63; Mich State Univ, MS, 66, PhD, 70. *Prof Exp:* Res assoc biol, Brookhaven Nat Lab, 70-72; asst prof, 72-80, ASSOC PROF ECOL, UNIV CONN, 80- *Mem:* AAAS; Ecol Soc Am; Am Soc Limnol & Oceanog; Int Asn Theoret & Appl Limnol. *Res:* Measurement of the functional, community parameters of the aquatic ecosystem, especially benthos; aquatic ecosystem energetics. *Mailing Add:* Biol Sci Group U-42 Univ of Conn Storrs CT 06268

RICH, RICHARD DOUGLAS, b Chicago, Ill, Nov 30, 36; m 59; c 2. ORGANIC CHEMISTRY. *Educ:* Rensselaer Polytech Inst, BChE, 58; Univ Md, PhD(org chem), 68. *Prof Exp:* Res chemist, US Naval Ord Lab, Md, 58-68; sr scientist, Bickford Res Labs, Inc, Ensign-Bickford Co, Conn, 68-70; res chemist, 70-78, res assoc, 78-79, SCIENTIST, LOCTITE CORP, 79- *Concurrent Pos:* Adj prof, Univ Hartford, 69-72. *Mem:* AAAS; Am Chem Soc; Adhesion Soc. *Res:* Organic chemistry of explosives; plastic binders for propellants and explosives; anaerobic and cyanoacrylate adhesives. *Mailing Add:* Loctite Corp 705 N Mountain Rd Newington CT 06111

RICH, ROBERT PETER, b Lowville, NY, Aug 28, 19; m 49; c 2. MATHEMATICS, COMPUTER SCIENCES. *Educ:* Hamilton Col, AB, 41; Johns Hopkins Univ, PhD(math), 50. *Prof Exp:* Mathematician, Appl Physics Lab, 50-56, ASSOC PROF BIOMED ENG & MEM APPL PHYSICS LAB, JOHNS HOPKINS UNIV, 69-, DIR COMPUT CTR, 56- *Mem:* AAAS; Am Math Soc; Asn Comput Mach; Soc Indust & Appl Math. *Res:* Digital computing. *Mailing Add:* Appl Physics Lab Johns Hopkins Univ Laurel MD 20810

RICH, ROBERT REGIER, b Newton, Kans, Mar 7, 41; m 74; c 2. IMMUNOBIOLOGY. *Educ:* Oberlin Col, AB, 62; Univ Kans, MD, 66. *Prof Exp:* Intern, Univ Wash, 66-67, asst resident, 67-68; clin assoc immunol, NIH, 68-71; NIH res fel immunol, Harvard Med Sch, 71-73; asst prof, 73-75, assoc prof, 75-78, PROF MICROBIOL & IMMUNOL, BAYLOR COL MED, 78-, PROF MED, 79-, HEAD, IMMUNOL SECT, 77-, CHIEF CLIN IMMUNOL, 78- *Concurrent Pos:* Asst med, Peter Bent Brigham Hosp, Boston, 72-73; attend physician, Vet Admin Hosp, Houston, 73-; adj asst prof, Grad Sch Biomed Sci, Univ Tex Health Sci Ctr, Houston, 75-79; prog dir, Gen Clin Res Ctr, Methodist Hosp, Houston, 75-77; NIH res career develop award, 75-77; investr, Howard Hughes Med Inst, 77-; mem immunobiol study sect, NIH, 77-81; assoc ed, J Immunol, 78-; adj prof, Grad Sch Biomed Sci, Univ Tex Health Sci Ctr, Houston, 79- *Mem:* Am Asn Immunologists; Am Asn Pathologists; fel Am Col Physicians; Am Soc Clin Invest; Asn Am Physicians. *Res:* Cell mediated immune responses in mice and humans. *Mailing Add:* Dept of Microbiol & Immunol Baylor Col of Med Houston TX 77030

RICH, RONALD LEE, b Washington, Ill, Mar 29, 27; m 53; c 4. INORGANIC CHEMISTRY. *Educ:* Bluffton Col, BS, 48; Univ Chicago, PhD(chem), 53. *Prof Exp:* Instr chem, Bethel Col, Kans, 50-51; mem staff, Los Alamos Sci Lab, 53; assoc prof chem, Bethel Col, Kans, 53-55; chemist, Nat Bur Stand, 55-56; prof chem, Bethel Col, Kans, 56-63; res fel, Harvard Univ, 63-64; prof chem, Bethel Col, Kans, 64-66; prof, Int Christian Univ, Tokyo, 66-69; prof chem & chmn div natural sci, Bethel Col, Kans, 69-71; prof chem, Int Christian Univ, Tokyo, 71-79; dean & prof chem, 79-80, SCHOLAR IN RESIDENCE, BLUFFTON COL, OHIO, 81- *Concurrent Pos:* Vis prof chem, Stanford Univ, 74, Univ Ill, 75 & Bethel Col, Kans, 76-77. *Res:* Qualitative analysis; correlation of chemical properties with electron structure. *Mailing Add:* 112 S Spring St Bluffton OH 45817

RICH, ROYAL ALLEN, b North Platte, Nebr, Aug 6, 34; m 56; c 4. REPRODUCTIVE PHYSIOLOGY. *Educ:* Univ Nebr, BS, 57; Utah State Univ, MS, 60, PhD(physiol), 65. *Prof Exp:* Instr zool & physiol, Utah State Univ, 62-64; assoc prof zool, 65-73, PROF ZOOL, UNIV NORTHERN COLO, 73- *Mem:* Soc Study Reproduction. *Res:* Mammalian physiology; influence of ovarian hormones on uterine biochemistry, especially deciduoma formation in the rat; post-partum involution. *Mailing Add:* Dept of Biol Sci Univ of Northern Colo Greeley CO 80631

RICH, SAUL, b Detroit, Mich, Nov 25, 17; m 46; c 2. PHYTOPATHOLOGY. *Educ:* Univ Calif, BS, 38, MS, 39; Ore State Col, PhD(plant path), 42. *Prof Exp:* Asst plant pathologist, Univ Wyo, 46; res assoc, Crop Protection Inst, 47-48; from asst plant pathologist to sr plant pathologist, 48-72, CHIEF DEPT PLANT PATH & BOT, CONN AGR EXP STA, 72- *Mem:* Fel AAAS; fel Am Phytopath Soc (treas, 52-58); Soc Indust Microbiol (pres, 66). *Res:* Air pollution; fungicides; vegetable diseases. *Mailing Add:* Conn Agr Exp Sta PO Box 1106 New Haven CT 06504

RICH, TRAVIS DEAN, b Ryan, Okla, Oct 5, 40; m 64; c 2. REPRODUCTIVE PHYSIOLOGY. *Educ:* Okla State Univ, BS, 62, MS, 67; Purdue Univ, Lafayette, PhD(animal sci), 70. *Prof Exp:* Beef herdsman, Okla State Univ, 62-65, teaching asst animal sci, 65-67; res asst, Purdue Univ, Lafayette, 67-70; asst prof, SDak State Univ, 70-72; researcher beef cattle reproduction, Res & Exten Ctr, Tex A&M Univ, 72-73; EXTEN BEEF CATTLE SPECIALIST, DEPT ANIMAL SCI, OKLA STATE UNIV, 73-, ASSOC PROF ANIMAL SCI & INDUST, 74- *Mem:* Am Soc Animal Sci; Soc Study Reproduction. *Res:* Beef cattle reproduction; endocrinology of postpartum period, puberty and superovulation; genetic improvement of beef cattle; physiology of reproduction. *Mailing Add:* Dept of Animal Sci Okla State Univ Stillwater OK 74074

RICH, WILEY FOSTER, physics, see previous edition

RICHARD, ALFRED JOSEPH, b Gardner, Mass, Mar 30, 28; m 54. PHYSICAL CHEMISTRY. *Educ:* Clark Univ, PhD(chem), 58. *Prof Exp:* Asst prof, 58-64, assoc prof chem, 64-76, PROF PHARMACEUT CHEM, MED COL VA, 76- *Mem:* Am Chem Soc. *Res:* Physical properties of proteins; compressibilities of pure liquids. *Mailing Add:* Dept of Chem Med Col of Va Richmond VA 23219

RICHARD, BENJAMIN H, b Phoenixville, Pa, May 6, 29. STRUCTURAL GEOLOGY, GEOPHYSICS. *Educ:* Va Polytech Inst, BS, 58; Ind Univ, MA, 61, PhD(geol), 66. *Prof Exp:* From instr to asst prof geol, Wittenberg Univ, 62-66; asst prof, 66-70, ASSOC PROF GEOL, WRIGHT STATE UNIV, 70- *Mem:* Nat Asn Geol Teachers. *Res:* Structural geology and geophysics; use of gravity to locate large pockets of gravel within glacial debris. *Mailing Add:* Dept of Geol Wright State Univ Dayton OH 45431

RICHARD, CLAUDE, b Quebec City, Que, Mar 18, 44; m 67; c 2. PHYTOPATHOLOGY. *Educ:* Laval Univ, BSc, 67, MSc, 69, DSc(phytopath), 73. *Prof Exp:* Prof bot, Laval Univ, 72-73; RES SCIENTIST AGR, AGR CAN, 73- *Mem:* Can Phytopath Soc; Am Phytopath Soc; Can Bot Asn; Can Asn Advan Sci; Agr Inst Can. *Res:* Foliar and root diseases of forage legumes mainly alfalfa; selection of alfalfa for persistance and disease resistance; survey of alfalfa diseases; mycorrhizae. *Mailing Add:* Agr Can Sta of Res 2560 Hochelaga Blvd Ste-Foy PQ G1V 2J6 Can

RICHARD, CLAUDE, b Trois-Rivieres, Que, Nov 28, 32; m 59; c 2. PLASMA PHYSICS, OPTICAL PHYSICS. *Educ:* Laval Univ, BASc, 59; Univ London, MSc & DIC, 61, PhD(microwave & plasma physics), 68. *Prof Exp:* Jr mem sci staff microwave & plasma physics, RCA Ltd, 61-65, mem sci staff optical & microwave physics, 65-68, sr mem sci staff space & plasma physics, 68-70; sr researcher laser plasma interaction, 70-71, sci dir basic res, 71-80, DIR RES & TESTING & PROD & CONSERV OF ENERGY, INST HYDRO RES, QUE, 80- *Mem:* Can Asn Physicists; Am Phys Soc; Inst Elec & Electronics Engrs; Fr-Can Asn Advan Sci. *Res:* Microwave optics; interaction of electromagnetic wave with plasmas; plasma diagnostics; focused microwave systems; electrochemical properties of reentry plasmas; negative ion generation in gas discharge; high resolution-multiple imaging optical systems; gaseous lasers; laser plasma interaction. *Mailing Add:* Dir Res & Test Prod & Conserv Energy PO Box 1000 Varennes PQ J0L 2P0 Can

RICHARD, JEAN-PAUL, b Quebec, Que, June 10, 36; m 63; c 2. EXPERIMENTAL PHYSICS. *Educ:* Laval Univ, BA, 56, BS, 60; Univ Paris, DSpec(physics), 63, DSc(physics), 65. *Prof Exp:* Res attache physics, Nat Ctr Sci Res, France, 63-65; res assoc, 65-68, from asst prof to assoc prof, 68-81, PROF PHYSICS, UNIV MD, COLLEGE PARK, 81- *Mem:* Am Inst Physics; Can Asn Physicists. *Res:* Gravity; astronomy; relativity; earth physics. *Mailing Add:* 5918 85th Ave New Carrollton MD 20784

RICHARD, JOHN L, b Melbourne, Iowa, May 19, 38; m 61; c 3. MYCOLOGY. *Educ:* Iowa State Univ, BS, 60, MS, 63, PhD(mycol), 68. *Prof Exp:* MICROBIOLOGIST, NAT ANIMAL DIS CTR, USDA, 63- *Mem:* Med Mycol Soc of the Americas; Am Soc Microbiol; Int Soc Human & Animal Mycol; Wildlife Dis Asn. *Res:* Fluorescent antibody, cultural techniques, transmission and electron microscopy of Dermatophilus congolensis; equine ringworm; mycotoxicoses; effects of mycotoxins on immunity; aerosol-toxins and infections fungal agents; avian aspergillosis. *Mailing Add:* Nat Animal Dis Ctr US Dept of Agr Box 70 Ames IA 50010

RICHARD, PATRICK, b Crowley, La, Apr 28, 38; m 60; c 2. ELECTRON PHYSICS, ATOMIC PHYSICS. *Educ:* Univ Southwestern La, BS, 61; Fla State Univ, PhD(physics), 64. *Prof Exp:* Res asst prof nuclear physics, Univ Wash, 65-68; from asst prof to prof physics, Univ Tex, Austin, 68-72; PROF PHYSICS, KANS STATE UNIV, 72- *Concurrent Pos:* Consult, Columbia Sci Res Inst, 69-71. *Mem:* Am Phys Soc. *Res:* Characteristic x-rays and Auger electons produced in collisions of energetic heavy ions with heavy atoms. *Mailing Add:* Dept of Physics Kans State Univ Manhattan KS 66502

RICHARD, PIERRE JOSEPH HERVE, b Montreal, Can, July 9, 46; m 70. PALYNOLOGY, PALEOECOLOGY. *Educ:* Univ Laval, BS, 67; Univ Paris, DEA, 68; Univ Montpellier, Dr Etat, 76. *Prof Exp:* Prof bot, Univ Que, Chicoutimi, 71-76; PROF GEOG, UNIV MONTREAL, 76- *Mem:* Palynology Asn Fr Lang; Bot Asn Can; Can Quaternary Asn; Int Soc Limnol. *Res:* Pollen analysis of late Pleistocene deposits, mainly in Quebec, for paleobiogeographic reconstruction; pollen morphology and methodology, organic sediments and other microfossils. *Mailing Add:* Dept of Geog Univ of Montreal CP 6128 Montreal PQ H3C 3J7 Can

RICHARD, RALPH MICHAEL, b South Bend, Ind, Dec 15, 30; m 61; c 3. STRUCTURAL ENGINEERING, SOLID MECHANICS. *Educ:* Univ Notre Dame, BSCE, 52; Washington Univ, MSCE, 56; Purdue Univ, PhD(civil eng), 61. *Prof Exp:* Instr civil eng, Washington Univ, 55-56; engr, McDonnell Aircraft, McDonnell Douglas Corp, 56-58; res asst, Purdue Univ, 59-61; asst prof civil eng, Univ Notre Dame, 61-63; assoc prof, 63-65, PROF CIVIL ENG, UNIV ARIZ, 65- *Concurrent Pos:* Consult, US Dept Defense, 63-65, General Dynamics Corp, 66-72, Kitt Peak Nat Observ, 68-70, City Investing Co, Los Angeles, 72-78, Welton Becket & Assoc, 74-76 & US Ballistics Lab, Md, 78. *Mem:* Am Soc Civil Engrs; Am Acad Mech. *Res:* Aseismic design; steel connection design; lightweight high resolution optical structural systems. *Mailing Add:* Dept Civil Eng & Eng Mech Univ of Ariz Tucson AZ 85721

RICHARD, RICHARD RAY, b Nederland, Tex, Sept 12, 27; m 55; c 2. REMOTE SENSING, THERMAL MANAGEMENT. *Educ:* Univ Tex, BS, 55. *Prof Exp:* Test engr instrumentation, Convair Div, Gen Dynamics Corp, 54-61; sr engr electronics, Brown Eng Co, Ala, 61-63; proj engr instrumentation, Manned Spacecraft Ctr, 63-65, head measurement sect, 65-67, head infrared sect, 67-81, HEAD ADV PROGS, JOHNSON SPACE CTR, NASA, 81- *Mem:* Instrument Soc Am. *Res:* Aircraft flutter prediction instrumentation; noncontacting vibration and measurement techniques; Saturn fuel measurement techniques; angular accelerometer and miscellaneous devices; development of digital sensing techniques; cryogenic refrigeration using molecular adsorption in zeolites for gas storage; raising operating temperature of photonic infrared defectors. *Mailing Add:* Johnson Space Ctr ED6 NASA Rd 1 Houston TX 77058

RICHARD, ROBERT H(ENRY), b Warrington, Fla, Sept 3, 27; m 53; c 6. ELECTRONIC & SYSTEMS ENGINEERING. *Educ:* Auburn Univ, BSEE, 50; Fla State Univ, MS, 51; Johns Hopkins Univ, MSE, 59, PhD(elec eng), 62. *Prof Exp:* Electronics aide, Nat Bur Standards, 49-50, electronic scientist, 50-51, physicist, 51-52; proj engr, Radiation Res Corp, 52-54; res staff asst electronics, Carlyle Barton Lab, Johns Hopkins Univ, 54-57, res assoc, 57-62, res scientist, 62-63; sr res engr, HRB-Singer, Inc, Pa, 63-65, staff engr, 65-68; mem prof staff, Systs Eval Group, Ctr Naval Anal, 68-75 & Opers Eval Group, 75-78, div dir, Opers Eval Group, 78-80; WITH BIRD & SON INC, 80- *Concurrent Pos:* Ctr Naval Anal fel, Admiralty Surface Weapons Estab, Eng, 72-73. *Mem:* Sr mem Inst Elec & Electronics Engrs; Opers Res Soc Am; Mil Opers Res Soc (pres, 78). *Res:* Systems analysis; operations research; sensor systems; electronic warfare. *Mailing Add:* Bird & Son Inc Washington St East Walpole MA 02032

RICHARD, TERRY GORDON, b Marshfield, Wis, Feb 25, 45; m 76; c 3. ENGINEERING MECHANICS, METALLURGY. *Educ:* Univ Wis-Madison, BS, 68, MS, 69, PhD(eng mech), 73. *Prof Exp:* Engr, Owen Ayers & Assoc, 66-67 & Naval Weapons Ctr, 68; teaching asst mech, Univ Wis-Madison, 68-72, fel, 73-75; prof eng mech, Ohio State Univ, 75-81; PROF ENG MECH, UNIV WIS-MADISON, 81- *Concurrent Pos:* Res scientist, Kimberly Clark Corp, 69-70; consult, Battelle Mem Inst-Columbus Div, 76-79, Al Lee Corp, 77-80, Columbia Gas Corp, 79, Joint Implant Surgeons Inc, 79-81 & Sensotec Inc, 79-81. *Mem:* Soc Exp Stress Anal; Soc Adv Eng Educ; Sigma Xi; Am Soc Mech Engrs. *Res:* Photoelasticity, holography, fatigue, fracture mechanics and cryogenic materials characterization. *Mailing Add:* Dept Eng Mech Univ Wis 1415 Johnson Dr Madison WI 53706

RICHARD, WILLIAM RALPH, JR, b Brooklyn, NY, Oct 13, 22; m 47; c 3. INDUSTRIAL ORGANIC CHEMISTRY, PAPER CHEMISTRY. *Educ:* Amherst Col, AB, 43; Univ Mich, MS, 47, PhD(org chem), 50. *Prof Exp:* Res chemist plastics div, Monsanto Chem Co, 43-44, chemist, Shawinigan Resins Corp, 44-45; res chemist, Plastics Div, Monsanto Co, 45-46, res & eng div, 50-55, group leader, 55-58, sect leader, 58-63, mgr res org div, 63-72, mgr res, Monsanto Indust Chem Co, 76, DIR TECHNOL, MONSANTO CHEM INTERMEDIATES CO, 76- *Mem:* AAAS; Am Chem Soc; Am Soc Lubrication Engrs; Tech Asn Pulp & Paper Indust; Soc Res Adminr. *Res:* Plasticizer theory; phases in polymer-plasticizer gels; vinyl monomer polymerization; stereospecific and pressure polymerization; synthetic lubricants; hydraulic, heat transfer and dielectric fluids; sizing and wet strength paper chemicals; maleic anhydride, phosphorus intermediates, halo aromatics, nitro and amino aromatics. *Mailing Add:* Monsanto Co 800 N Lindbergh Blvd St Louis MO 63166

RICHARDS, A(LVIN) M(AURER), b Akron, Ohio, Sept 24, 26; m 49; c 2. STRUCTURAL ENGINEERING. *Educ:* Univ Akron, BSCE, 48; Harvard Univ, MSCE, 49; Univ Cincinnati, PhD(struct), 68. *Prof Exp:* Designer, Barber & Magee, Ohio, 49; from asst prof to assoc prof, 49-66, PROF CIVIL ENG, UNIV AKRON, 68- *Concurrent Pos:* Consult. *Mem:* Am Soc Civil Engrs. *Res:* Computer applications to structural design and to the instructional process. *Mailing Add:* Dept Civil Eng Univ Akron Akron OH 44325

RICHARDS, ADRIAN F, b Worcester, Mass, Apr 1, 29; div; c 3. OCEAN ENGINEERING, OCEANOGRAPHY. *Educ:* Univ NMex, BS, 51; Univ Calif, Los Angeles, PhD(oceanog), 57. *Prof Exp:* Res asst submarine geol, Scripps Inst, Univ Calif, 51-55, grad res geologist, 55-57; geol oceanogr, US Navy Hydrographic Off, 57-60; actg exec secy, Div Earth Sci, Nat Res Coun, 60; liaison scientist, London Br Off, Off Naval Res, 61-64; from assoc prof to prof geol & civil eng, Univ Ill, Urbana, 64-69; adj prof oceanog & ocean eng, Depts Geol Sci & Civil Eng, Lehigh Univ, 68-69, prof, 69-82, dir, Marine Geotech Lab, 70-82; SR CONSULT, FUGRO BV, LEICHENDAM, HOLLAND, 82-; ADJ MEM STAFF, DEPT OCEAN ENG, WOODS HOLE OCEANOG INST, 82- *Concurrent Pos:* Instr, US Dept Agr Grad Sch, 59-60; Nat Acad Sci-Nat Res Coun resident res assoc, US Navy Electronics Lab, 60-61; Royal Norweg Coun Sci & Indust Res fel, Norweg Geotech Inst, 63-64; mem, Joint Oceanog Insts Deep Explor Sampling, Sedimentary, Petrol & Phys Properties Panel, 70-, chmn, 76-82; mem, Downhole Measurements Panel, 75-82; mem, US deleg on training, educ & mutual assistance, Intergovt Oceanog Comn, UNESCO, 71-73; co-chmn panel on undersea sci & technol, Nat Acad Sci-Nat Acad Eng, 72-73; mem adv coun, Univ-Nat Oceanog Lab Syst, 72-76, chmn, Alvin Rev Comt, 75-77, vchmn, 78-79; vis prof oceanog, Lafayette Col, 73; mem seafloor eng comt, Marine Bd, Nat Res Coun, 73-76; consult marine sci & technol, Govt of Iran, UNESCO, 74; ed-in-chief, Marine Geotechnol, 74-; mem vis comt, Dept Ocean Eng, Woods Hole Oceanog Inst, 74 & 76; Trans-Can lectr, Soil Mech Subcomt, Nat Res Coun Can, 74; rep eng comt on oceanic resources, Comt on Training Educ & Mutual Asstance, Intergovt Oceanog Comn, UNESCO, 75-; assoc ed, Ocean Eng, 75-; consult marine sci & technol, Adrian F Richards & Assocs, Inc, 75-, Marine Facil Panel, US-Japan Coop Prog Nat Resources, 72-, Sea-Bottom Surv Panel, 77- & Off Ocean Eng, Nat Oceanic & Atmospheric Admin, 77-81; Nat Res Coun rep, Int Prog & Int Coop Oceans, Dept State, 77-; mem ocean eng rev comt, Rosenstiel Sch Marine & Atmospheric Sci & Sch Eng & Environ Design, Univ Miami, 78. *Honors & Awards:* C A Hogentogler Award, Am Soc Testing & Mat, 73. *Mem:* Fel AAAS; fel Marine Technol Soc; fel Geol Soc Am; fel Geol Soc London; fel Am Soc Civil Engrs. *Res:* Geotechnical ocean engineering; marine sedimentology; ocean engineering education in developing nations. *Mailing Add:* Dept Ocean Eng Woods Hole Oceanog Inst Woods Hole MA 02543

RICHARDS, ALBERT GLENN, b Lake Forest, Ill, May 29, 09; m 35, 66; c 3. INSECT PHYSIOLOGY. *Educ:* Univ Ga, AB, 29; Cornell Univ, PhD(entom), 32. *Prof Exp:* Asst, Cornell Univ, 30-32; actg head dept entom, Ward's Nat Sci Estab, 32; asst zool, Univ Rochester, 33-36; asst, Am Mus Natural Hist, 36-37; instr biol, City Col New York, 37-39; from instr to asst prof zool, Univ Pa, 39-45; assoc prof entom & zool, 45-49, prof, 49-77, EMER PROF ENTOM & ZOOL, UNIV MINN, ST PAUL, 77- *Concurrent Pos:* Guggenheim fel & Fulbright res scholar, Max Planck Inst Biol, 57-58; vis lectr, Am Inst Biol Sci, 59-65; guest investr, Max Planck Inst Physiol Behav, 66-67; guest prof, Univ Munich, 66-67; mem, Marine Biol Lab, Woods Hole, Mass. *Mem:* Entom Soc Am (vpres, 49); Am Entom Soc (secy, 43-45); Am Soc Zool; Brit Soc Exp Biol; Electron Micros Soc Am. *Res:* Histology, ultrastructure and physiology of insects; arthropod cuticle; biological microscopy. *Mailing Add:* Dept Entom Fisheries & Wildlife Univ of Minn St Paul MN 55108

RICHARDS, ALBERT GUSTAV, b Chicago, Ill, Jan 7, 17; m 42; c 5. DENTAL RADIOLOGY. *Educ:* Univ Mich, BS, 40, MS, 43. *Prof Exp:* From instr to prof dent, Univ Mich, Ann Arbor, 40-74, Marcus L Ward prof, 74-82; RETIRED. *Concurrent Pos:* Consult, Vet Admin Hosp, Ann Arbor, 54-, Nat Res Coun, 58, dent health proj, Dept Health, Educ & Welfare, 62- & comt x-ray protection dent off, Nat Comn Radiation Protection, 63-; mem, Nat Adv Environ Coun, USPHS, 69-71. *Mem:* Am Dent Asn; Am Acad Dent Radiol (pres, Acad Oral Roentgenol, 62-63). *Res:* Electron microscopy, radiation hygiene and dosimetry in dentistry; radiographic technics for pedodontists and exodontists; erythema; dental and x-ray machine designs; invented dynamic tomography and dental x-ray technique trainer. *Mailing Add:* 395 Rock Creek Dr Ann Arbor MI 48104

RICHARDS, BERT LORIN, JR, b Fielding, Utah, July 8, 11; m 36; c 3. PLANT PATHOLOGY. *Educ:* Utah State Agr Col, BS, 35; Cornell Univ, PhD(plant path), 43. *Prof Exp:* Instr plant path, Cornell Univ, 42-44; sr res biologist, E I du Pont de Nemours & Co, Inc, 44-76; RETIRED. *Mem:* AAAS; Am Phytopath Soc; Am Hort Soc. *Res:* New virus diseases; bean virus strains; breeding for resistance; development methods for artificially inoculating plants with viruses; laboratory and greenhouse sorting and field evaluation; agricultural chemicals; fungicides. *Mailing Add:* 2402 Larchwood Rd Wilmington DE 19810

RICHARDS, CEDRIC W(ILLIAM), b Lincoln, Nebr, Mar 3, 13; m 45; c 4. CIVIL ENGINEERING. *Educ:* Univ Nebr, BS, 33; Stanford Univ, MS, 48, PhD(eng mech), 53. *Prof Exp:* Mgr, Richards Organ Co, 34-42; instr eng mech, Univ Nebr, 42-44; instr, Stanford Univ, 46-52; assoc prof, Univ Mass, 52-53; assoc prof, 53-70, prof, 70-78, EMER PROF CIVIL ENG, STANFORD UNIV, 78- *Concurrent Pos:* Consult, Stanford Res Inst, 53 & Swedish Cement & Concrete Res Inst, Sweden, 64; res fel, Eindhoven Technol Univ, 61-62. *Res:* Materials engineering; structural materials. *Mailing Add:* Dept of Civil Eng Stanford Univ Stanford CA 94305

RICHARDS, CHARLES DAVIS, b Cumberland, Md, May 14, 20; m 43; c 5. PLANT TAXONOMY. *Educ:* Wheaton Col, Ill, BA, 43; Univ Mich, MA, 47, PhD(bot), 52. *Prof Exp:* From instr to asst prof bot, Mich Col Mining & Technol, 47-50; instr, Univ Mich, 51; from instr to assoc prof, 52-63, PROF BOT, UNIV MAINE, ORONO, 63- *Res:* Flora and grasses of Maine; plant ecology of Mt Kathdin; aquatic flowering plants; plant geography; rare and endangered plants. *Mailing Add:* Dept of Bot & Plant Path Univ of Maine Orono ME 04473

RICHARDS, CHARLES NORMAN, b Buffalo, NY, Mar 3, 42. PHYSICAL ORGANIC CHEMISTRY. *Educ:* Canisius Col, BS, 64; Univ Hawaii, PhD(phys org chem), 68. *Prof Exp:* SR RES CHEMIST, CORN PROD RES, ANHEUSER-BUSCH, INC, 68- *Mem:* Am Chem Soc. *Res:* Pyrolysis gas chromatography applied to synthetic and natural polymers; thermodynamic activation parameters in mixed aqueous systems; modified food starches. *Mailing Add:* 12215 Country Manor Ln St Louis MO 63141

RICHARDS, CLYDE RICH, b Paris, Idaho, June 9, 21; m 46; c 3. DAIRY HUSBANDRY. *Educ:* Utah State Agr Col, BS, 43; Cornell Univ, MS, 49, PhD(dairy husb), 50. *Prof Exp:* Asst animal husb, Cornell Univ, 46-50; lectr animal breeding, Super Sch Agr, Athens, Greece, 50-51; from asst prof to assoc prof animal indust, Univ Del, 51-61; dep asst adminr, 71-72, PRIN ANIMAL NUTRITIONIST, COOP STATE RES SERV, USDA, 61- *Mem:* AAAS; Am Inst Nutrit; Am Soc Animal Sci; Am Dairy Sci Asn. *Res:* Roughage digestibility using indicator techniques; nutrient content of lima bean silage; ketosis in dairy cattle; agricultural research programs at land grant colleges of 1890; research administration. *Mailing Add:* Coop State Res Serv US Dept of Agr Washington DC 20250

RICHARDS, DALE OWEN, b Morgan, Utah, July 4, 27; m 55; c 3. STATISTICS. *Educ:* Utah State Univ, BS, 50; Iowa State Univ, MS, 57, PhD(statist, indust eng), 63. *Prof Exp:* Statistician, Gen Elec Co, 52-55; instr indust eng, Iowa State Univ, 55-59, asst prof, 59-63; assoc prof statist, 63-66, chmn dept, 66-69, PROF STATIST, BRIGHAM YOUNG UNIV, 67- *Concurrent Pos:* Consult, Am Can Co, 58; opers analyst, US Air Force contract, Iowa State Univ Standby Unit, 59-70; consult, Nuclear Div, Kaman Aircraft Corp, 60 & CEIR, Inc, 65-70. *Mem:* Am Statist Asn; Am Soc Qual Control. *Res:* Application of statistical and operations research techniques to industrial situations. *Mailing Add:* Dept of State Brigham Young Univ Provo UT 84601

RICHARDS, DEAN BOYD, forestry, see previous edition

RICHARDS, EARL FREDERICK, b Detroit, Mich, Mar 11, 23; m 46; c 2. ELECTRICAL ENGINEERING. *Educ:* Wayne State Univ, BS, 51; Mo Sch Mines & Metall, MS, 61; Univ Mo, PhD(elec eng), 71. *Prof Exp:* Engr elec, Electronic Control Corp, 51-52, Pa Salt Mfg Co, 52-54; instr elec, Mo Sch Mines & Metall, 58-61; from asst prof to assoc prof, 62-80, PROF ELEC ENG, UNIV MO-ROLLA, 80- *Concurrent Pos:* Lectr elec, Univ Detroit, 56-68; res cngr, Argonne Nat Lab, 63; consult, Ford Motor Co, 66-67, Emerson Elec Co, 78-80, Magnetic Peripherals, 80, Wanlass Corp, 81 & Public Serv Comn Mo, 82. *Mem:* Sigma Xi; Inst Elec & Electronic Engrs. *Res:* Linear and non-linear contract systems theory; simulation and modelling techniques; digital filtering; power system analysis and stability. *Mailing Add:* Dept Elec Eng Univ Mo Rolla MO 65401

RICHARDS, EDMUND A, b Grand Rapids, Mich, Jan 25, 35; m 56; c 2. PHYSIOLOGY, PHARMACOLOGY. *Educ:* Purdue Univ, BS, 57; Univ Ill, MS, 59, PhD(physiol), 65; Univ Stockholm, MD, 67. *Prof Exp:* Assoc pharmacologist, Eli Lilly Co, 59-61; res assoc physiol, Univ Ill, 63-65; guest scientist, Karolinska Inst, Sweden, 65-67; assoc prof physiol, Baylor Univ Col Med, 67-69; PROF PHYSIOL, UNIV NORTHERN COLO, 69- *Concurrent Pos:* Int lectr, Gt Brit & Scand, 72; consult, Astra Pharmaceut Co, Gen Mills, Inc, WHO & Int Drug Control. *Mem:* Am Gastroenterol Soc; Am Physiol Soc; Am Inst Biol Sci; fel Royal Soc; Int Pharmacol Cong; NY Acad Sci. *Res:* Gastroenterological research related to pancreatic and gastric secretion and peptic ulceration; the transfer of pharmacological active drugs across the human placental membranes; pharmacology of smooth muscle. *Mailing Add:* Dept of Biol Univ of Northern Colo Greeley CO 80639

RICHARDS, FRANCIS ASBURY, b Newton, Ill, May 26, 17; m 44; c 4. OCEANOGRAPHY. *Educ:* Univ Ill, BS, 39; Univ Nev, MS, 42; Univ Wash, PhD(chem), 50. *Prof Exp:* Sub-prof chemist, US Bur Mines, Nev, 41-42; res assoc, Univ Wash, 48-50; chem oceanogr, Woods Hole Oceanog Inst, 50-59; assoc prof oceanog, 59-64, asst chmn dept, 66-68, assoc chmn res, Dept Oceanog, 68-77, PROF OCEANOG, UNIV WASH, 64- *Concurrent Pos:* Guggenheim fel, Univ Oslo, 56-57; ed jour, Am Soc Limnol & Oceanog, 63-68; mem, US-Japan Coop Res Prog, Japan, 70-71; ed, Deep-Sea Res, 73-; sr liaison scientist, Off Naval Res, Tokyo, 77-79; sci dir, Off Naval Res, London, 81- *Mem:* Am Soc Limnol & Oceanog; Am Geophys Union; Oceanog Soc Japan. *Res:* Chemical oceanography; anoxic and sulfide-bearing marine environments; nutrient cycles; air gases; trace metals and organic compounds in the ocean; analysis of plankton pigments; analytical and physical chemistry of seawater. *Mailing Add:* 3914 48th Pl NE Seattle WA 98105

RICHARDS, FRANCIS RUSSELL, b Biloxi, Miss, Jan 19, 44; m 65; c 2. OPERATIONS RESEARCH, APPLIED STATISTICS. *Educ:* La Polytech Univ, BS, 65; Clemson Univ, MS, 67, PhD(math sci), 71. *Prof Exp:* Teaching asst math, Clemson Univ, 65-70; PROF OPERS RES, NAVAL POSTGRAD SCH, 70- *Mem:* Opers Res Soc Am; Inst Mgt Sci; Am Statist Asn. *Res:* Applications of multi-attribute utility theory to multi-criteria decision making; test and evaluation; constrained multi-item inventory analysis; reliability, maintenance and availability. *Mailing Add:* Naval Postgrad Sch Code 55Rh Monterey CA 93940

RICHARDS, FRANK FREDERICK, b London, Eng, Nov 14, 28; m 58; c 3. BIOCHEMISTRY, MEDICINE. *Educ:* Cambridge Univ, BA, 53, MS, BChir, 56, MD, 63. *Prof Exp:* Intern surg, St Mary's Hosp, London, 57-58; intern med, Oxford Univ, 58; resident, Brompton Hosp, 59; sr resident invest med, St Mary's Hosp Med Sch, 59-60, lectr, 60-64; res assoc biochem, Harvard Med Sch, 64-66; assoc med, Mass Gen Hosp, 66-68; assoc prof med & microbiol, 68-74, PROF INTERNAL MED, SCH MED, YALE UNIV, 74- *Concurrent Pos:* Res fel biochem, St Mary's Hosp, London, 58-59; Am Heart Asn adv res fel, 64-66; estab investr, Am Heart Asn, 66-71. *Mem:* Am Asn Immunol; Am Inst Chemists; Brit Biochem Soc. *Res:* Protein chemistry and molecular biology as applied to immunology, virology and parasitology; pulmonary disease. *Mailing Add:* Dept of Intern Med Yale Univ Sch of Med New Haven CT 06510

RICHARDS, FREDERIC MIDDLEBROOK, b New York, NY, Aug 19, 25; m 59; c 1. PROTEIN CHEMISTRY. *Educ:* Mass Inst Technol, SB, 48; Harvard Univ, PhD, 52. *Prof Exp:* Res fel phys chem, Harvard Univ, 52-53; from asst prof to assoc prof biochem, 54-62, chmn dept molecular biophys & biochem, 63-67 & 69-72, PROF BIOCHEM, YALE UNIV, 62-; DIR, JANE COFFIN CHILDS MEM FUND MED RES, 76- *Concurrent Pos:* Fels, Nat Res Coun, Carlsberg Lab, Copenhagen, Denmark, 54 & NSF, Cambridge Univ, 55. *Honors & Awards:* Pfizer-Paul Lewis Award Enzyme Chem, 65; Kai Linderstrom-Lang Award, 78. *Mem:* Nat Acad Sci; AAAS; Biophys Soc (pres, 72); Am Crystallog Asn; Am Soc Biol Chemists (pres, 79). *Res:* Proteins. *Mailing Add:* 69 Andrews Rd Guilford CT 06437

RICHARDS, GRAYDON EDWARD, b Gilmer Co, WVa, July 2, 33; m 56; c 2. SOIL FERTILITY. *Educ:* WVa Univ, BS, 55; Ohio State Univ, MSc, 59, PhD(agron), 61. *Prof Exp:* Teacher high sch, WVa, 55-57; res asst agron, Ohio State Univ, 57-61; res agronomist, Int Minerals & Chem Corp, 61-67; sr res scientist & proj leader agron, Continental Oil Co, 67-70; regional agronomist, Agr Div, Olin Corp, 70-79; chief agronomist, Smith-Douglass Div, Borden Inc, 80; acct supvr fertilizer, Doane Agr Serv, 80-81; MGR, AGR & TECH SERV, VISTRON CORP, 81- *Mem:* Am Soc Agron; Soil Sci Soc Am; Am Chem Soc. *Res:* Chemistry of soil potassium and essential micronutrient elements; plant growth regulators; micronutrient nutrition of plants; fertilization for optimum yields; efficient use of phosphatic fertilizer. *Mailing Add:* 3340 Rountree St Lima OH 45805

RICHARDS, HAROLD REX, b Timmins, Ont, Feb 9, 26; m 49; c 2. TEXTILE TECHNOLOGY. *Educ:* Univ Leeds, BSc, 49, PhD(textile sci), 54. *Prof Exp:* Sr phys chemist, Defence Res Bd, Can, 56-64; head dept textiles, clothing & design, Univ Guelph, 64-70; PROF TEXTILES & CLOTHING & HEAD DEPT, COLO STATE UNIV, 71- *Concurrent Pos:* Consult, Mich Chem Corp, 70- *Honors & Awards:* Textile Sci Award, Textile Tech Fedn Can, 68. *Mem:* Can Inst Textile Sci (pres, 65-66); fel Brit Textile Inst; fel Brit Plastics Inst; Fiber Soc. *Res:* Textile and polymer science. *Mailing Add:* Dept of Textiles & Clothing Colo State Univ Ft Collins CO 80523

RICHARDS, HORACE GARDINER, b Philadelphia, Pa, Mar 21, 06. PALEONTOLOGY. *Educ:* Univ Pa, AB, 27, MS, 29, PhD(zool, paleont), 32. *Prof Exp:* Sr sci aide, Div Mollusks, US Nat Mus, 31-32, asst cur, 32; res assoc, NJ State Mus, 34-42; res fel, Acad Natural Sci, Philadelphia, 37-42, assoc cur, 42-60, chmn dept geol, 60-72, emer cur geol, 72-75; RETIRED. *Concurrent Pos:* Assoc, NC State Mus, NC, 41-43; lectr, Univ Pa, 49-71; geologist, US Geol Surv, 49-61; res assoc, Lamont Geol Observ, 62-; hon res assoc, Del Mus Natural Hist, 73-; mem expeds, Mex, Cent Am, SAm, Mid E, Africa & Arctic Can. *Honors & Awards:* Pres Award, Am Asn Petrol Geol, 46. *Mem:* Fel Paleont Soc; fel Geol Soc Am; Am Asn Petrol Geol; Am Malacol Union; Int Asn Quaternary Res. *Res:* Geology and paleontology of the Atlantic coastal plain; Pleistocene geology and paleontology. *Mailing Add:* 2601 Parkway Apt 1012 Philadelphia PA 19130

RICHARDS, HUGH TAYLOR, b Baca Co, Colo, Nov 7, 18; m 44; c 6. NUCLEAR PHYSICS. *Educ:* Park Col, BA, 39; Rice Inst, MA, 40, PhD(physics), 42. *Prof Exp:* Asst physics, Rice Inst, 41-42, res assoc uranium proj, Off Sci Res & Develop, 42; scientist, Univ Minn, 42-43 & Manhattan Dist, Los Alamos Sci Lab, 43-46; res assoc nuclear physics, 46-47, from asst prof to assoc prof, 47-52, chmn dept physics, 61-63 & 66-68, assoc dean col lett & sci, 63-66, PROF NUCLEAR PHYSICS, UNIV WIS-MADISON, 52- *Mem:* Fel Am Phys Soc. *Res:* Nuclear scattering cross sections; yields and angular distributions of nuclear reactions; nuclear energy levels and reaction energies; isospin forbidden reactions; negative ion sources. *Mailing Add:* Dept of Physics Univ of Wis Madison WI 53706

RICHARDS, JACK LESTER, b Apr 29, 40; US citizen; m 64; c 2. ORGANIC CHEMISTRY, PHOTOGRAPHIC TECHNOLOGY. *Educ:* Rochester Inst Technol, BS, 65; Univ Rochester, PhD(org chem), 70. *Prof Exp:* sr res chemist, 69-76, tech assoc, 77-81, RES ASSOC, RES LABS, EASTMAN KODAK CO, 81- *Mem:* Am Chem Soc. *Res:* Synthesis of organic compounds for applications in image formation systems; chemistry of organosulfur and organosulfur-nitrogen compounds; research and development work on color photographic systems; production and quality control of color photographic products; worldwide coordination of complex technical programs. *Mailing Add:* 2259 Latta Rd Rochester NY 14612

RICHARDS, JAMES AUSTIN, JR, b Boston, Mass, Apr 15, 16; m 39; c 4. PHYSICS. *Educ:* Oberlin Col, BA, 38; Duke Univ, PhD(physics), 42. *Prof Exp:* Instr physics, Bucknell Univ, 42-46; tutor physics & math, Olivet Col, 46-49; asst prof physics, Univ Minn, Duluth, 49-51; res physicist, Am Viscose Corp, 51-55; prof physics, Drexel Inst Technol, 55-65; dean instr, Community Col Philadelphia, 65-68; prof physics, 68-82, INSTRNL DEVELOPER, STATE UNIV NY AGR & TECH COL DELHI, 82- *Mem:* Am Asn Physics Teachers. *Res:* Atomic physics; nuclear science. *Mailing Add:* Dept of Physics State Univ NY Agr & Tech Col Delhi NY 13753

RICHARDS, JAMES FREDERICK, b Amherst Island, Ont, Mar 15, 27; m 52; c 3. BIOCHEMISTRY. *Educ:* Queen's Univ, Ont, BA, 49, MA, 52; Univ Western Ont, PhD(biochem), 58. *Prof Exp:* Nat Res Coun Can overseas fel biochem, Glasgow Univ, 59-60; from instr to assoc prof, 60-75, PROF BIOCHEM, UNIV BC, 75- *Mem:* Can Biochem Soc. *Res:* Mechanism of action of peptide hormones-effects of prolactin. *Mailing Add:* Dept of Biochem Univ of BC Vancouver BC V6T 1W5 Can

RICHARDS, JAMES L, b Kankakee, Ill, Dec 26, 46; m 69; c 2. OPERATIONS RESEARCH, COMPUTER SCIENCE. *Educ:* Ill State Univ, BS, 68; Univ Mo-Rolla, MS, 72, PhD(math), 76. *Prof Exp:* asst prof math & comput sci, 76-81, ASSOC PROF COMPUT SCI, BEMIDJI STATE UNIV, 81- *Mem:* Asn Comput Mach. *Res:* Integer programming, optimization theory and programming languages. *Mailing Add:* Dept of Math & Comput Sci Bemidji State Univ Bemidji MN 56601

RICHARDS, JOANNE S, b Exeter, NH, Apr 23, 45. REPRODUCTIVE ENDOCRINOLOGY. *Educ:* Oberlin Col, BA, 67; Brown Univ, MAT, 68, PhD(physiol chem), 70. *Prof Exp:* Asst prof biol, Univ NDak, 70-71; fel, 71-73, instr, 73-74, ASST PROF REPROD ENDOCRINOL, UNIV MICH, 74- *Concurrent Pos:* Prin investr, NIH grants, 76-79; Nat Inst Child Health & Human Develop res career develop award, 78. *Res:* Mammalian reproductive endocrinology; mechanisms of hormone action; ovarian cell physiology. *Mailing Add:* Reprod Endocrinol Prog Univ of Mich Ann Arbor MI 48109

RICHARDS, JOHN HALL, b Berkeley, Calif, Mar 13, 30; m 54, 75; c 4. BIOCHEMISTRY. *Educ:* Univ Calif, BS, 51, PhD, 55; Oxford Univ, BSc, 53. *Prof Exp:* Instr chem, Harvard Univ, 55-57; from asst prof to assoc prof, 57-70, PROF CHEM, CALIF INST TECHNOL, 70- *Concurrent Pos:* Consult, E I du Pont de Nemours & Co. *Honors & Awards:* Lalor Award, 56. *Mem:* Am Chem Soc; NY Acad Sci; Royal Soc Chem. *Res:* Mechanism of protein function; molecular immunology. *Mailing Add:* Church Lab of Chem Biol Calif Inst of Technol Pasadena CA 91109

RICHARDS, JONATHAN IAN, b New York, NY, Dec 4, 36. MATHEMATICS. *Educ:* Univ Minn, BA, 57; Harvard Univ, MA, 59, PhD(math), 60. *Prof Exp:* Instr math, Mass Inst Technol, 60-62; asst prof, 62-67, assoc prof, 67-80, PROF MATH, UNIV MINN, MINNEAPOLIS, 80- *Mem:* Am Math Soc; Math Asn Am. *Res:* Functional analysis; functions of one complex variable; number theory. *Mailing Add:* Dept of Math Univ of Minn Minneapolis MN 55455

RICHARDS, JOSEPH DUDLEY, b Hanover, NH, Sept 13, 17; m 40; c 4. INDUSTRIAL CHEMISTRY. *Educ:* Dartmouth Col, AB, 39. *Prof Exp:* Analyst, Duraloy Co, Pa, 39-40 & Weirton Steel Co, WVa, 40-41; spectrogr, Am Steel & Wire Co, Mass, 40-44, US Bur Mines, 44-45 & Nat Bur Stand, Washington, DC, 45; res chemist in-chg instruments lab, Chem & Pigment Co, 45-50, res group leader chem pigments, Metals Div, Glidden Co, 50-57, asst to dir res pigments & color dept, 57-61, group leader new prod, 61-63, liaison mkt res, 63-66, mgr econ eval, Glidden-Durkee Div, SCM Corp, Baltimore, 66-67, mgr res serv, 67-70, MGR COM DEVELOP, GLIDDEN-DURKEE DIV, SCM CORP, BALTIMORE, 70-, MGR SPEC SALES, PIGMENTS GROUP, 80- *Mem:* Am Chem Soc; fel Am Inst Chemists. *Res:* Emission spectroscopy; electron microscopy; x-ray diffraction; pigment and inorganic chemistry; research planning. *Mailing Add:* 113 Tenbury Rd Lutherville MD 21093

RICHARDS, KENNETH JULIAN, b Long Beach, Calif, Nov 29, 32; m 58; c 3. CHEMICAL METALLURGY, METALLURGICAL ENGINEERING. *Educ:* Univ Utah, Salt Lake City, BS, 56, PhD(metall eng), 62. *Prof Exp:* Process eng refining, Union Oil, 56; process eng fractionation, C F Braun, 57; develop eng rare earth separation, US Intel Agency, 57-59; group leader metals & ceramics res, Aerospace Res Labs, 62-67; sr scientist chem metall, 67-70, sect head refining res, 70-72, mgr process metall, 72-74, RES DIR, METAL MINING DIV RES CTR, KENNECOTT COPPER CORP, 74- *Concurrent Pos:* Mat consult, Air Force Mat Lab, 65-67, Air Force Ballistics Missile Div, 65-67, & NASA, 65-67. *Mem:* Metall Soc; Am Inst Mining, Metal & Petrol Eng; Am Soc Metals; Am Inst Chem Eng; Soc Mining Engrs. *Res:* Extractive metallurgy; process development; technical planning; research management. *Mailing Add:* Kennecott Copper Corp 1515 Mineral Sq Salt Lake City UT 84147

RICHARDS, L(ORENZO) WILLARD, b Logan, Utah, July 11, 32; m 66; c 2. PHYSICAL CHEMISTRY. *Educ:* Calif Inst Technol, BS, 54; Harvard Univ, AM, 56, PhD, 60. *Prof Exp:* From instr to asst prof chem, Amherst Col, 59-66; indust res fel, Cabot Corp, 66-68, mem tech staff, 68-74; mem tech staff, Environ Monitoring & Serv Ctr, Rockwell Int, 74-79; SR PROJ MGR, METEROL RES, INC, 79- *Concurrent Pos:* USPHS fel, Univ Calif, Berkeley, 64-65; adj prof, Rensselaer Polytech Inst, 71-73. *Mem:* Am Chem Soc; Am Phys Soc; Optical Soc Am; Combustion Inst; Air Pollution Control Asn. *Res:* Atmospheric chemistry; aerosols; light scattering by particles; multiple scattering of light; gas phase chemical kinetics; atmospheric sciences. *Mailing Add:* Metereol Res Inc 3402 Mendocino Ave Santa Rosa CA 95401

RICHARDS, LAWRENCE PHILLIPS, b Honolulu, Hawaii, Jan 15, 24; m 53; c 2. MAMMALOGY, VERTEBRATE PALEONTOLOGY. *Educ:* Univ Calif, AB, 50; Univ Ill, PhD(zool), 57. *Prof Exp:* Asst zool, Univ Calif, 51-52; asst avian anat, Univ Ill, 53-54, asst zool, 54-57; res assoc avian physiol, State Col Wash, 57-58; from instr to asst prof zool, Idaho State Col, 58-62; vert zoologist, New Guinea & Bernice Pauahi Bishop Mus, Honolulu, Hawaii, 62-63; asst prof mammalian histol, Sch Dent, Temple Uni v, 63-64; vert paleontologist, Univ Ariz, 64-65; from asst prof to assoc prof, 65-77, PROF BIOL, EASTERN MICH UNIV, 77- *Concurrent Pos:* Ranger-naturalist, Yosemite Nat Park, US Nat Park Serv, Calif, 57-58; NSF res grants, 59-62. *Mem:* AAAS; Soc Vert Paleont; Am Soc Zool; Am Soc Mammal. *Res:* Natural history of Chanler's mountain reedbuck, Redunca fulvorfula chanleri in Nairobi National Park, Kenya, East Africa; functional anatomy and phylogeny of Hawaiian honeycreepers. *Mailing Add:* Dept of Biol Eastern Mich Univ Ypsilanti MI 48197

RICHARDS, LORENZO ADOLPH, b Fielding, Utah, Apr 24, 04; m 30; c 3. EXPERIMENTAL PHYSICS. *Educ:* Utah State Univ, BS, 26, MA, 27; Cornell Univ, PhD(physics), 31. *Hon Degrees:* DTechSc, Israel Inst Technol, 52; DSc, Utah State Univ, 74. *Prof Exp:* Asst physics, Cornell Univ, 27-29, instr, 29-35; physicist, Battelle Mem Inst, 35; from asst prof to assoc prof physics, Iowa State Univ, 35-39; sr soil physicist salinity lab, Bur Plant Indust, USDA, 39-42; Nat Defense Res fel & group supvr, Calif Inst Technol, 42-45; chief physicst salinity lab, Bur Plant Indust, USDA, Calif, 45-66; CONSULT PHYSICIST IN-CHG RES & DEVELOP, LARK INSTRUMENTS, 66- *Concurrent Pos:* Consult, Ministry Agr, Egypt, 52; vpres & dir, Moistomatic, Inc, 54-62; lectr, Univ Alexandria, 62; prof in residence, Univ Calif, Riverside, 68-69; consult, Ford Found. *Honors & Awards:* Ord Develop Award, Dept Navy, 45; Super Serv Award, USDA, 59. *Mem:* Fel AAAS; Am Soc Agron (pres, 65); Am Phys Soc; Soil Sci Soc Am (pres, 52); Am Geophys Union. *Res:* Physics of soil water; automatic irrigation; diagnosis and improvement of saline and alkali soils; electronic sensors for soil water matric suction and salinity. *Mailing Add:* 4455 Fifth St Riverside CA 92501

RICHARDS, MARVIN SHERRILL, b Somerville, NJ, Jan 27, 22. ORGANIC CHEMISTRY. *Educ:* Princeton Univ, BS, 43; Lehigh Univ, MS, 49; Rutgers Univ, PhD(chem), 53. *Prof Exp:* Res chemist, Johns-Manville Corp, 43; develop chemist, Am Cyanamid Co, 46-47; asst instr org chem, Lehigh Univ, 48-49; asst instr, Rutgers Univ, 49-52, instr, 52-54; from asst prof to prof phys chem, Drew Univ, 54-69; sr assoc prof chem, 69-73, PROF CHEM, MIAMI-DADE COMMUNITY COL, 73- *Mem:* Am Chem Soc. *Res:* Mechanism; diazoketones; halogenations; synthesis of pyrimidines. *Mailing Add:* Dept of Chem Miami-Dade Community Col Miami FL 33167

RICHARDS, NORMAN LEE, b New London, Conn, Apr 11, 35; m 56; c 3. MARINE BIOLOGY, TOXICOLOGY. *Educ:* Univ Conn, BA, 57, MS, 60; Univ RI, PhD(bacteriol), 70. *Prof Exp:* Res asst, Univ Conn, 56-59; biochemist, Gen Dynamics Corp, 59-61; bioscientist, Boeing Co, 61-64; prin microbiologist, Rep Aviation Corp, 64-65; SCIENTIST DIR, US ENVIRON PROTECTION AGENCY, 65- *Concurrent Pos:* Fel, NIH, 69-71; res collabr, US/USSR Sci Exchange Prog, 76-80 & US/Poland PL 480 Prog, 74-79. *Mem:* Estuarine Res Fedn; Am Soc Microbiol. *Res:* Research on environmental pollutants: fate and effects; environmental hazard asessment; human health risk assessment; bioaccumulation; chemical separation and characterization. *Mailing Add:* 18 Highpoint Dr Gulf Breeze FL 32561

RICHARDS, NORVAL RICHARD, b Ont, Can, July 2, 16; m 51; c 2. SOILS. *Educ:* Univ Toronto, BSA, 38; Mich State Univ, MS, 46. *Hon Degrees:* DSc, Laval Univ, 67. *Prof Exp:* Agr res officer soil classification, Agr Res Br, Can, 38-50; prof soils & head dept, Univ Guelph, 50-62, dean, 62-72, prof land resource sci, Ont Agr Col, 72-81; RETIRED. *Concurrent Pos:* Chmn, Can Agr Res Coun, 75- *Mem:* Int Soil Sci Soc; fel Soil Conserv Soc Am; Can Soc Soil Sci (pres, 56); fel Agr Inst Can (pres, 75). *Res:* Soil classification. *Mailing Add:* Dept Land Resource Sci Univ Guelph Guelph ON N1G 2W1 Can

RICHARDS, OLIVER CHRISTOPHER, b Jamesburg, NJ, Jan 13, 33; m 63; c 2. BIOCHEMISTRY. *Educ:* Syracuse Univ, BS, 55; Univ Ill, PhD(biochem), 60. *Prof Exp:* NSF fel, Univ Minn, Minneapolis, 62-63; NSF fel, Univ Calif, Los Angeles, 63-64, res assoc, 64-65; from instr to asst prof, 65-72, ASSOC PROF BIOCHEM, COL MED, UNIV UTAH, 72- *Mem:* Am Soc Biol Chemists. *Res:* Structure, replication and function of extranuclear DNAs in eukaryotes; replication of animal viruses. *Mailing Add:* 25 S 1100 E Salt Lake City UT 84102

RICHARDS, OSCAR WHITE, b Butte, Mont, Jan 4, 02; m 23; c 2. ENVIRONMENTAL PHYSIOLOGY. *Educ:* Univ Ore, BA, 23, MA, 25; Yale Univ, PhD(zool), 31. *Prof Exp:* Instr zool & med, Univ Ore, 25-26; asst prof biol, Clark Univ, 28-30; instr, Yale Univ, 31-37; res biologist, Spencer Lens Co, 37-45; chief biologist sci instrument div, Am Optical Co, 45-47, res supvr biol, NY, 47-50 & Mass, 50-57, chief biologist, 57-67; consult & resident lectr, 67-82, EMER CONSULT & RESIDENT LECTR ENVIRON VISION, PAC UNIV, 82- *Concurrent Pos:* Lectr, Woman's Col New Haven, 35-37, Allegany Sch Natural Hist, 38, eve sch, Univ Buffalo, 38-39 & med sch, 48-50; consult, Armed Forces Inst Path, 52-76. *Honors & Awards:* Schmidt Award, Biol Photog Asn, 53; Prentice Award, Am Acad Optom, 71. *Mem:* AAAS; Am Soc Zool; hon fel Royal Micros Soc; hon fel Am Micros Soc (pres, 53); fel Optical Soc Am. *Res:* Phase interference and fluorescence microscopy; human vision and color vision; growth of yeast and Mytilus. *Mailing Add:* Rt 1 Box 79F Oakland OR 97462

RICHARDS, PAUL BLAND, b North Attleboro, Mass, Aug 14, 24; m 45; c 5. EMERGENCY MANAGEMENT, DISASTER MANAGEMENT. *Educ:* US Naval Acad, BS, 45; Harvard Univ, MS, 50; Case Inst Technol, MS, 53, PhD(math), 59. *Prof Exp:* Res engr, Babcock & Wilcox Res Ctr, 50-54; instr math & supvr res proj, Case Inst Technol, 54-57; mgr systs anal, Thompson Ramo Wooldridge, Inc, 57-59; mathematician, Gen Elec Co, 59-62; mgr math, sci comput, mech & math physics, Aerospace Res Ctr, Gen Precision, Inc, 62-68; supt math & info sci div, 68-74, DIR FLEET MED SUPPORT PROJ, NAVAL RES LAB, 74- *Mem:* Fel Am Astronaut Soc (pres, 71-73); AAAS. *Res:* Pioneered research in the design and evaluation of emergency and disaster management systems; principal analytical tool is computer simulation; applications include natural disasters, man-made disasters and military medical operations. *Mailing Add:* 9715 Culver St Kensington MD 20895

RICHARDS, PAUL IRVING, physics, deceased

RICHARDS, PAUL LINFORD, b Ithaca, NY, June 4, 34; m 65; c 2. PHYSICS. *Educ:* Harvard Univ, AB, 56; Univ Calif, PhD(physics), 60. *Prof Exp:* NSF fel, Royal Soc Mond Lab, Cambridge Univ, 59-60; mem tech staff, Bell Labs, Inc, 60-66; PROF PHYSICS, UNIV CALIF, BERKELEY, 66- *Concurrent Pos:* Miller Inst fac fel, 70-71; Guggenheim fel, Cambridge Univ, 73-74; Alexander von Humboldt sr scientist, Max Planck Inst, Stuttgart, 82. *Mem:* Am Phys Soc. *Res:* Astrophysics; low temperature solid state physics; far infrared; superconductivity; magnetic resonance. *Mailing Add:* Dept Physics Univ Calif Berkeley CA 94720

RICHARDS, PETER MICHAEL, b San Jose, Calif, Dec 20, 34; m 59; c 3. MAGNETISM, HYDROGEN SOLIDS. *Educ:* Mass Inst Technol, BS, 57; Stanford Univ, PhD(physics), 62. *Prof Exp:* Imp Chem Industs res fel, Oxford Univ, 62-64; from asst prof to prof physics, Univ Kans, 64-71; mem staff, 71-74, div supvr, 74-80, MEM STAFF, SANDIA NAT LABS, 80- *Concurrent Pos:* Consult, US Army Missile Command, Ala, 70-72. *Mem:* Fel Am Phys Soc. *Res:* Magnetic properties of matter; ionic conductivity; metal hydrides. *Mailing Add:* Sandia Nat Labs Org 5151 Albuquerque NM 87185

RICHARDS, R RONALD, b Wenatchee, Wash, Nov 22, 37; m 61; c 3. PHYSICAL CHEMISTRY. *Educ:* Seattle Pac Col, BS, 59; Univ Wash, PhD(phys chem), 64. *Prof Exp:* Assoc prof, 64-77, PROF CHEM, GREENVILLE COL, 77- *Concurrent Pos:* Fel, NASA Langley Res Ctr, Old Dom Univ, 71-72; res fel, Argonne Nat Lab, 78-79. *Mem:* Am Chem Soc. *Res:* Thermodynamics; kinetics; analysis. *Mailing Add:* Dept of Chem Greenville Col Greenville IL 62246

RICHARDS, RALPH CHAMBERLAIN, surgery, deceased

RICHARDS, RICHARD DAVISON, b Grand Haven, Mich, Mar 10, 27; m 50; c 3. OPHTHALMOLOGY. *Educ:* Univ Mich, AB, 48, MD, 51; Univ Iowa, MSc, 57; Am Bd Ophthal, dipl, 58. *Prof Exp:* Asst prof ophthal, Col Med, Univ Iowa, 58-60; PROF OPHTHAL & HEAD DEPT, SCH MED, UNIV MD, BALTIMORE, 60- *Concurrent Pos:* Attend physician, Vet Admin Hosp, Iowa City, 58-60. *Mem:* AAAS; Asn Res Vision & Ophthal; Am Acad Ophthal & Otolaryngol; fel Am Col Surgeons; Am Ophthal Soc. *Res:* Radiation cataracts. *Mailing Add:* Dept of Ophthal Univ of Md Sch of Med Baltimore MD 21201

RICHARDS, RICHARD EARL, b New Haven, Conn, Feb 14, 34; m 80; c 2. ANIMAL PHYSIOLOGY. *Educ:* Colo Col, BA, 56; Univ NMex, MA, 58; Univ Northern Colo, DA, 76. *Prof Exp:* Teacher & counselor biol, Kennewick Sr High Sch & South High Sch, 58-65; from asst prof to assoc prof, 65-80, prof, 80-82, EMER PROF BIOL, WESTERN STATE COL COLO, 82- *Concurrent Pos:* Asst dir, Rocky Mountain Biol Lab Corp, 60-62, assoc dir, 67-78, exec dir, 79-80; wildlife consult, Dames & Moore Corp, Homestake Mining Co, Buttes Gas & Oil Corp & others, 76-80. *Mem:* Am Biol Teachers Asn. *Res:* Distribution, natural history and physiology of the ringtail Bassariscus astutus. *Mailing Add:* Rte 1 Box 79F Oakland OR 97462

RICHARDS, RICHARD KOHN, b Lodz, Poland, June 16, 04; nat US; m 46. PHARMACOLOGY, CLINICAL PHARMACOLOGY. *Educ:* Hamburg Univ, MD, 31. *Prof Exp:* Intern, St George Hosp, Ger, 30-31; asst pharmacol, Hamburg Univ, 31-33, res assoc med, 33-35, lectr, 35; fel physiol, Michael Reese Hosp, Ill, 35-36; dir pharmacol res, Abbott Labs, 37-49, assoc dir res, 49-57, dir exp ther, 57-66; prof, 59-72, EMER PROF PHARMACOL, NORTHWESTERN UNIV, 72-; vis prof anesthesia, pharmacol & med, 68-72, CONSULT PROF, STANFORD UNIV, 72- *Concurrent Pos:* Prof lectr, Northwestern Univ, 48-59; consult clin pharmacologist, Palo Alto Vet Admin Hosp, 67- *Mem:* Am Physiol Soc; Am Soc Pharmacol & Exp Therapeut; Am Soc Anesthesiol; fel Am Col Physicians. *Res:* Experimental and clinical pharmacology; hypnotics; anticonvulsants; local anesthetics; toxicology; metabolism. *Mailing Add:* 29 Los Altos Square Los Altos CA 94022

RICHARDS, ROBERT BENJAMIN, b Scranton, Pa, Nov 18, 16; m 43; c 2. CHEMICAL ENGINEERING. *Educ:* Pa State Col, BS, 39, MS, 41, PhD(org chem), 46. *Prof Exp:* Asst petrol eng & chem, Pa State Col, 41-46; chem engr, Hanford Works, Gen Elec Co, 47-51, mgr separations technol, 51-53 & 55-57, mgr pile technol, 53-55, mgr eng, Atomic Power Equip Dept, 57-68, mgr fuel eng, Nuclear Fuel Dept, San Jose, 68-71, mgr spec fuel progs,

71-73, mgr int bus develop, Int Opers, 73-74, GEN MGR, ADVAN REACTOR SYSTS DEPT, GEN ELEC CO, SUNNYVALE, 74- *Honors & Awards:* R E Wilson Award, Am Inst Chem Engrs, 70. *Mem:* Nat Acad Eng; Am Inst Chem Engrs; Am Nuclear Soc. *Res:* Distillation; solvent extraction; physical analysis; petroleum refining; nuclear engineering; reactor physics; process design; plant and equipment operation. *Mailing Add:* 15142 Sobey Rd Saratoga CA 95070

RICHARDS, ROBERTA LYNNE, b Salt Lake City, Utah, Apr 20, 45; m 76; c 1. BIOCHEMISTRY, IMMUNOLOGY. *Educ:* Bucknell Univ, BS, 67; Purdue Univ, PhD(biochem), 74. *Prof Exp:* Res chemist biochem & immunol lipids, Dept Immunol, 74-78, RES CHEMIST BIOCHEM & IMMUNOL LIPIDS, DEPT MEMBRANE BIOCHEM, WALTER REED ARMY INST RES, 78- *Mem:* AAAS; Am Oil Chemists Soc; Am Chem Soc; Am Asn Immunol. *Res:* Biological function and reactivity of membrane lipids using liposomal model membranes, particularly as related to complement activation and lysis, immunospecificity for lipid antigens and receptor functions of lipids. *Mailing Add:* Dept of Membrane Biochem Walter Reed Army Inst Res Washington DC 20012

RICHARDS, ROGER THOMAS, acoustics, physics, see previous edition

RICHARDS, ROWLAND, JR, civil engineering, see previous edition

RICHARDS, THOMAS CHARLES, biological structure, see previous edition

RICHARDS, THOMAS L, b Santa Monica, Calif, Feb 2, 42; m 65; c 4. MARINE BIOLOGY, ZOOLOGY. *Educ:* Calif State Univ, Long Beach, BS, 64, MA, 66; Univ Maine, PhD(zool), 69. *Prof Exp:* Tech asst biol, Calif State Univ, Long Beach, 62-64, asst marine biol, 64-66; asst zool, Univ Maine, 66-67; PROF BIOL, CALIF POLYTECH STATE UNIV, SAN LUIS OBISPO, 69- *Mem:* Marine Biol Asn UK; Sigma Xi; Am Soc Zool; Western Soc Naturalists. *Res:* Physiological ecology of intertidal invertebrates, adults and larvae, oyster mariculture; developmental biology of invertebrate meroplankton; fresh water prawn aquaculture. *Mailing Add:* Dept Biol Sci Calif Polytech State Univ San Luis Obispo CA 93407

RICHARDS, VICTOR, b Ft Worth, Tex, June 4, 18; m 41; c 4. SURGERY. *Educ:* Stanford Univ, AB, 35, MD, 39; Am Bd Surg, dipl, 45; Bd Thoracic Surg, dipl, 45. *Prof Exp:* From instr to prof surg, Sch Med, Stanford Univ, 42-59, chmn dept, 55-58, clin prof, 59-65; CLIN PROF SURG, UNIV CALIF, SAN FRANCISCO, 65-; CHIEF SURG, CHILDREN'S HOSP, 59- *Concurrent Pos:* Commonwealth res fel, Harvard Univ, 50-51; mem spec comt, USPHS, 58-62; ed, Oncology, 68-76; mem surg study sect B, NIH; consult, USPHS, Letterman Gen, Oak Knoll Naval & Travis AFB Hosps. *Honors & Awards:* Outstanding Man of Year, San Francisco, 53. *Mem:* Soc Exp Biol & Med; Sigma Xi; Pan-Pac Surg Asn (vpres, 72-); Am Cancer Soc; Soc Surg Alimentary Tract (vpres, 72-73). *Res:* Cancer; cardiovascular surgery; transplantation and preservation of tissues. *Mailing Add:* Children's Hosp 3838 California St San Francisco CA 94118

RICHARDS, WALTER BRUCE, b Warren, Ohio, Jan 29, 41; m 62; c 2. PHYSICS. *Educ:* Oberlin Col, AB, 61; Univ Calif, Berkeley, PhD(physics), 66. *Prof Exp:* Physicist, Lawrence Radiation Lab, 65-66; res assoc & lectr physics, Tufts Univ, 66-67; asst prof, 67-73, ASSOC PROF PHYSICS, OBERLIN COL, 73- *Concurrent Pos:* Vis assoc prof physics, Case Western Reserve Univ, 81-82. *Mem:* Am Phys Soc; Am Asn Physics Teachers. *Res:* Musical acoustics. *Mailing Add:* Dept Physics Oberlin Col Oberlin OH 44074

RICHARDS, WILLIAM JOSEPH, b Scranton, Pa, Apr 7, 36; m 58; c 3. ICHTHYOLOGY. *Educ:* Wesleyan Univ, BA, 58; State Univ NY, 60; Cornell Univ, PhD(vert zool), 63. *Prof Exp:* Fishery biologist, Biol Lab, US Bur Com Fisheries, DC, 63-65, res syst zoologist, 65, Trop Atlantic Biol Lab, 65-71; zoologist & prog mgr, 71-77, DIR, MIAMI LAB, NAT MARINE FISHERIES SERV, 77- *Concurrent Pos:* Mem working group, Food & Agr Orgn UN, 65-; adj asst prof, Inst Marine Sci, Univ Miami, 66-68, adj assoc prof, Rosenstiel Sch Marine & Atmospheric Sci, 68-74, adj prof, 74-; ed, Bull Marine Sci, 74- *Mem:* Soc Syst Zool; Am Soc Ichthyol & Herpet; Am Soc Zool; fel Am Inst Fishery Res Biologists; Sigma Xi. *Res:* Systematics of fishes, especially the study of larval pelagic fishes and the family Triglidae; recruitment mechanisms of reef fishes. *Mailing Add:* Miami Lab Nat Marine Fisheries 75 Virginia Beach Dr Miami FL 33149

RICHARDS, WILLIAM REESE, b Springfield, Mo, June 27, 38; m 66. BIOCHEMISTRY, BIO-ORGANIC CHEMISTRY. *Educ:* Univ Calif, Riverside, AB, 61; Univ Calif, Berkeley, PhD(org chem), 66. *Prof Exp:* NIH fel chem path, St Mary's Hosp Med Sch, Eng, 66-67; fel bact, Univ Calif, Los Angeles, 67-68; ASST PROF CHEM, SIMON FRASER UNIV, 68- *Concurrent Pos:* Sabbatical leave microbiol, Univ Freiburg, WGer, 77-78; Minna-James-Heineman-Stiftung fel, 77-78. *Mem:* Am Soc Photobiol; Can Biochem Soc. *Res:* Biosynthesis of bacterial chlorophylls and morphogenesis of the bacterial photosynthetic apparatus; chemistry of porphyrins and chlorophylls. *Mailing Add:* Dept of Chem Simon Fraser Univ Burnaby BC V5A 1S6 Can

RICHARDS, WINSTON ASHTON, b Trinidad, WI; m 64; c 8. MATHEMATICAL STATISTICS. *Educ:* Marquette Univ, BS, 59, MS, 61; Univ Western Ont, MA, 66, PhD(math), 71. *Prof Exp:* Instr math, Aquinas Col, 60-61; chmn dept high sch, Mich, 64-65; ASSOC PROF MATH & STATIST, PA STATE UNIV, CAPITOL CAMPUS, 69- *Concurrent Pos:* Pa State Univ res grant, 72-73; statist expert, Orgn Am States, 75-; consult training govt statisticians, Repub Trinidad, Tobago & eastern Caribbean, 76-81; consult, UN, 79; vis sr lectr, Univ West Indies, Trinidad, 80-81 & 81-82. *Mem:* Int Asn Surv Statisticians; Inst Math Statist; Math Asn Am; Can Math Cong. *Res:* Exact distribution theory; n-dimensional geometry; mathematical modeling; national income; applied statistics. *Mailing Add:* Dept of Math Pa State Univ Capitol Campus Middletown PA 17050

RICHARDSON, ALBERT EDWARD, b Lovelock, Nev, Feb 4, 29; m 59; c 7. NUCLEAR FISSION, GAMMA SPECTROMETRY. *Educ:* Univ Nev, BS, 50; Iowa State Univ, PhD(phys chem), 56. *Prof Exp:* Asst radiochem, Ames Lab, Iowa State Univ, 50-55; asst prof phys chem, 55-60, ASSOC PROF PHYS CHEM, NMEX STATE UNIV, 60- *Concurrent Pos:* Consult, White Sands Missile Range, 65-71, contractor, 73-74, chemist, 81-; US AEC fel, Univ Colo, 68-69; vis staff mem, Los Alamos Nat Lab, 75-80. *Mem:* Fel AAAS; Am Chem Soc; Nat Sci Teachers Asn. *Res:* Nuclear chemistry; activation analysis; hot atom chemistry; neutron radiography. *Mailing Add:* 710 Manor Way Las Cruces NM 88001

RICHARDSON, ALFRED, JR, b Jersey City, NJ, Feb 18, 32; m 56; c 4. ORGANIC CHEMISTRY. *Educ:* Rutgers Univ, BS, 53; Lehigh Univ, MS, 55, PhD(chem), 58. *Prof Exp:* Asst chem, Lehigh Univ, 53-58; proj leader med chem res, William S Merrell Co, 58-67, sect head org res, 67-71, mgr res info, Merrell-Nat Labs, 71-76, dir com develop, Richardson-Merrell Inc, 76-81, DIR SCI & COM DEVELOP, MERRELL DOW PHARMACEUT, INC, 81- *Concurrent Pos:* Lectr eve col, Univ Cincinnati, 66-70. *Mem:* AAAS; Am Chem Soc; Licensing Exec Soc; Am Inst Chemists; NY Acad Sci. *Res:* Medicinal chemistry; synthetic organic chemistry; interdisciplinary product development; licensing; health care products. *Mailing Add:* Merrell Dow Pharmaceut Inc 2110 E Galbraith Rd Cincinnati OH 45215

RICHARDSON, ALLAN CHARLES BARBOUR, b Toronto, Ont, July 14, 32; US citizen; m 56; c 3. NUCLEAR PHYSICS, RADIATION HEALTH. *Educ:* Col William & Mary, BS, 54; Univ Md, MS, 58. *Prof Exp:* Physicist, Nat Bur Stand, 58-69; exec secy radiol health sci training comt, Environ Control Admin & radiol health study sect, 69-72, spec asst sci coord & eval, Off Radiation Progs, US Environ Protection Agency, 72-73, asst for standard develop, 73-77, chief fed guid br, 77-80, CHIEF GEN RADIATION STANDARDS BR, OFF RADIATION PROGS, US ENVIRON PROTECTION AGENCY, 80- *Honors & Awards:* Bronze Medal, US Environ Protection Agency, 73. *Mem:* Am Nuclear Soc; Health Physics Soc; Am Phys Soc. *Res:* Radiation protection standards; fast neutron cross-sections; neutron age measurements. *Mailing Add:* Off Radiation Progs ANR 460 Environ Protection Agency 401 M St SW Washington DC 20460

RICHARDSON, ALLYN (ST CLAIR), b Edmonton, Alta, Nov 16, 18; nat US; m 41, 56; c 6. ENGINEERING. *Educ:* Univ BC, BASc, 41; Harvard Univ, SM, 49. *Prof Exp:* Asst chemist anal & process control, BC Pulp & Paper Co, Can, 41-42; from asst engr to sr engr, Can Dept Nat Health & Welfare, 42-46, dist engr pub health, 46-50; res engr hydraul, Harvard Univ, 50-53, res engr bact aerosol viability study, 53-54, res engr soil stabilization res, 54-55; sr engr radar dept, Raytheon Co, 55-58; asst prof civil eng & dir fluid network lab, Tufts Univ, 58-59; proj dir instrumentation res & develop, United Res, Inc, 59-61 & Trans-Sonics, Inc, 61-65; res proj engr, WHO, 65-67; DIR OFF RES PROGS, REGION I, ENVIRON PROTECTION AGENCY, 67- *Concurrent Pos:* Consult & vis prof sanit sci, Cent Univ Venezuela; staff adv res & educ projs, Am Region Hq, Washington, DC; consult, Univ Tehran. *Mem:* Math Asn Am; Inst Elec & Electronics Engrs; Water Pollution Control Fedn. *Res:* Methods for control and improvement of air, water and land environment; environmental needs and standards, especially water hygiene, water pollution control and solid wastes management; application of microcomputers in management of environmental control processes. *Mailing Add:* Environ Protection Agency Region I J F Kennedy Fed Bldg Boston MA 02203

RICHARDSON, ANNIE LOUISE, b Charlotte, NC, Mar 4, 23. SYSTEMATIC BOTANY. *Educ:* J C Smith Univ, BS, 44; Univ Ill, MS, 54, PhD, 59. *Prof Exp:* Asst prof biol, Southern Univ, 54-57; asst bot, Univ Ill, 57-59; assoc prof biol, NC Col, Durham, 59-61; prof, Va State Col, Norfolk, 61-66, actg head dept, 63-64; actg chmn dept, St Augustine's Col, 66-67; prof & chmn dept, J C Smith Univ, 67-69; PROF BIOL, NORFOLK STATE COL, 69- *Concurrent Pos:* NSF res partic grant, NC State Univ, 68; mem, NSF Conf, Yale Univ, 69, NSF panelist, 70. *Mem:* AAAS; Am Soc Plant Taxon; Nat Inst Sci; Int Asn Plant Taxon; Am Inst Biol Sci. *Res:* Floristic studies, especially in East Baton Rouge Parish, Louisiana and the flowering angiosperms of the Norfolk area of Virginia. *Mailing Add:* Dept of Biol Norfolk State Col Norfolk VA 23504

RICHARDSON, ARLAN GILBERT, b Beatrice, Nebr, Jan 23, 42; m 66. BIOCHEMISTRY, ORGANIC CHEMISTRY. *Educ:* Peru State Col, BA, 63; Okla State Univ, PhD(biochem), 68. *Prof Exp:* Teaching asst biochem, Okla State Univ, 67-68; asst prof chem, Fort Lewis Col, 68-69; NIH fel biochem, Univ Minn, St Paul, 69-71; asst prof chem, 71-75, ASSOC PROF CHEM & BIOL SCI, ILL STATE UNIV, 71- *Mem:* AAAS; Am Chem Soc; Am Soc Microbiol. *Res:* Bacterial transformation and genetics; protein synthesis, especially the effect of various diets upon polysome profiles and protein synthesis in rat liver. *Mailing Add:* Dept of Chem Ill State Univ Normal IL 61761

RICHARDSON, BILLY, b Channelview, Tex, June 20, 36; m 80. RESEARCH ADMINISTRATION. *Educ:* Tex A&M Univ, BS, 58, MS, 64, PhD(biol), 67. *Prof Exp:* Res technician, Tex A&M Univ, 58-59, instr floricult, 59-62; chief cellular physiol br, Environ Sci Div, 67-72, dep chief environ sci div, 72-73, chief crew environ br, 73-76, dep chief crew technol div, 76-78, chief biomet div, 78-79, dir spec proj, 79-80, dir chem defense prog off, 80-81, CHIEF, CREW TECHNOL DIV, US AIR FORCE SCH AEROSPACE MED, 81- *Concurrent Pos:* Consult, new fighter aircraft, Can Forces, 77-78. *Mem:* AAAS; fel Am Inst Chemists; assoc fel Aerospace Med Asn; Am Inst Biol Sci. *Res:* Steroid metabolism in plants; mechanism of oxygen toxicity; aerospace physiology; cellular and biochemical effects of environmental stresses; aircrew protection and life support systems. *Mailing Add:* Crew Technol Div US Air Force Sch Aerospace Med Brooks AFB TX 78235

RICHARDSON, BOBBIE L, b Detroit, Mich, May 24, 26; m 49; c 5. ENGINEERING. *Educ:* Purdue Univ, BS, 53, MS, 54, PhD(eng sci), 59. *Prof Exp:* Instr eng mech, Purdue Univ, 54-57; mech engr reactor eng div, Argonne Nat Lab, 57-58; from asst prof to assoc prof, 58-67, chmn dept, 59-67, PROF MECH ENG, MARQUETTE UNIV, 67- *Mem:* Am Soc Mech Engrs; Am Nuclear Soc; Am Soc Eng Educ. *Res:* Nuclear engineering; digital systems engineering; two-phase flow; heat transfer. *Mailing Add:* Dept of Mech Eng Marquette Univ Milwaukee WI 53233

RICHARDSON, CHARLES BONNER, b Dallas, Tex, Jan 18, 30; , 59; c 1. PHYSICS. *Educ:* Univ Pittsburgh, BS, 57, PhD(physics), 62. *Prof Exp:* Res asst prof physics, Univ Wash, 62-66; from asst prof to assoc prof, 66-74, PROF PHYSICS, UNIV ARK, FAYETTEVILLE, 74- *Mem:* Am Phys Soc. *Res:* Optics; atmospheric physics. *Mailing Add:* Dept of Physics Univ of Ark Fayetteville AR 72701

RICHARDSON, CHARLES CLIFTON, b Wilson, NC, May 7, 35; m 61; c 2. BIOCHEMISTRY. *Educ:* Duke Univ, BS, 59, MD, 60. *Hon Degrees:* AM, Harvard Univ, 67. *Prof Exp:* Intern med, Duke Univ, 60-61; res fel biochem, Med Sch, Stanford Univ, 61-62; from asst prof to assoc prof biochem, 64-69, PROF BIOCHEM, HARVARD MED SCH, 69-, FEL, 64-, CHMN, DEPT BIOL CHEM, 78- *Concurrent Pos:* Consult physiol chem study sect, NIH; assoc ed, Annual Rev Biochem; mem, Nat Bd Med Examrs & adv comt nucleic acids & protein synthesis, Am Cancer Soc; mem adv div, Max Plank Inst Moleculare Genetik, Berlin, 80- *Honors & Awards:* Biol Chem Award, Am Chem Soc, 68; Am Acad Arts & Sci Award, 75. *Mem:* Am Chem Soc; Am Soc Biol Chemists. *Res:* DNA metabolism. *Mailing Add:* Dept Biol Chem Harvard Med Sch Boston MA 02115

RICHARDSON, CLARENCE ROBERT, b Lovelock, Nev, Jan 10, 31; m 55; c 2. RESEARCH ADMINISTRATION, PHYSICAL SCIENCES PLANNING. *Educ:* Univ Nev, BS, 57; Johns Hopkins Univ, PhD(physics), 63. *Prof Exp:* Jr physicist, Naval Ord Test Sta, Calif, 57; physicist, Appl Physics Lab, Johns Hopkins Univ, 58-59; from asst physicist to assoc physicist, Brookhaven Nat Lab, 63-67; physicist high energy physics prof, Div Res, US AEC, 67-73, physicist nuclear sci prog, 73-75, dept mgr solar inst proj off, US Energy Res & Develop Admin, 75-76, dir prog planning div, 79, phys sci planning specialist, prog planning div, basic energy sci, 76-79, PROG MGR MEDIUM ENERGY NUCLEAR PHYSICS, DEPT ENERGY, 79- *Concurrent Pos:* Vis physicist, Europ Orgn Nuclear Res, Switz, 70-71; co-chmn, Bubble Chamber Working Group, 73-74 & 78-79. *Mem:* Am Phys Soc. *Res:* Elementary particle research using bubble chambers; eta meson and omega hyperon. *Mailing Add:* 20513 Topridge Dr Boyds MD 20841

RICHARDSON, CLARENCE WADE, b Temple, Tex, Nov 15, 42; m 64; c 3. HYDROLOGY, CIVIL ENGINEERING. *Educ:* Tex A&M Univ, BS, 64, MS, 66; Colo State Univ, PhD(civil eng), 76. *Prof Exp:* Agr engr, Tex Agr Exp Sta, 64-65 & Agr Res Serv, 66-77, AGR ENGR, SCI & EDUC ADMIN-FED RES, USDA, 78- *Mem:* Am Soc Agr Engrs; Soil Conserv Soc Am. *Res:* Deterministic hydrologic modeling; stochastic simulation of precipitation patterns; agricultural water quality. *Mailing Add:* Blackland Res Ctr PO Box 748 Temple TX 76501

RICHARDSON, CURTIS JOHN, b Gouverneur, NY, July 27, 44; m 72; c 1. WETLANDS ECOLOGY, ECOSYSTEM ANALYSIS. *Educ:* State Univ NY, Cortland, BS, 66; Univ Tenn, PhD(ecol), 72. *Prof Exp:* Asst prof resource ecol, Sch Natural Resources, Univ Mich, 72-77, asst prof plant ecol, Biol Sta, 73; ASSOC PROF RESOURCE ECOL, SCH FORESTRY & ENVIRON STUDIES, DUKE UNIV, 77- *Concurrent Pos:* Res ecologist, Atomic Energy Comn, 68; res fel ecol, Ecol Sci Div, Oak Ridge Nat Lab, 70-72; nat rep, Inst Ecol, 79- *Mem:* AAAS; Am Inst Biol Sci; Ecol Soc Am; Sigma Xi; Soil Sci Soc Am. *Res:* Ecosystem analysis of wetland and forest systems; linkages between terrestrial and aquatic ecosystems with an emphasis on primary productivity and biogeochemical cycles as influenced by man. *Mailing Add:* Sch Forestry & Environ Studies Duke Univ Durham NC 27706

RICHARDSON, DANIEL RAY, b Martinsville, Ind, May 5, 39; m 59; c 2. PHYSIOLOGY. *Educ:* Ind Univ, Bloomington, BA, 65, Ind Univ, Indianapolis, PhD(physiol), 69. *Prof Exp:* Fel, Univ Calif, San Diego, 69-70; asst prof, 70-74, ASSOC PROF PHYSIOL & BIOPHYS, SCH MED, UNIV KY, 74- *Mem:* Microcirc Soc; NY Acad Sci; Soc Exp Biol & Med; Am Heart Asn; Am Physiol Soc. *Res:* Studies of peripheral vascular dynamics in man and laboratory animal models. *Mailing Add:* Dept of Physiol & Biophys Univ of Ky Med Sch Lexington KY 40506

RICHARDSON, DAVID LOUIS, b New York, NY, Sept 27, 48. ORBITAL MECHANICS, PLANETARY MOTION. *Educ:* Ind Univ, AB, 70; Cornell Univ, MS, 72, PhD(space mech), 77. *Prof Exp:* Structural analyst, US Naval Surface Weapons Lab, 73-74; orbital analyst, Comput Sci Corp, 74-77; asst prof, 77-81, ASSOC PROF DYNAMICS & ORBITAL MECH, UNIV CINCINNATI, 81- *Concurrent Pos:* Prin investr, NSF, 78-80; res worker, Nat Bur Standards, 80- *Mem:* Am Astron Soc. *Res:* Planetary motion analysis; orbital dynamics of artificial satellites; application of analytical and semi-analytical methods to the problems of space mechanics; analytical investigations of nonlinear resonance phenomena. *Mailing Add:* Dept Aerospace Eng ML #70 Univ Cincinnati Cincinnati OH 45221

RICHARDSON, DAVID W, b Nanking, China, Mar 22, 25; US citizen; m 48; c 4. CARDIOLOGY. *Educ:* Davidson Col, BS, 47; Harvard Med Sch, MD, 51. *Prof Exp:* Intern, Yale-New Haven Med Ctr, 51-52, asst resident, 52-53; from asst resident to resident, Med Col Va, 53-55, NIH fel cardiovasc physiol, 55-56; chief cardiovasc sect & assoc chief staff res, Vet Admin Hosp, 56-62; vis fel cardiovasc dis, Oxford Univ, 62-63; assoc prof med, 63-67, actg chmn dept, 73-74, PROF MED, MED COL VA, 67-, CHMN DIV CARDIOL, 72- *Concurrent Pos:* Fel coun clin cardiol, Am Heart Asn; consult, Vet Admin Coop Study Antihypertensive Agents, 62-; Va Heart Asn Chair cardiovasc res, Med Col Va, 62-71; vis fel, Inst Cardiovasc Res, Univ Milan, 71-72. *Mem:* Am Fedn Clin Res; Am Clin & Climat Asn; Am Soc Clin Invest; fel Am Col Physicians; Am Col Cardiol. *Res:* Clinical hypertension and cardiology; prevention of myocardial infarction; neural control of circulation. *Mailing Add:* Med Col of Va Box 105 Richmond VA 23219

RICHARDSON, DON ORLAND, b Auglaize Co, Ohio, May 12, 34; m 52; c 4. ANIMAL SCIENCE, DAIRY SCIENCE. *Educ:* Ohio State Univ, BS, 56, MS, 57, PhD(animal breeding), 61. *Prof Exp:* Asst dairy breeding, Ohio State Univ, 56-58, instr, 60; dairy husbandman, Agr Res Serv, USDA, 58-61, dairy genetist, 61-63; asst prof dairy sci, 63-67, assoc prof dairying, 67-72, assoc prof, 72-75, PROF ANIMAL SCI, UNIV TENN, KNOXVILLE, 75- *Mem:* Am Dairy Sci Asn. *Res:* Evaluation of progress resulting from various selection schemes utilized with daity cattle, including an evaluation of correlated responses to single trait selection on milk yield. *Mailing Add:* Dept of Animal Sci Univ of Tenn PO Box 1071 Knoxville TN 37901

RICHARDSON, DONALD EDWARD, b Vicksburg, Miss, Oct 5, 31; m; c 4. NEUROSURGERY. *Educ:* Millsaps Col, BS, 53; Tulane Univ, MD, 57. *Prof Exp:* Assoc prof, 64-74, PROF & CHMN DEPT NEUROSURG, SCH MED, TULANE UNIV, 80-; ASSOC CLIN PROF NEUROSURG, LA STATE UNIV MED CTR, NEW ORLEANS, 74- *Concurrent Pos:* Consult, New Orleans Cancer Asn, 67-69. *Mem:* AAAS; AMA; Am Asn Neurol Surg; Am Col Surgeons; Int Soc Res Stereonencephalotomy. *Res:* Clinical and research neurosurgery; basic neurophysical research; electrophysiology of the sensory system of spinal cord and brain. *Mailing Add:* Sch Med Dept Neurosurg Tulane Univ 1430 Tulane Ave New Orleans LA 70112

RICHARDSON, EARL LEROY, b Lebanon, Mo, Mar 21, 17; m 42; c 1. COSMETIC CHEMISTRY. *Educ:* Drury Col, BSc, 38; Okla Agr & Mech Col, MSc, 39; Rutgers Univ, PhD(anal chem), 48. *Prof Exp:* Analyst, Procter & Gamble, 39; res chemist, Calco Chem Div, Am Cyanamid Co, NJ, 40-42; res chemist, Colgate-Palmolive-Peet Co, 42-48, group leader, 48-50; dir res, Whitehall Labs Div, Am Home Prod Co, NJ, 50-67; head tech serv, cosmetic chem, Union Carbide Corp, NY, 67-72; PROJ MGR, FOOD & DRUG ADMIN, 72- *Mem:* Am Chem Soc; Soc Cosmetic Chem; Am Pharmaceut Asn; Acad Pharmaceut Sci; Asn Official Anal Chemists. *Res:* Esterification; hydrolysis; esters; aluminum antiperspirant compositions; soaps, fats, oils and detergents; emulsions; cosmetics; proprietary drugs; dentifrices; natural and synthetic gums; hair care products. *Mailing Add:* Food & Drug Admin 200 C St SW Washington DC 20204

RICHARDSON, EDWARD HENDERSON, JR, b Baltimore, Md, Dec 24, 11; m 48; c 3. OBSTETRICS & GYNECOLOGY. *Educ:* Princeton Univ, AB, 34; Johns Hopkins Univ, MD, 38; Am Bd Obstet & Gynec, dipl, 47. *Prof Exp:* Instr, 43-59, ASST PROF GYNEC, SCH MED, JOHNS HOPKINS UNIV, 59- *Concurrent Pos:* Consult, Vet Admin Hosp, Baltimore, Md. *Mem:* Fel, Am Col Obstet & Gynec. *Res:* Female urology. *Mailing Add:* 9 E Chase St Baltimore MD 21202

RICHARDSON, ELISHA ROSCOE, b Monroe, La, Aug 15, 31; m 67; c 3. ORTHODONTICS, ANATOMY. *Educ:* Southern Univ, BS, 51; Meharry Med Col, DDS, 55; Univ Ill, MS, 63. *Prof Exp:* NIH fel, Univ Ill, 60-62; asst prof dent radiol, 62-63, from asst prof to assoc prof, 62-76, PROF ORTHOD, MEHARRY MED COL, 67-, DIR POSTGRAD EDUC, SCH DENT, 67-, ASSOC DEAN, SCH DENT, 77- *Concurrent Pos:* Prin investr, Nat Inst Child Health & Human Develop, res grant, 65-68; guest lectr, John F Kennedy Ctr Res Educ & Human Develop, 66-68 & George Peabody Col, 66-68; prin investr, Nat Inst Dent Res grant, 68; consult, Vet Admin Hosp, Nashville, Tenn, 68; pres, Craniofacial Biol Group, Int Asn Dent Res, 78-79. *Mem:* Am Dent Asn; Am Asn Orthod; fel Am Col Dentists; Int Asn Dent Res; NY Acad Sci. *Res:* Craniofacial region; maxillary growth; periodontal membrane; uvula and tongue; tooth size and eruption, growth of face and jaws. *Mailing Add:* Meharry Med Col Sch of Dent Nashville TN 37208

RICHARDSON, ERIC HARVEY, b Portland, Ore, Aug 14, 27; Can citizen; m 78. APPLIED OPTICS, ASTRONOMY. *Educ:* Univ BC, BA, 49, MA, 51; Univ Toronto, PhD(molecular spectros), 59. *Prof Exp:* Res asst, Gen Elec Co, Stanmore Labs, London, 52-53; res asst, 54-57, RES OFFICER, DOMINION ASTROPHYS OBSERV, 59- *Concurrent Pos:* Optical consult, Can-France-Hawaii Telescope Corp, 73-78; optical consult, Viking Satellite, 81- *Mem:* Int Astron Union. *Res:* Optical design of space and ground based telescopes and associated instruments. *Mailing Add:* Dominion Astrophys Observ 5071 W Saanich Rd Victoria BC V8X 4M6 Can

RICHARDSON, EUGENE STANLEY, JR, paleozoology, paleoecology, see previous edition

RICHARDSON, EVERETT V, b Scottsbluff, Nebr, Jan 5, 24; m 48; c 3. HYDRAULICS, HYDROLOGY. *Educ:* Colo State Univ, BS, 49, MS, 60, PhD(civil eng), 65. *Prof Exp:* Hydraul engr, Wyo Qual Water Br, US Geol Surv, 49-53 & Iowa Surface Water Br, 53-56, res hydraul engr, Water Resources Div, 56-68; assoc prof, 65-68, PROF CIVIL ENG, COLO STATE UNIV, 68-, ADMINR, ENG RES CTR, 68- *Concurrent Pos:* Consult, US Bur Pub Rd, 65-, US Corps Engrs, 67-, World Bank Reconstruct & Develop, 70-, Colo Hwy Dept, 74-, US Bur Reclamation, 74- & USAID, 76-; dir, USAID Prog, Colo State Univ, 74-76, proj dir, Egypt Water Use & Mgt, 77-; mem joint workshop on res mgt, Nat Acad Sci/Egypt Nat Acad Sci, 75. *Honors & Awards:* J C Stevens Award, Am Soc Civil Engrs, 61. *Mem:* Am Soc Civil Engrs; Int Cong Irrigation & Drainage; AAAS. *Res:* Internal structure of turbulent shear flow; diffusion of waste in natural streams; measurement of fluid flow; erosion and sedimentation, river mechanics, irrigation and water management. *Mailing Add:* Eng Res Ctr Colo State Univ Ft Collins CO 80521

RICHARDSON, F C, b Whitehaven, Tenn, Sept 22, 36; m 60; c 2. BOTANY. *Educ:* Rust Col, BA, 60; Atlanta Univ, MSc, 64; Univ Calif, Santa Barbara, PhD(bot), 67. *Prof Exp:* Asst prof bot, 67-71, assoc prof bot & chmn dept, 71-72, DEAN ARTS & SCI, IND UNIV NORTHWEST, 72- *Mem:* Am Inst Biol Sci; Bot Soc Am; Int Soc Plant Morphol; Am Asn Higher Educ. *Res:* Plant morphology; origin and evolution of the angiosperms using the anatomy and development of the flower, particularly the carpel, as the primary tool; nodal anatomy of elm species in connection with Dutch elm succeptibility in the family. *Mailing Add:* Dept of Biol Ind Univ Northwest Gary IN 46408

RICHARDSON, FRANCES MARIAN, b Roanoke, Va, May 6, 22. CHEMICAL & BIOMEDICAL ENGINEERING. *Educ:* Roanoke Col, BS, 43; Univ Cincinnati, MS, 47. *Prof Exp:* Chemist, E I du Pont de Nemours & Co, 43-45; asst chem, Univ Cincinnati, 45-47; res chemist, Leas & McVitty, Inc, 48-49; res assoc, 51-60, RES ASSOC PROF ENG RES, NC STATE UNIV, 60-, ASSOC DIR, ENG OPER PROG, 80- *Concurrent Pos:* Vis assoc prof, Case Western Reserve Univ, 67-68. *Mem:* AAAS; Royal Soc Health; Soc Women Engrs; Am Inst Chem Engrs; Am Soc Eng Educ. *Res:* Infrared imaging thermography; biomedical engineering; fluid flow; flow visualization. *Mailing Add:* Eng Oper Prog Sch Eng NC State Univ Raleigh NC 27650

RICHARDSON, FREDERICK S, b Carlisle, Pa, June 8, 39; m 59; c 3. THEORETICAL CHEMISTRY, PHYSICAL CHEMISTRY. *Educ:* Dickinson Col, BS, 61; Princeton Univ, PhD(chem), 66. *Prof Exp:* Instr chem, Princeton Univ, 65-66; fel, Univ Calif, San Diego, 68-69; from asst to assoc prof, 69-78, PROF CHEM, UNIV VA, 78- *Concurrent Pos:* Dreyfus Found scholar, 72. *Mem:* AAAS; Am Chem Soc; Am Phys Soc. *Res:* Theoretical and experimental aspects of molecular electronic spectroscopy; optical properties of molecular crystals; natural and magnetic optical activity in molecules and crystals; coupling of electronic states by molecular vibrations. *Mailing Add:* Dept of Chem Univ of Va Charlottesville VA 22901

RICHARDSON, GARY HAIGHT, b Grace, Idaho, Nov 30, 31; m 54; c 6. DAIRY CHEMISTRY, DAIRY MICROBIOLOGY. *Educ:* Utah State Agr Col, BS, 53; Univ Wis, PhD(dairy & food industs), 60. *Prof Exp:* Dairy chemist, Res Labs, Swift & Co, Ill, 59-61; res mgr, Dairyland Food Labs, Inc, Wis, 61-63, res dir, 63-67; prof dairy & food sci, 67-73, PROF NUTRIT & FOOD SCI, UTAH STATE UNIV, 73- *Concurrent Pos:* Dairyland Food Labs, Inc grant, 68-; USPHS grant, 69-72; Kellogg fel, Univ Col, Cork, Ireland, 81. *Mem:* Am Dairy Sci Asn; Inst Food Technol; Am Soc Microbiol; Inst Asn Milk, Food & Environ Sanit. *Res:* Dairy cultures; dehydration; accelerated cheese flavor development; enzyme utilization in production of dairy flavors; staphylococcal enterotoxin production in cheese products; prevention of defects in Swiss cheese; assay of milk constitutents. *Mailing Add:* Dept of Nutrit & Food Sci Utah State Univ Logan UT 84322

RICHARDSON, GEORGE S, b Boston, Mass, Dec 1, 21; m 58; c 3. ENDOCRINOLOGY, OBSTETRICS & GYNECOLOGY. *Educ:* Harvard Univ, BA, 43, MD, 46. *Prof Exp:* From intern to resident surg, Mass Gen Hosp, 46-55; instr surg, Harvard Med Sch, 54-55; asst, Mass Gen Hosp, 55-59; clin assoc, 59-71, asst prof, 71-74, ASSOC PROF SURG, HARVARD MED SCH, 74- *Concurrent Pos:* Res fel physiol, Harvard Med Sch, 47-48; NIH res grants, 58-; assoc vis surgeon, Mass Gen Hosp, 64-75, vis surgeon, 76-, gynecologist, 77-; Nat Cancer Inst spec fel, Southwest Found Res & Educ, 69-71. *Mem:* Am Fertil Soc; Endocrine Soc; Soc Pelvic Surgeons; Am Col Surgeons. *Res:* Steroid hormones in relation to neoplasia; human endometrium. *Mailing Add:* Mass Gen Hosp Boston MA 02114

RICHARDSON, GERALD LAVERNE, b Ft Morgan, Colo, Sept 21, 28. CHEMICAL ENGINEERING. *Educ:* Univ Colo, BS, 50. *Prof Exp:* Jr engr, Hanford Atomic Prod Div, Gen Elec Co, 50-55, engr, 55-62, sr engr, 62-65; sr develop engr, Pac Northwest Lab, Battelle Mem Inst, 65-69, res assoc, 69-70; prin engr, 70-79, FEL ENGR, WESTINGHOUSE HANFORD CO, 79- *Res:* Separation and purification of radioactive isotopes from irradiated uranium; development of solvent extraction processes and equipment; nuclear fuel cycle waste management. *Mailing Add:* Westinghouse Hanford Co W/C-35 PO Box 1970 Richland WA 99352

RICHARDSON, GLEN A(RTHUR), b Havensville, Kans, July 15, 15; m 44; c 2. ELECTRICAL ENGINEERING. *Educ:* Univ Kans, BS, 41, MS, 47; Iowa State Col, PhD(elec eng), 52. *Prof Exp:* Jr engr, Commonwealth Edison Co, Ill, 41-42; instr elec eng, Univ Kans, 42-47; from asst prof to assoc prof, Iowa State Col, 47-58; prof & head dept, Worcester Polytech Inst, 58-73; PROF & CHMN DIV PHYSICS, ELEC ENG & COMPUT SCI, ROSE-HULMAN INST TECHNOL, 73- *Concurrent Pos:* Consult, Wilcox Elec Co, Mo, 44-47, Lawrence Paper Co, Kans, 45 & Meredith Publ Co, Iowa, 56-58. *Mem:* Am Soc Eng Educ (vpres, 66-68); Inst Elec & Electronics Engrs. *Res:* Circuits and electronics. *Mailing Add:* Rose-Hulman Inst of Technol Terre Haute IN 47803

RICHARDSON, GRAHAM MCGAVOCK, b Emory, Va, Jan 10, 13; m 40; c 3. ORGANIC CHEMISTRY. *Educ:* Univ Tenn, BS, 34; Mass Inst Technol, PhD(org chem), 39. *Prof Exp:* Chemist, Acetate Yarn Div, Tenn Eastman Corp, 34-36; instr chem, Franklin Tech Inst, Boston, 38-39; chemist, E I Du Pont de Nemours & Co, Inc, 39-42 & 44-51, supvr, 42-44 & 51-62, specialist textile fibers, dyeing & finishing, 62-76; DIR RES & DEVELOP, LUTEX CHEM CORP, 76- *Mem:* Am Asn Textile Chem & Colorists; Am Asn Textile Technol (pres); Am Soc Testing & Mat. *Res:* Process development of dyes; dyeing; organo sodium compounds; detergents; wetting agents; textile processing and finishing; cosmetics; vinyl polymers; flammability test methods for textile materials. *Mailing Add:* Box 3654 Greenville Wilmington DE 19807

RICHARDSON, GRANT LEE, b Safford, Ariz, June 20, 19; m 43; c 6. AGRONOMY. *Educ:* Univ Ariz, BS, 47, MS, 48; Ore State Col, PhD(farm crops), 50. *Prof Exp:* Asst prof agron, Purdue Univ, 50 53; assoc prof, 53-57, PROF AGRON, ARIZ STATE UNIV, 57- *Concurrent Pos:* Team leader, Ariz State Univ-Kufra Agr Team, 73- *Mem:* Crop Sci Soc Am; Am Soc Agron. *Res:* Crop production in arid regions; crop physiology. *Mailing Add:* 1810 E Alameda Dr Tempe AZ 85282

RICHARDSON, HAROLD, b Ferryhill, Eng, Apr 13, 38; m 60; c 3. MEDICAL MICROBIOLOGY. *Educ:* Univ Durham, BSc, 59, MB, BS, 62; Univ Newcastle, Eng, MD, 68. *Prof Exp:* Demonstr bact, Univ Newcastle, Eng, 63-64, lectr, 64-69, sr lectr microbiol, 69-71; assoc prof, 71-76, PROF & DIR MICROBIOL, MED CTR, MCMASTER UNIV, 76- *Concurrent Pos:* Consult, United Newcastle Upon Tyne Hosps, 69-71. *Honors & Awards:* Officer, Order of St John of Jerusalem, 75. *Mem:* Am Soc Clin Path; Am Soc

Microbiol; Path Soc Gt Brit & Ireland. *Res:* Control of colicine production and role of colicinogeny in epidemiology of Escherichia coli infection. *Mailing Add:* Dept Microbiol Rm 2N30 Chedoke-McMaster Hosp Hamilton ON L8N 3Z5 Can

RICHARDSON, HARRY EDWARD, b Girardville, Pa, Jan 30, 37; m 62; c 3. COMPUTER SCIENCE, MANAGEMENT SCIENCE. *Educ:* Pa State Univ, BSEE, 61; Johns Hopkins Univ, Cert Bus Mgt, 64; Univ Md, MBA, 67. *Prof Exp:* Sr programmer, Westinghouse Elec Corp, 62-64; programmer/analyst, Dynalectron Corp, 64-65 & Comput & Software, Inc, 65-68; SR SCIENTIST, OPERS RES INC, 68- *Mem:* Asn Comput Mach. *Res:* Development of computer models to project various categories of military retirees and corresponding disbursements under varying actuarial assumptions. *Mailing Add:* 1400 Spring St Laurel MD 20708

RICHARDSON, HENRY HOWE, b Millis, Mass, Feb 22, 06; m 31; c 2. ENTOMOLOGY. *Educ:* Mass Col, BS, 26; Iowa State Col, MS, 29, PhD(entom), 31. *Hon Degrees:* MS, Univ NC, 69. *Prof Exp:* Jr entomologist, USDA, 26-28; asst, Iowa State Col, 28-29 & 31; from asst entomologist to assoc entomologist, Bur Entom & Plant Quarantine, USDA, 31-43, entomologist, 46-51, proj leader plant quarantine treatment res, 51-59, invests leader plant quarantine commodity treatments, 59-66; Air Pollution Control Inst fel, Univ Southern Calif, 67; Inst Environ Health Studies fel, Sch Pub Health, Univ NC, Chapel Hill, 68-69; Fulbright res fel, Australian-Am Educ Found, Canberra, Australia, 69-70; CONSULT, 70- *Mem:* AAAS; fel Entom Soc Am; Air Pollution Control Asn; NY Acad Sci. *Res:* Phosphine and ethylene oxide fumigation of overseas containers; methyl bromide fumigation for quarantinable insects; in transit cold sterilization of fruit; pyrethrum fly sprays; rearing media for housefly. *Mailing Add:* RD 3 Rummel Rd Milford NJ 08848

RICHARDSON, HERBERT HEATH, b Lynn, Mass, Sept 24, 30; m 73; c 1. MECHANICAL ENGINEERING. *Educ:* Mass Inst Technol, ScD(mech eng), 58. *Prof Exp:* Res engr dynamic anal & control lab, 53-57, from instr to assoc prof, 57-68, PROF MECH ENG, MASS INST TECHNOL, 68-, HEAD DEPT, 74- *Concurrent Pos:* Ord officer, Ballistics Res Lab, Aberdeen Proving Grounds, 58; sr consult, Foster-Miller Assocs, 58-; chief scientist, US Dept Transp, 70-72. *Honors & Awards:* Gold Medal, Pi Tau Sigma, 63; Moody Award, 70; Centennial Medal, Am Soc Mech Engrs, 80. *Mem:* Nat Acad Eng; Am Soc Eng Educ; NY Acad Sci; AAAS; fel Am Soc Mech Engrs. *Res:* Dynamics; automatic control; lubrication; transportation; fluid mechanics. *Mailing Add:* Rm 3-173 Dept of Mech Eng Mass Inst of Technol Cambridge MA 02139

RICHARDSON, IRVIN WHALEY, b Tulsa, Okla, May 28, 34; m 58. BIOPHYSICS, BIOMATHEMATICS. *Educ:* Stanford Univ, BS, 56; Univ Calif, Berkeley, PhD(biophys), 67. *Prof Exp:* Asst prof physiol, Inst Physiol, Aarhus Univ, 67-68 & 69-71; vis assoc prof biophys, Sch Med, Univ Calif, San Francisco, 71-73; dir biophys sect, 74-75, assoc prof, 73-78, PROF BIOPHYS, MED FAC, DALHOUSIE UNIV, 78- *Concurrent Pos:* Am Heart Asn vis scientist, Sch Med, Univ Calif, San Francisco, 71-72; assoc ed, Bull Math Biol, 73-79. *Mem:* Soc Math Biol; Am Phys Soc. *Res:* Irreversible thermodynamics; membrane transport theory; mathematical modeling of physiological systems. *Mailing Add:* Dept of Physiol & Biophys Dalhousie Univ Fac of Med Halifax NS B3H 3J5 Can

RICHARDSON, J MARK, b Duncan, Okla, Apr 27, 54. STOCHASTIC PROCESSES, MATHEMATICAL ANALYSIS. *Educ:* Okla State Univ, BS, 75, MS, 77, PhD(elec eng), 80. *Prof Exp:* Res assoc & teaching assoc circuit anal, Okla State Univ, 75-80; MEM TECH STAFF, SANDIA NAT LABS, 80- *Concurrent Pos:* Software engr, Halliburton Co, 77; mem tech staff, Sandia Nat Labs, 78. *Mem:* Inst Elec & Electronics Engrs. *Res:* Stochastic integration and its relation to numerical integration; nuclear safety and safeguards at operating nuclear power plants and fuel cycle facilities; signal processing; estimation theory and techniques. *Mailing Add:* 8418 Ironsides NE Albuquerque NM 87109

RICHARDSON, JAMES ALBERT, b Schenectady, NY, Jan 27, 15; m 49; c 4. PHARMACOLOGY. *Educ:* Univ SC, BS, 36; Univ Miss, MS, 40; Univ Tenn, PhD(physiol), 49. *Prof Exp:* Instr pharmacy, Univ Miss, 40-41; instr physiol & pharmacol, 42-47, assoc pharmacol, 48, from asst prof to assoc prof, 49-60, actg chmn dept, 71-72, PROF PHARMACOL, MED UNIV SC, 60- *Mem:* AAAS; Am Soc Pharmacol & Exp Therapeut; Soc Exp Biol & Med; Am Fedn Clin Res; Sigma Xi. *Res:* Autonomic drugs; cardiovascular drugs; spinal anesthesia; toxicology of kerosene and decaborane; blood coagulation; catecholamines. *Mailing Add:* Dept of Pharmacol Med Univ of SC Charleston SC 29425

RICHARDSON, JAMES T(HOMAS), b Gillingham, Eng, Aug 5, 28; nat US; m 50; c 2. CHEMICAL ENGINEERING. *Educ:* Rice Inst, BA, 50, MA, 54, PhD(physics), 55. *Prof Exp:* Jr chemist, Pan-Am Refining Corp, 50-52; Welch Found fel, Rice Inst, 55-56; res physicist, Humble Oil & Refining Co, 56-65, sr res physicist, Esso Res & Eng Co, 59-64, res specialist, 64-66, res assoc, 66-69; assoc prof, 69-70, PROF CHEM ENG, UNIV HOUSTON, 70- *Mem:* Am Phys Soc; Am Chem Soc; Sigma Xi; Am Inst Chem Engrs. *Res:* Mass and infrared spectroscopy; x-ray and electron diffraction; electron microscopy; adsorption; magnetism; low temperature physics; adiabatic demagnetization; catalysis; defect solid state; electron spin resonance. *Mailing Add:* 5004 Arrowhead Baytown TX 77520

RICHARDSON, JAMES WYMAN, b Sioux Falls, SDak, Aug 8, 30; m 52; c 4. QUANTUM CHEMISTRY. *Educ:* SDak Sch Mines & Technol, BS, 52; Iowa State Col, PhD(chem), 56. *Prof Exp:* Asst, Ames Lab, Iowa State Col, 53-56; res assoc physics, Univ Chicago, 56-57; from instr to assoc prof chem, 57-73, PROF CHEM, PURDUE UNIV, WEST LAFAYETTE, 73- *Concurrent Pos:* Visitor, Philips Res Labs, Neth, 67-68. *Mem:* Am Chem Soc; Am Phys Soc. *Res:* Theory of electronic properties of small molecules; transition-metal complex ions, and ionic solids. *Mailing Add:* Dept of Chem Purdue Univ West Lafayette IN 47907

RICHARDSON, JASPER E, b Memphis, Tenn, Nov 8, 22; m 47; c 5. ENGINEERING PHYSICS. *Educ:* Yale Univ, BS, 44; Rice Inst, MA, 48, PhD(physics), 50. *Prof Exp:* Instr physics, Univ Miss, 46-47; asst prof, Ala Polytech Inst, 50-51; physicist, Med Div, Oak Ridge Inst Nuclear Studies, 51-53, Univ Tex MD Anderson Hosp & Tumor Inst, 53-55 & Shell Develop Co, Tex, 55-69; sr engr, 69-72, STAFF ENGR, SHELL OIL CO, 72- *Mem:* Am Phys Soc; Soc Petrol Engrs. *Res:* Petrophysics; nuclear physics; medical physics and oil well logging; field testing new techniques for tertiary oil recovery. *Mailing Add:* Shell Oil Co PO Box 991 Houston TX 77001

RICHARDSON, JAY WILSON, JR, b Salt Lake City, Utah, Aug 1, 40. AQUATIC ENTOMOLOGY, AQUATIC ECOLOGY. *Educ:* Univ Utah, BS, 62, MS, 64. *Prof Exp:* Teaching asst invert zool, Univ Utah, 62-64; ENTOMOLOGIST, ACAD NAT SCI PHILADELPHIA, 64- *Concurrent Pos:* Biologist, Bur Com Fisheries, 62; asst to dir entom, Stroud Water Res Ctr, Acad Nat Sci Philadelphia, 69-73; entomologist, Coun Environ Qual, Exec Off President, 71-72, Savannah River Plant, E I du Pont de Nemours & Co, Inc, 71-75 & Nat Comn Water Qual, 74-75; proj mgr environ consult, Dept Limnol, Acad Nat Sci Philadelphia, 75- *Mem:* Sigma Xi; Entom Soc Am; Am Entom Soc; Ecol Soc. *Res:* Taxonomy and ecology of ephemeroptera; trichoptera; environmental pollution, especially fresh water biological monitoring. *Mailing Add:* RD 1 Box 512 Avondale PA 19311

RICHARDSON, JEFFERY HOWARD, b Oakland, Calif, Nov 23, 48; m 78. PHYSICAL CHEMISTRY. *Educ:* Calif Inst Technol, BS, 70; Stanford Univ, PhD(chem), 74. *Prof Exp:* CHEMIST, LAWRENCE LIVERMORE LAB, 74- *Concurrent Pos:* Consult, Mallinckrodt, 78. *Mem:* Am Chem Soc; Sigma Xi. *Res:* Applications of laser spectroscopy to analytical problems; oil shale chemistry; photoelectrochemistry. *Mailing Add:* Gen Chem Div L-325 Lawrence Livermore Lab Livermore CA 94550

RICHARDSON, JOHN CLIFFORD, b Owen Sound, Ont, Jan 10, 09; m 37; c 2. NEUROLOGY. *Educ:* Univ Toronto, MD, 32, BSc, 35; FRCP(C). *Prof Exp:* Intern, Toronto Gen Hosp, 32-34; house physician, Nat Hosp Nervous Dis, Queen Sq, London, 35-37; fel neuropath, Univ Toronto, 37-38, from asst prof to assoc prof, 50-63, prof med, 63-71, prof neurol, 74-76, EMER PROF MED & NEUROL, UNIV TORONTO, 76- *Mem:* Am Neurol Asn; Asn Res Nerv & Ment Dis; hon AMA; Am Acad Neurol; Can Neurol Soc (pres, 50). *Res:* Cerebral and spinal vascular diseases; epilepsy; poliomyelitis. *Mailing Add:* 170 St George St Toronto ON M5R 2M8 Can

RICHARDSON, JOHN L(LOYD), b Ventura, Calif, Jan 29, 35; m 57; c 5. TECHNICAL MANAGEMENT. *Educ:* Stanford Univ, BS, 56, PhD(chem eng), 64. *Prof Exp:* Res & develop engr, Aeronutronic Div, Ford Motor Co, 61-62, sr engr, 62-64, sect supvr, Chem Lab, Res Labs, Philco Corp, 64-65, mgr, Appl Chem Dept, Appl Res Labs, Aeronutronic Div, Philco-Ford Corp, Newport Beach, 65-71, mgr, Res & Eng Dept, Liquid Process Prod, 71-74; gen mgr, Recovery Systs, Oxy Metal Indust Corp, 74-78, mgr mkt, Vdylite Plating Systs, 78-80; PRES, SEAGOLD INDUSTS CORP, BURNABY, BC, 81- *Mem:* Am Inst Chem Engrs. *Res:* Energy and mass transfer in chemically reacting systems; ordinary and thermal diffusion in liquid solutions; membrane transport phenomena; reverse osmosis and ultrafiltration, desalination and water purification. *Mailing Add:* 1108 Connaught Dr Vancouver BC V6H 2H1 Can

RICHARDSON, JOHN MARSHALL, b Rock Island, Ill, Sept 5, 21; m 44; c 4. PHYSICS, TELECOMMUNICATIONS. *Educ:* Univ Colo, BA, 42; Harvard Univ, MA, 47, PhD(physics), 51. *Prof Exp:* Assoc head, Physics Div, Inst Indust Res, Univ Denver, 50-52; physicist, Nat Bur Stand, 52-60, chief, Radio Stand Lab, 60-67, dep dir, Inst Basic Stand, 66-67; dir, Off Stand Rev, US Dept Com, 67-68, actg dir, Off Telecommun, 69-70 & 72-76, dep dir, 70-72, dir, 76-78, chief scientist, Nat Telecommun & Info Admin, 78-80; SR STAFF OFFICER, NAT ACAD SCI, 80- *Concurrent Pos:* Nat Bur Stand rep, Consult Comt Definition of the Second, Int Comt Weights & Measures, 61-67; conf chmn, Int Conf Precision Electromagnetic Measurements, 62; chmn UC Comn I, Int Union Radio Sci, 64-67, mem at large, US Nat Comt, 69-72; exec secy, Comt Telecommun, Nat Acad Eng, 68-69; US mem, Panel Comput & Commun, Orgn Econ Coop & Develop, 70-77; vchmn, Working Party of Info, Comput & Communs Policy, 77- *Honors & Awards:* Gold Medal Award, US Dept Com, 64. *Mem:* Fel AAAS; fel Inst Elec & Electronics Engrs; fel Am Phys Soc. *Res:* Gaseous discharges; microwave spectroscopy; microwave physics; atomic time and frequency standards; precision electromagnetic measurements and standards; telecommunications technology, management and policy. *Mailing Add:* Nat Acad Sci 2101 Constitution Ave Washington DC 20418

RICHARDSON, JOHN MEAD, b San Francisco, Calif, Nov 25, 18; m 69; c 1. THEORETICAL PHYSICS, INFORMATION SCIENCES. *Educ:* Calif Inst Technol, BS, 41; Cornell Univ, PhD(phys chem), 44. *Prof Exp:* Res assoc, Cornell Univ, 44-45; mem tech staff, Bell Tel Labs, 45-49; phys chemist, US Bur Mines, Pa, 49-50, head kinetics sect, 50-53; physicist, Hughes Aircraft Co, 53-54; sr staff physicist, Ramo Wooldridge Corp, 54-56; sr staff physicist, Hughes Res Labs, Calif, 56-57, asst head physics lab, 57-58, sr staff consult, 58-61, mgr theoret studies dept, 61-68; MEM STAFF, SCI CTR, ROCKWELL INT CORP, 68- *Concurrent Pos:* Instr, Stevens Inst Technol, 47-48; vis prof, Univ Calif, Los Angeles, 62; ed, J Cybernet, 73-78 & Info Sci, 68- *Mem:* Am Phys Soc; Soc Eng Sci. *Res:* Mathematical physics; underwater explosions and damage; combustion and detonation waves; hypersonic flow; dielectrics and ferroelectrics; liquids, plasmas and order-disorder phenomena; irreversible statistical mechanics; mathematical methods in statistical mechanics; automatic pattern recognition and estimation theory. *Mailing Add:* Sci Ctr Rockwell Int Corp 1049 Camino Dos Rios Thousand Oaks CA 91360

RICHARDSON, JOHN PAUL, b Pittsfield, Mass, June 27, 38; m 66; c 3. BIOCHEMISTRY. *Educ:* Amherst Col, BA, 60; Harvard Univ, PhD(biochem), 66. *Prof Exp:* NIH fel, Inst Biol Physcio-Chimigene, Paris, 65-67; Am Cancer Soc fel, Inst Molecular Biol, Geneva, Switz, 67-69; res assoc molecular genetics, Univ Wash, 69-70; from asst prof to assoc prof, 70-78, PROF CHEM, IND UNIV, BLOOMINGTON, 78- *Concurrent Pos:* NIH res grant, Ind Univ, Bloomington, 71-82. *Res:* Enzymology and regulation of RNA biosynthesis; control of virus development. *Mailing Add:* Dept of Chem Ind Univ Bloomington IN 47405

RICHARDSON, JOHN REGINALD, b Edmonton, Alta, Oct 31, 12; nat US; m 38; c 2. NUCLEAR PHYSICS. *Educ:* Univ Calif, Los Angeles, AB, 33; Univ Calif, PhD(physics), 37. *Prof Exp:* Nat Res Coun fel physics, Univ Mich, 37-38; asst prof, Univ Ill, 38-42; physicist, Manhattan Proj, Univ Calif, 42-46; assoc prof, 46-52, PROF PHYSICS, UNIV CALIF, LOS ANGELES, 52- *Concurrent Pos:* Sci liaison officer, Off Naval Res, London, 53-54 & 56-57; mem comt sr reviewers, US AEC, 52-71; dir, Tri Univ Meson Facility, Univ BC, 71-76. *Mem:* Fel Am Phys Soc. *Res:* Nucleon-nucleon interaction; nuclear structure; cyclotrons. *Mailing Add:* Dept Physics Univ Calif Los Angeles CA 90024

RICHARDSON, JONATHAN L, b Philadelphia, Pa, May 15, 35; m 63; c 2. LIMNOLOGY. *Educ:* Williams Col, BA, 57; Univ NZ, MA, 60; Duke Univ, PhD(zool), 65. *Prof Exp:* Asst prof, 66-70, assoc prof, 70-80, PROF BIOL, FRANKLIN & MARSHALL COL, 80- *Concurrent Pos:* NSF res grant, EAfrican lakes & climatic hist, 69-72; US-Australia Coop sci fel, 80-81. *Mem:* AAAS; Int Soc Limnol; Ecol Soc Am; Am Inst Biol Sci. *Res:* Limnology and paleoecology of tropical lakes; ecology of diatoms; plant ecology of disturbed habitats; primary productivity of aquatic ecosystems. *Mailing Add:* Dept of Biol Franklin & Marshall Col Lancaster PA 17604

RICHARDSON, KATHLEEN SCHUELLER, b New York, NY, Sept 28, 38; m 70. ORGANIC CHEMISTRY. *Educ:* Bryn Mawr Col, BA, 60; Radcliffe Col, MA, 62; Harvard Univ, PhD(chem), 66. *Prof Exp:* Res scientist org chem, Bell Tel Labs, 66-68; asst prof, Vassar Col, 68-74; lectr, Ohio State Univ, 74-75; instr, 75-76, asst prof, 76-80, ASSOC PROF CHEM, CAPITAL UNIV, 80- *Mem:* AAAS; Am Chem Soc. *Res:* Cycloaddition reactions. *Mailing Add:* 415 Clinton Heights Columbus OH 43202

RICHARDSON, KEITH ERWIN, b Tucson, Ariz, Apr 22, 28; m 52; c 6. PHYSIOLOGICAL CHEMISTRY. *Educ:* Brigham Young Univ, BS, 52, MS, 55; Purdue Univ, PhD(biochem), 58. *Prof Exp:* Asst biochem, Purdue Univ, 55-58; fel agr chem, Mich State Univ, 58-60; from asst prof to assoc prof physiol chem, 60-67, PROF PHYSIOL CHEM & VCHMN DEPT, OHIO STATE UNIV, 67- *Mem:* AAAS; Am Chem Soc; Am Soc Plant Physiol; Am Soc Biol Chem; Am Inst Nutrit. *Res:* Enzymology; primary hyperoxaluria and oxalic acid metabolism; enzyme regulation; intermediate metabolism; metabolic inborn errors of metabolism. *Mailing Add:* Dept of Physiol Chem Ohio State Univ Columbus OH 43210

RICHARDSON, LAVON PRESTON, b Ranger, Tex, July 6, 25; m 50; c 2. MICROBIOLOGY. *Educ:* Tex Christian Univ, AB, 48; NTex State Univ, MA, 49; Okla State Univ, EdD, 58. *Prof Exp:* From instr to asst prof biol, Cent State Univ, Okla, 49-57; from instr to asst prof bact, Okla State Univ, 57-59; adminr, DeLeon Munic Hosp, Tex, 59-60; asst prof biol, Tarleton State Col, 60-61; asst prof microbiol, 61-64, co-dir sci teaching ctr, 67, ASSOC PROF MICROBIOL, OKLA STATE UNIV, 65- *Concurrent Pos:* Asst dir spec proj, NSF, 66-67; coordr, This Atomic World Prog. *Mem:* Am Soc Microbiol; Nat Asn Biol Teachers; Am Pub Health Asn; Am Inst Biol Sci. *Res:* Colony movement in Bacillus alvei. *Mailing Add:* Sch Biol Sci LSE 318 Okla State Univ Stillwater OK 74078

RICHARDSON, LEE S(PENCER), b Syracuse, NY, Mar 17, 29; m 56; c 2. PHYSICAL METALLURGY, MATHEMATICS. *Educ:* Mass Inst Technol, SB, 50, SM, 51, ScD(phys metall), 56. *Prof Exp:* Res asst oxidation & nitriding titanium, Mass Inst Technol, 50-51, res asst creep rupture titanium, 53-55; jr metallurgist, Oak Ridge Nat Lab, 51-52; res metallurgist, Westinghouse Elec Corp, 55-56; indust staff mem, Los Alamos Sci Lab, 56-58; res metallurgist, Westinghouse Elec Corp, 58-60, supvry metallurgist, 60-63; mgr ceramics & metall res, Foote Mineral Co, 63-69, dir res & eng, Ferroalloy Div, 69-71, dir res & develop, 72-77; MGR, MAT SCI, EG&G IDAHO INC, 77- *Mem:* Am Soc Metals; Am Inst Mining, Metall & Petrol Engrs. *Res:* High temperature materials; alloy development; ferroalloys; inorganic chemistry of lithium and manganese; computer simulation; materials for energy production and conversion. *Mailing Add:* 1991 Malibu Dr Idaho Falls ID 83401

RICHARDSON, LEONARD FREDERICK, b Brooklyn, NY, Nov 23, 44; m 72. MATHEMATICAL ANALYSIS. *Educ:* Yale Univ, BA & MA, 65, PhD(math), 70. *Prof Exp:* Instr math, Yale Univ, 70-71; CLE Moore instr math, Mass Inst Technol, 71-73; asst prof, 73-77, ASSOC PROF MATH, LA STATE UNIV, 77- *Concurrent Pos:* NSF res grant, 74-82; NSF Int travel grant, 75, 76. *Mem:* Am Math Soc. *Res:* Harmonic analysis on manifolds; projections, measures and distributions on nilmanifolds; representation theory. *Mailing Add:* Dept of Math La State Univ Baton Rouge LA 70803

RICHARDSON, LLOYD THOMAS, b Hamilton, Ont, Nov 19, 13; m 42; c 3. PLANT PATHOLOGY. *Educ:* McMaster Univ, BA, 37; Univ Toronto, MA, 38, PhD(plant path), 41. *Prof Exp:* Plant pathologist, Can Dept Agr, 41-49 & SDak State Col, 49-51; res scientist, Res Inst, Agr Can, 51-73, plant pathologist, 73-77; RETIRED. *Concurrent Pos:* Fel, Univ Calif, Riverside, 62-63. *Mem:* fel Am Phytopath Soc; Can Phytopath Soc. *Res:* Chemical and biological control of plant diseases. *Mailing Add:* 201 9 Grosvenor St Apt 201 London ON N6A 1Y3 Can

RICHARDSON, MARY ELIZABETH, b Los Angeles, Calif, June 3, 27; m 55. PATHOLOGY, ELECTRON MICROSCOPY. *Educ:* Univ Calif, Los Angeles, BA, 49, MS, 52; Woman's Med Col Pa, MD, 56; Am Bd Path, dipl & cert anat path, 62, cert clin path, 64. *Prof Exp:* Intern, Providence Hosp, Seattle, Wash, 56-57; resident path, Univ Wash & affil hosps, 57-61; resident, Barnes Hosp, St Louis, 61-62, asst path, Barnes Hosp & affil hosps, 62-64; asst prof path, Med Ctr, Univ Ark, Little Rock, 64-68; res pathologist & chief electron micros, Bur Sci, Food & Drug Admin, DC, 68-70; RES PATHOLOGIST, OFF PESTICIDES, ENVIRON PROTECTION AGENCY & CHIEF ELECTRON, MICRO BR, HEW, 70- *Concurrent Pos:* Trainee exp path, Washington Univ, 61-64; consult path, Maryvale Med Ctr & Maryvale Community Hosp, 67-68. *Mem:* Am Soc Clin Pathologists; Int Acad Pathologists; Am Soc Nephrology; Electron Micros Soc Am; Soc Pharmacol & Environ Path. *Res:* Histochemistry; experimental carcinogenesis; tissue culture; organ transplantation; trace metals; food additives; pesticides. *Mailing Add:* Tissue Reaction to Drug Registry Armed Forces Inst of Path Washington DC 20306

RICHARDSON, MARY FRANCES, b Barbourville, Ky, Sept 3, 41. INORGANIC CHEMISTRY, CRYSTALLOGRAPHY. *Educ:* Univ Ky, BS, 62, PhD(chem), 67. *Prof Exp:* Contractor, Aerospace Res Labs, Wright-Patterson AFB, 67-71; asst prof, 71-75, assoc prof, 75-81, chmn dept, 79-82, PROF CHEM, BROCK UNIV, 81- *Mem:* Am Chem Soc; Am Crystallog Asn; Chem Inst Can. *Res:* Coordination compounds; complexes of metals with vitamins and related compounds; asymmetric syntheses and stereochemical control of reactions on single crystals; x-ray crystal structures. *Mailing Add:* Dept of Chem Brock Univ St Catharines ON L2S 3A1 Can

RICHARDSON, NEAL A(LLEN), b Casper, Wyo, Mar 14, 26; m 52; c 2. ENGINEERING. *Educ:* Univ Calif, Los Angeles, BS, 49, MS, 53, PhD(eng), 62. *Prof Exp:* Lectr eng, Univ Calif, Los Angeles, 49-62; mgr, TRW Systs Group, 62-76, MGR COAL CONVERSION PROGS, TRW ENERGY SYSTS GROUP, 76- *Mem:* Soc Automotive Engrs. *Res:* Advanced energy conversion processes including electrochemical systems; vehicle power train development and engineering including power plant emissions characterization and control; chemical processes based on coal; new catalytic process to produce high BTU gas. *Mailing Add:* 30823 Cartier Dr Rancho Palos Verdes CA 90274

RICHARDSON, PAUL ERNEST, b Covington, Ky, Dec 29, 34; m 58; c 1. PLANT ANATOMY, PLANT MORPHOLOGY. *Educ:* Univ Ky, AB, 57; Univ Cincinnati, MEd, 62, MS, 66, PhD(bot), 68; Univ NC, Chapel Hill, MAT, 63. *Prof Exp:* Teacher, Lloyd Mem High Sch, Ky, 57-59 & Holmes High Sch, 59-62; asst prof, 68-73, ASSOC PROF BOT, OKLA STATE UNIV, 73- *Mem:* Bot Soc Am; Int Asn Plant Morphologists; Am Phytopath Soc; Torrey Bot Club; Am Inst Biol Sci. *Res:* Comparative and developmental morphology of flowering plants; abnormal and pathological plant structure. *Mailing Add:* Dept Bot Okla State Univ Stillwater OK 74074

RICHARDSON, PAUL FREDERICK, b Baltimore, Md, Jan 12, 22; m 53; c 6. MEDICINE. *Educ:* Univ Md, MD, 50; Am Bd Phys Med & Rehab, dipl, 60. *Prof Exp:* Chief div phys med & rehab serv, Vet Admin Hosp, Durham, NC, 54-55 & Ft Howard, Md, 56-58; from assoc prof to prof phys med & rehab, 58-70, head div phys med & rehab & med dir phys ther curric, 58-70, PROF REHAB MED & CHMN DEPT, SCH MED, UNIV MD, BALTIMORE CITY, 70- *Concurrent Pos:* Instr, Sch Med, Duke Univ, 54-55; consult, Vet Admin Hosps, Baltimore, Ft Howard & Perry Point, Md, 60- *Mem:* Am Cong Rehab Med; Am Acad Phys Med & Rehab; AMA. *Res:* Gait analysis and disturbances of motor function. *Mailing Add:* Dept of Rehab Med Univ of Md Sch of Med Baltimore MD 21201

RICHARDSON, PAUL NOEL, b Minneapolis, Minn, Mar 31, 25; m 46; c 3. ORGANIC CHEMISTRY. *Educ:* Univ Minn, BS, 49, PhD(org chem), 52. *Prof Exp:* Res chemist, 52-57, tech rep, 57-64, consult, 64-65, supvr, 66-70, sr res chemist, Plastic Dept, 71-80, RES ASSOC, POLYMER PROD DEPT, E I DU PONT DE NEMOURS & CO, INC, 80- *Concurrent Pos:* Instr, Univ Del. *Honors & Awards:* Pres Cup, Soc Plastic Engrs, 72. *Mem:* Am Chem Soc; Soc Plastic Engrs (treas, 70). *Res:* Polymer chemistry; plastics engineering. *Mailing Add:* 2408 Lanside Dr Foulkside Wilmington DE 19810

RICHARDSON, PETER DAMIAN, b West Wickham, Eng. BIOMEDICAL ENGINEERING. *Educ:* Univ London, BSc, 55, PhD(ent) & DIC, 58; City & Guilds of London Inst, ACGI, 55. *Hon Degrees:* MA, Brown Univ, 65; DSc, Univ London, 74. *Prof Exp:* Demonstr eng, Imp Col, Univ London, 55-58; res assoc, 58-60, from asst prof to assoc prof, 60-68, PROF ENG, BROWN UNIV, 68-, CHMN EXEC COMT, CTR BIOMED ENG, 72- *Concurrent Pos:* Sci Res Coun Eng sr res fel, 67; Humboldt Found award, 76. *Mem:* Am Soc Mech Engrs; Am Soc Eng Educ; Am Soc Artificial Internal Organs. *Res:* Heat and mass transfer, fluid dynamics; theory and technology of artificial internal organs; blood flow. *Mailing Add:* Div of Eng Box D Brown Univ Providence RI 02912

RICHARDSON, PHILIP LIVERMORE, b New York, NY, Oct 31, 40; m 66; c 2. PHYSICAL OCEANOGRAPHY, MARINE SCIENCE. *Educ:* Univ Calif, Berkeley, BS, 64; Univ RI, MS, 70, PhD(phys oceanog), 74. *Prof Exp:* Lieutenant jr grade, US Coast & Geod Surv, 64-66; asst, Sch Oceanog, Univ RI, 67-69, res asst, 69-73, asst prof, 73-74; asst scientist, 74-78, ASSOC SCIENTIST, WOODS HOLE OCEANOG INST, 78- *Concurrent Pos:* Vis scientist, Nat Mus Natural Hist, Oceanog Phys Lab, Paris, 78-79. *Mem:* AAAS; Am Geophys Union; Am Meteorol Soc. *Res:* General ocean circulation; gulf stream; oceanic eddies. *Mailing Add:* Woods Hole Oceanog Inst Woods Hole MA 02543

RICHARDSON, RALPH J, b Jamestown, NDak, Feb 28, 41; m 64; c 1. SOLID STATE PHYSICS. *Educ:* Rockhurst Col, AB, 62; St Louis Univ, MS, 64, PhD(physics), 69. *Prof Exp:* scientist, McDonnell Douglas Res Labs, McDonnell Douglas Corp, 69-81; MGT DIR, INT TECHNOL, SRI INT, 81- *Mem:* Am Phys Soc. *Res:* Electron spin resonance; combustion; chemical lasers. *Mailing Add:* 9981 Mangos Dr San Ramon CA 94583

RICHARDSON, RANDALL MILLER, b Santa Monica, Calif, Dec 29, 48; m 77; c 1. GEOPHYSICS, EARTH SCIENCE. *Educ:* Univ Calif, San Diego, BA, 72; Mass Inst Technol, PhD(geophysics), 78. *Prof Exp:* ASST PROF GEOSCIENCES, UNIV ARIZ, 78- *Mem:* Am Geophys Union; Seismol Soc Am; Sigma Xi. *Res:* Driving mechanism for plate tectonics through observation and finite element modeling of the state of stress away from plate boundaries due to present and past forces acting on the plates. *Mailing Add:* Dept of Geosci Univ of Ariz Tucson AZ 85721

RICHARDSON, RAYMAN PAUL, b Piedmont, Mo, May 17, 39; m 66; c 2 SCIENCE EDUCATION. *Educ:* Cent Methodist Col, AB, 61; Univ Mo, MST, 64; Ohio State Univ, PhD(sci educ), 71. *Prof Exp:* Teacher chem & math, St Clair Pub Schs, 61-64; teacher phys sci, Antilles Sch Syst, 64-67; instr, 71-78, PROF PHYS SCI & SCI EDUC, FAIRMONT STATE COL, 78- *Mem:* Am Chem Soc; Nat Asn Res Sci Teaching; Nat Sci Teachers Asn. *Res:* Measurement of scientific curiosity and interests of elementary school children. *Mailing Add:* Fairmont State Col Fairmont WV 26554

RICHARDSON, RAYMOND C(HARLES), b Junction City, Kans, Sept 26, 29; m 55; c 3. CHEMICAL ENGINEERING. *Educ:* Univ Colo, BS, 54; Kans State Univ, MS, 58; Iowa State Univ, PhD(chem eng), 63. *Prof Exp:* Sr tech serv rep, Spencer Chem Co, 54-56; instr chem eng, Iowa State Univ, 61-62; from asst prof to assoc prof, Univ Ariz, 62-67; hybrid simulation engr, Phillips Petrol Co, 67-69; mgr process br, 69-75, mgr admin & control div, 75-77, MGR PROCESS TECHNOL DIV, APPLIED AUTOMATION, INC, 77- *Mem:* Am Inst Chem Engrs; Simulation Coun. *Res:* Chemical and petroleum processes; modeling and simulation of processes; application of computer control. *Mailing Add:* Applied Automation Inc Pawhuska Rd Bartlesville OK 74003

RICHARDSON, RICHARD HARVEY, b Mexia, Tex, Mar 24, 38; m 57, 70; c 3. BIOLOGICAL PEST CONTROL, EVOLUTION. *Educ:* Tex A&M Univ, BS, 59; NC State Univ, MS, 62, PhD(genetics), 65. *Prof Exp:* Assoc res scientist, Genetics Found, 64-65, NIH fel zool, 65-67, from lectr to assoc prof, 65-79, PROF ZOOL, UNIV TEX, AUSTIN, 79- *Concurrent Pos:* USPHS career develop award, 70-75. *Mem:* Fel AAAS; Genetics Soc Am; Soc Study Evolution; Biomet Soc; Am Soc Naturalists. *Res:* Genetics of mating behavior and population structure; chromosomal, behavioral and biochemical changes during the evolution of the genus Drosophila; population genetics and ecology of natural and laboratory populations; genetics, evolutionary biology and biogeography of screwworms, Cochliomyia spp; ticks. *Mailing Add:* Dept of Zool Univ of Tex Austin TX 78712

RICHARDSON, RICHARD LAUREL, b Chelan, Wash, Aug 12, 26; m 48; c 6. APPLIED MATHEMATICS, ELECTRICAL ENGINEERING. *Educ:* Univ Colo, Boulder, BS, 53; Univ Idaho, MS, 61. *Prof Exp:* Tech grad, Gen Elec Co, 53-55, engr, 55-60, mathematician, 60-65; sr res scientist, Pac Northwest Labs, Battelle Mem Inst, 65-80; WITH UNC NUCLEAR INDUST INC, 80- *Concurrent Pos:* Instr, Columbia Basin Col; lectr, Joint Ctr Grad Study, Richland, Wash. *Mem:* Inst Elec & Electronics Engrs; Soc Indust & Appl Math. *Res:* Stress wave propagation, especially thermal diffusing applications of generalized functions; sphere packing and related molecular models, especially transmission and distribution of electrical energy and industrial control. *Mailing Add:* Unc Nuclear Indust Inc PO Box 490 Richland WA 99352

RICHARDSON, ROBERT COLEMAN, b Washington, DC, June 26, 37; m 62; c 2. LOW TEMPERATURE PHYSICS. *Educ:* Va Polytech Inst, MS, 60; Duke Univ, PhD(physics), 66. *Prof Exp:* Asst prof, 67-71, assoc prof, 71-74, PROF PHYSICS, CORNELL UNIV, 74- *Concurrent Pos:* NSF grant, 71-73. *Honors & Awards:* Buckley Prize, Am Phys Soc, 81. *Mem:* fel AAAS; Am Phys Soc. *Res:* Studies of thermal and magnetic properties of solid and liquid helium at very low temperatures. *Mailing Add:* Dept of Physics Cornell Univ Ithaca NY 14850

RICHARDSON, ROBERT ESPLIN, b Alameda, Calif, Nov 9, 24; m 46; c 6. PHYSICS, ELECTRICAL ENGINEERING. *Educ:* Univ Okla, BS, 45; Univ Calif, PhD(physics), 51. *Prof Exp:* Physicist, Radiation Lab, Univ Calif, 46-52; MEM STAFF, LINCOLN LAB, MASS INST TECHNOL, 52- *Mem:* AAAS; Am Phys Soc; Inst Elec & Electronics Eng. *Res:* Reentry physics; radar; electronics; computer systems and applications. *Mailing Add:* 159 Merriam St Weston MA 02193

RICHARDSON, ROBERT LLOYD, b Syracuse, NY, Oct 1, 29; m 57; c 6. ELECTRICAL ENGINEERING, NUCLEAR MEDICINE. *Educ:* Syracuse Univ, BEE, 51, MEE, 56, PhD(elec eng), 61. *Prof Exp:* Res asst elec eng, Syracuse Univ, 51-53, res assoc, 53-56, from instr to asst prof, 56-64; res engr, Syracuse Univ Res Corp, 64-70; ASSOC PROF RADIOL, STATE UNIV NY UPSTATE MED CTR, 70- *Concurrent Pos:* Lectr, Syracuse Univ, 71-76, adj prof, 76- *Mem:* Inst Elec & Electronic Engrs; Soc Nuclear Med. *Res:* Electronic circuits and electronics applied to medicine. *Mailing Add:* Div Nuclear Med State Univ NY Upstate Med Ctr Syracuse NY 13210

RICHARDSON, ROBERT LOUIS, b Lexington, Ky, Mar 19, 22; m 50; c 3. BACTERIOLOGY. *Educ:* Univ Louisville, DMD, 44; Univ Iowa, MS, 53. *Prof Exp:* Practicing dentist, Ky, 47-48; from instr to asst prof restorative dent, Univ Tex, 48-51; instr periodontia, 51-52, asst prof microbiol, Col Med, 53-64, ASSOC PROF MICROBIOL, COL MED, UNIV IOWA, 64- *Mem:* AAAS; Am Soc Microbiol; Int Asn Dent Res. *Res:* In vitro studies of dental caries; microorganisms in the mouth. *Mailing Add:* Dept of Microbiol Univ of Iowa Col of Med Iowa City IA 52241

RICHARDSON, ROBERT WILLIAM, b Sydney, Australia, Sept, 5, 35; US citizen; m 59; c 1. STATISTICAL MECHANICS, THEORETICAL NUCLEAR PHYSICS. *Educ:* Univ Mich, BS & MA, 58, PhD(physics), 63. *Prof Exp:* Asst res scientist, Courant Inst Math Sci, NY Univ, 63-65, from asst prof to assoc prof physics, 65-75, PROF PHYSICS, NY UNIV, 75- *Mem:* Am Phys Soc; Am Asn Physics Teachers. *Res:* Many-body problem; nuclear models; low temperature physics. *Mailing Add:* Dept of Physics NY Univ New York NY 10003

RICHARDSON, RUDY JAMES, b Winfield, Kans, May 13, 45; m 70; c 1. TOXICOLOGY, NEUROTOXICOLOGY. *Educ:* Wichita State Univ, BS, 67; Harvard Univ, ScM, 73, ScD(toxicol), 74. *Prof Exp:* NASA trainee chem, State Univ NY Stony Brook, 67-70; Nat Int Environ Health Sci trainee toxicol, Harvard Univ, 70-74; res biochem neurotoxicol, Med Res Coun, Eng, 74-75; asst prof, 75-79, ASSOC PROF TOXICOL, UNIV MICH, 79- *Concurrent Pos:* Consult, Environ Protection Agency, 76-; mem safe drinking water comt & toxicol subcomt, Nat Acad Sci, 78-79. *Mem:* Am Chem Soc; AAAS; Soc Environ Geochem & Health; Soc Toxicol; Sigma Xi. *Res:* Delayed neurotoxicity of organophosphorus compounds; neurotoxic esterase; models of neurological disease; maintenance and plasticity of neurons; biomembranes; biological functions of glutathione; transport of heavy metals; leukocytes as biomonitors and models of certain neuronal functions. *Mailing Add:* Toxicol Res Lab Sch of Pub Health Ann Arbor MI 48109

RICHARDSON, SALLY L, b Wilkes-Barre, Pa, July 22, 44; m 71. ICHTHYOLOGY. *Educ:* Wilkes Col, BS, 66; Va Inst Marine Sci, Col William & Mary, PhD(marine sci), 72. *Prof Exp:* Res assoc, Sch Oceanog, Ore State Univ, 71-76, from asst prof to assoc prof, 76-78; ASSOC ICHTHYOLOGIST, GULF COAST RES LAB, 78- *Concurrent Pos:* Prin investr contracts, Nat Oceanog & Atmospheric Admin-Marine Resources, Monitoring, Assessment & Prediction Prog, Narragansett Lab, RI, 72 & Nat Marine Fisheries Serv, Seattle, 76-79; prin investr, Nat Oceanog & Atmospheric Admin-sea grant, Ore State Univ, 72-79, Gulf Coast Res Lab, 78-82, Miss Dept Wildlife Conserv, Bur Marine Resources, 80-82, Nat Marine Fisheries Serv, Pascagoula, 80-81, Smithsonian Inst, NSF, 80-82. *Mem:* Am Soc Ichthyologists & Herpetologists; AAAS; Am Fisheries Soc; Am Soc Limnol & Oceanog; Sigma Xi. *Res:* Systematics and development of marine and estuarine larval fishes; ecology and population dynamics of ichthyoplankton; resource assessment; ichthyoplankton sampling; fish life histories; reproductive strategies of fishes. *Mailing Add:* Gulf Coast Res Lab East Beach Ocean Springs MS 39564

RICHARDSON, STEPHEN H, b Kalamazoo, Mich, June 30, 32; wid; c 2. MICROBIOLOGY, BIOCHEMISTRY. *Educ:* Univ Calif, Los Angeles, BA, 55; Univ Southern Calif, MS, 59, PhD(bact), 60. *Prof Exp:* Lectr, Univ Southern Calif, 59-61; res assoc, Tobacco Industs Res Comt, 60-61; trainee, Enzyme Inst, Univ Wis, 61-63; from asst prof to assoc prof, 63-71, PROF MICROBIOL, BOWMAN GRAY SCH MED, 71- *Concurrent Pos:* Mem cholera adv comt, NIH, 69-73, US-Japan Cholera Panel, 69-76; guest scientist, Cholera Res Lab, Bangladesh, 72-73; found lectr, Am Soc Microbiol, 71-72; consult, NIH Infectious Dis Comt, 77; pres NC br, Am Soc Microbiol, 77-78; mem, bacteriol/mycology study sect, NIH, 78- *Mem:* AAAS; Am Soc Microbiol. *Res:* Bacteriology; microbial physiology; biochemistry of membrane systems and virulence; biochemical mechanisms of microbial pathogenesis; physiology of Vibrio cholerae; pathogenic microorganisms; diarrheal diseases. *Mailing Add:* Dept Microbiol Bowman Gray Sch Med Winston-Salem NC 27103

RICHARDSON, THOMAS, b Ft Lupton, Colo, Dec 4, 31; m 54; c 2. FOOD CHEMISTRY, BIOCHEMISTRY. *Educ:* Univ Colo, Boulder, BS, 54; Univ Wis-Madison, MS, 56, PhD(biochem), 60. *Prof Exp:* Fel food chem, Univ Calif, Davis, 60-62; from asst prof to assoc prof, 62-69, PROF FOOD CHEM, UNIV WIS-MADISON, 70- *Mem:* Am Chem Soc; Inst Food Technol; Am Dairy Sci Asn. *Res:* Application of insoluble enzymes to food processing, analysis and structure; applied enzymology in general. *Mailing Add:* Dept of Food Sci Univ of Wis Madison WI 53706

RICHARDSON, VERLIN HOMER, b Gage, Okla, July 5, 30; m 51; c 3. CHEMISTRY, SCIENCE EDUCATION. *Educ:* Northwestern State Col, Okla, BS, 52; Phillips Univ, MEd, 57; Okla State Univ, MS, 58; Univ Okla, PhD(sci educ), 69. *Prof Exp:* Teacher, Pub Sch, Okla, 52-56; instr chem, El Dorado Jr Col, Kans, 58-62; assoc prof, 62-76, PROF CHEM, CENT STATE UNIV, OKLA, 76- *Mem:* Am Chem Soc. *Res:* Inorganic chemistry. *Mailing Add:* Dept of Chem Cent State Univ Edmond OK 73034

RICHARDSON, WALLACE LLOYD, b Santa Barbara, Calif, Sept 16, 27; m 51; c 4. ORGANIC CHEMISTRY. *Educ:* Univ Calif, BS, 51; Mass Inst Technol, PhD(org chem), 54. *Prof Exp:* Sr res assoc, Fuels, Asphalts & Spec Prods, 54-69, MGR FUEL CHEM DIV, CHEVRON RES CO, STAND OIL CO, CALIF, 69- *Mem:* Am Chem Soc. *Res:* Mechanism of combustion chemistry of knock and antiknock reactions; application of surfactants in hydrocarbon systems; wax crystal modification for improvement of low temperature flow. *Mailing Add:* Chevron Res Co 576 Standard Ave Richmond CA 94530

RICHARDSON, WILLIAM HARRY, b Los Angeles, Calif, Sept 15, 31; c 2. ORGANIC CHEMISTRY. *Educ:* Univ Calif, Los Angeles, BS, 55; Univ Ill, PhD(org chem), 58. *Prof Exp:* Fel, Univ Wash, 58-60; res chemist, Calif Res Corp, 60-63; from asst prof to PROF ORG CHEM, SAN DIEGO STATE UNIV, 63- *Concurrent Pos:* Petrol Res Fund grants, 63-64 & 69-71; US Army Res Off-Durham grants, 65-68, 71-74, 74-77, 77-80 & 80-83. *Mem:* Am Chem Soc; Royal Soc Chem. *Res:* Reaction mechanisms of organic peroxides and related chemiluminescence reactions; oxidation of organic compounds; neighboring group reactions. *Mailing Add:* Dept of Chem Calif State Univ San Diego CA 92115

RICHART, F(RANK) E(DWIN), JR, b Urbana, Ill, Dec 6, 18; m 45; c 3. CIVIL ENGINEERING. *Educ:* Univ Ill, BS, 40, MS, 46, PhD(appl mech), 48. *Hon Degrees:* DSc, Univ Fla, 72. *Prof Exp:* Asst, Univ Ill, 46-47, spec res assoc, 47-48; asst prof mech eng, Harvard Univ, 48-52; assoc prof, Univ Fla, 52-54, prof, 54-62; chmn dept, 62-69, prof, 62-67, W J EMMONS DISTINGUISHED PROF CIVIL ENG, UNIV MICH, ANN ARBOR, 77- *Concurrent Pos:* NSF fac fel, 59-60. *Honors & Awards:* Middlebrooks Award, Am Soc Civil Engrs, 56, 59, 60 & 66, Wellington Prize, 63; Karl Terzaghi Award, Am Soc Civil Engrs, 80. *Mem:* Nat Acad Eng; fel Am Soc Civil Engrs; Earthquake Eng Res Inst. *Res:* Soil dynamics; soil mechanics and foundations; stress analysis. *Mailing Add:* Dept of Civil Eng Univ of Mich Ann Arbor MI 48104

RICHART, RALPH M, b Wilkes Barre, Pa, Dec 14, 33; m; c 2. PATHOLOGY, OBSTETRICS & GYNECOLOGY. *Educ:* Johns Hopkins Univ, BA, 54; Univ Rochester, MD, 58. *Prof Exp:* Teaching fel path, Harvard Med Sch, 59-60; instr path & obstet & gynec, Med Col Va, 61-63; from asst prof to assoc prof path, 63-69, PROF PATH, COL PHYSICIANS & SURGEONS, COLUMBIA UNIV, 69-, DIR PATH & CYTOL, SLOANE HOSP, PRESBY HOSP, NEW YORK, 63- *Concurrent Pos:* USPHS spec res fel, 61-63, career res develop award, 61-63 & 65-69; asst vis obstetrician & gynecologist, Harlem Hosp, New York, 63; from asst attend pathologist to assoc attend pathologist, Presby Hosp, 63-69, attend pathologist, 69-; consult, Ford Found Pop Off, 69. *Mem:* Am Soc Cytol; Soc Gynec Invest; assoc fel Am Col Obstetricians & Gynecologists; Int Acad Cytol; Am Asn Path & Bact. *Res:* Cervical neoplasia; human reproduction. *Mailing Add:* Col of Physicians & Surgeons Columbia Univ New York NY 10032

RICHARZ, WERNER GUNTER, b Troisdorf, WGer, June 24, 48; Can citizen. AERO ACOUSTICS. *Educ:* Univ Toronto, BASc, 72, MASc, 74, PhD(aero acoust), 78. *Prof Exp:* ASST PROF, INST SPACE SCI, UNIV TORONTO, 78- *Mem:* Am Inst Aeronaut & Astronaut; Acoust Soc Am; Can Aeronaut & Space Inst. *Res:* Generation of sound by unsteady flows; stability of shear flows; unsteady aerodynamics. *Mailing Add:* 4925 Dufferin St Downsview ON M3H 5T6 Can

RICHASON, GEORGE R, JR, b Turners Falls, Mass, Apr 3, 16; m 40; c 3. INORGANIC CHEMISTRY. *Educ:* Univ Mass, BS, 37, MS, 39. *Prof Exp:* Instr high sch, Mass, 39-42, 46-47; from asst prof to assoc prof chem, 47-64, assoc head dept, 64-80, PROF CHEM, UNIV MASS, AMHERST, 64- *Mem:* Am Chem Soc; Sigma Xi. *Res:* Radiochemistry. *Mailing Add:* Dept of Chem Univ of Mass Amherst MA 01002

RICHBERG, CARL GEORGE, b Syracuse, NY, July 10, 28; m 55. FOOD SCIENCE. *Educ:* Syracuse Univ, BS, 51, MS, 53, PhD(microbiol), 56. *Prof Exp:* Asst indust microbiol, bact & food tech, Syracuse Univ, 51-56, effects of radiation on food, Inst Indust Res, 56; res assoc, Res Ctr, 57-72, DEVELOP SCIENTIST, RES CTR, LEVER BROS CO, 72- *Mem:* AAAS; NY Acad Sci; Sigma Xi; Inst Food Technol; Fedn Am Scientists. *Res:* Oral microbiology; emulsions and protein chemistry; industrial microbiology; submerged culture methods; germicides; sterilization; dairy science; baking science and technology. *Mailing Add:* Res Ctr Lever Bros Co 45 River Rd Edgewater NJ 07020

RICHELLE, LEON JOSEPH, b Liege, Belg, Sept 22, 35; m 59; c 3. BIOLOGY. *Educ:* Univ Liege, BS, 56, MD, 60, PhD(biomed sci), 67. *Prof Exp:* Res asst pharmacol, Univ Liege, 56-64, in chg res biomed sci, 64-67; assoc dean grad sch, Inst Mat Sci, Univ Conn, 72-74, prof oral biol, 67-75; prof biol & vpres acad affairs, Portland State Univ, 75-79; provost & vpres acad affairs & prof life sci, Clark Univ, 79-80; CHANCELLOR & PROF BIOL SCI, UNIV NEW ORLEANS, 80- *Concurrent Pos:* Mem, Inst Mat Sci, Univ Conn, 67-75; prog dir, USPHS Prog-Proj grant, Univ Conn, 69-76, exec dir long-range planning comt, 71-73. *Mem:* Orthop Res Soc; Soc Col & Univ Planning. *Res:* Biology of calcified tissues; biomaterials. *Mailing Add:* Univ New Orleans New Orleans LA 70122

RICHELSON, ELLIOTT, b Cambridge, Mass, Apr 3, 43; m 69; c 3. PSYCHOPHARMACOLOGY. *Educ:* Brandeis Univ, BA, 65; Johns Hopkins Univ, MD, 69; Am Bd Psychiat & Neurol, cert, 76. *Prof Exp:* Asst prof pharmacol & exp therapeut, Sch Med, Johns Hopkins Univ, 72-75; asst prof psychiat & pharmacol, 75-78, assoc prof, 78-81, PROF PSYCHIAT & PHARMACOL, MAYO MED SCH, 81-, CONSULT MAYO CLIN, 75- *Concurrent Pos:* Borden res award med, Sch Med, Johns Hopkins Univ, 69, NIMH res scientist develop award, 74; A E Bennet basic sci res award, Soc Biol Psychiat, 77. *Mem:* Am Psychiat Asn; Am Soc Neurochem; Am Soc Pharmacol & Exp Therapeut; Soc Biol Psychiat; Am Col Neuropsychopharmacol. *Res:* Psychiatry and pharmacology. *Mailing Add:* Mayo Found 200 Second St SW Rochester MN 55905

RICHENS, VOIT B, b Vernal, Utah, July 14, 27; m 52; c 3. WILDLIFE ECOLOGY. *Educ:* Wash State Col, BS, 57; Utah State Univ, MS, 61, PhD(wildlife biol), 67. *Prof Exp:* Wildlife biologist, Denver Wildlife Res Ctr, Bur Sport Fisheries & Wildlife, 63-68; asst prof wildlife resources, Univ Maine, Orono, 68-74, asst leader, Maine Coop Wildlife Res Unit, 68-80, assoc prof, 74-80; WILDLIFE BIOLOGIST, DENVER WILDLIFE RES CTR, US FISH & WILDLIFE SERV, 80- *Mem:* Am Soc Mammalogists; Ecol Soc Am; Wildlife Soc. *Res:* Effects of environment on big game animals; small mammal ecology and control; highway impact on northern forest ecosystems; coyote biology. *Mailing Add:* US Fish & Wildlife Serv Rural Housing Res Unit PO Box 792 Clemson SC 29631

RICHER, CLAUDE-LISE, b St Hyacinthe, Que, Nov 20, 28. MICROSCOPIC ANATOMY, ENDOCRINOLOGY. *Educ:* Univ Montreal, BA, 48, MD, 54, MS, 57. *Prof Exp:* Asst histol, 57-59, asst prof, 59-68, assoc prof, 68-80, PROF ANAT, UNIV MONTREAL, 80-, ASST DEAN FAC MED, 69- *Mem:* Endocrine Soc; Am Asn Anatomists; Can Asn Anat; Can Physiol Soc. *Res:* Neuroendocrinology; magnesium deficiency and its effect on adrenal function. *Mailing Add:* Fac of Med Univ of Montreal Montreal PQ H3C 3J7 Can

RICHER, HARVEY BRIAN, b Montreal, Que, Apr 7, 44. ASTRONOMY. *Educ:* McGill Univ, BS, 65; Univ Rochester, MS, 68, PhD(physics, astron), 70. *Prof Exp:* Assoc astron, Univ Rochester, 65-70; instr, 70-71, asst prof, 71-77, ASSOC PROF ASTRON, UNIV BC, 77- *Concurrent Pos:* Vis prof, Univ Uppsala, Sweden, 77-78. *Mem:* AAAS; Am Astron Soc; Can Astron Soc; Royal Astron Soc. *Res:* Carbon stars; galactic structure; white dwarf stars. *Mailing Add:* Dept of Geophys & Astron Univ of BC Vancouver BC V6T 1W5 Can

RICHER, JEAN-CLAUDE, b Montreal, Que, Feb 23, 33; m 55; c 4. ORGANIC CHEMISTRY. *Educ:* Univ Montreal, BSc, 54, MSc, 56, PhD(chem), 58. *Prof Exp:* Lectr chem, 57-58, from asst prof to assoc prof, 60-70, PROF CHEM, UNIV MONTREAL, 70- *Concurrent Pos:* Res assoc, Univ Notre Dame, 58-60; Herbert Lank Lectr, Univ Del, 66; invited prof, Univ Toulouse, 68-69; sci adv, Sci Coun Can, 71-72. *Mem:* Am Chem Soc; Chem Inst Can. *Res:* Organometallic derivatives; oxidation reactions; peptide synthesis; nuclear magnetic resonance; conformational analysis. *Mailing Add:* Dept of Chem Univ of Montreal Montreal PQ H3C 3J7 Can

RICHERSON, HAL BATES, b Phoenix, Ariz, Feb 16, 29; m 53; c 5. ALLERGY, IMMUNOLOGY. *Educ:* Univ Ariz, BS, 50; Northwestern Univ, MD, 54. *Prof Exp:* Resident internal med, Univ Iowa Hosps, 61-64, fel allergy, 64-66, from asst prof to assoc prof, 66-74, PROF INTERNAL MED & DIR, ALLERGY-IMMUNOL DIV, COL MED, UNIV IOWA, 74- *Concurrent Pos:* Consult, Vet Admin Hosp, Iowa City, 66-; vis lectr, Med Sch, Harvard Univ, 68-69; NIH spec fel immunol, Mass Gen Hosp, 68-69; mem task force res in respiratory dis, NIH, 71-72; mem, Merit Rev Bd Respiration, Veterans Admin, 81- *Mem:* Fel Am Col Physicians; fel Am Acad Allergy; Am Asn Immunol; Am Fedn Clin Res; Am Thoracic Soc. *Res:* Study of the lung as an immunologic target organ; cutaneous basophil hypersensitivity and its relationship to reaginic hypersensitivity. *Mailing Add:* Allergy-Immunol Sect Univ of Iowa Hosps & Clins Iowa City IA 52240

RICHERSON, JIM VERNON, b Bossier City, La, Sept 22, 43; m 65; c 1. ENTOMOLOGY. *Educ:* Univ Mo-Columbia, BA, 65, MSc, 68; Simon Fraser Univ, PhD(biol sci), 72. *Prof Exp:* Res technician, Biol Control Insects Lab, USDA, 65-68; res assoc entom, Pa State Univ, University Park, 72-76; fel entom, Tex A&M Univ, College Station, 76-79; ASST PROF BIOL, SUL ROSS STATE UNIV, ALPINE, TEX, 79- *Mem:* Entom Soc Am. *Res:* Behavior of insects as it relates to pest management and control programs; host-parasite relationships and sex pheromone biology and behavior; medical-veterinary entomology; aquatic entomology; bio-control of range and weeds. *Mailing Add:* Dept Biol Sul Ross State Univ Alpine TX 79830

RICHERSON, PETER JAMES, b San Mateo, Calif, Oct 11, 43. LIMNOLOGY, HUMAN ECOLOGY. *Educ:* Univ Calif, Davis, BS, 65, PhD(zool), 69. *Prof Exp:* Asst prof, 71-77, ASSOC PROF ECOL, DIV ENVIRON STUDIES, UNIV CALIF, DAVIS, 77- *Concurrent Pos:* Consult, Nat Water Comn, 70-71; co-investr, NSF grant, 72-82. *Mem:* AAAS; Am Soc Limnol & Oceanog; Ecol Soc Am. *Res:* Human ecology; theory of cultural evolution; plankton community ecology. tropical limnology. *Mailing Add:* Div of Environ Studies Univ of Calif Davis CA 95616

RICHERT, ANTON STUART, b Newton, Kans, May 19, 35; m 60; c 1. PARTICLE PHYSICS, NUCLEAR PHYSICS. *Educ:* Cornell Univ, PhD(exp physics), 62. *Prof Exp:* Res assoc high energy physics, Cornell Univ, 62-63; asst prof physics, Univ Pa, 63-69; assoc prof physics, Ore State Univ, 69-76; SR SYSTS ANALYST, SUN STUDS-VENEER, ROSEBURG, ORE, 76- *Mem:* Am Phys Soc. *Res:* Photo production and neutral decays of pion resonances; cosmic ray muons; lepton conservation; pion-nucleus interactions. *Mailing Add:* 1461 SE Virginia Ct Roseburg OR 97470

RICHES, RALPH HARVARD, genetics, biology, see previous edition

RICHES, WESLEY WILLIAM, b Mt Pleasant, Mich, Feb 13, 14; m 41; c 2. CHEMISTRY. *Educ:* Cent Mich Univ, AB, 35; Univ Mich, MS, 36, PhD(chem), 41. *Hon Degrees:* ScD, Cent Mich Univ, 63. *Prof Exp:* Res chemist pigments dept, E I Du Pont De Nemours & Co, 41-55, salesman, 55-63, tech serv chemist, 63-64, group supvr, 64-66, mgr, Chem Dyes, 66-79; RETIRED. *Mem:* Am Chem Soc; Tech Asn Pulp & Paper Inst. *Res:* Pigments; surface chemistry. *Mailing Add:* Cokesbury Village Hockessin DE 19707

RICHEY, CLARENCE B(ENTLEY), b Winnipeg, Man, Dec 28, 10; m 36; c 2. AGRICULTURAL ENGINEERING. *Educ:* Iowa State Univ, BSAE, 33; Purdue Univ, BSME, 39. *Prof Exp:* Time study engr, David Bradley Mfg Works, Ill, 33-36; instr farm power-mach, Purdue Univ, 36-41; asst prof, Ohio State Univ, 41-43; supvr adv develop eng, Elec Wheel Co, Ill, 43-46; proj engr, Harry Ferguson, Inc, Mich, 46-47; res eng, Dearborn Motors Corp, 47-53; supvr tractor & implement div, Ford Motor Co, 53-57, chief res engr, 57-62; chief engr & partner, Five Mfg Co, Ohio, 62-64; chief engr, Fowler Div, Massey-Ferguson Inc, Calif, 64-69, prod mgt engr, Massey-Ferguson Ltd, 70; assoc prof, 70-76, EMER PROF AGR ENG, PURDUE UNIV, 76- *Honors & Awards:* Cyrus Hall McCormick Gold Medal, Am Soc Agr Engrs, 77. *Mem:* Am Soc Agr Engrs. *Res:* Farm equipment; field machinery and tractors. *Mailing Add:* 2217 Delaware Dr West Lafayette IN 47906

RICHEY, HERMAN GLENN, JR, b Chicago, Ill, May 25, 32; m 62; c 3. ORGANIC CHEMISTRY. *Educ:* Univ Chicago, BA, 52; Harvard Univ, MA, 55, PhD(chem), 59. *Prof Exp:* NSF fel chem, Yale Univ, 58-59; from asst prof to assoc prof, 59-69, PROF CHEM, PA STATE UNIV, 69- *Concurrent Pos:* Sloan fel, 64-68; John Simon Guggenheim fel, 67-68; consult, Koppers Co, Inc, 63- *Mem:* Am Chem Soc; Royal Soc Chem. *Res:* Reaction mechanisms and intermediates; new synthetic methods; organometallic chemistry. *Mailing Add:* Dept Chem Pa State Univ University Park PA 16802

RICHEY, WILLIS DALE, b Bedford, Ohio, July 26, 30; m; c 1. PHYSICAL CHEMISTRY. *Educ:* Hiram Col, BA, 52; Univ Rochester, PhD(chem), 58. *Prof Exp:* Res chemist, Diamond Alkali Co, 57-58; from asst prof to assoc prof chem, Bethany Col, 58-62; vis assoc prof, Colby Col, 62-63; from asst prof to assoc prof, 63-74, Buhl prof, 76-77, PROF CHEM, CHATHAM COL, 74- *Concurrent Pos:* Vis scholar, Freer Gallery of Art, Smithsonian Inst, 69-70; fac res participant, Pittsburgh Energy Technol Ctr, Dept Energy, 78-79. *Mem:* AAAS; Am Chem Soc; Am Phys Soc; Royal Soc Chem; Int Inst Conserv Hist & Artistic Works. *Res:* Chemical aspects of the conservation of objects of historic and artistic value; thermodynamics of the conversions of inorganic constituents of coals during liquifaction and gasification processes. *Mailing Add:* Dept of Chem Chatham Col Pittsburgh PA 15232

RICHLEY, E(DWARD) A(NTHONY), b Cleveland, Ohio, Sept 5, 28; m 50; c 2. MECHANICAL ENGINEERING, PHYSICS. *Educ:* Cleveland State Univ, BME, 59; Case Western Reserve Univ, MS, 63. *Prof Exp:* Res scientist, Lewis Res Ctr, 59-62, head propulsion components sect, 62-68, chief ion physics br, 68-70, mem dir staff, 70-72, chief off oper anal & planning, 72-76, chief mgt opers officer, 76-80, DIR ADMIN, LEWIS RES CTR, NASA, 80- *Mem:* Assoc fel Am Inst Aeronaut & Astronaut. *Res:* Institutional and research and development operations analysis and planning. *Mailing Add:* 4801 W 229 St Cleveland OH 44135

RICHLIN, JACK, b New York, NY, Jan 17, 33. PHYSICAL CHEMISTRY. *Educ:* Brooklyn Col, BS, 54; Purdue Univ, MS, 57; Rutgers Univ, New Brunswick, PhD(chem), 64. *Prof Exp:* Sr res chemist, Allied Chem Corp, 62-65; asst prof, 65-69, ASSOC PROF PHYS CHEM, MONMOUTH COL, NJ, 69- *Mem:* Am Chem Soc. *Res:* Polymer physics; charge transfer complexes; solution and surface properties of detergents and surfactants. *Mailing Add:* Dept of Chem Monmouth Col West Long Branch NJ 07764

RICHMAN, ALEX, b Winnipeg, Man, Jan 23, 29; m 52; c 4. PSYCHIATRY, EPIDEMIOLOGY. *Educ:* Univ Man, MD, 53; McGill Univ, dipl psychiat, 57; Johns Hopkins Univ, MPH, 60. *Prof Exp:* Staff asst comt ment health serv, Can Ment Health Asn, 56-60; asst prof psychiat, Univ BC, 60; proj dir, Can Royal Comn Health Serv, 62-63; head sect social psychiat, Univ BC, 63-66; med officer, WHO, Geneva, 66-67; assoc prof epidemiol & dir training prog psychiat epidemiol, Columbia Univ, 67-69; prof psychiat, Mt Sinai Sch Med & chief utilization rev psychiat, Beth Israel Med Ctr, 69-78; PROF DEPT PSYCHIAT & PREV MED & DIR TRAINING & RES UNIT PSYCHIAT EPIDEMIOL, DALHOUSIE UNIV, 78- *Concurrent Pos:* Nat Ment Health res award, Can Ment Health Asn, 64; assoc prof psychiat, Univ BC, 64-66; consult, WHO, Ministry Health, Jamaica, 64-66; consult, Southern NB Ment Health Planning Comt, 80-82 & Policy & Planning Unit, Ment Health Br, Ont Ministry of Health, 81-; Nat Health Scientist award, 78-82. *Mem:* Am Psychiat Asn; Biomet Soc; Am Statist Asn; Can Psychiat Asn; Royal Col Psychiat. *Res:* Social psychiatry; epidemiology; mental disorders; quality assurance; evaluation; planning of mental health services. *Mailing Add:* Dept Preventive Med Dalhousie Univ 5849 University Ave Halifax NS B3H 4H7 Can

RICHMAN, DAVID M(ARTIN), b New York, NY, Mar 13, 32; m 60; c 2. CHEMICAL ENGINEERING, ENERGY SCIENCE. *Educ:* Columbia Univ, AB, 53, BA, 54, MS, 56. *Prof Exp:* Chem engr, Nuclear Eng Dept, Brookhaven Nat Lab, 55-58; radiation specialist, Div Isotope Develop, US Atomic Energy Comn, 58-60, chemist, Div Res, 60-71, chief, Eng Chem & Isotope Prep Br, Div Phys Res, 71-72; head, Indust Appln & Chem Sect, Int Atomic Energy Agency, 72-74; chief, Chem Energy & Geosci Br, ERDA, 74-76, sr prog analyst, Off Asst Admin for Solar & Geothermal Energy, 76-77; head Prog Planning & Implementation Off, Off Asst Secy Conserv & Solar Appln, 77-78, sr prog analyst, Off Asst Secy Energy Technol, 79-80, actg dir Res & Tech Assessment Div, 80, STAFF PHYS SCIENTIST, OFF BASIC ENERGY SCI, ENERGY RES, DEPT ENERGY, 80- *Mem:* Am Nuclear Soc; Am Chem Soc; Am Inst Chem Engrs. *Res:* Isotopic radiation source design; radiation chemistry; administration of basic research; isotope separations, transplutonium element production; separations chemistry; research materials distribution; solar energy. *Mailing Add:* Off Basic Energy Sci G-256 Dept Energy Washington DC 20545

RICHMAN, DAVID PAUL, b Boston, Mass, June 9, 43; m 69; c 2. NEUROIMMUNOLOGY, EXPERIMENTAL NEUROPATHOLOGY. *Educ:* Princeton Univ, AB, 65; Johns Hopkins Univ, MD, 69. *Prof Exp:* Intern & asst resident, Albert Einstein Col Med, 69-71; asst resident neurol, Mass Gen Hosp, 71-73, chief resident, 73-74, clin & res fel, 74-76; asst prof, 76-80, ASSOC PROF NEUROL, UNIV CHICAGO, 81- *Concurrent Pos:* Med, Med Avd Bd, Myasthenia Gravis Found; Instr neurol, Harvard Univ, 75-76. *Mem:* Sigma Xi; Am Acad Neurol; AAAS. *Res:* Cellular immunology of neurological diseases; myasthenia gravis and experimental myasthenia; monocloual anti-acetylcholine receptor antibodies and anti-idiotypic antibodies; cell membrane receptors; flow cytometry. *Mailing Add:* Dept Nurol Univ Chicago 950 E 59th St Chicago IL 60637

RICHMAN, ISAAC, b Havana, Cuba, Apr 3, 32; US citizen; m 60; c 2. ELECTROOPTICS, SPECTROSCOPY. *Educ:* Univ Calif, Los Angeles, BA, 54, MA, 58, PhD(physics), 63. *Prof Exp:* Res engr, Elec Div, Nat Cash Register Co, 56-58; mem tech staff crystal physics, Lab Div, Aerospace Corp, 63-66; SR STAFF SCIENTIST, McDONNELL DOUGLAS ASTRONAUTICS CO, 66- *Concurrent Pos:* Res physicist, Univ Calif, Los Angeles, 66; mem, Infrared Info Symposium. *Mem:* Am Phys Soc. *Res:* Research and development in the areas of infrared detection and imaging, radiometry, and spectroscopy; lattice vibration studies; infrared photoconductor studies, spectroscopy of dielectrics. *Mailing Add:* 1842 Port Manleigh Pl Newport Beach CA 92660

RICHMAN, JUSTIN LEWIS, b Providence, RI, Apr 12, 25; m 57; c 3. MEDICINE. *Educ:* Brown Univ, AB, 46; Tufts Univ, MD, 49; Am Bd Internal Med, dipl, 56. *Prof Exp:* Lectr, Harvard Univ, 52-53; lectr, Univ, 53-60, from instr to sr instr, 56-58, asst prof, 58-79, ASSOC PROF MED, SCH MED, TUFTS UNIV, 70- *Concurrent Pos:* USPHS fel cardiol, 52-53; physician-in-chg, Dept Med, Boston Dispensary, 56-68, chief electrocardiography lab, 57-68; consult, Mass Heart Asn, 57-60 & NH Heart Asn, 59-; physician-in-chief, Med Clin, New Eng Med Ctr Hosps, 56-68. *Mem:* AAAS; Am Heart Asn; Am Soc Internal Med; fel Am Col Cardiol. *Res:* Clinical cardiology; spatial vectorcardiography and electrocardiography. *Mailing Add:* 25 Boylston St Chestnut Hill MA 02167

RICHMAN, MARC H(ERBERT), b Boston, Mass, Oct 14, 36; m 63. METALLURGY, MATERIALS SCIENCE. *Educ:* Mass Inst Technol, BS, 57, ScD(metall), 63. *Prof Exp:* Instr metall, Mass Inst Technol, 57-60, res asst, 60-63; from asst prof to assoc prof, 63-70, PROF ENG & DIR ELECTRON MICROSCOPY FACILITY, BROWN UNIV, 70- *Concurrent Pos:* Instr, Dept Educ, Commonwealth of Mass, 58-62; consult engr, 58-; consult, Army Mat & Mech Res Ctr; adj staff, Dept Med, Miriam Hospital, Providence, RI, 74-; bioengr, Dept Orthop, RI Hosp, Providence, 79- *Honors & Awards:* Outstanding Young Faculty Award, Am Soc Eng Educ, 69; Albert Sauveur Award, Am Soc Metals, 69. *Mem:* Am Soc Metals; Am Crystallog Asn; Am Inst Mining, Metall & Petrol Engrs; fel Am Inst Chem; Am Ceramic Soc. *Res:* Study of phase transformations by optical, electron and field ion microscopy; relation of properties to structure; development of ceramic materials by microstructural design; biomaterials in orthopaedics and cardiovascular systems. *Mailing Add:* Div of Eng Brown Univ Providence RI 02912

RICHMAN, PAUL L(AWRENCE), computer science, see previous edition

RICHMAN, ROBERT MICHAEL, b Pasadena, Calif, Apr 27, 50; m 76. TRANSITION METAL PHOTOCHEMISTRY. *Educ:* Occidental Col, AB, 71; Univ Ill, Urbana, MS, 72, PhD(inorg chem), 76. *Prof Exp:* NSF fel, Calif Inst Technol, 76-77; ASST PROF CHEM, CARNEGIE-MELLON UNIV, 77- *Mem:* Am Chem Soc. *Res:* Transition metal photochemistry in homogeneous solution aimed at developing new strategies for solar energy conversion. *Mailing Add:* Dept Chem Carnegie-Mellon Univ Pittsburgh PA 15213

RICHMAN, ROGER HARRY, physical metallurgy, see previous edition

RICHMAN, SUMNER, b Boston, Mass, Dec 15, 29; m 52; c 3. AQUATIC ECOLOGY. *Educ:* Hartwick Col, AB, 51; Univ Mass, MA, 53; Univ Mich, PhD(zool), 57. *Prof Exp:* Instr biol, 57-60, from asst prof to assoc prof, 60-70, PROF BIOL, LAWRENCE UNIV, 70-, CHMN DEPT, 77- *Concurrent Pos:* Vis prof marine biol, Tel-Aviv Univ & Marine Lab, Eilat, Israel, 72 & Chesapeake Biol Lab, Univ Md, 74-75; col accreditation evaluator, N Cent Asn Col & Sec Schs, 72-; Smithsonian Inst Foreign Currency Grant, 72. *Mem:* AAAS; Ecol Soc Am; Am Soc Limnol & Oceanog; Sigma Xi; Int Cong Limnol. *Res:* Energy transformation in aquatic systems; secondary productivity and zooplankton feeding behavior. *Mailing Add:* Dept of Biol Lawrence Univ Appleton WI 54911

RICHMOND, ARTHUR DEAN, b Long Beach, Calif, Mar 13, 44; m 71. ATMOSPHERIC PHYSICS. *Educ:* Univ Calif, Los Angeles, BS, 65, PhD(meteorol), 70. *Prof Exp:* Asst res meteorologist, Univ Calif, Los Angeles, 70-71; Nat Acad Sci resident res assoc, Air Force Cambridge Res Labs, 71-72; res assoc upper atmospheric physics, High Altitude Observ, Nat Ctr Atmospheric Res, 72-76; res assoc, Coop Inst Res Environ Sci, Univ Colo, 76-77; res assoc, 77-80, SPACE SCIENTIST, NAT OCEANIC & ATMOSPHERIC ADMIN, 80- *Concurrent Pos:* Consult, Rand Corp, 66-69; NATO fel in sci, Lab Physique de l'Exosphere, Univ Paris, 73-74. *Mem:* AAAS; Am Geophys Union; Am Meteorol Soc. *Res:* Upper atmospheric electric fields and currents; geomagnetism; atmospheric dynamics. *Mailing Add:* NOAA Space Environ Lab Boulder CO 80303

RICHMOND, CHARLES WILLIAM, b New Martinsville, WVa, Jan 8, 38; m 66; c 3. ORGANIC CHEMISTRY. *Educ:* David Lipscomb Col, BA, 60; Univ Miss, PhD(org chem), 64. *Prof Exp:* Asst prof chem, David Lipscomb Col, 64-69; assoc prof, 69, PROF CHEM, UNIV NORTH ALA, 69- *Mem:* Am Chem Soc. *Res:* Preparation of heterocyclic compounds for use as potential drugs. *Mailing Add:* Dept of Chem Univ of N Ala Florence AL 35630

RICHMOND, CHESTER ROBERT, b South Amboy, NJ, May 29, 29; m 52; c 5. RADIOBIOLOGY. *Educ:* NJ State Col, Montclair, BA, 52; Univ NMex, MS, 54, PhD(biol), 58. *Prof Exp:* Asst physiol, Univ NMex, 54-55; asst, Los Alamos Sci Lab, 55-57, mem staff, 57-68; mem staff, Div Biol & Med, US AEC, 68-71; leader biomed res group, Los Alamos Sci Lab, 71-73, alternate health div leader, 73-74; ASSOC DIR BIOMED & ENVIRON SCI, OAK RIDGE NAT LAB, 74-; PROF BIOMED SCI, UNIV TENN-OAK RIDGE GRAD SCH BIOMED SCI, 75-, DIR HEALTH, SAFETY & ENVIRON AFFAIRS, 81- *Concurrent Pos:* Mem, Nat Coun Radiation Protection & Measurements, 74-; comt 2, Int Comn Radiol Protection, 77- *Honors & Awards:* E O Lawrence Award, US AEC, 74; G Failla lectr, 76. *Mem:* Fel AAAS; Health Physics Soc; Sigma Xi; Soc Risk Anal; Radiation Res Soc. *Res:* Water and electrolyte metabolism; comparative metabolism of radionuclides; anthropometry; biological effects of internal emitters; health & environ effects of energy production; radiobiology of actinide elements. *Mailing Add:* PO Box X Oak Ridge TN 37830

RICHMOND, F(RANCIS) M(ARTIN), b Washington, Pa, July 7, 22; m 44; c 1. METALLURGICAL ENGINEERING. *Educ:* Univ Pittsburgh, BS, 43, MS, 49, PhD, 66. *Prof Exp:* Lab instr metall, Univ Pittsburgh, 42-43, asst, 46; metall observer, US Steel Corp, Youngstown, 43; res engr, Res Labs, Westinghouse Elec Corp, 47-53; res assoc, 53-55, mgr mat res, 55-57, mgr res & develop, 57-60, dir res & develop, 60-61, TECH DIR, SPECIALTY STEEL DIV, UNIVERSAL CYCLOPS STEEL CORP, 61-, VPRES, 66-, VPRES RES & DEVELOP, 81- *Mem:* Fel Am Soc Metals; Brit Metals Soc; Am Inst Mining, Metall & Petrol Engrs; Am Iron & Steel Inst; Asn Iron & Steel Engrs. *Res:* Heat-resistant alloys for jet engines; gas turbines; austenitic stainless steels; precipitation hardening; corrosion resistant, tool, die and high-speed steels; vacuum melting; air melting. *Mailing Add:* 1127 Folkstone Dr Pittsburgh PA 15243

RICHMOND, GERALD MARTIN, b Providence, RI, July 30, 14; m 41, 67; c 4. QUATERNARY GEOLOGY. *Educ:* Brown Univ, BA, 36; Harvard Univ, MA, 39; Univ Colo, PhD, 54. *Prof Exp:* Instr geol, Univ Conn, 40; geologist, Spec Eng Div, Panama Canal, 41-42; SR GEOLOGIST, BR CENT GEN GEOL, US GEOL SURV, 42- *Concurrent Pos:* NSF grant, Alps, 60-61; mem qual adv group, US Comn Stratig Nomenclature; mem stratig comn, Int Union Quaternary Res, 77-; mem, US Nat Comt for Int Geol Correlation Prog, 74-78; US working group, Quaternary Glaciation in Northern Hemisphere, 74- *Honors & Awards:* Kirk Bryan Award, Geol Soc Am, 65; Albrecht Penck Medal, Deutsche Quartarvereinigung, 78. *Mem:* AAAS; Int Union Quaternary Res (secy gen, 62-65, pres, 65-69); fel Geol Soc Am; Am Quaternary Asn. *Res:* Glacial and surficial geology; quaternary stratigraphy and correlation; fossil soils; geomorphology. *Mailing Add:* Br of Cent Gen Geol US Geol Surv Box 25046 Fed Ctr MS 913 Denver CO 80225

RICHMOND, J(ACK) H(UBERT), b Kalispell, Mont, July 30, 22; m 46; c 3. ELECTRICAL ENGINEERING. *Educ:* Lafayette Col, BS, 50; Ohio State Univ, MSc, 52, PhD(elec eng), 55. *Prof Exp:* Res assoc, 52-54, asst supvr, 54-56, from asst prof to assoc prof, 55-62, PROF ELEC ENG, OHIO STATE UNIV, 62-, ASSOC SUPVR, 56- *Mem:* Fel Inst Elec & Electronics Engrs. *Res:* Electromagnetic field theory; antennas; radomes; scattering. *Mailing Add:* Dept of Elec Eng Ohio State Univ 1320 Kinnear Rd Columbus OH 43212

RICHMOND, JAMES FRANK, b Walla Walla, Wash, Dec 30, 08; m 32. GEOLOGY. *Educ:* Whitman Col, AB, 30; Claremont Col, MA, 51; Stanford Univ, PhD(geol), 54. *Prof Exp:* Instr, John Muir Col, 50-51; asst prof geol, Univ Redlands, 52-53, 54-55; from asst prof to prof, 55-75, EMER PROF GEOL, CALIF STATE UNIV, LOS ANGELES, 75- *Res:* Pleistocene terraces of North Oregon Coast. *Mailing Add:* Arch Cape OR 97102

RICHMOND, JAMES KENNETH, b Chattanooga, Tenn, June 23, 20; m 44; c 4. PHYSICS. *Educ:* Ga Inst Technol, BS, 42; Univ Pittsburgh, MS, 43, MA, 58. *Prof Exp:* Res engr, Westinghouse Elec Corp, 42-44, 47-49; asst nuclear physics, Univ Pa, 46-47; physicist combustion, US Bur Mines, 49-59; res specialist advan propulsion, Sci Res Labs, Boeing Co, 59-69; sr basic res scientist, 69-71; res physicist, 71-80, SUPVRY RES PHYSICIST, US BUR MINES, 80- *Concurrent Pos:* Instr, Carnegie Inst Technol, 55-59; consult, Comt Fire Res & Fire Res Conf, Nat Acad Sci-Nat Res Coun, 59. *Honors & Awards:* Award, US Dept Interior, 59 & 75. *Mem:* Am Phys Soc; Am Inst Aeronaut & Astronaut; Inst Elec & Electronics Eng. *Res:* Prevention of fires and explosions in coal mines, oil shale mines and other mines; supervision of group engaged in conducting research on full-scale explosions in experimental mines and the instrumentation thereof. *Mailing Add:* 3328 Ivanhoe Rd Pittsburgh PA 15241

RICHMOND, JONAS EDWARD, b Prentiss, Miss, July 17, 29; m 57; c 2. BIOCHEMISTRY. *Educ:* Univ Tenn, BS, 48; Univ Rochester, MS, 50, PhD(biochem, biophys), 53. *Prof Exp:* Res assoc biophys, Univ Rochester, 50-55, instr biophys & biochem, 56-57; estab investr, Am Heart Asn, Harvard Med Sch, 57-63; res biochemist, 63-69, BIOCHEMIST, UNIV CALIF, BERKELEY, 69- *Concurrent Pos:* NIH fel, Univ Rochester, 53-55; Commonwealth fel, Oxford Univ, 55-56; mem, Allergy & Immunol A Study Sect, NIH, 65-69; consult, US Dept Health, Educ & Welfare, 66- & NIH, 71, 74; pres, Alameda County Heart Asn, 74-; vpres, Am Heart Asn Calif affil. *Mem:* AAAS; Am Chem Soc; Radiation Res Soc; Am Soc Biol Chem; Biophys Soc. *Res:* Chemistry and biochemistry of proteins; protein and amino acid metabolism; transport and membrane function; intermediary metabolism; radiation chemistry; biochemistry and biophysics of growth; molecular biology; cell recognition and differentiation; cell surface chemistry. *Mailing Add:* 6870 Charing Cross Rd Berkeley CA 94705

RICHMOND, JONATHAN YOUNG, b Norwalk, Conn, Feb 10, 41; m 66; c 4. VIROLOGY, GENETICS. *Educ:* Univ Conn, BA, 62, MS, 64; Hahnemann Med Col, PhD(genetics), 68. *Prof Exp:* NSF-Nat Res Coun fel virol & cytol, 67-69, res microbiologist, 69-79, BIOL SAFETY OFFICER, PLUM ISLAND ANIMAL DIS CTR, US DEPT AGR, 79- *Concurrent Pos:* Seminar chmn, Plum Island Animal Dis Lab, 74-78, Biol Safety Comt, 75-76, Indust Safety Comt, 73-79, chmn, Blood Bank, 77-78; mem, Biol Safety Conf Steering Comt, 80-82. *Mem:* Am Soc Microbiol; Am Asn Vet Lab Diagnosticians; Biol Photog Asn; fel Am Acad Microbiol. *Res:* Mutants mammalian viruses; cytogenetics; host cell-virus interrelationships. *Mailing Add:* Plum Island Animal Dis Lab Cytology Sect Box 848 Greenport NY 11944

RICHMOND, JULIUS BENJAMIN, b Chicago, Ill, Sept 26, 16; m 37; c 2. MEDICINE. *Educ:* Univ Ill, BS, 37, MD & MS, 39; Am Bd Pediat, dipl. *Prof Exp:* Resident, Cook County Hosp, Chicago, Ill, 46; prof pediat, Col Med, Univ Ill, 46-53; prof & chmn dept, Col Med, State Univ NY Upstate Med Ctr, 53-71; prof child psychiat & human develop, Fac Pub Health & Fac Med, Harvard Med Sch, 71-73, prof prev & social med & chmn dept, 71-79; PROF HEALTH POLICY, HARVARD MED SCH, 81-,. *Concurrent Pos:* Markle Found scholar med sci, 48-53; supt inst juvenile res, Ill State Dept Pub Welfare, 52-53; dir, Proj Headstart, Off Econ Opportunity, 65-; dean med fac, State Univ NY Upstate Med Ctr, 65-71; psychiatrist in chief, Children's Hosp Med Ctr, Boston, 71-74; trustee, Child Welfare League Am; mem Nat Inst Med; asst secy for Health & Surgeon Gen, USPHS, HEW, 77-81; adv child health policy, Children's Hosp Med Ctr, 81- *Mem:* Hon mem Am Acad Child Psychiat; distinguished fel Am Psychiat Asn; Am Pub Health Asn; Soc Exp Biol & Med; Soc Pediat Res. *Res:* Pediatrics; psychological aspects of pediatrics; child development. *Mailing Add:* 79 Beverly Rd Chestnut Hill MA 02167

RICHMOND, MARTHA ELLIS, b Wilmington, Del, Sept 10, 41; m 69; c 2. BIOCHEMISTRY. *Educ:* Wellesley Col, Mass, AB, 62; Tufts Univ, PhD(biochem), 69. *Prof Exp:* Res fel bact & immunol, Harvard Med Sch, 69-70; res assoc med, Sch Med, Tufts Univ, 70-73; lectr, 73-74, asst prof biol, Univ Mass, Boston, 74-75; asst prof, 75-79, ASSOC PROF CHEM, SUFFOLK UNIV, 79- *Mem:* Sigma Xi; Am Chem Soc. *Res:* Biosynthesis of complex carbohydrates; regulation of complex carbohydrate synthesis in mammalian systems. *Mailing Add:* Dept of Chem Suffolk Univ Beacon Hill Boston MA 02114

RICHMOND, MILO EUGENE, b Cutler, Ill, Aug 29, 39. VERTEBRATE ZOOLOGY, REPRODUCTIVE BIOLOGY. *Educ:* Southern Ill Univ, Carbondale, BA & BS, 61; Univ Mo-Columbia, MS, 63, PhD(zool), 67. *Prof Exp:* Asst instr zool, Univ Mo-Columbia, 64-67; asst prof biol, ETenn State Univ, 67-68; ASST PROF WILDLIFE SCI, NY STATE COL AGR & LIFE SCI & ASST LEADER NY COOP WILDLIFE RES UNIT, CORNELL UNIV, 68- *Mem:* Am Soc Mammal; Wildlife Soc. *Res:* Ecology and physiology of reproduction of vertebrates; mammalian population dynamics, especially microtine rodents. *Mailing Add:* Dept of Natural Resources Cornell Univ Ithaca NY 14853

RICHMOND, ROBERT CHAFFEE, b New York, NY, May 3, 43; m 68. RADIOBIOLOGY. *Educ:* Univ NH, BA, 66; Univ Tex, Austin, MA, 70, PhD(radiation biol), 72. *Prof Exp:* Teacher biol & chem, Chester High Sch, Vt, 66-68; res assoc radiation biol, Univ Kans, Lawrence, 73-75; vis scientist radiation biol, US Army Natick Develop Ctr, 75-77; instr radiol & radiation med, Boston Univ Med Ctr, 77-79; RES ASST PROF, NORRIS COTTON CANCER CTR, DARTMOUTH-HITCHCOCK MED CTR, HANOVER NH, 79- *Concurrent Pos:* Nat Res Coun fel, 75-77. *Mem:* Radiation Res Soc;

Sigma Xi; AAAS; NY Acad Sci. *Res:* Chemical and thermal potentiation of cellular sensitivity to ionizing radiation; chemistry and biochemical consequences of radiation-induced damage to cellular DNA. *Mailing Add:* Norris Cotton Cancer Ctr Dartmouth Hitchcock Med Ctr Hanover NH 03755

RICHMOND, ROLLIN CHARLES, b Nairobi, Kenya, May 31, 44; US citizen; m 75. POPULATION GENETICS, BIOCHEMICAL GENETICS. *Educ:* San Diego State Univ, AB, 66; Rockefeller Univ, PhD(genetics), 71. *Prof Exp:* From asst prof to assoc prof zool, Ind Univ, 70-75; assoc prof genetics, NC State Univ, 76; assoc prof, 76-81, PROF, IND UNIV, 81- *Concurrent Pos:* Assoc ed, J Soc Study Evolution, 75-77, Genetica, 81- & J Heredity, 81- *Mem:* Sigma Xi; Genetics Soc Am; Soc Study Evolution; Am Soc Naturalists; Ecol Soc Am. *Res:* Population genetics of natural and artifical populations of Drosophila with particular emphasis on the adaptive significance of isozyme variants; behavioral genetics of Drosophila. *Mailing Add:* Dept Biol Ind Univ Bloomington IN 47405

RICHMOND, VIRGINIA, b Hominy, Okla, July 5, 27. BIOCHEMISTRY. *Educ:* Okla State Univ, BS, 49; Univ Okla, MS, 54; Univ Wash, PhD(biochem), 63. *Prof Exp:* Fel biochem, Univ Calif, Berkeley, 63-64, Nat Inst Dent Res trainee collagen, 64-67; res assoc chem, Univ Colo, 67-68; res assoc path, Univ Wash, 68-69, res assoc environ health, 69-71, res asst prof med, 72-77, res asst prof physiol nursing, 77-80. *Concurrent Pos:* Sr investr, Virginia Mason Res Ctr, 71-75. *Mem:* AAAS; Am Chem Soc; Am Inst Nutrit; Am Thoracic Soc; Am Fedn Clin Res. *Res:* In vivo effect of ascorbic acid on guinea pig skin collagens; elastic fiber components; lung collagen and elastin biosynthesis. *Mailing Add:* 4207 Bagley Ave N Seattle WA 98103

RICHMOND, WILLIAM D, b Denver, Colo, July 19, 25; m 48; c 5. MECHANICAL ENGINEERING. *Educ:* Univ Wis, BSME, 46. *Prof Exp:* Engr, Bur Reclamation, 46-47, & Hanford Atomic Proj Opers, 47, Gen Elec Co, 47-64, proj engr, 47-56, supvr proj engr, 56-59, plant mgr, 59-64; asst lab dir, 65-68, DIR PROJ & FACIL, PAC NORTHWEST DIV, BATTELLE MEM INST, 68- *Res:* Nuclear reactors. *Mailing Add:* Pac Northwest Div Battelle Mem Inst PO Box 999 Richland WA 99352

RICHSTONE, DOUGLAS ORANGE, b Alexandria, Va, Sept 20, 49. ASTRONOMY. *Educ:* Calif Inst Technol, BS, 71; Princeton Univ, PhD(astrophys), 75. *Prof Exp:* Res fel astron, Calif Inst Technol, 74-76; ASST PROF PHYSICS, UNIV PITTSBURGH, 77- *Mem:* Royal Astron Soc; Am Astron Soc. *Res:* Quasi-stellar objects; structure of galaxies and clusters of galaxies; stellar dynamics. *Mailing Add:* Dept Physics & Astron Univ Pittsburgh Pittsburgh PA 15206

RICHTER, BURTON, b Brooklyn, NY, Mar 22, 31; m 60; c 2. PHYSICS. *Educ:* Mass Inst Technol, BS, 52, PhD(physics), 56. *Prof Exp:* Res assoc physics, High Energy Physics Lab, 56-59, from asst prof to assoc prof, Linear Accelerator Ctr, 59-67, PROF PHYSICS, LINEAR ACCELERATOR CTR, STANFORD UNIV, 67-, PAUL PIGOTT PROF PHYSICS SCI, 79- *Concurrent Pos:* Consult, Dept of Energy, NSF. *Honors & Awards:* E O Lawrence Medal, 75; Nobel Prize (physics-shared), 76. *Mem:* Nat Acad Sci; fel AAAS; fel Am Phys Soc. *Res:* High energy physics; particle accelerators. *Mailing Add:* Stanford Linear Accelerator Ctr Stanford Univ Stanford CA 94305

RICHTER, CURT PAUL, b Denver, Colo, Feb 20, 94; m 36; c 1. PSYCHOBIOLOGY. *Educ:* Harvard Col, BS, 17; Johns Hopkins Univ, PhD, 21. *Hon Degrees:* LLD, Johns Hopkins Univ, 70; DSc, Univ Chicago, 68; DSc, Univ Pa, 76. *Prof Exp:* Prof, 57-59, EMER PROF PSYCHOBIOL, SCH MED, JOHNS HOPKINS UNIV, 59-, DIR PSYCHOBIOL LAB, PHIPPS PSYCHIAT CLIN, 22- *Concurrent Pos:* Harvey Soc lectr, 42-43; mem comts neurol, food habits & rodent control, Off Sci Res & Develop, 42-46; Gregory lectr, 52; Salmon lectr, 59; Bailey lectr, 64, Hamilton lectr, 65. *Honors & Awards:* Warren Medal, Soc Exp Psychol, 50; Passano Award, 77; Lashley Award, Am Philos Soc, 80. *Mem:* Nat Acad Sci; Am Philos Soc; Am Acad Arts & Sci. *Res:* Animal and human behavior; biological cycles. *Mailing Add:* Johns Hopkins Hosp Baltimore MD 21205

RICHTER, DONALD, b Brooklyn, NY, Sept 3, 30; c 2. STATISTICS. *Educ:* Bowdoin Col, AB, 52; Univ N C, PhD(statist), 59. *Prof Exp:* Asst prof statist, Univ Minn, 59-61; mem tech staff, Bell Tel Labs, 61-64; assoc prof statist, 64-72, dir doctoral off, 74-76, PROF STATIST, GRAD SCH BUS ADMIN, N Y UNIV, 72- *Mem:* Am Statist Asn; Inst Mgt Sci; Inst Math Statist; fel Royal Statist Soc. *Res:* Statistical inference. *Mailing Add:* Dept of Stat Grad Sch Bus Admin New York Univ 100 Trinity Pl New York NY 10006

RICHTER, EDWARD EUGENE, b Hebron, Ill, Oct 22, 19; m 41; c 2. ORGANIC CHEMISTRY, INORGANIC CHEMISTRY. *Educ:* DePauw Univ, BA, 41. *Prof Exp:* Chemist, Jones-Dabney Co, 41-44 & Am-Marietta Co, 46-50; chief chemist, Kay & Ess Co, 50-51; tech dir & spec projs engr, Moran Paint Co, 51-60; TECH DIR & VPRES, BLATZ PAINT CO, INC, 60- *Mem:* Am Chem Soc; Fedn Socs Coatings Technol. *Res:* Protective and decorative industrial type organic coatings. *Mailing Add:* 304 Old Farm Rd Louisville KY 40207

RICHTER, ERWIN (WILLIAM), b Ironwood, Mich, Jan 29, 34. BIOCHEMISTRY. *Educ:* Northern Mich Univ, BS, 56; Univ Northern Iowa, MS, 63; Univ Iowa, PhD(biochem), 70. *Prof Exp:* High sch teacher, Mich, 56-62; instr phys sci, 63-67, asst prof chem, 70-72, ASSOC PROF CHEM, UNIV NORTHERN IOWA, 72- *Res:* Particle analysis of atmospheric pollutants; structure of proteins. *Mailing Add:* Dept of Chem Univ of Northern Iowa Cedar Falls IA 50613

RICHTER, G PAUL, b Rahway, NJ, Aug 13, 37; m 61; c 2. INORGANIC CHEMISTRY. *Educ:* Grinnell Col, BA, 59; Univ Minn, PhD(inorg chem), 68. *Prof Exp:* Asst prof, 65-59, assoc prof, 69-78, PROF CHEM, WVA WESLEYAN COL, 78- *Mem:* AAAS; Am Chem Soc; Nat Wildlife Fedn; Nat Speleological Soc. *Res:* Sulfur-nitrogen chemistry; nonmetal compounds; inorganic aquatic chemistry. *Mailing Add:* Dept of Chem W Va Wesleyan Col Buckhannon WV 26201

RICHTER, GEORGE ALVIN, JR, b Berlin, NH, Apr 22, 19; m 40; c 2. CHEMISTRY. *Educ:* Harvard Univ, BS, 40; Mass Inst Technol, MS, 42. *Prof Exp:* Res chemist & chem engr, Am Viscose Corp, 42-51; group leader, Res Div, Rohm & Haas Co, 51-57, lab head, 57-64, tech asst to vpres mkt, 64-72, asst mgr, Govt Regulatory Relations Dept, 72-77, asst mgr chem standards, 77-81; RETIRED. *Mem:* Am Chem Soc; Am Inst Chem Eng; Am Soc Test & Mats. *Res:* Cellulose; cellulose esters and xanthate; viscose; viscose spinning; preparation of cellulose derivatives with modified physical properties; cross-linking; physical properties of polymers; synthetic fibers. *Mailing Add:* Rohm & Haas Co Independence Mall W Philadelphia PA 19105

RICHTER, GEORGE NEAL, b Denver, Colo, Mar 13, 30; m 60; c 5. CHEMICAL ENGINEERING. *Educ:* Yale Univ, BE, 51; Calif Inst Technol, MS, 52, PhD(chem eng), 57. *Prof Exp:* Res fel, Calif Inst Technol, 57-58; asst prof chem eng, 58-65; sr res chem engr, 65-80, TECHNOLOGIST, TEXACO INC, MONTEBELLO, 80- *Mem:* Am Inst Chem Engrs. *Res:* Synthesis gas and hydrogen generation by partial oxidation; coal gasification and conversion; alternate energy process development and commercialization; waste treatment and environmental impact measurements. *Mailing Add:* 1470 Granada Ave San Marino CA 91108

RICHTER, GOETZ WILFRIED, b Berlin, Ger, Dec 19, 22; nat US; m 46; c 3. PATHOLOGY, CELL BIOLOGY. *Educ:* Williams Col, AB, 43; Johns Hopkins Univ, MD, 48; Am Bd Path, dipl, 53. *Prof Exp:* Instr path, Med Col, Cornell Univ, 50-51, res assoc, 51-53, from asst prof to assoc prof, 53-67; PROF PATH, UNIV ROCHESTER, 67- *Concurrent Pos:* Ledyard fel, NY Hosp & Cornell Univ, 51-53; Rockefeller Found grant, 56-61; vis investr, Rockefeller Inst, 56-57; Health Res Coun New York career scientist, 61-67; consult, NIH, 63-67; ed, Int Rev Exp Path; ed, Beitraege zur Pathologie, 71-78; path res & pract, 78- *Mem:* Electron Micros Soc Am; Soc Exp Biol & Med; Am Asn Path; Am Soc Cell Biol; Int Acad Path. *Res:* Experimental pathology; cell biology; ferritin and iron metabolism; pathology of heart muscle; lead poisoning. *Mailing Add:* Univ of Rochester Dept of Path 601 Elmwood Ave Rochester NY 14642

RICHTER, HAROLD GENE, b Fontanet, Ind, Mar 5, 25; m 54; c 4. INORGANIC CHEMISTRY. *Educ:* Franklin Col, AB, 47; Mass Inst Technol, MS, 50, PhD(inorg chem), 52. *Prof Exp:* Jr physicist, Argonne Nat Lab, 47-48; instr chem, Univ Ore, 52-54; radiochemist, US Naval Radiol Defense Lab, Calif, 54-55; asst to pres, Nuclear Sci & Eng Corp, Pa, 55-58; chief radiochemist, Res Triangle Inst, 59-71; CHEMIST, OFF AIR PROGS, ENVIRON PROTECTION AGENCY, 71- *Mem:* AAAS; Am Chem Soc. *Res:* Radiochemistry of fission products; industrial applications of isotopes; analytical chemistry; biomedical instrumentation; atmospheric chemistry; air pollution control. *Mailing Add:* Off Air Prog Environ Protection Agency Research Triangle Park NC 27711

RICHTER, HELEN WILKINSON, b Biloxi, Miss. PHYSICAL CHEMISTRY. *Educ:* Woman's Col Ga, BA, 67; Ohio State Univ, MS, 70, PhD(phys chem), 74. *Prof Exp:* Res assoc radiation chem, Brookhaven Nat Lab, Upton, NY, 74-75; res chemist, Radiation Res Labs, 76, SR RES CHEMIST, DEPT CHEM, CARNEGIE-MELLON UNIV, 76- *Concurrent Pos:* Vis res assoc & vis scientist, Radiation Lab, Univ Notre Dame, 76-79. *Mem:* Am Chem Soc. *Res:* Application of physical chemistry and radiation chemistry to the study of biochemical reaction mechanisms. *Mailing Add:* Carnegie-Mellon Univ 4400 Fifth Ave Pittsburgh PA 15213

RICHTER, HERBERT PETER, b St Paul, Minn, Jan 22, 39; m 62; c 2. PHYSICAL CHEMISTRY, POLYMER CHEMISTRY. *Educ:* San Diego State Univ, BA, 65, MS, 67. *Prof Exp:* Teaching asst & res asst, Chem Dept, San Diego State Univ, 66-67; chemist, Electronic Warfare Dept, 67-70; res chemist, 70-79, RES COORDR, POLYMER CHEM, RES DEPT, NAVAL WEAPONS CTR, 79- *Mem:* Am Chem Soc; Sigma Xi. *Res:* Polymer and surface chemistry; physical and mechanical properties of polymers; photochemistry and photophysics; chemiluminescence. *Mailing Add:* Dept of Res Naval Weapons Ctr China Lake CA 93555

RICHTER, JOHN LEWIS, b Laredo, Tex, July 26, 33; m 58; c 2. NUCLEAR PHYSICS. *Educ:* Univ Tex, Austin, BS, 54, MS, 56, PhD(physics), 58. *Prof Exp:* STAFF MEM PHYSICS, LOS ALAMOS SCI LAB, 58-, GROUP LEADER, TD-4, 78- *Mem:* Am Phys Soc. *Res:* Nuclear weapon design. *Mailing Add:* Group TD 4 MS 250 Los Alamos Sci Lab Los Alamos NM 87545

RICHTER, JUDITH ANNE, b Wilmington, Del, Mar 4, 42. NEUROPHARMACOLOGY, NEUROCHEMISTRY. *Educ:* Univ Colo, BA, 64; Stanford Univ, PhD(pharmacol), 69. *Prof Exp:* Wellcome Trust fel biochem, Cambridge Univ, 69-70 & Inst Psychiat, Univ London, 70-71; asst prof pharmacol, 71-78, ASSOC PROF PHARMACOL & NEUROBIOL, MED SCH, IND UNIV, INDIANAPOLIS, 78- *Mem:* AAAS; Am Soc Neurochem; Int Soc Neurochem; Soc Neurosci; Am Soc Pharmacol Exp Therap. *Res:* Neurotransmission, especially cholinergic in central nervous system; mechanism of action of barbiturates. *Mailing Add:* Inst Psychiat Res Ind Univ Med Sch Indianapolis IN 46202

RICHTER, MAXWELL, b Montreal, Que, June 11, 33; m 58; c 2. IMMUNOLOGY, PATHOLOGY. *Educ:* McGill Univ, BSc, 54, PhD(biochem), 58, MD, 64. *Prof Exp:* From asst prof to assoc prof exp med, McGill Univ, 58-72; assoc prof immunol & allergy, 70-72; PROF PATH, UNIV OTTAWA, 72- *Concurrent Pos:* Mem staff, Dept Immunol & Allergy, Royal Victoria Hosp, Montreal, 68-; Med Res Coun scholar immunol, Univ Ottawa Clin, Victoria Hosp, 70- *Mem:* Am Acad Allergy; Am Asn Immunol; NY Acad Sci; Brit Soc Immunol; Can Soc Immunol. *Res:* Immunopathology. *Mailing Add:* Dept of Path Univ of Ottawa Ottawa ON K1N 6N5 Can

RICHTER, RAYMOND C, b Riverside, Calif, Apr 17, 18; m 40; c 3. GEOLOGY. *Educ:* Univ Calif, BA, 40, BS, 42. *Prof Exp:* Supv eng geologist, Calif Dept Water Resources, 46-66, staff geologist, Resources Agency, 66-75; CONSULT GEOLOGIST, 76- *Mem:* Geol Soc Am; Asn Eng Geologists. *Res:* Engineering geology; ground water geology. *Mailing Add:* 18309 S Van Allen Rd Escalon CA 95320

RICHTER, REINHARD HANS, b Reinswalde, Ger, Oct 3, 37; m 65. ORGANIC CHEMISTRY. *Educ:* Univ Tübingen, BS, 60; Stuttgart Tech Univ, MS, 62, PhD(org chem), 65. *Prof Exp:* NIH fel, Mellon Inst, 65-68; STAFF SCIENTIST, DONALD S GILMORE RES LABS, UPJOHN CO, 68- *Mem:* Am Chem Soc; Ger Chem Soc. *Res:* Organic synthesis; heterocycles; isocyanates; nitrile oxides. *Mailing Add:* Donald S Gilmore Res Labs Upjohn Co North Haven CT 06473

RICHTER, ROBERT FREELAND, industrial organic chemistry, see previous edition

RICHTER, STEPHEN L(AWRENCE), b Brooklyn, NY, Dec 29, 42; m 62. ELECTRICAL ENGINEERING. *Educ:* Columbia Univ, BS, 63, MS, 64, PhD(electromagnetic theory), 67. *Prof Exp:* Res asst elec eng, Columbia Univ, 63-66, preceptor, 66-67; asst prof, 67-68; res scientist, 68; asst prof, City Col New York, 68-71; sr engr, 71-73, PRIN ENGR, RAYTHEON CO, 73- *Concurrent Pos:* Consult, 64-67 & 70; reviewer proceedings, Inst Elec & Electronics Engrs, 68- *Mem:* Inst Elec & Electronics Engrs; Am Phys Soc; NY Acad Sci; Sigma Xi. *Res:* Systems analysis; signal processing; communication and information theory; radar; electronic-counter-counter-measures; software requirements; optical processing; stochastic processes; digital processing and computation; image processing; numerical methods; electromagnetic wave propagation; guided waves and antennas; applied mathematics and physics. *Mailing Add:* Raytheon Co Hartwell Rd Bedford MA 01730

RICHTER, WARD ROBERT, b Union Grove, Wis, Feb 27, 30; m 54; c 3. PATHOLOGY, ELECTRON MICROSCOPY. *Educ:* Iowa State Univ, DVM, 55, MS, 62. *Prof Exp:* Instr vet path, Iowa State Univ, 57-60; chief cellular path, US Army Med Res Lab, Ft Knox, Ky, 60-63; res assoc path, Univ Louisville, 61-63; head cellular path & electron micros, Abbott Labs, 63-68; assoc prof, 68-77, PROF COMP PATH & DIR RES FACIL, UNIV CHICAGO, 77- *Concurrent Pos:* Assoc prof, Iowa State Univ, 64-; dep dir, A J Carlson Animal Res Facil, Univ Chicago; consult, Argonne Nat Lab, US Dept Health, Educ & Welfare & Univs Assoc for Res & Educ in Path. *Mem:* Am Vet Med Asn; Am Col Vet Path; Int Acad Pathologists. *Res:* Electron microscopy applied to study of drug toxicity, drug action and laboratory animal diseases; cell biology; pathology of trauma and subcellular injury produced by physical environmental alterations. *Mailing Add:* A J Carleson Animal Res Facil Univ of Chicago Chicago IL 60637

RICHTER, WAYNE H, b New York, NY, June 7, 36; c 1. MATHEMATICS. *Educ:* Swarthmore Col, AB, 58; Princeton Univ, MA, 60, PhD(math), 63. *Prof Exp:* From instr to asst prof math, Rutgers Univ, 61-69; ASSOC PROF MATH, UNIV MINN, MINNEAPOLIS, 69- *Concurrent Pos:* Fac fel, Rutgers Univ, 64-65; NSF res grant, 66-68 & 70-75. *Mem:* Am Math Soc; Asn Symbolic Logic. *Res:* Theory of recursive functions; mathematical logic. *Mailing Add:* Dept of Math Univ of Minn Minneapolis MN 55455

RICHTERS, ARNIS, b Sauka, Latvia, Sept 23, 28; US citizen; c 1. EXPERIMENTAL PATHOLOGY. *Educ:* Univ Ariz, BS, 57, MS, 59; Univ Southern Calif, PhD(exp path), 67. *Prof Exp:* From instr to asst prof, 68-75, ASSOC PROF PATH, SCH MED, UNIV SOUTHERN CALIF, 75- *Concurrent Pos:* Site vis, Breast Cancer Task Force, Nat Cancer Inst, 72; reviewer, Monroe County Cancer & Leukemia Asn, 73- *Mem:* Tissue Cult Asn; Int Acad Path; AAAS; Am Soc Exp Path. *Res:* Correlation of in vivo and in vitro behavior of cancer and the lymphocyte responses in cancer draining lymph nodes; ultrastructure of lymphocyte-target cell interactions; air pollution and health. *Mailing Add:* 2205 Tall Pine Dr Duarte CA 91010

RICHTOL, HERBERT H, b New York, NY, Aug 3, 32; m 56; c 4. ANALYTICAL CHEMISTRY, PHOTOCHEMISTRY. *Educ:* St Lawrence Univ, BS, 54; NY Univ, PhD(chem), 61. *Prof Exp:* Instr chem, NY Univ, 60-61; from asst prof to assoc prof, 61-74, PROF CHEM, RENSSELAER POLYTECH INST, 74- *Mem:* AAAS; Am Chem Soc. *Res:* Photoelectrochemistry; luminescence; liquid crystals. *Mailing Add:* Dept of Chem Rensselaer Polytech Inst Troy NY 12181

RICHWINE, JOHN ROBERT, rubber chemistry, organic chemistry, see previous edition

RICK, CHARLES MADEIRA, JR, b Reading, Pa, Apr 30, 15; m 38; c 2. CYTOGENETICS, EVOLUTION. *Educ:* Pa State Col, BS, 37; Harvard Univ, AM, 38, PhD(genetics), 40. *Prof Exp:* Tech asst, Harvard Univ, 38; instr & jr geneticist, 40-44, asst prof & asst geneticist, 44-49, assoc prof & assoc geneticist, 49-55, PROF VEG CROPS & GENETICIST, UNIV CALIF, DAVIS, EXP STA, 55- *Concurrent Pos:* Guggenheim fel, 49, 51; Rockefeller res fel, 56-57; vis lectr, N C State Col, 56; fac res lectr, Univ Calif, 61; Carnegie vis prof, Univ Hawaii, 63; mem, Galapagos Int Sci Proj, 64; lectr, Univ Sao Paulo, 65; vis scientist, Univ P R, 68; centennial lectr, Ont Agr Col, Univ Guelph, 74; adj prof, Univ Rosario, Argentina, 80. *Honors & Awards:* Vaughan Award, Am Soc Hort Sci, 45; Campbell Award, AAAS, 59; M A Blake Award, Am Soc Hort Sci, 74. *Mem:* Nat Acad Sci; AAAS; Am Soc Nat; Genetics Soc Am; Bot Soc Am. *Res:* Natural relationships amongst the tomato, Lycopersicon, species are investigated via cytology, incompatibility, hybrid fertility, and genetic variability, including isozymes. *Mailing Add:* Dept Veg Crops Univ of Calif Davis CA 95616

RICK, CHRISTIAN E(DWARD), b Kansas City, Mo, Oct 9, 13; m 38. CHEMICAL ENGINEERING. *Educ:* Univ Kans, BS, 36; Univ Del, MS, 44. *Prof Exp:* Res chemist, Pigments Dept, E I du Pont de Nemours & Co, Inc, 36-58, res supvr, Staff Sect, 58-78; RETIRED. *Honors & Awards:* Citation, Off Sci Res & Develop, 45. *Mem:* Am Chem Soc. *Res:* Engineering economics; titanium metal, compounds and minerals; germanium, silicon and boron semiconductors; oxide ceramics and refractories; instruments; electronics; computers. *Mailing Add:* 1903 Greenhill Ave Wilmington DE 19806

RICKARD, CORWIN LLOYD, b Medina, Ohio, Sept, 26, 26; m 48; c 2. NUCLEAR ENGINEERING, HEAT TRANSFER. *Educ:* Univ Rochester, BS, 47, MS, 49; Cornell Univ, PhD(eng, math), 61. *Prof Exp:* Asst eng, Univ Rochester, 47-48, instr, 48-49, asst prof, 49-52; instr, Cornell Univ, 52-54; nuclear engr, Brookhaven Nat Lab, 54-56; res staff mem nuclear eng, Gen Atomic Div, Gen Dynamics Corp, 56-66, vpres, Gulf Gen Atomic Inc, 67-77, EXEC V PRES, GEN ATOMIC CO, 77- *Concurrent Pos:* Consult, Brookhaven Nat Lab, 49, Worthington Corp, NY, 50, Boeing Aircraft Co, Wash, 51, Adv Electronic Res Lab, Gen Elec Co, 53-54. *Mem:* Am Nuclear Soc (vpres, 80-81, pres, 81-82); Am Soc Mech Engrs; AAAS. *Res:* Thermodynamics; gas cooled nuclear reactor core and plant development, design and engineering; nuclear power plant economics and fuel cycles. *Mailing Add:* Gen Atomic Co PO Box 81608 San Diego CA 92138

RICKARD, DAVID ALAN, plant nematology, see previous edition

RICKARD, EUGENE CLARK, b Wichita, Kans, Oct 19, 43; m 70. ANALYTICAL CHEMISTRY. *Educ:* Wichita State Univ, BS, 65, MS, 67; Univ Wis-Madison, PhD(anal chem), 72. *Prof Exp:* Lectr anal chem, Univ Wis-Madison, 70-71; sr chemist, 71-76, RES SCIENTIST, ELI LILLY & CO, 77- *Mem:* Am Chem Soc; Sigma Xi. *Res:* Electroanalytical chemistry, especially the mechanism of electron transfer at electrodes, double layer properties, influence of potential gradients on electron transfer and homogeneous kinetic mechanisms involving electroactive species. *Mailing Add:* Dept M-769 Eli Lilly & Co 307 E McCarty St Indianapolis IN 46285

RICKARD, JAMES ALEXANDER, b Austin, Tex, July 9, 26; m 52; c 2. PHYSICS. *Educ:* Tex A&I Univ, BS & MS, 48; Univ Tex, PhD(physics), 54. *Prof Exp:* Res engr, Houston Res Lab, Humble Oil & Ref Co, 53-62, res mgr, Esso Prod Res Co, Tex, 63-71, sr adv, Exxon Corp, 71-76, PLANNING MGR, EXXON PROD RES CO, 76- *Mem:* Am Phys Soc; Marine Technol Soc (pres, 77-78); Am Inst Mining, Metall & Petrol Eng; Soc Naval Architects & Marine Engrs. *Res:* Petroleum; ocean engineering. *Mailing Add:* Exxon Prod Res Co Box 2189 Houston TX 77001

RICKARD, JAMES JOSEPH, b Seattle, Wash, Sept 20, 40; m 63. ASTRONOMY, COMPUTER SCIENCE. *Educ:* San Jose State Univ, BA, 62; Univ Md, MS, 65, PhD(astron), 67. *Prof Exp:* Teaching asst astron, Univ Md, 62-64, res asst radio astron, 64-67, res fel, 67-68; res fel astron, Calif Inst Technol-Hale Observ, 68-69; staff astronomer, Europ Southern Observ, 69-76; res scientist astron, Univ Iowa, 77-80; PARTNER/OWNER, BORREGO SOLAR SYSTS, 80-; SOLAR ASTRONR, UNIV MD CLRO, 82- *Concurrent Pos:* Earth resources consult, Terra Inst, 76- *Mem:* Am Astron Soc; Int Astron Union. *Res:* Galactic structure; physics of the interstellar medium; instrumentation; computer systems design; extragalactic radio sources. *Mailing Add:* PO Box 128 Borrego Springs CA 92004

RICKARD, JOHN TERRELL, b Humboldt, Tenn, Sept 17, 47; m 71; c 2. SIGNAL PROCESSING, INFORMATION THEORY. *Educ:* Fla Inst Technol, BS, 69, MS, 71; Univ Calif, San Diego, PhD(eng physics), 75. *Prof Exp:* Electronics engr, Harris Corp, Melbourne, Fla, 69-71; sr prin engr, 75-80, VPRES, ORINCON CORP, 80- *Mem:* Inst Elec & Electronics Engrs. *Res:* Random processes; adaptive signal processing; detection theory. *Mailing Add:* Orincon Corp 3366 N Torrey Pines Ct Suite 320 La Jolla CA 92037

RICKARD, LAWRENCE VROMAN, b Cobleskill, NY, July 10, 26; m 52; c 5. PALEONTOLOGY, STRATIGRAPHY. *Educ:* Cornell Univ, BA, 51, PhD(geol), 55; Univ Rochester, MS, 53. *Prof Exp:* Asst prof geol, St Lawrence Univ, 55-56; sr paleontologist, 56-73, assoc paleontologist, 73-77, PRIN PALEONTOLOGIST, MUS & SCI SERV, STATE GEOL SURV, NY, 77- *Concurrent Pos:* Mem, Paleont Res Inst. *Mem:* Geol Soc Am; Paleont Soc. *Res:* Stratigraphy and paleontology of the Silurian and Devonian rocks of New York. *Mailing Add:* Rm 3140 NY State Mus Cult Educ Ctr Albany NY 12230

RICKARD, LEE J, b Miami, Fla, Dec 24, 49; m 72. ASTROPHYSICS, RADIO ASTRONOMY. *Educ:* Univ Miami, BS, 69; Univ Chicago, MS, 72, PhD(astrophysics), 75. *Prof Exp:* Res assoc, Nat Radio Astron Observ, 75-77, asst scientist, 77-79, assoc scientist, 79-80; ASST PROF, DEPT PHYSICS & ASTRON, HOWARD UNIV, 80- *Mem:* Am Astron Soc; Int Astron Union. *Res:* Radio spectroscopy, specifically interstellar molecules, molecular constituents of galaxies, interstellar masers and atomic recombination lines; problems of active galactic nuclei. *Mailing Add:* Dept Physics & Astron Howard Univ Washington DC 20059

RICKARD, WILLIAM HOWARD, JR, b Walsenburg, Colo, May 15, 26; m 53; c 1. BOTANY. *Educ:* Univ Colo, BA, 50, MA, 53; Wash State Univ, PhD(bot), 57. *Prof Exp:* Asst prof bot, N Mex Highlands Univ, 57-60; biol scientist, Hanford Atomic Prod Opers, Gen Elec Co, 60-65; SR RES SCIENTIST, ECOL DEPT, PAC NORTHWEST LAB, BATTELLE MEM INST, 65- *Mem:* AAAS; Ecol Soc Am; Soc Range Mgt; Northwest Sci Asn. *Res:* Plant ecology; fate and behavior of trace elements and radionuclides in terrestrial ecosystems; primary productivity and mineral cycling in shrub steppe ecosystems. *Mailing Add:* 1904 Lassen Ave Richland WA 99352

RICKART, CHARLES EARL, b Osage City, Kans, June 28, 13; m 42; c 3. MATHEMATICS. *Educ:* Univ Kans, BA, 37, MA, 38; Univ Mich, PhD(math), 41. *Hon Degrees:* MA, Yale Univ, 59. *Prof Exp:* Peirce instr & tutor math, Harvard Univ, 41-43; from instr to assoc prof, 43-59, chmn dept, 59-65, PROF MATH, YALE UNIV, 59- *Mem:* AAAS; Am Math Soc; Math Asn Am. *Res:* Functional analysis; theory of Banach algebras; function algebras. *Mailing Add:* Dept of Math Yale Univ New Haven CT 06520

RICKBORN, BRUCE FREDERICK, b New Brunswick, NJ, Feb 23, 35; m 55; c 1. ORGANIC CHEMISTRY. *Educ:* Univ Calif, Riverside, BA, 56; Univ Calif, Los Angeles, PhD(chem), 60. *Prof Exp:* Asst prof chem, Univ Calif, Berkeley, 60-62; from asst prof to assoc prof, 62-71, provost, Col Creative Studies, 69-71, PROF CHEM, UNIV CALIF, SANTA BARBARA, 71- *Concurrent Pos:* NSF sr fel, 66-67; Alfred P Sloan fel, 67-69; Fulbright sr lectr, Bogata, Columbia, 70; assoc dean, Col Letters & Sci, Univ Calif, Santa Barbara, 71-73, dean, 73-78. *Mem:* Am Chem Soc; AAAS; Sigma Xi. *Res:* Mechanism and stereochemistry of small ring forming and opening reactions; organometallics; conformational analysis; photochemistry; hydride reduction; strong base induced reactions. *Mailing Add:* Dept of Chem Univ of Calif Santa Barbara CA 93106

RICKELS, KARL, b Wilhelmshaven, Ger, Aug 17, 24; US citizen; m 64; c 3. PSYCHIATRY, PSYCHOPHARMACOLOGY. *Educ:* Univ Munster, MD, 51. *Prof Exp:* PROF PSYCHIAT & PHARMACOL, UNIV PA, 69-, STUART & EMILY MUDD PROF HUMAN BEHAV IN REPROD, 77- *Concurrent Pos:* Dir psychopharmacol res, Univ Pa, 64-; chmn, OTC Sedatives, Tranquilizers and Sleep Aids Rev Panel, Food & Drug Admin, 72-75; chief psychiat, Phildelphia Gen Hosp, 75-77. *Mem:* Fel Acad Psychosom Med; fel Am Soc Clin Pharmacol & Therapeut; fel Am Col Neuropsychopharmacol; fel Am Psychiat Asn; fel Int Col Neuropsychopharmacol. *Res:* Clinical psychopharmacology; evaluation of psychotropic drugs in anxiety, depression and insomnia; study of the role of non-specific factors in drug and placebo response; assessment of emotional symptoms in various family practice and OB-GYN patients and their response to stress and hormonal treatment. *Mailing Add:* 203 Piersol Bldg Univ Hosp 3600 Spruce St Philadelphia PA 19104

RICKENBERG, HOWARD V, b Nuremberg, Ger, Feb 3, 22; nat US; m 53; c 3. DEVELOPMENTAL BIOLOGY. *Educ:* Cornell Univ, BS, 50; Yale Univ, PhD(microbiol), 54. *Prof Exp:* Am Cancer Soc fel, Pasteur Inst, Paris, 54-55 & Nat Inst Med Res, Eng, 55-56; from instr to asst prof microbiol, Univ Wash, 56-60; assoc prof bact, Ind Univ, 61-63, prof bact, 63-66; prof microbiol, 66-71, PROF BIOPHYS & GENETICS, SCH MED, UNIV COLO, DENVER, 71-; dir div, 66-80, CHMN DEPT, DIV MOLECULAR & CELLULAR BIOL, NAT JEWISH HOSP & RES CTR, 80- *Concurrent Pos:* Ida & Cecil Green investigatorship develop biochem, 75- *Mem:* Am Soc Microbiol; Am Soc Biol Chem; Soc Gen Physiol. *Res:* Gene-enzyme relationships and differentiation. *Mailing Add:* Div Molecular & Cellular Biol Nat Jewish Hosp & Res Ctr Denver CO 80206

RICKER, NEIL LAWRENCE, b Stambaugh, Mich, Oct 15, 48; m 71. CHEMICAL ENGINEERING. *Educ:* Univ Mich, Ann Arbor, BS, 70; Univ Calif, Berkeley, MS, 72, PhD(chem eng), 78. *Prof Exp:* Sci systs analyst, Air Prod & Chem, Inc, 72-75; ASST PROF CHEM ENG, UNIV WASH, 78- *Mem:* Am Inst Chem Engrs. *Res:* Wastewater treatment by physical and chemical methods; chemical process analysis and conceptual design; phase-equilibrium thermodynamics; process dynamics and control. *Mailing Add:* Dept Chem Eng BF-10 Univ Wash Seattle WA 98195

RICKER, RICHARD W(ILSON), b Galion, Ohio, Mar 30, 14; m 44; c 5. CERAMICS ENGINEERING. *Educ:* Alfred Univ, BS, 34; Pa State Col, MS, 50, PhD(ceramics), 52. *Prof Exp:* Mem staff res & develop, Libbey-Owens-Ford Glass Co, 34-48; res assoc, Pa State Col, 48-52; res engr, Alcoa Res Labs, Aluminum Co Am, 52-55, asst chief process metall div, 55-60; asst dir res, Ferro Corp, 60-66; tech dir ceramics, Harshaw Chem Co, 66-71; CERAMIC CONSULT, 71- *Concurrent Pos:* Consult refractories & whitewares projs, South Korea, Turkey, Mexico, Columbia, Brazil & Egypt. *Mem:* Fel Am Ceramic Soc; Sigma Xi; Nat Inst Ceramic Engrs. *Res:* Phase equilibria; refractories; porcelain enamel; ceramic color pigments; whitewares. *Mailing Add:* 5373 NE Sixth Ave Ft Lauderdale FL 33334

RICKERT, DAVID A, b Trenton, NJ, Mar 14, 40; m 62; c 3. ENVIRONMENTAL SCIENCES. *Educ:* Rutgers Univ, BS, 62, MS, 65, PhD(environ sci), 69. *Prof Exp:* Chemist urban hydrol prog, 69-72, res hydrologist, chief, Willamette River Basin Study, 72-75, res hydrologist, chief, Land-Use-River Qual Study, Water Resources Div, 75-77, chief, Ore 208 Assessment, Ore Dept Environ Qual, 77-79, coordr, River Qual Assessment Prog, 79-80, SR STAFF SCIENTIST, WATER RESOURCES DIV, US GEOL SURV, 80- *Concurrent Pos:* Vpres, Am Water Resources Asn, 82-; secy, Water Qual Comn, Int Asn Hydrological Sci, 81- *Honors & Awards:* W R Boggess Award, Am Water Resources Asn, 74. *Mem:* Sigma Xi; AAAS; Int Asn Hydrological Sci; Am Chem Soc; Am Water Resources Asn. *Res:* Development and implementation of large-scale interdisciplinary programs for land and water-resources assessment; environmental chemistry and biology; applied hydrology; environmental geology; land-use analysis. *Mailing Add:* Sr Staff Scientist US Geol Surv Reston VA 22090

RICKERT, DOUGLAS EDWARD, b Sioux City, Iowa, Jan 27, 46; m 81. TOXICOLOGY, PHARMACOLOGY. *Educ:* Univ Iowa, BS, 68, MS, 72, PhD(pharmacol), 74; Am Bd Toxicol, dipl, 80. *Prof Exp:* Asst prof pharmacol, Mich State Univ, 74-77; ANAL BIOCHEMIST, CHEM INDUST INST TOXICOL, 77- *Mem:* AAAS; Soc Toxicol; Am Soc Pharmacol & Exp Therapeut; Am Soc Mass Spectros. *Res:* Biological disposition of foreign compounds and their toxicity. *Mailing Add:* Chem Indust Inst Toxicol PO Box 12137 Research Triangle Park NC 27709

RICKERT, NEIL WILLIAM, b Perth, Australia, June 2, 39; m 65; c 2. MATHEMATICS. *Educ:* Univ Western Australia, BSc, 62; Yale Univ, PhD(math), 65. *Prof Exp:* From instr to asst prof math, Yale Univ, 65-68; ASSOC PROF MATH, UNIV ILL, CHICAGO CIRCLE, 68- *Concurrent Pos:* Mem, Inst Advan Study, 66-67. *Mem:* Am Math Soc. *Res:* Analysis; functional and harmonic analysis. *Mailing Add:* Dept of Math Univ Ill Chicago Circle Box 4348 Chicago IL 60680

RICKERT, RUSSELL KENNETH, b Chalfont, Pa, Feb 6, 26; m 49; c 3. PHYSICS. *Educ:* West Chester State Col, BS, 50; Univ Del, MS, 53; NY Univ, EdD(sci ed), 61. *Prof Exp:* Teacher high sch, Md, 50-52 & Del, 52-55; instr phys sci, Salisbury State Col, 55-56; from asst prof to prof phys sci, 56-74, chmn dept sci, 64-68, dean, Sch Sci & Math, 69-79, PROF PHYSICS, WEST CHESTER STATE COL, 74- *Mem:* AAAS; Am Asn Physics Teachers. *Res:* Physics teaching, especially the development of physical science courses for students who are not science majors; aerospace science education; solar energy research and development. *Mailing Add:* Dept Physics West Chester State Col West Chester PA 19380

RICKETT, FREDERIC LAWRENCE, b Woodridge, NJ, Mar 11, 39; m 63; c 2. BIOCHEMISTRY. *Educ:* Pa State Univ, BS, 61, MS, 63, PhD, 66. *Prof Exp:* Instr biochem, Pa State Univ, 63-66; res assoc, 66-74, SR RES ASSOC ANAL BIOCHEM, DEPT RES & DEVELOP, AM TOBACCO CO, 74- *Mem:* AAAS; Am Chem Soc; Am Oil Chem Soc. *Res:* Analytical methodology for lipids and other plant constituents, tobacco and tobacco smoke, flavoring agents; pesticide analysis and process development. *Mailing Add:* Dept of Res & Develop Am Tobacco Co PO Box 899 Hopewell VA 23860

RICKETTS, GARY EUGENE, b Willard, Ohio, Aug 2, 35; m 58; c 3. ANIMAL SCIENCE. *Educ:* Ohio State Univ, BS, 57, MS, 60, PhD(animal sci), 63. *Prof Exp:* LIVESTOCK EXTEN SPECIALIST SHEEP & BEEF CATTLE, UNIV ILL, URBANA, 64- *Mem:* Am Soc Animal Sci. *Mailing Add:* 326 Mumford Hall Univ Ill 1301 W Gregory Dr Urbana IL 61801

RICKETTS, JOHN ADRIAN, b Lakewood, Ohio, Feb 29, 24; m 48; c 2. PHYSICAL CHEMISTRY. *Educ:* Ind Univ, BS, 48; Western Reserve Univ, MS, 50, PhD(chem), 53. *Prof Exp:* Lectr, Fenn Col, 51; from asst prof to assoc prof, 52-62, dir grad studies, 66-69, PROF CHEM, DePAUW UNIV, 62- *Mem:* Am Chem Soc; Royal Soc Chem. *Res:* Electrochemistry; thermodynamics, chemical kinetics. *Mailing Add:* Dept of Chem DePauw Univ Greencastle IN 46135

RICKEY, FRANK ATKINSON, JR, b Baton Rouge, La, Nov 21, 38; m 62; c 2. NUCLEAR PHYSICS. *Educ:* La State Univ, Baton Rouge, BS, 60; Fla State Univ, PhD(physics), 66. *Prof Exp:* Res assoc nuclear physics, Los Alamos Sci Lab, 66-68; asst prof, 68-76 ASSOC PROF NUCLEAR PHYSICS, PURDUE UNIV, LAFAYETTE, 76- *Mem:* Am Phys Soc. *Res:* Low energy nuclear physics; charged particle reactions; nuclear structure. *Mailing Add:* Dept of Physics Purdue Univ Lafayette IN 47907

RICKEY, MARTIN EUGENE, b Memphis, Tenn, Aug 4, 27; c 3. NUCLEAR PHYSICS, MUSICAL ACOUSTICS. *Educ:* Southwestern at Memphis, BS, 49; Univ Wash, PhD(physics), 58. *Prof Exp:* From asst prof to assoc prof physics, Univ Colo, 58-65; assoc prof, 65-68, PROF PHYSICS, IND UNIV, 68- *Concurrent Pos:* Vis staff mem, Los Alamos Sci Lab, 69-; consult, Brookhaven Nat Lab, 71-72 & Hahn-Meitner Inst, Berlin, 72- *Honors & Awards:* Sr Scientist Award, Alexander von Humboldt Found, WGer, 75. *Mem:* Fel Am Phys Soc. *Res:* Cyclotron design and development; nuclear reactions at low and intermediate energies; acoustical properties of musical instruments. *Mailing Add:* Dept of Physics Ind Univ Bloomington IN 47401

RICKLEFS, ROBERT ERIC, b San Francisco, Calif, June 6, 43. ECOLOGY. *Educ:* Stanford Univ, AB, 63; Univ Pa, PhD(biol), 67. *Prof Exp:* Nat Res Coun vis res assoc, Smithsonian Trop Res Inst, 67-68; asst prof, 68-72, assoc prof, 72-80, PROF BIOL, UNIV PA, 80- *Mem:* Soc Study Evolution; Am Soc Naturalists; Ecol Soc Am; Am Ornithologists Union; Cooper Ornith Soc. *Res:* Evolutionary ecology; development and reproductive biology of birds; population and community ecology. *Mailing Add:* Dept of Biol Univ of Pa Philadelphia PA 19174

RICKLES, FREDERICK R, b Chicago, Ill, Sept 24, 42; m 64; c 2. HEMATOLOGY. *Educ:* Col Med, Univ Ill, MD, 67. *Prof Exp:* Intern & resident internal med, Univ Rochester-Strong Mem Hosp, 67-70, fel hemat, 70-71; dir coagulation res lab, Walter Reed Army Inst Res, 71-74; asst prof, 74-77, ASSOC PROF MED, UNIV CONN, 77-, CO-CHIEF, DIV HEMATOL-ONCOL, SCH MED, 81- *Concurrent Pos:* Clin asst prof med, George Washington Univ, 71-74; attend physician, Walter Reed Army Med Ctr, 71-74 & John Dempsey-Univ Conn Hosp, 74-; chief hemat sect, Vet Admin Hosp, Newington, Conn, 74-, chief hematol-oncol sect, 81-; consult, Artificial Kidney-Chronic Uremia Prog, Nat Inst Arthritis, Metab & Digestive Dis-NIH, 74-78; Vet Admin res grant, 74-; Nat Cancer Inst-NIH grant, 78; Nat Heart, Lung & Blood Inst-NIH grant, 78; med res serv assoc chief staff, Vet Admin Hosp, Newington, Conn, 78-81. *Mem:* AAAS; Am Fedn Clin Res; Am Asn Immunologists; Am Soc Hemat; Int Soc Thrombosis & Hemostasis. *Res:* Blood coagulation; cancer; delayed hypersensitivity; endotoxin biochemistry; membrane proteins. *Mailing Add:* Vet Admin Hosp Bldg S 555 Willard Ave Newington CT 06111

RICKLES, NORMAN HAROLD, b Seattle, Wash, May 8, 20; m 50; c 3. ORAL PATHOLOGY. *Educ:* Wash Univ, DDS, 47; Univ Calif, MS, 51. *Prof Exp:* Instr dent med, Col Dent, Univ Calif, 47-48, lectr, 48-52, asst clin prof, 52-56; assoc prof, 56-60, PROF DENT, DENT SCH, UNIV ORE, 60-, HEAD DEPT ORAL PATH, 56- *Concurrent Pos:* Fel, Armed Forces Inst Path, 54-56; consult to Surgeon Gen, Madigan Army Hosp, Ft Lewis, Wash, 58-; Fulbright prof, Sch Dent Med, Hebrew Univ, Israel, 66-67; sabbatical vis prof & consult, Guys Hosp, London, 77-78. *Mem:* Am Soc Clin Path; Am Dent Asn; Am Acad Oral Med; Am Acad Oral Path (pres, 62-63); Int Acad

Path. *Res:* Dental caries; allergy; methods of teaching dental students; screening tests for dental patients; histochemistry and methods of evaluation of oral disease; fluorescent microscopy; transplantation of dental pulp. *Mailing Add:* Dept of Dent Univ of Ore Portland OR 97201

RICKLIN, SAUL, b New York, NY, Sept 5, 19; m 47. CHEMICAL ENGINEERING. *Educ:* Columbia Univ, BS, 39, ChE, 40. *Prof Exp:* Process engr, Metal & Thermit Corp, NJ, 40-46; consult engr, 46-47; asst prof chem, Brown Univ, 47-54; consult engr, Ricklin Res Assocs, 54-59; vpres, Dixon Corp, 59-66, exec vpres, 66-70, pres, 70-77, CHMN, DIXON INDUSTS CORP, 77- *Concurrent Pos:* Dir, NTN Rulon Industs Co, Ltd, Japan, 66-; vpres, Valflon, SpA, Italy, 71-; vpres, G D Spencer Co, Ltd, Can, 71-; dir, Entwistle Corp, 76-, EFO Corp. *Mem:* AAAS; Soc Plastics Indust; Am Chem Soc; Electrochem Soc; Am Inst Chem Engrs. *Res:* Thermit reactions; aluminothermics; incendiaries; tracer ammunition; ceramic materials; metal organics; fine particle technology; electroplating; metal finishing; corrosion; friction and wear of dry bearings; fluorocarbon plastics. *Mailing Add:* Dixon Industs Corp Bristol RI 02809

RICKMAN, RONALD WAYNE, b Pomeroy, Wash, June 28, 40; m 63; c 3. SOIL CONSERVATION. *Educ:* Wash State Univ, BS, 63; Univ Calif, Riverside, PhD(soil physics), 66. *Prof Exp:* SOIL SCIENTIST, SCI & EDUC ADMIN-AGR RES, USDA, 66- *Mem:* Am Soc Agron; Am Soc Agr Engrs; Sigma Xi. *Res:* Dryland small grain growth simulation; wheat root growth and water use; water conservation; wheat production. *Mailing Add:* Sci & Educ Admin-Agr Res USDA Box 370 Pendleton OR 97801

RICKMERS, ALBERT D, b Benton, Pa, June 29, 23; m 45; c 4. APPLIED STATISTICS, PHOTOGRAPHY. *Educ:* Bloomsburg State Col, BS, 48; St Bonaventure Univ, MEd, 50; Rochester Inst Technol, MS, 69. *Prof Exp:* Teacher pub sch, 48-55; instr photog math, Rochester Inst Technol, 55-58, assoc prof photog sci, 58-66, prof, 66-81; CONSULT, 81- *Concurrent Pos:* Consult, Aerospace Corp, Calif, 62-64; R S T Assocs, NY, 62-80, Data Corp, Ohio, 64-80, Lord Corp, Pa, S C Johnson & Son Inc, Wis, Xerox Corp, Hershey Foods, Rogers Corp & Nimslo Corp. *Mem:* AAAS; Am Soc Qual Control; Am Statist Asn. *Res:* Imaging systems and evaluation; physical optics; statistical quality control. *Mailing Add:* 15 Emerald Course Ocala FL 32672

RICKOVER, HYMAN GEORGE, b Jan 27, 1900; m 72, 74; c 1. ELECTRICAL ENGINEERING. *Educ:* US Naval Acad, BS, 22; US Naval Postgrad Sch, MS, 29. *Prof Exp:* From comdg ensign to admiral, US Navy, 22-73; DIR DIV NAVAL REACTORS, ERDA, 73- *Concurrent Pos:* Head elec sect, Bur Ships, Dept Navy, Washington, DC, 39-45; mem staff atomic submarine proj, AEC, Oak Ridge, 46; dep comdr nuclear propulsion, Naval Sea Systs Command. *Honors & Awards:* Spec Gold Medal, US Cong, 59; Enrico Fermi Award, AEC, 65; numerous mil honors & awards. *Res:* Developed and constructed world's first atomic submarine. *Mailing Add:* US Energy Res & Develop Admin Washington DC 20545

RICKS, BEVERLY LEE, b Grand Chenier, La, Oct 10, 28; m 51; c 2. PHYSIOLOGY, ZOOLOGY. *Educ:* Miss State Univ, BS, 50, PhD(physiol), 69; Miss Col, MS, 53. *Prof Exp:* Teacher high schs, Miss, 51-65; asst prof, 65-70, ASSOC PROF BIOL, NORTHEAST LA UNIV, 70- *Honors & Awards:* OBTA Award, Nat Asn Biol Teachers, 63. *Mem:* Nat Asn Biol Teachers; Am Inst Biol Sci; Entom Soc Am. *Res:* Feeding preferences; seasonal changes in stored nutrients; distribution of digestive enzymes in the imported fire ant. *Mailing Add:* Dept of Biol Northeast La Univ 4001 De Saird Rd Monroe LA 71201

RICKSECKER, RALPH E, b Cleveland, Ohio, Sept 9, 12; m 38; c 2. CHEMICAL METALLURGY, METALLURGICAL ENGINEERING. *Educ:* Western Reserve Univ, BS, 44, MS, 50. *Prof Exp:* Anal chemist, Chase Brass & Copper Co, Inc, Cleveland, 30-35, asst chief chemist, 34-35, chief chemist, 35-45, process metallurgist, 45-48, chief metallurgist, 48-50, dir metall, 50-77; METALL CONSULT, 77- *Mem:* Am Chem Soc; Am Soc Test & Mat; Soc Automotive Eng; Am Inst Mining, Metall & Petrol Eng; Am Soc Metals. *Res:* Physical metallurgy of copper and copper alloys. *Mailing Add:* 130 E 196th St Euclid OH 44119

RICKTER, DONALD OSCAR, b Rio Dell, Calif, May 5, 31; m 59; c 2. ORGANIC CHEMISTRY, INFORMATION SCIENCE. *Educ:* Univ Calif, Davis, AB, 52, MS, 55; Mich State Univ, PhD(chem), 64. *Prof Exp:* Instr chem, Santa Ana Col, 57-59; res scientist, Res Labs, 64-80, SCIENTIST, RES DIV, POLAROID CORP, CAMBRIDGE, 80- *Mem:* Am Chem Soc. *Res:* photographic chemistry; information science; new synthesis of heterocycles, monomers and polymers; retrieval and communication of technical information. *Mailing Add:* 88 Hemlock St Arlington MA 02174

RICORD, LOUIS CHESTER, b Burbank, Calif, Aug 16, 51. BIOMEDICAL COMPUTING, INFORMATION SYSTEMS. *Educ:* Univ Utah, BS, 73, ME, 75, PhD(med biophys, comput), 78. *Prof Exp:* RES SCIENTIST BIOMED INFO SYSTS, BATTELLE COLUMBUS LABS, 78- *Concurrent Pos:* Res assoc, NIH, 74-78; adj asst prof, Ohio State Univ, 80- *Mem:* Inst Elec & Electronics Engrs; Comput Soc; Soc Comput Med; Asn Comput Mach. *Res:* Computer assisted decision making in health sciences; medical data base design and construction; computer applications in laboratory animal toxicology. *Mailing Add:* Columbus Labs Battelle Mem Inst 505 King Ave Columbus OH 43201

RIDDELL, JAMES, b Quill Lake, Sask, Sept 28, 33; m 57; c 3. MATHEMATICS. *Educ:* Univ Alta, BSc, 57, MSc, 61, PhD(math), 67. *Prof Exp:* Geophysicist, Shell Can Ltd, Calgary, 57-59; asst prof math, Eastern Mont Col, 62-64; asst prof, 67-73, ASSOC PROF MATH, UNIV VICTORIA, BC, 73- *Concurrent Pos:* Nat Res Coun grants, Univ Victoria, BC, 68- *Mem:* Math Asn Am; Can Math Cong; Am Math Soc. *Res:* Combinatorial number theory; combinatorics; additive prime number theory. *Mailing Add:* Dept of Math Univ of Victoria Victoria BC V8W 2Y2 Can

RIDDELL, JOHN EVANS, b Montreal, Que, May 21, 13; m 39; c 5. ECONOMIC GEOLOGY. *Educ:* McGill Univ, BEng, 35, MSc, 36, PhD(geol), 53. *Prof Exp:* Consult Univ Sask, 45-46, lectr geol, 47-49; lectr geol, McGill Univ, 49-50, from asst prof to assoc prof, 50-58; prof & chmn dept, Carleton Univ, Can, 58-62; pres & managing dir, Mt Pleasant Mines, Ltd, 62-65; pres & dir res, Int Geochem Assocs Ltd, 65-74; CONSULT, 74- *Concurrent Pos:* Pres & dir of various mining & mineral explor co. *Mem:* Am Inst Mining, Metall & Petrol Eng; fel Geol Soc Am; fel Royal Soc Can; fel Geol Asn Can; Can Inst Mining & Metall. *Res:* Mineral exploration, particularly use of geochemical techniques and development of integrated interpretation of field data using geotectonics, geophysics and geology. *Mailing Add:* PO Box 220 Bridgetown NS B0S 1C0 Can

RIDDELL, ROBERT HENRY, b Hampshire, Eng, Aug 28, 43; m 69; c 2. PATHOLOGY. *Educ:* Univ London, MB & BS, 67; Col Physicians & Surgeons, LRCP & MRCS, 67; Royal Col Pathologists, MRCPath, 73. *Prof Exp:* House surgeon, Royal Berkshire Hosp, Eng, 67; house physician, St Albans City Hosp, 68; sr house officer path, St Bartholomew's Hosp, 68-69, registr, 69-70; registr, Royal Postgrad Med Sch, 70-71; lectr & sr registr, St Bartholomew's & St Mark's Hosp, 71-74; asst prof, 75-79, ASSOC PROF PATH, UNIV CHICAGO, 79- *Res:* Pathogenesis of gastrointestinal carcinoma, particularly precarcinomatous changes associated with ulcerative colitis and its clinical implication; electron microscopy, especially scanning and transmission associated with these lesions. *Mailing Add:* Dept of Path Univ of Chicago Chicago IL 60637

RIDDELL, ROBERT JAMES, JR, b US, June 25, 23; m 50; c 3. THEORETICAL PHYSICS. *Educ:* Carnegie Inst Technol, BS, 44; Univ Mich, MS, 47, PhD(physics), 51. *Prof Exp:* From instr to asst prof physics, Univ Calif, 51-55, physicist, Radiation Lab, 55-58; physicist, AEC, 58-60; PHYSICIST, LAWRENCE BERKELEY LAB, 60- *Mem:* Am Phys Soc. *Res:* High energy physics and strong interactions. *Mailing Add:* Lawrence Berkeley Lab Berkeley CA 94720

RIDDELL, RONALD CAMERON, mathematics, deceased

RIDDICK, JOHN ALLEN, b Greenville, Tex, Dec 20, 03; m 36. ANALYTICAL CHEMISTRY. *Educ:* Southwestern Univ, Tex, AB & AM, 26; Univ Iowa, PhD(anal chem), 29. *Hon Degrees:* DSc, Southwestern Univ, Tex, 73. *Prof Exp:* Asst, Southwestern Univ, 24-26 & Univ Iowa, 26-28; asst prof chem, Univ Miss, 28-31; consult, 31-35; instr, Southern Methodist Univ, 35-36; anal chemist, Commercial Solvents Corp, Ind, 36-42, chief anal chemist, Res & Develop Div, 45-64, res chemist, 64-68; INDEPENDENT CONSULT & AUTHOR, 69- *Mem:* AAAS; Am Chem Soc. *Res:* Analysis in nonaqueous media; physical and thermodynamic properties of solvents; azeotropes. *Mailing Add:* 522 Centenary Dr Baton Rouge LA 70808

RIDDIFORD, LYNN MOORHEAD, b Knoxville, Tenn, Oct 18, 36; m 70. INSECT PHYSIOLOGY, DEVELOPMENTAL BIOLOGY. *Educ:* Radcliffe Col, AB, 58; Cornell Univ, PhD(develop biol, protein chem), 61. *Prof Exp:* NSF res fel biol, Harvard Univ, 61-63; instr, Wellesley Col, 63-65; res fel, Harvard Univ, 65-66, from asst prof to assoc prof, 66-73; assoc prof zool, 73-75, PROF ZOOL, UNIV WASH, 75- *Concurrent Pos:* NSF res grant, 64-85; mem trop med & parasitol study sect, NIH, 74-78, res grant, 75-; Guggenheim fel, 79-80. *Mem:* Fel AAAS; Am Chem Soc; Am Soc Zoologists; Soc Develop Biol; Am Soc Biol Chem. *Res:* Hormonal control of insect development and behavior; insect embryogenesis; olfaction; pheromones. *Mailing Add:* Dept of Zool Univ of Wash Seattle WA 98195

RIDDLE, DONALD LEE, b Vancouver, Wash, July 26, 45; m 69; c 2. DEVELOPMENTAL GENETICS. *Educ:* Univ Calif, Davis, BS, 68; Univ Calif, Berkeley, PhD(genetics), 71. *Prof Exp:* Fel, Univ Calif, Santa Barbara, 72-73; fel, MRC Lab Molecular Biol, Cambridge, Eng, 73-75; asst prof, 75-81, ASSOC PROF BIOL, UNIV MO, 81- *Concurrent Pos:* NIH prin investr res grant & career develop award, Nat Inst Child Health & Human Develop, 77- & Nat Inst Aging--Caenorhabditis Genetics Ctr, 79- *Mem:* Genetics Soc Am; Soc Develop Biol; Soc Nematologists; AAAS. *Res:* Genetic, microscopic, ultrastructural and biochemical methods are employed in detailed analysis of a post-embryonic developmental branch point in the life cycle of the soil nematode, Caenorhabditis elegans (dauer larvae). *Mailing Add:* Dept Biol Sci Tucker Hall Univ Mo Columbia MO 65211

RIDDLE, GEORGE HERBERT NEEDHAM, b New York, NY, Mar 29, 40; m 65; c 3. PHYSICS, ELECTRON OPTICS. *Educ:* Princeton Univ, AB, 62; Univ Ill, MS, 64; Cornell Univ, PhD(appl physics), 71. *Prof Exp:* Mem tech staff, RCA Labs, 64-66; res physicist, Esso Res & Eng Co, 71-73; MEM TECH STAFF, RCA LABS, 73- *Mem:* Sigma Xi. *Res:* Surface physics; electron optics and electron beam instrumentation; video-disc stylus technology. *Mailing Add:* David Sarnoff Res Ctr RCA Labs Princeton NJ 08540

RIDDLE, WAYNE ALLEN, b Madison, Wis, Nov 3, 45. INVERTEBRATE PHYSIOLOGY. *Educ:* Utah State Univ, BS, 68; Univ NMex, MS, 73, PhD(biol), 77. *Prof Exp:* Vis asst prof biol, Univ NMex, 76-77; ASST PROF PHYSIOL, ILL STATE UNIV, 77- *Mem:* Am Soc Zoologists; Ecol Soc Am; Am Physiol Soc. *Res:* Respiratory physiology; cold hardiness; water relations and osmoregulation of terrestrial arthropods and molluscs. *Mailing Add:* Dept Biol Ill State Univ Normal IL 61761

RIDEN, JOSEPH ROBERT, JR, b Gettysburg, Pa, Dec 13, 22; m 46; c 5. BIOCHEMISTRY. *Educ:* Pa State Univ, BS, 44, MS, 49, PhD(agr biochem), 51. *Prof Exp:* Res assoc, McCollum-Pratt Inst, Johns Hopkins Univ, 51-55; biochemist, Pittsburgh Coke & Chem Co, 55-57 & Spencer Chem Co, 57-66; res assoc, Gulf Res & Develop Co, 66-74, MGR CHEM RES, CROP PROTECTION PRODS, GULF OIL CHEM CO, 74- *Mem:* Am Chem Soc. *Res:* Pesticides; metabolism; microanalytical techniques. *Mailing Add:* Kans City Lab Gulf Oil Chem Co Merriam KS 66202

RIDENER, FRED LOUIS, JR, b El Reno, Okla, Sept 19, 44; m 71. ELEMENTARY PARTICLE PHYSICS. *Educ:* NMex State Univ, BS, 68; Iowa State Univ, PhD(physics), 76. *Prof Exp:* ASST PROF PHYSICS, PA STATE UNIV, 77- *Mem:* Am Phys Soc; AAAS. *Res:* Elementary particle theory, especially polarization, electromagnetic form factors and relativistic wave equations; response functions for nonlinear systems. *Mailing Add:* Dept Physics Pa State Univ New Kensington PA 15068

RIDENHOUR, RICHARD LEWIS, b Santa Rosa, Calif, July 13, 32; m 54; c 5. FISH BIOLOGY. *Educ:* Humboldt State Col, BS, 54; Iowa State Col, MS, 55, PhD(fisheries), 58. *Prof Exp:* Aquatic biologist com fisheries, State Fish Comn, Ore, 58-60; from asst prof to assoc prof, 60-70, asst dean acad affairs, 67-69, dean acad planning, 69-81 PROF FISHERIES, HUMBOLDT STATE UNIV, 70-, DEAN, COL NAT RES, 81- *Mem:* Am Fisheries Soc; Am Inst Fishery Res Biol. *Res:* Biometrics; ecology. *Mailing Add:* Col Nat Res Humboldt State Univ Arcata CA 95521

RIDEOUT, DONALD ERIC, b Burlington, Nfld, May 15, 42; m 65; c 2. MATHEMATICS. *Educ:* Mem Univ Nfld, BA, 63, BSc, 64; McGill Univ, PhD(math), 70. *Prof Exp:* Lectr math, McGill Univ, 66-70; asst prof, 70-74, ASSOC PROF MATH, MEM UNIV NFLD, 74- *Concurrent Pos:* Nat Res Coun Can fel, 70-72 & 72-74. *Mem:* Math Soc Can. *Res:* Algebraic number theory. *Mailing Add:* Dept of Math Mem Univ of Nfld St John's NF A1C 5S7 Can

RIDEOUT, JANET LITSTER, b Bennington, Vt, Jan 6, 39; m 73. CHEMISTRY. *Educ:* Mt Holyoke Col, AB, 61, MA, 63; State Univ NY Buffalo, PhD(chem), 68. *Prof Exp:* Res chemist, 68-70, sr res chemist, 70-79, GROUP LEADER, EXP THER DEPT, BURROUGHS WELLCOME CO, 79- *Mem:* Am Chem Soc; NY Acad Sci. *Res:* Organic synthesis; heterocyclic compounds; nucleosides; purines; pyrimidines; imidazoles; metabolites; cancer chemotherapy. *Mailing Add:* Exp Ther Dept Burroughs Wellcome Co Research Triangle Park NC 27709

RIDEOUT, SHELDON P, b Toronto, Ohio, Nov 5, 27; m 47; c 6. PHYSICAL METALLURGY. *Educ:* Mich Technol Univ, BS, 48; Univ Notre Dame, MS, 51. *Prof Exp:* Engr, Ladish Co, Wis, 48-49; works tech metall lab, Savannah River Plant, 51-63, process supvr, 53-55, sr supvr, 55-63, res supvr, Nuclear Mat Div, 63-78, CHIEF SUPVR, REACTOR MAT TECH, SAVANNAH RIVER LAB, E I DU PONT DE NEMOURS & CO, INC, 78- *Mem:* Am Soc Metals; Nat Asn Corrosion Engrs. *Res:* Metallurgy of materials for nuclear reactors; stress corrosion of stainless steel and titanium alloys; hydrogen effects in metals. *Mailing Add:* 245 Barnard Ave SE Aiken SC 29801

RIDEOUT, VINCENT C(HARLES), b Chinook, Alta, May 22, 24; nat US; m 39; c 4. ELECTRICAL ENGINEERING. *Educ:* Univ Alta, BSc, 38; Calif Inst Technol, MS, 40. *Prof Exp:* Mem tech staff elec eng, Bell Tel Labs, Inc, 39-46; asst prof, Univ Wis, 46-49, assoc prof, 49-54; vis prof, Indian Inst Sci, 54-55; PROF ELEC ENG, UNIV WIS-MADISON, 55- *Concurrent Pos:* Vis prof, Univ Colo, 63-64 & Inst Med Physics, Utrecht, Holland, 70-71; mem, Ball Mfrs Engrs Comt. *Mem:* AAAS; fel Inst Elec & Electronics Engrs. *Res:* Control systems, computing, bioengineering, socio-economics. *Mailing Add:* Dept of Elec Eng Univ of Wis Madison WI 53706

RIDER, BENJAMIN FRANKLIN, b Cleveland, Ohio, Dec 4, 21; m 44. ANALYTICAL CHEMISTRY. *Educ:* Mt Union Col, BS, 43; Purdue Univ, MS, 44, PhD(anal chem), 47. *Prof Exp:* Res assoc, Knolls Atomic Power Lab, 47-57, RES ASSOC, VALLECITOS NUCLEAR CTR, GEN ELEC CO, 57- *Mem:* Am Chem Soc; fel Am Inst Chem; Am Soc Test & Mat. *Res:* Spectrophotometry; radiochemistry; medical radioisotopes processing; nuclear fuel burnup analysis; fission yields compilation. *Mailing Add:* Vallecitos Nuclear Ctr Gen Elec Co Vallecitos Rd Pleasanton CA 94566

RIDER, DON KEITH, b Rockford, Ill, Feb 12, 18; m 47; c 3. ORGANIC POLYMER CHEMISTRY, MATERIALS ENGINEERING. *Educ:* Univ Mich, BS, 39, MS, 41. *Prof Exp:* Chemist resin develop, Rohm & Haas Co, 41-46, group leader ion exchange develop, 46-47; chemist binder res, Chicopee Mfg Corp Div, Johnson & Johnson, 47-48; chemist, Resins Laminates Develop, 48-59, head organic mat res & develop dept, 59-75, head organic mat eng dept, 75-78; RETIRED. *Concurrent Pos:* Mem tech panel, Mat Adv Bd, Nat Acad Sci-Nat Res Coun, 56-57, spec comt adhesive bonded struct components, Bldg Res Adv Bd, 63-65; consult, Archit Plastics Int, 64-66; mem ad hoc comt, Predictive Testing, Nat Acad Sci-Nat Res Coun, 70-72; consult, 78- *Mem:* AAAS; Am Chem Soc; Soc Advan Mat & Process Eng; fel Am Inst Chem; fel NY Acad Sci. *Res:* Adhesives, bonded structures and casting resins; laminates; structural plastics; laminated thermoset materials; printed circuits; fibrous reinforcements. *Mailing Add:* 788 Park Shore Dr B24 Naples FL 33948

RIDER, JOSEPH ALFRED, b Chicago, Ill, Jan 30, 21; m 43; c 2. GASTROENTEROLOGY. *Educ:* Univ Chicago, SB, 42, MD, 44, PhD(pharmacol), 51; Am Bd Internal Med, dipl; Am Bd Gastroenterol, dipl. *Prof Exp:* Intern internal med, Presby Hosp, Chicago, 44-45; asst resident med, Univ Tex, 47-49; resident, Univ Chicago, 49-50, instr, 51-52; asst prof, Med Ctr, Univ Calif, San Francisco, 53-59, asst clin prof, 59-66, asst chief gastrointestinal clin, 53-61; DIR GASTROINTESTINAL RES LAB, FRANKLIN HOSP, 63- *Mem:* Am Soc Pharmacol & Exp Therapeut; Soc Exp Biol & Med; Am Geriat Soc; fel Am Gastroenterol Asn; fel Am Col Physicians. *Res:* Tolerance of organic phosphates in men; hypersensitivity factors in ulcerative colitis; cytology in the diagnosis of gastrointestinal malignancies; gastric secretion and motility; color television endoscopy. *Mailing Add:* Suite 900 350 Parnassus San Francisco CA 94117

RIDER, PAUL EDWARD, b Des Moines, Iowa, Nov 22, 40; m 63; c 3. PHYSICAL CHEMISTRY. *Educ:* Drake Univ, BA, 62; Iowa State Univ, MS, 64; Kans State Univ, PhD(phys chem), 69. *Prof Exp:* Instr chem, Drake Univ, 64-66; vis prof, Coe Col, 69; asst prof, 69-73, assoc prof, 73-79, PROF CHEM, UNIV NORTHERN IOWA, 79- *Mem:* Am Chem Soc. *Res:* Thermodynamic studies of weak hydrogen bonds. *Mailing Add:* Dept of Chem Univ of Northern Iowa Cedar Falls IA 50613

RIDER, RONALD EDWARD, b Pasadena, Calif, June 11, 45; m 69; c 2. COMPUTER SCIENCE, PHYSICS. *Educ:* Occidental Col, AB, 67; Wash Univ, AM, 69, PhD(physics), 72. *Prof Exp:* Res scientist comput sci & physics, 72-77, MGR ELECTRONIC SUBSYST DEVELOP, XEROX CORP, 77- *Res:* Computer systems; word processing; image processing. *Mailing Add:* Xerox Corp 701 S Aviation Blvd El Segundo CA 90245

RIDER, ROWLAND VANCE, b Syracuse, NY, Aug 23, 15; m 48. BIOSTATISTICS. *Educ:* Amherst Col, AB, 37; Syracuse Univ, MA, 38; Johns Hopkins Univ, ScD(biostatist), 47. *Prof Exp:* From asst prof to assoc prof pub health admin, 50-65, PROF POP DYNAMICS, SCH HYG & PUB HEALTH, JOHNS HOPKINS UNIV, 65- *Mem:* AAAS; Pop Asn Am; Am Pub Health Asn; Am Statist Asn; Int Union Sci Study Pop. *Mailing Add:* Dept of Pop Dynamics Johns Hopkins Univ Sch of Hyg Baltimore MD 21205

RIDER, WILLIAM B, b St Louis, Mo, Nov 10, 22; m 43; c 3. DATA PROCESSING. *Educ:* Wash Univ, St Louis, AB, 43, MA, 49. *Prof Exp:* Appl sci rep, Int Bus Mach Corp, Mo, 49-53; sr res engr, Pan-Am Petrol Corp, Okla, 53-58; supvr anal group, Electrodata Div, Burroughs Corp, Calif, 58-59; specialist res, Autonetics Div, NAm Aviation, Inc, Anaheim, 59-68; sr engr-scientist, McDonnell Douglas Corp, 68-70; teacher, Bishop Amat High Sch, 71-73; sr programmer, Meteorol Res, Inc, 73-74; mem tech staff, Space Div, Rockwell Int Corp, 75-79; SYSTS ANALYST, RALPH M PARSONS CO, 80- *Mem:* Asn Comput Mach; Am Inst Aeronaut & Astronaut. *Res:* Scientific and engineering application on digital computers. *Mailing Add:* 319 Monte Vista Rd Arcadia CA 91007

RIDGE, DOUGLAS POLL, b Portland, Ore, Nov 9, 44; m 71; c 5. PHYSICAL CHEMISTRY. *Educ:* Harvard Col, AB, 68; Calif Inst Technol, PhD(chem), 72. *Prof Exp:* Asst prof, 72-79, ASSOC PROF CHEM, UNIV DEL, 79- *Mem:* Am Phys Soc; Am Chem Soc. *Res:* Reactive and nonreactive ion molecule interactions in the gas phase; ion cyclotron resonance spectroscopy; gas phase organometallic chemistry. *Mailing Add:* Dept of Chem Univ of Del Newark DE 19711

RIDGE, JOHN DREW, b Cincinnati, Ohio, July 3, 09; m 41; c 2. ECONOMIC GEOLOGY. *Educ:* Univ Chicago, SB, 30, SM, 32, PhD(econ geol), 35. *Prof Exp:* Res petrographer, Universal-Atlas Cement Co, Ind, 35-36; petrologist, US Nat Park Serv, Washington, DC, 36-37; geologist, Cerro de Pasco Copper Corp, Peru, 37-40 & NJ Zinc Co, 46-47; assoc prof econ geol, Pa State Univ, 47-51; prof mineral econ, 51-64, asst dean col mineral indust, 53-64, prof econ geol & mineral econ, 64-75, head dept mineral econ, 51-75. *Concurrent Pos:* mem, Earth Sci Div, Nat Res Coun, 67-70 & 68-71; mem panel mineral econ, Nat Acad Sci, 67-79; ed, Graton-Sales Volume, 68-72; Nat Acad Sci exchange scientist in Poland, 69 & 70, Romania, 73, USSR & Yugoslavia, 77; mem comt critical & strategic mat, Nat Mat Adv Bd, 69-71; exchange scientist, Nat Sci Found, 69 & 73 & Nat Res Coun, 70, 72, 74 & 77; adj prof geol, Univ Fla, 75-80, actg chmn dept, 80-81, vis prof, 80- *Honors & Awards:* Henry Krumb lectr, 71; Mineral Econ Award, 72. *Mem:* Int Asn Genesis Ore Deposits (pres, 76-80, past pres, 80-84); Soc Econ Geol; Am Soc Mining, Metall & Petrol Engrs; fel Am Mineral Soc; fel Geol Soc Am. *Res:* Geology and geochemistry of metallic ore deposits; chemistry of metasomatism, stable isotopes and ore genesis; politics and economics of mineral exploration and exploitation. *Mailing Add:* Int Asn Genesis Ore Deposits 1402 NW 18th St Gainesville FL 32605

RIDGE, WILLIAM CLAYTON, mathematics, see previous edition

RIDGEWAY, BILL TOM, b Columbia, Mo, Dec 23, 27; m 52; c 3. PARASITOLOGY, PROTOZOOLOGY. *Educ:* Friends Univ, AB, 52; Wichita State Univ, MS, 58; Univ Mo, PhD(zool), 66. *Prof Exp:* From instr to asst prof zool, Southwestern Col, 58-63; res asst parasitol, Univ Mo, 63-66, asst prof invert zool, 66; assoc prof, 66-71, PROF ZOOL & PARASITOL, EASTERN ILL UNIV, 71- *Concurrent Pos:* Vis prof, Inland Environ Lab, Univ Md, 74-75. *Mem:* Am Soc Parasitol; Am Micros Soc; Am Soc Protozoologists. *Res:* Protozoan ectosymbionts of freshwater invertebrates; helminth and protozoan parasites of wild rodents. *Mailing Add:* Dept Zool Eastern Ill Univ Charleston IL 61920

RIDGWAY, ELLIS BRANSON, b Philadelphia, Pa, May 14, 39; m 64, 80; c 3. PHYSIOLOGY, BIOPHYSICS. *Educ:* Mass Inst Technol, SB, 63; Univ Ore, PhD(biol), 68. *Prof Exp:* NATO fel, Univ Col, Univ London, 69; USPHS fel, Cambridge Univ, 69-70; USPHS fel, Friday Harbor Labs, Univ Wash, 70-72; asst prof, 72-77, ASSOC PROF PHYSIOL, MED COL VA, 77- *Mem:* AAAS; Soc Gen Physiol; Biophys Soc. *Res:* Role of calcium as an activator in muscle, nerve and synapse; biophysics of muscle contraction and membrane permeability. *Mailing Add:* Dept of Physiol Med Col of Va Richmond VA 23298

RIDGWAY, GEORGE JUNIOR, b Lincoln, Nebr, Aug 26, 22; m 47; c 3. MICROBIOLOGY, BIOCHEMISTRY. *Educ:* Univ Wash, Seattle, BS, 49, MS, 51, PhD(microbiol), 54. *Prof Exp:* Biochemist, US Bur Commercial Fisheries, 54-64; asst lab dir, 64-71, dir biol lab, Maine, 71-73, ASST CTR DIR, NORTHEAST FISHERIES CTR, NAT MARINE FISHERIES SERV, WOODS HOLE, 73- *Mem:* AAAS. *Res:* Comparative immunology, immunogenetics, immunochemistry and biochemical genetics of fishes and other animals as applied to discrimination of natural populations. *Mailing Add:* Northeast Fisheries Ctr Nat Marine Fisheries Serv Woods Hole MA 02543

RIDGWAY, HELEN JANE, b Ft Worth, Tex, Aug 10, 37. BIOCHEMISTRY. *Educ:* NTex State Col, BA, 59; Baylor Univ, MS, 63, PhD(chem), 68. *Prof Exp:* Chemist, 60-68, RES INVESTR BIOCHEM, WADLEY INSTS MOLECULAR MED, 68- *Mem:* Am Chem Soc; fel Int Soc Hemat. *Res:* Biochemistry of blood coagulation; blood disorders; leukemia and cancer chemotherapy; platelet function; protein chemistry; lipid chemistry. *Mailing Add:* Wadley Inst of Molecular Med 9000 Harry Hines Dallas TX 75235

RIDGWAY, JAMES STRATMAN, b Paintsville, Ky, July 27, 36; m 59; c 2. POLYMER CHEMISTRY. *Educ:* Univ Louisville, BS, 58, MS, 59, PhD(org chem), 61. *Prof Exp:* Technician, Girdler Co, 57; teaching asst gen chem & qual anal, Univ Louisville, 57-58; res asst org chem, 58-61; res chemist, Chemstrand Res Ctr, Inc, 61-66; sr res chemist, 66-67; sr res chemist, 68-69, res specialist, 69-76, SR RES SPECIALIST, MONSANTO TEXTILES CO, 76- *Mem:* Am Chem Soc; fel Am Inst Chemists. *Res:* Polymer structure-property relationships; synthesis of polyamides and copolyamides; synthetic fiber applications for textile and tire cords; melt and solution polycondensation reactions; high modulus organic fibers; fiber flammability, textile colorfastness; anti-soil fibers. *Mailing Add:* Monsanto Textiles Co PO Box 12830 Pensacola FL 32575

RIDGWAY, RICHARD L, b Brownfield, Tex, Nov 9, 35; m 57; c 2. ENTOMOLOGY. *Educ:* Tex Tech Col, BS, 57; Cornell Univ, MS, 59, PhD(entom), 60. *Prof Exp:* Exten entomologist, Tex A&M Univ, 60-63, res entomologist, Entom Res Div, 63-70, entomologist-in-charge, Cotton Inst, 70-72, entomologist, Univ, 71-72; mem grad fac, 65-75, res leader, 72-75; staff scientist cotton & tobacco insects, Agr Res Serv, US Dept Agr, Washington, DC, 75-80; MEM FAC, ENTOM DEPT, TEX A&M UNIV, 80- *Honors & Awards:* Geigy Recognition Award, Entom Soc Am, 72. *Mem:* AAAS; Entom Soc Am; Int Orgn Biol Control. *Res:* Methods of application of systematic insecticides; behavior of insecticides in plants and soil; selective insecticides; biological control of insect pests. *Mailing Add:* Tex A&M Univ College Station TX 77840

RIDGWAY, ROBERT WORRELL, b Hampton, Va, July 14, 39; m 60; c 1. ORGANIC CHEMISTRY. *Educ:* Drexel Univ, BS, 66; Univ NH, PhD(org chem), 70. *Prof Exp:* NSF fel & res assoc, Princeton Univ, 69-70; asst prof chem, J C Smith Univ, 70-72; asst prof chem, Rollins Col, 72-75, assoc prof, 75-80; MGR OFF COOP EDUC, AM CHEM SOC, 80- *Mem:* Am Chem Soc; Royal Soc Chem; Sigma Xi. *Res:* Organometallic stereochemistry, especially asymmetric reductions and biologically important systems; synthetic organic chemistry. *Mailing Add:* Off Coop Educ Am Chem Soc Washington DC 20036

RIDGWAY, SAM H, b San Antonio, Tex, June 26, 36; m 60. ENVIRONMENTAL PHYSIOLOGY. *Educ:* Tex A&M Univ, BS, 58, DVM, 60; Cambridge Univ, PhD(neurobiol), 73. *Prof Exp:* Res vet, US Naval Missile Ctr, 62-63, Univ Southern Calif, 63-65 & Univ Calif, Santa Barbara, 65-66; res vet, 66-72, HEAD BIOMED DIV, NAVAL UNDERSEA CTR, 72- *Concurrent Pos:* US Navy res sponsor, 62- & Univ Calif, Santa Barbara & Inst Environ Stress, 65-; sr res fel, Cambridge Univ, 70-72; sci adv, Marine Mammal Comn, 75-77, chmn, 77-78; coun mem, Inst Lab Animal Resources, Nat Acad Sci-Nat Res Coun, 75-78; mem res comt, San Diego Zoo, 73- *Honors & Awards:* Gilbert Curl Sci Award, Naval Undersea Ctr, 73. *Mem:* NY Acad Sci; AAAS; Am Vet Med Asn; Sigma Xi; Explorers Club. *Res:* Marine mammal physiology; neural control mechanisms; aquatic animal medicine; bioacoustics. *Mailing Add:* Biosci Dept Naval Ocean Systs Ctr San Diego CA 92152

RIDGWAY, STUART L, b Freeport, Ill, July 27, 22. ENERGY CONVERSION. *Educ:* Haverford Col, BS, 43; Princeton Univ, PhD(physics), 52. *Prof Exp:* Group leader fire control res, US Naval Res Lab, 43-46; instr physics, Princeton Univ, 50-52; res assoc, 52-53; res assoc, Brookhaven Nat Lab, 53-56; mem sr staff, TRW Inc, 56-62; mem sr tech staff, Gen Tech Corp, 62-66; sr physicist, Princeton Appl Res Corp, 66-73; SR RES SCIENTIST, R&D ASSOCS, 73- *Mem:* Am Phys Soc; Combustion Inst; Soc Automotive Engrs; NY Acad Sci; AAAS. *Res:* Beta decay; high energy physics; heat transfer; combustion dynamics; motor vehicle exhaust control; ocean thermal energy conversion. *Mailing Add:* 537 Ninth St Santa Monica CA 90402

RIDGWAY, WILLIAM C(OMBS), III, b Orange, NJ, Apr 28, 36; div; c 3. COMPUTING. *Educ:* Princeton Univ, BSE, 57; NY Univ, BEE, 59; Stanford Univ, PhD(elec eng), 62. *Prof Exp:* Mem tech staff, Bell Tel Labs, 57-68, head mil data systs eng dept, 68-70, head ocean data systs dept, 70-72, dir, PAR Software & Data Processing Ctr, 72-73, DIR, COMPUT TECHNOL & PROG DEVELOP CTR, BELL TEL LABS, 73- *Concurrent Pos:* Mem resource & technol panel, Comput Sci & Eng Bd, Nat Acad Sci. *Mem:* Asn Comput Mach; Inst Elec & Electronics Engrs. *Res:* Development of advanced computing services. *Mailing Add:* Bell Tel Labs Holmdel NJ 07733

RIDHA, R(AOUF) A, b Karbala, Iraq, Aug 25, 37; US citizen. ENGINEERING MECHANICS, STRUCTURAL ENGINEERING. *Educ:* Univ Baghdad, BS, 59; Univ Ill, Urbana, MS, 63, PhD(struct), 66. *Prof Exp:* Supv engr struct, Govt Iraq, 59-62; anal specialist, Energy Controls Div, Bendix Corp, 66-73; res assoc, Cent Res Labs, Firestone Tire & Rubber Co, 73-78; head, Eng Mech Sect, 78-80, SECT HEAD, PHYSICS & ENG MECH SECT, RES DIV, GEN TIRE & RUBBER CO, 80- *Concurrent Pos:* Lectr, Ind Univ, South Bend, 69 & Mich State Univ, 70-71; lectr IV, Univ Akron, 77- *Mem:* assoc fel Am Inst Aeronaut & Astronaut. *Res:* Engineering mechanics; structural optimization; stability; nonlinear analysis; finite element methods; composite materials; aerospace structures; numerical methods; tire mechanics; tire stresses and deformation; analysis and design of composite structures. *Mailing Add:* Gen Tire & Rubber Co 2990 Gilchrist Rd Akron OH 44305

RIDINGS, GUS RAY, b Arbyrd, Mo, Nov 22, 18; m 41; c 2. RADIOLOGY. *Educ:* Ark State Col, AB, 39; Vanderbilt Univ, MD, 50. *Prof Exp:* Instr radiol, Col Med, Vanderbilt Univ, 55-56; assoc prof, Sch Med, Univ Miss, 56-57; prof, Sch Med, Univ Okla, 57-62; prof, Sch Med, Univ Mo-Columbia, 63-67; clin prof radiother, Univ Tex Southwestern Med Sch Dallas & radiotherapist, St Paul Hosp, 67-71; dir, C J Williams Cancer Treatment Ctr, Baptist Mem Hosp, 71-75; DIR, SOUTHEAST HOSP RADIATION ONCOL CTR, 75- *Concurrent Pos:* Consult, Vet Admin Hosp. *Mem:* Soc Nuclear Med; Radiol Soc NAm; Am Asn Cancer Educ; Am Soc Therapeut Radiologists; Sigma Xi. *Res:* Radiation therapy. *Mailing Add:* Southeast Hosp Radiation Oncol Ctr 1701 Lacey St Cape Girardeau MO 63701

RIDLEN, SAMUEL FRANKLIN, b Marion, Ill, Apr 24, 16; m 46; c 3. POULTRY SCIENCE. *Educ:* Univ Ill, BS, 40; Mich State Univ, MS, 57. *Prof Exp:* Instr high sch, Ill, 40-43; asst prof poultry, Exten Div, Univ Ill, 46-53; gen mgr, Honegger Breeder Hatchery, Ill, 53-56; assoc prof poultry, Univ Conn, 57-58; assoc prof, 58-65, PROF POULTRY, COOP EXTEN SERV, UNIV ILL, URBANA, 65-, ASST HEAD DEPT ANIMAL SCI, 78- *Honors & Awards:* Poultry Sci Asn Exten Award, 65. *Mem:* Fel Poultry Sci Asn; World Poultry Sci Asn. *Res:* Poultry management and production economics; effect of different cage densities and protein levels on the performance of laying hens. *Mailing Add:* 321 Mumford Hall Univ Ill 1301 W Gregory Dr Urbana IL 61801

RIDLEY, ESTHER JOANNE, b Pittsburgh, Pa, Sept 5, 24. PLANT PHYSIOLOGY. *Educ:* Fisk Univ, BA, 45; Univ Pittsburgh, MS, 50; Okla State Univ, PhD(bot), 67. *Prof Exp:* Asst biol, Univ Pittsburgh, 49-50, lab technician, Med Ctr, 50-54, res asst immunol, 54-56, lab supvr blood procurement, Cent Blood Bank, 56-59; instr biol, Morgan State Col, 59-60, instr sci educ, 60-61; instr bot, Baltimore Jr Col, 61-62; asst prof, 62-65, assoc prof, 67-69, PROF SCI EDUC, MORGAN STATE COL, 70-, CHMN DEPT, 72- *Mem:* AAAS; NY Acad Sci; EAfrican Wildlife Soc. *Res:* Developmental physiology; plant anatomy and morphology. *Mailing Add:* Dept of Sci Educ Morgan State Col Morgan State Univ MD 21239

RIDLEY, PETER TONE, b Meriden, Conn, Nov 11, 36; m 59; c 3. PHYSIOLOGY, PHARMACOLOGY. *Educ:* Rutgers Univ, BA, 59; Univ Pa, PhD(physiol), 64. *Prof Exp:* Jr pharmacologist, Smith Kline & French Labs, 59-60; USPHS fel, Karolinska Inst, Sweden, 64-65; asst prof physiol, George Washington Univ, 65-67; asst dir pharmacol, 67-71, dir pharmacol, 71-75, dep dir res, 75-81, VPRES RES & DEVELOP, ALLERGAN PHARMACEUT, DIV SMITH KLINE & FRENCH LABS, 81- *Mem:* Am Physiol Soc; Am Gastroenterol Asn. *Res:* Physiology and pharmacology of the gastrointestinal tract; central neural control of gastrointestinal function. *Mailing Add:* Allergan Pharmaceut 2525 Dupont Dr Irvine CA 92713

RIDOLFO, ANTHONY SYLVESTER, b Montclair, NJ, Oct 27, 18; m 42; c 2. RHEUMATOLOGY, CLINICAL PHARMACOLOGY. *Educ:* Rutgers Univ, BS, 40; Ohio State Univ, MS, 42, PhD, 47, MD, 54; Am Bd Internal Med, dipl, 64. *Prof Exp:* Assoc prof pharm, Univ Toledo, 42-44; assoc prof, Ohio State Univ, 47-50; fel cardiol, Marion County Gen Hosp, Indianapolis, Ind, 57-58; from physician to sr physician, 58-73, SR CLIN PHARMACOLOGIST, ELI LILLY & CO, 73- *Concurrent Pos:* Instr, Sch Med, Ind Univ, Indianapolis, 57-60, from asst to assoc, 60-65, from asst prof to assoc prof, 65-75, clin prof med, 75-79, prof med, 79-; mem bd dirs, Ind Arthritis Found, 61-, pres, 71-72; chmn sect rheumatic dis & anti-inflammatory agent, Am Soc Clin Pharmacol & Therapeut, 74-77; mem, US Pharmacopeia Panel on Analgesics, Sedatives & Anti-Inflammatory Agents; mem, Comt Relationships Pharmaceut Houses, Nat Arthritis Found, 81- *Mem:* Fel Am Col Physicians; Am Fedn Clin Res; Am Rheumatism Asn; AMA; Am Soc Clin Pharmacol & Therapeut. *Mailing Add:* Lilly Lab Clin Res Wishard Mem Hosp Indianapolis IN 46202

RIE, JOHN E, b New York, NY, Aug 26, 44; m 71. POLYMER CHEMISTRY, PHOTOCHEMISTRY. *Educ:* Univ Vt, BA, 66; Wayne State Univ, PhD(chem), 72. *Prof Exp:* Res chemist photopolymers, Kalle Aktiengesellschaft Div, Hoechst AG, 71-72, prod mgr photoresist, 72-74; sr res chemist photopolymers, Photopolymer Systs, W R Grace & Co, 74-78; group leader, Dynacure Printed Circuit Prod, Thiokol/Dynachem Corp, 78-80; MGR MAT SCI, P C K TECHNOL DIV, KOLLMORGEN CORP, 80- *Mem:* Am Chem Soc; Sigma Xi. *Res:* Photopolymer research and development for coatings and photoresist applications. *Mailing Add:* P C K Technol Div Kollmmorgen Corp 322 L I E S Service Rd Melville NY 11747

RIEBESELL, JOHN F, b Oneida, NY, March 18, 48. PLANT ECOLOGY, POPULATION ECOLOGY. *Educ:* State Univ NY, Albany, BS, 70, MS, 71; Univ Chicago, PhD(biol), 75. *Prof Exp:* Vis asst prof biol, Col Wooster, 76-77; ASST PROF BIOL, UNIV MICH, DEARBORN, 77- *Concurrent Pos:* Dir, Adirondack Lab, 76- *Mem:* Ecol Soc Am; Sigma Xi; AAAS. *Res:* Population biology and physiological ecology; photosynthetic adaptations in plants; island biogeography of alpine ecosystems; effects of environmental modification on population densities and community stability. *Mailing Add:* Dept Natural Sci Univ Mich Dearborn MI 48128

RIEBMAN, LEON, b Coatesville, Pa, Apr 22, 20; m 42; c 2. ELECTRONIC ENGINEERING. *Educ:* Univ Pa, BSEE, 43, MSEE, 47, PhD(electronic eng), 51. *Prof Exp:* Sr engr, Philco Corp, 45-46; res assoc & part-time instr, Univ Pa, 48-51; PRES, AM ELECTRONIC LABS, INC, 51- *Concurrent Pos:* Mem bd eng educ, Univ Pa, 68; dir, Ampal, 70 & Butler Aviation Int, 71- *Mem:* Fel Inst Elec & Electronics Engrs. *Res:* Electronics, particularly antenna and microwaves; computers. *Mailing Add:* Am Electronic Labs Inc PO Box 552 Lansdale PA 19446

RIECHEL, THOMAS LESLIE, b Bakersfield, Calif, July 9, 50; m. ANALYTICAL CHEMISTRY, ELECTROCHEMISTRY. *Educ:* Univ Calif, Davis, BS, 72, Riverside, PhD(chem), 76. *Prof Exp:* Res assoc chem, State Univ NY Buffalo, 76-77 & Univ Del, 78; ASST PROF CHEM, MIAMI UNIV, 78- *Mem:* Am Chem Soc. *Res:* Electrochemical and spectroscopic studies of models for metalloenzymes. *Mailing Add:* Dept of Chem Miami Univ Oxford OH 45056

RIECHERT, SUSAN ELISE, b Milwaukee, Wis, Oct 20, 45. ZOOLOGY. *Educ:* Univ Wis-Madison, BA, 67, MS, 70, PhD(zool), 73. *Prof Exp:* asst prof, 73-77, ASSOC PROF ZOOL, UNIV TENN, 77- *Concurrent Pos:* Assoc cur invert, Univ Wis Zool Mus, 71-77; asst ed, J Arachnology. *Mem:* Ecol Soc Am; Animal Behav Soc; Sigma Xi; Am Arachnological Asn; Entom Soc Am. *Res:* Food-based spacing in spiders; underlying factors responsible for observed patterns of local animal distribution; game playing and interaction strategies in spiders. *Mailing Add:* Dept of Zool Univ of Tenn Knoxville TN 37916

RIECK, ALVIN FRANK, physiology, embryology, see previous edition

RIECK, H(ENRY) G(EORGE), b Eugene, Ore, Aug 30, 22; m 53; c 3. CHEMICAL ENGINEERING. *Educ:* Ore State Col, BS, 43, MS, 44. *Prof Exp:* Engr, Gen Elec Co, 47-65; SR RES SCIENTIST, PAC NORTHWEST LABS, BATTELLE MEM INST, 65- *Res:* Development and design of equipment used in air sampling (land, marine and aircraft based systems); water sampling (rivers, lakes and ocean based systems); collection and measurement of radionuclides in various sampling regimes. *Mailing Add:* Pac Northwest Lab Battelle Blvd Richland WA 99352

RIECK, JAMES NELSON, b Wheeling, WVa, Aug 7, 39; m; c 2. POLYMER CHEMISTRY. *Educ:* West Liberty State Col, BS, 61; WVa Univ, PhD(org chem), 73. *Prof Exp:* Res chemist, 60-73, group leader polymer chem, 73-81, SECT MGR POLYURETHANE RES, MOBAY CHEM CORP, 81- *Mem:* Am Chem Soc. *Res:* Polyurethane textile coatings; polyurethane adhesives; prepolymers; modified isocyanates; bonding agents; rubber adhesive agents. *Mailing Add:* Mobay Chem Corp New Martinsville WV 26155

RIECK, NORMAN WILBUR, b Union City, NJ, Feb 16, 23; m 53; c 1. ANATOMY. *Educ:* Hope Col, AB, 53; Univ Mich, MS, 56, PhD(anat), 57. *Prof Exp:* Instr anat, Sch Med, Temple Univ, 57-59 & Sch Med, Univ Mich, 59-62; ASSOC PROF BIOL, HOPE COL, 62- *Mem:* Am Asn Anat; Am Mus Natural Hist; Am Inst Biol Sci. *Res:* Neuroanatomy; stimulation of occipital lobe of monkey. *Mailing Add:* 52 E 25th St Holland MI 49423

RIECKE, EDGAR ERICK, b Spencer, Iowa, Dec 29, 44; m 66; c 1. ORGANIC POLYMER CHEMISTRY. *Educ:* Univ SDak, BA, 67; Univ Mo-Kansas City, PhD(chem), 71. *Prof Exp:* Fel chem, Univ Rochester, 72; RES CHEMIST, EASTMAN KODAK CO, 72- *Mem:* Am Chem Soc. *Mailing Add:* Res Labs Bldg 82 Eastman Kodak Co Rochester NY 14650

RIECKER, ROBERT E, b Chicago, Ill, Oct 31, 36. GEOLOGY, GEOPHYSICS. *Educ:* Univ Colo, BA, 58, PhD(geol), 61. *Prof Exp:* Gen physicist, Air Force Cambridge Res Labs, 64-72, geophysicist, 72-76; alt group leader geol res, 76-77, group leader, 77-79, PROG MGR BASIC RES GEOSCI, LOS ALAMOS NAT LAB, 76- *Concurrent Pos:* Lectr geol, Boston Col, 64-76; mem US Nat comn rock mech, Nat Acad Sci-Nat Res Coun, 70-73; adv panel geol-geophys, Los Alamos Sci Lab; adj prof geol, Grad Sch, Univ NMex, 77- & prof, Univ, 80- *Mem:* AAAS; fel Geol Soc Am; Am Geophys Union; Sigma Xi; Nat Wildlife Fedn. *Res:* Physical and mechanical properties and modes of deformation of rocks, minerals, and solids under geophysically realistic conditions of high pressure and temperature to gain insight into tectonophysical manifestations within the earth. *Mailing Add:* Los Alamos Nat Lab G6 MS570 Box 1663 Los Alamos NM 87545

RIECKHOFF, KLAUS E, b Weimar, Ger, Feb 8, 28; Can citizen; m 49; c 3. CHEMICAL PHYSICS, SOLID STATE PHYSICS. *Educ:* Univ BC, BSc, 58, MSc, 59, PhD(physics), 62. *Prof Exp:* Mem res staff physics, Res Lab, Int Bus Mach Corp, Calif, 62-65; assoc prof, 65-66, actg dean sci, 66-67, assoc dean grad studies, 73-76, PROF PHYSICS, SIMON FRASER UNIV, 66- *Concurrent Pos:* Vis prof, Inst Appl Physics, Univ Karlsruhe, 69-70; vis scientist res lab, Int Bus Mach Corp, 76-77. *Mem:* AAAS; Am Phys Soc; Can Asn Physicists; NY Acad Sci. *Res:* Low temperature solid state; magneto-optics; spin-lattice relaxation; nonlinear optics; multiphoton processes in organic molecules; intermolecular and intramolecular energy transfer; spontaneous and stimulated Brillouin and Raman scattering; molecular luminescence. *Mailing Add:* Dept of Physics Simon Fraser Univ Burnaby BC V5A 1S6 Can

RIEDEL, BERNARD EDWARD, b Provost, Alta, Sept 25, 19; m 44; c 3. PHARMACY. *Educ:* Univ Alta, BSc, 43, MSc, 49; Univ Western Ont, PhD(biochem), 53. *Prof Exp:* Assoc prof pharm, Univ Alta, 46-50, 52-58, prof, 58-62, exec asst to vpres, 62-67; PROF PHARMACEUT SCI & DEAN FAC, UNIV BC, 67-, COORDR HEALTH SCI, 77- *Mem:* AAAS; Am Chem Soc; Can Biochem Soc; Pharmacol Soc Can; Can Pharmaceut Asn. *Res:* Biochemistry; radioisotope technology. *Mailing Add:* Fac Pharmaceut Sci Univ BC Vancouver BC V6T 1W5 Can

RIEDEL, EBERHARD KARL, b Dresden, Ger, Dec 25, 39. STATISTICAL MECHANICS, THEORETICAL SOLID STATE PHYSICS. *Educ:* Univ Koln, Cologne, Ger, Physics Dipl, 64; Tech Univ Munchen, Munich, Ger, Dr rer nat, 66. *Prof Exp:* Res physicist, Max-Planck Inst Physics, Munich, Ger, 65-68 & Inst v Laue-Langevin, Munich, Ger & Grenoble, France, 69; res assoc physics, Cornell Univ, Ithaca, NY, 69-71; from asst prof to assoc prof physics, Duke Univ, Durham, NC, 71-75; assoc prof, 75-78, PROF PHYSICS, UNIV WASH, 78- *Mem:* Am Phys Soc. *Res:* Theories of condensed matter, especially phase transitions and critical phenomena. *Mailing Add:* Dept of Physics Univ of Wash Seattle WA 98195

RIEDEL, ERNEST PAUL, b New York, NY, July 30, 31; m 56; c 2. LASERS, OPTICAL PHYSICS. *Educ:* Cornell Univ, BEngPhys, 54; Univ Wis, MS, 57; Mich State Univ, PhD(physics), 61. *Prof Exp:* Scientist, Lockheed Aircraft Corp, 56-58; sr res scientist, 61-69, mgr quantum electronics, 69-72, adv scientist res labs, 72-74, mgr lasers & optical technol res labs, 74-78, MGR APPL PHYSICS, WESTINGHOUSE ELEC CORP, 78- *Mem:* AAAS. *Res:* Symmetry of antiferromagnetic crystals; spectroscopy of laser materials; electromagnetic wave propagation. *Mailing Add:* Westinghouse Elec Corp Res Labs Pittsburgh PA 15230

RIEDEL, RICHARD ANTHONY, b Milwaukee, Wis, Feb 26, 22; m 45; c 4. DENTISTRY. *Educ:* Marquette Univ, DDS, 45; Northwestern Univ, MS, 48; Am Bd Orthod, dipl, 57. *Prof Exp:* Instr orthod, Northwestern Univ, 48-49; from instr to assoc prof, 49-71, actg dean, 80-81, PROF ORTHOD, SCH DENT, UNIV WASH, 71-, ASSOC DEAN ACAD AFFAIRS, 77- *Concurrent Pos:* Pvt pract, 49-; dir, 72-, Am Bd Orthod, pres, 78-79. *Mem:* Am Dent Asn; Am Asn Orthod; fel Am Col Dentists; Asn Dent Res; Sigma Xi. *Res:* Orthodontics; cephalometric evaluation of the skeletal interrelationships of the human face and esthetics as related to clinical orthodontics. *Mailing Add:* Dept of Orthod Univ of Wash Sch of Dent Seattle WA 98195

RIEDEL, WILLIAM REX, b South Australia, Sept 5, 27; m 52, 63; c 3. MICROPALEONTOLOGY. *Educ:* Univ Adelaide, MSc, 52. *Hon Degrees:* DSc, Univ Adelaide, 76. *Prof Exp:* Paleontologist, SAustralian Mus, 48-50; res fel, Oceanog Inst, Sweden, 50-51; paleontologist, SAustralian Mus, 54-55; asst res geologist, 56-62, assoc res geologist, 62-68, RES GEOLOGIST, SCRIPPS INST OCEANOG, UNIV CALIF, SAN DIEGO, 68- *Concurrent Pos:* With US Geol Surv, 59; chmn, Geol Res Div, Scripps Inst Oceanog, 78- *Mem:* Paleont Soc; Australian Geol Soc. *Res:* Systematic and stratigraphic investigations of Mesozoic to Quaternary Radiolaria; deep sea sediments; stratigraphy of microscopic fish skeletal debris. *Mailing Add:* Scripps Inst Oceanog A-012 Univ Calif at San Diego La Jolla CA 92093

RIEDER, RONALD FREDERIC, b New York, NY, July 13, 33; m 64; c 2. MEDICINE, HEMATOLOGY. *Educ:* Swarthmore Col, BA, 54; NY Univ, MD, 58; Am Bd Internal Med, dipl & cert med & hemat. *Prof Exp:* Intern, III, NY Univ Med Div, Bellevue Hosp, 58-59, asst resident, 59-60, fel microbiol, NY Univ, 60-61; fel immunol, Pasteur Inst, Paris, 61-62; fel hemat, Sch Med, Johns Hopkins Univ, 62-64; asst resident, III & IV, NY Univ Med Div, 64-65; res assoc, Montefiore Hosp, 65-67; asst prof, 67-71, assoc prof, 71-76, PROF MED, STATE UNIV NY DOWNSTATE MED CTR, 76-, DIR HEMAT & ONCOL, 76- *Concurrent Pos:* Assoc med, Albert Einstein Col Med, 65-67; vis prof lectr, Nuffield Unit Med Genetics, Univ Liverpool, 68; WHO traveling fel, 68; Macy Found fac scholar, 75-76; vis fel, Wolfson Col, Oxford Univ, 75-76. *Mem:* Am Soc Clin Invest; Asn Am Physicians; Am Soc Hemat; fel Am Col Physicians; Am Physiol Soc. *Res:* Abnormal hemoglobins; hemoglobin synthesis; thalassemia. *Mailing Add:* Dept Med State Univ NY Downstate Med Ctr Brooklyn NY 11203

RIEDER, SIDNEY VICTOR, b Philadelphia, Pa, Oct 22, 21; m 49; c 2. BIOCHEMISTRY. *Educ:* Philadelphia Col Pharm, BS, 43; Univ Pa, MS, 48, PhD(biochem), 53. *Prof Exp:* Instr biochem, Univ Pa, 52-53; from instr to asst prof, Sch Med, Yale Univ, 53-61; ASST PROF BIOL CHEM, MASS GEN HOSP, HARVARD MED SCH, 61- *Mem:* AAAS. *Res:* Intermediary metabolism of amino sugars; carbohydrates. *Mailing Add:* Dept of Biol Chem Harvard Med Sch Boston MA 02115

RIEDER, WILLIAM G(ARY), b Williston, NDak, Oct 28, 34; m 62; c 2. MECHANICAL ENGINEERING. *Educ:* NDak State Univ, BSME, 56; Ohio State Univ, MSc, 62; Univ Nebr, Lincoln, PhD(mech eng), 71. *Prof Exp:* Design engr, Atomic Energy Div, Phillips Petrol Co, 56-59; prin mech engr, Battelle Mem Inst, Ohio, 59-65; asst prof mech eng, NDak State Univ, 65-68; consult, Dept Econ Develop, State of Nebr, 68-69; asst prof mech eng, 70-73, ASSOC PROF MECH ENG, NDAK STATE UNIV, 73- *Mem:* AAAS; Am Soc Mech Engrs; Am Soc Eng Educ. *Res:* Energy conversion; thermal sciences; fluid mechanics; nuclear experiments; vacuum and processing phenomena. *Mailing Add:* Dept of Mech Eng NDak State Univ Fargo ND 58105

RIEDERER-HENDERSON, MARY ANN, b Buffalo, NY, July 21, 43; m 67. MICROBIAL PHYSIOLOGY. *Educ:* Rosary Hill Col, BS, 64; Univ Wis-Madison, MS, 66; Univ Ga, PhD(biochem), 71. *Prof Exp:* Instr microbiol, Univ Fla, 71-72; asst prof, 72-76, ASSOC PROF BIOL, ROLLINS COL, 76- *Mem:* AAAS; Am Soc Microbiol. *Res:* Formate hydrogenlyase of sulfate-reducing bacteria; hydrogenase in algae. *Mailing Add:* Dept of Biol Rollins Col Winter Park FL 32789

RIEDERS, FREDRIC, b Vienna, Austria, July 9, 22; US citizen. TOXICOLOGY, PHARMACOLOGY. *Educ:* NY Univ, AB, 48, MS, 49; Jefferson Med Col, PhD(pharmacol & toxicol), 51. *Prof Exp:* Prod chemist, Myer's 1890 Soda, Inc, New York, 40-42; qual control chemist, Penetone Corp, NJ, 42-43; jr toxicologist forensic toxicol, Lab Chief Med Examr New York, 46-49; from instr to assoc prof, 51-56, PROF PHARMACOL, JEFFERSON MED COL, 56-; PRES, TOXICON ASSOC, LTD, 76- *Concurrent Pos:* Chief toxicologist forensic toxicol, Off Med Examr, Philadelphia, 56-70; ed bull, Int Asn Forensic Toxicol, 60-63; NIH fel, Jefferson Med Col, 63-68; NIH & Pa Health Dept fels, Off Med Examr, Philadelphia, 67-69; adj prof toxicol, Drexel Univ, 67-69; mem toxicol study sect, NIH, 69-70. *Mem:* Am Acad Forensic Sci; Am Bd Clin Chem; Am Soc Pharmacol & Exp Ther; Am Chem Soc; Int Asn Forensic Toxicol. *Res:* Bioanalytical and forensic toxicology; heavy metals; cyanogenetic and interactive mechanisms of toxic actions. *Mailing Add:* PO Box 605 Rushland PA 18956

RIEDESEL, CARL CLEMENT, b Ind, June 5, 10; m 39; c 2. PHARMACOLOGY. *Educ:* Univ Idaho, BS, 34; Univ Nebr, MS, 47; Univ Iowa, PhD(physiol), 52. *Prof Exp:* Retail pharmacist, 34-37; hosp pharmacist, 38-42; instr physiol, Univ Nebr, 47-48; assoc prof pharmacol, Idaho State Col, 48-56; chmn dept, 56-70, prof physiol & pharmacol, 56-80, EMER PROF PHYSIOL & PHARMACOL, UNIV OF THE PAC, 80-, ASST DEAN PHARMACEUT SCI, 70- *Mem:* Am Pub Health Asn; Am Pharmaceut Asn; Coun Med TV. *Res:* Toxicity of barbiturates; choline and carbohydrate metabolism; pharmacologic actions of natural products. *Mailing Add:* Dept of Physiol & Pharmacol Univ of the Pac Stockton CA 95211

RIEDESEL, MARVIN LEROY, b Iowa City, Iowa, Nov 8, 25; m 49; c 1. PHYSIOLOGY. *Educ:* Cornell Col, BA, 49; Univ Iowa, MS, 53, PhD, 55. *Prof Exp:* Asst, Col Dent, Univ Iowa, 50-53; fel physiol, 53-55; res assoc occup health, Grad Sch Pub Health, Univ Pittsburgh, 55-59; from asst prof to assoc prof, 59-71, PROF BIOL, UNIV N MEX, 71- *Mem:* AAAS; Am Physiol Soc; NY Acad Sci; Int Soc Biometeorol; Soc Cryobiol. *Res:* Environmental and comparative physiology; mammalian hibernation; electrolyte metabolism. *Mailing Add:* Dept Biol Univ NMex Albuquerque NM 87131

RIEDINGER, LEO LOUIS, b Brownwood, Tex, Nov 25, 44; m 66; c 1. NUCLEAR PHYSICS. *Educ:* Thomas More Col, AB, 64; Vanderbilt Univ, PhD(physics), 69. *Prof Exp:* NSF fel, Niels Bohr Inst, Copenhagen Univ, 68-69; res assoc nuclear physics, Univ Notre Dame, 69-71; asst prof, 71-76, ASSOC PROF PHYSICS, UNIV TENN, KNOXVILLE, 71- *Concurrent Pos:* Consult, Oak Ridge Nat Lab, 72-73. *Mem:* Am Phys Soc. *Res:* Low energy nuclear structure; radioactive decay experiments; in-beam coulomb-excitation and heavy-ion reaction experiments. *Mailing Add:* Dept Physics & Astron Univ Tenn Knoxville TN 37916

RIEDL, H RAYMOND, b Colorado Springs, Colo, Aug 25, 35; m 59; c 7. PHYSICS. *Educ:* Creighton Univ, BS, 57. PHYSICIST, SOLID STATE BR, NAVAL SURFACE WEAPONS CTR, 57- *Mem:* Am Phys Soc. *Res:* Solid state physics; semiconductors; epitaxial films; amorphous films. *Mailing Add:* Solid State Br Naval Surface Weapons Ctr White Oak Silver Spring MD 20910

RIEDL, JOHN ORTH, JR, b Milwaukee, Wis, Dec 9, 37; m 61; c 4. MATHEMATICS. *Educ:* Marquette Univ, BS, 58; Univ Notre Dame, South Bend, MS, 60, PhD(math), 63. *Prof Exp:* Asst prof, 65-70, assoc dean, 69-74, ASSOC PROF MATH, OHIO STATE UNIV, 70-, ASSOC DEAN COL MATH & PHYS SCI, 74- *Mem:* Am Math Soc; Math Asn Am. *Res:* Functional analysis. *Mailing Add:* Dept Math Ohio State Univ Columbus OH 43210

RIEDMAN, RICHARD M, b Long Beach, Calif, Sept 9, 33; m 57; c 2. AUDIOLOGY. *Educ:* Univ Redlands, BA, 55, MA, 56; Univ Pittsburgh, PhD(audiol), 62. *Prof Exp:* From asst prof to assoc prof speech & hearing, 62-68, PROF SPEECH PATH & AUDIOL, SAN DIEGO STATE UNIV, 68- *Mem:* Acoust Soc Am; Am Speech & Hearing Asn. *Res:* Clinical and experimental audiology. *Mailing Add:* Dept Speech San Diego State Univ San Diego CA 92182

RIEFFEL, MARC A, b New York, NY, Dec 22, 37; m 59; c 3. OPERATOR ALGEBRAS, GROUP REPRESENTATIONS. *Educ:* Harvard Univ, AB, 59; Columbia Univ, PhD(math), 63. *Prof Exp:* Lectr, 63-64; from actg asst prof to asst prof, 64-68, assoc prof, 68-73, PROF MATH, UNIV CALIF, BERKELEY, 73- *Mem:* Am Math Soc. *Res:* Functional analysis. *Mailing Add:* Dept of Math Univ of Calif Berkeley CA 94720

RIEG, LOUIS EUGENE, b Pittsburgh, Pa, July 25, 30; m 56; c 3. GEOLOGY. *Educ:* Univ Notre Dame, BS, 52; Univ Pittsburgh, PhD(geol), 58. *Prof Exp:* Asst, Pa State Univ, 52-54 & Univ Pittsburgh, 54-58; geologist, Gulf Res & Develop Co, Pa, 58-66, Explor Dept, Gulf Oil Corp, La, 66-68, sr geologist, 68-73, regional geologist & explor geol supvr, Gulf Oil Co, Nigeria, 73-76, geologist & geotechnologist, Gulf Oil Prod, La, 77-78, regional geologist, Gulf Oil Explor, La, 78-80, AREA GEOLOGIST, GULF OIL EXPLOR WYO, 81- *Concurrent Pos:* Asst geol, Whiterock Quarries, 53-55; asst, Pa State Geol Surv, 54-57. *Mem:* Am Asn Petrol Geologists; Soc Econ Paleontologists & Mineralogists; Am Inst Prof Geologists. *Res:* Petroleum exploration; environmental sedimentology. *Mailing Add:* Gulf Oil Explor & Prod Co PO Box 2619 Casper WY 82602

RIEGEL, CHRISTOPHER ALBERT, b Stassfurt, Ger, Sept 20, 28; US citizen; m 54; c 2. DYNAMIC METEOROLOGY. *Educ:* Univ Calif, Los Angeles, BA, 60, MA, 62, PhD(meteorol), 64. *Prof Exp:* Res meteorologist, Meteorol Int, Inc, Calif, 64-66; from asst prof to assoc prof, 66-71, PROF METEOROL, CALIF STATE UNIV, SAN JOSE, 71- *Mem:* AAAS; Am Meteorol Soc; Am Geophys Union. *Res:* Internal waves; numerical modelling of atmospheric flows; stratospheric mesospheric modelling. *Mailing Add:* Dept of Meteorol San Jose State Univ San Jose CA 95192

RIEGEL, GARLAND TAVNER, b Bowling Green, Mo, Aug 26, 14; m 41; c 4. ENTOMOLOGY. *Educ:* Univ Ill, BS, 38, MS, 40, PhD(entom), 47. *Prof Exp:* Asst entom, Ill Natural Hist Surv, 37-42; fel, Grad Col, Univ Ill, 47-48; from asst prof to assoc prof, 48-60, head dept, 63-76, prof zool, 60-78, EMER PROF ZOOL, EASTERN ILL UNIV, 78- *Mem:* AAAS; Entom Soc Am; Soc Syst Zool. *Res:* Classification of Braconidae, Alysiinae and Dacnusinae; insect ecology and morphology. *Mailing Add:* Dept of Zool Eastern Ill Univ Charleston IL 61920

RIEGEL, ILSE LEERS, b Berlin, Ger, June 16, 16; m 40; c 2. CANCER RESEARCH. *Educ:* Univ Wis, Madison, BA, 41, MA, 49, PhD(endocrinol), 52. *Prof Exp:* Fel, 52-54, managing ed, Cancer Res, 54-64, SR SCIENTIST, MCARDLE LAB CANCER RES, UNIV WIS-MADISON, 64- *Mem:* Sigma Xi. *Mailing Add:* McArdle Lab Cancer Res Univ Wis Madison WI 53706

RIEGEL, KURT WETHERHOLD, b Lexington, Va, Feb 28, 39; m 74; c 3. RESEARCH ADMINISTRATION. *Educ:* Johns Hopkins Univ, AB, 61; Univ Md, PhD(astron), 66. *Prof Exp:* Res fel astron, Univ Md, 66; asst prof, Univ Calif, Los Angeles, 66-74; mgr energy conserv prog, Fed Energy Admin, 74-75, chief, technol & consumer prod energy conserv, 75-77, DIR, CONSUMER PROD DIV, DEPT ENERGY, 77-; DIR ENVIRON ENG & TECHNOL, ENVIRON PROTECTION AGENCY, 80- *Concurrent Pos:* Consult, Aerospace Corp, 67-70; prof astron, Extens, Univ Calif, Los Angeles, 68-74; consult, Rand Corp, 73-74; vis fel, Univ Leiden, 72-73. *Mem:* AAAS; Am Phys Soc; Am Astron Soc; Int Astron Union; Int Radio Sci Union. *Res:* Environmental pollution control technology; galactic radio astronomy; interstellar medium; energy technology. *Mailing Add:* Box 2807 Washington DC 20013

RIEGELMAN, SIDNEY, b Milwaukee, Wis, July 19, 21; m 46; c 3. PHARMACY. *Educ:* Univ Wis, BS, 43, PhD(pharm), 48. *Prof Exp:* Asst prof pharm, 48-56, assoc prof pharm & pharmaceut chem, 56-67, PROF PHARM & PHARMACEUT CHEM & CHMN DEPT PHARM, COL PHARM, UNIV CALIF, SAN FRANCISCO, 67- *Mem:* Am Soc Hosp Pharmacists; Am Chem Soc; Am Pharmaceut Asn; NY Acad Sci. *Res:* Pharmacokinetics of drug absorption and metabolism; physical, chemical and biological properties, absorption of drugs through biological membranes. *Mailing Add:* Dept of Pharm Col Pharm Med Ctr Univ of Calif San Francisco CA 94143

RIEGER, ANNE LLOYD, b Philadelphia, Pa, Feb 6, 35; m 57; c 1. ORGANIC CHEMISTRY. *Educ:* Reed Col, BA, 56; Stanford Univ, MS, 59; Columbia Univ, PhD, 62. *Prof Exp:* Res assoc chem, 62-68, res assoc biol & med sci, 68-70, 71-74, res assoc chem, 74-77, ASST PROF RES, BROWN UNIV, 77- *Mem:* AAAS; Sigma Xi; Am Chem Soc. *Res:* Free radical chemistry and halogenating agents; synthesis of steroids; isolation and indentification of steroids from biological systems; electron transfer intermediates in photosynthetic systems. *Mailing Add:* 119 Congdon St Providence RI 02906

RIEGER, MARTIN MAX, b Braunschweig, Ger, Apr 12, 20; nat US; m 43; c 2. PHYSICAL ORGANIC CHEMISTRY. *Educ:* Univ Ill, BS, 41; Univ Minn, MS, 42; Univ Chicago, PhD(chem), 48. *Prof Exp:* Chemist, Transparent Package Co, 42-44; instr, DePaul Univ, 47; res chemist, Lever Bros Co, 48-55; sr res assoc, 55-60, dir toiletries & cosmetics res, 60-71, assoc dir chem-proprietary res, 71-75, dir chem-biol res, 75-77, DIR CHEM RES, CONSUMER PROD DIV, WARNER LAMBERT CO 77- *Concurrent Pos:* Ed, J Soc Cosmetic Chem, 62-67. *Mem:* Textile Res Inst; Am Chem Soc; Soc Cosmetic Chem (pres, 72-73); Fiber Soc; Soc Ger Chem. *Res:* Cosmetics; proprietaries; aging; skin; hair; antacids; oral hygiene; confections chewing gum. *Mailing Add:* 304 Mountain Way Morris Plains NJ 07950

RIEGER, PHILIP HENRI, b Portland, Ore, June 24, 35; m 57; c 1. PHYSICAL CHEMISTRY. *Educ:* Reed Col, BA, 56; Columbia Univ, PhD(chem), 62. *Prof Exp:* Instr chem, Columbia Univ, 61-62; from instr to assoc prof, 62-77, PROF CHEM, BROWN UNIV, 77- *Concurrent Pos:* Vis prof, Univ Othgo, Dunedin, New Zealand, 77-78. *Mem:* Am Chem Soc; Royal Soc Chem. *Res:* Solution physical chemistry of transition metal coordination and organometallic compounds; electron spin resonance; electrochemistry; chemistry of arsenic and vanadium. *Mailing Add:* Dept of Chem Brown Univ Providence RI 02912

RIEGER, SAMUEL, b New York, NY, Sept 29, 21; m 47; c 3. SOIL MORPHOLOGY. *Educ:* Cornell Univ, BS, 43; Univ Wis, MS, 47; State Col Wash, PhD(soils), 52. *Prof Exp:* Soil surveyor, State Geol & Natural Hist Surv, Wis, 46, 47; soil scientist, US Bur Reclamation, 47-49; asst soils, State Col Wash, 49-52; soil scientist, Soil Conserv Serv, USDA, 52-55, state soil scientist, 55-78; RETIRED. *Mem:* Soil Sci Soc Am; Am Soc Agron. *Res:* Soil morphology, genesis, and classification, particularly of arctic and subarctic soils. *Mailing Add:* Box 337 Palmer AK 99645

RIEGERT, PAUL WILLIAM, b Can, Dec 5, 23; m 48; c 4. INSECT PHYSIOLOGY. *Educ:* Univ Sask, BA, 44; Mont State Col, MSc, 48; Univ Ill, PhD(entom, physiol), 54. *Prof Exp:* Agr asst entom, Can Dept Agr, 44-47; lectr entom, Mont State Col, 47-48; entomologist, Entom Sect Res Lab, Can Dept Agr, 48-68; prof biol & chmn dept, Univ Sask, 68-72; head dept, 72-79, PROF BIOL, UNIV REGINA, 72- *Mem:* Fel Entom Soc Can; Assoc d'Aeridologie; Can Soc Zool; fel Royal Entom Soc London. *Res:* Sensory and behavioral aspects of insect physiology; bioenergetics; history of entomology. *Mailing Add:* Dept of Biol Univ of Regina Regina SK S4S 0A2 Can

RIEGERT, R(ICHARD) P(AUL), b Oradell, NJ, July 24, 27. COMPUTER SCIENCE, MATERIALS ENGINEERING. *Educ:* Alfred Univ, BS, 53, MS, 56. *Prof Exp:* Res fel cataphoresis of colloids, Air Force res proj, Alfred Univ, 50-53, res assoc metal & ceramic bonding, 53-56; res engr glass studies, Helipot Corp, 56-57; res scientist solid state chem, Servomechanisms, Inc, 57-61; dir res, Sloan Res Indust Eng, 60-62, pres, Sloan Instruments Corp, 62-73; OWNER & CONSULT, QUAD GROUP, 73- *Mem:* Am Soc Metals; Am Ceramic Soc; Am Crystallog Asn; fel Am Inst Chemists; Am Acad Arts & Sci. *Res:* Thin films; energy exploration and technology; crystal chemistry. *Mailing Add:* Quad Group 2030 Alameda Padre Serra Santa Barbara CA 93103

RIEGGER, OTTO K, b Howell, Mich, Dec 11, 35; m 60; c 3. METALLURGICAL ENGINEERING. *Educ:* Univ Mich, BSE, 58, MSE, 59, PhD(metall eng), 63. *Prof Exp:* Res engr appl res off, Ford Motor Co, 62-64; res engr, 64-67, DIR RES, RES LAB, TECUMSEH PROD CO, 67- *Mem:* Am Soc Metals; Am Foundrymen's Soc; Am Ceramic Soc; Soc Mfg Eng; Soc Die Casting Eng. *Res:* Applied research administration; computer aided product design and simulation; manufacturing engineering and process specification. *Mailing Add:* Res & Develop Lab 3869 Res Park Dr Ann Arbor MI 48104

RIEGLE, GAIL DANIEL, b De Soto, Iowa, Feb 19, 35; m 60; c 2. ENDOCRINOLOGY, REPRODUCTIVE PHYSIOLOGY. *Educ:* Iowa State Univ, BS, 57; Mich State Univ, MS, 60, PhD(physiol), 63. *Prof Exp:* Asst prof, 64-70, assoc prof, 70-76, PROF PHYSIOL, MICH STATE UNIV, 76-, ASST DEAN CURRICULUM, COL OSTEOPATHIC MED, 80- *Mem:* Geront Soc; Am Physiol Soc; Soc Exp Biol & Med. *Res:* Effects of stress and aging on endocrine and reproductive control systems. *Mailing Add:* Endocrine Res Unit Dept Physiol Mich State Univ East Lansing MI 48824

RIEHL, HERBERT, b Munich, Ger, Mar 30, 15; nat US; m 52; c 2. METEOROLOGY. *Educ:* NY Univ, MS, 42; Univ Chicago, PhD(meteorol), 47. *Prof Exp:* Instr meteorol, Univ Wash, 41-42; from instr to prof, Univ Chicago, 42-60; prof & head dept, Colo State Univ, 60-72; prof, Free Univ Berlin, 72-76; vis scientist, Nat Ctr Atmospheric Res, 76-79; PROF, COOP INST RES ENVIRON SCI, 79- *Concurrent Pos:* Consult, US Navy & US Weather Bur; consult, Sen, Berlin, 74-75. *Honors & Awards:* Losey Award, Am Inst Aeronaut & Astronaut, 60; Andrew G Clark Award, Colo State Univ, 72; Meisinger Award, Am Meteorol Soc, 47; Rossby Award, 79. *Mem:* AAAS; Am Meteorol Soc; Am Geophys Union; Royal Meteorol Soc; Ger Meteorol Soc. *Res:* General circulation; jet streams; tropical meteorology; climatology; hydrometeorology. *Mailing Add:* NOAA/ERL Colo State Univ Boulder CO 80521

RIEHL, JAMES PATRICK, b Toms River, NJ, Aug 6, 48; m 72; c 1. PHYSICAL CHEMISTRY, THEORETICAL CHEMISTRY. *Educ:* Villanova Univ, BS, 70; Purdue Univ, PhD(phys chem), 75. *Prof Exp:* Instr chem, Univ Va, 75-77; ASST PROF CHEM, UNIV MO-ST LOUIS, 77- *Concurrent Pos:* Res investr, Am Chem Soc Petrol Res Fund, 78-80 & Res Corp, 78. *Mem:* Am Chem Soc. *Res:* Molecular dynamics and structure of condensed phases; molecular spectroscopy; optical activity. *Mailing Add:* Dept of Chem Univ of Mo St Louis MO 63121

RIEHL, JERRY A, b Kalispell, Mont, July 25, 33; m 75. PHYSICS, CHEMISTRY. *Educ:* Seattle Univ, BS, 62; Wash State Univ, PhD(chem), 66. *Prof Exp:* Assoc prof physics, Seattle Univ, 66-74, chmn dept, 71-74; sr res specialist, Boeing Com Airline Co, 74-80; RES PROF CHEM, SEATTLE UNIV, 78-; SCIENTIST, PHYS DYNAMICS, 80- *Concurrent Pos:* Res consult, 74- *Res:* Air pollution control; gas-turbine emissions; nuclear analysis. *Mailing Add:* Phys Dynamics PO Box 3027 Bellevue WA 98009

RIEHL, MARY AGATHA, b Raleigh, NDak, Feb 17, 21. ORGANIC CHEMISTRY. *Educ:* Col St Scholastica, BA, 42; Inst Divi Thomae, MS, 45; Catholic Univ, PhD(chem), 66. *Prof Exp:* PROF CHEM, COL ST SCHOLASTICA, 45- *Concurrent Pos:* NSF sci fac fel, 62-63; NSF res participation grant, Argonne Nat Lab, 69, Ill Inst Technol, 71. *Mem:* AAAS; Am Chem Soc; Am Inst Chem. *Res:* Biochemical studies in cancer, especially enzyme systems in cancerous and normal tissue; chromic acid oxidations of organic compounds. *Mailing Add:* Col of St Scholastica Duluth MN 55811

RIEHM, CARL RICHARD, b Kitchener, Ont, May 2, 35; m 58; c 2. ALGEBRA. *Educ:* Univ Toronto, BA, 58; Princeton Univ, PhD(math), 61. *Prof Exp:* From lectr to asst prof math, McGill Univ, 61-63; from asst prof to assoc prof, Univ Notre Dame, 63-73; chmn dept, 73-79, PROF MATH, MCMASTER UNIV, 73- *Concurrent Pos:* Mem, Inst Advan Study, 66-67; vis prof, Harvard Univ, 67-68. *Mem:* Am Math Soc; Math Asn Am; Can Math Cong. *Res:* Integral quadratic forms; classical groups; orthogonal representations of finite groups. *Mailing Add:* Dept of Math McMaster Univ Hamilton ON L85 4L8 Can

RIEHM, JOHN P, b Fergus, Ont, Mar 24, 35; m 63; c 1. BIOCHEMISTRY. *Educ:* Ont Agr Col, BSA, 56; Mich State Univ, PhD(biochem), 62. *Prof Exp:* Fel, Cornell Univ, 62-65; asst prof biochem, Univ Calif, Santa Barbara, 65-70; assoc prof, 70-77, PROF BIOL & CHMN DEPT, UNIV WEST FLA, 77- *Res:* Chemical and physical properties of proteins. *Mailing Add:* Dept of Biol Univ of WFla Pensacola FL 32504

RIEKE, CAROL ANGER, b Milwaukee, Wis, Jan 17, 08; m 32; c 2. MATHEMATICS, ASTRONOMY. *Educ:* Northwestern Univ, BA, 28, MA, 29; Radcliffe Col, PhD(astron), 32. *Prof Exp:* Berliner fel, Radcliffe Col, 32-33, tutor astron, 33-36; instr, Johns Hopkins Univ, 37; asst physics, Univ Chicago, 38-42; computer, Mass Inst Tech, 42-46; instr, Purdue Univ, 47-52; INSTR MATH & ASTRON, THORNTON COMMUNITY COL, 57- *Concurrent Pos:* Asst, Mass Inst Tech, 33-36, computer, 33-38. *Mem:* Am Astron Soc. *Res:* Spectroscopic parallaxes; astronomical spectroscopy; molecular spectra; airplane propulsion; galactic clusters. *Mailing Add:* 2812 Tennyson Pl Hazel Crest IL 60429

RIEKE, GARL KALMAN, b Seattle, Wash, June 30, 42. ANATOMY, NEUROSCIENCE. *Educ:* Univ Wash, BS, 65, BS, 66; La State Univ, PhD(anat), 71. *Prof Exp:* Asst prof anat, Hahnemann Med Col & Hosp, 73-78; ASST PROF ANAT, COL MED, TEX A&M UNIV, 78- *Concurrent Pos:* Fel physiol, Univ Calif, Los Angeles, 71-73. *Mem:* AAAS; Sigma Xi; Soc Neurosci. *Res:* Neuronal interactions; local circuits; homing and magnetic fields. *Mailing Add:* Dept of Anat Olin E Teague Res Ctr College Station TX 77843

RIEKE, GEORGE HENRY, b Boston, Mass, Jan 5, 43. ASTRONOMY. *Educ:* Oberlin Col, AB, 64; Harvard Univ, MA, 65, PhD(physics), 69. *Prof Exp:* Fel astron, Smithsonian Astrophys Observ, 69-70; res assoc, Lunar & Planetary Lab, 70-73, asst prof, Steward Observ & Lunar & Planetary Lab, 73-75, assoc prof, 75-80, PROF ASTRON, STEWARD OBSERV & LUNAR & PLANETARY LAB, UNIV ARIZ, 80- *Concurrent Pos:* Alfred P Sloan Found fel, 76- *Res:* Infrared astronomy. *Mailing Add:* Lunar & Planetary Lab Univ Ariz Tucson AZ 85721

RIEKE, HERMAN HENRY, III, b Louisville, Ky, June 18, 37; m 64; c 6. PETROLEUM ENGINEERING, GEOLOGY. *Educ:* Univ Ky, BS, 59; Univ Southern Calif, MS, 64 & 65, PhD(petrol eng), 70. *Prof Exp:* Chief geologist, United Minerals, Inc, Los Angeles, 63-64; staff engr, Electro-Osmotics, Inc, Los Angeles, 64-66; lectr petrol eng, Univ Southern Calif, 66-68; res scientist, Res & Develop, Continental Oil Co, Ponca City, 69-71; asst prof petrol eng, Col Mineral & Energy Resources, WVa Univ, 71-76, assoc prof, 76-81; mem tech staff, TRW Inc, 77-81; PROD MGR, POI ENERGY, INC, CLEVELAND, OH, 81- *Concurrent Pos:* Eng scientist, Res Eng Exp Sta, WVa Univ, 71-81. *Honors & Awards:* Crown Medal, Shah of Iran, 76. *Mem:* Soc Petrol Engrs; Geol Soc Am; Soc Prof Well Long Analysts; Soc Econ Paleont & Mineral. *Res:* Abnormal subsurface pressure detection; reservoir engineering; formation evaluation; compaction of sediments; geothermal energy; in-situ coal liquefaction and mineral resources; oil and gas production. *Mailing Add:* 161 Poplar Dr Morgantown WV 26505

RIEKE, JAMES KIRK, b Barrington, Ill, Apr 15, 24; m 49; c 3. PHYSICAL CHEMISTRY. *Educ:* Univ Ill, BS, 49; Univ Wis, MS, 52, PhD(chem), 54. *Prof Exp:* Asst chem, Univ Wis, 49-54; res chemist, 54-57, proj leader, 57-62, group leader, 62-65; asst to dir plastics dept lab, 65-70, ASST TO DIR PHYS RES, DOW CHEM USA, 70- *Mem:* AAAS; Am Chem Soc; Soc Plastics Eng; Sigma Xi; Soc Rheol. *Res:* Luminescence properties induced in crystals by high energy radiation; physical properties of high polymers; graft copolymers. *Mailing Add:* 4715 Swede Rd Midland MI 48640

RIEKE, PAUL EUGENE, b Kankakee, Ill, May 13, 34; m 57; c 2. TURF MANAGEMENT, SOIL SCIENCE. *Educ:* Univ Ill, BS, 56, MS, 58; Mich State Univ, PhD(soil sci), 63. *Prof Exp:* From asst prof to assoc prof, 63-72, PROF SOIL SCI, MICH STATE UNIV, 72- *Mem:* Sigma Xi; Soil Sci Soc Am; Crop Sci Soc Am; Am Soc Agron. *Res:* Physical and chemical properties of soils affecting turf management. *Mailing Add:* Dept of Crop & Soil Sci Mich State Univ East Lansing MI 48824

RIEKE, REUBEN DENNIS, b Lucan, Minn, Mar 7, 39; m 62; c 2. ORGANIC CHEMISTRY. *Educ:* Univ Minn, Minneapolis, BCh, 61; Univ Wis-Madison, PhD(org chem), 66. *Prof Exp:* Assoc phys org chem, Univ Calif, Los Angeles, 65-66; from asst prof to prof phys org chem, Univ NC, Chapel Hill, 66-76; prof, NDak State Univ, 76-77; PROF CHEM, UNIV NEBR-LINCOLN, 77- *Concurrent Pos:* NIH res fel, 65-66; participant Am Chem Soc Course Molecular Orbital Theory, 68-70; fel, Alfred P Sloan Found, 73-77; fel, Alexander von Humboldt Found, 73-74. *Mem:* Am Chem Soc. *Res:* Preparation and study of chemistry of activated metals, electrochemical studies of organic and organometallic compounds; electron paramagnetic resonance studies on radical anions and cations; preparation and study of organic metals. *Mailing Add:* Dept of Chem Univ of Nebr Lincoln NE 68588

RIEKE, WILLIAM OLIVER, b Odessa, Wash, Apr 26, 31; m 54; c 3. MEDICAL ADMINISTRATION, ANATOMY. *Educ:* Pac Lutheran Univ, BA, 53; Univ Wash, MD, 58. *Prof Exp:* Instr anat, Sch Med, Univ Wash, 58-61, asst prof biol struct, 61-64, assoc prof, 64-66, admin officer, 63-66; prof anat, Univ Iowa, 66-71, chmn dept, 66-69, dean protem, 69-70; prof anat & exec vchancellor, Univ Kans Med Ctr, Kansas City, 71-76; PRES, DEPT ANAT, PAC LUTHERAN UNIV, 76- *Mem:* AAAS; Am Asn Anatomists; Am Soc Cell Biol. *Res:* Hematology; immunology; cell kinetics; metabolism. *Mailing Add:* Dept of Anat Pac Lutheran Univ Tacoma WA 98447

RIEKELS, JERALD WAYNE, b Muskegon, Mich, Oct 31, 32; m 58; c 3. PLANT PHYSIOLOGY, HORTICULTURE. *Educ:* Mich State Univ, BS, 59, MS, 60; Univ Calif, Davis, PhD(plant physiol), 64. *Prof Exp:* Asst prof, 64-68, ASSOC PROF HORT SCI, UNIV GUELPH, 68- *Concurrent Pos:* Grants, Nat Res Coun Can, 65-69, Ont Dept Univ Affairs, 69 & Potash Inst Can, 71. *Mem:* Am Soc Hort Sci; Am Soc Plant Physiol; Int Soc Hort Sci; Coun Agr Sci & Technol; Coun Soil Testing & Plant Anal. *Res:* Vegetable physiology, culture and production with emphasis on mineral nutrition. *Mailing Add:* Dept Hort Sci Univ Guelph Guelph ON N1G 2W1 Can

RIEKSTNIECE, EMILIJA KATRINA, pathology, endocrinology, see previous edition

RIEL, GORDON KIENZLE, b Columbus, Ohio, Oct 26, 34; m 54; c 3. NULCEAR ENGINEERING. *Educ:* Univ Fla, BChE, 56; Univ Md, MS, 61, PhD, 67. *Prof Exp:* Chem engr, 56-59, PHYSICIST, NAVAL ORD LAB, 59-, CONSULT, 69- *Mem:* Health Physics Soc; Instrument Soc Am; Nat Soc Prof Engrs. *Res:* Measurement of radiation in the ocean including cosmic rays, natural and artificial radioactive isotopes; neutron spectrometry and personnel dosimetry; radiation monitoring systems for nuclear reactors and environment. *Mailing Add:* Code R-41 Naval Surface Weapons Ctr White Oak MD 20910

RIEL, RENE ROSAIRE, b Sherrington, Que, Oct 21, 23; m 58; c 3. FOOD SCIENCE. *Educ:* Univ Montreal, BSA, 47, MSc, 49; Univ Wis, PhD(dairy indust, biochem), 52. *Prof Exp:* Prof dairy chem, Univ Montreal, 52-53; res officer, Chem Div, Sci Serv, 53-59; head chem sect, Dairy Tech Res Inst, Can Dept Agr, 59-62; dir dept food sci, Laval Univ, 62-71, prof food opers, 62-74; FOOD RES COORDR, CAN DEPT AGR, 74- *Honors & Awards:* David Prize, 60. *Mem:* Am Dairy Sci Asn; Inst Food Technologists; Can Inst Food Sci & Technol; Chem Inst Can; Fr-Can Asn Advan Sci. *Res:* Protein extraction; texturization; modified fats; freeze-drying. *Mailing Add:* Res Br Can Dept of Agr Ottawa ON K1A 0C5 Can

RIEMANN, HANS, b Harte, Denmark, Mar 11, 20; m 43, 65; c 2. VETERINARY MEDICINE. *Educ:* Royal Vet & Agr Col, Denmark, DVM, 43; Copenhagen Univ, PhD(microbiol), 63. *Prof Exp:* Private practice, 43; vet inspector food, Pub Health Serv, Denmark, 43-45; microbiologist, Tech Lab, Ministry Fisheries, 45-54; chief microbiologist, Danish Meat Res Inst, 54-57 & dir res planning, 60-64; res asst microbiol, Univ Ill, 57-60; res fel food microbiol, 64-65, from lectr to assoc prof, 65-69, prof pub health, 69-80, chief investr, Field Res & Training Prog, 71-80, PROF, UNIV CALIF, DAVIS, 80-, CHAIRPERSON DEPT EPIDEMIOL & PREV MED, 76-, DIR, MASTER PREV VET MED PROG, 81- *Concurrent Pos:* Lectr, Royal Vet & Agr Col, Denmark, 60-64. *Honors & Awards:* Dr C O Jensen's Food Microbiol Reward, 53. *Mem:* Am Vet Med Asn; Am Meat Sci Asn; Inst Food Technol; Am Pub Health Asn; Danish Vet Asn. *Res:* Veterinary epidemiology and preventive medicine. *Mailing Add:* Dept of Epidemiol & Prev Med Univ of Calif Davis CA 95616

RIEMANN, JAMES MICHAEL, b Philadelphia, Ill, Oct 14, 40; m 63; c 2. ORGANIC CHEMISTRY. *Educ:* Berea Col, BA, 62; Univ Ohio, PhD(chem), 68. *Prof Exp:* PROF CHEM, PFEIFFER COL, 66-, DIR ACAD COMPUT, 79-, CHMN, DIV NATURAL & HEALTH SCI, 82- *Concurrent Pos:* Vis prof gen chem, Iowa State Univ, 73-74. *Mem:* Am Chem Soc. *Res:* Flash vacuum pyrolysis in synthesis; ozonolysis of aqueous organic mixtures. *Mailing Add:* Dept Chem Pfeiffer Col Misenheimer NC 28109

RIEMANN, JOHN G, b Gladstone, NMex, June 18, 28; m 61. ENTOMOLOGY. *Educ:* Tex Tech Col, BA, 51; Univ Tex, MA, 54, PhD(zool), 61. *Prof Exp:* Asst prof biol, West Tex State Col, 57-60; vis asst prof zool, Tulane Univ, 61-62; res entomologist, Man & Animal Br, 62-64, RES ENTOMOLOGIST, METAB & RADIATION LAB, ENTOM RES DIV, US DEPT AGR, 64- *Mem:* Entom Soc Am; AAAS. *Res:* Radiation biology, cytology and reproductive physiology of insects. *Mailing Add:* Metab & Radiation Res Lab State Univ Sta Fargo ND 58102

RIEMENSCHNEIDER, ALBERT LOUIS, b Cody, Nebr, May 18, 36; m 62; c 3. ELECTRICAL ENGINEERING. *Educ:* SDak Sch Mines & Technol, BSEE, 59, MSEE, 62; Univ Wyo, PhD(elec eng), 69. *Prof Exp:* Engr, Sperry Utah Co, 59-60; instr elec eng, Univ Wyo, 62-67; asst prof, SDak Sch Mines & Technol, 67-74; gen mgr, Syncom, Inc, 74-80; ASSOC PROF, SDAK SCH MINES & TECHNOL, 80- *Concurrent Pos:* Res engr, Natural Resources Res Inst, 64-67; consult, Respec Corp, 70-74, Durham Assoc, 80- *Mem:* Inst Elec & Electronics Engrs; Nat Soc Prof Engrs. *Res:* Control systems; instrumentation; hybrid computations; computer aided design; computer aided instruction; microprocessors; digital control. *Mailing Add:* Suburban Rte Box 323 Rapid City SD 57701

RIEMENSCHNEIDER, PAUL ARTHUR, b Cleveland, Ohio, Apr 17, 20; m 45; c 6. MEDICINE, RADIOLOGY. *Educ:* Baldwin-Wallace Col, BS, 41; Harvard Univ, MD, 44; Am Bd Radiol, dipl. *Prof Exp:* Asst radiol, Harvard Med Sch, 49; from asst prof to assoc prof, Med Col, Syracuse Univ, 50-51; from assoc prof to prof, Col Med, State Univ NY Upstate Med Ctr, 52-65; DIR DIAG RADIOL, SANTA BARBARA COTTAGE HOSP, 64- *Concurrent Pos:* Consult, Oak Ridge Inst; mem bd trustees, Am Bd Radiol. *Mem:* Roentgen Ray Soc (pres, 80); Radiol Soc NAm; Am Col Radiol (pres, 75); Am Fedn Clin Res. *Res:* Diagnostic radiology with particular emphasis on cerebral angiography. *Mailing Add:* Santa Barbara Cottage Hosp 320 W Pueblo St Santa Barbara CA 93105

RIEMENSCHNEIDER, SHERMAN DELBERT, b Alliance, Ohio, Sept 11, 43; m 67; c 2. MATHEMATICS. *Educ:* Hiram Col, AB, 65; Syracuse Univ, MA, 67, PhD(math), 69. *Prof Exp:* Lectr math, Univ Wash, 69-70; Nat Res Coun grant & asst prof, 70-75, assoc prof, 75-82, PROF MATH, UNIV ALTA, 82- *Concurrent Pos:* Vis scholar, Univ Tex, 76-77; vis assoc prof, Univ SC, 80-81. *Mem:* Am Math Soc; Math Asn Am; Soc Indust & Appl Math; Can Math Soc. *Res:* Interpolation of operators; approximation theory; splines. *Mailing Add:* Dept of Math Univ of Alta Edmonton AB T6G 2G7 Can

RIEMER, DONALD NEIL, b Newark, NJ, Feb 14, 34; m 56; c 2. AQUATIC BIOLOGY. *Educ:* Rutgers Univ, BS, 56, PhD(weed control), 66; Auburn Univ, MS, 60. *Prof Exp:* Fisheries biologist, NJ Div Fish & Game, 61-62; instr aquatic weed control, 62-66, asst res prof, 66-69, ASSOC RES PROF AQUATIC WEED CONTROL, RUTGERS UNIV, NEW BRUNSWICK, 69-, CHMN DEPT SOILS & CROPS, 75- *Mem:* Weed Sci Soc Am; Soc Aquatic Plant Mgt; Asn Aquatic Vascular Plant Biologists. *Res:* Life histories, ecology and control of aquatic vegetation. *Mailing Add:* Dept of Soils & Crops Rutgers Univ New Brunswick NJ 08903

RIEMER, PAUL, b Poland, Mar 20, 24; nat US; m 49; c 3. ENGINEERING. *Educ:* Univ Sask, BE, 47. *Prof Exp:* From asst prof to assoc prof, 50-77, PROF CIVIL ENG, UNIV SASK, 77- *Concurrent Pos:* Consult, Eng Inst Can. *Res:* Structural engineering. *Mailing Add:* Dept of Civil Eng Univ of Sask Saskatoon SK S7N 0W0 Can

RIEMER, WILLIAM JOHN, b Los Angeles, Calif, Jan 25, 24; m 47; c 4. BIOLOGY, ECOLOGY. *Educ:* Univ Calif, BA, 49, MA, 53, PhD(zool), 56. *Prof Exp:* Asst zool, Univ Calif, 55; asst prof biol, Univ Fla, 55-63; Systs asst prog dir, Prog Syst Biol, 63, assoc prog dir, 65; planning officer, Div Biol & Med Sci, 66-79, SR STAFF ASSOC, DIV ENVIRON BIOL, NSF, 79- *Concurrent Pos:* Fulbright lectr, Tel Aviv Univ, 58-59; assoc cur in chg natural sci & herpet, Fla State Mus, 61-63. *Res:* Science policy and administration; evolutionary biology; public administration. *Mailing Add:* Div Environ Biol NSF Washington DC 20550

RIEMER-RUBENSTEIN, DELILAH, b Brooklyn, NY, Aug 28, 10; m 37; c 3. MEDICAL ADMINISTRATION, NEUROPSYCHIATRY. *Educ:* Tufts Univ, BS, 31; Med Col Pa, MD, 36. *Prof Exp:* Intern, Univ Hosp, Boston, Mass, 36-37; jr physician, Boston Dispensary, 37-47; ward physician, Vet Admin Hosp, Bedford, Mass, 48-53, chief phys med & rehab serv, 53-63; dir, John T Berry Rehab Ctr, Mass Dept Ment Health, 63-79; MED DIR, PENTUCKET CHRONIC HOSP, 79- *Concurrent Pos:* Physician in chg, Am Red Blood Donor Ctr, New Eng, Am Red Cross, 42-45; asst, Sch Med, Tufts Univ, 57-63, instr, 63-66; asst physician, Boston Dispensary, Mass, 58-66. *Honors & Awards:* Bronze Medal, Am Cong Phys Med, 55. *Mem:* Am Cong Rehab Med; Am Psychiat Asn; Am Asn Ment Deficiency. *Res:* Mental retardation in all its aspects from developmental to results of habilitation and rehabilitation; psychiatry; geriatrics. *Mailing Add:* 164 Ward St Newton Center MA 02159

RIEMERSMA, H(ENRY), b Neth, Nov 30, 28; US citizen; m 56; c 4. ELECTRICAL ENGINEERING, PHYSICS. *Educ:* Univ Mich, BS, 57; Carnegie Inst Technol, MS, 65. *Prof Exp:* Intermediate res engr, 58-61, res engr, 61-64, sr engr, 65-70, res prog adminr, 70-75, SR ENGR, RES & DEVELOP CTR, WESTINGHOUSE ELEC CORP, 75- *Res:* Attainment of ultrahigh vacua; superconducting equipment, magnets, transformers, generators; electrical breakdown in various environment. *Mailing Add:* Res & Develop Ctr Westinghouse Elec Corp Pittsburgh PA 15235

RIES, EDWARD RICHARD, b Freeman, SDak, Sept 18, 18; m 49, 64; c 2. PETROLEUM GEOLOGY, EXPLORATION GEOLOGY. *Educ:* Univ SDak, AB, 41; Univ Okla, MS, 43, PhD(geol), 51. *Prof Exp:* Geophys interpreter, Robert H Ray, Inc, 42; jr geologist, Carter Oil Co, 43-44, geologist, 46-49; sr geologist, Standard Vacuum Oil Co, 51-53, geol adv, 59-62; regional geologist, Standard Vacuum Petrol Co, 53-59; geol adv, Mobil Petrol Co, Inc, 62-65, staff geologist, Int Div, 65-71, regional explorationist, 71-73, sr regional explorationist, Int Div, 73-75 & Regional Geol Group, 75-77, sr geol adv, 77-79, ASSOC GEOL ADV, MOBIL OIL CORP, 79- *Concurrent Pos:* Vis lectr, Calcutta Univ, 52-53 & NY Univ, 65-70; assoc ed, Am Asn Petrol Geologists, 76-82. *Mem:* AAAS; Geol Soc Am; NY Acad Sci; Am Asn Petrol Geologists; Soc Explor Geophysicists. *Res:* Search for and evaluate the petroleum potential of hydrocarbon provenances and their specific prospects by use of applied geological and geophysical techniques. *Mailing Add:* 6009 Royal Crest Dr Dallas TX 75230

RIES, RICHARD RALPH, b New Ulm, Minn, Nov 16, 35; m 64; c 2. OPERATIONS MANAGEMENT. *Educ:* St Edward's Univ, BS, 57; Univ Minn, MS, 59, PhD(physics), 63. *Prof Exp:* Res assoc physics, Max Planck Inst Chem, 63-64; instr physics, Harvard Univ, 64-65; asst prog dir, US-Japan Coop Sci Prog, 65-66, staff assoc int sci activities, Tokyo Liaison Off, 66-70, prof assoc, Off Int Progs, 70-72, regional mgr Europ & Am sect, 72-74, dep head, Off Int Progs, 75-76, DIR OPERS & ANAL, SCI, TECHNOL & INT AFFAIRS, NSF, 77- *Mem:* AAAS; Am Phys Soc. *Res:* Mass spectroscopy; positive ion optics; precise measurement of atomic masses; administration of international cooperative science programs; science policy; allocation of science resources; operations management; planning and evaluation. *Mailing Add:* Off Asst Dir Sci Technol & Int Affairs NSF Washington DC 20550

RIES, RONALD EDWARD, b Powell, Wyo, Feb 7, 44; m 66; c 2. RANGE SCIENCE, RANGE ECOLOGY. *Educ:* Univ Mont, BS, 66, MS, 68; Univ Wyo, PhD(range mgt), 73. *Prof Exp:* Teaching & res asst forest grazing, Univ Mont, 66-68; nat resource specialist forestry & range, Bur Land Mgt, 68; res asst arid land ecol, Univ Wyo, 70-73, res assoc, 73-74; RANGE SCIENTIST RECLAMATION RES, AGR RES SERV, USDA, 74- *Mem:* Am Soc Agron; Soc Range Mgt; Soil Conserv Soc Am; Sci Res Soc NAm; Ecol Soc Am. *Res:* Principles and techniques important in revegetation of man-caused disturbed areas with emphasis on coal strip-mine land; effects of water on plant specie and community establishment; prairie hay as a seed source for revegetation. *Mailing Add:* Northern Great Plains Res Ctr Box 459 Mandan ND 58554

RIES, STANLEY K, b Kenton, Ohio, Sept 6, 27; m 49; c 3. HORTICULTURE, PLANT PHYSIOLOGY. *Educ:* Mich State Col, BS, 50; Cornell Univ, MS, 51, PhD(veg crops), 54. *Prof Exp:* From asst prof to assoc prof, 53-65, PROF HORT, MICH STATE UNIV, 65- *Concurrent Pos:* Consult, Int Atomic Energy Agency, Vienna, 72-82; coop researcher, Rockefeller Found & Ford Found in Mex, Costa Rica, Turkey & Asia. *Mem:* Fel AAAS; Am Soc Hort Sci; Weed Sci Soc Am; Am Soc Plant Physiol; Sigma Xi. *Res:* Plant growth regulation; herbicide physiology; crop physiology. *Mailing Add:* Dept of Hort Mich State Univ East Lansing MI 48824

RIES, STEPHEN MICHAEL, b Watertown, SDak, Apr 4, 44; m 66; c 3. PLANT PATHOLOGY. *Educ:* SDak State Univ, BS, 66; Mont State Univ, PhD(microbiol), 71. *Prof Exp:* Res assoc plant path, Mont State Univ, 71; res assoc chem, Univ Colo, 71-72; res assoc plant physiol, Univ Calif, Riverside, 72-73; asst prof, 73-80, ASSOC PROF PLANT PATH, UNIV ILL, URBANA, 80- *Mem:* Am Phytopath Soc. *Res:* Identification and control of diseases of fruit crops and the motility and chemotaxis of bacterial pathogens of fruit crops. *Mailing Add:* N427 Turner Hall Univ Ill 1102 S Goodwin Urbana IL 61801

RIESE, RUSSELL L(LOYD), b Kulm, NDak, June 20, 23; m 45; c 1. ELECTRICAL ENGINEERING. *Educ:* Univ Wash, BSEE, 46; Okla State Univ, MS, 50, PhD, 55. *Prof Exp:* With US Civil Serv, Sig Corps, US Dept Army, 42-43; res assoc, Phys Sci Lab, NMex State Univ, 46-47, from instr to assoc prof elec eng, 47-56; prof elec & comput eng & chmn depts, Ariz State Univ, 57-61; prof & assoc chmn, Sch Eng, San Fernando Valley State Col, 61-63; assoc dean acad planning, Off of Chancellor, Calif State Cols, 63-67; CHIEF HIGHER EDUC SPECIALIST & HEAD SECT ACAD PLANS & PROGS, CALIF POSTSECONDARY EDUC COMN, 67- *Concurrent Pos:* Consult, Daley Elec Co, 58-59, Gen Elec Co, 59-61, Western Mgt Consults, 60-63, Marquardt Corp, 61-62, Electronics Assocs Inc, 65- & W N Samarzich & Assocs, 79- *Mem:* Am Soc Eng Educ; Inst Elec & Electronics Engrs; Sigma Xi. *Res:* Network synthesis; reliability; radar; controls; computers; power systems. *Mailing Add:* Calif Postsecondary Educ Comn 1020 12th St Sacramento CA 98514

RIESE, WALTER CHARLES, b Newport, RI, June 8, 51; m 73. GEOCHEMISTRY. *Educ:* NMex Tech, BS, 73; Univ NMex, MS, 77, PhD(geol), 80. *Prof Exp:* Asst geologist, Vanguard Explor, 71 & NMex Bur Mines & Mineral Resources, 72-73; geologist, Technol Appln Ctr, Univ NMex, 73-74; proj geologist, Gulf Mineral Resources Co, 74-81; PROJ GEOCHEMIST, ANACONDA COPPER CO, ARCO, 81- *Concurrent Pos:* Res asst, Univ NMex, 79-81. *Mem:* Soc Econ Geologists; Am Inst Professional Geologists; Asn Explor Geochemists; Am Asn Petrol Geologists; Geol Soc Am. *Res:* Applied geochemical exploration research in the fields of biogeochemistry, arctic geochemistry and tropical geochemistry; uranium ore genesis; scanning electron microscopic alterations studies. *Mailing Add:* 7829 Waverly Mountain Littleton CO 80127

RIESELBACH, RICHARD EDGAR, b Milwaukee, Wis, Dec 5, 33; m 56; c 3. INTERNAL MEDICINE, PHYSIOLOGY. *Educ:* Univ Wis-Madison, BS, 55; Harvard Med Sch, MD, 58. *Prof Exp:* Fel nephrol, Washington Univ, 62-64, instr internal med, Med Sch, 64-65; from instr to assoc prof internal med, 65-73, chmn dept, 73-77, PROF MED, MED SCH, UNIV WIS-MADISON, 73-, CHIEF MED & COORDR ACAD AFFAIRS, MT SINAI MED CTR, 73- *Concurrent Pos:* Markle Found scholar, 69. *Mem:* Am Soc Clin Invest; Am Fedn Clin Res; Am Soc Nephrol. *Res:* Renal physiology and pathophysiology. *Mailing Add:* Dept of Med Univ of Wis Med Sch Milwaukee WI 53706

RIESEN, AUSTIN HERBERT, b Newton, Kans, July 1, 13; m 39; c 2. PHYSIOLOGICAL PSYCHOLOGY, COMPARATIVE PSYCHOLOGY. *Educ:* Univ Ariz, AB, 35; Yale Univ, PhD(psychol), 39. *Hon Degrees:* DSc, Univ Ariz, 81. *Prof Exp:* Res assoc psychobiol, Yale Univ, 39-49; aviation physiologist, US Army Air Corps, 43-46; from assoc prof to prof psychol, Univ Chicago, 49-62; prof, 62-80, EMER PROF PSYCHOL, UNIV CALIF, RIVERSIDE, 80- *Concurrent Pos:* Vis res prof, Univ Rochester, 51-53; NIH res grant, 62-75; chmn dept psychol, Univ Calif, Riverside, 63-68; mem career develop rev comt, NIMH, 64-69; consult primate resources adv comt, Nat Inst Child Health & Human Develop, 71-75, res grant, 76-82. *Mem:* Am Psychol Asn; Soc Neurosci; Int Soc Develop Psychobiol (pres, 70-71); Int Brain Res Orgn; Asn Res Vision & Ophthalmol. *Res:* Sensory deprivation; brain development; behavioral development; sensitive periods; primate behavior. *Mailing Add:* Dept of Psychol Univ of Calif Riverside CA 92521

RIESEN, JOHN WILLIAM, b Summit, NJ, Aug 18, 41; m 63; c 2. REPRODUCTIVE PHYSIOLOGY. *Educ:* Univ Mass, BS, 63; Univ Wis, MS, 65, PhD, 68. *Prof Exp:* Fel, Primate Ctr, Univ Wis, 68-70; asst prof, 70-73, ASSOC PROF ANIMAL INDUST, UNIV CONN, 74- *Mem:* Am Soc Animal Sci; Soc Study Reproduction; Am Dairy Sci Asn. *Res:* Physiology of follicular growth; physiology of the postpartum cow; control of ovulation; physiology and endocrinology of spermatogenesis. *Mailing Add:* Animal Indust U-40 Univ of Conn Storrs CT 06268

RIESENFELD, F(RED) C(HARLES), b Vienna, Austria, Apr 25, 13; nat US; m 39. CHEMICAL ENGINEERING. *Educ:* Univ Vienna, BS, 38. *Prof Exp:* Res fel biochem, Univ Paris, 38-39; org chemist, Harold L Simons, Inc, NY, 42-44; res chemist, Chem Processing Develop, Res Div, Fluor Corp, Ltd, 44-46, sr res chemist, 46-52, prin res chemist, 52-59, chief res chemist, 59-60; process develop coordr, Ralph M Parsons Co, 60-66, dir process eng, Europe, 66-69, dir process develop, 69-78; CONSULT, 78- *Mem:* AAAS; Am Chem Soc. *Res:* Applied chemistry; development of industrial processes for the manufacture of chemicals and petroleum refining; purification of industrial gases. *Mailing Add:* 3460 W Seventh St Los Angeles CA 90005

RIESENFELD, PETER WILLIAM, b Minneapolis, Minn, Sept 6, 45; m 72; c 2. NUCLEAR SCIENCE. *Educ:* Univ Calif, Berkeley, BS, 67; Princeton Univ, MS, 69, PhD(chem & physics), 71. *Prof Exp:* Res asst, Inst Theoret Physics, Univ Frankfurt, 72-74; instr physics, Ind Univ, Bloomington, 74-75; RESEARCHER, RI NUCLEAR SCI CTR, 75- *Concurrent Pos:* Consult, Res Inst Nuclear Physics, Ger, 72-74. *Mem:* Sigma Xi; Am Phys Soc; AAAS. *Res:* Heavy ion physics, nuclear techniques for chemical analysis. *Mailing Add:* Saunderstown RI 02874

RIESENFELD, RICHARD F, b Milwaukee, Wis, Nov 26, 44; m 74; c 2. COMPUTER SCIENCE. *Educ:* Princeton Univ, AB, 66; Syracuse Univ, MA, 69, PhD(comput sci), 73. *Prof Exp:* Asst prof elec eng, 72-74, asst prof, 74-76, assoc prof, 77-81, PROF COMPUT SCI & CHMN DEPT, UNIV UTAH, 81- *Concurrent Pos:* Consult comput aided design; adj asst prof math, Univ Utah, 74-76. *Mem:* Asn Comput Mach; Soc Indust & Appl Math; Math Asn Am. *Res:* Developing mathematical models for representing geometric shape information in a computer; computer graphics; an experimental computer-aided design/computer-aided manufacturing system. *Mailing Add:* Dept of Comput Sci Univ of Utah Salt Lake City UT 84112

RIESER, CHARLES ELY, urology, deceased

RIESER, LEONARD M, JR, b Chicago, Ill, May 18, 22; m 44; c 3. ATOMIC PHYSICS, NUCLEAR PHYSICS. *Educ:* Univ Chicago, BS, 43; Stanford Univ, PhD(physics), 52. *Prof Exp:* Asst physics, Metall Lab, Univ Chicago, 44 & Los Alamos Sci Lab, 45-46; asst, Stanford Univ, 46-51, res assoc, 51-52; from instr to assoc prof, 52-60, dept provost, 59-64, dean fac arts & sci, 64-69, provost, 67-71, PROF PHYSICS, DARTMOUTH COL, 60-, VPRES & DEAN FAC ARTS & SCI, 71- *Concurrent Pos:* Pres, New Eng Conf Grad Educ, 65-66. *Mem:* AAAS (pres 73-); Interciencia Asn (vpres, 76-); Am Phys Soc; Biophys Soc; Am Asn Physics Teachers. *Res:* Reflection of x-rays; x-ray microscopy; proportional counters; experimental nuclear physics; biophysics. *Mailing Add:* Dept of Physics Dartmouth Col 201 Wentworth Hanover NH 03755

RIESKE, JOHN SAMUEL, b Provo, Utah, Sept 25, 23; m 49; c 6. BIOCHEMISTRY. *Educ:* Brigham Young Univ, BA, 49; Univ Utah, PhD(biol chem), 56. *Prof Exp:* Biochemist, US Army Res & develop Command, 55-60; trainee respiratory enzymes, Inst Enzyme Res, Univ Wis, 60-64; asst prof, Inst enzyme Res, Univ Wis, 64-66; assoc prof, 66-75, PROF PHYSIOL CHEM, OHIO STATE UNIV, 75- *Concurrent Pos:* USPHS career develop award, 64-65. *Mem:* AAAS; Am Soc Biol Chemists. *Res:* Structure and function of respiratory enzymes; cholinesterase enzymes; photosynthesis. *Mailing Add:* Dept of Physiol Chem Ohio State Univ Col of Med Columbus OH 43210

RIESS, KARLEM, b New Orleans, La, Apr 17, 13. PHYSICS. *Educ:* Tulane Univ, BS, 33, MS, 35; Brown Univ, PhD(physics), 43. *Prof Exp:* Instr math, Tulane Univ, 33-35, reader, 35-36; prof, high sch, La, 36-42; jr chemist, US Navy Yard, Philadelphia, 42; instr physics, Brown Univ, 42-43; from asst prof to prof, 43-78, EMER PROF PHYSICS, TULANE UNIV, 78- *Mem:* Am Phys Soc; Am Chem Soc; Am Math Soc; Math Asn Am; Am Crystallog Asn. *Res:* Electromagnetic waves in a bent pipe of rectangular cross section; biophysics; mathematical physics. *Mailing Add:* 17 Audubon Blvd New Orleans LA 70118

RIESS, RONALD DEAN, b North English, Iowa, Sept 28, 40; m 62; c 1. MATHEMATICS. *Educ:* Iowa State Univ, BS, 63, MS, 65, PhD(numerical anal), 67. *Prof Exp:* Instr math, Iowa State Univ, 66-67; asst prof, 67-78, ASSOC PROF MATH, VA POLYTECH INST & STATE UNIV, 78- *Res:* Conditioning eigen value problems; numerical analysis of integration. *Mailing Add:* Dept Math Va Polytech Inst & State Univ Blacksburg VA 24061

RIESZ, G(EORGE) W, b Irvington, NJ, Dec 8, 28; m 53; c 2. ELECTRICAL ENGINEERING, SYSTEMS ENGINEERING. *Educ:* Princeton Univ, BSE, 50, MSE, 52. *Prof Exp:* Mem tech staff, 52-54 & 56-58, supvr systs eng, 58-62, dept head adv systs, 62-63, dept head discrimination measurements, Marshall Islands, 63-65, dept head, Nike X Anal, 65-70, dept head traffic network studies, 70-75, dept head network admin, 75-79, DEPT HEAD OPERS SYSTS IMPLEMENTATION PLANNING, BELL TEL LABS, 79- *Mem:* Sigma Xi. *Res:* Telephone network planning, administration and utilization studies. *Mailing Add:* Dept 59524 Bell Tel Labs Holmdel NJ 07733

RIESZ, PETER, b Vienna, Austria, Oct 2, 26; US citizen; m 53; c 3. PHYSICAL CHEMISTRY, RADIATION BIOLOGY. *Educ:* Oxford Univ, BA, 46, BSc, 47; Columbia Univ, PhD(phys chem), 53. *Prof Exp:* Res assoc phys chem, Pa State Univ, 53-54; res assoc, Brookhaven Nat Lab, 54-56; res assoc radiation chem, Argonne Nat Lab, 56-58; res chemist, 58-81, CHIEF, RADIATION BIOL SECT, LAB PATHOPHYSIOL, NAT CANCER INST, 81- *Mem:* Am Chem Soc; Radiation Res Soc; Biophys Soc; Am Soc Photobiol. *Res:* Kinetics and mechanisms of organic reactions; radiation chemistry; effects of ionizing and ultraviolet radiation on nucleic acids and proteins; electron spin resonance; free radical mechanisms; spin trapping. *Mailing Add:* Radiation Biol Sect Nat Cancer Inst Lab of Pathophysiol Bethesda MD 20205

RIETHOF, THOMAS ROBERT, b Teplice, Czech, July 29, 27; nat US; m 49. PHYSICAL CHEMISTRY, ELECTROOPTICS. *Educ:* Manchester Col, AB, 49; Purdue Univ, MSc, 51, PhD(phys chem), 54. *Prof Exp:* Physicist, Aerophys Applns, 56-63, mgr reentry physics, 64-68, MGR SENSOR SYSTS, SPACE SCI LAB, GEN ELEC CO, PHILADELPHIA, 68- *Mem:* AAAS; Am Chem Soc; Optical Soc Am; Am Inst Aeronaut & Astronaut. *Res:* Electrooptical sensors and experiments; remote sensing, optical and infrared, military and civilian; Lidar systems and laser atmosphere experiments; measurement of atmospheric constituents and contaminants; thermal radiation and its measurement. *Mailing Add:* 4124 Barberry Dr Lafayette Hill PA 19444

RIETVELD, WILLIS JAMES, b Harvey, Ill, Oct 30, 42. FOREST PHYSIOLOGY. *Educ:* Ore State Univ, BS, 65, MS, 67; Univ Ariz, PhD(plant physiol), 74. *Prof Exp:* Res plant physiologist, Rocky Mountain Forest & Range Exp Sta, US Forest Serv, Forestry Sci Lab, Northern Ariz Univ, 66-76; PRIN PLANT PHYSIOLOGIST, NORTH CENT FOREST EXP STA, FORESTRY SCI LAB, SOUTHERN ILL UNIV, 76- *Mem:* Soc Am Foresters; Sigma Xi. *Res:* Physiological quality of tree planting stock and post-planting seedling growth; water relations; allelopathy. *Mailing Add:* NCent Forest Exp Sta Southern Ill Univ Carbondale IL 62901

RIETZ, EDWARD GUSTAVE, b Chicago, Ill, Feb 24, 11. CHEMISTRY. *Educ:* Univ Chicago, SB, 33, SM, 35, PhD(org chem), 39. *Prof Exp:* Asst prof chem, Howard Col, 39; chemist, US Food & Drug Admin, Ill, 39-41; chemist, USDA, Calif, 41-46; asst prof chem, Univ Fla, 46, assoc prof, 47-52; from assoc prof to prof phys sci, Wright Col, 52-76, chmn dept, 65-72; asst prof, 56-78, PROF CHEM, UNIV ILL, CHICAGO, 78-, EDUC COORDR, RUSH MED COL, 80- *Concurrent Pos:* Vis assoc prof, St Louis Univ, 55; GD Searle Co, 56, 57. *Mem:* Am Chem Soc; Sigma Xi. *Res:* Sulfur compounds; carbohydrates; agricultural products; steroids. *Mailing Add:* 2948 N Laramie Ave Chicago IL 60641

RIEWALD, PAUL GORDON, b E Grand Rapids, Mich, Aug 31, 41; m 68; c 2. MATERIALS SCIENCE, METALLURGICAL ENGINEERING. *Educ:* Univ Mich, BS, 63, MS, 64, PhD(metall eng), 68. *Prof Exp:* Res engr mat eng & develop, 68-74, sr res engr, 74-77, RES ASSOC MAT ENG & DEVELOP, E I DU PONT DE NEMOURS & CO, INC, 77- *Mem:* Am Soc Metals. *Res:* Characterization and study of fibrous materials; end-use research and development of products from fibers including advanced composites; ropes and cables; industrial applications. *Mailing Add:* Chestnut Run Labs Bldg 701 E I duPont De Nemours & Co Inc Wilmington DE 19898

RIFE, DAVID CECIL, b Cedarville, Ohio, Jan 3, 01; m; c 1. GENETICS. *Educ:* Cedarville Col, BS, 22; Ohio State Univ, BS, 23, AM, 31, PhD(genetics), 33. *Prof Exp:* Instr sci & agr, Mission Sch, Sudan, 27-30; from instr to prof genetics, Ohio State Univ, 34-57; livestock adv, Int Coop Admin, Thailand, 57-59, dep sci attache, Am Embassy, New Delhi, India, 60-62; dir int rels, Am Inst Biol Sci, 62-63; sci adminr, Nat Inst Gen Med Sci, 63-65; vis prof genetics, Univ Fla, 66-71; CONSULT GENETICS, 71- *Concurrent Pos:* Consult geneticist, Ohio Agr Exp Sta, 44-52; Fulbright lectr, Univ Cairo, 51-52; Fulbright res scholar, Uganda, 55-56; mem panel selection awards, Fulbright Found, 56. *Mem:* Am Soc Human Genetics (secy, 55); Am Genetic Asn; Genetics Soc Am; AAAS; Int Soc Twin Studies. *Res:* Human population and behavioral genetics; dermatoglyphics; handedness; twins; genetics of coleus; bovine genetics. *Mailing Add:* 154 Avenida del Rio Clewiston FL 33440

RIFE, ROBERT SELDON, industrial organic chemistry, see previous edition

RIFE, WILLIAM C, b Chicago, Ill, Dec 29, 33; m 62, 70. ORGANIC CHEMISTRY. *Educ:* NCent Col, BA, 56; Univ Ill, PhD(chem), 60. *Prof Exp:* Assoc prof chem, Parsons Col, 60-62; patent chemist, Owens-Ill Glass Co, 62-64; prof chem, NCent Col, 64-72, chmn div humanities, 72-76; fel, Pa State Univ, 76-77; HEAD, DEPT CHEM, CALIF POLYTECH STATE UNIV, 77- *Mem:* AAAS; Am Chem Soc. *Res:* Organometallic compounds; isobenzofurans. *Mailing Add:* Dept of Chem Calif Polytech State Univ San Luis Obispo CA 93407

RIFFEE, WILLIAM HARVEY, b Steubenville, Ohio, Feb 17, 44; m 67; c 1. PHARMACOLOGY. *Educ:* WVa Univ, BS Pharm, 67; Ohio State Univ, PhD(pharmacol), 75. *Prof Exp:* Pharm officer, USPHS, 67-70; teaching & res assoc pharmacol, Col Pharm, Ohio State Univ, 71-75; ASST PROF PHARMACOL, UNIV TEX, AUSTIN, 75- *Mem:* Am Pharmaceut Asn. *Res:* Investigation of the effects of drugs on the central nervous systems with particular emphasis on neurotransmitter dynamics; the study of the mechanisms responsible for the development of tolerance to and physiological dependence on various drugs of abuse. *Mailing Add:* Col of Phar Univ of Tex Austin TX 78712

RIFFENBURGH, ROBERT HARRY, b Blacksburg, Va, June 19, 31; m 52; c 5. STATISTICS, BIOMEDICAL ENGINEERING. *Educ:* Col William & Mary, BS, 51, MS, 53; Va Polytech Inst, PhD, 57. *Prof Exp:* Asst, Univ Hawaii, 51-52; asst prof math, Va Polytech Inst, 55-57; asst prof, Univ Hawaii, 57-61; sr systs analyst, Lab for Electronics, Inc, Calif, 61-62; prof statist & head dept, Univ Conn, 62-70; SR SCIENTIST, NAVAL OCEAN SYSTS CTR, 70- *Concurrent Pos:* Math statistician, US Fish & Wildlife Serv, 58-61; res assoc, Scripps Inst Oceanog, Univ Calif, San Diego, 68-69; prof oceanog,

San Diego State Univ, 68-74 & 78-; lectr, Europ Div, Univ Md, 74-77. *Mem:* Am Statist Asn; Am Soc Qual Control; Biomet Soc; fel Biomed Soc. *Res:* Data exploration in medicine and oceanography; data salvage; time-dependent multivariate analysis. *Mailing Add:* 3069 Award Row San Diego CA 92122

RIFFER, RICHARD, b Chicago, Ill, Dec 3, 39. NATURAL PRODUCTS CHEMISTRY, AIR & WATER POLLUTION. *Educ:* Ind Univ, BS, 61; Univ Calif, Berkeley, MS, 63, PhD(agr chem), 67. *Prof Exp:* Asst specialist, natural prod chem, Forest Prod Lab, Univ Calif, Berkeley, 63-69; res chemist, US Forest Serv, 69-72; RES CHEMIST, CALIF & HAWAIIAN SUGAR CO, 72- *Concurrent Pos:* Res chemist, Statewide Air Pollution Res Ctr, Univ Calif, 69-72. *Mem:* Am Chem Soc. *Res:* Structure elucidation of natural products; pyrolysis mechanisms; cellulose biosynthesis; electrokinetic properties of colloids; ion exchange and reverse osmosis; flavor and aroma chemistry; light scattering; polysaccharides; toxicology, cancer and forensic chemistry. *Mailing Add:* 1401 Walnut St Berkeley CA 94709

RIFFEY, MERIBETH M, b Waukegan, Ill, Mar 18, 24. BIOLOGY. *Educ:* Northwestern Univ, BS, 46, MS, 48; Wash State Univ, PhD, 59. *Prof Exp:* Instr biol, DC Teachers Col, 49-52; Everett Jr Col, 53-54 & Grays Harbor Col, 56-57; asst prof, 57-67, ASSOC PROF BIOL, WESTERN WASH STATE COL, 67- *Res:* Avian physiology and ecology; integration of sciences in nursing. *Mailing Add:* Dept of Biol Western Wash State Col Bellingham WA 98225

RIFFLE, JERRY WILLIAM, b Mishawaka, Ind, Jan 7, 34; m 59; c 6. FOREST PATHOLOGY. *Educ:* Mich State Univ, BS, 57, MS, 59; Univ Wis-Madison, PhD(plant path), 62. *Prof Exp:* Res asst forest path, Mich State Univ, 57-58 & Univ Wis-Madison, 58-62; RES PLANT PATHOLOGIST, USDA FOREST SERV, ROCKY MOUNTAIN FOREST & RANGE EXP STA, 62- *Mem:* Am Phytopath Soc; Soc Nematologists; Mycological Soc Am. *Res:* Diseases of trees in plantings and natural stands; mycorrhizae of conifers; forest nematology. *Mailing Add:* Forestry Sci Lab E Campus Univ Nebr Lincoln NE 68583

RIFINO, CARL BIAGGIO, b New York, NY, Aug 21, 38; m 64; c 5. PHARMACEUTICAL CHEMISTRY. *Educ:* Fordham Univ, BS, 59; St John's Univ, NY, MS, 64; Purdue Univ, West Lafayette, PhD(med chem), 68. *Prof Exp:* Res investr, Olin Mathieson & Co, Inc, 67-68; res investr, Squibb-Beech Nut, Inc, 68-71, performulations sect, Squibb Corp, 71-72, process develop mgr, Topical & Parenteral Trade Prod, Squibb Corp, 72-76; sect chief new prod develop, Morton-Norwich Corp, 76-77; SUPVR PROCESS DEVELOP, J C I AMERICAS, INC, 77- *Mem:* Am Chem Soc; Am Pharmaceut Asn; Acad Pharmaceut Sci; Sigma Xi; Am Mgt Asn. *Res:* Physical pharmacy, especially suspension technology and dissolution characteristics of solid solutions; scaleup activities in solids and liquids. pharmaceutical science; process validation activities. *Mailing Add:* Stuart Pharmaceut Old Baltimore Pike PO Box 945 Newark DE 19711

RIFKIN, ARTHUR, b New York, NY, Apr 7, 37. PSYCHOPHARMACOLOGY. *Educ:* Columbia Col, BA, 57; State Univ NY Downstate Med Ctr, MD, 61. *Prof Exp:* Staff psychiatrist, Hillside Hosp, 67-69, dir, Aftercare Clin, 70-76; res psychiatrist, NY State Psychiat Inst, 76-79; DIR, DIV PSYCHOPHARMACOL RES & ASSOC PROF PSYCHIAT, MT SINAI SCH MED, 79- *Concurrent Pos:* Fel psychiat res, State Univ NY Downstate Med Ctr, 67-69. *Mem:* Fel Am Col Neuropsychopharmacol; Am Col Neuropsychopharmacol; Am Psychopath Asn; Psychiat Res Soc; fel Am Psychiat Asn. *Res:* Drug treatment of schizophrenia, affective disorders, panic disorders and character disorders; impairment of central nervous system in those disorders. *Mailing Add:* Mt Sinai Med Ctr New York NY 10029

RIFKIN, BARRY RICHARD, b Trenton, NJ, Mar 30, 40; div; c 2. EXPERIMENTAL PATHOLOGY, ORAL MEDICINE. *Educ:* Ohio State Univ, BS, 61; Univ Ill, MS, 64; Temple Univ, DDS, 68; Univ Rochester, PhD(path), 74. *Prof Exp:* Assoc prof path & dent res, Med Sch, Univ Rochester, 73-80, assoc pathologist, Strong Mem Hosp, 74-80; ASSOC PROF ORAL MED, PATHOBIOL & ORAL PATH, COL DENT, NY UNIV, 80-, CHMN, DEPT ORAL MED, 80-, ASSOC PROF BIOMED SCI, GRAD FAC, COL ARTS & SCI, 81- *Concurrent Pos:* Prin investr, Pathogenesis of Bone Loss in Peridontal Disease, Nat Inst Dent Res, 76-80. *Mem:* Int Acad Path; Int Asn Dent Res; Am Soc Bone & Mineral Res; Sigma Xi. *Res:* Inflammation and bone resorption; mechanisms of localized loss; pathogenesis of bone loss in periodontal disease; vitro structure of bone resorption. *Mailing Add:* Dept Oral Med Col Dent NY Univ 421 First Ave New York NY 10010

RIFKIN, ERIK, b Brooklyn, NY, Sept 13, 40; m 64; c 2. PATHOBIOLOGY. *Educ:* Rutgers Univ, BA, 64; Univ Hawaii, MS, 67, PhD(zool), 69. *Prof Exp:* Res asst biol, Rutgers Univ, 64-65; res asst, Univ Hawaii, 66-67; Nat Res Coun assoc pathobiol, Naval Med Res Inst, 69-70; dir ecol, Antioch Col, 70-72; consult environ planning, Urban Life Ctr, Columbia, Md, 72-73; dir environ studies prog, New Col, 73-74; dir, Environ Planning/Res Inst, 74-78; PRES, RIFKIN & ASSOCS, INC, 79- *Mem:* Am Inst Biol Sci; AAAS; Am Soc Zoologists; Soc Invert Path. *Res:* Pathobiology of invertebrates, with emphasis on those organisms cultured for aquaculture and/or mariculture systems; surface mining and the environment; environmental policy; analysis and evaluation of the adverse environmental effects caused by coal and nonfuel mining operations. *Mailing Add:* Environ Planning/Res Inst Suite 310 Columbia MD 21044

RIFKIND, ARLEEN B, b New York, NY, June 29, 38; m 61; c 2. PHARMACOLOGY, ENDOCRINOLGY. *Educ:* Bryn Mawr Col, BA, 60; NY Univ, MD, 64. *Prof Exp:* Intern med, III & IV Med Div, Bellevue Hosp, 64-65, first year resident, 65; clin assoc endocrine br, Nat Cancer Inst, 65-68; res assoc endocrine pharmacol, Rockefeller Univ, 68-71; asst prof pediat, 71-75 & pharmacol, 73-78, ASST PROF MED, MED COL, CORNELL UNIV, 71-, ASSOC PROF PHARMACOL, 78- *Concurrent Pos:* Staff fel, Nat Inst

Child Health & Human Develop, 65-68; USPHS spec fel, Rockefeller Univ, 68-70; USPHS spec fel, 71-72; adj asst prof, Rockefeller Univ, 71-74. *Mem:* AAAS; Am Soc Pharmacol & Exp Therapeut; Am Soc Clin Pharmacol; Endocrine Soc. *Res:* Heme, porphyrin and mixed function oxidase regulation; developmental pharmacology and toxicology; biochemical pharmacology. *Mailing Add:* Dept of Pharmacol Cornell Univ Med Col New York NY 10021

RIFKIND, DAVID, b Los Angeles, Calif, Mar 11, 29; m 57; c 2. INTERNAL MEDICINE, INFECTIOUS DISEASES. *Educ:* Univ Calif, Los Angeles, AB, 50, PhD(microbiol), 53; Univ Chicago, MD, 57. *Prof Exp:* Res asst, Univ Chicago, 55-57; clin assoc, Nat Inst Allergy & Infectious Dis, 59-61; from instr to asst prof med, Univ Colo Med Ctr, Denver, 62-67, head sect infectious dis, 66-67; PROF MICROBIOL & HEAD DEPT, COL MED, UNIV ARIZ, 67-, PROF MED, 71-, HEAD SECT INFECTIOUS DIS, 71- *Concurrent Pos:* Consult, Fitzsimons Gen Hosp, Denver, 64-; attend physician, Vet Admin Hosp, 66- *Mem:* Am Soc Microbiol; Am Fedn Clin Res; Infectious Dis Soc Am. *Res:* Infectious diseases complicating immunosuppressive drug therapy; mechanisms of action of endotoxin; respiratory, viral and mycoplasmal infections; viral latency and activation; antimicrobial drug therapy. *Mailing Add:* Dept of Microbiol Univ of Ariz Col of Med Tucson AZ 85721

RIFKIND, JOSEPH MOSES, b New York, NY, Jan 13, 40; m 64; c 4. PHYSICAL BIOCHEMISTRY. *Educ:* Yeshiva Univ, BA, 61; Columbia Univ, MA, 62, PhD(phys chem), 66. *Prof Exp:* Res assoc biophys chem, Univ Minn, 65-67; from staff fel to sr staff fel molecular biol, Geront Res Ctr, Nat Inst Child Health & Human Develop, 68-73, RES CHEMIST, NAT INST AGEING, 73- *Concurrent Pos:* Pegram hon fel, 65-66; NIH fel, 67. *Mem:* AAAS; Am Chem Soc; Biophys Soc. *Res:* Thermodynamics and kinetics of conformational transitions in polypeptides, proteins and nucleic acids; structure function relationships in proteins and nucleic acids; oxygenation of hemoglobin; interaction between proteins and nucleic acids; regulation of oxygen transport; hemolysis of the erythrocyte; the erythrocyte membrane; membrane fluidity. *Mailing Add:* Nat Inst of Ageing Baltimore City Hosps Baltimore MD 21224

RIFKIND, RICHARD A, b New York, NY, Oct 26, 30; m 56; c 2. MEDICINE, HEMATOLOGY. *Educ:* Yale Univ, BS, 52; Columbia Univ, MD, 55. *Prof Exp:* Intern med, Presby Hosp, New York, 55-56, resident, 56-57 & 60-61; assoc med, Col Physicians & Surgeons, Columbia Univ, 62-63, from asst prof to prof med & human genetics, 63-81; MEM, SLOAN-KETTERING INST & DIR, SLOAN-KETTERING DIV, GRAD SCH MED SCI, CORNELL UNIV, 81- *Concurrent Pos:* Nat Found fel, 59-60; USPHS trainee hemat, 61-62; Guggenheim fel, 65-66. *Mem:* Am Soc Cell Biol; Asn Am Physicians; Am Soc Clin Invest; Electron Micros Soc Am; Am Soc Hemat. *Res:* Developmental biology; molecular biology; hematology. *Mailing Add:* Mem Sloan-Kettering Cancer Ctr 1275 York Ave New York NY 10021

RIGANATI, JOHN PHILIP, b Mt Vernon, NY, Apr 11, 44; m 66; c 3. ELECTRICAL ENGINEERING, APPLIED MATHEMATICS. *Educ:* Rensselaer Polytech Inst, BEE, 65, MEng, 66, PhD(elec eng), 69. *Prof Exp:* Co-op engr commun systs, Advan Systs Develop Div, IBM Corp, 61-63, co-op engr thin films & CPU design, Res Div, 63-65; engr mini-comput control systs, Syst Sales & Eng, Gen Elec Co, 67; instr elec eng, Rensselaer Polytech Inst, 68-69; mem tech staff pattern recognition, Electronics Res Ctr, Rockwell Int Corp, 69-77, chief scientist identification systs, Collins Commun Switching Systs Div, Com Telecommun Group, 77-80; WITH SYST COMPONENT DIV, NAT BUR STANDARDS, 80- *Concurrent Pos:* Lectr, Inst Elec & Electronics Engrs, 75- *Mem:* Inst Elec & Electronics Engrs; Pattern Recognition Soc; Sigma Xi. *Res:* Pattern recognition applied to identification systems and image and speech processing; queueing and statistical sampling theory; distributed computer systems; microfilm information retrieval; digital signal processing; coding and decoding; cryptography; data base design; music theory. *Mailing Add:* Syst Component Div Nat Bur Standards Bldg 225 A219 Washington DC 20234

RIGAS, ANTHONY L, b Andros, Greece, May 3, 31; US citizen; m 59; c 1. ELECTRICAL ENGINEERING. *Educ:* Univ Kans, BSEE, 58, MSEE, 62; Univ Beverly Hills, PhD(eng), 78. *Prof Exp:* Elec engr, US Naval Missile Ctr, Point Mugu, 58-61; teaching fel, Univ Kans, 61-63; sr res engr, Lockheed Missile & Space Div, 63-65; sr res engr, Delmo Victor Co, 65-66; from asst prof to assoc prof, 66-73, PROF ELEC ENG & DIR ENG EDUC, OUTREACH DIV, UNIV IDAHO, 73- *Concurrent Pos:* Asst prof, Grad Prog, San Jose State Col, 63-65; NASA-Stanford faculty fel, 67; Nat Sci Found fel, Princeton Univ, 68; US Cong fel, AAAS, 75-76 & Inst Elec & Electronics Engrs; Cong fel, Inst Elec & Electronics Engrs. *Mem:* Am Soc Eng Educ; Simulation Coun; Sigma Xi. *Res:* Missiles and space vehicles guidance and control systems; biological and environmental systems analysis; computer simulation. *Mailing Add:* Dept of Elec Eng Univ of Idaho Moscow ID 83843

RIGAS, DEMETRIOS A, b Andros, Greece, Feb 2, 21; US citizen; m 55; c 2. BIOCHEMISTRY, BIOPHYSICS. *Educ:* Univ Eng Sci, Ahtens, ChE, PhD(phys chem), 41. *Prof Exp:* From res asst to res assoc biochem, 47-53, from asst prof to assoc prof, 53-63, PROF BIOCHEM, MED SCH, ORE HEALTH SCI UNIV, 63- *Concurrent Pos:* Vis prof, Med Sch, Univ Athens & Democritos Ctr Nuclear Res, 70-71. *Mem:* Sigma Xi; Am Asn Biol Chemists; Biophys Soc; Am Chem Soc; NY Acad Sci. *Res:* Biophysical chemistry of proteins; effects of ionizing radiations on mammalian cells; lymphocyte transformation and function; kinetics of cell proliferation. *Mailing Add:* Dept Biochem Ore Health Sci Univ Sch Med Portland OR 97201

RIGAS, HARRIETT B, b Winnipeg, Man, Apr 30, 34; US citizen; m 59; c 1. ELECTRICAL ENGINEERING. *Educ:* Queen's Univ, Ont, BSc, 56; Univ Kans, MS, 59, PhD(elec eng), 63. *Prof Exp:* Engr, Mayo Clin, 56-57; instr physics, math & eng, Ventura Col, 59-60; sr res engr, Lockheed Missile & Space Co, 63-65; from asst prof to assoc prof info sci & elec eng, 65-76, mgr hybrid facility, 68-80, PROF ELEC ENG, WASH STATE UNIV, 76-, CHMN ELEC ENG, 80- *Concurrent Pos:* Asst prof, San Jose State Col, 63-65 & Richland Grad Ctr, 66-67; proj dir, NSF, 75-76. *Mem:* Inst Elec & Electronics Engrs; Am Soc Eng Educ; Soc Comput Simulation; Soc Women Engrs. *Res:* Control system stability and optimization; computer systems; hybrid computer and automatic patching; logic design; parallel processing. *Mailing Add:* Dept Elec Eng Wash State Univ Pullman WA 99164

RIGASSIO, JAMES LOUIS, b Union City, NJ, Aug 13, 23; m 59; c 4. ENGINEERING. *Educ:* Newark Col Eng, BS, 48; Yale Univ, ME, 49. *Prof Exp:* Develop engr, Johnson & Johnson, 49-52, indust engr, Ethicon Inc Div, 52-55, chief engr, 55-58; asst prof, 58-59, assoc prof, 59-65, PROF INDUST ENG, NEWARK COL ENG, 65-, CHMN DEPT, 69- *Concurrent Pos:* Adj prof, Newark Col Eng, 56-58; grants, Newark Col Eng Res Found, 62-63 & 68-69; consult, NJ Sch Bds Asn, 68- & Nat Asn Advan Colored People, 71- *Mem:* Am Soc Mech Engrs; Am Inst Indust Engrs; Am Soc Eng Educ; Nat Soc Prof Engrs; Indust Relations Res Asn. *Res:* Queuing theory; production process design and control; scheduling theory; work methods; job evaluation. *Mailing Add:* 23 Colony Dr Summit NJ 07901

RIGAUD, MICHEL JEAN, b Paris, France, Oct 22, 39; Can citizen; m 63; c 3. MATERIALS SCIENCE. *Educ:* Polytech Sch, Montreal, BApplSc, 63, MApplSc, 64, Dr(metall), 66. *Prof Exp:* Asst prof metall, Polytech Sch, Montreal, 66-71, assoc prof & head dept, 71-74; assoc dir res, Sidbec-Dosco, 74-76; PROF METALL ENG & CHMN DEPT, POLYTECH SCH, MONTREAL, 76- *Mem:* Can Metall Soc (treas, 68-); Can Inst Mining & Metall (pres, Metall Soc, 76); Am Soc Metals. *Res:* Extractive metallurgy; steelmaking; direct reduction; refractories. *Mailing Add:* Dept Metall Eng Campus Univ Montreal Montreal PQ H3C 3A7 Can

RIGBY, CHARLOTTE EDITH, b Winnipeg, Man, July 9, 40. MICROBIOLOGY, HEALTH SCIENCES. *Educ:* Univ Man, BSc, 60, MSc, 63; Univ Ottawa, PhD(microbiol), 71; Univ Sask, dipl vet microbiol, 75. *Prof Exp:* Lectr med microbiol, Univ Man, 66-68; res scientist vet microbiol, Inst Animal Sci, Havana, Cuba, 71-73; resident, Univ Sask, 74-75; res scientist vet microbiol, Animal Dis Res Inst, 75-81, RES SCIENTIST VET MICROBIOL, ANIMAL PATH LAB, AGR CAN, 81- *Mem:* Am Soc Microbiol; Can Soc Microbiologists. *Res:* Salmonella infections of poultry; brucellosis of cattle. *Mailing Add:* Animal Path Lab Agr Can 116 Veterinary Rd Saskatoon SK S7N 2R3 Can

RIGBY, DONALD W, b Anaheim, Calif, Feb 14, 29; m 50; c 1. PARASITOLOGY. *Educ:* La Sierra Col, BA, 50; Walla Walla Col, MA, 56; Loma Linda Univ, PhD(biol, parasitol), 67. *Prof Exp:* Med technologist, USPHS Hosp, Ft Worth, Tex, 53-54; PROF PARASITOL, WALLA WALLA COL, 58- *Mem:* AAAS; Am Soc Parasitol; Am Soc Zool. *Res:* General parasitology; host-parasite relationships; invertebrate zoology. *Mailing Add:* Dept of Biol Walla Walla Col College Place WA 99324

RIGBY, E(UGENE) B(ERTRAND), b Provo, Utah, Apr 12, 30; m 55; c 4. CERAMIC ENGINEERING. *Educ:* Brigham Young Univ, BES, 56; Univ Utah, PhD(ceramic engr), 62. *Prof Exp:* Sr res engr, United Tech Ctr, United Aircraft Corp, 62-64; res chemist, E I du Pont de Nemours & Co, Inc, 64-69; staff engr, 69-72, ADV ENG INORG RES, IBM CORP, 72- *Mem:* Am Ceramic Soc. *Res:* Diffusion in ionic inorganic crystals; high strength ceramics; high wear resistant ceramics; magnetic materials for recording and computer technology. *Mailing Add:* Dept 76G Bldg 061-2 IBM Corp Tucson AZ 85744

RIGBY, F LLOYD, b Calgary, Alta, Nov 10, 18; m 63. AGRICULTURAL CHEMISTRY, BIOCHEMISTRY. *Educ:* Univ Alta, BSc, 42, MSc, 44; McGill Univ, PhD(agr chem), 48. *Prof Exp:* Sr res chemist, Res Div, Can Breweries, 48-63, dir res, 63-65; vpres, 69-79, TECH DIR, JOHN I HAAS, INC, 65-, EXEC VPRES, 80- *Mem:* Am Soc Brewing Chemists; Master Brewers Asn Am; Brit Inst Brewing; Am Chem Soc. *Res:* Plant biochemistry; fermentation biochemistry; food flavors; development of hop concentration. *Mailing Add:* John I Haas Inc PO Box 1441 Yakima WA 98907

RIGBY, FRED DURNFORD, b Missoula, Mont, Sept 11, 14; m 37; c 2. MATHEMATICS. *Educ:* Reed Col, BA, 35; Univ Iowa, MS, 38, PhD(math), 40. *Prof Exp:* Statistician, Pac Northwest Regional Planning Comn, Ore, 37; asst math, Univ Iowa, 36-40; instr, Tex Tech Col, 40-43; mathematician, US Off Naval Res, 46-49, head logistics br, 49-58, dir math sci div, 58-62, dep res dir, 62-63; dean grad sch, 63-68, assoc vpres acad affairs, 68-73, prof math, statist & comput sci, 68-80, dir, Instnl Studies & Res, 73-78, EMER PROF, TEX TECH UNIV, 80- *Mem:* AAAS; Am Math Soc; Math Asn Am. *Res:* Mathematical theories of decision making; mathematical statistics; theory of partially ordered systems; self-organizing systems. *Mailing Add:* 3822 53rd St Lubbock TX 79413

RIGBY, J KEITH, b Fairview, Utah, Oct 8, 26; m 45; c 3. PALEONTOLOGY. *Educ:* Brigham Young Univ, BS, 48, MS, 49; Columbia Univ, PhD(geol), 52. *Prof Exp:* Geologist, Carter Oil Co, 47-48; geologist, Humble Oil & Refining Co, 52-53, from asst prof to assoc prof geol, 53-62, PROF GEOL, BRIGHAM YOUNG UNIV, 62- *Concurrent Pos:* Consult geologist, Union Oil Co Can, 60-74 & Phillips Petrol Co, 75. *Mem:* Geol Soc Am; Paleont Soc; Am Asn Petrol Geologists; Geol Asn Can; Paleont Asn. *Res:* Carbonate deposition and paleoecology of reefs; Upper Paleozoic paleontology; regional geology of Utah, Nevada and Western Canada; fossil sponges and reefs of the world; paleoecology. *Mailing Add:* Room 361 Eyring Sci Ctr Brigham Young Univ Provo UT 84601

RIGBY, MALCOLM, b Hartford, Wash, Oct 26, 09; m 33; c 2. METEOROLOGY. *Prof Exp:* Coop weather man, US Weather Bur, Wash, 27-28, observer, 28-30, sr observer & first asst, Alaska, 30-31, officer in chg airport sta, Spokane, Wash, 32-38, North Head, 38-40, Mont, 41-42, climat res & reports, Washington, DC, 42-46 & climat res reports & abstracts, 46-49;

ed, Meteorol Abstracts & Bibliog, 49-59; ED, METEOROL & GEOASTROPHYS ABSTR, AM METEOROL SOC, 60-; CUR RARE BOOK COLLECTIONS, NAT OCEANIC & ATMOSPHERIC ADMIN, 75-, CONSULT, 80- *Concurrent Pos:* Librn, US Weather Bur, 54; mem, Nat Fedn Sci Abstracting & Indexing Serv, 58-70, vpres, 66-67; chmn subcomt mechanization of universal decimal classification, Int Fedn Documents, 63-70, mem cent classification comt, 62-, chmn comt geol-geophys, 62-65 & 70; chmn comt universal decimal classification, US Nat Comt, Nat Res Coun-Nat Acad Sci, 62-65 & 80-, mem-at-large, 63-66; mem comn hydrol, World Meteorol Orgn, 64-67, reporter, 67-, chmn comt universal decimal classification, 72-73, chmn working group bibliog prob, 73-; tech info specialist, Sci Info & Document Div, Environ Sci Serv Admin, 66-70, historian, Environ Sci Info Ctr, Nat Oceanic & Atmospheric Agency, 70-73. *Honors & Awards:* Am Meteorol Soc Spec Award, 72. *Mem:* AAAS; Am Meteorol Soc; Am Soc Info Sci; Am Geophys Union; Royal Meteorol Soc. *Res:* Scientific information documentation; multilingual vocabularies; preservation of rare books; library and document classification. *Mailing Add:* 5816 22nd St N Arlington VA 22205

RIGBY, PAUL HERBERT, b Humboldt, Ariz, Aug 6, 24; m 54; c 2. MANAGEMENT SCIENCES, APPLIED STATISTICS. *Educ:* Univ Tex, Austin, BBA, 45, MBA, 48, PhD(statist), 52. *Prof Exp:* Sr price economist, Regional Off, Off Price Stabilization, Wash, 51-52; res assoc & asst prof mkt & regional econ, Bur Bus Res, Univ Ala, 52-54; assoc prof statist & dir ctr res bus & econ, Ga State Univ, 54-56; prof econ & dir ctr res bus & econ, Univ Houston, 56-62; assoc prof mgt & dir bus studies, Ctr Res, Univ Mo-Columbia, 62-64; PROF MGT SCI, DIR CTR RES & DEAN RES, PA STATE UNIV, UNIVERSITY PARK, 64- *Concurrent Pos:* Fulbright fel, Nat Univ Mex, 62; vpres, Assoc Univs Bus & Econ Res, 66-67, pres, 67-68. *Mem:* Am Statist Asn; Inst Mgt Sci; Am Inst Decision Sci. *Res:* Cost benefit analysis; problem solving and decision making; program analysis and evaluation. *Mailing Add:* 801 Bus Admin Ctr for Res Pa State Univ Col of Bus Admin University Park PA 16802

RIGBY, PERRY G, b East Liverpool, Ohio, July 1, 32; m 57; c 4. INTERNAL MEDICINE, HEMATOLOGY. *Educ:* Mt Union Col, BS, 53; Western Reserve Univ, MD, 57; Am Bd Internal Med, dipl, 64. *Prof Exp:* Intern med, Univ Va Hosp, 58, resident, 60; clin asst, Boston City Hosp, 61-62; fel hamat, Mass Mem Hosp, 62; from asst prof to assoc prof, Univ Nebr Med Ctr, Omaha, 64-69, prof anat, 69-74, dir hemat, 68-74, asst dean curric, 71-72, assoc dean acad affairs, 72-74, prof internal med, 69-78, prof med educ, chmn dept med & educ admin & dean, Col Med, 74-78; PROF MED & ASSOC DEAN ACAD AFFAIRS, LA STATE UNIV, SHREVEPORT, 78-, ACTG DEAN, 81- *Concurrent Pos:* Head hemat, Eugene C Eppley Inst, 64-68; Markle scholar acad med, 65. *Mem:* Am Chem Soc; Am Soc Hemat; Am Asn Cancer Res; fel Am Col Physicians; Int Soc Hemat. *Res:* Immunology; cancer biology; RNA metabolism. *Mailing Add:* PO Box 33932 Shreveport LA 71130

RIGDEN, JOHN SAXBY, b Painesville, Ohio, Jan 10, 34; m 53; c 6. ACOUSTICS. *Educ:* Eastern Nazarene Col, BS, 56; Johns Hopkins Univ, PhD(phys chem), 60. *Prof Exp:* Res fel chem physics, Harvard Univ, 60-61; asst prof physics, Eastern Nazarene Col, 61-64, assoc prof & head dept, 64-67; assoc prof, Middlebury Col, 67-68; assoc prof, 68-74, PROF PHYSICS UNIV MO-ST LOUIS, 74- *Concurrent Pos:* Res assoc, Harvard Univ, 66-67; Nat Endowment Humanities grant, 70; US rep, Int Sci Exhib, Burma, 70; Fulbright fel, Burma, 71, Uruguay, 75; ed, Am J Physics, 78- *Mem:* Am Phys Soc; Am Asn Physics Teachers; Optical Soc Am. *Res:* Microwave spectroscopy; history and philosophy of science; teaching of science. *Mailing Add:* Dept Physics Univ Mo St Louis MO 63121

RIGDON, ORVILLE WAYNE, b Ashland, La, Aug 25, 32; m 55; c 2. ORGANIC CHEMISTRY, PETROLEUM CHEMISTRY. *Educ:* Northwestern State Col, La, BS, 58; Univ Va, PhD(org photo oxidation), 66. *Prof Exp:* SR PROJ CHEMIST, RES & TECH DEPT, TEXACO INC, PORT ARTHUR, 72- *Mem:* AAAS; Am Chem Soc. *Res:* Petrochemicals applied research; additives and commodity chemicals. *Mailing Add:* 3600 Graves Ave Groves TX 77619

RIGDON, ROBERT DAVID, b Louisville, Ky, Dec 11, 42. TOPOLOGY. *Educ:* Princeton Univ, AB, 65; Univ Calif, Berkeley, PhD(math), 70. *Prof Exp:* Asst prof math, Northwestern Univ, 70-72; vis asst prof, Univ Ky, 72-73; lectr, Calif State Univ, Dominguez Hills, 73-75; asst prof, 75-80, ASSOC PROF MATH, IND UNIV-PURDUE UNIV, INDIANAPOLIS, 80- *Mem:* Sigma Xi; Am Math Soc. *Res:* Obstruction theory in algebraic topology. *Mailing Add:* Dept Math Sci Ind Univ-Purdue Univ Indianapolis IN 46205

RIGERT, JAMES ALOYSIUS, b Beaverton, Ore, Feb 13, 35. ROCK MECHANICS. *Educ:* Univ Portland, BS, 57; Cornell Univ, MS, 60; Univ Ill, PhD(physics), 72; Tex A&M Univ, PhD(geophys), 80. *Prof Exp:* asst prof, 73-79, ASSOC PROF GEOPHYS, UNIV NOTRE DAME, 79- *Mem:* AAAS; Am Geophys Union; Geol Soc Am. *Res:* Deformation processes in rock; internal deformation, rock strength, and frictional properties of surfaces at high pressures. *Mailing Add:* Dept of Earth Sci Univ of Notre Dame Notre Dame IN 46556

RIGGI, STEPHEN JOSEPH, b Olyphant, Pa, Oct 11, 37; m 57; c 3. PHYSIOLOGY, PHARMACOLOGY. *Educ:* Univ Scranton, BS, 55; Univ Tenn, Memphis, MS, 61, PhD(physiol), 63. *Prof Exp:* Res scientist, Lederle Labs, Am Cyanamid Co, 63-66, group leader pharmacol, 66-74; head pharmacol, 74-77, dir biol res, 77-81, VPRES RES & DEVELOP, PENNWALT PHARMACEUT DIV, 81- *Mem:* AAAS; Am Heart Asn; Reticuloendothelial Soc; Am Soc Pharmacol & Exp Therapeut. *Res:* Lipid metabolism; atherosclerosis; diabetes; cardiovascular, central nervous system; research administration. *Mailing Add:* Biol Res Pennwalt Pharmaceut Div Rochester NY 14623

RIGGLE, EVERETT C, b Spokane, Wash, Aug 4, 32; m 52; c 3. NUMERICAL ANALYSIS. *Educ:* Eastern Wash State Col, AB, 52; Ore State Univ, MS, 58. *Prof Exp:* PROF MATH, CALIF STATE UNIV, CHICO, 58-, CHMN DEPT, 73- *Concurrent Pos:* NSF fac fel. *Mem:* Asn Comput Mach; Math Asn Am. *Res:* Gradient methods for the solution of linear systems; Tchcbycheff approximation. *Mailing Add:* Dept of Math Calif State Univ Chico CA 95926

RIGGLE, J(OHN) W(EBSTER), b Painesville, Ohio, Feb 6, 24; m 49. CHEMICAL & ELECTRICAL ENGINEERING. *Educ:* Carnegie Inst Technol, BSc, 45; Univ Mich, MS, 46; Univ Del, MSc, 61. *Prof Exp:* Res engr, 46-64, staff engr, Tenn, 64-69, sr res engr, WVa, 69-73, process engr, Design Div, Del, 73-76, sr develop engr, 76-78, PROJ COORDR, PHOTO PROD DEPT, E I DU PONT DE NEMOURS & CO INC, NIAGARA FALLS, 78- *Mem:* Am Chem Soc; Sigma Xi; Nat Soc Prof Engrs. *Res:* Fundamental engineering properties of materials; high vacuum fluid dynamics; mass transfer operations; photoelectric analysis; process dynamics; high polymer technology; water gel explosives technology; nitric acid technology; electronic thick film technology. *Mailing Add:* PO Box 370 Lewiston NY 14092

RIGGLE, JOHN H, b Avella, Pa, May 28, 26; m 51; c 2. MATHEMATICS. *Educ:* Washington & Jefferson Col, BA, 50; Univ Pittsburgh, MLitt, 52; Cent Mich Univ, MA, 64. *Prof Exp:* Teacher high sch, Pa, 50-64; ASSOC PROF MATH, CALIFORNIA STATE COL, PA, 64- *Mailing Add:* Dept of Math California State Col California PA 15419

RIGGLE, TIMOTHY A, b Coshocton, Ohio, Dec 24, 40; div; c 2. MATHEMATICS. *Educ:* Wittenberg Univ, AB, 62, MEd, 66; Ohio State Univ, PhD(math educ), 68. *Prof Exp:* Instr math, Lima Campus, Ohio State Univ, 66-68; assoc prof, 68-76, PROF MATH & GRAD FAC, BALDWIN-WALLACE COL, 76- *Mem:* Math Asn Am. *Res:* Mathematics education; operations research. *Mailing Add:* Dept Math Baldwin-Wallace Col Berea OH 44107

RIGGLEMAN, JAMES DALE, b Washington, DC, Feb 6, 33; m 54; c 2. HORTICULTURE, PLANT PHYSIOLOGY. *Educ:* Univ Md, BS, 55, MS, 61, PhD(hort, plant physiol), 64. *Prof Exp:* Res asst hort, Univ Md, 57-64; res biologist, Plant Res Lab, 64-67, sr sales res biologist, 67-72, prod develop mgr, 72-78, prod develop coordr, 78-79, mgr field stas, 79, mgr new prod develop, 79-81, MGR LICENSING & UNIV RELATIONS, E I DU PONT DE NEMOURS & CO, INC, 81- *Concurrent Pos:* Mem, North Cent Weed Control Conf; Coun Agr Sci & Technol. *Mem:* Weed Sci Soc Am; Sigma Xi; Int Weed Sci Soc. *Res:* Experimental insecticides and fungicides. *Mailing Add:* DuPont Biochem Dept Wilmington DE 19898

RIGGS, ARTHUR DALE, b Modesto, Calif, Aug 8, 39; m 60; c 2. MOLECULAR BIOLOGY. *Educ:* Univ Calif, Riverside, AB, 61; Calif Inst Technol, PhD(biochem), 66. *Prof Exp:* USPHS fel, Salk Inst Biol Studies, Calif, 66-69; SR RES SCIENTIST, CITY OF HOPE MED CTR, 69-, CHMN, BIOL DIV, 81- *Mem:* AAAS. *Res:* Chromosome structure; gene regulation; X chromosome inactivation; DNA methylation. *Mailing Add:* City Hope Med Ctr 1500 Duarte Rd Duarte CA 91010

RIGGS, AUSTEN FOX, II, b New York, NY, Nov 11, 24; m 52; c 3. BIOCHEMISTRY. *Educ:* Harvard Univ, AB, 48, AM, 49, PhD, 52. *Prof Exp:* Instr biol, Harvard Univ, 53-56; from asst prof to assoc prof zool, 56-65, PROF ZOOL, UNIV TEX, AUSTIN, 65- *Res:* Biochemistry of proteins. *Mailing Add:* 3327 Perry Lane Austin TX 78731

RIGGS, BENJAMIN C, b Stockbridge, Mass, May 11, 14; m 67; c 4. PSYCHIATRY, PSYCHOANALYSIS. *Educ:* Harvard Univ, AB, 36; Columbia Univ, MD, 40; Am Bd Psychiat & Neurol, cert psychiat, 51; Boston Psychoanal Inst, cert psychoanalyst, 64. *Prof Exp:* Intern med & surg, Bellevue Hosp, 40-41; resident gastroent, Hosp Univ Pa, 41-43; instr biochem, Univ Pa, 43-44, assoc, 44-45; resident psychiat, Baldpate Hosp, Mass, 45-47; resident, Metrop State Hosp, 47-48, asst supt, 49-50, clin dir, Adult Outpatient Clin, 49-50; asst instr, Dept Psychiat, Harvard Univ, 53-58, clin assoc, 58-66; asst clin prof, Emory Univ, 66-70; assoc clin prof, 68-70, actg chmn dept, 74-75, PROF PSYCHIAT, MED UNIV SC, 70- *Concurrent Pos:* Intern clin path, Germantown Hosp, 41; intern obstet & gynec, Hosp Univ Pa, 42; fel gastroent, Univ Pa, 42-43; resident psychiat, Mass Gen Hosp, 46-47; attend, Vet Admin Hosp, Charleston, 70-74, consult, 74- *Mem:* AAAS; Am Psychoanal Soc; Int Psychoanal Soc; fel Am Psychiat Asn; Am Acad Psychoanal. *Res:* Biochemistry of oxygen poisoning; general systems theory in psychiatry; analysis of interpersonal process. *Mailing Add:* Dept of Psychiat & Behav Sci Med Univ SC Charleston SC 29401

RIGGS, BYRON LAWRENCE, b Hot Springs, Ark, Mar 24, 31; m 55; c 2. INTERNAL MEDICINE. *Educ:* Univ Ark, BS, 51, MD, 55; Univ Minn, MS, 62. *Prof Exp:* Consult internal med, Mayo Clin, 62; from instr to assoc prof, 62-74, PROF MED & CHMN DIV ENDOCRINOL, MAYO MED SCH, UNIV MINN, 74- *Concurrent Pos:* Royal Soc Med traveling fel, 73. *Mem:* Am Fedn Clin Res; Endocrine Soc; Am Col Physicians; Am Soc Clin Invest; Am Diabetes Asn. *Res:* Bone and calcium metabolism. *Mailing Add:* Dept of Endocrinol Mayo Clin 200 First St SW Rochester MN 55905

RIGGS, CARL DANIEL, b Indianapolis, Ind, Dec 7, 20; m 54; c 4. ZOOLOGY. *Educ:* Univ Mich, BS, 44, MS, 46, PhD(zool), 53. *Prof Exp:* Asst, Univ Mich, 44-45, fel, 45-47; instr zool, Univ Okla, 48-49, asst prof & actg dir, Okla Biol Surv, 49-54, dir, 54-70, from assoc prof to prof zool, 54-71, dir, Univ Biol Sta, 50-69, cur, Mus Zool, 54-66, dean, Grad Col, 65-71, vpres grad studies, 66-71, actg provost, 70-71; vpres acad affairs & prof biol, 71-80, DEAN, GRAD SCH & COORDR UNIV RES, UNIV SOUTH FLA, 80- *Concurrent Pos:* Consult, Coun of Grad Schs, 65- *Mem:* AAAS; Am Fisheries Soc; Am Soc Ichthyologists & Herpetologists; Sigma Xi. *Res:* Taxonomy, natural history and distribution of North American fresh water fishes. *Mailing Add:* Univ of South Fla Tampa FL 33620

RIGGS, CHARLES LATHAN, b Bearden, Ark, Aug 13, 23; m 51. MATHEMATICS. *Educ:* Tex Christian Univ, BA, 44; Univ Mich, MA, 45, PhD(math, statist), 49. *Prof Exp:* Instr math, Univ Ky, 46-49; asst prof, Kent State Univ, 49-51; asst prof, East Tex State Univ, 51-53; assoc prof, 53-60, PROF MATH, TEX TECH UNIV, 60- *Mem:* Am Math Soc; Math Asn Am. *Res:* Mathematical statistics; probability. *Mailing Add:* 3805 61st St Lubbock TX 79413

RIGGS, CHARLES LEE, b Clayton, NMex, Aug 21, 46; m 67; c 2. PHYSICAL INORGANIC CHEMISTRY. *Educ:* Southwestern Okla State Univ, BS, 67; Okla State Univ, PhD(chem), 74. *Prof Exp:* asst prof & detergency res coordr, 74-79, ASSOC PROF, TEX WOMAN'S UNIV RES INST, 79- *Concurrent Pos:* Proposal rev for ISEP prog, NSF, 80. *Mem:* Am Chem Soc; Am Asn Textile Chemists & Colorists; Sigma Xi; Am Oil Chemists Soc; Am Asn Textile Chemists & Colorists. *Res:* Interactions between surfactants, alkalis and other detergent components and auxiliaries with textile fibers and finishes; coordination chemistry of lanthanides; toxicity of combustion products. *Mailing Add:* Col of Nutrit Textiles & Human Develop PO Box 23975 TWU Sta Denton TX 76204

RIGGS, DIXON L, b St Mary's, WVa, June 25, 24; m 52; c 2. HUMAN PHYSIOLOGY. *Educ:* Marietta Col, AB, 49; Univ Mich, MS, 50. *Prof Exp:* Res assoc ecol, Inst Human Biol, Univ Mich, 50; asst prof biol, Simpson Col, 51; assoc prof, Huron Col, 52-58; ASSOC PROF BIOL, UNIV NORTHERN IOWA, 58- *Mem:* AAAS; Nat Sci Teachers Asn; Am Soc Mammal. *Res:* Mammalian physiology and ecology; alcohol, particularly the ingestion, metabolism and effects on the body. *Mailing Add:* Dept Biol Univ Northern Iowa Cedar Falls IA 50613

RIGGS, HAMMOND GREENWALD, JR, b Drumright, Okla, July 30, 31; m 59; c 2. MICROBIOLOGY. *Educ:* Okla State Univ, BA, 55, MS, 65; Univ Tex Southwestern Med Sch Dallas, PhD(microbiol), 69. *Prof Exp:* Res technician & chemist oil prod anal, Jersey Prod Res Co, Okla, 55-62; asst prof med microbiol, 68-73, ASSOC PROF MED MICROBIOL, MED SCH, UNIV MO-COLUMBIA, 73- *Concurrent Pos:* Univ Mo assoc prof advan fel diag virol, Yale Univ, 69. *Honors & Awards:* O B Williams Award, Am Soc Microbiol. *Mem:* Am Soc Microbiol. *Res:* Bacterial genetics concerned with regulation of biosynthesis of cell wall and virulence factors; diagnostic medical microbiology. *Mailing Add:* 904 Cowan Dr Columbia MO 65201

RIGGS, JAMES LEAR, b Webster City, Iowa, Sept 23, 29; m 51; c 2. INDUSTRIAL ENGINEERING, ENGINEERING MANAGEMENT. *Educ:* Ore State Univ, BF, 51, MS, 58, PhD(indust eng), 62. *Prof Exp:* Asst prof mech eng, 58-59, assoc prof indust eng, 62-67, PROF INDUST ENG, ORE STATE UNIV, 67-, HEAD DEPT, 69- *Concurrent Pos:* Consult various industs & govt; consult ed, McGraw-Hill, 74- Fulbright lectr, Yugoslavia, 75; affil faculty, Japan-Am Inst Mgt Sci, Hawaii, 75-; dir, Ore Productivity Ctr, 80-; pres, World Confederation Productivity Sci, 81- *Mem:* Am Soc Eng Educ; Am Inst Indust Engrs; Inst Mgt Sci. *Res:* Engineering economics, production management, operations research. *Mailing Add:* Dept Indust & Gen Eng Ore State Univ Corvallis OR 97331

RIGGS, JAMES W, JR, b Houston, Tex, Mar 15, 14; m 40; c 2. PHYSICS. *Educ:* Loma Linda Univ, BA, 47; Tex A&M Univ, MS, 53, PhD(physics), 58. *Prof Exp:* From instr to asst prof math & physics, 47-53, assoc prof physics, 53-58, PROF PHYSICS, LIMA LINDA UNIV, 58-, HEAD DEPT, 59- *Mem:* Am Asn Physics Teachers; Optical Soc Am; Am Phys Soc; Am Geophys Union. *Res:* Molecular physics and spectroscopy. *Mailing Add:* Dept of Physics Loma Linda Univ Loma Linda CA 92354

RIGGS, JOHN L, b Kingman, Kans, Nov 26, 26; m 51; c 2. VIROLOGY. *Educ:* Univ Calif, Berkeley, AB, 54; Univ Kans, MA, 57, PhD(bact), 59. *Prof Exp:* Microbiol trainee virol, Univ Mich, 59-61, asst prof epidemiol, 61-62; VIROLOGIST, VIRAL & RICKETTSIAL DIS LAB, STATE DEPT HEALTH, CALIF, 62- *Mem:* Am Soc Microbiol; Am Asn Cancer Res; Am Asn Immunol; Soc Exp Biol & Med. *Res:* Application of fluorescent antibody techniques to virology; oncogenic viruses. *Mailing Add:* Viral & Rickettsial Dis Lab Calif State Dept Health Serv Berkeley CA 94704

RIGGS, KARL A, b Thomasville, Ga, Aug 12, 29; m 52; c 3. ECONOMIC GEOLOGY. *Educ:* Mich State Univ, BS, 51, MS, 52; Iowa State Univ, PhD(geol), 56. *Prof Exp:* Instr geol, Iowa State Univ, 52-56; sr res geologist, Mobil Field Res Lab, 56-59; consult geol, Tex, 59-66; asst prof, Western Mich Univ, 66-68; ASST PROF GEOL, MISS STATE UNIV, 68- *Concurrent Pos:* Consult, numerous firms, 52-81; abstractor, Mineral Abstr. *Mem:* Mineral Soc Am; Soc Econ Paleont & Mineral; Geochem Soc; fel Geol Soc Am; Asn Prof Geol Scientists. *Res:* Rock classification; mineralogy and petrology of serpentinite; carbonates; Pleistocene till and loess, stratigraphy and sedimentation. *Mailing Add:* Dept of Geol Miss State Univ Mississippi State MS 39762

RIGGS, LORRIN ANDREWS, b Harput, Turkey, June 11, 12; US citizen; m 37; c 2. PHYSIOLOGICAL PSYCHOLOGY. *Educ:* Dartmouth Col, AB, 33; Clark Univ, AM, 34, PhD(psychol), 36. *Prof Exp:* Nat Res Coun fel biol sci, Johnson Found Med Physics, Univ Pa, 36-37; instr psychol, Univ Vt, 37-38; res assoc, Brown Univ, 38-39; instr psychol, Univ Vt, 39-41; res assoc, 41-45, from asst prof to prof psychol, 45-68, Edgar J Marston prof, 68-77, EMER PROF PSYCHOL, BROWN UNIV, 77- *Concurrent Pos:* Assoc ed, J Optical Soc Am, Vision Res & Sensory Processes, 62-; Guggenheim fel, Cambridge Univ, 71-72. *Honors & Awards:* Warren Medal, 56; Friedenwald Award, 66; Edgar D. Tillyer Award, Optical Soc Am, 69; Prentice Medal, Am Acad Optom, 73; Distinguished Sci Contrib Award, Am Psychol Asn, 74; Kenneth Craik Award, St Johns Col, Cambridge Univ, 79. *Mem:* Nat Acad Sci; AAAS (vpres, 64); Asn Res Vision & Ophthal (pres, 77); Optical Soc Am; Soc Exp Psychol. *Res:* Human vision; vision in animals; stereoscopic vision; electrical recording of nerve impulses. *Mailing Add:* Dept Psychol Brown Univ Providence RI 02912

RIGGS, OLEN LONNIE, JR, b Bethany, Okla, Aug 25, 25; m 47; c 2. CORROSION, ELECTROCHEMISTRY. *Educ:* Eastern Nazarene Col, BS, 49. *Prof Exp:* Group supvr corrosion sci, Continental Oil Co, 52-68; res dir mat eng, Koch Industs, Inc, 68-69; sr res assoc mat, Getty Oil Co, 69-70; SR RES PROJ CHEMIST ELECTRO CHEM, KERR-McGEE CORP, 71- *Concurrent Pos:* Mem adv bd, Univ Okla Continuing Educ Div, 73- *Mem:* Electrochem Soc; Nat Asn Corrosion Engrs; fel Am Inst Chemists. *Res:* New electrolytic processes based on modern concepts; metal/solution interfaces, especially corrosion process and its control; design of electrolytic cells and their component parts. *Mailing Add:* Kerr-McGee Corp Tech Ctr PO Box 25861 Oklahoma City OK 73125

RIGGS, PHILIP SHAEFER, b Chicago, Ill, May 30, 06; m 39; c 2. ASTRONOMY. *Educ:* Carnegie Inst Technol, BS, 27; Univ Calif, PhD(astron), 44. *Prof Exp:* Asst prof astron, Washburn Univ, 37-38, from asst prof to prof physics & astron, 39-47; instr astron, Univ Ill, 38-39; from assoc prof to prof, 47-76, EMER PROF ASTRON, DRAKE UNIV, 76- *Concurrent Pos:* NSF sci fac fel, Univ Calif, 57-58; vis prof, Univ Mich, 54, Univ Ill, 60 & Univ Iowa, 64. *Mem:* AAAS; Fedn Am Sci; Am Astron Soc; Astron Soc Pac. *Res:* Stellar and galactic astronomy. *Mailing Add:* Dept Physics & Astron Drake Univ Des Moines IA 50311

RIGGS, RICHARD, b Polo, Ill, Oct 8, 38; m 61; c 1. MATHEMATICS EDUCATION. *Educ:* Knox Col, Ill, AB, 60; Rutgers Univ, MA, 64, EdD(math educ), 68. *Prof Exp:* High sch teacher, Mich, 60-61 & Tex, 61-63; from instr to assoc prof, 64-78, PROF MATH, JERSEY CITY STATE COL, 78- *Mem:* Nat Coun Teachers Math; Math Asn Am. *Res:* Mathematics education at the secondary and undergraduate level. *Mailing Add:* Dept of Math Jersey City State Col Jersey City NJ 07305

RIGGS, ROBERT D, b Pocahontas, Ark, June 15, 32; m 54; c 4. PHYTOPATHOLOGY. *Educ:* Univ Ark, BSA, 54, MS, 56; NC State Col, PhD(plant path), 58. *Prof Exp:* Asst plant path, Univ Ark, 54-55; asst, NC State Col, 55-58; from asst prof to assoc prof, 58-68, PROF PLANT PATH, UNIV ARK, FAYETTEVILLE, 68- *Mem:* Soc Nematologists. *Res:* Plant parasitic nematodes; variability, control and host range. *Mailing Add:* Dept of Plant Path Univ of Ark Fayetteville AR 72701

RIGGS, RODERICK D, b Racine, Wis, Apr 15, 31; m 55; c 3. NUCLEAR PHYSICS. *Educ:* Dubuque Univ, BS, 55; Iowa State Univ, MS, 57; Mich State Univ, PhD, 71. *Prof Exp:* Instr physics & chem, 58-61, dean men, 61-62, dean students, 62-65, chmn dept physics, 65-69, prof physics & eng & head dept, 69-73, PROF PHYSICS & CHAIRPERSON DEPT, JACKSON COMMUNITY COL, 73- *Concurrent Pos:* Lectr & consult physics curriculum, Spring Arbor Col, 65-69; consult, Sci Assocs, 65- *Mem:* Am Asn Physics Teachers. *Res:* Theory and development of training programs in nuclear reactor technology; physics curriculum development; comparative European science education; low energy gamma ray spectroscopy. *Mailing Add:* 2605 S St Anthony Dr Jackson MI 49203

RIGGS, SCHULTZ, b Owensboro, Ky, Feb 10, 41. MATHEMATICS. *Educ:* Univ Ky, BS, 62, MS, 64, PhD(math), 70. *Prof Exp:* Instr math, Western Ky Univ, 67-69; ASST PROF MATH, JACKSON STATE COL, 71- *Mem:* Am Math Soc; Math Asn Am. *Res:* Analysis. *Mailing Add:* Dept of Math Jackson State Col Jackson MS 39217

RIGGS, STANLEY R, b Watertown, Wis, May 20, 38; m 60; c 2. GEOLOGY. *Educ:* Beloit Col, BS, 60; Dartmouth Col, MA, 62; Univ Mont, PhD(geol), 67. *Prof Exp:* Res & explor geologist, Int Minerals & Chem Corp, 62-67; from asst prof to assoc prof, 67-77, PROF GEOL, EAST CAROLINA UNIV, 77- *Mem:* Geol Soc Am; Soc Econ Paleontologists & Mineralogists. *Res:* Modern nearshore and estuarine sediment studies in the southeastern United States; interpretation of the Atlantic Coastal Plain stratigraphy and sedimentary petrology. *Mailing Add:* Dept Geol E Carolina Univ Greenville NC 27834

RIGGS, STUART, b Port Arthur, Tex, Sept 23, 28; c 3. MEDICINE, MICROBIOLOGY. *Educ:* Rice Inst, 47-49; Univ Tex, MD, 53; Am Bd Internal Med, dipl, 61, cert, 74, cert infectious dis, 72. *Prof Exp:* Intern, Univ Iowa, 53-54, resident internal med, Univ Hosps, 54-57; instr med, Univ Tex Med Br Galveston, 59-61; res fel infectious dis, Univ Tex Southwestern Med Sch Dallas, 61-62; from asst prof to assoc prof, 62-69, CLIN ASSOC PROF MED, BAYLOR COL MED, 69-, ASST PROF MICROBIOL, 66- *Concurrent Pos:* Attend physician, John Sealy Hosp, Galveston, Tex, 59-61 & Parkland Mem Hosp, Dallas, 61-62; attend physician, Ben Taub Gen Hosp, Houston, 62-69, head sect infectious dis med serv & supvr clin microbiol lab, 66-69; consult, Vet Admin Hosp, Houston, 64-66; attend physician internal med, Methodist Hosp, Tex, 67-; attend physician internal med & chief infectious dis, St Luke's Episcopal Hosp, 73- *Mem:* AAAS; Am Fedn Clin Res; Am Soc Microbiol; fel Am Col Physicians; AMA. *Res:* Viral respiratory and central nervous system infections; mycoplasma serology; infectious diseases. *Mailing Add:* Kelsey-Seybold Clin 6624 Fannin Houston TX 77025

RIGGS, THOMAS ROWLAND, b Dallas, Ore, Oct 30, 21; m 58; c 2. BIOCHEMISTRY, NUTRITION. *Educ:* Ore State Col, BS, 44, MS, 45; Tufts Univ, PhD(biochem, nutrit), 50. *Prof Exp:* Instr biochem, Tufts Univ, 49-50, from instr to asst prof biochem & nutrit, Med & Dent Schs, 50-55; asst prof biol chem, 55-61, ASSOC PROF BIOL CHEM, UNIV MICH, ANN ARBOR, 61- *Mem:* Am Soc Biol Chemists; Am Inst Nutrit. *Res:* Amino acid transport, especially as altered by hormones and nutritional factors. *Mailing Add:* Dept Biol Chem Univ Mich Ann Arbor MI 48109

RIGGSBY, ERNEST DUWARD, b Nashville, Tenn, June 12, 25; m 62. SCIENCE EDUCATION, SCIENCE WRITING. *Educ:* Tenn Polytech Inst, BS, 48; George Peabody Col, BA, 55, MA, 56, EdS, 58, EdD, 64. *Prof Exp:* High sch teacher, 53-54; teacher math & sci, Univ of the South, 54-55; from instr to prof phys sci & sci educ, Troy State Col, 55-67; vis prof sci educ, Auburn Univ, 67-69; PROF SCI EDUC & PHYS SCI, COLUMBUS COL, 69- *Concurrent Pos:* Mem, Nat Aerospace Educ Adv Comt, 60-; educ consult,

Ark Proj, Int Paper Co, 61 & US Steel Corp, 62; vis scientist, Ala Acad Sci & NSF Coop High Sch-Col Sci Proj, 64-66; spec consult, Ala Proj, US Off Educ, 65-66; vis prof, Fla Inst Technol, 70-74; vis grad prof, Univ PR, 75-76. *Honors & Awards:* Gen Aviation Mfg Asn Cert Merit in Aerospace Sci, 75. *Mem:* Fel AAAS; Nat Asn Res Sci. *Res:* Philosophy of science and scientific methodology; programmed instruction for use in science education; science teacher education through newer media; dimensional analysis as applied to teacher education in science; aerospace science. *Mailing Add:* Dept of Educ Columbus Col Columbus GA 31993

RIGGSBY, WILLIAM STUART, b Ashland, Ky, July 25, 36; m 63; c 3. MOLECULAR BIOLOGY, BIOPHYSICS. *Educ:* George Washington Univ, AB, 58, Yale Univ, MS, 60, PhD(molecular biol), 64. *Prof Exp:* USPHS fel nucleic acids, Oak Ridge Nat Lab, 65-68, biochemist, 68-69; asst prof microbiol, 69-72, ASSOC PROF MICROBIOL, UNIV TENN, KNOXVILLE, 72- *Concurrent Pos:* NIH career develop award, 72- *Mem:* AAAS; Biophys Soc; Am Soc Microbiol. *Res:* Nucleic acid sequence homology; physical chemistry of nucleic acids and proteins; control of RNA synthesis in normal and malignant cells. *Mailing Add:* Dept Microbiol Univ Tenn Knoxville TN 37916

RIGHTHAND, VERA FAY, b Pittsfield, Mass, Sept 4, 30. VIROLOGY, MICROBIAL BIOCHEMISTRY. *Educ:* Univ Rochester, BA, 52; Rutgers Univ, PhD(microbiol), 63. *Prof Exp:* Jr biologist, Am Cyanamid Co, 52-55; res asst virol, Rockefeller Inst Med Res, 55-59; from instr to asst prof, State Univ NY Buffalo, 63-68; asst prof, 68-74, ASSOC PROF VIROL, SCH MED, WAYNE STATE UNIV, 74- *Mem:* AAAS; Am Soc Microbiol; Sigma Xi; Soc Exp Biol & Med; fel Am Acad Microbiol. *Res:* Host cell-virus interrelationship; picornaviruses; measles virus; virus plaque mutants; oncogenic viruses; SV40 and Rous sarcoma virus studies; biochemical replication of viruses; factor influencing cell susceptibility to virus infections. *Mailing Add:* Dept Immunol & Microbiol Wayne State Univ Sch Med Detroit MI 48201

RIGHTMIRE, GEORGE PHILIP, b Boston, Mass, Sept 15, 42; m 66; c 2. PALEO-ANTHRROPOLOY, SKELETAL BIOLOGY. *Educ:* Harvard Col, AB, 64; Univ Wis, MS, 66, PhD(human biol), 69. *Prof Exp:* Asst prof, 69-73, chmn dept, 76-78, assoc prof, 73-82, PROF ANTHROP, STATE UNIV NY BINGHAMTON, 82- *Concurrent Pos:* Nat Inst Gen Med Sci spec res fel, Osteological Res Lab, Univ Stockholm, 73; vis scientist, Archeol Dept, Univ Cape Town, 75-76. *Mem:* Am Asn Phys Anthrop; Human Biol Coun; Sigma Xi; Soc Syst Zool. *Res:* Biometric and statistical studies of living and subfossil human populations in Africa; early man in Africa and Asia; methods in physical anthropology. *Mailing Add:* Dept of Anthrop State Univ of NY Binghamton NY 13901

RIGHTMIRE, ROBERT, b Bedford, Ohio, Sept 28, 31; m 58; c 1. NUCLEAR CHEMISTRY. *Educ:* Hiram Col, BA, 53; Carnegie Inst Technol, MS, 56, PhD(chem), 57. *Prof Exp:* Tech specialist & electrochemist, 57-61, systs coordr, 61-64, res supvr, 64-69, mgr electrokinetics div, 69-71, petrol prod develop, 71-73, mgr petrol res & develop, 76-81, ENERGY & DIVERSIFICATION RES, STANDARD OIL CO, OHIO, 81- *Concurrent Pos:* Dir, Photosci & Energy Storage Lab. *Mem:* Am Chem Soc; Am Petrol Inst. *Res:* Energy conversion; battery research; coal and shale oil conversion process research; biochemistry; photochemistry; photovoltaic materials research; petroleum fuels and lubricants; geochemistry. *Mailing Add:* 4440 Warrensville Ctr Rd Cleveland OH 44128

RIGHTSEL, WILTON ADAIR, b Terre Haute, Ind, July 21, 21; m 46; c 2. BACTERIOLOGY. *Educ:* Ind Univ, AB, 42; Ind State Teachers Col, MS, 47; Univ Cincinnati, PhD(bact), 51; Am Bd Med Microbiol, dipl. *Prof Exp:* Med technologist, St Anthony's Hosp, Terre Haute, 46-47; lab asst bact, Univ Cincinnati, 48-51; med bacteriologist, Biol Labs, Chem Corps, Camp Detrick, 51-52; assoc res virologist, Parke, Davis & Co, 52-53; res virologist, 53-58, sr res virologist, 58-61, lab dir virol, 62-63, dir virol, 63-66; ASSOC PROF MICROBIOL, MED UNITS, UNIV TENN, MEMPHIS, 66-; TECH DIR MICROBIOL, BAPTIST MEM HOSP, MEMPHIS, 66-, CLIN ASSOC PROF MICROBIOL, 76- *Mem:* Am Soc Microbiol; Am Soc Clin Path; Tissue Cult Asn; Brit Soc Gen Microbiol; fel Am Acad Microbiol. *Res:* Medical bacteriology and immunology; tularemia; virology; chemotherapy of virus diseases and neoplasms; tissue culture; application of cell cultures in viruses and cancer. *Mailing Add:* Dept of Microbiol Univ of Tenn Col of Med Memphis TN 38163

RIGLER, A KELLAM, b Lincoln, Nebr, June 8, 29; m 52; c 4. NUMERICAL ANALYSIS, OPTICS. *Educ:* Simpson Col, BA, 50; Univ Nebr, MA, 52; Univ Pittsburgh, PhD(math). *Prof Exp:* Comput analyst, Douglas Aircraft Corp, 52-54; mathematician, Sandia Corp, 54-55; sr mathematician, Westinghouse Elec Corp, 59-69; PROF COMPUT SCI, UNIV MO-ROLLA, 69- *Concurrent Pos:* Lectr, Univ Conn, 58-59; sr lectr, Carnegie-Mellon Univ, 63-69; consult, Westinghouse Elec Corp, 69- *Mem:* Soc Indust & Appl Math; Asn Comput Mach; Math Prog Soc. *Res:* Nonlinear programming applied to engineering design. *Mailing Add:* Rte 4 Box 79 Rolla MO 65401

RIGLER, FRANK HAROLD, b Eng, June 9, 28; m 57; c 4. ZOOLOGY. *Educ:* Univ Toronto, PhD(limnol), 54. *Prof Exp:* Nat Res Coun Can fel, 55-56, from asst prof to prof zool, Univ Toronto, 57-76; PROF BIOL & CHMN DEPT, McGILL UNIV, 76- *Mem:* Am Soc Limnol & Oceanog; Int Asn Theoret & Appl Limnol. *Res:* Limnology, particularly nutrient cycles. *Mailing Add:* Dept Biol McGill Univ 853 Sherbrooke St W Montreal PQ H3A 2T6 Can

RIGLER, NEIL EDWARD, b Waco, Tex, Nov 2, 08; m 34; c 2. ENVIRONMENTAL CHEMISTRY. *Educ:* Trinity Univ, Tex, BS, 30; Univ Tex, MA, 32, PhD(org chem), 35. *Prof Exp:* From asst to instr, Univ Tex, 30-35; agent, Bur Plant Indust, USDA, 35-37; res chemist, E R Squibb & Sons, 37; assoc agronomist, Exp Sta, NC State Col, 37-38; plant physiologist, Exp Sta, Agr & Mech Col, Tex, 38-43; org chemist & group leader antibiotic res,

Heyden Chem Corp, 43-53; dir process develop antibiotics, Fine Chem Div, Am Cyanamid Co, 53-55, sr res chemist, Lederle Labs Div, 55-60, head, Anal Develop Dept, 60-73; CONSULT, HAVENS & EMERSON, INC, 73- *Mem:* Fel AAAS; fel Am Inst Chemists; Am Chem Soc; NY Acad Sci. *Res:* Isolation, purification, identification and determination of natural products; chemical process development; analytical instrumentation; pollution analysis; industrial waste treatment. *Mailing Add:* 548 Barnett Pl Ridgewood NJ 07450

RIGNEY, CARL JENNINGS, b Port Arthur, Tex, July 28, 25; m 48; c 5. PHYSICS. *Educ:* Univ Louisville, BS, 47; Northwestern Univ, MS, 48, PhD, 51. *Prof Exp:* Asst prof physics, Southern Ill Univ, 50-51; asst prof, Northern Ill Univ, 51-56; prof, Stephen F Austin State Col, 56-57; head dept, 57-78, PROF PHYSICS, LAMAR UNIV, 57- *Concurrent Pos:* Consult, Gen Elec Co, Ill, 54-55. *Mem:* Am Phys Soc; Am Asn Physics Teachers. *Res:* Measurements for thermal conductivity. *Mailing Add:* Dept of Physics Lamar Univ Beaumont TX 77710

RIGNEY, DAVID ARTHUR, b Waterbury, Conn, Aug 8, 38; m 65; c 2. PHYSICAL METALLURGY. *Educ:* Harvard Univ, AB, 60, SM, 62; Cornell Univ, PhD(mat sci, eng), 66. *Prof Exp:* Fac mem, 67-75, PROF METALL ENG, OHIO STATE UNIV, 75- *Concurrent Pos:* Vis researcher, Cambridge Univ, Eng, 81; deleg, US/China Bilateral meeting, 81. *Mem:* Am Soc Metals; AIME. *Res:* Solidification; liquid metals; magnetic resonance; electromigration; friction and wear (materials aspects, deformation, microstructure). *Mailing Add:* Dept of Metall Eng Ohio State Univ Columbus OH 43210

RIGNEY, DAVID ROTH, b Carbondale, Ill, Dec 27, 50. BIOPHYSICS, MOLECULAR BIOLOGY. *Educ:* Univ Tex, Austin, BA, 72, PhD(physics), 78. *Prof Exp:* RES SCIENTIST BIOPHYSICS, INST CANCER RES, 78- *Concurrent Pos:* NIH trainee, 78- *Res:* Theoretical biology; cell physiology; biochemical stochastics; biostatistics. *Mailing Add:* Inst for Cancer Res 7701 Burholme Ave Philadelphia PA 19111

RIGNEY, JAMES ARTHUR, b Flushing, NY, July 12, 31; m 58; c 4. ORGANIC CHEMISTRY, BIOCHEMISTRY. *Educ:* Fordham Univ, BS, 53; Va Polytech Inst, MS, 59, PhD(org chem), 61. *Prof Exp:* Res chemist, Am Cyanamid Co, 53-57; res chemist, Esso Res Labs, 61-66; sr chemist, Enjay Chem Co, La, 66-67; asst prof chem, 67-69, chmn dept, 72-77, assoc prof, 69-78, PROF CHEM, UNIV PRINCE EDWARD ISLAND, 78- *Mem:* Am Chem Soc; Chem Inst Can; NY Acad Sci. *Res:* Organosulfur chemistry; chemistry of marine plants; catalysis. *Mailing Add:* Dept Chem Univ Prince Edward Island Charlottetown PE C1A 4P3 Can

RIGNEY, MARY MARGARET, b Albany, Mo, Nov 10, 26. MEDICAL MICROBIOLOGY. *Educ:* Northwest Mo State Col, BS, 50; Univ Mo-Columbia, MS, 60, PhD(microbiol), 68. *Prof Exp:* Asst prof biol, 68-71, ASSOC PROF BIOL, UNIV WIS-OSHKOSH, 71- *Mem:* AAAS; Am Soc Microbiol. *Res:* Growth characteristics of aeromonas species; isolation and characterization of endotoxins and hemolysins of aeromonas species; pathogenicity of aeromonas species for warm and cold-blooded animals. *Mailing Add:* Dept of Biol Univ of Wis Oshkosh WI 54901

RIGOR, BENJAMIN MORALES, SR, b Rizal, Philippines, Oct 13, 36; US citizen; m 61; c 3. ANESTHESIOLOGY. *Educ:* Univ Philippines, BS, 57; Univ of the East, Manila, MD, 62; Am Bd Anesthesiol, dipl, 70. *Prof Exp:* Instr pharmacol, Univ of the East Med Sch, 62-63; res assoc, Univ Ky, 65-66, resident anesthesiol, Med Ctr, 66-68, asst prof, 68-69; assoc prof, 69-71, prof anesthesiol & chmn dept, Col Med, NJ, 71-74; prof anesthesiol & chmn dept, Med Sch, Univ Tex, Houston, 74-81, prof & med dir nurse anesthesiol educ, 76-81; PROF ANESTHESIOL & CHMN DEPT, SCH MED, UNIV LOUISVILLE, 81- *Concurrent Pos:* USPHS grant, Univ Ky, 63; Am Heart Asn grant, 66; chief obstet anesthesia, Naval Hosp, Portsmouth, Va, 71-73; consult anesthesiol, Vet Admin Hosp, East Orange, Newark Beth Israel Med Ctr & St Barnabas Med Ctr, NJ, 71-74; consult, M D Anderson Hosp & Univ Tex Cancer Systs, 74-81; chief anesthesia, Hermann-Univ Hosp, Houston, 74- & Univ Hosp, Louisville 81- *Mem:* Am Soc Anesthesiol; Int Anesthesia Res Soc; fel Am Col Anesthesiol; AMA; Acad Anesthesiol. *Res:* Biological transport of non-electrolytes and electrolytes in the blood brain barrier; clinical pharmacology of drugs; fluid and parenteral therapy; clinical anesthesia. *Mailing Add:* Sch Med Univ Louisville Health Sci Ctr Louisville KY 40292

RIGROD, WILLIAM W, b New York, NY, Mar 29, 13; m 39. ELECTRONICS. *Educ:* Cooper Union, BS, 34; Cornell Univ, MS, 41; Polytech Inst Brooklyn, DEE, 50. *Prof Exp:* Sci worker, All-Union Electrotech Inst, USSR, 35-39; develop engr, Westinghouse Elec Corp, NJ, 40-51; mem tech staff, Electronics Res Lab, Bell Labs, Inc, 51-77; CONSULT, LOS ALAMOS SCI LAB, 79- *Concurrent Pos:* Sr mem Inst Elec & Electronics Eng; Sigma Xi; Optical Soc Am. *Res:* Microwave electronics; physics of electron beams and gaseous discharges; lasers; physical optics. *Mailing Add:* Rt 3 Box 91-T Sunlit Hills Santa Fe NM 87501

RIGSBY, GEORGE PIERCE, b Wichita Falls, Tex, Nov 19, 15; m 43, 68; c 2. GEOLOGY. *Educ:* Calif Inst Technol, BS, 48, MS, 50, PhD(geol), 53. *Prof Exp:* Res scientist, Snow, Ice & Permafrost Res Estab, Corps Engrs, US Army, 53-56; res scientist, US Navy Electronics Lab, 56-59; staff scientist, Arctic Inst NAm, 59-68; assoc prof geol, US Int Univ, Elliott Campus, 68-74; GEOLOGIST, GEOTHERMAL SURV, INC, 74- *Mem:* Geol Soc Am; Am Mineral Soc; Am Geophys Union; Glaciol Soc; Sigma Xi. *Res:* Glaciology; field and laboratory investigation of ice; arctic field research; mineralogy; petrology; petrography; geothermal field research. *Mailing Add:* 1542 Alcala Pl San Diego CA 92111

RIHA, WILLIAM E, JR, b New Brunswick, NJ, Sept 15, 43; m 66; c 1. FOOD SCIENCE. *Educ:* Rutgers Univ, New Brunswick, BS, 65, MS, 69, PhD(food sci), 72. *Prof Exp:* Res asst food sci, Rutgers Univ, New Brunswick, 65-72; food scientist, Hunt-Wesson Foods, Inc, 72-74, group leader, 74-76, sect head, 76; dir tech serv, Cadbury North Am, Peter Paul Cadbury, 76-78, mgr food technol, 78-80; WITH RES & TECH SERV, PEPSICO INC, 80- *Concurrent Pos:* Consult food indust, 68- *Mem:* Inst Food Technologists; Can Inst Food Technologists; Am Soc Microbiologists; Sigma Xi. *Res:* Food product development and research; food microbiology. *Mailing Add:* Res & Tech Serv Pepsico Inc 100 Stevens Ave Valhalla NY 10595

RIHM, ALEXANDER, JR, b New York, NY, May 18, 16; m 40; c 2. SANITARY ENGINEERING. *Educ:* NY Univ, BS, 36, MS, 39. *Prof Exp:* Mem field party, Brader Construct Corp, 37-39; dist sanit engr, NY State Dept Health, 39-44, water supply engr, 47-49, water pollution control engr, 49-51, chief radiol health & air sanit sect, 52-57, exec secy air pollution control bd, 57-66, asst comnr health, 66-70; dir div air resources, NY State Dept Environ Conserv, 70-76; CONSULT, 76- *Concurrent Pos:* Adj prof, Rensselaer Polytech Inst; mem Nat Air Qual Criteria Adv Comt. *Mem:* Am Pub Health Asn; Air Pollution Control Asn (pres, 73-74). *Res:* Air pollution control. *Mailing Add:* 28 Euclid Ave Delmar NY 12054

RIJKE, ARIE MARIE, b Velsen, Neth, Apr 6, 34; US citizen; m 74. BIOMATERIALS, POLYMER SCIENCE. *Educ:* State Univ Leiden, BS, 56, MS & PhD(phys chem), 61; State Univ NY, MS, 60; Univ Amsterdam, MD, 78. *Prof Exp:* Res officer surface chem, Nat Defense Res Orgn, Neth, 61-64; res officer polymer, Coun Sci & Indust Res, 64-66; lectr chem, Univ Cape Town, 66-67; res assoc polymer physics, Inst Molecular Biophys, Fla State Univ, 67-69; lectr, Univ Witwatersrand, 69-70; SR SCIENTIST MAT SCI, UNIV VA, 70- *Mem:* Am Chem Soc; Opers Res Soc; AAAS. *Res:* Implant tissue response; development of new biomate rials for soft and hard tissue replacement; dental composites. *Mailing Add:* Dept Mat Sci Sch Eng & Appl Sci Univ of Va Charlottesville VA 22901

RIKANS, LORA ELIZABETH, b Grand Rapids, Mich, Feb 7, 40; m 62; c 2. BIOCHEMICAL PHARMACOLOGY. *Educ:* Mich State Univ, BS, 61, MS, 62; Univ Mich, Ann Arbor, PhD(pharmacol), 75. *Prof Exp:* Res assoc nutrit, Mich State Univ, 62-63; clin chemist, St Marys Hosp, Saginaw, Mich, 64-67; res asst pharmacol, Dow Chem Co, Midland, Mich, 67-69; fel, Univ Mich, 70-75, scholar pharmacol, 75-77; ASST PROF PHARMACOL, UNIV OKLA, 77- *Mem:* Am Soc Pharmacol & Exp Therapeut; Geront Soc Am. *Res:* Aging modification of drug metabolism; nutrition and cancer; cytochrome P-450 multiplicity. *Mailing Add:* Dept Pharmacol PO Box 26901 Oklahoma City OK 73190

RIKE, PAUL MILLER, b Duquesne, Pa, Feb 6, 13; m 45. CARDIOLOGY, INTERNAL MEDICINE. *Educ:* Univ Pittsburgh, BS, 36, MD, 38; Thiel Col, DSc, 71. *Prof Exp:* ASST PROF MED, SCH MED, UNIV PITTSBURGH, 48- *Concurrent Pos:* Active staff, Magee Womens Hosp & Presby Univ Hosp; consult, Western Psychiat Inst & Clin. *Mem:* Am Heart Asn; fel Am Col Physicians; fel Am Col Cardiol; fel Am Col Angiol. *Mailing Add:* Magee Womens Hosp Forbes & Halket Sts Pittsburgh PA 15213

RIKE, ZEB W, III, b Farmersville, Tex, Mar 29, 37; m 58; c 1. ORGANIC CHEMISTRY. *Educ:* ETex State Col, BA, 58; Univ Tex, PhD(org chem), 62. *Prof Exp:* CHEMIST, SABINE RIVER LAB, E I DU PONT DE NEMOURS & CO, INC, 62- *Res:* Quality control and process research. *Mailing Add:* E I du Pont de Nemours & Co Inc Box 1089 Orange TX 77630

RIKER, ALBERT JOYCE, b Wheeling, WVa, Apr 3, 94; m 22, 53, 65. PLANT PATHOLOGY. *Educ:* Oberlin Col, BA, 17; Univ Cincinnati, MA, 20; Univ Wis, PhD(plant path), 22. *Prof Exp:* Asst bot, Univ Cincinnati, 17-18, instr, 19-20; instr plant path, Univ, 22-23, fel biol, Nat Res Coun, 23-24, fel, Crop Protection Inst, 24-25, from asst prof to prof plant path, Univ, 25-64, EMER PROF PLANT PATH, UNIV WIS-MADISON, 64- *Concurrent Pos:* Fel, Int Ed Bd, London & Paris, 26-27; vpres, Forest Genetics Res Found, 53; Haight traveling fel, 59; chmn sect bot, Nat Acad Sci, 59-62; mem, Latin Am Sci Bd, 63-65. *Honors & Awards:* Medal, Int Bot Cong, Paris, 54. *Mem:* Nat Acad Sci; AAAS; Am Soc Microbiol; Am Phytopath Soc (vpres, 46, pres, 47). *Res:* Bacterial plant diseases; pathological growth; tissue culture; diseases of forest trees; developing disease resistant trees; publication problems. *Mailing Add:* 2760 E Eighth St Tucson AZ 85716

RIKER, WALTER FRANKLYN, JR, b Bronx, NY, Mar 8, 16; m 41; c 3. PHARMACOLOGY. *Educ:* Columbia Univ, BS, 39, Cornell Univ, MD, 43. *Hon Degrees:* DSc, Med Col Ohio, 80. *Prof Exp:* Res fel pharmacol, 41-44, from instr to assoc prof pharmacol, 44-56, instr med, 45-46, PROF PHARMACOL & CHMN DEPT, MED COL, CORNELL UNIV, 56- *Concurrent Pos:* Traveling fel, Am Physiol Soc Cong Oxford, Eng, 47; vis prof, Univ Kans, 53-54; mem pharmacol comt, Nat Bd Med Exam, 56-59; mem pharmacol study sect, USPHS, 56-59, mem pharmacol training grant comt, 58-61, chmn, 61-63; mem adv coun, Nat Inst Gen Med Sci, 63; mem toxicol panel, President's Sci Adv Comt, 65; mem pharmacol-toxicol rev comt, NIH, 65-; mem adv comts, Pharmaceut Mfrs Asn Found, 65-; vis scientist, Roche Inst Molecular Biol, 71-72, adj mem, 72-75; mem adv coun, Nat Inst Environ Health Sci, 72-75; dir, Richardson Vicks Inc, 79. *Honors & Awards:* John J Abel Prize, Am Pharmacol Soc, 51. *Mem:* Fel AAAS; Am Acad Neurol; Am Soc Pharmacol & Exp Therapeut; Sigma Xi; Am Soc Clin Pharmacol & Therapeut. *Res:* Neuromuscular transmission; neuropharmacology; general pharmacology. *Mailing Add:* Dept of Pharmacol Cornell Univ Med Col New York NY 10021

RIKER, WILLIAM KAY, b New York, NY, Aug 31, 25; m 47; c 3. PHARMACOLOGY. *Educ:* Columbia Univ, BA, 49; Cornell Univ, MD, 53. *Prof Exp:* Intern, II Med Div, Bellevue Hosp, New York, 53-54; instr pharmacol, Sch Med, Univ Pa, 54-57, assoc, 57-59, asst prof, 59-61; Nat Inst Neurol Dis & Blindness spec fel physiol, Sch Med, Univ Utah, 61-64; assoc prof, Woman's Med Col Pa, 64-68, prof & chmn dept, 68-69; PROF PHARMACOL & CHMN DEPT, MED SCH, UNIV ORE, 69- *Concurrent Pos:* Pa Plan scholar, 58-61; field ed neuropharmacol, J Pharmacol & Exp Therapeut, 68-; mem, Neurol Dis Prog Proj Rev Comt B, 75-79; chmn, Pharmacol-Morphol Adv Comt, Pharmaceut Mfrs Asn Found, 70- *Mem:* Am Soc Pharmacol & Exp Therapeut (secy-treas, 78-79); Japan Pharmacol Soc; Am Epilepsy Soc; NY Acad Sci. *Res:* Physiology and pharmacology of synaptic transmission. *Mailing Add:* Dept of Pharmacol Univ of Ore Med Sch Portland OR 97201

RIKERT, JOHN A, b Brooklyn, NY, Jan 8, 27; m 57; c 2. FOOD SCIENCE. *Educ:* Univ Mass, BS, 50; Rutgers Univ, MS, 52, PhD(food sci), 54. *Prof Exp:* Assoc technologist, G Res Ctr, Gen Foods Corp, 54-59 & Lever Bros Co, 59-61; proj leader, 61-71, assoc sci dir, 71-76, SECT MGR NUT & NUT PROD, FLEISCHMANN LABS DIV, STANDARD BRANDS, INC, 76- *Res:* Product and process development of various food products, especially cereals, new vegetable products, nut and snack items, dehydrated foods, frozen meat products, salad dressing, soup bases, pie fillings and candy; food and drug regulations; nutritional labeling. *Mailing Add:* Fleischmann Lab 15 River Rd Wilton CT 06897

RIKLI, ARTHUR EUGENE, b Naperville, Ill, Dec 2, 17; m 44; c 4. PREVENTIVE MEDICINE, PUBLIC HEALTH. *Educ:* N Cent Col, BA, 40; Univ Ill, BS, 42, MD, 44; Johns Hopkins Univ, MPH, 48. *Prof Exp:* Chief heart dis control br, HEW, 59-63; health attache, US Mission to UN Europ Off, Geneva, 63-64; asst dir progs, Div Hosp Med Facil, Silver Spring, Md, 65-68; PROF FAMILY & COMMUNITY MED, UNIV MO-COLUMBIA, 68- *Concurrent Pos:* Med surg adv, 63-64; coordr, Mo Regional Med Prog, 68-76 & Mo Kidney Prog, Columbia, 76-; dir consumer health info prog, Exten Div, Univ Mo, Columbia, 71-73; vis prof, Nippon Med Sch, Tokyo, 74-75; mem prof liability rev bd, State of Mo, 77-79. *Honors & Awards:* Meritorious Serv Award, Chicago Heart Asn, 54; Medal Commendation, USPHS, 63. *Mem:* Am Col Prev Med; Soc Comput Med (pres, 77); Pub Health Serv Club (pres, 66); Nat USPHS Com Officers Asn (pres, 58). *Res:* Resource forecasting by predictive model (End Stage Renal Disease); computer as a diagnostice aid. *Mailing Add:* Dept of Family & Community Med 107 Lewis Hall 406 Turner Ave Columbia MO 65201

RIKMENSPOEL, ROBERT, b Rotterdam, Netherlands, May 9, 30. BIOPHYSICS, INSTRUMENTATION. *Educ:* State Univ Utrecht, PhD(exp physics), 57. *Prof Exp:* Res asst biophys, Res Inst Animal Husb, 56-59; fel nuclear physics, Bartol Res Found, 59-60; res asst biophys, Univ Pa, 60-61 & Stanford Univ, 61-62; sr scientist, Pop Coun, Rockefeller Univ, 62-67; assoc prof, 67-70, PROF BIOPHYS, STATE UNIV NY ALBANY, 70- *Concurrent Pos:* NIH res grant, 64-67 & 70-; Pop Coun res grant, 67-69. *Mem:* AAAS; Biophys Soc; Am Phys Soc; Soc Gen Physiol. *Res:* Nuclear physics; optical instrumentation; flagellar motion; mathematical models. *Mailing Add:* Dept Biol Sci State Univ NY Albany NY 12222

RIKOSKI, RICHARD ANTHONY, b Kingston, Pa, Aug 13, 41; m 71. ELECTRICAL ENGINEERING, MATERIALS SCIENCE. *Educ:* Univ Detroit, BEE, 64; Carnegie-Mellon Univ, MSEE, 65, PhD(elec eng, appl space sci), 68. *Prof Exp:* Solid state engr, Electronic Defense Lab, Int Tel & Tel Corp, NJ, 62, solid state engr, Space Commun Lab, 63; guid engr, AC Electronics Div, Gen Motors Corp, Wis, 64; instr elec eng, Carnegie-Mellon Univ, 67-68; asst prof, Univ Pa, 68-74; ASSOC PROF ELEC ENG, ILL INST TECHNOL, 74-; PRES, TECH ANAL CORP, 74- *Concurrent Pos:* Engr, Hazeltine Res, Ill, 69; consult metroliner vehicle dynamics, Ensco Inc, Va, 70; NASA-Am Soc Eng Educ fel, Case Western Reserve Univ, 71; eng & mgt consult. *Mem:* Sr mem Inst Elec & Electronics Engrs; Franklin Inst; Am Phys Soc. *Res:* Circuit theory, simulations; thick film microelectronics; plasmas; fluid mechanics; energy conversion; magnetohydrodynamics; product liability; evaluation of new technological concepts; analysis of patent claims; management and engineering problem solving. *Mailing Add:* 2124 W 116th St Chicago IL 60643

RILA, CHARLES CLINTON, b Pittsburgh, Pa, Aug 1, 28; m 50; c 2. INORGANIC CHEMISTRY, ORGANIC CHEMISTRY. *Educ:* Col Wooster, BA, 50; Ill Inst Technol, PhD(chem), 55. *Prof Exp:* From instr to asst prof chem, Ohio Wesleyan Univ, 55-62; assoc prof, Parsons Col, 62-65; PROF CHEM & HEAD DEPT, IOWA WESLEYAN COL, 65-, CHMN DIV NATURAL SCI, 76- *Mem:* Am Chem Soc. *Res:* Transition metal complexes; hydrogen bonding; sewage treatment plant gases. *Mailing Add:* Dept of Chem Iowa Wesleyan Col Mt Pleasant IA 52641

RILES, JAMES BYRUM, b Dexter, Iowa, Feb 16, 38; m 60; c 3. ALGEBRA. *Educ:* Reed Col, BA, 59; Univ London, PhD(algebra), 67. *Prof Exp:* From asst prof to assoc prof, 67-76, PROF MATH, ST LOUIS UNIV, 76-, CONSULT, COLLEGIATE ASSISTANCE PROG, 70- *Mem:* Am Math Soc; London Math Soc. *Res:* Infinite group theory. *Mailing Add:* Dept Math St Louis Univ St Louis MO 63103

RILEY, BERNARD JEROME, b Eau Claire, Wis, Feb 15, 28; m 51; c 8. REGULATION LIAISON. *Educ:* St Mary's Col, Minn, BS, 48; Univ Detroit, MS, 50, MBA, 61. *Prof Exp:* Radioceramicist, Glass Div Res Labs, Pittsburgh Plate Glass Co, 54-55; sr res chemist, Isotope Lab, Res Labs, Gen Motors Tech Ctr, 55-65, sect chief, Mil Vehicles Oper, Detroit Diesel Allison Div, 65-77, STAFF DEVELOP ENGR, AUTO SAFETY ENG, GEN MOTORS TECH CTR, 77- *Mem:* Am Chem Soc. *Res:* Use of radioactive tracers in solution of research problems, principally in fields of electrochemistry and surface chemistry. *Mailing Add:* 365 Willowtree Lane Rochester MI 48063

RILEY, CHARLES MARSHALL, b Chicago, Ill, Aug 17, 20; m 46; c 4. ECONOMIC GEOLOGY. *Educ:* Univ Chicago, BS, 42; Univ Minn, MS, 48, PhD(geol), 50. *Prof Exp:* Asst geol, Univ Minn, 47-50; asst prof, Univ Nebr, 50-57; RES GEOLOGIST, EXXON PROD RES CO, 57- *Mem:* Geol Soc Am; Am Asn Petrol Geol. *Res:* Sedimentary petrography; organic geochemistry; dolomite; petroleum; economic minerals. *Mailing Add:* Exxon Prod Res Co PO Box 2189 Houston TX 77001

RILEY, CHARLES VICTOR, b Dover, Ohio, May 7, 21; m 45; c 2. BIOLOGY, ECOLOGY. *Educ:* Kent State Univ, BS, 42; Ohio State Univ, MS, 47, PhD(zool), 52. *Prof Exp:* From instr to assoc prof, 48-61, PROF BIOL SCI, KENT STATE UNIV, 61-, CHMN DEPT, 59- *Concurrent Pos:* Mem panel, Nat Acad Sci-Nat Acad Eng-Nat Res Coun, 68-69. *Mem:* AAAS; Sigma Xi; Soil Conserv Soc Am; Wildlife Soc; Am Fisheries Soc. *Res:* Limnology; conservation. *Mailing Add:* Dept of Biol Sci Kent State Univ Kent OH 44240

RILEY, CLAUDE FRANK, JR, b Milledgeville, Ga, Apr 24, 22; m 47; c 3. AERONAUTICAL & MECHANICAL ENGINEERING. *Educ:* Ga Inst Tech, BS, 43; Univ Mich, MS, 49. *Prof Exp:* Propulsion engr, Bell Aircraft Corp, 46-47; assoc prof, Univ Mich, 47-50; sr operating vpres, Booz, Allen & Hamilton, 50-71; corp & group vpres & mem exec comt, Auerbach Corp Sci & Technol, 71-72, gen mgr, Auerback Asn, Inc, 71-72; vpres & gen mgr, Computing & Software Corp, 72-74; V PRES, TRACOR INC, 74-, MEM BD DIRS, TRACOR-JITCO, 74- *Concurrent Pos:* Mem bd dir, Am Fedn Info Processing Socs; exec off, Ga Mil Col; chmn distinguished lect series, Nat Bd Trade; lectr, Int Telemetry Conf; chmn, Proj Aristolle, Nat Security Indust Asn. *Mem:* Assoc fel Am Inst Aeronaut & Astronaut; Prof Engrs Soc. *Res:* Aeronautics; propulsion; instrumentation; computer technology; scientific and general management and marketing. *Mailing Add:* 10825 Foxhunt Lane Potomac MD 20854

RILEY, CLYDE, b Niagara Falls, NY, Feb 19, 39; m 61. PHYSICAL CHEMISTRY. *Educ:* Univ Rochester, BS, 60; Fla State Univ, PhD. *Prof Exp:* proj assoc, Univ Wis-Madison, 65-67, asst prof, 67-68, assoc prof, 68-79, PROF CHEM, UNIV ALA, HUNTSVILLE, 79-, CHMN DEPT, 72- *Mem:* Am Chem Soc. *Res:* Laser induced chemistry; reactive scattering from crossed molecular beams; pyrolysis decomposition mechanisms by modulated molecular beam velocity; analysis mass spectrometry; electrodeposition in low gravity. *Mailing Add:* Dept of Chem Univ Ala Huntsville AL 35899

RILEY, DANNY ARTHUR, b Rhinelander, Wis, Nov 18, 44; m 70; c 1. ANATOMY. *Educ:* Univ Wis, BS, 66, PhD(anat), 71. *Prof Exp:* Muscular Dystrophy Asn Am fel, NIH, 72-73; ASST PROF ANAT, UNIV CALIF, SAN FRANCISCO, 73- *Mem:* Int Soc Electromyographic Kinesiology; Am Asn Anatomists. *Res:* Skeletal muscle, differentiation of fiber types; regeneration, neural dependence, hormonal dependence as studied histochemically, electronmicroscopically and physiologically. *Mailing Add:* Dept Anat Univ Calif San Francisco CA 94143

RILEY, DAVID WAEGAR, b Winchester, Mass, May 7, 21; m 45; c 3. RHEOLOGY, MATERIAL SCIENCE ENGINEERING. *Educ:* Tufts Col, BS, 43; Ohio State Univ, MSc, 49, PhD(chem), 51. *Prof Exp:* Res chemist, Res Ctr, Goodyear Tire & Rubber Co, 43-44 & 46; asst gen chem, Ohio State Univ, 46 & 49-51; res chemist, Polychem Dept, E I du Pont de Nemours & Co, 51-54; res chemist, Silicones Div, Union Carbide Corp, 54-60; sr develop engr, Western Elec Co, 60-67; res adv & group mgr technol, Gen Cable Res Ctr, 67-76; dir plastics eng, Sci Process & Res, 76-78; mat res specialist, Tenneco Chemicals, Inc, 78-81; CONSULT, EXTRUSION ENGRS, 81- *Mem:* Fel AAAS; fel Am Inst Chem; Am Chem Soc; Soc Plastics Engineers; Inst Elec & Electronics Engrs. *Res:* Polyethylene; silicone polymers; rheology of vinyl chloride compounds; thermal stability and extrusion of polymers; computer simulation of extrusion; coefficient of friction of plastics and solids convexing; calendering; theory of lubrication of polyvinyl chloride compounds. *Mailing Add:* 308 Pemberton Ave Plainfield NJ 07060

RILEY, DENNIS PATRICK, b Tiffin, Ohio, Jan 22, 47; m 73; c 1. CATALYTIC OXIDATION CHEMISTRY. *Educ:* Heidelberg Col, BS, 69; Ohio State Univ, PhD(chem), 75. *Prof Exp:* Staff indexer chem, Chem Abstracts Serv, 69-71; fel chem, Univ Chicago, 75-76; RES CHEMIST, TECHNOL DIV, PROCTER & GAMBLE CO, 76- *Mem:* Am Chem Soc; AAAS. *Res:* Catalytic asymmetric hydrogenations; better catalysts for molecular oxygen activation. *Mailing Add:* Miami Valley Lab Procter & Gamble Co PO Box 39175 Cincinnati OH 45247

RILEY, EDGAR FRANCIS, b Platteville, Wis, Nov 26, 14; m 43; c 4. RADIOBIOLOGY. *Educ:* Univ Wis, AB, 38; Univ Iowa, PhD(bot), 53. *Prof Exp:* Assoc biologist, Manhattan Proj, Oak Ridge, Tenn, 43-48; asst bot, 50-53, res assoc, Radiation Res Lab, 53-55, from asst prof to assoc prof, 55-69, PROF RADIOBIOL, RADIATION RES LAB, UNIV IOWA, 69- *Concurrent Pos:* Consult, AEC. *Mem:* AAAS; Radiation Res Soc; Am Inst Biol Sci; NY Acad Sci; Am Soc Plant Physiol. *Res:* Comparative biological effects of different ionizing radiations; effect of x-radiation on plant growth; radiation cataracts. *Mailing Add:* Radiation Res Lab Univ of Iowa Iowa City IA 52242

RILEY, EDWARD EDDY, JR, cell biology, histophysiology, deceased

RILEY, GENE ALDEN, b Wheeling, WVa, July 7, 30; m 53; c 3. PHARMACOLOGY. *Educ:* Duquesne Univ, BS, 52; Case Western Reserve Univ, PhD(pharmacol), 61. *Prof Exp:* From instr to asst prof pharmacol, Western Reserve Univ, 61-66; assoc prof, 66-72, PROF PHARMACOL, SCH PHARM, DUQUESNE UNIV, 72-, CHMN DEPT PHARMACOL & TOXICOL, 70- *Concurrent Pos:* NIH res grant, 64-69; mem teaching staff, St Francis Hosp, Pittsburgh, 67- *Mem:* ?Am Pharmaceut Asn; Acad Pharmaceut Sci. *Res:* Hormonal control of intermediary metabolism; drug mechanisms leading to intracellular variations in adenosine-phosphate. *Mailing Add:* Dept of Pharmacol & Toxicol Duquesne Univ Sch of Pharm Pittsburgh PA 15219

RILEY, HARRIS D, JR, b Clarksdale, Miss, Nov 12, 25; m 50; c 3. PEDIATRICS. *Educ:* Vanderbilt Univ, BA, 45, MD, 48. *Prof Exp:* Instr pediat, Sch Med, Vanderbilt Univ, 53-57; PROF PEDIAT, SCH MED, UNIV OKLA, 58- *Mem:* Soc Pediat Res; Am Acad Pediat; Am Pediat Soc; Infectious Dis Soc Am. *Res:* Infectious diseases, immunology and renal disease. *Mailing Add:* Children's Mem Hosp Dept Pediat Univ of Okla Med Ctr Oklahoma City OK 73190

RILEY, HERBERT PARKES, b Brooklyn, NY, June 28, 04; m 35; c 1. CYTOGENETICS. *Educ:* Princeton Univ, AB, 25, AM, 29, PhD(genetics), 31. *Hon Degrees:* DSc, Univ Ky, 76. *Prof Exp:* Asst biol, Princeton Univ, 28-30, Procter fel, 31-32; fel biol, Nat Res Coun, Bussey Inst, Harvard Univ, 32-34; asst prof, Newcomb Col, Tulane Univ, 34-38; from asst prof to assoc prof bot, Univ Wash, 38-42; from prof to distinguished prof, 42-74, head dept, 42-65, EMER DISTINGUISHED PROF BOT, UNIV KY, 74- *Concurrent Pos:* Ed plant genetics sect, Biol Abstracts, 50-; vis Fulbright lectr, Univ Pretoria, SAfrica, 55 & Univ Cape Town, 56; mem bd, Index to Plant Chromosome Numbers, 58-74; vis prof, Univ Calif, Irvine, 67-68; external examr, Univ Calcutta, India, 60-; vis prof, Chapman Col World Campus Afloat, 74; adj prof, Transylvania Univ, 79- *Mem:* Fel AAAS; Am Soc Naturalists; Genetics Soc Am; Bot Soc Am; Am Genetic Asn. *Res:* Chromosome aberrations in wild populations; cytogenetics of South African plants. *Mailing Add:* 1023 E Cooper Dr Lexington KY 40502

RILEY, JAMES A, b Minneapolis, Minn, May 26, 37; m 62; c 2. PHYSICS. *Educ:* Univ Minn, BS, 60; Temple Univ, MA, 64; Univ Minn, PhD(physics), 69. *Prof Exp:* Pub sch teacher, Mich, 60-63; instr physics, Mankato State Col, 64-65; from asst prof to assoc prof, 69-79, PROF PHYSICS, DRURY COL, 79- *Concurrent Pos:* Res Corp Fredrick Gardner Cottrell grant, 70. *Mem:* Am Asn Physics Teachers. *Res:* Interaction of atomic oxygen with solid surfaces; analysis of causes of failure of carbonated beverage bottles and closures. *Mailing Add:* Dept of Physics Drury Col Springfield MO 65802

RILEY, JAMES DANIEL, b Tuscola, Ill, June 25, 20; m 52; c 2. PURE MATHEMATICS. *Educ:* Park Col, AB, 42; Univ Kans, MA, 48, PhD(math), 52. *Prof Exp:* Asst instr math, Park Col, 46; asst, Univ Kans, 46-48; mathematician, Naval Res Lab, 48-49; asst, Univ Md, 49-50; mathematician, Naval Ord Lab, 52-54; asst prof math, Univ Ky, 54-55; asst prof, Iowa State Univ, 55-58; mem tech staff, Space Tech Labs, Inc Div, Thompson Ramo Wooldridge, Inc, 58-61; mem tech staff, Aerospace Corp, 61-66; staff mathematician, Hughes Aircraft Co, Calif, 66-67; sr exec adv, Western Div, McDonnell Douglas Astronautics Co, Huntington Beach, 67-72, sr staff scientist, 72-74; mem tech staff, TRW, Inc, 74-75; lectr math, Univ Kebangsaan, Malaysia, 75-77; mem staff, Abacus Prog Corp, 77-80; MEM STAFF, HONEYWELL, INC, 80- *Mem:* Am Math Soc; Soc Indust & Appl Math; Math Asn Am. *Res:* Complex variables; numerical analysis. *Mailing Add:* 6195 Sylvan Dr Simi Valley CA 93063

RILEY, JOHN ASTWOOD, b Belmont, Mass, Feb 19, 30; m 54; c 4. ALGEBRA, APPLIED MATHEMATICS. *Educ:* Fordham Univ, BS, 51; Boston Col, MA, 57; Brandeis Univ, MA, 59, PhD, 64. *Prof Exp:* Math analyst, Pratt & Whitney Aircraft Div, United Aircraft Corp, 52-55; res assoc math, Parke Math Labs Inc, 55-65; assoc prof, Lowell Technol Inst, 65-66, prof & head dept, 66-69; PROF MATH, STATE UNIV NY COL PLATTSBURGH, 69- *Mem:* Math Asn Am. *Res:* Ring theory; operations research. *Mailing Add:* Box 230 Main St Chazy NY 12921

RILEY, JOHN PAUL, b Celista, BC, June 27, 27; m 52; c 4. CIVIL ENGINEERING. *Educ:* Univ BC, BASc, 50; Utah State Univ, CE, 53, PhD(civil eng), 67. *Prof Exp:* Res fel civil eng, Utah State Univ, 51-52; asst hydraul engr, Water Rights Br, BC Prov Govt, 52-54; instr agr eng, Ore State Univ, 54-57; dist eng, Water Rights Br, BC Prov Govt, 57-62, proj eng, Water Invests Br, 62-63; res asst, 63-67, assoc prof, 67-71, PROF CIVIL ENG, UTAH STATE UNIV, 71- *Mem:* Am Soc Civil Engrs; Am Soc Agr Engrs; Am Soc Eng Educ; Am Water Resources Asn; Am Geophys Union. *Res:* Water rights and computer simulation of water resource systems. *Mailing Add:* Utah Water Res Lab Utah State Univ Logan UT 84321

RILEY, JOHN THOMAS, b Bardstown, Ky, Apr 2, 42; m 63; c 2. ANALYTICAL CHEMISTRY, COAL CHEMISTRY. *Educ:* Western Ky Univ, BS, 64; Univ Ky, PhD(inorg chem), 68. *Prof Exp:* From asst prof to assoc prof, 68-81, actg head dept, 81, PROF CHEM, WESTERN KY UNIV, 81- *Concurrent Pos:* Prin investr, four coal anal grants, 79-81; consult, area industs, 70- *Mem:* Am Chem Soc; Sigma Xi; Am Soc Testing & Mat. *Res:* Voltametric measurements, particularly anodic stripping and cyclic voltametry; determination of trace elements in coal, coal ash and coal-derived liquids; transition metal oxy-anions. *Mailing Add:* Dept of Chem Western Ky Univ Bowling Green KY 42101

RILEY, KENNETH LLOYD, b New Orleans, La, Feb 25, 41; m 61; c 2. CHEMICAL ENGINEERING. *Educ:* La State Univ, BS, 63, MS, 65, PhD(chem eng), 67. *Prof Exp:* Staff engr, 67-80, SR STAFF ENGR, EXXON RES & DEVELOP LABS, EXXON CO, USA, 80- *Concurrent Pos:* Adj prof chem eng, La State Univ, 78- *Mem:* Am Inst Chem Engrs; Am Chem Soc; Catalysis Soc. *Res:* Heterogeneous catalysis; development of hydroprocessing catalysts and processes; catalyst characterization; process modelling. *Mailing Add:* 1289 Rodney Dr Baton Rouge LA 70808

RILEY, LEE HUNTER, JR, b St Louis, Mo, May 21, 32; m 57; c 2. ORTHOPEDIC SURGERY. *Educ:* Univ Okla, BS, 54, MD, 57. *Prof Exp:* From instr to assoc prof, 63-73, PROF ORTHOP SURG, SCH MED, JOHNS HOPKINS UNIV, 73-, CHMN DEPT, 79- *Concurrent Pos:* Fel orthop surg, Armed Forces Inst Path, 61; consult, Perry Point Vet Admin Hosp, 63- & Loch Raven Vet Admin Hosp, 68-; mem subcomt rehab & related health serv personnel, Nat Res Coun, 68-71; orthop surgeon-in-chief, Johns Hopkins Hosp, 79- *Mem:* Am Acad Orthop Surg; Am Col Surgeons; Orthop Res Soc; Am Orthop Asn; Asn Acad Surg. *Res:* Intracellular calcification; orthopedic pathology; total joint replacement; cervical spine surgery. *Mailing Add:* Dept of Orthop Surg Johns Hopkins Univ Baltimore MD 21205

RILEY, MICHAEL VERITY, b Bradford, Eng, Dec 27, 33; m 63; c 4. BIOCHEMISTRY, OPHTHALMOLOGY. *Educ:* Cambridge Univ, BA, 55, MA, 60; Univ Liverpool, PhD(biochem), 61. *Prof Exp:* USPHS fel, Sch Med, Johns Hopkins Univ, 61-62; sr lectr biochem, Inst Ophthal, Univ London, 62-69; assoc prof, 69-78, PROF BIOMED SCI, INST BIOL SCI, OAKLAND UNIV, 78- *Concurrent Pos:* Lister travel fel, Royal Col Surgeons

Eng, 67; vis prof, Sch Med, Wash Univ, 67-68; NIH career develop award, 71; mem vision res & training comt, Nat Eye Inst, 71-75; vis prof, Welsh Nat Sch Med, Univ Wales, Cardiff, 75. *Mem:* Asn Res Vision & Ophthal; Sigma Xi; NY Acad Sci. *Res:* Transport processes and metabolism that relate to control of hydration and transparency of the cornea; other ocular transport and metabolism. *Mailing Add:* Inst of Biol Sci Oakland Univ Rochester MI 48063

RILEY, MICHAEL WALTERMIER, b Sedalia, Mo, Feb 11, 46; m 71; c 2. INDUSTRIAL ENGINEERING, HUMAN FACTORS. *Educ:* Univ Mo-Rolla, BS, 68; NMex State Univ, MS, 73; Tex Tech Univ, PhD(indust eng), 75. *Prof Exp:* Field engr oil prod, Shell Oil Co, 68-70; data analyst missile testing, US Army, 70-72; res asst measurement studies, NMex State Univ, 72-73; instr indust eng, Tex Tech Univ, 73-75; ASST PROF INDUST ENG, UNIV NEBR, 75- *Concurrent Pos:* NSF traineeship, 74-75. *Honors & Awards:* R R Teetor Award, Soc Automotive Engrs, 77. *Mem:* Am Inst Indust Engrs; Am Soc Eng Educ; Sigma Xi; Human Factors Soc; Soc Automotive Engrs. *Res:* Applied human factors; applied operations research. *Mailing Add:* 3701 Briarwood Ave Lincoln NE 68516

RILEY, MONICA, b New Orleans, La, Oct 4, 26; div; c 3. MOLECULAR GENETICS. *Educ:* Smith Col, AB, 47; Univ Calif, Berkeley, PhD(biochem), 60. *Prof Exp:* Asst prof bact, Univ Calif, Davis, 60-66; assoc prof biol, 66-75, PROF BIOCHEM, STATE UNIV NY STONY BROOK, 75- *Concurrent Pos:* USPHS fel, Stanford Univ, 61-62; vis scientist, Univ Brussels, 81. *Mem:* AAAS; Genetics Soc Am; Fedn Am Socs Exp Biol; Am Soc Microbiol. *Res:* Molecular mechanisms of genome evolution in enterobacteria. *Mailing Add:* Dept of Biochem State Univ of NY Stony Brook NY 11794

RILEY, N ALLEN, b Urbana, Ill, Aug 15, 15; m 42; c 1. EARTH SCIENCES, RESEARCH ADMINISTRATION. *Educ:* Univ Chicago, BS, 37, PhD(geol), 47. *Hon Degrees:* DSc Sci, Chapman Col, 76. *Prof Exp:* Field geophysicist, Magnolia Petrol Co, Tex, 37-38; res assoc, Univ Chicago, 42, from instr to asst prof geol & geophys, 46-48; supvr explor res, Chevron Res Co Div, Standard Oil Co Calif, 48-54, mgr explor res, 54-63, lab dir, 63-68, exec vpres, Chevron Oil Field Res Co, 68-71, pres, 71-80; DIR DEVELOP, GEOPHYS SYSTS CORP, 81-; DIR, WRIGHT ENERGY CORP, 81- *Mem:* Soc Explor Geophys; Am Geophys Union. *Mailing Add:* 1106 Miramar Pl Fullerton CA 92631

RILEY, PERRY STEPHEN, medical microbiology, see previous edition

RILEY, PETER JULIAN, b Kamloops, BC, July 6, 33; m 59; c 4. EXPERIMENTAL NUCLEAR PHYSICS. *Educ:* Univ BC, BASc, 56, MASc, 58; Univ Alta, PhD(nuclear physics), 62. *Prof Exp:* Res asst, Fla State Univ, 58-59; from asst prof to assoc prof, 62-76, PROF PHYSICS, UNIV TEX, AUSTIN, 76- *Concurrent Pos:* Res partic, Oak Ridge Nat Lab, 66; vis staff mem, Los Alamos Sci Lab, 74. *Mem:* Am Phys Soc. *Res:* Nuclear spectroscopy; reactions and scattering; direct nuclear reactions; nucleon-nucleon interactions, with emphasis on elastic and inelastic polarization measurements at medium energies. *Mailing Add:* Dept Physics Univ Tex Austin TX 78712

RILEY, REED FARRAR, b Chicago, Ill, Aug 5, 27; m 51; c 6. INDUSTRIAL CHEMISTRY. *Educ:* Univ Ill, BS, 49; Mich State Univ, PhD(chem), 54; Columbia Univ, JD, 71. *Prof Exp:* Asst prof, Bucknell Univ, 54-57; from asst prof to assoc prof, Polytech Inst Brooklyn, 57-65; eng specialist, Bayside Labs, Gen Tel & Electronics, Inc, 65-68; patent attorney, 71-74, sr patent attorney, 74-77, DIR TECH LIAISON, STANDARD OIL CO, INC, 77- *Concurrent Pos:* Res Corp grant, 56-57; NSF res grant, 63-65; AEC contract, 63-65; adj prof, NY Inst Technol, 69-71. *Mem:* Sigma Xi. *Res:* Activated carbons; catalysed processes. *Mailing Add:* 2411 N Burling Chicago IL 60614

RILEY, RICHARD CHARLES, radiation biophysics, see previous edition

RILEY, RICHARD FOWBLE, b South Pasadena, Calif, Mar 23, 17. PHYSIOLOGICAL CHEMISTRY. *Educ:* Pomona Col, BA, 39; Univ Rochester, PhD(biochem), 42. *Prof Exp:* Asst biochem & pharmacol, Sch Med & Dent, Univ Rochester, 39-42, instr pharmacol, 42-45; fel biochem, Sch Med, Buffalo, 45-47; asst prof pharmacol, Univ Rochester, 47-49; fel clin radiol, 49-53, fel physiol chem & radiol, 53-55, ASSOC PROF PHYSIOL CHEM & RADIOL, SCH MED, UNIV CALIF, LOS ANGELES, 55- *Concurrent Pos:* Rep from Univ California, Los Angeles, to tech info div, AEC, DC. *Mem:* AAAS; Am Chem Soc; Am Soc Pharmacol & Exp Med; Radiation Res Soc; Soc Exp Biol & Med. *Res:* Radiation biology; radioactive pharmaceuticals for nuclear medicine. *Mailing Add:* 649 Bienvenida Pacific Palisades CA 90272

RILEY, RICHARD KING, b Marshalltown, Iowa, June 4, 36; m 61; c 2. MECHANICAL ENGINEERING. *Educ:* State Univ Iowa, BS, 61, MS, 65; Univ Mo-Rolla, PhD(mech eng), 70. *Prof Exp:* Develop engr, Western Elec Corp, 65-66; from instr to asst prof mech eng, Univ Mo-Rolla, 66-76; prin engr, Dravo Corp, 76-78; res engr, 78-80, SR RES ENGR, PHILLIPS PETROL CO, 80- *Mem:* Am Soc Mech Engrs; Sigma Xi; Soc Automotive Engrs. *Res:* Petroleum fuels and combustion research. *Mailing Add:* Phillips Res Ctr 134-AL Phillips Petrol Co Bartlesville OK 73004

RILEY, RICHARD LORD, b North Plainfield, NJ, July 10, 11; m 47; c 3. MEDICINE. *Educ:* Harvard Univ, BS, 33, MD, 37. *Prof Exp:* Intern, St Luke's Hosp, NY, 38-40; asst resident, Chest Serv, Bellevue Hosp, New York, 40-42; researcher, Off Sci Res & Develop, 42-43; from assoc to asst prof med, Columbia Univ, 47-50; assoc prof, Inst Indust Med, NY Univ, 49-50; from assoc prof to prof med, 50-77, from assoc prof to prof environ med, Sch Hyg & Pub Health, 50-77, EMER PROF MED, JOHNS HOPKINS UNIV, 77-, EMER PROF ENVIRON HEALTH SCI, 77- *Mem:* Assoc Am Physiol Soc; assoc Am Thoracic Soc; assoc Am Soc Clin Ivest; assoc Asn Am Physicians. *Res:* Respiratory physiology; cardiovascular physiology; airborne infection. *Mailing Add:* Petersham MA 01366

RILEY, ROBERT C, b Brooklyn, NY, Aug 14, 28; m 53; c 2. ENTOMOLOGY. *Educ:* Hobart Col, BA, 51; Clemson Univ, MS, 59; Rutgers Univ, New Brunswick, PhD(entom), 64. *Prof Exp:* Qual control & formulation chemist, Geigy Agr Chem Div, Geigy Chem Corp, 51-55; anal chemist, Clemson Univ, 57-59; from res asst to res assoc entom, Rutgers Univ, 59-64, from asst res prof to assoc res prof entom, 64-68; PRIN ENTOMOLOGIST, COOP STATE RES SERV, USDA, 68- *Mem:* Entom Soc Am. *Res:* Integrated control of insects and pest management; economic entomology; pesticides; research information and retrieval systems. *Mailing Add:* 5013 Cedar Lane West Bethesda MD 20014

RILEY, ROBERT GENE, b Oakland, Calif, June 9, 46. ANALYTICAL CHEMISTRY, ORGANIC CHEMISTRY. *Educ:* Calif State Univ, Hayward, BS, 69; State Univ NY, PhD(org chem), 74. *Prof Exp:* Res assoc chem, Wash State Univ, 74-76; res scientist, 76-78, SR RES SCIENTIST ENVIRON CHEM, PAC NORTHWEST LABS, BATTELLE MEM INST, 78- *Mem:* Am Chem Soc. *Res:* Fate and effects of fossil fuels and their waste effluents in aquatic and terrestrial environments; distribution and fate of anthropogenic pollutants discharged to estuarine water bodies. *Mailing Add:* Battelle Northwest Battelle Blvd Richland WA 99352

RILEY, ROBERT LEE, b Iola, Kans, Jan 8, 35; m 58; c 1. POLYMER CHEMISTRY, ORGANIC CHEMISTRY. *Educ:* Regis Col, Colo, BS, 56. *Prof Exp:* Chemist, Convair Div, Gen Dynamics Corp, Tex, 57-58, res chemist, Gen Dynamics Sci Res Lab, Calif, 58-62, from staff assoc to staff mem, Gen Atomic Div, Gen Dynamics Corp, 62-67, staff mem, Gulf Gen Atomic, Inc, 67-72, mgr membrane res, Gulf Environ Systs Co, 72-74; DIR BASIC DEVELOP DEPT, FLUID SYSTS DIV, UNIVERSAL OIL PROD INC, 74- *Concurrent Pos:* Guest scientist, Max Planck Inst Biophys, 71. *Honors & Awards:* Indust Res, Inc Award, 72. *Mem:* AAAS; Am Chem Soc; Nat Water Supply Improv Asn. *Res:* Environmental science and technology; biomedical engineering; membrane research and development for desalination by reverse osmosis; seawater desalination; gas separation processes; membrane transport, structure and separations technology. *Mailing Add:* 5803 Cactus Way La Jolla CA 92037

RILEY, STEPHEN JAMES, b Washington, DC, July 17, 43. PHYSICAL CHEMISTRY. *Educ:* Oberlin Col, Ohio, BA, 65; Harvard Univ, MA, 67, PhD(chem), 70. *Prof Exp:* NIH fel chem, Univ Calif, San Diego, 70-72, res asst chem, 72-73; asst prof chem, Yale Univ, 73-80; CHEMIST, ARGONNE NAT LAB, 80- *Mem:* Am Phys Soc. *Res:* Molecular dynamics of photodissocation processes. *Mailing Add:* Chem Div Argonne Nat Lab 9700 S Cass Ave Argonne IL 60439

RILEY, THOMAS NOLAN, b Mishawaka, Ind, Dec 2, 39; m 60; c 2. MEDICINAL CHEMISTRY. *Educ:* Univ Ky, BS, 63; Univ Minn, Minneapolis, PhD(med chem), 69. *Prof Exp:* Res asst med chem, Univ Minn, 63-67, USPHS trainee, 67-69; asst prof, 69-72, assoc prof, 72-79, PROF MED CHEM, SCH PHARM, UNIV MISS, 79- *Mem:* AAAS; Am Chem Soc; Am Asn Cols Pharm; Sigma Xi. *Res:* Design, synthesis and evaluation of organic medicinal agents in an attempt to elucidate the molecular mechanisms of drug action. *Mailing Add:* Sch of Pharm Univ of Miss University MS 38677

RILEY, VERNON TODD, b Idaho Falls, Idaho, Sept 2, 14; m 36; c 4. STRESS, NON-IONIZING RADIATION. *Educ:* Sorbonne, DSc(microbiol), 66. *Prof Exp:* Sr res asst biochem, Univ Wash, 36-38, chemist & bacteriologist, 39; biologist, Nat Cancer Inst, 43-53; head lab, Mem Ctr, Sloan-Kettering Inst Cancer Res, 53-67; CHMN DEPT MICROBIOL, PAC NORTHWEST RES FOUND & MEM, FRED HUTCHINSON CANCER RES CTR, 67- *Concurrent Pos:* Prof exp animal med, Sch Med, Univ Wash; chmn Int Pigment Cell Group; Am Cancer Soc grant, 67-; grants, Res Corp, Seattle, 68-70, NY Cancer Res Inst, 69-, Nat Cancer Res Inst, 70-, Leukemia Res Found, 75 & Sloan-Kettering Inst Cancer Res. *Mem:* Harvey Soc; Am Asn Cancer Res; Am Soc Microbiol; Am Soc Cell Biol; fel NY Acad Sci. *Res:* Cancer melanomas; pigment cells; subcellular particulates; enzymes; virus; chromatography; manometry; photosynthesis; amino acids; asparaginase; physiology of stress. *Mailing Add:* Pac Northwest Res Found 1102 Columbia St Seattle WA 98104

RILEY, WILLIAM F(RANKLIN), b Allenport, Pa, Mar 1, 25; m 45; c 2. ENGINEERING MECHANICS, MECHANICAL ENGINEERING. *Educ:* Carnegie Inst Technol, BS, 51; Ill Inst Technol, MS, 58. *Prof Exp:* Mech engr, Mesta Mach Co, 51-54; assoc engr, Armour Res Found, 54-58, res engr, 58-61, sr res engr, 61, sect mgr, IIT Res Inst, 61-64, sci adv, 64-66; assoc prof, 66-69, PROF ENG MECH, IOWA STATE UNIV, 69- *Concurrent Pos:* Am consult, US Agency Int Develop Summer Inst Prog, Bihar Inst Technol, Sindri, India, 66, Indian Inst Technol, Kanpur, India, 70. *Mem:* Soc Exp Stress Anal. *Res:* Photoelasticity, especially the solution of three-dimensional and dynamic stress problems. *Mailing Add:* 206 Lab of Mech Iowa State Univ Ames IA 50011

RILEY, WILLIAM ROBERT, b Bellaire, Ohio, July 31, 22; m 49; c 2. PHYSICS. *Educ:* Hiram Col, AB, 44; Ohio State Univ, BSc, 51, MA, 52, PhD(sci ed, physics), 59. *Prof Exp:* Instr math & physics, Hiram Col, 46-48; asst physics, 48-50, instr, 51-53, instr in chg demonstrations, 53-59, asst prof, 59-64, ASSOC PROF PHYSICS, OHIO STATE UNIV, 64- *Concurrent Pos:* Consult, Bur Educ Res, Ohio State Univ, 57-58, res found mobile lab, 59-60; dir, In-serv Insts in Physics, NSF-Ohio State Univ, 60-67, 68-73 & 78-consult, North Bengal Univ, India, 64; NSF sci liaison staff, New Delhi, India, 67-68. *Mem:* Sigma Xi; AAAS; Nat Sci Teachers Asn; Am Asn Physics Teachers. *Res:* Science education. *Mailing Add:* Dept of Physics Ohio State Univ 174 W 18th Ave Columbus OH 43210

RILL, RANDOLPH LYNN, b Canton, Ohio, Oct 19, 44; m 66; c 2. PHYSICAL BIOCHEMISTRY. *Educ:* Franklin & Marshall Col, BA, 66; Northwestern Univ, Evanston, PhD(phys chem), 71. *Prof Exp:* USPHS fel biophys, Dept Biochem & Biophys, Ore State Univ, Corvallis, 70-72; asst prof phys biochem, 72-77, ASSOC PROF PHYS BIOCHEM, DEPT CHEM,

FLA STATE UNIV, TALLAHASSEE, 77- *Honors & Awards:* Career Develop Award, USPHS, 75. *Mem:* Biophys Soc; Am Soc Biol Chemists. *Res:* Physical and chemical studies of DNA-protein interactions; molecular structure and function of chromosomes; structure of chromatin subunits; conformational properties of DNA; histone chemistry. *Mailing Add:* Dept of Chem Fla State Univ Tallahassee FL 32306

RILLEMA, JAMES ALAN, b Grand Rapids, Mich, Nov 6, 42; m 68; c 3. ENDOCRINOLOGY, PHYSIOLOGY. *Educ:* Calvin Col, BS, 64; Mich State Univ, MS, 66, PhD(physiol), 68. *Prof Exp:* NIH fel, Emory Univ, 68-70, res assoc physiol, 70-71; asst prof, 71-75, assoc prof, 75-79, PROF PHYSIOL, SCH MED, WAYNE STATE UNIV, 79- *Concurrent Pos:* Fogarty Sr Int Fel, VanLeeuwenholtz Cancer Inst, Amsterdam, Neth, 80-81. *Mem:* AAAS; Endocrine Soc; Am Physiol Soc; Soc Exp Biol & Med; Sigma Xi. *Res:* Hormones, especially mechanism of action. *Mailing Add:* Dept of Physiol Wayne State Univ Sch of Med Detroit MI 48201

RILLING, HANS CHRISTOPHER, b Cleveland, Ohio, June 6, 33; m 55; c 3. BIOCHEMISTRY. *Educ:* Oberlin Col, BA, 55; Harvard Univ, PhD(biochem), 60. *Prof Exp:* Res assoc biochem, Univ Mich, 58-60, from instr to assoc prof, 60-71, PROF BIOCHEM, UNIV UTAH, 71- *Concurrent Pos:* USPHS res career develop award, 63-73. *Mem:* Am Soc Biol Chemists. *Res:* Enzymology and mechanism of the biosynthesis of terpenes. *Mailing Add:* Dept of Biochem 410 Chipeta Way Salt Lake City UT 84112

RILLINGS, JAMES H, b Mineola, NY, June 5, 42; m 78. AUTOMATIC CONTROL SYSTEMS. *Educ:* Rensselaer Polytech Inst, BSEE, 64, MSEE, 66, DEng, 68. *Prof Exp:* Instr elec eng, Rensselaer Polytech Inst, 66-68; engr, Electronics Res Ctr, NASA, 68-70; SR RES ENGR, GEN MOTORS RES LABS, 70- *Mem:* Inst Elec & Electronics Engrs; Soc Automotive Engrs. *Res:* Computer applications to automatic control. *Mailing Add:* General Motors Res Labs Mound Rd Warren MI 48090

RIM, DOCK SANG, b Korea, Oct 2, 28; m 59. MATHEMATICS. *Educ:* Seoul Nat Univ, BS, 54; Ind Univ, PhD(math), 57. *Prof Exp:* Res assoc math, Columbia Univ, 57-60; from asst prof to assoc prof, Brandeis Univ, 60-65; PROF MATH, UNIV PA, 65-, CHMN MATH DEPT, 75- *Concurrent Pos:* Ed, Transactions & Memoirs, Am Math Soc. *Mem:* Am Math Soc. *Res:* Homological and commutative algebra; class field theory; algebraic geometry. *Mailing Add:* Dept of Math Univ of Pa Philadelphia PA 19104

RIM, KWAN, b Korea, Nov 7, 34; m 62; c 3. ENGINEERING MECHANICS, BIOMEDICAL ENGINEERING. *Educ:* Tri-State Col, BS, 55; Northwestern Univ, MS, 58, PhD(theoret & appl mech), 60. *Prof Exp:* Engr, Int Bus Mach Corp, NY, 56; from asst prof to assoc prof, 60-68, PROF MECH, UNIV IOWA, 68, CHMN DEPT MECH & HYDRAUL, 72-, ASSOC DEAN ENG, 74-, ADJ PROF MED, DEPT ORTHOP SURG, 70- *Concurrent Pos:* Consult, Deere & Co, Ill, 64-66; actg chmn dept mech & hydraul, Univ Iowa, 71-72. *Honors & Awards:* Teetor Educ Fund Award, Soc Automotive Eng, 65. *Mem:* Soc Indust & Appl Math; Am Soc Mech Engrs; Am Soc Eng Educ. *Res:* Classical mechanics of deformable bodies, such as the theory of elasticity and viscoelasticity; optimal design; biomechanics. *Mailing Add:* Col of Eng Univ of Iowa Iowa City IA 52242

RIM, YONG SUNG, b Changryun, Korea, Mar 15, 35; m 59; c 2. ORGANIC CHEMISTRY. *Educ:* Yonsei Univ, Korea, BS, 57; Univ Tex, Austin, PhD(chem), 67. *Prof Exp:* Res chemist, 68-70, res scientist, 70-75, sr res scientist, Oxford Res Ctr, 75-78, sr group leader elastomer res, 78-80, MGR ETHYELENE-PROPYLENE-DIENE MONOMER RES & DEVELOP, UNIROYAL CHEM, UNIROYAL INC, 80- *Mem:* Am Chem Soc. *Res:* Nonbenzenoid aromatic chemistry; free radical chemistry; fire retardant polymer chemistry; elastomer syntheses and evaluation of elastomers. *Mailing Add:* Elastomer Res & Develop Uniroyal Chem Naugatuck CT 06770

RIMA, DONALD R, b Adams Center, NY, Nov 22, 25; m 50; c 2. GROUND WATER HYDROLOGY. *Educ:* Syracuse Univ, AB, 49. *Prof Exp:* Hydrologist, Water Resources Div, US Geol Surv, 50-54, proj chief geohydrol, 54-56, asst dist geologist, 56-59, dist geologist, 59-63, asst dist chief, 63-82. *Mem:* Geol Soc Am; Nat Water Well Asn. *Res:* Planning and execution of detailed hydrologic studies of area or topics concerned with ground water; ground water contamination. *Mailing Add:* US Geol Surv Fed Office Bldg Rm A413 Nashville TN 37203

RIMAI, DONALD SAUL, b New York City, NY, Oct 17, 49; m 77. SOLID STATE PHYSICS. *Educ:* Rensselaer Polytech Inst, BS, 71; Univ Chicago, MS, 73, PhD(physics), 77. *Prof Exp:* Res assoc, Purdue Univ, 77-79; SR RES SCIENTIST, EASTMAN KODAK, 79- *Mem:* Am Phys Soc; NY Acad Sci; Sigma Xi. *Res:* Electrical and photoconducting properties of organic insulators; ultrasonic properties. *Mailing Add:* PO Box 1001 Webster NY 14580

RIMAI, LAJOS, b Budapest, Hungary, Apr 10, 30; US citizen; m 54; c 3. NONLINEAR OPTICS, SPECTROSCOPY. *Educ:* Univ San Paulo, Brazil, EE, 52, BS, 53; Harvard Univ, PhD(appl physcis), 59. *Prof Exp:* Instr elec eng, Inst Aeronaut Technol, San Jose Campus, San Paulo, Brazil, 53-55; scientist physics, Res Div, Raytheon Co, 59-64; STAFF SCIENTIST, PHYSICS DEPT, FORD MOTOR CO, 54- *Mem:* Am Phys Soc. *Res:* Spectroscopic probes of molecular interactions, structure and combustion; nonlinear laser spectroscopic diagnostics of combustion; resonance effects in Raman spectroscopy; resonance Raman spectroscopy of biologically active chromophores (visual pigments); laser velocimetry. *Mailing Add:* Physics Dept Rm S-1021 Ford Motor Co PO Box 2053 Dearborn MI 48121

RIMBEY, PETER RAYMOND, b LaGrande, Ore, Aug 27, 47. THEORETICAL SOLID STATE PHYSICS. *Educ:* Eastern Ore State Col, BA, 69; Univ Ore, MS, 71, PhD(physics), 74. *Prof Exp:* Res assoc, Ind Univ, 73-74; fel, Ames Lab, Energy Res & Develop Admin, Iowa State Univ, 75-78;

fel, Univ Wis-Milwaukee, 78-80; MEM STAFF, BOEING AEROSPACE, 80- *Mem:* Am Phys Soc; Sigma Xi. *Res:* Many-body theory; condensed matter; optical properties of semiconductors, molecular crystals and metals; photoemission; surface physics; photo-electro-chemistry; excitons and polarons; transport in semiconductors; electro- and thermo-transport; atomic diffusion. *Mailing Add:* Boeing Aerospace PO Box 3999 M/S 8C-62 Seattle WA 98124

RIMES, WILLIAM JOHN, b Lake Providence, La, Mar 31, 18. ANALYTICAL CHEMISTRY. *Educ:* Spring Hill Col, BS, 43; Cath Univ, MS, 45; La State Univ, PhD(chem), 57. *Prof Exp:* Assoc prof, 56-73, chmn dept, 58-66, PROF CHEM, SPRING HILL COL, 73-, PRES, 66-, DIR CHEM, 77- *Mem:* Am Chem Soc. *Res:* Instrumental methods of analysis. *Mailing Add:* Dept of Chem Spring Hill Col Mobile AL 36608

RIMLAND, DAVID, b Havana, Cuba, Aug 8, 44; US citizen; m 71; c 2. INFECTIOUS DISEASES. *Educ:* Emory Univ, BS, 66 MD, 70; Am Bd Internal Med, dipl & cert infectious dis. *Prof Exp:* Intern & resident internal med, Barnes Hosp, 70-72; epidemic intel serv officer, Ctr Dis Control, 72-74; resident & fel, Emory Univ Affil Hosps, 74-77; ASST PROF MED INFECTIOUS DIS, SCH MED, EMORY UNIV, 77- *Concurrent Pos:* Staff physician, Vet Admin Med Ctr, Atlanta, 77- *Mem:* Am Soc Microbiol; Am Fedn Clin Res; Infectious Dis Soc Am. *Res:* Host defense mechanisms of alcoholics; epidemiology of hospital infections. *Mailing Add:* Med Serv Vet Admin Med Ctr Atlanta Decatur GA 30033

RIMM, ALFRED A, b Atlantic City, NJ, Apr 13, 34; m 58; c 4. GENETICS, STATISTICS. *Educ:* Rutgers Univ, 56, MS, 58, PhD(dairy sci), 62. *Prof Exp:* Sr res scientist, Roswell Park Mem Inst, 63-66; PROF BIOSTATIST, MED COL WIS, 66- *Mem:* Am Statist Asn; Biomet Soc; Am Pub Health Asn. *Res:* Controlled clinical trials; epidemiology studies in obesity and heart disease; public health statistics; teaching biostatistics in medical school; computers for medical research; immunobiology; disease registeries. *Mailing Add:* Med Col Wis PO Box 26509 Milwaukee WI 53226

RIMMER, MATTHEW PETER, optics, see previous edition

RIMMER, ROBERT W, organic chemistry, see previous edition

RIMOIN, DAVID (LAWRENCE), b Montreal, Que, Nov 9, 36; m 62; c 1. MEDICAL GENETICS. *Educ:* McGill Univ, BSc, 57, MSc, & MD, CM, 61; Johns Hopkins Univ, PhD(human genetics), 67. *Prof Exp:* Asst prof med & pediat, Wash Univ, 67-70; assoc prof, 70-73, PROF MED & PEDIAT, SCH MED, UNIV CALIF, LOS ANGELES, 73-; CHIEF MED GENETICS, HARBOR GEN HOSP, 70- *Concurrent Pos:* Lectr med, Sch Med, Johns Hopkins Univ, 67-71; consult, Orthop Hosp, Los Angeles, 70-, Fairview State Hosp, Costa Mesa, 71- & Cedars-Sinai Med Ctr, Los Angeles, 71- *Mem:* Am Soc Clin Invest; Am Fedn Clin Res (secy-treas, 73-76); Soc Pediat Res; Am Soc Human Genetics; fel Am Col Physicians. *Res:* Dwarfism; birth defects; genetic disorders of the endocrine glands. *Mailing Add:* Los Angeles County Harbor 1000 W Carson Torrance CA 90509

RIMROTT, F(RIEDRICH) P(AUL) J(OHANNES), b Halle, Ger, Aug 4, 27; m 55; c 4. ENGINEERING MECHANICS. *Educ:* Univ Karlsruhe, Dipl Ing, 51; Univ Toronto, MASc, 55; Pa State Univ, PhD(eng mech), 58; Tech Univ Darmstadt, DrIng, 61. *Prof Exp:* Design engr locomotives, Henschel-Werke Kassel, Ger, 51-52; instr mech eng, Univ Toronto, 53-55; from instr to asst prof eng mech, Pa State Univ, 55-60; from asst prof to assoc prof mech eng, 60-67, PROF MECH ENG, UNIV TORONTO, 67- *Concurrent Pos:* Vis prof, Wien Tech Univ, 69; Hannover Tech Univ, 70, Ruhr Univ, 71 & Univ Wuppertal, 78. *Honors & Awards:* Queen's Silver Anniversary Medal, 77. *Mem:* Can Soc Mech Engrs; fel Eng Inst Can; Int Cong Theoret & Appl Mech. *Res:* Plasticity; creep; fatigue; strain and stress measurement; vibrations; strength of materials; elasticity; machine design; robotics. *Mailing Add:* Dept Mech Eng Univ Toronto Toronto ON M5S 1A4 Can

RINALDI, LEONARD DANIEL, b Torrington, Conn, Feb 15, 24; m 50; c 3. MATHEMATICS. *Educ:* Univ Conn, BS, 45; Univ Buffalo, MS, 55. *Prof Exp:* Res mathematician, Cornell Aeronaut Labs, Inc, 45-55; dir, Arithmetion Consults, 55-58; PRES, RINALDI DATA PROCESSING CONSULTS, INC, 58- *Mem:* Math Asn Am; Asn Comput Mach; Am Mkt Asn; Am Math Soc; Inst Mgt Sci. *Res:* Probability and statistics; theory and practice of computation; mathematics of resource use; aeronautical engineering. *Mailing Add:* 506 Springfield Ave Cranford NJ 07016

RINALDI, ROBERT ARTHUR, b Modesto, Calif, Oct 24, 28; m 49; c 3. CELL PHYSIOLOGY. *Educ:* Univ Calif, Berkeley, AB, 54, MA, 57; Univ Calif, Los Angeles, PhD(cell physiol), 62. *Prof Exp:* Asst prof zool, Univ Tenn, 62-66; asst prof anat, Sch Med, Vanderbilt Univ, 66-68 & Sch Med, Georgetown Univ, 68-71; prog coordr, Biophys Res Lab, NY Univ, 70-75; consult, Nat Cancer Inst, NIH, 75-77; actg chmn physiol & pharmacol, 77-78; assoc prof physiol & anat, Sch Med, Cath Univ, PR, 77-80; MEM FAC ANAT, MED SCH, LA STATE UNIV, 80- *Concurrent Pos:* Grants, US AEC, 63-66, Tenn Heart Asn, 63-64; Life Ins Med Res Fund, 64-66, Wash Heart Asn, 68-69 & HEW Pub Health Serv, 70-75. *Mem:* AAAS; Am Soc Cell Biol; Am Soc Zoologists; Biophys Soc; Soc Protozoologists. *Res:* Cell physiology; cellular contractility; cell cleavage, collagen formation; biophysics of gelation and solation; growth and healing of cells. *Mailing Add:* Med Sch Anat La State Univ PO Box 33932 Shreveport LA 71130

RINARD, GILBERT ALLEN, b Denver, Colo, Dec 16, 39; m 61; c 4. PHYSIOLOGY, ENDOCRINOLOGY. *Educ:* George Fox Col, BA, 61; Ore State Univ, MS, 63; Cornell Univ, PhD(endocrinol), 66. *Prof Exp:* NIH fel pharmacol, Case Western Reserve Univ, 66-68; instr, 68-69, asst prof physiol, 69-76, ASSOC PROF PHYSIOL, SCH MED, EMORY UNIV, 76- *Mem:* NY Acad Sci; Am Thoracic Soc; Endocrine Soc; Am Physiol Soc. *Res:* Mechanism of action of drugs used in asthma therapy; cyclic nucleotides; smooth muscle; cellular mechanisms of asthma. *Mailing Add:* Dept Physiol Sch Med Emory Univ Atlanta GA 30322

RIND, DAVID HAROLD, b New York, NY, May 1, 48. GENERAL CIRCULATION MODELING, CLIMATE DYNAMICS. *Educ:* City Col, City Univ New York, BS, 69; Columbia Univ, MA, 73, PhD(meteorol & geophysics), 76. *Prof Exp:* Res assoc, Lamont Doherty Geol Observ, 76-81; SPACE SCIENTIST, GODDARD INST SPACE STUDIES, NASA, 81- *Concurrent Pos:* Lectr, Columbia Univ, 78-82, adj asst prof, 82-; consult, Goddard Inst Space Studies, NASA, 79-81. *Mem:* Am Meteorol Soc; Am Geophys Union. *Res:* Climate and upper atmosphere research using computer models of the atmosphere; observations of upper atmosphere parameters and geophysicsal wave propagation. *Mailing Add:* 201 W 70th St New York NY 10023

RINDERER, THOMAS EARL, b Dubuque, Iowa, Sept 16, 43; m 67, 80. GENETICS, INSECT BEHAVIOR. *Educ:* Loras Col, BS, 66; Ohio State Univ, MSc, 68, PhD(insect path), 75. *Prof Exp:* RES GENETICIST & RES LEADER, BEE BREEDING & STOCK CTR LAB, AGR RES SERV, USDA, 75- *Mem:* Entom Soc Am; Bee Res Asn; Soc Invert Path; Am Behav Soc. *Res:* Epigenetics of disease events, including breeding for resistance and susceptibility in insects and understanding the influence of environmental factors; behavior, behavior genetics, and pathogenetics of honey bees; nector foraging and defensive behavior of both European and Africanized honeybees. *Mailing Add:* Bee Breeding & Stock Ctr Lab Rt 3 Box 82B Ben Hur Rd Baton Rouge LA 70808

RINDERKNECHT, HEINRICH, b Zurich, Switz, Jan 21, 13; US citizen; m 39; c 4. BIOCHEMISTRY, ORGANIC CHEMISTRY. *Educ:* Swiss Fed Inst Technol, MSc, 36; Univ London, PhD(biochem), 39. *Prof Exp:* Res chemist, Roche Prod, Ltd, Eng, 39-47; assoc dir biochem res, Aligena Co, Switz, 47-49; res fel chem, Calif Inst Technol, 49-54; res dir org chem, Crookes Labs, London, Eng, 54-55; dir res & develop, Calbiochem, Calif, 55-62; sr res fel chem, Calif Inst Technol, 62-70; from assoc prof to prof, Sch Med, Univ Southern Calif, 64-70; PROF MED, UNIV CALIF, LOS ANGELES, 70-; CHIEF MED BIOCHEM, VET ADMIN HOSP, SEPULVEDA, 70- *Concurrent Pos:* Consult, Cilag A G, Switz, 49-54; Geigy Pharmaceut, 55-57 & Stuart Co, Calif, 59-61. *Mem:* AAAS; Am Chem Soc; Am Fedn Clin Res; Brit Biochem Soc; fel Royal Soc Health. *Res:* Development of synthetic analgesics and local anesthetics; synthesis of nucleotides, enzyme substrates and metabolites; ultrarapid method for fluorescent labeling of proteins; role of proteolytic enzymes in acute pancreatitis; radioimmunoassay of peptide hormones. *Mailing Add:* 1971 Cielito Lane Santa Barbara CA 93105

RINDLER, WOLFGANG, b Vienna, Austria, May 18, 24; m 59, 77. RELATIVITY THEORY. *Educ:* Univ Liverpool, BSc, 45, MSc, 47; Univ London, PhD, 56. *Prof Exp:* Asst lectr pure math, Univ Liverpool, 47-49; lectr math, Univ London, 49-56; instr, Cornell Univ, 56-58, asst prof 58-63; from assoc prof to prof, Southwest Ctr for Advan Studies, 63-69; prof math, 69-80, PROF PHYSICS, UNIV TEX, DALLAS, 80- *Concurrent Pos:* NSF fel, Hamburg & King's Col, Univ London, 61-62; Nat Res Coun Italy fel, Univ Rome, 68-69; vis prof, Univ Vienna, 75. *Mem:* Fel Am Phys Soc; fel Royal Astron Soc; Int Astron Union; Int Soc Gen Relativity & Gravitation. *Res:* Relativity; cosmology; spinors. *Mailing Add:* Dept Physics Univ of Tex at Dallas Richardson TX 75080

RINDONE, GUY E(DWARD), b Buffalo, NY, Aug 11, 22; m 43; c 2. CERAMICS. *Educ:* Alfred Univ, BS, 43; Pa State Univ, MS, 46, PhD(ceramics), 48. *Prof Exp:* Glass technologist, Sylvania Elec Prod, Inc, 43-45; glass technologist, Glass Sci Inc, 45-47; asst, 47-48, from asst prof to prof, 49-81, chmn sect, 69-80, EMER PROF CERAMIC SCI, PA STATE UNIV, UNIVERSITY PARK, 81-; PRES, MAT RES CONSULTS, INC, 81- *Concurrent Pos:* Prog chmn, Int Cong Glass, DC, 62; mem coun, Int Comn Glass; mem, Univs Space Res Asn, NASA, 72-; prog dir, Mats Processing Space, 81- *Honors & Awards:* Forrest Award, Am Ceramic Soc, 63. *Mem:* Fel Am Ceramic Soc (vpres, 77-78); fel Brit Soc Glass Technol. *Res:* Ceramic and glass science; solarization; gas evolution anelasticity, nucleation and crystallization processes and electrochemical behavior of glass; small angle x-ray scattering of glass; relaxation processes; glass strength; fluorescence; microstructure, laser light scattering; nuclear waste encapsulation. *Mailing Add:* 247 E McCormick Ave State College PA 16801

RINEHART, EDGAR A, b Guthrie, Okla, Oct 16, 28; m 59; c 2. MOLECULAR SPECTROSCOPY, LASERS. *Educ:* Cent State Col, Okla, BS, 52; Univ Okla, MS, 55, PhD(physics), 61. *Prof Exp:* Asst prof physics, Univ Idaho, 60-61; adj asst prof, Univ Okla, 61-64; asst prof, 64-67, assoc prof, 67-77, PROF PHYSICS & ASTRON, UNIV WYO, 77- *Concurrent Pos:* Consult, Lawrence Livermore Lab, 66- & Martin Marietta Corp, 78- *Mem:* Am Phys Soc; Am Chem Soc; Am Appl Spectros; AAAS; Optical Soc Am. *Res:* Microwave spectroscopy, line widths and intensities; free radicals; laser physics. *Mailing Add:* Dept Physics & Astron Univ Wyo Laramie WY 82071

RINEHART, FRANK PALMER, b Washington, DC, Mar 1, 44. BIOPHYSICAL CHEMISTRY. *Educ:* Western Md Col, BA, 66; Univ Calif, Berkeley, PhD(chem), 71. *Prof Exp:* Lectr chem, Univ Ife, Nigeria, 71 74; researcher biophys chem, Univ Calif, Davis, 74-77; lectr chem, 77; asst prof, 77-80, ASSOC PROF CHEM, COL VI, 80- *Mem:* Am Chem Soc. *Res:* Analysis of repetitive sequences in eucaryotic DNA; design of microcomputer software for chemistry courses. *Mailing Add:* Dept Chem Col VI St Thomas VI 00801

RINEHART, JAY KENT, b Xenia, Ohio, Apr 13, 40; m 61; c 2. CHEMISTRY. *Educ:* Univ Cincinnati, BS, 62; Univ Minn, Minneapolis, PhD(org chem), 67. *Prof Exp:* SR RES CHEMIST, PPG INDUSTS, INC, 67- *Mem:* Am Chem Soc. *Res:* Synthesis of new pesticides; structure-activity correlations as a tool for new pesticide design; carbene chemistry; small ring chemistry; bridged aromatic compounds; organic sulfur chemistry; heterocyclic chemistry; agricultural chemistry. *Mailing Add:* Res B PPG Industs Inc Barberton OH 44203

RINEHART, JOHN SARGENT, b Kirksville, Mo, Feb 8, 15; m 40; c 2. PHYSICS. *Educ:* Northeastern Mo State Teachers Col, BS, 34, AB, 35; Calif Inst Technol, MS, 37; Univ Iowa, PhD(physics), 40. *Prof Exp:* Asst physics, Calif Inst Technol, 35-37; asst, Univ Iowa, 37-40, Kans State Col, 40 & Wayne State Univ, 41-42; assoc physicist, Nat Bur Stand, 42; sect tech aide, Nat Defense Res Comt, 42-45; head physicist & supvr exp range, Res & Develop Div, NMex Sch Mines, 45-48; head terminal ballistics br, US Naval Ord Testing Sta, Inyokern, 49-50, mech br, 50-51, res physicist, 51-55; asst dir astrophys lab, Smithsonian Inst, 55-58; prof mining eng & dir mining res lab, Colo Sch Mines, 58-64; dir res, US Coast & Geod Surv, 64-65; dir sci & eng, Environ Sci Serv Admin, 65-66, sr res fel & dir univ rels, Inst Environ Res, 66-68, sr res fel, Nat Oceanic & Atmospheric Admin, 68-73; MEM STAFF, HYPERDYNAMICS, INC, SANTE FE, N MEX, 73- *Concurrent Pos:* Adj prof, Univ Colo, Boulder, 68-73. *Honors & Awards:* Presidential Cert Merit. *Res:* Interior, exterior and terminal ballistics; failure of metals under impulsive loading; hypersonics; rock physics; geysers; geothermal areas. *Mailing Add:* Hyperdynamics PO Box 392 Santa Fe NM 87501

RINEHART, KENNETH LLOYD, JR, b Chillicothe, Mo, Mar 17, 29; m 61; c 3. ORGANIC CHEMISTRY. *Educ:* Yale Univ, BS, 50; Univ Calif, PhD(chem), 54. *Prof Exp:* From instr to assoc prof, 54-64, PROF ORG CHEM, UNIV ILL, URBANA, 64- *Concurrent Pos:* Fels, Orgn Europ Econ Coop, 60, Guggenheim, 62 & Fulbright, 66; Squibb lectr, Rutgers Univ, 61; Werner lectr, Univ Kans, 65; A D Little lectr, Mass Inst Technol, 75; distinguished vis lectr, Tex A&M Univ, 80; Barnett lectr, Northeasteren Univ, 81; consult, Upjohn Co & NIH. *Mem:* Am Chem Soc; The Chem Soc; Am Soc Biol Chem; Am Soc Microbiol; fel AAAS. *Res:* Structure, biosynthesis and synthesis of natural products; antibiotics and marine natural products; mass spectrometry. *Mailing Add:* 454 Roger Adams Lab Univ Ill 1209 W California St Urbana IL 61801

RINEHART, ROBERT EUGENE, b Boise, Idaho, Jan 12, 30; m 61; c 2. ORGANIC CHEMISTRY. *Educ:* Univ Idaho, BS, 52; Univ Mich, MS, 54, PhD(chem), 57. *Prof Exp:* Res scientist, Res Ctr, US Rubber Co, NJ, 57-66, sr res scientist, 66-72, sr res scientist, Oxford Mgt & Res Ctr, Uniroyal Inc, 72-78; SR RES CHEMIST, LOCTITE CORP, 78- *Mem:* Am Chem Soc; Sigma Xi. *Res:* Homogeneous catalysis of organic reactions by metal complexes; transition metal-olefin complexes; polymer synthesis; organic mechanisms; adhesives. *Mailing Add:* Loctite Corp 705 N Mountain Rd Newington CT 06111

RINEHART, ROBERT FROSS, b Springfield, Ohio, May 31, 07; m 42; c 2. MATHEMATICS. *Educ:* Wittenberg Col, BA, 30; Ohio State Univ, MA, 32, PhD(math), 34. *Hon Degrees:* DSc, Wittenberg Col, 60. *Prof Exp:* Asst, Ohio State Univ, 30-34; prof math, Ashland Col, 34-37; from instr to prof, Case Inst Technol, 37-65; acad dean, 65-70, EMER DEAN, NAVAL POSTGRAD SCH, 70- *Concurrent Pos:* Exec secy, Res & Develop Bd, Dept Defense, 48-50; dir spec res & opers res, Duke Univ, 58-60; mem, Adv Bd Air Training Command, US Air Force, 61-65; mem, Nat Security Agency Sci Adv Bd, 60-65; dir weapons syts eval div, Inst Defense Anal, DC, 62-64; consult, Opers Res Off, Johns Hopkins Univ, Rand Corp & Off Ord Res. *Mem:* AAAS; Am Math Soc; Opers Res Soc Am (pres, 54); Soc Indust & Appl Math (pres, 60); Math Asn Am. *Res:* Matrices; functions on algebras; operations research. *Mailing Add:* 303 Mar Vista Dr Monterey CA 93940

RINEHART, ROBERT R, b Shenandoah, Iowa, Apr 5, 32; m 55; c 3. GENETICS, RADIATION BIOLOGY. *Educ:* San Diego State Col, AB, 58; Univ Tex, PhD(zool), 62. *Prof Exp:* USPHS fel genetics, Oak Ridge Nat Lab, 62-63; res assoc, Ind Univ, 63-64; assoc prof biol, 64-70, PROF BIOL, SAN DIEGO STATE UNIV, 70- *Concurrent Pos:* AEC res grant, 64-; res assoc, State Univ Leiden, Neth, 68-69. *Mem:* AAAS; Genetics Soc Am. *Res:* Radiation induced mutation repair of radiation damage; chromosome mechanics in Drosophila. *Mailing Add:* Dept of Biol San Diego State Univ San Diego CA 92182

RINEHART, RONALD EARL, b Wilkinsburg, Pa, Aug 16, 40; m 61; c 3. ATMOSPHERIC SCIENCE. *Educ:* Asbury Col, BA, 62; Ore State Univ, MS, 68; Colo State Univ, PhD, 79. *Prof Exp:* Res assoc radar meterol, Ill State Water Surv, Urbana, 65-69; prof meteorologist Kenya hail suppression prog, Atmospherics Inc, Fresno Calif, 69-70; proj dir Vaalharts hail suppression prog, Repub S Africa, 72-73; support scientist, 74-80, STAFF SCIENTIST RADAR METEOROL, NAT CTR ATMOSPHERIC RES, 80- *Mem:* Am Meteorol Soc; AAAS. *Res:* Radar meteorology; hail storms; hail suppression; weather modification; radar calibration; dual wavelength radar; Doppler radar. *Mailing Add:* Convective Storms Div PO Box 3000 Boulder CO 80307

RINEHART, ROY K, b NJ, Nov 23, 22; m 48; c 4. BIOCHEMISTRY. *Educ:* Rutgers Univ, BS, 47, MS, 56, PhD(physiol, biochem), 60. *Prof Exp:* Jr pharmacologist, 48-55, from asst pharmacologist to assoc pharmacologist, 55-61, sr biochemist, 62-77, SR STAFF SCIENTIST, CIBA-GEIGY CORP, 77- *Mem:* Am Chem Soc; NY Acad Sci. *Res:* Biochemical pharmacology; mechanism of drug action; neurotransmitters; cardiovascular pharmacology. *Mailing Add:* Ciba-Geigy Corp Summit NJ 07901

RINEHART, WALTER ARLEY, b Peoria, Ill, June 1, 36; m 59; c 2. ENGINEERING MANAGEMENT, AEROSPACE ENGINEERING. *Educ:* Univ Mo-Rolla, BS, 59. *Prof Exp:* Assoc engr thermodynamics, 59, from res asst to res assoc arc heaters, 59-64, res scientist, 64-69, group engr, 69-70, sr group engr gas dynamics, 70-72, sect mgr, 72-77, BR CHIEF, McDONNELL DOUGLAS CORP, 77- *Mem:* Am Inst Aeronaut & Astronaut. *Res:* Arc heater development for simulation of reentry heating environments encountered by spacecraft and missiles with application to heat protection systems evaluation. *Mailing Add:* McDonnell Douglas Corp PO Box 516 St Louis MO 63166

RINEHART, WILBUR ALLAN, b Mansfield, Ohio, Aug 17, 30; m 63; c 3. GEOPHYSICS, COMPUTER SCIENCE. *Educ:* Bowling Green State Univ, BS, 59; Univ Utah, MS, 62. *Prof Exp:* Geophysicist, US Coast & Geod Surv, 64-73; geophysicist, US Geol Surv, 74-75; GEOPHYSICIST, NAT OCEANIC & ATMOSPHERIC ADMIN, 76- *Mem:* Seismol Soc Am. *Res:* Solid earth geophysics data management; earthquake loss estimation to structures. *Mailing Add:* MS D622 EDIS/NGSDC Nat Oceanic & Atmospheric Admin Boulder CO 80302

RINER, JOHN WILLIAM, b Kansas City, Mo, July 29, 24; m 47; c 5. MATHEMATICS. *Educ:* Rockhurst Col, BS, 47; Univ Notre Dame, MS, 49, PhD(math), 53. *Prof Exp:* Instr math, Univ Notre Dame, 49-50 & St Peters Col, 53-56; asst prof, St Louis Univ, 56-59; from asst prof to assoc prof, 59-69, assoc, Systs Res Group, 60-64, PROF MATH, OHIO STATE UNIV, 69-, VCHMN DEPT, 70- *Mem:* Am Math Soc. *Res:* Topology; organization theory. *Mailing Add:* Dept of Math Ohio State Univ Columbus OH 43210

RING, B ALBERT, b Greenwood, Maine, Jan 7, 20; m 47 & 65; c 6. MEDICINE. *Educ:* Bates Col, BS, 42; Tufts Univ, MD, 46; Am Bd Radiol, dipl, 60. *Prof Exp:* Resident, Bellevue Hosp, New York, 50-51; resident, Col Med, Univ Vt, 55-58; trainee neuroradiol, Stockholm, Sweden, 58-59; from instr to assoc prof radiol, 59-72, PROF RADIOL, COL MED, UNIV VT, 72- *Concurrent Pos:* USPHS grant, 59- *Mem:* Am Col Radiol; Radiol Soc NAm. *Res:* Neuroradiology; occlusion of small intracranial arteries as diagnosed by angiography. *Mailing Add:* Radiol Dept Univ Vermont Burlington VT 05401

RING, HAROLD FRANCIS, b Chelsea, Mass, Dec 11, 20; m 48; c 3. PHYSICS. *Educ:* Mass Inst Technol, BS, 42; Duke Univ, PhD, 49. *Prof Exp:* Physicist, Savannah River Proj, 50-56, sect head, Eastern Lab, Explosives Dept, 56-60, res supvr, Cent Res Dept, 60-63, res mgr, Eastern Lab, 63-64, lab dir, Potomac River Develop Lab, 64-67, asst dir res, Explosives Dept, 67-72, SECT DIR, ATOMIC ENERGY DIV, E I DU PONT DE NEMOURS & CO, INC, 72- *Res:* Nuclear reactor physics; propellants and high explosives; shock waves and explosive metal working. *Mailing Add:* Atomic Energy Div Montcharin Bldg E I du Pont de Nemours & Co Wilmington DE 19898

RING, JAMES GEORGE, b Chicago, Ill, July 26, 38. SOLID STATE PHYSICS, OPTICS. *Educ:* Ill Inst Technol, BS, 60, PhD(physics), 66. *Prof Exp:* Res assoc physics, Univ Ill, Urbana, 65-68; vis asst prof, Univ Ill, Chicago Circle, 68-71; res physicist, 72-74, SR RES PHYSICIST, LAB, PACKARD INSTRUMENT CO, 74- *Mem:* Am Phys Soc; Am Asn Physics Teachers; Sigma Xi. *Res:* Optical properties of color centers in alkali halides; Borrmann effect in germanium and silicon; laser Raman scattering; applied research on radiation detectors; computer assisted spectral analysis. *Mailing Add:* Packard Instrument Co Lab 2200 Warrenville Rd Downers Grove IL 60515

RING, JAMES WALTER, b Worcester, NY, Feb 24, 29; m 59; c 1. CHEMICAL PHYSICS, SOLAR ENERGY. *Educ:* Hamilton Col, AB, 51; Univ Rochester, PhD(physics), 58. *Prof Exp:* From asst prof to assoc prof, 57-69, chmn dept, 68-80, PROF PHYSICS, HAMILTON COL, 69- *Concurrent Pos:* NSF sci fac fel, 65-66; attached physicist, Phys Chem Lab, Oxford Univ, UK, 73; vis fel, Princeton Univ, 81. *Mem:* Am Phys Soc; Am Asn Physics Teachers. *Res:* Dielectrics; inelastic neutron scattering; H-bonded liquids; vibrational modes; solar energy; energy conservation; passive solar heating. *Mailing Add:* Dept of Physics Hamilton Col Clinton NY 13323

RING, JOHN ROBERT, b Warsaw, Ind, Nov 19, 15; m 48; c 3. ANATOMY. *Educ:* Univ Ill, AB, 39; Brown Univ, ScM, 41, PhD(biol), 43. *Prof Exp:* Asst biol, Brown Univ, 39-42; instr anat, Sch Med, St Louis Univ, 43-47; from asst prof to assoc prof, 47-62, asst dean pre-clin instr & res, 67-72, chmn anat dept, 74-77, PROF ANAT, SCH DENT MED, WASH UNIV, 62-, DIR ADMIS, 72-, ASST DEAN BIOMED SCI & CHMN DEPT, 77- *Mem:* Am Asn Dent Schs; AAAS; Am Asn Anat; Int Asn Dent Res. *Res:* Sex endocrinology; gerontology; histology and histochemistry of endocrine organs and oral tissues. *Mailing Add:* Wash Univ Sch of Dent Med 4559 Scott Ave St Louis MO 63110

RING, LEON EDWARD, aeronautical engineering, see previous edition

RING, MOREY ABRAHAM, b Detroit, Mich, Aug 31, 32; m 60; c 4. INORGANIC CHEMISTRY. *Educ:* Univ Calif, Los Angeles, BS, 54; Univ Wash, PhD(chem), 60. *Prof Exp:* Fel chem, Johns Hopkins Univ, 60-61; sr engr, Rocketdyne Div, NAm Aviation, Inc, 61-62; from asst prof to assoc prof chem, 62-70, PROF CHEM, SAN DIEGO STATE UNIV, 70- *Mem:* Am Chem Soc. *Res:* Chemistry of group IV compounds, especially silicon hydrides. *Mailing Add:* Dept Chem San Diego State Univ San Diego CA 92182

RING, PAUL JOSEPH, b Winthrop, Mass, Dec 1, 28; m 66; c 4. PHYSICS. *Educ:* Boston Col, BS, 50; Rensselaer Polytech Inst, MS, 54; Brown Univ, PhD(physics), 63. *Prof Exp:* Scientist physics, Nuclear Magnetics Corp, Perkin-Elmer Corp, 56-57; res asst, Brown Univ, 57-60; consult, Metals & Controls, Inc, Mass, 60-61; res asst, Brown Univ, 61-63; scientist semiconductors, Transitron Electronics Corp, Mass, 63-64; scientist electrooptics, RCA, Mass, 64-67; ASSOC PROF PHYSICS, UNIV LOWELL 67- *Concurrent Pos:* Vis prof, Inst Educ Technol, Univ Surrey, Eng. *Mem:* Nat Sci Teachers Asn; Am Soc Eng Educ; Am Asn Physics Teachers; Am Asn Univ Professors. *Res:* Solid state and infrared physics; cathodoluminescence; minerals; nuclear magnetic resonance; education; ultrasonics. *Mailing Add:* Dept Physics & Appl Sci Univ Lowell Lowell MA 01854

RING, RICHARD ALEXANDER, b Glasgow, Scotland, Sept 24, 38; m 60; c 2. ENTOMOLOGY. *Educ:* Glasgow Univ, BSc, 61, PhD(entom), 65. *Prof Exp:* Asst prof entom, Univ BC, 64-65; Nat Res Coun Can fel, Entom Res Inst, Can Dept Agr, 65-66; asst prof, 66-72, ASSOC PROF ENTOM, UNIV VICTORIA, BC, 72- *Mem:* Soc Cryobiol; Can Soc Zool; Can Entom Soc. *Res:* Insect ecology and physiology; extrinsic and intrinsic control of diapause and coldhardiness in insects; intertidal insects. *Mailing Add:* Dept of Biol Univ of Victoria Victoria BC V8W 2Y2 Can

RING, ROBERT E, b Ragsdale, Ind, Aug 6, 22; m 44; c 2. AERONAUTICAL ENGINEERING. *Educ:* Purdue Univ, BS, 50; Denver Univ, MBA, 56. *Prof Exp:* Asst prof, Western Mich Univ, 51-62; assoc prof, 62-80, PROF AERONAUT, SAN JOSE STATE UNIV, 80- *Res:* Aircraft accident research and investigation; man power requirements in the aeronautics and aerospace industry. *Mailing Add:* Dept Aeronaut San Jose State Univ San Jose CA 95192

RING-CARROLL, ROSE, mathematics, see previous edition

RINGEISEN, RICHARD DELOSE, b Kokomo, Ind, Mar 18, 44; m 65; c 2. MATHEMATICS, GRAPH THEORY & APPLICATIONS. *Educ:* Manchester Col, BS, 66; Mich State Univ, MS, 68, PhD(math), 70. *Prof Exp:* Asst prof math, Colgate Univ, 70-74; asst profInd Univ-Purdue Univ, Ft Wayne, 74-77, assoc prof math, 77-79; ASSOC HEAD & ASSOC PROF MATH SCI, CLEMSON UNIV, SC, 79- *Concurrent Pos:* Vis scientist human eng, Aerospace Med Res Lab, Wright-Patterson AFB, 78-79. *Mem:* Am Math Soc; Math Asn Am; Soc Indust & Appl Math. *Res:* Graph theory, with special emphasis in applications, modelling and topological problems; network models for social sciences. *Mailing Add:* Dept Math Sci Clemson Univ Clemson SC 29631

RINGEL, SAMUEL MORRIS, b New York, NY, Nov 29, 24; m 51; c 3. CLINICAL PHARMACOLOGY, INFECTIOUS DISEASES. *Educ:* Hunter Col, BA, 50; Univ Mich, MS, 51; Mich State Univ, PhD(mycol), 56. *Prof Exp:* Jr microbiologist, Hoffmann-La Roche, 51-52; asst mycol, Mich State Univ, 53-56; from assoc plant pathologist to plant pathologist, Agr Mkt Serv, USDA, 56-61; sr scientist, Dept Microbiol & Immunol, Warner-Lambert Res Inst, 61-67, sr res assoc, 67-78; ASST DIR CLIN PHARMACOL, REVLON HEALTH CARE GROUP, 79- *Concurrent Pos:* Vis scientist, NJ Acad Sci, 65-67; consult numerous univs, industs & insts, 78-81. *Mem:* Int Soc Human & Animal Mycosis; Soc Indust Microbiol; Am Soc Clin Pharmacol & Therapeut; Am Soc Microbiol; NY Acad Sci. *Res:* Fungal enzymes; antifungal agents; post-harvest diseases of fruits and vegetables; medical and pharmaceutical microbiology; antibiotics; cardiovascular research. *Mailing Add:* 30 Cayuga Ave Rockaway NJ 07866

RINGEN, LEIF MATT, b Minot, NDak, July 31, 20; m 45. MICROBIOLOGY. *Educ:* NDak State Univ, BS, 43, MS, 48, PhD(bact), 52. *Prof Exp:* From instr to assoc prof, 52-66, PROF VET MICROBIOL, COL VET MED, WASH STATE UNIV, 66- *Mem:* AAAS; Am Soc Microbiol; NY Acad Sci; Int Soc Human & Animal Mycol. *Res:* Serology of leptospirosis. *Mailing Add:* Dept Vet Microbiol Wash State Univ Pullman WA 99163

RINGENBERG, LAWRENCE ALBERT, b Stryker, Ohio, Aug 21, 15; m 42; c 4. MATHEMATICS. *Educ:* Bowling Green State Univ, AB & BS, 37; Ohio State Univ, MA, 39, PhD(math), 41. *Prof Exp:* Asst math, Ohio State Univ, 37-40; asst prof, Tusculum Col, 41; asst prof, Univ Md, 46-47; prof & head dept, 47-67, DEAN COL ARTS & SCI, EASTERN ILL UNIV, 61- *Mem:* Am Asn Higher Educ; Math Asn Am. *Res:* Mathematical analysis. *Mailing Add:* Off Dean Col Arts & Sci Eastern Ill Univ Charleston IL 61920

RINGER, LARRY JOEL, b Cedar Rapids, Iowa, Sept 24, 37; m 60; c 3. STATISTICS. *Educ:* Iowa State Univ, BS, 59, MS, 62; Tex A&M Univ, PhD(statist), 66. *Prof Exp:* Res asst statist, Iowa State Univ, 59-61; from instr to assoc prof, 65-75, res scientist, Data Processing Ctr, 74-76, PROF STATIST & ASSOC DIR, INST STATIST, TEX A&M UNIV, 75- *Concurrent Pos:* Assoc res statistician, Tex Transportation Inst, 70- *Mem:* Am Statist Asn; Am Soc Qual Control; Sigma Xi. *Res:* Statistical methods and techniques as applied to problems in engineering and physical sciences. *Mailing Add:* Inst Statist Tex A&M Univ College Station TX 77843

RINGER, ROBERT KOSEL, b Ringoes, NJ, Feb 21, 29; m 51; c 1. PHYSIOLOGY. *Educ:* Rutgers Univ, BS, 50, MS, 52, PhD(physiol), 55. *Prof Exp:* Asst prof avian physiol, Rutgers Univ, 55-57; from asst prof to assoc prof, 57-64, PROF AVIAN PHYSIOL, MICH STATE UNIV, 64-, PROF PHYSIOL, 65- *Concurrent Pos:* On leave, Unilever Res Lab, Eng, 66-67; trustee, Am Asn Accreditation of Lab Animal Care. *Mem:* Am Asn Avian Path; Am Physiol Soc; Poultry Sci Asn; World Poultry Sci Asn; Soc Environ Toxicol & Chem. *Res:* Cardiovascular research; endocrinology. *Mailing Add:* Dept of Physiol Mich State Univ East Lansing MI 48824

RINGHAM, GARY LEWIS, b Boonville, Ind, Nov 11, 41; m 64; c 2. PHYSIOLOGY, PHARMACOLOGY. *Educ:* Butler Univ, BS, 63, MS, 66; Univ Utah, PhD(pharmacol), 71. *Prof Exp:* Fel physiol, Univ Colo Med Ctr, Denver, 71-73; res instr, 73-76, ASST PROF PHYSIOL, UNIV UTAH, 76- *Res:* Physiology and pharmacology of synaptic transmission; excitation-secretion coupling; impulse origin and conduction. *Mailing Add:* Dept of Physiol Univ of Utah Col of Med Salt Lake City UT 84132

RINGLE, DAVID ALLAN, b Wausau, Wis, Sept 28, 24; m 49. PHYSIOLOGY, IMMUNOLOGY. *Educ:* Univ Wis, BS, 49; Columbia Univ, MA, 52; NY Univ, PhD(cellular physiol), 60. *Prof Exp:* Scientist, Warner-Lambert Pharmaceut Co, NY, 52-53; biologist, Am Cyanamid Co, Conn, 53-54; USPHS fel, Col Physicians & Surgeons, Columbia Univ, 60-62; prin physiologist, Midwest Res Inst, 62-76; CONSULT IMMUNOPHYSIOL, 76- *Mem:* Harvey Soc; Am Soc Zoologists; Reticuloendothelial Soc; NY Acad Sci. *Res:* Tissue metabolism; reticuloendothelial system function; plasma protein alterations; amphibian yolk; shock; structure and function of cell membranes; cellular immunology; lymphocyte physiology; antilymphocyte serum; immunologic effects of morphine; immunologic detection methods. *Mailing Add:* PO Box 8013 Prairie Village KS 66208

RINGLE, JOHN CLAYTON, b Kokomo, Ind, Aug 28, 35; m 60; c 4. NUCLEAR ENGINEERING. *Educ:* Case Inst Technol, BS, 57, MS, 59; Univ Calif, Berkeley, PhD(nuclear eng), 64. *Prof Exp:* Res physicist, Cambridge Res Lab, 63-66; ASSOC PROF NUCLEAR ENG, RADIATION CTR, ORE STATE UNIV, 66- *Mem:* AAAS; Am Nuclear Soc; Am Phys Soc. *Res:* Reactor administration and operation, safety analysis and radiological engineering calculations for nuclear power plants, environmental effects of nuclear power, energy system analysis. *Mailing Add:* Radiation Ctr Ore State Univ Corvallis OR 97331

RINGLEE, ROBERT J, b Sacramento, Calif, Apr 23, 26; m 49; c 3. MECHANICS, ELECTRICAL ENGINEERING. *Educ:* Univ Wash, BS, 46, MS, 48; Rensselaer Polytech Inst, PhD(mech), 64. *Prof Exp:* Engr, Gen Elec Co, 48-55, supvr design, 55-60, sr engr, 60-67, mgr systs reliability, Elec Utility Eng Oper, 67-69; PRIN ENGR & DIR, POWER TECHNOL INC, 69- *Concurrent Pos:* Mem, Expert Adv Study Comt 32, Int Conf Large Elec Systs, 53-; adj prof, Polytech Inst Brooklyn, 65-66. *Mem:* Fel Inst Elec & Electronics Engrs; fel AAAS. *Res:* Systems sciences; vibration, noise; process modelling; system reliability; control theory. *Mailing Add:* Power Technologies Inc PO Box 1058 Schenectady NY 12301

RINGLER, DANIEL HOWARD, b Oberlin, Ohio, Aug 19, 41; m 63; c 2. LABORATORY ANIMAL MEDICINE, PATHOGENIC BACTERIOLOGY. *Educ:* Ohio State Univ, DVM, 65; Univ Mich, MS, 69; Am Col Lab Animal Med, dipl, 71. *Prof Exp:* Fel, 67-69, instr, 69-71, asst prof, 71-75, assoc prof, 75-79, PROF LAB ANIMAL MED, UNIV MICH, 79- *Concurrent Pos:* Consult, Animal Resources Br, Div Res Resources, NIH, 73-; mem, Am Asn Accreditation Lab Animal Care, 74-, Adv Coun, Inst Lab Animal Resource, Nat Res Coun-Nat Nat Acad Sci, 75-78. *Honors & Awards:* Griffin Award, Am Asn Lab Animal Sci. *Mem:* Am Asn Lab Animal Sci; Am Vet Med Asn. *Res:* Spontaneous diseases of laboratory animals; use of animals in biomedical research; diseases and husbandry of amphibians. *Mailing Add:* Unit Lab Animal Med Sch of Med Univ of Mich Ann Arbor MI 48109

RINGLER, IRA, b Brooklyn, NY, Feb 11, 28; m 54; c 3. BIOCHEMISTRY. *Educ:* Ohio State Univ, BS, 51; Cornell Univ, MNutrS, 53, PhD(biochem), 55. *Prof Exp:* Res fel endocrinol, Harvard Univ, 55-57; group leader, Exp Therapeut Res Sect, Lederle Labs, Am Cyanamid Co, 57-61, head dept metab chemother, 61-66, dir exp therapeut res sect, 66-69, dir res, 69-75; vpres res mgt & corp develop, 75-76; VPRES PHARMACEUT PROD RES & DEVELOP, ABBOTT LABS, 76- *Mem:* Am Chem Soc; Endocrine Soc; Am Soc Pharmacol & Exp Therapeut; Am Soc Biol Chem. *Res:* Biochemical aspects of endocrinology. *Mailing Add:* Abbott Labs 14th & Sheridan Rds North Chicago IL 60064

RINGLER, NEIL HARRISON, b Long Beach, Calif, Nov 12, 45; m 68. AQUATIC ECOLOGY. *Educ:* Calif State Univ, Long Beach, BA, 67; Ore State Univ, MS, 70; Univ Mich, PhD(fisheries biol), 75. *Prof Exp:* Res asst, Ore Game Comn, Ore State Univ, 68-69; teaching fel ichthyol & aquatic entom, Sch Natural Resources, Univ Mich, 71-74; asst prof, 75-79, ASSOC PROF ZOOL, STATE UNIV NY COL ENVIRON SCI & FORESTRY, 79- *Mem:* Sigma Xi; Am Fisheries Soc; Am Soc Ichthyologists & Herpetologists. *Res:* Foraging tactics and behavior of fishes; salmonid biology; population ecology of fishes and aquatic invertebrates; role of predation in structering aquatic communities; stream ecology; effects of forest particles on streambeds. *Mailing Add:* Dept of Environ & Forest Biol SUNY Col Environ Sci & Forestry Syracuse NY 13210

RINGLER, ROBERT L, b Chase, Mich, Mar 27, 22; m 47; c 1. BIOCHEMISTRY. *Educ:* Cent Mich Col, AB, 51; Mich State Univ, PhD(biochem), 55. *Prof Exp:* Asst prof biochem, NC State Col, 55-57; res assoc, Edsel B Ford Inst Med Res, Henry Ford Hosp, Detroit, 57-61; sci adminr, 61-62, chief prog projs br, 62-66, head task force cardiovasc res ctrs, 66-67, chief instnl res progs, 67-68, spec asst to dir, 68-69, actg assoc dir collab res & develop, 69-70, dep dir, Nat Heart & Lung Inst, 69-78, DEP DIR, NAT INST AGING, NIH, 78- *Concurrent Pos:* Mem, Nat Heart Inst Fel Bd, 62-66; mem, Bd US Civil Serv Examrs, 64-69; mem, Ad Hoc Comt Myocardial Infarction Study Ctrs, 67; staff dir, Nat Heart Inst Task Force Cardiac Replacement, 68-69; mem sci group path diag acute ischemic heart dis, WHO, Geneva, 69; chmn coronary drug proj adv comt, NIH, 69-71; mem subcomt med devices, Comt Drugs & Med Devices, Dept Health, Educ & Welfare, 69-70, coordr sickle cell dis prog, 71-72; staff dir, Nat Heart & Lung Inst Task Force Arteriosclerosis, 70-71; Dept Health, Educ & Welfare rep, Inter-Agency Coun Mat, 70-71; mem, US Deleg to USSR in Congenital Heart Dis, US-USSR Health Exchange, 72; chmn, Nat Heart, Blood Vessel, Lung & Blood Prog Plan Adv Comt, 72-73; chmn cardiovascular dis area, US-USSR Joint Comt Health, Moscow, 74. *Honors & Awards:* Superior Serv Award, Dept Health, Educ & Welfare, 70. *Mem:* Am Soc Biol Chemists; Am Heart Asn; fel Am Col Cardiologists. *Res:* Pub health administration. *Mailing Add:* Nat Inst Aging 9000 Rockville Pike Bethesda MD 20205

RINGO, GEORGE ROY, b Minot, NDak, Jan 19, 17; m 41; c 3. EXPERIMENTAL PHYSICS. *Educ:* Univ Chicago, BS, 36, PhD(physics), 40. *Prof Exp:* Physicist, US Rubber Co, RI, 41; physicist, Naval Res Lab, DC, 41-48; PHYSICIST, ARGONNE NAT LAB, 48- *Mem:* Am Phys Soc. *Res:* Neutron physics; ion microscopy. *Mailing Add:* 16 W 220 97th St Hinsdale IL 60521

RINGO, JOHN ALAN, b Spokane, Wash, Dec 29, 41; m 64; c 3. BIOENGINEERING, BIOMEDICAL ENGINEERING. *Educ:* Wash State Univ, BS, 64; Univ Wash, MS, 67, PhD(elec eng), 71. *Prof Exp:* Assoc engr, Douglas Aircraft Co, 64; assoc res engr, Boeing Co, 66-67; asst prof, 72-77, ASSOC PROF ELEC ENG, WASH STATE UNIV, 77- *Mem:* Sigma Xi. *Res:* Application of engineering principles for understanding the interactive heart-artery systems; development of instrumental techniques for monitoring oviduct motility; solid state device properties and their application in linear circuit design. *Mailing Add:* Dept Elec Eng 2210 Wash State Univ Pullman WA 99164

RINGO, JOHN MOYER, b Columbia, Mo, Nov 25, 43; m 69; c 1. BEHAVIORAL GENETICS. *Educ:* Univ Calif, Berkeley, AB, 69; Univ Calif, Davis, PhD(behav genetics), 73. *Prof Exp:* Asst prof, 74-80, ASSOC PROF ZOOL, UNIV MAINE, ORONO, 80- *Concurrent Pos:* Assoc ed, Behav Genetics, 78-81. *Mem:* Behav Genetics Asn; Soc Study Evolution; Genetics Soc Am; Animal Behav Soc; AAAS. *Res:* Genetic analysis of stereotyped behavior, speciation, phylogeny and reproductive isolating mechanisms in Drosophila. *Mailing Add:* Dept of Zool Univ of Maine Orono ME 04473

RINGOLD, HOWARD JOSEPH, b Seattle, Wash, Sept 7, 23; c 3. BIO-ORGANIC CHEMISTRY, MEDICINAL CHEMISTRY. *Educ:* Univ Wash, BS, 46, PhD(chem), 53. *Prof Exp:* Group leader, Syntex, SA, 51-55, assoc dir res, 55-57, dir chem res, 57-59; sr scientist, Worcester Found Exp Biol, Mass, 60-67; VPRES, SYNTEX RES, 67-, DIR INST BIOL SCI, 69-, SR VPRES & DIR BASIC RES, 79- *Concurrent Pos:* Consult, Syntex Res, 60-67. *Mem:* Am Chem Soc; Am Soc Biol Chemists; Endocrine Soc; fel NY Acad Sci; Royal Soc Chem. *Res:* Mechanism of hormone action; mechanism of drug action; mechanism of enzyme action; steroid and drug biological activity. *Mailing Add:* Syntex Res 3401 Hillview Palo Alto CA 94304

RINGS, ROY WILSON, b Columbus, Ohio, Aug 15, 16; m 42; c 3. ENTOMOLOGY. *Educ:* Ohio State Univ, BSc, 38, MSc, 40, PhD(entom), 46. *Prof Exp:* Asst, Ohio Exp Sta, 41-42; specialist in chg, Div Plant Indust, State Dept Agr, 46-47; asst entomologist, 47-53; assoc prof entom, Ohio Agr Exp Sta, 54-61; assoc chmn ctr, 61-73, prof entom, 61-77, EMER PROF ENTOM, OHIO AGR RES & DEVELOP CTR, 77- *Mem:* Entom Soc Am; Am Mosquito Control Asn. *Res:* Biology, ecology and behavior of cutworms and mosquitoes. *Mailing Add:* Ohio Agr Res & Develop Ctr Wooster OH 44691

RINGSDORF, WARREN MARSHALL, JR, b Elba, Ala, May 2, 30; m 55; c 2. DENTISTRY, NUTRITION. *Educ:* Asbury Col, AB, 51; Univ Ala, MS, 56; Univ Ala, Birmingham, DMD, 56; Am Bd Oral Med, dipl, 63. *Prof Exp:* Pvt dent pract, Ala, 58-59; asst prof, 59-64, assoc prof, 64-82, PROF CLIN DENT, UNIV ALA, BIRMINGHAM, 82- *Concurrent Pos:* Fel, Univ Ala, Birmingham, 60-62; attend oral med, Vet Admin Hosp, Birmingham, Ala, 60-; consult, Hq US Army Infantry Ctr, Ft Benning, Ga, 64- & Nutrotech Corp, Santa Barbara, 80- *Honors & Awards:* Chicago Dent Soc Res Award, 66 & 68; Angiol Res Found, Inc Honors Achievement Award, 68. *Mem:* Am Dent Asn; Am Acad Oral Med; Acad Orthomolecular Psychiat. *Res:* Role of diet and nutrition in host resistance and susceptibility and its relationship to prevention of disease occurrence and recurrence; author or coauthor of over 350 publications. *Mailing Add:* Dept of Oral Med Univ of Ala Birmingham AL 35294

RINK, GEORGE, b Riga, Latvia, Jan 17, 42; US citizen; m 66; c 2. FOREST GENETICS. *Educ:* NY Univ, BA, 63; Univ Tenn, MS, 71, PhD(forest genetics), 74. *Prof Exp:* ASST PROF FORESTRY, STEPHEN F AUSTIN STATE UNIV, 75- *Mem:* Sigma Xi; Nat Forestry Orgn; Nat Agr Orgn. *Res:* Proposal for research to describe inbreeding in loblolly pine as reflected by height growth depression and isozyme peroxidase variation. *Mailing Add:* Sch of Forestry Stephen F Austin State Univ Nacogdoches TX 75962

RINK, RICHARD DONALD, b Chicago, Ill, Mar 29, 41; m 62; c 2. HUMAN ANATOMY. *Educ:* Beloit Col, BA, 63; Tulane Univ, PhD(anat), 67. *Prof Exp:* From instr to asst prof, 67-74, assoc prof, 74-80, PROF ANAT, SCH MED, UNIV LOUISVILLE, 80- *Mem:* Am Physiol Soc; Am Asn Anatomists; Int Soc Oxygen Transport to Tissue. *Res:* Oxygen supply to tissue in relation to shock. *Mailing Add:* Dept Anat Health Sci Ctr Univ Louisville Sch Med Louisville KY 40292

RINKER, GEORGE ALBERT, JR, b Lubbock, Tex, Feb 7, 45; c 3. THEORETICAL NUCLEAR PHYSICS, ATOMIC PHYSICS. *Educ:* Franklin Col, BA, 67; Univ Calif, Irvine, MA, 70, PhD(physics), 71. *Prof Exp:* Fel, 71-73, STAFF MEM PHYSICS, LOS ALAMOS SCI LAB, 73- *Concurrent Pos:* Vis scientist, Nuclear Energy Res Inst, Jülich, WGer, 76-77; vis lectr, Univ Fribourg, Switzerland, 77. *Mem:* Am Phys Soc. *Res:* Exotic atoms; nuclear physics; quantum electrodynamics; electron transport. *Mailing Add:* T-4 MS212 Los Alamos Sci Lab Los Alamos NM 87545

RINKER, GEORGE CLARK, b Hamilton, Kans, Apr 8, 22; m 44; c 3. ANATOMY. *Educ:* Univ Kans, AB, 46; Univ Mich, MS, 48, PhD(zool), 51. *Prof Exp:* From instr to asst prof anat, Univ Mich, 50-62; assoc prof, 62-70, asst dean sch med, 70-73, PROF ANAT, SCH MED, UNIV SDAK, VERMILLION, 70-, ASSOC DEAN SCH MED, 73- *Mem:* Am Asn Anat. *Res:* Comparative mammalian and human gross anatomy. *Mailing Add:* Dept of Anat Univ of SDak Sch of Med Vermillion SD 57069

RINKER, JACK NOLL, physics, geology, see previous edition

RINKER, ROBERT G(ENE), b Vincennes, Ind, Dec 31, 29; m; c 3. CHEMICAL ENGINEERING. *Educ:* Rose Polytech Inst, BS, 51; Calif Inst Technol, MS, 55, PhD(chem eng), 59. *Prof Exp:* Res fel, Calif Inst Technol, 59-60, asst prof, 60-67; assoc prof, 67-73, chmn dept, 73-78, PROF CHEM ENG, UNIV CALIF, SANTA BARBARA, 73- *Concurrent Pos:* Consult, NAm Instrument Co, 55, Electro Optical Systs, Inc, 60, Dow Chem Co, 64-65, MHD Res, Inc, 65-67, Sci Appln, Inc, 70- & JRB Assocs, 70- *Mem:* AAAS; Am Inst Chem Engrs. *Res:* Chemical kinetics; reactor design; catalysis. *Mailing Add:* Dept of Chem & Nuclear Eng Univ of Calif Santa Barbara CA 93106

RINNE, JOHN NORMAN, b Pawnee City, Nebr, Mar 19, 44; m 66; c 1. FISHERY BIOLOGY, AQUATIC ECOLOGY. *Educ:* Peru State Col, BSE, 66; Ariz State Univ, MS, 69, PhD(zool), 73. *Prof Exp:* Chief field invest res, Ariz State Univ, 72-73; fishery res biologist, EAfrican Community, 73-75; fishery res biologist, US Fish Wildlife Serv, 76; FISHERY RES BIOLOGIST BIOLOGIST, US FOREST SERV, 76- *Concurrent Pos:* Consult, Squawfish Recovery Team, 76-77, Ariz Trout Recovery Team & Gila Trout Recovery

Team, 76-; area coordr, Desert Fishes Coun, 77- *Mem:* Am Fisheries Soc; Am Inst Fishery Res Biologists. *Res:* Habitat, biology and distribution of endangered fish in the southwestern United States; fisheries and ecology of desert and tropical resources. *Mailing Add:* Forestry Sci Lab Ariz State Univ Tempe AZ 85281

RINNE, ROBERT W, b Hammond, Ind, Jan 6, 32; m 56; c 4. PLANT PHYSIOLOGY. *Educ:* DePauw Univ, BA, 55; Purdue Univ, BS, 57, MS, 59, PhD(plant physiol), 61. *Prof Exp:* Asst plant physiol, Purdue Univ, 57-61; res assoc microbiol, Dartmouth Med Sch, 61-62; NIH fel biochem, Wayne State Univ, 62-64; PROF PLANT PHYSIOL, DEPT AGRON, UNIV ILL, URBANA, 64- *Mem:* Am Soc Plant Physiol; Crop Sci Soc Am. *Res:* Metabolism of the developing soybean seed. *Mailing Add:* Dept of Agron Univ of Ill Urbana IL 61801

RINNE, VERNON WILMER, b Pawnee City, Nebr, Dec 15, 25; m 48; c 5. DENTISTRY. *Educ:* Univ Nebr, BS & DDS, 53. *Prof Exp:* From instr to assoc prof oper dent, 53-68, chmn dept restorative dent, 69-72, PROF ADULT RESTORATION, COL DENT, UNIV NEBR-LINCOLN, 69- *Concurrent Pos:* Consult, USPHS, 60. *Res:* Dental materials. *Mailing Add:* Dept of Restorative Dent Univ of Nebr Col of Dent Lincoln NE 68583

RINNERT, HEINZ R, b Grunberg, Ger, July 17, 21; US citizen; m 66. ENGINEERING PHYSICS. *Educ:* Univ Calif, Berkeley, BS, 50. *Prof Exp:* Mech engr, Naval Radiol Defense Lab, Calif, 50-62, physicist, 62-69, Systs Anal Group, Naval Undersea Ctr, San Diego, 69-75, PHYSICIST, FLEET READINESS GROUP, NAVAL OCEAN SYSTS CTR, SAN DIEGO, 75- *Res:* Nuclear weapons effects and countermeasures; development of computer software and naval operations analysis. *Mailing Add:* Naval Ocean Systs Ctr Code 18 San Diego CA 92152

RINSE, JACOBUS, b Amsterdam, Neth, Apr 4, 00; m 31; c 3. PHYSICAL CHEMISTRY. *Educ:* Univ Amsterdam, PhD(chem), 27. *Prof Exp:* Instr phys chem, Univ Amsterdam, 23-27; fel, John Hopkins Univ, 27; res chemist, Int Paper Co, 28; chief chemist & asst dir, N V Pieter Schoen a Zn Zaandam, Neth, 28-38; founder & dir, Chem Tech Advice Bur, 38-49; DIR & OWNER, CHEM RES ASSOCS, 50- *Mem:* Am Chem Soc; Am Oil Chemists Soc; Asn Consult Chemists & Chem Engrs (treas); NY Acad Sci; Brit Oil & Colour Chemists Asn. *Res:* Allotropy of mercury sulfide and vapor pressure measurements of mercuric iodide; tung oil; alkyd resins; styrenated resins; vinyl esters; paints; degumming of fibers; exchange esterifications; pigments; thixotropy; organic metal compounds; greases; antiacids; metallic resins; atherosclerosis and aging. *Mailing Add:* East Dorset VT 05253

RINSLEY, DONALD BRENDAN, b New York, NY, Jan 31, 28; m 55. PSYCHOANALYTIC RESEARCH, MEDICAL EDUCATION. *Educ:* Harvard Univ, AB, 49; Washington Univ, MD, 54; Am Bd Psychiat & Neurol, dipl psychiat. *Hon Degrees:* Dipl child psychiat, Menninger Found, 75. *Prof Exp:* Asst pediat, Sch Med, Washington Univ, 54-55; resident psychiatrist, Topeka State Hosp, Kans, 55-56 & 58-60, asst chief psychiatrist, Adolescent Unit, Children's Sect, 60-68, chief psychiatrist, 68-75, dir children's sect, 70-75; ASSOC CHIEF PSYCHIAT EDUC, TOPEKA VET ADMIN HOSP, 75- *Concurrent Pos:* House officer pediat, St Louis Children's Hosp, 54-55; fel psychiat, Menninger Found, 55-56 & 58-60; mem, Fac Gen Psychiat, Menninger Sch Psychiat, 60-, Fac Child Psychiat, 68 & Exec & Training Fac Child Psychiat, 69-75 & 77-; assoc clin prof psychiat, Sch Med, Univ Kans, 70-78, clin prof, 78-; fel advan studies, Dept Educ, Menninger Found, 76-79; consult psychiatrist, C F Menninger Mem Hosp, 78- *Honors & Awards:* Edward A Strecker Mem Award, Inst Pa Hosp, 68. *Mem:* Fel Am Col Psychoanalysts; fel Royal Soc Health; fel NY Acad Sci; fel Am Psychiat Asn; fel AAAS. *Res:* Adolescent psychiatry; intensive residential treatment of adolescents; psychoanalytic ego psychology and object-relations theory; special education in residential treatment; borderline and narcissistic personality disorders. *Mailing Add:* Topeka Vet Admin Hosp 2200 Gage Blvd Topeka KS 66622

RINTAMAA, DAVID LEE, ecology, see previous edition

RINZEL, JOHN MATTHEW, b Milwaukee, Wis, July 18, 44; m 67; c 2. APPLIED MATHEMATICS. *Educ:* Univ Fla, BS, 67; NY Univ, MS, 68, PhD(math), 73. *Prof Exp:* Mathematician, Div Comput Res & Technol, NIH, 68-70 & 73-75, RES MATHEMATICIAN, MATH RES BR, NAT INST ARTHRITIS, METAB & DIGESTIVE DIS, NIH, 75- *Concurrent Pos:* Vis instr, Dept Math, Univ Md, College Park, 75- *Mem:* Soc Indust & Appl Math; Am Math Soc; Soc Neurosci. *Res:* Biomathematics; mathematical models for neuroelectric signaling; theoretical neurophysiology; numerical analysis. *Mailing Add:* Bldg 31 Rm 4B-54 NIH Bethesda MD 20205

RIO, SHELDON T, b Raymond, Mont, May 9, 27; m 50; c 2. MATHEMATICS. *Educ:* Westmar Col, BA, 50; Mont State Univ, MA, 54; Ore State Univ, PhD(anal), 59. *Prof Exp:* Chmn, Dept Math, Pac Univ, 55-57; assoc prof, Western Wash State Col, 59-63; chmn dept, 63-72, PROF MATH, SOUTHERN ORE COL, 63-, DIR, SCH SCI & MATH, 79- *Mem:* Am Math Soc; Math Asn Am. *Res:* Analysis; topology. *Mailing Add:* 570 Taylor St Ashland OR 97520

RIOCH, DAVID MCKENZIE, b Mussoorie, India, July 6, 00; nat US; m 38. NEUROPSYCHIATRY. *Educ:* Butler Col, BA, 20; Johns Hopkins Univ, MD, 24. *Hon Degrees:* HLD, Exp Col, Inst Behav Res, 73. *Prof Exp:* House officer surg, Peter Bent Brigham Hosp, Boston, 24-26; asst resident & instr med, Strong Mem Hosp & Sch Med & Dent, Univ Rochester, 26-28; Nat Res Coun fel anat, Univ Mich & Dutch Cent Inst Brain Res, 28-29 & Oxford Univ, 29-30; assoc physiol, Med Sch, Johns Hopkins Univ, 30-31; asst prof anat, Harvard Univ, 31-38; prof neurol, Sch Med, Washington Univ, 38-43, chmn dept neuropsychiat, 38-42; dir res, Chestnut Lodge Sanitarium, 43-51; dir neuropsychiat div, Walter Reed Army Inst Res, Washington, DC, 51-70; coordr, Adult Learning Ctr, Inst Behav Res, Inc, 70-72, sr scientist, 72-81; DISTINGUISHED CLIN PROF, DEPT PSYCHIAT, UNIFORMED SERV UNIV, HEALTH SCI MED SCH, 81- *Concurrent Pos:* Fel, Wash Sch Psychiat, 43-54; Salmon lectr, 57; mem, Inst Advan Study, NJ, 58-59; vis prof psychiat, Univ Chicago, 69-81, emer prof, 81-; lectr, Med Sch, Johns Hopkins Univ, 71-80, emer, 72- *Honors & Awards:* US Army Res & Develop Tech Award & Exceptional Civilian Serv Decoration, Secy US Army, 61; Distinguished Civilian Serv Award, Dept Defense, 62; Walter Reed Medal, Walter Reed Army Med Ctr, 70. *Mem:* Fel Am Psychiat Asn; Am Psychopath Asn (pres, 54); Asn Res Nerv & Ment Dis (pres, 62); Am Acad Arts & Sci; assoc Am Acad Neurol. *Res:* Neuroanatomy and neurophysiology of diencephalic and mesencephalic systems and others bearing on psychiatric concepts. *Mailing Add:* Inst for Behav Res Inc 2429 Linden Lane Silver Spring MD 20910

RIOPEL, JAMES L, b Kittery, Maine, May 24, 34; m 56; c 3. PLANT MORPHOLOGY. *Educ:* Bates Col, AB, 56; Harvard Univ, MS, 58, PhD(biol), 60. *Prof Exp:* Asst prof, 60-66, assoc dean grad sch arts & sci, 68-69, ASSOC PROF BIOL, UNIV VA, 66-, DIR MT LAKE BIOL STA, 60- *Concurrent Pos:* NSF Instnl grant, 62-63; Am Cancer Soc Instnl grant, 63-64; NSF grant, 65-67. *Mem:* Bot Soc Am; Torrey Bot Club; Soc Develop Biol; Int Soc Plant Morphol. *Res:* Developmental plant anatomy and morphogenesis; regulation on cell differentiation and organ origin and determination. *Mailing Add:* Dept of Biol Univ of Va Charlottesville VA 22904

RIORDAN, H(UGH) E(RNEST), b Brooklyn, NJ, July 23, 23; m 45; c 3. MECHANICAL ENGINEERING. *Educ:* Rensselaer Polytech Inst, BME, 44, MME, 47. *Prof Exp:* Res engr, Battelle Mem Inst, 47-48; res engr, Curtiss-Wright Corp, 48-50; from sr engr to asst supvr eng group, Appl Physics Lab, Johns Hopkins Univ, 50-58; sr staff engr, Kearfott Systs Div, Gen Precision, Inc, 58-59, head instrument lab, 59, mgr adv projs & res dept, 59-65, chief res & advan develop gyrodyn, NJ, 65-67; dir corp res ctr, Kelsey Hayes Co, Mich, 67-69, dir res & advan eng, 69-71; DIR ENG SERVS, MERCURY MARINE DIV, BRUNSWICK CORP, 71- *Mem:* AAAS; Audio Eng Soc; Soc Automotive Engrs; NY Acad Sci; Nat Soc Prof Engrs. *Res:* Servomechanisms, signal theory dynamics and physics, of materials as applied to transducers; specialized industrial and military instruments and control systems. *Mailing Add:* Mercury Marine Div 1939 Pioneer Dr Fond du Lac WI 54935

RIORDAN, JAMES F, b New Haven, Conn, Feb 6, 34; m 57; c 2. BIOLOGICAL CHEMISTRY. *Educ:* Fairfield Univ, BS, 55; Fordham Univ, MS, 57, PhD(enzym), 61. *Prof Exp:* Instr chem, US Merchant Marine Acad, 57-58 & Fordham Univ, 58-61; res fel biol chem, 61-64, res assoc, 64-65, assoc, 66-68, asst prof, 68-71, ASSOC PROF BIOL CHEM, HARVARD MED SCH, 71-; ASSOC BIOCHEMIST, BRIGHAM & WOMEN'S HOSP, 61-, ASST DIR, CLIN CHEM LAB, 66- *Concurrent Pos:* Nat Found fels, 62-63 & 64-65; NIH fel, 63-64; ed, J Inorg Biochem, 79-; exec ed, Anal Biochem, 79- *Mem:* Am Chem Soc; Am Soc Biol Chem; AAAS. *Res:* Chemical modification of proteins; mechanism of enzyme action; microscopic environment of functional groups of proteins; zinc metalloenzymen; angiotensin converting enzyme. *Mailing Add:* Steeley G Mudd Bldg 250 Longwood Ave Boston MA 02115

RIORDAN, JOHN RICHARD, b St Stephen, NB, Sept 2, 43; m 70. BIOCHEMISTRY. *Educ:* Univ Toronto, BSc, 66, PhD(biochem), 70. *Prof Exp:* Fel, Max Planck Inst Biophys, Frankfurt, 70-73; INVESTR BIOCHEM, RES INST, HOSP SICK CHILDREN, 73-; ASSOC PROF, DEPTS BIOCHEM & CLIN BIOCHEM, UNIV TORONTO, 74- *Concurrent Pos:* Can Cystic Fibrosis Found fel, 70; res grants, Med Res Coun Can, 81- & Can Cystic Fibrosis Found, 82- *Mem:* Can Fedn Biol Soc; Am Soc Biol Chem. *Res:* Studies of mammalian cell plasma membrane glycoproteins, particularly normal structure, function and aberrations thereof in genetic disease; studies of trace metal homeostasis in man. *Mailing Add:* Hosp for Sick Children 555 University Ave Toronto ON M5G 1X8 Can

RIORDAN, MICHAEL DAVITT, b Willimantic, Conn, Oct 21, 21; m 45; c 1. PETROLEUM CHEMISTRY. *Educ:* Col Holy Cross, BS, 43, MS, 44. *Prof Exp:* Anal chemist, 43-45, chemist, 45-54, proj leader fuels res, 54-57, asst supvr, 57-61, asst supvr process res, 61-67, res supvr chem res, 67-76, staff coordr, 76-79, MGR PETROL PROD RES STAFF, TEXACO, INC, 79- *Mem:* Am Chem Soc; Am Inst Chem Engrs. *Res:* Petroleum products; petroleum processing; petrochemicals. *Mailing Add:* Texaco Inc PO Box 509 Beacon NY 12524

RIORDAN, WILLIAM J, b Chicago, Ill, July 26, 25; m 49; c 6. MATHEMATICS. *Educ:* Mass Inst Technol, BS, 48; Univ Chicago, PhD, 55. *Prof Exp:* Instr math, Mass Inst Technol, 48 & Ill Inst Technol, 49-51; instr mil res, Univ Chicago, 51-56; MEM STAFF, BELL TEL LABS, 56- *Res:* Systems engineering. *Mailing Add:* Bell Tel Labs Holmdel NJ 07733

RIORDON, J(OHN) SPRUCE, b Springs, SAfrica, June 28, 36; Can citizen; m 63; c 3. COMPUTER SYSTEMS ENGINEERING, COMMUNICATIONS. *Educ:* McGill Univ, BEng, 57, MEng, 61; Univ London, PhD(automatic control eng), 67. *Prof Exp:* Res officer, Nat Res Coun Can, 57-68; sessional lectr, 70-73, asst prof eng, 68-70, assoc prof systs eng, 70-77, chmn dept systs eng & comput sci, 70-75, chmn dept systs eng & comput sci, 78-81, PROF SYSTS ENG, CARLETON UNIV, 77-, DEAN ENG, 81- *Concurrent Pos:* Nat Res Coun Can res grant, 69-; consult, Dept Energy, Mines & Resources, 71-73, Ministry of State for Urban Affairs, 75-76 & Dept Commun, 80- *Mem:* Inst Elec & Electronics Engrs; Can Info Processing Soc. *Res:* Mobile communications; computer networks; distributed databases; modelling and simulation; information systems design; application of digital computers to on-line process control; optimum control of stochastic processes; adaptive control systems; modelling of dynamic systems; information storage and retrieval; management information systems. *Mailing Add:* Dean Eng Carleton Univ Ottawa ON K1S 5B6 Can

RIOS, PEDRO AGUSTIN, b Havana, Cuba, Apr 26, 38; US citizen; m 60; c 2. CRYOGENICS. *Educ:* Mass Inst Technol, BS, 59 & 60, MS, 67, ScD(mech eng), 69. *Prof Exp:* Plant engr, Airco Indust Gases, 60-62, asst plant supt, 63-65; res assoc, Mass Inst Technol, 69-70; mech & proj engr, 70-73, mgr, Rotating Mach Unit, 73-77, MGR, ELECTRO-MECH BR, RES & DEVELOP CTR, GEN ELEC CO, 77- *Honors & Awards:* IR-100 Award Indust Res & Develop, 80. *Mem:* Am Soc Mech Engrs. *Res:* Application of cryogenics and superconductivity to rotating electrical machinery, electrical apparatus and magnets; computer aided engineering tools for electromagnetic and electromechanical devices and fluid flow. *Mailing Add:* Corp Res & Develop Bldg 37 Rm 361 Gen Elec Co Schenectady NY 12301

RIOUX, CLAUDE, b Mont-Joli, Que, June 4, 53; m 76; c 2. NUCLEAR STRUCTURE. *Educ:* Univ Laval, BAC, 75, MSc, 78, PhD(nuclear physics), 82. *Prof Exp:* NATURAL SCI & ENG RES COUN CAN FEL NUCLEAR PHYSICS, LAWRENCE BERKELEY LAB, 82- *Mem:* Am Phys Soc. *Res:* Polarization and analyzing-power measurements to check symmetry under time-reversal for nuclear structure information. *Mailing Add:* Bldg 88 Lawrence Berkeley Lab Univ Calif Berkeley CA 94720

RIOUX, ROBERT LESTER, b Natick, Mass, June 11, 27; m 58; c 6. GEOLOGY. *Educ:* Univ NH, BA, 53; Univ Ill, MS, 55, PhD(geol), 58. *Prof Exp:* Asst geol, Univ Ill, 54-55; GEOLOGIST, US GEOL SURV, 56- *Mem:* Geol Soc Am; Am Asn Petrol Geologists. *Res:* Structural geology; Mesozoic stratigraphy; economic geology of mineral fuels and fertilizaers; conservation of mineral lands. *Mailing Add:* US Geol Surv Conserv Div MS 640 12201 Sunrise Valley Dr Reston VA 22092

RIPARBELLI, CARLO, b Rome, Italy, Nov 15, 10; nat US; m 58. AERONAUTICAL ENGINEERING. *Educ:* Univ Rome, Italy, DSc(civil eng), 33, DSc(aeronaut eng), 34, libero docente, 40. *Prof Exp:* Design engr aircraft, S A Caproni, Italy, 35-37, chief designer, 41-43; asst prof aeronaut eng, Univ Rome, 37-41; res assoc, Princeton Univ, 47-48; from asst prof to assoc prof, Cornell Univ, 49-55; design specialist aircraft, Convair Div, Gen Dynamics Corp, 55-59, mem res staff space craft, Gen Atomic Div, 60-65, eng staff specialist, Pomona Div, 65-72; ENG CONSULT, 73- *Concurrent Pos:* Designer, Italian Air Ministry, 41-43; consult, Princeton Univ, 49-50, Aeronaut Macchi, Italy, 49-53, Cornell Aeronaut Lab, NY, 51, Bur Ships, US Navy, 53-55 & Aerospace Corp, Sci Applns, Inc, 73- *Mem:* Soc Exp Stress Anal; assoc fel Am Inst Aeronaut & Astronaut; Italian Aerotechnol Asn. *Res:* Dynamics of structures; impact problems; theoretical and experimental stress analysis; design of aircraft and space craft structures. *Mailing Add:* 4429 Arista Dr San Diego CA 92103

RIPIN, BARRETT HOWARD, b Troy, NY, Oct 27, 42. PLASMA PHYSICS. *Educ:* Rensselaer Polytech Inst, BS, 64; Univ Md, PhD(physics), 71. *Prof Exp:* Res asst plasma physics, Univ Md, 65-70; res assoc controlled thermonuclear res, Plasma Physics Lab, Princeton Univ, 70-71; asst prof physics, Univ Calif, Los Angeles, 71-73; RES PHYSICIST & SECT HEAD, NAVAL RES LAB, 73- *Mem:* Sr mem Inst Elec & Electronics Engrs; fel Am Phys Soc; AAAS. *Res:* Experimental investigations of laser-produced plasmas, laser fusion and controlled thermonuclear research; laser light scattering; self-generated magnetic fields; nonlinear wave interactions. *Mailing Add:* Code 4732 Naval Res Lab Washington DC 20375

RIPKA, WILLIAM CHARLES, b Los Angeles, Calif, June 2, 39; m 67; c 1. ORGANIC CHEMISTRY, PHARMACEUTICAL CHEMISTRY. *Educ:* Calif Inst Technol, BS, 61; Univ Ill, PhD(chem), 66. *Prof Exp:* RES CHEMIST, CENT RES DEPT, E I DU PONT DE NEMOURS & CO, INC, 65- *Mem:* Am Chem Soc. *Res:* Synthesis of fluorosteroids with modified hormonal actions and elaboration of partial morphine fragments as analgesic-narcotic antagonists. *Mailing Add:* Cent Res Dept E I du Pont de Nemours & Co Inc Wilmington DE 19898

RIPLEY, DENNIS LEON, b Joplin, Mo, Aug 30, 38; m 58; c 3. CHEMISTRY, ENGINEERING. *Educ:* Kans State Univ, BS, 59; Univ Tex, PhD(phys chem), 67. *Prof Exp:* Chem engr, Dow Chem Co, 59-61 & US Bur Mines, 61-63; res chemist, 66-69, sect mgr, 69-74, br mgr, Alt Fuels Br, 74-79, MGR PLANNING & ECON, PHILLIPS PETROL CO, 79-81. *Mem:* Am Chem Soc. *Res:* Synthetic fuels; catalysts and catalytic processes; petroleum processes; application of computer techniques. *Mailing Add:* 982 AB Phillips Petrol Co Bartlesville OK 74004

RIPLEY, EARLE ALLISON, b Sydney, NS, June 29, 33; m 67; c 1. BIOMETEOROLOGY, AGROMETEOROLOGY. *Educ:* Dalhousie Univ, BSc, 53; Univ Toronto, MA, 55. *Prof Exp:* Meteorologist, Meterol Br, Can, 55-60 & Nigerian Meteorol Serv, 60-62; agrometeorologist, EAfrican Agr & Forestry Res Orgn, 62-67; micrometeorologist, Matador Proj, 68-74, assoc prof, 74-78, PROF, PLANT ECOL DEPT, UNIV SASK, 74- *Mem:* Fel Can Meteorol Soc; fel Royal Meteorol Soc; Am Meteorol Soc. *Res:* Micrometeorology; agricultural meteorology; environmental impact analysis. *Mailing Add:* Dept of Plant Ecol Univ of Sask Saskatoon SK S7N 0W0 Can

RIPLEY, HERBERT SPENCER, b Galveston, Tex, June 29, 07; m 40; c 2. PSYCHIATRY. *Educ:* Univ Mich, AB, 29; Harvard Univ, MD, 33; Columbia Univ, cert training in psychoanal med, 49. *Prof Exp:* Intern med, Univ Chicago Clins, 34; jr asst resident psychiat, New York Hosp, 35, resident, 38, asst attend psychiatrist, 49; asst prof psychiat, Med Col, Cornell Univ, 35-37, from instr to asst prof, 37-49; chmn dept, 49-69, PROF PSYCHIAT, SCH MED, UNIV WASH, 49- *Concurrent Pos:* Consult, Vet Admin Hosp & Harborview Med Ctr, Seattle, Wash & Children's Orthop Hosp; attend psychiatrist, Univ Hosp, Seattle. *Mem:* Am Col Psychiatrists; Am Col Psychoanalysts; AMA; Am Psychiat Asn; Am Psychoanal Asn. *Res:* Psychiatric education; psychopathology, schizophrenia, suicide depression and psychophysiological reactions. *Mailing Add:* Dept of Psychiat Univ of Wash Sch of Med Seattle WA 98195

RIPLEY, ROBERT CLARENCE, b Attleboro, Mass, Oct 24, 40. ANATOMY, CELL BIOLOGY. *Educ:* Brown Univ, AB, 62; Univ Calif, Los Angeles, PhD(anat), 66. *Prof Exp:* From instr to asst prof biol med sci, 67-74, asst dean, 74-78, ASSOC DEAN HEALTH CAREERS, BROWN UNIV, 78- *Mem:* Am Asn Med Cols. *Res:* Electron microscopy. *Mailing Add:* Div of Biol Med Sci Brown Univ Providence RI 02912

RIPLEY, SIDNEY DILLON, II, b New York, NY, Sept 20, 13; m 49; c 3. ZOOLOGY. *Educ:* Yale Univ, BA, 36; Harvard Univ, PhD(zool), 43. *Hon Degrees:* MA, Yale Univ, 61; DHL, Marlboro Col, 65 & Williams Col, 72; DSc, George Washington Univ, 66, Cath Univ Am, 68, Univ Md, 70, Cambridge Univ, 74, Brown Univ, 75 & Trinity Col, 77; LLD, Dickinson Col, 67, Hofstra Univ, 68 & Yale Univ, 75; DEng, Stevens Inst Technol, 77. *Prof Exp:* Zool collector, Acad Natural Sci Philadelphia, 36-39; vol asst, Am Mus Natural Hist, NY, 39-40; asst, Harvard Univ, 41-42; asst cur birds, Smithsonian Inst, 42; lectr, Yale Univ, 46-52, from asst prof to assoc prof zool, 49-61, prof biol, 61-64; SECY, SMITHSONIAN INST, 64- *Concurrent Pos:* Fulbright fel, Northeast Assam, 50; Guggenheim fel, Yale Univ & NSF fel, Indonesia, 54; Tata Mem lectr, 75. From assoc cur to cur, Peabody Mus Natural Hist, Yale Univ, 46-64, dir, 59-64; dir, Pac War Mem, 46-50; trustee, White Mem Found; pres, Int Coun Bird Preserv, 58-; mem int comt, Int Ornith Cong, 62; bd trustees, World Wildlife Fund, 74-75, Leader exped, Yale Univ & Smithsonian Inst, India & Nepal, 46-47, Nat Geog Soc, Yale Univ & Smithsonian Inst, Nepal, 48-49, Neth New Guinea, 60 & Bhutan & India, 67-77; Deleg, UN Sci Conf Conserv Utilization Resources, 49; deleg, Int Union Preserv Nature, Caracas, 52, mem exec bd, 64; deleg, Stockholm Environ Conf, 72. *Honors & Awards:* Medals, NY Zool Soc, 66 & Zool Soc Belg, 70. *Mem:* Nat Acad Sci; Fel AAAS; Am Ornithologists Union; Soc Study Evolution; Soc Syst Zool. *Res:* Speciation and evolution in vertebrate zoology, primarily ornithology. *Mailing Add:* Smithsonian Inst Washington DC 20560

RIPLEY, THOMAS H, b Bennington, Vt, Nov 18, 27; m 48; c 3. BIOLOGY. *Educ:* Va Polytech Inst, BS, 51, PhD, 58; Univ Mass, MS, 54. *Prof Exp:* Wildlife consult res admin, Dept Fish & Game, Mass, 53-56; instr biol, Va Polytech Inst, 56-57; wildlife consult res admin, Dept Fish & Game, Mass, 57; res biologist, Comn Game & Inland Fisheries, Va, 57-58; asst dir, Southeast Forest Exp Sta, asst to dep chief for res & chief range & wildlife res, US Forest Serv, 58-69; dir forestry, fisheries & wildlife develop, 69-78, MGR, OFF NATURAL RESOURCES, TENN VALLEY AUTHORITY, 79- *Mem:* Wildlife Soc; Soc Am Foresters; Am Forestry Asn (pres, 81-82); Am Inst Biol Sci; Int Union Forestry Res Orgn. *Res:* Forest land management; wildlife, range, watershed and timber resources. *Mailing Add:* Tenn Valley Authority 219 Locust St Bldg Knoxville TN 37902

RIPLING, E(DWARD) J, b Lewistown, Pa, Feb 25, 21; m 43; c 3. METALLURGICAL ENGINEERING. *Educ:* Pa State Univ, BS, 42; Case Inst Technol, MS, 48, PhD(phys metall), 52. *Prof Exp:* Metallurgist, Westinghouse Elec Co, 42-43 & Copperweld Steel Co, 43-44; asst, Case Inst Technol, 46-52, asst prof & res dir, 52-55; lab dir mech metall, Continental Can Co, Inc, 55-60; PRES & DIR RES, MAT RES LAB, INC, 60- *Mem:* Fel Am Soc Metals; Am Inst Mining, Metall & Petrol Engrs. *Res:* Metal forming; mechanical properties of materials. *Mailing Add:* Mat Res Lab Inc One Science Rd Glenwood IL 60425

RIPMEESTER, JOHN ADRIAN, b Voorburg, Neth, Feb 11, 44; Can citizen; m 67; c 2. PHYSICAL CHEMISTRY. *Educ:* Univ BC, 65, PhD(chem), 70. *Prof Exp:* Res assoc chem, Univ Ill, Urbana-Champaign, 70-72; fel, 72-74, asst res officer, 74-78, ASSOC RES OFFICER CHEM, NAT RES COUN CAN, 78- *Res:* Molecular motion in solids; nuclear magnetic resonance. *Mailing Add:* 29 Delong Dr Ottawa ON K1A 0R6 Can

RIPPEN, ALVIN LEONARD, b Campbell, Nebr, Nov 6, 17; m 43; c 3. DAIRY SCIENCE. *Educ:* Univ Nebr, BSc, 40; Ohio State Univ, MSc, 41. *Prof Exp:* Sales engr, Creamery Package Mfg Co, 45-50; plant supt dairy processing, Kegle Dairy Co, Mich, 50-57; asst prof agr eng, Mich State Univ, 57-64, assoc prof food sci, 64-69, prof, 69-80, exten specialist, 57-80; RETIRED. *Mem:* Am Dairy Sci Asn. *Res:* Dairy products processing; dairy plant engineering. *Mailing Add:* Dept of Food Sci & Human Nutrit Mich State Univ East Lansing MI 48824

RIPPERE, RALPH ELLIOTT, b New York, NY, July 10, 12; m 40, 74; c 3. PHYSICAL CHEMISTRY. *Educ:* Columbia Univ, MA, 35, PhD(phys chem), 43; Am Inst Chem, cert, 69. *Prof Exp:* Sr chemist, Aerovox Wireless Co, NY, 34-37; teacher appl chem, Bd Educ New York, 38-41 & 46; res chemist, Plastics Lab, Gen Elec Co, 46-54, anal chemist, Gen Eng Lab, 54-62, sr res scientist, Comput Lab, Calif, 62-68, staff scientist, Processor Equip Dept, Ariz, 68-70; consult, Feed Recycling Co, Calif, 72-73 & Arc Labs, Sperry Flight Systs, 73-76; consult, Circuit Systs Div, Rogers Corp, 76-78; CONSULT, 78- *Mem:* Am Chem Soc; fel Am Inst Chemists; NY Acad Sci; Sigma Xi; Am Powder Metall Inst. *Res:* Borate compounds of glycols; production of silicon tetrafluoride; analytical use of infrared; photoresist etching of films; metals recovery from effluents; electrodeposition metal powders for powder metallurgy. *Mailing Add:* 2408 W Myrtle Ave Phoenix AZ 85021

RIPPERGER, EUGENE ARMAN, b Stover, Mo, July 7, 14; m 40; c 3. ENGINEERING MECHANICS. *Educ:* Kans State Col, BS, 39; Univ Tex, MS, 50; Stanford Univ, PhD(eng mech), 52. *Prof Exp:* Asst res engr, Portland Cement Asn, 39-42; asst engr, US War Dept, 42-43; from instr to asst prof, Univ Tex, 46-50; asst, Stanford Univ, 50-52; assoc dir eng mech res lab, 52-64, dir, 64-77, PROF AEROSPACE ENG & ENG MECH, UNIV TEX, AUSTIN, 52- *Mem:* Fel Am Soc Mech Engrs; Soc Exp Stress Anal; Inst Elec & Electronics Engrs; Am Acad Mech; Nat Soc Prof Engrs. *Res:* Wave propagation; impact; properties of materials; experimental mechanics; bioengineering. *Mailing Add:* Dept of Aerospace Eng & Eng Mech Univ of Tex Austin TX 78712

RIPPERTON, LYMAN ALONZO, biochemistry, deceased

RIPPIE, EDWARD GRANT, b Beloit, Wis, May 29, 31; m 55. PHARMACEUTICS. *Educ:* Univ Wis, BS, 53, MS, 56, PhD(pharm), 59. *Prof Exp:* Asst pharm, Univ Wis, 56; from asst prof to assoc prof, 59-66, head dept, 66-74, dir grad studies, 74-81, PROF PHARMACEUT, UNIV MINN, MINNEAPOLIS, 66- *Concurrent Pos:* Mem comt rev, US Pharmacopoeia, 70-80; res consult, Minn Mining & Mfg Co, 74- *Mem:* Am Chem Soc; Am Pharmaceut Asn; Am Asn Cols Pharm; fel Acad Pharmaceut Sci; fel Am Inst Chemists. *Res:* Pharmaceutics; physical chemical behavior of physiologically active chemical species within anisotropic solvents; mechanisms of mass transport within beds of particulate solids; viscoelasticity of pharmaceutical tablets during and after compression. *Mailing Add:* Univ Minn Col Pharm Minneapolis MN 55455

RIPPON, JOHN WILLARD, b Toledo, Ohio, May 19, 32. MEDICAL MYCOLOGY. *Educ:* Univ Toledo, BS, 53; Univ Ill, MS, 57, PhD(microbiol), 59. *Prof Exp:* Res asst biochem, Univ Ill, 57-59; res assoc, Northwestern Univ, 59-60; instr biol, Loyola Univ, Ill, 60-63; asst prof, 63-69, ASSOC PROF MED, UNIV CHICAGO, 70- *Concurrent Pos:* Res bacteriologist, Vet Admin Hosp, Hines, Ill, 59-60, consult biochemist, 60-62, consult mycologist, 73-; ed-in-chief Mycopathologia, 74- *Mem:* Am Soc Microbiol; Mycol Soc Am; Int Soc Human & Animal Mycol. *Res:* Mechanisms of fungal pathogenicity; physiology of dimorphism in pathogenic fungi. *Mailing Add:* 1148 E 48th St Chicago IL 60615

RIPPS, HARRIS, b New York, NY, Mar 9, 27; m 49; c 3. PHYSIOLOGY. *Educ:* Columbia Univ, BS, 50, MS, 53, MA, 56, PhD(physiol psychol), 59. *Prof Exp:* Assoc optom, Columbia Univ, 51-56; from asst prof to assoc prof ophthal, 59-67, PROF OPHTHAL & PHYSIOL, SCH MED, NY UNIV, 67- *Concurrent Pos:* Nat Inst Neurol Dis & Blindness spec fels, 62 & 63; USPHS career develop award, 63- *Mem:* AAAS; Biophys Soc; Harvey Soc; Am Asn Res Vision & Ophthal; NY Acad Sci. *Res:* Visual physiology, especially visual pigments; electrical activity of retina. *Mailing Add:* Dept of Ophthal NY Univ Sch of Med New York NY 10016

RIPS, E(RVINE) M(ILTON), b Tulsa, Okla, Mar 7, 21; m 48; c 3. ELECTRICAL ENGINEERING. *Educ:* Mass Inst Technol, BS, 42; Carnegie Inst Technol, MS, 47. *Prof Exp:* Asst exp historadiography, Sloan-Kettering Inst Cancer Res, 48-50; instr elec eng, Polytech Inst Brooklyn, 50-52; asst chief engr, Cent Transformer Co, Ill, 52-56; chief engr, Hamner Electronics Co, NJ, 56-58; asst prof, 58-61, ASSOC PROF ELEC ENG, NJ INST TECHNOL, 61- *Mem:* Sr mem Inst Elec & Electronics Engrs. *Res:* Circuit design by digital computers; regulated direct-current power supplies. *Mailing Add:* Dept of Elec Eng 323 High St Newark NJ 07102

RIPY, SARA LOUISE, b Lawrenceburg, Ky, July 22, 24. MATHEMATICAL ANALYSIS. *Educ:* Randolph-Macon Woman's Col, BA, 46; Univ Ky, MA, 49, PhD(math), 57. *Prof Exp:* Instr math, Univ Ky, 46-54, Randolph-Macon Woman's Col, 54-56, Univ Ky, 56-57 & Vassar Col, 57-58; from asst prof to assoc prof, 58-67, PROF MATH, AGNES SCOTT COL, 67-, CHMN DEPT, 70- *Mem:* Math Asn Am; Am Math Soc. *Res:* Summability theory; analytic continuation. *Mailing Add:* Dept of Math Agnes Scott Col Decatur GA 30030

RIRIE, DAVID, b Ririe, Idaho, Mar 20, 22; m 46; c 5. AGRONOMY. *Educ:* Brigham Young Univ, BS, 48; Rutgers Univ, PhD, 51. *Prof Exp:* Agronomist, Sugar Beet Proj, Univ Calif, 51-55; chmn dept agr, Church Col NZ, 55-63; soils & irrig farm adv, 63-80, DIR, MONTEREY COUNTY, AGR EXTEN SERV, UNIV CALIF, 81- *Concurrent Pos:* Consult, FMC Int, Eastern Europe. *Mem:* Am Soc Agron; Soil Sci Soc Am; Am Soc Hort Sci. *Res:* Nutrition studies with sugar beets; effects of growth regulators on sugar beets; peat land reclamation; vegetable crop culture; cereal crop fertilization. *Mailing Add:* 118 Wilgart Way Salinas CA 93901

RIS, HANS, b Bern, Switz, June 15, 14; nat US; m 80; c 2. CELL BIOLOGY. *Educ:* Columbia Univ, PhD(cytol), 42. *Prof Exp:* Asst zool, Columbia Univ, 39-40, lectr, 41-42; Seessel fel, Yale Univ, 42; instr biol, Johns Hopkins Univ, 42-44; asst physiol, Rockefeller Inst, 44-47, assoc, 47-49; assoc prof, 49-53, PROF ZOOL, UNIV WIS-MADISON, 53- *Mem:* Nat Acad Sci; fel Am Acad Arts & Sci; Am Soc Naturalists; Genetics Soc Am; Am Soc Cell Biol. *Res:* Chromosome structure and chemistry; physiology of cell nucleus; mitosis; cell metrastructure. *Mailing Add:* Dept of Zool Univ of Wis Madison WI 53706

RISBUD, SUBHASH HANAMANT, b New Delhi, India, Aug 3, 47; m 74; c 1. GLASS SCIENCE, REFRACTORY MATERIALS. *Educ:* Indian Inst Technol, BS, 69; Univ Calif, Berkeley, MS, 71, PhD(ceramic eng), 76. *Prof Exp:* Eng assoc mat res, Stanford Univ, 71-73; ceramic engr, GTE-WESGO Corp, Calif, 73-74; asst prof mech eng, Univ Nebr-Lincoln, 76-78; asst prof mat sci & eng, Lehigh Univ, 78-79; ASST PROF CERAMIC ENG, UNIV ILL, URBANA, 79- *Concurrent Pos:* Prin investr, Mat Res Lab, Univ Ill, Urbana, 79- *Honors & Awards:* Ross Coffin Purdy Award, Am Ceramic Soc, 79. *Mem:* Am Ceramic Soc; Am Soc Eng Educ. *Res:* Glasses and glass-ceramics: developing the scientific framework for new and unusual glasses in non-oxide ceramic systems, crystallization behavior, microstructure, and properties. *Mailing Add:* Dept Ceramic Eng Univ Ill 105 S Goodwin Urbana IL 61801

RISBY, EDWARD LOUIS, b Clarksdale, Miss, Sept 14, 33; m 57; c 3. PARASITOLOGY, CELL BIOLOGY. *Educ:* Lane Col, BS, 56; Southern Ill Univ, Carbondale, MA, 59; Tulane Univ, PhD(parasitol, cell biol), 68. *Prof Exp:* Asst prof biol, Lane Col, 58-61 & Southern Univ, 61-66; asst prof microbiol, Meharry Med Col, 68-78, asst dean grad studies, 71-78; PROF & HEAD, DEPT BIOL SCI, TENN STATE UNIV, 78- *Concurrent Pos:* Consult, United Negro Col Fund Premed Prog, Fisk Univ, 71- & premed prog, Dillard Univ, 72. *Mem:* Am Soc Parasitol; Soc Protozool; Am Soc Microbiol. *Res:* Comparative study of trypanosomal physiology and pathobiology observed in experimental trypanosomiasis. *Mailing Add:* Dept Biol Tenn State Univ Nashville TN 37203

RISBY, TERENCE HUMPHREY, b Essex, Eng, June 9, 47. ANALYTICAL CHEMISTRY. *Educ:* Imperial Col, Univ London, DIC, 68, PhD(chem), 70; Royal Inst Chem, MRIC CChem, 75. *Prof Exp:* Res fel chem, Univ Madrid, 70-71; res assoc, Univ NC, Chapel Hill, 71-72; asst prof chem, Pa State Univ, 72-80; MEM STAFF, USPHS HOSP, 80- *Concurrent Pos:* Europ fel, Royal Soc, 70-71; consult, Appl Sci Labs, 74- & Sci Res Instruments Corp, 75- *Mem:* Royal Inst Chem; Royal Inst Gt Brit; Am Chem Soc; Soc Appl Spectros; Am Soc Mass Spectros. *Res:* Mechanism of fragmentation and excitation of molecules in electrical discharges; ion-molecule reactions in various ionization sources for mass spectrometry; thermodynamics of solute-solvent interaction in chromatography. *Mailing Add:* CCOEH USPHS Hosp 3100 Wyman Park Dr Baltimore MD 21211

RISDON, THOMAS JOSEPH, b Detroit, Mich, Sept 22, 39; m 79; c 1. LUBRICANTS, TRIBOLOGY. *Educ:* Univ Detroit, BSChE, 62. *Prof Exp:* Res asst, 63-67, sr res asst, 67-70, res assoc, 70-75, sr res assoc, 75-78, SR RES SPECIALIST, CLIMAX MOLYBDENUM CO, AMAX, INC, 78- *Mem:* Am Soc Lubrication Engrs. *Res:* New uses and applications for molybdenum disulfide and other molybdenum compounds as lubricants or lubricant additives. *Mailing Add:* 4871 Dexter-Pinckney Rd Dexter MI 48130

RISEBERG, LESLIE ALLEN, b Malden, Mass, July 23, 43; m 64; c 2. PHYSICS. *Educ:* Harvard Univ, AB, 64; Johns Hopkins Univ, PhD(physics), 68. *Prof Exp:* Mem tech staff, Bell Tel Labs, 68; guest lectr physics, Hebrew Univ Jerusalem, 68-69; mem tech staff, Corp Res & Eng, Tex Instruments Inc, 70-72; mem tech staff, 72-75, res mgr, 75-81, DIR, LIGHTING TECHNOL CTR, GTE LABS, INC, 81- *Concurrent Pos:* Consult, Raytheon Co, 70- & Lawrence Livermore Lab, 74. *Mem:* Am Phys Soc; Inst Elec & Electronics Engrs; Sigma Xi; Optical Soc Am. *Res:* Quantum electronics; spectroscopy; solid state physics; optics; optical pumping; gas discharges; phosphors; solid state devices; lighting technology; materials science. *Mailing Add:* GTE Labs Inc 40 Sylvan Rd Waltham MA 02154

RISEN, WILLIAM MAURICE, JR, b St Louis, Mo, July 22, 40; m 64; c 2. PHYSICAL CHEMISTRY, INORGANIC CHEMISTRY. *Educ:* Georgetown Univ, ScB, 62; Purdue Univ, PhD(phys chem), 67. *Prof Exp:* From instr to assoc prof, 66-75, chmn dept, 70-80, PROF CHEM, BROWN UNIV, 75- *Concurrent Pos:* Consult, NSF. *Mem:* Am Chem Soc; Am Phys Soc; Am Ceramic Soc; Coun Clin Res. *Res:* Molecular spectroscopy; metal-metal bonding; metal carbonyls; far infrared and laser Raman spectra of ionic polymers and glasses; electron-delocalized materials; photoelectron spectroscopy. *Mailing Add:* Dept of Chem Brown Univ Providence RI 02912

RISER, MARY ELIZABETH, b Richland, Wash, Aug 1, 45; m 78. SOMATIC CELL GENETICS, ENDOCRINOLOGY. *Educ:* Newcomb Col, Tulane Univ, BS, 67; Univ Tex Grad Sch Biomed Sci, MS, 70, PhD(genetics & cell biol), 73. *Prof Exp:* Fel endocrinol, 74-77, ASST PROF CELL BIOL, BAYLOR COL MED, 77- *Concurrent Pos:* Fel, NIH, 74-77. *Mem:* Am Soc Cell Biol; Tissue Culture Asn; Sigma Xi. *Res:* Genetic controls in cells: in vitro techniques somatic cell hybridization, and chromosome banding; malignant characteristics of cells; hormone regulation of functions; controls involved in peptide hormone synthesis. *Mailing Add:* Dept Cell Biol Baylor Col Med Houston TX 77030

RISER, NATHAN WENDELL, b Salt Lake City, Utah, Apr 11, 20; m 43; c 3. INVERTEBRATE ZOOLOGY. *Educ:* Univ Ill, AB, 41; Stanford Univ, AM, 47, PhD, 49. *Prof Exp:* Actg instr biol, Stanford Univ, 49; instr zool, Univ Pa, 49-50; from assoc prof to prof biol, Fisk Univ, 50-56; res assoc marine biol, Woods Hole Oceanog Inst, 56-57; prof biol, 57-79, dir, Marine Sci Inst, 66-79, PROF MARINE BIOL, NORTHEASTERN UNIV, 79- *Concurrent Pos:* Vis prof, Univ NH, 50-52 & 53-58; instr, Marine Biol Lab, Woods Hole, 52; res assoc, Woods Hole Oceanog Inst, 57-59; assoc, Mus Comp Zool, Harvard Univ, 57- *Mem:* Am Micros Soc; Am Soc Zoologists. *Res:* Cestodes of mammals and cold blooded vertebrates; invertebrate systematics, morphology, histology and embryology. *Mailing Add:* Marine Sci Inst East Point Nahant MA 01908

RISHEL, RAYMOND WARREN, b Phillips, Wis, June 27, 30; m 57; c 2. MATHEMATICS. *Educ:* Univ Wis, BS, 52, MS, 53, PhD(math), 59. *Prof Exp:* Instr math, Brown Univ, 59-60; res specialist, Boeing Co, Wash, 60-68; assoc prof math, Wash State Univ, 68-69; mathematician, Bell Tel Labs, 69-72; PROF MATH, UNIV KY, 72- *Mem:* Soc Indust & Appl Math. *Res:* Optimal control theory; probability. *Mailing Add:* Dept of Math Univ of Ky Lexington KY 40506

RISHELL, WILLIAM ARTHUR, b Lock Haven, Pa, Mar 1, 40; m 60; c 2. POULTRY BREEDING. *Educ:* Univ Md, BS, 62; Iowa State Univ, MS, 65, PhD(poultry breeding), 68. *Prof Exp:* Geneticist & dir breeding res, Indian River Int, Tex, 67-75; res geneticist, 75-76, DIR RES, ARBOR ACRES FARM, INC, 76- *Mem:* Poultry Sci Asn; World Poultry Sci Asn; Am Genetic Asn. *Res:* Applied poultry breeding and research; statistical analyses of experiments; estimation of genetic parameters. *Mailing Add:* Arbor Acres Farm Inc Marlborough Rd Glastonbury CT 06033

RISING, EDWARD JAMES, b Troy, NY, Nov 10, 26; m 49; c 3. INDUSTRIAL ENGINEERING. *Educ:* Rensselaer Polytech Inst, BME, 50; Syracuse Univ, MME, 53; Univ Iowa, PhD(indust eng), 59. *Prof Exp:* Instr mech eng, Syracuse Univ, 51-54; asst prof, Kans State Univ, 54-56; instr mech & hydraul, Univ Iowa, 56-60; assoc prof indust eng & asst dean, 60-71, PROF INDUST ENG & OPERS RES, UNIV MASS, AMHERST, 71- *Concurrent Pos:* Consult, Mo River Div, US Corps Engrs, 58, Educ Testing Serv, NJ, 60, Package Mach Corp, Mass, 60, City of Gardner, 61, Franklin County Hosp, Greenfield, 64-66, Sprague & Carlton, NH, 66, Paper Serv Corp, Mass, 70 & US Pub Health Serv, 72; Joseph Lucas vis prof, Univ Birmingham. *Mem:* Am Soc Eng Educ; Am Inst Indust Engrs; Am Hosp Asn; Opers Res Soc Am. *Res:* Hospital systems; engineering education. *Mailing Add:* Dept of Indust Eng Univ of Mass Amherst MA 01003

RISING, JAMES DAVID, b Kansas City, Mo, Aug 10, 42; m 65; c 1. EVOLUTIONARY BIOLOGY, SYSTEMATIC ZOOLOGY. *Educ:* Univ Kans, BA, 64, PhD(zool), 68. *Prof Exp:* Fel, Cornell Univ, 68-69; ASSOC PROF ZOOL, UNIV TORONTO, 69- *Mem:* Am Ornithologists Union; Am Soc Naturalists; Soc Study Evolution; Ecol Soc Am; Soc Syst Zool. *Res:* Biology of birds; distribution, abundance, ecology, systematics, behavior and physiology of birds, especially systematic theory; interpopulational variation of vertebrate animals. *Mailing Add:* Dept Zool Univ Toronto Toronto ON M5S 1A1 Can

RISINGER, GERALD E, b Pekin, Ill, Nov 13, 33; m 53; c 2. CHEMISTRY. *Educ:* Bradley Univ, BS, 55; Iowa State Univ, PhD(org chem), 60. *Prof Exp:* Asst prof org chem, Arlington State Col, 60-62 & La Polytech Inst, 62-63; asst prof biochem, 63-71, ASSOC PROF BIOCHEM, LA STATE UNIV, BATON ROUGE, 71- *Concurrent Pos:* Petrol Res Fund grant, 63-66; USPHS res grant, 64-66. *Mem:* Am Chem Soc. *Res:* Bio-organic chemistry; characterization and synthesis of natural products; biogenesis of alkaloids and terpenes; biochemical mechanisms of coenzymatic and enzymatic reactions. *Mailing Add:* Dept of Biochem La State Univ Baton Rouge LA 70803

RISIUS, MARVIN LEROY, b Buffalo Center, Iowa, July 20, 31; m 59; c 2. PLANT BREEDING. *Educ:* Iowa State Univ, BS, 58; Cornell Univ, MS, 62, PhD(plant breeding), 64. *Prof Exp:* Res assoc corn breeding, Cornell Univ, 64-66; from asst prof to assoc prof, 66-77, prof forage breeding, 77-79, PROF SMALL GRAIN BREEDING, PA STATE UNIV, UNIVERSITY PARK, 79- *Mem:* Am Soc Agron; Crop Sci Soc Am. *Res:* Plant breeding and genetics with small grains. *Mailing Add:* Dept of Agron 119 Tyson Pa State Univ University Park PA 16802

RISK, MICHAEL JOHN, b Toronto, Ont, Feb 17, 40; m 65; c 2. MARINE ECOLOGY, PALEOECOLOGY. *Educ:* Univ Toronto, BSc, 62; Univ Western Ont, MSc, 64; Univ Southern Calif, 71. *Prof Exp:* ASST PROF GEOL, McMASTER UNIV, 71- *Mem:* AAAS; Soc Econ Paleontologists & Mineralogists; Geol Asn Can. *Res:* Species diversity and substrate complexity; coral reef diversity; trace fossils; early history of the invertebrate phyla; animal-sediment relationships. *Mailing Add:* Dept of Geol McMaster Univ Hamilton ON L8S 4L8 Can

RISKA, DAN OLOF, b Stockholm, Sweden, Mar 29, 44; m 68. NUCLEAR PHYSICS, THEORETICAL PHYSICS. *Educ:* Helsinki Univ Technol, MSc, 67, LicEng, 70, DrTech(theoret physics), 74. *Prof Exp:* Secy gen, Res Inst Theoret Physics, Helsinki, 68-69; grant, Nordita, Copenhagen, 69-71; vis asst prof physics, State Univ NY Stony Brook, 71-74; asst prof, 74-77, ASSOC PROF PHYSICS, MICH STATE UNIV, 77- *Mem:* Am Phys Soc; Finnish Phys Soc. *Res:* Theoretical nuclear physics; theory of the nuclear force; nuclear reactions. *Mailing Add:* Dept of Physics Mich State Univ East Lansing MI 48824

RISKIN, JULES, b Oakland, Calif, Aug 25, 26; m 60; c 2. PSYCHIATRY. *Educ:* Univ Chicago, PhB, 48, MD, 54. *Prof Exp:* Intern, Col Med, Univ Ill, 54-55; intern psychiat res, Cincinnati Gen Hosp, Ohio, 55-58; actg dir, 58, assoc dir, 59-76, DIR, MENT RES INST, 76- *Concurrent Pos:* NIMH res grant co-prin investr, Ment Res Inst, 61-65; prin investr, 66-69. *Mem:* Am Psychiat Asn; AMA. *Res:* Developing a methodology for studying whole family interaction; studying technique and theory of family therapy. *Mailing Add:* Ment Res Inst 555 Middlefield Rd Palo Alto CA 94301

RISLEY, JOHN STETLER, b Seattle, Wash, Mar 3, 42; m 64; c 3. ATOMIC PHYSICS. *Educ:* Univ Wash, BS, 65, MS, 66, PhD(physics), 73. *Prof Exp:* Teaching asst & res assoc physics, Univ Wash, 65-75; vis asst prof, Univ Nebr, 76; asst prof, 76-79, ASSOC PROF PHYSICS, NC STATE UNIV, 79- *Concurrent Pos:* Secy, Int Conf Physics of Electronic & Atomic Collisions, 77-; mem prog comt electronic & atomic physics, Am Phys Soc, 78- *Mem:* Am Phys Soc; Sigma Xi; AAAS. *Res:* Atomic collisions physics; negative ions; autodetaching states; vacuum ultraviolet radiation; synchrotron radiation. *Mailing Add:* Dept of Physics NC State Univ Raleigh NC 27650

RISLOVE, DAVID JOEL, b Rushford, Minn, Nov 16, 40; m 63; c 2. ORGANIC CHEMISTRY. *Educ:* Winona State Col, BA, 62; NDak State Univ, PhD(chem), 68. *Prof Exp:* Am Petrol Inst res asst, NDak State Univ, 65-68; assoc prof, 68-77, PROF CHEM, WINONA STATE UNIV, 77- *Mem:* Am Chem Soc. *Res:* Porphyrin chemistry; synthetic organic chemistry; kinetics and mechanisms of organic reactions; analytical organic methods. *Mailing Add:* Dept of Chem Winona State Univ Winona MN 55987

RISMAN, GEORGE CARL, b Roxbury, Mass, Dec 18, 19; m 50; c 2. MEDICINE. *Educ:* Univ Maine, BSc, 41; Brown Univ, MSc, 43; Univ Pa, PhD(zool), 47, MD, 50. *Prof Exp:* Instr zool, Univ Pa, 43-44; instr anat, Med Col Pa, 44-46; instr med, Tulane Univ, 53-54; ASST PROF MED, COL MED, UNIV ALA, BIRMINGHAM, 58- *Concurrent Pos:* Mem, Comn Occup Dis. *Mem:* Fel Am Col Chest Physicians; Am Col Physicians. *Res:* Internal medicine and pulmonary diseases. *Mailing Add:* 2715 S 18th Pl Birmingham AL 35209

RISS, WALTER, b New Britain, Conn, Jan 1, 25; m 51; c 4. NEUROANATOMY, PSYCHOLOGY. *Educ:* Univ Conn, BA, 49; Univ Rochester, PhD(psychol), 53. *Prof Exp:* Res assoc anat, Univ Kans, 52-53, USPHS fel, 53-54; from instr to assoc prof anat, 54-69, asst dean grad studies, 70-73, dir biol psychol, 71-75, PROF ANAT, STATE UNIV NY DOWNSTATE MED CTR, 70- *Concurrent Pos:* Prin founder & ed-in-chief, Brain, Behav & Evolution, 68- *Mem:* Am Psychol Asn; Am Asn Anatomists; Soc Neurosci. *Res:* Evolution of the nervous system and behavior; brain functions and behavior; endocrines and energetics of behavior. *Mailing Add:* Dept of Anat & Biol Psychol State Univ NY Downstate Med Ctr Brooklyn NY 11203

RISSANEN, JORMA JOHANNES, b Finland, Oct 20, 32; m 57; c 2. MATHEMATICS. *Educ:* Tech Univ Helsinki, dipl eng, 56, Techn Lic, 60, Techn Dr(control theory, math), 65. *Prof Exp:* MEM RES STAFF, INFO THEORY & MATH, IBM RES, 60- *Res:* Information theory; estimation; theory of data structures. *Mailing Add:* IBM Res 5600 Cottle Rd San Jose CA 95114

RISSE, GUENTER BERNHARD, b Buenos Aires, Arg, Apr 28, 32; US citizen. HISTORY OF MEDICINE. *Educ:* Univ Buenos Aires, MD, 58; Univ Chicago, MA, 66, PhD(hist), 71. *Prof Exp:* Asst med, Med Sch, Univ Chicago, 63-67; asst prof hist med, Med Sch, Univ Minn, 69-71; assoc prof hist med, 71-76, PROF HIST MED, CTR HEALTH SCI, UNIV WIS-MADISON, 76-, PROF HIST SCI, 80- *Concurrent Pos:* Am Philos Soc fel, 72 & 77; NIH grant, Univ Wis, 72-74. *Mem:* Am Asn Hist Med; Ger Soc Hist Med, Sci & Technol; Hist Sci Soc; Int Acad Hist Med; Brit Soc Social Hist Med. *Res:* History of eighteenth century medical theories and practices in Europe; history of the hospital and medicine in Latin America, especially the factors that have historically shaped the ecology of disease. *Mailing Add:* Dept Hist Med & Hist Sci Ctr Health Sci Univ Wis Madison WI 53706

RISSER, ARTHUR CRANE, JR, b Blackwell, Okla, July 8, 38; m 78; c 3. ORNITHOLOGY. *Educ:* Grinnell Col, BA, 60; Univ Ariz, MS, 63; Univ Calif, Davis, PhD(zool), 70. *Prof Exp:* Mus technician, Smithsonian Inst, US Nat Mus, 63-64; res assoc med ecol, Int Ctr Med Res & Training, Univ Md, 64-65; asst zool, Univ Calif, Davis, 65-67; lab technician, 67-70; asst prof biol, Univ Nev, Reno, 70-74; asst cur birds, 74-76, CUR BIRDS, SAN DIEGO ZOO, 76- *Concurrent Pos:* Adj prof zool, San Diego State Univ, 77- *Mem:* Am Asn Zool Parks & Aquariums; Am Pheasant & Waterfowl Soc; Cooper Ornith Soc; Am Fedn Aviculture. *Res:* Avian reproduction. *Mailing Add:* PO Box 551 San Diego Zoo San Diego CA 92112

RISSER, JACOB RUTT, b Lancaster, Pa, Aug 3, 10; m 37; c 2. PHYSICS. *Educ:* Franklin & Marshall Col, AB, 31; Princeton Univ, AM, 35, PhD(physics), 38. *Prof Exp:* Instr physics, Purdue Univ, 37-41, asst prof physics & group leader cyclotron res lab, 46; from asst prof to assoc prof, 46-58, prof, 58-80, EMER PROF PHYSICS, RICE UNIV, 80- *Concurrent Pos:* Consult, Radioisotope Unit, US Vet Admin; mem staff, Antenna Div, Radiation Lab, Mass Inst Technol, 41-46. *Mem:* Fel Am Phys Soc. *Res:* Disintegration and excitation of nuclei by deuterons, neutrons and alpha particles; charged particle scattering. *Mailing Add:* Dept of Physics Rice Univ Houston TX 77001

RISSER, PAUL GILLAN, b Blackwell, Okla, Sept 14, 39; m 61; c 4. ECOSYSTEMS. *Educ:* Grinnell Col, BA, 61; Univ Wis-Madison, MS, 65, PhD(bot & soils), 67. *Prof Exp:* Res asst, Jackson Lab, 61-63; asst prof bot, Univ Okla, Norman, 67-72, assoc prof, 72-77, chmn, Dept Bot & Microbiol & prog dir ecosyst studies, 77-81, prof, 78-81; CHIEF, ILL NATURAL HIST SURV, 81- *Mem:* Ecol Soc Am (secy, 78-82); Sigma Xi; Brit Ecol Soc; Soc Range Mgt. *Res:* Systems analysis of grassland ecosystems, particularly, dynamics of energy and material storage and transfer; studies of vegetation structure; natural resource planning. *Mailing Add:* Off Chief Ill Natural Hist Surv 607 E Peabody Champaign IL 61820

RISSLER, JANE FRANCINA, b Martinsburg, WVa, Jan 1, 46. PLANT PATHOLOGY. *Educ:* Shepherd Col, BA, 66; WVa Univ, MA, 68; Cornell Univ, PhD(plant path), 77. *Prof Exp:* Fel fungal physiol, Boyce Thompson Inst, 77-78; ASST PROF PLANT PATH, UNIV MD, 78- *Mem:* Am Phytopath Soc. *Res:* Phytopathogenic bacteria; diseases of ornamental plants and turf grass. *Mailing Add:* Dept of Bot Univ of Md College Park MD 20742

RISTENBATT, MARLIN P, b Lebanon, Pa, Oct 12, 28; m 57; c 1. ELECTRONICS. *Educ:* Pa State Univ, BS, 52, MS, 54; Univ Mich, PhD(elec eng), 61. *Prof Exp:* Instr elec eng, Pa State Univ, 52-54; sr engr, HRB-Singer, Inc, 54-56; assoc res engr, 56-61, res engr, 61-65, GROUP LEADER COMMUN, UNIV MICH, ANN ARBOR, 65- *Mem:* AAAS; sr mem Inst Elec & Electronics Engrs. *Res:* Application of communications theory, decision theory, estimation theory and computer methods to devise and evaluate new communication techniques and systems. *Mailing Add:* 3606 Terhune Rd Ann Arbor MI 48104

RISTIC, MIODRAG, b Serbia, Yugoslavia, May 16, 18. VETERINARY MEDICINE. *Educ:* Univ Munich, dipl, 50; Col Vet Med, Ger, Dr Vet Med, 50; Univ Wis, MS, 53; Univ Ill, PhD, 59. *Prof Exp:* Asst prof microbiol, Col Vet Med, Ger, 50-51; proj asst vet sci, Univ Wis, 51-53; from assoc pathologist to pathologist, Univ Fla, 53-60; PROF VET PATH & HYG, UNIV ILL, URBANA, 60-, PROF VET RES, 65- *Concurrent Pos:* Mem comt anaplasmosis & transmissible dis of swine, US Animal Health Asn; Anglo-Am fel, Europe; mem comt on rickettsia, Bergey's Manual; consult, Agency Int Develop & Rockefeller Found. *Mem:* Soc Immunol; Conf Res Workers Animal Dis; Am Vet Med Asn; Am Soc Trop Med & Hyg; Soc Protozool. *Res:* Infectious diseases of domestic animals, with special emphasis on blood diseases of man and animals. *Mailing Add:* Dept of Vet Path & Hyg Univ of Ill Col of Vet Med Urbana IL 61801

RISTIC, VELIMIR MIHAILO, b Skopje, Yugoslavia, Oct 10, 36; m 64; c 1. PLASMA PHYSICS, ELECTRICAL ENGINEERING. *Educ:* Univ Belgrade, BS, 60, MS, 64; Stanford Univ, MS, 66, PhD(elec eng), 69. *Prof Exp:* Res asst elec eng, Boris Kidric Inst Nuclear Sci, Belgrade, 61-62; lectr, Univ Belgrade, 62-65; res asst plasma physics, Stanford Univ, 66-68; asst prof, 68-72, assoc prof, 72-80, PROF ELEC ENG, UNIV TORONTO, 80- *Concurrent Pos:* Res assoc, Inst Geomagnetic Sci & lectr, Univ Nis, 62-65; Nat Res Coun Can & Defence Res Bd Can res grants, Univ Toronto, 68-72; Ont Dept Univ Affairs res grant, 69-70. *Mem:* Inst Elec & Electronics Engrs. *Res:* Microwave acoustics; acousto-optic signal processing; wave-wave and wave-particle interactions in acoustics, optics and electromagnetics; real-time signal processing. *Mailing Add:* Dept of Elec Eng Univ of Toronto Toronto ON M5S 1A1 Can

RISTOW, BRUCE W, b Chicago, Ill, June 24, 40; m 66. PHYSICAL CHEMISTRY. *Educ:* Northwestern Univ, BA, 62; Cornell Univ, PhD, 66. *Prof Exp:* NIH fel, Yale Univ, 66-67; asst prof, 67-72, ASSOC PROF CHEM & DEAN GRAD STUDIES, STATE UNIV NY COL GENESEO, 72- *Mem:* Am Chem Soc. *Res:* Electron spin resonance; electrochemistry. *Mailing Add:* 540 Antlers Rochester NY 14618

RISTVET, BYRON LEO, b Tacoma, Wash, Aug 22, 47; m 75. MARINE GEOCHEMISTRY. *Educ:* Univ Puget Sound, BS, 69; Northwestern Univ, PhD(geol), 76. *Prof Exp:* SCI ADV GEOL, AIR FORCE WEAPONS LAB, 73- *Honors & Awards:* Secy Air Force Res & Develop Award, 75. *Mem:* Geochem Soc; Soc Econ Paleontologists & Mineralogists; Clays & Clay Minerals Soc; Geol Soc Am; Am Mineral Soc. *Res:* Quaternary geology of Eniwetok Atoll; shock metamorphism of recent carbonates; reverse weathering reactions and their global implications. *Mailing Add:* Defense Nuclear Agency Kirtland AFB NM 87115

RITCEY, GORDON M, b Halifax, NS, May 17, 30; m 55; c 1. INORGANIC CHEMISTRY, ORGANIC CHEMISTRY. *Educ:* Dalhousie Univ, BSc, 52. *Prof Exp:* Chemist, Radioactivity Div, Mines Br, Dept Energy, Mines & Resources, Can, 52; chief chemist, Eldorado Mining & Refining Co, 52-57, chief chemist res & develop & res chemist, 57, chief chemist, 59-60, head chem res group, 60-67; res scientist & head hydrometall sect, Mineral Sci Div, 67-80, RES SCIENTIST & HEAD PROCESS METALL SECT, EXTEN METALL LABS, CANMET, DEPT ENERGY MINES & RESOURCES, 80- *Mem:* Am Inst Mining, Metall & Petrol Eng; Am Chem Soc; Chem Inst Can; Can Soc Chem Engrs; Can Inst Mining & Metall. *Res:* Solution chemistry relating to hydrometallurgy; recovery and separation of metals from leach solutions resulting from work on solvent extraction has resulted in plants for the recovery of uranium, cobalt, nickel, zirconium and hafnium; rare earth separations. *Mailing Add:* 258 Grandview Rd Nepean ON K2H 8A9 Can

RITCHEY, JOHN ARTHUR, b Camden, Ind, Nov 13, 19; m 41; c 2. INDUSTRIAL ENGINEERING. *Educ:* Purdue Univ, BSc, 41; Mass Inst Technol, ScM, 46; Univ Chicago, PhD(bus), 58. *Prof Exp:* Personnel asst, Revere Copper & Brass, 41-42; prod mgr, Procter & Gamble, 46-52; prof indust eng, Purdue Univ, 52-68; opers analyst, Stanford Res Inst, 68-70; PROF INDUST ENG & HEAD DEPT, MONT STATE UNIV, 70- *Concurrent Pos:* Indust develop specialist, Ford Found, Egypt, 65-67. *Mem:* Am Inst Indust Engrs. *Res:* Productivity analysis in private organizations and ways to improve productivity; management. *Mailing Add:* Dept Indust Eng Mont State Univ Bozeman MT 59717

RITCHEY, JOHN MICHAEL, b Wichita, Kans, Dec 14, 40; m 64; c 1. INORGANIC CHEMISTRY, ANALYTICAL CHEMISTRY. *Educ:* Univ Colo, PhD(inorganic chem), 68. *Prof Exp:* Clin chemist, Wesley Med Ctr, 62-63; asst prof chem, Furman Univ, 68-70 & Northern Ariz Univ, 70-72; asst prof, 72-73, chmn dept, 73-77, assoc prof, 74-77, PROF CHEM, FT LEWIS COL, 78- *Concurrent Pos:* Consult, Four Corners Environ Res Inst, 72-, dir, 73-; vis staff mem, Los Alamos Nat Lab, 81-82. *Mem:* AAAS; Am Chem Soc; Sigma Xi. *Res:* Organometallic chemistry, especially boroxines and zero valent metal-sulfur-oxygen complexes; trace metal analysis, especially in natural systems; synthetic inorganic and organic metallurgy. *Mailing Add:* Dept of Chem Ft Lewis Col Durango CO 81301

RITCHEY, KENNETH DALE, b Washington, DC, Oct 24, 44; m 71; c 2. SOIL FERTILITY. *Educ:* Carnegie Inst Technol, BS, 65; Cornell Univ, MS, 67, PhD(agron), 73. *Prof Exp:* Soil fertil specialist int agr progs, Univ Wis, 73-74; RES ASSOC SOIL FERTIL, CORNELL UNIV, 74- *Mem:* Int Soil Sci Soc; Am Soc Agron; Am Soil Sci Soc; Brazilian Soil Sci Soc. *Res:* Nitrogen, magnesium, micronutrient and potassium responses in highly weathered tropical soils; amelioration of subsoil acidity by leaching of calcium sulfate. *Mailing Add:* Dept of Agron Bradfield Hall Cornell Univ Ithaca NY 14853

RITCHEY, SANFORD JEWELL, b Columbia, Miss, Feb 6, 30; m 57; c 3. NUTRITION. *Educ:* La State Univ, BS, 51; Univ Ill, MS, 56, PhD(animal nutrit), 57. *Prof Exp:* Fel biochem, Tex A&M Univ, 57-59, asst prof food & nutrit, 59-63; assoc prof, 63-66, head dept nutrit & foods, 66-73, assoc dean, Col Home Econ, 73-80, PROF HUMAN NUTRIT, VA POLYTECH INST & STATE UNIV, 69-, DEAN, COL HOME ECON, 80- *Honors & Awards:* Borden Award, 79. *Mem:* AAAS; Am Chem Soc; Inst Food Technologists; Am Inst Nutrit. *Res:* Food science; nutritional relationships in growing children. *Mailing Add:* Col of Home Econ Va Polytech Inst & State Univ Blacksburg VA 24061

RITCHEY, THOMAS WILLIAM, b Altoona, Pa, Apr 25, 49; m 73. MICROBIOLOGY, DENTAL RESEARCH. *Educ:* Pa State Univ, BS, 71; Cornell Univ, PhD(microbiol), 74. *Prof Exp:* Teaching asst microbiol, Pa State Univ, 70-71 & Cornell Univ, 71-74; PRIN RES BIOLOGIST MICROBIOL, LEVER BROS CO, UNILEVER LTD, 74-; INVESTR, FAIRLEIGH DICKINSON UNIV, SCH DENT, 78- *Concurrent Pos:* Investr, Sch Dent, Fairleigh Dickinson Univ, 78- *Mem:* Am Soc Microbiol; Sigma Xi; NY Acad Sci; Int Asn Dent Res; Am Asn Dent Res. *Res:* Elucidate the development of dental plaque and calculus while seeking therapeutic agents; develop a Salmonella, mammalian, microsome mutagenicity test for detecting carcinogens and mutagens. *Mailing Add:* Res & Develop Div Unilever Ltd 45 River Rd Edgewater NJ 07020

RITCHEY, WILLIAM MICHAEL, b Mt Vernon, Ohio, June 2, 25; m 47; c 2. PHYSICAL CHEMISTRY. *Educ:* Ohio State Univ, BS, 50, MS, 53, PhD(phys chem), 55. *Prof Exp:* Chemist, Battelle Mem Inst, 52-55; sr res chemist, Res Dept, Standard Oil Co, Ohio, 55-66, group leader, 66-68; assoc prof phys chem, 68-69, assoc prof phys chem 69-79, ASSOC PROF MACROMOLECULAR SCI, CASE WESTERN RESERVE UNIV, 69-, PROF CHEM, 79- *Concurrent Pos:* Asst, Ohio State Univ, 50-54. *Mem:* AAAS; Am Chem Soc; Soc Appl Spectros. *Res:* Applications of nuclear magentic resonance in the solution and solid state, polymer characterization in structures, motion and morphology; x-ray spectroscopy and differential thermal analysis to petroleum chemistry, polymers and fossil fuels. *Mailing Add:* Dept of Chem Case Western Reserve Univ Cleveland OH 44106

RITCHIE, ADAM BURKE, b Waynesboro, Va, Sept 8, 39; m 61; c 2. THEORETICAL CHEMISTRY. *Educ:* Univ Va, BA, 60, MA, 61, PhD(chem), 68. *Prof Exp:* Air Force Off Sci Res fel chem, Harvard Univ, 68-69; Nat Acad Sci-Nat Res Coun-NASA resident res assoc atomic physics, Goddard Space Flight Ctr, 69-71; asst prof, 71-76, assoc prof, 76-80, PROF CHEM, UNIV ALA, 80- *Res:* Faraday effect; perturbation theory; correlation energies of molecules; atomic and molecular collision processes. *Mailing Add:* Dept Chem Univ Ala University AL 35486

RITCHIE, ALEXANDER CHARLES, b Auckland, NZ, Apr 2, 21; m 56. PATHOLOGY. *Educ:* Univ NZ, MB, ChB, 44; Oxford Univ, DPhil(path), 50; Royal Col Physicians Can, cert specialist path, 55; Am Bd Path, dipl, 56; FRCP(C), 64; FRCPath, 70; FRCP(Australia), 72. *Prof Exp:* Mem Brit Empire cancer campaign res unit, Oxford Univ, 47-49, Walker studentship path, Oxford Univ, 50-51; vis fel oncol, Chicago Med Sch, 51-52; lectr path, McGill Univ, 54-55, Douglas res fel, 55-56, asst prof, 55-58, Miranda Fraser assoc prof comp path, 58-61; head dept, 61-74, PROF PATH, UNIV TORONTO, 61- *Concurrent Pos:* Mem consult panel, Can Tumour Registry, 58-75; pathologist-in-chief, Toronto Gen Hosp, 62-75; consult, Wellesley Hosp, Hosp Sick Children & Women's Col Hosp, 63- & Ont Cancer Inst, 64-; chief examr lab med, Royal Col Physicians & Surgeons, Can, 73-77; hon consult, Toronto Western Hosp, 75-; secy, World Asn Soc Path, 75-81, pres, 81-, pres, World Path Found, 80- *Honors & Awards:* Jubilee Medal, Can, 77. *Mem:* Am Asn Cancer Res; Am Asn Path & Bact; fel Col Am Path; Can Asn Path (pres, 67-69); Int Acad Path. *Res:* Oncology; pathology of tumors and cancer; occupational lung disease. *Mailing Add:* Dept of Path 100 College St Toronto ON M5G 1L5 Can

RITCHIE, AUSTIN E, b Van Wert, Ohio, Feb 3, 18; m 42; c 4. AGRICULTURE, AGRICULTURAL EDUCATION. *Educ:* Ohio State Univ, BSc, 46, MSc, 51, PhD(agr educ), 55. *Prof Exp:* Teacher, Gibsonburg High Sch, 47-48 & Hilliard High Sch, 48-50; from instr to assoc prof, 48-62, asst dean & secy agr, 57-63 & 64-65, actg exec dean spec serv, 63-64, PROF AGR EDUC, OHIO STATE UNIV, 62-, ASST DEAN ACAD AFFAIRS AGR, 65- *Mem:* AAAS. *Res:* Administration college of agriculture and home economics; agriculture curricula; general education and teacher education. *Mailing Add:* Ohio State Univ 2120 Fyffe Rd Columbus OH 43210

RITCHIE, BETTY CARAWAY, b Dyersburg, Tenn, June 16, 29; m 66. AUDIOLOGY. *Educ:* La State Univ, BA, 50, MA, 51; Northwestern Univ, PhD(audiol), 64. *Prof Exp:* Speech correctionist, La Pub Schs, 51-53; dir, WTenn Hearing & Speech Ctr, 53-60; asst prof speech & dir hearing eval ctr, Univ Wis-Milwaukee, 63-70; assoc prof, Southern Ill Univ, 70-72; ASSOC PROF SPEECH PATH & AUDIOL, UNIV WIS-MILWAUKEE, 72- *Mem:* Am Audiol Soc; Am Speech & Hearing Asn; Acoust Soc Am. *Res:* Effects of compression amplication on speech intelligibility; evaluation of the efficiency of the verbal auditory screening for children. *Mailing Add:* Hearing Eval Ctr Univ Wis Milwaukee WI 53201

RITCHIE, BRENDA RACHEL (BIGLAND), b Jordans, Eng, Sept 23, 27; m 51; c 2. PHYSIOLOGY. *Educ:* Univ London, BSc, 49, PhD(physiol), 68. *Prof Exp:* Res asst physiol, Univ Col, Univ London, 49-51, asst lectr, 51-53; lectr pharmacol, Royal Free Hosp for Women, London, Eng, 55-56; res asst, Albert Einstein Col Med, 61-64; lectr biol, Lehman Col, 66-67; asst prof, Marymount Col, NY, 67-70; assoc prof, 70-73, PROF BIOL, QUINNIPIAC COL, 73-, NIH RES GRANT, 71- *Concurrent Pos:* Prin investr, NIH & Marking Device Asn grants; assoc fel, John B Pierce Found, Conn, 79- *Mem:* Brit Physiol Soc; Am Physiol Soc Neurosci; fel Am Col Sports Med. *Res:* Analysis of human muscle movement and exercise in terms of the physical properties of isolated muscle. *Mailing Add:* Dept of Biol Quinnipiac Col Hamden CT 06518

RITCHIE, CALVIN DONALD, b Arlington, Va, Jan 30, 30; m 52; c 4. ORGANIC CHEMISTRY. *Educ:* George Washington Univ, BS, 54, PhD(phys org chem), 60. *Prof Exp:* Org chemist, Food & Drug Admin, 56-60; Welch fel chem, Rice Univ, 60-61; PROF CHEM, STATE UNIV NY BUFFALO, 61- *Mem:* Am Chem Soc; Royal Soc Chem. *Res:* Physical organic chemistry, particularly dealing with solvent effects and substituent effects in organic chemistry. *Mailing Add:* Dept of Chem State Univ of NY Buffalo NY 14214

RITCHIE, DAVID MALCOLM, b Woodburg, NJ, April 13, 50; m 72; c 2. PULMONARY PHARMACOLOGY, HYPERSENSITIVITY DISEASES. *Educ:* Rutgers Univ, BA, 72; Hahnemann Med Col, MS, 74, PhD(pharmacol), 76. *Prof Exp:* Fel pharmacol, Hahnemann Med Col, 74-76; res assoc, Med Col Pa, 76-78; scientist, 78-80, SR SCIENTIST, ORTHO PHARMACEUT CORP, 80- *Concurrent Pos:* Mem, Am Heart Asn. *Mem:* Am Chem Soc; Int Soc Immunopharmacol. *Res:* Leukotriene and lipoxygenase pathway of arachidonic metabolism as they relate to hypersensitivity disease; role of leukotrienes and their management in asthma and allergic disorders. *Mailing Add:* Ortho Pharmaceut Corp Rte 202 Raritan NJ 08869

RITCHIE, DONALD DIRK, b Atlanta, Ga, Mar 28, 14; m 40; c 3. MYCOLOGY. *Educ:* Furman Univ, BA, 33, BS, 34; Univ NC, MA, 37, PhD(bot), 47. *Prof Exp:* From asst to instr biol, Furman Univ, 33-35; asst bot, Univ NC, 35-38; from instr to asst prof, WVa Univ, 38-48; from asst prof to assoc prof, 48-66, head dept, 51-66, prof & head dept, 66-79, EMER PROF BIOL, BARNARD COL, COLUMBIA UNIV, 80- *Concurrent Pos:* Mycologist, Naval Res Lab, 48, 55, 58 & 67, dir, Naval Res Lab Exposure Sta, Panama, 53-54; US Navy Submarine Habitability Prog, 58 & US Army Pershing Missile Test, 63; Fulbright lectr, Univ Col, Galway, 67-68; adj instr, Hunter Col, 81. *Honors & Awards:* Emily Gregory Award, 79. *Mem:* AAAS; Bot Soc Am; Torrey Bot Club; Am Soc Microbiol; Soc Indust Microbiol. *Res:* Cytology and growth of fungi, especially marine; cultivation of algae. *Mailing Add:* Dept of Biol Barnard Col Columbia Univ New York NY 10027

RITCHIE, GARY ALAN, b Washington, DC, Aug 23, 41. PHYSIOLOGICAL ECOLOGY. *Educ:* Univ Ga, BS, 64; Univ Wash, MF, 66, PhD(forest ecol), 71. *Prof Exp:* Environ engr, US Army Corps Engrs, 71-73; environ impact analyst, 73-74, tech planner forestry & raw mat res develop, 74-76, RES PROJ LEADER PLANT PHYSIOL, WEYERHAEUSER CO, 77- *Mem:* Sigma Xi; Soc Am Foresters. *Res:* Financial analysis of long and short-term research investments in forestry, forest regeneration, forest management and forest genetics; reforestation and tree seedling production technology. *Mailing Add:* Weyerhaeuser Co Centralia WA 98506

RITCHIE, HARLAN, b Albert City, Iowa, Aug 3, 35; m 57; c 3. ANIMAL HUSBANDRY. *Educ:* Iowa State Univ, BS, 57; Mich State Univ, PhD(animal husb), 64. *Prof Exp:* Asst instr, 57-64, from asst prof to assoc prof, 64-71, PROF ANIMAL HUSB, MICH STATE UNIV, 71- *Mem:* Am Soc Animal Sci. *Res:* Trace elements in swine nutrition; beef cattle management. *Mailing Add:* Dept of Animal Husb Mich State Univ East Lansing MI 48823

RITCHIE, JAMES CUNNINGHAM, b Aberdeen, Scotland, July 20, 29; m 54; c 3. BOTANY, ECOLOGY. *Educ:* Aberdeen Univ, BSc, 51, DSc(bot), 62; Sheffield Univ, PhD, 55. *Prof Exp:* Sr res demonstr, Univ Sheffield, 52-53; Royal Comn Exhib 1851 sr res scholar, Montreal Bot Gardens & Man, 54-55; Nat Res Coun Can fel, Man, 55-56, from asst prof to assoc prof bot, 56-65; prof biol, Trent Univ, 65-69; prof, Dalhousie Univ, 69-70; chmn dept, 70-75, PROF LIFE SCI DIV, SCARBOROUGH COL, UNIV TORONTO, 72- *Concurrent Pos:* Nat Res Coun Can exchange scientist, USSR, 61; Sr Killam Res scholar, 77-78. *Mem:* Ecol Soc Am; fel Arctic Inst NAm; Can Bot Soc (pres, 69); Brit Ecol Soc; Bot Soc Brit Isles. *Res:* Quaternary ecology, especially Holocene and Pleistocene vegetation and ecology of North West America and North Africa. *Mailing Add:* Life Sci Div Scarborough Col Westhill ON M1C 1A4 Can

RITCHIE, JERRY CARLYLE, b Richfield, NC, Dec 13, 37; m 66; c 2. ECOLOGY. *Educ:* Pfeiffer Col, BA, 60; Univ Tenn, Knoxville, MS, 62; Univ Ga, PhD(bot), 67. *Prof Exp:* Res asst ecol, Oak Ridge Nat Lab, 62; fel plant sci, Southeastern Watershed Res Ctr, Univ Ga, 67-68; botanist, US Sedimentation Lab, Agr Res Serv, USDA, Oxford, Miss, 68-78; SOIL SCIENTIST, USDA, BELTSVILLE, 78- *Mem:* Ecol Soc Am; Brit Ecol Soc; Am Inst Biol Sci; Am Soc Agron. *Res:* Radioecology, limnology, sedimentation; remote sensing. *Mailing Add:* Barc-West Bldg 005 Beltsville MD 20705

RITCHIE, JOE T, b Palestine, Tex, June 2, 37; m 59; c 1. SOIL PHYSICS, PHYSICAL CHEMISTRY. *Educ:* Abilene Christian Col, BS, 59; Tex Tech Col, MS, 61; Iowa State Univ, PhD(soil physics), 64. *Prof Exp:* Lab asst agr, Abilene Christian Col, 57-59; res asst, Tex Agr Exp Sta, 59-61; asst agron, Iowa State Univ, 61-64; physicist, Tex Res Found, 64-66; RES SOIL SCIENTIST, SOIL & WATER CONSERV RES DIV, AGR RES SERV, USDA, 66- *Concurrent Pos:* Consult, Tex Instruments, Inc, 65. *Mem:* Am Soc Agron; Soil Sci Soc Am; Am Chem Soc; Am Statist Asn; Am Geophys Union. *Res:* Application of gas-solid chromatography for analysis of soil gases; measurement of microclimate as related to evapotranspiration; soil moisture estimation under row crops. *Mailing Add:* Agr Res Serv Agr Res Serv USDA PO Box 748 Temple TX 76501

RITCHIE, JOSEPH MURDOCH, b Scotland, June 10, 25; m 51; c 2. PHARMACOLOGY, PHYSIOLOGY. *Educ:* Aberdeen Univ, BSc, 44; Univ London, BSc, 49, PhD(physiol), 52, DSc, 60. *Hon Degrees:* MA, Yale Univ, 68. *Prof Exp:* Lectr physiol, Univ London, 49-51; mem staff, Nat Inst Med Res, Eng, 51-56; from asst prof to prof pharmacol, Albert Einstein Col Med, 56-68; chmn dept pharmacol, 68-74, dir div biol sci, 75-78, EUGENE HIGGINS PROF PHARMACOL, SCH MED, YALE UNIV, 68- *Concurrent Pos:* Overseas fel, Churchill Col, Cambridge Univ, 64-65. *Mem:* Am Soc Pharmacol; Am Physiol Soc; Brit Physiol Soc; fel Royal Soc; Brit Pharmacol Soc. *Res:* Biophysics of muscle and nerve. *Mailing Add:* Dept Pharmacol Sch Med Yale Univ New Haven CT 06510

RITCHIE, KIM, b Korea, Apr 13, 36; US citizen; m 59; c 1. BIOCHEMISTRY. *Educ:* ETenn State Col, BA, 59; Univ Tenn, MS, 61; Ariz State Univ, PhD(chem), 67. *Prof Exp:* Res chemist, Tenn Eastman Co, 61-62; res biochemist, Parke-Davis Co, 62-64; res biochemist, Barrow Neurol Inst, St Joseph's Hosp, Phoenix, Ariz, 64-68; sr chemist, Motorola Inc, 68-76, lab mgr, Process Technol Lab, Semiconductor Res & Develop Lab, Semiconductor Prod Div, 76-80; WITH AUX CERAMICS, 80- *Mem:* Electrochem Soc; AAAS; Am Chem Soc; NY Acad Sci. *Res:* Neurochemistry; copper metabolism in central nervous system; organometallic interaction with biopolymers; solid state chemistry; polymer surface chemistry. *Mailing Add:* AUX Ceramics PO Box 867 Myrtle Beach SC 29577

RITCHIE, ROBERT OLIVER, b Plymouth, Eng, Jan 2, 48. MATERIALS SCIENCE, MECHANICAL ENGINEERING. *Educ:* Cambridge Univ, BA, 69, MA & PhD(metall, mat sci), 73. *Prof Exp:* Res assoc metall & mat sci, Churchill Col, Cambridge Univ, 72-74; lectr mat sci & eng, Univ Calif, Berkeley, 74-76, res metallurgist mat, Lawrence Berkeley Lab, 76; asst prof mech eng, Mass Inst Technol, 77-78, assoc prof, 78-81; ASSOC PROF METALL, UNIV CALIF, BERKELEY, 81- *Concurrent Pos:* Goldsmith's res fel, Churchill Col, Cambridge Univ, 72-74; Miller res fel, Univ Calif, Berkeley, 74-76. *Mem:* Am Soc Metals; AIME; Brit Metals Soc; assoc Brit Inst Metallurgists; Am Soc Mech Engrs. *Res:* Deformation and failure of engineering materials, especially metallurgy, toughness, fatigue and environmentally-assisted failure and wear of metals and alloys. *Mailing Add:* Dept Mat Sci & Mineral Eng 282 Hearst Mining Bldg Univ Calif Berkeley CA 02139

RITCHIE, ROBERT WELLS, b Alameda, Calif, Sept 21, 35; m 57; c 2. COMPUTER SCIENCE, MATHEMATICS. *Educ:* Reed Col, BA, 57; Princeton Univ, MA, 59, PhD(math), 61. *Prof Exp:* Res instr, Dartmouth Col, 60-62; from asst prof to assoc prof math, 62-69, assoc dean grad sch, 66-69, assoc math & comput sci & vprovost acad admin, 69-72, prof comput sci & vprovost & asst vpres acad affairs, 72-76, PROF & CHMN COMPUT SCI, UNIV WASH, 77- *Concurrent Pos:* Vis scientist, Xerox Palo Alto Res Ctr, 81-82. *Mem:* AAAS; Am Math Soc; Math Asn Am; Asn Symbolic Logic; Asn Comput Mach. *Res:* Mathematical logic and linguistics; computability theory; theory of algorithms; complexity theory. *Mailing Add:* Comput Sci Dept FR-35 Univ of Wash Seattle WA 98195

RITCHIE, RUFUS HAYNES, b Blue Diamond, Ky, Sept 24, 24; m 44; c 2. RADIATION PHYSICS. *Educ:* Univ Ky, BS, 47, MS, 49; Univ Tenn, PhD, 59. *Prof Exp:* Instr physics, Univ Ky, 48-49; PHYSICIST, HEALTH PHYSICS DIV, OAK RIDGE NAT LAB, 49-, DISTINGUISHED RES STAFF MEM, 78- *Concurrent Pos:* Vis res prof, Inst Physics, Aarhus Univ, 61-62; Ford Found prof physics, Univ Tenn, 65- prof, Univ Ky, 68-69; sr vis fel, Cavendish Lab, Cambridge Univ, 75-76, overseas fel, Churchill Col, 75-76; corp res fel, Union Carbide Corp, 79; guest res fel, Cavendish Lab, Cambridge Univ, 81; vis prof, Inst Physics, Odense Univ, Denmark, 80-81. *Mem:* AAAS; fel Am Phys Soc; Health Physics Soc; Radiation Res Soc. *Res:* Interaction of radiation with matter; health physics; collective interactions in condensed matter. *Mailing Add:* Health Physics Div Oak Ridge Nat Lab Oak Ridge TN 37830

RITCHIE, WALLACE PARKS, JR, b St Paul, Minn, Nov 4, 35; m 60; c 3. SURGERY. *Educ:* Yale Univ, BA, 57; Johns Hopkins Univ, MD, 61; Univ Minn, PhD(surg), 71. *Prof Exp:* From intern to resident surg, Yale-New Haven Med Ctr, 61-63; from resident to chief resident, SCh Med, Univ Minn, 64-69, instr, 69-70; chief dept surg gastroenterol, Div Surg, Walter Reed Army Inst Res, 70-73; from asst prof to assoc prof, 73-76, PROF SURG, SCH MED, UNIV VA, 76- *Concurrent Pos:* Consult, Vet Admin Hosp, Roanoke, Va, 73-; Am Heart Asn estab investr, Univ Va, 74- *Mem:* Am Fedn Clin Res; Am Gastroenterol Asn; Asn Acad Surg (pres, 76-77); Soc Univ Surgeons; Am Surg Asn. *Res:* Gastric mucosal resistance as a factor in ulcerative disease of the upper gastrointestinal tract. *Mailing Add:* Dept of Surg Univ of Va Sch of Med Charlottesville VA 22908

RITENOUR, GARY LEE, b Warsaw, Ind, Oct 5, 38; m 63; c 2. AGRONOMY, PLANT PHYSIOLOGY. *Educ:* Purdue Univ, West Lafayette, BS, 60; Univ Calif, Davis, MS, 62, PhD(plant physiol), 64. *Prof Exp:* Univ Ill res fel, Univ Ill, Urbana, 64-66 & farm adv agron crops, Agr Exten Serv, Univ Calif, 66-69; assoc prof, 69-74, PROF AGRON, CALIF STATE UNIV, FRESNO, 74- *Mem:* Am Soc Agron; Weed Sci Soc Am. *Res:* Weed control; field research on the effect of agronomic practices on yield and quality of field crops. *Mailing Add:* Dept Plant Sci Calif State Univ Fresno CA 93740

RITER, JOHN RANDOLPH, JR, b Denver, Colo, Apr 18, 33; m 55; c 4. PHYSICAL CHEMISTRY. *Educ:* Colo Sch Mines, PRE, 56; Univ Wash, PhD(chem), 62. *Prof Exp:* Jr engr, Boeing Co, 56-58, assoc res engr, 58-60; instr chem, Univ Wash, 61-62; from asst prof to assoc prof, 62-71, PROF CHEM, UNIV DENVER, 71- *Concurrent Pos:* Assoc Western Univ fac fel physics, Univ Calif, Berkeley, 68; vis prof, Math Inst, Oxford Univ, 71; consult, Colo Pathologists Regional Lab, 76- *Mem:* Am Chem Soc; Am Phys Soc. *Res:* Thermodynamics; high-temperature spectroscopy. *Mailing Add:* Dept Chem Univ Denver Denver CO 80208

RITER, STEPHEN, b Providence, RI, Mar 7, 40; m 64; c 2. ELECTRICAL ENGINEERING. *Educ:* Rice Univ, BA, 61, BSEE, 62; Univ Houston, MS, 67, PhD(elec eng), 68. *Prof Exp:* From asst prof to prof elec eng, Tex A&M Univ, 68-79, asst dir, Ctr Urban Progs, 72-76, assoc dir, Ctr Energy & Mineral Resources, 76-77, dir, Tex Energy Exten Serv, 77-79; PROF ELEC ENG, CHMN DEPT & DIR COMPUT SCI, UNIV TEX, EL PASO, 80- *Concurrent Pos:* Ed, Trans Geosci, Inst Elec & Electronics Engrs, 72. *Mem:* Inst Elec & Electronics Engrs; Marine Technol Soc; Sigma Xi; Technol Transfer Soc. *Res:* Communications theory and its applications to geophysical, marine and urban systems; energy system analysis and technology transfer. *Mailing Add:* Elec Eng Tex Univ El Paso TX 79968

RITGER, PAUL DAVID, b Orange, NJ, Sept 10, 25; m 57; c 4. APPLIED MATHEMATICS. *Educ:* Holy Cross Col, BS, 45; Univ Pa, MA, 48; NY Univ, PhD(math), 56. *Prof Exp:* Teacher, Phelps Sch, 47-48; instr math, Univ Mass, 48-50; asst, NY Univ, 51-54; from instr to assoc prof, Stevens Inst Technol, 54-68; MEM TECH STAFF, BELL LABS, 68- *Mem:* Math Asn Am. *Res:* Parabolic differential equations; free boundary problems; unsteady flow theory; missile trajectories and tracking; ocean acoustics. *Mailing Add:* Bell Labs Whippany NJ 07981

RITLAND, RICHARD MARTIN, b Grants Pass, Ore, July 3, 25; m 46; c 5. VERTEBRATE ZOOLOGY, PALEONTOLOGY. *Educ:* Walla Walla Col, BA, 46; Ore State Col, MS, 50; Harvard Univ, PhD, 54. *Prof Exp:* From instr to asst prof biol, Atlantic Union Col, 47-52; from instr to asst prof, Loma Linda Univ, 54-60; assoc prof, 60-65, PROF PALEONT, ANDREWS UNIV, 65-, PROF GEOL, 77- *Mem:* AAAS; Soc Study Evolution; Soc Vert Paleont; Paleont Soc; fel Brit Geol Soc. *Res:* Tertiary and cretaceous paleo-ecology. *Mailing Add:* Dept Geol Andrews Univ Berrien Springs MI 49104

RITSCHEL, WOLFGANG ADOLF, b Trautenau, Czech, Jan 10, 33; m 60; c 2. PHARMACOKINETICS. *Educ:* Innsbruck Univ, MPharm, 55; Univ Strasbourg, DPharm, 60; Univ Vienna, DPhil, 65. *Hon Degrees:* Prof, Nat Univ Mayor San Marcos, Lima, Peru, 73. *Prof Exp:* Chief pharmacist, Girol SA, Zurich, Switz, 58-59; head pharmaceut res, Biochemie AG, Kundl, Austria, 59-61; prof chem & pharmaceut, Notre Dame Col, Dacca, EPakistan, 61-64, head dept pharm, 62-64; head technol pharmaceut res, Siegfried AG Säckingen, Ger, 65-68; assoc prof, 69-72, prof biopharmaceut, 72-77, prof pharmacokinetics & biopharmaceut, 77-81, PROF PHARMACOL, MED COL, UNIV CINCINNATI, 81-, CO-DIR, CLIN PHARMACOKINETICS SERV, UNIV HOSP, 81- *Concurrent Pos:* Asst prof, Teaching Hosp, Kufstein, Austria, 59-61; adj prof, Univ Basel, 65-68; Nat Pharmaceut Coun grant biopharmaceut, Univ Cincinnati, 69-71; dir pharm serv-res, Cincinnati Gen Hosp, Med Ctr, Univ Cincinnati, 75. *Honors & Awards:* Theodor-Körner Prize, Pres of Repub Austria, 62 & Cross of Honor for Sci & Arts, 75; Hertha Heinemann Mem Prize, Ger Pharmaceut Indust, 65. *Mem:* Acad Pharmaceut Sci; Int Pharmaceut Fedn; Int Soc Chemother; Ger Asn Trop Med; fel Am Clin Pharmacol. *Res:* Pathways of absorption of drugs; bioavailability of drugs; development of testing procedures; pharmacokinetics of drugs; clinical pharmacokinetics. *Mailing Add:* Col of Pharm Univ of Cincinnati Med Ctr Cincinnati OH 45267

RITSKO, JOHN JAMES, b Pittston, Pa, July 8, 45; m 67; c 2. EXPERIMENTAL SOLID STATE PHYSICS. *Educ:* Mass Inst Technol, BS, 67; Princeton Univ, MS, 69, PhD(physics), 74. *Prof Exp:* SCIENTIST PHYSICS, XEROX CORP, 74- *Mem:* Am Phys Soc; Sigma Xi. *Res:* Study of electronic states and elementary excitations of organic and molecular solids by means of high energy inelastic electron scattering and ultraviolet photoemission spectroscopy. *Mailing Add:* Xerox Webster Res Ctr 800 Phillips Rd Webster NY 14580

RITSON, DAVID MARK, b London, Eng, Nov 10, 24; m 52; c 4. PHYSICS. *Educ:* Oxford Univ, BA, 44, DPhil(physics), 48. *Prof Exp:* Res fel physics, Dublin Inst Advan Studies, Ireland, 48-49; asst & instr, Univ Rochester, 49-52; lectr physics & res physicist, Mass Inst Technol, 52-64; assoc prof, 64-71, PROF PHYSICS, STANFORD UNIV, 71- *Res:* Cosmic rays; high energy accelerator physics; particularly properties of fundamental particles. *Mailing Add:* Dept of Physics Stanford Univ Stanford CA 94305

RITT, PAUL EDWARD, JR, b Baltimore, Md, Mar 3, 28; m 50; c 6. CHEMISTRY. *Educ:* Loyola Col, Md, BS, 50; Georgetown Univ, MS, 52, PhD(chem), 54. *Prof Exp:* Lab asst, Loyola Col, Md, 50; res asst, Harris Res Labs, Inc, 50-52; chemist, Melpar, Inc, Westinghouse Air Brake Co, 52-54; proj chemist, 54-56, chief chemist, 56-57, mgr chem lab, 57-59, mgr phys sci lab, 59-60, dir res, 60-62, vpres res, 62-67; pres, Appl Sci Div & Appl Technol Div, Litton Industs, 67-68; VPRES & DIR RES, GEN TEL & ELECTRONICS LABS, INC, 68- *Concurrent Pos:* Lectr, Univ Va, 57-59 & Am Univ, 58-; vpres & gen mgr, Training Corp Am, Melpar, Inc, 65-66, pres, 66-67. *Mem:* Am Chem Soc; Electrochem Soc; Am Ceramic Soc; Am Inst Chemists; NY Acad Sci. *Res:* Organometallic synthesis; rare earth ceramics; solid state phenomenon; thin films; integrated circuits; optical communications; plasma physics; high temperature measurements; space instrumentation; special purpose data processing; electron systems; systems integration; telecommunications; robotry; operations research. *Mailing Add:* 36 Sylvan Lane Weston MA 02193

RITT, ROBERT KING, b New York, NY, Dec 30, 24; m 50; c 4. APPLIED MATHEMATICS. *Educ:* Columbia Univ, AB, 44, PhD(math), 53. *Prof Exp:* Lectr math, Columbia Univ, 46-48; from instr to assoc prof, Univ Mich, 48-62; div mgr, Conductron Corp, 62-68; pres, Ritt Labs, Inc, 68-71; chmn dept, 71-76, PROF MATH, ILL STATE UNIV, 71- *Mem:* Am Math Soc; Math Asn Am. *Res:* Electromagnetic theory; foundations of statistical mechanics; perturbation theory of symetric operators. *Mailing Add:* Dept of Math Ill State Univ Normal IL 61761

RITTELMEYER, LOUIS FREDERICK, JR, b Mobile, Ala, Dec 23, 24; m 49; c 8. PSYCHIATRY. *Educ:* Spring Hill Col, BS, 45; Med Col Ala, MD, 47. *Prof Exp:* Instr prev med & asst dir dept gen pract, Col Med, Univ Tenn, 54-55; assoc prof & dir post-grad educ & student health serv, Med Ctr, Univ Miss, 55-59; assoc med dir, Mead Johnson & Co, 59-60, vpres & med dir, 60-63; from asst prof to assoc prof, 66-77, PROF PSYCHIAT, SCH MED, GEORGETOWN UNIV, 77- *Concurrent Pos:* Consult, Surgeon Gen, US Army, 57-65. *Mem:* Fel Am Psychiat Asn; Asn Acad Psychiat. *Res:* Psychiatry in primary care medicine; continuing education. *Mailing Add:* Dept of Psychiat Georgetown Univ Hosp Washington DC 20007

RITTENBERG, ALAN, b Nashville, Tenn, Dec 27, 38. PARTICLE PHYSICS. *Educ:* Yale Univ, BS, 60; Univ Calif, Berkeley, PhD(physics), 69. *Prof Exp:* RES PHYSICIST PARTICLE PHYSICS, LAWRENCE BERKELEY LAB, UNIV CALIF, 69- *Mem:* Am Phys Soc. *Res:* Compilation of experimental data on particle properties and reactions, in the field of particle physics. *Mailing Add:* Particle Data Group Univ Calif Lawrence Berkeley Lab Berkeley CA 94720

RITTENBERG, MARVIN BARRY, b Los Angeles, Calif, Sept 10, 31; m 54; c 2. IMMUNOLOGY, MICROBIOLOGY. *Educ:* Univ Calif, Los Angeles, AB, 54, MA, 57, PhD(microbiol), 61. *Prof Exp:* Inst Microbiol fel, Rutgers Univ, 61-63; NIH fel immunochem, Calif Inst Technol, 63-66; from asst prof to assoc prof med & microbiol, 66-73, PROF MICROBIOL & IMMUNOL, MED SCH, ORE HEALTH SCI UNIV, 73- *Concurrent Pos:* Leukemia Soc Am scholar, 67-71; consult diag immunol, United Med Labs, Portland, 68-73; vis prof zool, Univ Col London, 72-73; mem exec comt & bd dirs, Ore Comprehensive Cancer Ctr Prog, 72-76; assoc ed, J Immunol, 75-81; consult, Crime Detection Lab Syst, Ore State Police, 75-77 & NIH Immunobiol Study Sect, 77-81; vis prof zool, Univ Col London, 72-73 & 80-81; scholar, Am Cancer Soc, 80-81. *Mem:* AAAS; Am Asn Immunologists; Am Soc Microbiol; Reticuloendothelial Soc. *Res:* Development and control of immunological memory through differentiation of Blymohocytes. *Mailing Add:* Dept of Microbiol & Immunol Ore Health Sci Univ Portland OR 97201

RITTENBERG, SYDNEY CHARLES, b Chicago, Ill, Dec 19, 14; m 41; c 2. BACTERIOLOGY. *Educ:* Univ Calif, Los Angeles, AB, 35, MA, 37; Univ Calif, PhD(bact), 41. *Prof Exp:* Asst chem, Univ Calif, Los Angeles, 35-36; asst marine bact, Scripps Inst, Univ Calif, 37-41; res chemist, Technicolor Motion Picture Corp, 41-42; chief bacteriologist, Comt Infectious Wounds, Nat Res Coun, Tulane Univ, 42-43; chief microbiologist, Res Div, S B Penick

& Co, NY, 43-47; from asst prof to prof bact, Univ Southern Calif, 47-62; PROF BACT & CHMN DEPT, UNIV CALIF, LOS ANGELES, 62- *Honors & Awards:* Carski Found Distinguished Teaching Award, Am Soc Microbiol, 69. *Mem:* Am Soc Microbiol; Am Chem Soc; Brit Soc Gen Microbiol; Am Soc Biol Chemists. *Res:* Physiology and metabolism of bacterial chemolithotrophy; physiology of the Bdellovibrio. *Mailing Add:* Dept of Bact Univ of Calif Los Angeles CA 90024

RITTENBURY, MAX SANFORD, b Bailey, NC, Dec 16, 28; m 50; c 2. SURGERY, BIOCHEMISTRY. *Educ:* The Citadel, 46-49; Med Col Va, MD, 53. *Prof Exp:* Resident gen surg, Med Col Va, 56-62, from instr to asst prof, 62-66; from asst prof to assoc prof, 66-72, PROF GEN SURG, MED UNIV SC, 72- *Concurrent Pos:* Surg res fel, Med Col Va, 59-62, USPHS res grants, 59-, fel, 60-62, spec fel, 63-64. *Mem:* AAAS; Am Col Surgeons; Soc Surg Alimentary Tract; Am Asn Surg of Trauma; Am Fedn Clin Res. *Res:* Disease of the pancreas; immune and enzymatic response of the body to stress and thermal injury; surgical bacteriology. *Mailing Add:* Dept of Surg Med Univ of SC Charleston SC 29401

RITTENHOUSE, HARRY GEOGRE, b Spokane, Wash, Oct 19, 42. BIOLOGICAL CHEMISTRY. *Educ:* Univ Puget Sound, BS, 68; Wash State Univ, PhD(biochem), 72. *Prof Exp:* Am Cancer Soc fel biochem, Univ Calif, Los Angeles, 73-74; asst prof biochem, 75-78, SR RES ASSOC, MENT HEALTH RES INST, UNIV MICH, ANN ARBOR, 78- *Res:* Isolation and characterization of surface glycoproteins from cultured animal cells. *Mailing Add:* Ment Health Res Inst Univ of Mich Ann Arbor MI 48109

RITTENHOUSE, LARRY RONALD, b Lewellen, Nebr; c 4. RANGE SCIENCE. *Educ:* Utah State Univ, BS, 62; Univ Nebr, MS, 66, PhD, 69. *Prof Exp:* Asst, Univ Nebr, 64-69; from asst prof to assoc prof, Eastern Ore Agr Res Ctr, 69-74; assoc prof, Tex A&M Res & Exten Ctr, 75-78; ASSOC PROF, COLO STATE UNIV, 78- *Mem:* Am Soc Animal Sci; Soc Range Mgt. *Mailing Add:* Dept of Range Sci Colo State Univ Ft Collins CO 80523

RITTER, A(LFRED), b Brooklyn, NY, Mar 15, 23; m 47; c 3. AERODYNAMICS. *Educ:* Ga Inst Technol, BS, 43, MS, 47; Cornell Univ, PhD(aerodyn), 51. *Prof Exp:* Aerodynamicst, Glenn L Martin Co, 46; asst, Ga Inst Technol, 47-48; aeronaut res engr, Off Naval Res, 51-54; supvr aerophys, Armour Res Found, Ill Inst Technol, 54-58; vpres & dir res, Adv Res Div, Therm Inc, 58-64, pres, Therm Advan Res, Inc, NY, 64-68; asst head, Appl Mech Dept, Calspan Corp, 68-70, asst head, Aerodyn Res Dept, 70-78, head, Aerodyn Res Dept, 78-80; DIR TECHNOL, CALSPAN FIELD SERV & ARNOLD ENG DEVELOP CTR, ARNOLD AFB, 80- *Concurrent Pos:* Instr, Eve Div, Ill Inst Technol, 56-58; vis lectr, Cornell Univ, 65. *Mem:* AAAS; assoc fel Am Inst Aeronaut & Astronaut; NY Acad Sci. *Res:* Shock wave theory; high temperature gas dynamics; transonic aerodynamics; technical management. *Mailing Add:* Calspan Field Serv Arnold Eng Develop Ctr Arnold AFB Tulahoma TN 37389

RITTER, CRUM MARSHALL, b Washington, DC, June 7, 23; m 46; c 3. POMOLOGY. *Educ:* Univ WVa, BSAgr, 48, MS, 49; Ohio State Univ, PhD(pomol), 52. *Prof Exp:* From asst prof to assoc prof, 52-66, PROF POMOL, PA STATE UNIV, UNIVERSITY PARK, 66-, EXTEN SPECIALIST, 69- *Honors & Awards:* Carroll R Miller Award, Am Soc Hort Sci, 76. *Mem:* Am Soc Hort Sci; Am Pomol Soc; Plant Path Soc; Can Soc Hort Sci. *Res:* Nutrition and physiology of fruit crops. *Mailing Add:* Dept of Hort Pa State Univ Rm 4 Tyson Bldg University Park PA 16802

RITTER, DALE FRANKLIN, b Allentown, Pa, Nov 13, 32; m 53; c 4. GEOLOGY. *Educ:* Franklin & Marshall Col, AB, 55, BS, 59; Princeton Univ, MA, 63, PhD(geol), 64. *Prof Exp:* Asst prof geol, Franklin & Marshall Col, 64-72; PROF GEOL, SOUTHERN ILL UNIV, CARBONDALE, 72- *Mem:* AAAS; Geol Soc Am. *Res:* Geomorphology and Pleistocene geology specifically in analysis of processes. *Mailing Add:* Dept Geol Southern Ill Univ Carbondale IL 62901

RITTER, E GENE, b N Kansas City, Mo, Apr 2, 28; m 53; c 2. SPEECH PATHOLOGY. *Educ:* William Jewell Col, AB, 50; Univ Mo, MA, 56, PhD(speech path), 62. *Prof Exp:* Teacher speech & English, Lathrop Pub Schs, 51-53; supvr, Lab Schs, Univ Mo, 53-56; instr speech, Univ Hawaii, Hilo, 56-58; clinician speech path, Univ Mo, 58-62; assoc prof speech & hearing clin, Univ Hawaii, 62-69; ASSOC PROF SPEECH & HEARING CTR, IND UNIV, BLOOMINGTON, 69- *Concurrent Pos:* Consult speech path, var hosps, Honolulu, 62-69; Gov of Guam, 67 & Bloomington Hosp & Bloomington Convalescent Ctr, 69-; fel, Mayo Grad Sch Med, 66. *Mem:* Am Speech & Hearing Asn. *Res:* Diagnosis and treatment of aphasia and apraxia of speech. *Mailing Add:* Speech & Hearing Ctr Ind Univ Bloomington IN 47401

RITTER, EDMOND JEAN, b Cleveland, Ohio, Dec 11, 15; m; c 4. BIOCHEMISTRY. *Educ:* Ohio State Univ, BChE, 37; Univ Toledo, MS, 41; Univ Cincinnati, PhD, 70. *Prof Exp:* Chemist & chem engr, Sun Oil Co, 37-43; org res chemist, Sharples Chem, Inc, Pa Salt Mfg Co, 43-49; dir, Cimcool Lab, Cincinnati Milling Mach Co, 49-65; dir biol res, Laser Lab, 65-68, ASSOC PROF RES PEDIAT, CHILDREN'S HOSP RES FOUND, UNIV CINCINNATI, 68-, BIOCHEMIST, DIV PATH EMBRYOL, INST DEVELOP RES, 68- *Mem:* AAAS; Am Chem Soc; Teratology Soc; Soc Develop Biol. *Res:* Protein chemistry; experimental teratology and cytology; mental retardation; developmental biology; relationship of inhibition of DNA and ATP synthesis to death and differentiation of proliferating cells. *Mailing Add:* Children's Hosp Res Found Elland & Bethesda Aves Cincinnati OH 45229

RITTER, EDWARD, b New York, NY, June 28, 24; m 52; c 6. PROTOZOOLOGY. *Educ:* Ohio State Univ, BA, 48, MS, 50, PhD(zool), 53. *Prof Exp:* Asst zool, Ohio State Univ, 49-52, asst, 52, Muellhaupt fel biol, 53-54; from instr to prof biol & phys sci, Pace Col, 54-64; chmn dept biol, 64-73, chmn div nat sci, 65-68, PROF BIOL, STATE UNIV NY COL

GENESEO, 64- *Concurrent Pos:* Chmn dept natural sci, Pace Col, 55-64, dir, NSF Inst, 59-64; dir NSF Inst, State Univ NY Col Geneseo, 65-67. *Mem:* AAAS; Soc Syst Zool. *Res:* Protozoan parasites of frogs; taxonomy of colorless euglenid; cytology and cytochemistry of Heliozoa. *Mailing Add:* Dept Biol State Univ of NY Col Geneseo NY 14454

RITTER, ENLOE THOMAS, b Memphis, Tenn, June 21, 39; div. PHYSICS. *Educ:* Southwestern at Memphis, BS, 61; Johns Hopkins Univ, PhD(physics), 66. *Prof Exp:* Staff mem, P Div, Los Alamos Sci Lab, 66-68; physicist, 68-80, DIR, DIV NUCLEAR PHYSICS, US DEPT ENERGY, 80- *Mem:* Am Phys Soc. *Res:* Nuclear science. *Mailing Add:* Div of Nuclear Physics US Dept of Energy Washington DC 20545

RITTER, GARRY LEE, b Michigan City, Ind, Nov 14, 49; m 71. ANALYTICAL CHEMISTRY. *Educ:* Wabash Col, BA, 70; Univ NC, PhD(anal chem), 76. *Prof Exp:* Res assoc, Nat Bur Standards, 76-77; SR SCIENTIST, SCHERING CORP, 77- *Concurrent Pos:* Nat Acad Sci-Nat Res Coun fel, Nat Bur Standards, 76-77. *Mem:* Am Chem Soc; Am Statist Asn. *Res:* Interpretation of chemical data using optimization techniques and robust statistical techniques; numerical solutions to mixture problems; automation of laboratory instrumentation with active control and real time data acquisition and interpretation. *Mailing Add:* Schering Corp 60 Orange St Bloomfield NJ 07003

RITTER, HARRY WOODWARD, b Tipp City, Ohio, July 26, 19; m 50; c 2. INFECTIOUS DISEASES. *Prof Exp:* HEAD SECT BACT-MYCOL RES, MERRELL NAT LABS, 46- *Mem:* Am Soc Microbiol. *Res:* Experimental chemotherapy of infectious diseases. *Mailing Add:* Dept of Microbiol Merrell Nat Labs Cincinnati OH 45215

RITTER, HARTIEN SHARP, b Iola, Kans, Oct 13, 18; m 41; c 2. PHYSICAL CHEMISTRY. *Educ:* Univ Kans, AB, 41; Univ Akron, MS, 54, PhD, 64. *Prof Exp:* Res chemist, Olin Industs, Ill, 41-46; asst dir res, Calcium Carbonate Co, 46-48; sr res chemist, Chem Div, Pittsburgh Plate Glass Co, 48-59, supvr inorg chem, 60-64; sr supvr inorg chem, Chem Div, PPG Industs, Inc, 64-81; CONSULT COATINGS, 81- *Mem:* Am Chem Soc; Fedn Socs Plant Technol. *Res:* Colloid chemistry of pigments in paints and related products; application research in protective coatings. *Mailing Add:* 1495 Shanabrook Dr Akron OH 44313

RITTER, HOPE THOMAS MARTIN, JR, b Allentown, Pa, Sept 24, 19; m 46, 70; c 5. CELL BIOLOGY. *Educ:* Cornell Univ, AB, 43; Lehigh Univ, MS, 47, PhD, 55. *Prof Exp:* Instr zool & gen biol, Lehigh Univ, 48-55, asst prof zool, gen biol & comp physiol, 55-57; res fel, Biol Labs, Harvard Univ, 57-59, lectr biol, 59-61; asst prof, State Univ NY Buffalo, 61-66; PROF, UNIV GA, 66- *Mem:* AAAS; Soc Protozoologists; Am Soc Cell Biologists. *Res:* Biology of Cryptocercus and termite protozoa; insect blood cells; tissue culture; anaerobic metabolism. *Mailing Add:* Dept of Zool Univ of Ga Athens GA 30602

RITTER, HUBERT AUGUST, b St Louis, Mo, Aug 30, 24; m 49; c 1. OBSTETRICS & GYNECOLOGY. *Educ:* Westminster Col, Mo, AB, 45; St Louis Univ, MD, 48. *Prof Exp:* Actg chmn dept obstet & gynec, St Louis Univ, 76-78; PRES EDUC & RES FOUND, AM MED ASN, 77- *Concurrent Pos:* Trustee, Am Med Asn, 76-; comnr, Nat Joint Pract Comn, 77- *Mem:* Am Fertil Soc; Am Col Surgeons; Am Col Obstet & Gynec. *Res:* Incompetence of uterine cervix. *Mailing Add:* Am Med Asn 1035 Bellevue St Louis MO 63117

RITTER, JAMES CARROLL, b Denver, Colo, Apr 12, 35; m 59; c 4. NUCLEAR PHYSICS. *Educ:* Univ Colo, AB, 57; Purdue Univ, MS, 62. *Prof Exp:* Physicist, Radiation & Nucleonics Lab, Westinghouse Elec Corp, 59-60 & Nat Bur Standards, 61-62; res physicist, 62-73, HEAD, SATELLITE SURVIVABILITY SECT, US NAVAL RES LAB, 73- *Mem:* Am Phys Soc; Sigma Xi. *Res:* Nuclear reactions and spectroscopy; decay schemes; resonance neutron-capture gamma-ray studies; radiation hardening of electronic devices; satellite survivability; space radiation; single event upset; space dosimetry. *Mailing Add:* Code 6611 US Naval Res Lab Washington DC 20375

RITTER, JOHN EARL, JR, b Baton Rouge, La, July 17, 39. MATERIALS SCIENCE, METALLURGY. *Educ:* Mass Inst Technol, BS, 61, MS, 62; Cornell Univ, PhD(metall), 66. *Prof Exp:* Assoc prof, 65-76, PROF MECH ENG, UNIV MASS, AMHERST, 76- *Mem:* Am Ceramic Soc; Am Soc Metals; Am Soc Eng Educ; Am Inst Mining, Metall & Petrol Engrs. *Res:* Mechanical behavior of materials; adhesion between dissimilar materials. *Mailing Add:* Dept of Mech Eng Univ of Mass Amherst MA 01003

RITTER, JOSEPH JOHN, US citizen. SYNTHETIC INORGANIC CHEMISTRY, ELECTROCHEMISTRY. *Educ:* Siena Col, BS, 60; Univ Hawaii, MS, 63; Univ Md, PhD(inorg chem), 71. *Prof Exp:* RES CHEMIST, NAT BUR STANDARDS, 63- *Mem:* Am Chem Soc. *Res:* Reactivity of volatile boranes and silanes; inorganic chemistry of corrosive reactions on ferrous metals; nature of passive films on metals. *Mailing Add:* Mat Chem Div Nat Bur Standards Rm B254 Bldg 223 Washington DC 20234

RITTER, KARLA SCHWENSEN, b Detroit, Mich, Oct 30, 50; m 74. BIOCHEMISTRY. *Educ:* Ohio State Univ, BS, 71; Univ Calif, Berkeley, PhD(entom), 76. *Prof Exp:* Res fel, Harvard Univ, 76-77; vis asst prof, 78-79, ASST PROF BIOL & ENTOM, DREXEL UNIV, 79- *Mem:* Sigma Xi; Entom Soc Am; Am Entom Soc; Soc Invertebrate Path. *Res:* Function and metabolism of sterols in insects; physiological and histopathological effects of insect disease. *Mailing Add:* Dept Biol Sci Drexel Univ Philadelphia PA 19104

RITTER, MARK ALFRED, b San Francisco, Calif, May 11, 48; m 74. RADIATION BIOLOGY. *Educ:* Univ San Francisco, BS, 70; Univ Calif, MS, 72, PhD(nuclear eng), 76. *Prof Exp:* Res assoc, Sch Pub Health, Harvard Univ, 76-77; ASST PROF RADIATION THER, UNIV PA, 77- *Mem:* Radiation Res; Am Soc Photobiol; AAAS. *Res:* Mechanisms of DNA damage and repair; their relationship to cellular inactivation, mutagenesis, and transformation in normal or mutant human cells. *Mailing Add:* Dept of Radiation Ther 3400 Spruce St Philadelphia PA 19104

RITTER, PRESTON OTTO, b Memphis, Tenn, Mar 29, 41; m 61; c 2. BIOCHEMISTRY. *Educ:* Univ Calif, Berkeley, BS, 63; Univ Wis-Madison, MS, 65, PhD(biochem), 67. *Prof Exp:* Investr biochem, Biol Div, Oak Ridge Nat Lab, 67-69; res asst prof, Col Med, Baylor Univ, 69-70; asst prof, 70-78, PROF CHEM, EASTERN WASH UNIV, 78- *Concurrent Pos:* Vis staff, Health Res Lab, Los Alamos Sci Lab, NMex, 75-76. *Res:* Absorption and metabolism of antibiotics; protein and nucleic acid biochemistry. *Mailing Add:* Dept of Chem Eastern Wash Univ Cheney WA 99004

RITTER, R(OBERT) BROWN, b Winchester, Va, Jan 12, 21; m 45; c 2. CHEMICAL ENGINEERING. *Educ:* Ohio State Univ, BChE & MS, 50. *Prof Exp:* Chem engr, E I du Pont de Nemours & Co, 50-53; sr chem engr, C F Braun & Co, 53-59 & Chemet Engrs, Inc, 59-62; chief process engr, Aetron Div, Aerojet Gen Corp, 62-67; asst tech dir, Heat Transfer Res, Inc, Alhambra, 67-80; SUPRV ENG, FLUOR ENGRS & CONSTRUCTORS, INC, IRVINE, CALIF, 80- *Concurrent Pos:* Lectr, Long Beach State Univ, 80-81. *Honors & Awards:* Am Soc Eng Educ Div Eng Graphics Convair Award, 59. *Mem:* Am Inst Chem Engrs. *Res:* Heat transfer, condensation, fouling and rating methods; thermodynamics, chemical process, cryogenics and petroleum processes; process plant design, process equipment, instrumentation and controls. *Mailing Add:* 595 Old Ranch Rd Seal Beach CA 90740

RITTER, ROBERT L, b Louisville, Ky, June 13, 30; m 53; c 3. PHYSICAL CHEMISTRY. *Educ:* Univ Louisville, BChE, 53; Univ Tenn, PhD(chem), 64. *Prof Exp:* DEVELOP CHEMIST, MAT & SYSTS DEVELOP DEPT, NUCLEAR DIV, OAK RIDGE, UNION CARBIDE CORP, 53- *Res:* Gas-solid reaction kinetics; isotope separation; inorganic synthesis. *Mailing Add:* 3016 Waldridge Rd Knoxville TN 37921

RITTER, ROGERS C, b Pleasanton, Nebr, Oct 27, 29; m 50; c 3. EXPERIMENTAL GRAVITATIONAL PHYSICS, MEDICAL PHYSICS. *Educ:* Univ Nebr, BSc, 52; Univ Tenn, PhD(physics), 61. *Prof Exp:* Inst eng, Oak Ridge Gaseous Diffusion Plant, 52-59, Oak Ridge Inst Nuclear Studies fel physics, Oak Ridge Nat Lab, 59-61; from asst prof to assoc prof, 61-70, PROF PHYSICS, UNIV VA, 70- *Res:* Urology and cardiovascular medical physics; experimental gravitation. *Mailing Add:* Dept of Physics Univ of Va Charlottesville VA 22901

RITTER, WALTER PAUL, b Brooklyn, NY, Oct 8, 29; m 56; c 1. NEUROPSYCHOLOGY. *Educ:* City Col New York, BA, 53; Columbia Univ, PhD(psychol), 63. *Prof Exp:* Psychologist, Suffolk County Ment Health Bd, 62-64; supvr clin psychologist, NY Univ Med Ctr, Goldwater Hosp, 64-65; fel neurol, 65-68, from asst prof neurol to vis asst prof anat, Albert Einstein Col Med, 68-74; assoc prof, 71-80, PROF PSYCHOL, LEHMAN COL, 80- *Concurrent Pos:* Vis asst prof neurosci, Albert Einstein Col Med, 74- *Mem:* Am Psychol Asn; AAAS; Psychonomic Soc; Int Neuropsychol Soc. *Res:* Electrophysiological correlates of information processing. *Mailing Add:* Lehman Col City Univ New York Bedford Park Blvd Bronx NY 10468

RITTER, WILLIAM FREDERICK, b Stratford, Ont, Mar 25, 42; m 66; c 2. AGRICULTURAL ENGINEERING, ENVIRONMENTAL ENGINEERING. *Educ:* Univ Guelph, BSA, 65; Univ Toronto, BAS, 66; Iowa State Univ, MS, 68; Univ Toronto, PhD(agr, sanit eng), 71. *Prof Exp:* Res assoc agr eng, Iowa State Univ, 66-71; ASSOC PROF AGR ENG, UNIV DEL, 71- *Concurrent Pos:* Res grants, Hercules, Inc, 72-76, Del Water Resources Ctr, 74-76 & 78-, E I du Pont de Nemours & Co, Inc, 74-75 & 76-77; Univ Del Res Found, 74-75, 208 Prog, Environ Protection Agency, 76-81, Allied Chem Co, 77-78 & Clean Lakes Prog, Environ Protection Agency, 81- *Mem:* Am Soc Civil Engrs; Am Soc Agr Engrs; Water Pollution Control Fedn; Am Water Works Asn; Soil Sci Soc Am. *Res:* Agricultural waste management; water quality modeling; land disposal of industrial and municipal wastes; irrigation; groundwater pollution and lake eutrophication. *Mailing Add:* Dept of Agr Eng Univ of Del Newark DE 19711

RITTERHOFF, ROBERT J, b Dayton, Ohio, June 6, 10; m 34; c 3. MEDICINE. *Educ:* Univ Cincinnati, BS, 34, BM, 36, MD, 37. *Prof Exp:* From instr to asst prof, 38-71, ASSOC PROF PATH, COL MED, UNIV CINCINNNATI, 71-; dep coroner, Hamilton County, Ohio, 73-79; ASSOC PATHOLOGIST, DEACONESS HOSP, CINCINNATI, 71- *Concurrent Pos:* Dir lab, Dunham Hosp, Cincinnati, 38-47 & St Elizabeth Hosp, Covington, Ky, 47-70; consult, US Vet Hosp, Dayton, 46-, St Luke's Hosp, Ft Thomas, Ky, 52-70 & Kenton County Tuberc Hosp, Covington, 55-70; assoc pathologist, Mother of Mercy Hosp & Clermont County Hosp, Cincinnati, 73- *Mem:* Am Soc Clin Path; AMA; Am Asn Path & Bact; Am Acad Forensic Sci; AMA. *Res:* Diagnostic and clinical pathology; respiratory diseases. *Mailing Add:* 123 Hosea Cincinnati OH 45220

RITTERMAN, MURRAY B, b New York, NY, Oct 19, 14; m 44; c 4. APPLIED MATHEMATICS. *Educ:* NY Univ, PhD(math), 55. *Prof Exp:* Instr math, Long Island Univ, 47-52; engr, Sylvania Elec Prod Inc Div, Gen Tel & Electronics Corp, 52-59, eng specialist, GTE Labs, 59-72; asst prof math, York Col, NY, 72-77; ASST PROF MATH, HOFSTRA UNIV, 77- *Mem:* Am Math Soc; Math Asn Am. *Res:* Differential and difference equations; communication and information theory; electron optics. *Mailing Add:* 576 Marion Dr East Meadow NY 11554

RITTERSON, ALBERT L, b New Brunswick, NJ, Mar 13, 24; m 57; c 1. MEDICAL PARASITOLOGY. *Educ:* Rutgers Univ, BS, 45, MS, 48; Univ Calif, Los Angeles, PhD(zool), 52. *Prof Exp:* From instr to asst prof, 52-68, ASSOC PROF MICROBIOL & PARASITOL, SCH MED, UNIV ROCHESTER, 68- *Concurrent Pos:* China Med Bd fel, Cent Am, 57. *Mem:* AAAS; Am Soc Parasitologists; Am Soc Trop Med & Hyg. *Res:* Host parasite relationships; leishmaniasis, trichinosis and malaria in the golden and Chinese hamsters; innate resistance and parasite invasion; microbiology; immunology. *Mailing Add:* Dept Microbiol Sch Med Univ Rochester Rochester NY 14627

RITTNER, EDMUND SIDNEY, b Boston, Mass, May 29, 19; m 42; c 1. APPLIED PHYSICS, ENERGY CONVERSION. *Educ:* Mass Inst Technol, SB, 39, PhD(chem), 41. *Prof Exp:* Little fel chem, Mass Inst Technol, 41-42, res assoc, Div Indust Coop, 42-46; res physicist & sect chief, Philips Labs Div, NAm Philips Co, Inc, 46-62, dir dept physics, 62-69; mgr physics lab, 69-81, EXEC DIR PHYSICAL SCI, COMSAT LABS, 81- *Mem:* Fel Inst Elec & Electronics Engrs; fel Am Phys Soc. *Res:* Semiconductors; photoconductivity; infrared; thermionic emission; solid state devices. *Mailing Add:* 22300 Comsat Dr PO Box 115 Clarksburg MD 20871

RITTS, ROY ELLOT, JR, b St Petersburg, Fla, Jan 16, 29; m 53; c 3. MICROBIOLOGY, IMMUNOLOGY. *Educ:* George Washington Univ, AB, 48, MD, 51; Am Bd Microbiol, dipl. *Prof Exp:* Intern, DC Gen Hosp, 51-52; fel med, Sch Med, George Washington Univ, 52-53, resident, George Washington Univ Hosp, 53-54; res fel, Harvard Med Sch, 54-55; vis investr microbiol & path, Rockefeller Inst, 55-57, res assoc immunol, 57-58; from assoc prof microbiol to prof microbiol & trop med, Sch Med, Georgetown Univ, 58-64, chmn dept microbiol & trop med & prof lectr med, 59-64; dir inst biomed res, educ & res found, AMA, 64-68, dir med res, 66-68; chmn dept, Mayo Clin, 68-80, PROF MICROBIOL, MAYO MED SCH, UNIV MINN, 68-, PROF ONCOL & HEAD, MICROBIOL RES LAB, 80- *Concurrent Pos:* Life Ins Med Res Fund fel, 54-57; prof lectr, Sch Med, Univ Chicago, 64-68; mem, Am Bd Microbiol, 65-67; chmn ad hoc sci adv comt, USPHS-Food & Drug Admin, 70-71, consult, 71-; chmn adv comt diag prod, Food & Drug Admin, 72-75, Nat Food & Drug Adv Comt, 75-78; chmn stand comt, Int Union Immunol Socs Coun, 73-; mem carcinogenesis comt, Nat Comt Clin Lab Standards, Nat Cancer Inst, 80-; mem, Am Bd Med Lab Immunol, 76-; mem bd dirs, Int Assoc Study Lung Cancer, 74-76, secy, 76-78; chmn oral exam comt, Int Union Immunol Soc/WHO Standardization Prog, 79- *Mem:* Fel Am Col Physicians; fel Asn Clin Sci; fel Royal Soc Health; fel Am Col Chest Physicians; fel Am Acad Microbiol. *Res:* Host-parasite interaction; immune mechanisms in delayed hypersensitivity; immune surveillance; tolerance; cancer antigens; immunotherapy. *Mailing Add:* Microbiol Res Lab Mayo Clin Rochester MN 55901

RITTSCHOF, DANIEL, b Morenci, Ariz, Feb 26, 46; m 80; c 1. BEHAVIORAL ECOLOGY, CHEMICAL ECOLOGY. *Educ:* Univ Mich, BS, 68, MA, 70, PhD, 75. *Prof Exp:* Teaching asst, Univ Mich, 68-74, lectr zool, 74-75; fel, Univ Calif, Riverside, 75-78, res physiologist, Los Angeles, 78-80; MARINE SCIENTIST, UNIV DEL, 80- *Concurrent Pos:* Consult, Univ Chicago & Battelle Indust, Sequim, Wash; lectr, Univ Del. *Mem:* Am Soc Zoologists; Asn Chemoreception Sci; Nat Shellfisheries Asn. *Res:* Marine chemical sensing: molecules and mechanisms of chemoattraction of Urosalpinx cinerea, functions of chemical sensing in the integration of resource utilization in marine environments and in the gastropod shell habitat web, chemical camouflaging and inhibition/facilitation of chemoresponses, soluble pollutants, teratogenic effects, assays of behavioral toxicity. *Mailing Add:* Univ Del 700 Pilottown Lewes DE 19958

RITVO, EDWARD R, b Boston, Mass, June 1, 30; m 61; c 4. PSYCHIATRY. *Educ:* Harvard Col, BA, 51; Boston Univ, MD, 55. *Prof Exp:* From asst prof to assoc prof, 64-77, PROF IN RESIDENCE PSYCHIAT, SCH MED, UNIV CALIF, LOS ANGELES, 77- *Res:* Adult and child psychiatry, including psychoanalysis and neurophysiology. *Mailing Add:* 760 Westwood Plaza Univ Calif Los Angeles CA 90024

RITZ, VICTOR HENRY, b New York, NY, Apr 4, 34. SURFACE PHYSICS, RADIATION PHYSICS. *Educ:* Polytech Inst Brooklyn, BS, 55; Univ Md, College Park, MS, 62; Univ Sao Paulo, PhD(physics), 67. *Prof Exp:* Physicist, Nat Bur Standards, 56-59; RES PHYSICIST, US NAVAL RES LAB, 59- *Mem:* Am Phys Soc; Am Vacuum Soc; Sigma Xi. *Res:* Electron emission from solids; radiation effects in solids; radiation dosimetry. *Mailing Add:* Optical Sci Div US Naval Res Lab Washington DC 20375

RITZERT, ROGER WILLIAM, b Aurora, Ill, Jan 24, 36; m 62; c 3. BIOCHEMISTRY. *Educ:* NCent Col, Ill, BA, 58; Mich State Univ, MS, 61, PhD(biochem), 66. *Prof Exp:* Asst biochem, Mich State Univ, 58-65; res biochemist, Div Biochem & Microbiol, Battelle Mem Inst, 65-67; SR BIOCHEMIST, TECH CTR, OWENS-ILL, INC, 67- *Concurrent Pos:* Adj asst prof, Med Col Ohio, Toledo, 71- *Mem:* Am Soc Microbiol; Am Chem Soc; Tissue Cult Asn. *Res:* Biochemistry of plant growth and development; cellular responses responses to toxicants in vitro. *Mailing Add:* Owens-Ill Tech Ctr 1 Sea Gate Toledo OH 43666

RITZ-GOLD, CAROLYN JOYCE, b Cleveland, Ohio; m 78. ENERGY TRANSDUCING SYSTEMS. *Educ:* Calif State Univ, Long Beach, BS, 66, MS, 69; Univ Southern Calif, PhD(biochem), 78. *Prof Exp:* FEL, CARDIOVASCULAR RES INST, UNIV CALIF, SAN FRANCISCO, 78- *Concurrent Pos:* Advan res fel, Am Heart Asn, 80-81. *Mem:* Biophys Soc; Bioelectrochem Soc; Sigma Xi. *Res:* Self-organization in signal and energy transducing systems; dynamics and energetics of purposeful movement and structural change in protein assemblies and membrane arrays; changes in membrane structure and permeability triggered by light or voltage. *Mailing Add:* 38451 Timpanogas Circle Fremont CA 94536

RITZMAN, ROBERT L, b Peoria, Ill, Nov 19, 32; m 59; c 1. PHYSICAL CHEMISTRY, RADIOCHEMISTRY. *Educ:* Bradley Univ, BS, 55; Rensselaer Polytech Inst, PhD(phys chem), 61. *Prof Exp:* Sr scientist phys chem, Battelle-Columbus Labs, 59-75; sr scientist, 75-80, VPRES, SCI APPLICATIONS, INC, 80- *Mem:* AAAS; Am Chem Soc; Am Nuclear Soc. *Res:* Chemical separations; nuclear reactor safety and accident analysis; nuclear radiation effects; fission-product chemistry; fission-gas release; environmental impact analysis; nuclear fuel cycle risk analysis. *Mailing Add:* 829 Henderson Ave Sunnyvale CA 94086

RITZMANN, LEONARD W, b South Bend, Ind, Sept 8, 21; m 42; c 3. INTERNAL MEDICINE, CARDIOLOGY. *Educ:* Valparaiso Univ, AB, 42; Washington Univ, MD, 45; Am Bd Internal Med, dipl. *Prof Exp:* Intern internal med, Barnes Hosp, St Louis, 45-46; asst resident med, Salt Lake County Gen Hosp, 47-48, fel cardiol, 48-49, chief resident, 49-50; Am Heart Asn fel cardiol, Postgrad Med Sch London, Eng, 50-51; sect chief cardiol, 53-56, chief med, 56-60, sect chief cardiol, 60-70, STAFF CARDIOL, VET ADMIN HOSP, PORTLAND, 70-; PROF MED, SCH MED, UNIV ORE, 63- *Mem:* Am Heart Asn; Christian Med Soc (pres, 78-80). *Res:* Electrocardiography; vectorcardiography; cardiac arrhythmias; cor pulmonale; coronary heart disease; pacemakers. *Mailing Add:* Dept of Med Vet Admin Hosp Portland OR 97207

RITZMANN, RONALD FRED, b Cicero, Ill, June 16, 43. PSYCHOPHARMACOLOGY, DRUG ABUSE. *Educ:* Northern Ill Univ, BA, 65, MA, 68, PhD(neurosci), 73. *Prof Exp:* Res assoc, 77-78, ASST PROF PHYSIOL, DEPT PHYSIOL & BIOPHYSICS, UNIV ILL MED CTR, 78-, ASSOC FAC, DRUG & ALCOHOL ABUSE RES & TRAINING PROG, 80- *Mem:* Neurosci Soc; Am Soc Neurochem; Int Soc Biomed Res on Alcoholism. *Res:* Neurochemical basis for the development of tolerence and physical dependence on psychoactive drugs with particular interest in the modification of the addictive states by peptides. *Mailing Add:* Dept Physiol Univ Ill Med Ctr PO Box 6998 Chicago IL 60680

RITZMANN, STEPHAN E, b Thuringia, Ger, July 15, 28; m 58; c 3. IMMUNOLOGY, HEMATOLOGY. *Educ:* Univ Kiel, MSc, 49; Univ Heidelberg, MD, 52. *Prof Exp:* Res fel biochem & hemat, Med Sch, Univ Man, 57-58; instr, 60-63, res asst prof, 63-66, res assoc prof, 66-73, prof med, Univ Tex Med Br, Galveston, 73-76, prof path, 71-76; DIR CLIN CHEM, DEPT PATH, MED CTR, BAYLOR UNIV, 76- *Concurrent Pos:* Dir, Div Exp Path-Immunol & co-dir, Transplantation Immunol Lab, Univ Tex Med Br Galveston; res fel hemat, Univ Tex Med Br Galveston, 59-60, sr res fel, 60-65, Leukemia Soc scholar, 65-70; clin prof med, Irvine Med Sch, Irvine, Calif; clin prof path, Rutgers Med Sch, Piscataway, NJ; dir, Behring Consult Labs, Behring Diag, Somerville, NJ. *Mem:* Am Soc Hemat; Transplantation Soc; Am Fedn Clin Res; NY Acad Sci; Am Soc Clin Pathologists. *Res:* Immunology of transplantation; laboratory and clinical aspects of plasma cell, especially lymphocyte disorders; immunological aspects of man's space flight. *Mailing Add:* Dept of Path Baylor Univ Med Ctr Dallas TX 75246

RIVA, JOHN F, b Oltach, Italy, June 17, 29; US citizen; div; c 2. PALEONTOLOGY. *Educ:* Univ Nev, BA, 50, MSc, 57; Columbia Univ, PhD(geol), 62. *Prof Exp:* Res assoc geol, McGill Univ, 61-63; asst prof, Villanova Univ, 63-66; from asst prof to assoc prof, 66-77, TITULAR PROF LAVAL UNIV, 77- *Concurrent Pos:* Soc Sigma Xi res awards, 64, 65, 67 & 70; NSF res grant, 64-66 & 66-67; res assoc, Columbia Univ, 66-68 & 70-71; Nat Res Coun Can yearly grants, 67-; prin investr, res on graptolites. *Mem:* Geol Soc Am; Paleont Soc; Palaeont Asn. *Res:* Ordovician graptolites. *Mailing Add:* 1238 Rouville Ave Ste Foy PQ G1W 3T7 Can

RIVA, JOSEPH PETER, JR, b Chicago, Ill, Oct 31, 35; m 63; c 2. GEOLOGY, STRUCTURAL GEOLOGY. *Educ:* Carleton Col, BA, 57; Univ Wyo, MS, 59. *Prof Exp:* Geologist, Tenn Gas & Oil Co, 59; consult geologist, G H Otto Co, Chicago, 61-65 & Earth Sci Labs, Ohio, 65-66; geologist, Sci Info Exchange, Smithsonian Inst, 66-67, actg chief earth sci br, 67-69, chief, 69-74; SPECIALIST IN EARTH SCI, SCI POLICY RES DIV, CONG RES SERV, LIBR OF CONG, WASHINGTON, DC, 74- *Concurrent Pos:* Mem, US Geological Surv, 80. *Mem:* Am Asn Petrol Geologists; Am Inst Prof Geologists; Sigma Xi. *Res:* Petroleum geology; natural gas; underground gas storage; engineering geology; science policy; energy policy; geological information and retrieval; environmental geology, geothermal energy, editing and writing; author of over 70 publications in energy and the earth sciences. *Mailing Add:* 9705 Mill Run Dr Great Falls VA 22066

RIVARD, WILLIAM CHARLES, b Detroit, Mich, Sept 2, 42; m 64; c 2. FLUID PHYSICS. *Educ:* Univ Detroit, BS, 65, MS, 66; Ill Inst Technol, PhD(mech), 69. *Prof Exp:* MEM RES STAFF NUMERICAL FLUID DYNAMICS, LOS ALAMOS SCI LAB, UNIV CALIF, 68- *Concurrent Pos:* Consult, Battelle Columbus Labs, 75-77, Gen Elec Co, 78 & Bechtel Power Corp, 78- *Mem:* Am Phys Soc. *Res:* Development of numerical methodology for the computer simulation of fluid flows, particularly, chemically reactive and two-phase flows. *Mailing Add:* 536 Todd Los Alamos NM 87544

RIVAS, MARIAN LUCY, b New York, NY, May 6, 43. MEDICAL GENETICS, COMPUTER SYSTEMS. *Educ:* Marian Col, BS, 64; Ind Univ, MS, 67, PhD(med genetics), 69; Am Bd Med Genetics, cert, 82. *Prof Exp:* Fel med genetics, Dept Med, Johns Hopkins Hosp, 69-71; asst prof biol, Douglas Col, Rutgers Univ, 71-75; assoc prof, 75-82, dir genetic coun, Hemophilia Ctr, 77-79, PROF MED GENETICS, ORE HEALTH SCI UNIV, 82-; ASSOC SCIENTIST, NEUROL SCI INST, GOOD SAMARITAN HOSP, 78- *Concurrent Pos:* Lectr biol, Marian Col, 66-68; dir, Genetic Counseling Grad Prog, Rutgers Univ, 71-75; adj asst prof med genetics, Ind Univ, 71-75; mem, Mammalian Cell Lines Comt, Nat Inst Gen Med Sci, NIH, 75-76, adv comt, 76-80; consult, Interregional Cytogenetics Register Syst & Nat Mutant Cell Bank, 75-; staff mem, Emmanuel Hosp, Portland, 81-; mem, NIH-Venezuela Comn Huntington's Chorea, 82- *Mem:* Am Soc Human Genetics; Am Epilepsy Soc; NY Acad Sci; Sigma Xi. *Res:*

Human gene mapping; genetic aspects of epilepsy; human pedigree and segregation analyses; computer applications in clinical genetics and genetic counseling; population genetics; ethnic distribution of genetic disease. *Mailing Add:* Neurol Sci Inst Good Samaritan Hosp Med Ctr 1120 NW 20th Ave Portland OR 97209

RIVELA, LOUIS JOHN, b Brooklyn, NY, Feb 24, 42; m 64; c 1. INORGANIC CHEMISTRY. *Educ:* Rutgers Univ, New Brunswick, BS, 63; Univ NC, Chapel Hill, MS, 67, PhD(inorg chem), 69. *Prof Exp:* Asst prof, 69-77, ASSOC PROF INORG CHEM, WILLIAM PATERSON COL NJ, 77-, CHMN DEPT, 69- *Mem:* Am Chem Soc; AAAS. *Res:* Synthesis and characterization of coordination compounds containing organophophines. *Mailing Add:* William Paterson Col of NJ Wayne NJ 07470

RIVELAND, A(RVIN) R(OY), b Buxton, NDak, July 29, 23; m 52; c 3. CIVIL ENGINEERING. *Educ:* Univ NDak, BS, 45; Univ Nebr, MS, 54. *Prof Exp:* Engr, Lium & Burdick, Engrs, 45-57; from instr to assoc prof, 49-80, PROF CIVIL ENG, UNIV NEBR, LINCOLN, 80- *Mem:* Am Soc Civil Engrs; Am Soc Eng Educ; Am Concrete Inst. *Res:* Structures; ultimate strength design in reinforced concrete. *Mailing Add:* Dept of Civil Eng Univ of Nebr Lincoln NE 68508

RIVELLO, ROBERT MATTHEW, b Washington, DC, May 20, 21; m 50; c 4. AEROSPACE ENGINEERING. *Educ:* Univ Md, BS, 43, MS, 48. *Prof Exp:* From instr to asst prof mech eng, 46-49, from asst prof to assoc prof aeronaut eng, 49-67, prof, 67-79, EMER PROF AEROSPACE ENG, UNIV MD, COLLEGE PARK, 79-; ENGR, PRIN PROF STAFF, APPL PHYSICS LAB, JOHN HOPKINS UNIV, 79- *Concurrent Pos:* Engr, Fairchild Aircraft Co, 48; assoc engr, Appl Physics Lab, Johns Hopkins Univ, 53-54, consult, 54-79; sr engr, 56-79; mem spec struct subcomt, Panel Piloted Aircraft, Res & Develop Bd, 52-53; mem comt elevated temperature struct test facilities, US Air Force; consult, Smithsonian Inst, 57-58; struct subcomt, Navy Aeroballistics Comt, 80- *Mem:* Am Soc Mech Engrs; Am Inst Aeronaut & Astronaut. *Res:* Applied Mechanics; aircraft and missile structures; materials, dynamics, elasticity and thermal stresses. *Mailing Add:* 8502 Hunter Creek Trail Potomac MD 20854

RIVERA, AMERICO, JR, b New York, NY, Aug 22, 28; m 58; c 4. BIOCHEMISTRY, NEUROCHEMISTRY. *Educ:* Inter-Am Univ PR, San German, 52; Fordham Univ, MS, 56; Columbia Univ, PhD(biochem), 59. *Prof Exp:* USPHS fel, Univ Wis-Madison, 63-65; res chemist, NIH, San Juan, PR, 65-70 & Md, 70-75; HEALTH SCIENTIST ADMINR, NAT INST GEN MED SCI, 75- *Concurrent Pos:* Lectr, Med Sch, Univ PR, 71-72. *Mem:* AAAS; Am Chem Soc; Brit Biochem Soc. *Res:* Effects of energy deprivation on the carbohydrate metabolism of the monkey brain; intermediary metabolism and mechanisms of mitosis in microorganisms and cell cultures; administration of biomedical engineering research grants. *Mailing Add:* PO Box 583 Olney MD 20832

RIVERA, EVELYN MARGARET, b Hollister, Calif, Nov 10, 29. ENDOCRINOLOGY, CANCER. *Educ:* Univ Calif, Berkeley, AB, 52, MA, 60, PhD(zool), 63. *Prof Exp:* Am Cancer Soc fel biochem, Nat Inst Res Dairying, Reading, Eng, 63-65; from asst prof to assoc prof, 65-72, PROF ZOOL, MICH STATE UNIV, 72- *Concurrent Pos:* Sabbatical leave, Cancer Res Lab, 71-72; NIH res career develop award, 67-72 & res fel award, 78-79; mem exp biol comt, Breast Cancer Task Force, Nat Cancer Inst, 73-76, mem, Carcinogenesis Comt, 76-79, mem, Cancer Cause & Prev Comt, 79-81; sabbatical leave, Transplantation Biol Sect, Clin Res Ctr, Harrow, Eng, 78-79. *Honors & Awards:* UNESCO Award, Int Cell Res Orgn, 65. *Mem:* AAAS; Am Asn Can Res; Soc Exp Biol & Med; Tissue Cult Asn; Brit Soc Endocrinol. *Res:* Cell transformation; biology of tumors. *Mailing Add:* Dept of Zool Mich State Univ East Lansing MI 48824

RIVERA, EZEQUIEL RAMIREZ, b Alpine, Tex, Oct 17, 42; m 70; c 1. ELECTRON MICROSCOPY, ULTRASTRUCTURE. *Educ:* Sul Ross State Col, Tex, BS, 64; Purdue Univ, MS, 67; Univ Tex, Austin, PhD(biol sci & bot), 73. *Prof Exp:* Res technician plant & plant pathol, Purdue Univ, 66-67; clin lab technician clin chem, US Army, Ft Dix, NJ, 67; asst chief biochem & toxicol, 6th US Army Med Lab, Ft Baker, Calif, 68; chief biochem, 376th Med Lab, US Army Support, Thailand, 69-70; instr bot, Univ Tex, Austin, 72; asst prof biol, Univ Notre Dame, Ind, 73-74; asst prof, 74-80, ASSOC PROF BIOL SCI, UNIV LOWELL, MASS, 80- *Concurrent Pos:* Consult, Pathol Dept, Bon Secours Hosp, Mass, 80-; referee, Scanning Electron Micros, 80-, Protoplasma Inst J Cell Biol, 82- *Mem:* Bot Soc Am; Am Soc Plant Physiologists; Electron Micros Soc Am. *Res:* Ultrastructure of overwintering and desert xerophytic plants; cytochemistry of secretory components in marine snails; cytology of schistosome development; plant physiology of carbon 13/carbon 12 fractionation and calcuim oxalate. *Mailing Add:* Dept Biol Sci Univ Lowell Lowell MA 01854

RIVERA, WILLIAM HENRY, b El Paso, Tex, Jan 26, 31; m 58; c 5. ANALYTICAL CHEMISTRY. *Educ:* Univ Louisville, BS, 53, PhD(chem), 62. *Prof Exp:* Nuclear engr, Gen Dynamics/Ft Worth, 56-58; asst chem, Univ Louisville, 58-62, asst prof, 62-63, asst grad dean, 73-76, ASSOC PROF CHEM, UNIV TEX, EL PASO, 63- *Concurrent Pos:* Consult, Nuclear Effects Directorate, White Sands Missile Range, NMex, 64- *Mem:* Am Chem Soc; Am Soc Testing & Mat. *Res:* Radiation effects on organic materials, radiation induced polymerization; photon and neutron activation analysis; dosimetry; environmental analysis; radiation protection. *Mailing Add:* Dept Chem Univ Tex El Paso TX 79968

RIVERO, JUAN ARTURO, b Santurce, PR, Mar 5, 23; m; c 2. HERPETOLOGY. *Educ:* Univ PR, BS, 45; Harvard Univ, MA, 51, PhD(biol), 52. *Prof Exp:* Asst plant physiologist, Inst Trop Agr, PR, 45; from instr to assoc prof, 43-58, dir inst marine biol & zool garden, 54-63, dir dept biol, Univ, 59-60, actg dean arts & sci, 62-63, dean, 63-66, PROF ZOOL, UNIV PR, MAYAGUEZ, 58- *Concurrent Pos:* Assoc, Mus Comp Zool, Harvard Univ, 68; Guggenheim Found fel, 70; consult, Univ Consult Corp,

PR; temporary investr, Venezuelan Inst Sci Invests; Herpet League fel. *Mem:* AAAS; Asn Island Marine Labs, Caribbean (secy, 57-58, pres, 58-60); corresp mem Soc Venezolana de Ciencias Naturales; Soc Syst Zool; PR Acad Arts & Sci. *Mailing Add:* Dept of Biol Univ PR Mayaguez PR 00708

RIVERS, JERRY MARGARET, b Bogota, Tex, Sept 29, 29. NUTRITION. *Educ:* Tex Tech Univ, BS, 51, MS, 58; Pa State Univ, PhD(nutrit, biochem), 61. *Prof Exp:* Dietitian, USPHS, 51-53 & Methodist Hosp, 53-57; from asst prof to assoc prof, 62-72, PROF NUTRIT, CORNELL UNIV, 72- *Concurrent Pos:* Res grants, NIH, 63- & Nutrit Found, 66- *Mem:* Am Dietetic Asn; Am Inst Nutrit. *Res:* Ascorbic acid metabolism. *Mailing Add:* 104 Campbell Ave Ithaca NY 14850

RIVERS, JESSIE MARKERT, b Elizabeth City, NC, July 9, 49; m 71. ORGANIC CHEMISTRY, NATURAL PRODUCTS CHEMISTRY. *Educ:* Meredith Col, AB, 71; NC State Univ, PhD(org chem), 78. *Prof Exp:* SR RES CHEMIST TOBACCO CHEM, R J REYNOLDS TOBACCO CO, 77- *Mem:* Am Chem Soc; Sigma Xi. *Res:* Isolation, characterization and synthesis of naturally occurring tobacco constituents; relationship of tobacco chemistry to tobacco utilization. *Mailing Add:* Dept Res & Develop Bldg 611-1 R J Reynolds Tobacco Co Winston-Salem NC 27102

RIVERS, PAUL MICHAEL, b Schenectady, NY, July 18, 44; m 66; c 2. ORGANIC CHEMISTRY, ANALYTICAL CHEMISTRY. *Educ:* LeMoyne Col, BS, 66; Univ Notre Dame, Ind, PhD(org chem), 70. *Prof Exp:* Sr chemist, 70-71, DIR, QUAL CONTROL & DIR, ANAL DEPT, REILLY TAR & CHEM CORP, 71- *Mem:* Am Chem Soc; Am Soc Testing Mats. *Res:* Gas and liquid chromatographic separation of pyridine derivatives; analytical methods in air and water pollution control; isolation and identification of organic chemicals. *Mailing Add:* Reilly Tar & Chem Corp 1500 S Tibbs Ave Indianapolis IN 46241

RIVERS, WILLIAM J(ONES), b Lakeland, Fla, May 28, 36; m 58; c 2. MECHANICAL ENGINEERING. *Educ:* Univ Fla, BME, 59; Purdue Univ, MSME, 61, PhD(mech eng), 64; Univ Southern Calif, MSAE, 70. *Prof Exp:* Sr res engr, Rocketdyne Div, NAm Aviation, Inc, 64-65; ASSOC PROF THERMAL-FLUID SYSTS, CALIF STATE UNIV, NORTHRIDGE, 65- *Concurrent Pos:* Res engr, Rocketdyne Div, NAm Aviation, Inc, 65-66; develop engr, Marquardt Corp, 66-67; thermodynamics engr, Lockheed Calif Co, 68-69; NSF fac fel, Univ Southern Calif, 69-70; tech consult, Peerless Pump Co, 71- *Honors & Awards:* Ralph R Teetor Award, Soc Automotive Engrs, 70. *Mem:* Am Soc Mech Engrs; Am Soc Eng Educ. *Res:* Centrifugal pump performance and axial thrust. *Mailing Add:* Sch Eng Calif State Univ Northridge CA 91330

RIVES, JOHN EDGAR, b Birmingham, Ala; m 56; c 6. SOLID STATE PHYSICS. *Educ:* Auburn Univ, BS, 55; Duke Univ, PhD(physics), 62. *Prof Exp:* Asst prof physics, Univ Ga, 59-60; instr & res assoc, Duke Univ, 61-63; from asst prof to assoc prof, 63-76, PROF PHYSICS, UNIV GA, 76- *Concurrent Pos:* Res grants, Frederick Gardner Cottrell, 64-, Air Force Off Sci Res, 68-71 & NSF, 72-77, Army Res Off, Durham, NC, 78-; consult, Oak Ridge Nat Lab. *Mem:* fel Am Phys Soc; Am Asn Univ Professors. *Res:* Thermodynamics of magnetic phase transitions; laser induced phonon physics; heat transport in magnetic insulators. *Mailing Add:* Dept Physics & Astron Univ Ga Athens GA 30602

RIVEST, ROLAND, b Rawdon, Que, Apr 19, 23; m 53; c 4. CHEMISTRY. *Educ:* Univ Montreal, BA, 43, BSc, 46, MSc, 48, PhD(chem), 50. *Prof Exp:* Instr chem, Univ Calif, 50-51; lectr, 51-52; from asst prof to assoc prof, 52-64, head dept, 63-68, vdean sci, 68-72, vdean arts & sci, 72-79, PROF CHEM, UNIV MONTREAL, 64-, DEAN ARTS & SCI, 79- *Mem:* Fel AAAS; fel Chem Inst Can. *Res:* Coordination chemistry of halides of group elements; bioinorganic chemistry; preparations properties and structure of molecules of biological interest. *Mailing Add:* Fac of Arts & Sci Univ of Montreal PO Box 6128 Montreal PQ H3C 3J7 Can

RIVETT, ROBERT WYMAN, b Omaha, Nebr, Jan 20, 21; m 40; c 3. BIOCHEMISTRY. *Educ:* Univ Nebr, BS, 42, MS, 43; Univ Wis, PhD(biochem), 46. *Prof Exp:* Res microbiologist, Abbott Labs, 46-48, group leader antibiotic develop, 48-57, asst to dir develop, 57-58, mgr develop, 58-59, dir, 59-64, dir, Sci Admin & Serv, 64-71; dir, Corp Qual Assurance Standards & Audits, 71-76, dir, Qual Assurance Agr & Vet Div, 76-77, Sci Prod Div, 77-78, V PRES, ALPHA THERAPEUT CORP, QUAL ASSURANCE, 78- *Mem:* Am Chem Soc; Am Inst Chem Engr; Am Soc Qual Control. *Res:* Organic chemistry; nutrition of bacteria; natural products; streptolin; fermentation equipment. *Mailing Add:* Alpha Therapeut Corp 5555 Valley Blvd Los Angeles CA 90032

RIVETTI, HENRY CONRAD, b Feb 21, 24; US citizen; m 72; c 3. DENTISTRY, PROSTHODONTICS. *Prof Exp:* Assoc prof, 69-75, PROF PROSTHODONT, SCH DENT FAIRLEIGH DICKINSON UNIV, 75-, CHMN REMOVABLE PARTIAL DENTURE SECT, DEPT PROSTHODONT, 72-, ACTG CHMN DEPT PROSTHODONT, 75- *Concurrent Pos:* Grant, Sch Dent, Fairleigh Dickinson Univ, 71- *Mem:* Fel Am Col Dentists; Am Dent Asn; Am Prosthodont Soc. *Res:* Dental and psychological aspects involved in temporo-mandibular joint dysfunction syndrome. *Mailing Add:* Sch of Dent Fairleigh Dickinson Univ Hackensack NJ 07601

RIVIER, CATHERINE L, b Vaud, Switzerland, June 21, 43; m 67; c 2. REPRODUCTIVE ENDOCRINOLOGY. *Educ:* Univ Lausanne, Switzerland, Lic es Sci, 68, PhD, 72. *Prof Exp:* Fel, 72-74, sr res assoc, 74-79, ASST RES PROF, SALK INST, 79- *Mem:* Endocrine Soc; Am Physiol Soc; Soc Neurosci; Soc Study Reproduction; Res Soc Alcoholism. *Res:* Mechanism of control of prolactin, gonadotropin and adrenocorticotrophic hormone secretions. *Mailing Add:* Salk Inst PO Box 85800 San Diego CA 92138

RIVIER, JEAN E, b Casablanca, Morocco, July 14, 41; Swiss citizen; m 67; c 2. NEUROENDOCRINOLOGY. *Educ:* Univ Lausanne, PhD, 68. *Prof Exp:* Fel, Univ Lausanne, 69; fel, Rice Univ, Houston, Tex, 69-70; res assoc, 70-73, from asst res prof to assoc res prof, 73-82, ASSOC PROF, SALK INST, 82- *Mem:* Am Chem Soc; Swiss Chem Soc; Endocrine Soc. *Res:* Neuroendocrinology involved in isolation and analysis of new peptide hormones, their total synthesis and pharmacology. *Mailing Add:* Salk Inst PO Box 85800 San Diego CA 92138

RIVIERE, GEORGE ROBERT, b Decatur, Ill, Feb 26, 43; m 71; c 2. IMMUNOLOGY, DENTISTRY. *Educ:* Drake Univ, BA, 66; Univ Ill, Chicago Med Ctr, BSD, 66, DDS, 68, MS, 70; Univ Calif, Los Angeles, PhD(immunol), 73. *Prof Exp:* Researcher, Dent Res Inst, US Navy, 73-75; asst prof, 75-77, assoc prof, 77-81, PROF, SCH MED & DENT, DENT RES INST, UNIV CALIF, LOS ANGELES, 82- *Concurrent Pos:* USPHS fel, Nat Inst Dent Res, 73-75; prin investr, Nat Inst Dent res grant, 76-83 & NIH career res develop award, 77-82. *Mem:* Int Asn Dent Res; Sigma Xi; AAAS; Am Asn Immunologists. *Res:* Transplantation immunology; immunogenetics; regulation of immune responses, especially immunity to enteric microorganisms and role of immunity in development. *Mailing Add:* Sch of Dent Univ of Calif Los Angeles CA 90024

RIVIN, DONALD, b Brooklyn, NY, Oct 5, 34; m 56; c 4. SURFACE CHEMISTRY, PYROLYSIS & FLAME CHEMISTRY. *Educ:* Columbia Univ, BA, 55, MA, 57, PhD(chem), 60. *Prof Exp:* Res chemist, 59-61, group leader org chem, 61-69, sr res assoc, Fine Particle Technol Dept, 69-74, dir, Fine Particle Technol Dept, 74-80, corp res fel & dir environ health, 80-81, CORP RES FEL & CONSULT, CABOT CORP, BILLERICA, 81- *Mem:* AAAS; Am Chem Soc; Catalysis Soc; Am Carbon Soc. *Res:* Adsorption and reactions on carbon and oxide surfaces; heterogeneous catalysis; organic reaction mechanisms; rubber reinforcement; thermal dissociation processes; formation and properties of adsorbed polynuclear aromatic carbon. *Mailing Add:* 35 Oak Knoll Rd Natick MA 01760

RIVINGTON, DONALD ERSKINE, b Ottawa, Ont, Aug 9, 27; Can citizen. ANALYTICAL CHEMISTRY. *Educ:* Queen's Univ, Can, BSc, 48, MSc, 50; Univ Toronto, PhD(chem), 54. *Prof Exp:* Res chemist, 54-66, sr anal chemist, 66-76, RES ASSOC, CIP RES LTD, 76- *Mem:* Chem Inst Can; Can Pulp & Paper Asn. *Mailing Add:* 484 Smerdon St Hawkesbury ON K6A 2M8 Can

RIVKIN, ISRAEL, b Rochester, NY, Feb 14, 38; m 65; c 4. IMMUNOLOGY. *Educ:* Yeshiva Univ, BA, 59; NY Univ, MS, 68; Univ Conn, PhD(immunol), 74. *Prof Exp:* Res asst rheumatology, State Univ NY Downstate Med Ctr, 64-65; res assoc biochem pharmacol, 68-70, sr res investr immunol, Squibb Inst Med Res, 73-78; PRIN SCIENTIST, DEPT INFLAMMATION & ALLERGY, SCHERING CORP, 78- *Concurrent Pos:* Squibb sabbatical fel, 70. *Mem:* NY Acad Sci; AAAS. *Res:* The study of the effects of drugs on in vitro and in vivo neutrophil and monocycle chemotaxis; design biological systems for testing new anti-inflammatory drugs. *Mailing Add:* One Opatut Ct Edison NJ 08817

RIVKIN, MAXCY, b Columbia, SC, Mar 31, 37; m 59; c 2. CONTROL SYSTEMS, PAPER SCIENCE. *Educ:* Univ SC, BS, 59. *Prof Exp:* Group leader tech serv papermaking systs, Kraft Div, 63-70, group leader process systs, Covington Res Ctr, 70-78, DIR RES, LAUREL RES CTR, WESTVACO CORP, 78- *Mem:* Tech Asn Pulp & Paper Indust; Instrument Soc Am; AAAS; NY Acad Sci; Soc Rheology. *Res:* Development and implementation of experimental or prototype process control systems in the manufacture of pulp and paper and of allied products; development and implementation of systems for the management of research and innovation; properties of coated papers. *Mailing Add:* Laurel Res Ctr Johns Hopkins Rd Laurel MD 20707

RIVKIN, RICHARD BOB, b Brooklyn, NY, Nov 17, 49; m 72; c 2. BIOLOGICAL OCEANOGRAPHY. *Educ:* City Col New York, BS, 72, MS, 75; Univ RI, PhD(biol sci), 79. *Prof Exp:* ASSOC RES SCIENTIST PHYTOPLANKTON ECOL, JOHNS HOPKINS UNIV, 78- *Mem:* Am Soc Limnol & Oceanog; Phycol Soc Am; Am Soc Plant Physiologists; Sigma Xi. *Res:* Phytoplankton nutrient physiology and biochemistry; phytoplankton ecology; interactions of water motion and phytoplankton ecology. *Mailing Add:* Dept Biol Johns Hopkins Univ Baltimore MD 21218

RIVLIN, RONALD SAMUEL, b London, Eng, May 6, 15; m 48. APPLIED MATHEMATICS. *Educ:* Cambridge Univ, BA, 37, MA, 39, ScD(math), 52. *Hon Degrees:* Dr DSc, Univ Ireland & Univ Nottingham, Eng, 80. *Prof Exp:* Res scientist, Res Labs, Gen Elec Co, Ltd, 37-42; sci officer, Ministry Aircraft Prod, Telecommun Res Estab, 42-44; from physicist to supt res, Brit Rubber Producers Res Asn, 44-52; consult, US Naval Res Lab, 52-53; prof appl math, Brown Univ, 53-63, chmn div appl math, 58-63, L Herbert Ballou Univ Prof, 63-67; CENTENNIAL UNIV PROF & DIR CTR APPLN MATH, LEHIGH UNIV, 67- *Concurrent Pos:* Guest scientist, Nat Bur Standards, 46-47; res scientist, Davy-Faraday Lab, Royal Inst, London, 47-52; vis lectr, Calif Inst Technol, 53; Guggenheim fel, Univ Rome, 61-62; mem mech adv comt, Nat Bur Standards, 65-70; mem comt appln math, Nat Res Coun, 65-68; vis prof, Univ Paris, 66-67; mem, Nat Comt Theoret & Appl Mech, 72-, chmn, 76-78; Alexander von Humboldt sr award, 81. *Honors & Awards:* Bingham Medal, Soc Rheol, 58; Panetti Prize, Acad Sci of Turin, 75. *Mem:* Fel Am Acad Arts & Sci; Soc Rheology; Am Soc Mech Engrs; fel Am Acad Mech; fel Soc Eng Sci. *Res:* Finite elasticity; physics of rubber; continuum mechanics of viscoelastic solids and fluids. *Mailing Add:* Ctr Appln Math Lehigh Univ Bethlehem PA 18015

RIVLIN, THEODORE J, b Brooklyn, NY, Sept 11, 26. MATHEMATICS. *Educ:* Brooklyn Col, BA, 48; Harvard Univ, MA, 50, PhD(math), 53. *Prof Exp:* Instr math, Johns Hopkins Univ, 52-55; asst, Inst Math Sci, NY Univ, 55-56; sr math analyst, Engine Div, Fairchild Engine & Aircraft Corp, 56-59; MATHEMATICIAN, IBM CORP, 59- *Mem:* Am Math Soc; Soc Indust & Appl Math; Math Asn Am. *Res:* Approximation theory; function theory; numerical analysis. *Mailing Add:* Thomas J Watson Res Ctr IBM Corp Box 218 Yorktown Heights NY 10598

RIX, CECIL CHARLES, geology, see previous edition

RIXON, RAYMOND HARWOOD, b Vancouver, BC, July 17, 26; m 57; c 4. PHYSIOLOGY. *Educ:* Univ BC, BA, 48, MA, 50; Univ Western Ont, PhD(physiol), 55. *Prof Exp:* Fel physiol, Fac Med, Univ Western Ont, 55-56; asst res officer, Atomic Energy Can Ltd, 56-62, assoc res officer, 62-68; assoc res officer, 68-70, SR RES OFFICER, DIV BIOL, NAT RES COUN CAN, 70- *Res:* Electrolyte metabolism; physiology of starvation and cold adaptation; radiation injury in tissue cultures and animals; chemical protection against radiation damage; initiation and control of cell proliferation. *Mailing Add:* Div of Biol Nat Res Coun of Can Ottawa ON K1A 0R6 Can

RIZACK, MARTIN A, b New York, NY, Nov 19, 26; m 64; c 5. BIOCHEMISTRY, PHARMACOLOGY. *Educ:* Columbia Univ, MD, 50; Rockefeller Univ, PhD, 60; Am Bd Internal Med, dipl, 57, recertified, 74. *Prof Exp:* Intern, Cornell Med Div, Bellevue Hosp, 50-51, asst resident physician, 51; asst resident physician, St Luke's Hosp, 53-55, chief resident physician, 55-56, res assoc, 56-57; asst physician, 57-60, asst prof med & assoc physician, 60-65, assoc dean grad studies, 68-74, HEAD LAB CELLULAR BIOCHEM & PHARMACOL, ASSOC PROF & PHYSICIAN, ROCKEFELLER UNIV, 65- *Concurrent Pos:* Fel, Rockefeller Univ, 57-60; asst attend physician, St Luke's Hosp, 60-71, assoc attend physician, 71-80, adj attend physician, 80- *Mem:* Fel Am Col Physicians; Am Soc Pharmacol & Exp Therapeut; Am Soc Biol Chemists. *Res:* Biochemistry and physiology of hormone action; lipolytic enzymes; biochemical pharmacology. *Mailing Add:* Lab Cellular Biochem & Pharmacol Rockefeller Univ 1230 York Ave New York NY 10021

RIZKI, TAHIR MIRZA, b Hyderabad-Dn, India, Jan 8, 24; nat US; m 49; c 3. DEVELOPMENTAL GENETICS, CELL BIOLOGY. *Educ:* Osmania Univ, India, BSc, 44; Muslim Univ, MSc, 46; Columbia Univ, PhD(zool), 53. *Prof Exp:* Demonstr zool, Muslim Univ, 45-46, lectr, 46-48; asst, Columbia Univ, 51-52; Cramer res fel genetics, Dartmouth Col, 52-54; Am Cancer Soc fel, Yale Univ, 54-56; from asst prof to assoc prof biol, Reed Col, 56-61; assoc prof, 61-64, PROF BIOL, UNIV MICH, ANN ARBOR, 64- *Mem:* AAAS; Am Soc Zoologists; Am Soc Naturalists; Sigma Xi; Soc Invert Path. *Res:* Developmental genetics of Drosophila; biology of hemocytes and melanotic tumors in Drosophila; somatic cell mutations and neoplasia; cell surface properties and cell adhesion; cell death. *Mailing Add:* Div of Biol Sci Univ of Mich Ann Arbor MI 48109

RIZNYK, RAYMOND ZENON, b New York, NY, July 20, 42; m 60. BOTANY. *Educ:* Univ NMex, BS, 65; Ore State Univ, PhD(bot), 69. *Prof Exp:* Asst prof marine algology, Moss Landing Marine Labs, 69; asst prof, 69-77, PROF BOT, CALIF STATE POLYTECH UNIV, POMONA, 77- *Mem:* Phycol Soc Am; Int Phycol Soc; Brit Phycol Soc; Am Soc Limnol & Oceanog. *Res:* Physiological ecology and taxonomy of fresh water and marine algae, particularly benthic diatoms; aquaculture; water chemistry; water pollution. *Mailing Add:* Dept Biol Sci Calif State Polytech Univ Pomona CA 91768

RIZZI, GEORGE PETER, b Middletown, Conn, Sept 25, 37; m 59; c 2. ORGANIC CHEMISTRY. *Educ:* Worcester Polytech Inst, BS, 59, MS, 61, PhD(org chem), 63. *Prof Exp:* Res assoc chem, Stanford Univ, 63-64; RES CHEMIST, MIAMI VALLEY LABS, PROCTER & GAMBLE CO, 64- *Mem:* Am Chem Soc; The Chem Soc. *Res:* Organic synthesis; natural products; flavors; organic reactions involved in biochemical processes. *Mailing Add:* Miami Valley Labs Procter & Gamble Co Cincinnati OH 45247

RIZZO, ANTHONY AUGUSTINE, b Birmingham, Ala, June 8, 28; m 55, 73; c 5. DENTISTRY, MICROBIOLOGY. *Educ:* Birmingham-Southern Col, AB, 52; Univ Ala, DMD & MS, 56. *Prof Exp:* Instr chem, Lab, Univ Ala, 50-51; fel periodont, Sch Dent, 56-57, prin investr periodont dis, Lab, 57-68, chief mat sci & spec clin studies prog, 68-71, chief periodont dis prog, 70-73, SPEC ASST PROG COORDR, NAT INST DENT RES, 73- *Concurrent Pos:* Ed-in-chief, Ala Dent Rev, 55-56. *Mem:* Int Asn Dent Res. *Res:* Microbiology and immunopathology of periodontal disease; periodontology. *Mailing Add:* Extramural Progs Nat Inst Dent Res WB-507 Bethesda MD 20205

RIZZO, DONALD CHARLES, b Boston, Mass, June 10, 45. ENTOMOLOGY, PARASITOLOGY. *Educ:* Boston State Col, AB, 68; Cornell Univ, MS, 70, PhD(entom), 73. *Prof Exp:* Res asst insect path, Cornell Univ, 68-73; instr biol, Siena Heights Col, 73-74; asst prof, 74-78, ASSOC PROF BIOL, MARYGROVE COL, 78- *Mem:* Entom Soc Am; Nat Sci Teachers Asn; Am Asn Univ Prof; Nat Geog Soc; Am Inst Biol Sci. *Res:* Fungal pathogens of medically and economically important insects, especially dipterans. *Mailing Add:* Dept Biol Marygrove Col 8425 W McNichols Rd Detroit MI 48221

RIZZO, FRANK EARL, b Detroit, Mich, Dec 14, 38; m 60; c 2. METALLURGY. *Educ:* Univ Detroit, BChE, 61; Univ Cincinnati, MS, 63, PhD(metall), 64. *Prof Exp:* Actg instr metall eng, Univ Cincinnati, 62-63, instr, 63-64; res metallurgist, Aerospace Res Labs, US Air Force, 64-68; from assoc prof to prof metall eng, Univ Tex, El Paso, 68-77; dir res & educ, Harco Corp, 77-80; MEM FAC METALL, UNIV TEX, EL PASO, 80- *Mem:* Am Soc Metals; Am Inst Mining, Metall & Petrol Engrs. *Res:* Oxidation; thermodynamic measurements; stress corrosion; x-ray emission; diffusion. *Mailing Add:* 709 Educ Bldg Univ Tex El Paso TX 79968

RIZZO, PETER JACOB, b Gary, Ind, Dec 10, 40; m 66; c 1. PLANT PHYSIOLOGY, CELL BIOLOGY. *Educ:* Ind Univ, AB, 67, MA, 68; Univ Mich, PhD(plant physiol), 72. *Prof Exp:* Res assoc plant physiol, Purdue Univ, 72-75; lectr, 75-76, asst prof, 76-82, ASSOC PROF CELL BIOL, TEX A&M UNIV, 82- *Concurrent Pos:* NIH fel, 72. *Mem:* Soc Protozoologists; AAAS; Sigma Xi. *Res:* Role of chromosomal proteins and multiple ribonucleic acid polymerases in the regulation of gene activity in eukaryotes; histone occurance in lower eukaryotes; histone-like proteins in dinoflagellates; evolution of nucleosomes. *Mailing Add:* Biol Dept Tex A&M Univ College Station TX 77843

RIZZO, THOMAS GERARD, b New York, NY, June 22, 55. GRAND UNIFIED THEORIES, PHENOMENOLOGY. *Educ:* Fordham Univ, BS, 74; Columbia Univ, MA, 75; Univ Rochester, PhD(physics), 78. *Prof Exp:* Res assoc, Physics Dept, Brookhaven Nat Lab, 79-81; ASST PROF PHYSICS & ASSOC PHYSICIST, AMES LAB, IOWA STATE UNIV, 81- *Mem:* Am Phys Soc. *Res:* Phenomenological implications of grand unified theories--how low energy experiments can be used to distinguished between various schemes. *Mailing Add:* Dept Physics Iowa State Univ Ames IA 50011

RIZZUTO, ANTHONY B, b Baton Rouge, La, Sept 11, 30; m 57; c 4. MICROBIOLOGY, BIOCHEMISTRY. *Educ:* La State Univ, BS, 52; Miss State Univ, MS, 55; Nat Registry Microbiol, regist. *Prof Exp:* Plant microbiologist, Am Sugar Co, NY, 56-59, res microbiologist, 59-63, sr res scientist, Res & Develop Div, 63-69, asst dir, 69-74, asst dir, 74-80, DIR, AMSTAR CORP, 80- *Concurrent Pos:* Mem, Nat Comn Uniform Methods Sugar Anal, 60- & Int Comn, 62- *Mem:* Nat Acad Sci; Soc Indust Microbiol; Inst Food Technol; Am Soc Microbiol. *Res:* Industrial, agricultural, food, dairy and sanitation microbiology. *Mailing Add:* Amstar Corp 266 Kent Ave Brooklyn NY 11211

ROACH, ARCHIBALD WILSON KILBOURNE, b Omaha, Nebr, Sept 15, 20; m 42; c 3. BOTANY. *Educ:* Univ Colo, BA, 46, MA, 48; Ore State Univ, PhD, 51. *Prof Exp:* From asst prof to assoc prof, 50-57, prof bot, 57-77, PROF BIOL SCI, NTEX STATE UNIV, 77- *Concurrent Pos:* Mem, Int Bur Plant Taxon & Nomenclature. *Mem:* Ecol Soc Am. *Res:* Phytosociology; southwestern aquatic actinomycetes. *Mailing Add:* Dept Biol Sci NTex State Univ Denton TX 76203

ROACH, DAVID MICHAEL, b Detroit Lakes, Minn, Oct 10, 39; m 61; c 2. OCEANOGRAPHY. *Educ:* SDak Sch Mines & Technol, BS, 61, MS, 63; Ore State Univ, PhD(oceanog), 74. *Prof Exp:* Instr physics, SDak Sch Mines & Technol, 63-64; asst prof, Wis State Univ-Whitewater, 64-66; PROF PHYSICS, CALIF POLYTECH STATE UNIV, SAN LUIS OBISPO, 66- *Res:* Determination of refractive index distributions of oceanic particulates. *Mailing Add:* Dept of Physics Calif Polytech State Univ San Luis Obispo CA 93401

ROACH, DON, b Bono, Ark, Dec 10, 36; m 57; c 1. ANALYTICAL CHEMISTRY. *Educ:* Ark State Univ, BS, 59; Univ Ark, Fayetteville, MS, 63; Univ Mo-Columbia, PhD(anal biochem), 70. *Prof Exp:* Technician, Univ Ark, Fayetteville, 63-64; asst prof chem, Miami-Dade Jr Col, 64-67; chemist, Exp Sta Chem Labs, Univ Mo-Columbia, 67-68; assoc prof, 69-80, PROF & CHMN CHEM, MIAMI-DADE COMMUNITY COL, 80- *Concurrent Pos:* Consult, Precision Anal Labs, Inc, 65-67; res dir, 69- *Mem:* Am Chem Soc. *Res:* Gas-liquid chromatography of biologically important compounds. *Mailing Add:* Dept Chem Miami-Dade Community Col Miami FL 33176

ROACH, DONALD VINCENT, b Oak Grove, Mo, Jan 18, 32. PHYSICAL CHEMISTRY. *Educ:* Univ Mo, BS, 54, PhD(phys chem), 62. *Prof Exp:* Res assoc, Univ Calif, Berkeley, 62-63 & Univ Mo-Columbia, 63-64; res chemist, US Naval Weapons Lab, 64-65; asst prof, 65-72, ASSOC PROF CHEM, UNIV MO-ROLLA, 72- *Mem:* Am Chem Soc. *Res:* Gas-solid surface interactions; adsorption of gases on solids; exchange of energy between gases and solids. *Mailing Add:* Dept of Chem Univ of Mo Rolla MO 65401

ROACH, FRANCIS AUBRA, b Coleman, Tex, Apr 5, 35; m 56; c 2. MATHEMATICAL ANALYSIS. *Educ:* Univ Tex, BA, 59, MA, 60, PhD(math), 66. *Prof Exp:* Chemist, Tex Butadiene & Chem Corp, 57-58; programmer math, Shell Oil Co, 60-61; instr, San Jacinto Col, 61-62 & Univ Tex, 62-66; asst prof, Univ Ga, 66-69; asst prof, 69-72, ASSOC PROF MATH, UNIV HOUSTON, 72- *Mem:* Am Math Soc. *Res:* Mathematical analysis, especially continued fractions. *Mailing Add:* 6219 Fawnwood Spring TX 77379

ROACH, J ROBERT, b Stockton, Ill, Nov 24, 13; m 50; c 3. ORGANIC CHEMISTRY, FOOD CHEMISTRY. *Educ:* Iowa State Col, BS, 36; Purdue Univ, PhD(org chem), 42. *Prof Exp:* Pittsburgh Plate Glass Co fel, Northwestern Univ, 41-43; proj leader org chem, Gen Mills, Inc, 43-50, sect leader, Food Develop Dept, 50-56, dept head, 56-61, dir food develop activity, 61-69, vpres & dir res & develop food group, 69-77; RETIRED. *Mem:* Am Chem Soc; Am Asn Cereal Chemists; Inst Food Technologists. *Res:* Food development; convenience foods. *Mailing Add:* 24 Luverne Minneapolis MN 55419

ROACH, JOHN FAUNCE, b Boston, Mass, July 21, 12; m 39; c 1. RADIOLOGY. *Educ:* Harvard Univ, AB, 35, MD, 39. *Prof Exp:* From asst prof to assoc prof radiol, Sch Med, Johns Hopkins Univ, 47-50; chmn dept, 50-77, PROF RADIOL, ALBANY MED COL, 50-; CONSULT, NY STATE EDUC DEPT, 81- *Concurrent Pos:* Consult, Vet Admin Hosp, Albany; mem pub health coun, State Health Dept, NY; trustee, Am Bd Radiol; pres, Am Bd Med Specialties; exec secy, NY State Bd for Med, 77-81. *Mem:* Radiol Soc NAm; Am Roentgen Ray Soc; fel Am Col Radiologists. *Mailing Add:* Dept of Radiol Albany Med Col Albany NY 12208

ROACH, KENNETH ALPHONSA, b Brooklyn, NY, Apr 9, 19; m 55; c 2. PHYSICS. *Educ:* City Col New York, BChE, 44; Polytech Inst Brooklyn, MChE, 49. *Prof Exp:* Phys chemist, Kellex Corp, 44-46; develop engr, Process & Instruments, 46-62; proj engr, Transnuclear Corp, 62-63; MGR, ENVIRON ANAL GROUP, TELEDYNE-ISOTOPES, 63- *Mem:* AAAS; Inst Elec & Electronics Engrs. *Res:* Application of instruments for detection of stable and radioactive isotopes. *Mailing Add:* Qual Assurance Mgr Teledyne-Isotopes 50 Van Buren Ave Westwood NJ 07675

ROACH, MARGOT RUTH, b Moncton, NB, Dec 24, 34. BIOPHYSICS, MEDICINE. *Educ:* Univ NB, BSc, 55; McGill Univ, MD, CM, 59; Univ Western Ont, PhD(biophys), 63; FRCP(C), 65. *Hon Degrees:* DSc, Univ New Brunswick, 81. *Prof Exp:* Jr intern, Victoria Hosp, London, Ont, 59-60; Med Res Coun Can fel, Univ Western Ont, 60-62, Ont Heart Found fel cardiol,

Victoria Hosp, 62-63, asst resident med, 63-64; asst resident, Toronto Gen Hosp, Ont, 64-65; from asst prof to assoc prof med, 65-78, from asst prof to assoc prof biophys, 65-71, chmn dept, 70-78, PROF BIOPHYS, UNIV WESTERN ONT, 71-, PROF MED, 78- *Concurrent Pos:* Med Res Coun Can fel, Nuffield Inst Med Res, Oxford, Eng, 65-67; Med Res Coun Can scholar biophys & med, Univ Western Ont, 67-70; Med Res Coun res grants, 68-70 & 71-; Ont Heart Found res grant, 68-; Can Tuberc Asn res grant, 69-70; Ont Thoracic Soc res grant, 71-; Picker Found res grant, 71-73; mem active teaching staff med, Victoria Hosp, 67-72; Can rep, Adv Group Aeronaut Res & Develop, NATO, 69-71; mem comt on scholar, Med Res Coun Can, 71-72; res consult, Westminster Hosp, 71-73; mem adv comt biophys, Nat Res Coun, 71-78; consult, Univ Hosp, 72-; assoc ed, Can J Physiol Pharmacol, 73-79. *Honors & Awards:* Ciba Found Award, 59. *Mem:* Can Physiol Soc; Can Med Asn; Can Cardiovasc Soc; Can Soc Clin Invest; Biophys Soc. *Res:* Hemodynamics; elastic properties of tissues; effects of vibration on tissues; contraction of vascular smooth muscle; lung surfactant, atherosclerosis. *Mailing Add:* Dept Biophys Univ Western Ont London ON N6A 5C1 Can

ROACH, PETER JOHN, b Rangeworthy, UK, June 8, 48; m 75. GLYCOGEN METABOLISM, MECHANISMS OF HORMONE ACTION. *Educ:* Univ Glasgow, BSc, 69, PhD(biochem), 72. *Prof Exp:* Fel, Univ Calif, Los Angeles, 72-74, Univ Va, 74-75, Univ Pisa, Italy, 75-77; instr pharmacol, Univ Va, 77-79; ASST PROF BIOCHEM, SCH MED, IND UNIV, 79- *Res:* Mechanisms by which hormones regulate enzyme activity, with the main focus on covalent phosphorylation in the control of glycogen metabolism. *Mailing Add:* Dept Biochem Sch Med Ind Univ 1100 W Michigan St Indianapolis IN 46223

ROACH, WILLIAM KENNEY, b Cincinnati, Ohio, Feb 2, 42; m 64; c 2. ENTOMOLOGY. *Educ:* St Louis Univ, BS, 64; Ohio State Univ, PhD(entom), 71. *Prof Exp:* Surv entomologist, Ohio State Univ, 69-70; SPECIALIST-IN-CHARGE, PLANT PEST CONTROL SECT, OHIO DEPT AGR, 72- *Mem:* Entom Soc Am. *Res:* Taxonomy of Empidid flies. *Mailing Add:* Plant Pest Control Sect Ohio Dept Agr 8995 E Main Reynoldsburg OH 43068

ROACHE, LEWIE CALVIN, b Dalzell, SC, Oct 31, 25; m 59. ZOOLOGY. *Educ:* SC State Col, BS, 47, MS, 54; Cath Univ, PhD(zool), 60. *Prof Exp:* From instr to assoc prof, 47-69, from actg head to head dept, 56-69, chmn dept natural sci, 69-77, PROF BIOL, SC STATE COL, 69-, DEAN, SCH OF ARTS & SCI, 77- *Mem:* AAAS; Ecol Soc Am; Nat Inst Sci. *Res:* Systematics of the freshwater Cyclopoid Copepods. *Mailing Add:* Sch Arts & Sci SC State Col PO Box 1746 Orangeburg SC 29117

ROADS, JOHN OWEN, b Boulder, Colo, Jan 20, 50. METEOROLOGY, CLIMATOLOGY. *Educ:* Univ Colo, BA, 72; Mass Inst Technol, PhD(meteorol), 77. *Prof Exp:* Res asst, Nat Ctr Atmospheric Res, 70-72; NSF fel, 72-77, ASST RES METEOROLOGIST, SCRIPPS INST OCEANOG, UNIV CALIF, SAN DIEGO, 77- *Concurrent Pos:* Res asst, Mass Inst Technol, 75-77. *Mem:* Am Meteorol Soc. *Res:* Numerical modelling; dynamic meteorology; climate modelling. *Mailing Add:* Scripps Inst Oceanog Univ Calif San Diego La Jolla CA 92093

ROADSTRUM, WILLIAM H(ENRY), b Chicago, Ill, June 22, 15; m 43; c 2. ENGINEERING, ENGINEERING ECONOMICS. *Educ:* Lehigh Univ, BS, 38; Carnegie Inst Technol, MS, 48, PhD(elec eng), 55. *Prof Exp:* Elec engr, US Bur Mines, Pa, 39-41, 45-47; asst prof electronics, US Naval Postgrad Sch, 48-50, 52-53; syst engr, adv electronics ctr, Gen Elec Co, NY, 55-57, mgr missile systs eng, Hvy Mil Dept, 57-59, mgr detection & surveillance eng, 59-60, mgr info storage & retrieval, Adv Tech Labs, 60-63; adj prof, 63-64, PROF ELEC ENG, WORCESTER POLYTECH INST, 64- *Concurrent Pos:* Consult, eng practices & eng mgt, 64- *Mem:* Sigma Xi; sr mem Inst Elec & Electronics Engrs. *Res:* Systems engineering; engineering economy; management theory and techniques in engineering and development projects; education and development of engineers. *Mailing Add:* Dept of Elec Eng Worcester Polytech Inst Worcester MA 01609

ROAKE, WILLIAM EARL, b Oregon City, Ore, Sept 30, 19; m 42; c 2. NUCLEAR ENGINEERING, MATERIALS SCIENCE ENGINEERING. *Educ:* Ore State Col, BS, 41, MS, 42; Northwestern Univ, PhD, 49. *Prof Exp:* Chemist, Charleton Labs, Portland, Ore, 41; res chemist, Nat Defense Res Comt Contract, Cent Labs, Northwestern Univ, 42-45 & Calif Inst Technol, 45; res chemist, Hanford Atomic Prods Oper, Gen Elec Co, 48-58, sr engr, 58-62, mgr, Fuels Testing & Anal Unit, 62-65; mgr, Ceramics Res Unit, Pac Northwest Labs, Batelle Mem Inst, 65-66, mgr, Fast Reactor Fuels Sect, 65-70; mgr, FFTF Fuel Develop Sect, Wadco Corp, 66-68, dep mgr, 68-70, mgr, Core Components Subdiv, 70-73; mgr, Fuels Subdiv, 73-76, mgr, Fuels & Controls Subdept, 76-79, ASST MGR, APPL SYSTS DEVELOP DEPT, WESTINGHOUSE-HANFORD CO, 79- *Mem:* Am Chem Soc; Sigma Xi; fel Am Nuclear Soc; Am Inst Aeronaut & Astronaut. *Res:* Nuclear reactor fuels development, testing, design, fabrication and reprocessing. *Mailing Add:* Westinghouse-Hanford Co PO Box 1970 Richland WA 99352

ROALSVIG, JAN PER, b Stavanger, Norway, Mar 23, 28; m 54; c 5. EXPERIMENTAL NUCLEAR PHYSICS, HIGH ENERGY PHYSICS. *Educ:* Univ Oslo, BSc, 52, MSc, 55; Norweg Inst Pedag, BEd, 53; Univ Sask, PhD(physics), 59. *Prof Exp:* Asst prof physics, St John's Univ, NY, 59-62; asst prof, 62-67, ASSOC PROF PHYSICS, STATE UNIV NY BUFFALO, 67- *Concurrent Pos:* Res prof, Chalmers Univ Technol, Sweden, 69-70; docent, Norweg Tech Univ, 72-73. *Mem:* Am Phys Soc; Am Asn Physics Teachers; Can Asn Physicists; Norweg Phys Soc. *Res:* Pair-production; absolute beta-counting; photo-alpha and photo-neutron reactions; nuclear spectroscopy; gamma ray detectors; hyperfragments. *Mailing Add:* Dept Physics State Univ NY Buffalo NY 14260

ROAN, VERNON P, b Ft Myers, Fla, Nov 19, 35; m; c 2. MECHANICAL ENGINEERING, AEROSPACE ENGINEERING. *Educ:* Univ Fla, BS, 58, MS, 59; Univ Ill, PhD(mech eng), 66. *Prof Exp:* Assoc prof, 71-73, PROF MECH ENG, UNIV FLA, 73- *Concurrent Pos:* Consult, I E du Pont de Nemours & Co, Inc, 73-; chmn, Subcomt Univ Activities Elec & Hybrid Elec Vehicles, Inst Elec & Electronics Engrs, 77-; consult, Jet Propulsion Lab, 80-; mem staff, Brunel Univ, Uxbridge, Eng, 79-80. *Honors & Awards:* Nat Winner Urban Vehicle Design, Student Competition Relevant Eng, 72; Ralph R Tector Award, Soc Automotive Engrs, 75; Nat Winner Era II Wind Systs Design, Student Competition Relevant Eng, 77- *Mem:* Nat Soc Prof Engrs; Soc Automotive Engrs; Sigma Xi; Am Soc Mech Engrs. *Res:* Gasdynamics; propulsion systems; wind systems; electric and hybrid electric vehicles; development of first hybrid electric bus in US. *Mailing Add:* Dept of Mech Eng Univ Fla Gainesville FL 32611

ROANE, CURTIS WOODARD, b Norfolk, Va, Apr 19, 21; m 47; c 2. PLANT PATHOLOGY. *Educ:* Va Polytech Inst, BS, 43, MS, 44; Univ Minn, PhD(plant path), 53. *Prof Exp:* From asst plant pathologist to assoc plant pathologist, Exp Sta, 47-68, assoc prof, 48-68, PROF PLANT PATH, VA POLYTECH INST & STATE UNIV, 68- *Concurrent Pos:* Assoc ed, Phytopathology, 69-71; Plant Dis Reporter, 78-81; chmn, Southern Small Grain Worker's Conf, 70-72, Eastern Wheat Workers Conf, 78-81; chmn, NAm Barley Res Workers, 81-84. *Mem:* Sigma Xi; Am Phytopath Soc. *Res:* Control of cereal crops and soybean diseases through resistance; genetics of host-parasite interaction; education. *Mailing Add:* Dept of Plant Path & Physiol Va Polytech Inst & State Univ Blacksburg VA 24061

ROANE, MARTHA KOTILA, b Munising, Mich, Nov 1, 21; m 47; c 2. MYCOLOGY, TAXONOMIC BOTANY. *Educ:* Mich State Col, BS, 44; Univ Minn, MS, 46; Va Polytech Inst & State Univ, PhD(bot), 71. *Prof Exp:* Eng aide advan develop, Pratt & Whitney Aircraft Corp, 44-45; technician soils, Agr Eng, Va Polytech Inst, 47-48, instr math, 56-63; from instr to asst prof, Radford Col, 63-68, asst dir, Off Instnl Res, 68-69; coordr, Gen Biol Lab, 71-72, cur fungi, 72-75, adj asst prof bot, 75-77, ADJ PROF PLANT PATH, VA POLYTECH INST & STATE UNIV, 77- *Mem:* AAAS; Bot Soc Am; Mycol Soc Am; Int Asn Plant Taxon; Sigma Xi. *Res:* Monographic studies of Endothia and North American species of Rhododendron; morphology, taxonomy and development of the Chytridiales; role of fungal pigments, proteins and enzymes in taxonomy. *Mailing Add:* Dept of Plant Path & Physiol Va Polytech Inst & State Univ Blacksburg VA 24061

ROANE, PHILIP RANSOM, JR, b Baltimore, Md, Nov 20, 27. VIROLOGY, IMMUNOLOGY. *Educ:* Morgan State Col, BS, 52; Johns Hopkins Univ, MS, 60; Univ Md, PhD, 70. *Prof Exp:* Asst microbiol, Sch Med, Johns Hopkins Univ, 60-64; virologist, Microbiol Assocs, Inc, 64-72, dir qual control, 67-72; asst prof, 72-77, ASSOC PROF MICROBIOL, HOWARD UNIV, 78- *Concurrent Pos:* Mem, Virol Study Sect, NIH, 76-80, Viral & Rickettsial Rev Subcomt, 79-; consult, Hem Res Inc, Rockville Md, 81- *Mem:* AAAS; Am Soc Microbiol; Am Asn Immunologists. *Res:* Biophysical and immunological properties of viruses; biochemistry of tumor and transformed cells induced by a common virus. *Mailing Add:* Dept of Microbiol Howard Univ Sch of Med Washington DC 20001

ROANTREE, ROBERT JOSEPH, b Elko, Nev, Sept 11, 24. MEDICAL MICROBIOLOGY. *Educ:* Stanford Univ, AB, 45, MD, 48. *Prof Exp:* From instr to asst prof, 56-63, ASSOC PROF MED MICROBIOL, SCH MED, STANFORD UNIV, 63- *Concurrent Pos:* Bank of Am-Giannini fel, 55-56; Lederle med fac award, 57-60; vis fel, Lister Inst, 63-64. *Mem:* Am Soc Microbiol; NY Acad Sci. *Res:* Genetic changes affecting the bacterial cell wall and their effects upon virulence and susceptibility to antibiotics. *Mailing Add:* Dept of Med Microbiol Stanford Univ Stanford CA 94305

ROARK, BRUCE (ARCHIBALD), b New York, NY, Jan 19, 20; m 46, 77; c 7. PLANT PHYSIOLOGY, PLANT BREEDING. *Educ:* Univ Western Australia, BSc, 49 & 50; Univ Adelaide, PhD, 56. *Prof Exp:* Plant physiologist, Sci & Educ Admin, Agr Res, USDA, Mayaguez, PR, 56-58 & Miss, 58-70, supvry plant physiologist, 70-79; PLANT BREEDER, NORTHRUP KING SEED CO, 81- *Mem:* Am Soc Plant Physiologists; Am Soc Agron; Crop Sci Soc Am. *Res:* Water relations; stress resistance genotype and environment interactions; upland cotton; plant breeding. *Mailing Add:* Northrup King Res Ctr PO Drawer 272 Leland MS 38756

ROARK, JAMES L, b Kansas City, Mo, Mar 27, 43; m 67; c 2. ORGANIC CHEMISTRY, CHEMISTRY EDUCATION. *Educ:* Nebr Wesleyan Univ, BA, 65; Tex Christian Univ, PhD(chem), 69. *Prof Exp:* From asst prof to assoc prof chem, Kearney State Col, 69-75, prof & chmn dept, 76-81. *Concurrent Pos:* Robert Welch res fel, Tex Christian Univ, 67-69; NSF fel, Tufts Univ, 71; dir water anal lab, Kearney State Col, 72-76, proj dir water qual study, 73-75, high ability high sch students, 74-75 & 76-77, sec chem teachers, 77-; vis prof, Univ Va, 81-82. *Mem:* Am Chem Soc; Nat Sci Teachers Asn; Sigma Xi. *Res:* Non-traditional methods of instruction; computer based methods of instruction; chemistry curriculums for secondary education; natural products chemistry. *Mailing Add:* Dept Chem Univ Va Charlottesville VA 22904

ROARK, TERRY P, b Okeene, Okla, June 11, 38; m 63; c 1. ASTRONOMY, ASTROPHYSICS. *Educ:* Oklahoma City Univ, BA, 60; Rensselaer Polytech Inst, MS, 62, PhD(astron), 66. *Prof Exp:* from asst prof to assoc prof, 66-76, PROF ASTRON, OHIO STATE UNIV, 76-, ASST PROVOST, INSTRUCTION, 77- *Mem:* Am Astron Soc; Int Astron Union; Astron Soc Pac; Sigma Xi. *Res:* Observational and theoretical investigation of the solid interstellar medium, binary and white dwarf stars. *Mailing Add:* Dept of Astron Ohio State Univ 174 W 18th Ave Columbus OH 43210

ROARTY, JOSEPH D, b Philadelphia, Pa, Apr 6, 26; m 52; c 6. MECHANICAL ENGINEERING. *Educ:* Villanova Univ, BME, 50; Mass Inst Technol, SM, 51; Univ Pittsburgh, PhD(mech eng), 61. *Prof Exp:* Develop engr, Oak Ridge Nat Lab, 51-52; tech engr, US Atomic Energy Comn, 52-54; sr engr, 54-59, supvr reactor design, 59-65, mgr fuel element design, 65-72, mgr adv test core, 72-75, MGR NUCLEAR ENG, BETTIS ATOMIC POWER LAB, WESTINGHOUSE ELEC CORP, 75- *Mem:* Am Soc Mech Engrs. *Res:* Engineering. *Mailing Add:* 338 Cavan Dr Pittsburgh PA 15236

ROATH, WILLIAM WESLEY, b Torrington, Wyo, Dec 7, 34; m 55; c 6. PLANT BREEDING. *Educ:* Mont State Univ, BS, 57, PhD(genetics), 69. *Prof Exp:* res agronomist, Dekalb Agr Res, Inc, 71; RES GENETISIST, AGR RES SERV, USDA, 78- *Mem:* Am Soc Agron; Crop Sci Soc Am. *Res:* Sun flower genetics and breeding. *Mailing Add:* 1006 Third St N Fargo ND 58102

ROB, CHARLES G, b Weybridge, Eng, May 4, 13; nat US; m 41; c 4. SURGERY. *Educ:* Cambridge Univ, MA, 34, MB, BCh, 37, MCh, 41, MD, 60; FRCS, 39. *Hon Degrees:* MCh, Trinity Col, Dublin, 61. *Prof Exp:* Reader surg, Univ London, 46-50, prof, 50-60; prof surg & chmn dept, Sch Med, Univ Rochester, 60-78; PROF SURG, E CAROLINA SCH MED, GREENVILLE, NC, 78- *Concurrent Pos:* Consult, Brit Army, Royal Nat Orthop Hosp, London; mem court examr, Royal Col Surgeons. *Mem:* Asn Surg Gt Brit & Ireland (hon secy); Royal Soc Med; Int Soc Cardiovasc Surg (pres, 61); hon fel Venezuelan Surg Soc. *Mailing Add:* Dept of Surg E Carolina Univ Sch of Med Greenville NC 27834

ROBACK, SELWYN, b Boston, Mass, Aug 22, 24; m 49; c 2. ENTOMOLOGY. *Educ:* Cornell Univ, BS, 48; Univ Ill, MS, 49, PhD(entom), 51. *Prof Exp:* From asst cur to assoc cur, 51-62, CUR LIMNOL, ACAD NATURAL SCI, 62- *Mem:* Am Entom Soc (pres, 63-64); Entom Am; Soc Syst Zool; fel Royal Entom Soc London; NAm Benthological Soc. *Res:* Taxonomy and ecology of Chironomidae and aquatic insects. *Mailing Add:* Acad of Natural Sci 19th & The Parkway Philadelphia PA 19103

ROBB, ERNEST WILLARD, b Dodge City, Kans, Sept 4, 31; m 60; c 3. ORGANIC CHEMISTRY. *Educ:* Kans State Univ, BS, 52; Harvard Univ, MS, 54, PhD(chem), 56. *Prof Exp:* Fels, Iowa State Col, 56-57, Mass Inst Technol, 57-58 & Harvard Univ, 58-59; res chemist, Fritzsche Bros, Inc, 59-60; res scientist, Philip Morris Inc, 60-63, sr scientist, 63-65; assoc prof, 65-75, PROF ORG CHEM, STEVENS INST TECHNOL, 75- *Mem:* AAAS; Am Chem Soc. *Res:* Mechanism of organic reactions; organic stereochemistry. *Mailing Add:* Dept of Chem Stevens Inst of Technol Hoboken NJ 07030

ROBB, J PRESTON, b Montreal, Que, Apr 4, 14; m 40; c 4. NEUROLOGY. *Educ:* McGill Univ, BSc, 36, MD, CM, 39, MSc, 46. *Prof Exp:* Assoc prof, 55-69, PROF NEUROL, McGILL UNIV, 69- *Concurrent Pos:* Consult neurologist, Montreal Gen Hosp, 55-, Royal Victoria Hosp, 60- & Montreal Children's Hosp, 68-; neurologist-in-chief, Montreal Neurol Hosp, 55- *Honors & Awards:* Lennox Award, 79. *Mem:* Am Neurol Asn; Am Acad Neurol; Am Epilepsy Soc (pres, 65-66); Asn Res Nerv & Ment Dis; Can Med Asn; Can Neurol Soc (pres). *Mailing Add:* Dept of Neurol McGill Univ Fac of Med Montreal PQ N3A 2T5 Can

ROBB, JAMES ARTHUR, b Pueblo, Colo, Nov 13, 38; m 62; c 4. PATHOLOGY, VIROLOGY. *Educ:* Univ Colo, Boulder, BA, 60; Univ Colo, Denver, MD, 65, Am Bd Anatomic Pathol & Am Bd Dermatopathol, dipl. *Prof Exp:* Intern anat path, Yale Med Ctr, 65-66, resident, 66-68; res assoc molecular virol, Nat Inst Arthritis & Metab Dis, 68-71; from asst prof to assoc prof path, Univ Calif, San Diego, 71-78, STAFF PATHOLOGIST, GREEN HOSP OF SCRIPPS CLIN, LAJOLLA, CALIF, 78- *Concurrent Pos:* Assoc adj prof path, Sch Med, Univ Calif, 78-; fel Col Am Pathol. *Mem:* AAAS; Am Soc Cell Biol; Am Soc Microbiol; Am Asn Pathologists; Am Soc Clin Pathologists. *Res:* Molecular biology of oncogenic and neurotropic viruses; study of the animal virus-mammalian cell interactions resulting in cancer or chronic brain disease; detection of antigens in formalin-fixed, paraffin-embedded human tissues. *Mailing Add:* Dept Path Green Hosp Scripps Clin La Jolla CA 92037

ROBB, RICHARD A, b Price, Utah, Dec 2, 42. MEDICAL IMAGING, COMPUTED TOMOGRAPHY. *Educ:* Univ Utah, BA, 65, MS, 68, PhD(comput sci), 71. *Prof Exp:* DIR, RES COMPUT FACIL, MAYO FOUND, 72-, ASSOC PROF BIOPHYSICS, GRAD SCH MED, 79- *Concurrent Pos:* Prin investr & staff consult, Res Comput Facil, Mayo Found, 76- *Mem:* Am Physiol Soc; Biomed Eng Soc; AAAS; Asn Advan Technol in Biomed Sci; Sigma Xi. *Res:* Computerized processing, display and analysis of biomedical imagery; x-ray computed tomography; three dimensional image display. *Mailing Add:* Mayo Clin Rochester MN 55901

ROBB, THOMAS WILBERN, b Marshall, Mo, Apr 25, 53. RUMINANT NUTRITION, FORAGE EVALUATION. *Educ:* Central Mo State Univ, BS, 73; Univ Mo, Columbia, MS, 75; Univ Ky, PhD(animal sci), 80. *Prof Exp:* ASST PROF ANIMAL SCI, NC STATE UNIV, 81- *Res:* Ruminant nutrition research, primarily forages in Northeast Brazil, meat producing sheep and goats and with dairy goats. *Mailing Add:* Dept Animal Sci NC State Univ Raleigh NC 27607

ROBB, WALTER L(EE), b Harrisburg, Pa, Apr 25, 28; m 54; c 3. CHEMICAL ENGINEERING. *Educ:* Pa State Col, BS, 48; Univ Ill, MS, 49, PhD(chem eng), 51. *Prof Exp:* Engr, Knolls Atomic Power Lab, 51-56, res engr, Res Lab, 56-62, mgr chem process sect, 62-66, mgr res & develop, Silicone Prod Dept, 66-68, mgr med develop oper, Schenectady, 68-71, gen mgr silicone prod dept, Waterford, 71-73, gen mgr chem & metall div, 73, V PRES & GEN MGR, MED SYSTS OPER, GEN ELEC CO, 73- *Concurrent Pos:* Mem, Nat Adv Coun for Health Care Technol. *Res:* Permeable membranes; diagnostic imaging equipment. *Mailing Add:* 3665 Mary Cliff Lane Brookfield WI 53005

ROBB, WILLIAM DEREK, atomic physics, see previous edition

ROBBAT, ALBERT, JR, b Boston, Mass, Apr 11, 54. ELECTROCHEMISTRY, CHROMATOGRAPHY. *Educ:* Univ Mass, Boston, BA, 76; Pa State Univ, PhD(chem), 80. *Prof Exp:* ASST PROF CHEM, TUFTS UNIV, 80- *Concurrent Pos:* Res assoc anal chem, US Dept Energy, Pittsburgh, 81-82, prin investr, Anal Div. *Mem:* Am Chem Soc; Electrochem Soc. *Res:* Electroreactivity and affinity of biologically important species: iron, sulfur, molybdenum proteins, and condensed thiophenes; application of radio frequency, static and magnetic fields in chromatography. *Mailing Add:* Dept Chem Tufts Univ Medford MA 02155

ROBBEN, FRANKLIN ARTHUR, b Sacramento, Calif, Feb 12, 34; m 59, 81; c 3. COMBUSTION, DIAGNOSTICS. *Educ:* Univ Calif, BS, 54, PhD(physics), 63; Univ Calif, Los Angeles, MS, 56. *Prof Exp:* Scientist fluid dynamics, Lockheed Missiles & Space Co, 55-60; scientist, Magnetohydrodynamics, Missiles & Space Vehicles Div, Gen Elec Co, 60-61; asst res engr fluid dynamics, Univ Calif, Berkeley, 63-65; res engr plasma physics, A B Atomenergi, 65-68; lectr aeronaut sci, 68-71, assoc prof-in-residence mech eng, 71-76, SR SCIENTIST, LAWRENCE BERKELEY LAB, UNIV CALIF, BERKELEY, 75- *Mem:* Am Phys Soc; Optical Soc Am; Combustion Inst; Am Inst Aeronaut & Astronaut; AAAS. *Res:* Combustion fluid mechanics, chemistry and instrumentation. *Mailing Add:* Energy & Environ Div Lawrence Berkeley Lab Berkeley CA 94720

ROBBERS, JAMES EARL, b Everett, Wash, Oct 18, 34; m 57. PHARMACOGNOSY. *Educ:* Wash State Univ, BS & BPhar, 57, MS, 61; Univ Wash, PhD(pharmacog), 64. *Prof Exp:* Asst prof pharmacog, Univ Houston, 64-66; from asst prof to assoc prof, 66-75, PROF PHARMACOG, PURDUE UNIV, WEST LAFAYETTE, 75- *Honors & Awards:* Edwin Leigh Newcomb Award, 63. *Mem:* Am Soc Pharmacog; Am Pharmaceut Asn; Acad Pharmaceut Sci. *Res:* Isolation, physiology, biosynthesis and metabolic control of fungal metabolites. *Mailing Add:* Sch Pharm & Pharmacal Sci Purdue Univ West Lafayette IN 47907

ROBBIN, JOEL W, b Chicago, Ill, May 28, 41; m 66. MATHEMATICS. *Educ:* Univ Ill, BS, 62; Princeton Univ, MA, 64, PhD(math), 65. *Prof Exp:* Instr math, Princeton Univ, 65-67; asst prof, 67-73, PROF MATH, UNIV WIS-MADISON, 73- *Mem:* Am Math Soc; Asn Symbolic Logic. *Res:* Logic; differential equations. *Mailing Add:* Dept of Math Univ of Wis 313 Van Vleck Madison WI 53706

ROBBINS, ALLEN BISHOP, b New Brunswick, NJ, Mar 31, 30; m 79; c 4. PHYSICS. *Educ:* Rutgers Univ, BSc, 52; Yale Univ, MS, 53, PhD(physics), 56. *Prof Exp:* From instr to assoc prof, 56-68, PROF PHYSICS, RUTGERS UNIV, NEW BRUNSWICK, 68-; CHMN DEPT, 79- *Concurrent Pos:* Imp Chem Industs res fel, Univ Birmingham, 57-58, lectr, 60-61. *Mem:* AAAS; fel Am Phys Soc; Am Asn Physics Teachers. *Res:* Nuclear physics. *Mailing Add:* Dept of Physics Rutgers Univ New Brunswick NJ 08903

ROBBINS, CHANDLER SEYMOUR, b Belmont, Mass, July 17, 18; m 48; c 4. ORNITHOLOGY. *Educ:* Harvard Univ, AB, 40; George Washington Univ, MA, 50. *Prof Exp:* Chief scient, 61-76, WILDLIFE RES BIOLOGIST, MIGRATORY NON-GAME BIRD STUDIES, US FISH & WILDLIFE SERV, 46- *Concurrent Pos:* Ed, Md Birdlife, 47-; mem, Int Bird Census Comt; secy, Int Bird Ringing Comt, 71-; tech ed, Audubon Field Notes, 52-70 & Am Birds, 71-74 & 79- *Mem:* Fel Am Ornith Union; Wilson Ornith Soc; Cooper Ornith Soc; Am Meteorol Soc; Nat Audubon Soc. *Res:* Distribution, migration and abundance of North American birds; monitoring of bird population levels; analysis of records of banded birds; techniques of trapping birds for banding; field identification of birds. *Mailing Add:* US Fish & Wildlife Serv Laurel MD 20708

ROBBINS, CLARENCE RALPH, b Point Marion, Pa, Aug 25, 38; m 71; c 2. COSMETIC CHEMISTRY, ORGANIC CHEMISTRY. *Educ:* WVa Wesleyan Col, BS, 60; Purdue Univ, PhD(org chem), 64. *Prof Exp:* Res chemist hair res, 64-66; sect head, 66-72, sect head toiletries, 72-74, sr sect head hair & soap prod, 74-77, SR RES ASSOC SKIN & HAIR RES, COLGATE PALMOLIVE CO, 77- *Mem:* Soc Cosmetic Chemists. *Res:* Chemical and physical properties of human hair and skin, especially physical property changes of hair and skin to toiletry and surfactant treatments and to other environmental influences. *Mailing Add:* Colgate Palmolive Co 909 River Rd Piscataway NJ 08854

ROBBINS, D(ELMAR) HURLEY, b Elmira, NY, Dec 5, 37; m 68; c 1. ENGINEERING MECHANICS. *Educ:* Univ Mich, BSE(eng mech) & BSE(math), 60, MSE, 61, PhD(eng mech), 65. *Prof Exp:* Asst prof eng mech, Ohio State Univ, 65-67; RES ENGR, HWY SAFETY RES INST, UNIV MICH, ANN ARBOR, 67- *Honors & Awards:* Metrop Life Award, Nat Safety Coun, 70. *Mem:* Am Soc Mech Engrs; Acoust Soc Am; Soc Exp Stress Anal. *Res:* Theory of shells; mechanical properties of engineering and biological materials; analytical and experimental simulation of automotive crash impact; acoustics of musical instruments. *Mailing Add:* Hwy Safety Res Inst Huron Pkwy & Baxter Rd Ann Arbor MI 48109

ROBBINS, DAVID O, b Bryn Mawr, Pa, July 1, 43; m 71; c 2. VISION, ELECTROPHYSIOLOGY. *Educ:* Lycoming Col, BA, 65; Univ Del, MA, 68, PhD(physiol psychol), 70. *Prof Exp:* Fel vision, Eye Res Found, 69-70, prin investr, Dept Physiol, 70-73, dir res, 72-73; asst prof, 73-78, ASSOC PROF, DEPT PSYCHOL, OHIO WESLEYAN UNIV, 78- *Concurrent Pos:* Prin investr contracts, US Army Res & Develop Command, 70- *Mem:* Asn Res Vision & Ophthal; Sigma Xi. *Res:* Electrophysiological bases of color vision with emphasis on single cell receptive field organization to color and movement in reptiles; adverse effects of intense, coherent (laser) light on retinal physiology and function in rhesus monkeys. *Mailing Add:* Dept Psychol Ohio Wesleyn Univ 50 S Henry St Delaware OH 43015

ROBBINS, DONALD, physics, see previous edition

ROBBINS, DONALD EUGENE, b San Saba, Tex, July 4, 37; m 56; c 3. PHYSICS. *Educ:* Tex Christian Univ, BA, 60; Univ Houston, PhD(physics), 69. *Prof Exp:* Nuclear engr, Gen Dynamics/Ft Worth, 60-62; sr nuclear engr, Ling Temco Vought, Dallas, 62-63; PHYSICIST, JOHNSON SPACE CTR, NASA, 63- *Concurrent Pos:* Lectr, San Jacinto Col, Tex, 69-70; lectr, Univ Houston, 72-78. *Mem:* Am Phys Soc. *Res:* Atmospheric physics; catalytic attack of minor species on stratospheric ozone; institute measurements of ozone and other stratospheric species; measurement of vacuum ultraviolet photoabsorption cross section for gases of interest to atmospheric physics. *Mailing Add:* Mail Code SN3 NASA Lyndon B Johnson Space Ctr Houston TX 77058

ROBBINS, ERNEST ALECK, b Boy River, Minn, Mar 26, 26; m 46; c 6. BIOCHEMISTRY. *Educ:* Univ Minn, BChem, 51, PhD(biochem), 57. *Prof Exp:* Eng aide, State Hwy Dept, Minn, 49-51; asst, Univ Minn, 51-56; res chemist, Rohm and Haas Co, Pa, 56-71; head food biochem, 71-75, ASSOC DIR YEAST PROD RES, ANHEUSER-BUSCH INC, 75- *Mem:* Am Chem Soc; Am Asn Cereal Chem; Inst Food Technol. *Res:* Production, properties and utilization of enzymes from microorganisms; development of food and fermentation products. *Mailing Add:* 4429 Meadow Dr High Ridge MO 63049

ROBBINS, FREDERICK CHAPMAN, b Auburn, Ala, Aug 25, 16; m 48; c 2. PEDIATRICS. *Educ:* Univ Mo, BA, 36, BS, 38; Harvard Med Sch, MD, 40; Am Bd Pediat, dipl, 51. *Hon Degrees:* DSc, John Carroll Univ, 55 & Univ Mo, 58; LLD, Univ NMex, 68; DSc, Univ NC, Chapel Hill, 79. *Prof Exp:* Resident bact, Children's Hosp, 40-41, intern, 41-42, asst resident, 46-47, resident, 47-48; Nat Res Coun fel virus dis, Children's Hosp, Boston, 48-50; instr & assoc pediat, Harvard Med Sch, 50-52; prof pediat, Sch Med, Case Western Reserve Univ, 52-80, prof community health, 73-80, Dean, 66-80; PRES, INST MED-NAT ACAD SCI, 80- *Concurrent Pos:* Dir dept pediat, Cleveland Metrop Hosp, 52-66. *Honors & Awards:* Nobel Laureate Physiol & Med, 54. *Mem:* Nat Acad Sci; Am Philos Soc; Am Pediat Soc; Am Soc Clin Invest; Soc Exp Biol & Med. *Res:* Recognition and epidemiology of Q fever; immunology of mumps; tissue culture-poliomyelitis virus. *Mailing Add:* Inst Med-Nat Acad Sci 2101 Constitution Ave NW Washington DC 20418

ROBBINS, GORDON DANIEL, b Rocky Mount, NC, Feb 8, 40; m 67; c 2. ELECTROCHEMISTRY. *Educ:* Univ NC, BS, 62; Princeton Univ, MA, 64, PhD(electrochem), 66. *Prof Exp:* Fulbright fel, Molten Salts, Tech Univ Norway, 66-67; res chemist, 67-72, dir, Off Prof Univ Rels, 72-77, DIR, INFO DIV, OAK RIDGE NAT LAB, 78- *Mem:* Am Soc Info Sci. *Res:* Aqueous electrochemistry; thermodynamics, transport properties, electrochemistry and electrical conductivity of molten salts. *Mailing Add:* Oak Ridge Nat Lab Box X Oak Ridge TN 37830

ROBBINS, HERBERT ELLIS, b New Castle, Pa, Jan 12, 15; m 43, 66; c 5. MATHEMATICAL STATISTICS. *Educ:* Harvard Univ, AB, 35, AM, 36, PhD(math), 38. *Hon Degrees:* ScD, Purdue Univ, 74. *Prof Exp:* Instr & tutor math, Harvard Univ, 36-38; asst, Inst Advan Study, 38-39; instr math, NY Univ, 39-42; assoc prof math statist, Univ NC, 46-49, prof, 50-53; PROF MATH STATIST, COLUMBIA UNIV, 53- *Concurrent Pos:* Guggenheim fel, 52-53 & 75-76. *Mem:* Nat Acad Sci; fel Inst Math Statist (pres, 65-66); Int Statist Inst; Am Acad Arts & Sci. *Res:* Mathematical statistics, especially sequential experimentation; theory of probability. *Mailing Add:* Dept of Math Statist Columbia Univ New York NY 10027

ROBBINS, JACKIE WAYNE DARMON, b Spartanburg, SC, Feb 6, 40; m 63; c 2. AGRICULTURAL ENGINEERING, DRIP IRRIGATION. *Educ:* Clemson Univ, BS, 61, MS, 65; NC State Univ, PhD(biol & agr eng), 70. *Prof Exp:* E C McArthur fel, Clemson Univ, 62-63; asst prof agr eng, La State Univ, 63-65; res asst, NC State Univ, 65-68, res assoc biol & agr eng, 68-70; assoc prof agr eng, Univ Mo, 70-71; PROF AGR ENG & HEAD DEPT, LA TECH UNIV, 71- *Concurrent Pos:* NSF grant & vis prof, Univ Hawaii, 77-78; consult, Water Res Comn, Repub SAfrica, 81. *Mem:* Am Soc Agr Engrs; Am Soc Eng Educ; Sigma Xi; Irrigation Asn; Nat Soc Prof Engrs. *Res:* Agricultural waste and waste water management; soil and water conservation; groundwater hydrology; irrigation. *Mailing Add:* Dept of Agr Eng La Tech Univ Ruston LA 71272

ROBBINS, JACOB, b Yonkers, NY, Sept 1, 22; m 49; c 3. ENDOCRINOLOGY, MEDICAL RESEARCH. *Educ:* Cornell Univ, AB, 44, MD, 47; Am Bd Internal Med, dipl. *Prof Exp:* Intern med, NY Hosp, 47-48; res, Mem Hosp, 48-50; instr, Med Col, Cornell Univ, 50-54; res scientist, 54-62, CHIEF CLIN ENDOCRINOL BR, NAT INST ARTHRITIS, DIABETES, DIGESTIVE & KIDNEY DIS, 62- *Concurrent Pos:* Res fel, Sloan-Kettering Inst Cancer Res, 50-53, asst, 53-54, clin asst, Mem Ctr, 51-53, asst attend physician, 53-54; vis scientist, Calsberg Lab, Copenhagen, Denmark, 59-60. *Honors & Awards:* Van Meter Award, Am Thyroid Asn, 55. *Mem:* AAAS; Endocrine Soc; Am Soc Clin Invest; Am Physiol Soc; Am Thyroid Asn (pres, 74-75). *Res:* Thyroid physiology; biochemistry and disease. *Mailing Add:* Rm 8N315 Bldg 10 NIADDK/Nat Inst Health Bethesda MD 20014

ROBBINS, JAY HOWARD, b New York, NY, Feb 10, 34; m 61; c 3. CELL BIOLOGY, MEDICINE. *Educ:* Harvard Univ, AB, 56; Columbia Univ, MD, 60. *Prof Exp:* Intern, Mt Sinai Hosp, New York, 60-61, asst resident, 61-62, fel med, 63; res assoc, NIMH, 63-65; SR INVESTR, NAT CANCER INST, 65- *Mem:* Am Fedn Clin Res; Am Soc Cell Biol; AAAS; NY Acad Sci. *Res:* DNA repair and carcinogenesis; cell growth and differentiation; study of DNA-damaging agents of cultured cells from patients with degenerative neurological disease and/or with cancer. *Mailing Add:* Bldg 10 Rm 12 N-238 Nat Cancer Inst Bethesda MD 20014

ROBBINS, JOHN ALAN, b Syracuse, NY, Jan 19, 38; c 2. LIMNOLOGY, PHYSICS. *Educ:* Swarthmore Col, BA, 59; Univ Rochester, PhD(nuclear physics), 67. *Prof Exp:* Res assoc nuclear physics, Univ Rochester, 68-69; res assoc air chem, Dept Atmospheric Sci, Univ Mich, Ann

Arbor, 69-70; asst res physicist, Great Lakes Res Div, Univ Mich, Ann Arbor, 70-73, assoc res physicist, 73-76, sr res scientist limnol, 76-80; PHYSICIST, GREAT LAKES ENVIRON RES LAB, NAT OCEANIC & ATMOSPHERIC ADMIN, ANN ARBOR, MICH, 80- *Concurrent Pos:* Co-founder & consult, Environ Res Group, Inc, Ann Arbor, 70-; consult, Wildlife Supply Co, Saginaw, Mich, 74- & Radiol & Environ Res Div, Argonne Nat Lab, Ill, 78- *Mem:* AAAS; Am Soc Limnol & Oceanog; Int Asn Great Lakes; Sigma Xi. *Res:* Physics and chemistry of lakes; radiolimnology and sediment geochronology; radiotracer studies of animal-sediment interactions; mathematical modeling of limnological processes. *Mailing Add:* Great Lakes Environ Res Lab 2300 Washtenaw Ann Arbor MI 48104

ROBBINS, JOHN EDWARD, b Chamberlin, SDak, Apr 2, 35; m 58; c 1. BIOCHEMISTRY. *Educ:* Carroll Col, Mont, BA, 58; Mont State Univ, MS, 61, PhD(chem), 63. *Prof Exp:* NIH fel, Univ Ore, 63-66; asst prof, 67-70, assoc prof chem, 70-77, ASSOC PROF BIOCHEM, MONT STATE UNIV, 77- *Mem:* AAAS; Am Chem Soc. *Res:* Subunit structure of enzymes as related to their functional roles in enzyme functions of catalysis and control. *Mailing Add:* Dept of Chem Mont State Univ Bozeman MT 59715

ROBBINS, KENNETH CARL, b Chicago, Ill, Sept 1, 17; m 46; c 2. BIOCHEMISTRY. *Educ:* Univ Ill, BS, 39, MS, 40, PhD(biol chem), 44. *Prof Exp:* Asst physiol chem, Univ Ill, 41-44, instr biol chem, 44-47; asst prof immunochem, Western Reserve Univ, 47-51; head protein sect, Biochem Res Dept, Res Labs, Armour & Co, 51-56, sect head, Biochem Dept, Cent Labs, Res Div, 56-58; dir biochem res & develop dept, 58-73, SCI DIR, MICHAEL REESE RES FOUND, 73-; PROF MED & PATH, MICHAEL REESE RES FOUND, PRITZKER SCH MED, UNIV CHICAGO, 70- *Concurrent Pos:* Mem hemat study sect, Div Res Grants, NIH, 71-75 & 78-; chmn, Gordon Conf Hemostasis, 75; mem, Blood Diseases and Resources Adv Comt, Nat Heart, Lung & Blood Inst, NIH, 76-80; co-chmn, Subcom on Fibrinolysis, Int Comt on Thrombosis & Hemostasis, 77, chmn, 80- *Honors & Awards:* Elwood A Sharp Lect Award, Sch Med, Wayne State Univ; Prix Servier Medal & Prize, Fifth Int Congress Fibrinolysis, Malmo, Sweden, 80. *Mem:* Soc Exp Biol & Med; Am Chem Soc; Am Asn Immunol; Am Soc Biol Chem; Am Soc Hemat. *Res:* Blood coagulation and fibrinolysis; animal proteins and enzymes. *Mailing Add:* Michael Reese Res Found 530 E 31st St Chicago IL 60616

ROBBINS, LANNY ARNOLD, b Wahoo, Nebr, Apr 3, 40; m 62; c 2. CHEMICAL ENGINEERING. *Educ:* Iowa State Univ, BS, 61, MS, 63, PhD(chem eng), 66. *Prof Exp:* Chem engr, 66-67, res engr, 67-70, sr pilot plant engr, 70-72, res specialist, 72-73, sr res specialist, 73-76, assoc scientist, 76-79, SR ASSOC SCIENTIST, DOW CHEM CO, 79- *Concurrent Pos:* Adj prof, Mich State Univ, 82- *Mem:* Am Inst Chem Engrs; Sigma Xi. *Res:* Commercial separations and purification processes, with emphasis on melt crystallization, liquid-liquid extraction, packed tower strippers, absorbers and distillation; miniplant design and operation; commercial separation and purification processes. *Mailing Add:* Appl Process Res Dept Dow Chem USA Midland MI 48640

ROBBINS, LEONARD GILBERT, b Brooklyn, NY, Aug 10, 45; m 65; c 1. GENETICS. *Educ:* Brooklyn Col, BS, 65; Univ Wash, PhD(genetics), 70. *Prof Exp:* NIH trainee zool, Univ Tex, Austin, 70-72; asst prof, 72-76, ASSOC PROF ZOOL, MICH STATE UNIV, 77- *Concurrent Pos:* NIH-Fogarty sr int fel, Madrid, Spain, 80-81. *Mem:* Genetics Soc Am. *Res:* Formal and molecular genetics of higher organisms; maternal and zygotic gene action; genetic regulation of meiosis and of mitotic recombination in Drosophila. *Mailing Add:* 205 Biol Res Ctr Mich State Univ East Lansing MI 48824

ROBBINS, LOUISE MARIE, b Chicago, Ill, Oct 24, 28. PHYSICAL ANTHROPOLOGY. *Educ:* Ind Univ, AB, 60, MA, 63, PhD(anthrop), 68. *Prof Exp:* Instr anthrop, Univ Nebr, 63-64; instr, Univ Ky, 64-66, asst prof, 67-71; assoc prof, Miss State Univ, 71-74; ASSOC PROF ANTHROP, UNIV NC, GREENSBORO, 74- *Concurrent Pos:* Consult to var educ, law enforcement & sci orgn, 63-; Miss State Univ Off Res fac grant, Midwest USA, 72-73; res assoc, Dayton Mus Natural Hist, 75- *Mem:* AAAS; Am Asn Phys Anthrop; Soc Am Archaeol; Am Anthrop Asn; Am Acad Forensic Sci. *Res:* Human biocultural adaptation in prehistoric America; diet and disease relationships. *Mailing Add:* Dept of Anthrop Univ of NC Greensboro NC 27412

ROBBINS, MARION LERON, b Chesnee, SC, Aug 18, 41; m 65; c 4. HORTICULTURE, PLANT BREEDING. *Educ:* Clemson Univ, BS, 64; La State Univ, MS, 66; Univ Md, PhD(hort breeding), 68. *Prof Exp:* Asst prof hort, Iowa State Univ, 68-72; assoc prof, 72-79, PROF HORT, COASTAL EXP STA, CLEMSON UNIV, 79- *Concurrent Pos:* Assoc ed, Hort Res; contrib ed & columnist, Am Veg Grower & Greenhouse Grower; consult on veg prod & tea. *Mem:* Am Soc Hort Sci; Int Soc Hort Sci; Tropical Agr Asn. *Res:* Vegetable production research; breeding and physiology; influence of cultural practices on yield and quality of vegetables; tea as a crop for the United States. *Mailing Add:* Clemson Univ Coastal Exp Sta Box 30158 Charleston SC 29407

ROBBINS, MURRAY, b Brooklyn, NY, Mar 9, 31; m 54; c 1. INORGANIC CHEMISTRY. *Educ:* Brooklyn Col, BS, 53, MA, 54; Polytech Inst Brooklyn, PhD(inorg chem), 62. *Prof Exp:* Res chemist, Columbia Univ Mineral Beneficiation Labs, 53-54; instr inorg chem, Polytech Inst Brooklyn, 60-62; res chemist, David Sarnoff Res Labs, Radio Corp Am, 62-67; MEM TECH STAFF, BELL TEL LABS, INC, 67- *Mem:* Am Chem Soc; Am Phys Soc. *Res:* Synthesis and properties of solid state materials and crystal growth. *Mailing Add:* Bell Tel Labs Room 6F205 Murray Hill NJ 07974

ROBBINS, NAOMI BOGRAD, b Paterson, NJ, May 8, 37; m 62; c 2. STATISTICS. *Educ:* Bryn Mawr Col, AB, 58; Cornell Univ, MA, 62; Columbia Univ, PhD(math statist), 71. *Prof Exp:* MEM TECH STAFF, BELL LABS, 60- *Mem:* Am Statist Asn; Inst Math Statist. *Res:* Forecasting; data analysis. *Mailing Add:* 11 Christine Ct Wayne NJ 07470

ROBBINS, NORMAN, b Brooklyn, NY, Apr 15, 35. NEUROPHYSIOLOGY. *Educ:* Columbia Col, AB, 55; Harvard Univ, MD, 59; Rockefeller Univ, PhD(neurol), 66. *Prof Exp:* Intern med, 2nd Div, Bellevue Hosp, 59-60; jr asst resident med, Peter Bent Brigham Hosp, 60-61; fel neurobiol, Rockefeller Univ, 61-66; res assoc neurophysiol, Spinal Cord Div, Nat Inst Neurol Dis & Blindness, 66-69; vis scientist, Kyoto Prefectural Univ Med, 69-70; asst prof anat, 70-74, ASSOC PROF ANAT, SCH MED, CASE WESTERN RESERVE UNIV, 74- *Mem:* AAAS; Am Soc Cell Biol. *Res:* Neurobiology; physiology of development, plasticity and aging of the neuromuscular junction. *Mailing Add:* Dept of Anat Sch of Med Case Western Reserve Univ Cleveland OH 44106

ROBBINS, OMER ELLSWORTH, JR, b Detroit, Mich, Dec 18, 20; m 42; c 2. PHYSICAL CHEMISTRY. *Educ:* Univ Mich, BS, 42, MS, 47, PhD(phys chem), 50. *Prof Exp:* Res chemist, Dow Chem Co, 42-46 & Shell Oil Co, 50-53; vpres, Omer E Robbins Co, 53-58; asst prof chem, Heidelberg Col, 58-61; dean grad sch, 70-75 & 77-79, PROF CHEM, EASTERN MICH UNIV, 61- *Mem:* Am Chem Soc. *Mailing Add:* Dept of Chem Eastern Mich Univ Ypsilanti MI 48197

ROBBINS, PAUL EDWARD, b Camden, NJ, Apr 4, 28; m 54; c 3. ORGANIC CHEMISTRY. *Educ:* Univ Pa, BS, 52; Ga Inst Technol, PhD(chem), 56. *Prof Exp:* Res chemist, E I du Pont de Nemours & Co, 56-60; assoc prof textile chem, Clemson Univ, 60-66; assoc prof, 66-75, PROF CHEM, ARMSTRONG STATE COL, 75- *Mem:* Am Chem Soc; AAAS. *Res:* Catalytic hydrogenation; physical and synthetic organic chemistry; polymer chemistry and rheology; textile chemistry; films. *Mailing Add:* 14 Keystone Dr Savannah GA 31406

ROBBINS, PHILLIPS WESLEY, b Barre, Mass, Aug 10, 30; m 53; c 2. BIOCHEMISTRY. *Educ:* DePauw Univ, AB, 52; Univ Ill, PhD(biochem), 55. *Prof Exp:* Res assoc, Mass Gen Hosp, 55-57; asst prof, Rockefeller Inst, 57-59; from asst prof to assoc prof, 59-65, PROF BIOCHEM, MASS INST TECHNOL, 65- *Honors & Awards:* Eli Lilly Award Biol Chem, 66. *Mem:* Am Soc Biol Chem; Am Chem Soc; Am Acad Arts & Sci. *Res:* Sulfate activation; synthesis of complex polysaccharides; cell-virus relationships. *Mailing Add:* Dept of Biol Mass Inst of Technol Cambridge MA 02139

ROBBINS, R(OGER) W(ELLINGTON), b Belmont, Mass, July 25, 20; m 46; c 2. ELECTRICAL ENGINEERING. *Educ:* Univ Wis, BS, 42. *Prof Exp:* Elec draftsman, Jackson & Moreland, Mass, 42-43; field engr, Submarine Signal Co, 43, supvr tech div, Equip Dept, 43-45, asst admin engr, 45-46; res engr, Operadio Mfg Co, 46-51, proj engr, 51-53; mgr govt contracts div, 53-65, tech dir, Spec Prod Div, 65-70, ENG MGR, DUKANE CORP, 70- *Mem:* AAAS; Inst Elec & Electronics Engrs; Ultrasonic Indust Asn (pres, 75-77). *Res:* Devices which require the use of moving mechanical parts in conjunction with electrical circuits; optics; ultrasonics. *Mailing Add:* Dukane Corp 2900 Dukane Dr St Charles IL 60174

ROBBINS, RALPH COMPTON, b Spurrier, Tenn, Feb 7, 21; m 51. NUTRITION, PHYSIOLOGY. *Educ:* Tenn Technol Univ, BS, 52; Iowa State Univ, MS, 55; Univ Ill, PhD(nutrit), 58. *Prof Exp:* Res fel nutrit & biochem, Med Col SC, 58-59; asst prof nutrit, 59-66, ASSOC PROF NUTRIT, INST FOOD & AGR SCI, UNIV FLA, 66- *Mem:* Am Chem Soc. *Res:* Effectiveness in the diet of naturally occurring blood cell antiadhesive compounds against certain types of circulating dysfunction. *Mailing Add:* 409 FSB Univ of Fla Gainesville FL 32611

ROBBINS, RALPH ROBERT, b Wichita, Kans, Sept 2, 38. ASTROPHYSICS. *Educ:* Yale Univ, BA, 60; Univ Calif, Berkeley, PhD(astron), 66. *Prof Exp:* McDonald Observ fel, Univ Tex, Austin, 66-67; asst prof physics, Univ Houston, 67-68; asst prof astron, Univ Tex, 68-72, ASSOC PROF ASTRON, UNIV TEX, AUSTIN, 72- *Concurrent Pos:* Prin investr, NSF grant, Univ Tex Austin, 70-72; sci educ consult, AID. *Mem:* Am Astron Soc; Int Astron Union; fel Royal Astron Soc; Am Asn Physics Teachers. *Res:* Theoretical and observational astrophysics of gas nebulae and Seyfert galaxies; radiative transfer; atomic and plasma physics. *Mailing Add:* Dept Astron Univ Tex Austin TX 78712

ROBBINS, ROBERT, b Allentown, Pa, Feb 16, 18; m 44; c 2. MEDICINE. *Educ:* Temple Univ, AB, 40, MD, 43, MSc, 49. *Prof Exp:* Co-chmn dept radiol, Sch Med, 59-71, DIR RADIATION THER, UNIV HOSP, TEMPLE UNIV, 49-, PROF RADIOL, SCH MED, 56-, CHMN DEPT, 71- *Concurrent Pos:* Consult, St Christopher's Hosp Children & Skin & Cancer Hosp. *Mem:* AAAS; Radiol Soc NAm; Am Roentgen Ray Soc; Am Radium Soc. *Res:* Radiation therapy. *Mailing Add:* Temple Univ Hosp Broad & Ontario St Philadelphia PA 19140

ROBBINS, ROBERT JOHN, b Niles, Mich, May 10, 44. ECOLOGY. *Educ:* Stanford Univ, AB, 66; Mich State Univ, BS, 73, MS, 74, PhD(zool), 77. *Prof Exp:* Instr genetics, 76, ASST PROF BIOL SCI, MICH STATE UNIV, 77- *Concurrent Pos:* Fel, Univ Calif, Davis, 78-79. *Mem:* Am Inst Biol Sci; Ecol Soc Am; Philos Sci Asn; Psychonomic Soc. *Res:* Animal behavior; aspects of dietary selection with emphasis on learning. *Mailing Add:* Dept Zool Mich State Univ East Lansing MI 48824

ROBBINS, ROBERT KANNER, b New York, NY, Oct 26, 47. BIOLOGY, ECOLOGY. *Educ:* Brown Univ, AB, 69; Tufts Univ, PhD(biol), 78. *Prof Exp:* Fel biol, Smithsonian Trop Res Inst, 78-79; FEL BIOL, US NAT MUS, 81- *Mem:* Soc Study Evolution; Soc Am Naturalists; AAAS; Lepidopterists' Soc. *Res:* Evolution of insect species diversity; evolution of insect mating systems and predator-avoidance behaviors; heredity of behavior; statistical estimation of demographic parameters from field data; systematics of lepidoptera. *Mailing Add:* Dept Entom NHB 127 Smithsonian Inst Washington DC 20560

ROBBINS, ROBERT RAYMOND, b Des Moines, Iowa, May 28, 46. BOTANY, ULTRASTRUCTURE. *Educ:* Iowa State Univ, BS, 68; Univ Ill, Urbana, MS, 73. PhD(bot), 77. *Prof Exp:* Instr human anat, US Army Med Field Serv Sch, San Antonio, Tex, 69-71; lectr bot, Univ Ill, Urbana, 76, fel, 76-77; ASST PROF BOT, UNIV WIS-MILWAUKEE, 77- *Mem:* AAAS; Bot Soc Am; Am Bryol & Lichenological Soc; Am Inst Biol Sci; Am Fern Soc. *Res:* Ultrastructure of plant reproductive cells, especially bryophyte and lower vascular plant spermatogenesis; ragweed pollen development. *Mailing Add:* Dept of Bot PO Box 413 Milwaukee WI 53201

ROBBINS, WAYNE BRIAN, b Dayton, Ohio, Oct 12, 51; m 72. ANALYTICAL CHEMISTRY. *Educ:* Univ Cincinnati, BS, 75, MS, 77, PhD(anal chem), 78. *Prof Exp:* Asst prof chem, Utah State Univ, 78-79; RES SCIENTIST, UNION CAMP CORP, 79- *Mem:* Am Chem Soc; Soc Appl Spectros. *Res:* Methods development for atomic spectroscopic and chromatographic analyses. *Mailing Add:* Union Camp Corp PO Box 412 Princeton NJ 08540

ROBBINS, WILLIAM E, entomology, see previous edition

ROBBINS, WILLIAM PERRY, b Atlanta, Ga, May 29, 41; m 65. ELECTRICAL ENGINEERING. *Educ:* Mass Inst Technol, BSEE, 63, MSEE & Elec Engr, 65; Univ Wash, PhD(elec eng), 71. *Prof Exp:* Res engr, Boeing Co, 65-69; asst prof, 69-75, ASSOC PROF ELEC ENG, UNIV MINN, MINNEAPOLIS, 75- *Mem:* Am Inst Physics; Inst Elec & Electronics Engrs. *Res:* Acoustic surface wave properties and devices; active circuit design. *Mailing Add:* Dept of Elec Eng Univ of Minn 123 Church St Minneapolis MN 55455

ROBBLEE, ALEXANDER (ROBINSON), b Calgary, Alta, Jan 21, 19; m 44; c 4. POULTRY NUTRITION. *Educ:* Univ Alta, BSc, 44, MSc, 46; Univ Wis, PhD(poultry biochem), 48. *Prof Exp:* Govt agr fieldman, Dept Agr, Alta, 40-44; instr poultry nutrit, Univ Alta, 45-46 & Univ Wis, 47-48; from asst prof to assoc prof, 48-57, PROF POULTRY NUTRIT, UNIV ALTA, 57- *Mem:* Fel Poultry Sci Asn; fel Agr Inst Can; Worlds' Poultry Sci Asn; Can Soc Nutrit Sci. *Mailing Add:* Dept Animal Sci Univ Alta Edmonton AB T6G 2P5 Can

ROBE, THURLOW RICHARD, b Petersburg, Ohio, Jan 25, 34; m 55; c 4. ENGINEERING MECHANICS. *Educ:* Ohio Univ, BSCE, 55, MS, 62; Stanford Univ, PhD(eng), 66. *Prof Exp:* Engr, Lamp Div, Gen Elec Co, Ohio, 55, Locomotive & Car Equip Dept, Pa, 55-56, Flight Propulsion Lab, Ohio, 59-60; instr civil eng, Univ Ohio, 60-63; from asst prof to assoc prof eng mech, Univ KY, 65-75, prof, 75-80, assoc dean, Col Eng, 76-80. *Concurrent Pos:* Eng consult, Westinghouse Air Brake Co, 67-69; IBM Corp, 69-70. *Mem:* Am Soc Mech Engrs; Am Soc Eng Educ; Am Soc Civil Engrs. *Res:* Engineering mechanics with emphasis on analysis of dynamical systems. *Mailing Add:* 28 Canterbury Athens OH 45701

ROBEL, ROBERT JOSEPH, b Lansing, Mich, May 21, 33; m 60. APPLIED ECOLOGY. *Educ:* Mich State Univ, BS, 56; Univ Idaho, MS, 58; Utah State Univ, PhD(ecol), 61. *Prof Exp:* Biologist aide, Idaho Fish & Game Dept, 57-58; res asst ecol, Utah State Univ, 58-61; from asst prof to assoc prof biol, 61-71, PROF BIOL, KANS STATE UNIV, 71- *Concurrent Pos:* Aquatic biologist, Bear River Club Co, 58-61; governor's sci adv, 69-; chmn, Gov Energy & Natural Resources Coun; proj leader, US Congress Off of Technol Assessment. *Mem:* Fel AAAS; Wildlife Soc; Ecol Soc Am; Am Soc Mammal; Animal Behavior Soc. *Res:* Animal ecology with emphasis on avian population dynamics, comparative avian behavior, avian dispersal and movement patterns and avian bioenergetics; natural resources management; energy and environmental considerations, environmental assessments. *Mailing Add:* Div of Biol Kans State Univ Manhattan KS 66506

ROBEL, STEPHEN B(ERNARD), b Selah, Wash, Jan 29, 23; m 54; c 5. MECHANICAL ENGINEERING. *Educ:* Seattle Univ, BS, 48; Univ Notre Dame, MS, 51. *Prof Exp:* Instr math & physics, 48-49, from asst prof to assoc prof, 50-77, PROF MECH ENG, SEATTLE UNIV, 77- *Mem:* Am Soc Mech Engrs; Am Soc Eng Educ; Am Soc Artificial Internal Organs. *Res:* Thermodynamics; heat transfer; applied mechanics; cardiovascular research. *Mailing Add:* Dept of Mech Eng Seattle Univ Seattle WA 98122

ROBENS, JANE FLORENCE, b Utica, NY, July 23, 31. VETERINARY MEDICINE, TOXICOLOGY. *Educ:* Cornell Univ, DVM, 55; Am Bd Vet Toxicol, dipl. *Prof Exp:* Vet clinician, Ambassador Animal Hosp, 58-61; vet med officer, US Food & Drug Admin, 61-65; res vet, Div Toxicol Eval, 65-68; asst dir drug regulatory affairs, Hoffmann-La Roche Inc, 68-75; toxicologist, Cancer Bioassay Prog, Tracor Jitco, Inc, 75-79; chief, Animal Feed Safety Br, Food & Drug Admin, 79-80; PROG OFFICER FOOD SAFETY & HEALTH, AGR RES SERV, USDA, 81- *Concurrent Pos:* Assoc ed, Toxicol & Appl Pharmacol, 78- *Mem:* Am Vet Med Asn; Women's Vet Med Asn; Am Asn Lab Animal Sci; Soc Toxicol; Am Col Vet Toxicol. *Res:* Evaluation of the safety and efficacy of drugs used in veterinary medicine; teratological and carcinogenic potential of pesticides, drugs and other chemicals. *Mailing Add:* 5713 Lone Oak Dr Bethesda MD 20014

ROBERGE, ANDREE GROLEAU, b Quebec, Que, Aug 5, 38; m 60; c 4. BIOCHEMISTRY. *Educ:* Laval Univ, BSc, 60, DSc(biochem), 69. *Prof Exp:* Med Res Coun Can fel, McGill Univ, 69-70; Med Res Coun Can fel, 70-71, PROF NEUROCHEM, LABS NEUROBIOL, FAC MED & LAVAL UNIV, 71- *Concurrent Pos:* Med Res Coun Can grants, 71-76 & scholar, 73-78. *Mem:* AAAS; Can Biochem Soc; Am Soc Neurochem; Brit Biochem Soc; Soc Neurosci. *Res:* Catecholaminergic and serotoninergic metabolisms related to locomotor activity to stressfull situation and to treatment with L-Dopa and other drugs inhibiting or activating these metabolisms. *Mailing Add:* Dept Nutrit Humaine Laval Univ FSAA Quebec PQ G1K 7P4 Can

ROBERGE, FERNAND ADRIEN, b Thetford Mines, Que, June 11, 35; m 58; c 4. BIOMEDICAL ENGINEERING, CARDIOLOGY. *Educ:* Polytech Sch Montreal, BAS & Engr, 59, MScA, 60; McGill Univ, PhD(control eng, biomed eng), 64. *Prof Exp:* Develop engr numerical control, Sperry Gyroscope Co, Montreal, 60-61; lectr control eng, McGill Univ, 61-64, res assoc biophys, 64-65; from asst prof to assoc prof, 65-74, PROF PHYSIOL, FAC MED, UNIV MONTREAL, 74-, DIR BIOMED ENG, INST ECOLE POLYTECH, 78- *Concurrent Pos:* Mem res group neurol sci, Med Res Coun Can, Univ Montreal, 67-75; guest lectr, Univ Moncton, 71-72; mem, Sci Coun Can, 71-74; mem grant comt biomed eng, Med Res Coun Can, 71-76; mem sci comt, Can Heart Found, 74-77; mem, Killam Prog Can Coun, 74-77; mem elec eng comt, Nat Sci Eng Res Coun Can, 81-83. *Mem:* Inst Elec & Electronics Engrs; Can Physiol Soc; Can Med & Biol Eng Soc (vpres, 74-76); Int Fedn Med Electronics & Biol Eng; Biomed Eng Soc. *Res:* Membrane biophysics, oscillations and rhythms; physiology, especially cardiovascular regulation and control, cardiac arrhythmias; health care, especially computer applications, systems theory applications. *Mailing Add:* Inst de Genie Biomed PO Box 6208 Sta A Montreal PQ H3C 3T8 Can

ROBERGE, JAMES KERR, b Jersey City, NJ, June 13, 38; m 61; c 2. ELECTRICAL ENGINEERING. *Educ:* Mass Inst Technol, SB, 60, SM, 62, ScD(elec eng), 66. *Prof Exp:* Res asst, Mass Inst Technol, 60-62 & 63-66, staff mem, Lincoln Lab, 62-63, res assoc, 66-67, from asst prof to assoc prof, 67-76, PROF ELEC ENG, MASS INST TECHNOL, 76- *Concurrent Pos:* Consult, various companies, 60- *Mem:* Inst Elec & Electronics Engrs. *Res:* Electronic circuit design, particularly low power, high performance designs for difficult environments; control system design. *Mailing Add:* Dept of Elec Eng Mass Inst Technol Cambridge MA 02139

ROBERGE, MARCIEN ROMEO, b Quebec, PQ, Jan 19, 34; m 59; c 5. MICROBIOLOGY. *Educ:* Laval Univ, BSc, 59, MSc, 61, PhD(microbiol), 65. *Prof Exp:* RES SCIENTIST MICROBIOL OF FOREST SOILS, CAN FORESTRY SERV, DEPT ENVIRON, 59- *Mem:* Am Soc Agron; Can Soc Soil Sci; Can Soc Microbiol; Can Inst Forestry. *Res:* Effects of soil microbes and on their activities of various soil and forest treatments, such as fertilization, thinning, scarification and plantation. *Mailing Add:* Environ Can PO Box 3800 Ste-Foy PQ G1V 4C7 Can

ROBERSON, EDWARD LEE, b Tarboro, NC, June 10, 35; m 60; c 2. VETERINARY ANTHELMINTICS. *Educ:* Duke Univ, AB, 57, MAT, 65; Univ Ga, DVM, 61, PhD(parasitol), 72. *Prof Exp:* Teacher, Raleigh Pub Schs, NC, 63-66; NSF fel parasitol, NC State Univ, 66-67; res assoc path & parasitol, 67-70, instr parasitol, 70-73, asst prof parasitol, 73-77, ASSOC PROF PARASITOL, COL VET MED, UNIV GA, 77- *Mem:* Am Soc Parasitologists; Am Asn Vet Parasitologists (vpres, 77-79, pres, 79-81); Am Vet Med Asn; World Asn Advan Vet Parasitol. *Res:* Lactogenic and prenatal transmission and chemotherapy of veterinary helminths. *Mailing Add:* Dept Parasitol Univ Ga Col Vet Med Athens GA 30602

ROBERSON, ELBERT B, JR, organic chemistry, textiles, see previous edition

ROBERSON, HERMAN ELLIS, b Texarkana, Tex, Apr 27, 34; m 62; c 1. GEOLOGY, MINERALOGY. *Educ:* Univ Tex, BS, 55, MA, 57; Univ Ill, PhD(geol), 59. *Prof Exp:* From instr to assoc prof, 59-74, PROF GEOL & ENVIRON STUDIES, STATE UNIV NY BINGHAMTON, 74- *Mem:* AAAS; Mineral Soc Am; Soc Econ Paleont & Mineral; Mineral Soc Gt Brit. *Res:* Clay mineralogy; sedimentation. *Mailing Add:* Dept of Geol State Univ of NY Binghamton NY 13901

ROBERSON, JOHN A(RTHUR), b Woodland, Wash, June 4, 25; m 47; c 3. HYDRAULIC ENGINEERING. *Educ:* Wash State Univ, BS, 48; Univ Wis, MS, 50; Univ Iowa, PhD, 61. *Prof Exp:* Asst hydraul engr, Wash State Univ, 50-54; physicist hydrodyn res, US Naval Mine Defense Lab, 55-56; asst prof civil eng, Wash State Univ, 56-59, assoc prof, 59-66; prof, Seato Grad Sch Eng, Bangkok, 63-65; PROF CIVIL ENG, WASH STATE UNIV, 66-, ASSOC DEAN, RES & GRAD STUDIES, COL ENG, 81- *Mem:* Am Soc Civil Engrs; Am Soc Eng Educ; Int Asn Hydraulic Res. *Res:* Fluid mechanics and hydraulics. *Mailing Add:* Dept Civil Eng Wash State Univ Pullman WA 99163

ROBERSON, NATHAN RUSSELL, JR, b Robersonville, NC, Dec 13, 30; m 54; c 3. NUCLEAR PHYSICS. *Educ:* Univ NC, BS, 54, MS, 55; Johns Hopkins Univ, PhD(nuclear physics), 60. *Prof Exp:* Jr instr physics, Johns Hopkins Univ, 55-60; res assoc, Princeton Univ, 60-63; from asst prof to assoc prof, 63-74, PROF PHYSICS, DUKE UNIV, 74- *Concurrent Pos:* Mem bd dirs, Triangle Univs Comput Ctr, 75-80. *Mem:* Fel Am Phys Soc. *Res:* Nuclear spectroscopy; radiative capture reactions; use of electronic computers for data acquisition. *Mailing Add:* Dept of Physics Duke Univ Durham NC 27706

ROBERSON, PETER LEMMIE, nuclear physics, see previous edition

ROBERSON, ROBERT ERROL, b Cincinnati, Ohio, May 13, 23; m 43; c 3. DYNAMICS, SYSTEMS SCIENCE. *Educ:* Univ Chicago, BS, 43; George Washington Univ, MS, 46; Washington Univ, PhD(mech), 51. *Prof Exp:* PROF ENG SCI, UNIV CALIF, SAN DIEGO, 67- *Concurrent Pos:* Consult, 60- *Mem:* Fel AAAS; Am Inst Aeronaut & Astronaut; fel Am Astronaut Soc. *Res:* Dynamics and control of rotating systems; dynamic simulation. *Mailing Add:* Dept of Appl Mech & Eng Sci Univ of Calif San Diego La Jolla CA 92037

ROBERSON, ROBERT H, b Tuckerman, Ark, July 3, 28; m 51; c 6. POULTRY NUTRITION, BIOCHEMISTRY. *Educ:* Okla State Univ, BS, 51; Univ Ark, MS, 56; Mich State Univ, PhD(poultry nutrit, biochem), 59. *Prof Exp:* From asst prof to assoc prof, 59-74, PROF POULTRY NUTRIT, N MEX STATE UNIV, 74- *Mem:* Poultry Sci Asn; Am Inst Nutrit; World Poultry Sci Asn. *Res:* Mineral-zinc, calcium, protein and amino acids. *Mailing Add:* Dept of Animal Sci NMex State Univ Box 3I University Park NM 88003

ROBERSON, WARD BRYCE, b Hamilton, Ala, Jan 17, 39; m 68; c 1. PLANT PHYSIOLOGY. *Educ:* Harding Col, BA, 61; Utah State Univ, MS, 64, PhD(plant physiol), 67. *Prof Exp:* From asst prof to assoc prof, 66-78, PROF BIOL, HARDING UNIV, 78- *Mem:* AAAS. *Res:* Membrane permeability; plant water relations. *Mailing Add:* Dept of Biol Sci Harding Univ Searcy AR 72143

ROBERT, ANDRE, b Montreal, Que, Oct 6, 26; m 51; c 4. ENDOCRINOLOGY. *Educ:* Univ Montreal, BA, 44, MD, 50, PhD(exp med), 58. *Prof Exp:* Asst, Inst Exp Med & Surg, Univ Montreal, 50-52, asst prof endocrinol, Sch Med, 52-55; SR SCIENTIST, UPJOHN CO, 55- *Concurrent Pos:* Guest scientist, NIH, 60-61; vis scientist, Ctr Ulcer Res & Educ, Los Angeles, 80-81. *Mem:* Soc Exp Biol & Med; Am Gastroenterol Asn; Am Physiol Soc. *Res:* Peptic ulcer; hormones and inflammation; gastric secretion; prostaglandins; gastroenterology. *Mailing Add:* Upjohn Co Kalamazoo MI 49001

ROBERT, EMERY DEAN, neurology, radiology, see previous edition

ROBERT, KEARNY QUINN, JR, b Liberty, Tex, June 12, 43; m 68; c 3. PHYSICS, ENGINEERING. *Educ:* Tulane Univ, BA, 65, BS, 65, PhD(physics), 70. *Prof Exp:* Asst physics, Tulane Univ, 66-70; res physicist, Gulf South Res Inst, 70-76; RES PHYSICIST, USDA SOUTHERN REGIONAL RES CTR, 77- *Concurrent Pos:* Lectr physics, St Mary's Dominican Col, 66; res consult, Physics Dept, Tulane Univ, 72-76, adj asst prof, Sch Eng, 76- *Mem:* Am Phys Soc; Am Asn Physics Teachers; Health Physics Soc; Am Soc Nondestructive Testing; Int Asn Math & Comput Simulation. *Res:* Environmental health sciences; radiological health and health physics; industrial hygiene; medical diagnostics; nondestructive testing; computer simulation; textile engineering; dust control; nuclear physics. *Mailing Add:* USDA Sci & Educ Admin PO Box 19687 New Orleans LA 70179

ROBERTI, DOMINIC M, physical chemistry, see previous edition

ROBERTS, A(LBERT) S(IDNEY), JR, b Washington, NC, Sept 16, 35; m 57; c 4. MECHANICAL & NUCLEAR ENGINEERING. *Educ:* NC State Univ, BS, 57, PhD(nuclear eng, plasma physics), 65; Univ Pittsburgh, MS, 59. *Prof Exp:* Assoc engr, Bettis Atomic Power Lab, Westinghouse Elec Corp, 57-60; res asst exp plasma physics, Plasma Physics Lab, NC State Univ, 61-65; from asst prof to assoc prof thermal eng, chmn & grad prog dir, thermal eng group, 72, assoc dean eng, 74-77, PROF MECH ENG, OLD DOMINION UNIV, 72- *Concurrent Pos:* Consult, NASA, 66-; guest res engr, AB Atomenergi, Studsvik, Sweden, 68-69. *Mem:* AAAS; Am Soc Eng Educ; Am Soc Mech Engrs. *Res:* Thermodynamics; physical gas dynamics; plasma energy conversion methods; nuclear power reactors; solar energy conversion. *Mailing Add:* 5437 Glenhaven Crescent Norfolk VA 23508

ROBERTS, A WAYNE, b Chicago, Ill, Aug 29, 34; m 56; c 3. MATHEMATICS. *Educ:* Ill Inst Technol, BS, 56; Univ Wis, MS, 58, PhD(math), 65. *Prof Exp:* Instr math, Morton Jr Col, 58-62; teaching asst, Univ Wis-Madison, 62-65; PROF MATH, MACALESTER COL, 65- *Mem:* Math Asn Am; Am Math Soc. *Res:* Mathematical analysis; convex functions; optimization theory. *Mailing Add:* Dept of Math Macalester Col St Paul MN 55105

ROBERTS, ALFRED NATHAN, b Welsh, La, Nov 6, 17; m 39; c 3. HORTICULTURE. *Educ:* Ore State Univ, BS, 39, MS, 41; Mich State Univ, PhD(hort), 53. *Prof Exp:* Asst, 39-41, from instr to assoc prof, 41-57, prof, 57-80, EMER PROF HORT, ORE STATE UNIV, 80- *Honors & Awards:* Alex Laurie Award, Am Soc Hort Sci, 65; Stark Award, 68; Colman Award, 72; J H Gourley Medal, 77. *Mem:* Fel Am Soc Hort Sci; Int Plant Propagator's Soc; Int Hort Soc; Scand Soc Plant Physiol. *Res:* Ornamental plant physiology, growth and development; bulbcrop physiology; root regeneration physiology. *Mailing Add:* Dept of Hort Ore State Univ Corvallis OR 97331

ROBERTS, AMMARETTE, b Oakalla, Tex, June 24, 23. CHEMISTRY. *Educ:* Mary Hardin-Baylor Col, BA, 43. *Prof Exp:* Asst chemist, Magnolia Petrol Co, Tex, 43-46; jr chemist, Socony Oil Co, NJ, 46-47, Tex Res Found, 47-51 & Wadley Res Inst & Blood Bank, 51-56; librn-abstractor, Lone Star Gas Co, 56-66; mgr info serv, 66-69; MGR TECH INFO, MOBIL RES & DEVELOP CORP, 69- *Mem:* Am Chem Soc; Sigma Xi; Am Soc Info Sci; Spec Libr Asn; Am Rec Mgt Asn. *Res:* Organic synthesis using radioactive tracers; chemical studies of oil bearing seeds; blood coagulation; clinical applications of radioisotopes; information sciences; development of computerized system for retrieving scientific information with emphasis on internal information not appearing in open literature. *Mailing Add:* Mobil Res & Develop Corp PO Box 900 Dallas TX 75221

ROBERTS, AUDREY NADINE, b Lawrence, Kans, Jan 12, 35. IMMUNOLOGY, VIROLOGY. *Educ:* Univ Kans, AB, 55, MA, 57, PhD(microbiol biol, biochem), 59. *Prof Exp:* Asst microbiol, Univ Kans, 55-59; USPHS res assoc, Ind Univ, 59-61; instr immunol & virol, Col Med, 61-62; asst prof prev med, 62-66, assoc prof microbiol, 66-73, PROF MICROBIOL, UNIV TENN MED UNITS, MEMPHIS, 73-, DEP CHMN, 77- *Concurrent Pos:* Prin investr, Nat Inst Allergy & Infectious Dis grants, 61-, Nat Inst Allergy & Infectious Dis career develop award, 64- *Mem:* AAAS; Am Soc Microbiol; Am Pub Health Asn; Am Asn Immunol; NY Acad Sci. *Res:* Quantitation of mechanisms of immune responses in vivo and in vitro utilizing autoradiography, immunochemistry, radiochemistry, tissue culture, cytochemistry and fluorescence microscopy; enterovirus and respiratory virus diseases; cellular immunity and cytochemistry of virus infected cells. *Mailing Add:* Dept of Microbiol Univ of Tenn Med Units Memphis TN 38163

ROBERTS, BENJAMIN WASHINGTON, JR, solid state physics, deceased

ROBERTS, BRADLEY LEE, b Bristol, Va, Aug 11, 46. INTERMEDIATE ENERGY PHYSICS. *Educ:* Univ Va, BS, 68; Col William & Mary, MS, 70, PhD(physics), 74. *Prof Exp:* Res assoc medium energy nuclear physics, Sci Res Coun, Rutherford Lab, Chilton, Eng, 74-76 & Lab Nuclear Sci, Mass Inst Technol, 76-77; ASST PROF PHYSICS, BOSTON UNIV, 77- *Concurrent Pos:* Guest asst physicist, Brookhaven Nat Lab, 76-; co-prin investr, NSF grant photopion studies in complex nuclei, 77-; res affil, Lab Nuclear Sci, Mass Inst Technol, 78-; co prin investr, NSF grant exotic atom studies. *Mem:* AAAS; Am Phys Soc; Fedn Am Scientists; Sigma Xi. *Res:* Intermediate energy nuclear and particle physics; exotic atoms; photopion reactions; high energy photo proton studies; pion physics; kaon physics. *Mailing Add:* Dept of Physics 111 Cummington St Boston MA 02215

ROBERTS, BRUCE R, b Leonia, NJ, May 19, 33; m 56; c 2. PLANT PHYSIOLOGY. *Educ:* Gettysburg Col, AB, 56; Duke Univ, MF, 60, PhD(plant physiol), 63. *Prof Exp:* RES PLANT PHYSIOLOGIST, SHADE TREE LAB, USDA, 63- *Concurrent Pos:* Adj prof, Ohio Wesleyan Univ. *Honors & Awards:* Int Soc Arboricult Res Award, 75. *Mem:* Am Soc Plant Physiol; Sigma Xi; Am Soc Hort Sci; hon life mem Int Soc Arboricult. *Res:* Plant and tree physiology; water relations; physiological response to plant stress. *Mailing Add:* USDA Agr Res Serv Box 365 Delaware OH 43015

ROBERTS, BRYAN WILSON, b Pinehurst, NC, Feb 12, 38; m 60; c 2. ORGANIC CHEMISTRY. *Educ:* Univ NC, BS, 60; Stanford Univ, PhD(org chem), 64. *Prof Exp:* Nat Acad Sci-Nat Res Coun fel, Calif Inst Technol, 63-64; asst prof chem, Univ Southern Calif, 64-67; asst prof, 67-70, assoc prof, 70-81, asst chmn dept chem, 73-77, PROF CHEM, UNIV PA, 81-, CHMN DEPT, 81- *Mem:* Am Chem Soc; Royal Soc Chem. *Res:* Synthetic organic chemistry; synthesis of natural products and of molecular systems of theoretical interest. *Mailing Add:* Dept of Chem Univ of Pa Philadelphia PA 19104

ROBERTS, C SHELDON, b Rupert, Vt, Oct 27, 26; m 50; c 3. MATERIALS SCIENCE & ENGINEERING. *Educ:* Rensselaer Polytech Inst, BMetE, 48; Mass Inst Technol, SM, 49, ScD(metall), 52. *Prof Exp:* Res metallurgist, Dow Chem Co, Mich, 51-56; mem sr staff, Semiconductor Lab, Beckman Instrument Corp, Calif, 56-57; head mat res & develop, Fairchild Semiconductor Corp, 57-61; head mat, Amelco Semiconductor Div, Teledyne, Inc, 61-63; CONSULT MAT & PROCESSES, 63- *Concurrent Pos:* Pres, Timelapse Inc, 71-74; trustee, Rensselaer Polytech Inst, 72- *Honors & Awards:* Alfred Noble Award, 54. *Mem:* Metall Soc; Electrochem Soc; Am Phys Soc; Inst Elec & Electronics Engrs; Sigma Xi. *Res:* Deformation and fracture of metals; materials processing technology; magnesium and its alloys; semiconductor materials development; material processing technology; behavior of solid state electronic devices; failure analysis of engineering materials. *Mailing Add:* 8074 Winery Ct San Jose CA 95135

ROBERTS, CARLETON W, b Brooklyn, NY, Apr 29, 21; m 56; c 3. ORGANIC CHEMISTRY. *Educ:* NY Univ, BA, 43; Polytech Inst Brooklyn, MS, 47, PhD(org chem), 50. *Prof Exp:* Chemist, E Bilhuber, Inc, 43-46; asst, Polytech Inst Brooklyn, 46-49; sr res chemist, Colgate-Palmolive-Peet Co, 50-51; researcher biochem, Med Col, Cornell Univ, 51-53; asst prof chem, Purdue Univ, 53-56; assoc scientist, Polymer & Chem Res Lab, Dow Chem Co, 56-70; assoc prof textiles, 70-76, prof, 76-81, EMER PROF POLYMERS & TEXTILE CHEM, CLEMSON UNIV, 82- *Concurrent Pos:* Mem adv bd mil personnel supplies, Comt Textile Functional Finishing, 60-74 & 78-81; mem adv sci comt, Saginaw Valley Col, 66-70. *Mem:* Fel AAAS; Am Chem Soc; fel NY Acad Sci; Harvey Soc; Royal Soc Chem. *Res:* Halogen-containing carbon compounds; nitrogen heterocycles; polymers and plastics; polyesters; fire-retardant chemicals and plastics; agricultural chemicals; structure and physical properties; textile dyeing and finishing; polymer degradation. *Mailing Add:* Dept of Textiles Clemson Univ Clemson SC 29631

ROBERTS, CARLYLE JONES, b Philadelphia, Pa, Apr 13, 28; m 50; c 4. HEALTH PHYSICS. *Educ:* Lehigh Univ, BS, 50; Univ Rochester, PhD(biophys), 54. *Prof Exp:* Asst, Univ Rochester, 50-51, res assoc, 53-54; health physicist, Nuclear Power Dept, Curtiss-Wright Corp, 54-57, chief res reactor div, 57-58; res assoc prof appl biol & assoc dir reactor proj, Ga Inst Technol, 58-63, head nuclear res ctr, 63-65, prof nuclear eng, dir sch & chief nuclear sci div, Eng Exp Sta, 65-71, chief biol sci div, 70-71; chief training sect, Int AEC, 71-73; prof nuclear eng, Ga Inst Technol, 73-77; MEM STAFF, ARGONNE NAT LAB, 77- *Concurrent Pos:* Mem, Am Bd Health Physics, 75- *Mem:* AAAS; Health Physics Soc; Am Nuclear Soc. *Res:* Radiobiology; nuclear engineering. *Mailing Add:* Argonne Nat Lab 9700 S Cass Ave Argonne IL 60439

ROBERTS, CARMEL MONTGOMERY, b Atherton, Australia, Apr 5, 28; m 60; c 2. PHARMACOLOGY. *Educ:* Univ Queensland, BS, 48; Univ Southern Calif, MS, 50, PhD, 56. *Prof Exp:* Lectr biochem, Univ Melbourne, 57; asst prof pharmacol, 58-65, ASSOC PROF PHARMACOL, SCH MED, UNIV SOUTHERN CALIF, 65- *Concurrent Pos:* Consult, Los Angeles County Hosp; mem pharmacol-toxicol res prog comt, NIH, 77-81. *Mem:* Am Soc Cell Biol. *Res:* Pharmacology in relationship to mechanism of drug action at the cellular level; metabolism of fetal heart and drug effects on fetal heart metabolism; ionic basis of the electrical potential of cardiac cells; metabolism of the cardiac cell membrane; topography of receptor groups for acetylcholine on cardiac cell. *Mailing Add:* Dept of Pharmacol & Nutrit Univ of Southern Calif Sch of Med Los Angeles CA 90033

ROBERTS, CHARLES A, JR, b Changsha, China, Oct 21, 25; US citizen; m; c 5. THEORETICAL PHYSICS. *Educ:* Univ Calif, Los Angeles, BS, 49; Univ Southern Calif, MS, 51; Univ Md, PhD(physics), 56. *Prof Exp:* Physicist, Physics Naval Res Lab, Washington, DC, 52-53; chmn dept, 56-70, PROF PHYSICS, CALIF STATE UNIV, LONG BEACH, 56- *Concurrent Pos:* Res Corp grant theoret physics, 58-60; NSF grant, 62-64; NSF fel, Brussels, 64-65; consult, Naval Ord Lab, Calif, Douglas Aircraft Co & Aeroneutronics; sr Fulbright award, Dept State, 74- *Mem:* Am Phys Soc. *Res:* Nonequilibrium statistical mechanics applied to the field of plasma physics; equilibrium statistical mechanics; interaction of electromagnetic waves with plasmas; elastic surface waves in solids. *Mailing Add:* Dept of Physics Calif State Univ Long Beach CA 90804

ROBERTS, CHARLES BROCKWAY, b Kansas City, Mo, July 31, 18; m 46; c 3. INORGANIC CHEMISTRY, ANALYTICAL CHEMISTRY. *Educ:* Univ Alta, BSc, 40; Univ Ark, MS, 50; Univ Ill, PhD(anal chem), 56. *Prof Exp:* Explosives chemist, Kankakee Ord Works, US Civil Serv, 41-43; chemist, Ethyl Corp, 43-46; teacher & prin pub schs, Ark, 47-53; asst anal chem, Univ Ill, 53-56; anal chemist, Dow Chem Co, 56-59, anal specialist, 59-63, sr res chemist, 63-72, sr res specialist, 72-79, quality control supvr, 79-82; RETIRED. *Mem:* Am Chem Soc; Sigma Xi. *Res:* analytical methods development. *Mailing Add:* Dow Chem Co Bldg 1038 Midland MI 48640

ROBERTS, CHARLES DEWITT, b Atlanta, Ga, Nov 17, 38; m 63. MATHEMATICAL STATISTICS, APPLIED STATISTICS. *Educ:* Ga Inst Technol, BS, 60; Univ NC, PhD(math statist), 63. *Prof Exp:* Teacher, Dept Math, Ga Inst Technol, 59-60; fel, Dept Biostatist, Univ NC, 63; statistician, Nat Inst Arthritis & Metab Dis, 63-65 & Inst Nutrit Cent Am & Panama, 65-67; asst prof statist, Grad Sch Bus Admin, NY Univ, 67-69; math statistician, Div Statist, Bur Drugs, Food & Drug Admin, 69-73; STATISTICIAN, SMITHSONIAN INST, 73- *Concurrent Pos:* Mem, Inter-Am Statist Inst. *Mem:* Am Statist Asn; Biomet Soc; Sigma Xi. *Res:* Pure mathematical research, applications to biology, natural sciences, health, business and associated fields. *Mailing Add:* Smithsonian Inst 900 Jefferson Dr SW Washington DC 20560

ROBERTS, CHARLES SHELDON, b Newark, NJ, Sept 25, 37; m 59; c 2. OPERATING SYSTEMS, DATA MANAGEMENT. *Educ:* Carnegie Inst Technol, BS, 59; Mass Inst Technol, PhD(physics), 63. *Prof Exp:* Mem tech staff, 63-69, head comput technol dept, 69-70 & info processing res dept, 70-72, HEAD INTERACTIVE COMPUT SYSTS RES DEPT, BELL LABS, 72- *Mem:* Am Phys Soc; Asn Comput Mach; Inst Elec & Electronics Engrs; Sigma Xi. *Res:* Theory of molecular scattering; theory of plasmas; physics of the Van Allen belts and the earth's magnetosphere; experiments aboard earth satellites to measure particles and electromagnetic waves; computer operating systems and software systems. *Mailing Add:* Bell Labs Holmdel NJ 07733

ROBERTS, CLARENCE RICHARD, b Cushing, Okla, May 4, 26; m 51; c 4. HORTICULTURE, PLANT PHYSIOLOGY. *Educ:* Okla State Univ, BS, 49, MS, 51; Tex A&M Univ, PhD(hort), 64. *Prof Exp:* Asst county agt, Okla State Univ, 50-54; exten horticulturist, Kans State Univ, 54-67; EXTEN HORTICULTURIST, UNIV KY, 67- *Mem:* Am Soc Hort Sci. *Res:* Nutrition of vegetable crops; post harvest physiology studies. *Mailing Add:* Dept of Hort Univ of Ky Lexington KY 40506

ROBERTS, DANIEL ALTMAN, b Micanopy, Fla, Jan 8, 22; m 44; c 3. PLANT PATHOLOGY. *Educ:* Univ Fla, BS, 43, MS, 48; Cornell Univ, PhD(plant path), 51. *Prof Exp:* Asst plant path, Cornell Univ, 48-51, from asst prof to assoc prof, 51-59; assoc prof, 59-64, PROF PLANT PATH, UNIV FLA, 64- *Concurrent Pos:* Guggenheim fel, 58. *Mem:* Am Phytopath Soc. *Res:* Physiology of plant viral infections; diseases of alfalfa. *Mailing Add:* Dept of Plant Path Univ of Fla Gainesville FL 32611

ROBERTS, DANIEL KEITH, obstetrics & gynecology, see previous edition

ROBERTS, DARRELL LYNN, b Xenia, Ohio, Oct 8, 39; m 61; c 3. AGRICULTURAL & HUMAN ENGINEERING. *Educ:* Univ Fla, BAE, 62; NC State Univ, MS, 64, PhD(agr eng), 70. *Prof Exp:* Sr engr, Martin Co, Md, 65-66; res instr agr eng, NC State Univ, 66-70; from asst prof to assoc prof, La State Univ, Baton Rouge, 70-76; assoc prof, 76-80, PROF AGR ENG, CLEMSON UNIV, 80- *Mem:* Am Soc Agr Engrs; Sigma Xi. *Res:* Safety for agricultural workers; man-machine engineering; machinery management; environmental control; energy management and renewable energy. *Mailing Add:* 222 McAdams Hall Clemson Univ Clemson SC 29631

ROBERTS, DAVID, biomechanics, see previous edition

ROBERTS, DAVID CRAIG, b Madison, Wis, Feb 21, 48; m 79. PEPTIDE CHEMISTRY, BIOPHYSICAL CHEMISTRY. *Educ:* Univ Wis, BA, 70; Mass Inst Technol, PhD(org chem), 75. *Prof Exp:* Fel, Univ Calif, Los Angeles, 75-77; ASST PROF CHEM, RUTGERS UNIV, 77- *Mem:* Am Chem Soc; Synthesis of peptide hormone analogs with unusual side-chain and backbone functionality; development of peptidase inhibitors; statistical studies of protein crystal structure data; synthesis of conformationally restricted polymers. *Mailing Add:* Dept Chem Rutgers Univ New Brunswick NJ 08903

ROBERTS, DAVID HALL, b Washington, DC, Feb 4, 47; m 74; c 1. RADIO ASTRONOMY, THEORETICAL ASTROPHYSICS. *Educ:* Amherst Col, AB, 69; Stanford Univ, PhD(physics), 73. *Prof Exp:* Res assoc physics, Univ Ill, Urbana, 73-75; res physicist, Univ Calif, San Diego, 75-78; res scientist, Res Lab Electronics, Mass Inst Technol, 78-79; ASST PROF ASTROPHYSICS, BRANDEIS UNIV, 79- *Concurrent Pos:* Vis scientist, Res Lab Electronics, Mass Inst Technol, 79- *Mem:* Am Phys Soc; Am Astron Soc; Sigma Xi; Int Astron Union. *Res:* Non-thermal phenomena in galactic and extragalactic objects; radio astronomy; interferometry; pulsars, quasars, radio sources. *Mailing Add:* Dept Physics Brandeis Univ Waltham MA 02254

ROBERTS, DAVID LLEWELLYN, astrophysics, physics, see previous edition

ROBERTS, DAVID WILFRED ALAN, b Yeadon, Eng, Sept 21, 21; m 60; c 1. PLANT PHYSIOLOGY, BIOCHEMISTRY. *Educ:* Univ Toronto, BA, 42, PhD(plant physiol), 48. *Prof Exp:* Res assoc, Nat Cancer Inst Can, Toronto, 48-49; PLANT PHYSIOLOGIST, RES STA, CAN DEPT AGR, 49- *Mem:* AAAS; Am Soc Plant Physiol; Soc Cryobiol; Can Soc Plant Physiol. *Res:* Enzymology; cold resistance. *Mailing Add:* Can Agr Res Sta Lethbridge AB T1J 4B1 Can

ROBERTS, DEWAYNE, b Okla, Sept 7, 27; m 51; c 3. BIOCHEMICAL PHARMACOLOGY. *Educ:* Okla State Univ, BS; Wash Univ, PhD. *Prof Exp:* Res scientist, Roswell Park Mem Inst, 57-62; asst chief biochem pharmacol, Children's Cancer Res Found, Boston, 62-68; MEM, DEPT PRECLIN & CLIN PHARMACOL, ST JUDE CHILDREN'S RES HOSP, 68- *Concurrent Pos:* Res assoc, Grad Dept Biochem, Brandeis Univ, 62-65; res assoc, Harvard Med Sch, 62-68; adj prof biol, Northeastern Univ, 66-67; assoc prof pharmacol, Univ Tenn, Memphis, 68- *Mem:* Am Asn Cancer Res; Am Soc Pharmacol & Exp Therapeut; Am Fedn Clin Res. *Res:* Biochemistry of nucleic acid precursors and the effect of drugs on their biosyntheses in relation to cancer chemotherapy. *Mailing Add:* St Jude Children's Res Hosp PO Box 318 Memphis TN 38101

ROBERTS, DONALD DUANE, b Jamestown, NDak, Feb 18, 29; m 52; c 5. PHYSICAL ORGANIC CHEMISTRY. *Educ:* Jamestown Col, BS, 50; Loyola Univ, MS, 57, PhD(org chem), 62. *Prof Exp:* Res chemist, Sherwin Williams Co, 52-54; group leader polymer chem, Borg-Warner Corp, 54-58; asst proj chemist, Am Oil Co, 58-60; res assoc org chem, Plastics Div, Allied Chem Corp, 62-63; assoc prof chem, 63-74, PROF CHEM, LA TECH UNIV, 74- *Concurrent Pos:* Res Corp grant, 64-65; Petrol Res Fund grant, 66-68; NSF grant, 69-71. *Mem:* Am Chem Soc; Sigma Xi. *Res:* Cyclopropylcarbinyl system; solvent effects; medium size rings; linear free energy relationships. *Mailing Add:* Dept of Chem La Tech Univ Ruston LA 71270

ROBERTS, DONALD RAY, b Purcell, Okla, Mar 26, 42; m 67; c 2. MEDICAL ENTOMOLOGY, POPULATION DYNAMICS. *Educ:* Univ Mo-Columbia, BA, 65, MS, 66; Univ Tex, PhD(entom), 73. *Prof Exp:* Staff entomologist, USARSUPTHAI Command, Thailand, 68-69; med entomologist, US Army Environ Hyg Agency, Md, 69-70; med entomologist, US Army Med Res Unit, Belem, Brazil, 73-75, chief med res, 75-78, entomologist, US Army Med Res Unit, Brasilia, Brazil, 78-80; CHIEF, DEPT ENTOM, WALTER REED ARMY INST, 80- *Concurrent Pos:* Consult med entom, Pan Am Health Orgn, 73-78; prof med entom, Univ Brasilia, 78- *Mem:* Am Soc Trop Med & Hyg; Entom Soc Am; Am Mosquito Control Asn; Soc Brasileira Medicina Tropical; Soc Brasiliera Entomologia. *Mailing Add:* USAMRU-Brasilia c/o Am Embassy APO Miami FL 34030

ROBERTS, DONALD RAY, b Trenton, Tenn, Dec 21, 29; m 57; c 3. PLANT PHYSIOLOGY, WEED SCIENCE. *Educ:* Univ Tenn, BSA, 52, MS, 59; Auburn Univ, PhD(bot), 66. *Prof Exp:* Instr agron, Univ Tenn, 57-59; asst bot, Auburn Univ, 60-63; PLANT PHYSIOLOGIST, SOUTHEASTERN FOREST EXP STA, US FOREST SERV, 63- *Mem:* Am Soc Plant Physiologists; Soc Am Foresters. *Res:* Lightwood induction research; herbicide physiology, especially metabolism of atrazine; biosynthesis of oleoresin in slash pine and physiology of pine oleoresin extraction. *Mailing Add:* Southeastern Forest Exp Sta PO Box 70 Olustee FL 32072

ROBERTS, DONALD WILSON, b Phoenix, Ariz, Jan 20, 33; m 59; c 2. INSECT PATHOLOGY. *Educ:* Brigham Young Univ, BS, 57; Iowa State Univ, MS, 59; Univ Calif, Berkeley, PhD(entom), 64. *Prof Exp:* NSF fel, Swiss Fed Inst Technol, 64-65; asst entomologist, 65-69, assoc insect pathologist, 70-73, INSECT PATHOLOGIST, BOYCE THOMPSON INST PLANT RES, 74-, COORDR, INSECT PATH RESOURCE CTR, 79- *Concurrent Pos:* USPHS res grants, 66-76; consult, WHO, 74-78, res grants, 75-82; USDA res grants, 76-82; US-India exchange scientist, 78; consult, Brazil gov, 78-82, US Nat Acad Sci-Nat Res Coun, 76-77, US Agency Int Develop grant, 81-85. *Mem:* AAAS; Entom Soc Am; Am Soc Microbiol; Mycol Soc Am; Int Orgn Biol Control. *Res:* Insect mycoses, particularly mechanisms used by fungi to overcome insects; toxins produced by insect-infecting fungi; pathogens of mosquito larvae; pox-like viruses of insects; integration of pathogens into pest management programs in developing nations. *Mailing Add:* Boyce Thompson Inst Plant Res Cornell Univ Tower Rd Ithaca NY 14853

ROBERTS, DORIS EMMA, b Toledo, Ohio, Dec 28, 15. PUBLIC HEALTH. *Educ:* Peter Bent Brigham Sch Nursing, dipl nursing, 38; Geneva Col, BS, 44; Univ Minn, MPH, 58; Univ NC, PhD, 67. *Prof Exp:* Staff nurse, Vis Nurse Asn, New Haven, 38-40; sr nurse, Neighborhood House, Millburn, NJ, 42-45; supvr tuberc, Baltimore County Dept Health, Towson, Md, 45-46; tuberc consult, Md State Dept Health, 46-50; consult & chief nurse tuberc prog, USPHS, 50-57, consult div nursing, 58-63; chief nursing pract br, Health Resources Admin, HEW, 66-75; CONSULT, 75- *Concurrent Pos:* Comt officer, USPHS, 45-75; adj prof pub health nursing, Univ NC, Chapel Hill, 75-; consult, WHO. *Mem:* Inst Med-Nat Acad Sci; fel Am Pub Health Asn. *Mailing Add:* 6111 Kennedy Dr Chevy Chase MD 20015

ROBERTS, DURWARD THOMAS, JR, b Chattanooga, Tenn, Jan 1, 42; m 62; c 3. ORGANIC POLYMER CHEMISTRY. *Educ:* Univ NC, Chapel Hill, BA, 64, PhD(org chem), 68. *Prof Exp:* Chemist, Esso Res Labs, Humble Oil & Refining Co, La, 67-70; sr res scientist, 70-71, group leader, 71-76, MGR, CENT RES LABS, FIRESTONE TIRE & RUBBER CO, 76- *Mem:* Am Chem Soc. *Res:* Catalytic polymerization of monomers; polyurethane polymer synthesis; stabilization of polymer systems; flammability of polymers; urethane coatings; tire research; catalytic reactions of petroleum hydrocarbons. *Mailing Add:* Cent Res Labs Firestone Tire & Rubber Co Akron OH 44317

ROBERTS, EARL C(HAMPION), b Butte, Mont, Nov 3, 21; m 55; c 4. PHYSICAL METALLURGY. *Educ:* Mont Sch Mines, BS, 43; Mass Inst Technol, SM, 50, ScD, 52. *Prof Exp:* Metallographer, Aluminum Co Am, 43-44; asst metall, Armour Res Found, Ill Inst Technol, 46-47 & Mass Inst Technol, 47-52; asst prof, Mont Sch Mines, 52-54; from assoc prof to prof, Univ Wash, 54-63; consult, 55-63, CHIEF METALL LAB, AEROSPACE GROUP, BOEING CO, 63- *Mem:* Fel Am Soc Metals; Am Inst Mining, Metall & Petrol Engrs; Int Metallog Soc. *Res:* Phase transformation in metals; hardening and tempering of steels; corrosion of metals. *Mailing Add:* 24914 SE 422nd Enumclaw WA 98022

ROBERTS, EARL JOHN, b Magee, Miss, May 14, 13; m 44; c 2. CHEMISTRY. *Educ:* Miss Col, BA, 39; La State Univ, MS, 42. *Prof Exp:* High sch teacher, Miss, 39-40; analyst, Miss Testing Lab, 40-41; asst chem, La State Univ, 41-42; jr chemist, Southern Utilization Res Br, 42-44, from asst chemist to chemist, 44-62, res chemist, Southern Res & Develop Div, 62-72, SR CHEMIST, CANE SUGAR REFINING RES PROJ, SCI & EDUC ADMIN-AGR RES, USDA, 72- *Concurrent Pos:* Teaching fel, Tulane Univ, 48- *Res:* Organic chemistry of the by-products of the sugar industry; composition of sugar cane juice; structure of modified cellulose; identification and determination of minor constituents in refined cane sugar. *Mailing Add:* USDA Southern Res Ctr 1100 Robert E Lee Blvd New Orleans LA 70179

ROBERTS, EDGAR D, b Odessa, Tex, Mar 23, 31; m 50; c 2. VETERINARY PATHOLOGY. *Educ:* Colo State Univ, BS, 57, DVM, 59; Iowa State Univ, MS, 62, PhD(vet path), 65. *Prof Exp:* Res asst vet path, Vet Med Res Inst, 59-62; pathologist, Nat Animal Dis Lab, 62-63; asst prof vet path, Iowa State Univ, 63-65; vet pathologist, Rockefeller Found, 65-69; head animal health, Int Ctr Trop Agr, Colombia, 69-71; PROF VET PATH & HEAD DEPT, SCH VET MED, LA STATE UNIV, BATON ROUGE, 71- *Mem:* Am Vet Med Asn; Am Col Vet Path; Int Acad Path. *Res:* Pathogenesis of nutritional and infectious diseases of the swine and equine species; naturally occurring diseases of the tropics. *Mailing Add:* Dept of Path Sch of Vet Med La State Univ Baton Rouge LA 70803

ROBERTS, EDWIN KIRK, b Marlton, NJ, Nov 15, 22; m 49; c 2. PHYSICAL CHEMISTRY. *Educ:* Earlham Col, BA, 49; Harvard Univ, PhD(chem physics), 53. *Prof Exp:* From instr to assoc prof chem, Middlebury Col, 52-67, prof, 67-81; DIR LABS & LECTR CHEM, STANFORD UNIV, 82- *Concurrent Pos:* NSF fac fel, Stanford Univ, 69-70. *Mem:* Am Chem Soc. *Res:* Free radical kinetics; chemistry of coordination complexes. *Mailing Add:* Dept Chem Stanford Univ Stanford CA 94305

ROBERTS, ELIOT COLLINS, b Camden, NJ, Apr 25, 27; m 51; c 3. PLANT SCIENCE. *Educ:* Univ RI, BS, 50; Rutgers Univ, MS, 52, PhD(soil, plant physiol), 55. *Prof Exp:* From asst prof to assoc prof agron, Univ Mass, 54-59; from assoc prof to prof hort & agron, Iowa State Univ, 59-67; prof ornamental hort & chmn dept, Univ Fla, 67-70; chmn dept plant & soil sci, 70-73, PROF PLANT & SOIL SCI, UNIV RI, 70- *Concurrent Pos:* Ed, Proc Second Int Turfgrass Res Conf, 72-75. *Mem:* Fel Am Soc Agron; Am Soc Hort Sci. *Res:* Physiology of grasses under close clipping practices; factors related to arrested development and summer dormancy of grasses; microclimate-disease relationships of turfgrass species and strains. *Mailing Add:* 317 Woodward Hall Univ of RI Kingston RI 02881

ROBERTS, ELLIOTT JOHN, b Kalispell, Mont, Aug 7, 04; m 28; c 3. PHYSICAL INORGANIC CHEMISTRY. *Educ:* Yale Univ, BS, 25, PhD(chem), 28. *Prof Exp:* Instr chem, Yale Univ, 27-30; from res chemist to chem engr, Dorr Co, 30-41, res dir, 41-53, vpres res & develop, 54-55, dir res & develop, Dorr-Oliver, Inc, 55-58, tech adv, 58-61, chief scientist, 61-69, sci consult, 69-80; RETIRED. *Mem:* AAAS; Am Chem Soc; fel Am Inst Chemists. *Res:* Thermodynamics of solutions; sedimentation and classification; ion exchange; fluidization; waste water treatment, phosphorus and nitrogen removal; phosphoric acid manufacturing. *Mailing Add:* 8 Lyons Plain Rd Westport CT 06880

ROBERTS, EUGENE, b Krasnodar, Russia, Jan 19, 20; US citizen; m 77; c 3. BIOCHEMISTRY. *Educ:* Wayne State Univ, BS, 40; Univ Mich, MS, 41, PhD(biochem), 43. *Prof Exp:* Asst head inhalation sect uranium compounds res, Univ Rochester, 43-46; res assoc, Barnard Free Skin & Cancer Hosp, St Louis & Med Sch, Wash Univ, 46-54; chmn, Dept Biochem, 54-68, DIR DIV NEUROSCI, CITY OF HOPE RES INST, 68- *Concurrent Pos:* Mem psychopharmacol study sect, Div Res Grants, NIH, 61-66, mem, NIMH Scientist Exchange Group to USSR, 62, mem neurol B study sect, Div Res Grants, NIH, 67-69, mem bd sci counrs, Nat Inst Neurol Dis & Stroke, 69-73; mem comt brain sci, Div Med Sci, Nat Res Coun-Nat Acad Sci, Washington, DC, 66-70; res comt prof adv sect, Scottish Rite Res Found, 66-; mem res adv comt, Calif Dept Ment Hyg, 68-69; mem res adv comt, Nat Asn Ment Health, Inc, 69-71, adj prof, Sch Med, Univ Southern Calif, 70-; mem inst sci adv bd, Israel Ctr Psychobiol, Tel Aviv, 72-; mem bd sci counrs, Nat Inst Neurol & Commun Dis & Stroke, 80-84. *Honors & Awards:* Distinguished Serv Award, Wayne State Univ, 66. *Mem:* Am Chem Soc; Am Soc Biol Chemists; Soc Exp Biol & Med; Am Asn Cancer Res; Int Asn Study Pain. *Res:* Neurochemistry; biochemistry of cancer; comparative biochemistry; general metabolism. *Mailing Add:* Div Neurosci City Hope Res Inst Duarte CA 91010

ROBERTS, FLOYD EDWARD, JR, b Philadelphia, Pa, Dec 2, 34; m 56; c 3. ORGANIC CHEMISTRY. *Educ:* Franklin Col, AB, 56; Pa State Univ, MS, 58; Purdue Univ, PhD(org chem), 63. *Prof Exp:* Chemist, Merck & Co, Inc, 62-64, sr chemist, 64-69, res fel, 69-79, SR RES FEL, MERCK SHARPE & DOHME RES LABS, 79- *Mem:* Am Chem Soc. *Res:* Steroids and other medicinals; antibiotics; natural product isolation. *Mailing Add:* 220 Valley Rd Princeton NJ 08540

ROBERTS, FRANCIS DONALD, b Utica, NY, Jan 18, 38; m 64; c 4. ORGANIC CHEMISTRY. *Educ:* Syracuse Univ, BA, 59; Cornell Univ, PhD(org chem), 64. *Prof Exp:* Res chemist, New York, 64-66, sect head, 66-70, tech coordr toilet articles, Pharmaceut Div, 70-72, asst mgr oral res, 72-73, dir purchasing raw mat, 73-76, dir res & develop, 76-81, VPRES RES & DEVELOP, KENDALL CO DIV, COLGATE-PALMOLIVE CO, 81- *Mem:* AAAS; Am Chem Soc. *Res:* Synthesis of new organo-sulfur compounds; condensed aromatics; oral research, especially treatment of caries and periodontal disease; nonwoven fabrics, acrylic and rubber based pressure sensitive adhesives, medical devices, surgical dressings, urological products. *Mailing Add:* Kendall Co One Federal St Boston MA 02101

ROBERTS, FRANKLIN LEWIS, b Waterboro, Maine, Feb 21, 34; m 57; c 5. CYTOLOGY, GENETICS. *Educ:* Univ Maine, BS, 57; NC State Univ, PhD(genetics), 64. *Prof Exp:* Instr sci, Gorham State Teachers Col, 58-59; instr zool, NC State Univ, 59-64; from asst prof to assoc prof, 64-74, Coe Fund res grant, 65-66, PROF ZOOL, UNIV MAINE, ORONO, 74-, CHMN DEPT, 75- *Concurrent Pos:* NSF res grant, 66-69 & City of Hope Med Ctr, Duarte, Calif, 68. *Mem:* Am Soc Nat; AAAS; Am Soc Ichthyol & Herpet; Genetics Soc Am. *Res:* Cytotaxonomy and cytogenetics of cold blooded vertebrates, particularly fishes; cell culture of cold blooded vertebrate tissues; genetics of parthenogenesis. *Mailing Add:* Dept of Zool Murray Hall Univ of Maine Orono ME 04973

ROBERTS, FRED STEPHEN, b New York, NY, June 19, 43; m. DISCRETE MATHEMATICS, MATHEMATICAL MODELING. *Educ:* Dartmouth Col, AB, 64; Stanford Univ, MS, 67, PhD(math), 68. *Prof Exp:* NIH traineeship math psychol, Univ Pa, 68; mathematician, Rand Corp, 68-72; assoc prof, 72-76, PROF MATH, RUTGERS UNIV, 76- *Concurrent Pos:* Mem, Inst Advan Study, Princeton Univ, 71-72; vis prof oper res, Cornell Univ, 79-80; consult, Rand Corp, Orgn Econ Coop & Develop, Construct Eng Res Lab, Inst Gas Technol. *Mem:* Am Math Soc; Math Asn Am; Soc Indust & Appl Math; Oper Res Soc Am; Soc Math Psychol. *Res:* Mathematical models in the social, biological and environmental sciences; combinatorial mathematics and graph theory; theory of measurement; energy modeling. *Mailing Add:* Dept of Math Rutgers Univ New Brunswick NJ 08903

ROBERTS, FREDDY LEE, b Dermott, Ark, Dec 29, 41; m 64; c 2. CIVIL ENGINEERING. *Educ:* Univ Ark, Fayetteville, BSCE, 64, MSCE, 66; Univ Tex, Austin, PhD(civil eng), 70. *Prof Exp:* Soils engr, Grubbs Consult Engrs, Inc, Ark, 65; res engr, Univ Ark, Fayetteville, 64-66; consult piles, Hudson, Matlock, Dawkins & Panak Res Engrs, 66-67; res engr & teaching asst hwy roughness, Univ Tex, Austin, 66-69; from asst prof to assoc prof civil eng, Clemson Univ, 69-75; vis assoc prof, Univ Tex, Austin, 75-78; chief engr, Austin Res Engrs, Inc, 78-81; RES ENGR, UNIV TEX, AUSTIN, 81- *Concurrent Pos:* Mem, Hwy Res Bd, Nat Acad Sci-Nat Res Coun; mat & design consult, Rawhut Eng, Austin, 81- *Mem:* Am Soc Civil Engrs; Am Soc Testing & Mat. *Res:* Highway roughness, its measure and effect on highway user and vehicle; pavement material evaluation and use in design; highway geometric design; development of pavement evaluation and management systems; design and evaluation design procedure development; recycled mixture design; evaluation of stripping test methods. *Mailing Add:* 1504 Weyford Dr Austin TX 78758

ROBERTS, GEORGE A(DAM), b Uniontown, Pa, Feb 18, 19; m 71; c 3. METALLURGY. *Educ:* Carnegie Inst Technol, BSc, 39, MSc, 41, DSc, 42. *Prof Exp:* Res metallurgist, Vanadium-Alloys Steel Co, 41-45, chief metallurgist, 45-53, vpres, 53-61, pres, Vasco Metals Corp, Pa, 61-66; PRES, TELEDYNE, INC, 66- *Mem:* Nat Acad Eng; fel Am Soc Metals (vpres, 53, pres, 54); Soc Mfg Eng; Am Chem Soc; fel Am Inst Mining, Metall & Petrol Engrs. *Res:* Metallurgy of tool steels; heat treatment of hardenable steels; powder metallurgy of ferrous alloys; mechanical properties of steels. *Mailing Add:* Teledyne Inc 1901 Ave of the Stars Los Angeles CA 90067

ROBERTS, GEORGE E(DWARD), b Portsmouth, Eng, Sept 25, 26; m 50; c 1. SYSTEMS ANALYSIS. *Educ:* Portsmouth Naval Col Eng, BSc, 45. *Prof Exp:* Apprentice elec eng, Portsmouth Dockyard, Brit Admiralty, 42-47, design draftsman, 47-51; design draftsman, Can Vickers Ltd, 51-52; elec engr, Tech Prods Dept, RCA Victor Co, Ltd, 52-56 & Defense Dept, 56-58, sr mem sci staff, Res Labs, 58-66; mem tech staff, Gen Res Corp, 66-74; systs analyst, Litton Mellonics, 74-76; mem prof staff, 76-80, MGR, GEODYNAMICS CORP, 80- *Res:* Probability and statistics; antennas; mathematical analysis. *Mailing Add:* Geodynamics Corp 55 Hitchcock Way Santa Barbara CA 93105

ROBERTS, GEORGE P, b Barton, Vt, Dec 25, 37; m 59; c 4. POLYMER CHEMISTRY. *Educ:* Univ Vt, BS, 59; Northwestern Univ, PhD(phys chem), 64. *Prof Exp:* Res scientist, Corp Res Ctr, NJ, 64-69, group leader acrylonitrile-butadiene-styrene res, Chem Div, Conn, 69-74, MGR POLYMER APPL RES, CORP RES & DEVELOP, UNIROYAL, INC, 74- *Mem:* Am Chem Soc; Soc Plastics Engr. *Res:* Polymer characterization, relationship of properties of polymers to morphology and molecular structure; process development and polymer applications. *Mailing Add:* Oxford Mgt & Res/Develop Ctr Uniroyal Inc Middlebury CT 06749

ROBERTS, GEORGE W(ILLARD), b Bridgeport, Conn, Aug 9, 38; m 63; c 2. CHEMICAL ENGINEERING, PHYSICAL CHEMISTRY. *Educ:* Cornell Univ, BChE, 61; Mass Inst Technol, ScD, 65. *Prof Exp:* Instr heat transfer, Mass Inst Technol, 63; chem engr, Rohm & Haas Co, 65-67, projs supvr, 68-69; assoc prof chem eng, Washington Univ, 69-71; mgr chem & chem eng, Engelhard Industs Div, Engelhard Minerals & Chem Corp, 72-77; DIR, CORP RES & DEVELOP DEPT, AIR PROD & CHEM, INC, 77-, GEN MGR, COMMERCIAL DEVELOP DIV, PROCESS SYSTS GROUP, 81- *Mem:* Am Chem Soc; Am Inst Chem Engrs. *Res:* Chemical reaction engineering; heterogeneous catalysis; polymerization kinetics; tracer kinetics; research management. *Mailing Add:* Air Prod & Chem Inc PO Box 538 Allentown PA 18105

ROBERTS, GLENN DALE, b Gilmer, Tex, Apr 9, 43; m 73. CLINICAL MICROBIOLOGY, MEDICAL MYCOLOGY. *Educ:* NTex State Univ, BS, 67; Univ Okla, MS, 69, PhD(med mycol), 71; Am Bd Med Microbiol, cert, 79. *Prof Exp:* Fel clin mycol, Col Med, Univ Ky, 71-72; instr microbiol & lab med, Mayo Med Sch, 72-77, asst prof, 77-81, CONSULT, MAYO CLIN & MAYO FOUND, 72-, ASSOC PROF MICROBIOL & LAB MED, MAYO MED SCH, 81- *Mem:* Med Mycol Soc of the Americas; Int Soc Human & Animal Mycol; Am Soc Clin Path; Am Soc Microbiol; Am Thoracic Soc. *Res:* Diagnostic and clinical mycobacteriology and mycology; mycotic serology. *Mailing Add:* Sect of Clin Microbiol Mayo Clin Rochester MN 55901

ROBERTS, HAROLD R, b Four Oaks, NC, Jan 4, 30; m 58; c 2. INTERNAL MEDICINE, HEMATOLOGY. *Educ:* Univ NC, BS, 52, MD, 55. *Prof Exp:* Instr path, 60-62, assoc prof path & med, 62-70, chief div hemat, dept med, 68-77, PROF PATH & MED, SCH MED, UNIV NC, CHAPEL HILL, 70- *Res:* Blood coagulation; hemorrhage; thrombosis. *Mailing Add:* Dept of Med Univ of NC Sch of Med Chapel Hill NC 27514

ROBERTS, HARRY EDWARD, b Jacksonville, Fla, Jan 31, 20; m 41; c 2. PHOTOGRAPHIC CHEMISTRY, INFORMATION RETRIEVAL. *Prof Exp:* Univ Rochester, BS, 54. *Prof Exp:* Lab technician photog chem, 41-50, chemist, 50-59, res assoc, 59-72, SR TECH ASSOC, EASTMAN KODAK CO, 72- *Mem:* Am Chem Soc; Soc Photog Sci & Eng. *Res:* Preparation and coating of silver halide emulsions; design of information retrieval systems for published references in the field of photographic chemistry. *Mailing Add:* Emulsion Res Div Bldg 83 Kodak Park Eastman Kodak Co Rochester NY 14650

ROBERTS, HARRY HEIL, b Huntington, WVa, Feb 2, 40; m 63; c 1. GEOLOGY. *Educ:* Marshall Univ, BS, 62; La State Univ, Baton Rouge, MS, 66, PhD(geol), 69. *Prof Exp:* Asst prof geol res, 69-74, assoc prof marine sci, 74-78, PROF MARINE SCI, COASTAL STUDIES INST, LA STATE UNIV, BATON ROUGE, 78- *Mem:* Soc Econ Paleontologists & Mineralogists; Am Geophys Union; Coastal Soc; Geol Soc Am; Int Asn Sedimentol. *Res:* Sedimentology associated with reef and deltaic environments; dynamics and ecology of reefs. *Mailing Add:* Coastal Studies Inst La State Univ Baton Rouge LA 70803

ROBERTS, HARRY VIVIAN, b Peoria, Ill, May 1, 23; m 43; c 2. STATISTICS. *Educ:* Univ Chicago, BA, 43, MBA, 47, PhD(bus), 55. *Prof Exp:* Mkt res analyst, McCann-Erickson, Inc, 46-49; from instr to assoc prof, 49-59, PROF STATIST, UNIV CHICAGO, 59- *Concurrent Pos:* Assoc ed, Am Statistician News, 53-73 & J Am Statist Asn, 76-; Ford Found fel, 59-60. *Mem:* AAAS; Am Econ Asn; fel Am Statist Asn; Inst Math Statist; Royal Statist Soc. *Res:* Statistical theory and applications, especially interactive data analysis; statistical decision theory and applications, especially to medical diagnosis and treatment. *Mailing Add:* Grad Sch of Bus Univ of Chicago Chicago IL 60637

ROBERTS, HOWARD C(REIGHTON), b Wayne Co, Ill, Nov 1, 10; m 37; c 2. ENGINEERING. *Educ:* Univ Ill, AB, 33, EE, 44. *Prof Exp:* Asst physics, Univ Ill, 30-32; asst, Div Physics, State Geol Surv, Ill, 32-37; asst comput, Gen Geophys Co, Tex, 38-39; asst, res staff, Asn Am Railroads, Ill, 39-42 & 42-46; assoc prof civil eng, Univ Ill, Urbana, 46-53, assoc prof, Eng Exp Sta, 53-54, prof eng, 54-68, prof elec eng, 68; INDEPENDENT CONSULT PHYSICIST, 68- *Concurrent Pos:* Spec res assoc, Off Sci Res & Develop, 42-44; vis prof archit & acoust, Univ Ill, Urbana, 72-77; vis lectr, Univ Colo, Denver, 78- *Mem:* Fel AAAS; fel Instrument Soc Am. *Res:* Industrial measurements; automatic weighing and proportioning; noise and vibration control; architectural acoustics. *Mailing Add:* 7199 S Vine Circle W Littleton CO 80122

ROBERTS, HOWARD RADCLYFFE, b Villanova, Pa, Mar 26, 06; m 33; c 3. ENTOMOLOGY. *Educ:* Princeton Univ, BS, 29; Univ Pa, PhD(zool), 41. *Prof Exp:* Res assoc, 34-46, dir, 47-72, RES FEL ENTOM, ACAD NATURAL SCI PHILADELPHIA, 72- *Concurrent Pos:* Instr, Univ Pa, 35-41; hon lectr, 56-, trustee & secy, Wistar Inst. *Mem:* AAAS; Soc Study Evolution; Soc Syst Zool; Entom Soc Am. *Res:* Taxonomy of orthoptera. *Mailing Add:* Acad of Natural Sci of Phila 19th St & Parkway Philadelphia PA 19103

ROBERTS, IRVING, b Brooklyn, NY, Jan 9, 15; m 38, 66; c 2. CHEMICAL ENGINEERING. *Educ:* City Col New York, BS, 34; Columbia Univ, MS, 35, PhD(phys chem), 37. *Prof Exp:* Asst chem, Columbia Univ, 35-39; chem engr, Weiss & Downs, Inc, NY, 39-43; group leader, Manhattan proj, 43-45; div engr, Process Div, Res & Develop Dept, Elliott Co, 45-50; consult, 50-56; dir planning, Reynolds Metals Co, 56-61, vpres, 61-78; CONSULT ENGR, 78- *Mem:* Am Chem Soc; Am Inst Chem Engrs; Am Soc Mech Engrs. *Res:* Long-range planning and economic evaluation; the aluminum industry; oxygen and other low temperature plants; new chemical processes. *Mailing Add:* 3 Westwick Rd Richmond VA 23233

ROBERTS, J(ASPER) KENT, b Ryan, Okla, Jan 15, 22; m 43; c 2. ENGINEERING. *Educ:* Univ Okla, BSCE, 47; Univ Mo, MSCE, 50. *Prof Exp:* From instr to assoc prof, 47-57, asst dean eng, 70-80, PROF CIVIL ENG, UNIV MO-ROLLA, 57- *Mem:* Am Soc Civil Engrs; Nat Soc Prof Engrs; Am Soc Eng Educ. *Mailing Add:* Dept of Civil Eng Univ of Mo Rolla MO 65401

ROBERTS, JAMES C, JR, b New York, NY, Feb 13, 26; m 49; c 4. PATHOLOGY. *Educ:* Wesleyan Univ, AB, 45; Univ Rochester, MD, 49. *Prof Exp:* Asst path, Washington Univ, 49-51; instr, Univ Pittsburgh, 53-55, asst prof, 55-58; pathologist & dir med educ, ETenn Baptist Hosp, 58-60; PATHOLOGIST & DIR RES, LITTLE CO OF MARY HOSP, 60-, DIR, CETACEAN RES LAB, 62- *Concurrent Pos:* Hartford fel, Arteriosclerosis Res, 55-58; prin investr, Res Grants, 57-; consult, Los Angeles County Harbor Hosp, 62-; co-chmn conf comp arteriosclerosis, Nat Heart Inst, Calif, 64-65; Nuffield traveling fel, Zool Soc London, 65. *Mem:* Am Heart Asn; Am Soc Mammal; Am Med Asn; Am Asn Path & Bact; fel Col Am Path. *Res:* Immunopathology; arteriosclerosis; comparative arteriosclerosis and morphology. *Mailing Add:* 15 Portuguese Bend Rd Rolling Hills CA 90274

ROBERTS, JAMES ERNEST, SR, b Newport, Ark, May 17, 24; m 46; c 3. ECONOMIC ENTOMOLOGY. *Educ:* Univ Ark, BSA, 54, MS, 55; Kans State Univ, PhD(entom), 63. *Prof Exp:* High sch teacher, Ark, 47-52; jr entomologist, Univ Ark, 55-56; asst entomologist, Ga Exp Sta, Univ Ga, 56-65; exten entomologist, Agr Exten Serv, Univ Ark, Fayetteville, 65-69; EXTEN SPECIALIST ENTOM, COL AGR & LIFE SCI, VA POLYTECH INST & STATE UNIV, 69- *Concurrent Pos:* Consult, Nat Park Serv, 75.

Mem: Entom Soc Am; Agr & Life Sci Fac Asn. *Res:* Field testing of insecticides for the control of insects affecting crops and livestock in Virginia. *Mailing Add:* Dept Entom 215 Price Hall Va Polytech Inst & State Univ Blacksburg VA 24061

ROBERTS, JAMES HERBERT, b Tucson, Ariz, Oct 27, 15; m 42; c 4. EXPERIMENTAL NUCLEAR PHYSICS. *Educ:* Univ Ariz, BS, 37, MS, 38; Univ Chicago, PhD(physics), 46. *Prof Exp:* Lab asst physics, Univ Chicago, 38-39, asst, Metall Lab, 42-43, res assoc, 43-44; demonstr, Mus Sci & Indust, 39-42; res scientist, Los Alamos Sci Lab, Univ Calif, 44-46, actg group leader, 46-48; from asst prof to prof physics, Northwestern Univ, 48-69; prof physics, Macalester Col, 69-79, chmn, Dept Physics & Astron, 75-76; CONSULT, WESTINGHOUSE-HANFORD CO, 76- *Concurrent Pos:* Vis prof physics, Pahlavi Univ, Iran, 72. *Mem:* Fel Am Phys Soc; Am Asn Physics Teachers; Am Nuclear Soc. *Res:* Neutron physics involving fissionable material; neutron yields of light elements bombarded with alpha particles; neutron energy measurements with nuclear research emulsions; hyper fragments; detection of fission fragments and other charged particles with solid state track recorders; thermal annealing of mica and quartz solid state track recorders. *Mailing Add:* Westinghouse-Harford Co W/C 39 PO Box 1970 Richland WA 99352

ROBERTS, JAMES LEWIS, b Lima, Peru, Oct 23, 51; US citizen. BIOCHEMISTRY, MOLECULAR BIOLOGY. *Educ:* Colo State Univ, BS, 73; Univ Ore, PhD(chem), 78. *Prof Exp:* Res technician biochem, Colo State Univ, 70-73; teaching asst, Univ Ore, 73-74; fel biochem, Univ Calif, 78-79; MEM STAFF, DEPT BIOCHEM, COL PHYSICIANS & SURGEONS, COLUMBIA UNIV, 79- *Mem:* AAAS; Am Chem Soc. *Res:* Biosynthesis and regulation of the Adrenocorticotropin-endorphin precursor; recombinant DNA cloning of pituitary and brain Adrenocorticotropin-endorphin; glucocorticoid and thyroid hormone regulation of gene expression; gene structure. *Mailing Add:* Dept of Biochem 630 W 168th St New York NY 10032

ROBERTS, JAMES RICHARD, b Flint, Mich, July 1, 37; m 60; c 3. PHYSICS. *Educ:* Univ Mich, BS, 59, MS, 61, PHD(physics), 64. *Prof Exp:* PHYSICIST, NAT BUR STAND, 64- *Concurrent Pos:* Nat Bur Stand training grant & vis scientist, Aarhus Univ, 70-71. *Mem:* Am Inst Physics. *Res:* Plasma spectroscopy; experimental determination of atomic transition probabilities; stark broadening parameters and other atomic parameters of ionized plasmas. *Mailing Add:* A59 221 Nat Bur Stand Washington DC 20234

ROBERTS, JANE CAROLYN, b Malden, Mass, Nov 14, 32. PHYSIOLOGY. *Educ:* Univ Mass, Amherst, BS, 54; Univ Calif, Los Angeles, MA, 56, Univ Calif, Santa Barbara, PhD(physiol), 71. *Prof Exp:* Res physiologist, Med Ctr, Univ Calif, Los Angeles, 57-63, asst specialist physiol, 63-64, asst res physiologist, 64-67; assoc specialist, Dept Ergonomics, Univ Calif, Santa Barbara, 67-71; res worker, Dept Ophthal Res, Columbia Univ, 71-72; asst prof, 72-79, ASSOC PROF, DEPT BIOL, CREIGHTON UNIV, 79- *Mem:* AAAS; Am Physiol Soc; Int Hibernation Soc; Am Soc Zoologists; Soc Exp Biol & Med. *Res:* Metabolic and biochemical changes in hibernation and temperature acclimation. *Mailing Add:* Dept of Biol Creighton Univ Omaha NE 68178

ROBERTS, JAY, b New York, NY, July 15, 27; m 50; c 2. PHARMACOLOGY. *Educ:* Long Island Univ, BS, 49; Cornell Univ, PhD(pharmacol), 53. *Prof Exp:* Instr physiol, Hunter Col, 53; res fel pharmacol, Med Col, Cornell Univ, 53-54, from instr to assoc prof, 54-66; prof, Univ Pittsburgh, 66-70; PROF PHARMACOL & CHMN DEPT, MED COL PA, 70- *Concurrent Pos:* Asst ed, Biol Abstr, 56-72; Lederle fac award, 57-60; mem study sect pharmacol, USPHS, 68-72; mem, Geriat Adv Panel, US Pharmacopeia. *Mem:* AAAS; Am Soc Pharmacol & Exp Therapeut; fel Am Col Cardiol; Soc Exp Biol & Med; Cardiac Muscle Soc (secy-treas, 65-67, pres, 67-69). *Res:* Neuromuscular and cardiovascular pharmacology; aging. *Mailing Add:* Dept of Pharmacol Med Col of Pa Philadelphia PA 19129

ROBERTS, JEFFREY WARREN, b Flint, Mich, Feb 16, 44; m 68; c 2. MOLECULAR BIOLOGY, BIOCHEMISTRY. *Educ:* Univ Tex, BA, 64; Harvard Univ, PhD(biophys), 70. *Prof Exp:* NSF fel, Lab Molecular Biol, Med Res Ctr, 70-71; jr fel, Harvard Soc Fels, 71-73; asst prof, 74-80, ASSOC PROF BIOCHEM, CORNELL UNIV, 80- *Res:* Regulation of gene expression, especially mechanism of lysogenic induction and the mechanism of positive control in the life cycle of bacteriophage lambda. *Mailing Add:* Biochem Molecular & Cell Biol Cornell Univ Ithaca NY 14853

ROBERTS, JERRY ALLAN, b Landis, NC, July 31, 31; m 55; c 4. APPLIED MATHEMATICS. *Educ:* NC State Univ, BEngPhys, 58, MS, 60, PhD(appl math), 64. *Prof Exp:* Res asst, NC State Univ, 61-63, instr, 63-65; asst prof, 65-69, ASSOC PROF MATH, DAVIDSON COL, 69- *Mem:* Math Asn Am; Soc Indust & Appl Math; Asn Comput Mach. *Res:* Use of numerical analysis and digital computers to obtain approximate solutions of boundary-value problems arising from problems in fracture mechanics; experimental statistics. *Mailing Add:* Dept of Math Davidson Col Davidson NC 28036

ROBERTS, JOAN MARIE, b Wall, Pa, Sept 28, 32; m 66. RADIOBIOLOGY, EXPERIMENTAL PSYCHOLOGY. *Educ:* Wayne State Univ, BS, 54, MA, 57, PhD(psychol), 62. *Prof Exp:* Exp psychologist, Henry Ford Hosp, Detroit, 54-55; from res asst to res assoc animal behav, Lafayette Clin, 56-63; instr radiobiol, Sch Med, Wayne State Univ, 63-66; asst prof, 66-71, ASSOC PROF ORAL BIOL, SCH DENT, UNIV DETROIT, 71- *Concurrent Pos:* Consult, Detroit Mem Hosp, 63-66; USPHS res grant, Wayne State Univ & Univ Detroit, 64-71; Seed grant, Univ Detroit, 72-75. *Mem:* AAAS; Am Psychol Asn; Radiation Res Soc. *Res:* Effects of whole-body radiation on prenatal organisms, especially postnatal development and behavior; protection of the prenatal animal against irradiation by chemical agents administered to the pregnant animal. *Mailing Add:* Dept of Physiol & Pharmacol Univ of Detroit Sch of Dent Detroit MI 48207

ROBERTS, JOEL LAURENCE, b Denver, Colo, Sept 5, 40; m 64; c 3. MATHEMATICS. *Educ:* Mass Inst Technol, BS, 63; Harvard Univ, MA, 64, PhD(math), 69. *Prof Exp:* Asst prof math, Purdue Univ, Lafayette, 68-72; asst prof, 72-74, assoc prof, 74-80, PROF MATH, UNIV MINN, MINNEAPOLIS, 80- *Concurrent Pos:* Vis lectr, Nat Univ Mex, 69; NSF res grant, Purdue Univ, Lafayette, 70-72, Univ Minn, 72-; vis scholar, Univ Calif, Berkeley, 80. *Mem:* Am Math Soc. *Res:* Algebraic geometry; properties of algebriac varieties in projective spaces; rational equivalence ring and theory of Chern classes; commutative algebra. *Mailing Add:* Sch Math Univ Minn Minneapolis MN 55455

ROBERTS, JOHN BURNHAM, b Manchester, NH, Apr 29, 13; m 45; c 2. CHEMICAL ENGINEERING. *Educ:* Dartmouth Col, AB, 34; Mass Inst Technol, MS, 36. *Prof Exp:* Chem engr, E I du Pont de Nemours & Co, Inc, 36-40, gen group supvr, Jackson Lab, 40-48, res engr, Eng Res Lab, 48-50, res supvr, 50-52, staff asst, 53, res mgr, 54-60, asst dir, 60-62, sect mgr, Eng Res Div, 63-65, eng fel, Eng Develop Lab, 66-69, eng fel, Eng Technol Lab, 70-74, sr eng fel, 74-78; CONSULT, 78- *Concurrent Pos:* Mem, Franklin Inst. *Mem:* Am Chem Soc; Am Inst Chem Engrs; Inst Elec & Electronics Engrs; NY Acad Sci. *Res:* Pollution abatement; environmental engineering; solar energy; coal conversion and feedstocks technology. *Mailing Add:* 2302 W 11th St Wilmington DE 19805

ROBERTS, JOHN D, b Los Angeles, Calif, June 8, 18; m 42; c 4. ORGANIC CHEMISTRY. *Educ:* Univ Calif, Los Angeles, BA, 41, PhD(chem), 44. *Hon Degrees:* Dr rer nat, Univ Munich, 62; DrSci, Temple Univ, 64. *Prof Exp:* Instr chem, Univ Calif, Los Angeles, 44-45; Nat Res Coun fel, Harvard Univ, 45-46, instr, 46; from instr to assoc prof, Mass Inst Technol, 46-53; prof org chem, 53-72, chmn div chem & chem eng, 53-67, actg chmn, 72-73, inst prof chem, 72-80, VPRES, PROVOST & DEAN FAC, CALIF INST TECHNOL, 80- *Concurrent Pos:* Guggenheim fel, 52-53 & 55; consult, E I du Pont de Nemours & Co, 49- & Union Carbide Corp, 49-62; lectureships and professorships at var cols & univs, US & abroad, 56-; mem adv panel chem, NSF, 57-59 & 61, chmn, 59-60, mem div comt math, phys & eng sci, 62-64, mem adv comt math & phys sci, 65-66; mem adv panel, Off Sci Res, Air Force, 58-; dir & consult ed, W A Benjamin, Inc, 62-67; chmn chem sect, Nat Acad Sci, 68-71. *Honors & Awards:* Award, Am Chem Soc, 54, Harrison Howe Award, 57, Roger Adams Award Org Chem, 67, Nichols Medal, 71, Tolman Medal, 75, Michelson-Morley Award, 76, Norris Award, 79. *Mem:* Nat Acad Sci; Am Philos Soc; AAAS; Am Chem Soc; Am Acad Arts & Sci. *Res:* Small-ring organic compounds; mechanisms of rearrangement reactions; relation between structure and reactivity; nuclear magnetic resonance spectroscopy. *Mailing Add:* Div of Chem & Chem Eng Calif Inst of Technol Pasadena CA 91125

ROBERTS, JOHN EDWIN, b Laconia, NH, Mar 6, 20; m 44; c 2. CHEMISTRY. *Educ:* Univ NH, BS, 42, MS, 44; Cornell Univ, PhD(inorg chem), 47. *Prof Exp:* Asst chem, Univ NH, 42-44 & Cornell Univ, 44-46; from asst prof to assoc prof, 46-62, PROF CHEM, UNIV MASS, AMHERST, 62- *Concurrent Pos:* Fel fluorine chem, Univ Wash, 58-59; vis prof, Univ Cairo, 61-62; sabbatical, Anal Inst, Univ Vienna, 71. *Mem:* Am Chem Soc. *Res:* Molar refraction; indium fluoride systems; rare earth chemistry; fluorides of less familiar elements; the system indium trifluoride-water and the tendency of indium to form fluoanions; peroxydisulfuryldifluoride; fluorosulfonates; trifluoracetates; microchemistry and chemical microscopy; chemistry of art and archaeology. *Mailing Add:* Dept of Chem Univ of Mass Amherst MA 01002

ROBERTS, JOHN ENGLAND, b Los Angeles, Calif, Dec 27, 22; m 57; c 2. PHYSICS. *Educ:* Univ Calif, BS, 44, PhD(chem), 50. *Prof Exp:* Tech asst chem, Univ Calif, 43-44, jr scientist, Manhattan Dist, 44-46, asst, Dept Chem, 46-50, physicist, Lawrence Radiation Lab, 50-70; CHMN DEPT SCI & MATH, PARKS COL, ST LOUIS UNIV, 70- *Concurrent Pos:* Lectr physics, St Mary's Col, Calif, 67-70. *Mem:* Am Phys Soc; Math Asn Am; Am Asn Physics Teachers. *Res:* Physics and mathematics. *Mailing Add:* Dept of Sci & Math Parks Col of St Louis Univ Cahokia IL 62206

ROBERTS, JOHN FREDRICK, b Gallup, NMex, Oct 12, 28; m 51; c 4. ZOOLOGY, CELL BIOLOGY. *Educ:* Univ Ariz, BS, 56, PhD(zool), 64. *Prof Exp:* Asst prof biol, NMex Highlands Univ, 61-65; from asst prof to assoc prof zool, 65-74, PROF ZOOL, NC STATE UNIV, 74- *Concurrent Pos:* USPHS res grants, 64-65 & 69-72. *Mem:* Sigma Xi; Soc Protozool; Am Soc Cell Biol. *Res:* Regulation of respiration and mitochondrial biogenesis; mitochondrial nucleic acids; morphogenesis; trypanosomes. *Mailing Add:* Dept of Zool NC State Univ Raleigh NC 27650

ROBERTS, JOHN HENDERSON, b Raywood, Tex, Sept 2, 06; m 28; c 1. MATHEMATICS. *Educ:* Univ Tex, AB, 27, PhD(math), 29. *Prof Exp:* Nat Res Coun fel, Univ Pa, 29-30; adj prof pure math, Univ Tex, 30-31; from asst prof to prof, 31-71, chmn dept, 66-68, EMER PROF MATH, DUKE UNIV, 71- *Concurrent Pos:* Lectr, Princeton Univ, 37-38. *Mem:* AAAS; Am Math Soc (secy, 54); Math Asn Am. *Res:* Point-set topology; integral equations. *Mailing Add:* Dept of Math Duke Univ Durham NC 27706

ROBERTS, JOHN LEWIS, b Waukesha, Wis, May 23, 22; m 50; c 2. COMPARATIVE PHYSIOLOGY. *Educ:* Univ Wis, BS, 47, MS, 48; Univ Calif, Los Angeles, PhD, 53. *Prof Exp:* Asst zool, Univ Wis, 47-48 & Univ Calif, Los Angeles, 48-51; from instr to assoc prof physiol, 52-69, PROF PHYSIOL, UNIV MASS, AMHERST, 70- *Concurrent Pos:* With zool inst & mus, Univ Kiel, 59-60; USPHS spec fel, 66-67; mem corp, Marine Biol Lab, Woods Hole; guest lectr, Dept Zool, Univ Bristol, 66-67; sr res assoc, Nat Res Coun-Nat Oceanog & Atmospheric Admin, La Jolla, Calif, 73-75; panelist, NSF, 77-80; vis prof zool, Univ Hawaii, Manoa, Honolulu, 80. *Mem:* Fel AAAS; Soc Gen Physiol; Am Fisheries Soc; Am Soc Zool (secy, 76-79); Brit Soc Exp Biol. *Res:* Physiological adaptations of poikilotherms; respiratory and cardiac physiology of fish; neural control of respiration and swimming in fish. *Mailing Add:* Dept of Zool Univ of Mass Amherst MA 01003

ROBERTS, JOHN MELVILLE, b Toronto, Ont, Feb 16, 31; US citizen; div; c 2. PHYSICAL METALLURGY, MATERIALS SCIENCE. *Educ:* Univ Toronto, BASc, 53, MASc, 54; Univ Pa, PhD(phys metall), 60. *Prof Exp:* Metallurgist, Aluminum Labs Ltd, Ont, 54-56; from asst prof to assoc prof mech eng, 59-65, assoc prof mat sci, 65-70, PROF MAT SCI, RICE UNIV, 70- *Concurrent Pos:* Guggenheim fel, Univ Paris, 64-65; guest prof, Max-Planck Inst Metall forschung, Inst Physik, Stuttgart, W Ger, 72-73; vis prof & Nat Res Coun fel, Eng Mat Dept, Fed Univ Sao Carlos, Brasil, 79-80. *Mem:* Am Phys Soc; Am Soc Metals; Sigma Xi. *Res:* Microstrain and microcreep of metal crystals; plastic deformation and internal friction of metals; electroplating and anodizing of aluminum and aluminum alloys; internal friction in body centered cubic refractory metals; metallurgical studies on the fabrication of superconducting multifalamentary wires. *Mailing Add:* Dept Mech Eng & Mat Sci Rice Univ PO Box 1892 Houston TX 77001

ROBERTS, JOHN STEPHEN, b Apr 9, 37; m 59; c 2. PHYSIOLOGY, ENDOCRINOLOGY. *Educ:* Dartmouth Col, BA, 59; Duke Univ, PhD(zool), 65. *Prof Exp:* NIH fel, Sch Med, Case Western Reserve Univ, 64-67, Pop Coun res grant, 68-71, from sr instr to assoc prof physiol, 72-75; vis scientist, 73-75, SR SCIENTIST, WORCESTER FOUND EXP BIOL, 75- *Concurrent Pos:* NIH res grant, 71- *Mem:* AAAS; Am Physiol Soc; Endocrine Soc; Soc Study Reproduction. *Res:* Neuropharmacological studies of interactions among reproductive neuroendocrine control functions in intact animals using the systems analysis approach. *Mailing Add:* Worcester Found for Exp Bio! 222 Maple Ave Shrewsbury MA 01545

ROBERTS, JOSEPH, b Czech, May 24, 36; Can citizen; m 64; c 2. BIOCHEMISTRY. *Educ:* Univ Toronto, BScPharm, 59; Univ Wis, MSc, 62; McGill Univ, PhD(biochem), 64. *Prof Exp:* Fel enzym, Johns Hopkins Univ, 63-64; asst prof biochem, Grad Res Inst, Baylor Univ, 64-69; res asst prof, Sch Med, Univ Wash, 69-73; ASSOC MEM, MEM SLOAN-KETTERING CANCER CTR, 73-; ASSOC PROF BIOCHEM, GRAD SCH MED SCI, CORNELL UNIV, 74- *Concurrent Pos:* Leukemia Soc Am scholar, 65-70; NIH career develop award, 71-76. *Mem:* AAAS; Am Asn Cancer Res; Am Chem Soc. *Res:* Use of asparaginase, glutaminase and other selected enzymes as antitumor agents; isolation and physico-chemical characterization of new antitumor enzymes; development of new modes of therapy with enzymes; experimental oncology. *Mailing Add:* Sloan-Kettering Inst 145 Boston Post Rd Rye NY 10580

ROBERTS, JOSEPH BUFFINGTON, b Albany, NY, Sept 9, 23; m 44; c 3. MATHEMATICS. *Educ:* Case Inst Technol, BS, 44; Univ Colo, MA, 50; Univ Minn, PhD(math), 55. *Prof Exp:* Jr scientist radiochem, Manhattan Proj, Univ Calif, 45-46; asst math biol, Univ Chicago, 46-48; instr chem & math, Univ Wyo, 48-49; asst math, Univ Minn, 50-52; from instr to assoc prof, 52-70, PROF MATH, REED COL, 70- *Concurrent Pos:* Vis asst prof, Wesleyan Univ, 56-57; NSF res grant, 58-67; res assoc, Univ London, 62-63; Agency Int Develop vis prof, Univ Col, Dar es Salaam, 65-67; vis prof, Dalhousie Univ, 69-70; consult, Bonneville Power Admin, 58-61. *Mem:* Am Math Soc; Math Asn Am; Fedn Am Sci; Indian Math Soc; London Math Soc. *Res:* Number theory; summability; orthogonal functions. *Mailing Add:* Dept of Math Reed Col Portland OR 97202

ROBERTS, JOSEPH LINTON, b Atlanta, Ga, Nov 13, 29; m 53; c 3. PHYSICAL CHEMISTRY, BIOCHEMISTRY. *Educ:* Oglethorpe Univ, BS, 53; Univ SDak, MA, 55; Univ Cincinnati, PhD(theoret chem), 64. *Prof Exp:* Res asst systs anal, Biostatist Dept, Kettering Lab, Col Med, Univ Cincinnati, 59, res asst anal chem, Dept Toxicol, 59-61; res chemist, Dept Med Res, Vet Hosp, Cincinnati, 61-66; asst prof biochem & exp med, Col Med, Univ Cincinnati, 65-66; from asst prof to assoc prof chem, 66-74, PROF CHEM, MARSHALL UNIV, 74- *Mem:* Am Chem Soc. *Res:* Chemistry of fire supression; computer modeling of fire supression systems; models for effect of solvent or reactions. *Mailing Add:* Dept of Chem Marshall Univ Huntington WV 25701

ROBERTS, JULIAN LEE, JR, b Columbia, Mo, June 15, 35; m 65. ANALYTICAL CHEMISTRY. *Educ:* Univ Southern Calif, BA, 57; Northwestern Univ, PhD(anal chem), 62. *Prof Exp:* Instr chem, Univ Redlands, 61-63; res chemist & vis lectr, Univ Calif, Riverside, 63-64; from asst prof to assoc prof chem, 64-73, PROF CHEM, UNIV REDLANDS, 73- *Concurrent Pos:* NSF sci fac fel, Calif Inst Technol, 68-69; vis scientist, Lab Org & Anal Electrochem, Ctr Nuclear Studies, Grenoble, France, 75-76. *Mem:* AAAS; Am Chem Soc; NY Acad Sci. *Res:* Structural and electroanalytical chemistry; mechanisms of electrochemical reactions; electrochemistry of dissolved gases and coordination compounds. *Mailing Add:* Dept of Chem Univ of Redlands Redlands CA 92373

ROBERTS, KENNETH BRYSON, b London, Eng, Sept 7, 23; m 45; c 4. PHYSIOLOGY, HISTORY OF MEDICINE. *Educ:* Univ London, MB & BS, 45; Oxford Univ, BA, 49, DPhil, 52. *Prof Exp:* Lectr physiol, Exeter Col, Oxford Univ, 52-55; assoc prof, Med Col, Baghdad, Iraq, 55-56; sr lectr, Univ Edinburgh, 56-62; reader, Univ London, 62-68; prof physiol, 68-78, JOHN CLINCH PROF HIST MED & PHYSIOL, MEM UNIV NFLD, 78- *Concurrent Pos:* Assoc dean basic med sci, Mem Univ Nfld, 68-75. *Mem:* Can Physiol Soc; Physiol Soc Gt Brit; Can Soc Hist Med. *Mailing Add:* Med Sch Health Sci Ctr Mem Univ Nfld St John's NF A1C 5S7 Can

ROBERTS, KENNETH DAVID, b Montreal, Que, Nov 20, 31; m 60; c 1. BIOCHEMISTRY, ENDOCRINOLOGY. *Educ:* George Williams Col, BSc, 55; McGill Univ, PhD(biochem), 60. *Prof Exp:* Chemist, Charles E Frosst & Co, 49-55; Jane C Childs Mem Fund fel, Univ Basel, 61-63; asst prof biochem, Columbia Univ, 63-69; assoc prof, 69-77, PROF BIOCHEM, UNIV MONTREAL, 77- *Concurrent Pos:* Corresp ed, Steroids, 63-; consult, Endocrine Lab, Maisonneuve Hosp, Montreal, 69- mem grants comt, Med Res Coun Can, 71- *Mem:* AAAS; NY Acad Sci; Can Fertility Soc; Endocrine Soc; Can Biochem Soc. *Res:* Biochemistry of steroids and steroid conjugates; reproduction. *Mailing Add:* 2084 de la Regence St Bruno PQ J3V 4B6 Can

ROBERTS, LARRY SPURGEON, b Texon, Tex, June 30, 35; m 62; c 4. ZOOLOGY, PARASITOLOGY. *Educ:* Southern Methodist Univ, BSc, 56; Univ Ill, MSc, 58; Johns Hopkins Univ, ScD(parasitol), 61. *Prof Exp:* USPHS-NIH trainee, McGill Univ, 61-62; trainee, Univ Mass, Amherst, 62-63, from asst prof zool to prof 62-79; PROF & CHAIRPERSON BIOL SCI, TEX TECHNOL UNIV, LUBBOCK, 79- *Concurrent Pos:* USPHS-NIH spec fel, Johns Hopkins Univ, 69-70. *Honors & Awards:* Henry Baldwin Ward Medal, Am Soc Parasitol, 71. *Mem:* Am Soc Parasitol; Soc Protozoologists; Am Soc Trop Med Hyg; Am Micros Soc (vpres, 75). *Res:* Developmental biochemistry of helminth parasites, expecially cestodes; regulation of carbohydrate and energy metabolism in cestodes; systematics and morphology of parasitic copepods. *Mailing Add:* Dept Biol Sci Tex Technol Univ Lubbock TX 79409

ROBERTS, LEIGH M, b Jacksonville, Ill, June 9, 25; m 46; c 4. PSYCHIATRY. *Educ:* Univ Ill, BS, 45, MD, 47. *Prof Exp:* Intern med, St Francis Hosp, Peoria, Ill, 47-48; pvt pract, 48-50; resident, Univ Hosps, 53-56, clin instr, Sch Med, 56-58, from asst prof to assoc prof, 59-71, actg chmn dept, 72-75, PROF PSYCHIAT, SCH MED, UNIV WIS-MADISON, 71- *Concurrent Pos:* Staff psychiatrist, Mendota State Hosp, Madison, 56-58, consult, 60-; consult, Wis Child Ctr, Sparta, 56-58, Cent State Hosp, 62-70 & State Ment Health Planning, 63-; mem spec rev bd, Wis Div Corrections, 63-; mem bd, Methodist Hosp, Madison, 65- & Goodwill Industs, 71- *Mem:* AAAS; fel Am Psychiat Asn; AMA. *Res:* Community psychiatry; psychiatry and law. *Mailing Add:* Dept of Psychiat Univ of Wis Sch of Med Madison WI 53706

ROBERTS, LEONARD, b Prestatyn, North Wales, UK, Sept 27, 29; US citizen; m 55; c 2. APPLIED MATHEMATICS, AERODYNAMICS. *Educ:* Univ Manchester, BSc, 52, MSc, 54, PhD, 55. *Prof Exp:* Res assoc, Mass Inst Technol, 55-57; aerospace res engr theoret, Mech Div, Langley Res Ctr, NASA, 57-59, head math physics br, Dynamic Loads Div, 59-66, dir mission anal div, NASA Hq, 66-69; Stanford Sloan fel, 69-70; DIR AERONAUT & FLIGHT SYSTS, AMES RES CTR, NASA, 70- *Concurrent Pos:* Consult prof aeronaut & astronaut, Stanford Univ, 75- *Mem:* Am Inst Aeronaut & Astronaut; Am Helicopter Soc. *Res:* Aerodynamics; flight dynamics; guidance and control; aeronautical vehicles; aviation systems; research using wind tunnels, simulators and experimental aircraft; management of aeronautical research and development. *Mailing Add:* Aeronaut & Flight Systs NASA Ames Res Ctr Moffett Field CA 94035

ROBERTS, LEONIDAS HOWARD, b Garard's Ft, Pa, Feb 27, 21; m 45; c 2. PHYSICAL SCIENCES, ASTRONOMY. *Educ:* Waynesburg Col, BS, 48; WVa Univ, MS, 49; Univ Fla, PhD(appl math), 58. *Prof Exp:* From instr to asst prof phys sci, 49-61, assoc prof phys sci & astron, 61-71, PROF PHYS SCI & ASTRON, UNIV FLA, 71- *Mem:* Am Astron Soc. *Res:* Astronomy. *Mailing Add:* Rm 460 Winston Little Hall Univ Fla Dept of Phys Sci Gainesville FL 32611

ROBERTS, LESLIE GORDON, b Flin Flon, Man, Aug 16, 41; m 67. MATHEMATICS. *Educ:* Univ Man, BSc, 63; Harvard Univ, PhD(math), 68. *Prof Exp:* asst prof, 68-76, ASSOC PROF MATH, QUEEN'S UNIV, ONT, 76- *Mem:* Am Math Soc; Can Math Cong. *Res:* Algebraic K-theory; algebraic geometry. *Mailing Add:* Dept of Math Queen's Univ Kingston ON K7L 3N6 Can

ROBERTS, LORIN WATSON, b Clarksdale, Mo, June 28, 23; m 67; c 3. PLANT PHYSIOLOGY. *Educ:* Univ Mo, AB, 48, MA, 50, PhD(bot), 52. *Prof Exp:* Asst bot, Univ Mo, 49-52; asst prof biol, Agnes Scott Col, 52-56, assoc prof, 56-57; from asst prof to assoc prof bot, 57-67, PROF BOT, UNIV IDAHO, 67- *Concurrent Pos:* Vis asst prof, Emory Univ, 52-55; pres bot sect, Int Cong Histochem & Cytochem, Paris, 60; Fulbright res prof, Kyoto Univ, 67-68; vis prof, Bot Inst, Univ Bari, 68; Maria Moors Cabot res fel, Harvard Univ, 74; Fulbright vis lectr, NEastern Hill Univ, Shillong, Meghalaya, India, 77; Fulbright sr scholar & vis fel, Australian Nat Univ, Canberra, 80. *Honors & Awards:* Chevalier de l'Ordre du Merite Agricole, France, 61. *Mem:* Fel AAAS; Bot Soc Am; Am Soc Plant Physiol; Histochem Soc; Int Asn Plant Tissue Cult. *Res:* Plant histochemistry; physiology of vascular differentiation; physiological action of plant hormones. *Mailing Add:* Dept of Biol Sci Univ of Idaho Moscow ID 83843

ROBERTS, LOUIS DOUGLAS, b Charleston, SC, Jan 27, 18; m 42; c 1. SOLID STATE PHYSICS. *Educ:* Howard Col, AB, 38; Columbia Univ, PhD(phys chem), 41. *Prof Exp:* Nat Res Coun fel, Cornell Univ, 41-42; res physicist, Gen Elec Co, NY, 42-46; physicist, Oak Ridge Nat Lab, 46-68; PROF PHYSICS, UNIV NC, CHAPEL HILL, 68- *Concurrent Pos:* Prof, Univ Tenn, 63-68. *Mem:* Fel Am Phys Soc. *Res:* Semiconductors; vacuum tube design and ion optics; neutron diffusion theory and measurement; low temperature physics; low energy nuclear and solid state physics; high pressure physics. *Mailing Add:* Dept of Physics & Astron Univ of NC Chapel Hill NC 27514

ROBERTS, LOUIS REED, b Wray, Colo, July 8, 23; m 48; c 3. CHEMICAL ENGINEERING. *Educ:* Univ Colo, BS, 49, Rice Univ, MA, 51; Univ Tex, PhD(chem eng), 63. *Prof Exp:* Jr chemist, Gulf Oil Corp, 51-53, chemist, 53-56; chem engr, Southwest Res Inst, 56-58; sr chem engr, Union Tex Petrol Div, Allied Chem Corp, 62-63, engr, Cent Res Lab, 63-70, res chem engr, Chem Res Lab, 70-76; DIV DIR, STATE OF TEX, 76- *Mem:* Fel Am Inst Chem Engrs. *Res:* Vapor-liquid equilibria of hydrocarbon fixed-gas systems; high temperature chemistry; petrochemical and polymer processes. *Mailing Add:* 8611 Honeysuckle Austin TX 78759

ROBERTS, LOUIS W, b Jamestown, NY, Sept 1, 13; m 38; c 2. PHYSICS. *Educ:* Fisk Univ, AB, 35; Univ Mich, MS, 37. *Prof Exp:* Teaching asst physics & math, Fisk Univ, 35-36; instr, St Augustine's Col, 37-40, assoc prof physics, 41-43; asst prof, Howard Univ, 43-44; sr engr, Sylvania Elec Prod, Inc, 44-46, sect head tubes, 46-47, mgr tube develop, 47-50; pres, dir & founder, Microwave Assocs, 50-51, vpres, 51-55; eng specialist, Bomac Labs, Inc Div, Varian Inc, 55-59; vpres, dir & founder, Metcom Inc, 59-67; consult optics & microwaves, Electronic Res Ctr, NASA, 67, chief, Microwave Lab, 67-68, chief, Optics & Microwave Lab, 68-70; from dep dir to actg dir technol, 70-72, dir technol, 72-77, dir energy & environ, 77-79, Dep Dir, 79, DIR DATA SYSTS & TECHNOL, TRANSPORTATION SYSTS CTR, US DEPT TRANSPORTATION, 80- *Concurrent Pos:* Res assoc, Stand Oil NJ, 35-36; prof, A&T State Univ, NC, 41-43; instr, US Signal Corps Sch, 42; prof, Shaw Univ, 42-43 & Army Specialized Training Prog, Washington, DC, 43-44; staff mem, Res Lab Electronics, Mass Inst Technol, 50-51; pres, Elcon Lab, Inc, Metcom Inc & consult, Addison-Wesley Press, 63-67; mem, US-Japan Natural Resources Comt, US Dept Interior, 69-78, adv group aerospace res & develop, Nato, 73-79; vis engr & lectr, Mass Inst Technol, 79-80. *Mem:* AAAS; fel Inst Elec & Electronics Engrs; Am Phys Soc; Am Math Soc; Am Inst Aeronaut & Astronaut. *Res:* Microwave and optical techniques and components; plasma research and solid state component and circuit development. *Mailing Add:* Transportation Systs Ctr 55 Broadway Cambridge MA 02142

ROBERTS, MARTIN, b Brooklyn, NY, May 8, 20; m 49; c 4. BIOCHEMISTRY. *Educ:* City Col New York, BS, 42; Brooklyn Col, MA, 47; Univ Southern Calif, PhD(biochem), 51. *Prof Exp:* Res org chemist, Schwarz Labs, Inc, 43-47; sr clin res biochemist, Don Baxter, Inc, 51-66; mgt & med dir, Artificial Kidney Supply Div, Sweden Freezer Mfg Co, Seattle, 66-71; dir clin invest, 71-74, vpres mkt, CCI Life Systs Inc, Van Nuys, 74-76; vpres, 76-80, DIR MED & REGULATORY AFFAIRS, REDY LABS, ORGANON TEKNIKA, 80- *Mem:* AAAS; Am Soc Artificial Internal Organs; Asn Advan Med Instrumentation; Am Soc Nephrol; Int Cong Nephrol. *Res:* Nucleic acid derivatives; parenteral and nutritional solutions, peritoneal and hemodialysis. *Mailing Add:* 16022 Parthenia St Sepulveda CA 91343

ROBERTS, MARY FEDARKO, b Pittsburgh, Pa, July 11, 47; m 74; c 1. BIOCHEMISTRY, PHYSICAL CHEMISTRY. *Educ:* Bryn Mawr Col, AB, 69; Stanford Univ, PhD(chem), 74. *Prof Exp:* Res assoc biochem, Univ Ill, Urbana-Champaign, 74-75; NIH trainee biol, Univ Calif, San Diego, 75-77, NIH fel chem, 77-78; ASST PROF CHEM, MASS INST TECHNOL, 78- *Mailing Add:* Dept of Chem 18-023 Mass Inst Technol Cambridge MA 02139

ROBERTS, MERVIN FRANCIS, b New York, NY, June 7, 22; m 49; c 5. ANIMAL BEHAVIOR. *Educ:* Alfred Univ, BS, 47. *Prof Exp:* Sr inspector, New York Port Authority, 47-56; lab mgr, De Lackner Helicopters, NY, 56-58 & Irco Corp, 58-59; assoc ed, McGraw Hill Publ Co, 59-60; ed supvr, Anco Tech Writing Serv, 60-61; mgr res & develop, T F H Publ, Inc, 61-67, asst to pres res & develop, 67-68; MGR RES & DEVELOP, WIDGET CO OLD LYME, 68- *Concurrent Pos:* Fish behav consult, Northeast Utilities Serv Corp, 70-; mem, Govr's Coun Marine Resources, Conn, 70-, chmn, 71. *Mem:* Am Ceramic Soc; Am Soc Ichthyol & Herpet. *Res:* Photography of high speed animal movements; photography of high temperature ceramics, flames and plasmas; design of ion beam generators and laboratory equipment; glass-metal interface relations; small animal maintenance; fish culture; tidemash ecosystems; author or coauthor of over 20 publications on care of caged animals and on tidemarsh life. *Mailing Add:* Duck River Lane Old Lyme CT 06371

ROBERTS, MICHAEL FOSTER, b Guatemala, Guatemala, Aug 8, 43; US citizen; m 66. PHYSIOLOGY, ZOOLOGY. *Educ:* Univ Calif, Berkeley, BA, 66; Univ Wis-Madison, MA, 68, PhD(zool), 72. *Prof Exp:* NIH spec fel, 74-75; ASST PROF, DEPT EPIDEMIOL, SCH MED, YALE UNIV, 76- *Concurrent Pos:* Asst fel, John B Pierce Found Lab. *Mem:* AAAS; Sigma Xi; Am Physiol Soc. *Res:* Peripheral circulation and temperature regulation. *Mailing Add:* Sch Med Yale Univ 290 Congress Ave New Haven CT 06519

ROBERTS, MORTON SPITZ, b New York, NY, Nov 5, 26; m 51; c 1. RADIO ASTRONOMY. *Educ:* Pomona Col, BA, 48; Calif Inst Technol, MS, 50; Univ Calif, PhD(astron), 58. *Hon Degrees:* DSc, Pomona Col, 79. *Prof Exp:* Asst prof physics, Occidental Col, 49-52; physicist underwater ord, US Naval Ord Testing Sta, 52-53; jr res astronr, Univ Calif, 57-58, NSF fel, 58-59, lectr astron & asst res astronr, Radio Astron Lab, 59-60; lectr astron & res assoc, Observ, Harvard Univ, 60-64; asst dir, 69-70, scientist, 64-78, SR SCIENTIST & DIR, NAT RADIO ASTRON OBSERV, 78- *Concurrent Pos:* Vis prof, Univ Calif, Berkeley, 68, State Univ NY, Stony Brook, 68, Inst Theoret Astron, Cambridge, 72 & Univ Groningen, 72; Sigma Xi nat lectr, 70-71; assoc ed, Astron J, 77- *Mem:* AAAS; Int Union Radio Sci; Am Astron Soc (vpres, 71-72); Int Astron Union. *Res:* Galaxies; galactic structure; interstellar and intergalactic matter. *Mailing Add:* Nat Radio Astron Observ Edgemont Rd Charlottesville VA 22901

ROBERTS, NORBERT JOSEPH, b Alabama, NY, June 6, 16; m 43; c 5. MEDICINE. *Educ:* Canisius Col, 34-36; Univ Buffalo, MD, 40; Univ Minn, MS, 49; Am Bd Internal Med, dipl, 50; Am Bd Prev Med, dipl, 55. *Prof Exp:* Physician, Exxon Corp, 49-52; med dir, Pa RR Co, 52-55; assoc med dir, 55-73, med dir, 73-81, VPRES MED & ENVIRON HEALTH, EXXON CORP, 81- *Concurrent Pos:* Asst prof, Sch Med, Univ Pa, 53-73; mem US deleg, Permanent Comn & Int Asn Occup Health, 57-; lectr, Inst Environ Med, NY Univ, 58-; assoc clin prof, Mt Sinai Sch Med. *Honors & Awards:* Knudsen Award, 76; Robert Kehoe Award, 80. *Mem:* Fel Am Occup Med Asn (pres, 71-72); fel Am Col Prev Med; fel Am Col Physicians; fel Am Acad Occup Med; NY Acad Med (pres, 81-). *Res:* Internal and occupational medicine; preventive medicine. *Mailing Add:* 688 Key Royale Dr Holmes Beach FL 33510

ROBERTS, NORMAN HAILSTONE, b Seattle, Wash, Mar 3, 22; m 48; c 3. APPLIED STATISTICS. *Educ:* Univ Wash, BS, 46, PhD(physics), 57. *Prof Exp:* Asst physicist, Appl Physics Lab, 55, instr mech eng, Univ, 56-57, from assoc physicist to physicist, Appl Physics Lab, 57-65, actg assoc prof mech eng, Univ, 66-68, ASSOC PROF MECH ENG, UNIV WASH, 68-, SR PHYSICIST, APPL PHYSICS LAB, 66- *Concurrent Pos:* Consult to adv comt reactor safeguards, AEC, 69- *Mem:* AAAS; Am Asn Physics Teachers; NY Acad Sci; Syst Safety Soc. *Res:* Electron energy loss; ferroelectricity; statistics, reliability and systems analysis; physics of the oceans. *Mailing Add:* Dept of Mech Eng Univ of Wash Seattle WA 98195

ROBERTS, PAUL ALFRED, b Chicago, Ill, Dec 22, 31; m 57, 71; c 5. GENETICS. *Educ:* Univ Ill, Urbana, BS, 53, Univ Ill, Chicago, MD, 57; Univ Chicago, PhD(zool), 62; Chicago Teachers Col, MEd, 62. *Prof Exp:* Res assoc biol, Oak Ridge Nat Lab, 62-63, biologist, 63-66; assoc prof zool, 66-73, PROF ZOOL, ORE STATE UNIV, 73- *Mem:* Genetics Soc Am. *Res:* Chromosome behavior; developmental biology; cytogenetics; aging in Drosophila. *Mailing Add:* Dept Zool Ore State Univ Corvallis OR 97331

ROBERTS, PAUL OSBORNE, JR, b Memphis, Tenn, Mar 6, 33; m 57; c 3. TRANSPORTATION MANAGEMENT. *Educ:* Tex A&M Univ, BS, 55; Mass Inst Technol, SM, 57; Northwestern Univ, PhD(transp eng), 65. *Prof Exp:* Engr in charge electronic comput ctr, Michael Baker, Jr, Inc, Pa, 57-60; asst prof civil eng, Mass Inst Technol, 60-66; lectr transp, Harvard Univ, 66-69, assoc prof transp & logistics, Bus Sch, Harvard Univ, 69-72; prof transp eng & sr lectr, Sloan Sch Mgt, 72-76, PROF CIVIL ENG & DIR CTR TRANSP STUDIES, MASS INST TECHNOL, 76- *Concurrent Pos:* Mem, Hwy Res Bd, Nat Acad Sci-Nat Res Coun. *Mem:* Opers Res Soc Am; Inst Traffic Engrs. *Res:* Economic and engineering analysis of transportation systems, particularly as related to economic development; engineering project analyses; decision theory; business logistics; industry location; urban growth. *Mailing Add:* Dept of Civil Eng Mass Inst of Technol Cambridge MA 02139

ROBERTS, RALPH JACKSON, b Rosalia, Wash, Jan 31, 11; m 42; c 3. GEOLOGY. *Educ:* Univ Wash, BS, 35, MS, 37; Yale Univ, PhD, 49. *Prof Exp:* Geologist, US Geol Surv, 39-42, Cent Am, 42-45 & Nev-Utah, 45-71, tech adv econ geol, US Geol Surv, Saudi Arabia, 72-78, Nev, 78-80; CONSULT, 81- *Mem:* Geol Soc Am; Soc Econ Geologists. *Res:* Economic and structural geology of Nevada; geology of Cordilleran fold-belt; volcanogenic ore deposits in Arabian Shield; economic geology, western United States. *Mailing Add:* Box 136 Lilliwaup WA 98555

ROBERTS, REGINALD FRANCIS, b Baton Rouge, La, Feb 14, 23. PHYSICAL CHEMISTRY. *Educ:* La State Univ, AB, 42, BS, 47, MS, 50. *Prof Exp:* From asst res chemist to sr res chemist, Kaiser Aluminum & Chem Corp, 50-58, sr develop chemist, 59-63; SR RES CHEMIST, DOW CHEM CO, PLAQUEMINE, 64- *Mem:* Am Chem Soc. *Res:* Chemical kinetics; reaction mechanisms; physical organic chemistry; structural theory; effect of structure on reactivity; relationship between physical properties and molecular structure; thermodynamics. *Mailing Add:* La Div Res & Develop Dow Chem Co Rinir Rd PO Box 150 Plaquemine LA 70764

ROBERTS, RICHARD, b Atlantic, City, NJ, Feb 16, 38; m 60; c 3. MECHANICAL ENGINEERING. *Educ:* Drexel Univ, BS, 61; Lehigh Univ, MS, 62, PhD(mech eng), 64. *Prof Exp:* From asst prof to assoc prof, 64-77, PROF MECH ENG, LEHIGH UNIV, 77- *Honors & Awards:* Spraragen Award, Am Welding Soc, 72. *Mem:* Am Soc Mech Engrs; Am Soc Testing & Mat; Am Soc Eng Educ; Am Welding Soc; Am Soc Metals. *Res:* Fracture mechanics; material behavior; experimental stress analysis. *Mailing Add:* Mat Res Ctr Lehigh Univ Bethlehem PA 18015

ROBERTS, RICHARD A, b San Diego, Calif, Feb 27, 35. ELECTRICAL ENGINEERING. *Educ:* Univ Calif, Berkeley, BS, 57; Univ Mich, MS, 61, PhD(elec eng), 65. *Prof Exp:* Res assoc radar, Willow Run Lab, Univ Mich, 57-59, res assoc signal detection, Cooley Electronics Lab, 59-65; asst prof elec eng & comput sci, 65-70, assoc prof elec eng, 70-73, PROF ELEC ENG, UNIV COLO, BOULDER, 73- *Concurrent Pos:* NSF grants, 66-68, 68-70 & 75-77; Army Res Off Durham grants, 70-80 & 80-82; Univ Colo fac fel, Duke Univ, 72-73 & 78-79; Croft fel, 82. *Mem:* Inst Elec & Electronics Engrs. *Res:* Detection and extraction of signals from noise; computer applications to decision processes; digital filtering in biomedical applications; digital filtering structures; low noise structures; efficient hardware realizations; microcomputer realizations of digital signal processors; very large scale intergration implementation of digital signal processing tasks. *Mailing Add:* Dept of Elec Eng Univ of Colo Boulder CO 80302

ROBERTS, RICHARD CALVIN, b Akron, Ohio, May 26, 25; m 49; c 1. APPLIED MATHEMATICS. *Educ:* Kenyon Col, AB, 46; Brown Univ, ScM, 46, PhD(appl math), 49. *Prof Exp:* Asst appl math, Brown Univ, 46-48, res assoc, 48-50; fel, Univ Md, 50-51; mathematician, US Naval Ord Lab, 51-66, chief math dept, 60-66; div chmn, 66-74, dean div math & physics, 74-78, PROF MATH, UNIV MD BALTIMORE COUNTY, 78- *Mem:* Am Math Soc; Math Asn Am. *Res:* Fluid dynamics; numerical methods; finite differences. *Mailing Add:* Dept of Math Univ of Md Baltimore County Baltimore MD 21228

ROBERTS, RICHARD HARRIS, b Buffalo, NY, Oct 24, 24; m 54; c 3. MEDICAL ENTOMOLOGY, VETERINARY ENTOMOLOGY. *Educ:* Univ Buffalo, BA, 50, MA, 52; Univ Wis, PhD(med & vet entom), 56. *Prof Exp:* Asst invert zool, Univ Buffalo, 50-52; vet entom, Univ Wis, 52-56; RES ENTOMOLOGIST, SCI & EDUC ADMIN-FED RES, USDA, 56- *Concurrent Pos:* Adj assoc prof entom, Miss State Univ, 65-; adj prof entom, Univ Fla, 76- *Mem:* Entom Soc Am; Am Mosquito Control Asn; Am Soc Trop Med & Hyg. *Res:* Livestock-affecting insects, especially biology, control and taxonomy of Tabanidae and the vectors of bovine anaplasmosis; pesticide development on mosquitoes, houseflies, stableflies, ticks and chiggers. *Mailing Add:* Insects Affecting Man Res Lab PO Box 14565 Gainesville FL 32604

ROBERTS, RICHARD JOHN, b Derby, Eng, Sept 6, 43; m 65; c 2. MOLECULAR BIOLOGY. *Educ:* Sheffield Univ, BSc, 65, PhD(chem), 68. *Prof Exp:* Fel chem, Sheffield Univ, 68-69; fel biochem, Harvard Univ, 69-70, res assoc, 71-72; SR STAFF INVESTR MOLECULAR BIOL, COLD SPRING HARBOR LAB, 72- *Concurrent Pos:* Consult, New Eng Biolabs, 75- & Genex Corp, 78-; John Simon Guggenheim fel, 79-80. *Mem:* The Chem Soc; AAAS; Am Soc Microbiol; Fedn Am Soc Exp Biol. *Res:* Restriction endonucleases and their application for DNA sequence analysis and genetic engineering; molecular biology of adenovirus -2. *Mailing Add:* Cold Spring Harbor Lab Cold Spring Harbor NY 11724

ROBERTS, RICHARD NORMAN, b Lockport, NY, Sept 3, 30; m 61; c 1. BIOCHEMISTRY. *Educ:* Univ Buffalo, BA, 57, MA, 59, PhD(biochem), 62. *Prof Exp:* Fel biochem, Rutgers Univ, 62-64; res assoc, Cornell Univ, 64-65; res biochemist, 65-69, ANAL CHEMIST, GEN ELEC CO, SYRACUSE, 69- *Mem:* AAAS; Am Chem Soc; Sigma Xi. *Res:* Intermediary metabolism; metabolic pathways; products of microbial metabolism on synthetic and natural substrates; related organic-analytical techniques especially gas chromatography and infrared spectrophotometry; gas chromatographic identification of micro-organisms. *Mailing Add:* 117 North Way Camillus NY 13031

ROBERTS, RICHARD W, b Milwaukee, Wis, Dec 9, 21; m 43; c 2. ORGANIC CHEMISTRY. *Educ:* Marquette Univ, BS, 43; Lawrence Univ, MS, 49, PhD, 51. *Prof Exp:* Instr chem, Marquette Univ, 47; res chemist, Int Paper Co, 51-52 & Marathon Corp, 52-63; RES SUPVR & COMPUTER MGR, WAUSAU PAPER MILLS CO, 63- *Mem:* Am Chem Soc; Tech Asn Pulp & Paper Indust; Am Soc Qual Control. *Res:* Computer process control; pulp bleaching; product development; statistical techniques. *Mailing Add:* Wausau Paper Mills Brokaw WI 54417

ROBERTS, ROBERT ABRAM, b Iowa City, Iowa, Oct 28, 23; m 49; c 3. MATHEMATICS. *Educ:* WVa Wesleyan Col, BS, 45; Univ WVa, MS, 48; Univ Mich, PhD, 54. *Prof Exp:* Asst prof math, Univ WVa, 52-53; asst prof, Univ Miami, 53-58; sr mathematician, Bettis Plant, Westinghouse Elec Corp, Pa, 58-59; assoc prof math, Ohio Wesleyan Univ, 59-61; from assoc prof to prof, Denison Univ, 61-72; chmn dept, 72-77, PROF MATH, WASHINGTON & LEE UNIV, 72- *Concurrent Pos:* NSF fel, 65-66. *Mem:* AAAS; Am Math Soc; Math Asn Am; Soc Indust & Appl Math. *Res:* Mathematical physics; atomic structure; numerical analysis; computing machinery; educational use of machines. *Mailing Add:* Dept of Math Washington & Lee Univ Lexington VA 24450

ROBERTS, ROBERT EARL, physical chemistry, atmospheric physics, see previous edition

ROBERTS, ROBERT MICHAEL, b Ilkley, Eng, Oct 23, 40; m 61; c 2. BIOCHEMISTRY, PLANT PHYSIOLOGY. *Educ:* Oxford Univ, BA, 62, DPhil(plant physiol, biochem), 65. *Prof Exp:* Res assoc biol, State Univ NY Buffalo, 65-67, asst prof, 67-68; UK Atomic Energy Authority sr res fel, Radiochem Ctr, Amersham, Eng, 68-69; asst prof biochem, 70-72, assoc prof, 72-77, PROF BIOCHEM, UNIV FLA, 77- *Concurrent Pos:* Grants, Nat Cystic Fibrosis Res Found, Univ Fla, 71-72, NSF, 70-72 & NIH, 71-74 & 75-84. *Mem:* AAAS; Am Soc Biol Chem; Soc Study Reprod; Am soc Cell Biol. *Res:* Dynamics of membrane polypeptides in cultured mammalian cells; function and hormonal control of protein secretion in the mammalian uterus; blustolyst-uterus interactions in early pregnancy; iron-binding proteins. *Mailing Add:* Dept of Biochem Univ of Fla Gainesville FL 32611

ROBERTS, ROBERT RUSSELL, b Fitchburg, Mass, Mar 4, 31; m 53; c 3. MICROBIOLOGY, MOLECULAR BIOLOGY. *Educ:* Brigham Young Univ, BS, 70, MS, 72, PhD(microbiol), 75. *Prof Exp:* MICROBIOLOGIST, HAWAIIAN SUGAR PLANTERS ASN, 76- *Mem:* AAAS; Am Soc Microbiol; Am Chem Soc; Soc Indust Microbiol. *Res:* Molecular biology; recombinant DNA; microbial and yeast genetics; industrial fermentations; general applied microbiology. *Mailing Add:* Hawaiian Sugar Planters Asn Aiea HI 96701

ROBERTS, ROBERT WILLIAM, b Riverside, Ill, July 24, 23; m 46; c 3. CHEMICAL ENGINEERING. *Educ:* Washington Univ, St Louis, BSChE, 48; Univ Iowa, MS, 60, PhD(chem eng), 62. *Prof Exp:* Develop engr, Aluminum Ore Co, 48, prod engr, 49-51; foreman extrusion, Cryovac Div, W R Grace & Co, 51-52, plant engr, 52-57, tech dir, Western Div, 57-59; group supvr process res, Allegany Ballistics Lab, Hercules, Inc, 62-64; dir res & develop, Cadillac Plastics & Chem Co, 64-66; from assoc prof to prof, 66-77, head dept, 70-77, ROBERT IREDELL PROF CHEM ENG & RES ASSOC, INST POLYMER SCI, UNIV AKRON, 77- *Concurrent Pos:* Dean, Plastics Eng Prog, Algerian Inst Petrol, 79-80. *Mem:* Am Inst Chem Engrs; Soc Plastics Engrs; Am Soc Eng Educ. *Res:* Process design and economics; plastic processing; thermodynamics; research administration. *Mailing Add:* Dept of Chem Eng Univ of Akron Akron OH 44325

ROBERTS, RONALD C, b Meadville, Pa, Jan 28, 36; m 60; c 2. PHYSICAL BIOCHEMISTRY. *Educ:* Pa State Univ, BS, 57; Univ Minn, PhD(biochem), 64. *Prof Exp:* Res asst biochem, Univ Minn, 57-64, NIH fel & res assoc, 64-66; RES BIOCHEMIST, MARSHFIELD MED FOUND, 66- *Concurrent Pos:* Adj assoc prof chem, Univ Wis-Stevens Pt, 78-; adj prof, Biol Dept, Univ Wis-Oshkosh, 80- *Mem:* Am Chem Soc; Am Soc Clin Res; Am Acad Allergy; Am Soc Biol Chemists; Reticuloendothelial Soc. *Res:* Physical and chemical characterization of proteins, particularly blood serum proteins; chemical and immunological studies on the antigens of hypersensitivity pneumonitis. *Mailing Add:* Marshfield Med Found 510 N St Joseph's Ave Marshfield WI 54449

ROBERTS, RONALD FREDERICK, b Brooklyn, NY, Mar 26, 44; m 66; c 2. SURFACE CHEMISTRY. *Educ:* St John's Univ, BS, 65; Long Island Univ, MS, 67; NY Univ, PhD(phys chem), 72. *Prof Exp:* MEM TECH STAFF RES, BELL LABS, 71- *Mem:* AAAS; Am Chem Soc; Soc Appl Spectroscopy. *Res:* Electron spectroscopic investigation of the adsorption of chemical species onto inorganic surfaces as related to corrosion inhibition, and the chemical modification of polymer surfaces as related to adhesion and other phenomena. *Mailing Add:* Eight Winston Dr Somerset NJ 08873

ROBERTS, RONNIE SPENCER, b Pascagoula, Miss, June 5, 43. CHEMICAL ENGINEERING, BIOCHEMICAL ENGINEERING. *Educ:* Univ Miss, BSChE, 66; Univ Tenn, Knoxville, MS, 72, PhD(chem eng), 76. *Prof Exp:* Tech serv engr, Monsanto Co, 66-69; ASST PROF CHEM ENG, GA INST TECHNOL, 76- *Concurrent Pos:* Consult, Milliken & Co, 77-78. *Mem:* Am Inst Chem Engrs; Am Soc Eng Educ. *Res:* In vitro production of mammalian cells-cellular products; microbial processes; transport phenomena. *Mailing Add:* Sch of Chem Eng Ga Inst of Technol Atlanta GA 30332

ROBERTS, ROYSTON MURPHY, b Sherman, Tex, June 11, 18; m 43; c 4. ORGANIC CHEMISTRY. *Educ:* Austin Col, BA, 40; Univ Ill, MA, 41, PhD(org chem), 44. *Hon Degrees:* DSc, Austin Col, 65. *Prof Exp:* Asst, Comt Med Res, Off Sci Res & Develop, Univ Ill, 43-45; res chemist, Merck & Co, 45-46; fel, Univ Calif, Los Angeles, 46-47; from asst prof to assoc prof chem, 47-61, PROF CHEM, UNIV TEX, AUSTIN, 61- *Concurrent Pos:* Fel, Petrol Res Fund, Zurich, 59-60; consult. *Mem:* Am Chem Soc; The Chem Soc. *Res:* Organic synthesis; reaction mechanisms; reactions of ortho esters; imidic esters and amidines; new Friedel-Crafts chemistry; thermal rearrangement reactions. *Mailing Add:* Dept of Chem Univ of Tex Austin TX 78712

ROBERTS, RUFUS WINSTON, b Birmingham, Ala, Aug 9, 16; m 47; c 3. OPHTHALMOLOGY. *Educ:* Duke Univ, MD, 40; Am Bd Ophthal, dipl, 49. *Prof Exp:* From instr to prof ophthal, Bowman Gray Sch Med, 47-75, chief serv, 48-75; head opthal, LaMotte Clin & Hilton Head Hosp, 75-81; CONSULT, 81- *Concurrent Pos:* Mem, Josiah Macy, Jr Conf Glaucoma, 55-60. *Mem:* Am Acad Ophthal & Otolaryngol; Asn Res Vision & Ophthal; Pan Am Asn Ophthal. *Res:* Glaucoma, especially early and low tension glaucoma, diagnostic techniques, date retrieval, cataloguing early natural history, aqueous dynamics. *Mailing Add:* 25 Heritage Rd Hilton Head Island SC 29928

ROBERTS, SANFORD B(ERNARD), b New York, NY, Feb 20, 34; m 55; c 3. BIOMECHANICS, STRUCTURAL MECHANICS. *Educ:* City Col New York, BCE, 56; Univ Southern Calif, MSCE, 59; Univ Calif, Los Angeles, PhD(eng), 65. *Prof Exp:* Engr, Struct Space Div, N Am Aviation, Inc, 56-57; asst prof civil eng, Univ Southern Calif, 57-61; assoc eng, Univ Calif, Los Angeles, 61-63; design specialist, Rocketdyne Div, N Am Aviation, Inc, 63-65; asst prof eng, 65-71, ASSOC PROF ENG, UNIV CALIF, LOS ANGELES, 71- *Concurrent Pos:* Pres, Asn Sci Adv, 71-; consult, Civil & Aerospace Eng Co. *Mem:* Am Soc Civil Engrs. *Res:* Biomechanics, especially the structural dynamic behavior of the human body under normal and traumatic conditions; structural mechanics, theory of plates and shells. *Mailing Add:* Dept of Mech & Struct Univ of Calif Los Angeles CA 90024

ROBERTS, SHEPHERD (KNAPP DE FOREST), b Princeton, NJ, Mar 15, 32; m 55; c 4. COMPARATIVE PHYSIOLOGY. *Educ:* Princeton Univ, AB, 54, MA, 57, PhD(biol), 59. *Prof Exp:* Instr biol, Princeton Univ, 59-61; from asst prof to assoc prof, 61-75, PROF BIOL, TEMPLE UNIV, 75- *Concurrent Pos:* Prin investr, Bermuda Biol Sta, Off Naval Res, 59-60. *Mem:* AAAS; Animal Behav Soc; Int Soc Chromobiol. *Res:* Biological chronometry; diurnal rhythmic activities in animals. *Mailing Add:* Dept of Biol Temple Univ Philadelphia PA 19122

ROBERTS, SIDNEY, b Boston, Mass, Mar 11, 18; m 43. BIOLOGICAL CHEMISTRY, NEUROCHEMISTRY. *Educ:* Mass Inst Technol, SB, 39; Univ Minn, MS, 42, PhD(biochem), 43. *Prof Exp:* Instr physiol, Sch Med, Univ Minn, 43-44; instr, Sch Med, George Washington Univ, 44-45; res assoc, Worcester Found Exp Biol, 45-47; asst prof physiol chem, Sch Med, Yale Univ, 47-48; from asst prof to assoc prof, 48-57, PROF BIOL CHEM, SCH MED, UNIV CALIF, LOS ANGELES, 57- *Concurrent Pos:* Consult, Vet Admin Hosp, Long Beach, Calif, 51-55, NSF, 55-59, Vet Admin Hosp, Los Angeles, 58-62 & NIH, 60-62; Guggenheim fel, Univ London, 57; ed, Brain Res & Neurochem Res. *Honors & Awards:* Ciba Award, Endocrine Soc, 53. *Mem:* AAAS; Endocrine Soc (vpres, 68-69); Am Soc Biol Chemists; Am Soc Neurochem; Am Physiol Soc. *Res:* Biochemistry of information transfer and storage in the central nervous system; role of protein synthesis and protein modifiacation. *Mailing Add:* Dept of Biol Chem Sch of Med Univ of Calif Los Angeles CA 90024

ROBERTS, THEODORE S, b Waukesha, Wis, July 29, 26; m 53; c 4. NEUROSURGERY. *Educ:* Univ Wis, BS, 50, MS, 52, MD, 55. *Prof Exp:* Instr neurosurg & neuroanat, Sch Med, Univ Wis, 60-61; from instr to assoc prof neurosurg, 61-75, PROF NEUROSURG, COL MED, UNIV UTAH, 75-, CHMN DIV NEUROL SURG, 64- *Concurrent Pos:* Clin investr, Vet Admin Hosp, 61-63. *Mem:* Am Asn Neurol Surg; fel Am Col Surgeons; AMA. *Res:* Neuroanatomy and neurophysiology. *Mailing Add:* Div of Neurol Surg Univ of Utah Med Ctr Salt Lake City UT 84312

ROBERTS, THOMAS D, b New York, NY, June 21, 35; m 57; c 3. ELECTROPHYSICS. *Educ:* Ore State Univ, PhD(physics), 65. *Prof Exp:* Physicist, US Bur Mines, Ore, 59-64 & Nat Bur Stand, Colo, 65-66; assoc prof physics, 66-74, PROF PHYSICS & ELEC ENG, UNIV ALASKA, COLLEGE, 74- *Mem:* Am Phys Soc; Inst Elec & Electronics Engrs; Nat Asn Physics Teachers. *Res:* Propagation of electromagnetic radiation. *Mailing Add:* Dept of Elec Eng Univ of Alaska College AK 99701

ROBERTS, THOMAS DAVID, b Quanah, Tex, July 11, 38; m 57; c 3. ORGANIC CHEMISTRY. *Educ:* Abilene Christian Col, BS, 59; Ohio State Univ, PhD(chem), 67. *Prof Exp:* Res chemist, Explor Group, Pittsburgh Plate Glass Co, Ohio, 59-62; from asst prof to assoc prof chem, Univ Ark, Fayetteville, 67-77, prof, 77-79; CHEMIST, TEX EASTMAN CO, 79- *Concurrent Pos:* Petrol Res Fund grant, 67-79, 71-73 & 75-79; Res Corp grant, 69; vis assoc prof, Univ Fla, 73. *Mem:* Royal Soc Chem; Am Chem Soc. *Res:* Synthesis of strained small ring and pseudo-aromatic compounds; synthetic photochemistry; new synthetic reactions. *Mailing Add:* Res Labs Tex Eastman Co Longview TX 75607

ROBERTS, THOMAS GEORGE, b Ft Smith, Ark, Apr 27, 29; m 58; c 2. LASERS, PLASMA PHYSICS. *Educ:* Univ Ga, BS, 56, MS, 57; NC State Univ, PhD(physics), 67. *Prof Exp:* Instr physics, Univ Ga, 56-57; physicist, Army Rocket & Guided Missile Agency, 57-62; PHYSICIST, US ARMY MISSILE COMMAND, 62- *Concurrent Pos:* Consult, Ballistic Missile Defense Technol Ctr & Southeastern Inst Technol, 75-80. *Honors & Awards:* Dept Army-Army Missile Command Sci & Eng Achievement Award, 68. *Mem:* Am Phys Soc; Optical Soc Am; Sr mem Inst Elec & Electronic Engrs. *Res:* Behavior of very intense relativistic electron beams in plasmas; effects of short duration pulses of high energy on materials; high power laser technology where the active medium is a plasma or aerodynamic gases. *Mailing Add:* DRSMI-RHS US Army Missile Command Redstone Arsenal AL 35898

ROBERTS, THOMAS GLASDIR, b Clintonville, Wis, Aug 3, 18. MICROPALEONTOLOGY, STRATIGRAPHY. *Educ:* Univ Wis, PhB, 40; Columbia Univ, PhD(geol), 49. *Prof Exp:* Stratigrapher, Shell Oil Co, 41-46; instr geol, Univ Kans, 46-47; geologist & lab chief, Arctic Coastal Area Subsurface Invests, US Geol Surv, Alaska, 49-52, subsurface stratigrapher, Four Corners area, NMex, 52-55; asst prof geol, 56-59, ASSOC PROF GEOL, UNIV KY, 59- *Concurrent Pos:* Lectr, Univ Tulsa, 44-45; Fulbright & AID lectr, Ecuador, 71. *Mem:* Geol Soc Am; Am Asn Petrol Geologists; Sigma Xi. *Res:* Subsurface stratigraphy; Fusulinidae; phylogeny of Mississippian Archaediscidae of western Kentucky. *Mailing Add:* Dept of Geol Univ of Ky Lexington KY 40506

ROBERTS, THOMAS L, b Key West, Fla, Apr 17, 32; c 3. MICROBIAL BIOCHEMISTRY, GENETICS. *Educ:* Talladega Col, AB, 57; Trinity Univ, Tex, MS, 61; Clark Univ, PhD(microbiol, biochem), 65. *Prof Exp:* Res asst physiol, Med Br, Univ Tex, Galveston, 57-58; microbiologist, US Air Force Sch Aerospace Med, 59-63; from asst prof to assoc prof biol, 65-69, chmn dept biol, 72-76, PROF BIOL, WORCESTER STATE COL, 69-, EDUC DIR, NUCLEAR MED TECHNOL PROG, MASS MED SCH, 76- *Concurrent Pos:* Res assoc, Clark Univ, 65-67, res affiliate, 67-68; trustee, Rehab Ctr Worcester County, Inc, 75-81, pres, 77-81. *Mem:* Fel Sigma Xi; AAAS; NY Acad Sci; Am Soc Microbiol; fel Am Inst Chemists. *Res:* Immunochemistry related to learning under physical stresses. *Mailing Add:* Dept of Biol Worcester State Col Worcester MA 01602

ROBERTS, VERNE LOUIS, b Kansas City, Mo, Aug 11, 39; m 57; c 3. BIOMECHANICS, MECHANICAL ENGINEERING. *Educ:* Univ Kans, BS, 60; Univ Ill, MS, 61, PhD(eng mech), 64. *Prof Exp:* From asst prof to assoc prof eng mech, Wayne State Univ, 63-66, assoc prof neurosurg, 66; head dept biomech, Univ Mich, Ann Arbor, 66-73; ADJ PROF, DEPT MECH ENG, DUKE UNIV, 73-, DIR, INST PROD SAFETY, 79- *Concurrent Pos:* Assoc urol, Wayne State Univ, 64-66, fac res fel, 65; consult, Vet Admin, 64-66; mem engrs Joint Coun Comt Interaction Eng with Med & Biol, 65-66; co-ed in chief, J Biomech, 67-; mem, Comt Head Protection, Unified Space Appln Mission Standards Inst, 68-; mem, Adv Comt, Stapp Car Crash Conf, 68-; dir, Nat Driving Ctr, 73-78. *Honors & Awards:* Res Award, Am Soc Testing & Mat, 66. *Mem:* Am Soc Mech Engrs; Am Soc Safety Engrs; Syst Safety Soc; Am Soc Biomech; Europ Soc Biomech. *Res:* Safe product design. *Mailing Add:* Inst for Prod Safety 1410 Duke University Rd Durham NC 27701

ROBERTS, W(ILLIAM) NEIL, b Prince Albert, Sask, May 27, 31; m 58; c 1. METALLURGY. *Educ:* Univ Sask, BA, 52, Hons, 53, MA, 54; Univ Leeds, PhD(metall), 61. *Prof Exp:* Patent examr, Can Govt Patent & Copyright Off, 55-56; sci officer, Can Dept Mines & Tech Surv, 57-58, res scientist, Metal Physics Sect, 61-72, HEAD METAL PHYSICS SECT, PHYS METALL RES LABS, CAN DEPT ENERGY, MINES & RESOURCES, 72- *Mem:* Am Soc Metals; Am Inst Mining, Metall & Petrol Engrs; Am Soc Testing & Mat. *Res:* Development of improved sutures for microsurgery; evaluation of steels for line pipe; transmission electron microscopy of austenitic steels and chromium molybdenum steels for fuel conversion; transmission electron microscopy of dual phase steels for automotive applications. *Mailing Add:* 74 Rothwell Dr Ottawa ON K1J 7G6 Can

ROBERTS, WALDEN KAY, b Independence, Mo, July 1, 34; m 66; c 2. MICROBIOLOGY, BIOCHEMISTRY. *Educ:* Iowa State Univ, BS, 56; Univ Calif, Berkeley, PhD(biochem), 60. *Prof Exp:* NSF fel, Univ Newcastle, Eng, 60-62; asst prof molecular biol, Univ Calif, Berkeley, 62-67; assoc prof microbiol, PROF MICROBIOL, MED SCH, UNIV COLO, DENVER, 76- *Mem:* Am Soc Biol Chem. *Res:* RNA and protein synthesis in animal cells; animal virology. *Mailing Add:* Dept of Microbiol Univ of Colo Med Ctr Denver CO 80227

ROBERTS, WALTER HERBERT B, b Field, BC, Jan 24, 15; US citizen; m; c 3. ANATOMY. *Educ:* Loma Linda Univ, MD, 39. *Prof Exp:* Med dir, Rest Haven Hosp, Sidney, BC, 40-53; PROF ANAT, LOMA LINDA UNIV, 56- *Mem:* Am Asn Anatomists. *Res:* Gross anatomy. *Mailing Add:* Dept of Anat Loma Linda Univ Loma Linda CA 92354

ROBERTS, WALTER ORR, b West Bridgewater, Mass, Aug 20, 15; m 40; c 4. SOLAR PHYSICS. *Educ:* Amherst Col, AB, 38; Harvard Univ, MA, 40, PhD(astrophys), 43. *Hon Degrees:* DSc, Ripon Col, 58, Amherst Col, 59, Colo Col, 62, Long Island Univ, 64, Carleton Col, 66, Southwestern at Memphis, 68, Univ Colo, 68, Univ Denver, 69, Univ Alaska, 75 & Colo Sch Mines, 80. *Prof Exp:* Researcher, Eastman Kodak Co, 38-39; observer, Coronographic Sta, Harvard Univ, 42-46; supt high altitude observ, Univ Colo, 47-52, dir, 52-61; head dept astro-geophys, 56-60; dir, Nat Ctr Atmospheric Res, Colo, 60-68, pres & chief exec officer, Univ Corp Atmospheric Res, 68-73, trustee & past pres, 73-75; PROF ASTRO-GEOPHYS, UNIV COLO, 75-, EMER PRES, UNIV CORP ATMOSPHERIC RES, 80- *Concurrent Pos:* Instr, Harvard Univ & Radcliffe Col, 47-48; res assoc, Harvard Univ & Nat Ctr Atmospheric Res, 75-; trustee, Mitre Corp, 60-, Kettering Found, 64-70, Amherst Col, 64-70, Fleischmann Found, 67-79, Int Fedn Inst Advan Study & Upper Atmosphere Res Corp, 71-74; trustee Aspen Inst Humanistic Studies, mem, Soc Fels, 73-, secy, Marconi Int Fel Coun, 74-; chmn, Tech Panel Solar Activity, US Nat Comt, Int Geophys Yr, 56-59 & Tech Adv Comt, Mitre Corp, 68-71; mem, Adv Comt Res Grants, Res Corp, 57-65, Geophys Res Bd, 60-71, Adv Comt, World Meteorol Orgn, 63-67, US-Japan Comt Sci Coop, 68-74, Bd, Int Inst Environ Affairs, 71, Defense Sci Bd, Dept Defense, 72-75, Bd Dirs, Worldwatch Inst, 75-, Bur Comt Effects Solar Terrestrial Disturbances Lower Atmosphere, Spec Comt Solar-Terrestrial Physics, 72-, Bd Dirs, Air Force Acad Found, 73-, Sub-Comt US-USSR Coop Prog Man's Impact Environ, Dept State, 73-, Vis Comt, Smithsonian Astrophys Observ, 75-, Environ Group, UN Asn, 70-75 & Comt Consult, UN Stockholm Corp, 72; mem, Comt Int Environ Progs, Nat Acad Sci, 71-, chmn, Comt Arctic Sci & Technol, 72-73; dir & mem exec comt, Air Force Acad Found, 73- *Honors*

& Awards: Cleveland Abbe Award, Am Meteorol Soc, 70; Hodgkins Medal, Smithsonian Inst, 73; Mitchell Prize, 79. *Mem:* NY Acad Sci; Am Astron Soc; fel Am Meteorol Soc; Am Inst Aeronaut & Astronaut; AAAS (vpres & chmn, Astron Sect, 64-65, pres, 68). *Res:* Solar corona; solar spicules and prominences; origin of geomagnetic disturbances; influence of variable solar activity on the earth's ionsophere and weather; effects of climate on world food production. *Mailing Add:* 1919 14th St Suite 811 Boulder CO 80302

ROBERTS, WARREN WILCOX, b Lincoln, Nebr, Oct 22, 26; m 67; c 2. NEUROPSYCHOLOGY. *Educ:* Stanford Univ, BA, 48, MA, 53; Yale Univ, PhD(psychol), 56. *Prof Exp:* Fel psychol, Yale Univ, 56-57; asst res anatomist, Univ Calif, Los Angeles, 57-59; asst prof psychol, Syracuse Univ, 59-62; assoc prof, 62-64, PROF PSYCHOL, UNIV MINN, MINNEAPOLIS, 64- *Mem:* Soc Neurosci; Psychonomic Soc; Am Psychol Asn; Am Physiol Soc. *Res:* Brain mechanisms of motivation; thermoregulation. *Mailing Add:* N218 Elliott Hall Univ Minn Minneapolis MN 55455

ROBERTS, WILLARD LEWIS, b Milton Junction, Wis, Mar 24, 04; m 28; c 3. NUTRITIONAL BIOCHEMISTRY. *Educ:* Milton Col, BA, 27; Univ Wis, MA, 32, PhD(biochem), 37. *Prof Exp:* Chemist, State Regulatory Dept, NDak, 28-30; asst chem, Univ Wis, 30-32; chemist, State Regulatory Dept, NDak, 32-35; asst biochem, Univ Wis, 35-37; dir cereal res, Post Prod Div, Gen Foods Corp, 37-41, dir biochem & anal chem res, Cent Labs, 42-45, tech dir, Gaines Div, 45-47; gen mgr & secy, Fed Foods, Inc, Wis, 47-70; MGR RES, AGR-PROD, BEATRICE FOODS RES CTR, 70- *Mem:* Am Chem Soc. *Res:* Research, development and production of human foods and pet and fur bearing animal foods. *Mailing Add:* Beatrice Foods Res Ctr 1526 S State St Chicago IL 60605

ROBERTS, WILLIAM JOHN, b Philadelphia, Pa, June 5, 18; m 48; c 2. CHEMISTRTY, FIBER TECHNOLOGY. *Educ:* Univ Pa, AB, 42, MS, 44, PhD(org chem), 47. *Prof Exp:* Asst chemist, United Gas Improv Co, Pa, 36-41, res chemist, 41-44, asst to mgr, 44-45; asst to dir, Pa Indust Chem Corp, 46-47, from asst dir res to dir res, 48-57; dir res, Summit Res Labs, 57-64, vpres & tech dir, Celanese Corp, 65-74; vpres & tech dir, Fiber Div, FMC Corp, 74-76; CONSULT, 76- *Concurrent Pos:* Asst instr, Univ Pa, 42-44. *Mem:* Am Chem Soc; Brit Soc Chem Indust; Fiber Soc; Asn Res Dirs. *Res:* Organic synthesis; hydrocarbons; polymerization; isomerization; pyrolysis and petrochemicals; polymers; plastics; fibers, especially man-made fibers; oxygenated chemicals; research management. *Mailing Add:* 65 Peachcroft Rd Bernardsville NJ 07924

ROBERTS, WILLIAM JOSEPH, b Union Grove, Ala, Mar 5, 28; m 54; c 3. NUCLEAR ENGINEERING, SOLID STATE PHYSICS. *Educ:* Auburn Univ, BS, 47, MS, 49. *Prof Exp:* Head dept physics, Curtiss-Wright Corp, 56-59; supvr snap reactor physics, 59-61, group leader, 61-64, group leader reactor physics & safety, 64-67, prog mgr nuclear snap progs, 67-73, mgr design eng, Atomics Int Div, 73-76, dir, Clinch River Breeder Reactor Proj Prog, 76-79, VPRES RES & ENG, ROCKWELL INT, 79- *Mem:* Am Nuclear Soc; Am Soc Mech Engrs. *Mailing Add:* Energy Systs Group Rockwell Int PO Box 309 Canoga Park CA 91304

ROBERTS, WILLIAM KENNETH, b Provo, Utah, Dec 10, 28; m 56; c 3. RUMINANT NUTRITION. *Educ:* Calif State Polytech Col, BS, 52; Wash State Univ, MS, 57, PhD(animal nutrit), 59. *Prof Exp:* Res asst animal sci, Wash State Univ, 55-59; fel nutrit & biochem, Grad Sch Pub Health, Univ Pittsburgh, 59-60; asst prof animal nutrit, Univ Manitoba, 60-63, assoc prof, 63-66; res specialist, Kern County Land Co, Calif, 66-68; NUTRITIONIST, E S ERWIN & ASSOCS, 68- *Concurrent Pos:* Nat Res Coun Can res grants, 61-66. *Mem:* Am Soc Animal Sci; Can Soc Animal Sci; Sigma Xi. *Res:* Ruminant nutrition concerning fat deposition and volatile fatty acid metabolism; vitamin A utilization; the role of potassium in ruminant nutrition. *Mailing Add:* E S Erwin & Assocs Box 237 Tolleson AZ 85353

ROBERTS, WILLIAM WOODRUFF, JR, b Huntington, WVa, Oct 8, 42; m 67; c 2. APPLIED MATHEMATICS, ASTRONOMY. *Educ:* Mass Inst Technol, SB, 64, PhD(appl math), 69. *Prof Exp:* Asst prof, 69-74, ASSOC PROF APPL MATH, UNIV VA, 74- *Mem:* Am Astron Soc; Soc Indust & Appl Math; Int Astron Union. *Res:* Flud mechanics; dynamics of galaxies of gas and stars; shock waves; star formation; nonlinear wave motion; computational mathematics; computational fluid dynamics. *Mailing Add:* Dept Appl Math & Comput Sci Univ Va Thornton Hall Charlottesville VA 22901

ROBERTSEN, JOHN ALAN, b Kenosha, Wis, June 21, 26; m 57; c 2. MEDICAL MICROBIOLOGY. *Educ:* Univ Wis, BS, 52, MS, 56, PhD(med microbiol), 58. *Prof Exp:* Chief microbiol sect, Leprosy Res, USPHS Hosp, Carville, La, 58-62; leader infectious diseases group, Pitman-Moore Div, Dow Chem Co, 62-65, leader microbiol group, Biohazards Dept, Dow Chem Co, 65-69; dir microbiol, St Francis Hosp & Thornton-Haymond Labs, Indianapolis, 69-71; dir tech mkt, Kallestad Labs, Inc, Minneapolis, 71-73; VPRES, EXTENSOR CORP, 73- *Concurrent Pos:* Former US contrib ed, Int J Leprosy; founder & pres, Robertsen Biomed Consults; prin, Robertson & Assocs. *Mem:* AAAS; Int Leprosy Asn; Am Asn Contamination Control; Am Soc Trop Med & Hyg; Am Asn Lab Animal Sci. *Res:* Immunodiagnostics; host-parasite relationships in tropical diseases, especially leprosy; control and containment of biological hazards; hospital environmental control; time allocation, behavior and task analyses of persons in health-care-related and administrative positions. *Mailing Add:* 17273 Hampton Ct Minnetonka MN 55343

ROBERTSHAW, JOSEPH EARL, b Providence, RI, Apr 19, 34. SYSTEMS ANALYSIS, ENERGY MANAGEMENT. *Educ:* Providence Col, BS, 56; Mass Inst Technol, MS, 58, PhD(physics), 61. *Prof Exp:* Assoc prof, 61-72, PROF PHYSICS, PROVIDENCE COL, 72- *Concurrent Pos:* Vis prof systs eng, Ga Inst Technol, 70-71; consult, GTE Labs, Waltham, Mass, 81-82. *Mem:* Am Phys Soc; Nat Asn Physics Teachers; Inst Elec & Electronic Engrs; Asn Energy Eng; Am Soc Eng Educ. *Res:* Systems analysis and engineering; systems approach to problem solving in engineering designs; socio-technical fields; energy management; factory productivity improvement; control theory; optimization. *Mailing Add:* Dept Physics Eng Systs Providence Col Providence RI 02918

ROBERTS-MARCUS, HELEN MIRIAM, b Panama City, Panama, June 22, 43; US citizen. BIOSTATISTICS. *Educ:* City Col New York, BS, 64; Johns Hopkins Univ, PhD(biostatist), 70. *Prof Exp:* Asst prof statist, Univ Calif, Riverside, 70-72; asst prof, Montclair State Col, 72-77, assoc prof math, 77-80. *Concurrent Pos:* Consult, Pac State Hosp, Pomona, Calif, 70-72, Loma Linda Univ Hosp, Calif, 70-72, Hosp Res Assoc, Fanwood, NJ, 77-79 & Boyle-Midway, Cranford, NJ, 81-; vis assoc prof, Oper Res & Indust Eng, Cornell Univ, 79-80. *Mem:* Am Statist Asn; Math Asn Am; Soc Indust Appl Math. *Res:* Stochastic models in biology; mathematical genetics. *Mailing Add:* Dept Math Comput Sci Montclair State Col Upper Montclair NJ 07043

ROBERTSON, A(LEXANDER) F(RANCIS), b Vancouver, BC, Aug 31, 12; nat US; m 46; c 3. MECHANICAL ENGINEERING. *Educ:* Univ Wis, BS, 35, MS, 38, PhD(mech eng), 40. *Prof Exp:* Engr, Fairbanks, Morse & Co, Wis, 35-37, res engr, 40-41; asst, Univ Wis, 37-38; engr, US Naval Ord Lab, DC, 41-46 & Manhattan Dist, Chicago, 46; res engr, Battelle Mem Inst, 46-47; res assoc, Inst Textile Technol, 47-50; chief fire res sect, 50-68, tech asst dir inst appl technol, 68-70, tech asst chief fire technol div, 70-73, SR SCIENTIST, CTR FIRE RES, NAT BUR STANDARDS, 73- *Concurrent Pos:* N Am ed, Fire & Mat. *Mem:* Am Phys Soc; Combustion Inst. *Res:* Diesel and gaseous combustion; heat transfer; electromechanical transducers; problems relating to unwanted fires. *Mailing Add:* 4228 Butterworth Pl NW Washington DC 20016

ROBERTSON, ABEL ALFRED LAZZARINI, JR, b Argentina, July 21, 26; m 58. PATHOLOGY. *Educ:* Cambridge Col, Arg, BA, 42; Univ Buenos Aires, MD, 51; Cornell Univ, PhD, 59. *Prof Exp:* Instr, Inst Parasitol, Med Sch, Univ Buenos Aires, 48-50, resident, 49-51, lectr, 50-51; from asst prof to assoc prof res surg, Postgrad Med Sch, NY Univ, 55-60, assoc prof path, 60-63; prof exp path, Cleveland Clin Found & mem staff, Cleveland Clin, 63-73; PROF PATH & DIR INTERDISCIPLINARY CARDIOVASC RES, INST PATH, CASE WESTERN RESERVE UNIV, 73- *Concurrent Pos:* Instr, Navy Hosp, Buenos Aires, Arg, 47-49; dir tissue bank, Buenos Aires Dept Pub Health, 48-51; asst vis surgeon, Bellevue Hosp, NY, 55 & NY Univ Hosp, 55; Am Heart Asn estab investr, 56-; estab investr, Am Heart Asn, 56-61; res career develop award, NIH, 61-63, mem path study sect, 75-; lectr, Univs Caracas, Rio de Janeiro, Sao Paulo, Riberao Preto, Buenos Aires & La Plata; assoc clin prof, Sch Med, Case Western Reserve Univ, 69-73; mem exec comt, Inter-Am Asn Atherosclerosis; deleg, Int Cong Hemat & Pan-Am Cong of Am Col Surgeons; chmn, Gordon Res Conf Arteriosclerosis, 73; chmn & host, Hugh Lofland Conf Arterial Wall Metab, 78. *Mem:* AAAS; Tissue Cult Asn; Am Asn Path; Am Soc Cell Biol; Am Col Cardiol. *Res:* Cytopathology in relation to cardiovascular research and tissue transplantation immunity. *Mailing Add:* Inst of Path Case Western Reserve Univ Cleveland OH 44106

ROBERTSON, ALAN ROBERT, b Wakefield, Eng, Sept 3, 40; m 64; c 2. OPTICS, COLORIMETRY. *Educ:* Univ London, BSc, 62, PhD(physics), 65. *Prof Exp:* RES OFFICER PHYSICS, NAT RES COUN CAN, 65- *Concurrent Pos:* Assoc ed, Color Res & Appln, 78- *Mem:* Can Soc Color (pres, 79-81); Inter-Soc Color Coun; Optical Soc Am; Illum Eng Soc NAm; Int Color Asn. *Res:* Colour-difference evaluation, colour measurment, spectrophotometry, colour rendering, reflectance standards. *Mailing Add:* Nat Res Coun Montreal Rd Ottawa ON K1A 0R6 Can

ROBERTSON, ALEX F, b Staunton, Va, Dec 5, 32; m 57; c 3. PEDIATRICS, BIOCHEMISTRY. *Educ:* Univ Va, BA, 53, MD, 57; Univ Mich, MA, 62. *Prof Exp:* From instr to asst prof pediat, Univ Mich, 63-65; from asst prof to assoc prof, Ohio State Univ, 65-71, dir div neonatology, 65-71; chmn dept, 71-81, PROF PEDIAT, MED COL GA, 71- *Mem:* Soc Pediat Res; Am Pediat Soc; Am Acad Pediat. *Res:* Neonatology; bilirubin-albumin binding in neonates. *Mailing Add:* Eugene Talmadge Mem Hosp Med Col of Ga Augusta GA 30902

ROBERTSON, ALEXANDER ALLEN, b Edmonton, Alta, Jan 6, 19; m 49. PHYSICAL CHEMISTRY. *Educ:* Univ Alta, BSc, 40; McGill Univ, PhD(chem), 49. *Prof Exp:* prin scientist, 49-80, DIR APPL CHEM DIV, PULP & PAPER RES INST CAN, 80- *Concurrent Pos:* Phys chemist, Swed Forest Prod Res Lab, 53-54; res assoc, McGill Univ, 56- *Mem:* Can Pulp & Paper Asn; Sigma Xi. *Res:* Pulp and paper technology; physical properties of fibers and suspensions; polymer cellulose interactions; latexes. *Mailing Add:* Dept of Chem McGill Univ Pulp & Paper Bldg Montreal PQ H3A 2T5 Can

ROBERTSON, ANDREW, b Port Huron, Mich, Sept 15, 36; m 65; c 2. AQUATIC ECOLOGY. *Educ:* Univ Toledo, BS, 58; Univ Mich, MA, 61, PhD(zool), 64. *Prof Exp:* Asst res limnologist, Univ Mich, Ann Arbor, 64-67, assoc res limnologist, 67-68; assoc prof zool, Univ Okla, 68-71; fishery biologist, IFYGL Proj Off, 71-74, HEAD BIOL CHEM GROUP, GREAT LAKES ENVIRON RES LAB, NAT OCEANIC & ATMOSPHERIC ADMIN, 74- *Mem:* Am Soc Limnol & Oceanog; Ecol Soc Am; Int Soc Limnol; Int Asn Great Lakes Res. *Res:* Great Lakes ecology; systematics and distribution of calanoid copepods; modeling of Great Lakes ecosystems. *Mailing Add:* NOAA Gt Lakes Environ Res Labs 2300 Washtenaw Ann Arbor MI 48104

ROBERTSON, BALDWIN, b Los Angeles, Calif, Sept 26, 34; m 62; c 3. THEORETICAL PHYSICS. *Educ:* Stanford Univ, BS, 56, MS, 57, PhD(physics), 65. *Prof Exp:* Instr & res assoc, Cornell Univ, 64-66; res assoc, 66-68, PHYSICIST, NAT BUR STANDARDS, 68- *Mem:* Am Phys Soc. *Res:* Statistical mechanics; experimental and theoretical fluid mechanics. *Mailing Add:* FM 105 Nat Bur of Standards Washington DC 20234

ROBERTSON, BEVERLY ELLIS, b Fredericton, NB, Feb 5, 39; m 58; c 2. CRYSTALLOGRAPHY. *Educ:* Univ NB, BSc, 61; McMaster Univ, MSc, 65, PhD(physics), 67. *Prof Exp:* Assoc chem, Cornell Univ, 67-69; from asst prof to assoc prof physics & astron, 69-76, PROF PHYSICS & ASTRON, UNIV REGINA, 76-, ASSOC MEM DEPT CHEM, 72- *Concurrent Pos:* Vis prof, Univ Stuttgart, 76-77; mem, Sci Coun Can, 78-; energy consult, 81- *Mem:* Am Crystallog Asn; Can Asn Physicists; fel Chem Inst Can; Sigma Xi; Am Chem Soc. *Res:* Crystal structure determination; gamma molecular complexes, bridged diphenyl, metal hydrides, polyhedial geometry, nitrogen-nitrogen nitrosodesulphantes, permangametes nitrogen fixation. *Mailing Add:* Dept Physics & Astron Univ Regina Regina SK S4S 0A2 Can

ROBERTSON, BOBBY KEN, b Reed, Okla, June 20, 38. PHYSICAL CHEMISTRY. *Educ:* WTex State Univ, BA, 60; Tex A&M Univ, PhD, 65. *Prof Exp:* Asst prof, 65-74, ASSOC PROF PHYS CHEM, UNIV MO-ROLLA, 74- *Mem:* Am Chem Soc; Am Crystallog Asn. *Res:* Interpretation of molecular structure by use of x-ray crystallography. *Mailing Add:* Dept of Chem Univ of Mo Rolla MO 65401

ROBERTSON, CHARLES WILLIAM, JR, b Memphis, Tenn, Mar 2, 43; m 69. PHYSICS. *Educ:* Southwestern at Memphis, BS, 65; Fla State Univ, PhD(physics), 69. *Prof Exp:* Res assoc physics, Kans State Univ, 70-73; RES PHYSICIST, E I DU PONT DE NEMOURS & CO, INC, 73- *Mem:* Optical Soc Am. *Res:* Application of optical and spectroscopic techniques to the measurement of material properties in the infrared, visible and ultraviolet. *Mailing Add:* 1905 Gravers Lane Wilmington DE 19810

ROBERTSON, CLYDE HENRY, b Heath Springs, SC, Aug 8, 29; m 51; c 2. ENTOMOLOGY. *Educ:* Wofford Col, BS, 50; Duke Univ, MA, 52, PhD(zool), 55. *Prof Exp:* Asst prof biol, 56-66, head dept, 56-74, PROF BIOL, PFEIFFER COL, 56-, CHMN DIV NATURAL SCI, 74- *Res:* Vertebrate morphology; development and metamorphosis of insectan respiratory systems. *Mailing Add:* Div of Natural Sci Pfeiffer Col Misenheimer NC 28109

ROBERTSON, DALE NORMAN, b Whittier, Calif, Jan 8, 25; m 51. ORGANIC CHEMISTRY. *Educ:* Pomona Col, BA, 49; Univ Wis, MS, 51, PhD(biochem), 53. *Prof Exp:* Asst biochem, Univ Wis, 49-53; fel, Mellon Inst, 53-54; res chemist biochem dept, Dow Chem Co, 54-60; res chemist, Arapahoe Chem, Inc, 60-66, asst dir res, Arapahoe Chem Div, Syntex Corp, 66-72; staff scientist, 72-76, scientist, 76-82, SR SCIENTIST, POP COUN, ROCKEFELLER UNIV, 82- *Mem:* AAAS; Sigma Xi; Am Chem Soc; NY Acad Sci. *Res:* Porphyrins; 4-hydroxycoumarins; isolation, characterization and synthesis of porphyrins in bitumens and petroleum; agricultural and medicinal chemicals; process development research on organic and medicinal chemicals; analytical chemistry; liquid scintillation spectrometry; contraceptive development; clinical studies; regulatory affairs. *Mailing Add:* Pop Coun Rockefeller Univ York Ave & 66th St New York NY 10021

ROBERTSON, DAVID ANTHONY, chemistry, see previous edition

ROBERTSON, DAVID C, b Pittston, Pa, May 2, 37; m 65; c 1. CHEMICAL ENGINEERING. *Educ:* Lehigh Univ, BS, 58; Pa State Univ, MS, 60, PhD(chem eng), 65. *Prof Exp:* Res engr, 63-65, PROCESS ENGR, ORCHEM DEPT, CHAMBERS WORKS, E I DU PONT DE NEMOURS & CO, INC, 65- *Mem:* Am Inst Chem Engrs. *Res:* Solids separation; statistical analysis; distillation; mass transfer; process development; economic analysis. *Mailing Add:* Lauren Farms 132 Walls Way Delaware City DE 14706

ROBERTSON, DAVID MURRAY, b Melville, Sask, May 4, 32; m 56; c 3. NEUROPATHOLOGY, PATHOLOGY. *Educ:* Queen's Univ, Ont, MD, CM, 55, MSc, 60; Royal Col Physicians, cert, 60, fel neuropath, 68; Am Bd Path, cert anatomic path & neuropath, 77. *Prof Exp:* From asst prof to assoc prof, 62-69, PROF PATH, QUEEN'S UNIV, ONT, 69-, HEAD DEPT, 79- CHIEF PATHOLOGIST, KINGSTON GEN HOSP, 79- *Concurrent Pos:* Neuropathologist, Kingston Gen Hosp, 62-79. *Mem:* Am Asn Neuropath; Can Asn Path; Can Asn Neuropath; Int Acad Path. *Res:* Nutritional diseases of nervous system; diabetic neuropathy; cerebrovascular disease. *Mailing Add:* Richardson Lab Dept of Path Queen's Univ Kingston ON K7L 3N6 Can

ROBERTSON, DONALD, b Baltimore, Md, Nov 29, 10; m 55; c 1. MECHANICAL ENGINEERING. *Educ:* Cornell Univ, ME, 32. *Prof Exp:* Foreman copper furnace, Am Smelting & Refining Co, 33-36; eng specification writer, Leeds & Northrup Co, 36-37, engr, 37-45, head pyrometer sect, 45-55, chief res & develop, pyromet group, 55-62, head temperature measurements sect, Res & Develop Ctr, 62-68, mgr standard prod eng, Sensor Div, 68-69, mgr develop & eng, 69-73; temperature measurement expert, 73-76; INDEPENDENT TEMPERATURE CONSULT, 76- *Mem:* Instrument Soc Am; Am Soc Metals; Solar Energy Soc; Inst Elec & Electronics Engrs. *Res:* Temperature primary elements. *Mailing Add:* 619 McKean Rd RD1 Ambler PA 19002

ROBERTSON, DONALD CLAUS, b Rockford, Ill, Mar 5, 40; m 62; c 2. BIOCHEMISTRY, MICROBIOLOGY. *Educ:* Univ Dubuque, BS, 62; Iowa State Univ, PhD(biochem), 67. *Prof Exp:* Chemist, Nat Animal Dis Lab, Ames, Iowa, 62-67; res assoc biochem, Mich State Univ, 67-70; asst prof microbiol, 70-77, assoc prof, 77-80, PROF MICROBIOL, UNIV KANS, 80- *Concurrent Pos:* NIH trainee, 67-70. *Mem:* Am Soc Microbiol; AAAS; Sigma Xi; Am Asn Univ Professors. *Res:* Microbial physiology; protein chemistry; biochemistry of host-parasite relationships. *Mailing Add:* Dept of Microbiol Univ of Kans Lawrence KS 66045

ROBERTSON, DONALD EDWIN, b Edmonton, Alta, Jan 8, 29; nat US; m 52; c 1. ORGANIC CHEMISTRY. *Educ:* Univ Alta, BSc, 51; Univ Utah, PhD(chem), 59. *Prof Exp:* Res org chemist, US Gypsum Co, 60-62; res org chemist, Interchem Corp, 62-65; res org chemist, Com Solvents Corp, 65-75, RES ORG CHEMIST, COM SOLVENTS CORP & INT MINERALS & CHEM CORP, 75- *Mem:* Am Chem Soc; Chem Inst Can; fel Am Inst Chemists. *Res:* Synthesis of natural and pharmaceuticals; carbohydrate and polymer chemistry; process and product development. *Mailing Add:* 4951 Dixie Bee Rd Apt 6 Terre Haute IN 47802

ROBERTSON, DONALD HUBERT, b Monmouth, Maine, June 6, 34. ANALYTICAL CHEMISTRY. *Educ:* Bates Col, BS, 56; Univ Glasgow, PhD(chem), 73. *Prof Exp:* Researcher, Gen Foods Corp Res Ctr, 56-57, Natick Labs, US Army, 57-59 & Gen Foods Corp Res Ctr, 59-62; RESEARCHER, NATICK LABS, US ARMY, 62- *Mem:* AAAS; Am Chem Soc; Pattern Recognition Soc. *Res:* Chromatography; mass spectrometry; computer processing as related to natural products, especially foodstuffs. *Mailing Add:* Food Sci Labs Natick Labs US Army Natick MA 01760

ROBERTSON, DONALD SAGE, b Oakland, Calif, June 27, 21; m 42; c 3. MAIZE GENETICS. *Educ:* Stanford Univ, AB, 47; Calif Inst Technol, PhD, 51. *Prof Exp:* Head dept sci, Biola Bible Col, 51-57; from asst prof to assoc prof genetics, 57-63, chmn dept, 75-80, PROF GENETICS, IOWA STATE UNIV, 63- *Mem:* Genetics Soc Am; AAAS; Am Genetic Asn. *Res:* Genetic control of mutation in maize. *Mailing Add:* Dept of Genetics Iowa State Univ Ames IA 50010

ROBERTSON, DOUGLAS REED, b Buffalo, NY, Sept 11, 38; m 67; c 2. ANATOMY, ENDOCRINOLOGY. *Educ:* Univ Buffalo, BA, 61; State Univ NY Buffalo, MA, 63; State Univ NY Upstate Med Ctr, PhD(anat), 66. *Prof Exp:* Asst prof anat, Col Med, Univ Fla, 66-70; assoc prof, 70-76, PROF ANAT, STATE UNIV NY UPSTATE MED CTR, 76- *Concurrent Pos:* NIH res grant, Inst Arthritis, Metab & Digestive Dis, 67-; NSF grant, Div Biol & Med Sci. *Mem:* Am Asn Anatomists; Am Soc Cell Biol; Am Soc Zoologists; Sigma Xi. *Res:* Neuroendocrine mechanisms of the ultimobranchial body; endocrinology and physiology of the hormones, calcitonin and parathormone in amphibians; annual and diurnal rhythms of calcitonin secretion and plasma calcium; development of an enzyme immunoassay for frag calcitonin. *Mailing Add:* Dept of Anat State Univ of NY Upstate Med Ctr Syracuse NY 13210

ROBERTSON, DOUGLAS SCOTT, b Three Rivers, Mich, Dec 29, 45; m 72; c 1. GEOPHYSICS, ASTRONOMY. *Educ:* Principia Col, BS, 68; Mass Inst Technol, PhD(geophys), 75. *Prof Exp:* Mem tech staff, Comput Sci Corp, 75-77; GEODESIST, NAT GEODETIC SURV, NAT OCEAN SURV, NAT OCEANIC & ATMOSPHERIC ADMIN, 77- *Concurrent Pos:* Consult, Geophys Br, NASA Goddard Space Flight Ctr, 75- *Mem:* Am Geophys Union; Am Astron Soc; AAAS. *Res:* Use of very-long-baseline radio interferometry to study polar motion, earth rotation, precession, nutation, earth tides, tectonic crustal deformations and astrometry. *Mailing Add:* Nat Geodetic Surv Nat Ocean Surv Nat Ocean & Atmospheric Admin C124 Rockville MD 20852

ROBERTSON, DOUGLAS WELBY, b Crawford, Ga, June 13, 24; m 49; c 3. ELECTRONICS. *Educ:* Ga Inst Technol, BS, 51, MS, 57. *Prof Exp:* Electronic technician, US Civil Serv, 42-44 & 46-47; res asst eng exp sta, Ga Inst Technol, 50-53, res engr, 53-57; mem tech staff, ITT Labs, Int Tel & Tel Corp, 57-59; res engr, Ga Inst Technol, 59-62, head commun br, 62-72, chief commun div, 72-75, dir, Electronics Technol Lab, Eng Exp Sta, 75-80; CONSULT, 80- *Mem:* AAAS; sr mem Inst Elec & Electronics Engrs; Acoust Soc Am. *Res:* Voice intelligibility; speech communication systems; electromagnetic compatibility; piezoelectric crystals and oscillators; antennas; electronic measurements; solid state components; radar systems; research management. *Mailing Add:* 2937 Henderson Rd Tucker GA 30084

ROBERTSON, ELIZABETH CHANT, b Toronto, Ont, Apr 17, 99; m 26; c 2. NUTRITION. *Educ:* Univ Toronto, BA, 21, MD, 24, PhD(nutrit), 37. *Prof Exp:* Asst hyg, Univ Toronto, 26-28, asst pediat, 28-42, jr clinician, 43-48, clin teacher, 48-58, assoc, 59-62; clin asst, 42-43, assoc physician, 48-62, CLIN CONSULT, HOSP FOR SICK CHILDREN, 62- *Mem:* Soc Res Child Develop; Am Pub Health Asn; Am Inst Nutrit; Can Pediat Soc (secy & treas, 39-47). *Res:* Air-borne infections; nutrition in relation to resistance to infection; effects of diets deficient in minerals; diagnosis of early vitamin A deficiency; effects of thiamine on intelligence. *Mailing Add:* Hosp for Sick Children Toronto ON M5G 1X8 Can

ROBERTSON, EUGENE CORLEY, b Tucumcari, NMex, Apr 9, 15; m 72; c 2. GEOLOGY. *Educ:* Univ Ill, BS, 36; Harvard Univ, MA, 48, PhD(geol), 52. *Prof Exp:* Mining geologist, Anaconda Co, 36-42; GEOPHYSICIST, US GEOL SURV, 49- *Mem:* Am Inst Mining, Metall & Petrol Eng; Am Geophys Union; Geol Soc Am; Mineral Soc Am. *Res:* Deformation of rocks; experimental geology. *Mailing Add:* US Geol Surv 922 Nat Ctr Reston VA 22092

ROBERTSON, FORBES, b New Haven, Conn, May 24, 15; m 43; c 3. ECONOMIC GEOLOGY. *Educ:* Principia Col, BA, 38; Wash Univ, MS, 40; Univ Wash, PhD, 56. *Prof Exp:* Geologist, Reynolds Mining Co & Reynolds Metals Co, 41-45; geologist, Stand Oil Co NJ, 45-46; econ geologist, Mo State Geol Surv, 46-47; assoc prof geol, Mont Sch Mines, 47-55; lectr, Univ Wash, 55-57; prof petrol, Petrobras Sch Geol, Brazil, 57-59; prof geol & head dept, Principia Col, 59-78; pres, Western Minerals Inc, 78-80; RETIRED. *Concurrent Pos:* Geologist, Mont Bur Mines & Geol, 47-55. *Mem:* Geol Soc Am; Am Asn Petrol Geol; Mineral Soc Am. *Res:* Petrology and geology of mineral deposits. *Mailing Add:* 1743 Eagles Nest Dr Belleair FL 33516

ROBERTSON, FREDERICK JOHN, b Aberdeen, Scotland, Nov 29, 31; Can citizen; m 69; c 2. VETERINARY MEDICINE, SEROLOGY. *Educ:* Univ Aberdeen, BSc Hons, 54; Univ Cambridge, MSc, 56; Univ Edinburgh, DVMS & MRCVS, 65. *Prof Exp:* Agr adv animal prod, Commonwealth Rels Off, London, 56-60; asst gen vet med, Vet Hosp, Falmouth, Eng, 65-67; asst vet, Univ Aberdeen, 67-69; invest officer, Brucellosis Diag & Res Lab, 69-75; RES SCIENTIST, ANIMAL DIS RES INST, FED GOVT CAN, 75- *Mem:* Brit Vet Asn. *Res:* Brucellosis in animals and as public health hazard. *Mailing Add:* Animal Dis Res Inst PO Box 11300 Postal Sta H Ottawa ON K1A 0Y9 Can

ROBERTSON, GEORGE GORDON, b St John, NB, Jan 30, 16; nat; m 46; c 2. ANATOMY. *Educ:* Acadia Univ, BSc, 36, BA, 37; Yale Univ, PhD(zool), 41. *Prof Exp:* Asst biol, Yale Univ, 38-41; fel anat, Sch Med, Univ Ga, 41-42; instr anat, La State Univ, 42-43; from instr to assoc prof, Baylor Univ Col Med, 43-52; prof anat, 52-80, chmn dept, 61-80, EMER PROF ANAT, COL MED, UNIV TENN, 80- *Concurrent Pos:* Vis assoc prof anat, Col Basic Med Sci, Univ Tenn, Memphis, 48 & 51. *Mem:* Am Asn Anatomists. *Res:* Developmental genetics; ovarian transplantation; human embryology; experimental teratology. *Mailing Add:* 105 Whitetail Ct Sun City Center FL 33570

ROBERTSON, GEORGE HARCOURT, b Evergreen Park, Ill, Jan 30, 43; m 78. CHEMICAL ENGINEERING. *Educ:* Univ Ill, Urbana, BS, 65; Univ Calif, Berkeley, PhD(chem eng), 70. *Prof Exp:* RES CHEM ENGR AGR & FOOD ENG, WESTERN REGIONAL RES LAB, SCI & EDUC ADMIN-AGR RES, USDA, 69- *Mem:* AAAS; Inst Food Technologists; Am Inst Chem Engrs; Am Chem Soc; Nat Sweetcorn Breeders Asn. *Res:* Textile (wool) and food (sweetcorn) process modifications to reduce energy use, waste or pollutant generation; ethylalcohol fuels separation and generation. *Mailing Add:* Western Regional Res Ctr US Dept Agr 800 Buchanan St Berkeley CA 94710

ROBERTSON, GEORGE LEVEN, b Alexandria, La, Feb 7, 21; m 43; c 3. ANIMAL SCIENCE. *Educ:* La State Univ, BS, 41; Tex A&M Univ, MS, 47; Univ Wis, PhD(animal husb, genetics), 51. *Prof Exp:* Asst animal husb, Tex A&M Univ, 41-42, instr, 46-48, from asst prof to assoc prof, 48-55; prof animal sci & head dept, 55-77; EXEC DIR, HONOR SOC PHI KAPPA PHI, LA STATE UNIV, BATON ROUGE, 77- *Mem:* Fel AAAS; Am Soc Animal Sci. *Res:* Physiology of reproduction in farm animals. *Mailing Add:* La State Univ PO Box 16000 Baton Rouge LA 70893

ROBERTSON, GEORGE WILBER, b Strome, Alta, Dec 20, 14; m 41; c 2. AGRICULTURAL METEOROLOGY. *Educ:* Univ Alta, BSc, 39; Univ Toronto, MA, 48. *Prof Exp:* Weather observer, Meteorol Serv Can, 38-41, instr meteorol, 41-44, aviation & pub weather forecaster, 44-50, forecaster res & develop, Cent Anal Off, 50-51; res & meteorol adv, Can Dept Agr, 51-59, chief agro-meteorol res sect, Plant Res Inst, 56-69; World Meteorol Orgn res & training expert climat & agr meteorol, Manila, Philippines, 69-71; head environ sect, Swift Current Res Sta, Can Dept Agr, 71-73; proj mgr & expert agr meteorol, Food & Agr Orgn, Tech Assistance Proj, Govt of Malaysia, 74-76; consult, World Meteorol Orgn & Food & Agr Orgn, Philippines, India, Malaysia, Bangladesh, Pakistan, Rome & Geneva, 76-81; CONSULT AGR METEOROL, 82- *Concurrent Pos:* Consult interagency group agr biometeorol, Food & Agr Orgn-World Meteorol Orgn-UNESCO, Southeast Asia, 71-72; mem comn agr meteorol, World Meteorol Orgn, 62-69; consult agr meteorol, Can Wheat Bd & World Meteorol Orgn, 73-74. *Mem:* AAAS; Am Meteorol Soc; Can Meteorol & Oceanog Soc; Royal Meteorol Soc; Can Cult Agrologists Asn. *Res:* Crop-weather modelling; systems analysis; agro-climatic analysis; weather-based crop-yield surveillance systems. *Mailing Add:* PO Box 1120 Kemptville ON K0G 1J0 Can

ROBERTSON, GLENN D(AVID), JR, b Los Angeles, Calif, July 10, 24; m 51; c 3. CHEMICAL ENGINEERING, APPLIED PHYSICS. *Educ:* Rice Univ, BS, 49; Calif Inst Technol, MS, 50, ChE, 53. *Prof Exp:* Engr mat res & develop, 53-61, SR STAFF ENGR, HUGHES AIRCRAFT CO, 61- *Concurrent Pos:* Adj fac physics, Pepperdine Univ, 77- *Mem:* Inst Elec & Electronics Engrs; Sigma Xi. *Res:* Applications of materials in electronics, missiles and aircraft; plastics; ceramics; radiation detection and dosimetry; chemical kinetics; mass and energy transport; infrared detection systems; fiber-optic waveguides; high purity silicon. *Mailing Add:* 6202 Frondosa Dr Malibu CA 90265

ROBERTSON, HAMISH ALEXANDER, b Edinburgh, Scotland, Nov 10, 20; Brit & Can citizen. REPRODUCTIVE ENDOCRINOLOGY. *Educ:* Univ Edinburgh, BSc, 41, PhD(physiol), 50. *Prof Exp:* Sci officer biochem, Animal Dis Res Inst, Edinburgh, 47-52; asst lectr, Dept Biol Chem, Univ Aberdeen, 53-54, sr lectr, 57-67; lectr, Sch Agr, Univ Nottingham, 54-57; PRIN RES SCIENTIST REPROD PHYSIOL, ANIMAL RES INST, 67- *Concurrent Pos:* Adj prof, Dept Biol, Carleton Univ, 70-; fel, Kellog Found & Fulbright fel, Nat Acad Sci, 61; fel, Lalor Found, 62-65; sr scientist exchange fel USSR, Nat Res Coun Can, 75. *Mem:* Fel Royal Soc Edinburgh; fel Royal Inst Chem; Biochem Soc; Soc Endocrinol; Soc Study Fertility; Soc Study Reprod. *Res:* Comparative aspects of mammalian reproduction; follicular growth and ovulation; endocrinology of the pre-attachment chorionic vesicle; the role of chorionic-somatomammotrophins during pregnancy. *Mailing Add:* Reproductive Physiol Animal Res Inst Ottawa ON K1S 5B6 Can

ROBERTSON, HARRY STROUD, b Montgomery, Ala, Sept 26, 21; m 43; c 3. PLASMA PHYSICS, STATISTICAL MECHANICS. *Educ:* Univ NC, BS, 42; Johns Hopkins Univ, PhD(physics), 49. *Prof Exp:* Radio engr, US Naval Res Lab, 42-46; asst physics, Johns Hopkins Univ, 47-49; from asst prof to assoc prof, 49-56, chmn dept, 52-62, 72-74, PROF PHYSICS, UNIV MIAMI, FLA, 56- *Concurrent Pos:* Vis lectr, Johns Hopkins Univ, 56-57; consult, Oak Ridge Nat Lab, 58-69 & Princeton Plasma Physics Lab, 61; vis prof, Univ Edinburgh, 71. *Mem:* AAAS; Fedn Am Scientists; Am Phys Soc; Sigma Xi. *Res:* Plasma transport properties; plasma stability and oscillations; cesium plasmas; moving striations; physics and society; statistical thermodynamics; solar energy conversion. *Mailing Add:* Dept Physics Univ Miami Coral Gables FL 33124

ROBERTSON, HUGH ELBURN, b Sask, Can, Oct 2, 19; m 42; c 5. BIOCHEMISTRY, MICROBIOLOGY. *Educ:* Univ Sask, MA, 43; Univ Minn, PhD(biochem), 53. *Prof Exp:* Res chemist, Int Nickel Co, Can, 40-46; provincial analyst, Sask Dept Pub Health, 46-49, dir provincial labs, 50-52; instr bact & immunol, Univ Minn, 52-53, asst prof, 54; DIR PROVINCIAL LABS, SASK DEPT HEALTH, 55- *Concurrent Pos:* Adj prof dept chem, Univ Sask, Regina. *Mem:* fel Chem Inst Can; Eng Inst Can; Can Pub Health Asn. *Res:* Evaluation of clinical diagnostic laboratory procedures for metabolic and infectious diseases; economics of delivery systems for automated laboratory procedures with particular emphasis on clinical chemistry. *Mailing Add:* Provincial Labs Sask Dept of Health Regina SK S4S 5W6 Can

ROBERTSON, J(OHN) A(RCHIBALD) L(AW), b Dundee, Scotland, July 4, 25; Can citizen; m 54; c 3. MATERIALS SCIENCE. *Educ:* Cambridge Univ, BA, 50, MA, 53. *Prof Exp:* Sci officer metall, Atomic Energy Res Estab, UK Atomic Energy Authority, 50-55, sect leader, 55-57; res officer, Chalk River Nuclear Labs, 57-63, head reactor mat br, 63-70, dir fuels & mat div, 70-76, ASST TO V PRES & GEN MGR, CHALK RIVER NUCLEAR LABS, ATOMIC ENERGY CAN LTD, 76- *Concurrent Pos:* Co-ed, J Nuclear Mat, 67-71. *Mem:* Royal Soc Can. *Res:* Research and development programs for nuclear reactor systems; irradiation effects in nuclear fuels. *Mailing Add:* Chalk River Nuclear Labs Atomic Energy of Can Ltd Chalk River ON K0J 1J0 Can

ROBERTSON, J(AMES) M(UELLER), b Champaign, Ill, Apr 18, 16; m 43; c 2. ENGINEERING. *Educ:* Univ Ill, BS, 38; Univ Iowa, MS, 40, PhD(hydraul), 41. *Prof Exp:* Asst, Univ Iowa, 38-41; asst physicist, David Taylor Model Basin, US Navy, DC, 41-42; from asst prof to assoc prof eng mech, Pa State Univ, 42-47, assoc prof civil eng, 47-49, prof engr res & asst dir ord res lab, 49-54; PROF THEORET & APPL MECH, UNIV ILL, URBANA, 54- *Concurrent Pos:* Res engr, Douglas Aircraft Co, Calif, 44-45; mem proj Monte, Nat Acad Sci-Nat Res Coun, 57; consult, Waterways Exp Sta, 57, res & develop, Consol Papers, 60-61, Goodyear Aircraft Corp, 62, Caterpillar Tractor Co, 63-72, Kennecott Explor, Westvaco Res, 66-68 & Nat Distillers & Chem, 72; sr res scientist, Intersci Res Inst, 66-73; short course instr, TAPPI, 69; short course lectr, Univ Tenn Space Inst, 73; vis prof, Colo State Univ, 74-76; vis lectr, Kans State Univ, 74. *Honors & Awards:* Hilgard Prize, Am Soc Civil Engrs, 55. *Mem:* Fel Am Soc Civil Engrs; fel Am Soc Mech Engrs; Am Inst Aeronaut & Astronaut; Int Asn Hydraul Res; AAAS. *Res:* Hydrodynamics; turbulent boundary layers in adverse pressure gradient; cavitation; hydraulics; fluid mechanics; hemodynamics. *Mailing Add:* 125 Talbot Lab Univ of Ill Urbana IL 61801

ROBERTSON, JACK M, b Clovis, NMex, Sept 26, 37; m 57; c 3. MATHEMATICS. *Educ:* Eastern NMex Univ, BS, 59; Univ Utah, MS, 61, PhD(math), 64. *Prof Exp:* Teaching asst math, Univ Utah, 59-64; asst prof, 64-70, assoc prof, 70-77, PROF MATH, WASH STATE UNIV, 77- *Concurrent Pos:* Assoc dir, NSF Summer Inst Sec Teachers, Wash State, 66-67, dir, 68-69. *Mem:* Am Math Soc; Math Asn Am. *Res:* Topology; analysis; mathematics education. *Mailing Add:* Dept of Math Wash State Univ Pullman WA 99163

ROBERTSON, JACQUELINE LEE, b Petaluma, Calif, July 9, 47. INSECT PHYSIOLOGY, INSECT TOXICOLOGY. *Educ:* Univ Calif, Berkeley, BA, 69, PhD(entom), 73. *Prof Exp:* RES ENTOMOLOGIST, PAC SOUTHWEST FOREST & RANGE EXP STA, INSECTICIDE EVAL PROJ, FOREST SERV, BERKELY, CALIF, 70- *Concurrent Pos:* Teaching asst, Univ Calif, Berkeley, 70-72, res asst, 72-73. *Mem:* Entom Soc Can; Entom Soc Am; AAAS; Am Inst Biol Sci; Am Soc Zoologists. *Res:* Influence of insect hormones and hormone mimics on morphogenesis; toxicology of insecticides to forest insect pests; toxicological biostatistics. *Mailing Add:* Pac Southwest Forest & Range Sta 1960 Addison St Berkeley CA 94701

ROBERTSON, JAMES ALDRED, b Knoxville, Tenn, July 13, 31; m 54; c 2. CHEMISTRY. *Educ:* Univ Tenn, BS, 53, MS, 57; Ohio State Univ, PhD(dairy technol), 62. *Prof Exp:* Chemist, M&R Dietetic Labs, Inc, 62-63; res chemist, Southern Utilization Res & Develop Div, New Orleans, La, 63-69, RES LEADER, RICHARD B RUSSELL, SCI & EDUC ADMIN-AGR RES, USDA, ATHENS, GA, 69- *Mem:* Am Oil Chem Soc; Sigma Xi. *Res:* Purification and specificity of lipase in milk; distribution of fatty acids in blood lipids; toxic fungal metabolites; composition, flavor and oxidative stability of sunflower seed and oil; methods of analysis of sunflower seed; field and storage damage of soybeans and sunflower. *Mailing Add:* Richard B Russell Agr Res Ctr Agr Res Serv Sci & Educ Admin-Agr Res USDA PO Box 5677 Athens GA 30613

ROBERTSON, JAMES ALEXANDER, b Basswood, Man, Apr 15, 31; m 57; c 2. SOIL FERTILITY, SOIL CHEMISTRY. *Educ:* Univ Man, BSA, 53, MSc, 55; Purdue Univ, PhD, 63. *Prof Exp:* Assoc prof soil sci, 55-71, PROF SOIL SCI, UNIV ALTA, 71- *Concurrent Pos:* Mem, Alta Inst Agrology. *Mem:* Can Soc Soil Sci (secy-treas, 58-60, pres, 72-73); Am Soc Agron. *Res:* Phosphorus sorption by Alberta soils; plant uptake of phosphorus from various soil horizons; methods of measuring phosphorus availability. *Mailing Add:* Dept of Soil Sci Univ of Alta Edmonton AB T6G 2E1 Can

ROBERTSON, JAMES BYRON, b Spiceland, Ind, Mar 29, 37; m 61; c 2. MATHEMATICS. *Educ:* Mass Inst Technol, SB, 59; Ind Univ, PhD(math), 64. *Prof Exp:* From instr to asst prof math, Cornell Univ, 63-66; from asst prof to assoc prof, 66-77, PROF MATH, UNIV CALIF, SANTA BARBARA, 77- *Concurrent Pos:* NSF grant, 70-73; Fulbright lectr, Tbilisi, USSR, 77. *Mem:* Inst Math Statist; Am Math Soc; Math Asn Am. *Res:* Ergodic theory; prediction theory. *Mailing Add:* Dept of Math Univ of Calif Santa Barbara CA 93106

ROBERTSON, JAMES DAVID, b Tuscaloosa, Ala, Oct 13, 22; m 46; c 3. ANATOMY. *Educ:* Univ Ala, BS, 42; Harvard Med Sch, MD, 45; Mass Inst Technol, PhD(biochem), 52. *Prof Exp:* Asst biol, Univ Ala, 40-42; intern, Boston City Hosp, 45-46; asst physician, Vet Admin Hosp, Ala, 48; asst physician, Med Dept, Mass Inst Technol, 48-49; asst prof path & oncol, Univ Kans Med Ctr, Kansas City, 52-55; hon res assoc anat, Univ Col, Univ London, 55-60; from asst prof to assoc prof neuropath, Harvard Med Sch, 60-66; prof anat, 66-75, JAMES B DUKE PROF ANAT, SCH MED, DUKE UNIV, 75-, CHMN DEPT, 66- *Concurrent Pos:* Assoc biophysicist, McLean Hosp, Boston, 60-63, biophysicist, 64-67; mem cell biol study sect, NIH,

67-71; vis prof physiol chem inst, Univ Wurzburg, Germany, 78-79; Alexander von Humboldt sr scientist award; consult, Dept Defense; chmn search comt anat dept, Uniformed Servs Univ Health Sci. *Mem:* Electron Micros Soc Am; Physiol Soc Gt Brit & Ireland; Am Asn Anatomists; Am Soc Cell Biol; Int Soc Neurochem. *Res:* Tissue ultrastructure, especially electron microscope studies of nerve junctional tissues and cell membranes. *Mailing Add:* Dept of Anat Duke Univ Med Ctr Box 3011 Durham NC 27710

ROBERTSON, JAMES DOUGLAS, b New Rochelle, NY, Feb 15, 48; m 75. SEISMIC INTERPRETATION. *Educ:* Princeton Univ, BSE, 70; Univ Wis, MS, 72, PhD(geophysics), 75. *Prof Exp:* Sr res geophysicist, 75-79, RES DIR GEOPHYSICS, ARCO OIL & GAS CO, DIV OF ATLANTIC RICHFIELD CO, 79- *Concurrent Pos:* Vis lectr, Dept Geosci, Univ Tex, Dallas, 80- *Mem:* Soc Explor Geophysicists; Am Asn Petrol Geologists; Am Geophys Union. *Res:* Shear wave seismic technology; seismic modeling; stratigraphic interpretation methods; interactive computer graphics for seismic analysis. *Mailing Add:* Arco Oil & Gas Co PO Box 2819 Dallas TX 75221

ROBERTSON, JAMES E(VANS), b Fairfax, Okla, Mar 30, 24; m 56; c 4. ELECTRICAL ENGINEERING. *Educ:* Okla Agr & Mech Col, BS, 47; Univ Ill, MS, 48, PhD(elec eng), 52. *Prof Exp:* Res asst prof elec eng, 52-56, res assoc prof, 56-59, PROF ELEC ENG & COMPUT SCI, UNIV ILL, URBANA, 59- *Concurrent Pos:* Fulbright scholar, Univ Sydney, 63. *Mem:* Inst Elec & Electronics Engrs. *Res:* Design of electronic digital computers. *Mailing Add:* Dept of Comput Sci Univ Ill 1304 W Springfield Ave Urbana IL 61801

ROBERTSON, JAMES MAGRUDER, b Port Clinton, Ohio, Sept 24, 43; m 70. ECONOMIC GEOLOGY. *Educ:* Carleton Col, BA, 65; Univ Mich, Ann Arbor, MS, 68, PhD(econ geol), 72. *Prof Exp:* Asst prof geol, Mich Technol Univ, 72-74; MINING GEOLOGIST, NMEX BUR MINES & MINERAL RESOURCES, 74- *Mem:* Geochem Soc; Sigma Xi; Geol Soc Am; Soc Econ Geol. *Res:* Evaluating the geology, petrology and mineral resource potential of the Precambrian rocks of New Mexico. *Mailing Add:* NM Bur Mines & Mineral Resources Campus Sta Socorro NM 87801

ROBERTSON, JAMES SYDNOR, b Richmond, Va, Nov 27, 20; m 44; c 3. MEDICAL PHYSICS, NUCLEAR MEDICINE. *Educ:* Univ Minn, BS, 43, MB, 44, MD, 45; Univ Calif, PhD(physiol), 49. *Prof Exp:* Asst physiol, Univ Calif, 46-47, asst physiologist, 47-50; biophysicist & asst physician, Brookhaven Nat Lab, 50-51, head med physics div & physician, 51-74; CONSULT NUCLEAR MED, MAYO CLIN, 75- *Mem:* AAAS; Am Physiol Soc; Radiation Res Soc; Soc Nuclear Med; Health Physics Soc. *Res:* Electrolyte metabolism, neutron capture therapy; tracer theory; radiation dosimetry; emission tomography. *Mailing Add:* Diag Nuclear Med Sect Mayo Clin Rochester MN 55905

ROBERTSON, JAMES THOMAS, b McComb, Miss, Apr 5, 31; m 52; c 6. NEUROSURGERY. *Educ:* Univ Tenn, Memphis, MD, 55. *Prof Exp:* Teaching fel surg, Harvard Med Sch, 59-60; from instr to assoc prof neurosurg, 64-74, PROF NEUROSURG & CHMN DEPT, CTR FOR HEALTH SCI, UNIV TENN, MEMPHIS, 74- *Concurrent Pos:* Consult, Calif Med Facil, 60-63, Jackson-Madison County Gen Hosp, Tenn & Southeast Mo & St Francis Hosps, Cape Girardeau, Mo; pvt pract, Semmes-Murphey Clin, 64- *Mem:* Cong Neurol Surg (treas, 69-74, pres, 74-75); Am Asn Neurol Surg; fel Am Col Surgeons; Asn Acad Surg; Soc Univ Neurosurg (pres, 65). *Res:* Profound hypothermia; work with prostaglandins and the vasospasm phenomenon; platelet activity in experimental subarachnoid hemorrhage; pathogenesis and treatment of stoke; studies on cerebral vasospasm. *Mailing Add:* Rm 231 Univ Tenn 858 Madison Ave Memphis TN 38103

ROBERTSON, JEROLD C, b Provo, Utah, Mar 20, 33; m 53; c 3. PHYSICAL ORGANIC CHEMISTRY. *Educ:* Brigham Young Univ, BS, 58, PhD(org chem), 62. *Prof Exp:* From instr to asst prof, 61-74, ASSOC PROF ORG CHEM, COLO STATE UNIV, 74- *Mem:* Am Chem Soc. *Res:* Mechanisms of organic reactions, specifically aromatic electrophic substitution, Baeyer-Villiger oxidation and Schmidt reaction with olefins; molecular orbital calculations on chemisorption of small molecules on metal surfaces. *Mailing Add:* Dept of Chem Colo State Univ Ft Collins CO 80521

ROBERTSON, JERRY EARL, b Detroit, Mich, Oct 25, 32; m 55; c 3. ORGANIC CHEMISTRY, MEDICINAL CHEMISTRY. *Educ:* Miami Univ, BS, 54; Univ Mich, MS, 56, PhD(org chem), 59. *Prof Exp:* Sr chemist, Lakeside Labs, Colgate-Palmolive Co, Wis, 59-60; group leader cardiovasc med chem, 60-61, sect chief, 61-63; sr chemist, Riker Labs, Inc, 63-64; supvr synthetic med res, Cent Res Labs, 64-67, mgr, Synthetic Med Res Sect, 67-70, dir tech planning and coord, 70-71, dir, Chem Res Dept, 71-73, mgr, Surg Prod Dept, 74-75, gen mgr, Surg Prod Div, 75-79, div vpres surg, 79-80. *Mem:* Am Chem Soc. *Res:* Medicinal chemistry of cardiovascular and psychopharmacologic agents. *Mailing Add:* 3M Co 3M Ctr Bldg 220 St Paul MN 55144

ROBERTSON, JERRY L(EWIS), b Tulsa, Okla, Oct 25, 33; m 56; c 2. CHEMICAL ENGINEERING. *Educ:* Okla State Univ, BS, 55; Northwestern Univ, PhD(chem eng), 62. *Prof Exp:* Chem engr, Esso Res & Eng Co, 55-65, sr engr, 65-69, eng assoc, 69-71, sect head, 71-74, mgr process & systs eng, Centrifuge Enrichment, Exxon Nuclear Co, Inc, 74-78, SR ENG ASSOC, EXXON RES & ENG CO, 78- *Mem:* Am Inst Chem Engrs; Am Chem Soc. *Res:* Mass transfer in porous media; process design and economics; plant start up; liquified natural gas processing; uranium enrichment; energy conservation/efficiency. *Mailing Add:* Exxon Res & Eng Co PO Box 101 Florham Park NJ 07932

ROBERTSON, JOHN CONNELL, b Carrollton, Ky, Nov 24, 31; m 56; c 4. ANIMAL NUTRITION. *Educ:* Univ Ky, BS, 53, MS, 57, PhD(animal nutrit), 60. *Prof Exp:* Area livestock specialist, 60-63, state exten livestock specialist, 63-66, PROF ANIMAL SCI, UNIV KY, 66-, ASSOC DEAN COL AGR, 69- *Mem:* Am Soc Animal Sci. *Res:* Interrelationships of certain minerals, mainly calcium, phosphorous, zinc, and amino acids. *Mailing Add:* Rm N6 Agr Sci Bldg Univ of Ky Lexington KY 40506

ROBERTSON, JOHN HARVEY, b Cheyenne, Wyo, Dec 6, 41; m 66; c 2. ANALYTICAL CHEMISTRY, MICROBIOLOGY. *Educ:* Univ Wyo, BS, 68. *Prof Exp:* Design draftsman, Dynaelectron Corp, 63 & Wyott Mfg, Wyo, 64-65; design engr & draftsman, State of Wyo Engrs Off, 65-66; res microbiologist, 68-78, BIOENGR, THE UPJOHN CO, 78- *Mem:* Am Chem Soc; Int Soc Pharmaceut Engrs. *Res:* Development of chemical or microbiological assay methods for new product candidates or products; development of new sterilization and process methods for production. *Mailing Add:* Process Validation-Microbiol Unit Upjohn Co Kalamazoo MI 49001

ROBERTSON, JOSEPH HENRY, b Carrington, NDak, Jan 10, 06; m 33; c 5. RANGE CONSERVATION. *Educ:* Nebr State Teachers Col, Peru, AB, 28; Univ Nebr, MS, 32, PhD(bot), 39. *Prof Exp:* Teacher, pub schs, Nebr, 25-27 & Idaho, 28-30; instr biol, plant anat, bot & zool, Wis State Teachers Col, River Falls, 32-35; asst instr plant ecol, Univ Nebr, 36-39; jr range examr, Range Res, US Forest Serv, 40-42; forest ecologist, Range Exp Sta, 42-47; from assoc prof to prof agron & range mgt, 47-67, chmn dept, 52-64, range ecologist, 51-71, head Div Plant Sci, 59-65, prof range sci, 67-71, actg assoc dir, Agr Exp Sta, 75, actg assoc dean, Col Agr, 76, EMER PROF RANGE SCI, UNIV NEV, RENO, 71- *Concurrent Pos:* Lectr range mgt & chief of party, WVa Univ-USAID contract team & head, Dept Range Mgt, Egerton Col, Kenya, 65-67; consult watershed revegetation, Develop & Resources Corp, Khorramabad, Iran, 71-73; prin investr native shrub proj, Foresta Inst Ocean & Mountain Studies, 74-76, mem bd dirs, 75-79; leader, watershed veg surv, Nev Div Forestry, 76 & agr collection, Arch, Nev Univ, 78; consult, Desert Res Inst, Univ Nev, 80 & Res Mgt Co, 81. *Honors & Awards:* Frederic Renner Award, 77. *Mem:* Soc Range Mgt. *Res:* Artificial revegetation of range land; ecology of sagebrush-grass zone; domestication of native shrubs. *Mailing Add:* 920 Evans Ave Reno NV 89512

ROBERTSON, KENNETH RAY, b Detroit, Mich, July 26, 41; c 1. TAXONOMIC BOTANY. *Educ:* Univ Kans, BS, 64, MA, 66; Wash Univ, PhD(bot), 71. *Prof Exp:* Teaching asst bot & biol, Univ Kans, 64-66; instr biol, Forest Park Community Col, 69-70; asst cur, Arnold Arboretum, Harvard Univ, 71-76; asst scientist, 76-80, ASSOC SCIENTIST, ILL NAT HIST SUV, 80-, CUR HERBARIUM, 76- *Mem:* Am Soc Plant Taxonomists; New Eng Bot Club. *Res:* Classification and evolution of the Rosaceae; fruits and seeds, especially form, structure and dispersal; systematics of Jacquemontia (Convolvulaceae); flora of the southeastern United States. *Mailing Add:* Ill Nat Hist Surv 172 Nat Resources Bldg 607 E Peabody Dr Champaign IL 61820

ROBERTSON, LARRY DEE, plant breeding, see previous edition

ROBERTSON, LESLIE EARL, b Los Angeles, Calif, Feb 12, 28; m 69; c 3. STRUCTURAL ENGINEERING. *Educ:* Univ Calif, Berkeley, BS, 52. *Prof Exp:* Struct engr, Kaiser Engrs, Oakland, Calif, 52-54; John A Blume, San Francisco, 54-57 & Raymond Int Co, New York, 57-58; MANAGING PARTNER & STRUCT ENGR, SKILLING, HELLE, CHRISTIANSEN, ROBERTSON, 58- *Concurrent Pos:* Chmn comt risks & liabilities, Kinetic Energies Resource Coun, 75- *Honors & Awards:* Raymond C Reese Res Prize, Am Soc Civil Engrs, 74. *Mem:* Nat Acad Eng; fel Am Soc Civil Engrs. *Mailing Add:* 211 East 46th St New York NY 10017

ROBERTSON, LYLE PURMAL, b Vancouver, BC, Aug 15, 33; m 55; c 2. NUCLEAR PHYSICS, INTERMEDIATE ENERGY PHYSICS. *Educ:* Univ BC, BA, 55, MA, 58, PhD(nuclear physics), 63. *Prof Exp:* Res officer reactor physics, Atomic Energy Can Ltd, 57-60; Nat Res Coun Can overseas fel, 63-65; sr res officer nuclear physics, Rutherford High Energy Lab, Eng, 65-66; assoc prof physics, 66-72, PROF PHYSICS, UNIV VICTORIA, BC, 72- *Concurrent Pos:* Royal Soc Can Rutherford Mem fel, 63-64. *Mem:* Can Asn Physicists; Am Phys Soc. *Res:* Intermediate energy nuclear and particle physics, associated with triumf; nucleon-nucleon interaction at intermediate energy. *Mailing Add:* Dept of Physics Univ of Victoria Victoria BC V8N 2Y2 Can

ROBERTSON, LYNN SHELBY, JR, b Ind, Sept 19, 16; m 41; c 3. SOIL SCIENCE. *Educ:* Purdue Univ, BS, 40, MS, 41; Mich State Univ, PhD, 55. *Prof Exp:* Asst soil sci, Mich State Univ, 41-43, soil surveyor, 43, asst instr, 44-46, asst prof, 46-52; asst prof, Nat Univ Colombia, 52-53; assoc prof, 58-62, EXTEN SPECIALIST SOIL SCI, MICH STATE UNIV, 54-, PROF, 62- *Concurrent Pos:* Consult micronutrients, Taiwan, 71. *Mem:* AAAS; fel Soil Sci Soc Am; fel Soil Conserv Soc Am; fel Am Soc Agron; Int Soil Sci Soc. *Res:* Soil management, especially as related to systems of farming, tillage and economic use of commercial fertilizer. *Mailing Add:* Dept of Crop & Soil Sci Mich State Univ East Lansing MI 48824

ROBERTSON, MALCOLM SLINGSBY, b Brantford, Ont, July 18, 06; US citizen; m 34; c 2. MATHEMATICS. *Educ:* Univ Toronto, BA, 29, MA, 30; Princeton Univ, PhD(math), 34. *Prof Exp:* Nat Res Coun Can fel, Univ Chicago, 34-35; instr math, Yale Univ, 35-37; instr, Rutgers Univ, 37-40, from asst prof to prof, 40-66; prof, Univ Del, 74-78, unidel prof math, 77-80, EMER PROF, UNIV DEL, 80- *Mem:* Math Asn Am; Am Math Soc. *Res:* Theory of functions of complex variable; conformal mapping; univalent functions; multivalent and typically real functions. *Mailing Add:* 1116 Lawson Ave West Vancouver BC V7T 2E5 Can

ROBERTSON, MERTON M, b Scobey, Mont, Aug 16, 24; m 57; c 1. EXPERIMENTAL PHYSICS. *Educ:* Univ Mont, BA, 51; Univ Wis, MS, 56, PhD(physics), 60. *Prof Exp:* Proj assoc physics, Univ Wis, 60-61; mem tech staff, Sandia Lab, AEC, 61-66, tech div supvr, 66-72, PROJ LEADER, SANDIA LAB, DEPT ENERGY, 72- *Concurrent Pos:* Sci comdr, Sandia Lab Airborn Solar Eclipse Exped, Argentina, 66. *Mem:* Am Phys Soc. *Res:* Optical spectroscopy and instrumentation; interferometry; hyperfine structure; nuclear moments of radioactive atoms; optical studies of missile reentries; solar physics; plasma physics; high speed radiometry, photography and photometry. *Mailing Add:* 6608 Natalie NE Albuquerque NM 87110

ROBERTSON, NAT CLIFTON, b Atlanta, Ga, July 23, 19; m 46; c 3. PHYSICAL CHEMISTRY, RESOURCE MANAGEMENT. *Educ:* Emory Univ, AB, 39; Princeton Univ, PhD(phys chem), 42. *Hon Degrees:* ScD, Emory Univ, 70. *Prof Exp:* Asst chem, Princeton Univ, 40-41; res assoc, Nat Defense Res Comt, 42-43; res chemist, Standard Oil Develop Co, 43-47; group leader, Celanese Corp Am, 47-51; dir petrochem dept, Nat Res Corp, 51-55; vpres & dir res, Escambia Chem Corp, 55-58; vpres res & develop, Spencer Chem Co & Spencer Chem Div, Gulf Oil Corp, 58-66; vpres res, Air Prod & Chem, Inc, 66-69; sr vpres & dir, 69-77; DIR & SCI ADV, MARION LABS, INC, 77- *Res:* Kinetics of gas reactions; catalysis; physical methods of separation; free radicals. *Mailing Add:* 156 Philip Dr Princeton NJ 08540

ROBERTSON, PHILIP ALAN, b Sept 9, 38; US citizen; m 67; c 2. PLANT ECOLOGY. *Educ:* Colo State Univ, BS, 62, MS, 64, PhD(plant ecol), 68. *Prof Exp:* Instr range sci, Colo State Univ, 67-68; asst prof biol, State Univ NY Col Oneonta, 68-70; asst prof bot, 70-77, ASSOC PROF BOT, SOUTHERN ILL UNIV, CARBONDALE, 77- *Mem:* Ecol Soc Am; AAAS; Am Inst Biol Sci; Soc Range Mgt. *Res:* Analysis of structure and function of terrestrial plant communities. *Mailing Add:* Dept of Bot Southern Ill Univ Carbondale IL 62901

ROBERTSON, RALEIGH JOHN, b Reinbeck, Iowa, Nov 8, 42; m 66; c 2. ORNITHOLOGY. *Educ:* Grinnell Col, BA, 65; Univ Iowa, MSc, 67; Yale Univ, PhD(ecol), 71. *Prof Exp:* Assoc prof biol, 71, DIR, BIOL STA, QUEENS UNIV, 72- *Mem:* Am Ornithologists Union; Ecol Soc Am; Can Soc Zoologists. *Res:* Behavioral ecology of reproduction in birds including mating systems, sexual selection, parental investment and competition. *Mailing Add:* Biol Dept Queens Univ Kingston ON K7L 3N6 Can

ROBERTSON, RANDAL MCGAVOCK, b Tampa, Fla, Mar 12, 11; m 39; c 3. PHYSICS. *Educ:* Glasgow Univ, MA, 32; Mass Inst Technol, PhD(physics), 36. *Prof Exp:* Asst, Columbia Univ, 36-37; res assoc, Norton Co, Mass, 37-42; staff mem radiation lab, Mass Inst Technol, 42-46; head mech & mat br, US Off Naval Res, DC, 46-48, dir phys sci div, 48-51, dep natural sci, 51-52, sci dir, 52-58; asst dir math, phys & eng sci, NSF, 58-61, assoc dir res, 61-70; dean res div & prof physics, 70-76, EMER DEAN RES DIV, VA POLYTECH INST & STATE UNIV, 76- *Mem:* Fel AAAS; fel Am Phys Soc; Soc Am Foresters. *Res:* Arc cathode phenomena; nuclear magnetic moments; physics of solid materials, especially abrasives and refractories; microwave linear array scanning antennas; radar; research administration. *Mailing Add:* 1404 Highland Circle SE Blacksburg VA 24060

ROBERTSON, RAYMOND E(LIOT), b St Louis, Mo, Aug 17, 40; m 77. ORGANIC CHEMISTRY, PETROLEUM CHEMISTRY. *Educ:* Cent Mo State Col, BS, 62; Colo State Univ, MS, 71; Univ Wyo, PhD(chem), 76. *Prof Exp:* Res chemist org synthesis, Tretolite Co, Petrolite Corp, Webster Groves, Mo, 63-69; instr chem, Eastern Wyo Col, 75-76; RES CHEMIST PHYS & ORG CHEM, LARAMIE ENERGY TECHNOL CTR, US DEPT ENERGY, 76- *Mem:* Am Chem Soc; Sigma Xi. *Res:* Micellar catalysis; petroleum recovery and demulsification chemistry; asphalt chemistry and relationships between asphalt physical and chemical properties; acyloin condensation chemistry. *Mailing Add:* Laramie Energy Technol Ctr Box 3395 University Station Laramie WY 82071

ROBERTSON, REED S, b Philadelphia, Pa, Aug 19, 21; m 44; c 1. WATER CHEMISTRY, CHEMICAL ENGINEERING. *Educ:* Ill Inst Technol, BSChE, 56, MS, 69. *Prof Exp:* Chemist, Chambers Works, E I du Pont de Nemours & Co, 41-42; sr group leader water treatment, Clearing Labs, 46-67, sr group leader indust waste treatment, Res Ctr, 67-68, sr group leader, Pollution Control Lab, 68-69, pollution control specialist, 69-75, sect head Environ Sci, 75-77, mgr consult serv, 77-80, SR CONSULT WATER TREATMENT CHEM, NALCO CHEM CO, 81- *Mem:* Nat Asn Prof Engrs; Water Pollution Control Fedn; Am Soc Mech Engrs; Am Chem Soc; Am Inst Chemists. *Res:* New process development; air and water pollution control; problem solving, contract consulting; development of analytical methods for water chemistry; development and application of chemicals to treatment of water. *Mailing Add:* Nalco Chem Co 2901 Butterfield Rd Oak Brook IL 60521

ROBERTSON, RICHARD EARL, b Long Beach, Calif, Nov 12, 33; m 55, 74; c 2. PHYSICAL CHEMISTRY. *Educ:* Occidental Col, BA, 55; Calif Inst Technol, PhD(chem), 60. *Prof Exp:* NSF fel, Wash Univ, 59-60; phys chemist, Gen Elec Res & Develop Ctr, 60-70; STAFF SCIENTIST, FORD MOTOR CO, 70- *Mem:* AAAS; fel Am Phys Soc; Am Chem Soc. *Res:* Mechanical properties and structure of polymers; adhesion; structure and mechanical properties of polymers; behavior of fiber composites. *Mailing Add:* Metall Res Dept Ford Motor Co PO Box 2053 Dearborn MI 48121

ROBERTSON, RICHARD THOMAS, b Spokane, Wash, July 25, 45. NEUROBIOLOGY. *Educ:* Wash State Univ, BS, 67; Univ Calif, Irvine, MS, 68, PhD(biol sci), 72. *Prof Exp:* Res assoc neuroanat, Univ Oslo, 71-72; res scientist neurobiol, Fels Res Inst, 72-76; ASST ASSOC PROF ANAT & BIOL SCI, UNIV CALIF-IRVINE, 76- *Concurrent Pos:* Adj mem, Psychol Dept, Antioch Col, 73-76. *Mem:* Soc Neurosci; Am Asn Anatomists; Psychonomic Soc. *Res:* Neuroanatomical and neurophysiological studies of nonspecific sensory systems of the brainstem, thalamus and cerebral cortex. *Mailing Add:* Dept Anat Col Med Univ Calif Irvine CA 92717

ROBERTSON, ROBERT, b Suffolk, Eng, Nov 14, 34; c 1. MALACOLOGY. *Educ:* Stanford Univ, AB, 56; Harvard Univ, PhD(biol), 60. *Prof Exp:* Asst cur mollusks, 60-65, chmn dept, 69-72, assoc cur mollusks, 65-76, CUR MALACOL, ACAD NATURAL SCI PHILADELPHIA, 76-, HENRY A PILSBRY CHAIR MALACOL, 69- *Concurrent Pos:* Secy, Inst Malacol, 65-70, pres-elect, 70-73, pres, 73-74, co-ed-in-chief, Malacologia, 73- *Mem:* Fel AAAS; Am Malacol Union (vpres, 81-); Marine Biol Asn UK; Malacol Soc Japan; Australia Soc Malacol. *Res:* Marine mollusks of Western Atlantic and Indo-Pacific; taxonomy; larvae; anatomy; life histories; ecology, especially foods and reproduction of gastropods; paleontology; marine zoogeography. *Mailing Add:* Acad Natural Sci of Philadelphia Dept of Malacol 19th & Pkwy Philadelphia PA 19103

ROBERTSON, ROBERT GRAHAM HAMISH, b Ottawa, Ont, Oct 3, 43. PHYSICS. *Educ:* Oxford Univ, BA, 65; McMaster Univ, PhD(nuclear physics), 71. *Prof Exp:* Res assoc, 71-72, asst res prof nuclear physics, 72-73, asst prof, 73-78, assoc prof, 78-81, PROF PHYSICS, CYCLOTRON LAB, MICH STATE UNIV, 81- *Concurrent Pos:* Res assoc, Princeton Univ, 75-76. *Mem:* Brit Inst Physics; Can Asn Physicists; Am Phys Soc. *Res:* Weak interactions; atomic beam magnetic resonance; nuclear astrophysics; isobaric multiplets; nuclei far from stability. *Mailing Add:* MS-456 Los Alamos Nat Lab Mich State Univ Los Alamos NM 87544

ROBERTSON, ROBERT JAMES, b Hazleton, Pa, Oct 7, 43; m 67; c 1. EXERCISE PHYSIOLOGY. *Educ:* West Chester State Col, BS, 66; Univ Pittsburgh, MA, 67, PhD(health & phys educ), 73. *Prof Exp:* Asst dir, Phys Fitness Res Lab, Univ Health Ctr, 71-73; asst prof & dir, Phys Fitness Res Lab, Dept Health Educ, Nebr Ctr Health Educ, Univ Nebr, 73-76; ASSOC PROF & DIR, HUMAN ENERGY RES LAB, DEPT HEALTH & PHYS EDUC, UNIV PITTSBURGH, 76- *Mem:* Am Alliance Health Phys Educ & Recreation; Am Heart Asn; Am Col Sports Med. *Res:* Physiological and perceptual correlates of exercise stress; exercise as a therapeutic modality in coronary heart disease; exercise effect on epilepsy; energy cost of load carriage; effect of red blood cell reinfusion and bicarbonate ingestion on physical working capacity. *Mailing Add:* Human Energy Res Lab Univ of Pittsburgh Pittsburgh PA 15261

ROBERTSON, ROBERT L, b Blountsville, Ala, July 20, 25; m 64; c 1. ENTOMOLOGY. *Educ:* Auburn Univ, BS, 50, MS, 54. *Prof Exp:* Asst county agr agent, Auburn Univ, 50-52, res asst entom, 52-54, asst prof, 54-57; entomologist, Am Cyanamid Co, 57-58; exten entomologist, Univ Ga, 58-60; assoc prof entom, 60-69, EXTEN PROF ENTOM, NC STATE UNIV, 69- *Mem:* Entom Soc Am. *Res:* Insects of economic importance on tobacco, cotton, peanuts, ornamentals and turf. *Mailing Add:* Dept Entom NC State Univ 2309 Gardner Hall Raleigh NC 27607

ROBERTSON, RODERICK FRANCIS, b Vancouver, BC, Sept 9, 20; m 58; c 1. PHYSICAL CHEMISTRY. *Educ:* Univ BC, BA, 44, MA, 46; McGill Univ, PhD(chem), 55. *Prof Exp:* Lectr chem, Univ BC, 46-47; lectr, 48-50, 55-56, from asst prof to assoc prof, 57-72, PROF CHEM, McGILL UNIV, 72- *Concurrent Pos:* Res chemist, Med Treat Serv, Can Dept Vet Affairs, 54-60. *Mem:* Chem Inst Can. *Res:* Surface and colloid chemistry; films at air-water interface; sorption at gas-solid interface; solution properties of polymer systems. *Mailing Add:* Dept of Chem 801 Sherbrooke St W Montreal PQ H3A 2K6 Can

ROBERTSON, ROSS ELMORE, b Kennetcook, NS, Oct 5, 15; m 45; c 4. PHYSICAL CHEMISTRY, ORGANIC CHEMISTRY. *Educ:* Mt Allison Univ, BSc, 41, MSc, 42; McGill Univ, PhD(chem), 44. *Prof Exp:* From mem staff to prin res officer, Nat Res Coun Can, 44-69; prof chem, 69-81, AOSTRA res prof, 80-82, EMER PROF CHEM, UNIV CALGARY, 81- *Mem:* Am Chem Soc; fel Chem Inst Can; fel Royal Soc Can; Royal Soc Chem. *Res:* Detailed mechanisms of solvolysis; solvent isotope effects in kinetics and equilibria; secondary deuterium isotope effects; water-oil emulsions; water purification. *Mailing Add:* Dept of Chem Univ of Calgary Calgary AB T2N 1N4 Can

ROBERTSON, SCOTT HARRISON, b Washington, DC, Nov 6, 45; m 73. PLASMA PHYSICS. *Educ:* Cornell Univ, BS, 68, PhD(appl physics), 72. *Prof Exp:* Sr res assoc plasma physics, Columbia Univ, 72-74; asst res physicist, 75-80, ASSOC RES PHYSICIST PLASMA PHYSICS, UNIV CALIF, IRVINE, 80- *Mem:* Am Phys Soc; AAAS; Inst Elec & Electronics Engrs. *Res:* Experimental investigations of the propagation of intense ion and electron beams, and their interaction with magnetically confined target plasma, particularly heating, focusing, and microwave emission due to collective processes. *Mailing Add:* Dept of Physics Univ of Calif Irvine CA 92664

ROBERTSON, STUART DONALD TREADGOLD, b Lethbridge, Alta, June 4, 35; m 59; c 2. ELECTRICAL ENGINEERING. *Educ:* Queen's Univ, Ont, BSc, 58; Univ London, DIC, 60; Univ Toronto, MASc, 62, PhD(elec eng), 65. *Prof Exp:* From asst prof to assoc prof, 66-76, PROF ELEC ENG, UNIV TORONTO, 76- *Concurrent Pos:* Consult, Fed Pac Elec, 65- & Elec Eng Consociates, Inc, 68-; mem Int Conf Large Elec Systs, 69-72; pres, Vehicle Res Ltd, 70- *Mem:* Inst Elec & Electronics Engrs; Am Soc Eng Educ. *Res:* Electrical vehicles; power semiconductor circuits; electric power systems; relay protection; low frequency electromagnetic fields. *Mailing Add:* Dept of Elec Eng Univ of Toronto Toronto ON M5S 2R8 Can

ROBERTSON, T(HOMAS) M(ILLS), b Tallula, Ill, Oct 1, 22; m 43; c 2. ELECTRICAL ENGINEERING. *Educ:* Univ Ill, BS, 43. *Prof Exp:* Electronic engr, Farnsworth TV & Radio, 46-47 & Kellex Corp, 47-48; sect leader, Labs, Vitro Corp Am, 48-53, group leader, 53-54, asst dept head, 54-57, dept head, 57-69, dept head, Vitro Labs Div, 69-76, DEPT HEAD DIV CUSTOMER RELS, VITRO LABS DIV, AUTOMATION INDUSTS, INC, 76- *Concurrent Pos:* Chmn anti-submarine warfare adv comt, Nat Security Indust Asn. *Mem:* Sr mem Inst Elec & Electronics Engrs; Nat Soc Prof Engrs. *Res:* Ordnance equipment; weapons and systems for undersea warfare. *Mailing Add:* Vitro Labs Div 14000 Georgia Ave Silver Spring MD 20910

ROBERTSON, THOMAS N, b St Andrews, Scotland, Oct 22, 31; US citizen; m 58; c 2. MATHEMATICS. *Educ:* Univ St Andrews, BSc, 53; Col Aeronaut, MSc, 55; Univ Southern Calif, MA, 60. *Prof Exp:* Aerodynamicist, Eng Elec Co, 55-57; lectr math, Univ Southern Calif, 58-60; from instr to assoc prof math, 60-79, chmn dept, 69-75, PROF MATH, OCCIDENTAL COL, 79-, CHMN DEPT, 78- *Concurrent Pos:* Danforth teacher grant, 63-64; Fulbright lectr, Turkey, 73-74. *Mem:* Math Asn Am. *Res:* Supersonic aerodynamics; numerical analysis. *Mailing Add:* Dept of Math Occidental Col 1600 Campus Rd Los Angeles CA 90041

ROBERTSON, THOMAS W, developmental neurobiology, see previous edition

ROBERTSON, TIM, b Denver, Colo, Oct 4, 37; m 59; c 4. MATHEMATICAL STATISTICS. *Educ:* Univ Mo, BA, 59, MA, 61, PhD(statist), 65. *Prof Exp:* Asst prof math, Cornell Col, 61-63; from asst prof to assoc prof statist, 65-74, PROF STATIST, UNIV IOWA, 74- *Concurrent Pos:* Vis prof, Univ NC, 74-75. *Mem:* Fel Inst Math Statist; fel Am Statist Asn; Math Asn Am. *Res:* Mathmatical statistics with particular interests in the theory and applications of order restricted estimates, hypothesis tests and related problems. *Mailing Add:* Dept Statistics & Actuarial Sci Univ Iowa Iowa City IA 52242

ROBERTSON, W(ILLIAM) D(ONALD), b Montreal, Que, Dec 23, 13; nat US; m 38; c 2. MATERIALS SCIENCE. *Educ:* Mass Inst Technol, BSc, 42, DSc(metall), 48. *Hon Degrees:* MA, Yale Univ, 57. *Prof Exp:* Res metallurgist, Aluminum Labs, Ltd, 42-45; res assoc, Inst Study Metals, Chicago, 48-50; from assoc prof to prof metall & chmn dept, 50-63, prof appl sci, 63-78, EMER PROF APPL SCI, YALE UNIV, 78- *Concurrent Pos:* Fulbright sr res scholar, Cambridge Univ & overseas fel, Churchill Col, 64-65; vis prof, Univ Sussex, 71; sr res fel, Univ Warwick, Eng, 74-75; sr scientist in residence, Univ Va, 78- *Honors & Awards:* Willis R Whitney Award, Nat Asn Corrosion Engrs, 65. *Mem:* Int Inst Conserv Hist & Artistic Works Eng. *Res:* Physical metallurgy; corrosion of metals; crystal plasticity and fracture; structure and properties of surfaces by low energy electron diffraction techniques and electron spectroscopy; preservation of architectural monuments (cathedrals); physical techniques for evaluating durability of limestone masonry used in restoration of Westminster Abbey. *Mailing Add:* 2107 Minor Rd Charlottesville VA 22903

ROBERTSON, WALTER VOLLEY, b Malakoff, Tex, Apr 6, 31; m 57; c 5. VERTEBRATE ZOOLOGY. *Educ:* Stephen F Austin State Col, BS, 51; Tex A&M Univ, MS, 59, PhD(zool), 64. *Prof Exp:* Instr zool, Tex A&M Univ, 60-64; from asst prof to assoc prof, 64-73, PROF BIOL & ADMIN ASST, STEPHEN F AUSTIN STATE UNIV, 73- *Mem:* Am Soc Zoologists. *Res:* Comparative vertebrate anatomy, osteology of North American clupeid fishes and brain morphology of rodents. *Mailing Add:* Dept of Biol Stephen F Austin State Univ Nacogdoches TX 75961

ROBERTSON, WAYNE MARVIN, b Fremont, Mich, Feb 14, 36; m 57; c 4. PHYSICAL METALLURGY. *Educ:* Mich State Univ, BS, 57, MS, 59; Carnegie Inst Technol, PhD(metall eng), 63. *Prof Exp:* NSF fel metall, Univ Leeds, 62-63; mem tech staff phys metall, Rockwell Int Sci Ctr, 63-81; ASSOC PROG DIR METALL, NSF, 81- *Concurrent Pos:* Mat engr, US Army Armament Command, Rock Island, Ill, 74-75. *Mem:* Am Inst Mining, Metall & Petrol Engrs; Am Soc Metals; Am Soc Testing & Mat. *Res:* Mechanical properties of solids; surface energy and surface diffusion on solids; interaction of solids and liquids; gas, liquid and solid diffusion; environmental effects on fracture of metals. *Mailing Add:* Div Mat Res Nat Sci Found 1800 G St Washington DC 20550

ROBERTSON, WILBERT JOSEPH, JR, b Washington, DC, Mar 28, 28; m 55; c 4. INORGANIC CHEMISTRY. *Educ:* George Washington Univ, BS, 50; Univ Wis, PhD(inorg chem), 55. *Prof Exp:* Chemist, Uranium Div, Mallinckrodt Chem Works, 55-60, res supvr uranium processing, 60-66, chemist, Opers Div, 66-67; sr staff engr, Nuclear Div, 67-70, RES PROJ CHEMIST, TECH DIV, KERR-McGEE CORP, 70- *Mem:* Am Chem Soc; Am Nuclear Soc. *Res:* Hydrometallurgy; solvent extraction; mineral processing and purification; extractive metallurgy. *Mailing Add:* Tech Ctr Kerr-McGee Corp Oklahoma City OK 73125

ROBERTSON, WILLIAM, IV, b Glen Ridge, NJ, Sept 12, 43; m 71; c 2. SCIENCE POLICY, ENVIRONMENTAL MANAGEMENT. *Educ:* Parsons Col, BS, 66; Sam Houston State Univ, MA, 69. *Prof Exp:* Tutor biol, Parsons Col, 66-67; res technician biochem, Med Ctr, NY Univ, 67-68; sci secy, Comt Water Qual Criteria, Nat Acad Sci, 71-72; staff officer, Environ Studies Bd, 72-73, tech asst, Comn Natural Resources, 73-78, exec secy, Int Environ Progs Comt, 74-78; PROG DIR, ANDREW W MELLON FOUND, 79- *Mem:* AAAS; Am Soc Limnol & Oceanog. *Res:* Bringing scientific knowledge and understanding effectively to bear upon natural resource management and science policy issues. *Mailing Add:* Andrew W Mellon Found 140 East 62nd St New York NY 10021

ROBERTSON, WILLIAM G, b Bethesda, Md, Dec 2, 29; m 55; c 2. MEDICAL PHYSIOLOGY. *Educ:* Shepherd Col, BS, 54; WVa Univ, MS, 55; State Univ NY Buffalo, PhD(physiol), 63. *Prof Exp:* Instr zool, WVa Univ, 55-57; instr aviation physiol, Sch Aerospace Med, US Air Force, 57-62, res physiologist respiratory physiol, 62-63, chief sealed environ sect, 63-66; proj scientist, Garrett Corp, Calif, 66-70; sr staff scientist, Inhalation Toxicol Dept, Hazelton Labs, Inc, 70-71; chief environ physiol br, US Air Force Sch Aerospace Med, 71-73; PROF PHYSIOL & CHMN MED BIOL DIV, OKLA COL OSTEOP MED & SURG, 73- *Mem:* AAAS; Am Physiol Soc; Aerospace Med Asn. *Res:* Respiratory and environmental physiology. *Mailing Add:* Med Biol Div Okla Col Osteopath Med & Surg Tulsa OK 74101

ROBERTSON, WILLIAM O, b New York, NY, Nov 24, 25; m 52; c 5. PEDIATRICS, MEDICAL ADMINISTRATION. *Educ:* Univ Rochester, BA, 46, MD, 49. *Prof Exp:* From instr to assoc prof pediat, Col Med, Ohio State Univ, 56-63, asst dean, 62-63; from asst dean to assoc dean, 63-72, assoc prof, 63-72, PROF PEDIAT, SCH MED, UNIV WASH, 72- *Concurrent Pos:* Consult, US Army Madigen Hosp, 64- *Mem:* AAAS; Am Med Writers' Asn; Am Asn Poison Control Ctr (treas, 63-64). *Res:* Child development; nutrition; accidental poisoning; education. *Mailing Add:* Dept Pediat Univ Wash Sch Med Seattle WA 98105

ROBERTSON, WILLIAM VAN BOGAERT, b New York, NY, Sept 15, 14; m 41, 68; c 3. BIOCHEMISTRY. *Educ:* Stevens Inst Technol, ME, 34; Univ Freiburg, PhD(chem), 37. *Prof Exp:* Res chemist, Mass Gen Hosp, Boston, 38-41; res fel, Nat Cancer Inst, 41-44; res assoc, Univ Chicago, 44-45; asst prof exp med, Univ Vt, 45-48, assoc prof biochem & exp med, 48-52, prof biochem, 52-61; from assoc prof to prof, 61-79, EMER PROF BIOCHEM, STANFORD UNIV, 79-; DIR RES & EDUC, CHILDREN'S HOSP AT STANFORD, 62- *Concurrent Pos:* Vis prof biochem, Univ del Valle, Cali, Colombia, 67-68 & Univ Saigon, Viet-Nam, 74; consult nutrit, Nat Inst Child Health & Human Develop, Bethesda, Md, 78; prog mgr human nutrit, NSF, 79-81, prog mgr metabolic biol, 81- *Mem:* AAAS; Am Chem Soc; Inst Food Technol; Am Soc Biol Chemists; Am Soc Clin Nutrit. *Res:* Biochemistry of connective tissue; nutritional biochemistry. *Mailing Add:* 733 Mayfield Ave Stanford CA 94305

ROBERTS-PICHETTE, PATRICIA RUTH, b Hamilton, NZ, Dec 22, 30; m 67; c 2. ECOLOGY. *Educ:* Univ NZ, BSc, 53, MSc, 54; Duke Univ, PhD, 57. *Prof Exp:* Asst prof biol, Pfeiffer Col, 57-58; from asst prof to assoc prof, Univ NB, 58-67; consult & pvt researcher, 67-73; EXEC SECY, MAN & BIOSPHERE PROG IN CAN, LIAISON & COORD DIRECTORATE, ENVIRON CAN, 73- *Concurrent Pos:* Consult dept natural resources, Prov NB, 66-68 & dept agr, 68-71, Can Dept Forestry, 68 & Environ Can, 71-72. *Mem:* AAAS; Ecol Soc Am; Can Bot Asn. *Res:* Community ecology; vegetation and floras of specific regions; plant succession and distribution; pollution biology. *Mailing Add:* 430 Besserer St Ottawa ON K1N 6N5 Can

ROBERTSTAD, GORDON WESLEY, b Madison, Wis, Sept 29, 23; m 48; c 4. BACTERIOLOGY. *Educ:* Lniv Wis, BS, 49, MS, 51; Colo State Univ, PhD(bact), 59. *Prof Exp:* Instr bact, Univ Wyo, 49-50; proj asst, Univ Wis, 51-52; instr bact, Univ Wyo, 52-57, asst prof, 57-59, assoc prof microbiol, 59-64; prof bact & head dept, SDak State Univ, 64-68; dir health related prog, 75-81, PROF MICROBIOL, UNIV TEX, EL PASO, 68- *Concurrent Pos:* NIH fel, Commun Dis Ctr, Atlanta, Ga, 62-63. *Mem:* Fel Am Acad Microbiol; Am Soc Allied Health Professions; Sigma Xi; Mycol Soc Am; Int Soc Human & Animal Mycol. *Res:* Antigenic studies of Vibrio fetus; taxonomy of microaerophilic Actionomycetes; epidemiology of dermatophytic and systemic fungi; aeromycology. *Mailing Add:* Dept of Biol Sci Biol Bldg 212 Univ of Tex El Paso TX 79968

ROBEY, ROBERT ELLIS, microbiology, immunology, see previous edition

ROBEY, ROGER LEWIS, b Fairmont, WVa, June 18, 46; m 68; c 2. SYNTHETIC ORGANIC CHEMISTRY. *Educ:* Marietta Col, BS, 68; Princeton Univ, MS, 71, PhD(org chem), 72. *Prof Exp:* Assoc, Ohio State Univ, 72-74; SR ORG CHEMIST, ELI LILLY & CO, 74- *Mem:* Am Chem Soc; Royal Soc Chem. *Res:* Oxidative processes; thallium chemistry; synthesis of heterocycles. *Mailing Add:* Dept MC 742 Eli Lilly & Co Indianapolis IN 46206

ROBIE, NORMAN WILLIAM, b Washington, DC, Jan 21, 42; m 64; c 1. PHARMACOLOGY. *Educ:* Auburn Univ, BS, 64, MS, 69; Med Univ SC, PhD(pharmacol), 72. *Prof Exp:* Fel clin pharmacol, Sch Med, Emory Univ, 72-75; asst prof pharmacol, Univ Tex Health Sci Ctr, San Antonio, 75-77; asst prof, 77-79, ASSOC PROF PHARMACOL, LA STATE UNIV MED CTR, 79- *Mem:* Am Fed Clin Res; Am Soc Pharmacol & Exp Therapeut. *Res:* Autonomic cardiovascular pharmacology. *Mailing Add:* Dept Pharmacol La State Univ Med Ctr 1100 Florida Ave New Orleans LA 70119

ROBIE, RICHARD ALLEN, b Winchendon, Mass, Oct 13, 28; m 68. MINERALOGY. *Educ:* Dartmouth Col, AB, 50; Univ Chicago, MS, 53, PhD(geochem), 57. *Prof Exp:* Chemist, Univ Chicago, 54-56; GEOPHYSICIST, US GEOL SURV, 57- *Concurrent Pos:* Prin investr, Lunar Samples Prog. *Mem:* AAAS; Mineral Soc Am; Am Chem Soc; Am Geophys Union; Geochem Soc. *Res:* Thermodynamic properties of minerals; low temperature heat capacities and aqueous solution calorimetry of carbonates and silicates; elastic constants of single crystals; specific heats of lunar soils. *Mailing Add:* US Geol Surv Stop 959 Exp Geochem Br Reston VA 22092

ROBILLARD, EUGENE, b Montreal, Que, Mar 20, 10; m 41; c 5. PHYSIOLOGY. *Educ:* Univ Montreal, MD, 36. *Hon Degrees:* DM, Sherbrooke Univ, 77. *Prof Exp:* Prof physiol, Univ Montreal, 39-70, vdean fac med, 64-70, dean, 68-70, dir serv med studies, Col Physicians & Surgeons Prov Que, 70-75, EMER PROF PHYSIOL, UNIV MONTREAL, 75- *Concurrent Pos:* Mem panel aviation med, Defence Res Bd Can, 53-59; mem med adv comt, Nat Res Coun Can, 55-58; mem, Spec Comt Govt Support Med Res, 58-60. *Honors & Awards:* Duncan Graham Award, 76. *Mem:* Am Physiol Soc; Geront Soc; Can Physiol Soc (pres, 54); Fr-Can Asn Advan Sci (pres, 59); Fr Soc Biol Chem. *Res:* Respiration; gerontology. *Mailing Add:* Col Physicians & Surgeons PQ 1440 St Catherine St W Suite 914 Montreal PQ H3G 1S5 Can

ROBILLARD, GEOFFREY, b Niagara Falls, NY, Feb 25, 23; m 63; c 2. CHEMICAL ENGINEERING. *Educ:* Mass Inst Technol, BS, 44, MS, 47. *Prof Exp:* Chemist, Carbide & Carbon Chem Co Div, Union Carbide Corp, 47-52; res engr, 52-53, sect chief, 53-59, div chief, 59-63, dep proj mgr, 63-68, mgr, Eng Mech Div, 68-73, dep asst lab dir, 73-76, asst lab dir planning & rev, 76-78, ASST LAB DIR ENERGY & TECHNOL APPLICATIONS, JET PROPULSION LAB, CALIF INST TECHNOL, 78- *Mem:* Am Inst Aeronaut & Astronaut. *Res:* Propulsion; structures; materials; system design and development; Ranger, Mariner & Voyager projects; energy. *Mailing Add:* Calif Inst of Technol 4800 Oak Grove Pasadena CA 91109

ROBILLIARD, GORDON ALLAN, b Victoria, BC, May 19, 43; m 72; c 2. MARINE ECOLOGY. *Educ:* Univ Victoria, BSc, 65; Univ Wash, MS, 67, PhD(zool), 71. *Prof Exp:* SR AQUATIC ECOLOGIST, WOODWARD-CLYDE CONSULTS, 71- *Mem:* AAAS; Ecol Soc Am; Am Soc Limnol & Oceanog; Am Soc Zoologists; Sigma Xi. *Res:* Ecology and feeding habits of opisthobranch molluscs; ecological consequences of predation by fish and large motile invertebrates in marine benthic communities; polar marine ecology. *Mailing Add:* Woodward-Clyde Consults 3 Embarcadero Ctr Suite 700 San Francisco CA 94111

ROBIN, BURTON HOWARD, b Chicago, Ill, Mar 19, 26; m 47; c 3. ORGANIC CHEMISTRY. *Educ:* Roosevelt Univ, BS, 48; Univ Chicago, MS, 49. *Prof Exp:* Res chemist, Corn Prod Co, 49-51; res chemist, Swift & Co, 51-57; res chemist, Visking Corp, 58-59; res chemist, Nalco Chem Co, 59-63; chmn dept phys sci, 69-74, assoc prof, 63-76, PROF CHEM, KENNEDY-KING COL, 76- *Mem:* AAAS; Am Chem Soc; Sigma Xi. *Res:* Coagulants; surfactants; corrosion and rust inhibitors; flotation agents; vinyl polymers; emulsion polymerization; fats and fatty acids and derivatives; qualitative analysis; physical science. *Mailing Add:* Dept Phys Sci Kennedy-King Col 6800 S Wentworth Ave Chicago IL 60621

ROBIN, EUGENE DEBS, b Detroit, Mich, Aug 23, 19; m; c 2. PHYSIOLOGY. *Educ:* George Washington Univ, SB, 46, SM, 47, MD, 51. *Prof Exp:* Res fel med, Harvard Med Sch, 52-53; sr asst resident med serv, Peter Bent Brigham Hosp, Boston, 53-54; asst med, Harvard Med Sch, 54-55, instr, 55-58, assoc, 58-59; from assoc prof to prof, Sch Med, Univ Pittsburgh, 59-70; actg chmn dept med, 71-73, PROF MED & PHYSIOL, SCH MED, STANFORD UNIV, 70-, ACTG CHMN & CURRIC & ACAD CONSULT, DEPT PHYSIOL, 80- *Concurrent Pos:* Asst, Peter Bent Brigham Hosp, 52-53, chief med resident, 54-55, jr assoc, 55-57, assoc, 57-59, assoc dir, Cardiovasc Training Prog, 58-59; chmn pulmonary adv comt, Nat Heart & Lung Inst, 71-74. *Mem:* Am Physiol Soc; Am Soc Clin Invest; Am Thoracic Soc (pres, 70-71); Am Heart Asn; Am Col Physicians. *Res:* Clinical physiology; intracellular acid-base metabolism; intracellular gas exchange; comparative physiology and biochemistry. *Mailing Add:* Dept of Med Stanford Univ Sch of Med Stanford CA 94305

ROBIN, JAMES EDMOND, physics, lasers, see previous edition

ROBIN, MICHAEL, b New York, NY, May 17, 19; m 43; c 2. ORGANIC CHEMISTRY. *Educ:* City Col New York, BS, 40; NY Univ, ChE, 44; Brooklyn Col, MS, 50. *Prof Exp:* Sr org chemist org & pharmaceut res & develop, Nepera Chem Co, Inc, NY, 46-51; res & develop chemist metallic soap, Nuodex Prod Co, Inc, NJ, 51-53; chief chemist org & pharmaceut, Simpson Labs, Simpson Coal & Chem Co, 53-56; group leader chem org res & develop, Catalin Corp Div, 56-68, mgr chem prod div lab, 68-73, plant mgr fine chem dept, 73-74, mgr, Mfg Servs, Ashland Chem Co, Ashland Oil & Refining Co, 74-76; TECH DIR, CTR FOR PROF ADVAN, WEST BRUNSWICK, NJ, 77- *Mem:* AAAS; Am Chem Soc; Am Inst Chem; Soc Plastics Eng; NY Acad Sci. *Res:* Fine organic and pharmaceutical product and process research and development; organic synthesis; antioxidants and stabilizers for organic materials. *Mailing Add:* 1508 Ashbrook Dr Scotch Plains NJ 07076

ROBINETTE, CHARLES DENNIS, b Conway, Ark, June 23, 35; m 67; c 1. RADIOBIOLOGY, STATISTICS. *Educ:* State Col Ark, BS, 57; Colo State Univ, MS, 65, PhD(radiation biol), 71. *Prof Exp:* Statistician med, Southern Res Support Ctr, Vet Admin, 68-72; PROF ASSOC STATIST, MED FOLLOW-UP AGENCY, NAT ACAD SCI, 72- *Concurrent Pos:* Instr div biometry med ctr, Univ Ark, Little Rock, 68-72; statistician, Radiation Effects Res Found, Hiroshima, Japan, 77-79. *Mem:* Am Statist Asn; Radiation Res Soc. *Res:* Application of statistics methods to medical research. *Mailing Add:* Nat Acad of Sci Washington DC 20418

ROBINETTE, HILLARY, JR, b Wilmington, Del, Jan 27, 13; m 34; c 2. CHEMISTRY. *Educ:* Temple Univ, AB, 34. *Prof Exp:* Res chemist, Rohm and Haas Co, Pa, 33-39; pres, W H & F Jordon Jr Co, 39-41; mem res staff, Com Solvents Corp, Ind, 41-42; mgr mkt develop, Publicker Industs, Inc, Pa, 45-48; res dir, Amalgamated Chem Corp, 48-52; PRES, ROBINETTE RES LABS, INC, 52- *Mem:* AAAS; Am Asn Textile Chem & Colorists; Am Chem Soc; Am Soc Testing & Mat; fel Am Inst Chemists. *Res:* Organic chemistry; textile chemicals. *Mailing Add:* Robinette Res Labs Inc PO Box 68 Youngtown AZ 85363

ROBINETTE, MARTIN SMITH, b Sacramento, Calif, Sept 18, 39; m 65; c 3. AUDIOLOGY. *Educ:* Univ Utah, BS, 65, MS, 67; Wayne State Univ, PhD(audiol), 70. *Prof Exp:* Asst prof audiol, Univ Wyo, 70-74; assoc prof audiol, 74-80, ASSOC PROF COMMUN, UNIV UTAH, 80- *Mem:* Acoust Soc Am; Int Soc Audiol; Am Speech & Hearing Asn. *Res:* Lateralization of sound image from intensity cues; binaural detection ability at large interaural intensity differences; test for functional hearing loss; diplacusis. *Mailing Add:* Dept of Audiol Univ of Utah Salt Lake City UT 84112

ROBINOVITCH, MURRAY R, b Brandon, Man, Jan 17, 39; m 64. ORAL BIOLOGY, EXPERIMENTAL PATHOLOGY. *Educ:* Univ Minn, BS, 59, DDS, 61; Univ Wash, PhD(salivary gland protein synthesis), 67. *Prof Exp:* From instr to assoc prof, 66-75, PROF ORAL BIOL, UNIV WASH, 75-, MEM, CTR RES ORAL BIOL, 71-, ACTG CHMN DEPT ORAL BIOL, 73- *Mem:* AAAS; Am Soc Cell Biol; Am Dent Asn; Int Asn Dent Res. *Res:* Protein synthesis in salivary and other exocrine glands; secretion and the secretory product; oral histology and pathology. *Mailing Add:* Dept of Oral Biol Univ of Wash Seattle WA 98105

ROBINOW, CARL FRANZ, b Hamburg, Ger, Apr 10, 09; m 38; c 2. MICROBIOLOGY. *Educ:* Univ Hamburg, MD, 35. *Prof Exp:* Researcher, Copenhagen, Denmark, 35-37, St Bartholomew's Hosp, London, 37-40, Strangeways Lab, Cambridge Univ, 40-47; vis lectr, US univs, 47-49; assoc prof, 49-56, PROF BACT & IMMUNOL, UNIV WESTERN ONT, 56- *Mem:* Am Soc Microbiol; Bot Soc Am; fel Royal Soc Can. *Res:* Cytology of bacteria and fungi. *Mailing Add:* Dept Microbiol & Immunol Univ Western Ont London ON N6A 5C1 Can

ROBINS, CHARLES RICHARD, b Harrisburg, Pa, Nov 25, 28; m 65; c 3. ICHTHYOLOGY. *Educ:* Cornell Univ, BA, 50, PhD(ichthyol), 54. *Prof Exp:* Asst gen zool, Cornell Univ, 50-51, ichthyol & taxon, 51-54; from asst prof to prof, 56-69, chmn dept marine sci, 61-63, MAYTAG PROF MARINE BIOL, SCH MARINE & ATMOSPHERIC SCI, UNIV MIAMI, 69-, CUR FISHES, 66-, PROF ICHTHYOLOGY, 74-, CHMN, DIV BIOL & LIVING RESOURCES, 78-, ACTG DEAN, ROSENTIEL SCH MARINE & ATMOSPHERIC SCI, 81- *Concurrent Pos:* Res assoc, Cornell Univ, 52; ed, Bull Marine Sci & Gulf & Caribbean, 61-62; mem panel syst biol, NSF, 66-69; proj & prog rev comn, Marine Lab, Duke Univ, 68-70; comt inshore & estuarine pollution, Hoover Found, 69; mem ecol adv comt, Environ Protection Agency, 75-78. *Mem:* AAAS; Am Soc Ichthyologists & Herpetologists (vpres, 64 & pres-elect, 82); Am Soc Syst Zool; Am Soc Zool; Am Inst Fishery Res Biol. *Res:* Taxonomy, morphology, ecology and behavior of fishes. *Mailing Add:* Sch of Marine & Atmospheric Sci 4600 Rickenbacker Causeway Miami FL 33149

ROBINS, ELI, b Houston, Tex, Feb 22, 21; m 46; c 4. BIOCHEMISTRY, PSYCHIATRY. *Educ:* Rice Inst, BA, 40; Harvard Med Sch, MD, 43. *Prof Exp:* Asst psychiat, Harvard Med Sch, 44-45; asst neurol, Sch Med, Boston Univ, 48; USPHS fel Sch Med, 49-51, instr neuropsychiat, 51-53, from asst prof to prof psychiat, 53-66, head dept, 63-75, WALLACE RENARD PROF PSYCHIAT, SCH MED, WASHINGTON UNIV, 66- *Concurrent Pos:* Fel psychiat, New Eng Ctr Hosp, 48. *Honors & Awards:* Salmon Medalist, NY, 81. *Mem:* Am Soc Clin Invest; Histochem Soc; Am Soc Biol Chemists; AMA; Am Psychiat Asn. *Res:* Biochemistry of the nervous system; psychiatric disease. *Mailing Add:* Dept of Psychiat Wash Univ Sch of Med St Louis MO 63110

ROBINS, JACK, b Roselle, NJ, Feb 17, 19; m 49; c 2. PHYSICAL CHEMISTRY, POLYMER CHEMISTRY. *Educ:* City Col New York, BS, 40; Univ Buffalo, MA, 48; Polytech Inst Brooklyn, PhD(phys chem), 59. *Prof Exp:* Chemist, Vandium Corp Am, 44-48; chemist, Am Electrometal Corp, 48-49; chemist, Bd Transport, NY, 49-54; chemist, Wilmot & Cassidy, Inc, 55-56; res chemist, ICI Am, Inc, 59-75, RES CHEMIST, ATLAS POWDER CO, 75- *Mem:* AAAS; Am Chem Soc. *Res:* Analytical chemistry; inorganic solutions; gas chromatography of gases, etc; thermodynamics and material properties; microcomputers, software, hardware and interfacing with instruments; scientific programmer. *Mailing Add:* Atlas Powder Co Tamaqua PA 18252

ROBINS, JANIS, b Riga, Latvia, Aug 3, 25; nat US; m 51; c 4. POLYMER CHEMISTRY, CATALYSIS. *Educ:* Univ Wash, Seattle, BS, 52, PhD(chem), 57. *Prof Exp:* Anal chemist, Wash Farmers Coop, 52; anal chemist, State Dept Agr, Wash, 52-53; anal chemist, Am-Marietta Co, 54, res chemist, 55-57; res chemist, Minn Mining & Mfg Co, 57-65; res assoc, Archer Daniels Midland Co, 65-67; res assoc, Ashland Chem Co, 67-72; SR RES SPECIALIST, 3M CO, 72- *Concurrent Pos:* Asst prof chem, Macalester Col, 60-65. *Mem:* Am Chem Soc; Sigma Xi. *Res:* Physical organic chemistry; polymer synthesis; metal ion catalysis; polyurethane, furan, epoxy and phenolic resin technology; foundry binder technology; adhesives technology. *Mailing Add:* 3M Ctr 3M Co Bldg 209 IN-13 St Paul MN 55144

ROBINS, MORRIS JOSEPH, b Nephi, Utah, Sept 28, 39; m 60, 73; c 6. ORGANIC CHEMISTRY, NUCLEIC ACID COMPONENTS-ANALOGUES. *Educ:* Univ Utah, BA, 61; Ariz State Univ, PhD(org chem), 65. *Prof Exp:* Cancer res scientist biochem, Roswell Park Mem Inst, 65-66; res assoc org chem, Univ Utah, 66-69; from asst prof to assoc prof, 69-78, PROF ORG CHEM, UNIV ALTA, 78- *Concurrent Pos:* Mem adv comt chemother & hemat, Am Cancer Soc, 77-80; vis prof med chem, Univ Utah, 81-82. *Mem:* Am Chem Soc; Chem Inst Can; Am Asn Cancer Res. *Res:* Chemistry of nucleic acid components, nucleoside antibiotics, hormonal messenger cyclic nucleotides, and related biomolecules; synthetic transformations of natural product nucleosides, chemical structure-conformation studies, and biological activity investigations. *Mailing Add:* Dept of Chem Univ of Alta Edmonton AB T6G 2G2 Can

ROBINS, NORMAN ALAN, b Chicago, Ill, Nov 19, 34; m 56; c 2. CHEMICAL ENGINEERING, MATHEMATICS. *Educ:* Mass Inst Technol, BS, 55, MS, 56; Ill Inst Technol, PhD, 72. *Prof Exp:* Metallurgist, 56-60, res metallurgist, 60-62, asst mgr, Res Dept, 62-67, assoc mgr, 67-72, dir process res, 72-77, V PRES RES, INLAND STEEL CO, 77- *Mem:* Am Inst Mining, Metall & Petrol Engrs; Am Inst Chem Engrs; Math Asn Am. *Res:* Process research and computer process control. *Mailing Add:* 3001 E Columbus Dr East Chicago IL 46312

ROBINS, RICHARD DEAN, b North Manchester, Ind, Nov 19, 42; m 69. ORGANIC CHEMISTRY. *Educ:* Manchester Col, BA, 64; Ohio State Univ, MS, 66, PhD(org chem), 68. *Prof Exp:* RES CHEMIST, LUBRIZOL CORP, 69- *Mem:* Am Chem Soc. *Res:* Physical organic and polymer chemistry. *Mailing Add:* 18432 Lynton Shaker Heights OH 44122

ROBINS, ROLAND KENITH, b Scipio, Utah, Dec 13, 26; m 48; c 6. ORGANIC CHEMISTRY. *Educ:* Brigham Young Univ, AB, 48, MA, 49; Ore State Col, PhD(chem), 52. *Prof Exp:* Res assoc, Wellcome Res Labs, Burroughs Wellcome & Co, Inc, NY, 52-53; from asst prof chem to assoc prof chem, N Mex Highlands Univ, 53-57; assoc prof, Ariz State Univ, 57-60, prof, 60-64; prof, Univ Utah, 65-69; vpres res & develop & dir, Nucleic Acid Res Inst, Int Chem & Nuclear Corp, 69-74, sr vpres res & develop, 74-77; PROF CHEM & BIOCHEM, BRIGHAM YOUNG UNIV, 77-, DIR, CANCER RES CTR, 78- *Concurrent Pos:* Consult, Parke, Davis & Co, Mich, 55-60, Midwest Res Inst, Mo, 58-64, Nat Cancer Inst, 59-69 & Merck Sharp & Dohme Div, Merck & Co Inc, 57-65; mem chem panel, Cancer Chemother, Nat Serv Ctr, NIH, 60-62. *Mem:* Am Chem Soc; Am Asn Cancer Res. *Res:* Synthesis of purines and pyrimidines; purine nucleosides; condensed pyrimidine systems, especially in cancer research. *Mailing Add:* Dept Chem Brigham Young Univ Provo UT 84602

ROBINSON, A(UGUST) R(OBERT), b Tex, Apr 24, 21; m 51; c 2. AGRICULTURAL & HYDRAULIC ENGINEERING. *Educ:* Univ Iowa, BS, 47; Colo State Univ, MS, 51. *Prof Exp:* Hydraul engr, US Bur Reclamation & US Geol Surv, 47-50; res engr, Colo State Univ, 50-51; irrig & agr engr, USDA Sci & Educ Amin, Agr Res, 51-63, dir Snake River Conserv Res Ctr, Idaho, 63-69, dir sedimentation lab, 69-74, staff scientist, Beltsville, 74-79; CONSULT ENG, 79- *Mem:* Am Soc Civil Engrs; Am Soc Agr Engrs; Nat Soc Prof Engrs. *Res:* Agricultural engineering as it applies to hydraulics; flow of water as it pertains to irrigation; hydraulic engineering as it applies to erosion and the sedimentation process. *Mailing Add:* 8473 Imperial Dr Laurel MD 20708

ROBINSON, ALBERT DEAN, b Sherman Mills, Maine, Mar 28, 39; m 61; c 1. GENETICS, MYCOLOGY. *Educ:* Univ Maine, BA, 61; Johns Hopkins Univ, MAT, 62; Univ Iowa, PhD(bot), 68. *Prof Exp:* Teacher high sch, Nyack, NY, 62-65; asst prof genetics, 68-74, assoc prof genetics, 74-80, ASSOC PROF BIOL, STATE UNIV NY COL POTSDAM, 80- *Mem:* AAAS; Am Inst Biol Sci; Bot Soc Am; Genetics Soc Am. *Res:* Genetics of Basidiomycetes. *Mailing Add:* Dept of Biol State Univ of NY Col Potsdam NY 13676

ROBINSON, ALFRED GREEN, b Thomasville, Ga, Feb 19, 28; m 51; c 4. PETROLEUM CHEMISTRY. *Educ:* Emory Univ, AB, 49, MS, 51, PhD(chem), 55. *Prof Exp:* Chemist, Hercules Powder Co, 51-52; chemist, Tenn Eastman Co Div, 55-58, chemist, Tex Eastman Co Div, 58-73, develop assoc, 73-74, head develop div, 74-77, DIR RES DIV, TEX EASTMAN CO DIV, EASTMAN KODAK CO, 77- *Mem:* Am Chem Soc. *Res:* Chemical properties of aliphatic carbonyl compounds; synthesis of polymers by condensation polymerization. *Mailing Add:* Texas Eastman Co PO Box 7444 Longview TX 75601

ROBINSON, ALLAN RICHARD, b Lynn, Mass, Oct 17, 32; m 55; c 3. PHYSICAL OCEANOGRAPHY. *Educ:* Harvard Univ, BA, 54, MA, 56, PhD(physics), 59. *Prof Exp:* NSF fel meteorol & oceanog, Cambridge Univ, 59-60; from asst prof to assoc prof, 60-68, dir, Ctr Earth & Planetary Physics, 72-75, GORDON McKAY PROF GEOPHYS FLUID DYNAMICS & MEM CTR EARTH & PLANETARY PHYSICS, HARVARD UNIV, 68-, CHMN, COMT OCEANOG, 72-; ASSOC PHYS OCEANOGR WOODS HOLE OCEANOG INST, 60- *Concurrent Pos:* Co-chmn, Mid-Ocean Dynamics Exp I Sci Coun, NSF, 71-74; Guggenheim fel, Cambridge Univ, Eng, 72-73; Co-ed-in-chief, Dynamics of Atmospheres & Oceans, 76- *Mem:* Fel Am Acad Arts & Sci. *Res:* Oceanography; dynamics of oceanic motions and geophysical fluid dynamics. *Mailing Add:* Pierce Hall Harvard Univ Cambridge MA 02138

ROBINSON, ARTHUR, b New York, NY, Jan 12, 14; m 41; c 2. PEDIATRICS, GENETICS. *Educ:* Columbia Univ, AB, 34; Univ Chicago, MD, 38. *Prof Exp:* Assoc prof pediat & biophys, 63-66, PROF PEDIAT, SCH MED, UNIV COLO, DENVER, 66-, PROF BIOPHYS & GENETICS & CHMN DEPT, 71- *Concurrent Pos:* Dir prof serv, Nat Jewish Hosp & Res Ctr, 75- *Mem:* AAAS; Am Pediat Soc; Am Acad Pediat; Am Soc Human Genetics. *Res:* Cytogenetics. *Mailing Add:* Dept of Biophys & Genetics Univ of Colo Sch of Med Denver CO 80220

ROBINSON, ARTHUR BROUHARD, medicinal chemistry, see previous edition

ROBINSON, ARTHUR GRANT, b Wadena, Sask, July 7, 16; m 42; c 1. ENTOMOLOGY. *Educ:* Univ Man, BSA, 50, PhD(entom), 61; McGill Univ, MSc, 52. *Prof Exp:* Agr Res officer, Can Dept Agr, 50-53; assoc prof entom, Univ Man, 53-66, prof, 66-81, head dept, 77-81; RETIRED. *Mem:* Entom Soc Am; fel Entom Soc Can; Agr Inst Can. *Res:* Biology and taxonomy of aphids. *Mailing Add:* Dept Entom Univ Man Winnipeg MB R3T 2N2 Can

ROBINSON, ARTHUR R(ICHARD), b Brooklyn, NY, Oct 28, 29. STRUCTURAL MECHANICS. *Educ:* Cooper Union, BCE, 51; Univ Ill, MS, 53, PhD(civil eng), 56. *Prof Exp:* Res assoc mech & mat, Univ Minn, 55-57, asst prof, 57-58, asst prof aeronaut eng, 58-60; assoc prof civil eng, 60-63, PROF CIVIL ENG, UNIV ILL, URBANA, 63- *Honors & Awards:* Walter Leroy Huber Res Prize, Am Soc Civil Engrs, 69, Moisseiff Award, 70. *Mem:* Am Soc Civil Engrs; Am Soc Mech Engrs. *Res:* Numerical methods; stress waves in solids; analysis of structural systems; earthquake engineering. *Mailing Add:* 2129 Newmark Civil Eng Lab 208 N Romins St Urbana IL 61801

ROBINSON, ARTHUR ROBIN, b Montreal, Que, May 26, 43; m 68; c 4. AGRICULTURAL CHEMISTRY, ENDOCRINOLOGY. *Educ:* McGill Univ, BSc, 67, MSc, 70, PhD(agr chem), 75. *Prof Exp:* ASSOC PROF CHEM, NS AGR COL, 75- *Concurrent Pos:* Proj leader res, NS Dept Agr & Mkt, 76-79, Can Dept Agr, 77-78 & Dept Supply & Serv, 78-81. *Res:* Animal reproduction with particular reference to hormones and plant estrogens. *Mailing Add:* PO Box 550 Truro NS B2N 5E3 Can

ROBINSON, BEATRICE BARBARA, b Bloomsburg, Pa, June 6, 41; m 63; c 2. PHYCOLOGY. *Educ:* Bloomsburg State Col, BS, 63; Syracuse Univ, PhD(bot), 68. *Prof Exp:* Instr, Syracuse Univ, 68-75; asst prof biol, 55-80, ASSOC ACAD DEAN, LE MOYNE COL, 80- *Concurrent Pos:* Instr, Le Moyne Col, 68-75. *Mem:* AAAS; Phycol Soc Am. *Res:* Development in blue-green algae, specifically, photomorphogenesis in Nostoc. *Mailing Add:* Le Moyne Col Le Moyne Heights Syracuse NY 13214

ROBINSON, BEROL L(EE), b Highland Park, Mich, June 25, 24; m 48; c 3. NUCLEAR PHYSICS, SCIENCE EDUCATION. *Educ:* Harvard Univ, AB, 48; Johns Hopkins Univ, PhD(physics), 53. *Prof Exp:* Asst prof physics, Univ Ark, 52-56; assoc prof, Western Reserve Univ, 60-67; assoc prof, Case Western Reserve Univ, 67-71; PROG SPECIALIST, UNIV SCI EDUC, UNESCO, 71- *Concurrent Pos:* Res fel, Israel AEC, 61-62; vis prof, Rensselaer Polytech Inst, 64; asst to dir, Educ Res Ctr, Mass Inst Technol, 69-71; dir educ component, US Metric Study, 70-71; mem adv comt educ, Europ Phys Soc, 75-80; assoc mem int comn physics educ, Int Union Pure & Appl Physics, 74-80. *Mem:* AAAS; Am Phys Soc; Am Asn Physics Teachers. *Res:* Nuclear and x-ray spectroscopy; Mössbauer effect; physics laboratory instruction equipment; science education; international science administration. *Mailing Add:* Sci Sector UNESCO F-75700 Paris France

ROBINSON, BRIAN HOWARD, b Derby, UK, Sept 24, 44. BIOCHEMISTRY, GENETICS. *Educ:* Bristol Univ, BSc, 65, PhD(biochem), 68. *Prof Exp:* Can Med Res Coun fel biochem, 68-70; lectr, Univ Sheffield, 70-73; SCIENTIST BIOCHEM & GENETICS, RES INST, HOSP FOR SICK CHILDREN, TORONTO, 73- *Concurrent Pos:* Assoc prof, Dept Pediat, Univ Toronto, 73-, Dept Biochem, 74-; Can Med Res Coun grants, 75-80. *Mem:* Brit Biochem Soc; Can Biochem Soc. *Res:* Nitochondrial metabolite transport; neonatal hypoglycemia; keto acid dehydrogenases; hereditary disorders of metabolism leading to lactic acidosis and keto acidosis; branched-chain amino acid metabolism. *Mailing Add:* Res Inst Hosp for Sick Children 555 University Ave Toronto ON M5G 1X8 Can

ROBINSON, BRUCE B, b Chester, Pa, Oct 13, 33; m 60; c 2. PLASMA PHYSICS. *Educ:* Drexel Inst, 56; Princeton Univ, MA, 58, PhD(plasma transport properties), 61. *Prof Exp:* Res asst gen relativity, Yerkes Observ, Univ Chicago, 61; res asst plasma stability, Univ Calif, San Diego, 61-63; mem tech staff atomic physics & solid state plasmas, RCA Labs, 63-75; asst dir prog strategies, US Energy Res & Develop Admin, 75-77; DIR TECHNOL IMPLEMENTATION ANAL, US DEPT ENERGY, 77- *Concurrent Pos:* Exec dir com tech adv bd, US Dept Com, 73-75. *Mem:* Inst Elec & Electronics Engrs; Am Phys Soc. *Res:* Relativistic cosmology; plasma transport theory; atomic collision theory; plasma stability theory; solid-state device physics; energy research and development planning. *Mailing Add:* Off of Energy Res US Dept of Energy Washington DC 20545

ROBINSON, C PAUL, b Detroit, Mich, Oct 9, 41; m 63; c 2. LASERS, CHEMICAL PHYSICS. *Educ:* Christian Bros Col, BS, 63; Fla State Univ, Tallahassee, PhD(physics), 67. *Prof Exp:* Chief test operator nuclear reactor tests, Nev, 67-70, res physicist, Advan Concepts Group, NMex, 70-71, alt group leader chem laser res & develop, 71-73, proj dir laser isotope separation, 73-76, appl photochem div leader, 76-80, ASSOC DIR, LOS ALAMOS NAT LAB, 80- *Mem:* Am Phys Soc; AAAS. *Res:* Laser isotope separation research including work on uranium enrichment, laser spectroscopy, laser induced chemistry and tunable lasers; weapons physics; arms control issues. *Mailing Add:* AP-DO Los Alamos Nat Lab Los Alamos NM 87545

ROBINSON, CAMPBELL WILLIAM, b Edmonton, Alta, June 22, 33; c 3. CHEMICAL ENGINEERING. *Educ:* Univ BC, BASc, 61; Univ Calif, Berkeley, PhD(chem eng), 71. *Prof Exp:* Process engr, Gulf Oil Can Ltd, 57-62, process unit supt, 62-64, sr process engr, 64-65, tech serv supvr, 65-66; asst prof, 71-74, assoc prof, 74-81, PROF CHEM ENG, UNIV WATERLOO, 81- *Mem:* Can Soc Chem Eng; Chem Inst Can; Am Chem Soc; Can Inst Food Sci & Technol; Soc Indust Microbiol. *Res:* Mass transfer; biochemical engineering, fermentation and waste treatment process design; food processing operations. *Mailing Add:* Dept of Chem Eng Univ of Waterloo Waterloo ON W2L 3G1 Can

ROBINSON, CASEY PERRY, b Idabel, Okla, Oct 10, 32; m 55; c 3. PHARMACOLOGY. *Educ:* Univ Okla, BS, 54, MS, 67; Vanderbilt Univ, PhD(pharmacol), 70. *Prof Exp:* Sr sci investr pharmacol, Am Heart Asn, Med Sch, Univ Calif, Los Angeles, 70-71; assoc prof pharmacol, Col Med, 71-80, from asst prof to assoc prof pharmacodynamics, Col Pharm, 71-81, PROF PHARMACOL, COL MED, UNIV OKLA, 80-, PROF PHARMACODYNAMICS, COL PHARM, 81- *Concurrent Pos:* co-prin investr, NSF grant, 74-76; prin investr, EPA grant, 77- *Mem:* AAAS; Soc Exp Biol & Med; Am Soc Pharmacol & Exp Therapeut; Soc Toxicol. *Res:* Pesticide and drug effects on cardiovascular responses; neuroeffector mechanisms of blood vessels. *Mailing Add:* Col Pharm Health Sci Ctr Univ Okla Oklahoma City OK 73122

ROBINSON, CECIL HOWARD, b London, Eng, Nov 5, 28; m 56; c 5. ORGANIC CHEMISTRY, PHARMACOLOGY. *Educ:* Univ London, BSc, 50, PhD(chem), 54. *Prof Exp:* NSF fel, Wayne State Univ, 54-55; chemist, Glaxo Labs Ltd, 55-56; from chemist to sr chemist, Schering Corp, 56-63; from asst prof to assoc prof pharmacol, 63-77, PROF PHARMACOL, SCH MED, JOHNS HOPKINS UNIV, 77- *Mem:* AAAS; Am Chem Soc; The Chem Soc; Am Soc Pharmacol & Exp Therapeut. *Res:* Synthetic steroids; enzyme inhibitors; design and synthesis of chemotherapeutic agents; schistosomiasis. *Mailing Add:* Dept of Pharmacol Johns Hopkins Univ Sch of Med Baltimore MD 21205

ROBINSON, CHARLES ALBERT, b Newton, Mass, July 22, 21; m 54; c 1. ORGANIC CHEMISTRY. *Educ:* Brown Univ, ScB, 43; Mass Inst Technol, PhD(org chem), 50. *Prof Exp:* Develop res chemist, Merck & Co, 43-47; asst chem, Mass Inst Technol, 47-50; res chemist, Arnold, Hoffman & Co, 50-53, res sect leaoer, 53-57, mem staff develop dept, 57-59, sect leader tech serv, 59-63; sr res scientist, Wyeth Labs, Inc, 63-70, asst to dir, Biol & Chem Develop Div, 70-77, assoc dir chem develop, Res & Develop Dept, 77-81; RETIRED. *Mem:* Am Chem Soc. *Res:* Synthesis of organic compounds; process development; pharmaceuticals. *Mailing Add:* 1402 Carroll Brown Way West Chester PA 19380

ROBINSON, CHARLES C(ANFIELD), b East Orange, NJ, Oct 18, 32; m 61; c 2. ELECTRICAL ENGINEERING. *Educ:* Miami Univ, BS, 55; Mass Inst Technol, BS, 55, MS, 57, EE, 59, PhD(elec eng), 60. *Prof Exp:* Asst prof elec eng, Mass Inst Technol, 61-62; sr physicist, Res Ctr, Am Optical Corp, 62-77; TECH SPECIALIST & PROJ MGR, XEROX CORP, 77- *Mem:* Inst Elec & Electronics Engrs; Optical Soc Am. *Res:* Photoconductivity; optical properties of materials; xerographic instrumentation; optical thin films; rare earth studies in glass; magneto-optical effects. *Mailing Add:* Xerox Corp Webster NY 14580

ROBINSON, CHARLES DEE, b Dallas, Tex, July 16, 32; m 54. MATHEMATICS. *Educ:* Hardin-Simmons Univ, BA, 56; Univ Tex, MA, 61, PhD(math), 64. *Prof Exp:* Instr math, Hardin-Simmons Univ, 56-59; asst prof, Ariz State Univ, 64-65; assoc prof, Univ Miss, 65-68; chmn, Div Sci, 69-80, PROF MATH & HEAD DEPT, HARDIN-SIMMONS UNIV, 68-, DIR INSTNL RES, 80- *Concurrent Pos:* Dir student sci training projs math, NSF, 67-68, 70-71 & 74-80. *Mem:* Am Math Soc; Math Asn Am. *Res:* Banach spaces and operators on Banach spaces. *Mailing Add:* Dept of Math Hardin-Simmons Univ Abilene TX 79698

ROBINSON, CHARLES NELSON, b Fayetteville, Tenn, Nov 18, 28. ORGANIC CHEMISTRY. *Educ:* Maryville Col, BS, 49; Univ Tenn, MS, 51, PhD(org chem), 53. *Prof Exp:* Asst, Univ Tenn, 49-50; asst chemist org res, Oak Ridge Nat Lab, 52; fel & asst, Univ Ill, 53-54; from asst prof to assoc prof chem, La Polytech Inst, 56-61; assoc prof, 61-66, PROF CHEM, MEMPHIS STATE UNIV, 66- *Mem:* Am Chem Soc. *Res:* Structure proof and synthesis of alkaloids and related compounds; organophosphorus chemistry. *Mailing Add:* Dept of Chem Memphis State Univ Memphis TN 38152

ROBINSON, CLARK, b Seattle, Wash, Dec 29, 43; m 66. MATHEMATICAL ANALYSIS. *Educ:* Univ Wash, BS, 66; Univ Calif, Berkeley, PhD(math), 69. *Prof Exp:* Vis prof math, Inst Pure & Appl Math, Rio de Janeiro, Brazil, 70-71; from asst prof to assoc prof, 69-78, PROF MATH, NORTHWESTERN UNIV, 78- *Mem:* Am Math Soc; Math Asn Am. *Res:* Differential dynamical systems; global analysis. *Mailing Add:* Dept of Math Northwestern Univ Evanston IL 60201

ROBINSON, CLARK SHOVE, JR, b Reading, Mass, May 13, 17; m 42; c 2. PHYSICS. *Educ:* Mass Inst Technol, SB, 38, PhD(physics), 42. *Prof Exp:* Res assoc radiation lab, Mass Inst Technol, 41-43; res asst prof physics, Univ Ill, Urbana, 46-51, res assoc prof, 51-55, prof, 55-76; TRANSLR & ED, SOVIET J NUCLEAR PHYSICS, 76- *Concurrent Pos:* Adj prof physics, Mont State Univ, Bozeman, 76- *Mem:* Am Phys Soc. *Res:* X-ray study of glass structure; crystal growth in tungsten wire; microwave and other vacuum tubes; development of betatrons; nuclear physics; mesons; Russian translation. *Mailing Add:* Dept of Physics Mont State Univ Bozeman MT 59715

ROBINSON, CURTIS, b Wilmington, NC, May 12, 34; m 68; c 3. PLANT PHYSIOLOGY. *Educ:* Morgan State Col, BS, 60; Howard Univ, MS, 68; Univ Md, PhD(bot), 73. *Prof Exp:* Teacher sci & math, Lincoln High Sch, Leland, NC, 60-61 & Williston Sr High Sch, Wilmington, 61-62; res biologist, Radiation Biol Lab, Smithsonian Inst, 62-69; res technician immunol, Microbiol Assocs, 65-67; ASSOC PROF BIOL, EDINBORO STATE COL, 73- *Mem:* Am Soc Plant Physiologists. *Res:* Studies of light, hormonal, and mineral interactions in etiolated mung bean seedlings. *Mailing Add:* Dept of Biol Edinboro State Col Edinboro PA 16444

ROBINSON, D(ENIS) M(ORRELL), b London, Eng, Nov 19, 07; nat US; m 32; c 2. ENGINEERING. *Educ:* Univ London, BS, 27, PhD(elec eng), 29; Mass Inst Technol, MS, 31. *Prof Exp:* Mem staff eng res, Callender's Cable Co, 31-35; mem staff TV develop, Scophony, Ltd, 39; radar develop assignments, Ministry Aircraft Prod, 39-45; prof elec eng, Univ Birmingham, 45-46; pres, 46-70, CHMN BD, HIGH VOLTAGE ENG CORP, BURLINGTON, 70- *Concurrent Pos:* Chmn bd trustees, Marine Biol Lab, Woods Hole, 71- *Honors & Awards:* Order of the Brit Empire; Medal of Freedom, 47. *Mem:* Nat Acad Eng; Am Acad Arts & Sci (secy, 70-); Am Phys Soc; Brit Inst Elec Engrs. *Res:* High-voltage behavior of solids; television; radar; particle accelerators. *Mailing Add:* 19 Orlando Ave Arlington MA 02174

ROBINSON, DAN D, b Sacramento, Calif, May 28, 16; m. FORESTRY. *Educ:* Ore State Col, BS, 40; Syracuse Univ, MSF, 42. *Prof Exp:* Forest guard, US Forest Serv, Ore, 36-40; farm forester, Ore State, 42-44, exten forester, 44-46; from asst prof to assoc prof forest mgt, Ore State Univ, 46-65, prof, 65-81; RETIRED. *Mem:* Soc Am Foresters. *Res:* Meteorology; agriculture; hardwood utilization in Oregon. *Mailing Add:* Sch of Forestry Ore State Univ Corvallis OR 97331

ROBINSON, DANIEL ALFRED, b Schenectady, NY, Apr 9, 32; m 58; c 3. ALGEBRA. *Educ:* NY State Teachers Col Albany, BA, 53; Rensselaer Polytech Inst, MS, 54; Univ Wis-Madison, PhD(math), 64. *Prof Exp:* From asst prof to assoc prof math, 59-76, PROF MATH, GA INST TECHNOL, 76- *Mem:* Am Math Soc; Math Asn Am. *Res:* General algebraic structures; loop theory. *Mailing Add:* Sch of Math Ga Inst of Technol Atlanta GA 30332

ROBINSON, DANIEL E, b Philadelphia, Pa, Apr 30, 25; m 51; c 3. INSTRUMENTATION. *Educ:* Howard Univ, BS, 50; Polytech Inst Brooklyn, MS, 55. *Prof Exp:* Asst res engr, 50-52, res engr, 52-56, res supvr, 56-65, sr instrument engr, 65-67, chief instrument engr, 67-71, res & develop mgr wire assembly & instrumentation, 71-73, ASST DIR RES, GEN CABLE CORP, 73- *Concurrent Pos:* Owner, Specialized Electronic Instruments Co. *Mem:* Inst Elec & Electronics Engrs. *Res:* Electromagnetic shielding; crosstalk and common mode rejection in balanced and unbalanced transmission lines; fiber optic transmission. *Mailing Add:* 38 Orchard St Metuchen NJ 08840

ROBINSON, DANIEL OWEN, b Colonia Dublan, Mex, Jan 28, 18; m 42; c 6. SOIL SCIENCE. *Educ:* Brigham Young Univ, AB, 42; Univ Ariz, MS, 47; Ohio State Univ, PhD(soil physics), 49. *Prof Exp:* Instr agron, Ohio State Univ, 49-50; assoc prof agron & head dept agr, 50-55, prof agron & dir div agr, 55-70, PROF AGR, ARIZ STATE UNIV, 70- *Mem:* AAAS; Soil Sci Soc Am; Am Soc Agron. *Res:* Soils; soil physics; plant nutrition. *Mailing Add:* Div of Agr Ariz State Univ Tempe AZ 85281

ROBINSON, DAVID, b Larne, Ireland, Jan 13, 29; US citizen; m 59; c 4. PHYSICS. *Educ:* Queen's Univ, Belfast, BSc, 51, MSc, 53; Univ Western Ont, PhD(physics), 57. *Prof Exp:* Asst lectr physics, Queen's Univ, Belfast, 52-54; res assoc, Univ Western Ont, 54-58; res assoc, Univ Southern Calif, 58-60, asst prof elec eng, 62-64; assoc prof physics, Univ Windsor, 64-68; assoc prof, 68-70, PROF PHYSICS, DRAKE UNIV, 70-, CHMN DEPT, 68- *Concurrent Pos:* Consult, Northrop Space Labs, Calif, 62-64. *Res:* Molecular spectroscopy; plasmas in hypersonic flow; diagnostic techniques in high-current plasmas and plasma accelerators for space applications. *Mailing Add:* Dept of Physics Drake Univ Des Moines IA 50311

ROBINSON, DAVID ADAIR, b Boston, Mass, Dec 9, 25; m 80. NEUROPHYSIOLOGY. *Educ:* Brown Univ, BA, 47; Johns Hopkins Univ, MSc, 56, DrEng(elec eng), 59. *Prof Exp:* From proj engr to vpres res, Airpax Electronics, Inc, Md, 51-56, Fla, 58-61; from instr to assoc prof med, 61-70, from asst prof to assoc prof elec eng, 63-75, assoc prof biomed eng, 70-75, assoc prof ophthal, 71-75, PROF OPHTHAL & PROF BIOMED ENG, SCH MED, JOHNS HOPKINS UNIV, 75- *Concurrent Pos:* Consult visual sci study sect, Div Res Grants, NIH, 66-70, consult eng in biol & med training comt, 71-73; consult comt vision, Nat Res Ctr, Nat Acad Sci, 77-81 & consult planning comt, Nat Eye Inst, NIH, 76 & 81; NIH res grant, Sch Med, Johns Hopkins Univ, 69- *Mem:* Asn Res Vision & Ophthal; Soc Neurosci. *Res:* Neurophysiology of the eye movement control system. *Mailing Add:* Dept Ophthal Johns Hopkins Univ Sch Med Baltimore MD 21205

ROBINSON, DAVID BANCROFT, b Bellefonte, Pa, Feb 4, 24; m 45; c 5. PSYCHIATRY. *Educ:* Pa State Univ, BS, 44; Univ Pa, MD, 49; Univ Minn, MS, 57. *Prof Exp:* Intern, Geisinger Mem Hosp Foss Clin, Danville, Pa, 49-50, resident med, 50-51; staff psychiatrist, Rochester State Hosp, Minn, 55-56; instr psychiat, Mayo Clin, Mayo Grad Sch Med, Univ Minn, 57-58; from asst prof psychiat, to assoc prof psychiat, 58-68, actg chmn dept psychiat, 64-68 & 77-78, dir Adult Psychiat In-Patient Unit, 69-81, PROF PSYCHIAT, STATE UNIV NY UPSTATE MED CTR, 68-, CONSULT-LIAISON PSYCHIAT, 81- *Concurrent Pos:* Fel med, Mayo Found, Sch Med, Univ Minn, 52-55; sr psychiatrist, Syracuse Vet Admin Hosp & Crouse-Irving Mem Hosp, Syracuse, 58-61; coordr, Psychiat State Hosp Residents, NY State Dept Ment Hyg, 61-64; coordr, Grad Training Prof, Dept Psychiat, State Univ NY Upstate Med Ctr, 61-64; attend psychiatrist, Crouse-Irving Mem Hosp, Syracuse, 61-71 & Syracuse Vet Admin Hosp, 61-; proj dir, Nat Inst Ment Health Training Grants, State Univ NY Upstate Med Ctr, 64-68, pres, Med Col Assembly, 71-73. *Honors & Awards:* Silver Award, Psychiat Asn, 67. *Mem:* Fel Am Psychiat Asn. *Res:* Psychotherapy; psychosomatic medicine; determinants of deviant behavior and psychosis; methods of teaching psychotherapy. *Mailing Add:* Dept of Psychiat 750 E Adams St State Univ NY Upstate Med Ctr Syracuse NY 13210

ROBINSON, DAVID LEE, b St Louis, Mo, May 2, 43; Div; c 2. NEUROPHYSIOLOGY. *Educ:* Springfield Col, BS, 65; Wake Forest Univ, MS, 68; Univ Rochester, PhD(neurosci), 72. *Prof Exp:* Fel neurophysiol, Lab Neurobiol, Nat Inst Ment Health, 71-74; res physiologist, Neurobiol Dept, Armed Forces Radiobiol Res Inst, 74-78; RES PHYSIOLOGIST, LAB SENSORIMOTOR RES, NAT EYE INST, 78- *Concurrent Pos:* Fel psychiat, Nat Inst Ment Health, 73-74, guest scientist, Lab Neurobiol, 74-78. *Mem:* Soc Neurosci; Asn Res Vision & Ophthal. *Res:* Neural control of eye movements; information processing the visual system; influence of eye movements on the visual system. *Mailing Add:* Lab of Sensorimotor Res Nat Eye Inst Bethesda MD 20014

ROBINSON, DAVID MASON, b Eccles, Eng, July 7, 32; m 65; c 2. CELL BIOLOGY, CRYOBIOLOGY. *Educ:* Durham Univ, BSc, 55, PhD(zool), 58. *Prof Exp:* Sect head entom, Cotton Res Sta, Uganda, 59-61; res officer, Hope Dept Zool, Oxford Univ, 61-63; mem sci staff, Med Res Coun Radiobiol Res Unit, Atomic Energy Res Estab, Eng, 63-66; prin sci officer & head cell biol, Microbiol Res Estab, Eng, 66-69; asst res dir, Blood Res Lab, Am Red Cross, 69-74; prof biol, 74-80, PROF SOCIAL SCI, GEORGETOWN UNIV, 81-; EXPERT CONSULT, NAT HEART, LUNG & BLOOD INST, NIH, 80- *Mem:* Soc Cryobiol (secy, 75-76); Biophys Soc; Brit Asn Cancer Res; Am Soc Cell Biol; Brit Soc Low Temperature Biol (treas, 68). *Res:* Functional role of water in living systems; nature and repair of freezing injury in mammalian cells; nature and role of animal cell surface macromolecules. *Mailing Add:* 7919 Kentbury Dr Bethesda MD 20014

ROBINSON, DAVID NELSON, b Malden, Mass, July 14, 33. APPLIED MECHANICS, RHEOLOGY. *Educ:* Northeastern Univ, BSci, 61; Brown Univ, MSci, 63, PhD(appl mech), 66. *Prof Exp:* Prof appl mech, Dept Theoret & Appl Mech, Cornell Univ, 66-74; consult appl mech, IBM Corp, 68-72; RES STAFF MEM APPL MECH, OAK RIDGE NAT LAB, 74- *Mem:* Am Soc Mech Eng; Sigma Xi. *Res:* Development of constitutive equations representing the mechanical behavior of metals at elevated temperature. *Mailing Add:* Oak Ridge Nat Lab PO Box X Oak Ridge TN 37830

ROBINSON, DAVID WEAVER, b Kansas City, Mo, Nov 15, 14; m 40; c 4. SURGERY. *Educ:* Univ Kans, AB, 35, MS, 47; Univ Pa, MD, 38; Am Bd Plastic Surg, dipl. *Prof Exp:* Instr anat, 35-36, from instr to assoc prof surg, 41-54, chmn, Sect Plastic Surg, 46-72, prof surg, 54-78, DISTINGUISHED PROF SURG, COL HEALTH SCI, UNIV KANS, KANSAS CITY, 74- *Concurrent Pos:* VChancellor clin affairs-actg exec vchancellor, Am Bd Plastic Surg, 61-67, chmn, 67. *Mem:* Am Soc Plastic & Reconstruct Surg (pres, 66-67); Am Surg Asn (2nd vpres, 65-66); Am Asn Plastic Surg; Am Col Surgeons. *Mailing Add:* Sect of Plastic Surg Univ of Kans Med Ctr Kansas City KS 66103

ROBINSON, DAVID ZAV, b Montreal, Que, Sept 29, 27; nat US; m 54; c 2. PHYSICS. *Educ:* Harvard Univ, AB, 46, AM, 47, PhD(chem physics), 50. *Prof Exp:* Physicist, Baird Assocs, Inc, 49-52, asst dir res, 52-59; sci liaison officer, US Off Naval Res, London, Eng, 59-60; asst dir res, Baird-Atomic, Inc, 60-61; tech asst, Off Sci & Technol, Exec Off of President, Washington, DC, 61-62, tech specialist, 62-67; vpres acad affairs, NY Univ, 67-70; vpres, 70-80, EXEC VPRES, CARNEGIE CORP NEW YORK, CARNEGIE FOUND ADVAN TEACHING, 80- *Concurrent Pos:* US del, Int Comn Optics, 59-63, chmn, 61-63; mem comt physics & soc, Am Inst Physics, 67-; consult, President's Sci Adv Comt, 67-74; mem, NY State Energy Res & Develop Auth, 71-76; consult, NSF, 71-74 & Nat Acad Sci, 73- *Mem:* Optical Soc Am. *Res:* Optics; government and science. *Mailing Add:* Carnegie Corp 437 Madison Ave New York NY 10022

ROBINSON, DEAN WENTWORTH, b Boston, Mass, July 22, 29; div; c 3. PHYSICAL CHEMISTRY. *Educ:* Univ NH, BS, 51, MS, 52; Mass Inst Technol, PhD(infra-red spectros), 55. *Prof Exp:* From asst prof to assoc prof chem, 55-66, PROF CHEM, JOHNS HOPKINS UNIV, 66-, CHMN DEPT, 76- *Concurrent Pos:* Fulbright res grant & Guggenheim fel, 66-67. *Mem:* Am Chem Soc. *Res:* Far infrared and low temperature spectroscopy; electronic spectra of small molecules; magnetic rotation spectroscopy; far infrared chemically-pumped lasers. *Mailing Add:* Dept Chem Johns Hopkins Univ Baltimore MD 21218

ROBINSON, DEREK JOHN SCOTT, b Montrose, Scotland, Sept 25, 38. MATHEMATICS. *Educ:* Univ Edinburgh, BSc, 60; Cambridge Univ, PhD(math), 63. *Prof Exp:* Lectr math, Queen Mary Col, Univ London, 65-68; from asst prof to assoc prof, 68-74, PROF MATH, UNIV ILL, URBANA, 74- *Concurrent Pos:* Sir Edmund Whitaker Mem Prize, Edinburgh Math Soc, 71; Alexander von Humbolt prize, 79. *Mem:* Am Math Soc; London Math Soc. *Res:* Theory of groups. *Mailing Add:* Dept of Math Univ of Ill Urbana IL 61801

ROBINSON, DONALD ALONZO, b Joliet, Ill, Aug 4, 20; m 49; c 6. ORGANIC CHEMISTRY. *Educ:* Iowa State Col, BS, 42; Univ Wis, PhD(org chem), 48. *Prof Exp:* Res chemist, Naugatuck Chem Div, US Rubber Co, 42-46; res chemist, Mallinckrodt Chem Works, 48-51, mfg improvement supvr, 51-56, asst to opers mgr, 56-62, mkt res mgr, 62-65, asst dir com develop, 65-68, asst to pres, St Louis, 68-72, asst to vchmn, 72-79, ASST TO PRES, MALLINCKRODT, INC, 79- *Mem:* Am Chem Soc; Chem Mkt Res Asn. *Res:* Halogenation of amines; catalytic dehydrogenation; claisen condensations. *Mailing Add:* 2301 St Clair Ave Brentwood MO 63144

ROBINSON, DONALD KEITH, b Truro, NS, Aug 29, 32; m 65. PARTICLE PHYSICS. *Educ:* Dalhousie Univ, BSc, 54, MSc, 56; Oxford Univ, DPhil(physics), 60. *Prof Exp:* Res assoc high energy physics, Brookhaven Nat Lab, 60-62; from asst physicist to assoc physicist, 62-66; assoc prof high energy physics, 66-71, PROF HIGH ENERGY PHYSICS, CASE WESTERN RESERVE UNIV, 71- *Mem:* Am Phys Soc. *Res:* High energy particle interactions in bubble chambers; resonance production and decay; exchange processes; polarization measurements; counter experiments; K-meson interactions; anti-proton interactions. *Mailing Add:* Dept of Physics Case Western Reserve Univ Cleveland OH 44106

ROBINSON, DONALD NELLIS, b New Brunswick, NJ, Nov 21, 33; m 60; c 2. ORGANIC CHEMISTRY, POLYMER CHEMISTRY. *Educ:* Cornell Univ, AB, 55; Univ Minn, PhD(org chem), 59. *Prof Exp:* Res chemist elastomers dept, E I du Pont de Nemours & Co, Del, 59-64, develop chemist, Ky, 64-67; asst prof chem, Ky Southern Col, 67-69, actg chmn dept, 68-69; SR RES CHEMIST, PENNWALT CO, 69- *Mem:* Am Chem Soc. *Res:* Thermoplastics (synthesis, blends, physical evaluation); elastomers; indoles. *Mailing Add:* Pennwalt Co 900 First Ave King of Prussia PA 19406

ROBINSON, DONALD STETSON, b Pittsfield, Mass, Aug 14, 28; m 55; c 4. PHARMACOLOGY, MEDICINE. *Educ:* Rensselaer Polytech Inst, BChemEng, 49; Univ Pa, MD, 59; Univ Vt, MS, 66; Am Bd Internal Med, dipl, 66. *Prof Exp:* Sr investr, Nat Heart Inst, 66-68; from asst prof to assoc prof med & pharmacol, Col Med, Univ Vt, 70-77; PROF PHARMACOL & MED & CHMN DEPT PHARMACOL, SCH MED, MARSHALL UNIV, 77- *Concurrent Pos:* Pharmaceut Mfrs Asn fac develop award, 68-70; Burroughs Wellcome Fund scholar clin pharmacol, 71. *Mem:* Am Soc Pharmacol & Exp Therapeut; Am Fedn Clin Res. *Res:* Clinical and biochemical pharmacology; drug interactions; psychopharmacology; narcotic antagonists. *Mailing Add:* Dept of Pharmacol Marshall Univ Sch of Med Huntington WV 25701

ROBINSON, DONALD W(ALLACE), JR, b Minocqua, Wis, Sept 28, 21; m 47; c 4. MECHANICAL & AEROSPACE ENGINEERING. *Educ:* Northeastern Univ, BS, 47; Rensselaer Polytech Inst, MS, 68. *Prof Exp:* Aerodynamicist, Chance Vought Aircraft, 47-50; aerodynamicist, Kaman Aircraft, 50-52, flight test engr, 52-53, chief test & develop, 53-56, proj engr, 56-58, proj mgr res & develop, 58-60, chief res engr, 60-69, dir res & develop, 69-76, vpres eng, 76-78, V PRES PLANNING & MKT, KAMAN AEROSPACE CORP, 78- *Mem:* Am Inst Aeronaut & Astronaut; Am Helicopter Soc; Sigma Xi. *Res:* Fluid mechanics; vibrations; systems analysis; statistical forecasting. *Mailing Add:* Kaman Aerospace Corp Old Windsor Rd Bloomfield CT 06002

ROBINSON, DONALD WILFORD, b Salt Lake City, Utah, Feb 29, 28; m 52; c 7. MATHEMATICS. *Educ:* Univ Utah, BS, 48, MA, 52; Case Western Reserve Univ, PhD(math), 56. *Prof Exp:* From asst prof to assoc prof math, 56-62, PROF MATH, BRIGHAM YOUNG UNIV, 62- *Concurrent Pos:* NSF fac sr res fel, Calif Inst Technol, 62-63; vis prof math, Naval Postgrad Sch, 69-70; Fulbright-Hays Lectureship, Univ Carabobo, Valencia, Venezuela, 76-77. *Mem:* Am Math Soc; Math Asn Am; Sigma Xi. *Res:* Linear algebra and matrix theory. *Mailing Add:* Dept of Math Brigham Young Univ Provo UT 84602

ROBINSON, DOUGLAS WALTER, b Niagara Falls, NY, Oct 22, 34; m 63; c 2. ANALYTICAL CHEMISTRY. *Educ:* Hamilton Col, AB, 56; Cornell Univ, MS, 59; Univ RI, PhD(anal chem), 64. *Prof Exp:* Chemist, Cadet Chem Corp, 58-59; chemist, Hooker Chem Corp, 59-61; res chemist, E I du Pont de Nemours & Co, 64-66; PROJ LEADER, PENNWALT CORP, KING OF PRUSSIA, 66- *Mem:* Soc Appl Spectros; Am Chem Soc. *Res:* Mass spectroscopy; gas chromatography. *Mailing Add:* 401 Riverview Ave Swarthmore PA 19081

ROBINSON, EDWARD ARTHUR, inorganic chemistry, physical chemistry, see previous edition

ROBINSON, EDWARD J, b New York, NY, June 16, 36; m 59; c 2. PHYSICS. *Educ:* Queens Col, NY, BS, 57; NY Univ, PhD(physics), 64. *Prof Exp:* Substitute in physics, Queens Col, NY, 58-59; lectr, City Col New York, 59-61; instr, NY Univ, 61-63; res assoc, Joint Inst Lab Astrophys, Nat Bur Stand & Univ Colo, 64-65; asst prof, 65-69, ASSOC PROF PHYSICS, NY UNIV, 69- *Res:* Theoretical atomic physics, including atomic structure, scattering, and the interaction of laser radiation with atoms. *Mailing Add:* NY Univ Dept of Physics 4 Washington Pl New York NY 10003

ROBINSON, EDWARD LEE, b Clanton, Ala, Nov 6, 33; m 54; c 3. NUCLEAR PHYSICS. *Educ:* Samford Univ, AB, 54; Purdue Univ, MS, 58, PhD(physics), 62. *Prof Exp:* From asst prof to prof, Samford Univ, 61-67, head dept, 61-67; dir, Radiation Biol Lab, 67-80, PROF PHYSICS, UNIV ALA, BIRMINGHAM, 67- *Concurrent Pos:* Consult, Hayes Int Corp, 63-68, Accident Reconstruction & Applied Physics Problems. *Mem:* AAAS; Am Phys Soc; Am Asn Physics Teachers. *Res:* Nuclear spectroscopy; hypervelocity phenomena. *Mailing Add:* Dept of Physics Univ of Ala University Sta Birmingham AL 35294

ROBINSON, EDWARD LEWIS, b Pittsburgh, Pa, Aug 29, 45. ASTRONOMY. *Educ:* Univ Ariz, BA, 69; Univ Tex, Austin, PhD(astron), 73. *Prof Exp:* Astronomer, Lick Observ, Univ Calif, Santa Cruz, 73-74; asst prof, 74-80, ASSOC PROF ASTRON, UNIV TEX, AUSTIN, 80- *Concurrent Pos:* Alfred P Sloan Found fel, 78-80. *Mem:* Am Astron Soc. *Res:* Observational astrophysics, especially white dwarfs, neutron stars and black holes; interacting binary stars; accretion. *Mailing Add:* Dept of Astron Univ of Tex Austin TX 78712

ROBINSON, EDWIN ALLIN, b Denver, Colo, Nov 17, 07; m 33; c 3. CHEMISTRY. *Educ:* Univ Denver, AB, 28, MS, 29; Columbia Univ, PhD(org chem), 33. *Prof Exp:* Instr chem, Univ Denver, 28-29; asst, Columbia Univ, 30-32; res chemist, Tenn Eastman Corp, Tenn, 33-36; tech dir indust div, Nopco Chem Co, 36-48; asst vpres, 48-53, vpres, 53-67, dir, 58-67, vpres, Nopco Chem Div, Diamond Shamrock Corp, 67-69; INT CHEM CONSULT, 69- *Mem:* Am Chem Soc. *Res:* Textile fiber processing lubricants; surface active chemical production and evaluation; female sex hormones; substituted benzocinchoninic acids; polyurethane foams; metallic soaps and vinyl stabilizers; defoamers; water soluble polymers. *Mailing Add:* 105 Fairmount Ave Chatham NJ 07928

ROBINSON, EDWIN HOLLIS, b Florence, Ala, Dec 16, 42; m 65; c 2. NUTRITION, FISHERIES. *Educ:* Samford Univ, BS, 69; Auburn Univ, MS, 72, PhD(nutrit), 77. *Prof Exp:* res assoc biochem, Miss State Univ, 77-81; ASST PROF WILDLIFE & FISHERIES SCI, TEX A&M UNIV, 81- *Mem:* Am Inst Nutrit; Am Fisheries Soc; Sigma Xi. *Res:* Nutritional requirements of various aquatic animals. *Mailing Add:* Wildlife & Fisheries Sci Tex A&M Univ College Station TX 77843

ROBINSON, EDWIN JAMES, JR, b Wilkes-Barre, Pa, Feb 7, 16; m 48; c 6. PARASITOLOGY. *Educ:* Dartmouth Univ, AB, 39; NY Univ, MS, 41, PhD(biol), 49. *Prof Exp:* Asst biol, NY Univ, 39-48; instr parasitol med col, Cornell Univ, 48-51; sr asst scientist, USPHS, 51-54; from asst prof to assoc prof biol, Kenyon Col, 54-60, prof, 60; PROF BIOL, MACALESTER COL, 63- *Mem:* AAAS; Am Micros Soc; Am Soc Parasitol; Soc Protozool. *Res:* Ecology and life cycles of trematodes and filarial nematodes. *Mailing Add:* 5122 Garfield Ave S Minneapolis MN 55419

ROBINSON, EDWIN S, b Saginaw, Mich, Apr 29, 35; m 62; c 1. GEOPHYSICS, GEOLOGY. *Educ:* Univ Mich, BS, 57, MS, 59; Univ Wis, PhD(geophys, geol), 64. *Prof Exp:* Res asst geophys, Willow Run Labs, Univ Mich, 56-57; asst geophysicist, Arctic Inst NAm, 57-58; res asst geophys, Willow Run Labs, Univ Mich, 58-59; proj assoc geophys & polar res ctr, Univ Wis, 59-64; asst prof geophys, Univ Utah, 64-67; assoc prof, 67-72, PROF GEOPHYSICS, VA POLYTECH INST & STATE UNIV, 72- *Mem:* Am Geophys Union; Soc Explor Geophys; Glaciol Soc. *Res:* Studies of seismic waves; exploration seismology in Antarctica; regional gravity and magnetic surveys interaction of earth tides and ocean tides; characteristics of seismic waves from nuclear explosions. *Mailing Add:* Dept of Geol Sci Va Polytech Inst & State Univ Blacksburg VA 24061

ROBINSON, FARREL RICHARD, b Wellington, Kans, Mar 23, 27; m 49; c 4. VETERINARY PATHOLOGY, TOXICOLOGY. *Educ:* Kans State Univ, BS, 50, BS, DVM & MS, 58; Tex A&M Univ, PhD(vet path), 65. *Prof Exp:* Res vet, Aerospace Med Res Lab, Wright-Patterson AFB, US Air Force, 58-62, chief path br, 64-68, mem staff, Armed Forces Inst Path, 68-71, chief vet path, 72-74, registrar, Am Registries Vet & Comp Path, 72-74; PROF TOXICOL-PATH, PURDUE UNIV, 74-, DIR, ANIMAL DIS DIAG LAB, 78- *Concurrent Pos:* Vpres, Am Bd Vet Toxicol, 71-73, pres, 76-79; head, Int Ref Ctr Comp Oncol, WHO, 72-74, collab, Tumors of the Eye, 72-74. *Honors & Awards:* Meritorious Serv Medal, US Air Force, 74. *Mem:* Am Vet Med Asn; Am Col Vet Path; Soc Toxicol; Am Bd Vet Toxicol; Am Asn Vet Lab Diag. *Res:* Pathology of the respiratory system; pathology of laboratory animals; oxygen toxicity; beryllium toxicity; pathology of toxicologic diseases; oncology. *Mailing Add:* Sch of Vet Med Purdue Univ West Lafayette IN 47906

ROBINSON, FRANK ERNEST, b Oaklyn, NJ, Oct 29, 30; m 56; c 3. AGRONOMY. *Educ:* Rutgers Univ, BS, 52; Purdue Univ, PhD(soil physics), 58. *Prof Exp:* Asst, Purdue Univ, 55-58; assoc agronomist exp sta, Hawaiian Sugar Planters Asn, 58-64; from asst water scientist to assoc water scientist, 64-73, WATER SCIENTIST, DEPT LAND, AIR & WATER RESOURCES, UNIV CALIF, 73- *Concurrent Pos:* Mem, Int Comn Irrig & Drainage. *Honors & Awards:* Man of Year, Sprinkle Irrigation Asn, 73. *Mem:* AAAS; Am Soil Sci Soc; Am Soc Agr Eng; Am Geophys Union; Am Soc Agron. *Res:* Irrigation management and salinity control; nitrate mobility, soil drainage, sprinkler irrigation of vegetable crops; growth of plants with geothermal water. *Mailing Add:* 1004 E Holton Rd El Centro CA 92243

ROBINSON, GENE CONRAD, b Hurricane, La, July 31, 28; m 59; c 2. ORGANIC CHEMISTRY. *Educ:* Univ Chicago, PhB, 47, MS, 49; Univ Ill, PhD(org chem), 52. *Prof Exp:* Res chemist, Univ Calif, Los Angeles, 52-54; res chemist & res assoc, 54-73, SUPVR, ETHYL CORP, 73- *Mem:* Am Chem Soc; Oceanog Soc; Int Oceanog Found. *Res:* Physical organic chemistry; organometallic chemistry. *Mailing Add:* 1064 N Leighton Dr Baton Rouge LA 70806

ROBINSON, GEORGE DAVID, b Leeds, Eng, June 8, 13; m 48; c 2. ATMOSPHERIC PHYSICS. *Educ:* Leeds Univ, BSc, 33, PhD(physics), 36. *Prof Exp:* Res asst chem, Leeds Univ, 35-36; tech officer, UK Meteorol Off, 37-44; sci officer atmospheric physics, Kew Observ, Eng, 46-57; dep dir, UK Meteorol Off, 57-68; RES FEL ATMOSPHERIC PHYSICS, CTR ENVIRON & MAN, INC, 68- *Honors & Awards:* Buchan Prize, Royal Meteorol Soc, 52. *Mem:* Fel Brit Inst Physics; hon mem Royal Meteorol Soc (pres, 65-67); fel Am Meteorol Soc. *Res:* Radiative transfer in the earth's atmosphere; predictability of weather and climate; artificial modification of climate. *Mailing Add:* 676 Fern West Hartford CT 06107

ROBINSON, GEORGE EDWARD, JR, b Cary, Miss, May 4, 16; m 51; c 3. PHYSIOLOGY. *Educ:* Alcorn Agr & Mech Col, BS, 42; Univ Ill, MS, 45, PhD(animal sci), 50. *Prof Exp:* Head animal husb dept, Alcorn Agr & Mech Col, 45-47; assoc prof animal husb, 50-63, PROF ANIMAL SCI, SOUTH UNIV, BATON ROUGE, 63-, CHMN DEPT, 74- *Mem:* AAAS; Am Soc Animal Sci; Sigma Xi. *Res:* Physiology of reproduction; poultry and swine nutrition. *Mailing Add:* Dept of Animal Sci Southern Univ Baton Rouge LA 70813

ROBINSON, GEORGE H(ENRY), b Detroit, Mich, June 27, 24; m 50; c 7. METALLURGY. *Educ:* Univ Detroit, BChE, 49; Carnegie Inst Technol, BS, 50. *Prof Exp:* Asst metall res, 46-49, jr engr, 50-51, res metallurgist, 51-53, sr res metall, 53-56, supvr ferrous metall res, 56-62, asst head, Metall Eng Dept, 62-71, head, Emissions Res Dept, 71-73, HEAD, METALL DEPT, RES LABS, GEN MOTORS, 73- *Mem:* Fel Am Soc Metals; Am Soc Automotive Engrs. *Res:* Friction, wear and fatigue behavior of metals; physical metallurgy. *Mailing Add:* Metall Dept Gen Motors Res Labs 12 Mile & Mound Rds Warren MI 48090

ROBINSON, GEORGE WALLER, b Winchester, Ky, Mar 29, 41; m 67; c 2. BIOCHEMISTRY. *Educ:* Centre Col Ky, BA, 63; Duke Univ, PhD(biochem), 68. *Prof Exp:* Res assoc protein chem, Rockefeller Univ, 67-70; asst prof biochem, Univ Ky, 70-77; assoc prof chem, Centre Col Ky, 78-81. *Concurrent Pos:* Vis asst prof, Ga Inst Technol, 81-82. *Mem:* Am Chem Soc. *Res:* Structure-function relationships in proteins and enzymes; electrochemical detectors for high performance liquid chromatography, amino acid analysis. *Mailing Add:* 2886 Cherokee St Kennesaw GA 30144

ROBINSON, GEORGE WILSE, b Kansas City, Mo, July 27, 24; m 50. PICOSECOND SPECTROSCOPY. *Educ:* Ga Inst Technol, BS, 47, MS, 49; Univ Iowa, PhD(chem), 52. *Prof Exp:* Asst phys chem, Univ Iowa, 50-52; fel, Univ Rochester, 52-54; asst prof, Johns Hopkins Univ, 54-59; assoc prof chem, Calif Inst Technol, 59-61, prof phys chem, 61-75; ROBERT A WELCH PROF PHYS CHEM, TEX TECH UNIV, 76- *Concurrent Pos:* Prof phys chem & chmn dept, Univ Melbourne, Australia, 75-76. *Mem:* Am Chem Soc; NY Acad Sci; Inter-Am Photochem Soc; fel Am Phys Soc. *Res:* Molecular structure; low temperature spectroscopy and chemistry; frozen free radicals; environmental effects on energy levels and spectral intensities; energy transfer phenomena; excited states of organic crystals; quantum processes in photobiology; nucleation and liquid structure; ultrafast molecular processes. *Mailing Add:* Dept of Chem PO Box 4260 Lubbock TX 79409

ROBINSON, GERALD ARTHUR, b Hamilton, Ont, Apr 8, 29; m 53; c 6. RADIOBIOLOGY. *Educ:* Univ Western Ontario, BSc, 52, MSc, 54, PhD(biochem), 58. *Prof Exp:* Res asst biochem med sch, Univ Western Ont, 52-57; lectr, 57-58, from asst prof to assoc prof biomed sci, 58-70, PROF BIOMED SCI, ONT VET COL, UNIV GUELPH, 70- *Res:* Avian endocrinology and mineral metabolism. *Mailing Add:* Dept of Biomed Sci Univ of Guelph Guelph ON N1G 2W1 Can

ROBINSON, GERALD DEAN, JR, nuclear medicine, see previous edition

ROBINSON, GERALD GARLAND, b St Louis Co, Minn, May 8, 33; m 60; c 2. ZOOLOGY, PHYSIOLOGY. *Educ:* Univ Minn, BS, 55, PhD(zool), 60. *Prof Exp:* From instr to assoc prof, 60-77, PROF BIOL SCI, UNIV SOUTH FLA, 77- *Mem:* Am Soc Pharmacog. *Mailing Add:* Dept of Biol Sci Univ of SFla Tampa FL 33620

ROBINSON, GERSHON DUVALL, b Tulsa, Okla, Apr 2, 18; m 76; c 4. GEOLOGY. *Educ:* Northwestern Univ, BS, 39; Univ Calif, MA, 41. *Prof Exp:* Asst geol, Univ Calif, 39-41; petrol geologist, Tide Water Assoc Oil Co, Tex, 41-42; geologist field geol, Alaska, 42-45, in charge volcano invests, 45-48, asst chief gen geol br, Colo, 48-51, actg chief, 51-52, field geologist, Mont, 52-60, chief, Northern Rocky Mt Br, 60-64, res geologist, Rocky Mt Environ Geol Br, Colo, 64-72, RES GEOLOGIST, GEOL DIV, US GEOL SURV, 72- *Concurrent Pos:* Consult, Res & Develop Bd, 47-50; assoc ed, Geol Soc Am, 67-74; consult, Earth Sci Adv Comt, NSF, 76-80; chmn, Fed Geothermal Environ Adv Panel, Dept Interior, 78- *Mem:* Fel Mineral Soc Am; Soc Econ Geol; fel Geol Soc Am. *Res:* Ore deposits; volcanology; structural geology; geology applied to urban problems; disposal of radioactive waste. *Mailing Add:* Mail Stop 19 US Geol Surv 345 Middlefield Rd Menlo Park CA 94025

ROBINSON, GERTRUDE EDITH, b Peoria, Ill, Apr 28, 23. MATHEMATICS EDUCATION. *Educ:* Ill State Univ, BS, 45; Univ Wis-Madison, MS, 51, PhD(math educ), 64. *Prof Exp:* Teacher high sch, Ill, 45-57 & Wis, 57-60; asst prof, Univ Ga, 63-69, assoc prof math, 69-77; EXAMINER, EDUC TESTING SERV, PRINCETON, NJ, 77- *Concurrent Pos:* Consult, Ga Educ TV & Ga State Dept Educ, 64-77; Training Teacher Trainers Proj fel, NY Univ, 70-71. *Mem:* Math Asn Am; Res Coun Diagnostic & Prescriptive Math; Nat Coun Teachers Math. *Res:* Diagnostic testing in mathematics for elementary school children; problem-solving abilities of young children. *Mailing Add:* Educ Testing Serv Princeton NJ 08541

ROBINSON, GILBERT C(HASE), b Lykens, Pa, July 19, 19; m 47. CERAMICS ENGINEERING. *Educ:* NC State Col, BCerE, 40. *Hon Degrees:* DSc, Alfred Univ, 70. *Prof Exp:* Geol aide, Tenn Valley Authority, 40-41, jr chemist, 41, jr chem engr, 41-42, asst chem engr, Wilson Dam, Ala, 42-44; PROF CERAMICS ENG & HEAD DEPT, CLEMSON UNIV, 46- *Honors & Awards:* Wilson Award, Am Ceramic Soc, 57. *Mem:* Fel Am Ceramic Soc; Am Soc Testing & Mat; Nat Inst Ceramic Engrs. *Res:* Acoustic emission; analysis of clay minerals; ceramic raw materials; fundamentals of drying and firing; factory systems for preassembled masonry buildings; ceramic forming processes. *Mailing Add:* Dept of Ceramic Eng Clemson Univ Clemson SC 29631

ROBINSON, GILBERT DE BEAUREGARD, b Toronto, Ont, June 3, 06; m 35; c 2. MATHEMATICS. *Educ:* Univ Toronto, BA, 27; Cambridge Univ, PhD, 31. *Prof Exp:* Lectr math, 31-34, from asst prof to assoc prof, 34-54, vpres res, 65-71, PROF MATH, UNIV TORONTO, 54- *Concurrent Pos:* With Nat Res Coun Can, 41-45; vis prof, Mich State Univ, 53-54, Univ BC, 63 & Univ NZ, 68. *Honors & Awards:* Mem, Order British Empire, 46. *Mem:* Am Math Soc; Math Asn Am; Royal Soc Can; Can Math Cong (pres, 53-57); London Math Soc. *Res:* Theory of groups, especially representation theory. *Mailing Add:* Dept Math Univ Toronto Toronto ON M5S 1A1 Can

ROBINSON, GLEN MOORE, III, b El Dorado, Ark, July 23, 43; m 67; c 2. PHYSICAL CHEMISTRY. *Educ:* La Polytech Inst, BS, 65; Tulane Univ, La, PhD(phys chem), 70. *Prof Exp:* Chemist, E I du Pont de Nemours & Co, Inc, 66; sr chemist, 69-76, RES SPECIALIST, DATA RECORDING PROD DIV, 3M CO, 76- *Concurrent Pos:* Assoc prof, Bethel Col, 72. *Honors & Awards:* Harlan Vergin Award, 3M Co, 74. *Mem:* Am Chem Soc. *Res:* Magnetic tape; ceramics; surface chemistry; molecular spectroscopy; natural and magnetically induced optical activity; applied statistics; computerization of laboratory instruments; computer analysis of micrographs, optical and electron. *Mailing Add:* Data Recording Prod Div Bldg 236-3C 3M Co 3M Ctr St Paul MN 55114

ROBINSON, GLENN HUGH, b Rosedale, Ind, May 20, 12; m 40; c 3. SOILS. *Educ:* Purdue Univ, BS, 38, MS, 40; Univ Wis, PhD(soils), 50. *Prof Exp:* Asst agron, Purdue Univ, 38-42; assoc soil surveyor, US Forest Serv, 42-43, assoc soil surveyor, Bur Plant Indust, Soils & Agr Eng, USDA, NC, 43-46 & Wis, 46-51, soil correlator, 51-54, sr soil correlator, Soil Conserv Serv, 54-61; sr soil scientist, Food & Agr Orgn, UN, Brit Guiana, 61-64, sr soil scientist & proj mgr, Wad Medani, Sudan, 64-69, Land Develop Dept, Thailand, 69-73 & Indonesia, 73-75; sr scientist, econ res sect, USDA, Saudi Arabia, 76-80; CONSULT SOILS, 80- *Concurrent Pos:* Consult, Food & Agr Orgn, Malawi, 65 & Sudan, 70. *Mem:* Am Soc Agron; Soil Sci Soc Am; Sigma Xi; Int Soc Soil Sci. *Res:* Soil and land classification, mapping and utilization; agriculture development in new areas. *Mailing Add:* RR 1 Box 210 Carbon IN 47837

ROBINSON, GORDON HEATH, b Detroit, Mich, Oct 23, 31. HUMAN FACTORS ENGINEERING. *Educ:* Wayne State Univ, BS, 54; Univ Mich, Ann Arbor, MS, 55, PhD(instrumentation, eng, psychol), 62. *Prof Exp:* Asst res engr & lectr, Dept Indust Eng & Opers Res, Univ Calif, Berkeley, 61-66; from asst prof to assoc prof indust eng, 66-75, PROF INDUST ENG, UNIV WIS-MADISON, 75- *Mem:* Am Psychol Asn; Am Asn Univ Professors; Human Factors Soc; Brit Ergonomics Res Soc. *Res:* Human performance models; accident causation; sociotechnical systems; quality of working life. *Mailing Add:* Dept of Indust Eng Univ of Wis 1513 University Ave Madison WI 53706

ROBINSON, GUNER SUZEK, b Nazilli, Turkey, Feb 5, 37; US citizen; div; c 2. ELECTRICAL ENGINEERING. *Educ:* Istanbul Tech Univ, BS, 60, MS, 61; Polytech Inst Brooklyn, PhD(elec eng), 66. *Prof Exp:* Asst prof elec eng, Middle East Tech Univ, Ankara, Turkey, 66-68; mem tech staff, Comsat Labs, Commun Satellite Corp, 68-73; res scientist image processing, Image Processing Inst, Univ Southern Calif, 73-76; mem res & tech staff, 76-77, MGR SIGNAL PROCESSING LAB, NORTHROP RES & TECHNOL CTR, NORTHROP CORP, 77- *Concurrent Pos:* Consult, Re-transfer Technol to Turkey, UN Develop Prog, Turkey, 77-78 & 81. *Mem:* Inst Elec & Electronics Engrs; Soc Photo Instrumentation Engrs. *Res:* Education in electrical engineering and computer science; digital signal processing; image signal processing, compression and transmission; applications of image processing to military problems and industrial automation. *Mailing Add:* Northrop Res & Technol Ctr One Research Park Palos Verdes Peninsula CA 90274

ROBINSON, HAMILTON BURROWS GREAVES, b Philadelphia, Pa, Feb 16, 10; m 29; c 3. PATHOLOGY, HISTOLOGY. *Educ:* Univ Pa, DDS, 34; Univ Rochester, MS, 36. *Hon Degrees:* ScD, Georgetown Univ, 75. *Prof Exp:* Rockefeller & Carnegie fel, Univ Rochester, 36-37; from asst prof to assoc prof oral histol & path, Washington Univ, 37-44; prof dent, Ohio State Univ, 44-58; prof dent & dean sch dent, 58-75, EMER PROF DENT & EMER DEAN SCH MED, UNIV MO-KANSAS CITY, 75-; VIS PROF DENT, UNIV CALIF, LOS ANGELES, 75- *Concurrent Pos:* Ed, J Dent Res, 36-58 & Dent World, 75-; dir post-grad div, Col Dent, Ohio State Univ, 47-53, assoc dean, 53-58; pres, Am Asn Dent Schs, 67; actg chancellor, Univ Mo-Kansas City, 67-68; past pres, Am Bd Oral Path. Former consult to Surgeon Gen, USPHS, US Army, US Navy & Vet Admin Hosps, Kansas City & Wadsworth, Kans. *Honors & Awards:* Fauchard Medal, 51; Callahan Gold Medal, 64; Jarvis-Burkhart Medal, 67; Hinman Distinguished Serv Medal, 80. *Mem:* AAAS; Am Dent Asn (vpres, 71-72); fel Am Acad Oral Path (past pres); hon mem Am Acad Oral Med; hon mem Am Soc Oral Surg; Int Asn Dent Res (pres, 59-60). *Res:* Oral tumors and cysts; dental caries; relationship of oral and systemic diseases; diseases of dental pulp. *Mailing Add:* 3243 1B San Amadeo Laguna Hills CA 92653

ROBINSON, HAROLD ERNEST, b Syracuse, NY, May 22, 32. BOTANY, ENTOMOLOGY. *Educ:* Ohio Univ, BS, 55; Univ Tenn, MA, 57; Duke Univ, PhD(bot), 60. *Prof Exp:* Asst prof biol, Wofford Col, 60-62; CUR BOT, SMITHSONIAN INST, 62- *Mem:* Bot Soc Am; Am Soc Plant Taxon; Am Bryol & Lichenological Soc. *Res:* Bryophytes of Latin American and India; Asteraceae; Dolichopodidae. *Mailing Add:* Dept of Bot Smithsonian Inst Washington DC 20560

ROBINSON, HAROLD FRANK, b Bandana, NC, Oct 28, 18; m 44; c 2. QUANTITATIVE GENETICS, PLANT BREEDING. *Educ:* NC State Col, BS, 39, MS, 40; Univ Nebr, PhD(agron), 48. *Hon Degrees:* DSc, Univ Nebr, 66. *Prof Exp:* Seed improv specialist, NC Crop Improv Asn, 41-42; asst prof exp statist, Inst Statist, NC State Univ, 45-48, from assoc prof to prof statist, 48-58, head dept genetics, 58-62, dir inst biol sci, 62-65, prof genetics & admin dean res, 65-68; vchancellor, Univ Syst Ga, 68-71, officer bd regents, 70-71; prof biol sci & statist & provost, Purdue Univ, 71-74; CHANCELLOR, WESTERN CAROLINA UNIV, 74- *Concurrent Pos:* Mem comt plant breeding & genetics, Nat Res Coun-Nat Acad Sci; consult int maize prog, Rockefeller Found; mem consult bur, Nat Comn Undergrad Educ Biol Sci; mem, USPHS Environ Sci Res Rev Comt, 67-68; exec dir, President's Sci Adv Comt Panel World Food Supply, 66-68, mem, Panel Int Tech Coop & Assistance, 67-68; chmn bd trustees, Agron Sci Found, 67-70; mem, Nat Acad Sci Bd Sci & Technol Int Develop, 68-72, chmn panel food crisis Indonesia, 68, mem panel Korea tech assistance study, 69, mem world food & nutrit study, 76-77; mem bd trustees, Col Entrance Exam Bd, 71-75, chmn presidential search & nominating comt, 73, mem finance comt, 75; Purdue Univ rep, Univ Corp Atmospheric Res, 71-74; mem, Selection Comt for Tyler Award, 73-74; mem planning comt world food, health & pop, Nat Acad Sci-NSF, 74-; mem bd dir, Mountain Area Health Educ Found, Inc, Asheville, NC, 75-; mem, Nat Plant Genetics Resources Bd, 75-81; mem joint comt agr develop, Bd Int Food & Agr Develop, 77-; mem & Am Asn State Cols & Univs rep, Joint Comt USDA Policy Discussions, 77-78; chmn study comt tertiary educ, Govt Jamaica, 75; mem, Joint Coun Food & Agr Sci, 78, mem orgn study group, Exec Comt, 78-; mem world food & nutrit study, Nat Acad Sci, 76-77; chmn & mem, bd dirs, Ctr Pvt Vol Orgn/Univ Int Tech Assistance Rural Develop; mem bd, Int Food & Agr Develop. *Honors & Awards:* Crop Sci Award, Am Soc Agron, 59. *Mem:* Fel AAAS; fel Am Soc Agron; Biomet Soc; Am Soc Naturalists; Genetics Soc Am. *Res:* Population and quantitative genetics; quantitative inheritance and maize. *Mailing Add:* Western Carolina Univ Cullowhee NC 28723

ROBINSON, HARRY, b Oldham, Lancashire, Eng, Apr 7, 25; US citizen; m 46; c 2. BIOSTATISTICS. *Educ:* Univ Manchester, BSc, 51; Univ Pittsburgh, MS, 64, ScD(biostatist), 68. *Prof Exp:* Biostatistician, Hillsboro County, Fla, 59-61; from asst prof to assoc prof dept prev & community med, 68-75, prog dir arthritis res, Sect Rheumatol, 68-75, prof dept community med, Col Med, Univ Tenn, Memphis, 75-76; MED SYSTS DIR, MED DEPT, NY TEL CO, 76- *Concurrent Pos:* Mem criteria for scleroderma subcomt, Diag & Therapeut Criteria Comt, Arthritis Found, 70-, mem subcomt data on nat needs, 72-, mem comt criteria govt subcomt, 72-; consult arthritis suppl to Nat Health Interview Surv, HEW; chief sect biostatist, 71-76, assoc prin investr, Arthritis Res Prog, Sect Rheumatol, 72-76. *Mem:* Am Statist Asn; Am Pub Health Asn; Asn Teachers Prev Med. *Res:* Multi-disciplinary studies; evaluation of medical care delivery systems; federal study to develop an experiment to assess the influence of variables on total cancer mortality; federal study of panencephalitis; federal study of transient ischemic attacks in the University of Tennessee Cerebral Vascular Research Center. *Mailing Add:* NY Tel Co Rm 2527 New York NY 10036

ROBINSON, HARRY JOHN, b Elizabeth, NJ, July 30, 13; m 39; c 3. MEDICINE. *Educ:* NY Univ, AB, 40; Rutgers Univ, PhD(microbiol), 43; Columbia Univ, MD, 48. *Hon Degrees:* DSc, Bucknell Univ, 74. *Prof Exp:* Res assoc, Merck Inst Therapeut Res, 33-43, asst dir, 43-50, assoc dir, 50-56, exec dir, 56-65, pres & dir res, Quinton Co Div, Merck & Co, Inc, NJ, 65-68, sr vpres med affairs, Merck Sharp & Dohme Res Labs, Pa, 68-71, vpres sci affairs, Merck Sharp & Dohme Res Labs, NJ, 71-76; VPRES MED AFFAIRS, ALLIED CORP, 76- *Concurrent Pos:* Prof microbiol & chmn dept, Col Med & Dent NJ, 57-58, assoc clin prof, 60-76 & clin prof med, 76-; assoc attend physician, Bellevue Hosp, 60-; chmn, NJ Pub Health Coun, 53-77; chmn res comn, St Barnabas Med Ctr; mem, Int Adv Bd Prostaglandins, 75- *Mem:* Am Soc Pharmacol & Exp Therapeut; Soc Exp Biol & Med; Am Soc Clin Invest; AMA; Royal Soc Med Founds Inc (pres, 71-76). *Res:* Pharmacological and clinical investigations of antibiotics; hormones and chemotherapeutic agents; studies of bacterial endotoxins; functions of reticuloendothelial system; non-specific resistance; prostaglandins; continuing medical education; drug abuse; medical care; toxicology. *Mailing Add:* Allied Corp Morristown NJ 07960

ROBINSON, HENRY WILLIAM, b Chicago, Ill, Apr 26, 24; m 50; c 5. TROPICAL PUBLIC HEALTH. *Educ:* Brigham Young Univ, BA, 47; Univ Southern Calif, MA, 49; Stanford Univ, PhD(trop pub health), 62. *Prof Exp:* Instr zool, 52-55, from asst prof to assoc prof, 55-66, PROF MICROBIOL & ZOOL, SAN JOSE STATE UNIV, 66- *Mem:* Am Soc Parasitol; Royal Soc Trop Med & Hyg; Am Soc Trop Med & Hyg. *Res:* Antigenic analysis of blood and tissue flagellates, insect tissue culture-parasite models; epidemiology of parasitic diseases. *Mailing Add:* Dept of Biol Sci 125 S Seventh St San Jose CA 95114

ROBINSON, HUGH GETTYS, b New Orleans, La, Oct 30, 28. PRECISION MEASUREMENT, ATOMIC PHYSICS. *Educ:* Emory Univ, AB, 50; Duke Univ, PhD(physics), 54. *Prof Exp:* Res assoc physics, Duke Univ, 54-55; res assoc, Univ Md, 55-56; res assoc, Univ Wash, Seattle, 56-57; instr, Yale Univ, 57-58, asst prof, 58-63; lectr, Harvard Univ, 63-64; assoc prof, 64-70, PROF PHYSICS, DUKE UNIV, 70- *Mem:* AAAS; fel Am Phys Soc. *Res:* Atomic physics; precision measurements in atomic and molecular physics, including fundamental constants; design and construction of appropriate apparatus. *Mailing Add:* Dept of Physics Duke Univ Durham NC 27706

ROBINSON, IVAN MAXWELL, b Lakeville, NS, May 26, 20; nat US; m 44; c 4. ORGANIC CHEMISTRY. *Educ:* Univ Acadia, BSc, 40 & 41; Univ Toronto, MA, 42; Purdue Univ, PhD(chem), 49. *Prof Exp:* Res chemist, Can Indust, Ltd, 42-43 & 45-46; res chemist, 49-52, supvr, 52-54, sect mgr, 54-61, mgr tech sales, 61-64, lab dir, 64-73, res assoc, 73-75, RES FEL, E I DU PONT DE NEMOURS & CO, INC, 75- *Mem:* Am Chem Soc. *Res:* Vapor-phase nitration; polymers; polyimides; polybenzimidozoles; polybenzoxazoles; polyolefins; polyols for polyurethanes; new industrial chemicals. *Mailing Add:* 1805 Shipley Rd Wilmington DE 19803

ROBINSON, IVOR, b Liverpool, Eng, Oct 7, 23; m 63; c 3. MATHEMATICS, THEORETICAL PHYSICS. *Educ:* Cambridge Univ, BA, 47. *Prof Exp:* Lectr math, Univ Col Wales, 50-58; res assoc physics, Univ NC, 59-60; res assoc, Syracuse Univ, 60-61, 62-63; vis prof physics & astron, Cornell Univ, 61-62; prof, Southwest Ctr Advan Studies, 63-69; prof physics, 69-73, PROF MATH SCI, UNIV TEX, DALLAS, 73- *Concurrent Pos:* Res assoc, King's Col, Univ London, 59; vis lectr, Inst Theoret Physics, Polish Acad Sci, 59; vis prof, Univ Sydney, 65-66 & Tel-Aviv Univ, 66 & 70; state chair reserved for foreign scholars, Col France, 70. *Mem:* Int Astron Union; Am Astron Soc; Am Math Soc; Am Phys Soc. *Res:* Gravitational radiation. *Mailing Add:* Math Sci Prog PO Box 688 Univ of Tex at Dallas Richardson TX 75080

ROBINSON, J(AMES) MICHAEL, b Shreveport, La, Oct 13, 43; m 70; c 2. ORGANIC CHEMISTRY, MEDICINAL CHEMISTRY. *Educ:* La Tech Univ, BS, 67, MS, 69; La State Univ, Baton Rouge, PhD(org chem), 73. *Prof Exp:* Res assoc med chem, Purdue Univ, 73-74, NIH res fel, 74-75; res assoc org chem, Tulane Univ, 75-76; ASST PROF CHEM, UNIV TEX OF THE PERMIAN BASIN, 76- *Mem:* Am Chem Soc. *Res:* Organic, medicinal and analytical chemistry of enamines, imines, pyrdines and thiazyls; novel heterocyclic systems, especially 1,2-thiazines and 1,4-thiazocines; mechanisms and drug design. *Mailing Add:* Dept of Chem Univ of Tex of the Permian Basin Odessa TX 79762

ROBINSON, JACK BERT, JR, b Miami, Okla, Sept 8, 49. BIOCHEMISTRY. *Educ:* Okla State Univ, BS, 71, PhD(biochem), 75. *Prof Exp:* Res asst biochem, Okla State Univ, 71-75; fel biochem, Univ Tex Health Sci Ctr, Dallas, 75-80; MEM FAC, DEPT BIOCHEM, UNIV IOWA, 80- *Mem:* Sigma Xi. *Res:* Structure and function of enzymes, especially hydrolases; regulations of such systems at tissue level; biochemical transformations of acetate. *Mailing Add:* Dept Biochem Univ Iowa Iowa City IA 52240

ROBINSON, JACK LANDY, b Durant, Okla, Jan 6, 40; m 61; c 2. ANALYTICAL CHEMISTRY. *Educ:* Southeastern State Col, BA, 62; Univ Okla, PhD(chem), 66. *Prof Exp:* From asst prof to assoc prof, 66-77, PROF CHEM, SOUTHEAST STATE UNIV, 77- *Mem:* Am Chem Soc. *Res:* Analysis of polycyclic aromatic hydrocarbons and microbes by chromatographic methods; analysis of oxalic acid in body fluids; chromatography of polymeric adsorbents. *Mailing Add:* Dept of Phys Sci Southeastern State Univ Durant OK 74701

ROBINSON, JAMES EUGENE, b Parawan, Utah, Jan 4, 25. MEDICAL PHYSICS. *Educ:* Utah State Agr Col, BS, 47; Wash Univ, MA, 49, PhD(physics), 55. *Prof Exp:* Lab & res asst, Wash Univ, 47-49; instr, Kans State Teachers Col, Emporia, 49-51; res & lab asst, Wash Univ, 52-53, res asst med physics, Med Sch, 53-55; res assoc, Dept Radiol, Stanford Univ, 55-58, res assoc biophysics, 58-59, lectr, 59-61; from asst prof to assoc prof, 61-75, PROF RADIOL, UNIV MD, BALTIMORE, 75-, HEAD SECT PHYSICS & RADIOBIOL, 64- *Concurrent Pos:* Consult radiother comt, NIH. *Mem:* AAAS; Am Phys Soc; Am Asn Physicists Med & Biol; Sigma Xi; Inst Radiol. *Res:* Use of hyperthermia as an adjunct to radiation therapy for cancer; bio-effects of ionizing radiation at elevated temperatures, production and measurement of thermal fields in living systems, and interactions between thermal and non-thermal damage on bio-systems. *Mailing Add:* Dept Radiol-Oncol Sch Med Univ of Md Baltimore MD 21201

ROBINSON, JAMES EVERETT, solid state physics, see previous edition

ROBINSON, JAMES H, geophysics, physics, see previous edition

ROBINSON, JAMES LAWRENCE, b Boston, Mass, Feb 23, 42; m 63; c 3. BIOCHEMISTRY, NUTRITION. *Educ:* Univ Redlands, BS, 64; Univ Calif, Los Angeles, PhD(biochem), 68. *Prof Exp:* Teaching asst anal chem & biochem, Univ Calif, Los Angeles, 65-66; NIH res fel, Inst Cancer Res, Philadelphia, 68-70; asst prof, 70-76, ASSOC PROF BIOCHEM, UNIV ILL, URBANA, 76- *Concurrent Pos:* Mem nutrit sci fac, Univ Ill, 72; researcher, Nutrit Res Ctr, Meudon, France, 78-79. *Res:* Enzyme mechanisms; metabolic regulation; specific interests in orotate metabolism associated with lactation in the bovine and with consumption of orotic acid. *Mailing Add:* Dept of Dairy Sci Univ Ill 1207 W Gregory Dr Urbana IL 61801

ROBINSON, JAMES MCOMBER, b Petoskey, Mich, Aug 22, 20; m 44; c 4. CLINICAL BIOCHEMISTRY. *Educ:* DePauw Univ, AB, 42; Ind Univ, PhD(org chem), 44. *Prof Exp:* Res assoc, Off Sci Res & Develop, Ind Univ, 44-45; res assoc res found, Ohio State Univ, 46; org chemist, Merck & Co, Inc, 47-55; org chemist, Aero-Jet-Gen Corp Div, Gen Tire & Rubber Co, 55-65; org chemist autonetics div, NAm Aviation, Inc, Anaheim, 65-70; ORG CHEMIST CLIN BIOCHEM, LOS ANGELES COUNTY/UNIV SOUTHERN CALIF MED CTR, 71- *Mem:* Fel AAAS; fel Am Inst Chem; Am Chem Soc; Am Asn Clin Chemists. *Mailing Add:* 525 Baughman Ave Claremont CA 91711

ROBINSON, JAMES VANCE, b Corsicana, Tex, July 27, 43; m 62; c 3. ENTOMOLOGY. *Educ:* Tex A&M Univ, BS, 67, MS, 71; Miss State Univ, PhD(entom), 75. *Prof Exp:* Surv entomologist, Miss Agr & Forestry Exp Sta, 71-75; EXTEN ENTOMOLOGIST, TEX AGR EXTEN SERV, 75- *Mem:* Entom Soc Am. *Mailing Add:* Tex A&M Univ Res & Exten Ctr PO 220 Overton TX 75684

ROBINSON, JAMES WILLIAM, b Syracuse, NY, Apr 4, 38; m 64; c 4. ELECTRICAL ENGINEERING. *Educ:* Univ Mich, Ann Arbor, BSE, 59, MSE, 61, PhD(elec eng), 65. *Prof Exp:* Res asst elec eng, Univ Mich, Ann Arbor, 64-65, res engr, 65-66; asst prof, 66-70, assoc prof, 70-80, PROF ENG, PA STATE UNIV, 80- *Mem:* Inst Elec & Electronics Engrs. *Res:* Electric arcs and discharges; charged particle dynamics; instrumentation for fast transients. *Mailing Add:* Dept of Elec Eng Pa State Univ University Park PA 16802

ROBINSON, JAMES WILLIAM, b Kidderminster, Eng, July 12, 23; nat US; m 46; c 3. ANALYTICAL CHEMISTRY. *Educ:* Univ Birmingham, BSc, 49, PhD(anal chem), 52, DSc, 77. *Prof Exp:* Sr sci officer, Brit Civil Serv, 52-55; res assoc, La State Univ, 55-56; sr chemist res labs, Esso Standard Oil Co, 56-63; tech adv, Ethyl Corp, 63-64; assoc prof chem, 64-66, PROF CHEM, LA STATE UNIV, BATON ROUGE, 66-, ASST DIR ENVIRON INST, 71- *Concurrent Pos:* Ed, Spectros Letters, Environ Sci & Health & CRC Handbook Spectros; asst ed, Anal Chimica Acta & Appl Spectros Reviews; Guggenheim fel, 74; chmn, Anal Gordon Conf, 74. *Mem:* Am Chem Soc; The Chem Soc; Soc Appl Spectros; fel Royal Soc Chem. *Res:* Analysis of trace metals; atomic absorption; molecular spectroscopy; light structure; air quality control; air pollution analysis. *Mailing Add:* Dept Chem La State Univ Baton Rouge LA 70803

ROBINSON, JEROME DAVID, b Stamford, Conn, Jan 30, 41; m 64; c 2. CHEMICAL ENGINEERING. *Educ:* City Univ New York, BChE, 63; Univ Del, MChE, 66, PhD(chem eng), 68. *Prof Exp:* Res & develop chem engr, E I du Pont de Nemours & Co, 63-64; instr chem eng, Univ Del, 67; from process engr to MGR PROCESS ENG & TECHNOL, AM CYANAMID CO, 68- *Concurrent Pos:* Adj prof, Newark Col Eng, 69-70. *Mem:* Am Inst Chem Engrs. *Res:* Chemical and environmental process and systems design, analysis and control. *Mailing Add:* Am Cyanamid Co Wayne NJ 07470

ROBINSON, JERRY ALLEN, b Danville, Ill, Dec 18, 39; m 69; c 2. REPRODUCTIVE PHYSIOLOGY, ENDOCRINOLOGY. *Educ:* Wabash Col, BA, 63; Univ Cincinnati, MS, 66, PhD(zool), 70. *Prof Exp:* Trainee, 70-72, res assoc, 72-73, asst scientist, 73-78, ASSOC SCIENTIST, WIS REGIONAL PRIMATE RES CTR, UNIV WIS-MADISON, 78- *Mem:* Am Soc Primatologists; Soc Study Reprod; Am Soc Zool; Endocrine Soc; Sigma Xi. *Res:* Steroid hormone secretion, metabolism and mechanism of action. *Mailing Add:* 1223 Capitol Court Madison WI 53706

ROBINSON, JOHN, b Vancouver, BC, Apr 25, 22; m 46; c 4. BACTERIOLOGY. *Educ:* Univ BC, BSA, 44; McGill Univ, MSc, 45, PhD(bact), 50. *Prof Exp:* Res officer, Nat Res Coun Can, 46-48 & 49-50; res officer, Can Dept Agr, 50-56; bacteriologist, Dept Nat Health & Welfare, 56-65; assoc prof, 65-73, PROF MICROBIOL & IMMUNOL, UNIV WESTERN ONT, 73- *Mem:* Soc Gen Microbiol; Soc Appl Bact; Am Soc Microbiol; Can Soc Microbiol (secy-treas, 59-61, 72-74, first vpres, 76-77, pres, 77-78). *Res:* Production of antibiotics by fungi; metabolism of halphillic bacteria; isolation and characterization of toxins produced by Staphylococcus aureus; mode of action of lysis of specific bacteria by the predaceous bacterium Bdellovibrio; Bdellovibrio and the ecology of polluted water. *Mailing Add:* Dept of Microbiol & Immunol Univ of Western Ont London ON N6A 5C1 Can

ROBINSON, JOHN BERTRAM, b Toronto, Ont, June 7, 26; m 48; c 3. MICROBIAL ECOLOGY. *Educ:* Univ Toronto, BSA, 50, MSA, 52; Univ Canterbury, PhD, 63. *Prof Exp:* Assoc bacteriologist, Sci Serv, Can Dept Agr, 52-56; asst prof microbiol, Ont Agr Col, 56-60; Commonwealth scholar, NZ, 60-62; assoc prof microbiol, Ont Agr Col, 63-71, PROF ENVIRON BIOL, UNIV GUELPH, 71- *Mem:* Soil Sci Soc Am; Can Soc Microbiologists; Can Soc Soil Sci. *Res:* Soil microbiology; microbiology of agricultural wastes; nitrogen transformations in streams. *Mailing Add:* Dept of Environ Biol Univ of Guelph Guelph ON N1G 2W1 Can

ROBINSON, JOHN E, JR, b Kearny, NJ, Nov 27, 24; m 46. DENTISTRY. *Educ:* State Univ NY Buffalo, DDS, 52. *Prof Exp:* Asst dent surg, 57, from instr to prof dent, 57-80, EMER PROF DENT, ZOLLER DENT CLIN, UNIV HOSPS & CLINS, UNIV CHICAGO, 80- *Concurrent Pos:* Lectr, Col Dent, Univ Ill, 65-; consult, Ctr Craniofacial Anomalies, 69-; deleg, Fedn Prosthodontic Orgns, 65-68, secy, 68-71, vpres, 71- *Honors & Awards:* Ackerman Award, Am Acad Maxillofacial Prosthetics, 81. *Mem:* Fel NY Acad Sci; fel Am Col Dent; Am Prosthodont Soc; Fedn Prosthodontic Orgn (pres, 73-74); Am Acad Maxillofacial Prosthetics (pres, 70-71). *Res:* Maxillofacial prosthetic rehabilitation of the head and neck cancer patient utilizing new materials and techniques to provide better, longer-lasting prostheses. *Mailing Add:* 220 Fernwood Circle Seminole FL 33543

ROBINSON, JOHN FRANK, b Columbia, La, Mar 24, 43. ECONOMIC ENTOMOLOGY. *Educ:* La State Univ, BS, 65; Iowa State Univ, PhD(entom), 74. *Prof Exp:* Res entom, Europ Corn Borer Lab, 67-75, res entom, Veg Insects Lab, 75-77, RES ENTOM RICE PROD & INSECTS, SCI & EDUC ADMIN-AGR RES USDA, 77- *Mem:* Entom Soc Am; Sigma Xi. *Res:* Integrated pest management of rice insects. *Mailing Add:* La State Univ Rice Exp Sta PO Box 1429 Crowley LA 70526

ROBINSON, JOHN PAUL, b Providence, RI, Jan 1, 39; m 60; c 1. COMMUNICATION ENGINEERING. *Educ:* Iowa State Univ, BSEE, 60; Princeton Univ, MSE, 62, PhD(elec eng), 66. *Prof Exp:* Mem tech staff, RCA Labs, 60-62 & Int Bus Mach Labs, 71; from asst prof to assoc prof info eng, 65-72, PROF INFO ENG, UNIV IOWA, 72- *Concurrent Pos:* Consult various orgn. *Res:* Digital systems; switching theory; privacy and data security; codes for error detection and correction. *Mailing Add:* 5408 Eng Bldg Univ of Iowa Iowa City IA 52240

ROBINSON, JOHN PRICE, b Charlotte, Tenn, Dec 1, 27; m 60; c 2. MICROBIOLOGY. *Educ:* Univ Tenn, BS, 54; Vanderbilt Univ, PhD(microbiol), 61. *Prof Exp:* Instr, 61-63, asst prof, 63-68, ASSOC PROF MICROBIOL, SCH MED, VANDERBILT UNIV, 68- *Concurrent Pos:* USPHS sci res grants, 64-65 & NSF, 66-67. *Mem:* Electron Micros Soc; Am Soc Microbiol. *Res:* Mechanism of antibody-antigen complex formation; biochemical approach and visualization in the electron microscopy. *Mailing Add:* 906 Estes Rd Nashville TN 37215

ROBINSON, JOSEPH DEWEY, b Ottumwa, Iowa, Mar 22, 28. PHYSICAL CHEMISTRY, PHYSICS. *Educ:* Drake Univ, AB, 49; Univ NMex, MSc, 52; Wash Univ, PhD, 56. *Prof Exp:* Chemist, 56-60, res assoc physics, 60-71, sr res assoc, 71-72, sr staff res physicist, 72-78, PROJ LEADER BOREHOLE PHYSICS, SHELL DEVELOP CO DIV, SHELL OIL CO, 78- *Mem:* Soc Petrol Eng; Am Phys Soc. *Res:* Molecular physics; theoretical chemistry; petrophysics. *Mailing Add:* Shell Develop Co PO Box 481 Houston TX 77001

ROBINSON, JOSEPH DOUGLASS, b Asheville, NC, Nov 28, 34; m 58; c 2. PHARMACOLOGY. *Educ:* Yale Univ, MD, 59. *Prof Exp:* Intern med, Stanford Univ Hosp, 59-60; res assoc neurochem, NIH, 60-62; fel pharmacol, Sch Med, Yale Univ, 62-64; from asst prof to assoc prof pharmacol, 64-72, PROF PHARMACOL, STATE UNIV NY UPSTATE MED CTR, 72- *Concurrent Pos:* NSF sr fel pharmacol, Cambridge Univ, 71-72; mem pharmacol study sect, NIH, 80- *Mem:* AAAS; Am Soc Pharmacol & Exp Therapeut; NY Acad Sci; Am Soc Neurochem; Biophys Soc. *Res:* Membrane structure, permeability and transport; neurochemistry; history and philosophy of science. *Mailing Add:* Dept of Pharmacol State Univ of NY Upstate Med Ctr Syracuse NY 13210

ROBINSON, JOSEPH EDWARD, b Regina, Sask, June 25, 25; m 52, 75; c 3. PETROLEUM EXPLORATION, COMPUTER APPLICATIONS. *Educ:* McGill Univ, BEng, 50, MSc, 51, PhD(geol), 68. *Prof Exp:* Geophysicist, Imp Oil Ltd, 51-66; sr geologist, Union Oil Can, 68-76; PROF GEOL, SYRACUSE UNIV, 76- *Concurrent Pos:* Vis indust assoc, Kans Geol Surv, 70-72; vis prof, Syracuse Univ, 74; asst ed, Int Asn Math Geol, 76-80; prin investr, US Dept Energy, 79-81; geol consult, J E Robinson & Assoc, 76- *Mem:* Soc Explor Geophysists; Am Asn Petrol Geologists; Can Soc Petrol Geologists; Int Asn Math Geol. *Res:* Geologic data base construction; management and computer applications in exploration for petroleum, natural gas and other economic minerals. *Mailing Add:* Dept Geol Heroy Geol Lab Syracuse Univ Syracuse NY 13210

ROBINSON, JOSEPH ROBERT, b New York, NY, Feb 16, 39; m 59; c 3. PHARMACEUTICS. *Educ:* Columbia Univ, BS, 61, MS, 63; Univ Wis, PhD(pharm), 66. *Prof Exp:* From asst prof to assoc prof pharm, 66-74, PROF PHARM, UNIV WIS-MADISON, 74- *Mem:* Am Pharmaceut Asn; Am Chem Soc; fel Acad Pharmaceut Sci. *Res:* Biopharmaceutics; ophthalmic pharmacology; mechanisms of drug transport and activity in the eye. *Mailing Add:* Sch of Pharm Univ of Wis Madison WI 53706

ROBINSON, JULIA (BOWMAN), b St Louis, Mo, Dec 8, 19; m 41. MATHEMATICAL LOGIC, NUMBER THEORY. *Educ:* Univ Calif, Berkeley, AB, 40, MA, 41, PhD, 48. *Prof Exp:* Jr mathematician, Rand Corp, 49-50; lectr, 60-64, 66-67, 69-70 & 75, PROF MATH, UNIV CALIF, BERKELEY, 76- *Mem:* Nat Acad Sci; Am Math Soc; Asn Symbolic Logic. *Res:* Number theoretical decision problems; recursive functions. *Mailing Add:* 243 Lake Dr Berkeley CA 94708

ROBINSON, KEN KESSLER, chemical engineering, catalysis, see previous edition

ROBINSON, KENNETH ROBERT, b Akron, Ohio, Nov 17, 21; m 47; c 4. ORGANIC CHEMISTRY. *Educ:* Ohio Northern Univ, BA, 43; Purdue Univ, MS, 46; Mich State Univ, PhD(chem), 50. *Prof Exp:* Res chemist, E I du Pont de Nemours & Co, 50-55; sr chemist, Koppers Co, Inc, 55-61; res chemist, Maumee Chem Co, 61-63; group leader, 64-71, res assoc res & develop dept, 71-74, mgr govt contracts, 74, MGR CENT CODING CONTROL, ASHLAND OIL, INC, 74- *Mem:* AAAS; Am Chem Soc. *Res:* Petroleum chemistry; hydrocarbon oxidation; ozonation; custom chemical synthesis; coal; coal tar chemicals; aromatic chemicals; cellulose and viscose chemistry; synthetic monomer and polymer chemistry; research planning; fuel science; computer sciences. *Mailing Add:* Cent Coding Control Dept Ashland Oil Inc PO Box 2458 Columbus OH 43216

ROBINSON, KENNETH RONALD, developmental biology, see previous edition

ROBINSON, KENT, b Reese, NC, June 22, 24; m 48; c 2. BIOLOGY, SCIENCE EDUCATION. *Educ:* Appalachian State Teachers Col, BS, 50, MA, 52; Ohio State Univ, PhD(sci educ, biol), 66. *Concurrent Pos:* Teacher pub schs, NC, 50-56; PROF BIOL, APPALACHIAN STATE UNIV, 56- *Res:* Botany. *Mailing Add:* Dept of Biol Appalachian State Univ Boone NC 28607

ROBINSON, LARRY EUGENE, microbiology, biochemistry, see previous edition

ROBINSON, LAWRENCE BAYLOR, b Tappahannock, Va, Sept 14, 19; m 56; c 3. PHYSICS. *Educ:* Va Union Univ, BS, 39; Harvard Univ, MA, 41, PhD(chem physics), 46. *Prof Exp:* Instr math & physics, Va Union Univ, 41-42; teacher math, USSignal Corps Schs, Md, 42; tester radio parts, Victor Div, Radio Corp Am, NJ, 43; asst prof chem & physics, Va Union Univ, 44; asst prof physics, Howard Univ, 46-47, instr phys sci, 47-48, assoc prof physics, 48-51; res physicist, Atomic Energy Res Div, US Naval Res Lab, 53-54; asst prof physics, Brooklyn Col, 54-56; mem tech staff, Space Tech Labs, Inc Div, Thompson Ramo Wooldridge, Inc, 56-60; lectr, 57-60, from assoc prof to prof eng, 60-74, asst dean, Sch Eng & Appl Sci, 69-74, PROF ENG & APPL SCI, UNIV CALIF, LOS ANGELES, 74- *Concurrent Pos:*

NSF fel, 66-67; guest prof, Aachen Tech Univ, 66-67. *Mem:* Am Phys Soc; Am Asn Physics Teachers. *Res:* Zeta potentials of solutions of electrolytes; surface tension of electrolytes; neutron physics; reactor theory; collision between electrons and atoms; interatomic forces and collisions; magnetic properties of solids; nonequilibrium thermodynamics. *Mailing Add:* Dept of Eng & Appl Sci Unif of Calif Los Angeles CA 90024

ROBINSON, LEONARD H, b Woonsocket, RI, Sept 6, 16; m 53; c 4. DENTISTRY, ACADEMIC ADMINISTRATION. *Educ:* Brown Univ, AB, 37; Tufts Col, DMD, 43, MS, 49; Univ Ala, MD, 54. *Prof Exp:* Instr oral path & surg, Sch Dent, Tufts Col, 47-50; from asst prof to prof dent, Sch Dent, Univ Ala, Birmingham, 50-70, from asst prof to prof path, Med Ctr, 59-70; prof path, Health Ctr, Univ Conn, 70-74; assoc dean acad affairs, Sch Dent, 75-78, PROF PATH, MED CTR, 75-, PROF DENT & DEAN, SCH DENT, UNIV ALA, BIRMINGHAM, 78- *Concurrent Pos:* Consult, Vet Admin Hosps, Tuskegee, 50-70 & Birmingham, 60-; pathologist in chief, Bristol Hosp, Conn, 72-74. *Res:* Histochemical studies of bone formation and resorption. *Mailing Add:* Sch of Dent Univ of Ala Birmingham AL 35294

ROBINSON, LEWIS HOWE, b Cody, Wyo, Sept 11, 30; m 71. AIR QUALITY MODELING, APPLIED STATISTICS. *Educ:* San Jose State Col, BA, 52; Univ Calif, Berkeley, MA, 59. *Prof Exp:* Meteorologist, Pac Southwest Forest & Range Exp Sta, US Forest Serv, 57-60; meteorologist, Pac Gas & Elec Co, 61-66; meteorologist, WeatherMeasure Corp, 66; meteorologist, Aerojet-Gen Corp Div, Gen Tire & Rubber Co, 66-67; pres, Robinson Assocs, 68-71; air pollution meteorologist, 72-73, sr air pollution meteorologist, 73-76, chief res & planning sect, 76-79, DIR PLANNING DIV, BAY AREA AIR QUALITY MGT DIST, 79- *Mem:* Am Meteorol Soc; Am Statist Asn; Asn Comput Mach. *Res:* Air pollution; diffusion; atmospheric turbulence; continuum mechanics; numerical prediction. *Mailing Add:* Bay Area Air Quality Mgt Dist 939 Ellis St San Francisco CA 94109

ROBINSON, LLOYD BURDETTE, b Gravelburg, Sask, Aug 28, 29; US citizen; c 2. ELECTRONIC INSTRUMENTATION, ASTRONOMY. *Educ:* Univ Sask, BA, 53, MA, 54; Univ BC, PhD(physics), 57. *Prof Exp:* Res officer electronics, Atomic Energy Can Ltd, 57-62; electronics engr, Lawrence Radiation Lab, Univ Calif, 62-69; RES PHYSICIST & ASTRONOMER INSTRUMENTATION & ASTRON, LICK OBSERV, UNIV CALIF, SANTA CRUZ, 69- *Concurrent Pos:* NSF grants astron, 71- *Mem:* AAAS; Int Astronomers Union; Am Astron Soc. *Res:* Development of electronic and optical instruments for observational optical astronomy; use of small computers as an aid in control and data acquisition. *Mailing Add:* Lick Observ NS-2 Univ of Calif Santa Cruz CA 95064

ROBINSON, LOUIS, b Chelsea, Mass, May 7, 26; m 55; c 2. MATHEMATICS, COMPUTER SCIENCES. *Educ:* Univ Mass, BS, 49; Syracuse Univ, MA, 51, PhD(math), 53. *Prof Exp:* Instr math, Syracuse Univ, 52-53; appl sci rep, 53-56, mgr, Math & Applns Dept, 56-58, Mkt Develop Dept, 58-59, mkt anal, 59-61, systs eng, 61-62, sci comput, 63-65, mgr systs develop, 65-69, dir standards & systs eval, 69-72, standards & systs anal, 72-75, DIR SCI CENTERS, IBM CORP, NY, 75- *Mem:* AAAS; Am Math Soc; Opers Res Soc; Economet Soc; Math Asn Am. *Res:* Application of data processing machines to mathematical problems of science, engineering and business; design of data processing systems. *Mailing Add:* 1133 Westchester Ave White Plains NY 10604

ROBINSON, M JOHN, b Monroe, Mich, June 19, 38; m 60; c 4. NUCLEAR ENGINEERING. *Educ:* Univ Mich, BS, 60, MS, 62, PhD(nuclear eng), 65. *Prof Exp:* Res asst nuclear eng, Univ Mich, 60-63, asst res eng, 63-64, res assoc nuclear eng, 64-65, lectr, 65-69; assoc prof nuclear eng, Kans State Univ, 69-72; nuclear engr, 72-77, proj mgr, 77-78, PARTNER, BLACK & VEATCH CONSULT ENGRS, 79- *Concurrent Pos:* Inst Sci & Technol res fel, 65-66; Int Atomic Energy Agency tech asst expert, heat transfer adv Govt Brazil, 70-71. *Mem:* Am Nuclear Soc. *Res:* Fluid flow and heat transfer; nuclear power systems; reactor physics; shielding; fuel management; radiological effects. *Mailing Add:* Black & Veatch Consult Engrs Power Div 11401 Lamar Overland Park KS 66211

ROBINSON, MCDONALD, b Martinez, Calif, Aug 21, 38; m 61; c 2. CERAMICS. *Educ:* Univ Calif, Berkeley, BS, 61, MS, 62; Mass Inst Technol, ScD(ceramics), 67. *Prof Exp:* Res & develop coordr, US Army Mat & Mech Res Ctr, Mass, 67-68; MEM TECH STAFF, BELL LABS, 69- *Mem:* Am Ceramic Soc. *Res:* Crystal growth of magnetic and dielectric films. *Mailing Add:* RD 1 Box D-27-A Cora Lane Chester NJ 07930

ROBINSON, MARK TABOR, b Oak Park, Ill, June 23, 26; m 47; c 2. RADIATION EFFECTS, COMPUTATIONAL PHYSICS. *Educ:* Univ Ill, BS, 46; Okla State Univ, MS, 49, PhD(chem), 51. *Prof Exp:* Instr chem, Okla State Univ, 47-49, res assoc, 49-51; RES STAFF MEM, SOLID STATE DIV, OAK RIDGE NAT LAB, 51- *Concurrent Pos:* Vis scientist, Metall Div, Atomic Energy Res Estab, Eng, 64-65 & Inst Solid State Res, Nuclear Res Estab, Ger, 71-72; western hemisphere regional ed, Radiation Effects, 80- *Mem:* Am Chem Soc; Am Phys Soc. *Res:* Theory of radiation effects in solids; atomic collisions in solids; digital computer applications. *Mailing Add:* 112 Miramar Circle Oak Ridge TN 37830

ROBINSON, MARTIN ALVIN, b New York, NY, Sept 12, 30; m 56; c 3. INORGANIC CHEMISTRY. *Educ:* NY Univ, BA, 52; Univ Buffalo, MS, 54; Ohio State Univ, PhD(inorg chem), 61. *Prof Exp:* Sr chemist, Battelle Mem Inst, 56-61; group supvr inorg res & develop, Olin Corp, 61-69; dept mgr indust fine chem, J T Baker Chem Co, NJ, 69-71; MGR RES & DEVELOP, SPECIALTY CHEM DIV, ALLIED CHEM CORP, 72- *Concurrent Pos:* Asst prof, Southern Conn State Col, 62-69. *Mem:* Am Chem Soc; Sigma Xi; fel Am Inst Chemists. *Res:* Catalysis; transition metal complexes. *Mailing Add:* Buffalo Res Lab Allied Chem Corp Box 1069 Buffalo NY 14240

ROBINSON, MERTON ARNOLD, b Los Angeles, Calif, Sept 13, 25; m 49; c 3. SCIENTIFIC INSTRUMENTATION, ANALYTICAL CHEMISTRY. *Educ:* Univ Calif, Los Angeles, BS, 49. *Prof Exp:* Head anal lab, Riker Labs, Inc, 49-53 & Carnation Res Lab, 53-59; MGR PROD ASSURANCE, BECKMAN INSTRUMENTS, INC, ANAHEIM, 59- *Mem:* Am Chem Soc. *Res:* Optical instruments for satellites; gas chromatography for trace contaminant analysis. *Mailing Add:* 1041 Brookwood Dr La Habra CA 90631

ROBINSON, MYRON, b Bronx, NY, Mar 4, 28; m 63; c 4. AIR POLLUTION, ENVIRONMENTAL SCIENCE. *Educ:* City Col New York, BS, 49; NY Univ, MS, 58; Cooper Union, PhD(physics), 75. *Prof Exp:* Physicist, Nat Bur Stand, 50-53; physicist, US Army Biol Warfare Labs, 54-56; electronic scientist, US Navy Appl Sci Lab, 53-54 & 56-58; asst dir res, Res-Cottrell, Inc, 58-68; aerosol physicist, Health & Safety Lab, US AEC, New York, 68-75; vis prof, Hebrew Univ, Jerusalem, 75-76; prin sci assoc, Dart Indust, 78-80; PROF, QUEENSBOROUGH COMMUNITY COL, 81- *Concurrent Pos:* Consult air pollution control, Res-Cottrell, Inc, Precipitair Pollution Control, Seversky Electronatom, Environ Protect Agency, Energy Res Co, FluiDyne Eng Corp, Israel Environ Protection Agency & India Ministry Energy, 68-; adj prof, Cooper Union, 70-75; vis lectr, Univ Western Ont, 70-71 & Nehru, Madras & Madurai Univs, 76; Fulbright-Hayes fel, 75. *Mem:* Inst Elec & Electronics Engrs; Air Pollution Control Asn; Electrostatic Soc Am (pres, 71-73). *Res:* Particulate air pollution control mechanisms, particularly the extension of electrostatic precipitation to untried areas of application; aerosol technology in industrial hazard evaluation. *Mailing Add:* 73-32 136th St Flushing NY 11367

ROBINSON, NEAL CLARK, b Seattle, Wash, March 6,42; m 68. MEMBRANE BIOCHEMISTRY. *Educ:* Univ Wash, BS, 64, PhD(biochem), 71. *Prof Exp:* Res assoc & fel, Duke Univ, 71-74; res assoc, Univ Ore, 74-75; lectr biochem, Univ Calif, Davis, 75-77; ASST PROF BIOCHEM, UNIV TEX HEALTH SCI CTR, 77- *Mem:* Biophys Soc; Am Chem Soc; Sigma Xi; Am Soc Biol Chemists. *Res:* Protein-phospholipid and protein-detergent interactions with solubilized membrane protein complexes isolated from the inner mitochondrial membrane. *Mailing Add:* Dept Biochem Univ Tex Health Sci Ctr 7703 Floyd Curl Dr San Antonio TX 78284

ROBINSON, NORMAN EDWARD, b Tadley, Eng, Oct 12, 42; m 67; c 2. PULMONARY PATHOPHYSIOLOGY. *Educ:* Univ London, Eng, BVetMed, 65; Univ Calif, Davis, PhD(physiol), 72. *Prof Exp:* Vet Surgeon, Pvt Practice, Eng, 65-66; intern large animal med, Univ Pa, 66-67; assoc vet med, Univ Calif, Davis, 67-70; assoc prof, 72-78, PROF PHYSIOL & LARGE ANIMAL MED, MICH STATE UNIV, 78- *Concurrent Pos:* Prin investr, Develop Collateral Ventilation, 75-82 & Model Brondual Hyperactivity, 81-; ed, Current Therapy Equine Med, 82- *Mem:* Am Physiol Soc; Am Thoracic Soc; Am Vet Med Asn. *Res:* Pathophysiology of lung disease in the large domestic mammals, particularly chronic airway disease in the horse and pneumonia in cattle; species variations in collateral ventilation. *Mailing Add:* L117 Vet Clin Ctr Mich State Univ East Lansing MI 48824

ROBINSON, PAUL RONALD, b Philadelphia, Pa, Aug 6, 50. INORGANIC CHEMISTRY, COORDINATION CHEMISTRY. *Educ:* Univ Mo-Columbia, BS, 72, AM, 73; Univ Calif, San Diego, PhD(chem), 77. *Prof Exp:* Res assoc chem kinetics, Univ Ill, Urbana-Champaign, 76-77, vis asst prof chem, 77-78; staff res assoc inorg chem, Oak Ridge Nat Labs, 78-81; RES CHEMIST, UNION OIL CO CALIF, 81- *Mem:* AAAS; Sigma Xi; Am Chem Soc. *Res:* Preparation, characterization and testing of catalysts for synthesis gas conversion; synthesis and reactions of transition metal complexes; chemical kinetics. *Mailing Add:* Union Oil Co Calif Sci & Technol Div PO Box 76 Brea CA 92621

ROBINSON, PAUL THORNTON, b Saginaw, Mich, Apr 15, 34; m 56; c 3. GEOLOGY. *Educ:* Univ Mich, BS, 59; Univ Calif, Berkeley, PhD(geol), 64. *Prof Exp:* Asst prof geol, Ore State Univ, 63-69; asst prof, 69-70, assoc prof, 70-80, PROF GEOL, UNIV CALIF, RIVERSIDE, 80- *Mem:* Geol Soc Am. *Res:* Igneous petrology. *Mailing Add:* Dept of Geol Sci Univ of Calif Riverside CA 92502

ROBINSON, PETER, b New York, NY, July 19, 32; m 54; c 2. PALEONTOLOGY, GEOLOGY. *Educ:* Yale Univ, BS, 54, MS, 58, PhD(geol), 60. *Prof Exp:* Instr geol, Harpur Col, 55-57; res assoc paleont, Yale Peabody Mus, 60-61; cur mus, 61-71, from asst prof to assoc prof, 61-71, PROF NATURAL HIST & DIR MUS, UNIV COLO, BOULDER, 71-, CUR GEOL, 80- *Concurrent Pos:* NSF grants Eocene Insectivora res, 60-61 & co-recipient for salvage archaeol, Aswan Reservoir, Sudan, 64-67; res assoc, Carnegie Mus Natural Hist, 66-; Smithsonian grant paleont res, Tunisia, 67-; dir, Colo Paleont Exped to Tunisia, 67- *Mem:* AAAS; Soc Vert Paleont; Australian Soc Mammal. *Res:* Vertebrate paleontology, especially fossil mammals. *Mailing Add:* Dept of Natural Hist Univ of Colo Museum Boulder CO 80309

ROBINSON, PETER, b Hanover, NH, July 9, 32; m 57; c 3. STRUCTURAL GEOLOGY, PETROLOGY. *Educ:* Dartmouth Col, AB, 54; Univ Otago, NZ, MSc, 58; Harvard Univ, PhD(geol), 63. *Prof Exp:* Raw mat engr, Columbia Iron Mining Co, US Steel Corp, 56-58; from instr to asst prof, 62-69, assoc prof, 69-76, PROF GEOL, UNIV MASS, AMHERST, 76- *Concurrent Pos:* Petrologists Club lectr, Carnegie Inst Geophys Lab, 65; Am Geol Inst vis scientist, Maine & Dalhousie Univs, 66; NSF res grants & joint res grants with H W Jaffe, 66-71, 72-74; mem exped, Metamorphic Rocks, Chatham Island, NZ Plateau, 68; subsurface mapping, Northfield Mountain Pumped Storage Hydroelec Proj, 68-70; geol consult, Metrop Dist Comn, Boston, 72- *Mem:* Geol Soc Am; fel Mineral Soc Am; Am Geophys Union. *Res:* Structural geology and stratigraphy of metamorphic rocks in New England and New Zealand; metamorphic mineral facies; crystal chemistry and exsolution in amphiboles and pyroxenes. *Mailing Add:* Dept of Geol Univ of Mass Amherst MA 01003

ROBINSON, PETER JOHN, b Kinston, UK, July 4, 44; m 68; c 2. CLIMATOLOGY, ATMOSPHERIC RADIATION. *Educ:* Univ London, BSc, 65, MPhil, 68; McMaster Univ, PhD(climat), 72. *Prof Exp:* Asst prof, 71-76, ASSOC PROF CLIMAT, UNIV NC, CHAPEL HILL, 76- *Concurrent Pos:* Intergovt climate prog officer, Nat Climate Prog Off, Nat Oceanic & Atmospheric Admin, 80-82. *Mem:* Am Meteorol Soc; Am Asn State Climatologists (secy-treas, 79-80). *Res:* Techniques and benefits of using climate data and information in solution of operational planning problems of commercial enterprises; studies of electromagnetic radiation at the Earths' surface. *Mailing Add:* Dept Geog Univ NC Chapel Hill NC 27514

ROBINSON, PRENTISS NOBLE, b Salt Lake City, Utah, July 28, 36; m 66. ELECTRICAL ENGINEERING. *Educ:* Rensselaer Polytech Inst, BEE, 59; Univ Calif, Berkeley, MS, 60; Polytech Inst Brooklyn, PhD(controls), 65. *Prof Exp:* Res engr, Autonetics Div, NAm Aviation, Inc, Calif, 60-62 & Appl Physics Lab, Johns Hopkins Univ, 62-63; asst prof elec eng, George Washington Univ, 65-66, MidE Tech Univ, Ankara, 66-68 & Univ Md, 69-72; mem tech staff, 73-80, SR SCIENTIST, HUGHES AIRCRAFT CO, 80- *Mem:* Inst Elec & Electronics Engrs. *Res:* Stochastic optimal control theory. *Mailing Add:* Hughes Aircraft Co PO Box 92426 Los Angeles CA 90009

ROBINSON, PRESS L, b Florence, SC, Aug 2, 37; m 64; c 2. PHYSICAL CHEMISTRY. *Educ:* Morehouse Col, BS, 59; Howard Univ, MS, 62, PhD(phys chem), 63. *Prof Exp:* Chemist, NIH, 61; from asst prof to assoc prof, 63-68, PROF PHYS CHEM, SOUTHERN UNIV, BATON ROUGE, 68- *Concurrent Pos:* Res grants, 64-68. *Mem:* Am Chem Soc. *Res:* Molten salt chemistry; explosive metal forming of liquid alloys. *Mailing Add:* Dept of Chem Southern Univ Box 10155 Baton Rouge LA 70813

ROBINSON, RALPH M(YER), b Terre Haute, Ind, Aug 17, 26; m 56; c 2. CHEMICAL ENGINEERING, ORGANIC CHEMISTRY. *Educ:* Univ Ill, BS, 49; Univ Mich, MSE, 50. *Prof Exp:* Chem engr res & develop, Argonne Nat Labs, 51-53; chem engr, 53-60, group leader develop, High Pressure Lab, 60-62, mgr eng develop dept, 62-68, OPERS MGR ORAL & TOPICALS PROD, PHARMACEUT MFG DIV, ABBOTT LABS, 68- *Mem:* Am Chem Soc; Sigma Xi; Am Inst Chem Engrs. *Res:* Administration and evaluation of research and development; economic and financial analysis; process development in fermentation, pharmaceutical and chemical areas. *Mailing Add:* Pharmaceut Mfg Div Abbott Labs 14th at Sheridan Rd North Chicago IL 60064

ROBINSON, RAPHAEL MITCHEL, b National City, Calif, Nov 2, 11; m 41. MATHEMATICS. *Educ:* Univ Calif, AB, 32, MA, 33, PhD(math), 35. *Prof Exp:* Instr math, Brown Univ, 35-37; from instr to prof, 37-73, EMER PROF MATH, UNIV CALIF, BERKELEY, 73- *Mem:* Am Math Soc; Math Asn Am. *Res:* Functions of a complex variable; theory of numbers; foundations of mathematics; geometry. *Mailing Add:* Dept of Math Univ of Calif Berkeley CA 94720

ROBINSON, RAYMOND FRANCIS, b Albany, Ore, Sept 25, 14; m; c 9. GEOLOGY. *Educ:* Union Col, NY, BSc, 36; McGill Univ, MSc, 38. *Prof Exp:* Eng asst, NY State Dept Pub Works, Utica, 39-40; underground sampler, Anaconda Copper Mining Co, Butte, Mont, 41-43, asst mining engr, 43-45; resident geologist & engr, Am Smelting & Refining Co & Fed Mining & Smelting Co, Wallace, Idaho, 45-47; chief geologist, Sunshine Mining Co, Kellogg, Idaho, 47-53; actg dist supvr, Tucson Off Surv, US Geol Surv, 53; sr explor geologist, Bear Creek Mining Co, 53-56, supv geologists, 56-58, sr explor geologist, Develop Div, 58-64; field geologist, Phelps Dodge Corp, Douglas, Ariz, 64-65; dist mgr, Northwest Explor Div Duval Corp, 65-69, dist mgr, Holt McPhar, 69-71; CONSULT GEOL ENG, RAYMOND F ROBINSON, INC, RENO, NEV, 71- *Mem:* Am Inst Mining, Metall & Petrol Engrs; Soc Econ Geologists. *Res:* Metal exploration, evaluation and development; surface and underground; regional to specific mining properties; surface and underground; all phases of reconnaissance, detailed examination, evaluation and development; planning, administration and field execution; world-wide operation. *Mailing Add:* 180 W Laramie Dr Reno NV 89511

ROBINSON, REX JULIAN, b Maxwell, Ind, Nov 15, 04; m 32; c 3. ANALYTICAL CHEMISTRY. *Educ:* DePauw Univ, AB, 25; Univ Wis, MA, 27, PhD(chem), 29. *Prof Exp:* Asst, Univ Wis, 26-29; from instr to prof, 29-71, from instr to assoc prof, Oceanog Labs, 32-41, EMER PROF CHEM, UNIV WASH, 71- *Mem:* Am Chem Soc. *Res:* Colorimetric and micro quantitative methods of analysis. *Mailing Add:* Dept of Chem BG 10 Univ of Wash Seattle WA 98195

ROBINSON, RICHARD ALAN, b Monroe, Mich, Oct 4, 42; c 1. NUCLEAR ENGINEERING, MECHANICAL ENGINEERING. *Educ:* Univ Mich, BSE, 64, MSE, 66. *Prof Exp:* Res scientist nuclear technol, Battelle Columbus Labs, 67-78, DEPT MGR NUCLEAR WASTE ISOLATION, PROJ MGT DIV, BATTELLE MEM INST, 78- *Mem:* Am Nuclear Soc. *Res:* Nuclear technology; advanced fuel development; experimental reactor engineering; PWR and BWR LOCA analysis and experimental studies; nuclear material shipping and transportation; nuclear waste disposal and isolation. *Mailing Add:* Off Nuclear Waste Isolation 505 King Ave Columbus OH 43201

ROBINSON, RICHARD C(LARK), b Seattle, Wash, Nov 4, 37; m 60; c 3. CHEMICAL ENGINEERING. *Educ:* Univ Wash, BS, 59; Univ Wis-Madison, MS, 61, PhD(chem eng), 65. *Prof Exp:* Res engr, Chevron Res Co, Standard Oil Co, Calif, 65-70, sr res engr, 70-72; asst prof, Colo Sch Mines, 72-74; SR RES ENGR, CHEVRON RES CO, 74- *Mem:* Am Inst Chem Engrs; Am Chem Soc. *Res:* Diffusion in compressed fluids; diffusion coefficient correlation by corresponding states; chemical reaction kinetics; catalytic reforming of naphtha; hydrofining of oils; fluidized catalytic cracking. *Mailing Add:* Chevron Res Co 576 Standard Ave Richmond CA 94804

ROBINSON, RICHARD CARLETON, JR, b Walton, NY, Aug 29, 27; m 49; c 4. OPERATIONS RESEARCH, PROBABILITY STATISTICS. *Educ:* Alfred Univ, BA, 50; Kent State Univ, MA, 52. *Prof Exp:* Physicist, Argonne Nat Lab, 52-53 & Savannah River Lab, E I du Pont de Nemours & Co, 53-57; analyst, Opers Res Off, Johns Hopkins Univ, 58-61; sr opers res analyst, Res Anal Corp, Va, 61-72 & Gen Res Corp, Va, 72-75; sr opers res analyst, Ketron Inc, Va, 75-77; SR OPERS ANALYST, US NUCLEAR REGULATORY COMN, WASHINGTON, DC, 77- *Mem:* Am Asn Physics Teachers; Opers Res Soc Am. *Res:* Experimental research with nuclear reactors and exponential assemblies; electronic instrumentation design for nondestructive testing; systems analysis; computer simulation and programming; mathematical modeling, applied probability; nuclear safeguards; probabilistic risk analysis. *Mailing Add:* 4013 Cleveland St Kensington MD 20895

ROBINSON, RICHARD DAVID, JR, b Corvallis, Ore, Nov 8, 46; m 76; c 1. SOLAR ASTRONOMY. *Educ:* Univ Wash, BSc, 69; Univ Colo, PhD(astrogeophysics), 77. *Prof Exp:* Res asst astron, Univ Colo, 71-76; res scientist solar radio astron, Commonwealth Sci & Indust Res Orgn, Australia, 74-75; scientist, 76-78, ASST ASTRONOMER, SACRAMENTO PEAK OBSERV, 78- *Res:* Solar activity, especially flares, surges and sunspots; meter wavelength solar radio activity; stellar flares; magnetic field measurements; activity cycles. *Mailing Add:* Sacramento Peak Observ Sunspot NM 88349

ROBINSON, RICHARD WARREN, b Los Angeles, Calif, Apr 14, 30; m 63; c 2. HORTICULTURE. *Educ:* Univ Calif, Davis, BS, 52, MS, 53; Cornell Univ, PhD(veg crops), 62. *Prof Exp:* PROF SEEDS & VEG SCI, NY STATE AGR EXP STA, 61- *Res:* Vegetable breeding, genetics and physiology. *Mailing Add:* NY State Agr Exp Sta Dept Seeds & Veg Sci Geneva NY 14456

ROBINSON, ROBERT EARL, b Covington, Ky, Aug 3, 27; m 51; c 3. SYNTHETIC ORGANIC CHEMISTRY, ORGANOMETALLIC CHEMISTRY. *Educ:* Berea Col, BA, 49; Purdue Univ, MS, 51, PhD, 53. *Prof Exp:* Proj leader, Nat Distillers & Chem Corp, 53-64; group leader, Stauffer Chem Co, 64-66; dir res & develop, Cardinal Chem Co, 66-67; EXEC VPRES & DIR, LINDAU CHEM INC, 67- *Concurrent Pos:* Consult synthetic organic & organometallic chemistry. *Mem:* Am Chem Soc; fel Am Inst Chemists. *Res:* Organometallic compounds; transition metal catalysts; synthetic resins; resin additives; epoxy curing agents; alkali metals; pharmaceutical intermediates; quaternary ammonium compounds. *Mailing Add:* Lindau Chem Inc PO Box 641 Columbia SC 29202

ROBINSON, ROBERT EUGENE, b Provo, Utah, Jan 9, 27; m 51; c 1. ANALYTICAL CHEMISTRY. *Educ:* Univ Okla, BS, 49, MS, 52; Univ Mich, PhD(chem), 59. *Prof Exp:* Chemist asphalt prod develop, Kerr-McGee Oil Co, 49-50; chemist oil prod res, Sun Oil Co, 52-54; res chemist, 58-69, SR RES CHEMIST, SHELL OIL CO, 69- *Mem:* Am Chem Soc. *Res:* Raman, infrared and molecular spectroscopy; Raman spectra of fluorocarbon derivatives; catalytic process research and development; separation sciences; gas and supercritical chromatography. *Mailing Add:* 11631 Jaycreek Houston TX 77070

ROBINSON, ROBERT GEORGE, b Beacon, NY, Aug 13, 37; m 60; c 3. CHEMICAL ENGINEERING. *Educ:* Clarkson Tech Univ, BChE, 58, MChE, 60; Pa State Univ, PhD(chem eng), 64. *Prof Exp:* Scientist, 64-77, sr scientist, 77-80, RES MGR, CHEM PROCESS RES & DEVELOP, UPJOHN CO, KALAMAZOO, 80- *Mem:* Am Inst Chem Engrs; Am Chem Soc; AAAS. *Res:* Controlled cycling mass transfer; countercurrent crystallization; separation and purification. *Mailing Add:* 8056 Greenfield Shores Scotts MI 49088

ROBINSON, ROBERT GEORGE, b Minneapolis, Minn, Jan 26, 20. AGRONOMY. *Educ:* Iowa State Univ, BS, 41; Univ Minn, MS, 46, PhD(agron, soils), 48. *Prof Exp:* Teacher high sch, Iowa, 41-42; asst, 42-47, from asst prof to assoc prof, 48-73, PROF AGRON, UNIV MINN, ST PAUL, 73- *Mem:* Am Soc Agron; Weed Sci Soc Am; Sigma Xi; Soc Econ Bot. *Res:* Field crop production; new and special field crops. *Mailing Add:* Dept of Agron Univ of Minn St Paul MN 55108

ROBINSON, ROBERT L(OUIS), JR, b Muskogee, Okla, June 14, 37; m 58. CHEMICAL ENGINEERING. *Educ:* Okla State Univ, BS, 59, MS, 62, PhD(chem eng), 64. *Prof Exp:* Sr res engr, Pan Am Petrol Corp, Okla, 64-65; from asst prof to assoc prof chem eng, 65-72, PROF CHEM ENG, OKLA STATE UNIV, 72- *Mem:* Am Inst Chem Engrs; Am Chem Soc; Am Soc Eng Educ. *Res:* Thermodynamic and transport properties. *Mailing Add:* Dept of Chem Eng Okla State Univ Stillwater OK 74074

ROBINSON, ROBERT LEO, b Kansas City, Mo, Mar 14, 26; m 55; c 2. PHARMACOLOGY. *Educ:* Univ Kans, MA, 54, PhD(physiol), 58. *Prof Exp:* From instr to assoc prof, 59-74, PROF PHARMACOL, MED CTR, WVA UNIV, 74- *Mem:* Am Soc Pharmacol & Exp Therapeut. *Res:* Adrenal medullary physiology; pharmacology of autonomic drugs. *Mailing Add:* Dept of Pharmacol WVa Univ Med Ctr Morgantown WV 26506

ROBINSON, ROBERT REID, physical chemistry, see previous edition

ROBINSON, ROSCOE ROSS, b Oklahoma City, Okla, Aug 21, 29; m 52; c 2. INTERNAL MEDICINE, NEPHROLOGY. *Educ:* Cent State Univ, BS, 49; Univ Okla, MD, 54; Am Bd Internal Med, dipl, 62. *Prof Exp:* Intern med, Duke Univ, 54-55, asst resident, 55-56; Am Heart Asn res fel, Columbia-Presby Med Ctr, 56-57; instr, 57-58, assoc, 60-62, from asst prof to assoc prof, 62-69, dir Div Nepthrol, 62-80, PROF MED, DUKE UNIV, 69-, CHIEF, DIV NEPHROL, 80- *Concurrent Pos:* Chief resident, Vet Admin Hosp, Durham, NC, 57-58, clin investr, 60-62, attend physician, 62-; sr investr, NC Heart Asn, 62-; mem exec comt, Coun Kidney & Cardiovasc Dis, Am Heart Asn; nat consult internal med, US Air Force Surgeon Gen; mem sci adv bd, Nat Kidney Found; ed, Kidney Int. *Mem:* Am Physiol Soc; Am Clin & Climat Asn; Europ Dialysis & Transplant Soc; Am Soc Clin Invest; Am Soc Artificial Internal Organs. *Res:* Renal disease and physiology. *Mailing Add:* Dept of Med Duke Univ Med Ctr Box 3014 Durham NC 27710

ROBINSON, ROSLYN QUINBY, bacteriology, virology, deceased

ROBINSON, ROSS UTLEY, b Minneapolis, Minn, July 30, 28; m 53; c 6. ANALYTICAL BIOCHEMISTRY. *Educ:* Colgate Univ, BA, 49; Wesleyan Univ, MA, 51; Mass Inst Technol, MS, 53. *Prof Exp:* Physical chemist, Abbott Labs, 53-58, sci instrumentation group leader, 58-62, sect mgr, 62-67, res & develop coordr, 67-69, advan technol mgr, 69-71, prod planning & develop, 71-73, dir contract res & develop, 73-75, dir advan systs res, 75-80; WITH BOEHRINGER MANNHEIM CORP, 80- *Mem:* AAAS; Am Chem Soc; NY Acad Sci; Asn Advan Med Instrumentation. *Res:* Physical, analytical and medical instrumentation; technological forecasting. *Mailing Add:* Boehringer Mannheim Corp 2742 Dow Ave Tustin CA 92680

ROBINSON, ROY GARLAND, JR, b Arkansas City, Kans, Mar 14, 21; m 74; c 1. PHYSIOLOGY, HISTOLOGY. *Educ:* Univ Ariz, BS, 48; Univ Southern Calif, MS, 54, PhD(biol), 65. *Prof Exp:* Instr histol, Sch Dent, Univ Southern Calif, 53-65, asst prof physiol, 65-69, chmn dept, 60-69; PROF ZOOL, McNEESE STATE UNIV, 69- *Mem:* AAAS; Am Soc Mammal. *Res:* Metabolic effects of thyroxin; carbohydrate metabolism of Ascaris lumbricoides; tooth development of lepisosteus. *Mailing Add:* Dept of Biol McNeese State Univ Lake Charles LA 70609

ROBINSON, RUSSELL LEE, b Louisville, Ky, July 30, 31; m 53; c 3. NUCLEAR PHYSICS. *Educ:* Univ Louisville, BA, 53; Ind Univ, MS, 55, PhD(physics), 58. *Prof Exp:* Asst physics, Ind Univ, 53-58; PHYSICIST, OAK RIDGE NAT LAB, 58- *Mem:* Fel Am Phys Soc. *Res:* Gamma-ray spectroscopy; coulomb excitation; heavy-ion induced reactions. *Mailing Add:* Oak Ridge Nat Lab PO Box X Oak Ridge TN 37830

ROBINSON, STEPHEN MICHAEL, b Columbus, Ohio, Apr 12, 42; m 68. MATHEMATICAL PROGRAMMING, SYSTEMS ANALYSIS. *Educ:* Univ Wis-Madison, BA, 62, PhD(comput sci), 71; NY Univ, MS, 63. *Prof Exp:* Mem staff, Comput & Numerical Anal Div, Sandia Corp, 62; instr math, US Mil Acad, 68-69; asst dir, Math Res Ctr, 71-74, asst prof comput sci, 72-75, assoc prof math res & comput sci, 75-76, assoc prof, 76-79, PROF INDUST ENG & COMPUT SCI, UNIV WIS-MADISON, 79- *Concurrent Pos:* Assoc ed, Opers Res, 74-, Math Opers Res, 75-, Mathematische Operations Forschung und Statistik, 77-; ed, Math Opers Res, 81- *Mem:* Am Math Soc; Math Prog Soc; Opers Res Soc Am. *Res:* Mathematical programming; mathematical economics. *Mailing Add:* Dept of Indust Eng 1513 University Ave Madison WI 53706

ROBINSON, STEWART MARSHALL, b Schenectady, NY, Jan 7, 34; m 60; c 3. MATHEMATICS. *Educ:* Union Col, BS, 55; Duke Univ, PhD(math), 59. *Prof Exp:* Asst prof math, Univ RI, 59-61; asst prof, Smith Col, 61-64; asst prof, Union Col, NY, 64-66, assoc prof, 66-68; ASSOC PROF MATH, CLEVELAND STATE UNIV, 68- *Mem:* Am Math Soc; Math Asn Am. *Res:* Partial differential equations; topology. *Mailing Add:* Dept Math Cleveland State Univ 1983 E 24th St Cleveland OH 44115

ROBINSON, TERRANCE EARL, b Rochester, NY, May 22, 49. PHYSIOLOGICAL PSYCHOLOGY, NEUROSCIENCE. *Educ:* Univ Lethbridge, BA, 72; Univ Sask, MA, 74; Univ Western Ont, PhD(psychol), 78. *Prof Exp:* Lectr psychol, Univ Western Ont, 76-77; fel psychobiol, Univ Calif, Irvine, 77-78; ASST PROF PSYCHOL, UNIV MICH, ANN ARBOR, 78- *Concurrent Pos:* Nat Res Coun Can fel, Univ Calif, Irvine, 77-78; asst prof, Univ Mich, Ann Arbor, 78- *Mem:* AAAS; Soc Neurosci. *Res:* Electrophysiological correlates of behavior; gender and hormonal influences on brain activity and behavior; brain lateralization. *Mailing Add:* Neurosci Lab Bldg Univ of Mich 1103 E Huron Ann Arbor MI 48109

ROBINSON, THANE SPARKS, b Kansas City, Kans, Apr 8, 28; m 54, 67; c 2. ECOLOGY. *Educ:* Univ Kans, AB, 51, PhD(zool), 56. *Prof Exp:* Asst state biol survr, Univ Kans, 51-54, from asst instr to instr zool, 54-57; from asst prof to assoc prof, Western Mich Univ, 57-63; assoc prof, 63-66, chmn dept biol, 66-68, assoc dean, Col Arts & Sci, 68-72, PROF BIOL, UNIV LOUISVILLE, 66- *Concurrent Pos:* Dir, Adams Ctr Ecol Studies, 59-63. *Mem:* AAAS; Wilson Ornith Union; Am Ornith Union; Am Soc Zoologists. *Res:* Terrestial and micro-environmental ecology; microclimatology and bioclimatology of homoiotherms. *Mailing Add:* Dept of Biol Univ of Louisville Louisville KY 40292

ROBINSON, THOMAS FRANK, b Port Chester, NY, Jan 9, 44; m 67; c 3. BIOPHYSICS, MUSCULAR PHYSIOLOGY. *Educ:* State Univ NY Albany, BS, 65, MS, 68; Rensselaer Polytech Inst, PhD(biophys), 74. *Prof Exp:* Instr physics, St Rose Col, 67-68; NDEA Title IV biophys, Rensselaer Polytech Inst, 69-71; fel res assoc muscle biophys, Dept Physiol, Sch Med, Univ Pa, 74-78; ASST PROF MED & ANAT, ALBERT EINSTEIN COL MED, 78-, ASST PROF PHYSIOL & BIOPHYSICS, 81- *Concurrent Pos:* USPHS fel, Nat Heart & Lung Inst, 74-76; USPHS res career develop award, 79-84. *Mem:* Am Biophys Soc; Electron Micros Soc Am; AAAS; Biophys Soc; Electron Microscopic Soc Am. *Res:* Heart muscle contractility and ultrastructural aspects of contractile filament and cellular organization related to tissue function; molecular basis of Molluscan muscle catch contraction. *Mailing Add:* Cardiovasc Res Labs Albert Einstein Col of Med Bronx NY 10461

ROBINSON, THOMAS JOHN, b Volga, Iowa, May 7, 35; m 59; c 2. MATHEMATICS. *Educ:* Luther Col, BA, 56; Iowa State Univ, MS, 58, PhD(math), 63. *Prof Exp:* Instr math, Univ NDak, 58-60 & Iowa State Univ, 60-63; from asst prof to assoc prof, 63-72, PROF MATH, UNIV N DAK, 72- *Concurrent Pos:* Fel, Sch Behav Studies, Univ NDak, 71-72. *Mem:* Am Math Soc; Math Asn Am; Nat Coun Teachers Math. *Res:* Topology; algebra. *Mailing Add:* Dept of Math Univ of NDak Grand Forks ND 58202

ROBINSON, TREVOR, b Springfield, Mass, Feb 20, 29; m 52; c 3. BIOCHEMISTRY. *Educ:* Harvard Univ, AB, 50, AM, 51; Univ Mass, MS, 53; Cornell Univ, PhD(biochem), 56. *Prof Exp:* Res assoc bact & bot, Syracuse Univ, 56-60; from asst prof to assoc prof chem, 61-66, ASSOC PROF BIOCHEM, UNIV MASS, AMHERST, 66- *Mem:* Am Soc Plant Physiol; Photochem Soc NAm; AAAS. *Res:* Plant biochemistry; alkaloids; tannins; history of science. *Mailing Add:* Dept of Biochem Univ of Mass Amherst MA 01003

ROBINSON, WILBUR EUGENE, b Viola, Kans, Aug 27, 19; m 42; c 2. CHEMISTRY, FUEL SCIENCE. *Educ:* Sterling Col, BA, 41. *Prof Exp:* Teacher high sch, 41-42; chemist, US Bur Mines, Nev, 42-44, supvry chemist, Wyo, 47-64; sect supvr, Laramie Energy Technol Ctr, US Dept Energy, 64-80; RETIRED. *Mem:* Am Chem Soc; Sigma Xi. *Res:* Constitution and properties of oil-shale kerogen. *Mailing Add:* 1516 Sheridan Laramie WY 82070

ROBINSON, WILLARD BANCROFT, b State College, Pa, Apr 19, 18; m 42; c 5. FOOD SCIENCE. *Educ:* Pa State Col, BS, 40; Univ Ill, MS, 42, PhD(animal nutrit), 43. *Prof Exp:* Spec asst, Univ Ill, 40-42; res assoc, NY State Col Agr & Life Sci, Cornell Univ, 43-45, from asst prof to assoc prof, 45-55, prof chem, Exp Sta, 55-82, chmn, Dept Food Sci & Technol, 67-82, head, Food Sci Inst, 75-81; RETIRED. *Concurrent Pos:* Mem, Tech Secy, Food Protection Comt, Nat Res Coun, 53-54, Comt GRAS List Surv, 70-, chmn, Subcomt Specifications Food Chem Codex, 71-; consult, Interdept Comt Nutrit for Nat Defense, 59-68 & Nutrit Surv, Colombia, 60, Bolivia, 62 & Honduras, 66; mem, Food & Nutrit Bd, Nat Res Coun, 77-82. *Honors & Awards:* Award Merit, Am Wine Soc, 74. *Mem:* Inst Food Technologists; Am Soc Enol. *Res:* Chemical additives in foods; food processing with respect to quality control and nutritive value; enology. *Mailing Add:* NY State Agr Exp Sta Cornell Univ Geneva NY 14456

ROBINSON, WILLIAM COURTNEY, JR, b Weatherford, Tex, July 4, 37; m 64; c 2. METALLURGY, CHEMICAL ENGINEERING. *Educ:* Univ Tex, BS, 59; Iowa State Univ, PhD(metall), 64. *Prof Exp:* Jr chem engr, Humble Oil & Refining Co, 59; asst, Ames Lab, 60-64; metallurgist, Oak Ridge Nat Lab, 64-69; sr res scientist, Lockheed-Calif Co, 69-70, GROUP LEADER, UNION CARBIDE ELECTRONICS, 70- *Mem:* Am Soc Metals. *Res:* Vapor deposition of refractory metals; corrosion and adhesive bonding problems on aircraft; high temperature sinterins and powder metallurgical fabrication; anodization; capacitor manufacture. *Mailing Add:* Components Dept Union Carbide Corp PO Box 5928 Greenville SC 29606

ROBINSON, WILLIAM H, b Philadelphia, Pa, Feb 15, 43; m 64; c 3. ENTOMOLOGY. *Educ:* Kent State Univ, BA, 64, MA, 66; Iowa State Univ, PhD(entom), 70. *Prof Exp:* Asst prof, 70-80, ASSOC PROF ENTOM, VA POLYTECH INST & STATE UNIV, 80- *Mem:* Entom Soc Am; Entom Soc Can; Am Entom Soc. *Res:* Biology and immature stages of Phoridae; Diptera biology and taxonomy; insects associated with thermal water. *Mailing Add:* Dept of Entom Va Polytech Inst & State Univ Blacksburg VA 24061

ROBINSON, WILLIAM JAMES, b Erie, Pa, Feb 19, 29; m 57; c 2. DENDROCHRONOLOGY. *Educ:* Univ Ariz, BA, 57, MA, 59, PhD(anthrop), 67. *Prof Exp:* From res asst to res assoc, 63-69, from asst prof to assoc prof, 69-76, PROF DENDROCHRONOLOGY, LAB TREE-RING RES, UNIV ARIZ, 76-, ASST DIR LAB, 72- *Mem:* Am Anthrop Asn; Soc Am Archaeol; Am Quaternary Asn; Tree-Ring Soc. *Res:* Application of special techniques of dendrochronology to archaeology, especially the non-chronological aspect which views the material as an artifact, and reconstruction of past environments. *Mailing Add:* Lab of Tree-Ring Res Univ of Ariz Tucson AZ 85721

ROBINSON, WILLIAM JOHN, b Tulsa, Okla, Feb 10, 24; m 45; c 4. PETROLEUM GEOLOGY, GEOPHYSICS. *Educ:* Univ Tulsa, BS, 49. *Prof Exp:* Jr geologist, Sinclair Oil & Gas Co, Okla, 49-51, geophysicist, 51-54, div geophysicist, 54-59, staff geophysicist, 59-60, div geophysicist, 60-65, geophys specialist, 65-69; area geophysicist, 69-74, regional geophysicist, 74-76, dir, Geophys Anal & Processing, 76-81, MGR GEOPHYS DATA PROCESSING, ATLANTIC RICHFIELD CO, 81- *Mem:* Soc Explor Geophysicists. *Res:* Solid earth geophysics; exploration seismology and geophysics; structural and field geology. *Mailing Add:* Atlantic Richfield Co PO Box 2819 Dallas TX 75221

ROBINSON, WILLIAM KIRLEY, b Syracuse, NY, Apr 1, 25; m 50; c 4. PHYSICS. *Educ:* Univ Mo, BS, 45; Carnegie Inst Technol, MS, 54, PhD(physics), 59. *Prof Exp:* Instr math, Brevard Col, 48-51; assoc prof, 59-71, prof physics, 71-80, HENRY PRIEST PROF PHYSICS & CHMN DEPT, ST LAWRENCE UNIV, 80- *Mem:* Am Phys Soc; Am Asn Physics Teachers. *Res:* Nuclear measurements. *Mailing Add:* Dept of Physics St Lawrence Univ Canton NY 13617

ROBINSON, WILLIAM LAUGHLIN, b Ironwood, Mich, Mar 29, 33; m 59; c 2. WILDLIFE ECOLOGY. *Educ:* Mich State Univ, BS, 54; Univ Maine, MS, 59; Univ Toronto, PhD(zool, ecol), 63. *Prof Exp:* Asst leader, Maine Coop Wildlife Res Unit, Maine, 63; asst prof biol, Middlebury Col, 63-64; asst prof, 64-69, PROF BIOL, NORTHERN MICH UNIV, 69- *Concurrent Pos:* NSF res grants, 66-69; sci fac fel, San Diego State Col, 71-72; Huron Mt Wildlife Found res grant, 72-78; US Forest Serv res contracts, 72-79; Nat Audubon Soc res grant, 73-75; US Fish & Wildlife Serv contracts, 78-81. *Mem:* Sigma Xi; Wildlife Soc; Am Soc Mammal. *Res:* Winter shelter requirements, social behavior and populations of white-tailed deer; homing behavior of meadow mice; ecology of spruce grouse; ecology of wolves; effects of winter shipping on mammal movements. *Mailing Add:* Dept of Biol Northern Mich Univ Marquette MI 49855

ROBINSON, WILLIAM ROBERT, b Longview, Tex, May 30, 39; m 62; c 3. INORGANIC CHEMISTRY. *Educ:* Tex Technol Col, BS, 61, MS, 62; Mass Inst Technol, PhD(chem), 66. *Prof Exp:* NSF fel, Univ Sheffield, 66-67; asst prof, 67-72, assoc prof, 72-79, PROF CHEM, PURDUE UNIV, LAFAYETTE, 79- *Concurrent Pos:* Adj assoc prof, Dept Earth & Space Sci, State Univ NY Stony Brook, 73. *Mem:* AAAS; Am Chem Soc; Am Crystallog Asn. *Res:* X-ray crystallographic studies of inorganic compounds; solid state chemistry; synthesis and characterization of transition metal oxides, sulfides, and related compounds. *Mailing Add:* Dept of Chem Purdue Univ West Lafayette IN 47907

ROBINSON, WILLIAM SIDNEY, b Bloomington, Ind, Nov 24, 33; m 65. INTERNAL MEDICINE, MOLECULAR BIOLOGY. *Educ:* Ind Univ, AB, 56; Univ Chicago, MS & MD, 60. *Prof Exp:* Intern internal med, Columbia-Presby Med Ctr, NY, 60-61, jr asst resident, 61-62; sr asst resident, Univ Chicago Hosps, 62-63, resident, 63-64; NIH spec fel, Univ Calif, Berkeley, 64-65, asst prof molecular biol & res biologist, Virus Lab, 65-67; from asst prof to assoc prof med, 67-76, PROF MED, DIV INFECTIOUS DIS, SCH MED, STANFORD UNIV, 76- *Concurrent Pos:* Res fel biochem, Argonne Cancer Res Hosp & Univ Chicago, 62-64; mem cancer res training comt, NIH, 71- *Mem:* AAAS; Am Soc Microbiol; Am Soc Clin Invest. *Res:* Biochemistry of virus infection and replication; malignant transformation of cells by tumor viruses; nucleic acid metabolism; infectious diseases. *Mailing Add:* Dept of Med Div Infectious Dis Stanford Univ Sch of Med Stanford CA 94304

ROBINTON, ELIZABETH DOROTHY, b Woburn, Mass, June 27, 10. MICROBIOLOGY, PUBLIC HEALTH. *Educ:* Columbia Univ, BS, 38; Smith Col, MA, 42; Yale Univ, PhD(pub health), 50. *Prof Exp:* Microbiologist, Div Labs, State Dept Health, Conn, 31-42; instr bact, Woman's Col NC, 42-43; instr, Goucher Col, 43-44; from instr to asst prof bact, 44-56, assoc prof bact & pub health, 56-62, prof microbiol & pub health, 62-65, prof biol sci, 65-73, chmn dept, 66-69, EMER PROF BIOL SCI, SMITH COL, 73- *Concurrent Pos:* WHO fel, 65; ed-in-chief, Health Lab Sci, 66-74. *Mem:* Med Mycol Soc of the Americas; Conf State & Prov Pub Health Lab Dirs; Am Soc Microbiol; fel Am Pub Health Asn; fel Am Acad Microbiol. *Res:* Environmental and public health microbiology; medical mycology. *Mailing Add:* 7 Phillips Ave Rockport MA 01966

ROBISON, D(ELBERT) E(ARL), b Weiser, Idaho, June 11, 20; m 41; c 1. MECHANICAL ENGINEERING. *Educ:* Univ Idaho, BS, 50; Purdue Univ, MS, 52, PhD(jet propulsion), 55. *Prof Exp:* Instr mech eng & res engr, Exp Sta, Univ Idaho, 46-50; asst, Purdue Univ, 50-51, instr & res assoc, 51-55, asst prof, 55-56; gas dynamicist & actg supvr rocket engine sect, Gen Elec Co, 56-57, mgr combustion unit, 57-58, supvr rocket systs & processes, 58-61; mgr thrust chamber tech staff, Aerojet Gen Corp, 61-63, asst div mgr, 63-64, prog mgr, 64-70, vpres eng, Aerojet Liquid Rocket Co, Sacramento, 70-72, dir advan prod develop, Aerojet Energy Conversion Co, 72-76; PROF MECH ENG, CALIF POLYTECH STATE UNIV, SAN LUIS OBISPO, 76- *Mem:* Am Inst Aeronaut & Astronaut. *Res:* Rocket and space flight research and development; theory and procedures for evaluating rocket propulsion systems; comparison of liquid and solid propellant missile systems. *Mailing Add:* Dept of Mech Eng Calif Polytech State Univ San Luis Obispo CA 93407

ROBISON, GEORGE ALAN, b Lethbridge, Alta, Nov 4, 34; m 56; c 2. BIOCHEMICAL PHARMACOLOGY, ENDOCRINOLOGY. *Educ:* Univ Alta, BSc, 57; Tulane Univ, MS, 60, PhD(pharmacol), 62. *Prof Exp:* Res fel pharmacol, Sch Med, Western Reserve Univ, 62-63; res assoc physiol, Sch Med, Vanderbilt Univ, 63-64, instr physiol & pharmacol, 64-66, asst prof pharmacol, 66-69, assoc prof pharmacol & physiol, 69-72; PROF PHARMACOL & CHMN DEPT, UNIV TEX MED SCH HOUSTON, 72- *Concurrent Pos:* Investr, Howard Hughes Med Inst, 70-72; co-ed, Advances Cyclic Nucleotide Res, 72- *Honors & Awards:* J Murray Luck Award, Nat Acad Sci, 79. *Mem:* Am Chem Soc; Am Soc Pharmacol & Exp Therapeut; Endocrine Soc; NY Acad Sci; Soc Neurosci. *Res:* Biochemical basis of hormone action; biochemical basis of animal behavior. *Mailing Add:* Dept of Pharmacol Univ of Tex Med Sch Houston TX 77025

ROBISON, HENRY WELBORN, b Albany, Ga, Mar 24, 45; m 66; c 2. ICHTHYOLOGY. *Educ:* Ark State Univ, BS, 67, MS, 68; Okla State Univ, PhD(zool), 71. *Prof Exp:* Res asst fish social behav, Okla State Univ, 70-71; asst prof zool, Southern Ill Univ, Carbondale, 71; assoc prof, 71-77, PROF BIOL, SOUTHERN ARK UNIV, 78- *Concurrent Pos:* Hon prof, Southern Ark Univ, 81. *Mem:* Am Soc Ichthyologists & Herpetologists; Animal Behav Soc; Am Fisheries Soc; Soc Am Zoologists. *Res:* Taxonomy; ecology and behavior of cyprinid and perciform fishes; social behavior of anabantoid fishes; fishes of Arkansas; evolution of reproductive behavior in fishes. *Mailing Add:* Dept of Biol Southern Ark Univ Magnolia AR 71753

ROBISON, LAREN R, b Georgetown, Idaho, Mar 25, 31; m 55; c 6. PLANT GENETICS, WEED SCIENCE. *Educ:* Brigham Young Univ, BS, 57, MS, 58; Univ Minn, PhD(plant genetics), 62. *Prof Exp:* Res leader new crops, Univ Nebr-Lincoln, 62-65, res leader exten weed control, vchmn & exten leader, Agron Dept, 65-71; prof agron & hort & chmn dept, 71-82, ASSOC DEAN, COL BIOL & AGR SCI, BRIGHAM YOUNG UNIV, 82- *Mem:* Am Soc Agron; Crop Sci Soc Am; Weed Sci Soc Am. *Res:* Plant and soil relationships; forage breeding and research; weed control methods, including herbicides used, dissipation and crop tolerance. *Mailing Add:* Dept of Agron & Hort Brigham Young Univ Provo UT 84601

ROBISON, NORMAN GLENN, b Littlefield, Tex, Oct 5, 38; m 63; c 3. GENETICS, STATISTICS. *Educ:* Tex Tech Col, BS, 61; Univ Nebr, MS, 63, PhD(agron), 67. *Prof Exp:* RES AGRONOMIST, DEKALB AGRES, INC, NE, 65- *Mem:* Am Soc Agron. *Res:* Development and testing of hybrid grain sorghums for commerical distribution. *Mailing Add:* 2430 N Elm Hastings NE 68901

ROBISON, ODIS WAYNE, b Lawton, Okla, Aug 23, 34; m 56; c 3. GENETICS, REPRODUCTIVE PHYSIOLOGY. *Educ:* Okla State Univ, BS, 55; Univ Wis, MS, 57, PhD(genetics, animal husb), 59. *Prof Exp:* From asst prof to assoc prof, 59-74, PROF ANIMAL SCI & GENETICS, NC STATE UNIV, 74- *Concurrent Pos:* NSF travel grant, NATO Conf, 62 & 68; mem, AID Mission to Peru; lectr several foreign countries. *Mem:* AAAS; Am Soc Animal Sci; Biomet Soc; Sigma Xi; Am Genetic Asn. *Res:* Genetic control of developmental and physiological processes; formulation of selection schemes and breeding systems for efficient manipulation of populations; interaction of genetics and maternal influence on developing processes. *Mailing Add:* 226 Polk Hall NC State Univ Raleigh NC 27607

ROBISON, RICHARD ASHBY, b Fillmore, Utah, Jan 10, 33; m 53; c 3. GEOLOGY, PALEONTOLOGY. *Educ:* Brigham Young Univ, BS, 57, MS, 58; Univ Tex, PhD(geol), 62. *Prof Exp:* Geologist, US Geol Surv, 59-60; asst prof geol, Univ Utah, 62-66; assoc cur invert paleont, Smithsonian Inst, 66-67; from assoc prof to prof geol, Univ Utah, 67-74; HEDBERG PROF GEOL, UNIV KANS, 74-, DIR, PALEONT INST, 75- *Mem:* Int Paleont Asn; Am Asn Petrol Geologists; Palaeont Asn London; Geol Soc Am; Paleont Soc. *Res:* Paleontology, particularly Cambrian trilobites and stratigraphy. *Mailing Add:* Dept of Geol Univ of Kans Lawrence KS 66045

ROBISON, WENDALL C(LOYD), b Des Moines, Iowa, July 31, 23; m 47; c 3. ELECTRICAL ENGINEERING. *Educ:* Iowa State Univ, BSc, 47, MSc, 48, PhD(elec eng), 57. *Prof Exp:* Engr, Gen Elec Co, 48-49; from instr to assoc prof elec eng, 49-71, PROF ELEC ENG, UNIV NEBR, LINCOLN, 71- *Mem:* AAAS; Am Soc Eng Educ; Inst Elec & Electronics Engrs. *Res:* Electric network theory including both linear and nonlinear networks; system theory. *Mailing Add:* Dept of Elec Eng Univ of Nebr Lincoln NE 68588

ROBISON, WILBUR GERALD, JR, b Cheyenne, Wyo, Dec 27, 33; m 57; c 4. CELL BIOLOGY, EXPERIMENTAL PATHOLOGY. *Educ:* Brigham Young Univ, AB, 58, MA, 61; Univ Calif, Berkeley, PhD(genetics), 65. *Prof Exp:* Res geneticist, Univ Calif, Berkeley, 63-65; res fel anat, Harvard Med Sch, 65-66; asst prof biol, Univ Va, 66-72; sr staff fel, 72-76, GENETICIST & CELL BIOLOGIST, LAB VISION RES, NAT EYE INST, 76- *Concurrent Pos:* US Air Force Off Sci Res-Nat Acad Sci res fel, 65-66. *Mem:* Am Soc Cell Biol; Asn Res Vision & Ophthal. *Res:* Experimental pathology of the eye; ultrastructural and functional interrelationships between the pigment epithelium and the visual cells of the retina; turnover and fate of photoreceptor membranes in relation to vitamin A, vitamin E, and aging pigments; studies on ceroid-lipofuscinosis and retinitis pigmentosa. *Mailing Add:* Bldg 6 Rm 211 Nat Eye Inst Lab of Vision Res Bethesda MD 20014

ROBISON, WILLIAM LEWIS, b Grinnell, Iowa, June 18, 38; m 59; c 3. ECOLOGY, RADIOBIOLOGY. *Educ:* Cornell Col, AB, 56; Univ Calif, Berkeley, MS, 62, PhD(biophysics), 66. *Prof Exp:* SR RES SCIENTIST ENVIRON SCI, UNIV CALIF, LAWRENCE LIVERMORE LAB, 65- *Mem:* AAAS. *Res:* Environmental science; radionuclide and stable element transport and fate; radiation biology; uptake, retention, dose assessment to populations via food chains. *Mailing Add:* Univ of Calif Environ Div L-453 Livermore CA 94550

ROBITAILLE, HENRY ARTHUR, b Washington, DC, Sept 2, 43; m 68; c 3. HORTICULTURE. *Educ:* Univ Md, BS, 66; Mich State Univ, MS, 67, PhD(hort), 70. *Prof Exp:* Asst prof hort, Okla State Univ, 70-72; from asst prof to assoc prof hort, Purdue Univ, 72-81; MANAGING SCIENTIST, LAND-EPCOT CTR, 81- *Concurrent Pos:* Plant physiologist, USAID/Brazil, 73-75. *Mem:* Am Soc Hort Sci; Am Soc Plant Physiologists; Sigma Xi. *Res:* World agriculture and food production; developing new crops, especially for desert and tropical environments. *Mailing Add:* Land-Epcot Ctr PO Box 40 Lake Buena Vista FL 32830

ROBITSCHER, JONAS BONDI, psychiatry, law, deceased

ROBKIN, MAURICE, b New York, NY, Apr 25, 31; m 62; c 3. NUCLEAR ENGINEERING, BIOENGINEERING. *Educ:* Calif Inst Technol, BS, 53; Oak Ridge Sch Reactor Technol, dipl, 54; Mass Inst Technol, PhD(nuclear eng), 61. *Prof Exp:* Physicist, Bettis Atomic Power Lab, Westinghouse Elec Co, 54-56 & Valecitos Atomic Lab, Gen Elec Co, 61-67; assoc prof, 67-79, PROF NUCLEAR ENG, UNIV WASH, 79-, PROF ENVIRON HEALTH, 81- *Concurrent Pos:* Vis scientist, Cambridge Univ, 76; consult nuclear eng & health physics. *Mem:* AAAS; NY Acad Sci; Am Nuclear Soc; Radiation Res Soc; Health Physics Soc. *Res:* In vitro culturing and studies of mammalian embryos; neutron activation analysis of biological material; neutrography; health physics. *Mailing Add:* Dept Nuclear Eng Univ Wash Seattle WA 98195

ROBL, HERMANN R, b Vienna, Austria, Aug 7, 19; nat US; m 42; c 1. THEORETICAL PHYSICS. *Educ:* Univ Vienna, PhD, 48, Dr habil, 52. *Prof Exp:* Asst, Inst Theoret Physics, Vienna, 48-52, asst prof, 52-55; asst, Phys Sci Div, Off Ord Res, 55-56, assoc dir, Physics Div, 56-57, dir, 57-62; dep chief scientist, 62-73, chief scientist, 73-75, TECH DIR, US ARMY RES OFF, 75- *Concurrent Pos:* From vis asst prof to vis assoc prof, Duke Univ, 59-65, adj prof, 66-; Army Res Off-Durham res & study proj scholar, 65. *Honors & Awards:* Korner Award, 54. *Mem:* Am Phys Soc. *Res:* Quantum optics and mechanics. *Mailing Add:* US Army Res Off PO Box 12211 Research Triangle Park NC 27709

ROBL, ROBERT F(REDRICK), JR, b Pittsburgh, Pa, Feb 19, 28; m 53; c 3. ELECTRICAL ENGINEERING, ALUMINUM ELECTROLYSIS. *Educ:* Carnegie Inst Technol, BS, 53, MS, 54, PhD(elec eng), 58. *Prof Exp:* Asst, Carnegie Inst Technol, 51-55, instr elec eng, 55-58; res engr instrumentation & automatic control, Alcoa Res Labs, New Kensington, 58-72, sci assoc, Phys Chem Div, 72-80, SR ENG ASSOC, INSTRUMENTATION & AUTOMATIC CONTROL, PROCESS CONTROL & COMPUT TECHNOL DIV, ALCOA TECH CTR, ALUMINUM CO AM, 80- *Concurrent Pos:* Technician, Int Bus Mach Corp, 52; mem tech staff, Bell Tel Labs, Inc, 53. *Mem:* Inst Elec & Electronics Engrs; Sigma Xi. *Res:* Chemical, optical, metallurgical and electrical instrumentation; automatic control; analog and digital computers; electronics; spectroscopy; dielectric and magnetic phenomena; radar spark gap modulator; coaxial cable shielding effectiveness. *Mailing Add:* Process Control & Comput Technol Div Alcoa Tech Ctr Alcoa Center PA 15069

ROBLEE, LELAND H S, JR, chemical engineering, see previous edition

ROBLIN, JOHN M, b Sagada, Philippines, Feb 20, 31; US citizen; m 65; c 7. ENGINEERING MANAGEMENT, CHEMICAL ENGINEERING. *Educ:* Princeton Univ, BSE, 53; Mass Inst Technol, MS, 55; Case Inst Technol, PhD(chem eng), 62. *Prof Exp:* Asst dir pract sch, Mass Inst Technol, 55-56; res technologist extractive metall, 56-58, supvr coal chem, Res Lab, Independence, 58-60, asst chief coal & coal chem, 60-64, asst div head new prod, 64-65, div head, 65-75, mgr process & raw mat planning, 75-78, DIR, RESOURCE ADMIN & DEVELOP, REPUB STEEL CORP, CLEVELAND, OHIO, 78-, DIR CORP PLANNING, 80- *Mem:* Am Electroplaters Soc; Am Iron & Steel Inst; Am Inst Chem. *Res:* Application of chemical engineering techniques to metals processing, particularly iron and steel. *Mailing Add:* 37275 Windy Hill Lane Solon OH 44139

ROBOCK, ALAN, b Boston, Mass, Sept 7, 49; m 80. CLIMATE DYNAMICS, CLIMATOLOGICAL DATA ANALYSIS. *Educ:* Univ Wis, Madison, BA, 70; Mass Inst Technol, SM, 75, PhD(meteorol), 77. *Prof Exp:* Volunteer meteorol, US Peace Corps, Philippines, 70-72; ASST PROF, DEPT METEOROL, UNIV MD, 77- *Mem:* Am Meteorol Soc; AAAS; Am Geophys Union; Fedn Am Scientists. *Res:* Numerical modeling of the climate system; causes of climate change, especially volcanic eruptions, carbon dioxide and natural variability; snow and ice-albedo feedback; climatological data analysis-surface temperature and snow cover; broadcast meteorology. *Mailing Add:* Dept Meteorol Univ Md College Park MD 20742

ROBOLD, ALICE ILENE, b Daleville, Ind, Feb 7, 28; m 55; c 1. MATHEMATICS. *Educ:* Ball State Univ, BS, 55, MA, 60, EdD, 65. *Prof Exp:* Asst prof math, 64-69, assoc prof, 69-76, PROF MATH SCI, BALL STATE UNIV, 76- *Mem:* Nat Coun Teachers Math. *Res:* Background of college instructors of mathematics for prospective elementary school teachers. *Mailing Add:* Dept of Math Sci Ball State Univ Muncie IN 47306

ROBOZ, JOHN, b Budapest, Hungary, Oct 14, 31; US citizen; m 61; c 2. PHYSICAL CHEMISTRY. *Educ:* Eotvos Lorand, Budapest, BS, 55; NY Univ, MS, 60, PhD(phys chem), 62. *Prof Exp:* Sr engr, Gen Tel & Electronics Res Labs, NY, 57-63; group leader gas anal res, Cent Res Labs, Air Reduction Co, 63-69; res assoc prof clin chem, 69-74, ASSOC PROF NEOPLASTIC DIS, MT SINAI SCH MED, 74- *Mem:* Am Chem Soc; Am Soc Mass Spectrometry; Soc Appl Spectros. *Res:* Identification and quantification of antineoplastic agents in body fluids and tissues; biological markers of cancer; mass spectrometry, high performance liquid chromatography, and other instrumental techniques in clinical chemistry. *Mailing Add:* Dept of Neoplastic Fifth Ave at 100th St New York NY 10029

ROBSON, DONALD, b Leeds, Eng, Mar 19, 37; m 60, 71; c 3. NUCLEAR PHYSICS. *Educ:* Univ Melbourne, BSc, 59, MSc, 61, PhD(nuclear physics), 63. *Prof Exp:* Res assoc nuclear physics, 63-64, from asst prof to prof physics, 64-67, PROF PHYSICS, FLA STATE UNIV, 67- *Honors & Awards:* Tom W Bonner Prize, Am Phys Soc, 72. *Mem:* Fel Am Phys Soc. *Res:* Theoretical nuclear physics mainly low energy scattering phenomena. *Mailing Add:* Dept of Physics Fla State Univ Tallahassee FL 32306

ROBSON, DOUGLAS SHERMAN, b St John, NDak, July 30, 25; m 49; c 3. BIOMETRICS. *Educ:* Iowa State Col, BS, 49; Cornell Univ, MS, 51, PhD(statist), 55. *Prof Exp:* Biometrician, 49-54, res assoc plant breeding, 54-55, from asst prof to assoc prof, 55-62, PROF PLANT BREEDING & BIOMET, CORNELL UNIV, 62- *Concurrent Pos:* NIH career develop award, Cornell Univ, 62-72. *Mem:* fel Am Statist Asn; fel Am Inst Fishery Res Scientists; Am Fisheries Soc; Biomet Soc; Eastern NAm Region Biomet Soc (pres, 70). *Res:* Biological statsitics. *Mailing Add:* Dept of Plant Breeding & Biometry Cornell Univ Ithaca NY 14850

ROBSON, HARRY EDWIN, b Kans, July 19, 27; m 50; c 3. PHYSICAL CHEMISTRY. *Educ:* Univ Kans, BS, 49, PhD(chem), 59. *Prof Exp:* Res assoc, Esso Res Labs, Humble Oil & Refining Co, 57-72, res assoc, 72-78, SR RES ASSOC, EXXON RES & DEVELOP LABS, 78- *Res:* Petroleum process catalysts; inorganic synthesis. *Mailing Add:* Exxon Res & Develop Lab PO Box 2226 Baton Rouge LA 70821

ROBSON, HOPE HOWETH, b Bronxville, NY, Feb 28, 22. SOIL MICROBIOLOGY. *Educ:* Columbia Univ, AB, 44, PhD(bot), 53. *Prof Exp:* Asst biol, Princeton Univ, 44-45, bot, Columbia Univ, 45-52 & genetics, Smith Col, 53-54; res assoc biol, Amherst Col, 54-67; res assoc biol, Univ Mass, Amherst, 67-82; RETIRED. *Mem:* AAAS; Am Soc Plant Physiologists; Bot Soc Am; Torrey Bot Club; Am Soc Microbiol. *Res:* Physiological effects of an organophosphate, diazinon, on soil microbes. *Mailing Add:* 97 Mechanic St Amherst MA 01002

ROBSON, JOHN HOWARD, b East Liberty, Ohio, July 26, 40; m 61; c 2. POLYMER CHEMISTRY, ORGANIC CHEMISTRY. *Educ:* Ohio Northern Univ, BS, 62; Ohio State Univ, PhD(org chem), 67. *Prof Exp:* proj chemist, 66-77, mgr tech recruiting & mgr tech & managerial educ, 77-80, RES SCIENTIST, UNION CARBIDE CORP, 80- *Mem:* Am Chem Soc. *Res:* Development of intermediates and application technology for flexible, high-resiliency and rigid polyurethane foams; chemical process innovation & development. *Mailing Add:* Union Carbide Corp South Charleston WV 25303

ROBSON, JOHN MICHAEL, b London, Eng, Mar 26, 20; m 50; c 3. NUCLEAR PHYSICS. *Educ:* Cambridge Univ, BA, 42, MA, 46, ScD, 63. *Prof Exp:* Physicist, Radar Res & Develop Estab, Eng, 42-45, Atomic Energy Res Estab, 45-50 & Atomic Energy Can, Ltd, 50-60; prof physics, Univ Ottawa, 60-69; PROF PHYSICS, McGILL UNIV, 69- *Honors & Awards:* Gold Medal, Can Assoc Physicists, 78. *Mem:* Fel Am Phys Soc; Royal Soc Can; Can Asn Physicists (past pres). *Res:* Radioactive decay of the neutron; inelastic scattering of fast neutrons; shielding of nuclear reactors; ultra cold neutrons. *Mailing Add:* 3600 University St Dept Physics McGill Univ Montreal PQ H3A 2T8 Can

ROBSON, JOHN ROBERT KEITH, b Darlington, Eng, Oct 9, 25; m 21; c 4. NUTRITION, PUBLIC HEALTH. *Educ:* Univ Durham, MB, BS, 48; Univ Edinburgh, DTM&H, 56; Univ London, DPH, 59; Univ Newcastle, MD, 68. *Prof Exp:* Physician, hosp & pvt med pract, 48-52; spec grade med officer, Tanganyika Govt, 52-62; nutrit adv, WHO, Philippines, 62-64 & Egypt, 64-67; from assoc prof to prof human nutrit, Sch Pub Health, Univ Mich, Ann Arbor, 67-75; PROF NUTRIT, DEPT FAMILY PRACT, MED UNIV SC, 75- *Concurrent Pos:* Ed, Ecol of Food & Nutrit, 70. *Mem:* Fel Royal Soc Trop Med & Hyg. *Res:* Evaluation of nutritional status in communities and individuals; ethno-nutrition and nutritive value of prehistoric foods. *Mailing Add:* Dept of Family Pract Med Univ of SC Charleston SC 29401

ROBSON, JOHN WILLIAM, b Coshocton, Ohio, Sept 6, 23; m 48; c 2. PHYSICS. *Educ:* Oberlin Col, BA, 49; Case Inst Technol, MS, 52, PhD(physics), 54. *Prof Exp:* Asst physics, Case Inst Technol, 49-51, instr, 51-54; asst prof, 54-58, assoc prof, 58-74, PROF PHYSICS, UNIV ARIZ, 74- *Mem:* AAAS; Am Phys Soc; Am Asn Physics Teachers; Nat Sci Teachers Asn. *Res:* Low energy nuclear physics; applied optics and acoustics. *Mailing Add:* Dept of Physics Univ of Ariz Tucson AZ 85721

ROBSON, RICHARD MORRIS, b Atlantic, Iowa, Dec 9, 41; div; c 2. BIOCHEMISTRY, ANIMAL SCIENCE. *Educ:* Iowa State Univ, BS, 64, MS, 66, PhD(biochem), 69. *Prof Exp:* NIH fel biochem, Iowa State Univ, 65-69; asst prof biochem & animal sci, Univ Ill, 69-72; assoc prof, 72-77, PROF BIOCHEM & ANIMAL SCI, IOWA STATE UNIV, 77- *Mem:* AAAS; Am Heart Asn; Am Soc Animal Sci; Biophys Soc; Am Soc Cell Biol. *Res:* Biochemistry of muscle tissue with emphasis on the chemistry, structure, function and turnover of the myofibrillar proteins of heart, skeletal and smooth muscle cells. *Mailing Add:* Muscle Biol Group Iowa State Univ Ames IA 50011

ROBSON, RONALD D, b Leicester, Eng, Oct 21, 33; m 57; c 2. PHARMACOLOGY. *Educ:* Univ Leeds, BSc, 54 & 55, PhD(pharmacol), 58. *Prof Exp:* Mem staff pharmacol, Beecham Res Labs, UK, 58-61; mem staff pharmacol, Wellcome Res Labs, 61-66; group leader, Merck-Frosst Labs, Can, 66-67; sect head & sr scientist, Warner-Lambert Res Inst, 68-71; mgr cardiovasc res, 71-72, dir pharmacol, Pharmaceut Div, 72-78, exec dir biol res, 78-81, SCIENTIFIC ADV, CIBA-GEIGY CORP, 81- *Mem:* Am Soc Pharmacol & Exp Therapeut; Brit Pharmacol Soc; Am Pharm Asn; NY Acad Sci. *Res:* Pharmacology applied to the search for improved therapies for cardiovascular and psychotic disorders. *Mailing Add:* Pharmaceut Div Res Dept Ciba-Geigy Corp Summit NJ 07901

ROBUSTO, C CARL, b Bridgeport, Conn, Nov 29, 16; m 44; c 2. MATHEMATICS, PHYSICS. *Educ:* St John's Univ, NY, BS, 39; Columbia Univ, MA, 46; NY Univ, MS, 50; Fordham Univ, PhD, 54. *Prof Exp:* Assoc prof, 46-56, acad vpres, Queens, 78-80, PROF MATH & PHYSICS, ST JOHN'S UNIV, NY, 56-, EXEC VPRES, 80- *Concurrent Pos:* Dean jr col, St John's Univ, 62-67, dean gen studies, 68-71; acad vpres, Staten Island & dean, Notre Dame Col, 71-78. *Mailing Add:* St John's Univ Jamaica NY 11439

ROBYT, JOHN F, b Moline, Ill, Feb 17, 35; m 58; c 2. BIOCHEMISTRY. *Educ:* St Louis Univ, BS, 58; Iowa State Univ, PhD(biochem), 62. *Prof Exp:* Asst prof biochem, La State Univ, 62-63; NIH fel, Lister Inst Prev Med, London, Eng, 63-64; res assoc, 64-67, asst prof, 67-73, ASSOC PROF BIOCHEM, IOWA STATE UNIV, 73- *Concurrent Pos:* Consult, E I du Pont de Nemours & Co, 70- *Mem:* Am Soc Biol Chemists; Am Chem Soc. *Res:* Study of the mechanisms of carbohydrase action, the mode of substrate binding, the sequence of catalytic events, the types of groups involved, especially with the polysaccharide synthesizing and degrading enzymes. *Mailing Add:* Dept of Biochem Iowa State Univ Ames IA 50010

ROCCO, GREGORY GABRIEL, b Lawrence, Mass, Sept 16, 26; m 50; c 3. RADIOCHEMISTRY. *Educ:* Boston Univ, BA, 49; Univ Mich, MS, 50. *Prof Exp:* Radiochemist, Tracerlab, Inc, 49-63; staff chemist, Wentworth Inst, 63-66; mgr radiochem, 66-72, MGR NUCLIDES & SOURCES DIV, NEW ENG NUCLEAR CORP, NORTH BILLERICA, MASS, 72- *Res:* Development of radiochemical procedures for the separation and decontamination of reactor and cyclotron produced isotopes; development of the use of isotopes for medicine, industry and research. *Mailing Add:* 22 Harding Rd Wakefield MA 01880

ROCEK, JAN, b Prague, Czech, Mar 24, 24; US citizen; m 47; c 2. PHYSICAL ORGANIC CHEMISTRY. *Educ:* Prague Tech Univ, ChemE, 49, PhD(chem), 53. *Prof Exp:* Chemist, Inst Chem, Czech Acad Sci, Prague, 53-60; res fel chem, Harvard Univ, 60-66; from assoc prof to prof chem, Cath Univ, 62-66; dean grad sch, 70-79, actg head dept, 80-81, PROF CHEM, UNIV ILL, CHICAGO, 66-, HEAD DEPT, 81- *Concurrent Pos:* Act dean grad sch, Univ Ill, 69-70; vis scholar, Stanford Univ & Univ Cambridge, Eng, 79-80. *Mem:* AAAS; Am Chem Soc; Royal Soc Chem; Sigma Xi. *Res:* Mechanisms of oxidation reactions; acidity functions; acid catalyzed reactions; reactivities in small and medium-sized ring compounds. *Mailing Add:* Box 4348 Dept Chem Univ Ill Chicago IL 60680

ROCHBERG, RICHARD HOWARD, b Baltimore, Md, May 15, 43; m 68; c 2. MATHEMATICS. *Educ:* Princeton Univ, AB, 64; Harvard Univ, MA, 66, PhD(math), 70. *Prof Exp:* Res assoc, Inst for Future, 69-70; from asst prof to assoc prof, 70-81, PROF MATH, WASHINGTON UNIV, 81- *Concurrent Pos:* Sr vis fel, Univ Col, London, 78-79. *Mem:* Am Math Soc. *Res:* Function theory, spaces of analytic functions. *Mailing Add:* Dept of Math Washington Univ St Louis MO 63130

ROCHE, ALEXANDER F, b Melbourne, Australia, Oct 17, 21; m 45; c 3. CHILD GROWTH, ANTHROPOMETRICS. *Educ:* Univ Melbourne, MB, BS, 46, PhD(anat), 54, DSc(child growth), 66, MD, 69; FRACP, 80. *Prof Exp:* Intern med, St Vincent's Hosp, Melbourne, 46-48, asst to outpatients surgeon, 48-50; lectr anat, Univ Melbourne, 50-52, sr lectr, 52-62, reader,

62-68; chmn dept growth genetics, 68-71, chief sect phys growth & genetics, Sect Fels Longitudinal Study & Families, Sect Measurement Growth & Maturity, Fels Res Inst, Ohio, 71-77; PROF PEDIAT, OBSTET & GYNEC, WRIGHT STATE UNIV, 77- *Concurrent Pos:* Demonstr, Univ Melbourne, 48-50; Smith-Mundt & Fulbright fels, 52-53; teaching fel, Western Reserve Univ, 52-53; Rockefeller traveling grant, 52-; consult, Royal Children's Hosp, Melbourne, 67-68, Barney Children's Hosp, Dayton, Ohio, 69-, Hamilton County Diag Clin Ment Retarded, 69-, Univ Cincinnati Affil Prog Ment Retarded, 69-, US Air Force, Pan-Am Health Orgn, WHO, Inst Nutrit Cent Am & Panama, Nat Health & Nutrit Exam Surv, 71- & Nat Pituitary Agency, 72-; vis prof, Ohio State Univ, 76, Univ Md, 78; mem, Pediat Adv Sub-comt, Food & Drug Admin, 78; fels prof pediat, fels prof obstet & gynecol, Wright State Univ Sch Med; consult, Health Exam Surv, Dept HEW, 71; pres, Human Biol Coun; assoc ed, Am Journal Phys Anthrop. *Mem:* Am Asn Phys Anthrop; Soc Res Child Develop; Brit Soc Study Human Biol; Anat Soc Gt Brit & Ireland; fel Human Biol Coun. *Mailing Add:* Fels Res Inst Yellow Springs OH 45387

ROCHE, BEN F, JR, b Winona, Miss, Feb 2, 24; m 50; c 2. RANGE MANAGEMENT. *Educ:* Univ Calif, Davis BS, 51; Wash State Univ, MS, 60; Univ Idaho, PhD(range ecol), 65. *Prof Exp:* County exten agent land develop, 51-54, veg mgt, 54-57, weed specialist, 58-65, asst prof range ecol, 65-66, assoc prof, 66-71, PROF RANGE ECOL, WASH STATE UNIV, 71- *Concurrent Pos:* Coordr res, Colockum Multiple Use Res Ctr, 66- *Mem:* Weed Sci Soc Am; Soc Range Mgt. *Res:* Ecology of secondary succession as created by man's disorder of the primary, particularly the exotic species that seem preadapted to the site. *Mailing Add:* Dept Forestry 311 Johnson Hall Wash State Univ Pullman WA 99163

ROCHE, EDWARD BROWINING, b Stamford, Conn, Apr 29, 38; c 2. MEDICINAL CHEMISTRY, CHEMICAL PHARMACOLOGY. *Educ:* Butler Univ, BS, 61, MS, 63; Ohio State Univ, PhD(med chem), 66. *Prof Exp:* Asst prof, 66-71, ASSOC PROF BIOMED CHEM, COL PHARM, UNIV NEBR MED CTR, OMAHA, 71-, ASST DEAN, 80- *Mem:* AAAS; Am Pharmaceut Asn; Acad Pharmaceut Sci; Am Chem Soc. *Res:* Design of compounds for analgesic drug-receptor interaction studies; synthetic organic medicinal chemistry; the application of physical organic chemistry to the study of mechanism of biological activity. *Mailing Add:* Col of Pharm Univ of Nebr Med Ctr Omaha NE 68105

ROCHE, EDWARD TOWNE, b Buenos Aires, Arg, Mar 8, 25; nat US; m 52; c 3. INVERTEBRATE ZOOLOGY. *Educ:* San Diego State Col, AB, 48; Univ Southern Calif, MS, 52, PhD(zool), 57. *Prof Exp:* Asst & assoc, Univ Southern Calif, 53-57; instr life sci, Compton Jr Col, 57-59; from asst prof to assoc prof, 59-69, PROF BIOL SCI, CALIF STATE POLYTECH UNIV, 69- *Res:* Histology; parasitology; biological education; venomous fishes. *Mailing Add:* Dept of Biol Sci Calif State Polytech Univ Pomona CA 91766

ROCHE, GEORGE WILLIAM, b San Francisco, Calif, May 27, 21; m 54; c 2. FORENSIC SCIENCE. *Educ:* Univ Calif, Berkeley, AB, 42; Univ Minn, Minneapolis, MS, 52. *Prof Exp:* Crime lab analyst, Bur Criminal Apprehension, State Minn, 46-54, lab dir, 54-62; criminalist, Dept Justice, State Calif, 62-64, supvy criminalist, 64-69; assoc prof, 69-71, PROF DEPT CRIMINAL JUSTICE, CALIF STATE UNIV, SACRAMENTO, 71- *Mem:* Am Acad Forensic Sci; Am Chem Soc; Soc Appl Spectros; Am Soc Criminol; Inst Asn Identification. *Res:* Recognition, individualization and evaluation of physical evidence by application of the natural sciences to law-science matters. *Mailing Add:* 7233 Milford St Sacramento CA 95822

ROCHE, JAMES NORMAN, b Ithaca, NY, Oct 14, 98; m 37; c 1. CHEMISTRY. *Educ:* Univ Pittsburgh, BS, 24, PhD(chem), 27. *Prof Exp:* Asst, Univ Pittsburgh, 24-27, instr, 27-30; res chemist, Am Tar Prod Co, Pa, 30-44, mgr, Tech Sect, Tar Prod Div, Koppers Co, Inc, 44-49, mgr creosote & pitch sales, 49-52, mgr sales develop, 53-63, tech sales consult, 63-75; RETIRED. *Concurrent Pos:* Dir, Am Wood Preservers Inst, 50-63. *Honors & Awards:* Award Merit, Am Wood Preservers Asn, 72. *Mem:* Emer mem Am Chem Soc; Forest Prod Res Soc; hon mem Am Wood Preservers Asn; Am Chem Soc. *Res:* Glycerides; disinfectants; coal tar chemicals; creosote; pitches. *Mailing Add:* 1554 Fox Chapel Rd Pittsburgh PA 15238

ROCHE, LIDIA ALICIA, b Havana, Cuba, May 9, 39; m 61; c 3. NUCLEAR WASTE DISPOSAL, HEATH PHYSICS. *Educ:* The Am Univ, BS, 69, PhD(phys chem), 75. *Prof Exp:* Res technician biomed, Georgetown Univ, 63-69; chemist, Gellette Res Inst, 70-72, res chemist, 75-78; RES ANALYST, US NUCLEAR REGULATORY COMN, 78- *Mem:* Am Chem Soc. *Res:* Medical uses of radio isotopes; fuel production through waste management and disposal. *Mailing Add:* 623 Wardield Dr Rockville MD 20850

ROCHE, MARCEL, b Caracas, Venezuela, Aug 15, 20; m 47, 72; c 4. ENDOCRINOLOGY, PARASITOLOGY. *Educ:* St Joseph's Col, Pa, BS, 42; Johns Hopkins Univ, MD, 46. *Hon Degrees:* DSc, Case Western Reserve Univ, 63 & Univ of the Andes, Venezuela, 71. *Prof Exp:* Intern med, Osler Serv, Johns Hopkins Hosp, Baltimore, Md, 46-47; asst resident, Peter Bent Brigham Hosp, Boston, Mass, 47-48; res fel, Harvard Med Sch, 48-50; asst biochem, NY Pub Health Res Inst, 50-51; asst prof med, Cent Univ Venezuela, 51-53; dir, Inst Med Invests, 53-58; INVESTR, INST SCI INVEST, 58- *Concurrent Pos:* Vpres, Inter-Am Comn Atomic Energy, 59; mem, Coun Higher Educ in Am Repub, 62-65, co-pres, 65-69; sci attache Venezuelan deleg, UNESCO, 63-64; mem adv comt med res, Pan Am Health Orgn, 63-66 & WHO, 66; mem, Acad du Monde Latin, 67; pres, Nat Coun Sci & Technol Res, 69-72; mem, Coun UN Univ, 74-80; mem bd trustees, Int Found Sci, Stockholm, 75; mem coun, Pugwash Confs, 76; pres coun, UN Univ, Tokyo, 78. *Mem:* Venezuelan Asn Advan Sci (secy gen, 58); cor mem Venezuelan Nat Acad Med; cor mem Venezuelan Acad Phys, Math & Natural Sci; Pontif Acad Sci; Brazilian Acad Sci. *Res:* Thyroid physiology in endemic goiter; physiology and biochemistry of hookworm; isotopic tracers; history and sociology of science; sociology of science. *Mailing Add:* Apartado 1827 Caracas Venezuela

ROCHE, RODNEY SYLVESTER, b Oxford, Eng, July 9, 36; m 57; c 3. BIOPHYSICAL CHEMISTRY, POLYMER CHEMISTRY. *Educ:* Univ Glasgow, BSc, 57, PhD(polymer chem), 65. *Prof Exp:* Sci officer, Chem Div, UK Atomic Energy Authority Exp Reactor Estab, Scotland, 57-61; asst lectr chem, Univ Glasgow, 62-65; from asst prof to assoc prof, 65-78, PROF CHEM, UNIV CALGARY, 78- *Concurrent Pos:* Vis scientist, Weizmann Inst Sci, 71-72. *Mem:* AAAS; Am Chem Soc; The Chem Soc; fel Royal Inst Chem; fel Chem Inst Can. *Res:* Physical chemistry of macromolecules; conformational studies of polypeptides and proteins; calcium binding proteins; calmodulin. *Mailing Add:* Dept of Chem Univ of Calgary Calgary AB T2N 1N4 Can

ROCHE, THOMAS EDWARD, b Denver, Colo, Feb 17, 44; m 66; c 2. BIOCHEMISTRY. *Educ:* Regis Col, Colo, BS, 66; Wash State Univ, PhD(chem), 70. *Prof Exp:* NIH res fel, Clayton Found Biochem Inst, Univ Tex, Austin, 70-72, res assoc, 72-74; asst prof, 74-78, ASSOC PROF BIOCHEM, KANS STATE UNIV, 78- *Mem:* Am Chem Soc; Fedn Am Socs Exp Biol; AAAS. *Res:* Structure and function of 2-ketoacid dehydrogenase complexes; regulation of mammalian pyruvate dehydrogenase complex by enzymatic interconversion; cellular organization. *Mailing Add:* Dept of Biochem Willard Hall Kans State Univ Manhattan KS 66506

ROCHE, THOMAS STEPHEN, b New York, NY, Apr 9, 46; m 70; c 1. INORGANIC CHEMISTRY, PHYSICAL CHEMISTRY. *Educ:* Manhattan Col, BS, 67; State Univ NY, Buffalo, PhD(inorganic chem), 72. *Prof Exp:* Res assoc inorganic chem, Wayne State Univ, 72-73; res assoc organometallic chem, Univ Chicago, 73-75; res chemist, Pullman Kellogg Res & Develop Lab, 75-80; RES ASSOC, OLIN CHEM, 80- *Mem:* Am Chem Soc; Sigma Xi. *Res:* Inorganic and organometallic chemistry; reaction mechanisms; catalysis; new process research. *Mailing Add:* Pullman Kellogg Res & Develop Ctr 16200 Park Row Houston TX 77084

ROCHEFORT, JOHN S, b Boston, Mass, June 15, 24; m 52; c 5. ELECTRICAL ENGINEERING. *Educ:* Northeastern Univ, BS, 48; Mass Inst Technol, SM, 51. *Prof Exp:* Asst, Servomech Lab, Mass Inst Technol, 48-49, staff engr, 49; res assoc elec eng, 49-52, asst prof commun, 52-54, assoc prof, 54-62, acting chmn dept elec eng, 72-73, PROF ELEC ENG, NORTHEASTERN UNIV, 62-, CHMN DEPT, 77- *Concurrent Pos:* Vis prof elec eng, Univ Alaska, 74-75. *Mem:* Am Soc Eng Educ; sr mem Inst Elec & Electronics Engrs. *Res:* Analysis and instrumentation in information theory, networks and radio telemetry. *Mailing Add:* Dept of Elec Eng 360 Huntington Ave Boston MA 02115

ROCHEFORT, JOSEPH GUY, b Astroville, Ont, July 5, 29; m 54; c 2. BIOCHEMISTRY, ENDOCRINOLOGY. *Educ:* Laurentian Univ, BA, 51; McGill Univ, BSc, 54, MSc, 56, PhD(biochem), 58. *Prof Exp:* Biochemist, Regional Labs, Dept Health & Welfare, NB, 54-55; Nat Mutiple Sclerosis Soc fel, 58-60; sr scientist, Dept Pharmacol, 60-65 & Dept Biochem, 66-69, asst dir, Dept Clin Pharmacol, 69-77, DIR DEPT CLIN PHARMACOL, AYERST LABS, 77- *Concurrent Pos:* Lectr, Concordia Univ, 64- *Mem:* Endocrine Soc; Can Physiol Soc; Can Fertil Soc; Am Fertil Soc; Can Soc Clin Invest. *Res:* Anterior pituitary-adrenocorticotrophic hormone distribution and release; adrenal responses to stress; bioassay of synthetic and natural steroid hormones; adrenal steriodogenesis; biochemistry of inflammation; bioavailability; pharmacokinetics; clinical investigation of new drugs. *Mailing Add:* Dept of Clin PHarmacol Ayerst Labs PO Box 6115 Montreal PQ H3G 1Y6 Can

ROCHELLE, ROBERT W(HITE), b Nashville, Tenn, June 23, 23; m 49; c 4. ELECTRICAL ENGINEERING. *Educ:* Univ Tenn, BS, 47; Yale Univ, ME, 49; Univ Md, PhD(elec eng), 63. *Prof Exp:* Electronic scientist, US Naval Res Lab, 49-55, head magnetic amplifier sect, 55-58; br head flight data systs br, Goddard Space Flight Ctr, NASA, 58-71, assoc chief commun & navig div, 71-73; PROF ELEC ENG, UNIV TENN, 73- *Concurrent Pos:* Lectr, Univ Md, 57-59. *Honors & Awards:* Medaille du CNES, France, 65. *Mem:* AAAS; fel Inst Elec & Electronics Engrs; Am Soc Eng Educ; Sigma Xi. *Res:* Application of microcomputers in space and industrial instrumentation. *Mailing Add:* 4042 Kingston Pike SW Knoxville TN 37919

ROCHESTER, EUGENE WALLACE, b Greenville, SC, July 15, 43; m 68; c 2. AGRICULTURAL ENGINEERING. *Educ:* Clemson Univ, BS, 65; NC State Univ, MS, 68, PhD(biol & agr eng), 70. *Prof Exp:* ASST & ASSOC PROF AGR ENG, AUBURN UNIV, 70- *Concurrent Pos:* Consult, Irrig Syst Design, 78-; William Howard Smith fac fel award, Sch Agr & Agr Exp Sta, Auburn Univ, 76. *Mem:* Am Soc Agr Engrs; Irrig Asn. *Res:* Field crop irrigation, especially machinery types, energy requirements and systems for irregular fields. *Mailing Add:* Dept of Agr Eng Auburn Univ Auburn AL 36830

ROCHESTER, MICHAEL GRANT, b Toronto, Ont, Nov 22, 32; m 58; c 3. GEOPHYSICS, ASTRONOMY. *Educ:* Univ Toronto, BA, 54, MA, 56; Univ Utah, PhD(physics), 59. *Prof Exp:* Lectr physics, Univ Toronto, 59-60, asst prof, 60-61; from asst prof to assoc prof, Univ Waterloo, 61-67; assoc prof, 67-70, PROF PHYSICS, MEM UNIV NFLD, 70- *Concurrent Pos:* Mem, Working Group Physical Processes in Earth's Interior, Int Geodynamics Proj, 71-, Comn Rotation of Earth, Int Astron Union, 73- & Can Subcomt Geodynamics, 74-79; vis prof, York Univ, 74-75 & Univ Queensland, 77. *Mem:* AAAS; Am Geophys Union; Can Asn Physicists; Royal Astron Soc; Can Geophys Union. *Res:* Rotation of the earth; earth tides; dynamics of the earth's core; geomagnetism; planetary physics. *Mailing Add:* Dept Physics Mem Univ Nfld St John's NF A1B 3X7 Can

ROCHLIN, PHILLIP, b New York, NY, Mar 24, 23; m 54; c 2. CHEMISTRY, INFORMATION SCIENCE & RETRIEVAL. *Educ:* City Col New York, BS, 43; NY Univ, MS, 49; Rutgers Univ, MLS, 60. *Prof Exp:* Anal chemist, var cos, 43-49; res chemist, Picatinny Arsenal, NJ, 50-63; sci analyst, Nat Referral Ctr Sci & Technol, Libr Cong, DC, 63; supvry chemist & mgr tech libr, Naval Propellant Plant, Indian Head, 63-68; chief accessions

& indexing br, Nat Hwy Safety Inst Doc Ctr, 68-69; supvry chemist & dir tech info div, 69-79, CHEMIST & TECH INFO SPECIALIST, ENVIRON & ENERGY OFF, NAVAL ORD STA, INDIAN HEAD, 79- *Concurrent Pos:* Instr library Sci, Charles County Community Col, 73- *Mem:* Am Chem Soc; Spec Libr Asn; Am Inst Aeronaut & Astronaut. *Res:* Explosives and propellants; information storage and retrieval; missiles and rockets. *Mailing Add:* Environ & Energy Off Naval Ord Sta Indian Head MD 20640

ROCHLIN, ROBERT SUMNER, b Yonkers, NY, June 25, 22; m 50; c 2. NUCLEAR PHYSICS, ARMS CONTROL. *Educ:* Cornell Univ, BEE, 44, PhD(physics), 52. *Prof Exp:* Radio engr, US Naval Res Lab, 44-45; physicist, Gen Elec Co, 51-63; with US Arms Control & Disarmament Agency, 63-77, DEP ASST DIR, US ARMS CONTROL & DISARMAMENT AGENCY, 77- *Concurrent Pos:* Mem US del, US-Soviet Strategic Arms Limitation Talks, Vienna, Austria, 70 & Nuclear Fuel Cycle Eval, 78-80. *Res:* Arms control; negotiations, research and policy formulation. *Mailing Add:* US Arms Control & Disarm Agency Washington DC 20451

RO-CHOI, TAE SUK, b Seoul, Korea, May 8, 37; m 67; c 2. BIOCHEMISTRY, PHARMACOLOGY. *Educ:* Soo Do Med Col, Korea, MD, 62; Baylor Col Med, MS, 64, PhD(pharmacol), 68. *Prof Exp:* Teaching asst, 62-67, from instr to asst prof, 67-72, RES ASSOC PROF PHARMACOL, BAYLOR COL MED, 72- *Mem:* AAAS; Am Soc Biol Chemists; Am Soc Pharmacol & Exp Therapeut; Am Asn Cancer Res. *Res:* Nuclear RNA of cancer and normal cells; primary sequence of nuclear low molecular weight RNA; nuclear and nucleolar RNA transcription and control mechanism of gene expression; ribonucleoprotein complex and their functions. *Mailing Add:* Dept of Pharmacol Baylor Col of Med Houston TX 77025

ROCHOVANSKY, OLGA MARIA, b New York, NY. BIOCHEMISTRY, VIROLOGY. *Educ:* Queens Col, BS, 50; NY Univ, PhD(biochem), 60. *Prof Exp:* From asst to assoc biochem, Pub Health Res Inst New York, Inc, 60-71, assoc virol, 71-75, assoc mem virol, 75-77; MEM, CHRIST HOSP INST MED RES, 77- *Concurrent Pos:* Fel, Univ Calif, Berkeley, 61-62; Nat Inst Allergy & Infectious Dis grant, 79. *Mem:* Am Soc Microbiol; AAAS; Am Soc Biol Chemists; Harvey Soc. *Res:* Studies on influenza viral RNA and protein synthesis in vitro. *Mailing Add:* Christ Hosp Inst of Med Res 2141 Auburn Ave Cincinnati OH 45219

ROCHOW, EUGENE GEORGE, b Newark, NJ, Oct 4, 09; m 52; c 3. CHEMISTRY. *Educ:* Cornell Univ, BChem, 31, PhD(chem), 35. *Hon Degrees:* MA, Harvard Univ, 48; Dr rer nat, Brunswick Tech Univ, 66. *Prof Exp:* Res chemist, Halowax Corp, NJ, 31-32; asst chem, Cornell Univ, 33-35; chemist, Res Lab, Gen Elec Co, 35-48; from assoc prof to prof, 48-70, EMER PROF INORG CHEM, HARVARD UNIV, 70- *Concurrent Pos:* Mem, Nat Res Coun, 48. *Honors & Awards:* Baekeland Medal, 49; Matiello Award, 58; Perkin Medal, 62; Kipping Award, 65; Norris Award, Am Chem Soc, 74. *Mem:* AAAS; Am Chem Soc; Am Inst Chemists; French Soc Indust Chemists; Int Acad Law & Sci. *Res:* Organosilicon chemistry and silicones; inorganic chemistry. *Mailing Add:* Dept of Chem Harvard Univ Cambridge MA 02138

ROCHOW, WILLIAM FRANTZ, b Lancaster, Pa, Mar 12, 27; m 53; c 2. PLANT PATHOLOGY. *Educ:* Franklin & Marshall Col, BS, 50; Cornell Univ, PhD(plant path), 54. *Prof Exp:* Asst plant path, Cornell Univ, 50-54; from asst prof to assoc prof, 55-63, PROF PLANT PATH, CORNELL UNIV, 63-; PLANT PATHOLOGIST, USDA, 55- *Concurrent Pos:* Nat Found fel, Univ Calif, 54-55. *Honors & Awards:* Superior Serv Award, USDA, 66. *Mem:* AAAS; fel Am Phytopath Soc. *Res:* Plant virology, especially virus-vector relationships. *Mailing Add:* Dept Plant Path Cornell Univ Ithaca NY 14853

ROCK, BARRETT NELSON, b Warren, Ohio, Sept 8, 42; m 67; c 2. PLANT ANATOMY. *Educ:* Univ Vt, BA, 66; Univ Md, MS, 70, PhD(bot), 72. *Prof Exp:* Asst prof, 72-78, ASSOC PROF BIOL, ALFRED UNIV, 78- *Concurrent Pos:* Field Botanist, Columbia Gas Corp, Ohio, 78-; sabbatical leave, Dept Bot, Univ Calif, Davis, 80. *Mem:* Bot Soc Am; Int Asn Wood Anatomists. *Res:* Anatomical study of vegetative plant tissue, including wood, leaves, and stem tips; megaphytic members of the Asteraceae (compositae); remote sensed vegetation data. *Mailing Add:* Dept Biol Alfred Univ Alfred NY 14802

ROCK, CHET A, b Vancouver, Wash, Dec 8, 44; m 77; c 2. WATER POLLUTION, WATER QUALITY. *Educ:* Wash State Univ, BS, 68; Stanford Univ, MS, 71; Univ Wash, PhD(environ eng), 74. *Prof Exp:* Sanitary eng, Environ Sanitation Prog, US Pub Health Serv, 68-70; res assoc, Dept Civil Eng, Univ Wash, Seattle, 71-74; sanitary eng, Lake Restoration Sect, Water Quality Div, Dept Ecol, State Wash, 74-76 & Indust Waste Div, 76-79; ASST PROF ENVIRON ENG, DEPT CIVIL ENG, UNIV MAINE, 79- *Concurrent Pos:* Co-prin investr, US Environ Protection Agency & Off Water Res & Technol, US Dept Interior, 80-82. *Mem:* Am Soc Civil Engrs; Water Pollution Control Fedn; Asn Environ Eng Prof; Am Soc Limnol & Oceanog. *Res:* Onsite wastewater treatment; treatment of industrial wastes; ecological effects of wastewater; restoration of eutrophic lakes. *Mailing Add:* Dept Civil Eng Univ Maine 457 Aubert Hall Orono ME 04469

ROCK, ELIZABETH JANE, b Plattsburgh, NY, Dec 14, 24. PHYSICAL CHEMISTRY. *Educ:* Col Mt St Vincent, BS, 46; Smith Col, MA, 48; Pa State Col, PhD(chem), 51. *Prof Exp:* Asst, Cryogenic Lab, Pa State Col, 48-51, res assoc, Solid State Lab, 51-52; instr chem, Vassar Col, 52-55; from assoc prof to prof textiles, Univ Tenn, 55-59; lectr, 59-61, from assoc prof to prof, 61-70, chmn dept, 67-70, dir sci ctr, 73-75 & 76-78, ARTHUR J & NELLIE Z COHEN PROF CHEM, WELLESLEY COL, 70- *Concurrent Pos:* Textile chemist, Exp Sta, Univ Tenn, 55-59; NSF sci fac fel thermochem, Oxford Univ, 66-67; extramural assoc, NIH, 79; vis res prof, Tufts Univ, 81-82. *Mem:* Am Chem Soc. *Res:* Physical chemistry of conservation of stone in monuments; infrared laser induced reactions. *Mailing Add:* Dept of Chem Wellesley Col Wellesley MA 02181

ROCK, GEORGE CALVERT, b Roanoke, Va, May 26, 34; m 70. ENTOMOLOGY. *Educ:* Bob Jones Univ, BS, 57; Va Polytech Inst & State Univ, MS, 60; Cornell Univ, PhD(entom), 63. *Prof Exp:* Asst prof entom, Va Poltech Inst & State Univ, 64-67; from asst prof to assoc prof, 67-76, PROF ENTOM, NC STATE UNIV, 76- *Mem:* Entom Soc Am. *Res:* Nurtitional requirements of insects; pest population management in apple orchards; insect resistance to insecticides. *Mailing Add:* Dept of Entom NC State Univ Raleigh NC 27607

ROCK, MICHAEL KEITH, b Milwaukee, Wis, Aug 26, 51; m 78. NEUROSCIENCE. *Educ:* Univ Dallas, BA, 73; Univ Tex Med Br, Galveston, PhD(physiol), 77. *Prof Exp:* Res assoc neurophysiol, Sch Med, Washington Univ, 77-79 & Univ Va, 79-80; assoc mem neurophysiol, Marine Biomet Inst, 80-81; ASST PROF, SCH ALLIED HEALTH SCI, UNIV TEX MED BR GALVESTON, 81- *Mem:* Soc Neurosci. *Res:* Neurophysiology of simple nervous systems. *Mailing Add:* Sch Allied Health Sci Univ Tex Med Br Galveston TX 77550

ROCK, PETER ALFRED, b New Haven, Conn, Sept 29, 39; m 59; c 3. ELECTROCHEMISTRY. *Educ:* Boston Univ, AB, 61; Univ Calif, Berkeley, PhD(chem), 64. *Prof Exp:* From asst prof to assoc prof, 64-75, PROF CHEM, UNIV CALIF, DAVIS, 75-, CHMN DEPT, 80- *Concurrent Pos:* Nat Inst Neurol Dis & Stroke fel, Ind Univ, 70-71; consult, Dorland Med Dictionaries. *Mem:* Electrochem Soc; Am Chem Soc. *Res:* Electrochemical thermodynamics and kinetics; isotope effects; oscillatory phenomena; energy utilization and conversion. *Mailing Add:* Dept of Chem Univ of Calif Davis CA 95616

ROCKAFELLAR, RALPH TYRRELL, b Milwaukee, Wis, Feb 10, 35; m 65; c 1. MATHEMATICS. *Educ:* Harvard Univ, AB, 57, PhD(math), 63. *Prof Exp:* Teaching fel math, Harvard Univ, 60-62; mem res staff, Mass Inst Technol, 62-63; asst prof, Univ Tex, 63-65; vis asst prof, Princeton Univ, 65-66; from asst prof to assoc prof, 66-73, PROF MATH & ADJ PROF COMPUT SCI, UNIV WASH, 73- *Concurrent Pos:* Univ Tex res grant, Math Inst, Copenhagen, 64; Air Force Off Sci Res grants, Princeton Univ, 66 & Univ Wash, 66-68. *Mem:* Am Math Soc. *Res:* Convex sets and functions; linear programming; functional analysis. *Mailing Add:* Dept of Math Univ of Wash Seattle WA 98105

ROCKAWAY, JOHN D, b Cincinnati, Ohio, Mar 7, 38; m 61; c 4. GEOLOGICAL ENGINEERING. *Educ:* Colo Sch Mines, GeolE, 61; Purdue Univ, MSE, 63, PhD(civil eng), 68. *Prof Exp:* From asst to assoc prof, 68-76, PROF GEOL ENG, UNIV MO-ROLLA, 76-, CHMN DEPT, 81- *Mem:* Asn Eng Geol; Am Inst Mining, Metall & Petrol Engrs; Int Asn Eng Geol. *Res:* Development of techniques for mapping geological factors influencing urban growth; geotechnical evaluations of coal mine stability; microseismic zonation and response of surficial materials to earthquakes. *Mailing Add:* Dept Geol Eng Univ Mo Rolla MO 65401

ROCKCASTLE, VERNE NORTON, b Rochester, NY, Jan 1, 20; m 43; c 2. ECOLOGY. *Educ:* Syracuse Univ, AB, 42; Mass Inst Technol, SM, 44; Cornell Univ, PhD, 55. *Prof Exp:* Instr meteorol, Mass Inst Technol, 43-44; from asst prof biol to assoc prof biol, State Univ NY, Brockport, 47-56; assoc prof, 56-59, PROF SCI & ENVIRON EDUC, CORNELL UNIV, 59- *Mem:* Am Nature Study Soc (pres, 65); fel AAAS. *Res:* Elementary science education; concept development in science. *Mailing Add:* Div of Sci & Environ Educ Cornell Univ 18 Stone Hall Ithaca NY 14853

ROCKE, DAVID M, b Chicago, Ill, June 4, 46; m 71; c 1. MATHEMATICS. *Educ:* Shimer Col, AB, 66; Univ Ill, Chicago Circle, MA, 68, PhD(math), 72. *Prof Exp:* Vis lectr math, Univ Ill, Chicago Circle, 72-74; univ prof bus admin, Col Bus & Pub Serv, Goveners State Univ, 74-80; ASSOC PROF, GRAD SCH ADMIN, UNIV CALIF, DAVIS, 80- *Mem:* Math Asn Am; Am Math Soc; Am Statist Asn; AAAS; Inst Math Statist. *Res:* Finite p-groups; actuarial mathematics and statistical life testing; mathematical sociology. *Mailing Add:* Grad Sch Admin Univ Calif Davis CA 95616

ROCKETT, JOHN A, b Philadelphia, Pa, Aug 6, 22; m 56; c 2. FLUID MECHANICS. *Educ:* Mass Inst Technol, BS, 44; Brown Univ, MS, 51; Harvard Univ, PhD(appl physics), 57. *Prof Exp:* Res engr, Nat Adv Comt Aeronaut, 47-49; res engr, Dept Aeronaut, Mass Inst Technol, 50-53; res engr, United Aircraft Corp res proj, Harvard Univ, 53-57; chief fuel cell technol, United Aircraft Corp, 57-65; dir basic res, Factory Mutual Eng Corp, Mass, 65-68; spec asst to dir, Inst Appl Technol, 68, chief, Off Fire Res & Safety, 68-72, chief fire physics res, 73-80, SR SCIENTIST, OFF FIRE RES & SAFETY, NAT BUR STANDARDS, 81- *Concurrent Pos:* Vis prof, Tokyo Sci Univ, 82. *Honors & Awards:* Silver Medal, Dept Commerce, 77. *Mem:* Fire Protection Engrs. *Res:* Internal and external aerodynamics; hydrodynamics; combustion and flames; solid state physics; electrochemistry; mass-heat transfer. *Mailing Add:* Off Fire Res & Safety Nat Bur Standards Washington DC 20234

ROCKETT, THOMAS JOHN, b Medford, Mass, June 4, 31; m 64; c 1. MINERALOGY, CERAMICS. *Educ:* Tufts Univ, BS, 56; Boston Col, MS, 58; Ohio State Univ, PhD(mineral), 63. *Prof Exp:* Res mineralogist, Ohio State Univ, 59-61; res ceramist, Wright-Patterson AFB, 61-65; sr res ceramist, Monsanto Res Co, Mass, 65-67; scientist, New Enterprises Div, Monsanto Corp, 67-72; ASSOC PROF MAT & CHEM ENG, UNIV RI, 72- *Concurrent Pos:* NSF fel, 63; lectr, Univ Dayton, 63-65 & Boston Col, 65- *Mem:* Mineral Soc Am; Am Ceramic Soc; Am Chem Soc. *Res:* High temperature phase equilibria; oxide and silicate systems; silica reactions; glass systems and phase separation in glasses; ceramic composites; dental cement chemistry; oxide fiber; whisker formation; glass-metal seals. *Mailing Add:* Dept of Mat & Chem Eng Univ of RI Kingston RI 02881

ROCKETTE, HOWARD EARL, JR, b Baltimore, Md, Feb 6, 44; m 68; c 3. BIOSTATISTICS. *Educ:* Franklin & Marshall Col, BA, 65; Pa State Univ, MA & PhD(statist), 72. *Prof Exp:* Res asst, Ballistics Anal Lab, Johns Hopkins Univ, 65-66; asst math statist, Pa State Univ, 66-72; asst res prof, 72-78, ASSOC PROF BIOSTATIST, UNIV PITTSBURGH, 78- *Mem:* Am Statist Asn; Biomet Soc; Inst Math Statist; Am Pub Health Asn; Soc Occup & Environ Health. *Res:* Development of methodological techniques and the evaluation and collection of data in the fields of biology, medicine and health, particularly in the areas of clinical trial evluation and occupational health. *Mailing Add:* Dept Biostatist A320 Crabtree Hall Univ of Pittsburgh GSPH Pittsburgh PA 15261

ROCKEY, JOHN HENRY, b Madison, Wis, Feb 2, 31. OPHTHALMOLOGY, IMMUNOCHEMISTRY. *Educ:* Univ Wis, BS, 52, MD, 55; Univ Pa, PhD(molecular biol), 68. *Prof Exp:* Intern, Hosp Univ Pa, 55-56; asst resident path, Cornell Med Sch-New York Hosp, 58-59; res assoc & asst physician, Rockefeller Inst Hosp, 59-62; asst prof microbiol, 62-69, assoc med, 66-70, from asst prof to assoc prof ophthal, 69-73, PROF OPHTHAL, SCH MED, UNIV PA, 73- *Concurrent Pos:* Prin investr, USPHS-NIH grants, 62-75; mem grad group molecular biol, Univ Pa, 69-, mem grad group path, 71- & mem grad group immunol, 72-; mem sci staff med res coun molecular pharmacol unit, Med Sch, Cambridge Univ, 70; co-investr, NSF grant, 70-72. *Honors & Awards:* William J Bleckwenn Award, 55. *Mem:* Am Asn Immunol. *Res:* Reaginic antibodies; primary structural studies of visual pigments; multiple molecular forms of antibodies. *Mailing Add:* Dept of Ophthal Univ of Pa Sch of Med Philadelphia PA 19104

ROCKHILL, THERON D, b Malone, NY, Feb 9, 37; m 58; c 2. MATHEMATICS. *Educ:* Houghton Col, BA, 59; Syracuse Univ, MS, 62; State Univ NY Buffalo, EdD(math & educ), 69. *Prof Exp:* Teacher math, Newfield Cent Sch, 59-61; from asst prof to assoc prof, 62-72, PROF MATH, STATE UNIV COL BROCKPORT, 72-, CHMN DEPT, 77- *Concurrent Pos:* Res assoc, Ctr Res Col Instr Sci & Math, Fla State Univ, 71. *Mem:* Am Math Soc; Math Asn Am; Nat Coun Teachers Math; Soc Indust & Appl Math. *Res:* Numerical analysis and the use of computers in teaching mathematics. *Mailing Add:* Dept of Math State Univ of NY Col Brockport NY 14420

ROCKLAND, LOUIS B, b NY, July 14, 19; m 43; c 3. AGRICULTURAL CHEMISTRY, FOOD SCIENCE. *Educ:* Univ Calif, Los Angeles, BA, 40, MA, 47, PhD(phys & biol sci, chem), 48. - *Prof Exp:* Asst chem, Univ Calif, Los Angeles, 40-47, res assoc filter paper chromatog, 49-50; res chemist, Fruit & Veg Chem Lab, Western Utilization Res & Develop Div, Agr Res Serv, USDA, Calif, 49-70, res chemist, Western Regional Res Ctr, 70-80; PROF & CHMN, DEPT FOOD SCI & NUTRIT, CHAPMAN COL, 80- *Concurrent Pos:* Chmn, Second Int Symp Properties of Water, Osaka, Japan, 78. *Mem:* Fel AAAS; Am Chem Soc; fel Inst Food Technologists; Am Soc Biol Chemists; Am Asn Cereal Chemists. *Res:* Chemical, biological and physical properties of dry legume seeds; chemical properties of amino acids and proteins; methods for filter paper, thin layer and gas chromatography; citrus fruits and walnuts; lemon oil; moisture sorption; water activity-stability relationships in foods and natural products. *Mailing Add:* 45 Corliss Dr Moraga CA 94556

ROCKLIN, ALBERT LOUIS, b Toronto, Ont, May 28, 21; nat US; m 46; c 2. PHYSICAL CHEMISTRY, INDUSTRIAL CHEMISTRY. *Educ:* Univ Toronto, BA, 43, MA, 44, PhD(phys chem), 46. *Prof Exp:* Asst prof chem, exten, Purdue Univ, 46-47, univ, 47-50; res chemist, Western Div, Dow Chem Co, 51-58; chemist, 58-72, SR RES CHEMIST, SHELL DEVELOP CO, 72- *Honors & Awards:* Roon Found Awards Coatings Technol, 76, 78 & 80. *Mem:* Fel AAAS; fel Am Chem Soc; Fedn Socs Coatings Technol. *Res:* Applied solution theory relating to surface coatings, solubility, solvent evaporation from thin films, and solution viscosity; development of performance materials. *Mailing Add:* Shell Develop Co PO Box 1380 Houston TX 77001

ROCKLIN, ROY DAVID, b San Francisco, Calif, Aug 3, 53. ELECTROANALYTICAL CHEMISTRY, ION CHROMATOGRAPHY. *Educ:* Univ Calif, Santa Cruz, AB, 75; Univ NC, Chapel Hill, PhD(anal chem), 80. *Prof Exp:* RES CHEMIST, DIONEX CORP, 80- *Mem:* Am Chem Soc. *Res:* Electrochemical detectors for liquid chromatography; electroanalytical instrumentation; chemically modified electrodes. *Mailing Add:* 220-C Red Oak Dr W Sunnyvale CA 94086

ROCKMORE, RONALD MARSHALL, b New York, NY, Aug 10, 30; m 60; c 2. THEORETICAL MEDIUM ENERGY PHYSICS. *Educ:* Brooklyn Col, BS, 51; Columbia Univ, PhD(physics), 57. *Prof Exp:* Asst physics, Columbia Univ, 52-55; NSF fel, 57-58; res assoc, Brookhaven Nat Lab, 58-60; asst prof, Brandeis Univ, 60-63; assoc prof, 63-79, PROF PHYSICS, RUTGERS UNIV, 79- *Concurrent Pos:* Mem, Inst Advan Study, 57-58; vis lectr, Univ Minn, 58; consult, Repub Aviation Corp, 59-60, Rand Corp, 61-72 & Inst Defense Anal, 62-64; vis physicist, Brookhaven Nat Lab, 64 & 71; visitor, Neils Bohr Inst, Copenhagen, Denmark, 66 & Stanford Linear Accelerator Ctr, 67; vis staff mem, Los Alamos Sci Lab, 67 & 72-75, Argonne Nat Lab, 67 & Ctr Theoret Physics, Trieste, 68; vis mem staff, Theoret Physics Inst, Univ Alta, 72-80; vis theorist, SIN, Villigen, 78; Rutgers Univ fac fel, Imp Col, Univ London, 68-69; Rutgers foreign affairs & scholars prog fel, State Univ NY, Stony Brook, 78; vis theorist, Saclay, Gif-sur-Yvette, 79 & 81. *Mem:* Fel Am Phys Soc. *Res:* Field theory; pion physics; many-body problem; strong and weak interactions; medium-energy physics. *Mailing Add:* Dept of Physics Rutgers Univ Piscataway NJ 08854

ROCKOFF, MAXINE LIEBERMAN, b Gary, Ind, July 15, 38; m 56; c 3. MATHEMATICS. *Educ:* George Washington Univ, BS, 58; Univ Pa, MA, 60, PhD(math), 64. *Prof Exp:* Programmer, Univ Pa, 58-60, res fel physiol, 60-61; mathematician, Comput Lab, Nat Bur Standards, 61-64; res assoc, Comput Sci Ctr & Inst Fluid Dynamics, Univ Md, 64-65; res assoc epidemiol & pub health, Yale Univ, 65-68; asst prof, Appl Math, Comput & Biomed Comput Lab, Washington Univ, 68-71; health scientist adminr, Nat Ctr Health Serv Res 71-75, prog analyst, Off Planning, Eval & Legis, 75-76, health scientist adminr, Nat Ctr Health Serv Res, 76-78, prog analyst, Off Planning & Eval, Dept Energy, 78-79; vpres planning & res, Corp Pub Broadcasting, 79-80; MGR MKT TECHNOL, MERRILL LYNCH, PEIRCE, FENNER & SMITH, 80- *Concurrent Pos:* Mem, Panel Impact Comput, Math Curriculum, Comt Undergrad Prog Math, 71-72; mem bd trustees, Soc Indust & Appl Math, 76-78, chmn bd, 78; mem, Biotechnol resources Adv Comt, NIH, 78-81. *Mem:* AAAS; Asn Comput Mach; Soc Indust & Appl Math. *Res:* Development of mathematical models for physiological systems; numerical analysis; analysis of health care systems; application of technology and manpower innovations in health care delivery; evaluation of public programs; application of emerging electronic technologies to financial services delivery. *Mailing Add:* 310 W 56th St Apt 2 B New York NY 10019

ROCKOFF, SEYMOUR DAVID, b Utica, NY, July 21, 31; c 3. RADIOLOGY. *Educ:* Syracuse Univ, AB, 51; Albany Med Col, MD, 55; Univ Pa, MSc, 61. *Prof Exp:* Staff radiologist, Clin Ctr, NIH, 61-65; from asst prof to assoc prof radiol, Sch Med, Yale Univ, 65-68; assoc prof, Mallinckrodt Inst Radiol, Sch Med, Wash Univ, 68-71; chmn dept, 71-77, PROF RADIOL, GEORGE WASHINGTON UNIV MED CTR, 71-, HEAD SECT CHEST RADIOL, 77- *Concurrent Pos:* Asst attend radiologist, Yale-New Haven Med Ctr, Conn, 65-68; ed-in-chief, Investigative Radiol, 66-76, emer ed-in chief, 76-; asst radiologist, Barnes & Allied Hosps, St Louis, Mo; consult radiologist, Homer G Phillips Hosp, St Louis & Vet Admin Hosp, 69-71, NIH, Nat Naval Med Ctr, Bethesda, Md & Washington Vet Admin Hosp, DC, 73- & immunodiagnosis, Nat Cancer Inst, NIH, Bethesda, Md, 77. *Mem:* Fel Am Col Radiol; Am Fedn Clin Res; Asn Univ Radiol; AMA; Radiol Soc NAm. *Res:* Contrast media toxicity; image analysis of radiographs. *Mailing Add:* Dept Radiol George Washington Univ Med Ctr Washington DC 20037

ROCKOWER, EDWARD BRANDT, b Philadelphia, Pa, May 29, 43; m 64; c 2. PHYSICS, OPERATIONS RESEARCH. *Educ:* Univ Calif, Los Angeles, BS, 64; Brandeis Univ, MA, 67, PhD(physics), 75. *Prof Exp:* Res assoc physics, LTV Res Ctr, Western Div, 64-65; vpres, Univ Home Serv, Inc, 71-74; sr opers analyst oper res, Gen Dynamics Corp, 75-77, Ketron, Inc, 77-79; PHYSICIST, LASER ISOTOPE SEPARATION PROG, LAWRENCE LIVERMORE NAT LAB, 79- *Concurrent Pos:* Adj prof mgt sci, MBA prog, LaSalle Col, 77-78. *Mem:* Opers Res Soc Am. *Res:* Generalized Cherenkov radiation of massive fields in plasmas or by faster-than-light particles; applied stochastic processes in lasers and queueing systems; economic and financial analysis. *Mailing Add:* L466 PO Box 808 Livermore CA 94550

ROCKS, LAWRENCE, b New York, NY, Aug 27, 33. CHEMISTRY. *Educ:* Queens Col, NY, BS, 55; Purdue Univ, MS, 57; Vienna Tech Univ, Dr Tech, 64. *Prof Exp:* Asst prof, 58-72, ASSOC PROF CHEM, C W POST COL, LONG ISLAND UNIV, 58- *Mailing Add:* Dept of Chem C W Post Col Long Island Univ Greenvale NY 11548

ROCKSTAD, HOWARD KENT, b Ada, Minn, Aug 5, 35. SOLID STATE PHYSICS. *Educ:* St Olaf Col, BA, 57; Univ Ill, Urbana, MS, 59, PhD(physics), 63. *Prof Exp:* Res physicist, Corning Glass Works, NY, 63-70; res physicist, Energy Conversion Devices, Inc, 71-73; proj engr, Micro-Bit Corp, 74-80; PRIN SCIENTIST, ARCO SOLAR INDUST, 81- *Concurrent Pos:* Lectr, Elmira Col, 67. *Mem:* Am Phys Soc. *Res:* Physics of electron-beam-accessed management operating system memories; management operating system charge storage; semiconductor device physics; high-electric-field transport; physics of amorphous semiconductors; optical and electronic properties of semiconductors and insulators; color centers; thermoelectricity. *Mailing Add:* Arco Solar Indust 20717 Prairie Chatsworth CA 91311

ROCKSTEIN, MORRIS, b Toronto, Ont, Jan 8, 16; nat US; wid; c 2. PHYSIOLOGY. *Educ:* Brooklyn Col, BA, 38; Columbia Univ, MA, 41; Univ Minn, PhD(insect physiol & biochem), 48. *Prof Exp:* Asst entom, Univ Minn, 41-42; from asst prof to assoc prof zoophysiol, Wash State Univ, 48-53; from asst prof to assoc prof physiol, Sch Med, NY Univ, 53-61; prof physiol & biophys, 61-81, chmn dept, Sch Med, 67-71, PROF NURSING, UNIV MIAMI, 81- *Concurrent Pos:* Instr, Marine Biol Lab, Woods Hole, 54-60, trustee, 62-65; mem sci coun, Geront Res Found, 60-63; adv, Nat Inst Aging, 61; consult, Am Pub Health Asn, 61-74; adv study sect trop med, NIH, 62-66; abstractor, Excerpta Medica & Chem Abstr; ed, Biol Sci Bannerstone Lectr Ser Geriat & Geront, 64-72; ed biol sci, Acad Press, 72-; vpres, Int Asn Prolong Human Lifespan; mem adv coun, Weizmann Inst, 74- *Mem:* Fel AAAS; fel Entom Soc Am; Sigma Xi; Soc Gen Physiol; fel Geront Soc (pres, 65-66). *Res:* Insect physiology and enzymology; biochemistry of flight; physiology of aging; radiobiology; marine biology. *Mailing Add:* 335 Fluvia Ave Coral Gables FL 33134

ROCKWELL, DAVID ALAN, b Chicago, Ill, Nov 11, 45; m 67. OPTICAL PHYSICS. *Educ:* Univ Ill, Urbana, BS, 67; Mass Inst Technol, PhD(physics), 73. *Prof Exp:* Res assoc laser mat, Physics Dept, Univ Southern Calif, 73-75; head, Laser Physics Sect, Laser Div, Hughes Aircraft Co, 75-81, SR STAFF PHYSICIST, HUGHES RES LABS, 81- *Mem:* Am Phys Soc. *Res:* Research and development of solid state laser devices; nonlinear and electrooptic devices; high energy laser sources. *Mailing Add:* 15614 Roselle Ave Lawndale CA 90260

ROCKWELL, DONALD O, b Canton, Pa, Oct 2, 42; m 72. FLUID MECHANICS. *Educ:* Bucknell Univ, BS, 64; Lehigh Univ, MS, 65, PhD(mech eng), 68. *Prof Exp:* NSF trainee mech eng, Lehigh Univ, 64-67; group leader fluid syst, Harry Diamond Labs, 68-70; asst prof mech eng, Lehigh Univ, 70-72, assoc prof, 72-74; guest prof & Von Humboldt fel, Univ Karlsruhe, Ger, 74-75; PROF MECH ENG, LEHIGH UNIV, 76- *Concurrent Pos:* Co-dir, Volkswagen Found Prog, Univ Karlsruhe & Lehigh Univ, 77-82; NSF grant, Lehigh Univ, 78-83, NASA grant, 78-81; overseas fel, Churchill Col, Cambridge Univ, 81; consult fluid induced vibration &

noise generation, var firms in US, Ger, France, Austria & Switz. *Mem:* Am Phys Soc; Am Inst Aeronaut & Astronaut; Am Soc Mech Engrs; Ger Soc Air & Space Travel. *Res:* Unsteady fluid mechanics. *Mailing Add:* Bldg 19 Lehigh Univ Bethlehem PA 18015

ROCKWELL, HARRIET ESTHER, b Oneida, NY, Apr 16, 16. THERAPEUTICS. *Educ:* Keuka Col, BS, 37; Univ Ill, PhD(biochem), 46. *Prof Exp:* Sr investr org chem, Sterling-Winthrop Res Inst Div, Sterling Drugs, Inc, 46-49; lit scientist, Smith Kline & French Labs, 49-56, head info group, 56-61, proprietaries group leader, 61-64; head sci info dept, Menley & James Labs, 65-69; sr lit scientist, Med Doc Serv, Col Physicians Philadelphia, 70-80; RETIRED. *Mem:* Fel AAAS. *Res:* Documentation. *Mailing Add:* 400 Gypsy Lane Apt 523 Philadelphia PA 19144

ROCKWELL, JULIUS, JR, b Taunton, Mass, July 25, 18; m 64; c 5. FISHERIES, ENVIRONMENTAL MANAGEMENT. *Educ:* Univ Mich, BS, 40; Univ Wash, PhD(fisheries), 56. *Prof Exp:* Sci asst, Int Pac Halibut Fisheries Comn, 46; from jr res asst to res assoc, Fisheries Res Inst, Univ Wash, 46-54; fisheries res biologist & proj leader, Biol Lab Seattle, Bur Com Fisheries, US Fish & Wildlife Serv, 54-59, chief, Fish Counting Prog, 59-62, chief, Oceanog Instrumentation Unit, 62-67, spec asst, Br Marine Fisheries, 67-70; STAFF FISHERY BIOLOGIST, ALASKA PIPELINE OFF & OFF SPECIAL PROJ, BUR LAND MGT, US DEPT INTERIOR, 70- *Concurrent Pos:* Adj prof biol, Alaska Pac Univ. *Honors & Awards:* Superior Performance Award, Bur Com Fisheries, 62. *Mem:* AAAS; Am Fisheries Soc; Am Inst Fishery Res Biologists; Marine Technol Soc. Nat Speleol Soc. *Res:* Developing methods for environmental habitat protection, evaluation and restoration; research, development, test and evaluation of oceanographic equipment; data handling and processing systems; operations research; statistical analysis; mineral metabolism of fishes. *Mailing Add:* 2944 Emory St Anchorage AK 99504

ROCKWELL, KENNETH H, b Huntington, Pa, Jan 27, 36; m 58; c 3. ZOOLOGY. *Educ:* Juniata Col, BS, 57; Brown Univ, MS, 60; Pa State Univ, PhD(zool), 67. *Prof Exp:* From instr to assoc prof, 60-72, chmn dept, 69-74, PROF BIOL, JUNIATA COL, 72-, CHMN DEPT, 79- *Concurrent Pos:* Vis scholar, Stanford Univ, 74-75. *Mem:* AAAS; Am Inst Biol Sci. *Res:* Histology of endocrine organs; physiology of altitude exposure. *Mailing Add:* Dept of Biol Juniata Col Huntingdon PA 16652

ROCKWELL, ROBERT FRANKLIN, b Dayton, Ohio, Dec 19, 46. POPULATION BEHAVIOR GENETICS, POPULATION ECOLOGY. *Educ:* Wright State Univ, BS, 69, MS, 71; Queen's Univ, Ont, PhD(biol), 75. *Prof Exp:* Fel, City Univ New York, 75-76; asst prof, 76-80, ASSOC PROF BIOL, CITY COL NEW YORK, 81- *Mem:* Genetic Soc Am; Soc Study Evolution; Biomet Soc; Behav Genetics Soc; Am Soc Genetics. *Res:* Effect of behavior on genetic structure of natural populations; substructured populations; biostatistical methods; population ecology of migratory waterfowl. *Mailing Add:* City Col NY Dept of Biol Convent Ave at 138th New York NY 10031

ROCKWELL, ROBERT LAWRENCE, b Portsmouth, NH, Nov 18, 35; m 60; c 3. AEROSOL FLUID DYNAMICS. *Educ:* Univ Calif, Berkeley, AB, 59; Stanford Univ, MS, 64, PhD(aeronaut & astronaut), 70. *Prof Exp:* Physicist, 58-81, AERONAUT ENGR, NAVAL WEAPONS CTR, CHINA LAKE, 81- *Concurrent Pos:* Lectr mech eng, Univ Southern Calif, 72-74; elec eng, Calif State Univ, Northridge, 80- *Mem:* Am Asn Aerosol Res. *Res:* Nonlinear modeling of arterial blood flow, with emphasis on viscous and viscoelastic effects; mechanics of aerosols, particularly fluid dynamic effects on coagulation of chain aggregates. *Mailing Add:* Spec Proj Br Code 3542 Naval Weapons Ctr China Lake CA 93555

ROCKWELL, THEODORE, III, b Chicago, Ill, June 26, 22; m 47; c 4. NUCLEAR & CHEMICAL ENGINEERING. *Educ:* Princeton Univ, BSE, 43, MS, 45. *Hon Degrees:* ScD, Tri-State Col, 60. *Prof Exp:* Engr, Electromagnetic Separation Plant, Clinton Engr Works, Tenn, 44-45; head shield eng group, Oak Ridge Nat Lab, 45-49; nuclear engr naval reactors, Atomic Energy Comn & nuclear propulsion, Bur Ships, 49-53, dir nuclear technol div, 53-54, tech dir, 54-64; PRIN OFFICER & DIR, MPR ASSOCS, INC, WASHINGTON, DC, 64- *Concurrent Pos:* Chmn nat shield eng group, Atomic Energy Comn, 48-49; mem reactor safety panel, &chmn, Reactor Safety Task Force, Atomic Indust forum, 66-68; mem adv group, NIH, 66; mem adv comt, Dept Chem Eng, Princeton Univ, 67-72; res assoc, Wash Ctr Foreign Policy Res, Johns Hopkins Univ, 65-67; consult, Joint Cong Comt Atomic Energy, 67. *Honors & Awards:* Atomic Energy Comn Distinguished Serv Medal & Navy Distinguished Civilian Serv Medal, 60. *Mem:* Parapsychol Asn; Am Soc Phys Res. *Res:* Criteria, procedures and facilities for safe operation of naval and central station nuclear power plants; nuclear, oceanographic and marine engineering. *Mailing Add:* 3403 Woolsey Dr Chevy Chase MD 20815

ROCKWELL, THOMAS H, b Loma Linda, Calif, May 2, 29; m 53; c 5. INDUSTRIAL ENGINEERING. *Educ:* Stanford Univ, BS, 51; Ohio State Univ, MS, 53, PhD(indust eng), 57. *Prof Exp:* Design engr, Standard Oil Co Calif, 53-54; res assoc opers res, 55-57, from asst prof to assoc prof indust eng, 57-65, PROF INDUST ENG, OHIO STATE UNIV, 65- *Concurrent Pos:* USPHS grants, accident prev res, 62-, transp res, 66-; mem road user characteristics & traffic safety comt, Hwy Res Bd, 64-, chmn road user characteristics comt, 72; consult, Nationwide Ins, 64-; mem, Gov Traffic Comt; consult indust environ. *Mem:* Fel AAAS; Am Soc Eng Educ; Am Soc Safety Engrs; Inst Elec & Electronics Engrs; fel Human Factors Soc. *Res:* Operations research; human factors engineering; transportation accident prevention; human performance experimental design. *Mailing Add:* Dept of Indust & Systs Eng Ohio State Univ Columbus OH 43210

ROCKWOOD, STEPHEN DELL, b Ft Scott, Kans, Apr 8, 43; m 64; c 2. LASERS. *Educ:* Grinnell Col, BA, 65; Calif Inst Technol, MS, 67, PhD(physics), 69. *Prof Exp:* Res officer laser develop, Air Force Weapons Lab, 70-72; staff mem laser develop, 72-75, group leader tunable lasers, 75-80, DEP ASSOC DIR INERTIAL FUSION, LOS ALAMOS NAT LAB, 80- *Concurrent Pos:* Adj prof, Univ NMex Inst Modern Optics; vpres, Advan Technol Assocs; dir, Los Alamos Laser Fusion Prog; consult problems in laser develop & indust applications. *Honors & Awards:* US Air Force Sci Achievement Award, 71. *Mem:* Am Phys Soc. *Res:* Development of tunable ir lasers for isotope separation; sulfur, boron, carbon and silicon isotopes. *Mailing Add:* NSP/Inertial Fusion MS 527 Los Alamos Nat Lab Los Alamos NM 87545

ROCKWOOD, SUSAN WILLIAMS, b Cincinnati, Ohio, Nov 26, 24. MICROBIOLOGY. *Educ:* Denison Univ, AB, 46; Univ Cincinnati, MS, 58, PhD(microbiol), 62. *Prof Exp:* Chief technologist, Med Lab, Bethesda Hosp, Cincinnati, 47-53; bacteriologist, Robert A Taft Sanit Eng Ctr, USPHS, 53-56; instr bact, Univ Cincinnati, 56-57; fel, Cincinnati Gen Hosp, 58-59; from asst prof to assoc prof, 62-72, PROF MICROBIOL, MIAMI UNIV, 72-, UNIV BACTERIOLOGIST, 77- *Mem:* Am Soc Microbiol; S Cent Asn Microbiologists. *Res:* Tularemia. *Mailing Add:* 311 Upham Hall Miami Univ Oxford OH 45056

ROCKWOOD, WILLIAM PHILIP, b Albany, NY, Dec 7, 30; m 53; c 5. ENDOCRINOLOGY, PHYSIOLOGY. *Educ:* Boston Col, BS, 57; Syracuse Univ, MS, 59; NY Univ, PhD(endocrine physiol), 68. *Prof Exp:* From instr to assoc prof, 61-76, PROF BIOL, RUSSELL SAGE COL, 76- *Concurrent Pos:* Lectr & consult alcoholism, NY State Dept Correctional Serv, 72-; dir, SAGE proj alcoholism & drug abuse. *Mem:* AAAS; Int Soc Exp Hemat; Sigma Xi; NY Acad Sci. *Res:* Hematology; toxicological effects of drugs on mammals. *Mailing Add:* Dept of Biol Sci Russell Sage Col Troy NY 12180

ROD, DAVID LAWRENCE, b Gardner, Mass, Apr 23, 38; m 66. MATHEMATICS. *Educ:* Mass Inst Technol, BS, 60; Univ Wis-Madison, MS, 62, PhD(math), 71. *Prof Exp:* Asst prof, 66-75, ASSOC PROF MATH, UNIV CALGARY, 75- *Mem:* Am Math Soc. *Res:* Hamiltonian systems of differential equations and dynamical systems theory. *Mailing Add:* Dept of Math Univ of Calgary Calgary AB T2N 1N4 Can

RODABAUGH, DAVID JOSEPH, b Kansas City, Mo, Jan 14, 38; m 59; c 3. ALGEBRA, COMPUTER SCIENCE. *Educ:* Univ Chicago, SB, 59, SM, 60; Ill Inst Technol, PhD(math), 63. *Prof Exp:* Instr math, Ill Inst Technol, 62-63; asst prof, Vanderbilt Univ, 63-65; from asst prof to assoc prof, 65-78, PROF MATH, UNIV MO-COLUMBIA, 78- *Concurrent Pos:* Consult, NASA, 65-66; NSF grant, Univ Mo-Columbia, 67-68; prof, Calif State Univ, Northridge; staff scientist & engr, Lockheed Corp, 81- *Mem:* Asn Comput Mach; Inst Elec & Electronics Engrs; Soc Indust & Appl Math; Sigma Xi. *Mailing Add:* Dept Math Univ Mo Columbia MO 65201

RODAHL, KAARE, b Bronnoysund, Norway, Aug 17, 17; nat US; m 46; c 2. PHYSIOLOGY. *Educ:* Univ Oslo, MD, 48, Dr med, 50. *Prof Exp:* Spec consult, US Dept Air Force, 49, chief dept physiol, Arctic Aeromed Lab, Ladd AFB, Alaska, 50-52, dir res, 54-57; asst prof physiol, Univ Oslo, 52-54; dir res, Lankenau Hosp, 57-65; DIR, INST WORK PHYSIOL, 65-; PROF PHYSIOL, NORWEG COL PHYS EDUC, 66- *Concurrent Pos:* Hon mem staff & fac, Command Gen Staff Col, US Army. *Mem:* Am Physiol Soc. *Res:* Environmental physiology and medicine; work physiology; metabolism nutrition; vitamins. *Mailing Add:* Inst of Work Physiol Gydas vei 8 Oslo Norway

RODAN, GIDEON ALFRED, b Rumania, June 14, 34; m 72; c 2. CELL BIOLOGY. *Educ:* Hebrew Univ, Hadassah, MD, 64; Weizmann Inst Sci, PhD(chem), 70. *Prof Exp:* Asst prof, 70-75, assoc prof, 75-78, PROF & HEAD ORAL BIOL, SCH DENT MED, UNIV CONN, 78- *Res:* Cell biology of hard tissues; hormonal control of growth and differentiation in bone-derived cells and the transduction of hormone signals. *Mailing Add:* Oral Biol Dept Health Ctr Univ Conn Farmington CT 06032

RODBARD, DAVID, b Chicago, Ill, July 6, 41; m 77. MEDICINE, BIOPHYSICS. *Educ:* Univ Buffalo, BA, 60; Western Reserve Univ, MD, 64. *Prof Exp:* Intern med, King County Hosp, Seattle, 64-65; resident, Hahnemann Hosp, Philadelphia, 65-66; clin assoc med res, NIH, 66-69, sr investr, 69-78, SECT HEAD MED RES, BIOPHYS ENDOCRINOL SECT, ENDOCRINOL & REPRODUCTION RES BR, NAT INST CHILD HEALTH & HUMAN DEVELOP, 79- *Concurrent Pos:* Consult, Int Atomic Energy Agency, 70- & WHO, 74-; assoc ed, Am J Physiol, 76- *Honors & Awards:* Young Investr Award, Clin Radioassay Soc, 79; Ayerst Award, Endocrine Soc, 81. *Mem:* Endocrine Soc; Am Physiol Soc; Am Soc Biol Chemists; Biomet Soc; Am Soc Clin Invest. *Res:* Endocrinology; physiology; biomathematics; biochemistry; radio immunoassay; physical-chemistry of proteins; neurotransmitters. *Mailing Add:* Biophys Endocrinol Sect Nat Inst Child Health & Human Dev Bethesda MD 20205

RODBELL, MARTIN, biochemistry, see previous edition

RODDA, BRUCE EDWARD, b Schenectady, NY, June 21, 42; m 62; c 2. MEDICAL STATISTICS, CLINICAL PHARMACOLOGY. *Educ:* Alfred Univ, BA, 65; Tulane Univ, MS, 67, PhD(biostatist), 69; Fairleigh Dickinson Univ, MBA, 82. *Prof Exp:* Res scientist med statist, Eli Lilly & Co, 69-76; DIR, CBARDS INT, MERCK & CO, RAHWAY, NJ, 76- *Concurrent Pos:* Asst prof pharmacol, Ind Univ Med Ctr, 72-76; asst prof biostatist, Rockford Med Sch, 78-; guest investr, Rockefeller Univ, 77-; consult, Vet Admin, NIH. *Mem:* Am Statist Asn; Am Soc Clin Pharmacol & Therapeut; Biomet Soc; Sigma Xi; fel Royal Statist Soc. *Res:* Pharmacokinetic modeling; general statistical methodology; design of clinical trials. *Mailing Add:* Merck & Co PO Box 2000 Rahway NJ 08836

RODDA, ERROL DAVID, b Platteville, Wis, June 3, 28; m 55; c 2. AGRICULTURAL & STRUCTURAL ENGINEERING. *Educ:* Univ Ill, Urbana, BS, 51, MSCE, 60, MS, 64; Purdue Univ, PhD(agr eng), 65. *Prof Exp:* Engr, Caterpillar Tractor Co, Ill, 51-58; res assoc agr eng, Univ Ill, Urbana-Champaign, 58-62; asst prof, Univ Calif, Davis, 64-68; assoc prof, 68-75, PROF AGR ENG & FOOD ENG, UNIV ILL, URBANA-CHAMPAIGN, 75- *Concurrent Pos:* USAID-Univ Ill adv agr eng, Uttar Pradesh Agr Univ, India, 68-70. *Mem:* Am Soc Agr Engrs; Am Soc Eng Educ; AAAS. *Res:* Grain processing and storage; agricultural structures; engineering systems design; food engineering; fuel alcohol. *Mailing Add:* Dept Agr Eng Univ Ill 1208 W Peabody Dr Urbana IL 61801

RODDA, PETER ULISSE, b Albuquerque, NMex, Nov 18, 29; m 55. GEOLOGY. *Educ:* Univ Calif, Los Angeles, AB, 52, PhD(geol), 60. *Prof Exp:* Asst geol, Univ Calif, Los Angeles, 54-57, instr, 57; lectr geol, Univ Tex, Austin, 63-66, res scientist, Bur Econ Geol, 58-71; CUR & CHMN DEPT GEOL, CALIF ACAD SCI, 71- *Mem:* Geol Soc Am; Paleont Soc; Am Asn Petrol Geol. *Res:* Stratigraphy and invertebrate paleontology of the Cretaceous and Cenozoic. *Mailing Add:* Dept of Geol Calif Acad of Sci San Francisco CA 94118

RODDEN, ROBERT MORRIS, b Roswell, NMex, June 28, 22; m 46; c 2. PHYSICS, BIOLOGY. *Educ:* US Mil Acad, BS, 44; Univ Calif, Berkeley, MS, 54. *Prof Exp:* Chief weapons develop div, Defense Nuclear Agency, Dept Defense, 44-64; asst dir opers eval, SRI Int, 64-72, dir opers eval, 72-74, dir, Ctr Resources & Environ, 74-77; prin consult, 77-80, PRES, RMR ASSOCS, 80- *Concurrent Pos:* Dir, Systs eng task group, Nat Indust Pollution Control Coun, 70-72. *Mem:* Asn Energy Engrs; Soc Petrol Engrs; Int Cogeneration Soc. *Res:* Energy analysis; planning; environmental analysis; information systems; research and development management; energy, environment, nuclear and technology assessment. *Mailing Add:* RMR Assocs 750 Welch Rd Palo Alto CA 94304

RODDICK, JAMES ARCHIBALD, b New Westminster, BC, Feb 23, 25; m 63; c 2. GEOLOGY. *Educ:* Univ BC, BASc, 48; Calif Inst Technol, MS, 50; Univ Wash, PhD, 55. *Prof Exp:* GEOLOGIST, DEPT ENERGY, MINES & RESOURCES GEOL SURV, CAN, 50- *Mem:* Geol Soc Am; Geol Asn Can; Can Inst Mining & Metall. *Res:* Cordilleran geology; granitic rocks. *Mailing Add:* Dept of Energy Mines & Resources Geol Surv Can 100 W Pender St Vancouver BC V6B 1R8 Can

RODDICK, JOHN WILLIAM, JR, b Dallas, Tex, June 13, 26; m 49; c 3. OBSTETRICS & GYNECOLOGY. *Educ:* Northwestern Univ, BS, 47, BM, 49, MD, 50, MS, 56. *Prof Exp:* Resident obstet & gynec, Chicago Wesley Mem Hosp, 52-56; clin asst, Northwestern Univ, 56-57, instr, 57-59, assoc, 59-62, asst prof, 62-64; from assoc prof to prof, Univ Ky, 64-71; PROF OBSTET & GYNEC & CHMN DEPT, SCH MED, SOUTHERN ILL UNIV, 72- *Concurrent Pos:* Fel surg, Mem Ctr Cancer & Allied Dis, 61-62. *Mem:* AMA; Am Col Obstet & Gynec; Soc Gynec Invest; Am Col Surg; Soc Gynec Oncol. *Res:* Gynecologic oncology, clinical and laboratory. *Mailing Add:* Dept of Obstet & Gynec PO Box 3926 Springfield IL 62708

RODDIS, LOUIS HARRY, JR, b Charleston, SC, Sept 9, 18; m 41, 64; c 9. MARINE & ENERGY ENGINEERING. *Educ:* US Naval Acad, BS, 39; Mass Inst Technol, MS, 44. *Prof Exp:* Dep dir, Div Reactor Develop, US Atomic Energy Comn, 55-58; pres & dir, Pa Elec Co, 58-67, chmn bd, 67-69; pres & trustee, Consolidated Edison Co NY, Inc, 69-74; CONSULT ENGR, 74- *Concurrent Pos:* Pres, Atomic Indust Forum, 62-64; chmn, NY Power Pool Exec Comt, 72-73; chmn, Res Adv Bd, US Dept Energy, 81- *Honors & Awards:* Outstanding Serv Award, US Atomic Energy Comn, 57. *Mem:* Nat Acad Eng; fel Am Nuclear Soc (pres, 69-70); fel Am Soc Mech Engrs; Inst Elec & Electronics Engrs; Am Soc Heating, Refrig & Air-Conditioning Engrs. *Res:* Active in development of extended research and development program in United States electric utility industry. *Mailing Add:* 110 Broad St Charleston SC 29401

RODDY, DAVID JOHN, b Springfield, Ohio, May 27, 32; c 3. GEOLOGY, GEOPHYSICS. *Educ:* Miami Univ, AB, 55, MS, 57; Calif Inst Technol, PhD(physics, geol), 66. *Prof Exp:* Instr geol, Miami Univ, 54-57; geologist, Jet Propulsion Lab, Calif Inst Technol, 60-64; GEOLOGIST, US GEOL SURV, 66- *Concurrent Pos:* Geologist, Calif Oil Co, 55; instr, US Air Force Inst Technol, 66. *Mem:* Geol Soc Am; Am Geophys Union; Mineral Soc Am; Sigma Xi. *Res:* Large-scale impact cratering mechanics related to the earth and planets; shock metamorphic studies of very high pressure shock wave deformed natural materials. *Mailing Add:* US Geol Surv 2255 N Gemini Dr Flagstaff AZ 86001

RODDY, MARTIN THOMAS, b Washington, DC, Dec 17, 46; m 73. CELL BIOLOGY. *Educ:* St Ambrose Col, BS, 69; Cath Univ Am, MS, 72, PhD(cell biol), 75; Am Bd Toxicol, dipl. *Prof Exp:* Instr human anat, Cath Univ Am, 73-75; med rev officer, 75-81, SR TOXICOLOGIST, GILLETTE MED EVAL LAB, 81- *Mem:* Sigma Xi; AAAS; Am Soc Cell Biol; Tissue Cult Asn Am; Am Bd Toxicol. *Res:* The potential of various organic metal compounds to cause sister chromated exchanges in vitro. *Mailing Add:* Gillette Med Eval Lab 1415 Research Blvd Rockville MD 20850

RODE, DANIEL LEON, b Delphos, Ohio, Aug 10, 42; m 67. SOLID STATE PHYSICS, PLASMA PHYSICS. *Educ:* Univ Dayton, BS, 64; Case Western Reserve Univ, MS, 66, PhD(appl physics), 68. *Prof Exp:* Mem tech staff semiconductor microwave devices, Bell Tel Labs, 68-70, supvr semiconductor mat, 70-80; SR VPRES, WASHINGTON UNIV, 80- *Concurrent Pos:* Fel, Max-Planck Inst, 77. *Mem:* Am Phys Soc; AAAS; Inst Elec & Electronics Engrs. *Res:* Electron theory of crystals; band structure of solids; semiconductor crystal growth; thermonuclear plasmas. *Mailing Add:* Campus Box 1127 Washington Univ St Louis MO 63130

RODE, JONATHAN PACE, b Worcester Mass, Oct 2, 48; m 69. ELECTRICAL ENGINEERING, INFRARED IMAGING. *Educ:* Univ Ore, BA, 70, PhD(physics), 76. *Prof Exp:* MEM TECH STAFF INFRARED, ROCKWELL INT SCI CTR, 76- *Mem:* Am Phys Soc. *Res:* Development of high performance; two-dimensional arrays of infrared detectors and their incorporation into infrared imaging systems. *Mailing Add:* Rockwell Sci Ctr 1049 Camino Dos Rios Thousand Oaks CA 91360

RODEBACK, GEORGE WAYNE, b Soda Springs, Idaho, Aug 12, 21; m 57; c 2. PHYSICS. *Educ:* Univ Idaho, BS, 43; Univ Ill, MS, 47, PhD(physics), 51. *Prof Exp:* Mem staff radiation lab, Mass Inst Technol, 42-45; from res engr to sr tech specialist, Atomics Int Div, NAm Aviation Inc, 51-60; ASSOC PROF PHYSICS, NAVAL POSTGRAD SCH, 60- *Mem:* Am Phys Soc; Am Asn Physics Teachers. *Res:* Nuclear and reactor physics; analytical mechanics. *Mailing Add:* Dept of Physics Naval Postgrad Sch Monterey CA 93940

RODELL, CHARLES FRANKLIN, b La Crosse, Wis, Aug 1, 42; m 67; c 1. POPULATION GENETICS. *Educ:* Univ Wis, BS, 65; Univ Minn, MS, 67, PhD(genetics), 72. *Prof Exp:* Fel systs ecol, Natural Resource Ecol Lab, Colo State Univ, 72-74; asst prof biol, Vanderbilt Univ, 74-80; asst prof, 79-81, ASSOC PROF BIOL, COL ST BENEDICT, ST JOHN'S UNIV, 82- *Mem:* AAAS; Genetics Soc Am; Soc Study Evolution; Sigma Xi. *Res:* Development and analysis of life history parameters and demographic patterns on the genetic structure of populations. *Mailing Add:* Dept Biol Col St Benedict St John's Univ Collegeville MN 56321

RODELL, MICHAEL BYRON, b Brooklyn, NY, Sept 4, 32; m 80; c 2. PHARMACY, ANALYTICAL CHEMISTRY. *Educ:* Univ Md, BS, 58; Univ Tex, MS, 64, PhD(pharm), 66. *Prof Exp:* Res assoc, Dorsey Labs, Wander Co, 66-67, mgr pharmaceut & anal res, Dorsey Labs, Sandoz-Wander, Inc, 67-72; mgr regulatory affairs, 72-74, dir regulatory affairs & clin develop, Hyland Div, 74-81, VPRES, REGULATORY AFFAIRS, HYLAND THERAPEUT DIV, TRAVENOL LABS, INC, 82- *Mem:* Am Pharmaceut Asn; Am Chem Soc; Acad Pharmaceut Sci; NY Acad Sci; AAAS. *Res:* Development of pharmaceutical dosage forms; design of stability protocols; analytical methodology. *Mailing Add:* Hyland Labs 3300 Hyland Ave Costa Mesa CA 92626

RODEMEYER, STEPHEN A, b Freeport, Ill, Oct 2, 40; m 65; c 2. PHYSICAL ORGANIC CHEMISTRY. *Educ:* Col St Thomas, BS, 62; Univ Calif, Berkeley, PhD(chem), 66. *Prof Exp:* NSF res assoc chem, Radiation Lab, Univ Notre Dame, 66-67; from asst prof to assoc prof, 67-74, chmn dept, 71-77, PROF CHEM, CALIF STATE UNIV, FRESNO, 74- *Mem:* Am Chem Soc. *Res:* Kinetics and mechanism; radiation and photochemistry. *Mailing Add:* Dept of Chem Calif State Univ Fresno CA 93740

RODEMS, JAMES D, b Springfield, Ill, Apr 30, 26; m 47; c 3. ELECTRICAL ENGINEERING, ELECTRONICS. *Educ:* Univ Louisville, BEE, 47; Univ Ill, MS, 50. *Prof Exp:* Test engr, Gen Elec Co, 47-48; asst elec eng, Univ Ill, 48-50; instr, Ohio State Univ, 50-51; control systs engr, Bell Aircraft Corp, 51-53; res assoc radar & control systs, Univ Ill, 53-57; res engr radar & control systs, Defense Systs Lab, Syracuse Univ Res Corp, 57-78, dir, 61-78; PRES, JDR SYST CORP, 78- *Concurrent Pos:* Consult, US Navy Dept, 62- *Mem:* Inst Elec & Electronics Engrs. *Res:* Radar systems; detection; tracking; fire control; feedback; control systems; hybrid real time analog-digital control; maintenance and test engineering; production and process control engineering. *Mailing Add:* 701 Nottingham Rd Syracuse NY 13224

RODEN, CARL NILS LENNART, b Stockholm, Sweden, Nov 16, 29; m 50; c 4. BIOCHEMISTRY. *Educ:* Karolinska Inst, Sweden, MD, 65. *Prof Exp:* Teacher biochem, Karolinska Inst, Sweden, 52-56; asst prof, Univ Stockholm, 58-59; asst prof, Univ Uppsala, 59-61; from asst prof to assoc prof biochem, Pritzker Sch Med, La Rabida-Univ Chicago Inst, 61-70, prof pediat & biochem, 70-77; PROF MED & BIOCHEM, SCH MED, UNIV ALA, BIRMINGHAM, 77- *Mem:* Am Soc Biol Chem. *Res:* Structure and biosynthesis of acid mucopolysaccharides and their protein complexes. *Mailing Add:* Pritzker Sch of Med La Rabida-Univ of Chicago Inst Chicago IL 60649

RODEN, GUNNAR IVO, b Tallinn, Estonia, Dec 27, 28; m 58; c 3. PHYSICAL OCEANOGRAPHY, CLIMATOLOGY. *Educ:* Univ Calif, Los Angeles, MS, 56. *Prof Exp:* Res oceanographer, Univ Calif, San Diego, 56-64; asst specialist oceanog, 65-66; res assoc, 66-68; SR RES ASSOC PHYS OCEANOG, UNIV WASH, 68- *Concurrent Pos:* NSF res grants, 64-65 & 81-; Off Naval Res grants, 68- *Mem:* Am Geophys Union; Am Meteorol Soc. *Res:* Oceanic fronts; meso-scale and large-scale thermohaline ocean structure and circulation; air-sea interaction; remote sensing of the ocean environment; regional oceanography; sea level and climatic change. *Mailing Add:* Dept Oceanog WB-10 Univ Wash Seattle WA 98195

RODENBERG, SIDNEY DAN, b St Louis, Mo, Apr 5, 26; m 50; c 3. ALLIED HEALTH PROFESSION EDUCATION. *Educ:* Washington Univ, AB, 48, AM, 50, PhD(bot), 53. *Hon Degrees:* MA, Univ Pa, 71. *Prof Exp:* From instr to prof microbiol, Univ Pa, 53-75, dean sch allied med profs, 69-75; PROF HEALTH SCI & DEAN COL HEALTH REL PROFS, WICHITA STATE UNIV, 76- *Concurrent Pos:* NSF sci fac fel, Univ Wis, 66-67; mem, Nat Accrediting Agency Clin Lab Sci, 77-79, Comt Allied Health Educ & Accreditation, 79-; adj prof path, Sch Med, Univ Kans, 80. *Honors & Awards:* Lindback Found Award, 64. *Mem:* AAAS; fel Am Soc Allied Health Professions (pres, 76-79); Am Soc Microbiol; Am Inst Biol Sci. *Res:* Variation in microorganisms; tobacco mosaic virus biosynthesis; growth; protein synthesis, cellular physiology, growth and differentiation in microorganisms; bacterial sporulation and germination. *Mailing Add:* Col of Health Related Profs Wichita State Univ Wichita KS 67206

RODENBERGER, CHARLES ALVARD, b Muskogee, Okla, Sept 11, 26; m 49; c 2. ENGINEERING. *Educ:* Okla State Univ, BS, 48; Southern Methodist Univ, MS, 59; Univ Tex, Austin, PhD(aerospace eng), 68. *Prof Exp:* Jr petrol engr, Amoco Prod Co, 48-51; chief engr, McGregor Bros, Inc, 53-54; petrol engr, Gen Crude Oil Co, 54; sr design engr aircraft struct, Gen Dynamics/Convair, 54-60; Halliburton prof eng, 66-78, asst dean, Col Eng, 77-80, PROF AEROSPACE ENG, TEX A&M UNIV, 60- *Concurrent Pos:* Consult, Gen Motors Defense Res Labs, 65-66, Meiller Res, Inc, 66- & Southwest Res Inst, 67. *Mem:* Am Inst Aeronaut & Astronaut; Am Soc Eng Educ. *Res:* Problem definition in systems engineering; engineering innovation; oil spill containment; bioengineering orthotic devices; hypervelocity devices; composite structures. *Mailing Add:* Dept Aerospace Eng Tex A&M Univ College Station TX 77843

RODENHUIS, DAVID ROY, b Michigan City, Ind, Oct 5, 36; m 58; c 2. DYNAMIC METEOROLOGY. *Educ:* Univ Calif, Berkeley, BS, 59; Pa State Univ, BS, 60; Univ Wash, PhD(atmospheric sci), 67. *Prof Exp:* From asst prof to assoc prof fluid dynamics & appl math, 72-76, ASSOC PROF METEOROL, UNIV MD, COLLEGE PARK, 76- *Concurrent Pos:* Exec scientist, US Comt Global Atmospheric Res Prog, Nat Acad Sci, 72; sci officer, World Meteorol Orgn, 75-; US-USSR exchange scientist, 80. *Mem:* Am Geophys Union; Am Meteorol Soc. *Res:* Tropical meteorology; convection models; dynamic climate models. *Mailing Add:* Grad Meteorol Prog Univ of Md College Park MD 20742

RODER, HANS MARTIN, b Schenectady, NY, June 30, 30; m 51; c 3. FLUID THERMODYNAMICS. *Educ:* Univ Colo, BA, 55. *Prof Exp:* Physicist cryog, 55-66, supvr physicist data compilation, 66-75, EXP PHYSICIST, THERMOPHYS PROPERTIES DIV, NAT BUR STANDARDS, 75- *Concurrent Pos:* Mem quantum fluids panel, Int Union Pure & Appl Chem, Thermodyn Tables Proj Ctr, 67- *Honors & Awards:* Gold Medal, US Dept Com, 66; Russell B Scott Mem Award, Cryogenic Eng Conf, 70. *Mem:* Am Phys Soc; Res Soc Am. *Res:* Experimental research on the equilibrium and transport properties of simple fluids; correlation and derivation of thermodynamic functions from the experimental results. *Mailing Add:* Thermophys Properties Div Nat Bur Standards Boulder CO 80302

RODERICK, GILBERT LEROY, b Waukon, Iowa, Aug 18, 33; m 62. SOIL ENGINEERING. *Educ:* Iowa State Univ, BS, 60, MS, 63, PhD(soil eng), 65. *Prof Exp:* Engr, US Bur Reclamation, 60-61; res assoc soil eng, Iowa Eng Exp Sta, Iowa State Univ, 63-65; asst prof, Univ RI, 65-68; asst prof, 68-70, ASSOC PROF CIVIL ENG, UNIV WIS-MILWAUKEE, 70- *Concurrent Pos:* Mem, Hwy Res Bd, Nat Acad Sci-Nat Res Coun. *Mem:* Am Soc Civil Engrs. *Res:* Soil stabilization with chemicals; physicochemical properties of soils by x-ray diffraction and adsorption isotherm studies; frost action in soils; ground water flow; lake bottom sediments; disposal of dredging spoil. *Mailing Add:* Dept of Civil Eng Univ of Wis Milwaukee WI 53201

RODERICK, HILLIARD, nuclear physics, see previous edition

RODERICK, THOMAS HUSTON, b Grand Rapids, Mich, May 10, 30; m 58; c 2. GENETICS. *Educ:* Univ Mich, AB, 52, BS, 53; Univ Calif, Berkeley, PhD(genetics), 59. *Prof Exp:* Asst psychol, Univ Calif, 55-58; from assoc staff scientist to sr staff scientist, Jackson Lab, 59-73; geneticist, Energy Res & Develop Admin, 73-75; SR STAFF SCIENTIST, JACKSON LAB, 75- *Concurrent Pos:* Lectr, Univ Maine, 65-; vis lectr, Univ Calif, Berkeley, 68; staff consult, Maine Genetic Coun Ctr, 69-, pres bd dirs, 74-77; adj prof, Univ RI, 70-73. *Mem:* AAAS; Genetics Soc Am; Am Soc Human Genetics; Environ Mutagen Soc. *Res:* Mammalian genetics; mutagenesis in mammals; population and cytogenetics. *Mailing Add:* Jackson Lab Bar Harbor ME 04609

RODERICK, WILLIAM RODNEY, b Chicago, Ill, Aug 6, 33; m 65. ORGANIC CHEMISTRY, MEDICINAL CHEMISTRY. *Educ:* Northwestern Univ, BS, 54; Univ Chicago, SM, 55, PhD(chem), 57. *Prof Exp:* Res fel chem, Harvard Univ, 57-58; asst prof, Univ Fla, 58-62; sr res chemist, Abbott Labs, 62-70, assoc res fel, 70-71; asst prof natural sci, 72-73, ASSOC PROF NATURAL SCI & CHEM, ROOSEVELT UNIV, 73- *Mem:* Am Chem Soc; AAAS; Sigma Xi. *Res:* Structural and synthetic organic chemistry; synthesis of antiviral agents. *Mailing Add:* 15193 W Redwood Lane Libertyville IL 60048

RODERUCK, CHARLOTTE ELIZABETH, b Walkersville, Md, Dec 2, 19. NUTRITION. *Educ:* UNiv Pittsburgh, BS, 40; State Col Wash, MS, 42; Univ Iowa, PhD(biochem), 49. *Prof Exp:* Res chemist, Children's Fund Lab, Mich, 42-46; from asst prof to prof nutrition, 48-73, asst dean grad col, 71-73, assoc dean col home econ, 73-77, MARY B WELCH DISTINGUISHED PROF HOME ECON, IOWA STATE UNIV, 72-, DIR, WORLD FOOD INST, 77- *Concurrent Pos:* Vis prof, Univ Baroda, 64-66. *Mem:* Soc Exp Biol & Med; Am Chem Soc; Am Inst Nutrit; Am Home Econ Asn; Soc Nutrit Educ. *Res:* Nutrition education; nutritional status; intermediary metabolism. *Mailing Add:* World Food Inst 102 E O Bldg Ames IA 50011

RODESILER, PAUL FREDERICK, b Adrian, Mich, Sept 10, 41; m 65; c 1. INORGANIC CHEMISTRY, X-RAY CRYSTALLOGRAPHY. *Educ:* Capital Univ, BS, 63; Univ Western Ont, MSc, 66; Queen Mary Col, Univ London, PhD(chem), 68. *Prof Exp:* Res asst chem & crystallog, Univ SC, 69-71, asst prof chem, 71-72, res asst chem & crystallog, 72-73; asst prof math & sci, 73-77, ASSOC PROF CHEM, COLUMBIA COL, SC, 77- *Concurrent Pos:* Instr, Midland Tech Sch, 72-73. *Mem:* Am Chem Soc; Am Crystallog Asn. *Res:* Preparation, structure and bonding of metallo-organic compounds, including the use of x-ray diffraction techniques. *Mailing Add:* Dept of Chem Columbia Col Colmbia SC 29203

RODEWALD, LYNN B, b Norcatur, Kans, Nov 15, 39; m 63; c 2. ORGANIC CHEMISTRY. *Educ:* Whittier Col, BA, 61; Iowa State Univ, PhD(org chem), 64. *Prof Exp:* NIH fel chem, Princeton Univ, 64-65; asst prof, Univ Tex, Austin, 65-72; vis asst prof, Univ Okla, 72-75; ASST PROF CHEM, TOWSON STATE UNIV, 75- *Concurrent Pos:* Petrol Res fund grant, 65-66. *Mem:* Am Chem Soc; Sigma Xi. *Res:* Organic reaction mechanisms; electroorganic chemistry; small ring chemistry. *Mailing Add:* Dept of Chem Towson State Univ Towson MD 21204

RODEWALD, PAUL GERHARD, JR, b Pittsburgh, Pa, May 15, 36; m 58; c 4. CATALYSIS. *Educ:* Haverford Col, BA, 58; Pa State Univ, PhD(organosilicon chem), 62. *Prof Exp:* Res chemist, 63-66, sr res chemist, 66-78, ASSOC, CENT RES DIV LAB, MOBIL OIL CORP, 76- *Mem:* Am Chem Soc. *Res:* Organosilicon chemistry; electrophilic aromatic substitution; organic synthesis; catalysis. *Mailing Add:* Mobil Res & Develop Corp Box 1025 Princeton NJ 08540

RODEWALD, RICHARD DAVID, b Nyack, NY, Mar 20, 44; m 69. CELL BIOLOGY. *Educ:* Harvard Univ, BA, 66; Univ Pa, PhD(biochem), 70. *Prof Exp:* NSF fel, 70; fel biol, Univ Calif, San Diego, 70-71; fel path, Harvard Med Sch, 71-73; ASST PROF BIOL, UNIV VA, 73- *Concurrent Pos:* Instr physiol, Marine Biol Lab, Woods Hole, 74. *Mem:* Am Soc Cell Biol; AAAS. *Res:* Selective transport of immunoglobulins across the small intestine; glomerular permeability to macromolecules. *Mailing Add:* Dept of Biol Gilmer Hall Univ of Va Charlottesville VA 22901

RODEY, GLENN EUGENE, b Mansfield, Ohio, Mar 25, 36; m 58; c 4. HUMAN HISTOCOMPATIBILITY, TRANSPLANTATION IMMUNOLOGY. *Educ:* Ohio Univ, BS, 57; Ohio State Univ, MD, 61. *Prof Exp:* Resident internal med, Milwaukee County Gen Hosp & Med Col, Wis, 62-63 & 65-67; fel immunol, Univ Minn, 67-69; dir histocompatibility, Milwaukee Blood Ctr, 70-74; assoc prof path & med, Med Col, Wis, 74-76; assoc prof, 76-81, PROF MED & PATH, SCH MED, WASHINGTON UNIV, MO, 81- *Concurrent Pos:* NIH mem, Transplantation Immunol Comt, Nat Inst Allergy & Infectious Dis, 74-78; mem, Transplantation Comt, Am Nat Red Cross, 79-; managing ed, Human Immunol, 79- *Mem:* Am Asn Clin Histocompatibility Testing (pres, 82-83); Am Asn Immunologists; Am Soc Hemat; Cent Soc Clin Res; Transplantation Soc. *Res:* Structure and function of human lymphocyte antigens, genetic complex and gene products; how these factors contribute to disease susceptibility and their functions in generating effective immune responses. *Mailing Add:* Dept Path Sch Med Box 8118 Washington Univ St Louis MO 63110

RODGER, ALAN JOHNSON, b Montreal, Que, Oct 2, 40; m 62; c 4. CHEMICAL ENGINEERING, THERMODYNAMICS. *Educ:* Royal Mil Col Can, BE, 62; Mass Inst Technol, SM, 63; Queen's Univ, Ont, PhD(chem eng), 68. *Prof Exp:* Lectr chem eng, Royal Mil Col Can, 65-67, asst prof, 67-69; RES ENGR, PLASTICS DEPT, E I DU PONT DE NEMOURS & CO, 69- *Res:* Vapor-liquid equilibrium. *Mailing Add:* Plastics Dept E I du Pont de Nemours & Co Inc 1007 Market St Wilmington DE 19898

RODGER, WALTON A, b Detroit, Mich, Mar 18, 18; m 72; c 4. CHEMICAL ENGINEERING. *Educ:* Univ Mich, BSChE & BSMetE, 39, MS, 40; Ill Inst Technol, PhD, 56. *Prof Exp:* Chem engr, Parke, Davis & Co, Mich, 40-42; res assoc, Metall Lab, Univ Chicago, 42-43; shift supvr, Clinton Labs, Oak Ridge, 43-44, chief supvr, 44-46, sect chief, 46-47; sr chem engr, Argonne Nat Lab, 47-54, assoc div dir, 54-60; consult, McLain Rodger Assocs, 60-62; vpres res & develop, Nuclear Fuel Serv, Inc, 62-64; gen mgr, W Valley Oper, 64-65; consult, Nuclear Safety Asn, 65-79; CONSULT, EDS NUCLEAR, 79- *Honors & Awards:* Robert E Wilson Award, Am Inst Chem Engrs, 81. *Mem:* Am Nuclear Soc; Atomic Indust Forum; fel Am Inst Chem Engrs. *Res:* Separations processes in field of atomic energy; disposal of radioactive wastes. *Mailing Add:* 5101 River Rd Bethesda MD 20016

RODGERS, ALAN SHORTRIDGE, b St Louis, Mo, Oct 23, 31; div; c 5. PHYSICAL CHEMISTRY. *Educ:* Princeton Univ, AB, 53; Univ Colo, PhD(phys chem), 60. *Prof Exp:* Sr chemist, Minn Mining & Mfg Co, 60-65; phys chemist, Stanford Res Inst, 65-67; ASSOC PROF CHEM, TEX A&M UNIV, 67- *Mem:* Am Chem Soc. *Res:* Chemical kinetics; free radical thermochemistry; structure and bond dissociation energy. *Mailing Add:* Dept of Chem Tex A&M Univ College Station TX 77843

RODGERS, AUBREY, b Lexington, Miss, June 11, 29; m 55; c 3. PHYSICS, MATHEMATICS. *Educ:* Miss Col, BS, 57; Rensselaer Polytech Inst, dipl, 67; Univ Calif, Los Angeles, dipl 68. *Prof Exp:* Physicist electronics, Naval Coastal Syst Lab, Fla, 57-60; physicist, mech, 60-62 & gen, 62-64, PHYSICIST RES, US ARMY MISSILE COMMAND, ALA, 64- *Res:* Investigates revolutionary concepts and techniques of gyroscopic instrumention used in Army inertial guidance, stabilization and navigation systems. *Mailing Add:* DRSMI-RGL Redstone Arsenal AL 35897

RODGERS, BILLY RUSSELL, b Fitzgerald, Ga, Sept 5, 36; c 4. COAL CONVERSION. *Educ:* Univ Fla, BSChE, 66, MSE, 67; Univ Tenn, PhD(chem eng), 80. *Prof Exp:* Task leader petrol res, Shell Develop Co, 68-72; mgr filter develop, Fluid Handling Div, Keene Corp, 72-74; MGR COAL CONVERSION, OAK RIDGE NAT LAB, 74- *Concurrent Pos:* Lectr, Univ Tenn, 80- *Mem:* Am Inst Chem Engrs; AAAS; Am Chem Soc. *Res:* Conversion of heavy petroleum residues to lighter products followed by conversion of coal to lighter products; physical chemistry of seperating solids from liquids in heavy media. *Mailing Add:* PO Box X Bldg 4500N Oak Ridge Nat Lab Oak Ridge TN 37830

RODGERS, BRADLEY MORELAND, b Montclair, NJ, Jan 16, 42; m 69; c 2. PEDIATRIC SURGERY. *Educ:* Dartmouth Col, BA, 63, Dartmouth Med Sch, BS, 64; Johns Hopkins Univ, MD, 66. *Prof Exp:* Asst prof surg & pediat, Med Ctr, Univ Fla, 74-76, assoc prof, 76-78, prof & assoc chief, Div Pediat Surg, 78-81; PROF SURG & PEDIAT & CHIEF, DIV PEDIAT SURG,

MED SCH, UNIV VA, 81-, CHIEF CHILDREN'S SURG, UNIV VA HOSP, 81- *Mem:* Am Col Surgeons; Asn Acad Surg. *Res:* Neonatal gastric physiology. *Mailing Add:* Dept Surg Box 181 Sch Med Univ Va Charlottesville VA 22908

RODGERS, CHARLES H, b Sept 5, 32; US citizen; m 66; c 3. PHYSIOLOGICAL PSYCHOLOGY. *Educ:* Los Angeles State Col Arts & Sci, BA, 58, MS, 61; Claremont Grad Sch, PhD(psychol), 66. *Prof Exp:* Nat Inst Child Health & Human Develop fel physiol & neuroendocrinol, Sch Med, Stanford Univ, 66-68; asst prof psychol, physiol & pharmacol, Iowa State Univ, 68-70; asst prof, 70-72, ASSOC PROF PSYCHOL, PHYSIOL & PHARMACOL, COL MED, UNIV ILL, 72- *Concurrent Pos:* Nat Inst Child Health & Human Develop grant, Iowa State Univ & Univ Ill Col Med, 68-71; Vet Admin grant, West Side Vet Admin Hosp, Chicago, 70-73, psychologist, 70-74; consult, Cook County Hosp, Ill, 74. *Mem:* AAAS; Am Physiol Soc; Endocrine Soc. *Res:* Reproduction in the male and female. *Mailing Add:* Biol Labs Dept of Psychiat Univ of Ill Col of Med Chicago IL 60680

RODGERS, CHARLES LELAND, b Fork Shoals, SC, May 31, 18; m 42; c 2. BOTANY. *Educ:* Furman Univ, BS, 39; Duke Univ, MA, 42; Univ NC, PhD(bot), 50. *Prof Exp:* Teacher high sch, SC, 39-40; prof biol, North Greenville Col, 40-44, 46-48 & 50-53; instr bot, Univ NC, 48-50; prof biol, Carson-Newman Col, 53-56; PROF BIOL, FURMAN UNIV, 56- *Concurrent Pos:* Ecol consult, 72- *Honors & Awards:* Sewell Award, 51. *Mem:* Southern Appalachian Bot Club (pres, 75-76). *Res:* Ecology; taxonomy. *Mailing Add:* Dept of Biol Furman Univ Greenville SC 29613

RODGERS, DON HALL, b Ft Smith, Ark, Oct 5, 40. WILDLIFE BIOLOGY. *Educ:* Univ Mo, BS, 67, MS, 69. *Prof Exp:* Biologist ecol serv, 69-78, STAFF SPECIALIST ENDANGERED SPECIES, US FISH & WILDLIFE SERV, 78- *Res:* Endangered species. *Mailing Add:* Denver Fed Ctr PO Box 25486 Denver CO 80225

RODGERS, EARL GILBERT, b Trenton, Fla, Jan 27, 21; m 43; c 2. AGRONOMY, WEED SCIENCE. *Educ:* Univ Fla, BS, 43, MS, 49; Iowa State Univ, PhD(plant physiol), 51. *Prof Exp:* Asst county agent, Wauchula, Fla, 46-47; from instr to assoc prof, 47-59, grad coordr agron, 69-81, PROF AGRON, UNIV FLA, 59-, COORDR AGRON TEACHING, 65- *Concurrent Pos:* Consult, US Air Force, Eglin AFB, Fla, 57. *Mem:* Fel Weed Sci Soc Am (pres, 73); fel Am Soc Agron. *Res:* Crop production; weed science. *Mailing Add:* 611 S W 16th Pl Gainesville FL 32601

RODGERS, EDWARD J(OHN), b McKees Rocks, Pa, June 10, 23; m 46; c 5. ENGINEERING, DYNAMICS. *Educ:* Univ Mich, BS, 50, MS, 52; Pa State Univ, PhD(eng mech), 63. *Prof Exp:* Res assoc aerodyn, Willow Run Res Ctr, Univ Mich, 49-53; engr, Martin Co, Md, 53-55; res assoc aerodyn & stability & control, Dept Aeronaut Eng & Ord Res Lab, Pa State Univ, 55-63, asst prof, 63-65; prin res engr & mgr mech & thermodyn dept, Res Labs, Brown Eng Co, 65-69; tech consult, Missile Develop Div & Optics Div, US Army Advan Ballistic Missile Defense Agency, Huntsville Off, 69-70; PROF AERONAUT ENG & CHMN DEPT, WICHITA STATE UNIV, 70- *Concurrent Pos:* Guest lectr, distinguished vis prof prog, Auburn Univ, 66; consult, US Army Advan Ballistic Missile Defense Agency. *Honors & Awards:* Ralph R Teetor Award, Soc Auto Engrs, 80. *Mem:* Am Inst Aeronaut & Astronaut; Am Soc Mech Engrs; Am Astronaut Soc; Nat Soc Prof Engrs; Am Soc Eng Educ. *Res:* Aerodynamics; stability and control of airplanes and missiles; flight mechanics; aerodynamic interference effects. *Mailing Add:* Dept of Aeronaut Eng Wichita State Univ Wichita KS 67208

RODGERS, GLEN ERNEST, b Farmington, Maine, Dec 27, 44; m 66; c 3. INORGANIC CHEMISTRY. *Educ:* Tufts Univ, BS, 66; Cornell Univ, PhD(chem), 71. *Prof Exp:* Asst prof chem, Muskingum Col, 70-75; asst prof, 75-81, ASSOC PROF CHEM, ALLEGHENY COL, 81- *Concurrent Pos:* Vis prof chem, Univ Cincinnati, 77 & Boston Univ, 78; NSF fac develop fel, Univ BC, 81-82. *Mem:* Am Chem Soc; Smithsonian Assocs. *Res:* Infrared analysis of the interaction between amino acids and heavy metal cations; synthesis and characterization of metal complexes of homoanular ferrocene derivatives; topics in chemical education and interdisciplinary studies. *Mailing Add:* Dept of Chem Allegheny Col Meadville PA 16335

RODGERS, JAMES EARL, b Los Angeles, Calif, Aug 19, 43; div; c 1. MEDICAL PHYSICS. *Educ:* Calif State Univ, Long Beach, BS, 66; Univ Calif, Riverside, PhD(physics), 72. *Prof Exp:* Res physicist, Naval Weapons Ctr-Corona, 67-68; res assoc theoret physics, State Univ NY, Albany, 72-76; asst prof therapeut radiol, Tufts Univ Sch Med, radiation oncol res fel & spec & sci staff, 76-80; DIR RADIATION PHYSICS DIV, DEPT RADIATION MED, GEORGETOWN UNIV HOSP, 80-; ASST PROF RADIATION MED, SCH MED, GEORGETOWN UNIV, 81- *Mem:* Am Phys Soc; Fedn Am Scientists; Radiation Res Soc; Am Asn Phys Med; AAAS. *Res:* Medical applications of nuclear magnetic resonance imaging; thermal dosimetry for hyperthermia in cancer therapy; modes of energy deposition for localized and systemic hyperthermia; radiation dosimetry. *Mailing Add:* Dept Radiation Med Georgetown Univ Hosp Washington DC 20007

RODGERS, JAMES EDWARD, b Boise, Idaho, Jan 13, 38; m 58; c 2. PHYSICAL ORGANIC CHEMISTRY. *Educ:* Westmont Col, BA, 60; Univ Calif, Berkeley, PhD(chem), 64. *Prof Exp:* Res asst chem, Univ Calif, Berkeley, 60-64; from instr to asst prof, North Park Col, 64-66; from asst prof to assoc prof, Bethel Col, 66-73; vis prof, Westmont Col, 73-74; prof, Bethel Col, 74-75; assoc prof, 75-78, PROF CHEM & CHMN DIV SCI & MATH, AZUSA PAC COL, 78- *Concurrent Pos:* NSF res grant, North Park Col, 65-66. *Mem:* Am Chem Soc; Royal Soc Chem; Royal Inst Chem; Sigma Xi. *Res:* Organic synthesis; photochemistry of allylic systems; reaction mechanisms of the saturated carbon; free radical chemistry. *Mailing Add:* Dept of Chem Azusa Pac Col Azusa CA 91702

RODGERS, JOHN, b Albany, NY, July 11, 14. GEOLOGY. *Educ:* Cornell Univ, BA, 36, MS, 37; Yale Univ, PhD(geol), 44. *Prof Exp:* Asst geol, Cornell Univ, 35-36, instr, 36-37; field geologist, US Geol Surv, 40-46; from instr to prof, 46-62, SILLIMAN PROF GEOL, YALE UNIV, 62- *Concurrent Pos:* Asst ed, Am J Sci, 48-54, ed, 54-; secy, Comn Stratig, Int Geol Cong, 52-60; sr fel, NSF, 59-60; vis lectr, Col France, 60; comnr, Conn Geol & Natural Hist Surv, 60-71; Nat Acad Sci exchange scholar, USSR, 67; Guggenheim fel, Australia, 73-74. *Honors & Awards:* Medal of Freedom, US Army, 47; Penrose Medal, Geol Soc Am, 81. *Mem:* Nat Acad Sci; AAAS; Geol Soc Am (pres, 70); Am Asn Petrol Geologists; Am Geophys Union. *Res:* Field geology in deformed sedimentary rocks; stratigraphy and structural geology of Appalachian Mountains; comparative anatomy of mountain ranges. *Mailing Add:* Dept of Geol Yale Univ New Haven CT 06520

RODGERS, JOHN BARCLAY, JR, b Cleveland, Ohio, Jan 5, 33; m 55; c 3. INTERNAL MEDICINE, GASTROENTEROLOGY. *Educ:* Denison Univ, BA, 55; Harvard Med Sch, MD, 59. *Prof Exp:* Clin & res fel gastroenterol, Mass Gen Hosp, 64-66; from asst prof to assoc prof med, 66-74, PROF MED, ALBANY MED COL, 74-, CHIEF SECT GASTROENTEROL, 81- *Mem:* Am Fedn Clin Res; Am Gastrointestinal Asn; Am Asn Study Liver Dis; Am Soc Clin Invest. *Res:* Small bowel function and lipid absorption; factors influencing sterol absorption. *Mailing Add:* Dept Med Albany Med Col Albany NY 12208

RODGERS, JOHN JAMES, b Glasgow, Scotland, Mar 31, 30; US citizen; m 53; c 1. LUBRICATION ENGINEERING, RESEARCH ENGINEERING. *Educ:* Wayne State Univ, BS, 52, MS, 53. *Prof Exp:* Res engr, 52-59, sr res engr, 59-81, STAFF RES ENGR, RES LABS, GEN MOTORS CORP, 81- *Honors & Awards:* Henry Ford Mem Award, Soc Automotive Engrs, 61. *Mem:* Soc Automotive Engrs; Am Soc Lubrication Engrs. *Res:* Friction in lubricated sliding systems, primarily clutch plate systems in automatic transmissions and controlled-slip rear axles; lubricant-seal compatibility. *Mailing Add:* Fuels & Lubricants Dept 12 Mile & Mound Rds Warren MI 48090

RODGERS, LAWRENCE RODNEY, SR, b Clovis, NMex, Mar 9, 20; m 43; c 3. MEDICINE. *Educ:* WTex State Col, BS, 40; Univ Tex, MD, 43; Am Bd Internal Med, dipl, 57, cert, 74. *Prof Exp:* Intern, Philadelphia Gen Hosp, Pa, 43-44, resident internal med, 46-49; asst prof, 49-72, ASSOC PROF CLIN MED, BAYLOR COL MED, 72-; PROF CLIN MED, UNIV TEX MED SCH HOUSTON, 72- *Concurrent Pos:* Attend physician, Hermann Hosp, 49-66, chmn dept med, 66-71; assoc internist, Univ Tex M D Anderson Hosp & Tumor Inst, 49- *Mem:* AMA; Am Col Physicians; fel Royal Soc Health. *Res:* Internal medicine; inheritable disorders. *Mailing Add:* 1232 Hermann Prof Bldg Houston TX 77025

RODGERS, MICHAEL A J, b Chesterfield, Eng, Oct 10, 36. RADIATION CHEMISTRY, PHOTO CHEMISTRY. *Educ:* Univ Manchester, Eng, MSc, 64, PhD(chem), 66. *Prof Exp:* Fel, Lawrence Berkeley Lab, 66-67; sr res assoc, Univ Manchester, Eng, 68-69, lectr chem, 69-76; RES COORDR, CTR FAST KINETICS RES, UNIV TEX, AUSTIN, 76- *Mem:* Am Chem Soc; Royal Soc Chem; Am Soc Photobiol; Radiation Res Soc. *Res:* Nature and properties of unstable, short-lived reaction intermediates in chemistry; application of time-resolved techniques in chemistry and biology. *Mailing Add:* Ctr Fast Kinetics Res PAT 131 Univ Tex Austin TX 78712

RODGERS, NELSON EARL, b Fredonia, Pa, May 18, 15; m 37; c 1. MICROBIOLOGY, BIOCHEMISTRY. *Educ:* Allegheny Col, AB, 37; Univ Wis, AM, 40, PhD(bact), 42. *Prof Exp:* Asst biol, Allegheny Col, 36-37 & bact, Univ Wis, 37-42; chief bacteriologist, Western Condensing Co, 42-46, res mgr, 46-56, assoc dir res, Foremost Dairies, Inc, Calif, 56-64; res assoc, Pillsbury Co, 64-76; CONSULT MICROBIOL & BIOCHEM, 76- *Concurrent Pos:* Bacteriologist, Natural Hist Surv, Wis, 38-39. *Mem:* AAAS; Am Soc Microbiol; Am Chem Soc. *Res:* Industrial fermentations; vitamin synthesis by microorganisms; unidentified growth factors in animal nutrition; biochemistry of milk and whey products; microbial polysaccharides; cereal products. *Mailing Add:* 4262 Circle Dr Wayzata MN 55391

RODGERS, RICHARD MICHAEL, b Scranton, Pa, Nov 12, 45. BIOCHEMISTRY. *Educ:* Univ Scranton, BS, 67; Columbia Univ, PhD(biochem), 71. *Prof Exp:* Fel virol, Div Infectious Dis, Stanford Univ, 71-73; SR CHEMIST BIOCHEM, SYVA RES INST, 73- *Mem:* AAAS; Am Chem Soc; Sigma Xi. *Res:* Mechanism of enzyme action; use of enzymes in immunoassays; protein purification; fluorescence immunoassays. *Mailing Add:* 557 Irven Ct Palo Alto CA 94306

RODGERS, ROBERT STANLEIGH, b Kew Gardens, NY, Jan 5, 45; m 75. ANALYTICAL CHEMISTRY. *Educ:* Polytech Inst Brooklyn, BS & MS, 66; Clarkson Col Technol, PhD(chem), 71. *Prof Exp:* Res asst chem, Calif Inst Technol, 70-72; asst prof chem, Mich State Univ, 72-73; asst prof chem, Lehigh Univ, 73-80; MEM STAFF, PRINCETON APPL RES, EG&G, INC, 80- *Mem:* Am Chem Soc. *Res:* Electrode kinetics; laboratory microprocessors. *Mailing Add:* EG&G Princeton Appl Res PO Box 2565 Princeton NJ 08540

RODGERS, SHERIDAN JOSEPH, b Ellwood City, Pa, Mar 26, 29; m 50; c 4. ANALYTICAL CHEMISTRY, ENVIRONMENTAL HEALTH. *Educ:* Geneva Col, BS, 54. *Prof Exp:* Res chemist, 52-60, SECT HEAD ANAL CHEM, MSA RES CORP, 60- *Mem:* Am Nuclear Soc; Am Soc Test & Mat; Am Indust Hyg Asn. *Res:* Aerosol generation and sampling; air pollution monitoring; measurement and control of dust and toxic fumes in underground mines and vehicular tunnels; development and testing of protective clothing; monitoring and control of workplace health and safety hazards. *Mailing Add:* MSA Res Corp Evans City PA 16033

RODGMAN, ALAN, b Aberdare, Wales, Feb 7, 24; nat US; m 47; c 3. ORGANIC CHEMISTRY. *Educ:* Univ Toronto, BA, 49, MS, 51, PhD(org chem), 53. *Prof Exp:* Asst, Banting & Best, Dept Med Res, Toronto, 47-53, res assoc, 53-54; chemist, 54-65, head, Natural Prod Chem Sect, 65-72 & 74-

75, actg mgr chem res, 73, mgr anal res, 75-76, dir res, 76-80, DIR FUND RES, R J REYNOLDS TOBACCO CO, 80- *Mem:* Am Chem Soc; NY Acad Sci; Chem Inst Can. *Res:* Composition of tobacco smoke; tobacco smoke and health. *Mailing Add:* 2828 Birchwood Dr Winston-Salem NC 27103

RODIA, JACOB STEPHEN, b Chicago, Ill, Apr 7, 23; m 49; c 5. BIO-ORGANIC CHEMISTRY. *Educ:* Loyola Univ, Ill, BS, 47; Univ Ill, MS, 48, PhD(org chem), 52. *Prof Exp:* Res chemist, Int Minerals & Chem Corp, Ill, 52-54; assoc prof org chem, Drake Univ, 54-56; res chemist, Westinghouse Labs, 56-60 & 3M Res Labs, 60-63; assoc prof, 63-70, PROF CHEM, ST JOSEPH'S COL, IND, 70-, CHMN DEPT CHEM, 81- *Mem:* Am Chem Soc. *Res:* Polymer chemistry; synthesis, mechanism of formation, properties and reactions of new organic and polymeric materials. *Mailing Add:* Dept of Chem St Joseph's Col Rensselaer IN 47978

RODIECK, ROBERT WILLIAM, b Highland Falls, NY, Apr 17, 37; m 61. VISION. *Educ:* Mass Inst Technol, BS, 58, MS, 61; Univ Sydney, PhD(physiol), 65. *Prof Exp:* Lectr physiol, Univ Sydney, 62-67, sr lectr, 67-72, reader physiol, 72-78; BISHOP PROF, UNIV WASH, 78- *Res:* Neurophysiology; retinal neurophysiology. *Mailing Add:* Dept Ophthal RJ-10 Univ Wash Seattle WA 98195

RODIG, OSCAR RUDOLF, b Rahway, NJ, Nov 15, 29; m 64; c 2. ENZYME CHEMISTRY, BIOSYNTHESIS. *Educ:* Rutgers Univ, BS, 51; Univ Wis, PhD(chem), 54. *Prof Exp:* Fulbright fel, Univ Manchester, 54-55; USPHS fel, Swiss Fed Inst Technol, 55-56; asst prof chem, 56-61, ASSOC PROF CHEM, UNIV VA, 61- *Concurrent Pos:* Ramsay Mem fel, 54-55; vis assoc prof, Univ Strasbourg, 61, Swiss Fed Inst Technol, 73 & Max Planck Inst Biochem, Munich, 74. *Honors & Awards:* J Shelton Horsley Award, Va Acad Sci, 67. *Mem:* Am Chem Soc; Sigma Xi. *Res:* Chemistry of natural products, especially steroids and antibiotics; mechanisms of enzymic reactions. *Mailing Add:* Dept Chem Univ Va Charlottesville VA 22901

RODIN, ALVIN E, b Winnipeg, Man, Mar 25, 26; m 51; c 4. PATHOLOGY. *Educ:* Univ Man, MD, 50, MSc, 59; FRCP(C), 59. *Prof Exp:* Teaching fel path, Queen's Univ, Ont, 56-57; res assoc, Univ Man, 57-59; assoc dir path, Royal Alexandra Hosp, Edmonton, Alta, 59-60; dir path, Misericordia Hosp, 61-63; from asst prof to prof path, Univ Tex Med Br Galveston, 63-75; CHMN DEPT POSTGRAD MED & CONTINUING EDUC, SCH MED, WRIGHT STATE UNIV, 75- *Concurrent Pos:* Consult pathologist, Med-Surg Res Inst, Univ Alta, 59-63. *Mem:* Fel Col Am Path; Asn Am Med Cols; Am Osler Soc; Int Acad Path; fel Royal Soc Med. *Res:* Mercury nephrotoxicity; relationship of pineal to tumor growth; ultrastructure of pineal; radiation induced tumors; congenital heart disease; perinatal disease; medical education. *Mailing Add:* Sch of Med Wright State Univ Dayton OH 45431

RODIN, BURTON, b St Louis, Mo, June 19, 33; m 62; c 2. MATHEMATICS. *Educ:* Univ Calif, Los Angeles, BA, 55, PhD(math), 61; Univ Chicago, MS, 58. *Prof Exp:* Asst prof math, Harvard Univ, 61-63, Univ Minn, 63-64, Univ Calif, San Diego, 64-65 & Stanford Univ, 65-66; from asst prof to assoc prof, 66-72, PROF MATH, UNIV CALIF, SAN DIEGO, 72-, CHMN DEPT, 77- *Mem:* Am Math Soc. *Res:* Complex analysis. *Mailing Add:* Dept of Math Univ of Calif at San Diego La Jolla CA 92037

RODIN, ERVIN Y, b Budapest, Hungary, Jan 17, 32; US citizen; m 56; c 3. APPLIED MATHEMATICS. *Educ:* Univ Tex, Austin, BA, 60, PhD(math), 64. *Prof Exp:* Spec instr math, Univ Tex, Austin, 60-64; sr mathematician, Wyle Labs, 64-66; assoc prof, 66-77, PROF APPL MATH, WASH UNIV, 77- *Concurrent Pos:* Organizer & Ed Proceedings, Symp Apollo Appln, 65; mem, Adv Comt Data Processing Systs Antiballistic Missile Defense, Nat Acad Sci, 68-71 & Adv Bd, RETA Consult Environ Engrs, 71-; organizer & gen chmn, Symp Eng Sci in Biomed, 69; chmn, Aleph Found, 71-; organizer & gen chmn, Int Meeting Pollution, Eng & Sci Solutions, Israel, 72; organizer & dir, Appl Finite Element Technol in RR Indust, 75; ed-in-chief, Int J Comput & Math with Appln & Int Series Monographs on Modern Appl Math & Comput Sci. *Mem:* AAAS; Am Math Soc; Math Asn Am; Soc Indust & Appl Math; Soc Eng Sci. *Res:* Applied mathematics, particularly applications to air, water and noise pollution, to population studies and to the growth of tumors; nonlinear partial differential and similar equations. *Mailing Add:* Box 1045 Dept of Systs Sci & Math Washington Univ St Louis MO 63130

RODIN, MARTHA KINSCHER, b New York, NY, May 18, 29; m 51; c 3. ANATOMY, NEUROPHYSIOLOGY. *Educ:* Wagner Col, BS, 52; Wayne State Univ, MS, 65, PhD(anat), 67. *Prof Exp:* From instr to asst prof, 67-73, ASSOC PROF ANAT, COL MED, WAYNE STATE UNIV, 73- *Concurrent Pos:* Anat consult & assoc psychiat, Lafayette Clin, 72- *Honors & Awards:* Sigma Xi Res Award, 67. *Mem:* AAAS; Am Asn Anat. *Res:* Autonomic nerve endings; mechanisms of convulsive disorders; fluorescent mapping of catacholamines in brain. *Mailing Add:* 773 Balfour Grosse Pointe MI 48230

RODIN, MIRIAM BETH, b Chicago, Ill, Sept 21, 47. EPIDEMIOLOGY, MEDICAL ANTHROPOLOGY. *Educ:* Univ Ill, Urbana, AB, 69, AM, 73, PhD(anthrop), 77. *Prof Exp:* Instr anthrop, Univ Ill, Urbana, 76; ASST PROF EPIDEMIOL, SCH PUB HEALTH, UNIV ILL MED CTR, 76- *Concurrent Pos:* Investr, State Ill DMHOD extramural res grant, 77-80; assoc dir, NIMH training grant psychosocial epidemiol, 79-84. *Mem:* Am Anthrop Asn; AAAS; Am Pub Health Asn; Soc Epidemiol Res; Soc Med Anthrop. *Res:* Alcoholism; social psychiatry studies in support systems; urban anthropology of local community dynamics. *Mailing Add:* Sch Pub Health Box 6998 Univ of Ill Med Ctr Chicago IL 60680

RODINE, ROBERT HENRY, b West Pittston, Pa, Nov 9, 29; m 53; c 3. MATHEMATICS. *Educ:* Mansfield State Col, BSEd, 52; Purdue Univ, MS, 57, PhD, 64. *Prof Exp:* Chemist, Westinghouse Elec Corp, 52-55; instr math & statist, Purdue Univ, 57-64; asst prof statist, State Univ NY Buffalo, 64-68; ASSOC PROF MATH, NORTHERN ILL UNIV, 68- *Mem:* Am Statist Asn; Opers Res Soc Am; NY Acad Sci; Inst Math Statist. *Res:* Applied probability; applications of probability to the natural sciences and engineering. *Mailing Add:* Dept of Math Northern Ill Univ DeKalb IL 60115

RODINI, BENJAMIN THOMAS, JR, b Philadelphia, Pa, Feb 26, 47; m 75; c 2. COMPOSITE MATERIALS. *Educ:* Drexel Univ, BS, 70, MS, 72, PhD(appl mech), 75. *Prof Exp:* Sr structures engr, Fort Worth Div, Gen Dynamics, 75-79; STRUCTURAL ENGR, SPACE SYST DIV, GEN ELEC, 79- *Concurrent Pos:* Adj prof, Drexel Univ, 75. *Res:* Characterization, development, analysis and design of advanced composite structures (polymer and metal matrix); analysis and design of high voltage potted electronic modules for preclusion of arc over failures due to time-dependent crack growth in the potting compound. *Mailing Add:* Space Syst Div Gen Elec Co PO Box 8555 M4018 Philadelphia PA 19101

RODKEY, FREDERICK LEE, biochemistry, see previous edition

RODKEY, LEO SCOTT, b Topeka, Kans, Jan 18, 41; m 63; c 1. IMMUNOLOGY. *Educ:* Univ Kans, BA, 64, PhD(microbiol), 68. *Prof Exp:* NIH fel immunochem, Col Med, Univ Ill, 68-70; asst prof, 70-75, ASSOC PROF BIOL, KANS STATE UNIV, 75- *Concurrent Pos:* Mem, Basel Inst Immunol, 77-78; NIH res career develop award. *Mem:* AAAS; Am Asn Immunologists; Am Genetic Asn; NY Acad Sci; Am Soc Microbiol. *Res:* Isotypic, allotypic and idiotypic determinants of antibodies, autoantiidiotypic regulation of immune processes, allotype evolution and subgroup characterization. *Mailing Add:* Div of Biol Kans State Univ Manhattan KS 66506

RODKIEWICZ, CZESLAW MATEUSZ, b Turka, Poland; m. MECHANICAL ENGINEERING. *Educ:* Polish Univ Col, London, dipl ing, 50; Univ Ill, MSc, 63; Case Inst Technol, PhD(mech eng), 67. *Prof Exp:* Res engr trans-sonic wind tunnel, English Elec Co, 52-54; tech asst mech eng, Dowty Equip Ltd, Can, 54-55; lectr, Ryerson Inst Technol, Toronto, 55-58; from asst prof to assoc prof, 58-63, PROF, DEPT MECH ENG, UNIV ALTA, 72- *Mem:* Fel NY Acad Sci; fel Am Soc Mech Engrs; Can Soc Mech Engrs; Sigma Xi. *Res:* Fluid mechanics and heat transfer, especially hypersonic flight, lubrication, blood flow and ice formations. *Mailing Add:* Dept Mech Eng Univ Alta Edmonton AB T6G 2G7 Can

RODMAN, CHARLES WILLIAM, b Delaware, Ohio, Mar 27, 28; m 48; c 1. ENVIRONMENTAL NOISE, ACOUSTIC INSTRUMENTATION. *Educ:* Ohio State Univ, BSc, 71. *Prof Exp:* Res technician mech eng, 51-59, PRIN RES ENGR ACOUSTICS, BATTELLE MEM INST, 59- *Honors & Awards:* Wallace Waterfall Award, Am Soc Testing & Mat. *Mem:* Acoust Soc Am; Am Soc Testing & Mat; sr mem Instrument Soc Am; Inst Noise Control Eng. *Res:* Community noise; environmental noise; architectural acoustics; machinery noise control; dynamics instrumentation and analysis. *Mailing Add:* Battelle Mem Inst 505 King Ave Columbus OH 43201

RODMAN, HARVEY MEYER, b New York, NY, Sept, 8, 40. ENDOCRINOLOGY, DIABETES. *Educ:* Columbia Col, BA, 62; Univ Chicago, MD, 66. *Prof Exp:* Asst prof, 72-80, ASSOC PROF MED, SCH MED, CASE WESTERN RESERVE UNIV, 80-, RES FEL & DIR, CLIN RES CTR, 72- *Mem:* Am Diabetes Asn; Endocrine Soc; Am Fedn Clin Res. *Res:* Immunology of diabetes; diabetes in pregnancy; secondary causes of diabetes. *Mailing Add:* Dept Med Univ Hosps 2074 Abington Rd Cleveland OH 44106

RODMAN, JAMES PURCELL, b Alliance, Ohio, Nov 11, 26; m 50; c 4. ASTROPHYSICS. *Educ:* Mt Union Col, BS, 49; Washington Univ, MA, 51; Yale Univ, PhD(astrophysics), 63. *Prof Exp:* Part-time instr physics & math, 51-59, assoc prof physics, 62-66, dir comput ctr, 66-74, PROF PHYSICS & ASTRON & CHMN DEPT, MT UNION COL, 66-, DIR CLARKE OBSERV, 53- *Concurrent Pos:* From vpres to pres, Alliance Tool Co, 51-59; physicist, Alliance Ware Inc, 51-55, corp secy, 54-55; physicist, Alliance Mach Co, 57-; consult engr astron instrumentation, Yale Univ, 62-, res assoc, 63-69; dir, Mt Union Bank, 67-71; dir, United National Bank & Trust Co, 71- *Mem:* Am Phys Soc; Am Astron Soc; Am Geophys Union; Royal Astron Soc; Optical Soc Am. *Res:* Observational astrophysics of unstable stellar atmospheres; astrophysical-physical instrumentation design; x-ray and beta-spectroscopy. *Mailing Add:* Dept of Physics & Astron Mt Union Col Alliance OH 44601

RODMAN, MORTON JOSEPH, b Boston, Mass, Jan 28, 18; m 43; c 5. PHARMACOLOGY. *Educ:* Mass Col Pharm, BS, 39; Georgetown Univ, PhD, 50. *Prof Exp:* Asst prof biol sci, Univ, 50-53, assoc prof pharmacol, Col Pharm, 53-57, chmn, Dept Biol Sci, Univ, 53-71, chmn dept, Col Pharm, 71-81, PROF PHARMACOL, COL PHARM, RUTGERS UNIV, PISCATAWAY, 57- *Concurrent Pos:* Consult accident prev prog, USPHS, 57-64; consult, Dept Neurol & Psychiat, US Vet Admin, 58-80, Bur Maternal & Child Welfare, NJ State Dept Health, 60-64, New York City Dept Health, 60-64 & Dept Drugs, Coun on Drugs, AMA, 63-; NSF vis scientist, Am Asn Cols Pharm, 63-; comnr, Narcotic Drug Study Comn, NJ Legis, 63-70. *Honors & Awards:* Lindback Found Award, 62. *Mem:* Fel AAAS; Am Pharmaceut Asn; sci affil AMA; Am Pub Health Asn; Walter Reed Soc. *Res:* Physiology and pharmacology of thermoregulation; toxicology of plant products; organic chemicals in household products; neuropharmacology; psychopharmacology; evaluation of therapeutic efficacy and safety of drugs in clinical use. *Mailing Add.* Dept Pharmacol Rutgers Univ Col Pharm Busch Campus Piscataway NJ 08854

RODMAN, NATHANIEL FULFORD, JR, b Norfolk, Va, July 24, 26; m 51, 70; c 4. PATHOLOGY. *Educ:* Princeton Univ, AB, 47; Univ Pa, MD, 51. *Prof Exp:* Intern, Lankenau Hosp, Philadelphia, 51-52; fel & resident path, Sch Med, Univ NC, Chapel Hill, 52-53 & 55-58, from instr to assoc prof, 58-70; prof, Col Med, Univ Iowa, 70-74; PROF PATH & CHMN DEPT, MED CTR, WVA UNIV, 74- *Concurrent Pos:* Nat Heart & Lung Inst res career develop award, 67-70; mem coun thrombosis, Am Heart Asn. *Mem:* AAAS; Electron Micros Soc Am; AMA; Int Acad Path; Soc Exp Biol & Med. *Res:* Ultrastructural aspects of problems in thrombosis and atherosclerosis; cytopathology and surgical pathology. *Mailing Add:* Dept of Path WVa Univ Med Ctr Morgantown WV 26506

RODMAN, TOBY C, b Philadelphia, Pa. CHROMOSOME STRUCTURES. *Educ:* Philadelphia Col Pharm & Sci, BSc, 37; NY Univ, MS, 61, PhD(biol), 64. *Prof Exp:* USPHS fel, Columbia Univ, 64-67; res assoc biol sci, 67-69; from instr to asst prof, 69-76, ASSOC PROF ANAT, MED COL, CORNELL UNIV, 76- *Concurrent Pos:* Vis assoc prof, Rockefeller Univ, 76-77, adj assoc prof, 77- *Mem:* AAAS; Am Soc Cell Biol; Am Asn Anat; Soc Study of Reproduction. *Res:* Molecular organization of mammalian gametes and fertilized eggs. *Mailing Add:* Dept of Anat Cornell Univ Med Col New York NY 10021

RODNAN, GERALD PAUL, b New York, NY, Oct 3, 27; m 50; c 3. MEDICINE. *Educ:* State Univ NY, MD, 49. *Prof Exp:* House officer med, Maimonides Hosp, Brooklyn, 49-51; house officer, Duke Hosp, 51-53; clin investr, Nat Inst Arthritis & Metab Dis, 53-55; from instr to assoc prof, 55-67, PROF MED, UNIV PITTSBURGH, 67- *Concurrent Pos:* Ed, Bull Rheumatic Dis, 66- & Primer Rheumatic Dis, 72; mem bd gov, Am Bd Internal Med, 76-78. *Mem:* AAAS; Am Asn Hist Med; Am Rheumatism Asn (pres, 75-76); Am Fedn Clin Res. *Res:* Rheumatic disease. *Mailing Add:* Dept of Med Univ of Pittsburgh Pittsburgh PA 15261

RODNEY, DAVID ROSS, b Jane, Mo, May 15, 19; m 42; c 3. HORTICULTURE. *Educ:* Univ Mo, BS, 40; Ohio State Univ, MSc, 46, PhD(hort), 50. *Prof Exp:* Asst prof pomol, State Univ NY Col Agr, Cornell, 48-53; asst horticulturist, Citrus Exp Sta, Univ Calif, 53-57; assoc horticulturist, 57-63, HORTICULTURIST, EXP STA, UNIV ARIZ, 63- *Mem:* Am Soc Hort Sci. *Res:* Citrus rootstocks; tree physiology; plant nutrition. *Mailing Add:* 2025 Cotton Tail Ave Yuma AZ 85364

RODNEY, EARNEST ABRAM, b Scranton, Pa, Mar 30, 17; m 43; c 2. METEOROLOGY, MATHEMATICS. *Educ:* East Stroudsburg State Col, Pa, BS, 40. *Prof Exp:* Meteorologist, Com US Weather Bur, Washington, DC, 45-46; air traffic control meteorol, US Air Force, 46, meteorologist, Pope Field, NC, 46-48; meteorologist, Com US Weather Bur, Jacksonville, Fla, 48-49, prin asst, Asheville, NC, 49-51, prin asst, Greensboro, NC, 51-56; meteorologist hurricane res & radiomarine, Nat Weather Serv, Washington, DC, 56-61, meteorologist in chg, Com Nat Ocean & Atmospheric Admin, Fletcher, 61-79; RETIRED. *Concurrent Pos:* Teacher math & sci, Pender County Bd Educ, Burgaw, NC, 40-42; meteorologist & opers officer, US Air Force, 42-45. *Mem:* Am Meteorol Soc. *Res:* Hurricane research and quantitative precipitation research; operational field. *Mailing Add:* 28 Westridge Dr Asheville NC 28803

RODNEY, PAUL FREDERICK, electromagnetics, mathematical physics, see previous edition

RODNEY, WILLIAM STANLEY, b Scranton, Pa, Dec 20, 26; m 49; c 4. NUCLEAR PHYSICS, ASTROPHYSICS. *Educ:* Univ Scranton, BS, 49; Cath Univ, MS, 53, PhD, 55. *Prof Exp:* Physicist optics, Nat Bur Stand, 49-56; Guggenheim fel, Royal Inst Technol, Sweden, 56-57; physicist optics, Nat Bur Stand, 57-58; physicist, Off Sci Res, US Air Force, 58-62; PROG DIR, NUCLEAR PHYSICS PROG, NSF, 62- *Concurrent Pos:* Lectr, Cath Univ, 53; vis prof, Calif Inst Technol, 73-74; adj prof, Georgetown Univ, Washington, DC, 81. *Mem:* Fel AAAS; fel Am Phys Soc; fel Optical Soc Am. *Res:* Nuclear astrophysics using non-resonant proton radiative capture. *Mailing Add:* 8112 Whites Ford Way Potomac MD 20854

RODOLFO, KELVIN S, b Manila, Philippines, Dec 20, 36; US citizen; m 73; c 2. MARINE GEOLOGY. *Educ:* Univ Philippines, BS, 58; Univ Southern Calif, MS, 64, PhD, 67. *Prof Exp:* Geologist, San Jose Oil Co, 59-60; asst, Univ Southern Calif, 61-64, res assoc, 64-66; asst prof, 66-70, ASSOC PROF GEOL SCI, UNIV ILL, CHICAGO CIRCLE, 70- *Concurrent Pos:* Geologist, Tidewater Oil Co, 62-63; geol oceanogr, Int Indian Ocean Exped, 64; oceanogr, Environ Sci Serv Admin Res Vessel Oceanographer Global Cruise, 67; lithologist, Leg 16, Deep Sea Drilling Proj, 71, Leg 26, 72 & Leg 59, 78; NSF res grants; Danforth Found Assoc, 80- *Mem:* Fel AAAS; fel Geol Soc Am; Soc Econ Paleont & Mineral; Am Geophys Union. *Res:* Regional tectonics of Southeast Asia; deep-sea sedimentology. *Mailing Add:* Dept of Geol Sci Univ of Ill Chicago Circle Chicago IL 60680

RODOWSKAS, CHRISTOPHER A, JR, b Baltimore, Md, July 26, 39. PHARMACY, PHARMACY ADMINISTRATION. *Educ:* Fordham Univ, BS, 61; Purdue Univ, MS, 63, PhD(pharm), 68. *Prof Exp:* Asst prof pharm, Univ Conn, 64-68; from asst prof to assoc prof, Ohio State Univ, 68-73; vis dir, Pharm Manpower Info Proj, Am Asn Cols Pharm, 72, dir, Off Res & Develop, 73-74, exec dir, 75-81; PROF & CHMN, DEPT PHARM PRACT, HOWARD UNIV, 81- *Concurrent Pos:* Mem, Nat Adv Coun Health Professions Educ, Dept Health, Educ & Welfare, 76-79 & Bd Dirs, Am Found Pharmaceut Educ, 75-81. *Mem:* AAAS; Am Pharmaceut Asn; Am Pub Health Asn; Am Soc Hosp Pharmacists. *Res:* Application of administrative sciences to health care delivery systems with emphasis on drugs and pharmaceutical services. *Mailing Add:* 1103 Meurilee Lane Silver Springs MD 20901

RODRICK, GARY EUGENE, b McPherson, Kans, Oct 5, 43; m 67; c 2. PARASITOLOGY, INVERTEBRATE PHYSIOLOGY. *Educ:* Kans State Col Pittsburg, BA, 66, MS, 67; Univ Okla, PhD(zool), 71. *Prof Exp:* NIH fel parasitol, Univ Mass, Amherst, 71-73; res assoc pathobiol, Liverpool Univ, 73-75; asst prof biol, Dodge City Col, 75-78; ASST PROF COMP MED, UNIV SOUTH FLA, 78- *Mem:* Sigma Xi; Am Soc Parasitol; Am Micros Soc; Am Soc Trop Med & Hyg; Am Soc Zoologists. *Res:* Public health aspects of edible shellfish and fish; invertebrate immunobiology and biochemistry. *Mailing Add:* Sch of Med 12901 N 30th St Tampa FL 33612

RODRICKS, JOSEPH VICTOR, b Brockton, Mass, Feb 25, 38; m 75; c 2. RISK ASSESSMENT. *Educ:* Mass Inst Technol, BS, 60; Univ Md, PhD(biochem), 68; Am Bd Toxicol, dipl, 81. *Prof Exp:* Res chemist, Food & Drug Admin, 65-69; fel, chem Univ Calif, Berkeley, 69-70; chief, Biochem Br, Food & Drug Admin, 70-72, assoc dir, Div Toxicol, 73-77, dep assoc comnr

sci, 78-80; VPRES & DIR LIFE SCI, CLEMENT ASSOCS, 80-; ASSOC PROF CHEM, UNIV MD, 65- *Concurrent Pos:* Mem, Comt Toxicol, Nat Acad Sci-Nat Res Coun, 78-82. *Mem:* Acad Toxicol Sci; Soc Risk Analysis; Am Col Toxicol; Am Chem Soc. *Res:* Review and evaluation for toxicity and exposure data for purposes of estimating the risk to public health associated with exposures to environmental pollutants, occupational hazards, food additives, pesticides, industrial chemicals and natural toxins. *Mailing Add:* Dept Chem Univ Md College Park MD 20742

RODRIGUE, GEORGE PIERRE, b Paincourtville, La, June 19, 31; m 55; c 6. ELECTRICAL ENGINEERING. *Educ:* La State Univ, BS, 52, MS, 54; Harvard Univ, PhD(appl physics), 58. *Prof Exp:* Sr staff engr, Sperry-Rand Corp, 58-61, res consult, 61-68; prof, 68-77, REGENTS PROF ELEC ENG, GA INST TECHNOL, 77- *Concurrent Pos:* Consult, Sperry-Rand Corp, 68-72; US Army Missle Command, 70-73; Airtron, Inc, 76-82; bd dir, Electromagnetic Sci Inc, 69-73. *Mem:* Fel Inst Elec & Electronics Engrs. *Res:* Ferrites; application of ferrites to microwave devices; microwave acoustic phenomena and devices; near field antenna measurements. *Mailing Add:* 1090 Kingston Dr Atlanta GA 30342

RODRIGUEZ, ARGELIA VELEZ, b Havana, Cuba, Nov 23, 36; US citizen; m 54; c 2. MATHEMATICS, PHYSICS. *Educ:* Marianao Inst, Cuba, BS, 55; Univ Havana, PhD(math), 60. *Prof Exp:* Asst prof math, Marianao Inst, Cuba, 58-61; asst prof math & physics & head dept, Tex Col, 62-64; from asst prof to assoc prof, 64-72, PROF MATH & DEPT HEAD, BISHOP COL, 72-, CHAIRPERSON, DIV NATURAL & MATH SCI, 75- *Concurrent Pos:* Lectr mod math, NSF In-Serv Inst Sec Teachers, Bishop Col, 65-67; fel comput assisted instruct, Tex Christian Univ, 67-68; dir & coordr, US Off Educ Proj Elem Math Teachers & Teacher Trainers, 70-73; NSF Coop Col Sch Sci Prog Jr High Sch Teachers Math, 72-73; dir & coordr, NSF Math Instrnl Improv Implementation Prog for High Sch Teachers, Dallas Independent Sch Dist, 73-76; liaison officer, Argonne Nat Lab, 75- *Mem:* AAAS; Am Math Soc; Nat Coun Teachers Math; Math Asn Am. *Res:* Classical analysis; solutions of partial differential equations; teaching strategies in mathematics and curriculum development for disadvantaged college students. *Mailing Add:* 838 Foxboro Lane Dallas TX 75241

RODRIGUEZ, CARLOS EDUARDO, b San Antonio, Tex, Apr 23, 41. COMPUTER SCIENCE. *Educ:* Univ Tex, BS, 62, PhD(chem), 66. *Prof Exp:* Res assoc, Univ Tex, 66-68; staff asst comput animation films, Adv Coun Col Chem, 67-68; asst prof comput sci, 68-73, ASSOC PROF COMPUT SCI, E TEX STATE UNIV, 73- *Concurrent Pos:* Coun Libr Resources fel, 74-75. *Mem:* Asn Comput Mach; Asn Develop Comput Based Instrnl Systs. *Res:* Computer-assisted instruction; computer science curriculum development. *Mailing Add:* Dept of Comput Sci ETex State Univ Commerce TX 75428

RODRIGUEZ, CHARLES F, b San Antonio, Tex, July 1, 38; m 62; c 4. ANALYTICAL CHEMISTRY. *Educ:* St Mary's Univ, Tex, BS, 61. *Prof Exp:* Asst chemist, 61-64, res chemist, 64-74, SR RES CHEMIST, SOUTHWEST RES INST, 74- *Mem:* Am Chem Soc (treas, 68); Sigma Xi; Soc Appl Spectros; Am Soc Mass Spectrometry. *Res:* Analytical characterization of petroleum distillate fuels and their synthetic crude oil sources; development of chromatographic and spectroscopic analytical methods for applications in energy technology; enhanced recovery of synfuels. *Mailing Add:* 8500 Culebra Rd PO Drawer 28510 San Antonio TX 78284

RODRIGUEZ, DENNIS MILTON, b Tampa, Fla, July 21, 43; m 70. MATHEMATICS. *Educ:* Univ S Fla, BA, 65; Univ Calif, Riverside, MA, 66, PhD(math), 69. *Prof Exp:* Asst prof, 69-76, ASSOC PROF MATH, UNIV HOUSTON DOWNTOWN COL, 76- *Mem:* Math Asn Am. *Res:* Probability theory; stochastic processes. *Mailing Add:* Dept of Math Univ of Houston Downtown Col Houston TX 77002

RODRIGUEZ, EUGENE, b New York, NY, Mar 26, 33; m 58; c 4. IMMUNOLOGY. *Educ:* Queen's Col, NY, BS, 54; Johns Hopkins Univ, ScM, 59, ScD(microbiol), 66. *Prof Exp:* Instr microbiol, Med Sch, Johns Hopkins Univ, 66-67; mem field staff, Rockefeller Found, 67-70; IMMUNOLOGIST, DIV RES PATH, DEPT LAB MED, ST JOHN'S MERCY MED CTR, 70- *Concurrent Pos:* Vis prof, Mahidol Univ, Bangkok, Thailand, 67-69. *Res:* Mechanism of antigen-antibody reactions; biological consequences of antigen-antibody reactions such as immediate and delayed hypersensitivity and complement fixation; immunopath of glomerulas diseases. *Mailing Add:* St John's Mercy Med Ctr 615 S New Ballas Rd St Louis MO 63141

RODRIGUEZ, FERDINAND, b Cleveland, Ohio, July 8, 28; m 51; c 2. CHEMICAL ENGINEERING, POLYMER SCIENCE. *Educ:* Case Inst Technol, BS, 50, MS, 54; Cornell Univ, PhD(chem eng), 58. *Prof Exp:* Develop engr, Ferro Chem Corp, Ohio, 50-54; from asst prof to assoc prof chem eng, 58-71, PROF CHEM ENG, CORNELL UNIV, 71- *Concurrent Pos:* Consult, Union Carbide Corp, 60-69. *Mem:* Am Chem Soc; Am Inst Chem Engrs; Soc Rheology. *Res:* Formation, fabrication and evaluation of polymeric materials. *Mailing Add:* Sch of Eng Olin Hall Cornell Univ Ithaca NY 14850

RODRIGUEZ, GILBERTO, b Caracas, Venezuela, May 12, 29; m 59; c 5. BIOLOGICAL OCEANOGRAPHY, ECOLOGY. *Educ:* Cent Univ Venezuela, BSc, 55; Univ Miami, MSc, 57; Univ Wales, PhD(zool), 70. *Prof Exp:* Investr marine biol, Univ of the Orient, 59-60; INVESTR BIOL, VENEZUELAN INST SCI RES, 67-; assoc prof biol, Cent Univ Venezuela, 67-77; HEAD, CTR ECOL, VENEZUELAN INST SCI RES, 81- *Concurrent Pos:* Mem, Venezuelan Coun Agr Res, 67-68. *Mem:* Brit Soc Exp Biol; Venezuelan Soc Natural Sci. *Res:* Ecology of estuaries; taxonomy of freshwater crabs; biological rhythms. *Mailing Add:* Venezuelan Inst for Sci Res PO Box 1827 Caracas Venezuela

RODRIGUEZ, HAROLD VERNON, b New Orleans, La, Aug 30, 32; m 56; c 4. CHEMICAL ENGINEERING. *Educ:* La State Univ, BS, 54, MS, 58, PhD(chem eng), 62. *Prof Exp:* Engr trainee, Natural Gas Dept, Magnolia Petrol Co, 54-55; instr chem eng, La State Univ, 60-61; sr res technologist, Mobil Oil Corp, 61-69; assoc prof chem eng, 69-71, dir div eng, 71-76, DEAN, COL ENG, UNIV S ALA, 76- *Mem:* Am Inst Chem Engrs; Sigma Xi; Am Soc Eng Educ; Soc Am Military Engrs; Nat Soc Prof Engrs. *Res:* Application of heat to underground formations for oil recovery. *Mailing Add:* Col Eng Univ South Ala Mobile AL 36688

RODRIGUEZ, HAYDEE C, physics, mathematics, see previous edition

RODRIGUEZ, JOAQUIN, b New York, NY, Jan 9, 34; m 66. GEOLOGY. *Educ:* Hunter Col, BA, 55; Ohio State Univ, MSc, 57; Univ Ind, PhD(geol), 60. *Prof Exp:* Lectr, 59-62, from instr to asst prof, 62-70, assoc prof, 70-79, PROF GEOL, HUNTER COL, 79- *Mem:* AAAS; fel Geol Soc Am; Paleont Soc; Nat Asn Geol Teachers; Int Paleont Asn. *Res:* Invertebrate paleontology; paleoecology; palichnology; Devonian-Mississippian brachiopods; biostratigraphy. *Mailing Add:* Dept of Geol & Geog Hunter Col 695 Park Ave New York NY 10021

RODRIGUEZ, JOSE ENRIQUE, b San Juan, PR, Oct 16, 33; m 61; c 2. VIROLOGY. *Educ:* Yale Univ, BS, 55; Univ Pa, PhD(microbiol), 63. *Prof Exp:* Res asst virol, Children's Hosp, Philadelphia, 63-65; NIH fel, Inst Virol, Univ Wurzburg, 65-68; asst prof, 68-74, ASSOC PROF MICROBIOL, UNIV IOWA, 74- *Res:* Mechanisms of viral interference. *Mailing Add:* Dept of Microbiol Univ of Iowa Iowa City IA 52240

RODRIGUEZ, JUAN GUADALUPE, b Espanola, NMex, Dec 23, 20; m 48; c 4. ENTOMOLOGY. *Educ:* NMex State Univ, BS, 43; Ohio State Univ, MS, 46, PhD(entom), 49. *Prof Exp:* Asst, Ohio State Univ, 46-47, Exp Sta, 48-49; from asst entomologist to assoc entomologist, 49-59, assoc prof entom, 59-61, PROF ENTOM, UNIV KY, 61- *Concurrent Pos:* Adv entom, Univ San Carlos, Guatemala, 61; ed, Insect & Mite Nutrit, 72 & Recent Advances Acarol, 79; co-ed, Current Topics Insect Endorinol & Nutrit, 81. *Honors & Awards:* Alumni Asn Award Distinguished Res, 63; Thomas Poe Cooper Award Distinguished Achievement Res, Col Agr, Univ Ky, 72. *Mem:* AAAS; Am Inst Biol Sci; Entom Soc Can; Sigma Xi; Acarol Soc Am. *Res:* Axenic culture of arthropods; insect/mite nutrition; insect pest management; host-plant resistance to insects/mites; nutritional ecology. *Mailing Add:* Dept of Entom Univ of Ky Lexington KY 40506

RODRIGUEZ, LORRAINE DITZLER, b Ava, Ill, July 4, 20; m 48; c 4. MICROBIOLOGY, TOXICOLOGY. *Educ:* Southern Ill Norm Univ, BEduc, 43; Ohio State Univ, MS, 44; Univ Ky, PhD(microbiol), 73. *Prof Exp:* Asst nutritionist, Ohio Agr Res & Develop Ctr, 44-49; fel, Dept Entom, Univ Ky, 73-74; consult, 74-79; EXTENSION SPECIALIST, DEPT ENTOM, UNIV KY, 79- *Mem:* Am Chem Soc; Soc Environ Toxicol & Chem. *Res:* Acaricide resistance; relation of fungi to acarines; biodegradation of pesticides; pesticide impact assessment. *Mailing Add:* 1550 Beacon Hill Rd Lexington KY 40504

RODRIGUEZ, SERGIO, b Lautaro, Chile, Dec 12, 30; m 59; c 2. SOLID STATE PHYSICS. *Educ:* Univ Calif, Berkeley, AB, 55, MA, 56, PhD, 58. *Prof Exp:* Asst prof physics, Univ Wash, 58-59; res asst prof, Univ Ill, 59-60; asst prof, Purdue Univ, 60-61; asst prof, Princeton Univ, 61-62; assoc prof, 62-64, PROF PHYSICS, PURDUE UNIV, LAFAYETTE, 64- *Concurrent Pos:* Consult, Ford Motor Co, Mich, IBM Corp & Argonne Nat Lab; John Simon Guggenheim Mem fel, 67-68. *Honors & Awards:* Alexander von Humboldt Sr US Scientist Award, Alexander von Humboldt Stiftung, Bonn, Fed Repub Ger, 74. *Mem:* Fel Am Phys Soc. *Res:* Solid state theory; statistical mechanics. *Mailing Add:* Dept of Physics Purdue Univ Lafayette IN 47907

RODRIGUEZ-FRAGA, ANDRES, b Havana, Cuba, July 20, 29; m 56; c 3. NUCLEAR PHYSICS, RADIOCHEMISTRY. *Educ:* Univ Havana, Dr es Sci(phys chem), 55. *Prof Exp:* Asst physics, Univ Havana, 52-55, instr, 55-59, asst prof, 59-61; lectr radioisotopes, Nuclear Energy Comn, Mex, 62-63; lectr physics, Univ PR, Humacao, 63-64; from asst prof to assoc prof, 64-74, PROF PHYSICS & CHMN DEPT, UNIV OF THE PAC, 74- *Concurrent Pos:* Am States scholar nuclear physics, Inst Physics, Bariloche, Arg, 60 & fel, Inst Physics, Nat Univ Mex, 61-63; consult, Int Latin Am Prog, Oak Ridge Assoc Univs. *Mem:* AAAS; Am Asn Physics Teachers; Am Phys Soc; Mex Phys Soc. *Res:* Radioisotopes; natural radioactivity; fallout; solids under very high pressures. *Mailing Add:* Dept of Physics Univ of the Pac Stockton CA 95204

RODRIGUEZ-SIERRA, JORGE F, b Havana, Cuba, Sept 18, 45. NEUROENDOCRINOLOGY, NEUROSCIENCE. *Educ:* Calif State Col, Los Angeles, BA, 70; Calif State Univ, Los Angeles, MA, 72; Rutgers Univ, PhD(psychobiol), 76. *Prof Exp:* Fel neuroendocrinol, Wis Regional Primate Ctr, 76-77; ASST PROF ANAT, MED CTR, UNIV NEBR, 78- *Concurrent Pos:* Fel anat, Med Ctr, Univ Nebr, 78; asst prof, Dept Psychol, Univ Nebr at Omaha, 79- *Mem:* Endocrine Soc; Soc Neurosci; Soc Study Reproduction; Int Soc Neuroendocrinol. *Res:* Control of pituitary gland hormonal release by the brain; control of neural development by hormones; development of contraceptives; role of prostaglandins in behavior and pituitary function; neuroendocrinology of behavior. *Mailing Add:* Dept Anat Med Ctr Univ Nebr Omaha NE 68105

RODRIQUEZ, MILDRED SHEPHERD, b Sterling, Okla, Mar 31, 23; m 43; c 1. NUTRITION, BIOCHEMISTRY. *Educ:* Okla State Univ, BS, 43; Univ Ariz, MS, 63, PhD(agr biochem, nutrit), 69. *Prof Exp:* Res assoc biol chem, Georgetown Univ, 68-69; res nutritionist, Human Nutrit Inst, Agr Res Serv, USDA, 69-72; prof nutrit, Calif State Univ, Northridge, 73-74; PROF NUTRIT, CALIF STATE UNIV, LONG BEACH, 74- *Mem:* AAAS; Am Chem Soc; Am Dietetic Asn; Latin Am Nutrit Soc; Nutrit Ed Soc. *Res:* Human nutrition; metabolism and requirements for proteins, vitamin A and folic acid; developing sensitive criteria for evaluating nutritional status; evaluating nutrition intervention programs; obesity. *Mailing Add:* Dept of Dietetics & Food Admin Calif State Univ Long Beach CA 90840

RODWELL, JOHN DENNIS, b Boston, Mass, Oct 9, 46; m 71; c 2. MOLECULAR IMMUNOLOGY. *Educ:* Univ Mass, Amherst, BA, 68; Lowell Tech Inst, MS, 71; Univ Calif, Los Angeles, PhD(biochem), 76. *Prof Exp:* Fel, Univ Pa Sch Med, 76-80, asst prof microbiol, 80-81; SR SCIENTIST, CYTOGEN CORP, 81- *Concurrent Pos:* Adj asst prof microbiol, Univ Pa Sch Med, 81- *Mem:* Am Asn Immunologists; Am Chem Soc; AAAS. *Res:* Utilizing monoclonal antibodies, the restriction of the immunoglobulin macro class of immunoglobulins to germ-line genes is under investigation. *Mailing Add:* Cytogen Corp 201 College Rd E Princeton Forrestal Ctr Princeton NJ 08540

RODWELL, VICTOR WILLIAM, b London, Eng, Sept 10, 29; US citizen; m 52; c 4. BIOCHEMISTRY. *Educ:* Wilson Teachers Col, BS, 51; George Washington Univ, MS, 52; Univ Kans, PhD(biochem), 56. *Prof Exp:* USPHS fel biochem, Univ Calif, Berkeley, 56-58; asst prof, Med Ctr, Univ San Francisco, 58-65; assoc prof, 65-71, PROF BIOCHEM, PURDUE UNIV, LAFAYETTE, 72- *Mem:* Am Soc Biol Chem. *Res:* Regulation of 3-hydroxy-3-methylglutaryl-coenzyme A reductase and cholesterol biosynthesis; transport and metabolism of amino acids by bacteria. *Mailing Add:* Dept of Biochem Purdue Univ Lafayette IN 47907

ROE, ARNOLD, b New York, NY, June 13, 25; m 61; c 5. ENGINEERING. *Educ:* NY Univ, BS, 47; Univ Calif, Los Angeles, MS, 59, PhD(eng), 64. *Prof Exp:* Engr, Am Creosoting Co, 47-48; supt eng, Am & Foreign Power, 48-53; consult, TAMS-Turkish Govt, 53-58; assoc, Univ Calif, Los Angeles, 58-64, proj dir teaching systs lab, 59-64; chmn dept mech & mat, 64-67, PROF ENG, CALIF STATE UNIV, NORTHRIDGE, 67- *Concurrent Pos:* UNESCO consult higher educ, 65-; consult, Technomics, 66. *Honors & Awards:* Award, Am Soc Eng Educ, 59. *Mem:* Am Soc Mech Engrs; Am Soc Eng Educ. *Res:* Programmed learning; computer-aided instruction; adaptive learning systems; power engineering; hydroelectric dams; engineering education. *Mailing Add:* Sch of Eng 18111 Nordhoff St Northridge CA 91330

ROE, BENSON BERTHEAU, b Los Angeles, Calif, July 7, 18; m 45; c 2. CARDIO-THORACIC SURGERY. *Educ:* Univ Calif, AB, 39; Harvard Univ, MD, 43; Am Bd Surg, dipl; Am Bd Thoracic Surg, dipl. *Prof Exp:* Intern surg, Mass Gen Hosp, 43-44, from asst resident to resident, 46-50; asst clin prof, 52-59, assoc prof, 59-68, chief thoracic & cardiac surg, 66, chief cardiac surg, 58-76, PROF SURG, SCH MED, UNIV CALIF, SAN FRANCISCO, 68- *Concurrent Pos:* Nat Res Coun fel, Harvard Med Sch, 47-48; Moseley traveling fel, Univ Edinburgh, 51; vis thoracic surgeon, Vet Admin Hosp, Ft Miley; consult thoracic surgeon, St Luke's Hosp; vis surgeon, San Francisco Gen Hosp; dir & chmn, Am Bd Thoracic Surg. *Mem:* Soc Vascular Surg (vpres); Soc Univ Surg; AMA; Am Asn Thoracic Surgeons (vpres & pres, 72-73); fel Am Col Surg. *Res:* Cardiopulmonary physiology. *Mailing Add:* Dept of Surg Univ of Calif Sch of Med San Francisco CA 94143

ROE, BRUCE ALLAN, b New York, NY, Jan 01, 42; m 63; c 2. BIOCHEMISTRY, MOLECULAR BIOLOGY. *Educ:* Hope Col, BA, 63; Western Mich Univ, MA, 67, PhD(chem), 70. *Prof Exp:* Teacher chem & physics, Marshall Pub Sch, Mich, 63-68; teaching fel chem & biochem, Western Mich Univ, 68-70; fel biochem, State Univ NY, Stony Brook, 70-73; asst prof chem, Kent State Univ, 73-77, assoc prof, 77-81; PROF CHEM, UNIV OKLA, 81- *Concurrent Pos:* NIH fel, State Univ NY, Stony Brook, 71-72; NIH res grants, Kent State Univ, 74-81, Univ Okla, 81-, NIH res career develop fel, 76-81; res assoc prof, Col Med, Northeastern Ohio Univ, 77-81; Sabbatical res assoc, Med Res Coun, Cambridge, Eng, 78-79. *Mem:* AAAS; Am Soc Biol Chemists. *Res:* The role of modified nucleotides in mammalian transfer ribonucleic acids; structure of mammalian transfer ribonucleic acids; structure of mammalian transfer ribonucleic acid genes; structure and function of tumor transfer ribonucleic acids. *Mailing Add:* Dept Chem Univ Okla Norman OK 73019

ROE, BYRON PAUL, b St Louis, Mo, Apr 4, 34; m 61; c 2. PHYSICS. *Educ:* Wash Univ, AB, 54; Cornell Univ, PhD, 59. *Prof Exp:* From instr to assoc prof, 59-69, PROF PHYSICS, UNIV MICH, ANN ARBOR, 69- *Mem:* Fel Am Phys Soc. *Res:* High energy physics; fundamental particles; weak interactions. *Mailing Add:* Dept Physics Univ Mich Ann Arbor MI 48109

ROE, DAPHNE A, b London, Eng, Jan 4, 23; US citizen; m 54; c 3. NUTRITION, MEDICINE. *Educ:* Univ London, MB, BS, 46, MD, 50. *Prof Exp:* Asst pathologist, Royal Free Hosp, London, Eng, 45-46, house physician, 46-47, A M Bird scholar path, 47-48; house surgeon dermat, Bristol Gen Hosp, 48; registr, St John's Hosp Dis Skin, 48-52, first asst, 53-54; res assoc, Univ Pa, 54-57; res assoc, 61-63, asst prof, 63-70, ASSOC PROF CLIN NUTR'T, CORNELL UNIV, 70- *Concurrent Pos:* Res fel, Harvard Univ, 53-54; proj dir health & nutrit eval & rehab of men & women in poverty groups, Dept of Labor. *Mem:* AMA; Am Acad Dermat; Soc Invest Dermat. *Res:* Keratinization of skin in health and disease; drug induced malnutrition; effects of oral contraceptives on folate status; prenatal malnutrition caused by drugs; cutaneous losses of nutrients; sulfur metabolism with special reference to sulfur requirements for detoxication. *Mailing Add:* Div of Nutrit Sci Cornell Univ Ithaca NY 14853

ROE, DAVID KELMER, b Gig Harbor, Wash, Jan 9, 33; m 56; c 3. ELECTROCHEMISTRY, ANALYTICAL CHEMISTRY. *Educ:* Pac Lutheran Col, BA, 54; State Col Wash, MS, 56; Univ Ill, PhD, 59. *Prof Exp:* NSF fel, 59-60; chemist, Shell Develop Co, 60-62; asst prof, Mass Inst Technol, 62-68; assoc prof, Ore Grad Ctr, 68-72; assoc prof, 72-77, PROF CHEM, PORTLAND STATE UNIV, 77- *Mem:* AAAS; Am Chem Soc; Electrochem Soc. *Res:* Electroanalytical methods; chemical instrumentation. *Mailing Add:* Dept Chem Portland State Univ Portland OR 97207

ROE, GLENN DANA, b Danbury, Conn, Mar 5, 31; m 53; c 2. GEOCHEMISTRY. *Educ:* Tex Christian Univ, BA, 59, MA, 61; Mass Inst Technol, PhD(geochem), 65. *Prof Exp:* Asst astron, Mass Inst Technol, 62-63, asst geol, 63, asst geochronology, 63-64; sr res geologist, 64-71, supvr, Geochem Sect, 71-73, dir, 73-78, DIR MINERALS & GEOCHEM SECTS,

ATLANTIC RICHFIELD CO, 78- *Mem:* Am Asn Petrol Geologists. *Res:* Isotopic study of earth mantle rocks, origin and age; geochemical study of sedimentary rocks and their correlation. *Mailing Add:* Atlantic Richfield Co Geochem Sect PO Box 2819 Dallas TX 75221

ROE, KENNETH A, b Perry, NY, 1916; m; c 5. INDUSTRIAL ENGINEERING. *Educ:* Columbia Univ, BA, 36; Mass Inst Technol, BS, 38; Univ Pa, MS, 40. *Prof Exp:* Mech engr, chem engr, exec admin engr & exec vpres, 38-71, PRES & CHMN BD, BURNS & ROE INC, 71- *Concurrent Pos:* Chmn exec comt, Columbia Univ. *Mem:* Nat Acad Eng; sr mem Am Chem Soc; AAAS; Am Inst Chem Engrs; fel Am Soc Mech Engrs. *Res:* Designing efforts for the application of new fields of technology in power generation. *Mailing Add:* Burns & Roe Inc 550 Kinderkamack Rd Oradell NJ 07649

ROE, LAWRENCE A(LBERT), b Cassville, Wis, Feb 15, 16; m 41; c 3. METALLURGY. *Educ:* Univ Mo, BS, 39; Univ Wis, MS, 59. *Hon Degrees:* EMines, Univ Mo-Rolla, 65. *Prof Exp:* Flotation operator & chemist, Nev Consol Copper Corp, 37-38; chem plant supvr & res engr, Am Potash & Chem Corp, 39-44; res engr, Minerals Processing Div, Battelle Mem Inst, 44-46; tech supvr, Ore Res Div, Jones & Laughlin Steel Corp, 46-51; dir mining & metal sect, Bjorksten Res Labs, Inc, 51-55; dir eng, Int Minerals & Chem Corp, Ill, 55-62; proj mgr, Arthur G McKee Co, Calif, 63-64 & Parsons-Jurden Corp, NY, 65-69; pres, Mintec Assocs, 69-70; mgr inorg res & develop, R T Vanderbilt Co Inc, Norwalk, 70-73; sr consult engr, Brown & Root, Inc, Oak Brook, 73-81; PRES & COGNISANT OPERS ENGR, ROECO, INC, DOWNER'S GROVE, ILL, 82- *Mem:* Am Inst Mining, Metall & Petrol Engrs; Can Inst Mining & Metall. *Res:* Processing ferrous ores and industrial minerals; application of froth flotation to chemical and waste processing; international engineering feasibility studies. *Mailing Add:* 1080 39th St Downer's Grove IL 60515

ROE, PAMELA, b San Angelo, Tex, Oct 18, 42. ZOOLOGY. *Educ:* Univ Tex, Austin, BA, 65; Univ Wash, MS, 67, PhD(zool), 71. *Prof Exp:* ASSOC PROF BIOL SCI, CALIF STATE COL, STANISLAUS, 71- *Mem:* AAAS; Ecol Soc Am; Am Soc Zoologists; Am Soc Naturalists. *Res:* Marine invertebrate natural history and ecology; invertebrate zoology. *Mailing Add:* Dept of Biol Sci Calif State Col Stanislaus Turlock CA 95380

ROE, PETER HUGH O'NEIL, b Birmingham, Eng, May 18, 34; m 58; c 2. ELECTRICAL & SYSTEMS ENGINEERING. *Educ:* Univ Toronto, BASc, 59; Univ Waterloo, MSc, 60, PhD(elec eng), 63. *Prof Exp:* Lectr math, 60, lectr elec eng, 60-63, asst prof, 63-64, asst prof design & elec eng, 65, assoc prof, 65-69, assoc dean, eng, 77-78, PROF SYSTS DESIGN, UNIV WATERLOO, 69- *Concurrent Pos:* Vis asst prof, Thayer Sch Eng, Dartmouth Col, 63-64; consult, Inst Design, Univ Waterloo, 65-; vis assoc prof, NS Tech Univ, 68-69; vis prof, Technol Univ Compiegne & Advan Sch Eng Marseille, France, 74-75. *Mem:* Inst Elec & Electronics Engrs. *Res:* Network synthesis; lumped parameter system theory; probabilistic system theory; linear graph theory; role and theory of value and utility in engineering design. *Mailing Add:* Dept of Systs Design Univ of Waterloo Waterloo ON N2L 3G1 Can

ROE, RYONG-JOON, b Pyongyang, Korea, Mar 22, 29; m 61; c 3. POLYMER SCIENCE, PHYSICAL CHEMISTRY. *Educ:* Seoul Nat Univ, BS, 52, MS, 55; Univ Manchester, PhD(polymer chem), 57. *Prof Exp:* Res chemist, Arthur D Little Res Inst, Inveresk, Scotland, 57-60; res assoc polymer chem, Duke Univ, 60-63; res chemist, E I du Pont de Nemours & Co, Inc, 63-68; mem tech staff, Bell Labs, Inc, 68-75; assoc prof, 75-80, PROF MAT SCI & METALL ENG, UNIV CINCINNATI, 80- *Mem:* Am Phys Soc; Am Chem Soc; NY Acad Sci. *Res:* Physics and chemistry of polymers; thermodynamics of polymers; surface properties of polymers; application of x-ray diffraction to study of polymers. *Mailing Add:* 595 Abilene Trail Cincinnati OH 45215

ROE, WILLIAM P(RICE), b Dover, Del, Aug 25, 23; m 43; c 2. METALLURGY. *Educ:* Vanderbilt Univ, AB, 47, MS, 48, PhD(metall, inorg chem), 52. *Prof Exp:* Process develop chemist, Carbide & Carbon Chems Co Div, Union Carbide Corp, 48-49; res metallurgist, Titanium Div, Nat Lead Co, 51-56; sr metallurgist, Southern Res Inst, 56-57; sect leader, Cent Res Labs, 57-60, res supt, 60-63, mgr, 63-69, dir, 69-74, VPRES, ASARCO, INC, 74- *Mem:* AAAS; Am Soc Metals; Am Inst Mining, Metall & Petrol Engrs; NY Acad Sci; Sigma Xi. *Res:* Metallurgy of nonferrous metals. *Mailing Add:* 1041 Minisink Way Westfield NJ 07090

ROEBBER, JOHN LEONARD, b Bonne Terre, Mo, Mar 23, 31; m 55; c 3. PHYSICAL CHEMISTRY. *Educ:* Wash Univ, AB, 53; Univ Calif, PhD(chem), 57. *Prof Exp:* Sr chemist, Res Ctr, Texaco, Inc, NY, 57-64; asst prof, 64-70, ASSOC PROF CHEM, NORTHEASTERN UNIV, 70-, EXEC OFFICER, 76- *Mem:* Am Chem Soc. *Res:* Photochemistry; reaction kinetics; free radicals; infrared and ultraviolet spectroscopy; low temperature chemistry. *Mailing Add:* Dept of Chem 360 Huntington Ave Boston MA 02115

ROEBKE, HEIDE, organic chemistry, see previous edition

ROEBUCK, ISAAC FIELD, b Graham, Tex, Sept 6, 30; m 57; c 1. PETROLEUM ENGINEERING. *Educ:* Univ Tex, BS, 53, MS, 55. *Prof Exp:* From instr to asst prof petrol eng, Univ Tex, 54-57; petrol reservoir engr, Core Lab, Inc, 57-58; sr reservoir engr, 58-59; supv petrol engr, 59-61; asst mgr eng, 61-70; vpres & gen mgr, Eng Numerics Corp, 71-73; mgr educ serv, Core Labs, Inc, 74-78; PRES, ROEBUCK-WALTON, INC, 79- *Mem:* Nat Soc Prof Engrs; Am Asn Petrol Geologists; Am Inst Mining, Metall & Petrol Engrs; Am Mgt Asn. *Res:* Flow through porous media; improved oil recovery; computer science. *Mailing Add:* PO Box 25024 Roebuck-Walton Inc Dallas TX 75225

ROECKER, ROBERT MAAR, b US, Nov 30, 22; m 58. VERTEBRATE ZOOLOGY. *Educ:* Cornell Univ, BS, 47, MS, 48, PhD(zool), 51. *Prof Exp:* Biologist, NY State Dept Conserv, 50-62; assoc prof, 62-70, PROF BIOL, STATE UNIV NY COL GENESEO, 70- *Mem:* Am Soc Mammal; Wildlife Soc; Am Soc Ichthyologists & Herpetologists. *Res:* Life history of gray squirrel; life history and management work on New York waters; mammalogy; ichthyology; herpetology; wildlife and natural resource conservation; vertebrate taxonomy. *Mailing Add:* 4309 Reservoir Geneseo NY 14454

ROEDDER, EDWIN WOODS, b Monsey, NY, July 30, 19; m 45; c 2. GEOCHEMISTRY. *Educ:* Lehigh Univ, BA, 41; Columbia Univ, AM, 47, PhD(geol), 50. *Hon Degrees:* DSc, Lehigh Univ, 76. *Prof Exp:* Res engr, Bethlehem Steel Co, Pa,41-46; asst geol, Columbia Univ, 46-49; from asst prof to assoc prof mineral, Univ Utah, 50-55; chief solid state group, Geochem & Petrol Br, 55-60, staff geologist, 60-62, GEOLOGIST, US GEOL SURV, 62- *Concurrent Pos:* Mem comt geochem res, NSF, 54-55. *Honors & Awards:* Except Sci Achievement Medal, NASA, 73; Distinguished Serv Medal, Dept Interior, 78. *Mem:* Geochem Soc (pres, 76-77); Soc Econ Geol; Mineral Soc Am (vpres, 81-82); Am Geophys Union (pres, Volcanology, Geochem & Petrol Sect, 78-80). *Res:* Ore deposition; fluid inclusions in minerals; studies of lunar materials; nuclear waste storage problems. *Mailing Add:* Exp Geochem & Mineral Br US Geol Surv 959 Nat Ctr Reston VA 22092

ROEDEL, GEORGE FREDERICK, b Saginaw, Mich, July 1, 16; m 42; c 3. POLYMER CHEMISTRY. *Educ:* Valparaiso Univ, BS, 38; Purdue Univ, MS, 40, PhD(agr chem), 42. *Prof Exp:* Asst, Purdue Univ, 42; assoc, Res Lab, Gen Elec Co, 43-50; vpres, Tewes-Roedel Plastics Corp, 50-55; prod engr, Chem Mat Dept, 55-56, mgr chem & insulation, AC Motor & Generator Lab, 56-60, SPECIALIST SILICONE RESIN CHEM, SILICONE PROD DEPT, GEN ELEC CO, 60- *Concurrent Pos:* Assoc prof, Carroll Col, Wis, 50-55. *Mem:* Am Chem Soc. *Res:* Composition and properties of oils and fats; methyl silicone resins; silicone rubber; copolymerization of vinyl silicon compounds; boron chemistry; suspension polymerization of chlorotrifluoroethylene; research and development on silicone resins. *Mailing Add:* 2178 Apple Tree Lane Schenectady NY 12309

ROEDER, DAVID WILLIAM, b Philadelphia, Pa, June 19, 39; m 66; c 2. PURE MATHEMATICS. *Educ:* Univ NMex, BS, 60; Univ Calif, Berkeley, MA, 62, PhD(math), 68. *Prof Exp:* John Wesley Young Res Instr Math, Dartmouth Col, 68-70; asst prof, 70-77, ASSOC PROF MATH, COLO COL, 77-, CHMN DEPT, 75- *Mem:* Am Math Soc; Math Asn Am. *Res:* Duality theory of locally compact groups and topological groups; number theory. *Mailing Add:* Dept of Math Colo Col Colorado Springs CO 80903

ROEDER, EDWARD A, b Sellersville, Pa, Apr 25, 39. SOLID STATE PHYSICS. *Educ:* Lafayette Col, BS, 61; Lehigh Univ, MS, 63, PhD(physics), 67. *Prof Exp:* Asst prof, 67-74, ASSOC PROF PHYSICS, MORAVIAN COL, 74- *Mem:* Am Asn Physics Teachers. *Res:* Transport number measurements in silver chloride at high temperatures. *Mailing Add:* Dept of Physics Moravian Col Bethlehem PA 18018

ROEDER, MARTIN, b Long Branch, NJ, Aug 19, 25; m 57; c 2. PHYSIOLOGY, BIOCHEMISTRY. *Educ:* Queens Col, NY, BS, 48; Univ NMex, MS, 51; Univ NC, PhD(zool), 54. *Prof Exp:* Asst biol, Univ NMex, 49-51; US Atomic Energy Comn fel, Univ NC, 51-53, asst zool, 53-54; asst prof chem, Woman's Col NC, 54-56, biol, 56-59, assoc prof, 59-64; from asst dean to actg dean arts & sci, 66-74, ASSOC PROF BIOL SCI, FLA STATE UNIV, 64- *Mem:* Fel AAAS; Am Soc Zoologists; Soc Gen Physiol; Asn Southeastern Biologists. *Res:* Cellular physiology; enzyme induction; gene-enzyme relationships; respiratory activity of tumor cells; mineral nutrition; bioluminescence and evolutionary significance of bioluminescence. *Mailing Add:* Dept of Biol Sci Fla State Univ Tallahassee FL 32306

ROEDER, PETER LUDWIG, b Medford, Mass, Mar 6, 32; m 53; c 3. GEOCHEMISTRY, PETROLOGY. *Educ:* Tufts Univ, BS, 54; Pa State Univ, PhD(geochem), 60. *Prof Exp:* Fel geochem, Pa State Univ, 60-61 & NMex Inst Mining & Technol, 61-62; assoc prof, 62-70, PROF GEOCHEM & HEAD GEOL DEPT, QUEEN'S UNIV, ONT, 70- *Mem:* Mineral Soc Am. *Res:* High temperature phase euqilibrium studies in systems analogous to basic igneous rocks; analytical problems in petrology. *Mailing Add:* Miller Hall Queen's Univ Kingston ON K7L 3N6 Can

ROEDER, ROBERT CAYLE, b Boonville, Ind, June 3, 42; m 64; c 2. NUCLEIC ACID BIOCHEMISTRY. *Educ:* Wabash Col, Ind, BA, 64; Univ Ill, Urbana, MS, 65; Univ Wash, Seattle, PhD(biochem), 69. *Prof Exp:* Asst prof biol chem, Sch Med, Washington Univ, 71-75, assoc prof, 75-76, prof, 76-82; PROF BIOCHEM & MOLECULAR BIOL, ROCKEFELLER UNIV, 82- *Concurrent Pos:* Fel, Am Cancer Soc, Carnegie Inst Washington, 69-71; mem, Molecular Biol Study Sect, NIH, 75-79; prof genetics, Sch Med, Wash Univ, 78-82, James S McDonnell prof, 79-82. *Mem:* Am Soc Biol Chemists; Am Soc Microbiologists; AAAS; Am Chem Soc; NY Acad Sci. *Res:* Regulation of gene expression during cell growth and differentiation and in cells infected or transformed by DNA tumor viruses; enzymology, mechanism and regulation of genetic transcription. *Mailing Add:* Rockefeller Univ 1230 York Ave New York NY 10021

ROEDER, ROBERT CHARLES, b Stratford, Ont, Oct 7, 37; m 61; c 2. ASTRONOMY, PHYSICS. *Educ:* McMaster Univ, BSc, 59, MSc, 60; Univ Ill, Urbana, PhD(astron), 63. *Prof Exp:* Asst prof astron, Univ Ill, Urbana, 62-63; lectr physics, Queen's Univ, Ont, 63-64; from asst prof to assoc prof, 64-75, PROF ASTRON, UNIV TORONTO, 75- *Concurrent Pos:* Consult, Kitt Peak Nat Observ, 71-72; vis prof physics, Univ Tex, 79-80. *Mem:* Am Astron Soc; Can Astron Soc; Royal Astron Soc Can; Int Astron Union; Int Soc Gen Relativity & Gravitation. *Res:* Cosmology determination of models of universe; quasars investigations of the nature of redshifts; relativistic optics. *Mailing Add:* Scarborough Col Univ of Toronto West Hill ON M1C 1A4 Can

ROEDER, STEPHEN BERNHARD WALTER, b Dover, NJ, Aug 26, 39; m 69; c 2. NUCLEAR MAGNETIC RESONANCE, CHEMICAL PHYSICS. *Educ:* Dartmouth Col, BA, 61; Univ Wis, PhD(chem), 65. *Prof Exp:* Mem tech staff, Bell Labs, Inc, 65-66; instr physics, Univ Ore, 66-68; from asst prof to assoc prof, 68-74, chmn dept, 75-78, prof physics, 74-79, CHMN DEPT CHEM, SAN DIEGO STATE UNIV, 79- *Concurrent Pos:* Fel chem, Univ Ore, 66-68; vis prof, Univ BC, 74-75; vis staff mem, Los Alamos Sci Lab, 74- *Mem:* AAAS; Am Chem Soc. *Res:* Pulsed nuclear magnetic resonance. *Mailing Add:* Dept of Physics San Diego State Univ San Diego CA 92182

ROEDERER, JUAN GUALTERIO, b Trieste, Italy, Sept 2, 29; m 52; c 4. SPACE PHYSICS, PSYCHOACOUSTICS. *Educ:* Univ Buenos Aires, PhD(physics), 52. *Prof Exp:* Teaching asst physics, Univ Buenos Aires, 52-53; res asst high energy physics, Max Planck Inst, 53-55; prof physics, Univ Buenos Aires, 56-67; prof, Univ Denver, 67-77; DIR, GEOPHYS INST, UNIV ALASKA, 77- *Concurrent Pos:* Mem ICSU Special Comn Solar Terrestrial Physics, 66-82; vis staff mem, Dept Energy, Los Alamos Sci Lab, 68-81; mem polar res bd, Nat Acad Sci, 80- *Mem:* Fel Am Geophys Union; Argentine Geophys Soc; Acoustical Soc Am; Int Asn Geomag and Aeronomy (pres, 75-79); fel AAAS. *Res:* Physics of the Magnetosphere, particularly radiation belts, diffusion of trapped particles; physics of music; perception of musical sounds. *Mailing Add:* Geophys Inst Univ Alaska Fairbanks AK 99701

ROEFS, THEODORE GEORGE, b Mineola, NY, May 5, 36. COMPUTER SCIENCE, WATER RESOURCES PLANNING. *Educ:* Polytech Inst New York, BCE, 58; Stanford Univ, MS, 63. *Prof Exp:* From jr water res engr to assoc water res engr, Calif Dept Water Resources, 58-68; mem res staff opers res, Wash Sci Ctr, IBM Corp, 67-69; assoc prof hydrol & water resources, Univ Ariz, 69-74; WATER RES SCIENTIST OFF WATER RES & TECHNOL, US DEPT INTERIOR, 74- *Concurrent Pos:* Res fel, Univ Calif, Los Angeles, 64-68; adj prof, Univ Ariz, 74-77; prof environ sci, Univ Va, 81-82. *Mem:* Am Soc Civil Engrs. *Res:* Natural resources management; operations research information systems. *Mailing Add:* Off of Water Res & Technol US Dept of the Interior Washington DC 20240

ROEGER, ANTON, III, b Philadelphia, Pa, Oct 19, 35; m 67; c 2. CHEMICAL ENGINEERING, FUEL TECHNOLOGY. *Educ:* Lehigh Univ, BS, 57; Pa State Univ, MS, 59; Univ Va, DSc(chem eng), 63. *Prof Exp:* Res engr, Indust Chem Div, Res & Develop Lab, Shell Chem Co, Deer Park, 62-71; sr engr, 71-77, res adv, 77-78, coordr, Res & Technol Div, 78-80, TECH MGR, SYNFUELS DIV, TEX EASTERN CORP, 80- *Mem:* Am Inst Chem Engrs. *Res:* Synthetic gaseous and liquid fuels; chemicals; two phase flow; radiation chemistry; process research and development. *Mailing Add:* 4618 Shatner Dr Houston TX 77066

ROEHL, PERRY OWEN, b Detroit, Mich, Jan 2, 25; m 52; c 4. PETROLEUM GEOLOGY. *Educ:* Ohio State Univ, BS, 50; Stanford Univ, MS, 52; Univ Wis, PhD(geol), 55. *Prof Exp:* Exploitation engr, Shell Oil Co, 55-57, from prod geologist to sr prod geologist, 57-62, sr prod geologist, Shell Oil Co Can, Ltd, 62, res geologist, Shell Develop Co, 62-66; res assoc, Union Oil Co Calif, 66-75; consult, 75-81; HERNDON DISTINGUISHED PROF GEOL, TRINITY UNIV, SAN ANTONIO, TEX, 81- *Concurrent Pos:* Chmn carbonate adv comt, Am Petrol Inst, 70-75. *Mem:* Fel Geol Soc Am; Am Asn Petrol Geol; Soc Econ Paleont & Mineral; Am Inst Prof Geol; Am Inst Mining, Metall & Petrol Geol. *Res:* Carbonate geology, recent sedimentation; petroleum geology; paleoecology; sedimentary petrography; petrophysics; invertebrate paleontology; stratigraphy; marine geology; geological engineering. *Mailing Add:* Dept Geol Trinity Univ 715 Stadium Dr San Antonio TX 78284

ROEHRIG, FREDERICK KARL, b Peoria, Ill, June 25, 42; m 67. PHYSICAL METALLURGY, METALLURGICAL ENGINEERING. *Educ:* Bradley Univ, BS, 65; Univ Ill, MS, 67; Ohio State Univ, PhD(metall eng), 76. *Prof Exp:* Res metallurgist, Battelle-Columbus Lab, 67-72; RES ASSOC METALLURGY, OWENS-CORNING FIBERGLAS TECH CTR, 76- *Mem:* Sigma Xi; Am Soc Metals; Am Inst Mining, Metall & Petrol Eng; Am Powder Metall Inst; Nat Soc Prof Eng. *Res:* Physical metallurgy of high temperature alloys, particularly powder metallurgy; research and development of high performance material systems; work in field-freezing and electrotransport as well. *Mailing Add:* 4800 Hayden Blvd Columbus OH 43220

ROEHRIG, GERALD RALPH, b Aurora, Ill, Nov 2, 41; m 63; c 3. ORGANIC CHEMISTRY, PHYSICAL CHEMISTRY. *Educ:* Aurora Col, BS, 63; Univ Ky, MS, 65; Ind Univ, PhD(org chem), 70. *Prof Exp:* Asst prof chem, Aurora Col, 65-75, prof, 75-79; ASST PROF, ORAL ROBERTS UNIV, 79- *Concurrent Pos:* Chmn, Dept Chem, Aurora Col, 70-79, chmn, Div Natural Sci, 74-79, res dir, Res Corp, 76-79; educ consult, Argonne Nat Lab, 71-77; consult, Process Systs Div, John Zink Co, 80- *Mem:* AAAS; Am Chem Soc. *Res:* Synthesis of potential antitumor agents. *Mailing Add:* Dept Nat Sci Oral Roberts Univ 7777 S Lewis Tulsa OK 74171

ROEHRIG, JIMMY RICHARD, b Yokohama, Japan, Oct 12, 49. COLLIDING BEAM PHYSICS. *Educ:* Univ Chicago, BA, 71, PhD(physics), 77. *Prof Exp:* Res assoc, Univ Chicago, 77-78; RES ASSOC, STANFORD LINEAR ACCELERATOR CTR, 78- *Mailing Add:* Bin 65 Stanford Linear Accelerator Ctr PO Box 4349 Stanford CA 94305

ROEHRIG, KARLA LOUISE, b Sycamore, Ill, Aug 18, 46; m 67. BIOCHEMISTRY, NUTRITION. *Educ:* Univ Ill, BS, 67; Ohio State Univ, PhD(phys chem), 77. *Prof Exp:* Res asst nutrit biochem, Inst Nutrit, Ohio State Univ, 67-71 & Dept Food Sci & Nutrit, 71-75; res assoc biochem, Sch Med, Ind Univ, 77-78; ASST PROF NUTRIT BIOCHEM, DEPT FOOD SCI & NUTRIT, OHIO STATE UNIV, 78- *Concurrent Pos:* Showalter fel, Dept Biochem, Sch Med, Ind Univ, 77-78. *Mem:* AAAS; Am Diabetes Asn; Am Heart Asn; Biochem Soc; NY Acad Sci. *Res:* Metabolic regulation, especially dietary and hormonal control of enzymes involved in carbohydrate and lipid metabolism; mechanisms of insulin action; enzyme control mechanisms; mitochondrial malicenzymes. *Mailing Add:* Dept Food Sci & Nutrit 2121 Fyffe Rd Columbus OH 43210

ROEL, LAWRENCE EDMUND, b Brooklyn, NY, Aug 19, 49. NEUROCHEMISTRY, NEUROPHARMACOLOGY. *Educ:* Princeton Univ, AB, 71; Mass Inst Technol, PhD(nutrit biochem), 76. *Prof Exp:* Fel neurosci, Univ Calif, San Diego, 76-78; ASST PROF ANAT, MED SCH, NORTHWESTERN UNIV, 78- *Mem:* Soc Neurosci; Am Chem Soc; NY Acad Sci; Sigma Xi. *Res:* Regulation of protein synthesis in neurons and glia; effects of neurotransmitter release; neuronal recognition and synaptogenesis. *Mailing Add:* Dept Anat Med Sch Northwestern Univ 303 E Chicago Ave Chicago IL 60611

ROELFS, ALAN PAUL, b Stockton, Kans, Nov 18, 36; m 56; c 3. PLANT PATHOLOGY. *Educ:* Kans State Univ, BS, 59, MS, 64; Univ Minn, St Paul, PhD(plant path), 70. *Prof Exp:* Plant pathologist, Coop Rust Lab, Plant Protection Div, Agr Res Serv, 65-69, res plant pathologist, Cereal Rust Lab, Plant Protection Progs, Animal & Plant Health Inspection Serv, 69-75, RES PLANT PATHOLOGIST, CEREAL RUST LAB, AGR RES SERV, USDA, 75- *Concurrent Pos:* Assoc prof, Univ Minn. *Mem:* Am Phytopath Soc; AAAS; Int Asn Aeriobiol; US Fedn Culture Collections; Int Soc Plant Path. *Res:* Cereal rust epidemiology and physiological race distribution. *Mailing Add:* Cereal Rust Lab Univ Minn St Paul MN 55108

ROELLIG, HAROLD FREDERICK, b Detroit, Mich, Apr 23, 30; m 59; c 4. PALEONTOLOGY. *Educ:* Concordia Col, Mo, BA, 54; Concordia Sem, dipl theol, 57; Columbia Univ, PhD(geol), 67. *Prof Exp:* Campus chaplain, Lutheran Church, Mo Synod, 60-69; chmn earth sci dept, 78-81, ASSOC PROF GEOL, ADELPHI UNIV, 69- *Mem:* Geol Soc Am; Paleont Soc; Soc Vert Paleont. *Res:* Philosophical and theological interpretation of evolutionary phenomena; evolution and paleoecological interpretation of marine faunas. *Mailing Add:* Dept Earth Sci Adelphi Univ Garden City NY 11530

ROELLIG, LEONARD OSCAR, b Detroit, Mich, May 17, 27; m 52; c 3. ELECTRON PHYSICS. *Educ:* Univ Mich, AB, 50, MS, 55, PhD(physics), 59. *Prof Exp:* Asst, Univ Mich, 53-58; from asst prof to prof physics, Wayne State Univ, 58-78, dean acad admin, 71-72, assoc provost physics, 72-76; VCHANCELLOR ACAD AFFAIRS & PROF PHYSICS, CITY COL NEW YORK, 78- *Concurrent Pos:* Consult, High Energy Physics Div, Argonne Nat Lab, 59-62, Space Tech Lab, 62-63 & Gen Motors Res Lab, 69-71; dir sci res prog, Inner City High Sch Students, 67-71. vis prof, Univ Col, Univ London, 68-69 & Tata Inst Fundamental Res, Bombay, India, 73; pres, Cent Solar Energy Res Corp, 77. *Honors & Awards:* Res Recognition Award, Wayne State Fund, 63. *Mem:* Am Phys Soc. *Res:* Bubble nucleation by ionizing radiations; elementary particle detecting devices; positron annihilation; positron-atom scattering; low temperature physics; positron-atom interactions. *Mailing Add:* City Univ of New York 535 E 80 St New York NY 10021

ROELOFS, TERRY DEAN, b Manistique, Mich, Nov 3, 42. FISHERIES. *Educ:* Mich State Univ, BS, 65; Univ Wash, MS, 67; Ore State Univ, PhD(fisheries), 71. *Prof Exp:* Asst prof, 71-74, assoc prof, 74-78, PROF FISHERIES, HUMBOLDT STATE UNIV, 78- *Mem:* AAAS; Am Fisheries Soc; Am Soc Limnol & Oceanog. *Res:* Water pollution biology; fisheries ecology and limnology; anadromous salmonid ecology and management techniques designed to increase the natural production of these fishes through habitat rehabilitation and enhancement. *Mailing Add:* Sch of Natural Resources Humboldt State Univ Arcata CA 95521

ROELOFS, THOMAS HARWOOD, b Arlington, Va, Oct 10, 37; m 62; c 2. ELECTRICAL ENGINEERING. *Educ:* Cornell Univ, BEE, 60, MEE, 61, PhD(elec eng), 64. *Prof Exp:* Asst prof, 64-70, assoc prof, 68-72, PROF ELEC ENG, UNIV HAWAII, 72- *Concurrent Pos:* Mem staff, Adtech Inc, Honolulu, 69- *Mem:* Am Geophys Union. *Res:* Clear air radar echoes; ionospheric total electron content. *Mailing Add:* Dept of Elec Eng Univ of Hawaii Honolulu HI 96822

ROELOFS, WENDELL LEE, b Orange City, Iowa, July 26, 38; div; c 4. ORGANIC CHEMISTRY. *Educ:* Cent Col, Iowa, BA, 60; Univ Ind, PhD(med chem), 64. *Prof Exp:* NIH fel org chem, Mass Inst Technol, 64-65; from asst prof to assoc prof chem, 65-75, PROF INSECT BIOCHEM, STATE UNIV NY COL AGR, CORNELL UNIV, 76- *Honors & Awards:* J Everett Bossert Entom Award, 73; Alexander Von Humboldt Agr Award, 77. *Mem:* Am Chem Soc; Entom Soc Am; AAAS; Sigma Xi; NY Acad Sci. *Res:* Synthetic organic chemistry; isolation and characterization of sex, food and oviposition attractants of insects. *Mailing Add:* Dept of Entom NY State Agr Exp Sta Geneva NY 14456

ROELS, OSWALD A, biochemistry, marine biology, see previous edition

ROEMER, ELIZABETH, b Oakland, Calif, Sept 4, 29. ASTRONOMY. *Educ:* Univ Calif, BA, 50, PhD, 55. *Prof Exp:* Asst astron, Univ Calif, 50-52, lab technician, Lick Observ, 54-55; res astronr, univ, 55-56; res assoc, Yerkes Observ, Univ Chicago, 56; astronr, Flagstaff Sta, US Naval Observ, 57-66; assoc prof, 66-69, PROF ASTRON, LUNAR & PLANETARY LAB, UNIV ARIZ, 69-, ASTRONOMER, STEWARD OBSERVATORY, 80- *Concurrent Pos:* Partic, prog vis profs in astron, Am Astron Soc & NSF, 60-75; Donohoe Lecturer, Astron Soc Pac, 62; mem panel planetary astron, Nat Acad Sci, 67; mem adv comt astron, Off Naval Res, 69-70; chmn comt, Dept Planetary Sci, Univ Ariz, 72-73; mem, Space Sci Rev Panel Associateship Prog, Off Sci Personnel, Nat Res Coun, 73-75; chmn, 75; mem subcomt space telescope, Space Sci Steering Comt, NASA, 77-78; consult, Comet Sci Working Group, Jet Propulsion Lab, Calif Inst Technol, 79. *Honors & Awards:* Mademoiselle Merit Award, 59; Benjamin Apthorp Gould Prize, Nat Acad Sci, 71. *Mem:* Fel AAAS; Am Astron Soc; Am Geophys Union; fel Royal Astron Soc; Sigma Xi. *Res:* Comets and minor planets; astrometry and practical astronomy; computation of orbits; astrometric and astrophysical investigations of comets, minor planets and satellites; dynamical astronomy. *Mailing Add:* Lunar & Planetary Lab Univ of Ariz Tucson AZ 85721

ROEMER, LOUIS EDWARD, b Washington, DC, July 5, 34; m 58; c 3. ELECTRICAL ENGINEERING, PHYSICS. *Educ:* Univ Del, BS, 55, MS, 63, PhD(appl sci), 67. *Prof Exp:* Assoc engr, Sperry Gyroscope Co, Sperry Rand Corp, 60-63; from instr to asst prof elec eng, Univ Del, 63-68; PROF ELEC ENG, UNIV AKRON, 68- *Mem:* Inst Elec & Electronics Engrs. *Res:* Wave propagation in plasma; time domain reflectometry. *Mailing Add:* Dept of Elec Eng Univ of Akron Akron OH 44325

ROEMER, MILTON IRWIN, b Paterson, NJ, Mar 24, 16; m 39; c 2. PUBLIC HEALTH, PREVENTIVE MEDICINE. *Educ:* Cornell Univ, BA, 36, MA, 39; NY Univ, MD, 40; Univ Mich, MPH, 43. *Prof Exp:* Med officer venereal dis, NJ State Dept Health, 41-42; med officer med care, USPHS, 43-49; assoc prof pub health, Yale Univ, 49-51; sect chief social med, WHO, Geneva, 51-53; dir bur med care, Sask Dept Health, 53-56; prof admin med, Cornell Univ, 57-61; PROF PUB HEALTH, UNIV CALIF, LOS ANGELES, 62- *Honors & Awards:* Henry E Sigerist lectr, Yale Univ, 80. *Mem:* Inst Med-Nat Acad Sci; Am Pub Health Asn. *Res:* Organization of medical care; health insurance; rural health; international health care systems; health manpower. *Mailing Add:* Sch of Pub Health Univ of Calif Los Angeles CA 90024

ROEMER, RICHARD ARTHUR, b Minneapolis, Minn, Sept 12, 39; m 72; c 6. NEUROSCIENCE, COMPUTER SCIENCE. *Educ:* Calif State Univ, Northridge, BA, 68; Univ Calif, Irvine, PhD(psychobiol), 73. *Prof Exp:* Sr eng aide digital comput, Litton Data Systs, 62-64; comput specialist reentry systs, Gen Elec Co, 64-66; sr elec engr digital comput, Calif State Univ, Northridge, 66-67; analyst mgt systs, Syst Develop Corp, 67-69; comput syst consult, Enki Res Inst, 69-73; res asst & res assoc, Univ Calif, Irvine, 69-73; res fel psychol, Harvard Univ, 73-75; med res scientist, 75-80, ASSOC PROF, DEPT PSYCHIAT, TEMPLE UNIV, 81- *Concurrent Pos:* Analyst mgt systs, 69; clin asst prof, Dept Psychiat, Temple Univ, 75-77, res assoc prof, 77-; lectr psychol, Univ Pa & Rutgers Univ, 77-; sr Fulbright scholar, 81. *Mem:* Soc Neurosci; Inst Elec & Electronics Engrs; Nat Asn On-Line Comput Psychol; Soc Systs, Man & Cybernet; Soc Eng Med & Biol. *Res:* Assessment of neuropsychological and neuropharmacological relationships in mentally ill patients; development of multivariate statistical applications in neurobiology. *Mailing Add:* Eastern Pa Psychiat Inst Henry Ave & Abbottsford Rd Philadelphia PA 19129

ROEMHILD, GEORGE R, b Dimock, Pa, Oct 15, 23; m 48; c 2. ENTOMOLOGY. *Educ:* Pa State Univ, BS, 52; Mont State Univ, MS, 53, PhD(entom), 61. *Prof Exp:* Asst state entomologist, Univ Mont, 54-60, from asst prof to assoc prof, 60-73, PROF ENTOM, MONT STATE UNIV, 73- *Res:* Water quality; ecology of high altitude streams; aquatic invertebrates, especially physiology. *Mailing Add:* Dept of Entom Mont State Univ Bozeman MT 59715

ROENIGK, WILLIAM J, b Cleveland, Ohio, Jan 26, 29; m 53; c 4. VETERINARY MEDICINE. *Educ:* Ohio State Univ, DVM, 54; Baylor Univ, MSc, 58; Am Col Vet Radiol, ACVR, 66. *Prof Exp:* From asst prof to prof vet radiol, Vet Clin, Ohio State Univ, 58-67; assoc prof comp radiol & lab animal med, Col Med & dir, Div Vet Med, Children's Hosp Res Found, Univ Cincinnati, 67-72; prof vet radiol, NY State Vet Col, Cornell Univ, 72-75; PROF VET RADIOL & HEAD DEPT, COL VET MED, TEX A&M UNIV, 75- *Concurrent Pos:* NIH grant, 62-65. *Mem:* Am Vet Med Asn; Am Col Vet Radiol (pres, 70); Educ Vet Radiol Sci (pres, 66); Radiol Soc NAm; Am Vet Radiol Soc. *Res:* Diagnostic radiology; radiation therapy; nuclear medicine. *Mailing Add:* Col of Vet Med Tex A&M Univ College Station TX 77843

ROEPKE, HARLAN HUGH, b Rochester, Minn, Nov 14, 30; m 58; c 2. SEDIMENTARY PETROLOGY. *Educ:* Univ Minn, Minneapolis, BA, 53, MS, 58; Univ Tex, Austin, PhD(geol), 70. *Prof Exp:* Res asst geol, Minn Geol Surv, 56-58; geologist, Paleont & Stratig Br, US Geol Surv, 58-60, Alaskan Br, summer 60; from asst prof to assoc prof, 65-77, PROF GEOL, BALL STATE UNIV, 77- *Concurrent Pos:* Geol consult. 73- *Mem:* AAAS; Geol Soc Am; Soc Econ Paleont & Mineral; Sigma Xi. *Res:* Petrology of carbonate rocks; x-ray florescence study of Indiana chert. *Mailing Add:* Dept Geol Ball State Univ Muncie IN 47306

ROEPKE, RAYMOND ROLLIN, b Bodaville, Kans, Jan 5, 11; m 42; c 1. BIOCHEMISTRY. *Educ:* Kans State Col, BS, 33, MS, 34; Univ Minn, PhD(biophys), 38. *Prof Exp:* Asst, Agr Exp Sta, Kans State Col, 33-35; asst physiol, Univ Minn, 39-40; asst chem, Lafayette Col, 40-41; res biochemist, Am Cyanamid Co, 42-56; group leader pharmacol res, Lederle Labs, 56-76; RETIRED. *Mem:* AAAS; Am Chem Soc; Am Soc Pharmacol & Exp Therapeut; NY Acad Sci. *Res:* Osmotic pressures of biologic fluids; intestinal absorption of electrolytes; rheology of the blood; bacterial mutation and metabolism; chemotherapy; toxicology and safety evaluation; biochemical pharmacology. *Mailing Add:* 139 Mar Vista Dr Vista CA 92083

ROESCH, WILLIAM CARL, b Saginaw, Mich, Nov 11, 23; m 46; c 3. PHYSICS. *Educ:* Miami Univ, Ohio, AB, 45; Calif Inst Technol, PhD(physics), 49. *Prof Exp:* Mgr, Radiol Physics, Gen Elec Co, 49-64; mgr, Radiol Physics, 65, sr res assoc, 66-70, STAFF SCIENTIST, BATTELLE-NORTHWEST, 70- *Mem:* Am Phys Soc; Radiation Res Soc; Health Phys Soc; Am Asn Physicists in Med. *Res:* Radiological physics; instrumentation and dosimetry methods for alpha, beta and gamma rays and neutrons; physics of radiobiology and radiation protection. *Mailing Add:* 1646 Butternut Richland WA 99352

ROESEL, CATHERINE ELIZABETH, b Augusta, Ga, Feb 6, 20. IMMUNOLOGY. *Educ:* Vanderbilt Univ, BA, 41; Wash Univ, PhD(bact), 51. *Prof Exp:* Fel, Carnegie Inst, 50-51; from instr to assoc prof, 51-76, PROF CELL & MOLECULAR BIOL, MED COL GA, 76- *Mem:* AAAS; Am Soc Microbiol; Asn Am Med Cols. *Res:* Antibody formation; Rubella virus; tissue culture. *Mailing Add:* Dept of Cell & Molecular Biol Med Col of Ga Augusta GA 30902

ROESEL, OSCAR FRED, physiology, biomedical engineering, see previous edition

ROESER, ROSS JOSEPH, b Louisville, Ky, Nov 14, 42; m 63; c 3. AUDIOLOGY. *Educ:* Western Ill Univ, BS, 66; Northern Ill Univ, MA, 67; Fla State Univ, PhD(audiol), 72. *Prof Exp:* CHIEF AUDIOL, UNIV TEX, DALLAS, 72- *Concurrent Pos:* Clin asst prof otolaryngol, Med Sch, Univ Tex Southwestern, 73-; assoc prof grad prog, Univ Tex, Dallas, 73-; HEW grant cent auditory processing children, 77-79; NASA grant, Hearing Aid Malfunction Detection Unit; consult, Independent Sch Dists, McKinney, Dallas & Houston, Tex, NASA, Houston & West Tex Rehab Ctr, Abilene. *Mem:* Am Speech & Hearing Asn; Acoust Soc Am; Am Auditory Soc (secy-treas, 73-); fel Soc Ear, Nose & Throat Advan Children. *Res:* Central auditory processing in children and other audiology related areas. *Mailing Add:* Callier Ctr for Commun Dis Univ of Tex 1966 Inwood Dallas TX 75235

ROESING, TIMOTHY GEORGE, b Abington, Pa, May 14, 47; m 69; c 2. VIROLOGY, IMMUNOLOGY. *Educ:* Univ Md, BS, 69; Hahnemann Med Col, MS, 73, PhD(microbiol & immunol), 76. *Prof Exp:* Sr res scientist microbiol, Smith Kline Diag Div, Smith Kline Corp, 76-77; SR PROJ DEVELOP BIOLOGIST MICROBIOL, MERCK SHARP & DOHME DIV, MERCK & CO, 77- *Concurrent Pos:* Fel, Smith Kline Diag, 76-77. *Mem:* Am Soc Microbiol; Brit Soc Gen Microbiol; Tissue Cult Asn; Am Asn Tissue Banks. *Res:* Virus-cell interactions with coxsackieviruses; role of coxsackieviruses in heart disease and pancreatitis; enzyme linked immunoassays and fluorescent immunoassays for human viruses. *Mailing Add:* Merck Sharp & Dohme W1-10 West Point PA 19486

ROESKE, ROGER WILLIAM, b Valders, Wis, July 30, 27; m 55; c 2. BIO-ORGANIC CHEMISTRY. *Educ:* Univ Wis, BA, 48; Univ Ill, PhD(org chem), 51. *Prof Exp:* Merck fel, Swiss Fed Inst Tech, 51-52; res assoc biochem, Med Col, Cornell Univ, 52-55; sr chemist, Eli Lilly & Co, Ind, 55-61; from asst prof to assoc prof, 62-66, PROF BIOCHEM, SCH MED, IND UNIV, 77- *Concurrent Pos:* Res Career Develop Award, USPHS, 62-71. *Mem:* AAAS; Am Chem Soc; Royal Soc Chem; Swiss Chem Soc. *Res:* Mechanism of enzyme action; synthesis of peptides; membrane-active peptides. *Mailing Add:* Dept of Biochem Ind Univ Sch Med Indianapolis IN 46223

ROESLER, FREDERICK LEWIS, b Milwaukee, Wis, Feb 26, 34; m 57, 68; c 5. ATOMIC PHYSICS, OPTICAL SPECTROSCOPY. *Educ:* St Olaf Col, BA, 56; Univ Wis, MS, 58, PhD(physics), 62. *Prof Exp:* Res assoc physics, Univ Wis, 62-63; NSF fel, Bellevue Labs, France, 63-64; from asst prof to assoc prof, 64-70, PROF PHYSICS, UNIV WIS-MADISON, 70- *Concurrent Pos:* Consult, Los Alamos Sci Lab, 65-69 & Argonne Nat Lab, 77-; mem comt line spectra of elements, Nat Acad Sci-Nat Res Coun, 67-72; vis assoc prof physics, Univ Ariz, 70; von Humboldt Found Sr US Scientist Award, 75-; vis prof physics, Univ Munich, 76. *Mem:* Optical Soc Am. *Res:* Interference spectroscopy; astronomy; aeronomy. *Mailing Add:* Dept Physics 1150 University Ave Madison WI 53706

ROESLER, JOSEPH FRANK, b Chicago, Ill, Dec 15, 30; m 61; c 2. PHYSICAL CHEMISTRY, SANITARY ENGINEERING. *Educ:* Roosevelt Univ, BS, 54; Okla State Univ, MS, 61; Univ Cincinnati, MS, 70. *Prof Exp:* Res chemist, Ill Inst Technol, 56-59, Okla State Univ, 60-61 & Rauland Corp, 61-62; res chemist, Div Air Pollution, USPHS, 62-67; sanit engr & mgr instrumentation & automation of waste water systs, Nat Environ Res Ctr, 67-78, ENVIRON ENGR, REGIONAL LIAISON OFFICER, OFF RES & DEVELOP, US ENVIRON PROTECTION AGENCY, 78- *Mem:* Instrument Soc Am; Water Pollution Control Fedn; Am Soc Civil Engrs; Sigma Xi. *Res:* Mathematical modeling of advanced waste water treatment processes; environmental health engineering; aerosols and chemical instrumentation pertaining to air pollution; kinetics and photoemissive surfaces. *Mailing Add:* Environ Res Ctr US Environ Protection Agency Cincinnati OH 45268

ROESMER, JOSEF, b Konigsberg, Ger, Aug 29, 28; m 59; c 1. NUCLEAR SCIENCE. *Educ:* Univ Mainz, BS, 52, MS, 55; Clark Univ, PhD(radiochem), 64. *Prof Exp:* Adv scientist, Nuclear Sci & Eng Corp, 60-64; sr scientist, Astronuclear Lab, 64-71, FEL SCIENTIST, NUCLEAR ENERGY SYSTS, WESTINGHOUSE ELEC CORP, 71- *Mem:* NY Acad Sci; Am Chem Soc. *Res:* Nuclear reactions; corrosion products in reactor coolant systems; radiochemical studies of nuclear fission processes; low-level counting techniques; fission product diffusion from nuclear fuels; applications of computers to radiochemistry; high-temperature chemistry; primary and secondary coolant system chemistry of nuclear power reactors. *Mailing Add:* 969 Holly Lyme Dr Pittsburgh PA 15236

ROESS, WILLIAM B, b Evanston, Ill, Sept 8, 38; m 57; c 4. GENETICS, MOLECULAR BIOLOGY. *Educ:* Blackburn Col, BA, 61; Fla State Univ, PhD(genetics), 66. *Prof Exp:* From asst prof to assoc prof, 66-74, PROF BIOL, ECKERD COL, 75-, CHMN, COLLEGIUM NATURAL SCI, 76- *Concurrent Pos:* NIH spec fel, Oak Ridge Nat Labs, 71. *Mem:* AAAS; Tissue Cult Asn; Sigma Xi. *Res:* Mechanisms and genetic control of amino acid transport in human tissue culture cells; genetic control of membrane synthesis. *Mailing Add:* Collegium of Natural Sci Eckerd Col St Petersburg FL 33733

ROESSLER, BARTON, b Toledo, Ohio, Nov 19, 32; m 59; c 3. METALLURGY, ENGINEERING. *Educ:* Mass Inst Technol, SB, 55, ScD(metall), 60. *Prof Exp:* NSF fel, X-ray Inst, Stuttgart Tech Univ, 59-60; sr metallurgist, Westinghouse Res Labs, 61-64; from asst prof to assoc prof eng, 64-76, PROF ENG, BROWN UNIV, 76- *Concurrent Pos:* Fulbright-Hays res grant, Fritz Haber Inst, Berlin, Ger, 71-72. *Mem:* Am Soc Metals; Am Inst Metall Engrs; Nat Asn Corrosion Engrs. *Res:* X-ray diffraction; imperfections in crystalline solids; magnetic domains. *Mailing Add:* Dept of Eng Brown Univ Providence RI 02912

ROESSLER, CHARLES ERVIN, b Elysian, Minn, May 1, 34; m 56; c 7. HEALTH PHYSICS, RADIOLOGICAL HEALTH. *Educ:* Mankato State Col, AB, 55; Univ Rochester, MS, 56; Univ Pittsburgh, MPH, 59; Univ Fla, PhD(environ eng), 67; Am Bd Health Physics, cert, 61. *Prof Exp:* Health physicist, Nuclear Power Dept, Res Div, Curtiss-Wright Corp, 56-58; radiol physicist, Fla State Bd Health, 59-65; asst prof radiation biophys, 67-72, asst prof environ eng, 72-73, assoc prof, 73-79, PROF ENVIRON ENG, UNIV FLA, 79- *Mem:* AAAS; Health Physics Soc; Am Pub Health Asn; Am Indust Hyg Asn; Am Conf Govt Indust Hygienists. *Res:* Environmental radiation, particularly naturally occurring radioactivity; radiation exposure in the healing arts. *Mailing Add:* 525 NE Fourth St Gainesville FL 32601

ROESSLER, DAVID MARTYN, b London, Eng, Apr 29, 40. PHYSICS, SPECTROSCOPY. *Educ:* Univ London, BSc, 61, PhD(physics), 66. *Prof Exp:* Fel, Univ Calif, Santa Barbara, 66-68; temp mem tech staff spectroscopy, Bell Labs, 68-70; ASSOC & SR RES PHYSICIST, SPECTROSCOPY, GEN MOTORS RES LABS, 70- *Mem:* Brit Inst Physics; Sigma Xi; Optical Soc Am; Int Solar Energy Soc. *Res:* Optical Properties of solids and aerosols; reflection; luminescence; photoacoustic spectroscopy. *Mailing Add:* Dept Physics Gen Motors Res Labs Warren MI 48090

ROESSLER, MARTIN A, b Hempstead, NY, Apr 7, 39. FISH BIOLOGY. *Educ:* Univ Miami, BS, 61, MS, 64, PhD(marine sci), 67. *Prof Exp:* Instr fisheries biol, Inst Marine Sci, Univ Miami, 66-69, from asst prof to assoc prof, Rosenstiel Sch Marine & Atmospheric Sci, 69-73; PROG DIR, TROP BIOINDUST DEVELOP CO, 73- *Mem:* Am Fisheries Soc; Am Soc Ichthyologists & Herpetologists; Am Soc Limnol & Oceanog. *Res:* Ecology of estuaries in Florida; biology of pink shrimp Penaeus duorarum; ecology of fishes; power plant siting and environmental effects of coastal zone development. *Mailing Add:* Trop BioIndust Co 9869 East Fern St Miami FL 33157

ROESSLER, ROBERT L, b Neillsville, Wis, Sept 2, 21; m 46; c 3. PSYCHIATRY. *Educ:* Univ Wis, PhB, 42; Columbia Univ, MD, 45; Am Bd Psychiat & Neurol, dipl, 51. *Prof Exp:* Intern, Englewood Hosp, NJ, 45-46; resident psychiat, Vet Admin Hosp, Madison, Wis, 46-48; resident, Strong Mem Hosp, Rochester, NY, 48-49; instr, Sch Med, Univ Rochester, 49-50; from asst prof to prof, Sch Med, Univ Wis, 50-63, from actg chmn dept to chmn dept, 56-61, dir psychiat inst, 60-61; PROF PSYCHIAT, BAYLOR COL MED, 63- *Concurrent Pos:* Consult, US Info Agency, 59-61 & Vet Admin Hosp, Madison, 59-61. *Mem:* AAAS; fel Am Psychiat Asn; Am Psychosom Soc; Soc Psychophysiol Res; NY Acad Sci. *Res:* Psychophysiology; psychosomatic medicine. *Mailing Add:* Dept of Psychiat Baylor Col of Med Houston TX 77030

ROEST, ARYAN INGOMAR, b Chicago, Ill, June 13, 25; m 50; c 4. VERTEBRATE ZOOLOGY, TAXONOMY. *Educ:* Univ Va, BS, 45; Ore State Col, BS, 48, MS, 49, PhD(zool), 54. *Prof Exp:* Asst, Ore State Col, 49; instr biol & math, Cent Ore Col, 52-55; PROF BIOL, CALIF POLYTECH STATE UNIV, SAN LUIS OBISPO, 55- *Mem:* Am Soc Mammal. *Res:* Vertebrate field zoology, including mammals, birds, reptiles and amphibians; systematic studies of sea otter, red fox, kit fox & kangaroo rat; mammal studies. *Mailing Add:* Dept Biol Sci Calif Polytech State Univ San Luis Obispo CA 93401

ROETH, FREDERICK WARREN, b Houston, Ohio, Aug 21, 41; m 68; c 3. WEED SCIENCE. *Educ:* Ohio State Univ, BS, 64; Univ Nebr, Lincoln, MS, 67, PhD(agron), 70. *Prof Exp:* Res asst weed sci, Univ Nebr, Lincoln, 64-69; asst prof, Purdue Univ, W Lafayette, 69-75; asst prof, 75-76, ASSOC PROF AGRON, UNIV NEBR, LINCOLN, 76- *Mem:* Weed Sci Soc Am; Am Soc Agron; Coun Agr Sci and Technol. *Res:* Weed biology and control in agronomic crops and pastures. *Mailing Add:* Box 66 S Cent Sta Clay Center NE 68933

ROETLING, PAUL G, b Buffalo, NY, Sept 12, 33; m 60. PHYSICS, OPTICS. *Educ:* Univ Buffalo, BA, 55, PhD(physics), 60. *Prof Exp:* Consult, Cornell Aeronaut Lab, 59-60, physicist, 60-63, sect head optics, 63-68; prin scientist, 68-70, mgr optics res area, 70-74, mgr image processing area, 74-78, RES FEL, XEROX CORP, 78- *Mem:* Am Phys Soc; fel Optical Soc Am; Inst Elec & Electronics Engrs. *Res:* Optical image formation and image processing. *Mailing Add:* Xerox Corp 800 Phillips Rd Webster NY 14580

ROETMAN, ERNEST LEVANE, b Chandler, Minn, Sept 18, 36; m 62; c 2. APPLIED MATHEMATICS, ANALYTICAL MECHANICS. *Educ:* Univ Minn, BA, 57; Ore State Univ, PhD(math & mech eng), 63. *Prof Exp:* Asst math, Aachen Tech Univ, 63; tech specialist, Bell Tel Labs, 63-65; asst prof, Stevens Inst Technol, 65-68; assoc prof math, Univ Mo-Columbia, 68-75, prof, 75-80; PROF ENGR, BOEIN COMPUT SERV, 80- *Concurrent Pos:* Guest prof, Aachen Tech Univ, 75-76; von Humboldt fel, 76; guest prof, Ore State Univ, 79-80. *Mem:* Soc Indust & Appl Math; Soc Natural Philos; Int Soc Oxygen Transport Tissue. *Res:* Biofluid mechanics; partial differential equations; irregular boundary value problems; numerical analysis; fluid flow. *Mailing Add:* 4205 93 Ave SE Mercer Island WA 98040

ROFFMAN, STEVEN, b New York, NY, April 29, 44. BIOCHEMICAL PHARMACOLOGY. *Educ:* Queens Col, NY, BA, 65; New York Univ, MS, 68, PhD(biochem), 74. *Prof Exp:* Fel biochem, Albert Einstein Col Med, NY, 73-75; res assoc, 75-78, assoc, 78-79, asst prof pharmacol, 79-81, RES ASSOC MED, COL PHYSICIANS & SURGEONS, COLUMBIA UNIV, 81- *Mem:* AAAS. *Res:* Role of prokolytic enzymes in the pathophysiology of inflammation and carcinogenesis; role of vasoactive peptides released in inflammatory disease of lung and skin. *Mailing Add:* Dept Med Col Physicians & Surgeons Columbia Univ New York NY 10032

ROFFWARG, HOWARD PHILIP, b New York, NY, June 9, 32; m; c 1. PSYCHIATRY. *Educ:* Columbia Univ, AB, 54, MD, 58. *Prof Exp:* Res assoc, Mt Sinai Hosp, 61-62; instr psychiat, Columbia Univ, 62-66; asst prof, 66-71, ASSOC PROF PSYCHIAT, ALBERT EINSTEIN COL MED, 71- *Concurrent Pos:* NIMH career res scientist awards & res proj grants, 62-76; dir sleep EEG lab, NY State Psychiat Inst, 62-66, asst attend psychiatrist, 63-66; adj attend psychiatrist, Montefiore Hosp & Med Ctr, 66-71, assoc attend psychiatrist, 71-77. *Mem:* Asn Res Nerv & Ment Dis; Am Psychosom Soc; Asn Psychophysiol Study Sleep. *Res:* Sleep physiology; clinical psychiatry. *Mailing Add:* Dept of Psychiat 5323 Harry Hines Dallas TX 75235

ROGAK, EARL, mathematics, see previous edition

ROGAN, ELEANOR GROENIGER, b Cincinnati, Ohio, Nov 25, 42; div; c 1. BIOCHEMISTRY. *Educ:* Mt Holyoke Col, AB, 63; Johns Hopkins Univ, PhD(biochem), 68. *Prof Exp:* Lectr biol sci, Goucher Col, 68-69; fel biochem, Univ Tenn, 69-71, res assoc cancer res, 71-73; res assoc, 73-76, asst prof, 76-80, ASSOC PROF CHEM CARCINOGENESIS, EPPLEY INST & DEPT BIOMED CHEM, MED CTR, UNIV NEBR, 80- *Mem:* Am Asn Cancer Res; AAAS; Sigma Xi. *Res:* Mechanism of carcinogenesis by polycyclic aromatic hydrocarbons; nuclear monooxygenase enzyme activities especially those catalyzing activation of hydrocarbons; binding of hydrocarbons to DNA and structure of hydrocarbon-nucleic acid base derivatives. *Mailing Add:* Eppley Inst Univ of Nebr Med Ctr Omaha NE 68105

ROGAN, JOHN B, b Kansas City, Kans, Sept 3, 30; m 66. ORGANIC CHEMISTRY, POLYMER CHEMISTRY. *Educ:* Univ Wyo, BS, 52; Univ Calif, Berkeley, PhD(chem), 55. *Prof Exp:* Res chemist, Elastomer Chem Dept, E I du Pont de Nemours & Co, 55-59; res assoc org chem, Univ Wyo, 59; asst prof chem, Colo State Univ, 59-62; assoc prof, Univ Nev, Reno, 62-66; res chemist, 66-69, group leader, Res & Develop Dept, 69-73, RES ASSOC, RES & DEVELOP DEPT, AMOCO CHEM CORP, 73- *Concurrent Pos:* Res grants, NSF, 60-62, Am Chem Soc Petrol Res Fund, 64-66 & Desert Res Inst, Univ Nev, 66. *Mem:* AAAS; Am Chem Soc; Am Inst Chem Eng. *Res:* Polymer synthesis; property-structure relationships. *Mailing Add:* Res & Develop Dept Amoco Chem Corp PO Box 400 Naperville IL 60540

ROGATZ, PETER, b New York, NY, Aug 5, 26; m 49; c 2. PUBLIC HEALTH. *Educ:* Columbia Univ, BA, 46, MPH, 56; Cornell Univ, MD, 49. *Prof Exp:* Dir study home care prog, Hosp Coun Greater New York, 53-55; Commonwealth Fund fel, Columbia Univ, 55-56; assoc med dir, Health Ins Plan Greater New York, 56-57; med adminr, East Nassau Med Group, 57-58; assoc dir hosp & health agency study, Fedn Jewish Philanthropies of NY, 58-59; dep dir, Montefiore Hosp, New York, 60-63; dir, Long Island Jewish Hosp, 64-68; PROF CLIN COMMUNITY MED, SCH MED & HEALTH CARE ADMIN, SCH ALLIED HEALTH PROFESSIONS, STATE UNIV NY STONY BROOK, 68- *Concurrent Pos:* Lectr, Sch Pub Health, Columbia Univ, 58-; dir univ hosp, State Univ NY Stony Brook, 68-71, co-dir grad prog health care admin, 69-71; sr vpres, Blue Cross & Blue Shield of Greater New York, 71-76 & Peter Rogatz & Donald Meyers Assocs, Inc, 76- *Mem:* Fel Am Col Physicians; fel Am Col Hosp Adminr; fel Am Col Prev Med; fel Am Pub Health Asn; Asn Teachers Prev Med. *Res:* Medical care organization and delivery of health services; community health planning; medical care administration. *Mailing Add:* P Rogatz & D Meyers Assocs Inc 142 Mineola Ave Roslyn Heights NY 11577

ROGAWSKI, ALEXANDER S, b Jaslo, Austria, May 11, 13; nat US; m 47; c 2. PSYCHIATRY. *Educ:* Univ Vienna, MD, 38, PhD, 78. *Prof Exp:* training supv analyst, Psychoanal Inst, 60-80, lectr psychoanat, 55-80, EMER PROF, SCH MED, UNIV SOUTHERN CALIF, 80-; CLINICAL PROF, PSYCHIATRY & BEHAV SCI, UNIV CALIF, LOS ANGELES, 80- *Concurrent Pos:* Sr attend physician, Los Angeles County, Univ Southern Calif Med Ctr, Gen Hosp, 54-; res assoc, Ford Found Proj & attend physician, Mt Sinai Hosp, 57-65; consult, Vet Admin, 58-61; chief ment health consult, Los Angeles County Bur Pub Assistance, 60-78. *Mem:* Am Psychosom Soc; fel Am Col Psychiatrists; fel Am Psychiat Asn; Am Psychoanal Asn; fel Group Advan Psychiat. *Res:* Psychoanalysis; nature of psychotherapeutic process; psychiatry and public welfare, chronic patients. *Mailing Add:* 11665 W Olympic Blvd Los Angeles CA 90064

ROGAWSKI, MICHAEL ANDREW, b Los Angeles, Calif, April 8, 52. NEUROSCIENCE, NEUROPHARMACOLOGY. *Educ:* Amherst Col, BA, 74; Sch Med, Yale Univ, MD & PhD(pharmacol), 80. *Prof Exp:* MED STAFF FEL, LAB NEUROPHYSIOL, NAT INST NEUROL & COMMUN DISORDERS & STROKE, NIH, 81- *Mem:* Sigma Xi; Soc Neurosci; Am Soc Pharmacol & Exp Therapeut. *Res:* Neurophysiological studies on the mechanism of action of neurotransmitters and neuroactive drugs, with emphasis on those agents used in the treatment of neurological and psychiatric disorders. *Mailing Add:* Lab Neurophysiol NIH Bldg 36 Rm 2C-02 Bethesda MD 20205

ROGER, WILLIAM ALEXANDER, b Toronto, Ont, Apr 6, 47; m 69; c 1. ELECTRONICS, COMPUTER SCIENCES. *Educ:* Univ Toronto, BASc, 68, MSc, 70; Univ Alta, PhD(physics), 74. *Prof Exp:* Killam fel physics, Dalhousie Univ, 74-77; DEFENSE SCIENTIST ELECTRONICS & SIGNAL PROCESSING, DEFENSE RES ESTAB (ATLANTIC), 77- *Res:* Design and fabrication of electronic instruments for the armed forces; signal processing and analysis of oceanographic acoustic data. *Mailing Add:* Defense Res Estab (Atlantic) PO Box 1012 Dartmouth NS B2Y 3Z7 Can

ROGERS, ADRIANNE ELLEFSON, b Aberdeen, Wash, Feb 18, 33; m 54; c 3. EXPERIMENTAL PATHOLOGY. *Educ:* Radcliffe Col, AB, 54; Harvard Med Sch, MD, 58. *Prof Exp:* Intern med, Beth Israel Hosp, Boston, 58-59; res fel path, Boston City Hosp & Harvard Med Sch, 60-62; USPHS res fel, Mallory Inst Path, 62-64, res fel, 64-65; res assoc, 66-72, SR RES SCIENTIST NUTRIT & FOOD SCI, MASS INST TECHNOL, 72-, LECTR, 73- *Concurrent Pos:* Asst, Harvard Med Sch, 64-67, instr, 68-73; sr resident path, Peter Bent Brigham Hosp, Boston, Mass, 76-77, clin fel, 77- *Mem:* Am Asn Study Liver Dis; Am Soc Exp Path; Am Inst Nutrit. *Res:* Liver regeneration; nutritional liver disease, including fatty liver and cirrhosis; interaction between diet and chemical carcinogenesis. *Mailing Add:* Dept of Nutrit & Food Sci Mass Inst of Technol Cambridge MA 02139

ROGERS, ALAN BARDE, b Sergeant Bluffs, Iowa, Nov 11, 18; m 41; c 3. CHEMISTRY. *Educ:* Iowa State Col, BSc, 42. *Prof Exp:* Res chemist, 41-42, chem process develop, 45-48, chem mkt develop, 48-53, head dairy, poultry & specialty prods res, 53-60, assoc tech dir, Food Res Div, 60-64, asst mgr, Food Res Div, 64-67, ASST DIR RES, FOOD RES DIV, ARMOUR & CO, 67- *Concurrent Pos:* Mem, Nat Turkey Fedn Res Comt. *Mem:* Poultry Sci Asn; Inst Food Technol. *Res:* Poultry; frozen foods; dehydrated and dairy products. *Mailing Add:* Food Res Div Armour & Co 15101 N Scottsdale Rd Scottsdale AZ 85260

ROGERS, ALAN ERNEST EXEL, b Salisbury, Zimbabwe, Oct 3, 41; US citizen; m 68. RADIO ASTRONOMY. *Educ:* Univ Col Rhodesia & Nyasaland, BSc, 62; Mass Inst Technol, SM, 64, PhD(elec eng), 67. *Prof Exp:* MEM STAFF, HAYSTACK OBSERV, MASS INST TECHNOL, 67- *Honors & Awards:* Rumford Medal, Am Acad Arts & Sci, 71. *Mem:* AAAS; Inst Elec & Electronics Engrs; Am Astron Soc; Am Geophys Union. *Res:* Emission and absorption of microwave radiation by interstellar hydroxl radical; radar mapping of Venus; very long baseline interferometry; radiometric instrumentation. *Mailing Add:* Haystack Observ Westford MA 01886

ROGERS, ALVIN LEE, b Houston, Tex, Jan 18, 29. MEDICAL MYCOLOGY, MEDICAL MICROBIOLOGY. *Educ:* Southeastern State Col, BS, 48; Mich State Univ, PhD(med mycol, mycol), 67. *Prof Exp:* Teacher high sch, Tex, 48-59; instr biol, comp anat & microbiol, Bay City Jr Col, 59; instr biol bot, zool & microbiol, Port Huron Jr Col, 59-61; from instr to asst prof med mycol, 65-78, ASSOC PROF MED MYCOL, MICH STATE UNIV, 78- *Concurrent Pos:* Res assoc, Belo Horizonte Vet Sch, Brazil, 60; Bot Inst Sao Paulo, Brazil, 61; Nat Univ Colombia, 68; co-dir, Mycol Sect Health Ctr & Animal Diag Lab, Mich State Univ, 77- *Mem:* Int Soc Human & Animal Mycol; Med Mycol Soc of the Americas; Am Soc Microbiol; Mycol Soc Am; Soc Gen Microbiol. *Res:* Medical mycology; pathogenicity of fungi pathogenic in man and animals and metabolic products produced by these fungi; adherance of Candida Albisans to biological surfaces; protein low diets and the development of mycoses. *Mailing Add:* Dept Microbiol & Pub Health Mich State Univ East Lansing MI 48824

ROGERS, ANDREW JACKSON, b Perry, Fla, Jan 7, 16; m 41; c 3. MEDICAL ENTOMOLOGY. *Educ:* Univ Fla, BSA, 41, MS, 43; Univ Md, PhD(entom), 53. *Prof Exp:* Entomologist, USPHS, 42-44; assoc prof entom, Univ Fla, 46-56; chief control res, Entom Res Ctr, Fla State Bd Health, 56-64, dir, West Fla Arthropod Res Lab, 64-76, dir, Off Entom, 76-79; RETIRED. *Concurrent Pos:* Consult, La Mosquito Control Asn, 61 & CZ Govt, 62. *Mem:* Entom Soc Am; Am Mosquito Control Asn (pres, 71-72). *Res:* Arthropods of medical importance, especially mosquitoes and other biting flies. *Mailing Add:* Off of Entom PO Box 210 Jacksonville FL 32231

ROGERS, BENJAMIN LANHAM, b Roebuck, SC, June 26, 20; m 51; c 2. HORTICULTURE. *Educ:* Clemson Col, BS, 43; Univ Minn, MS, 47; Univ Md, PhD(hort), 50. *Prof Exp:* Asst horticulturist, USDA, 50-54; from asst prof to assoc prof hort, Univ Md, College Park, 54-71, prof, 71-80; RETIRED. *Mem:* Am Soc Hort Sci. *Res:* Chemical thinning of apples and peaches; irrigation; pruning; weed control. *Mailing Add:* 110 Concord Ave Berkeley Springs WV 25411

ROGERS, BEVERLY JANE, b Pasadena, Tex, Sept 24, 43; m 72; c 1. BIOCHEMISTRY, REPRODUCTIVE BIOLOGY. *Educ:* Univ Tex, Austin, BA, 64; Univ Wis-Madison, MS, 70; Univ Hawaii, PhD(biochem), 72. *Prof Exp:* NIH fel reproductive biol, Dept Anat & Reproductive Biol, 74-76, ASST PROF, DEPT OBSTET & GYNEC, SCH MED, UNIV HAWAII, 76- *Mem:* AAAS; Am Soc Cell Biol; Soc Study Reproduction. *Res:* Biochemistry of capacitation of mammalian spermatozoa; metabolism of spermatozoa and occurrence of acrosome reaction in the presence of various energy sources and inhibitors; in vitro fertilization. *Mailing Add:* Dept of Obstet & Gynec Kapiolani Hosp Rm 829 Honolulu HI 96826

ROGERS, BRUCE G(EORGE), b Houston, Tex, Feb 20, 25. CIVIL ENGINEERING. *Educ:* Univ Houston, BS, 57; Univ Ill, MS, 58, PhD(civil eng), 61. *Prof Exp:* Engr geophys, Robert H Ray Co, Tex, 47-52; engr asst, Tex Hwy Dept, 53-54, sr draftsman, 54-56, assoc design engr, 56; consult civil eng, Turner & Collie, 56-57; teaching asst theoret & appl mech, Univ Ill, 57-59, instr, 59-61; from asst prof to assoc prof civil eng, 61-67, PROF CIVIL ENG, LAMAR UNIV, 67- *Mem:* Am Soc Civil Engrs; Am Soc Mech Engrs; Am Soc Testing & Mat; Am Concrete Inst; Soc Exp Stress Anal. *Res:* Behavior of tapered beam-columns under ultimate loads; plastic design and analysis of non-prismatic members. *Mailing Add:* Dept of Civil Eng Lamar Univ Box 10024 Beaumont TX 77710

ROGERS, BRUCE JOSEPH, b Pasadena, Calif, June 21, 24; m 56; c 4. PLANT PHYSIOLOGY, SCIENCE WRITING. *Educ:* Univ Calif, BSF, 49, MSF, 50; Calif Inst Technol, PhD(plant physiol), 55. *Prof Exp:* From asst prof to assoc prof plant physiol, Purdue Univ, 54-61; assoc plant physiologist, Univ Hawaii, 61-66; prof bot, NDak State Univ, 66-67; plant physiologist, Agr Res Serv, USDA, Pasadena, Calif, 67-69, Riverside, 69-71; consult & sci writer, 71-74; HEAD CLIN RES & DOC, LEE PHARMACEUT, 73- *Mem:* Am Inst Biol Sci; Soc Am Foresters; Sigma Xi. *Res:* Abscission; ethylene enzymology; herbicide action; ecology; dental and medical materials and devices. *Mailing Add:* 17372 Lido Lane Huntington Beach CA 92647

ROGERS, CHARLES C, b Crawfordsville, Ind, Jan 27, 31; m 54; c 3. ELECTRICAL ENGINEERING. *Educ:* Purdue Univ, BSEE, 53, MSEE, 57, PhD(elec eng), 60. *Prof Exp:* Res asst elec eng, Mass Inst Technol, 55; supt elec power, Crawfordsville Elec Light & Power Co, Ind, 56; teaching asst elec eng, Purdue Univ, 56-57, instr, 57-60; res engr electromagnetics, Collins Radio Co, 60-61; from asst prof to prof elec eng, 61-70, chmn dept, 65-70, PROF PHYSICS & ELEC ENG & CHMN DIV, ROSE-HULMAN INST TECHNOL, 72- *Concurrent Pos:* Mem adv bd, Aerospace Res Appl Ctr, Indiana Univ, 65- *Mem:* Inst Elec & Electronics Engrs; Am Soc Eng Educ. *Res:* Electromagnetic theory. *Mailing Add:* Div of Physics & Elec Eng Rose-Hulman Inst of Technol Terre Haute IN 47803

ROGERS, CHARLES EDWIN, b Rochester, NY, Dec 29, 29; m 54; c 3. PHYSICAL CHEMISTRY, MEMBRANE MATERIALS. *Educ:* Univ Syracuse, BS, 54; Univ Syracuse & State Univ NY, PhD(phys chem), 57. *Prof Exp:* Goodyear res fel & res assoc chem, Princeton Univ, 57-59; mem tech staff polymer chem, Bell Labs, 59-65; PROF MACROMOLECULAR SCI, CASE WESTERN RESERVE UNIV, 65- *Mem:* Am Chem Soc; Am Phys Soc; Soc Plastics Engr; Soc Coatings Tech. *Res:* Polymer science; solubility and diffusion in polymers; kinetics and mechanism of polymerization; polymer rheology and properties; polymer degradation; environmental effects on polymers; membrane separation processes and materials. *Mailing Add:* Dept of Macromolecular Sci Case Western Reserve Univ Cleveland OH 44106

ROGERS, CHARLES GRAHAM, b Summerside, PEI, Mar 13, 29; m 61; c 1. BIOCHEMISTRY, MICROBIOLOGY. *Educ:* McGill Univ, BSc, 52, MSc, 54; Univ Wis, PhD(microbiol), 63. *Prof Exp:* Chemist, 54-64, RES SCIENTIST, DEPT NAT HEALTH & WELFARE, CAN, 65- *Mem:* Am Soc Microbiol; Can Biochem Soc; Can Soc Microbiol; Nutrit Soc Can; Can Inst Food Sci & Technol. *Res:* Dietary stress in relation to lipid composition and metabolism in rat liver tissue and cardiac muscle cells in tissue culture; enzymes of lipid metabolism in cultured heart cells. *Mailing Add:* Res Labs Health Protection Br Dept of Nat Health & Welfare Ottawa ON K1A 0L2 Can

ROGERS, CHARLES HENRY, biomedical engineering, medical electronics, see previous edition

ROGERS, CHARLIE ELLIC, b Booneville, Ark, Aug 13, 38; m 71; c 2. ENTOMOLOGY. *Educ:* Northern Ariz Univ, BS, 64; Univ Ky, MS, 67; Okla State Univ, PhD(entom), 70. *Prof Exp:* Teacher biol & social studies, Dysart Pub Schs, Ariz, 64-65; res assoc entom, Okla State Univ, 70-71; asst prof, Agr Exp Sta, Tex A&M Univ, 71-75; res entomologist, Southwestern Great Plains Res Ctr, Sci & Educ Admin-Fed Res, USDA, 75-80; SUPVR RES ENTOMOLOGIST & RES LEADER, CONSERVATION & PROD RES CTR, AGR RES SERV, USDA, 80- *Concurrent Pos:* Assoc ed, Insect World Dig, Biol Sci Res Inst, 73-77. *Mem:* Entom Soc Am; Am Registry Prof Entom; Southwest Entom Soc. *Res:* Biology, ecology and control of insect pests of sunflower and guar; biological control of agricultural pests. *Mailing Add:* Sci & Educ Admin-Fed Res USDA Southwestern Gt Plains Res Ctr Bushland TX 79012

ROGERS, CLAUDE MARVIN, b Bloomington, Ind, Sept 22, 19; m 44; c 4. BOTANY, TAXONOMY. *Educ:* Ind Univ, AB, 40; Univ Mich, MA, 47, PhD, 50. *Prof Exp:* Stockroom custodian, Univ Okla, 43-44; instr biol, Univ Tex, 48-49; from asst prof to assoc prof, 49-71, PROF BIOL, WAYNE STATE UNIV, 71- *Mem:* AAAS; Am Soc Plant Taxon; Bot Soc Am; Int Asn Plant Taxon. *Res:* Taxonomy of flowering plants, especially family Linaceae. *Mailing Add:* Dept of Biol Wayne State Univ Detroit MI 48202

ROGERS, DAVID ELLIOTT, b New York, NY, Mar 17, 26; m 72; c 3. INTERNAL MEDICINE. *Educ:* Cornell Univ, MD, 48. *Prof Exp:* Intern, Osler Med Serv, Johns Hopkins Hosp, 48-49, asst resident, 49-50; NIH fel med, Med Col, Cornell Univ, 50-51; chief resident physician, New York Hosp, 51-52; from asst prof to assoc prof, Cornell Univ, 54-59; prof & chmn dept, Sch Med, Vanderbilt Univ, 59-68; vpres med & dean med sch, Johns Hopkins Univ, 68-72; PRES, ROBERT WOOD JOHNSON FOUND, 72- *Concurrent Pos:* Vis investr, Rockefeller Inst, 54-55; dir comn staphylococcus dis, Armed Forces Epidemiol Bd, 58-69. *Mem:* Inst of Med of Nat Acad Sci; Am Soc Clin Invest; Asn Am Physicians; Am Clin & Climat Asn. *Res:* Host-parasite relationships in infectious diseases. *Mailing Add:* Robert Wood Johnson Found PO Box 2316 Princeton NJ 08540

ROGERS, DAVID FREEMAN, b Theresa, NY, Sept 3, 37. FLUID DYNAMICS, AEROSPACE ENGINEERING. *Educ:* Rensselaer Polytech Inst, BAeroE, 59, MS, 60, PhD(aeronaut, astronaut), 67. *Prof Exp:* Res assoc aeronaut eng, Rensselaer Polytech Inst, 62-64; asst prof, 64-67, ASSOC PROF AERONAUT ENG, US NAVAL ACAD, 67-, OFF OF NAVAL RES PROF & DIR CAD/IG, 71- *Concurrent Pos:* Sr consult, Cadcom, Inc, 70-; hon res fel, Univ Col London, 77-78. *Mem:* Am Inst Aeronaut & Astronaut; Am Phys Soc; Soc Naval Archit & Marine Engrs; Asn Comput Mach. *Res:* Computer graphics; computer aided manufactoring; curve and surface description; compressible boundary layers; aerodynamics of nonrigid airfoils; computer aided design and interactive graphics; numerical methods; nonlinear two point asymptotic boundary value problems. *Mailing Add:* Dept of Aerospace Eng US Naval Acad Annapolis MD 21402

ROGERS, DAVID JAMES, b De Funiak Springs, Fla, Oct 19, 18; m 45; c 3. ECONOMIC BOTANY. *Educ:* Univ Fla, BS, 41; Wash Univ, MA, 49, PhD(bot), 51. *Prof Exp:* Asst bot, Wash Univ, 49; from asst prof to assoc prof biol, Allegheny Col, 51-57; ed, Econ Bot & cur, NY Bot Garden, 57-65; prof bot, Colo State Univ, 65-67; prof biol, 67-80, EMER PROF BIOL, UNIV COLO, BOULDER, 80- *Concurrent Pos:* Vis fel, Food Res Inst, Stanford Univ & proj coordr, Environ Info Mgt Ctr, Gulf Univs Res Consortium, 71-72; genetic resources doc officer, Crop Ecol & Genetic Resources Unit, Food & Agr Orgn, Rome, Italy, 74. *Mem:* Soc Econ Bot (treas, 58-60); Int Soc Plant Taxon. *Res:* Taxonomy of phanerogams, vitis, particularly the North American species. *Mailing Add:* Dept of EPO Biol Univ of Colo Boulder CO 80309

ROGERS, DAVID K, b Auburn, Calif, Mar 17, 43; m 67. ENGINEERING GEOLOGY, ECONOMIC GEOLOGY. *Educ:* Univ Nev, BS, 67, MS, 76. *Prof Exp:* Staff geologist econ geol, Utah Int, Inc, 67-73; staff geologist eng geol, Converse Davis Dixon, 75-76; sr staff geologist, Woodward Clyde Consult, 76-77; proj geologist, 76-77, SR GEOLOGIST ENG GEOL, CONVERSE WARD DAVIS DIXON, 77- *Mem:* Asn Eng Geologists; Geol Soc Am; Soc Mining Engrs. *Res:* Active fault morphology; recurrance of active faulting; geomorphology of landslides; quaternary geology; analysis of rock discontinuities; mining reclamation. *Mailing Add:* Converse Ward Davis Dixon 101 Howard St Suite A San Francisco CA 94105

ROGERS, DAVID T, JR, b Foley, Ala, Apr 10, 35; m 58; c 2. ECOLOGY. *Educ:* Huntington Col, AB, 58; Univ Ga, MS, 63, PhD(bird migration), 65. *Prof Exp:* Teacher, Marbury High Sch, 59-61 & Southern Union Jr Col, 61-62; from asst prof to assoc prof, 65-77, PROF BIOL, UNIV ALA, TUSCALOOSA, 77- *Concurrent Pos:* US Dept Interior grant, 70-71; NSF grant, 71; US Corps Eng grant, 72-73. *Mem:* Ecol Soc Am; Am Ornithologists Union. *Res:* Ornithology, especially population and community aspects; bird migration in Latin America. *Mailing Add:* Dept of Biol Univ of Ala in Tuscaloosa University AL 35486

ROGERS, DAVID WILLIAM OLIVER, b Toronto, Ont, Aug 11, 45; m 71; c 2. NUCLEAR PHYSICS, RADIATION DOSIMETRY. *Educ:* Univ of Toronto, BSc, 68, MSc, 69, PhD(physics), 72. *Prof Exp:* Res assoc, Oxford Nuclear Physics Lab, UK, 72-73, RES OFFICER RADIATION DOSIMETRY, NAT RES COUN CAN, 73- *Mem:* Can Asn Physicists; Health Physics Soc; Asn Sci, Eng & Technol Community Can; Am Asn Physicists Med; Can Radiation Protection Asn. *Res:* Radiation dosimetry for medical and radiation protection purposes. *Mailing Add:* Nat Res Coun Can Physics Div Montreal Rd Ottawa ON K1A 0R6 Can

ROGERS, DEXTER, b Kyoto, Japan, Dec 14, 21; m 45; c 4. BIOCHEMISTRY. *Educ:* Univ Mich, BS, 44, MS, 46; Ore State Univ, PhD(biochem), 54. *Prof Exp:* Res chemist, Western Condensing Co, Appleton, Wis, 45-51; NSF fel, Stanford Univ, 54-55; instr biochem, Univ Mich, 55-58; instr & res assoc chem, Univ Ore, 58-60; asst prof food & nutrit, Utah State Univ, 60-62, chem, 62-65; asst prof, Univ Mont, 65-66; USPHS spec fel, Ore State Univ, 66-68; prof, State Univ NY Col Cortland, 68-69; lectr, Portland State Univ, 69-70; prof & chmn dept, William Paterson Col NJ, 70-75; prof chem, Bloomfield Col, 75-77; applns & develop chemist, KONTES, 77-79; CONSULT TECH MGT & ENVIRON REGULATIONS, 80- *Mem:* AAAS; Am Chem Soc; Am Soc Microbiol. *Res:* Biochemistry of microorganisms; sugar transport mechanisms. *Mailing Add:* 535 Harding Hwy Mays Landing NJ 08330

ROGERS, DILWYN JOHN, b Chicago, Ill, Aug 18, 29; m 53; c 4. ECOLOGY. *Educ:* Wheaton Col, Ill, BS, 51; Univ Wis, MS, 57, PhD(bot), 59. *Prof Exp:* Asst plant ecol, Univ Wis, 56-59; from asst prof to assoc prof, 59-72, chmn dept, 72-77, PROF BIOL, AUGUSTANA COL, SDAK, 77- *Concurrent Pos:* Vis prof, Univ Natal & Geobotanical Inst, Switz, 67-68; Fulbright vis prof, Univ Sci & Technol, Ghana, 72-73. *Mem:* AAAS; Ecol Soc Am; Brit Ecol Soc; Wilderness Soc. *Res:* Phytosociology. *Mailing Add:* Dept of Biol Augustana Col Sioux Falls SD 57102

ROGERS, DONALD EUGENE, b Los Angeles, Calif, Aug 27, 32; m 55; c 2. FISH BIOLOGY. *Educ:* Calif State Polytech, San Luis Obispo, BS, 58; Univ Wash, MS, 61, PhD(fisheries), 67. *Prof Exp:* Fishery biologist, 60-68, mem fac fisheries, 69-77, RES ASSOC PROF FISHERIES, FISHERIES RES INST, UNIV WASH, 77- *Mem:* Am Inst Fishery Res Biologists; Am Fisheries Soc. *Res:* Fish population dynamics; biology of sockeye salmon. *Mailing Add:* Fisheries Res Inst Univ of Wash Seattle WA 98195

ROGERS, DONALD PHILIP, b Toledo, Ohio, Feb 5, 08; m 34; c 1. BOTANY. *Educ:* Oberlin Col, BA, 29; Univ Iowa, PhD(mycol), 35. *Prof Exp:* Asst bot, Univ Nebr, 29-30 & Univ Iowa, 31-35; instr, Ore State Col, 36-40 & Brown Univ, 41-42; assoc prof biol, Am Int Col, 42-45; asst prof bot, Univ Hawaii, 45-47; cur, NY Bot Garden, 47-57; prof bot & cur mycol collections, 57-76, EMER PROF BOT, UNIV ILL, URBANA, 76- *Concurrent Pos:* Nat Res Coun fel bot, Harvard Univ, 35-36; managing ed, Mycologia, 48-57, ed-in-chief, 58-60. *Mem:* Mycol Soc Am (vpres, 54, pres, 56-57); Torrey Bot Club (rec secy, 48-55); Bot Soc Am; Brit Mycol Soc; Int Asn Plant Taxon. *Res:* Cytology, comparative morphology, phylogeny of fungi; taxonomy of lower Basidiomycetes; nomenclature; history of mycology. *Mailing Add:* Dept of Bot Univ of Ill Urbana IL 61801

ROGERS, DONALD RICHARD, b Richmond, Ky, Apr 27, 32; m 61. INORGANIC CHEMISTRY. *Educ:* Univ Ky, BS, 59, MS, 61, PhD(chem), 68. *Prof Exp:* Res chemist, 61-64, group leader chem, 64-65 & 68-71, sr res specialist, 72-79, FEL NUCLEAR OPERS DEPT, MOUND LAB, MONSANTO RES CORP, MIAMISBURG, 79- *Mem:* AAAS; Am Chem Soc; Sigma Xi. *Res:* Coordination chemistry of lanthanide and actinide elements; solvent extraction equilibria; radioisotopic fuels; environmental chemistry of plutonium; nuclear safeguards; uranium and plutonium measurement methods. *Mailing Add:* 975 Fernshire Dr Centerville OH 45459

ROGERS, DONALD WARREN, b Hackensack, NJ, Sept 10, 32; m 56; c 2. PHYSICAL CHEMISTRY, ANALYTICAL CHEMISTRY. *Educ:* Princeton Univ, BA, 54; Wesleyan Univ, MA, 56; NC Univ, PhD(chem, mamath), 60. *Prof Exp:* Asst prof chem, Robert Col, Istanbul, 60-63 & Long Island Univ, 63-64; master teacher chem & physics, Am Madrid, Spain, 64-65; from asst prof to assoc prof, 65-71, PROF CHEM, LONG ISLAND UNIV, 71- *Concurrent Pos:* NIH res grants, 71-73, 74-76 & 77-81; vis prof chem, Univ Ga, 76-77 & Barnard Col, 80-81. *Mem:* Am Chem Soc. *Res:* Heats of hydrogenation; thermochemistry; molecular structure; enthalpimetry; solution theory; applications of phase separations to analytical problems. *Mailing Add:* Dept of Chem Long Island Univ Brooklyn NY 11201

ROGERS, DOUGLAS HERBERT, b Wolfville, NS, June 2, 26; m 51; c 3. OPTICS, METAL PHYSICS. *Educ:* Dalhousie Univ, BSc, 47, MSc, 49; Mass Inst Technol, PhD(physics), 53. *Prof Exp:* Fel low temperature & solid state physics, Nat Res Coun, Can, 52-54; from asst prof to assoc prof, 54-65, PROF PHYSICS, ROYAL MIL COL CAN, 65- *Mem:* Optical Soc Am; Am Phys Soc; Am Asn Physics Teachers; Can Asn Physicists. *Res:* Attenuation of ultra sound; dislocations; acoustic emission; liquid crystals; holographic interferometry. *Mailing Add:* Dept Physics Royal Mil Col Can Kingston ON K7L 2W3 Can

ROGERS, EDWIN HENRY, b Newton, Mass, Nov 5, 36; m 60; c 3. APPLIED MATHEMATICS. *Educ:* Carnegie-Mellon Univ, BS, 58, MS, 60, PhD(math), 62. *Prof Exp:* Teaching asst & instr math, Carnegie Inst Technol, 58-62; Leverhulme vis fel, Univ Strathclyde, Scotland, 62-63; from asst prof to assoc prof, 65-75, PROF MATH, RENSSELAER POLYTECH INST, 75- *Concurrent Pos:* Ed, Siam News, Soc Indust & Appl Math, 75-; vis res prof, Univ Waterloo, 76-77. *Mem:* AAAS; Am Math Soc; Soc Indust & Appl Math; Asn Comput Mach; Inst Elec & Electronics Engrs. *Res:* Computer science; numerical analysis; biomathematics; nonlinear and multiparameter eigenproblems; educational computer systems. *Mailing Add:* Dept of Math Sci Rensselaer Polytech Inst Troy NY 12181

ROGERS, EMERY HERMAN, b Los Angeles, Calif, Mar 31, 21; m; c 3. PHYSICS. *Educ:* Stanford Univ, AB, 43, PhD(physics), 51. *Prof Exp:* Asst physics, Stanford Univ, 42-43; physicist, US Naval Res Lab, 43-45; engr nuclear magnetic resonance, Varian Assocs, 49-53, mgr instrument field eng, 53-60, vpres & mgr instrument div, 60-63, vpres instrument group, 63-67; gen mgr, 67-75, gen mgr, Anal Instrument Group, Hewlett-Packard Co, 75-79, EXEC DIR, HEWLETT-PACKARD CO FOUND, 79- *Mem:* AAAS; Am Phys Soc; Instrument Soc Am; Sci Apparatus Makers Asn. *Res:* Nuclear magnetic resonance; electron paramagnetic resonance; magnetism; analytical instrumentation. *Mailing Add:* Hewlett-Packard Co Found 3000 Harover St 20AH Palo Alto CA 94304

ROGERS, ERIC MALCOLM, b Bickley, Eng, Aug 15, 02; m 30; c 1. PHYSICS. *Educ:* Cambridge Univ, BA, 24, MA, 30. *Hon Degrees:* DSc, Col Wooster, 68. *Prof Exp:* Demonstr, Cavendish Lab, Eng, 24-25; teacher physics, Clifton Col, 25-28 & Bedales, Eng, 28-30; instr & tutor, Harvard Univ, 30-32 & Charterhouse, Eng, 32-37; instr, Mt Holyoke Col, 40-41 & St Pauls Sch, 41-42; from asst prof to prof, 42-71, EMER PROF PHYSICS, PRINCETON UNIV, 71- *Concurrent Pos:* Mem staff, Phys Sci Study Comt, Mass Inst Technol, 58-59; vis prof exp physics, Univ Sussex, 63-64; organizer physics, Nuffield Found sci teaching proj, 63- & rev physics proj, 71-; Ford Found grant sociol of exam, 67; adj prof, Univ Miami, 72- *Honors & Awards:* Oersted Medal, 69. *Mem:* Fel Am Phys Soc; Am Asn Physics Teachers; fel Brit Inst Physics; Europ Physics Soc. *Res:* Design of apparatus; methods of teaching in science; radioactivity; physics education; sociology of examinations. *Mailing Add:* Dept of Physics Princeton Univ Princeton NJ 08540

ROGERS, FRANCES ARLENE, b Northfield, Minn, Jan 24, 23; m 56; c 2. PROTOZOOLOGY, VERTEBRATE ZOOLOGY. *Educ:* Drake Univ, BA, 44; Univ Chicago, MS, 46; Univ Iowa, PhD(zool), 53. *Prof Exp:* Instr biol, Earlham Col, 46-49; asst prof biol, Cornell Col, 54 & Shimer Col, 55-56; asst prof 66-74, ASSOC PROF BIOL, DRAKE UNIV, 74- *Res:* Parasitic protozoology. *Mailing Add:* Dept of Biol Drake Univ Des Moines IA 50311

ROGERS, FRANK BRADWAY, b Norwood, Ohio, Dec 31, 14; m 42; c 3. MEDICINE. *Educ:* Yale Univ, BA, 36; Ohio State Univ, MD, 42; Columbia Univ, MS, 49. *Prof Exp:* Mem staff, Walter Reed Army Hosp, 47-48; dir, Nat Libr Med, Washington, DC, 49-63; librn, Univ Colo Med Ctr, Denver, 63-74; CONSULT MED LIBR, 75- *Mem:* Med Libr Asn (pres, 62-63); Am Asn Hist Med (pres, 66-68). *Res:* Bibliography of medicine; preservation and rebinding of rare books. *Mailing Add:* 1135 Grape St Denver CO 80220

ROGERS, FRED BAKER, b Trenton, NJ, Aug 25, 26. PREVENTIVE MEDICINE, PUBLIC HEALTH. *Educ:* Temple Univ, MD, 48; Univ Pa, MS, 54; Columbia Univ, MPH, 54; Am Bd Prev Med, dipl, 57. *Prof Exp:* Rotating intern, Univ Hosp, 48-49, chief resident med, 53-54, USPHS fel, Univ, 54-55, from asst prof to assoc prof prev med, Sch Med, 56-60, chmn dept family pract & community health, 70-77, PROF PREV MED, SCH MED, TEMPLE UNIV, 60- *Concurrent Pos:* Lectr epidemiol, Sch Pub Health, Columbia Univ, 57-68; lectr pub health, Sch Nursing, Univ Pa, 64-67; consult med, US Naval Hosp, Philadelphia, 64-73. *Mem:* AMA; Am Pub Health Asn; fel Am Col Physicians. *Res:* Epidemiology; immunization. *Mailing Add:* Dept Family Pract & Community Health Sch Med Temple Univ Philadelphia PA 19140

ROGERS, GARY ALLEN, b Compton, Calif, Jan 22, 45. BIOCHEMISTRY. *Educ:* Univ Calif, Los Angeles, BS, 68, Univ Calif, Santa Barbara, PhD(org chem), 73. *Prof Exp:* Fel biochem, Univ Calif, Los Angeles, 73-76; ASST PROF CHEM, UNIV TEX, DALLAS, 76- *Concurrent Pos:* NIH fel, Molecular Biol Inst, Univ Calif, Los Angeles, 73-75. *Mem:* Am Chem Soc. *Res:* Mechanisms of enzymic catalysis; protein modification reagents; mechanism of uncouplers of oxidative phosphorylation. *Mailing Add:* Dept of Chem Univ of Tex Richardson TX 75080

ROGERS, GERALD STANLEY, b Reading, Pa, Feb 29, 28. MATHEMATICAL STATISTICS. *Educ:* Muhlenberg Col, BS, 48; Univ Wash, MA, 51; Univ Iowa, PhD(math), 58. *Prof Exp:* Instr, Lafayette Col, 54-55; asst prof math, Univ Ariz, 58-65; assoc prof, 65-76, PROF MATH, NMEX STATE UNIV, 76- *Mem:* Am Math Soc; Am Statist Asn; Inst Math Statist. *Res:* Statistical distribution theory. *Mailing Add:* Dept of Math NMex State Univ Las Cruces NM 88001

ROGERS, H(ARRY) C(ARTON), JR, b Patchogue, NY, Oct 3, 23; m 47; c 3. PHYSICAL & MECHANICAL METALLURGY, METALWORKING. *Educ:* Cornell Univ, AB, 47; Rensselaer Polytech Inst, PhD(metall), 56. *Prof Exp:* Res metallurgist, Gen Elec Co, 48-69; PROF MAT ENG, DREXEL UNIV, 69- *Mem:* Am Soc Metals; Am Welding Soc; Am Inst Mining, Metall & Petrol Engrs. *Res:* Materials processing; mechanical behavior and fracture of solids; hydrogen embrittlement of metals; high pressure processing of metals; powder metallurgy. *Mailing Add:* Dept of Mat Eng Drexel Univ Philadelphia PA 19104

ROGERS, HARTLEY, b Buffalo, NY, July 6, 26; m 54; c 3. MATHEMATICS, PROBABILITY. *Educ:* Yale Univ, AB, 46, MS, 50; Princeton Univ, PhD(math), 52; Cambridge Univ, MA, 68. *Prof Exp:* Asst instr math, Princeton Univ, 50-52; Benjamin Pierce instr, Harvard Univ, 52-55; vis lectr, 55-56, from asst prof to assoc prof, 56-64, chmn faculty, 71-73, assoc provost, 74-80, PROF MATH, MASS INST TECHNOL, 64- *Concurrent Pos:* Guggenheim fel, 60-61; vis fel, Clare Hall, Cambridge Univ & NSF sr fel, 67-68; ed, Annals Math Logic & J Comput & Syst Sci, 69- & J Symbolic Logic, 63-67; trustee, Buckingham, Browne & Nichols Sch, 75-81 & Kingsley Trust Assoc, 76-78; consult, NSF, 80- *Honors & Awards:* Ford Award, Math Asn Am. *Mem:* Am Math Soc; Math Asn Am; Asn Symbolic Logic (vpres, 64-67). *Res:* Mathematical logic and recursion theory; probability and statistics, mathematical models; mathematics education; physics and applied mechanics. *Mailing Add:* Mass Inst Technol Rm 2-249 Cambridge MA 02139

ROGERS, HOLLIS JETTON, b Murray, Ky, Oct 7, 11; m 45; c 3. BOTANY. *Educ:* Murray State Col, BS, 33; Univ Ky, MS, 41; Duke Univ, PhD, 49. *Prof Exp:* Prin schs, Ky, 33-37, teacher, 37-40; instr bot, Univ Ky, 41-42; from asst prof to assoc prof, 47-79, EMER ASSOC PROF BOT, UNIV NC, GREENSBORO, 79- *Mem:* Bot Soc Am. *Res:* Taxonomy of the genus Galactia in the United States. *Mailing Add:* Dept Biol Univ NC Greensboro NC 27412

ROGERS, HORACE ELTON, b Philadelphia, Pa, Dec 5, 02; m 26; c 2. PHYSICAL CHEMISTRY, ANALYTICAL CHEMISTRY. *Educ:* Dickinson Col, BSc, 24; Lafayette Col, MSc, 25; Princeton Univ, PhD(chem), 30. *Prof Exp:* Instr sci, Dickinson Col, 25-27; asst chem, Princeton Univ, 27-29; assoc prof, 29-41, prof anal chem, 41-52, Alfred Victor duPont prof, 52-71, chmn dept, 58-65, EMER ALFRED VICTOR DUPONT PROF ANAL CHEM, DICKINSON COL, 71- *Concurrent Pos:* Head dept, Pa Area Col, Harrisburg, 46-48. *Mem:* Emer mem Am Chem Soc. *Res:* Gas chromatography of metal chelates; metal analysis by thin-layer chromatography. *Mailing Add:* 900 W South St Carlisle PA 17013

ROGERS, HOWARD GARDNER, b Houghton, Mich, June 21, 15; m 40; c 5. PHYSICS, CHEMISTRY. *Prof Exp:* Prod asst mfg light polarizers, 36-37, res asst new light polarizers, 37-41, Nat Defense Res Coun contract, 41-44, res mgr optical plastics, 44-47, sr scientist, 47-54, dept mgr color photog res, 54-66, dir, 66-68, vpres, 68-78, assoc dir res, 75-80, SR RES FEL, POLAROID CORP, 68-, SR VPRES, 78-, DIR RES, 80- *Honors & Awards:* Wetherill Medal, Franklin Inst, 66. *Mem:* AAAS; fel Soc Photog Scientists & Engrs; fel Optical Soc Am; fel Am Inst Chemists; fel Am Acad Arts & Sci. *Res:* New one step color photographic processes; new light polarizing materials; fabrication of optical plastics. *Mailing Add:* Polaroid Corp 549 Technol Sq Cambridge MA 02139

ROGERS, HOWARD H, b New York, Dec 26, 26; m 54; c 3. CHEMISTRY, ELECTRONICS. *Educ:* Univ Ill, BS, 49; Mass Inst Technol, PhD(inorg chem), 53. *Prof Exp:* Res asst chem, Mass Inst Technol, 51-52; from res chemist to res group leader inorg chem, Res Div, Allis-Chalmers Mfg Co, 52-61; from res specialist to sr tech specialist, Res Div, Rocketdyne Div, NAm Rockwell Corp, 61-70; CHIEF RES SCIENTIST, MARTEK INSTRUMENTS, INC, 70- *Mem:* Am Chem Soc; Electrochem Soc; Instrument Soc Am. *Res:* Chemical instrumentation; electrochemistry; electronics; fluorine chemistry; high temperature chemistry; advanced wastewater treatment. *Mailing Add:* 18361 Van Ness Ave Torrance CA 90504

ROGERS, HOWARD TOPPING, b Savedge, Va, July 22, 08; m 37; c 1. SOIL SCIENCE, AGRONOMY. *Educ:* Va Polytech Inst, BS, 30; Mich State Col, MS, 36; Iowa State Col, PhD(soil fertility), 42. *Prof Exp:* Instr high schs, Va, 30-34; asst soil surv, Mich State Col, 35; asst soil technologist, Exp Sta, Va Polytech Inst, 36-41; assoc soil chemist, Ala Polytech Inst, 42-46; agronomist & chief, Soil & Fertilizer Res Br, Tenn Valley Authority, 47-51; head dept, 51-66, prof agron & soils, 66-76, EMER PROF AGRON & SOILS, AUBURN UNIV, 76- *Concurrent Pos:* Consult, Tenn Valley Authority, 80. *Mem:* Soil Sci Soc Am; fel Am Soc Agron. *Res:* Availability of organic phosphorus to plants; soil and water conservation; effect of lime on physicochemical properties of soils and crop yields; boron requirements of legumes and boron fixation in soils; summary and analysis of data on crop response to phosphates; agri-chemicals; new fertilizer practices. *Mailing Add:* Dept Agron & Soils Funchess Hall Auburn Univ Auburn AL 36849

ROGERS, HOWELL WADE, b Ripley, Miss, Nov 26, 43; m 63; c 3. MEDICAL MICROBIOLOGY, VIROLOGY. *Educ:* Univ Miss, BA, 65, MA, 67; Univ Okla, PhD(med microbiol), 70. *Prof Exp:* Instr microbiol, Med Ctr, Univ Miss, 70-72, actg asst prof, 72; ASST PROF MICROBIOL & IMMUNOL, EVANSVILLE CTR MED EDUC, SCH MED, IND UNIV, 72- *Mem:* AAAS; Am Soc Microbiol. *Res:* Viral enzymes; Herpes virus immunology; cell-mediated immunity to Herpes simplex virus. *Mailing Add:* Ind Univ Ctr for Med Educ 8600 Univ Blvd Evansville IN 47712

ROGERS, HUGO H, JR, b Atmore, Ala, Aug 2, 47; m 70. AIR POLLUTION, PLANT PHYSIOLOGY. *Educ:* Auburn Univ, BS, 69, MS, 71; Univ NC, Chapel Hill, PhD(air pollution), 75. *Prof Exp:* Environ engr air pollution & veg, Res Triangle Inst, 75-76; asst prof bot, 76-80, ASSOC PROF BOT, NC STATE UNIV, 80-, PLANT PHYSIOLOGIST, AGR RES SERV, USDA, 76- *Concurrent Pos:* Res assoc air pollutant uptake by veg, NC State Univ, 75-76; adj assoc prof, Dept Environ Sci & Eng, Sch Pub Health, Univ NC, Chapel Hill, 78- *Mem:* Air Pollution Control Asn; Am Soc Plant Physiologists; Am Soc Agr Eng; Agron Soc Am; Crop Sci Soc Am. *Res:* Interaction of vegetation with atmospheric chemicals, especially plant gas exchange and effects of air pollutants on plants; carbon dioxide and field studies; design of research equipment for such work. *Mailing Add:* Bot ARS-USDA NC State Univ Raleigh NC 27650

ROGERS, JACK CREE, mathematics, see previous edition

ROGERS, JACK DAVID, b Point Pleasant, WVa, Sept 3, 37; m 58; c 2. MYCOLOGY, PLANT PATHOLOGY. *Educ:* Davis & Elkins Col, BS, 60; Duke Univ, MF, 60; Univ Wis, PhD(plant path), 63. *Prof Exp:* Asst prof forestry & asst plant pathologist, 63-68, assoc prof plant path, 68-72, PROF PLANT PATH, WASH STATE UNIV, 72- *Mem:* Mycol Soc Am (vpres, 75-76, pres-elect, 76-77, pres, 77-78); Am Phytopath Soc; Bot Soc Am. *Res:* Forest pathology; botany; cytology; genetics; evolution of Ascomycetes. *Mailing Add:* Dept Plant Path Wash State Univ Pullman WA 99164

ROGERS, JACK WYNDALL, JR, b Austin, Tex, Jan 13, 43; m 62; c 2. TOPOLOGY. *Educ:* Univ Tex, BA, 63, MS, 65, PhD(math), 66. *Prof Exp:* From asst prof to assoc prof math, Emory Univ, 66-73; assoc prof, 73-76, PROF MATH, AUBURN UNIV, 76- *Mem:* Am Math Soc; Math Asn Am. *Mailing Add:* Dept of Math Auburn Univ Auburn AL 36830

ROGERS, JAMES ALBERT, b Sault Ste Marie, Ont, July 4, 40; m 66; c 2. PHARMACEUTICS, PHYSICAL PHARMACY. *Educ:* Univ Toronto, BS, 63, MS, 66; Univ Strathclyde, Scotland, PhD(pharmaceut technol), 69. *Prof Exp:* Pharmacist, Tamblyn Drug Co, Ltd, 63; asst prof, 69-74, ASSOC PROF PHARM, UNIV ALTA, 74- *Mem:* Asn Faculties Pharm Can; Am Pharmaceut Asn. *Mailing Add:* Fac Pharm & Pharmaceut Sci Univ of Alta Edmonton AB T6G 2G7 Can

ROGERS, JAMES JOSEPH, b Salem, NJ, Oct 30, 42; m 65; c 3. HYDROLOGY, SYSTEM MODELING. *Educ:* Utah State Univ, BS, 64; Univ Ariz, MS, 71, PhD(hydrol), 73. *Prof Exp:* Forester mgt, Apache Nat Forest, 65-71; forester watershed, Rocky Mountain Forest & Range Exp Sta, 71-72, hydrologist, 72-74; hydrologist, Pac Northwest Forest & Range Exp Sta, 74-76; HYDROLOGIST WATERSHED, ROCKY MOUNTAIN FOREST & RANGE EXP STA, 76- *Mem:* Sigma Xi; Am Geophys Union. *Res:* Development of computer systems for understanding and predicting effects of land management activities on resource outputs and productivity of southwestern forest ecosystems. *Mailing Add:* Forest Sci Lab Ariz State Univ Tempe AZ 85281

ROGERS, JAMES SAMUEL, b Cassville, Ga, Aug 20, 34; m 56; c 1. AGRICULTURAL ENGINEERING, SOIL PHYSICS. *Educ:* Univ Ga, BSAE, 55, MS, 62; Univ Ill, Urbana, PhD(soil physics), 69. *Prof Exp:* Agr engr, Agr Res Serv, USDA, Univ Ga, 57-64 & Univ Ill, 64-68; AGR ENGR SCI & EDUC ADMIN-AGR, USDA, UNIV FLA, 68-, ASST PROF AGR ENG, 77- *Mem:* Am Soc Agr Engrs; Am Soc Agron; Soil Sci Soc Am. *Res:* Water management in wet soils to include drainage, irrigation, climate modification and more efficient use of water in agriculture. *Mailing Add:* Soil & Water Conserv Res Div Rogers Hall Univ of Fla Gainesville FL 32611

ROGERS, JAMES STEWART, b Santa Maria, Calif, Apr 5, 32; Can citizen; m 56; c 4. EXPERIMENTAL SOLID STATE PHYSICS. *Educ:* Univ Sask, BEng, 54; Univ Alta, MSc, 62, PhD(physics), 64. *Prof Exp:* Fel, Commonwealth Sci & Indust Res Orgn, Australia, 64-66; ASSOC PROF PHYSICS, UNIV ALTA, 68- *Mem:* Australian Inst Physics. *Res:* Electron tunneling into superconductors and ferromagnetic materials. *Mailing Add:* Dept Physics Univ Alta Edmonton AB T6G 2E1 Can

ROGERS, JAMES TED, JR, b Statesville, NC, July 26, 42; m 66; c 2. MATHEMATICS. *Educ:* Univ NC, Chapel Hill, BS, 64; Univ Calif, Riverside, MA, 66, PhD(math), 68. *Prof Exp:* From asst prof to assoc prof, 68-77, PROF MATH, TULANE UNIV, 77- *Mem:* AAAS; Am Math Soc. *Res:* Point set topology. *Mailing Add:* Dept of Math Tulane Univ of La New Orleans LA 70118

ROGERS, JAMES TERENCE, (JR), b Montreal, Que, Nov 19, 26; m 57; c 4. MECHANICAL ENGINEERING. *Educ:* McGill Univ, BEng, 48, MEng, 50, PhD(mech eng), 53. *Prof Exp:* Res engr, Can Dept Mines & Tech Surv, 50-51; asst prof mech eng, Royal Mil Col Can, 53-55; engr & design specialist, Nuclear Div, Canadair Ltd, 55-59; res engr, Gen Atomic Div, Gen Dynamics Corp, 59-60; tech counsr, Atomic Power Dept, Can Gen Elec, 60-70; PROF MECH ENG, CARLETON UNIV, 70-; CONSULT, ATOMIC ENERGY CONTROL BD, 77- *Concurrent Pos:* Mem assoc comt heat transfer, Nat Res Coun Can, 66-71; Can deleg, Assembly Int Heat Transfer Conf, 67; mem comt energy sci policies, Sci Coun Can, 76-79; Can Nat Comt Heat Transfer, 79-; mem sci coun, Int Ctr Heat & Mass Transfer, Yugoslavia, 68; consult, Atomic Energy Can Ltd, 70-; ed, Trans, Can Soc Mech Engrs, 70- *Honors & Awards:* Robert W Angus Medal, Eng Inst Can, 64. *Mem:* Can Soc Mech Engrs; Eng Inst Can; Am Soc Mech Engrs. *Res:* Coolant mixing in nuclear reactor fuel bundles; two-phase flow and heat transfer problems in nuclear reactors; nuclear reactor safety; combined-purpose use of nuclear reactors; effective utilization of energy; solar energy. *Mailing Add:* Fac of Eng Carleton Univ Ottawa ON K1S 5B6 Can

ROGERS, JAMES VIRGIL, JR, b Johnson City, Tenn, Oct 7, 22; m 45; c 4. RADIOLOGY. *Educ:* Emory Univ, BS, 43, MD, 45. *Prof Exp:* CHIEF SECT DIAG RADIOL, UNIV HOSP, EMORY UNIV, 59-, PROF RADIOL, SCH MED, 65- *Concurrent Pos:* Vis radiologist, Grady Mem Hosp, 51-; attend radiologist, Atlanta Vet Admin Hosp, 51- *Mem:* Radiol Soc NAm; Am Roentgen Ray Soc; AMA; fel Am Col Radiol. *Res:* Pulmonary vasculature in heart and lung diseases; mammography. *Mailing Add:* Sect of Diag Radiol Emory Univ Clin Atlanta GA 30322

ROGERS, JAMES WESLEY, physical chemistry, textile chemistry, see previous edition

ROGERS, JERRY DALE, b Nebo, WVa, Mar 27, 54. PHYSICAL CHEMISTRY. *Educ:* WVa Univ, BS, 76; Univ Fla, PhD(chem), 80. *Prof Exp:* NAT RES COUN FEL, GODDARD SPACE FLIGHT CTR, NASA, 80- *Mem:* Coblentz Soc; Am Inst Chemists; Am Chem Soc; Am Geophys Union. *Res:* Infrared spectroscopy; calculation and measurement of spectroscopic properties of molecules found in planetary atmospheres and interstellar space. *Mailing Add:* Infrared & Radioastron Br Goddard Space Flight Ctr NASA Greenbelt MD 20771

ROGERS, JESSE WALLACE, b Littlefield, Tex, June 8, 41; m 62; c 1. PHYSICAL CHEMISTRY. *Educ:* Univ Tex, Arlington, BS, 63; Tex Christian Univ, PhD(phys chem), 68. *Prof Exp:* From asst prof to assoc prof, 67-77, chmn dept, 69-78, actg vpres acad affairs, 78-80, PROF CHEM, MIDWEST UNIV, 77-, PRES ACAD AFFAIRS, 80- *Mem:* Am Chem Soc. *Res:* Electrochemical kinetics. *Mailing Add:* Dept Chem Midwestern Univ Wichita Falls TX 76308

ROGERS, JOHN ERNEST, b Ames, Iowa, May 15, 47; c 1. MICROBIOLOGY, BIOCHEMISTRY. *Educ:* Univ Ill, BS, 69; Wash State Univ, PhD(biochem), 74. *Prof Exp:* NIH fel, Nat Inst Environ Health Sci, 75; RES SCIENTIST MICROBIOL, PAC NORTHWEST LABS, BATTELLE MEM INST, 77- *Mem:* AAAS; Am Soc Microbiol; Am Soc Agron. *Res:* Microbiology of fates and effects of trace metals, radionuclides and organic pollutants in the environment. *Mailing Add:* Pac Northwest Labs Battelle Blvd Richland WA 99352

ROGERS, JOHN GILBERT, JR, b New York, NY, Sept 13, 41; m 68; c 2. WILDLIFE ECOLOGY. *Educ:* Cornell Univ, BS, 63; NMex State Univ, MS, 66; NC State Univ, PhD(wildlife ecol), 71. *Prof Exp:* Wildlife specialist, NC Agr Exten Serv, 66-67; wildlife biologist, 69-78, Pa, STAFF BIOLOGIST, DIV WILDLIFE RES, US FISH & WILDLIFE SERV, 78- *Mem:* Am Soc Mammalogists; Ecol Soc Am; Wildlife Soc. *Res:* The chemical senses in animal depredations control. *Mailing Add:* 5207 Dalby Lane Burke VA 22015

ROGERS, JOHN JAMES WILLIAM, b Chicago, Ill, June 27, 30; m 56; c 2. GEOLOGY, GEOCHEMISTRY. *Educ:* Calif Inst Technol, BS, 52, PhD(geol), 55; Univ Minn, MS, 52. *Prof Exp:* From instr to prof geol, Rice Univ, 54-74, chmn dept, 71-74; W R KENAN, JR PROF GEOL, UNIV NC, CHAPEL HILL, 75- *Mem:* Am Asn Petrol Geologists; Geol Soc Am; Mineral Soc Am; Soc Econ Paleont & Mineral; Geophys Union. *Res:* Igneous, metamorphic and sedimentary petrology; sedimentation. *Mailing Add:* Dept of Geol Univ of NC Chapel Hill NC 27514

ROGERS, JOHN LANGLEY, solid state physics, see previous edition

ROGERS, JOHN PATRICK, b Watertown, Mass, Mar 20, 24; m 59; c 2. MIGRATORY BIRD MANAGEMENT, WILDLIFE ECOLOGY. *Educ:* Univ Mass, BS, 50; Univ Mo, PhD(zool), 62. *Prof Exp:* Game researcher, Mass Div Fisheries & Game, 51-55; from instr to asst prof zool, Univ Mo, 61-66; staff specialist wetland ecol, Bur Sport Fisheries & Wildlife, 66-68, asst dir migratory bird pop sta, Patuxent Wildlife Res Ctr, 68-72; CHIEF, OFF MIGRATORY BIRD MGT, WASHINGTON, DC, 72- *Mem:* Am Soc Mammal; Wildlife Soc; Nat Audubon Soc. *Res:* Environmental effects of reproduction of game animals; population ecology of birds, especially waterfowl; wetland ecology; management of migratory birds. *Mailing Add:* US Fish & Wildlife Serv Dept of Interior Washington DC 20240

ROGERS, JOSEPH WOOD, b Jamaica, NY, Mar 7, 37; m 60; c 2. ELECTRICAL ENGINEERING. *Educ:* Cornell Univ, BEE, 59; Univ Mich, PhD(elec eng), 65. *Prof Exp:* Asst prof, 65-71, ASSOC PROF ELEC ENG, BUCKNELL UNIV, 65- *Mem:* AAAS. *Res:* Electrical circuit theory; mathematics; education. *Mailing Add:* Dept of Elec Eng Bucknell Univ Lewisburg PA 17837

ROGERS, KENNETH CANNICOTT, b Teaneck, NJ, Mar 21, 29; m 56; c 3. PHYSICS. *Educ:* St Lawrence Univ, BS, 50, MA, 52; Columbia Univ, PhD(physics), 56. *Hon Degrees:* MEng, Stevens Inst Technol, 64. *Prof Exp:* Res scientist, Lab Nuclear Studies, Cornell Univ, 55-57; from asst prof to assoc prof, 57-64, head dept physics, 68-72, actg provost & dean fac, 72, PROF PHYSICS, STEVENS INST TECHNOL, 64-, PRES, 72- *Concurrent Pos:* Vis prof, City Col New York, 65-66; consult, Stanford Res Inst, 59-62, Grumman Aircraft Eng Corp, 62-63 & Vitro Labs, 62- *Mem:* Fel Royal Soc Arts; Inst Elec & Electronics Engrs; NY Acad Sci; Newcomen Soc; Sigma Xi. *Res:* Plasma, particle accelerator and high energy particle physics; physical electronics. *Mailing Add:* Off of the Pres Stevens Inst of Technol Hoboken NJ 07030

ROGERS, KENNETH D, b Cincinnati, Ohio, May 23, 21. PREVENTIVE MEDICINE. *Educ:* DePauw Univ, AB, 42; Univ Cincinnati, MD, 45; Univ Pittsburgh, MPH, 52. *Prof Exp:* From asst prof to assoc prof maternal child health, Grad Sch Pub Health, 52-60, PROF COMMUNITY MED, SCH MED, UNIV PITTSBURGH, 60-, CHMN, 80- *Res:* Public health; pediatrics. *Mailing Add:* Dept of Community Med Univ of Pittsburgh Sch of Med Pittsburgh PA 15261

ROGERS, KENNETH L, mechanical engineering, see previous edition

ROGERS, KENNETH SCIPIO, b Lafayette, Ind, Oct 8, 35; m 57; c 2. BIOCHEMISTRY. *Educ:* Purdue Univ, BSA, 57, MS, 59, PhD(biochem), 62. *Prof Exp:* USPHS fel, Sch Med, Johns Hopkins Univ, 61-64; from asst prof to assoc prof, 64-76, PROF BIOCHEM, MED COL VA, VA COMMONWEALTH UNIV, 77- *Mem:* AAAS; Am Soc Biol Chem; Soc Exp Biol & Med; Sigma Xi; Int Soc Quantum Biol. *Res:* Physical biochemistry; mechanisms of enzyme inhibition and glutamate dehydrogenase; experimental diabetes and membrane function; molecular interactions of hydrophobic cations and anions with mitochondria, DNA and proteins. *Mailing Add:* 8506 Rivermont Dr Richmond VA 23229

ROGERS, LEE EDWARD, b Haxtun, Colo, Sept 12, 37; m 58; c 3. ECOLOGY, ENTOMOLOGY. *Educ:* Univ Nebr, Bachelors, 67, Masters, 69; Univ Wyo, PhD(entom), 72. *Prof Exp:* Teaching asst biol, Univ Nebr, Omaha, 66-69, instr, 69; SR RES SCIENTIST ECOL, PAC NORTHWEST LAB, BATTELLE MEM INST, 72- *Concurrent Pos:* Lectr, Wash State Univ, 77- *Mem:* Entom Soc Am. *Res:* Ecology of semi-arid regions; insect ecology; bioenergetics; effects of electric fields on the environment. *Mailing Add:* Ecosyst Dept Battelle Mem Inst Richland WA 99352

ROGERS, LEO ABBOTT, metallurgy, applied physics, see previous edition

ROGERS, LEWIS HENRY, b DeFuniak Springs, Fla, Oct 1, 10; m 34; c 2. ANALYTICAL CHEMISTRY. *Educ:* Univ Fla, BS, 32, MS, 34; Cornell Univ, PhD(chem), 41. *Prof Exp:* Spectrochem analyst, Exp Sta, Univ Fla, 34-39, from assoc chemist to chemist, 39-48; res chemist, Carbide Nuclear Co Div, Union Carbide Corp, 48-52; leader, Anal Div, Kraftco Res Lab, 52-54; sr chemist, Air Pollution Found, 54-58; from assoc dir to dir, West Orange Lab, Automation Industs, Inc, 58-69; dir corp res & develop, Automation Industs, Inc, Calif, 69-71; exec vpres, Air Pollution Control Asn, 71-78; SR STAFF CONSULT ENVIRON SCI & ENG, 78- *Mem:* AAAS; Am Chem Soc; hon mem Air Pollution Control Asn. *Res:* Society administration; spectrochemistry; soil and nuclear chemistry; photochemistry; trace elements in agriculture; air pollution; high temperature reactions; research management. *Mailing Add:* 2607 NW 22nd Ave Gainesville FL 32605

ROGERS, LLOYD SLOAN, b Waukegan, Ill, Apr 23, 14. SURGERY. *Educ:* Trinity Col, Conn, BS, 36; Univ Rochester, MD, 41; Am Bd Surg, dipl, 51. *Prof Exp:* Instr chem, Trinity Col, Conn, 36-37; intern surg, Strong Mem Hosp, Rochester, NY, 41-42; asst resident surgeon & resident, Strong Mem & Genesee Hosps, 46-50; asst chief surg serv, Crile Vet Admin Hosp, Cleveland, Ohio, 51-53; from asst prof to assoc prof surg, 53-65, actg chmn dept, 67-70, head div gen surg, Univ Hosp, 67-77, PROF SURG, COL MED, STATE UNIV NY UPSTATE MED CTR, 65- *Concurrent Pos:* Chief surgeon, Vet Admin Hosp, 53-81; attend surgeon, Univ Hosp, State Univ NY Upstate Med Ctr, 54-; attend surgeon, Crouse-Mem Hosp, 58-; chmn surg adjuvant cancer chemother infustion study group, Vet Admin, 61-80, nat partic surg consult comt, 65-69, mem surg res prog comt, 65-69; mem surg study sect, NIH, 62-67; consult, St Joseph & Community Hosp, 66- *Mem:* Am Soc Colon & Rectal Surgeons; Am Col Surg; Soc Surg Alimentary Tract; Cent Surg Asn; Asn Vet Admin Surgeons (pres, 67). *Res:* Cancer surgery, research and chemotherapy; hyperbaric medicine; gastrointestinal physiology and surgery. *Mailing Add:* Dept of Surg State Univ of NY Upstate Med Ctr Syracuse NY 13210

ROGERS, LOCKHART BURGESS, b Manchester, Conn, July 16, 17; m 52; c 2. ANALYTICAL CHEMISTRY. *Educ:* Wesleyan Univ, BA, 39; Princeton Univ, MA, 40, PhD(anal chem), 42. *Prof Exp:* Instr anal chem, Stanford Univ, 42-43, asst prof, 43-46; group leader, Oak Ridge Nat Lab, 46-48; from asst prof to prof, Mass Inst Technol, 48-61; prof, Purdue Univ, West Lafayette, 61-74; GRAHAM PERDUE PROF CHEM, UNIV GA, 74- *Concurrent Pos:* Mem adv comt anal chem div, Oak Ridge Nat Lab; mem, Anal Chem Comt, Nat Res Coun; consult, Lawrence Livermore Lab, Oak Ridge Nat Lab, US Air Force Off Sci Res, NSF, Nat Bur Standards, US Army Res Off-Durham, US Environ Protection Agency & NIH; mem, Comn Equilibrium Data, Int Union Pure & Appl Chem, 67-71 & Comn Nomenclature, 75-78. *Honors & Awards:* Anal Chem Award, Am Chem Soc, 68, Chromatography Award, 74; Stephen dal Nogare Award, Chromatography Forum, 72. *Mem:* Am Chem Soc; Electrochem Soc; Am Acad Arts & Sci; Instrument Soc Am. *Res:* Instrumental methods of chemical analysis; separation processes; trace analysis. *Mailing Add:* 219 Rolling Wood Dr Athens GA 30605

ROGERS, LORENE LANE, b Prosper, Tex, Apr 3, 14; m 35. BIOCHEMISTRY. *Educ:* NTex State Col, BA, 34; Univ Tex, MA, 46, PhD(chem), 48. *Hon Degrees:* DSc, Oakland Univ, 72; LLD, Austin Col, 77. *Prof Exp:* Instr high sch, Tex, 34-35; asst, Clayton Found Biochem Inst, Univ Tex, 46-47; prof chem, Sam Houston State Col, 47-49; Eli Lilly & Co fel, Univ Tex, Austin, 49-50, res scientist, Clayton Found Biochem Inst, 50-64, exec asst, 51-57, asst dir, 57-64, assoc dean grad sch, 64-71, vpres univ, 71-74, pres ad interim, 74-75, prof nutrit, 62-79, pres univ, 75-79; RETIRED. *Mem:* AAAS; Am Chem Soc; Am Inst Nutrit; fel Am Inst Chem. *Res:* Synthesis of hydantoins; metabolic interrelationships of vitamins and amino acids; metabolic patterns; alcoholism; mental retardation; congenital malformations. *Mailing Add:* 4 Nob Hill Circle Austin TX 78746

ROGERS, LYNN LEROY, b Grand Rapids, Mich, Apr 9, 39. ETHOLOGY, ECOLOGY. *Educ:* Mich State Univ, BS, 68; Univ Minn, MS, 70, PhD(ecol), 77. *Prof Exp:* Res asst black bears, Bell Mus Natural Hist, Univ Minn, 68-72; dir, Wildlife Res Inst, 72-76; WILDLIFE RES BIOLOGIST, USDA FOREST SERV, N CENT FOREST EXP STA, 76- *Honors & Awards:* Anna M Jackson Award, Am Soc Mammalogists, 74. *Mem:* Wildlife Soc; Am Soc Mammalogists. *Res:* Determining habitat use, food habits, social behavior, travels, physiology and population dynamics of black bears, white-tailed deer and moose in the upper midwest. *Mailing Add:* NCent Forest Exp Sta Star Rte 1 Box 7200 Ely MN 55731

ROGERS, MARION ALAN, b Columbus, Ind, Nov 4, 36; div; c 4. GEOCHEMISTRY, PETROLEUM GEOLOGY. *Educ:* Earlham Col, AB, 58; Univ Minn, MS, 62, PhD(geol), 65. *Prof Exp:* Res geologist, Exxon Prod Res Co, Tex, 65-68; res specialist, Serv & Res Labs, Imp Oil, Ltd, Alta, 68-72; res supvr petrol geochem, Exxon Prod Res Co, 73-78, sr supvr geologist, Lafayette Prod Dist, Exxon Co, 78-80, dist geologist, Cent Dist, SE Explor Div, New Orleans, 80-81, DIV MGR, RESERVOIR EVAL DIV, EXXON PROD RES CO, 81- *Mem:* Fel Geol Soc Am; Am Asn Petrol Geologists; Am Chem Soc; Geochem Soc; Can Soc Petrol Geologists. *Res:* Petroleum geochemistry; light hydrocarbons; carbon isotopes; biodegradation and water-washing; deasphalting; reservoir bitumens and asphalts; sulfur in oils. *Mailing Add:* Exxon Prod Res Co PO Box 2189 Houston TX 77001

ROGERS, MARLIN NORBERT, b Mexico, Mo, Dec 18, 23; m 56; c 2. FLORICULTURE. *Educ:* Univ Mo, BS, 48, MS, 51; Cornell Univ, PhD(plant path), 56. *Prof Exp:* Assoc prof, 60-67, PROF HORT, UNIV MO-COLUMBIA, 67- *Concurrent Pos:* Vis prof, Univ Fla, Gainesville, 81-82. *Mem:* Am Soc Hort Sci. *Res:* Plant growth regulators; physiological responses of herbaceous ornamentals to environment; diseases of ornamental plants. *Mailing Add:* 1-40 Agr Bldg Univ Mo Columbia MO 65211

ROGERS, MAX TOFIELD, b Edmonton, Alta, Jan 12, 17; nat US; m 43; c 2. PHYSICAL CHEMISTRY. *Educ:* Univ Alta, BSc, 37, MSc, 38; Calif Inst Technol, PhD(phys chem), 41. *Prof Exp:* Fel, Calif Inst Technol, 41-42; instr chem, Univ Calif, Los Angeles, 42-46; from asst prof to assoc prof, 46-55, PROF CHEM, MICH STATE UNIV, 55- *Concurrent Pos:* Res assoc, Argonne Nat Lab, 50; Guggenheim fel, 54-55; NSF fel, 62-63. *Mem:* Fel AAAS; Am Chem Soc; Am Phys Soc; The Chem Soc. *Res:* Molecular structure; nuclear magnetic resonance; electron spin resonance; nuclear quadrupole resonance spectroscopy. *Mailing Add:* Dept of Chem Mich State Univ East Lansing MI 48824

ROGERS, MICHAEL JOSEPH, b Buffalo, NY, Dec 22, 44; m 70. BIOCHEMISTRY, IMMUNOLOGY. *Educ:* Cornell Univ, BS, 67; Purdue Univ, PhD(biochem), 71. *Prof Exp:* Fel biochem, Health Ctr, Univ Conn, 71-74; staff fel biochem, 74-78, RES CHEMIST, NIH, 79- *Concurrent Pos:* NIH fel, Health Ctr, Univ Conn, 71-72. *Res:* Histocompatability antigens of the mouse and tumor specific transplantation antigens in mouse tumors. *Mailing Add:* Bldg 8 Rm 217 NIH Bethesda MD 20014

ROGERS, MORRIS RALPH, b Poughkeepsie, NY, Feb 28, 24; m 54; c 2. INDUSTRIAL MICROBIOLOGY. *Educ:* Syracuse Univ, BS, 50; Hofstra Univ, MA, 52. *Prof Exp:* Bacteriologist, Nat Dairy Res Labs, Inc, NY, 50-52; microbiologist, Appl Microbiol Group, Pioneering Res Div, 52-70, RES MICROBIOLOGIST, ENVIRON PROTECTION GROUP, SCI & ADV TECHNOL LAB, US DEPT ARMY NATICK LABS, 70- *Concurrent Pos:* Gov bd, Am Inst Biol Sci, 72-75. *Honors & Awards:* Award, US Dept Army Natick Labs, 58; Charles Porter Award, Soc Indust Microbiol, 75. *Mem:* Soc Indust Microbiol (pres, 69-70); Sigma Xi; Am Soc Microbiol; Am Inst Biol Sci. *Res:* Germicides and fungicides, including inter-disciplinary microbiological and chemical problems; interaction of fungicides with base materials; synergism; effects of microorganisms and insects on prevention of deterioration of materials; biodegradable detergents; biodegration of organic compounds; biodegradation of petroleum products. *Mailing Add:* Environ Protection Group Sci & Advan Technol Lab US Army Natick Res & Develop Command Natick MA 01760

ROGERS, NELSON FLOYD, b Baldwinsville, NY, Jan 14, 11; m 34; c 4. FORESTRY. *Educ:* State Univ NY, BS, 32. *Prof Exp:* Cultural foreman, Ozark Nat Forest, Ark, US Forest Serv, 33; jr forester, Ouachita Nat Forest, 34; from prin forest ranger to dist forest ranger, Pisgah Nat Forest, NC, 34-39, asst forester & sr dist proj supvr, NH, 39-40, dist forest ranger, Ottawa Nat Forest, Mich, 40-43, forester, Ohio, 43-45, silviculturist, Cent States Forest Exp Sta, Ohio, 45-49, res forester, North Ozark Br, 49-52 & Columbia Forest Res Ctr, 52-59, supt, Sinkin Exp Forest, 59-65, res forester forest mgt, North Cent Forest Exp Sta, 66-73; CONSULT, 73- *Mem:* Soc Am Foresters. *Res:* Forest tree species adaption tests on coal spoil banks; silvicultural and forest management studies in Missouri Ozark region. *Mailing Add:* 901 E First St Salem MO 65560

ROGERS, NELSON K, b Flushing, NY, May 17, 28; m 53; c 3. INDUSTRIAL & MARINE ENGINEERING. *Educ:* US Naval Acad, BS, 50; Ga Inst Technol, MS, 56. *Prof Exp:* Instr indust eng, Ga Inst Technol, 54-56; proj engr, Waterman Steamship Corp, 56-58; mgr, Pan-Atlantic Steamship Corp, 58-59; asst to pres, Sea-Land Serv, Inc, 59-60, vpres marine opers, 60-61, vpres construct opers, 61-63; lectr indust eng, 65-69, ASSOC PROF INDUST ENG, GA INST TECHNOL, 69- *Concurrent Pos:* Sr mem, N K Rogers, Inc, 63- *Mem:* Am Inst Indust Engrs; Am Soc Eng Educ; Soc Am Mil Engrs; Soc Adv Mgt. *Res:* Design of transportation systems; design and simulation of economic systems; organizational and physical development of transportation enterprises; financial and economic analysis. *Mailing Add:* Sch of Indust Eng Ga Inst of Technol Atlanta GA 30332

ROGERS, OWEN MAURICE, b Worcester, Mass, July 4, 30; m 56; c 2. GENETICS, PLANT BREEDING. *Educ:* Univ Mass, BVA, 52; Cornell Univ, MS, 54; Pa State Univ, PhD(genetics, plant breeding), 59. *Prof Exp:* Asst prof hort, 59-65, assoc prof plant sci, 65-72, actg chmn dept, 78-79, PROF PLANT SCI, UNIV NH, 72-, CHMN DEPT, 79- *Mem:* Am Soc Hort Sci; Genetics Soc Am. *Res:* Genetics and plant breeding of Syringa and Pelargonium. *Mailing Add:* Dept of Plant Sci Univ of NH Durham NH 03824

ROGERS, PALMER, JR, b New York, NY, Sept 7, 27; m 51; c 4. BIOCHEMISTRY, MICROBIOLOGY. *Educ:* Johns Hopkins Univ, PhD(biol), 57. *Prof Exp:* Am Cancer Soc fel biochem, Biol Div, Oak Ridge Nat Lab, 57-59; asst prof agr biochem, Ohio State Univ, 59-63; assoc prof, 63-68, PROF MICROBIOL, UNIV MINN, MINNEAPOLIS, 68- *Mem:* AAAS; Am Soc Microbiol; Am Soc Biol Chemists. *Res:* Mechanisms of biosynthesis of enzymes in bacteria; regulation of bacterial protein and desoxyribonucleic acid synthesis in Escherichia coli. *Mailing Add:* Dept of Microbiol Univ of Minn Minneapolis MN 55455

ROGERS, PETER H, b New York, NY, Jan 8, 45; m 66; c 3. PHYSICS. *Educ:* Mass Inst Technol, SB, 65; Brown Univ, PhD(physics), 70. *Prof Exp:* Res physicist acoust, Washington, DC, 69-75; supvry res physicist, Underwater Sound Res Div, Naval Res Lab, 75-81, SCI OFFICER, OFF NAVAL RES, 81- *Honors & Awards:* A B Wood Award & Prize, Inst Acoust, 79; Biennial Award, Acoust Soc Am, 80. *Mem:* Fel Acoust Soc Am. *Res:* Nonlinear acoustics; acoustic radiation theory; acoustic measurement theory. *Mailing Add:* Off Naval Res Code 425 UA Arlington VA 22217

ROGERS, PHIL H, b McKinney, Tex, Apr 13, 24; m 46; c 4. ELECTRICAL ENGINEERING. *Educ:* Univ Tex, BS, 44, MS, 47; Univ Mich, PhD, 56. *Prof Exp:* Design engr, Westinghouse Elec Co, 47-48; instr elec eng, Univ Mich, 48-53, assoc res engr, Eng Res Inst, 53-55, asst prof elec eng, 55-56; prof, Univ Ariz, 56-59; asst dir res, Collins Radio Co, Iowa, 59-62; dir prog software develop, State of Tex, 63-67; mgr comput systs, 67-76, dir, 76-80, VPRES ELECTRONIC SYSTS SOFTWARE, E-SYSTS, 80- *Mem:* Inst Elec & Electronics Engrs. *Res:* Circuit theory; computer, computer systems and programming systems design; electronic systems embedded software development. *Mailing Add:* E-Systs 1200 Jupiter Rd Garland TX 75040

ROGERS, PHILIP VIRGILIUS, b Utica, NY, Feb 7, 07; m 32; c 3. ENDOCRINOLOGY, EMBRYOLOGY. *Educ:* Hamilton Col, AB, 30, MA, 34; Yale Univ, PhD(anat), 37. *Prof Exp:* Asst biol, Hamilton Col, 32-34; lab asst anat, Yale Univ Sch Med, 34-37; from instr to asst prof biol, Hamilton Col, 37-45; fel, Johns Hopkins Univ, 45-46; from assoc prof to prof, 47-72, chmn dept, 60-72, EMER PROF BIOL, HAMILTON COL, 72- *Concurrent Pos:* Ford Found fel & res assoc, Stanford Univ, 53-54; trustee, Kirkland Col, 69- *Mem:* AAAS; Soc Endocrinol; assoc Am Soc Zool; Am Asn Anat. *Res:* Electrical potential changes during the reproductive cycle; comparative studies of the adrenal gland; effect of sulfa drugs on reproduction. *Mailing Add:* 29 Bristol Rd Clinton NY 13323

ROGERS, QUINTON RAY, b Palco, Kans, Nov 24, 36; m 56; c 4. NUTRITION, BIOCHEMISTRY. *Educ:* Univ Idaho, BS, 58; Univ Wis, MS, 60, PhD(biochem), 63. *Prof Exp:* Res assoc with Dr A E Harper, Mass Inst Technol, 62-63; instr nutrit, 63-64, asst prof physiol chem, 64-66; from asst prof to assoc prof, 66-74, PROF PHYSIOL CHEM, SCH VET MED, UNIV CALIF, DAVIS, 74- *Mem:* AAAS; Am Inst Nutrit; Am Physiol Soc. *Res:* Amino acid nutrition and metabolism; feline nutrition; food intake regulation. *Mailing Add:* Dept of Physiol Sci Sch Vet Med Univ of Calif Davis CA 95616

ROGERS, RALPH LOUCKS, b Wilkensburg, Pa, Feb 2, 22; m 47; c 4. INDUSTRIAL ORGANIC CHEMISTRY. *Educ:* Juniata Col, BS, 46; Univ Pa, MS, 48, PhD(org chem), 56. *Prof Exp:* From assoc chemist to res chemist, 51-69, SR RES CHEMIST, ATLANTIC REF CO, 69- *Mem:* Am Chem Soc. *Res:* Unnatural amino acids; effects of ionizing radiation on chemicals; physical testing of polymers. *Mailing Add:* 22 Ridgeway Ave Norwood PA 19074

ROGERS, RAYMOND N, b Albuquerque, NMex, July 21, 27; m 48; c 2. ANALYTICAL CHEMISTRY. *Educ:* Univ Ariz, BS, 48, MS, 51. *Prof Exp:* Chemist, Infilco, Inc, Ariz, 51-52; staff mem anal, 52-63, sect leader anal & stability, 63-64, alternate group leader, 64-74, GROUP LEADER, EXPLOSIVES RES, LOS ALAMOS SCI LAB, UNIV CALIF, 74- *Concurrent Pos:* Consult, Petrol Technol Corp, 72- *Mem:* Am Chem Soc. *Res:* Isotope dilution methods as applied to agricultural chemical problems; analytical chemistry, physical chemistry and thermal stability of organic high explosives, polymers and adhesives; analysis of archeological samples. *Mailing Add:* Los Alamos Sci Lab Univ of Calif Box 1663 WX-2 Los Alamos NM 87545

ROGERS, RICHARD BREWER, b Paris, Tex, Oct 20, 44; m 66; c 2. AGRICULTURAL CHEMISTRY. *Educ:* Tulane Univ, BS, 66; Univ Wis, MS, 68; Univ Ala, PhD(org chem), 72. *Prof Exp:* Fel, Ind Univ, 71-73; sr res chemist org chem, Mich, 73-77, RES SPECIALIST, DOW CHEM CO, 77- *Mem:* Am Chem Soc. *Res:* Heterocyclic chemistry; specifically biologically active derivatives of pyridine and fused pyridines, naphtheridine, quinazoline and benzo thiophene. *Mailing Add:* Agr Prod Dept Dow Chem Co 2800 Mitchell Dr Walnut Creek CA 94598

ROGERS, RICHARD C, b Burbank, Calif, June 29, 53; m 75; c 1. NEUROSCIENCE, AUTONOMIC NERVOUS SYSTEM. *Educ:* Univ Calif, Los Angeles, BA, 74, PhD(neurosci), 79. *Prof Exp:* Fel gastroenterol, Ctr Ulcer Res & Educ, 79-80; ASST PROF PHYSIOL, SCH MED, NORTHWESTERN UNIV, 80- *Concurrent Pos:* Vis scientist, Dept Physiol, Sch Med, Fukuoka Univ, Japan, 80; prin investr, NIH, 81- *Mem:* Soc Neurosci. *Res:* Central neural elaboration of the autonomic nervous system; physiological and anatomical details of visceral afferent control over ingestive behavior, gastrointestinal function and neuroendocrine function. *Mailing Add:* Dept Physiol Sch Med Northwestern Univ 303 E Chicago Ave Chicago IL 60611

ROGERS, ROBERT LARRY, b Lawrence Co, Miss, Feb 10, 42; m 64; c 2. PLANT PHYSIOLOGY, BIOCHEMISTRY. *Educ:* Miss State Univ, BS, 64; Auburn Univ, PhD(plant physiol, biochem), 68. *Prof Exp:* From asst prof to assoc prof, 67-74, PROF PLANT PHYSIOL, PLANT PATH DEPT, LA STATE UNIV, BATON ROUGE, 80-, SUPT, NORTHEAST EXP STA, 74- *Mem:* Am Chem Soc; Am Soc Plant Physiol; Weed Sci Soc Am; Am Soc Agron. *Res:* Chemical weed control in agronomic crops; metabolism and mode of action of herbicides; vigor tests of planting seed. *Mailing Add:* Northeast La Exp Sta PO Box 438 St Joseph LA 71366

ROGERS, ROBERT MERRILL, marine biology, biological oceanography, see previous edition

ROGERS, ROBERT N, b San Francisco, Calif, Nov 4, 33; m 55; c 4. SOLID STATE PHYSICS, ACADEMIC ADMINISTRATION. *Educ:* Stanford Univ, BS, 56, PhD(physics), 62. *Prof Exp:* Res assoc appl sci, Yale Univ, 65-66; asst prof physics, Wesleyan Univ, 60-67; from assoc prof to prof, Univ Colo, Boulder, 67-76, spec asst to pres, 73-75; ASSOC DEAN GRAD SCH & COORDR RES, UNIV COLO, DENVER, 76- *Concurrent Pos:* Consult, Sandia Lab, 65-66, 67-70, tech staff mem, 66-67; admin fel, Am Coun Educ, 73-74. *Mem:* AAAS; Am Phys Soc; Am Asn Physics Teachers. *Res:* Magnetic interactions in solids; paramagnetic resonance in solids and liquids; optical pumping; ion implantation. *Mailing Add:* State Govt Sci Adv Grad Sch Univ of Colo Denver CO 80202

ROGERS, ROBERT WAYNE, b Russellville, Ky, Aug 6, 38; m 61; c 3. ANIMAL SCIENCE. *Educ:* Univ Ky, BS, 60, MS, 62, PhD(animal sci), 64. *Prof Exp:* Assoc prof, 64-74, PROF ANIMAL SCI, MISS STATE UNIV, 74- *Mem:* Am Soc Animal Sci; Am Meat Sci Asn; Inst Food Technol. *Res:* Curing and processing of pork and beef; methods of extending shelf-life of fresh meats; beef tenderness; efficient production of meat; live animal and carcass evaluation methods. *Mailing Add:* Dept of Animal Sci Miss State Univ PO Drawer 5228 Mississippi State MS 39762

ROGERS, RODDY R, b Baytown, Tex, Jan 19, 34; m 64; c 2. METEOROLOGY. *Educ:* Univ Tex, BS, 55; Mass Inst Technol, SM, 57; NY Univ, PhD(meteorol), 64. *Prof Exp:* Asst res scientist, Nat Adv Comt Aeronaut, 57-58; asst physicist, Cornell Aeronaut Lab, 59-60, assoc physicist, 61-62, res physicist, 63-66; assoc prof, 66-74, PROF METEOROL, MCGILL UNIV, 74-, CHMN DEPT, 78- *Res:* Am Meteorol Soc. Res: Radar meteorology; cloud physics; precipitation physics. *Mailing Add:* Dept of Meteorol Burnside Hall McGill Univ Montreal PQ H3A 2K6 Can

ROGERS, RODNEY ALBERT, b Lucas, Iowa, Aug 24, 26; m 56; c 2. BIOLOGY. *Educ:* Drake Univ, BA, 49, MA, 51; Univ Iowa, PhD(zool), 55. *Prof Exp:* From asst prof to assoc prof, 55-65, PROF BIOL, DRAKE UNIV, 65-, CHMN DEPT, 66- *Concurrent Pos:* Assoc prog dir, NSF, 67-68. *Mem:* AAAS; Am Soc Parasitol; Soc Protozool; Am Soc Trop Med & Hyg; Am Soc Zool. *Res:* Parasitology, especially helminthology; cytology; immunology; microbiology. *Mailing Add:* 4203 40th St Des Moines IA 50310

ROGERS, SAMUEL JOHN, b Florence, Ariz, Nov 5, 34; m 61; c 2. BIOCHEMISTRY. *Educ:* Univ Calif, Davis, BS, 56, DVM, 58; Univ Calif, Berkeley, PhD(biochem), 64. *Prof Exp:* Fel chem, Univ Ore, 64-66; asst prof, 66-71, ASSOC PROF BIOCHEM, MONT STATE UNIV, 71- *Mem:* Am Chem Soc. *Res:* Chemical modification of the ribiosome; dye-sensitized photooxidation mechanism of action; environmental mutagenesis, metal in mutagenesis. *Mailing Add:* Dept of Chem Mont State Univ Bozeman MT 59717

ROGERS, SEDGWICK COOKERLY, b Chicago, Ill, Mar 24, 19; m 43; c 3. WOOD TECHNOLOGY. *Educ:* Univ Minn, BS, 41, MS, 42; Pa State Col, PhD(biol & org chem), 44. *Prof Exp:* Asst wood utilization, Univ Minn, 41-42; asst plant biochem, Pa State Col, 42-43, asst bact, 43-44; chemist forest prod lab, US Forest Serv, Wis, 44-47; RES CHEMIST, KIMBERLY CLARK CORP, 47- *Mem:* Forest Prod Res Soc. *Res:* Saturation and coating of paper with synthetic resins; tissue paper manufacturing; synthetic non-woven textile-like materials manufacturing. *Mailing Add:* Kimberly-Clark Corp Winchester Rd Neenah WI 54956

ROGERS, SENTA S(TEPHANIE), b Braila, Romania, May 30, 23; US citizen. ENVIRONMENTAL HEALTH. *Educ:* Hunter Col, City Univ NY, AB, 45; Purdue Univ, MS, 48; George Washington Univ, PhD(org phys chem), 67. *Prof Exp:* Res fel anal instrumentation, Georgetown Univ, Washington, DC, 66-67; assoc prof chem forensic sci, Northern Va Community Col, 67-69; res chemist, Bur Customs, 70; sr staff scientist, George Washington Univ, 71-75, asst res prof, Univ & dir, Occup Cancer Proj, Med Ctr, 75-78; COORDR, TOXIC SUBSTANCES PROJ, NAT WILDLIFE FEDN, WASHINGTON, DC, 80- *Mem:* Am Chem Soc; AAAS; NY Acad Sci; fel Am Inst Chemists; Sigma Xi. *Res:* The relationship between environmental pollutants and health; correlations of chemical structure-reactivity-physiological properties in toxic substances (simple and complex). *Mailing Add:* 3001 Veazey Terrace NW Washington DC 20008

ROGERS, SPENCER LEE, b Topeka, Kans, Mar 28, 05; m 35; c 3. PHYSICAL ANTHROPOLOGY, ETHNOLOGY. *Educ:* San Diego State Univ, BA, 27; Claremont Grad Sch, MA, 30; Univ Southern Calif, PhD(anthrop), 37. *Prof Exp:* from instr to prof, 30-71, EMER PROF ANTHROP, SAN DIEGO STATE UNIV, 71- *Concurrent Pos:* Sci dir, San Diego Mus Man, 71-77, res anthropologist, 77- *Mem:* Am Asn Phys Anthrop. *Res:* Aboriginal medicine and surgery; ancient California populations; paleopathology. *Mailing Add:* San Diego Mus Man 1350 El Prado Balboa Park San Diego CA 92101

ROGERS, STANFIELD, b Dyersburg, Tenn, Nov 14, 19; m 46; c 3. PATHOLOGY. *Educ:* Duke Univ, BS, 42, MD, 44. *Prof Exp:* Intern path, Duke Hosp, 44-45; resident, Inst Path, Univ Tenn, 47; Childs fel, Rockefeller Inst, 47-48, asst, 48-52; assoc path, Sch Med, Duke Univ, 52-53; from asst prof to assoc prof, 53-58; dir, Mem Res Ctr, Univ Tenn, 58-64; head carcinogenesis group, Biol Div, Oak Ridge Nat Lab, 64-72; PROF BIOCHEM, SCH MED, UNIV TENN, MEMPHIS, 72-, PROF MICROBIOL & IMMUNOL, 81- *Concurrent Pos:* Consult biol div, Oak Ridge Nat Lab, 55-; consult cell biol study sect, USPHS, 60-; consult adv coun instnl res grants, Am Cancer Soc; consult, Tenn Bd Basic Sci Exam, 60-61; consult biochem, Yr Bk of Cancer, 61- *Honors & Awards:* Parke-Davis Award, Am Soc Exp Path, 59. *Mem:* Fel AAAS; Am Asn Cancer Res; Am Asn Path & Bact; Am Soc Biol Chemists; Am Chem Soc. *Res:* Experimental pathology; genetics. *Mailing Add:* Dept Biochem Sch Med Univ Tenn Memphis TN 38103

ROGERS, STEARNS WALTER, b Alva, Okla, July 28, 34; m 55; c 2. BIOCHEMISTRY, ORGANIC CHEMISTRY. *Educ:* Northwestern State Col, BS, 56; Okla State Univ, PhD(biochem), 61. *Prof Exp:* Prof chem, Northwestern State Col, Okla, 61-76; ASSOC PROF CHEM, McNEESE STATE UNIV, 76- *Mem:* Am Chem Soc; Am Inst Chemists. *Res:* Utilization of amino acid analogs in the synthesis of bacterial proteins; synthesis of mannans in Pseudonomas auregenosia; topic sporulation in Bacillus cereus organization; interaction of blood platlets with basement membrane and insoluble collagen; chemical modification of basement membranes. *Mailing Add:* Dept of Chem McNeese State Univ Lake Charles LA 70609

ROGERS, STEFFEN HAROLD, b Madison, Wis, Apr 17, 41; m 64. CELL BIOLOGY, PARASITOLOGY. *Educ:* Ga Southern Col, BS, 65; Vanderbilt Univ, PhD(biol), 68. *Prof Exp:* NIH training grant, Sch Pub Health & Hyg, Johns Hopkins Univ, 68-70; asst prof, 70-77, ASSOC PROF ZOOL, UNIV TULSA, 77-, ASSOC DEAN, 81- *Mem:* Am Soc Parasitol. *Res:* Ultrastructure physiology and chemotherapy of parasites and gastropods. *Mailing Add:* Dept of Natural Sci Univ of Tulsa Tulsa OK 74104

ROGERS, TERENCE ARTHUR, b London, Eng, Oct 8, 24; nat US; m 45; c 4. PHYSIOLOGY. *Educ:* Univ BC, BS, 52; Univ Calif, PhD, 55. *Prof Exp:* Instr physiol, Sch Med, Univ Rochester, 55-59; asst prof, Sch Med, Stanford Univ, 59-63; chmn dept physiol & assoc dean sch med, 67-71, PROF PHYSIOL, SCH MED, UNIV HAWAII, MANOA, 63-, DEAN SCH MED, 71- *Concurrent Pos:* Lederle med fac award, 58-59; USPHS sr res fel, 59; dir res & anal, Presidential Comn World Hunger, 79-80. *Mem:* AAAS; Am Physiol Soc; Aerospace Med Asn. *Res:* Fluid and electrolyte metabolism; starvation; arctic survival. *Mailing Add:* Univ Hawaii Sch Med 1960 East West Rd Honolulu HI 96822

ROGERS, THOMAS D, b Long Beach, Calif, Sept 22, 39; m 62; c 2. CELL BIOLOGY, BIOCHEMISTRY. *Educ:* Sul Ross State Univ, BS, 61, MA, 64; NTex State Univ, PhD(biol), 69. *Prof Exp:* Res assoc virol, M D Anderson Hosp & Tumor Inst, 63-65 & NTex State Univ, 65-69; NASA fel Cell, Pres Med Div, 69-72, SR SCIENTIST, NORTHROP SERV, INC, JOHNSON SPACE CTR, NASA, 72-, BIOMED LAB MGR, 77- *Concurrent Pos:* NASA grant, 69-72; prin investr, USA-USSR joint biol exp, Apollo Soyuz Test Proj; adj prof biol, Univ Houston, Clear Lake City, 77- *Res:* Application of cytospectrophotometry, automated cellular analysis and computer processing of cell image data for characterization of cells. *Mailing Add:* Northrop Serv Inc Space Sci Lab PO Box 34416 Houston TX 77034

ROGERS, THOMAS EARL, b Saline, La, Oct 25, 33; m 53; c 3. MICROBIOLOGY, IMMUNOLOGY. *Educ:* Northwestern State Col La, BS, 57, MS, 59; La State Univ, PhD(microbiol), 63; Am Bd Med Microbiol, dipl. *Prof Exp:* Instr animal dis res, La State Univ, 59-63; asst prof microbiol & immunol, Med Col SC, 63-68; DIR MICROBIOL & IMMUNOL, PATH DEPT, ST LUKES EPISCOPAL HOSP, 68- *Concurrent Pos:* Consult, Vet Admin Hosp, Charleston, SC, 66-68; lectr combined med technol prog, Tex Med Ctr, 68-; consult, Lind, Milam & Assoc Path Lab, 70-, Med Clin Houston, 72- & Vet Admin Hosp, Temple, Tex, 79- *Mem:* Fel Am Soc Microbiol; Am Soc Clin Path; Am Soc Exp Biol & Med; NY Acad Sci; Sigma Xi. *Res:* Clinical microbiology and immunology; immunopathology. *Mailing Add:* St Lukes Episcopal Hosp Tex Med Ctr Houston TX 77025

ROGERS, THOMAS EDWIN, b Mt Vernon, Iowa, Mar 19, 17; m 41; c 2. ZOOLOGY. *Educ:* Cornell Col, BA, 39; Univ Okla, MS, 41, PhD(zool, plant sci). *Prof Exp:* Instr zool sci, Univ Okla, 46-49; assoc prof biol, Baylor Univ, 49-55; prof & chmn dept, Cornell Col, 55-64; mem Rockefeller Found spec field staff, Univ Valle, Colombia, 64-66; prof biol, Cornell Col, 66-82. *Res:* Cardiovascular studies on lower vertebrates; arthropod soil fauna. *Mailing Add:* Dept of Biol Cornell Col Mt Vernon IA 52314

ROGERS, THOMAS F, b Providence, RI, Aug 11, 23; m 46; c 3. PHYSICS, ELECTRONICS. *Educ:* Providence Col, BSc, 45; Boston Univ, AM, 49. *Prof Exp:* Res assoc, Radio Res Lab, Harvard Univ, 44-45; TV proj engr, Bell & Howell Co, 45-46; electronic scientist, Air Force Cambridge Res Ctr, Mass, 46-54, supvry physicist, 54-59; assoc head radio physics div, Lincoln Lab, Mass Inst Technol, 59-63; head commun div & mem steering comt, 63-64; asst dir defense res & eng, Off Secy Defense, US Dept Defense, 64-65, dep dir, 65-67; dir urban technol & res, US Dept Housing & Urban Develop, 67-69; vpres urban affairs, Mitre Corp, 69-72; PRES, SOPHRON FOUND, 80- *Concurrent Pos:* Assoc group leader, Lincoln Lab, Mass Inst Technol, 51-53; mem & later panel chmn, Commun Comt, Dept Navy Polaris Command, 60-64; mem, President's Sci Adv Comt Commun Satellite, 61-63, Commun Satellite Panel, Inst Defense Anal, 61-63, Dept Defense-NASA Tech Comt Commun Satellite, 61-64, US Nat Comt, UN Conf Appl Sci & Technol to Lesser Developed Nations, 63, Aeronaut & Astronaut Coord Bd, 65-67, NASA Space & Terrestrial Appl Adv Comt, 71-, Space Appln Bd, Nat Res Coun, 74- & Regional Emergency Med Commun Comt, Nat Acad Sci, 76-79. *Mem:* Fel Inst Elec & Electronics Engr; Am Phys Soc; Am Geophys Union; Sigma Xi; Brit Inst Physics. *Res:* Research, development and engineering in electronics; communications; command control; intelligence; reconnaissance; radio wave propagation; electronic memory devices; ultrasonics; molecular physics; housing; city planning and administration. *Mailing Add:* Colshire Dr McLean VA 22102

ROGERS, THOMAS OLIN, microbiology, see previous edition

ROGERS, TOMMIE GENE, organic chemistry, see previous edition

ROGERS, VERN CHILD, b Salt Lake City, Utah, Aug 28, 41. NUCLEAR PHYSICS, NUCLEAR ENGINEERING. *Educ:* Univ Utah, BS & MS, 65; Mass Inst Technol, PhD(nuclear eng), 69. *Prof Exp:* Technician radiation physics, Cancer Res Wing, Univ Utah, 64-65; asst nuclear engr, Argonne Nat Lab, 68-69; assoc prof physics, Lowell Technol Inst, 70-71; assoc prof chem eng & physics, Brigham Young Univ, 69-70 & 71-73; dept mgr nuclear & appl sci, IRT Corp, 73-76; mgr nuclear & advan systs, Ford, Bacon & Davis, 76-77, vpres, 77-80; MEM STAFF, ROGERS & ASSOCS ENG CORP, 80- *Concurrent Pos:* Adj assoc prof, Univ Utah, 76- *Mem:* Am Nuclear Soc; Am Phys Soc; Am Chem Soc; Health Physics Soc. *Res:* Fast reactor physics; low energy nuclear physics; radiation pathway and risk analysis. *Mailing Add:* Rogers & Assocs Systs Eng Corp PO Box 330 Salt Lake City UT 84110

ROGERS, WAID, b New York, NY, Sept 7, 27; m 51; c 3. SURGERY. *Educ:* Yale Univ, BA, 50; Cornell Univ, MD, 57; Univ Minn, MS, 66, PhD(surg & oncol), 67. *Prof Exp:* Instr surg, Univ Minn, 67; from asst prof to assoc prof surg, 67-74, PROF SURG, UNIV TEX HEALTH SCI CTR, 74-; CHIEF SURG, AUDIE MURPHY VET ADMIN HOSP, 73- *Concurrent Pos:* NIH spec fel, 63-; consult gen surg, San Antonio State Tuberc Hosp, 70- *Mem:* Sigma Xi; Am Soc Transplant Surgeons; Am Col Angiol; Transplantation Soc; AAAS. *Res:* Tumor blood flow; transplantation; parenteral nutrition. *Mailing Add:* 7703 Floyd Curl Dr San Antonio TX 78284

ROGERS, WALLACE EDWARD, plant pathology, see previous edition

ROGERS, WILLARD L(EWIS), b Ottumwa, Iowa, Apr 14, 17; m 44; c 2. MECHANICAL ENGINEERING. *Educ:* Iowa State Col, BS, 42; Northwestern Univ, MS, 49; Stanford Univ, PhD(mech eng), 60. *Prof Exp:* Inspector hwy construct, State Hwy Comn, Iowa, 41; instr mech eng, Iowa State Col, 42-46; from lectr to assoc prof, Northwestern Univ, 46-59; PROF MECH ENG, UNIV ARIZ, 59- *Mem:* Am Soc Mech Engrs; Am Soc Eng Educ; Sigma Xi; Int Solar Energy Soc. *Res:* Machine dynamics; energy systems; solar systems; thermodynamics; vibration and noise in liquid piping systems. *Mailing Add:* 5744 E Holmes Tucson AZ 85711

ROGERS, WILLIAM ALAN, b Trenton, NJ, Feb 22, 21; m 47; c 4. PHYSICS. *Educ:* Oberlin Col, AB, 47; Univ NMex, MS, 51; Univ Pittsburgh, PhD(physics), 58. *Prof Exp:* Res physicist, Res Lab, Westinghouse Elec Corp, 51-60; from assoc prof to prof physics, Thiel Col, 60-66; prof physics, Univ Petrol & Minerals, Dhahran, Saudi Arabia, 66-80, chmn dept, 66-70 & 71-74; MEM FAC, DEPT PHYSICS, TRINITY UNIV, 80- *Concurrent Pos:* Vis fel, Sch Eng & Appl Sci, Princeton Univ, 75-76. *Mem:* Am Phys Soc; Am Asn Physics Teachers. *Res:* Atomic physics; microwave discharge and plasmas; undergraduate teaching. *Mailing Add:* Phys Dept Trinity Univ San Antonio TX 78204

ROGERS, WILLIAM EDWARD, JR, biochemistry, nutrition, see previous edition

ROGERS, WILLIAM EDWIN, b Carlisle, Pa, Apr 5, 36; m 60; c 3. ZOOLOGY, PARASITOLOGY. *Educ:* Dickinson Col, BS, 58; Pa State Univ, MS, 61; Univ Minn, PhD(zool), 69. *Prof Exp:* Asst prof biol, Shippensburg State Col, 64-65; asst prof, Lycoming Col, 65-70; assoc prof, 70-77, PROF BIOL, SHIPPENSBURG STATE COL, 77- *Mem:* Soc Protozool; Am Soc Parasitol. *Res:* Morphogenesis and ultrastructure of trypanosomatids found in muscoid flies. *Mailing Add:* Dept of Biol Shippensburg State Col Shippensburg PA 17257

ROGERS, WILLIAM IRVINE, b Brooklyn, NY, Dec 10, 27; m 54; c 2. BIOCHEMISTRY, RESEARCH MANAGEMENT. *Educ:* Adelphi Col, BA, 49; Univ Vt, MS, 52; Univ Iowa, PhD(biochem), 56. *Prof Exp:* Asst, Univ Vt, 50-52 & Univ Iowa, 52-54; assoc technologist, Res Ctr, Gen Foods Corp, 56-59, proj leader, 59; consult biochem & sect leader, Life Sci Div, 59-70, SR STAFF MEM, ORGN DEVELOP SECT, ARTHUR D LITTLE, INC, 69- *Mem:* Am Chem Soc; Int Transactional Anal Asn. *Res:* Application of organic, analytical and physical chemistry to the problems of biochemistry and the physiological disposition and mechanisms of action of drugs; isolation and characterization of natural products; nutrition; organization development at interfaces of technical and other operations in academic, industrial and governmental agencies. *Mailing Add:* Arthur D Little Inc Orgn Develop Sect Acorn Park Cambridge MA 02140

ROGERS, WILLIAM LESLIE, b Boston, Mass, Mar 27, 34; m 62; c 3. MEDICINE, MEDICAL PHYSICS. *Educ:* Ohio Wesleyan Univ, AB, 55; Case Western Reserve, MS, 61, PhD(physics), 67. *Prof Exp:* Engr, Hughes Aircraft Co, 55-58; instr physics, Univ Wyo, 61-62; fel, Case Western Reserve, 67-68; staff engr, Bendix Aerospace Systs, 68-70; res assoc, 70-72, ASST PROF INTERNAL MED, UNIV MICH, ANN ARBOR, 72- *Mem:* Soc Nuclear Med. *Res:* Improved nuclear medicine imaging techniques and instrumentation. *Mailing Add:* 1425 Cambridge Rd Ann Arbor MI 48104

ROGERS, WILMER ALEXANDER, b Mt Dora, Fla, Aug 17, 33; m 61; c 4. FISH PATHOLOGY, FISHERIES MANAGEMENT. *Educ:* Univ Southern Miss, BS, 58; Auburn Univ, MS, 60, PhD(fish mgt), 67. *Prof Exp:* Biologist aide, Miss Game & Fish Comn, 57-58; fishery biologist, Ala Dept Conserv, 60-62, US Fish & Wildlife Serv, 62-64; from instr to assoc prof, 64-77, PROF FISHERIES, AUBURN UNIV, 77- *Concurrent Pos:* Leader, Southeastern Coop Fish Dis Proj, 68-; ed, Southeastern Game and Fish Proc, 74-77. *Mem:* Am Fisheries Soc; Am Soc Parasitol; Wildlife Dis Asn. *Res:* General parasites and diseases of fish, especially taxonomy of monogenea; intensive culture of fish. *Mailing Add:* Dept Fisheries & Allied Aquacult Auburn Univ Auburn AL 36830

ROGERSON, ALLEN COLLINGWOOD, b Stoke-on-Trent, Eng, Dec 9, 40; US citizen; m 60; c 2. NITROGEN FIXATION, MICROBIAL PHYSIOLOGY. *Educ:* Haverford Col, BA, 64; Dartmouth Col, PhD(molecular biol), 69. *Prof Exp:* NIH fel molecular biol, Albert Einstein Med Ctr, Philadelphia, Pa, 68-70; asst prof biol, Bryn Mawr Col, 70-76; res assoc & head, Biol Nitrogen Fixation Group, Div Agr, Fort Valley State Col, Ga, 76-79; ASSOC PROF & CHMN, BIOL DEPT, ST LAWRENCE UNIV, 79- *Concurrent Pos:* NIH grant, 71-74; vis res prof, Univ Copenhagen, Denmark, 73-74 & Univ Dundee, Scotland, 77. *Mem:* AAAS; Am Soc Microbiol. *Res:* Regulation of nitrogen fixation and heterocyst formation in blue-green bacteria; physiology and molecular biology of blue-greens; regulation of macromolecular synthesis and growth in microorganisms. *Mailing Add:* Biol Dept St Lawrence Univ Canton NY 13617

ROGERSON, ASA BENJAMIN, b Williamston, NC, Oct 24, 39; m 65; c 2. PLANT PHYSIOLOGY, AGRONOMY. *Educ:* NC State Univ, BS, 62; Va Polytech Inst, MS, 65, PhD(plant physiol), 68. *Prof Exp:* Asst prof crop sci, NC State Univ, 68-70; REGIONAL MGR RES & DEVELOP, UNIROYAL CHEM, 70- *Mem:* Weed Sci Soc Am. *Res:* Agricultural chemical products involving tobacco, soybeans, cotton, fruits, ornamentals and growth regulants. *Mailing Add:* Uniroyal Chem Co Elm St Naugatuck CT 06770

ROGERSON, CLARK THOMAS, b Ogden, Utah, Oct 2, 18. MYCOLOGY. *Educ:* Utah State Agr Col, BS, 40; Cornell Univ, PhD(mycol), 50. *Prof Exp:* Asst plant path, Utah State Agr Col, 39-41; asst mycol, Cornell Univ, 46-50; asst prof bot, Kans State Col & asst mycologist, Exp Sta, 50-56, assoc prof & assoc mycologist, 56-57; cur cryptogamic bot, 58-66, SR CUR, NY BOT GARDEN, 67- *Concurrent Pos:* Ed, Mem NY Bot Garden, N Am Flora & Flora Neotropica. *Mem:* AAAS; Mycol Soc Am; Am Phytopath Soc; Bot Soc Am; Torrey Bot Club. *Res:* Taxonomy of pyrenomycetous Ascomycetes, particularly Hypocreales; fungi of Kansas, New York and Utah. *Mailing Add:* NY Bot Garden Bronx NY 10458

ROGERSON, JOHN BERNARD, JR, b Cleveland, Ohio, Sept 3, 22; m 43; c 3. ASTROPHYSICS. *Educ:* Case Univ, BS, 51; Princeton Univ, PhD(astron), 54. *Prof Exp:* Carnegie fel astron, Mt Wilson Observ, 54-56; from res assoc & lectr to assoc prof, 56-67, PROF ASTRON, PRINCETON UNIV, 67- *Mem:* Am Astron Soc; Int Astron Union. *Res:* Solar atmosphere; photoelectric spectrophotometry; high altitude astronomy with balloon and satellite borne telescopes and equipment. *Mailing Add:* Peyton Hall Princeton Univ Princeton NJ 08540

ROGERSON, PETER FREEMAN, b Stoke-on-Trent, Eng, Mar 12, 44; US citizen; m 66; c 2. ANALYTICAL CHEMISTRY. *Educ:* Univ Vt, BS, 66; Univ NC, Chapel Hill, PhD(anal chem), 71. *Prof Exp:* Res assoc, Cornell Univ, 70-71; RES CHEMIST, ENVIRON RES LAB, ENVIRON PROTECTION AGENCY, 71- *Mem:* Am Soc Mass Spectrometry; Am Chem Soc. *Res:* Analytical chemistry as applied to pollution control research. *Mailing Add:* Environ Res Lab S Ferry Rd Narragansett RI 02882

ROGERSON, ROBERT JAMES, b Lancaster, Eng, July 4, 43; Can citizen; m 68; c 1. GLACIER MASS BALANCE, QUATERNARY HISTORY. *Educ:* Liverpool Univ, BA, 65; McGill Univ, MSc, 67; Macquarie Univ, Australia, PhD(earth sci), 79. *Prof Exp:* Sci officer, Glaciology Div, Inland Waters Br, Ottawa, 67-69; lectr, 69-72, asst prof, 72-78, ASSOC PROF GEOL & GEOG, MEM UNIV NFLD, ST JOHN'S, 78- *Concurrent Pos:* Consult, Ice Eng, 81-82, Westfield Minerals, 79 & Mus Can, 75; mem subcomt glaciers, Assoc Comt Hydrol, Nat Res Coun Can, 75- *Mem:* Int Glaciol Soc; Geol Asn Can; Can Quaternary Asn; Can Asn Geographers. *Res:* Mass-balance and dynamics of cirque glaciers in Torngat Mountains of Labrador and the Yoho region of Canadian Rockies; glacial geology and quaternary history of Labrador, Newfoundland and the Arctic. *Mailing Add:* Geol Dept Mem Univ Nfld St John's NF A1B 3X5 Can

ROGERSON, THOMAS DEAN, b Salt Lake City, Utah, Oct 31, 46; m 68; c 2. ORGANIC CHEMISTRY, AGRICULTURAL CHEMISTRY. *Educ:* Mich State Univ, BS, 68; Cornell Univ, MS, 71, PhD(org chem), 74. *Prof Exp:* sr chemist, 74-81, RESISTRATION MGR, ROHM AND HAAS CO, 81- *Concurrent Pos:* NIH fel, Dept Entom & Limnol, Cornell Univ, 73-74. *Res:* Synthesis and structure-activity relationships of biologically-active compounds; terpenes, alkaloids and toxins; pesticide metabolism and residue analysis; pesticide registration. *Mailing Add:* Rohm & Haas Co Spring House Res Lab Spring House PA 19477

ROGGE, THOMAS RAY, b Oelwein, Iowa, Oct 29, 35; m 60; c 3. ENGINEERING MECHANICS, APPLIED MATHEMATICS. *Educ:* Iowa State Univ, BS, 58, MS, 61, PhD(appl math), 64. *Prof Exp:* Asst prof math, Univ Ariz, 64-65; from asst prof to assoc prof eng mech, 65-76, PROF ENG SCI & MECH, IOWA STATE UNIV, 76- *Mem:* Soc Indust & Appl Math; Soc Eng Sci. *Res:* Elastic wave propagation in bounded media. *Mailing Add:* Dept of Eng Mech Iowa State Univ Ames IA 50010

ROGGENKAMP, PAUL LEONARD, b Jefferson Co, Ky, May 3, 27; m 50; c 5. REACTOR PHYSICS, NUCLEAR ENGINEERING. *Educ:* Louisville Univ, BA, 49; Univ Ind, MS, 51, PhD(physics), 53. *Prof Exp:* Res physicist, 52-57, sr supvr, 57-59, sr physicist 59-61, chief supvr, 61-64, RES MGR, E I DU PONT DE NEMOURS & CO INC, AIKEN, 64- *Mem:* Am Phys Soc; fel Am Nuclear Soc; Am Chem Soc. *Res:* Beta decay; operational planning. *Mailing Add:* 1418 Socastee Dr North Augusta SC 29841

ROGGEVEEN, VINCENT, civil engineering, business administration, see previous edition

ROGIC, MILORAD MIHAILO, b Belgrade, Yugoslavia, July 23, 31; US citizen; m 56; c 3. ORGANIC CHEMISTRY. *Educ:* Univ Belgrade, BS, 56, PhD(org chem), 61. *Prof Exp:* Asst prof chem, Univ Belgrade, 58-61; res assoc steroidal chem, Worcester Found Exp Biol, 61-62, org chem & stereochem, Univ Notre Dame, 62-64 & org chem, Univ Sask, 65-66; asst prof organoborane chem, Purdue Univ, 66-69; res group leader, 69-77, res supvr, 77-80, SR RES ASSOC ORG CHEM, ALLIED CORP, 80- *Mem:* Am Chem Soc. *Res:* Organic reaction mechanism; metal catalyzed oxidations; organic chemistry of sulfur dioxide; electrophilic additions; nitrogen containing organic compounds; organoborane chemistry; stereochemistry and conformational analysis. *Mailing Add:* Corp Res & Develop Lab Allied Corp PO Box 1021-R Morristown NJ 07960

ROGLER, JOHN CHARLES, b Providence, RI, Sept 21, 27; m 51; c 2. ANIMAL NUTRITION. *Educ:* Univ RI, BS, 51; Purdue Univ, MS, 53, PhD(poultry nutrit), 58. *Prof Exp:* Res asst, 51-53 & 55-57, from asst prof to assoc prof, 57-66, PROF ANIMAL NUTRIT, PURDUE UNIV, W LAFAYETTE, 66- *Mem:* AAAS; Am Inst Nutrit; Poultry Sci Asn. *Res:* Study requirements, interactions and biochemical functions of nutrients. *Mailing Add:* Dept of Animal Sci Purdue Univ West Lafayette IN 47906

ROGNLIE, DALE MURRAY, b Grand Forks, NDak, July 12, 33; m 55; c 4. MATHEMATICS. *Educ:* Concordia Col, Moorhead, Minn, BA, 55; Univ NDak, MS, 58; Iowa State Univ, PhD(appl math), 69. *Prof Exp:* Instr math, Univ NDak, 56-60; res engr, Boeing Co, Wash, 60-66, supvr math group, 66; assoc prof, 69-77, PROF MATH, SDAK SCH MINES & TECHNOL, 77- *Concurrent Pos:* Eve lectr, Seattle Univ, 61 & Pac Lutheran Univ, 61-63. *Mem:* Soc Indust & Appl Math; Sigma Xi; Math Asn Am. *Res:* Special functions; integral transforms; numerical analysis. *Mailing Add:* Dept of Math SDak Sch Mines & Technol Rapid City SD 57701

ROGNLIEN, THOMAS DALE, b June 2, 45; US citizen; m 71; c 1. PLASMA PHYSICS, IONOSPHERIC PHYSICS. *Educ:* Univ Minn, BEE, 67; Stanford Univ, MS, 69, PhD(elec eng), 73. *Prof Exp:* Res assoc ionospheric plasma physics, Nat Oceanic & Atmospheric Admin, 72-74; res assoc plasma physics, Univ Colo, 74-75; PHYSICIST PLASMA PHYSICS, LAWRENCE LIVERMORE LAB, 75- *Concurrent Pos:* Nat Res Coun fel, 72-74. *Mem:* Am Phys Soc. *Res:* Linear and nonlinear waves in plasmas; real space and velocity space transport of particles in plasmas via theoretical and computational models. *Mailing Add:* Lawrence Livermore Lab MS L-630 PO Box 5511 Livermore CA 94550

ROGOFF, GERALD LEE, b New Haven, Conn, June 7, 39; m 62. PLASMA PHYSICS. *Educ:* Yale Univ, BA, 61; Mass Inst Technol, PhD(physics), 69. *Prof Exp:* Res asst physics, Mass Inst Technol, 61-66; sr scientist, 69-78, FEL SCIENTIST, RES & DEVELOP CTR, WESTINGHOUSE ELEC CORP, 78- *Concurrent Pos:* Lectr, Carnegie-Mellon Univ, 73-75; mem exec comt & treas, Gaseous Electronics Conf, 76-80. *Mem:* AAAS; Am Phys Soc; Sigma Xi. *Res:* Physics of electrical discharges in gases; gaseous electronics; optical diagnostics of ionized gases. *Mailing Add:* Westinghouse Res & Develop Ctr 1310 Beulah Rd Pittsburgh PA 15235

ROGOFF, JOSEPH BERNARD, b Brockton, Mass, July 13, 08; m 41; c 1. MEDICINE. *Educ:* Univ Paris, MD, 40; Univ Aix-Marseille, dipl, 42; Am Bd Phys Med & Rehab, dipl. *Prof Exp:* Intern, Lincoln Hosp, New York, 43-44; admitting physician, City Hosp, 44; practicing physician, 44-45; surgeon, UNRRA & USPHS, Europe, 45-47; chief med officer, Joint Distrib Comt, Austria, 47; ward surgeon, Marine Hosp, USPHS, 48-51; from instr to clin prof phys med & rehab, New York Med Col, 52-67; prof rehab med, Mt Sinai Sch Med, 67-76; PROF REHAB MED, NEW YORK MED COL, 76- *Concurrent Pos:* Resident, Vet Admin Hosp, NY, 51-53, asst chief resident, Brooklyn, 53-54; attend physician, Bird S Coler & Metrop Hosps, 52-; dir phys med & rehab, Jewish Chronic Dis Hosp, Brooklyn, 54-67; dir rehab med, Beth Israel Hosp, 67-76; consult, Vet Admin Hosps, Montrose, NY; attend rehab med, Bird S Coler Hosp, 76-79. *Mem:* AMA; fel Am Acad Phys Med & Rehab; Am Cong Rehab Med; fel NY Acad Sci; fel NY Acad Med. *Res:* Clinical neurology and medicine; physical medicine and rehabilitation; electrophysiology. *Mailing Add:* Dept Rehab Med New York Med Col Valhalla NY 10595

ROGOFF, STANLEY MYRON, radiology, see previous edition

ROGOFF, WILLIAM MILTON, b New York, NY, Mar 15, 16; m 47; c 2. VETERINARY ENTOMOLOGY. *Educ:* Univ Conn, BS, 37; Cornell Univ, PhD(insect morphol), 43. *Prof Exp:* Assoc, Exp Sta, Univ Calif, 46-47; asst prof entom & zool & asst entomologist, Exp Sta, SDak State Univ, 47-49, assoc prof & assoc entomologist, 49-53, prof & entomologist, 53-62; res entomologist, Agr Res Serv, Ore, 62-68, res leader western insects affecting man & animals, 68-78, res entomologist & prof entom, 78-80, EMER PROF ENTOM, LIVESTOCK INSECT RES UNIT, AGR RES SERV, UNIV NEBR, USDA, 80- *Concurrent Pos:* Fulbright res scholar, Commonwealth Sci & Indust Res Orgn, Australia, 55-56. *Mem:* Fel AAAS; Entom Soc Am; Am Soc Zool; Am Micros Soc; Am Mosquito Control Asn. *Res:* Insect morphology and behavior; pheromones; veterinary entomology; systemic insecticides in livestock; insect vectors of disease organisms. *Mailing Add:* Agr Res Serv USDA Univ Nebr Lincoln NE 68583

ROGOL, ALAN DAVID, b New Haven, Conn, March 9, 41; m 68; c 2. PEDIATRICS, CLINICAL PHARMACOLOGY. *Educ:* Mass Inst Technol, BS, 63; Duke Univ, PhD(physiol), 70, MD, 70. *Prof Exp:* Intern pediat, Johns Hopkins Hosp, 70-71, resident, 71-72 & 74-75; fel endocrinol, Nat Inst Health, 72-74; asst prof pediat, 75-79, ASST PROF PHARMACOL, SCH MED, UNIV VA, 77-, ASSOC PROF PEDIAT, 79- *Concurrent Pos:* Co-dir, Blue Ridge Poison Control Ctr, 81- *Mem:* Am Acad Pediat; Am Fedn Clin Res; Endocrin Soc; Soc Pediat Res. *Res:* Mechanism of action of an insulin antagonistic pituitary peptide; control of prolactin secretion by human decidua tissue; control of luteinizing hormone release. *Mailing Add:* Dept Pediat Sch Med Box 386 Univ Va Charlottesville VA 22908

ROGOLSKY, MARVIN, b Passaic, NJ, Apr 17, 39. MICROBIOLOGY. *Educ:* Rutgers Univ, BA, 60; Northwestern Univ, MS, 62; Syracuse Univ, PhD(microbiol), 65. *Prof Exp:* Asst biol, Northwestern Univ, 60-62; NIH fel microbiol, Scripps Clin & Res Found, 65-67; from instr to assoc prof microbiol, Col Med, Univ Utah, 67-76; ASSOC PROF BIOL & MED, UNIV MO-KANSAS CITY, 77- *Concurrent Pos:* Gen Res Support Fund grant & Am Cancer Soc inst grant, 67-68; NIH res grants, 68-71, 72-75 & 76-79; Gen Res Support Fund grant, Univ Utah, 71-72. *Mem:* Am Soc Microbiol. *Res:* Genetic studies with mammalian tissue culture cells; genetic and physiological studies with a system of morphogenesis at the unicellular level; genetic mapping in staphylococcus aureus; genetic control of staphylococcal exfoliative toxin production; staphylococcal plasmids. *Mailing Add:* Dept Biol Univ Mo Kansas City MO 64110

ROGOSA, GEORGE LEON, physics, see previous edition

ROGOVIN, DANIEL NOEL, solid state physics, laser optics, see previous edition

ROGOWSKI, A(UGUSTUS) R(UDOLPH), b Shelton, Conn, June 18, 05; m 29; c 1. ENGINEERING. *Educ:* Yale Univ, BS, 27; Mass Inst Technol, SM, 28. *Prof Exp:* Engr, Curtiss Aeroplane & Motor Co, 28-34 & Fleetwings, Inc, 34-36; res assoc, 36-40, from asst prof to prof, 40-68, EMER PROF MECH ENG, MASS INST TECHNOL, 70- *Concurrent Pos:* Sloan automotive fel. *Mem:* Soc Automotive Engrs; fel Am Soc Mech Engrs; Am Soc Eng Educ. *Res:* Alcohol fuel blends; two-stroke engine development; combustion of fuel sprays; laboratory equipment. *Mailing Add:* Box 92 Needham MA 02192

ROGOWSKI, ANDREW S, soil physics, hydrology, see previous edition

ROGOWSKI, ROBERT STEPHEN, b Batavia, NY, Oct 7, 38; m 58; c 3. PHYSICAL CHEMISTRY, MOLECULAR SPECTROSCOPY. *Educ:* Canisius Col, BS, 60; Mich State Univ, PhD(phys chem), 68. *Prof Exp:* CHEMIST, NASA LANGLEY RES CTR, 68- *Concurrent Pos:* Adj prof chem, Christopher Newport Col, 69-79. *Mem:* AAAS; Am Chem Soc; Am Phys Soc. *Res:* High resolution infrared spectroscopy; atmospheric chemistry; heterogeneous reactions; magnetic resonance; detection of trace atmospheric species. *Mailing Add:* 232 Chickamauga Pike Hampton VA 23669

ROGUSKA-KYTS, JADWIGA, b Warsaw, Poland, May 11, 32; m 60. INTERNAL MEDICINE, NEPHROLOGY. *Educ:* Univ Poznan, Poland, MA, 52; Poznan Med Sch, MD, 58. *Prof Exp:* Intern, 58-59, resident, 59-63, NIH fel, 64-66, asst prof, 70-74, ASSOC PROF MED, MED SCH, NORTHWESTERN UNIV, CHICAGO, 74- *Concurrent Pos:* Attend physician, Cook County Hosp, Chicago, 64-68, Passavant Mem Hosp, 66-, Med Sch, Northwestern Univ, Chicago, 66- & Vet Admin Res Hosp, 70-; assoc chief div med, Northwestern Mem Hosp, Chicago. *Mem:* AAAS; Am Fedn Clin. *Res:* Am Soc Nephrol; Am Heart Asn; fel Am Col Physicians. *Res:* Hypertension; renal pressor system; uremia. *Mailing Add:* Dept of Med Northwestern Univ Med Sch Chicago IL 60611

ROHA, MAX EUGENE, b Meadville, Pa, Apr 14, 23; m 46; c 3. ORGANIC CHEMISTRY. *Educ:* Allegheny Col, BS, 44; Harvard Univ, AM, 47, PhD, 49. *Prof Exp:* Sr tech man, Res Ctr, B F Goodrich Co, 49-59, mgr plastics res, 60-62, dir sci liaison, 62-78, dir explor new prods, 78-81, DIR NEW SPEC POLYMERS & CHEM, RES & DEVELOP, B F GOODRICH CHEM CO, CLEVELAND, 81- *Mem:* Am Chem Soc; Soc Ger Chem. *Res:* Organometallic catalysis; polymers; plastics; research and development planning; technological forecasting. *Mailing Add:* 8205-A Parkview Rd Brecksville OH 44141

ROHACH, ALFRED F(RANKLIN), b Toledo, Iowa, Jan 30, 34; m 61; c 4. NUCLEAR ENGINEERING. *Educ:* Iowa State Univ, BS, 59, MS, 61, PhD(nuclear eng), 63. *Prof Exp:* Asst prof nuclear eng, 63-69, assoc prof, 69-79, PROF NUCLEAR ENG, IOWA STATE UNIV, 79- *Concurrent Pos:* AEC fel, 64-66; fac improvement leave, Southern Calif Edison Co, 77-78. *Mem:* Am Soc Eng Educ; Am Nuclear Soc. *Res:* Radiation shielding; numerical analysis in nuclear reactor theory; nuclear power economics; nuclear fuel management. *Mailing Add:* 261 Sweeney Hall Iowa State Univ Ames IA 50011

ROHAN, PAUL E(DWARD), b Evergreen Park, Ill, May 5, 43; m 70. NUCLEAR ENGINEERING. *Educ:* Univ Detroit, BS, 65; Univ Ill, Urbana, MS, 66, PhD(nuclear eng), 70. *Prof Exp:* Sr staff physicist, 70-72, supvr nuclear eng, 72-74, sect mgr, 74-77, task area mgr physics, 77-79, MGR COMPUTER ANALYSIS, COMBUSTION ENG, INC, 79- *Mem:* Sigma Xi; Am Nuclear Soc. *Res:* Computational methods for nuclear reactor analyses; reactor physics; numerical analysis. *Mailing Add:* 76 Overlook Dr Windsor CT 06095

ROHATGI, UPENDRA SINGH, b Kanpur, India, Mar 3, 49; m 75; c 1. MECHANICAL ENGINEERING. *Educ:* Indian Inst Technol, Kanpur, BTech, 70; Case Western Reserve Univ, MS, 72, PhD(fluid & thermal sci), 75. *Prof Exp:* MECH ENGR THERMOHYDRAUL REACTORS, BROOKHAVEN NAT LAB, 75- *Concurrent Pos:* Engr aircraft fuel pumps, TRW Inc, Cleveland, 74 & Chandler-Evans, 81. *Mem:* Am Soc Mech Engrs; Sci Res Soc NAm. *Res:* Nonequilibrium two-phase flow; thermohydraulic of reactors and rotating machines. *Mailing Add:* Bldg 130 Brookhaven Nat Lab Upton NY 11973

ROHATGI, VIJAY, b Delhi, India, Feb 1, 39; m 71. MATHEMATICAL STATISTICS, PROBABILITY. *Educ:* Univ Delhi, BSc, 58; MA, 60; Univ Alta, MS, 64; Mich State Univ, PhD(math statist), 67. *Prof Exp:* From asst prof to assoc prof math, Cath Univ Am, 67-72; assoc prof, 72-73, PROF MATH, BOWLING GREEN STATE UNIV, 73- *Mem:* Am Math Soc; Am Statist Asn; Int Statist Inst; Inst Math Statist. *Res:* Probability limit laws; statistical inference; sequential methods; stochastic processes. *Mailing Add:* Dept Math Bowling Green State Univ Bowling Green OH 43403

ROHDE, CHARLES RAYMOND, b Glasgow, Mont, Sept 3, 22; m 45; c 5. PLANT BREEDING. *Educ:* Mont State Col, BS, 47; Univ Minn, PhD(plant genetics), 53. *Prof Exp:* Asst prof agron & small grain breeder, Univ Wyo, 50-51; assoc prof, 52-70, supt, Pendleton Exp Sta, 70-76, PROF AGRON, ORE STATE UNIV, 70-, WHEAT BREEDER, PENDLETON EXP STA, 52- *Mem:* Am Soc Agron. *Res:* Wheat breeding and genetics. *Mailing Add:* PO Box 370 Pendleton OR 97801

ROHDE, FLORENCE VIRGINIA, b Davenport, Iowa, May 15, 18. APPLIED MATHEMATICS. *Educ:* Univ Northern Iowa, AB, 39; Univ Rochester, MM, 40; Miami Univ, AM, 45; Univ Ky, PhD(math), 50. *Prof Exp:* Teacher pub schs, Iowa, 40-45; instr music & math, Miami Univ, 42-45; asst math, Ohio State Univ, 45-46; instr math & astron, Univ Ky, 46-50; instr math & astron, Univ Fla, 50-52, from asst prof to assoc prof, 52-57; prof math, Univ Chattanooga, 57-66; PROF MATH, MISS STATE UNIV, 66- *Concurrent Pos:* Mathematician, Tenn Valley Authority, 59-62. *Mem:* Soc Indust & Appl Math; Am Math Soc; Math Asn Am. *Res:* Engineering and actuarial mathematics; numerical analysis. *Mailing Add:* Box 5172 Mississippi State MS 39762

ROHDE, RICHARD ALLEN, b Peekskill, NY, Sept 28, 29; m S5; c 4. PLANT PATHOLOGY. *Educ:* Drew Univ, AB, 51; Univ Md, MS, 56, PhD(plant path), 58. *Prof Exp:* Asst plant path, Univ Md, 58-59; from asst prof to assoc prof, 59-68, head dept, 68-81, PROF PLANT PATH, UNIV MASS, AMHERST, 68- *Concurrent Pos:* Vis scientist, Rothamsted Exp Sta, Eng, 67; vis prof, Univ Ariz, 74; nematologist, Coop State Res Serv, USDA, 81. *Mem:* AAAS; Am Phytopath Soc; Soc Nematol. *Res:* Ecology and physiology of plant parasitic nematodes; plant diseases caused by nematodes. *Mailing Add:* Dept Plant Path Univ Mass Amherst MA 01003

ROHDE, RICHARD WHITNEY, b Salt Lake City, Utah, Dec 23, 40; m 61; c 5. MATERIALS SCIENCE, TRIBOLOGY. *Educ:* Univ Utah, BS, 63, PhD(metall), 67. *Prof Exp:* Staff mem shock wave physics div, 67-69, SUPVR PHYS & MECH METALL DIV, SANDIA NAT LABS, 69- *Mem:* Metall Soc; Am Inst Mining, Metall & Petrol Engrs; Am Soc Metals; Am Soc Testing & Mat. *Res:* Dislocation dynamics in shock loaded materials; shock loading equation of state; phase transformation in metals; dislocation dynamics; stress corrosion cracking; friction, lubrication and wear; inleastic deformation modeling. *Mailing Add:* Phys Metall Div 5832 Sandia Nat Lab Albuquerque NM 87185

ROHDE, STEVE MARK, b Newark, NJ, May 18, 46; m 68; c 2. APPLIED MATHEMATICS, TRIBOLOGY. *Educ:* NJ Inst Technol, BS, 67; Lehigh Univ, MS, 69, PhD(math), 70. *Prof Exp:* res scientist appl math, 70-79, STAFF RES SCIENTIST & SUPVR, VEHICLE SIMULATION & CONTROL GROUP, 79- *Honors & Awards:* Henry Hess Award, Am Soc Mech Engrs, 73; Harry Kummer Mem Award, Am Soc Testing & Mat, 76; Burt L Newkirk Tribology Award, Am Soc Mech Engrs, 77. *Mem:* Math Asn Am; Soc Indust & Appl Math; Am Soc Mech Engrs; Am Soc Lubrication Engrs. *Res:* Optimization of distrubuted parameter systems; calculus of variations; hydrodynamic lubrication; friction and wear; finite element methods; computer aided engineering; control of mechanical systems. *Mailing Add:* Gen Motors Res Labs GM Tech Ctr Warren MI 48090

ROHEIM, PAUL SAMUEL, b Kiskunhalas, Hungary, July 11, 25; US citizen; m 57; c 1. PHYSIOLOGY, MEDICINE. *Educ:* Med Sch Budapest, MD, 51. *Prof Exp:* Demonstr physiol, Med Sch Budapest, 47-51, asst prof, 51-56; res assoc, Hahnemann Med Col, 57-58; instr med, Albert Einstein Col Med, 58-62, assoc in med, 62-63, from asst prof physiol to prof physiol & med, 63-77; PROF PHYSIOL, MED & PATH, LA STATE UNIV MED CTR, 77- *Concurrent Pos:* Intern, Univ Budapest Clins, 51-52; NIH fel, Albert Einstein Col Med, 58-62, New York Health Res Coun career scientist award, 68-73; estab investr, Am Heart Asn, 63-68, mem coun on arteriosclerosis. *Mem:* Am Physiol Soc; Fedn Am Socs Exp Biol; Hungarian Physiol Soc. *Res:* Lipid and lipoprotein metabolism; arteriosclerosis. *Mailing Add:* Dept of Physiol Bldg 112 1190 Florida Ave New Orleans LA 70119

ROHLF, F JAMES, b Blythe, Calif, Oct 24, 36; m 59; c 2. BIOMETRY, POPULATION BIOLOGY. *Educ:* San Diego State Col, BS, 58; Univ Kans, PhD(entom), 62. *Prof Exp:* Asst prof biol, Univ Calif, Santa Barbara, 62-65; assoc prof statist biol, Univ Kans, 65-69; assoc prof biol, 69-72, chmn, Dept Ecol & Evolution, 75-80, PROF BIOL, STATE UNIV NY STONY BROOK, 72- *Concurrent Pos:* Statist consult, NY Pub Serv Comn, 75-, IBM, 77- & US Environ Protection Agency, 78-; vis scientist, IBM, Yorktown Heights, NY, 76-77 & 80-81. *Mem:* Biomet Soc; Asn Comput Mach; Soc Syst Zool; Classification Soc (pres NAm br, 75-78). *Res:* Applications of cluster and factor analysis to systematics and population biology. *Mailing Add:* Dept of Ecol & Evolution State Univ NY Stony biology NY 11794

ROHLFING, DUANE L, b Cape Girardeau, Mo, Nov 18, 33; m 56; c 4. BIOCHEMISTRY, EVOLUTION. *Educ:* Drury Col, BS, 55; Fla State Univ, MS, 60, PhD(biochem), 64. *Prof Exp:* Nat Acad Sci res assoc enzyme models, Ames Res Ctr, NASA, Calif, 64-66; Med Found Boston sr res fel enzymes, Mass Inst Technol, 66-68; from asst prof to assoc prof, 68-76, PROF BIOL, UNIV SC, 76- *Mem:* AAAS; Am Chem Soc; Am Soc Biol Chem; Int Soc Study Origins Life. *Res:* Molecular and cellular evolution; polyamino acids; protocells; catalysis. *Mailing Add:* Dept of Biol Univ of SC Columbia SC 29208

ROHLFING, STEPHEN ROY, b Toledo, Ohio, July 25, 36; m 59; c 2. MICROBIOLOGY, INFECTIOUS DISEASES. *Educ:* Bowling Green State Univ, BS, 58; Miami Univ, MS, 60; Western Reserve Univ, PhD(microbiol), 65. *Prof Exp:* Assoc microbiol, Chicago Med Sch, 65-66, asst prof, 66-70; instr pharmacog, 70-74, asst prof, 74-80, ASSOC PROF PHARMACOL, COL PHARM, UNIV MINN, MINNEAPOLIS, 80- *Concurrent Pos:* Sr scientist, Riker Res Labs, Minn Mining & Mfg Co, 70-72, res specialist, Riker Labs, Inc, 72-75, supvr microbiol, 75-78, proj leader, Antiinfective Drug Res, 78- *Mem:* AAAS; Tissue Cult Asn; Am Soc Microbiol; Brit Soc Antimicrobial Chemother. *Res:* Gene-enzyme relationships; molecular characteristics of lymphomas; anti-infective research and development. *Mailing Add:* Riker Labs Inc 3M Ctr Bldg 270-2 St Paul MN 55144

ROHLICH, GERARD A(DDISON), b Brooklyn, NY, July 8, 10; m 41; c 10. ENVIRONMENTAL ENGINEERING, HYDRAULICS. *Educ:* Cooper Union, BS, 34; Univ Wis, BS, 36, MS, 37, PhD(sanit eng), 40. *Prof Exp:* Instr civil eng, Carnegie Inst Technol, 37-39, 40-41; asst prof sanit eng, Pa State Col, 41-42, from assoc prof to prof, 45-46; chief proj engr, Esna Corp, NJ, 44-45; prof sanit eng, Univ Wis-Madison, 46-72; C W COOK PROF ENVIRON ENG & PROF PUB AFFAIRS, LYNDON B JOHNSON SCH, UNIV TEX, AUSTIN, 72- *Concurrent Pos:* Chmn water qual criteria comt, Nat Acad Sci; mem sci adv bd, Environ Protection Agency, 77-; mem, Potomac River Water Supply Rev Comn, Nat Acad Eng, 77- *Honors & Awards:* Eddy Medal, Waste Pollution Control Fedn, 55. *Mem:* Nat Acad Eng; AAAS; Am Soc Civil Engrs; Am Soc Eng Educ; Am Water Works Asn. *Res:* Removal of nutrients from sewage effluents; lakes and streams pollution investigations; water quality. *Mailing Add:* Dept of Civil Eng 8-6 Cockrell Hall Univ of Tex Austin TX 78712

ROHMAN, MICHAEL, b New York, NY, Nov 21, 25; m 48; c 2. CARDIOVASCULAR SURGERY, THORACIC SURGERY. *Educ:* Boston Univ, MD, 50. *Prof Exp:* From intern to chief resident surg, Mass Mem Hosp, 50-55; asst & chief resident thoracic surg, Bronx Munic Hosp Ctr, 55-58; from instr to asst prof cardio-thoracic surg, Albert Einstein Col Med, 58-64, from asst clin prof to assoc clin prof, 64-70; PROF SURG, NEW YORK MED COL, 70-; CHIEF CARDIOTHORACIC SURG & TRAUMA SURG, LINCOLN MED & MENTAL HEALTH CTR, 79- *Concurrent Pos:* Nat Tuberc Asn fel, Albert Einstein Col Med, 57-59; consult cardio-thoracic surg, Northern Westchester Hosp, Yonkers Gen Hosp, United Hosp & Montrose Vet Admin Hosp, 66-; dir surg, Westchester County Med Ctr, 64-79. *Mem:* Am Col Chest Physicians; Am Heart Asn; fel Am Col Surg; Soc Thoracic Surg. *Res:* Small arterial anastamoses; pulmonary hemodynamics, particularly bronchial artery circulation. *Mailing Add:* Dept Surg Lincoln Med & Mental Health Ctr Bronx NY 10451

ROHN, ROBERT JONES, b Lima, Ohio, June 16, 18; m 42; c 4. MEDICINE. *Educ:* DePauw Univ, AB, 40; Ohio State Univ, MD, 43. *Prof Exp:* Intern, Ohio State Univ Hosp, 43-44, resident internal med, 44-46, resident hemat, 48-50; from instr to asst prof med, 50-55, assoc med & coordr cancer educ, 55-68, prof med, 68-74, BRUCE KENNETH WISEMAN PROF MED, SCH MED, IND UNIV, INDIANAPOLIS, 74-, CANCER COORDR, 68- *Concurrent Pos:* Consult, Vet Admin & Army Hosps, 52- *Mem:* Am Soc Hemat; Reticuloendothelial Soc; fel Am Col Physicians; Am Fedn Clin Res; Int Soc Hemat. *Res:* Cytological and clinical hematology. *Mailing Add:* Dept Med Ind Univ Sch Med Indianapolis IN 46223

ROHNER, MARY CHRISTOPHER, b Akron, Ohio, Apr 16, 23. EXPERIMENTAL EMBRYOLOGY, NEUROPHYSIOLOGY. *Educ:* Notre Dame Col, Ohio, BS, 43; Fordham Univ, MS, 56, PhD(biol), 58. *Prof Exp:* Jr physicist, Goodyear Res, Ohio, 43-45; from instr to prof biol, Notre Dame Col, Ohio, 46-69; PROV ASST, NOTRE DAME EDUC CTR, 69- *Concurrent Pos:* Mem bd trustees, Notre Dame Col, Ohio, 69-, pres, 73-, prov super, Notre Dame Educ Ctr, 73- *Mem:* AAAS. *Res:* Neurophysiology of medial forebrain bundle by means of electrode implantations; biochemical pathways in embryological morphogenesis. *Mailing Add:* Notre Dame Educ Ctr 13000 Auburn Rd Chardon OH 44024

ROHNER, THOMAS JOHN, b Trenton, NJ, Jan 1, 36; c 2. UROLOGY. *Educ:* Yale Univ, BA, 57; Univ Pa, MD, 61. *Prof Exp:* Resident gen surg, Hosp, Univ Pa, 62-64, resident urol, 64-67, USPHS spec fel, Dept Pharm, Sch Med, 69-70; from asst prof to assoc prof, 70-75, PROF SURG, MILTON S HERSHEY MED CTR, PA STATE UNIV, 75-, CHIEF DIV UROL, 70- *Concurrent Pos:* Consult urol, Vet Admin Hosp, Lebanon, Pa, 70- & Elizabethtown Hosp Children & Youth, Pa, 70- *Mem:* Am Urol Asn; Am Col Surgeons; Soc Pediat Urol; Asn Acad Surg. *Res:* In vitro contractile mechanisms of bladder and ureteral smooth muscle. *Mailing Add:* Div of Urol M S Hershey Med Ctr Pa State Univ 500 University Dr Hershey PA 17033

ROHOLT, OLIVER A, JR, b Preston, Idaho, May 30, 16; m 44; c 2. IMMUNOLOGY. *Educ:* Univ Mont, BA, 39; Univ Calif, PhD(biochem), 53. *Prof Exp:* Asst, Utah State Agr Col, 40-41; asst, Univ Calif, 47-50; instr, State Col Wash, 50-56; sr cancer res scientist, 56-63, assoc cancer res scientist, 63-65, prin cancer res scientist, 65-79, CANCER RES SCIENTIST VI, ROSWELL PARK MEM INST, 79-, ACTG DEPT CHMN, MOLECULAR IMMUNOL, 80- *Concurrent Pos:* Assoc res prof, Roswell Park Div, Grad Sch, State Univ NY Buffalo, 66-; mem grad fac, Niagara Univ, 68- *Mem:* AAAS; Am Chem Soc; Am Asn Immunol; Am Soc Biol Chem. *Res:* Immunochemistry. *Mailing Add:* Roswell Park Mem Inst Buffalo NY 14263

ROHOVSKY, MICHAEL WILLIAM, b Youngstown, Ohio, Feb 26, 37; m 65; c 2. PATHOLOGY. *Educ:* Ohio State Univ, DVM, 60, MSc, 65, PhD(vet path), 67; Am Col Vet Path, dipl. *Prof Exp:* Res assoc vet path, Ohio State Univ, 62-63, NIH trainee, 63-67, asst prof vet path, 67-69; sect head path, Dept Path & Toxicol, Merrell-Nat Labs, 69-72; head lab path, Arthur D Little, Inc, 72-77; V PRES RES, PITMAN-MOORE, INC, PA, 77-; DIR, ORTHOP RES & DEVELOP, JOHNSON & JOHNSON PRODS CO, INC, 80- *Concurrent Pos:* Adj asst prof, Univ Cincinnati, 69- *Mem:* Am Vet Med Asn; fel Am Col Vet Pharmacol & Therapeut; Int Acad Path. *Res:* Infectious diseases of animals; neoplastic diseases; antiviral therapy; toxicology and drug safety. *Mailing Add:* Johnson & Johnson Prod Co Inc PO Box -344 Washington Crossing NJ 08901

ROHR, DAVID M, b Portsmouth, Va, Sept 9, 47. PALEONTOLOGY, STRATIGRAPHY. *Educ:* Col William & Mary, BS, 69; Ore State Univ, PhD(geol), 77. *Prof Exp:* Asst prof geol, Univ Ore, 77-79; asst prof geol, Univ Wash, 79-80; ASST PROF GEOL, SUL ROSS STATE UNIV, 80- *Mem:* Paleont Soc; Geol Soc Am; Paleont Res Inst. *Res:* Lower Paleozoic (Ordovician through Lower Devonian) gastropods; paleoecology; lower Paleozoic stratigraphy. *Mailing Add:* Dept Geol Sul Ross State Univ Alpine TX 79830

ROHR, ROBERT CHARLES, b Leonia, NJ, Feb 27, 22; m 46; c 3. PHYSICS. *Educ:* Guilford Col, BS, 43; Univ Wis, MS, 47; Univ Tenn, PhD(physics), 55. *Prof Exp:* Physicist, Union Carbide Nuclear Co, div, Union Carbide Corp, 47-53; physicist, 55-59, mgr cold water assembly, 59-66, mgr cold water assembly/adv test reactor, 66-72, mgr chem & radiol controls navy training support, 72-74, sr proj engr, Prototype Opers & Eng, Guided Missile Cruiser Ship & Prototype Testing, 74-77, MGR REACTOR ENG OPER SHIP & PROTOTYPE TESTING, KNOLLS ATOMIC POWER LAB, GEN ELEC CO, 77- *Mem:* Am Phys Soc; Am Nuclear Soc. *Res:* Critical assembly experiments; beta ray spectroscopy; radiation and particle detectors. *Mailing Add:* RD 3 161 A Gordon Rd Schenectady NY 12306

ROHR, THOMAS EUGENE, biochemistry, see previous edition

ROHRBACH, KENNETH G, b Ashland, Ohio, Oct 16, 40; m 62; c 3. PLANT PATHOLOGY. *Educ:* Ohio State Univ, BS, 62; Univ Idaho, MS, 64; Colo State Univ, PhD(plant path), 67. *Prof Exp:* Res asst plant dis, Univ Idaho, 62-64 & Colo State Univ, 64-67; plant pathologist, Dole Co, 67-70 & Pineapple Res Inst, 70-73; assoc plant pathologist, 73-77, PLANT PATHOLOGIST, UNIV HAWAII, MANOA, 77- *Mem:* Am Phytopath Soc. *Res:* Diseases of tropical crops. *Mailing Add:* Dept of Plant Path Univ of Hawaii at Manoa Honolulu HI 96822

ROHRBACH, ROGER P(HILLIP), b Canton, Ohio, Oct 12, 42; m 65; c 3. AGRICULTURAL ENGINEERING. *Educ:* Ohio State Univ, PhD(agr eng), 68. *Prof Exp:* From asst prof to assoc prof biol & agr eng, 68-78, PROF BIOL & AGR ENG, AGR EXP STA, NC STATE UNIV, 78- *Mem:* Am Soc Agr Engrs. *Res:* Fruit production mechanization; blueberries and grapes; fluidics applied to agriculture; seed metering mechanisms development and research. *Mailing Add:* Dept of Biol & Agr Eng NC State Univ Box 5906 Raleigh NC 27650

ROHRER, DOUGLAS C, b Cleveland, Ohio, Dec 24, 42; m 66; c 2. X-RAY CRYSTALLOGRAPHY. *Educ:* Western Reserve Univ, BA, 66; Case Western Reserve Univ, PhD(chem), 70. *Prof Exp:* Res assoc crystallog, Crystallog Dept, Univ Pittsburgh, 70-73; res assoc, 73-74, res scientist cyrstallog, 74-78, ASSOC RES SCIENTIST, MOLECULAR BIOPHYS DEPT, MED FOUND BUFFALO, 78- *Concurrent Pos:* Vis prof, Sch Pharm, Oregon State Univ, 79. *Mem:* Am Chem Soc; Am Crystallog Asn; Am Inst Physics. *Mailing Add:* Med Found of Buffalo 73 High St Buffalo NY 14203

ROHRER, ROBERT HARRY, b Philadelphia, Pa, Sept 20, 18; m 42; c 4. PHYSICS. *Educ:* Emory Univ, BS, 39, MS, 42; Duke Univ, PhD(physics), 54. *Prof Exp:* From instr to asst prof eng, 40-51, from asst prof to assoc prof physics, 51-61, assoc prof radiol, 56-62, chmn dept physics, 63-69, PROF PHYSICS, EMORY UNIV, 61-, RADIOL, SCH MED, 62- *Mem:* Am Phys Soc; Health Physics Soc; Soc Nuclear Med (vpres, 71-72); Am Asn Physicists in Med; Am Asn Physics Teachers. *Res:* Nuclear radiation spectroscopy; radiation dosimetry; low energy neutron spectroscopy. *Mailing Add:* Dept of Physics Emory Univ Atlanta GA 30322

ROHRER, WESLEY M, JR, b Johntown, Pa, Sept 12, 21; m 43; c 3. MECHANICAL ENGINEERING, FLUID MECHANICS. *Educ:* Univ Pittsburgh, BS, 47; Mass Inst Technol, SM, 61. *Prof Exp:* Instr eng, Johnstown Ctr, 47-49, from instr to asst prof mech eng, Univ, 49-55, ASSOC PROF MECH ENG, UNIV PITTSBURGH, 55- *Concurrent Pos:* Consult, IBM Corp, 61-63, Adv Bd Hardened Elec Systs, Nat Acad Sci, 64-67 & World Bank, 80; vpres eng & natural sci, Univ Sci Ctr, Inc, 68-71, eng consult, 71-; vpres, Hosp Utility Mgt, Inc, 80-81. *Mem:* Combustion Inst (treas, 64-); Am Soc Eng Educ; Am Inst Aeronaut & Astronaut; AAAS; Sigma Xi. *Res:* Radiative heat transfer; air pollution abatement; combustion; two-phase flow; boiling heat transfer; efficient energy utilization. *Mailing Add:* Dept Mech Eng Univ Pittsburgh 648 Benedum Hall Pittsburgh PA 15213

ROHRER, WILLIAM GLEN, b Redlands, Calif, July 28, 16; m 38. ASTRONOMY, PHYSICS. *Educ:* Univ Redlands, BA, 42. *Prof Exp:* Chmn dept astron & aeronaut, Riverside Col, 45-51; develop engr, Aerojet-Gen Corp Div, Gen Tire & Rubber Co, 51-52; engr & field serv rep, Redstone Arsenal, Northrop Aircraft, Inc, 52-53; from asst to chief prod eng, Missiles Div, Firestone Tire & Rubber Co, 53-54; prin astrophysicist, Appl Res & Develop Div, Repub Aviation Corp, 58-60; sr res specialist, Space & Info Div, NAm Aviation, Inc, Calif, 60-61; staff scientist, Space Sci Dept, Res & Adv Develop Div, Avco Corp, Mass, 62; CONSULT SPACE SCI & AEROSPACE EDUC, 63- *Concurrent Pos:* Consult, Riverside Flight Acad, Inc, Corona Flight Acad, Redlands Flight Acad, Cal-Brown Flight Acad, 46-69, Missile Div Repub Aviation, X-15 Prog, Aircraft Div & SNAP Progs, Atomics Int; mem spec aviation comt, Joint Liaison Comt Higher Educ, 50-52; Calif Aviation Adv Comt, 52-53; secy bd trustees, Edison Tech Col, Calif. *Mem:* AAAS; Am Astronaut Soc; Int Platform Asn; fel Intercontinental Biog Asn; fel Int Lunar Soc. *Res:* Solar radiation; planetary and lunar environment; interplanetary navigation techniques; astronomical instrumentation for lunar and satellite observatories; astrophysical problems pertaining to astronautics; interplanetary and interstellar navigation; aerospace education. *Mailing Add:* PO Box 16 Redlands CA 92373

ROHRIG, NORMAN, b Creston, Iowa, Oct 28, 44; m 67; c 2. RADIOLOGICAL PHYSICS. *Educ:* Iowa State Univ, BS, 66; Univ Wis-Madison, MS, 68, PhD(nuclear physics), 73. *Prof Exp:* Res scientist, Radiol Res Labs, Col Physicians & Surgeons, Columbia Univ, 72-74; ASSOC SCIENTIST, MED DEPT, BROOKHAVEN NAT LAB, 74- *Mem:* Radiation Res Soc; Am Phys Soc; AAAS; Sigma Xi. *Res:* Measurements of W, energy required to create an ion pair, in gases relevant to neutron dosimetry; development of hardware for irradiation of mammalian cells with charged particles. *Mailing Add:* Bldg 535 Brookhaven Nat Lab Upton NY 11973

ROHRINGER, ROLAND, b Nürnberg, Ger, Aug 12, 29; nat Can; m 58; c 2. PLANT PATHOLOGY. *Educ:* Univ Göttingen, PhD(agr), 56. *Prof Exp:* Fel plant path, Univ Göttingen, 56, res asst, 58-59; res asst biochem, Univ Wis, 56-58; res officer agr, Pesticide Res Inst, 59, head, Cereal Rust Sect, 63-73, HEAD CEREAL DIS SECT, CAN DEPT AGR, 74- *Mem:* Phytochem Soc NAm. *Res:* Physiology of parasitism in plants; molecular biology of cereal rust diseases. *Mailing Add:* Agr Can Res Sta 195 Dafoe Rd Winnipeg MB R3T 2M9 Can

ROHRL, HELMUT, b Straubing, Ger, Mar 22, 27. MATHEMATICS. *Educ:* Univ Munich, DSc(math), 49, Habilitation, 53. *Prof Exp:* Asst prof math, Univ Würzburg, 49-51; asst prof, Univ Munich, 51-53, 54-55, docent, 55-58; asst prof, Univ Münster, 53-54; res assoc, Univ Chicago, 58-59; from assoc prof to prof, Univ Minn, 59-64; vis prof, Harvard Univ, 62-63; chmn dept, 68-71, PROF MATH, UNIV CALIF, SAN DIEGO, 64- *Concurrent Pos:* Vis prof, Princeton Univ, 67-68, Univ Munich, 72-73 & Univ Nagoya, 76. *Mem:* Am Math Soc; Ger Math Asn. *Res:* Pure mathematics. *Mailing Add:* Univ Calif San Diego PO Box 109 La Jolla CA 92037

ROHRLICH, FRITZ, b Vienna, Austria, May 12, 21; nat US; m 51; c 2. RELATIVISTIC PARTICLE DYNAMICS. *Educ:* Inst Technol, Israel, ChemE, 43; Harvard Univ, MA, 47, PhD(physics), 48. *Prof Exp:* Mem staff, Inst Adv Study, 48-49; res assoc physics, Nuclear Studies Lab, Cornell Univ, 49-51; lectr, Princeton Univ, 51-53; from assoc prof to prof, Univ Iowa, 53-63; PROF PHYSICS, SYRACUSE UNIV, 63- *Concurrent Pos:* Vis prof, Johns Hopkins Univ, 58-59; vis prof, Tel-Aviv Univ, 67; consult, Nat Bur Standards, 58-61; vis prof, Poland, 77, Bulgaria, 78, Univ Calif, Irvine, 81 & Stanford Univ, 81. *Honors & Awards:* Fulbright lectr, US Dept State, Cent Europ, 74. *Mem:* NY Acad Sci; fel Am Phys Soc; Fedn Am Sci. *Res:* Quantum field theory and elementary particles; quantum electrodynamics; relativistic particle dynamics. *Mailing Add:* Dept of Physics Syracuse Univ Syracuse NY 13210

ROHRMANN, CHARLES A(LBERT), b Pendleton, Ore, Dec 17, 11; m 39; c 4. CHEMICAL ENGINEERING. *Educ:* Ore State Univ, BS, 34; Ohio State Univ, PhD(chem eng), 39. *Prof Exp:* Res chem engr, Grasselli Chem Dept, E I du Pont de Nemours & Co, Ohio, 39-43; plant process supvr, Pa, 43-48; chem engr, Gen Elec Co, 48-64; sr res assoc, Battelle Northwest, 65-68, consult, Chem & Metall Div, Pac Northwest Labs, 68-70, staff engr, Chem Tech Dept, 70-77, RESIDENT CONSULT, PAC NORTHWEST LABS, BATTELLE MEM INST, 77- *Mem:* Am Chem Soc; fel Am Inst Chem Engrs; AAAS. *Res:* Heavy inorganic and organic chemicals; sulfur-nitrogen chemicals; applications in the atomic energy industry; production and application of radioisotopes; air pollution control; biomass conversion. *Mailing Add:* Pac Northwest Labs Battelle Mem Inst PO Box 999 Richland WA 99352

ROHRS, HAROLD CLARK, b Alexandria, Ky, Sept 23, 40; m 62; c 2. CELL PHYSIOLOGY. *Educ:* Transylvania Col, AB, 61; Univ Ky, PhD(physiol), 66. *Prof Exp:* Asst prof, 66-72, assoc prof, 72-79, PROF ZOOL, DREW UNIV, 79- *Concurrent Pos:* Vis res prof, Univ Oslo, 73-74. *Mem:* Am Physiol Soc; Am Soc Zoologists. *Res:* Transport-process in blood and bone marrow cells. *Mailing Add:* Dept of Zool Drew Univ Madison NJ 07940

ROHRSCHNEIDER, LARRY RAY, b Minneapolis, Minn, Oct 2, 44; m 71; c 2. VIROLOGY, ONCOLOGY. *Educ:* Univ Minn, BS, 67; Univ Wis, PhD(oncol), 73. *Prof Exp:* Res fel, Nat Cancer Inst, NIH, 73-76; asst mem tumor virol, 76-80, ASSOC MEM TUMOR VIROL, FRED HUTCHINSON CANCER RES CTR, 81- *Concurrent Pos:* Res grant, HEW, USPHS, 77-; res asst prof microbiol, Univ Wash, 78- *Mem:* AAAS; Sigma Xi; Am Soc Cell Biol. *Res:* Investigation of the mechanism of transformation by avian RNA tumor virus; biochemistry of transforming proteins and expression of tumor specific cell surface antigens. *Mailing Add:* Fred Hutchinson Cancer Res Ctr 1124 Columbia St Seattle WA 98104

ROHSENOW, WARREN M(AX), b Chicago, Ill, Feb 12, 21; m 46; c 1. ENGINEERING. *Educ:* Northwestern Univ, BS, 41; Yale Univ, MEng, 43, DEng(heat power), 44. *Prof Exp:* Lab asst mech eng, Yale Univ, 41-43, instr, 43-44; from asst prof to assoc prof mech eng, 46-56, PROF MECH ENG, MASS INST TECHNOL, 56- *Concurrent Pos:* Consult engr, 46-; dir, Dynatech Corp, 57- *Honors & Awards:* Gold Medal, Am Soc Mech Engrs, 51, Jr Award, 52; Yale Eng Asn Award, 52; Heat Transfer Div Mem Award, Am Soc Mech Engrs, 67, Max Jakob Mem Award, 71. *Mem:* Fel Nat Acad Eng; fel Am Soc Mech Engrs; fel Am Acad Arts & Sci. *Res:* Gas turbines; heat transfer; thermodynamics. *Mailing Add:* Dept of Mech Eng 77 Massachusetts Ave Cambridge MA 02139

ROHT, LEWIS HOWARD, b New York, NY, Oct 9, 38; m 72; c 1. EPIDEMIOLOGY, PREVENTIVE MEDICINE. *Educ:* Union Col, BS, 60; New York Med Col, MD, 64; Johns Hopkins Univ, MPH, 70. *Prof Exp:* Clinician, US Air Force, Japan, 65-68, Mem Hosp, NY, 68-69; res fel, Med Sch, Okayama Univ, Japan, 70-71; resident preventive med, Univ Md, 71-73; ASSOC PROF EPIDEMIOL, SCH PUBLIC HEALTH, UNIV TEX, 73- *Concurrent Pos:* Assoc investr, Am Nat Red Cross, 77- *Mem:* Soc Epidemiol Res; Am Col Preventive Med; Am Public Health Asn. *Res:* Environmental and occupational health epidemiology; clinical therapeutic trials; maternal and child health (particularly induced abortion). *Mailing Add:* Sch Public Health Univ Tex PO Box 20186 Houston TX 77025

ROHWEDDER, WILLIAM KENNETH, b Williston Park, NY, June 15, 32. MASS SPECTROMETRY. *Educ:* Lehigh Univ, BS, 54, MS, 57, PhD(chem), 60. *Prof Exp:* Sr engr, Bendix Corp, 60-61; CHEMIST, NORTHERN REGIONAL RES LAB, SCI & EDUC ADMIN, AGR RES, USDA, 62- *Mem:* Am Chem Soc; Am Oil Chemists Soc; Am Soc Mass Spectrometry; AAAS. *Res:* Mass spectrometry of natural and isotopically labeled chemical derivatives from oilseeds and other natural products. *Mailing Add:* 3900 North Stable Ct Apt 205 Peoria IL 61614

ROHWEDER, DWAYNE A, b Marshalltown, Iowa, Aug 12, 26; m 48; c 2. AGRONOMY. *Educ:* Iowa State Univ, BS, 48, MS, 56, PhD(crop prod & soil mgt), 63. *Prof Exp:* Co Exten dir, Exten Div, Iowa State Univ, 48-54, area exten agronomist, 55-59, exten agronomist, 59-63; PROF FORAGE CROPS & EXTEN AGRONOMIST, EXTEN DIV, UNIV WIS-MADISON, 63- *Concurrent Pos:* Agronomist & chief of party, Univ Wis-US Agency Int Develop univ develop contract, Univ Rio Grande do Sul, Brazil, 67-69. *Honors & Awards:* Merit Award, Am Forage & Grassland Coun, 74. *Mem:* Am Forage & Grassland Coun; fel Am Soc Agron; Crop Sci Soc; Soil Conserv Soc Am. *Res:* Forage crop production; forage quality and evaluation. *Mailing Add:* 153 Agron Univ Wis Madison WI 53706

ROHWER, ROBERT G, b Ft Calhoun, Nebr, Nov 20, 20; m 43; c 4. CEREAL CHEMISTRY. *Educ:* Univ Nebr, BS, 43. *Prof Exp:* Chemist, Am Cyanamid Co, 43-48; plant supt, KrimKo Corp, 48-49; res chemist, Clinton Corn Processing Co, Standard Brands, Inc, 49-51, supvr sugar res, 51-59; res chemist, 59-62, sales mgr, 62-66, vpres, 66-78, SR VPRES & DIR MKT, GRAIN PROCESSING CORP, 78- *Mem:* Am Chem Soc; Tech Asn Pulp & Paper Indust; Inst Food Technol; Am Asn Cereal Chem. *Res:* Corn wet milling; starch, sugars and syrups; ion exchange. *Mailing Add:* Grain Processing Corp 1600 Oregon St Muscatine IA 52761

ROHY, DAVID ALAN, b Santa Barbara, Calif, July 30, 40; m 64; c 3. SOLID STATE PHYSICS. *Educ:* Univ Calif, Santa Barbara, BA, 62; Cornell Univ, PhD(physics), 68. *Prof Exp:* Physicist instrumentation, Lawrence Livermore Labs, Univ Calif, 67-70; res engr instrumentation & energy storage, Solar Turbines, 70-76, prog mgr, energy storage, hydrogen & instrumentation int harvester, 76-80, MGR APPLIED SCI SOLAR TURBINE INC, CATERPILLAR, 81- *Mem:* Int Asn Hydrogen Energy; Am Phys Soc. *Res:* Development of waste heat recovery; thermal energy storage and thermal energy conversion systems using metal hydrides; hydrogen energy systems; instrumentation for gas turbine engines, particularly gas and solid temperature measurement. *Mailing Add:* Solar Turbines Inc PO Box 80966 San Diego CA 92138

ROIA, FRANK COSTA, JR, b New Bedford, Mass, June 5, 36; m 60; c 3. ECONOMIC BOTANY, MICROBIOLOGY. *Educ:* Mass Col Pharm, BS, 58, MS, 60, PhD(biol sci), 67. *Prof Exp:* Assoc prof, 67-77, PROF BIOL, PHILA COL PHARM & SCI, 77- *Honors & Awards:* Award, Soc Cosmetic Chem, 67. *Mem:* Soc Cosmetic Chem; Sigma Xi; Am Soc Microbiol. *Res:* Antimicrobial activity of plants; microbial flora and its relationship to dandruff. *Mailing Add:* Phila Col of Pharm & Sci Philadelphia PA 19104

ROISTACHER, SEYMOUR LESTER, b New York, NY, May 21, 22; m 46; c 3. DENTISTRY. *Educ:* City Col New York, BS, 41; NY Univ, DDS, 44. *Prof Exp:* DIR DENTISTRY, QUEENS HOSP CTR, LONG ISLAND JEWISH-HILLSIDE MED CTR, 64-; PROF DENT MED, STATE UNIV

NY STONY BROOK, 70- *Concurrent Pos:* Attend dentist, Long Island Jewish-Hillside Med Ctr, 60-; mem sect oral surg, anesthesia & hosp dent, Am Asn Dent Schs, 68-, chmn coun hosp dent serv, 69-, vpres coun hosp, 70- *Mem:* Fel Am Col Dent; Am Asn Hosp Dent; fel Int Col Dent. *Res:* Myofascial pain in the facial areas. *Mailing Add:* 82-64 164 St Dept Dent Queens Hosp Ctr New York NY 11432

ROITMAN, JAMES NATHANIEL, b Providence, RI, June 29, 41; m 72. ORGANIC CHEMISTRY. *Educ:* Brown Univ, BA, 63; Univ Calif, PhD(org chem), 69. *Prof Exp:* RES CHEMIST, WESTERN REGIONAL LAB, US DEPT AGR, 69- *Mem:* Am Chem Soc. *Res:* Isolation, characterization, and synthesis of naturally occurring compounds possessing biological activity. *Mailing Add:* Western Regional Res Ctr US Dept Agr Albany CA 94710

ROITMAN, JUDY, b New York, NY, Nov 12, 45; m 78; c 1. TOPOLOGY, MATHEMATICAL LOGIC. *Educ:* Sarah Lawrence Col, BA, 66; Univ Calif, Berkeley, MA, 72, PhD(math), 74. *Prof Exp:* Asst prof math, Wellesley Col, 74-77; mem, Inst Advan Study, 77; asst prof, 78-80, ASSOC PROF MATH, UNIV KANS, 80- *Mem:* Am Math Soc; Math Asn Am; Asn Women Math; Asn Women Sci. *Res:* Applications of set theory to topology; consistency results. *Mailing Add:* Dept of Math Univ of Kans Lawrence KS 66045

ROITMAN, PETER, b Boston, Mass, Aug 30, 49. ELECTRONICS, SOLID STATE PHYSICS. *Educ:* Dartmouth Col, BA, 72; Princeton Univ, PhD(elec eng), 76. *Prof Exp:* NAT RES COUN FEL PHYSICS, NAT BUR STANDARDS, 76- *Mem:* Am Phys Soc; Am Vacuum Soc; Inst Elec & Electronics Engrs; Sigma Xi. *Mailing Add:* Nat Bur Standards Washington DC 20234

ROITSCH, CAROLYN ANN, biochemistry, cell biology, see previous edition

ROIZIN, LEON, b Dubossare, Russia, Dec 31, 12; nat US; m 41; c 2. NEUROPATHOLOGY. *Educ:* Univ Milan, MD, 36. *Prof Exp:* Fel neuropsychiat, Univ Pavia, 36, resident, 36-39; asst, St Paul Univ, Brazil, 39-40; vol asst, NY State Psychiat Inst, 40-41; actg assoc & instr psychiat, 41-43, assoc res neuropathologist, 43-59, chief res neuropathologist, 59-69, from asst prof to assoc prof neuropath, 51-69, PROF NEUROPATH, COL PHYSICIANS & SURGEONS, COLUMBIA UNIV, 69-; CHIEF PSYCHIAT RES, NY STATE PSYCHIAT INST, 72- *Concurrent Pos:* Mem staff, NY State Psychiat Inst, 41-72; sr consult, US Vet Admin, 46-; dir neurotoxicol res unit, Bronx State Hosp, 65- *Mem:* Am Asn Neuropath; AMA; Am Neurol Asn; Am Psychiat Asn. *Res:* Neuropsychiatry; human and experimental histometabolism of the nervous system; ultracellular central nervous system pathogenic mechanisms. *Mailing Add:* NY State Psychiat Inst 722 W 168th St New York NY 10032

ROIZMAN, BERNARD, b Chisinau, Romania, Apr 17, 29; nat US; m 50; c 2. VIROLOGY. *Educ:* Temple Univ, BA, 52, MS, 54; Johns Hopkins Univ, ScD(virol), 56. *Prof Exp:* Instr microbiol, Sch Med & Sch Hyg & Pub Health, Johns Hopkins Univ, 56-57, res assoc, 57-58, asst prof, 58-65; assoc prof, 65-69, PROF MICROBIOL & CHMN COMT VIROL, UNIV CHICAGO, 69-, PROF BIOPHYS & THEORET BIOL, 70-, PROF VIROL, 81- *Concurrent Pos:* Lederle med fac award, 60; Am Cancer Soc scholar, Pasteur Inst, France, 61-62; USPHS career develop award, 63-65; Am Cancer Soc fac res assoc award, 66-71; mem develop res working group, Spec Virus Cancer Prog, Nat Cancer Inst, 67-71, consult, 67-73; Int Agency Res Against Cancer traveling fel, Karolinska Inst, Sweden, 70; mem steering coun, Human Cell Biol Prog, NSF, 71-74; mem sci adv coun, NY Cancer Inst, 71-; chmn herpesvirus study group, Int Comn Nomenclature of Viruses, 71-; consult, Nat Sci Fedn, 72-74; mem med adv bd, Leukemia Res Found, 72-77; lectr, Am Found Microbiol, 74-75; mem bd sci consult, Sloan Kettering Inst, NY, 75-81; mem, Task Force Virol, Nat Inst Allergy & Infectious Dis, 76-77; mem, Study Sect Virol & Res Grants Rev Bd, NIH, 76-80; mem bd trustees, Goodwin Inst Cancer Res, 77-; mem adv bd, Northwestern Univ Cancer Ctr, 79- *Honors & Awards:* Esther Langer Award Achievement Cancer Res, 74. *Mem:* Nat Acad Sci; Am Asn Immunol; Soc Exp Biol & Med; Am Soc Microbiol; Am Soc Biol Chemists. *Res:* Biochemistry and genetics of viral replication; viral oncology; biochemistry and molecular biology of herpes viruses, especially genosome structure and function. *Mailing Add:* Univ of Chicago 910 E 58th St Chicago IL 60637

ROJANSKY, VLADIMIR, physics, deceased

ROJAS, RICHARD RAIMOND, b New York, NY, Sept 25, 31; m 54; c 2. UNDERWATER ACOUSTICS, SIGNAL PROCESSING. *Educ:* Col City New York, BEE, 52; Drexel Inst Technol, Philadelphia, MEE, 61. *Prof Exp:* Proj engr guided missile fuzing, Philco Corp, 52-60; dept mgr undersea warfare, Magnovox Gen Atronic Corp, 60-69; assoc div head undersea surveillance, 69-76, ASSOC DIR RES, NAVAL RES LAB, 76- *Concurrent Pos:* Lectr, Pa State Univ, 63-69. *Mem:* Sigma Xi; Acoust Soc Am; Marine Technol Soc; Inst Elec & Electronics Engrs. *Res:* Ocean engineering; physical oceanography; radar; electronic warfare; application of signal processing and statistical techniques to sonar. *Mailing Add:* Naval Res Lab Code 5000 Washington DC 20375

ROJIANI, KAMAL B, b Bombay, India, Oct 22, 48; Pakistan citizen. STRUCTURAL RELIABILITY. *Educ:* Univ Karachi, BE, 71; Univ Ill, Urbana, MS, 73, PhD(civil eng), 77. *Prof Exp:* Comput programmer, Dept Finance, State Ill, 74; teaching & res asst, Dept Civil Eng, Univ Ill, 73-77; ASST PROF STRUCT, DEPT CIVIL ENG, VA POLYTECH INST & STATE UNIV, 78- *Concurrent Pos:* Struct engr, Bechtel Power Corp, 80; co-prin investr, US Dept Interior, Bur Surface Mines, 80-82; prin investr, Res Initiation Grant, NSF, 81-83; mem, Comt Load Resistance Factor Design, Am Soc Civil Engrs, 82- *Mem:* Am Soc Civil Engrs. *Res:* Application of probabilistic concepts to the solution of civil engineering problems, and specifically in the area of structural reliability. *Mailing Add:* Dept Civil Eng Va Polytech Inst State Univ 300 Norris Hall Blacksburg VA 24061

ROJO, ALFONSO, b Burgos, Spain, Jan 22, 21; Can citizen; m 56; c 3. ICHTHYOLOGY. *Educ:* Univ Valladolid, BSc & BA, 43; Univ Madrid, MSc, 53, PhD(ichthyol), 56. *Prof Exp:* Biologist, Spanish Dept Fisheries, 54-58; asst scientist, Fisheries Res Bd Can, 58-61; from asst prof to assoc prof, comp anat & ichthyol, St Mary's Univ, NS, 61-68; assoc prof expert fisheries & oceanog, Food & Agr Orgn, UN, 68-70; assoc prof, 70-72, PROF ICHTHYOL, ST MARY'S UNIV, NS, 72- *Concurrent Pos:* Sci adv for Spain, Int Comn Northwest Atlantic Fisheries, 54-58; sci adv for Can, Int Comn Great Lakes, 58-61. *Mem:* Am Fisheries Soc; Can Soc Zool; Soc Syst Zool. *Res:* Problems of systematics at the species level in relation to larval forms of commerical fishes; study of a possibility of linking sciences and humanities through bioethics. *Mailing Add:* Dept of Biol St Mary's Univ Halifax NS B3H 1J3 Can

ROKACH, JOSHUA, b Cairo, Egypt, Sept 17, 35; Can citizen. LEUKOTRIENES, PROSTAGLANDINS. *Educ:* Hebrew Univ, MSC, 62; Weizmann Inst Sci, Israel, PhD, 64. *Prof Exp:* Fel, Weizmann Inst Sci, 64-65, Max-Planck Inst, 65-66; sr res chemist, Merck Frosst Labs, 66-74, group leader, 74-77, sr res fel, 77-79, dir med chem, 79-81, EXEC DIR RES, MERCK FROSST CAN INC, 81- *Mem:* Am Chem Soc; Chem Inst Can; Can Res Mgt Asn. *Res:* Syntheses of various metabolites of the lipoxygenase pathway of arachidonic acid and the biological properties of these metabolites with special emphasis on their relation to allergic and respiratory diseases. *Mailing Add:* Merck Frosst Can Inc PO Box 1005 Pointe Claire-Dorval PQ H9R 4P8 Can

ROKAW, STANLEY N, b Brooklyn, NY, June 22, 21; m 46; c 3. MEDICINE. *Educ:* City Col New York, BBA, 43; Wash Univ, BS, MSc & MD, 49; Am Bd Internal Med, dipl. *Prof Exp:* Intern, Ward Med Serv, Barnes Hosp, 49-50, resident, 50-51; fel med & cardiol, Sch Med, Wash Univ, 53-54; fel res physiol, Harvard Med Sch, 54-55; res assoc pulmonary res, Rancho Los Amigos Hosp, 55-57, chief pulmonary res coord & head phys pulmonary respiratory serv, 57-68; instr chest dis & asst prof med, 63-69, ASSOC CLIN PROF MED, UNIV CALIF, IRVINE-CALIF COL MED, 69-, MED DIR, TUBERC & RESPIRATORY DIS ASN LOS ANGELES COUNTY & MED DIR BREATHMOBILE PROJ, 70- *Concurrent Pos:* Instr, Loma Linda Univ, 55-57, asst clin prof, 57-62, asst prof, 62-71; chief pulmonary physiol, Vet Admin Hosp, Long Beach, Calif, 68-71; assoc clin prof med, Univ Southern Calif & Univ Calif, Los Angeles; attend physician, Los Angeles County Gen & White Mem Hosps, 57-; attend physician active staff med, St Francis Hosp, 61-; consult, City of Hope & Rio Hondo Hosp, 62-, pulmonary dis, Orange County Med Ctr, 68-71, US Naval Hosp, Long Beach, statewide adv comt, Statewide Air Pollution Res Ctr, Univ Calif, Riverside & toxicol info prog, Div Med Sci, Nat Acad Sci-Nat Res Coun; consult-contrib, Nat Air Pollution Control Admin, Dept Health, Educ & Welfare; task force consult, Univ Calif Proj Clean Air, 70-; dir pulmonary lab & inhalation ther serv, Downey Community Hosp, 72-; mem subcomt air qual stand & res, Calif Dept Pub Health, 63-; ad hoc comt respiratory dis ctrs, State of Calif, 64 & Air Conserv Comn, chmn, 68-71; mem comt environ health, Nat Air Conserv Comn, chmn bd dirs area IV coun, Calif Regional Med Prog & nominating comt, Comt Air Conserv, Southern Planning Coun. *Mem:* AAAS; Am Thoracic Soc. *Res:* Effects of positive pressure breathing on ventilatory mechanics; gas distribution and blood-gas exchange; air pollution and chronic respiratory disease; pulmonary manifestations in scoliosis; pollutants and human functions; environment control. *Mailing Add:* Lung Asn of Los Angeles Co 1670 Beverly Blvd Los Angeles CA 90026

ROKEBY, THOMAS R(UPERT) C(OLLINSON), b Port Rowan, Ont, May 9, 21; nat US; m 46; c 3. AGRICULTURAL ENGINEERING. *Educ:* Ont Agr Col, BSA, 48; Univ Toronto, MSA, 50; Okla State Univ, PhD, 68. *Prof Exp:* Asst agr eng, Ont Agr Col, 48-50, asst res, 50-51; asst prof, SDak State Col, 51-55; from asst prof to assoc prof, 55-64, PROF AGR ENG, UNIV ARK, FAYETTEVILLE, 64- *Concurrent Pos:* NSF fel, Okla State Univ, 64-65. *Mem:* Am Soc Agr Engrs; Int Solar Energy Soc. *Res:* Solar energy for heating farm and residential buildings; design and construction of farm buildings, particularly houses and poultry housing; design of grain and bulk materials storage; materials and energy research. *Mailing Add:* Dept of Agr Eng Univ of Ark Fayetteville AR 72701

ROKOSKE, THOMAS LEO, b Danville, Ill, Feb 25, 39; m 61; c 3. SOLID STATE PHYSICS. *Educ:* Loyola Univ, La, BS, 61; Fla State Univ, MS, 63; Auburn Univ, PhD(physics), 73. *Prof Exp:* Instr physics, Fla State Univ, 64; from instr to asst prof, 64-67 & 71-74, ASSOC PROF PHYSICS, APPALACHIAN STATE UNIV, 74- *Concurrent Pos:* Vchmn, NC Adv Coun Metrication, 74-75, chmn, 75-76; dir, Indust Metric Educ Conf, 74-75. *Mem:* Am Phys Soc; Am Asn Physics Teachers. *Res:* Electrical conduction in thin films. *Mailing Add:* Dept of Physics Appalachian State Univ Boone NC 28608

ROL, PIETER KLAAS, b Netherlands, Nov 22, 27; m 52; c 3. PHYSICS. *Educ:* Univ Amsterdam, Drs, 53, PhD(physics), 60. *Prof Exp:* Group leader isotope separation, Inst Atomic & Molecular Physics, Found Fundamental Res in Matter, Amsterdam, 53-60; fel, Space Sci Lab, Gen Dynamics/ Convair, Calif, 60-62; res leader atomic collisions, Inst Atomic & Molecular Physics, Found Fundamental Res in Matter, 62-66; staff scientist, Convair Div, Gen Dynamics, 66-69; dir res, Inst Eng Sci, 74-76, assoc dean, Col Eng, 76-78, assoc provost acad planning, 78-81, PROF CHEM & METALL ENG, COL ENG, WAYNE STATE UNIV, 69- *Concurrent Pos:* Consult, Appl Res Labs, 68-69. *Mem:* Am Phys Soc; Am Vacuum Soc; AAAS; Netherlands Vacuum Soc; Sigma Xi. *Res:* Atomic and molecular physics; surface physics. *Mailing Add:* Dept Chem & Metall Eng Wayne State Univ Detroit MI 48202

ROLAND, CHARLES GORDON, b Winnipeg, Man, Jan 25, 33. HISTORY OF MEDICINE, COMMUNICATION SCIENCE. *Educ:* Univ Man, BSc & MD, 58. *Prof Exp:* Physician pvt pract, 59-64; sr ed jour, AMA, 64-69; prof biomed commun & chmn dept & assoc prof hist med, Mayo Med Sch & Mayo Found, 69-77; JASON A HANNAH PROF HIST MED, McMASTER UNIV, 77- *Mem:* Am Med Writers Asn (pres, 69-70); Coun Biol Ed; Am Asn

Hist Med (secy-treas, 76-79); Am Osler Soc (secy-treas, 75-); Can Soc Hist Med. *Res:* Variety of investigations into the sociology and history of scientific communication; history of medicine in the nineteenth century. *Mailing Add:* 3N10-HSC McMaster Univ Hamilton ON L8N 3Z5 Can

ROLAND, DAVID ALFRED, SR, b Cochran, Ga, Jan 2, 43; m 65; c 1. NUTRITIONAL BIOCHEMISTRY. *Educ:* Univ Ga, BS, 66, PhD(nutrit), 70. *Prof Exp:* Res asst nutrit, Univ Ga, 66-67; assoc prof mgt & poultry & asst poultry scientist, Univ Fla, 70-76; ALUMNI ASSOC PROF POULTRY NUTRIT, AUBURN UNIV, 76- *Honors & Awards:* Research Award, Poultry Sci Asn, 73 & Egg Sci Award, 74. *Mem:* AAAS; Poultry Sci Asn; World Poultry Sci Asn. *Res:* Mineral metabolism; egg shell quality; poultry management; lipid metabolism; reproductive physiology. *Mailing Add:* Dept Poultry Sci Auburn Univ Auburn AL 38630

ROLAND, DENNIS MICHAEL, b New Castle, Ind, July 16, 49; m 71. PHARMACEUTICAL CHEMISTRY. *Educ:* Ball State Univ, BS, 71; Univ Vt, PhD(org chem), 77. *Prof Exp:* Fel org synthesis, Colo State Univ, 77-79; SR SCIENTIST MED CHEM, PHARMACEUT DIV, CIBA-GEIGY, CORP, 79- *Concurrent Pos:* Nar Res Serv Award, NIH, 77-79. *Mem:* Am Chem Soc. *Res:* Design and synthesis of new biologically active molecules for use as theraputic agents. *Mailing Add:* RFD #1 Drewville Rd Carmel NY 10512

ROLAND, GEORGE WARREN, geology, chemistry, see previous edition

ROLAND, JOHN FRANCIS, b Denver, Colo, June 17, 20; m 43; c 2. MICROBIAL BIOCHEMISTRY. *Educ:* Purdue Univ, BS, 42. *Prof Exp:* Res chemist & head nutrit & fermentation sects, Armour & Co, 42-50; group leader, 50-76, SR SCIENTIST MICROBIOL, KRAFT, INC, 50-, SR GROUP LEADER, 76- *Mem:* Am Chem Soc. *Res:* Utilization of enzyme technology in the development of new chemical and food processes. *Mailing Add:* Kraft Inc Res & Develop 801 Waukegan Rd Glenview IL 60025

ROLDAN, LUIS GONZALEZ, b Garafia, Spain, Aug 8, 25; m 61; c 4. CRYSTALLOGRAPHY, CHEMISTRY. *Educ:* Univ Seville, Lic Chem, 50, DSc, 57. *Prof Exp:* Chemist, Celulosa Andaluza, Ltd, 52-53; adj prof exp physics, Univ Seville, 53-57; from res physicist to sr res physicist, Brit Rayon Res Asn, Manchester, Eng, 57-61; sr res chemist, Cent Res Lab, Allied Chem Corp, 61-63; from scientist to sr scientist, 63-68; res assoc, 68-76, MGR PHYSICS & MICROS DEPT, TECH CTR, J P STEVENS & CO, INC, GREENVILLE, SC, 76- *Mem:* AAAS; Am Chem Soc; Am Crystallog Asn; Royal Span Soc Phys & Chem; NY Acad Sci. *Res:* Structure of organic compounds, macromolecules and polymers by x-ray diffraction techniques; morphology of these compounds by electron microscopy; relationship of structure and morphology with physical properties; metallography; ceramics structure; fiber physics. *Mailing Add:* 124 Becky Don Dr Greer SC 29651

ROLETT, ELLIS LAWRENCE, b New York, NY, July 10, 30; m 56; c 3. INTERNAL MEDICINE, CARDIOLOGY. *Educ:* Yale Univ, BS, 52; Harvard Univ, MD, 55. *Prof Exp:* Intern med, Mass Gen Hosp, Boston, 55-56; asst resident, New York Hosp, 56-57; resident, Mass Gen Hosp, 59-60, clin fel cardiol, 60-61; asst med, Peter Bent Brigham Hosp, 61-63; from asst prof to prof, Univ NC, Chapel Hill, 63-74; prof med, Univ Calif, Los Angeles, 74-77; PROF MED, DARTMOUTH MED SCH, 77-; CHIEF CARDIOL, DARTMOUTH-HITCHCOCK MED CTR, 77- *Concurrent Pos:* Am Heart Asn res fel, 61-63; res grant, USPHS, 64-77; career develop award, 67-72; Lederle med fac award, 65-67; chief cardiol, Vet Admin Wadsworth Hosp Ctr, 74-77; mem, Merit Rev Bd Cardiovasc Studies, Vet Admin, chmn, 76-79. *Mem:* AAAS; Am Col Cardiol; Am Physiol Soc. *Res:* Cardiodynamics; influence of catecholamines on cardiac muscle function; contractile behavior of isolated myocytes. *Mailing Add:* Cardiol Sect Dartmouth-Hitchcock Med Ctr Hanover NH 03755

ROLF, CLYDE NORMAN, b Dayton, Ky, June 26, 37; c 2. HYPERTENSION, NEPHROLOGY. *Educ:* Univ Ky, AB, 63, MD, 67. *Prof Exp:* Pvt practice nephrol, 72-77; assoc group dir, 77-79, group dir, 79-81, SR MED SPECIALIST, MERRELL RES CTR, 81- *Concurrent Pos:* Fel med nephrol, Good Samaritan Hosp, Cincinnati, 72; asst clin prof med, Col Med, Univ Cincinnati, 75- *Mem:* Am Nephrol Soc; Int Nephrol Soc; Am Col Physicians; Am Soc Artificial Internal Organs; Am Soc Clin Pharmacol & Therapeut. *Res:* Development, conduct and analysis of clinical trials with investigational antihypertensive agents and other investigational drugs. *Mailing Add:* Merrell Res Ctr 2110 E Galbraith Rd Cincinnati OH 45215

ROLF, HOWARD LEROY, b Laverne, Okla, Nov 25, 28. MATHEMATICS. *Educ:* Okla Baptist Univ, BS, 51; Vanderbilt Univ, MA, 53, PhD(math), 56. *Prof Exp:* Instr math, Vanderbilt Univ, 54-56; asst prof, Baylor Univ, 56-57; assoc prof, Georgetown Col, 57-59; asst prof & dir comput cent, Vanderbilt Univ, 59-64; PROF MATH, BAYLOR UNIV, 64-, CHMN DEPT, 71- *Concurrent Pos:* Vis assoc, Calif Inst Technol, 67-68. *Mem:* Am Math Soc; Math Asn Am. *Res:* Lattice theory; abstract algebra. *Mailing Add:* Dept of Math Baylor Univ Waco TX 76703

ROLF, LESTER LEO, JR, b San Antonio, Tex, Nov 30, 40; m 64; c 3. PHARMACOLOGY, PHYSIOLOGY. *Educ:* St Mary's Univ, BA, 64; Tex A&M Univ, MS, 67, PhD(physiol), 69. *Prof Exp:* NIH fel, Col Med, Univ Fla, 69-71, from instr to asst prof pharmacol, 71-74; ASST PROF PHYSIOL SCI, OKLA STATE UNIV, 74- *Mem:* Am Physiol Soc; Sigma Xi; AAAS. *Res:* Formation and characteristics of pleural fluids in animal models; pulmonary disposition of drugs in large animals; synthesis of acrosin inhibitors of the benzamidine type; steroidogenesis (ovarian) in catfish exposed to water pollutants. *Mailing Add:* Dept of Physiol Sci Okla State Univ Stillwater OK 74074

ROLF, RICHARD L(AWRENCE), b Milwaukee, Wis, Nov 4, 35; m 61; c 1. STRUCTURAL MECHANICS, STRUCTURAL ENGINEERING. *Educ:* Marquette Univ, BS, 58; Univ Ill, Urbana, MS, 60. *Prof Exp:* Res asst civil eng, Univ Ill, Urbana, 58-60; res engr, Eng Design Div, Res Labs, 60-75, sr engr, 75-81, STAFF ENGR, ENG PROPERTIES & DESIGN DIV, ALCOA LABS, ALUMINUM CO AM, 81- *Honors & Awards:* J James R Croes Medal, Am Soc Civil Engrs, 66. *Mem:* Sigma Xi; Soc Automotive Engrs; Am Acad Mech; Am Soc Civil Engrs. *Res:* Analysis and testing of various structural members; development of design rules for aluminum and for brittle materials (ceramics); design and analysis of equipment used in smelting of aluminum. *Mailing Add:* Eng Properties & Design Div Alcoa Tech Ctr Alcoa Center PA 15069

ROLFE, GARY LAVELLE, b Paducah, Ky, Sept 5, 46; m 68. ECOLOGY, BIOLOGY. *Educ:* Univ Ill, BS, 68, MS, 69, PhD(ecol), 71. *Prof Exp:* Dir metals task force, 71-77, asst prof, 72-75, assoc prof forest ecol, 75-80, PROF FORESTRY & CHMN DEPT, UNIV ILL, 80- *Concurrent Pos:* Asst dir, Ill Agr Exp Sta, 76-80. *Mem:* Ecol Soc Am; Soil Sci Soc Am; Soc Am Foresters. *Res:* Nutrient cycling in forest ecosystems; water quality; trace contaminants in the environment. *Mailing Add:* 211 Mumford Univ of Ill Urbana IL 61801

ROLFE, JOHN, b London, Eng, Feb 15, 27; Can citizen; m 53; c 3. SOLID STATE PHYSICS. *Educ:* Univ London, BSc, 50, PhD(physics), 53. *Prof Exp:* Res physicist, A E I Res labs, Aldermaston, Eng, 53-55; fel, Radio & Elec Eng Div, 55-57, res officer solid state physics, 57-75, SR RES OFFICER, PHYSICS DIV, NAT RES COUN CAN, 75- *Mem:* Am Phys Soc; Can Asn Physicists. *Res:* Electrical and optical properties of insulating crystals, especially alkali halide crystals; color centers in alkali halide crystals. *Mailing Add:* 11 Appleford St Ottawa ON K1J 6V1 Can

ROLFE, STANLEY THEODORE, b Chicago, Ill, July 7, 34; m 56; c 3. CIVIL ENGINEERING. *Educ:* Univ Ill, Urbana, BS, 56, MS, 58, PhD(civil eng), 62. *Prof Exp:* Res assoc civil eng, Univ Ill, Urbana, 56-62; sect supvr & div chief, US Steel Appl Res Lab, 62-69; ROSS H FORNEY PROF CIVIL ENG, UNIV KANS, 69-, CHMN CIVIL ENG, 80- *Concurrent Pos:* Chmn, Metall Studies Panel, Nat Acad Sci, 68-71; chmn low cycle fatigue comt, Pressure Vessel Res Coun, 68-70. *Honors & Awards:* Sam Tour Award, Am Soc Testing & Mat, 71. *Mem:* Am Soc Civil Engrs; Am Soc Mech Engrs; Soc Exp Stress Anal; Am Soc Eng Educ; Am Soc Testing & Mat. *Res:* Fracture mechanics; failure analysis; fatigue and fracture of structural materials as related to design; experimental stress analysis. *Mailing Add:* Dept of Civil Eng Univ of Kans Lawrence KS 66044

ROLKE, ROGER WILLIAM, chemical engineering, see previous edition

ROLL, BARBARA HONEYMAN HEATH, b Portland, Ore, Apr 4, 10; m 77. PHYSICAL ANTHROPOLOGY. *Educ:* Smith Col, BA, 32. *Prof Exp:* Res assoc & exec dir, Constitution Lab, Col Physicians & Surgeons, NY, 48-53; instr phys anthrop, Monterey Peninsula Col, 66-74; RES ASSOC, DEPT ANTHROP, UNIV PA, 75- *Mem:* Fel AAAS; Am Asn Phys Anthrop; fel Am Anthrop Asn; Brit Soc Study Human Biol; Int Asn Human Biol. *Res:* Child development; somatotype methodology and interpretation of somatotype data. *Mailing Add:* 26030 Rotunda Dr Carmel CA 93923

ROLL, DAVID BYRON, b Miles City, Mont, Mar 16, 40; m 70; c 2. MEDICINAL CHEMISTRY. *Educ:* Univ Mont, BS, 62; Univ Wash, PhD(med chem), 66. *Prof Exp:* Res chemist, Pesticides Res Lab, Dept Health, Educ & Welfare, 66-67; asst prof med chem, 67-76, PROF MED CHEM, COL PHARM, UNIV UTAH, 76-, ASSOC DEAN ACAD AFFAIRS, 77- *Mem:* Am Pharmaceut Asn. *Res:* Nuclear magnetic resonance and its applications to stereochemical and biochemical problems; medicinal chemistry. *Mailing Add:* Col of Pharm Univ of Utah Salt Lake City UT 84112

ROLL, FREDERIC, b New York, NY, Sept 10, 21; m 50. CIVIL ENGINEERING. *Educ:* City Col New York, BCE, 44; Columbia Univ, MS, 49, PhD(civil eng), 57. *Hon Degrees:* MA, Univ Pa, 71. *Prof Exp:* Civil engr, W S Briggs, NY, 50; stress analyst, Chance Vought Aircraft Corp, Conn, 44; civil engr, Andrews & Clarke, NY, 44-45; asst civil eng, Columbia Univ, 45-46, instr, 46-50, assoc, 50-57; assoc prof, 57-67, prof civil eng, 67-80, FOUND PROF TRANSP, DEPT CIVIL ENG, TOWNE SCH CIVIL & MECH ENG, UNIV PA, 80- *Concurrent Pos:* NSF fel, Eng & Port, 63-64; grant, 66-; mem res staff, Cement & Concrete Asn, 70-71. *Mem:* Am Concrete Inst; Am Soc Civil Engrs; Am Soc Testing & Mat; Soc Exp Stress Anal. *Res:* Creep of plain concrete; shear and diagonal tension in reinforced concrete beams and slabs; structural model analysis; structural and materials testing; reinforced and prestressed concrete. *Mailing Add:* Towne Sch of Civil & Mech Eng Univ of Pa Philadelphia PA 19104

ROLL, JOHN DONALD, b Newport, Ky, June 25, 12. NUCLEAR PHYSICS. *Educ:* Loyola Univ, AB, 35; St Louis Univ, MS, 39; Fordham Univ, PhD(physics), 50. *Prof Exp:* Instr philos & speech, John Carroll Univ, 39-40; from instr to prof, 49-79, dir, Seismol Lab, 58-79, chmn dept, 52-70, EMER PROF PHYSICS, LOYOLA UNIV, CHICAGO, 79- *Honors & Awards:* Merit Award, Chicago Tech Soc Coun, 60. *Res:* Seismology. *Mailing Add:* Dept of Physics Loyola Univ 6525 Sheridan Rd Chicago IL 60626

ROLL, PETER GUY, b Detroit, Mich, Apr 13, 33; m 55; c 3. PHYSICS. *Educ:* Yale Univ, BS, 54, MS, 58, PhD(physics), 60. *Prof Exp:* Jr scientist nuclear reactor design, Westinghouse Atomic Power Div, 54-56; res asst physics, Yale Univ, 56-58, instr, 59-60; from instr to asst prof, Princeton Univ, 60-65; staff physicist, Comn Col Physics, Univ Mich, 65-66; ASSOC PROF PHYSICS, UNIV MINN, MINNEAPOLIS, 66-, SPEC ASST TO VPRES ACAD ADMIN, 71- *Mem:* AAAS; Am Asn Physics Teachers. *Res:* Low energy nuclear physics; gravity experiments; cosmic background radiation measurements; musical acoustics. *Mailing Add:* 217 Morrill Hall Univ Minn Minneapolis MN 55455

ROLLAND, WILLIAM WOODY, b Asheville, NC, June 8, 31; m 50; c 4. NUCLEAR PHYSICS. *Educ:* King Col, BA, 53; Duke Univ, PhD, 63. *Prof Exp:* Instr math, King Col, 55-56, assoc prof physics, 59-68; ASSOC PROF COMPUT SCI & DIR COMPUT CTR, ST ANDREW'S PRESBY COL, 68- *Mem:* Am Asn Physics Teachers. *Res:* Nuclear spectroscopy, particularly direct nuclear interactions; studies of variable stars, both eclipsing and intrinsic variables. *Mailing Add:* Comput Ctr St Andrews Presby Col Laurinberg NC 28352

ROLLASON, GRACE SAUNDERS, b New York, NY, Sept 14, 19; m 44; c 2. EMBRYOLOGY. *Educ:* Hunter Col, AB, 40; NY Univ, MS, 42, PhD(exp embryol), 48. *Prof Exp:* Asst, Harvard Univ, 44-45; assoc, Amherst Col, 46-47; res assoc, 47-56, from instr to asst prof, 56-73, ASSOC PROF ZOOL, UNIV MASS, AMHERST, 73- *Concurrent Pos:* Hunter Col scholar, Woods Hole Marine Biol Lab. *Mem:* AAAS. *Res:* Mammalian and amphibian embryology. *Mailing Add:* Dept of Zool Univ of Mass Amherst MA 01002

ROLLASON, HERBERT DUNCAN, b Beverly, Mass, Mar 20, 17; m 44; c 2. HISTOLOGY. *Educ:* Middlebury Col, AB, 39; Williams Col, AM, 41; Harvard Univ, MA, 43, PhD(biol), 49. *Prof Exp:* Instr anat, L I Col Med, 45-46; instr biol, Amherst Col, 46-48; from asst prof to assoc prof, 48-72, asst dean, 65-71, assoc dean, Col Arts & Sci, 72-73, PROF ZOOL, UNIV MASS, AMHERST, 72-, ASSOC CHMN DEPT, 76- *Mem:* AAAS; Am Soc Zool; Am Inst Biol Sci. *Res:* Kidney histology and cytology; compensatory hypertrophy; cellular ultrastructure. *Mailing Add:* Morrill Sci Ctr Univ of Mass Amherst MA 01002

ROLLE, F ROBERT, b Jamaica, NY, May 21, 39; m 74; c 1. ANALYTICAL CHEMISTRY. *Educ:* Pratt Inst, BS, 61; Purdue Univ, MS, 65, PhD(phys org chem), 66. *Prof Exp:* Res fel kinetics, Univ London, 66-67; res chemist, 67-68, group leader, 68-71, asst mgr, 71-75, mgr anal chem, 75-79, asst dir cent lab, 79-80, ASST DIR TECH & ADV SERV, JOHNSON & JOHNSON, 80- *Honors & Awards:* P B Hoffman Res Scientist Award, Johnson & Johnson, 73. *Mem:* The Chem Soc; Am Chem Soc. *Res:* Talc analysis in bulk and airborn state; analytical aspects of industrial hygiene. *Mailing Add:* Johnson & Johnson 501 George St New Brunswick NJ 08903

ROLLEFSON, RAGNAR, b Chicago, Ill, Aug 23, 06; m 36; c 4. PHYSICS. *Educ:* Univ Wis, BA, 26, MA, 27, PhD(physics), 30. *Prof Exp:* Asst, physics 27-30, from instr to assoc prof, 30-46, chmn dept, 47-51, 52-56 & 57-61, prof, 46-76, EMER PROF PHYSICS, UNIV WIS-MADISON, 76- *Concurrent Pos:* Mem staff, Radiation Lab, Mass Inst Technol, 42-46; chief scientist, Naval Res Lab, Boston, Mass, 46; mem staff, Proj Charles, Mass Inst Technol, 51, Lincoln Lab, 51-52; tech capabilities panel, Off Defense Mobilization, 54-55; chief scientist, US Army, 56-57; actg dir lab, Midwestern Univs Res Asn, 57-60; dir int sci affairs, Dept State, Washington, DC, 62-64. *Mem:* Fel Am Phys Soc. *Res:* Continuous spectrum of mercury vapor; radar; infrared dispersion of gases. *Mailing Add:* Dept of Physics Univ of Wis Madison WI 53706

ROLLEFSON, ROBERT JOHN, b Madison, Wis, Sept 9, 41; m 65; c 2. LOW TEMPERATURE PHYSICS, SURFACE PHYSICS. *Educ:* Univ Wis, BA, 63; Cornell Univ, PhD(physics), 70. *Prof Exp:* Res assoc physics, Univ Wash, 70-73; asst prof physics, 73-80, ASSOC PROF PHYSICS, WESLEYAN UNIV, 80- *Mem:* Am Phys Soc. *Res:* Properties of absorbed monolayer gas films; use of nuclear magnetic resonance spectroscopy to study the phases existing at various densities and dynamics of phase changes; investigations of the effects of surface structure on film properties. *Mailing Add:* Dept of Physics Wesleyan Univ Middletown CT 06457

ROLLER, DUANE HENRY DUBOSE, b Eagle Pass, Tex, Mar 14, 20; m 42; c 1. HISTORY OF SCIENCE. *Educ:* Columbia Univ, AB, 41; Purdue Univ, MS, 49; Harvard Univ, PhD(hist sci), 54. *Prof Exp:* Asst physics, Purdue Univ, 46-49; vis fel gen educ, Harvard Univ, 49-50, teaching fel, 51-54; asst prof hist sci & cur DeGolyer Collection, 54-58, assoc prof hist sci, 58-63, asst dir, Univ Okla Libr, 71-79, CUR HIST SCI COLLECTIONS, UNIV OF OKLA LIBR, 59-, MCCASLAND PROF, UNIV OKLA, 63-, DAVID ROSS BOYD PROF, 81- *Concurrent Pos:* Vis prof, Univ Colo, 60 & Univ Ore, 66; NSF sr fel, 61-62; mem, Nat Comt Hist & Philos Sci, 60-61, 63-68, chmn, 64-65; res fel, Am Sch Classical Studies, 69-70 & 77-78; Sigma Xi nat lectr, 77-78 & 78-82; NSF Chautauqua lectr, 78-79. *Mem:* Fel AAAS; Hist Sci Soc; cor mem Int Acad Hist Sci; Sigma Xi. *Res:* Bibliography; history of electricity and magnetism; history of Greek and Renaissance science. *Mailing Add:* Hist Sci Collections Univ Okla 401 W Brooks Norman OK 73019

ROLLER, HERBERT ALFRED, b Magdeburg, Ger, Aug 2, 27; m 57. ZOOLOGY, BIOLOGICAL CHEMISTRY. *Educ:* Georg August Univ, Gottingen, PhD(zool), 62. *Prof Exp:* Proj assoc zool, Univ Wis-Madison, 62-65, asst prof pharmacol, 65-66, res assoc zool, 66-67, assoc prof, 67-68; prof biol, 68-77, head invert res, Inst Life Sci, 68-73, alumni prof, 80-85, DIR INST DEVELOP BIOL, TEX A&M UNIV, 73-, PROF BIOCHEM & BIOPHYS, 74-, DISTINGUISHED PROF BIOL, 77- *Concurrent Pos:* Vpres & dir res, Zoecon Corp, Calif, 68-72, sci adv, 72-; mem adv panel regulatory biol, NSF, 69-72; res dir, Int Ctr Insect Physiol & Ecol, Nairobi, Kenya, 70-75; consult, Syntex Res Div, Calif, 67-68. *Mem:* AAAS; Am Soc Zool; Entom Soc Am; Soc Develop Biol; Sigma Xi. *Res:* Physiology and biochemistry of morphogenetic hormone systems in insects; development of metamerism in insects; biology and chemistry of pheromonesystems in pyralid moths. *Mailing Add:* Tex A&M Univ Inst of Develop Biol College Station TX 77843

ROLLER, MICHAEL HARRIS, b Soldier, Kans, Apr 20, 22; m 44; c 3. ANIMAL PHYSIOLOGY. *Educ:* Kans State Univ, BS & DVM, 50, PhD(physiol), 66; cert biophys, Baylor Univ, 63. *Prof Exp:* Private practice, 50-61; Nat Defense Educ Act fel, 61-64; instr surg & med, Col Vet Med, Kans State Univ, 64; USPHS res fel, 64-65; instr physiol, Col Vet Med, Kans State Univ, 65-66; assoc prof, 66-73, prof entom & zool, 73-79, PROF VET SCI, SDAK STATE UNIV, 79- *Concurrent Pos:* Moorman res grant zool, 68-69. *Mem:* Am Vet Med Asn; Sigma Xi. *Res:* Ammonia intoxication in cattle, sheep and rabbits, especially blood and tissue changes and reproductive performance. *Mailing Add:* 1011 Forest St Brookings SD 57006

ROLLER, PAUL S, b New York, NY, Apr 2, 02; m 29; c 3. CHEMISTRY. *Educ:* Polytech Inst Brooklyn, BS, 23; Columbia Univ, AM, 25, PhD(chem), 29. *Prof Exp:* Chemist & chem engr, Res Div, Combustion Utilities Corp, 23-24; asst chem, Columbia Univ, 24-28; from asst chemist to sr chemist, Non-metallic Minerals Exp Sta, US Bur Mines, 28-47, sr chemist res & develop, 47-49; tech dir, Gen Hydro Corp, 49-58; TECH DIR, LIDQUIDS PROCESS CO, 58- *Concurrent Pos:* Abstr, Chem Abstracts, 33-72. *Mem:* Fel AAAS; Am Chem Soc; Water Pollution Control Fedn; Am Water Works Asn. *Res:* Law of size distribution; particle size analyzer; alumina from clay; plasticity of dispersions; theory of acidimetry; origin of the solar system and related properties; water treatment; recovery of reuse and pure water. *Mailing Add:* 1440 N St NW No 1011 Washington DC 20005

ROLLER, PETER PAUL, b Debrecen, Hungary, Nov 16, 40; US citizen; m 67; c 3. ORGANIC CHEMISTRY. *Educ:* Univ BC, BSc, 63, MSc, 65; Stanford Univ, PhD(org chem), 69. *Prof Exp:* NIH fel, Univ Hawaii, 70 & Univ Va, 71-72; RES CHEMIST, NAT CANCER INST, NAT INSTS HEALTH, 72- *Mem:* Am Chem Soc; Am Soc Mass Spectrometry. *Res:* Organic mass spectrometry of natural products, biochemical applications; mass spectrometry instrumentation; molecular biochemistry of carcinogenesis; organics and pharmaceuticals from the ocean. *Mailing Add:* Nat Cancer Inst Nat Inst Health Bldg 37 Rm 1E-22 Bethesda MD 20205

ROLLER, WARREN L(EON), b Logansport, Ind, May 31, 29; m 51; c 5. AGRICULTURAL ENGINEERING. *Educ:* Purdue Univ, BS, 51, MS, 55, PhD(agr eng), 61. *Prof Exp:* Res fel agr eng, Purdue Univ, 53-54; jr agr engr, Agr Res Serv, USDA, 54-55; from instr to asst prof agr eng, Ohio Agr Exp Sta, 55-63, assoc prof, Ohio Agr Res & Develop Ctr, 63-68, assoc chmn dept, 68-81, PROF AGR ENG, OHIO AGR RES & DEVELOP, 68-, CHMN DEPT, 81- *Concurrent Pos:* Nat Acad Sci-Nat Res Coun sr vis scientist, US Army Res Inst Environ Med, 67- *Honors & Awards:* Am Soc Agr Engrs Jour Award, 64, 70 & 78, Nat Award, 75. *Mem:* Sigma Xi; Am Soc Agr Engrs. *Res:* Automatic feeding systems for animal production; environmental control for animal production; effect of thermal environment upon animal reproduction; energy efficiencies in agricultural production systems; biomass production for fuel. *Mailing Add:* 873 Ashwood Dr Wooster OH 44691

ROLLESTON, FRANCIS STOPFORD, b Montreal, Que, June 1, 40; m 64; c 3. BIOCHEMISTRY. *Educ:* Queen's Univ, Ont, BSc, 62; Oxford Univ, DPhil(biochem), 66. *Prof Exp:* Fel physiol, Univ Chicago, 66-67, res assoc biochem, 67-68; asst prof, Banting & Best Dept Med Res, Univ Toronto, 68-75; asst dir grants prog, 75-77, DIR SPEC PROG, MED RES COUN CAN, 77- *Concurrent Pos:* Med Res Coun Can oper grants, 68-75. *Mem:* Can Biochem Soc. *Res:* Functional differences between membrane bound and free ribosomes; control of intermediary metabolism. *Mailing Add:* Spec Prog Med Res Coun of Can Ottawa ON K1A 0W9 Can

ROLLETSCHEK, HEINRICH FRANZ, b Gmunden, Austria, Mar 9, 54. RECURSIVE FUNCTION THEORY. *Educ:* Johannes Kepler Univ, dipl ing, 77, PhD(tech math), 81. *Prof Exp:* Vis asst prof, Rensselaer Polytech Inst, 80-81; VIS ASST PROF COMPUT SCI, UNIV DEL, 81- *Mem:* Asn Comput Mach. *Res:* Recursive function theory, especially variants of the notoon of creative set and other properties of recursively enumerable sets; polynomial time complexity. *Mailing Add:* Dept Comput & Info Sci Univ Del 103 Smith Hall Newark DE 19711

ROLLINGER, CHARLES N(ICHOLAS), b Chicago Heights, Ill, Aug 5, 34; m 57; c 5. COMPUTER SCIENCE, ENGINEERING MANAGEMENT. *Educ:* Univ Detroit, BME, 57; Northwestern Univ, MS, 59, PhD(mech eng), 61. *Prof Exp:* Res engr, Roy C Ingersoll Res Ctr, Borg-Warner Corp, 60-61; from instr to asst prof math, US Air Force Acad, 61-63; res engr, Frank J Seiler Res Lab, Off Aerospace Res, US Air Force, 64; sr res engr, Res Labs, Whirlpool Corp, 64-66, corp mgr eng & sci comput, 66-68, dir comput sci & technol, 68-72, dir eng res, 72-74; DIR COMPUT SERV, BERRIEN COUNTY GOVT, 75- *Concurrent Pos:* Lectr, Univ Denver, 64; lectr, Univ Notre Dame, 66, adj asst prof mgt, 78-; sr lectr, Mich State Univ, 64-66; consult, R C Ingersoll Res Ctr, Borg-Warner Corp, 61-64; adj assoc prof indust eng, Univ Mich, 70-71. *Mem:* Opers Res Soc Am; Inst Mgt Sci; Am Soc Mech Engrs; Data Processing Mgt Asn. *Res:* Information systems design; management science; decision support systems. *Mailing Add:* Berrien County Courthouse 811 Port St St Joseph MI 49085

ROLLINO, JOHN A, b Brooklyn, NY, Oct 11, 44; m 70; c 1. PHYSICAL CHEMISTRY. *Educ:* St Francis Col, NY, BS, 66; Mass Inst Technol, PhD(chem), 69. *Prof Exp:* ASST PROF CHEM & PHYSICS, ST FRANCIS COL, NY, 69- *Mem:* Am Chem Soc; Am Inst Physics. *Res:* Low temperature thermodynamics; solid state charge transfer complexes. *Mailing Add:* 8424 Doran Ave Glen Dale NY 11385

ROLLINS, EARL ARTHUR, b Portland, Ore, Mar 6, 40; m 61; c 2. DEVELOPMENTAL BIOLOGY. *Educ:* Willamette Univ, BS, 61; Purdue Univ, MS, 64; State Univ NY Buffalo, PhD(develop biol), 67. *Prof Exp:* Fel biochem, C F Kettering Res Lab, 66-67; asst prof biol sci, State Univ NY Albany, 67-72; assoc prof biol, Sangamon State Univ, 72-80; MEM FAC, DEPT BIOL, AQUINAS COL, 80- *Concurrent Pos:* State of NY Res Found fac fel, 68, grant-in-aid, 68-69; Am Cancer Soc res grant, 68-70; adj assoc prof, Sch Med, Southern Ill Univ, 73- *Mem:* AAAS; Am Soc Cell Biol; Soc Develop Biol; Int Soc Develop Biol; NY Acad Sci. *Res:* Chemical and physical properties of embryonic chromatin; structure of chromasomes. *Mailing Add:* Dept of Biol Aquinas Col Grand Rapids MI 49506

ROLLINS, GILBERT HORACE, b Wellington, Va, June 22, 19; m 44; c 3. DAIRY HUSBANDRY. *Educ:* Va Polytech Inst, BS, 43, MS, 48; Univ Ill, PhD(dairy sci), 58. *Prof Exp:* Asst prof, 48-51, ASSOC PROF ANIMAL & DAIRY SCI & ASSOC DAIRY HUSBANDMAN, AGR EXP STA, AUBURN UNIV, 54- *Mem:* Am Dairy Sci Asn. *Res:* Dairy cattle nutrition. *Mailing Add:* Dept of Dairy Sci Auburn Univ Auburn AL 36830

ROLLINS, HAROLD BERT, b Hamilton, NY, Feb 1, 39; m 60; c 1. INVERTEBRATE PALEONTOLOGY, PALEOECOLOGY. *Educ:* Colgate Univ, BA, 60; Univ Wis-Madison, MA, 63; Columbia Univ, PhD(geol, invert paleont), 67. *Prof Exp:* NSF-Great Lakes Col Asn teaching intern earth sci & biol, Antioch Col, 67-68, asst prof, 68-69; asst prof, 69-73, ASSOC PROF EARTH SCI, UNIV PITTSBURGH, 73- *Concurrent Pos:* Res assoc, Am Mus Natural Hist, NY & Carnegie Mus, Pa; mem Paleont Res Inst. *Mem:* Paleont Soc; Soc Syst Zool; Geol Soc Am; Brit Paleont Asn. *Res:* Phylogeny and functional morphology of Paleozoic Gastropoda; Devonian paleontology and stratigraphy; Paleozoic Monoplacophora; Pennsylvanian peleoecology. *Mailing Add:* Dept of Earth & Planetary Sci Univ of Pittsburgh Pittsburgh PA 15260

ROLLINS, HOWARD A, JR, b Dover, NH, July 12, 27; m 52; c 4. HORTICULTURE. *Educ:* Univ Conn, BS, 50; Univ NH, MS, 51; Ohio State Univ, PhD, 54. *Prof Exp:* Assoc prof hort, Winchester Fruit Res Lab, Va Polytech Inst & State Univ, 54-56, prof, 56-67, prof & head dept, 67-70; PROF HORT & CHMN DEPT, OHIO STATE UNIV & OHIO AGR RES & DEVELOP CTR, 70- *Mem:* Am Soc Hort Sci. *Res:* Winter hardiness of apple; apple production, harvest efficiency and tree fruit culture. *Mailing Add:* Dept of Hort Ohio State Univ Columbus OH 43210

ROLLINS, ORVILLE WOODROW, b Sybial, WVa, Dec 4, 23; m 47; c 1. INORGANIC CHEMISTRY, ANALYTICAL CHEMISTRY. *Educ:* Univ WVa, MS, 50; Georgetown Univ, PhD(chem), 66. *Prof Exp:* Instr & Asst prof chem, Moravian Col for Men, 49-51; from asst prof to assoc prof, 51-65, PROF CHEM, US NAVAL ACAD, 65- *Concurrent Pos:* Consult, Chem Div, Air Force Off Sci Res. *Mem:* Am Chem Soc. *Res:* Isopoly and heteropoly molybdates and tungstates; analytical methods. *Mailing Add:* Dept of Chem US Naval Acad Annapolis MD 21402

ROLLINS, REED CLARK, b Lyman, Wyo, Dec 7, 11; m 39; c 2. BOTANY. *Educ:* Univ Wyo, AB, 33; State Col Wash, SM, 36; Harvard Univ, PhD(bot), 41. *Prof Exp:* From instr to assoc prof biol, Stanford Univ, 40-48; assoc prof bot, 48-54, chmn inst res plant morphol, 55-66, inst plant sci, 65-69, dir Gray Herbarium, 48-78, supvr Bussey Inst, 67-78, chmn admin comt, Farlow Libr & Herbarium, 74-78, ASA GRAY PROF SYST BOT, HARVARD UNIV, 54- *Concurrent Pos:* Asst cur, Dudley Herbarium, Stanford Univ, 40-41, cur, 41-48; assoc geneticist, Guayule Res Proj, US Dept Agr, 43-45, geneticist, Div Rubber Plant Invests, 47-48; prin geneticist, Stanford Res Inst, 46-47; ed-in-chief, Rhodora, 50-61; pres, Orgn Trop Studies, Inc, 64-65. *Honors & Awards:* Congress Medal, XII Int Bot Cong, Leningrad, 75. *Mem:* Nat Acad Sci; Am Acad Arts & Sci; Am Soc Nat (vpres, 60, pres, 66); Genetics Soc Am; Int Asn Plant Taxon (vpres, 50-54, pres, 54-59). *Res:* Cytology and systematics of the Cruciferae; cytogenetics of the guayule rubber plant and related species of Parthenium. *Mailing Add:* Gray Herbarium Harvard Univ 22 Divinity Ave Cambridge MA 02138

ROLLINS, ROGER WILLIAM, b Columbia City, Ind, Jan 23, 39; m 61; c 2. EXPERIMENTAL SOLID STATE PHYSICS, LOW TEMPERATURE PHYSICS. *Educ:* Purdue Univ, BS, 61; Cornell Univ, PhD(appl physics), 67. *Prof Exp:* From asst prof to assoc prof, 66-78, PROF PHYSICS, OHIO UNIV, 78- *Concurrent Pos:* Vis scientist, Inst Exp Nuclear Physics, Univ Karlsruhe, Germany, 72-73. *Mem:* AAAS; Am Phys Soc; Am Asn Physics Teachers. *Res:* Superconductivity-hysteresis effects in type II superconductors, alternating current losses, bulk and surface effects; specific heat and magnetic properties of superconductors. *Mailing Add:* Dept of Physics Ohio Univ Athens OH 45701

ROLLINS, RONALD ROY, b Tooele, Utah, Oct 2, 30; m 57; c 5. PHYSICAL CHEMISTRY, EXPLOSIVES. *Educ:* Univ Utah, BS, 59, PhD(metall), 62. *Prof Exp:* Staff mem direct energy conversion, Vallecitos Atomic Lab, Gen Elec Co, Calif, 62-64; asst prof theory high explosives, Univ Mo-Rolla, 64-69, assoc prof, 69-79; PROF EXPLOSIVES/MINING, WVA UNIV, 79-, CHMN MINERAL PROCESSING ENG DEPT, 81- *Concurrent Pos:* Univ Mo-Rolla vis lectr, 65-, sr investr, Rock Mech & Explosives Res Ctr, 64-79. *Mem:* AAAS; Am Inst Mining, Metall & Petrol Engrs; Am Chem Soc; Am Soc Eng Educ; Am Nuclear Soc. *Res:* Hot wire initiation of secondary explosives; factors that sensitize primary and secondary explosives; factors plowshare program and activities; theory of high explosives; shaped charge explosive effects. *Mailing Add:* COMER/White Hall WVa Univ Morgantown WV 26506

ROLLINS, WADE CUTHBERT, b Jersey City, NJ, Feb 12, 12; m 41; c 1. BIOLOGY. *Educ:* Univ Calif, AB, 33, MA, 35, PhD(genetics), 48. *Prof Exp:* Asst, 45-48, instr & jr animal husbandryman, 48-50, asst prof & asst animal husbandryman, 50-56, assoc prof & assoc animal husbandryman, 56-64, prof & geneticist, 64-78, EMER PROF ANIMAL SCI, UNIV CALIF, DAVIS, 78- *Mem:* Biomet Soc; Am Soc Animal Sci. *Res:* Application of genetics to livestock breeding; population genetics. *Mailing Add:* 442 University Ave Davis CA 95616

ROLLMAN, WALTER F(UHRMANN), b Des Moines, Iowa, Feb 7, 13; m 46; c 3. CHEMICAL ENGINEERING. *Educ:* Iowa State Col, BS, 34, MS, 35, PhD(chem eng), 38. *Prof Exp:* Asst, Exp Sta, Univ Iowa, 34-38; res engr, Esso Res & Eng Co, 38-63, eng assoc, 63-78; PRES, TECH-SEARCH, 78- *Mem:* Am Chem Soc; Am Inst Chem Engrs. *Res:* Petroleum refining; petroleum in the steel industry; information retrieval; engineering. *Mailing Add:* 37 Byron Rd Short Hills NJ 07078

ROLLMANN, LOUIS DEANE, b Kingman, Kans, Apr 26, 39; m 67; c 3. INORGANIC CHEMISTRY, PETROLEUM. *Educ:* Univ Kans, BA, 60, PhD(inorg chem), 67. *Prof Exp:* NIH fel phys chem, Calif Inst Technol, 67-68; res chemist, 68-70, sr res chemist, 70-75, assoc chem & prog leader, 75-77, res assoc, 77-80, GROUP MGR, MOBIL RES & DEVELOP CORP, 80- *Mem:* AAAS; Am Chem Soc; Am Soc Test & Mat. *Res:* Electrochemistry and electron spin resonance; zeolite synthesis; catalysis; hydrodesulfurization; metals in petroleum; petroleum processing; petroleum research management. *Mailing Add:* 3 Dorann Ave Princeton NJ 08540

ROLLO, FRANK DAVID, b Endicott, NY, Apr 15, 39; m 60; c 1. PHYSICS, MEDICINE. *Educ:* Harpur Col, BS, 59; Univ Miami, MSc, 65; Johns Hopkins Univ, PhD(physics), 68; State Univ NY Upstate Med Ctr, MD, 72; Am Bd Nuclear Med, dipl, 74. *Prof Exp:* Res physicist, Dept Appl Res, Int Bus Mach Corp, NY, 59-60; assoc prof math & physics, Dept Eng Physics, Broome Tech Community Col, 60-64; radiol consult, Sinai Hosp, Greater Baltimore Med Ctr & Md Gen Hosp, Baltimore, 65-68; res assoc med physics & nuclear med, State Univ NY Upstate Med Ctr, 68-72; resident radiol & nuclear med, Med Ctr, Univ Calif, San Francisco, 72-74, asst prof med & radiol, 74-77; ASSOC PROF RADIOL & DIR NUCLEAR MED, UNIV HOSP, VANDERBILT UNIV, 77- *Concurrent Pos:* Sci lectr, Radiol Health Ctr, Rockville, Md, 66-68; res consult radiol, Duke Univ, 68-72; res consult appl physics lab, Johns Hopkins Univ, 68-; res consult, Univ Tex, Galveston, 73-; assoc dir nuclear med, Vet Admin Hosp, San Francisco, 74-77 & Vet Admin Hosp, Nashville, 77- *Honors & Awards:* Achievement Award, Am Math Soc, 63; Bronze Medal, Soc Nuclear Med, 75. *Mem:* Asn Physicists in Med; Am Math Soc; Soc Nuclear Med; Asn Univ Radiologists; Radiol Soc NAm. *Res:* Calorimetry of Grenz rays; pulse height selection in scintigraphic imaging systems; frequency response analysis of imaging systems; determination of organ volumes with imaging systems; depth correction in organ imaging; thyroid uptake methodology; radionuclide evaluation of renal and cardiac function. *Mailing Add:* Dept Radiology Sci Vanderbuilt Univ Med Nashville TN 37232

ROLLO, IAN MCINTOSH, b Aberdeen, Scotland, May 28, 26; m 49; c 1. PHARMACOLOGY, MICROBIOLOGY. *Educ:* Aberdeen Univ, BSc, 45; Univ Man, PhD(pharmacol), 68. *Prof Exp:* Exp officer chem, Ministry of Food, Brit Civil Serv, 46-48; res asst chemother, Sch Trop Med, Univ Liverpool, 48-49; res scientist, Wellcome Labs Trop Med, London, 49-58; res scientist, Distillers Co, Ltd, 58-61; PROF PHARMACOL, FAC MED, UNIV MAN, 61- *Mem:* Am Soc Pharmacol & Exp Therapeut; Can Soc Microbiol; Pharmacol Soc Can; Brit Pharmacol Soc; Am Soc Trop Med & Hyg. *Res:* Chemotherapy of protozoal and bacterial infections; drug resistance and drug potentiation; relation between physicochemical properties of drugs and their physiological disposition; secretion of drugs by the renal tubule and the choroid plexus. *Mailing Add:* Dept of Pharmacol & Therapeut Univ of Man Fac of Med Winnipeg MB B3E 0W3 Can

ROLLOSSON, GEORGE WILLIAM, b Lake Charles, La, Oct 13, 23; m 58; c 2. PHYSICS. *Educ:* Univ Southwestern La, BS, 45; Mass Inst Technol, MS, 47; Univ NMex, PhD(physics), 52. *Prof Exp:* Asst prof physics, Univ Southwestern La, 47-48; staff mem physics instrumentation, Sandia Corp, NMex, 51-55, div supvr instrumentation, 55-65; group head, Field Exp Dept, Stanford Res Inst, 65-66, sr res engr, 67-69; dean sci & math, 74-78, dean letters & sci, 78-81, PROF PHYSICS, MENLO COL, 69-, CHMN, DEPT SCI & ENG, 71-, DEAN SCI & MATH, 74- *Concurrent Pos:* Lectr, Univ NMex, 60, part-time prof, 61; consult, Thomas Bede Found, 70- *Mem:* Am Asn Physics Teachers. *Res:* Instrumentation; field experimentation; computers in education. *Mailing Add:* Dept Sci Menlo Col Menlo Park CA 94025

ROLLWITZ, WILLIAM LLOYD, b Dooley, Mont, Apr 28, 22; m 43; c 2. MAGNETIC RESONANCE, ELECTRONIC INSTRUMENTATION. *Educ:* Mass Inst Technol, SB, 50, SM, 52. *Prof Exp:* Res engr, Philco Corp, 49-52; sr res physicist, 52-59, mgr electronic instrumentation, 60-70, staff scientist, 70-72, INST SCIENTIST, SOUTHWEST RES INST, 72- *Mem:* Sigma Xi; Instrument Soc Am; Inst Elec & Electronics Eng. *Res:* Biomedical electronics; nuclear magnetic, electron paramagnetic and nuclear quadrupole resonance; transistor electronics; quality control instrumentation; nondestructive testing with magnetobsorption; resonance detection of hidden explosives; nuclear magnetic resonance and electron magnetic resonance in live animals. *Mailing Add:* 213 Halbart Dr San Antonio TX 78213

ROLNICK, WILLIAM BARNETT, b Brooklyn, NY, Aug 20, 36; m 62; c 2. PHYSICS. *Educ:* Brooklyn Col, BS, 56; Columbia Univ, AM, 60, PhD(physics), 63. *Prof Exp:* Asst prof physics, US Merchant Marine Acad, 63-64; res assoc, Case Inst Technol, 64-66; from asst prof to assoc prof, 66-80, PROF PHYSICS, WAYNE STATE UNIV, 80- *Mem:* Am Phys Soc. *Res:* Elementary particle theory; scattering theory; electromagnetic theory; quantum coherence and particle beams; quantum electrodynamics; tachyons. *Mailing Add:* Dept of Physics Wayne State Univ Detroit MI 48202

ROLOFSON, GEORGE LAWRENCE, b Lincoln, Nebr, July 16, 38. TOXICOLOGY, ENTOMOLOGY. *Educ:* Univ Nebr, BSc, 61, MSc, 64; Va Polytech Inst, PhD(entom & toxicol), 68. *Prof Exp:* Staff specialist insecticide develop, Ciba-Geigy Corp, 68-70, group leader plant protectants, 70-72, toxicologist, 72-75, sr toxicologist, 75-78, mgr toxicol, 78-79; CONSULT TOXICOL & REGULATORY AFFAIRS, 79- *Mem:* Entom Soc Am. *Res:* Toxicology required for Federal Insecticide, Fungicide and Rodenticide Act and Toxic Substance Control Act. *Mailing Add:* 5119-A Lawndale Dr Greensboro NC 27405

ROLSTON, CHARLES HOPKINS, b Harrisonburg, Va, July 25, 27; m 53; c 3. INDUSTRIAL ORGANIC CHEMISTRY. *Educ:* Hampden-Sydney Col, BS, 48; Univ Md, MS, 53. *Prof Exp:* Res org chemist, Westvaco Chlorine-Alkali Div, Food Mach & Chem Corp, 52-54; res chem, Eastern Lab, Gibbstown, 56-72, sr res chemist, Exp Sta, 72-81, SR RES CHEMIST, JACKSON LAB, E I DU PONT DE NEMOURS & CO, INC, 81- *Mem:* Am Chem Soc; AAAS; Sigma Xi. *Res:* Synthetic organic chemistry; developmental research on organic intermediates; application of catalytic processes. *Mailing Add:* Jackson Lab E I du Pont de Nemours & Co Inc Deepwater NJ 08023

ROLSTON, DENNIS EUGENE, b Burke, SDak, June 20, 43; m 69; c 1. SOIL PHYSICS. *Educ:* SDak State Univ, BS, 65; Iowa State Univ, MS, 67; Univ Calif, Davis, PhD(soils), 70. *Prof Exp:* Lab technician, 68-70, asst prof soils, 70-77, assoc prof, 77-81, PROF SOILS & ASSOC DEAN, UNIV CALIF, DAVIS, 81- *Mem:* Am Soc Agron; Soil Sci Soc Am; Indian Soc Agron; Indian Soil Sci Soc. *Res:* Water movement in soils; diffusion and displacement of ions in soil; denitrification; drip irrigation. *Mailing Add:* Dept of Land Air & Water Univ of Calif Davis CA 95616

ROLSTON, LAWRENCE H, b Parkersburg, WVa, Apr 14, 22; m 41; c 4. ENTOMOLOGY. *Educ:* Marietta Col, AB, 49; Ohio State Univ, MS, 50, PhD, 55. *Prof Exp:* Jr entomologist & cur, Entom Mus, Univ Ark, 52-55; asst prof entom, Exp Sta, Ohio State Univ, 55-58; from assoc prof to prof, Univ Ark, 58-66, mem exp sta, 58-66; entom specialist, Tex A&M Univ, 66-68; PROF ENTOM, LA STATE UNIV, BATON ROUGE, 68- *Res:* Truck insects; agricultural entomology; taxonomy of pentatomidae. *Mailing Add:* Dept Entom Life Sci Bldg La State Univ Baton Rouge LA 70803

ROLWING, RAYMOND H, b Toledo, Ohio, Mar 22, 31; m 56; c 4. MATHEMATICS. *Educ:* Christian Bros Col, BS, 55; Univ Notre Dame, MS, 58; Univ Cincinnati, PhD(math), 63. RPXInstr math, Christian Bros Col, Tenn, 58-60; from instr to asst prof, 58-70, asst dean, McMicken Col Arts & Sci, 68-71, ASSOC PROF MATH, UNIV CINCINNATI, 70- *Concurrent Pos:* Dir acad year in-serv summer inst sec teachers math & sci, NSF, 65-73; dir leadership develop proj, NSF, 73-75. *Mem:* Am Math Soc; Math Asn Am; Nat Coun Teachers Math. *Res:* Ordinary differential equations; existence and uniqueness theorems; quadratic nonlinear integral equations; calculus of variations; isoperimetric problems; econometrics; learning theories in mathematics; history of mathematics. *Mailing Add:* Dept of Math Sci Univ of Cincinnati Cincinnati OH 45221

ROM, ROY CURT, b Milwaukee, Wis, Jan 29, 22; m 50; c 4. HORTICULTURE, POMOLOGY. *Educ:* Univ Wis-Madison, BS, 48, PhD(hort soils), 58. *Prof Exp:* Asst hort, Univ Wis-Madison, 54-58; PROF HORT, UNIV ARK, FAYETTEVILLE, 58- *Concurrent Pos:* Consult, Corp Farms, 70- & USAID prog; vis scientist, Nat Acad Sci, Poland & Czech, 75; sabbatical study, France, 79. *Mem:* Am Pomol Soc (secy, 80); Int Dwarf Fruit Tree Asn; fel Am Soc Hort Sci. *Res:* Nutrition, physiology, pruning and cultural practices in fruit production; weed control; breeding of apples and peaches; rootstock growth and development. *Mailing Add:* Dept of Hort Univ of Ark Fayetteville AR 72701

ROMACK, FRANK ELDON, b Jennings, Okla, Dec 26, 24; m 44; c 4. CARDIOVASCULAR DISEASES, ANIMAL PHYSIOLOGY. *Educ:* Univ Mo, BS, 51, MS, 61, PhD, 63. *Prof Exp:* Asst animal husb, Univ Mo, 59-61, from instr to asst prof vet anat, 60-65; asst prof, 65-67, ASSOC PROF VET BIOSCI & VET PROGS IN AGR, COL VET MED, UNIV ILL, URBANA, 67- *Concurrent Pos:* US Atomic Energy Comn contract, 65- *Mem:* Am Asn Vet Anat; World Asn Vet Anat; Am Asn Anat; Am Soc Animal Sci; Soc Study Reproduction. *Res:* Endocrine metabolism and function; surgical anesthesia; circulatory dysfunction and tissue culture systems; atherosclerosis. *Mailing Add:* RR 2 Box 234 St Joseph IL 61873

ROMAGNOLI, ROBERT JOSEPH, b Chicago, Ill, Aug 16, 31. ELECTROMAGNETICS. *Educ:* Ill Inst Technol, BS, 53, MS, 54, PhD(physics), 57. *Prof Exp:* Instr physics, Ill Inst Technol, 57-59; lectr, El Camino Col, 59-60; from asst prof to assoc prof, 60-72, PROF PHYSICS, CALIF STATE UNIV, NORTHRIDGE, 72- *Mem:* Am Phys Soc; Am Asn Physics Teachers. *Res:* Electromagnetic radiation; optical propagation; photovoltaic devices; electron optics; magneto-optics; nonlinear magneto-optics. *Mailing Add:* Dept of Physics & Astron Calif State Univ Northridge CA 91330

ROMAIN, CHARLES B, organic chemistry, deceased

ROMAN, ANN, b Tampa, Fla, Sept 8, 45; m 74; c 1. VIROLOGY, MOLECULAR GENETICS. *Educ:* Reed Col, BA, 67; Univ Calif, San Diego, PhD(biol), 73. *Prof Exp:* Fel immunol, Ore Health Sci Ctr, 73-75; ASST PROF MICROBIOL & IMMUNOL, SCH MED, IND UNIV, 75- *Concurrent Pos:* Lectr, 75-; prin investr, Nat Cancer Inst, NIH, 76-80, 81- *Mem:* AAAS; Am Soc Microbiol. *Res:* Elucidation of factors regulating the papovavirus replication cycle with particular emphasis on the regulatory switch between replication and maturation pathways; role of intracellular environment in the outcome of viral infection. *Mailing Add:* Dept Microbiol & Immunol Sch Med Ind Univ Indianapolis IN 46223

ROMAN, BERNARD JOHN, b Kingston, Pa, June 26, 40; m 65; c 3. PHYSICS. *Educ:* Carnegie-Mellon Univ, BSc, 62; Northwestern Univ, PhD(physics), 69. *Prof Exp:* Jr engr electronics, Radio Corp Am, 61, 62 & 63; MEM STAFF MAGNETIC DEVICES, BELL LABS, 69- *Mem:* Am Phys Soc. *Res:* Fabrication techniques for magnetic domain (bubble) devices. *Mailing Add:* Bell Labs 600 Mountain Ave Murray Hill NJ 07974

ROMAN, HERSCHEL LEWIS, b Szumsk, Poland, Sept 29, 14; nat US; m 38; c 2. GENETICS. *Educ:* Univ Mo, AB, 36, PhD(genetics), 42. *Prof Exp:* From instr to assoc prof bot, 42-44 & 46-52, prof bot, 52-59, chmn dept, 59-80, PROF GENETICS, UNIV WASH, 59- *Concurrent Pos:* Gosney fel, Calif Inst Technol, 46-48; Guggenheim fel, 52-53; Fulbright res scholar, France, 56-57; vis investr, Carlsberg Lab, Copenhagen, Denmark, 60; ed, Annual Rev Genetics, 65-; vis fel, Australian Nat Univ, 66; mem adv comt, Oak Ridge Nat Lab, 66-70; Goldschmidt mem lectr, Hebrew Univ Jerusalem, 71; consult, USPHS & NSF. *Honors & Awards:* Gold Medal, Emil Christian Hansen Found, Copenhagen, 80. *Mem:* Nat Acad Sci; fel AAAS; Am Acad Arts & Sci; Genetics Soc Am (vpres, 64 & 67, pres, 68); Am Soc Naturalists. *Res:* Cytogenetics of maize; genetics of yeast. *Mailing Add:* Dept of Genetics Univ of Wash Seattle WA 98195

ROMAN, JANET MEINCER, immunology, virology, see previous edition

ROMAN, JESSE, b Cabo Rojo, PR, June 18, 31; m 56; c 1. PLANT NEMATOLOGY. *Educ:* Univ PR, BS, 56; Auburn Univ, MS, 59; NC State Univ, PhD(nematol), 68. *Prof Exp:* Asst nematologist, 56-73, nematologist & head dept entom & nematol, 73-77, TECH ASST TO DIR, AGR EXP STA, UNIV PR, RIO PIEDRAS, 77- *Mem:* Soc Nematol; Orgn Trop Am Nematol (pres, 71); Caribbean Food Crop Soc; Am Soc Agr Sci (pres, 74). *Res:* Taxonomy; morphology; cytology; biology; population dynamics; reproduction and control of plant parasitic nematodes. *Mailing Add:* Off of the Dir Agr Exp Sta Univ of P R Rio Piedras PR 00928

ROMAN, NANCY GRACE, b Nashville, Tenn, May 16, 25. ASTRONOMY. *Educ:* Swarthmore Col, BA, 46; Univ Chicago, PhD(astron), 49. *Hon Degrees:* DSc, Russell Sage Col, 66, Hood Col, 69, Bates Col, 71 & Swarthmore Col, 76. *Prof Exp:* Asst astron & astrophys, Univ Chicago, 46-48, res assoc, 49-52, instr, 52-54, asst prof, 54-55; astronr, Radio Astron Br, US Naval Res Lab, 55-56, head, Microwave Spectros Sect, 56-57, consult, 58-59; head observational astron prog, NASA Hq, 59-60, chief astron & astrophys progs, 60-61, chief astron & solar physics, 61-63, chief astron, 63-72, chief astron & relativity, 72-79; CONSULT, 79- *Concurrent Pos:* Trustee, Russell Sage Col, 73-78 & Swarthmore Col, 80- *Honors & Awards:* Fed Woman's Award, 62; NASA Except Sci Achievement Award, 69. *Mem:* Int Union Radio Sci; Int Astron Union; fel Am Astron Soc; Astron Soc Pac. *Res:* Spectral classification; stellar motions; photoelectric photometry; space research. *Mailing Add:* 4620 N Park Ave Apt 306W Chevy Chase MD 20815

ROMAN, PAUL, b Budapest, Hungary, Aug 20, 25; nat US; m 47, 62; c 4. THEORETICAL PHYSICS, MATHEMATICAL PHYSICS. *Educ:* Eotvos Lorand Univ, MSc, 47, PhD(physics), 48; Hungarian Acad Sci, DSc, 56. *Prof Exp:* Asst lectr physics, Eötvös Lorand Univ, Budapest, 47-48, lectr, 48-50, sr lectr, 50-51, sr res worker, 54-56; dept chmn, Tech Pedag Col, Budapest, 51-52; res fel, Moscow State Univ, 52-53; dept chmn, Agr Univ, Budapest, 53-54; lectr, Univ Manchester, 57-61; assoc prof physics, Boston Univ, 60-62, prof, 62-78; DEAN GRAD STUDIES & RES, STATE UNIV NY PLATTSBURGH, 78- *Concurrent Pos:* Vis prof, Mex, 72, 74, 75 & 77 & Max Planck Inst, 76, 78, 80 & 82; assoc ed, J Math Physics, 78-81. *Mem:* Fel Am Phys Soc; Am Asn Physics Teachers; Int Asn Math Physicists; Nat Coun Univ Res Adminrs; Soc Res Admin. *Res:* Theory of elementary particles and quantum field theory; mathematical physics; science education and research administration. *Mailing Add:* Off Dean Grad Studies & Res State Univ NY Plattsburgh NY 12901

ROMANCIER, ROBERT MARSHALL, b Springfield, Mass, June 12, 35; m 58; c 2. FOREST ECOLOGY. *Educ:* Univ Mass, BS, 57; Yale Univ, MF, 58; Duke Univ, PhD(forest ecol), 71. *Prof Exp:* Res forester, Southeastern Forest Exp Sta, 57-69, asst br chief conifer ecol, Timber Mgt Res, Wash Off, 69-72, ASST DIR FORESTRY RES, PAC NORTHWEST FOREST & RANGE EXP STA, FOREST SERV, USDA, 72- *Mem:* Soc Am Foresters; Sigma Xi. *Res:* Administration of research programs, including silviculture, genetics, ecology, prescribed burning, insect and disease, watershed, management, and wildlife habitat. *Mailing Add:* Forestry Sci Lab USDA 3200 Jefferson Way Corvallis OR 97331

ROMANI, ROGER JOSEPH, b Sacramento, Calif, Dec 17, 19; m 59; c 4. PLANT PHYSIOLOGY, BIOCHEMISTRY. *Educ:* Univ Calif, BS, 51, PhD(plant physiol, biochem), 55. *Prof Exp:* Asst, Univ Calif, Los Angeles, 51-55, asst food scientist, 57-59, lectr pomol, 70-74, ASSOC POMOLOGIST, UNIV CALIF, DAVIS, 59-, PROF POMOL, 74- *Concurrent Pos:* Mem food irradiation adv comt, AEC-Am Inst Biol Sci, 61-63. *Mem:* AAAS; Am Soc Plant Physiol; Radiation Res Soc. *Res:* Cellular aspects of maturation and senescence; radiation biochemistry; molecular biology. *Mailing Add:* Dept of Pomol Univ of Calif Davis CA 95616

ROMANKIW, LUBOMYR TARAS, b Zhowkwa, Ukraine, Apr 17, 31; Can citizen. MATERIALS ENGINEERING, ELECTROCHEMISTRY. *Educ:* Univ Alta, BSc, 55; Mass Inst Technol, MSc & PhD(metall), 62. *Prof Exp:* Mem res staff electrochem, Thomas J Watson Res Ctr, 62-63, mgr magnetic mat group, Components Div, 63-64, mem res staff mat & processes, 65-68, mgr magnetic mat & devices, 68-78, consult, IBM E Fishkill Develop Lab & Mfg, 78-80, MGR MAT & PROCESS STUDIES, THOMAS J WATSON RES CTR, IBM CORP, 81- *Concurrent Pos:* Instr, Mass Inst Technol, 59-61. *Honors & Awards:* Outstanding Contrib Award, IBM Corp, 70. *Mem:* Electrochem Soc (secy-tres, 79-80 & chmn, 81); Am Electroplaters Soc; Inst Elec & Electronics Engrs; Sigma Xi. *Res:* Magnetic thin films; deposition of thin films; dielectrics; magnetic device design; material selection and fabrication; electrodeposition; magnetic materials; electronic and magnetic device fabrication; chemical engineering; metallurgy. *Mailing Add:* Thomas J Watson Res Ctr IBM Corp PO Box 218 Yorktown Heights NY 10598

ROMANKO, RICHARD ROBERT, b Cortland, NY, Dec 18, 25; m 54; c 3. PLANT PATHOLOGY. *Educ:* Univ NH, BS, 53; Univ Del, MS, 55; La State Univ, PhD(plant path), 57. *Prof Exp:* Asst fruit fungicides, Univ Del, 53-55; ASSOC PLANT PATHOLOGIST, EXP STA, UNIV IDAHO, 57- *Mem:* AAAS; Potato Asn Am; Am Phytopath Soc. *Res:* Physiology of parasitism; microbial genetics; hop diseases. *Mailing Add:* Highland Addition Parma ID 83660

ROMANO, ALBERT, b New York, NY, Feb 2, 27. MATHEMATICAL STATISTICS. *Educ:* Brooklyn Col, BA, 50; Wash Univ, St Louis, MA, 54; Va Polytech Univ, PhD, 61. *Prof Exp:* Asst prof math, Ariz State Univ, 58-60; staff statistician, Semiconductor Prod Div, Motorola Inc, 60-63; NSF res assoc, Nat Bur Standards, 62-63; assoc prof, 63-78, PROF MATH, SAN DIEGO STATE UNIV, 78- *Mem:* AAAS; Am Math Soc; Am Statist Soc; Inst Math Statist. *Res:* Evolution and population genetics; statistical models. *Mailing Add:* Dept Math San Diego State Univ 5402 College Ave San Diego CA 92182

ROMANO, ANTONIO HAROLD, b Penns Grove, NJ, Mar 6, 29; m 53; c 3. MICROBIOLOGY. *Educ:* Rutgers Univ, BS, 49, PhD(microbiol), 52. *Prof Exp:* Assoc microbiologist, Ortho Res Found Div, Johnson & Johnson, 52-54; instr microbial biochem, Rutgers Univ, 54-56; from sr asst scientist to sr scientist, Taft Sanit Eng Ctr, USPHS, Ohio, 56-59; from assoc prof to prof bact, Univ Cincinnati, 59-71; PROF BIOL, UNIV CONN, STORRS, 71-, HEAD, MICROBIOL SECT, 74- *Concurrent Pos:* NSF sr fel, Univ Leicester, 67-68; vis fel, Cambridge Univ, 79. *Mem:* AAAS; Am Soc Microbiol; Am Acad Microbiol. *Res:* Microbial physiology and biochemistry; regulation of sugar uptake in microorganisms and mammalian cells. *Mailing Add:* Biol Sci Group Univ Conn Storrs CT 06268

ROMANO, JOHN, b Milwaukee, Wis, Nov 20, 08; m 33; c 1. PSYCHIATRY. *Educ:* Marquette Univ, BS, 32, MD, 34. *Hon Degrees:* DSc, Med Col Wis, 71; Hahnemann Med Col, 74 & Univ Cincinnati, 79. *Prof Exp:* Extern psychiat, Milwaukee County Asylum Ment Dis, 32-33; intern med, Milwaukee County Hosp, 33-34; asst psychiat, Sch Med, Yale Univ, 34-35; Commonwealth Fund fel, Sch Med, Univ Colo, 35-38; Rockefeller fel neurol, Harvard Med Sch, 38-39; Freud fel, 39-42, asst med, 39-40, instr, 40-42; prof psychiat, Col Med, Univ Cincinnati, 42-46; prof, 46-68, chmn dept, 46-71, distinguished univ prof psychiat, 68-79, EMER PROF, SCH MED & DENT, UNIV ROCHESTER, 79- *Concurrent Pos:* Intern & asst resident, New Haven Hosp, 34-35; asst psychiatrist, Colo Psychopath Hosp, Denver, 35-38; fel, Boston City Hosp, 38-39; assoc, Peter Bent Brigham Hosp, 39-42; dir dept psychiat, Cincinnati Gen Hosp, 42-46; mem nat adv ment health coun, USPHS, 46-49, chmn ment health career investr selection comt, 56-61; consult, NIMH, 46-61; psychiatrist-in-chief, Strong Mem Hosp, 46-71; mem adv comt, Behav Sci Div, Ford Found, 55-58; Commonwealth Fund advan fel Europ study, 59-60. *Mem:* Sr mem Inst Med-Nat Acad Sci; Am Soc Clin Invest; Am Epilepsy Soc; fel Am Psychiat Asn; Am Neurol Asn. *Res:* Medical and psychiatric education; studies of schizophrenic patients and their families; general clinical psychiatry; psychosomatic medicine. *Mailing Add:* Sch Med & Dent Dept Psychiat Univ of Rochester Rochester NY 14642

ROMANO, JOHN EMILIO, chemical engineering, see previous edition

ROMANO, PAULA JOSEPHINE, b Rochester, NY, Mar 19, 40. IMMUNOLOGY, MICROBIOLOGY. *Educ:* Cath Univ Am, AB, 61; Duke Univ, PhD(microbiol, immunol), 74. *Prof Exp:* USPHS fel immunol, Nat Cancer Inst, 75-76; instr, Georgetown Univ, 76-79; dir, Histocompatibility Lab, Found Blood Res, 79-81; DIR, HISTOCOMPATIBILTIY LAB, MILTON S HERSHEY MED CTR, 81- *Mem:* Am Asn Clin Histocompatibility Testing; Am Soc Microbiol; AAAS. *Res:* Understanding of mechanisms of cellular immune reactions; role of histomcompatibility cell surface antigens in disease processes. *Mailing Add:* Dept Surg Milton S Hershey Med Ctr Hershey PA 17033

ROMANO, SALVATORE JAMES, b Highland Park, NJ, June 2, 41; m 63; c 2. ANALYTICAL CHEMISTRY. *Educ:* Mt St Mary's Col, BS, 63; Rutgers Univ, PhD(anal chem), 68. *Prof Exp:* Res chemist, Colgate-Palmolive Res Lab, 68-71; prin scientist & supvr, Ethicon Inc, 71-74, mgr, 74-78, assoc dir res, 78-79; VPRES RES & DEVELOP, DEVRO INC, 79- *Mem:* Am Chem Soc. *Res:* Chemical separations, particularly optical isomer separations; high pressure liquid chromatography. *Mailing Add:* Devro Inc Somerville NJ 08876

ROMANOFF, ELIJAH BRAVMAN, b Clinton, Mass, Feb 15, 13; m 42. PHYSIOLOGY. *Educ:* Worcester Polytech Inst, BS, 34, MS, 36; Tufts Univ, PhD, 52. *Prof Exp:* Jr chemist, Commonwealth Mass, 35-38; jr chemist, Worcester State Hosp, 38-40, asst chemist, 40-41, dir lab, 46-47; res assoc, Worcester Found Exp Biol, 47-60, scientist, 60-62, assoc dir training prog physiol reprod, 62-68, sr scientist, 62-69; PROG DIR METAB BIOL, NAT SCI FOUND, 69- *Concurrent Pos:* Chemist, Texol Chem Works, 38-41; instr, Univ Exten, State Dept Educ, Mass, 38-42; vis prof, Med Sch, Univ PR, 57-60; lectr, Brown Univ, 65-69. *Mem:* AAAS; Am Physiol Soc; NY Acad Sci; Brit Soc Endocrinol. *Res:* Steroid metabolism; reproduction. *Mailing Add:* Nat Sci Found Washington DC 20550

ROMANOVICZ, DWIGHT KEITH, b Newport News, Va, Sept 1, 48; m 72. CELL BIOLOGY, ENZYME CYTOCHEMISTRY. *Educ:* Dickinson Col, BS, 70; Univ NC, Chapel Hill, PhD(bot), 75. *Prof Exp:* Res assoc cytochem, Dent Res Ctr, Sch Dent, Univ NC, 75-80; asst prof, 78-82, ASSOC PROF BIOL, WGA COL, 82- *Mem:* Am Soc Cell Biol; Electromicro Soc Am; Am Soc Plant Physiol. *Res:* Cytochemical localization of plant carbonic anhydrase; ultrastructural investigation of cell wall formation. *Mailing Add:* Dept Biol WGa Col Carrollton GA 30117

ROMANOWSKI, CHRISTOPHER ANDREW, b London, Eng, July 23, 53. MOLTEN METAL FILTRATION. *Educ:* Univ Surrey, Eng, BS Hons, 75, PhD (metall), 81. *Prof Exp:* RES ASSOC MAT ENG, DREXEL UNIV, 79- *Concurrent Pos:* Consult, Alloa Tech Ctr, 79- *Mem:* Metall Soc; Am Soc Metals; Inst Metallurgists. *Res:* Industrial filter media and optimising filter systems for aluminum, steels and superalloys; aluminum alloy recrystallization, metallography and powder processing technology. *Mailing Add:* Dept Mat Eng Drexel Univ Philadelphia PA 19104

ROMANOWSKI, ROBERT DAVID, b Chicago, Ill, Oct 4, 31; m 51; c 5. BIOCHEMISTRY. *Educ:* SDak State Univ, BS, 56, MS, 57; Purdue Univ, PhD(biochem), 61. *Prof Exp:* Asst, Purdue Univ, 57-61; asst prof vet biochem, Vet Res Lab, Mont State Univ, 61-66; res chemist, Beltsville Parasitol Lab, 66-72, RES BIOCHEMIST, ANIMAL PARASITOL INST, NAT AGR RES CTR, US DEPT AGR, 72- *Mem:* Am Soc Parasitol. *Res:* Disease resistance of plants; urinary calculi; biochemistry, enzymology and immunology of nematodes; separation and isolation of antigens from nematodes. *Mailing Add:* Animal Parasitol Inst Nat Agr Res Ctr US Dept of Agr Beltsville MD 20705

ROMANOWSKI, THOMAS ANDREW, b Warsaw, Poland, Apr 17, 25; nat US; m 52; c 2. EXPERIMENTAL HIGH ENERGY PHYSICS. *Educ:* Mass Inst Technol, BS, 52; Case Inst Technol, MS, 55, PhD(physics), 57. *Prof Exp:* Physicist, Nat Bur Standards, Washington, DC, 52; instr, Case Inst Technol, 55-56; res physicist, Carnegie Inst Technol, 57-60; physicist, High Energy Physics Div, Argonne Nat Lab, 60-78; PROF PHYSICS, OHIO STATE UNIV, 64- *Mem:* Fel Am Phys Soc. *Res:* Nuclear physics; photonuclear reactions; radio propagation and upper atmospheric physics. *Mailing Add:* Smith Lab Ohio State Univ 174 W 18th Ave Columbus OH 43210

ROMANS, ALICE YVONNE, b Wayne, WVa, June 27, 47. BIOPHYSICAL CHEMISTRY. *Educ:* Marshall Univ, BS, 69; Duke Univ, PhD(biophys chem), 74. *Prof Exp:* Instr biochem, Med Ctr, Univ Ala, 74-77; res scientist biochem, 77-81, PROD DEVELOP SCIENTIST, KIMBERLY-CLARK CORP, 81- *Mem:* Am Chem Soc; Biophys Soc; Sigma Xi. *Res:* Biological membranes and protein-lipid interactions; plasma lipoproteins; physical chemistry of biological macromolecules. *Mailing Add:* Kimberly-Clark Corp PO Box 999 Neenah WI 54956

ROMANS, JAMES BOND, b Monroe, Iowa, Jan 24, 14; m 39; c 3. PHYSICAL CHEMISTRY. *Educ:* Cent Col, Iowa, BA, 35. *Prof Exp:* Teacher sci, Beaver Consol Sch, Iowa, 36-38; chemist oils & fuels, Nat Bur Standards, 38-46; chemist phys & surface chem, Naval Res Lab, Dept Navy, 46-80; CONSULT FIRE SUPPRESSIVE FLUIDS, 80- *Mem:* Am Chem Soc; Sigma Xi; AAAS. *Res:* Surface analysis; wettability of surfaces; lubricants; dielectric liquids; friction and wear; fatigue resistance of reinforced plastics in water; desensitization of explosives; frictional electrification of polymers; gas adsorption properties of charcoal; fire suppressive fluids. *Mailing Add:* 9111 Louis Ave Silver Spring MD 20910

ROMANS, JOHN RICHARD, b Montevideo, Minn, Mar 4, 33; m 56; c 4. ANIMAL SCIENCE, BIOCHEMISTRY. *Educ:* Iowa State Univ, BS, 55; SDak State Univ, MS, 64, PhD(animal sci), 67. *Prof Exp:* Asst mgr agr serv dept, John Morrell & Co, 55-56; hog buyer, 58-62; res asst meat & animal sci, SDak State Univ, 62-67; asst prof, 67-73, ASSOC PROF ANIMAL SCI, UNIV ILL, URBANA, 73- *Mem:* Am Soc Animal Sci; Am Meat Sci Asn; Inst Food Technol. *Res:* Increase efficiency of high-quality nutritious food production via meat animals. *Mailing Add:* 132 Davenport Hall Univ of Ill Urbana IL 61801

ROMANS, ROBERT CHARLES, b Hawthorne, Wis, Oct 12, 37; m 63; c 1. BOTANY. *Educ:* Univ Wis-Superior, BS, 65, MST, 66; Ariz State Univ, PhD(bot), 69. *Prof Exp:* Asst biol, Univ Wis-Superior, 65-66; asst prof, 69-75, ASSOC PROF BIOL, BOWLING GREEN STATE UNIV, 75- *Concurrent Pos:* Ohio Biol Surv grant, 71-72. *Mem:* Bot Soc Am; Am Asn Stratig Palynologists; Int Soc Plant Morphologists. *Res:* Palynology; paleobotany; plant anatomy and morphology. *Mailing Add:* Dept of Biol Sci Bowling Green State Univ Bowling Green OH 43403

ROMANS, ROBERT GORDON, b Waverley, NS, Aug 19, 09; m 39; c 3. PROTEIN CHEMISTRY. *Educ:* Univ Toronto, BA, 33, MA, 34, PhD(chem), 42. *Prof Exp:* Asst chem, Univ Toronto, 33-38; tech asst, 38-39, res asst, 39-46, res assoc, 46-61, res mem, 61-73, dir, Insulin Div, Connaught Med Res Labs, 73-74; consult, 74-78; RETIRED. *Mem:* AAAS; fel Chem Inst Can. *Res:* Raman effect; photochemistry; insulin. *Mailing Add:* 9 Tresillian Rd Downsview Can

ROMANSKY, MONROE JAMES, b Hartford, Conn, Mar 16, 11; m 43; c 4. INTERNAL MEDICINE. *Educ:* Univ Maine, AB, 33; Univ Rochester, MD, 37. *Prof Exp:* Intern med, Strong Mem Hosp, NY, 37-38, asst resident, 38-39; Gleason res fel, Univ Rochester, 39-40; chief resident, Strong Mem Hosp, 40-41; instr med, Off Sci Res & Develop Proj, Univ Rochester, 41-42; assoc prof, 46-57, chief univ med div, DC Gen Hosp, 50-69, PROF MED, SCH MED, GEORGE WASHINGTON UNIV, 57- *Concurrent Pos:* Consult, Walter Reed Army Hosp & Cent Off, US Vet Admin, 46-; consult, USPHS, 46- & Clin Ctr, NIH, 53-; consult, Wash Hosp Ctr, 58- *Mem:* Am Fedn Clin Res; Soc Med Consults Armed Forces; Soc Exp Biol & Med; Am Soc Microbiol; Infectious Dis Soc Am; AMA; Am Col Physicians. *Res:* Infectious diseases; chemotherapy and antibiotics; immunology; nutrition in obesity. *Mailing Add:* 5480 Wisconsin Ave Washington DC 20015

ROMARY, JOHN KIRK, b Topeka, Kans, July 26, 34; div; c 3. PHYSICAL CHEMISTRY. *Educ:* Washburn Univ, BS, 56; Kans State Univ, PhD(phys chem), 61. *Prof Exp:* Asst prof phys chem, Univ Nev, 61-63; from asst prof to assoc prof, Washburn Univ, 63-68; PROF CHEM & CHMN DEPT, UNIV WIS-WHITEWATER, 68- *Concurrent Pos:* Asst prog dir, NSF, 67-68; mem, Gov Comn Educ, State of Wis, 69-70. *Mem:* Am Chem Soc; Royal Soc Chem. *Res:* Polarographic, potentiometric, thermodynamic and calorimetric studies of coordination compound formation; synthesis of pyridyl polyamine ligands; development of computer programs for analysis of coordination data. *Mailing Add:* Dept of Chem Univ of Wis Whitewater WI 53190

ROMBERGER, JOHN ALBERT, b Northumberland Co, Pa, Dec 25, 25; m 51; c 2. PLANT PHYSIOLOGY. *Educ:* Swarthmore Col, BA, 51; Pa State Univ, MS, 53; Univ Mich, PhD(bot), 58. *Prof Exp:* Res fel plant physiol, Calif Inst Technol, 58-59; PLANT PHYSIOLOGIST, US FOREST SERV, 59- *Concurrent Pos:* Vis scholar, Univ Silesia, Poland, 81. *Mem:* Am Soc Plant Physiol; Bot Soc Am; Scand Soc Plant Physiol; Int Soc Plant Morphol; Int Asn Wood Anatomists. *Res:* Tree physiology; growth and development in woody plants; developmental biology; morphogenesis; wood anatomy; morphogenesis and development in higher organisms. *Mailing Add:* Forest Physiol Lab US Forest Serv Beltsville MD 20705

ROMBERGER, KARL ARTHUR, b Orwin, Pa, Sept 13, 34; m 58; c 4. ANALYTICAL CHEMISTRY, PHYSICAL CHEMISTRY. *Educ:* Lebanon Valley Col, BS, 56; Pa State Univ, PhD(anal chem), 67. *Prof Exp:* Res chemist, Oak Ridge Nat Lab, 64-70; GROUP LEADER CHEM, KAWECKI-BERYLCO INDUSTS, 70- *Mem:* AAAS; Am Chem Soc. *Res:* Beryllium extraction, purification and metallurgy. *Mailing Add:* 100 Martin Ave Gilbertsville PA 19525

ROMBERGER, SAMUEL B, b Harrisburg, Pa, June 12, 39; m 66; c 1. GEOCHEMISTRY, ECONOMIC GEOLOGY. *Educ:* Pa State Univ, BS, 62, PhD(geochem), 68. *Prof Exp:* Asst prof geol, Mich State Univ, 66-69 & Univ Wis-Madison, 69-75; MEM FAC, COLO SCH MINES, 75- *Concurrent Pos:* Assoc prof geol, Off Water Resources grants, 66-69. *Mem:* Mineral Soc Am; Soc Econ Geologists; Geol Soc Am; Sigma Xi. Mineral Asn Can. *Res:* Determination of the nature, particularly the chemistry, of the processes responsible for the formation of metallic, and uranium ore deposits. *Mailing Add:* Colo Sch of Mines Golden CO 80401

ROME, DORIS SPECTOR, b Albany, NY, Feb 10, 26; m 47; c 3. CYTOLOGY, PATHOLOGY. *Educ:* Skidmore Col, BA, 47; Albany Med Col, MD, 50; Am Bd Path, dipl, 72. *Prof Exp:* Dir, Cytol Lab, Albany Med Col, 51-80, from instr to assoc prof med, 53-80, dir, Cytol Lab, 77-80; DIR, ALBANY CYTOPATH LABS, INC, 81- *Concurrent Pos:* Am Cancer Soc fel, Albany Med Ctr, 51-52, univ fel, 52-53, univ fel path, 70-72, attend physician, Albany Med Ctr Hosp, 62-72, attend pathologist, 75-81. *Mem:* Am Soc Cytol; fel Am Col Path; Int Acad Path; AMA; fel Int Acad Cytol. *Res:* Diagnostic procedures for early detection of cancer by cytologic methods. *Mailing Add:* 736 Madison Ave Albany NY 12208

ROME, JAMES ALAN, b New York, NY, Oct 12, 42. PLASMA PHYSICS. *Educ:* Mass Inst Technol, SB, 65, SM, 67, ScD, 71. *Prof Exp:* Instr elec eng, Mass Inst Technol, 67-71; PHYSICIST, FUSION ENERGY DIV, OAK RIDGE NAT LAB, 71- *Concurrent Pos:* Assoc ed, Physics Fluids, 79-82. *Mem:* Fel Phys Soc; Inst Elec & Electronics Engrs. *Res:* Particle containment in magnetic fusion devices; optimization of magnetic configurations; theory of neutral beam heating of tokamaks. *Mailing Add:* Bldg 9201-2 Fusion Energy Div Oak Ridge Nat Lab PO Box Y Oak Ridge TN 37830

ROME, MARTIN, b New York, NY, June 20, 25; m 50; c 2. PHYSICAL CHEMISTRY. *Educ:* Brooklyn Col, AB, 47; Columbia Univ, AM, 49; Polytech Inst Brooklyn, PhD(phys chem), 51. *Prof Exp:* Sr engr, Electronic Tube Div, Westinghouse Elec Corp, 51-55; chief engr, Photosensitive Tube Div, Machlett Labs, Inc, 55-63; dir res & develop, Electro-Mech Res, Inc, 63-68; vpres & gen mgr, EMR Div, 68-71, VPRES & GEN MGR, EMR PHOTOELEC, WESTON INSTRUMENTS, INC, 71- *Mem:* AAAS; Optical Soc Am; Inst Elec & Electronics Engrs. *Res:* Photoelectric television camera tubes; semiconductor photoemissive and photoconducting layers; vacuum technology; x-ray image intensifying devices; ultraviolet and visible image converter and intensifier tubes; multiplier phototubes. *Mailing Add:* EMR Photoelec PO Box 44 Princeton NJ 08540

ROMEO, JOHN THOMAS, b Plattsburgh, NY, July 4, 40; m 66; c 1. PLANT CHEMISTRY, CHEMICAL ECOLOGY. *Educ:* Hamilton Col, AB, 62; Univ Idaho, MS, 70; Univ Tex, Austin, PhD(bot), 73. *Prof Exp:* Teacher biol, East Syracuse-Minoa High Sch, 66-69; res assoc phytochem, Inst Biomed Res, Univ Tex, 73; chemist, Tex Air Control Bd, 74; asst prof biol, Oakland Univ, 74-77; asst prof, 77-79, ASSOC PROF BIOL, UNIV SOUTH FLA, TAMPA, 80- *Mem:* Sigma Xi; Phytochem Soc NAm. *Res:* Non-protein amino acids, alkaloids and flavonoids of various plant species, application to taxonomic and ecological problems. *Mailing Add:* Dept of Biol Univ of South Fla Tampa FL 33620

ROMER, ALFRED, b Pleasantville, NY, Aug 9, 06; m 33; c 3. PHYSICS, SCIENCE EDUCATION. *Educ:* Williams Col, BA, 28; Calif Inst Technol, PhD(physics), 35. *Hon Degrees:* ScD, St Lawrence Univ, 79. *Prof Exp:* Asst chem, Williams Col, 28-29; from asst prof to prof physics, Whittier Col, 33-43; assoc prof, Vassar Col, 43-46; from assoc prof to prof, 46-73, EMER PROF PHYSICS, ST LAWRENCE UNIV, 73- *Concurrent Pos:* Fel, Harvard Univ, 40-41; vis fel, Princeton Univ, 55-56; actg ed, Am J Physics, 62; vis staff mem, Educ Serv Inc, 62-63; consult, AID & Univ Grants Comn, India, 64 & 65; vis prof hist, Univ Calif, Santa Barbara, 75. *Mem:* AAAS; Am Phys Soc; Hist Sci Soc; Soc Hist Technol; Am Asn Physics Teachers (secy, 66-70). *Res:* History of physics; history of technology. *Mailing Add:* Dept of Physics St Lawrence Univ Canton NY 13617

ROMER, I(RVING) CARL, JR, b Rochester, NY, Nov 23, 31; m 56; c 3. MECHANICAL ENGINEERING. *Educ:* Univ Rochester, BS, 52; Northwestern Univ, MS, 55; Univ Wis, PhD, 65. *Prof Exp:* Combustion res engr, Flight Propulsion Div, Gen Elec Co, Ohio, 56-59; instr mech eng, Univ Wis-Madison, 59-61 & 63-65; asst prof mech eng, 65-68, chmn energetics dept, 66-71, ASSOC PROF MECH ENG, UNIV WIS-MILWAUKEE, 68-, ASST DEAN UNDERGRAD STUDIES, 77- *Mem:* Sigma Xi; AAAS; Am Soc Eng Educ; Am Soc Mech Engrs. *Res:* Thermodynamics, especially properties of combustion gases and applications to environmental problems; propagation of acoustic waves through gases; noise reduction. *Mailing Add:* Col of Appl Sci & Eng Univ of Wis Milwaukee WI 53201

ROMER, ROBERT HORTON, b Chicago, Ill, Apr 15, 31; m 53; c 3. LOW TEMPERATURE PHYSICS. *Educ:* Amherst Col, BA, 52; Princeton Univ, PhD(physics), 55. *Prof Exp:* From instr to assoc prof, 55-66, PROF PHYSICS, AMHERST COL, 66- *Concurrent Pos:* Res assoc, Duke Univ, 58-59; vis physicist, Brookhaven Nat Lab, 63-; NSF fel, Univ Grenoble, 64-65; vis prof, Voorhees Col, 69-70; assoc ed, Am J Physics. *Mem:* AAAS; Am Phys Soc; Am Asn Physics Teachers; Solar Energy Soc. *Res:* Nuclear magnetic resonance; environmental physics. *Mailing Add:* Dept of Physics Amherst Col Amherst MA 01002

ROMERO, JACOB B, b Las Vegas, NMex, July 10, 32; m 61; c 2. CHEMICAL & NUCLEAR ENGINEERING. *Educ:* Univ NMex, BS, 54; Univ Wash, MS, 57, PhD(chem eng), 59. *Prof Exp:* Res specialist, Aerospace Group, Boeing Co, Wash, 59-66; assoc prof chem & nuclear eng, Univ Idaho, 66-69; specialist engr aerospace group, Boeing Co, Wash, 69-72; mem fac, 72-80, NATURAL SCI INSTR, EVERGREEN STATE COL, 80- *Res:* Fluid flow in fluidized beds; analysis of advanced nuclear reactor concepts; cryogenic fluid storage using superinsulations; transient behavior of heat pipes; lasers. *Mailing Add:* 2101 Beverly Beach Dr NW Olympia WA 98502

ROMERO-SIERRA, CESAR AURELIO, b Madrid, Spain, Nov 29, 31; Can citizen; c 5. ANATOMY. *Educ:* Univ Granada, BA & BSc, 49, MD, 59; Univ Zaragoza, MD, 60, DSc, 61. *Prof Exp:* Intern dermat, Univ Granada, 59; asst prof anat, Univ Zaragoza, 59-61; Swed Ministry Foreign Affairs fel, 61-62; scholar, Swed Inst, 62; NIH fel, Univ Calif, Los Angeles, 64-65; asst prof anat, Univ Ottawa, 65-67; assoc prof, 67-76, PROF ANAT, QUEEN'S UNIV, ONT, 76- *Concurrent Pos:* Researcher, Nat Health & Welfare, Ont, 68. *Mem:* AAAS; Am Soc Cell Biol; Can Asn Lab Animal Sci; Can Fedn Biol Socs; Pan-Am Asn Anat. *Res:* Interaction of electromagnetic fields with living organisms; a modeling of neural behavior; biomedical instrumentation. *Mailing Add:* Dept of Anat Queen's Univ Kingston ON K7L 3N6 Can

ROMESBERG, FLOYD EUGENE, b Garrett, Pa, Jan 31, 27; m 48; c 3. CHEMICAL ENGINEERING, PHYSICAL CHEMISTRY. *Educ:* Pa State Univ, BS, 49; Bucknell Univ, MS, 50; Univ Cincinnati, PhD(phys chem), 53. *Prof Exp:* Chemist, 53-56, proj leader fibers, 56-59, group leader, 59-63, lab dir films, 63-65, asst to tech dir films res & develop, 65-78, MEM STAFF, GRANVILLE RES & DEVELOP, DOW CHEM CO, 78- *Mem:* Am Chem Soc. *Res:* Technology support of manufacturing and research and development for the industrial polymeric films, including polyethylene, polystyrene, saran, copolymer and multilayer and for the consumer products, including Handiwrap and Saranwrap films and Ziploc bags; long range product development for films, foam and composites. *Mailing Add:* Eastern Div Res Dow Chem Co Box 515 Granville OH 43023

ROMEY, WILLIAM DOWDEN, b Richmond, Ind, Oct 26, 30; m 55; c 3. GEOLOGY, SCIENCE EDUCATION. *Educ:* Ind Univ, AB, 52; Univ Calif, Berkeley, PhD(geol), 62. *Prof Exp:* From asst prof to assoc prof geol & sci teaching, Syracuse Univ, 62-69, exec dir, Earth Sci Educ Prog, 69-72; chmn dept geol & geog, 71-76, PROF GEOL, ST LAWRENCE UNIV, 71- *Concurrent Pos:* Consult, Earth Sci Curriculum Proj, 63-72; vis geol scientist, Am Geol Inst, 64-72 & NY State Educ Dept, 65-69; NSF sci fac fel, Univ Oslo Geol Mus, 67-68; earth sci consult, Compton's Encycl, 71; assoc ed, Geol Soc Am Bulletin, 79- & J Geol Educ, 80- *Mem:* Fel AAAS; fel Geol Soc Am; Nat Asn Geol Teachers (vpres, 71-72, pres, 72-73); Asn Am Geographers; Am Geophys Union. *Res:* Igneous and metamorphic petrology; structural, Precambrian and general field geology; humanistic learning theory and human potential. *Mailing Add:* Dept Geol & Geog St Lawrence Univ Canton NY 13617

ROMICK, GERALD J, b Ennis, Tex, Jan 26, 32. AERONOMY. *Educ:* Univ Alaska, BS, 52, PhD(geophys), 64; Univ Calif, Los Angeles, MS, 54. *Prof Exp:* Spectroscopist, US Naval Ord Lab, Calif, 54-56; res asst auroral studies, 56-58, asst geophysicist, 58-64, from asst prof to assoc prof, 64-75, PROF GEOPHYS, GEOPHYS INST, UNIV ALASKA, 75- *Concurrent Pos:* Consult, Lockheed Missiles & Space Co, 66-67. *Mem:* Am Geophys Union; Int Asn Geomag & Aeronomy. *Res:* Physics of the upper atmosphere; studies of the excitation of the constituents by energetic particle, solar radiation and chemical processes. *Mailing Add:* Geophys Inst Univ of Alaska Fairbanks AK 99701

ROMICK, KENNETH M(ONROE), chemical engineering, deceased

ROMIG, ALTON DALE, JR, b Bethlehem, Pa, Oct 6, 53. ELECTRON MICROSCOPY, SOLID STATE DIFFUSION. *Educ:* Lehigh Univ, BS, 75, MS, 77, PhD(metall), 79. *Prof Exp:* MEM TECH STAFF, WESTERN ELEC, SANDIA NAT LABS, 79-; ASST PROF METALL, NMEX INST MINING & TECHNOL, 81- *Concurrent Pos:* Key reader, Metall Transactions, 80-; lectr, Lehigh Univ, 78- *Mem:* Am Inst Mining Metall & Petrol Engrs; Am Soc Metals; Microbeam Anal Soc; Electron Microscope Soc Am; Sigma Xi. *Res:* Diffusion controlled phase transformations and phase equilibrium in multicomponent metallic alloy systems theoretically and by several experimental techniques including analytical electron microscopy. *Mailing Add:* Div 5832 Phys Metall Sandia Nat Labs PO Box 5800 Albuquerque NM 87185

ROMIG, PHILLIP RICHARDSON, b Dennison, Ohio, July 24, 38; m 62; c 2. GEOPHYSICS, SEISMOLOGY. *Educ:* Univ Notre Dame, BS, 60; Colo Sch Mines, MS, 67, PhD(geophys), 69. *Prof Exp:* System engr, A C Electronics Div, Gen Motors Corp, 63-64; res assoc, earthquake seismol, 69-74, asst prof, 74-78, ASSOC PROF, COLO SCH MINES, 78- *Concurrent Pos:* Sr geophysicist, Westinghouse Geores Lab, 69-74; staff seismologist, E D'Appolonia Consult Engrs, 75- *Mem:* Siesmol Soc Am; Am Geophys Union; Inst Elec & Electronics Eng; Soc Explor Geophysicists; Earthquake Eng Res Inst. *Res:* Engineering geophysics and evaluation of seismic hazards for major projects, particularly nuclear power plant site evaluation. *Mailing Add:* Dept of Geophys Colo Sch of Mines Golden CO 80401

ROMIG, ROBERT P, b Eugene, Ore, May 1, 36; m 65; c 2. CHEMICAL ENGINEERING. *Educ:* Ore State Univ, BS, 59, MS, 61; Carnegie Inst Technol, PhD(chem eng, fluid flow), 64. *Prof Exp:* ASSOC PROF CHEM ENG, SAN JOSE STATE UNIV, 64- *Mem:* Am Inst Chem Engrs; Am Comput Mach. *Res:* Applied mathematics; computer simulation of chemical processes. *Mailing Add:* Dept of Chem Eng San Jose State Univ San Jose CA 95114

ROMIG, ROBERT WILLIAM MCCLELLAND, b Cornwall, Ont, July 17, 29; m 52; c 2. PLANT PATHOLOGY. *Educ:* Drew Univ, BA, 53; Purdue Univ, MS, 55, PhD(plant path), 57. *Prof Exp:* Asst geneticist, Agr Prog, Rockefeller Found, Colombia, 57-59, assoc geneticist, Chile, 59-62; res plant pathologist, USDA, Univ Minn, St Paul, 62-69; GENETICIST & WHEAT PROJ LEADER, NORTHRUP KING & CO, 69-, DIR, WHEAT RES, 78- *Mem:* AAAS; Am Phytopath Soc; Am Soc Agron. *Res:* Small grains; disease resistance; epidemiology; wheat breeding. *Mailing Add:* Northrup King & Co 1340 Research Rd Eden Prairie MN 55344

ROMIG, WILLIAM D(AVIS), b Victor, Iowa, Aug 19, 14; m 39; c 2. CIVIL ENGINEERING, WATER RESOURCES. *Educ:* Univ Colo, BS, 36. *Prof Exp:* Levelman, US Bur Reclamation, Colo, 36, jr hydraul engr, State Water Conserv Bd, Colo, 37-41; from jr engr to engr, US Bur Reclamation, Colo, 41-45, Washington, DC, 45-53, planning engr, US Foreign Opers, Costa Rica, 53-55 & Washington, DC, 55-63; water resources engr, Near East & SAsia, USAID, Washington, DC, 63-72; CONSULT, 72- *Concurrent Pos:* Mem, Int Comn Irrig & Drainage. *Mem:* Am Soc Civil Engrs. *Res:* Hydrology; multi-purpose water projects, including municipal water and groundwater; agricultural water management. *Mailing Add:* 100 Inca Pkwy Boulder CO 80303

ROMIG, WILLIAM ROBERT, b Hope, Ark, Mar 4, 26; m 58; c 1. BACTERIOLOGY. *Educ:* Southwestern State Col, BA, 48; Univ Okla, MS, 54; Univ Tex, PhD(bact), 57. *Prof Exp:* From instr to asst prof, 57-70, PROF BACT, UNIV CALIF, LOS ANGELES, 70- *Mem:* Am Soc Microbiol; Brit Soc Gen Microbiol. *Res:* Bacteriophage; radiation effects on bacteria; bacterial genetics and endospore formation; transformation. *Mailing Add:* Dept of Bact Univ of Calif Los Angeles CA 90024

ROMINGER, JAMES MCDONALD, b Charleston, Ill, May 19, 28; m 52; c 2. SYSTEMATIC BOTANY. *Educ:* Eastern Ill Univ, BS, 50; Univ NMex, MS, 55; Univ Ill, PhD(bot), 59. *Prof Exp:* Asst biol, Univ NMex, 50-52; instr, Univ Jacksonville, 55-56; asst bot, Univ Ill, 56-59; instr biol, Black Hills State Col, 59-61; asst prof, Western State Col Colo, 61-63; ranger-naturalist, Grand Teton Nat Park, 63; assoc prof bot, 63-74, PROF BIOL, NORTHERN ARIZ UNIV, 74-, CURATOR, DEAVER HERBARIUM, 63- *Mem:* Am Soc Plant Taxon. *Res:* Agrostology; vascular flora of northern Arizona, especially grass flora; genus Setaria in North America. *Mailing Add:* Dept of Biol Northern Ariz Univ Flagstaff AZ 86001

ROMINGER, JOSEPH FRANKLIN, b Glendale, Calif, Dec 8, 19; m 48, 65; c 5. GEOLOGY. *Educ:* Calif Inst Technol, BS, 41; Northwestern Univ, MS, 43, PhD(geol), 50; Harvard Univ, AM, 47. *Prof Exp:* Asst geol, Northwestern Univ, 41-43; from jr geologist to asst geologist, US Geol Surv, 43-44, 46-49; from res geologist to res group leader, Petrol Geol Res Lab, Carter Oil Co, 48-53; from regional study geologist to head geol sect, Int Petrol Colombia, Ltd, 53-58; chief geologist, Esso Standard Libya, Inc, 58-64; consult geologist, 64-66; vpres, Podesta, Meyers, Rominger & Clift, Inc, 69-71; pres, W Manor Co, Inc, 71-73; pres, Geo-Resources Discovery Inc, 73-78; pres, Manor Energy Corp, 78-81; PRES, GEO-ENERGY CORP, 81- *Mem:* Am Asn Petrol; Am Inst Prof Geologists; Geol Soc Am. *Res:* Sedimentary petrography; use of soil mechanics techniques in geology; grain size, grain orientation and plasticity relationships of sediments; quantitative relationships of oil occurrence to stratigraphic facies; petroleum geology. *Mailing Add:* Geo-Energy Corp 7520 N Lakeside Lane Scottsdale AZ 85253

ROMINGER, MICHAEL COLLINS, b Indianapolis, Ind, July 9, 44; m 78. CONTROL SYSTEMS, CHEMICAL ENGINEERING. *Educ:* Purdue Univ, Lafayette, BSChE, 66; Ohio State Univ, MS, 68, PhD(chem eng), 71. *Prof Exp:* Consult, 70-72, sr biochemist, 72-76, ENG ASSOC, ELI LILLY & CO, 76- *Mem:* Am Inst Chem Engrs; Instrument Soc Am; Am Chem Soc. *Res:* Control of chemical and fermentation processes. *Mailing Add:* Dept K833 Eli Lilly & Co 307 E McCarty St Indianapolis IN 46206

ROMMEL, FREDERICK ALLEN, b Carlisle, Pa, Feb 27, 35; m 57; c 1. MEDICAL MICROBIOLOGY, IMMUNOPATHOLOGY. *Educ:* Univ Miami, BS, 57, PhD(immunol), 67. *Prof Exp:* Res asst infectious dis, Med Sch, Univ Miami, 57-60; USPHS fel immunol, Med Sch, Johns Hopkins Univ, 66-69; asst prof pediat, Immunol-Allergy Sect & Dept Microbiol, Univ Tex Health Sci Ctr San Antonio, 70-75; assoc prof path, Med Sch, Univ Mo-Kansas City, 75-76; res chemist, Plum Island Animal Dis Ctr, Diag Res, USDA, 76-81; VPRES & ASSOC DIR SCI RES & DEVELOP, IMMUNO GENETICS, INC, DOVER, NH, 81- *Concurrent Pos:* Nat Inst Allergy & Infectious Dis & Nat Inst Environ Health Sci grants, 71-75; chief clin microbiol & immunol, Dept Path, Kansas City Gen Hosp, 75-76. *Mem:* Am Asn Immunol; AAAS; NY Acad Sci; Am Soc Microbiol; World Mariculture Soc. *Res:* Mechanism of action of complement; enzyme systems; veterinary immunology; pathobiology of inflammation these are separate invertebrate immunity; primitive foreign recognition systems; immunochemistry; aquaculture diseases. *Mailing Add:* Immuno Genetics Inc 50 Chestnut St Dover NH 03820

ROMMEL, MARJORIE ANN, b Denver, Colo, Apr 23, 33; m 55. ANALYTICAL CHEMISTRY. *Educ:* Univ Colo, Boulder, BA, 55; Univ Ariz, PhD(chem), 64. *Prof Exp:* Chemist, Martinez Ref, Shell Oil Co, Calif, 55-61; tech specialist, Rocketdyne Div, NAm Rockwell Corp, 64-68; dir res, Gen Monitors, Inc, 68-69; tech specialist, Rocketdyne Div, NAm Rockwell Corp, 69-70; chemist, 70-73, res chemist tech serv div, Washington, DC, 73-75, LAB DIR, US CUSTOMS LAB, DEPT TREAS, CHICAGO, 75- *Mem:* Am Chem Soc. *Res:* Characterization of materials; gas detection; environmental chemistry. *Mailing Add:* US Customs Lab 610 South Canal St Rm 714 Chicago IL 60607

ROMNEY, CARL FREDRICK, b Salt Lake City, Utah, June 5, 24; m 46; c 2. SEISMOLOGY. *Educ:* Calif Inst Technol, BS, 45; Univ Calif, PhD(geophys), 56. *Prof Exp:* Asst seismol, Univ Calif, 47-49; from seismologist to chief seismologist, Beers & Heroy, 49-54, consult, 54-55; supvry geophysicist, Air Force Off Atomic Energy, 55-58, asst tech dir, Air Force Tech Applns Ctr, 58-73; dep dir, 73-75, dir, Nuclear Monitoring Res Off, 75-79, DEP DIR RES, DEFENSE ADVAN RES PROJ AGENCY, 79- *Concurrent Pos:* Mem panel seismic improv, Off Spec Asst to President for Sci & Tech, 59; mem US deleg, Negotiations Limiting Peaceful Nuclear Explosions, Moscow, 74-75; comprehensive nuclear test ban negotiations, Geneva, 77-78. *Honors & Awards:* Decoration, US Air Force, 59; Distinguished Civilian Serv Award, US Dept Defense, 64; President's Award for Distinguished Fed Civilian Serv, 67. *Mem:* Soc Explor Geophys; Seismol Soc Am; Am Geophys Union. *Res:* Explosion seismology; seismic detection methods and instruments; seismicity; differences between earthquake and explosion signals. *Mailing Add:* 4105 Sulgrave Dr Alexandria VA 22309

ROMNEY, EVAN M, b Duncan, Ariz, Jan 13, 25; m 48; c 4. PLANT NUTRITION, SOILS. *Educ:* Brigham Young Univ, BS, 50; Rutgers Univ, PhD(soils), 53. *Prof Exp:* Asst res soil scientist, Atomic Energy Proj, 53-60, assoc res soil scientist, 60-65, RES SOIL SCIENTIST, LAB BIOMED & ENVIRON SCI, UNIV CALIF, LOS ANGELES, 66-, ASSOC DIR, LAB BIOMED & ENVIRON SCI, 79-; ELEMENT MGR, NEV APPL ECOL GROUP, US DEPT ENERGY, 72- *Mem:* Soil Sci Soc Am; Am Soc Agron. *Res:* Cycling of radioactive materials in plants and soils; trace elements in plants and soils; soil chemistry of rare earth elements; fate and persistence of radioactive fallout in natural environment. *Mailing Add:* Lab Nuclear Med & Radiation Biol Univ of Calif 900 Veteran Ave Los Angeles CA 90024

ROMNEY, SEYMOUR L, b New York, NY, June 8, 17; m 45; c 3. OBSTETRICS & GYNECOLOGY. *Educ:* Johns Hopkins Univ, AB, 38; NY Univ, MD, 42. *Prof Exp:* Resident gynecologist, Free Hosp for Women, 49; 49; resident obstetrician, Boston Lying-in-Hosp, 50; instr gynec & obstet, Harvard Med Sch, 50-51, assoc, 52-56; PROF OBSTET & GYNEC, ALBERT EINSTEIN COL MED, 57-, DIR GYNEC CANCER RES, 72- *Concurrent Pos:* Consult, Nat Cancer Inst, WHO Planned Parenthood-World Pop & NY State Family Planning Asn. *Mem:* AAAS; Am Gynec Soc; Soc Gynec Invest; Am Soc Clin Cancer Res; NY Acad Sci. *Res:* Human reproduction; population and fertility regulation; medical education; delivery of health care; nutrition and female genital tract malignancy. *Mailing Add:* 1081 Orienta Ave Mamaroneck NY 10543

ROMO, WILLIAM JOSEPH, b Oregon City, Ore, Jan 17, 34; m 67. PHYSICS. *Educ:* Univ Ore, 60, MS, 61; Univ Wis-Madison, PhD(theoret physics), 67. *Prof Exp:* Res assoc theoret physics, Univ Wis-Madison, 67-68 & Physics Div, Argonne Nat Lab, 68-70; asst prof, 70-74, ASSOC PROF PHYSICS, CARLETON UNIV, 74- *Mem:* Am Phys Soc; Can Asn Physicists. *Res:* Nuclear reaction theory; continuum shell model; resonances; nuclear structure. *Mailing Add:* Dept of Physics Carleton Univ Ottawa ON K1S 5B6 Can

ROMOSER, WILLIAM SHERBURNE, b Columbus, Ohio, Oct 18, 40; m 73; c 2. ENTOMOLOGY. *Educ:* Ohio State Univ, BSc, 62, PhD(entom), 64. *Prof Exp:* Res assoc entom, Ohio State Univ, 65; from asst prof to assoc prof entom, 65-76, PROF ZOOL, OHIO UNIV, 76- *Mem:* AAAS; Entom Soc Am; Am Mosquito Control Asn; Am Inst Biol Sci. *Res:* Alimentary morphology and physiology of blood-feeding insects, particularly mosquitoes; development and metamorphosis of insects, particularly mosquitoes. *Mailing Add:* Dept of Zool & Microbiol Ohio Univ Athens OH 45701

ROMOVACEK, GEORGE R, b Prague, Czech, May 17, 23; div; c 2. CHEMISTRY, FUEL TECHNOLOGY. *Educ:* Univ Chem Technol, Prague, MSc, 49, PhD(fuel technol), 55. *Prof Exp:* Sr lectr fuel technol, Univ Chem Technol, Prague, 51-62, assoc prof, 62-69; sr scientist, Coal Tar & Pitch, 69-72, RES MGR, INDUST PROD, KOPPERS CO, INC, 72- *Concurrent Pos:* Brit Coun res fel, Univ Strathclyde, 65-66; NSF res assoc, Pa State Univ, 67-68. *Mem:* Am Chem Soc; Am Ceramic Soc; Am Inst Metall Engrs. *Res:* Chemistry and chemical technology of petroleum, coal, natural and manufactured gas; air pollution. *Mailing Add:* Koppers Co Inc 440 College Park Dr Monroeville PA 15146

ROMRELL, LYNN JOHN, b Idaho Falls, Idaho, Oct 20, 44; m 80; c 3. REPRODUCTIVE BIOLOGY, HUMAN ANATOMY. *Educ:* Idaho State Univ, BS, 67; Utah State Univ, PhD(zool), 71. *Prof Exp:* NIH res fel anat, Harvard Med Sch, 71-73, instr anat & mem lab human reproduction & reproductive biol, 73-75; asst prof path, 75-76, asst prof, 76-79, ASSOC PROF ANAT, COL MED, UNIV FLA, 79- *Mem:* Sigma Xi; Soc Study Reproduction; Am Asn Anat; Soc Exp Biol & Med; Am Soc Cell Biol. *Res:* Reproductive biology; cytology; cell biology; ultrastructure and function of isolated cells; genetic, biochemical and physiological factors which influence sperm development. *Mailing Add:* Dept of Anat Univ of Fla Col of Med Gainesville FL 32610

ROMSDAHL, MARVIN MAGNUS, b Hayti, SDak, Apr 2, 30; m 58; c 1. SURGERY, BIOLOGY. *Educ:* Univ SDak, AB, 52, BS, 54; Univ Ill, MD, 56; Univ Tex, PhD(biomed sci), 68. *Prof Exp:* Intern, Res & Educ Hosps, Univ Ill, 56-57; resident surg, Vet Admin Hosp, Hines, Ill, 57-58; clin assoc surg br, Nat Cancer Inst, 58-60; resident, Res & Educ Hosps, Univ Ill, 60-63, instr, 63-64; from asst prof to assoc prof, 67-75, PROF SURG, UNIV TEX M D ANDERSON HOSP & TUMOR INST, 75- *Concurrent Pos:* USPHS trainee, Univ Ill, 63-64; univ fel, Univ Tex, 64-67; assoc dir sci opers, Nat Large Bowel Cancer Proj, Houston, 77- *Honors & Awards:* Mead Johnson Award, Am Col Surg, 66-69. *Mem:* AMA; Am Asn Cancer Res; Am Col Surg; Soc Surg Alimentary Tract; Asn Acad Surg. *Res:* Management and surgical treatment of cancer; dissemination of cancer and metastases in experimental systems; cancer cells in human blood-identification and incidence; human malignant melanoma grown in vitro; immunology of human solid tumors. *Mailing Add:* Univ of Tex MD Anderson Hosp & Tumor Inst Houston TX 77030

ROMSOS, DALE RICHARD, b Rice Lake, Wis, Nov 19, 41. NUTRITION. *Educ:* Univ Wis, BS, 64; Iowa State Univ, PhD(nutrit), 70. *Prof Exp:* Fel, Univ Ill, Urbana, 70-71; asst prof, 71-75, assoc prof, 75-79, PROF NUTRIT, MICH STATE UNIV, 79- *Concurrent Pos:* NIH res career develop award; Sigma Xi junior res award, Mich State Univ; Mead Johnson res award, Am Inst Nutrit. *Mem:* Brit Nutrit Soc; Soc Exp Biol & Med; Am Inst Nutrit; NY Acad Sci; Inst Food Technologists. *Res:* Lipid and carbohydrate metabolism; obesity; cardiovascular disease. *Mailing Add:* Dept of Food Sci & Human Nutrit Mich State Univ East Lansing MI 48824

ROMSTAD, KARL MARTIN, structural engineering, see previous edition

ROMUALDI, JAMES P, b New York, NY, June 30, 29; m 58; c 3. CIVIL ENGINEERING. *Educ:* Carnegie Inst Technol, BS, 51, MS, 53, PhD, 54. *Prof Exp:* Fulbright fel, Karlsruhe Tech Univ, 54-55; from asst prof to assoc prof civil eng, Carnegie-Mellon Univ, 55-65, prof, 65-79, dir, Trans Res Inst, 66-79; VPRES, GAI CONSULTANTS, INC & PRES, FORENSIC CONSULTANTS & ENGRS, INC, 79- *Mem:* Am Soc Civil Engrs; Am Soc Testing & Mat; Am Concrete Inst; Am Soc Eng Educ. *Res:* Fracture mechanics, especially design and applications to reinforced concrete; applied mechanics and structural analysis; transportation engineering and planning. *Mailing Add:* 5737 Wilkins Ave Pittsburgh PA 15217

RONA, ELIZABETH, radio chemistry, nuclear chemistry, deceased

RONA, GEORGE, b Budapest, Hungary, Mar 8, 24; Can citizen; m 54; c 2. PATHOLOGY. *Educ:* Med Univ Budapest, MD, 49; Hungarian Acad Sci, PhD(diabetes), 53; FRCP(C), 60; FRCPath. *Prof Exp:* From asst prof to assoc prof path, Med Univ Budapest, 50-54, dep dir, 54-56; resident, St Mary's Hosp, Montreal, 57-59; sr pathologist, Ayerst Res Labs, 59-61; from asst pathologist to assoc pathologist, St Mary's Hosp, 61-64; assoc prof, 67-71, PROF PATH, McGILL UNIV, 71-; pathologist & dir labs, 65-79, SR CONSULT PATHOLOGIST, LAKESHORE GEN HOSP, 79- *Concurrent Pos:* Med Res Coun Can grant, 67-; pres Am sect, Int Study Group Res Cardiac Metab; vis prof, Univ Geneva, 73-74; dir & pres, Lakeshore Diag Serv, 76- *Mem:* Am Asn Pathologists; Int Acad Path; fel Col Am Path; Can Asn Path. *Res:* Tuberculous meningitis; diabetic vascular lesions; experimental and human myocardial infarction. *Mailing Add:* Lakeshore Gen Hosp Labs Montreal PQ H9R 2Y2 Can

RONA, PETER ARNOLD, b Trenton, NJ, Aug 17, 34. MARINE GEOLOGY, GEOPHYSICS. *Educ:* Brown Univ, AB, 56; Yale Univ, MS, 57, PhD(marine geol, geophys), 67. *Prof Exp:* Explor geologist, Standard Oil Co, NJ, 57-59; res asst Hudson Labs, Columbia Univ, 60-61, marine geologist, 61-67, res assoc marine geol & geophys & prin investr, Ocean Bottom Studies, 67-69; prin investr, Metallogenesis Proj, 75-80, SR GEOPHYSICIST & CHIEF SCIENTIST, TRANS-ATLANTIC GEOTRAVERSE, ATLANTIC OCEANOG & METEOROL LABS, NAT OCEANIC & ATMOSPHERIC ADMIN, 69-, PRIN INVESTR, MARINE MINERALS PROJ, 80- *Concurrent Pos:* Consult sea floor resources, UN, 70-; adj prof, Univ Miami, 74-; mem vis comt geol sci, Brown Univ, 74-77; trustee, Mus Sci, Miami, Fla, 74-, gov & vpres, 77-, chmn, 79-80 & trustee, Int Oceanog Found, 81-; assoc ed, The Geol Soc Am, 75-; mem, Sierra Club Adv Comt, Ocean Environ, 75-; mem, Nat Oceanic & Atmospheric Admin, Marine Minerals Task Force, 76-; Penrose Medal Comt, Geol Soc Am, 81-; chmn metallogenesis panel, Manganese Proj, Int Geol Correlation Prog, 76-, chmn, NATO Advan Res Inst, 80-; tech expert sea floor resources, US Dept State, -; adv, Tectonic Map NAm Proj, 81-; adj prof, Fla Int Univ, 78-79. *Mem:* Fel Geol Soc Am; Am Geophys Union; Soc Explor Geophysicists; fel AAAS; Am Asn Petrol Geologists. *Res:* Structure and development of continental margins and ocean basins; marine energy and mineral resources; author or coauthor of over 100 publications. *Mailing Add:* NOAA 4301 Rickenbacker Causeway Miami FL 33149

RONALD, ALLAN ROSS, b Portage la Prairie, Man, Aug 24, 38; m 62; c 3. INFECTIOUS DISEASES, MICROBIOLOGY. *Educ:* Univ Man, BSc & MD, 61; FRCP(C), 67; Am Bd Microbiol, dipl, 70. *Prof Exp:* Fel infectious dis, Univ Wash, 65-67, res asst, 67-68; from asst prof to assoc prof microbiol & internal med, 68-77, PROF INTERNAL MED, PROF MED MICROBIOL & HEAD DEPT, UNIV MAN, 77- *Mem:* Fel Am Col Physicians; Infectious Dis Soc Am; Can Soc Clin Invest; Am Soc Microbiol. *Res:* Pathogenesis of recurrent urinary infection; antimicrobial susceptibility testing and resistance; chancroid, and hemophilus ducreyi. *Mailing Add:* Univ Man Health Sci Ctr 730 William Ave Winnipeg MB R3E 0W3 Can

RONALD, BRUCE PENDER, b Chicago, Ill, Nov 22, 39; m 67. ORGANIC CHEMISTRY. *Educ:* Portland State Col, BS, 62; Univ Wash, PhD(chem), 68. *Prof Exp:* Asst prof, 68-77, ASSOC PROF CHEM, IDAHO STATE UNIV, 77- *Mem:* Am Chem Soc; Royal Soc Chem. *Res:* Carbonium ion reactions; stereochemistry of reactions in asymmetric environments; chemical kinetic applications of nuclear magnetic resonance spectrometry. *Mailing Add:* Dept of Chem Idaho State Univ Pocatello ID 83201

RONALD, KEITH, b Llandaff, Wales, Aug 24, 28; m 54; c 1. ZOOLOGY. *Educ:* McGill Univ, BSc, 53, MSc, 56, PhD(parasitol), 58. *Prof Exp:* Marine pathologist, Que Dept Fisheries, 54-58, sr biologist & actg dir, 58; prof parasitol, Ont Agr Col, 58-62; sr scientist, Fisheries Res Bd Can, 62-64; prof zool & head dept, 64-71, DEAN COL BIOL SCI, UNIV GUELPH, 71- *Concurrent Pos:* Pres & chmn, Huntsman Marine Lab, 67-73; mem Nat Res Coun Grants Comt (Animal), 70-72; mem adv bd, Atlantic Regional Lab, Nat Res Coun, 70-72; mem, Fisheries Res Bd Can, 72-77; chmn, Sci Adv Comt, World Wildlife Fund, Can, 72-76; chmn seal group, Int Union Conserv Nature & Natural Resources, 77- *Honors & Awards:* Fry Medal Res, Can Soc Zoologists, 81. *Mem:* Can Soc Zool (pres, 72); fel Royal Geog Soc; fel Inst Biol; Sigma Xi. *Mailing Add:* Col of Biol Sci Univ of Guelph Guelph ON N1G 2W1 Can

RONALD, ROBERT CHARLES, b Blue Island, Ill, Apr 22, 44. ORGANIC CHEMISTRY. *Educ:* Portland State Col, BS, 66; Stanford Univ, PhD(org chem), 70. *Prof Exp:* Vis prof chem, Univ Sao Paulo, 70-72; sr res chemist & sect mgr chem, Syva Res Inst, Calif, 72-74; ASST PROF CHEM, WASH STATE UNIV, 74- *Concurrent Pos:* Nat Acad Sci overseas fel, 70-72. *Mem:* Am Chem Soc. *Res:* Synthetic organic chemistry; structure and synthesis of natural products and other biologically significant molecules; development of new methods and reagents for synthetic purposes. *Mailing Add:* Dept of Chem Wash State Univ Pullman WA 99164

RONAN, MICHAEL THOMAS, b Fall River, Mass, Jan 15, 49; m 76; c 2. ELEMENTARY PARTICLE PHYSICS. *Educ:* Southeastern Mass Univ, BS, 70; Northeastern Univ, MS, 73, PhD(physics), 76. *Prof Exp:* RES ASSOC EXP HIGH ENERGY PHYSICS, LAWRENCE BERKELEY LAB, 76- *Mem:* Am Phys Soc. *Mailing Add:* Rm 5239 Bldg 50B Lawrence Berkeley Lab Berkeley CA 94530

RONCA, LUCIANO BRUNO, b Trieste, Italy, Apr 26, 35; US citizen; m 58; c 3. GEOLOGY. *Educ:* Univ Kans, MS, 55, PhD(geol), 63. *Prof Exp:* Res assoc geochem, Univ Kans, 63-64; res scientist, Air Force Cambridge Res Labs, 64-67; assor prof, 70-74, PROF GEOL, WAYNE STATE UNIV, 74- *Concurrent Pos:* Vis scientist, Lunar Sci Inst, Houston, Vernadsky Inst Acad Sci, USSR, Univ Bern, Switz, Observ de Paris, France; ed, Modern Geol, 70-; assoc ed, The Moon, 72-; exchange scientist, Acad Sci USSR-USA, 76 & 79-80. *Honors & Awards:* Superior Performance Award, Air Force Cambridge Res Labs, 66; Mt Ronca

Antarctica Award, 66. *Mem:* AAAS; fel Geol Soc Am; Am Geophys Union; Am Polar Soc. *Res:* Thermoluminescence; radiation damage in geological material; lunar and planetary geology; geostatistics. *Mailing Add:* Dept of Geol Wayne State Univ Detroit MI 48202

RONCADORI, RONALD WAYNE, b Centerville, Pa, Nov 19, 35; m 59; c 3. PLANT PATHOLOGY. *Educ:* Waynesburg Col, BS, 57; Univ WVa, MS, 59, PhD(plant path), 62. *Prof Exp:* Plant pathologist, US Forest Serv, 62-66; asst plant pathologist, 66-69, ASSOC PROF PLANT PATH, UNIV GA, 69- *Mem:* Am Phytopath Soc; Mycol Soc Am. *Res:* General plant pathology, especially cotton diseases; mycorrhizae. *Mailing Add:* Dept Plant Path & Plant Genetics Univ of Ga Athens GA 30602

RONCO, FRANK, JR, b Pueblo, Colo, Sept 23, 26; m 48; c 2. FOREST MANAGEMENT. *Educ:* Colo State Univ, BS, 51, MS, 60; Duke Univ, DF, 68. *Prof Exp:* Forester, 51-56, RES FORESTER, ROCKY MOUNTAIN FOREST & RANGE EXP STA, US FOREST SERV, USDA, 56- *Mem:* Soc Am Foresters. *Res:* Artificial regeneration and silviculture of Engelmann Spruce; tree physiology. *Mailing Add:* 1500 Edgewood St Flagstaff AZ 86001

RONDEAU, DANIEL BERTRAND, b St-Hyacinthe, Que, July 27, 49. BIOPSYCHOLOGY, NEUROPHARMACOLOGY. *Educ:* Univ Que, Baccalaureat, 72, MA, 75; Syracuse Univ, PhD(biopsychol), 76. *Prof Exp:* Teaching asst, Dept Psychol, Syracuse Univ, 73-76; MED RES COUN CAN FEL, CLIN RES INST MONTREAL, 77- *Concurrent Pos:* Lectr, Dept Psychol, Univ Que, 78. *Res:* Neuropharmacological and behavioral studies on the possible interactions between brain peptides and transmitter mechanisms in the basal ganglia in relation to the pathophysiology of motor disorders. *Mailing Add:* Clin Res Inst 110 Pine Ave W Montreal PQ H2W 1R7 Can

RONDESTVEDT, CHRISTIAN SCRIVER, JR, b Minneapolis, Minn, July 13, 23; m 44; c 2. INDUSTRIAL ORGANIC CHEMISTRY. *Educ:* Univ Minn, BS, 43; Northwestern Univ, PhD(org chem), 48. *Prof Exp:* Asst, Northwestern Univ, 43-44; instr chem, Univ Mich, 47-52, asst prof, 52-56; Guggenheim fel, Univ Munich, 56-57; res chemist, 57-63, sr res chemist, 63-68, RES ASSOC, E I DU PONT DE NEMOURS & CO, 68- *Concurrent Pos:* Consult, US Rubber Co, 52-56; assoc prof, Univ Del, 60-61. *Mem:* Am Chem Soc. *Res:* New low-cost synthesis of industrial organic chemicals, especially acid chlorides, amines, and halogenated compounds; mechanisms of organic reactions; organic sulfur compounds; olefins; free radicals; organic fluorine compounds; organometallic chemistry. *Mailing Add:* Jackson Lab E I du Pont de Nemours & Co Wilmington DE 19898

RONEL, SAMUEL HANAN, b Metz, France. BIOMEDICAL ENGINEERING. *Educ:* Israel Inst Technol, BSc, 64, MSc, 66, DSc(polymers), 69. *Prof Exp:* Asst prof, Israel Inst Technol, 66-69; NIH fel, Clarkson Col Technol, 69-70; res chemist, Hydron Labs, Nat Patent Develop Corp, 70-71; group leader biomat, Hydro Med Sci, Inc, 71-74; dir res & develop, 74-75; VPRES RES & DEVELOP, NAT PATENT DEVELOP CORP, 75-; PRES, INTERFERON SCIENCES, 80- *Mem:* Am Chem Soc; Soc Biomat; Soc Plastics Engrs; Asn Advan Med Instrumentation; NY Acad Sci. *Res:* Biocompatible synthetic materials useful for implantation; non-thrombogenic materials for use in the vascular system; prosthetic devices; production and clinical testing of interferon. *Mailing Add:* 27 Turner Ct Princeton NJ 08540

RONEY, ROBERT K(ENNETH), b Newton, Iowa, Aug 5, 22; m 51; c 2. ELECTRICAL ENGINEERING, SPACE SYSTEMS. *Educ:* Univ Mo, BS, 44; Calif Inst Technol, MS, 47, PhD(elec eng), 50. *Prof Exp:* Res engr, Calif Inst Technol, 48-50; mgr systs anal, 50-60, tech dir res & develop labs, 60-61, from assoc mgr to mgr, Space Systs Div, 61-70, asst group exec, Space & Commun Group, 70, VPRES, HUGHES AIRCRAFT CO, 73- *Mem:* Fel Inst Elec & Electronics Engrs; Am Inst Aeronaut & Astronaut. *Res:* Dynamic systems analysis and feedback control. *Mailing Add:* 1105 Georgina Ave Santa Monica CA 90402

RONGONE, EDWARD LAUREL, b Cuyahoga Falls, Ohio, June 17, 26; m 58; c 4. BIOCHEMISTRY. *Educ:* Kent State Univ, BS, 50; St Louis Univ, PhD(biochem), 56. *Prof Exp:* Asst prof biochem, Sch Med, Tulane Univ, 56-63; assoc prof, 63-68, PROF BIOCHEM, SCH MED, CREIGHTON UNIV, 68- *Concurrent Pos:* Res biochemist, Ochsner Med Found, 56-63; consult, Baker Maid, Inc, La, 57-63. *Mem:* Am Chem Soc; Brit Soc Endocrinol; Am Soc Biol Chemists; Soc Exp Biol & Med; NY Acad Sci. *Res:* Steroid metabolism by in vitro and vivo methods; mechanism of steroid metabolism and steroid isolation; steroid metabolism by skin; protein isolation. *Mailing Add:* Dept of Biol Chem Creighton Univ Sch of Med Omaha NE 68178

RONGSTAD, ORRIN JAMES, b Northfield, Wis, Apr 22, 31; m 62; c 3. WILDLIFE ECOLOGY. *Educ:* Univ Minn, BS, 59; Univ Wis, Madison, MS, 63, PhD(wildlife ecol & zool), 65. *Prof Exp:* Fel mammal res, Univ Minn, 65-67; asst prof & wildlife exten specialist, 67-71, assoc prof, 71-78, PROF WILDLIFE ECOL, UNIV WIS-MADISON, 78- *Mem:* Am Soc Mammal; Wildlife Soc. *Res:* Mammalian ecology, especially hares, rabbits and deer. *Mailing Add:* Dept of Wildlife Ecol Univ of Wis Madison WI 53706

RONIS, MAX LEE, b May 8, 30; US citizen; m 54; c 3. OTOLARYNGOLOGY. *Educ:* Muhlenberg Col, BS, 52; Temple Univ, MD & MS, 56. *Prof Exp:* PROF OTORHINOL & CHMN DEPT, HEALTH SCI CTR, TEMPLE UNIV, 69-; DIR OTORHINOL, ST CHRISTOPHER'S HOSP FOR CHILDREN, 69- *Mem:* Am Otol Soc; Am Acad Ophthal & Otolaryngol; Am Laryngol, Rhinol & Otol Soc. *Res:* Anatomy and pathophysiology of diseases of the cochlea-vestibular apparatus. *Mailing Add:* Dept of Otorhinol Temple Univ Hosp Philadelphia PA 19140

RONKIN, R(APHAEL), R(OOSER), b Los Angeles, Calif, July 8, 19; m 49; c 2. PHYSIOLOGY. *Educ:* Stanford Univ, AB, 39; Univ Calif, MA, 41, PhD(zool), 49. *Prof Exp:* Aquatic biologist, US Fish & Wildlife Serv, 41-42; asst zool, Univ Calif, 46-49; from asst prof to assoc prof biol sci, Univ Del, 49-67; mem sci liaison staff, New Delhi, 67-69, assoc prog dir course content improvement sect, 63-64, mgr spec for currency prog, 72-74, mgr, Africa & Asia Sect, 74-76, STAFF ASSOC, DIV INT PROGS, NAT SCI FOUND, 76- *Concurrent Pos:* Merck sr fel & guest investr, Biol Inst, Carlsberg Found, Denmark, 57-58; mem corp, Marine Biol Lab, Woods Hole. *Mem:* Fel AAAS; Soc Gen Physiol. Am Physiol Soc; Sigma Xi. *Res:* Energy in living systems; instrumentation; international cooperative science programs; science education. *Mailing Add:* Div of Int Progs Nat Sci Found Washington DC 20550

RONN, AVIGDOR MEIR, b Tel-Aviv, Israel, Nov 17, 38; m 63; c 2. CHEMICAL PHYSICS. *Educ:* Univ Calif, Berkeley, BSc, 63; Harvard Univ, AM, 64, PhD(phys chem), 66. *Prof Exp:* Res chemist, Nat Bur Standards, 66-68; from asst prof to assoc prof phys chem, Polytech Inst Brooklyn, 68-72; assoc prof chem, 73-76, PROF CHEM, BROOKLYN COL, 76- *Concurrent Pos:* Vis prof, Tel-Aviv Univ Israel, 71-72; Alfred P Sloan fel, 71-73; vis prof, Univ Sao Paulo, 73; vpres & gen mgr, LIC Indust, Inc, 79-81. *Mem:* AAAS; Am Phys Soc. *Res:* Double resonance and energy transfer in rotational and vibrational spectra; infrared lasers; relaxation phenomena in gas lasers; laser catalyzed chemical reactions and laser induced isotope separation. *Mailing Add:* Dept of Chem Brooklyn Col New York NY 11210

RONNINGEN, REGINALD MARTIN, b Frederic, Wis, Aug 19, 47. NUCLEAR PHYSICS. *Educ:* Univ Wis-River Falls, BS, 69; Vanderbilt Univ, PhD(physics), 75. *Prof Exp:* Res assoc physics, Vanderbilt Univ & Oak Ridge Nat Lab, 74-77; res assoc physics, Max-Planck für Kernphysik, Heidelberg, 77-78; res asst prof physics, 78-81, SPECIALIST, MICH STATE UNIV, EAST LANSING, 81- *Mem:* Sigma Xi. *Res:* In-beam gamma ray spectroscopy, light and heavy ion Coulomb excitation, in elastic scattering. *Mailing Add:* Nat Superconducting Cyclotron Lab Mich State Univ East Lansing MI 48824

RONNINGEN, THOMAS SPOONER, b Hammond, Wis, Oct 3, 18; m 45; c 3. AGRONOMY, CROP BREEDING. *Educ:* Univ Wis, River Falls, BS, 39; Univ Wis, Madison, MS, 47, PhD(agron), 49. *Prof Exp:* Teacher high sch, Ind, 39-41; chemist, E I du Pont de Nemours & Co, Ind, 41-43; asst agron, Univ Wis, 46-49; from asst prof to assoc prof, Univ Md, 49-56; prin agronomist, 56-63, asst to adminstr, 63-65, asst adminstr, 65-73, assoc adminr, Coop State Res Serv, 73-77, assoc dep dir coop res, Sci & Educ Admin, 77-79, DIR-AT-LARGE, NORTHEAST STATE AGR EXP STAS, USDA, 79- *Concurrent Pos:* Partic, Fed Exec Inst, Va, 70; dir, Turkish Exec Mgt Seminar, 70-71. *Mem:* Fel AAAS; fel Am Soc Agron; Am Inst Biol Sci. *Res:* Forage breeding and management; microclimatology. *Mailing Add:* 1919 Blackbriar St Silver Spring MD 20903

RONY, PETER R(OLAND), b Paris, France, June 29, 39; US citizen; m 62; c 3. PHYSICAL CHEMISTRY, CHEMICAL ENGINEERING. *Educ:* Calif Inst Technol, BS, 60; Univ Calif, Berkeley, PhD(chem eng), 65. *Prof Exp:* Res specialist, Monsanto Co, 65-70; sr res engr, Esso Res & Develop Co, 70-71; assoc prof chem eng, 71-76, PROF CHEM ENG, VA POLYTECH INST & STATE UNIV, 76- *Honors & Awards:* Dreyfuss Found Teacher-Scholar grant, 74. *Mem:* Am Chem Soc; Am Inst Chem Engrs; Inst Elec & Electronics Engrs; Am Soc Elec Engrs. *Res:* Microcomputers; digital electronics; digital controls; chemical microengineering; multiphase catalysis; homogeneous and heterogeneous catalysis; guerilla science; computer sciences; hardware systems. *Mailing Add:* Dept of Chemical Eng Va Polytech Inst & State Univ Blacksburg VA 24061

RONZIO, ROBERT A, b Boulder, Colo, Jan 24, 38. BIOCHEMISTRY, NUTRITION. *Educ:* Reed Col, BA, 60; Univ Calif, Berkeley, PhD(biochem), 66. *Prof Exp:* NIH fel biochem, Med Sch, Tufts Univ, 65-67; Am Cancer Soc fel, Univ Wash, 67-69; asst prof biochem, Mich State Univ, 69-74, assoc prof, 74-77. *Concurrent Pos:* USPHS res career develop award, 72-77; adj prof, Evergreen State Col, 80- *Mem:* Am Chem Soc; Soc Nutrit Educ; Sigma Xi; Soc Complex Carbohydrates; Soc Health & Human Values. *Res:* Formation and function of mammalian cell membranes; embryology. *Mailing Add:* Evergreen State Col Olympia WA 98505

ROOBOL, NORMAN R, b Grand Rapids, Mich, Aug 19, 34; m 55; c 4. ORGANIC CHEMISTRY, MATERIALS SCIENCE. *Educ:* Calvin Col, BS, 58; Mich State Univ, PhD(org chem), 62. *Prof Exp:* Chemist, Shell Develop Co, 62-65; asst prof org chem, 65-68, assoc prof mat sci, 68-71, PROF MAT SCI, GEN MOTORS INST, 71- *Concurrent Pos:* Consult coatings appln, 79-; Rodes prof, Rüsselsheim, WGermany. *Res:* paints and coatings application. *Mailing Add:* Gen Motors Inst 1700 W Third Ave Flint MI 48502

ROOD, JOSEPH LLOYD, b May 2, 22; m 49; c 4. PHYSICS. *Educ:* Univ Calif, AB, 43, MA, 47, PhD(physics), 48. *Prof Exp:* Asst physics, Univ Calif, 43-48; from instr to assoc prof, Univ San Francisco, 48-56; head mat physics lab, Bausch & Lomb, Inc, 56-67; PROF PHYSICS, UNIV LETHBRIDGE, 67- *Mem:* AAAS; Am Phys Soc; Optical Soc Am; Am Ceramic Soc; Am Asn Physics Teachers. *Res:* Optical and solid state properties of materials, especially glass and other ceramics. *Mailing Add:* Dept of Physics Univ of Lethbridge Lethbridge AB T0L 0Z0 Can

ROOD, ROBERT THOMAS, b Raleigh, NC, Mar 30, 42. ASTROPHYSICS. *Educ:* NC State Univ, BS, 64; Mass Inst Technol, PhD(physics), 69. *Prof Exp:* Res assoc physics, Mass Inst Technol, 69-71; res fel, Kellogg Lab, Calif Inst Technol, 71-73; asst prof, 73-78, ASSOC PROF ASTRON, UNIV VA, 78- *Mem:* AAAS; Am Astron Soc; Int Astron Union. *Res:* Stellar interiors. *Mailing Add:* Dept of Astron Univ of Va Charlottesville VA 22903

ROODMAN, STANFORD TRENT, b St Louis, Mo, Sept 17, 39; m 61; c 2. IMMUNOLOGY, BIOCHEMISTRY. *Educ:* Purdue Univ, BS, 61; Univ Mich, PhD(biochem), 68. *Prof Exp:* NIH fel, Univ Calif, San Diego, 68-70; asst prof biochem, 70-74, ASST PROF PATH, MED SCH, ST LOUIS UNIV, 74- & DIR GRAD PROG PATH, 78- *Concurrent Pos:* Vis asst prof, Med Sch, Washington Univ, 81-82. *Mem:* AAAS; Am Chem Soc. *Res:* Characterization of nuclear ribonucleoprotein antigens uninvolved in diagnosis of autoimmune diseases; clinical immunology; pathology. *Mailing Add:* Dept Path St Louis Univ Med Sch St Louis MO 63104

ROOF, BETTY SAMS, b Columbia, SC, Apr 13, 26; div; c 4. INTERNAL MEDICINE. *Educ:* Univ SC, BS, 44; Duke Univ, MD, 49. *Prof Exp:* Vol vis investr, Rockefeller Inst, New York, 49-50; from intern to asst resident med, Presby Hosp, New York, 50-53; vis fel, Col Physicians & Surgeons, Columbia Univ, 53-55; clin & res fel, Mass Gen Hosp, Boston, 55-56; asst, Rockefeller Inst, 56-57; res fel, Mass Gen Hosp, 57-59; asst res physician, Cancer Res Inst, Univ Calif, San Francisco, 62-63, assoc res physician, 67-71, lectr med, Dept Med & assoc res physician, Cancer Res Inst, 71-74, assoc clin prof med, Dept Med, 74; assoc prof, 74-80, PROF MED, MED UNIV SC, 80- *Honors & Awards:* Cert of Merit, AMA, 74; Pres Award, Am Col Obstet-Gynec, 75. *Mem:* Endocrine Soc; Int Endocrine Soc; Western Soc Clin Res; Am Soc Bone & Mineral Res; Am Asn Cancer Res. *Res:* Parathyroid hormone produced by non-endocrine tumors; metabolic bone disease; post-menopausal osteoporosis; breast cancer therapy with hormone; hyperparathyroidism. *Mailing Add:* Med Univ of SC 171 Ashley Ave Charleston SC 29425

ROOF, JACK GLYNDON, b Cleburne, Tex, June 17, 13; m 41; c 3. PHYSICAL CHEMISTRY. *Educ:* Univ Calif, Los Angeles, BA, 34, MA, 35; Univ Wis, PhD(phys chem), 38. *Prof Exp:* From instr to asst prof chem, Ore State Col, 38-46; sr chemist, Shell Develop Co, 46-63, res assoc, 63-70; INSTR CHEM, GALVESTON COL, 70- *Concurrent Pos:* Chemist, Nat Defense Res Comt, Northwestern Univ, 42-45; consult, Univ Calif, 46; mem, Joint Task Force One, Bikini, 46. *Mailing Add:* Galveston Col 4015 Ave Q Galveston TX 77550

ROOF, RAYMOND BRADLEY, JR, b Battle Creek, Mich, Mar 3, 29; m 51; c 2. CRYSTALLOGRAPHY. *Educ:* Univ Mich, BS(chem eng) & BS(metall eng), 51, MS, 52, PhD(mineral, crystallog), 55. *Prof Exp:* Sr engr, Atomic Power Div, Westinghouse Elec Corp, 55-57; CRYSTALLOGRAPHER, LOS ALAMOS SCI LAB, 57- *Concurrent Pos:* Vis lectr, Univ Western Australia, 70; adj prof, Univ NMex, 71-72; mem, Joint Comt on Powder Diffraction Stands, 75- *Mem:* Am Crystallog Asn. *Res:* Crystallographic structure analysis; powder patterns; computer programming; metallurgical identifications; synthetic minerals. *Mailing Add:* 128 Bandelier White Rock Los Alamos NM 87544

ROOFE, PAUL GIBBONS, b Gainesville, Mo, Dec 25, 99; m 28; c 1. ANATOMY. *Educ:* Kans State Col, BS, 24; Meadville Theol Sch, BD, 29; Univ Chicago, PhD(anat), 34. *Prof Exp:* Dir, Thessalonica Agr & Indust Inst, Greece, 24-25; instr chem, Haskell Inst, 25-27; dairy chemist, Sidney Wanzer & Sons, Ill, 30-34; asst anat, Univ Louisville, 34-35; from instr to asst prof, 35-45; prof anat, 45-61, chmn dept, 45-70, prof anat & zool, 63-70, EMER PROF ANAT & ZOOL, UNIV KANS, 70- *Concurrent Pos:* Spec res fel, NIH, 57-58. *Mem:* AAAS; Am Asn Anat; Am Soc Zool; Soc Gen Syst Res; Asn Res Nerv & Ment Dis. *Res:* Endocranial blood vessels and histology of paraphysis of Amphibians; effect of radium chloride and protein deficiencies upon hematopoiesis; chemical patterns in neurogenesis; blood flow in the brain capillaries. *Mailing Add:* 1400 Lilac Lane Apt 302 Lawrence KS 66044

ROOK, HARRY LORENZ, b Middletown, Conn, May 31, 40; m 63; c 2. ANALYTICAL CHEMISTRY. *Educ:* Worcester Polytech Inst, BS, 62, MS, 67; Tex A&M Univ, PhD(anal chem), 69. *Prof Exp:* Anal chemist, Monsanto Res Corp, 62-65; res chemist, 69-75, sect chief neutron activation anal, 75-78, CHIEF GAS & PARTICULATE SCI DIV, CTR ANAL CHEM, NAT BUR STANDARDS, 78- *Concurrent Pos:* Sci consult to subcomt on environ & atmosphere, Comt Sci & Technol, US House of Representatives, 75; chmn radioactivity, Off Water Data Coord, 75- *Mem:* Am Chem Soc; Sigma Xi; Am Soc Testing & Mats. *Res:* Analytical methodology using nuclear techniques; studies into proper methods of sampling, storage and preservation of analytical samples; environmental analysis. *Mailing Add:* Off of Environ Measurements Nat Bur of Standards Washington DC 20234

ROOKS, H CORBYN, b Grand Rapids, Mich, Feb 9, 10; m 37; c 2. ENERGY, HEAT TRANSFER. *Educ:* Univ Mich, BS, 32, MS, 33. *Prof Exp:* Engr, Trane Co, 34-35, mgr coil sales, 35-37, mgr heat transfer sales, 37-51, vpres, 51-59, vpres eng, 59-68, vpres eng & res, 68-75; ENERGY CONSULT, US DEPT ENERGY, 75- *Concurrent Pos:* Consult, Dept of Appl Sci, Brookhaven Nat Lab, 76-, Off Technol Assessment, US Cong, 76-78 & Energy & Environ Div, Lawrence Berkeley Lab, 77- *Mem:* Am Soc Heating, Refrig & Air-Conditioning Engrs; Int Solar Energy Soc; Am Soc Eng Educ; Am Soc Mech Engrs; AAAS. *Res:* Solar energy. *Mailing Add:* 2607 Cass St La Crosse WI 54601

ROOKS, WENDELL HOFMA, II, b Ann Arbor, Mich, Oct 2, 31; m 55; c 5. PHARMACOLOGY. *Educ:* Calvin Col, AB, 53; Univ Mich, MS, 54. *Prof Exp:* Staff scientist, Worcester Found Exp Biol, Shrewsbury, Mass, 56-64; asst dept head bioassay, Inst Hormone Biol, Syntex Corp, 64-65, head dept bioassay, 65-73, ASST DIR INST BIOL SCI, RES DIV, SYNTEX USA INC, 73- *Mem:* Am Soc Pharmacol & Exp Therapeut. *Res:* Steroid and prostaglandin bioassay; anti-inflammatory and immuno-suppressive pharmacology; reproductive physiology; acne vulgaris. *Mailing Add:* Dept Bioassay R1-177 Syntex Corp 3401 Hillview Ave Palo Alto CA 94304

ROON, ROBERT JACK, b Grand Rapids, Mich, Nov 3, 43; m 66; c 1. BIOCHEMISTRY, MICROBIOLOGY. *Educ:* Calvin Col, BS, 65; Univ Mich, Ann Arbor, MS, 67, PhD(biochem), 69. *Prof Exp:* Teaching asst biochem, Univ Mich, Ann Arbor, 65-69; Am Cancer Soc fel, Univ Calif, Berkeley, 70-71; asst prof, 71-77, ASSOC PROF BIOCHEM, UNIV MINN,

MINNEAPOLIS, 77- *Concurrent Pos:* NSF fel, Univ Calif, Berkeley, 78. *Res:* Regulation of nitrogen metabolism in saccharomyces mechanism of amino acid transport in saccharomyces; biochemistry of protein secretion in saccharomyces. *Mailing Add:* Dept of Biochem Univ of Minn Minneapolis MN 55455

ROONEY, JAMES ARTHUR, b Springfield, Vt, Sept 15, 43; m 67; c 1. PHYSICS. *Educ:* Clark Univ, Mass, BA, 65; Univ Vt, MS, 67, PhD(physics), 70. *Prof Exp:* Res assoc physics, Univ Vt, 71-72; asst prof, 72-76, ASSOC PROF PHYSICS, UNIV MAINE, 76- *Mem:* Am Asn Advan Med Instrumentation; Am Inst Ultrasound in Med; Acoust Soc Am; AAAS. *Res:* Biomedical ultrasonics concerning biological effects of ultrasound on membranes and enzymes as well as applications of sound and ultrasound to dispersal of cell aggregates; blood pressure measurements and coagulation studies. *Mailing Add:* Dept of Physics Univ of Maine Orono ME 04473

ROONEY, LAWRENCE FREDERICK, b Conrad, Mont, Nov 21, 26; m 56. ECONOMIC GEOLOGY. *Educ:* Univ Mont, BA, 48, MA, 50; Ind Univ, PhD(geol), 56. *Prof Exp:* Jr geologist, Mobil Oil Can, 56-58; asst prof geol, Univ Tex, 58-59; geologist, Humble Oil & Refining Co, 60-62 & Ind Geol Surv, 62-70; prof geol, Flathead Valley Community Col, 70-75; GEOLOGIST, US GEOL SURVEY, 75- *Mem:* Geol Soc Am; Am Inst Mining, Metall & Petrol Eng. *Res:* Geology of industrial minerals. *Mailing Add:* US Geol Surv c|o Am Embassy APO New York NY 22092

ROONEY, LLOYD WILLIAM, b Atwood, Kans, July 17, 39; m 63; c 3. FOOD SCIENCE. *Educ:* Kans State Univ, BS, 61, PhD(cereal chem), 66. *Prof Exp:* Res asst grain sci, Kans State Univ, 63-65; from asst prof to assoc prof cereal chem, 65-77, PROF AGRON, TEX A&M UNIV, 77- *Mem:* AAAS; Am Asn Cereal Chemists; Inst Food Technologists; Am Chem Soc; Am Soc Agron. *Res:* Research program on determination of physical, chemical, nutritional and processing properties of cereal grains, especially sorghum and wheat, involving close cooperation with plant breeders to use genetic material for cereal improvement. *Mailing Add:* Dept Agron Tex A&M Univ College Station TX 77843

ROONEY, PAUL GEORGE, b New York, NY, July 14, 25; Can citizen; m 50; c 5. MATHEMATICS. *Educ:* Univ Alta, BSc, 49; Calif Inst Technol, PhD(math), 52. *Prof Exp:* Lectr math, Univ Alta, 52-54; asst prof, 54-55; from asst prof to assoc prof, 55-62, PROF MATH, UNIV TORONTO, 62- *Concurrent Pos:* Ed-in-chief, Can J Math, 71-75. *Mem:* Am Math Soc; Math Asn Am; Can Math Soc (vpres, 79-81, pres, 81-); fel Royal Soc Can. *Res:* Functional analysis. *Mailing Add:* Dept Math Univ Toronto Toronto ON M5S 1A1 Can

ROONEY, SEAMUS AUGUSTINE, b Cork, Ireland, Dec 19, 43; US citizen; m 68; c 3. LIPID BIOCHEMISTRY, LUNG BIOCHEMISTRY. *Educ:* Nat Univ, Ireland, BSc, 64, MSc, 66; Dublin Univ, PhD(biochem), 69. *Prof Exp:* Fel lipid chem, Dept Microbiol, Univ Pa, 69-72; res assoc 72-77, sr res assoc, 77-81, SR RES SCIENTIST, DEPT PEDIAT, SCH MED, YALE UNIV, 81- *Mem:* Am Soc Biol Chemists; Soc Pediat Res; Perinatal Res Soc; Am Thoracic Soc; Am Physiol Soc. *Res:* Hormonal control of pulmonary surfactant production during fetal development. *Mailing Add:* Dept of Pediat Sch of Med Yale Univ New Haven CT 06510

ROONEY, THOMAS PETER, b New York, NY, June 29, 32; m 65; c 2. GEOLOGY. *Educ:* City Col New York, BS, 59; Columbia Univ, MA, 62, PhD(geol), 65. *Prof Exp:* GEOPHYSICIST, TERRESTRIAL SCI DIV, AIR FORCE Geophysics Lab, 66- *Mem:* Geol Soc Am; Am Geophys Union. *Res:* Satellite altimetry; remote sensing; rock deformation. *Mailing Add:* Terrestrial Sci Div Air Force Geophysics Lab Hanscom AFB MA 01731

ROONEY, VICTOR MARTIN, b Paris, Ill, Oct 9, 37; m 60; c 1. ELECTRONIC ENGINEERING. *Educ:* Univ Dayton, BEE, 65; Ohio State Univ, MSc, 70. *Prof Exp:* From instr to assoc prof, 70-78, PROF ELECTRONIC ENG, UNIV DAYTON, 78- *Concurrent Pos:* Bioeng consult, Miami Valley Hosp, 73-; ad hoc visitor, Engrs Coun Prof, 73- *Mem:* Inst Elec & Electronics Engrs. *Res:* Mocroprocessors; bioengineering; analysis of linear circuits; passive and active components. *Mailing Add:* Dept of Electronic Eng Technol 300 College Park Dayton OH 45469

ROOP, ROBERT DICKINSON, b Plainfield, NJ, Sept 23, 49. BIOLOGY, ECOLOGY. *Educ:* Hiram Col, BA, 71; State Univ NY Stony Brook, MA, 75. *Prof Exp:* Staff ecologist, Inst Ecol, 74-76; RES ASSOC, OAK RIDGE NAT LAB, 76- *Mem:* AAAS; Am Inst Biol Sci; Ecol Soc Am; Water Pollution Control Fedn. *Res:* Environmental impact assessment for energy programs and facilities. *Mailing Add:* Bldg 2001 Oak Ridge Nat Lab Oak Ridge TN 37830

ROORDA, JOHN, b Tzummarum, Neth, June 22, 39; Can citizen; m 62; c 4. CIVIL ENGINEERING, APPLIED MECHANICS. *Educ:* Univ Waterloo, BASc, 62; Univ London, PhD(struct eng), 65. *Prof Exp:* Fel, civil eng, Northwestern Univ, 65-66; from asst prof to assoc prof, 66-74, PROF CIVIL ENG, UNIV WATERLOO, 74- *Concurrent Pos:* Sr vis fel, Sci Res Coun, Eng, 68; vis prof, Cranfield Inst Technol, Eng, 71 & Univ Col, London, 74 & 78. *Res:* Structural analysis; stability of structures; dynamic response of structures; vibration problems; theory of elasticity. *Mailing Add:* 569 Glen Manor Blvd Waterloo ON H2L 4T7 Can

ROOS, ALBERT, b Leyden, Neth, Nov 22, 14; nat US; m 46; c 2. PHYSIOLOGY. *Educ:* State Univ Groningen, MD, 40. *Prof Exp:* Fel cardiol, 46-47, from instr to asst prof physiol, 47-54, assoc prof physiol & surg, 54-61, assoc prof physiol, 61-70, PROF PHYSIOL & BIOPHYS, SCH MED, WASH UNIV, 70-, RES PROF ANESTHESIOL, 61- *Mem:* AAAS; Am Physiol Soc. *Res:* Physiology of respiration; membrane transport. *Mailing Add:* Dept of Physiol & Biophys Wash Univ Sch of Med St Louis MO 63110

ROOS, C(HARLES) WILLIAM, b Cairo, Ill, July 2, 27; m 50; c 3. CHEMICAL ENGINEERING. *Educ:* Wash Univ, BS, 48, MS, 49, DSc(chem eng), 51. *Prof Exp:* Asst chem eng, Wash Univ, 50-51; res chem engr, 51-56, group leader chem eng res, 56-59, sect leader, 59-63, technologist, 63-66, mgr res & develop pioneering res, 66-68, mgr petrol additives res, 68-70, dir technol planning & eval, 70-75, gen mgr, New Enterprise Div, 75-77, dir, Corp Res Labs, 77-79, DIR, TECHNOL ADMIN, MONSANTO CO, 79- *Concurrent Pos:* Lectr, Wash Univ, 51- & St Louis Univ, 59- *Mem:* Am Inst Chem Engrs; Nat Soc Prof Engrs. *Res:* Catalysis; biochemistry; analytical chemistry; chemical process development; reaction kinetics; research project evaluation; resource allocation. *Mailing Add:* Monsanto Co 800 N Lindbergh Blvd St Louis MO 63166

ROOS, CHARLES EDWIN, b Chicago, Ill, Apr 23, 27; m 52; c 4. NUCLEAR PHYSICS. *Educ:* Univ Tex, BA, 48; Johns Hopkins Univ, PhD(physics), 53. *Prof Exp:* Assoc res staff, Johns Hopkins Univ, 53; from instr to asst prof physics, Univ Calif, 53-59; vis assoc prof, 58-59, assoc prof, 59-65, PROF PHYSICS, VANDERBILT UNIV, 65- *Concurrent Pos:* Res fel, Calif Inst Technol, 56-59; guest physicist, Brookhaven Nat Lab. *Mem:* Am Phys Soc; NY Acad Sci. *Res:* Auger transitions; x-rays; nuclear emulsions; photo mesonic reactions; high field magnets; superconductivity; hyperon magnetic moments. *Mailing Add:* Dept of Physics & Astron Vanderbilt Univ Nashville TN 37240

ROOS, FREDERICK WILLIAM, b Sault Ste Marie, Mich, June 4, 40; m 63; c 1. AEROSPACE ENGINEERING. *Educ:* Univ Mich, BSE, 63, MSE, 65, PhD(aerospace eng), 68. *Prof Exp:* SCIENTIST, FLIGHT SCI DEPT, McDONNELL DOUGLAS RES LABS, McDONNELL DOUGLAS CORP, 68- *Mem:* Am Inst Aeronaut & Astronaut. *Res:* Unsteady separated fluid flows with emphasis on aircraft buffeting at low and transonic speed. *Mailing Add:* Flight Sci Dept PO Box 516 St Louis MO 63166

ROOS, HENRY, b Jersey City, NJ, Dec 25, 21; m 54; c 1. MICROSCOPIC ANATOMY, PHYSIOLOGY. *Educ:* City Col New York, BS, 43; Columbia Univ, MA, 46, EdD(sci educ), 61; Univ NC, MPH, 52. *Prof Exp:* Asst prof biol, Westfield State Teachers Col, 47-48; instr, Springfield Col, 48-49; asst prof, ECarolina Col, 49-50; health educator, Hudson County Tuberc & Health Asn, 52-54; instr biol, Westchester Community Col, 55-61; assoc prof, 61-68, PROF BIOL, EASTERN CONN STATE COL, 68- *Mem:* AAAS; Nat Asn Biol Teachers. *Res:* hematopoiesis in mouse spleen; energy potential of Connecticut farm wastes. *Mailing Add:* Dept of Biol Eastern Conn State Col Willimantic CT 06226

ROOS, JOHN FRANCIS, b Seattle, Wash, Jan 18, 32; m 56; c 3. FISHERIES MANAGEMENT. *Educ:* Univ Wash, BS, 55. *Prof Exp:* Proj leader chignik sockeye salmon studies, Fisheries Res Inst, Univ Wash, 55-60; asst dir, 71-82, DIR, INT PAC SALMON FISHERIES COMN, 71-, CHIEF BIOLOGIST, 68- *Mem:* Am Fisheries Soc; Am Inst Fishery Res Biologists; Pac Fishery Biologists. *Mailing Add:* Int Pac Salmon Fisheries Comn New Westminister BC V3A 4X9 Can

ROOS, LEO, b Amsterdam, Neth, Nov 10, 37; US citizen; m 61; c 3. PHYSICAL ORGANIC CHEMISTRY, PHOTOCHEMISTRY. *Educ:* City Col New York, BS, 61; Univ Cincinnati, PhD(phys org chem), 65. *Prof Exp:* Res chemist, Photoproducts Dept, E I du Pont de Nemours & Co, Inc, 65-71, sr res chemist, 71-76; DIR NEW IMAGING SYSTS, XIDEX CORP, 76- *Mem:* AAAS; Am Chem Soc; Soc Photog Sci & Eng. *Res:* Photopolymerization; homogeneous catalysis, specifically reaction of cobalt carbonyls with olefins. *Mailing Add:* 6427 Berwickshire Way San Jose CA 95120

ROOS, PHILIP G, b Wauseon, Ohio, May 16, 38; m 63; c 1. NUCLEAR PHYSICS. *Educ:* Ohio Wesleyan Univ, BA, 60; Mass Inst Technol, PhD(physics), 64. *Prof Exp:* Vis asst prof physics, Univ Md, 64-65; AEC fel nuclear physics, Oak Ridge Nat Lab, 65-70; from asst prof to assoc prof nuclear physics, 71-75, PROF PHYSICS & ASTRON, UNIV MD, COLLEGE PARK, 75- *Res:* Study of nuclear reactions and nuclear structure using particle accelerators. *Mailing Add:* Dept of Physics Univ of Md College Park MD 20740

ROOS, RAYMOND PHILIP, b Brooklyn, NY, Apr 5, 44; m 67; c 1. NEUROLOGY, VIROLOGY. *Educ:* Columbia Col, BA, 64; State Univ NY Downstate Med Ctr, MD, 68. *Prof Exp:* Intern med, State Univ NY, Kings County Hosp, Brooklyn, 68-69; staff assoc spec chronic dis study sect, Nat Inst Neurol Dis & Stroke, 69-71; resident neurol, Johns Hopkins Univ, 71-74, instr neurol & NIH fel neurovirol, 74-78; MEM STAFF, DEPT NEUROL, MED CLINS, UNIV CHICAGO, 78- *Concurrent Pos:* Consult neurol, Moore Genetics Clin, Johns Hopkins Univ, 75. *Mem:* Am Acad Neurol. *Res:* Relationship of virus infections, especially defective, slow or unconventional infections to neurological degenerative diseases; virological etiology to certain neurological heritable diseases. *Mailing Add:* Dept Neurol 950 E 59th St Chicago IL 60637

ROOS, THOMAS BLOOM, b Peoria, Ill, Mar 19, 30; m 53; c 2. ZOOLOGY. *Educ:* Harvard Univ, AB, 51; Univ Wis, MS, 53, PhD(zool), 60. *Prof Exp:* Instr zool, Univ Wis, 60; from instr to prof zool, 60-71, CHMN DEPT, 69-70, 78- PROF BIOL, DARTMOUTH COL, 71- *Concurrent Pos:* USPHS spec fel, 66-67; mem comn undergrad educ biol sci, NSF, 66-70; hon res fel, Univ Col, London, 74-75. *Mem:* AAAS; Am Soc Zool. *Res:* Phylogenetic and ontogenetic development of hormonal secretory function and responsivity; theoretical biology; use of computers in biology. and teaching of biology; automation of data collection and anylsis. *Mailing Add:* Dept of Biol Sci Dartmouth Col Hanover NH 03755

ROOSA, ROBERT ANDREW, b Manila, Philippines, June 18, 25; US citizen; m 52; c 3. MEDICAL MICROBIOLOGY, GENETICS. *Educ:* Univ Conn, BA, 50; Univ Pa, PhD(med microbiol), 57. *Prof Exp:* Res asst, Sch Med, Yale Univ, 50-52; Nat Found fel, 57; fel, Nat Cancer Inst, 57-60; res assoc, 60-64, dept dir sci serv, 69-74, ASSOC PROF, WISTAR INST ANAT & BIOL, 64-, CUR MUS, 69-, SCI ADMINR, 75- *Concurrent Pos:* Eleanor Roosevelt Int Cancer Res fel, Med Res Coun Exp Virus Res Unit, Univ Glasgow, 67-68; ed, Info Newslett Somatic Cell Genetics, 69-73. *Mem:* AAAS; Tissue Cult Asn; Am Asn Cancer Res; Radiation Res Soc; Am Assoc Lab Animal Sci. *Res:* Nuclear cytology; cancer chemotherapy; mechanisms of drug resistance; nutritional requirements of cells in culture; somatic cell genetics; tumor transplantation; role of the thymus in immunobiology; slow virus diseases of mammals. *Mailing Add:* Wistar Inst of Anat & Biol 36th & Spruce Sts Philadelphia PA 19104

ROOSENRAAD, CRIS THOMAS, b Lansing, Mich, July 28, 41; m 64. MATHEMATICS. *Educ:* Univ Mich, BSc, 63, MSc, 64; Univ Wis, PhD(math), 69. *Prof Exp:* Asst prof math, 69-75, ASSOC DEAN & LECTR MATH, WILLIAMS COL, 75- *Mem:* Am Math Soc; Math Asn Am. *Res:* Orthogonal polynomials; special functions. *Mailing Add:* Dept of Math Williams Col Williamstown MA 01267

ROOSEVELT, C(ORNELIUS) V(AN) S(CHAAK), b New York, NY, Oct 23, 15. MINING ENGINEERING, ELECTRONICS. *Educ:* Mass Inst Technol, BS, 38. *Prof Exp:* Engr, Am Smelting & Refining Co, Mex, 38-41; mgr, Mining Div, William Hunt & Co, China, 46-49, pres & dir, 49-50; res administr, Off Naval Res, 52-62; pres & dir, Linderman Eng Co, 54-68; vpres, US Banknote Co, Philadelphia, 65-70. *Concurrent Pos:* Pres & dir, Int Industs, Inc, Hong Kong, 49-50; vpres, Security Banknote Co, Philadelphia, 49-65; consult, US Intel Bd, 64-74; dir, Columbia Res Corp, DC, 68-; mem bd trustees, The Aerospace Corp, Los Angeles, 78- *Mem:* AAAS; Soc Indust Archaeol; NY Acad Sci. *Res:* Industrial electronic control equipment; industrial archaeology; naval electronic equipment; scuba equipment. *Mailing Add:* 2500 Que St NW Apt 604 Washington DC 20007

ROOT, ALLEN WILLIAM, b Philadelphia, Pa, Sept 24, 33; m 58; c 3. PEDIATRIC ENDOCRINOLOGY. *Educ:* Dartmouth Col, AB, 55; Harvard Univ, MD, 58; Am Bd Pediat, dipl, 64, dipl endocrinol, 78. *Prof Exp:* Intern. Strong Mem Hosp, Rochester, NY, 58-60; resident pediat, Hosp Univ Pa, Philadelphia, 60-62; fel pediat endocrinol, Children's Hosp Philadelphia, 62-65; assoc physician pediat, Sch Med, Univ Pa, 64-66, asst prof, 66-69; from assoc prof to prof, Sch Med, Temple Univ, 69-73; PROF PEDIAT & HEAD SECT PEDIAT ENDOCRINOL, COL MED, UNIV S FLA, 73-; DIR UNIV SERV, ALL CHILDREN'S HOSP, ST PETERSBURG, 73- *Concurrent Pos:* Asst physician endocrinol, Children's Hosp Philadelphia, 65-66; USPHS career develop award, 68-69; chmn, Div Pediat, Albert Einstein Med Ctr, Philadelphia, 69-73; consult ed, J Pediat, 73-81 & J Adolescent Health Care, 79-; mem med adv bd, Nat Pituitary Agency, 74- *Mem:* Endocrine Soc; AAAS; Am Pediat Soc; Am Acad Pediat; Soc Pediat Res. *Res:* Investigation of factors which regulate function of the hypothalamic-pituitary unit and the mechanisms of pubertal maturation and the effects of prenatal events upon development of the hypothalamic-pituitary axis. *Mailing Add:* 4916 St Croix Dr Tampa FL 33609

ROOT, CHARLES ARTHUR, b Rochester, NY, Aug 25, 38; m 63; c 2. INORGANIC CHEMISTRY. *Educ:* Ohio Wesleyan Univ, BA, 60; Ohio State Univ, MSc, 62, PhD(chem), 65. *Prof Exp:* Instr chem, 65-66, asst prof, 66-72, ASSOC PROF CHEM, BUCKNELL UNIV, 72- *Concurrent Pos:* NSF fac fel, Calif Inst Technol, 71-72, vis assoc prof, 79-80. *Mem:* AAAS; Am Chem Soc; Soc Environ Geochem & Health. *Res:* Reactions at coordinated sulfur and coordinated aziridines; aziridine and N-substituted aziridine complexes with transition metal ions. *Mailing Add:* Dept of Chem Bucknell Univ Lewisburg PA 17837

ROOT, DAVID HARLEY, b Columbus, Ohio, Oct 10, 37; m 67; c 2. MATHEMATICS, ENERGY RESOURCES. *Educ:* Mass Inst Technol, BS, 59; Univ Wash, PhD(math), 68. *Prof Exp:* Asst prof math & statist, Purdue Univ, 68-74; MATHEMATICIAN, US GEOL SURV, 74- *Mem:* AAAS. *Res:* Study of the methods of extimation of the remnants of fossil fuels and of the potentials of various non-fossil fuel energy resources. *Mailing Add:* US Geol Surv Nat Ctr Mail Stop 922 Reston VA 22092

ROOT, HARLAN D, b Riders Mills, NY, Feb 16, 26; m 53; c 4. SURGERY. *Educ:* Cornell Univ, AB, 50, MD, 53; Univ Minn, PhD(surg), 61, Am Bd Surg, dipl, 61. *Prof Exp:* Univ fel, Univ Minn, 54-60, Nat Cancer Soc fel, 55-59, Am Cancer Soc fel, 59-61, instr surg, Med Sch, 60-66, instr surg, Med Sch, 61, asst prof, 61-66; assoc dir surg, Ancker Hosp, St Paul, Minn; asst chmn & assoc prof, 66-67, PROF SURG & ASST CHMN UNIV TEX HEALTH SCI CTR SAN ANTONIO, 67- *Concurrent Pos:* Consult, San Antonio State Chest Hosp, 66-, Audie L Murphy Mem Vet Admin Hosp, San Antonio, 73-; surg test comt, Nat Bd Med Examiners, 77-; dist comt applicants, 77- & comt trauma, Am Col Surg, 77-80. *Mem:* AMA; fel, Am Col Surg; Am Trauma Soc; Am Asn Surg of Trauma; Western Surg Asn. *Res:* Peripheral vasular surgery. *Mailing Add:* Dept of Surg 7703 Floyd Curl Dr San Antonio TX 78284

ROOT, JOHN WALTER, b Kansas City, Mo, Oct 5, 35; m 60; c 2. PHYSICAL CHEMISTRY, RADIOCHEMISTRY. *Educ:* Univ Kans, BA, 58, PhD(chem), 64; Univ Calif, Los Angeles, cert, 66. *Prof Exp:* From asst prof to assoc prof chem, 66-75, assoc dir, Crocker Nuclear Lab, 74-77, PROF CHEM, UNIV CALIF, DAVIS, 75- *Concurrent Pos:* Consult, Gen Elec Co, 68-70; John Simon Guggenheim fel, 72-73. *Mem:* Am Chem Soc; Am Phys Soc; Am Nuclear Soc; AAAS; Sigma Xi. *Res:* Radiochemistry; hot-atom chemistry; chemical kinetics; radiation, isotope and physical chemistry. *Mailing Add:* Dept of Chem Univ of Calif Davis CA 95616

ROOT, L(EONARD) EUGENE, b Lewiston, Idaho, July 4, 10; m 35; c 3. AERONAUTICS. *Educ:* Col Pac, BA, 32; Calif Inst Technol, MS, 33 & 34. *Hon Degrees:* ScD, Col Pac, 58. *Prof Exp:* Asst chief aerodyn sect, Douglas Aircraft Co, Inc, Calif, 34-39, chief sect, 39-46, mem staff, Spec Eng Proj, 46-48; chief aircraft div, Rand Corp, 48-53; dir develop planning dept, Lockheed Aircraft Corp, 53-56, gen mgr missile & space div & vpres corp, 56-59, group vpres missiles & electronics, 59-61, pres, Lockheed Missiles & Space Co, 61-69, group vpres, Lockheed Aircraft Corp, 69-70; RETIRED. *Concurrent Pos:* Lectr, Calif Inst Technol, 37-38; consult, Hughes Aircraft Co, 42-43; mem aerodyn comt, Nat Adv Comt Aeronaut, 44-50; chmn aerodyn adv panel, Atomic Energy Comn, Sandia Corp, 48-50; mem sci adv bd, Chief Staff, US Air Force, 48-59; adv, US Air Force Inst Air Weapons Res, Univ Chicago, 50-52; spec asst to dep chief staff, Develop Hqs, US Air Force, 51-52; mem defense sci bd, Dir Defense, Res & Eng, 57-70. *Honors & Awards:* Except Serv Award, Dept Air Force, 48 & 56; Distinguished Pub Serv Award, US Dept Navy, 60; Pub Serv Award, Gemini, NASA, 66. *Mem:* Fel Am Astronaut Soc; fel Am Inst Aeronaut & Astronaut (vpres, 58, pres, 62); fel Royal Aeronaut Soc. *Res:* Aircraft design; aerodynamics; dynamic longitudinal stability; empennage design; flying qualities; systems and operational analyses in military sciences; development planning methods; missiles and spacecraft; aerospace management. *Mailing Add:* 1340 Hillview Dr Menlo Park CA 94025

ROOT, MARY AVERY, b Hartford, Conn, Oct 28, 18. PHARMACOLOGY. *Educ:* Oberlin Col, AB, 40; Radcliffe Col, MA, 49, PhD, 50. *Prof Exp:* Pharmacologist, 50-63, RES ASSOC, RES LABS, ELI LILLY & CO, 63- *Mem:* Endocrine Soc; Am Soc Pharmacol & Exp Therapeut; Soc Exp Biol & Med; Am Diabetes Asn; NY Acad Sci. *Res:* Carbohydrate metabolism; insulin, diabetes. *Mailing Add:* Res Labs Eli Lilly & Co Indianapolis IN 46285

ROOT, RICHARD BRUCE, b Dearborn, Mich, Sept 7, 36; div; c 2. ECOLOGY. *Educ:* Univ Mich, BS, 58; Univ Calif, Berkeley, PhD(zool), 64. *Prof Exp:* Assoc zool, Univ Calif, Berkeley, 60-62; from asst prof to assoc prof, 64-79, PROF ECOL, CORNELL UNIV, 79- *Concurrent Pos:* Mem field staff, Rockefeller Found, Colombia, 70-71; vis prof, Univ Valle, Colombia, 70-71; ed, Ecol & Ecol Monogr, 71-73; res assoc, Mus Vert Zool, Univ Calif, Berkeley, 75; bd dir, Orgn Trop Studies, 76- *Honors & Awards:* Howell Award, Cooper Ornith Soc, 63. *Mem:* Org Tropical Studies; Ecol Soc Am (vpres, 79-80); Brit Ecol Soc; Am Ornith Union; Royal Entom Soc London; Entom Soc Am. *Res:* Comparative ecology of insects; adaptive syndromes of birds and insects; structure of arthropod faunae associated with various plants; agricultural ecology; functional classifications. *Mailing Add:* Sect Ecol & Systematics Cornell Univ Ithaca NY 14853

ROOT, SAMUEL I, b Winnipeg, Man, Mar 1, 30; m 52; c 3. GEOLOGY. *Educ:* Univ Man, BSc, 52, MSc, 56; Ohio State Univ, PhD(geol), 58. *Prof Exp:* Geologist, Seaboard Oil Co, Can, 52-53; sr geologist, Int Petrol Co Ltd, 57-63; sr geologist, Pa State Geol Surv, 63-65, staff geologist, 65-66, chief field geologist, 66-80; MEM STAFF, ESSO PROSPECCAO LTD, BRAZIL, 80- *Mem:* Geol Soc Am; Am Asn Petrol Geologists; Soc Econ Paleontologists & Mineralogists. *Res:* Areal and structural geology; stratigraphy; nonmetallic mineral deposits. *Mailing Add:* Esso Prospeccao Ltd Caixa Postal 16153 Rio De Janeiro RJ CEP 22 210 Brazil

ROOT, WILLIAM L(UCAS), b Des Moines, Iowa, Oct 6, 19; m 40; c 2. ENGINEERING. *Educ:* Mass Inst Technol, PhD(math), 52. *Prof Exp:* Instr math, Mass Inst Technol, 47-51, mem staff, Instrumentation Lab, 51-52 & Lincoln Lab, 52-56, asst leader, Systs Res Group, 57-59, leader anal group, 59-61; PROF AEROSPACE ENG, UNIV MICH, ANN ARBOR, 61- *Concurrent Pos:* Vis lectr, Harvard Univ, 58-59; vis prof, Univ Calif, Berkeley, 66-67; NSF sr fel & vis fel, Clare Hall, Univ Cambridge, 70; mem, Army Sci Bd, 71- *Mem:* Fel Inst Elec & Electronics Engrs; Am Math Soc; Soc Indust & Appl Math. *Res:* Stochastic processes, statistical theory of communications and general system theory; system modelling and identification; estimation and detection theory; information theory. *Mailing Add:* Dept Aerospace Eng Univ Mich Ann Arbor MI 48109

ROOTARE, HILLAR MUIDAR, b Tallinn, Estonia, Apr 26, 28; US citizen; m 59; c 6. DENTAL MATERIALS, SURFACE CHEMISTRY. *Educ:* Wagner Col, BS, 52; Univ Mich, PhD(dent mat & pharmaceut chem), 73. *Prof Exp:* Chemist & res assoc, Bone Char Res Proj, Inc, Nat Bur Stand, 57-63; dir, Mat Technol Lab, Am Instrument Co, Inc, div Travenol Labs, 63-66; NIH trainee & res asst, Univ Mich, Ann Arbor, 66-73; dir tech res, L D Caulk Co, div Dentsply Int Inc, 73-75; sr res assoc, Dept Dent Mat, Sch Dent, Univ Mich, Ann Arbor, 75-77; RES SCIENTIST, MICROMERITICS INSTRUMENT CORP, 78- *Mem:* Int Asn Dent Res; Am Chem Soc; Am Soc Metals; Fine Particle Soc; Sigma Xi. *Res:* Physical and surface chemistry applied to use of hydroxyapatite as synthetic bone, in characterizing of surfaces, compaction and sintering of powders to reproduce the porous structures of bone for possible use as implants; design and construction of microprocessor controlled instrumentation for automatic measurements and analysis of pore size distributions of porous materials. *Mailing Add:* Micromeritics Instrument Corp 5680 Goshen Springs Rd Norcross GA 30093

ROOTENBERG, JACOB, b Afula, Israel, Mar 23, 36; m 68; c 2. ELECTRICAL ENGINEERING. *Educ:* Israel Inst Technol, BSc, 60, MSc, 62, PhD(elec eng), 67. *Prof Exp:* Asst elec eng, Israel Inst Technol, 60-62, instr, 62-65, lectr, 65-67; asst prof, Columbia Univ, 67-72, assoc prof, 72-76; PROF DEPT COMPUT SCI, QUEENS COL, NY, 76- *Mem:* Inst Elec & Electronics Engrs. *Res:* Control systems; optimal control; stability of nonlinear systems; simulation and bioengineering problems. *Mailing Add:* Dept of Comput Sci 65-30 Kissena Blvd Flushing NY 11367

ROOTHAAN, CLEMENS CAREL JOHANNES, b Nymegen, Neth, Aug 29, 18; US citizen; m 50; c 5. PHYSICS. *Educ:* Inst Technol, Delft, MS, 45; Univ Chicago, PhD(physics), 50. *Prof Exp:* Instr, Cath Univ Am, 47-49; res assoc, 49-50, from instr to prof, 50-68, prof commun & info sci, 65-68, dir comput ctr, 62-68, LOUIS BLOCK PROF PHYSICS, UNIV CHICAGO, 68- *Concurrent Pos:* Guggenheim fel, Cambridge Univ, 57; consult, Argonne Nat Lab, 58-66, Lockheed Missiles & Space Co, 60-65, Union Carbide Corp, 65- & IBM Corp, 65- *Mem:* Asn Comput Mach; fel Am Phys Soc. *Res:* Theory of atomic and molecular structure; application of digital computers to scientific problems. *Mailing Add:* Dept of Physics Univ of Chicago Chicago IL 60637

ROOTS, BETTY IDA, b South Croydon, Eng. ZOOLOGY. *Educ:* Univ Col, Univ London, BSc, 49, dipl educ, 50, PhD(zool), 53, DSc, 81. *Prof Exp:* Asst lectr biol, Royal Free Hosp Sch Med, Univ London, 53-59; vis asst prof physiol, Univ Ill, Urbana, 59-61; asst lectr biol, Royal Free Hosp Sch Med, Univ London, 61-62, lectr anat, Univ Col, 62-66; vis scientist physiol, Univ Ill, Urbana, 66-67; res neuroscientist, Univ Calif, San Diego, 68-69; assoc prof zool, 69-72, PROF ZOOL, UNIV TORONTO, 72- *Concurrent Pos:* Rose Sidgwick Mem fel, Univ Ill, Urbana, 59-60. *Mem:* Am Soc Neurochem; Am Oil Chem Soc; Soc Neurosci; Can Soc Zool; Int Soc Develop Neurosci. *Res:* Structural and chemical changes in nervous system in relation to environmental factors; cell isolation techniques; structure and function of glial cells. *Mailing Add:* Dept of Zool Univ of Toronto Toronto ON M5S 1A1 Can

ROOTS, ERNEST FREDERICK, b Salmon Arm, BC, July 5, 23; m 55; c 5. GEOLOGY. *Educ:* Univ BC, MASc, 47; Princeton Univ, PhD(geol), 49. *Prof Exp:* Surveyor, Nat Parks Serv, Can, 41-42; asst, Geol Surv Can, 43-44, tech officer, 45-47, geologist, 48-49; asst prof geol, Princeton Univ, 52-54; geologist, Geol Surv Can, 55-58, coordr, Polar Continetal Shelf Proj, 58-72; sr adv, Dept Energy Mines & Resources, 72-73; SCI ADV, ENVIRON DEPT ENVIRON, 73- *Concurrent Pos:* Sr Geologist, Norweg-Brit-Swed Antarctic Exped, 49-52, 54-55; pres, Int Comn Snow & Ice, 79-; mem coun, Comt Arctique, 80- *Honors & Awards:* King Haakon VII Distinguished Serv Medal, Norway, 52; Queen Elizabeth II Polar Medal, UK, 56; Patron's Medal, Royal Geog Soc, 65; Massey Medal, Royal Can Geog Soc, 79. *Mem:* Geol Soc Am; Am Geophys Union; Glaciol Soc; Arctic Inst NAm. *Res:* Tectonics and mineral deposits of Canadian cordillera; geology of Antarctica and the Himalayas; glaciology; geology and geophysics of Arctic North America and the Arctic Ocean basin. *Mailing Add:* Dept Environ Fontaine Bldg Ottawa ON K1A 0N3 Can

ROOVERS, JACQUES ELVIRE, b Deurne, Belg, June 3, 37; m 63; c 3. POLYMER CHEMISTRY, PHYSICAL CHEMISTRY. *Educ:* Cath Univ Louvain, BSc, 59, PhD(polymer chem), 62. *Prof Exp:* Nat Res Coun Can fel, 63-64; assoc pharmacol, Cath Univ Louvain, 65-66; assoc res officer, 67-77, SR RES OFFICER POLYMER CHEM, NAT RES COUN CAN, 77- *Mem:* Am Chem Soc; Can High Polymer Forum (secy, 77). *Mailing Add:* Div of Chem Nat Res Coun of Can Ottawa ON K1A 0R9 Can

ROOZEN, KENNETH JAMES, b Milwaukee, Wis, Jan 17, 43; m 66; c 3. GENETICS, MOLECULAR BIOLOGY. *Educ:* Lakeland Col, BS, 66; Univ SDak, MA, 68; Univ Tenn, Knoxville, PhD(microbial genetics), 71. *Prof Exp:* NIH fel pediat, Med Sch, Wash Univ, 71-74; asst prof, 74-80, vchmn, Dept Microbiol, 77-81, assoc dean, 78-81, ASSOC PROF MICROBIOL & DEAN & CO-DIR, GRAD SCH, UNIV ALA, BIRMINGHAM, 81- *Mem:* AAAS; Am Soc Microbiol; Sigma Xi; Am Soc Cell Biologists. *Res:* Mammalian cell genetics and biochemistry, specifically mutant isolation, correction of genetic defects, gene mapping and nucleic acid metabolism. *Mailing Add:* Dept of Microbiol Univ of Ala Birmingham AL 35226

ROPER, CLYDE FORREST EUGENE, b Ipswich, Mass, Oct 1, 37; m 58; c 2. BIOLOGICAL OCEANOGRAPHY, SYSTEMATIC ZOOLOGY. *Educ:* Transylvania Col, AB, 59; Univ Miami, Fla, MS, 62, PhD(marine sci), 67. *Prof Exp:* Sr res asst oceanog, Inst Marine Sci, Univ Miami, 64-66; assoc cur, 66-72, supvr mollusks, 68-70, CUR, SMITHSONIAN INST, 72- *Concurrent Pos:* Adj assoc prof, Inst Marine Sci, Univ Miami, 67-; adj lectr, George Washington Univ, 68-; affil grad fac, Dept Oceanog, Univ Hawaii, 75-76; chmn, Dept Invertebrate Zool, Nat Museum Natural Hist, Smithsonian Inst, 80- *Mem:* Soc Syst Zool; Australian Malacol Soc; Am Malacol Union; Marine Biol Asn UK; Inst Malacol. *Res:* Systematics and ecology of recent Cephalopoda of the world, particularly oceanic forms; phylogenetic relationship of families and orders; functional anatomy of bioluminescent organs. *Mailing Add:* Dept Invert Zool-Mollusca Nat Mus Nat Hist Smithsonian Inst Washington DC 20560

ROPER, GERALD C, b Tewksbury, Mass, Dec 18, 33; m 57; c 3. PHYSICAL CHEMISTRY. *Educ:* Univ Boston, AB, 56, PhD(phys chem), 66. *Prof Exp:* From asst prof to assoc prof phys chem, 62-74, PROF CHEM, DICKINSON COL, 74-, CHMN DEPT, 71- *Mem:* Am Chem Soc. *Res:* Inorganic synthesis; transition metal chemistry. *Mailing Add:* Dept of Chem Dickinson Col Carlisle PA 17013

ROPER, JOHN GORDON, experimental solid state physics, see previous edition

ROPER, LEON DAVID, b Shattuck, Okla, Dec 13, 35; m 55; c 2. THEORETICAL PARTICLE PHYSICS, BIOPHYSICS. *Educ:* Okla Baptist Univ, AB, 58; Mass Inst Technol, PhD(pion-nucleon interaction), 63. *Prof Exp:* Asst, Mass Inst Technol, 58-63; fel, Lawrence Radiation Lab, Univ Calif, 63-65; asst prof physics, Ky Southern Col, 65-67; asst prof, 67-70, assoc prof, 70-74, actg head dept, 77-78, PROF PHYSICS, VA POLYTECH INST & STATE UNIV, 74- *Concurrent Pos:* Instr, Eastern Nazarene Col, 62-63; mem staff, KEK Nat Lab High Energy Physics, Japan, 80-81. *Mem:* Fel Am Phys Soc; Am Asn Physics Teachers; Biophys Soc; World Future Soc. *Res:* Particle scattering phenomenology; membrane electrodiffusion; modeling excitable membranes, nonrenewable resource depletion. *Mailing Add:* Dept Physics Va Polytech Inst & State Univ Blacksburg VA 24061

ROPER, PAUL JAMES, b Detroit, Mich, June 29, 39; m 80. STRUCTURAL GEOLOGY, FUEL TECHNOLOGY. *Educ:* Univ Mich, Ann Arbor, BS, 62; Univ Nebr, Lincoln, MS, 64; Univ NC, Chapel Hill, PhD(geol), 70. *Prof Exp:* Instr geol, 69-70, asst prof geol, Lafayette Col, 70-76; lectr, Univ Wis, Oshkosh, 76-77; assoc prof, Univ SW La, 77-78; prod geologist, Superior Oil Co, 78-80; exp geologist, Ramco Explor, 80-81; PRES, AALPHA EXPLOR CO, 81- *Mem:* Geol Soc Am; Am Geophys Union; Am Geol Inst; Am Asn Petrol Geologists; Earthquake Eng Res Inst. *Res:* Geology and tectonics of Brevard zone, Southern Appalachian Mountains, Motagua fault zone and Sierra de las Minas Mountains, Guatemala; proposed theory of plastic plate tectonics; post jurassic tectomism in eastern North America. *Mailing Add:* PO Box 53709 OCS 118 Audubon Lafayette LA 70505

ROPER, ROBERT, b Vienna, Austria, Jan 1, 28; US citizen; m 58; c 2. POLYMER CHEMISTRY. *Educ:* City Col New York, BS, 51; NY Univ, PhD(org chem), 57. *Prof Exp:* Chemist, Esso Res & Eng Co, 57-60, sr chemist, 60-65, res assoc surface coatings, Rubbers, Adhesives & Sealants, 65-78, RES ASSOC INFO ANALYSIS, EXXON RES & ENG CO, 78- *Mem:* Am Chem Soc. *Res:* Development of polymers for elastomers, sealants and coatings; effect of polymer structure on properties; polymer synthesis; information retrieval and analysis; patent and technical literature. *Mailing Add:* Exxon Res & Eng Co Box 121 Linden NJ 07036

ROPER, ROBERT GEORGE, b Adelaide, Australia, Apr 30, 33; m 58; c 4. ATMOSPHERIC PHYSICS. *Educ:* Univ Adelaide, BSc, 57 & 58, PhD(physics), 63. *Prof Exp:* Demonstr physics, Univ Adelaide, 58, Radio Res Bd grant & res officer upper atmosphere, 62-63; Nat Acad Sci-Nat Res Coun resident res assoc, NASA, Goddard Space Flight Ctr, Md, 64-65; assoc prof aerospace eng, Ga Inst Technol, 65-66; sr res scientist, Australian Defence Sci Serv, 66-69; assoc prof to prof aerospace eng, 69-76, prof aerospace eng & geophys sci, 77-80, PROF GEOPHYS SCI, GA INST TECHNOL, 80- *Concurrent Pos:* Pres, Int Comt Meteorol Upper Atmosphere, Int Asn Meteorol & Atmospheric Physics, 79- *Mem:* Am Geophys Union; Am Meteorol Soc; Australian Inst Physics; Int Asn Geomagnetism & Aeronomy; fel Royal Meteorol Soc. *Res:* Design and construction of instrumentation for the measurement of upper atmosphere winds and shears using radio meteor technique; analysis and interpretation of upper atmosphere wind data from various sources. *Mailing Add:* Sch of Aerospace Eng Ga Inst Technol Atlanta GA 30332

ROPER, STEPHEN DAVID, b Rock Island, Ill, May 30, 45; m 67; c 2. DEVELOPMENTAL NEUROBIOLOGY, NEUROPLASTICITY. *Educ:* Harvard Col, BA, 67; Univ Col, London, PhD(physiol), 70. *Prof Exp:* Fel neurobiol, Harvard Med Sch, 70-73; asst prof anat, 73-79, asst prof physiol, 76-79, ASSOC PROF ANAT & PHYSIOL, MED SCH, UNIV COLO, 79- *Concurrent Pos:* Fulbright fel, 67-69; instr neurobiol, Harvard Med Sch, 71-73; NIH res career develop award; consult, NIH Site Visit Teams, 77-; mem, NIH Neurobiol Study Sect, 81- *Mem:* Am Asn Anat; Soc Neurosci; Am Physiol Soc. *Res:* Development and maintenance of synaptic connections in the vertebrate, focusing on trophic interactions between neurons and their targets and upon the regeneration of neural connections after damage. *Mailing Add:* Dept Anat Box B111 Univ Colo Med Ctr Denver CO 80262

ROPP, GUS ANDERSON, b Columbia, SC, July 31, 18; m 66. ORGANIC CHEMISTRY. *Educ:* Univ SC, BS, 40; Univ Tenn, PhD(org chem), 49. *Prof Exp:* Prod chemist, Gen Chem Co, 41-43; res chemist, Rohm & Haas Co, Pa, 43-45; res chemist, Oak Ridge Nat Lab, 48-61; res scientist & group leader, Union Carbide Corp, 61-64; PROF CHEM, COKER COL, 65- *Concurrent Pos:* USPHS res fel, Phys Chem Lab, Oxford Univ, 55-56. *Mem:* Am Inst Chemists; Am Chem Soc. *Res:* Effect of isotopes on reaction rates; isotopic tracers and organic reaction mechanisms; Diels-Alder reactions and synthesis of dienes; applications of mass spectrometry; gas chromatography; electroorganic chemistry. *Mailing Add:* 301 Park Ave Hartsville SC 29550

ROPP, RICHARD C, b Detroit, Mich, Mar 26, 27; m 52; c 4. SOLID STATE CHEMISTRY. *Educ:* Franklin Col, AB, 50; Purdue Univ, West Lafayette, MS, 52; Rutgers Univ, Newark, PhD(phys chem), 71. *Prof Exp:* Adv develop engr, Sylvania Elec Prod, Pa, 52-63; mgr luminescence, Westinghouse Elec, NJ, 63-71; pres, Luminescence Technol, 71-73; consult, Allied Chem Corp, 72-73, staff scientist solid state chem, 73-77; dir technol, 78-79, VPRES, PETREX CORP, 80- *Concurrent Pos:* Res specialist chem, Rutgers Univ, Newark, 71- *Mem:* Am Chem Soc; Am Inst Chemists; AAAS. *Res:* Luminescent materials; laser hosts; phosphate glass; nuclear waste encapsulation; petroleum recovery. *Mailing Add:* 138 Mountain Ave Warren NJ 07060

ROPP, WALTER SHADE, b Lakeland, Fla, Oct 15, 22; m 49; c 3. CHEMISTRY. *Educ:* Fla Southern Col, BS, 43; Pa State Col, MS, 44, PhD, 48. *Prof Exp:* Asst, Pa State Col, 43-44 & 45-47; res chemist, Exp Sta, 47-52, res supvr, 52-55, sr tech rep, 56-57, sr res chemist, Coatings Div, Res Ctr, 58-61, supvr coatings develop, Polymers Dept, 61-65, sr res chemist, Mat Res Div, 66-68, res assoc, 68-79, SR RES ASSOC, MAT SCI DIV, HERCULES INC, 79- *Concurrent Pos:* Instr, Pa State Col, 46-47. *Mem:* Am Chem Soc. *Res:* Plastics, elastomers, organic coatings and water soluble polymers. *Mailing Add:* Res Ctr Hercules Inc Wilmington DE 19899

ROQUES, ALBAN JOSEPH, b Paulina, La, Feb 3, 41; m 66; c 2. MATHEMATICAL ANALYSIS. *Educ:* Nicholls State Univ, BS, 63; La State Univ, MS, 65, PhD(math), 74. *Prof Exp:* Math analyst comput sci, Space Div, Chrysler Corp, 65-68; instr math, Southeastern La Univ, 68-69; instr, La State Univ, 71-72, instr math & comput sci, 74-75; instr, 75-78, asst prof math & computer sci, 78-80, ASSOC PROF MATH, LA STATE UNIV, 80- *Mem:* Math Asn Am. *Res:* Evolution equations in general Banach spaces. *Mailing Add:* Dept of Math La State Univ Eunice LA 70535

ROQUITTE, BIMAL C, b Calcutta, India, Sept 29, 31; m 61; c 2. PHYSICAL CHEMISTRY. *Educ:* Univ Calcutta, BSc, 52, MSc, 55; Univ Rochester, PhD(phys chem), 61. *Prof Exp:* Res assoc chem, Res Found, Ohio State Univ, 61-62; vis fel phys chem, Mellon Inst, 62; fel, Nat Res Coun Can, 62-64 & Mellon Inst, 64-66; ASSOC PROF PHYS CHEM, UNIV MINN, MORRIS, 66- *Mem:* Am Chem Soc. *Res:* Unimolecular decomposition of cyclobutane carboxaldehyde; photochemistry of bicyclic hydrocarbons; energy transfer in cyclopentanone both in the gas and solid phase; flash photolysis of hydrocarbon in the far ultraviolet. *Mailing Add:* Dept of Chem Univ of Minn Morris MN 56267

RORABACHER, DAVID BRUCE, b Ypsilanti, Mich, June 8, 35; m 58; c 4. ANALYTICAL CHEMISTRY, INORGANIC CHEMISTRY. *Educ:* Univ Mich, BS, 57; Purdue Univ, PhD(anal chem), 63. *Prof Exp:* Res engr, Ford Motor Co, 57-59; PROF ANAL CHEM, WAYNE STATE UNIV, 63- *Concurrent Pos:* Wayne State Univ fac res fel, 64; NIH fel, Max Planck Inst

Phys Chem, 64-65. *Mem:* Am Chem Soc. *Res:* Kinetics and mechanisms of coordination reactions and electron transfer reactions; nonaqueous solvation effects; analytical selectivity. *Mailing Add:* Dept of Chem Wayne State Univ Detroit MI 48202

RORABAUGH, M(ATTHEW) I(RVIN), b Salina, Pa, Apr 12, 16; m 40; c 3. HYDRAULIC ENGINEERING. *Educ:* Pa State Col, BS, 37. *Prof Exp:* Draftsman, Am Bridge Co, Pa, 37-38; hydraul eng, Surface Water Div, 38, Ky, 39-44 & Utilization Br, Washington, DC, 44-45, engr in chg, Ground Water Br, Ky, 45-48, dist engr, 48-54, dist engr, Fla, 54-62, res engr, Wash, 62-64, res hydrologist, Gen Hydrol Br, 64-67, REGIONAL RES HYDROLOGIST, US GEOL SURV, 67- *Concurrent Pos:* US rep, Int Asn Sci Hydrol, Dijon, France, 56; lectr, Fla State Univ, 58-60. *Mem:* Nat Soc Prof Engrs; Am Soc Civil Engrs; Am Water Works Asn; Am Geophys Union. *Res:* Ground water hydraulics; induced infiltration; bank storage. *Mailing Add:* 2077 Luray Ct Dunwoody GA 30338

RORER, DAVID COOKE, b Darby, Pa, Oct 25, 37; m 61; c 3. NUCLEAR ENGINEERING, RESEARCH ADMINISTRATION. *Educ:* Mass Inst Technol, BS, 59; Univ Ill, MS, 61; Duke Univ, PhD(physics), 64. *Prof Exp:* Res assoc physics, Duke Univ, 63-65; assoc physicist, Brookhaven Nat Lab, 65-72; reactor engr nuclear eng, Long Island Lighting Co, 72-75; DEP DIV MGR, REACTOR DIV, BROOKHAVEN NAT LAB, 80- *Concurrent Pos:* Adj prof, Polytech Inst New York, 76- *Mem:* Am Phys Soc; Am Nuclear Soc. *Res:* Neutron physics; nuclear cryogenics. *Mailing Add:* Reactor Div Brookhaven Nat Lab Upton NY 11973

RORIG, KURT JOACHIM, b Bremerhaven, Ger, Dec 1, 20; US citizen; m 49; c 3. MEDICINAL CHEMISTRY, ORGANIC CHEMISTRY. *Educ:* Univ Chicago, BS, 42; Carleton Col, MA, 44; Univ Wis, PhD(chem), 47. *Prof Exp:* Chemist, J Seagram & Sons, 42-43; res chemist, 47-60, asst dir, 60-74, assoc dir chem res, 74-79, SECT HEAD CARDIOVASC & RENAL RES, G D SEARLE & CO, 74- *Concurrent Pos:* Lectr, Loyola Univ Chicago, 50-60. *Mem:* AAAS; Am Chem Soc; NY Acad Sci; Am Soc Pharmacol & Exp Therapeut. *Res:* Cardiovascular and psychotropic drugs; aldol condensations; synthesis of aliphatic disulfonic acids, pyrimidines, imidazoles, oxazolines, steroids and steroid analogs. *Mailing Add:* G D Searle & Co PO Box 5110 Chicago IL 60680

RORK, EUGENE WALLACE, b Beatrice, Nebr, Mar 22, 40; m 71; c 4. SPACE SURVEILLANCE, ELECTRO OPTICS. *Educ:* Ohio State Univ, BS, 62, MS, 65, PhD(physics), 71. *Prof Exp:* Vis res assoc & lectr physics, Dept Physics, Ohio State Univ, 71-73; physicist, US Air Force Avionics Lab, 73-75; MEM STAFF, LINCOLN LAB, MASS INST TECHNOL, 75- *Res:* Ground-based electro optical sensor systems and techniques for detection of artificial satellites in space from reflected sunlight at night and in daytime; photoelectronic imaging devices; computer-controlled telescopes; atmospheric optical phenomena; Mössbauer-effect spectroscopy of gadolinium and dysprosium nuclei. *Mailing Add:* 246 Central St Concord MA 01742

RORK, GERALD STEPHEN, b Horton, Kans, Feb 12, 47; m 69; c 1. PHARMACEUTICAL CHEMISTRY. *Educ:* Univ Kans, BS, 69, MS, 73, PhD(pharmaceut chem), 74. *Prof Exp:* Jr chemist, Cook Paint & Varnish Co, 69-71; sr res scientist pharmaceut res & develop, Wyeth labs, Inc, 74-80; WITH RIKER LABS INC, 80- *Mem:* Am Chem Soc; Am Pharmaceut Asn. *Res:* Improvement of drug bioavailability and dosage from stability; physical organic chemistry; mechanisms of elimination reactions and nucleophilic addition reactions involving slow proton transfer steps. *Mailing Add:* Bldg 270-45-02 3M Ctr Riker Labs Inc St Paul MN 55101

RORKE, LUCY BALIAN, b St Paul, Minn, June 22, 29; m 60. NEUROPATHOLOGY. *Educ:* Univ Minn, BA, 51, MA, 52, BS, 55, MD, 57. *Prof Exp:* Intern med, 57-58, resident physician path, 58-61, NIH fels neuropath, 61-62 & neonatal brain path, 63-69, asst neuropathologist & pediat pathologist, 62-68, chief neuropathologist, 68-69, chmn dept anat path, 69-73, pres med staff, 73-75, chmn dept path, Philadelphia Gen Hosp, 73-77; PROF PATH, SCH MED, UNIV PA, 73-, CLIN PROF NEUROL, 79- *Concurrent Pos:* Consult neuropathologist, Wyeth Res Labs, 62-, Wistar Inst Anat & Biol, 67- & Inst Merieux, Lyons, France, 69-70; neuropathologist, Children's Hosp Philadelphia, 65- *Mem:* Am Asn Neuropath (pres, 81-82); Am Neurol Asn; Am Acad Neurol; Col Am Path. *Res:* Pediatric neuropathology and viral diseases of the nervous system; health sciences. *Mailing Add:* Dept of Path Children's Hosp of Philadelphia Philadelphia PA 19104

RORRES, CHRIS, b Philadelphia, Pa, Jan 2, 41. MATHEMATICS. *Educ:* Drexel Univ, BS, 63; NY Univ, MS, 65, PhD(math), 69. *Prof Exp:* asst prof, 68-80, ASSOC PROF MATH, DREXEL UNIV, 80- *Mem:* AAAS; Sigma Xi; Soc Indust & Applied Math; Am Math Soc; Math Asn Am. *Res:* Population dynamics; harvesting of renewable resources; solar energy. *Mailing Add:* Dept of Math Drexel Univ Philadelphia PA 19104

RORSCHACH, HAROLD EMIL, JR, b Tulsa, Okla, Nov 5, 26; m 51; c 2. PHYSICS. *Educ:* Mass Inst Technol, BS, 49, MS, 50, PhD(physics), 52. *Prof Exp:* From instr to assoc prof physics, 52-61, prof, 61-81, chmn dept, 66-73, SAM & HELEN WORDEN PROF PHYSICS, RICE UNIV, 81- *Concurrent Pos:* Guggenheim fel, 61; vis prof, Baylor Col Med. *Mem:* Fel Am Phys Soc. *Res:* Low temperature and solid state physics; biophysics. *Mailing Add:* Dept of Physics Rice Univ Houston TX 77001

ROSA, CASIMIR JOSEPH, b Poland, 1933; US citizen. OXIDATION, DIFFUSION. *Educ:* Acad Mining & Metall, Cracow, Poland, BS & MS, 56; McMaster Univ, Hamilton, Can, PhD(metall), 65. *Prof Exp:* Res metallurgist, Atlas Steels Ltd, Can, 60-62; sr res metallurgist, Westinghouse Co, Can, 65-66; fel metall, Univ Denver, 66-68; PROF METALL, UNIV CINCINNATI, OHIO, 68- *Concurrent Pos:* Alexander von Humboldt-Stiftung, US Sr Scientist, Ger, 78. *Honors & Awards:* Fulbright Lectr, Fulbright-Hays Comn & Korean Ministry Educ, 80. *Mem:* Am Inst Mining,

Metall & Petrol Engrs; Electrochem Soc; Sigma Xi. *Res:* High temperature oxidation of metals, diffusion of gases in metals; surface properties as related to initial stages of oxidation; thermodynamics of solutions. *Mailing Add:* Dept Mat Sci & Metall Eng Univ Cincinnati Cincinnati OH 45221

ROSA, EUGENE JOHN, b Sacramento, Calif, May 25, 37; m 59. CHEMICAL PHYSICS. *Educ:* Univ Calif, Berkeley, BS, 59; Univ Wash, PhD(chem), 64. *Prof Exp:* Chemist, Shell Develop Co, 64-67, supvr appl physics, 67-72; gen mgr, Veekay Ltd, 72-78; V PRES & GEN MGR, ONDYNE, INC, 78- *Res:* Development of analytical and process control instrumentation; development, manufacture and sales of process instrumentation. *Mailing Add:* 913 Tarvan East Dr Martinez CA 94553

ROSA, NESTOR, b Myrnam, Alta, Jan 15, 36; m 57; c 4. PLANT PHYSIOLOGY, BIOCHEMISTRY. *Educ:* Univ Alta, BSc, 58, MSc, 60; Dalhousie Univ, PhD(biol), 66. *Prof Exp:* Horticulturist, 60-63, PLANT PHYSIOLOGIST, RES BR, RES STA, CAN DEPT AGR, 66- *Mem:* Can Soc Plant Physiol; Am Soc Plant Physiol; Am Soc Agron. *Res:* Physiological and biochemical studies related to growth and development and chemical changes in Nicotiana tabacum and other plants. *Mailing Add:* Can Dept Agr Res Sta PO 186 Delhi ON N4B 2W9 Can

ROSA, RICHARD JOHN, b Detroit, Mich, Mar 19, 27; m 50; c 3. MAGNETOHYDRODYNAMICS. *Educ:* Cornell Univ, BEP, 53, PhD(eng physics), 56. *Prof Exp:* Res assoc, Cornell Univ, 55-56; prin res scientist, Avco-Everett Res Lab Div, Avco Corp, 56-71, chief scientist, MHD Generator Proj, 71-75; PROF MECH ENG, MONT STATE UNIV, 75- *Concurrent Pos:* Vis lectr, Stanford Univ, 66; magnetohydrodyn ed, J Adv Energy Conversion; vis prof, Univ Sydney, Australia, 78, Tokyo Inst Technol, Japan, 81. *Mem:* AAAS; Inst Elec & Electronics Eng; Am Inst Aeronaut & Astronaut; Am Soc Mech Eng. *Res:* Applied physics; magnetohydrodynamics, particularly the development of magnetohydrodynamic generators for large-scale production of electric power from chemical or nuclear fission heat sources. *Mailing Add:* Dept of Mech Eng Mont State Univ Bozeman MT 59715

ROSADO, JOHN ALLEN, b Baton Rouge, La, June 15, 36; c 2. PHYSICS. *Educ:* Harvard Univ, AB, 58. *Prof Exp:* Physicist microwaves, 61-65, physicist nuclear weapons effects, 65-74, supvry physicist, 74-77, chief, Tactical Nuclear Warfare Br, 77-79, CHIEF, NUCLEAR RADIATION EFFECTS LAB, HARRY DIAMOND LABS, 79- *Mem:* Am Phys Soc; Inst Elec & Electronic Engrs. *Res:* Nuclear weapons effects; fiber optic systems; microwave systems; high power technology; semi-conductor components; computer software; operations research. *Mailing Add:* 10519 Edgemont Dr Adelphi MD 20783

ROSALES-SHARP, MARIA CONSOLACION, b Manila, Philippines, Jan 1, 27; m 50; c 2. DEVELOPMENTAL BIOLOGY, TISSUE CULTURE. *Educ:* Univ Philippines, BS, 50; Univ Ill, MS, 66, PhD(develop biol, insect bionomics), 68. *Prof Exp:* Instr zool, Univ of the East, Manila, 51-55, asst prof embryol, comp anat & gen entom, 56-63; asst embryol, Univ Ill, Urbana, 63-65, asst entom, 65-68, res assoc insect bionomics & develop biol, 68-69, AID contract res assoc zool, 69-72, AID contract res assoc biologist, clin prof & res scientist, Univ NMex, 72-75; VIS ASST PROF ENTOM, UNIV ILL, URBANA, 75- *Concurrent Pos:* NIH fel entom, Univ Ill, Urbana, 68-69; mem, Smithsonian Inst. *Mem:* Sigma Xi; Am Inst Biol Scientist; NY Acad Sci; Entom Soc Am; Soc Develop Biol. *Res:* Establishment of primary tissue culture of anopheline mosquitoes; cultivation of the sporogonic forms of the malarial parasites in vitro; cell movement in vitro using mosquito tissues; histochemistry of mosquito tissues in vivo and in vitro; postembryonic development of aedine mosquitoes; application of tissue culture to problems in malariology. *Mailing Add:* Dept of Entom Univ of Ill Urbana IL 61801

ROSAN, ALAN MARK, b Buffalo, NY, Oct 6, 48; m 69; c 2. CATALYSIS. *Educ:* Earlham Col, BS, 70; Brandeis Univ, PhD(chem), 75. *Prof Exp:* Fel chem, Yale Univ, 75-77; SR RES CHEMIST CORP RES & TEHCNOL, ALLIED CORP, 82- *Concurrent Pos:* Res chemist, Allied Corp, 77- *Mem:* Am Chem Soc; Catalysis Soc; Sigma Xi; NY Acad Sci; AAAS. *Res:* Applied and exploratory organometallic chemistry including catalysis, photochemistry, reaction mechanism, and synthesis. *Mailing Add:* Allied Corp PO Box 1021R Morristown NJ 07960

ROSAN, BURTON, b New York, Aug 18, 28; m 51; c 3. MEDICAL MICROBIOLOGY. *Educ:* City Col New York, BS, 50; Univ Pa, DDS, 57, MSc, 62. *Prof Exp:* NIH fel, 57-59; res assoc microbiol, 59-62, from asst prof to assoc prof periodont, 62-68, from asst prof to assoc prof microbiol, 62-75, PROF MICROBIOL, SCH DENT MED, UNIV PA, 75- *Concurrent Pos:* Partic, World Conf Periodont, Mich, 66; co-prin investr, NIH grant, 59-68 & Ctr Oral Health Res, 68-, prin investr, 70-; vis assoc prof, State Univ NY Downstate Med Ctr, 71-72; mem study sect oral biol & med, NIH, Div Res Grants, 75-79; assessor, Australian Med Res Coun, 77-; vis scientist, Nat Inst Dent Res, Sydney, Australia. *Mem:* AAAS; Int Asn Dent Res; Am Soc Microbiol; NY Acad Sci. *Res:* Serology and immunochemistry of the oral streptococci and relationship to other adherence to oral tissues; extracellular polysaccharides of the actinomycetes. *Mailing Add:* Dept Microbiol 4001 Spruce St Univ of Pa Sch Dent Med Philadelphia PA 19104

ROSANO, HENRI LOUIS, b Nice, France, Feb 29, 24; US citizen; m 53; c 3. CHEMISTRY. *Educ:* Sorbonne Univ, Lic es phys sc, 46, Dr Sc Eng, 51. *Prof Exp:* Fel, Columbia Univ, 54-55; sr res assoc, Lever Brothers Co, NJ, 55-59; res assoc mineral eng, Columbia Univ, 59-62; PROF CHEM, CITY COL NEW YORK, 62- *Honors & Awards:* Prize, Fatty Acid Mat Inst Paris, 51; Prize, Soc Cosmetic Chem, 73. *Mem:* Am Chem Soc; Sigma Xi. *Res:* Surface and colloid chemistry. *Mailing Add:* Dept of Chem City Univ NY 139th St-Convent Ave New York NY 10031

ROSANO, THOMAS GERARD, b Albany, NY, Oct 22, 48; m 70; c 1. CLINICAL CHEMISTRY, BIOCHEMISTRY. *Educ:* State Univ NY Albany, BS, 70; Albany Med Col, PhD(biochem), 75; Am Bd Clin Chem, dipl, 78. *Prof Exp:* Fel clin chem, Dept of Lab Med, Univ Wash, 74-76; ASSOC DIR CLIN CHEM, ALBANY MED CTR, 76- *Concurrent Pos:* Asst prof biochem, Albany Med Col, 76-; mem exam comt, Nat Registry Clin Chem, 77-; consult, Vet Admin Hosp, Albany, NY, 78- *Mem:* Am Asn Clin Chem; Acad Clin Lab Physicians & Scientists. *Res:* Development of new methodology and techniques in the area of clinical biochemistry; chromatography; radioimmunoassay; enzymology; endocrine testing. *Mailing Add:* 65 Lawnridge Ave Albany NY 12208

ROSATI, ROBERT LOUIS, b Providence, RI, Mar 3, 42; m 66; c 2. MEDICINAL CHEMISTRY. *Educ:* Providence Col, BS, 64; Mass Inst Technol, PhD(org chem), 69. *Prof Exp:* NIH fel chem, Harvard Univ, 69; res chemist, 70-80, SR RES INVESTR, MED RES LAB, PFIZER, INC, 80- *Mem:* Am Chem Soc. *Mailing Add:* Pfizer Cent Res Groton CT 06340

ROSATO, FRANK JOSEPH, b Somerville, Mass, Feb 28, 25; m 50; c 4. APPLIED PHYSICS. *Educ:* Northeastern Univ, BS, 47; Tufts Univ, MS, 49; Harvard Univ, SM, 50, PhD(applied physics), 53. *Prof Exp:* Engr electronics, Polaroid Corp, Mass, 48-49; mathematician, Snow & Schule, Inc, 50; tech dir, 53-73, CHIEF SCIENTIST, GTE SYLVANIA, INC, GEN TEL & ELECTRONICS CORP, 73- *Concurrent Pos:* Teaching fel, Tufts Univ, 48-49; fel, Harvard Univ, 53; vis lectr, Lowell Tech Inst, 56-61; consult, Inst Naval Studies, 61-65 & Inst Defense Anal, 62; dir naval commun, US Navy, 64-69. *Mem:* Acoust Soc Am; Am Asn Physics Teachers; sr mem Inst Elec & Electronics Engrs. *Res:* Communication satellite systems; defense communication systems; electronic countermeasures; electromechanical transducers; electroacoustics. *Mailing Add:* 12 Blueberry Lane Lexington MA 02173

ROSAUER, ELMER AUGUSTINE, b Chicago, Ill, Dec 21, 30; m 60; c 3. MATERIALS SCIENCE. *Educ:* Purdue Univ, BS, 53; Univ Bonn, Dr rer nat(mineral), 57. *Prof Exp:* Res assoc mat, Eng Res Inst, 58-61, asst prof ceramics & mat, Dept Mat Sci & Eng & Eng Res Inst, 61-69, ASSOC PROF CERAMICS & MAT, DEPT MAT SCI & ENG & ENG RES INST, IOWA STATE UNIV, 69- *Concurrent Pos:* Fulbright-Hays Travel award, 71. *Mem:* Am Ceramic Soc; Clay Minerals Soc; Electron Micros Soc Am; Geochem Soc; Electron Probe Anal Soc Am. *Res:* Protective coatings on metals; sedimentation phenomena in colloidal suspensions; lightweight waste-ash insulation. *Mailing Add:* 110 Eng Annex Iowa State Univ Ames IA 50011

ROSAZZA, JOHN PAUL, b Torrington, Conn, Dec 25, 40; m 62; c 2. PHARMACOGNOSY, BIO-ORGANIC CHEMISTRY. *Educ:* Univ Conn, BS, 62, MS, 66, PhD(org pharmacog), 69. *Prof Exp:* NIH trainee natural prod res, Univ Conn, 65-68; fel pharmaceut biochem, Univ Wis, 68-69; from asst prof to assoc prof pharmacog, 69-73, assoc prof pharm, 73-77, PROF PHARM, UNIV IOWA, 77-, HEAD MED CHEM, NATURAL PROD DIV, COL PHARM, 77- *Mem:* Am Chem Soc; Am Soc Microbiologists; Am Soc Pharmacog. *Res:* Investigations of the chemical constituents of fungi and higher plants; microbial transformations of natural or synthetic products; synthesis of natural products. *Mailing Add:* Col of Pharm Univ of Iowa Iowa City IA 52240

ROSBERG, DAVID WILLIAM, b Superior, Wis, Jan 3, 19; m; c 2. PLANT PATHOLOGY. *Educ:* St Olaf Col, BS, 41; Ohio State Univ, MS, 47, PhD(plant path), 49. *Prof Exp:* Asst bot & plant path, Ohio State Univ, 46-47, res found, 48-49; from asst prof to prof plant path, 49-60, prof plant physiol & path & head dept plant sci, 60-74, PROF PLANT PATH, TEX A&M UNIV, 74- *Concurrent Pos:* Mem, President's Cabinet Comt on Environ, Subcomt on Pesticides, Task Group on Training Objectives & Stand as Resource Contact, 71- *Mem:* Fel AAAS; Am Phytopath Soc. *Mailing Add:* Dept of Plant Sci Tex A&M Univ College Station TX 77843

ROSBOROUGH, JOHN PAUL, b Chicago, Ill, June 23, 30; m 54; c 3. PHYSIOLOGY. *Educ:* Univ Ill, Urbana, BS, 51, MS, 53, BS, 54, DVM, 56, PhD(vet med sci), 69. *Prof Exp:* Res asst physiol, Univ Ill, Urbana, 61-64; NIH fel biophys, 69-70, asst prof, 71-76, ASSOC PROF PHYSIOL, BAYLOR COL MED, 76- *Mem:* Am Asn Lab Animal Sci; Am Soc Vet Anesthesiol; Am Soc Vet Physiol & Pharmacol. *Res:* Cardiopulmonary physiology. *Mailing Add:* Dept of Physiol Baylor Col of Med Tex Med Ctr Houston TX 77030

ROSCHER, DAVID MOORE, b Mt Vernon, NY, Mar 28, 37; m 64. PHOTOCHEMISTRY, PHYSICAL ORGANIC CHEMISTRY. *Educ:* Rutgers Univ, BS, 59; Purdue Univ, PhD(org chem), 66. *Prof Exp:* Robert A Welch fel, Univ Tex, 65-67; res chemist, Celanese Res Co, 67-70; sci instr, Matawan High Sch, 70-75; SCI INSTR, ALEXANDRIA CITY SCH DIST, 75- *Mem:* AAAS; Am Chem Soc; Nat Sci Teachers Asn. *Res:* Gas-phase photochemical processes; photochemical polymerization and solvolysis reactions. *Mailing Add:* 10400 Hunter Ridge Dr Oakton VA 22124

ROSCHER, NINA MATHENY, b Uniontown, Pa, Dec 8, 38; m 64. PHYSICAL ORGANIC CHEMISTRY. *Educ:* Univ Del, BS, 60; Purdue Univ, PhD, 64. *Prof Exp:* Eli Lilly fel & instr chem, Purdue Univ, 64-65; instr, Univ Tex, 65-67; sr staff chemist, Coca-Cola Export Corp, 68; asst prof chem, Douglass Col, Rutgers Univ, 68-74, asst dean col, 71-74; dir acad admin, 74-76, assoc prof chem, 74-79, assoc dean grad affairs & res, 76-79, PROF CHEM, AM UNIV, 79-, VPROVOST ACAD SERV, 79-, DEAN FAC AFFAIRS, 81- *Concurrent Pos:* mem, Sci Manpower Comn, 79-84, pres, 81-82. *Mem:* AAAS; Am Chem Soc; fel Am Inst Chemists; NY Acad Sci. *Res:* Reaction mechanisms in organic chemistry, particularly in inorganic ion, free radical and light catalysis; structures of organic molecules. *Mailing Add:* Dept Chem American Univ Washington DC 20016

ROSCHLAU, WALTER HANS ERNEST, b Sonneberg, Ger, Feb 14, 24; Can citizen; m 51; c 1. PHARMACOLOGY. *Educ:* Univ Heidelberg, MD, 51. *Prof Exp:* Res asst exp med, W P Caven Mem Res Found, Toronto, Ont, 51-55; res asst, Gardiner Med Res Found, 55-60; sr res asst pharmacol, Connaught Med Res Labs, Univ Toronto, 60-62; res assoc, 62-66, assoc prof, Fac Med, 66-69, PROF PHARMACOL, FAC MED, UNIV TORONTO, 69- *Concurrent Pos:* Mem coun thrombosis, Am Heart Asn. *Mem:* AAAS; Pharmacol Soc Can; Int Soc Thrombosis & Haemostasis. *Res:* Blood coagulation; fibrinolytic enzymes; clinical pharmacology. *Mailing Add:* Dept Pharmacol Univ Toronto Fac Med Toronto ON M5S 1A8 Can

ROSCOE, CHARLES WILLIAM, b Pocatello, Idaho, Nov 22, 24; m 55; c 1. PHARMACEUTICAL CHEMISTRY. *Educ:* Idaho State Col, BS, 48; Univ Wash, MS, 54, PhD(pharmaceut chem), 58. *Prof Exp:* Asst prof pharmaceut chem, Univ Mont, 58-62; res suprv, NSF Prog, 60-61; assoc prof, 62-71, PROF PHARMACEUT CHEM, UNIV OF THE PAC, 71- *Concurrent Pos:* Vis scholar, Univ Wash, 70. *Mem:* AAAS; Am Chem Soc; Am Pharmaceut Asn. *Res:* Medicinal chemistry; organic syntheses; relationships between chemical constitution and biologic activity. *Mailing Add:* Dept Pharmaceut Chem Univ of Pac 751 Brookside Rd Stockton CA 95207

ROSCOE, HENRY GEORGE, b Bridgeport, Conn, Nov 24, 30; m 55; c 3. BIOCHEMISTRY, SCIENCE ADMINISTRATION. *Educ:* Columbia Univ, AB, 52; Cornell Univ, PhD(biochem), 60. *Prof Exp:* Sr res biochemist, Lederle Labs, 60-72; assoc, 72-73, health scientist adminr, Grants Assoc Off, 73-74 & Nat Inst Neurol & Commun Disorders & Stroke, 74-79, CHIEF, REFERRAL BR, DIV RES GRANTS, NIH, 79- *Concurrent Pos:* Exec secy, Res Rev Comt B, Nat Heart, Lung & Blood Inst, 79- *Mem:* Am Chem Soc; fel Am Inst Chemists. *Res:* Lipid biochemistry and cardiovascular biochemistry. *Mailing Add:* Referral Br Div Res Grants NIH 5333 Westbard Ave Bethesda MD 20014

ROSCOE, JOHN MINER, b Halifax, NS, Dec 31, 43; m 68. CHEMICAL KINETICS. *Educ:* Acadia Univ, BSc, 65, MSc, 66; McGill Univ, PhD(chem), 70. *Prof Exp:* Fel appl physics lab, Johns Hopkins Univ, 69-70; ASST PROF CHEM, ACADIA UNIV, 70- *Mem:* Chem Inst Can; Royal Soc Chem. *Res:* Chemical kinetics of reactions of atoms, molecules, free radicals and excited molecules in the gas phase; solvent effects on reactions in solution. *Mailing Add:* PO Box 878 Wolfville NS B0P 1X0 Can

ROSCOE, JOHN STANLEY, JR, b Dakota Co, Minn, Oct 12, 22; m 46; c 6. PHYSICAL INORGANIC CHEMISTRY. *Educ:* Univ Chicago, PhB, 47, MS, 51; St Louis Univ, PhD(chem), 54. *Prof Exp:* Res assoc, St Louis Univ, 52-53; mem staff, Res Dept, Mathieson Chem Corp, 53-59, mem staff, Energy Div, Olin Mathieson Chem Corp, 59-61, res assoc, Chem Div, 61-68; dir res, Quantum Inc, 68-71; SR PARTNER, J S ROSCOE ASSOCS, 72- *Mem:* Fel AAAS; fel Am Inst Chemists; Am Chem Soc. *Res:* Synthetic and physical chemistry of the hydrides of aluminum and boron; organometallics; compounds of phosphorus, nitrogen and sulfur; high performance epoxy, urethane and polyimide coatings; urethane and silicone elastomers; glass reinforced plastics. *Mailing Add:* 267 Lanyon Dr Cheshire CT 06410

ROSE (RAUEN), MARY, mathematics, see previous edition

ROSE, AARON, b Clarksburg, WVa, Oct 28, 20; m 45. CHEMICAL ENGINEERING. *Educ:* Univ WVa, BS, 40, MS, 46; Ohio State Univ, PhD(chem eng), 49; San Fernando Valley State Col, MS, 67. *Prof Exp:* Instr chem eng, Ohio State Univ, 46-49; asst prof, Wash Univ, St Louis, 49-53, assoc prof, 54-55; Fulbright lectr, Univ Nancy, France, 53-54; chief technologist, Olin Mathieson Chem Corp, 56, mgr process develop, 57-58; prof chem eng, Tex A&M Univ, 58-60; mgr process opers, United Tech Ctr, 60-62; chief engr aerospace equip dept, Marquardt Corp, 62-67; ASSOC EXEC DIR FAC AFFAIRS, INST SAFETY & SYSTS MGT & PROF SYSTS TECHNOL, PUB ADMIN & INDUST & SYSTS ENG, UNIV SOUTHERN CALIF, 67- *Mem:* Am Inst Aeronaut & Astronaut; Am Soc Eng Educ; Am Inst Cost Eng; Am Inst Chem Eng; Am Soc Eng Mgt. *Res:* Engineering development management; development economics. *Mailing Add:* Dept of Safety & Systs Mgt Univ of Southern Calif Los Angeles CA 90007

ROSE, ALBERT, b New York, NY, Mar 30, 10; m 40; c 2. PHYSICS. *Educ:* Cornell Univ, AB, 31, PhD(physics), 35. *Prof Exp:* Asst physics, Cornell Univ, 31-34; asst physics, Elec Res Labs, Radio Corp Am, 35-55, dir res labs, Radio Corp Am, Ltd, Switz, 55-57, PHYSICIST, RCA LABS, 57- *Concurrent Pos:* Vis lectr, Univ Ill, 53; Princeton Univ, 61, NATO, State Univ Ghent, 61, Univ PR, 66, Cornell Univ, 67, Polytech Inst, Mexico City, 68 & Hebrew Univ Jerusalem, 68; Fairchild distinguished scholar, Calif Inst Technol, 75-76. *Honors & Awards:* Liebman Award, 46; TV Broadcasters Award, 46; Soc Motion Picture & TV Eng Award, 47; Sarnoff Gold Medal, 58. *Mem:* Nat Acad Eng; fel Am Phys Soc; fel Inst Elec & Electronics Eng; Swiss Phys Soc. *Res:* Electronic processes in vacuum and in solids; noise limitations of photo detectors, including the human eye; television pick up tubes. *Mailing Add:* RCA Labs Princeton NJ 08540

ROSE, ARTHUR L, b Cracow, Poland, July 21, 32; US citizen; c 2. NEUROLOGY, PEDIATRICS. *Educ:* Univ Bristol, MB ChB, 57; Royal Col Physicians & Surgeons, dipl child health, 59; Am Bd Pediat, dipl, 63; Am Bd Psychiat & Neurol, dipl & cert neurol, 69, cert child neurol, 73. *Prof Exp:* Res fel pediat, Med Sch, Harvard Univ, 61-63; instr neuropath, Col Physicians & Surgeons, Columbia Univ, 66-67; from asst prof to assoc prof neurol & pediat, Albert Einstein Col Med, 67-75; assoc prof, 75-80, PROF NEUROL, STATE UNIV NY DOWNSTATE MED CTR, 80-, DIR, DIV PEDIAT NEUROL, 75- *Concurrent Pos:* Fel behav & neurol sci, Albert Einstein Col Med, 67-69, Nat Inst Neurol Dis & Stroke fels, 69-77; assoc attend neurologist, Bronx Munic Hosp & Montefiore Hosp, 74-; assoc attend neurologist & pediatrician, Albert Einstein Col Hosp, 74- *Mem:* Am Acad Neurol; Child Neurol Soc. *Res:* Investigation of neurotoxic substances on the development of the nervous system using pathological techniques. *Mailing Add:* State Univ NY Downstate Med Ctr Box 118 Brooklyn NY 11203

ROSE, ARTHUR WILLIAM, b Bellefonte, Pa, Aug 8, 31; m 71; c 3. GEOCHEMICAL EXPLORATION, ECONOMIC GEOLOGY. *Educ:* Antioch Col, BS, 53; Calif Inst Technol, MS, 55, PhD(geol & geochem), 58. *Prof Exp:* From geologist to sr geologist mineral explor, Bear Creek Mining Co, Kennecott Copper Co, 57-64; mining geologist geol mapping, Div Mines & Minerals, State Alaska, 64-67; from asst prof to assoc prof, 67-75, PROF GEOCHEM, PA STATE UNIV, 75-, DIR MINERAL CONSERV SECT, 78- *Concurrent Pos:* Mem, Nat Comt Geochem, Nat Res Coun, 78-81. *Mem:* Asn Explor Geochemists (pres, 80-81); Geochem Soc; Soc Econ Geologists; Geol Soc Am; Soc Mining Engrs. *Res:* Geochemical exploration; geology and geochemistry of metallic ore deposits; environmental geochemistry; economics of mineral resources. *Mailing Add:* Pa State Univ Dept of Geosci 332 Deike Bldg University Park PA 16802

ROSE, AUGUSTUS STEELE, b Fayetteville, NC, July 14, 07; m 32; c 4. CLINICAL NEUROLOGY. *Educ:* Univ NC, BS, 30; Harvard Med Sch, MD, 32; Am Bd Psychiat & Neurol, dipl, 40. *Prof Exp:* Intern med, Mass Gen Hosp, 32-34; assoc prof anat, Univ NC, 34-37; resident physician neurol, Mass Gen Hosp, 37-39; instr neurol & psychiat, Harvard Med Sch, 43-52; prof neurol, 51-74, chmn dept, 70-74, EMER PROF NEUROL, SCH MED, UNIV CALIF, LOS ANGELES, 74- *Concurrent Pos:* From jr physician to sr physician, Boston Psychopath Hosp, 39-51; consult, Los Angeles Vet Admin Hosp, 51-74, Vet Admin Distinguished physician in neurol, 74-; consult, Nat Inst Neurol Dis & Blindness, 52-60; mem med adv comt, Cent Off, Vet Admin Psychiat & Neurol Serv, 60-64; dir, Am Bd Psychiat & Neurol, 60-68; mem, Nat Adv Neurol Dis & Stroke Coun, 68-72. *Mem:* Am Neurol Asn (pres, 68-69); fel Am Psychiat Asn; Am Acad Neurol (vpres, 55-57, pres, 59-61). *Res:* Syphilis of the nervous system; demyelinating disease and tissue culture of the central nervous system. *Mailing Add:* 625 N Crescent Dr Beverly Hills CA 90210

ROSE, BIRGIT, b Tegernsee, WGer, Aug 21, 43; m 72. PHYSIOLOGY, CELL PHYSIOLOGY. *Educ:* Univ Munich, PhD(natural sci), 70. *Prof Exp:* Lab technician, Med Sch, Stanford Univ, 62-63; lab technician, Stanford Res Inst, 63-64; from res asst to res assoc physiol, Columbia Univ, 67-71; res asst prof, 71-77, RES ASSOC PROF PHYSIOL & BIOPHYS, MED SCH, UNIV MIAMI, 77- *Res:* Intercellular communication, its basis of mechanism and role in differentiation; role of calcium in membrane physiology; membrane structure; cell differentiation. *Mailing Add:* Dept of Physiol & Biophys PO Box 016430 Miami FL 33101

ROSE, BRAM, b Montreal, Que, Apr 21, 07; m 41; c 3. MEDICINE. *Educ:* McGill Univ, BA, 29, MD, 33, MSc, 37, PhD, 39. *Prof Exp:* Jr intern med, Royal Victoria Hosp, Montreal, Que, 33-34, asst med resident, 34-35; asst in med, Guy's Hosp, London, 35-36; physician & assoc in med, Royal Victoria Hosp, 41, from asst prof to assoc prof med, Univ, 45-63, prof exp med & dir, div immunochem & allergy, Royal Victoria Hosp, 63-75, EMER PROF MED, MCGILL UNIV, 75- *Mem:* Am Soc Clin Invest; fel Aerospace Med Asn; fel Am Col Physicians; Am Asn Immunologists; fel Am Acad Allergy (past pres). *Res:* Investigations of allergy; metabolism of histamine; naturally occurring antihistaminics; immunoglobulins and antigen antibody mechanisms. *Mailing Add:* RR 3 Magog PQ J1X 3W4 Can

ROSE, CARL MARTIN, JR, b Macon, Ga, Aug 31, 36; m 60; c 2. PHYSICS. *Educ:* Yale Univ, BS, 58; Univ Chicago, SM, 62, PhD(physics), 67. *Prof Exp:* Res assoc physics, Duke Univ, 66-67, asst prof, 67-74; mem staff, 74-78, SUPVR, BELL LABS, 78- *Mem:* Am Phys Soc; Asn Comput Machinists; Inst Elec & Electronic Engrs. *Res:* Electron beam lithography; real-time computing; pattern recognition; numerical computing techniques. *Mailing Add:* Bell Labs 600 Mountain Ave Murray Hill NJ 07974

ROSE, CHARLES BUCKLEY, b Washington, DC, Feb 8, 38; m 61; c 3. ORGANIC CHEMISTRY. *Educ:* Brigham Young Univ, BS, 60; Harvard Univ, AM, 63, PhD(org chem), 66. *Prof Exp:* Asst prof chem, 66-73, ASSOC PROF CHEM, UNIV NEV, RENO, 73- *Mem:* Am Chem Soc; The Chem Soc; fel Am Inst Chemists. *Res:* Structure elucidation of natural products; development of new synthetic methods; model systems of physiologically active compounds. *Mailing Add:* PO Box 8936 Univ Sta Reno NV 89507

ROSE, CHARLES WILLIAM, b Columbus, Ohio, May 20, 40; m 63; c 2. COMPUTER ENGINEERING, INFORMATION SCIENCE. *Educ:* Duke Univ, BS, 62, MS, 63; Case Western Reserve Univ, PhD(comput & info sci), 70. *Prof Exp:* Sr engr, Tex Instruments, Inc, 63-70; from asst prof to assoc prof, 70-79, asst to pres univ comput servs, 78-79, PROF & CHMN, DEPT COMPUT ENG & SCI, CASE WESTERN RESERVE UNIV, 79- *Concurrent Pos:* Chmn spec interest group on design automation, 75-77; consult, US Govt, Nat Eng Consortium & var indust corp. *Mem:* Inst Elec & Electronics Engrs; Asn Comput Mach. *Res:* Computer system architecture; design automation of computer systems. *Mailing Add:* Dept of Systs & Comput Eng Case Western Reserve Univ Cleveland OH 44106

ROSE, DAVID, b Chicago, Ill, Nov 13, 21; m 44; c 2. PHYSICS. *Educ:* Univ NDak, BS, 42; Carnegie Inst Technol, DSc, 52. *Prof Exp:* Control chemist, Chicago Sanit Dist, 42; jr physicist, Metall Lab, Chicago, 44; jr engr, Manhattan Engrs, Tenn, 44-45; jr scientist, Los Alamos Sci Lab, Univ Calif, 45-46, asst engr, 46; asst res physicist, Carnegie Inst Technol, 47-52; assoc physicist, Argonne Nat Lab, 52-56; physicist, Gen Atomic Div, Gen Dynamics Corp, 56-66; consult engr, United Engrs & Constructors, 66-67; SR NUCLEAR ENGR, ARGONNE NAT LAB, 67- *Res:* Nuclear physics; power reactors; reactor safety. *Mailing Add:* Argonne Nat Lab 9700 Cass Ave Argonne IL 60439

ROSE, DAVID JOHN, b Victoria, BC, May 8, 22; US citizen; m 73; c 4. ENERGY, NUCLEAR ENGINEERING. *Educ:* Univ BC, BASc, 47; Mass Inst Technol, PhD(physics), 50. *Prof Exp:* Mem staff physics, BC Res Coun, 50-51; mem tech staff, Bell Labs, 51-58; assoc prof, 58-60, PROF NUCLEAR ENG, MASS INST TECHNOL, 60- *Concurrent Pos:* Consult, Oak Ridge Nat Lab, 59-67, vis scientist, 67-68, dir long range planning, 69-71; vis scientist, UK Atomic Energy Authority, 67-68; chmn energy panel, Nat Acad Eng, 72; mem, Rev Panel Energy, Pres Off Sci & Technol, 72-73; fac mem, Salzburg Sem Am Studies, Austria, 73; mem steering comt, Nuclear & Alternative Energy Syst, Nat Acad Sci, 75-79; res fel, East-West Ctr, Honolulu, Hawaii, 81- *Honors & Awards:* Arthur Holly Compton Award, Am Nuclear Soc, 75; Killian Award lectr, Mass Inst Technol, 79-80. *Mem:* Fel Am Acad Arts & Sci; fel Am Phys Soc; fel AAAS; Am Nuclear Soc. *Res:* Energy policy and technology; national science and environmental policy; controlled nuclear fusion. *Mailing Add:* Dept of Nuclear Eng Mass Inst of Technol Cambridge MA 02139

ROSE, DONALD CLAYTON, b Clearmont, Mo, Apr 30, 20; m 42; c 5. MATHEMATICS. *Educ:* Transylvania Col, AB, 45; Univ Ky, MA, 48, PhD(math), 54. *Prof Exp:* Instr astron & math, Univ Ky, 45-54; chmn Dept Math, Transylvania Col, 54-60; from asst prof to prof, Univ SFla, 60-75, chmn dept, 61-75; prof math, Hillsborough Community Col, 75-77; PROF MATH, UNIV S FLA, 77- *Mem:* Am Math Soc; Math Asn Am. *Mailing Add:* Dept of Math Univ of S Fla Tampa FL 33620

ROSE, DONALD GLENN, b Colton, Calif, May 6, 22; m 52. NUCLEAR ENGINEERING. *Educ:* Univ Calif, BS, 44; Northwestern Univ, MS, 49; Ind Univ, PhD(chem), 54. *Prof Exp:* Jr chemist, Oak Ridge Nat Lab, 44-46; sr staff chemist, Appl Physics Labs, Johns Hopkins Univ, 53-56; mem staff, Los Alamos Sci Lab, 56-57; sr fel, Mellon Inst, 57-58; MEM STAFF, LOS ALAMOS NAT LAB, 58- *Mem:* Am Chem Soc; Am Phys Soc; Instrument Soc Am. *Res:* Aerosols; kinetics; high temperature and uranium chemistry; remote systems engineering; physical security; data systems; nuclear power plant safety; technical management. *Mailing Add:* 4895 Trinity Los Alamos NM 87544

ROSE, DONALD JAMES, b Santa Ana, Calif, May 25, 44. APPLIED MATHEMATICS, COMPUTER SCIENCE. *Educ:* Univ Calif, Berkeley, BA, 66; Harvard Univ, AM, 67, PhD(appl math), 70. *Prof Exp:* Asst prof math, Univ Denver, 70-72; from asst prof to assoc prof appl math, Harvard Univ, 72-77; prof comput sci & chmn dept, Vanderbilt Univ, 77-78; MEM TECH STAFF MATH, BELL LABS, 78- *Concurrent Pos:* Consult, Argonne Nat Lab, 73-78. *Mem:* Soc Indust & Appl Math; Am Math Soc; Math Asn Am; Asn Comput Mach. *Res:* Numerical mathematics; combinatorics; algorithms; linear algebra. *Mailing Add:* Math Ctr Bell Labs 600 Mountain Ave Murray Hill NJ 07974

ROSE, EARL FORREST, b Isabel, SDak, Sept 23, 26; m 51; c 6. PATHOLOGY. *Educ:* Yankton Col, BA, 49; Univ SDak, BSM, 51; Univ Nebr, MD, 53; Southern Methodist Univ, LLB, 67. *Prof Exp:* Resident path, Med Ctr, Baylor Univ, 56-58; resident DePaul Hosp, St Louis, 58-60; fel forensic path, Med Col Va, 61, lectr forensic path, 61-63; prof path, Univ Tex Southwestern Med Sch, Dallas, 63-68; PROF PATH, COL MED, UNIV IOWA, 68- *Concurrent Pos:* Dep chief med examr, Commonwealth Va, 61-63; dep chief, Dallas County Med Examrs, 63-68; lectr, Col Law, Univ Iowa, 71. *Mem:* Fel Col Am Pathologists; fel Am Soc Clin Pathologists; Am Acad Forensic Sci; AMA. *Res:* Forensic pathology; surgical and autopsy pathology; application of pathology to law. *Mailing Add:* Dept of Path Univ of Iowa Col of Med Iowa City IA 52240

ROSE, FRANCIS L, b Augusta, Ga, Dec 20, 35; m 55; c 4. ZOOLOGY. *Educ:* Univ Ga, BS, 60, MS, 62; Tulane Univ, PhD, 65. *Prof Exp:* NIH fel, Fla State Mus, 65-66; asst prof, 66-74, PROF BIOL, TEX TECH UNIV, 74- *Concurrent Pos:* Am Philos Soc grant, 65-66. *Mem:* Am Soc Ichthyologists & Herpetologists. *Res:* Anatomy, ecology, behavior and systematics. *Mailing Add:* Dept of Biol Tex Tech Univ Lubbock TX 79409

ROSE, FRANK EDWARD, b Junction City, Kans, Mar 11, 27; m 48; c 4. SOLID STATE PHYSICS. *Educ:* Greenville Col, BS, 49; Univ Mich, AM, 57; Cornell Univ, PhD(exp physics), 65. *Prof Exp:* Teacher high sch, 49-54; instr physics & electronics, Gen Motors Inst, 54-58; res asst physics, Cornell Univ, 60-62; from lectr to asst prof, 63-68, chmn, Dept Physics & Astron, 78-80, ASSOC PROF PHYSICS, UNIV MICH-FLINT, 68- *Mem:* Am Phys Soc; Am Asn Physics Teachers; Am Sci Affil. *Res:* Research at cryogenic temperatures on the electron properties of metals; electrical magnetoresistance of the alkali metals; helicon mode of wave propagation and resonances; computer assisted instruction; astronomy instructions; forensic physics; computer text processing. *Mailing Add:* Dept of Physics & Astron Univ of Mich Flint MI 48503

ROSE, FREDERICK LOUIS, JR, b Salem, Ore, Aug 1, 35; m 56; c 3. AQUATIC BIOLOGY, BOTANY. *Educ:* Willamette Univ, BA, 57; Ore State Univ, MS, 64, PhD(bot), 68. *Prof Exp:* Res asst bot, Ore State Univ, 65-67; AEC fel aquatic ecol, Pac Northwest Labs, Battelle Mem Inst, 68-69; asst prof, 69-74, ASSOC PROF BIOL, IDAHO STATE UNIV, 74- *Concurrent Pos:* Consult natural resources. *Mem:* Am Soc Limnol & Oceanog; Ecol Soc Am; Int Asn Theoret & Appl Limnol. *Res:* Accumulation or concentration of pesticide residues, heavy metals, and radionuclides by aquatic biota. *Mailing Add:* Dept of Biol Idaho State Univ Pocatello ID 83201

ROSE, GENE FUERST, b Erie, Pa, Mar 15, 18; m 40; c 1. MATHEMATICS, COMPUTER SCIENCE. *Educ:* Case Inst Technol, BS, 38; Univ Wis, MA, 47, PhD(math), 52. *Prof Exp:* Chemist, Copperweld Corp, Ohio & Pa, 40-42; res engr, Res Labs, Westinghouse Elec Corp, 42-45; res assoc, Allegany Ballistics Lab, George Washington Univ, 45; asst & actg instr math, Univ Wis, 45-52; mem staff, Sandia Corp, 52-55; mem tech staff, Space Tech Labs, Inc, Thompson Ramo Wooldridge, Inc, 55-60; sr scientist, Syst Develop Corp, Calif, 60-68; prof math & info sci, Case Western Reserve Univ, 68-77; prof & chmn Dept Comput Sci, Calif State Univ, Fullerton, 77-78. *Concurrent Pos:* Guest prof, Munich Tech Univ, 66-67; guest lectr, Imp Col Sci & Technol, Univ London, 66; Alexander von Humboldt Found grant, Ges für Math und Datenverarbeitung MBH Bonn, 72-73. *Mem:* Am Math Soc; Math Asn Am; Asn Symbolic Logic. *Res:* Recursive function theory; foundations of mathematics; formal language theory; mathematical machine theory; relational data bases. *Mailing Add:* 1565 Sherwood Village Circle Placentia CA 92670

ROSE, GEORGE G, b Liberty, Ind, Aug 7, 22; m 45; c 2. MEDICINE. *Educ:* Univ Tex, BA, 47, MD, 51. *Prof Exp:* Res assoc tissue cult lab, Med Br, 54-60, from asst prof to assoc prof, 60-71, PROF MED, UNIV TEX DENT BR, HOUSTON, 71- *Concurrent Pos:* Asst biologist, M D Anderson Hosp & Tumor Inst Houston, 55-66, assoc biologist, 66-67. *Mem:* Tissue Cult Asn; Am Soc Cell Biol; fel Royal Micros Soc; Int Asn Dent Res. *Res:* Tissue culture and electron microscopy, principally oral research. *Mailing Add:* Univ of Tex Dent Br PO Box 20068 Houston TX 77025

ROSE, GORDON WILSON, b Elmira, NY, Apr 25, 24; m 51; c 3. EPIDEMIOLOGY, CLINICAL MICROBIOLOGY. *Educ:* Wayne State Univ, AB, 50; Univ Detroit, MS, 54; Univ Mich, PhD(epidemiol sci), 65. *Prof Exp:* Asst chem, Wayne State Univ, 47-48, chem, gross anat & histol, Dept Mortuary Sci, 50-54, instr bact, histol & chem, 54-56; spec instr bact, Univ Detroit, 56-57; from asst prof to assoc prof, 57-80, PROF BACT, HISTOL & CHEM, WAYNE STATE UNIV, 80- *Concurrent Pos:* Spec instr, Providence Hosp, Detroit, 57-58; assoc dir dept mortuary sci, Wayne State Univ, 57-65, spec instr, Sch Med, 65; asst dir dept, Deaconess Hosp, 65-66. *Mem:* Am Asn Bioanalysts; Am Soc Clin Pathologists; Am Pub Health Asn; Am Soc Microbiol. *Res:* Clinical and post-mortem microbiology; histopathogenesis of infectious diseases; hospital epidemiology. *Mailing Add:* Univ Curriculums Wayne State Univ Detroit MI 48202

ROSE, HAROLD D, b Kansas City, Mo, June 24, 24; m 49; c 4. INTERNAL MEDICINE. *Educ:* Univ SDak, BS, 46; George Washington Univ, MD, 48. *Prof Exp:* Intern med, St Elizabeth's Hosp, Washington, DC, 48-50; resident internal med, 50-52 & 54-56, chief, Med Chest Sect, 56-60, CHIEF, INFECTIOUS DIS SECT, VET ADMIN HOSP, WOOD, WIS, 60-, ASST CHIEF MED SERV, 64- *Concurrent Pos:* From instr to assoc prof med, Sch Med, Marquette Univ, 56-72, prof, 72-; Vis consult, Milwaukee County Hosp, 68- *Mem:* Fel Am Col Physicians; Infectious Dis Soc Am; AMA. *Res:* Infectious diseases. *Mailing Add:* Vet Admin Ctr Wood WI 53193

ROSE, HAROLD WAYNE, b Telluride, Colo, Jan 11, 40; m 64; c 4. ELECTRONIC ENGINEERING, COMPUTER SCIENCE. *Educ:* Univ Colo, Boulder, BS, 62, MS, 64; Ohio State Univ, PhD(elec eng), 72. *Prof Exp:* Res engr, 66-71, ELECTRONICS ENGR, AVIONICS LAB, AIR FORCE SYSTS COMMAND, WRIGHT-PATTERSON AFB, 71- *Honors & Awards:* Technical Achievement Award, Air Force Systs Command, Andrews AFB, 74. *Mem:* Optical Soc Am; Am Inst Physics. *Res:* Holography; holographic optical elements; coherent optics; lasers; missile guidance techniques; electro-optical trackers; laser trackers. *Mailing Add:* 636 N Galloway St Xenia OH 45385

ROSE, HARVEY ARNOLD, b New York, NY, Nov 9, 47. FLUID DYNAMICS. *Educ:* City Col New York, BS, 68; Harvard Univ, MA, 69, PhD(physics), 75. *Prof Exp:* Health serv officer radiol health, USPHS, 70-72, fel fluid turbulence, Nat Ctr Atmospheric Res, 75-76; vis scientist turbulence res, Observ Nice, France, 76-77; fel, 77-79, MEM STAFF, LOS ALAMOS NAT LAB, 79- *Mem:* Sigma Xi. *Res:* Calculate properties of turbulence, using methods of quantum field theory in high temperature plasmas and in fluids. *Mailing Add:* 2111-C 34th St Los Alamos NM 87544

ROSE, IRA MARVIN, b Brooklyn, NY, Feb 22, 21; c 1. ORGANIC CHEMISTRY, ANALYTICAL CHEMISTRY. *Educ:* Brooklyn Col, BA, 41; Columbia Univ, AM, 49, PhD(org chem), 52. *Prof Exp:* Anal chemist, Wallerstein Labs, NY, 41-42; anal chemist, War Dept, Edgewood Arsenal, Md, 42-44, org chemist, Chem Corps, 44-47; sr org chemist, US Vitamin Corp, NY, 52-58; group leader res & develop indust org chem, Nopco Chem Co, 58-71 & Nopco Div, 71-74, SR RES ASSOC, PROCESS CHEM DIV, DIAMOND SHAMROCK CHEM CO, MORRISTOWN, 74- *Mem:* Am Chem Soc. *Res:* Fine chemical synthesis; industrial organic synthesis, research, product and process development and general analytical chemistry; synthesis, research, development and analysis of chemical warfare agents. *Mailing Add:* 55 Greenwood Dr Millburn NJ 07041

ROSE, IRWIN ALLAN, b Brooklyn, NY, July 16, 26; m 55; c 4. BIOCHEMISTRY. *Educ:* Univ Chicago, PhD(biochem), 52. *Prof Exp:* Asst prof biochem, Sch Med, Yale Univ, 55-60, assoc prof, 60-63; SR MEM, BIOCHEM DIV, INST CANCER RES, 63- *Concurrent Pos:* Affil phys biochem, Grad Sch, Univ Pa, 63-70. *Mem:* AAAS; Am Chem Soc; Soc Biol Chemists; Am Acad Arts & Sci. *Res:* Mechanisms of transfer enzyme; protein degradation; regulation of metabolism. *Mailing Add:* Inst for Cancer Res 7701 Burholme Ave Philadelphia PA 19111

ROSE, ISRAEL HAROLD, b New Britain, Conn, May 17, 17. MATHEMATICS. *Educ:* Brooklyn Col, AB, 38, AM, 41; Harvard Univ, PhD(math), 51. *Prof Exp:* Tutor & instr math, Brooklyn Col, 38-41; instr, Pa State Univ, 42-46; from asst prof to assoc prof, Univ Mass, 48-60; from assoc prof to prof math, Hunter Col, 60-68, chmn dept, 66-68; chmn dept, 68-72 & 80-82, PROF MATH, LEHMAN COL, 68- *Concurrent Pos:* Vis asst prof, Mt Holyoke Col, 51-52, vis assoc prof, 54-55 & 58-59; fel, Ford Found, 52-53. *Mem:* Am Math Soc; Math Asn Am. *Res:* Abstract algebra. *Mailing Add:* Dept Math Lehman Col City Univ NY Bronx NY 10468

ROSE, JAMES DAVID, b Ann Arbor, Mich, Mar 31, 42; m 66; c 2. NEUROSCIENCE, BIOPSYCHOLOGY. *Educ:* Cent Mich Univ, BS, 64; Ind Univ, PhD(psychol), 70. *Prof Exp:* Fel, Sch Med, Emory Univ, 69-71; asst prof psychol, Dartmouth Col, 71-74; asst prof neurophysiol & anat, Sch Med, Emory Univ, 74-76; assoc prof, 76-80, PROF PSYCHOL, UNIV WYO, 80- *Concurrent Pos:* Prin investr, NIH res grants, 72- *Mem:* Soc Neurosci; Am Asn Anatomists; Soc Psychoneuroendocrinol. *Res:* Neurological bases of behavior; neurophysiology; neuroanatomy. *Mailing Add:* Dept Psychol Univ Wyo Laramie WY 82071

ROSE, JAMES STEPHENSON, b Halifax, NS, Can, July 9, 26. ORGANIC CHEMISTRY. *Educ:* Dalhousie Univ, BSc, 48, MSc, 50; Yale Univ, PhD(chem), 55. *Prof Exp:* Asst prof chem, NS Tech Univ, 54-55; sr res chemist, Olin-Mathieson Chem Corp, 55-62; sr res chemist, Naval Res Estab, NS, 62-64; SR RES CHEMIST, UPJOHN CO, 64- *Res:* Organic reaction mechanisms; synthetic organic chemistry; structure-spectra correlation of organic compounds. *Mailing Add:* 1820 Durham Rd RFD 2 Guilford CT 06437

ROSE, JERZY EDWIN, b Buczacz, Poland, Mar 5, 09; nat US. NEUROPHYSIOLOGY. *Educ:* Jagiellonian Univ, MD, 34. *Prof Exp:* Asst neurol & psychiat, Stefan Batory Univ, Poland, 34-36; fel, Emperor William Inst Brain Res, Ger, 36-37 & Ger Inst Brain Res, 37-38; sr instr neurol & psychiat, Stefan Batory Univ, 38-39; res assoc neuropath, Johns Hopkins Univ, 40-43; from asst prof to assoc prof physiol & psychiat, 46-60; prof, 60-80, EMER PROF NEUROPHYSIOL, UNIV WIS-MADISON, 80- *Mem:* Nat Acad Sci; Soc Exp Biol & Med; Am Physiol Soc; Am Asn Anatomists; Am Neurol Asn. *Res:* Anatomy and physiology of the mammalian central nervous system. *Mailing Add:* Dept of Neurophysiol Univ of Wis Madison WI 53706

ROSE, JOHN CHARLES, b New York, NY, Dec 13, 24; m 48; c 5. PHYSIOLOGY. *Educ:* Fordham Univ, BS, 46; Georgetown Univ, MD, 50. *Prof Exp:* From instr to asst prof med, 54-58, assoc prof physiol & biophys, 58-60, chmn dept biophys, 59-63, dean, Sch Med, 63-73, PROF PHYSIOL & BIOPHYS, SCH MED, GEORGETOWN UNIV, 60- *Concurrent Pos:* Estab investr, Am Heart Asn, 54-57, coordr med educ, 57-58; med ed, Am Family Physician. *Mem:* Am Physiol Soc; Biophys Soc; Soc Exp Biol & Med; Am Col Physicians; Am Fedn Clin Res. *Res:* Cardiovascular physiology; medical education. *Mailing Add:* 5710 Surrey St Chevy Chase MD 20015

ROSE, JOHN CREIGHTON, b Milwaukee, Wis, July 27, 22; div; c 4. GEOPHYSICS. *Educ:* Univ Wis, BS, 48, MS, 50, PhD(geol), 55. *Prof Exp:* Res assoc, Woods Hole Oceanog Inst, 50-55; from instr to asst prof geol & geophys, Univ Wis, 55-64; assoc geophysicist, 64-68, prof geosci, 68-74, PROF GEOPHYS, UNIV HAWAII, 74-, GEOPHYSICIST, 76- *Concurrent Pos:* Consult, Aero Div, Minneapolis-Honeywell Regulator Co. *Mem:* Am Geophys Union; Europ Asn Explor Geophys. *Res:* International pendulum gravity reference standard; absolute gravity measurements by pulse recycling and laser interferometer; geodesy; explosion seismology; marine gravity. *Mailing Add:* Inst of Geophys Univ of Hawaii Honolulu HI 96822

ROSE, JOSEPH EDWARD, biochemistry, see previous edition

ROSE, JOSEPH LAWRENCE, b Philadelphia, Pa, July 5, 42; m 63; c 3. MECHANICS, MECHANICAL ENGINEERING. *Educ:* Drexel Inst Technol, BSME, 65, MS, 67; Drexel Univ, PhD(appl mech), 70. *Prof Exp:* Engr, Hale Fire Pump Co, 61-62 & SKF Industs, Inc, 63-64; instr mech eng, 65-69, asst prof, 70-73, assoc prof, 73-78, PROF MECH ENG, DREXEL UNIV, 78- *Mem:* Am Soc Mech Engrs; Soc Exp Stress Anal; Am Soc Nondestruct Test; Am Soc Testing & Mat; Acoust Soc Am. *Res:* Nondestructive testing; experimental mechanics; stress analysis; wave propagation; composite materials; biomechanics. *Mailing Add:* Dept of Mech Eng & Mech 32nd & Chestnut Sts Philadelphia PA 19104

ROSE, KATHLEEN MARY, b St Paul, Minn, Sept 5, 45. NUCLEIC ACID SYNTHESIS, ENZYMOLOGY. *Educ:* Mich State Univ, BS, 66, MS, 69; Pa State Univ, PhD(genetics), 77. *Prof Exp:* NIH fel biochem, Mich State Univ, 67-69; res asst, 72-78, asst prof, 78-82, ASSOC PROF PHARMACOL, M S HRESHEY MED CTR, PA STATE UNIV, 82- *Concurrent Pos:* Consult, Alcoa Found Award, Grad Prof Opportunities Prog, US Dept Educ, 81-82 & US Pub Health Serv, Res Career Develop Award, Nat Cancer Inst, 80-; prin investr, US Pub Health Serv & Nat Inst Gen Med Sci, 79- *Mem:* Am Soc Biol Chemists; Am Soc Cell Biol; Sigma Xi. *Res:* Regulation of ribosomal RNA synthesis; role of protein phosphorylation in gene expression; control of cell growth and transformation. *Mailing Add:* Dept Pharmacol M S Hershey Med Ctr 500 Univ Dr Hershey PA 17033

ROSE, KENNETH, b Bloomington, Ind, Apr 21, 35; m 59; c 2. ELECTRICAL ENGINEERING, PHYSICS. *Educ:* Univ Ill, BS, 55, MS, 57, PhD(elec eng), 61. *Prof Exp:* Physicist, Gen Elec Res Lab, 61-65; assoc prof elec eng, 65-71, PROF ELEC ENG, RENSSELAER POLYTECH INST, 71- *Concurrent Pos:* Consult, US Naval Res Lab, 66-69 & Gen Elec Co, 76-78. *Mem:* AAAS; Inst Elec & Electronics Engrs; Am Phys Soc. *Res:* Semiconductors; superconductors; thin films; microwave and optical studies; telecommunications; microprocessor reliability; microprocessor testing and reliability; very-large-scale integration fabrication, computers, thin film growth and characterization; telecommunications. *Mailing Add:* Elec Comput & Systs Eng Dept Rensselaer Polytech Inst Troy NY 12181

ROSE, KENNETH DAVID, b Newark, NJ, June 21, 49; m 81. MAMMALIAN EVOLUTION. *Educ:* Yale Univ, BS, 72; Harvard Univ, MA, 74; Univ Mich, PhD(geol & paleont), 79. *Prof Exp:* Fel paleobiol, Smithsonian Nat Mus Natural Hist, 79-80; ASST PROF ANAT, SCH MED, JOHNS HOPKINS UNIV, 80- *Concurrent Pos:* Res collab, Dept Paleobiol, Smithsonian Nat Mus Natural Hist, 81- *Mem:* Soc Vert Paleont; Paleont Soc; Am Soc Mammalogists; Soc Syst Zool; Sigma Xi. *Res:* Early Cenozoic mammals, with emphasis on systematics and evolution, functional anatomy of the teeth and skeleton, bistratigraphy and biochronology (use of fossil mammals for stratigraphic correlation and determination of relative age of strata), and species diversity. *Mailing Add:* Dept Cell Biol & Anat Sch Med Johns Hopkins Univ Baltimore MD 21205

ROSE, KENNETH E(UGENE), b Winfield, Kans, Oct 20, 15; m 39; c 2. METALLURGY, MATERIALS SELECTION & PROCESSING. *Educ:* Colo Sch Mines, EMet, 39; Cornell Univ, MS, 43. *Prof Exp:* Jr engr, US Govt, 36-37; engr trainee, Caterpillar Tractor Co, 39-41; instr mech & metall, Cornell Univ, 41-43; res engr, Battelle Mem Inst, 43-46; asst prof mech &

metall, Univ Okla, 46-47; from assoc prof to prof metall eng, 47-75, chmn dept metall eng, 47-68, assoc dean eng, 68-75, PROF MECH ENG, UNIV KANS, 75- *Concurrent Pos:* Consult, 48-; mem, State Bd Eng Examr, 56-59; Fulbright lectr, Nat Univ Eng, Peru, 60. *Mem:* fel Am Soc Metals; Am Inst Mining, Metall & Petrol Engrs; Nat Asn Corrosion Engrs. *Res:* Metallurgy of cast metals; science of materials and materials processing; service failures; engineering education; corrosion. *Mailing Add:* Dept of Mech Eng Univ of Kans Lawrence KS 66045

ROSE, LAWRENCE LYON, b Hyannis, Mass, Jan 30, 44; m 67. COMPUTER SCIENCE. *Educ:* Va Mil Inst, BA, 65; Pa State Univ, MS, 67, PhD(comput sci), 73. *Prof Exp:* Instr comput sci, Pa State Univ, 71-73; asst prof, State Univ NY Binghamton, 73-75; ASST PROF COMPUT SCI, OHIO STATE UNIV, 75- *Concurrent Pos:* Consult, United Steelworkers Am, 75- *Mem:* Asn Comput Mach; Sigma Xi. *Res:* Information storage and retrieval, especially file organization and storage hierarchies; simulation techniques and methodology; programming languages. *Mailing Add:* Dept of Comput & Info Sci Ohio State Univ Columbua OH 43210

ROSE, MICHAEL ROBERTSON, b Iserlohn, WGer, July 25, 55; Can citizen; m 76. EVOLUTIONARY ECOLOGY, THEORETICAL POPULATION BIOLOGY. *Educ:* Queen's Univ, BSc, 75, MSc, 76; Univ, Sussex, DPhil, 79. *Prof Exp:* NATO Sci fel, Univ Wis, Madison, 79-81; ASST PROF BIOL, DALHOUSIE UNIV, 81- *Concurrent Pos:* Univ res fel, Dalhousie Univ, 81- *Mem:* Am Soc Zoologists; Genetics Soc Am; Soc Study Evolution. *Res:* Drosophila life-history evolution, including fitness-components and senescence; evolutionary game theory; evolution with antagonistic pleiotropy; evolution of sex; genome evolution; selfish DNA. *Mailing Add:* Dept Biol Dalhousie Univ Halifax NS B3H 4J1 Can

ROSE, MILTON EDWARD, b Newark, NJ, May 22, 25; m 48; c 3. MATHEMATICS. *Educ:* NY Univ, AB, 47, PhD, 53. *Prof Exp:* Res assoc, Inst Math Sci, NY Univ, 50-55; mathematician, Off Naval Res, 55-57; head appl math div, Brookhaven Nat Lab, 57-60; mathematician, Lawrence Radiation Lab, Univ Calif, 60-63; head math sci sect, NSF, 63-67, head off comput activities, 67-69; head dept math & statist, Colo State Univ, 69-70; vis prof, Univ Denver, 70-71; chief math & comput prog, USERDA, 71-77; DIR, INST COMPUT APPLNS SCI & ENG, NASA LANGLEY RES CTR, 77-; CHIEF MATH & COMPUT PROG, ENERGY RES & DEVELOP ADMIN, 71- *Concurrent Pos:* Consult, NSF. *Mem:* Am Math Soc; Soc Indust & Appl Math; Asn Comput Mach. *Res:* Applied mathematics; computer science. *Mailing Add:* ICASE MS 132C NASA Langley Res Ctr Hampton VA 23665

ROSE, MITCHELL, b Cleveland, Ohio, Mar 10, 51; m 74; c 4. GAS PHASE PHOTOCHEMISTRY, X-RAY FLUORESCENCE. *Educ:* Maimonides Col, BA, 75; Cleveland State Univ, MS, 77; Case Western Univ, PhD(chem), 79. *Prof Exp:* Anal lab mgr, Mogul Corp, Div Dexter Corp, 79-81; RES ADV, MASTER BUILDERS CO, DIV MARTIN MARIETTA CORP, 81- *Mem:* Am Chem Soc. *Res:* Gas phase reaction kinetics; x-ray diffraction, and x-ray fluorescence spectroscopy; computer interfacing for laboratories. *Mailing Add:* 3788 Shannon Rd Cleveland Heights OH 44118

ROSE, NICHOLAS JOHN, b Ossining, NY, Apr 21, 24; m 46; c 4. MATHEMATICS. *Educ:* Stevens Inst Technol, ME, 44; NY Univ, MS, 49, PhD(math), 56. *Prof Exp:* From instr to prof math, Stevens Inst Technol, 46-68, head dept, 60-68, consult, 48-54; head dept, 68-77, PROF MATH, NC STATE UNIV, 68- *Concurrent Pos:* Consult, Bell Tel Labs, Inc, 54-60. *Mem:* Am Math Soc; Math Asn Am; Soc Indust & Appl Math. *Res:* Differential equations; matrix theory. *Mailing Add:* Dept of Math NC State Univ PO Box 5126 Raleigh NC 27607

ROSE, NOEL RICHARD, b Stamford, Conn, Dec 3, 27; m 51; c 4. MICROBIOLOGY, IMMUNOLOGY. *Educ:* Yale Univ, BS, 48; Univ Pa, AM, 49, PhD(microbiol), 51; State Univ NY Buffalo, MD, 64; Am Bd Microbiol, dipl; Am Bd Path, dipl. *Prof Exp:* From instr to assoc prof bact & immunol, State Univ NY Buffalo, 51-66, prof microbiol, Sch Med, 66-73; PROF IMMUNOL & MICROBIOL & CHMN DEPT, SCH MED, WAYNE STATE UNIV, 73- *Concurrent Pos:* Consult, Niagara Sanatorium, NY, 53-56 & Edward J Meyer Mem Hosp, Buffalo, 56-73, Vet Admin Hosp, Oak Park, Mich & Sinai Hosp, Detroit, 73-; from assoc dir to dir, Erie County Lab, 64-70; asst prof med, State Univ NY Buffalo, 64-73, dir ctr immunol, 70-73. *Mem:* Fel Am Pub Health Asn; Tissue Cult Asn; fel Am Acad Allergy; fel Col Am Path; fel Am Acad Microbiol. *Res:* Organ specificity; allergy; cancer; autoantibodies. *Mailing Add:* Dept of Immunol & Microbiol Wayne State Univ Sch of Med Detroit MI 48201

ROSE, NORMAN CARL, b Seattle, Wash, Mar 15, 29; m 54; c 4. ORGANIC CHEMISTRY. *Educ:* Univ Calif, BS, 50; Univ Kans, PhD(chem), 57. *Prof Exp:* From asst prof to assoc prof chem, Tex A&M Univ, 56-66; from assoc prof to prof, 66-78, ASST DEAN, COL SCI, PORTLAND STATE UNIV, 78- *Mem:* Am Chem Soc. *Res:* Learning theories. *Mailing Add:* Dept of Chem Portland State Univ Portland OR 97207

ROSE, PETER HENRY, b Lincoln, Eng, Jan 16, 25; m 52; c 2. PHYSICS. *Educ:* Univ London, BSc, 45, PhD(physics), 55. *Prof Exp:* Sci officer, Nat Gas Turbine Estab, 45-47; asst lectr physics, Univ Leicester, 47-48; res assoc, Mass Inst Technol, 51-52, physicist, Proj Lincoln, 52-53; lectr physics, Birmingham Univ, 55-56; vpres & dir res, High Voltage Eng Corp, 56-70; pres, Ion Physics Corp, 70-71; pres, Extrion Corp, 71-75; gen mgr, Varian Extrion Div, Varian Assocs, 75-77; pres, Nova Assoc, Inc, 78-80; PRES, ION IMPLANTATION DIV, EATON CORP, 80- *Mem:* Fel Am Phys Soc; fel Brit Inst Physics. *Res:* Low energy nuclear physics; accelerators; theoretical and experimental ion optics; plasma and atomic physics as related to the accelerator; ion implantation. *Mailing Add:* Ion Implantation Div 16 Tozer Rd Beverly MA 01915

ROSE, PETER R, b Austin, Tex, July 3, 35; m 56; c 3. PETROLEUM GEOLOGY, STRATIGRAPHY. *Educ:* Univ Tex, BS, 57, MA, 59, PhD(geol), 68. *Prof Exp:* Geologist, Shell Oil Co, 59-66; asst prof geol, State Univ NY Stony Brook, 68-69; staff geologist, Shell Oil Co, 69-73; chief Br Oil & Gas Resources, US Geol Surv, 73-76; chief geol, Energy Reserves Group, Inc, 76-80; WITH TELEGRAPH EXPLORATION, 80- *Concurrent Pos:* State Univ NY Res Found grant-in-aid & fel, 68-69. *Mem:* Am Asn Petrol Geologists; fel Geol Soc Am; Soc Econ Paleontologists & Mineralogists. *Res:* Petrology and paleoecology of carbonate rocks; carbonate reservoir rocks; analysis of petroleum basins; petroleum resource prediction. *Mailing Add:* Telegraph Exploration PO Box 2 Telegraph TX 76883

ROSE, PHILIP I, b New York, NY, Apr 3, 39; m 59; c 2. PHYSICAL CHEMISTRY. *Educ:* Univ Ariz, BS, 60; Purdue Univ, PhD(phys chem), 64. *Prof Exp:* Sr res chemist, Res Labs, 64-73, RES ASSOC, RES LABS, EASTMAN KODAK CO, 73- *Mem:* AAAS; Am Chem Soc; Soc Photog Scientists & Engrs. *Res:* Molecular structure and intermolecular interactions; nuclear magnetic resonance spectroscopy of biopolymers; molecular characterization and physical chemistry of biopolymers. *Mailing Add:* 125 Summit Dr Rochester NY 14620

ROSE, RALPH, b Detroit, Mich, Dec 27, 17; m 41; c 5. CERAMICS. *Educ:* Ohio State Univ, BE, 42. *Prof Exp:* Res engr, Battelle Mem Inst, 46-51 & E J Lavino & Co, 52-57; proj engr, Refractories Div, H K Porter Co, Inc, 57-60, mgr basic prod, 60-66, gen mat mgr, 66-68, gen mgr admin & tech serv, 68-76; sr vpres, Laclede Christy Clay Prods Co, 76-81; RETIRED. *Concurrent Pos:* Indust group mgr, Pullman Swindell Div, Pullman, Inc, 77-79. *Mem:* AAAS; fel Am Ceramic Soc; Am Soc Testing & Mat; Am Inst Ceramic Engrs. *Res:* Refractories; raw materials processing and utilization; management and administration; purchasing; traffic; engineering research; quality assurance; kilns and plants for the refractories and technical ceramic fields. *Mailing Add:* R1 Box 294 Huddleston VA 24104

ROSE, RAYMOND EDWARD, b Canton, Ohio, July 17, 26; c 4. AERODYNAMICS, MATHEMATICS. *Educ:* Univ Kans, BSAE, 51; Univ Minn, MSAE, 56, PhD(aerodyn), 66. *Prof Exp:* From jr engr to scientist aerodyn, Rosemount Aero Labs, Univ Minn, 51-59, scientist, 59-62, res fel, Univ Minn, 62-66; prin res scientist to proj staff engr/supvr, Aerodyn & Fluid Dynamics, Res Dept, Systs & Res Ctr, Honeywell, Inc, 66-76; prog mgr, Aerodyn & Active Controls, Aircraft Energy Efficiency Prog Off, 76-79, PROG MGR, GEN AVIATION PROG OFF, NASA, 79- *Concurrent Pos:* Consult, EDO Corp, NY, 62, Pioneer Parachute Co, 65 & Pillsbury Co, Minn, 65; prof math dept, Southeastern Univ, Washington, DC, 81- *Mem:* Am Inst Aeronaut & Astronaut. *Res:* Shock swallowing and control concepts for air data sensing; jet-flap aerodynamics; laminar flow for general aviation aircraft; general aviation crash dynamics (structural design for occupant survivability); single pilot instrument flight rules operations (pilot workload reduction). *Mailing Add:* NASA Code RJG 600 Independence Ave SW Washington DC 20546

ROSE, RAYMOND WESLEY, JR, b Cleveland, Ohio, July 5, 41; m 65; c 2. MOLECULAR GENETICS. *Educ:* Bucknell Univ, BS, 63, MS, 65; Temple Univ, PhD(biol), 70. *Prof Exp:* Asst prof, 70-77, ASSOC PROF BIOL, BEAVER COL, 77- CHMN DEPT, 74- *Mem:* Genetics Soc Am; AAAS; Am Soc Zoologists. *Res:* Genetic control of protein synthesis and nucleic acid synthesis in Drosophila; protein and nucleic acid synthesis during early development in Xenopus; effect of environmental pollutants on mammalian development. *Mailing Add:* Dept of Biol Beaver Col Glenside PA 19038

ROSE, RICHARD CARROL, b Minneapolis, Minn, Jan 2, 40. PHYSIOLOGY. *Educ:* Augsburg Col, 65; Mich State Univ, MS, 67, PhD(physiol), 69. *Prof Exp:* USPHS fel, Sch Med, Univ Pittsburgh, 70-71; asst prof, 71-74, assoc prof, 74-80, PROF PHYSIOL & SURG, COL MED, PA STATE UNIV, 81- *Concurrent Pos:* Fogarty sr int fel, 81. *Mem:* Am Physiol Soc; Am Gastroenterol Asn; Biophys Soc. *Res:* Membrane physiology; electrophysiology of epithelial tissues; transport in intestine and gallbladder; vitamin absorption/metabolism. *Mailing Add:* Dept of Physiol Pa State Univ Hershey Med Ctr Hershey PA 17033

ROSE, ROBERT LEON, b San Francisco, Calif, Sept 3, 20; m 42; c 3. GEOLOGY. *Educ:* Univ Calif, AB, 48, MA, 49, PhD(geol), 57. *Prof Exp:* Geologist, Shell Oil Co, 49-53; assoc geol, Univ Calif, 53-56; actg asst prof geol, Stanford Univ, 56-57; asst econ geologist, Nev Bur Mines, 57-59; from asst prof to assoc prof geol, 59-68, PROF GEOL, SAN JOSE STATE UNIV, 68- *Mem:* Geol Soc Am; Mineral Soc Am; Am Asn Petrol Geologists. *Res:* Petrology and petrography of igneous and metamorphic rocks; geology of California and the Franciscan Formation. *Mailing Add:* 3911 Balcom Rd San Jose CA 95148

ROSE, ROBERT M(ICHAEL), b New York, NY, Apr 15, 37; m 61; c 3. PHYSICAL METALLURGY, SOLID STATE PHYSICS. *Educ:* Mass Inst Technol, SB, 58, ScD(phys metall), 61. *Prof Exp:* Ford Found fel eng, 61-63, from asst prof to assoc prof metall, 61-76, PROF METALL, MASS INST TECHNOL, 76- *Mem:* AAAS; Am Phys Soc; Am Inst Mining, Metall & Petrol Engrs; Am Soc Metals; Orthop Res Soc. *Res:* Electrical, magnetic, mechanical and thermodynamic properties of metals at cryogenic and high temperatures; theoretical and practical solid state physics; statistical thermodynamics; surgical implant materials; mammalian bone. *Mailing Add:* Dept of Metall Rm 4-132 Mass Inst of Technol Cambridge MA 02139

ROSE, SETH DAVID, b Dayton, Ohio, Nov 11, 48. BIO-ORGANIC CHEMISTRY, MOLECULAR BIOLOGY. *Educ:* Univ Calif, Berkeley, BS, 70; Univ Calif, San Diego, PhD(chem), 74. *Prof Exp:* NIH fel biophys, Johns Hopkins Univ, 74-76; asst prof, 76-80, ASSOC PROF CHEM, ARIZ STATE UNIV, 81- *Mem:* Am Chem Soc. *Res:* Nucleic acid chemistry; electron microscopy; physical organic chemistry. *Mailing Add:* Dept of Chem Ariz State Univ Tempe AZ 85287

ROSE, STUART ALAN, b Dayton, Ohio, Sept 17, 42; m 65; c 2. ANALYTICAL CHEMISTRY. *Educ:* Univ Cincinnati, BA, 64; Wayne State Univ, PhD(anal chem), 69. *Prof Exp:* Finished prod chemist, Wm S Merrell Div, Richardson-Merrell, Inc, 64-66; res chemist, Cent Res Div, 69-73, dept head-group leader, Lederle Labs Div, 73-76, asst to dir qual control, 76-77, mgr Pearl River qual control, 77-81, DIR PHARMACEUT CONTROL, LEDERLE LABS DIV, AM CYANAMID CO, PEARL RIVER, 81- *Mem:* Am Chem Soc; Water Pollution Control Fedn. *Res:* General analytical problem solving; technical management. *Mailing Add:* Lederle Labs Middletown Rd Pearl River NY 10965

ROSE, TIMOTHY LAURENCE, b Cleveland, Ohio, July 6, 41; m 63; c 3. CHEMICAL PHYSICS, CHEMICAL KINETICS. *Educ:* Haverford Col, BA, 63; Yale Univ, MS, 64, PhD(phys chem), 67. *Prof Exp:* NATO fel physics, Univ Freiburg, 68; from asst prof to assoc prof chem, Tex A&M Univ, 69-78; Nat Res Coun sr res assoc, Air Force Geophys Lab, 76-78; SR SCIENTIST, EIC CORP, 78- *Concurrent Pos:* Welch Found grant, 71-76. *Mem:* AAAS; Am Chem Soc; Am Phys Soc; Am Soc Mass Spectrometry; fel Am Inst Chemists. *Res:* Gas phase methylene reactions and chemical activation; molecular and ion beam photodissociation processes; photochemical and photovoltaic solar energy conversion. *Mailing Add:* EIC Corp 55 Chapel St Newton MA 02158

ROSE, VINCENT C(ELMER), b Fall River, Mass, July 31, 30; m 59; c 3. CHEMICAL ENGINEERING. *Educ:* Univ RI, BS, 52, MS, 58; Univ Mo, PhD(chem eng), 64. *Prof Exp:* Pilot plant supvr, Lindsay Chem Co, 54-56; asst prof chem eng, 63-67, asst prof nuclear & ocean eng, 67-70, ASSOC PROF NUCLEAR & OCEAN ENG, UNIV RI, 70-, ASSOC DEAN GRAD SCH, 71- *Mem:* Am Inst Chem Engrs; Am Soc Eng Educ. *Res:* Power plant siting; marine corrosion; water pollution control. *Mailing Add:* Grad Sch Univ of RI Kingston RI 02881

ROSE, WALTER DEANE, petroleum engineering, surface chemistry, see previous edition

ROSE, WAYNE BURL, b Lamar, Colo, Dec 23, 32; m 56; c 3. PHYSICAL CHEMISTRY, PHARMACY. *Educ:* Adams State Col, BA, 55, MEd, 57; Kans State Univ, MS, 61, PhD(phys chem), 64. *Prof Exp:* Assoc chemist, Midwest Res Inst, 63-67; res chemist, Chemagro Corp, 67-68, sr res chemist, 68-69, mgr formulations res, 69-74; MGR CHEM RES, BAYVET CORP, 74- *Mem:* Sigma Xi; Royal Soc Chem; Am Chem Soc. *Res:* Oxygen fluoride and nitrogen fluoride chemistry; metal ligand complexes in deuterium oxide; histamine heparin interactions in aqueous solutions; surface chemistry; kinetics of decomposition; preparation of pharmaceutical products and their registration; analytical methods and packaging. *Mailing Add:* Bayvet Corp PO Box 390 Shawnee KS 66203

ROSE, WILLIAM CUMMING, b Greenville, SC, Apr 4, 87; m 13. BIOCHEMISTRY. *Educ:* Davidson Col, BS, 07; Yale Univ, PhD(biochem), 11. *Hon Degrees:* ScD, Davidson Col, 47, Yale Univ, 47, Univ Chicago, 56 & Univ Ill, 62. *Prof Exp:* Instr, Univ Pa, 11-13; assoc prof biochem, Sch Med, Univ Tex, 13-14, prof & head dept, 14-22; prof, 22-53, actg head dept chem, 42-46, res prof, 53-55, EMER RES PROF BIOCHEM, UNIV ILL, URBANA, 55- *Concurrent Pos:* Mem adv bd, Wistar Inst Anat & Biol, Univ Pa, 36-40; Hektoen lectr, Inst Med Chicago, 38; mem food & nutrit bd, Nat Res Coun, 40-47; sci adv comt, Nutrit Found, 43-57; mem nat adv health coun & consult, USPHS, 44-49; lectr, Univ Calif, Los Angeles, 58. *Honors & Awards:* Grocery Mfrs Am Award, 47; Osborne-Mendel Award, Am Inst Nutrit, 49; Gibbs Medal, 52 & Spencer Award, 57, Am Chem Soc; 20th Anniversary Award, Nutrit Found, 61; Nat Medal of Sci, 66. *Mem:* Nat Acad Sci; Am Soc Biol Chemists (vpres, 37-39, pres, 39-41); Am Chem Soc; hon mem Harvey Soc; fel Am Inst Nutrit (vpres, 44-45, pres, 45-46). *Res:* Pepsin; creatine and creatinine; metabolism of mucic acid; origin of uric acid; enzymes in marine organisms; purine metabolism; nephrotoxic action of dicarboxylic acids; replacement of amino acids by synthetic products; significance of amino acids in growth; discovery, isolation, identification and spatial configuration of threonine; amino acid requirements of animals and man. *Mailing Add:* 405 W University Ave Champaign IL 61820

ROSE, WILLIAM DAKE, b Nashville, Tenn, Mar 15, 28; m 52; c 2. PETROLEUM GEOLOGY. *Educ:* Vanderbilt Univ, AB, 50, MS, 53. *Prof Exp:* Geologist, Gulf Oil Corp, 53-56 & Ky Geol Surv, 56-70; GEOLOGIST-ED, OKLA GEOL SURV, 70- *Mem:* Geol Soc Am; Am Asn Petrol Geol; Am Inst Prof Geologists; Asn Earth Sci Ed (secy-treas, 68-71). *Res:* Areal geology; stratigraphy. *Mailing Add:* Okla Geol Surv 830 Van Vleet Oval Rm 163 Norman OK 73019

ROSE, WILLIAM INGERSOLL, JR, b Detroit, Mich, Oct 4, 44; m 67; c 1. VOLCANOLOGY. *Educ:* Dartmouth Col, AB, 66, PhD(geol), 70. *Prof Exp:* Res asst geol, Dartmouth Col, 66-68; res asst geochronology, Univ Ariz, 68-69; res asst geol, Dartmouth Col, 69-70; asst prof, 70-74, ASSOC PROF GEOL, MICH TECHNOL UNIV, 74- *Concurrent Pos:* NSF grants, Guatemala, El Salvador & Nicaragua, 70-72, Guatemalan volcanoes, 73-74 & 78-80 & volcanic ash, 75-77; vis scientist, Nat Ctr Atmospheric Res, 77-78. *Mem:* AAAS; Int Asn Volcanology & Chem Earth's Interior; Geochem Soc; Am Geophys Union; fel Geol Soc Am. *Res:* Volcanic gas geochemistry; igneous petrology; volcanic domes; active Central American volcanoes; volcanic ash. *Mailing Add:* Dept of Geol & Geol Eng Mich Technol Univ Houghton MI 49931

ROSE, WILLIAM K, b Ossining, NY, Aug 10, 35; m 61; c 3. ASTROPHYSICS. *Educ:* Columbia Col, AB, 57; Columbia Univ, PhD(physics), 63. *Prof Exp:* Res staff astrophys, Princeton Univ, 63-67; asst prof, Mass Inst Technol, 67-70, assoc prof, 71; PROF ASTROPHYS, UNIV MD, 76- *Mem:* Am Astron Soc; AAAS; Am Asn Univ Prof; Int Astron Union. *Res:* Stellar evolution; plasma astrophysics; radio astronomy. *Mailing Add:* Dept of Physics & Astron Univ of Md College Park MD 20742

ROSEBERRY, JOHN L, b Riverton, Ill, Sept 24, 36. WILDLIFE RESEARCH. *Educ:* Univ Ill, Urbana, BS, 58; Southern Ill Univ, Carbondale, MA, 61. *Prof Exp:* Res asst zool, 58-60, RESEARCHER ZOOL, COOP WILDLIFE RES LAB, SOUTHERN ILL UNIV, CARBONDALE, 61- *Concurrent Pos:* Consult controlled deer hunt, Crab Orchard Nat Wildlife Refuge, 66, 78 & 79; biol adv deer permit task force, Ill Dept Conserv, 77 & 78. *Mem:* Wildlife Soc; Am Ornithologists' Union; Am Soc Mammalogists; Sigma Xi. *Res:* Vertebrate ecology and population dynamics, especially regulation, exploitation, computer simulation, habitat inventory and analysis. *Mailing Add:* Coop Wildlife Res Lab Southern Ill Univ Carbondale IL 62901

ROSEBERY, DEAN ARLO, b Stahl, Mo, Sept 23, 19; m 43; c 2. FISHERIES. *Educ:* Northeast Mo State Teachers Col, BS, 41; Va Polytech Inst, PhD(zool), 50. *Prof Exp:* Instr biol, Va Polytech Inst, 46-48; asst chief fish div, State Comn Game & Inland Fisheries, Va, 48-52; prof sci, 52-72, PROF BIOL & HEAD DIV SCI, NORTHEAST MO STATE UNIV, 70- *Mem:* AAAS; Am Fisheries Soc; Wildlife Soc; Am Soc Limnol & Oceanog. *Res:* Freshwater fish management; fisheries biology. *Mailing Add:* Div of Sci Northeast Mo State Univ Kirksville MO 63501

ROSEBOOM, EUGENE HOLLOWAY, JR, b Columbus, Ohio, Sept 21, 26; m 58; c 4. NUCLEAR WASTE DISPOSAL, EXPERIMENTAL PETROLOGY. *Educ:* Ohio State Univ, BS, 49, MS, 51; Harvard Univ, PhD(geol), 58. *Prof Exp:* Res fel, Geophys Lab, Carnegie Inst, 56-59; geologist, Washington, DC, 59-74, regional geologist, Eastern Region, 74-79, PROG COORDR NUCLEAR WASTER DISPOSAL, GEOL DIV, US GEOL SURV, 80- *Mem:* Mineral Soc Am; Soc Econ Geol. *Res:* Phase equilibria among arsenides, sulfides, silicates; geologic applications; theory of phase equilibria diagrams. *Mailing Add:* US Geol Surv Stop 959 Reston VA 22092

ROSECRANS, JOHN A, b Brooklyn, NY, July 30, 35; m 58; c 3. PHARMACOLOGY. *Educ:* St John's Univ, BS, 57; Univ RI, MS, 60, PhD(pharmacol), 63. *Prof Exp:* NIMH fel, Univ Mich, Ann Arbor, 63-64; res asst prof pharmacol, Univ Pittsburgh, 64-65; trainee, Yale Univ, from asst prof to assoc prof, 67-78, PROF PHARMACOL, MED COL VA, 78- *Mem:* AAAS; Am Soc Pharmacol & Exp Therapeut; Soc Neurosci. *Res:* Behavioral and biochemical basis of drug dependence. *Mailing Add:* Dept of Pharmacol Med Col of Va Richmond VA 23219

ROSEGAY, AVERY, b New York, NY, Sept 3, 29; c 1. RADIOCHEMISTRY, ORGANIC CHEMISTRY. *Educ:* Columbia Univ, BS, 50, MS, 53; NY Univ, PhD(org chem), 60. *Prof Exp:* Res fel, 60-80, SR RES FEL, MERCK, SHARP & DOHME RES LABS, RAHWAY, 80- *Mem:* Am Chem Soc. *Res:* Synthesis of radioactive pharmaceuticals; hydrogen exchange reactions. *Mailing Add:* 20 Berkeley Pl Cranford NJ 07016

ROSEHART, ROBERT GEORGE, b Owen Sound, Ont, July 29, 43; m 67. CHEMICAL ENGINEERING. *Educ:* Univ Waterloo, BASc, 67, MASc, 68, PhD(chem eng), 70. *Prof Exp:* Fluids & heat transfer engr, Atomic Energy Can, 66 & Can Gen Elec, 67; COORDR CHEM ENG GROUP, LAKEHEAD UNIV, 70-, DEAN UNIV SCHS, 77- *Concurrent Pos:* Consult, Atomic Energy Can, 67- *Mem:* Am Inst Chem Engrs; Am Soc Mech Engrs; Chem Inst Can; Can Soc Chem Engrs; Am Soc Eng Educ. *Res:* Nuclear technology; heat transfer; two-phase flow; water treatment processes; simulation. *Mailing Add:* Dean Univ Schs Lakehead Univ Thunder Bay ON P7B 5E1 Can

ROSELLE, DAVID PAUL, b Vandergrift, Pa, May 30, 39; m 67. MATHEMATICS. *Educ:* West Chester State Col, BS, 61; Duke Univ, PhD(number theory), 65. *Prof Exp:* Asst prof math, Univ Md, 65-68; from assoc prof to prof, La State Univ, Baton Rouge, 68-74; prof math 74-79, dean grad sch, 79-81, DEAN RES & GRAD STUDIES, VA POLYTECH INST & STATE UNIV, 81- *Concurrent Pos:* Chief investr, NSF grants, 66-71 & 73-75; Nat Res Coun Can fel, 68; assoc ed, Am Math Monthly, 73-75. *Mem:* Am Math Soc; Math Asn Am (secy, 75-); Nat Coun Teachers Math. *Res:* Combinatorial analysis; number theory. *Mailing Add:* Dept Math Va Polytech Inst & State Univ Blacksburg VA 24061

ROSEMAN, ARNOLD S(AUL), b Boston, Mass; US citizen. FOOD SCIENCE & TECHNOLOGY. *Educ:* Northeastern Univ, BS, 52; Univ Mass, MS, 54, PhD(food technol), 56. *Prof Exp:* Biochemist rice, Southern Regional Lab, Agr Res Serv, USDA, 56-60; sr scientist, Res & Develop Div, Kraft Co, 60-68; res mgr meats, Res & Develop Dept, John Morrell & Co, 68-74; DIR RES & DEVELOP FOOD TECHNOL, CFS CONTINENTAL, INC, CHICAGO, 74- *Mem:* Inst Food Technologists; Am Chem Soc; Am Asn Cereal Chemists. *Res:* Food product development, especially institutional items; organoleptic evaluation of foods; utilization of products by food service; effects of processing and storage on the chemical, physical and organoleptic properties; research management. *Mailing Add:* 437 Hill Ave Glen Ellyn IL 60137

ROSEMAN, EPHRAIM, b Baltimore, Md, Jan 1, 13; m 60. MEDICINE. *Educ:* Johns Hopkins Univ, AB, 33; Univ Md, MD, 37. *Prof Exp:* Intern, Baltimore City Hosps, 37-38; resident, Montreal Gen Hosp, 38-39, asst resident, 39; resident, Cincinnati Gen Hosp, 39-40 & Boston City Hosp, 40-41; asst psychiat & asst, Neuropsychiat Inst, Univ Ill, 41-42; instr neurol, Univ Cincinnati, 42-46; asst prof, Med Sch, Univ Calif, 46-47; assoc prof, 47-49, PROF NEUROL, MED SCH, UNIV LOUISVILLE, 49- *Concurrent Pos:* Teaching fel neurol, Med Sch, McGill Univ, 38-39; fel neuropath, Cincinnati Gen Hosp, 39-40; teaching fel neurol, Col Med, Univ Cincinnati, 39-40 & Harvard Med Sch, 40-41; Rockefeller fel, Neuropsychiat Inst, Med Sch, Univ Ill, 41-42; from asst attend neurologist to attend neurologist, Hosps, 42-; asst dir, Neurol Clin, Univ Calif, 46-47; consult, Hosps, 46-; dir neurol clin & lab EEG, Louisville Gen Hosp, 47-; consult & dir lab EEG, Vet Admin Hosp, Louisville, 47-; civilian consult, Surgeon Gen Off, Letterman Gen Hosp, 47 & Surgeon Gen, US Army, 48- *Mem:* AAAS; Am EEG Soc; Am Epilepsy Soc; Asn Res Nerv & Ment Dis. *Res:* Electroencephalography; epilepsy; use and abuse of cerebrospinal fluid; intracranial blood flow; infectious polyneuritis; cerebral vascular accident; lateral medullary syndrome; tetanus; infectious neuronitis. *Mailing Add:* 323 E Chestnut St Louisville KY 40202

ROSEMAN, JOSEPH JACOB, b Brooklyn, NY, Nov 11, 35. MATHEMATICS. *Educ:* Mass Inst Technol, BS, 57; Polytech Inst Brooklyn, MS, 61; NY Univ, PhD(math), 65. *Prof Exp:* Chem engr, Gen Elec Co, 57-59; asst prof math, Univ Wis-Madison, 65-67; assoc prof, Polytech Inst Brooklyn, 67-74; sr lectr, 74-79, ASSOC PROF, TEL AVIV UNIV, 79- *Mem:* Am Math Soc; Math Asn Am; Soc Natural Philos. *Res:* Mathematical elasticity; fluid dynamics. *Mailing Add:* Tel Aviv Univ Ramat Aviv Tel Aviv Israel

ROSEMAN, SAUL, b New York, NY, Mar 9, 21; m 41; c 3. BIOCHEMISTRY. *Educ:* City Col New York, BS, 41; Univ Wis, MS, 43, PhD(biochem, org chem), 48. *Prof Exp:* Res assoc biochem & pediat, Univ Chicago, 48-51, asst prof, 51-53; res assoc, Rackham Arthritis Res Unit, Univ Mich Hosp, 53-54, from asst prof to prof biol chem, 54-65; chmn dept biol & dir McCollum-Pratt Inst, 69-73, PROF BIOL, JOHNS HOPKINS UNIV, 65- *Concurrent Pos:* Sci counr, Nat Cancer Inst, 72- *Honors & Awards:* T Duckett Jones Mem Award, Helen Hay Whitney Found, 73; Rosenstiel Award, Brandeis Univ, 74. *Mem:* Nat Acad Sci; Am Acad Arts & Sci; Am Chem Soc; Am Soc Biol Chemists. *Res:* Chemistry and metabolism of complex carbohydrates; polysaccharides; glycoproteins; glycolipids. *Mailing Add:* Johns Hopkins Univ Charles & 34th Sts Baltimore MD 21218

ROSEMAN, THEODORE JONAS, b Chicago, Ill, Aug 2, 41; m 63; c 2. PHARMACEUTICAL CHEMISTRY. *Educ:* Univ Ill, BS, 63; Univ Mich, MS, 65, PhD(pharmaceut chem), 67. *Prof Exp:* Pharmacist, Westridge Med Ctr, 63; teaching asst pharm, Univ Mich, 63-64; res scientist, 67-80, SR SCIENTIST PHARM, UPJOHN CO, 80- *Mem:* Am Pharmaceut Asn; Am Chem Soc; Control Release Soc; Parenteral Drug Asn; fel Acad Pharmaceut Sci. *Res:* Physical-chemical properties of therapeutic agents; controlled release delivery systems; package-product interactions; drug release mechanisms. *Mailing Add:* 301 Henrietta St Pharmaceut Res Upjohn Co Kalamazoo MI 49001

ROSEMOND, GEORGE P, b Hilsboro, NC, Aug 23, 10; m 37; c 1. SURGERY. *Educ:* Univ NC, BS, 32; Temple Univ, MD, 34, MS, 39; Am Bd Surg, dipl, 42; Am Bd Thoracic Surg, dipl, 60. *Prof Exp:* From instr to assoc prof surg, 39-47, clin prof, 47-50, prof clin surg, 50-60, co-chmn dept surg, 60-63, chmn div surg, 63-73, PROF SURG & CHMN DEPT, SCH MED, TEMPLE UNIV, 63- *Concurrent Pos:* Mem adv comt & consult physician, Wilkes-Barre Vet Admin Hosp. *Mem:* Am Asn Thoracic Surg; Am Col Chest Physicians; Am Surg Asn; fel Am Col Surg; Am Cancer Soc (pres, 74). *Res:* Cancer, especially cancer of the breast. *Mailing Add:* Dept of Surg Temple Univ Sch of Med Philadelphia PA 19140

ROSEN, ALAN, b Tel Aviv, Israel, Aug 19, 27; nat US; m 56; c 1. SPACE PHYSICS, BIOMEDICAL ENGINEERING. *Educ:* Univ Southern Calif, BA, 51, MA, 54, PhD(nuclear physics), 58. *Prof Exp:* Asst, Univ Southern Calif, 51-55, lectr physics, 55-58; geophysicist, Space Tech Lab, Inc, Thompson Ramo Wooldridge, Inc, 58-68, DIR SPACE SCI LAB, TRW SYSTS GROUP, 68- *Mem:* Am Phys Soc; Am Asn Physics Teachers; Am Geophys Union; Am Inst Aeronaut & Astronaut. *Res:* Space physics, especially terrestrial radiation belt studies by means of earth satellites and space probes; studies of the magnetic characteristics of man; magnetocardiographic research; spacecraft charging by magnetospheric plasmas. *Mailing Add:* TRW R5/1291 DSSG One Space Park Redondo Beach CA 90278

ROSEN, ARTHUR LEONARD, b Chicago, Ill, Apr 30, 34; m 56; c 2. BIOPHYSICS, APPLIED MATHEMATICS. *Educ:* Roosevelt Univ, BS, 57; Univ Chicago, MS, 64, PhD(physics), 71. *Prof Exp:* Res assoc, Dept Cardiovasc Res, Michael Reese Hosp, Chicago, 55-58, res assoc, Dept Surg Res, 60-64; asst dir dept surg res, Hektoen Inst Med Res, 64-78; RES ASSOC, DEPT SURG, MICHAEL REESE HOSP, CHICAGO, 78-; RES ASSOC, DEPT SURG, UNIV CHICAGO, 81- *Concurrent Pos:* Asst prof biophys, Dept Surg, Col Med, Univ Ill, 67-78. *Mem:* Am Phys Soc; Biophys Soc; Soc Rheol; Inst Elec & Electronics Engrs; Am Asn Physicists in Med. *Res:* Physics of the circulation; biomathematics. *Mailing Add:* Dept of Surg 2929 S Ellis Chicago IL 60616

ROSEN, ARTHUR ZELIG, b Oil City, Pa, Feb 5, 20; m 41. PHYSICS. *Educ:* Univ Calif, BA, 41, PhD(physics), 52. *Prof Exp:* Engr, Permanente Shipyards, 41-42; jr physicist radiation lab, Univ Calif, 42-45, asst physics, 46-51; engr, Berkeley Sci Co, 46; lectr physics, Santa Barbara Col, 51-53; from instr to assoc prof, 53-64, PROF PHYSICS, CALIF POLYTECH STATE UNIV, SAN LUIS OBISPO, 64- *Concurrent Pos:* NSF sci fac fel, 59. *Mem:* Am Phys Soc; Am Asn Physics Teachers. *Res:* Mass spectrograph development; cosmic ray studies at sea level and mountain altitudes; experimental nuclear physics; health physics. *Mailing Add:* Dept of Physics Calif Polytech State Univ San Luis Obispo CA 93407

ROSEN, BARRY PHILIP, b Hartford, Conn, June 18, 44. BIOCHEMISTRY. *Educ:* Trinity Col, BS, 65; Univ Conn, MS, 68, PhD(biochem), 69. *Prof Exp:* USPHS fel, Cornell Univ, 69-71; ASSOC PROF BIOCHEM, SCH MED, UNIV MD, BALTIMORE CITY, 71- *Mem:* Am Soc Microbiol; Am Soc Biol Chemists. *Res:* Structure and function of biological membranes; energy transduction and active transport in microorganisms. *Mailing Add:* Dept of Biol Chem Univ of Md Sch of Med Baltimore MD 20201

ROSEN, BERNARD, b New York, NY, June 6, 30; m 62; c 2. PLASMA PHYSICS. *Educ:* NY Univ, AB, 50, PhD(physics), 59. *Prof Exp:* Engr, Fed Tel & Radio Co, 51-52 & Bendix Aviation Co, 52-53; instr physics, NY Univ, 55-58; engr, Radio Corp Am, 58-60; from asst prof to assoc prof physics, 60-73, PROF PHYSICS, STEVENS INST TECHNOL, 73- *Concurrent Pos:* Consult, Plasma Physics Lab, Princeton Univ, 72-75. *Mem:* Am Phys Soc. *Res:* Computational plasma physics. *Mailing Add:* Dept of Physics Stevens Inst of Technol Hoboken NJ 07030

ROSEN, BRUCE IRWIN, b Chicago, Ill, July 8, 52. ORGANIC CHEMISTRY. *Educ:* Northwestern Univ, BA, 74; Univ Southern Calif, PhD(org chem), 77. *Prof Exp:* sr res chemist org chem, 3M Co, 77-79; SR RES CHEMIST, ORG CHEM, UOP INC, 79- *Mem:* Am Chem Soc; Sigma Xi. *Res:* synthetic organic chemistry, organometallic chemistry (heterogeneous and homogeneous catalysis) and polymer chemistry; organometallic chemistry; polymer chemistry. *Mailing Add:* UOP Inc UOP Pl Des Plaines IL 60016

ROSEN, C(HARLES) A(BRAHAM), b Toronto, Ont, Dec 7, 17; nat US; m 41; c 4. ELECTRICAL ENGINEERING. *Educ:* Cooper Union, BEE, 40; McGill Univ, MEng, 50; Syracuse Univ, PhD(elec eng), 56. *Prof Exp:* Sr examr, Brit Air Comn, NY, 40-43; proj engr, Fairchild Aircraft, Ltd, Can, 43-47; co-owner, Electrolabs Regist, 47-50; consult engr, Gen Elec Co, 50-57; mgr appl physics lab, 57-70, MGR ARTIFICIAL INTEL GROUP, INFO SCI LAB, SRI INT, 70- *Concurrent Pos:* Co-founder & pres, Machine Intel Corp, 78-80, chmn, 80- *Honors & Awards:* Taylor Award, Inst Elec & Electronics Engrs, 75. *Mem:* Am Phys Soc; Sigma Xi; fel Inst Elec & Electronics Engrs; AAAS. *Res:* Learning machines; pattern recognition; artificial intelligence; electron-beam-activated micromachining processes; ferroelectric and piezoelectric devices; programmable automation; robotics. *Mailing Add:* 139 Tuscaloosa Ave Atherton CA 94026

ROSEN, CAROL ZWICK, b Brooklyn, NY; m 62; c 2. LOW TEMPERATURE PHYSICS, METALLURGY. *Educ:* Brooklyn Col, BS, 53; NY Univ, MS, 55; Stevens Inst Technol, PhD(physics), 65. *Prof Exp:* Fel nuclear magnetic resonance, IBM Watson Lab, 65-67; res assoc, Stevens Inst Technol, 67-70; staff physicist, Am Inst Physics, 70-74; asst prof physics, York Col, NY, 74-75; staff physicist, Am Phys Soc, 75-76, nonwoven web technol, Johnson & Johnson, 76-79 & composite superconductors, Airco Superconductors, 79-80; STAFF PHYSICIST, ADVAN TECHNOL SYSTS INC, DIV OF AUSTIN CO, 80- *Concurrent Pos:* Consult index ed, Phys Rev A, B1, B17, Am Inst Physics, 74-; adj asst prof physics, Queen's Col, NY, 75-77; adj prof, 77- *Mem:* Am Phys Soc; Soc Women Engrs. *Res:* Selectively thermalized low pressure rf sputtering to synthesize a generalized (Nb1-x Tx) 3Ge system, the goal being to space the T atoms periodically along the Nb chains; physical adsorption and absorption; paper and nonwoven web technology; electroplating; heat treatment; superconducting wire and braid from in-situ copper-niobium wire. *Mailing Add:* 934 Red Rd Teaneck NJ 07666

ROSEN, DAVID, b New Haven, Conn, Jan 26, 21; m 46; c 4. MATHEMATICS. *Educ:* NY Univ, AB, 42; Univ Pa, AM, 49, PhD(math), 52. *Prof Exp:* Asst instr math, Univ Pa, 49-52; from instr to assoc prof, 52-67, PROF MATH, SWARTHMORE COL, 67- *Concurrent Pos:* NSF fac fel, 61-62; Fulbright-Hays lectr, Ireland, 71-72. *Mem:* Am Math Soc; Math Asn Am; Sigma Xi. *Res:* Automorphic functions; continued fractions. *Mailing Add:* Dept of Math Swarthmore Col Swarthmore PA 19081

ROSEN, DAVID A, b Montreal, Que, Apr 18, 26; m 47; c 2. OPHTHALMOLOGY. *Educ:* McGill Univ, BSc, 47, MD, CM, 49; FRCS(C), 54. *Prof Exp:* From asst prof to assoc prof ophthal, Queen's Univ, Ont, 54-57, prof, 57-78; PROF OPHTHAL, STATE UNIV NY, STONY BROOK, 78- *Concurrent Pos:* Markle scholar, 54-59; chmn dept ophthal, Kingston Gen Hosp, 54-73; chmn, Dept Ophthal, Long Island Jewish-Hillside Med Ctr, 78- *Mem:* Asn Res Vision & Ophthal; Am Acad Ophthal & Otolaryngol; fel Am Col Surgeons; Can Soc Ophthal; Can Med Asn. *Res:* Ophthalmic pathology; retinal vessel physiology and angiology; photocoagulation; health care delivery; medical education. *Mailing Add:* Dept Ophthal Med Ctr New Hyde Park NY 11040

ROSEN, DONN ERIC, b New York, NY, Jan 9, 29; m 54; c 2. ICHTHYOLOGY. *Educ:* NY Univ, BS, 55, MS, 57, PhD, 59. *Prof Exp:* Systematist, NY Zool Soc, 54-59; asst prof biol, Univ Fla, 60-61; asst cur, Dept Ichthyol, 61-65, assoc cur, 65-69, chmn dept, 65-75, CUR, DEPT ICHTHYOL, AM MUS NATURAL HIST, 69- *Concurrent Pos:* Frederick Stoye Ichthyol Award, 52-54; NSF fel, 59; asst cur biol sci, Fla State Mus, 60-61, res assoc, 61-65; adj prof biol, City Univ New York, 65- *Honors & Awards:* Leidy Medal, Acad Natural Sci, 67. *Mem:* Am Soc Ichthyologists & Herpetologists; Am Fisheries Soc; Am Soc Naturalists; Linnean Soc; Soc Syst Zool (pres, 75-77). *Res:* Systematic ichthyology; comparative and functional morphology; evolution; biogeography. *Mailing Add:* Am Mus of Natural Hist New York NY 10024

ROSEN, EDWARD M(ARSHALL), b Chicago, Ill, Jan 28, 30; m 65; c 2. CHEMICAL ENGINEERING. *Educ:* Ill Inst Technol, BS, 51, MS, 53; Univ Ill, PhD(chem eng), 59. *Prof Exp:* SCI FEL CHEM ENG, MONSANTO CO, 59- *Concurrent Pos:* Monsanto acad leave chem eng, Stanford Univ, 62-63; lectr, Univ Mo, 72-; affil prof, Wash Univ, 74. *Mem:* Am Inst Chem Engrs; Asn Comput Mach. *Res:* Process simulation and design. *Mailing Add:* Monsanto Co 800 N Lindbergh St Louis MO 63166

ROSEN, FRED, b Newark, NJ, Dec 18, 21; m 49; c 2. BIOCHEMISTRY, NUTRITION. *Educ:* Univ Wis, BS, 44; Duke Univ, PhD(biochem), 49. *Prof Exp:* Jr chemist, Hoffmann La Roche Inc, 44-45; res assoc nutrit, Ortho Res Found, 50-56; res assoc cancer res scientist to prin cancer res scientist, Roswell Park Mem Inst, 56-71, assoc chief cancer res scientist, 71-79, assoc dir, Cancer Drug Ctr, 72-79, assoc inst dir, 79-81; RETIRED. *Concurrent Pos:* NIH fel nutrit, 49-50. *Mem:* AAAS; Am Chem Soc; Am Soc Biol Chemists; Am Asn Cancer Res; Am Inst Nutrit. *Res:* Mechanics of action of drugs and hormones; chemotherapy; metabolic fate of drugs. *Mailing Add:* 3245-58 Via Allicante La Jolla CA 92037

ROSEN, GERALD HARRIS, b Mt Vernon, NY, Aug 10, 33; m 63; c 2. THEORETICAL PHYSICS. *Educ:* Princeton Univ, BSE, 55, MA, 56, PhD(physics), 58. *Prof Exp:* Res assoc dept aeronaut eng, Princeton Univ, 58-59; NSF fel, Inst Theoret Physics, Stockholm, Sweden, 59-60; prin scientist, Martin-Marietta Aerospace Div, 60-63; consult basic & appl res,

Southwest Res Inst, 63-66; prof physics, 66-73, M RUSSELL WEHR PROF PHYSICS & ATMOSPHERIC SCI, DREXEL UNIV, 73- Concurrent Pos: Mem tech staff, Weapons Systs Eval Div, The Pentagon, 60. Mem: Fel AAAS; fel Am Phys Soc. Res: Theories of relativistic quantum and classical fields; theories of compressible, viscous and combustible fluid flows; turbulence phenomena; nonlinear reaction and transport processes; space-charge-limited currents; biomathematics; nonlinear partial differential equations. Mailing Add: Dept of Physics Drexel Univ Philadelphia PA 19104

ROSEN, HAROLD A, b New Orleans, La, 1926. ASTRONAUTICS. Educ: Tulane Univ, BE, 44; Calif Inst Technol, PhD, 50. Prof Exp: VPRES ENG & MGR COM SYSTS DIV, SPACE & COMMUN GROUP, HUGHES AIRCRAFT CO, 50- Concurrent Pos: Astronaut engr, Nat Space Coun, 64. Honors & Awards: Commun Award, Am Inst Aeronaut & Astronaut, 68; Mervin J Kelly Award, Inst Elec & Electronics Engrs, 71. Mem: Nat Acad Eng. Res: Conceived spin stabilized synchronous communication satellite. Mailing Add: Hughes Aircraft Co PO Box 92919 Airport Sta Los Angeles CA 90009

ROSEN, HARRY MARK, b Philadelphia, Pa, Mar 19, 46. MEDICAL ADMINISTRATION. Educ: Univ Pa, BS, 68; Columbia Univ, MS, 70; Cornell Univ, PhD, 76. Prof Exp: Dir hosp stud, New York City Health Serv Admin, 72-73; from asst prof to assoc prof, 73-80, PROF, MT SINAI SCH MED, 80-, VCHMN, DEPT HEALTH CARE MGT, 79- Mem: Am Pub Health Asn; Am Hosp Asn; Am Col Hosp Adminr. Res: Evaluation of health care services; quantitative methods in health care management; the quality assurance function. Mailing Add: Baruch Col-Mt Sinai Prog 17 Lexington Ave New York NY 10010

ROSEN, HOWARD, b Chicago, Ill, July 25, 39; m 64; c 2. DNA REPAIR, GENETIC RECOMBINATION. Educ: Univ Calif, Los Angeles, BS, 61, MS, 65, PhD(bot sci), 68. Prof Exp: Fel, Dept Human Genetics, Univ Mich, 69-70; PROF BIOL, CALIF STATE UNIV, LOS ANGELES, 70- Concurrent Pos: Res assoc, Carnegie-Mellon Univ, 72. Res: Mechanism of repair of ultraviolet induced damage in chlamydomonas reinhardtii. Mailing Add: Calif State Univ Dept Biol 5151 State Univ Dr Los Angeles CA 90032

ROSEN, HOWARD NEAL, b Takoma Park, Md, June 25, 42; m 69; c 2. CHEMICAL ENGINEERING, WOOD TECHNOLOGY. Educ: Univ Md, BS, 64; Northwestern Univ, MS, 66, PhD(chem eng), 69. Prof Exp: Develop engr petrol res, Shell Develop Co, 69-70; res chem engr, 70-77, PROJ LEADER WOOD UTILIZATION, US FOREST SERV, NCENT FOREST EXP STA, USDA, 77- Concurrent Pos: Adj asst prof, Forestry Dept, Southern Ill Univ, 71- Mem: Am Inst Chem Engrs; Forest Prod Res Soc; Soc Wood Sci & Technol. Res: Drying, energy conservation, wood utilization, treated wood products, wood physics, crystallization. Mailing Add: USDA Forest Serv Southern Ill Univ Carbondale IL 62901

ROSEN, IRVING, b New York, NY, Apr 3, 24; m 48; c 2. POLYMER CHEMISTRY. Educ: Brooklyn Col, BA, 47; Ind Univ, MS, 49, PhD(chem), 51. Prof Exp: Res phys chemist, Reaction Motors, Inc, 51-52; sr chemist, Diamond Alkali Co, 52-55, res group leader polymer & radiation chem, 55-66, sr group leader polymer chem, 66-67; res supvr, 67-81, ADV TO CORP DIR RES, STANDARD OIL CO, OHIO, 81- Mem: Am Chem Soc; Soc Plastics Engrs. Res: Free radical and ionic polymerization; thermoplastic and thermoset polymers; structure-property relations; monomer synthesis; catalysis; chemicals; synfuels. Mailing Add: Standard Oil Co Ohio 4440 Warrensville Ctr Rd Cleveland OH 44128

ROSEN, IRWIN GARY, b Long Beach, NY, Feb 19, 54. NUMERICAL ANALYSIS, CONTROL THEORY. Educ: Brown Univ, ScB, 75, ScM, 76, PhD(appl math), 80. Prof Exp: ASST PROF MATH, BOWDOIN COL, 80- Concurrent Pos: Vis scientist, Inst Comput Appln Sci & Eng, 81, consult, 81- Mem: Am Math Soc; Soc Indust & Appl Math. Res: Numerical approximation methods for the solution of parameter identification and optimal control problems for distributed parameter systems. Mailing Add: Dept Math Bowdoin Col Brunswick ME 04011

ROSEN, JAMES MARTIN, b Waseca, Minn, Mar 9, 39; m 67; c 2. PHYSICS. Educ: Univ Minn, BS, 61, MS, 63, PhD(physics), 67. Prof Exp: Res assoc, Univ Minn, 67-68; from asst prof to assoc prof, 68-78, PROF PHYSICS, UNIV WYO, 78- Mem: Am Geophys Union; Optical Soc Am. Res: Stratospheric constituents; atmospheric research, especially aerosols. Mailing Add: Dept of Physics & Astron Univ of Wyo Laramie WY 82071

ROSEN, JEFFREY KENNETH, b Middletown, NY, Dec 27, 41; m 70; c 2. DATA PROCESSING. Educ: Dartmouth Col, BA, 63; Brown Univ, MA & PhD(physiol), 72. Prof Exp: Teacher gen sci, Middletown Bd Educ, NY, 66-68; partner biol consult, L M Kraft Assocs, Goshen, NY, 68-69; asst prof physiol, Univ Dar es Salaam, Tanzania, 72-74; res investr & admin asst to dir, Animal Physiol & Husb, Amphibian Facil, 74-77; sr procedures analyst, data processing, Med Serv Plan Off, 78-80, PROGRAMMER/ANALYST, HOSP DATA SYSTS CTR, UNIV MICH HOSP, 80- Concurrent Pos: Fel, Brown Univ, 72. Mem: Am Asn Lab Animal Sci; AAAS. Mailing Add: Hosp Data Systs Ctr Univ Mich Hosp Ann Arbor MI 48109

ROSEN, JEFFREY MARK, b New York, NY, Jan 5, 45; m 70. BIOCHEMISTRY, ENDOCRINOLOGY. Educ: Williams Col, BA, 66; State Univ NY Buffalo, PhD(biochem), 71. Prof Exp: Res assoc obstet & gynec, Sch Med, Vanderbilt Univ, 72-73; asst prof, 73-77, ASSOC PROF CELL BIOL, BAYLOR COL MED, 77- Concurrent Pos: NIH career develop award, 75-80. Mem: AAAS; Am Chem Soc; Endocrine Soc; Am Soc Biol Chemists; Am Soc Cell Biol. Res: Mechanism of steroid and peptide hormone action; hormonal regulation of mammary gland growth and differentiation; hormonal regulation of breast cancer. Mailing Add: Dept of Cell Biol Baylor Col of Med Houston TX 77030

ROSEN, JOHN FRIESNER, b New York, NY, June 3, 35; m 63; c 2. BIOCHEMISTRY, METABOLISM. Educ: Harvard Col, AB, 57; Columbia Univ, MD, 61. Prof Exp: Intern med, Montefiore Hosp, Bronx, NY, 61-62; resident pediat, Columbia-Presby Med Ctr 62-65; guest investr, Rockefeller Univ, 65-66, res assoc pediat endocrinol, 66-69, asst physician, Univ Hosp, 65-69; asst prof, 69-76, ASSOC PROF PEDIAT, ALBERT EINSTEIN COL MED & MONTEFIORE HOSP & MED CTR, 76- DIR PEDIAT METAB SERV & LABS, HOSP & CTR, 69- Mem: AAAS; Am Chem Soc; Am Fedn Clin Res; fel Am Acad Pediat. Res: Biochemical research in mineral metabolism; extraction and purification of human thyrocalcitonin; clinical research in pediatric mineral metabolism; vitamin D dependent rickets; basic and clinical research in mechanisms of lead's interaction with bone. Mailing Add: Dept of Pediat 111 E 210th St Bronx NY 10467

ROSEN, JOSEPH DAVID, b New York, NY, Feb 26, 35; m 62; c 4. FOOD CHEMISTRY, PESTICIDE CHEMISTRY. Educ: City Col New York, BS, 56; Rutgers Univ, PhD(org chem), 63. Prof Exp: Res chemist, E I du Pont de Nemours & Co, Inc, 63-65; from asst res prof to assoc res prof food sci, 65-74, RES PROF FOOD SCI, RUTGERS UNIV, NEW BRUNSWICK, 74- Concurrent Pos: Sci adv, Food & Drug Admin, 74-78, 81-; adv bd, J Agr & Food Chem, 76-78; vis prof pesticide chem, Univ Calif, Berkeley, 78-79; co ed, J Food Safety, 78- Mem: Am Chem Soc; AAAS. Res: Analysis of mycotoxins and industrial chemicals in food by mass spectrometry; metabolism of xenobiotics; photochemistry of pesticides. Mailing Add: Dept of Food Sci Cook Col Rutgers Univ New Brunswick NJ 08903

ROSEN, JUDAH BEN, b Philadelphia, Pa, May 5, 22; m 43; c 2. COMPUTER SCIENCE. Educ: Johns Hopkins Univ, BS, 43; Columbia Univ, PhD(appl math), 52. Prof Exp: Jr engr, Gen Elec Co, 43-44; develop engr, Manhattan Proj, 44-47; develop engr, Brookhaven Nat Lab, 47-48; res assoc, Princeton Univ, 52-54; head appl math dept, Shell Develop Co, 55-62; vis prof comput sci, Stanford Univ, 62-64; prof & chmn dept, Univ Wis-Madison, 65-71, prof math res ctr, 64-71; PROF COMPUT SCI & HEAD DEPT, UNIV MINN, MINNEAPOLIS, 71- Concurrent Pos: Consult, Argonne Nat Labs, 76-; Lady Davis vis prof, Technion, Israel, 80. Mem: Comput Sci Bd; Soc Indust & Appl Math; Asn Comput Mach; Math Prog Soc. Res: Mathematical programming; numerical analysis; interactive graphical solution of boundary value problems. Mailing Add: 1904 W 49th St Minneapolis MN 55409

ROSEN, LAWRENCE, b July 25, 24; US citizen; m; c 3. CHEMISTRY. Educ: Washington & Jefferson Col, BS, 48; Univ Ala, University, MS, 52, PhD, 57. Prof Exp: Asst biochem, Med Ctr, Univ Ala, University, 52-54; assoc, Duke Univ, 57-58; asst prof, Mem Res Ctr, Univ Tenn, 58-62; USPHS spec fel, Oak Ridge Nat Lab, 62-70; PROF CHEM, UNIV ALA, BIRMINGHAM, 70- Mem: AAAS; Am Chem Soc; Sigma Xi. Res: Biochemical mechanisms; intermediary metabolism; biosynthesis; nucleic acids. Mailing Add: Dept of Chem Univ of Ala Birmingham AL 35294

ROSEN, LEON, b Los Angeles, Calif, Oct 4, 26; m 52; c 3. EPIDEMIOLOGY. Educ: Univ Calif, AB, 45, MD, 48, MPH, 50; Johns Hopkins Univ, DrPH, 53. Prof Exp: Intern, Gorgas Hosp, Panama, CZ, 48-49; med dir & head Pac Res Sect, Nat Inst Allergy & Infectious Dis, 50-78, dir, Pac Res Unit, Res Corp, 78-80, DIR ARBOVIRUS PROG, PAC BIOMED RES CTR, UNIV HAWAII, 80- Honors & Awards: Dist Serv Medal & Meritorious Serv Medal, USPHS; Ashford Medal, Am Soc Trop Med & Hyg. Mem: Am Epidemiol Soc; Am Soc Trop Med & Hyg; Royal Soc Trop Med & Hyg; Infectious Dis Soc Am. Res: Virology; arthropod-borne viruses; nematode infections; medical entomology. Mailing Add: Arbovirus Prog Pac Biomed Res Ctr Univ Hawaii PO Box 1680 Honolulu HI 96806

ROSEN, LEONARD CRAIG, b New York, NY, Apr 14, 36; m 59; c 2. ENVIRONMENTAL PHYSICS, ENERGY CONVERSION. Educ: Cornell Univ, AB, 57; Columbia Univ, MBA, 58, MA, 64, PhD(physics), 68. Prof Exp: Asst prof physics & astron, Dartmouth Col, 69-76; MEM STAFF, LAWRENCE LIVERMORE NAT LAB, UNIV CALIF, 76- Concurrent Pos: Consult, Lawrence Livermore Lab, Univ Calif, 68-76 & Arthur D Little, Inc, 75-76. Res: Nucleosynthesis; mathematical models of air pollution; development of energy conversion systems. Mailing Add: 85 Montell St Oakland CA 94611

ROSEN, LOUIS, b New York, NY, June 10, 18; m 41; c 1. PHYSICS. Educ: Univ Ala, BA, 39, MS, 41; Pa State Univ, PhD(physics), 44. Prof Exp: Asst physics, Univ Ala, 39-40, instr, 40-41; from asst to instr, Pa State Univ, 41-44; mem staff, 44-46, alt group leader cyclotron group, 46-49, group leader, Nuclear Plate Lab, 49-65, alt div leader, 62-65, DIV LEADER, LOS ALAMOS SCI LAB, 65- Concurrent Pos: Guggenheim fel, 59-60; mem nuclear sci panel & chmn subpanel accelerators, President's Off Sci & Technol & Nat Acad Sci, 70-; mem, Gov Comn Tech Excellence in NMex, 70-; dir, Los Alamos Meson Physics Facil, 71-; ad hoc comt nuclear sci, Nat Acad Sci, 75-77; mem, NMex Cancer Control Adv Comn, NIH. Honors & Awards: E O Lawrence Award, 63; Golden Plate Award, Nat Acad Achievement, 64. Mem: Fel AAAS; fel Am Phys Soc. Res: High hydrostatic pressures; x-ray; cosmic rays; nuclear physics; particle accelerators; nuclear and particle physics; accelerators; cancer treatment. Mailing Add: Los Alamos Sci Lab PO Box 1663 Los Alamos NM 87544

ROSEN, MARVIN, b Newark, NJ, Jan 28, 27; m 49; c 2. ORGANIC CHEMISTRY, POLYMER CHEMISTRY. Educ: NY Univ, BA, 48, PhD(chem), 53. Prof Exp: Res chemist, Otto B May, Inc, 53-58; chief chem prod lab, Nuodex Chem Prod Co, 58-66, mgr res, Nuodex Div, Tenneco Chem, Inc, 66-69, vpres res & develop, 69-70, mgr res & develop, Tenneco Intermediates Div, 70-71, dir res & develop, Tenneco Organics & Polymers Div, 71-75, mgr polymer appln, 75-77; MGR ORG RES, GLYCO CHEM, 77- Mem: Am Chem Soc; Soc Plastics Engrs. Res: Terpenes; dyes and intermediates; protective coatings; vinyls; fungicides; polyvinyl chloride applications and development; hydantoin chemistry. Mailing Add: 50 Cliffside Dr Williamsport PA 17701

ROSEN, MICHAEL IRA, b Brooklyn, NY, Mar 7, 38; m 60. MATHEMATICS. *Educ:* Brandeis Univ, BA, 59; Princeton Univ, PhD(math), 63. *Prof Exp:* From instr to assoc prof math, 62-73, PROF MATH, BROWN UNIV, 73- *Concurrent Pos:* NSF res grants, 63-78; Off Naval Res fel, 65-66. *Mem:* Am Math Soc. *Res:* Algebraic numbers, algebraic functions, arithmetic algebraic geometry, cohomology of groups. *Mailing Add:* Dept of Math Brown Univ Providence RI 02912

ROSEN, MILTON JACQUES, b Brooklyn, NY, Feb 11, 20; m 48; c 3. SURFACE CHEMISTRY, APPLIED CHEMISTRY. *Educ:* City Col New York, BS, 39; Univ Md, MS, 41; Polytech Inst Brooklyn, PhD(org chem), 49. *Prof Exp:* Chemist, Jewish Hosp, Brooklyn, 40-42, Glyco Prod Co, 42-44 & Publicker Commercial Alcohol Co, Pa, 44; tutor chem, 46-50, from instr to assoc prof, 50-66, PROF CHEM, BROOKLYN COL, 66- *Concurrent Pos:* Fel, Lenox Hill Hosp, 41; chem consult to indust & US govt, 46-; vis prof, Hebrew Univ, Israel, 58-59, 64-65, 71-72 & 80; grants, City Univ New York, 62-64, NSF, 63-71 & 79-82 & Yamada Sci Found, Japan, 79; NIH spec fel, 64-65; Pilot Chem Co Calif grant, 76-78; assoc ed, J Am Oil Chemists Soc, 81- *Mem:* Am Chem Soc; Am Oil Chem Soc. *Res:* Surface active agents--correlations between structure and properties, utilization, synthesis, analysis; reactions at interfaces; qualitative organic analysis. *Mailing Add:* Dept of Chem Brooklyn Col City Univ NY Brooklyn NY 11210

ROSEN, MILTON W(ILLIAM), b Philadelphia, Pa, July 25, 15; m 48; c 3. PROPUSION, GUIDANCE & CONTROL. *Educ:* Univ Pa, BS, 37. *Prof Exp:* Radio engr guided missiles, Naval Res Lab, 40-45, head rocket sect, Rocket-Sonde Br, 47-52, head, Rocket Develop Br, 53-55, tech dir, Proj Vanguard, 55-58; physicist, Liquid Rocket Sect, Jet Propulsion Lab, Calif Inst Technol, 46-47; chief, Rocket Vehicle Develop, NASA, 58-60, dep dir, Off Launch Vehicle Prog, 60-61, dir, Launch Vehicles & Propulsion, Off Manned Space Flight, 61-63, sr scientist, Off Dept Defense & Interagency Affairs, 63-72, dep assoc, Admin Space Sci, 72-74; exec secy, Space Sci Bd, 74-78, exec secy, Comt Impacts Stratospheric Change, 78-80, EXEC SECY, COMT UNDERGROUND COAL MINE SAFETY, NAT ACAD SCI, 80- *Honors & Awards:* James H Wyld Award for Propulsion, Am Inst Aeronaut & Astronaut, 54. *Mem:* Fel Am Inst Aeronaut & Astronaut. *Res:* Radio and radar systems for control of guided missiles; ceramic liners for rocket combustion chambers; Viking high-altitude sounding rocket; conception of Vanguard earth satellite vehicle. *Mailing Add:* 5610 Alta Vista Rd Bethesda MD 20034

ROSEN, MORDECAI DAVID, b Brooklyn, NY, Nov 23, 51; m 73; c 2. PLASMA PHYSICS, LASER-PLASMA INTERACTIONS. *Educ:* Hebrew Univ, Jerusalem, BSc, 72; Princeton Univ, PhD(astrophysics), 76. *Prof Exp:* From res asst to res assoc, Plasma Physics Lab, Princeton Univ, 72-76; prof mgr shiva physics, 78-82 STAFF PHYSICIST PLASMA PHYSICS & LASER FUSION TARGET DELAY, UNIV CALIF, LAWRENCE LIVERMORE LAB, 76- *Concurrent Pos:* Lectr, Dept Appl Sci, Univ Calif, Davis. *Mem:* Am Phys Soc. *Res:* Laser fusion target design; laser-plasma interactions; magnetohydrodynamic stability of tokamaks, shock waves in plasmas; radiation transport; suprathernal electron transport; physics of high energy density. *Mailing Add:* L-477 Lawrence Livermore Lab Livermore CA 94550

ROSEN, MORTIMER GILBERT, b Brooklyn, NY, Dec 31, 31; m 55; c 2. OBSTETRICS & GYNECOLOGY. *Educ:* Univ Wis, BS, 52; NY Univ, MD, 55. *Prof Exp:* Intern, Bellevue Hosp, New York, 55-56, resident med & surg, 56-57; resident obstet & gynec, Genesee Hosp, Rochester, NY, 59-62; from instr to assoc prof obstet & gynec, Sch Med & Dent, Univ Rochester, 62-73, dir res, 68-73; PROF REPRODUCTIVE BIOL & DIR PERINATAL RES UNIT, SCH MED, CASE WESTERN RESERVE UNIV, 73-; DIR DEPT OBSTET & GYNEC & DIR MATERNITY & INFANT CARE PROJ, CLEVELAND METROP GEN HOSP, 73- *Mem:* Am Col Obstetricians & Gynecologists; Royal Soc Med; Soc Neurosci; Soc Psychophysiol Res. *Res:* Neurologic function and development of the fetus and newborn infant; antepartum and intrapartum human fetal monitoring systems; delivery of improved health care systems to obstetrics patients. *Mailing Add:* Cleveland Metrop Gen Hosp 3395 Scranton Rd Cleveland OH 44109

ROSEN, NATHAN, b Brooklyn, NY, Mar 22, 09; m 32; c 2. THEORETICAL PHYSICS. *Educ:* Mass Inst Technol, SB, 29, SM, 30, ScD(physics), 32. *Prof Exp:* Nat Res Coun fel, Univ Mich, 32-33 & Princeton Univ, 33-34; res worker, Inst Advan Study, 34-36; prof theoret physics, Kiev State Univ, 36-38; assoc spectros res, Mass Inst Technol, 38-40; asst prof physics, Black Mountain Col, 40-41; from asst prof to prof, Univ NC, 41-52; prof physics, 52-77, res prof, 77-79, EMER PROF PHYSICS, ISRAEL INST TECHNOL, 79- *Honors & Awards:* Weizmann Res Prize, Tel-Aviv Munic, 68; Landau Res Prize, 75. *Mem:* Fel AAAS; fel Am Phys Soc; Am Asn Physics Teachers; Israel Acad Sci; Phys Soc Israel (vpres, 54-56, pres, 56-58). *Res:* Relativity and unified field theory; quantum theory; gravitation and cosmology. *Mailing Add:* Dept of Physics Israel Inst of Technol Haifa Israel

ROSEN, NORMAN CHARLES, b Cleveland, Ohio, Oct 8, 41; m 64; c 2. PETROLEUM GEOLOGY, SEDIMENTOLOGY. *Educ:* Ohio State Univ, BSc, 63, MSc, 64; La State Univ, PhD(geol), 68. *Prof Exp:* Ed publs, Geol Surv Iran, 68-69; explor geologist, Texaco Inc, 69-74; sr geologist, Deminex A G, 74-78; proj geologist, Tenneco Oil Co, 78-80, sr geol specialist, 80-81; EXEC VPRES, ROBERTSON RES, 81- *Mem:* Am Asn Petrol Geologists; Soc Econ Paleontologists & Mineralogists; Sigma Xi. *Res:* Carbonate depositional environments; lithologic interpretation from wire-line logging techniques. *Mailing Add:* 3526 Aspen Rd Houston TX 77068

ROSEN, ORA MENDELSOHN, b New York, NY, Oct 26, 35; m 56; c 2. ENZYMOLOGY, ENDOCRINOLOGY. *Educ:* Columbia Univ, BA, 56, MD, 60. *Prof Exp:* Asst prof med, 66-67, from asst prof to assoc prof med & molecular biol, 67-75, PROF MED & MOLECULAR BIOL, ALBERT EINSTEIN COL MED, 75-, DIR DIV ENDOCRINOL, DEPT MED, 72-, PROF & CHMN, DEPT MOLECULAR PHARMACOL, 76- *Concurrent Pos:* USPHS res career develop award, 66-76; mem, Bd Sci Counrs, Nat Heart & Lung Inst, 75-79; Irma T Hirschl Trust Career sci award, 75-80. *Honors & Awards:* Achievement Award, Am Med Women's Asn, 60; Spirit of Achievement Award, Albert Einstein Col Med, 74. *Mem:* Am Soc Biol Chemists; Endocrine Soc; Am Diabetes Asn; Am Soc Clin Invest; Am Col Physicians. *Res:* Molecular mechanisms of hormone action; characterization of proteins involved in cyclic nucleotide synthesis, function and degradation; mechanism of insulin and growth factor action. *Mailing Add:* Albert Einstein Col Med 1300 Morris Park Ave Bronx NY 10461

ROSEN, PAUL, b New York, NY, Apr 2, 28; m 51; c 4. PHYSICS, ELECTRONICS. *Educ:* City Col New York, BS, 53; NY Univ, MS, 66. *Prof Exp:* Res physicist, Patterson Moos Div, Universal Coil Winding Mach, Inc, 53-56; res engr, Fairchild Camera & Instrument Corp, 56-58; res assoc, 58-70, AFFIL BIOPHYS, ROCKEFELLER UNIV, 70- *Concurrent Pos:* Instr, Brooklyn Polytech Inst, 62-71; mem adj fac, Fairleigh Dickinson Univ, 71- *Mem:* AAAS; Am Phys Soc. *Res:* Biomedical instrumentation; electro-optics; analytical chemistry instrumentation; digital computer interfacing and programming. *Mailing Add:* Electronics Lab Rockefeller Univ New York NY 10021

ROSEN, PERRY, b Bronx, NY, Oct 2, 30; m 60; c 1. ORGANIC CHEMISTRY. *Educ:* City Col New York, BS, 53; Columbia Univ, MS & PhD(chem), 60. *Prof Exp:* Fel, Columbia Univ, 61-62; sr chemist, 62-70, res fel, 70-72, group chief, 72-76, sect chief, 76-80, ASSOC DIR, HOFFMANN-LA ROCHE, INC, 80- *Mem:* Am Chem Soc; NY Acad Sci; Am Inst Chemists. *Res:* Synthetic organic chemistry; development of new chemical reactions. *Mailing Add:* Hoffman-La Roche Inc Nutley NJ 07110

ROSEN, PHILIP, b New York, NY, Oct 31, 22; m 46, 66; c 3. BIOPHYSICS. *Educ:* Yale Univ, MS, 46, PhD(physics), 49. *Prof Exp:* Physicist, Nat Adv Comt Aeronaut, 44; asst high polymers, Polytech Inst Brooklyn, 45; lab asst, Yale Univ, 46-48; from instr to asst prof physics, Rensselaer Polytech Inst, 48-51; sr theoret physicist, Appl Physics Lab, Johns Hopkins Univ, 51-54; asst prof physics, Univ Conn, 54-57; PROF PHYSICS, UNIV MASS, AMHERST, 57- *Concurrent Pos:* Consult, Gen Elec Co, 56-57, appl physics lab, Johns Hopkins Univ, 58, 62-63 & Boeing Airplane Co, 59; vis prof, Univ Wis, 65; vis fel, Yale Univ, 65-66; Nat Cancer Inst spec fel biol, Oak Ridge Nat Lab, 72-73; guest scientist, Biol Dept, Brookhaven Nat Lab, 79-80. *Mem:* Fel Am Phys Soc; Biophys Soc; Am Soc Photobiol. *Res:* Microwaves; molecular quantum mechanics; kinetic theory; irreversible thermodynamics; plasma physics; electronic structure of nucleic acids and proteins, particularly the energy band structure; theory of radiation carcinogenesis. *Mailing Add:* Dept of Physics & Astron Univ of Mass Amherst MA 01003

ROSEN, ROBERT, b Brooklyn, NY, June 27, 34; m 58; c 3. MATHEMATICAL BIOLOGY. *Educ:* Brooklyn Col, BS, 55; Columbia Univ, MA, 56; Univ Chicago, PhD(math biol), 59. *Prof Exp:* Asst analyst, Chicago Midway Labs, Ill, 56-57; asst math biol, Univ Chicago, 57-60, res assoc, 60-62, asst prof, 62-67; from assoc prof to prof math & biophys, State Univ NY Buffalo, 67-75, vis assoc prof, Ctr Theoret Biol, 66-67, assoc dir, 69-75; I W KILLAM PROF PHYSIOL & BIOPHYSICS, DALHOUSIE UNIV, 75- *Concurrent Pos:* Vis fel, Ctr Study Democratic Insts, 71-72. *Mem:* Am Math Soc; Am Soc Cell Biol; Biophys Soc. *Res:* Relational aspects of general biological systems; quantum-theoretic mechanisms involved in the utilization of primary genetic information; morphogenesis and stability in biological systems. *Mailing Add:* Sir Charles Tupper Med Bldg Dalhousie Univ Halifax NS B3H 3J5 Can

ROSEN, RONALD HAIAM, b Cleveland, Ohio, June 13, 33. MATHEMATICS. *Educ:* Western Reserve Univ, BA, 55; Univ Wis, MA, 57, PhD, 59. *Prof Exp:* From instr to asst prof math, 59-66, ASSOC PROF MATH, UNIV MICH, ANN ARBOR, 66- *Concurrent Pos:* Partic topology inst, Univ Ga, 61; res assoc, Off Naval Res, Columbia Univ, 62-63; consult & reviewer, Math Reviews, Ann Arbor, 62-; reviewer, Zentralblatt fur Mathematik, West Berlin, 63-; NSF fel, Int Advan Study, 63-64. *Mem:* Am Math Soc. *Res:* Point set topology; combinatorial topology; topology of manifolds, continua and continuous mappings; chess and its relationship to computer programming. *Mailing Add:* 3222 Bolgos Circle Ann Arbor MI 48105

ROSEN, SAMUEL, b New York, NY, Apr 14, 23; m 54; c 2. MICROBIOLOGY. *Educ:* Brooklyn Col, BA, 48; Univ Ill, MS, 49; Mich State Univ, PhD(microbiol), 53. *Prof Exp:* Technician microbiol, Pyridium Corp, 49-50; res assoc, Mich State Univ, 52-61; PROF MICROBIOL, OHIO STATE UNIV, 61- *Concurrent Pos:* Consult, Battelle Mem Inst, 62-, Procter & Gamble Co, 70-, Dent Res Inst, Great Lakes, 70, Southern Ill Univ, 72- & Nat Inst Dent Res, 75-; NIH career develop award, Ohio State Univ, 67-72. *Mem:* AAAS; Am Soc Microbiol; Int Asn Dent Res; Am Asn Dent Schs; Gnotobiotics Asn. *Res:* Experimental dental caries; experimental periodontal disease; microbial taxonomy. *Mailing Add:* Ohio State Univ Col of Dent Columbus OH 43210

ROSEN, SAUL, b Port Chester, NY, Feb 8, 22; m 50; c 4. COMPUTER SCIENCE. *Educ:* City Col, BS, 41; Univ Cincinnati, MA, 42; Univ Pa, PhD, 50. *Prof Exp:* Instr math, Univ Del, 46-47; lectr, Univ Calif, Los Angeles, 48-49; asst prof, Drexel Inst Technol, 49-51; assoc res engr, Burroughs Corp, 51-52, mgr eastern appl math sect, Electrodata Div, 56-58; asst prof elec eng, Univ Pa, 52-54; assoc prof math, Comput Lab, Wayne Univ, 54-56; mgr comput prog & serv, Philco Corp, 58-60, consult, Comput & Prog Systs, 60-62; prof comput sci, Purdue Univ, 62-66; prof eng & assoc, Comput Ctr, State Univ NY Stony Brook, 66-67; PROF MATH & COMPUT SCI, PURDUE UNIV, 67-, DIR UNIV COMPUT CTR, 68- *Mem:* Asn Comput Mach; Computer Soc; Inst Elec & Electronics Eng. *Res:* Operating systems, computer performance measurement and evaluation; history of computing; applications of electronic digital computers, programming systems and automatic programming. *Mailing Add:* Comput Ctr Purdue Univ West Lafayette IN 47907

ROSEN, SAUL W, b Boston, Mass, July 29, 28; m 59; c 3. INTERNAL MEDICINE, ENDOCRINOLOGY. *Educ:* Harvard Univ, AB, 47; Northwestern Univ, PhD(chem), 55; Harvard Med Sch, MD, 56; Am Bd Internal Med, dipl endocrinol, 65. *Prof Exp:* From intern med to asst resident, Univ Calif Med Ctr, San Francisco, 56-58; clin assoc, Nat Inst Arthritis & Metab Dis, 58-60; sr resident med, Med Ctr, Univ Calif, 60-61; SR INVESTR, CLIN ENDOCRINOL BR, NAT INST ARTHRITIS, METAB & DIGESTIVE DIS, 61- *Mem:* Am Chem Soc; Am Fedn Clin Res; fel Am Col Physicians; Endocrine Soc. *Res:* Clinical endocrinology; ectopic tumor gonadotropins. *Mailing Add:* Nat Inst Arthritis, Diabetes, Digestive & Kidney Dis Clin Ctr Rm 8N315 Bethesda MD 20014

ROSEN, SIDNEY, b Boston, Mass, June 5, 16; m 44; c 1. HISTORY OF SCIENCE. *Educ:* Univ Mass, AB, 39; Harvard Univ, MAT, 52, PhD(phys sci), 55. *Prof Exp:* From instr to asst prof phys sci, Brandeis Univ, 53-58; assoc prof sci educ, 58-60, assoc prof phys sci, 60-64, PROF PHYS SCI, UNIV ILL, URBANA, 64- *Concurrent Pos:* Consult, Comnr Educ, Mass, 57-58 & Am Humanities Sem, 58; vis lectr, Harvard Univ, 58; spec sci consult, Ford Found, Colombia, SAm, 63-64 & 66; Fulbright fel, UK, 63; consult, Encycl Britannica Films, Inc, 64- *Honors & Awards:* Clara Ingram Judson Mem Award, 70. *Mem:* Fel AAAS; Nat Asn Res Sci Teaching; Hist Sci Soc; Nat Sci Teachers Asn; Am Asn Physics Teachers. *Res:* History of learning; problems of science teaching. *Mailing Add:* 341 Astron Univ Ill 1011 W Springfield Ave Urbana IL 61801

ROSEN, SIMON PETER, b London, Eng, Aug 4, 33; m 58; c 2. PHYSICS. *Educ:* Oxford Univ, BA, 54, PhD(physics), 57. *Prof Exp:* Res assoc physics, Washington Univ, 57-59; scientist, Midwestern Univ Res Asn, 59-61; NATO fel, Oxford Univ, 61-62; from asst prof to assoc prof physics, 62-66, PROF PHYSICS, PURDUE UNIV, 66- *Concurrent Pos:* Tutorial fel, Univ Sussex, 69; sr theoret physicist, High Energy Physics Prog, Div Phys Res, US Energy Res & Develop Admin, Washington, DC, 75-77; prog assoc theoret physics, NSF, 81- *Mem:* Fel Am Phys Soc. *Res:* Symmetry theories of elementary particles; theory of weak interactions; high energy physics. *Mailing Add:* Dept Physics Purdue Univ West Lafayette IN 47907

ROSEN, SOL, b New York, NY, Oct 12, 32; m 55; c 3. METALLURGY. *Educ:* City Col New York, BChE, 54; Columbia Univ, MS, 57; NY Univ, EngScDr, 62. *Prof Exp:* Scientist nuclear metall, Tech Res Corp, 56-58; engr, Sylvania-Corning Nuclear Corp, 58-59; asst scientist actinide alloy chem, Argonne Nat Lab, 59-62; sr res assoc struct mat, x-ray diffraction & electron micros, Pratt & Whitney Aircraft Div, United Aircraft Corp, Conn, 63-66; group leader, 66-67; metallurgist nuclear fuels & mat, US Atomic Energy Comn, 67-73, USAEC/ERDA sci rep, US Mission to Europ Communities, Belg, 73-76; US Dept Energy sci adv energy, US Mission to Orgn Econ Coop & Develop, France, 76-78; int tech adv, Off Nuc Progs, 78-79, DIR, INT NUCLEAR PROGS DIV, DEPT ENERGY, 79- *Res:* Nuclear and alternative energy technology; international relations. *Mailing Add:* Off of Nuclear Progs Dept of Energy Washington DC 20545

ROSEN, STEPHEN, b New York, NY, May 3, 34; m 59; c 2. HUMAN BIOMETEOROLOGY, CONSUMER SCIENCE. *Educ:* Queens Col, NY, BS, 55; Bryn Mawr Col, MA, 58; Adelphi Univ, PhD(physics), 66. *Prof Exp:* Physicist, Int Bus Mach Corp, 58-60; asst prof physics, State Univ NY Maritime Col, 60-67; res adv, Gen Res Labs, NJ, 67-69; mem prof staff, Hudson Inst, 69-70; dir res, Mkt & Planning Group, Inc, 72-76; PRES, FUTURE FACTS, INC, 76- *Concurrent Pos:* Sr engr & scientist, Ford Instrument Co Div, Sperry Rand Corp, 63; res assoc, Astrophys Inst, Paris & Nuclear Studies Ctr, Saclay, France, 68; consult, Xerox Corp, Gen Tel & Electronics Corp & Carnegie Corp, 70-; consult, NSF, 73-74 & Fed Energy Admin, 74-75. *Mem:* AAAS; Am Phys Soc; Am Astron Soc; NY Acad Sci. *Res:* Beta and gamma ray spectroscopy; nuclear reactors; radiation effects; operational tactics; high energy interactions; origin and astrophysics of cosmic rays; technological and social forecasting; long-range planning; market planning for high-technology products and services; electronic and print journalism. *Mailing Add:* 150 West End Ave Suite 29P New York NY 10023

ROSEN, STEPHEN I, b Brooklyn, NY, Feb 4, 43; m 64; c 2. PHYSICAL ANTHROPOLOGY, PRIMATOLOGY. *Educ:* Univ Southern Calif, BA, 65; Univ Kans, PhD(phys anthrop), 69. *Prof Exp:* Phys anthropologist, Univ Ariz, 64; res asst phys anthrop, Univ Kans, 66-69; asst prof, 69-72, ASSOC PROF ANTHROP, UNIV MD, COLLEGE PARK, 72- *Concurrent Pos:* NSF grant, Univ Kans, 68-69; collabr surg neurol sect, Nat Inst Neurol Dis & Stroke, 70-; fac res award, Univ Md, College Park, 70-72, asst provost, 73-77. *Mem:* AAAS; Am Asn Phys Anthrop; Am Acad Forensic Sci; Int Primatological Soc; fel Royal Anthrop Inst. *Res:* Primate biology; human paleontology. *Mailing Add:* Dept of Anthrop Univ of Md College Park MD 20742

ROSEN, STEPHEN L(OUIS), b New York, NY, Nov 25, 37. CHEMICAL ENGINEERING. *Educ:* Cornell Univ, BChE, 60, PhD(chem eng), 64; Princeton Univ, MS, 61. *Prof Exp:* From asst prof to assoc prof chem eng, Carnegie-Mellon Univ, 64-74, prof, 74-81; PROF CHEM ENG & CHMN DEPT, UNIV TOLEDO, 81- *Mem:* Am Chem Soc; Am Inst Chem Engrs; Soc Plastics Engrs. *Res:* Polymeric materials; rheology; polymerization. *Mailing Add:* Dept of Chem Eng Univ Toledo Toledo OH 43606

ROSEN, STEVEN DAVID, b New York, NY, Oct 20, 43. CELL BIOLOGY. *Educ:* Univ Calif, Berkeley, AB, 66; Cornell Univ, PhD(neurobiol), 72. *Prof Exp:* Fel cell biol, Dept Psychiat, Sch Med, Univ Calif, San Diego, 72-76; ASST PROF CELL BIOL, DEPT ANAT, UNIV CALIF, SAN FRANCISCO, 76- *Concurrent Pos:* Am Cancer Soc fel, Dept Psychiat, Univ Calif, San Diego, 72-74. *Mem:* AAAS; Am Soc Cell Biol. *Res:* Molecular basis of specific cell adhesion in cellular slime molds and higher systems. *Mailing Add:* Dept of Anat Univ of Calif San Francisco CA 94143

ROSEN, WALTER GEORGE, plant physiology, see previous edition

ROSEN, WILLIAM EDWARD, b New York, NY, Jan 29, 27; m 53; c 5. ORGANIC CHEMISTRY, MICROBIOLOGY. *Educ:* NY Univ, BA, 48; Harvard Univ, MA, 50, PhD(chem), 52. *Prof Exp:* Fel, Univ Southern Calif, 52 & Yale Univ, 52-53; sr res chemist, Ciba Pharmaceut Prod, Inc, 53-64; vpres res, Cambridge Res, Inc, 64-68; EXEC VPRES, SUTTON LABS, INC, 68- *Mem:* Am Chem Soc; Soc Cosmetic Chem; Soc Indust Microbiologists. *Res:* Cosmetic preservation; pharmaceuticals and fine chemicals; process research and development; organic synthesis; steroids; alkaloids. *Mailing Add:* 116 Summit Ave Chatham NJ 07928

ROSEN, WILLIAM G, b Portsmouth, NH, May 13, 21; c 2. MATHEMATICS. *Educ:* Univ Ill, MS, 47, PhD(math), 54. *Prof Exp:* Instr math, Univ Md, 54-56, asst prof, 56-61; from asst prof dir to assoc prof dir sci educ, 61-64, staff assoc sci develop, 64-66, spec asst to dir, 66-70, prog dir, Mod Anal & Probability Prog, 70-79, HEAD, MATH SCI SECT, NSF, 79- *Res:* Science administration. *Mailing Add:* Nat Sci Found Washington DC 20550

ROSEN, WILLIAM M, b Lynn, Mass, Dec 27, 41; m 64; c 2. CHEMISTRY. *Educ:* Univ Calif, Los Angeles, BS, 63; Univ Calif, Riverside, PhD(chem), 67. *Prof Exp:* Teaching asst chem, Univ Calif, Riverside, 63-65, res assoc, 65-66; assoc, 66-67; res assoc, Ohio State Univ, 67-69; asst prof, Purdue Univ, 69-70; asst prof, 70-74, ASSOC PROF CHEM, UNIV RI, 74- *Concurrent Pos:* NIH fel, 67-69; assoc res chemist, Scripps Inst oceanog, 76-77. *Mem:* Am Chem Soc; The Chem Soc. *Res:* Synthesis of interesting organic and inorganic chemical systems. *Mailing Add:* Dept of Chem Univ of RI Kingston RI 02881

ROSENAU, JOHN (RUDOLPH), b Sheboygan, Wis, Feb 25, 43; m 65; c 2. AGRICULTURAL & FOOD ENGINEERING. *Educ:* Univ Wis-Madison, BSAgr, 65, BSME, 66; Mich State Univ, PhD(agr eng), 70. *Prof Exp:* Asst prof food sci & indusits, Univ Minn, St Paul, 70-73; ASSOC PROF FOOD ENG, UNIV MASS, AMHERST, 73- *Mem:* Am Soc Agr Engrs; Inst Food Technol; Sigma Xi. *Res:* Utilization of protein components; new systems for cheese production, soy protein utilization. *Mailing Add:* Dept Food Eng Univ Mass Amherst MA 01003

ROSENAU, WERNER, b June 28, 29; US citizen. PATHOLOGY, IMMUNOLOGY. *Educ:* Univ Calif, San Francisco, MD, 56. *Prof Exp:* From asst prof to assoc prof, 61-72, PROF PATH, UNIV CALIF, SAN FRANCISCO, 72- *Mem:* Am Soc Exp Path; AAAS. *Mailing Add:* Dept of Path Univ of Calif Med Ctr San Francisco CA 94122

ROSENAU, WILLIAM ALLISON, b Redding, Conn, Nov 25, 26; m 62; c 3. PLANT NUTRITION. *Educ:* Yale Univ, BS, 48; Univ Conn, MS, 50; Pa State Univ, PhD(agron), 60. *Prof Exp:* Res asst forage crops, Eastern State Farmers Exchange, 50-51 & 54-56; asst prof, 60-69, res asst prof soils, Waltham Field Sta, 60-66, assoc prof, 69-77, PROF PLANT & SOIL SCI, UNIV MASS, AMHERST, 77- *Mem:* Am Soc Agron. *Res:* Nitrogen fertilization and calcium nutrition of corn; calcium-boron relationships in soils and crops. *Mailing Add:* Dept Plant & Soil Sci Univ of Mass Amherst MA 01003

ROSENBAUM, DAVID MARK, b Boston, Mass, Feb 11, 35; m 64. RISK ANALYSIS, SYSTEMS ANALYSIS. *Educ:* Brown Univ, ScB, 56; Rensselaer Polytech Inst, MS, 58; Brandeis Univ, PhD(physics), 64. *Prof Exp:* Mem staff, Mitre Corp, 60-64; asst res prof physics, Boston Univ, 64-65; mem staff, Inst Defense Anal, 65-67; expert commun & network anal, Off Emergency Planning, Exec Off President, 67-68; assoc prof elec eng, Polytech Inst Brooklyn, 68-69; sr staff mem, Mitre Corp, 70-72; asst dir anal & asst dir admin, systs & computerization, Off Nat Narcotics Intel, US Dept Justice, 72-73; consult, US AEC, 73-74; consult, Perm Subcomt Invests, US Senate, 74; sr staff mem, Mitre Corp, 74-76; consult to the comptroller gen, US Gen Accounting Off, 76-79; dep asst adminr, Radiation Progs, US Environ Protection Agency, 79-81; PRES, TECH ANALYSIS CORP, 81- *Concurrent Pos:* Consult, Off Emergency Planning, Exec Off President, 68-69; pres, Network Anal Corp, 68-70; mem, Bd Dirs, Beta Instrument Corp, 68-72; chmn, Eng Found Conf Vulnerability Urban Areas Subversive Disruption, 72; consult, Perm Subcomt Invests, US Sen, 74- *Honors & Awards:* Cert Appreciation, Off President, 68. *Mem:* Am Phys Soc; Soc Indust & Appl Math. *Res:* Plasma physics; history of guerilla warfare; network analysis; elementary particles and mathematical foundations of quantum mechanics; energy and environmental policy studies; nuclear safeguards; nuclear proliferation; epidemiology. *Mailing Add:* 4620 Dittmar Rd Arlington VA 22207

ROSENBAUM, EUGENE JOSEPH, b New York, NY, July 22, 07; m 32; c 2. PHYSICAL CHEMISTRY. *Educ:* Univ Chicago, SB, 29, PhD(chem), 33. *Prof Exp:* Instr chem, Univ Chicago, 31-40; Lalor Found fel, Harvard Univ, 40-41; res chemist, Sun Oil Co, 41-58; prof chem, 58-72, EMER PROF CHEM, DREXEL UNIV, 72- *Mem:* AAAS; Am Chem Soc; Am Soc Testing & Mat; Soc Appl Spectros (pres, 52). *Res:* Applied spectroscopy; Raman spectra and molecular structure. *Mailing Add:* 60 Pilgrim Lane Drexel Hill PA 19026

ROSENBAUM, FRED J(EROME), b Chicago, Ill, Feb 15, 37; m 60; c 2. ELECTRICAL ENGINEERING. *Educ:* Univ Ill, Urbana, BS, 59, MS, 60, PhD(elec eng), 63. *Prof Exp:* Res asst ultramicrowave group, Dept Elec Eng, Univ Ill, Urbana, 59-63; res scientist, McDonnell Aircraft Corp, Mo, 63-65; from asst prof to assoc prof elec eng, 65-71, PROF ELEC ENG, WASH UNIV, 71- *Concurrent Pos:* Ed, Transactions on Microwave Theory & Techniques, 72-74. *Mem:* Fel Inst Elec & Electronics Engrs (pres, 81). *Res:* Electromagnetic theory; microwave devices and quantum electronics; microwave propagation in ferrites; ferrite phase shifters; microwave solid state devices and circuits; millimeter wave solid state devices and circuits. *Mailing Add:* Dept of Elec Eng Box 1127 Wash Univ St Louis MO 63130

ROSENBAUM, H(ERMAN) S(OLOMON), b Philadelphia, Pa, Oct 24, 32; m 53; c 3. METALLURGY. *Educ:* Univ Pa, BS, 53, MS, 56; Rensselaer Polytech Inst, PhD(metall). 59. *Prof Exp:* Lab asst, Sam Tour & Co, 52 & Franklin Inst, 53-56; metallurgist, Res Lab, 56-64, mgr mat struct & properties, Nucleonics Lab, Vallecitos Nuclear Ctr, 64-76, prin engr & prog mgr, 76-78, SR PROG MGR, NUCLEAR ENERGY ENG DIV, GEN ELEC CO, 78- *Mem:* Am Soc Metals; Am Inst Mining, Metall & Petrol Engrs; Am Nuclear Soc. *Res:* Crystal imperfections; precipitation kinetics in solids; radiation damage; microstructures and properties of irradiated materials; physical metallurgy. *Mailing Add:* Gen Elec Co 175 Curtner Ave Mail Code 138 San Jose CA 95125

ROSENBAUM, HAROLD DENNIS, b Fairplay, Ky, Aug 17, 21; m 70; c 6. MEDICINE. *Educ:* Berea Col, AB, 41; Harvard Univ, MD, 44. *Prof Exp:* Instr med, Sch Med, Univ Colo, 47-48; res fel pediat & radiol, Harvard Med Sch & Children's Med Ctr, Boston, 52; radiologist, John Graves Ford Hosp, Georgetown, Ky, 53-60; PROF DIAG RADIOL & CHMN DEPT, MED CTR, UNIV KY, 60- *Concurrent Pos:* Radiologist, Clark County Hosp, Winchester, Ky, 53-55, Eastern State Hosp, Lexington, 54-60, Woodford County Mem Hosp, Versailles, 55-60 & Proj Hope, Corinto, Nicaragua, 66-; consult cardioroentgenologist, St Joseph's Hosp, Lexington, Ky, 53-; US Dept Health, Educ & Welfare grant, Univ Ky, 70-; CARE-Medico prof, Honduras, 71- *Mem:* Am Roentgen Ray Soc; Radiol Soc NAm; AMA; Am Heart Asn; fel Am Col Radiol. *Res:* Congenital heart disease; radiology; medical and radiological education and clinical service. *Mailing Add:* Dept of Diag Radiol Univ of Ky Med Ctr Lexington KY 40506

ROSENBAUM, IRA JOEL, b New York, NY, June 5, 41; c 2. PHYSICS. *Educ:* Queen's Col, NY, BS, 62; Am Univ, MS, 67, PhD(physics), 71. *Prof Exp:* Physicist, Nat Bur Standards, 64-66; PHYSICIST, WHITE OAK LAB, NAVAL SURFACE WEAPONS CTR, 66- *Mem:* Am Phys Soc; Acoust Soc Am. *Res:* Acoustic properties of liquid metals at high pressures. *Mailing Add:* White Oak Lab Naval Surface Weapons Ctr Silver Spring MD 20910

ROSENBAUM, JOE B(EYUM), b Denver, Colo, Mar 1, 12; m 35; c 3. METALLURGY. *Educ:* Colo Sch Mines, EMet, 34. *Prof Exp:* Off engr, Pub Works Admin, 34-38; metallurgist, Walker Mining Co, 39-41; supv metallurgist, Salt Lake Metall Res Ctr, 41-61, dir metall res, Md, 62-67, res dir, Salt Lake City Metall Res Ctr, 67-74; CONSULT METALLURGIST, 75- *Concurrent Pos:* Adj prof, Univ Utah, 67- *Mem:* Nat Acad Eng; Am Inst Mining, Metall & Petrol Engrs; Am Soc Metals. *Res:* Programming and management of research in minerals; metals processing and utilization. *Mailing Add:* 1149 Mercedes Way Salt Lake City UT 84108

ROSENBAUM, JOSEPH HANS, b Hannover, Ger, July 1, 25; nat US; m 59; c 1. PHYSICS. *Educ:* Lowell Technol Inst, BS, 47; Clark Univ, PhD(chem), 50. *Prof Exp:* Phys chemist, US Naval Ord Lab, 50-53; asst prof textile chem, Lowell Technol Inst, 53-54; phys chemist, US Naval Ord Lab, 54-56; PHYSICIST, SHELL DEVELOP CO, 56- *Mem:* Am Chem Soc; Am Asn Textile Chemists & Colorists; Acoust Soc Am; Am Geophys Union; Soc Explor Geophys. *Res:* Elastic waves; thermodynamics; hydrodynamics; electrochemistry; applied mathematics. *Mailing Add:* 1308 Castle Court Blvd Houston TX 77006

ROSENBAUM, MANUEL, b Detroit, Mich, Sept 13, 29; m 55; c 3. MICROBIOLOGY, GRANT ADMINISTRATION. *Educ:* Univ Mich, BS, 51, MS, 53, PhD(bact), 56. *Prof Exp:* Asst microbiol, Univ Mich, 53-55; instr med col, Cornell Univ, 56-58; res assoc, Wistar Inst Anat & Biol, Univ Pa, 58-60; chief microbiologist, Wayne County Gen Hosp, Mich, 60-63; res microbiologist, Parke, Davis & Co, 64-71; res assoc, Child Res Ctr, Mich, 71-76; GRANT & CONTRACT ADMINR, MICH CANCER FOUND, 76- *Mem:* AAAS; Am Soc Microbiol; Soc Res Adminrs. *Res:* Protein synthesis in development of bacteriophage; nucleic acid metabolism in normal and virus-infected animal cells; viral oncogenesis. *Mailing Add:* Mich Cancer Found 110 E Warren Ave Detroit MI 48201

ROSENBAUM, MARCOS, b Mexico, DF, Feb 26, 35; m 65; c 1. MATHEMATICAL PHYSICS. *Educ:* Nat Univ Mex, BS, 57; Univ Mich, MSE, 59, PhD(nuclear sci), 63. *Prof Exp:* From res asst to res assoc neutron physics, Univ Mich, Ann Arbor, 61-64; mem res staff physics & appl math, Ctr Advan Studies, G E Tempo, 64-71; head dept physics & math, 74-76, RES PROF MATH PHYSICS, NAT UNIV MEX, 71-, DIR CTR NUCLEAR STUDY, 76- *Concurrent Pos:* Consult, Nat Inst Nuclear Energy, 71-; mem scholar comt nuclear sci, Nat Coun Sci Technol, 75- *Mem:* Sigma Xi; Am Phys Soc; AAAS; Acad Sci Res Mex; NY Acad Sci. *Res:* Abstract tensor and spinor techniques applied to gravitation and general relativity theory. *Mailing Add:* Ctr Nuclear Study UNAM Circuito Exterior Ciudad Universitaria Mexico 20 DF Mexico

ROSENBAUM, MAX J, virology, microbiology, see previous edition

ROSENBAUM, ROBERT ABRAHAM, b New Haven, Conn, Nov 14, 15; m 42; c 3. MATHEMATICS. *Educ:* Yale Univ, BA, 36, PhD(math), 47. *Hon Degrees:* MA, Wesleyan Univ, 54, LHD, 81; LHD, St Joseph Col, Conn, 70. *Prof Exp:* From instr to prof math, Reed Col, 40-53; PROF MATH, WESLEYAN UNIV, 53-, PROF MATH & SCI, 77- *Concurrent Pos:* NSF fel, Math Inst, Oxford Univ, 58-59; dean sci, Wesleyan Univ, 63-65; provost, 65-67, acad vpres, 67-69, actg pres, 69-70, chancellor, 70-73; vis scholar, Univ Calif, Berkeley, 62; ed, Math Asn Am, 66-68; vis prof, Univ Mass, 73-74; mem adv coun, Braitmayer Found, 74- *Mem:* Fel AAAS; Am Math Soc; Math Asn Am (2nd vpres, 61-62). *Res:* Classical analysis; geometry; subadditive functions. *Mailing Add:* Wesleyan Univ Middletown CT 06457

ROSENBAUM, ROBERT MORRIS, experimental biology, see previous edition

ROSENBERG, ABRAHAM, b New York, NY, Aug 12, 24; m 48; c 2. BIOCHEMISTRY. *Educ:* Univ Ill, BS, 47; Polytech Inst Brooklyn, MS, 52; Columbia Univ, PhD(biochem), 56. *Prof Exp:* Jr biochemist, Jewish Hosp Brooklyn, 47, res asst, 48-49, supvr clin chem, 49-51, res biochemist, 51-53; res assoc biochem, Columbia Univ, 57-61, asst prof, 61-68; assoc prof biol chem, 68-71, PROF BIOL CHEM, COL MED, PA STATE UNIV, HERSHEY MED CTR, 71- *Concurrent Pos:* USPHS fel, 56; NY Heart Asn res fel, 57-58, sr fel, 59-61; Health Res Coun New York career investr, 61-66; Fulbright prof & res scholar, 74; master res, Nat Inst Health & Med Res, France, 75. *Mem:* Am Soc Biol Chemists; Am Chem Soc; Am Soc Neurochem; Soc Protozool; fel Am Inst Chemists. *Res:* Fat-soluble vitamin; analysis, absorption, transport and conversion of provitamin; structure and isolation of complex glycolipids of nervous tissues; lipids in photosynthesis; neurochemistry; synaptic structure-function; cell surface enzymes. *Mailing Add:* Dept of Biol Chem Pa State Univ Hershey Med Ctr Hershey PA 17033

ROSENBERG, ALBURT M, b Hollywood, Calif, Oct 26, 27; m 58; c 4. BIOPHYSICS. *Educ:* Harvard Univ, AB, 49; Univ Fla, MS, 51; Univ Pa, PhD(gen physiol), 58. *Prof Exp:* Fel, Basic Res Div, Eastern Pa Psychiat Inst, 58-59; instr biol, 59-60, asst prof natural sci, 60-66, ASSOC PROF NATURAL SCI, SWARTHMORE COL, 66- *Mem:* Am Asn Physics Teachers. *Res:* Marine egg physiology; role of cellular water; x-ray sensitivity of yeast; growing giant chromosomes; general education in physics; computers in physics teaching; divalent ions and cell division; sunflower seed order. *Mailing Add:* Dept of Physics Swarthmore Col Swarthmore PA 19081

ROSENBERG, ALEX, b Berlin, Ger, Dec 5, 26; nat US; m 52; c 2. MATHEMATICS. *Educ:* Univ Toronto, BA, 48, MA, 49; Univ Chicago, PhD(math), 51. *Prof Exp:* Res assoc math, Univ Mich, 51-52; from instr to assoc prof, Northwestern Univ, 52-61; chmn dept math, 66-69, PROF MATH, CORNELL UNIV, 61- *Concurrent Pos:* Mem, Inst Advan Study, 55-57; algebra ed, Proc, Am Math Soc, 60-65, trustee, 74-83; vis prof, Univ Calif, Berkeley, 61; researcher, Queen Mary Col, Univ London, 63-64; vis researcher, Univ Calif, Los Angeles, 69-70; ed, Math Asn Am, 74-78; Alexander V Humboldt-Stifbung sr US scientist award, Univ Munich, 75-76; vis prof, Univ Calif, Berkeley, 79 & Univ Calif, Los Angeles, 82. *Mem:* Am Math Soc; Math Asn Am. *Res:* Homological algebra; structure theory of rings; quadratic forms; Witt rings. *Mailing Add:* Dept of Math Cornell Univ Ithaca NY 14853

ROSENBERG, ALEXANDER F, b Frankfurt am Main, Mar 8, 27; nat US; m 54; c 3. ANALYTICAL CHEMISTRY. *Educ:* City Col New York, BS, 51; Duke Univ, AM, 53, PhD(chem), 55. *Prof Exp:* Asst, Duke Univ, 51-54; res chemist, Shell Oil Co, 54-59; sr engr, Aircraft Nuclear Propulsion Dept-Nuclear Mat & Propulsion Opers, 59-63; prin chemist, 63-68, chemist, Major Appliance Labs, Major Appliance Bus Group, 68-71, mgr chem anal, Major Appliance Labs, 71-79, MGR CHEM ANAL, APPLD SCI & TECHNOL LAB, MAJOR APPLIANCE BUS GROUP, GEN ELEC CO, 79- *Concurrent Pos:* Instr, Univ Houston, 55-59. *Mem:* Chem Soc. *Res:* Development of analytical methods; gas chromatography; mass spectrometry; thermal analysis. *Mailing Add:* Appliance Park 35-1301 Gen Elec Co Louisville KY 40225

ROSENBERG, ALLAN (HERBERT), b Brooklyn, NY, Dec 18, 38; m 62; c 3. PHYSICAL CHEMISTRY. *Educ:* City Col NY, BS, 59; Yale Univ, MS, 62, PhD(chem), 64. *Prof Exp:* Res chemist, Allied Chem Corp, 64-69; SR RES INVESTR, BRISTOL-MYERS CORP, 69- *Mem:* AAAS; Am Chem Soc; Am Pharmaceut Asn; Royal Soc Chem. *Res:* Kinetics of drug decomposition; foam stabilization; wetting and adsorption phenomena with respect to human skin; dissolution and absorption of drugs. *Mailing Add:* Dept Phys Chem 1350 Liberty Ave Bristol-Myers Products Hillside NJ 07207

ROSENBERG, ARNOLD LEONARD, b Boston, Mass, Feb 11, 41; m 64; c 2. INFORMATION SCIENCE, SYSTEMS THEORY. *Educ:* Harvard Col, AB, 62; Harvard Univ, AM, 63, PhD(appl math), 66. *Prof Exp:* Res staff mem, T J Watson Res Ctr, IBM Corp, 65-81; PROF COMPUT SCI, DUKE UNIV, 81- *Concurrent Pos:* Vis asst prof, Polytech Inst Brooklyn, 67-69; adj assoc prof math, NY Univ, 70-73, adj prof comput sci, 80-81; vis lectr, Yale Univ, 78-79; vis prof comput sci, Univ Toronto, 79-80. *Mem:* Asn Comput Mach; Soc Indust & Appl Math; Sigma Xi; Inst Elec & Electronics Engrs. *Res:* Mathematical theory of computation, with emphasis on computational structures and complexity of computation; concrete complexity; applications to very large scale integration and data structures. *Mailing Add:* Dept Comput Sci Duke Univ Durham NC 27706

ROSENBERG, ARNOLD MORRY, b Boston, Mass, Mar 18, 34; m 55; c 3. CONSTRUCTION CHEMICALS & MATERIALS. *Educ:* Boston Univ, AB, 55; Purdue Univ, PhD(phys chem), 60. *Prof Exp:* Chemist, Dewey & Almy Div, W R Grace & Co, 60-62, group leader, Construct Prod Div, 63-66; sr supvr, Polaroid Corp, 66-69; res mgr, Construction Prod Div, 69-71, res dir, 71-74, RES MGR, RES DIV, W R GRACE & CO, 74- *Honors & Awards:* IR-100 Award, Indust Res Mag, 80. *Mem:* Am Soc Testing & Mat; Am Concrete Inst; Am Chem Soc; Nat Asn Corrosion Engrs; Transp Res Bd. *Res:* Product development in concrete admixtures, fire proof coatings, insulation, roofing and corrosion control; author or coauthor of 40 publications. *Mailing Add:* 11836 Goya Dr Potomac MD 20854

ROSENBERG, ARTHUR, marine microbiology, soil microbiology, see previous edition

ROSENBERG, BARBARA HATCH, b New York, NY; m. MOLECULAR BIOLOGY. *Educ:* Cornell Univ, BA, 50, PhD(biochem), 62; Columbia Univ, MA, 57. *Prof Exp:* Res assoc, 62-64, assoc, 64-69, ASSOC MEM, SLOANKETTERING INST CANCER RES, 69-; ASSOC PROF, COL MED SCI, CORNELL UNIV, 71- *Concurrent Pos:* Am Cancer Soc grant, Inst Sci Res in Cancer, France, 71. *Mem:* Am Soc Biol Chemists; Biophys Soc; Am Soc Cell Biol. *Res:* SV40 virus (DNA tumor virus); DNA replication. *Mailing Add:* Walker Lab Sloan-Kettering Inst Rye NY 10580

ROSENBERG, DAN YALE, b Stockton, Calif, Jan 8, 22; m 54; c 1. PHYTOPATHOLOGY. *Educ:* Col of the Pac, AB, 49; Univ Calif, Davis, MS, 52. *Prof Exp:* Jr plant pathologist, Bur Plant Path, 52-55, asst plant pathologist, 55-59, plant pathologist, 59-63, prog supvr dis detection, 63-72, chief exclusion & detection, 72-76, CHIEF NURSERY & SEED SERV, DIV PLANT INDUST, CALIF DEPT FOOD & AGR, 76- *Mem:* Nat Acad Sci; Am Phytopath Soc. *Res:* Seed-borne plant diseases; regulatory plant pathology involving detection of new or rarely occurring plant diseases to California; regulatory agricultural pests including plant pathology, entomology, weeds occurring in nurseries; vertebrates; seed law enforcement; certification programs for fruit trees, citrus, avocado, and so on. *Mailing Add:* Calif Dept Food & Agr 1220 N St Rm A-350 Sacramento CA 95814

ROSENBERG, DAVID MICHAEL, b Edmonton, Alta, Aug 24, 43; m 65; c 2. FRESH WATERS. *Educ:* Univ Alta, BSc, 65, PhD(entom), 73. *Prof Exp:* RES SCIENTIST, FRESHWATER INST, CAN DEPT FISHERIES & OCEANS, 71- *Concurrent Pos:* Mem sci comt, Biol Survey Can Terrestrial Anthropods, 77-; adj prof dept entom, Univ Man, 78- *Mem:* NAm Benthological Soc; Entom Soc Can; Can Soc Limnol. *Res:* Design of environmental impact studies; use of zoobenthic invertebrates as indicators of environmental upset; effects of sedimentation, oil contamination, etc, on freshwater invertebrates; ecology of Chironomidae; sampling methods; freshwater wetlands. *Mailing Add:* Environ Can Freshwater Inst 501 University Crescent Winnipeg MB R3T 2N6 Can

ROSENBERG, DENNIS MELVILLE LEO, b Johannesburg, SAfrica, Jan 27, 21; nat US; m 47. THORACIC SURGERY, CARDIOVASCULAR SURGERY. *Educ:* Univ Witwatersrand, BSc, 41 & 44, MB, BCh, 45; Am Bd Surg, dipl, 53; Bd Thoracic Surg, dipl, 54. *Prof Exp:* Asst surg, Tulane Univ, 46-47, instr, 48-52; surgeon, Biggs Hosp, Ithaca, NY, 53-54; ASSOC PROF CLIN SURG, SCH MED, TULANE UNIV, 56- *Concurrent Pos:* Resident, Ochsner Found, 48-52; registr, Children's Hosp, Johannesburg, SAfrica, 52; sr vis physician, Charity Hosp, 57-; prin investr, Touro Res Inst. *Mem:* Asn Thoracic Surg; fel Am Col Surg; fel Am Col Chest Physicians; Am Surg Asn; Soc Vascular Surg. *Res:* Development of open heart surgical apparatus; embolism; assisted circulation; arterial heterografts. *Mailing Add:* Tulane Med Ctr Tulane Univ New Orleans LA 70112

ROSENBERG, EDITH E, b Berlin, Ger, Jan 24, 28; Can citizen. PHYSIOLOGY. *Educ:* Univ Toronto, MA, 52; Univ Pa, PhD(physiol), 59. *Prof Exp:* Asst biophys, Univ Western Ont, 52-55; asst instr physiol, Sch Med, Univ Pa, 56-57; asst prof, Med Sch, Univ Montreal, 59-63; asst prof exp surg & lectr physiol, McGill Univ, 63-68; ASSOC PROF PHYSIOL, COL MED, HOWARD UNIV, 68- *Concurrent Pos:* Univ res fel physiol, Sch Med, Univ Pa, 59; grants, Nat Res Coun Can, Univ Montreal, 60-63 & Mc Gill Univ, 64-68, Washington Heart Asn, 70-71; asst instr, Sch Med, Hebrew Univ, Israel, 54-55. *Mem:* Am Physiol Soc; Biophys Soc; Can Physiol Soc; NY Acad Sci; Am Thoracic Soc. *Res:* Respiration and circulation, particularly pulmonary circulation and Va/Q distribution; alveolar-arterial tension differences; pulmonary surfactant; pulmonary diffusing capacity; immunological reactions of lung tissue; effect of hyperbaric oxygen. *Mailing Add:* Dept of Physiol Howard Univ Col of Med Washington DC 20059

ROSENBERG, ELI IRA, b Brooklyn, NY, Feb 19, 43; m 65; c 2. ELEMENTARY PARTICLE PHYSICS. *Educ:* City Col New York, BS, 64; Univ Ill, Urbana, MS, 66, PhD(physics), 71. *Prof Exp:* Enrico Fermi fel physics, Enrico Fermi Inst, Univ Chicago, 71-72, res assoc, 72, instr, 72-74, asst prof, 74-79; asst prof, 79-81, ASSOC PROF PHYSICS, IOWA STATE UNIV, 81- *Concurrent Pos:* assoc physicist, Ames Lab, US Dept Energy, 79-81, physicist, 81- *Mem:* AAAS; Fedn Am Scientists; NY Acad Sci; Sigma Xi; Am Phys Soc. *Res:* Experimental high energy physics; study of asymptotic behavior of scattering processes with counter techniques; direct production of leptons in hadron interactions. *Mailing Add:* Dept Physics Iowa State Univ Ames IA 50011

ROSENBERG, EUGENE, b New York, NY, Oct 10, 35; m 58; c 3. BIOCHEMISTRY, BACTERIOLOGY. *Educ:* Univ Calif, Los Angeles, BS, 57; Columbia Univ, PhD(biochem), 61. *Prof Exp:* NIH fel, Univ Cambridge, 61-62; asst prof bact, Univ Calif, Los Angeles, 62-70; PROF MICROBIOL, TEL-AVIV UNIV, 70- *Mem:* Am Soc Microbiol; Am Soc Biol Chemists. *Res:* Nucleic acid biosynthesis; biochemistry of myxobacteria; petroleum microbiology; antibiotics. *Mailing Add:* Dept of Microbiol Tel-Aviv Univ Tel-Aviv Israel

ROSENBERG, FRANKLIN J, b Brooklyn, NY, Dec 6, 27; m 48; c 1. PHARMACOLOGY. *Educ:* Princeton Univ, BA, 48; Univ Rochester, PhD(pharmacol), 61. *Prof Exp:* Res asst physiol, US Army Med Labs, Edgewood Arsenal, Md, 54-57; asst pharmacol, Sch Med, Univ Rochester, 57-61; assoc res biologist, 61-62, res biol group leader, 62-65, sect head pharmacol, 65-69, dir dept pharmacol, 69-71, ASST DIR BIOL DIV, STERLING-WINTHROP RES INST, 71-, VPRES PROD DEVELOP, 77- *Concurrent Pos:* Lectr, Albany Med Col, 62-74. *Mem:* AAAS; Am Soc Pharmacol & Exp Therapeut; NY Acad Sci; Soc Clin Pharmacol & Therapeut. *Res:* Pharmacology of psychotropic agents, analgesics and anti-convulsants; pharmacology of muscle relaxants; actions of epinephrine and histamine in the central nervous system; prevention of thrombosis. *Mailing Add:* Prod Develop Div Sterling-Winthrop Res Inst Rensselaer NY 12144

ROSENBERG, FRED A, b Berlin, Ger, Mar 19, 32; nat US; m 57; c 1. MICROBIOLOGY. *Educ:* NY Univ, AB, 53; Rutgers Univ, PhD(sanit), 60. *Prof Exp:* Asst bact, Univ Fla, 54-57; asst sanit, Rutgers Univ, 57-60; res assoc physiol aspects water qual, Grad Sch Pub Health, Univ Pittsburgh, 60-61; from asst prof to assoc prof, 61-77, PROF MICROBIOL, NORTHEASTERN UNIV, 77- *Mem:* Fel Am Pub Health Asn; Am Soc Microbiol; fel Am Acad Microbiol; Biodeterioration Soc England. *Res:* Bacterial cellulases; marine and freshwater microbiology. *Mailing Add:* Dept Biol Northeastern Univ Boston MA 02115

ROSENBERG, HARRY, b Feb 14, 40; Can citizen; m 64; c 2. BIOCHEMISTRY, IMMUNOLOGY. *Educ:* Univ Toronto, BSc, 61; Univ Mich, BS & PharmD, 68, MS, 70, PhD(pharmacog), 72. *Prof Exp:* Res asst pharmacog, Col Pharm, Univ Mich, 65-69; asst prof, Univ Pittsburgh, 71-72; assoc prof, 72-80, PROF BIOMED CHEM, UNIV NEBR MED CTR, 80-; PHARMACIST, LINCOLN GEN HOSP, 74- *Mem:* Am Asn Cols Pharm; Am Pharmaceut Asn; AAAS; Sigma Xi. *Res:* Altered drug metabolism in diabetic state; synthesis and screening of antiarrythmic agents; enzymatic and non-enzymatic glucosylation of biological macromolecules. *Mailing Add:* Col of Pharm Univ of Nebr Omaha NE 68105

ROSENBERG, HENRY MARK, b Chicago, Ill, Jan 29, 14; m 39; c 1. RADIOLOGY, PERIODONTOLOGY. *Educ:* Northwestern Univ, DDS, 36. *Prof Exp:* From res asst to res assoc dent, 54-57, asst prof mat med & therapeut, 58-59, from asst prof to assoc prof radiol, 59-65, assoc head dept, 63-65, actg head dept, 65-67, PROF RADIOL, COL DENT, UNIV ILL MED CTR, 66-, HEAD DEPT, 67- *Concurrent Pos:* Consult, Ill State Psychiat Inst, 60- & div biol & med res, Argonne Nat Lab, 61-; co-prin investr, Nat Inst Dent Res, 62-65. *Mem:* Fel Am Col Dent; Am Dent Asn; Am Acad Periodontics; Int Asn Dent Res; Am Acad Dent Radiol. *Res:* Aging of bone in human masticatory apparatus; dosimetry in radiology. *Mailing Add:* 763 La Crosse Wilmette IL 60091

ROSENBERG, HERBERT IRVING, b Brooklyn, NY, Oct 2, 39; c 2. VERTEBRATE MORPHOLOGY. *Educ:* City Col New York, BS, 61; State Univ NY Buffalo, PhD(biol), 68. *Prof Exp:* Fel insect behav, Cornell Univ, 67-69; asst prof vert zool, 69-73, asst dean fac arts & sci, 71-74, ASSOC PROF VERT ZOOL, UNIV CALGARY, 73- *Concurrent Pos:* Vis assoc prof zool, Univ Mich, 75-76. *Mem:* AAAS; Am Soc Zoologists; Am Soc Ichthyologists & Herpetologists; Can Soc Zool; Sigma Xi. *Res:* Comparative anatomy and histology of vertebrate organ systems. *Mailing Add:* Dept of Biol Univ of Calgary Calgary AB T2N 1N4 Can

ROSENBERG, HERMAN, b Jersey City, NJ, Aug 27, 20. MATHEMATICS. *Educ:* NY Univ, BA, 39, MA, 48, PhD(math), 55. *Prof Exp:* Instr math, Jersey City Pub Sch Syst, 40-60; assoc prof, 60-61, PROF MATH, JERSEY CITY STATE COL, 61-, COORDR GRAD STUDIES MATH, 66-, CHMN DEPT, 76- *Concurrent Pos:* Assoc dir, Esso-Educ Found, Math Inst, NY Univ, 59-60; NSF lectr, Math Inst, Montclair State Col, 63- & Rutgers Univ, 70- *Mem:* Math Asn Am. *Res:* The impact of modern mathematics on trigonometry; modern applications of exponential and logarithmic functions; alternative structures for trigonometry and geometry. *Mailing Add:* Dept of Math Jersey City State Col Jersey City NJ 07305

ROSENBERG, HOWARD C, b Atlantic City, NJ, Apr 17, 47; m 69; c 2. NEUROPHARMACOLOGY, DRUG ABUSE. *Educ:* Ithaca Col, BA, 69; Cornell Univ, PhD(pharmacol), 75, MD, 76. *Prof Exp:* Fel pharmacol, Med Col, Cornell Univ, 76-77; asst prof, 77-82, ASSOC PROF PHARMACOL, MED COL OHIO, 82- *Mem:* Am Soc Pharmacol & Exp Therapeut; Soc Neurosci; Sigma Xi; AAAS. *Res:* Mechanisms for drug tolerance and dependence, and other effects of chronically administered barbiturates and benzodiazepines. *Mailing Add:* Dept Pharmacol Med Col Ohio CS #10008 Toledo OH 43699

ROSENBERG, IRA EDWARD, b New York, NY, Sept 25, 41; m 64; c 1. PHOTOCHEMISTRY, PHYSICAL ORGANIC CHEMISTRY. *Educ:* Hunter Col, BA, 63; Univ Md, College Park, MS, 66; George Washington Univ, PhD(org chem), 70. *Prof Exp:* Res fel photchem, Mich State Univ, 69-70; prin res scientist, 70-76, sect head, 76-78, MGR ADVAN INSTRUMENTATION, CLAIROL INC, 78- *Mem:* Am Chem Soc. *Mailing Add:* Clairol Inc 2 Blachley Rd Stamford CT 06902

ROSENBERG, IRWIN HAROLD, b Madison, Wis, Jan 6, 35; m 64; c 2. GASTROENTEROLOGY, NUTRITION. *Educ:* Univ Wis-Madison, BS, 56; Harvard Univ, MD, 59. *Prof Exp:* Instr med, Harvard Med Sch, 65, assoc med, 67; res assoc, Thorndike Mem Lab-Boston City Hosp, 67; vis scientist, Dept Biophys, Weizmann Inst Sci, Israel, 68-69; asst prof med, Harvard Med Sch, 69-70; assoc prof med, 70, CHIEF, SECT GASTROENTEROL, UNIV CHICAGO, 71-, PROF MED, 75-, DIR, CLIN NUTRIT RES CTR, 79- *Concurrent Pos:* NIH career develop award, 68-74; Josiah Macy fac scholar award, 74; chmn Food Drug Admin Panel OTC Vitamin, Mineral & Hematinics Consult Nutrit Prog, US Govt, 75-; mem, Training Grants Study Sect, Gen Med Study Sect, 76-; chmn, Food & Nutrit Bd, Nat Res Coun. *Mem:* Am Gastroenterol Asn; Am Soc Clin Invest; Am Soc Clin Nutrit. *Res:* Study of intestinal absorption and malabsorption; human nutrition with emphasis on metabolic and nutritional aspects of gastrointestinal disease. *Mailing Add:* Dept Med Univ Chicago Box 400 950 E 59th St Chicago IL 60637

ROSENBERG, ISADORE NATHAN, b Boston, Mass, May 19, 19; m 54; c 2. MEDICINE. *Educ:* Harvard Univ, AB, 40, MD, 43. *Prof Exp:* Intern med, Boston City Hosp, 44, asst res & resident, 47-49; asst, Med Sch, Tufts Col, 49-51, instr, 51-54; from asst prof to assoc prof, 54-71, PROF, DEPT MED, SCH MED, BOSTON UNIV, 71- *Concurrent Pos:* Asst med, Boston Univ, 49; res assoc, New Eng Ctr Hosp, 49-54; physician-in-chg endocrine unit, 5th & 6th Med Servs, Boston City Hosp, 54-72, physician-in-chief, 6th Med Serv, 63-72; chief med, Framingham Union Hosp, 72- *Honors & Awards:* Van Meter Prize, Am Goiter Soc, 51; Ciba Award, Endocrine Soc, 54. *Mem:* Am Soc Clin Invest; Endocrine Soc; AMA; Am Thyroid Asn; NY Acad Sci. *Res:* Chemical and metabolic studies of thyroid, pituitary and adrenal. *Mailing Add:* Dept Med Framingham Union Hosp 115 Lincoln St Framingham MA 01701

ROSENBERG, IVO GEORGE, b Brno, Czech, Dec 13, 34; m 66; c 2. MATHEMATICS. *Educ:* Purkyne Univ, Brno, MSc, 58, CandSc, 65, Dr rer nat(math), 66; Brno Tech Univ, Habil Dozent, 66. *Prof Exp:* From lectr to dozent math, Brno Tech Univ, 58-66; from lectr to sr lectr, Univ Khartoum, 66-68; assoc prof, Univ Sask, 68-71; ASSOC MEM, CTR MATH RES, UNIV MONTREAL, 71- *Mem:* Can Math Cong; Am Math Soc. *Res:* Zero to one programming; universal algebra. *Mailing Add:* Math Res Ctr Univ of Montreal Montreal PQ H3C 3J7 Can

ROSENBERG, JEROME LAIB, b Harrisburg, Pa, June 20, 21; m 46; c 2. BIOPHYSICAL CHEMISTRY. *Educ:* Dickinson Col, AB, 41; Columbia Univ, MA, 46, PhD(phys chem), 48. *Prof Exp:* Lectr chem, Columbia Univ, 42-44, res scientist, SAM Labs, 44-46, instr chem, Univ, 46-48; AEC fel, Univ Chicago, 48-50, res assoc, 50-53; from asst prof to prof chem, 53-69, chmn dept biophys & microbiol, 69-71, prof molecular biol, 69-76, DEAN FAC ARTS & SCI, UNIV PITTSBURGH, 69-, PROF CHEM & BIOL SCI, 76-, VPROVOST, 78- *Concurrent Pos:* NSF sr fel, 62-63. *Mem:* Am Chem Soc; AAAS. *Res:* Photochemistry; photosynthesis; luminescence; molecular spectroscopy. *Mailing Add:* Fac of Arts & Sci Univ of Pittsburgh Pittsburgh PA 15260

ROSENBERG, JERRY C, b New York, NY, Apr 23, 29; m 55; c 2. SURGERY, TRANSPLANTATION IMMUNOLOGY. *Educ:* Wagner Col, BS, 50; Chicago Med Sch, MD, 54; Univ Minn, Minneapolis, PhD(surg), 63. *Prof Exp:* Fulbright fel, Univ Vienna, 55-56; univ fel, Univ Minn, Minneapolis, 60-61; asst chief surg, USPHS Hosp, Staten Island, 61-63; instr, Univ Ky, 64-65; adj asst prof pharm, Univ Toledo, 67-68; dir surg, Maumee Valley Hosp, 65-68; assoc prof, 68-72, PROF SURG, SCH MED, WAYNE STATE UNIV, 72- *Concurrent Pos:* Consult, Vet Admin Hosp, 68-; chief surg, Hutzel Hosp. *Mem:* Transplantation Soc; Am Asn Hist Med; Am Soc Artificial Internal Organs; Soc Univ Surg. *Res:* Mechanisms of immune damage to transplanted organs; biochemical and physiological responses to shock and trauma; renal failure. *Mailing Add:* Dept of Gen Surg Wayne State Univ Sch of Med Detroit MI 48202

ROSENBERG, JOSEPH, b New York, NY, Sept 8, 26; m 48; c 3. ORGANIC CHEMISTRY. *Educ:* City Col New York, BS, 48; Kans State Univ, MS, 49; Wayne State Univ, PhD(org chem), 51. *Prof Exp:* Polymer chemist, Gen Elec Co, 51-60; head org chem dept, Tracerlab, Inc, 60-62, mgr, Tracerlab Tech Prod Div, Lab for Electronics, Inc, Mass, 62-69; group vpres, Int Chem & Nuclear Corp, 70-71; PRES, INTEREX CORP, 71- *Mem:* Am Chem Soc. *Res:* Synthetic organic chemistry; pyrolysis of esters; monomer synthesis; polymer chemistry; epoxy resins; polyurethanes; polyesters; addition and condensation polymers; acrylonitrile copolymers; synthesis of radiochemicals. *Mailing Add:* 46 Maugus Hill Rd Wellesley MA 02181

ROSENBERG, LAWSON LAWRENCE, b Hagerstown, Md, Apr 3, 20. PHYSIOLOGICAL CHEMISTRY. *Educ:* Johns Hopkins Univ, AB, 40, PhD, 51. *Prof Exp:* Asst physiol chem, Sch Med, Johns Hopkins Univ, 51-52, instr pediat, 52-53; jr res biochemist, 53-56, asst res biochemist, 56-65, assoc prof, 65-70, PROF PHYSIOL, UNIV CALIF, BERKELEY, 70- *Mem:* Am Soc Biol Chemists. *Res:* Binding of metalloporphyrins to protein; enzymes; pituitary hormones and target organ relationships. *Mailing Add:* Dept of Physiol Univ of Calif Berkeley CA 94720

ROSENBERG, LEON EMANUEL, b Madison, Wis, Mar 3, 33; m 54; c 3. GENETICS. *Educ:* Univ Wis, BA, 54, MD, 57. *Prof Exp:* From intern to resident med, Columbia-Presby Hosp, 57-59; clin assoc metab, Nat Cancer Inst, 59-61, sr invest, 61-62 & 63-65; resident med, Yale-New Haven Hosp, 62-63; from asst prof to assoc prof, 65-72, PROF HUMAN GENETICS, MED & PEDIAT, SCH MED, YALE UNIV, 72- *Concurrent Pos:* John Hartford Found grant, 65-68; NIH res grant, 65-81; Nat Inst Arthritis & Metab Dis res career develop award, 65-70. *Mem:* AAAS; Am Fedn Clin Res; Am Soc Human Genetics; Am Soc Clin Invest; Asn Am Physicians. *Res:* Medical genetics; membrane function; biogenesis of mitochondrial enzymes; inherited disorders of amino acid metabolism; mechanism of vitamin transport and coenzyme synthesis. *Mailing Add:* Dept Human Genetics Sch Med Yale Univ New Haven CT 06510

ROSENBERG, LEON T, b New York, NY, Feb 11, 28; m 50; c 2. IMMUNOLOGY. *Educ:* City Col New York, BSc, 46; Ohio State Univ, MSc, 48; NY Univ, PhD(biol), 58. *Prof Exp:* Res bacteriologist, Bellevue Hosp, 53-55; res assoc immunol, Bronx Hosp, 55-59; from asst prof to assoc prof immunol, 61-81, PROF MED MICROBIOL, STANFORD UNIV, 81- *Concurrent Pos:* NIH fel immunol, Stanford Univ, 59-60, Giannini Found fel, 60-61; Eleanor Roosevelt fel, Int Union Against Cancer, Karolinski Inst, Stockholm, 69-70. *Mem:* AAAS; Am Asn Immunologists; Am Soc Microbiol. *Res:* Biological functions of antibody and complement; microbiology. *Mailing Add:* Dept of Med Microbiol Stanford Univ Stanford CA 94305

ROSENBERG, LEONARD, b New York, NY, Mar 11, 31. PHYSICS. *Educ:* City Col New York, BS, 52; NY Univ, MS, 54, PhD(physics), 59. *Prof Exp:* Assoc res scientist, NY Univ, 59-61 & Univ Pa, 61-63; from asst prof to assoc prof, 63-70, PROF PHYSICS, NY UNIV, 70- *Mem:* Am Phys Soc. *Res:* Scattering theory; low-energy atomic and nuclear physics. *Mailing Add:* Dept of Physics NY Univ New York NY 10003

ROSENBERG, MARVIN J, b New York, NY, Aug 27, 31; m 54; c 2. BIOLOGY, MOLECULAR GENETICS. *Educ:* City Col New York, BS, 52; Cornell Univ, MS, 54; Columbia Univ, PhD(molecular biol), 67. *Prof Exp:* Teacher sec sch, NY, 54-60; asst prof biol, State Univ NY Stony Brook, 60-68; assoc prof, 68-74, PROF BIOL, CALIF STATE UNIV, FULLERTON, 74-, CHMN DEPT BIOL SCI, 76- *Concurrent Pos:* State of NY Res Found grant in aid, 67-69. *Mem:* AAAS; Genetics Soc Am; Bot Soc Am. *Res:* Chromosome structure; radiomimetic effects on chromosome breakage and reunion; density gradient studies of DNA replication after treatment with thymidine analogs; exogenous DNA uptake by tumor cells. *Mailing Add:* Dept of Biol Calif State Univ Fullerton CA 92634

ROSENBERG, MURRAY DAVID, b Boston, Mass, Jan 7, 25; m 47; c 3. CELL BIOLOGY, MEDICINE. *Educ:* Harvard Univ, AB, 47, MA, 48, MES, 50, PhD(appl physics), 52, MD, 56; Am Bd Family Physicians, dipl, 74. *Prof Exp:* Res assoc acoust, Harvard Univ, 52-54; consult biophys, NIH, 57-59; res assoc & asst prof develop biol, Rockefeller Inst, 59-65; PROF CELL BIOL, UNIV MINN, ST PAUL, 65-, PROF GENETICS, 77- *Concurrent Pos:* Res assoc, Mass Inst Technol, 58-59; consult div biol & med sci, NSF, 61-67, Off Sci & Technol, Exec Off President, 61-67 & med adv

comt, State of Minn, 69-; Health Res Coun New York career scientist, 62-65; MacAulay nonresident fel inst animal genetics, Univ Edinburg, 63-66; mem exec comt & coun, Int Cell Res Orgn, 62; fel comt div biol & agr, Nat Acad Sci-Nat Res Coun, 63-67; mem cell biol study sect, NIH, 65-69; prog dir human cell biol, NSF, 71-72. *Mem:* Am Phys Soc; Acoust Soc Am; Biophys Soc; fel Am Acad Family Physicians; Asn Am Vol Physicians. *Res:* Physics and chemistry of cell in growth and development; cell contact relations; cell membranes; surface physics; reproductive biology. *Mailing Add:* Dept of Genetics & Cell Biol Univ of Minn St Paul MN 55101

ROSENBERG, NORMAN J, b Brooklyn, NY, Feb 22, 30; m 50; c 2. MICROMETEOROLOGY, SOIL PHYSICS. *Educ:* Mich State Univ, BS, 51; Okla State Univ, MS, 58; Rutgers Univ, PhD(soil physics), 61. *Prof Exp:* Soil scientist, Israel Soil Conserv Serv, 53-55 & Israel Water Authority, 55-57; res asst soil physics, Okla State Univ, 57-58; from asst prof to assoc prof, 61-67, PROF AGR CLIMAT, UNIV NEBR-LINCOLN, 67-, LEADER AGR METEOROL SECT, INST AGR & NATURAL RESOURCES, 74-, DIR, CTR AGR METEOROL & CLIMAT, 79-, GEORGE HOLMES PROF AGR METEOROL, 81- *Concurrent Pos:* Consult, Nat Oceanic & Atmospheric Admin, 62-, Great Western Sugar Co, 64-68, Water Resources Res Inst, US Dept Interior, 65- & US AID; vis prof, Israel Inst Technol, 68; NATO sr fel sci, 68; NSF grant, 71-; NASA grant, 72-; mem comt atmospheric sci, Nat Res Coun, 75-78 & Oak Ridge Assoc Univ, 80- *Honors & Awards:* Centennial Medal, Nat Oceanic & Atmospheric Admin, 70; Award Outstanding Achievement Biometeorol, Am Meteorol Soc, 78. *Mem:* Fel AAAS; Am Meteorol Soc; fel Am Soc Agron. *Res:* Microclimatology; ground level micrometeorology; evapotranspiration and windbreak influences on crop growth and development; global carbon dioxide balance and its interaction with plant growth; remote sensing of evapotranspiration in large regions; impact of drought on social, political and physical environment; development of strategies to cope with extended drought. *Mailing Add:* Inst of Agr & Natural Resources Univ of Nebr Lincoln NE 68503

ROSENBERG, PAUL, b New York, NY, Mar 31, 10; m 43; c 1. PHYSICS, ENGINEERING. *Educ:* Columbia Univ, AB, 30, AM, 33, PhD, 41. *Prof Exp:* Chemist, Hawthorne Paint & Varnish Corp, NJ, 30-33; asst physics, Columbia Univ, 34-39; instr, Hunter Col, 39-41; res assoc, Mass Inst Technol, 41, mem staff, Radiation Lab, 41-45; PRES, PAUL ROSENBERG ASSOCS, 45- *Concurrent Pos:* Lectr, Columbia Univ, 40-41; mem maritime res adv panel, Nat Acad Sci-Nat Res Coun, 59-60, chmn navig & traffic control panel, Space Appln Study, 68, chmn cartog & mapping panel, Comt Remote Sensing Progs for Earth Resources Surv, 73-77; chmn, Nat Conf Clear Air Turbulence, 66; mem navig adv comt, NASA, 69-70; mem bd dirs, Ctr Environ & Man, 76-78; gen chmn, Joint Conf, Radio Tech Comn Aeronaut, Radio Tech Comn Marine & Inst Navig. *Honors & Awards:* Abrams Award, Am Soc Photogram, 55. *Mem:* Nat Acad Eng; fel AAAS (vpres, 66-69); Am Inst Navig (pres, 50-51); fel Inst Elec & Electronics Engrs; NY Acad Sci. *Res:* Molecular beams; kinetic theory of gases; geometric and physical optics; ultrasonics; radar; navigation of land, marine, air and space vehicles; industrial electronics; photogrammetry; space technology; earth satellites; aeronautics; electrophotography; remote sensing. *Mailing Add:* 53 Fernwood Rd Larchmont NY 10538

ROSENBERG, PHILIP, b Philadelphia, Pa, July 28, 31; m 56; c 3. TOXINOLOGY, NEUROCHEMISTRY. *Educ:* Temple Univ, BS, 53; Univ Kans, MS, 55; Jefferson Med Col, PhD(pharmacol), 57. *Prof Exp:* Instr pharmacol, Jefferson Med Col, 57-58; res asst neurol & biochem, Col Physicians & Surgeons, Columbia Univ, 58-62, res assoc, 63, asst prof neurol, 63-68; asst dean grad studies, 71-75, PROF PHARMACOL & TOXICOL & CHMN SECT, SCH PHARM, UNIV CONN, 68- *Concurrent Pos:* USPHS spec fel, Nat Inst Neurol Dis & Blindness, 60-62 & career develop award, 64-68; ed, Toxicon, 70-; WHO spec consult & vis prof, Sch Med, Tel Aviv Univ, 74-75. *Mem:* Am Pharmaceut Asn; Am Chem Soc; Am Soc Pharmacol; Int Soc Toxinology; Am Soc Neurochem. *Res:* Pharmacodynamics of drugs affecting the nervous system; actions of phospholipases; venom action on biological tissue; membranal permeability; actions of organophosphorus anticholinesterases. *Mailing Add:* Sect of Pharmacol & Toxicol Univ of Conn Sch of Pharm Storrs CT 06268

ROSENBERG, PHILIP E, b Atlantic City, NJ, Dec 19, 28; m 54; c 2. AUDIOLOGY. *Educ:* Univ Md, BA, 49, MA, 51; Northwestern Univ, PhD(audiol), 56. *Prof Exp:* From asst prof to assoc prof audiol, 56-66, PROF AUDIOL & SPEECH, SCH MED, TEMPLE UNIV, 66-, DIR AUDIOL DEPT, UNIV HOSP, 56- *Concurrent Pos:* Consult, Pa Dept Health, 59-, Pa Bur Voc Rehab, 60-, Pa Acad Ophthal & Otolaryngol, 60-77, US Off Educ, 70- & Philadelphia Bd Educ, 70- *Mem:* AAAS; Am Speech & Hearing Asn; Acoust Soc Am; Am Acad Otolaryngol; Int Soc Audiol. *Res:* Physiological acoustics; deafness; hearing aids; auditory rehabilitation; middle ear impedance; noise; tinnitus. *Mailing Add:* Dept of Audiol Temple Univ Health Sci Ctr Philadelphia PA 19140

ROSENBERG, REINHARDT M, b Tübingen, Ger, Dec 17, 12; nat US; m 37; c 1. MECHANICS. *Educ:* Univ Pittsburgh, BS, 41; Purdue Univ, MS, 47. *Hon Degrees:* Dr, Univ Besancon, 62. *Prof Exp:* Engr, Flutter Group, Bell Aircraft Co, 42-44; design specialist, Consol Vultee Aircraft Corp, 44-46; from instr to asst prof aeronaut eng, Purdue Univ, 46-48; assoc prof, Univ Wash, 48-51; design specialist, Boeing Airplane Co, 51-53; prof appl mech, Univ Toledo, 53-58; prof eng mech, 58-64, Miller res prof, 64-76, PROF ENG MECH, UNIV CALIF, BERKELEY, 76- *Concurrent Pos:* Guggenheim fel, 60-; ed, Int J Nonlinear Mech & J Franklin Inst. *Res:* Nonlinear oscillations; vibration theory; biomechanics; dynamics; applied mathematics; theoretical and applied mechanics. *Mailing Add:* Dept of Mech Eng Univ of Calif Berkeley CA 94720

ROSENBERG, RICHARD CARL, b Chicago, Ill, Mar 14, 43; m 69; c 3. MECHANICAL ENGINEERING, MATERIAL SCIENCE. *Educ:* Gen Motors Inst, BS, 66; Rensselaer Polytech Inst, MS, 67. *Prof Exp:* Res engr, 67-75, sr res engr mech eng, 75-80, STAFF RES ENGR, GEN MOTORS

RES LABS, 80- *Mem:* Am Soc Mech Engrs; Soc Automotive Engrs. *Res:* Friction and wear mechanisms, especially bearing alloy development, rolling element bearings, lubricant additive effects and engine friction. *Mailing Add:* Mech Res Dept GM Res Labs GM Res Ctr Warren MI 48090

ROSENBERG, RICHARD H(ARVEY), b New York, NY, Feb 26, 30; m 52; c 3. CHEMICAL ENGINEERING, RESEARCH ADMINISTRATION. *Educ:* Purdue Univ, BSChE, 52. *Prof Exp:* Chem engr, Corn Prod Co, 52-53 & Victor Chem Works, Stauffer Chem Co, 56-62; mgr chem & environ eng, R C Ingersoll Res Ctr, Borg-Warner Corp, 62-77, MGR REGULATORY AFFAIRS/SAFETY, BORG-WARNER CHEM INC, 77- *Mem:* Am Inst Chem Engrs; Am Mgt Asn. *Mailing Add:* Borg-Warner Chem Inc Wolf & Algonquin Rds Des Plaines IL 60018

ROSENBERG, RICHARD MARTIN, b New York, NY, Jan 13, 33; m 55; c 3. INORGANIC CHEMISTRY, RESEARCH ADMINISTRATION. *Educ:* Brooklyn Col, BS, 54; Pa State Univ PhD(chem), 59. *Prof Exp:* Res chemist, Cent Res Dept, 59-69, & Electrochem Dept, 69-70, res supvr, 70-75, res mgr, 75-80, PROD MKT MGR ELECTRONIC MAT, PHOTO PROD DEPT, E I DU PONT DE NEMOURS & CO, INC, 80- *Mem:* Am Chem Soc; Fel Am Ceramic Soc; Int Soc Hybrid Microelectronics. *Res:* Solid state materials; hybrid microelectronics. *Mailing Add:* Photo Prod Dept E I du Pont de Nemours & Co Inc Wilmington DE 19898

ROSENBERG, RICHARD STUART, b Toronto, Ont, Aug 12, 39; m 78; c 1. COMPUTER SCIENCE. *Educ:* Univ Toronto, BASc, 61, MASc, 64; Univ Mich, PhD(comput sci), 67. *Prof Exp:* Lab instr physics, Univ Toronto, 61-62; res asst elec eng, 62; asst in res eng, Univ Mich, 62-65, res asst math, 65-68, asst prof comput sci, 67-68; asst prof, 68-76, ASSOC PROF COMPUT SCI, UNIV BC, 76- *Mem:* AAAS; Asn Comput Mach; Can Soc Computational Studies Intel (pres, 76-78); Sigma Xi. *Res:* Artificial intelligence, natural language understanding by computer; dialogue; reference problems; question-answering systems; bibliographic information; retrieval. *Mailing Add:* Dept of Comput Sci Univ of BC Vancouver BC V6T 1N5 Can

ROSENBERG, ROBERT, b Philadelphia, Pa, Aug 17, 32; m 55; c 2. PHYSICAL METALLURGY. *Educ:* Drexel Inst, BS, 56; NY Univ, MS, 59, EngScD(environ embrittlement), 62. *Prof Exp:* Engr tech serv, E I du Pont de Nemours & Co, Del, 56-57; res metallurgist res labs, Merck & Co, NJ, 62-63; asst prof mat sci, State Univ NY Stony Brook, 63-66; staff scientist, Thomas J Watson Res Ctr, IBM Corp, 66-71; mgr dept thin films & metall, 71-76; MEM STAFF, BELL LABS, 76- *Concurrent Pos:* NSF res grant, 64-65; consult, Western Elec Co, 65; Off Naval Res grant, 65-67. *Mem:* AAAS; Am Phys Soc; Am Vacuum Soc. *Res:* Embrittlement of metals by liquid metal environments; electron microscopy of fatigue damage and surface dislocation configurations; surface induced elastic energy absorption; structure and properties of thin films. *Mailing Add:* Bell Labs 4b 525 Holmdel NJ 07733

ROSENBERG, ROBERT, b Brooklyn, NY, Jan 3, 30; m 52; c 2. PHYSICS. *Educ:* Columbia Univ, BS, 51, MS, 52, State Univ NY, OD, 73. *Prof Exp:* MEM FAC, DEPT BASIC OPTOM SCI, STATE UNIV NY COL OPTOM, 74- *Res:* Optics. *Mailing Add:* Dept of Basic Optom Sci 100 E 24th St New York NY 10010

ROSENBERG, ROBERT BRINKMANN, b Chicago, Ill, Mar 19, 37; m 59; c 2. ENERGY TECHNOLOGY, CHEMICAL ENGINEERING. *Educ:* Ill Inst Technol, BS, 58, MS, 61, PhD(gas technol), 64. *Prof Exp:* Assoc chem engr, 62-64, chem engr, 64-65, supvr utilization res, 65-66, mgr, 66-68, asst dir, Eng Res, 68-71, dir, 71-77, vpres, 74-77, vpres res & develop, 77-78, EXEC VPRES, INST GAS TECHNOL, 78- *Concurrent Pos:* Adj asst prof, Ill Inst Technol, 65-70; US dir, Atlantic Gas Res Info Exchange, 77-; mem, Study Standards Panel, Nat Res Coun & Comt Advan Energy Storage Systs. *Mem:* Am Gas Asn; Combustion Inst; Am Inst Chem Engrs; Am Chem Soc; Air Pollution Control Asn. *Res:* Development of new processes and equipment and consulting and environmental studies; new supplies and efficient utilization of natural gas and other gaseous fuels. *Mailing Add:* Gas Res Inst 10 W 35th St Chicago IL 60616

ROSENBERG, ROBERT MELVIN, b Hartford, Conn, Mar 9, 26; m 51; c 4. PHYSICAL BIOCHEMISTRY. *Educ:* Trinity Col, Conn, BS, 47; Northwestern Univ, PhD(chem), 51. *Prof Exp:* Res assoc chem, Cath Univ Am, 50-51; asst dermat, Harvard Univ, 51-53; asst prof chem, Wesleyan Univ, 53-56; from asst prof to assoc prof chem, 56-67, chmn dept, 61-62, 66-67 & 79-81, assoc dean, Lawrence & Downer Cols, 68-75, PROF CHEM, LAWRENCE UNIV, 67- *Concurrent Pos:* NSF sci fac fel, Oxford Univ, 62-63; Am Chem Soc vis scientist, 63-74; resident dir, Assoc Cols Midwest Argonne Sem Prog, Argonne Nat Lab, 67-68; res assoc chem, Univ Wis-Madison, 75-76 & 81-82. *Mem:* AAAS; Am Chem Soc; Royal Soc Chem. *Res:* Physical chemistry of proteins. *Mailing Add:* Dept of Chem Lawrence Univ Appleton WI 54911

ROSENBERG, RONALD C(ARL), b Philadelphia, Pa, Dec 15, 37; m 59; c 4. MECHANICAL ENGINEERING, SYSTEMS SCIENCE. *Educ:* Mass Inst Technol, BSc & MSc, 60, PhD(mech eng), 65. *Prof Exp:* Asst prof mech eng, Mass Inst Technol, 66-69; assoc prof, 69-73, PROF MECH ENG, MICH STATE UNIV, 73- *Concurrent Pos:* Ford Found fel, Mass Inst Technol, 66-68; consult, Bolt, Beranek & Newman, Inc, 66-69. *Mem:* Am Soc Mech Engrs; Inst Elec & Electronics Engrs; Asn Comput Mach. *Res:* Dynamic system modeling and behavior; computer-aided design. *Mailing Add:* Dept Mech Eng Eng Bldg Mich State Univ East Lansing MI 48824

ROSENBERG, RONALD LOWELL, b Newark, NJ, Jan 5, 41; m 69. SPACE PHYSICS. *Educ:* Case Inst Technol, BS, 62; Univ Calif, BerkeleY, MA, 66. *Prof Exp:* Physicist, Lawrence Radiation Lab, Calif, 62-64; analYst physics, Space Systs Div, TRW, Calif, 66-68; RES GEOPHYSICIST, INST GEOPHYS & PLANETARY PHYSICS, UNIV CALIF, LOS ANGELES, 68- *Mem:* Am Geophys Union. *Res:* Magnetic fields research, spacecraft utilization. *Mailing Add:* Inst Geophys & Planetary Physics 405 Hilgard Ave Los Angeles CA 90024

ROSENBERG, SANDERS DAVID, b New York, NY, Dec 21, 26; m 46; c 2. FUELS SCIENCE, ORGANOMETALLIC CHEMISTRY. *Educ:* Middlebury Col, AB, 48; Iowa State Univ, PhD(org chem), 52. *Prof Exp:* Sr chemist & group leader org res dept, Rahway Res Lab, Metal & Thermal Corp, NJ, 53-58; prin chemist & mgr fuels & combustion res dept, Chem Prod Div, Aerojet Gen Corp, 58-68, mgr fuels & combustion res, 68-70, mgr chem processing & mat, Aerojet Liquid Rocket Co, 70-73, MGR ADVAN PROGS, AEROJET LIQUID ROCKET CO, 73- *Mem:* Am Inst Aeronaut & Astronaut. *Res:* Development of high energy liquid propellants; research on nature of combustion in chemical rocket engines, development of materials for advanced applications, and development and production of liquid rocket engine systems. *Mailing Add:* 628 Commons Dr Sacramento CA 95825

ROSENBERG, SAUL A, b Cleveland, Ohio, Aug 2, 27; c 3. INTERNAL MEDICINE, ONCOLOGY. *Educ:* Western Reserve Univ, BS, 48, MD, 53; Am Bd Internal Med, dipl. *Prof Exp:* Spec fel, Med Neoplasia, Mem Ctr Cancer & Allied Dis, NY, 57-58; Henry A & Camillus Christian fel med & instr med, Harvard Med Sch, 60-61; from asst prof to assoc prof, 61-69, PROF MED & RADIOL, STANFORD UNIV, 69-, CHIEF DIV ONCOL, 65- *Concurrent Pos:* Chief resident physician, Peter Bent Brigham Hosp, Boston, 60-61; mem, Am Bd Internal Med. *Mem:* Radiation Res Soc; fel Am Col Physicians. *Res:* Clinical investigation of malignant lymphomas; cancer chemotherapy. *Mailing Add:* Div of Oncol S025 Stanford Univ Med Ctr Stanford CA 94304

ROSENBERG, SAUL H, biostatistics, see previous edition

ROSENBERG, STEVEN LOREN, b Oakland, Calif, Sept 27, 41; m 68. MICROBIOLOGY. *Educ:* Univ Calif, Berkeley, AB, 63, PhD(bact), 70. *Prof Exp:* Fel bact, Univ Mass, Amherst, 70-71, NIH fel, 71-72; microbiologist, Phys Chem Lab, Gen Elec Res & Develop Ctr, 72-76; mem staff, Lawrence Berkeley Lab, Univ Calif, 76-81; SR MICROBIOLOGIST, SRI INT, 81- *Mem:* Am Chem Soc; Mycol Soc Am; Am Soc Microbiol. *Res:* Experimental study of bacterial evolution; enzymology of lignocellulose degradation; production of fuels and chemicals from cellulosic materials by fermentation. *Mailing Add:* SRI Int 333 Ravenswood Ave Menlo Park CA 94025

ROSENBERG, THEODORE JAY, b New York, NY, May 24, 37; m 60; c 2. SPACE PHYSICS. *Educ:* City Col New York, BEE, 60; Univ Calif, Berkeley, PhD(physics), 65. *Prof Exp:* Royal Norweg Coun Sci & Indust Res grant, Univ Bergen, 65-66; res assoc & lectr space sci, Rice Univ, 66-68; from res asst prof to res assoc prof, 71-75, res prof, Inst Fluid Dynamics & Appl Math, 75-76, RES PROF, INST PHYS SCI & TECHNOL, UNIV MD, COLLEGE PARK, 76- *Concurrent Pos:* Royal Norweg Coun Sci & Indust Res fel, Norweg Inst Cosmic Physics, 75-76. *Mem:* Am Geophys Union; Am Phys Soc. *Res:* Magnetosphere and ionosphere of earth. *Mailing Add:* Inst for Phys Sci & Technol Univ of Md College Park MD 20742

ROSENBERGER, ALBERT THOMAS, b Butte, Mont, Jan 27, 50. QUANTUM OPTICS. *Educ:* Whitman Col, AB, 71; Univ Chicago, MS, 72; Univ Ill, Champaign-Urbana, PhD(physics), 79. *Prof Exp:* Vis asst prof physics, Drexel Univ, 79-80; ASST PROF PHYSICS, WESTERN ILL UNIV, 80- *Concurrent Pos:* Consult, Battelle Columbus Labs, 76-79. *Mem:* Am Phys Soc; Am Asn Physics Teachers; Optical Soc Am; Inst Elec & Electronics Engrs. *Res:* Quantum optics and laser physics, especially coherent optical effects and superradiance; atomic and molecular spectroscopy. *Mailing Add:* Western Ill Univ Macomb IL 61455

ROSENBERGER, ALFRED L, b New York, NY, Nov 30, 49; m 79. PRIMATOLOGY, EVOLUTIONARY BIOLOGY. *Educ:* City Col New York, BA, 72; City Univ New York, PhD(anthrop), 79. *Prof Exp:* Lectr & fel, Dept Anat Sci, State Univ NY Stony Brook, 79-81; ASST PROF, DEPT ANTHROP, UNIV ILL, CHICAGO, 81- *Mem:* Am Asn Phys Anthropologists; Am Asn Primatologists; Int Soc Primatology; Soc Syst Zool. *Res:* Primate evolution, particularly evolution and adaptation of South and Central American monkeys and higher primates as a whole. *Mailing Add:* Dept Anthrop Univ Ill Box 4348 Chicago IL 60680

ROSENBERGER, FRANZ, b Salzburg, Austria, May 31, 33; m 59; c 3. CHEMICAL PHYSICS. *Educ:* Stuttgart Univ, MS, 64; Univ Utah, PhD, 69. *Prof Exp:* res scientist, 69-70, asst res prof, 70-73, asst prof, 73-78, assoc prof, 78-81, PROF PHYSICS, UNIV UTAH, 81-, DIR, CRYSTAL GROWTH LAB, 66- *Concurrent Pos:* Adj assoc prof mat sci & eng, Univ Utah, 71- *Mem:* Am Asn Crystal Growth; Am Phys Soc. *Res:* Mass and heat transfer phenomena in vapor and solution crystal growth. *Mailing Add:* Dept of Physics Univ of Utah Salt Lake City UT 84112

ROSENBERGER, JOHN KNOX, b Wilmington, Del, Dec 8, 42; m 64; c 2. ANIMAL VIROLOGY, AVIAN PATHOLOGY. *Educ:* Univ Del, BS, 64, MS, 66; Univ Wis-Madison, PhD(virol, immunol), 72. *Prof Exp:* Virologist, US Army Biol Labs, 67-69; asst prof, 72-75, assoc prof, 75-81, PROF VIROL & IMMUNOL, COL AGR SCI, UNIV DEL, 81-, CHAIRPERSON, DEPT ANIMAL SCI & AGR BIOCHEM, 78- *Mem:* Wildlife Dis Asn; Am Soc Microbiol; assoc Am Asn Avian Pathologists; AAAS; Sigma Xi. *Res:* Studies involving various type-A influenza virus isolants as pathogens in various species; viral arthritis; virus induced immuno suppression; characterization of avian adenoviruses. *Mailing Add:* Dept of Animal Sci & Agr Biochem Col of Agr Sci Univ of Del Newark DE 19711

ROSENBERRY, TERRONE LEE, b Ft Wayne, Ind, Mar 15, 43; m 65; c 2. BIOCHEMISTRY, NEUROCHEMISTRY. *Educ:* Oberlin Col, AB, 65; Univ Ore, PhD(biochem), 69. *Prof Exp:* Res assoc biochem, Columbia Univ, 69-72, asst prof, 72-79; ASSOC PROF PHARMACOL, CASE WESTERN RESERVE UNIV, 79- *Concurrent Pos:* Prin investr, NSF grant, 79-82 & NIH grant, 81-84, Muscular Dystrophy Asn grant, 79-82. *Mem:* Am Chem Soc. *Res:* Proteins involved in nerve excitation; membrane biochemistry. *Mailing Add:* Dept Pharmacol Case Western Reserve Univ 2119 Abington Rd Cleveland OH 44106

ROSENBLATT, CHARLES STEVEN, b Brooklyn, NY, Aug, 23, 52. LIGHT SCATTERING & OPTICS. *Educ:* Mass Inst Technol, SB, 74; Harvard Univ, PhD, 78. *Prof Exp:* Res fel physics, Lawrence Berkeley Lab, Univ Calif, 78-80; RES STAFF PHYSICS, FRANCIS BITTER NAT MAGNET LAB, MASS INST TECHNOL, 80- *Mem:* Am Phys Soc; Sigma Xi. *Res:* Optical, magnetic, and mechanical studies of liquid crystals, liquids, and colloids; phase transitions; light scattering from small biological organisms. *Mailing Add:* Francis Bitter Nat Magnet Lab Mass Inst Technol Cambridge MA 02139

ROSENBLATT, DAVID, b New York, NY, Sept 5, 19; m 50. MATHEMATICAL STATISTICS. *Educ:* City Col New York, BS, 40. *Prof Exp:* Assoc statistician, Off Price Admin, DC, 41-44; sr economist, Div Statist Stand, US Bur Budget, 44-47, 48-49; asst prof econ, Carnegie Inst Technol, 49-51; consult, 51-53; assoc prof statist, Am Univ, 53-55; prin investr, Off Naval Res, 53-57; res consult, Industs, 55-61; consult, Info Tech Div, Nat Bur Stand, 61-63, mathematician, 63-67; RES CONSULT, 68- *Concurrent Pos:* Littauer fel, Harvard Univ, 47-48; statist consult, Div Statist Standards, US Bur Budget, 49-53; consult, George Washington Univ, 55, 59-61, 68-; adj prof math & statist, Am Univ, 59-61. *Mem:* Fel AAAS; Am Math Soc; fel Am Statist Asn. *Res:* Applied stochastic processes; theory of graphs and theory of relations; mathematical theory of organizations and complex systems; design of statistical information systems; history of mathematical and symbolic methods in resource and social sciences; relation and Boolzan algebraic methods. *Mailing Add:* 2939 Van Ness St NW Washington DC 20008

ROSENBLATT, DAVID HIRSCH, b Trenton, NJ, July 24, 27; m 49; c 3. CHEMISTRY. *Educ:* Johns Hopkins Univ, BA, 46; Univ Conn, PhD(chem), 50. *Prof Exp:* Res & develop chemist, Baltimore Paint & Color Works, 50-51; chemist, Chem Warfare Labs, US Dept Army, 51-56; org chemist, Johns Hopkins Univ, 56-57; chemist, Chem Res & Develop Labs, US Dept Army, 57-63, chief decontamination res sect, Chem Lab, Edgewood Arsenal, 63-72, RES CHEMIST, ENVIRON PROTECTION RES DIV, US ARMY MED BIOENG RES & DEVELOP LAB, FT DETRICK, MD, 72- *Concurrent Pos:* Instr eve col, Johns Hopkins Univ, 57-70. *Mem:* AAAS; Am Chem Soc; Sigma Xi; NY Acad Sci; Soc Environ Toxicol Chem. *Res:* Nucleophilic displacements; mechanisms of oxidation of amines and other organics in aqueous solution; halogens and halogen oxides; decomposition and complexing of toxic chemical agents; specific analytical methods; risk assessment of environmental pollutants. *Mailing Add:* US Army Med Bioeng Res & Develop Fort Detrick MD 21701

ROSENBLATT, DAVID SYDNEY, b Montreal, Que, July 14, 46; m 69; c 2. BIOCHEMICAL GENETICS, PEDIATRICS. *Educ:* McGill Univ, BSc, 68, MDCM, 70. *Prof Exp:* Intern pediat med, Montreal Children's Hosp, 70-71; clin & res fel pediat & genetics, Mass Gen Hosp, Harvard Med Sch, 71-73; fel biol, Mass Inst Technol, 73-74; asst resident pediat, Children's Hosp Med Ctr, Harvard Med Sch, 74-75; asst prof, 75-80, assoc prof, Ctr Human Genetics, 80, AUXILIARY PROF BIOL, MCGILL UNIV, 78-, ASSOC PROF PEDIAT, 80- *Concurrent Pos:* Prin investr, Med Res Coun Can, Genetics Group, McGill Univ, 75-; mem genetics comt, Med Res Coun Can, 78-81; vchmn res comt, McGill Univ, Montreal Children's Hosp Res Inst, 80- *Mem:* Am Soc Human Genetics; Can Soc Clin Invest; Soc Pediat Res. *Res:* Inborn errors of folate metabolism in cultured human cells; methotrexate metabolism. *Mailing Add:* Montreal Children's Hosp 2300 Tupper St A-709 Montreal PQ H3H 1P3 Can

ROSENBLATT, DORRIE ELLEN, neurochemistry, see previous edition

ROSENBLATT, GERD MATTHEW, b Leipzig, Ger, July 6, 33; US citizen; m 57; c 2. PHYSICAL CHEMISTRY. *Educ:* Swarthmore Col, BA, 55; Princeton Univ, PhD(phys chem), 60. *Prof Exp:* Chemist, Inorg Mat Res Div, Lawrence Radiation Lab, Univ Calif, 60-63; from asst prof to assoc prof chem, Pa State Univ, University Park, 63-70, prof, 70-81; ASSOC DIV LEADER, CHEM-MAT SCI DIV, LOS ALAMOS NAT LAB, 81- *Concurrent Pos:* Lectr, Univ Calif, Berkeley, 62-63; guest scientist & consult, Inorg Mat Res Div, Lawrence Berkeley Lab, Univ Calif, 68, 70, 72, 75 & 77; mem Nat Res Coun Comt High Temperature Sci & Technol, 72-; vis prof, Vrije Univ, Brussels, Belg, 73; mem rev comt, Chem Eng Div, Argonne Nat Lab, 74-79; consult, Hooker Chem Co, 76-, Xerox Corp, 77-78, Los Alamos Sci Lab, 78, 80 & 81, Solar energy Res Inst, 80-81 & Aerospace Corp, 79-; mem rev Comn, High Temperature Mat Lab, Oak Ridge Nat Lab, 78-; US nat rep, Int Union Pure Appl Chem Comn, High Temperature & Refractory Mat, 78- *Mem:* Am Phys Soc; Am Chem Soc; AAAS; NY Acad Sci; Am Metall Soc. *Res:* Solid-vapor kinetics and equilibria; high temperature and surface chemistry; Raman spectroscopy and thermodynamics of high temperature gaseous molecules. *Mailing Add:* Chem Mat Sci Div MS-G756 Los Alamos Nat Lab Los Alamos NM 87545

ROSENBLATT, JOAN RAUP, b New York, NY, Apr 15, 26; m 50. MATHEMATICAL STATISTICS. *Educ:* Columbia Univ, AB, 46; Univ NC, PhD(statist), 56. *Prof Exp:* Statist analyst, US Bur Budget, 48; asst statist, Univ NC, 53-54; mathematician, 55-69, chief statist eng lab, 69-78, DEP DIR CTR APPL MATH, NAT BUR STAND, 78- *Honors & Awards:* Fed Woman's Award, 71; Gold Medal, Dept Commerce, 76. *Mem:* Fel AAAS; Am Math Soc; Int Statist Inst; fel Am Statist Asn (vpres, 81-83); fel Inst Math Statist. *Res:* Nonparametric statistical theory; applications of statistical techniques in physical and engineering sciences; reliability of complex systems. *Mailing Add:* 2939 Van Ness St NW Washington DC 20008

ROSENBLATT, JUDAH ISSER, b Baltimore, Md, Feb 12, 31; m 56; c 1. BIOMETRICS, BIOSTATISTICS. *Educ:* Johns Hopkins Univ, BA, 51; Columbia Univ, PhD, 59. *Prof Exp:* Asst prof math & statist, Purdue Univ, 56-60; assoc prof math, Univ NMex, 60-68, dir math comput lab, 67-68; prof math, 68-76, PROF BIOMET, CASE WESTERN RESERVE UNIV, 76- *Concurrent Pos:* Consult, Sandia Corp, Albuquerque, NMex, 60-68, Gen Elec Co, 77- *Mem:* Am Math Soc; Inst Math Statist; Math Asn Am; Soc Critical Care Med. *Res:* Stochastic processes, numerical analysis, biostatistical modelling and analysis. *Mailing Add:* Dept of Biomet Case Western Reserve Univ Cleveland OH 44106

ROSENBLATT, MURRAY, b New York, NY, Sept 7, 26; m 49; c 2. APPLIED MATHEMATICS, MATHEMATICAL STATISTICS. *Educ:* City Col New York, BS, 46; Cornell Univ, MS, 47, PhD(math), 49. *Prof Exp:* Res assoc math, Cornell Univ, 49-50; from instr to asst prof statist, Univ Chicago, 50-55; assoc prof math, Ind Univ, 56-59; prof appl math, Brown Univ, 59-64; PROF MATH, UNIV CALIF, SAN DIEGO, 64- *Concurrent Pos:* Off Naval Res grant, 49-50; Guggenheim fels, 65-66, 71-72; fel, Univ Col London, 66, 72 & Australian Nat Univ, 76; overseas fel, Churchill Col, 79. *Mem:* Am Math Soc; fel Inst Math Statist; fel AAAS; Int Statist Inst. *Res:* Probability theory; stochastic processes; time series analysis; turbulence. *Mailing Add:* Dept Math Univ Calif at San Diego La Jolla CA 92037

ROSENBLATT, N(AFTALI) WALTER, b Ilsenberg, Ger, Oct 6, 26; m 56; c 2. CHEMICAL ENGINEERING. *Educ:* Israel Inst Technol, BSc, 53, Ing, 54; Univ Birmingham, PhD(chem eng), 59. *Prof Exp:* Engr, Israel Mining Indust, 54-56; res engr, Textile Fibers Dept, 59-64, sr res engr, 64-66, res assoc, Permasep Prod, 66-74, res fel, 74-76, SR TECH CONSULT, CENT RES DEVELOP DEPT, E I DU PONT DE NEMOURS & CO, INC, 76- *Res:* Membrane technology; water desalination; new products; new processes. *Mailing Add:* Cent Res & Develop Dept E I du Pont de Nemours & Co Inc Wilmington DE 19898

ROSENBLATT, RICHARD HEINRICH, b Kansas City, Mo, Dec 21, 30; m 52; c 2. ZOOLOGY. *Educ:* Univ Calif, Los Angeles, AB, 53, MA, 54, PhD, 59. *Prof Exp:* Asst zool, Univ Calif, Los Angeles, 53-56; asst res zoologist, Inst, 58-65, from asst prof to assoc prof, 65-73, PROF MARINE BIOL, SCRIPPS INST OCEANOG, PROF, GRAD DEPT & RES ZOOLOGIST, SCI SUPPORT DIV, UNIV CALIF, 73-, VCHMN DEPT, 70-, CUR MARINE VERT, 58-, CHMN, GRAD DEPT, 80- *Mem:* AAAS; Soc Syst Zool; Am Soc Ichthyol & Herpet; Soc Study Evolution; Am Soc Zool. *Res:* Systematics, evolution, ecology and zoogeography of fishes. *Mailing Add:* Grad Dept Scripps Inst of Oceanog La Jolla CA 92093

ROSENBLITH, WALTER ALTER, b Vienna, Austria, Sept 21, 13; nat US; m 41; c 2. BIOPHYSICS. *Educ:* Univ Bordeaux, ing radiotelegraphiste, 36; Ecole Superieure d'Elec, Univ Paris, ing radioelectricien, 37. *Prof Exp:* Res engr, France, 37-39; res asst physics, NY Univ, 39-40; from asst prof to assoc prof, SDak Sch Mines, 43-47, actg head dept, 44-47; res fel, Psychoacoust Lab, Harvard Univ, 47-51; assoc prof, 51-57, staff mem res lab electronics, 51-69, chmn fac, 67-69, assoc provost, 69-71, provost, 71-80, PROF COMMUN BIOPHYS, MASS INST TECHNOL, 57-, INST PROF, 75- *Concurrent Pos:* Lectr otol, Harvard Med Sch & Mass Eye & Ear Infirmary, 57-; inaugural lectr, Tata Inst Fundamental Res, Bombay, 62; mem sci adv bd, US Air Force, 61-62; consult, Life Sci Panel, President's Sci Adv Comt, 61-66; consult, WHO, 64-65; chmn comt electronic comput in life sci, Nat Acad Sci/Nat Res Coun, 60-64, mem brain sci comt, 65-68, chmn, 66-67; mem cent coun exec comt, Int Brain Res Orgn, 60-68, hon treas, 62-67; mem coun, Int Union Pure & Appl Biophys, 61-69 & pres comn biophys commun & control processes, 64-69; mem bd med, Nat Acad Sci, 67-70; mem, President's Comn Urban Housing, 67-68; chmn sci adv coun, Callier Ctr Commun Disorders, 68-; mem bd gov, Weizmann Inst Sci, 73-; dir, Kaiser Industs, 68-76; adv comt dir, NIH, 70-74; mem comt on scholarly commun, People's Repub China, 77-; mem, Bd Foreign Scholar, 78-81, chmn, 80-81; co-chmn comt for study on saccharin & food safety policy, Nat Res Coun-Inst Med, 78-79; mem bd trustees, Brandeis Univ, 79- *Honors & Awards:* Weizmann lectr, Weizmann Inst Sci, Israel, 62. *Mem:* Nat Acad Sci; Nat Acad Eng; Inst Med-Nat Acad Sci; Inst Elec & Electronics Engrs; Biophys Soc. *Res:* Electrical activity of the nervous system and brain function; sensory communication. *Mailing Add:* Rm E51-232 Mass Inst of Technol Cambridge MA 02139

ROSENBLOOM, ALFRED A, JR, b Pittsburgh, Pa, Apr 5, 21; m; c 2. OPTOMETRY. *Educ:* Pa State Col, BA, 42; Ill Col Optom, OD, 48; Univ Chicago, MA, 53. *Hon Degrees:* DOS, Ill Col Optom, 54. *Prof Exp:* Instr neural physiol, 46-48, dir contact lens & subnorm vision clins, 47-48, lectr, 49-54, dean, 55-72, PRES, ILL COL OPTOM, 72-, PROF OPTOM, 77- *Concurrent Pos:* Am Optom Found fel, 52-54; reading clinician & res assoc, Dept Educ, Univ Chicago, 53-54; consult, Chicago Lighthouse for Blind, 55-; chmn adv res coun, Am Optom Found, 69-76; lectr, Brit Optical Asn, 70; mem, Optom Exten Prog; mem optom rev comt, Bur Health Prof Educ & Manpower, US Dept Health, Educ & Welfare, Region III; mem state contract task force, Am Optom Found. *Mem:* AAAS; fel Am Acad Optom; Am Optom Asn; Nat Soc Study Educ; Asn Schs & Cols Optom. *Res:* Visual problems of children and youth and the partially sighted; reading problems. *Mailing Add:* Ill Col of Optom 3241 S Michigan Ave Chicago IL 60616

ROSENBLOOM, ARLAN LEE, b Milwaukee, Wis, Apr 15, 34; m 58; c 4. PEDIATRICS, ENDOCRINOLOGY. *Educ:* Univ Wis-Madison, BA, 55, MD, 58. *Prof Exp:* Intern, Los Angeles County Gen Hosp, 58-59; resident, Ventura County Hosp, Calif, 59-60; physician & chief, Medico Hosp, Kratie, Cambodia, 60-61, med officer, Medico, Inc, Pahang, Malaysia, 61-62; resident pediat, Univ Wis-Madison, 62-63, chief resident, 64-65; tech adv epidemiol, Commun Dis Ctr, USPHS, 66-68; from asst prof to assoc prof, 68-74, PROF PEDIAT ENDOCRINOL, COL MED, UNIV FLA, 74-, DIR CLIN RES CTR, 74- *Concurrent Pos:* USPHS training grants pediat, Univ Wis-Madison, 63-64 & 65-66. *Mem:* Am Diabetes Asn; Am Acad Pediat; Pediat Endocrine Soc; Soc Pediat Res; Endocrine Soc. *Res:* Natural history of diabetes mellitus; hypoglycemoses in childhood. *Mailing Add:* Dept of Pediat Univ of Fla Col of Med Gainesville FL 32610

ROSENBLOOM, ARNOLD, b Chicago, Ill, Apr 27, 29; m 51; c 3. ENGINEERING. *Educ:* Ill Inst Technol, BSEE, 50; Stanford Univ, MSEE, 51; Univ Calif, Los Angeles, PhD(eng), 54. *Prof Exp:* Engr, Hughes Aircraft Co, 51-52 & Univ Calif, Los Angeles, 52-54; mem tech staff guided missile res div, Ramo Wooldridge Corp, 54-57, assoc mgr guid & navig dept, Space Tech Labs, 57-59, mgr comput & guid dept, TRW Space Tech Labs, 59-61, dir guid lab, 61-63, assoc dir syst res & anal div, 63-65, mgr, Houston Opers, TRW Systs Group, TRW Inc, 65-69, asst dir civil systs, 69-73, vpres transp & environ opers, 73-75; mgr systs staff, Strategic Systs Div, 75-78, ASST

MGR, SPACE ELECTRO-OPTICAL SYSTS LABS, SPACE SENSOR DIV, HUGHES AIRCRAFT CO, 78- *Mem:* Am Inst Aeronaut & Astronaut. *Res:* Statistical control theory; space guidance; astrodynamics; simulation. *Mailing Add:* Strategic Systs Div Centinela & Teale St Culver City CA 90230

ROSENBLOOM, JOEL, b Denver, Colo, July 18, 35; m 58; c 2. BIOCHEMISTRY, BIOPHYSICS. *Educ:* Harvard Univ, AB, 57; Univ Pa, MD, 62, PhD(biochem), 65. *Prof Exp:* Asst prof biochem & med, Sch Med, 65-71, assoc prof biochem, Sch Dent Med, 71-74, PROF EMBRYOL & HISTOL & CHMN DEPT, SCH DENT MED, UNIV PA, 74- *Concurrent Pos:* Biochemist, Clin Res Ctr, Philadelphia Gen Hosp, 65-73; dir, Ctr Oral Health Res, 78- *Mem:* AAAS; NY Acad Sci; Am Chem Soc; Biophys Soc; Am Soc Biol Chemists. *Res:* Structure of macromolecules; ultracentrifugation; structure and biosynthesis of macromolecules, particularly collagen and elastin. *Mailing Add:* Dept of Embryol & Histol Univ of Pa Sch of Dent Med Philadelphia PA 19104

ROSENBLOOM, PAUL CHARLES, b Portsmouth, Va, Mar 31, 20; m 48, 55; c 2. MATHEMATICS. *Educ:* Univ Pa, AB, 41; Stanford Univ, PhD(math), 44. *Prof Exp:* Asst math, Stanford Univ, 41-43; from instr to asst prof, Brown Univ, 43-46; from asst prof to assoc prof, Univ Syracuse, 46-51; from assoc prof to prof, Univ Minn, 51-65; PROF MATH, TEACHERS COL, COLUMBIA UNIV, 65- *Concurrent Pos:* Dir math sect, Minn Nat Lab, State Dept Educ & Minn Sch Math & Sci Ctr, 58-65; Guggenheim fel & asst prof, Univ Lund, 47-48; vis prof, Columbia Univ, 52, Univ Kans, 53 & Harvard Univ, 56; mem, Inst Advan Study, 53; mem, Adv Panel Math Sci, NSF, 54-57; mem, Div Math, Nat Res Coun, 58-; vis prof, Univ Denver, 70, Sir George Williams Univ, Montreal, 72-74 & Israel Inst Technol, 78-79. *Honors & Awards:* Frechet Prize, Math Soc France, 50. *Mem:* Am Math Soc; Inst Advan Study; Math Asn Am. *Res:* Mathematical logic; function of complex variables; absolutely monotonic functions; Banach spaces; differential equations; mathematical education. *Mailing Add:* Dept of Math Teachers Col Columbia Univ New York NY 10027

ROSENBLUH, MICHAEL, atomic & molecular physics, see previous edition

ROSENBLUM, ANNETTE TANNENHOLZ, b Brooklyn, NY, Oct 3, 42; m 66; c 2. SCIENCE POLICY, CHEMICAL SCIENCES. *Educ:* Queens Col, BS, 64; Univ Rochester, MS, 67; Ohio State Univ, PhD(org chem), 71. *Prof Exp:* Teaching asst chem, Univ Rochester, 64-66; teaching asst, Ohio State Univ, 66-67, res asst, 67-71; staff writer chem sci, News Serv, 72-74, asst for res & coordr govt affairs, 74-79, ASST TO DIR, DEPT PUB AFFAIRS, AM CHEM SOC, WASHINGTON, DC, 79- *Concurrent Pos:* NY State Col teaching fel, Univ Rochester, 64-66; res chemist, Naval Ord Lab, Dept Navy, 72; interim co-adminr govt affairs, Dept Chem & Pub Affairs, Am Chem Soc, 77-78. *Mem:* AAAS; Am Chem Soc; Soc Occup & Environ Health. *Res:* Science policy; legislation; federal regulations; chemical safety and health; environmental improvement. *Mailing Add:* 12008 Trailridge Dr Potomac MD 20854

ROSENBLUM, ARTHUR H, b Chicago, Ill, Feb 11, 09; m 38; c 3. PEDIATRICS, ALLERGY. *Educ:* Univ Chicago, SB, 30, MS, 32, MD, 33. *Prof Exp:* DIR PEDIAT ALLERGY, MICHAEL REESE HOSP, 71- *Concurrent Pos:* Sr attend pediat, Michael Reese Hosp, 66-; chmn penicillin study group, Am Acad Allergy, 68-74; pediat staff, Weiss Mem Hosp, 70-; pvt pract pediat & allergy, 71-; clin prof med, Univ Chicago Pritzger Sch Med & consult allergy, St James Hosp, Chicago Heights, 74-; consult, HEW, 77. *Mem:* Fel Am Acad Allergy; fel Am Acad Pediat; AMA; Asn Cert Allergists. *Res:* Penicillin allergy, studies and management; drug allergy, ACTH, sulfa, silk; nephrosis studies and therapy; group therapy bronchial asthma. *Mailing Add:* 1010 Dixie Hwy Chicago Heights IL 60411

ROSENBLUM, BRUCE, b New York, NY, May 20, 26; div; c 3. PHYSICS. *Educ:* NY Univ, BS, 49; Columbia Univ, PhD(physics), 59. *Prof Exp:* Res physicist, Dept Physics, Univ Calif, Berkeley, 57-58; mem tech staff, Radio Corp Am Labs, 58-65, head, Gen Res Group, 65-66; chmn dept physics, Univ Calif, Santa Cruz, 66-70, dep provost, Stevenson Col, 68-73, PROF PHYSICS, UNIV CALIF, SANTA CRUZ, 66-, ASSOC DIR, CTR INNOVATION & ENTREPRENEURIAL DEVELOP, 78- *Concurrent Pos:* VPres, Rev & Critique, 80- *Mem:* Am Phys Soc; Am Asn Physics Teachers. *Res:* Molecular and atmospheric physics; microwave spectroscopy; plasmas and transport in semiconductors; superconductivity; biophysics. *Mailing Add:* Dept of Physics Univ of Calif Santa Cruz CA 95064

ROSENBLUM, CHARLES, b Brooklyn, NY, Sept 19, 05; m 33; c 1. PHYSICAL CHEMISTRY. *Educ:* Univ Rochester, BS, 27; Univ Minn, PhD(phys chem), 31. *Prof Exp:* Asst chem, Univ Minn, 27-30, assoc, 31-35; fel, Comn Relief Belg Educ Found Louvain, 35-37; instr chem, Princeton Univ, 37-41; sr chemist, Merck & Co, Inc, 41-42; sect head, Kellex Corp, NY, 44; sect head, Merck & Co, Inc, 46-50, head radioactivity lab, 50-65, sr investr & dir, 65-70; VIS SR RES BIOCHEMIST, PRINCETON UNIV, 70- *Honors & Awards:* Levy Medal, Franklin Inst, 40. *Mem:* Fel AAAS; Am Chem Soc; Soc Exp Biol & Med; fel Am Inst Chemists; Belg Am Educ Found. *Res:* Photochemistry; radiochemistry; radioactive indicators; activation analysis; adsorption; physical methods of analysis; structure of precipitates; stability of pharmaceuticals. *Mailing Add:* Moffett Labs Princeton Univ Princeton NJ 08540

ROSENBLUM, EUGENE DAVID, b Brooklyn, NY, Oct 13, 20; m 56; c 2. MICROBIOLOGY, GENETICS. *Educ:* Brooklyn Col, BA, 41; Univ Wis, MS, 48, PhD(bact), 50. *Prof Exp:* Bacteriologist, Biol Lab, Cold Spring Harbor, 50-52; res assoc microbiol, May Inst Med Res, Cincinnati, 52-53; from asst prof to assoc prof, 53-74, PROF MICROBIOL, UNIV TEX HEALTH SCI CTR, DALLAS, 53-, DIR MICROBIOL GRAD PROG, 72- *Mem:* AAAS; Am Soc Microbiol; Soc Gen Microbiol. *Res:* Genetics of pathogenic bacteria; antibiotic resistance; extrachromosomal inheritance; bacteriophage. *Mailing Add:* Dept of Microbiol Univ of Tex Health Sci Ctr Dallas TX 75235

ROSENBLUM, HAROLD, b Paterson, NJ, Mar 30, 18; m 41; c 3. ELECTRONIC ENGINEERING. *Educ:* Cooper Union, BChE, 43; NY Univ, MEE, 51. *Prof Exp:* Head, Radar Systs Sect, NY Naval Shipyard, 47-54; head, Flight Trainers Br, Naval Training Device Ctr, 54-57, Air Tactics Br, 57-60, Strike-Air Defense Systs Trainers Div, 60-65 & Aerospace Systs Trainers Dept, 65-67, asst tech dir eng, 67-69, dep dir, 69-74; dir tech sales, Appl Devices Corp, Kissimmee, Fla, 77-78; ENG CONSULT, 74-; SR STAFF CONSULT, LINK SIMULATION SYSTS DIV, SINGER CO, SILVER SPRING, MD, 80- *Mem:* Sr mem Inst Elec & Electronics Engrs; NY Acad Sci; Sigma Xi. *Res:* Training devices, research techniques and instructional technology for simulation of air, surface underwater and land warfare weapon systems. *Mailing Add:* 1310 Webster St Orlando FL 32804

ROSENBLUM, HOWARD EDWIN, b Brooklyn, NY, Apr 28, 28; m 50; c 4. COMMUNICATIONS ENGINEERING, ACOUSTICS. *Educ:* City Col New York, BS, 50. *Prof Exp:* Chief proj engr commun systs, Sanders Assocs, 61-62; div chief res & develop secure speech systs, 63-71, asst dir res & develop, 71-73, asst dep dir res & eng, 73-74, dep dir, 74-78, DEP DIR COMMUN SECURITY, NAT SECURITY AGENCY, FT GEORGE G MEADE, 78- *Concurrent Pos:* Consult, Defense Sci Bd, 76-77; mem, Mil Commun Electronics Bd & Defense Telecommun Coun, 78- *Honors & Awards:* Except Civilian Serv Award, Nat Security Agency, 72. *Mem:* AAAS; Armed Forces Commun-Electronics Asn. *Res:* Cryptography; speech compression and digitalization; microelectronics; computer and information science. *Mailing Add:* 1809 Franwall Ave Silver Spring MD 20902

ROSENBLUM, IRA, b Brooklyn, NY, Feb 23, 25; m 51; c 1. PHARMACOLOGY, TOXICOLOGY. *Educ:* Long Island Univ, BS, 48; Yale Univ, PhD, 53. *Prof Exp:* Instr pharmacol, Sch Med, Creighton Univ, 52-54; from asst prof to assoc prof, 54-69, PROF PHARMACOL, ALBANY MED COL, 69-, PROF TOXICOL & ADMIN DIR INST COMP & HUMAN TOXICOL, 75- *Concurrent Pos:* Assoc dir Inst Comp & Human Toxicol, 70-75, dir Int Ctr Environ Safety, 73-75, DIR INT CTR ENVIRON SAFETY, 73- *Mem:* Am Soc Pharmacol & Exp Therapeut; Soc Toxicol; Soc Exp Biol & Med. *Res:* Res: Toxicology of central nervous system. *Mailing Add:* Inst Comp & Human Toxicol Albany Med Col Albany NY 12208

ROSENBLUM, LAWRENCE JAY, b New York, NY, Jan 25, 44; m 66; c 2. COMPUTER SYSTEM DEVELOPMENT, MATHEMATICAL MODELING. *Educ:* Queens Col, NY, BA, 64; Ohio State UniV, MS, 66, PhD(math), 71. *Prof Exp:* Mathematician, Dept Navy, 71-73, prog mgr ocean environ, 73-77; MATHEMATICIAN, NAVAL RES LAB, 77- *Mem:* AAAS; Am Math Soc; Acoust Soc Am. *Res:* Application of computers to oceanographic experiments; mathematical modeling of oceanographic phenomena. *Mailing Add:* Naval Res Lab Code 5003 4555 Overlook Ave SW Washington DC 20375

ROSENBLUM, LEONARD ALLEN, b Brooklyn, NY, May 18, 36; m 56; c 2. ETHOLOGY. *Educ:* Brooklyn Col, BA, 56, MA, 58; Univ Wis-Madison, PhD, 61. *Prof Exp:* Res asst psychol, Brooklyn Col, 56-58; res asst psychol, Univ Wis, 58-61, teaching fel, 61; from instr to assoc prof, 61-72, PROF PSYCHIAT, STATE UNIV NY DOWNSTATE MED CTR, 72- *Concurrent Pos:* NIMH career develop award, 64-71; reviewer small grants, NIMH, 74-77, basic behavioral sci, 78-82. *Mem:* Am Psychol Asn; Am Soc Primatol; Int Acad Sex Res; Int Primatol Soc; Int Soc Develop Psychobiol (pres, 80). *Res:* Mother-infant relations and effects of early experience on development in primates; sexual behavior and its development and control. *Mailing Add:* Primate Behav Lab State Univ NY Downstate Med Ctr 450 Clarkson Ave Brooklyn NY 11203

ROSENBLUM, MARTIN JACOB, b Stamford, Conn, Dec 6, 28; m 55; c 2. COMPUTER SCIENCE, APPLIED MATHEMATICS. *Educ:* Yale Univ, BA, 50, MA, 51; State Univ NY Stony Brook, MS, 75; Stevens Inst Technol, MS, 81. *Prof Exp:* Asst physics, Yale Univ, 54-59, res assoc, 59-61; from assoc physicist to physicist, Brookhaven Nat Lab, 61-75; mem tech staff, Bell Labs, 75-80; MEM STAFF INFO SYSTS, WESTERN ELEC CO, 80- *Concurrent Pos:* Ford fel, Europ Orgn Nuclear Res, Switz, 63-64. *Mem:* AAAS; Asn Comput Mach; Inst Elec & Electronics Engrs. *Res:* Computer sciences; communication science; digital systems; data analysis. *Mailing Add:* Western Elec Co 6 Corporate Pl Piscataway NJ 08854

ROSENBLUM, MARVIN, b Brooklyn, NY, June 30, 26; m 59; c 5. MATHEMATICS. *Educ:* Univ Calif, BS, 49, MA, 51, PhD(math), 55. *Prof Exp:* Actg instr math, Univ Calif, 54-55; from asst prof to assoc prof, 55-65, chmn dept, 69-72, prof math, 65-78, COMMONWEALTH PROF MATH, UNIV VA, 78- *Concurrent Pos:* Mem, Inst Advan Study, 59-60. *Mem:* Am Math Soc; Math Asn Am; Soc Indust & Appl Math. *Res:* Hilbert space; harmonic analysis. *Mailing Add:* Dept of Math Univ of Va Charlottesville VA 22903

ROSENBLUM, MYRON, b New York, NY, Oct 20, 25; m 58. ORGANIC CHEMISTRY. *Educ:* Columbia Univ, AB, 49; Harvard Univ, AM, 50, PhD(chem), 54. *Prof Exp:* Res assoc, Columbia Univ, 53-55; asst prof chem, Ill Inst Technol, 55-58; from asst prof to assoc prof, 58-66, PROF CHEM, BRANDEIS UNIV, 66- *Concurrent Pos:* Guggenheim fel, 65-66; vis prof, Israel Inst Technol, 66. *Mem:* Am Chem Soc; Royal Soc Chem. *Res:* Organometallic chemistry of the transition elements; reaction mechanisms; synthesis. *Mailing Add:* Dept of Chem Brandeis Univ Waltham MA 02154

ROSENBLUM, SAM, b New York, NY, Jan 25, 23; m 47; c 2. GEOCHEMISTRY. *Educ:* City Col New York, BS, 49; Stanford Univ, MS, 51. *Prof Exp:* Geologist, US Bur Reclamation, 51; geologist, Br Mineral Deposits, US Geol Surv, 52-57, Br Foreign Geol, Taiwan, 57-61, Geochem Census Unit, 61-63, Br Mil Geol, 63-65, Br Foreign Geol, Bolivia, 65-67, Off Int Geol, Liberia, 67-72, mineralogist, Br Explor Res, 72-80; CONSULT GEOL, 80- *Mem:* Geol Soc Am; Mineral Soc Am; Int Asn Geochem & Cosmochem; Soc Environ Geochem & Health; Asn Explor Geochemists. *Res:* Mineralogy; petrography; geochemistry; economic and exploration geology; rare-earth element mineralogy; application of geochemistry to health studies. *Mailing Add:* 12165 W Ohio Pl Lakewood CO 80228

ROSENBLUM, STEPHEN SAUL, b Brooklyn, NY, Sept 26, 42; m 72; c 2. EXPERIMENTAL SOLID STATE PHYSICS, PARTICLE ACCELERATOR DESIGN. *Educ:* Columbia Univ, AB, 63; Univ Calif, Berkeley, PhD(chem), 69. *Prof Exp:* Res fel physics, Calif Inst Technol, 69-70; guest lectr physics, Freie Univ, Berlin, 70-72; vis staff mem, Hahn-Meitner Inst, Berlin, 72-74; staff mem cryogenics, Los Alamos Sci Lab, 74-77; staff scientist physics, 77-78, STAFF SCIENTIST ELEC ENG, LAWRENCE BERKELEY LAB, 78- *Mem:* Am Phys Soc; Am Chem Soc; Inst Elec & Electron Engrs. *Res:* Investigation of magnetic interactions in solids; principally using hyperfine interactions as a probe; investigation of materials pertinent to accelerator construction. *Mailing Add:* Bldg 47 Lawrence Berkeley Lab Berkeley CA 94720

ROSENBLUM, WILLIAM I, b New York, NY, July 6, 35; m 59; c 3. NEUROPATHOLOGY, PATHOLOGY. *Educ:* Swarthmore Col, BA, 57; NY Univ, MD, 61. *Prof Exp:* USPHS fel path & neuropath & intern & resident path, Sch Med, NY Univ, 61-66; assoc prof neuropath, Northwestern Univ, 68-69; PROF PATH & CHMN, DIV NEUROPATH, MED COL VA, 69-, VCHMN, DEPT PATH, 79- *Concurrent Pos:* Assoc pathologist, Clin Ctr, NIH, 66-68; asst pathologist, Passavant Mem Hosp, Chicago, 68-69; consult neuropath, Evanston Hosp, 68-69; mem exec comt, Coun on Stroke, Am Heart Asn. *Mem:* Am Asn Path & Bact; Am Asn Neuropath; Am Soc Exp Path; Am Physiol Soc; Microcirc Soc. *Res:* Cerebral circulation in health and disease. *Mailing Add:* Box 17 Div of Neuropath Med Col of Va Richmond VA 23298

ROSENBLUM, WILLIAM M, US citizen. PHYSICS, OPTOMETRY. *Educ:* Univ Miami, BS, 58; Fla State Univ, MS, 60; Tufts Univ, PhD(physics), 67. *Prof Exp:* Asst, Fla State Univ, 58-60; instr physics, Univ Miami, 60-62 & Tufts Univ, 62-66; sr scientist, Phys Optics Dept, Tech Opers, Inc, 66-68, Optical Eng Dept, Polaroid Corp, Mass, 68-69 & NASA Electronics Res Ctr, 69-70; ASSOC PROF PHYSICS & OPTOM, UNIV ALA, BIRMINGHAM, 70- *Concurrent Pos:* Instr, Harvard Exten Ser, 67-68 & Northeastern Univ, 69-70. *Mem:* Am Phys Soc; Soc Photog Sci & Eng; Nat Security Indust Asn. *Mailing Add:* Dept of Optom Univ of Ala Med Ctr Birmingham AL 35294

ROSENBLUTH, JACK, b New York, NY, Nov 8, 30; m 60; c 3. CYTOLOGY. *Educ:* Columbia Univ, AB, 52; NY Univ, MD, 56. *Prof Exp:* Intern & asst resident med, Bellevue Hosp, New York, 56-58; Nat Found fel, Nat Inst Neurol Dis & Blindness, 58-59, sr asst surgeon, 59-61; USPHS spec fel, Med Ctr, Univ Calif, San Francisco, 61-62; instr anat, Harvard Med Sch, 62-63; asst prof, Albert Einstein Col Med, 63-66; assoc prof, 66-71, PROF PHYSIOL, SCH MED, NY UNIV, 71- *Concurrent Pos:* Mem, Neurol Study Sect B, NIH, 79-; vis prof, Univ London, 81-82. *Mem:* AAAS; Am Asn Anatomists; Soc Neurosci; Am Soc Cell Biol. *Res:* Comparative cytology and physiology of nerve and muscle tissues; neurobiology. *Mailing Add:* Dept Physiol Sch Med NY Univ New York NY 10016

ROSENBLUTH, MARSHALL N, b Albany, NY, Feb 5, 27; m 51; c 2. THEORETICAL PHYSICS. *Educ:* Harvard Univ, BS, 45; Univ Chicago, PhD, 49. *Prof Exp:* Instr physics, Stanford Univ, 49-50; mem staff, Los Alamos Sci Lab, Univ Calif, 50-56; sr res adv, Gen Dynamics Corp, 56-60; prof physics, Univ Calif, San Diego, 60-67; vis prof astrophys sci, Sch Natural Sci, Inst Advan Study, Princeton Univ, 67-80, vis res physicist, Plasma Physics Lab, 67-80; WITH INST FUSION STUDIES, UNIV TEX, 80- *Mem:* Nat Acad Sci; fel Am Phys Soc. *Res:* Physics of plasmas. *Mailing Add:* Inst Fusion Studies Univ Tex Austin TX 78712

ROSENBLUTH, SIDNEY ALAN, b Deport, Tex, Nov 20, 33; m 62; c 2. PHARMACY. *Educ:* Univ Okla, BS, 55; Univ Tex, MS, 62, PhD(pharm), 66. *Prof Exp:* Pharmacist, Swindle Pharm, Tex, 55-56; hosp pharm resident, Med Ctr Pharm Serv, Univ Ark, 60-61; exchange pharmacist, Univ Hosp Pharm, Copenhagen, 61-62; res assoc, Drug-Plastic Res & Toxicol Lab, Univ Tex, 62-66; res fel, Univ Bath, 66; from asst prof to assoc prof pharmaceut, Col Pharm, Univ Tenn, Memphis, 66-71, prof, 71-75, asst dean clin affairs & chief clin pharm, 73-75, asst dean student affairs, 75-79, assoc dean, 79-81; PROF & DEAN, SCH PHARM, WVA UNIV, 81- *Concurrent Pos:* Mead Johnson Labs res grant pharm, 68-69; NIMH res grant & prin investr, 71-73, 76-79, 78-82; Am Cancer Soc, Tenn Div & Regional Med Prog, res grant & prin investr, 73-75; Vet Admin, training grant & prin investr, 74-78; NIMH, training grant & prin investr, 74-78; NIH Bur Health Manpower Educ, res grant & prin investr, 75-78; training grant & prin investr, NIMH, 76-80 & 78-82 & Dept Educ, 80-83. *Mem:* AAAS; Am Acad Pharmaceut Sci; Tissue Cult Asn; NY Acad Sci. *Res:* Use of tissue cultures in investigations of pharmacological and toxicological actions of drugs and chemicals; development and evaluation of new roles and education units for pharmacists in health care delivery. *Mailing Add:* Sch Pharm Med Ctr WVa Univ Morgantown WV 26506

ROSENBROOK, WILLIAM, JR, b Omaha, Nebr, Mar 28, 38; m 69; c 2. ORGANIC CHEMISTRY. *Educ:* Univ Omaha, BA, 60; Mont State Univ, PhD(org chem), 64. *Prof Exp:* Fel, Univ Calif, Berkeley, 64-65; sr res chemist, Dept Biochem Res, 65-70 & Dept Microbial Chem, 70-74, SR RES CHEMIST, DEPT CHEM RES, ABBOTT LABS, 74- *Mem:* AAAS; Am Chem Soc. *Res:* Natural products chemistry; isolation, characterization and modification of biologically active microbial products. *Mailing Add:* Dept Chem Res Abbott Labs North Chicago IL 60064

ROSENBURG, DALE WEAVER, b Hannibal, Mo, Dec 2, 27; m 54; c 3. ORGANIC CHEMISTRY. *Educ:* Culver-Stockton Col, AB, 50; Univ Mo, AM, 51, PhD(org chem), 58. *Prof Exp:* Jr chemist, Merck & Co, Inc, NJ, 51-55, chemist, Pa, 58-60, sr chemist & sect leader process develop org chem, Va, 60-64, sect leader process res org chem, NJ, 64-66; from asst prof to assoc prof, 66-73, PROF CHEM, NORTHWEST MO STATE UNIV, 73- *Mem:* Am Chem Soc. *Res:* Process research and development in the synthesis and manufacture of organic compounds of biological interest. *Mailing Add:* Dept of Chem Northwest Mo State Univ Maryville MO 64468

ROSENCRANS, STEVEN I, b Brooklyn, NY, Mar 13, 38; m 67; c 2. MATHEMATICS. *Educ:* Mass Inst Technol, SB, 60, ScD(math), 64. *Prof Exp:* Instr math, Mass Inst Technol, 64-65; from asst prof to assoc prof, 65-75, PROF MATH, TULANE UNIV, 75. *Concurrent Pos:* Vis assoc prof, Univ NMex, 71-72. *Res:* Mathematical physics; partial differential equations; stochastic processes. *Mailing Add:* Dept Math Tulane Univ New Orleans LA 70118

ROSENCWAIG, ALLAN, b Poland, Jan 1, 41; US citizen. PHYSICS. *Educ:* Univ Toronto, BASc, 63, MA, 65, PhD(physics), 69. *Prof Exp:* Mem tech staff solid state res, Bell Labs, 69-76; sr scientist, Gilford Instrument Labs, 76-77; physicist, Lawrence Livermore Labs, 77-82; PRES, THERMA-WAVE INC, 82- *Concurrent Pos:* Ed, J Photoacoust. *Mem:* Am Chem Soc; Am Optical Soc; Mem: Am Phys Soc. *Res:* Thermal-wave imaging; photoacoustics. *Mailing Add:* Therma-Wave Inc 47734 Westinghouse Dr Fremont CA 94539

ROSENDAHL, GOTTFRIED R, b Borna, Ger, Mar 25, 11; nat US; m 39; c 4. OPTICS. *Educ:* Dresden Tech, Dipl Eng, 35, Dr Eng, 38; Johns Hopkins Univ, MA, 36. *Prof Exp:* Res asst, Dresden Tech, 38-40; head optics lab, E Leitz, Inc, Ger, 40-42, sr scientist, Peenemuende, Ger, 43-46; head optics lab, E Leitz, Inc, 46-53; consult physics, Air Defense Command, Holloman AFB, NMex, 53-54; tech dir, E Leitz, Inc, NY, 54-57; sr scientist, Ball Bros Res Corp, Colo, 58-60, Gen Elec Co, 60-62, Fed Lab, Int Tel & Tel Corp, 63-64 & Link Group, Gen Precision, Inc, NY, 64-67; res physicist, Naval Training Equip Ctr, 67-78; RETIRED. *Concurrent Pos:* Lectr, Univ Pa, 61-62, Exten Ctr, Purdue Univ, 63-64, State Univ NY Binghamton, 66-67 & Univ Cent Fla, 79. *Mem:* Fel Optical Soc Am. *Res:* Physical and geometrical optics; optical systems and instruments; photometry and radiometry; metrology. *Mailing Add:* 2329 Westminster Ct Winter Park FL 32789

ROSENE, CLARENCE JAMES, b Cherokee, Iowa, June 7, 29; m 51; c 2. ORGANIC CHEMISTRY, ANALYTICAL CHEMISTRY. *Educ:* Coe Col, BA, 51. *Prof Exp:* Res chemist, Reynolds Metals Co, 56-57; res chemist, 58-60, group leader anal chem, 61-67, area supvr, 68-76, head, Res Div, 76-79, RES SCIENTIST, BROWN & WILLIAMSON TOBACCO CORP, 80- *Mem:* AAAS; Am Chem Soc; Am Inst Chemists. *Res:* Absorption and nuclear magnetic resonance spectroscopy; analytical methods for cigarette smoke research. *Mailing Add:* Brown & Williamson Tobacco Corp PO Box 539 Louisville KY 40201

ROSENE, HILDA FLORENCE (MRS E J LUND), electrophysiology, see previous edition

ROSENE, ROBERT BERNARD, b Novelty, Wash, Sept 1, 23; m 47; c 6. ORGANIC CHEMISTRY. *Educ:* Whittier Col, AB, 44; Purdue Univ, PhD(chem), 51. *Prof Exp:* Asst instr chem, Purdue Univ, 47-50; res chemist, Plantation Div, US Rubber Co, 50-52; lab group leader, Dowell, Inc, 52-54, lab dir, Dowell Div, Dow Chem Co, Tulsa, 54-74, HYDROCARBONS BUS MGR, DOW CHEM USA, 74- *Mem:* Am Inst Mining, Metall & Petrol Eng. *Res:* Action of nitric oxide on ketones; emulsions; corrosion; gels; plastics; surfactants. *Mailing Add:* PO Box 150 Plaguermine LA 70764

ROSENE, WALTER, JR, b Ogden, Iowa, May 15, 12; m 37; c 2. WILDLIFE ECOLOGY, WILDLIFE MANAGEMENT. *Educ:* Iowa State Univ, BS, 34; Auburn Univ, MS, 37. *Prof Exp:* Game technician, Iowa State Planning Bd, 34-35; technician, Ala State Conserv Comn, 38; proj biologist, Soil Conserv Serv, USDA, 38-39, area biologist, 39-40, conservationist, 40-46; biologist, US Fish & Wildlife Serv, 46-69; CONSULT WILDLIFE MGT, 69- *Concurrent Pos:* Spec writing proj, NAm Wildlife Found, 64-70; vis prof, Miss State Univ, 78. *Mem:* Wildlife Soc. *Res:* Ecology and population dynamics of the bobwhite quail and mourning dove in the southeast; evaluation of introduced plants in wildlife management; evaluation of effects of insecticides on wildlife. *Mailing Add:* 127 Oak Circle Gadsden AL 35901

ROSENFELD, ARTHUR H, b Birmingham, Ala, June 22, 26; m 55; c 3. NUCLEAR PHYSICS. *Educ:* Va Polytech Univ, BS, 44; Univ Chicago, PhD(physics), 54. *Prof Exp:* Res assoc, Inst Nuclear Studies, Univ Chicago, 54-55; from asst prof to assoc prof, 57-63, actg chmn dept comput sci, 67-68, PROF PHYSICS, UNIV CALIF, BERKELEY, 63-, RES ASSOC, LAWRENCE BERKELEY LAB, 56-, DIR PARTICLE DATA GROUP, 64-, LEADER RES GROUP A, 71- *Concurrent Pos:* Mem comt uses comput, Nat Acad Sci-Nat Res Coun, 62-65 & statist data panel, Physics Surv Comt, 70-; mem panel univ comput facil, NSF, 63-66, chmn, 65-66, chief investr, Univ Comput Facil Grant, 70-; mem subpanel B, High Energy Physics Adv Panel, AEC, 67-69; mem physics info comt, Am Inst Physics, 69-71. *Mem:* Fel Am Phys Soc; Fedn Am Sci. *Res:* Physics of elementary particles; use of digital computers to process data. *Mailing Add:* Dept of Physics Univ of Calif Berkeley CA 94720

ROSENFELD, AZRIEL, b New York, NY, Feb 19, 31; m 59; c 3. COMPUTER SCIENCE. *Educ:* Yeshiva Univ, BA, 50, MHL, 53, MS, 54, DHL, 55; Columbia Univ, MA, 51, PhD(math), 57. *Prof Exp:* Physicist, Fairchild Controls Corp, 54-56; engr, Ford Instrument Co, 56-59; mgr res, Budd Electronics, Inc, 59-64; RES PROF COMPUT SCI, UNIV MD, COLLEGE PARK, 64- *Concurrent Pos:* Vis asst prof, Grad Sch Math, Yeshiva Univ, 58-63. *Mem:* Math Asn Am, fel Inst Elec & Electronics Engrs; Asn Comput Mach. *Res:* Computer processing of pictorial information. *Mailing Add:* 847 Loxford Terr Silver Spring MD 20901

ROSENFELD, DANIEL, b Brooklyn, NY, May 7, 33; m 57; c 2. PETROLEUM CHEMISTRY. *Educ:* Brooklyn Col, BS, 55; Univ Pa, MS, 57, PhD(org chem), 61. *Prof Exp:* Res chemist, Esso Res & Eng Co, 60-66, sr res chemist, 66-71, res assoc, 71-72, head aromatics tech serv, 72-79, HEAD, AROMATICS LAB, EXXON CHEM CO, 79- *Mem:* Am Chem Soc. *Res:* Synthesis of solid rocket propellants; reactions in aprotic solvents; synthesis and screening of agricultural pesticides; process development; ketone solvents; hydotreating desulphurization studies; catalyst evaluations; zeolite adsorption. *Mailing Add:* Exxon Chem Co PO Box 4900 Baytown TX 77520

ROSENFELD, GEORGE, b Cambridge, Mass, Nov 6, 19; m 59. BIOCHEMISTRY, MEDICAL RESEARCH. *Educ:* Mass Inst Technol, BS, 40, MS, 41; Geogetown Univ, PhD(biochem), 52. *Prof Exp:* Asst chemist, Mass State Dept Pub Health, 41-42; asst toxicologist, Med Res Div, US War Dept, 42; mem staff, Med Sch, Cornell Univ, 43-46; officer-in-chg, Navy Chem Warfare Sch, Calif, 46-50 & Naval Med Res Inst, 50-57; assoc res physiologist, Univ Calif, Berkeley, 57-60, res biochemist, 60-63; BIOMED CONSULT, 64- *Honors & Awards:* Res Commendation, US Navy, 56. *Mem:* Endocrine Soc; Am Physiol Soc; Sigma Xi; fel AAAS. *Res:* Stress physiology; endocrinopathy; acute and chronic alcoholism; neurohormones; radiation medicine. *Mailing Add:* 50 Vista Del Mar Ct Oakland CA 94611

ROSENFELD, IRENE, b Austria-Hungary, Oct 13, 08; US citizen. TOXICOLOGY, PATHOLOGICAL PHYSIOLOGY. *Educ:* Ohio State Univ, BS, 35, MS, 36, PhD(path), 42. *Prof Exp:* Asst, Ohio State Univ, 35-36, 38-40, instr path, 42; instr, Mt Sinai Hosp, Chicago, 36-38; from asst prof to prof biochem, 42-67, pharmacologist, 50-67, EMER PROF BIOCHEM, UNIV WYO, 67-, CONSULT, 69- *Concurrent Pos:* Res fels, AEC, 48-49 & Nat Inst Res, 56-57. *Mem:* AAAS; Soc Exp Biol & Med; Am Soc Biol Chem; NY Acad Sci. *Res:* Pathological and biochemical changes produced by various poisonous substances in the tissues. *Mailing Add:* 5966 Whitman Rd Columbus OH 43213

ROSENFELD, JACK LEE, b Pittsburgh, Pa, June 6, 35; m 69; c 2. COMPUTER SCIENCE, OFFICE AUTOMATION & MICROPROCESSOR SYSTEMS. *Educ:* Mass Inst Technol, SB & SM, 57, ScD(elec eng), 61. *Prof Exp:* RES STAFF MEM COMPUT SCI, T J WATSON RES CTR, IBM CORP, 61- *Concurrent Pos:* Adj prof, Columbia Univ, 65-72. *Honors & Awards:* Silver Core, Int Fedn Info Processing, 77. *Mem:* Asn Comput Mach; Inst Elec & Electronics Engrs. *Res:* Computer architecture; office automation; microprocessor system design; parallel processing; distributed systems. *Mailing Add:* IBM Res Ctr PO Box 218 Yorktown Heights NY 10598

ROSENFELD, JEROLD CHARLES, b New Haven, Conn, Apr 13, 43; m 67; c 2. ORGANIC CHEMISTRY, POLYMER CHEMISTRY. *Educ:* Clark Univ, BA, 65; Yale Univ, PhD(chem), 70. *Prof Exp:* SR RES CHEMIST, HOOKER CHEM CORP DIV, OCCIDENTAL PETROL CORP, GRAND ISLAND, 70- *Mem:* Am Chem Soc. *Res:* Preparation of non-burning and high temperature plastics. *Mailing Add:* 18 Willow Green Dr Tonawanda NY 14150

ROSENFELD, JOHN L, b Portland, Ore, July 14, 20; m 43; c 2. GEOLOGY. *Educ:* Dartmouth Col, AB, 42; Harvard Univ, AM, 49, PhD(geol), 54. *Prof Exp:* Asst prof geol, Mo Sch Mines, 49-55; vis asst prof, Wesleyan Univ, 55-57; from asst prof to assoc prof, 57-70, PROF GEOL, UNIV CALIF, LOS ANGELES, 70- *Concurrent Pos:* Guggenheim fel, 63; res assoc, Harvard Univ, 71-72. *Mem:* AAAS; fel Geol Soc Am; fel Mineral Soc Am; Am Geophys Union. *Res:* Structure, petrology and stratigraphy of metamorphic rocks in western New England; application of physical and chemical properties of minerals to petrology; structural petrology; solid inclusion piezothermometry. *Mailing Add:* 2401 Arbutus Dr Los Angeles CA 90049

ROSENFELD, LEONARD M, b Philadelphia, Pa, June 28, 38; m 62; c 3. PHYSIOLOGY, BIOCHEMISTRY. *Educ:* Univ Pa, AB, 59; Jefferson Med Col, PhD(physiol), 64. *Prof Exp:* Instr physiol, Jefferson Med Col, 64-68, physiol coordr, Sch Nursing, Col Allied Health Sci, 74-75, physiol coorder, Jefferson Med Col, 75-80, coordr, Struct & Function Course Anat & Physiol, 77-79, ASST PROF PHYSIOL, JEFFERSON MED COL, THOMAS JEFFERSON UNIV, 68- *Concurrent Pos:* Vis lectr, Pa State Univ, Ogontz Campus, 69-71, vis prof, 71-74. *Mem:* AAAS; Soc Exp Biol & Med; Am Physiol Soc; Sigma Xi. *Res:* Electrolyte interactions in metabolic systems; factors influencing the phosphatase enzyme system; environmental biology; biological effects of air pollution; acute biochemical changes following myocardial infarction; intestinal integrity; alteration in intestinal blood flow; malnutrition. *Mailing Add:* Dept Physiol Jefferson Med Col 1020 Locust St Philadelphia PA 19107

ROSENFELD, LEONARD SIDNEY, b New York, NY, Aug 30, 13; m 42; c 1. MEDICINE, PUBLIC HEALTH. *Educ:* NY Univ, BS, 33, MD, 37; Johns Hopkins Univ, MPH, 42. *Prof Exp:* Res asst, Col Med, NY Univ, 40; chief field party, Inst Inter-Am Affairs, 42-46; dir regional health serv & Sask Hosp Serv, Can, 46-48; co-dir study regional orgn, Sch Pub Health, Columbia Univ, 54; dir med care eval studies, United Community Serv, Boston, Mass, 54-57; assoc dir, Community Health Asn, Detroit, Mich, 57-60; gen dir, Metrop Hosp, 60-65; mem staff, Hosp Rev & Planning Coun Southern NY, 65-70; prof community & prev med & vpres planning, New York Med Col, 70-73; PROF PUB HEALTH ADMIN, SCH PUB HEALTH, UNIV NC, CHAPEL HILL, 73- *Concurrent Pos:* Rockefeller Found spec fel, 46; lectr, Sch Hyg, Johns Hopkins Univ, 49-53; consult, Venezuelan Dept Health & Welfare, 51-52, NIH, 62-66, Latin-Am Sci Bd, Nat Acad Sci, 64-65, PR Dept Pub Health, 66- & Nat Ctr Health Servs Res & Develop, 67-71. *Honors & Awards:* Distinguished Serv Medal, Nicaragua, 45. *Mem:* NY Acad Med; Int Epidemiological Asn; Am Pub Health Asn; Am Hosp Asn. *Res:* Epidemiology; measurement of values of public health effort and research into the distribution of illness and medical care among various socioeconomic groups; medical administration. *Mailing Add:* Dept Health Admin Univ NC Sch Pub Health Chapel Hill NC 27514

ROSENFELD, LOUIS, b Brooklyn, NY, Apr 8, 25. BIOCHEMISTRY. *Educ:* City Col New York, BS, 46; Ohio State Univ, MS, 48, PhD(physiol chem), 52. *Prof Exp:* Asst instr physiol chem, Ohio State Univ, 52; res assoc biochem, Univ Va, 52-53; biochemist, Wayne County Gen Hosp, 54-56 & Beth-El Hosp, 56-61; asst prof, 61-67, dir chem, Univ Hosp, 61-73, ASSOC PROF CLIN PATH, MED CTR, NY UNIV, 67-, DIR SPEC CHEM, UNIV HOSP, 73- *Concurrent Pos:* Instr sci, Rutgers Univ, Newark, 57-63. *Mem:* AAAS; Am Soc Clin Pathologists; Asn Clin Sci; Nat Acad Clin Biochem; Am Asn Clin Chemists; NY Acad Sci. *Res:* Fibrinogen; plasma coagulation; heparin; electrophoresis; protein analysis. glycosaminoglycans; history of chemistry. *Mailing Add:* Dept Path 560 First Ave NY Univ Med Ctr New York NY 10016

ROSENFELD, MARTIN HERBERT, b Rockaway Beach, NY, May 30, 26; m 52; c 2. MICROBIOLOGY, CLINICAL BIOCHEMISTRY. *Educ:* Brooklyn Col, BA, 50; St John's Univ, MS, 62, PhD(microbiol), 72; Nat Registry Microbiologists, registered, 65. *Prof Exp:* Supvr labs, A Angrist, 50-55 & Horace Harding Hosp, 55-60; lab adminr, Montefiore-Morrisania Hosp Affil, 63-70; assoc prof, 70-74, chmn div diag progs, 70-77, PROF MED TECHNOL, SCH ALLIED HEALTH PROF, STATE UNIV NY, STONY BROOK, 74-, CHMN DEPT MED TECHNOL, 70-, ASST DEAN GRAD PROGS, 73- *Concurrent Pos:* Mem & chmn nat comt instnl orgn, Asn Schs Allied Health Prof, 71-74; mem sci lab technol adv comt, State Univ NY Agr & Tech Col, Cobleskill, 71-; mem med technol adv comt, Sch Allied Health Prof, Univ Lowell, 75-; mem bd adv, NY City Dept Lab Supvrs, 79-, mem, Nat Acad Clin Biochem, 81-; med technologist, Am Soc Clin Pathologists, 52-; clin lab scientist, Nat Cert Agency Med Lab Personnel, 79- *Mem:* Am Asn Clin Chem; NY Acad Sci; Am Soc Microbiol; Am Asn Bioanalysts; Am Inst Biol Sci. *Res:* Detection of microorganisms and quantitative assay of blood constituents by automated chemiluminescent technique; ratios by intra-red spectroscopy. *Mailing Add:* Div of Diag Progs State Univ of NY Health Sci Ctr Stony Brook NY 11790

ROSENFELD, MELVIN, b New York, NY, Apr 19, 34; m 57; c 1. MATHEMATICS. *Educ:* Univ Calif, Los Angeles, BA, 56, MA, 62, PhD(math), 63. *Prof Exp:* Lectr math, Univ Calif, Los Angeles, 63-64; from lectr to asst prof, 64-70, ASSOC PROF MATH, UNIV CALIF, SANTA BARBARA, 70- *Concurrent Pos:* NSF grant, 66-67. *Mem:* Am Math Soc; Math Asn Am. *Res:* Functional analysis. *Mailing Add:* Dept of Math Univ of Calif Santa Barbara CA 93106

ROSENFELD, MELVIN ARTHUR, b Chicago, Ill, Dec 26, 18; m 46; c 2. SEDIMENTOLOGY, ACADEMIC ADMINISTRATION. *Educ:* Univ Chicago, BS, 40; Pa State Univ, MS, 50, PhD(sedimentology, statist), 53. *Prof Exp:* Instr & map draftsman, Univ Chicago, 40-42, instr map interpretation, 46; petrol geologist, H D Hadley & I E Stewart, Consult, 46-47; from res asst to res assoc sedimentary petrog, Pa State Univ, 47-53; sr res geologist, Field Res Labs, Magnolia Petrol Co, 53-57; dir explor res div, Pure Oil Co, 57-65, leader corp model opers res team, 64-65; sr scientist & mgr info processing ctr, Woods Hole Oceanog Inst, 65-81; RETIRED. *Concurrent Pos:* Mem data mgt panel, Comt Oceanog, Nat Acad Sci, 67-71; chmn panel info handling, Joint Oceanog Inst Deep Earth Sampling Proj, 68-; mem US deleg, Working Group Int Exchange Oceanog Data, Int Oceanog Comn, Rome, 71. *Mem:* AAAS; Sigma Xi. *Res:* Application of statistics and computers to geology and oceanography. *Mailing Add:* PO Box 758 Damariscotta MA 04543

ROSENFELD, NORMAN SAMUEL, b New York, NY, July 21, 34; m; c 2. MATHEMATICS. *Educ:* Yeshiva Univ, BA, 54; Univ Syracuse, MA, 56; Yale Univ, PhD(math), 59. *Prof Exp:* Res asst, Yale Univ, 57-58; lectr, City Col New York, 58-59; asst res scientist, Courant Inst Math Sci, NY Univ, 59-61; from asst prof to assoc prof, NY Univ, 61-68; assoc prof, 68-79, PROF MATH, BELFER GRAD SCH, YESHIVA UNIV, 80-, DEAN COL, 80- *Concurrent Pos:* Vis asst prof, Belfer Grad Sch Sci, Yeshiva Univ, 60-61. *Mem:* Am Math Soc; Math Asn Am. *Res:* Functional analysis. *Mailing Add:* Yeshiva Univ 500 W 185th St New York NY 10033

ROSENFELD, ROBERT L, b New York, NY, Aug 6, 37; m 59; c 2. APPLIED MECHANICS, COMPUTER SCIENCE. *Educ:* Mass Inst Technol, SB, 59; Calif Inst Technol, PhD(appl mech), 62. *Prof Exp:* Engr, Components Div, IBM Corp, 62-64; mem tech staff, RCA Labs, 64-69; mgr applns dept, Appl Logic Corp, 69-70; staff analyst, Computer Servs Dept, 70-74, reliability & performance adminr elec prod, 74-81, NUCLEAR PLANNING ADMINR NUCLEAR OPERS, CONSUMERS POWER CO, 81- *Mem:* Am Soc Mech Engrs; Inst Elec & Electronics Engrs; Asn Comput Mach. *Mailing Add:* Prod & Transmission Dept Consumers Power Co Jackson MI 49201

ROSENFELD, ROBERT SAMSON, b Richmond, Va, June 24, 21; m 44; c 3. BIOCHEMISTRY. *Educ:* Univ Pittsburgh, PhD(chem), 50. *Prof Exp:* Asst prof biochem, Sloan-Kettering Div, Med Col, Cornell Univ, 50-63; INVESTR, INST STEROID RES, MONTEFIORE HOSP & MED CTR, 63-; PROF BIOCHEM, ALBERT EINSTEIN COL MED, 72- *Concurrent Pos:* Asst, Sloan-Kettering Inst Cancer Res, 50-56, assoc mem, 56-63. *Mem:* Am Chem Soc; Endocrine Soc; Am Heart Asn. *Res:* Steroid chemistry. *Mailing Add:* Inst of Steroid Res Montefiore Hosp & Med Ctr Bronx NY 10467

ROSENFELD, SHELDON, b New York, NY, Dec 28, 21; m 53; c 4. PHYSIOLOGY. *Educ:* Middlesex Sch Vet Med, DVM, 45; Brooklyn Col, BA, 48; Univ Calif, MS, 55; Univ Southern Calif, PhD(physiol), 64. *Prof Exp:* Asst med, Med Col, Cornell Univ, 46-48; res assoc aviation med, Sch Med, Univ Southern Calif, 48-50, instr & res assoc physiol, 50-53, asst prof, 50-53; SR RES ASSOC, CEDARSSINAI MED RES INST, MT SINAI HOSP, 53- *Mem:* Am Physiol Soc; Am Heart Asn; Soc Exp Biol & Med; Int Soc Nephrology; Am Soc Nephrology. *Res:* Renal physiology; hypertension. *Mailing Add:* Cedars-Sinai Med Res Inst Mt Sinai Hosp Los Angeles CA 90048

ROSENFELD, STEPHEN I, b New York, NY, May 8, 39; m 60; c 2. IMMUNOLOGY. *Educ:* Univ Rochester, BA, 59, MD, 63. *Prof Exp:* Instr med, Sch Med, Boston Univ, 70-72; asst prof, 72-78, ASSOC PROF MED, SCH MED, UNIV ROCHESTER, 78- *Mem:* Am Acad Allergy; Am Fedn Clin Res; Am Rheumatism Asn. *Res:* Biological functions and genetics of the human complement system; clinical immunology. *Mailing Add:* Univ of Rochester Med Ctr 601 Elmwood Ave Rochester NY 14642

ROSENFELD, STUART MICHAEL, b New Haven, Conn, Jan 28, 48. PHYSICAL ORGANIC CHEMISTRY. *Educ:* Colby Col, BA, 69; Brown Univ, PhD(org chem), 73. *Prof Exp:* Fel chem, Dept Chem, Brandeis Univ, 72-73 & Dyson Perrins Lab, Oxford Univ, 73-74; asst prof, Dept Chem, Univ RI, 75-77 & Univ Mass, 77-78; asst prof chem, Brandeis Univ, 78-79; ASST

PROF CHEM, WELLESLEY COL, 79- *Res:* Mechanistic studies of free radical reactions; observation and study of transient intermediates formed during chemical reactions; synthesis and structural studies of spirocyclopropyl compounds and B-keto acids. *Mailing Add:* Dept Chem Wellesley Col Wellesley MA 02181

ROSENFIELD, ALAN R(OBERT), b Chelsea, Mass, Sept 7, 31; m 60; c 2. FRACTURE MECHANICS. *Educ:* Mass Inst Technol, SB, 53, SM, 55, ScD, 59. *Prof Exp:* Metallurgist, Mass Inst Technol, 59-61; fel metall, Univ Liverpool, 61-62; SR SCIENTIST, BATTELLE MEM INST, 62- *Concurrent Pos:* Consult, Open Univ, 74. *Mem:* Am Soc Metals; Am Inst Mining, Metall & Petrol Engrs; Iron & Steel Inst Japan; Am Soc Testing & Mat. *Res:* Fracture mechanics; physical metallurgy; experimental and analytical studies of fracture resistance of engineering materials, principally steels and ceramics; relations between strength and microstructure; advanced techniques to measure strength and toughness. *Mailing Add:* Battelle Mem Inst 505 King Ave Columbus OH 43212

ROSENFIELD, CHRISTINE ANN CULP, b Lansing, Mich, May 6, 36; m 57. AGRICULTURAL CHEMISTRY. *Educ:* Univ Mich, BS, 57; Univ Alta, PhD(chem), 60. *Prof Exp:* Teaching asst chem, Univ Alta, 57-59; res chemist, Dow Chem Co, 60-68; agr field officer, 68-75, OFFICER-IN-CHG, FOOD & AGR ORGN, UN, 75- *Concurrent Pos:* Abstractor, Chem Abstr, 60- *Mem:* Am Chem Soc. *Res:* Pesticide formulation and specifications; catalytic decomposition of pesticides; particle sizing; surface phenomena. *Mailing Add:* PO Box 99 Clarkston MI 48016

ROSENFIELD, DANIEL, b Philadelphia, Pa, Jan 3, 32; m 71. NUTRITION. *Educ:* Univ Mass, BS, 53; Rutgers Univ, MS, 55, PhD(food sci, biochem), 59. *Prof Exp:* Dir quality control & res, Engelhorn Meat Packing Co, 59-60; sr food technologist, Gen Foods Tech Ctr, 60-62; group leader food proteins & plant physiol, Union Carbide Res Inst, 62-68; dep dir nutrit & agribus group, USDA, 68-71, dir nutrit & tech serv, staff, Food & Nutrit Serv, 71-73; dir nutrit affairs, Miles Labs Inc, 73-79; DIR SCI AFFAIRS, M&M/MARS, 79- *Concurrent Pos:* Sr food technologist, Off Tech Coop & Res, US AID, 65-67; US deleg workshop food, US Nat Acad Sci-Indonesian Inst Sci, 68; mem new foods panel, White House Conf Food, Nutrit & Health, 69; partic workshop prepare guidelines nat prog food enrichment & fortification, Pan Am Health Orgn, 71; mem, World Soy Protein Conf, 73 & Xth Int Cong Nutrit, 75; adj prof nutrit, Sch Med, Ind Univ, 78- *Mem:* AAAS; Inst Food Technologists; Am Chem Soc; Am Asn Cereal Chemists; Soc Nutrit Educ. *Res:* Nutritional equivalency of new food analogs; technology of fortification and fabrication of protein foods; availability of food nutrients effectiveness of dietary supplements; relationship of diets to illness. *Mailing Add:* M&M/Mars High St Hockettstown NJ 07840

ROSENFIELD, JOAN SAMOUR, b Boston, Mass, Aug 12, 39. ATMOSPHERIC CHEMISTRY, PHYSICS. *Educ:* Brandeis Univ, AB, 61; Univ Minn, Minneapolis, PhD(phys chem), 69. *Prof Exp:* Res asst chem, Children's Cancer Res Found, Boston, 61-62; res specialist phys chem, Univ Minn, Minneapolis, 69-71, teaching fel, 71-72; staff fel physics, Nat Inst Arthritis, Metab & Digestive Dis, 73-77; SCI PROGRAMMER & ANALYST, SIGMA DATA SERV, NASA GODDARD SPACE FLIGHT CTR, 77- *Honors & Awards:* Eastman Kodak Sci Award, 65-66. *Mem:* Am Chem Soc; Am Phys Soc; AAAS. *Res:* Atmospheric radiation; theoretical chemistry; electronic structue of molecules; optical activity. *Mailing Add:* Apt T-1 8461 Greenbelt Rd Greenbelt MD 20770

ROSENFIELD, RICHARD ERNEST, b Pittsburgh, Pa, Apr 7, 15; m 44; c 2. HEMATOLOGY, IMMUNOLOGY. *Educ:* Univ Pittsburgh, BS, 36, MD, 40. *Prof Exp:* Resident hemat, Mt Sinai Hosp, 47-48, res asst, 48-51, clin asst, Outpatient Dept, Med Div, Hemat Clin, 48-53, res asst med, Blood Bank, 51-53, asst hematologist, 53-57, assoc hematologist, 57-61, dir, Blood Bank, 57-80, prof med, Mt Sinai Sch Med, 66-71, ATTEND HEMATOLOGIST, MT SINAI HOSP, 61-, EMER DIR, DEPT BLOOD BANK & CLIN MICROS, 81-, PROF PATH, MT SINAI SCH MED, 72-, PROF MED, 79- *Concurrent Pos:* Asst physician, Willard Parker Hosp, New York, 50-56; NIH res fel ABO erythroblastosis, Mt Sinai Hosp, New York, 59-70, NIH blood bank dirs training fel, 62-77, NIH contract hepatitis, New York & Boston, 72-73; ed-in-chief, Transfusion, Am Asn Blood Banks, 67-71. *Honors & Awards:* Landsteiner Award, Am Asn Blood Banks; Philip Levine Award, Am Soc Clin Pathologists, 75. *Mem:* Am Asn Immunologists; Am Soc Clin Pathologists; Int Soc Hemat; Int Soc Blood Transfusion; NY Acad Sci. *Res:* Study, largely immunochemical, of human blood types and the clinical significance of allogeneic immune responses. *Mailing Add:* Dept of Blood Bank & Clin Micros Mt Sinai Hosp New York NY 10029

ROSENFIELD, ROBERT LEE, b Robinson, Ill, Dec 16, 34. PEDIATRIC ENDOCRINOLOGY. *Educ:* Northwestern Univ, Evanston, BA, 56; Northwestern Univ, Chicago, MD, 60. *Prof Exp:* Intern, Philadelphia Gen Hosp, 60-61; resident pediat, Children's Hosp Philadelphia, 61-63; instr, Med Sch, Univ Pa, 65-68; asst prof to assoc prof, 68-78, PROF PEDIAT & MED, MED SCH, UNIV CHICAGO, 78- *Concurrent Pos:* USPHS trainee, Children's Hosp Philadelphia, 65-68; Fogarty sr int fel, 77- *Mem:* Endocrine Soc; Soc Pediat Res; Am Pediat Soc; Soc Gynec Invest. *Res:* Androgen physiology; reproductive endocrinology; growth disorders. *Mailing Add:* Dept of Pediat Univ of Chicago Med Sch Chicago IL 60637

ROSENGREN, JACK WHITEHEAD, b Chula Vista, Calif, Oct 2, 26; m 49; c 2. PHYSICS. *Educ:* Univ Calif, AB, 48, PhD(physics), 52. *Prof Exp:* Physicist, Radiation Lab, Univ Calif, 48-52; from instr to asst prof physics, Mass Inst Technol, 52-55; head reactor physics sect, Missile Systs Div, Lockheed Aircraft Corp, 55-57; staff physicist, Aeronutronic Systs, Inc, Ford Motor Co, 57; physicist, Lawrence Livermore Lab, Univ Calif, 57-63, head large weapons physics div, 63-64, assoc dir nuclear design, 64-67 & spec projs, 67-72; dep dir sci & technol, Defense Nuclear Agency, 72-74; SR PHYSICIST, R&D ASSOCS, 74- *Concurrent Pos:* Mem, Polaris Re-entry Body Coord Comt, 58-60; mem Mark 11 re-entry vehicle joint working group, US Air Force, 60-63, penetration prog panel, Ballistic Systs Div, 62-64 & ballistic missile re-entry systs consult group, 66-68; mem sci adv comt, Defense Intel Agency, 65-71; mem sci adv panel, US Army, 66-68, consult, 68-70; assoc ed, J Defense Res, 67-70; mem defense sci bd, Nuclear Test Detection Task Force, 67-72; mem Bethe Panel, Foreign Weapons Eval Group, 67-72; mem comt sr reviewers, AEC, 69-72 & Energy Res & Develop Admin, 76-77; consult, Tech Eval Panel (classification), Dept Energy, 77- *Mem:* Am Phys Soc. *Res:* Experimental nuclear physics; nuclear weapon effects; nuclear weapon security; nuclear materials safeguards; nuclear weapon requirements studies. *Mailing Add:* R&D Assocs Suite 500 1401 Wilson Blvd Arlington VA 22209

ROSENGREN, JOHN, b Wooster, Ohio, Sept 29, 28; m 55; c 3. FRESHWATER BIOLOGY. *Educ:* Col Wooster, BA, 49; Columbia Univ, MA, 55, EdD, 58. *Prof Exp:* Instr biol, Am Univ Beirut, 49-53; instr, High Sch, 55-58; assoc prof, 59-63, PROF BIOL, WILLIAM PATERSON COL NJ, 64- *Mem:* AAAS; Nat Sci Teachers Asn; Nat Asn Biol Teachers. *Res:* Freshwater Porifera. *Mailing Add:* 332 Eastside Ave Ridgewood NJ 07450

ROSENHEIM, D(ONALD) E(DWIN), b New York, NY, Mar 23, 26; m 58; c 2. ELECTRICAL ENGINEERING. *Educ:* Polytech Inst Brooklyn, BS, 49; Columbia Univ, MS, 57. *Prof Exp:* Develop engr, Servo Corp Am , 49-51; engr, Develop Labs, IBM Corp, 51-53, res staff mem, Thomas J Watson Res Ctr, 53-60, mgr circuits & systs, 60-63, mgr solid state electronics, 63-66, dir appl res, 66-72, asst IBM dir res, 72-73, DIR IBM SAN JOSE RES LAB, IBM CORP, 73- *Concurrent Pos:* Lectr, City Col New York, 55-56 & Columbia Univ, 57-58. *Mem:* Sr mem Inst Elec & Electronics Engrs. *Res:* Digital systems and technology, especially solid state materials, devices and circuits for logic, storage and input/output applications in data processing systems. *Mailing Add:* IBM San Jose Res Lab 5600 Cottle Rd San Jose CA 95193

ROSENHOLTZ, IRA N, b New York, NY, May 14, 45; c 2. TOPOLOGY. *Educ:* Brandeis Univ, BA, 67; Univ Wis, MA & PhD(math), 72. *Prof Exp:* Asst prof math, Grinnell Col, Iowa, 72-73; ASST PROF MATH, UNIV WYO, 73- *Concurrent Pos:* NDEA Title IV fel, Univ Wis, 71-72. *Mem:* Math Asn Am; Am Math Soc. *Res:* Continua; fixed point problems; remetrization. *Mailing Add:* Univ of Wyo Laramie WY 82071

ROSENKILDE, CARL EDWARD, b Yakima, Wash, Mar 16, 37; m 63; c 2. FLUID DYNAMICS, ATMOSPHERIC PHYSICS. *Educ:* Wash State Univ, BS, 59; Univ Chicago, MS, 60, PhD(physics), 66. *Prof Exp:* Fel physics, Argonne Nat Lab, 66-68; asst prof math, NY Univ, 68-70; asst prof physics, 70-76; assoc prof physics, Kans State Univ, 76-79; PHYSICIST, LAWRENCE LIVERMORE NAT LAB, 79- *Concurrent Pos:* Vis scientist, Lawrence Livermore Lab, 77-78. *Mem:* AAAS; Am Astron Soc; Am Phys Soc; Soc Indust & Appl Math; Am Geophys Union. *Res:* Fluid dynamics; aerosol scavenging; atmospheric electrical phenomena; nuclear weapon effects. *Mailing Add:* Lawrence Livermore Nat Lab PO Box 808 Livermore CA 94550

ROSENKRANTZ, HARRIS, b Brooklyn, NY, Mar 23, 22; m 51; c 2. BIOCHEMICAL PHARMACOLOGY. *Educ:* Brooklyn Col, AB, 43; NY Univ, MS, 46; Cornell Univ, MS, 48; Tufts Univ, PhD(physiol), 52. *Prof Exp:* Asst infrared anal of steroids, NY Hosp, 43-46, res assoc biochem, 48-51; res biochemist, Worcester Found Exp Biol, 52-60; DIR BIOCHEM & VPRES, MASON RES INST, EG&G, INC, 60- *Concurrent Pos:* Affil prof, Clark Univ, 59-; adj prof, Sch Vet Med, Tufts Univ, 81- *Mem:* Am Chem Soc; Am Soc Biol Chemists; Endocrine Soc; Am Soc Pharmacol & Exp Therapeut; Soc Toxicol. *Res:* Biochemistry of steroid hormones; vitamin E and muscular dystrophy; infrared spectroscopic analysis of biologically important compounds; biochemistry of the prostate; biochemical pharmacology, toxicology and endocrinology of marihuana, narcotic antagonists, antineoplastic, contraceptive agents and iron chelators. *Mailing Add:* Dept Biochem Mason Res Inst EG&G Inc 57 Union St Worcester MA 01608

ROSENKRANTZ, JACOB ALVIN, b New York, NY, Feb 12, 14; m 36; c 4. MEDICINE, HOSPITAL ADMINISTRATION. *Educ:* City Col New York, BS, 33; Columbia Univ, MA, 34, MD, 38. *Prof Exp:* Res asst, Columbia Univ, 41-42, 46; chief outpatient serv, Bronx Vet Admin Hosp, 47-49, asst chief prof servs, 49-52, attend, Med Serv, 52; chief prof servs, Vet Admin Hosp, East Orange, NJ, 52-56; adminr, Southern Div, Albert Einstein Med Ctr, 56-59; exec dir, Newark Beth Israel Hosp, 59-68; chief, Outpatient Clin, Vet Admin, 71-82. *Concurrent Pos:* Fel, Postgrad Med Sch, NY Univ, 41-42 & 46, asst physician, 41-, instr, 54-; clin assoc prof community & prev med & exec dir & assoc dean hosp admin, New York Med Col Flower & Fifth Ave Hosps, 68-71. *Mem:* Fel Am Geriat Soc; fel Am Pub Health Asn; fel Am Col Physicians; fel Am Col Prev Med; fel Am Col Hosp Adminr. *Res:* Hypertension; galactose and glucose tolerance; arteriosclerosis; infectious mononucleosis; bilateral nephrectomy in rats; potassium and electrocardiograms; thyroid diseases; benign paroxysmal peritonitis; Paget's disease; puperperal sepsis. *Mailing Add:* Outpatient Clin Vet Admin 20 Washington Pl Newark NJ 07102

ROSENKRANTZ, JENS GEORG, b Elsinore, Denmark, Aug 10, 29; m 52; c 3. SURGERY, PHYSIOLOGY. *Educ:* Yale Univ, AB, 49; Harvard Med Sch, MD, 53. *Prof Exp:* From intern to resident surg, Mass Gen Hosp, 53-61; asst prof, Med Ctr, Univ Colo, 62-67, assoc prof surg & asst prof physiol, 67-69; prof surg, Sch Med, Univ Southern Calif, 69-74; surgeon-in-chief, Children's Hosp Los Angeles, 69-74; PROF SURG, UNIV CINCINNATI, 74-; MEM STAFF, CINCINNATI CHILDREN'S HOSP, 74- *Concurrent Pos:* Resident, Children's Hosp Med Ctr, 59-61; mem courtesy staff, Children's Hosp, Denver, 62-66, mem consult staff, 67-69 & Denver Gen Hosp, 67-69; USPHS grants, 66-71; Colo Heart Asn grant, 68-69. *Mem:* AMA; Am Heart Asn; fel Am Col Surg; affil fel Am Acad Pediat; Soc Univ Surg. *Res:* Production of ventricular septal defects in pigs by administration of trypan blue; production of an experimental model for the study of pulmonary hypertension by exposure of the pig to chronic hypoxia and by ligation of a single pulmonary artery in the antenatal or postnatal period. *Mailing Add:* Dept of Surg Children's Hosp Cincinnati OH 45229

ROSENKRANTZ, LAWRENCE JAY, lasers, experimental solid state physics, see previous edition

ROSENKRANZ, EUGEN EMIL, b Wilno, Poland, July 9, 31; US citizen. PLANT PATHOLOGY. *Educ:* Univ Wis, BS, 56, MS, 57, PhD(plant path), 61. *Prof Exp:* Fel microbial genetics, Univ Wis, 61-62, res assoc plant path, 63-64; ADJ PROF PLANT PATH, MISS STATE UNIV, 71- *Mem:* Am Phytopath Soc. *Res:* Diseases of maize caused by viruses and mycoplasma-like organisms; insect transmission of mycoplasma-like organisms and viruses affecting corn and other graminaceous plants. *Mailing Add:* Dept of Plant Path & Weed Sci Miss State Univ Mississippi State MS 39762

ROSENKRANZ, GEORGE, b Budapest, Hungary, Aug 20, 16; nat Mex citizen; m 45; c 3. ORGANIC CHEMISTRY. *Educ:* Swiss Fed Inst Technol, dipl, 38, DrScTech, 39. *Prof Exp:* Res assoc org chem, Swiss Fed Inst Technol, 39-41; tech dir, Vieta Plasencia Lab, Cuba, 41-45; vpres, 49-56, pres & chmn bd,56-76, chmn bd & chief exec officer, 76-81, SCI DIR, SYNTEX SA, 45-, CHMN BD & DIR, 81- *Concurrent Pos:* Lectr, Havana, Cuba, 41-45; mem bd gov, Tel Aviv Univ & Weizmann Inst Sci. *Honors & Awards:* Comdr Order of Vasco Nunez de Balboa, Govt Panama. *Mem:* AAAS; Am Chem Soc; Royal Soc Chem; Swiss Chem Soc. *Res:* Higher terpenes; steroids; sex hormones; pharmaceuticals; natural substances. *Mailing Add:* Syntex SA PO Box 10063 Apartado 2679 Mexico DF Mexico

ROSENKRANZ, HERBERT S, b Vienna, Austria, Sept 27, 33; US citizen; m 59; c 7. MICROBIOLOGY, ONCOLOGY. *Educ:* City Col New York, BS, 54; Cornell Univ, PhD(biochem), 59. *Prof Exp:* Res assoc biochem, Univ Pa, 60-61; from asst prof to prof microbiol, Col Physicians & Surgeons, Columbia Univ, 61-76; prof microbiol & pediat & chmn dept microbiol, NY Med Col, 76-81; DIR CTR ENVIRON HEALTH SCI & PROF EPIDEMIOL & COMMUNITY HEALTH, BIOCHEM & RADIOL, CASE WESTERN RES UNIV, 81- *Concurrent Pos:* Nat Cancer Inst fel, Sloan-Kettering Inst, 59-60; NIH res career develop award, Columbia Univ, 65-75; vis prof, Hadassah Med Sch, Hebrew Univ, Jerusalem, 71-72; Int Comn for Protection Against Environ Mutagens & Carcinogens, 77-; del, Fifth Soviet-Am Symp Environ Mutagenesis & Carcinogenesis, 78; chmn DNA panel, Gene & Toxicol Prog, Environ Protection Agency, 79-, scientific review panel health effects, 80-; guest investr, Nat Coun Res Ct Japan, 80. *Mem:* Am Soc Photobiol; Am Asn Cancer Res; Am Chem Soc; Am Soc Biol Chemists; Am Soc Microbiol. *Res:* Chemistry and biology of nucleic acids; biochemical basis of mutagenicity and carcinogenecity. *Mailing Add:* Ctr Environ Health Sci Sch Med Case Western Res Univ Cleveland OH 44106

ROSENKRANZ, PHILIP WILLIAM, b Buffalo, NY, Oct 30, 45. REMOTE SENSING. *Educ:* Mass Inst Technol, SB, 67, SM, 68, PhD(elec eng), 71. *Prof Exp:* Resident res assoc, Jet Propulsion Lab, Calif Inst Technol, 71-73; RES ASSOC, MASS INST TECHNOL, 73- *Mem:* AAAS; Am Geophys Union; Inst Elec & Electronics Engrs. *Res:* Remote sensing of earth; radio astronomy. *Mailing Add:* Rm 26-339 Mass Inst of Technol Cambridge MA 02139

ROSENLICHT, MAXWELL, b Brooklyn, NY, Apr 15, 24; m 53; c 3. MATHEMATICS. *Educ:* Columbia Univ, AB, 47; Harvard Univ, PhD(math), 50. *Prof Exp:* Nat Res Coun fel, Univ Chicago & Princeton Univ, 50-52; from asst prof to assoc prof math, Northwestern Univ, 52-59; PROF MATH, UNIV CALIF, BERKELEY, 59- *Concurrent Pos:* Fulbright fel, Univ Rome, 54-55; Guggenheim fel, 57-58; mem, Inst Advan Sci Studies, France, 62-63. *Honors & Awards:* Cole Prize, Am Math Soc, 60. *Mem:* Am Math Soc. *Res:* Algebraic groups; differential algebra. *Mailing Add:* Dept of Math Univ of Calif Berkeley CA 94720

ROSENMAN, IRWIN DAVID, b Brooklyn, NY, Apr 9, 23; m 50; c 3. ORGANIC CHEMISTRY. *Educ:* Univ Pa, BA, 45; Univ Conn, MS, 48; PhD(biochem), 51. *Prof Exp:* Asst instr anal chem, Univ Conn, 48-50; chemist, Ames Aromatics, Inc, 51-53; CHEMIST & PRES, AMES LABS, INC, 53- *Mem:* Sigma Xi; Am Chem Soc. *Res:* Organic synthesis of aliphatic and aromatic amines, oximes and other nitrogen containing compounds; antiskinning agents; electrophoresis; antioxidants and additives for paint and inks; amines. *Mailing Add:* Ames Labs Inc 200 Rock Lane Milford CT 06460

ROSENMAN, RAY HAROLD, b Akron, Ohio, Nov 17, 20; m 45, 78; c 2. MEDICINE. *Educ:* Univ Mich, AB, 41, MD, 44. *Prof Exp:* Intern, Michael Reese Hosp, Chicago, 44-45; resident path, Wayne County Gen Hosp, Eloise, Mich, 45-46; resident internal med & cardiovasc dis, Michael Reese Hosp, 48-50; ASSOC CHIEF DEPT MED, MT ZION HOSP & MED CTR, SAN FRANCISCO, CALIF, 51-; SR RES PHYSICIAN, STANFORD RES INST, SRI INT, MENLO PARK, CALIF, 78- *Concurrent Pos:* Mem coun arteriosclerosis & coun high blood pressure res, Am Heart Asn; consult, Sch Aerospace Med, San Antonio, Brooks AFB, USAF, 74-79; mem, Nat Task Force Epidemiol of Heart Dis, Nat Heart, Lung & Blood Inst, 78; Am Heart Asn fel, 59-60, assoc chief, Harold Brunn Inst, Mt Zion Hosp & Med Ctr, San Francisco, Calif, 51-78; mem study sect, Behav Med, NIH, 81-; mem adv bd, Stress & Cardiovasc Res Ctr, Eckerd Col, St Petersburg, Fla, 81-, med adv bd coun, High Blood Pressure Res, Am Heart Asn, 66- & expert adv counc, Health Econ, Basel, 81-; trustee, Am Inst Stress, Yonkers, NY, 81-; co-chmn, Int Symp Psychophysiol Risk Factors, Carlsbad, Czech, 81; mem rev panel, Coronary-Prone Behav, Jacksonville, Fla & Workshop, Cholesterol & Non-Cardiovasc Mortality, Nat Heart, Lung & Blood Inst, Bethesda, Md, 81-; guest lectr, Australia, Sydney & Canberra, 74, 78 & 80; guest lectr, Klinik Hohenreid, Munich, Ger & Ciba Symp, Stratford, Eng, 78, Charing Cross Hosp, London, Eng, 79, Ciba Symp, Montsoult, France, Netherlands Inst Adv Study Humanities & Social Sci, Amsterdam, Holland, conf, Coronary-Prone Behav, Univ Freiburg, Ger & Univ SFla, Tampa, 80, conf, Psychol Factors Before & After Myocardial Infarction, Europ Soc Cardiol, Nice, France, Ger Conf, Coronary-Prone Behav, Altenberg, Ger & Switzerland, Univ Hosps, Basel, Zurich, Bern, Geneva & Lausanne, 81. *Mem:* AAAS; Soc Exp Biol & Res; Am Soc Clin Invest; Am Soc Internal Med; Am Physiol Soc. *Res:* Lipid metabolism; internal medicine and cardiology; pathogenesis of coronary heart disease; hypertension and the predictive role of rish factors; role of type-A behavior pattern in coronary heart disease; author and coauthor of 245 scientific publications and 45 chapters in scientific texts. *Mailing Add:* SRI Int 333 Ravenswood Ave 2S-368 Menlo Park CA 94025

ROSENOW, EDWARD CARL, JR, b Chicago, Ill, Apr 7, 09; m 31; c 2. MEDICINE. *Educ:* Carleton Col, BA, 31; Harvard Med Sch, MD, 35; Univ Minn, MSc, 39; Am Bd Internal Med, dipl, 46; FRCP, 68. *Hon Degrees:* DSc, Carleton Col, 67 & MacMurray Col, 73. *Prof Exp:* Exec dir, Los Angeles County Med Asn, 57-59; exec vpres, 60-77, EMER EXEC VPRES, AM COL PHYSICIANS, 77- *Concurrent Pos:* Clin prof, Sch Med, Univ Pa, 60-66, emer clin prof, 66-; trustee, Carleton Col, 68-; dir med educ, Grad Hosp, Philadelphia, 78- *Honors & Awards:* Stengel Award, Am Col Physicians, 76. *Mem:* Int Soc Internal Med (pres elec, 78-); Am Clin & Climat Asn; Am Fedn Clin Res; hon fel Am Col Chest Physicians; Am Med Writers Asn (pres, 65). *Res:* Postgraduate education; medical administration. *Mailing Add:* 1901 Walnut St Philadelphia PA 19103

ROSENQUIST, BRUCE DAVID, b Chicago, Ill, June 19, 34; m 56; c 2. VETERINARY VIROLOGY. *Educ:* Iowa State Univ, DVM, 58; Univ Mo-Columbia, PhD(microbiol), 68. *Prof Exp:* Vet, Morton Grove Animal Hosp, Ill, 60-61 & Dempster Animal Clin, Skokie, Ill, 61-64; res assoc vet microbiol, Sch Vet Med, 64-68, from asst prof to assoc prof, Univ, 68-73, res assoc, Space Sci Res Ctr, 65-66, PROF VET MICROBIOL, UNIV MO-COLUMBIA, 73- *Concurrent Pos:* NIH fel, 66-68; mem working team for bovine & equine picornaviruses, WHO-Food & Agr Orgn Prog Comp Virol, 73- *Mem:* Conf Res Workers Animal Dis; Am Vet Med Asn; Am Soc Microbio; Am Col Vet Microbiol. *Res:* Bovine viral respiratory disease; interferon; bovine rhinoviruses. *Mailing Add:* Dept Vet Microbiol Univ Mo Columbia MO 65211

ROSENQUIST, EDWARD P, b Dayton, Ohio, Feb 28, 38; m 64; c 3. ORGANIC CHEMISTRY, PHYSICAL CHEMISTRY. *Educ:* Denison Univ, BS, 60; Purdue Univ, PhD(org chem), 65. *Prof Exp:* Res chemist, Shell Oil Co, Ill, 65-69, chemist, Head Off Mfg Res, NY, 69-70, sr engr, Mkt Lubricants, Tex, 70-73, supvr staff, Shell Develop Co, Wood River, Ill & Houston, Tex, 73-78, mgr res recruitment, 78-80, MGR RES & DEVELOP COORD-LUBES/FUELS, SHELL OIL CO, HOUSTON, TEX, 80- *Mem:* Am Chem Soc. *Res:* Organic synthesis and lubricants research. *Mailing Add:* 5614 Bermuda Dunes Lane Houston TX 77069

ROSENQUIST, GLENN CARL, b Lincoln, Nebr, Aug 29, 31; m 53; c 6. MEDICINE. *Educ:* Univ Nebr, BA, 53, MD, 57. *Prof Exp:* USPHS fel embryol, Carnegie Inst Washington, 63-65; fel pediat cardiol, Johns Hopkins Univ, 65-67, asst prof pediat, 67-71, assoc prof, 71-76; prof pediat & chmn, Col Med, Univ Nebr, 76-80; PROF CHILD HEALTH & DEVELOP, GEORGE WASHINGTON UNIV, 80-; ASSOC DIR RES, CHILDREN'S HOSP, NAT MED CTR, 80- *Concurrent Pos:* Prof path, Johns Hopkins Univ, 72-76; mem, Human Embryol & Develop Study Sect, 75-79. *Mem:* Am Asn Anatomists; Soc Develop Biol; Teratol Soc; Am Col Cardiol; Am Acad Pediat. *Res:* Early development of organ systems in the chick embryo; embryology of the heart and lung; pathology of congenital heart disease. *Mailing Add:* Res Found Children's Hosp 111 Michigan Ave NW Washington DC 20010

ROSENQUIST, GRACE LINK, b Los Angeles, Calif; m 60; c 2. IMMUNOLOGY. *Educ:* Willamette Univ, BA, 54; Univ Wis-Madison, MS, 58, PhD(zool), 61. *Prof Exp:* Fel, Calif Inst Technol, 61-64; USPHS fel, Sch Med, Wash Univ, 64-66; instr med microbiol, 66-68, res assoc, 68-70, res assoc med & microbiol, Sch Med, Stanford Univ, 70-74; lectr, 75-80, PROF ANIMAL PHYSIOL, UNIV CALIF, DAVIS, 80- *Concurrent Pos:* Vis scientist, Inst Animal Physiol, Cambridge, 72-73, Ctr Ulcer Res & Educ, Los Angeles, 74-; vis scientist, Nat Inst Med Res, London, 81-82. *Mem:* AAAS; Am Asn Immunol. *Res:* Phylogeny of the immune response; cholecystokinin; evolution of gastrointestinal hormones; radioimmunoassay of gastrin; peptide purification and snythesis. *Mailing Add:* Dept of Animal Physiol Univ of Calif Davis CA 95616

ROSENSHEIN, JOSEPH SAMUEL, b Kimball, WVa, Apr 19, 29; m 51; c 3. HYDROLOGY, GEOHYDROLOGY. *Educ:* Univ Conn, BA, 52; Johns Hopkins Univ, MA, 53; Univ Ill, Urbana, PhD(geol), 67. *Prof Exp:* Geologist, Ind Dist, 53-63, subdist chief, RI & NY Dist, 64-66, R I & Cent New Eng Dist, 66-67 & Tampa Subdist, Fla Dist, 67-75, CHIEF KANS DIST, WATER RESOURCES DIV, US GEOL SURV, 75- *Mem:* Am Geophys Union; Geol Soc Am; Am Water Resources Asn; Soc Econ Geol; Am Soc Hydrogeol. *Res:* Hydrology of aquifer systems; estuarine hydrology; environmental hydrology; subsurface storage of wastes; hydraulic characteristics and modeling of aquifer systems; remote sensing of the environment. *Mailing Add:* US Geol Surv 1950 Ave A W Campus Univ Kans Lawrence KS 66045

ROSENSHEIN, JOSEPH STANLEY, b Middletown, NY, July 2, 36; m 67. LOW TEMPERATURE PHYSICS, BIOPHYSICS. *Educ:* Mass Inst Technol, BS, 57, PhD(physics), 63. *Prof Exp:* Appointment physics, Mass Inst Technol, 63-64; res scholar, Rome, 64-66; asst prof, 66-74, DIR, OFF PREPROF EDUC, UNIV FLA, 74-, LECTR PHYSICS, 75- *Concurrent Pos:* Fulbright res fel, 64-65; consult psychol, Vet Admin Hosp, Gainesville, Fla, 72-; mem, Asn Am Med Cols Nat Test Comt for New Med Col Admis Test. *Mem:* Am Asn Physics Teachers; Sigma Xi; AAAS; Am Phys Soc. *Res:* Low temperature cooperative phenomena; phase transitions; interaction of ions with liquid helium; superfluid properties of liquid helium; remote monitoring of and interaction with ambulatory patients; application of computer techniques to behavioral medicine. *Mailing Add:* Off of Preprof Educ Univ Fla 113 Anderson Hall Gainesville FL 32611

ROSENSHINE, MATTHEW, b New York, NY. OPERATIONS RESEARCH, MATHEMATICS. *Educ:* Columbia Univ, AB, 52, MA, 53; Univ Ill, MS, 56; State Univ NY Buffalo, PhD(opers res), 66. *Prof Exp:* Engr aerodyn, Bell Aircraft Corp, 53-56; instr, Univ Ala, Huntsville, 57; prin math, Aeronaut Lab, Cornell Univ, 58-68; PROF INDUST ENG, PA STATE UNIV, 68- *Concurrent Pos:* Instr, Univ Buffalo, 53-55 & NMex State Univ, 58; lectr, State Univ NY Buffalo, 66-68; consult, Aeronaut Lab, Cornell Univ, 69-70, Xerox Corp, 72, Fed Energy Admin, 73-76 & Fed RR Admin, 78-80. *Mem:* AAAS; Opers Res Soc Am; Inst Mgt Sci; Am Inst Indust Engrs. *Res:* Queueing theory and control applied to large scale systems, especially air traffic and railroads. *Mailing Add:* 207 Hammond Bldg Pa State Univ University Park PA 16802

ROSENSON, LAWRENCE, b Brooklyn, NY, May 20, 31; m 63; c 2. ELEMENTARY PARTICLE PHYSICS, EXPERIMENTAL PHYSICS. *Educ:* Univ Chicago, AB, 50, MS, 53, PhD(physics), 56. *Prof Exp:* Res assoc physics, Univ Chicago, 56-58; from instr to assoc prof, 58-67, PROF PHYSICS, MASS INST TECHNOL, 67- *Mem:* Fel Am Phys Soc. *Res:* Experimental elementary particle physics; particle spectroscopy; weak and strong interactions. *Mailing Add:* Rm 520 Bldg 24 Mass Inst of Technol Cambridge MA 02139

ROSENSTARK, SOLOMON, b Pionki, Poland, May 13, 36; US citizen; m 60; c 2. ELECTRICAL ENGINEERING. *Educ:* City Col New York, BEE, 58; NY Univ, MEE, 61, PhD(elec eng), 66. *Prof Exp:* Jr engr, Polarad Electronics Corp, 58-59; assoc develop engr, Norden Labs, Div United Aircraft Corp, 59-61; lectr, City Col New York, 61-63; teaching fel, NY Univ, 64-65, res asst, 65-66; mem tech staff, Bell Tel Labs, 66-68; ASST PROF ELEC ENG, NJ INST TECHNOL, 68- *Mem:* Inst Elec & Electronics Engrs. *Res:* Communication theory; electronics; microprocessors. *Mailing Add:* Dept of Elec Eng NJ Inst of Technol 323 High St Newark NJ 07102

ROSENSTEIN, A(LLEN) B, b Baltimore, Md, Aug 25, 20; m; c 3. ENGINEERING. *Educ:* Univ Ariz, BS, 40; Univ Calif, Los Angeles, MS, 50, PhD, 58. *Prof Exp:* Elec engr, Convair Div, Gen Dynamics Corp, 40-41; sr elec engr, Lockheed Aircraft Corp, 41-42; chief plant engr, Utility Appliance Co, 42-44; lectr eng, 46-58, PROF ENG & APPL SCI, UNIV CALIF, LOS ANGELES, 58- *Concurrent Pos:* Consult, Atomic Energy Comn, US Air Force, US Corps Eng, Douglas Aircraft Co, Beckman Instruments & Marquardt Aircraft Co, 46-; chmn bd, Inet, Inc, 47-53, consult engr, 54-; dir, Pioneer Magnetics, Inc, Int Transformer Co, Inc & Foreign Resource Serv. *Mem:* AAAS; Am Soc Eng Educ; Inst Elec & Electronics Engrs; NY Acad Sci. *Res:* Magnetic amplifiers; ferromagnetic systems; automatic controls; system design; engineering organization; education; computer aided design; educational planning. *Mailing Add:* 314 S Rockingham Ave Los Angeles CA 90024

ROSENSTEIN, ALAN HERBERT, b Baltimore, Md, July 4, 36; m 61; c 2. METALLURGY. *Educ:* Drexel Inst Technol, BS, 59; George Washington Univ, MA, 63; Colo Sch Mines, MS, 65, DSc(metall eng), 66. *Prof Exp:* Physical metallurgist ferrous & nonferrous, Naval Ship Res & Develop Ctr, Annapolis, 59-68, br chief ferrous metall, 68-71; PROG MGR STRUCT MAT, AIR FORCE OFF SCI RES, BOLLING AFB, WASHINGTON, DC, 71- *Mem:* Am Soc Metals; Sigma Xi; Am Welding Soc; Am Soc Testing & Mat; Am Inst Mining, Metall & Petrol Engrs. *Res:* Structural materials research and development, especially metallurgy and mechanics of ferrous, titanium, aluminum, nickel and copper alloys; administration of federal contracts and grants program in industry and universities dealing with above. *Mailing Add:* 12217 Wynmore Lane Bowie MD 20715

ROSENSTEIN, GEORGE MORRIS, JR, b Philadelphia, Pa, Feb 27, 37; m 59; c 1. MATHEMATICS, HISTORY OF MATHEMATICS. *Educ:* Oberlin Col, AB, 59; Duke Univ, MA, 62, PhD(math), 63. *Prof Exp:* Asst prof math, Western Reserve Univ, 63-67; asst prof, 67-69, assoc prof, 69-80, PROF MATH, FRANKLIN & MARSHALL COL, 80- *Mem:* AAAS; Math Asn Am; Am Math Soc; Hist Sci Soc. *Res:* History of 19th Century mathematics, focusing on the evolution of calculus; point-set topology; metric topology. *Mailing Add:* Dept Math Franklin & Marshall Col Lancaster PA 17604

ROSENSTEIN, JOSEPH GEOFFREY, b London, Eng, Feb 8, 41; US citizen; m 69; c 2. MATHEMATICAL LOGIC. *Educ:* Columbia Univ, BA, 61; Cornell Univ, PhD(math logic), 66. *Prof Exp:* Instr & res assoc math, Cornell Univ, 66; asst prof, Univ Minn, Minneapolis, 66-69; from asst prof to assoc prof, 69-79, PROF MATH, RUTGERS UNIV, NEW BRUNSWICK, 79-, VCHMN DEPT, 81- *Concurrent Pos:* Mem Sch Math, Inst Advan Study, 76, 77. *Mem:* Am Math Soc; Math Asn Am; Asn Symbolic Logic. *Res:* Recursion theory; model theory. *Mailing Add:* Dept of Math Rutgers Univ New Brunswick NJ 08903

ROSENSTEIN, LAURENCE S, b Philadelphia, Pa, Aug 19, 41; m 62; c 2. TOXICOLOGY, PHYSIOLOGY. *Educ:* Drexel Univ, BS, 64, MS, 65; Univ Cincinnati, PhD(toxicol), 70. *Prof Exp:* Toxicologist, Ins Inst Hwy Safety, 71-72; sr toxicologist, Environ Protection Agency, 72-77; sr toxicologist, SRI Int, 77-79; SR TOXICOLOGIST, ENVIRON PROTECTION AGENCY, 79- *Concurrent Pos:* Consult, Environ Defense Fund, 71-; vis scientist, Environ Protection Agency, 71-72; adj prof, Univ Miami, 72-73 & NC State Univ, 73-; coord dir, Clearing House on Phthalata Ester, Nat Toxicol Prog/Environ Protection Agency, 81- *Mem:* AAAS; Soc Toxicol; Am Asn Lab Animal Sci; Am Pub Health Asn; Am Col Toxicol. *Res:* Regulatory toxicology; chemical carcinogenesis; microscopic calcium metabolism. *Mailing Add:* 412 Feather Rock Dr Rockville MD 20850

ROSENSTEIN, ROBERT, b New York, NY, Aug 7, 33; m 65; c 2. PHARMACOLOGY. *Educ:* Columbia Univ, BS, 55, MS, 57; Univ Utah, PhD(pharmacol), 62. *Prof Exp:* Teaching asst biol, Col Pharm, Columbia Univ, 55-57; res asst pharmacol, Col Med, Univ Utah, 57-58; res instr, Sch Med, Univ Okla, 62-65, asst res prof, 65; from instr to asst prof, 65-77, ASSOC PROF PHARMACOL, DARTMOUTH MED SCH, 77-, PHARMACOLOGIST, RES SERV, VET ADMIN CTR, 65 *Concurrent Pos:* Res pharmacologist, Civil Aeromed Res Inst, Fed Aviation Agency, 62-65. *Mem:* AAAS; Am Physiol Soc; Am Soc Pharmacol & Exp Therapeut; Soc Neurosci. *Res:* Respiratory pharmacology and physiology; actions of drugs upon brain stem; blood platelet pharmacology; pathology. *Mailing Add:* Res Serv Vet Admin Ctr White River Junction VT 05001

ROSENSTEIN, SHELDON WILLIAM, b Chicago, Ill, Oct 16, 27; m 55; c 3. ORTHODONTICS. *Educ:* Northwestern Univ, DDS, 51, MSD, 55. *Prof Exp:* Attend orthodontist, Children's Mem Hosp, Chicago, 55-74; PROF ORTHOD, DENT SCH, NORTHWESTERN UNIV, 74- *Concurrent Pos:* Prof orthod, Sch Med, St Louis Univ, 69-74. *Res:* Growth and development of orthodontics; clinical cleft lip and palate. *Mailing Add:* 3500 W Peterson Ave Chicago IL 60659

ROSENSTOCK, HERBERT BERNHARD, b Vienna, Austria, Dec 5, 24; nat US; m 50; c 3. SOLID STATE PHYSICS. *Educ:* Clemson Col, BS, 44; Univ NC, MS, 50, PhD(physics), 52. *Prof Exp:* theoretical physicist, US Naval Res Lab, 51-80; RES PHYSICIST, SACHS & FREEMAN ASSOCS, BOWIE, MD, 80- *Concurrent Pos:* Res contract adv, Off Naval Res, 65-66; vis prof, Univ Utah, 70-71. *Mem:* AAAS; Am Phys Soc; fel Sigma Xi; Fedn Am Sci. *Res:* Solid state theory, especially lattice dynamics, energy transfer, color centers, multiphonon absorption, amorphous solids and dislocations; atmospheric physics and light propagation; probability theory. *Mailing Add:* Sachs & Feeman Assocs Bowie MD 20715

ROSENSTOCK, PAUL DANIEL, b Brooklyn, NY, Apr 1, 35; m 56; c 2. ORGANIC CHEMISTRY. *Educ:* Polytech Inst Brooklyn, BS, 56; Pa State Univ, PhD(chem), 60. *Prof Exp:* Chemist, Ethyl Corp, Mich, 60; med chemist, Nat Drug Co, Pa, 63-64; chemist, 64-67, group leader plant trouble-shooting lab, 67-70, head chem process develop lab, 70-74, mgr process develop dept, Rohm and Haas Co, 74-81, MANAGER DEVELOP & ENVIRON CONTROL, ROHM AND HAAS DELAWARE VALLEY, INC, 81- *Mem:* Soc Plastics Engrs. *Res:* Process development and design; predominantly on polymers and extrusion; environmental sciences; sanitary and environmental engineering. *Mailing Add:* 3598 Neshaminy Valley Dr Cornwells Heights PA 19020

ROSENSTRAUS, MAURICE JAY, b Brooklyn, NY, Mar 13, 51; m 77. BIOLOGY. *Educ:* Rensselaer Polytech Inst, BS, 72; Columbia Univ, PhD(biol), 77. *Prof Exp:* Fel develop genetics, Princeton Univ, 76-78; ASST PROF BIOL, RUTGERS UNIV, NEW BRUNSWICK, 78- *Mem:* AAAS; Genetics Soc Am; Sigma Xi. *Res:* Somatic cell genetic studies of mammalian development using cultured murine teratocarcinoma cells. *Mailing Add:* Dept of Biol Sci Douglass Col Rutgers Univ New Brunswick NJ 08903

ROSENSTREICH, DAVID LEON, b New York, NY, Nov 16, 42; m 65; c 3. CELLULAR IMMUNOLOGY, ALLERGY. *Educ:* City Col New York, BS, 63; Sch Med, NY Univ, MD, 67. *Prof Exp:* Clin assoc, Nat Inst Allergy & Infectious Dis, 69-72; sr investr, Nat Inst Dent Res, 72-79; ASSOC PROF, DEPT MED, ALBERT EINSTEIN COL MED, 80-, DIR, DIV ALLERGY & IMMUNOL, 81- *Concurrent Pos:* Vis assoc prof, Rockefeller Univ, 78-79. *Mem:* Am Asn Immunologists; Am Soc Clin Invest; Am Fedn Clin Res; Am Acad Allergy. *Res:* Genetic regulation of the immune response and resistance to infection. *Mailing Add:* Dept Med Albert Einstein Col Med 1300 Morris Park Ave Bronx NY 10461

ROSENSWEIG, JACOB, b Montreal, Que, Dec 1, 30; m 52; c 3. THORACIC SURGERY, CARDIOVASCULAR SURGERY. *Educ:* McGill Univ, BSc, 51, MD, CM, 55, PhD(exp surg), 60. *Prof Exp:* Fel cardio-thoracic surg, Jewish Gen Hosp, Montreal, 61-62, jr asst, 62-66, assoc surgeon, 66-71, dir clin teaching unit surg, 69-71; assoc prof surg, Sch Med, Univ Conn, 71-74; clin assoc prof surg, Med Sch, Univ Tenn, Memphis, 74-77; CLIN ASSOC PROF SURG, UNIV ARK HEALTH SCI, 77- *Concurrent Pos:* Clin fel cardiac surg, Royal Victoria Hosp, 61-63; consult thoracic surg, Mt Sinai Hosp, Ste Agathe, Que, 62-71 & thoracic & cardiovasc surg, Maimonides Hosp, Montreal, 66-71; Que Heart Found grant, Jewish Gen Hosp, Montreal, 63-70; Med Res Coun Can grant, Lady Davis Inst Med Res, Montreal, 67-73, head surg div, Exp Surg, 67-68, sr investr, 68-71; vis consult, Nat Heart Inst, Md, 68; lectr surg, McGill Univ, 70; chief surg, Mt Sinai Hosp, Hartford, Conn, 71-74; consult cardiovasc surg, Vet Admin Hosp, Newington, Conn, 72-74; mem staff, Baptist Mem, St Joseph & Methodist Hosps, Memphis, 74-, St Francis Hosp, Memphis, 76-, chmn, Cardiovasc Surg & Thoracic Surg, 81-82; mem coun thrombosis, Am Heart Asn. *Mem:* Am Col Surgeons; Am Asn Thoracic Surg; Soc Thoracic Surg. *Res:* Circulatory and pulmonary support systems; transplantation, specifically role of platelets in rejection. *Mailing Add:* 6005 Park Ave Suite 406 Memphis TN 38138

ROSENSWEIG, RONALD E(LLIS), b Hamilton, Ohio, Nov 8, 32; m 54; c 3. CHEMICAL ENGINEERING, FLUID MECHANICS. *Educ:* Univ Cincinnati, ChE, 55; Mass Inst Technol, SM, 56, ScD(chem eng), 59. *Prof Exp:* Asst prof chem eng, Mass Inst Technol, 59-62; sect chief, Avco Corp, Mass, 62-69; pres & tech dir, 69-72, chmn, treas & tech dir, 72-73, MEM BD DIRS, FERROFLUIDICS CORP, 69-; group leader fluid physics, 73-80, SR RES ASSOC, CORP RES LABS, EXXON RES & ENG CO, 73- *Concurrent Pos:* Indust consult, Nat Res Corp, Linde Speedway Res Labs, Dynatech Corp, 59-62; vis prof chem eng, Univ Minn, 80. *Honors & Awards:* IR-100 Awards, 65, 68, 70 & 72. *Mem:* Am Inst Chem Engrs; Inst Elec & Electronics Engrs. *Res:* Magnetic fluid technology; turbulent mixing; reentry ablation; colloids; energy conversion; hydrodynamic stability. *Mailing Add:* 34 Gloucester Rd Summit NJ 07901

ROSENTHAL, ALEX, b Scollard, Alta, Oct 16, 14; m 47; c 4. ORGANIC CHEMISTRY. *Educ:* Univ Alta, BSc, 43, BEd, 47, MSc, 49; Ohio State Univ, PhD(chem), 52. *Prof Exp:* Teacher pub sch, Can, 34-37; prin & teacher high sch, 38-41, 44-46; instr, War Vet Sch, 46-47; fel, Univ Utah, 52-53; from asst prof to assoc prof, 53-64, PROF CHEM, UNIV BC, 65- *Concurrent Pos:* Vis prof, Cambridge Univ, 63-64; Killam sr res fel, 75-76; vis scientist, Salk Inst, Sloan Kettering Inst, 75-76. *Mem:* Am Chem Soc; fel Chem Inst Can. *Res:* Photoamidation studies; branched-chain sugar nucleosides; glycosyl amino acids; synthesis of analogs of nucleoside antibiotics. *Mailing Add:* Dept of Chem Univ of BC Vancouver BC V6T 1W5 Can

ROSENTHAL, ALLAN LAWRENCE, b Montreal, Que, Feb 16, 48; m 71; c 2. ANTIBIOTICS, ANTI-INFLAMMATORIES. *Educ:* McGill Univ, BS, 69; Fla State Univ, MS, 72; State Univ NY Upstate Med Ctr, PhD(microbiol), 75. *Prof Exp:* Fel, Brookhaven Nat Lab, 75-78; asst prof biol, Tex Christian Univ, 78-80; SCIENTIST, ALCON LABS, INC, 80- *Concurrent Pos:* Adj prof, Tex Christian Univ, 80- *Res:* Genetic transformation of streptococcus pneumoniae and the acholeplasmas, with specific reference to the role of nucleuses; ocular anti-infective and anti-inflammatory agents. *Mailing Add:* Alcon Labs Inc Box 1959 Ft Worth TX 76101

ROSENTHAL, ARNOLD JOSEPH, b New York, NY, July 9, 22; m 47; c 4. PHYSICAL CHEMISTRY, ORGANIC CHEMISTRY. *Educ:* Polytech Inst Brooklyn, PhD, 58. *Prof Exp:* Sr res chemist, Celanese Corp, Cumberland, Md, 41-44, 47, SR RES ASSOC, CELANESE RES CO, SUMMIT, NJ, 47- *Concurrent Pos:* Ed, Qual Control & Appl Statist, 56- & Opers Res & Mgt Sci, 61- *Mem:* Am Chem Soc; Opers Res Soc Am; Am Soc Qual Control; Biomet Soc; Am Statist Asn. *Res:* Synthetic fibers; mechanisms of chemical reactions; physical chemistry of polymers; statistical design and analysis of experiments; operations research; flame retardant polymers. *Mailing Add:* 8 Ford Hill Rd Whippany NJ 07981

ROSENTHAL, ARTHUR FREDERICK, b Brooklyn, NY, Aug 3, 31; m 67; c 3. BIOCHEMISTRY. *Educ:* Antioch Col, BS, 54; Harvard Univ, AM, 56, PhD(biochem), 60; Am Bd Clin Chem, dipl, 74. *Prof Exp:* Fel chem, Univ Birmingham, 61-62 & Auburn Univ, 62; CHIEF BIOCHEM, LONG ISLAND JEWISH-HILLSIDE MED CTR, 62-; ASSOC PROF PATH, STATE UNIV NY STONY BROOK, 72- *Concurrent Pos:* Prin investr, NIH Proj Grant, 63-; adj prof biochem, PhD Prog Biochem, City Univ New York, 74-; adj prof, City Univ NY; exten assoc prof, Univ Puerto Rico, 76- *Mem:* Am Chem Soc; The Chem Soc; Am Asn Clin Chemists; Am Soc Biol Chemists. *Res:* Phospholipid chemistry and biochemistry; synthetic organophosphorus chemistry; lipid chemistry and metabolism; clinical chemistry; protein modification. *Mailing Add:* L I Jewish-Hillside Med Ctr New Hyde Park NY 11042

ROSENTHAL, DAVID (WALTER), b Detroit, Mich, July 1, 31; m 52; c 4. SOFTWARE SYSTEMS, MASS SPECTROMETRY. *Educ:* Univ Calif, Los Angeles, BS, 52; Mass Inst Technol, PhD(chem), 56. *Prof Exp:* USPHS fel, Weizmann Inst, 56-57; fel chem, Harvard Univ, 58; sr res chemist, Squibb Inst Med Res, 59-63; sr chemist, Res Triangle Inst, 63-71, asst dir chem & life sci div, 71-77, sr mass spectrometrist, 77-81; SR SOFTWARE ENGR, GCA BURLINGTON DIV, 81- *Concurrent Pos:* Adj assoc prof, Duke Univ, 68-77. *Mem:* AAAS; Am Soc Mass Spectrometry; Am Chem Soc. *Res:* Software systems; robotics; microelectronics. *Mailing Add:* GCA Burlington Div 209 Burlington Rd Bedford MA 01730

ROSENTHAL, DONALD, b Princeton, NJ, July 16, 26; m 55; c 4. ANALYTICAL CHEMISTRY, PHYSICAL CHEMISTRY. *Educ:* Princeton Univ, AB, 49; Columbia Univ, AM, 50, PhD(chem), 55. *Prof Exp:* Instr chem, Columbia Univ, 54-55 & Univ Minn, 55-56; from instr to asst prof, Univ Chicago, 56-61; assoc prof, 61-66, PROF CHEM, CLARKSON COL, 66-, EXEC OFFICER, DEPT CHEM, 81- *Concurrent Pos:* Sr res assoc, Brandeis Univ, 70-71; ed, Comput Chem Educ Newslett, 81- *Mem:* AAAS; Am Chem Soc; NY Acad Sci. *Res:* Solution chemistry; equilibria, acidity and kinetics in aqueous and non-aqueous solutions; potentiometry and spectrophotometry; instrumental methods of analysis; chromatography; computer simulation. *Mailing Add:* Dept of Chem Clarkson Col Potsdam NY 13676

ROSENTHAL, F(ELIX), b Munich, Ger, Feb 6, 25; nat US; c 3. MECHANICS. *Educ:* Ill Inst Technol, BS, 47, MS, 48, PhD(appl mech), 52. *Prof Exp:* Instr, Ill Inst Technol, 47-50, res engr, Armour Res Found, 48-54; proj engr & head, Math Sect, Res Ctr, Clevite Corp, 54-58; staff scientist, Raytheon Co, 58-61; adv engr, Fed Systs Div, IBM Corp, 61-68; vpres res & develop, Oceanog, Inc, 68-69; independent consult mech design, underwater acoust & signal processing, 69-71; head appl mech br, 71-78, HEAD OCEAN ENG SECT, NAVAL RES LAB, 78- *Mem:* Am Soc Mech Engrs; Fedn Am Sci, sr mem Inst Elec & Electronics Engrs. *Res:* Applied mechanics; elasticity, dynamics; acoustics; high speed automatic machines; piezoelectric transducers; wave propagation; oceanography; acoustic and seismic signal processing; structural dynamics; fluid mechanics; underwater engineering; computer structural design analysis methods. *Mailing Add:* Code 5843 Naval Res Lab Washington DC 20375

ROSENTHAL, FRED, b Breslau, Ger, Feb 26, 31; US citizen; m 57; c 2. NEUROPHYSIOLOGY. *Educ:* Univ Calif, Berkeley, BA, 52, PhD(psychol), 56; Stanford Univ, MD, 60. *Prof Exp:* Res physiologist, Univ Calif, Berkeley, 60-62; fel neurophysiol, Univ Wash, 62-64; asst prof, New York Med Col, Flower & Fifth Ave Hosps, 64-69, assoc prof, 69-70; ASSOC RES PHYSIOLOGIST, CARDIOVASC RES INST, MED SCH, UNIV CALIF, SAN FRANCISCO, 70- *Mem:* Am Physiol Soc; Biophys Soc. *Res:* Description of the extracellular electric field around cortical pyramidal tract neurons; effects of radiation on brain function; relations between somatic motor systems and cardiovascular changes. *Mailing Add:* Cardiovasc Res Inst Univ of Calif Med Sch San Francisco CA 94143

ROSENTHAL, FRITZ, b Wuerzburg, Ger, July 4, 11; nat US; m 38; c 2. INDUSTRIAL CHEMISTRY. *Educ:* Univ Bern, PhD(chem), 35. *Prof Exp:* Res chemist, Gen Elec Co, 36-38 & Forest Prod Chem Co, 38-39; plastics technologist, Univ Tenn, 39-42; chem engr, Radio Corp Am, 42-46; dir res, Nat Plastics, Inc, 46-49; sr res chemist, Nashua Corp, 49-54; proj leader, Armour Res Found, Ill Inst Technol, 54-56; dir prod develop, Knowlton Bros, Inc, NY, 56-68; sr assoc res & develop dept, Riegel Paper Corp, NJ, 68-70; SR ASSOC, SCM CORP, 70- *Mem:* Am Chem Soc; Tech Asn Pulp & Paper Indust; Am Inst Chemists. *Res:* Plastics and paper technology; high polymer literature; Electrofax; Xerography. *Mailing Add:* Cherry Hill Apt 402 E 2151 Rte 38 Cherry Hill NJ 08002

ROSENTHAL, GERALD A, b New York, NY, Jan 9, 39; m 60; c 3. PLANT BIOCHEMISTRY, CHEMICAL ECOLOGY. *Educ:* Syracuse Univ, BS, 62; Duke Univ, MF, 63, PhD(plant physiol, biochem), 66. *Prof Exp:* NIH fel biochem, Med Col, Cornell Univ, 66-69; asst prof biol, Case Western Reserve Univ, 69-73; from asst prof to assoc prof, 73-80, PROF BIOL, UNIV KY, 80- *Concurrent Pos:* NIH grant, 70-73, 74-78, 79-82; NSF grants, 73-75, 76-79 & 80-83; Lady Davis prof agr entomol, Hebrew Univ Jerusalem, 79. *Mem:* Am Soc Plant Physiologists; Entomol Soc Am; Phytochem Soc NAm; AAAS; Phytochem Soc Europe. *Res:* Plant amino acid metabolism and enzymology; biochemistry of plant-insect interaction. *Mailing Add:* T H Morgan Sch Biol Sci Univ of Ky Lexington KY 40506

ROSENTHAL, GERSON MAX, JR, b Pittsfield, Mass, Mar 13, 22; m 54; c 1. ECOLOGY, ZOOLOGY. *Educ:* Dartmouth Col, AB, 43; Univ Calif, MS, 51, PhD(zool), 54. *Prof Exp:* Asst zool, Univ Chicago, 46-48; asst, Univ Calif, 49-51, assoc, 52-53; Ford fel, 54, instr natural sci, 54-56, asst prof, 57-58, asst prof biol, 59-63, assoc prof biol, 63-76, PROF BIOL, SOCIAL SCI & GEOG, UNIV CHICAGO, 76- *Concurrent Pos:* Consult ecol, Oak Ridge Inst Nuclear Res, 63-76; vis scientist, Argonnne Nat Lab, 69-70, consult ecol, 70-74. *Honors & Awards:* Quantrell Award, 63. *Mem:* AAAS; Ecol Soc Am; Am Inst Biol Sci; Soc Study Evolution. *Res:* Physiological ecology; energetics of ecosystems; radioecology; biogeography; relationship of organisms to microclimates; animal populations. *Mailing Add:* 17 Gates-Blake Hall 5845 S Ellis Ave Univ Chicago Chicago IL 60637

ROSENTHAL, HAROLD LESLIE, b Elizabeth, NJ, Mar 26, 22; m 47; c 2. BIOCHEMISTRY. *Educ:* Univ NMex, BSc, 44; Rutgers Univ, PhD(biochem), 51. *Prof Exp:* Res biochemist, Rutgers Univ, 49-51; res biochemist, Philadelphia Gen Hosp, 51; instr med, Tulane Univ, 51-53; chief biochem, Rochester Gen Hosp, 53-58; from asst prof to assoc prof, 58-64, chmn dept, 58-74, PROF PHYSIOL CHEM, SCH DENT, WASHINGTON UNIV, 65- *Concurrent Pos:* Res assoc, Minerva Found Med Res, Helsinki, Finland, 66; Nat Acad Sci exchange scientist, Inst Nutrit, Budapest, Hungary, 73-74. *Mem:* Soc Exp Biol & Med; Am Chem Soc; Am Inst Nutrit; Am Inst Biol Sci; Am Inst Chemists; Am Soc Biol Chemists. *Res:* Intermediary metabolism; vitamins and radioactive isotopes. *Mailing Add:* 7541 Teasdale University City MO 63130

ROSENTHAL, HOWARD, b Brooklyn, NY, Sept 15, 24; m 51; c 2. CHEMICAL ENGINEERING. *Educ:* City Col New York, BChE, 44; NY Univ, MChE, 49. *Prof Exp:* Res engr, Sunray Elec Co, 46-47; asst chem eng, NY Univ, 48-49; mem tech staff, RCA Labs, 49-59, indust hyg & safety engr, 59-63, sr tech adminr, 63-66, mgr tech admin, 66-68, adminr staff serv, Res & Eng, 68-70, dir, 70-72, STAFF VPRES ENG, RCA CORP, 72- *Mem:* Am Chem Soc; Inst Elec & Electronics Engrs. *Res:* Engineering management. *Mailing Add:* David Sarnoff Res Ctr Radio Corp of Am Princeton NJ 08540

ROSENTHAL, IRA MAURICE, b New York, NY, June 11, 20; m 43; c 2. PEDIATRICS. *Educ:* Univ Ind, AB, 40, MD, 43. *Prof Exp:* From asst prof to assoc prof, 53-63, PROF PEDIAT, ABRAHAM LINCOLN SCH MED, UNIV ILL COL MED, 67-, HEAD DEPT, 74- *Mem:* Soc Pediat Res; Endocrine Soc; AMA; Am Acad Pediat; Am Fedn Clin Res; Am Pediat Soc. *Res:* Pediatric endocrinology and metabolism. *Mailing Add:* Abraham Lincoln Sch of Med Univ Ill Col Med 840 S Wood St Chicago IL 60612

ROSENTHAL, J WILLIAM, b New Orleans, La, Oct 30, 22; m 45; c 2. OPHTHALMOLOGY, SURGERY. *Educ:* Tulane Univ, BS, 43, MD, 45; Univ Pa, MSc, 52, DSc, 62; Am Bd Ophthal, dipl, 54. *Prof Exp:* From instr to assoc clin prof, 52-71, CLIN PROF OPHTHAL, MED SCH, TULANE UNIV, 71- *Concurrent Pos:* Sr ophthal surg, Touro Infirmary & Eye, Ear, Nose & Throat Hosp, 52-; chief opthal, Sara Mayo Hosps & St Claude Gen Hosp. *Mem:* French Ophthal Soc; fel Am Col Surgeons; Am Acad Ophthal & Otolaryngol; fel Royal Soc Med; fel Int Col Surgeons. *Res:* Tularemia; pterygia; glaucoma with brachydactyly and spherophakia; trachoma; accident prone children; microsurgery. *Mailing Add:* 3715 Prytania St New Orleans LA 70115

ROSENTHAL, JEFFREY, b El Paso, Tex, Sept 18, 53; m 75; c 1. PHOTOELECTROCHEMISTRY. *Educ:* Univ Minn, Duluth, BS, 75; Purdue Univ, PhD(anal chem), 80. *Prof Exp:* Asst prof, Oakland Univ, 80-82; ASST PROF ANAL CHEM, UNIV WIS, RIVER FALLS, 82- *Mem:* Am Chem Soc; Electrochem Soc. *Res:* Semiconductor photoelectrochemistry; design of instrumentation (optimized for transient measurements). *Mailing Add:* Dept Chem Univ Wis River Falls WI 54022

ROSENTHAL, JENNY EUGENIE (MRS ARTHUR BRAMLEY), b Moscow, Russia, July 31, 09; nat US; m 43; c 3. PHYSICS. *Educ:* Univ Paris, ScB, 26; NY Univ, ScM, 27, PhD(physics), 29. *Prof Exp:* Nat Res Coun fel, Johns Hopkins Univ, 29-31; res assoc physics, NY Univ, 31-33; mem staff, Harvard Observ, 34; Am Asn Univ Women Berliner res fel, Columbia Univ, 35-36; instr, Grad Div, Brooklyn Col, 37-42; physicist, Signal Corps, US Army, 42-44, 48-50, consult physicist, 50-53; proj engr, Du Mont Labs, Inc, 53-58; consult, Bramley Consults, 58-62; sect head, Melpar, Inc, 62-67; SUPVRY PHYSICIST, NIGHT VISION LAB, DEPT ARMY, FT BELVOIR, 67- *Concurrent Pos:* Lectr, NY Univ, 41-42. *Mem:* Am Math Soc; fel Am Phys Soc; fel Inst Elec & Electronics Engrs; Optical Soc Am; Soc Info Display. *Res:* Band spectra; polyatomic molecules; applied mathematics; secondary emission; dark trace tubes; electron optics; cathode ray tube design; color television; solid state storage panels and high intensity light sources. *Mailing Add:* 7124 Strathmore St Falls Church VA 22042

ROSENTHAL, JOEL WILLIAM, b Newark, NJ, Apr 3, 42; m 63; c 2. FUEL SCIENCE, PETROLEUM CHEMISTRY. *Educ:* Univ Calif, Berkeley, BS, 64; Yale Univ, MS, 66, MPh, 67, PhD(chem), 68. *Prof Exp:* Fel, Univ Calif, Los Angeles, 68-69; res chemist, 69-74, sr res chemist, 74-77, SR RES ASSOC, CHEVRON RES CO, 77- *Mem:* Am Chem Soc; Royal Soc Chem. *Res:* Petroleum processing; catalysis; novel materials for petroleum products; reaction mechanisms in hydrocarbon chemistry; synthetic fuels; coal conversion chemistry. *Mailing Add:* Chevron Res Co 576 Standard Ave Richmond CA 94801

ROSENTHAL, JOHN WILLIAM, b New York, NY, Sept 6, 45; m 68. MATHEMATICS. *Educ:* Mass Inst Technol, BS, 65, PhD(math), 68. *Prof Exp:* Asst prof math, State Univ NY Stony Brook, 68-71, NSF res contract, 69-71; asst prof, 71-74, ASSOC PROF MATH, ITHACA COL, 74- *Concurrent Pos:* Vis assoc prof, Mich State Univ, 77-78; vis lectr, Univ Sydney, Australia, 78. *Mem:* Math Asn Am; Am Math Soc; Asn Symbolic Logic. *Res:* Mathematical logic; model theory; categoricity and stability; infinitary languages; set theory; computational complexity; algebraically closed fields; asymptotic methods in combinatorics. *Mailing Add:* Dept of Math Ithaca Col Ithaca NY 14850

ROSENTHAL, JUDITH WOLDER, b New York, NY, May 12, 45. ENDOCRINOLOGY. *Educ:* Brown Univ, BA, 67, PhD(physiol chem), 71. *Prof Exp:* Fel cholesterol synthesis adipose tissue, Univ Toronto, 71-72; fel insulin effects human fibroblasts, McMaster Univ, 72-73; ASST PROF BIOL, KEAN COL NJ, 74- *Concurrent Pos:* Am Philos Soc grant, 76-78. *Mem:* Endocrine Soc; Asn Women Sci; Sigma Xi. *Res:* Mechanism of action of hormones and their effects on fat cell metabolism. *Mailing Add:* Dept of Biol Kean Col of NJ Union NJ 07083

ROSENTHAL, KENNETH LEE, b Chicago, Ill, Nov 29, 50; m 77; c 1. CELL MEDIATED IMMUNITY, VIROLOGY. *Educ:* Univ Ill, Urbana, BSc, 72, MSc, 74; McMaster Univ, Can, PhD(med sci), 78. *Prof Exp:* Fel immunol, Scripps Clin Res Found, Calif, 78-80 & Univ Zurich, Switz, 80-81; ASST PROF IMMUNOL, MCMASTER UNIV, CAN, 81- *Concurrent Pos:* Damon Runyon Fel, Walter Winchell Cancer Found, 78 & Swiss Nat Sci Found, 80; scholar, Med Res Coun Can, 82. *Mem:* Am Asn Immunologists; Can Soc Immunol. *Res:* Role, specificity and receptors of cytotoxic T lymphocytes; role and mechanism of natural killer cells; virus-lymphocyte interactions. *Mailing Add:* Dept Path McMaster Univ Health Sci Ctr Hamilton ON L8N 3Z5 Can

ROSENTHAL, LEE, b Brooklyn, NY, Nov 28, 37; m 70; c 1. ELECTRICAL & SYSTEMS ENGINEERING. *Educ:* Polytech Inst Brooklyn, BEE, 58, PhD(elec eng), 67; Calif Inst Technol, MS, 59. *Prof Exp:* Engr, Hughes Aircraft Co, 58-59; lectr elec eng, City Col New York, 62-66; asst prof, Stevens Inst Technol, 66-70; asst prof, Hofstra Univ, 70-72; assoc prof, 72-80, PROF, FAIRLEIGH DICKINSON UNIV, 80- *Honors & Awards:* Dow Outstanding Young Fac Award, Am Soc Eng Educ, 73. *Mem:* Am Soc Eng Educ; NY Acad Sci; Sigma Xi. *Res:* Linear integrated circuits; process control. *Mailing Add:* Dept of Eng Technol Fairleigh Dickinson Univ Teaneck NJ 07666

ROSENTHAL, LEONARD JASON, b Boston, Mass, June 23, 42; m 76; c 2. VIROLOGY, MOLECULAR BIOLOGY. *Educ:* Univ Vermont, BA, 64; Souther Ill Univ, MA, 66; Kans State Univ, PhD(bact), 69. *Prof Exp:* Res fel, Harvard Med Sch, 69-71, instr, 72-73; Europ Molecular Biol Orgn fel, Univ Geneva, 73-74 & Leukemia Soc Am Spec fel, NIH, 74-75; asst prof, 75-82, ASSOC PROF, GEORGETOWN UNIV, 82- *Concurrent Pos:* Consult, Bethesda Res Labs, 76; Leukemia Soc Am Scholar, 80. *Mem:* Am Soc Microbiol; Sigma Xi. *Res:* Determining the association of human herpes viruses with cancer. *Mailing Add:* Dept Microbiol Sch Med & Dent Georgetown Univ 3900 Reservoir Rd Washington DC 20007

ROSENTHAL, LOIS C, b Boston, Mass, Mar 20, 46. PHYSICAL CHEMISTRY. *Educ:* Simmons Col, BS, 68; Univ Calif, Berkeley, PhD(chem), 75. *Prof Exp:* Instr chem, Diablo Valley Col, 75-77; ASST PROF CHEM, UNIV SANTA CLARA, 77- *Mem:* Am Chem Soc. *Res:* Molecular motion in fluids; infrared and Raman spectroscopy; resonance Raman spectroscopy. *Mailing Add:* Dept of Chem Univ of Santa Clara Santa Clara CA 95053

ROSENTHAL, LOUIS, b New York, NY, Aug 16, 22; m 46; c 3. ELECTRICAL ENGINEERING. *Educ:* City Col New York, BEE, 43; Polytech Inst Brooklyn, MEE, 47. *Prof Exp:* Elec engr, Star Elec Motor Co, NJ, 43; instr elec eng, Lehigh Univ, 44; assoc prof, 44-54, prof, 54-81, EMER PROF ELEC ENG, RUTGERS UNIV, NEW BRUNSWICK, 81- *Concurrent Pos:* Consult, Union Carbide Plastics Co, 54-, Esso Res & Eng Co, NJ, 56-65; US Naval Ord Lab, Md, 58-, Atlas Chem Industs, Pa, 64-70, Johnson & Johnson, NJ, 65-68, Sandia Corp, NMex, 66-68, Jet Propulsion Lab, 67-77, US Naval Surface Weapons Ctr & US Army Armament Res & Develop Command. *Mem:* Sr mem Inst Elec & Electronics Engrs. *Res:* Instrumentation in the chemical, processing and nonelectrical industries; electronic applications to industry for measurement and control. *Mailing Add:* Dept of Elec Eng Rutgers Univ Piscataway NJ 08854

ROSENTHAL, MARCIA WHITE, b Chicago, Ill, July 11, 21; m 54; c 1. RADIATION BIOLOGY, BIOLOGICAL EDITOR. *Educ:* Cornell Univ, AB, 43; Univ Chicago, PhD(zool), 49. *Prof Exp:* Assoc biologist, 49-56, consult, 56-60, ASSOC SCIENTIST, ARGONNE NAT LAB, 60-, ED, DIV BIOL & MED RES, 74- *Concurrent Pos:* Clin assoc prof, Sch Dent, Loyola Univ, 72-74. *Mem:* Am Inst Biol Sci; Am Soc Zool; Radiation Res Soc. *Res:* Therapy of experimental metal poisonings; metabolism of radiocolloids; carcinogenicity of plutonium. *Mailing Add:* Div of Biol & Med Res Argonne Nat Lab Argonne IL 60439

ROSENTHAL, MICHAEL DAVID, b Brooklyn, NY, Dec 30, 43; m 81. SOLID STATE PHYSICS. *Educ:* Wesleyan Univ, BA, 65; Cornell Univ, PhD(physics), 72. *Prof Exp:* Res assoc sci policy, Prog Sci, Technol & Soc, Cornell Univ, 71-73; instr physics, Dept Physics, Rutgers Univ, 73-74; asst prof physics, Swarthmore Col, 74-77; phys sci officer, Non Proliferation Bur, US Arms Control & Disarmament Agency, 77-81; FIRST OFFICER, INT ATOMIC ENERGY AGENCY, 81- *Mem:* Sigma Xi; Am Phys Soc; Am Nuclear Soc; Fedn Am Scientists. *Res:* Radiofrequency size effects in metals and electrical properties of metal-ammonia compounds and solutions; international safeguards. *Mailing Add:* Int Atomic Energy Agency Wagramer St 5 PO Box 100 A-1400 Vienna 20451 Austria

ROSENTHAL, MICHAEL R, b Youngstown, Ohio, Dec 2, 39; m 63; c 3. PHYSICAL INORGANIC CHEMISTRY, ENVIRONMENTAL SCIENCES. *Educ:* Western Reserve Univ, AB, 61; Univ Ill, MS, 63, PhD(chem), 65. *Prof Exp:* From asst prof to assoc prof, 65-73, PROF CHEM, BARD COL, 73-, ASSOC DEAN ACAD AFFAIRS, 80- *Mem:* AAAS; Am Chem Soc; Royal Soc Chem. *Res:* Coordination chemistry; water chemistry in the natural environment; water pollution. *Mailing Add:* Dept Chem Bard Col Annandale-on-Hudson NY 12504

ROSENTHAL, MURRAY WILFORD, b Greenville, Miss, Feb 25, 26; m 49; c 2. CHEMICAL ENGINEERING. *Educ:* La State Univ, BS, 49; Mass Inst Technol, ScD(chem eng), 53. *Prof Exp:* Develop engr, Oak Ridge Nat Lab, 53-55, lectr, Oak Ridge Sch Reactor Technol, 55-56, leader reactor anal group, 65-61, proj engr, Pebble Bed Reactor Exp, 61-63, head long range planning sect, 63-65, dir, Molten Salt Reactor Prog, 66-73, actg dep lab dir, 73-74, ASSOC LAB DIR, ADVAN ENERGY SYSTS, OAK RIDGE NAT LAB, 74- *Concurrent Pos:* Vis prof, Mass Inst Technol, 61; tech asst to asst gen mgr reactors, Atomic Energy Comn, 65-66; US deleg, Panel Utilization Thorium in Power Reactors, Int Atomic Energy Agency, Vienna, 65, Manila Conf Probs & Prospects of Nuclear Power Appln Develop Countries, 66 & Int Conf on Nuclear Energy, Geneva, 71; adv panel fusion energy, Energy Res & Prod Subcomt, Comt Sci & Technol, US House Representatives, 81-; adv ed, Eng Sci & Technol News, 80- *Mem:* AAAS; fel Am Nuclear Soc. *Res:* Energy research and development, especially fossil, magnetic fusion, conservation, solar and geothermal. *Mailing Add:* Oak Ridge Nat Lab Oak Ridge TN 37830

ROSENTHAL, MURRAY WILLIAM, b Stamford, Conn, Aug 15, 18; m 47; c 2. PHARMACEUTICAL CHEMISTRY. *Educ:* Pa State Univ, BS, 41, MS, 42. *Prof Exp:* Chemist, Philadelphia Qm Depot, 42-43 & Edcan Labs, 46-48; asst res dir, McKesson-Robbins, 48-51; from asst res dir to res dir, 51-62, VPRES RES & DEVELOP, BLOCK DRUG CO, INC, 62- *Concurrent Pos:* Dir, Therapeut Res Found. *Mem:* AAAS; Soc Cosmetic Chemists; Am Chem Soc; Proprietary Asn; Am Pharmaceut Asn. *Res:* Development of proprietary pharmaceuticals and toiletries. *Mailing Add:* Block Drug Co Inc 257 Cornelison Ave Jersey City NJ 07302

ROSENTHAL, NATHAN RAYMOND, b Washington, DC, Oct 29, 25; m 55; c 4. BIOCHEMISTRY. *Educ:* Georgetown Univ, BS, 49, MS, 51, PhD(biochem), 57. *Prof Exp:* Chemist, NIH, 51-54; biochemist, Walter Reed Army Inst Res, 54-58; CHEMIST, BUR DRUGS, FOOD & DRUG ADMIN, 58- *Honors & Awards:* Meritorious Achievement Award, US Dept Army, 57. *Mem:* Am Chem Soc; Asn Off Anal Chem; Sigma Xi. *Res:* Biochemistry of endocrine glands and their regulation; metabolism and biological activity of organophosphorus pesticides; manufacturing controls on radiopharmaceutical, antineoplastic and psychopharmacologic new drugs and investigational new drugs. *Mailing Add:* 18708 Bloomfield Rd Olney MD 20832

ROSENTHAL, PETER (MICHAEL), b New York, NY, June 1, 41; m 60; c 3. MATHEMATICS. *Educ:* Queens Col, NY, BS, 62; Univ Mich, Ann Arbor, MA, 63, PhD(math), 67. *Prof Exp:* Instr math, Univ Toledo, 66-67; from asst prof to assoc prof, 67-76, PROF MATH, UNIV TORONTO, 76- *Mem:* Am Math Soc; Can Math Cong. *Res:* Operators on Hilbert and Banach spaces. *Mailing Add:* Dept of Math Univ of Toronto Toronto ON M5S 1A1 Can

ROSENTHAL, RICHARD ALAN, b Newark, NJ, Aug 29, 36; m 62; c 2. MECHANICAL & OPTICAL ENGINEERING. *Educ:* Mass Inst Technol, BSME, 58, MSME, 59. *Prof Exp:* Mem tech staff, Bell Tel Labs, 59-64; sr engr, Itek Corp, 64-65; staff engr, 65-68; sr optical engr, 68-71, sect mgr, 71-79, TECHNICAL MGR, INSTRUMENTATION & ELECTRONICS ENG DIV, POLAROID CORP, 79- *Mem:* Sr mem Am Soc Mech Engrs. *Res:* Electrooptical and electromechanical instruments and instrumentation systems. *Mailing Add:* Eng Instrumentation Develop Polaroid Corp Cambridge MA 02139

ROSENTHAL, ROBERT WERNICK, b Philadelphia, Pa, July 8, 44; m 71. OPERATIONS RESEARCH, ECONOMICS. *Educ:* Johns Hopkins Univ, BA, 66; Stanford Univ, MS, 68, PhD(opers res), 71. *Prof Exp:* From asst prof to assoc prof, Indust Eng & Mgt Sci, Northwestern Univ, Evanston, 70-76; MEM STAFF, DIV MATH ECON, BELL LABS, 76- *Concurrent Pos:* Assoc ed, Oper Res & Math Oper Res. *Res:* Game theory; mathematical economics; mathematical programming. *Mailing Add:* Econ Res Ctr Bell Labs Murray Hill NJ 07974

ROSENTHAL, RUDOLPH, b Atlantic City, NJ, Mar 24, 23; m 60; c 2. ORGANIC CHEMISTRY. *Educ:* Temple Univ, AB, 44, MA, 48; Univ Southern Calif, PhD(chem), 51. *Prof Exp:* Res chemist, Allied Chem Corp, 51-61; sr res chemist, Glenolden, 61-81, SR RES CHEMIST, ATLANTIC RICHFIELD CO, NEWTOWN SQUARE, 81- *Mem:* Am Chem Soc. *Res:* Olefin oxides; catalytic oxidation; nitration of olefins; isocyanates. *Mailing Add:* 484 Hilldale Ave Broomall PA 19008

ROSENTHAL, SAUL HASKELL, b Brooklyn, NY, Nov 14, 36; m 64; c 2. PSYCHIATRY. *Educ:* Harvard Univ, BA, 58, Harvard Med Sch, MD, 62; Am Bd Psychiat & Neurol, dipl, 69. *Prof Exp:* Intern med, Boston City Hosp, Harvard Med Sch, 62-63, resident psychiat, Mass Ment Health Ctr, 63-66; psychiatrist, US Air Force, 66-68; asst prof, 68-69, coordr residency training, 68-72, assoc prof psychiat, Univ Tex Med Sch San Antonio, 69-73; PRIV PRACT, 73- *Concurrent Pos:* Assoc clin prof psychiat, Univ Tex Med Sch, San Antonio, 73- *Mem:* Fel Am Psychiat Asn; AMA. *Res:* Depression; electrosleep. *Mailing Add:* Oak Hills Med Bldg 7711 Louis Pasteur Dr San Antonio TX 78229

ROSENTHAL, SAUL W, b New York, NY, Aug 13, 18; m 54; c 2. ELECTROPHYSICS, ELECTRICAL ENGINEERING. *Educ:* Polytech Inst Brooklyn, BEE, 48, MEE, 52. *Prof Exp:* ASSOC PROF ELECTROPHYS, POLYTECH INST NEW YORK, 61-, ASST DIR, MICROWAVE RES INST, 78- *Concurrent Pos:* Chmn, Comt C-95 RF Radiation Hazards, Am Nat Standards Inst, 68-; chmn, Int Working Group Measurements Related Interaction Electromagnetic Fields Biol Systs, Int Union Radio Sci, 76-; mem, Satellite Power Syst Microwave Health & Ecol Rev Group, Environ Protection Agency, 78- *Mem:* Sigma Xi; NY Acad Sci; Inst Elec & Electronics Engrs; Bioelectromagnetics Soc; Int Union Radio Sci. *Res:* Interaction of electromagnetic fields with biological systems and microwave measurements. *Mailing Add:* Polytech Inst of New York Rte 110 Farmingdale NY 11735

ROSENTHAL, SOL ROY, b Russia; nat US; m 50, 72; c 2. PATHOLOGY, IMMUNOLOGY. *Educ:* Univ Ill, BS, MD, MS, PhD(path). *Prof Exp:* Intern, Cook County Hosp, 27-29, resident path; instr, Univ Ill Col Med, 30-32, instr bact & pub health, 34-36, assoc, 36-40, asst prof, 40-49, assoc prof prev med, 49-65, prof prev med & community health, 65-72; dir, Inst Tuberc Res, 48-72; med dir, Res Found, Chicago, 48-75; DIR, RES FOUND, 75- *Concurrent Pos:* Lectr, SAm, Cuba, China, 80, Japan, 80; Pasteur Inst Paris consult, USPHS, 47-53. *Mem:* Soc Exp Biol & Med; Am Soc Exp Pathologists; Am Physiol Soc; Am Thoracic Soc; Am Asn Path & Bact. *Res:* Experimental pathology and medicine; immunology; bacillus-Calmette-Guerin vaccination against tuberculosis and neoplasia; chemical mediator of pain; atherosclerosis; thermal and radiation injury; competetin; risk exercise. *Mailing Add:* Box F Rancho Santa Fe CA 92067

ROSENTHAL, STANLEY ARTHUR, b Paterson, NJ, July 9, 26; m 48; c 2. MEDICAL MYCOLOGY, MICROBIOLOGY. *Educ:* Rutgers Univ, BS, 48; Univ Maine, MS, 50; Pa State Col, PhD(bact), 52. *Prof Exp:* USPHS spec fel, Prince Leopold Inst Trop Med, Antwerp, Belg, 60-61; from asst microbiol to asst prof dermat, 52-71, ASSOC PROF EXP DERMAT, MED CTR, NY UNIV, 61- *Mem:* Am Soc Microbiol; Med Mycol Soc Am; Int Soc Human & Animal Mycol. *Res:* Dermatophytosis; transmission of ringworm; identification of fungi. *Mailing Add:* Dept of Dermat NY Univ Med Ctr New York NY 10016

ROSENTHAL, STANLEY LAWRENCE, b Brooklyn, NY, Dec 6, 29; m 53; c 3. METEOROLOGY. *Educ:* Fla State Univ, MS, 53, PhD(meteorol), 58. *Prof Exp:* Instr meteorol, Fla State Univ, 57-58; mem staff, Los Alamos Sci Lab, 58-59; asst prof meteorol, Fla State Univ, 59-60; mem staff, 60-75, chief modeling group, 75-78, DIR, NAT HURRICANE RES LAB, NAT OCEANIC & ATMOSPHERIC ADMIN, 78- *Concurrent Pos:* Adj prof, Univ Miami; chmn, Oceans & Atmospheres Sect, Fla Acad Sci, 78-79. *Honors & Awards:* Gold Medal, Dept Com, 70. *Mem:* AAAS; fel Am Meteorol Soc. *Res:* Application of dynamic meteorology ot the tropical portions of the atmosphere; application of numerical weather prediction techniques to the tropics; dynamics and numerical simulation of hurricanes. *Mailing Add:* 13301 SW 99th Pl Miami FL 33156

ROSENTHAL, THEODORE BERNARD, b New Haven, Conn, June 12, 14. MICROSCOPIC ANATOMY, PHYSIOLOGY. *Educ:* Yale Univ, BS, 35, PhD(physiol), 41. *Prof Exp:* Res assoc cancer, Barnard Free Skin & Cancer Hosp, St Louis, 46-47; res assoc & instr anat, Sch Med, Washington Univ, 47-54; assoc prof, Sch Med, Univ Ind, 54-55 & Sch Med, Emory Univ, 55-56; ASSOC PROF ANAT, SCH MED, UNIV PITTSBURGH, 56- *Concurrent Pos:* Vis fel, Carlsberg Lab, Copenhagen Univ, 48. *Mem:* AAAS; Am Asn Anatomists. *Res:* Aging; arteriosclerosis; cancer. *Mailing Add:* Dept of Anat & Cell Biol Univ of Pittsburgh Sch of Med Pittsburgh PA 15213

ROSENTHAL, WALDEMAR ARTHUR, b Milwaukee, Wis, Jan 19, 24; m 48; c 1. CLINICAL CHEMISTRY. *Educ:* Marquette Univ, BS, 50, MS, 57; Nat Registry Clin Chem, dipl, 68. *Prof Exp:* Mgr new prod, Am Bio-Synthesis Corp, 50-57; vpres, Milwaukee Res Inst, 57-59; group leader geriat res, Vet Admin, Downey, Ill, 59-63, supvr spec chem, Wood Vet Admin Ctr, 63-72, clin res chemist, 72, RES & DEVELOP CHEMIST, LAB SERV, WOOD VET ADMIN CTR, 72- *Mem:* Fel Am Inst Chemists; Am Chem Soc; Am Asn Clin Chem; NY Acad Sci. *Res:* Organic and microchemical analytical aspects of biochemistry. *Mailing Add:* Wood Vet Admin Ctr Wood WI 53193

ROSENTHAL, WILLIAM S, b New York, NY, June 21, 25; m 54; c 2. GASTROENTEROLOGY, PHYSIOLOGY. *Educ:* Univ Minn, BA, 46; State Univ NY, 50. *Prof Exp:* Intern, Michael Reese Hosp, Chicago, 50-51; resident med, Vet Admin Hosp, Brooklyn, 51-52 & 53-55; res asst liver dis, Postgrad Med Sch, Univ London, 55-56; res asst gastroenterol, Mt Sinai Hosp, New York, 57-61; from asst prof to assoc prof med, 61-69, PROF MED & CHIEF SECT, NEW YORK MED COL, 69-, RES PROF PHYSIOL, 73- *Concurrent Pos:* Chief sect gastroenterol, Westchester County Med Ctr, 77- *Mem:* Am Gastroenterol Asn; Am Asn Study Liver Dis; Am Col Physicians; Am Col Gastroenterol (pres, 77-78); Am Soc Human Genetics. *Res:* Clinical and laboratory investigation of the pathological physiology of gastrointestinal and liver disease. *Mailing Add:* Westchester County Med Ctr Valhalla NY 10595

ROSENTHALE, MARVIN E, b Philadelphia, Pa, Dec 13, 33; m 59; c 2. PHARMACOLOGY. *Educ:* Philadelphia Col Pharm & Sci, BSc, 56, MSc, 57; Hahnemann Med Col, PhD(pharmacol), 60. *Prof Exp:* Pharmacologist, Lawall & Harrison Res & Control Labs, 51-60; pharmacologist, Wyeth Labs, Inc, 60-69, mgr immunoinflammatory pharmacol, 69-77, dir div pharmacol, 77-79, DIR DIV BIOL RES, ORTHO PHARMACEUT CORP, 79- *Concurrent Pos:* Vis asst prof, Hahnemann Med Col, 63-; instr, Univ Pa, 64-67; lectr, Philadelphia Col Pharm & Sci, 65- *Mem:* Am Soc Pharmacol & Exp Therapeut; Soc Exp Biol & Med; Am Rheumatism Asn. *Res:* Inflammation and allergy, particularly autoimmune diseases; cardiovascular and renal pharmacology. *Mailing Add:* Div Biol Res Ortho Pharmaceut Corp Raritan NJ 08869

ROSENTHALL, EDWARD, b Montreal, Que, June 3, 16; m 42; c 3. MATHEMATICS. *Educ:* McGill Univ, BSc, 37, MSc, 38; Calif Inst Technol, PhD(math), 44. *Prof Exp:* From lectr to asst prof math, McGill Univ, 40-47; mem staff, Inst Advan Study, NJ, 47-48; from assoc prof to prof, 48-77; assoc prof, 48-54, Peter Redpath prof pure math, 77-81, chmn dept, 60-79, EMER PROF MATH, MCGILL UNIV, 81- *Concurrent Pos:* Mem, Ctr Res, Univ Montreal, 79. *Res:* Number theory, especially diophantine analysis. *Mailing Add:* Dept Math McGill Univ 805 Sherbrooke St W Montreal PQ H3A 2K6 Can

ROSENWALD, GARY W, b Manhattan, Kans, Jan 10, 41; m 65; c 4. CHEMICAL ENGINEERING, PETROLEUM ENGINEERING. *Educ:* Univ Kans, BS, 64; Kans State Univ, MS, 66; Univ Kans, PhD(chem eng), 72. *Prof Exp:* High sch teacher math, Dickinson County Community High Sch,

64-66; res engr, 70-73, SR RES ENGR PETROL PROD, CITIES SERV CO, 73- *Mem:* Am Inst Mining, Metall & Petrol Engrs; Am Chem Soc; Am Inst Chem Engrs; AAAS. *Res:* Petroleum production, especially oil recovery by thermal and chemical flooding methods, reservoir performance and numerical simulation. *Mailing Add:* Energy Resources Group Cities Serv Co PO Box 50408 Tulsa OK 74150

ROSENWASSER, HYMAN, b Brooklyn, NY, Aug 18, 14; m 51; c 3. PHYSICAL CHEMISTRY. *Educ:* Brooklyn Col, BA, 36; George Washington Univ, PhD, 65. *Prof Exp:* Inspector naval mat, US Dept Navy, 41-46; anal chemist, US Geol Surv, 47-48; chemist, Nat Bur Stand, 48-53; chemist, Picatinny Arsenal & guest scientist, Brookhaven Nat Lab, 53-55; chemist & chief radiation unit, Naval Powder Factor, US Dept Navy, 55-56; chemist & chief chem div, Basic Res Lab, Eng Res & Develop Lab, US Army, 56-67; RES ADMINR, NAVAL AIR SYSTS COMMAND, 67- *Mem:* Am Chem Soc. *Res:* Jet fuels; pyrotechnics; azides. *Mailing Add:* 6325 Gentele Ct Alexandria VA 22310

ROSENWINKEL, EARL RICHARD, plant ecology, see previous edition

ROSENZWEIG, DAVID YATES, b Detroit, Mich, June 9, 33; m 58; c 5. INTERNAL MEDICINE, PULMONARY DISEASE. *Educ:* Wayne State Univ, BS, 54, MD, 57. *Prof Exp:* Intern, Sinai Hosp, Detroit, 57-58; resident internal med, Vet Admin Hosp, Denver, 58-60; fel pulmonary dis, Univ Colo, 60-62; from instr to asst prof, 62-72, ASSOC PROF MED, MED COL WIS, 72- *Concurrent Pos:* Consult, Vet Admin Hosp, Wood, Wis, 66-; fel pulmonary physiol, Postgrad Med Sch, Univ London, 67-68. *Mem:* Am Thoracic Soc; Am Fedn Clin Res; Int Union against Tuberculosis; fel Am Col Physicians; Am Physiol Soc. *Res:* Pulmonary disease and physiology; distribution of pulmonary ventilation and perfusion; exercise physiology; mycobacterial infections. *Mailing Add:* Dept of Med Med Col of Wis Milwaukee WI 53226

ROSENZWEIG, MARK RICHARD, b Rochester, NY, Sept 12, 22; m 47; c 3. NEUROSCIENCES. *Educ:* Univ Rochester, BA, 43, MA, 44; Harvard Univ, PhD(psychol), 49. *Hon Degrees:* Dr, Univ Rene Descartes, Sorbonne, 80. *Prof Exp:* Res assoc, Psycho-Acoust Lab, Harvard Univ, 49-51; from asst prof to assoc prof psychol, 50-60, res prof, Miller Inst Basic Res in Sci, 58-59, 65-66, PROF PSYCHOL, UNIV CALIF, BERKELEY, 60- *Concurrent Pos:* Fulbright res fel & Soc Sci Res Coun fel, Paris, 60-61; Am Psychol Asn rep, Int Union Psychol Sci, 70-72; vis prof, Univ Paris, 73-74. mem exec comt, 72-80; vpres, Int Union Psychol Sci, 80-84. *Mem:* Nat Acad Sci; fel Am Psychol Asn; Int Brain Res Orgn; Am Physiol Soc; Soc Neurosci. *Res:* Neurophysiology and behavior; neural processes in learning and memory; history of psychology. *Mailing Add:* Dept of Psychol Tolman Hall Univ of Calif Berkeley CA 94720

ROSENZWEIG, MICHAEL LEO, b Philadelphia, Pa, June 25, 41; m 61; c 3. POPULATION ECOLOGY, MAMMALOGY. *Educ:* Univ Pa, AB, 62, PhD(zool), 66. *Prof Exp:* Asst prof biol, Bucknell Univ, 65-69 & State Univ NY Albany, 69-71; assoc prof, Univ NMex, 71-75; dept head, 75-76, PROF ECOL & EVOLUTIONARY BIOL, UNIV ARIZ, 74- *Mem:* Ecol Soc Am; Soc Study Evolution; Am Soc Mammal; Am Soc Naturalists; Japanese Soc Pop Ecol. *Res:* Theory of predation; theory of habitat selection; speciation dynamics; population ecology of desert rodent communities. *Mailing Add:* Dept of Ecol & Evolutionary Biol Univ of Ariz Tucson AZ 85721

ROSENZWEIG, NORMAN, b New York, NY, Feb 28, 24; m 45; c 1. PSYCHIATRY. *Educ:* Univ Chicago, MB, 47, MD, 48; Univ Mich, MS, 54; Am Bd Psychiat & Neurol, dipl, 54. *Prof Exp:* From instr to assoc prof psychiat, Med Sch, Univ Mich, 53-61; from asst prof to assoc prof, 62-73, PROF PSYCHIAT, WAYNE STATE UNIV, 73-, CHMN DEPT, SINAI HOSP OF DETROIT, 61- *Concurrent Pos:* Dir joint res proj, Univ Mich & Ypsilanti State Hosp, 57-59. *Honors & Awards:* Rush Gold Medal Award, Am Psychiat Asn. *Mem:* NY Acad Sci; fel Am Col Psychiat; AMA; fel Am Psychiat Asn; AAAS. *Res:* Schizophrenia; mind-brain relationships; perceptual integration and isolation; clinical drugs; psychological consequences of physical illness; social attitudes. *Mailing Add:* Dept Psychiat Sinai Hosp Detroit Detroit MI 48235

ROSENZWEIG, WALTER, b Vienna, Austria, Sept 23, 27; US citizen; m 49; c 3. PHYSICS. *Educ:* Rutgers Univ, BS, 50; Univ Rochester, MS, 52; Columbia Univ, PhD(physics), 60. *Prof Exp:* Assoc health physicist, Brookhaven Nat Lab, 51-53; res physicist, Radiol Res Lab, Columbia Univ, 53-60; mem tech staff semiconductor physics, 60-72, SUPVR SEMICONDUCTOR MEMORIES, BELL LABS, 72- *Mem:* Radiation Res Soc; Inst Elec & Electronics Engrs. *Res:* Radiation dosimetry; radiation damage to semiconductors and devices; semiconductor memory design, large scale integrated circuit design; semiconductor device physics. *Mailing Add:* Bell Labs 555 Union Blvd Allentown PA 18103

ROSENZWEIG, WILLIAM DAVID, b New York, NY, Feb 6, 46. MICROBIOL ECOLOGY. *Educ:* St John's Univ, BS, 69; Long Island Univ, MS, 71; NY Univ, PhD(biol), 78. *Prof Exp:* Instr microbiol, NY Univ, 74-78; res fel microbiol, Rutgers Univ, 78-80; ASST PROF MICROBIOL, DREXEL UNIV, 80- *Mem:* Am Soc Microbiol. *Res:* Environmental biology; interactions between microorganisms and abiotic soil factors. *Mailing Add:* Dept Biol Sci Drexel Univ Philadelphia PA 19104

ROSETT, THEODORE, b Baltimore, Md, Aug 13, 23. BIOCHEMISTRY. *Educ:* Columbia Univ, BA, 49; Univ London, PhD(microbiol), 55. *Prof Exp:* Fel, Duke Univ, 55-57, USPHS fel, 57-59, assoc biochem, 59-66, asst prof, 66-67; asst prof, Med Col Ga, 67-70; ASSOC PROF BIOCHEM, SCH DENT, TEMPLE UNIV, 70- *Mem:* Am Soc Biol Chemists; Biochem Soc; Int Asn Dent Res; Soc Invest Dermat; Am Inst Chemists. *Res:* Biochemistry of skin and oral tissue. *Mailing Add:* Dept of Biochem Temple Univ Sch of Dent Philadelphia PA 19140

ROSEVEAR, JOHN WILLIAM, b Glenns Ferry, Idaho, Feb 19, 27; m 49; c 4. BIOCHEMISTRY. *Educ:* Ore State Col, BS, 49; Northwestern Univ, MD, 53; Univ Utah, PhD(biochem), 58. *Prof Exp:* Intern, Evanston Hosp Asn, 54; asst to staff, Sect Biochem, Mayo Clin, 58-59, consult, 59-69; assoc prof, Div Health Comput Sci, Univ Minn, Minneapolis, 69-71; med dir & dir clin chem, Kallestad Labs Inc, 71-74, dir labs, 74-75, vpres sci affairs, 76-79; PRES, BIO-METRIC SYSTS, INC, 79- *Concurrent Pos:* Clin assoc prof, Univ Minn, Minneapolis, 71- *Mem:* AAAS; Am Chem Soc; AMA. *Res:* Carbohydrate groups of proteins; diabetes mellitus; biochemical monitoring of patients; chromatographic analyses of organic acids; cancer detection tests; radioimmunoassay systems. *Mailing Add:* Bio-Metric Systs Inc 6316 Barrie Rd #1A Minneapolis MN 55435

ROSEWATER, JOSEPH, b Claremont, NH, Sept 18, 28; m 51; c 3. MALACOLOGY. *Educ:* Univ NH, BS, 50, MS, 55; Harvard Univ, PhD(biol), 60. *Prof Exp:* Instr zool, Mt St Mary Col, NH, 53-54; malacologist, 60-61, assoc cur div mollusks, 61-65, cur-in-chg, 65-68, CUR DIV MOLLUSKS, NAT MUS NATURAL HIST, 68- *Mem:* AAAS; Soc Syst Zool (treas, 63-65); Am Malacol Union, (pres, 69). *Res:* Systematics and zoogeography of mollusks. *Mailing Add:* Div of Mollusks Nat Mus of Natural Hist Washington DC 20560

ROSHAL, JAY YEHUDIE, b Chicago, Ill, Aug 27, 22. BOTANY. *Educ:* Univ Chicago, PhB, 48, SB, 49, SM, 50, PhD(bot), 53. *Prof Exp:* Instr bot, Oberlin Col, 53-55; res assoc, Ben May Lab, Univ Chicago, 55-56; asst prof bot, Eastern Ill Univ, 57-58; from instr to assoc prof, 58-63, chmn div sci & math, 62-64, PROF BOT, UNIV MINN, MORRIS, 63- *Concurrent Pos:* Mem secretariat, Space Sci Bd, Nat Acad Sci, 62-63; lectr, Univ Tex, 65-66; hon res assoc, Harvard Univ, 68-69. *Mem:* AAAS; Bot Soc Am; Mycol Soc Am; Am Soc Plant Physiol. *Res:* Mycology; physiology; microbial genetics. *Mailing Add:* Div of Sci Univ of Minn Morris MN 56267

ROSHKO, ANATOL, b Bellevue, Alta, July 15, 23; nat US; m 57; c 2. MECHANICS. *Educ:* Univ Alta, BSc, 45; Calif Inst Technol, MS, 47, PhD(aeronaut), 52. *Prof Exp:* Instr math, Univ Alta, 45-46, lectr eng, 49-50; res fel, 52-55, from asst prof to assoc prof, 55-62, PROF AERONAUT, CALIF INST TECHNOL, 62- *Concurrent Pos:* Sci liaison officer, Off Naval Res, London, 61-62; consult, McDonnell Douglas Corp, 54-; Dryden Res Lectr, Am Inst Aeronaut & Astronaut, 76. *Mem:* Nat Acad Eng; fel AAAS; fel Am Inst Aeronaut & Astronaut; Am Phys Soc; fel Can Aeronaut & Space Inst. *Res:* Gas dynamics; separated flow; turbulence. *Mailing Add:* Calif Inst of Technol 1201 E California Blvd Pasadena CA 91125

ROSHWALB, IRVING, b New York, NY, Jan 24, 24; m 47; c 4. STATISTICS. *Educ:* City Col New York, BSS, 43; Columbia Univ, MA, 46. *Prof Exp:* Chief statistician, Opinion Res Corp, 50-55; SR VPRES, AUDITS & SURV, INC, 55- *Concurrent Pos:* Adj prof statist, Grad Sch Bus, City Univ New York, 46- *Mem:* Am Asn Pub Opinion Res; fel Am Statist Asn; Am Mkt Asn; AAAS. *Res:* Survey sampling procedures; applications to areas of marketing and public opinion research; data analysis. *Mailing Add:* Audits & Surv Inc One Park Ave New York NY 10016

ROSI, DAVID, b Utica, NY, Apr 22, 32; m 56; c 4. BIOLOGY, MUTASYNTHESIS. *Educ:* Utica Col, BS, 54; Univ NH, MS, 56. *Prof Exp:* Jr bacteriologist & jr sanit chemist, Div Labs & Res Water Pollution, NY State Dept Health, 56-58, sanit chemist, 58-60; from asst res biologist to res biologist, 60-70, SR RES BIOLOGIST, STERLING WINTHROP RES INST, 70-, GROUP LEADER, 66- *Mem:* Am Soc Microbiol. *Res:* Microbial conversion, isolation and characterization of synthetic organic compounds of pharmaceutical interest; in vivo and in vitro drug metabolism studies; new antibiotics via mutagenesis; natural products. *Mailing Add:* Sterling Winthrop Res Inst Rensselaer NY 12144

ROSIER, RONALD CROSBY, b Baltimore, Md, Jan 23, 43; m 65; c 3. MATHEMATICS. *Educ:* Boston Col, AB, 65; Univ Md, PhD(math), 70. *Prof Exp:* ASST PROF MATH, GEORGETOWN UNIV, 70- *Mem:* Math Asn Am; Am Math Soc. *Res:* Functional analysis. *Mailing Add:* Dept of Math Georgetown Univ Washington DC 20007

ROSIN, ROBERT FISHER, b Chicago, Ill, Mar 19, 36; m 63; c 2. COMPUTER SCIENCE. *Educ:* Mass Inst Technol, BS, 57; Univ Mich, MS, 60, PhD(commun sci), 64. *Prof Exp:* From asst prof to assoc prof eng & appl sci, Yale Univ, 64-68; assoc prof comput sci & vchmn dept, State Univ NY Buffalo, 68-70, prof, 70-74; prof comput sci, Iowa State Univ, 74-76; mem tech staff, 76-78, CONSULT, BELL LABS, HOLMDEL, NJ, 78- *Concurrent Pos:* Nat Sci Found res grant, 70-72; NATO res grant, 72-73; vis prof, Univ Aarhus, 72-74. *Mem:* Asn Comput Mach; Comput Soc Inst Elec & Electronics Engrs. *Res:* Software and communication systems; realization of computer systems via software, hardware and firmware. *Mailing Add:* Bell Labs Holmdel NJ 07733

ROSIN, SEYMOUR, physics, deceased

ROSING, WAYNE C, b Kenosha, Wis, Oct 6, 47. FUNGAL ULTRASTRUCTURE. *Educ:* Univ Wis, Madison, BS, 69; Univ Tex, Austin, PhD(bot & mycol), 75. *Prof Exp:* Asst prof, George Peabody Col, 76-80; ASST PROF BIOL, MIDDLE TENN STATE UNIV, 80- *Mem:* Mycol Soc Am; Sigma Xi. *Res:* Ultrastructural studies of fungi; ascomycete spore formation. *Mailing Add:* Dept Biol Middle Tenn State Univ Murfreesboro TN 37132

ROSINGER, EVA LIBUSE JAROSLAVA, b July 21, 41; Can citizen; m 69. RADIOACTIVE WASTE MANAGEMENT, CHEMICAL ENGINEERING. *Educ:* Tech Univ, Prague, MSc, 63, PhD(chem), 68. *Prof Exp:* Researcher indust res, 67-68; fel chem eng, Univ Toronto, 68-70; res librarian tech info, Tech Univ, Aachen, Ger, 71-72; res officer environ comput modelling, 73-79, head, Systs Assessment Sect, 79, SCI ASSISTANT TO THE DIR, WASTE MGT DIV, ATOMIC ENERGY CAN, 80- *Mem:* Chem Inst Can; Can Nuclear Soc; Mat Res Soc; Asn Prof Engrs Manitoba. *Res:* Environmental assessment studies for radioactive waste disposal; computer simulation of environmental systems; developing scientific and organizational strategies, documenting optims, providing scientific advice and liason in nuclear waste management. *Mailing Add:* Whiteshell Nuclear Res Estab Atomic Energy of Can Ltd Pinawa MB R0E 1L0 Can

ROSINGER, HERBERT EUGENE, b Ger, Apr 18, 42; Can citizen; m 69. METALLURGY, MATERIALS SCIENCE. *Educ:* Univ Toronto, BASc, 66, MASc, 67, PhD(metall & materials sci), 70. *Prof Exp:* Humboldt fel, Gen Inst Metal Physics & Metall, Aachen WGer, 70-72; res officer metall, 72-78, head, Fuel Model Verification & Assessment Sect, 79-80, HEAD, FUEL TRANSIENT BEHAVIOUR SECT, ATOMIC ENERGY CAN LTD, 80- *Concurrent Pos:* Vis scientist at Kernforschungszentrum Karlsruhe, WGer, 79. *Mem:* Asn Prof Engrs Manitoba. *Res:* Nuclear safety studies; severe reactor core damage studies; high temperature materials behaviour; reactor fuel behaviour. *Mailing Add:* Atomic Energy of Can Ltd Pinawa Can

ROSINSKI, EDWARD J(OSEPH), inorganic chemistry, chemical engineering, see previous edition

ROSINSKI, JAN, b Warsaw, Poland, Feb 10, 17; nat US; m 45; c 1. ATMOSPHERIC CHEMISTRY. *Educ:* Warsaw Inst Technol, dipl, 49; Univ Warsaw, PhD. *Hon Degrees:* Libera docenza, Univ Bologna, 70; Dr habil, Univ Warsaw, 80. *Prof Exp:* Res chemist, Brit Celanese, Ltd, 48-51; chief chemist, Poray, Inc, Ill, 51-52; sr engr, IIT Res Inst, 52-62; SCIENTIST, NAT CTR ATMOSPHERIC RES, 62- *Mem:* AAAS; Am Meteorol Soc. *Res:* Fine particles; radiochemistry; colloids; geochemistry. *Mailing Add:* Nat Ctr for Atmospheric Res PO Box 3000 Boulder CO 80303

ROSINSKI, JOANNE, b Milwaukee, Wis. ELECTRON MICROSCOPY. *Educ:* Marquette Univ, BS, 66; State Univ NY, Buffalo, PhD(biol), 70. *Prof Exp:* Res fel, Harvard Univ, 71-73; asst prof biol, Williams Col, 73-78; res assoc, Brookhaven Nat Lab, 78-80; ASST PROF BIOL, SWEET BRIAR COL, 80- *Concurrent Pos:* NIH fel, Harvard Univ, 71-73. *Mem:* Am Soc Plant Physiologists; Bot Soc Am; Am Inst Biol Sci; AAAS. *Res:* Chloroplast development; ultrastructural and biochemical characterization of pigment-protein complexes in cyanobacteria and aigher plants. *Mailing Add:* Biol Dept Sweet Briar Col Sweet Briar VA 24595

ROSINSKI, MARTIN ALBIN, b Chicago, Ill, Aug 5, 27; m 51; c 3. MYCOLOGY, BOTANY. *Educ:* Univ Ill, BS, 50; Cornell Univ, PhD(mycol), 55. *Prof Exp:* From asst prof to assoc prof bot, Univ Maine, 55-62; from assoc prof to prof, Univ Iowa, 62-72; PROF ENVIRON SCI, UNITY COL, 72- *Concurrent Pos:* Chmn environ sci ctr, Unity Col, 73-75, dean fac, 75- 76. *Mem:* Mycol Soc Am. *Res:* Cytological, genetic and life history studies of higher fungi, especially ascomycetes, basidiomycetes. *Mailing Add:* Ctr of Environ Sci Unity Col Unity ME 04988

ROSKA, FRED JAMES, b Sheboygan, Wis, May 7, 54. RHEOLOGY, X-RAY SCATTERING. *Educ:* Univ Wis, BS, 76, PhD(chem), 81. *Prof Exp:* SR CHEMIST, MINN MINING & MFG CO, 81- *Concurrent Pos:* mem, Nat Ctr Small-Angle Scattering Res. *Res:* Structure and related physical properties of fibrin clots and oriented polymeric films by techniques such as small angle x-ray scattering, tensile properties and theoretical approaches. *Mailing Add:* Bldg 236 3M Ctr St Paul MN 55144

ROSKAM, JAN, b The Hague, Neth, Feb 22, 30; US citizen; m 56. AEROSPACE ENGINEERING. *Educ:* Delft Technol Univ, MS, 54; Univ Wash, PhD(aeronaut, astronaut), 65. *Prof Exp:* Asst chief designer, Aviolanda Aircraft Co, Neth, 54-56; aerodyn engr, Cessna Aircraft Co, 57-59; sr group engr, Boeing Co, 59-67; from assoc prof to prof aerospace eng, 67-76, ACKERS PROF AEROSPACE ENG, UNIV KANS, 76-, CHMN DEPT, 72- *Concurrent Pos:* Consult, Gates Learjet Corp. *Mem:* Assoc fel Am Inst Aeronaut & Astronaut; assoc fel Royal Aeronaut Soc; Neth Royal Inst Engrs. *Res:* Airplane stability, control and design; effects of aeroelasticity on stability, control and design; automatic flight controls. *Mailing Add:* Dept of Eng Univ of Kans Lawrence KS 66045

ROSKAMP, GORDON KEITH, b Quincy, Ill, July 4, 50; m 74; c 2. WEED SCIENCE, AGRONOMY. *Educ:* Western Ill Univ, BS, 71; Univ Mo-Columbia, MS, 73, PhD(agron), 75. *Prof Exp:* Res asst weed sci, Western Ill Univ, 70-71 & Univ Mo-Columbia, 71-75; asst prof agron, 75-81, ASSOC PROF AGR, WESTERN ILL UNIV, 81- *Concurrent Pos:* Grants from var chem co, Ill Soybean Operating Bd & Nat Crop Ins Asn. *Mem:* Weed Sci Soc Am; Am Soc Agron. *Res:* Weed control, especially in corn, soybeans and pastures; hail damage to corn; control of multiflora rose; herbicide damage to soybeans. *Mailing Add:* Dept of Agr Western Ill Univ Macomb IL 61455

ROSKIES, RALPH ZVI, b Montreal, Que, Nov 24, 40; m 63; c 3. THEORETICAL PHYSICS. *Educ:* McGill Univ, BSc, 61; Princeton Univ, MA, 63, PhD(math), 66. *Prof Exp:* Instr physics, Yale Univ, 65-67; I Meyer Segals fel, Weizmann Inst, 67-68; asst prof, Yale Univ, 68-72; assoc prof, 72-78, PROF PHYSICS, UNIV PITTSBURGH, 78- *Concurrent Pos:* Yale jr fac fel, Stanford Linear Accelerator Ctr, 71-72. *Mem:* Am Phys Soc; Asn Comput Mach. *Res:* High energy theoretical physics; quantum electrodynamics; symbolic calculation techniques; Yang-Mills fields; lattice field theory. *Mailing Add:* Dept of Physics Univ of Pittsburgh Pittsburgh PA 15260

ROSKOS, ROLAND R, b Arcadia, Wis, July 9, 40; m 66; c 2. PHYSICAL CHEMISTRY. *Educ:* Wis State Univ, La Crosse, BS, 62; Iowa State Univ, MS, 64, PhD(phys chem), 66. *Prof Exp:* Asst prof, 66-69, assoc prof, 69-76, PROF CHEM, UNIV WIS-LA CROSSE, 76- *Concurrent Pos:* Consult, Gunderson Clin, Ltd, La Crosse, Wis, 67- *Mem:* Am Chem Soc. *Res:* Chemical and medical instrumentation; physical and chemical properties as related to structure; applications and theory of lasers; isotope effects. *Mailing Add:* Dept of Chem Cowley Hall Univ of Wis La Crosse WI 54601

ROSKOSKI, JOANN PEARL, b Paterson, NJ, June 18, 47. ECOLOGY, MICROBIOLOGY. *Educ:* Rutgers Univ, BA, 69, MS, 72; Yale Univ, PhD(forest ecol), 77. *Prof Exp:* Res asst microbiol, E R Squibb Corp, 69-71; Rockefeller found fel, Res Inst Biotic Resources, 77-80; MEM FAC, PLANT SCI DEPT, UNIV ARIZ, 80- *Mem:* Ecol Soc Am; Sigma Xi; Int Soc Trop Ecol. *Res:* Nutrient cycling in tropical ecosystems, especially the role of nitrogen fixation in tropical agroecosystems. *Mailing Add:* Plant Sci Dept Univ Ariz Tucson AZ 85721

ROSKOSKI, ROBERT, JR, b Elyria, Ohio, Dec 10, 39; m 75. BIOCHEMISTRY. *Educ:* Bowling Green State Univ, BS, 61; Univ Chicago, MD, 64, PhD(biochem), 68. *Prof Exp:* USPHS fel biochem, Univ Chicago, 64-66; sr investr, US Air Force Sch Aerospace Med, 67-69; USPHS spec fel, Rockefeller Univ, 69-72; asst prof biochem, Univ Iowa, 72-75, assoc prof, 75-79; PROF & HEAD BIOCHEM DEPT, LA STATE UNIV MED CTR, 79- *Concurrent Pos:* Mem, Biochem Test Comt, Nat Bd Med Examiners, 81- *Mem:* Am Chem Soc; NY Acad Sci; Am Soc Neurochem; Am Soc Biol Chemists; Soc Neurosci. *Res:* Charcterization of cyclic adenosine monophosphate dependent protein kinase and tyrosine hydroxylase activity in the central nervous system; characterization of the actylcholine receptor in the heart. *Mailing Add:* Dept Biochem La State Univ Med Ctr 1900 Perdido St New Orleans LA 70112

ROSLER, LAWRENCE, b Brooklyn, NY, Feb 20, 34; m 65; c 2. COMPUTER SCIENCES. *Educ:* Cornell Univ, BA, 53; Yale Univ, MS, 54, PhD(physics), 58. *Prof Exp:* Jr physicist, Cornell Aeronaut Labs, 53, jr mathematician, 54; mem tech staff, 57-67, supvr comput graphics systs group, 67-76, SUPVR LANG & LIBR DEVELOP GROUP, BELL LABS, 76- *Mem:* AAAS; Am Phys Soc. *Res:* Man-machine graphical interaction; small-computer systems; computer languages. *Mailing Add:* Bell Labs Murray Hill NJ 07974

ROSLER, RICHARD S(TEPHEN), b Spokane, Wash, Jan 29, 37; m 61; c 4. CHEMICAL ENGINEERING. *Educ:* Gonzaga Univ, BS, 59; Northwestern Univ, PhD(chem eng), 62. *Prof Exp:* Sr aerothermo engr, United Aircraft Corp, 62-64; from asst prof to assoc prof chem eng, Gonzaga Univ, 64-68; process engr, Shell Develop Co, Calif, 68-69; dir res & develop, Applied Mat, Inc, 69-77; mgr semiconductor mat res, Motorola, Inc, 77-79; CORP DIR RES & DEVELOP, ADVAN SEMICONDUCTOR MAT AM, 79- *Mem:* Am Vacuum Soc; Electrochem Soc. *Res:* Technical management of development of equipment and processes on low pressure chemical vapor deposition reactors and plasma reactors for the processing of semiconductor wafers for the semiconductor industry. *Mailing Add:* 6700 E Solano Dr Paradise Valley AZ 85253

ROSLINSKI, LAWRENCE MICHAEL, b Detroit, Mich, May 28, 42; m 64; c 3. TOXICOLOGY, ENVIRONMENTAL HEALTH. *Educ:* Univ Mich, BS, 64; Wayne State Univ, MS, 66, PhD(pharmacol, physiol), 68. *Prof Exp:* Indust hygienist, Prof Exp: Indust Bur Indust Hyg, Detroit, Mich, 64; fel toxicol, Sch Pub Health, Univ Mich, 68-69; prof assoc, Nat Acad Sci, 69-72; toxicologist, Environ Protection Agency, 72-73; INDUST TOXICOLOGIST, FORD MOTOR CO, 73- *Concurrent Pos:* Comnr, Toxic Substances Control Comn, State Mich, 79- *Mem:* AAAS; Am Indust Hyg Asn; Am Bd Indust Hyg; Soc Toxicol; Am Bd Toxicol. *Res:* Pharmacology; industrial hygiene; physiology; biochemistry; toxicology. *Mailing Add:* Ford Motor Co PLTW-900 Dearborn MI 48121

ROSLOFF, BARRY NOEL, b New York, NY, May 25, 45. PHARMACOLOGY, PSYCHO-PHARMACOLOGY. *Educ:* Clark Univ, AB, 66; Vanderbilt Univ, PhD(pharmacol), 75. *Prof Exp:* PHARMACOLOGIST, FOOD & DRUG ADMIN, 75- *Res:* Mechanism of action of antidepressant drugs; neurotransmitters; toxicology of psychotropic and neurologic drugs; geriatric drugs. *Mailing Add:* 11203 Rokeby Ave Garrett Park MD 20766

ROSLYCKY, EUGENE BOHDAN, b Tovste, Ukraine, May 8, 27; Can citizen; m 71. MICROBIOLOGY. *Educ:* Univ Man, BSc, 53, MSc, 55; Univ Wis-Madison, PhD(microbiol), 60. *Prof Exp:* Asst microbiol, Univ Man, 53-55; asst bact, Univ Wis-Madison, 55-59; RES SCIENTIST MICROBIOL, RES INST, AGR CAN, 59- *Concurrent Pos:* Hon lectr fac med & dent, Univ Western Ont, 65-, lectr dept Russ studies, 71-74; chmn, Int Subcomt Agrobacterium & Rhizobium, Int Asn Microbiol Socs, 74- *Mem:* Can Soc Microbiol; Am Soc Microbiol; Soc Gen Microbiol; Ukrainian Free Acad Sci; Shevchenko Sci Soc. *Res:* Characterization of bacteriophages; bacteriocins; serological reactions; herbicides in relation to microbes. *Mailing Add:* 195 Tarbart Terrace London ON N6H 3B3 Can

ROSMAN, BERNARD HARVEY, mathematics, computer science, see previous edition

ROSMAN, HOWARD, b New York, NY, July 17, 29; m 52; c 2. PHYSICAL CHEMISTRY. *Educ:* State Univ NY, BA, 51, MA, 52; Columbia Univ, PhD(chem), 58. *Prof Exp:* Asst chem, Columbia Univ, 52-56; from instr to assoc prof chem, 56-72, chmn dept, 67-75 & 77-80, PROF CHEM, HOFSTRA UNIV, 72- *Concurrent Pos:* Lectr gen studies sch, Columbia Univ, 57-60. *Mem:* Am Chem Soc; AAAS; Sigma Xi. *Res:* Diffusion controlled and exchange reactions; photochemistry. *Mailing Add:* Dept of Chem Hofstra Univ Hempstead NY 11550

ROSNER, ANTHONY LEOPOLD, b Greensboro, NC, Nov 13, 43; m 66. ENZYMOLOGY, ENDOCRINOLOGY. *Educ:* Haverford Col, BS, 66; Harvard Univ, PhD(med sci), 72. *Prof Exp:* Teaching fel biochem, Harvard Univ, 69-72; fel molecular biol, Nat Inst Neurol Dis & Stroke, NIH, 72-73, staff fel, 73-74; res fel endocrinol, Med Sch, Tufts Univ, 74-75; res fel, 75-77, res assoc, 75-81, INSTR PATH, BETH ISRAEL HOSP, BOSTON, 81-; INSTR PATH, HARVARD MED SCH, 81- *Concurrent Pos:* Fel, Nat Inst Gen Med Sci, 72; res assoc biol chem, Harvard Med Sch, 78-81; dir, Estrogen Receptor Assay Lab & tech dir, Clinical Chem Lab, Beth Israel Hosp, Boston, 81- *Mem:* AAAS; Am Chem Soc; Am Soc Microbiol; Am Soc Cell Biol. *Res:*

Kinetics and control mechanisms attendant upon the binding of steroid hormones to receptor proteins in target tissues, comprised of either normal or cancerous cells. *Mailing Add:* Dept Path Beth Israel Hosp 330 Brookline Ave Boston MA 02215

ROSNER, DANIEL E(DWIN), b New York, NY, Oct 30, 33; m 58; c 2. CHEMICAL ENGINEERING, MECHANICAL ENGINEERING. *Educ:* City Col New York, BME, 55; Princeton Univ, MA, 57, PhD, 61. *Prof Exp:* Head interface kinetics & transport group, AeroChem Res Labs, Inc, 58-69; assoc prof, 69-74, PROF ENG & APPL SCI, YALE UNIV, 74- *Concurrent Pos:* Vis prof mech eng, Polytech Inst Brooklyn, 64-67; consult, Gen Elec Corp, Exxon & AeroChem Res Labs. *Mem:* AAAS; Am Inst Chem Engrs; Am Inst Aeronaut & Astronaut; Sigma Xi; Combustion Inst. *Res:* Energy and mass transfer in chemically reacting flow systems; experimental and theoretical studies in heterogeneous chemical kinetics; combustion; aerosol deposition, nucleation, growth, dispersion and coagulation. *Mailing Add:* Dept Chem Eng Yale Univ Box 2159 YS New Haven CT 06520

ROSNER, JOHN C, b Speedway, Ind, Oct 13, 35; m 58; c 2. CIVIL ENGINEERING, SOIL MECHANICS. *Educ:* Purdue Univ, BSCE, 59, PhD(soil mech), 69; Lehigh Univ, MSCE, 61. *Prof Exp:* Asst prof civil eng, Bradley Univ, 61-63; proj engr, Clyde E Williams & Assocs, Inc, 63-64; asst civil eng, Purdue Univ, 64-69; from asst prof to assoc prof, Ariz State Univ, 69-74; vpres, Engrs Testing Labs, Inc, 74-78; VPRES, WESTERN TECHNOLOGIES, INC, 78- *Mem:* Am Soc Civil Engrs; Am Soc Eng Educ; Am Inst Mining Engrs; Am Concrete Inst; Am Soc Testing & Mat. *Res:* Waste materials--fly ash; engineering properties of soils; performance of earth supported structures; earth retaining structures; shallow foundations. *Mailing Add:* Western Technologies Inc 3737 E Broadway Rd Phoenix AZ 85040

ROSNER, JONATHAN LINCOLN, b New York, NY, July 23, 41; m 65; c 1. PHYSICS. *Educ:* Swarthmore Col, AB, 62; Princeton Univ, MA, 63, PhD(physics), 65. *Prof Exp:* Res asst prof physics, Univ Wash, 65-67; vis lectr, Tel-Aviv Univ, 67-69; from asst prof to assoc prof, 69-75, PROF PHYSICS, UNIV MINN, MINNEAPOLIS, 75- *Concurrent Pos:* Consult, Argonne Nat Lab, 71-74; Fermi Nat Accelerator Lab, 75-78 & Brookhaven Nat Lab, 79-82; transl, Am Inst Physics, 71-73 & 78-; Alfred P Sloan res fel, Univ Minn, Minneapolis, Europ Orgn Nuclear Res, Geneva & Stanford Linear Accelerator Ctr, 71-73; mem, Inst Advan Study, 72, 76-77; vis res assoc, Calif Inst Technol, 70, 72 & 75; mem, High Energy Physics adv panel, 75; subpanel on new facil, 77 & subpanel on long range planning, 81; mem bd trustees, Aspen Ctr Physics, 78-; mem natural sci & eng grant selection comt, High Energy Physics, Can, 80-82. *Mem:* Fel Am Phys Soc. *Res:* Theoretical and elementary particle physics. *Mailing Add:* Physics 148 Univ of Minn Minneapolis MN 55455

ROSNER, JUDAH LEON, b New York, NY, Oct 18, 39; m 65; c 1. MOLECULAR BIOLOGY. *Educ:* Columbia Col, BA, 60; Yale Univ, MS, 64, PhD(biol), 67. *Prof Exp:* Biologist, 67, scientist, 67-70, staff fel, 70-74, RES BIOLOGIST, NIH, 74- *Mem:* Am Soc Microbiol. *Res:* Molecular biology and genetics of bacteria, bacterial viruses and transposable genetic elements. *Mailing Add:* Bldg 2 Rm 210 Nat Insts of Health Bethesda MD 20014

ROSNER, ROBERT, b Garmisch-Partenkirchen, WGer, June 26, 47; US citizen; m 71. PLASMA ASTROPHYSICS, SOLAR PHYSICS. *Educ:* Brandeis Univ, BA, 69; Harvard Univ, PhD(physics), 75. *Prof Exp:* Instr, 77-78, ASST PROF ASTRON, HARVARD UNIV, 78- *Concurrent Pos:* Woodrow Wilson Found fel, 69; res fel solar x-ray astron, Harvard Col Observ, 76-78. *Mem:* Am Phys Soc. *Res:* Solar and stellar x-ray astronomy; plasma heating, transport processes, diagnostics; astrophysical magnetic field generation and diffusion. *Mailing Add:* Harvard-Smithsonian Ctr Astrophys 60 Garden St Cambridge MA 02138

ROSNER, SHELDON DAVID, b Toronto, Ont, Feb 19, 41; m 67; c 2. PHYSICS. *Educ:* Univ Toronto, BSc, 62; Harvard Univ, AM, 63, PhD(physics), 68. *Prof Exp:* Nat Res Coun Can fel, Clarendon Lab, Oxford Univ, 69-71; ASST PROF PHYSICS & NAT RES COUN CAN GRANT, UNIV WESTERN ONT, 71- *Concurrent Pos:* Vis fel, Univ Colo, 78-79. *Mem:* Am Phys Soc; Can Asn Physicists. *Res:* Atomic physics; optical pumping; atomic and molecular beams; precise resonance measurements of atomic and molecular structure of fundamental interest. *Mailing Add:* Dept of Physics Univ of Western Ont London ON N6A 3K7 Can

ROSNER, WILLIAM, b Brooklyn, NY, Jan 7, 33. ENDOCRINOLOGY. *Educ:* Univ Wis, BA, 54; Albert Einstein Col Med, MD, 62. *Prof Exp:* Instr med, 67-69, assoc, 69-70, asst clin prof med, 70-72, asst prof, 72-73, assoc prof, 73-82, PROF MED, COL PHYSICIANS & SURGEONS, COLUMBIA UNIV, 82- *Concurrent Pos:* Asst attending physician, Roosevelt Hosp, 67-79, assoc attending physician, 69-72, attending physician & dir, Div Endocrinol, 72- *Mem:* Fel Am Col Physicians; Am Fedn Clin Res; Am Soc Biol Chemists; Am Soc Clin Invest; Endocrine Soc. *Res:* Steroid hormones, including the steroids secreted by the adrenal cortex, the ovaries, and the testis, their transport in plasma and the specific plasma proteins to which they are bound. *Mailing Add:* Dept Med St Luke's-Roosevelt Hosp Ctr 428 W 59 St New York NY 10019

ROSOFF, BETTY, b New York, NY, May 28, 20; m 42; c 1. ENDOCRINOLOGY. *Educ:* Hunter Col, BA, 42, MA, 60; City Univ New York, PhD(biol), 66. *Prof Exp:* Res chemist, Nat Aniline Div, Allied Chem Corp, NY, 43-48; res assoc cancer, Montefiore Hosp, Bronx, 52-62; instr biol, Bronx Community Col, 64-65; lectr, Hunter Col, 65-67; assoc prof, Paterson State Col, 67-68; from asst prof to assoc prof, 68-74, PROF BIOL, STERN COL, YESHIVA UNIV, 74- *Concurrent Pos:* Lectr physiol, Hunter Col, 61-64, adj prof, 68-75; mem working cadre, Nat Prostatic Cancer Proj, 74-79; vis investr, Am Mus Natural Hist, 81-82. *Mem:* AAAS; NY Acad Sci; Am Physiol Soc; Sigma Xi. *Res:* Zinc and trace metal metabolism; zinc and prostatic pathology; gonadotrophic control of prostate; thymus gland in development; radioactive isotope decontamination. *Mailing Add:* Dept Biol Stern Col 245 Lexington Ave New York NY 10016

ROSOFF, LEONARD, b Grand Forks, NDak, May 5, 12; m 35; c 1. SURGERY. *Educ:* Univ Southern Calif, AB, 31; Univ Tex, MD, 35; Am Bd Surg, dipl, 47. *Prof Exp:* Intern, Los Angeles County Hosp, 35-37, resident physician surg, 37-41; dir surg, Los Angeles County-Univ Southern Calif Med Ctr, 56-79, assoc prof, 56-66, prof, 66-79, chmn dept, 70-79, EMER PROF SURG, SCH MED, UNIV SOUTHERN CALIF, 79- *Concurrent Pos:* Mem staff, Hosp Good Samaritan; mem hon staff, Cedars of Lebanon Hosp, Los Angeles; mem bd dirs, Am Bd Surg, 70-76, sr mem, 76- *Mem:* Am Surg Asn; fel Am Col Surgeons (2nd vpres, 81-82); Am Asn Surg of Trauma; Soc Surg Alimentary Tract (pres, 79). *Res:* Studies of shock; peptic ulcer disease surgery; parathyroid and thyroid surgery. *Mailing Add:* Rm 9900 Dept Surg Sch Med Univ Southern Calif 1200 N State St Los Angeles CA 90033

ROSOFF, MORTON, b Brooklyn, NY, Feb 19, 22. PHYSICAL CHEMISTRY, SURFACE CHEMISTRY. *Educ:* Brooklyn Col, BA, 42, MA, 49; Duke Univ, PhD(chem), 55. *Prof Exp:* Res assoc & lectr colloid chem, Columbia Univ, 52-54; adj asst prof biophys chem, Sloan Kettering Inst Cancer Res, 54-58; sr scientist, IBM Watson Labs, NY, 60-64; sr scientist surface chem, Columbia Univ, 64-68, assoc prof phys chem & chmn dept, Col Pharmaceut Sci, 68-76; GROUP LEADER PHYS PHARM, USV PHARMACEUT CORP, 76- *Concurrent Pos:* Adj prof, City Univ New York, 56-75; sr scientist, Lever Bros Inc, NJ, 59-60; consult, Vet Admin Hosp, East Orange, NJ, 64, Dr Madaus Inc, WGer, 65-68, Am Stand & Testing, NY, 66-69 & Carter Wallace Inc, NJ, 69-74. *Mem:* Am Chem Soc; fel AAAS. *Res:* Physical chemistry of biological macromolecules; surface chemistry of biological macromolecules, microemulsions; metastable colloidal systems; lyotropic liquid crystals; physical pharmacy. *Mailing Add:* 15 Wellesley Ave Yonkers NY 10705

ROSOLOWSKI, JOSEPH HENRY, b Fall River, Mass, May 18, 30; m 52; c 2. PHYSICAL PROPERTIES OF CERMAICS. *Educ:* Rensselaer Polytech Inst, BS, 52, PhD(solid state physics), 61. *Prof Exp:* Assoc physicist, Res & Develop Ctr, Vitro Corp Am, 52-54; PHYSICIST, CORP RES & DEVELOP CTR, GEN ELEC CO, 60- *Concurrent Pos:* AEC exchange scientist, Poland, 62-63. *Honors & Awards:* Ross Coffin Purdy Award, Am Ceramic Soc, 76. *Mem:* Am Phys Soc; Am Ceramic Soc. *Res:* Diffusion in solids; physical properties of ceramics; radiation effects in metals; technical management. *Mailing Add:* Gen Elec Corp Res & Develop Ctr PO Box 8 Schenectady NY 12301

ROSOMOFF, HUBERT LAWRENCE, b Philadelphia, Pa, Apr 11, 27; m 50; c 2. MEDICINE. *Educ:* Univ Pa, AB, 48; Hahnemann Med Col, MD, 52; Columbia Univ, DMedSci, 60. *Prof Exp:* Intern, Hahnemann Hosp, Pa, 52-53; asst resident surgeon, Presby Hosp, New York, 53-54, asst resident neurosurgeon, 54-55; asst resident neurosurgeon, Neurol Inst, New York, 57-58, resident neurosurgeon, 58-59; from asst prof to assoc prof neurol surg, Sch Med, Univ Pittsburgh, 59-66; prof & chmn dept, Albert Einstein Col Med & chief hosp, 66-71; PROF NEUROL SURG & CHMN DEPT, SCH MED, UNIV MIAMI, 71- *Concurrent Pos:* Neurosurgeon, Presby Hosp & chief neurosurg, Vet Admin Hosp, Pittsburgh, 59-66; chief neurol surg, Bronx Munic Hosp Ctr & chief, Montefiore Hosp & Med Ctr, 66-71; chief neurosurg sect, Vet Admin Hosp, Miami, 71-; chmn dept neurol surg, Jackson Mem Hosp, Miami, 71- *Mem:* AMA; Am Col Surg; Cong Neurol Surg; Soc Neurol Surg; NY Acad Sci. *Res:* Neurological surgery; physiology; hypothermia; transplantation. *Mailing Add:* Dept of Neurol Surg Univ of Miami Sch of Med Miami FL 33101

ROSOWSKY, ANDRE, b Lille, France, Mar 3, 36; US citizen; m 62; c 3. ORGANIC CHEMISTRY. *Educ:* Univ Calif, Berkeley, BS, 57; Univ Rochester, PhD(org chem), 61. *Prof Exp:* NSF res fel, Harvard Univ, 61-62; res assoc path, Children's Cancer Res Found & Children's Hosp Med Ctr, 62-74, ASSOC SCIENTIST, SIDNEY FARBER CANCER CTR, 74-; ASSOC BIOL CHEM, HARVARD MED SCH, 64- *Mem:* Am Chem Soc. *Res:* Design and synthesis of new biologically active compounds, especially nitrogen heterocycles; medicinal chemistry. *Mailing Add:* Lab of Bioorg Chem 44 Binney St Boston MA 02115

ROSS, ALAN, b Hamilton, Ohio, Aug 25, 26; m 50; c 3. BIOSTATISTICS. *Educ:* Brown Univ, AB, 50; Iowa State Univ, MS, 52, PhD(statist), 60. *Prof Exp:* Res assoc biostatist, Sch Pub Health, Univ Pittsburgh, 54-56; from asst prof to assoc prof behav sci, Sch Med, Univ Ky, 56-64; assoc prof, 64-67, PROF BIOSTATIST & CHMN DEPT, SCH HYGIENE & PUB HEALTH, JOHNS HOPKINS UNIV, 67- *Concurrent Pos:* Prin investr, Med Comput Planning grant, HEW, 62- 63; chief biostatist consult, Off Aviation Med, Fed Aviation Admin, 66-70; statist adv, Int Collab Study Med Care, WHO, 66-73; prog dir, Biostatist Training grant, Nat Inst Gen Med Sci, 66-76 & Pub Health Statist Training grant, HEW, 69-74; chief statistician, Afghan Demog Study, USAID proj, 71-76. *Mem:* Fel Am Statist Asn; Biomet Soc. *Res:* Sampling theory and methods. *Mailing Add:* Dept Biostatist Johns Hopkins Univ Baltimore MD 21205

ROSS, ALAN MALCOLM, b London, Eng, July 21, 30; m 53; c 2. PHYSICAL METALLURGY, CERAMICS. *Educ:* Univ London, BSc, 53. *Prof Exp:* Asst, Res Labs, GEC Co, Ltd, UK, 48-53, res asst, 53-57; jr res officer, 57-60, asst res officer, 60-65, ASSOC RES OFFICER, ATOMIC ENERGY CAN LTD, 65- *Mem:* Am Ceramic Soc; Can Nuclear Soc. *Res:* Nuclear material inventory and criticality control by computer; fabrication of mixed-oxide recycle fuels; neutron radiography of reactor fuels and components. *Mailing Add:* Fuel Mat Branch Atomic Energy Can Ltd Chalk River ON K0J 1J0 Can

ROSS, ALBERTA B, b Moores Hill, Ind, July 26, 28; m 56; c 4. CHEMISTRY, INFORMATION SCIENCE. *Educ:* Purdue Univ, BS, 48; Wash Univ, BS, 51; Univ Md, PhD(chem), 57. *Prof Exp:* Tech librn, Monsanto Chem Co, 48-53; res assoc, Univ Mich, 57-58; consult, 71-72, SUPVR, RADIATION CHEM DATA CTR, UNIV NOTRE DAME, 64-71 & 72- *Mem:* Am Chem Soc; Am Soc Info Sci. *Res:* Radiation chemistry; chemical kinetics; data compilation; chemical literature. *Mailing Add:* Radiation Chem Data Ctr Radiation Lab Univ Notre Dame Notre Dame IN 46556

ROSS, ALEX R, b Cleveland, Ohio, June 30, 19; m 42; c 6. PHYSICAL GEOLOGY, GEOMORPHOLOGY. *Educ:* Colgate Univ, BA, 41; Univ Mich, MA, 47, PhD(geol), 50. *Prof Exp:* Instr geol, Univ Mich, 49-50; from asst prof to assoc prof, 50-57, PROF GEOL, OKLA STATE UNIV, 57-, CHAIRPERSON DEPT, 77- *Mem:* Geol Soc Am. *Res:* General geology; earth science education. *Mailing Add:* Dept of Geol Okla State Univ Stillwater OK 74074

ROSS, ALEXANDER, b St Louis, Mo, Feb 7, 20; m 47; c 1. ORGANIC CHEMISTRY. *Educ:* Wayne Univ, BS, 42; Univ Mich, MS, 50, PhD(org chem), 53. *Prof Exp:* Control chemist, Swift & Co, 42; instr chem, Univ Mich, 51; res chemist, Ethyl Corp, 52-55, asst res supvr, 55; sr res chemist, Olin-Mathieson Chem Corp, Conn, 56-57, sect chief, 57-59; head org res, Metal & Thermit Corp, 59-61, Europ tech mgr, M&T Chem Inc, Switz, 61-63, mgr org chem res & develop, NJ, 63-64, mgr chem res & develop, 64-65, dir res, 65-68, tech dir, 68-74; dir res & develop, 74-76, VPRES RES & DEVELOP, SPENCER KELLOGG DIV, TEXTRON INC, 77- *Mem:* AAAS; Am Chem Soc; Soc Plastics Engrs; Asn Res Dirs; NY Acad Sci. *Res:* Mechanism of antiknock action; organic phosphorus and agricultural chemistry; stereochemistry of carbocyclic systems; organohydrazine compounds; organometallics; stabilizers for polymers; organotin biocides; urethane chemicals; metal treatment; ceramics; polymers; catalysts; resins for coatings, inks, adhesives; urethanes, polyesters. *Mailing Add:* 216 Wood Acres Dr East Amherst NY 14051

ROSS, ALTA CATHARINE, b Santa Monica, Calif, Jan 19, 47; m 69. VITAMIN METABOLISM, ATHEROSCLEROSIS. *Educ:* Univ Calif, Davis, BS, 70; Cornell Univ, MNS, 72, PhD(biochem), 76. *Prof Exp:* Staff & res assoc med, Columbia Univ, 76-78; ASST PROF BIOCHEM & PEDIAT, MED COL PA, 78- *Concurrent Pos:* Coun fel, Am Heart Asn, 81- *Mem:* AAAS; Sigma Xi; Am Inst Nutrit. *Res:* Vitamin A transport and metabolism particularly during lactation; cholesterol transport and storage; relation of maternal diet to milk composition; diet and experimental atherosclerosis. *Mailing Add:* 3300 Henry Ave Philadelphia PA 19129

ROSS, ANTHONY, zoology, entomology, see previous edition

ROSS, ARTHUR LEONARD, b New York, NY, Mar 9, 24; m 48; c 2. ENGINEERING & SOLID MECHANICS. *Educ:* NY Univ, BAeE, 48, MAeE, 50, EngScD(aeronaut eng), 54. *Prof Exp:* Consult engr struct anal methods, Aircraft Nuclear Propulsion Dept, 54-61, mgr S5G struct eval, Knolls Atomic Power Lab, 61-66, STAFF ENGR STRUCT MECH, RE-ENTRY SYSTS DIV, GEN ELEC CO, 66- *Concurrent Pos:* Reviewer, Appl Mech Reviews, 55- *Mem:* Am Soc Mech Engrs; Am Acad Mech; Sigma Xi; Am Inst Aeronaut & Astronaut. *Res:* Research and development of mechanical stress analysis, shock and vibration, thermal stress, pressure vessels and composite materials; consultation and design reviews for failure prevention and mechanical design support. *Mailing Add:* Re-Entry Systs Div RM 5722 PO Box 7722 Philadelphia PA 19101

ROSS, BERNARD, b Montreal, Que, Nov 10, 34; US citizen; m 68. MECHANICAL & STRUCTURAL ENGINEERING. *Educ:* Cornell Univ, BME, 57; Stanford Univ, MSc, 59, PhD(aeronaut eng), 65; Nat Sch Advan Aeronaut Studies, France, dipl aeronaut eng, 60; Univ Edinburgh, dipl eng mech, 61. *Prof Exp:* Assoc engr, Marquardt Aircraft Co, 57-58; res asst aeronaut eng, Standord Univ, 60-64, res assoc, 64-65; eng physicist, Stanford Res Inst, 65-70; sr mem staff & exec, 70-78, PRES, FAILURE ANAL ASSOCS, 78- *Concurrent Pos:* Consult, Failure Anal Assocs, 68-70; vis lectr, Univ Santa Clara, 70-78. *Mem:* AAAS; Am Soc Mech Engrs; Am Inst Aeronaut & Astronaut; Sigma Xi; Nat Soc Prof Engrs. *Res:* Experimental and theoretical research in the buckling of thin shell structures and the penetration of solids by projectiles; structural and mechanical analysis of failures; fracture mechanics; design analysis. *Mailing Add:* Failure Anal Assocs 2225 E Bayshore Rd Palo Alto CA 94303

ROSS, BERND, b Munich, Ger, Dec 23, 24; nat US; m 59; c 2. SOLID STATE PHYSICS, SOLID STATE ELECTRONICS. *Educ:* Univ Ky, BS, 49, MS, 50; Ill Inst Technol, PhD(physics), 57. *Prof Exp:* Asst physics, Univ Ky, 49-50; dir res physics & chem, Radiation Counter Labs, Inc, 50-53; assoc physicist, Armour Res Found, Ill Inst Technol, 53-54; chief physicist, Semiconductor Div, Hoffman Electronics Corp, 54-58; dir res, Wesson Metal Corp, 58-61; chief scientist, Semiconductor Div, Hoffman Electronics Corp, 61-64, sr scientist, Electro Optical Systs, 65-66; prin res physicist, Bell & Howell Res Ctr, 66-69, mgr semiconductor dept, 69-71; mgr product develop, Emcon Div, Ill Tool Works, 71-76; PRESIDENT'S CONSULT TO USAF, 76-; PRES BERND ROSS ASSOC, 76- *Mem:* Am Phys Soc; Inst Elec & Electronics Engrs. *Mailing Add:* 2154 Blackmore Dr San Diego CA 92109

ROSS, BRADLEY ALFRED, b Broolyn, NY, June 5, 52. COMPUTER SIMULATION & MODELING. *Educ:* Univv Pa, BS, 74, MS, 76, PhD(chem eng), 79. *Prof Exp:* SR ENGR, MONSANTO CO, 79- *Mem:* Am Inst Chem Engrs; Sigma Xi. *Res:* Computer programs to aid in design, maintenance and operation of chemical plants, with emphasis on steady-state simulation. *Mailing Add:* Monsanto Co 800 N Lindbergh Blvd St Louis MO 63167

ROSS, BRUCE BRIAN, b Bryn Mawr, Pa, June 30, 44; m 68; c 2. DYNAMIC METEOROLOGY. *Educ:* Brown Univ, ScB, 66; Princeton Univ, MA, 68, PhD(aerospace eng), 71. *Prof Exp:* PHYSICIST METEOROL, GEOPHYS FLUID DYNAMICS LAB, NOAA PRINCETON UNIV, 71- *Concurrent Pos:* NSF fel, 66-70. *Mem:* Am Meteorol Soc; Sigma Xi; Am Geophys Union. Res; Mesoscale meteorology; particularly, numerical modeling of generation and maintenance of severe storm systems. *Mailing Add:* Geophys Fluid Dynamics Lab Princeton Univ PO Box 308 Princeton NJ 08540

ROSS, CAMILLA BREMS, b Chicago, Ill, Nov 21, 30; m; c 1. ORGANIC CHEMISTRY. *Educ:* Carthage Col, BA, 52; Univ Chicago, SM, 56, PhD(org chem), 58. *Prof Exp:* Group leader, 58-77, SR GROUP LEADER RES & DEVELOP, FILMS PACKAGING DIV, UNION CARBIDE CORP, 77- *Mem:* Am Chem Soc. *Res:* Food casings. *Mailing Add:* Films Packaging Div 6733 W 65th St Chicago IL 60638

ROSS, CHARLES ALEXANDER, b Urbana, Ill, Apr 16, 33; m 59. GEOLOGY, PALEOBIOLOGY. *Educ:* Univ Colo, BA, 54; Yale Univ, MS, 58, PhD(geol), 59. *Prof Exp:* Res assoc, Yale Univ, 59-60; from asst geologist to assoc geologist, Ill State Geol Surv, 60-64; from asst prof to assoc prof, 64-67, PROF GEOL, WESTERN WASH UNIV, 67-, CHMN DEPT, 77- *Concurrent Pos:* NSF res grants late Paleozoic fusulinaceans, 64-68; fel, Cushman Found Foraminiferal Res; consult petrol explor, Geol Surv Can, 75; mem, Int Subcomn Permian Stratig, 75-82. *Mem:* Fel AAAS; fel Geol Soc Am; Soc Econ Paleont & Mineral (secy-treas, 82-84); Am Asn Petrol Geol; Soc Study Evolution. *Res:* Biostratigraphy and paleontology, including foraminiferal faunas; paleoclimatology; paleoecology; recent large calcareous Foraminifera; paleobiogeography. *Mailing Add:* Dept of Geol Western Wash Univ Bellingham WA 98225

ROSS, CHARLES BURTON, b Rochester, NY, July 23, 34; m 62; c 2. PHYSICS. *Educ:* Villanova Univ, BS, 57; Purdue Univ, Lafayette, MS, 63, PhD(physics), 69. *Prof Exp:* AEC fel, Los Alamos Sci Lab, 69-71; asst prof, 71-80, ASSOC PROF COMPUT SCI, WRIGHT STATE UNIV, 80- *Mem:* Optical Soc Am. *Res:* High resolution optical atomic spectroscopy. *Mailing Add:* Dept of Comput Sci Wright State Univ Dayton OH 45435

ROSS, CHARLES W(ARREN), b Richard City, Tenn, Nov 2, 20; m 42; c 2. ELECTRICAL ENGINEERING. *Educ:* Univ Ala, BS, 43; Harvard Univ, MS, 49, DSc(elec eng), 52. *Prof Exp:* Chief elec engr, US Army Hqs, Frankfurt, Ger, 47-48; res engr, James G Biddle Co, 52-55; staff scientist, Res & Develop Ctr, 56-68, DIR SYSTS ANAL DEPT, TECH CTR, LEEDS & NORTHRUP CO, 68- *Honors & Awards:* IR-100 Award, Indust Res Mag, 65; John Vaaler Award, Chem Processing Mag, 68. *Mem:* Fel & sr mem Instrument Soc Am; Simulation Coun; fel Inst Elec & Electronics Engrs. *Res:* Instruments; measurements; primary measuring elements; process dynamic characteristics and control systems. *Mailing Add:* Systs Anal Dept Tech Ctr Dickerson Rd North Wales PA 19454

ROSS, CLAY CAMPBELL, JR, b Lexington, Ky, June 17, 36; m 64. MATHEMATICS. *Educ:* Univ Ky, BS, 59; Univ NC, MA, 61, PhD(math), 64. *Prof Exp:* From asst prof to assoc prof math, Emory Univ, 67-73; assoc prof, 73-81, dir acad comput, 77-81, PROF MATH & CONSULT, FAC COMPUT, UNIV OF THE SOUTH, 81- *Concurrent Pos:* Vis prof math, Univ Mo-Rolla, 79-80. *Mem:* Math Asn Am; Soc Indust & Appl Math; Asn Comput Mach. *Res:* Singular differential equations and systems. *Mailing Add:* Univ of the South Sewanee TN 37375

ROSS, CLEON WALTER, b Driggs, Idaho, May 27, 34; m 56; c 3. PLANT PHYSIOLOGY, PLANT BIOCHEMISTRY. *Educ:* Brigham Young Univ, BS, 56; Utah State Univ, MS, 59, PhD(plant physiol), 61. *Prof Exp:* From asst prof to assoc prof, 60-70, PROF BOT & PLANT PATH, COLO STATE UNIV, 70- *Mem:* Am Soc Plant Physiol. *Res:* Mechanisms of hormone-induced plant growth. *Mailing Add:* Dept of Bot & Plant Path Colo State Univ Ft Collins CO 80523

ROSS, DANIEL LOUIS, b New York, NY, June 10, 33; m 61. ORGANIC CHEMISTRY. *Educ:* Swarthmore Col, BA, 55; Mass Inst Technol, PhD(org chem), 59. *Prof Exp:* Scientist, Polaroid Corp, Mass, 59-63; mem tech staff, 64-73, GROUP HEAD ORG MAT & DEVICES RES, RCA LABS, 73- *Mem:* AAAS; Sigma Xi. *Res:* Cope elimination reaction; photographic chemistry; structure and color in dyes; lanthanide chelate lasers and coordination compounds; deuterium labeling; organic photochromic compounds; indigoid dyes; photochemistry; electron beam-sensitive materials; liquid crystals; microlithography; photoresists. *Mailing Add:* RCA Labs David Sarnoff Res Ctr Princeton NJ 08540

ROSS, DAVID A, b New York, NY, Aug 8, 36. GEOLOGICAL OCEANOGRAPHY. *Educ:* City Col New York, BS, 58; Univ Kans, MS, 60; Univ Calif, San Diego, PhD(oceanog), 65. *Prof Exp:* Res asst geol, Univ Kans, 58-60; res oceanogr, Scripps Inst Oceanog, Calif, 60-65; asst scientist, 65-68, assoc scientist, 68-78, SR SCIENTIST & DIR, MARINE POLICY & OCEAN MGT PROG, WOODS HOLE OCEANOG INST, 78- *Concurrent Pos:* Instr, Mass Inst Technol, 71-78 & Fletcher Sch Law & Diplomacy, Tufts Univ, 71-78; mem exec bd, Law of the Sea Inst, 74-; Ocean Affairs Adv Comn, Dept of State, 75-; Sea Grant Coordr, 77-; Ocean Policy Comt, Nat Acad Sci, 77- *Mem:* AAAS; Geol Soc Am; Am Geophys Union. *Res:* Distribution and movement of sediments on the continental shelf and deep sea; Black Sea, Mediterranean Sea, Red Sea and Persian Gulf; geology and geophysics of marginal seas; marine affairs. *Mailing Add:* Woods Hole Oceanog Inst Woods Hole MA 02543

ROSS, DAVID I, geophysics, see previous edition

ROSS, DAVID PAUL, institutional research, plasma physics, see previous edition

ROSS, DAVID SAMUEL, b Los Angeles, Calif, Dec 5, 37; m 66; c 3. PHYSICAL ORGANIC CHEMISTRY. *Educ:* Univ Calif, Los Angeles BS, 59; Univ Wash, PhD(org chem), 64. *Prof Exp:* PHYS ORG CHEMIST, STANFORD RES INST, 64- *Mem:* Am Chem Soc. *Res:* Chemical reaction kinetics; thermochemistry and mechanism gas and solution phases; acid-base catalysis; coal dissolution and liquefaction; chemistry related to synthetic fuels; fundamental studies in aromatic nitration and oxidation. *Mailing Add:* A063 Stanford Res Inst 333 Ravenswood Ave Menlo Park CA 94025

ROSS, DAVID STANLEY, b DuBois, Pa, Apr 16, 47; m 69; c 2. AGRICULTURAL ENGINEERING. *Educ:* Pa State Univ, BS, 69, MS, 71, PhD(agr eng), 73. *Prof Exp:* Res asst agr eng, Pa State Univ, 69-71, NSF trainee, 71-72; asst prof, 73-78, ASSOC PROF AGR ENG, UNIV MD, 78- *Concurrent Pos:* Exten agr engr, Univ Md, 73-; 1977 & 1978 Yearbk Agr Comt, USDA, 76-78; mem, Coun Agr Sci & Technol. *Honors & Awards:* Blue Ribbon Awards, Am Soc Agr Engrs, 77, 78 & 80. *Mem:* Am Soc Agr Engrs. *Res:* Extension education programs in nursery and greenhouse structures, environment and equipment; equipment for turf, fruit and vegetable producers; trickle irrigation; energy conservation. *Mailing Add:* Dept of Agr Eng Univ of Md College Park MD 20742

ROSS, DAVID WARD, b Detroit, Mich, Aug 11, 37; m 59; c 2. THEORETICAL PHYSICS. *Educ:* Univ Mich, BS, 59; Harvard Univ, AM, 60; PhD(physics), 64. *Prof Exp:* Res assoc physics, Univ Ill, Urbana, 64-66; univ fel, 66-67, asst prof physics, 66-70, res scientist, 66-74, ASST DIR THEORET PROG, FUSION RES CTR, UNIV TEX, AUSTIN, 74-, ASST DIR, INST FUSION STUDIES, 80- *Concurrent Pos:* Mem, Inst Advan Study, Princeton Univ, 70-71. *Mem:* AAAS; Am Phys Soc. *Res:* Linear and nonlinear stability theory and radio frequency heating of fusion plasmas; quantum many-body theory. *Mailing Add:* Fusion Res Ctr Univ of Tex Austin TX 78712

ROSS, DENNIS KENT, b Hebron, Nebr, May 4, 42; m 66; c 1. THEORETICAL PHYSICS. *Educ:* Calif Inst Technol, BS, 64; Stanford Univ, PhD(physics), 68. *Prof Exp:* From instr to assoc prof, 68-79, PROF ASTROPHYS, IOWA STATE UNIV, 79- *Mem:* Am Phys Soc; Int Astron Union. *Res:* Radar reflection test of general relativity; absorption in high energy photo production; large angle multiple scattering; magnetic monopoles; scalar-tensor theory of gravitation; charge quantization; Weyl geometry and quantum electrodynamics; gauge supersymmetry; fiber bundles and supergravity; holonomy groups and spontaneous symmetry breaking. *Mailing Add:* Dept of Physics Iowa State Univ Ames IA 50011

ROSS, DONALD, b New York, NY, June 9, 22; m 42; c 3. ACOUSTICS. *Educ:* Harvard Univ, BS, 42, MA, 43, PhD, 53. *Prof Exp:* Asst, Underwater Sound Lab, Harvard Univ, 45; assoc prof eng res & proj engr, Ord Res Lab, Pa State Col, 45-53; mem tech staff, Bell Tel Labs, Inc, 53-58; sr consult, Bolt, Beranek & Newman, Inc, Mass, 58-66, vpres, 66-67; head, Acoust Vibrations Lab, Naval Ships Res & Develop Ctr, 67-71; asst to pres, Tetra Tech Inc, 71-76; dep dir, Supreme Allied Command Atlantic, Acoustic Surface Wave Ctr, La Spezia, Italy, 76-80; WITH TETRA TECH SERVICES, 80- *Concurrent Pos:* Acoust liaison scientist, Off Naval Res, London, 64-65; chmn, Ad Hoc Group, Chief Naval Opers, 68-69. *Honors & Awards:* Karl Emil Hilgard Hydraul Prize, Am Soc Civil Eng, 55 & 57; Distinguished Civilian Serv Award, US Navy, 71. *Mem:* Fel Acoust Soc Am. *Res:* Underwater sound; ship and submarine noise control; oceanology. *Mailing Add:* Tetra Tech Services 3559 Kenyon St San Diego CA 92110

ROSS, DONALD ALEXANDER, b Montreal, Que, May 22, 22; nat US; m 50; c 1. PHYSICS. *Educ:* McGill Univ, BEng, 47; Yale Univ, MSc, 55, PhD(physics), 57. *Prof Exp:* X-ray physicist, Gen Elec Co, 48-50; engr, High Voltage Eng Corp, 50-53 & 58; res physicist, Indust Reactor Lab, Radio Corp Am, 58-62, mgr, PhD Recruiting, 62-64, head, Electronic Printing Labs, 64-75, HEAD, MFG TECHNOL RES LABS, RCA CORP, 75- *Mem:* Am Phys Soc. *Res:* Solid state physics; electrophotography; printing-graphic arts; electrical engineering. *Mailing Add:* RCA Labs Princeton NJ 08540

ROSS, DONALD CLARENCE, b Buffalo, NY, Mar 15, 24; m 48; c 3. GEOLOGY. *Educ:* Univ Iowa, BA, 48, MS, 49; Univ Calif, Los Angeles, PhD(geol), 52. *Prof Exp:* Asst, Univ Iowa, 48-49; geologist, State Geol Surv, Iowa, 49; asst, Univ Calif, Los Angeles, 49-52; GEOLOGIST, US GEOL SURV, 52- *Res:* Igneous and metamorphic petrology; granitic rocks of the White and Inyo Mountains, California; granitic basement of the San Andreas fault region, Coast and Tranverse Ranges; tectonic framework, Southern Sierra Nevada, California. *Mailing Add:* MS-77 US Geol Surv 345 Middlefield Rd Menlo Park CA 94025

ROSS, DONALD JOSEPH, b Brooklyn, NY, Mar 26, 28; m 51; c 3. PHYSIOLOGICAL CHEMISTRY. *Educ:* Fordham Univ, BS, 49, PhD(physiol), 56; Boston Col, MS, 50. *Prof Exp:* Asst biol, Boston Col, 49-50; from instr to assoc prof, 50-64, chmn dept, 60-70, prof biol, 64-78, DECAMP PROF BIOL, FAIRFIELD UNIV, 79- *Concurrent Pos:* Dir biochem lab, St Vincent's Hosp, Bridgeport, Conn, 57-59, consult, 59- *Mem:* AAAS; NY Acad Sci; fel Am Inst Chem; Am Inst Biol. *Res:* Biochemistry of insect metamorphosis; invertebrate physiology; cardiac enzymology; enzyme induction of cardiac and vascular atherosclerotic lesions. *Mailing Add:* Dept of Biol Fairfield Univ Fairfield CT 06430

ROSS, DONALD K(ENNETH), b St Louis, Mo, Apr 15, 25; m 51; c 1. ELECTRICAL & INDUSTRIAL ENGINEERING. *Educ:* Univ Minn, BSEE, 46; Mass Inst Technol, MSEE, 48; Wash Univ, DSc(indust eng), 60. *Prof Exp:* Asst, Mass Inst Technol, 46-48; PRES, ROSS & BARUZZINI, INC, 62- *Concurrent Pos:* Prof assoc, Bldg Res Adv Bd, Nat Acad Sci, 70- *Mem:* Inst Elec & Electronics Engrs; fel Am Consult Engrs Coun. *Res:* Effects of illumination on task performance. *Mailing Add:* Ross & Baruzzini Inc 7912 Bonhomme Clayton MO 63105

ROSS, DONALD LEWIS, b Paris, Tex, Aug 11, 36. ORGANIC CHEMISTRY. *Educ:* Univ Tex, BA, 58, PhD(chem), 63; Golden Gate Univ, MBA, 79. *Prof Exp:* Chemist, 62-70, GROUP MGR, SRI INT, 70- *Mem:* Am Chem Soc. *Res:* Synthesis of propellant ingredients; chemistry of organic fluorine and nitro compounds; synthesis of metabolite antagonists; process development. *Mailing Add:* SRI Int Menlo Park CA 94025

ROSS, DONALD MORRIS, b Kenosha, Wis, Aug 22, 23; m 46; c 6. INDUSTRIAL HYGIENE. *Educ:* Univ Tex, BS, 43; Univ Pittsburgh, MPH, 53, ScD(indust hyg), 56. *Prof Exp:* Tech supvr, Tenn Eastman Co, 43-46; res assoc physics, Carbide & Carbon Chem Co Div, Union Carbide & Carbon Corp, 46-48, indust hygienist, 48-52; res assoc, Univ Pittsburgh, 56-58, indust hygienist, 58-62, chief health protection br, US Energy Res & Develop Admin, 62-77, chief, 77-81, DIR DIV OCCUP SAFETY & HEALTH BR, US DEPT ENERGY, 81- *Concurrent Pos:* Fel indust hyg, AEC, Pa, 52-53, res fel, 53-56. *Mem:* Health Physics Soc; Am Indust Hyg Asn; Am Conf Govt Indust Hygienists. *Res:* Radiation protection; human engineering; control of industrial environment. *Mailing Add:* Occup Safety & Health Br US Dept Energy Washington DC 20545

ROSS, DONALD MURRAY, b Sydney, NS, May 21, 14; m 41; c 2. ZOOLOGY. *Educ:* Dalhousie Univ, BA, 34, MA, 36; Cambridge Univ, PhD(zool), 41, ScD(zool), 66. *Prof Exp:* Res assoc pest control, Sch Agr, Cambridge Univ, 41-46; lectr zool, Univ Col, London, 46-60; prof, 61-79, head dept, 61-64, dean sci, 64-76, EMER PROF ZOOL, UNIV ALTA, 79- *Honors & Awards:* Fry Medal, Can Soc Zool, 80. *Mem:* Fel AAAS; fel Royal Soc Can; Am Soc Zool; Can Soc Zool; Zool Soc London. *Res:* Neuromuscular activities and behavior of sea anemones; ecological and behavioral interactions between sea anemones and crustacean and molluscan partners and predators; control of color change and activity rhythms in fish. *Mailing Add:* Dept Zool Univ Alta Edmonton AB T6G 2G7 Can

ROSS, DORIS LAUNE, b Thorndale, Tex, Apr 20, 26. BIOCHEMISTRY. *Educ:* Tex Woman's Univ, BS, 47; Baylor Univ, MS, 58; Univ Tex, PhD(biochem), 67. *Prof Exp:* Med technologist, 47-54, sect head chem, Clin Labs, 54-56, chief med technologist & teaching supvr, 56-64, clin biochemist, Hermann Hosp & asst prof clin lab sci, Med Sch, Univ Tex Health Sci Ctr, 67-77, ASSOC PROF PATH & LAB MED & PROG DIR SCH ALLIED HEALTH SCI, MED SCH, UNIV TEX, 77- *Concurrent Pos:* Chief med technologist, Care Medico, Algeria, 62. *Mem:* Am Soc Med Technol; Am Asn Clin Chemists. *Res:* Clinical chemistry; clinical laboratory methodology; protein structure; immunoglobulins. *Mailing Add:* Dept of Path & Lab Med Main Bldg Univ Tex Med Sch Houston TX 77025

ROSS, EDWARD WILLIAM, JR, b Jackson Heights, NY, July 3, 25; m 55; c 5. MATHEMATICS, APPLIED MATHEMATICS. *Educ:* Webb Inst Naval Archit, BSc, 45; Brown Univ, ScM, 49, PhD(appl math), 54. *Prof Exp:* Fel, Exp Towing Tank, Stevens Inst Technol, 46-47; res engr, 51-52; mathematician, US Army Res Agency, Watertown Arsenal, 55-68; STAFF MATHEMATICIAN, NATICK RES & DEVELOP COMMAND, US ARMY, 68- *Concurrent Pos:* Secy Army res & study fel, 60-61. *Res:* Plasticity; elasticity; thin shell theory; differential equations; asymptotic theory; mechanical vibrations; biological statistics. *Mailing Add:* Natick Res & Develop Command US Army Kansas St Natick MA 01760

ROSS, ELDON WAYNE, b Elana, WVa, Oct 7, 34; m 59; c 2. FOREST PATHOLOGY. *Educ:* WVa Univ, BS, 57, MS, 58; Syracuse Univ, PhD(forest path), 64. *Prof Exp:* Instr forest bot, State Univ NY Col Forestry, Syracuse Univ, 63-64; plant pathologist, Forestry Sci Lab, Ga, 64-71, forest pathologist, Div Forest Insect & Disease Res, 71-73, asst dir forest insect & disease res, 73-74, asst dir continuing res, Northeast Forest Exp Sta, 74-79, DIR, SOUTHEASTERN FOREST EXP STA, FOREST SERV, USDA, 79- *Mem:* Am Phytopath Soc; Soc Am Foresters. *Res:* Dieback diseases of forest trees; Fomes annosus root rot; research administration. *Mailing Add:* USDA Forest Serv PO Box 2570 Asheville NC 28802

ROSS, ERNEST, b New York, NY, Dec 23, 20; m 49; c 4. POULTRY NUTRITION. *Educ:* Ohio State Univ, PhD(poultry nutrit), 55. *Prof Exp:* Asst poultry nutrit, Ohio State Univ, 51-55; asst poultry scientist, 57-60, assoc poultry scientist, 60-65, POULTRY SCIENTIST, UNIV HAWAII, 65- *Mem:* Poultry Sci Asn; World Poultry Sci Asn. *Res:* Physiological aspects of nutrition; tropical feedstuffs; environmental housing; management. *Mailing Add:* Dept Animal Sci Univ Hawaii 1800 East-West Rd Honolulu HI 96822

ROSS, FREDERICK KEITH, b Red Oak, Iowa, Nov 11, 42; m 64. STRUCTURAL CHEMISTRY, CRYSTALLOGRAPHY. *Educ:* Western Wash State Col, AB, 64; Univ Ill, Urbana, MS, 66, PhD(chem), 69. *Prof Exp:* Res assoc chem, Brookhaven Nat Lab, 69-71, State Univ NY Buffalo, 71-72; asst prof, Va Polytech Inst & State Univ, 72-79; SR RES SCIENTIST, UNIV MO, 79- *Concurrent Pos:* Adj assoc prof chem, Univ Mo-Columbia. *Mem:* Am Chem Soc; The Chem Soc; Am Crystallog Asn. *Res:* X-ray, neutron and gamma-ray diffraction; electronic distributions in solids by diffraction methods; diffraction physics of materials; low temperature x-ray and neutron diffraction. *Mailing Add:* Res Reactor Univ Mo Columbia MO 65211

ROSS, GERALD FRED, b New York, NY, Dec 14, 30; m 53; c 3. ELECTRONICS. *Educ:* City Col New York, BEE, 52; Polytech Inst Brooklyn, MEE, 55, PhD(electronics), 63. *Prof Exp:* Res asst microwave receivers, Univ Mich, 52-53; sr staff engr, W L Maxson Corp, NY, 54-58; res sect head phased array radar, Sperry Gyroscope Co, NY, 58-65, mem res staff microwaves, Sperry Rand Res Ctr, 65-68, mgr sensory systs dept, Sperry Rand Res Ctr, Sudbury, 68-81; PRES, ANRO ENG CONSULT, INC, BEDFORD, 81- *Mem:* Fel Inst Elec & Electronics Engrs; Sigma Xi. *Res:* Transient behavior studies related to microwave devices and high resolution radar systems; subnanosecond pulse technology and baseband radar. *Mailing Add:* 22 Suzanne Rd Lexington MA 02173

ROSS, GILBERT STUART, b New York, NY, Nov 4, 30; m 56; c 3. NEUROLOGY. *Educ:* Franklin & Marshall Col, AB, 51; State Univ NY, MD, 55. *Prof Exp:* From instr to asst prof neurol, Univ Minn, 61-64; assoc prof, 64-66, PROF NEUROL & CHMN DEPT, STATE UNIV NY UPSTATE MED CTR, 66- *Concurrent Pos:* Consult, Vet Admin Hosps, Hot Springs, SDak, 61-63 & Syracuse, NY, 64-; Nat Inst Neurol Dis & Stroke res & training grants, 64- *Mem:* AAAS; Am Acad Neurol; Animal Behav Soc. *Res:* Electroencephalography; pain perception in subhuman forms by the use of operant conditioning techniques. *Mailing Add:* Dept Neurol State Univ NY Upstate Med Ctr Syracuse NY 13210

ROSS, GORDON, b London, Eng, Sept 24, 30; m 54; c 2. PHYSIOLOGY, INTERNAL MEDICINE. *Educ:* Univ London, BSc, 51, MB, BS, 54. *Prof Exp:* Demonstr pharmacol, St Bartholomew's Hosp, London, 51-55; house physician & surgeon, St Mary Abbot's Hosp, 55-56; med registr, Mayday Hosp, 58-60 & King's Col Hosp, 60-63; from asst to assoc res pharmacologist, 63-66, from asst prof to assoc prof physiol & med, 66-72, PROF PHYSIOL & MED, SCH MED, UNIV CALIF, LOS ANGELES, 72- *Mem:* Am Fedn Clin Res; Am Physiol Soc. *Res:* Coronary circulation; adrenergic mechanisms. *Mailing Add:* Dept of Physiol Univ of Calif Sch of Med Los Angeles CA 90024

ROSS, GRIFF TERRY, SR, b Mt Enterprise, Tex, July 17, 20; m 45; c 2. ENDOCRINE PHYSIOLOGY, MEDICINE. *Educ:* SF Austin State Teachers Col, BA, 39; Univ Tex Med Br Galveston, MD, 45; Univ Minn, PhD(med), 60. *Prof Exp:* Med officer & sr investr, Endocrinol Br, Nat Cancer Inst, NIH, 60-67, asst chief, 67-70; asst chief, Reprod Res Br, Nat Inst Child Health & Human Develop, NIH, 70-75, chief, 75-76; clin dir, Nat Inst Child Health & Human Develop, NIH, 72-76; DEP DIR, CLIN CTR, NIH, 76- *Concurrent Pos:* Assoc ed, J Nat Cancer Inst, 67-68; mem Gonadotropin Subcomt, Nat Pituitary Agency, 67-70, mem Med Adv Bd, 71-74; assoc ed, J Clin Endocrinol & Metab, 68-72; mem Sci Adv Staff, Med Res Inst, Worcester, Mass, 69- *Mem:* Endocrine Soc (pres, 77-78); Am Col Physicians; Asn Am Physicians. *Res:* Endocrinology of reproduction. *Mailing Add:* Clinical Ctr Bethesda MD 20205

ROSS, HARLEY HARRIS, b Chicago, Ill, Apr 18, 35; m 59; c 2. RADIO ANALYTICAL CHEMISTRY, CHEMICAL INSTRUMENTATION. *Educ:* Univ Ill, Urbana, BS, 57; Wayne State Univ, MS, 58, PhD(radiochem), 60. *Prof Exp:* Scientist, Spec Training Div, Oak Ridge Inst Nuclear Studies, 60-63, chemist, Oak Ridge Nat Lab, 63-66, asst group leader nuclear & radiochem, 66-72, GROUP LEADER ANAL INSTRUMENTATION, OAK RIDGE NAT LAB, 72- *Honors & Awards:* IR-100 Award, 67. *Mem:* Sigma Xi. *Res:* Analytical applications of radioisotopes; liquid scintillator technology; organic luminescent properties; analytical instrumentation; radioisotope energy conversion; atomic and molecular spectroscopy; spectroscopic instrumentation. *Mailing Add:* Anal Chem Div Oak Ridge Nat Lab Box X Oak Ridge TN 37830

ROSS, HOWARD PERSING, b Stockbridge, Mass, Oct 26, 35; m 58; c 3. GEOPHYSICS, ECONOMIC GEOLOGY. *Educ:* Univ NH, BA, 57; Pa State Univ, MS, 63, PhD(geophys), 65. *Prof Exp:* Computer, United Geophys Corp, Calif, 58-60; res gen phys scientist, Air Force Cambridge Res Lab Mass, 65-67; sr res geophysicist, Explor Serv Div, Kennecott Explor, Inc, 67-77; PROJ MGR & SR GEOPHYSICIST, EARTH SCI LAB, UNIV UTAH RES INST, 77-; GEOPHYS CONSULT, 80- *Concurrent Pos:* Investr, Apollo Appln Prog, NASA, 66-67, mem peer rev panels, 77- *Mem:* Am Geophys Union; Soc Explor Geophys; Europ Asn Explor Geophys. *Res:* Rock magnetism; potential theory; research geophysics; mathematical models of geologic and geophysical processes; remote sensing; porphyry copper geology; geoelectric studies; mineral exploration; geothermal research; nuclear waste isolations studies. *Mailing Add:* Earth Sci Lab Univ Utah Res Inst Suite 120 420 Chipeta Way Salt Lake City UT 84108

ROSS, IAN KENNETH, b London, Eng, May 22, 30; m 56; c 2. MYCOLOGY, CELL BIOLOGY. *Educ:* George Washington Univ, BS, 52, MS, 53; McGill Univ, PhD(bot), 57. *Prof Exp:* Lectr bot, McGill Univ, 57; res assoc mycol, Univ Wis, 57-58; from instr to asst prof bot, Yale Univ, 58-64; from asst prof to assoc prof, 64-73, PROF BIOL, UNIV CALIF, SANTA BARBARA, 73- *Mem:* AAAS; Mycol Soc Am; Am Soc Cell Biol; Am Soc Microbiol. *Res:* Cytology and morphogenesis of fungi and the slime molds; cell communication and surfaces; fungal viruses. *Mailing Add:* Dept Biol Sci Univ Calif Santa Barbara CA 93111

ROSS, IAN M(UNRO), b Southport, Eng, Aug 15, 27; nat US; m 55; c 3. ELECTRICAL ENGINEERING. *Educ:* Cambridge Univ, BA, 48, MA & PhD(elec eng), 52. *Prof Exp:* Mem tech staff, Bell Tel Labs, Inc, 52-64, dir, Semiconductor Device & Electron Tube Lab, 62-64, managing dir, Bellcommun, Inc, 64-68, pres, 68-70 & 71-72, exec dir network planning, Bell Tel Labs, Inc, 71-73, vpres network planning & customer servs, 73-76, exec vpres systs eng & develop, 76-79, PRES, BELL TEL LABS, 79- *Honors & Awards:* Mem Prize Award in Honor of Morris N Liebmann, Inst Radio Engrs, 63; Pub Serv Award & Pub Serv Group Achievement Award, NASA, 69 & 75. *Mem:* Fel Inst Elec & Electronics Engrs; Nat Res Coun; fel Am Acad Arts & Sci. *Res:* Systems engineering and development. *Mailing Add:* Bell Tel Labs Inc 600 Mountain Ave Murray Hill NJ 07974

ROSS, IRA JOSEPH, b Live Oak, Fla, Apr 8, 33; m 55; c 3. AGRICULTURAL ENGINEERING. *Educ:* Univ Fla, BAgE, 55; Purdue Univ, MS, 57, PhD, 60. *Prof Exp:* Asst, Purdue Univ, 55-56, instr & asst in agr eng, 56-59; asst prof agr eng & asst agr engr, Univ Fla, 59-65, assoc prof & assoc agr engr, 65-67; assoc prof, 67-70, PROF AGR ENG, UNIV KY, 70- *Res:* Electric power and processing. *Mailing Add:* Dept of Agr Eng Univ of Ky Lexington KY 40506

ROSS, JAMES F(RANCIS), chemical engineering, see previous edition

ROSS, JAMES GEORGE, b Elgin, Man, Mar 12, 16; nat US; m 43; c 2. AGRICULTURE. *Educ:* Univ Alta, BSc, 41, MSc, 43; Univ Wis, PhD(bot), 47. *Prof Exp:* From asst prof to assoc prof, 47-54, PROF PLANT SCI, S DAK STATE UNIV, 54- *Concurrent Pos:* Guggenheim fel, Inst Genetics, Univ Lund, 58-59; Univ Nebr-USAID contract, Ataturk Univ, Turkey, 66-68. *Mem:* Genetics Soc Can; Am Genetic Asn; fel Am Soc Agron. *Res:* Breeding of wheat, barley and flax; cytology of flax, Taraxacum kok-saghyz and Canadian Taraxacums; cytotaxonomy of native Wisconsin flora including hybrid Juniperus; origin of homozygous diploid growth from colchicine induced tumors; breeding of forage grasses suitable to South Dakota; tissue culture of forage grasses. *Mailing Add:* Dept of Plant Sci SDak State Univ Brookings SD 57007

ROSS, JAMES NEIL, JR, b Akron, Ohio, Dec 18, 40; m 64; c 3. CARDIOVASCULAR PHYSIOLOGY, VETERINARY CARDIOLOGY. *Educ:* Ohio State Univ, DVM, 65, MSc, 67; Baylor Col Med, PhD(physiol), 72. *Prof Exp:* Res asst, Dept Vet Physiol & Pharm, Ohio State Univ, 61-65, res assoc vet cardiol, 65-67, lectr clin cardiol, 65-67; from instr to asst prof, Dept Surg & Physiol, Baylor Col Med, 67-74, asst dir vivarium, 67-69, asst chief exp surg, Taub Labs Mech Circulatory Support, 70-74; assoc prof physiol, Med Col Ohio, 74-81; PROF & CHMN, DEPT MED, SCH VET MED, TUFTS UNIV, 81- *Concurrent Pos:* Consult, Vet Admin Hosp, Houston, 70-73; mem coun clin cardiol, Am Heart Asn. *Mem:* Acad Vet

Cardiol (pres, 73-75); Am Soc Artificial Internal Organs; Am Asn Lab Animal Sci; Am Vet Med Asn; Am Col Vet Internal Med. *Res:* Hemodynamics; circulatory assist-replacement devices and techniques; biomaterials for blood interfacing; cardiovascular models; congenital heart disease; veterinary cardiology; cardiovascular surgery. *Mailing Add:* Dept Med Sch Vet Med Tufts Univ Boston MA 02111

ROSS, JAMES WILLIAM, b Ft Lewis, Wash, June 23, 28; m 70; c 3. ANALYTICAL CHEMISTRY, PHYSICAL CHEMISTRY. *Educ:* Univ Calif, Berkeley, BA, 51; Univ Wis-Madison, PhD(chem), 57. *Prof Exp:* Chemist, Tidewater Assoc Oil Co, 51-53; asst prof chem, Mass Inst Technol, 57-62; V PRES & DIR RES, ORION RES INC, 62- *Concurrent Pos:* Dir bd, Orion Res Inc, 62-; A D Williams distinguished vis scholar, Med Col Va, Va Commonwealth Univ, 72-73. *Mem:* Am Chem Soc; Am Electrochem Soc; AAAS. *Res:* Ion selective electrodes; theory, modes of fabrication and application to chemical and medical analysis. *Mailing Add:* Orion Res Inc 380 Putnam Ave Cambridge MA 02139

ROSS, JEFFREY, b St Louis, Mo, Feb 25, 43; m 68; c 2. MOLECULAR BIOLOGY. *Educ:* Princeton Univ, BA, 65; Wash Univ, MD, 69. *Prof Exp:* Intern med, Cedars-Sinai Med Ctr, Los Angeles, Calif, 69-70; res assoc, NIH, 70-74; asst prof, 74-78, ASSOC PROF, MCARDLE LAB CANCER RES, UNIV WIS-MADISON, 78- *Res:* Mechanism of synthesis of messenger RNA in eukaryotes with emphasis on the characterization of a precursor of globin messenger RNA; role of heme in development of authentic erythroid cells and of cultured erythroleukemic, Friend cells; mRNA synthesis and stability in the thalassemias. *Mailing Add:* McArdle Lab for Cancer Res Univ of Wis Madison WI 53706

ROSS, JOHN, b Vienna, Austria, Oct 2, 26; nat US; m 50; c 2. PHYSICAL CHEMISTRY. *Educ:* Queens Col, NY, BS, 48; Mass Inst Technol, PhD, 51. *Prof Exp:* Res assoc phys chem, Mass Inst Technol, 50-52; res fel, Yale Univ, 52-53; from asst prof to prof chem, Brown Univ, 53-66; prof & chmn dept, Mass Inst Technol, 66-71, Frederick George Keyes prof chem, 71-80. *Concurrent Pos:* Fel, NSF, 52-53, Guggenheim Found, 59-60 & Sloan Found, 60-64; vis Van der Waals prof, Univ Amsterdam, 66; mem bd govs, Weizmann Inst Sci, 71-; mem, NSF Adv Panel, 74-; chmn fac, Mass Inst Technol, 75-77. *Mem:* Nat Acad Sci; Am Chem Soc; fel Am Phys Soc; fel Am Acad Arts & Sci. *Res:* Kinetic theory; statistical and quantum mechanics; chemical kinetics; molecular beams. *Mailing Add:* Dept Chem Stanford Univ Stanford CA 94305

ROSS, JOHN, JR, b New York, NY, Dec 1, 28; m 58; c 3. MEDICINE, CARDIOLOGY. *Educ:* Dartmouth Col, AB, 51; Cornell Univ, MD, 55. *Prof Exp:* Clin assoc & sr investr, Nat Heart Inst, 56-60; asst resident, Columbia-Presby Med Ctr, 60-61 & Med Col, Cornell Univ, 61-62; attend physician & chief sect cardiovasc diag, Cardiol Br, Nat Heart Inst, 62-68; PROF MED & DIR CARDIOVASC DIV, SCH MED, UNIV CALIF, SAN DIEGO, 68- *Concurrent Pos:* Consult, Nat Conf Cardiovasc Dis, 63; mem cardiol adv comt, Nat Heart & Lung Inst, 74- *Mem:* Am Physiol Soc; fel Am Col Cardiol (trustee & vpres, 72-73); Am Soc Clin Invest; fel Am Col Physicians; Asn Am Physicians. *Res:* Cardiovascular research; cardiac catheterization techniques; mechanics of cardiac contraction; physiology of coronary circulation. *Mailing Add:* Dept of Med Univ of Calif at San Diego La Jolla CA 92093

ROSS, JOHN B(YE), b St Louis, Mo, June 14, 39; m 72; c 2. ELECTRICAL ENGINEERING. *Educ:* Pa State Univ, BS, 61, MS, 63, PhD(elec eng), 67. *Prof Exp:* Sr physicist, 67-80, RES ASSOC, EASTMAN KODAK CO, 80- *Mem:* Inst Elec & Electronics Engrs. *Res:* Applications of instrumentation and computers to analysis of the quality of film emulsion systems. *Mailing Add:* Res Labs Eastman Kodak Co Rochester NY 14650

ROSS, JOHN BRANDON ALEXANDER, b Suffern, NY, Feb 18, 47. BIOCHEMISTRY. *Educ:* Antioch Col, BA, 70; Univ Wash, PhD(biochem), 76. *Prof Exp:* Res assoc, Dept Chem, Univ Wash, 76-78; assoc res scientist, Dept Biol, Johns Hopkins Univ, 78-80; sr res fel, Dept Lab Med, Sch Med, Univ Wash, 80-82; ASST PROF, DEPT BIOCHEM, MOUNT SINAI SCH MED, 82- *Mem:* Sigma Xi; Am Chem Soc; Am Soc Photobiol; Biophys Soc. *Res:* Time resolved luminescence of biomolecules; structure of polypetides and proteins in solution; lipid, protein, and steroid interactions; luminescence assay in medicine. *Mailing Add:* Dept Biochem Mount Sinai Sch Med 5th Ave & 100th St New York NY 10029

ROSS, JOHN EDWARD, b Swissvale, Pa, Jan 1, 29; m 60; c 4. INDUSTRIAL HYGIENE, HEALTH PHYSICS. *Educ:* Univ Pittsburgh, BS, 49, MS, 59; Am Bd Health Physics, cert, 64; Bd Cert Safety Prof, cert, 72. *Prof Exp:* Indust hygienist, Bettis Atomic Power Lab, Westinghouse Elec Corp, 53-61; sr health & safety engr, Nuclear Mat & Equip Corp, 61-62; mgr reactor serv, Controls for Radiation, Inc, 62-65, gen mgr occup health, 65-67, GEN MGR, TELEDYNE ISOTOPES, 67- *Mem:* Am Indust Hyg Asn; Health Physics Soc. *Res:* Sample collection, analysis, evaluation and corrective action for industrial health hazards; heat and noise stress; occupational health program development; nuclear facility decommissioning. *Mailing Add:* Teledyne Inc PO Box 2304 Sandusky OH 44870

ROSS, JOHN FRANKLIN, b Guinda, Calif, June 19, 00; m 31; c 2. CHEMISTRY. *Educ:* Univ Mich, BS, 21, MS, 22, PhD(chem), 24. *Prof Exp:* Res chemist, Kodak Co, NY, 25-29; dir anal lab, J T Baker Co, NJ, 29-31, chief chemist, 40-43; res chemist, Mallinckrodt Chem Works, Mo, 31-40, Gen Elec Co, 43-65; CONSULT, CHEM & PHARMACEUT INDUSTS, 65- *Mem:* Am Chem Soc. *Res:* Analytical and inorganic chemistry; photographic, pharmaceutical and pure inorganic chemicals; phosphors. *Mailing Add:* 3053 Warrington Rd Cleveland OH 44120

ROSS, JOHN PAUL, b New Rochelle, NY, Apr 29, 27; m 51; c 4. PLANT PATHOLOGY. *Educ:* Univ Vt, BS, 52; Cornell Univ, PhD(plant path), 56. *Prof Exp:* Asst plant path, Cornell Univ, 52-56; from asst prof to assoc prof, 56-67, PROF PLANT PATH, NC STATE UNIV, 67-; PLANT PATHOLOGIST, SCI & EDUC ADMIN-AGR RES, USDA, 56- *Mem:* Am Phytopath Soc; Crop Sci Soc Am. *Res:* Diseases of soybeans caused by nematodes, viruses, fungi and bacteria. *Mailing Add:* Dept of Plant Path NC State Univ PO Box 5397 Raleigh NC 27650

ROSS, JOHN STONER, b Ames, Iowa, Sept 28, 25; m 48; c 8. ATOMIC SPECTROSCOPY. *Educ:* DePauw Univ, BA, 47; Univ Wis, MS, 48, PhD(physics), 52. *Prof Exp:* Res physicist, Ansco Res Lab Div, Gen Aniline & Film Corp, 51-53; from asst prof to assoc prof, 53-62, PROF PHYSICS, ROLLINS COL, 63- *Concurrent Pos:* Consult, Radio Corp Am, 55-58; res div, Radiation, Inc, 58-63. *Mem:* Am Phys Soc; Optical Soc Am; Am Asn Physics Teachers. *Res:* Isotope shifts in atomic spectra. *Mailing Add:* Dept of Physics Rollins Col Winter Park FL 32789

ROSS, JOSEPH C, b Tompkinsville, Ky, June 16, 27; m 52; c 5. INTERNAL MEDICINE. *Educ:* Univ Ky, BS, 50; Vanderbilt Univ, MD, 54; Am Bd Internal Med, dipl & cert pulmonary dis. *Prof Exp:* Intern med, Vanderbilt Univ Hosp, 54-55; resident, Duke Univ Hosp, 55-57, USPHS fel, 57-58; from instr to prof, Sch Med, Ind Univ, 58-70; prof med & chmn dept, Med Univ SC, 70-80; PROF MED, VANDERBILT UNIV, 81-, ASST VPRES, MED AFFAIRS, 82- *Concurrent Pos:* Mem, President's Nat Adv Panel on Heart Dis, 72, Vet Admin Merit Rev Bd Respiration, 72-76, Cardiovasc Study Sect, Nat Heart Inst, 66-70, Comt Respiratory Physiol, Nat Acad Sci 66-67, Prog Proj Comt, NIH, 71-75; mem bd gov pulmonary dis, Am Bd Internal Med, 72-81, Adv Coun, Nat Heart, Lung & Blood Inst, NIH, 81- *Mem:* Am Fedn Clin Res; Am Soc Clin Invest; Am Physiol Soc; Am Heart Asn; Am Col Physicians. *Res:* Pulmonary physiology, diffusion, function tests and capillary bed; emphysema. *Mailing Add:* D-3300 Med Ctr N Vanderbilt Univ Nashville TN 37232

ROSS, JOSEPH HANSBRO, b Houston, Tex, May 24, 25; m 56; c 4. ORGANIC CHEMISTRY. *Educ:* Rice Inst, BS, 46; Univ Tex, MA, 48; Univ Md, PhD(chem), 57. *Prof Exp:* Res assoc & fel chem, Univ Mich, 57-58; res chemist, Stamford Labs, Am Cyanamid Co, 58-63; asst prof, 63-67, from asst chmn to chmn dept, 67-73, ASSOC PROF CHEM, IND UNIV, SOUTH BEND, 67- *Mem:* Am Chem Soc; AAAS; Royal Soc Chem. *Res:* Reaction mechanisms; amine oxidations and condensations; nitrogen heterocycles; chromatography and solvent interactions; dyes. *Mailing Add:* Dept of Chem Ind Univ South Bend IN 46615

ROSS, JUNE ROSA PITT, b Taree, NSW, Australia, 31; m 59. MARINE SCIENCES, PALEOBIOGEOGRAPHY. *Educ:* Univ Sydney, BSc, 54, PhD(geol), 59, DSc(evolution), 74. *Prof Exp:* Res fel, Yale Univ, 57-60; res assoc, Univ Ill, 60-65; res assoc, 65-67, assoc prof, 67-70, PROF BIOL, WESTERN WASH UNIV, 70- *Concurrent Pos:* NSF res grants, 60-71. *Mem:* Soc Study Evolution; Marine Biol Asn UK; Int Bryozool Asn; Australian Marine Sci Asn; Electron Microscope Soc Am. *Res:* Ectoprocta; evolution and ecology; evolution of marine invertebrates and marine communities. *Mailing Add:* Dept of Biol Western Wash Univ Bellingham WA 98225

ROSS, KENNETH ALLEN, b Chicago, Ill, Jan 21, 36; c 2. MATHEMATICS. *Educ:* Univ Utah, BS, 56; Univ Wash, Seattle, MS, 58, PhD(math), 60. *Prof Exp:* Res instr math, Univ Wash, 60-61; asst prof, Univ Rochester, 61-64; assoc prof, 64-70, PROF MATH, UNIV ORE, 70- *Concurrent Pos:* Vis asst prof, Yale Univ, 64-65; Alfred P Sloan Found fel, 67-70; vis prof, Univ BC, 80-81. *Mem:* Am Math Soc; Math Asn Am. *Res:* Abstract harmonic analysis over topological groups. *Mailing Add:* Dept of Math Univ of Ore Eugene OR 97403

ROSS, LAWRENCE JAMES, b Brooklyn, NY, Sept 4, 29; m 59; c 3. PHYSICAL ORGANIC CHEMISTRY. *Educ:* Fordham Univ, BS, 50; Rutgers Univ, PhD(chem), 61. *Prof Exp:* Chemist, Nat Starch & Chem Corp, 50-55, supvr control methods lab, 55-57; from res chemist to sr res chemist, 60-75, group leader, 75-78, MGR FORMULATIONS, AM CYANAMID AGR CTR, 78- *Mem:* Am Chem Soc; fel Am Inst Chem. *Res:* Preparation and characterization of starch derivatives; mechanism of organic reactions; preparation of sulfonamides; preparation of brighteners of the styryl benzoxazole type; organic intermediates; process development; agricultural chemicals. *Mailing Add:* 1789 Woodfield Rd Martinsville NJ 08836

ROSS, LEONARD LESTER, b New York, NY, Sept 11, 27; m 51; c 2. ANATOMY, NEUROBIOLOGY. *Educ:* NY Univ, AB, 46, MS, 49, PhD(anat), 54. *Prof Exp:* Res assoc, NY Univ, 49-52; asst prof anat, Med Col Ala, 52-57; from assoc prof to prof, Med Col, Cornell Univ, 57-73; PROF ANAT & CHMN DEPT, MED COL PA, 73- *Concurrent Pos:* NIH fel, Cambridge Univ, 67-68. *Mem:* Electron Micros Soc Am; Histochem Soc; Am Asn Anatomists; Am Soc Cell Biol; Soc Neurosci. *Res:* Nervous system; electron microscopy; histochemistry; biogenic amines; neuroembryology. *Mailing Add:* Dept of Anat Med Col of Pa Philadelphia PA 19129

ROSS, LOUIS, b Akron, Ohio, Mar 24, 12; m 42; c 1. MATHEMATICS, STATISTICS. *Educ:* Univ Akron, AB, 34, BS, 35, MAEd, 39; Western Reserve Univ, PhD, 55. *Prof Exp:* Teacher pub sch, Ohio, 35-41; assoc prof math, 46-77, EMER PROF MATH, UNIV AKRON, 77- *Concurrent Pos:* Dir Ohio-Ky-Tenn region, US Metric Asn, Inc, 72- *Mem:* Math Asn Am; Am Statist Asn; fel Am Soc Qual Control; Sigma Xi. *Res:* Quality control and reliability; impact of metrication on education, business, and industry in the US. *Mailing Add:* 2400 Burnham Rd Akron OH 44313

ROSS, MALCOLM, b Washington, DC, Aug 22, 29; m 56; c 2. GEOCHEMISTRY, CRYSTALLOGRAPHY. *Educ:* Utah State Univ, BS, 51; Univ Md, MS, 59; Harvard Univ, PhD(geol), 62. *Prof Exp:* PHYS CHEMIST GEOCHEM, US GEOL SURV, 54-59 & 61- *Mem:* AAAS; fel Mineral Soc Am (treas, 76-80); fel Geol Soc Am; Clay Minerals Soc; Am Geophys Union. *Res:* Mineralogy, petrology and crystallography of rock-forming silicates, clay minerals and the asbestos minerals; subsolidus phase changes in silicates; pyroxene and amphibole geothermometry; relationships between human health and exposure to mineral particulates. *Mailing Add:* US Geol Surv Nat Ctr 959 Reston VA 22092

ROSS, MARC HANSEN, b Baltimore, Md, Dec 24, 28; m 49; c 3. THEORETICAL PHYSICS. *Educ:* Queens Col, NY, BS, 48; Univ Wis, PhD, 52. *Prof Exp:* NSF fel, Cornell Univ, 52-53; assoc physicist, Brookhaven Nat Lab, 53-55; from asst prof to prof physics, Ind Univ, 55-63; dir residential col, 74-77, PROF PHYSICS, UNIV MICH, ANN ARBOR, 63- *Concurrent Pos:* NSF fel, Univ Rome, 60-61. *Mem:* Am Phys Soc. *Res:* Elementary particle physics; environmental physics. *Mailing Add:* Dept of Physics Univ of Mich Ann Arbor MI 48109

ROSS, MARTIN RUSSELL, b New York, NY, Aug 23, 22; m 46; c 3. VIROLOGY, IMMUNOLOGY. *Educ:* Univ Conn, BA, 50; Univ Mich, MS, 52; George Washington Univ, PhD(virol), 57. *Prof Exp:* Res virologist, US Army Biol Labs, 52-56; asst prof virol, WVa Univ, 56-58; res microbiologist, 58-59, CHIEF VIROLOGIST, CONN STATE DEPT HEALTH, 59- *Honors & Awards:* J Howard Brown Award, Am Soc Microbiol, 56. *Mem:* Am Soc Microbiol. *Res:* Antigenic structure of psittacosis group of agents; development of fluorescent antibody techniques; epidemiology and laboratory diagnosis of viral diseases. *Mailing Add:* 115 Downey Dr Manchester CT 06040

ROSS, MARVIN, b Brooklyn, NY, June 27, 31; m 58; c 2. HIGH PRESSURE PHYSICS. *Educ:* Brooklyn Col, BS, 55; Pa State Univ, PhD(chem), 60. *Prof Exp:* Res assoc, Univ Calif, Berkeley, 60-63; PHYS CHEMIST, LAWRENCE LIVERMORE LAB, 63- *Mem:* Am Phys Soc; Sigma Xi. *Res:* Theoretical studies of condensed media at high pressures and temperatures; applications of shock waves to high pressure and high temperature research. *Mailing Add:* Lawrence Livermore Lab L-355 Univ of Calif Livermore CA 94550

ROSS, MARY HARVEY, b Albany, NY, Apr 1, 25; m 47; c 3. ENTOMOLOGY. *Educ:* Cornell Univ, BA, 45, MA, 47, PhD(paleont), 50. *Prof Exp:* Biologist, Oak Ridge Nat Lab, 51; from instr to assoc prof, 59-80, PROF ENTOM, VA POLYTECH INST & STATE UNIV, 80- *Concurrent Pos:* NSF grants, 71-73 & 80-83; Naval Facilities Eng Command grant, 74; Off Naval Res grant, 77-82; adj assoc prof, NC State Univ, 77-79; mem orgn comt, Genetics Sect, XV Int Cong Entom. *Mem:* Am Genetic Asn; Entom Soc Am; Genetics Soc Am; Sigma Xi. *Res:* Genetics and cytogenetics of the cockroach. *Mailing Add:* Dept of Entom Va Polytech Inst & State Univ Blacksburg VA 24061

ROSS, MERRILL ARTHUR, JR, b Montrose, Colo, June 2, 35; m 55, 73; c 5. WEED SCIENCE. *Educ:* Colo State Univ, BS, 57, MS, 59, PhD(plant physiol), 65. *Prof Exp:* Instr bot & plant path & jr plant physiologist, Colo State Univ, 59-65; asst prof bot, 65-69, assoc prof plant physiol, 69-75, ASSOC PROF BOT & PLANT PATH, PURDUE UNIV, WEST LAFAYETTE, 75-, EXTEN WEED SPECIALIST, 65- *Mem:* Weed Sci Soc Am. *Res:* Weed control; agronomy; botany; control of Johnson grass, Canada thistle and other perennial weeds in Indiana crop production systems. *Mailing Add:* Dept of Bot & Plant Path Purdue Univ West Lafayette IN 47907

ROSS, MICHAEL H, b Jamaica, NY, Oct 23, 30; m 58; c 3. ANATOMY, CELL BIOLOGY. *Educ:* Franklin & Marshall Col, BS, 51; NY Univ, MS, 59, PhD(biol), 60. *Prof Exp:* From instr to assoc prof anat, Sch Med, NY Univ, 60-71; prof path & dir, 71-77, CHMN DEPT ANAT, SCH MED, UNIV FLA, 77- *Concurrent Pos:* Chmn, Fla State Anat Bd, 71-; assoc ed, Am J Anat, 70-73 & Anat Record, 73- *Mem:* Am Asn Anatomists; Am Soc Cell Biol; Pan-Am Asn Anat; Soc Study Reprod; hon mem Bolivian Soc Anat. *Res:* Cell biology; tissue development; testicular function and developmental changes. *Mailing Add:* Dept of Anat Univ of Fla Sch of Med Gainesville FL 32610

ROSS, MICHAEL RALPH, b Middletown, Ohio, Apr 19, 47; m 70; c 2. AQUATIC ECOLOGY, FISH BIOLOGY. *Educ:* Miami Univ, BS, 69; Ohio State Univ, MS, 71, PhD(zool), 75. *Prof Exp:* Asst prof, 75-80, ASSOC PROF FISHERIES BIOL, UNIV MASS, 80- *Concurrent Pos:* Vis asst prof, Itasca Biol Sta, 79-81. *Mem:* Sigma Xi; Am Soc Ichthyologists & Herpetologists; Ecol Soc; AAAS; Am Fisheries Soc. *Res:* Behavior, mating systems, life history and population dynamics of fishes. *Mailing Add:* Dept of Forestry & Wildlife Mgt Univ of Mass Amherst MA 01003

ROSS, MONTE, b Chicago, Ill, May 26, 32; m 57; c 3. COMMUNICATIONS. *Educ:* Univ Ill, BSEE, 53; Northwestern Univ, MSEE, 62. *Prof Exp:* Elec engr, Chance-Vought Corp, 53-54 & Corps of Engrs, 54-56; electronic engr, Motorola, Inc, 56-57; sr engr, Hallicrafters Co, 57-59, group mgr electronics res & develop, 59-61, from assoc dir res to dir res, 61-66; mgr laser technol, 66-74, prog mgr, 74-81, DIR, LASER COMMUN SYSTS, MCDONNELL DOUGLAS ASTRONAUTICS CO, 81- *Concurrent Pos:* Adv ed, Laser Focus Mag, 66-70; tech ed, Laser Appln Ser, Acad Press, 70-; reviewer of grants, Nat Sci Found, 75-; affil prof, Washington Univ, 80- *Mem:* Fel Inst Elec & Electronics Engrs; Am Inst Aeronaut & Astronaut. *Res:* Laser communications systems; fiber optic systems; space communications; laser research and development, especially communications and guidance. *Mailing Add:* 19 Beaver Dr St Louis MO 63141

ROSS, MORRIS H, b Philadelphia, Pa, Jan 3, 17; m 49; c 3. BIOLOGY. *Educ:* Univ Pa, VMD, 43. *Prof Exp:* Jr biologist exp sta, Univ Tex, 43-44 & USDA, Ark, 44; res biologist, Biochem Res Found, 44-56, chief div cancer enzym, 56-66; SR MEM, INST CANCER RES, 66- *Concurrent Pos:* Mem staff, Franklin Inst, 46-56; assoc ed, Growth, Cancer & Nutrit; res award, Am Aging Asn, 79. *Honors & Awards:* J B Allison Mem Award, Rutgers Univ, 69. *Mem:* Gerontol Soc; Am Inst Nutrit. *Res:* Gerontology; pathology; nutrition; role of nutrition on the regulation of tumor susceptibility. *Mailing Add:* Inst Cancer Res 7701 Burholme Fox Chase Philadelphia PA 19111

ROSS, MYRON JAY, b Winthrop, Mass, June 10, 42; m 68; c 2. ELECTRICAL ENGINEERING. *Educ:* Northeastern Univ, BS, 64, MS, 66, PhD(elec eng), 70. *Prof Exp:* Staff engr, Proj Apollo, Draper Lab, Mass Inst Technol, 63-66; test dir test & eval, Mat Testing Directorate, Aberdeen Proving Ground, Md, 70-72; advan res & develop engr secure voice systs, GTE Sylvania, Needham, Mass, 72-74; eng specialist secure voice systs, CNR Inc, Newton, Mass, 74; ENG SPECIALIST TELECOMMUN SWITCHING, GTE SYLVANIA, 74- *Concurrent Pos:* NASA trainee fel, 66-69; lectr elec eng, Northeastern Univ, 68-70; NDEA fel, 70; assoc prof & lectr mgt sci, George Washington Univ, 71-72; lectr comput sci, Boston Univ, 78. *Honors & Awards:* NASA Commendation, Apollo Prog. *Mem:* Inst Elec & Electronics Engrs; Sigma Xi. *Res:* Telecommunications switching systems; data communication systems; integrated digital voice and data switching; secure voice systems; military communications networks. *Mailing Add:* 43 Condor Rd Sharon MA 02067

ROSS, NORTON MORRIS, b Rockville, Conn, Sept 29, 25; m 49; c 4. CLINICAL PHARMACOLOGY. *Educ:* Univ Conn, BA, 49; Univ Md, DDS, 54; Loyola Univ, MA, 67. *Prof Exp:* Assoc prof pharmacol, Sch Dent, Univ Md, 62-67; asst clin res dir, Squibb & Diamond Pin Awards, Fairleigh Dickinson Univ, 78- Med Res, 67-69; chief dent, Multiphasic Health Screening Ctr, Brookdale Hosp Ctr, Brooklyn, 69-70; assoc prof oral biol, pharmacol & oral med, Sch Dent, Med Col Ga, 70-73; prof pharmacol, chmn dept & dir divs oral biol & res & res coordr, Sch Dent, Fairleigh Dickinson Univ, 73-78; DIR, DEPT DENT CLIN RES, WARNER-LAMBERT CO, 78- *Concurrent Pos:* Clin prof, Dept Pharmacol, Sch Dent, 78-81. *Honors & Awards:* Distinguished Serv & Diamond Pin Awards, Am Acad Oral Med. *Mem:* AAAS; fel Royal Soc Health; fel Am Acad Oral Med (past-pres); fel Am Col Dent; Int Asn Dent Res. *Res:* Clinical investigation of analgesics; antibiotics; local and topical anesthetics; intra-oral adhesives; clinical investigation of plaque-suppressing agents. *Mailing Add:* Dept of Dent Sci 170 Tabor Rd Morris Plains NJ 07950

ROSS, PETER A, b Detroit, Mich, June 25, 31; m 58; c 3. MECHANICAL ENGINEERING. *Educ:* Univ Detroit, BME, 54; Northwestern Univ, MSEng, 56; Univ Wis, PhD(mech eng), 60. *Prof Exp:* Instr thermodyn & heat transfer, Univ Wis, 58-60; res specialist high temperature fluid dynamics, Aerospace Div, 60-64, chief combustion & flow, Turbine Div, 64-66, chief inlet res, Airplane Div, 66-68, ASST CHIEF PROPULSION LAB, BOEING CO, 68- *Res:* High temperature fluid mechanics; combustion and gas dynamics. *Mailing Add:* 12136 SE 23rd St Bellevue WA 98004

ROSS, PHILIP, b Newton, Mass, Nov 2, 26; m 52; c 2. ECOLOGY. *Educ:* Brown Univ, AB, 49; Univ Mass, MS, 51; Harvard Univ, PhD(plant ecol & geog), 58, MPH, 68. *Prof Exp:* Fulbright res scholar trop agr, Imperial Col, 57-58; botanist, Mil Geol Br, US Geol Surv, DC, 58-62; asst chief training grants sect, Nat Inst Dent Res, 62-63, chief res grants sect, 63-65, asst head spec int progs sect, Off Int Res, NIH, 65-68; pres, Int Sugar Res Found, Inc, 68-70; exec secy, Comt Effects of Herbicides in Vietnam, 70-74, EXEC SECY, BD AGR & RENEWABLE RESOURCES, NAT ACAD SCI-NAT RES COUN, 74- *Concurrent Pos:* Prof lectr, Am Univ, 59- *Mem:* Ecol Soc Am; Int Soc Trop Ecol. *Res:* Plant ecology and geography; vegetation mapping; microclimate; human ecology; science administration; agriculture. *Mailing Add:* 9108 Seven Locks Rd Bethesda MD 20817

ROSS, PHILIP N, b Boston, Mass, Mar 2, 16. ENGINEERING. *Educ:* Harvard Univ, BS, 38, MS, 39. *Prof Exp:* Tech asst to dir power pile div, Oak Ridge Nat Lab, from Westinghouse Elec Corp, 46-48, asst dir res, Bettis Atomic Power Lab, 48-50, mgr proj dept, 50-52, mgr reactor dept, 52-54, asst mgr surface ship proj, 54-58, mgr div reactor eng, 58-59, vpres & gen mgr, 59-66, mgr elec utility hq dept, 66-69, mgr power systs planning, 69-75; RETIRED. *Honors & Awards:* Order of Merit Award, Westinghouse Elec Corp, 52. *Mem:* Nat Acad Eng; Am Soc Mech Engrs; Am Nuclear Soc; Inst Elec & Electronics Engrs. *Res:* Nuclear power; systems engineering; marketing of power generation, transmission and distribution apparatus. *Mailing Add:* PO Box 336 Irvington VA 22480

ROSS, PHILIP NORMAN, JR, b Washington, DC, Oct 31, 43; m 66; c 1. CHEMICAL ENGINEERING, ELECTROCHEMISTRY. *Educ:* Yale Univ, BS, 65; Univ Del, MS, 69; Yale Univ, PhD(eng, appl sci), 72. *Prof Exp:* Proj engr chem eng, Explor Develop Div, Procter & Gamble Corp, 66-69; sr res assoc electrochem, Pratt & Whitney Aircraft & Power Systs Div, United Technol Corp, 72-76, sr scientist, United Technol Res Ctr, 76-78; PRIN INVESTR ELECTROCHEM, LAWRENCE BERKELEY LAB, UNIV CALIF, BERKELEY, 78- *Mem:* Am Chem Soc; Am Vacuum Soc. *Res:* Electrochemical energy conversion and storage systems; applied research in hydrogen production from fossil fuels. *Mailing Add:* Mat & Molecular Res Div Lawrence Berkeley Lab Berkeley CA 94720

ROSS, REUBEN JAMES, JR, b New York, NY, July 1, 18; m 42; c 4. PALEONTOLOGY, STRATIGRAPHY SEDIMENTATION. *Educ:* Princeton Univ, AB, 40; Yale Univ, MS, 46, PhD(geol), 48. *Prof Exp:* Field asst, Newfoundland Geol Surv, 38; asst prof geol, Wesleyan Univ, 48-52; geologist, Paleont & Stratig Br, US Geol Surv, 52-80. *Concurrent Pos:* Chmn subcomn Ordovician Stratigraphy, Int Union Geol Sci, 76-; adj prof geol, Colo Sch Mines, 80- *Mem:* Paleont Soc; Geol Soc Am; Am Asn Petrol Geologists; Brit Palaeontograph Soc; Soc Econ Paleont & Mineral. *Res:* Invertebrate paleontology and Ordovician stratigraphy of Basin Ranges. *Mailing Add:* Dept Geol Colo Sch Mines Golden CO 80401

ROSS, RICHARD FRANCIS, b Washington, Iowa, Apr 30, 35; m 57; c 2. VETERINARY MICROBIOLOGY. *Educ:* Iowa State Univ, DVM, 59, MS, 60, PhD(vet microbiol), 65; Am Col Vet Microbiol, dipl, 67. *Prof Exp:* Res assoc vet microbiol, Iowa State Univ, 59-61; operating mgr, Vet Labs, Inc, Iowa, 61-62; from instr to asst prof vet path, 62-65, assoc prof, 66-72, PROF VET MICROBIOL, IOWA STATE UNIV, 72- *Concurrent Pos:* NIH fel, Rocky Mt Lab, Nat Inst Allergy & Infectious Dis, Mont, 65-66; vis prof, Tierarztl Hochschule, Hanover & sr fel Humboldt Found, WGer, 75-76.

Mem: Am Vet Med Asn; Conf Res Workers Animal Dis; Am Soc Microbiol; Int Orgn Mycoplasmology; Am Col Vet Microbiologists. *Res:* Investigations on pneumonia in swine due to mycoplasma hypneumoniae and haemophilus pheuropneumoniae; agalactia in swine caused by coliform mastitis. *Mailing Add:* Vet Med Res Inst Iowa State Univ Ames IA 50011

ROSS, RICHARD HENRY, b Centre Hall, Pa, Sept 19, 16; m 43; c 3. DAIRY SCIENCE. *Educ:* Pa State Univ, BS, 38, PhD(dairy), 47; WVa Univ, MS, 40. *Prof Exp:* Asst dairy, WVa Univ, 38-40 & Pa State Univ, 40-42; from assoc prof to prof dairy husb, 47-53, head dept dairy sci, 60-70, prof dairy sci, Univ Idaho, 53-78; RETIRED. *Concurrent Pos:* Exten dairyman, Univ Idaho, 74-78. *Mem:* Am Soc Animal Sci; Am Dairy Sci Asn. *Res:* Dairy cattle nutrition and management; pasture. *Mailing Add:* 1464 Alpowa Ave Moscow ID 83843

ROSS, RICHARD STARR, b Richmond, Ind, Jan 18, 24; m 50; c 3. CARDIOLOGY. *Educ:* Harvard Med Sch, MD, 47. *Prof Exp:* From instr to assoc prof, 54-65, PROF MED, SCH MED, JOHNS HOPKINS UNIV, 65-, DEAN MED FAC & VPRES MED 75- *Concurrent Pos:* Consult, Nat Heart & Lung Inst, 61-78, training grant comt, 71 & adv coun, 74; chmn cardiovasc study sect, NIH, 66. *Mem:* Am Soc Clin Invest; Asn Am Physicians; Am Physiol Soc; master Am Col Physicians; Am Fedn Clin Res. *Res:* Cardiology utilizing physiological and radiological techniques. *Mailing Add:* Off of the Dean Johns Hopkins Univ Sch of Med Baltimore MD 21205

ROSS, ROBERT ANDERSON, b Auchinleck, Scotland, Sept 6, 31; m 58; c 3. SURFACE CHEMISTRY, APPLIED CHEMISTRY. *Educ:* Univ Glasgow, BS, 54, PhD(phys chem), 58; Univ Strathyclyde, ARCST, 54, DSc, 78. *Prof Exp:* Res engr, Marconi's Res Labs, Chelmsford, Eng, 57-59; asst res mgr, Joseph Crosfields Ltd, Warrington, 59-60; lectr inorg chem, Univ Strathyclyde, 60-64; head dept chem, Col Technol, Univ Belfast, 64-69; dean sci, 70-75, PROF CHEM, LAKEHEAD UNIV, 69- *Concurrent Pos:* Grants, Nat Res Coun Can, Dept Energy, Imperial Oil Ltd, Ont Dept Environ & Int Nickel Co Ltd. *Mem:* Royal Soc Chem; Can Inst Chem; Can Soc Chem Eng. *Res:* Heterogeneous catalysis and adsorption; technological and combustion chemistry; air and water pollution studies. *Mailing Add:* Dept of Chem Lakehead Univ Thunder Bay ON P7B 5E1 Can

ROSS, ROBERT EDGAR, b Trenton, NJ, Aug 25, 48; m 79. FOOD SCIENCE. *Educ:* Rutgers Univ, BS, 70; Univ Mass, MS, 72, PhD(food sci), 73. *Prof Exp:* Res asst prod develop, PepsiCo, Inc, 68; food technologist, Prod Develop, Hunt-Wesson Foods, Inc, 73-74, sr food technologist, 74-75, group leader, 75-77; mgr corp new prod, 78-79, asst dir, 79-81, ASSOC DIR FOOD RES, NABISCO, INC, 81- *Mem:* Inst Food Technologists; Sigma Xi; Am Asn Cereal Chemists. *Res:* New product development and brand maintenance; technical evaluation of new business opportunities, joint ventures, technology licensing, applied ingredient research, technical service and quality control for Nabisco Flour Mills. *Mailing Add:* 201 Farmingdale Rd Wayne NJ 07470

ROSS, ROBERT EDWARD, b Rochester, NY, Nov 19, 37; m 59. ORGANIC CHEMISTRY. *Educ:* St John Fisher Col, BS, 61; Princeton Univ, MA, 63, PhD(org chem), 66. *Prof Exp:* RES ASSOC, EASTMAN KODAK CO, 66- *Mem:* Am Chem Soc; AAAS; Royal Soc Chem. *Res:* Organic synthesis of heterocyclic compounds, photographic couplers and redox materials; evaluation of photographically useful fragments in a film format. *Mailing Add:* Res Labs Eastman Kodak Co 1669 Lake Ave Rochester NY 14650

ROSS, ROBERT GORDON, b Oxford, NS, July 14, 22; m 52; c 2. PHYTOPATHOLOGY. *Educ:* McGill Univ, BSc, 49, MSc, 54; Univ Western Ont, PhD(bot), 56. *Prof Exp:* Res officer & plant pathologist, 49-76, ASST DIR RES STA, AGR CAN, KENTVILLE, NS, 76- *Mem:* Am Phytopath Soc; Can Phytopath Soc (pres, 75-76); Agr Inst Can. *Res:* Tree fruit diseases. *Mailing Add:* 54 Southview Ave Kentville NS B4N 1W2 Can

ROSS, ROBERT TALMAN, b San Diego, Calif, Oct 10, 40; m 62; c 3. BIOPHYSICAL CHEMISTRY. *Educ:* Calif Inst Technol, BS, 62; Univ Calif, Berkeley, PhD(chem), 66. *Prof Exp:* Lectr chem, Univ Calif, Berkeley, 66-67; asst prof, Am Univ Beirut, 67-70; assoc prof biophys, 70-75, assoc prof, 75-81, PROF BIOCHEM, OHIO STATE UNIV, 81- *Concurrent Pos:* Chemist, Lawrence Berkeley Lab, Univ Calif, 66-67; dir, Beirut Study Ctr, Univ Calif, 69-70 & Biophys Prog, Ohio State Univ, 81- *Mem:* Biophys Soc; Am chem Soc. *Res:* Thermodynamics, statistical mechanics and kinetics of biological systems; photosynthesis. *Mailing Add:* Dept of Biochem Ohio State Univ 484 W 12th Ave Columbus OH 43210

ROSS, RODERICK ALEXANDER, b Ottawa, Ont, June 27, 26. APPLIED MATHEMATICS. *Educ:* Univ Toronto, PhD(math), 58. *Prof Exp:* From lectr appl math to asst prof math, 57-71, ASSOC PROF MATH, UNIV TORONTO, 71- *Res:* Wave propagation; differential equations. *Mailing Add:* Dept of Math Univ of Toronto Toronto ON M5S 2R8 Can

ROSS, RODNEY JAMES, b Sault Ste Marie, Ont, May 10, 42; m 64; c 2. BIOLOGY, SENSORY PHYSIOLOGY. *Educ:* Univ Toronto, BSc, 64, MSc, 67, PhD(zool), 77. *Prof Exp:* Fel insect neurobiol, Univ NB, 77-80; BIOL & STATIST CONSULT, 80- *Mem:* Can Soc Zoologists. *Res:* Sensory neurophysiology of vertebrate vibration detectors and of insect chemical detectors. *Mailing Add:* 240 Parkside Dr #9 Fredericton NB E3B 5V7 Can

ROSS, RONALD D, chemistry, see previous edition

ROSS, RONALD RICKARD, b Minneapolis, Minn, July 11, 31; m 52; c 3. HIGH ENERGY PHYSICS. *Educ:* Univ Calif, Berkeley, BA, 56, PhD(physics), 61. *Prof Exp:* Res physicist, Lawrence Radiation Lab & lectr physics, 61-63, asst prof, 63-67, assoc prof, 67-72, PROF PHYSICS, UNIV CALIF BERKELEY, 72- *Concurrent Pos:* Vis prof, Inst High Energy Physics, Univ Heidelberg, 66-67. *Mem:* AAAS; Am Phys Soc; Am Asn Physics Teachers. *Res:* Electron-positron interactions; fundamental interactions of particles. *Mailing Add:* Dept of Physics Univ of Calif Berkeley CA 94720

ROSS, RUSSELL, b St Augustine, Fla, May 25, 29; m 56; c 2. EXPERIMENTAL PATHOLOGY, CELL BIOLOGY. *Educ:* Cornell Univ, AB, 51; Columbia Univ, DDS, 55; Univ Wash, PhD(exp path), 62. *Prof Exp:* Intern, Presby Hosp, New York, 55-56; staff mem in chg oral surg sect, USPHS Hosp, Seattle, 56-58; from asst prof to assoc prof, 62-69, assoc dean sci affairs, 71-78, PROF PATH, SCH MED, UNIV WASH, 69-, ADJ PROF BIOCHEM, 78- *Concurrent Pos:* NIH career develop res award, 62-67; Guggenheim fel, 66-67; vis fel, Clare Hall, Cambridge Univ, 66-68; mem cell biol study sect B, NIH, 66-69, mem, Molecular Biol Study Sect, 69-71, chmn, 74-76; mem adv coun, Nat Heart, Lung & Hl Blood Inst, 78-81. *Honors & Awards:* Gordon Wilson Medal, Am Clin & Climatol Asn, 81. *Mem:* Am Soc Cell Biol; Histochem Soc; Electron Micros Soc Am; Am Soc Exp Pathologists; Am Asn Pathologists & Bacteriologists. *Res:* Wound healing; connective tissue; inflammation and arteriosclerosis electron microscopy; autoradiography and biochemical analyses. *Mailing Add:* Dept Path SM-30 Univ Wash Sch Med Seattle WA 98195

ROSS, SAM JONES, JR, b Tompkinsville, Ky, July 4, 31; m 56; c 3. SOIL MORPHOLOGY. *Educ:* Western Ky State Col, BS, 58; Univ Ky, MS, 61; Purdue Univ, PhD(soil), 73. *Prof Exp:* Asst soils, Univ Ky, 59-61; soil scientist, Va Polytech Inst, 61 & Soil Surv Lab, 62-68; instr soils, Purdue Univ, 68-73; soil scientist, Soil Surv Invest Lab, 73-75; SOIL SCIENTIST, NAT SOIL SURV LAB, 75- *Mem:* Am Soc Agron; Soil Sci Soc Am. *Res:* Field hydraulic conductivity work and soil physical work in laboratory. *Mailing Add:* Nat Soil Surv Lab USDA Eagle NE 68347

ROSS, SHEPLEY LITTLEFIELD, b Sanford, Maine, Nov 5, 27; m 54; c 4. MATHEMATICS. *Educ:* Univ Boston, AB, 49, AM, 50, PhD(math), 53. *Prof Exp:* Lectr math, Univ Boston, 50-53; instr, Northeastern Univ, 53-54 & Univ Boston, 54-55; from instr to assoc prof, 55-70, PROF MATH, UNIV NH, 70- *Mem:* Am Math Soc; Math Asn Am. *Res:* Ordinary differential equations. *Mailing Add:* Dept of Math Univ of NH Durham NH 03824

ROSS, SIDNEY, b Philadelphia, Pa, May 12, 26; m 48; c 3. PHYSICS, RESEARCH ADMINISTRATION. *Educ:* Pa State Univ, BS, 48; Univ Pa, MS, 53; Temple Univ, PhD(physics), 61. *Prof Exp:* Physicist interior ballistics res, Pitman-Dunn Labs, US Dept Army, 48-50, weapon systs res, 51-52, chief interior ballistics br, 53-54, ballistics div, 55-56, tech asst dir labs group, 57, asst dir physics res lab, 58-66, dir appl sci lab, 66-68, tech dir, Frankford Arsenal, 68-77; STAFF TECH ADV, GOVT SYSTS DIV ENG, RCA CORP, 77- *Mem:* Am Phys Soc; Sigma Xi. *Res:* Plasma physics; magnetohydrodynamics; hyperballistic propulsion and impact systems; advanced weapon systems; solid state physics; lasers; defense sciences and engineering. *Mailing Add:* 1042 Camas Dr Philadelphia PA 19115

ROSS, SIDNEY DAVID, b Lynn, Mass, Jan 31, 18; m 42; c 1. CHEMISTRY. *Educ:* Harvard Univ, AB, 39, PhD(org chem), 44; Boston Univ, MA, 40. *Prof Exp:* Asst chem, Boston Univ, 39-40; asst, Harvard Univ, 40-41, res assoc, Naval Ord Res Coun, 41-45, Comt Med Res, 45 & Pittsburgh Plate Glass Co fel, 46; dir org res, 46-56, res assoc, 56-71, DIR CORP RES & DEVELOP, SPRAGUE ELEC CO, 71- *Mem:* Am Chem Soc; Electrochem Soc; The Chem Soc. *Res:* Mechanism of organic reactions; polymerization; kinetics; dielectrics; synthetic organic chemistry. *Mailing Add:* Sprague Electric Co North Adams MA 01247

ROSS, STANLEY ELIJAH, b Paterson, NJ, Nov 27, 22; m 61; c 1. ORGANIC POLYMER CHEMISTRY, TEXTILES. *Educ:* Rutgers Univ, BS, 43; NY Univ, MS, 49. *Prof Exp:* Res chemist, Cent Res Lab, Celanese Corp Am, 47-52 & Allied Chem Corp, 52-59; head polymer dept, 60-65, head process develop dept, 65-67, res assoc, Explor Tech, 67-75, prod develop mgr, 71-74, mgr nonwoven tech, 75-79, MGR FIBER TECHNOL, RES & DEVELOP DIV, J P STEVENS & CO, INC, 79- *Mem:* Am Chem Soc; Soc Plastics Eng; Fiber Soc (vpres, 74; pres, 75); NY Acad Sci. *Res:* Polymers, fibers and textiles and their characterizations; mechanical behavior; thermoanalysis; extrusion and orientation of thermoplastics; crystallinity behavior; carbonization and pyrolysis of cellulose; development of nonwoven textile structures; cotton dust and its measurement. *Mailing Add:* J P Stevens & Co Inc Stevens Ctr PO Box 2850 Greenville SC 29602

ROSS, STEPHEN T, b Chicago, Ill, Mar 21, 31; m 52; c 2. MEDICINAL CHEMISTRY. *Educ:* Univ Ill, BS, 53; Rutgers Univ, MS, 60, PhD(org chem), 61. *Prof Exp:* Chemist, Johnson & Johnson, 55-59; assoc sr investr, 61-74, SR INVESTR, SMITH KLINE & FRENCH LABS, 74- *Mem:* Am Chem Soc; AAAS; NY Acad Sci. *Res:* Structure and activity relationships; synthetic heterocyclic chemistry; organo-analytical chemistry; organophosphorus chemistry; infrared and nuclear magnetic resonance spectroscopy; mass spectrometry; high-performance liquid and gas chromatography. *Mailing Add:* Smith Kline & French Labs 1500 Spring Garden St Philadelphia PA 19101

ROSS, STEPHEN THOMAS, b Hollywood, Calif, Nov 9, 44; m 69; c 1. ICHTHYOLOGY, FISH BIOLOGY. *Educ:* Univ Calif, Los Angeles, BA, 67, Calif State Univ, Fullerton, MA, 70; Univ SFla, PhD(biol), 74. *Prof Exp:* Teaching asst biol, Calif State Univ, Fullerton, 67-69; teaching asst, Univ SFla, 70-71, instr, 72; asst prof, 74-78, ASSOC PROF BIOL, UNIV SOUTHERN MISS, 78- *Concurrent Pos:* Vis res prof, Univ Okla Biol Sta, 81-82. *Mem:* Am Soc Ichthyologists & Herpetologists; Am Fisheries Soc; Soc Study Evolution; Soc Systematic Zool; Ecol Soc Am. *Res:* Ecological and evolutionary relationships of fishes. *Mailing Add:* Dept Biol SS Box 5018 Univ of Southern Miss Hattiesburg MS 39401

ROSS, STEWART HAMILTON, b Stanstead, Que, May 26, 03; nat US; m 30; c 1. GEOLOGY. *Educ:* McGill Univ, BSc, 25; Syracuse Univ, MS, 28, PhD(geol), 51; Harvard Univ, MA, 49. *Prof Exp:* Instr mineral, Syracuse Univ, 25-30; prof physics, Montreal Tech Sch, 31-44; instr physics, Agr & Mech Col, Tex, 44; assoc prof & chmn dept, Trinity Univ, 44-49; instr geol, Syracuse Univ, 49-50; prof & chmn dept, Univ Houston, 50-54; consult mining & geol, 53-61; geologist & proj mgr tech assistance team, US Opers

Mission-USAID & adv Nat Govt Vietnam, Paul Wier Co, 61-63; prof earth sci & dir earth sci prog, Adelphi Univ, 64-69; PROF PHYSICS & CHMN DEPT, MOLLOY COL, 69- Concurrent Pos: Geologist, Can Geol Surv, 25-29; prov geologist, Que Dept Mines, 37-51; chief geologist, Latin Am, Nat Bulk Carriers Inc, 54-60; consult geologist, Behre Dolbear & Cadillac Explors, Northwest Territories, 69, G V Lloyd Explor, Dist of Keewatin, 70, Rosario Explor, Dist of MacKenzie, 71, Mineral Serv, Cleveland, Coal Deposits, Hazard, Ky & Ky Prince Coal Mines; sr geologist, Geochem Reconnaissance Surveys, Resource Assocs Alaska, Fairbanks, 74; geologist/prospector, Pan Ocean Oil Ltd, Uranium explor, Barren Grounds, Baker Lake & Northwest Territories, Can, 80-81. Mem: Geol Soc Am; Nat Soc Prof Eng; Am Asn Petrol Geol; Am Inst Mining, Metall & Petrol Eng; fel Explorers Club. Res: Geological exploration; economic geology of oil, gas and other minerals; geophysical exploration; direct iron reduction. Mailing Add: Roxbury CT 06783

ROSS, STUART THOM, b Green Bay, Wis, July 6, 23; m 49; c 2. MECHANICAL METALLURGY, MATERIALS SCIENCE. Educ: Purdue Univ, BSMetE, 47, MSMetE, 49, PhD(metall), 50. Prof Exp: Asst chief metallurgist, Harrison Radiator Div, Gen Motors Corp, 50-52; head metall res, Eng Div, Chrysler Corp, 52-59; chief mat engr, Aeronutronic Div, Ford Motor Corp, 59-61; vpres eng & res, Brooks & Perkins, Inc, 61-65; dir eng & develop, Wolverine Tube Div, Universal Oil Prod, 65-69; vpres & tech dir, Crucible Specialty Metals Div, Colt Industs, 69-74 & Int Mill Serv, IU Int, 74-76; V PRES & TECH DIR, ITT MEYER INDUSTS, 76- Mem: Sigma Xi; fel Am Soc Metals; Am Inst Metall Engrs; Am Nuclear Soc; Brit Iron & Steel Inst. Res: Hot isostatic compaction; prealloyed powders; shapes/cavities; mechanical metallurgy of steel; fracture toughness; failure analysis and causation. Mailing Add: 2247 Hallquist Ave Red Wing MN 55066

ROSS, SYDNEY, b Glasgow, Scotland, July 6, 15. COLLOID CHEMISTRY. Educ: McGill Univ, BSc, 36; Univ Ill, PhD(chem), 40. Prof Exp: Instr chem, Monmouth Col, 40-41; res assoc & fel chem, Stanford Univ, 41-45; assoc prof phys chem, Univ Ala, 45-46; sr chemist, Oak Ridge Nat Lab, Tenn, 46-48; assoc prof, 48-51, PROF COLLOID SCI, RENSSELAER POLYTECH INST, 51- Concurrent Pos: Mem adv bd, Gordon Res Conf, 54; vis prof, Univ Strathclyde, Scotland, 75-78. Mem: Am Chem Soc; Royal Soc Chem. Res: Foams and antifoams; electrokinetic phenomena; dispersions and emulsions; adsorption of gases by solids. Mailing Add: Dept Chem Rensselaer Polytech Inst Troy NY 12181

ROSS, THEODORE WILLIAM, b Oak Park, Ill, May 9, 35; m 62; c 2. GEOLOGY. Educ: Ind Univ, BS, 57, MA, 62; Wash State Univ, PhD(geol), 69. Prof Exp: Instr, 66-67, chmn dept, 67-70, ASST PROF GEOL, LAWRENCE UNIV, 70-, CHMN DEPT, 74- Mem: Soc Econ Geol; Nat Asn Geol Teachers; Geol Soc Am. Res: Economic geology of metals; determination of pre-Pleistocene bedrock topography of Wisconsin. Mailing Add: Dept of Geol Lawrence Univ Appleton WI 54911

ROSS, WILLIAM D(ANIEL), b Elmira, NY, Nov 22, 17; m 61; c 1. LIGHT SCATTERING. Educ: Columbia Univ, BA, 38, BS, 39. Prof Exp: RES CHEMIST, E I DU PONT DE NEMOURS & CO, INC, 39-, RES FEL, 68- Honors & Awards: Roon Awards, Fedn Socs Paint Technol, 69 & 71, Bruning Award, 78. Mem: AAAS; Am Chem Soc; Optical Soc Am; Am Inst Chem Engrs; NY Acad Sci. Res: Titanium pigments; optics of pigments; chemistry of titanium; surface chemistry; thermodynamics; heat transfer; light scattering. Mailing Add: C & P Dept Exp Sta Bldg 336 E I du Pont de Nemours & Co Inc Wilmington DE 19898

ROSS, WILLIAM DONALD, b Hamilton, Ont, Sept 13, 13; nat US; m 39, 79; c 1. PSYCHIATRY. Educ: Univ Man, BSc(med) & MD, 38; McGill Univ, dipl, 49; FRCP(C); Am Bd Psychiat & Neurol, dipl, 49; Chicago Inst Psychoanal, cert, 58. Prof Exp: Demonstr histol, Univ Man, 33-34, demonstr physiol, 35-38, demonstr clin path & med, 38-39; demonstr neurol, McGill Univ, 40-43, demonstr psychiat, 43-48; asst prof, Univ Cincinnati, 48-53; prof, Univ BC, 53; assoc prof, 54-60, assoc prof environ health, 61-76, PROF PSYCHIAT & PROF ENVIRON HEALTH, COL MED, UNIV CINCINNATI, 76- Concurrent Pos: Attend psychiatrist & clinician, Outpatient Dept, Cincinnati Gen Hosp, dir & psychiat consult-liaison serv; consult, Vet Admin Hosp, Cincinnati. Honors & Awards: Franz Alexander Prize psychoanal res, Chicago Inst Psychoanal. Mem: AAAS; fel Soc Personality Assessment; Am Sociol Asn; Am Psychiat Asn; Am Psychoanal Asn. Res: Industrial mental health; psychosomatic medicine; psychopharmacology; psychoanalysis. Mailing Add: Dept of Psychiat Univ of Cincinnati Col of Med Cincinnati OH 45267

ROSS, WILLIAM J(OHN), b Auckland, NZ, June 11, 30; m 59; c 1. ELECTRICAL ENGINEERING. Educ: Univ Auckland, BSc, 51, MSc, 53, PhD(physics), 55. Prof Exp: Res asst, Ionosphere Res Lab, 55-56, from asst prof to assoc prof elec eng, 56-63, PROF ELEC ENG, PA STATE UNIV, UNIVERSITY PARK, 63-, HEAD DEPT, 71- Mem: Am Geophys Union; Inst Elec & Electronics Engrs; Am Soc Eng Educ. Res: Ionospheric radio propagation; ionospheric theory. Mailing Add: Dept of Elec Eng Pa State Univ University Park PA 16802

ROSS, WILLIAM MAX, b Farmington, Ill, Mar 20, 25; m 52; c 5. PLANT BREEDING, CROP PRODUCTION. Educ: Univ Ill, BS, 48, MS, 49, PhD(agron), 52. Prof Exp: Res asst agron, Univ Ill, 49-51, Kans State Univ, 51-52; res agronomist & res geneticist, Ft Hays Exp Sta, Kans, 52-69, RES GENETICIST & PROF, USDA, DEPT AGRON, UNIV NEBR, LINCOLN, 69- Concurrent Pos: Assoc ed, Crop Sci, 80-82. Mem: Fel Am Soc Agron; Crop Sci Soc Am. Res: Production, breeding and genetics of sorghum; population improvement for yield, grain quality and insect resistance. Mailing Add: RFD 13 Karlee Dr Lincoln NE 68527

ROSS, WILLIAM MICHAEL, b Vancouver, BC, Oct 14, 45. RESOURCE MANAGEMENT. Educ: Univ BC, BEd, 67; Univ Toronto, MA, 68; Univ Wash, PhD(geog), 72. Prof Exp: Asst prof geog, Kent State Univ, 72-73; asst prof, Rutgers Univ, 73-74; asst prof, 74-80, ASSOC PROF GEOG, UNIV VICTORIA, 80- Mem: Can Asn Geogr; Am Asn Geogr. Res: Externality and common property resource management problems in coastal zone areas and the availability of natural resources, including the impact of transferring them from place to place. Mailing Add: Dept of Geog Univ of Victoria Victoria BC V8W 2Y2 Can

ROSSA, ROBERT FRANK, b Kankakee, Ill, Aug 17, 42; m 69. ALGEBRA. Educ: Univ Okla, BA, 63, MA, 66, PhD(math), 71. Prof Exp: Asst math, Univ Okla, 63-69; asst prof, 69-74, ASSOC PROF MATH, ARK STATE UNIV, 74- Mem: Am Math Soc; Asn Comput Mach; Inst Elec & Electronics Engrs; Math Asn Am. Res: Ring theory; radicals. Mailing Add: Div of Math Ark State Univ State University AR 72467

ROSSALL, RICHARD EDWARD, b Lytham St Annes, Eng, Jan 11, 26; Can citizen; m 52; c 2. INTERNAL MEDICINE, CARDIOLOGY. Educ: Univ Leeds, BSc, 47, MB, ChB, 50, MD, 59; FRCPS(C), 58. Prof Exp: House physician internal med, Gen Infirmary, Leeds, Eng, 50, Postgrad Med Sch, Univ London, 50-51 & Brompton Hosp, London, 51; asst chest physician, Bromley & Farnboro, Kent, 51-52; registr, Hull & East Riding Hosp Bd, 54; registr, Gen Infirmary, Leeds, 54-55, sr registr, 55-57; from instr to assoc prof internal med, 57-70, asst dean, 69-74, assoc dean, 74-78, INTERNAL MED, UNIV ALTA, 70-, HEAD, DIV CARDIOL, 69-, CARDIOLOGIST, UNIV HOSP, 57- Concurrent Pos: Consult cardiologist, Edmonton Gen, Royal Alexandria & Misericordia Hosps, 57- & Dept Vet Affairs, 59-; fel coun clin cardiol, Am Heart Asn. Mem: Fel Am Col Cardiol; Can Soc Clin Invest; fel Am Col Physicians; Can Cardiovasc Soc (pres, 80-82). Res: Pulmonary lymphatic and blood circulation in health and disease. Mailing Add: Rm 6-122 Clin Sci Bldg Univ of Alta Edmonton AB T6G 2G7 Can

ROSSAN, RICHARD NORMAN, b Chicago, Ill, May 15, 28; m 66; c 1. PARASITOLOGY. Educ: Univ Ill, BS, 49, MS, 51; Rutgers Univ, PhD(zool), 59. Prof Exp: Mem staff, Naval Med Res Inst, 52-56; res training assoc, Howard Univ, 59-60; res assoc, Inst Med Res, Christ Hosp, 60-63; asst prof biol & res parasitologist, Nat Ctr for Primate Biol, Univ Calif, Davis, 63-69; MEM PROF STAFF, GORGAS MEM LAB, 69- Concurrent Pos: WHO traveling fel, 65. Mem: AAAS; Am Soc Parasitol; Soc Protozool; Am Soc Trop Med & Hyg; Sigma Xi. Res: Biology, chemotherapy and immunity of avian and primate malarias; serum changes and immunity associated with visceral leishmaniasis. Mailing Add: Gorgas Mem Lab PO Box 935 APO Miami FL

ROSSANO, AUGUST THOMAS, b New York, NY, Feb 1, 16; m 44; c 8. SANITARY ENGINEERING. Educ: Mass Inst Technol, BS, 38; Harvard Univ, SM, 41, ScD(air sanit), 54; Am Bd Indust Hyg, dipl, 58. Prof Exp: Asst civil eng, Univ Ill, 39-40; sanit engr, USPHS, 41-62; vis prof environ health eng, Calif Inst Technol, 60-63; PROF CIVIL ENG, AIR RESOURCE PROG, UNIV WASH, 63- Concurrent Pos: Consult, WHO, World Bank, 12 foreign govts, US govt & various pvt corps, 60- Honors & Awards: Spec Serv Award, USPHS, 58. Mem: Am Pub Health Asn; Am Indust Hyg Asn; Air Pollution Control Asn; Am Acad Environ Engrs. Res: Industrial hygiene; air pollution; radiological health. Mailing Add: Dept of Civil Eng FX-10 Univ of Wash Seattle WA 98105

ROSSANT, JANET, b Chatham, UK, July 13, 50; m 76. MAMMALIAN DEVELOPMENT, FETAL IMMUNOLOGY. Educ: Oxford Univ, BA, 72; Cambridge Univ, PhD(embryol), 76. Prof Exp: Vis prof, Dept Immunol, Univ Alta, 77; asst prof, 77-81, ASSOC PROF BIOL, BROCK UNIV, 81- Concurrent Pos: Asst prof, Dept Path, McMaster Univ, 81- Mem: Brit Soc Develop Biol; Can Soc Cell Biol. Res: Early mammalian development, using micromanipulative and cell culture approaches to studying early differentiation; immunlogy of pregnancy; teratocarinoma differentiation. Mailing Add: Dept Biol Sci Brock Univ St Catharines ON L2S 3A1 Can

ROSSBACHER, LISA ANN, b Fredericksburg, Va, Oct 10, 52; m 79. PLANETARY GEOLOGY, SCIENCE WRITING. Educ: Dickinson Col, BS, 75; State Univ NY Binghamton, MA, 78; Princeton Univ, MA, 79, PhD(geol), 82. Prof Exp: Geologist archeol dig, Dickinson Col & Hartwick Col, 74-75; instr geol, Dickinson Col, 76-77; RES ASSOC, WHITTIER COL, 79- Concurrent Pos: Consult, Repub Geothermal Inc, 79-81. Mem: AAAS; Am Geophys Union; Asn Earth Sci Ed; Geol Soc Am; Sigma Xi. Res: Geomorphology of planetary surfaces, especially solutional landforms (karst and thermokarst) on Earth and Mars. Mailing Add: Dept Geol Whittier Col Whittier CA 90608

ROSSBY, HANS THOMAS, b Boston, Mass, June 8, 37; c 2. PHYSICAL OCEANOGRAPHY. Educ: Royal Inst Technol, Sweden, BS, 62; Mass Inst Technol, PhD(oceanog), 66. Prof Exp: Res asst, Swedish Nat Defense Res Inst, 61-62 & Mass Inst Technol, 62-66; from asst prof to assoc prof, Yale Univ, 68-75; PROF OCEANOG, UNIV RI, 75- Mem: AAAS; Sigma Xi. Mailing Add: Grad Sch of Oceanog Univ of RI Kingston RI 02881

ROSSBY, THOMAS, b Boston, Mass, June 8, 37; m 62; c 2. PHYSICAL OCEANOGRAPHY. Educ: Royal Inst Technol, Sweden, BS, 62; Mass Inst Technol, PhD(oceanog), 66. Prof Exp: Res asst mech physics, Royal Inst Technol, Sweden, 60-62; res asst geophys, Mass Inst Technol, 62-66, res assoc oceanog, 66-68; from asst prof to assoc prof geophys, 68-75; PROF OCEANOG, UNIV RI, 75- Mem: AAAS; Marine Technol Soc; Am Geophys Union. Res: Structure and variability of deep ocean currents; temporal evolution of the vertical structure of horizontal motions; oceanic microstructure. Mailing Add: Grad Sch of Oceanog Univ of RI Kingston RI 02881

ROSSE, CORNELIUS, b Csorna, Hungary, Jan 13, 38. ANATOMY, IMMUNOLOGY. *Educ:* Bristol Univ, MB, ChB, 64, MD, 74. *Prof Exp:* House surgeon, United Hosps, Bristol Univ, 64-65, demonstr anat, Univ, 65-67; from asst prof to assoc prof biol struct, 67-75, PROF BIOL STRUCT, SCH MED, UNIV WASH, 75-, CHMN BIOL STRUCTURE, 81- *Mem:* Exp Hemat Soc; Am Asn Anatomists; Anat Soc Gt Brit & Ireland. *Res:* Experimental hematology; problems relating to hemopoietic stem cell and to the role of the bone marrow in producing potentially immunocompetent cells. *Mailing Add:* Dept of Biol Struct Univ of Wash Sch of Med Seattle WA 98195

ROSSE, WENDELL FRANKLYN, b Sidney, Nebr, June 5, 33; m 59; c 4. MEDICINE, IMMUNOLOGY. *Educ:* Univ Omaha, AB, 53; Univ Nebr, MS, 56; Univ Chicago, MD, 58. *Prof Exp:* NIH clin assoc, Nat Cancer Inst, 60-63; vis res fel, Med Sch, Univ London, 63-64; sr investr med, Nat Cancer Inst, 64-66; from asst prof to assoc prof, 66-72, assoc prof immunol, 70-74, chief immuno-hemat, 71-76, PROF MED, MED CTR, DUKE UNIV, 72-, PROF IMMUNOL, 74-, DIR BLOOD BANK, 71-, CHIEF HEMAT-MED ONCOL, 76- *Mem:* Am Soc Hemat; Am Asn Physics; Am Soc Clin Invest; Am Fedn Clin Res. *Res:* Immune hemolytic anemia and thrombocytopenia; complement-dependent mechanisms of hemolysis. *Mailing Add:* Box 3934 Duke Univ Med Ctr Durham NC 27710

ROSSEN, JACK L(EOPOLD), b Detroit, Mich, Oct 11, 29; m 55; c 3. CHEMICAL ENGINEERING, FOOD SCIENCE. *Educ:* George Washington Univ, BS, 51, MS, 52; Columbia Univ, MSChE, 57; Rutgers Univ, PhD(food sci), 74. *Prof Exp:* Chem engr, Corp Res Ctr, Gen Foods Corp, 56-61; res assoc & sr res assoc foods sect, Res Ctr, Lever Bros Co, 61-66; head process eng, Res Ctr, Nabisco, Inc, 66-73, mgr process technol, 73-75; DIR ENG RES & DEVELOP, KRAFT, INC, 75- *Mem:* Am Inst Chem Engrs; Inst Food Technol; Sigma Xi. *Res:* New food processes, with emphasis on separations, extrusion techniques, continuous processing, process control and instrumentation. *Mailing Add:* Kraft Inc 801 Waukegan Rd Glenview IL 60025

ROSSEN, JOEL N(ORMAN), b Detroit, Mich, June 22, 27; m 52; c 3. CHEMICAL ENGINEERING. *Educ:* Mass Inst Technol, BS, 48, MS, 49. *Prof Exp:* Res engr adhesives, Div Indust Coop, Mass Inst Technol, 49-50; chem engr, Tracerlab, Inc, 50-51; chem engr, Atlantic Res Corp, 51-56, proj engr, 56-57, head, Rocket Ballistics Group, 57-58, asst dir, Solid Propellant Div, 58-60, dir, 60-62; asst mgr, Solid Rocket Br, United Tech Ctr, United Aircraft Corp, 62-64, tech asst, Opers Dept, 64, asst chief engr, Solid Rockets, 64-65, asst prod develop mgr, 65-66, mgr advan technol br, 66-67, mgr ICM progs, 67-71, mgr FMB propulsion progs, 71-73, mgr ballistic missile progs, 73-78, MGR SOLID ROCKET PROGS, CHEM SYSTS DIV, UNITED TECHNOLOGIES CORP, 78- *Mem:* Am Chem Soc; Am Inst Aeronaut & Astronaut; Am Inst Chem Engrs. *Res:* Solid and hybrid rocket propulsion technology development and design; systems development; solid rocket propulsion systems management. *Mailing Add:* Chem Systs Div United Technologies Corp Sunnyvale CA 94088

ROSSEN, ROGER DOWNEY, b Cleveland, Ohio, June 4, 35; m 61; c 3. IMMUNOLOGY, INTERNAL MEDICINE. *Educ:* Yale Univ, BA, 57; Western Reserve Univ, MD, 61. *Prof Exp:* From intern to asst resident internal med, Columbia-Presby Hosp, New York, 61-63; from clin assoc to clin investr, Lab Clin Invest, Nat Inst Allergy & Infectious Dis, 63-66; sr resident internal med, Columbia-Presby Hosp, 66-67; from instr to assoc prof, 67-73, PROF MICROBIOL, IMMUNOL & MED, BAYLOR COL MED, 73-; CHIEF CLIN IMMUNOL, VET ADMIN HOSP, 72- *Concurrent Pos:* Nat Inst Allergy & Infectious Dis spec res fel, Baylor Col Med, 67-68; mem adv comt transplantation & immunol, Nat Inst Allergy & Infectious Dis, 70-74. *Mem:* Am Asn Immunologists; Am Soc Microbiol; Soc Exp Biol & Med; Central Soc Clin Res; Am Soc Pathologists. *Res:* Soluble components of human external secretions; factors mediating host resistance to infectious agents, particularly the immunoglobulins; transplantation immunology; auto-allergic diseases. *Mailing Add:* Dept of Microbiol & Immunol Baylor Col of Med Houston TX 77030

ROSSER, EDWARD BARRY, b Athens, Ohio, June 28, 11; m 39; c 1. INORGANIC CHEMISTRY. *Educ:* Ohio Univ, BS, 32, MA, 34; Western Reserve Univ, PhD(chem), 52. *Prof Exp:* Instr, Pub Schs, Ohio, 32-34 & 34-46; assoc prof, 46-52, prof, 52-77, chmn sci div, 58-75, EMER PROF CHEM, HIRAM COL, 77- *Concurrent Pos:* Tech specialist, Standard Oil Co Ohio, 56-65. *Mem:* AAAS; Nat Sci Teachers Asn; Am Chem Soc; Am Inst Chem. *Res:* Solvent systems. *Mailing Add:* 11866 Kenyon Dr Hiram OH 44234

ROSSER, JOHN BARKLEY, b Jacksonville, Fla, Dec 6, 07; m 35; c 2. MATHEMATICS. *Educ:* Univ Fla, BS, 29, MS, 31; Princeton Univ, PhD(math), 34. *Hon Degrees:* DSc, Univ Fla, 70 & Otterbein Col, 71. *Prof Exp:* Procter fel, Princeton Univ, 33-35; Nat Res Coun fel, Harvard Univ, 35-36; from instr to prof math, Cornell Univ, 36-63; dir math res ctr, 63-73, PROF MATH & COMPUT SCI, MATH RES CTR, UNIV WIS-MADISON, 63- *Concurrent Pos:* Lectr, Princeton Univ, 39-40; chief theoret ballistics sect, Allegany Ballistics Lab, Md, 44-46; consult, Appl Physics Lab, Johns Hopkins Univ, 45-63; dir res Inst Numerical Anal, 49-50; mem comt eval, Nat Bur Stand, 53, adv panel, 62-68; dir commun res div, Inst Defense Anal, 59-61; chmn math div, Nat Res Coun, 60-62, conf bd math sci, 62-64; mem space technol panel, President's Sci Adv Comt, 64-66; ed jour, Asn Symbolic Logic, 36-80. *Mem:* Am Math Soc; Math Asn Am; Asn Symbolic Logic (pres, 50-53); Soc Indust & Appl Math (pres, 64-66); Asn Comput Mach. *Res:* Symbolic logic; analytic theory of numbers; rocket ballistics. *Mailing Add:* Math Res Ctr Univ of Wis Madison WI 53706

ROSSER, ROBERT WILLIAM, fluorine chemistry, polymer chemistry, see previous edition

ROSSETTI, LOUIS MICHAEL, b Chicago, Ill, Aug 20, 48; m 72; c 1. SPEECH PATHOLOGY, DEVELOPMENTAL PSYCHOLOGY. *Educ:* Northern Mich Univ, BS, 70, MA, 72; Southern Ill Univ, PhD(speech path), 78. *Prof Exp:* Chief speech pathologist, Children's Develop Ctr, 72-74; res asst, Southern Ill Univ, 74-76; ASST PROF SPEECH PATH, NORTHEAST MO STATE UNIV, 76- *Concurrent Pos:* Lectr & consult, Kirksville Col Osteop Med, 77-; diag consult, Kirksville Diag Ctr, 77- & Head Start Prog Mo, 78; assoc ed, Mo Speech & Hearing Asn J, 78-; res consult, Knoxville Vet Admin Hosp, 78- *Mem:* Am Speech & Hearing Asn. *Res:* Clinical application of distinctive feature theory; infant screening, especially high risk infants. *Mailing Add:* 1401 E Meadow Lane Kirksville MO 63501

ROSSETTOS, JOHN N(ICHOLAS), b Nisyros, Greece, Mar 11, 32; US citizen; m 63; c 2. SOLID MECHANICS, APPLIED MATHEMATICS. *Educ:* Mass Inst Technol, BS & MS, 56; Harvard Univ, MA, 60, PhD(solid mech), 64. *Prof Exp:* Staff engr, Mass Inst Technol, 54-56; res engr, United Aircraft Res Ctr, 56-57; sr engr, Allied Res, Inc & Am Sci & Eng, Inc, 57-59; res scientist appl mech, Langley Res Ctr, NASA, 64-66; sr staff scientist, Mech & Comput, Avco Corp, 66-69; assoc prof mech & appl math, 69-77, PROF MECH & APPL MATH, NORTHEASTERN UNIV, 77- *Concurrent Pos:* Lectr, Univ Va, 64-66; adj prof, Boston Univ, 67-69; vis assoc prof, Mass Inst Technol, 70; NASA res grant, Northeastern Univ, 71-; consult mech, Houghton Mifflin Publ Co, 72-; hon res assoc struct mech, Harvard Univ, 79-80. *Mem:* Am Acad Mech; assoc fel Am Inst Aeronaut & Astronaut; Am Soc Mech Engrs; Soc Exp Stress Anal. *Res:* Mechanics of deformable solids; composite materials; application of finite element method and computers in engineering science; vibration of structural components. *Mailing Add:* Dept of Mech Eng Northeastern Univ Boston MA 02115

ROSSI, BRUNO B, b Venice, Italy, Apr 13, 05; nat US; m 38; c 3. PHYSICS. *Educ:* Bologna Univ, PhD(physics), 27. *Hon Degrees:* PhD, Univ Palermo, 64, Dr, Univ Palermo, 64, Univ Durham, Eng, 74 & Univ Chicago, 77. *Prof Exp:* Asst physics, Univ Florence, 28-32; prof, Univ Padua, 32-38; res assoc, Victoria Univ, 38-39; res assoc, Univ Chicago, 39-40; assoc prof, Cornell Univ, 40-43; mem staff, Los Alamos Proj, Univ Calif, 43-46; prof, 46-71, EMER PROF PHYSICS, MASS INST TECHNOL, 71- *Concurrent Pos:* Hon prof, La Paz; consult, AEC & NASA; mem space sci bd, Nat Acad Sci. *Honors & Awards:* Gold Medal, Italian Phys Soc, 78; Int Feltrinelli Award, Accademia dei Lincei, 71; Cresson Medal, Franklin Inst, 74; Rumford Prize Award, Am Acad Arts & Sci, 76. *Mem:* Nat Acad Sci; AAAS; Am Philos Soc; Am Phys Soc; Nat Acad Lincei. *Res:* Cosmic rays; space research. *Mailing Add:* Ctr for Space Res Mass Inst of Technol Rm 37-66 Cambridge MA 02139

ROSSI, EDWARD P, b Cleveland, Ohio, Jan 28, 34; div; c 1. ORAL PATHOLOGY, DENTISTRY. *Educ:* Kent State Univ, BA, 57; Western Reserve Univ, DDS, 62, MS, 65. *Prof Exp:* Intern, Crile Vet Admin Hosp, 62-63; from instr to asst prof, 64-71, ASSOC PROF ORAL PATH & CHMN DEPT, SCH DENT & ASST PROF, SCH MED, CASE WESTERN RESERVE UNIV, 71- *Concurrent Pos:* Am Cancer Soc clin fel, 65-66, advan clin fel, 66-69; consult, Cleveland Vet Admin Hosp; mem fel awards comt, Am Fund Dent Educ. *Mem:* Am Dent Asn; Am Acad Oral Path; Am Asn Cancer Educ; Int Acad Path. *Res:* Teaching oral pathology; oral pathology diagnostic laboratory; programmed instruction in dental education. *Mailing Add:* Dept of Oral Path Sch of Dent Case Western Reserve Univ Cleveland OH 44106

ROSSI, ENNIO CLAUDIO, b Madison, Wis, Apr 3, 31; m 57; c 2. MEDICINE. *Educ:* Univ Wis, BA, 51, MD, 54; Am Bd Internal Med, dipl, 64. *Prof Exp:* Intern, Ohio State Univ, 54-55; Fulbright scholar, Univ Rome, 55-56; resident med, Univ Wis, 58-61, res fel hemat, 61-63; from instr to asst prof, Marquette Univ, 63-66; assoc prof, 66-72, PROF MED, SCH MED, NORTHWESTERN UNIV, CHICAGO, 72- *Mem:* Am Fedn Clin Res; Am Soc Hemat. *Res:* Hematology; platelet metabolism and function; abnormal hemoglobins. *Mailing Add:* Northwestern Univ Sch of Med 303 E Chicago Chicago IL 60611

ROSSI, GEORGE VICTOR, b Ardmore, Pa, Mar 8, 29; m 56; c 1. PHARMACOLOGY. *Educ:* Philadelphia Col Pharm & Sci, BSc, 51, MSc, 52; Purdue Univ, Lafayette, PhD(pharmacol), 54. *Prof Exp:* Res assoc pharmacol, Nat Drug Co, 54-55; assoc prof, 55-61, dir, Dept Biol Sci, 65-81, PROF PHARMACOL, PHILADELPHIA COL PHARM & SCI, 61-, ASSOC DEAN RES & GRAD STUDIES, 77-, DIR, DEPT PHARMACOL & TOXICOL, 81- *Concurrent Pos:* Lindback Found Award, 81. *Mem:* AAAS; Am Soc Pharmacol & Exp Therapeut; Am Phamarceut Asn; fel Acad Pharmaceut Sci; NY Acad Sci. *Res:* cardiovascular pharmacology; antihypertensive, antiarrhythmic and antianginal drug mechanisms; histamine receptor mechanisms; gastric secretory mechanisms. *Mailing Add:* Dept Pharmacol & Toxicol Philadelphia Col of Pharm & Sci Philadelphia PA 19104

ROSSI, HARALD HERMAN, b Vienna, Austria, Sept 3, 17; US citizen; m 46; c 3. RADIATION BIOPHYSICS. *Educ:* Johns Hopkins Univ, PhD(physics), 42. *Prof Exp:* Instr physics, Johns Hopkins Univ, 40-45; res scientist radiol physics, 46-60, from asst prof to assoc prof radiol, 49-60, PROF RADIOL, COL PHYSICIANS & SURGEONS, COLUMBIA UNIV, 60- *Concurrent Pos:* Res physicist, Nat Bur Stand, 45; physicist & radiation protection officer, Presby Hosp, 54-60; mem, Nat Coun Radiation Protection, 54-, bd dirs, 71-76; chmn, Health Comnrs, Tech Adv Comn Radiation, New York, 58-; dir Dept Energy contract radiation physics, biophysics & radiation biol, 60-; mem, Int Comn Radiation Units, 59-, chmn liaison comt, 75-77; chmn radiation study sect, NIH, 62-67; consult, Off Radiation Control, New York, 63-; consult, Defense Atomic Support Agency, Armed Forces Radiol Res Inst, 65-70; consult, Brookhaven Nat Lab, 65-; consult & chmn adv comn radiation aspects SST, Fed Aviation Agency, 68-74; chmn rev comn biol & med res, Argonne Nat Lab, 71-76; consult med use nuclear powered pacemakers, AEC, 71-; mem, Comt Biol Effects of Iionizing Radiations, Nat Res Coun, 76- *Mem:* Radiation Res Soc (pres, 74); Am Radium Soc; Radiol Soc NAm; Am Col Radiol; Sigma Xi. *Res:* Radiation dosimetry; radiobiology; radiation protection; biophysics. *Mailing Add:* Radiol Res Lab Columbia Univ Col of Phys & Surg New York NY 10032

ROSSI, JOHN JOSEPH, b Washington, DC, July 8, 46; m 69; c 3. MOLECULAR GENETICS. *Educ:* Univ NH, BA, 69; Univ Conn, MS, 71, PhD(genetics), 76. *Prof Exp:* Res assoc, Div Biol & Med, Brown Univ, 76-80; ASST RES SCIENTIST, DEPT MOLECULAR GENETICS, CITY OF HOPE RES INST, 80- *Mem:* Am Soc Microbiol; AAAS. *Res:* Mechanisms of gene regulation in prokaryotic and simple eukaryotic systems; messenger RNA splicing; RNA processing. *Mailing Add:* Dept Molecular Genetics City of Hope Res Inst 1450 E Duarte Rd Duarte CA 91010

ROSSI, LOUIS J, b South Hackensack, NJ, Dec 9, 38; m 65; c 2. ORGANIC CHEMISTRY. *Educ:* Worcester Polytech Inst, BS, 61, MS, 63. *Prof Exp:* SR RES CHEMIST, EASTMAN KODAK CO RES LABS, 65- *Res:* Synthesis of heterocyclic compounds. *Mailing Add:* 49 Yates Rochester NY 14609

ROSSI, NICHOLAS PETER, b Philadelphia, Pa, July 17, 27; m 57; c 4. CARDIOVASCULAR SURGERY. *Educ:* Univ Pa, 51; Hahnemann Med Col, MD, 55. *Prof Exp:* Instr surg, Univ Iowa, 60-61, assoc, 61-62; instr, Univ Ky, 63-64; from asst prof to assoc prof, 64-72, PROF SURG, UNIV IOWA, 72- *Concurrent Pos:* Fel cardiovasc surg, Univ Ky, 63-64; consult, Oakdale State Sanatorium, 64- *Mem:* AAAS; Am Col Cardiol; AMA; Am Col Surg; Am Col Chest Physicians. *Mailing Add:* Dept Surg Univ Hosp Iowa City IA 52242

ROSSI, ROBERT DANIEL, b Philadelphia, Pa, Nov 4, 50; m 77. ORGANIC CHEMISTRY. *Educ:* Philadelphia Col Pharm & Sci, BS, 72; Temple Univ, PhD(chem), 78. *Prof Exp:* Sr chemist, Borg-Warner Chem, 77-80; PROJ SUPVR, NAT STARCH & CHEM CORP, 80- *Mem:* Am Chem Soc. *Res:* Preparation of unique monomers and their respective homo- and copolymers; chemistry of organophosphorus compounds. *Mailing Add:* Nat Starch & Chem Corp 10 Finderne Ave Birdgewater NJ 08807

ROSSI, RONALD CHARLES, b North Tonawanda, NY, June 17, 34; m 58; c 2. MATERIALS SCIENCE, CERAMICS. *Educ:* Alfred Univ, BS, 60; Univ Calif, Berkeley, MS, 62, PhD(eng sci), 64. *Prof Exp:* Sr ceramist engr, Aeronutronic Div, Philco Corp, 64-65; mem tech staff ceramics, Aerospace Corp, 65-70, mgr ceramics & graphite sect, Non-Metallic Mat Dept, 70-73, head dept, 73-77; DIR MAT, TYLAN CORP, 77- *Honors & Awards:* IR 100 Award, Indust Res Mag, 76. *Mem:* Am Ceramics Soc. *Res:* Research and development of carbon based refractory materials including glassy carbon glaze and metal-carbide composites. *Mailing Add:* Tylan Corp 233301 S Wilmington Ave Carson CA 90745

ROSSIER, ALAIN B, b Lausanne, Switz, Nov 29, 30; m 58. PHYSICAL MEDICINE, REHABILITATION. *Educ:* Univ Lausanne, BS, 50, Med Sch, Fed Dipl, 57, MD, 58. *Prof Exp:* Asst chief, Univ Hosp Geneva & chief paraplegic ctr, Beau-Sejour Hosp, Univ Hosp Geneva, 64-73; CHIEF SPINAL CORD INJURY SERV, VET ADMIN MED CTR, 73-; PROF SPINAL CORD REHAB, HARVARD MED SCH, 73- *Concurrent Pos:* Fel, Spinal Cord Injury Serv, Vet Admin Hosp, Long Beach, Calif & Swiss Acad Med Sci, 62-63; consult neurosurg & orthopaedic surg, Children's Hosp Med Ctr, 73-, spinal cord injury, Braintree Hosp & Mass Rehab Hosp; assoc staff mem, New England Med Ctr Hosp, Boston. *Mem:* Int Med Soc Paraplegia; Am Asn Neurol Surg; Am Urol Asn; Am Cong Rehab Med; Int Continence Soc. *Res:* Spinal cord regeneration, heterotopic bone ossification; urodynamic problems in neurogenic bladder; deep venous thrombosis; spinal fusion; wheelchair bioengineering. *Mailing Add:* Vet Admin Med Ctr 1400 Vet Foreign Wars Pkwy West Roxbury MA 02132

ROSSIER, EDMOND, medical microbiology, see previous edition

ROSSIGNOL, PHILIPPE ALBERT, b Sherbrooke, Que, Jan 15, 50; m 82. MEDICAL ENTOMOLOGY. *Educ:* Univ Ottawa, BSc, 71; Univ Toronto, MSc, 75, PhD(parasitol), 78. *Prof Exp:* Res fel, 78-81, RES ASSOC MED ENTOM, DEPT TROP PUB HEALTH, SCH PUB HEALTH, HARVARD UNIV, 81- *Mem:* AAAS; Am Soc Trop Med & Hyg; Royal Soc Trop Med & Hyg. *Res:* Physiology of salivatim, oogenesis and parasite transmission of mosquitoes. *Mailing Add:* Dept Trop Pub Health Harvard Univ Cambridge MA 02138

ROSSIN, A DAVID, b Cleveland, Ohio, May 5, 31; m 66; c 2. METALLURGY, NUCLEAR ENGINEERING. *Educ:* Cornell Univ, BS, 54; Mass Inst Technol, MS, 55; Northwestern Univ, MBA, 63; Case Western Reserve Univ, PhD(metall), 66. *Prof Exp:* Sr scientist metall, Argonne Nat Lab, 55-72; syst nuclear res engr, Commonwealth Edison Co, 72-78, dir res, 78-81; DIR, NUCLEAR SAFETY ANALYSIS CTR, ELEC POWER RES INST,78- *Concurrent Pos:* Fel Adlai Stevenson Inst, 67-68. *Mem:* Am Nuclear Soc; Am Soc Testing & Mat; AAAS. *Res:* Reliability of nuclear reactor piping and pressure vessels; radiation embrittlement of reactor materials; nuclear reactor safety systems; nuclear waste disposal and spent fuel management; nuclear nonproliferation policy. *Mailing Add:* PO Box 10412 Palo Alto CA 94303

ROSSIN, P(ETER) C(HARLES), b New York, NY, Sept 29, 23; m 46; c 2. PHYSICAL METALLURGY. *Educ:* Lehigh Univ, BS, 48; Yale Univ, MS, 50. *Prof Exp:* Res metallurgist, Remington Arms Co, 48-51; res assoc, Gen Elec Co, 51-55; from gen mgr refractomet div to works mgr, Titusville Plant, Universal-Cyclops Steel Corp, 55-64; vpres opers, Fansteel Metall Corp, 64-65; asst vpres prod, Crucible Steel Co Am, 65-67, PRES, DYNAMET INC, 67- *Mem:* Am Soc Metals; Electrochem Soc; Am Inst Mining, Metall & Petrol Engrs. *Res:* Metallurgical processes associated with reactive and refractory metals. *Mailing Add:* Dynamet Inc 195 Museum Rd Washington PA 15301

ROSSING, BARRY ROBERT, b Jamestown, NY, May 16, 38; m 62; c 1. CERAMICS. *Educ:* Alfred Univ, BS, 59; Mass Inst Technol, ScD(ceramics), 66. *Prof Exp:* Sr scientist ceramic-metal adherence, 66-70, sect mgr ceramic sci, 70-74, PROJ MGR, WESTINGHOUSE RES LABS, 74- *Mem:* Am Ceramic Soc. *Res:* Mechanisms of ceramic-metal adherence; solid state bonding; high temperature electrical materials; MHD materials. *Mailing Add:* Westinghouse Res Labs Beulah Rd Pittsburgh PA 15235

ROSSING, THOMAS D(EAN), b Madison, SDak, Mar 27, 29; m 52; c 5. PHYSICS, ACOUSTICS. *Educ:* Luther Col, BA, 50; Iowa State Univ, MS, 52, PhD(physics), 54. *Prof Exp:* Res assoc, Iowa Eng Exp Sta, 52-54; physicist, Univac Div, Sperry Rand Corp, 54-57; prof physics, St Olaf Col, 57-71; PROF PHYSICS, NORTHERN ILL UNIV, 71- *Mem:* Am Phys Soc; Am Asn Physics Teachers; fel Acoust Soc Am. *Res:* Magnetic materials and devices; ferromagnetic resonance; surface effects in fusion reactors; ultrasonic dispersion in gases; musical acoustics. *Mailing Add:* Dept of Physics Northern Ill Univ DeKalb IL 60115

ROSSINGTON, DAVID RALPH, b London, Eng, July 13, 32; US citizen; m 55; c 4. PHYSICAL CHEMISTRY. *Educ:* Bristol Univ, BSc, 53, PhD(chem), 56. *Prof Exp:* Res fel phys chem, State Univ NY Col Ceramics, Alfred Univ, 56-58; tech officer paints div, Imp Chem Industs, Eng, 58-60; from asst prof to assoc prof, 60-69, head, Div Eng & Sci, 76-79, PROF PHYS CHEM, STATE UNIV NY COL CERAMICS, ALFRED UNIV, 69- *Concurrent Pos:* Fulbright traveling fels, 56 & 58. *Mem:* Am Chem Soc; Am Ceramic Soc; Nat Inst Ceramic Engrs. *Res:* Surface chemistry; catalysis; adsorption phenomena; chemistry of cement hydration. *Mailing Add:* Div of Eng & Sci Alfred Univ Alfred NY 14802

ROSSINI, FREDERICK DOMINIC, b Monongahela, Pa, July 18, 99; m 32; c 1. PHYSICAL CHEMISTRY. *Educ:* Carnegie Inst Technol, BS, 25, MS, 26; Univ Calif, Berkeley, PhD(phys chem), 28. *Hon Degrees:* DSc, Carnegie Inst Technol, 48, Univ Notre Dame, 59, Loyola Univ, Ill, 60, Univ Portland, 65; DEngSc, Duquesne Univ, 55; LittD, St Francis Col, Pa, 62; PhD, Univ Lund, Sweden, 74. *Prof Exp:* Phys chemist, Nat Bur Standards, 28-36, chief sect thermochem & hydrocarbons, 36-50; Silliman prof chem, head dept & dir chem & petrol res lab, Carnegie Inst Tech, 50-60; prof chem, dean col sci & assoc dean grad sch, 60-67, vpres res, 67-71, EMER PROF CHEM, UNIV NOTRE DAME, 71-; prof, 71-78, EMER PROF CHEM, RICE UNIV, 78- *Concurrent Pos:* Marburg lectr, Am Soc Test Mat, 53; lectr, Indian Sci Cong, Madras, 58 & New Mex Highlands Univ, 61; Harkins lectr, Univ Chicago, 63; lectr, Welch Found, Tex, McCauley lectr, St Joseph Col, Wimmer lectr, St Vincent Col & Freud-McCormack lectr, Ill Inst Tech, 64; Albertus Magnus lectr, Marist Col, 65-; USA-USSR Acad exchange lectr, 67; USA-Romania Acad exchange lectr, 69; Strosacker prof, Baldwin-Wallace Col, 73; mem comt thermochem, Int Union Pure & Appl Chem, 34-51, chmn, 48-51, chmn comt chem thermodyn, 51-61, mem sect phys chem & mem exec comt, 53-61, comt thermodyn thermochem, 65-73, Rossini lectr, Int Conf Chem Thermodyn, 75, US del, Zurich & chmn comt, 55, Paris 57 & Munich, 59; chmn petrol chem, Gordon Res Conf, 44, geochem-origin petrol, 63; chmn comt phys chem, Nat Res Coun, 48-58, mem comt fund constants, 48-70, vchmn div chem tech, 53-55, chmn, 55-58, mem exec comt, Off Critical Tables, 57-70, chmn, 65-70; mem panel chem, NSF, 51-54, comt div math phys eng sci, 54-58, panel grad facilities, 58-62; adv coun, Rock Island Arsenal, 54-61; policy adv bd, Argonne Nat Lab, 58-67, consult, 64-78; mem, US Nat Comt, World Petrol Conf, 65-67 & 75-79; panel res mat, US-Japan Coop Sci Prog, 65; comt data sci technol, Int Coun Sci Unions, 65-72, chmn, 66-70; mem comt USSR & Eastern Europe, Nat Acad Sci, 66-71, chmn, 70-71; pres, World Petrol Cong, 67-75; consult tech adv comt, Petrol Indust War Coun, Off Rubber Res, Off Sci Res & Develop & AEC Prog; prof chem, Rice Univ, 71-78. *Honors & Awards:* Hillebrand Prize, Chem Soc Wash, 34; Gold Medal Excep Serv Award, US Dept Commerce, 50; Wetherill Medal, Franklin Inst, 65; Pittsburgh Award, Am Chem Soc, 59, Nichols Medal, 66 & Priestley Medal, 71; Redwood Medal, Brit Inst Petrol, 72; Carl Engler Medal, Deut Ges Mincralolwissenschaft und Kohlechemie, Ger, 76; Nat Medal Sci, 77. *Mem:* Nat Acad Sci; fel AAAS; Am Acad Arts & Sci; Sigma Xi (pres, 63-64, treas, 72-); fel Am Inst Chem. *Res:* Thermodynamics and thermochemistry; numerical data for science and technology; physical chemistry of hydrocarbons and petroleum; author of over 260 publications. *Mailing Add:* 2131 NE 58th Ct Ft Lauderdale FL 33308

ROSSIO, JEFFREY L, b Cleveland, Ohio, May 22, 47; m 72; c 2. IMMUNOLOGY, MICROBIOLOGY. *Educ:* Univ Mich, BS, 69; Ohio State Univ, MS, 71, PhD(microbiol), 73. *Prof Exp:* Instr biochem, Univ Tex Med Br, 76-78; asst prof immunol, Wright State Univ, 78-81; SCIENTIST, NAT CANCER INST, 81- *Mem:* Sigma Xi; Reticuloendothelial Soc; Am Soc Microbiol. *Res:* Thymic hormones; immune regulation; immunotherapy. *Mailing Add:* Biol Response Modifiers Prog NCI NIH Frederick Cancer Res Ctr Frederick MD 21701

ROSSITER, BRYANT WILLIAM, b Ogden, Utah, Mar 10, 31; m 51; c 8. ORGANIC CHEMISTRY. *Educ:* Univ Utah, BA, 54, PhD(org chem), 57. *Prof Exp:* Res assoc, 57-69, assoc head, 69-70, DIR CHEM DIV, RES LABS, EASTMAN KODAK CO, 70- *Concurrent Pos:* Mem, US Nat Comt, Int Union Pure & Appl Chem, 73-81, chmn, 77-80; mem bd trustees, Eastman Dent Ctr, 74- & Eyring Res Inst, 78-79; mem, Int Finance Comt, 75-79; mem, US Nat Acad Adv Comt, Int Coun Sci Unions, 81- *Mem:* Am Chem Soc; fel AAAS. *Res:* Chemistry of photographic processes; mechanisms of organic reactions; research management; photochemical processes, chemical instrumentation. *Mailing Add:* Chem Div Eastman Kodak Co Kodak Park Rochester NY 14650

ROSSITTO, CONRAD, b Siracusa, Italy, Sept 4, 26; m 53; c 3. POLYMER & ORGANIC CHEMISTRY. *Educ:* Univ Palermo, Dr(chem), 51. *Prof Exp:* Res chemist, BB Chem Co, 54-59; sr res chemist, USM Chem Co, 60-68, mgr polymer synthesis group, 68-70, sr tech adv, 70-73, sr res chemist, USM Corp, 73-78, GROUP LEADER, BOSTIC DIV, EMHART CORP, 78- *Mem:* Am Chem Soc. *Res:* Synthesis of polymers to be used in adhesives and coatings. *Mailing Add:* Bostik Div Emhart Corp Middleton MA 01949

ROSSMAN, DOUGLAS ATHON, b Waukesha, Wis, July 4, 36; m 57; c 2. SYSTEMATIC HERPETOLOGY. *Educ:* Southern Ill Univ, BA, 58; Univ Fla, PhD(zool), 61. *Prof Exp:* Instr zool, Univ NC, 61-63; from asst prof to assoc prof zool, 63-74, assoc prof zool & physiol & assoc cur, Mus Zool, 74-76, PROF ZOOL & PHYSIOL, LA STATE UNIV, 76-, CUR, MUS ZOOL, 76- *Concurrent Pos:* Res grants, Am Philos Soc, 63, NSF, 65-67. *Mem:*

Herpetologists League; Am Arachnological Soc; Am Soc Ichthyol & Herpet; Soc Study Amphibians & Reptiles. *Res:* Taxonomy and evolution of colubrid snake subfamily Natricinae (garter snakes); taxonomy of other colubrid snakes, especially Neotropical; snake osteology. *Mailing Add:* Mus of Zool La State Univ Baton Rouge LA 70893

ROSSMAN, ELMER CHRIS, b Rawlins, Wyo, Nov 17, 19; m 42; c 3. PLANT BREEDING. *Educ:* Oregon State Univ, BS, 41; Mich State Univ, MS, 43; Iowa State Univ, PhD(plant breeding & physiol), 48. *Prof Exp:* From asst to assoc prof, 41-57, PROF CROP SCI, MICH STATE UNIV, 57- *Mem:* Fel AAAS; Am Soc Agron; Am Soc Plant Physiol; Genetics Soc Am; Am Genetic Asn. *Res:* Corn breeding, genetics, physiology and production. *Mailing Add:* Dept of Crop & Soil Sci Mich State Univ East Lansing MI 48823

ROSSMAN, GEORGE ROBERT, b LaCrosse, Wis, Aug 3, 44. MINERALOGY, INORGANIC CHEMISTRY. *Educ:* Wis State Univ, BS, 66; Calif Inst Technol, PhD(chem), 71. *Prof Exp:* From instr to asst prof, 71-77, ASSOC PROF MINERAL, CALIF INST TECHNOL, 77- *Mem:* Mineral Soc Am. *Res:* Physical and chemical properties of minerals and related synthetic materials; color; spectroscopy; radiation effects; role of trace water. *Mailing Add:* 170-25 Calif Inst Technol Pasadena CA 91125

ROSSMAN, ISADORE, b Elizabeth, NJ, Mar 29, 13; m 43; c 1. GERIATRICS. *Educ:* Univ Wis, BA, 33; Univ Chicago, PhD(anat), 37, MD, 42. *Prof Exp:* MED DIR DEPT HOME CARE & EXTENDED SERV, MONTEFIORE HOSP, NEW YORK, 54-; assoc prof, 70-80, PROF COMMUNITY HEALTH, ALBERT EINSTEIN COL MED, 80- *Honors & Awards:* Jos Freeman Award, Geront Soc Am, 81. *Res:* Mortality studies; patterns of medical care. *Mailing Add:* Montefiore Hosp and Med Ctr 111 E 210th St New York NY 10467

ROSSMAN, TOBY GALE, b Weehawken, NJ, June 3, 42; m 62. GENETIC TOXICOLOGY. *Educ:* Washington Sq Col, AB, 64; NY Univ, PhD(microbiol), 68. *Prof Exp:* Assoc res scientist, 71-73, asst prof, 73-78, ASSOC PROF ENVIRON MED, SCH MED, NY UNIV, 78- *Concurrent Pos:* NIH trainee, Med Ctr, NY Univ, 69-71. *Mem:* AAAS; Am Soc Microbiol; Asn Women Sci; Am Soc Cell Biol; Environ Mutagen Soc. *Res:* DNA repair and mutagenesis; genetic toxicology; environmental carcinogenesis. *Mailing Add:* Dept of Environ Med NY Univ Med Ctr New York NY 10016

ROSSMANN, KURT, physics, deceased

ROSSMANN, MICHAEL G, b Frankfurt, Ger, July 30, 30; m 54; c 3. CRYSTALLOGRAPHY. *Educ:* Univ London, BSc, 50, hons, 51, MSc, 53; Univ Glasgow, PhD(chem), 56. *Prof Exp:* Asst lectr physics, Univ Strathclyde, 52-56; Fulbright traveling fel chem, Univ Minn, Minneapolis, 56-58; res worker, M R C Lab Molecular Biol, Eng, 58-64; from assoc prof to prof biol, 64-67, prof biol sci, 67-78, PROF BIOCHEM, 75- & HANLEY DISTINGUISHED PROF BIOL SCI, PURDUE UNIV, 78- *Mem:* Am Crystallog Asn; Am Chem Soc; Am Soc Biol Chemists; Biophys Soc; Brit Inst Physics. *Res:* Determination of the structure of biological macromolecules, particularly proteins and viruses, by means of x-ray crystallography. *Mailing Add:* Dept of Biol Sci Purdue Univ Lafayette IN 47907

ROSSMASSLER, STEPHEN ATWATER, physical chemistry, science administration, deceased

ROSSMILLER, JOHN DAVID, b Elkhorn, Wis, Mar 12, 35; m 57. BIOCHEMISTRY. *Educ:* Univ Wis, BS, 56, MS, 62; PhD(biochem), 65. *Prof Exp:* Asst prof, 65-71, ASSOC PROF BIOCHEM, WRIGHT STATE UNIV, 71-, DEPT CHMN, 80- *Mem:* AAAS. *Res:* Biochemical physiological mechanisms of regulation. *Mailing Add:* Dept of Biol Sci Wright State Univ Dayton OH 45431

ROSSMOORE, HAROLD W, b New York, NY, June 15, 25; m 46; c 4. BACTERIOLOGY. *Educ:* Univ Mich, BS, 49, MS, 51, PhD(bact), 55. *Prof Exp:* From instr to assoc prof, 54-68, PROF BIOL, WAYNE STATE UNIV, 68- *Concurrent Pos:* Fulbright & NSF fels, 64-65; consult. *Mem:* AAAS; Soc Indust Microbiol; Am Soc Microbiol; Soc Invert Path; fel Royal Soc Health. *Res:* Environmental microbiology, especially detection and control of deterioration water and oil systems; mechanisms of infection and resistance, especially in insects. *Mailing Add:* Dept of Biol Wayne State Univ Detroit MI 48202

ROSSNAGEL, BRIAN GORDON, b Gladstone, Man, May 19, 52. PLANT BREEDING, AGRONOMY. *Educ:* Univ Man, BSAgr, 73, PhD(plant breeding, agron), 78. *Prof Exp:* FEED GRAIN BREEDER BARLEY & OATS, CROP DEVELOP CTR, UNIV SASK, 77- *Mem:* Agr Inst Can; Can Soc Agron; Am Soc Agron; Crop Sci Soc Am. *Res:* Breeding and development of genotypes and agronomic practices for the optimum production of barley and oats in Saskatchewan. *Mailing Add:* Crop Develop Ctr Univ of Sask Saskatoon SK S7N 0W0 Can

ROSSNER, KENNETH LESLIE, b Brookline, Mass, Apr 11, 47. PHYSIOLOGY. *Educ:* Univ Wis, BA, 70; Clark Univ, MA, 72, PhD(muscle physiol), 76. *Prof Exp:* Res assoc physiol, Univ Ill Med Ctr, 76-78; ASST PROF BIOL, UNIV HARTFORD, 78- *Mem:* Am Asn Zoologists; AAAS. *Res:* Examination, by means of intracellular electrophysiology, of characteristics of the cardiac action potential in a strain of hamster which develops a hereditary cardiomyopathy. *Mailing Add:* Dept Biol Univ Hartford West Hartford CT 06117

ROSSNER, LAWRENCE FRANKLIN, b St Louis, Mo, Dec 17, 38; m 60; c 3. ASTROPHYSICS. *Educ:* Univ Chicago, SB, 60, SM, 61, PhD(astrophys & astron), 66. *Prof Exp:* Res assoc astron, Columbia Univ, 66-68; asst prof physics, Brown Univ, 68-75; DIR COMPUT CTR, EPA ENVIRON RES LAB, NARRAGANSETT, RI, 75- *Mem:* Am Astron Soc. *Res:* Application of fluid dynamics to problems of astrophysical interest, particularly galactic structure. *Mailing Add:* 50 Montague St Providence RI 02906

ROSSO, PEDRO, b Genoa, Italy, Aug 27, 41; Chilean citizen; m 67; c 3. PERINATAL BIOLOGY. *Educ:* Cath Univ Chile, BS, 63; Univ Chile, MD, 66. *Prof Exp:* Intern & resident pediat, Univ Chile, 66-69; fel growth & develop, Dept Pediat, Col Med, Cornell Univ, 70-72; adj asst prof nutrit, 72-73, ASST PROF PEDIAT, INST HUMAN NUTRIT, COLUMBIA UNIV, 73- *Concurrent Pos:* Consult, Regional Grad Appl Nutrit Course, Seameo Proj, Djakarta, Indonesia, 72 & Nutrit Prog, Univ PR, 75; NIH career develop award, 75. *Mem:* Soc Pediat Res; Am Inst Nutrit; Am Soc Clin Nutrit; Harvey Soc. *Res:* Control of prenatal growth and the influence of maternal nutrition on fetal growth and development. *Mailing Add:* Inst of Human Nutrit Columbia Univ 630 W 168th St New York NY 10032

ROSSOL, FREDERICK CARL, b New York, NY, Feb 6, 33; m 54; c 1. MAGNETISM. *Educ:* Univ Calif, Berkeley, BSEE, 59; NY Univ, MEE, 61; Harvard Univ, MA, 63, PhD(appl physics), 66. MEM TECH STAFF, BELLLABS, INC, 59- *Mem:* Inst Elec & Electronics Engrs; Am Phys Soc. *Res:* Magnetic properties of materials. *Mailing Add:* Bell Labs Inc Murray Hill NJ 07974

ROSSON, H(AROLD) F(RANK), b San Antonio, Tex, Apr 4, 29; m 51; c 3. CHEMICAL ENGINEERING. *Educ:* Rice Inst Technol, BS, 49, PhD, 58. *Prof Exp:* From asst prof to assoc prof chem eng, 57-66, chmn dept chem & petrol eng, 64-70, PROF CHEM ENG, UNIV KANS, 66- *Mem:* Am Chem Soc; Am Inst Chem Engrs. *Res:* Rate processes. *Mailing Add:* Dept of Chem & Petrol Eng Univ of Kans Lawrence KS 66045

ROSSON, REINHARDT ARTHUR, b Santa Monica, Calif, Oct 5, 49; m 77. BIOGEOCHEMISTRY, MARINE MICROBIAL ECOLOGY. *Educ:* Univ Calif, Los Angeles, AB, 71, PhD(microbiol), 78. *Prof Exp:* Res biologist, Scripps Inst Oceanog, 78-81; ASST PROF MARINE MICROBIOL, DEPT MARINE STUDIES, MARINE SCI INST, UNIV TEX, AUSTIN, 81- *Mem:* AAAS; Am Geophys Union; Am Soc Microbiol. *Res:* Laboratory studies on the physiology (biochemistry, mechanisms, and regulation), of bacterial manganese oxidation and combined area field studies in local bays, lagoons, nearshore Gulf of Mexico, and the deep sea on tracemetal cycling catalyzed by bacteria. *Mailing Add:* Marine Sci Inst Univ Tex Port Aransas TX 78373

ROSSOW, PETER WILLIAM, b Los Angeles, Calif, Dec 10, 48. CELL CYCLE REGULATION, HORMONE ACTION. *Educ:* Mass Inst Technol, SB, 71; Harvard Univ, PhD(microbiol & molecular genetics), 76. *Prof Exp:* Fel pharmacol, Med Sch, Harvard Univ, 75-79; res assoc, Sidney Farber Cancer Inst, 79-80; ASSOC STAFF SCIENTIST, JACKSON LAB, 80- *Concurrent Pos:* Coop prof zool, Univ Maine, Orono, 81- *Mem:* Am Soc Cell Biol; AAAS; NY Acad Sci. *Res:* Hormonal regulation of normal cell growth and the earliest events in the acquisition of the malignant phenotype in model cell culture systems. *Mailing Add:* Jackson Lab Bar Harbor ME 04609

ROSSOW, VERNON J, b Danbury, Iowa, July 22, 26; m 48; c 4. FLUID DYNAMICS. *Educ:* Iowa State Col, BS, 47; Univ Mich, MS, 49; Swiss Fed Inst Technol, DrTechSci, 57. *Prof Exp:* Res scientist, 49-70, STAFF SCIENTIST, AMES RES CTR, NASA, MOFFETT FIELD, 70- *Concurrent Pos:* Mem res adv comt fluid mech, NASA, 63-69. *Mem:* Am Phys Soc; Am Geophys Union; assoc fel Am Inst Aeronaut & Astronaut; Am Meteorol Soc. *Res:* Aerodynamics. *Mailing Add:* 549 Arboleda Dr Los Altos CA 94022

ROST, ERNEST STEPHAN, b Breslau, Ger, June 3, 34; US citizen; m 63; c 2. NUCLEAR PHYSICS. *Educ:* Princeton Univ, AB, 56; Univ Pittsburgh, PhD(physics), 61. *Prof Exp:* From instr to asst prof physics, Princeton Univ, 61-66; assoc prof, 66-70, PROF PHYSICS, UNIV COLO, BOULDER, 70- *Concurrent Pos:* Vis staff mem, Los Alamos Sci Lab, 67- *Mem:* Am Phys Soc. *Res:* Theoretical nuclear physics; nuclear structure and reactions. *Mailing Add:* Dept of Physics Univ of Colo Boulder CO 80302

ROST, THOMAS LOWELL, b St Paul, Minn, Dec 28, 41; m 63; c 3. PLANT ANATOMY, PLANT CYTOLOGY. *Educ:* St John's Univ, BS, 63; Mankato State Univ, MA, 66; Iowa State Univ, PhD(bot), 71. *Prof Exp:* Asst prof, 72-78, ASSOC PROF BOT, UNIV CALIF, DAVIS, 78- *Concurrent Pos:* Vis fel, Australia Nat Univ, Canberra, 79-80; co ed, Mech & Control Cell Div, 77. *Mem:* Sigma Xi; Bot Soc Am; Am Inst Biol Sci. *Res:* Structure of mature and germinating seeds; tissue culture studies; the cell cycle in root meristems and the effects of stress factors on structure and cell cycle progression. *Mailing Add:* Dept of Bot Univ of Calif Davis CA 95616

ROST, WILLIAM JOSEPH, b Fargo, NDak, Dec 8, 26; m 51; c 3. PHARMACEUTICAL CHEMISTRY. *Educ:* Univ Minn, BS, 48, PhD(pharmaceut chem), 52. *Prof Exp:* From asst prof to assoc prof, 52-60, PROF PHARMACEUT CHEM, UNIV MO-KANSAS CITY, 60- *Mem:* Am Chem Soc; Am Pharmaceut Asn. *Res:* Synthesis of chemicals that have possible medicinal activity. *Mailing Add:* Sch Pharm Univ Mo Kansas City 5100 Rockhill Rd Kansas City MO 64110

ROSTAMIAN, ROUBEN, b Tehran, Iran, Oct 27, 49. APPLIED MATHEMATICS. *Educ:* Arya-Mehr Univ, Tehran, BS, 72; Brown Univ, PhD(appl math), 78. *Prof Exp:* Asst prof, Purdue Univ, 77-81; ASST PROF MATH, PA STATE UNIV, 81- *Mem:* Am Math Asn. *Res:* Qualitative study of solutions of degenerate parabolic equations; asymptotic behavior of solutions in large time; linear and nonlinear elasticity, existence of solutions for problems with internal constraints. *Mailing Add:* Dept Math Pa State Univ University Park PA 16802

ROSTENBACH, ROYAL E(DWIN), b Buffalo, Iowa, Sept 20, 12; m 40. CHEMISTRY, ENGINEERING. *Educ:* St Ambrose Col, BS, 35; Univ Iowa, MS, 37, PhD(chem, eng), 39. *Prof Exp:* Asst chem, Catholic Univ, 35-36; sanit eng, Univ Iowa, 37-39; consult engr, Clark, Stewart & Wood Co, 39-40; chem & pub health engr, USPHS, 40-42; engr, Chem Div, US War Prod Bd, 42-43; chief, Copolymer Br, Off Rubber Reserve, Reconstruct Finance Corp, 43-53; sr engr & specialist, Hanford Atomic Prod Oper, Gen Elec Co, 53-59;

sr proj engr, Bendix Aviation Corp, 59-60; res dir, Mast Develop Co, 60-61; PROG DIR, DIV ENG, NAT SCI FOUND, 62- Mem: Am Chem Soc; fel Am Inst Chem; Am Inst Chem Engrs; Water Pollution Control Fedn; Am Nuclear Soc. Mailing Add: 6111 Wiscasset Rd Bethesda MD 20816

ROSTOKER, GORDON, b Toronto, Ont, July 15, 40; m 66; c 3. SPACE PHYSICS. Educ: Univ Toronto, BSc, 62, MA, 63; Univ BC, PhD(geophys), 66. Prof Exp: Nat Res Coun Can fel space physics, Royal Inst Technol, Sweden, 66-68; asst prof physics, 68-73, assoc prof, 73-79, PROF PHYSICS, UNIV ALTA, 79- Concurrent Pos: Int Union Geod & Geophys appointee, Steering Comt, Int Magnetospheric Study, 73-79; mem grant selection comt space & astron, Nat Res Coun Can, 73-76, chmn, 75-76, mem assoc comt space res, 75-80; Nat Res Coun Can travel fel, 74; ed, Can J Phys, 80- Mem: Am Geophys Union; Can Asn Physicist; Can Geophys Union (secy-treas, 73-74). Res: Study of the solar-terrestrial interaction, with emphasis on the investigation of magnetospheric substorms and magnetosphere-ionosphere coupling using magnetometer arrays. Mailing Add: Inst Earth & Planetary Physics Univ of Alta Edmonton AB T6G 2J1 Can

ROSTOKER, NORMAN, b Toronto, Ont, Aug 16, 25; m 48; c 2. PHYSICS. Educ: Univ Toronto, BASc, 46, MA, 47; Carnegie Inst Technol, DSc(physics of solids), 50. Prof Exp: Res physicist, Carnegie Inst Technol, 48-53, Armour Res Found, 53-56 & Gen Atomic Div, Gen Dynamics Corp, 56-62; prof physics, Univ Calif, San Diego, 62-65; res physicist, Gen Atomic Div, Gen Dynamics Corp, 65-67; IBM prof eng, Cornell Univ, 67-73, chmn Dept Appl Physics, 67-70; PROF PHYSICS, UNIV CALIF, IRVINE, 73- Mem: Fel Am Phys Soc. Res: Band theory; design of fission reactors; plasma physics; controlled thermonuclear research; intense electron beams. Mailing Add: Dept of Physics Univ of Calif Irvine CA 92717

ROSTOKER, WILLIAM, b Hamilton, Ont, June 21, 24; nat US; m 49; c 4. METALLURGY, BIOMATERIALS. Educ: Univ Toronto, BASc, 45, MASc, 46; Lehigh Univ, PhD(metall eng), 48. Prof Exp: Res fel indust metall, Univ Birmingham, 48-49, lectr, 49-50; asst prof, Ill Inst Technol, 50-51, from res metallurgist to sr metall adv, Metals Div, IIT Res Inst, 51-65; actg dean grad col, 68-70, PROF METALL & BIOENG, UNIV ILL, CHICAGO CIRCLE, 65- Concurrent Pos: Consult, Frankfort Arsenal, 58-73, mem refractory metals panel, Mat Adv Bd, 59-63, chmn metal-working processes comt, 63-69; chmn rev comts eng metall, Idaho Facility, Argonne Nat Lab, 65-68; mem nat mat adv bd, 69-71; mem & consult, Army Sci Adv Panel, 71-; prof orthopedic surg, Rush Med Sch, Chicago, 72- Honors & Awards: Kappa Delta Award, Am Acad Orthop Surg, 70. Mem: Fel Am Soc Metals. Res: Fracture processes; powder metallurgy; biomedical engineering; brittle fracture; refractory metals; physical metallurgy; metal processing; skeletal reconstruction; alloy development; ancient metallurgical processes. Mailing Add: Dept of Mat Eng Box 4348 Chicago IL 60680

ROSTRON, ROBERT W(ALTHER), nuclear & systems engineering, see previous edition

ROSWELL, DAVID FREDERICK, b Evansville, Ind, Dec 5, 42; m 65; c 2. CHEMISTRY. Educ: Johns Hopkins Univ, AB, 64, PhD(chem), 68. Prof Exp: From asst prof to assoc prof, 68-74, PROF CHEM, LOYOLA COL, MD, 74-, DEAN, COL ARTS & SCI, 80- Concurrent Pos: Cottrell Res Corp grant, Loyola Col, 69-70; asst prof, Evening Col, Johns Hopkins Univ, 70-79, res scientist, 71- Mem: Am Chem Soc. Res: Chemiluminescence; photochemistry; biochemistry. Mailing Add: Col Arts & Sci Loyola Col Baltimore MD 21210

ROSZEL, JEFFIE FISHER, b Amarillo, Tex, Apr 5, 26; m 49; c 1. CYTOPATHOLOGY, VETERINARY PATHOLOGY. Educ: Univ Pa, VMD, 63; Okla State Univ, PhD(comp path), 75. Prof Exp: NIH fel, Hahnemann Med Col & Hosp, 63-65; from instr to asst prof path, Sch Vet Med, Univ Pa, 65-70; vis prof, 71-72, from asst prof to assoc prof, 72-78, PROF PATH, COL VET MED, OKLA STATE UNIV, 78- Concurrent Pos: Res assoc, Hahnemann Med Col & Hosp, 66-68; lectr path, Philadelphia Col Pharm & Sci, 68-70; mem vet med rev comt, Bur Health Manpower Educ, NIH, 72 & co-prin investr, Registry Canine & Feline Neoplasms, 72-78. Mem: Am Soc Cytol; Vet Cancer Soc. Res: Comparative cytopathology of neoplasms. Mailing Add: Dept of Path Col of Vet Med Okla State Univ Stillwater OK 74074

ROSZKOWSKI, ADOLPH PETER, b Chicago, Ill, July 27, 28; m 51; c 4. PHARMACOLOGY. Educ: DePaul Univ, BS, 51, MS, 54; Loyola Univ, PhD(pharmacol), 56. Prof Exp: Mem staff, Dept Pharmacol, G D Searle & Co, 52-53; asst dir biol res, McNeil Labs, Inc, Div Johnson & Johnson, 57-66; head pharmacol, Kendall Res Ctr, Ill, 66-67; dir dept pharmacol & asst dir inst clin med, 67-77, DIR, INST PHARMACOL & METABOL, SYNTEX RES DIV, SYNTEX CORP, 77- Concurrent Pos: McNeil fel, Univ Pa, 56-57; instr, Sch Med, Temple Univ, 57-64; lectr, Sch Med, Stanford Univ, 75- Honors & Awards: Johnson Medal Award, 65. Mem: AAAS; Am Soc Pharmacol & Exp Therapeut; Am Soc Clin Pharmacol & Therapeut; Soc Toxicol. Res: Psychopharmacology; autonomic pharmacology; immunopharmacology; toxicology. Mailing Add: Syntex Res Div Syntex Corp 3401 Hillview Ave Palo Alto CA 94304

ROSZMAN, LARRY JOE, b Marion, Ohio, June 9, 44; m 66. ATOMIC PHYSICS, PLASMA PHYSICS. Educ: Bowling Green State Univ, BS, 66; Univ Fla, PhD(physics), 71. Prof Exp: Teaching asst physics, Univ Fla, 66-70, res asst physics, 70-71; PHYSICIST, NAT BUR STANDS, 71- Mem: Am Phys Soc; AAAS. Res: Calculation of electron-atom/ion collision cross sections and rates for important processes in thermonuclear plasmas; calculation of plasma line broadening effects; analysis of plasma-ion interaction; theoretical physics; thermal physics. Mailing Add: Nat Bur Stands Washington DC 20234

ROTA, GIAN-CARLO, b Italy, Apr 27, 32; nat US; m 56. MATHEMATICS. Educ: Princeton Univ, BA, 53; Yale Univ, MA, 54, PhD(math), 56. Prof Exp: Fel, Courant Inst Math Sci, NY Univ, 56-57; Benjamin Pierce instr math, Harvard Univ, 57-59; from asst prof to assoc prof, Mass Inst Technol, 59-65; prof, Rockefeller Univ, 65-67; prof math, 67-74, PROF APPL MATH & PHILOS, MASS INST TECHNOL, 74- Concurrent Pos: Sloan fel, 62-64; mem comt math adv, Off Naval Res, 63-67; Hedrick lectr, Am Math Asn, 67; ed-in-chief, Advan in Math, 68-; vis prof, Univ Colo, 69-; Andre Aisenstadt vis prof, Univ Montreal, 71; Taft lectr, Univ Cincinnati, 71; fel, Los Alamos Sci Lab, 71-; Hardy lectr, London Math Soc, 73; fel, Los Alamos Nat Lab, 63- & Rand Corp, 64-71; ed, Studies Appl Math, 70-, J Math Anal & Applns & J Combinatorial Theory. Mem: Fel Am Acad Arts & Sci; Am Math Soc; fel Academia Argentina de Ciencias; Soc Indust & Appl Math (vpres, 75); fel Inst Math Statist. Res: Combinatorial theory; probability; phenomenology. Mailing Add: Dept of Math Mass Inst of Technol Cambridge MA 02139

ROTAR, PETER P, b Omaha, Nebr, June 9, 29; m 56; c 4. CROP BREEDING, CYTOGENETICS. Educ: Washington State Univ, BSc, 54, MSc, 57; Univ Nebr, PhD(agron), 60. Prof Exp: Asst prof biol, Salve Regina Col, 60-62; asst prof agron & asst agronomist, 62-72, PROF AGRON & AGRONOMIST, UNIV HAWAII, 72-, CHMN, DEPT AGRON & SOIL SCI, 76- Mem: Crop Sci Soc Am; Am Soc Agron; Bot Soc Am; Sigma Xi. Res: Cytology; cytogenetics of tropical legumes and grasses used for forage and pasture; taxonomy of grasses. Mailing Add: Dept Agron & Soil Sci Univ Hawaii Honolulu HI 96822

ROTARIU, GEORGE JULIAN, b Los Angeles, Calif, Aug 24, 17; m 48; c 3. PHYSICAL CHEMISTY, INSTRUMENTATION. Educ: Univ Chicago, BS, 39, MS, 40; Univ Ill, PhD(chem), 50. Prof Exp: Asst chem & pharmacol, Univ Chicago, 41-45; res chemist, Lever Bros Co, 45-46; instr phys sci, Univ Chicago, 46-48; asst phys chem, Univ Ill, 48-50; res assoc, Univ Calif, 50-52; asst prof phys chem, Loyola Univ, Ill, 52-55; dir inland testing labs & nuclear eng, Cook Elec Co, 55-57; dir, Nuclear Tech & Phys Chem, Booz-Allen Appl Res Inc, Ill, 57-62; chief anal & appl br, Div Isotopes Develop, US AEC, 62-64, systs eng sect, Radiation & Thermal Appl Br, 64-66, prog mgr, Process Radiation Staff, 66-72, prog mgr, Radiation Applns Br, Div Applns Technol, 72-73, prog mgr instrumentation, Div Biomed & Environ Res, US Energy Res & Develop Admin, 73-76, PROG MGR ENVIRON PROGS, DIV TECHNICAL ASSESSMENTS, DEPT OF ENERGY, 76- Concurrent Pos: US Rep Int Atomic Energy Agency Conf, Warsaw, Poland & panel, Cracow, Poland, 65 & Munich, 69; Comn Europ Communities Conf, Brussels, Belg, 71. Mem: Am Chem Soc; Am Nuclear Soc; Sigma Xi. Res: Nuclear radiation testing; nuclear radiation effects on materials; high altitude environments; environmental testing; lubricants; films and coatings; radioisotope applications in industry and government; environmental assessments for magnetohydrodynamics, enhanced gas recovery, enhanced oil recovery and oil shale technologies. Mailing Add: Environ Progs US Dept Energy Washington DC 20545

ROTEM, CHAVA EVE, b Jan 15, 28; wid; c 2. CARDIOLOGY, EXPERIMENTAL MEDICINE. Educ: Univ Lausanne, cert bact, 50, MD, 52; MRCP(Edin), 58, MRCP(L), 58, FRCP(C), 68. Prof Exp: House officer pediat, Kantonsspital, Zurich, Switz, 52-53; sr house surgeon, Leicester Chest Univ, UK, 54-55; med registr, Leicester Isolation Hosp & Chest Univ, 55-59, sr med registr cardiol, Cardiac Invest Ctr, 59-60; consult physician, Scottish Mission Hosp, Nazareth, 60-61; cardiologist, NIH Surv Ischeamic & Hypertensive Heart Dis, Rambam Govt Hosp, Haifa, Israel, 62-63; res fel cardiol, Stanford Univ, 63-64; cardiologist, St Paul's Hosp, Vancouver, BC, 64-65; cardiol, 65-68, head, Div Cardiol, 78-82, IN CHG INTENSIVE CORONARY CARE UNIT & CARDIAC CATHETERIZATION LAB, SHAUGHNESSY HOSP, VANCOUVER, BC, 68- Concurrent Pos: Physician, Rothschild Hadassa Munic Hosp, Haifa, 62-63. Mem: Can Cardiovasc Soc; Soc Microcirc; Israel Soc Cardiol; NY Acad Sci; fel Am Col Cardiol. Res: Investigative cardiology; hydrodynamics of the great blood vessels, especially clinical applications; clinical investigation of new cardiac drugs. Mailing Add: Dept Cardiol Shaughnessy Hosp 4500 Oak St Vancouver BC V6H 3N1 Can

ROTENBERG, A DANIEL, b Toronto, Ont, July 21, 34; m 62; c 4. MEDICAL PHYSICS. Educ: Univ Toronto, PhD(med biophys), 62. Prof Exp: Biophysicist, Montreal Gen Hosp, 63-66, physicist, 66-69; lectr therapeut radiol, Sch Med, McGill Univ, 69-71; head dept biomed physics & physicist, Jewish Gen Hosp, 69-77; asst prof diag radiol, Sch Med, McGill Univ, 70-77; DIR RES & DEVELOP, COINAMATIC INC, MONTREAL, 77- Concurrent Pos: Consult, Jewish Gen Hosp, 66-69; Queen Elizabeth Hosp, 68-; St Mary's Hosp, 68-; Reedy Mem Hosp, 69- & Etobicoke Gen Hosp, 72-; assoc scientist, Royal Victoria Hosp, 70- & Northwestern Gen Hosp, 74-; vpres, Beique, Rotenberg & Radford Inc, 66-80; dir, BRRCM Inc, 80- Mem: Soc Nuclear Med; Can Asn Physicists (secy-treas, 66-69); Asn Advan Med Instrumentation. Res: Hospital physics and instrumentation; microprocessor developments; laser photocoagulation; diagnostic radiology. Mailing Add: 6616 Fleet Rd Montreal PQ H4V 1A9 Can

ROTENBERG, DON HARRIS, b Portland, Ore, Mar 31, 34; m 58; c 2. POLYMER CHEMISTRY, RESEARCH ADMINISTRATION. Educ: Univ Ore, BA, 55; Harvard Univ, AM, 56; Cornell Univ, PhD(org chem), 60. Prof Exp: Res chemist, Enjay Chem Intermediate Div, 60-67, sr res chemist, Enjay Polymer Lab, Esso Res & Eng Co, 68-71; mgr polymer sci & eng, 71-75, dir polymer res & develop, 75-78, dir mat sci & process lab, 78-80, VPRES RES & DEVELOP, AM OPTICAL CO, 80- Mem: Am Chem Soc; AAAS. Res: Optical plastics; optical and abrasion resistant coatings; photochromic materials; polyethylene-propylene, butyl and chlorobutyl elastomers; vinyl plasticizers; polyesters; polyurethanes; chemical and polymer synthesis, analysis, characterization and physical properties; product and process development; heterocyclics; contact and ophthalmic lenses. Mailing Add: 13 Hundreds Rd Westborough MA 01581

ROTENBERG, KEITH SAUL, b San Francisco, Calif, Oct 10, 50; m 76; c 1. PHARMACOKINETICS, BIOPHARMACEUTICS. *Educ:* Univ Calif, Berkeley, BA, 72; Univ Md, PhD (pharmacokinetics & biopharmaceut), 77. *Prof Exp:* reviewer, 77-80, TECH SUPVR BIOAVAILABILITY & BIOEQUIVALENCY, FOOD & DRUG ADMIN, 80- *Mem:* Am Pharmaceut Asn; Acad Am Pharmaceut Asn; AAAS; NY Acad Sci; Am Chem Soc. *Res:* Pharmacokinetics of nicotine in animals and man; pharmacokinetics and bioavailability of drugs in man; in vivo-in vitro correlations; formulation factors which affect a drugs bioavailability and in vitro dissolution. *Mailing Add:* Div of Biopharmaceut 5600 Fishers Lane Rockville MD 20857

ROTENBERG, MANUEL, b Toronto, Ont, Mar 12, 30; nat US; m 52; c 2. ATOMIC PHYSICS, BIOPHYSICS. *Educ:* Mass Inst Technol, SB, 52, PhD(physics), 55. *Prof Exp:* Staff mem, Los Alamos Sci Lab, 55-57; instr physics, Princeton Univ, 57-58, staff mem, Proj Matterhorn, 58; asst prof physics, Univ Chicago & Inst Comput Res, 50-61; asst prof physics, 61-65, asst dir inst radiation physics & aerodyn, 65-67, assoc prof, 67-70, assoc dean grad studies & res, 71-75, PROF APPL PHYSICS, UNIV CALIF, SAN DIEGO, 70-, DEAN GRAD STUDIES & RES, 75- *Mem:* Fel Am Phys Soc; Sigma Xi; AAAS. *Res:* Atomic theory; scattering theory; numerical techniques; population theory; cell kinetics. *Mailing Add:* Dept of Appl Phys Univ of Calif San Diego La Jolla CA 92093

ROTERMUND, ALBERT J, JR, b St Louis, Mo, June 20, 40; m 68; c 3. CELL BIOLOGY, CELL PHYSIOLOGY. *Educ:* St Louis Univ, BS, 62, MS, 66; State Univ NY Buffalo, PhD(biol), 69. *Prof Exp:* NIH fel, Brookhaven Nat Lab, 68-70; asst prof, 70-76, ASSOC PROF BIOL, LOYOLA UNIV, CHICAGO, 77- *Mem:* Am Soc Zool, Sigma Xi. *Res:* Cellular physiology and biochemistry; metabolic regulation of mammalian red blood cell metabolism in acclimation to low temperature. *Mailing Add:* Dept of Biol Loyola Univ 6525 N Sheridan Rd Chicago IL 60626

ROTH, ALLAN CHARLES, b St Joseph, Mo, Dec 23, 46; m 68; c 2. PHYSIOLOGY, BIOMEDICAL ENGINEERING. *Educ:* Iowa State Univ, BS, 69, MS, 74, PhD(biomed eng), 77. *Prof Exp:* Design engr, Rockwell Int, Calif, 69-72; res asst, Biomed Eng Prog, Iowa State Univ, 72-74, teaching asst, Dept Zool, 74-77; res assoc, Dept Physiol & Biophys, Univ Wash, 77-80; ASST PROF, DIV BIOMED ENG, UNIV VA, 80- *Mem:* Sigma Xi; Biomed Eng Soc Am. *Res:* Fluid mechanics of arterial stenosis; comparative circulatory hemodynamics; gas transport in the tissue; circulatory transport and instrumentation. *Mailing Add:* Div Biomed Eng Med Ctr Box 377 Univ Va Charlottesville VA 22908

ROTH, ARIEL A, b Geneva, Switz, July 16, 27; nat US; m 52; c 2. BIOLOGICAL OCEANOGRAPHY. *Educ:* Pac Union Col, BA, 48; Univ Mich, MS, 49, PhD(zool), 55. *Prof Exp:* From instr to assoc prof biol, Pac Union Col, 50-57; res assoc, Loma Linda Univ, 57-58; from assoc prof to prof biol & chmn dept, Andrews Univ, 58-63; chmn, Dept Biol, 63-73, PROF BIOL, LOMA LINDA UNIV, 63-, DIR, GEOSCI RES INST, 80- *Concurrent Pos:* Mem, Geosci Res Inst, 73-; ed, Origins. *Mem:* Sigma Xi; AAAS; Geol Soc Am; Soc Econ Paleontologists & Mineralogists; Am Asn Petrol Geologists. *Res:* Factors affecting rate of coral growth; parasitology; schistosomiasis; invertebrate zoology; coral reef development. *Mailing Add:* Dept of Biol Loma Linda Univ Loma Linda CA 92350

ROTH, ARTHUR JASON, b Brooklyn, NY, Oct 8, 49; m 72; c 1. MATHEMATICAL STATISTICS. *Educ:* Cornell Univ, BA, 71; Univ Minn, PhD(statist), 75. *Prof Exp:* Asst prof statist, Carnegie-Mellon Univ, 75-77; asst prof math, Syracuse Univ, 77-80; MEM STAFF, CIBA-GEIGY, CORP, 80- *Mem:* Inst Math Statist. *Res:* Group testing, particularly Bayesian and sequential aspects; sequential analysis; nonparametric statistics; ranking and selection problems. *Mailing Add:* CIBA-GEIGY CORP 556 Morris Ave Summit NJ 07901

ROTH, BARBARA, b Milwaukee, Wis, June 9, 16. ORGANIC CHEMISTRY. *Educ:* Beloit Col, BS, 37; Northwestern Univ, MS, 39, PhD(org chem), 41. *Prof Exp:* Lab asst, Northwestern Univ, 38-41; res chemist, Calco chem div, Am Cyanamid Co, 41-51; group leader keratin res, Toni div, Gillette Co, 51-55; sr res chemist, NY, 55-71, GROUP LEADER, WELLCOME RES LABS, BURROUGHS WELLCOME CO, RES TRIANGLE PARK, NC, 71- *Concurrent Pos:* Instr, Lake Forest Col, 40-41; adj prof sch pharm, Univ NC, 71- *Mem:* AAAS; Am Chem Soc; NY Acad Sci; Royal Soc Chem. *Res:* Pyrimidine and medicinal chemistry; synthetic organic chemistry. *Mailing Add:* 7 Lone Pine Rd Chapel Hill NC 27514

ROTH, BEN G, b Bloomington, Ill, Oct 5, 42; m 69; c 2. MATHEMATICS. *Educ:* Occidental Col, AB, 64; Dartmouth Col, AM, 66, PhD(math), 69. *Prof Exp:* From asst prof to assoc prof, 69-79, PROF MATH, UNIV WYO, 79- *Mem:* Am Math Soc; Math Asn Am. *Res:* Spaces of continuous and differentiable functions; spaces of distributions; rigidity. *Mailing Add:* Dept of Math Univ of Wyo Laramie WY 82071

ROTH, BENJAMIN, b New York, NY, Feb 6, 09; m 41; c 1. ELEMENTARY PARTICLE PHYSICS. *Educ:* City Col New York, BS, 29; Columbia Univ, MA, 31; Polytech Inst Brooklyn, BEE, 47; Cornell Univ, PhD(physics), 51. *Prof Exp:* Instr physics, Univ Conn, 51-56; from asst prof to assoc prof, Okla State Univ, 57-61; from assoc prof to prof, 62-76, EMER PROF PHYSICS, BROOKLYN COL, 76- *Mem:* Am Phys Soc. *Res:* S-matrix theory. *Mailing Add:* Dept of Physics Brooklyn Col Brooklyn NY 11210

ROTH, BERNARD, b New York, NY, May 28, 33; m 55; c 2. MECHANICAL ENGINEERING. *Educ:* City Col New York, BS, 56; Columbia Univ, MS, 58, PhD(mech eng), 62. *Prof Exp:* Lectr mech eng, City Col New York, 56-58; from asst prof to assoc prof, 62-71, PROF MECH ENG, STANFORD UNIV, 71- *Concurrent Pos:* Consult, Atlantic Design Co, 57; Columbia Univ, 62-64; Int Bus Mach Corp, 64-67; Univ Neger, Israel, 73 & Atomic Energy Comn, France, 76; prin investr, NSF Grants, 63-; vis

prof, Technol Univ Delft, 68-69; Kanpur, India, 77 & Shanghai, China, 79. *Honors & Awards:* Melville Medal, Am Soc Mech Engrs, 67. *Mem:* Am Soc Mech Engrs; Int Fedn Theory Mach & Mechanisms (pres, 81-). *Res:* Robotics; interpersonal relations; kinematics; numerical methods, especially computer aided design; machine design, especially analytical techniques. *Mailing Add:* Dept of Mech Eng Stanford Univ Stanford CA 94305

ROTH, CHARLES, b Huncovce, Czech, Dec 25, 39; Can citizen; m 63; c 2. APPLIED MATHEMATICS, THEORETICAL PHYSICS. *Educ:* McGill Univ, BSc, 61, MSc, 62; Hebrew Univ, Israel, PhD(theoret physics), 65. *Prof Exp:* Lectr math & physics, Hebrew Univ, Israel, 63-65; asst prof, 65-70, ASSOC PROF MATH, MCGILL UNIV, 70- *Mem:* Can Math Cong. *Res:* Applications of group representations and irreducible tensorial sets to atomic and nuclear spectroscopy. *Mailing Add:* Dept of Math McGill Univ Montreal PQ H3A 2T5 Can

ROTH, CHARLES BARRON, b Columbia, Mo, Apr 27, 42; m 64; c 2. AGRONOMY, SOIL SCIENCE. *Educ:* Univ Mo, BS, 63, MS, 65; Univ Wis, PhD(soil sci), 69. *Prof Exp:* Res assoc, 68-70, asst prof, 70-75, ASSOC PROF SOIL CHEM & MINERAL, PURDUE UNIV, 75- *Concurrent Pos:* Vis assoc prof, Tex A&M Univ, 78-79. *Mem:* AAAS; Am Soc Agron; Int Asn Study Clays; Soil Sci Soc Am; Int Soc Soil Sci. *Res:* Physical and chemical effects of iron, aluminum and silica sesquioxides on the physicochemical properties of soils and clays; redox reactions of iron in clay mineral structures; prediction of soil erosion from reclaimed minelands. *Mailing Add:* Dept of Agron Purdue Univ West Lafayette IN 47907

ROTH, DANIEL, b New York, NY, Oct 27, 20; m 50; c 2. MEDICINE, PATHOLOGY. *Educ:* Columbia Univ, AB, 40; New York Med Col, MD, 43. *Prof Exp:* Asst pathologist, United Hosp, 51-56; asst prof path, Med Ctr, NY Univ, 56-59; dir lab, Bergen Pines County Hosp, 59-62 & St Barnabas Hosp, Bronx, 62-67; assoc prof path, Med Ctr & Univ Hosp, NY Univ, 67-73, assoc clin prof environ med, 73-80; PATHOLOGIST, GOODWIN INST CANCER RES, 74- *Mem:* Am Asn Path & Bact; Am Soc Exp Path; Am Soc Photobiol; NY Acad Sci; Environ Mutagen Soc. *Res:* Photobiology; experimental carcinogenesis; cancer cytodiagnosis; physical chemistry of DNA in cancer. *Mailing Add:* 8 Glenwood Lane Roslyn Heights NY 11577

ROTH, DONALD ALFRED, b Slinger, Wis, July 31, 18; m 51; c 4. MEDICINE. *Educ:* Univ Wis, PhD(chem), 44; Marquette Univ, MD, 52; Am Bd Internal Med, dipl, 63; Am Bd Nephrol, dipl, 76. *Prof Exp:* Asst chem, Univ Wis, 41-44, instr, 46-48; physiologist, 53-54; from instr to asst prof, 61-68, ASSOC PROF MED, MED COL WIS, 69-; CHIEF RENAL SECT, WOOD VET ADMIN HOSP, 58- *Mem:* AMA; Am Diabetes Asn; Am Fedn Clin Res; Am heart Asn; fel Am Col Physicians. *Res:* Renal disease; hemodialysis; hypertension, including retinal photography and ultrastructure of kidney. *Mailing Add:* 1620 Revere Dr Brookfield WI 53005

ROTH, ELDON SHERWOOD, b St Paul, Minn, Nov 7, 29; m 56. GEOMORPHOLOGY. *Educ:* Univ Calif, Los Angeles, BA, 53; Univ Southern Calif, MS, 59, PhD(higher educ), 69. *Prof Exp:* Instr geol & chem, Barstow Col, 60-69; ASSOC PROF EARTH SCI, NORTHERN ARIZ UNIV, 69- *Mem:* Geol Soc Am; Nat Asn Geol Teachers. *Res:* Local and regional geomorphology; delineation of geomorphic regions by quantitative means; adaptation of computer methods to geomorphic research; energy resources and utilization. *Mailing Add:* Dept of Earth Sci Northern Ariz Univ Flagstaff AZ 86001

ROTH, ELMER ALFRED, b York, Nebr, Nov 18, 20; m 41; c 2. BOTANY. *Educ:* Ottawa Univ, Kans, BA, 53; Univ Kans, MA, 54. *Hon Degrees:* MHL, Ottawa Univ, 70. *Prof Exp:* Asst prof, 54-65, ASSOC PROF BOT & BIOL, OTTAWA UNIV, 65- *Res:* Plant taxonomy; plant and animal ecology; paleobotany. *Mailing Add:* Dept of Biol Ottawa Univ Ottawa KS 66067

ROTH, FRANK J, JR, b Garwood, NJ, Feb 15, 18; m 46; c 3. MICROBIOLOGY, MYCOLOGY. *Educ:* Ohio Univ, BS, 42; Univ NC, MS, 47; Univ Minn, PhD(microbiol), 55. *Prof Exp:* Instr bact, Univ Minn, 49-55; asst prof, 56-60, ASSOC PROF MICROBIOL & DERMAT, UNIV MIAMI, 60- *Mem:* Am Soc Microbiol; Soc Invest Dermat; Int Soc Human & Animal Mycol. *Res:* Medical mycology; antifungal antibiotics; marine yeasts; mechanisms of natural resistance; electron microscopy. *Mailing Add:* Dept Microbiol Univ Miami Miami FL 33101

ROTH, FRIEDA, b Niagara Falls, NY, Nov 25, 27; m 49; c 3. MICROBIOLOGY, VIROLOGY. *Educ:* Syracuse Univ, BS, 49, MS, 51; State Univ NY Upstate Med Ctr, PhD(microbiol), 69. *Prof Exp:* Res asst allergy, State Univ NY Upstate Med Ctr, 51-52, med, 58-62, microbiol, 62-65, res assoc, 68-72; assoc microbiol, 72-75, ASSOC MED, UNIV ROCHESTER, 75- *Res:* Viral immunology; viral infectious diseases. *Mailing Add:* Dept of Med Univ of Rochester Rochester NY 14627

ROTH, GEORGE STANLEY, b Honolulu, Hawaii, Aug 5, 46; m 72; c 2. GERONTOLOGY, ENDOCRINOLOGY. *Educ:* Villanova Univ, BS, 68; Temple Univ, PhD(microbiol), 71. *Prof Exp:* Asst microbiol, Sch Med, Temple Univ, 68-71; fel biochem, Fels Res Inst, 71-72; staff fel, Geront Res Ctr, 72-76, RES BIOCHEMIST GERONT, NAT INST AGING, 76- *Concurrent Pos:* Res consult, George Washington Univ, 77-; co-ed, Chem Rubber Co Press, 77-; ed, Neurobiol Aging, 80-; exchange scientist, Nat Acad Sci, 77-80; Ann Res Award, Am Aging Asn, 81. *Mem:* Fel Geront Soc. *Res:* Effect of aging on hormone action; molecular mechanisms of aging. *Mailing Add:* Geront Res Ctr Baltimore City Hosp Baltimore MD 21224

ROTH, HAROLD, b Wilkes-Barre, Pa, Jan 26, 31; m 52; c 3. SOLID STATE PHYSICS. *Educ:* Mass Inst Technol, BS, 52; Univ Pa, MS, 54, PhD(physics), 59. *Prof Exp:* Asst physics, Univ Pa, 53-54; res assoc, Gen Atomic Div, Gen Dynamics Corp, Calif, 56-59; staff scientist, 59; staff scientist, Raytheon Res Div, Mass, 59-63; prin scientist, 63-65; chief adv res br, Electronics Res Ctr, NASA, 65-68, chief electronic components lab, 68-70; dir res & advan develop, 70-73; dir res & eng, Electronics Div, Allen-Bradley Co, 73-82; DIR, SOLID STATE SCI DIV, ROME AIR DEVELOP CTR, HANSCOM AFB, MASS, 82- *Concurrent Pos:* Mem adv subcomt electrophys, NASA, 68-70. *Mem:* Am Phys Soc; Sigma Xi; Inst Elec & Electronics Eng; Am Inst Physics. *Res:* Semiconductors; galvanomagnetic effects; radiation damage; electrical properties of junctions; passive electronic components. *Mailing Add:* Solid State Sci Div Rome Air Develop Ctr Hanscom AFB MA 01731

ROTH, HAROLD PHILMORE, b Cleveland, Ohio, Aug 2, 15; m 52; c 2. GASTROENTEROLOGY. *Educ:* Western Reserve Univ, BA, 36, MD, 39; Harvard Univ, MS, 67. *Prof Exp:* Intern, Cincinnati Gen Hosp, 39-40; house officer, Fifth Med Serv, Boston City Hosp, 40-42; asst resident med, Barnes Hosp, St Louis, Mo, 42-43; from clin instr to sr clin instr med, Case Western Reserve Univ, 49-55, from asst prof to assoc prof, 55-74, assoc prof community health, 71-74; ASSOC DIR DIGESTIVE DIS & NUTRIT, NAT INST ARTHRITIS, DIABETES, DIGESTIVE & KIDNEY DIS, 74- *Concurrent Pos:* Asst med, Wash Univ, 42-43; asst physician, Out-Patient Dept, Univ Hosps, 49-, Med Staff, 57-, assoc physician, Dept Med, 69-; chief gastroenterol sect, Vet Admin Hosp, 47-74, dir gastroenterol training prog, Univ Hosps & Vet Admin Hosp, 63-74; USPHS spec fel, Sch Pub Health, Harvard Univ, 66-67. *Mem:* Am Gastroenterol Asn; fel Am Col Physicians; Am Asn Study Liver Dis; Soc Clin Trials (pres, 78-80); Cent Soc Clin Res. *Res:* Formation of gallstones; patient care, factors influencing patients' cooperation with medical regimens. *Mailing Add:* Bldg 31 Rm A 23 NIH Bethesda MD 20014

ROTH, HEINZ DIETER, b Rheinhausen, Ger, Oct 25, 36; m 64; c 2. PHYSICAL ORGANIC CHEMISTRY. *Educ:* Univ Karlsruhe, BS, 58; Univ Cologne, MS, 62, Dr rer nat, 65. *Prof Exp:* Fel org chem, Yale Univ, 65-67; MEM TECH STAFF ORG CHEM, BELL LABS, 67- *Mem:* Am Chem Soc; Ger Chem Soc. *Res:* Reactivity and structure of carbenes, radicals and radical ions; photochemistry; chemically induced magnetic polarization; nuclear magnetic resonance; electron paramagnetic resonance. *Mailing Add:* Bell Labs 1A219 Murray Hill NJ 07974

ROTH, HOWARD, b New York, NY, Oct 11, 25; m 43; c 2. FOOD CHEMISTRY. *Educ:* City Col New York, BS, 53. *Prof Exp:* Sr proj mgr, 53-75, assoc dir res & develop, Cent Res Lab, 75-77, DIR CORP RES CTR, DCA FOOD INDUSTRIES, INC, 77- *Mem:* Am Chem Soc; Am Oil Chem Soc; Int Microwave Power Inst (treas); Am Asn Cereal Chem. *Res:* Chemistry and physics of fats, oils and cereals; confectionary and bakery products; microwave applications; food product and machine development. *Mailing Add:* Corp Res Ctr 330 W 34th St New York NY 10001

ROTH, IVAN LAMBERT, b Nixon, Tex, Feb 21, 28; m 51; c 2. MICROBIOLOGY. *Educ:* Tex Lutheran Col, BA, 50; Univ Tex, MA, 56; Baylor Univ, PhD(microbiol), 63. *Prof Exp:* Anal chemist, Texaco Inc, Tex, 51-54; instr biol, Univ Houston, 58-62; asst prof microbiol, Med Ctr, Univ Ala, 62-66; assoc prof, 66-75; PROF MICROBIOL, UNIV GA, 75- *Mem:* AAAS; Am Soc Microbiol; Electron Micros Soc Am; Brit Soc Gen Microbiol. *Res:* Ultrastructure of animal tissue infected with bacteria; bacterial virulence, avirulence and pathogenesis in animals; ultrastructure of microbial cells; ultrastructure of bacterial capsules and slime; scanning electron microscopy of slime molds (myxomycetes). *Mailing Add:* Dept of Microbiol Univ of Ga Athens GA 30602

ROTH, J(OHN) REECE, b Washington, Pa, Sept 19, 37; m 72. PLASMA SCIENCE, ENGINEERING PHYSICS. *Educ:* Mass Inst Technol, SB, 59; Cornell Univ, PhD(eng physics), 63. *Prof Exp:* Aerospace res scientist, Phys Sci Div, Lewis Res Ctr, NASA, 63-78; PROF ELEC ENG, UNIV TENN, KNOXVILLE, 78- *Mem:* AAAS; Am Nuclear Soc; fel Inst Elec & Electronics Engrs; Am Phys Soc; Am Inst Aeronaut & Astronaut. *Res:* High temperature plasma science related to controlled fusion; plasma heating and confinement; effects of electric fields on toroidal plasmas. *Mailing Add:* Dept Elec Eng Univ Tenn Knoxville TN 37996

ROTH, JAMES FRANK, b Rahway, NJ, Dec 7, 25; m 50; c 3. PHYSICAL CHEMISTRY. *Educ:* WVa Univ, BA, 47; Univ Md, PhD(chem), 52. *Prof Exp:* Sr res chemist, Franklin Inst, 51-54; res chemist, Lehigh Paints & Chem Inc, 54-56 & cent res lab, Gen Aniline & Film Corp, 56-59; mgr chem br, Franklin Inst, 59-60; mgr catalysis res, Cent Res Dept, Monsanto Co, 60-69, mgr catalysis res, 69-73, dir catalysis res, 73-76, dir process sci, Corp Res Labs, 76-80; CORP CHIEF SCIENTIST, AIR PRODUCTS & CHEMICALS, INC, 80- *Honors & Awards:* E V Murphree Award in Indust & Eng Chem, Am Chem Soc, 76; R J Kokes Award, Johns Hopkins Univ, 77. *Mem:* Nat Acad Eng; Catalysis Soc NAm; Am Chem Soc. *Res:* Heterogeneous and homogeneous catalysis. *Mailing Add:* Sci Ctr Air Prod PO Box 538 Allentown PA 18105

ROTH, JAMES LUTHER AUMONT, b Milwaukee, Wis, Mar 8, 17; m 38; c 3. GASTROENTEROLOGY. *Educ:* Carthage Col, BA, 38, Univ Ill, MA, 39; Northwestern Univ, MD, 44, PhD(physiol), 45; Am Bd Internal Med, dipl, 54; Am Bd Gastroenterol, dipl, 55. *Hon Degrees:* DSc, Carthage Col, 57; MSc, Univ Pa. *Prof Exp:* Instr physiol, Med Sch Northwestern Univ, 42-44; intern med, Mass Gen Hosp, 44-45; resident physician, Grad Hosp, Philadelphia, 45-46; resident physician, Univ Hosp, 48-49, from instr to assoc gastroenterol, Div Grad Med, 50-54, asst prof physiol, 53-66, from asst prof to assoc prof, 54-59, prof clin gastroenterol, 59-68, PROF CLIN MED, SCH MED, UNIV PA, 68-, CHIEF GASTROENTEROL SERV & DIR, INST GASTROENTEROL, PRESBYUNIV PA MED CTR, 65- *Concurrent Pos:* Res fel med, Grad Hosp, Philadelphia, 49-50; dir, gastrointestinal res lab, Grad Hosp, 50-66, chief, gastrointestinal clin, 58-66; spec consult, Off Surgeon Gen, US Army, 48-49; mem adv comt rev, US Pharmacopeia XV, 50-60, 70-; exchange prof, Med Sch, Pontif Univ Javeriana, 60, prof extraordinary, 60-; dir grad div gastroenterol, Univ Pa, 61-69; consult, subcomt digestive syst, AMA, 62-64; mem drug efficacy panel, Food & Drug Admin, 66-68; consult, US Navy, Bethesda & Philadelphia Navy Hosps, 67-; mem bd dirs & chmn prog comt, Digestive Dis Found, 69-72; assoc ed, Bockus' Gastroenterology. *Honors & Awards:* Bronze Medal, AMA, Sigma Xi Prize, Joseph Capps Award, Inst Med, Chicago, 44; Order of Christopher Columbus, Govt Dominican Repub, 69. *Mem:* AMA; Am Gastroenterol Asn; fel Am Col Physicians; Pan-Am Med Asn; Bockus Int Soc Gastroenterol (secy-gen, 58-67, vpres, 67-71, pres elect, 71-73, pres, 73-75). *Res:* Intermediary metabolism of phenylalanine; caffeine potentiation of gastric secretion; caffeine gastric analysis; cold environment metabolic balances; penetration and hemorrhage in peptic ulcer; pancreatitis; hepatic coma; hazards of anti-cholinergic drugs; salicylate erosion and ulceration; ulcerative colitis. *Mailing Add:* Inst of Gastroenterol Suite 3233 Presby-Univ of Pa Med Ctr Philadelphia PA 19104

ROTH, JAN JEAN, b Rocky Ford, Colo, Sept 17, 43; m 75; c 2. ENVIRONMENTAL PHYSIOLOGY, PALEONTOLOGY. *Educ:* Univ Colo, BA, 69, MA, 73, PhD(biol), 74. *Prof Exp:* Jr staff fel neuroanat, 77-79, SR STAFF FEL BRAIN EVOLUTION, NAT INST MENTAL HEALTH, 79- *Concurrent Pos:* Biol instr, Arapahow Community Col, 71-72; res asst, Univ Colo, 72-74; fel, Colo State Univ & NSF, 74-76, Smithsonian Inst, 76-77; Smithsonian res collabr paneobiol, Smithsonian Inst, 77- *Mem:* AAAS; Soc Vertebrate Paleontol; Am Soc Zoologists. *Res:* Neuroanatomy, endocrinology and physiology of parietal-pineal complex in reptiles; neuroanatomy and brain evolution in fossil reptiles, especially mammal-like reptiles. *Mailing Add:* Lab Brain Evolution & Behav NIMH PO Box 289 Poolesville MD 20837

ROTH, JAY SANFORD, b New York, NY, June 10, 19; m 51, 72; c 8. BIOCHEMISTRY. *Educ:* City Col New York, BS, 40; Cornell Univ, MS, 41; Purdue Univ, PhD(org chem), 44. *Prof Exp:* Asst, Purdue Univ, 41-44; asst prof chem, Univ Idaho, 44-47 & Rutgers Univ, 47-50; from asst prof to assoc prof biochem, Hahnemann Med Col, 50-60; PROF BIOCHEM, UNIV CONN, 60- *Concurrent Pos:* Brit-Am Cancer Res fel, Strangeways Res Lab, Cambridge, 53-54; assoc, Marine Biol Lab, Woods Hole; Nat Cancer Inst career fel, 62-; assoc ed, Cancer Res, 71-76. *Mem:* AAAS; Am Soc Biol Chem; Soc Exp Biol & Med; Am Chem Soc; Am Asn Cancer Res. *Res:* Nucleic acids and nucleases in relation to cell division; control mechanisms in cancer; deoxynucleotide metabolism in growth; virus tumor biochemistry. *Mailing Add:* Sect of Biochem & Biophys Biol Sci Group Univ of Conn Storrs CT 06268

ROTH, JEROME A, b Springfield, Ill, Aug 13, 40; m 64; c 2. ORGANIC CHEMISTRY. *Educ:* Loyola Univ, Ill, BS, 62; Ill Inst Technol, PhD(org chem), 66. *Prof Exp:* Assoc catalysis chem, Northwestern Univ, 66-67, instr org chem, 67-68; asst prof, 68-72, assoc prof, 72-78, PROF CHEM, NORTHERN MICH UNIV, 78- *Concurrent Pos:* Am Chem Soc res grant, 68-71. *Mem:* Am Chem Soc; Org Reactions Catalysis Soc. *Res:* Organic chemical synthesis; mechanisms; transition-metal organic chemical compounds; heterogeneous and homogeneous catalysis. *Mailing Add:* Dept of Chem Northern Mich Univ Marquette MI 49855

ROTH, JEROME ALLAN, b New York, NY, Aug 20, 43; m 69; c 2. BIOCHEMISTRY, NEUROPHARMACOLOGY. *Educ:* State Univ NY Col New Paltz, BS, 65; Cornell Univ, MNS, 67, PhD(biochem), 71. *Prof Exp:* Res assoc biochem, Vanderbilt Univ, 71-72; res assoc to asst prof anesthesiol, Sch Med, Yale Univ, 72-76; asst prof, 76-79, ASSOC PROF, DEPT PHARMACOL & THERAPEUT, STATE UNIV NY, BUFFALO, 79- *Mem:* Am Chem Soc; Am Soc Pharmacol & Exp therapeut; Am Soc Neurochem. *Res:* Structure and properties ofmanomine oxidase, catechol-o-methyltransferase and phenolsulfotransferase; effect of drugs on enzymes involved in biosynthesis and degradation of biogenic amines; effect of drugs on microsomal enzymes. *Mailing Add:* Dept of Pharmacol & Therapeutics State Univ NY Buffalo NY 14214

ROTH, JESSE, b New York, NY, Aug 5, 34. ENDOCRINOLOGY. *Educ:* Columbia Univ, BA, 55; Albert Einstein Col Med, MD, 59. *Hon Degrees:* Dr, Univ Uppsala, 80. *Prof Exp:* From intern to asst resident, Barnes Hosp, Wash Univ, 59-61; Am Diabetes Asn res fel, Radioisotope Serv, Vet Hosp, Bronx, NY, 61-63; clin assoc, 63-65, sr investr, 65-66, chief diabetes sect, Clin Endocrinol Br, 66-74, CHIEF DIABETES BR, NAT INST ARTHRITIS, METAB & DIGESTIVE DIS, NIH, 74- *Honors & Awards:* Eli Lilly Award, Am Diabetes Asn, 74; Ernst Oppenheimer Mem Award, Endocrine Soc, 74; Spec Achievement Award, US Dept Health, Educ & Welfare, David Rumbough Mem Award, Juvenile Diabetes Found, 77; Regents' lectr, Univ Calif, 77; G. Burroughs Mider lectr, NIH, 78; Diaz Cristobal Prize, Int Diabetes Fedn, 79; Gairdner Found Annual Award, 80; A Cressy Morrison Award, NY Acad Sci, 80; Joslin Medal, New Eng Diabetes Asn, 81. *Mem:* Endocrine Soc; Am Diabetes Asn; Am Fedn Clin Res; Am Soc Clin Invest (pres, 78-80). *Res:* Diabetes; clinical research. *Mailing Add:* Diabetes Br Nat Inst Arthritis Metab & Digestive Dis Bethesda MD 20014

ROTH, JOHN AUSTIN, b Louisville, Ky, May 14, 34; m 59; c 2. CHEMICAL ENGINEERING, ENVIRONMENTAL ENGINEERING. *Educ:* Univ Louisville, BChE, 56, MChE, 57, PhD(chem eng), 61. *Prof Exp:* Teaching asst chem eng, Univ Louisville, 56-59; from asst prof to prof chem eng, 62-74, from asst dean to assoc dean sch eng, 68-72, CHMN CHEM FLUID & THERMAL SCI DIV, VANDERBILT UNIV, 71-, PROF CHEM & ENVIRON ENG & DIR, CTR ENVIRON QUAL MGT, 74- *Concurrent Pos:* Year-in-indust partic, Savannah River Lab, E I du Pont de Nemours & Co, Inc, Del, 67-68; comnr, Ky Bur Environ Protection, 77-78. *Mem:* Water Pollution Control Fedn; Am Inst Chem Engrs; Am Chem Soc; Nat Soc Prof Engrs; Am Inst Chemists. *Res:* Water and waste water treatment by ozonation; carbon adsorption; chemical engineering kinetics; mass transfer processes; hazardous materials; mixing processes. *Mailing Add:* Ctr Environ Qual Mgt Vanderbilt Univ Nashville TN 37235

ROTH, JOHN L, JR, b Trenton, NJ, July 5, 49; m 73; c 3. ANGIOSPEAM EVOLUTION, PALYNOLOGY. *Educ:* Brigham Young Univ, BS, 73, MS, 75; Ind Univ, MA, 79, PhD(bot), 81. *Prof Exp:* Vis lectr bot, Ind Univ, 80; RES ASSOC BOT, UNIV MASS, AMHERST, 81- *Mem:* Bot Soc Am; Am Soc Plant Toxonomists; Int Asn Angiosperm Paleobotany; AAAS; Sigma Xi. *Mailing Add:* Dept Bot Univ Mass Amherst MA 01003

ROTH, JOHN PAUL, b Detroit, Mich, Dec 16, 22; m 48; c 2. COMPUTER SCIENCE, MATHEMATICS. *Educ:* Univ Detroit, BME, 46; Univ Mich, MS, 48, PhD(math), 54. *Prof Exp:* Instr math, Wayne State Univ, 46-47; res assoc appl math, Univ Mich, 47-53; Pierce instr math, Univ Calif, 53-55; staff mathematician, Inst Adv Study, 55-56; MEM RES STAFF, THOMAS J WATSON RES CTR, IBM CORP, 56- *Concurrent Pos:* Res engr, Continental Aviation & Eng Corp, 46-47; consult, Shell Develop Co, 54-55; adj prof, City Univ New York, 81-82. *Mem:* Am Math Soc; Soc Indust & Appl Math; fel Inst Elec & Elec Engrs. *Res:* Mathematical computer design; combinatorial topology, especially conceptual and practical use in the solution of physical problems. *Mailing Add:* IBM Thomas J Watson Res Ctr Box 218 Yorktown Heights NY 10598

ROTH, JOHN R, b Winona, Minn, Mar 14, 39; m 61; c 2. BACTERIAL GENETICS. *Educ:* Harvard Univ, BS, 61; Johns Hopkins Univ, PhD(biol), 65. *Prof Exp:* USPHS fel, Lab of Bruce N Ames, NIH, 65-67; from asst prof to prof molecular biol, Univ Calif, Berkeley, 67-76; PROF BIOL, UNIV UTAH, 76- *Mem:* Genetics Soc Am; Am Soc Microbiol. *Res:* Gene regulation in bacteria; informational suppressors. *Mailing Add:* Dept of Biol Univ of Utah Salt Lake City UT 84112

ROTH, JONATHAN NICHOLAS, b Albany, Ore, Mar 2, 38; m 59; c 3. PLANT PATHOLOGY, MARINE BIOLOGY. *Educ:* Goshen Col, AB, 59; Ore State Univ, PhD(plant path), 62. *Prof Exp:* From asst prof to assoc prof, 62-70, PROF BIOL, GOSHEN COL, 70-, CHMN DEPT BIOL, 80- *Concurrent Pos:* NIH fel, Inst Marine Sci, Miami, Fla, 64-65. *Mem:* Am Inst Biol Sci. *Res:* Phytopathology, mycology; marine algae; invertebrate zoology; development of termperature independent substitute for agar-agar as a microbiological medium gelling agent. *Mailing Add:* Dept of Biol Goshen Col Goshen IN 46526

ROTH, LAURA MAURER, b Flushing, NY, Oct 11, 30; m 52; c 2. SOLID STATE PHYSICS. *Educ:* Swarthmore Col, BA, 52; Radcliffe Col, MA, 53, PhD(physics), 57. *Prof Exp:* Staff physicist, Lincoln Lab, Mass Inst Technol, 56-62; prof physics, Tufts Univ, 62-67; physicist, Res & Develop Ctr, Gen Elec Co, 67-72; Abby Rockefeller Mauze vis prof physics, Mass Inst Technol, 72-73; res prof sci & math, 73-77, PROF PHYSICS, STATE UNIV NY, ALBANY, 77- *Concurrent Pos:* Consult, Lincoln Lab, Mass Inst Technol, 62-67. *Mem:* Fel Am Phys Soc. *Res:* Band structure of solids; Bloch electrons in magnetic fields; magnetooptics; magnetism; liquid and amorphous metals. *Mailing Add:* Dept of Physics State Univ of NY Albany NY 12222

ROTH, LAWRENCE MAX, b McAlester, Okla, June 25, 36; m 65; c 2. PATHOLOGY, ELECTRON MICROSCOPY. *Educ:* Vanderbilt Univ, BA, 57; Harvard Med Sch, MD, 60; Am Bd Path, dipl & cert anat path, 66, cert clin path, 68, cert dermatopath, 74. *Prof Exp:* Intern, Univ Ill Res & Educ Hosps, Chicago, 60-61; resident anat path, Barnes Hosp, St Louis, Mo, 61-63, resident surg path, 63-64; resident clin path, Univ Calif Med Ctr, San Francisco, 67-68; from asst prof to assoc prof path, Sch Med, Tulane Univ, 68-71; assoc prof, 71-72, PROF PATH & DIR SURG PATH DIV, SCH MED, IND UNIV, INDIANAPOLIS, 72- *Concurrent Pos:* Nat Inst Gen Med Sci sr res trainee, Hormone Lab, Karolinska Inst, Stockholm, Sweden, 64-65; asst path, Sch Med, Wash Univ, 61-64; series ed, Contemporary Issues Surg Pathol. *Mem:* Am Asn Path & Bact; Am Soc Clin Path; Int Acad Path; Int Soc Gynec Pathologists. *Res:* Gynecological and endocrine pathology; steroid chemistry; electron microscopy; ovarian tumors. *Mailing Add:* Dept Path Ind Univ Med Ctr Indianapolis IN 46223

ROTH, LAWRENCE O(RVAL), b Hillsboro, Wis, June 7, 28; m 54; c 2. AGRICULTURAL ENGINEERING. *Educ:* Univ Wis, BS, 49 & 51; Okla State Univ, MS, 56, PhD(eng), 65. *Prof Exp:* From instr to assoc prof, 51-72, PROF AGR ENG, OKLA STATE UNIV, 72- *Concurrent Pos:* Ford Found residency eng pract fel, 67-68. *Mem:* Am Soc Agr Eng; Am Soc Eng Educ; Weed Sci Soc Am; Nat Soc Prof Engrs. *Res:* Farm power and machinery; machine design and development for drift control of pesticides and mechanization of horticultural crop production. *Mailing Add:* Dept of Agr Eng Okla State Univ Stillwater OK 74074

ROTH, LEWIS FRANKLIN, b Poplar, Mont, Apr 12, 14; m 45; c 2. FOREST PATHOLOGY, MYCOLOGY. *Educ:* Miami Univ, BA, 36; Univ Wis, PhD(plant path), 40. *Prof Exp:* Asst plant path, Univ Wis, 36-38; from instr to assoc prof, 40-57, prof, 57-79, EMER PROF BOT & PLANT PATH, ORE STATE UNIV, 79-, CONSULT. *Concurrent Pos:* Sci aide, Forest Prod Lab, US Forest Serv, 40, collab, 58-; fel, Harvard Univ, 46-47. *Mem:* Fel Am Phytopath Soc; Mycol Soc Am; Soc Am Foresters. *Res:* Epidemiology; life history and control of forest diseases; root diseases; dwarf mistletoe; pine needle blight; aquatic fungi. *Mailing Add:* Dept Bot & Plant Path Ore State Univ Corvallis OR 97331

ROTH, LINWOOD EVANS, b Ft Wayne, Ind, Mar 8, 29; m 49; c 2. CELL BIOLOGY. *Educ:* Univ Ind, AB, 50; Northwestern Univ, MS, 55; Univ Chicago, PhD(zool), 57. *Prof Exp:* Electron microscopist, Med Sch, Univ Ind, 50-52; sr res technician, Div Biol & Med Res, Argonne Nat Lab, 52-54, asst scientist, 54-60; from assoc prof to prof biochem & biophys, Iowa State Univ, 60-67, asst dean grad col, 62-67; prof biol & dir, div biol, Kans State Univ, 67-76; PROF ZOOL & V CHANCELLOR GRAD STUDIES & RES, UNIV TENN, KNOXVILLE, 76- *Concurrent Pos:* Ed, European J Cell Biol, 74- *Mem:* AAAS; Am Soc Cell Biol; Sigma Xi; Am Sci Affil. *Res:* Cell biology; educational administration; research education. *Mailing Add:* 404 Holt Tower Univ Tenn Knoxville TN 37996

ROTH, MARIE M, b Boston, Mass, Apr 30, 26; m 51; c 4. ORGANIC & GENERAL CHEMISTRY. *Educ:* Mt Holyoke Col, BA, 45, MA, 47; Univ Wis, PhD(org chem), 52. *Prof Exp:* Res librn, Pittsburgh Plate Glass Co, 51-52; abstractor, Chem Abstr, 52-59; lectr, Univ Wis Ctr Syst, Waukesha County, 71 & 73, lectr gen chem, Washington County, 72-79; LECTR, MARQUETTE UNIV, 81- *Concurrent Pos:* Adj asst prof, Univ Wis-Milwaukee, 81. *Mem:* Am Chem Soc. *Res:* Heterocyclic compounds and synthesis of antimalarials; synthesis of steroid intermediates. *Mailing Add:* 1620 Revere Dr Brookfield WI 53005

ROTH, MICHAEL WILLIAM, b Davenport, Iowa, June 30, 52; m 73. PHYSICAL OCEANOGRAPHY, SIGNAL PROCESSING. *Educ:* MacMurray Col, BA, 71; Univ Ill, Urbana, MS, 72, PhD(physics), 75. *Prof Exp:* Res assoc, Fermi Nat Accelerator Lab, 75-77; SR PHYSICIST, APPL PHYSICS LAB, JOHNS HOPKINS UNIV, 77- *Concurrent Pos:* NATO travel grant, NSF, 76; proj mgr, Appl Physics Lab, Johns Hopkins Univ, 80-, sect supvr & proj dir, 81- *Mem:* Am Asn Artificial Intelligence. *Res:* Physical oceanography; internal waves; fine structure; signal processing. *Mailing Add:* Appl Physics Lab Johns Hopkins Univ Johns Hopkins Rd Laurel MD 20707

ROTH, NILES, b New York, NY, Sept 27, 25; m 52; c 3. PHYSIOLOGICAL OPTICS, OPTOMETRY. *Educ:* Univ Calif, Berkeley, BS, 55, MOpt, 56, PhD(physiol optics), 61. *Prof Exp:* Asst res biophysicist, Univ Calif, Los Angeles, 61-69; assoc prof, 69-76, PROF PHYSIOL OPTICS, COL OPTOM, PAC UNIV, 76- *Concurrent Pos:* Res grants, USPHS, 61-65, Am Cancer Soc, 66-67; consult, Long Beach Vet Admin Hosp, 61-69. *Mem:* AAAS; Am Optom Asn; Optical Soc Am; fel Am Acad Optom; Sigma Xi. *Res:* Factors affecting resting ocular refractive state and pupil size; psychophysical and photometric aspects of vision testing. *Mailing Add:* Col of Optom Pac Univ Forest Grove OR 97116

ROTH, NORMAN GILBERT, b Chicago, Ill, Dec 11, 24; m 50; c 6. MICROBIOLOGY. *Educ:* Univ Chicago, BS, 47; Univ Ill, MS, 49, PhD(bact), 51. *Prof Exp:* Bacteriologist, Ft Detrick, Md, 51-57; sr res bacteriologist, 57-60, dir life support, 60-73, dir waste mgt, 73-77, DIR RES & ENG SPEC PROJS, WHIRLPOOL CORP, 77- *Res:* Aerospace life support, Gemini, Apollo; food, waste, water, sanitation management systems; microbial deterioration; appliance sanitation; psychrophilic bacteria; bacterial spores. *Mailing Add:* 1801 Briarcliff St Joseph MI 49085

ROTH, PETER HANS, b Zurich, Switz, June 25, 42; m 69; c 2. MICROPALEONTOLOGY, MARINE GEOLOGY. *Educ:* Swiss Fed Inst Technol, Zurich, dipl, 65, PhD(geol), 70. *Prof Exp:* Asst res geologist, Scripps Inst Oceanog, 71-75; ASSOC PROF GEOL & GEOPHYS, UNIV UTAH, 75- *Mem:* Am Geophys Union; AAAS; Geol Soc Am; Swiss Geol Soc. *Res:* Biostratigraphy, paleoecology and preservation of calcareous nannofossil; early diagenesis of deep-sea carbonates; paleoceanography. *Mailing Add:* Dept Geol & Geophys Univ Utah Salt Lake City UT 84112

ROTH, PHILIP MARTIN, chemical engineering, environmental science, see previous edition

ROTH, RAYMOND EDWARD, b Rochester, NY, Oct 29, 18; m 42; c 5. STATISTICS. *Educ:* St Bonaventure Univ, BS, 40, MS, 42; Rochester Univ, PhD(statist), 63. *Prof Exp:* Consult, Gen Elec Co, 43-46; res assoc, Univ Notre Dame, 46-47; asst prof physics, Univ Dayton, 47-49; physicist, Wright-Patterson Air Force Base, 49-50; res assoc atomic energy proj, Med Sch, Rochester Univ, 53-57; assoc prof math & head dept, St Bonaventure Univ, 58-63, prof & chmn dept, 63-66; prof statist & dir comput ctr, State Univ NY Col Geneseo, 66-68; ARCHIBALD GRANVILLE BUSH PROF MATH, ROLLINS COL, 68- *Concurrent Pos:* Vis staff med sch & math dept, Univ Okla, 62-63; consult, Civil Aeromed Res Inst, Fed Aviation Agency, Oklahoma City, 62-63 & Med Div, Oak Ridge Inst Nuclear Studies, 64-65. *Mem:* Am Chem Soc; Am Statist Asn; Math Asn Am; Royal Statist Soc; Biomet Soc. *Res:* Flash burn effects; quantal response in a Latin square design of experiment; models. *Mailing Add:* Dept of Math Rollins Col Winter Park FL 32789

ROTH, RENE ROMAIN, b Timisoara, Romania, Feb 24, 28; Can citizen; m 61; c 3. ENDOCRINOLOGY, HISTORY OF BIOLOGY. *Educ:* Univ Cluj, MSc, 50; Univ Alta, PhD(comp endocrinol), 69. *Prof Exp:* Lectr bact, Inst Vet Med, Bucharest, Romania, 50-52; lectr zool & parasitol, Inst Vet Med, Arad, 52-56; res fel endocrinol, Univ Timisoara Hosp, 56-60 & Sch Med, Hebrew Univ, Israel, 60-62; ASST PROF ZOOL, UNIV WESTERN ONT, 66- *Mem:* AAAS; Am Inst Biol Sci; NY Acad Sci; Can Soc Zool; Can Soc Endocrinol & Metab. *Res:* Influence of light and temperature on gonad activity and nutrition in the red-back vole; effect of protein intake levels on reproduction and dietary self-selection in rats; theoretical biology; history of biology; comparative physiology of growth and nutrition. *Mailing Add:* Dept Zool Univ Western Ont London ON N6A 5B7 Can

ROTH, RICHARD FRANCIS, b St Louis, Mo, Jan 18, 38; m 63; c 2. PHYSICS. *Educ:* Rockhurst Col, BS, 59; Princeton Univ, MA, 61, PhD(physics), 64. *Prof Exp:* Fel physics, Princeton Univ, 63-64, res assoc, 64-65, instr, 65-66; staff physicist, Comn Col Physics, Univ Mich, 66-69; ASSOC PROF PHYSICS & ASTRON, EASTERN MICH UNIV, 69- *Mem:* Am Phys Soc; Am Asn Physics Teachers. *Res:* Experimental elementary particle physics; use of computers. *Mailing Add:* Dept of Physics & Astron Eastern Mich Univ Ypsilanti MI 48197

ROTH, RICHARD LEWIS, b New York, NY, Feb 24, 36. MATHEMATICS. *Educ:* Harvard Univ, BA, 58; Univ Calif, Berkeley, MA, 60, PhD(math), 63. *Prof Exp:* Asst prof, 63-68, ASSOC PROF MATH, UNIV COLO, BOULDER, 68- *Concurrent Pos:* Regional specialist, NSF, Cent Am, 65-66. *Mem:* Am Math Soc; Math Asn Am. *Res:* Representations of finite groups; algebra; color symmetry. *Mailing Add:* Dept Math Univ Colo Boulder CO 80309

ROTH, ROBERT ANDREW, JR, b McKeesport, Pa, Aug 15, 46; m 70. BIOCHEMICAL PHARMACOLOGY, ENVIRONMENTAL MEDICINE. *Educ:* Duke Univ, BA, 68; Johns Hopkins Univ, PhD(biochem toxicol), 75; Am Bd Toxicol, dipl. *Prof Exp:* Toxicol test specialist, US Army Environ Hyg Agency, 69-71; res fel pulmonary pharmacol, Dept Anesthesiol, Yale Univ, 75-77; ASST PROF PHARMACOL & TOXICOL, MICH STATE UNIV, EAST LANSING, 77- *Mem:* Am Soc Pharmacol Exp Therapeut; Soc Toxicol. *Res:* Removal and metabolism of drugs and hormones by lung; pulmonary toxicology; effect of carbon monoxide and of hypoxic hypoxia on hepatic drug metabolism. *Mailing Add:* Dept of Pharmacol Mich State Univ East Lansing MI 48824

ROTH, ROBERT EARL, b Wauseon, Ohio, Mar 30, 37; m 59; c 2. SCIENCE EDUCATION, NATURAL RESOURCES. *Educ:* Ohio State Univ, BS, 59 & 61, MS, 60; Univ Wis, PhD(environ educ), 69. *Prof Exp:* Teacher & conserv educ supvr, Ethical Cult Schs, 61-63; teacher & naturalist, Edwin Gould Found for Children, 63-65; instr outdoor teacher educ, Northern Ill Univ, 65-67; res asst environ educ, Wis Res & Develop Ctr for Cognitive Learning, 67-69; asst prof natural resources, 69-72, assoc prof, 72-78, PROF, ENVIRON EDUC DIV, SCH NATURAL RES, OHIO STATE UNIV, 79-, CHMN DEPT, 72- *Concurrent Pos:* Res assoc, Educ Resources Info Ctr Environ Educ, 70-74; from assoc prof to prof, Ohio Agr Res & Develop Ctr & Fac Sci & Math Educ. *Honors & Awards:* Publ Prize, J Environ Educ, 73. *Mem:* Nat Asn Environ Educ (pres elect, 75-76, pres, 76-77); Nat Sci Teachers Asn; Asn Interpretive Naturalists; Conserv Educ Asn. *Res:* Concept development and attitude formation in environmental management; curriculum development; program modeling and interpretive skill development and evaluation; information analysis in environmental education; program and international environmental education development. *Mailing Add:* 570 Morning St Worthington OH 43085

ROTH, ROBERT EARL, b Springfield, Ill, Mar 3, 25; m 48; c 5. RADIOLOGY. *Educ:* Univ Ill, BS, 47, MD, 49. *Prof Exp:* Intern, St Louis County Hosp, Clayton, Mo, 49-50; resident, US Naval Hosp, San Diego, Calif, US Vet Admin Hosp, Nashville, Tenn & Vanderbilt Univ Hosp, 50-54, asst chief radiol, US Vet Admin Hosp, 54-55; from asst prof to assoc prof, 55-59, prof radiol & chmn dept, 59-69, PROF RADIATION ONCOL & CHMN DEPT, MED COL, UNIV ALA, BIRMINGHAM, 69- *Concurrent Pos:* Actg chief radiol, Vet Admin Hosp, Birmingham, Ala; consult, Vet Admin Hosps, Birmingham & Tuskegee, Ala. *Mem:* AAAS; fel Am Col Radiol; Soc Nuclear Med; Radiol Soc NAm; NY Acad Sci. *Res:* Radiation therapy. *Mailing Add:* Univ of Ala Med Ctr Birmingham AL 35233

ROTH, ROBERT HENRY, JR, b Hackensack, NJ, Sept 18, 39; m 63; c 2. NEUROPHARMACOLOGY. *Educ:* Univ Conn, BS, 61; Yale Univ, PhD(pharmacol), 65. *Prof Exp:* From instr to asst prof, 66-69, assoc prof pharmacol, 69-77, PROF PSYCHIAT & PHARMACOL, YALE UNIV, 77- *Concurrent Pos:* Nat Inst Gen Med Sci fel physiol, Karolinska Inst, Sweden, 65-66; USPHS res grants, 66-72. *Mem:* Am Soc Pharmacol & Exp Therapeut. *Res:* Neuropharmacology and neurochemsitry, especially related to central nervous system depressants and sleep; monoamines and chemical transmission in the nervous system; endogenous factors in control of neurohumors in the nervous system. *Mailing Add:* Dept of Pharmacol Yale Univ New Haven CT 06510

ROTH, ROBERT MARK, b Brooklyn, NY, Apr 9, 43; m 64; c 3. BIOLOGY, GENETICS. *Educ:* Brooklyn Col, BS, 63; Brandeis Univ, PhD(biol), 67. *Prof Exp:* Fel biol, Univ Wis-Madison, 68; from asst prof to assoc prof, 68-76, PROF BIOL, ILL INST TECHNOL, 76-, CHMN DEPT, 78- *Concurrent Pos:* Res assoc, Univ Calif, Berkeley, 70; USPHS res career develop award, 72; vis lectr biol chem, Harvard Med Sch, 73-74. *Mem:* Genetics Soc Am; Am Soc Photobiol; Am Soc Microbiol. *Res:* Biochemical genetics of developing microorganisms, including slime molds and yeast; photodynamic action and photosensitivity in microorganisms. *Mailing Add:* Dept of Biol Ill Inst of Technol Chicago IL 60616

ROTH, ROBERT S, b Chicago, Ill, Aug 21, 26; m 54; c 3. GEOLOGY. *Educ:* Coe Col, BA, 47; Univ Ill, MS, 50, PhD(geol), 51. *Prof Exp:* Res assoc, Eng Exp Sta, Univ Ill, 51; geologist, 51-56, solid state physicist, 57-61, res chemist, 62-68, supvr chemist, 69-81, RES CHEMIST, NAT BUR STANDARDS, 81- *Mem:* Geol Soc Am; Mineral Soc Am; Am Crystallog Asn; Mineral Soc Gt Brit & Ireland; Am Ceramic Soc. *Res:* X-ray crystallography and phase equilibria of ceramic materials. *Mailing Add:* Nat Bur of Standards 561 Washington DC 20234

ROTH, ROBERT STEELE, b Philadelphia, Pa, July 3, 30; m 66; c 1. APPLIED MECHANICS. *Educ:* Kenyon Col, AB, 53; Carnegie-Mellon Univ, MS, 54; Harvard Univ, PhD(appl math), 62. *Prof Exp:* Engr math, Aberdeen Proving Ground, 54-56; scientist & group leader mech, Systs Div Avco Corp, 62-74; TECH STAFF APPL MATH, CHARLES STARK DRAPER LAB, INC, CAMBRIDGE, 74- *Concurrent Pos:* Assoc ed, Math Biosci, 72-76. *Mem:* Sigma Xi; Am Inst Aeronaut & Astronaut; Am Acad Mech. *Res:* Structural mechanics; dynamic buckling of thin shells; plastic buckling of thin shells; numerical analysis; nonlinear differential equations; system identification; segmental differential approximation; bioengineering analysis. *Mailing Add:* 192 Commonwealth Ave Boston MA 02116

ROTH, RODNEY J, b Brockway, Pa, Mar 13, 27; m 54; c 2. MATHEMATICS. *Educ:* Pa State Univ, BA, 51; Univ Iowa, MFA, 53; Duke Univ, PhD(math), 62. *Prof Exp:* Asst prof math, Univ Ky, 61-63 & Univ SFla, 63-66; assoc prof & chmn dept, Upsala Col, 66-70; assoc prof, 71-77, PROF MATH, RAMAPO COL, NJ, 77- *Mem:* Am Math Soc; Math Asn Am. *Res:* Algebra; applications of mathematics in behavioral and social science. *Mailing Add:* Dept of Math Ramapo Col of NJ Mahwah NJ 07430

ROTH, ROLAND RAY, b Stuttgart, Ark, Jan 9, 43; m 64; c 3. ECOLOGY, VERTEBRATE BIOLOGY. *Educ:* Univ Ark, Fayetteville, BS, 66; Univ Ill, Urbana, MS, 67, PhD(zool), 71. *Prof Exp:* Res assoc zool, Univ Ill, Urbana, 71; asst prof, 71-77, ASSOC PROF ECOL & ORNITH, UNIV DEL, 77- *Mem:* AAAS; Am Inst Biol Sci; Ecol Soc Am; Am Ornith Union; Brit Ornith Union. *Res:* Community structure; habitat selection and use, especially of birds; yellowjacket ecology; urban wildlife. *Mailing Add:* Dept of Entom & Appl Ecol Univ of Del Newark DE 19711

ROTH, RONALD JOHN, b New York, NY, Feb 1, 47. ORGANIC CHEMISTRY. *Educ:* City Col NY, BS, 67; Columbia Univ, PhD(chem), 72. *Prof Exp:* Res assoc chem, Univ Chicago, 72-73; instr chem, Brown Univ, 74-75; asst prof, 75-80, ASSOC PROF CHEM, GEORGE MASON UNIV, 81- *Mem:* Am Chem Soc; Sigma Xi. *Res:* Synthesis of small strained hydrocarbons and their metal catalyzed transformations. *Mailing Add:* George Mason Univ Dept of Chem 4400 University Dr Fairfax VA 22030

ROTH, ROY WILLIAM, b Collingswood, NJ, May 27, 29; m 55; c 3. POLYMER CHEMISTRY. *Educ:* Mass Inst Technol, BS, 50; Univ Mich, MS, 51; Mass Inst Technol, PhD(chem), 55. *Prof Exp:* Res chemist, Stamford Labs, Am Cyanamid Co, Conn, 55-60, group leader, 60-64, mgr prod res sect, 64-67, mgr prod develop, Davis & Geck Dept, Lederle Labs, 68-75; dir prod develop, Kendall Co, Colgate-Palmolive, 76-78; res assoc, Pall Corp, 78-79; CHIEF FIBER & FABRIC TECH, NATICK LABS, US ARMY, 79- *Mem:* Am Chem Soc; Soc Plastics Eng. *Res:* Polymer chemistry; medical specialties; product development; non-woven fabrics; specialty filters; sterile-disposable products. *Mailing Add:* US Army Natick Labs Natick MA 01760

ROTH, SANFORD IRWIN, b McAlester, Okla, Oct 14, 32; m 61; c 4. PATHOLOGY, ELECTRON MICROSCOPY. *Educ:* Harvard Univ, MD, 56. *Prof Exp:* From intern to asst resident, Mass Gen Hosp, 56-58, actg asst resident, 58-60, asst, 62-64, asst pathologist, 64-70, assoc pathologist, 70-75; prof path & chmn dept, Col Med, Univ Ark, 75-80; PROF, DEPT PATH, MED SCH, NORTHWESTERN UNIV, 80- *Concurrent Pos:* USPHS res trainee, Mass Gen Hosp, 58-60, teaching fel, Harvard Med Sch, 58-60; instr, Sch Med, Tufts Univ, 58-60; asst, Harvard Med Sch, 62-63, instr, 63-64, assoc, 64-67, from asst prof to assoc prof path, 67-75; Am Cancer Soc fac res assoc, 67-72. *Mem:* Electron Micros Soc Am; Int Acad Pathologists; Am Soc Cell Biol; Soc Invest Dermat; Am Asn Pathologists. *Res:* Experimental pathology; pathology of the parathyroid glands; dermatopathology; molecular biology of parathyroids and skin. *Mailing Add:* Dept Path Northwestern Univ Col Med 303 E Chicago Ave Chicago IL 60611

ROTH, SHIRLEY H, b Brooklyn, NY. CHEMISTRY. *Educ:* NY Univ, AB, 58, PhD(phys chem), 62. *Prof Exp:* Instr chem, NY Univ, 62; from instr to asst prof, Temple Univ, 62-64; res scientist, Res Div, Am Stand Inc, 64-66; sr res chemist, Cities Serv Co, 67-74, res assoc, 74-77; mgr mat synthesis design, 77-81, MGR MAT ANALYSIS, XEROX CORP, 81- *Mem:* Am Chem Soc. *Res:* Physical and polymer chemistry; intumescent coatings; styrenic polymers; synthesis and characterization of specialty chemicals and polymers; techniques of polymerization; photoconductors. *Mailing Add:* Xerox Corp 800 Phillips Rd W 139 Webster NY 14580

ROTH, STEPHEN (ALLEN), developmental biology, see previous edition

ROTH, STEPHEN, b New York, NY, Sept 3, 42; m 81; c 2. MEMBRANE BIOCHEMISTRY, CARBOHYDRATE BIOCHEMISTRY. *Educ:* Johns Hopkins Univ, AB, 64; Case Western Reserve Univ, PhD(embryol), 68; Univ Pa, MA, 80. *Prof Exp:* Fel biochem, Johns Hopkins Univ, 68-70, from asst prof to assoc prof develop biol, 70-80; PROF DEVELOP BIOL, UNIV PA, 80- *Concurrent Pos:* Mem, Cell Biol Study Sect, NIH, 74-78. *Mem:* Am Soc Develop Biol; NY Acad Sci; Soc Gen Physiologists; AAAS; Int Soc Develop Biol. *Res:* Biochemical mechanisms for the acquisition of form in biological systems specifically, membrane biochemistry as it controls morphogenesis in vertebrate embryos. *Mailing Add:* Dept Biol Univ Pa Philadelphia PA 19104

ROTH, THOMAS ALLAN, b Cudahy, Wis, Dec 12, 37; m 67. METALLURGICAL ENGINEERING, MATERIALS SCIENCE. *Educ:* Univ Wis, BS, 60, MS, 61, PhD(metall eng), 67. *Prof Exp:* Teaching asst metall eng, Univ Wis, 61-62, instr, 64-65; from asst prof to assoc prof indust eng, 65-76, ASSOC PROF CHEM ENG, KANS STATE UNIV, 76- *Concurrent Pos:* Prin investr, Kans State Univ Res Coord Coun grants, 66-68; proj dir, Nat Sci Found Instr Sci Equip grant, 68-70; acad year res grant, Kans State Univ, 68-70; Kans State Univ Bur Gen Res grant, 70; prin investr, US Air Force Off Sci Res grant, 75-77; bk reviewer, J Electrochem Soc, 77- *Mem:* AAAS; Am Soc Metals; Metall Soc; Electrochem Soc. *Res:* Physical metallurgy; influence of adsorbed gases on the surface properties of metals; hydrogen embrittlement of iron and steel; ionic thermoconductivity. *Mailing Add:* Dept of Chem Eng Kans State Univ Manhattan KS 66506

ROTH, THOMAS FREDERIC, b Detroit, Mich, Feb 28, 32; m 63. CELL BIOLOGY, DEVELOPMENTAL BIOLOGY. *Educ:* Tufts Univ, BS, 54; Harvard Univ, MA, 59, PhD(biol), 64. *Prof Exp:* USPHS fel biol, Harvard Univ, 64; fel, Univ Calif, San Diego, 64-66, asst res biologist, 66-67, asst prof biol, 67-72; assoc prof, 72-77, PROF BIOL, UNIV MD BALTIMORE COUNTY, 77- *Mem:* AAAS; Soc Develop Biol; Soc Study Reproduction; Am Soc Cell Biol; Electron Micros Soc Am. *Res:* Physiology, biochemistry and ultra structure of receptor mediated protein transport in the oocyte and yolk sac; assembly of coated vesicles. *Mailing Add:* Dept Biol Sci Univ Md Baltimore Co Baltimore MD 21228

ROTH, VINCENT DANIEL, b Portland, Ore, Feb 12, 24; m 61; c 3. ARACHNOLOGY. *Educ:* Ore State Col, BS, 49, MS, 50. *Prof Exp:* Cur, Ore State Col, 48-52; surv entomologist, State Dept Agr, 53-54; asst entomologist, Univ Ariz, 55-56; entomologist, USDA, 56-60; farm adv entomologist, Univ Calif, 60-62, RESIDENT DIR, SOUTHWESTERN RES STA, 62-; RES ASSOC BIOL SCI, UNIV ARIZ, 71- *Mem:* Entom Soc Am; Am Arachnology Soc. *Res:* Taxonomy of spiders; Agelenidae of world. *Mailing Add:* Southwestern Res Sta Portal AZ 85632

ROTH, WALTER, b New York, NY, Dec 4, 22; m 47; c 2. PHYSICAL CHEMISTRY. *Educ:* City Col New York, BS, 44; NY Univ, MS, 47; Rensselaer Polytech Inst, PhD(chem), 54. *Prof Exp:* Chemist, Kellex Corp, NJ, 44-45; chemist, Carbide & Carbon Chem Co, Tenn, 45-46; phys chemist, US Bur Mines, Pa, 48-53; phys chemist, Res Lab, Gen Elec Co, NY, 54-59; sr physicist, Armour Res Found, Ill Inst Technol, 59-63; mgr gaseous electronics res, Xerox Corp, 63-68; mgr, San Diego Opers, KMS Technol Ctr, 68-70; vpres & tech dir, Diag Instruments, Inc, 70-73; INDEPENDENT CONSULT, 73- *Concurrent Pos:* Mem, Sci Adv Coun, Rensselaer Polytech Inst, 64-66. *Mem:* Am Chem Soc; Am Phys Soc; Optical Soc Am. *Res:* Chemical kinetics and mechanisms of light emission; relaxation processes behind shock waves in gases; combustion kinetics and spectroscopy; processes in gas discharges; photochemistry. *Mailing Add:* 8241 El Paseo Grande La Jolla CA 92037

ROTH, WALTER JOHN, b Ann Arbor, Mich, July 20, 39; m 59; c 2. OPERATIONS RESEARCH. *Educ:* Univ Mich, Ann Arbor, BS, 61; Univ NMex, MS, 63, PhD(math), 71. *Prof Exp:* Engr, Bendix Systs Div, Bendix Corp, 59-61; staff mem, Sandia Corp, 61-65; ASST PROF MATH, UNIV NC, CHARLOTTE, 68- *Mem:* Am Math Soc; Oper Res Soc Am. *Res:* Partial differential equations. *Mailing Add:* Dept of Math Univ of NC Charlotte NC 28223

ROTH, WILFRED, b New York, NY, June 24, 22; m 44; c 4. ELECTRONICS. *Educ:* Columbia Univ, BS, 43; Mass Inst Technol, PhD(physics), 48. *Prof Exp:* Mem staff, Radiation Lab, Mass Inst Technol, 43-45, assoc, Res Lab Electronics, 46-47; chief physicist, Rieber Res Lab, NY, 48; develop group leader, Harvey Radio Labs, Mass, 48-49; sect head, Res Div, Raytheon Mfg Co, 49-50; co-dir, Rich-Roth Labs, 50-55; dir, Roth Lab Phys Res, 55-64; chmn dept, 64-80, PROF ELEC ENG, UNIV VT, 64- *Concurrent Pos:* Partner, Rich Roth Labs, 50-55; treas & dir res, Ultra Viscoson Corp, 52-53; chmn bd dirs, Roth Lab Phys Res, 55-68. *Mem:* AAAS; fel Acoust Soc Am; fel Inst Elec & Electronics Engrs. *Res:* Transducers; biomedical engineering; ultrasonic engineering; system dynamics. *Mailing Add:* Dept of Elec Eng Univ of Vt Burlington VT 05401

ROTHAUGE, CHARLES HARRY, b Baltimore, Md, Sept 8, 19. ELECTRICAL ENGINEERING. *Educ:* Johns Hopkins Univ, BE, 40, DrEngr(elec eng), 49. *Prof Exp:* Instr elec eng, Johns Hopkins Univ, 46-49; from asst prof to assoc prof, 49-56, chmn dept, 62-69, PROF ELEC ENG, NAVAL POSTGRAD SCH, 56- *Mem:* Inst Elec & Electronics Engrs; Am Soc Eng Educ. *Res:* Electrical measurements and magnetics. *Mailing Add:* Dept of Elec Eng Naval Postgrad Sch Monterey CA 93940

ROTHAUS, OSCAR SEYMOUR, b Baltimore, Md, Oct 21, 27; m 53; c 1. MATHEMATICS. *Educ:* Princeton Univ, AB, 48, PhD(math), 58. *Prof Exp:* Mathematician, Dept Defense, 53-60; mathematician, Inst Defense Anal, 60-65, dep dir, 63-65; vis prof math, Yale Univ, 65-66; chmn dept, 73-76, PROF MATH, CORNELL UNIV, 66- *Mem:* Am Math Soc. *Res:* Lie groups; geometry; several complex variables. *Mailing Add:* Dept of Math White Hall Cornell Univ Ithaca NY 14850

ROTHBALLER, ALAN BURNS, b New York, NY, May 15, 26. NEUROANATOMY. *Educ:* Univ Pa, MD, 48; McGill Univ, MSc, 55; Am Bd Neurol Surg, dipl, 59. *Prof Exp:* From asst prof to assoc prof anat & neurol surg, Albert Einstein Col Med, 56-65; PROF NEUROSURG & CHMN DEPT, NEW YORK MED COL, 65-, RES PROF PHYSIOL, 65- *Concurrent Pos:* USPHS res fel, 54-55; USPHS sr res fel, 56-60, res career develop award, 61-64. *Mem:* AMA; Am Asn Neurol Surg; Am Physiol Soc; fel Am Col Surg; fel NY Acad Med. *Res:* Neuroendocrinology; neurophysiology; neuropharmacology; clinical neurosurgery. *Mailing Add:* Dept of Neurosurg New York Med Col Valhalla NY 10595

ROTHBART, HAROLD A(RTHUR), b Newark, NJ, Dec 17, 17; m 43; c 3. MECHANICAL ENGINEERING. *Educ:* Newark Col Eng, BS, 39; Univ Pa, MS, 42; Munich Tech Univ, DEng, 59. *Prof Exp:* Marine engr, Philadelphia Navy Yard, 39-43; chief engr, Trought Assocs, NJ, 43-46; prof mech eng, City Col New York, 46-61; dean, Col Sci & Eng, Fairleigh Dickinson Univ, 61-72; CHMN INDUST MGT DEPT, CALIF STATE UNIV, DOMINGUEZ HILLS, 72- *Mem:* Am Soc Mech Engrs; Am Soc Eng Educ. *Res:* High speed machinery, cams, complex mechanical systems. *Mailing Add:* Sch of Mgt Calif State Univ Dominguez Hills Carson CA 90747

ROTHBART, HERBERT LAWRENCE, b Feb 5, 37; US citizen; m 61; c 1. PHYSICAL CHEMISTRY, ANALYTICAL CHEMISTRY. *Educ:* Brooklyn Col, BS, 58; Rutgers Univ, PhD(chem), 63. *Prof Exp:* From instr to asst prof chem, Rutgers Univ, 62-66; head separation & compos invests, 66-76, chief phys chem lab, 76-80, DIR EASTERN REGIONAL RES LAB, USDA, 80- *Concurrent Pos:* Consult. *Mem:* Am Chem Soc; Inst Food Technol; AAAS. *Res:* Study of the fundamentals of separation processes including equilibrium and transport phenomena; molecular spectroscopy; mass spectrometry; electron microscopy; computer applications; development of mathematical representations to describe systems and predict efficient separations. *Mailing Add:* Eastern Regional Res Ctr 600 E Mermaid Ln USDA Philadelphia PA 19118

ROTHBERG, GERALD MORRIS, b NJ, May 14, 31; m 54; c 2. SOLID STATE PHYSICS. *Educ:* Mass Inst Technol, BS, 52; Columbia Univ, PhD(physics), 59. *Prof Exp:* Adams res fel, Univ Leiden, 58-59; asst prof physics, Rutgers Univ, 59-66; assoc prof, 66-70, head metallurgy dept & dir, Cryogenics Ctr, 74-77, prof physics, 70-80, PROF MAT & METALL ENG, STEVENS INST TECHNOL, 80- *Concurrent Pos:* Fulbright lectr & res, Univ Barcelona, 64-65, Fulbright sr lectr, 72-73. *Honors & Awards:* Jess H Davis Mem Res Award, Stevens Inst Technol, 75. *Mem:* AAAS; Am Phys Soc; Sigma Xi; Am Soc Metals. *Res:* Mossbauer effect; high pressures; cryogenics. *Mailing Add:* Dept of Physics Stevens Inst of Technol Hoboken NJ 07030

ROTHBERG, JOSEPH ELI, b Philadelphia, Pa, May 15, 35; m 58. PHYSICS. *Educ:* Univ Pa, BA, 56; Columbia Univ, MA, 58, PhD(physics), 63. *Prof Exp:* Res assoc physics, Yale Univ, 63-64, from instr to asst prof, 64-69; assoc prof, 69-74, PROF PHYSICS, UNIV WASH, 74- *Mem:* Fel Am Phys Soc. *Res:* Elementary particle physics; muon physics; experimental physics. *Mailing Add:* Dept of Physics Univ of Wash Seattle WA 98195

ROTHBERG, RICHARD MARTIN, b New York, NY, July 15, 33; m 55; c 3. IMMUNOLOGY, PEDIATRICS. *Educ:* Univ Rochester, BA, 55; Univ Chicago, MD, 58. *Prof Exp:* Resident pediat, Univ Pittsburgh, 60-61, 62; from asst prof to assoc prof, 66-74, PROF PEDIAT, UNIV CHICAGO, 74- *Concurrent Pos:* Res fels immunol, Univ Pittsburgh, 59, 61; res fel immunol, Scripps Clin & Res Found, 64-66; Nat Inst Allergy & Infectious Dis res career develop award, 68-73. *Mem:* AAAS; Am Acad Allergy; Am Acad Pediat; Am Fedn Clin Res; Am Asn Immunol. *Res:* Process by which mammals become immunized to ingested protein and polysaccharide antigens; immune responses of the newborn; immunedeficiency diseases. *Mailing Add:* Dept of Pediat Univ of Chicago Chicago IL 60637

ROTHBERG, SIMON, b New York, NY, Mar 7, 21; m 46; c 3. BIOCHEMISTRY. *Educ:* Columbia Univ, BS, 48; Georgetown Univ, MS, 52, PhD(biochem), 56. *Prof Exp:* Phys chemist, Nat Bur Stand, 48-53; biochemist, Nat Heart Inst, 53-56; biochemist, Nat Cancer Inst, 57-70; res prof, 70-81, EMER PROF, MED COL VA, VA COMMONWEALTH UNIV, 81- *Concurrent Pos:* NIH res grants, 71-74, 74-78; vis scientist, Cambridge, 64-65; Med Col Va support grants, 78-80. *Mem:* AAAS; Am Chem Soc; Am Soc Biol Chem; Brit Biochem Soc; Sigma Xi. *Res:* Mechanisms of enzymatic reactions; decarboxylation; oxygenases; structure of normal and abnormal keratin; enzymes of epidermis; biochemical regulation of epidermal proliferation and keratinization in normal and pathological skin; role of chalone; DNA catabolism. *Mailing Add:* Box 127 Med Col of Va Va Commonwealth Univ Richmond VA 23298

ROTHBLAT, GEORGE H, b Willimantic, Conn, Oct 6, 35; m 57; c 2. BIOCHEMISTRY. *Educ:* Univ Conn, BA, 57; Univ Pa, PhD(microbiol), 61. *Prof Exp:* Assoc, Wistar Inst, 61-66, assoc mem, 66-71, mem, 71-76; PROF BIOCHEM, MED COL PA, 76- *Concurrent Pos:* Asst prof, Sch Med, Univ Pa, 66-71, assoc prof, 71-76; estab investr, Am Heart Asn, 70-75, fel coun arteriosclerosis. *Mem:* AAAS; Tissue Cult Asn; Am Soc Biol Chemists. *Res:* Cellular lipid metabolism; cholesterol metabolism in tissue culture cells. *Mailing Add:* Dept Physiol/Biochem 3300 Henry Ave Philadelphia PA 19129

ROTHCHILD, IRVING, b New York, NY, Dec 2, 13; m 35, 58; c 1. REPRODUCTIVE ENDOCRINOLOGY. *Educ:* Univ Wis, BA, 35, MA, 36, PhD, 39; Ohio State Univ, MD, 54. *Prof Exp:* Asst dir chem, Michael Reese Hosp, Chicago, Ill, 41-43; physiologist, USDA, Md, 43-48; asst prof physiol, Sch Med, Univ Md, 48-49; asst prof physiol & obstet & gynec, Ohio State Univ, 49-53; assoc prof obstet & gynec, 55-66, PROF REPROD BIOL, SCH MED, CASE WESTERN RESERVE UNIV, 66- *Mem:* Fel AAAS; Am Soc Zool; Am Physiol Soc; Endocrine Soc; Soc Study Reproduction. *Res:* Physiology of reproduction. *Mailing Add:* Univ Hosp 2065 Adelbert Rd Cleveland OH 44106

ROTHCHILD, ROBERT, b New York, NY, May 12, 46. ORGANIC CHEMISTRY, INSTRUMENTATION. *Educ:* City Col New York, BS, 67; Columbia Univ, MA, 68, MPhil, 74, PhD(org chem), 75. *Prof Exp:* Instr org chem, Schwartz Col Pharm & Health Sci, Long Island Univ, 68-72; res asst org chem & instrumentation, Columbia Univ, 72-73; adj asst prof adv pharmaceut synthesis, Schwartz Col Pharm & Health Sci, Long Island Univ, 75-76; lectr org chem, Tex A&M Univ, 76-77; adj asst prof, org chem, Brandeis Univ, 77-78; ASST PROF ORG CHEM, JOHN JAY COL CRIMINAL JUSTICE, CITY UNIV NEW YORK, 78- *Res:* Organic mass spectrometry; organic mechanism and synthesis; nuclear magnetic resonance; chromatographic techniques. *Mailing Add:* Rm 4416-N Dept Sci City Univ New York 445 W 59th St New York NY 10019

ROTHE, CARL FREDERICK, b Lima, Ohio, Feb 6, 29; m 52; c 2. PHYSIOLOGY, AGRICULTURAL ENGINEERING. *Educ:* Ohio State Univ, BSc, 51, MSc, 52, PhD(physiol), 55. *Prof Exp:* Sr asst scientist, USPHS, 55-58; from instr to assoc prof, 58-70, PROF PHYSIOL, IND UNIV SCH MED, IND UNIV-PURDUE UNIV, INDIANAPOLIS, 70- *Concurrent Pos:* Estab investr, Am Heart Asn, 63-69; indust consult biomed instrumentation, 67-; consult, NIH, 71-75, mem cardiovasc renal study sect, Nat Heart & Lung Inst. *Mem:* Am Physiol Soc; Microcirulatory Soc; Biomed Eng Soc; AAAS; Am Asn Univ Prof. *Res:* Cardiovascular physiology; instrumentation for physiological research; computer simulation of physiological systems; bioengineering; control of venous pressure and capacity vessels. *Mailing Add:* Dept Physiol Ind Univ Sch Med Ind Univ-Purdue Univ Indianapolis IN 46202

ROTHE, ERHARD WILLIAM, b Breslau, Ger, Apr 15, 31; US citizen; m 59; c 2. CHEMICAL PHYSICS. *Educ:* Univ Mich, BS, 52, MS, 54, PhD(chem), 59. *Prof Exp:* Staff scientist physics, Gen Dynamics Convair, 59-69; PROF ENG, RES INST ENG SCI, WAYNE STATE UNIV, 69- *Concurrent Pos:* Lectr, San Diego State Col, 65-66; consult, Phys Dynamics, Inc, 75- *Mem:* AAAS; Am Chem Soc; fel Am Phys Soc; Sigma Xi. *Res:* Physics and chemistry of atomic and molecular collisions; laser-driven chemistry. *Mailing Add:* Dept of Chem Eng Wayne State Univ Detroit MI 48202

ROTHE, KAROLYN REGINA, b Fayetteville, NC, Jan 28, 47. LIMNOLOGY, ECOLOGY. *Educ:* Univ Fla, BS, 67, PhD(zool), 70. *Prof Exp:* ASST PROF PHYS SCI, CALIF STATE UNIV, CHICO, 71- *Mem:* Ecol Soc Am; Am Soc Limnol & Oceanog. *Res:* Limnology, especially of Littoral Zone; water resources management. *Mailing Add:* Dept of Geol & Phys Sci Calif State Univ Chico CA 95929

ROTHEIM, MINNA B, b New York, NY, Dec 27, 33. MICROBIAL GENETICS, DEVELOPMENTAL GENETICS. *Educ:* Queens Col NY, BS, 54; Amherst Col, MA, 56; Univ Rochester, PhD(biol), 61. *Prof Exp:* Nat Cancer Inst res fel microbial genetics, Univ Rochester, 61-62, res assoc, 62-68, asst prof, 64-68; res assoc, Rockefeller Univ, 68-70; ASSOC PROF MICROBIAL GENETICS, STATE UNIV NY UPSTATE MED CTR, 70- *Concurrent Pos:* Nat Inst Allergy & Infectious Dis fel, 61-62. *Mem:* Genetics Soc Am; Am Soc Microbiol; NY Acad Sci; Sigma Xi. *Res:* Biochemical genetics of mating type recognition in Tetrahymena thermophila. *Mailing Add:* Dept Microbiol SUNY Upstate Med Ctr Syracuse NY 13210

ROTHENBACHER, HANSJAKOB, b Blaubeuren, WGer, Jan 21, 28; US citizen; m 69; c 2. VETERINARY PATHOLOGY, VETERINARY MICROBIOLOGY. *Educ:* Univ Munich, dipl vet med, 52, DMV, 53; Mich State Univ, MS, 55, PhD(path), 62; Am Col Vet Pathologists, dipl, 62. *Prof Exp:* Asst prof vet sci, Univ Ark, 55-58; res vet path, Mich State Univ, 58-61, pathologist in chg necropsy, 61-63; assoc prof, 63-74, PROF VET SCI, PA STATE UNIV, UNIVERSITY PARK, 74- *Mem:* Am Asn Avian Path; Wildlife Dis Asn; Int Acad Path; Am Vet Med Asn. *Res:* Ecologic pathology; diseases of fish; pathology of viral, bacterial and nutritional diseases of animals; endocrine pathology. *Mailing Add:* Dept of Vet Sci Pa State Univ University Park PA 16802

ROTHENBERG, ALAN S, b Harvey, Ill, Jan 30, 51. ORGANIC CHEMISTRY. *Educ:* Univ Utah, BS, 72; Pa State Univ, PhD(org chem), 77. *Prof Exp:* Res chemist monomer synthesis, 77-80, RES GROUP LEADER PROD & PROCESS DEVELOP, STAMFORD RES LABS, AM CYANAMID CO, 81- *Mem:* Am Chem Soc. *Res:* Organic synthesis; natural products chemistry; iso- quinoline alkaloids; monomer synthesis; cationic monomers; water treating chemicals. *Mailing Add:* Stamford Res Labs Am Cyanamid Co 1937 W Main St Stamford CT 06904

ROTHENBERG, ALBERT, b New York, NY, June 2, 30; m 70; c 3. PSYCHIATRY. *Educ:* Harvard Univ, AB, 52; Tufts Univ, MD, 56; Am Bd Psychiat & Neurol, Dipl Psychiat, 65. *Prof Exp:* Intern, Pa Hosp, 56-57; resident, Dept Psychiat, Sch Med, Yale Univ, 57-60, instr psychiat, 60-61 & 63-64, from asst prof to assoc prof, 64-74; prof psychiat, Sch Med, Univ Conn & chief psychiat serv, Univ Health Ctr, 75-79, DIR RES, AUSTEN RIGGS CTR, SCH MED, UNIV CONN, 79- *Concurrent Pos:* Chief resident, Yale Psychiat Inst, 60-61; asst med dir, 63-64; attend psychiatrist, PR Inst Psychiat, 61-63; asst attend psychiatrist, Yale New Haven Hosp, 63-68, attend psychiatrist, 68-; USPHS res career develop awards, Dept Psychiat, Yale Univ, 64-69 & 69-74; attend psychiatrist, West Haven Vet Admin Hosp, 68-; vis prof, Pa State Univ, 71; clin prof psychiat, Yale Univ Sch Med, 74-; Guggenheim Found fel, 74-75; attend physician, Dempsey Hosp, Farmington, Conn, 75- *Mem:* Fel Am Psychiat Asn; Am Soc Aesthetics; fel Royal Soc Health; Pan-Am Med Asn; Sigma Xi. *Res:* Psychological basis of the creative process in literature, visual and graphic arts, music and science; psychology of aesthetics; psychotherapy; schizophrenia. *Mailing Add:* Austen Riggs Ctr Inc Stockbridge MA 01262

ROTHENBERG, HERBERT CARL, b Brooklyn, NY, Mar 9, 19; m 45; c 3. SOLID STATE PHYSICS. *Educ:* Univ Minn, AB, 38; Pa State Col, PhD(physics), 49. *Prof Exp:* Geophysicist & mathematician, Standard Oil Co, Venezuela, 40-42; res engr, Div Phys War Res, Duke Univ, 42-45; res assoc, Acoust Lab, Pa State Univ, 45-49; fel, Mellon Inst, 49-51; physicist & mgr, Electronic Devices Lab, Gen Elec Co, 51-66; PHYS SCIENTIST, CENT INTEL AGENCY, 66- *Concurrent Pos:* Mem res proj, Off Sci Res & Develop. *Mem:* Am Phys Soc; Sigma Xi. *Res:* Geophysics; acoustics; electronics; microwaves; solid state. *Mailing Add:* 918 Leigh Mill Rd Great Falls VA 22066

ROTHENBERG, LAWRENCE NEIL, b Philadelphia, Pa, July 30, 40; m 71; c 2. MEDICAL PHYSICS. *Educ:* Univ Pa, BA, 62; Univ Wis-Madison, MS, 64, PhD(nuclear physics), 70; Am Bd Radiol, cert radiol physics, 76. *Prof Exp:* Teaching asst physics, Univ Wis-Madison, 62-63, from res asst to res assoc nuclear physics, 66-70; from instr to asst prof, 71-79, ASSOC PROF PHYSICS IN RADIOL, MED COL, CORNELL UNIV, 79-; ASSOC ATTEND PHYSICIST MED PHYSICS, MEM HOSP, MEM SLOAN-KETTERING CANCER CTR, 78- *Concurrent Pos:* Am Cancer Soc fel med physics, Mem Hosp, 70; asst physicist, Mem Hosp, Sloan-Kettering Cancer Ctr, 70-73, asst attend physicist, 73-78; asst attend physicist, NY Hosp, 71-; assoc ed, Med Physics. *Mem:* NY Acad Sci; Am Col Radiol; Health Physics Soc; Am Phys Soc; Am Asn Physicists in Med. *Res:* Diagnostic x-ray physics; development of x-ray test methods for United States Public Health Service; computer tomography and mammography. *Mailing Add:* Dept of Med Physics Mem Hosp Mem-Sloan Kettering Cancer Ctr New York NY 10021

ROTHENBERG, MELVIN G, mathematics, see previous edition

ROTHENBERG, MORTIMER ABRAHAM, b New York, NY, June 3, 20; m 44; c 4. NEUROCHEMISTRY, ENVIRONMENTAL SCIENCES. *Educ:* Univ Louisville, BA, 41; NY Univ, MS, 42; Columbia Univ, PhD(biochem), 49. *Prof Exp:* Res assoc neurol & biochem, Columbia Univ, 47-49; res assoc & asst prof, Inst Radiobiol & Biophys, Univ Chicago, 49-51; chief biochemist, Chem Corps Proving Ground, US Dept Army, 51-53, chief chem div, 53-55, dir res, 55-57, sci dir, 57-63, sci dir, Dugway Proving Ground, 63-68, sci dir, Deseret Test Ctr, Ft Douglas, 68-73, sci dir, Dugway Proving Ground, 73-81; CONSULT ENVIRON SCI, 81- *Concurrent Pos:* Mem corp, Woods Hole Marine Biol Lab, Mass. *Mem:* Fel AAAS; Am Chem Soc; fel Am Inst Chemists; NY Acad Sci. *Res:* Physiology and biochemistry of nerve conduction and transmission using inhibitors, drugs pesticides; enzymology and protein isolation and purification; transport and dilution of gases and aerosols in the atmosphere; atmospheric dynamics. *Mailing Add:* 2233 East 3980 S Salt Lake City UT 84117

ROTHENBERG, RONALD ISAAC, b New York, NY. MATHEMATICS, OPERATIONS RESEARCH. *Educ:* City Col New York, BSChE, 58; Northwester Univ, Evanston, MS, 60; Univ Calif, Davis, PhD(eng), 64. *Prof Exp:* Lectr, 60-62 & 64-66, asst prof, 66-80, ASSOC PROF MATH, QUEEN'S COL, NY, 80- *Mem:* Math Asn Am; Sigma Xi. *Res:* Ordinary and partial differential equations; probability and statistics; engineering mathematics; mathematics for optimization; applied mathematics. *Mailing Add:* Dept of Math Queens Col Flushing NY 11367

ROTHENBERG, SHELDON PHILIP, b New York, NY, May 28, 29; m 56; c 2. HEMATOLOGY, INTERNAL MEDICINE. *Educ:* NY Univ, AB, 50; Chicago Med Sch, MD, 55. *Prof Exp:* From instr to assoc prof, 61-71, PROF MED, NEW YORK MED COL, 71-, CHIEF HEMAT/ONCOL SECT, 69- *Mem:* Am Soc Clin Oncol; Am Soc Hemat; Am Soc Clin Invest; Am Fedn Clin Res; NY Acad Sci. *Res:* Study of metabolism and adsorption of vitamin B-12 and folic acid and the interrelationship of these cofactors in enzymatic reactions in health and disease. *Mailing Add:* Dept of Med New York Med Col 1249 Fifth Ave New York NY 10029

ROTHENBERG, STEPHEN, b New York, NY, Feb 3, 41; m 64; c 1. COMPUTER SYSTEMS. *Educ:* Carnegie Inst Technol, BS, 62; Univ Wash, PhD(phys chem), 66. *Prof Exp:* Res assoc, Princeton Univ, 66-68; mgr chem applns, Univ Comput Co, 68-71; mgr tech serv, Info Systs Design, 71-73, vpres comput servs, 73-76; PRES, ROTHENBERG INFO SYSTS, INC, 76- *Concurrent Pos:* Nat Ctr Atmospheric Res fel, 68. *Mem:* Int Word Processing Asn. *Res:* Computer calculation of molecular electronic structure; chemical information systems; programming languages; computer-based office systems; computer systems and applications. *Mailing Add:* 117 Pinon Portola Valley CA 94025

ROTHENBUHLER, WALTER CHRISTOPHER, b Monroe Co, Ohio, May 4, 20; m 44; c 4. ZOOLOGY. *Educ:* Iowa State Col, BS, 50, MS, 52, PhD(genetics, zool), 54. *Prof Exp:* Res assoc genetics, Iowa State Univ, 50-54, from asst prof to prof apicult, 54-62; PROF APICULT, ETHOLOGY & BEHAV GENETICS, OHIO STATE UNIV, 62- *Concurrent Pos:* Mem comt on African honey bee, Nat Res Coun. *Mem:* Animal Behav Soc; Am Genetics Asn; Entom Soc Am; Am Soc Naturalists; Bee Res Asn. *Res:* Biology of honey bees, particularly genetics, gynandromorphism, behavior and disease resistance; animal behavior; behavior genetics of honey bees and other animals. *Mailing Add:* Dept of Entom Ohio State Univ Columbus OH 43210

ROTHENBURY, RAYMAND ALBERT, b London, Eng, May 14, 37; m 63; c 2. ACADEMIC ADMINISTRATION. *Educ:* Univ Exeter, BSc, 58; Univ London, PhD(chem), 61. *Prof Exp:* Fel inorg chem with Prof R J Gillespie, McMaster Univ, 61-63; res chemist, Dow Chem Can Ltd, 63-66; lectr chem, 66-68, chmn technol, 68-75, dir technol & appl arts, 75-81, DIR TECHNOL & INDUST TRAINING, LAMBTON COL APPL ARTS & TECHNOL, 81- *Mem:* Fel Chem Inst Can. *Mailing Add:* LambtonCol Appl Arts & Technol Box 969 Sarnia ON N7T 7K4 Can

ROTHER, ANA, b Brandenburg/Havel, Ger, July 14, 31. PHARMACOGNOSY. *Educ:* Nat Univ Colombia, BS, 51; Univ Munich, Dr rer nat(pharm), 58. *Prof Exp:* Teaching asst pharm chem, Nat Univ Colombia, 51-53; chemist-analyst, Beneficencia, Bogota, 53-54 & Squibb & Sons, Cali, 58-59; fel, 59-61, res asst, 61-64, from instr to asst prof, 64-70, RES ASSOC PHARMACOG, SCH PHARM, UNIV CONN, 70- *Mem:* Am Chem Soc; Am Soc Pharmacog; NY Acad Sci. *Res:* Isolation, structure and biosynthesis of secondary plant constitutents; metabolic studies of tissue and cell cultures of selected drug-producing plants. *Mailing Add:* Sch of Pharm Univ of Conn U-92 Storrs CT 06268

ROTHERHAM, JEAN, b Pompton Lakes, NJ, Jan 4, 22. BIOCHEMISTRY. *Educ:* Montclair State Teachers Col, BA, 41; Univ NC, MS, 52, PhD, 54. *Prof Exp:* Fel, Nat Cancer Inst, 54 & Nat Heart & Lung Inst, 55, biochemist, Nat Cancer Inst, 56-81. *Mem:* AAAS; Sigma Xi. *Res:* Nucleic acids; intermediary metabolism of normal and tumor tissue; proteins. *Mailing Add:* 1307 Noyes Dr Silver Spring MD 20910

ROTHERMEL, JOSEPH JACKSON, b Reading, Pa, Nov 4, 18; m 43; c 5. CHEMISTRY, GLASS TECHNOLOGY. *Educ:* Franklin & Marshall Col, BS, 40; Univ Pittsburgh, PhD(chem), 48. *Prof Exp:* Asst chem, Univ Pittsburgh, 40-44; res chemist, Manhattan proj, Sch Med & Dent, Univ Rochester, 44-46; asst chem, Univ Pittsburgh, 46-48; res chemist, Res Labs, 48-58, mgr chem serv, 58-66, mgr tech anal, 66-68, SR ENG ASSOC, MFG & ENG DIV, CORNING GLASS WORKS, 68- *Honors & Awards:* Eugene C Sullivan Award, Corning Sect, Am Chem Soc, 73. *Mem:* Am Chem Soc; Am Ceramic Soc; Soc Glass Technol. *Res:* Non-silicate glass compositions; glass melting; borate and phosphate glasses; x-ray absorbing transparent barriers. *Mailing Add:* Powderhouse Rd RD 2 Box 540 Corning NY 14830

ROTHFELD, LEONARD B(ENJAMIN), b New York, NY, Feb 20, 33; m 67; c 1. COAL TECHNOLOGY, ENGINEERING & CONSTRUCTION. *Educ:* Cornell Univ, BChE, 55; Univ Wis, MS, 56, PhD(chem eng), 61. *Prof Exp:* Res engr, Emeryville Res Ctr, Shell Develop Co, 61-62; group leader eng res, Houston Res Lab, Shell Oil Co, 62-67, sr engr, NY, 67-70, spec assignment, Shell Int Petrol Maatschapij, The Hague, Holland, 70-71, group leader, Martinez Refinery, Shell Oil Co, Calif, 71-72, spec assignment, Bellaire Res Ctr, Shell Develop Co, 72-73; dir process eng, Synthetic Crude & Minerals Div, Atlantic Richfield Co, Los Angeles, 73-74, mgr process eng, 74-81, MGR GEN ENG, SYNTHETIC CRUDE & MINERALS DIV, ARCO COAL CO, 81- *Mem:* Am Inst Chem Engrs; Soc Mining Engrs-Inst Mining Engrs. *Res:* Synthetic fuels; shale oil; coal processing; coal mine facilities. *Mailing Add:* Arco Coal Co 555 17th St Denver CO 80202

ROTHFELS, KLAUS HERMANN, b Berlin, Ger, May 25, 19; Can citizen; m 45; c 4. CYTOLOGY. *Educ:* Univ Toronto, BA, 44, PhD, 48. *Prof Exp:* Lectr cytol, 47, from asst prof to assoc prof, 50-70, PROF BOT, UNIV TORONTO, 70- *Mem:* Am Soc Naturalists; Genetics Soc Am. *Res:* Cytology of insects; microbial genetics. *Mailing Add:* Dept of Bot Univ of Toronto Toronto ON M5S 2R8 Can

ROTHFIELD, LAWRENCE I, b New York, NY, Dec 30, 27; m 53; c 4. MICROBIOLOGY, BIOCHEMISTRY. *Educ:* Cornell Univ, AB, 47; NY Univ, MD, 51. *Prof Exp:* From intern to asst resident internal med, Bellevue Hosp, New York, 51-53; asst resident, Presby Hosp, New York, 55-56; asst prof med, NY Univ, 62-64; from asst prof to assoc prof molecular biol, Albert Einstein Col Med, 64-68; chmn dept, 68-80, PROF MICROBIOL, SCH MED, UNIV CONN, 68- *Concurrent Pos:* Consult molecular biol sect, NIH, 70-74; mem microbiol & immunol adv comt, President's Biomed Res Panel, 75; Josiah Macy Found grant, 76-77. *Mem:* Am Soc Biol Chem; Am Soc Microbiol. *Res:* Membrane molecular biology. *Mailing Add:* Dept of Microbiol Univ of Conn Health Ctr Farmington CT 06032

ROTHFIELD, NAOMI FOX, b New York, NY, Apr 5, 29; m 53; c 4. MEDICINE. *Educ:* Bard Col, BA, 50; NY Univ, MD, 55. *Prof Exp:* Clin asst med, Sch Med, Univ Frankfurt, 54-55; intern, Lenox Hill Hosp, New York, 55-56; asst in med, Sch Med, NY Univ, 59-61, from instr to asst prof med, 61-68; assoc prof, 68-73, PROF MED, SCH MED, UNIV CONN, 73-, HEAD ARTHRITIS SECT, 71- *Concurrent Pos:* Fel, Sch Med, NY Univ, 56-59, Arthritis Found clin scholar, 64-68; consult, Hartford Hosp, 71- *Mem:* Am Soc Clin Invest; Am Rheumatism Asn; Am Asn Immunol; Am Fedn Clin Res. *Res:* Connective tissue diseases and their pathogenesis; antinuclear and anti-DNA antibodies. *Mailing Add:* Dept of Med Univ of Conn Sch of Med Farmington CT 06107

ROTHFUS, JOHN ARDEN, b Des Moines, Iowa, Dec 25, 32; m 59; c 2. BIOCHEMISTRY. *Educ:* Drake Univ, BA, 55; Univ Ill, PhD(chem), 60. *Prof Exp:* Asst biochem, Univ Ill, 55-59; USPHS fel, Col Med, Univ Utah, 59-61, instr, 61-63; asst prof, Sch Med, Univ Calif, Los Angeles, 63-65; prin res chemist, 65-70, invest head, Sci & Educ Admin-Agr Res, 70-73, RES LEADER, NORTHERN REGIONAL RES CTR, AGR RES SERV, USDA, 73- *Mem:* AAAS; Am Chem Soc; NY Acad Sci; Am Asn Cereal Chem; Am Soc Plant Physiologists. *Res:* Protein chemistry; structure and function of conjugated macromolecules; lipid chemistry; plant cell and tissue culture; plant biochemistry. *Mailing Add:* Northern Regional Res Ctr 1815 N Univ Peoria IL 61604

ROTHFUS, ROBERT R(ANDLE), b Rochester, NY, May 13, 19; m 42; c 3. CHEMICAL ENGINEERING. *Educ:* Univ Rochester, BS, 41; Carnegie Inst Technol, MS, 42, DSc(chem eng), 48. *Prof Exp:* Chem engr, Eastman Kodak Co, NY, 42-46; from instr to assoc prof chem eng, 47-59, head dept, 71-78, PROF CHEM ENG, CARNEGIE-MELLON UNIV, 59- *Mem:* Am Chem Soc; Am Soc Mech Engrs; Am Inst Chem Engrs. *Res:* Flow of fluids in conduits; heat transfer by convection; fine particle technology; process dynamics and control. *Mailing Add:* Dept of Chem Eng Carnegie-Mellon Univ Pittsburgh PA 15213

ROTHKOPF, MICHAEL H, b New York, NY, May 20, 39; m 60; c 2. OPERATIONS RESEARCH. *Educ:* Pomona Col, BA, 60; Mass Inst Technol, MS, 62, PhD(opers res), 64. *Prof Exp:* Mathematician, Shell Develop Co, Shell Oil Co, 64-67, res supvr, 67-71, head planning methods & models div, Shell Int Petrol Co, 71-73; SCIENTIST, XEROX PALO ALTO RES CTR, 73- *Concurrent Pos:* Instr, Univ Calif Exten, 66-78; asst prof math, Calif State Univ, Hayward, 67-69, lectr, Sch Bus & Econ, 74, 76-78; lectr, Dept Med Info Sci, Univ Calif, San Francisco, 74-75; consult, assoc prof, Dept Eng, Econ Syst, Stanford Univ, 80-; lectr, Grad Sch Bus, Univ Santa Clara, 80. *Mem:* Opers Res Soc Am; Inst Mgt Sci. *Res:* Mathematical modeling useful for improving decisions; management science generally. *Mailing Add:* Xerox Palo Alto Res Ctr 3333 Coyote Hill Rd Palo Alto CA 94304

ROTHLEDER, STEPHEN DAVID, b New York, NY, Mar 7, 37; m 60; c 2. UNDERWATER ACOUSTICS. *Educ:* NY Univ, BS, 57; Mass Inst Technol, SM, 59, PhD(plasma physics), 62. *Prof Exp:* Res assoc plasma physics lab, Princeton Univ, 62-66; MEM TECH STAFF, OCEAN SYSTS RES DEPT, BELL LABS, INC, 66- *Mem:* Am Phys Soc. *Res:* Plasma physics; reentry physics; ocean physics; nuclear engineering. *Mailing Add:* Bell Labs Inc Whippany Rd Whippany NJ 07981

ROTHLISBERGER, HAZEL MARIE, b Elgin, Iowa, May 10, 11. MATHEMATICS. *Educ:* Iowa State Teachers Col, BA, 38; Univ Wis, MA, 50. *Prof Exp:* Actg prin & teacher high sch, Owasa, Iowa, 40-43; prof & head dept, 43-76, EMER PROF MATH, UNIV DUBUQUE, 76- *Mem:* Math Asn Am; Nat Coun Teachers Math. *Mailing Add:* Dept Math Univ Dubuque Dubuque IA 52001

ROTHMAN, ALAN BERNARD, b Pittsburgh, Pa, July 5, 27; m 63; c 1. PHYSICAL CHEMISTRY, NUCLEAR ENGINEERING. *Educ:* Univ Pittsburgh, BS, 49; Carnegie Inst Technol, MS, 52, PhD(chem), 54. *Prof Exp:* Sr scientist, Bettis Atomic Power Lab, Westinghouse Elec Co, 53-54; res chemist, Glass Div Res Lab, Pittsburgh Plate Glass Corp, 54-57; assoc chemist, Argonne Nat Lab, 57-60; sr scientist, Astronuclear Lab, Westinghouse Elec Corp, 60-61, mgr flight safety sect, 61-62, adv engr, 62-64, adv scientist, Bettis Atomic Power Lab, 64-65; assoc scientist, Space Div, Chrysler Corp, 65-68, assoc chemist, 68-80, CHEMIST, REACTOR ANAL & SAFETY DIV, ARGONNE NAT LAB, ARGONNE, 80- *Mem:* Am Nuclear Soc. *Res:* Fields of reactor safety experiments; materials research and development. *Mailing Add:* Apt 403 301 Lake Hinsdale Dr Willowbrook IL 60514

ROTHMAN, ALAN MICHAEL, b Philadelphia, Pa, July 7, 43; m 72; c 2. ANALYTICAL CHROMATOGRAPHY, RADIOTRACER CHEMISTRY. *Educ:* Purdue Univ, BS, 65; Pa State Univ, PhD(org chem), 69. *Prof Exp:* Instr radiation safety, Defense Atomic Support Agency Nuclear Weapons Sch, 69-71; instr chem, Pa State Univ, Ogontz Campus, 71-73; SR CHEMIST, ROHM AND HAAS RES LABS, 73- *Mem:* Am Chem Soc; Health Physics Soc. *Res:* Utilization of radiotracers to further research goals of all company research groups, including major fields of plastics, agricultural products, health products, and analysis. *Mailing Add:* 519 Pine Tree Rd Jenkintown PA 19046

ROTHMAN, ALBERT J(OEL), b Brooklyn, NY, Jan 16, 24; m 47; c 3. NUCLEAR WASTE ISOLATION, OIL SHALE PROCESSING. *Educ:* Columbia Univ, BS, 44; Polytech Inst Brooklyn, MChE, 50; Univ Calif, Berkeley, PhD(chem eng), 53. *Prof Exp:* Chem engr, Stamford Res Labs, Am Cyanamid Co, 44-48; process design engr, Colgate-Palmolive Co, 48-50; res chem engr, Shell Oil Co, 53-56; proj mgr & res assoc corrosion of metals, Eng Res Labs, Columbia Univ, 56-58; chemist ceramic res & develop, 58-59, group leader, 59-61, assoc div leader, Inorg Mat, 61-72, dep proj leader, Oil Shale, 72-81, PROJ LEADER, NUCLEAR WASTE ISOLATION, LAWRENCE LIVERMORE LAB, UNIV CALIF, 81- *Mem:* Am Chem Soc. *Res:* Nuclear waste isolation; research and development shale oil recovery from oil shale, especially in-situ oil shale pyrolysis; ceramic materials; chemical process development; heat transfer and thermal conductivity of gases. *Mailing Add:* L-204 Lawrence Livermore Lab Livermore CA 94550

ROTHMAN, ALVIN HARVEY, b Brooklyn, NY, Feb 25, 30; m 54; c 3. BIOLOGY. *Educ:* Univ Calif, Los Angeles, BA, 52, MA, 54; Johns Hopkins Univ, ScD(pathobiol), 58. *Prof Exp:* USPHS fel, Johns Hopkins Univ, 59-60; res assoc biol, Rice Univ, 60-64; asst prof, 64-73, PROF BIOL, CALIF STATE UNIV, FULLERTON, 73- *Mem:* Soc Protozool; Am Soc Parasitol; Soc Syst Zool; Wildlife Dis Asn. *Res:* Parasite physiology; functional-ultrastructural relationships of helminths. *Mailing Add:* Dept of Biol Calif State Univ Fullerton CA 92631

ROTHMAN, ARTHUR I, b Montreal, Que, Apr 8, 38; m 60; c 3. MEDICAL EDUCATION. *Educ:* McGill Univ, BSc, 59; Univ Maine, MS, 65; State Univ NY Buffalo, EdD(sci educ), 68. *Prof Exp:* Res assoc sci educ, Grad Sch Educ, Harvard Univ, 67-68; res assoc med educ, Educ Res Unit, 68-69, DIR & PROF MED EDUC, DIV STUDIES MED EDUC, FAC MED, UNIV TORONTO, 69-; PROF HIGHER EDUC GROUP, ONT INST STUDIES EDUC, 76- *Concurrent Pos:* Hon lectr med educ, Dept Internal Med, Univ Toronto, 69- consult, Can Asn Can Coun fel, 75-76; vis scholar, Univ Teaching Methods Univ, Inst Educ, Univ London, 75-76. *Mem:* Am Educ Res Asn; Nat Conf Measurement Educ; Can Soc Study Higher Educ; Asn Study Med Educ. *Res:* Examination of programs directed at the development of faculty as teachers; relationships between student characteristics, learning and career selection in medicine; methods of curriculum evaluation in medicine; programs of patient education. *Mailing Add:* Div of Studies in Med Educ Fac of Med Univ of Toronto Toronto ON M5S 2R8 Can

ROTHMAN, EDWARD SAMUEL, organic chemistry, see previous edition

ROTHMAN, FRANCOISE, b Paris, France; US citizen. MEDICINE. *Educ:* Paris Med Sch, MD, 51. *Prof Exp:* Asst med dir, Med Tribune, 65-73; asst dir clin res, Sandoz Labs, 74-75; area med dir, Abbott Int, 76-77; assoc dir clin res, Merrell Int, 78; ASST MED DIR, AYERST LABS, 79- *Mem:* Am Asn for Study of Headache. *Mailing Add:* 115 E 87th St New York NY 10028

ROTHMAN, FRANK GEORGE, b Budapest, Hungary, Feb 2, 30; US citizen; m 53; c 4. BIOCHEMISTRY, GENETICS. *Educ:* Univ Chicago, AB, 48, MS, 51; Harvard Univ, PhD(chem), 55. *Prof Exp:* Res assoc chem, Univ Wis, 57; res assoc biol, Mass Inst Technol, 57-61; from asst prof to assoc prof, 61-70, PROF BIOL, BROWN UNIV, 70- *Concurrent Pos:* NSF fel, 56-58; Am Cancer Soc fel, 67-68. *Mem:* Genetics Soc Am; Soc Develop Biol; AAAS; Soc Gen Physiologists. *Res:* Biochemical genetics; mechanisms of cell differentiation. *Mailing Add:* Div Biol & Med Brown Univ Providence RI 02912

ROTHMAN, HOWARD BARRY, b New York, NY, July 17, 38; m 72; c 2. SPEECH & HEARING SCIENCE. *Educ:* City Col New York, BA, 61; NY Univ, MA, 64; Stanford Univ, PhD(speech & hearing sci), 71. *Prof Exp:* Clinician aphasia, Inst Phys Med & Rehab, 63-64; res instr, Commun Sci Lab, 69-70, asst prof, 71-76, ASSOC PROF ACOUST PHONETICS, DEPT SPEECH, INST ADVAN STUDY COMMUN PROCESSES, UNIV FLA, 76- *Concurrent Pos:* Consult, Speech Transmission Lab, Royal Inst Technol, Sweden, 72, Defense Res Bd, Defense & Civil Inst Environ Med, Ont, 72, Swed Develop Corp & Swed Nat Defense Works on Underwater Commun, 73, Harbor Br Found/Smithsonian Inst, 73, US Dist Court, Western Dist Tenn, 75 & Alachua County Sheriff's Dept, 75. *Mem:* Acoust Soc Am; Am Asn Phonetic Sci; Am Speech & Hearing Asn; NY Acad Sci; Sigma Xi. *Res:* Acoustic and perceptual aspects of speaker identification; underwater speech communication; acoustic and electromyographic aspects of atypical speech behavior; tape decoding and authentication. *Mailing Add:* Inst Advan Study Commun Process ASB 63 Univ of Fla Gainesville FL 32611

ROTHMAN, JAMES EDWARD, b Haverhill, Mass, Nov 3, 50; m 71; c 1. BIOCHEMISTRY. *Educ:* Yale Univ, BA, 71; Harvard Univ, PhD(biochem), 76. *Prof Exp:* Fel, Dept Biol, Mass Inst Technol, 76-78; asst prof, 78-81, ASSOC PROF, DEPT BIOCHEM, STANFORD UNIV, 81- *Mem:* Am Soc Biol Chemists. *Mailing Add:* Dept Biochem Stanford Univ Stanford CA 94305

ROTHMAN, LAURENCE SIDNEY, b New York, NY, Jan 20, 40. ATOMIC PHYSICS, ATMOSPHERIC CHEMISTRY. *Educ:* Mass Inst Technol, BS, 61; Boston Univ, MA, 64, PhD(physics), 71. *Prof Exp:* Res physicist infrared physics, Block Assoc Inc, Cambridge, Mass, 61-63; ATOMIC & MOLECULAR PHYSICIST ATMOSPHERIC TRANSMISSION, OPTICAL PHYSICS DIV, AIR FORCE GEOPHYSICS LAB, 68- *Mem:* Sigma Xi; Optical Soc Am. *Res:* Development of theoretical and analytical methods for the study of molecular physics and infrared absorption; study of mechanisms of attenuation and emission of infrared radiation in model atmospheres. *Mailing Add:* Optical Physics Div Hanscom AFB Bedford MA 01731

ROTHMAN, MILTON A, b Philadelphia, Pa, Nov 30, 19; m 50; c 2. PLASMA PHYSICS. *Educ:* Ore State Col, BS, 44; Univ Pa, MS, 48, PhD(physics), 52. *Prof Exp:* Physicist, Bartol Res Found, Franklin Inst, Pa, 52-59 & Plasma Physics Lab, Princeton Univ, 59-68; prof physics, Trenton State Col, 68-79; SR RES SCIENTIST, FRANKLIN RES CTR, 79- *Mem:* Am Phys Soc; AAAS. *Res:* Nuclear physics. *Mailing Add:* 2020 Chancellor St Philadelphia PA 19103

ROTHMAN, NEAL JULES, b Philadelphia, Pa, Nov 20, 28; m 55; c 3. MATHEMATICAL ANALYSIS. *Educ:* Univ Del, BA, 51; Tulane Univ, MS, 54; La State Univ, PhD, 58. *Prof Exp:* Sr comput analyst, Burroughs Corp, 54-56; instr & asst math, La State Univ, 56-58; from instr to asst prof, Univ Rochester, 58-62; from asst prof to prof math, Univ Ill, Urbana, 62-82; prog dir modern anal, NSF Washington, 79-82; PROF & CHMN, MATH DEPT, IND UNIV PURDUE UNIV-INDIANAPOLIS, 82- *Concurrent Pos:* Vis prof Israel Inst Technol, Haifa, Israel, 71-72, 76-77. *Mem:* Am Math Soc; Math Asn Am; Asn Women Math. *Res:* Topological algebra. *Mailing Add:* Rm 304 NSF Math Wahsington DC 20550

ROTHMAN, PAUL GEORGE, b Detroit, Mich, Apr 16, 23; m 51; c 5. AGRONOMY. *Educ:* Mich State Univ, BS, 50, MS, 52; Univ Ill, PhD, 55. *Prof Exp:* Asst farm crops, Mich State Univ, 50-52; asst agron, Univ Ill, 52-55; agronomist, 55-67, RES PATHOLOGIST, SCI & EDUC ADMIN-AGR RES, USDA, 67- *Mem:* Am Soc Agron; Am Phytopath Soc. *Res:* Plant breeding and pathology. *Mailing Add:* Cereal Rust Lab Univ of Minn St Paul MN 55108

ROTHMAN, RICHARD HARRISON, b Philadelphia, Pa, Dec 2, 36; m 60; c 2. ORTHOPEDIC SURGERY, ANATOMY. *Educ:* Univ Pa, BA, 58, MD, 62; Jefferson Med Col, PhD(anat), 65. *Prof Exp:* NIH fel, Jefferson Med Col, 63-65, dir orthop res lab, 65-71; asst prof, 71-73, ASSOC PROF ORTHOP SURG, SCH MED, UNIV PA, 73- *Mem:* Am Asn Anat. *Res:* Blood flow in tendon and bone. *Mailing Add:* Dept of Orthop Surg Univ of Pa Sch of Med Philadelphia PA 19104

ROTHMAN, SAM, b Brooklyn, NY, Feb 1, 20; m 43; c 2. PHYSICAL CHEMISTRY, RESEARCH ADMINISTRATION. *Educ:* Long Island Univ, BS, 43; Am Univ, MA, 54, PhD, 59. *Prof Exp:* Chemist, Nat Bur Standards, 46-55; dep res coordr, Off Naval Res, 55-61, asst res & eng off, Bur Naval Weapons, 61-63, dep dir explor develop, Hq, Naval Mat Command, 63-70, dep dir prog mgt off, 70-74; res prof, 74-75, PROF & CHMN ENG ADMIN, GEORGE WASHINGTON UNIV, 75- *Concurrent Pos:* Prof lectr, Am Univ, 59-67, adj prof, 68- *Mem:* AAAS; Am Chem Soc; Sigma Xi. *Res:* Polymers in solution; adsorption of macromolecules; research and development management. *Mailing Add:* Dept Eng Admin George Washington Univ Washington DC 20052

ROTHMAN, SARA WEINSTEIN, b Winthrop, Mass, July 29, 29; m 50; c 2. BACTERIAL TOXINS, PATHOGENESIS. *Educ:* Simmons Col, BS, 65; Boston Univ, AM, 67, PhD(microbiol), 70. *Prof Exp:* Am Cancer Soc fel, Dept Biochem & Pharmacol, Sch Med, Tufts Univ, 70-73; res assoc, Dept Path, Boston Univ, 73-74, res asst prof, 74-75, res asst prof, Dept Microbiol, Sch Med, Boston Univ, 75-78; RES CHEMIST, DEPT BIOL CHEM, WALTER REED ARMY INST RES, 78- *Concurrent Pos:* Res assoc, Mallory Inst Path, 76-; mem spec sci staff, Boston City Hosp, 76- *Mem:* Am Soc Microbiol; Sigma Xi; Asn Women in Sci. *Res:* Detection by bacterial mutation of carcinogens in humans and animals; effect of diet; macromolecular transport by mammalian cells in tissue culture; calorimetry of bacterial enzymes; genetic basis of bacterial pathogenesis. *Mailing Add:* Div Biochem Walter Reed Army Inst Res Washington DC 20012

ROTHMAN, STEPHEN SUTTON, b New York, NY, July 10, 35; m 57; c 2. PHYSIOLOGY. *Educ:* Univ Pa, AB, 56, DDS, 61, PhD(physiol), 64. *Prof Exp:* Instr physiol, Univ Pa, 64-65; instr, Harvard Med Sch, 65-66, assoc, 66-67, from asst prof to assoc prof, 67-71; PROF PHYSIOL, UNIV CALIF, SAN FRANCISCO, 71- *Concurrent Pos:* NIH res grants, 61- *Mem:* AAAS; Am Physiol Soc; Am Inst Biol Sci; NY Acad Sci; Biophys Soc. *Res:* Gastrointestinal and cellular physiology. *Mailing Add:* Dept of Physiol Univ Calif Med Ctr San Francisco CA 94143

ROTHMAN, STEVEN J, b Giessen, Ger, Dec 18, 27; US citizen; m 51; c 2. PHYSICAL METALLURGY. *Educ:* Univ Chicago, PhB, 47; Stanford Univ, BS, 51, MS, 53, PhD(metall eng), 55. *Prof Exp:* Asst metallurgist, 54-60, assoc metallurgist, 60-77, METALLURGIST, ARGONNE NAT LAB, 77- *Concurrent Pos:* NSF fel, 62-63. *Mem:* AAAS; Am Inst Mining, Metall & Petrol Engrs; Am Phys Soc. *Res:* Diffusion in metals. *Mailing Add:* Argonne Nat Lab Bldg 212-C 226 Argonne IL 60439

ROTHMAN-DENES, LUCIA B, b Buenos Aires, Arg, Feb 17, 43; US citizen; m 66; c 2. BIOCHEMISTRY, MOLECULAR BIOLOGY. *Educ:* Univ Buenos Aires, Lic, 64, PhD(biochem), 67. *Prof Exp:* Fel biochem, Res Inst Biochem, Buenos Aires, 67; fel, Nat Inst Arthritis, Metab & Digestive Dis, 67-69, vis fel genetics, 69-70; fel molecular biol, Dept Biophys, 70-72, res assoc, 72-74, asst prof molecular biol, dept biophys & theoret biol, 74-80, ASSOC PROF DEPT BIOPHYS & THEORETICAL BIOLOGY, UNIV CHICAGO, 80- *Concurrent Pos:* Nat Res Coun fel, Buenos Aires, 67; NIH spec res fel, 70-72, NIH res career develop award, 75-80. *Mem:* Am Soc Biol Chemists; Am Soc Microbiol; AAAS. *Res:* Biochemistry and regulation of transcription and DNA replication in bacteriophage infected bacteria. *Mailing Add:* Dept Biophys & Theoret Biol 920 E 58th St Chicago IL 60637

ROTHMEIER, JEFFREY, b Milwaukee, Wis, Jan 7, 41; m 62; c 2. MEDICINE, COMPUTER SCIENCE. *Educ:* Univ Wis, BSEE, 62; Cornell Univ, PhD(physiol), 69. *Prof Exp:* Asst prof pharmacol, Sch Med, Univ Pittsburgh, 70-71; asst prof med, Dartmouth Med Sch, 71-74; assoc prof biomed comput, Univ Mass, Worcester, 74-79; res assoc, Harvard Med Sch, 80-81; VPRES, HCW CORP FINANCE, 81- *Concurrent Pos:* Res fel psychiat, Mass Gen Hosp, 69-70. *Mem:* AAAS; Asn Comput Mach; Inst Elec & Electronics Eng. *Res:* Use of computers in medicine. *Mailing Add:* HCW Corp Finance One Boston Place Boston MA 02108

ROTHROCK, GEORGE MOORE, b Columbus, Ohio, May 5, 19; m 46; c 3. CHEMISTRY. *Educ:* De Pauw Univ, AB, 41; Purdue Univ, PhD(org chem), 45. *Prof Exp:* SR PATENT CHEMIST, E I DU PONT DE NEMOURS & CO, INC, 45- *Mem:* Am Chem Soc. *Res:* Chlorination and fluorination of hydrocarbons; polymer chemistry; polymer solvents; synthetic fibers; non-woven textiles. *Mailing Add:* 816 Spruce Ave West Chester PA 19380

ROTHROCK, HENRY SHIRLEY, b Bloomington, Ind, Sept 17, 06; m 32; c 1. CHEMISTRY. *Educ:* Ind Univ, AB, 26; Purdue Univ, MS, 28; Pa State Univ, PhD(org chem), 31. *Prof Exp:* Asst chem, Purdue Univ, 26-28; res chemist, Chem Dept, E I du Pont de Nemours & Co, 30-37, res supvr, 37-60, liaison mgr, Cent Res Dept, 60-71; CONSULT, 71- *Mem:* Am Chem Soc. *Res:* Organic chemistry; synthetic polymers. *Mailing Add:* 3 Red Oak Rd Wilmington DE 19806

ROTHROCK, JOHN WILLIAM, b Bangor, Pa, Jan 6, 20; m 46; c 2. BIOCHEMISTRY. *Educ:* Pa State Col, BS, 41; Univ Ill, PhD(biochem), 49. *Prof Exp:* RES CHEMIST, MERCK SHARP & DOHME RES LABS, MERCK & CO, 49- *Mem:* Am Chem Soc. *Res:* Antibiotics; growth factors; steroids; enzymes. *Mailing Add:* Merck Sharp & Dohme Res Labs Merck & Co Rahway NJ 07065

ROTHROCK, PAUL E, b Newark, NJ, Oct 17, 48; m 73; c 1. BOTANY, PHYTOPATHOLOGY. *Educ:* Rutgers Univ, BA, 70; Pa State Univ, MS, 73, PhD(bot), 76. *Prof Exp:* Prof biol, Montreat-Anderson Col, 76-81; ASST PROF BIOL, TAYLOR UNIV, 81- *Mem:* Nat Asn Biol Teachers. *Res:* Systematics of the genus Carex (Cyperaceae). *Mailing Add:* Dept Biol Taylor Univ Upland IN 46989

ROTHROCK, THOMAS STEPHENSON, b Springdale, Ark, Sept 7, 28; m 54; c 2. ORGANIC CHEMISTRY. *Educ:* Univ Ark, BA, 50, MS, 56, PhD(org chem), 58. *Prof Exp:* Res chemist, Tenn Eastman Corp, 53-54; sr res chemist, Celanese Corp Am, Tex, 57-63; RES CHEMIST, MONSANTO CO, ST LOUIS, 63- *Mem:* Am Chem Soc. *Res:* Carbon-14 tracer studies. *Mailing Add:* Monsanto Res Ctr 800 Lindbergh Blvd St Louis MO 63166

ROTHSCHILD, BRIAN JAMES, b Newark, NJ, Aug 14, 34; m 62; c 2. FISH BIOLOGY, AQUATIC ECOLOGY. *Educ:* Rutgers Univ, BS, 57; Univ Maine, MS, 59; Cornell Univ, PhD(vert zool), 62. *Prof Exp:* Asst fishery biol, NJ Div Fish & Game, 54-57, zool, Univ Maine, 57-59 & vert zool, Cornell Univ, 59-62; chief skipjack tuna ecol prog, Honolulu Biol Lab, Bur Com Fisheries, 62-68; from assoc prof to prof, Fishery Res Inst & Ctr Quant Sci, Univ Wash, 68-71; dep dir, Northwest Fisheries Ctr, Nat Marine Fisheries Serv, 71-72, dir Atmospheric Admin, 72-75, dir, Extended Jurisdiction Prog Staff, 75-76, dir, Off Policy & Long-Range Planning, 76-77; sr policy adv, Off Admin, Nat Oceanic & Atmospheric Admin, 77-80; PROF, CTR ENVIRON & ESTUARINE STUDIES, CHESAPEAKE BIOL LAB, UNIV MD, 80- *Concurrent Pos:* Asst, Inst Fishery Res, Univ NC, 59; affil grad fac, Univ Hawaii, 64-, lectr, 66-67; vis fel biomet, Cornell Univ, 65-66. *Mem:* Fel AAAS; Am Am Fisheries Soc. *Res:* Ecology of fishes; marine ecology; biology and population dynamics; resource policy. *Mailing Add:* Chesapeake Biol Lab Univ Md Box 38 Solomons MD 20688

ROTHSCHILD, BRUCE LEE, b Los Angeles, Calif, Aug 26, 41. MATHEMATICS. *Educ:* Calif Inst Technol, BS, 63; Yale Univ, PhD(math), 67. *Prof Exp:* Instr math, Mass Inst Technol, 67-69; asst prof, 69-73, assoc prof, 73-77, PROF MATH, UNIV CALIF, LOS ANGELES, 77- *Concurrent Pos:* US Air Force grant, Mass Inst Technol, 67-69; consult, Bell Tel Labs, 68-71 & Network Anal Corp, 69; NSF grant, Univ Calif, Los Angeles, 69-; ed, J Combinatorial Theory, 70-; Sloan Found fel, 73-75. *Mem:* AAAS; Am Math Soc; Math Asn Am; Soc Indust & Appl Math. *Res:* Combinatorial theory; finite geometries; asymptotic enumeration; Ramsey theory; graph theory; network flows. *Mailing Add:* Dept of Math Univ of Calif Los Angeles CA 90024

ROTHSCHILD, DAVID (SEYMOUR), b New York, NY, Nov 28, 41; m 74. ELECTRICAL ENGINEERING, SYSTEMS SCIENCE. *Educ:* City Col New York, BEE, 63; NY Univ, MSEE, 66, PhD(elec eng), 71. *Prof Exp:* Asst engr, Sperry Gyroscope Corp, 63; electronics engr, Grumman Aerospace Corp, 63-66, res scientist control systs res, 66-75; cash mgt systs consult, Chase Manhattan Bank, 75-81; DECISION SUPPORT SYSTS ANALYST, LEHMAN BROS, KUHN LOEB, 81- *Mem:* Inst Elec & Electronics Engrs. *Res:* Linear optimal control theory; sensitivity analysis; nonlinear stability; estimation theory; research on the design of flight control systems which meet specified goals despite existing disturbances. *Mailing Add:* 3231 Nantucket Lane Oceanside NY 11572

ROTHSCHILD, GILBERT ROBERT, b Chicago, Ill, Dec 21, 15. ELECTRICAL ENGINEERING. *Educ:* Armour Inst Technol, BS, 36. *Prof Exp:* Jr engr, Repub Flow Meters Co, 36-37; test engr, Electromotive Div, Gen Motors Corp, 38-42; welding engr, Goodyear Aircraft Corp, 42-46; res engr welding res, Air Reduction Co, Inc, 46-52, sect head, 52-56, asst mgr, 56-57, asst dir, 57-62, asst mgr process & equip develop dept, Air Reduction Sales Co, 62-63, mgr eng & develop dept, Airco Indust Gases Div, Air Reduction Co, Inc, 63-66, gen mgr advan prod develop dept, Airco Welding Prod Div, Airco, Inc, 66-67, tech consult, 67-68, chief welding engr, 68-71, sr staff engr, Cent Res Labs, 71-80; CONSULT. *Mem:* Am Welding Soc; Am Soc Metals; Brit Inst Welding. *Mailing Add:* 198 Hillside Ave Berkeley Heights NJ 07922

ROTHSCHILD, HENRI CHARLES, bionucleonics, see previous edition

ROTHSCHILD, HENRY, b Horstein, Ger, June 5, 32; US citizen. MOLECULAR BIOLOGY, MEDICINE. *Educ:* Cornell Univ, BA, 54; Univ Chicago, MD, 58; Johns Hopkins Univ, PhD(biol), 68. *Prof Exp:* Intern, Univ Chicago, 58-59; asst resident, Univ Hosp, Baltimore, 59-61; asst physician, Johns Hopkins Univ, 63-66; instr med, Mass Gen Hosp, 70-71; assoc prof med, 71-75, assoc prof anat, 72-75, ASSOC GRAD FAC, MED CTR, LA STATE UNIV, NEW ORLEANS, 73-, PROF MED, 75-, PROF ANAT, 75- *Concurrent Pos:* Fel, Johns Hopkins Univ, 67-68; USPHS spec fel, Mass Gen Hosp, 68-70; King Trust Award, 70-71; vis physician, Charity Hosp, New Orleans, 72-; dir, La Ethnogenetic Dis Screening Prog; consult, La Sickle Cell Educ & Screening Prog; Wellcome res travel grant, 79; vis prof, Fac Med, Univ Anonoma Nuevo Leon, Mex, 81; med dir, New Orleans Home & Rehab Ctr & St Margaret's Daughters Home. *Mem:* Am Fedn Clin Res; Am Col Physicians; Am Asn Cancer Res; Am Soc Human Genetics; Am Soc Exp Path. *Res:* Molecular medicine; oncogenic virology; genetics; gerontology. *Mailing Add:* Dept of Med La State Univ Med Ctr New Orleans LA 70112

ROTHSCHILD, KENNETH J, b New York, NY, Feb 9, 48; m 74. BIOPHYSICS. *Educ:* Rensselaer Polytech Inst, BS, 69; Mass Inst Technol, PhD(physics), 73. *Prof Exp:* Res assoc biophys, Harvard-Mass Inst Technol Prog Health Sci & Technol, 73-75; asst prof physiol, Sch Med & asst prof physics, 76-81, ASSOC PROF PHYSIOL, SCH MED & ASSOC PROF PHYSICS, BOSTON UNIV, 82- *Concurrent Pos:* NIH fel, Nat Eye Inst, 74, coprin investr, 75; NIH fel, 72-75; established investr, Am Heart Asn; vis scientist, Neth Found Basic Sci. *Honors & Awards:* Whitaker Found Award. *Mem:* Biophys Soc; Sigma Xi; AAAS. *Res:* Molecular mechanisms of membrane transport; conformational analysis of photoreceptor membranes using raman spectroscopy, fourier transform IR spectroscopy; purple membrane; nonequilibrium thermodynamics. *Mailing Add:* Boston Univ Boston MA 02215

ROTHSCHILD, MARCUS ADOLPHUS, b New York, NY, June 2, 24; m 65; c 2. INTERNAL MEDICINE. *Educ:* Yale Univ, BS, 45; NY Univ, MD, 49; Am Bd Nuclear Med, dipl, 75. *Prof Exp:* Intern, Beth Israel Hosp, New York, 49-50; resident med, Mt Sinai Hosp, New York, 50-51; resident, Beth Israel Hosp, Boston, Mass, 51-52; chief med resident, Beth Israel Hosp, New York, 52-53; from clin instr to assoc prof med, 55-71, PROF MED, SCH MED, NY UNIV, 71-; SECT CHIEF GEN MED, VET ADMIN HOSP, NEW YORK, 55-, CHIEF RADIOISOTOPE SERV, 55- *Concurrent Pos:* Dazian Found fel, Radioisotope Serv, Vet Admin Hosp, New York, 53-55; USPHS grants, 56-78, 74-; lectr physiol, Hunter Col, 54-55; adj prof, Rockefeller Univ, 77-; spec asst dir med res, Vet Admin Alcohol Res, 78- *Mem:* Fel Am Col Physicians; Am Soc Clin Invest; Am Asn Study Liver Diseases (secy-treas, 76-); Soc Nuclear Med; Asn Am Physicians. *Res:* Protein metabolism. *Mailing Add:* Radioisotope Serv Vet Admin Hosp New York NY 10010

ROTHSCHILD, WALTER GUSTAV, b Berlin, Ger, Aug 18, 24; nat US. CHEMICAL PHYSICS. *Educ:* Tech Univ Berlin, BS, 49; Max Planck Inst, 50; Columbia Univ, MA, 58, PhD, 61. *Prof Exp:* Res scientist, Electronized Chem Corp, NY, 50-52, Tracerlab, Inc, Mass, 52-54, Brookhaven Nat Lab, 54-57 & Columbia Univ, 57-61; SR SCIENTIST, FORD MOTOR CO, 61- *Concurrent Pos:* Guest prof, Dept Physics, Univ Buenos Aires, 69; Fulbright fel, 76-77, NATO res fel, 79-81; guest prof, Univ Bordeaux, France, 76-77 & Univ Vienna, 77; vis prof, Univ Paris V, France, 79, 80 & 82. *Mem:* Am Phys Soc; Am Chem Soc. *Res:* Molecular interactions, dynamics and structure; liquid-state phenomena; surface properties and dynamics; hydrogen-bonding; infrared, and Raman spectroscopy; combustion and flames. *Mailing Add:* Sci Res Staff Ford Motor Co Dearborn MI 48121

ROTHSTEIN, ASER, b Vancouver, BC, Apr 29, 18; nat US; m 40; c 3. BIOPHYSICS, CELL PHYSIOLOGY. *Educ:* Univ BC, BA, 38; Univ Rochester, PhD(biol), 43. *Prof Exp:* Asst biol, Univ Rochester, 40-42, asst physiol, Off Sci Res & Develop Contract, 43, asst, Manhattan Proj, 44-45, assoc, 46-47, from instr to assoc prof pharmacol, 46-72, prof radiation biol, 59-72, co-chmn dept, 65-72, chief physiol sect, 48-60, assoc dir Atomic Energy Proj, 60-65, co-dir, 65-72; DIR RES INST, HOSP SICK CHILDREN, 72-; PROF MED BIOPHYS, UNIV TORONTO, 73-, UNIV PROF, 80- *Concurrent Pos:* NSF sr fel, 59-60; vis prof, Dept Radiation Biol & Biophys, Med Sch, Univ Rochester. *Mem:* Am Physiol Soc; Biophys Soc; Int Union Physiol Sci; Soc Gen Physiologists. *Res:* Structure and function of cell membranes, especially role of membrane proteins; role of membrane in cell growth and differentiation. *Mailing Add:* Res Inst Hosp for Sick Children Toronto ON M5G 1X8 Can

ROTHSTEIN, EDWIN C(ARL), b Brooklyn, NY, Nov 17, 33; m 58; c 2. CHEMICAL ENGINEERING, POLYMER CHEMISTRY. *Educ:* Brooklyn Col, BA, 54; Mass Inst Technol, MS, 56; Polytech Inst Brooklyn, PhD(chem eng), 64. *Prof Exp:* Res technologist, Cent Res Labs, Socony Mobil Oil Co, 56-59; res engr, Res Labs, Keuffel & Esser Co, 59-65; asst tech develop mgr, Indust Chem Div, Geigy Chem Corp, 65-67; chief chemist, Sinclair & Valentine Div, Martin-Marietta Corp, 67-69, dir res & develop, 69-70; tech dir, Equitable Bag Co, Inc, Long Island City, 70-75; tech dir, Century Chem Corp, 75-78; TECH DEVELOP MGR, SUN CHEM CORP, 78- *Honors & Awards:* Roon Award, Fedn Paint Socs, 64. *Mem:* AAAS; Am Chem Soc; Soc Plastics Engrs; Soc Rheol; Am Soc Testing & Mat. *Res:* Printing inks and coatings; pigment dispersion rheology; photographic processes; plastics stabilization and testing. *Mailing Add:* Sun Chem Corp 631 Central Ave Carlstadt NJ 07072

ROTHSTEIN, HOWARD, b Brooklyn, NY, Aug 25, 35; m 56; c 3. CELL PHYSIOLOGY. *Educ:* Johns Hopkins Univ, BA, 56; Univ Pa, PhD(gen physiol), 60. *Prof Exp:* Asst instr zool, Univ Pa, 57-60; fel ophthal, Col Physicians & Surgeons, Columbia Univ, 60-62; from asst prof to prof zool, Univ Vt, 62-77; assoc prof ophthal, Kresge Eye Inst, Wayne State Univ Sch Med, Detroit, 77-81; PROF & CHMN, DEPT BIOL SCI, BRONX, NY, 81- *Res:* Cell division; hormonal control of growth; vitro culture and wound healing of ocular tissues. *Mailing Add:* Dept Biol Sci Bronx NY 10458

ROTHSTEIN, JEROME, b New York, NY, Dec 14, 18; m 41; c 3. PLASMA PHYSICS, SOLID STATE PHYSICS. *Educ:* City Col New York, BS, 38; Jewish Theol Sem Am, BHL, 39; Columbia Univ, AM, 40. *Prof Exp:* Res assoc, Columbia Univ, 41-42; physicist, Evans Signal Corps Lab, US Dept Army, 42-57; sr sci exec, Edgerton, Germeshausen & Grier, Inc, 57-61; vpres & dir res, Maser Optics, 61-62; sr staff scientist, Lab For Electronics, Inc, Mass, 62-67; PROF COMPUT & INFO SCI & BIOPHYS, OHIO STATE UNIV, 67- *Concurrent Pos:* Tutor, City Col New York, 41-42; distinguished lectr, Inst Elec & Electronics Engrs, 81-82. *Mem:* AAAS; Am Phys Soc; Biophys Soc; Inst Elec & Electronics Eng. *Res:* Physical electronics; vacuum techniques; plasma and arc spot; solid state and radiation physics; lasers; photography; statistical mechanics; methodology, biophysics; neural modeling; information and systems theory; computer and information science; formal languages; automata theory; pattern recognition; artificial intelligence. *Mailing Add:* Dept Comput & Info Sci Ohio State Univ Columbus OH 43210

ROTHSTEIN, LEWIS ROBERT, b New York, NY, Oct 4, 20; m 46; c 2. CHEMISTRY. *Educ:* Queens Col NY, BS, 42; Ill Inst Technol, MS, 44, PhD(chem), 49. *Prof Exp:* Tech dir, Mason & Hanger-Silas Mason Co, 48-60; dir spec projs, Amcel Propulsion, Inc, 60-65; dir chem & munitions dept, Northrop-Carolina Inc, 65-71; spec asst, 71-74, ASST TECH DIR NAVAL WEAPONS STA, YORKTOWN, VA, 74- *Mem:* Am Chem Soc. *Res:* Physical organic chemistry. *Mailing Add:* 124 Selden Rd Newport News VA 23606

ROTHSTEIN, MORTON, b Vancouver, BC, Sept 8, 22; nat US; m 47; c 3. BIOCHEMISTRY. *Educ:* Univ BC, BA, 46; Univ Ill, MS, 47, PhD(org chem), 49. *Prof Exp:* Res assoc tracer chem, Sch Med, Univ Rochester, 49-54; from asst res biochemist to assoc res biochemist, Sch Med, Univ Calif, San Francisco, 54-60; assoc res scientist, Res Inst, Kaiser Found, 60-65; chmn dept, 69-70, PROF CELL & MOLECULAR BIOL, STATE UNIV NY BUFFALO, 65- *Concurrent Pos:* Lectr, Sch Med, Univ Calif, San Francisco, 58-65; Nat Inst Child Health & Human Develop res grant, 72-77; Nat Inst Aging res grant, 77- *Mem:* AAAS; Am Soc Biol Chem; fel Geront Soc. *Res:* Biochemistry of invertebrates; biochemistry of aging. *Mailing Add:* Div Cell & Molecular Biol State Univ of NY Buffalo NY 14260

ROTHSTEIN, ROBERT, b Philadelphia, Pa, Sept 22, 25; m 46; c 2. MEDICAL ADMINISTRATION, AGRICULTURAL SCIENCES. *Educ:* Brooklyn Col, BA, 47, MA, 53. *Prof Exp:* Head labs, Brooklyn Women's Hosp, NY, 47-57; dir labs, Key Clin Labs Inc, 57-60; lectr biol, Brooklyn Col, 60-61; teacher, Farmingdale High Sch, 61-64; from asst prof to assoc prof, State Univ NY Agr & Tech Col, 64-68, prof biol & coordr, Med Lab Technol, 68-71, chmn dept, 71-75, chmn div human serv, 75-78, PROF MED LAB TECHNOL, STATE UNIV NY AGR & TECH COL FARMINGDALE, 71-, DEAN SCH AGR & HEALTH SCI, 78- *Concurrent Pos:* Lectr, Sch Gen Studies, Brooklyn Col, 53-73; vis prof, Univ RI, 64-77. *Mem:* AAAS; Am Inst Biol Sci; Nat Asn Biol Teachers; Am Asn Higher Educ; Am Soc Allied Health Professions. *Res:* Histochemical identification of phospholipid in situ in frog adrenal cortices under varying physiological conditions utilizing carbowax techniques; behavior of Japanese quail, especially nesting activity in captivity; utilization of classroom interaction analysis as an instrument to determine effective teaching. *Mailing Add:* Schs Agr & Health Sci State Univ NY Agr & Tech Col Farmingdale NY 11735

ROTHSTEIN, RODNEY JOEL, b Seattle, Wash, Nov 4, 47; m 69; c 2. MOLECULAR GENETICS. *Educ:* Univ Ill, Chicago, BS, 69; Univ Chicago, PhD(genetics), 75. *Prof Exp:* Fel molecular genetics, Dept Radiation Biol & Biophys, Sch Med & Dent, Univ Rochester, 75-77; fel biochem, Sect Biochem, Cell & Molecular Biol, Cornell Univ, 77-79; ASST PROF MICROBIOL, NJ MED SCH, NEWARK, 79- *Mem:* Genetics Soc Am. *Res:* Investigations into the regulation and biosynthesis of eukaryotic genes; investigation of the mechanisms of genetic recombination and gene rearrangements in eukaryotic genomes. *Mailing Add:* Dept Microbiol Cornell Univ Newark NJ 07103

ROTHSTEIN, SAMUEL, b New York, NY, Aug 21, 17; m 41; c 3. MATERIALS SCIENCE, CORROSION. *Educ:* City Col New York, BS, 40. *Prof Exp:* Instr aircraft mat, Air Forces Tech Sch, Biloxi, Miss, 41-44; staff consult mat & finishes, Fairchild Camera & Instrument Corp, 44-58; chief metallurgist, Stamford Div, Am Mach & Foundry Co, 58-64, York Div, Pa, 64-70; consult metallurgist, 70-71; PRIN ENGR, MECH ENG DEPT, CONSOL EDISON CO, NY, 71- *Concurrent Pos:* Mem tech adv comn, Metal Properties Coun & Steam Generator Owners Group; mem, EPRI Corrosion Adv Comn; US deleg, Int Atomic Energy Asn Sepcialists Group on Irradiation Embrittlement Reactor Pressure Components. *Mem:* Am Soc Metals; Am Welding Soc. *Res:* Ausforging steels to ultrahigh strengths; special welding techniques; electroplating magnesium and titanium alloys; beryllium-aluminum alloy developments; studies on corrosion materials in mechanical equipment in nuclear and fossil-fuel fired power plants; studies on irradiation embrittlement of metals. *Mailing Add:* 79-19 269th St New Hyde Park NY 11040

ROTHWARF, ALLEN, b Philadelphia, Pa, Oct 1, 35; m 57; c 3. THEORETICAL SOLID STATE PHYSICS. *Educ:* Temple Univ, AB, 57; Univ Pa, MS, 60, PhD(physics), 64. *Prof Exp:* Instr physics, Rutgers Univ, 60-62; mem tech staff, RCA Labs, 64-72; fel Sch Metall & Mat Sci, Univ Pa, 72-73; sr scientist, Mgr, Inst Energy Conversion, Univ Del, 73-79; ASSOC PROF ELEC ENG, DREXEL UNIV, PHILADELPHIA, PA, 79- *Mem:* Am Phys Soc; Am Vacuum Soc; Electrochem Soc; sr mem Inst Elec & Electronics Engrs. *Res:* Theory of superconductivity; transport properties of fermion systems; energy losses in solids; theory of amorphous solids; photovoltaics; localized wave functions in metals; modeling of new solar cell structures and materials; amorphous silicon hydride; metal-insulator-semiconductor solar cells. *Mailing Add:* 1206 Tyson Ave Philadelphia PA 19111

ROTHWARF, FREDERICK, b Philadelphia, Pa, Apr 23, 30; m 51; c 4. SOLID STATE PHYSICS, MATERIALS SCIENCE. *Educ:* Temple Univ, AB, 51, AM, 53, PhD(physics), 60. *Prof Exp:* Physicist antisubmarine warfare, US Naval Air Develop Ctr, Pa, 51-52; asst, Temple Univ, 52-56; physicist, Frankford Arsenal, 56-71; PHYSICIST SOLID STATE PHYSICS, ELECTRONICS TECHNOL & DEVICES LAB, US ARMY, FT MONMOUTH, 71- *Concurrent Pos:* Physicist thin film res, Burroughs Corp, Philadelphia, 52-53; health physicist, Radiobiol & X-ray Dept, Temple Univ Hosp, 54-55; instr physics, Ogontz Ctr, Pa State Univ, 55-56; consult, Dept Otolaryngol, Presby Hosp, Philadelphia, 62-70; Secy of Army fel, Univ Paris-Orsay, France, 65-66; consult superconductivity, Naval Ships Res & Develop Ctr, Annapolis, Md, 68-72; pres, Terra Systs, Inc, Toms River, 70-; consult magnetics, Harry Diamond Labs, Washington, DC, 72-74. *Honors & Awards:* Sci Achievement Award, Secy of Army, 74. *Mem:* Am Phys Soc; Inst Elec & Electronics Engrs; Electrochem Soc; Int Asn Hydrogen Energy. *Res:* Semiconductor technology of silicon and gallium arsenide; rare earth-cobalt and amorphous magnetic materials; magnetic circuit designs; superconductivity; metal physics; metal hydrides; cryogenics; electronics; health physics. *Mailing Add:* US Army R&S Group Box 65 FPO NY 09510

ROTHWELL, FREDERICK MIRVAN, b Arena, Wis, May 7, 23; m 45; c 3. MYCOLOGY, PHYSIOLOGICAL ECOLOGY. *Educ:* Eastern Ky Univ, BS, 49; Univ Ky, MS, 51; Purdue Univ, PhD(mycol), 55. *Prof Exp:* USPHS fel, Purdue Univ, 55-56; res microbiologist, Buckman Labs, Inc, Tenn, 56-57, tech rep, 59-61; assoc prof animal dis, Agr Exp Sta, Miss State Univ, 57-59; prof life sci, Ind State Univ, Terre Haute, 61-74; consult, 74-75; MICROBIOLOGIST, US FOREST SERV, 75- *Concurrent Pos:* Res grants, Com Solvents Corp, 64-66, Tenn Valley Auth, 65-68 & USDA, 67-68; adj prof, Ind Univ Sch Med, Terre Haute Ctr Med Educ & Ind State Univ, 72-75. *Mem:* AAAS; Soil Sci Soc Am. *Res:* Microbiology associated with revegetation of surface-mined lands; mycorrhizal associates and asymbiotic and symbiotic nitrogen-fixing bacterial species. *Mailing Add:* Box 375 Rte 5 Berea KY 40403

ROTHWELL, NORMAN VINCENT, b Passaic, NJ, Sept 30, 24. CYTOGENETICS. *Educ:* Rutgers Univ, BS, 49; Univ Ind, PhD(bot), 54. *Prof Exp:* From lectr to instr bot, Univ Ind, 53-54; assoc prof biol, Southeastern Mo State Col, 54-55; lab instr, Cancer Inst, Univ Miami, Fla, 55-56; PROF BIOL, LONG ISLAND UNIV, 56- *Concurrent Pos:* Fulbright lectr, Univ Ceylon, 65-66 & 68-69. *Res:* Cytogenetic studies on Claytonia virginica; cellular differentiation in the grass root tip of epidermis. *Mailing Add:* Dept of Biol Long Island Univ Brooklyn NY 11201

ROTHWELL, PAUL L, b Norwood, Mass, Apr 2, 38; m 65; c 1. SPACE SCIENCE. *Educ:* Harvard Univ, BA, 60; Northeastern Univ, MS, 62, PhD(physics), 67. *Prof Exp:* Res fel elementary particles, Northeastern Univ, 62-67, RES PHYSICIST, AIR FORCE GEOPHYSICS LABS, 67- *Mem:* Am Geophys Union; Am Phys Soc. *Res:* Validity of quantum electrodynamics and the decay modes of the boson resonances; trapped radiation in the Van Allen belts; solar particles. *Mailing Add:* 15 George St Littleton MA 01460

ROTHWELL, RICHARD LEE, watershed management, forestry, see previous edition

ROTHWELL, WILLIAM STANLEY, b Wabasha, Minn, May 3, 24; m 46; c 4. PHYSICS. *Educ:* US Naval Acad, BS, 45; Univ Wis, MS, 48, PhD(physics), 54. *Prof Exp:* Instr influence mines, US Navy Explosive Ord Disposal Sch, 46-47; instr physics, Racine Exten Ctr, Univ Wis, 49-52; res physicist, Corning Glass Works, 54-57; res group leader, Res Labs, Allis-Chalmers Mfg Co, 57-62; staff scientist, 62-81, SR STAFF SCIENTIST, LOCKHEED PALO ALTO RES LAB, 81- *Mem:* Am Phys Soc. *Res:* Solid state physics; small angle x-ray scattering; materials science; aerospace sciences. *Mailing Add:* Lockheed Palo Alto Res Lab Or 52-35 Bl 204 3251 Hanover St Palo Alto CA 94304

ROTI ROTI, JOSEPH LEE, b Newport, RI, Oct 12, 43; div. RADIATION BIOPHYSICS, THEORETICAL BIOLOGY. *Educ:* Mich Technol Univ, BS, 65; Univ Rochester, PhD(biophys), 72. *Prof Exp:* Res instr, 73-76, asst prof, 76-79, ASSOC PROF RADIOL, UNIV UTAH, 79- *Concurrent Pos:* Res collabr, Brookhaven Nat Lab, 73-75. *Mem:* Cell Kinetics Soc; Radiation Res Soc. *Res:* Simulation of cell kinetics in vitro and in vivo using matrix algebra; studies of the effects of x-irradiation and hyperthermia on DNA, chromosomal proteins and cell progression through the cell cycle. *Mailing Add:* Sect of Radiation & Tumor Biol Dept of Radiol Univ of Utah Salt Lake City UT 84132

ROTKIN, ISADORE DAVID, b Chicago, Ill, June 26, 21; m 42; c 3. EPIDEMIOLOGY, CANCER. *Educ:* Univ Chicago, BS, 46; Univ Calif, Berkeley, MS, 49, PhD(genetics), 54. *Prof Exp:* Researcher, Cancer Res Lab, Univ Calif, Berkeley, 50-54; consult sci & indust, 55-59; dir cancer res, Res Inst, Kaiser Found, 59-68; dep chief oper studies, Nat Cancer Control Prog, USPHS, 68; consult, Calif Regional Med Progs, 68-70; assoc prof, 70-73, PROF PREV MED & COMMUNITY HEALTH, UNIV ILL COL MED, 73- *Concurrent Pos:* Consult bd med, Nat Acad Sci, Vet Admin Hosp, WSide, Chicago, Zellerbach-Saroni Tumor Inst, Mt Zion Hosp, San Francisco, unit epidemiol & biostatist, WHO, France, inst behav res, Tex Christian Univ, med dept, Pac Tel Co, San Francisco, Dept Chronic Dis, State of Conn & Stanford Res Inst; lectr epidemiol & community health, Sch Med, Univ Calif, San Diego, 70-72; consult, Am Cancer Soc, Alameda & San Francisco Counties, Calif, Oak Forest Hosp, Oak Forest, Ill, Ill Cancer Coun, Comprehensive Cancer Ctr, Chicago, Head & Neck Cancer Network, Rush Med Cancer Ctr, Chicago & Northwestern Univ Med Sch, Chicago, Ill Inst Technol, Chicago & Pan Am Health Orgn, WHO, Washington, DC; chmn, Task Force on Epidemiol & Statist, Ill Comprehensive Cancer Coun, Chicago, 73-; chmn, Panel Anal Epidemiol, XI Int Cancer Congress, Italy, 74; chmn, Legis & Tumor Registry Panels, Ill Cancer Coun, Chicago, 74-; mem, Comt Comprehensive Cancer Ctr Patient Data Syst, Nat Cancer Inst, NIH, 74-; vis prof, Univ Calif, Los Angeles, 80-81. *Mem:* Am Asn Cancer Res; Soc Epidemiol Res; Am Soc Human Genetics; Genetics Soc Am; Soc Study Social Biol. *Res:* Cancer and chronic disease epidemiology; multidimensional risk studies; survey research strategy; disease prevention and control; medical systems; community health; graduate and continuing education; sexual data and counseling; human cancer genetics. *Mailing Add:* Dept of Prev Med & Community Health Univ of Ill Col of Med Chicago IL 60680

ROTMAN, BORIS, b Buenos Aires, Arg, Dec 4, 24; nat US; wid; c 1. MICROBIOLOGY, IMMUNOLOGY. *Educ:* Valparaiso Tech Univ, Chile, MS, 48; Univ Ill, PhD(bact), 52. *Prof Exp:* Res assoc, Univ Ill, 52-53; Enzyme Inst, Madison, Wis, 53-56; vis prof, Sch Med, Univ Chile, 56-59; res dir, Radioisotope Serv, Vet Admin Hosp, Albany, NY, 59-61; res assoc genetics, Sch Med, Stanford Univ, 61; head biochem sect, Syntex Inst Molecular Biol, Calif, 61-66; PROF MED SCI, BROWN UNIV, 66- *Concurrent Pos:* Am Soc Microbiol pres fel, 58; fel, Harvard Univ, 58. *Mem:* Am Soc Biol Chem; Am Soc Microbiol; Am Soc Cell Biol. *Res:* Transport and cellular membrane; enzyme chemistry at the molecular level; immune response genes; antibody-mediated activation of enzymes. *Mailing Add:* Div of Biol & Med Sci Brown Univ Providence RI 02912

ROTMAN, JOSEPH JONAH, b Chicago, Ill, May 26, 34; m 78; c 1. MATHEMATICS. *Educ:* Univ Chicago, AB, 54, MS, 56, PhD(math), 59. *Prof Exp:* Res assoc, 59-61, from asst prof to assoc prof, 61-68, PROF MATH, UNIV ILL, URBANA, 68- *Concurrent Pos:* Vis prof, Queen Mary Col, Univ London, 65-66 & Hebrew Univ, Jerusalem, 70, 78; ed, Proc, Am Math Soc, 70-73; Lady Davis fel & vis prof, Israel Inst Technol, Haifa, 77 & Tel Aviv Univ, 82. *Mem:* Math Asn Am; Am Math Soc. *Res:* Algebra. *Mailing Add:* 327 Altgeld Hall Univ of Ill 1409 W Green St Urbana IL 61801

ROTMAN, WALTER, b St Louis, Mo, Aug 24, 22; m 54; c 2. ELECTRICAL ENGINEERING. *Educ:* Mass Inst Technol, BS, 47, MS, 48. *Prof Exp:* Asst elec eng, Res Lab Electronics, Mass Inst Technol, 47-48; electronic scientist, Air Force Cambridge Res Labs, 48-76; electronic scientist, Rome Air Development Ctr, 76-80; ELECTRONIC STAFF ENGR, LINCOLN LAB, MASS INST TECHNOL, 80- *Concurrent Pos:* Mem comn VI, Int Sci Radio Union. *Mem:* Sigma Xi; fel Inst Elec & Electronics Engrs. *Res:* Development of microwave antennas for radar and communications; millimeter wave satellite communication antennas. *Mailing Add:* Lincoln Lab Rm D-410 Mass Inst Technol PO Box 73 Lexington MA 02173

ROTT, NICHOLAS, b Budapest, Hungary, Oct 6, 17; nat US; m 44; c 2. AERODYNAMICS, ACOUSTICS. *Educ:* Swiss Fed Inst Technol, MME, 40, Dr Sc Tech, 43. *Prof Exp:* Res assoc, Swiss Fed Inst Technol, 43-47, privat-docent, 47-51; from assoc prof to prof aeronaut eng, Cornell Univ, 51-59; prof eng, Univ Calif, Los Angeles, 59-67; PROF ENG, SWISS FED INST TECHNOL, 67- *Mem:* Am Phys Soc; Am Inst Aeronaut & Astronaut; Acoust Soc Am. *Res:* High speed aerodynamics; boundary layers; rotating flow; acoustics, particularly thermal effects and non-linear effects. *Mailing Add:* Inst of Aerodynamics Swiss Fed Inst of Technol Zurich Switzerland

ROTTER, JEROME ISRAEL, b Los Angeles, Calif, Feb 24, 49; m 70; c 2. MEDICAL GENETICS, INTERNAL MEDICINE. *Educ:* Univ Calif, Los Angeles, BS, 70, MD, 73. *Prof Exp:* Intern, Harbor Gen Hosp, Torrance, Calif, 73-74; med resident, Wadsworth Vet Admin Hosp, 74-75; fel med genetics, Los Angeles County Harbor-Med Ctr, Univ Calif, Los Angeles, 75-77, sr res fel, 77-78, asst res pediatrician med genetics, 78-79, ASST PROF MED & PEDIAT, DIV MED GENETICS, SCH MED, UNIV CALIF, LOS ANGELES, 79- *Concurrent Pos:* Res fel, Ctr Ulcer Res & Educ, 76-77, investr, 77-80, key investr, 80-; res fel, Nat Inst Arthritis, Metab & Digestive Dis, USPHS, 77-79, clin investr, 79-82. *Mem:* Am Soc Human Genetics; fel Am Col Physicians; Am Fedn Clin Res; Am Gastroenterol Asn; Am Diabetes Asn. *Res:* Genetics of the gastrointestinal disorders and of common diseases, with special interest in peptic ulcer and diabetes. *Mailing Add:* Div Med Genetics 1000 W Carson Torrance CA 90509

ROTTINK, BRUCE ALLAN, b Minneapolis, Minn, Feb 15, 47; m 71. TREE PHYSIOLOGY, PLANT ECOLOGY. *Educ:* Univ Minn, St Paul, BS, 69; Mich State Univ, PhD (forestry), 74. *Prof Exp:* Res biologist, Dow Corning Corp, 73-75; RES FORESTER, CROWN ZELLERBACH CORP, 75- *Mem:* Am Soc Plant Physiologists; Soc Am Foresters; Sigma Xi. *Res:* Plant water relations; reproductive biology of conifers; physiological differences between genotypes of trees; biological nitrogen fixation. *Mailing Add:* Forestry Res Div Crown Zellerbach Corp PO 368 Wilsonville OR 97070

ROTTMAN, FRITZ M, b Muskegon, Mich, Mar 29, 37; m 59; c 3. BIOCHEMISTRY. *Educ:* Calvin Col, BA, 59; Univ Mich, PhD(biochem), 63. *Prof Exp:* From asst prof to assoc prof, 66-74, PROF BIOCHEM, MICH STATE UNIV, 74- *Concurrent Pos:* NIH fel, 63-64; Am Cancer Soc fel, NIH, 64-66; vis prof biochem, Univ BC, 74-75. *Mem:* AAAS; Am Soc Biol Chem; Am Chem Soc. *Res:* RNA chemistry; protein biosynthesis; RNA processing and the presence and role of trace nucleotides in RNA molecules. *Mailing Add:* Dept of Biochem Mich State Univ East Lansing MI 48824

ROTTMAN, GARY JAMES, b Denver, Colo, Sept 21, 44; m 78. ASTROPHYSICS, ATMOSPHERIC SCIENCE. *Educ:* Rockhurst Col, BA, 66; Johns Hopkins Univ, MS, 69, PhD (physics), 72. *Prof Exp:* Res asst physics, Johns Hopkins Univ, 69-72, teaching asst, 72; RES ASSOC PHYSICS, LAB ATMOSPHERIC & SPACE PHYSICS, UNIV COLO, 72-, LECTR, DEPT PHYSICS & ASTROPHYS, 74- *Concurrent Pos:* Scientist, NASA Sounding Rocket Exp, Johns Hopkins Univ & Colo Univ, 69-; co-investr, NASA Orbiting Solar Observ-8, 75-; proj scientist, Solar Mesosphere Explorer Satellite Prog, Lab Atmospheric & Space Physics, NASA, 75-, prin investr, Solar Extreme Ultraviolet Rocket Prog, 77-; consult, Univ Space Res Asn, 77. *Honors & Awards:* Group Achievement Award, Nat Aeronaut & Space Admin, 77. *Mem:* AAAS; Am Geophys Union. *Res:* Study of the solar atmosphere, in particular the measurement of persistant flows and oscillatory motions in the chromosphere and corona, these observations are made using ultraviolet spectrophotometry from sounding rockets and satellite platforms. *Mailing Add:* Lab Atmospheric & Space Physics Univ of Colo Boulder CO 80309

ROTTMANN, WARREN LEONARD, b New York, NY, Dec 23, 43; m 65; c 1. CELL BIOLOGY. *Educ:* State Univ NY Binghamton, BA, 65; Col William & Mary, MA, 67; Univ Ore, PhD(biol), 71. *Prof Exp:* NIH fel cell biol, Johns Hopkins Univ, 71-73, assoc res fel, 73-74; asst prof zool, Univ Minn, Minneapolis, 74-76; ASST PROF GENETICS & CELL BIOL, UNIV MINN, ST PAUL, 76- *Res:* Role of cell surface and plasma membrane in growth control and differentiation; biochemical and cellular mechanisms of intercellular adhesion and cellular invasiveness. *Mailing Add:* Dept of Genetics & Cell Biol Univ of Minn St Paul MN 55108

ROTTY, RALPH M(CGEE), b St Louis, Mo, Aug 1, 23; m 44; c 4. ENGINEERING THERMODYNAMICS, METEOROLOGY. *Educ:* Univ Iowa, BS, 47; Calif Inst Technol, MS, 48 & 49; Mich State Univ, PhD(mech eng), 53. *Prof Exp:* From instr to assoc prof mech eng, Mich State Univ, 49-58; prof & head dept, Tulane Univ, 58-66; prof eng & dean, Old Dominion Univ, 66-72; CHIEF SCIENTIST, INST ENERGY ANAL, OAK RIDGE ASSOC UNIVS, 74- *Concurrent Pos:* Nat Res Coun resident res assoc, Nat Oceanic & Atmospheric Admin, 72-73. *Mem:* Am Soc Mech Engrs; AAAS; Am Meteorol Soc. *Res:* Irreversible and atmospheric thermodynamics; energy policy analysis, especially relation of energy use to global and regional climate; atmospheric consequences of anthropogenic activities, fossil fuels and atmospheric CO2 energy requirements in the developing world. *Mailing Add:* Inst for Energy Anal PO Box 117 Oak Ridge TN 37830

ROTZ, CHRISTOPHER ALAN, b Van Nuys, Calif, Feb 29, 48; m 73; c 2. POLYMER ENGINEERING, MANUFACTURING PROCESSING. *Educ:* Mass Inst Technol, BS, 73, SM, 76, PhD(mech eng), 78. *Prof Exp:* ASST PROF MECH ENG, UNIV TEX, AUSTIN, 78- *Mem:* Assoc mem Am Soc Mech Engrs; Soc Plastics Engrs. *Res:* Modeling and analysis of polymer mixing processes; characterization and prediction of viscoelastic properties; injection molding of polymer blends; designing with polymeric materials; modeling and control of extrusion of polymers. *Mailing Add:* Taylor Hall 167 Mech Eng Dept Univ Tex Austin TX 78712

ROUBAL, RONALD KEITH, b Omaha, Nebr, Mar 22, 35; wid; c 3. INORGANIC CHEMISTRY. *Educ:* Creighton Univ, BS, 57, MS, 59; Univ Iowa, PhD(chem), 65. *Prof Exp:* Assoc prof, 64-76, PROF CHEM, UNIV WIS-SUPERIOR, 76- *Mem:* Am Chem Soc. *Res:* Synthesis and studies of new borazine compounds; preparation of coordination compounds; natural waters chemistry. *Mailing Add:* Dept of Chem Univ of Wis Superior WI 54880

ROUBAL, WILLIAM THEODORE, b Eugene, Ore, Dec 20, 30; m 53; c 4. BIO-ORGANIC CHEMISTRY. *Educ:* Ore State Univ, BA, 54, MS, 59; Univ Calif, Davis, PhD(biochem), 64. *Prof Exp:* RES CHEMIST, ENVIRON CONSERV DIV, NAT MARINE FISHERIES SERV, 60- *Concurrent Pos:* Affil prof, Col Fisheries, Univ Wash, 74- *Mem:* Sigma Xi; NY Acad Sci. *Res:* Spin-labeling studies on lipid-protein and pollutant-host interaction; studies on uptake, depuration and metabolism of xenobiotics in aquatic organisms. *Mailing Add:* Nat Marine Fisheries Serv Environ Conserv Div 2725 Montlake Blvd E Seattle WA 98102

ROUBICEK, CARL BEN, animal genetics, see previous edition

ROUDABUSH, ROBERT LEE, b Mt Carmel, Pa, Mar 20, 09; m 32; c 2. ZOOLOGY. *Educ:* Lebanon Valley Col, AB, 31; Iowa State Col, MS, 32, PhD(zool), 36. *Prof Exp:* Zool technician, Iowa State Col, 33-34, instr, 34-38; head microscope slide dept, Ward's Nat Sci Estab, 38-49, dir res & develop, 49-51; asst to dir, Lab Indust Med, Eastman Kodak Co, 51-66, asst dir, 66-72, from assoc dir to dir, Health & Safety Lab, 72-74; RETIRED. *Concurrent Pos:* Fel, Rochester Mus, 48; instr parasitol, Sch Med & Dent, Univ Rochester, 43-64; sr instr, 64-69, asst prof, 69- *Mem:* Am Soc Parasitol; Am Micros Soc; Am Soc Trop Med & Hyg; Am Indust Hyg Asn; Soc Toxicol (treas, 65-68, pres, 70). *Res:* Regeneration in hydra; parasitology; malaria; microscopical technique; toxicology. *Mailing Add:* 709 N Landing Rd Rochester NY 14625

ROUF, MOHAMMED ABDUR, b Dacca, Bangladesh, May 2, 33; m 65. BACTERIOLOGY. *Educ:* Univ Dacca, BS, 54, MS, 55; Univ Calif, Davis, MA, 59; Wash State Univ, PhD(bact, biochem), 63. *Prof Exp:* Lectr bot, Govt Col Sylhet, Bangladesh, 55-57; asst bacteriologist, Pullman Div Indust Res, Wash State Univ, 63-64; from asst prof to assoc prof, 64-68, PROF BACT, UNIV WIS-OSHKOSH, 68-, CHMN DEPT BIOL, 70- *Concurrent Pos:* Received grants from various state and fed agencies; NSF fac sci fel, 75. *Mem:* AAAS; Am Soc Microbiol; Sigma Xi. *Res:* Microbial physiology; degradation of uric acid by bacteria; iron and manganese oxidizing bacteria; jute retting; red leg disease of frogs. *Mailing Add:* Dept of Biol Univ of Wis Oshkosh WI 54901

ROUFA, DONALD JAY, b St Louis, Mo, Apr 8, 43; m 67; c 2. BIOCHEMISTRY, GENETICS. *Educ:* Amherst Col, AB, 65; Johns Hopkins Univ, PhD(biol), 70. *Prof Exp:* Chemist, Nat Inst Child Health & Human Develop, 69-70; res scientist biochem, NY State Dept Health, Albany, 70-71; instr, 71-73, asst prof biochem & med, Baylor Col Med, 73-75; assoc prof biol, 75-81, PROF BIOL, KANSAS STATE UNIV, 81- *Res:* Biochemical mechanisms involved in protein synthesis; molecular mechanisms participating in genetic processes; animal cell somatic genetics. *Mailing Add:* Div Biol Kans State Univ Manhattan KS 66506

ROUFFA, ALBERT STANLEY, b Boston, Mass, Mar 30, 19; m 43; c 3. BOTANY. *Educ:* Mass State Col, BS, 41; Rutgers Univ, MS, 47, PhD(bot), 49. *Prof Exp:* Asst bot, Rutgers Univ, 41-42 & gen biol, 46-49; from asst prof to assoc prof, 49-60, PROF BIOL SCI, UNIV ILL, CHICAGO CIRCLE, 60- *Concurrent Pos:* Exec secy, Dept Biol Sci, 64-68; dir James Woodworth Prairie Preserve, 69- *Mem:* Am Fern Soc; Bot Soc Am; Ecol Soc Am; Explorers Club. *Res:* Developmental plant morphology and anatomy; woody ornamentals. *Mailing Add:* Dept of Biol Sci Univ Ill Chicago Cir Box 4348 Chicago IL 60680

ROUGH, GAYLORD EARL, b Cochranton, Pa, Nov 17, 24; m 49; c 3. ZOOLOGY. *Educ:* Univ Pittsburgh, BS, 50, MS, 52, PhD(animal ecol), 61. *Prof Exp:* Instr biol, Alfred Univ, 52-56; asst, Univ Pittsburgh, 56-57, spec lectr, 57-58; from asst prof to chmn dept, 69-74, dir environ studies prog, 78-81, PROF BIOL, ALFRED UNIV, 66- *Mem:* AAAS; Ecol Soc Am; Am Soc Ichthyologists & Herpetologists; Sigma Xi. *Res:* Radioecology; physiological ecology; respiratory metabolism and thyroid activity in small mammals; animal ecology, especially behavior; limnology, aquatic productivity; population dynamics and meristic characters of freshwater fishes. *Mailing Add:* Dept of Biol Alfred Univ Alfred NY 14802

ROUGHGARDEN, JONATHAN DAVID, b Paterson, NJ, Mar 13, 46; m 69. POPULATION BIOLOGY. *Educ:* Univ Rochester, AB & BS, 68; Harvard Univ, PhD(biol), 71. *Prof Exp:* Asst prof biol, Univ Mass, Boston, 70-72; asst prof, 72-77, assoc prof, 77-81, PROF BIOL, STANFORD UNIV, 81- *Res:* Theoretical population biology; population ecology and genetics; mathematical theory of density-dependent natural selection, niche width, community structure, faunal buildup, population spatial structure and species borders; field work on anolis lizards; intertidal marine community ecology. *Mailing Add:* Dept Biol Stanford Univ Stanford CA 94305

ROUGHLEY, PETER JAMES, b Doncaster, Eng, July 22, 47. CARTILAGE PROTEOGLYCAN BIOCHEMISTRY. *Educ:* Nottingham Univ, BSc, 69, PhD(chem), 72. *Prof Exp:* Fel, Charing Cross Hosp, Eng, 72-74, Strangeways Res Lab, Eng, 74-77; RES SCIENTIST, SHRINERS HOSP, CAN, 77- *Concurrent Pos:* Asst prof, McGill Univ, 77- *Mem:* Biochem Soc Eng; Orthopaedic Res Soc. *Res:* Structure and function of the proteoglycans isolated from human articular cartilage; proteinases and proteinase inhibitors present in cartilage; biochemistry of human articular cartilages. *Mailing Add:* Joint Dis Lab Shriners Hosp 1529 Cedar Ave Montreal PQ H3G 1A6 Can

ROUGVIE, MALCOLM ARNOLD, b Newton, Mass, Feb 4, 28; m 59. BIOPHYSICS. *Educ:* Mass Inst Technol, SB & SM, 51, PhD(biophys), 54. *Prof Exp:* Instr biophys, Mass Inst Technol, 54-55; res assoc, 55-56, asst prof physics, 57-60, asst prof biophys, 60-62, ASSOC PROF BIOPHYS, IOWA STATE UNIV, 62- *Mem:* Biophys Soc; AAAS. *Res:* Structure of proteins by optical and physicochemical methods. *Mailing Add:* Dept of Biochem & Biophys Iowa State Univ Ames IA 50011

ROULEAU, WILFRED T(HOMAS), b Quincy, Mass, May 3, 29; m 54; c 2. MECHANICAL ENGINEERING. *Educ:* Carnegie Inst Technol, BS, 51, MS, 52, PhD(mech eng), 54. *Prof Exp:* From asst prof to assoc prof mech eng, 54-65, PROF MECH ENG, CARNEGIE-MELLON UNIV, 65- *Concurrent Pos:* Consult, Gulf Res & Develop Co, 59, Bituminous Coal Res, Inc, 65 & Westinghouse Res Labs, 70-76, Celanese Fibers Corp, 79, Colt Industs, 80. *Mem:* Am Soc Mech Engrs; Sigma Xi. *Res:* Hydrodynamic stability; wave propagation in viscous fluids; viscous flows; biological flows; hydrodynamic lubrication; porous bearings; numerical analysis of fluid flow; jet mixing; magnetohydrodynamics; flow and erosion in turbomachinery; energetics. *Mailing Add:* Dept Mech Eng Carnagie-Mellon Univ Schenley Park Pittsburgh PA 15213

ROULIER, JOHN ARTHUR, b Cohoes, NY, May 3, 41; m 62; c 4. MATHEMATICS. *Educ:* Siena Col, NY, BS, 63; Syracuse Univ, MS, 66, PhD(math), 68. *Prof Exp:* Technician, Gen Elec Co, 63-64; asst prof math, Mich State Univ, 68; NSF res assoc math, Rensselaer Polytech Inst, 69; asst prof, Union Col, NY, 69-73; asst prof, 73-75, ASSOC PROF MATH, NC STATE UNIV, 75- *Mem:* Math Asn Am; Am Math Soc. *Res:* Approximation theory; approximation by polynomials satisfying linear restrictions; weighted approximation; Chebyshev rational approximation on infinite line segments; shape preserving spline interpolation. *Mailing Add:* Dept of Math NC State Univ Raleigh NC 27607

ROULSTON, DAVID J, b London, Eng, Nov 3, 36; m 61; c 3. SEMICONDUCTORS. *Educ:* Queen's Univ, Belfast, BSc, 57; Univ London, PhD(elec eng) & DIC, 62. *Prof Exp:* Sci officer, Civil Serv, Portland, Eng, 57-58; engr, CSF Dept, RPC, France, 62-67; assoc prof, 67-72, PROF ELEC ENG, UNIV WATERLOO, 72- *Concurrent Pos:* Vis assoc prof, Univ Waterloo, 66-67; consult engr, Thomson-CSF, Orsay, France, 73- & Res & Develop Labs in US & Can, 77-; mem elec eng grants comt, Nat Res Coun Can, 75-78. *Mem:* Inst Elec Engrs UK; sr mem Inst Elec & Electronics Engrs. *Res:* Semiconductor devices and circuits; device characterization and modeling using computer aided techniques, microwave bipolar and field effect transistors integrated circuit modelling; photo and photoparametric diodes and related circuits. *Mailing Add:* Dept of Elec Eng Univ of Waterloo Waterloo ON N2L 3G1 Can

ROULSTON, THOMAS MERVYN, b Armagh, Northern Ireland, July 23, 20; m 47; c 3. OBSTETRICS & GYNECOLOGY. *Educ:* Queen's Univ Belfast, MB, BCh & BAO, 43; FRCOG, 64; FRCS(C). *Prof Exp:* Chmn dept, 64-76, PROF OBSTET & GYNEC UNIV MAN, 64- *Concurrent Pos:* Obstetrician & gynecologist, Health Sci Ctr, Winnipeg, 56-; consult, Misericordia Gen, Grace, St Boniface Gen & Children's Hosps, Winnipeg, 64-; pres, Family Planning Fedn Can, 70-72; mem, Cent Coun, Int Planned Parenthood Fedn. *Honors & Awards:* Queen Elizabeth II Silver Jubilee Medal; Alan Guttmacher Mem Medal. *Mem:* Fel Am Col Obstet & Gynec; NY Acad Sci; Soc Obstet & Gynaec Can (pres, 72); Can Med Asn; Brit Med Asn. *Res:* Fertility regulation; population problems; genital cancer; medical education; ultrasonics in obstetrics and gynecology. *Mailing Add:* Dept of Obstet and Gynec Univ Man 59 Emily St Winnipeg MB R3E 0W3 Can

ROUND, G(EORGE) F(REDERICK), b Worcestershire, Eng, Jan 31, 32; m 56; c 5. CHEMICAL & MECHANICAL ENGINEERING. *Educ:* Univ Birmingham, BSc, 54, PhD(chem eng), 57, DSc(chem eng), 74. *Prof Exp:* Asst res officer, Res Coun Alta, 57-61, assoc res officer, 61-67, sr res officer, 67-68; assoc prof, 68-71, PROF MECH ENG, McMASTER UNIV, 71- *Concurrent Pos:* Prof chem eng, Kuwait Univ, 78-80. *Honors & Awards:* H R Worthington Tech Achievement Award, 77. *Mem:* Chem Inst Can; Int Asn Hydraul Res; Royal Soc Arts. *Res:* Fluid dynamics; thermodynamics; biomedical engineering. *Mailing Add:* Fac of Eng McMaster Univ Hamilton ON L8S 4L7 Can

ROUNDS, BURTON WARD, b Milan, NH, May 6, 24; m 46; c 3. WILDLIFE MANAGEMENT, NATURAL RESOURCE CONSERVATION. *Educ:* Colo A&M Col, BS, 48. *Prof Exp:* Wildlife res biologist effects fed projs wildlife, US Fish & Wildlife Serv, 48-58; supvry wildlife res biologist determination causes wetland losses, Bur Sport Fisheries & Wildlife, US Dept Interior, 58-61, supvry wildlife biologist wetlands protection, 61-68, wetlands prog coordr, 68-72, regional supvr wildlife serv, 72; area mgr fish & wildlife admin, US Fish & Wildlife Serv, 72-79; CONSERV CONSULT, 79- *Concurrent Pos:* Vchmn fish & wildlife resources div, Soil Conserv Soc Am, 72, chmn, 73; fac mem gyroscope, US Fish & Wildlife Serv, 75 & 76, mem pathfinder, 78; mem adv coun to dean sch forestry, Univ Mont, 77-79. *Honors & Awards:* Spec Achievement Awards, US Fish & Wildlife Serv, 75 & 76; Meritorious Serv Award, Secy US Dept Interior, 78. *Mem:* Wildlife Soc; Am Soc Mammalogists; Soil Conserv Soc Am; Trumpeter Swan Soc. *Res:* Ecology of prairie wetlands; ecology of wild canids. *Mailing Add:* Star Rte 2 Box 7C Columbus MT 59019

ROUNDS, DONALD EDWIN, b Maywood, Ill, Jan 17, 26; m 51; c 2. EMBRYOLOGY. *Educ:* Occidental Col, BA, 51; Univ Calif, Los Angeles, PhD(zool), 58. *Prof Exp:* Lab technician, AEC Proj, 51-54; res assoc exp embryol, Univ Calif, Los Angeles, 54-56; investr tissue cult, Med Br, Univ Tex, 58-59; investr, Tissue Cult Lab, 59-60, assoc dir div cell biol, 60-64, RES COORDR, PASADENA FOUND MED RES, 64- *Concurrent Pos:* Adj asst prof anat, Univ Southern Calif, 62-70, adj assoc prof, 70-; consult, air & indust hyg lab, Dept Pub Health, Calif, 64-66; biomed consult, Electro-Optical Systs, Inc, 65-68; asst clin prof path, Sch Med, Loma Linda Univ, 65-74, clin prof, 74-; mem bd dirs, Laser Inst Am, 73- *Mem:* Fel AAAS; Tissue Cult Asn; Am

Soc Cell Biol; Soc Gen Physiol; Am Sci Film Asn. *Res:* Cellular and molecular effects of laser energy; tissue culture; cell physiology; laser research. *Mailing Add:* Pasadena Found for Med Res 99 North El Molino Ave Pasadena CA 91101

ROUNDS, FRED G, JR, b Colfax, Wash, June 4, 25; m 59; c 2. CHEMICAL ENGINEERING. *Educ:* State Col Wash, BS, 49. *Prof Exp:* From jr res engr to sr res engr, 49-75, DEPT RES ENGR, RES LABS, GEN MOTORS CORP, 75- *Honors & Awards:* Alfred E Hunt Award, Am Soc Lubrication Engrs, 64. *Mem:* Am Chem Soc; Am Soc Lubrication Engrs. *Res:* Automotive engine exhaust gas emissions; diesel odor; engine combustion; additive mechanisms; lubricant coking; lubricant composition effects on rolling contact fatigue, friction and wear; diesel soot effects on wear. *Mailing Add:* Fuels & Lubricants Dept Gen Motors Res Labs 12 Mile & Mound Rds Warren MI 48090

ROUNDS, RICHARD CLIFFORD, b Rockford Ill, Feb 16, 43; m 65; c 2. BIOGEOGRAPHY, RESOURCE GEOGRAPHY. *Educ:* Ill State Univ, BSc, 65, MSc, 67; Univ Colo, Boulder, PhD(geog), 71. *Prof Exp:* Teaching assoc phys geog, Ill State Univ, 66-67; asst prof, 70-78, ASSOC PROF GEOG, BRANDON UNIV, 78- *Res:* Wildlife resources; tourism and recreation. *Mailing Add:* Dept of Geog Brandon Univ 270 18th St Brandon MB R7A 6A9 Can

ROUNSLEY, ROBERT R(ICHARD), b Detroit, Mich, Jan 11, 31; m 53; c 5. CHEMICAL ENGINEERING. *Educ:* Mich Technol Univ, BS, 52, MS, 54; Iowa State Univ, PhD(chem eng), 57. *Prof Exp:* Res asst, Argonne Nat Lab, 53-54; instr, Iowa State Univ, 54-57; sr res engr, 57-79, RES FEL, MEAD CORP, 79- *Mem:* Soc Comput Simulation; Am Inst Chem Engrs; Am Chem Soc; Coun Continuing Prof Educ; Tech Asn Pulp & Paper Indust. *Res:* Application of computer control in process industries; process simulation; statistics; training programs; drying of paper products. *Mailing Add:* Cent Res Labs Mead Corp Chillicothe OH 45601

ROUQUETTE, FRANCIS MARION, JR, b Aransas Pass, Tex, Dec 25, 42; m 64; c 4. AGRONOMY. *Educ:* Tex A&I Univ, BS, 65; Tex Tech Univ, MS, 67; Tex A&M Univ, PhD(soil & plant sci), 70. *Prof Exp:* Asst prof, 70-74, ASSOC PROF FORAGE PHYSIOL, AGR RES & EXTEN CTR, TEX A&M UNIV, 74- *Mem:* Am Soc Agron; Sigma Xi; Am Soc Range Sci. *Res:* Investigation of quantity and quality parameters of forages under various levels of grazing intensity. *Mailing Add:* Agr Res & Exten Ctr Drawer E Tex A&M Univ Overton TX 75684

ROURKE, ARTHUR W, b Boston, Mass, Oct 8, 42; m 65; c 2. CELL PHYSIOLOGY. *Educ:* Lafayette Col, AB, 64; Univ Conn, PhD(cell biol), 70. *Prof Exp:* Fel cell physiol, Univ Conn, 70-72; asst prof biol, 72-77, ASSOC PROF ZOOL & BIOCHEM, UNIV IDAHO, 77- *Concurrent Pos:* Muscular Dystrophy Asn Am grant, 73; Heart Asn grant, 75. *Mem:* Biophys Soc; Sigma Xi; AAAS; Am Soc Cell Biologists. *Res:* Cellular turnover in eukaryotes. *Mailing Add:* Dept of Life Sci Univ of Idaho Moscow ID 83843

ROUS, STEPHEN N, b New York, NY, Nov 1, 31; m 66; c 2. UROLOGY. *Educ:* Amherst Col, AB, 52; New York Med Col, MD, 56; Univ Minn, MS, 63. *Prof Exp:* Fel, Mayo Grad Sch Med, Univ Minn, 60-63; assoc prof urol, New York Med Col, 68-72, asst dean, 68-70, assoc dean, 70-72; prof surg & chief div urol, Col Human Med, Mich State Univ, 72-75; PROF & CHMN DEPT UROL, MED UNIV SC, 75-; UROLOGIST-IN-CHIEF, MED UNIV & CHARLESTON COUNTY HOSPS, 75- *Concurrent Pos:* Chief urol, Metrop Hosp Ctr, New York, 68-72; consult, Vet Admins, Roper & St Francis Hosps, Charleston, 75- *Mem:* Am Urol Asn; Am Col Surg; Soc Univ Urol; Pan-Pac Surg Asn; Int Soc Urol. *Mailing Add:* Dept of Urol Med Univ of SC Charleston SC 29403

ROUSE, BARRY TYRRELL, b Jan 9, 42; Brit & Can citizen; m 65; c 2. IMMUNOLOGY, VIROLOGY. *Educ:* Bristol Univ, BVSc, 65; Univ Guelph, MSc, 67, PhD(immunol), 70. *Prof Exp:* Houseman vet med, Bristol Univ, 65-66; fel immunol, Walter & Eliza Hall, Inst Med Sci, Melbourne, Australia, 70-72; asst prof, Univ Sask, 72-73, assoc prof, 77-78, PROF IMMUNOL, UNIV TENN, KNOXVILLE, 78- *Concurrent Pos:* Med Res Coun Can fel, 70-72, mem study sect immunol & transplantation, Med Res Coun Can, 74- 77; ad hoc mem, Study Sect Exp Virol, NIH, 78; mem grant rev panel, Morris Animal Found, 78-80; grants, NIH, Morris Animal Found, Nat Hog Producers. *Mem:* Royal Col Vet Surgeons; Am Asn Immunologists; Infectious Dis Soc Am; Reticuloendothelial Soc; Can Soc Immunol. *Res:* Mechanisms of recovery from herpesvirus infections; treatment methods for canine allergy; immunological diseases of domestic animals. *Mailing Add:* Dept of Microbiol Univ of Tenn Knoxville TN 37996

ROUSE, CARL ALBERT, b Youngstown, Ohio, July 14, 26; m 55; c 3. THEORETICAL ASTROPHYSICS, THEORETICAL NUCLEAR PHYSICS. *Educ:* Case Western Reserve Univ, BS, 51; Calif Inst Technol, MS, 53, PhD(physics), 56. *Prof Exp:* Sr res engr, NAm Aviation Inc, 56-57; theoret physicist, Lawrence Radiation Lab, Univ Calif, 57-65, res assoc theoret physics, Space Sci Lab, Univ Calif, Berkeley, 65-68; staff physicist, Gulf Radiation Technol, 68-74; STAFF SCIENTIST, GEN ATOMIC CO, 74- *Concurrent Pos:* Instr, Exten Div, Univ Calif, Los Angeles, 57; NSF res assoc, E O Hulburt Ctr Space Res, US Naval Res Lab, 65-68; instr, Exten Div, Univ Calif, San Diego, 75; prin investtr, NSF grant, 81- *Mem:* AAAS; fel Am Phys Soc; Am Astron Soc; Int Astron Union. *Res:* Ionization equilibrium equations of state for monatomic matter; exploding wire phenomena; numerical solutions to the Schrodinger equations; solar and stellar interiors; radiation transport; solar oscillations; original theoretical studies of new shielding materials for fission and fusion nuclear reactors. *Mailing Add:* Gen Atomic Co PO Box 81608 San Diego CA 92138

ROUSE, GEORGE ELVERTON, b Chugwater, Wyo, May 4, 34; m 61; c 3. GEOCHEMISTRY. *Educ:* Colo Sch Mines, Geol Engr, 61, DSc, 68. *Prof Exp:* Mining geologist, Anglo Am Corp SAfrica, Ltd, 61-64; proj mgr, 68-71, VPRES & SR PROJ MGR, MINERAL EXPLOR, EARTH SCI, INC, 71- *Mem:* AAAS; Am Geophys Union. *Res:* Global tectonics; gas geochemistry for mineral exploration; geochemistry of metalliferous shales; hydrometallurgy. *Mailing Add:* 9254 Fern Way Blue Mountain Estates Golden CO 80401

ROUSE, GLENN EVERETT, b Hamilton, Ont, Aug 1, 28; m 52; c 1. PALYNOLOGY, PALEOBOTANY. *Educ:* McMaster Univ, BA, 51, MSc, 52, PhD(palynology, paleobot), 56. *Prof Exp:* From instr to assoc prof, 57-68, PROF PALYNOLOGY & PALEOBOT, UNIV BC, 68- *Concurrent Pos:* Palynology consult, Oil & Coal Explor. *Mem:* Am Asn Stratig Palynologists; Geol Asn Can; Can Bot Soc; fel Linnaean Soc London. *Res:* Palynology of Upper Cretaceous and Tertiary strata of Arctic and Western Canada. *Mailing Add:* 3529 6270 Univ Blvd Dept Bot Univ BC Vancouver BC V6T 2B1 Can

ROUSE, HUNTER, b Toledo, Ohio, Mar 29, 06; m 32; c 3. FLUID MECHANICS, HYDRAULICS. *Educ:* Mass Inst Technol, SB, 29, SM, 32; Karlsruhe Tech Hoschsch, Ger, Dr Ing(hydraul eng), 32; Univ Paris, Dr es Sci(fluid mech), 59. *Hon Degrees:* Dr Ing(eng hydraul), Univ Karlsruhe, 75. *Prof Exp:* Asst hydraul, Mass Inst Technol, 31-33; instr civil eng, Columbia Univ, 33-35; asst prof fluid mech, Calif Inst Technol, 35-39; prof, 39-72, assoc dir, Inst Hydraul Res, 42-44, dir, 44-66, dean, Col Eng, 66-72, Carver Prof hydraul, 72-74, EMER CARVER PROF HYDRAUL, UNIV IOWA, 74-, EMER DEAN ENG, 72- *Concurrent Pos:* Assoc hydraul engr, Soil Conserv Serv, USDA, 36-39; consult, US Off Naval Res, 48-66 & Waterways Exp Sta, US Corps Engrs, 49-68; Fulbright exchange prof, Univ Grenoble, 52-53; NSF sr fel, Univs Gottingen, Rome, Cambridge & Paris, 58-59; sr scholar, Australian-Am Educ Found, 73; vis prof, Col State Univ, 75- *Honors & Awards:* Norman Medal, Am Soc Civil Engrs, 38, Von Karman Medal, 63, Hist & Hertiage Award, 80; Westinghouse Award, Am Soc Eng Educ, 48, Bendix Award, 58; Outstanding Civilian Serv Medal, US Army, 73. *Mem:* Nat Acad Eng; hon mem Am Soc Civil Engrs; Am Soc Eng Educ; fel Am Acad Arts & Sci; hon mem Am Soc Mech Engrs. *Res:* Engineering hydraulics; history of hydraulics; engineering education; human ecology. *Mailing Add:* 10814 Mimosa Dr Sun City AZ 85373

ROUSE, JOHN THOMAS, b Covington, Ky, Oct 6, 06; m 32; c 2. GEOLOGY. *Educ:* Univ Cincinnati, AB, 29, MA, 30; Princeton Univ, PhD(geol), 32. *Prof Exp:* Asst geol, Princeton Univ, 30-31; instr, Hamilton Col, 32-36 & Ohio State Univ, 36-38; from geologist to staff geologist, Magnolia Petrol Co, Socony Mobil Oil Co, Inc, 38-52, mgr explor, Pegasus Div, 52-54, vpres, Mobil Producing Co, 54-60, dist explor supt, Mobil Oil Co, 60-66, region geologist, Mobil Oil Corp, Tex, 66-70; CONSULT GEOLOGIST, 70- *Mem:* Fel Geol Soc Am; hon mem Am Asn Petrol Geologists. *Res:* Petrology; physiography; structural geology; stratigraphy; petroleum exploration; volcanology. *Mailing Add:* 2026 Pryor Lane Billings MT 59102

ROUSE, JOHN WILSON, JR, b Kansas City, Mo, Dec 7, 37; m 56; c 1. ELECTRICAL ENGINEERING. *Educ:* Purdue Univ, BS, 59; Univ Kans, MS, 65, PhD(elec eng), 68. *Prof Exp:* Engr, Bendix Corp, 59-64; res coordr, Ctr Res, Inc, Univ Kans, 64-68; from asst prof & actg dir to prof elec eng & dir, Remote Sensing Ctr, Tex A&M Univ, 68-78; distinguished prof elec eng, chmn dept & dir, Bioeng Prog, Univ Mo-Columbia, 78-81; DEAN ENG, UNIV TEX, ARLINGTON, 81- *Concurrent Pos:* Mem comn F, Int Union Radio Sci, 69- *Mem:* Inst Elec & Electronics Engrs; AAAS. *Res:* Electromagnetic and acoustic scattering; radar systems; remote sensor systems; geoscience applications. *Mailing Add:* Dean Eng Univ Tex Arlington TX 76019

ROUSE, ROBERT ARTHUR, b St Louis, Mo, Sept 4, 43; m 66; c 2. THEORETICAL CHEMISTRY. *Educ:* Wash Univ, AB, 65; Northwestern Univ, PhD(chem), 68. *Prof Exp:* Res assoc chem, Harvard Univ, 68-69; asst prof chem, Univ Mo-St Louis, 69-76; ASST PROF CHEM, WASHINGTON UNIV, 77- *Mem:* Am Chem Soc; Am Phys Soc; Soc Comput Mach. *Res:* Molecular quantum mechanics; interacting molecular systems; reactions in theoretical organic chemistry. *Mailing Add:* Washington Univ Box 1141 St Louis MO 63130

ROUSE, ROBERT S, b Northampton, Mass, Sept 2, 30; m 51; c 4. ORGANIC CHEMISTRY. *Educ:* Yale Univ, BS, 51, MS, 53, PhD(chem), 57. *Prof Exp:* Lab asst, Yale Univ, 51-53 & 55, asst instruction, 56; asst prof chem, Lehigh Univ, 56-62; group leader, Plastics Div, Allied Chem Corp, NJ, 62-66, tech supvr, 66-67; assoc dean fac, 68-73, chmn dept, 67-73, PROF CHEM, MONMOUTH COL, 67-; dean fac, 73-80, VPRES, ACAD AFFAIRS, 73-, PROVOST, 80- *Concurrent Pos:* Consult, Allied Chem Corp, 68-70; Sabbatical leave, 81-82. *Mem:* Am Chem Soc; fel NY Acad Sci. *Res:* Organic reactions and synthesis, oxidation, alkylations, energy, educational administration. *Mailing Add:* Monmouth Col West Long Branch NJ 07764

ROUSE, ROY DENNIS, b Andersonville, Ga, Sept 20, 20; m 46; c 2. SOIL CHEMISTRY. *Educ:* Univ Ga, BSA, 42, MSA, 47; Purdue Univ, PhD(soil chem), 49. *Prof Exp:* Assoc soil chemist, 49-56, prof soils, 56-66, assoc dir, Agr Exp Sta & asst dean, Sch Agr, 66-72, dir, 72-81, EMER DIR, AGR EXP STA, AUBURN UNIV, 81-, DEAN, SCH AGR, 72- *Concurrent Pos:* Chmn Exp Sta Comt on Org and Policy, 77; mem Food Adv Comt, Off Tech Assessment, 78. *Mem:* Fel Soil Sci Soc Am; fel Am Soc Agron. *Res:* Soil chemistry of potassium; potassium nutrition of agronomic plants; resource allocation and research administration. *Mailing Add:* Agr Exp Sta Sch Agr Auburn Univ Auburn AL 36830

ROUSE, THOMAS C, b Milwaukee, Wis, Sept 24, 34; m 71. PARASITOLOGY, PHYSIOLOGY. *Educ:* Univ Wis-Milwaukee, BS, 59; Univ Wis-Madison, MS, 63, PhD(zool), 67. *Prof Exp:* Asst prof, Wis State Univ, Platteville, 65-67; asst prof, 67-74, ASSOC PROF BIOL, UNIV WIS-EAU CLAIRE, 74- *Mem:* Sigma Xi. *Res:* Effect of exercise on the normal and diseased cardiovascular system. *Mailing Add:* Dept of Biol Univ of Wis Eau Claire WI 54701

ROUSE, WILLIAM BRADFORD, human factors engineering, operations research, see previous edition

ROUSEK, EDWIN J, b Burwell, Nebr, Sept 8, 17; m 45; c 2. AGRICULTURE. *Educ:* Univ Nebr, BSc, 40; Cornell Univ, MSc, 43. *Prof Exp:* Chmn dept animal sci, 48-63, PROF ANIMAL SCI, CALIF STATE UNIV, FRESNO, 63- *Concurrent Pos:* Chmn univ senate, Calif State Univ, Fresno, 69-71. *Mem:* Am Meat Sci Asn. *Res:* Animal nutrition and meats. *Mailing Add:* Dept Animal Sci Calif State Univ Fresno CA 93710

ROUSELL, DON HERBERT, b Winnipeg, Man, Sept 4, 31; m 57; c 2. STRUCTURAL GEOLOGY. *Educ:* Univ Man, BSc, 52, Univ BC, MSc, 59; Univ Man, PhD(geol), 65. *Prof Exp:* Geologist, Tidewater Oil Co, 52-53 & Chevron Oil Co Venezuela, 56-59; asst prof, 63-66, ASSOC PROF GEOL, LAURENTIAN UNIV, 66- chmn dept, 77-78. *Concurrent Pos:* Nat Res Coun Can grants, 68-69 & 71-73; Ont Dept Univ Affairs grant, 68-69; fel, Ctr Tectonophys, Tex A&M Univ, 69-70; indust grants, 74-75, 79-80. *Mem:* Geol Soc Am; Fel Geol Asn Can. *Res:* Geology of Northwestern Venezuela; Precambrian geology of Northern Manitoba; geology of the Sudbury Basin. *Mailing Add:* Dept of Geol Laurentian Univ Sudbury ON P3E 2C6 Can

ROUSELL, GERALD, insect physiology, see previous edition

ROUSER, GEORGE, b Austin, Tex, June 2, 23; m 51; c 4. BIOCHEMISTRY. *Educ:* Southwestern Univ, Tex, BS, 44; Univ Rochester, PhD(biochem), 52. *Prof Exp:* Instr biol, Southwestern Univ, Tex, 47-48; res chemist, Sch Med, Vanderbilt Univ & Meharry Med Col, 48-49; USPHS fel biochem, Univ Rochester, 52-54; sr res biochemist, 54-67, HEAD SECT LIPID RES, DIV NEUROSCI, CITY OF HOPE MED CTR, 67- *Mem:* Am Oil Chem Soc. *Res:* Lipid chemistry and metabolism; neurochemistry; chemical composition and metabolism of blood cells. *Mailing Add:* 1512 S 3rd Ave Arcadia CA 91006

ROUSH, ALLAN HERBERT, b Hardin Mont, Feb 24, 18; m 44; c 2. BIOCHEMISTRY. *Educ:* Mont State Col, BS, 40; Univ Wash, PhD(biochem), 51. *Prof Exp:* From asst prof to assoc prof, 51-62, PROF BIOCHEM, ILL INST TECHNOL, 62- *Mem:* Am Chem Soc; Am Soc Biol Chemists; Mycol Soc Am. *Res:* Enzymology; nucleic acid metabolism; active transport. *Mailing Add:* Dept of Biol Ill Inst of Technol Chicago IL 60616

ROUSH, FRED WILLIAM, b Brooklyn, NY, May 7, 47. MATHEMATICS. *Educ:* Univ NC, AB, 66; Princeton Univ, PhD(math), 72. *Prof Exp:* Asst prof math, Univ Ga, 70-74; ASST PROF MATH, ALA STATE UNIV, 76- *Mem:* Am Math Soc. *Res:* Boolean matrix theory; combinatorics. *Mailing Add:* Dept Math Ala State Univ Montgomery AL 36104

ROUSH, MARVIN LEROY, b Topeka, Kans, Dec 26, 34; m 55; c 3. RISK ASSESSMENT. *Educ:* Ottawa Univ, BSc, 56; Univ Md, PhD(nuclear physics), 64. *Prof Exp:* Asst prof physics, Baker Univ, 59-61 & Tex A&M Univ, 65-66; asst prof, 66-70, assoc prof physics, 70-80, ASSOC PROF NUCLEAR ENG, UNIV MD, COLLEGE PARK, 80- *Mem:* AAAS; Am Phys Soc; Am Asn Physics Teachers; Am Nuclear Soc. *Res:* Risk assessment of nuclear power plants; neutron, gamma-ray and charged particle spectroscopy; trace-element analysis by x-ray fluorescence spectroscopy. *Mailing Add:* Dept Physics & Astron Univ of Md College Park MD 20742

ROUSH, WILLIAM BURDETTE, b Sheridan, Wyo, Apr 26, 45; m 73; c 2. ANIMAL HUSBANDRY. *Educ:* Brigham Young Univ, BS, 72, MS, 75; Ore State Univ, PhD(poultry sci), 79- *Prof Exp:* ASST PROF POULTRY SCI, PA STATE UNIV, 79- *Mem:* Poultry Sci Asn. *Res:* Management systems analysis for the biological and economical optimization of poultry production. *Mailing Add:* 201 Animal Indust Bldg Dept Poultry Sci Pa State Univ University Park PA 16802

ROUSLIN, WILLIAM, b Providence, RI, Nov 10, 38; m 70. BIOCHEMISTRY. *Educ:* Brown Univ, AB, 60; Univ Conn, PhD(biochem), 68. *Prof Exp:* NIH res fel, Cornell Univ, 68-70; asst prof biol, Douglass Col, Rutgers Univ, New Brunswick, 70-77; ASST PROF PHARMACOL & CELL BIOPHYSICS, COL MED, UNIV CINCINNATI, 77- *Res:* Mitochondrial inner membrane changes in ischemic heart disease; mitochondrial inner membrane structure, function, regulation and biogenesis. *Mailing Add:* Dept of Pharmacol & Cell Biophysics 231 Bethesda Ave Cincinnati OH 45267

ROUSSEAU, CECIL CLYDE, b Philadelphia, Pa, Jan 13, 38; m 65; c 2. MATHEMATICS, PHYSICS. *Educ:* Lamar Univ, BS, 60; Tex A&M Univ, MS, 62, PhD (physics), 68. *Prof Exp:* Asst prof physics, Baylor Univ, 68-70; asst prof math, Memphis State Univ, 70-75; Carnegie fel, Univ Aberdeen, 75-76; from asst prof to assoc prof, 76-81, PROF MATH, MEMPHIS STATE UNIV, 81- *Concurrent Pos:* Collaborating ed, Probs & Solutions, Soc Indust & Appl Math, 73- *Mem:* Math Asn Am; Soc Indust & Appl Math; Am Math Soc. *Res:* Graph theory; analysis; mathematical physics. *Mailing Add:* Dept Math Sci Memphis State Univ Memphis TN 38152

ROUSSEAU, DENIS LAWRENCE, b Franklin, NH, Nov 18, 40; m 63. BIOLOGICAL PHYSICS, PHYSICAL CHEMISTRY. *Educ:* Bowdoin Col, BA, 62; Princeton Univ, PhD(phys chem), 67. *Prof Exp:* Res fel, Univ Southern Calif, 67-69; MEM STAFF, CHEM PHYSICS, BELL LABS, INC, 69- *Mem:* Biophys Soc; Am Phys Soc; AAAS. *Res:* Raman scattering from biological materials; heme proteins; molecular physics. *Mailing Add:* Bell Labs Inc Murray Hill NJ 07974

ROUSSEAU, PAUL ROYAL, microbiology, industrial genetics, see previous edition

ROUSSEAU, RONALD WILLIAM, b Sept 28, 43; US citizen; m 63; c 3. CHEMICAL ENGINEERING. *Educ:* La State Univ, BS, 66, MS, 68, PhD(chem eng), 69. *Prof Exp:* Instr chem eng, La State Univ, 67; res engr, Westvaco Corp, 69; asst prof, 69-74, assoc prof, 74-80, PROF CHEM ENG, NC STATE UNIV, 80- *Honors & Awards:* Forest Prod Award, Am Inst Chem Engrs, 80. *Mem:* Am Inst Chem Engrs; Am Chem Soc. *Res:* Mass transfer and crystallization processes; applied polymer chemistry; cleaning gases produced from coal. *Mailing Add:* Dept of Chem Eng NC State Univ Raleigh NC 27607

ROUSSEAU, VIATEUR, b Baie des Sables, Que, July 5, 14; nat US; m 58; c 3. ORGANIC CHEMISTRY. *Educ:* Am Int Col, BS, 39; NY Univ, PhD(org chem), 48. *Prof Exp:* Anal chemist, Chapman Valve Mfg Co, Mass, 40-42; asst chem, NY Univ, 42-47; instr, Col Mt St Vincent, 47-50, asst prof, 50-56; assoc prof, 56-58, chmn sci div, 66-68, PROF CHEM, IONA COL, 58- *Mem:* Am Chem Soc. *Res:* Chemistry of indazoles; synthesis; structural relationships; absorption spectra. *Mailing Add:* Dept of Chem Iona Col New Rochelle NY 10801

ROUSSEL, JOHN S, b Hester, La, Nov 23, 21; m 46; c 5. ENTOMOLOGY, AGRONOMY. *Educ:* La State Univ, BS, 42, MS, 48; Tex A&M Univ, PhD(entom), 50. *Prof Exp:* From asst prof to assoc prof, 49-57, PROF ENTOM, LA STATE UNIV, BATON ROUGE, 57-, COORDR COTTON RES & ASST TO DIR AGR EXP STA, 61- *Concurrent Pos:* NSF grant, 57-60. *Mem:* AAAS; Entom Soc Am; Am Inst Biol Sci. *Res:* Cotton production practices and insects. *Mailing Add:* La State Univ Agr Exp Sta Drawer E Baton Rouge LA 70803

ROUSSEL, JOSEPH DONALD, b Paulina, La, Apr 28, 29; m 58; c 2. REPRODUCTIVE PHYSIOLOGY. *Educ:* La State Univ, BS, 58, MS, 60, PhD(reprod physiol), 63. *Prof Exp:* Res asst, La State Univ, 59-63; res assoc, Univ Ark, 63-65 & Delta Regional Primate Res Ctr, 66-72; PROF REPROD PHYSIOL, LA STATE UNIV, BATON ROUGE, 72- *Concurrent Pos:* Res grant, 63-66. *Mem:* Am Fertil Asn; Am Dairy Sci Asn; Int Fertil Asn; Brit Soc Study Fertil; Am Soc Animal Sci. *Res:* Environmental reproductive physiology; semen metabolism; enzyme activity in spermatogenesis and physiology factors influencing reproduction; reproduction in primates; nutritional influence in reproduction; ovulation; semen preservation and articicial insemination. *Mailing Add:* Dept of Dairy Sci La State Univ Baton Rouge LA 70803

ROUSSEL, PHILIP ANDREW, chemistry, see previous edition

ROUSSELLE, GILLES L, b Iberville, Que, Oct 30, 45; m 68; c 2. PLANT BREEDING, TREE FRUITS. *Educ:* Montreal Univ, BA, 65; Laval Univ, BSc, 69, MSc, 73; Rutgers Univ, PhD(plant breeding), 74. *Prof Exp:* RES SCIENTIST PLANT BREEDING, AGR CAN RES STA, 70- *Concurrent Pos:* Mem, Can Expert Comt Plant Gene Resources, 78- *Mem:* Can Soc Hort Sci; Am Soc Hort Sci; Am Pomol Soc; Int Dwarf Fruit Tree Asn; Que Soc Protection Plants. *Res:* Breeding apple cultivars and root stocks for disease and insect resistance and resistance to extremes in temperature and dwarfing potential; propagation of tree fruits. *Mailing Add:* Agr Can Res Sta PO Box 457 St-Jean-Sur-Richelieu PQ J3B 6Z8 Can

ROUSSIN, ROBERT WARREN, b Columbia, Mo, Jan 27, 39; m 62. NUCLEAR ENGINEERING, INFORMATION SCIENCE. *Educ:* Univ Mo-Rolla, BS, 62; Univ Ill, MS, 64, PhD(nuclear eng), 69. *Prof Exp:* Co-op student mech eng, McDonnell Aircraft Corp, 57-62; engr mech & nuclear eng, Allis Chalmers, 62; RES STAFF MEM NUCLEAR ENG, RADIATION SHIELDING INFO CTR, OAK RIDGE NAT LAB, UNION CARBIDE CORP, 68- *Concurrent Pos:* Chmn shielding subcomt, Cross Sect Eval Working Group, 75- *Mem:* Am Nuclear Soc. *Res:* Promote the exchange of information and computing technology in the field of radiation transport. *Mailing Add:* Radiation Shielding Info Ctr PO Box X Oak Ridge TN 37830

ROUTBORT, JULES LAZAR, b San Francisco, Calif, May 15, 37; m 66; c 2. MATERIALS SCIENCE. *Educ:* Univ Calif, Berkeley, BS, 60; Cornell Univ, PhD(eng physics), 65. *Prof Exp:* Sci Res Coun fel physics, Cavendish Lab, Cambridge Univ, 64-66; AEC fel, Rensselaer Polytech Inst, 66-68; PHYSICIST, MAT SCI DIV, ARGONNE NAT LAB, 68- *Concurrent Pos:* Humboldt fel, Res Inst for Transurane, Karlsruhe, Ger, 73-74. *Mem:* Am Ceramic Soc; Am Phys Soc. *Res:* Mechanical properties of ceramics; diffusion and elastic properties of ceramics. *Mailing Add:* Mat Sci Div Argonne Nat Lab 9700 S Cass Ave Argonne IL 60439

ROUTH, JOSEPH ISAAC, b Logansport, Ind, May 8, 10; m 37, 76; c 2. CLINICAL BIOCHEMISTRY, PATHOLOGY. *Educ:* Purdue Univ, BSChE, 33, MS, 34; Univ Mich, PhD(biochem), 37. *Prof Exp:* From instr to assoc prof biochem, 37-51, dir, Clin Biochem Lab, 52-64, PROF BIOCHEM, UNIV IOWA, 51-, dir spec clin chem lab & prof path, 70-78, EMER PROF BIOCHEM, UNIV IOWA, 78- *Concurrent Pos:* Consult clin chem, Vet Admin Hosp, Iowa City, Iowa, 52- *Mem:* Am Chem Soc; Am Soc Biol Chemists; Am Asn Clin Chem (pres, 57-58); Am Bd Clin Chem (pres, 59-73); fel Am Inst Chem. *Res:* Purification and properties of trypsin inhibitor, levodopa metabolites in Parkinson's disease, enzyme inhibitors; methodology, metabolism and protein binding of analgesic drugs; effects of drugs on clinical chemistry parameters. *Mailing Add:* Dept of Biochem Univ of Iowa Iowa City IA 52242

ROUTIEN, JOHN BRODERICK, b Mt Vernon, Ind, Jan 23, 13; m 44, 67. MICROBIOLOGY. *Educ:* DePauw Univ, AB, 34; Northwestern Univ, AM, 36; Mich State Col, PhD(mycol), 40. *Prof Exp:* Instr bot, Univ Mo, 39-42; mycologist, Chemotherapeut Res Labs, 46-73, res adv, Cent Res, Pfizer Inc, 73-77; RETIRED. *Concurrent Pos:* Mem, Antimicrobial Agents & Chemother, 74- *Honors & Awards:* Com Solvents Award, 50. *Mem:* Bot Soc Am; Mycol Soc Am; Am Soc Microbiol; Soc Indust Microbiol; NY Acad Sci. *Res:* Isolation of microorganisms; culture collection; taxonomy of microorganisms. *Mailing Add:* Grassy Hill Rd Box 363 RR3 Lyme CT 06371

ROUTLEDGE, RICHARD DONOVAN, b Toronto, Ont, Aug 15, 48; m 70; c 2. STATISTICAL METHODOLOGY. *Educ:* Queen's Univ, Kingston, Ont, BSc, 70; Univ Alta, Edmonton, MSc, 72; Dalhousie Univ, Halifax, PhD(biol), 75. *Prof Exp:* Killam fel math, Univ Alta, 75-77, asst prof, 75-80; ASST PROF MATH, SIMON FRASER UNIV, 80- *Mem:* Biomet Soc; Statist Soc Can. *Res:* Development of statistical methodology and use of mathematical optimization to study problems in population ecology and resource management. *Mailing Add:* Dept Math Simon Fraser Univ Burnaby BC V5A 1S6 Can

ROUTLEY, DOUGLAS GEORGE, b BC, Apr 26, 29; m 58; c 2. HORTICULTURE. *Educ:* Univ BC, BSA, 52; Pa State Univ, MS, 55, PhD(agr, biol chem), 57. *Prof Exp:* Asst prof biochem, 57-64, assoc prof biochem & plant sci, 64-70, PROF PLANT SCI, UNIV NH, 70- *Concurrent Pos:* NIH spec fel, 66-67. *Mem:* Am Soc Hort Sci. *Res:* Plant growth regulators; greenhouse crops. *Mailing Add:* Dept of Plant Sci Univ of NH Durham NH 03824

ROUTLY, PAUL MCRAE, b Chester, Pa, Jan 4, 26; m 51; c 2. ASTROPHYSICS. *Educ:* McGill Univ, BSc, 47, MSc, 48; Princeton Univ, AM, 50, PhD(astrophys), 51. *Prof Exp:* Nat Res Coun Can fel, 51-53; res fel, Calif Inst Technol, 53-54; chmn dept & dir observ, 54-63, from asst prof to prof astron, Pomona Col, 54-63; exec off, Am Astron Soc, 62-68; dir div astrometry & astrophys, 68-77, HEAD EXPLOR DEVELOP STAFF, US NAVAL OBSERV, 77- *Concurrent Pos:* Vpres, Comn 38, Int Astron Union; 38; vis prof, Rutgers In-Serv Inst, 66; pres, Comn 38, Int Astron Union, 73- *Mem:* Am Astron Soc; Int Astron Union. *Res:* Astrometry; molecular spectroscopy; absolute and relative atomic transition probabilities; stellar parallaxes. *Mailing Add:* Explor Develop Staff US Naval Observ Washington DC 20390

ROUTSON, RONALD C, b Chewelah, Wash, Dec 12, 33; m 58; c 1. SOIL CHEMISTRY & MINERALOGY. *Educ:* Wash State Univ, BS, 58, PhD(soil chem), 70. *Prof Exp:* Sr res scientist & prog mgr, Battelle Pac Northwest Labs, 65-77; STAFF SCIENTIST SOIL CHEM, ROCKWELL HANFORD CO, 77- *Mem:* Am Soc Agron; Soil Sci Soc Am; Clay Minerals Soc. *Res:* Modeling the movement of radionuclides through soil systems; disposal and fate of wastes in soil. *Mailing Add:* Rockwell Hanford Co Richland WA 99352

ROUTTENBERG, ARYEH, b Reading, Pa, Dec 1, 39; m; c 2. NEUROSCIENCE. *Educ:* McGill Univ, BA, 61; Northwestern Univ, MA, 63; Univ Mich, PhD(neurosci & behav), 65. *Prof Exp:* PROF PSYCHOL & NEUROBIOL/PHYSIOL & DIR UNDERGRAD NEUROSCI PROG, COL ARTS & SCI & GRAD NEUROSCI PROG, PSYCHOL DEPT, NORTHWESTERN UNIV, 73- *Concurrent Pos:* Mem res adv bd, NIMH, 76-80. *Mem:* Neurosci Soc; Am Physiol Soc; Am Soc Neurochem; Am Asn Anatomists; Int Soc Neurochem. *Res:* Memory and learning. *Mailing Add:* Cresap Neurosci Lab 2021 Sheridan Rd Evanston IL 60201

ROUX, JACQUES F, b Geneva, Switz, Mar 27, 30; US citizen; m 53; c 3. OBSTETRICS & GYNECOLOGY. *Educ:* Col Geneva, BA, BS, 49; Geneva Med Sch, MD, PhD(med), 60; Am Bd Obstet & Gynec, dipl, 69. *Prof Exp:* Resident, Lying-in-Hosp, Geneva, 55-57; from asst resident to chief resident gynec & obstet, Jacobi Hosp & Albert Einstein Col Med, 60-64, asst prof, 64-67; assoc attend obstetrician-gynecologist, Cleveland Metrop Gen Hosp, 67; prof obstet & gynec & dir perinatal clinical ctr, Sch Med, Case Western Reserve Univ, 67-71; prof obstet & gynec & head perinatol, Univ Montreal, 71-77; dir dept obstet & gynec, St Justine Hosp, Hoteldieu, 71-77; PROF OBSTET & GYNEC, MICH STATE UNIV, 77- *Concurrent Pos:* Fel med, Boston Lying-In Hosp, 57; fel endocrinol, Free Hosp Women, Brookline, 58; vis asst prof, Okayama Med Sci, 66; attend physician obstet & gynec & dir perinatal res ctr, Cleveland Metrop Gen Hosp, 67-70, assoc osbstetrician & gynecologist, asst dir dept & dir perinatal clin res ctr, 70-71; vis scientist, NIH, San Juan, 69; consult fetal & maternal health, State Mich, 77- *Mem:* Soc Gynec Invest; Soc Study Reproduction; NY Acad Sci; Am Col Surg; Am Col Obstet & Gynec. *Res:* Fetal lipid metabolism during development; fetal monitoring; teaching; perinatology; biomedicine and biochemistry. *Mailing Add:* 316 Clin Life Sci Bldg East Lansing MI 48823

ROUX, KENNETH H, b Philadelphia, Pa, May 12, 48; m 70; c 1. IMMUNOGENTICS, IMMUNOREGULATION. *Educ:* Del Valley Col, BS, 70; Tulane Univ, MS, 72, PhD(immunol), 74. *Prof Exp:* Fel immunol, Univ Ill Med Ctr, 75-78; ASST PROF IMMUNOL, DEPT BIOL SCI, FLA STATE UNIV, 78-, DIR, HYBRIDOMA LAB, 81- *Concurrent Pos:* Prin investr, Dept Biol Sci, Fla State Univ, 79- *Mem:* Fedn Am Soc Exp Biol; Am Asn Immunologists; AAAS. *Res:* Genetics and regulation of immunoglobulin molecules; electronmicroscopy of immunoglobulin molecules; monoclonal antibody (hybridoma) production. *Mailing Add:* Dept Biol Sci Fla State Univ Tallahassee FL 32306

ROUX, STANLEY JOSEPH, b Houston, Tex, Feb 9, 42; m 75; c 2. PHOTOBIOLOGY, MEMBRANE BIOLOGY. *Educ:* Spring Hill Col, BS, 66; Loyola Univ, New Orleans, 68; Yale Univ, PhD(biol), 71. *Prof Exp:* Fel, Yale Univ, 71-73; asst prof biol, Univ Pittsburgh, 73-78; asst prof, 78-80, ASSOC PROF BOT, UNIV TEX, AUSTIN, 80- *Mem:* AAAS; Am Soc Plant Physiologists; Am Soc Photobiol. *Res:* Identifying cellular mechanisms for the control of plant growth and development by light and for the control of plant tropisms by light and gravity. *Mailing Add:* Dept Bot Univ Tex Austin TX 78712

ROUZE, STANLEY RUPLE, b Haxtun, Colo, May 15, 19; m 40; c 1. METAL PHYSICS, ELECTRON MICROSCOPY. *Educ:* Univ Colo, Boulder, BS, 49. *Prof Exp:* Mem staff electron micros, Gen Motors Res Labs, 49-58 & thermionic emission micros, 58-72, sr res physicist photoemission electron micros, 72-81; RETIRED. *Mem:* Electron Micros Soc (treas, 64-66); Int Metall Soc; Sigma Xi. *Res:* Fatigue in metals; exoelectron microscopy is used to detect fatigue before actual failure, and to study fatigue crack initiation and propagation. *Mailing Add:* 13306 Langtry San Antonio MI 78248

ROVAINEN, CARL (MARX), b Virginia, Minn, Mar 13, 39; m 66; c 3. NEUROPHYSIOLOGY. *Educ:* Calif Inst Technol, BS, 62; Harvard Univ, PhD(physiol), 67. *Prof Exp:* NIH training fel biochem, 67-68, from instr to asst prof physiol & biophys, 68-73, assoc prof, 73-79, PROF PHYSIOL & BIOPHYS, SCH MED, WASHINGTON UNIV, 79- *Concurrent Pos:* Nat Inst Neurol Dis & Stroke res grant, 73- *Mem:* Soc Neurosci; Soc Gen Physiol. *Res:* Physiological and anatomical organization of lamprey brain and spinal cord. *Mailing Add:* Dept of Physiol & Biophys Wash Univ Sch of Med St Louis MO 63110

ROVE, LOUIS CLAUDE, JR, b Milwaukee, Wis, Jan 6, 28; div; c 5. GEOLOGY. *Educ:* Colo Sch Mines, GeolE, 51. *Prof Exp:* Geologist, US Geol Surv, Climax Molybdenum Co, E J Longyear Co & Utah Construct & Mining Co, 51-66; chief geologist, Vitro Minerals Corp, 66-68; staff geologist, 68-78, DIV GEOLOGIST, MINERALS DIV, GETTY OIL CO, 78- *Mem:* Soc Econ Geologists; Am Inst Mining Engrs; Geol Soc Can. *Res:* Continental drift and its effect on the formation and location of mineral deposits. *Mailing Add:* Getty Oil Co 3810 Wilshire Blvd Los Angeles CA 90010

ROVEE, DAVID THOMAS, b Cape Girardeau, Mo, July 13, 39; m 64; c 2. BIOLOGY. *Educ:* Memphis State Univ, BS, 62; La State Univ, MS, 64; Brown Univ, PhD(biol), 67. *Prof Exp:* SR SCIENTIST, RES DIV, JOHNSON & JOHNSON, NEW BRUNSWICK, 65- *Concurrent Pos:* Lectr, Trenton State Col, 70-71; course chmn continuing med educ, Med Ctr, Univ Calif, 71- *Res:* Wound healing physiology; cell kinetics; methodology development applicable to human wound studies. *Mailing Add:* 30 Chelsea Way Bridgewater NJ 08807

ROVELSTAD, GORDON HENRY, b Elgin, Ill, May 19, 21. DENTISTRY. *Educ:* Northwestern Univ, DDS, 44, MSD, 48, PhD(dent), 60; Am Bd Pedodont, dipl. *Prof Exp:* Instr dent, Northwestern Univ, 46-49, asst prof pedodont & consult, Cleft Palate Inst, 49-53; res officer, Dent Res Lab, Dent Corps, US Navy, 54-58, head res & sci div, Dent Sch, 60-65, dir dent res, Dent Res Facil, Training Ctr, 65-67, officer in charge & sci dir, Naval Dent Res Inst, Ill, 67-69, prog mgr dent res, Dent Div, Bur Med & Surg, Washington, DC, 69-74; prof pediat dent & assoc prof physiol & biophysics, Sch Dent, Univ Miss Med Ctr, Jackson, 74-81, actg chmn, Dept Pediat Dent & assoc dean educ prog, 77-81; EXEC DIR, AM COL DENTISTS, 81- *Concurrent Pos:* chief dent staff, Children's Mem Hosp, Chicago, 49-53; consult, Herrick House Rheumatic Fever Inst, 51-53. *Mem:* AAAS; Am Soc Dent for Children; Am Dent Asn; Am Acad Pedodontics; NY Acad Sci. *Mailing Add:* Am Col Dentists 7315 Wisconsin Ave Suite 352N Bethesda MD 20014

ROVELSTAD, RANDOLPH ANDREW, b Elgin, Ill, Mar 11, 20; m 45; c 5. MEDICINE. *Educ:* St Olaf Col, BA, 40; Northwestern Univ, MD, 44; Univ Minn, PhD(med), 54. *Prof Exp:* Instr, 53-59, asst prof, 59-73, ASSOC PROF MED, MAYO MED SCH, 73- *Concurrent Pos:* Consult, Mayo Clin, 52- *Mem:* Am Gastroenterol Asn. *Res:* Gastroenterology; gastric secretion; gastric and duodenal pH; enterocutaneous potentials; Composition of ascitic fluid. *Mailing Add:* Mayo Clin Rochester MN 55901

ROVERA, GIOVANNI, b Cocconato, Italy, Sept, 23, 40; m 79; c 1. HEMATHOLOGY. *Educ:* Univ Torino, Italy, MD, 64. *Prof Exp:* Fel biochem, Fels Inst, 68-70; resident path, Temple Univ, 70-73, asst prof, 73-75; assoc prof, 75-78, PROF CANCER RES, WISTAR INST, 79- *Concurrent Pos:* Scholar, Leukemia Soc Am, 74-79; mem, Molecular Biol Grad Group, Univ Pa, 77-; assoc ed, J Cellular Physiol, 78- *Res:* Proliferation and differentiation of leukemia cells; expression of globin genes; mechanisms of tumor pomotion. *Mailing Add:* Wistar Inst 3601 Spruce St Philadelphia PA 19104

ROVETTO, MICHAEL JULIEN, b Challis, Idaho, Mar 20, 43; m 67; c 2. PHYSIOLOGY, BIOCHEMISTRY. *Educ:* Utah State Univ, BS, 65; Univ Idaho, MS, 68; Univ Va, PhD(physiol), 70. *Prof Exp:* Res assoc physiol, Hershey Med Ctr, Pa State Univ, 71-73, asst prof, 73-74; from asst prof to assoc prof physiol, Jefferson Med Col, 74-80; ASSOC PROF PHYSIOL, SCH MED, UNIV MO, 80- *Concurrent Pos:* NIH fel, Hershey Med Ctr, Pa State Univ, 70-71. *Mem:* Am Physiol Soc; Biophys Soc; Cardiac Muscle Soc; Int Soc Heart Res. *Res:* Myocardial energy metabolism; regulation of cardiovascular function; adenine nucleotide metabolism. *Mailing Add:* Dept of Physiol Sch Med Univ Mo Columbia MO 65212

ROVICK, ALLEN ASHER, b Chicago, Ill, Feb 11, 28; m 49; c 4. PHYSIOLOGY. *Educ:* Roosevelt Univ, BS, 51; Univ Ill, MS, 54, PhD(physiol), 58. *Prof Exp:* Instr physiol, Stritch Sch Med, Loyola Univ Chicago, 58-59, assoc, 59, from asst prof to assoc prof, 66-67; Univ Ill Proj, Thailand, 67-68; assoc prof physiol, Univ Ill Med Sch, 69-70; exec secy cardiovasc study sect, Div Res Grants, NIH, 70-71, chief cardiac dis br, Nat Heart & Lung Inst, 71-72; ASSOC PROF BIOMED ENG, COL HEALTH SCI, RUSH UNIV, 75- *Mem:* AAAS; Am Physiol Soc; Am Heart Asn. *Res:* Metabolic control of local blood circulation; influence of hemodynamics on tissue water partition; local control of blood flow; effect of arterial pulse on blood flow. *Mailing Add:* Dept of Physiol Rush-Presby-St Lukes Med Ctr Chicago IL 60612

ROVIT, RICHARD LEE, b Boston, Mass, Apr 3, 24; m 53; c 3. NEUROSURGERY. *Educ:* Jefferson Med Col, MD, 50; McGill Univ, MSc, 61; Am Bd Neurol Surg, dipl, 62. *Prof Exp:* Asst neurosurgeon, Montreal Neurol Inst, 60-61; assoc prof & surgeon, Jefferson Med Col & Hosp, 61-66, head div neurosurg, 61-65; assoc prof neurosurg, 66-71, PROF CLIN NEUROSURG, SCH MED, NY UNIV, 71-; DIR DEPT, ST VINCENT'S HOSP, NEW YORK & ATTEND NEUROSURGEON, UNIV HOSP, NEW YORK, 66- *Concurrent Pos:* Consult, US Vet Admin Hosps, Philadelphia, 62-64 & Coatesville, 62-66; chief sect neurosurg, Philadelphia Gen Hosp, New York, Columbus Hosp & St Vincent's Hosp. *Mem:* AAAS; Am Acad Neurol; Am Epilepsy Soc; Asn Res Nerv & Ment Dis; Am Asn Neurol Surg. *Res:* Surgery of epilepsy and neuroendocrinology. *Mailing Add:* Dept Neurosurg NY Univ Sch Med New York NY 10016

ROVNER, DAVID RICHARD, b Philadelphia, Pa, Sept 20, 30. ENDOCRINOLOGY, METABOLISM. *Educ:* Temple Univ, AB, 51, MD, 55. *Prof Exp:* Intern, San Francisco Hosp, Univ Calif Serv, 55-56; resident med, Med Ctr, Univ Mich, 56-57; internist radiobiol, US Air Force Sch Avaition Med, 57-59; resident med, Med Ctr, Univ Mich, 59-60, from fel to prof endocrinol & metab, 60-71; vchmn dept med, 71-80, PROF ENDOCRINOL & METAB, COL HUMAN MED, MICH STATE UNIV, 71-, CHIEF DIV ENDROCRINOL & METAB, 80- *Mem:* Endocrine Soc; Am Fedn Clin Res; fel Am Col Physicians; Am Soc Nephrology; Cent Soc Clin Res. *Res:* Decision analysis as applied to clinical medicine; endocrine hypertension; control of aldosterone biosynthesis; sodium and potassium metabolism control. *Mailing Add:* 8220 Life Sci Mich State Univ East Lansing MI 48824

ROVNER, JEROME SYLVAN, b Baltimore, Md, July 15, 40; m 62; c 1. ARACHNOLOGY, ANIMAL BEHAVIOR. *Educ:* Univ Md, BS, 62, PhD(zool), 66. *Prof Exp:* NSF fel zool, Univ Mainz, 66-67; asst prof, 67-71, assoc prof, 71-77, PROF ZOOL, OHIO UNIV, 77- *Concurrent Pos:* Res grant, NSF, 72 & 74. *Mem:* AAAS; Animal Behav Soc; Am Arachnological Soc; Sigma Xi; Brit Arachnological Soc. *Res:* Predatory behavior in wandering spiders; acoustic communication in wolf spiders. *Mailing Add:* Dept of Zool Ohio Univ Athens OH 45701

ROVNYAK, GEORGE CHARLES, b Ford City, Pa, Jan 31, 41; m 63; c 3. MEDICINAL CHEMISTRY, ORGANIC CHEMISTRY. *Educ:* St Vincent Col, AB, 62; Univ Pittsburgh, BS, 65, PhD(chem), 70. *Prof Exp:* Chemist, Neville Chem Co, 63-66; res investr, 70-80, SR RES INVESTR MED CHEM, E R SQUIBB & SONS, INC, 80- *Mem:* Am Chem Soc; NY Acad Sci; Sigma Xi. *Res:* Synthesis and structure-activity relationship of biologically active organic compounds; reaction mechanisms; application of small ring compounds to chemical synthesis; heterocyclic chemistry. *Mailing Add:* E R Squibb & Sons Inc Box 4000 Princeton NJ 08540

ROVNYAK, JAMES L, b Ford City, Pa, Jan 9, 39; m 63; c 2. MATHEMATICS. *Educ:* Lafayette Col, AB, 60; Yale Univ, MA, 62, PhD(math), 63. *Prof Exp:* Asst prof math, Purdue Univ, 63-67; assoc prof, 67-73, PROF MATH, UNIV VA, 73- *Concurrent Pos:* NSF fel, Inst Advan Study, 66-67; Alexander von Humboldt Award, US Sr Scientist, Fed Repub Ger, 79. *Mem:* Am Math Soc. *Res:* Hilbert space; complex analysis. *Mailing Add:* Dept of Math Univ of Va Charlottesville VA 22904

ROW, CLARK, b Washington, DC, July 24, 34; m 72. FOREST ECONOMICS. *Educ:* Yale Univ, BS, 56; Duke Univ, MF, 58; Tulane Univ La, PhD(econ), 73. *Prof Exp:* Res forester, Southern Forest Exp Sta, US Forest Serv, 58-62; proj leader forest prod & mkt res, 62-65; chief, Forest Prods Demand & Price Anal Br, 65-67, chief, Forest Econ Br, 68-75, LEADER, EVAL METHODS RES GROUP, US FOREST SERV, 75- *Concurrent Pos:* Spec lectr, Duke Univ, 81. *Mem:* Am Econ Asn; Soc Am Foresters. *Res:* Economics of forest, range, watershed outdoor recreation wilderness management; pest control economics; demand for forest products; economics of forest products industries. *Mailing Add:* Forest Econ Res USDA Forest Serv PO Box 2417 Washington DC 20013

ROW, THOMAS HENRY, b Blacksburg, Va, Feb 9, 35; m 75; c 4. NUCLEAR ENGINEERING. *Educ:* Roanoke Col, BS, 57; Va Polytech Inst & State Univ, MS, 59. *Prof Exp:* Instr math, Roanoke Col, 57; res staff, 59-67, nat prog coordr, Reactor Containment Spray Syst Prog, Atomic Energy Comn, 67-71, dir, Environ Statements Proj, 71-75, head, Environ Impact Sect, Energy Div, 75-81, DIR, NUCLEAR WASTE PROG, OAK RIDGE NAT LAB, 81- *Concurrent Pos:* Consult, Adv Comt Reactor Safeguards, US Atomic Energy Comn, 68-71; mem Standard Comt, Am Nat Standards Inst, 71-72. *Mem:* Nat Asn Environ Prof; Am Nuclear Soc. *Res:* Nuclear waste. *Mailing Add:* Oak Ridge Nat Lab Oak Ridge TN 37830

ROWAN, DIGHTON FRANCIS, b Amsterdam, NY, Dec 31, 14; m. MEDICAL VIROLOGY. *Educ:* San Jose State Col, BA, 48; Stanford Univ, MA, 53, PhD(bact & exp path), 54. *Prof Exp:* Instr microbiol virol, Stanford Univ Sch Med, 53-56; instr epidemiol, Sch Trop Med & Pub Health, Tulane Univ, 56-57; asst prof microbiol & virol, Sch Med, Univ Vt, 57-59; prin virologist develop & res, NJ State Dept Health, 59-61; dir virol lab, Mont State Bd Health, 61-63; prof dir virol dept, Col Dent, Baylor Univ & Med Ctr, 63-73; PROF DIR MICROBIOL VIROL, ADV MICROBIOL INFECTIOUS DIS DIV, SCH MED, SOUTHERN ILL UNIV, 73- *Honors & Awards:* Sect Award, Am Pub Health Asn, 61; Outstanding Serv in Educ Recognition Award, Am Soc Clin Pathologists, 68. *Mem:* Fel Am Acad Microbiol; fel Am Pub Health Asn; Am Soc Microbiol; AAAS; Sigma Xi. *Res:* The role of the herpesviruses in vulvitis; birth defects and sudden infant death; role of coxsackieviruses in adult myocarditis and pericarditis; respiratory disease and encephalitis surveillance. *Mailing Add:* 2313 Westchester Blvd Springfield IL 62704

ROWAN, NANCY STILES, b Plainfield, NJ, Apr 6, 46; wid; c 2. INORGANIC CHEMISTRY. *Educ:* Mt Holyoke Col, AB, 68; Boston Univ, PhD(inorg chem), 74. *Prof Exp:* Vis asst prof chem, Carnegie-Mellon Univ, 73-74; ASST PROF CHEM, AM UNIV, 78- *Mem:* Am Chem Soc. *Res:* Kinetics of transition metal reactions; models for metal binding sites in proteins. *Mailing Add:* Dept of Chem Am Univ Washington DC 20016

ROWAN, ROBERT, III, nuclear magnetic resonance, deceased

ROWAN, SAMUEL JAMES, forest pathology, plant physiology, see previous edition

ROWAND, WILL H, b 1908. ENGINEERING. *Educ:* Cornell Univ, ME, 29. *Prof Exp:* Mem staff, Babcock & Wilcox, 29-48, chem engr, 48-53, vpres eng, 53-61, vpres mkt, 61-66, vpres nuclear power, 66-72; RETIRED. *Honors & Awards:* Newcomen Medal, 54. *Mem:* Nat Acad Eng; fel Am Soc Mech Engrs. *Mailing Add:* PO Box 6485 Litchfield Park AZ 85340

ROWE, ALLEN MCGHEE, JR, b Columbus, Ohio, May 15, 32. THERMODYNAMICS. *Educ:* Ohio State Univ, BPetrolEng & MS, 56; Univ Tex, PhD(petrol eng), 64. *Prof Exp:* Jr engr, Texaco, Inc, 56-57, res engr, 57-58; res engr, Esso Prod Res Co, 58-61 & Tex Petrol Res Comt, 61-64; asst prof petrol eng, Okla State Univ, 64-71, assoc prof mech eng, 71-76; SR RES ENGR, ATLANTIC RICHFIELD CO, 76- *Concurrent Pos:* Consult, Continental Oil Co, Okla, 64; Intercomp, Tex, 71 & Marathon Oil Co, 74; NASA fel, 67 & 68; lectr, Stanford Univ, 74. *Mem:* Inst Mining, Metall & Petrol Engrs. *Res:* Calculation of equilibrium compositions of hydrocarbon mixtures; desalination research. *Mailing Add:* Atlantic Richfield Co PO Box 2819 Dallas TX 75221

ROWE, ANNE PRINE, b Detroit, Mich, Feb 1, 27; m 50; c 2. PHYSICAL CHEMISTRY. *Educ:* Univ Mich, BS, 50, MS, 68, PhD(mat eng), 73. *Prof Exp:* Asst res chem, Chem Dept, Univ Mich, 61-68, res assoc, Lab Metall & Mat Eng, 68-71, sr res assoc dent mat, 71-75; res mat engr, NASA Lewis Res Ctr, 76-78; ASSOC PROF MECH ENG, FLA INST TECHNOL, 79- *Concurrent Pos:* Mat engr, NASA Kennedy Space Ctr, 80- *Mem:* Am Soc Metals; Electron Micros Soc Am; Am Vacuum Soc; Soc Women Engrs. *Res:* Electon metallography of a cobalt-chromium-nickel-tantalum alloy; dental amalgams; corrosion and erosion of superalloys for application in a pressurized fluidized bed coal combustor and turbine combined cycle system; corrosion testing of candidate paint systems for resistance to marine environment corrosion of ground support systems. *Mailing Add:* Mech Eng Dept Fla Inst Technol Melbourne FL 32901

ROWE, ARTHUR WILSON, b Newark, NJ, Sept 14, 31; m 57; c 2. BIOCHEMISTRY, CRYOBIOLOGY. *Educ:* Duke Univ, AB, 53; Rutgers Univ, PhD, 60. *Prof Exp:* Asst chem, Rutgers Univ, 57, 58-60; res chemist, Linde Div, Union Carbide Corp, 60-64; INVESTR & HEAD LAB CRYOBIOL, NY BLOOD CTR, 64-; ASSOC PROF, SCH MED, NY UNIV, 69- *Concurrent Pos:* Consult, Acute Leukemia Task Force, Nat Cancer Inst, 62-66; consult, Lab Exp Med & Surg in Primates, Sch Med, NY Univ, 67-; assoc ed, J Cryobiol, 72-73, ed-in-chief, 73- *Mem:* Fel AAAS; Am Chem Soc; Soc Cryobiol (treas, 69-72, vpres, 73-76, gov, 76-); fel Am Inst Chemists; Transplantation Soc; NY Acad Sci. *Res:* Low temperature preservation of bone marrow, blood, leukocytes, platelets and tissues; cryobiology; cellular metabolism and isotopic techniques; immunohematology; cryogenics. *Mailing Add:* Lab of Cryobiol NY Blood Ctr 310 E 67th St New York NY 10021

ROWE, CARLETON NORWOOD, b Halifax, Pa, Apr 1, 28; m 56; c 3. PHYSICAL CHEMISTRY. *Educ:* Juniata Col, BS, 51; Pa State Univ, MS, 53, PhD(phys chem), 55. *Prof Exp:* Res chemist, Tex Co, 55-60; sr res chemist, 60-65, res assoc, Princeton, 65-80, RES ASSOC, MOBIL RES & DEVELOP CORP, PAULSBORO, NJ, 81- *Mem:* Am Chem Soc; fel Am Soc Lubrication Engrs; Soc Automotive Engrs. *Res:* Lubrication; friction and wear; additive chemistry; contact fatigue. *Mailing Add:* 7 E Sch Lane Yardley PA 19067

ROWE, CHARLES DAVID, b Winchester, Ind, Dec 6, 39; m 61; c 1. POLYMER CHEMISTRY. *Educ:* Purdue Univ, BS, 61, MS, 64; Univ Mich, PhD(chem), 69. *Prof Exp:* Group leader plastics, Rohm & Haas Co, 68-72; MGR POLYMER PROD ADHESIVES, DAUBERT CHEM CO, 72- *Mem:* Am Chem Soc. *Mailing Add:* Daubert Chem Co 4700 S Central Ave Chicago IL 60638

ROWE, CLEMENT E, b Maryborough, Ireland, Nov 29, 11; US citizen; m 43; c 2. CHEMICAL ENGINEERING. *Educ:* Univ Ill, BSc, 35. *Prof Exp:* Prod engr, Monsanto Chem Co, 35-42, tech adv, Monsanto Pty, Ltd, Australia, 43, res group leader, Monsanto Chem Co, US, 44-45, actg chief chem engr, Monsanto Chem, Ltd, Brit, 45-48, staff engr, Monsanto Chem Co, US, 49; mgr prod coord, Mathieson Hydrocarbon Chem Co, 50-54, dir res & develop, 55-56; dir develop, Org Div, Olin Corp, 57-62, tech mgr, Doe Run Works, 63-76; CONSULT INDUST CHEM TECHNOL, 76- *Mem:* Am Chem Soc; Am Inst Chem Engrs; Brit Inst Chem Engrs. *Res:* Technical development of chemical processes and the design and operation of economical and commercial manufacturing plants, principally in the production of organic chemical products. *Mailing Add:* 929 Dontaos Dr St Louis MO 63131

ROWE, DAVID JOHN, b Totnes, Eng, Feb 4, 36; m 58; c 2. PHYSICS. *Educ:* Cambridge Univ, BA, 59; Oxford Univ, BA, 59, MA & DPhil(nuclear physics), 62. *Prof Exp:* Ford Found fel, Niels Bohr Inst, Copenhagen, Denmark, 62-63; UK Atomic Energy Authority res fel, Atomic Energy Res Estab, Harwell, Eng, 63-65; res assoc, Univ Rochester, 65-68; assoc prof, 68-74, PROF PHYSICS & ASSOC CHMN DEPT, UNIV TORONTO, 74- *Concurrent Pos:* Alfred P Sloan Found fel, 70; vis prof, Univ Sao Paulo, 71-72. *Mem:* Can Asn Physicists. *Res:* Theory of nuclear structure and reactions; collective motion; group theory. *Mailing Add:* Dept Physics Univ Toronto Toronto ON M5S 1A7 Can

ROWE, DONALD R, b Vantage, Sask, Oct 12, 26; m 45; c 2. CIVIL ENGINEERING, ENVIRONMENTAL ENGINEERING. *Educ:* Univ Sask, BS, 48; Univ Tex, MS, 62, PhD(civil eng), 65. *Prof Exp:* Dist engr, Dept Hwy, Sask, 48-53, spec proj engr, 53-55, chief munic engr, Munic Rd Auth, 55-56, dir rd prog, 56-57; pres, D R Rowe Eng Serv, Ltd, 57-61; assoc prof environ eng, Tulane Univ, 64-69; PROF ENG TECHNOL, WESTERN KY UNIV, BOWLING GREEN, 69- *Concurrent Pos:* Dir, Larox Corp. *Honors & Awards:* Fulbright-Hayes Award, Ege Univ, Turkey, 80. *Mem:* Am Soc Civil Engrs; Am Water Works Asn; Water Pollution Control Fedn. *Res:* Radiological health; water and waste water treatment; air pollution control. *Mailing Add:* Dept Indust Eng Technol Western Ky Univ Bowling Green KY 42101

ROWE, EDWARD BARRY, b Navasota, Tex, Oct 8, 20; m 43; c 1. SURGERY. *Educ:* Southern Methodist Univ, BA, 41; Univ Tex, MD, 44. *Prof Exp:* Instr, 51-53, from instr to asst prof, 51-69, ASSOC PROF SURG, UNIV TEX MED BR, GALVESTON, 69- *Mem:* AMA; Am Col Surg; Am Asn Surg of Trauma. *Mailing Add:* Dept of Surg Univ of Tex Med Br Galveston TX 77550

ROWE, EDWARD C, b Oakland, Calif, Dec 23, 33; m 55; c 3. NEUROPHYSIOLOGY. *Educ:* Wesleyan Univ, BA, 55; Univ Mich, MS, 57, PhD(zool), 64. *Prof Exp:* Assoc prof, 61-73, PROF BIOL, EMPORIA STATE UNIV, 73- *Concurrent Pos:* NIH res grant physiol ganglia, 66-71. *Mem:* AAAS; Am Soc Zool. *Res:* Comparative neurophysiology. *Mailing Add:* Dept of Biol Emporia State Univ Emporia KS 66802

ROWE, EDWARD JOHN, b Racine, Wis, Dec 28, 10; m 43. PHARMACY. *Educ:* Univ Wis, BS, 37, PhD(pharm), 41. *Prof Exp:* From asst prof to assoc prof, 41-45, PROF PHARM & HEAD DEPT, COL PHARM, BUTLER UNIV, 45- *Mem:* Acad Pharmaceut Sci. *Res:* Pharmaceutical chemistry and dispensing. *Mailing Add:* 5332 Brendonridge Rd Indianapolis IN 46226

ROWE, ELIZABETH SNOW, b Seattle, Wash, Dec 28, 43; m 66; c 2. PHYSICAL BIOCHEMISTRY. *Educ:* Duke Univ, BA, 66, PhD(biochem), 71. *Prof Exp:* Fel calorimetry, Med Sch, Johns Hopkins Univ, 71-72; res assoc elec birefringence, Georgetown Univ, 72-75; fel membrane phys chem, Chem Dept, Johns Hopkins Univ, 76-77; asst prof biochem, Univ Kans Med Sch, 77-78; DIR, MOLECULAR MECH ALCOHOLISM LAB, KANSAS CITY VET ADMIN MED CTR, 78- *Concurrent Pos:* Adj asst prof biochem, Med Sch, Univ Kans, 80- *Mem:* Sigma Xi. *Res:* Physical properties of membrane components; effect of anesthetics on membranes; thermodynamics of protein structure and function. *Mailing Add:* Phys Biochem Res Lab Vet Admin Med Ctr 4801 Linwood Blvd Kansas City MO 64128

ROWE, ENGLEBERT L, b Highland Park, Mich, Dec 18, 25; m 49; c 5. PHYSICAL PHARMACY. *Educ:* Wayne State Univ, BS, 50, MS, 58. *Prof Exp:* Chemist, City of Dearborn, 49-53 & Minn Mining Mfg Co, 53-58; RES ASSOC PROD RES & DEVELOP, UPJOHN CO, 58- *Mem:* Am Chem Soc; Am Pharmaceut Asn; Sigma Xi; Acad Pharmaceut Sci. *Res:* Coagulation of colloids; kinetics of drug degradation; surface tension measurement and correlation with drug activity; sustained action dosage forms; particle size and surface area of emulsions and solids. *Mailing Add:* Upjohn Co Kalamazoo MI 49001

ROWE, GEORGE G, b Vulcan, Alta, May 17, 21; nat US; m 47; c 3. INTERNAL MEDICINE. *Educ:* Univ Wis, BA, 43, MD, 45; Am Bd Internal Med, dipl, 55; Am Bd Cardiovasc Dis, dipl, 69. *Prof Exp:* Instr anat, Sch Med, Wash Univ, 48-50; resident, Med Sch, Univ Wis, 50-52, res assoc med, 54-55; voluntary res assoc, Hammersmith Hosp, London, 56-57; from asst prof to assoc prof, 57-64, PROF MED, MED SCH, UNIV WIS, MADISON, 64- *Concurrent Pos:* Am Heart Asn fel, Univ Wis, 52-54; Markle scholar, 55-60. *Mem:* Am Physiol Soc; Am Soc Pharmacol & Exp Therapeut; fel Am Col Physicians; Am Fedn Clin Res; Am Soc Clin Invest. *Res:* Hemodynamics of the systemic and coronary circulations; congenital and acquired heart disease. *Mailing Add:* Dept of Med Med Sch Univ Wis 600 N Highland Ave Madison WI 53792

ROWE, GILBERT THOMAS, biological oceanography, see previous edition

ROWE, H(ARRISON) E(DWARD), b Chicago, Ill, Jan 29, 27; m 51; c 4. ELECTRICAL ENGINEERING. *Educ:* Mass Inst Technol, BS, 48, MS, 50, ScD(elec eng), 52. *Prof Exp:* MEM TECH STAFF, BELL TEL LABS, INC, 52- *Concurrent Pos:* Mem comn 6, Int Union Radio Sci; vis lectr, Univ Calif, Berkeley, 63 & Imperial Col, Univ London, 68 & 81. *Honors & Awards:* David Sarnoff Award, Inst Elec & Electronics Engrs, 77. *Mem:* Fel Inst Elec & Electronics Engrs; Sigma Xi. *Res:* Communications systems; wave guides; optical communication systems. *Mailing Add:* Bell Tel Labs Inc Box 400 Holmdel NJ 07733

ROWE, IRVING, b Brooklyn, NY, Nov 1, 13; m 39; c 3. PHYSICS, ELECTRONICS. *Educ:* Columbia Univ, BS, 34, BS, 35, EE, 36; Polytech Inst Brooklyn, PhD(physics), 57. *Prof Exp:* Inspection engr, Signal Corps, US Army, 36-45; prog planning engr, Watson Labs, US Air Force, 45-46; phys sci adminr, Off Naval Res, 46-75, dep chief scientist, 75-80; RETIRED. *Concurrent Pos:* Instr, Polytech Inst Brooklyn, 60-66. *Honors & Awards:* Superior Accomplishment Award, US Dept Navy, 63. *Mem:* Am Phys Soc; Inst Elec & Electronics Engrs. *Res:* X-ray diffraction; laser physics. *Mailing Add:* 35 Ridge Dr Port Washington NY 11050

ROWE, JAMES LINCOLN, b Chicago, Ill, Nov 14, 17; m 48; c 3. ORGANIC CHEMISTRY. *Educ:* Princeton Univ, BA, 39; Univ Chicago, PhD(org chem), 46; Ind Univ, DJ, 68. *Prof Exp:* Chemist, Nat Defense Res Comt, Univ Chicago, 42 & Off Sci Res & Develop, 44-46; res chemist, 46-54, patent agent, 54-68; PATENT ATTORNEY, ELI LILLY & CO, 68- *Mem:* AAAS; Am Chem Soc. *Res:* Mechanisms of organic reactions; free radical reactions; synthesis of synthetic drugs; war gases; nitrogen mustards; decomposition of di-acetyl peroxide in alcohols. *Mailing Add:* Eli Lilly & Co 307 E McCarty St Indianapolis IN 46285

ROWE, JAY ELWOOD, b Tacoma, Wash, Jan 10, 47; m 65; c 3. INDUSTRIAL ORGANIC CHEMISTRY. *Educ:* Bucknell Univ, BS, 68; Lehigh Univ, PhD(org chem), 73. *Prof Exp:* Instr chem, Muhlenberg Col, 72-73, asst prof, 73-74; RES ASSOC, CROMPTON & KNOWLES CORP, 74- *Mem:* Am Chem Soc; Am Asn Textile Chemists & Colorists; Sigma Xi. *Res:* Chemistry and theory of acid dyes. *Mailing Add:* Crompton & Knowles Corp PO Box 341 Reading PA 19601

ROWE, JOHN EDWARD, b Jacksonville, Fla, Sept 25, 41; m 65; c 3. SURFACE PHYSICS, EXPERIMENTAL SOLID STATE PHYSICS. *Educ:* Emory Univ, BS, 63; Brown Univ, PhD(physics), 71. *Prof Exp:* Mem tech staff, 69-80, RES HEAD SURFACE PHYSICS, BELL LABS, 80- *Concurrent Pos:* Mem, Synchrotron Users Exec Comt, Brookhaven Nat Lab. *Mem:* Am Phys Soc; Am Vacuum Soc. *Res:* Electron spectroscopy on surfaces and bulk solids using photoemission, electron energy loss and Auger spectroscopies; low energy electron diffraction; studies of chemisorption and of film growth; synchrotron radiation. *Mailing Add:* Rm 1C-318 Bell Labs Murray Hill NJ 07974

ROWE, JOHN JAMES, b Washington, DC, Aug 12, 44; m 68; c 1. MICROBIAL BIOCHEMISTRY, MICROBIAL ECOLOGY. *Educ:* Colo State Univ, BS, 67; Ariz State Univ, MS, 71; Univ Kans, PhD(microbiol), 75. *Prof Exp:* Fel microbiol, Dept Biol, Univ Ga, 75-77; ASST PROF MICROBIOL, DEPT BIOL, UNIV DAYTON, 77- *Mem:* Sigma Xi; Am Soc Microbiol. *Res:* Physiological and genetic studies of sporeforming thermophilic bacteria; physiological studies of bacteria in the genus Pseudomonas; denitrification; microbial differentiation; inorganic nitrogen metabolism; antimicrobial agents produced by Pseudomanas aeruginosa. *Mailing Add:* Dept Biol Univ Dayton Dayton OH 45469

ROWE, JOHN MICHAEL, b Oakville, Ont, Apr 9, 39. SOLID STATE PHYSICS. *Educ:* Queen's Univ, Ont, BSc, 62; McMaster Univ, PhD(solid state physics), 66. *Prof Exp:* Fel physics, Argonne Nat Lab, 66-67, asst staff physicist, 67-72, assoc physicist, 72-73; RES PHYSICIST, NAT BUR STANDARDS, 73- *Mem:* AAAS; Am Phys Soc. *Res:* Study of lattice and liquid dynamics by slow neutron scattering. *Mailing Add:* Nat Bur Standards Washington DC 20234

ROWE, JOHN STANLEY, b Hardisty, Alta, June 11, 18; m 54; c 2. PLANT ECOLOGY. *Educ:* Univ Alta, BSc, 41; Univ Nebr, MSc, 48; Univ Man, PhD(ecol), 56. *Prof Exp:* Forest ecologist, Can Dept Forestry, 48-67; PROF PLANT ECOL, UNIV SASK, 67- *Mem:* Can Inst Forestry; Can Bot Asn; Ecol Soc Am. *Res:* Ecology of northern Canada; boreal forest, tundra and peatlands. *Mailing Add:* Dept of Plant Ecol Univ of Sask Saskatoon SK S7N 0W0 Can

ROWE, JOHN WESTEL, b New York, NY, Sept 3, 24; m 49; c 3. WOOD CHEMISTRY. *Educ:* Mass Inst Technol, BS, 48; Univ Colo, MS, 52; Swiss Fed Inst Technol, Zurich, ScD(org chem), 56. *Prof Exp:* PROJ LEADER, FOREST PRODS LAB, USDA, 57- *Concurrent Pos:* Mem, Nat Acad Sci Corrim Comt, 74-75. *Mem:* AAAS; Soc Econ Bot Am Chem Soc; Phytochem Soc NAm; Am Inst Chemists; fel Int Acad Wood Sci. *Res:* Natural products, especially extractives of wood and bark; higher terpenoids and steroids; improved chemical utilization of wood. *Mailing Add:* Forest Prod Lab USDA Madison WI 53705

ROWE, JOSEPH E(VERETT), b Highland Park, Mich, June 4, 27; m 50; c 2. ELECTRICAL & COMPUTER ENGINEERING. *Educ:* Univ Mich, BSE(elec eng) & BSE(math), 51, MSE, 52, PhD(elec eng), 55. *Prof Exp:* Asst, Electron Tube Lab, Eng Res Inst, Univ Mich, Ann Arbor, 51-53, lectr, 52-55, res assoc, 53-55, dir electron physics lab, 58-68, from asst prof to prof elec eng, 55-74, chmn dept elec & comput eng, 68-74; vprovost & dean eng, Case Inst Technol, 74-76, provost, 76-78; vpres technol, 78-81, VPRES & GEN MGR, HARRIS CONTROLS DIV, HARRIS CORP, 81- *Honors & Awards:* Curtis W McGraw Res Award, Am Soc Eng Educ, 64. *Mem:* Nat Acad Eng; fel Inst Elec & Electronics Engrs; Am Phys Soc; Am Soc Eng Educ; fel AAAS. *Res:* Microwave circuits; traveling-wave tubes; crossed-field devices; electromagnetic field theory; noise; masers; lasers; solid state devices; plasmas. *Mailing Add:* Harris Corp Melbourne FL 32919

ROWE, KENNETH EUGENE, b Canon City, Colo, Feb 8, 34; m 70; c 4. EXPERIMENTAL STATISTICS, BIOMETRY. *Educ:* Colo State Univ, BS, 57; NC State Univ, MS, 60; Iowa State Univ, PhD(animal breeding), 66. *Prof Exp:* Geneticist, Regional Swine Breeding Lab, USDA, Ames, Iowa, 61-64; from asst prof to assoc prof exp statist, 64-70, assoc prof, 70-80, PROF STATIST, ORE STATE UNIV, 80- *Concurrent Pos:* NSF fac develop fel, NC State Univ, 69-70; sr statist adv, Special Studies Staff, IERL, US Environ Protection Agency, NC, 78-79. *Mem:* Biomet Soc; Am Statist Asn; Sigma Xi. *Res:* Applications of statistics, particularly biological problems and quantitative genetics; statistical computation. *Mailing Add:* Dept of Statist Ore State Univ Corvallis OR 97331

ROWE, LEONARD C, b Dearborn, Mich, Jan 22, 22; m 44; c 3. CORROSION. *Educ:* Mich State Univ, BS, 43, MS, 47. *Prof Exp:* Jr anal chemist, 48-49, res chemist, 49-54, sr res chemist, 54-73, supvr res chemist, 73-77, dept res scientist, 77-81, SR STAFF RES SCIENTIST, RES LABS, GEN MOTORS CORP, 81- *Concurrent Pos:* Hon mem, Am Soc Testing & Mats, 81. *Honors & Awards:* Citation of Recognition, Nat Asn Corrosion Engr, 73, R A Brannon Award, 76; D H Green Award, Am Soc Testing & Mat, 74; Award of Merit, 76. *Mem:* Nat Asn Corrosion Engr (vpres-elect, 76-77, pres 77-78); Am Chem Soc; hon mem Am Soc Testing & Mat. *Res:* Inhibition of engine coolants; prevention of automobile corrosion; study of metals corrosion. *Mailing Add:* Phys Chem Dept Gen Motors Res Labs Warren MI 48090

ROWE, MARK J, b Oakland, Calif, July 16, 43; m 66; c 5. BIOCHEMISTRY. *Educ:* Brigham Young Univ, BS, 68, PhD(biochem), 72. *Prof Exp:* Fel molecular biol, Stanford Univ, 72-73; asst prof, 73-78, ASSOC PROF BIOCHEM, EASTERN VA MED SCH, 78- *Concurrent Pos:* NIH fel, Dept Biol, Stanford Univ, 72-73. *Mem:* Am Chem Soc; AAAS; Sigma Xi. *Res:* Nucleic acids; Protein biosynthesis; mitochondrial membrane biogenesis, protein synthesis and genetics and biochemical genetics; ovarian molecular endocrinology. *Mailing Add:* Dept of Biochem Eastern Va Med Sch Box 1980 Norfolk VA 23507

ROWE, MARVIN W, b Amarillo, Tex, July 6, 37; m 57; c 4. NUCLEAR GEOCHEMISTRY. *Educ:* NMex Inst Mining & Technol, BS, 59; Univ Ark, PhD(chem), 66. *Prof Exp:* Res asst radioactiv, Los Alamos Sci Lab, 60-63; Miller res fel physics, Univ Calif, Berkeley, 66-68; asst prof chem, Univ Wash, 68-69; asst prof, 69-75, ASSOC PROF CHEM, TEX A&M UNIV, 75- *Mem:* AAAS; Am Geophys Union; fel Meteoritical Soc; Int Asn Geochem & Cosmochem; Geochem Soc. *Res:* Radioactivity, magnetism and noble gas mass spectrometry in meteorites; chronology of early solar system; effect of magnetism on reaction rates. meteoritics. *Mailing Add:* Dept of Chem Tex A&M Univ College Station TX 77843

ROWE, MARY BUDD, b Jersey City, NJ, Mar 24, 25. SCIENCE EDUCATION. *Educ:* NJ State Col Montclair, BA, 47; Univ Calif, Berkeley, MA, 55; Stanford Univ, PhD(sci educ), 64. *Prof Exp:* Teacher, Am High Sch, Munich Ger, 55-58; sonsult, Colo State Dept Educ, 59-61; lectr sci educ, Stanford Univ, 64-65; assoc prof sci, Teachers Col, Columbia Univ, 65-72; assoc prof, 72-73, PROF SCI EDUC, INST DEVELOP HUMAN RESOURCES, UNIV FLA, 73- *Concurrent Pos:* Fel, Univ Fla, 70-71; prog dir, RISF, NSF, 78-80. *Honors & Awards:* Outstanding Res Award in Sci Educ, Nat Asn Res Sci Teaching, 74. *Mem:* Fel AAAS; Nat Asn Res Sci Teaching; Nat Sci Teachers Asn; Am Educ Res Asn; Sigma Xi. *Res:* Influence of pausing phenomena on quality of enquiry; rewards as a factor in inquiry; relation of science to fate control orientations. *Mailing Add:* Inst Develop Human Resources Univ of Fla Gainesville FL 32611

ROWE, NATHANIEL H, b Hibbing, Minn, May 26, 31; div; c 4. ORAL PATHOLOGY. *Educ:* Univ Minn, BS, DDS, 55, MSD, 58; Am Bd Oral Path, dipl. *Prof Exp:* Instr, Univ Minn, 58-59; from asst prof to assoc prof gen & oral path, Sch Dent, Wash chmn Univ & chmn dept, 59-69; assoc prof path, 69-76, assoc dir, Dent Res Inst, 70-77, PROF DENT & ORAL PATH, SCH DENT, UNIV MICH, ANN ARBOR, 68-, PROF PATH, SCH MED, 76-SR RES SCIENTIST, DENT RES INST, 77- *Concurrent Pos:* Res fel oral path, Univ Minn, 55-58; consult, Vet Admin, 64- & Ellis Fischel State Cancer Hosp, 66-; assoc res scientist, Cancer Res Ctr, Columbia, Mo, 67-; mem sci adv bd, Cancer Res Ctr, Columbia Mo, 75-79; civilian prof consult, Off Surgeon, Fifth US Army, 67-; mem prof adv coun cancer, Mich Asn Regional Med Progs, 69-, comt cancer control, Mich Dent Asn, 71-77 & coun dent educ, Am Dent Asn, 71-77, coun on hosp & inst dent, 79- *Honors & Awards:* Tiffany Div Nat Award, Am Cancer Soc, 79. *Mem:* AAAS; Am Cancer Soc; Am Dent Asn; fel Am Acad Oral Path (pres, 77-78); Am Asn Cancer Res. *Res:* Effect of environmental variables upon oral cancer induction; etiology and pathogenesis of dental caries; Herpes Simplex virus, antiviral chemotherapy. *Mailing Add:* Dent Res Inst Univ of Mich Sch of Dent Ann Arbor MI 48104

ROWE, PAUL E, b Marlboro, Mass, Nov 16, 27; m 53; c 3. PHYSICAL ORGANIC CHEMISTRY. *Educ:* Mass Inst Technol, SB, 48; Boston Univ, PhD(chem), 59. *Prof Exp:* Proj chemist, Nat Northern Div, Am Potash & Chem Co, 53-59; head, Org Develop Dept, Emerson & Cuming, Inc, 69-74, chief chemist, 74-78, dir res & develop, 78-80, partner, Cuming Corp, 80-81; CONSULT, 81- *Mem:* Am Chem Soc. *Res:* Research and development in the explosive and propellant fields and in the plastics and ceramic fields with emphasis on electronic and microwave materials. *Mailing Add:* 34 Summit Ave Sharon MA 02067

ROWE, R(ICHARD) G(REGOR), b Tacoma, Wash, Sept 7, 13; m 42; c 3. CHEMICAL ENGINEERING, ENVIRONMENTAL SCIENCE. *Educ:* Univ Minn, BChE, 35; Yale Univ, MEng, 42. *Prof Exp:* Chemist, Swift & Co, Ill, 35-38, process engr, 38-40; res fel, Dictaphone Corp, Conn, 40-43, chief chem engr, 44-53; dir varnish res, Calif Ink Co, 43-44; chief chemist, Waterman Pen Co, Conn, 53-57; consult engr, R G Rowe & Assocs, Conn, 57-60; vpres & tech dir, Martin Cantine Co, 60-65; CONSULT CHEM, R G ROWE & ASSOCS, 65- *Concurrent Pos:* Abstractor, Chem Abstr, 43-; vis lectr, State Univ NY Col New Paltz, 66- *Mem:* Am Chem Soc; Nat Soc Prof Engrs; Am Inst Chem Engrs; Am Soc Testing & Mat; fel Am Inst Chemists. *Res:* Hydrogenation of fats and oils; alkyd resins; metallic soaps; sound recording media; organic synthesis; thermoplastics; writing inks; consumer product development. *Mailing Add:* RD 2 Box 461 Rocktown Rd Ringoes NJ 08551

ROWE, RANDALL CHARLES, b Baltimore, Md, Sept 26, 45; m 67; c 2. VEGETABLE PATHOLOGY, POTATO PATHOLOGY. *Educ:* Mich State Univ, BS, 67; Ore State Univ, PhD(plant path), 72. *Prof Exp:* Res assoc peanut path, NC State Univ, 72-74; asst prof, 74-79, ASSOC PROF VEG PATH, OHIO AGR RES & DEVELOP CTR & OHIO STATE UNIV, 79- *Mem:* Am Phytopath Soc; Potato Asn Am. *Res:* Biology, ecology and control of potato and vegetable diseases with emphasis on soil-borne fungi, verticillium, fusarium, rhizoetonia, fungal-nematode interactions, and fungicide evaluation. *Mailing Add:* Dept of Plant Path Ohio Agr Res & Develop Ctr Wooster OH 44691

ROWE, RAYMOND GRANT, b Seattle, Wash, Oct 24, 41; m 71; c 2. METALLURGY, SURFACE PHYSICS. *Educ:* Wash State Univ, BS, 65; Univ Ill, MS, 68, PhD(metall eng), 75. *Prof Exp:* Scientist metall, Battelle-Northwest Labs, 65-67; fels, Jones & Laughlin Steel Co, 67-68 & Am Vacuum Soc, 70-72; adv eng metall, Westinghouse-Hanford Co, 74-76; staff metallurgist, 76-78, MGR PROPERTIES BR, RES & DEVELOP CTR, GEN ELEC CORP, 78- *Mem:* Am Inst Mining, Metall & Petrol Engrs; Metall Soc; Am Vacuum Soc; AAAS; Microbeam Anal Soc. *Res:* Grain boundary segregation effects in metals; high resolution scanning; auger microscopy; grain growth in metals. *Mailing Add:* Res & Develop Ctr Gen Elec Corp Schenectady NY 12301

ROWE, RICHARD J(AY), b Lackawanna, NY, June 12, 30; m 53; c 4. AGRICULTURAL ENGINEERING. *Educ:* Cornell Univ, BS, 52, PhD, 69; Iowa State Univ, BS, 57, MS, 59. *Prof Exp:* Agr engr, Agr Res Serv, USDA, 57-59; PROF AGR ENG, UNIV MAINE, ORONO, 59- *Mem:* Am Soc Agr Engrs; Am Soc Eng Educ. *Res:* Power and mechanization of agricultural operations. *Mailing Add:* Dept Agr Eng Univ Maine Orono ME 04473

ROWE, ROBERT S(EAMAN), b Wilmington, Del, Jan 31, 20; m 42; c 2. CIVIL ENGINEERING. *Educ:* Univ Del, BCE, 42; Columbia Univ, MS, 49; Yale Univ, MEng, 50, DEng, 51. *Prof Exp:* Design engr, Triumph Explosives, Inc, 38-42; from instr to assoc prof civil eng, Princeton Univ, 46-56, dir rivers & harbors sect, 51-56; J A Jones prof eng & chmn dept civil eng, Duke Univ, 56-60; dean eng, 60-70, PROF CIVIL, ENVIRON & WATER RESOURCES ENG, VANDERBILT UNIV, 70- *Concurrent Pos:* Vis prof, Univ Del, 48-49; asst to dean, NY Univ, 51-52; indust educator, E I du Pont de Nemours & Co, Inc, 55-56; consult scientist, Land Locomotion Res Lab, Detroit Arsenal; consult & mem adv panel, Off Ord Res, US Army. *Mem:* Am Soc Civil Engrs; Am Soc Eng Educ; Soc Am Mil Engrs; Nat Soc Prof Engrs; Am Concrete Inst. *Res:* Structural engineering; land mobility. *Mailing Add:* Box 1626 Sta B Vanderbilt Univ Nashville TN 37235

ROWE, RONALD KERRY, b Univ Sydney, BSc, 73, BE, 75, PhD(geotech eng), 79. SOIL MECHANICS, ROCK MECHANICS. *Prof Exp:* Cadet engr, Australian Dept Construct, 71-74, engr, 75-78; asst prof, 78-82, ASSOC PROF CIVIL ENG, UNIV WESTERN ONT, 82- *Mem:* Inst Engrs Australia; Asn Prof Engrs Ont; Int Soc Soil Mech & Found Eng; Can Geotech Soc; Eng Inst Can. *Res:* Geotechnical engineering, with particular emphasis on design and analysis involving soil and rock-structure interaction, including tunnelling, shallow foundations and embankments, geotextiles, piles and anchors. *Mailing Add:* Fac Eng Sci London ON N6A 5B9 Can

ROWE, THOMAS DUDLEY, b Missoula, Mont, June 25, 10; m 34; c 1. PHARMACY. *Educ:* Univ Mont, BS, 32, MS, 33; Univ Wis, PhD(pharm), 41. *Prof Exp:* Instr pharm, Univ Nebr, 34-35; from instr to asst prof, Med Col Va, 35-40, assoc prof & actg chmn dept, 40-43, asst dean & chmn dept, 43-45; prof & chmn dept, Rutgers Univ, 45-51; dean, 51-75, PROF PHARM, COL PHARM, UNIV MICH, ANN ARBOR, 51-, EMER DEAN, 75- *Concurrent Pos:* From asst dean to dean col pharm, Rutgers Univ, 45-51; consult, Off Surgeon Gen, US Dept Army, 58- *Mem:* Am Asn Cols Pharm (pres, 57-58); Am Pharmaceut Asn (1st vpres, 52). *Res:* Plant chemistry; pharmacology of medicinal plants; phytochemical and pharmacological investigation of fresh Aloe leaves; pharmacy education; socio-economic problems in pharmacy; ethics. *Mailing Add:* Col of Pharm Univ of Mich Ann Arbor MI 48104

ROWE, VERALD KEITH, b Warren, Ill, Oct 5, 14; m 37; c 2. TOXICOLOGY, INDUSTRIAL HYGIENE. *Educ:* Cornell Col, AB, 36; Univ Iowa, MS, 38. *Hon Degrees:* ScD, Cornell Col, 71. *Prof Exp:* Biochemist, Dow Chem Co, 37-44, proj leader, Dow Chem USA, 44-49, toxicologist, 49-52, tech expert, 52-54, lab div leader, 54-64, asst dir, 64-70, dir toxicol & indust hyg, Chem Biol Res, 70-74, dir toxicol affairs & health & environ sci, 74-79; CONSULT INDUST TOXICOL, 79- *Concurrent Pos:* Mem comt toxicol, Nat Acad Sci-Nat Res Coun, 64-72; mem hazardous mat adv comt, Environ Protection Agency, 75-76, res fel, 77- *Honors & Awards:* Cummings Award, Am Indust Hyg Asn, 79. *Mem:* Am Soc Pharmacol & Exp Therapeut; Soc Toxicol (pres, 66-67); Am Chem Soc; Am Indust Hyg Asn; Am Acad Indust Hyg (pres, 72-73). *Res:* Determination of physiological effects of chemicals on animals and man; metabolism of chemicals. *Mailing Add:* 9605 Sandstone Dr Dow Chem USA 1803 Bldg Sun City AZ 85351

ROWE, VERNON DODDS, b Washington, DC, July 11, 44; m 66; c 2. DEVELOPMENTAL NEUROBIOLOGY. *Educ:* Duke Univ, BS, 65, MD, 69. *Prof Exp:* Resident neurol, Johns Hopkins Hosp, 71-72 & 75-77; res assoc develop neurobiol, Nat Inst Child Health & Human Develop, 72-75; ASST PROF NEUROL, UNIV KANS MED CTR, 77- *Concurrent Pos:* Staff neurologist, Kansas City Vet Admin Hosp, 77-; Basil O'Connor Starter Grant, Nat Found, 78-80. *Res:* Tissue culture of sympathetic and pineal tissue; developmental neurotoxicology. *Mailing Add:* Univ of Kans Med Ctr 39th & Rainbow Kansas City KS 66103

ROWE, WALLACE PRESCOTT, b Baltimore, Md, Feb 20, 26; m 48, 81; c 2. VIROLOGY. *Educ:* Johns Hopkins Univ, MD, 48. *Prof Exp:* Intern internal med, NC Baptist Hosp, Winston-Salem, 48-49; virologist, Naval Med Res Inst, Bethesda, 49-52; chief oncolytic & oncogenic virus unit, Lab Infectious Dis, 57-68, CHIEF LAB VIRAL DIS, NAT INST ALLERGY & INFECTIOUS DIS, 68- *Concurrent Pos:* Mary Scott Newbold lectr, Col Physicians Philadelphia, 61; Esther Langer-Bertha Teplitz Award, Ann Langer Cancer Res Found, Chicago, 65; J Howard Mueller Mem lectr, Harvard Univ, 70. *Honors & Awards:* Eli Lilly Award, Soc Am Bacteriologists, 60; Rockefeller Pub Serv Award, 72; Howard Taylor Ricketts Award, 74; Selman A Waksman Award microbiol, Nat Acad Sci, 76; Virus Cancer Prog Award, Nat Cancer Inst, 76, Ehrlich-Darmstaedter Award, Fed Repub Ger, 79; Alfred P Sloan Award, Gen Motors Cancer Res Found. *Mem:* Nat Acad Sci; Am Soc Clin Invest; AAAS. *Res:* Tumor viruses; chronic and latent virus infections. *Mailing Add:* Bldg 7 Rm 304 Nat Inst of Allergy & Infect Dis Bethesda MD 20014

ROWE, WILLIAM A, b Detroit, Mich, July 21, 23; m 55; c 4. ANALYTICAL CHEMISTRY, TECCHNICAL MANAGEMENT. *Educ:* Univ Wis, BS, 48, MS, 49. *Prof Exp:* Res chemist, Res Ctr, Pure Oil Co, 49-65; MGR RES SERV, RES DIV, GOULD, INC, 65- *Mem:* Am Chem Soc; Soc Appl Spectros; Am Soc Test & Mat. *Res:* Chemical analysis in fields of emission spectrography, x-ray spectrometry and flame emission spectrometry; petroleum materials and products; electrochemical power sources, materials and product analysis; environmental health and safety; quality assurance. *Mailing Add:* Gould Inc 40 Gould Ctr Rolling Meadows IL 60008

ROWE, WILLIAM BRUCE, b Canon City, Colo, Nov 12, 35; m 78; c 2. BIOCHEMISTRY. *Educ:* Colo State Univ, BS, 57; Univ Rochester, MS, 59, PhD(biochem), 67. *Prof Exp:* Instr, 69-72, asst prof biochem, med col, Cornell Univ, 72-78; ASSOC DIR, BIOCHEM, BAXTER-TRAVENOL LABS, 78- *Concurrent Pos:* Fel, Sch Med, Tufts Univ, 67; fel, Med Col, Cornell Univ, 67-69. *Mem:* AAAS; Am Chem Soc; Sigma Xi; NY Acad Sci; Harvey Soc. *Res:* Amino acid and protein metabolism; enzymology and control mechanisms of intermediary metabolism; mechanism of glutamine synthetase and the effect of methionine sulfoximine; parenteral nutrition; immunochemistry. *Mailing Add:* Dept of Biochem Baxter-Travenol Labs Morton Grove IL 60053

ROWE, WILLIAM DAVID, b Orange, NJ, Jan 7, 30; c 4. RISK ANALYSIS, MANAGEMENT SCIENCE. *Educ:* Wesleyan Univ, BS, 52; Univ Pittsburgh, MS, 52; Univ Buffalo, MBA, 61; Am Univ, PhD(bus admin), 73. *Prof Exp:* Jr engr, Westinghouse Elec Corp, 52-53, asst engr anal dept, 53-55, assoc engr, 55-56, engr, 56-57, supv engr systs control dept, 57-61; eng specialist, Advan Systs Lab, Sylvania Electronic Systs, Mass, 61-62, mgr digital systs dept & Minuteman syst task mgr, 62-63, tech dir, Minuteman WS-133B Prog, 63, mem info processing staff, 63-64, sr eng specialist, 63-66, dir advan technol, 66-68; head, Spec Studies Subdept, Mitre Corp, Washington Oper, 68-69, dept head & assoc, 69-72; dep asst adminr radiation progs, US Environ Protection Agency, 72-80; PROF DECISIONS & RISK ANAL, CTR TECHNOL OF ADMIN, AM UNIV, WASHINGTON, DC, & DIR, INST RISK ANAL, 80- Concurrent Pos: Treas, Am Fedn Info Processing Socs, 66-67; head environ systs dept, Mitre Corp, 69-72; adj prof, Am Univ, 72-80. Mem: AAAS; Systs, Man & Cybernet Soc; Soc Risk Anal; sr mem Inst Elec & Electronics Engrs; Am Risk & Ins Asn. Res: Environmental science and radiation protection; radiation protection and risk analysis philosophy and application. Mailing Add: 6423 Woodville Dr Falls Church VA 22044

ROWELL, ALBERT JOHN, b Ely, Eng, July 19, 29; m 54; c 4. INVERTEBRATE PALEONTOLOGY. Educ: Univ Leeds, BSc, 50, PhD(geol), 53. Prof Exp: From asst lectr to lectr geol, Univ Nottingham, 55-64, reader, 64-67; PROF GEOL, UNIV KANS, 67- Concurrent Pos: Vis prof, Univ Kans, 64-65. Mem: Geol Soc Am; Am Paleont Soc; Soc Syst Zool; Geol Soc London; Brit Paleont Asn. Res: Application of numerical methods in paleontology; Cambrian stratigraphy and biogeography; paleozoic inarticulate brachiopods. Mailing Add: Dept of Geol Univ of Kans Lawrence KS 66045

ROWELL, CHARLES FREDERICK, b Lowville, NY, May 29, 35; m 55; c 2. PHYSICAL ORGANIC CHEMISTRY. Educ: Syracuse Univ, BS, 56; Iowa State Univ, MS, 59; Ore State Univ, PhD(org chem), 64. Prof Exp: From asst prof to assoc prof, US Naval Postgrad Sch, 62-79, PROF CHEM & CONSULT FORENSIC SCI, US NAVAL ACAD, 79-, ASSOC CHMN DEPT, 81- Concurrent Pos: Vis scientist, Chicago Br, Off Naval Res, 74-75; vis prof, US Naval Acad, 75-76. Mem: AAAS; Am Chem Soc; The Chem Soc. Res: Photochemistry; cyclopropane reactions; water pollution; nitramine chemistry; liquid propellants; uzulene derivations. Mailing Add: Dept of Chem US Naval Acad Annapolis MD 21402

ROWELL, CHESTER MORRISON, JR, b Burnet, Tex, Dec 2, 25. TAXONOMY. Educ: Univ Tex, BS, 47; Agr & Mech Col, Tex, MS, 49; Okla State Univ, PhD, 67. Prof Exp: Asst herbarium, Univ Mich, 53-54; asst prof biol, Agr & Mech Col, Tex, 49-57, assoc prof, Tex Tech Univ, 57-70; PROF BIOL & HEAD DEPT, ANGELO STATE UNIV, 70- Res: Seedplants of Texas and Mexico. Mailing Add: Dept of Biol Angelo State Univ San Angelo TX 76901

ROWELL, JOHN BARTLETT, b Pawtucket, RI, Nov 26, 18; m 44; c 3. CEREAL RUST PATHOLOGY. Educ: RI State Col, BS, 41; Univ Minn, PhD(plant path), 49. Prof Exp: Jr res asst plant path, Exp Sta, RI State Col, 40; asst, Univ Minn, St Paul, 41-42 & 46-47; asst, Exp Sta, RI State Col, 47-48, asst res prof, 48-49; res assoc, Univ Minn, St Paul, 49-55, assoc prof, 55-69; plant physiologist, Crops Res Div, USDA, 55-69, res plant pathologist & leader cereal rust lab, Sci & Educ Admin-Agr Res, 69-80; PROF PLANT PATH, UNIV MINN, ST PAUL, 80- Concurrent Pos: Consult, Ford Found, 71. Mem: Fel AAAS; fel Am Phytopath Soc; Bot Soc Am; Indian Phytopath Soc. Res: Control of cereal rusts. Mailing Add: Cereal Rust Lab Univ of Minn St Paul MN 55108

ROWELL, JOHN MARTIN, b Linslade, Eng, June 27, 35; m 59; c 3. PHYSICS. Educ: Univ Oxford, BA, 57, DPhil(physics) & MA, 61. Prof Exp: Mem tech staff, 61-69, dept head solid state electronics res, 69-77, dept head solid state & physics metals, Bell Tel Labs, 77-81, DIR CHEM PHYSICS RES, BELL LABS, 81- Honors & Awards: Fritz London Mem Award, 78. Mem: Fel Am Phys Soc. Res: Conduction in semiconductors at low temperatures; superconductivity; tunneling in superconductor junctions and in normal metal junctions; the Josephson effect; superconducting materials. Mailing Add: Rm 1D-367 Bell Tel Labs PO Box 261 Murray Hill NJ 07974

ROWELL, LORING B, b Lynn, Mass, Jan 27, 30; m 56; c 2. PHYSIOLOGY. Educ: Springfield Col, BS, 53; Univ Minn, PhD(physiol), 62. Prof Exp: NIH fel cardiovasc physiol & cardiol, 62-63; from res instr to res asst prof med, 63-68, assoc prof physiol, biophys & med, 70-72, PROF PHYSIOL & BIOPHYS, SCH MED, UNIV WASH, 72-, ADJ PROF MED, 72- Concurrent Pos: Estab investr, Am Heart Asn, 66-71. Mem: Am Physiol Soc. Res: Human cardiovascular function; total and regional blood flow; temperature regulation; skeletal muscle and hepatic metabolism; hemodynamics-pressure regulation. Mailing Add: Dept of Physiol & Biophys Univ of Wash Sch of Med Seattle WA 98195

ROWELL, LYMAN SMITH, b Colebrook, NH, May 8, 04; m 32; c 1. EMBRYOLOGY. Educ: Univ Vt, BS, 25, MS, 30. Hon Degrees: LHD, St Michael's Col, 68; LLD, Univ Vt, 71. Prof Exp: From instr to assoc prof zool, 25-69, actg dir, Fleming Mus, 34-35, dir adult educ, 55-56, dean admin, 56-61, actg pres univ, 64-65, from vpres to pres, 65-70, EMER PRES, UNIV VT, 71- Concurrent Pos: Vt comnr, Educ Comn of States, 68-71. Mem: Soc Develop Biol. Res: Institutional research; regeneration in Lumbricus; zoology. Mailing Add: Pinehurst Dr Shelburne VT 05482

ROWELL, NEAL POPE, b Mobile, Ala, Jan 11, 26; m 47; c 5. PHYSICS. Educ: Univ Ala, BS, 49, MS, 50; Univ Fla, PhD(physics), 54. Prof Exp: Instr physics, Univ Ala, 50-51; physicist, Mine Countermeasures Sta, US Navy, 51-52; instr physics, Univ Fla, 53-54; physicist, Courtaulds, Inc, 54-68; dir div eng, 68-72, prof eng, 72-74, PROF PHYSICS, UNIV S ALA, 74- Mem: Am Phys Soc; Am Asn Physics Teachers. Res: Physical properties of viscose rayon; electron diffraction study of alloys produced by simultaneous vacuum evaporation of aluminum and copper. Mailing Add: 354 McDonald Ave Mobile AL 36604

ROWELL, ROBERT LEE, b Quincy, Mass, July 29, 32; m 56; c 4. PHYSICAL CHEMISTRY, COLLOID SCIENCE. Educ: Mass State Col Bridgewater, BS, 54; Boston Col, MS, 56; Ind Univ, PhD(phys chem), 60. Prof Exp: From instr to assoc prof, 60-78, dir, Res Comput Ctr, 61-64, PROF CHEM, UNIV MASS, AMHERST, 78- Concurrent Pos: Int Bus Mach Corp fel, Comput Ctr, Mass Inst Technol, 63-64; res assoc, Clarkson Col, 66-70; vis prof, Univ Bristol, Eng, 73-74, Unilever vis prof, 80. Mem: Am Chem Soc. Res: Laser light scattering by molecules, macromolecules and colloidal particles; characterization of particle shape and particle size distribution; stability, structure and rheology of coal slurry fuels. Mailing Add: Dept Chem GRC Twr 1 Univ Mass Amherst MA 01003

ROWEN, BURT, b New York, NY, Mar 30, 21; m 42; c 3. AEROSPACE MEDICINE. Educ: Lafayette Col, BA, 42; NY Univ, MD, 45; Am Bd Prev Med, dipl, 65. Prof Exp: With Med Corps, US Air Force, 46-, instr, US Air Force Sch Aviation Med, 49-51, asst air attache, Stockholm, Sweden, 52-55, med dir, X-15 Proj, US Air Force Flight Test Ctr, 56-62, med dir, Dynasoar Proj, Aeronaut Syst Div, 62-64, dep comdr, Aerospace Med Res Labs, 64-65, flight surgeon, Vietnam, 65-66, Hq, 12th Air Force, Waco, Tex, 66-68 & Hq, 17th Air Force, Ramstein, Ger, 68-69, dep surgeon, Hq, US Air Forces Europ, Wiesbaden, Ger, 69-72, comdr, US Air Force Sch Health Care Sci, Sheppard AFB, 72-74, mem phys eval bd, Air Force Military Personnel Ctr, 74-81, CHIEF MED STANDARDS DIV, MILITARY MANPOWER CTR, US AIR FORCE, RANDOLPH AFB, 81- Mem: Fel Aerospace Med Asn; Am Col Prev Med; Int Acad Aerospace Med. Res: Devleopment of life support systems, including air to ground telemetry of life support parameters and real time ground readout; health care training and management of health care resources; medical Manpower & support of tactical air operations; adjudication of medical conditions in relation to the USAF Disability Retirement System; medical standards management of USAF active and reserve forces. Mailing Add: Air Force Mil Personnel Ctr MPCAR Randolph AFB TX 78148

ROWEN, WILLIAM H(OWARD), b Milwaukee, Wis, June 22, 18; m 42; c 2. ELECTRICAL & NUCLEAR ENGINEERING. Educ: US Naval Acad, BS, 41; Mass Inst Technol, MS, 47. Prof Exp: Res asst weapon physics, Los Alamos Sci Lab, 48-49 & 50-51; mem staff weapons res & develop, US Atomic Energy Comn, 53-56; naval weapons asst, Lawrence Radiation Lab, Univ Calif, 58-60; proj mgr nuclear rocket test, 62-63, mem staff automated space vehicle checkout, 63-65, proj mgr, weapon effects test, 65-67, proj engr, Poseidon Automated Checkout Equip, 68-70, STAFF ENGR, SATELLITE ORBIT OPERS, LOCKHEED MISSILES & SPACE CO, SUNNYVALE, 70- Mem: AAAS. Res: Nuclear weapon and rocket development and test; instrumentation; real time computer control of space vehicle checkout and operation; effects of nuclear weapons. Mailing Add: Lockheed Missiles & Space Co PO Box 504 Sunnyvale CA 94088

ROWIN, GERALD L, b Aurora, Ill, Apr 28, 37; c 3. SYNTHETIC ORGANIC CHEMISTRY. Educ: NCent Col, BA, 59; Univ Ill, MS, 63, PhD(biochem), 65. Prof Exp: Chemist, Northern Regional Res Lab, US Dept Agr, 65-67; res chemist, Squibb Inst, 67-69; sr chemist, Wallace Labs, Carter-Wallace Inc, 69-74; sr res chemist, 75-80, RES FEL, MERCK SHARPE & DOHME RES LABS, 80- Mem: Am Chem Soc. Res: Chemistry and enzymology of aminosugars; isolation and structure of bacterial polysaccharides; isolation of cell particles; natural product isolation-antibiotics, antifungal agents, enzyme inhibitors, secondary metabolites with pharmacological activity. Mailing Add: Merck & Co Inc PO Box 2000 Ramway NJ 07065

ROWLAND, ALEX THOMAS, b Kingston, NY, Feb 25, 31; m 53; c 2. STEROID CHEMISTRY. Educ: Gettysburg Col, AB, 53; Brown Univ, PhD(chem), 58. Prof Exp: From asst prof to assoc prof, 58-67, PROF CHEM, GETTYSBURG COL, 67-, CHMN DEPT, 68- Mem: Am Chem Soc; AAAS. Res: Synthesis of modified steroids; reactions of certain steroidal oxides; chemistry of highly substituted cyclohexanones; steroidal oxetanones. Mailing Add: Dept of Chem Gettysburg Col Gettysburg PA 17325

ROWLAND, DAVID LAWRENCE, b Philadelphia, Pa, Sept 30, 50. NEUROENDOCRINOLOGY, ETHOLOGY. Educ: Southern Ill Univ, BA, 72; Univ Chicago, MA, 75, PhD(biopsychol), 77. Prof Exp: Asst prof psychol & dir, Psychol Animal Lab, Millikin Univ, 76-80; res fel, State Univ NY, Stony Brook, 80-81; ASST PROF PSYCHOL, VALPARAISO UNIV, 81- Concurrent Pos: Proj dir, NSF grants, 79-81. Mem: Soc Neurosci; Am Asn Univ Prof. Res: Neural and hormonal basis of reproductive behavior. Mailing Add: Dept Psychol Valparaiso Univ Valparaiso IN 46383

ROWLAND, E(LBERT) S(ANDS), b Olney, Ill, Dec 12, 08; m 32, 68. METALLURGY. Educ: Wayne State Univ, BSE, 30; Univ Mich, MS, 32, PhD(metall eng), 34. Prof Exp: Instr in charge exten activities in metall, Pa State Col, 33-35; res metallurgist, Timken Co, 35-51, chief metall engr, 51-64, dir res, 64-73; RETIRED. Mem: AAAS; Am Soc Metals; Soc Automotive Engrs (vpres, 58); Am Inst Mining, Metall & Petrol Engrs; Brit Iron & Steel Inst. Res: Metallography and heat treatment of bearing steels; metallurgy of engineering alloy steels; bearing technology. Mailing Add: 1608 Radcliff NW Massillon OH 44646

ROWLAND, FRANK SHERWOOD, b Delaware, Ohio, June 28, 27; m 52; c 2. CHEMICAL KINETICS, ATMOSPHERIC CHEMISTRY. Educ: Ohio Wesleyan Univ, AB, 48; Univ Chicago, MS, 51, PhD(chem), 52. Prof Exp: Instr, Princeton Univ, 52-56; from asst prof to prof chem, Univ Kans, 56-64; chmn dept, 64-70, PROF CHEM, UNIV CALIF, IRVINE, 64- Concurrent Pos: Guggenheim fel, 62 & 74; Humboldt Sr Scientist prize, WGer, 81; vis sr scientist, Japan, 80; Snider Vis Prof, Univ Toronto, 80; Erskine Fel, Univ Canterbury, NZ, 78; mem, Int Comn Atmospheric Chem & Global Pollution, Int Asn Meteor & Atmospheric Phys, 79- & Ozone Comn, 80-; chmn sci adv bd, High Altitude Pollution Prog, Fed Aviation Agency, 79-; mem, US Nat Comt, CODATA, Nat Acad Sci, 76- & chmn, 79-, mem comt atmospheric sci, 79- & mem comt solar-terrestrial relationships, 79-; mem sci adv bd, Max

Planck Inst Cosmochem & Geochem, WGer, 81- *Honors & Awards:* Billard Award in Environ Sci, NY Acad Sci; Tolman Award, Am Chem Soc; John Wiley Jones Award in Environ Chem, Rochester Inst Technol; E F Smith Lectr Award, Am Chem Soc, 80; Aimmermann Award, Am Chem Soc, 80; Leo Szilard Award, Am Phys Soc, 79; Venable Lectr, Univ NC, 79. *Mem:* Nat Acad Sci; Am Chem Soc; Am Phys Soc; fel Am Geophys Union; fel Am Acad Arts & Sci. *Res:* Stratospheric chlorine chemistry; chemical effects of nuclear transformations; radiation chemistry; tracer reactions; isotopes applied to geochemistry; tropospheric chemistry of halocarbons, methane and other hydocarbons. *Mailing Add:* 4807 Dorchester Rd Corona del Mar CA 92625

ROWLAND, IVAN W, b Pocatello, Idaho, Apr 1, 10; m 58; c 1. PHARMACY, MICROBIOLOGY. *Educ:* Idaho State Col, BS, 32; Univ Colo, MS, 47; Univ Wash, PhD(pharm), 54. *Prof Exp:* Dean col pharm, Idaho State Col, 54-56; dean sch pharm, 56-81, EMER DEAN, UNIV OF THE PAC, 81- *Mem:* Am Pharmaceut Asn. *Res:* Antiseptics; germicides; antibiotics; pharmacognosy; pharmaceutical chemistry; pharmacy administration. *Mailing Add:* Sch of Pharm Univ of the Pac Stockton CA 95207

ROWLAND, JAMES RICHARD, b Muldrow, Okla, Jan 24, 40; m 63; c 2. ELECTRICAL ENGINEERING. *Educ:* Okla State Univ, BS, 62; Purdue Univ, Lafayette, MS, 64, PhD(elec eng), 66. *Prof Exp:* Instr elec eng, Purdue Univ, Lafayette, 64-66; from asst prof to assoc prof, Ga Inst Technol, 66-71; assoc prof, 71-76, PROF ELEC ENG, OKLA STATE UNIV, 76- *Concurrent Pos:* Consult, Lockheed-Ga Co, 66-71 & US Army Missile Command, 69-79. *Mem:* Inst Elec & Electronics Engrs; Am Soc Eng Educ; Nat Soc Prof Engrs. *Res:* Stochastic systems simulation and control; optimal and adaptive control systems; computer and control applications; nonlinear systems stability; computer systems analysis and design. *Mailing Add:* Sch Elec Eng Okla State Univ Stillwater OK 74078

ROWLAND, JOHN H, b Bellefonte, Pa, Feb 20, 34; m 56; c 4. MATHEMATICS, COMPUTER SCIENCE. *Educ:* Pa State Univ, BS, 56, PhD(math), 66; Univ Wash, MS, 58. *Prof Exp:* Instr math, Univ Nev, 58-61; staff mathematician, HRB Singer, Inc, 61-66; assoc prof math & comput sci, 66-77, head dept comput sci, 73-79, PROF MATH & COMPUT SCI, UNIV WYO, 77- *Concurrent Pos:* NSF fac residency in comput sci, Santa Monica, Calif, 70-71. *Mem:* Am Math Soc; Soc Indust & Appl Math; Asn Comput Mach. *Res:* Approximation theory; numerical analysis; theory of program testing. *Mailing Add:* Dept Comput Sci Univ Wyo Laramie WY 82071

ROWLAND, LENTON O, JR, b Mobile, Ala, Sept 29, 43. POULTRY NUTRITION. *Educ:* Univ Fla, BSA, 65, MS, 67, PhD(animal nutrit), 72. *Prof Exp:* Poultry serviceman layers & pullets, Cent Soya Inc, 65-66; staff mem res & develop animal nutrit, Dow Chem Co, USA, 72-73; mem tech serv, Dow Chem Co, Latin Am, 73-74; ASST PROF POULTRY NUTRIT, TEX A&M UNIV, 75- *Mem:* Poultry Sci Asn; Am Soc Animal Sci; World Poultry Sci Asn. *Res:* Basic hen and broiler nutrition with particular emphasis on new feed ingredients, energy and amino acid requirements of poultry. *Mailing Add:* Dept of Poultry Sci Tex A&M Univ College Station TX 77843

ROWLAND, LEWIS PHILLIP, b Brooklyn, NY, Aug 3, 25; m 52; c 3. NEUROLOGY. *Educ:* Yale Univ, BS, 45, MD, 48. *Prof Exp:* Res asst neuroanat, Columbia Univ, 48; asst med, Yale Univ, 49-50; asst resident, Columbia Univ, 50-52; asst neurol, Col Physicians & Surgeons, 53; clin instr, Georgetown Univ, 53-54; instr, Col Physicians & Surgeons, Columbia Univ, 54-56, assoc, 56-57, from asst prof to prof, 56-67; prof neurol & chmn dept, Univ Pa, 67-73; PROF NEUROL & CHMN DEPT, COL PHYSICIANS & SURGEONS, COLUMBIA UNIV, 73-, DIR NEUROL SERV, PRESBY HOSP, 73- *Concurrent Pos:* Clin investr, Nat Inst Neurol Dis & Blindness, 53-54; asst neurologist, Montefiore Hosp, New York, 54-57; neurologist, Presby Hosp, 54-67; vis fel, Med Res Coun Labs, London, Eng, 56; co-dir, Neurol Clin Res Ctr, Columbia Univ, 61-67; mem med adv bd, Myasthenia Gravis Found, 63-, pres, 71-73; sci adv bd, Muscular Dystrophy Asns Am, 69-; med adv bd, Multiple Sclerosis Soc; mem neurol res training comt B, Nat Inst Neurol Dis & Stroke, 71-73, bd sci counr, Nat Inst Neurol Commun Dis Stroke, 78-82, chmn, 81-82; ed-in-chief, Neurol, 77- *Mem:* AAAS; Asn Res Nerv & Ment Dis (pres, 69, vpres, 80); Am Neurol Asn (pres, 80-81); Am Acad Neurol; Soc Neurosci. *Res:* Biochemistry of human muscle disease. *Mailing Add:* Neurol Inst Columbia-Presby Med Ctr 710 West 168th St New York NY 10032

ROWLAND, NEIL WILSON, b Singapore, July 5, 19; US citizen; m 43; c 3. BOTANY. *Educ:* Union Col, Nebr, BA, 47; Univ Nebr, MA, 52, PhD, 61. *Prof Exp:* Head dept, 52-67, acad dean, 67-77, PROF BIOL, UNION COL, NEBR, 52- *Mem:* Am Asn Higher Educ. *Res:* Plant physiology and ecology. *Mailing Add:* Union Col Lincoln NE 68506

ROWLAND, RICHARD LLOYD, b Delaware, Ohio, May 31, 29; m 64. PHYSICAL CHEMISTRY. *Educ:* Ohio Wesleyan Univ, BA, 51; Univ Chicago, PhD(chem), 60. *Prof Exp:* Res chemist, Stand Oil Co, Ohio, 61-62, sr res chemist, 62-64; asst prof, Robert Col, Istanbul, 64-67, assoc prof, 67-71; assoc prof, Univ Calif, Irvine, 71-72; MEM FAC CHEM, COSUMNES RIVER COL, 72- *Mem:* Am Chem Soc. *Res:* Solid state diffusion; electrochemistry. *Mailing Add:* 8756 Leo-Virgo Ct Elk Grove CA 95624

ROWLAND, RICHARDS ATWELL, b Richmond, Va, Dec 20, 10; m 43; c 2. CLAY MINERALOGY. *Educ:* Univ Cincinnati, GeolE, 34; Cornell Univ, PhD(struct geol), 38. *Prof Exp:* With US Coast & Geod Surv, 34-35; asst petrographer, Ill Geol Surv, 37-42; sect leader, Shell Develop Co, 46-51, sr geologist, 51-65, sr staff geologist, Shell Can Explor, 66-68; sr res assoc, Baroid Div, NL Industs, Houston, 69-73; consult, Dresser Minerals, Houston, 75-77. *Concurrent Pos:* Vis prof, Univ Fla, 64-66; lectr, Univ Houston, 67-; adj prof, Univ Houston, 73-; Ed-in-chief, Clays & Clay Minerals, 74-78. *Mem:* Fel Geol Soc Am; fel Am Mineral Soc; Am Asn Petrol Geol; Clay Minerals Soc (pres, 64); Am Inst Mining, Metall & Petrol Engrs. *Res:* Petrofabrics; clay mineralogy; thermal analysis, x-ray structure and ion exchange of clays;

petrofabrics of clastic quartz; clay mineral technique in exploration and production of petroleum; carbonate mineralogy and textures; mineral exploration; natural and synthetic zeolites; clay organic complexes. *Mailing Add:* 5405 Pine Bellaire TX 77401

ROWLAND, ROBERT EDMUND, b St Charles, Ill, Jan 10, 23; m 44; c 3. RADIATION BIOPHYSICS. *Educ:* Cornell Col, BS, 47; Univ Ill, MS, 49; Univ Rochester, PhD, 64; Univ Chicago, MBA, 75. *Prof Exp:* Assoc physicist, Argonne Nat Lab, 50-62; sr tech assoc, Univ Rochester, 62-64; assoc dir, Radiol Physics Div, 64-67, dir Radiol & Environ Res Div, 67-81, SR BIOPHYSICIST, ARGONNE NAT LAB, 66-, INTERIM ASSOC LAB DIR, BIOMED & ENVIRON RES, 81- *Concurrent Pos:* Mem, Nat Coun Radiation Protection & Measurements, 71- *Mem:* Radiation Res Soc; Health Physics Soc. *Res:* Radiation biology; epidemiology and toxicology of internally deposited radioisotopes. *Mailing Add:* Off Dir Argonne Nat Lab 9700 SCass Ave Argonne IL 60439

ROWLAND, SATTLEY CLARK, b San Jose, Calif, May 15, 38; m 61; c 2. MATERIALS SCIENCE, PHYSICS. *Educ:* Pac Union Col, BA, 60; Univ Utah, PhD(mat sci), 66. *Prof Exp:* Assoc prof, 66-74, PROF PHYSICS, ANDREWS UNIV, 74- *Concurrent Pos:* NSF grant, Andrews Univ, 69-72. *Mem:* AAAS; Am Asn Physics Teachers; Am Phys Soc. *Res:* X-ray diffraction studies of the structure of amorphous and crystalline semiconductors; lattice parameter measurements; high pressure studies of fatigue in metals. *Mailing Add:* Dept of Physics Andrews Univ Berrien Springs MI 49104

ROWLAND, STANLEY PAUL, b LaCrosse, Wis, Feb 25, 16; m 43; c 4. CELLULOSE CHEMISTRY, POLYMER CHEMISTRY. *Educ:* Univ Minn, BChem, 38; Univ Ill, PhD(org chem), 43. *Prof Exp:* Res chemist, Rohm and Haas Co, 43-56; res supvr, US Indust Chem Co, 56-59, asst mgr org chem, 59-61, mgr explor polymer res, 61-63; res leader, crosslink struct, 63-74, RES LEADER, NAT POLYMER STRUCT RES, SOUTHERN REGIONAL RES CTR, 74- *Concurrent Pos:* Instr, Tulane Univ, 65-68. *Mem:* Am Chem Soc; Soc Plastics Eng; Chem Mkt Res Asn; Fiber Soc; The Chem Soc. *Res:* Chemical modification of cellulose; structural characterization of chemically modified and crosslinked celluloses; chemical reactivity of cellulose and synthetic polymers; synthesis of intermediates, resins and polymers; plasticizers; plastics; fabrication; characterization and testing of polymers and plastics; dehydration of hydrobenzoins. *Mailing Add:* Southern Regional Res Ctr PO Box 19687 New Orleans LA 70179

ROWLAND, THEODORE JUSTIN, b Cleveland, Ohio, May 15, 27; m 52, 68; c 3. ELECTRONIC STRUCTURE, PROPERTIES OF SOLIDS. *Educ:* Western Reserve Univ, BS, 48; Harvard Univ, MA, 49, PhD(appl physics), 54. *Prof Exp:* Res physicist, Res Labs, Union Carbide Metals Co Div, Union Carbide Corp, 54-61; PROF PHYS METALL, UNIV ILL, URBANA, 61- *Concurrent Pos:* Fac res participant, Argonne Nat Lab, 78-; prin investr, Mats Res Lab, Univ Iowa, Ames Lab, 81-82. *Mem:* Fel Am Phys Soc; Am Soc Metals; Am Chem Soc; Am Inst Mining, Metall & Petrol Eng; AAAS. *Res:* Radiospectroscopy; nuclear magnetic resonance in metals; physics of metals, especially solid solutions; polymer physics; nuclear relaxation in elastomers. *Mailing Add:* Dept of Metall & Mining Eng Univ Ill 1304 W Green St Urbana IL 61801

ROWLAND, VERNON, b Clevelend Heights, Ohio, Aug 11, 22; m 49; c 2. PSYCHIATRY. *Educ:* Harvard Med Sch, MD, 46; Am Bd Psychiat & Neurol, dipl. *Prof Exp:* From intern to asst resident med, Univ Hosps, Cleveland, Ohio, 46-48, resident neuropsychiat, 52-53; resident, Cleveland Vet Admin Hosp, 50-52; assoc prof, 60-71, PROF PSYCHIAT, MED SCH, CASE WESTERN UNIV, 71- *Concurrent Pos:* NIMH & univ res fels psychiat, Western Reserve Univ, 53-55; NIMH career develop award, 55-60; assoc physician, Univ Hosps, 54- *Mem:* AAAS; Pavlovian Soc NAm; Am Psychiat Asn. *Res:* Conditioned electrographic response in the brain. *Mailing Add:* Dept of Psychiat Case Western Reserve Univ Cleveland OH 44106

ROWLAND, WALTER FRANCIS, b Decatur, Ill, Nov, 9, 31; c 3. CIVIL ENGINEERING, WATER RESOURCES. *Educ:* Univ Ill, BS, 54, MS, 57; Stanford Univ, PhD(civil eng), 67. *Prof Exp:* Instr civil eng, Univ Ill, 56-59; actg instr, Stanford Univ, 59-61; actg asst prof, Univ Calif, Berkeley, 63-64; asst prof, Colo State Univ, 64-67; assoc prof, 67-72, PROF CIVIL ENG, CALIF STATE UNIV, FRESNO, 72- *Concurrent Pos:* Dir atmospheric water resources res, Fresno State Col Found, 71-73. *Mem:* Am Soc Civil Engrs. *Res:* Surface and atmospheric water resources research and development. *Mailing Add:* 1156 W Ellery Way Fresno CA 93740

ROWLAND, WILLIAM JOSEPH, b Brooklyn, NY, Dec 15, 43; m 71; c 1. ETHOLOGY, BEHAVIORAL ECOLOGY. *Educ:* Adelphi Univ, BA, 65; State Univ NY Stony Brook, PhD(biol), 70. *Prof Exp:* Sci co-worker ethol, Zool Lab, Rijksuniversiteit te Groningen, Haren, Neth, 70-71; asst prof, 71-77, ASSOC PROF ZOOL, IND UNIV, BLOOMINGTON, 77- *Mem:* Sigma Xi; Animal Behav Soc; AAAS; Int Asn Fish Ethologists. *Res:* Causation, evolution and function of species-typical behavior in fishes and other lower vertebrates; social behavior and behavioral ecology of fishes. *Mailing Add:* Dept Biol Ind Univ Bloomington IN 47401

ROWLANDS, DAVID T, JR, b Wilkes-Barre, Pa, Mar 22, 30; m 58; c 2. PATHOLOGY, IMMUNOLOGY. *Educ:* Univ Pa, MD, 55. *Prof Exp:* Asst prof path, Univ Colo, 62-64; asst prof biochem, Rockefeller Univ, 64-66; assoc prof path, Duke Univ, 66-70; chmn dept, 73-78, PROF PATH, SCH MED, UNIV PA, 70- *Mem:* Am Asn Path & Bact; Fedn Am Socs Exp Biol; Int Acad Path; Am Soc Clin Path. *Res:* Developmental immunology; transplantation immunity. *Mailing Add:* Dept of Path Univ of Pa Sch of Med Philadelphia PA 19104

ROWLANDS, JOHN ALAN, b Altrincham, Eng, May 4, 45. SOLID STATE PHYSICS, MEDICAL PHYSICS. *Educ:* Leeds Univ, BSc, 66, PhD(physics), 71. *Prof Exp:* Killam fel physics, Univ Alta, 71-73, res assoc physics, 71-77; vis asst prof dept physics, Mich State Univ, 77-78, vis prof, 78-79; ASST PROF, DEPT RADIOL, UNIV TORONTO, 79- *Mem:* Can Asn Physicists; Am Asn Physicists Med; Am Phys Soc; Soc Photo-Optical Instrumentation Engrs. *Res:* Physics of diagnostic radiology. *Mailing Add:* Radiol Res Labs Med Sci Bldg Univ Toronto Toronto ON 48824 M5S 1A8 Can

ROWLANDS, JOHN RHYS, biophysical chemistry, see previous edition

ROWLANDS, R(ICHARD) O(WEN), b Llangefni, Wales, Apr 26, 14; nat US; m 39; c 2. MATHEMATICS, ELECTRICAL ENGINEERING. *Educ:* Univ Wales, BS, 36, MS, 50. *Prof Exp:* Head filter design group, Gen Elec Co, Eng, 37-48; sr lectr studio sect, Eng Training Dept, Brit Broadcasting Co, 48-57; assoc prof elec eng, 57-58, assoc prof eng res, 58-64, chmn dept eng acoust, 67-70, prof eng res, 64-79, EMER PROF ENG RES, PA STATE UNIV, 79- *Concurrent Pos:* Liaison scientist, US Off Naval Res, Eng, 70-71. *Mem:* Acoust Soc Am; Inst Elec & Electronics Engrs; Brit Inst Elec Engrs. *Res:* Circuit theory; communications; information theory as applied to signal detection; electroacoustics; acoustic telemetry. *Mailing Add:* Appl Res Lab PO Box 30 State College PA 16801

ROWLANDS, ROBERT EDWARD, b Trail, BC, July 7, 36; m 59; c 2. STRESS ANALYSIS, FAILURE-STRENGTH. *Educ:* Univ BC, BASc, 59; Univ Ill, Urbana, MS, 64, PhD(mech), 67. *Prof Exp:* From res engr to sr res engr, IIT Res Inst, 67-74; from asst prof to assoc prof, 74-80, PROF MECH, UNIV WIS-MADISON, 74- *Concurrent Pos:* Consult various orgns, 67- *Honors & Awards:* Hetenyi Award, Soc Exp Stress Anal, 70 & 76. *Mem:* Am Soc Testing & Mat; Am Acad Mech; Am Soc Mech Engrs; Soc Exp Stress Anal; NAm Photonics Asn. *Res:* Experimental stress analysis; photomechanics; fatigue; fracture; composite and advanced materials; numerical processing of experimental data; energy storage; materials at cryogenic environments; wood and paper engineering. *Mailing Add:* Dept Eng Mech Univ Wis 1415 Johnson Dr Madison WI 53706

ROWLANDS, STANLEY, b Liverpool, Eng, July 30, 18; m 42; c 2. MEDICAL BIOPHYSICS, NUCLEAR MEDICINE. *Educ:* Univ Liverpool, BSc, 39, PhD(physics), 42; Univ London, LRCP & MRCS, 56. *Prof Exp:* Lectr physics, Univ Liverpool, 42-44; sr lectr, Univ London, 45-48; lectr med physics, Univ Edinburgh, 48-52; reader physics, Univ London, 52-67; PROF MED BIOPHYS & HEAD DEPT, UNIV CALGARY, 67-, HON PROF PHYSICS, 77- *Concurrent Pos:* Consult physician, St Mary's Hosp, 60-67. *Mem:* Biophys Soc; Soc Nuclear Med; Brit Physiol Soc; Microcirc Soc. *Res:* Cardiovascular biophysics; microcirculation, particularly the mechanical and rheological properties of human erythrocytes. *Mailing Add:* Div Med Biophysics Fac Med Univ Calgary Calgary AB T2N 1N4 Can

ROWLES, CHARLES A, b Crandal, Man, May 8, 15; m 38; c 2. PEDOLOGY. *Educ:* Univ Sask, BSA, 36, MSc, 38; Univ Minn, PhD(soils), 40. *Prof Exp:* Asst, Univ Sask, 35-38, lectr, 40; chief chemist & inspecting officer, Chem & Explosives Div, Inspection Bd, UK & Can, 41-45; assoc prof soil sci, Ont Agr Col, 45-46; prof soil sci & chmn dept, 46-80, hon prof & spec lectr, 80-82, EMER PROF SOIL SCI, UNIV BC, 80- *Concurrent Pos:* UN tech adv, Govt Venezuela, 62-63. *Mem:* Can Soc Soil Sci (secy, 52, treas 53, vpres, 54, pres, 55); Chem Inst Can; Agr Inst Can; Int Soc Soil Sci; Soil Sci Soc Am. *Res:* Formation, chemical and physical properties, cartography, utilization and conservation of soils and documentation of results in the form of journal articles, reports and talks to scientific organizations and the public. *Mailing Add:* Dept Soil Sci Univ BC Vancouver BC V6T 1W5 Can

ROWLETT, ROGER SCOTT, b Chickasha, Okla, Jan 1, 55. ENZYMOLOGY, PHYSICAL BIOCHEMISTRY. *Educ:* Univ Ala, BS, 76, PhD(chem), 81. *Prof Exp:* FEL, DEPT PHARMACOL, COL MED, UNIV FLA, 81- *Mem:* Am Chem Soc. *Res:* Mechanistic studies of zinc-mettaloenzymes (carbonic anhydrase, thermolysin) primarily by examination of steady-state kinetics using microcomputer techniques. *Mailing Add:* Dept Pharmacol Col Med Univ Fla Box J-267 J Hillis Miller Health Ctr Gainesville FL 32610

ROWLETT, RUSSELL JOHNSTON, JR, b Richmond, Va, Sept 19, 20; m 43; c 2. INFORMATION SCIENCE. *Educ:* Univ Va, BS, 41, MS, 43, PhD(org chem), 45. *Prof Exp:* Asst chem, Univ Va, 40-42, assoc, 42-46; chemist, E I du Pont de Nemours & Co, Del, 46; asst ed, Chem Abstr, Ohio State Univ, 47-48, assoc ed, 49-52; patent coordr, Va-Carolina Chem Corp, 52-55, asst dir res, 55-57, asst dir res & develop, 57-60, dir, 60; asst dir, Va Inst Sci Res, 60-67; ed, Chem Abstr Serv, 67-78, ED & DIR PUBL & SERV, CHEM ABSTR SERV, 79- *Concurrent Pos:* Mem comt chem info, Nat Res Coun, 68-73; chmn, Gordon Conf Sci Info Prob Res, 74. *Honors & Awards:* Miles Conrad Award, Nat Fedn Abstracting & Indexing Serv, 80. *Mem:* Fel AAAS; Am Chem Soc; Sigma Xi; Nat Fedn Abstr & Indexing Serv (secy, 74-76, pres 77-78). *Res:* Synthetic organic chemistry; antimalarial drugs; organic chemical nomenclature; patents; chemistry of phosphorus compounds; scientific information storage and retrieval. *Mailing Add:* 3607 Prestwick Ct N Columbus OH 43220

ROWLETT, RUSSELL JOHNSTON, III, b Charlottesville, Va, June 26, 45; m 67; c 1. TOPOLOGY. *Educ:* Univ Va, BA, 67, PhD(math), 70. *Prof Exp:* Instr math, Princeton Univ, 70-74; asst prof, 74-78, ASSOC PROF MATH, UNIV TENN, 78-, DIR, LIBERAL ARTS CO-OP PROG, 79- *Mem:* Am Math Soc; Math Asn Am; Am Soc Eng Educ. *Res:* Classification of smooth actions of compact lie groups on compact manifolds; related questions in the theory of compact transformation groups. *Mailing Add:* Dept of Math Univ of Tenn Knoxville TN 37916

ROWLEY, DAVID ALTON, b Rochester, NY, July 21, 40; m 62; c 2. PHYSICAL INORGANIC CHEMISTRY. *Educ:* State Univ NY Albany, BS, 63, MS, 64; Univ Ill, Urbana, PhD(inorg chem), 68. *Prof Exp:* From asst prof to assoc prof, 68-81, PROF CHEM, GEORGE WASHINGTON UNIV, 81-, ASST DEAN, GRAD SCH ARTS & SCI, 74- *Mem:* Am Chem Soc. *Res:* Inorganic electronic absorption spectroscopy; reaction mechanism and reactions of coordinated ligands. *Mailing Add:* Dept of Chem George Washington Univ Washington DC 20006

ROWLEY, DONALD ADAMS, b Owatonna, Minn, Feb 4, 23; m 48; c 4. EXPERIMENTAL PATHOLOGY, IMMUNOLOGY. *Educ:* Univ Chicago, BS, 45, MS, MD, 50. *Prof Exp:* Sr res surgeon, Nat Inst Allergy & Infectious Dis, 51-54; from instr to asst prof, 54-69, PROF PATH & PEDIAT, UNIV CHICAGO, 69-, dir res, 74-77, DIR, LA RABIDA CHILDREN'S HOSP & RES CTR, LA RABIDA-UNIV CHICAGO INST, 77- *Concurrent Pos:* USPHS sr res fel, 59-69; vis scientist, Sir William Dunn Sch Path, Oxford Univ, 61-62, 70-71. *Mem:* Am Soc Exp Path; Am Asn Path & Bact; Am Asn Immunol. *Res:* Immunologic networks and regulation of the immune responses, specific enhancement and suppression by antigen and antibody. *Mailing Add:* La Rabida Res Ctr East 65th St at Lake Michigan Chicago IL 60649

ROWLEY, DURWOOD B, b Walton, NY, Aug 11, 29; m 50; c 3. FOOD MICROBIOLOGY. *Educ:* Hartwick Col, BS, 51; Syracuse Univ, MS, 53, PhD(microbiol), 62. *Prof Exp:* Asst prof biol, Hartwick Col, 56-59; asst microbiol, Syracuse Univ, 59-62; asst prof, Univ Mass, 62-63; res microbiologist, US Army Natick Labs, 63-70, chief microbiol div, Food Lab, 70-74, HEAD FOOD MICROBIOL GROUP, SCI & TECHNOL LAB, US ARMY NATICK RES & DEVELOP LABS, 74- *Concurrent Pos:* Mem comt nitrate & alternative curing agents in food, Nat Acad Sci. *Mem:* Sigma Xi; Am Soc Microbiol; Inst Food Technol; Brit Soc Appl Bact. *Res:* Bacterial spores; radiation microbiology; microbiological safety of mass feeding systems; rapid recovery and estimation of injured and uninjured food borne bacteria. *Mailing Add:* Food Microbiol Sci & Adv Tech Lab US Army Natick Res & Develop Lab Natick MA 01760

ROWLEY, GEORGE RICHARD, b Rahway, NJ, Aug 21, 23. BIOCHEMISTRY, PHYSIOLOGY. *Educ:* Upsala Col, AB, 49; Rutgers Univ, PhD(biochem), 55. *Prof Exp:* Chem qual control chemist, E R Squibb & Sons, 49-51; USPHS grant psychiat, Coatesville Vet Admin Hosp & Med Sch, Univ Pa, 55-56; assoc res specialist agr chem, Rutgers Univ, 56-57; instr physiol, Col Physicians & Surgeons, Columbia Univ, 57-60; sr res chemist, Colgate-Palmolive Res Lab, 60-64; asst prof, 64-68, ASSOC PROF BIOCHEM & ACTG CHMN DEPT, SCH DENT, FAIRLEIGH DICKINSON UNIV, 68- *Mem:* AAAS; Int Asn Dent Res; Am Chem Soc; NY Acad Sci. *Res:* Blood coagulation and platelet aggregation during hyperlipemia and effects of lipolytic activity; metabolism of vitamin E and vitamin C. *Mailing Add:* 14 Thrumont Rd West Caldwell NJ 07006

ROWLEY, GERALD L(EROY), b New York, NY, May 6, 38; m 61; c 5. BIOCHEMISTRY, ORGANIC CHEMISTRY. *Educ:* Univ Calif, Los Angeles, BS, 61; Calif State Univ, San Diego, MS, 63; Univ Calif, Berkeley, PhD(chem), 71. *Prof Exp:* Res engr chem, Rocketdyne Div, NAm-Rockwell Corp, 63-67; fel, 71-72, sr res chemist, 72-74; proj leader, 74-75, res mgr chem, 75-80, ASST DIR RES, SYVA RES INST, 80- *Concurrent Pos:* Spec fel, NIH, 68-71. *Mem:* Am Chem Soc. *Res:* Enzyme mechanisms especially substrate inter- actions; chemistry of protein labeling; design of new immunoassay methods; immunochemistry. *Mailing Add:* Syva Res Inst PO Box 10058 Palo Alto CA 94303

ROWLEY, JANET DAVISON, b New York, NY, Apr 5, 25; m 48; c 4. CYTOGENETICS. *Educ:* Univ Chicago, BS, 46, MD, 48. *Prof Exp:* Intern med, Marine Hosp, 50-51; instr neurol & neurol surg, Col Med, Univ Ill, 58-61; res assoc, 62-69, assoc prof, 69-77, PROF MED, SCH MED, UNIV CHICAGO, 77- *Concurrent Pos:* Julian D Levinson Res Found fel, 55-58; USPHS spec trainee, 61-62; vis scientist, Lab Chem, Oxford Univ, 70-71. *Mem:* Am Soc Human Genetics. *Res:* Human chromosomes; chromosome abnormalities in pre-leukemia as well as in leukemia and lymphoma; quinacrine and Giemsa stains to identify chromosmes in hybrid cells; hybrids in somatic cell genetics. *Mailing Add:* Dept of Med Box 420 Univ of Chicago Chicago IL 60637

ROWLEY, PETER DEWITT, b Providence, RI, Dec 6, 42; m 81; c 2. GEOLOGY. *Educ:* Carleton Col, BA, 64; Univ Tex, Austin, PhD(geol), 68. *Prof Exp:* Temp instr geol, Kent State Univ, 68-69; asst prof, Carleton Col, 69-70; GEOLOGIST, US GEOL SURV, 70- *Honors & Awards:* Antarctic Serv Medal, US Govt, 72. *Mem:* Soc Econ Geologists; fel Geol Soc Am; Am Polar Soc; Am Geol Inst; Rocky Mountain Asn Geologists. *Res:* Geology of Antarctic Peninsula, Antarctica; Antarctic mineral deposits; geology of Iron Springs Mining District, Utah; structural geology and volcanic stratigraphy of High Plateaus of Utah; geology of eastern Uinta Mountains, Utah-Colorado; geology of Marysvale mining district, Utah; geology of Mount St Helen's volcano. *Mailing Add:* US Geol Surv Box 25046 Fed Ctr Denver CO 80225

ROWLEY, PETER TEMPLETON, b Greenville, Pa, Apr 29, 29; m 67; c 1. HUMAN GENETICS, INTERNAL MEDICINE. *Educ:* Harvard Col, AB, 51; Columbia Univ, MD, 55. *Prof Exp:* Intern med, NY Hosp-Cornell Med Ctr, 55-56; resident, Boston City Hosp, 58-60; asst prof med, Stanford Univ, 63-70; assoc prof, 70-75, PROF MED, PEDIAT, GENETICS & MICROBIOLOGY & ACTG CHMN, DIV GENETICS, SCH MED, UNIV ROCHESTER, 75- *Concurrent Pos:* Hon res asst, Univ Col, Univ London, 60-61; physician & pediatrician, Strong Mem Hosp, 70- *Mem:* Am Soc Human Genetics; Am Fedn Clin Res; Am Col Physicians. *Res:* Human biochemical genetics; thalassemia; abnormal human hemoglobins; genetic counseling. *Mailing Add:* Div of Genetics Univ of Rochester Sch of Med Rochester NY 14642

ROWLEY, RICHARD L, b Salt Lake City, UT, Sept 1, 51; m 72; c 6. THERMODYNAMICS, TRANSPORT PHENOMENA. *Educ:* Brigham Young Univ, BS, 74; Mich State Univ, PhD(phys chem), 78. *Prof Exp:* Res asst thermodynamics, Ctr Thermochem Studies, 74; ASST PROF CHEM ENG, RICE UNIV, 78- *Concurrent Pos:* Consult, Eng Dept, Texaco, Inc, 81. *Mem:* Am Chem Soc; Am Inst Chem Engrs; AAAS; Sigma Xi. *Res:* Measurement and prediction of thermophysical properties, particularly transport coefficients, in liquid mixtures; formulation of liquid mixture models and theories as related to thermodynamic properties. *Mailing Add:* Dept Chem Eng Rice Univ PO Box 1892 Houston TX 77251

ROWLEY, RODNEY RAY, b Cedar City, Utah, Mar 25, 34; m 61; c 4. AUDIOLOGY, PSYCHOACOUSTICS. *Educ:* Brigham Young Univ, BS, 59; Univ Md, MA, 61; Univ Okla, PhD, 66. *Prof Exp:* Assoc prof speech, Univ Utah, 63-73; DIR AUDIOL, MED CTR, LOMA LINDA UNIV, 73- *Concurrent Pos:* Res audiologist, Vet Admin Hosp, Oklahoma City, 65-66; consult, Utah State Training Sch, 68-73, Mt Fuel Supply, 71-73 & Patton State Hosp, 74- *Mem:* Am Speech & Hearing Asn. *Res:* Loudness; noise and man; behavior modification and hearing loss. *Mailing Add:* Dept of Audiol Rm 5406 Loma Linda Univ Med Ctr Loma Linda CA 92350

ROWLEY, WAYNE A, b Spring Glen, Utah, Aug 27, 33; m 57; c 3. ENTOMOLOGY. *Educ:* Utah State Univ, BS, 60, MS, 62; Wash State Univ, PhD(med entom), 65. *Prof Exp:* Res entomologist, US Army Biol Labs, Ft Detrick, Md, 65-67; asst prof, 67-71, assoc prof, 71-75, PROF ENTOM, IOWA STATE UNIV, 75- *Mem:* Sigma Xi; Entom Soc Am; Am Mosquito Control Asn. *Res:* Insect transmission of vertebrate pathogen; mosquito biology and flight; biology and taxonomy of bloodsucking midges. *Mailing Add:* Dept of Entom Iowa State Univ Ames IA 50010

ROWND, ROBERT HARVEY, b Chicago, Ill, July 4, 37; m 59; c 3. BIOCHEMISTRY, MOLECULAR BIOLOGY. *Educ:* St Louis Univ, BS, 59; Harvard Univ, MA, 61, PhD(biophys), 63. *Prof Exp:* USPHS fel molecular biol, Med Res Coun Unit, Cambridge Univ, Eng, 63-65; Nat Acad Sci-Nat Res Coun res fel biochem, Pasteur Inst, Paris, France, 65-66; from asst prof to assoc prof biochem & molecular biol, Univ Wis-Madison, 66-73, chmn, Molecular Biol Lab, 70-81, prof, 73-81; PROF & CHMN, DEPT MOLECULAR BIOL, MED & DENT SCH, NORTHWESTERN UNIV, 81- *Concurrent Pos:* Mem, NSF adv panel for develop biol, 68-71; USPHS res career develop award, NIH, 68-73; mem adv panel grad fel, NSF, 74-77, chmn, 76-77, NATO fel, 79; mem, NIH Microbial Biochem Study Sect, 78-; mem comt human health effects subtherapeut antibiotic use in animal feed, Nat Res Coun, 79-81; ed, J Bacteriol, 81- *Mem:* Am Soc Biol Chem; Am Soc Microbiol; Am Acad Microbiol; NY Acad Sci. *Res:* Structure, function and replication of nucleic acids; cellular regulatory mechanisms; genetics and mechanism of drug resistance in bacteria; macromolecular chemistry and biology. *Mailing Add:* Dept Molecular Biol Northwestern Univ 303 E Chicago Ave Chicago IL 60611

ROWNTREE, ROBERT FREDRIC, b Columbus, Ohio, Feb 8, 30; m 56; c 2. TECHNOLOGY BASE MANAGEMENT, LABORATORY PLANNING. *Educ:* Miami Univ, BA, 52; Syracuse Univ, MPA, 53; Ohio State Univ, PhD(physics), 63. *Prof Exp:* Physicist, Wright Air Develop Ctr, Wright-Paterson AFB, Ohio, 53; asst physics, Ohio State Univ, 56-58, Univ Res Found, 58-59, res assoc, 61-63; physicist, 63-64, assoc missions anal, 64-68, prog dir air strike warfare, 68-72, prog dir res & develop planning, Weapons Planning Group, 72-75, head regt group, Off Resource & Technol, 75-76, head, Off Plans & Progs, 76-78, TECHNOL BASE COORDR, LAB DIRECTORATE, NAVAL WEAPONS CTR, CHINA LAKE, CALIF, 78- *Mem:* Optical Soc Am; Am Phys Soc. *Res:* Optical properties of solids; instrumentation for infrared spectroscopy; arms control research; military operations research; laboratory management science policy. *Mailing Add:* 1920 Halsey St Ridgecrest CA 93555

ROWOTH, OLIN ARTHUR, b Trenton, Mo, May 6, 21; m 46; c 3. POULTRY NUTRITION, POULTRY HUSBANDRY. *Educ:* Univ Mo, BA, 43, MA, 48. *Prof Exp:* Vitamin chemist, Beacon Milling Co, Spencer Kellogg & Sons, Inc, 47-50, poultry nutritionist, 50-59, asst dir poultry & small animal res, 59-64, dir poultry res, Beacon Feeds, Textron Inc, 64-66, DIR RES & TECH SERV, BEACON MILLING CO, INC, 66-, VPRES SERV, 68- *Mem:* Poultry Sci Asn; Animal Nutrit Res Coun; World Poultry Sci Asn; Am Soc Animal Sci; Am Poultry Hist Soc. *Res:* Nutrition of chickens, ducks, turkeys, game birds and dogs; feeding systems; nutrient requirements of poultry. *Mailing Add:* Beacon Milling Co Inc Cayuga NY 13034

ROWSELL, HARRY CECIL, b Toronto, Ont, May 29, 21; m 46; c 4. VETERINARY PATHOLOGY. *Educ:* Univ Toronto, DVM, 49, DVPH, 50; Univ Minn, PhD(vet path), 56. *Prof Exp:* Asst res bact, Ont Vet Col, Univ Guelph, 50-51, asst prof path, 53-56, prof res, 56-57 & physiol sci, 58-65; prof vet path, Univ Sask, 65-68; exec dir, Can Coun Animal Care, 68-70; PROF PATH, FAC MED, UNIV OTTAWA, 70- *Concurrent Pos:* Consult, Blood & Vasc Dis Res Unit, Dept Med, Univ Toronto, 58-64 & Med Sci Complex, 64-65, res assoc, 64-65; permanent secy, Can Coun Animal Care, 70- *Mem:* Am Heart Asn; Am Soc Exp Path; Can Vet Med Asn; Can Physiol Soc; Can Fedn Biol Sci. *Res:* Comparative medicine; pathogenesis of bacterial and mycotic infections; comparative pathology and cardiology; hemostatic mechanism; coagulation defects in animals; experimental and naturally occuring atherosclerosis; laboratory animal science, care and management. *Mailing Add:* Dept of Path Fac of Med Univ of Ottawa Ottawa ON K1N 9A9 Can

ROWTON, RICHARD LEE, b Springfield, Mo, May 29, 28; m 51; c 2. ORGANIC CHEMISTRY. *Educ:* Univ Mo-Rolla, BS, 50, MS, 52; Okla State Univ, PhD(org chem), 59. *Prof Exp:* sr res chemist, Jefferson Chem Co, 59-77, SR TECH SERV REP, TEXACO CHEM CO, 77- *Mem:* Am Chem Soc. *Res:* Petrochemicals epoxide reaction mechanisms and isotope effects in chemical reactions; urethane chemistry, foams and elastomers; urethane foam seating. *Mailing Add:* Texaco Chem Co PO Box 15730 Austin TX 78761

ROWZEE, E(DWIN) R(ALPH), b Washington, DC, May 17, 08; m 35; c 3. CHEMICAL ENGINEERING. *Educ:* Mass Inst Technol, MS, 31. *Hon Degrees:* DSc, Laval Univ, 55. *Prof Exp:* Chem engr, Goodyear Tire & Rubber Co, 31-35, in charge synthetic rubber develop, 35-42; with copolymer plant, Can Synthetic Rubber, Ltd, 42-44; dir res, 44-47, mgr prod eng & res, 47-51, mem bd dirs, 50, vpres & mgr, 51-57, pres & managing dir, 57-71, chmn bd dirs, Polymer Corp, 71-78, CHMN BD DIRS, URBAN TRANS DEVELOP CORP, LTD, 73- *Concurrent Pos:* Purvis Mem lectr, Soc Chem Indust, 47; R S Jane Mem lectr, Chem Inst Can, 60; Found lectr, Brit Inst Rubber Indust, 63; mem bd gov, Univ Windsor & Ont Res Found; mem, Sci Coun Can, 66-69. *Mem:* Am Chem Soc; Chem Inst Can (pres, 54-55); Soc Chem Indust. *Mailing Add:* 580 Woodrowe Ave Sarnia ON N7V 2W2 Can

ROXBURGH, JAMES MAXWELL, b Ft Saskatchewan, Alta, Sept 9, 21; m 44; c 2. BIOMEDICAL ENGINEERING. *Educ:* Univ Alta, BSc, 42, MSc, 47; McGill Univ, PhD(chem), 49. *Prof Exp:* Lectr chem, Univ Alta, 45-47; assoc res officer, Prairie Regional Lab, Nat Res Coun Can, 49-61, sci liaison officer, 61-65; sci counsr, Can Embassy, 65-67; assoc awards officer, Nat Res Coun Can, 67-68; secy, 68-75, DIR GRANTS, MED RES COUN CAN, 75- *Res:* Biomedical engineering. *Mailing Add:* Med Res Coun of Can Ottawa ON K1A 0W9 Can

ROXBY, ROBERT, b Abington, Pa, June 4, 40; m 65; c 2. BIOCHEMISTRY. *Educ:* Gettysburg Col, BA, 62; Univ NC, Chapel Hill, MA, 65; Duke Univ, PhD(biochem), 70. *Prof Exp:* Fel biochem & biophys, Ore State Univ, 70-72; asst prof biochem, Temple Univ Sch Med, 72-75; ASST PROF BIOCHEM, UNIV MAINE, ORONO, 75- *Res:* Protein structure and interactions. *Mailing Add:* Dept of Biochem Univ of Maine Orono ME 04473

ROXIN, EMILIO O, b Buenos Aires, Arg, Apr 6, 22; m 62; c 2. MATHEMATICS. *Educ:* Univ Buenos Aires, Engr, 47, Dr(math), 58. *Prof Exp:* Asst math & physics, Univ Buenos Aires, 48-56, prof math, 56-67; PROF MATH, UNIV RI, 67- *Concurrent Pos:* Researcher, AEC, Arg, 53-60 & Res Inst Advan Study, Md, 60-64; res assoc, Brown Univ, 64-65; vis prof, Univ Mich, 67. *Mem:* Am Math Soc; Arg Math Union; Math Asn Am; Soc Indust & Appl Math. *Res:* Ordinary differential equations, especially applied to control theory. *Mailing Add:* Dept of Math Univ of RI Kingston RI 02881

ROY, AMEDEE, metallurgical engineering, see previous edition

ROY, ARUN K, b Ganraganj, India, Dec 29, 38; m 68. BIOCHEMISTRY, ENDOCRINOLOGY. *Educ:* Univ Calcutta, BSc, 58, MSc, 60; Wayne State Univ, PhD(biochem), 65. *Prof Exp:* Asst biochem, Wayne State Univ, 61-65 & molecular biol, Columbia Univ, 65-66; res assoc biochem, Univ Pittsburgh, 66-69; asst prof, 69-74, assoc prof, 74-79, PROF BIOL SCI, OAKLAND UNIV, 79- *Concurrent Pos:* Vis asst prof, Dept Cell Biol, Baylor Col Med, Houston, Tex, 74 & Dept Chem, Univ Nebr, Lincoln, 75; NIH res career develop award, 75. *Honors & Awards:* Lillehei Award Biomed Res, Oakland Med Ctr, 72. *Mem:* Am Physiol Soc; Endocrine Soc; Soc Exp Biol & Med; Am Soc Biol Chemists. *Res:* Molecular endocrinology. *Mailing Add:* Dept of Biol Sci Oakland Univ Rochester MI 48063

ROY, CLAUDE CHARLES, b Quebec City, Que, Oct 21, 28; m 62; c 3. PEDIATRICS, GASTROENTEROLOGY. *Educ:* Laval Univ, BA, 49, MD, 54, FRCPS(C), 59. *Prof Exp:* NIH res fel, Med Ctr, Univ Colo, Denver, 64-66, from asst prof to assoc prof pediat, 66-70; asst to dir, Dept Pediat, 77-80, DIR, PEDIAT RES CTR, STE JUSTINE HOSP, 80-; PROF PEDIAT, UNIV MONTREAL, 70- *Mem:* Can Pediat Soc; Can Soc Clin Invest; Soc Pediat Res; Am Gastroenterol Asn. *Res:* Bile salt metabolism and function; bile salt in clinical and experimental disorders of the liver, pancreas and gastrointestinal tract. *Mailing Add:* Ste Justine Hosp 3175 Ste Catherine Rd Montreal PQ Can

ROY, DEBDUTTA, b Calcutta, India, Jan 20, 40; c 2. BIOCHEMISTRY. *Educ:* Univ Calcutta, BSc, 59, MSc, 61, DPhil(chem), 66. *Prof Exp:* Sr biochemist, Univ Calcutta, 66-68; asst res biochemist, Univ Calif, Berkeley, 68-69; res assoc, Yale Univ, 69-73; RES ASSOC, COLUMBIA UNIV, 73- *Mem:* Asn Res Vision & Ophthal. *Res:* Mechanism of senile cataract formation and its prevention. *Mailing Add:* Dept Ophthal 630 W 168th St New York NY 10032

ROY, DELLA M(ARTIN), b Merrill, Ore, Nov 3, 26; m 48; c 3. GEOCHEMISTRY, MATERIALS SCIENCE. *Educ:* Univ Ore, BS, 47; Pa State Univ, MS, 49, PhD(mineral), 52. *Prof Exp:* Asst mineral, 49-52, res assoc geochem, 52-59, sr res assoc, 59-69, sr res assoc, Mat Res Lab, 63-69, assoc prof mat sci, 69-77, PROF MAT SCI, MAT RES LAB, PA STATE UNIV, UNIVERSITY PARK, 77- *Concurrent Pos:* Mem comn A2E06, Hwy Res Bd, Nat Acad Sci; ed, Cement & Concrete Res. *Honors & Awards:* Jeppeson Medal, Am Ceramic Soc, 82. *Mem:* Fel AAAS; Geochem Soc; fel Mineral Soc Am; Am Soc Eng Educ; Am Ceramics Soc. *Res:* Phase equilibria in fluoride and oxide systems at elevated temperatures and pressures; mineral synthesis; crystal chemistry and phase transitions; crystal growth; cement chemistry, hydration and microstructure; concrete durability; biomaterials; special glasses; radioactive waste management; geologic isolation. *Mailing Add:* 217 Mat Res Lab Pa State Univ University Park PA 16802

ROY, DIPAK, b WBengal, India, Aug 4, 46; m 75; c 1. HAZARDOUS WASTE MANAGEMENT, WATER & WASTE TREATMENT. *Educ:* Jadavpur Univ, India, BCE, 68; Indian Inst Technol, MTech, 71; Univ Ill, Urbana, PhD(civil & environ eng), 79. *Prof Exp:* Scientist Res Environ Eng, Nat Environ Eng Res Inst, 71-73; design engr civil eng, Catalytic, Inc, 73-74, Air Pollution Control, Johns & March, 74-75; ASST PROF, ENVIRON ENG, LA STATE UNIV, 79- *Concurrent Pos:* Consult, NY Assoc, New Orleans, 80. *Mem:* Water Pollution Control Fedn; Am Water Works Asn; Am Soc Civil Engrs; Asn Environ Eng Prof. *Res:* Destruction of hazardous wastes by photolytic ozonation; removal and inactivation of viruses from water and wastewater; methane generation from waste and organic biomass; mathematical modelling of environmental engineering processes. *Mailing Add:* Dept Civil Eng La State Univ Baton Rouge LA 70803

ROY, DIPANKAR, b Calcutta, India, July 4, 52. AERONAUTICAL & ASTRONAUTICAL ENGINEERING. *Educ:* Indian Inst Technol, Kharagpur, BTechnol, 74; Univ Toronto, MASc, 76, PhD(aerospace eng), 79. *Prof Exp:* Res asst aeroacoust, Inst Aerospace Studies, Univ Toronto, 80; contract engr, 80-81, specialist engr, 81, SR SPECIALIST ENGR NOISE TECHNOL, BOEING COMMERICAL AIRPLANE CO, SEATTLE, 81- *Mem:* Acoust Soc Am; Am Inst Aeronaut & Astronaut. *Res:* Aircraft noise propagation effects-especially refraction, Doppler and turbulence mechanisms introduced by wind and temperature variations in the atmosphere; acoustics of thunder. *Mailing Add:* 6216 S 153rd St #209 Seattle WA 98188

ROY, DONALD H, b Raleigh, NC, July 13, 36; m 65. NUCLEAR PHYSICS, REACTOR PHYSICS. *Educ:* NC State Univ, BS, 58, PhD(nuclear eng), 62; Mass Inst Technol, MS, 59. *Prof Exp:* Reactor physicist, 59-60, sr reactor physicist, 62-63, GROUP SUPVR THEORET PHYSICS & EXP PHYSICS ANAL, BABCOCK & WILCOX CO, 63- *Res:* Advanced computational methods for resonance absorption calculations and prediction of high energy nuclear reaction cross sections and distribution matrices. *Mailing Add:* 1221 Langhorne Rd Lynchburg VA 24503

ROY, DOUGLASS FIELDING, b San Francisco, Calif, June 11, 19; m 47; c 4. FORESTRY. *Educ:* Univ Calif, BS, 46, MS, 62. *Prof Exp:* Forester forest mgt res, Calif, Forest & Range Exp Sta, 46-47, silviculturist, 48-49, res forester, 50-55, PRIN SILVICULTURIST & PROJ LEADER, PAC SOUTHWEST FOREST & RANGE EXP STA, US FOREST SERV, 56- *Mem:* AAAS; Ecol Soc Am; Soc Am Foresters. *Res:* Silviculture, mensuration and regeneration; effects of harvest cutting, stand improvement and other treatments on the growth, yield, quality, mortality and regeneration of pure and mixed forest stands in California; effects of climatic and soil factors and subordinate vegetation. *Mailing Add:* 2400 Washington Ave Redding CA 96001

ROY, GABRIEL L, b Otterburne, Man, Apr 27, 38; c 2. ANIMAL BREEDING, GENETICS. *Educ:* Univ Man, BSA, 64, MSc, 66; Univ Sask, PhD(animal breeding), 73. *Prof Exp:* Supt swine prod, Govt Nfld & Labrador, 66-69; RES SCIENTIST ANIMAL BREEDING, RES STA AGR CAN, 72- *Mem:* Am Soc Animal Sci; Can Soc Animal Sci. *Res:* Dairy protein yield, lifetime production, crossbreeding and mating scheme; dairy-beef crossbreeding; cow productivity; carcass fat distribution; dystocia. *Mailing Add:* Agr Can Res Sta PO Box 90 Lennoxville PQ J1M 1Z3 Can

ROY, GUY, b Que, Apr 10, 39; m 63; c 3. BIOPHYSICS. *Educ:* Univ Laval, BSc, 64; Univ Calif, PhD(biophys), 69. *Prof Exp:* Asst prof, 68-74, assoc prof, 74-80, PROF BIOPHYS, UNIV MONTREAL, 80- *Concurrent Pos:* Vis prof, Dept Physiol, Kyoto Univ, Kyoto, Japan, 75-76. *Mem:* Biophys Soc. *Res:* Ionic currents across artificial and biological membranes; theory and experiments. *Mailing Add:* Dept Physics Univ Montreal Box 6128 Montreal PQ H3C 3J7 Can

ROY, HARRY, b Cincinnati, Ohio, Aug 29, 43. PLANT BIOCHEMISTRY. *Educ:* Brown Univ, AB, 65, ScM, 66; Johns Hopkins Univ, PhD(cell biol), 70. *Prof Exp:* Fel plant biochem, Johns Hopkins Univ, 70-71; NIH fel plant physiol, Cornell Univ, 71-74; asst prof life sci, Polytech Inst New York, 74-76; asst prof, 76-80, ASSOC PROF BIOL, RENSSELAER POLYTECH INST, 80- *Mem:* Biophys Soc; Am Soc Plant Physiologists; NY Acad Sci; AAAS. *Res:* Synthesis and assembly of chloroplast proteins. *Mailing Add:* Dept of Biol Rensselaer Polytech Inst Troy NY 12181

ROY, JEAN-CLAUDE, b Quebec, Que, Jan 6, 27; m 56; c 2. RADIOCHEMISTRY, ANALYTICAL CHEMISTRY. *Educ:* Univ Laval, BA, 47, BSc, 51; Univ Notre Dame, PhD(chem), 54. *Prof Exp:* Vis chemist, Carnegie Inst Technol, 54-55; res officer radiochem, Atomic Energy Can, 55-62 & Int Bur Weights & Measures, France, 62-64; prof radiochem, 64-74, PROF CHEM, UNIV LAVAL, 74- *Mem:* Chem Inst Can. *Res:* Methodology and measurement of radioactivity in waters and sediments; x-ray fluorescence analysis; analytical studies on asbestos and asbestos tailings. *Mailing Add:* Dept of Chem Fac of Sci Univ of Laval Quebec PQ G1K 7P4 Can

ROY, LELAND F(REDERIC), b Passaic, NJ, July 11, 15; m 51; c 2. CHEMICAL ENGINEERING. *Educ:* Ohio State Univ, BChE, 36, MSc, 37, PhD(chem eng), 39. *Prof Exp:* Res chemist, Carnegie-Ill Steel Co, Pa, 39-41; chem engr, Tenn Valley Authority, 41-53; from assoc prof to prof chem eng, Univ Miss, 53-80; RETIRED. *Concurrent Pos:* Actg asst prof, Ohio State Univ, 45. *Mem:* Am Chem Soc; Am Inst Chem Engrs. *Res:* Development of fertilizer processes; phosphates; heat transfer tests of a glass-lined condenser. *Mailing Add:* Dept of Chem Eng Univ of Miss University MS 38677

ROY, MARIE LESSARD, b Fall River, Mass, Mar 1, 44; m 69. TOXICOLOGY, OCCUPATIONAL MEDICINE. *Educ:* Albertus Magnus Col, BA, 65; Univ Conn, PhD(org chem), 69, MD, 79. *Prof Exp:* Lectr org chem & chem eng, Univ Toronto, 69-73, lectr pharmacol, 73-77; internship, 79-80, resident internal med, 80-81, TOXICOLOGIST, MINISTRY LABOR, 81- *Mem:* Am Chem Soc; Sigma Xi. *Mailing Add:* 89 Poyntz Ave Willowdale ON M2N 1J3 Can

ROY, PAUL-H(ENRI), b Quebec City, Que, Apr 19, 24, m 56. CHEMICAL ENGINEERING. *Educ:* Laval Univ, BASc, 48; Univ Mich, MSE, 49; Ill Inst Technol, PhD(chem eng), 55. *Prof Exp:* Proj engr, Res Inst, Univ Mich, 49-51; res engr, E I du Pont de Nemours & Co, Inc, 55-60; from asst prof to assoc prof chem eng, 60-64, vdean fac sci, 61-69, PROF CHEM ENG, LAVAL UNIV, 64- *Concurrent Pos:* Consult, E I du Pont de Nemours & Co, Inc, 64-69; mem, Hydro-Que Res Comt, 65-66 & Laval Admin Comn, 65-69; Laval rep, Can Res Mgt Asn, 67-72; rep sci adv planning br, Ministry of State Sci & Technol, Govt Can, 72- *Mem:* Am Inst Chem Engrs; Can Chem Eng Soc; Can Coun Prof Engrs. *Res:* Mixing of liquids as related to dynamics of chemical reactors; mechanism of liquid; liquid dispersion; waste water treatment; chemical process economics. *Mailing Add:* 380 CH St Louis Apt 503 Quebec PQ C1K 7P4 Can

ROY, PRABIR, b Calcutta, India, Nov 24, 37. TOPOLOGY. *Educ:* Univ NC, Chapel Hill, BS, 57, MA, 59, PhD(math), 61. *Prof Exp:* Instr math, Univ NC, Chapel Hill, 58-61; mem, Inst Advan Studies, 61-62; asst prof, Univ Ill, Urbana, 62-63; asst prof, Univ Wis, 63-66; assoc prof, Rutgers Univ, 66-68; PROF MATH, STATE UNIV NY BINGHAMTON, 68- *Res:* Point-set theoretic investigation of continua; dimension theory of sets in the Hilbert Cube; normality and its variations; composition of functions. *Mailing Add:* Dept Math Sci State Univ NY Binghamton NY 13901

ROY, PRODYOT, b Calcutta, India; US citizen; m 63; c 2. MATERIALS SCIENCE, PHYSICAL CHEMISTRY. *Educ:* Univ Calcutta, BS, 57; Univ Calif, Berkeley, MS, 59, PhD(mat sci), 63. *Prof Exp:* Res engr surface chem, Univ Calif, Berkeley, 63-65, res engr chem, 67-68; res fel, Max Planck Inst Phys Chem, 65-67; engr chem, 68-80, MGR PLANT MAT, GEN ELEC CO, SUNNYVALE, 80- *Mem:* Am Inst Mining, Metall & Petrol Engrs; Am Soc Metals. *Res:* Thermodynamics of metals and alloys; surface chemistry and adsorption phenomenon; solid state electrochemistry; fast breeder coolant chemistry; mechanical properties of materials; corrosion and stress corrosion. *Mailing Add:* 12980 Foot Hill Lane Saratoga CA 95070

ROY, RABINDRA (NATH), b July 31, 39; m 68. PHYSICAL CHEMISTRY, ANALYTICAL CHEMISTRY. *Educ:* Jadavpur Univ, India, BSc, 59, MSc, 61; La State Univ, Baton Rouge, PhD(chem), 66. *Prof Exp:* Indian Dept Health res scholar phys chem, Jadavpur Univ, India, 61-63; teaching asst chem, La State Univ, Baton Rouge, 65-66; from asst prof to assoc prof phys & anal chem, Drury Col, 66-71; petrol res fund res assoc phys chem, Univ Fla, 71-73; PROF CHEM & CHMN DEPT, DRURY COL, 73- *Mem:* Am Chem Soc; Royal Soc Chem; Am Soc Test & Mat. *Res:* Thermodynamics and analytical processes of electrolytes and nonelectrolytes in aqueous mixed and nonaqueous solvents from physicochemical measurements; buffer solutions; ion-selective electrode and mixed strong electrolytes. *Mailing Add:* Dept of Chem Drury Col Springfield MO 65802

ROY, RADHA RAMAN, b Calcutta, India, Feb 8, 21; US citizen; m 56; c 2. NUCLEAR PHYSICS. *Educ:* Univ Calcutta, BS, 40, MS, 42; Univ London, PhD(nuclear physics), 46. *Prof Exp:* AEC fel, Univ London, 43-49; in chg courses nuclear physics & dir nuclear lab, Free Univ Brussels, 49-57; from asst prof to prof nuclear physics, Pa State Univ, 58-63, dir nuclear physics lab, 58-63; PROF NUCLEAR PHYSICS, ARIZ STATE UNIV, 63- *Mem:* Fel Am Phys Soc. *Res:* Interactions of photons and leptons with matter; nuclear structure; fission; pair and triplet production; scattering of light particles; nuclear instrumentation. *Mailing Add:* Dept of Physics Ariz State Univ Tempe AZ 85257

ROY, RAM BABU, b Patna, India, Jan 15, 33; US citizen; m; c 3. ORGANIC CHEMISTRY, ANALYTICAL CHEMISTRY. *Educ:* Univ Bihar, India, BSc, 56; Patna Univ, MSc, 58; Univ Newcastle, Eng, PhD(org chem), 67. *Prof Exp:* Head dept chem, Magadh Univ, India, 60-68; vis prof, Univ Mich, Ann Arbor, 68-69 & Univ Wash, 69-71; sr res fel biochem sci, Princeton Univ, 71-72; res chemist food eng, Mass Inst Technol, 72-73; SR RES SCIENTIST, TECHNICON INSTRUMENT CORP, 73- *Mem:* Am Chem Soc; fel Am Inst Chemists; fel Inst Food Technol; Royal Inst Chem. *Res:* Application of autoanalyzer in analytical works, especially development of methods for food, agriculture, pharmaceutical and water samples; use of NMR, ESR and MS for determining structures of organic compounds. *Mailing Add:* Technicon Indust Systs Tarrytown NY 10591

ROY, ROB, b Brooklyn, NY, Jan 2, 33; m 59; c 2. ELECTRICAL & BIOMEDICAL ENGINEERING. *Educ:* Cooper Union, BSEE, 54; Columbia Univ, MSEE, 56; Rensselaer Polytech Inst, DEngSci(elec eng), 62. *Prof Exp:* Sr engr character recognition, Control Instrument Div, Burroughs Corp, 56-60; from instr to assoc prof elec eng, 60-68, PROF SYSTS ENG, RENSSELAER POLYTECH INST, 68- *Concurrent Pos:* Consult, Raytheon Corp, 66-, US Air Force, 67- & Cornell Aeronaut Lab, 67-; NIH spec fel, 72-74. *Mem:* Inst Elec & Electronics Engrs. *Res:* Pattern recognition; digital signal processing; process identification; adaptive control systems; biomedical research; radar systems. *Mailing Add:* Dept of Systs Eng Rensselaer Polytech Inst Troy NY 12181

ROY, ROBERT FRANCIS, b Boston, Mass, Aug 13, 30; m 60; c 4. GEOPHYSICS. *Educ:* Harvard Univ, AB, 52, MS, 60, PhD(geophys), 63. *Prof Exp:* Geologist, Anaconda Co, 52-57; res fel geophys, Harvard Univ, 63-66; sr res fel, Calif Inst Technol, 66-68; assoc prof, Univ Minn, Minneapolis, 68-71; prof geophys, Purdue Univ, Lafayette, 71-77; L A NELSON PROF GEOL SCI, UNIV TEX EL PASO, 77- *Mem:* Am Geophys Union; Soc Econ Geol; Soc Explor Geophysicists. *Res:* Geothermal studies; economic geology; geochemistry; petrology. *Mailing Add:* Dept Geol Sci Univ Tex El Paso TX 79968

ROY, RUSTUM, b Ranchi, India, July 3, 24; nat US; m 48; c 3. MATERIALS SCIENCE. *Educ:* Univ Patna, India, BSc, 42, MSc, 44; Pa State Univ, PhD(ceramics), 48. *Prof Exp:* Res asst, Pa State Univ, 48-49; sr sci officer, Nat Ceramic Lab, India, 50; from asst prof to assoc prof, 50-57, chmn solid state tech prog, 60-67, prof solid state, 67-80, PROF GEOCHEM, PA STATE UNIV, 57-, DIR MAT RES LAB, 62-, CHMN SCI, TECHNOL & SOCIAL PROG, 77-, EVAN PUGH PROF SOLID STATE, 80 *Concurrent Pos:* Dir, Tem-Pres Res Inc, 60-68 & Kirkridge Inc, 60-; mem, Nat Res Coun, 62-71, Exec Comt, Chem Div, 67-70; chmn, Comt Sci Technol & Church, Planning Strategy Comt, Nat Coun Churches, 64-70; mem, Pa Govr's Sci Adv Comt & chmn, Mat Adv Panel, 65-; ed in chief, Mat Res Bull, 66- & Bull Sci, Technol & Soc, 81-; mem, Comt Mineral Sci Technol, Nat Acad Sci, 67-69, Comt Surv Mat Sci Technol, 70-74; mem, Adv Comt Eng, NSF, 68-72, Adv Comt Ethical & Human Value Implications Sci & Technol, 74-77 & Adv Comt Div Mat Res, 74-77; mem, Bd Trustees, Dag Hammarskjold Col, 68-75, chmn, 73-75; mem, Nat Mat Adv Bd, 70-76; chmn sci, tech & soc prog, Pa State Univ, 70-72 & 77-; mem, Comt Radioactive Waste, Nat Acad Sci-Nat Res Coun-Nat Acad Eng, 74- & Comt USSR & Eastern Europe, 74-, chmn, 75-; consult, Xerox Corp, Bausch & Lomb Inc & Carborumdum Co. *Honors*

& Awards: Mineral Soc Am Award, 57. Mem: Nat Acad Eng; fel AAAS; fel Am Ceramic Soc; fel Mineral Soc Am; Mat Res Soc (vpres, 75, pres, 77). Res: Materials science, especially synthesis and preparation of new materials, in particular non-crystalline and polyphasic materials; high temperature high pressure chemistry and phase transitions; studies in science, technology and values; sex ethics. Mailing Add: Materials Res Lab Pa State Univ University Park PA 16802

ROY, WILLIAM ARTHUR, b Elkins, WVa, July 24, 48. TERATOLOGY, BONE BIOLOGY. Educ: Fairmont State Col, BS, 70; WVa Univ, PhD(anat), 76. Prof Exp: Nat res serv award anat, Univ Va, 76-78; ASST PROF ANAT & EMBRYOLOGY, SCH DENT, MARQUETTE UNIV, 78- Mem: Teratology Soc; AAAS; Am Asn Anatomists. Res: Normal and abnormal craniofacial development during the prenatal and early postnatal periods; pathogenesis and treatment of craniofacial anomalies such as premature craniosynostosis and cleft palate. Mailing Add: Dept Basic Sci Sch Dent Marquette Univ 604 N 16th St Milwaukee WI 53233

ROYAL, GEORGE CALVIN, JR, b Williamston, SC, Aug 5, 21; c 6. MEDICAL MICROBIOLOGY. Educ: Tuskegee Inst, BS, 43; Univ Wis, MS, 47; Univ Pa, PhD, 57. Prof Exp: Instr bact, Tuskegee Inst, 47-48; asst immunol, Ohio Agr Exp Sta, 50-52; asst prof bact, Agr & Tech Col NC, 52-53, prof, 57-65; ASSOC PROF MICROBIOL, COL MED, HOWARD UNIV, 66- Concurrent Pos: Fel, Jefferson Med Col, 65-66; dir, Sr Res Proj, US AEC, 58-65; dir, Undergrad Res Partic Prog, NSF, 59-61; mem, Nat Adv Food Comt, Food & Drug Admin, 72- Mem: NY Acad Sci; Am Soc Microbiol; fel Am Acad Microbiol. Res: Allergy and immunology; chemical and physical properties of univalent-reaginic-type immunoglobulins and their production and demonstration in man and animals. Mailing Add: Dept of Microbiol Howard Univ Col of Med Washington DC 20059

ROYALL, NORMAN NORRIS, JR, b Whiteville, NC, Oct 29, 08; m 31; c 1. MATHEMATICS. Educ: Stetson Univ, BS & MS, 29; Emory Univ, AM, 35, Brown Univ, PhD(math), 40. Prof Exp: Instr math, Ga Sch Technol, 29-35 & Brown Univ, 35-37; asst prof, The Citadel, 37-40; assoc prof, Winthrop Col, 40-42; dean, Col Lib Arts, 47-53, prof math & phys sci, 53-75, EMER PROF, COL ARTS & SCI, UNIV MO-KANSAS CITY, 75- Mem: Am Math Asn. Res: Mathematical analysis; Laplace transforms; history and philosophy of science; physical science; educational and technical motion pictures. Mailing Add: 635 E 63rd Terr Kansas City MO 64110

ROYALL, RICHARD MILES, b Elkin, NC, Aug 13, 39; m 59; c 2. BIOSTATISTICS. Educ: NC State Univ, BS, 62; Stanford Univ, MS, 64, PhD(statist), 66. Prof Exp: From asst prof to assoc prof biostatist, 66-74, assoc prof math sci, 74-77, PROF BIOSTATIST, JOHNS HOPKINS UNIV, 77- Mem: Int Statist Inst; Biomet Soc; Am Statist Asn. Res: Finite population sampling theory; foundations of statistical inference. Mailing Add: Dept of Biostatist Johns Hopkins Univ Baltimore MD 21205

ROYALS, EDWIN EARL, b Climax, Ga, Jan 23, 19; m 42; c 4. ORGANIC CHEMISTRY. Educ: Emory Univ, AB, 40, MS, 41; Univ Wis, PhD(org chem), 44. Prof Exp: Instr chem, Ga Inst Technol, 44-46; from asst prof to assoc prof, Emory Univ, 46-62; res chemist, Heyden Newport Chem Corp, 62-65; PROF CHEM, PENSACOLA JR COL, 65-, HEAD DEPT, 67- Concurrent Pos: Consult citrus indust. Mem: Am Chem Soc. Res: Base catalyzed condensations; terpene and epoxide chemistry; reactions of olefinic linkage. Mailing Add: Dept of Chem Pensacola Jr Col Pensacola FL 32504

ROY-BURMAN, PRADIP, b Comillah, India, Nov 12, 38; m 63; c 2. BIOCHEMISTRY, MOLECULAR BIOLOGY. Educ: Univ Calcutta, BSc, 56, MSc, 58, PhD(chem), 63. Prof Exp: Sr res chemist, Dept Bot, Univ Calcutta, 62-63; res assoc biochem, 63-66, asst prof, 67-70, asst prof biochem & path, 70-71, assoc prof path & biochem, 72-78, SECY, GRAD COMT EXP PATH, MED SCH, UNIV SOUTHERN CALIF, 74-, PROF PATH & BIOCHEM, 78- Mem: AAAS; Am Soc Biol Chem; Am Soc Microbiol; Int Asn Comp res leukemia & Related Dis; Am Asn Univ Prof. Res: Molecular biology of viral neoplasia; understanding of RNA tumor viral oncogenesis at the molecular level; investigating potential immunological approaches in controlling neoplasia. Mailing Add: Dept Path Univ Southern Calif Med Sch Los Angeles CA 90033

ROYCE, BARRIE SAUNDERS HART, b Bishop's Stortford, Eng, Jan 10, 33; US citizen; m 64; c 2. SOLID STATE PHYSICS. Educ: Univ London, BSc, 54, PhD(physics), 57. Prof Exp: Res assoc physics, Carnegie Inst Technol, 57-60; res assoc, 60-61; asst prof, 61-66, assoc prof, 66-77, PROF SOLID STATE SCI, PRINCETON UNIV, 77- Concurrent Pos: Vis prof, Univ Sao Paulo, 62 & 69 & Nat Polytech Inst, Mex, 67 & 78; Sci Res Coun sr fel, Clarenden Labs, Oxford Univ, Eng, 69-70; vis prof, Solid State Physics Lab, Orsay, France, 73 & 78. Mem: Am Phys Soc; Sigma Xi. Res: Radiation damage in ionic solids; color centers and radiation induced reactions; molecular solids; optical properties; physical properties of biological materials; surface properties of insulators; photoacoustic spectroscopy of solids; photothermal deflectrai spectroscopy; catalytic material. Mailing Add: Mat Lab Princeton Univ D416 Duffield Hal Princeton NJ 08540

ROYCE, GEORGE JAMES, b Petoskey, Mich, Sept 30, 38. ANATOMY. Educ: Mich State Univ, BA; Ohio State Univ, MA, 63, PhD(anat), 67. Prof Exp: NIH fel, Case Western Reserve Univ, 68-69; instr, Albany Med Col, 69-70, asst prof anat, 70-74; ASSOC PROF ANAT, UNIV WIS-MADISON, 74- Mem: Soc Neurosci. Res: Neuroanatomy. Mailing Add: Dept of Anat Univ of Wis Madison WI 53706

ROYCE, JOSIAH, b Waltham, Mass, July 19, 20; m 73; c 3. ECONOMIC GEOLOGY, MINING ENGINEERING. Educ: Mich Technol Univ, BS, 43. Prof Exp: From asst chief geologist to chief geologist, Pickands, Mather & Co Inc, Ohio, 46-60; geologist, USAID, Ankara, Turkey, 61-64; chief mining & transp div, New Delhi, India, 64-72, mining engr, Washington, DC & engr/mgr, Mineral Projs World-Wide, 72-75, mining engr & actg chief engr,

Regional Econ Develop Serv Off WAfrica, 75-77, gen eng adv, 77-79, mgr regional projs, 79-81, PHYSICAL SCIENTIST, US BUR MINES, AID, 81- Mem: Soc Mining Engrs; Am Inst Mining, Metall & Petrol Engrs; Geol Soc Am. Mailing Add: Div Minerals Availability US Bur Mines Dept State AID 2401 E St NW Washington DC 20241

ROYCE, PAUL CHADWICK, b Minneapolis, Minn, July 2, 28; m 56; c 3. MEDICINE, ENDOCRINOLOGY. Educ: Univ Minn, BA, 48, MD, 52; Western Reserve Univ, PhD(physiol), 59. Prof Exp: Asst prof med, Albert Einstein Col Med, 61-69; dir med educ, Robert Packer Hosp, 70-81; assoc prof med, Hahnemann Med Col, 73-81; PROF PHYSIOL & CLIN SCI & DEAN, SCH MED, UNIV MINN, 82- Concurrent Pos: Clin prof med, Upstate Med Ctr at Syracuse, 77-81. Mem: Am Physiol Soc; Harvey Soc. Res: Endocrinology; medical education and internal medicine. Mailing Add: Sch Med Univ Minn Duluth MN 55812

ROYCE, WILLIAM FRANCIS, b DeBruce, NY, Jan 5, 16; m 40; c 3. FISHERIES, RESOURCE MANAGEMENT. Educ: Cornell Univ, BS, 37, PhD(vert zool), 43. Prof Exp: From aquatic biologist to fishery res biologist, US Fish & Wildlife Serv, 42-58; prof fisheries, Univ Wash, 58-72, dir fisheries res inst, 58-67, assoc dean col fisheries, 67-72; assoc dir, Nat Marine Fisheries Serv, 72-76; CONSULT, FISHERIES SCI & DEVELOP, AQUATIC ENVIRON, 76- Mem: Fel AAAS; Am Fisheries Soc; Am Soc Limnol & Oceanog. Res: Population studies of fish; biological oceanography; life history of fishes; measurement and sampling techniques of fisheries. Mailing Add: 10012 Lake Shore Blvd NE Seattle WA 98125

ROYCHOUDHURI, CHANDRASEKHAR, b Barisal, India, Apr 7, 42; m 77. PHYSICS, OPTICS. Educ: Jadavpur Univ, BSc, 63, MSc, 65; Univ Rochester, PhD(optics), 73. Prof Exp: Sr lectr physics, Univ Kalyani, W Bengal, India, 65-68; scientist optics, Nat Inst Astrophys & Optics, Puebla, Mex, 74-78; SCIENTIST, TRW SYSTS, 78- Mem: Optical Soc Am; Soc Photo-optical Instrumentation Engrs. Res: Interferometry; holography; Fourier optics; spectroscopy; interference, diffraction and spectroscopy with ultra-short pulses; conceptual foundations of quantum mechanics; lasers; laser communication. Mailing Add: TRW Defense & Space Systs Group One Space Park Redondo Beach CA 90278

ROYDEN, HALSEY LAWRENCE, b Phoenix, Ariz, Sept 26, 28; m 48; c 3. MATHEMATICAL ANALYSIS. Educ: Stanford Univ, BS, 48, MS, 49; Harvard Univ, PhD(math), 51. Prof Exp: From asst prof to assoc prof, 51-58, assoc dean, 62-65, actg dean, 68-69, dean, Sch Humanities & Sci, 73-81, PROF MATH, STANFORD UNIV, 58-, . Concurrent Pos: Ed, Pac J Math, 54-58 & 67-69; NSF fel, 58-59; vis prof, Mid East Tech Univ, Ankara, 66; mem math sci div, Nat Res Coun, 71-75 & adv comt res, NSF, 74-76; adv coun, NSF, 78-81. Mem: Am Math Soc; Math Asn Am. Res: Functions of a complex variable; conformal mapping; Riemann surfaces; differential geometry. Mailing Add: Dept Math Stanford Univ Stanford CA 94305

ROYE, GERALD STEPHEN, b Brooklyn, NY, July 19, 37; m 60; c 2. ANALYTICAL CHEMISTRY, COMPUTER SCIENCE. Educ: Hunter Col, BA, 60; Southern Conn State Col, MS, 70; Univ New Haven, MBA, 74. Prof Exp: Chemist, NORDA Essential Oil & Chem Co, NY, 60-62 & Denver Chem Mfg Co, Conn, 62-64; sr chemist, 64-70, group leader tech serv, 70-73, sect head sci info, 73-77, MGR QUAL ASSURANCE, PACKAGE FOODS, CHESEBROUGH-POND'S RES LABS, 77- Mem: Soc Cosmetic Chemists; Am Chem Soc; Instrument Soc Am; Am Soc Testing Mat; Inst Food Technologists. Res: Computerized color matching and analytical instrumentation. Mailing Add: Chesebrough-Pond's Res Labs Trumbull CT 06611

ROYER, ANTOINE JEAN, b Montreal, Can, Oct 13, 45; m 67; c 3. PHYSICS, PHYSICAL CHEMISTRY. Educ: Univ Montreal, BSc, 65, MSc, 66; Yale Univ, PhD(physics), 69. Prof Exp: Fel physics, Ctr Res Atom Molecules, Laval Univ, 70-71; RES ASSOC PHYSICS, CTR RES MATH, UNIV MONTREAL, 71- Mem: Am Phys Soc. Res: Shape of pressure broadened spectral lines; foundations of quantum mechanics. Mailing Add: Ctr Res Math Univ Montreal Montreal PQ H3C 3J7 Can

ROYER, DENNIS JACK, b Lock Haven, Pa, May 24, 41; c 2. CHEMICAL ENGINEERING. Educ: Pa State Univ, BS, 62, PhD(chem eng), 67; Carnegie Inst Technol, MS, 64. Prof Exp: dir, Continental Oil Co, 68-80, DIR ENG RES, CHEM RES DIV, CONOCO INC, 80- Mem: Am Inst Chem Engrs. Res: Petrochemical processes; production scale gas chromatography. Mailing Add: 813 Edgewood Ponca City OK 74601

ROYER, DONALD JACK, b Newton, Kans, May 7, 28. INORGANIC CHEMISTRY. Educ: Univ Kans, PhD(chem), 56. Prof Exp: From asst prof to assoc prof, 56-78, PROF CHEM, GA INST TECHNOL, 78- Mem: AAAS; Am Chem Soc. Res: Complex inorganic compounds and inorganic stereochemistry. Mailing Add: Dept of Chem Ga Inst of Technol Atlanta GA 30332

ROYER, GARFIELD PAUL, b Waynesboro, Pa, Dec 2, 42; m 66; c 3. BIOCHEMISTRY. Educ: Juniata Col, BS, 64; WVa Univ, PhD(biochem), 68. Prof Exp: NIH fel, Northwestern Univ, 68-70; asst prof, 70-74, ASSOC PROF BIOCHEM, OHIO STATE UNIV, 74- Honors & Awards: Res Career Develop Award, Nat Inst Gen Med Sci, 75. Mem: Am Soc Biol Chemists; Am Chem Soc. Res: Enzymology; immobilized enzymes and synthetic enzyme models. Mailing Add: Dept of Biochem Ohio State Univ Columbus OH 43210

ROYER, THOMAS CLARK, b Battle Creek, Mich, Jan 2, 41; m 68; c 2. PHYSICAL OCEANOGRAPHY. Educ: Albion Col, AB, 63; Tex A&M Univ, MS, 66, PhD(phys oceanog), 69. Prof Exp: Asst prof, 69-74, assoc prof, 74-81, PROF PHYS OCEANOG, UNIV ALASKA, FAIRBANKS, 81- Mem: Am Geophys Union; Am Meteorol Soc; Sigma Xi; AAAS. Res: Ocean circulation, especially the Alaskan Gyre; measurement of currents, water masses and air-sea interactions; long period ocean waves including tsunamis and storm surges. Mailing Add: Inst of Marine Sci Univ of Alaska Fairbanks AK 99701

ROYO, CARLOS MANUEL, b San Juan, PR, Sept 30, 44; m 66; c 1. CHEMICAL ENGINEERING, PETROLEUM ENGINEERING. *Educ:* Univ Fla, BS, 67; Tulane Univ, MS, 70, PhD(chem eng), 71. *Prof Exp:* SR RES ENGR, CITIES SERV CO, 71- *Mem:* Soc Petrol Engrs. *Res:* Numerical simulation; enhanced oil recovery methods. *Mailing Add:* Cities Serv Co Box 50408 Tulsa OK 74150

ROYS, CHESTER CROSBY, b Milwaukee, Wis, Nov 19, 12. INVERTEBRATE PHYSIOLOGY. *Educ:* Univ Mich, BS, 34, MS, 35; Univ Iowa, PhD(zool), 50. *Prof Exp:* Asst zool, Mus Zool, Univ Mich, 35; asst entom, Chicago Natural Hist Mus, 36; independent collector insects, Mex, Cent Am & WIndies, 36-37; vpres, Osborn & Roys, Inc, 38-42; res assoc, 50-78, EMER RES ASSOC BIOL, TUFTS UNIV, 78- *Concurrent Pos:* Rockefeller Found res fel, Univ Sao Paulo, 54. *Mem:* AAAS; Entom Soc Am; Am Soc Zool; Am Inst Biol Sci. *Res:* Sensory physiology, particularly chemical senses of insects and marine invertebrates. *Mailing Add:* Dept Biol Tufts Univ Medford MA 02155

ROYS, PAUL ALLEN, b Evanston, Ill, Apr 3, 26; m 52; c 4. PHYSICS. *Educ:* Ill Inst Technol, BS, 48, MS, 50, PhD(physics), 58. *Prof Exp:* Instr physics, Ill Inst Technol, 51-52; sr scientist, Atomic Power Div, Westinghouse Elec Corp, 52-57; from asst prof to assoc prof physics, Univ Wichita, 57-61; PROF PHYSICS & CHMN DEPT, CARROLL COL, WIS, 61- *Concurrent Pos:* Consult, Beech Aircraft Corp, 58-61 & Dynex Co, 62-65. *Mem:* Am Phys Soc; Am Asn Physics Teachers. *Res:* Low energy nuclear physics; mechanics; instrumentation. *Mailing Add:* Dept of Physics Carroll Col Waukesha WI 53186

ROYSE, DANIEL JOSEPH, b Olney, Ill, Aug 31, 50; m 72; c 1. PLANT PATHOLOGY, MYCOLOGY. *Educ:* Eastern Ill Univ, BS, 72, MS, 74; Univ Ill, Urbana, PhD(plant path), 78. *Prof Exp:* Res asst plant path, Univ Ill, 74-78, teaching asst, 75; teaching asst air pollution, Nat Univ Bogota, Colombia, 75; instr plant path, 78, ASST PROF PLANT PATH, PA STATE UNIV, 78- *Mem:* Am Phytopath Soc; Mycol Soc Am; Am Mushroom Inst. *Res:* Mushroom spawn; mushroom diseases; edible mushroom cultivation; disease management; fungal genetics; epidemiology; biochemical systematics and selective breeding of Agaricus brunnescens; cultivation of Shutake on artifical substrate. *Mailing Add:* 117 Buckhout Lab Pa State Univ University Park PA 16802

ROYSTER, L(ARRY) H(ERBERT), b Durham Co, NC, Sept 22, 36; m 57; c 2. ENGINEERING. *Educ:* NC State Univ, BS, 59, PhD(eng), 68. *Prof Exp:* Res engr, NC State Univ, 59-61; sr dynamics engr, N Am Aviation, Inc, 61-64; res engr, 64-67, from instr to prof eng, 67-76, PROF MECH ENG & AEROSPACE ENG, NC STATE UNIV, 76- *Concurrent Pos:* Consult to numerous industs. *Mem:* Fel Acoust Soc Am. *Res:* Vibrations, noise control, hearing conservation. *Mailing Add:* Dept Mech & Aerospace Eng NC State Univ Raleigh NC 27650

ROYSTER, WIMBERLY CALVIN, b Robards, Ky, Jan 12, 25; m 50; c 2. MATHEMATICS. *Educ:* Murray State Col, BS, 46; Univ Ky, MA, 48, PhD(math), 52. *Prof Exp:* Asst math, Univ Ky, 46-48, instr, 48-52; asst prof, Ala Polytech Inst, 52-56; from asst prof to assoc prof, 56-62, chmn dept math, 63-69, dean col arts & sci, 69-72, PROF MATH, UNIV KY, 62-, DEAN GRAD SCH, 72- *Concurrent Pos:* Mem, Inst Advan Study, 62 & Nat Res Coun, 72-75; mem bd dirs, Oak Ridge Assoc Univs, 78- *Mem:* AAAS; Am Math Soc; Math Asn Am. *Res:* Geometric function theory; univalent function theory; expansion in orthonormal functions; approximate methods in difference equations; summability. *Mailing Add:* 133 Vanderbilt Dr Lexington KY 40503

ROYSTON, RICHARD JOHN, b Windlesham, Eng, June 18, 31; m 58; c 2. COMPUTER SCIENCE. *Educ:* Oxford Univ, BA, 52, MA, 58; Univ London, BSc, 66. *Prof Exp:* Sci officer appl math, Atomic Energy Res Estab, 52-61; asst mathematician comput sci, Argonne Nat Lab, 62-65; vis scientist, Europ Orgn Nuclear Res, 65-66; assoc mathematician, Argonne Nat Lab, 66-69; sr consult, Scicon Ltd, 69-71; DIV DIR APPL MATH, ARGONNE NAT LAB, 71- *Mem:* Asn Comput Mach; fel Brit Comput Soc. *Res:* Computer center operation; networking; pattern recognition; operating systems. *Mailing Add:* Argonne Nat Lab Appl Math Div 9700 S Cass Ave Argonne IL 60439

ROYT, PAULETTE ANNE, b Brooklyn, NY, June 14, 45; m 71. MICROBIOLOGY. *Educ:* Am Univ, BS, 67, MS, 71; Univ Md, PhD(microbiol), 74. *Prof Exp:* Fel metab, Nat Heart, Lung & Blood Inst, 75-77; ASST PROF DEPT BIOL, GEORGE MASON UNIV, 77- *Mem:* Am Soc Microbiol. *Res:* Protein degradation in microorganisms; glucose transport in yeast. *Mailing Add:* Dept of Biol 4400 University Blvd Fairfax VA 22030

ROZANSKI, GEORGE, b Bronx, NY, Apr 21, 12; m 51; c 3. GEOLOGY. *Educ:* City Col New York, BS, 36; Columbia Univ, AM, 38. *Prof Exp:* Inspector construct, Tenn Valley Authority, 41-42; geologist, Empresa Petrolera Fiscal Peru, 46-48 & US Geol Surv, 49-65; geologist, US Corps Engrs, 65-77; ENG GEOLOGIST & CONSULT, 77- *Mem:* Asn Eng Geologists. *Res:* Engineering geology. *Mailing Add:* 10503 Hutting Pl Silver Spring MD 20902

ROZDILSKY, BOHDAN, b Wola Ceklynska, Ukraine, Nov 22, 16; m 59; c 3. NEUROPATHOLOGY. *Educ:* Univ Lvov, MD, 41; McGill Univ, MSc, 56; Univ Sask, PhD(neuropath), 58; FRCP(C). *Prof Exp:* Assoc prof, 64-73, PROF NEUROPATH, UNIV SASK, 73-, RES ASSOC PATH, 56- *Concurrent Pos:* Mem staff, Univ Sask Hosp, 57-, neuropathologist, 62-; lectr, Univ Sask, 59-64; consult, Ment Hosps, Sask. *Mem:* Am Asn Neuropath; Am Acad Neurol; fel Am Soc Clin Path; Can Asn Neuropath; Int Acad Path. *Res:* Cerebrovascular permeability; kernicterus; mental subnormality. *Mailing Add:* Dept of Path Univ of Sask Saskatoon SK S7H 0W0 Can

ROZE, ULDIS, b Riga, Latvia, Jan 3, 38; US citizen; m 66. ECOLOGY. *Educ:* Univ Chicago, BS, 59; Washington Univ, PhD(pharm), 64. *Prof Exp:* Instr, 64-70, asst prof, 70-76, ASSOC PROF BIOL, QUEENS COL, NY, 76- *Mem:* AAAS; Ecol Soc Am. *Res:* Natural history of New York State. *Mailing Add:* Dept of Biol Queens Col Flushing NY 11367

ROZEBOOM, LLOYD EUGENE, b Orange City, Iowa, Oct 17, 08; m 39; c 2. MEDICAL ENTOMOLOGY. *Educ:* Iowa State Col, SB, 31; Johns Hopkins Univ, ScD(med entom), 34. *Prof Exp:* Asst med entom, Sch Hyg & Pub Health, Johns Hopkins Univ, 31-34; med entomologist, Gorgas Mem Lab, Panama, 34-37; assoc prof med entom, Okla Agr & Mech Col, 37-39; assoc prof parasitol, 39-58, prof 58-77, EMER PROF MED ENTOM, SCH HYG & PUB HEALTH, JOHNS HOPKINS UNIV, 77- *Concurrent Pos:* Guggenheim fel, 54; exchange prof, Univ Philippines, 54-55. *Honors & Awards:* Ashford Award, 41. *Mem:* AAAS; fel Am Soc Trop Med & Hyg (pres, 74). *Res:* Taxonomy, genetics and biology of mosquitoes; transmission and epidemiology of arthropodborne diseases. *Mailing Add:* 3196 Laverne Circle Hampstead MD 21074

ROZEE, KENNETH ROY, b Halifax, NS, Feb 7, 31. MICROBIOLOGY, VIROLOGY. *Educ:* Dalhousie Univ, BSc, 53, MSc, 55, PhD(microbiol), 58; Univ Toronto, dipl bact, 58. *Prof Exp:* Res asst biol, Dalhousie Univ, 55-59, asst prof, 59-62; assoc prof microbiol, Univ Toronto, 62-67; PROF MICROBIOL, DALHOUSIE UNIV, 68-, HEAD DEPT, 74- *Mailing Add:* Dept of Microbiol Dalhousie Univ Tupper Med Bldg Halifax NS B3H 4H7 Can

ROZELLE, LEE THEODORE, physical chemistry, water treatment, see previous edition

ROZELLE, RALPH B, b West Wyoming, Pa, July 9, 32; m 57; c 3. PHYSICAL CHEMISTRY. *Educ:* Wilkes Col, BS, 54; Alfred Univ, PhD(chem), 61. *Prof Exp:* Instr chem, Alfred Univ, 60-62; asst prof, 62-65, assoc prof, 65-66, chmn dept chem, 65-70, dir grad studies, 67-72, chmn div natural sci & math, 67-77, PROF CHEM, WILKES COL, 66-, DEAN HEALTH SCI, 74-, PROJ DIR, WILKES-HAHNAMANN COOP MED EVAL PROG FAMILY MED, 77- *Mem:* Am Chem Soc. *Res:* Fuel cells; heterogeneous catalysis; inorganic chemistry of water pollution. *Mailing Add:* Stark Sci Hall Wilkes Col SRiver St Wilkes-Barre PA 18703

ROZEMA, EDWARD RALPH, b Chicago, Ill, Nov 16, 45; m 74; c 1. APPROXIMATION THEORY. *Educ:* Calvin Col, AB, 67; Purdue Univ, MS, 69, PhD(math), 72. *Prof Exp:* Vis asst prof math, Purdue Univ, Calumet Campus, 72-73; ASSOC PROF MATH, UNIV TENN, CHATTANOOGA, 73- *Mem:* Am Math Soc; Math Asn Am; Soc Indust & Appl Math. *Res:* Numerical analysis; methods of teaching. *Mailing Add:* Dept of Math Univ of Tenn Chattanooga TN 37402

ROZEN, JEROME GEORGE, JR, b Evanston, Ill, Mar 19, 28; m 48; c 3. SYSTEMATIC ENTOMOLOGY, ACADEMIC ADMINISTRATION. *Educ:* Univ Kans, BA, 50; Univ Calif, Berkeley, PhD, 55. *Prof Exp:* Asst instr biol, Univ Kans, 50, instr, 51; asst, Univ Calif, Berkeley, 51-55; entomologist, USDA, US Nat Mus, 56-58; asst prof entom, Ohio State Univ, 58-60; assoc cur hymenoptera, 60-65, chmn dept entom, 60-71, CUR, AM MUS NATURAL HIST, 65-, DEP DIR RES, 72- *Concurrent Pos:* Ed pub, Entom Soc Am, 59-60. *Mem:* AAAS; Entom Soc Am; Soc Syst Zool; Soc Study Evolution. *Res:* Ethology, taxonomy and phylogeny of bees; taxonomy, ethology, phylogeny and morphology of Coleoptera larvae; evolution; insect morphology; zoogeography. *Mailing Add:* Am Mus Natural Hist Cent Park W at 79th St New York NY 10024

ROZENBERG, J(UDA) E(BER), b Bocicoul-Mare, Romania, Oct 12, 22; US citizen; m 55; c 4. STRUCTURAL ENGINEERING, CIVIL ENGINEERING. *Educ:* Berchem Tech Sch Com & Admin, Antwerp, dipl, 39; Univ Notre Dame, BSCE, MSCE, 65, PhD(civil eng), 67. *Prof Exp:* Traffic mgr int freight, Reliable Shipping Co, New York, 55-61; asst prof civil eng, Univ Notre Dame, 67-68 & Christian Bros Col, 68-70; assoc prof, 70-79, PROF CIVIL ENG, TENN STATE UNIV, 80- *Concurrent Pos:* Consult, Wright-Patterson AFB Mat Lab, 78-79. *Mem:* Am Soc Civil Engrs; Biblical Archeol Soc; Asn Archit & Eng Israel. *Res:* Systems analysis of structures; composites. *Mailing Add:* Dept of Civil Eng 3500 Centennial Blvd Nashville TN 37203

ROZENDAL, DAVID BERNARD, b Chamberlain, SDak, Feb 4, 37; m 57; c 2. CIVIL ENGINEERING. *Educ:* SDak Sch Mines & Technol, BS, 58; Univ Minn, MS, 60; Purdue Univ, PhD(struct eng), 74. *Prof Exp:* Asst prof, 60-65, ASSOC PROF CIVIL ENG, UNIV TEX, EL PASO, 69- *Mem:* Am Soc Eng Educ. *Res:* Stress analysis; structural engineering. *Mailing Add:* Dept of Civil Eng Univ of Tex El Paso TX 79968

ROZET, DAVID, b Poland, Apr 18, 11; US citizen; m 44; c 1. METALLURGY, CHEMISTRY. *Educ:* Free Univ Brussels, BSc & MSc, 34, DSc(phys chem), 36. *Prof Exp:* Res assoc welding, Free Univ Brussels, 36-39; chief chemist, Arcos Corp, Philadelphia, 42-46, res chemist welding metall, 46-51; dir res, Weldvire Co, Philadelphia, 51-54; sr res engr, Alloy Rods Co, York-Hanover, Pa, 54-76; DIR RES & DEVELOP WELDING METALL, REID AVERY DIV, TECHALLOY MD INC, 76- *Concurrent Pos:* Consult welding metall. *Mem:* Am Welding Soc; Am Soc Metals. *Res:* Welding metallurgy; development of wires and electrodes for electric welding. *Mailing Add:* Reid Avery Div Techalloy Md Inc Chesapeake & Cleveland Ave Baltimore MD 21222

ROZETT, RICHARD WALTER, analytical chemistry, environmental chemistry, see previous edition

ROZGONYI, GEORGE A, b Brooklyn, NY, Apr 24, 37; m 63; c 3. MATERIALS SCIENCE. *Educ:* Univ Notre Dame, BS, 58, MS, 60; Univ Ariz, PhD(field emission micros), 64. *Prof Exp:* Teaching fel eng sci, Univ Notre Dame, 58-60; instr mech eng, Univ Ariz, 60-61, res assoc, Field Emission Lab, 61-63; MEM TECH STAFF STRUCT ANAL & THIN FILM MAT, BELL TEL LABS, 63- *Concurrent Pos:* Electronics ed, J Electrochem Soc, 77-; vis scientist, Max Plank Inst, Stuttgart, WGer, 79-80, Ctr Nat d'Etudes Sci, Microelectronics Lab, Grenoble, France, 81. *Mem:* Am Phys Soc; Electrochem Soc; Am Asn Crystal Growth. *Res:* Application of x-ray diffraction and optical microscopy to the study of native and process-induced defects in films and substrates of metals and semiconductors; thin film growth; vacuum physics; crystal defects. *Mailing Add:* Rm 2A-142 Bell Tel Labs Murray Hill NJ 07974

ROZHIN, JURIJ, b Kharkiv, Ukraine, USSR, Mar 19, 31; US citizen; m 60; c 1. BIOCHEMISTRY. *Educ:* Wayne State Univ, BS, 55, PhD(biochem), 67. *Prof Exp:* Res assoc biochem, Child Res Ctr Mich, Detroit, 61-63; fel biochem, 67-69, instr, 71-77, ASST PROF, DEPT SURG, MED SCH, WAYNE STATE UNIV, 77- *Concurrent Pos:* Res scientist, Mich Cancer Found, 69-81. *Mem:* Am Chem Soc; Sigma Xi; Am Asn Cancer Res. *Res:* Sulfation of steroids in normal and tumor tissue. *Mailing Add:* Dept Surg Wayne State Univ Med Sch Detroit MI 48201

ROZIER, CAROLYN K, b Fulton, Mo, Aug 17, 44; div; c 1. ANATOMY. *Educ:* Univ Mo, BS, 66; Univ Okla, MS, 71, PhD(anat sci), 72. *Prof Exp:* Staff phys therapist, Gen Leonard Wood Army Hosp, Mo, 66-67; educ coordr & phys therapist, St Anthony Hosp, Oklahoma City, 67-69; asst anat sci, Med Ctr, Univ Okla, 70-72; asst prof anat, Sch Med, Tex Tech Univ, 72-73; DEAN, SCH PHYS THER, TEX WOMAN'S UNIV, 73-, PROVOST, INST HEALTH SCI, 80- *Concurrent Pos:* Res asst, Civil Aeromed Inst, Fed Aviation Admin, Dept Transp, Oklahoma City, 72; instr, Oscar Rose Jr Col, 72. *Mem:* Am Phys Ther Asn. *Res:* Functional and neuroanatomical problems and problems in the field of rehabilitation. *Mailing Add:* Sch Phys Ther Tex Woman's Univ Denton TX 76204

ROZMAN, ROBERT SANFORD, b Washington, DC, Dec 28, 31; m 57; c 1. PHARMACOLOGY. *Educ:* George Washington Univ, BS, 55, MS, 58, PhD(pharmacol), 62. *Prof Exp:* Res assoc hemat, George Washington Univ, 61-62; res assoc pharmacol, Sch Med, Univ Md, 62-64, asst prof, 63-66; RES PHARMACOLOGIST, WALTER REED ARMY INST RES, 66- *Mem:* Am Col Clin Pharmacol; AAAS; Am Soc Pharmacol & Exp Therapeut; Am Chem Soc; Lepidop Soc. *Res:* Antimalarial and antiradiation drug development; autonomic pharmacology; toxicology; drug metabolism. *Mailing Add:* Div of Exp Therapeut Walter Reed Inst of Res Washington DC 20012

ROZSNYAI, BALAZS, b Szekesfehervar, Hungary, Nov 24, 29; US citizen. PHYSICS, MATHEMATICS. *Educ:* Eotvos Lorand Univ, Budapest, MS, 52; Univ Calif, Berkeley, PhD(physics), 60. *Prof Exp:* Physicist, Cent Res Inst Physics, Budapest, Hunagry, 52-56 & Int Bus Mach Corp, Calif, 60-64; SR PHYSICIST, LAWRENCE LIVERMORE LAB, UNIV CALIF, 64- *Concurrent Pos:* Asst prof, San Jose State Col, 61-63. *Mem:* Am Phys Soc. *Res:* Quantum chemistry; electron-molecular scattering; scattering theory; nuclear physics, especially nuclear shell model; optics; thermodynamics; mathematical physics. *Mailing Add:* Lawrence Livermore Lab Univ of Calif PO Box 808 Livermore CA 94550

ROZZELL, THOMAS CLIFTON, b Gastonia, NC, Apr 5, 37; m 59; c 3. ENVIRONMENTAL BIOLOGY, RADIATION BIOLOGY. *Educ:* Fisk Univ, BS, 59; Univ Cincinnati, MS, 60; Univ Pittsburgh, ScD(environ radiation), 68. *Prof Exp:* Radiochemist, USPHS, 60-65; res assoc environ radiation, Univ Pittsburgh, 66-68, asst prof, 68-71; ENVIRON SCIENTIST, OFF NAVAL RES, 71- *Concurrent Pos:* Consult, Bur Health, Manpower & Educ, USPHS, 69-71; spec asst to vchancellor health professions, Univ Pittsburgh, 70-71. *Mem:* Health Physics Soc; Int Microwave Power Inst; Bioelectromagnetics Soc. *Res:* Radioecology; effect of environmental radiation on man; biological effects of electromagnetic energy, including microwaves, lasers and radio frequency fields. *Mailing Add:* Off of Naval Res 800 N Quincy St Arlington VA 22217

RUARK, ANNETTE, see Hazen, Annette

RUBATZKY, VINCENT E, b New York, NY, Oct 24, 32; m 56; c 2. PLANT PHYSIOLOGY, HORTICULTURE. *Educ:* Cornell Univ, BS, 56; Va Polytech Inst, MS, 60; Rutgers Univ, PhD(plant physiol, biochem, hort), 64. *Prof Exp:* EXTEN VEG CROPS SPECIALIST, UNIV CALIF, DAVIS, 64-, AGRICULTURALIST, COOP EXTEN SERV, 73-, VPRES AGR SCI, VEG CROPS EXTEN, 73- *Mem:* AAAS; Am Soc Hort Sci. *Res:* Herbicidal selectivity; biochemistry of tomato internal browning related to tobacco mosaic virus; spacing relating to mechanization and use of growth regulating chemicals. *Mailing Add:* Veg Crop Exten Univ of Calif Davis CA 95616

RUBAYI, NAJIM, b Baghdad, Iraq, June 18, 27; m 59. ENGINEERING MECHANICS, MECHANICAL ENGINEERING. *Educ:* Wolverhampton Polytech Inst, BS, 51; Univ Wis, Madison, MS, 56, PhD(eng mech), 66. *Prof Exp:* Develop engr, Wooden Transformer Co, Ltd, Eng, 50-51; asst chief mech engr, Iraqi Rwy, 51-60; instr theoret & appl mech, Univ Ill, Urbana, 60-61; instr eng mech, Univ Wis, Madison, 63-66; from asst prof to assoc prof eng, 66-75, PROF ENG, SCH ENG, SOUTHERN ILL UNIV, CARBONDALE, 75- *Concurrent Pos:* Lectr, Univ Baghdad, 51-55; instr, Univ Wis, Madison, 56; vis prof, Aachen Tech Univ, WGer & Heinrich-Hertz fel, Ger Ministry Sci & Res, 72-73. *Mem:* Am Soc Mech Engrs; Am Soc Eng Educ; Soc Exp Stress Anal; Am Acad Mech; Sigma Xi. *Res:* Buckling and bending of orthotropic core sandwich plates; elasticity; plates and shells; experimental stress analysis; photoelasticity. *Mailing Add:* Sch of Eng Southern Ill Univ Carbondale IL 62901

RUBBERT, PAUL EDWARD, b Minneapolis, Minn, Feb 18, 37; m 58; c 3. AERODYNAMICS. *Educ:* Univ Minn, BS, 58, MS, 60; Mass Inst Technol, PhD(aerodynamics), 65. *Prof Exp:* Res scientist aerodynamics, 60-62 & 65-72, SUPVR AERODYNAMICS RES, BOEING CO, 72- *Concurrent Pos:* Assoc ed, J Am Inst Aeronaut & Astronaut, 75-78. *Honors & Awards:* Arch T Colwell Merit Award, Soc Automotive Engrs, 68. *Mem:* Fel Am Inst Aeronaut & Astronaut; Sigma Xi. *Res:* Computational fluid dynamics including hydrodynamics; subsonic, transonic and supersonic flows; viscous and inviscid phenomena; steady and unsteady flows. *Mailing Add:* 2001-86 Ave NE Bellevue WA 98004

RUBEGA, ROBERT A, b Blackstone, Mass, Aug 2, 27; m 54; c 8. ACOUSTICS. *Educ:* Univ RI, BS, 51; Univ Rochester, MS, 61, PhD(elec eng), 66. *Prof Exp:* Physicist, US Navy Underwater Sound Lab, 51-56; staff mem res acoust, Gen Dynamics/Electronics, 56-63, mgr acoust labs, 63-65, mgr info sci lab, 65-68; dir marine tech serv, Marine Resources Inc, 68-71; SUPVR PHYSICIST, US NAVAL UNDERWATER SYSTS CTR, 71- *Concurrent Pos:* Asst, Univ Rochester, 63-65. *Honors & Awards:* Stromberg Carlson Award, 59. *Mem:* Acoust Soc Am; Inst Elec & Electronics Engrs. *Res:* Acoustics and techniques of signal processing. *Mailing Add:* 27 Tormberg Lane Groton CT 06340

RUBEL, DANIEL NICHOLAS, petrology, volcanology, see previous edition

RUBEL, EDWIN W, b Chicago, Ill, May 8, 42; m 63; c 1. NEUROBIOLOGY. *Educ:* Mich State Univ, BS, 64, MA, 67, PhD(psychol), 69. *Prof Exp:* Asst physiol psychol, Mich State Univ, 64-66, res asst neurobiol, 66-68; NIMH fel, Univ Calif, Irvine, 69-71; asst prof psychobiol, Yale Univ, 71-77; ASSOC PROF OTOLARYNGOL & PHYSIOL, UNIV VA MED CTR, 77- *Mem:* AAAS; Am Asn Anatomists; Psychonomic Soc. *Res:* Neuroembryology; behavior development; ethology. *Mailing Add:* Dept of Otolaryngol Univ of Va Med Ctr Charlottesville VA 22908

RUBEL, LEE ALBERT, b New York, NY, Dec 1, 28; m 54; c 2. MATHEMATICS. *Educ:* City Col, BS, 50; Univ Wis, MS, 51, PhD(math), 54. *Prof Exp:* Instr math, Cornell Univ, 54-56; mem, Inst Advan Study, 56-58; asst prof, 58-65, mem ctr advan studies, 64-65 & 73-74, PROF MATH, UNIV ILL, URBANA, 65- *Concurrent Pos:* NSF fel, 56-58; vis assoc prof, Columbia Univ, 60-62; NSF sr fel, Univ Paris, 65-66; vis prof, Princeton Univ, 67-68, mem inst advan study, 67-68; vis prof, Inst Math Sci, Madras, India, 68; ed proc, Am Math Soc, 72-73; vis prof, Flinders Univ SAustralia, 74; ed, Ill J Math, 73-81, Int J Math & Math Sci, 78 & Transactions Ill State Acad Sci, 81. *Mem:* Am Math Soc. *Res:* Complex variables; harmonic and functional analysis; number theory; logic and topology; differential equations. *Mailing Add:* Dept of Math Univ of Ill Urbana IL 61801

RUBEN, JOHN ALEX, b Los Angeles, Calif, Jan 5, 47; m 73. MORPHOLOGY. *Educ:* Humboldt State Col, BS, 68; Univ Calif, Berkeley, MA, 70. *Prof Exp:* ASST PROF ZOOL, ORE STATE UNIV, 75- *Mem:* Soc Vert Paleontologists; AAAS. *Res:* Functional morphology and physiology of reptiles. *Mailing Add:* Dept of Zool Ore State Univ Corvallis OR 97331

RUBEN, LAURENS NORMAN, b New York, NY, May 14, 27; m 50; c 3. IMMUNOLOGY. *Educ:* Univ Mich, AB, 49, MS, 50; Columbia Univ, PhD(zool), 54. *Prof Exp:* Asst, Columbia Univ, 50-53; Nat Cancer Inst fel, Princeton Univ, 54-55; from instr to assoc prof, 55-67, PROF BIOL, REED COL, 67-, CHMN DEPT, 73- *Mem:* AAAS; Am Soc Zool; Soc Develop Biol; Int Soc Develop Biol; Am Asn Immunologists. *Res:* The evolution and development of humoral immune responses; hapten-carrier immunization of amphibian model systems which represent evolutionary, developmental, anatomical and physiological immunologic progressions. *Mailing Add:* Dept of Biol Reed Col Portland OR 97202

RUBEN, MORRIS P, b East Liverpool, Ohio, Aug 27, 19; m 43; c 1. PERIODONTOLOGY, ORAL BIOLOGY. *Educ:* Ohio State Univ, BSc, 40; Loyola Univ, La, DDS, 43; Univ Pa, cert periodont & Boston Univ, cert periodont oral med, 61; Am Bd Periodont, dipl, 66. *Prof Exp:* From asst prof to prof stomatol, 60-73, asst dean, Sch Grad Dent, 61-64, assoc dean grad studies, 69-77, PROF ORAL BIOL & CHMN DEPT & PROF PERIODONT, SCH GRAD DENT, BOSTON UNIV, 73- *Concurrent Pos:* Nat Inst Dent Res fel periodont, Grad Sch Med, Univ Pa, 59-60 & fel stomatol, Sch Med, Boston Univ, 60-61; consult pediat periodont, Kennedy Mem Hosp, Boston; attend dent surgeon, Beth Israel Hosp, Boston. *Mem:* Fel Am Col Dent; Am Acad Periodont; Am Dent Asn; fel Am Acad Dent Sci; fel Int Col Dent. *Mailing Add:* Dept of Oral Biol Boston Univ Sch of Grad Dent Boston MA 02118

RUBEN, REGINA LANSING, b Newark, NJ, Jan 2, 50; m 75; c 1. EXPERIMENTAL ONCOLOGY, TISSUE CULTURE. *Educ:* Univ Rochester, BA, 72; Ohio State Univ, MS, 74, PhD(anat), 75. *Prof Exp:* Fel anat, Col Med, Univ Ill, 75-78; sr instr, 78-79, ASST PROF ANAT, HAHNEMANN MED COL, 79- *Mem:* Tissue Culture Asn; Am Asn Anatomists; Sigma Xi; NY Acad Sci. *Res:* Invitro characterization of human tumor cells; assessment of differential invivo susceptibility of mammals in different physiological states to topically applied carcinogen; carcinogen susceptibility of cells cultured from mammals in different phases of their normal physiological cycles. *Mailing Add:* Dept Anat Hahnemann Med Col & Hosp MS 408 230 N Broad St Philadelphia PA 19102

RUBEN, ROBERT JOEL, b New York, NY, Aug 2, 33; m 56; c 4. OTOLARYNGOLOGY, CELL BIOLOGY. *Educ:* Princeton Univ, AB, 55; Johns Hopkins Univ, MD, 59. *Prof Exp:* Dir neurophysiol, Sch Med Johns Hopkins Univ, 58-64; res assoc exp embryol, NIH, 65-68; asst prof otolaryngol, Med Ctr, NY Univ, 66-70; PROF OTOLARYNGOL & CHMN DEPT, ALBERT EINSTEIN COL MED, 70- *Concurrent Pos:* Attend otolaryngol surg, Montefiore & Morrisania Hosps, 70-; attend & chmn, Dept Otolaryngol, Lincoln Hosp, 71-77; chmn dept, Bronx Munic Hosp Ctr, 71-;

attend & chmn dept, Hosp, Albert Einstein Col Med, 71- *Mem:* Acoust Soc Am; Am Asn Anat; Am Acad Ophthal & Otolaryngol; Am Otological Soc; Am Asn Hist Med. *Res:* Normal and diseased states of the inner ear, particularly physiological, genetic, cellular pathological, embryological and behavior aspects of genetic deafness. *Mailing Add:* Albert Einstein Col of Med 1300 Morris Park Ave Bronx NY 10461

RUBEN, SAMUEL, b Harrison, NJ, July 14, 00; m 25; c 1. ELECTROCHEMISTRY. *Hon Degrees:* DSc, Butler Univ, 59; DEng, Polytech Inst Brooklyn, 66; DSc, Columbia Univ, 81. *Prof Exp:* DIR, RUBEN LABS, 23- *Concurrent Pos:* Consult, Duracell Int Co, Inc, 30- *Honors & Awards:* Cert Appreciation, US Sig Corps, 44; Golden Plate Award, Am Acad Achievements, 65; Inventor of Year Award, George Washington Univ, 65; Acheson Gold Medal & Prize, Am Electrochem Soc, 70; Edward Longstreth Medal, Franklin Inst, 72. *Mem:* Fel AAAS; fel Am Inst Chem; life fel, Franklin Inst; Am Electrochem Soc. *Res:* Dry electrolytic capacitors; primary and secondary mercury dry cells; electrophoretic deposition of insulating materials; sealed zinc/mercuric oxide/alkaline cell. *Mailing Add:* Ruben Labs 271 NAve New Rochelle NY 10801

RUBENFELD, LESTER A, b New York, NY, Dec 30, 40; m 64. MATHEMATICAL PHYSICS. *Educ:* Polytech Inst Brooklyn, BS, 62; NY Univ, MS, 64, PhD(math), 66. *Prof Exp:* Fel, Courant Inst Math Sci, NY Univ, 66-67; asst prof, 67-72, ASSOC PROF MATH, RENSSELAER POLYTECH INST, 72- *Mem:* Am Math Soc; Soc Indust & Appl Math. *Res:* Wave propagation in elasticity and electromagnetic theory and asymptotic expansions arising from these fields. *Mailing Add:* Dept of Math Rensselaer Polytech Inst Troy NY 12181

RUBENS, SIDNEY MICHEL, b Spokane, Wash, Mar 21, 10; m 44; c 1. PHYSICS. *Educ:* Univ Wash, BS, 34, PhD(physics), 39. *Prof Exp:* Instr physics, Univ Southern Calif, 39-40; res assoc, Univ Calif, Los Angeles, 40-41; from assoc physicist to physicist, US Naval Ord Lab, 41-46; sr physicist, Eng Res Assocs, Inc, 46-51, staff physicist, 51-52; dir physics, Univac Div, Sperry Rand Corp, 52-55, mgr physics dept, 55-60, mgr phys res, 60-61, dir res, 61-66, staff scientist, Defense Systs Div, 66-69, dir spec projs, Univac Fed Systs Div, 69-71, dir spec tech activities, Defense Systs Div, 71-75; CONSULT, S M RUBENS ASSOCS, 75- *Concurrent Pos:* Mem res & technol adv subcomt instrumentation & data processing, NASA, 67-69; hon fel, Univ Minn, 77- *Honors & Awards:* Meritorious Civilian Serv Award, US 45. *Mem:* AAAS; Am Phys Soc; Optical Soc Am; Am Geophys Union; fel inst Elec & Electronics Eng. *Res:* Plasma physics; solid state; ferromagnetism; thin films; optics; magnetic measurements; digital computer components; information processing. *Mailing Add:* Apt 506 1077 Sibley Mem Hwy St Paul MN 55118

RUBENSON, J(OSEPH), G(EORGE), b Newburgh, NY, Aug 7, 20; m 43; c 3. ELECTRONIC & SYSTEMS ENGINEERING. *Educ:* City Col New York, BS, 40; Polytech Inst Brooklyn, MEE, 46. *Prof Exp:* Proj engr, Nat Union Radio Corp, 41-46 & Polytech Res & Develop Corp, 46-51; sect head, Airborne Instruments Lab, Inc, 51-58; eng specialist, Sylvania Elec Prod, Inc, Gen Tel & Electronics Corp, 58-60; mgr systs div, Watkins-Johnson Co, 60-64; sr res engr, Stanford Res Inst, SRI Int, Calif, 64-70, dir syst eval dept, 70-71, dir, Washington, 71-78; PROG MGR, SYST PLANNING CORP, 78- *Concurrent Pos:* Instr, Polytech Inst Brooklyn, 46-50. *Mem:* Sigma Xi; Inst Elec & Electronics Engrs. *Res:* Electron tubes; industrial electronics; electronic countermeasures; microwave components; electronic reconnaisance; electronic systems; radar systems. *Mailing Add:* 5211 Worthington Dr Bethesda MD 20816

RUBENSTEIN, ABRAHAM DANIEL, b Lynn, Mass, Nov 19, 07; m 37; c 3. PUBLIC HEALTH. *Educ:* Harvard Univ, AB, 28, MPH, 40; Boston Univ, MD, 33; Am Bd Prev Med, dipl. *Prof Exp:* Intern & res med, Brockton Hosp, 33-35; house officer internal med, Boston City Hosp, 35-36; epidemiologist, 37-42, dist health officer, 42-47, dir, Div Hosp Surv & Construct, 47-50, dir, Div Hosps, 50-54, dir, Bur Hosp Facils & dep comnr, 54-69, HOSP CONSULT, MASS DEPT PUB HEALTH, 69- *Concurrent Pos:* From asst prof to assoc clin prof, Sch Pub Health, Harvard Univ, 48-60, Simmons Col, 50-59, Boston Col, 50-71 & Sch Med, Tufts Univ, 71-73; sr lectr food sci & nutrit, Mass Inst Technol, 71-74, vis prof, 68-70; pres & trustee, New Eng Sinai Hosp; consult, Jewish Mem Hosp & Beth Israel Hosp, Boston. *Mem:* AMA; Am Pub Health Asn; Am Hosp Asn; Asn Teachers Prev Med; fel Am Col Prev Med. *Res:* Epidemiology of Salmonellosis; medical care programs. *Mailing Add:* 164 Ward St Newton Center MA 02159

RUBENSTEIN, ALBERT HAROLD, b Philadelphia, Pa, Nov 11, 23; m 49; c 2. INDUSTRIAL ENGINEERING, MANUFACTURING ENGINEERING. *Educ:* Lehigh Univ, BS, 49; Columbia Univ, MS, 50, PhD(indust eng & mgt), 54. *Prof Exp:* Asst to pres, Perry Equip Corp, 40-43; res assoc indust eng, Columbia Univ, 50-53; asst prof indust mgt, Mass Inst Technol, 54-59; PROF INDUST ENG & MGT SCI, NORTHWESTERN UNIV, 59- *Concurrent Pos:* Ed, Transactions, Inst Elec & Electronics Engrs, 59-; dir studies col res & develop, Inst Mgt Sci, 60; dir, Narragansett Capital Corp, 60-; vis prof, Sch Bus, Univ Calif, Berkeley, 64; pres, Int Appl Sci & Technol Assocs, Inc, 77- *Mem:* Fel Soc Appl Anthrop; Inst Elec & Electronics Engrs; Inst Mgt Sci. *Res:* Organization, economics and management of research and development and innovation; field research on organizational behavior. *Mailing Add:* Dept of Indust Eng & Mgt Sci Northwestern Univ Evanston IL 60201

RUBENSTEIN, ALBERT MARVIN, b New York, NY, May 9, 18; m 44; c 2. PHYSICS. *Educ:* Brooklyn Col, BA, 39; Univ Md, MS, 49. *Prof Exp:* Lab asst & specifications engr, Micamold Radio Corp, NY, 41-42; unit head submarine radar design, Bur Ships, US Dept Navy, 45-51, mem planning staff in charge of air defense & atomic warfare, Electronics Div, 51-54; head planning staff, 54-56, surveillance warfare syst coordr, Off Naval Res, 56-59; asst chief, Ballistic Missile Defense Br, Adv Res Projs Agency, US Dept Defense, 59-60, actg & asst dir, Ballistic Missile Defense Off, 60-61, asst dir, Ballistic Missile Defense Eng Off, 61-64; tech staff mem, Inst Defense Anal, 64-68; asst dir, Advan Sensor Off, Advan Res Proj Agency, 68-71, dep dir, 71-73; RES STAFF MEM SCI & TECHNOL DIV, INST DEFENSE ANAL, 73- *Concurrent Pos:* Lectr exten div, Univ Md, 53 & Dept Agr grad sch, 54-60; lectr exten div, Univ Va, 58-59. *Honors & Awards:* Civilian Meritorious Awards, US Navy Bur Ships, 54 & Off Naval Res, 59. *Mem:* Am Phys Soc. *Res:* Electronics; radar; air defense; ballistic missile defense systems and space technology; advanced sensors; optics; electro-optics solid state detectors; space systems; reconnaissance and systems analyses. *Mailing Add:* 2709 Navarre Dr Chevy Chase MD 20815

RUBENSTEIN, ARTHUR HAROLD, b Germiston, SAfrica, Dec 28, 37; m 62; c 2. MEDICINE, ENDOCRINOLOGY. *Educ:* Univ Witwatersrand, MBBCh(med), 60. *Prof Exp:* From asst prof to assoc prof, 68-74, assoc chmn dept, 74-81, PROF MED, UNIV CHICAGO, 74-, CHMN DEPT, 81- *Concurrent Pos:* Smith & Nephew fel, Postgrad Sch Med, Univ London, 65-66; Schweppe Award, Schweppe Found, 70-73; estab investr, Am Diabetes Asn, 75; mem adv coun, Nat Inst Health, Arthritis, Metab Diabetes & Digestive Dis, 77-80 & chmn, Nat Ciabetes Adv Bd, 81- *Honors & Awards:* Lilly Award, Am Diabetes Asn, 73; Sci Award, Juv Diabetes Found, 77. *Mem:* Am Diabetes Asn; fel Am Col Physicians; Asn Am Physicians; Endocrine Soc; Am Soc Clin Invest. *Res:* Diabetes mellitus; insulin biosynthesis and secretion; proinsulin; c-peptide; obesity; insulin resistance; immunoassay of hormones and lipoprotein peptides; lipoprotein metabolism. *Mailing Add:* Dept of Med Univ of Chicago Chicago IL 60637

RUBENSTEIN, EDWARD, b Cincinnati, Ohio, Dec 5, 24; m 54; c 3. INTERNAL MEDICINE. *Educ:* Univ Cincinnati, MD, 47. *Prof Exp:* Asst, Univ Cincinnati, 46-47; intern internal med, Cincinnati Gen Hosp, Ohio, 47-48, asst resident, 48-50; asst resident internal med, Ward Serv, Barnes Hosp, 52-53; clin instr, Univ Cincinnati, 53-54; lectr & clin prof med, 54-77, ASSOC DEAN POSTGRAD MED EDUC, SCH MED, STANFORD UNIV, 72-, PROF CLIN MED, 77- *Concurrent Pos:* Fel metab, May Inst Med Res, Jewish Hosp, Cincinnati, Ohio, 50; head dept clin physiol, San Mateo County Gen Hosp, 57-70, chief med, 60-70; ed-in-chief, Sci Am Med. *Mem:* Nat Acad Sci; Inst Med-Nat Acad Sci; Assoc Am Col Physicians. *Res:* Synchrotron radiation; thromboembolism. *Mailing Add:* Dept of Med Stanford Univ Sch of Med Stanford CA 94305

RUBENSTEIN, HOWARD STUART, b Chicago, Ill, June 14, 31; m 68; c 4. EXPERIMENTAL PATHOLOGY, BEHAVIOR ETHOLOGY. *Educ:* Carleton Col, BA, 53; Harvard Univ, MD, 57. *Prof Exp:* Intern & resident med, Los Angeles County Gen Hosp, Calif, 57-60; res fel exp surg & bact, Harvard Med Sch, 60-62, Harold C Ernst fel bact, 62-64; res assoc bact, 64-65, res assoc path, 65-67, CLIN INSTR MED, HARVARD UNIV, 67-, PHYSICIAN, UNIV HEALTH SERV, 66-, CHIEF ALLERGY SERV, 67- *Mem:* Am Acad Allergy; AMA; Am Col Allergists. *Res:* Mechanism of lethal action of endotoxin; differentiating reticulum cell in antibody formation; influence of environmental temperature on resistance; controlling behavior of patients with bronchial asthma and their overcontrolling mothers; ethical problems posed by bee stings; immunology. *Mailing Add:* Harvard Univ Health Serv 75 Mt Auburn St Cambridge MA 02138

RUBENSTEIN, IRWIN, b Kansas City, Mo, Sept 6, 31; m 56; c 3. MOLECULAR BIOLOGY. *Educ:* Calif Inst Technol, BS, 53; Univ Calif, Los Angeles, PhD(biophys), 60. *Prof Exp:* Fel, Johns Hopkins Univ, 60-62; from asst prof to assoc prof molecular biophys, Yale Univ, 62-70; PROF GENETICS & CELL BIOL, COL BIOL SCI, UNIV MINN, ST PAUL, 70- *Concurrent Pos:* NIH fel, Carnegie Inst Wash, 69-70; mem biol sci comt, World Book Encyclop. *Mem:* AAAS; Biophys Soc; Genetics Soc Am; Am Soc Microbiol; Am Soc Plant Physiologists. *Res:* Molecular biology of plants. *Mailing Add:* Dept of Genetics & Cell Biol Univ of Minn St Paul MN 55108

RUBENSTEIN, KENNETH E, b Passaic, NJ, July 26, 41; div; c 1. ORGANIC CHEMISTRY, BIOCHEMISTRY. *Educ:* Fairleigh Dickinson Univ, BS, 62; Univ Wis, PhD(org chem), 66. *Prof Exp:* Chemist, Rohm and Haas Co, 66-68; res biochemist, Sch Med, Univ Pa, 68-70; proj leader, Syva Res Inst, 70-74, asst dir res, 74-75; mgr advan res, Smith Kline Instruments, Inc, 75-76; asst dir develop, 76-78, VPRES SCI AFFAIRS, SYVA CO, 79- *Mem:* Am Asn Clin Chemists. *Res:* Clinical chemistry; immuno-assay techniques; enzyme modification; immunochemistry. *Mailing Add:* Syva Co 3181 Porter Dr Palo Alto CA 94304

RUBENTHALER, GORDON LAWRENCE, b Gothenburg, Nebr, Sept 30, 32; m 53; c 4. CEREAL CHEMISTRY. *Educ:* Kans State Univ, BS, 60, MS, 62. *Prof Exp:* Phys sci aid, 58-62, cereal technologist, 62-66, res cereal technician, 66-68, RES CEREAL TECHNICIAN IN CHG WHEAT RES, WHEAT QUAL LAB, AGR RES SERV, USDA, 68- *Mem:* Sigma Xi; Am Asn Cereal Chemists; Crop Sci Soc Am. *Res:* Improvement of milling, baking, protein and amino acid balance of experimental wheat varieties; efforts to improve nutritional value and utilization of wheat for human consumption in domestic and foreign market. *Mailing Add:* Western Wheat Qual Lab WSU Agr Res Serv USDA Pullman WA 99163

RUBER, ERNEST, b Berlin, Ger, Aug 21, 34; US citizen; m 55; c 2. ECOLOGY. *Educ:* Brooklyn Col, BA, 59; Rutgers Univ, PhD(zool), 65. *Prof Exp:* Instr biol, Franklin & Marshall Col, 64-65; asst prof zool, Howard Univ, 65-68; assoc prof, 68-80, PROF BIOL, NORTHEASTERN UNIV, 80- *Mem:* AAAS; Am Soc Limnol & Oceanog; Ecol Soc Am. *Res:* Coastal ecology; ecology and taxonomy of salt marsh Microcrustacea; effects of pesticides. *Mailing Add:* Dept of Biol Northeastern Univ Boston MA 02115

RUBIN, ALAN, b Philadelphia, Pa, Nov 10, 23; m 47; c 3. MEDICINE. *Educ:* Univ Pa, MD, 47; Am Bd Obstet & Gynec, dipl, 56. *Prof Exp:* Intern, Univ Hosp, 47-48, resident obstet & gynec, 49-51, instr, 51-52, res assoc, 52-72, assoc, 72-79, CLIN ASSOC PROF OBSTET & GYNEC, SCH MED, UNIV PA, 80-; CLIN PROF OBSTET & GYNEC, MED SCH, TEMPLE UNIV, 81- *Concurrent Pos:* Res fel pharmacol, Sch Med, Univ Pa, 48-49; Nat Cancer Inst trainee, 51-52; res fel & chief resident, Gynecean Hosp Inst Gynec Res,

Univ Pa, 51-52, res assoc, 53-; assoc, Albert Einstein Med Ctr, 55, asst dir, Div Gynec, 68-, actg chmn, Div Obstet & Gynec, 78-80; gynecologist, Grad Hosp Univ Pa, 73-; mem, Am Comn Maternal & Infant Health; dir gynec div, Wills Eye Hosp, 77-80; actg chmn dept gynec, Grad Hosp, 77-78, chmn, 79-; clin assoc prof obstet & gynec, Med Sch, Univ Pa, 80- *Mem:* Am Geriat Soc; Am Fertil Soc; Am Soc Human Genetics; AMA; Am Col Obstet & Gynec. *Res:* Obstetrics and gynecology; infertility; cancer. *Mailing Add:* 1905 Spruce St Philadelphia PA 19103

RUBIN, ALAN, b Boston, Mass, Mar 4, 38; m 61; c 2. PHARMACOLOGY. *Educ:* Univ Mass, BS, 59; Univ Wis, PhD(pharmacol), 64. *Prof Exp:* Pharmacologist, Smith Kline & French Labs, 64-66; sr pharmacologist, Midwest Res Inst, 66-68; sr pharmacologist, 68-73, RES PHARMACOLOGIST, LILLY LABS CLIN RES, 73- *Concurrent Pos:* Instr, Dept Pharmacol, Sch Med, Ind Univ, Indianapolis, 68-74, asst prof & assoc mem grad fac, 74-78. *Mem:* Am Soc Pharmacol & Exp Therapeut; Am Soc Clin Pharmacol & Therapeut; Sigma Xi. *Res:* Drug metabolism and disposition; biochemical pharmacology. *Mailing Add:* Lilly Labs for Clin Res William Wishard Mem Hosp Indianapolis IN 46202

RUBIN, ALAN A, b Brooklyn, NY, July 10, 26; m 53; c 3. PHARMACOLOGY. *Educ:* NY Univ, BA, 49, MS, 53, PhD(biol), 59. *Prof Exp:* Pharmacologist, Schering Corp, 53-64; dir pharmacol, Endo Labs, 64-71, vpres res, 71-74; DIR RES, DUPONT PHARMACEUT, 74- *Mem:* AAAS; Am Soc Pharmacol & Exp Therapeut; Am Heart Asn; NY Acad Sci; Soc Exp Biol Med. *Res:* Characterization and evaluation of drugs with special emphasis on the cardiovascular system and central and autonomic nervous systems; drug research management. *Mailing Add:* Stine Lab Newark DE 19711

RUBIN, ALAN BARRY, b Brooklyn, NY, Mar 24, 41; m 63; c 3. ORGANIC CHEMISTRY. *Educ:* Cornell Univ, BA, 62; Univ Rochester, PhD(org chem), 67. *Prof Exp:* Teaching asst org chem, Univ Rochester, 62-66; res chemist, Walter Reed Army Inst Res, Walter Reed Army Med Ctr, 67-69; HEAD SPEC CHEM, BRADLEE MED LABS, 69-; CHIEF RES CHEMIST, ADAMS LABS, INC, 69- *Mem:* Am Chem Soc. *Res:* Free radical chemistry; synthesis of antimalarials; medicinal chemistry. *Mailing Add:* 3304 Mill Cross Ct Oakton VA 22124

RUBIN, ALAN J, b Yonkers, NY, Mar 20, 34; m 62; c 1. ENVIRONMENTAL CHEMISTRY, SANITARY ENGINEERING. *Educ:* Univ Miami, BSCE, 59; Univ NC, Chapel Hill, MSSE, 62, PhD(environ chem), 66. *Prof Exp:* Civil engr, Fed Aviation Agency, Tex, 59-60; asst prof environ chem, Univ Cincinnati, 65-68; assoc prof, Water Resources Ctr, 68-74, PROF CIVIL ENG, OHIO STATE UNIV, 74- *Mem:* Am Chem Soc; Am Water Works Asn; Water Pollution Control Fedn. *Res:* Water chemistry, coagulation and colloid stability; foam separations and flotation; adsorption; coagulation and colloid stability; aluminum(III) and metal ion hydrolysis; disinfection and chlorine dioxide, dewatering of inorganic sludges; physical-chemical water and waste treatment. *Mailing Add:* Dept of Civil Eng 1791 Neil Ave Columbus OH 43210

RUBIN, ALBERT LOUIS, b Memphis, Tenn, May 9, 27; m 53; c 1. INTERNAL MEDICINE. *Educ:* Cornell Univ, MD, 50; Am Bd Internal Med, dipl, 57. *Prof Exp:* Assoc prof med, 59-68, PROF BIOCHEM & SURG, MED COL, CORNELL UNIV, 69-, PROF MED, 76-; DIR, ROGOSIN LABS, NY HOSP CORNELL MED CTR, 63-, DIR ROGOSIN KIDNEY CTR, 71- *Concurrent Pos:* Estab investr, Am Heart Asn, 58-63; attend surgeon, NY Hosp, 69- *Res:* Heart and kidney diseases. *Mailing Add:* Rogosin Lab Cornell Univ Med Col New York NY 10021

RUBIN, ALLEN GERSHON, b Lewiston, Maine, July 4, 30. SPACE PHYSICS. *Educ:* Boston Univ, PhD(physics), 57. *Prof Exp:* Physicist, Oak Ridge Nat Lab, 57-58 & Williamson Develop Co, 58-63; PHYSICIST, AIR FORCE CAMBRIDGE RES LABS, 63- *Mem:* Am Phys Soc. *Res:* Nuclear spectroscopy and reactions; plasma acceleration; laboratory astrophysics; lasers. *Mailing Add:* Air Force Geophys Lab Hanscom AFB Bedford MA 01731

RUBIN, ARTHUR I(SRAEL), b New York, NY, Dec 3, 27; m 50; c 2. COMPUTER SCIENCES. *Educ:* City Col New York, BS, 49; Stevens Inst Technol, MS, 53. *Prof Exp:* Physicist, Picatinny Arsenal, Ord Corps, 50-55; appln engr, Electronic Assocs, Inc, NJ, 55-56, supvr, 57-59, dir comput ctr, 59-62; chief automatic comput, Martin Co, 62-67, mgr hybrid comput sci dept, Orlando Div, Martin Marietta Corp, 67-69; sr tech staff consult, Electronic Assocs, Inc, 69, dir comput ctr, 69-70, mgr anal eng dept, 71-77; dir planning, 78-80, DIR PROJ CONTROL, AUTODYNAMICS, INC, 80- *Concurrent Pos:* Chmn libr comt, Simulation Coun, 64-77; mem surv comt, Am Fedn Info Processing Socs, 66-69, secy, 68-69. *Mem:* Inst Elec & Electronics Engrs; sr mem Soc Comput Simulation; assoc fel Am Inst Aeronaut & Astronaut. *Res:* Analog and hybrid computer programming and design; thermal physics. *Mailing Add:* 917 Stuart Rd Princeton NJ 08540

RUBIN, BARNEY, b Kansas City, Mo, Jan 1, 24; m 48; c 2. CHEMICAL ENGINEERING, TECHNICAL MANAGEMENT. *Educ:* Univ Calif, BS, 46, MS, 48, PhD(chem eng), 50. *Prof Exp:* Res chem engr, Radiation Lab, Univ Calif, 50-51 & Calif Res & Develop Co, 51-53; leader, Process & Mat Develop Div, 53-71, sr staff scientist, 71-81, ASST ASSOC DIR, LAWRENCE LIVERMORE NAT LAB, UNIV CALIF, 81- *Mem:* Am Chem Soc. *Res:* Computer networking assessment; energy technology research and development assessment. *Mailing Add:* Lawrence Livermore Nat Lab PO Box 808 Livermore CA 94550

RUBIN, BENJAMIN ARNOLD, b New York, NY, Sept 27, 17; m 51. MICROBIOLOGY. *Educ:* City Col, BS, 37; Va Polytech Inst, MS, 38; Yale Univ, PhD(microbiol), 47. *Prof Exp:* Asst bacteriologist, US War Dept, 40-44; res microbiologist, Schenley Res Inst, Ind, 44-45; microbiol chemist, Off Sci Res & Develop, Yale Univ, 45-47; assoc microbiologist, Brookhaven Nat Lab,

47-52; chief microbiologist, Syntex SAm, Mex, 52-54; asst prof pub health, Col Med, Baylor Univ, 54-60; MGR, BIOL PROD DEVELOP DEPT, WYETH LABS, INC, AM HOME PROD, 60- *Honors & Awards:* John Scott Award & Medal. *Mem:* Am Soc Microbiol; Am Asn Immunol; Harvey Soc; Genetics Soc Am; Radiation Res Soc. *Res:* Immunogenetics; virology; chemical and viral carcinogenesis; bioengineering; immunosuppressants; vaccine development; epidemiology and public health; radiobiology; chemotherapy. *Mailing Add:* 50 Belmont Ave Bala-Cynwyd PA 19004

RUBIN, BERNARD, physical chemistry, research administration, see previous edition

RUBIN, BERNARD, b New York, NY, Feb 15, 19; m 45; c 2. PHARMACOLOGY. *Educ:* Brooklyn Col, BA, 39; Yale Univ, PhD(pharmacol), 50. *Prof Exp:* Bact asst respiratory dis, Bur Labs, New York City Health Dept, 40-42, food & drug inspector, Bur Food & Drugs, 44-45; med lab technician path, Marine Hosp, USPHS, 43-44; res asst pharmacol & chemother, Nepera Chem Co, 45-48; SR RES GROUP LEADER PHARMACOL, SQUIBB INST MED RES, 50- *Concurrent Pos:* Mem, Am Heart Asn. *Mem:* AAAS; Am Soc Pharmacol; Soc Exp Biol & Med; NY Acad Sci. *Res:* Bioassay of natural products, as veratrum viride and Rauwolfia; chemotherapeutic agents (isoniazid, etc) and their pharmacological characteristics; anesthetics; analgetics; antihistaminics; biometrics; phenothiazine tranquilizers; central nervous system stimulants; antiserotonins; polypeptides; autonomic, vascular and gastrointestinal pharmacology; (teprotide and captopril) inhibitors of angiotensin-converting enzyme. *Mailing Add:* Pharmacol Dept Squibb Inst for Med Res Princeton NJ 08540

RUBIN, BRUCE JOEL, b Brooklyn, NY, Nov 24, 42; m 64; c 2. ELECTROPHOTOGRAPHY. *Educ:* City Univ New York, BEchE, 64; Polytech Univ Brooklyn, MchE, 65; Univ Rochester, MBA, 73. *Prof Exp:* Chemist, 65-73, sr chemist, 73-78, RES ASSOC, EASTMAN KODAK CO, 79- *Mem:* Am Inst Chem Engrs; Am Chem Soc. *Res:* Theory of electrophotographic systems; testing techniques to accurately describe new electrophotographic processes. *Mailing Add:* Eastman Kodak Co Kodak Park Res Labs Rochester NY 14650

RUBIN, BYRON HERBERT, b Chicago, Ill, July 25, 43. BIOPHYSICAL CHEMISTRY. *Educ:* Reed Col, BA, 65; Duke Univ, PhD(chem), 71. *Prof Exp:* Fel, Dept Biochem, Duke Univ Med Ctr, 70-73; assoc, Inst Cancer Res, 73-77; ASST PROF CHEM, EMORY UNIV, 77- *Mem:* Am Chem Soc; Am Crystallog Asn. *Res:* X-ray defraction. *Mailing Add:* Dept Chem Emory Univ Atlanta GA 30322

RUBIN, CHARLES STUART, b Scranton, Pa, Nov 24, 43; m 67. BIOCHEMISTRY. *Educ:* Univ Scranton, BS, 65; Cornell Univ, PhD(biochem), 71. *Prof Exp:* asst prof neurosci & molecular biol, 72-77, ASSOC PROF MOLECULAR PHARMACOL, ALBERT EINSTEIN COL MED, 78- *Concurrent Pos:* Damon Runyon fel, Albert Einstein Col Med, 70-72; City of New York Health Res Coun career scientist award, 73; NIH res career develop award, 76. *Mem:* AAAS; Am Chem Soc; Am Soc Biol Chemists. *Res:* Enzymology; enzymes involved in the metabolism and action of cyclic AMP; structure and function of membrane-associated enzymes, especially in the central nervous system; biochemical genetics. *Mailing Add:* Dept of Molecular Pharmacol Albert Einstein Col of Med Bronx NY 10461

RUBIN, CYRUS E, b Philadelphia, Pa, July 20, 21; m 47; c 2. MEDICINE, GASTROENTEROLOGY. *Educ:* Brooklyn Col, AB, 43; Harvard Med Sch, MD, 45. *Prof Exp:* Intern, Beth Israel Hosp, Boston, Mass, 45-46, resident radiol, 50-51; resident med, Cushing Vet Admin Hosp, Framingham, Mass, 48-50; from instr to assoc prof, 54-62, PROF MED, UNIV WASH, 62- *Concurrent Pos:* Dazian fel, Univ Chicago, 51-52, Runyon res fel, 52-53; Nat Cancer Inst career res award, 62-; consult, Univ, Children's Orthop, Vet Admin, King County & USPHS Hosps, Seattle, Wash. *Mem:* Am Soc Clin Invest; Am Soc Cell Biol; Am Fedn Clin Res; Am Gastroenterol Asn; Asn Am Physicians. *Res:* Structure and function of the human gastrointestinal tract. *Mailing Add:* Dept of Med Univ of Wash Seattle WA 98105

RUBIN, DANIEL JUSTIN, b Pensacola, Fla, Apr 19, 39; m 61; c 2. IMMUNOLOGY, ONCOLOGY. *Educ:* Harvard Univ, AB, 60; NY Univ, PhD(immunopath), 67. *Prof Exp:* Extern, Baptist Hosp, Pensacola, Fla, 62-63; res assoc immunochem, Sch Med & Dent, Univ Rochester, 63-64; staff fel immunochem, Biol Br, Nat Cancer Inst, 67-69, staff fel Viral Leukemia & Lymphoma Br, sr staff fel & sci coordr collab res, Off Assoc Sci Dir Viral Oncol, 70-72, res planning officer, Off Assoc Dir Prog Planning & Anal, 72-76, spec asst to dir sci coord, Off Dir, Div Cancer Treatment, 76-79; chief, Planning & Coord Br, Off Dir, Nat Heart, Lung & Blood Inst, NIH, 79-81; PRES, DANAR ASSOCS, HEALTH CARE SYSTS, CONSULTS, 81- *Mem:* AAAS; Reticuloendothelial Soc; Am Asn Cancer Res; Am Asn Immunol; NY Acad Sci. *Res:* Immunology, immunochemistry; role of complement in humoral immunity; etiology, pathogenesis of viral induced cancer and role of immune mechanisms in determination of hosp susceptibility and resistance. *Mailing Add:* 6000 Folkstone Rd Bethesda MD 20817

RUBIN, DAVID CHARLES, b Brooklyn, NY, Feb 9, 43; m 68; c 2. HERPETOLOGY, ECOLOGY. *Educ:* Cornell Univ, BS, 63; Ind State Univ, Terre Haute, MA, 65, PhD(systs & ecol), 69. *Prof Exp:* Actg instr biol, Ind State Univ, 66-67; proj writer interrelated math-sci proj, Broward County, Fla, 69-70; asst prof, 70-76, ASSOC PROF BIOL, CENT STATE UNIV, OHIO, 76- *Concurrent Pos:* Consult interrelated math-sci proj, Broward County, Fla 71 & interdisciplinary environ educ proj, 72; mem interuniv comt environ qual, Ohio Bd Regents, 72-75; mem adv bd, Ohio Biol Surv, 75- *Mem:* Am Soc Ichthyol & Herpet; Soc Study Amphibians & Reptiles; Soc Study Evolution; Herpetologists League; Soc Syst Zoologists. *Res:* Systematics of Plethodontid salamanders; amphibian and reptile distribution; amphibian and reptile food habits. *Mailing Add:* Dept Biol Cent State Univ Wilberforce OH 45384

RUBIN, DONALD BRUCE, b Washington, DC, Dec 22, 43. STATISTICS. *Educ:* Princeton Univ, AB, 65; Harvard Univ, MS, 66, PhD(statist), 70. *Prof Exp:* Lectr statist, Harvard Univ, 70-71; res statistician, Educ Testing Serv, 71-80, chmn statist group, 75-80; MEM STAFF, MATH RES CTR, UNIV WIS, 80- *Concurrent Pos:* Vis lectr statist, Princeton Univ, 71-74; assoc ed jour, Am Statist Asn, 75-, J Educ Statist, 76-; vis scholar, Univ Calif, Berkeley, 75; vis assoc prof, Univ Minn, 76 & Harvard Univ, 78; Guggenheim fel, 77-78. *Mem:* Fel Am Statist Asn; Biomet Soc; fel Inst Math Statist; Psychometric Soc. *Res:* Inference for causal effects in randomized and non-randomized studies; analysis of incomplete data. *Mailing Add:* Math Res Ctr Univ Wis Madison WI 53706

RUBIN, EDWARD S, b New York, NY, Sept 19, 41; m; c 2. MECHANICAL ENGINEERING, ENERGY. *Educ:* City Col New York, BE, 64; Stanford Univ, MS, 65, PhD(mech eng), 69. *Prof Exp:* NSF trainee & res assoc, High Temp Gas Dynamics Lab, Dept Mech Eng, Stanford Univ, 64-68; asst prof mech eng, 69-72, asst prof mech eng & pub affairs, 72-74, assoc prof mech eng & eng & pub policy, 74-79, PROF MECH ENG & ENG & PUB POLICY, CARNEGIE-MELLON UNIV, 79- *Concurrent Pos:* Consult to various pub & pvt orgn, 70-; mem energy systs task group, Gov Energy Coun, Harrisburg, Pa, 74-76; vis mech engr, Ctr Energy Policy Anal, Brookhaven Nat Lab, 75 & 77; mem air & water qual tech adv comt, Pa Dept Environ Resources, 77-; mem US steering comt-coal task force, Int Inst Appl Syst Anal, Laxenburg, Austria, 77-78; dir, Ctr Energy & Environ Studies, Carnegie-Mellon Univ, 78. *Res:* Environmental impacts of coal conversion and utilization; modelling of energy and environmental systems; air quality management; technology assessment and public policy. *Mailing Add:* Scaife Hall Carnegie-Mellon Univ Pittsburgh PA 15213

RUBIN, EMANUEL, b New York, NY, Dec 5, 28; m 55; c 4. PATHOLOGY. *Educ:* Villanova Univ, BS, 50; Harvard Univ, MD, 54. *Prof Exp:* Asst pathologist, Col Physicians & Surgeons, Columbia Univ, 61-64; assoc attend pathologist, Mt Sinai Hosp, 62-68, attend pathologist, 69-77, prof path, Mt Sinai Sch Med, 66-77, chmn dept, 72-76; PROF & CHMN, DEPT PATH & LAB MED, HAHNEMANN MED COL & HOSP, 77- *Concurrent Pos:* Consult, Path B Study Sect, NIH & Cardiomyopathies Study Sect, Nat Heart, Lung & Blood Inst, 81-86; ed, Lab Invest, 81- *Mem:* Int Acad Path; Am Soc Biol Chemists; Am Asn Path; Am Col Physicians; Am Asn Study Liver Dis. *Res:* Function and structure in human and experimental liver disease; effects of ethanol on the liver, heart and other organs. *Mailing Add:* Dept of Path & Lab Med Hahnemann Med Col Philadelphia PA 19102

RUBIN, G A, b Leipzig, Ger, Dec 30, 26; m 55; c 3. PHYSICS. *Educ:* Univ Heidelberg, BA, 46; Univ Saarlandes, dipl, 53, PhD(physics), 55. *Prof Exp:* Instr physics, Univ Saarlandes, 53-56; res scientist, Roechling Steelworks, 56-57; proj group leader mat res, Union Carbide Corp, 57-60; assoc prof physics, Clarkson Tech, 60-65; sr physicist, IIT Res Inst, 65-67; PROF PHYSICS & CHMN DEPT, LAURENTIAN UNIV, 67- *Concurrent Pos:* Consult, Steinzeug A G, Ger, 62-64; NASA & Nat Res Coun Can grants, 65-; consult, IIT Res Inst, 67-72. *Mem:* Am Phys Soc; Am Ceramic Soc; NY Acad Sci; Can Phys Soc; Ger Phys Soc. *Res:* Acoustic emissions from particulate matter; surface and fine particle physics; charge transportion in solids. *Mailing Add:* Dept of Physics Laurentian Univ Sudbury ON P3E 2C6 Can

RUBIN, HARRY, b New York, NY, June 23, 26; m 52; c 4. CELL BIOLOGY, VIROLOGY. *Educ:* Cornell Univ, DVM, 47. *Prof Exp:* Veterinarian, Foot & Mouth Dis Proj, Mex, 47-48; sr asst veterinarian, Virus Lab, USPHS, Ala, 48-52; res fel virol, Nat Found Infantile Paralysis, Biochem & Virus Lab, Calif, 52-53; res fel, Biol Div, Calif Inst Technol, 53-55, sr res fel, 55-58; assoc prof, 58-60, PROF VIROL, UNIV CALIF, BERKELEY, 60-, RES VIROLOGIST MOLECULAR BIOL, 73- *Concurrent Pos:* Dyer lectr, NIH, 64; Harvey lectr, NY Acad Med, 66. *Honors & Awards:* Rosenthal Award, AAAS, 59; Eli Lilly Award, 61; Lasker Award, 64; Mod Med Distinguished Achievement Award, 67. *Mem:* Nat Acad Sci; AAAS. *Res:* Cell growth regulation and malignancy. *Mailing Add:* Dept of Molecular Biol Univ of Calif Berkeley CA 94720

RUBIN, HARVEY LOUIS, b San Diego, Calif, Apr 28, 14; m 41; c 2. VETERINARY MICROBIOLOGY, PATHOLOGY. *Educ:* Auburn Univ, DVM, 39; Univ Ky, MS, 40; Johns Hopkins Univ, MPH, 52; Am Col Vet Prev Med, dipl. *Prof Exp:* Sr technician, Univ Ky, 40; instr vet anat & histol, Agr & Mech Col, Tex, 40-42; instr, Vet Corps, US Army, 42-68; dir, Animal Dis Diag Lab, Live Oak, Fla, 68-77; CHIEF, BUR DIAG LABS, FLA DEPT AGR, 77- *Concurrent Pos:* Adj prof, Col Vet Med, Univ Fla, 77- *Mem:* Am Vet Med Asn; Am Asn Vet Lab Diagnosticians; Am Col Vet Toxicol. *Res:* Salmonella in hogs; immunology; leptospirosis; zoonoses. *Mailing Add:* Animal Dis Diag Lab PO Box 460 Kissimmee FL 32741

RUBIN, HERBERT, b New York, NY, Oct 9, 23; m 53; c 2. PHYSICAL CHEMISTRY. *Educ:* NY Univ, BA, 44; Polytech Inst Brooklyn, MS, 49, PhD(phys chem), 53. *Prof Exp:* Res assoc radiation chem, Syracuse Univ, 53-54; sr chemist, Ozalid Div, Gen Aniline & Film Corp, 54-56; sr res engr, Schlumberger Well Surv Corp, 56-63; specialist phys chem, Repub Aviation Corp, 63-64; sr res chemist, Reaction Motors Div, Thiokol Chem Corp, 64-66; prin scientist, 66-75, RES ASSOC, INMONT CORP, 75- *Mem:* AAAS; Am Chem Soc; Sigma Xi. *Res:* Wide-line nuclear magnetic resonance; electrochemistry; photoreproductive processes; photopolymerization and ultraviolet absorption of inks and coatings; ultraviolet lamp photometry; solvent-polymer solution behavior. *Mailing Add:* 35 Byron Pl Livingston NJ 07039

RUBIN, HERBERT, b New York, NY, June 11, 30; m 57; c 3. COMMUNICATIONS, SPEECH PATHOLOGY. *Educ:* Queens Col, NY, BA, 51; Brooklyn Col, MA, 55; Harvard Univ, PhD(psychol), 59. *Prof Exp:* Clin coord speech & audiol, 59-65, assoc prof speech, 65-72, dir commun prog, 70-74, PROF SPEECH, UNIV PITTSBURGH, 72-, ASSOC DEAN GRAD FAC ARTS & SCI, 78- *Concurrent Pos:* Asst dean, Grad Fac Arts & Sci, Univ Pittsburgh, 73-78. *Mem:* Acoust Soc Am; fel Am Speech & Hearing Asn; Speech Commun Asn; Am Psychol Asn. *Res:* Psychoacoustics; psycholinguistics; language development; self-communication. *Mailing Add:* Dept of Speech Univ of Pittsburgh Pittsburgh PA 15260

RUBIN, HERMAN, b Chicago, Ill, Oct 27, 26; m 52; c 2. STATISTICS, MATHEMATICS. *Educ:* Univ Chicago, BS, 44, MS, 45, PhD(math), 48. *Prof Exp:* Res asst, Cowles Comn Res Econ, Chicago, 44-46, res assoc, 46-47 & 48-49; asst prof statist, Stanford Univ, 49-55; assoc prof math, Univ Ore, 55-59; prof statist, Mich State Univ, 59-67; PROF STATIST, PURDUE UNIV, LAFAYETTE, 67- *Mem:* AAAS; Am Math Soc; Math Asn Am; fel Inst Math Statist. *Res:* Mathematical statistics; statistical decision theory; mathematical logic and set theory; stochastic processes. *Mailing Add:* Dept of Statist Purdue Univ West Lafayette IN 47907

RUBIN, HOWARD ARNOLD, b Baltimore, Md, Jan 4, 40; m 65; c 2. PHYSICS. *Educ:* Mass Inst Technol, SB, 61; Univ Md, College Park, PhD(physics), 67. *Prof Exp:* Asst prof, 66-72, ASSOC PROF PHYSICS, ILL INST TECHNOL, 72- *Mem:* Am Phys Soc. *Res:* High energy physics, using bubble chamber and electronic techniques. *Mailing Add:* Dept of Physics Ill Inst Technol Chicago IL 60616

RUBIN, ISAAC D, b Krakow, Poland, Nov 8, 31; US citizen; m 57; c 1. POLYMER CHEMISTRY, ORGANIC CHEMISTRY. *Educ:* Brooklyn Col, BS, 54; Brooklyn Polytech Inst, MS, 57, PhD(polymer chem), 61. *Prof Exp:* Chemist, Acralite Co, Inc, 54-56, plant mgr, 56-57; develop chemist, Gen Elec Co, 60-62; sr chemist, 62-64, res chemist, 64-67, group leader, 67-78, TECHNOLOGIST, TEXACO, INC, 78- *Mem:* NY Acad Sci. *Res:* Polymerization mechanisms; structure-property relationships in polymers; synthetic lubricants; lubricant and fuel additives. *Mailing Add:* Texaco Inc PO Box 509 Beacon NY 12508

RUBIN, IZHAK, b Haifa, Israel, May 22, 42; m 65; c 3. ELECTRICAL ENGINEERING. *Educ:* Israel Inst Technol, BS, 64, MS, 68; Princeton Univ, PhD(elec eng), 70. *Prof Exp:* Electronics engr, Signal Corps, Israel Defense Army, 64-67; electronics engr, Israel Aircraft Industs, 67-68; res asst elec eng, Princeton Univ, 69-70; from asst prof to assoc prof, 70-80, PROF ENG & APPL SCI, UNIV CALIF, LOS ANGELES, 80- *Concurrent Pos:* Off Naval Res grant, Univ Calif, Los Angeles, 72-, NSF res grant, 75-, Naval Res Lab grant, 78-; actg chief scientist, Xerox Telecoms Network, 79-80; pres, IRI Corp, 80- *Mem:* Inst Elec & Electronics Engrs. *Res:* Data and computer communication networks; satellite communication networks; queueing systems; network flows; communication and information theory; stochastic processes. *Mailing Add:* Dept of Syst Sci 4531 Boelter Hall Univ of Calif Los Angeles CA 90024

RUBIN, JACOB, b Wloclawek, Poland, Feb 1, 19; US citizen; m 43; c 3. SOIL PHYSICS, HYDROLOGY. *Educ:* Univ Calif, Berkeley, BS, 42, PhD(soil sci), 49. *Prof Exp:* Soil physicist, Agr Res Sta, Rehovoth, Israel, 50-61, chmn div irrig & soil physics, 56-58, dir inst soils & water, 59-61; adv solute transport, 74-76, SOIL PHYSICIST, WATER RESOURCES DIV, US GEOL SURV, 62- 74- *Concurrent Pos:* Adj lectr, Israel Inst Technol, 52-55, adj sr lectr, 56-58, adj assoc prof, 59-61; external lectr, Fac Agr, Hebrew Univ, Israel, 52-61; leader, UN Proj Tech Assistance to Cyprus Govt, 57; consult, Govt Israel, 57-61 & Italian Ministry Agr, 60; consult prof, Stanford Univ, Calif, 75- *Honors & Awards:* O E Meinzer Award, Geol Soc Am, 77. *Mem:* AAAS; Soil Sci Soc Am; Am Geophys Union. *Res:* Movement of water and solutes in the unsaturated zone; flow of fluids and transport of reacting solutes in porous media; evapotranspiration; irrigation practices; soil physical properties in relation to plant growth. *Mailing Add:* Water Resources Div MS 21 US Geol Surv 345 Middlefield Rd Menlo Park CA 94025

RUBIN, JEAN E, b New York, NY, Oct 29, 26; m 52; c 2. MATHEMATICS. *Educ:* Queens Col, NY, BS, 48; Columbia Univ, MA, 49; Stanford Univ, PhD(math), 55. *Prof Exp:* Tutor math, Queens Col, NY, 49-51; instr, Stanford Univ, 53-55; lectr, Univ Ore, 55-59; asst prof, Mich State Univ, 61-68; assoc prof, 68-75, PROF MATH, PURDUE UNIV, 75- *Mem:* Am Math Soc; Asn Symbolic Logic; Math Asn Am. *Res:* Set theory; axiom of choice; cardinal and ordinal numbers; models of set theory. *Mailing Add:* Dept of Math Purdue Univ West Lafayette IN 47907

RUBIN, JOEL E(DWARD), b Cleveland, Ohio, Sept 5, 28; m 53; c 3. ELECTRICAL ENGINEERING. *Educ:* Case Inst Technol, BS, 49; Yale Univ, MFA, 51; Stanford Univ, PhD(theatre eng), 60. *Prof Exp:* VPRES ILLUMINATING ENG, KLIEGL BROS LIGHTING, LONG ISLAND CITY, 54- *Concurrent Pos:* Mem comt theatre eng, US Inst Theatre Technol, 60- *Honors & Awards:* Founder's Award, US Inst Theatre Technol, 72. *Mem:* US Inst Theatre Technol; Illum Eng Soc; Int Orgn Scenographers & Theatre Technicians (pres, 71-79); fel Am theatre Asn. *Res:* Theatre technology and illuminating engineering. *Mailing Add:* 24 Edgewood Ave Hastings-on-Hudson NY 10706

RUBIN, JOHN RONALD, biophysical chemistry, see previous edition

RUBIN, KENNETH, b New York, NY, Feb 28, 28; m 51; c 3. PHYSICS. *Educ:* NY Univ, BS, 50, MS, 52, PhD(physics), 59. *Prof Exp:* Asst panel electron tubes, Res Div, NY Univ, 52-53 & Radiation Lab, Columbia Univ, 53-54; instr physics, City Col New York, 54-55; from instr to asst prof, NY Univ, 55-66; assoc prof, 64-72, PROF PHYSICS, CITY COL NEW YORK, 72- *Mem:* Am Phys Soc. *Res:* Atomic beam resonance and atomic scattering experiments utilizing atomic beam techniques. *Mailing Add:* Dept of Physics City Col of New York New York NY 10031

RUBIN, LAWRENCE G, b Brooklyn, NY, Sept 17, 25; m 51; c 3. PHYSICS, INSTRUMENTATION. *Educ:* Univ Chicago, BS, 49; Columbia Univ, MA, 50. *Prof Exp:* Staff mem solid state physics, Res Div, Raytheon Co, Mass, 50-58, mgr instrumentation group, 58-64; GROUP LEADER INSTRUMENTATION & OPERS, NAT MAGNET LAB, MASS INST TECHNOL, 64-, DIV HEAD, 77- *Concurrent Pos:* Mem adv panel, Nat Acad Sci, Nat Bur Standards, 77-82. *Mem:* Fel Am Phys Soc; fel Inst Elec & Electronics Eng; Instrument Soc Am; Am Vacuum Soc. *Res:* Instrumentation in electronics; vacuum, cryogenics and visible and infrared spectrometry; temperature measurement and control; bulk properties of semiconductors; low level signal processing; high field magnetometry. *Mailing Add:* Nat Magnet Lab Bldg NW14 Mass Inst Technol 170 Albany St Cambridge MA 02139

RUBIN, LEON E, b Winthrop, Mass, Apr 24, 21; m 47; c 3. ANALYTICAL CHEMISTRY. *Educ:* Mass Inst Technol, BS, 42; Boston Univ, MS, 47; Columbia Univ, PhD(chem), 51. *Prof Exp:* Res assoc phys org chem, Columbia Univ, 51-52; scientist, 52-65, res group leader, 65-67, MGR ANAL CHEM, POLAROID CORP, 67- *Mem:* Am Chem Soc. *Res:* Spectrophotometry; titrimetry; chromatography; absorption spectroscopy; kinetics of reactions; photographic chemistry; polymer analysis. *Mailing Add:* Polaroid Corp Res Labs 750 Main St Cambridge MA 02139

RUBIN, LEON JULIUS, b Poland, Nov 22, 13; Can citizen; m 37; c 2. FOOD SCIENCE, FOOD ENGINEERING. *Educ:* Univ Toronto, BASc, 38, MASc, 39, PhD(org chem), 45. *Prof Exp:* Lectr chem eng, Univ Toronto, 39-45; res chemist, Res Ctr, Can Packers Ltd, 45-49, res dir, 49-78; PROF FOOD ENG, DEPT CHEM ENG & APPL CHEM, UNIV TORONTO, 79- *Concurrent Pos:* Mem, Can Comt Food, Expert Comt Meats & chmn, Indust/ Govt Nitrites & Nitrosamines. *Honors & Awards:* Montreal Medal, Chem Inst Can, 70, Charles Honey Award, 75; William J Eva Award, Can Inst Food Sci & Technol, 78; John Labatt Award, Chem Inst Can, 80. *Mem:* Am Chem Soc; Inst Food Technologists; fel Chem Inst Can; Can Inst Food Sci & Technol; Indust Res Inst. *Res:* Food chemistry; food processes and products; food additives; lipid chemistry; oilseed processing, meat curing. *Mailing Add:* Dept Chem Eng & Appl Chem Univ Toronto Toronto ON M5S 1A4 Can

RUBIN, LEONARD ROY, b Brooklyn, NY, Nov 16, 39; m 60; c 2. TOPOLOGY. *Educ:* Tulane Univ, BS, 61; Univ Miami, MS, 63; Fla State Univ, PhD(math), 65. *Prof Exp:* From asst prof to assoc prof, 67-78, PROF MATH, UNIV OKLA, 78- *Concurrent Pos:* Staff mem, Okla Univ Res Inst, 68; vis assoc prof, Univ Utah, 73-74. *Mem:* Am Math Soc. *Res:* Geometric topology and dimension theory. *Mailing Add:* Dept of Math Rm 423 Univ Okla 601 Elm Ave Norman OK 73019

RUBIN, LEONARD SIDNEY, b New York, NY, Aug 27, 22; m 50; c 3. PSYCHOPHYSIOLOGY, PSYCHOPHARMACOLOGY. *Educ:* NY Univ, PhD(psychol), 51. *Prof Exp:* Asst instr biochem, NY Med Col, 44-45; tutor psychol, City Col New York, 45; instr, Wash Sq Col, NY Univ, 47-50, res assoc col eng, 50-53; chief psychol & human eng br, Med Labs, US Chem Corps, 53-57; head psychobiol, Eastern Pa Psychiat Inst, 57-80; PROF PHYSIOL & PHARM, PHILADELPHIA COL OSTEOP, 80- *Concurrent Pos:* Asst prof psychiat, Sch Med, Univ Pa, 59-65, assoc prof, 65-; adj prof, Sch Med, Temple Univ, 70-; foreign exchange scholar, Nat Acad Sci, Yugoslavia, 74. *Honors & Awards:* Soc Sci Res Coun Award, Inst Math, Stanford Univ, 55; Hon Award, Soc Biol Psychiat, 59. *Mem:* Fel Acad Psychosomat Med; Soc Biol Psychiat; fel Am Psychol Asn; Am Psychopathol Asn; Sco Psychophysiol Res. *Res:* Autonomic neurohumoral concomitants of schizophrenia; other behavior disorders; chronic alcoholism; drug abuse; migraine. *Mailing Add:* 706 Powder Mill Lane Philadelphia PA 19151

RUBIN, LOUIS, b New York, NY, Aug 19, 22; m 46; c 2. CHEMISTRY. *Educ:* NY Univ, AB, 43; Univ Mo, AM, 47, PhD(chem), 50. *Prof Exp:* Asst chem, Univ Mo, 47-49; chemist, Winthrop Labs, 51-52, dir, Process Develop Lab, 52-59; sr chemist, Rohr Aircraft Corp, 59-61, chief tech staff, 61-64; mem tech staff, 64-75, STAFF SCIENTIST, AEROSPACE CORP, 75- *Concurrent Pos:* Lectr, Univ Calif, Los Angeles & Exten Div, 63-64. *Mem:* Am Chem Soc; NY Acad Sci; Soc Plastics Engrs. *Res:* Organic chemistry; reinforced plastics; adhesives; polymer chemistry; ablative materials; hypervelocity erosion; metal-matrix composites. *Mailing Add:* 2502 E Willow St Signal Hill CA 90806

RUBIN, MARTIN ISRAEL, b New York, NY, Nov 2, 15; m 42; c 4. BIOCHEMISTRY. *Educ:* City Col New York, BS, 36; Columbia Univ, PhD(org chem), 42. *Hon Degrees:* DSc, Univ Louis Pasteur, France, 76. *Prof Exp:* Hernscheim fel, Mt Sinai Hosp, 39-40; res chemist, Wallace & Tiernan Prod, Inc, NJ, 41-46 & Schering Corp, 46-48; prof bioclin chem, Med Sch, 48-52, PROF BIOCHEM, GRAD SCH, GEORGETOWN UNIV, 52-, SCH MED & DENT, 58- *Concurrent Pos:* US Chem; consult, WHO, Pan Am Health Orgn, Food & Drug Admin & NIH. Comn Clin Chem, Int Union Pure & Appl Chem; pres, Int Fedn Clin Chem. *Honors & Awards:* Smith Kline & French Award, Fisher Award, Roe Award & Gemlot Award, Am Asn Clin Chemists. *Mem:* AAAS; Am Chem Soc; Soc Exp Biol & Med; Am Asn Clin Chem; Am Rheumatism Asn. *Res:* Synthetic drugs; use of radioisotopes in biochemistry and medicine; steroid chemistry; clinical chemistry; synthesis of unsaturated lactones related to the cardiac aglycones; chelate compounds; mineral metabolism. *Mailing Add:* Dept of Biochem Georgetown Univ Sch Med & Dent Washington DC 20007

RUBIN, MAX, b New York, NY, Jan 6, 16; m 42; c 2. ANIMAL NUTRITION, BIOCHEMISTRY. *Educ:* Rutgers Univ, BS, 38; Univ Md, MS, 40, PhD(poultry nutrit), 42. *Prof Exp:* Chemist, Chem Warfare Serv, 42-43; physiologist, 43-44; biologist, US Bur Animal Indust, 44-46; nutritionist, Schenley Distillers Corp, 46-47; fel, 69-72, FAC RES ASSOC ANIMAL NUTRIT, UNIV MD, COLLEGE PARK, 72- *Concurrent Pos:* Fel animal nutrit, Univ Md, 42-43. *Mem:* AAAS; Poultry Sci Asn; World Poultry Sci Asn; Am Chem Soc. *Res:* Amino acid metabolism; buphthalmos as it is related to glycine in the diet; lysine and tryptophane from grains which have genetically improved amino acid composition. *Mailing Add:* 7333 New Hampshire Ave Hyattsville MD 20783

RUBIN, MELVIN LYNNE, b San Francisco, Calif, May 10, 32; m 53; c 3. MEDICINE, OPHTHALMOLOGY. *Educ:* Univ Calif, Berkeley, BS, 53; Univ San Francisco, MD, 57; Univ Iowa, MS, 61; Am Bd Ophthal, cert. *Prof Exp:* Exec secy vision res training comn, Nat Inst Neurol Dis & Blindness, 61-63; from asst prof to assoc prof, 63-67, PROF OPHTHAL, COL MED, UNIV FLA, 67-, CHMN DEPT, 79- *Mem:* Asn Res Vision & Ophthal (pres); Am Acad Ophthal (secy); Am Ophthal Soc. *Res:* Visual physiology and visual optics; retinal anatomy; microscopic histology and photochemistry; effects of therapy for retinal detachment surgery on the microstructrue of the eye. *Mailing Add:* Dept of Ophthal Univ of Fla Med Ctr Gainesville FL 32610

RUBIN, MEYER, b Chicago, Ill, Feb 17, 24; m 44; c 3. GEOLOGY. *Educ:* Univ Chicago, BS, 47, MS, 49, PhD, 56. *Prof Exp:* Asst geol, Univ Chicago, 49-50; geologist, Mil Geol Br, 50-53, GEOLOGIST, C-14 LAB, ISOTOPE GEOL BR, US GEOL SURV, 53- *Concurrent Pos:* Instr, Ill Inst Technol, 49 & USDA Grad Sch, 51-52. *Mem:* AAAS; Geol Soc Am; Am Geophys Union; Am Quaternary Asn. *Res:* Radiocarbon age determinations of Wisconsin glaciations; sea-level changes; dating groundwater. *Mailing Add:* US Geol Surv Nat Ctr 971 Reston VA 22092

RUBIN, MILTON D(AVID), b Boston, Mass, July 4, 14; m 44; c 2. SYSTEMS ENGINEERING. *Educ:* Harvard Univ, BS, 35. *Prof Exp:* Proj engr, Raytheon Corp, Mass, 44-48; res dir comput, Philbrick Res, Inc, 48-49; proj leader radar & comput, Lab Electronics, Inc, Mass, 49-51; group leader radar, Lincoln Lab, Mass Inst Technol, 51-55; dept mgr anal, Sylvania Elec Prod, Inc, 55-57; systs engr, Lincoln Lab, Mass Inst Technol, 57-59 & Mitre Corp, Mass, 59-69; consult scientist, Raytheon Co, 69-75; pres, Energy Conserv Res Inst, 75-77; STAFF MEM, LINCOLN LAB, MASS INST TECHNOL, 77- *Mem:* Fel AAAS; Inst Elec & Electronics Engrs; Soc Gen Systs Res (secy-treas, 64-67, pres, 68-69); Inst Mgt Sci; Opers Res Soc Am. *Res:* Radar engineering; printed circuit techniques; computer and radar circuits; radar design; analysis of networks of radars for detection of aircraft, missiles and satellites; general systems research; air traffic control; organization theory and technology; impact on ecology of the technology of improvement of equipment; energy utilization efficiency. *Mailing Add:* 19 Dorr Rd Newton MA 02158

RUBIN, MITCHELL IRVING, b Charleston, SC, Apr 1, 02; m 34; c 2. PEDIATRICS, NEPHROLOGY. *Educ:* Med Col SC, MD, 25. *Hon Degrees:* Dr(humane letters), Med Univ SC, 75. *Prof Exp:* Instr pediat, Med Sch, Johns Hopkins Univ, 30-31; assoc clin prof, Univ Pa, 38-45; prof pediat, 45-72, EMER PROF PEDIAT, STATE UNIV NY, BUFFALO, 72- *Concurrent Pos:* Pediatrician-in-chief & attend pediatrician, Children's Hosp Buffalo, 45-72; ed, Am J Dis Children & Pediat; consult, Dept Pediat, Med Univ SC, 72-; ed, Pediatric Nephrol, 75; Spanish ed, Ed Pediat, Barcelona, 78. *Mem:* Am Pediat Soc (vpres, 69-70); Soc Pediat Res (secy, 39-46, pres, 47); AMA; Am Acad Pediat; Sigma Xi. *Res:* Physiology of renal functions in childhood. *Mailing Add:* 22 Charlestowne Court Charleston SC 29401

RUBIN, MORDECAI B, organic chemistry, see previous edition

RUBIN, MORTON HAROLD, b Albany, NY, Mar 10, 38; m 65; c 2. THEORETICAL PHYSICS. *Educ:* Mass Inst Technol, SB, 59; Princeton Univ, PhD(physics), 64. *Prof Exp:* Jr scientist physics, Avco-Everett Res Corp, 60-61; fel physics, Univ Wis, 64-66, instr, 66-67; asst prof physics, Univ Pa, 67-73; vis asst prof physics, Pahlavi Univ, Shiraz, Iran, 70-71; ASSOC PROF PHYSICS, UNIV MD BALTIMORE COUNTY, 73- *Mem:* Am Phys Soc; Am Asn Physics Teachers. *Res:* Critical phenomena; nucleation and condensation; statistical mechanics; non-equilibrium thermodynamics; quantum theory of scattering. *Mailing Add:* Dept Physics Univ Md Baltimore County Baltimore MD 21228

RUBIN, MORTON JOSEPH, b Philadelphia, Pa, May 15, 17; m 40, 75; c 3. METEOROLOGY. *Educ:* Pa State Univ, BA, 42; Mass Inst Technol, MS, 52. *Prof Exp:* Meteorologist, Pan-Am Grace Airways, 42-49; res assoc meteorol, Mass Inst Technol, 49-52; res meteorologist, US Weather Bur, Environ Sci Serv Admin, 52-65; sr staff scientist meteorol, 65-67, dep chief plans & requirements div, 67-69, chief off spec studies, 67-69, chief res group, Nat Oceanic & Atmospheric Admin, 69-74; sci officer, World Meteorol Orgn, 74-81; VIS SCHOLAR, SCOTT POLAR RES INST, 81- *Concurrent Pos:* Mem heat & water panel, Comn Polar Res, Nat Acad Sci, 63-65; chmn, Working Group Antarctic Meteorol, Sci Comt Antarctic Res, 64-; pres, Int Comn Polar Meteorol, 64-72. *Honors & Awards:* Antarctic Serv Medal, 65; Am Meteorol Soc Spec Award, 65. *Mem:* Am Meteorol Soc; Am Geophys Union. *Res:* Polar meteorology; heat and water budget; southern hemisphere atmospheric circulation and climate. *Mailing Add:* c/o Scott Polar Res Inst Lensfield Rd Cambridge CB2 7ER Eng

RUBIN, NATHAN, b Philadelphia, Pa, Dec 20, 12; m 40; c 2. ORGANIC CHEMISTRY. *Educ:* Phila Col Pharm, BSc, 34; Univ Pa, MS, 35, PhD(org chem), 39. *Prof Exp:* PROF CHEM, PHILA COL PHARM & SCI, 59-, DEAN STUDENTS, 75- *Mem:* Acad Pharmaceut Sci; Am Chem Soc; Am Pharmaceut Asn; NY Acad Sci. *Res:* Synthetic medicinals. *Mailing Add:* Dept of Chem Phila Col of Pharm & Sci Philadelphia PA 19104

RUBIN, RICHARD MARK, b Pensacola, Fla, July 26, 37; m 63; c 2. NUCLEAR ENGINEERING, PHYSICS. *Educ:* Univ Mich, BSE, 59; Univ Okla, MNE, 61; Kans State Univ, PhD(nuclear eng), 70. *Prof Exp:* Exp supvr Off Civil Defense contract, Nuclear Eng Shielding Facil, Kans State Univ, 67-69, instr nuclear eng, 69; asst prof, Miss State Univ, 70-77; PROJ PHYSICIST, RADIATION RES ASSOCS, INC, 77- *Concurrent Pos:* Adj mem grad fac, Tex Christian Univ, 77- *Mem:* Am Nuclear Soc; Am Soc Eng Educ; Sigma Xi. *Res:* Radiation shielding; radiation transport; neutron activation analysis; dosimetry. *Mailing Add:* 3550 Hulen St Ft Worth TX 76107

RUBIN, ROBERT, veterinary parasitology, see previous edition

RUBIN, ROBERT JAY, b Boston, Mass, Mar 25, 32; Wid; c 3. TOXICOLOGY, BIOCHEMISTRY. *Educ:* Univ Mass, BS, 53; Boston Univ, AM, 55, PhD(pharmacol), 60. *Prof Exp:* Asst prof, Univ Kans, 63-64; from asst prof to assoc, 64-73, dir, Div Toxicol, 77-79, PROF ENVIRON HEALTH SCI, SCH HYG & PUB HEALTH, JOHNS HOPKINS UNIV, 73- *Concurrent Pos:* USPHS fel pharmacol, Sch Med, Yale Univ, 60-63; Res Career Develop Award, Nat Inst Environ Health Sci, 69-74. *Mem:* AAAS; Soc Occup & Environ Health; Soc Toxicol; Am Soc Pharmacol & Exp Therapeut. *Res:* Biochemical toxicology; biochemical mechanisms of action of pharmacologic and toxic agents; drug metabolism and disposition; carcinogenesis. *Mailing Add:* Dept of Environ Health Sci Johns Hopkins Sch of Hyg & Pub Health Baltimore MD 21205

RUBIN, ROBERT JOSHUA, b New York, NY, Aug 17, 26; m 48; c 4. PHYSICAL CHEMISTRY. *Educ:* Cornell Univ, AB, 48, PhD(phys chem), 51. *Prof Exp:* Sr mem staff, Appl Physics Lab, Johns Hopkins Univ, 51-55; vis asst prof phys chem, Univ Ill, 55-57; PHYSICIST, NAT BUR STANDARDS, 57- *Concurrent Pos:* NSF sr fel, 63-64; res physicist, NIH, 76-77; vis prof chem eng, Univ Calif, Berkeley, 81. *Mem:* Am Phys Soc; Am Chem Soc; Biophys Soc; Soc Indust & Appl Math. *Res:* Chemical physics; statistical and quantum mechanics; mathematical physics; biophysics. *Mailing Add:* 3308 McKinley St NW Washington DC 20015

RUBIN, ROBERT TERRY, b Los Angeles, Calif, Aug 26, 36; m 62; c 3. PSYCHIATRY. *Educ:* Univ Calif, Los Angeles, AB, 58; Univ Calif, San Francisco, MD, 61; Am Bd Psychiat & Neurol, dipl & cert psychiat, 68; Univ Southern Calif, PhD, 77. *Prof Exp:* Intern, Philadelphia Gen Hosp, 61-62; resident psychiat, Sch Med, 62-65, asst prof, 65-71, vis prof, 72-74, adj prof, 74-77, PROF PSYCHIAT, SCH MED, UNIV CALIF, LOS ANGELES, 77-, MEM, BRAIN RES INST, 69- *Concurrent Pos:* Prof psychiat, Col Med, Pa State Univ, 71-74. *Mem:* Fel Am Psychiat Asn; Am Psychosom Soc; fel Am Col Psychiat; Int Soc Psychoneuroendocrinol; fel AAAS. *Res:* Biochemical and neuroendocrine correlates of stress and mental illness. *Mailing Add:* Harbor Hosp Univ Calif Los Angeles Med Ctr Torrance CA 90509

RUBIN, SAMUEL H, b New York, NY, July 24, 16; m 43; c 2. INTERNAL MEDICINE. *Educ:* Brown Univ, AB, 38; Univ Chicago, MS, 55; St Louis Univ, MD, 43; Am Bd Internal Med, dipl. *Prof Exp:* Assoc prof, 60-65, dir cardiovasc training prog, 66-71, assoc dean, 71-72, vpres acad affairs, 75-77, PROF INTERNAL MED, NY MED COL, 65-, EXEC DEAN, 72-, DEAN COL, 75-, PROVOST, 77- *Concurrent Pos:* Consult, Jersey Shore Med Ctr, Neptune, NJ, 62- *Mem:* Fel Am Col Physicians; Asn Am Med Cols; NY Acad Sci. *Res:* Clinical and internal medicine. *Mailing Add:* NY Med Col Elmwood Hall Valhalla NY 10595

RUBIN, SAUL H, b Cleveland, Ohio, Nov 24, 23; m 47; c 4. ENGINEERING. *Educ:* Case Inst Technol, BS, 44, MS, 47. *Prof Exp:* Res engr, Nat Adv Comt Aeronaut, Ohio, 44-45; asst, Case Inst Technol, 45-46; sci engr, Joy Mfg Co, 47-50; sci engr, 50-64, PRES, TYROLER METALS, INC, 64- *Res:* Test and analysis of aircraft compressors and navy refrigeration coils; analytical design and analysis of axial-flow fans and compressors; design of equipment for salvage and reclamation. *Mailing Add:* 2445 Queenston Rd Cleveland Heights OH 44118

RUBIN, SAUL HOWARD, b New York, NY, Oct 15, 12; m 32; c 2. BIOCHEMISTRY. *Educ:* City Col, BS, 31; NY Univ, MS, 32, PhD(biochem), 39. *Prof Exp:* Biochemist, Littauer Res Fund, Harlem Hosp, New York, 32-34; res biochemist, Metab Lab, NY Univ, 36-41; dir, Nutrit Labs, Hoffman-LaRoche, Inc, 41-49, coordr pharmaceut res, 49-53, dir new prods div, 53-58, corp dir prod develop, 58-77. *Concurrent Pos:* Mem liaison & sci adv bd, Quartermaster Corps Food & Container Inst, US Army. *Mem:* Asn Res Dirs (past pres); Am Soc Clin Nutrit; Am Pharm Asn; Am Soc Biol Chemists; Am Inst Nutrit. *Res:* Acid base and lipid metabolism; vitamin assays and metabolism; drug formulation and metabolism. *Mailing Add:* 62 Beech St Nutley NJ 07110

RUBIN, SHELDON, b Chicago, Ill, July 19, 32; m 55; c 3. STRUCTUAL DYNAMICS. *Educ:* Calif Inst Technol, BS , 53, MS, 54, PhD(mech eng, physics), 56. *Prof Exp:* Res engr sound & vibration, Lockheed Aircraft Co, 56-58; head tech eng sect, Hughes Aircraft Co, 58-62; SR PROJ ENGR VEHICLE ENG, AEROSPACE CORP, LOS ANGELES, 62- *Concurrent Pos:* Consult, 56-; lectr, Univ Calif, Los Angeles, 64- *Honors & Awards:* Cert Appreciation, Soc Automotive Engrs, 65. *Mem:* Am Inst Aeronaut & Astronaut; Soc Automotive Engrs; An Nat Standards Inst. *Res:* Detection of structural damage by vibration monitoring; influence of propulsion system on vibration stability of liquid rocket vehicles. *Mailing Add:* 3531 Alana Dr Sherman Oaks CA 91403

RUBIN, STANLEY G(ERALD), b Brooklyn, NY, May 11, 38; m 63; c 3. COMPUTATIONAL FLUID MECHANICS, VISCOUS FLOWS. *Educ:* Polytech Inst Brooklyn, BAE, 59; Cornell Univ, PhD(aerospace eng), 63. *Prof Exp:* Res scientist, Boeing Airplane Co, 63; NSF fel, Henri Poincare Inst, Univ Paris, 63-64; from asst prof to assoc prof eng & appl mech, Polytech Inst New York, 64-73, prof mech & aerospace eng, 73-79, assoc dir, Aerodyn Labs, 77-79; PROF AEROSPACE & APPL MECH & HEAD DEPT, UNIV CINCINNATI, 79- *Concurrent Pos:* Vis prof mech eng, Old Dominion Univ, 73-74; consult, Aerospace Corp, 77-; ed, Int J Comput & Fluids, 79- *Mem:* Am Soc Mech Engrs; Soc Indust & Appl Math; Am Soc Eng Educ; Assoc fel Am Inst Aeronaut & Astronaut. *Res:* High-speed gasdynamics; three-dimensional viscous interactions; asymptotic expansions in viscous flow; numerical analysis of flow problems. *Mailing Add:* 10695 Deershadow Lane Cincinnati OH 45242

RUBIN, VERA COOPER, b Philadelphia, Pa, July 23, 28; m 48; c 4. ASTRONOMY. *Educ:* Vassar Col, BA, 48; Cornell Univ, MA, 51; Georgetown Univ, PhD(astron), 54. *Hon Degrees:* DSc, Creighton Univ, 78. *Prof Exp:* Instr math & physics, Montgomery County Jr Col, 54-55; res assoc astron, Georgetown Univ, 55-65, lectr, 59-62, asst prof, 62-65; STAFF MEM, DEPT TERRESTRIAL MAGNETISM, CARNEGIE INST, 65- *Concurrent Pos:* Assoc ed, Astron J, 72-; mem space astron comt, Nat Acad Sci, 72-, US Nat Comt, Int Astron Union, 72-76, Bd of Dirs, Asn Univs Res Astron, Inc, 73-76 & space sci bd, Nat Acad Sci, 74-76; mem vis comn, Dept Astron, Harvard Univ, 76-82, Nat Radio Astron Observ, 75-79 & Aura Observ, 80-; assoc ed, Astrophys J Letters, 77-; mem, Smithsonian Coun, 79-; distinguished vis astron, Cerro Tololo, 78; Chancellor's distinguished prof astron, Univ Calif, Berkeley, 81. *Mem:* Nat Acad Sci; Int Astron Union; Am Astron Soc. *Res:* External galaxies; galactic dynamics; spectroscopy. *Mailing Add:* Carnegie Inst Dept Terr Magnet 5341 Broad Branch Rd Washington DC 20015

RUBIN, WALTER, b Worcester, Mass, Aug 15, 33; m 58; c 5. GASTROENTEROLOGY, CELL BIOLOGY. *Educ:* Mass Inst Technol, BS, 55; Cornell Univ, MD, 59. *Prof Exp:* From instr to asst prof med, Med Col, Cornell Univ, 64-69, asst prof anat, 68-69; assoc prof med, 69-70, assoc prof anat, 69-75, PROF MED, MED COL PA, 70-, PROF ANAT, 75-, CHIEF GASTROENTEROL, 69- *Concurrent Pos:* Res fel med, Med Col, Cornell Univ, 62-64; Nat Inst Arthritis & Metab Dis res grant & Am Cancer Soc res grant, Med Col, Cornell Univ, 66-69 & Med Col Pa, 69-; consult gastroenterol, Mem Hosp, New York, 69-70 & Vet Admin Hosp, Philadelphia, 69-; mem gastrointestinal syst res eval comt, US Vet Admin, 69-71, mem merit rev bd gastroenterol, 72-74; mem gastroenterol adv panel, Subcomt Scope of US Pharmacopeia Comt of Revision, 75- *Mem:* Am Soc Cell Biol; Histochem Soc; fel Am Col Physicians; Am Gastroenterol Asn; Am Soc Clin Invest. *Res:* Gastrointestinal epithelia, particularly their fine structure, ontogenesis, differentiation and function in health and disease. *Mailing Add:* Dept of Med Med Col of Pa Philadelphia PA 19129

RUBINO, ANDREW M, b Brooklyn, NY, Apr 30, 22; m 44; c 3. INORGANIC CHEMISTRY, PHYSICAL CHEMISTRY. *Educ:* St Johns's Col, NY, BS, 49. *Prof Exp:* Res chemist, Reheis Co Inc, NJ, 51-56, mgr tech serv, 56-60 & res & develop, 60-65; vpres & tech dir, Dragoco Inc, 65-66; dir res & develop, 66-73, vpres-tech dir, 73-78, CONSULT, REHEIS CHEM CO DIV, ARMOUR PHARMACEUT CO, 78- *Mem:* AAAS; Am Chem Soc; Soc Cosmetic Chem; NY Acad Sci. *Res:* Aluminum chemistry; chelates; cosmetics; pharmaceuticals and other fine chemicals. *Mailing Add:* Reheis Chem Co Berkeley Heights NJ 07922

RUBINOFF, IRA, b New York, NY, Dec 21, 38; m 78; c 1. ZOOLOGY. *Educ:* Queens Col, BS, 59; Harvard Univ, AM, 61, PhD(biol), 63. *Prof Exp:* Fel evolutionary biol, Harvard Univ, 64, asst cur ichthyol, Mus Comp Zool, 65; asst dir sci, 65-73, DIR, SMITHSONIAN TROP RES INST, 73- *Concurrent Pos:* Res grants, Am Philos Soc & Harvard Univ Milton Fund, 64, NSF, 65 & Smithsonian Res Award Prog, 65-67; assoc ichthyol, Mus Comp Zool, Harvard Univ, 65-; mem adv sci bd, Gorgas Mem Inst, 74-; mem bd dirs, Charles Darwin Res Found; trustee, Rare Animal Relief Effort; vis fel, Wolfson Col, Oxford Univ, 80-81. *Mem:* AAAS; Am Soc Nat; Am Soc Ichthyol & Herpet; Soc Study Evolution; fel Linnean Soc London. *Res:* Biological implications of the construction of a sea level canal; zoogeography of the Eastern Tropical Pacific; strategies for preservation of world's tropical forests. *Mailing Add:* Smithsonian Trop Res Inst Box 2072 Balboa Panama

RUBINOFF, MORRIS, b Toronto, Ont, Aug 20, 17; nat US; m 41; c 3. ELECTRICAL ENGINEERING. *Educ:* Univ Toronto, BA, 41, MA, 42, PhD(external ballistics), 46. *Prof Exp:* Teach tech sch, Ont, 41; asst, Univ Toronto, 42-44; res fel & instr physics, Harvard Univ, 46-48; res engr, Inst Advan Study, 48-50; from asst prof to assoc prof, 50-63, PROF ELEC ENG, MOORE SCH ELEC ENG, UNIV PA, 63-; PRES, PA RES ASSOCS, 60- *Concurrent Pos:* Asst dir, Naval Ord Eng, 43-44; chief engr, Philco Corp, 57-59; trustee, Eng Index, 67-; mem res adv comt commun, instrumentation & data processing, NASA. *Honors & Awards:* Inst Elec & Electronics Engrs Award, 55. *Mem:* Asn Comput Mach; Inst Elec & Electronics Engrs. *Res:* Computer logical design; electronic circuit design; mathematical analysis; information retrieval. *Mailing Add:* Moore Sch Elec Eng Univ of Pa Philadelphia PA 19066

RUBINOFF, ROBERTA WOLFF, b New York, NY, Aug 26, 39. MARINE BIOLOGY, EVOLUTIONARY BIOLOGY. *Educ:* Queen's Col, BS, 59. *Prof Exp:* Biologist res, 66-75, marine sci coordr admin & res, Smithsonian Trop Res Inst, 75-80; ASST DIR, OFF FEL & GRANTS ADMIN, SMITHSONIAN INST, 80- *Mem:* Am Soc Ichthyologists & Herpotologists; Soc Study Evolution. *Res:* Behavior and evolution of transisthmian species of intertidal organisms; taxonomic group speciality is tropical marine inshore fishes. *Mailing Add:* Smithsonian Inst 3300 LEnfant Plaza Balboa DC 20560

RUBINOW, SOL ISAAC, biomathematics, deceased

RUBINS, ROY SELWYN, b Manchester, Eng, Nov 11, 35; m 63. MAGNETIC RESONANCE. *Educ:* Oxford Univ, BA, 57, MA & DPhil(physics), 61. *Prof Exp:* Res physicist, Hebrew Univ Jerusalem, 61-63; vis physicist, Battelle Mem Inst, Geneva, 63; res assoc physics, Syracuse Univ, 64-66; asst res physicist & asst prof in residence physics, Univ Calif, Los Angeles, 66-68; lectr Calif State Col, Los Angeles, 69; asst prof, 69-71, ASSOC PROF PHYSICS, UNIV TEX, ARLINGTON, 71- *Concurrent Pos:* Michael & Anna Wix fel, Hebrew Univ Jerusalem, 61-62. *Mem:* Am Phys Soc; Am Asn Physics Teachers. *Res:* Experimental and theoretical treatment of electron paramagnetic resonance in solids; nuclear relaxation in solid hydrogen deuteride. *Mailing Add:* Dept Physics Box 19059 Univ of Tex Arlington TX 76019

RUBINSON, KALMAN, b New York, NY, Dec 24, 41; m 60; c 2. NEUROANATOMY. *Educ:* Columbia Univ, AB, 62; State Univ NY Downstate Med Ctr, PhD(anat), 68. *Prof Exp:* Vis asst prof anat, Sch Med, Univ PR, San Juan, 67-68; vis prof, Sch Med, Univ PR, San Juan, 69; asst prof, 69-74, assoc prof cell biol, 74-78, ASSOC PROF PHYSIOL & BIOPHYS, SCH MED, NY UNIV, 78- *Concurrent Pos:* Nat Inst Neurol Dis & Stroke fel, Lab Perinatal Physiol, PR, 68-69; Nat Inst Neurol Dis & Stroke res grants, Sch Med, NY Univ, 70-72 & Pub Health Res Inst NY, 74-76; assoc, Dept Neurobiol & Behav, Pub Health Res Inst, NY, 69-76. *Mem:* AAAS; Soc Neurosci; Am Asn Anat. *Res:* Comparative neuroanatomy; development of sensory pathways and retina. *Mailing Add:* Dept Physiol & Biophys Sch Med NY Univ New York NY 10016

RUBINSTEIN, ASHER A, b Kishinev, USSR, Sept 16, 47; m 80. FRACTURE MECHANICS. *Educ:* Leningrad Polytech Inst, Dipl, 72; Israel Inst Technol, MSc, 77; Brown Univ, PhD(eng), 81. *Prof Exp:* Design engr equip design, Lenigrad Turbine Blades Plant, 72-74; res engr mat testing, Israel Inst Metals, 74-75; ASST PROF SOLID MECH, STATE UNIV NY, STONY BROOK, 81- *Mem:* Soc Eng Sci. *Res:* Application of theoretical mechanics of materials to problems at interface of continuum mechanics and material science, especially the analysis of problems in the deformation and fracture of solids at both macro and micro scales. *Mailing Add:* Dept Mech Eng State Univ NY Stony Brook NY 11794

RUBINSTEIN, CHARLES B(ENJAMIN), b New York, NY, Dec 25, 33; m 57; c 3. ELECTRICAL ENGINEERING, PSYCHOLOGY. *Educ:* City Col New York, BEE, 59; NY Univ, MEE, 61. *Prof Exp:* Mem tech staff, 59-77, HEAD, HUMAN FACTORS DEPT, BELL TEL LABS, 77- *Honors & Awards:* Leonard G Abraham Prize Paper Award, Inst Elec & Electronics Engrs Commun Socs, 73. *Mem:* Fel Optical Soc Am; Asn Res Vision & Ophthal. *Res:* Magneto, electro, geometrical and physical optics; optical properties of materials; crystallographic properties of rare earth crystals; holography; color perception and rendition in complex scenes; digital coding of color pictures; visual threshold; human factors. *Mailing Add:* Bell Tel Labs Rm 3E-537 Holmdel NJ 07733

RUBINSTEIN, DAVID, biochemistry, deceased

RUBINSTEIN, EDUARDO HECTOR, b Buenos Aires, Arg, July 10, 31; c 2. PHYSIOLOGY. *Educ:* Univ Buenos Aires, BS, 48, MD, 58, PhD(med), 61. *Prof Exp:* Asst physiol, Sch Med, Univ Buenos Aires, 56-58, asst med, Med Res Inst, 58-61, head neurophysiol sect, 64-67, assoc researcher, 66-67; from asst prof physiol to assoc prof, 67-77, PROF ANESTHESIOL & PHYSIOL IN RESIDENCE, UNIV CALIF, LOS ANGELES, 77- *Concurrent Pos:* Res fel physiol, Sch Med, Yale Univ, 61-62; res fel physiol, Sch Med, Gotenburg Univ, 62-64; WHO med res grant, Med Res Inst, Univ Buenos Aires, 65-67; estab investr, Nat Res Coun, Arg, 64; asst researcher & lectr, Cardiovasc Res Inst, Univ Calif, San Francisco, 65; sr res investr, Los Angeles County Heart Asn, 67; prin investr, Am Heart Asn grant, Univ Calif, Los Angeles, 69-72. *Mem:* Am Physiol Soc; Soc Neurosci. *Res:* Central nervous control of autonomic functions, especially cardiovascular and gastrointestinal. *Mailing Add:* Dept of Physiol Univ of Calif Sch of Med Los Angeles CA 90024

RUBINSTEIN, HARRY, b Cologne, Ger, Dec 19, 30; nat US; m 54; c 1. ORGANIC CHEMISTRY. *Educ:* Brooklyn Col, BS, 53; Purdue Univ, MS, 56, PhD(org chem), 58. *Prof Exp:* Res chemist, Wyandotte Chem Corp, 58-59, Keystone Chemurgic Corp, 59-60 & Merck & Co, 60-63; asst prof chem, Springfield Col, 64-65; PROF CHEM, UNIV LOWELL, 65-, DEAN GRAD SCH, 77- *Mem:* Am Chem Soc; Sigma Xi. *Res:* Heterocyclic compounds; natural products; general organic syntheses; mass spectroscopy. *Mailing Add:* 15 Fairbanks Rd Chelmsford MA 01824

RUBINSTEIN, LUCIEN JULES, b Antwerp, Belg, Oct 15, 24; m 50; c 3. NEUROPATHOLOGY. *Educ:* Univ London, MB, BS, 48, MD, 52. *Prof Exp:* Asst path, London Hosp, Eng, 49-50, demonstr chem path, Med Col, 51-52, lectr morbid anat, 54-59, sr lectr, 59-61; attend neuropathologist, Montefiore Hosp, New York, 61-64; assoc prof neuropath, Col Physicians & Surgeons, Columbia Univ, 61-64; prof path & neuropath, Sch Med, Stanford Univ, 64-81; PROF PATH & DIR, DIV NEUROPATH, UNIV VA, 81- *Concurrent Pos:* Vis asst prof, Univ Minn, 59-60; vis scientist, Nat Inst Neurol Dis & Blindness, 60; consult, lab serv, Vet Admin Hosp, Palo Alto, Calif, 64-81. *Honors & Awards:* T A M, Ross Prize Clin Med & Path, London Hosp, 48. *Mem:* Am Asn Neuropath (pres, 70-71); Brit Neuropath Soc; Path Soc Gt Brit & Ireland. *Res:* Biology and pathology of human and experimental nervous system tumors. *Mailing Add:* Div Neuropath Sch Med Stanford Univ Sch of Med Charlottesville VA 22901

RUBINSTEIN, LYDIA, b Buenos Aires, Arg, Jan 30, 36; m 59; c 2. ENDOCRINOLOGY, NEUROENDOCRINOLOGY. *Educ:* Univ Buenos Aires, MD, 59, PhD(physiol), 61. *Prof Exp:* Estab investr, Inst Biol & Exp Med, 61-76; asst prof, 76-81, ASSOC PROF, DEPT OBSTET & GYNEC, SCH MED, UNIV CALIF, 81- *Concurrent Pos:* Nat Coun Sci Res fel anat, Med Sch, Yale Univ, 61-62 & fel physiol, Gotenburg Univ, 62-64; Ford Found fel anat, Med Sch, Univ Calif, Los Angeles, 68-69. *Mem:* Endocrine Soc; Arg Biol Soc; NY Acad Sci. *Res:* Regulatory mechanisms of reproduction and growth processes. *Mailing Add:* 1100 Glendon Ave Suite 950 Los Angeles CA 90024

RUBINSTEIN, MARK, b Brooklyn, NY, Dec 26, 35; m 57; c 3. SOLID STATE PHYSICS. *Educ:* Univ Colo, BA, 57; Univ Calif, PhD(physics), 63. *Prof Exp:* Res assoc solid state physics, Atomic Energy Res Estab, Eng, 63; RES PHYSICIST, US NAVAL RES LAB, 64- *Mem:* Am Phys Soc. *Res:* Nuclear magnetic resonance in magnetically ordered systems. *Mailing Add:* US Naval Res Lab 4555 Overlook Ave SW Washington DC 20375

RUBINSTEIN, MOSHE FAJWEL, b Miechow, Poland, Aug 13, 30; nat US; m 53; c 2. STRUCTURAL DYNAMICS. *Educ:* Univ Calif, Los Angeles, BS, 54, MS, 57, PhD, 61. *Prof Exp:* Designer, Murray Erick Assocs, 54-56; struct designer, Victor Gruen Assocs, 56-61; from asst prof to assoc prof eng, 61-69, coord prof & prog dir continuing educ, Mod Eng for Execs Prog, 65-70, chmn eng systs dept, 70-75, PROF ENG, UNIV CALIF, LOS ANGELES, 69- *Concurrent Pos:* Consult, Pac Power & Light Co, Ore, Northrop Corp, US Army, NASA Res Ctr, Langley, Tex Instruments Co, Hughes Space Syst Div, US Army Sci Adv Comn, Kaiser Aluminum & Chem Corp & IBM; Sussmann chair distinguished vis, Technion Israel Inst Technol, 67-68; Fulbright-Hays fel, Yugoslavia & Eng, 75-76. *Mem:* Am Soc Chem Engrs; Am Soc Eng Educ; Seismol Soc Am; Sigma Xi. *Res:* Use of computers in structural systems, analysis and synthesis; problem solving and decision theory. *Mailing Add:* Dept of Eng Systs Univ of Calif Los Angeles CA 90024

RUBINSTEIN, ROY, b Darlington, Eng, Sept 12, 36; m 68. EXPERIMENTAL HIGH ENERGY PHYSICS. *Educ:* Cambridge Univ, BA, 58; Birmingham Univ, PhD(physics), 61. *Prof Exp:* Res assoc, Birmingham Univ, 61-62; res assoc & actg asst prof physics, Cornell Univ, 62-66; from assoc physicist to physicist, Brookhaven Nat Lab, 66-73; PHYSICIST, FERMI NAT ACCELERATOR LAB, 73- *Mem:* Am Phys Soc. *Res:* Elastic scattering and total cross sections of nucleons and mesons on nucleons in the 100 GeV region. *Mailing Add:* Fermi Nat Accelerator Lab PO Box 500 Batavia IL 60510

RUBIO, RAFAEL, b Queretaro, Mex, Feb 15, 28; m 55, 79; c 5. CARDIOVASCULAR PHYSIOLOGY. *Educ:* Univ Mex, BS, 63; Univ Va, PhD(physiol), 68. *Prof Exp:* Res assoc physiol, Syntex, Mex, 52-55; res assoc, Inst Nac Cardiol, Mex, 55-63; res assoc, Case Western Reserve Univ, 64-66; asst prof, 69-72, assoc prof, 72-76, PROF PHYSIOL, UNIV VA, 76- *Concurrent Pos:* NIH fel, Univ Va, 68-69; Am Heart Asn fel, 74. *Mem:* Mex Physiol Sci Soc; Am Physiol Soc; Biophys Soc; Soc Gen Physiol. *Res:* Blood flow regulation; muscle contraction and metabolism. *Mailing Add:* Dept of Physiol Univ of Va Charlottesville VA 22901

RUBIS, DAVID DANIEL, b Jackson, Minn, May 30, 24; m 59; c 3. PLANT BREEDING, GENETICS. *Educ:* Univ Minn, BS, 48; Iowa State Univ, MS, 50, PhD(crop breeding), 54. *Prof Exp:* Res asst, Corn Breeding Proj, Iowa State Univ, 48-52; agent-agronomist, Spec Crops Sect, Agr Res Serv, USDA, 52-56; from asst prof agron & asst agronomist to assoc prof & assoc agronomist, 56-64, PROF AGRON & AGRONOMIST, UNIV ARIZ, 64- *Mem:* Am Soc Agron; Crop Sci Soc Am; Am Genetic Asn; Genetics Soc Am; Soc Econ Bot. *Res:* Genetics and breeding of safflower, soybeans, guayule and plantago; development of new crops; pollination of entomphilous plants; genetics of water use of plants. *Mailing Add:* Dept of Plant Sci Univ of Ariz Tucson AZ 85721

RUBISON, RICHARD MICHAEL, b Quincy, Ill, Sept 16, 48; m 70; c 3. MATHEMATICS, STATISTICS. *Educ:* Quincy Col, BS, 70; Southern Ill Univ, Edwardsville, MS, 71; Ind Univ, MA, 74, PhD(math), 76. *Prof Exp:* ASST PROF STATIST, KANS STATE UNIV, 76- *Concurrent Pos:* Coun rep, Am Statist Asn, 78-79. *Mem:* Am Math Soc; Am Statist Asn; Inst Math Statist; Math Asn Am. *Res:* Nonparametric statistics; design of experiments; applications of statistics to physical and social science. *Mailing Add:* 3425 Cardinal Rd Manhattan KS 66502

RUBNITZ, MYRON ETHAN, b Omaha, Nebr, Mar 2, 24; m 52; c 4. PATHOLOGY. *Educ:* Univ Nebr, BSc, 45, MD, 47. *Prof Exp:* Assoc path, Med Sch, Northwestern Univ, 55-59, asst prof, 59-63; assoc prof, 63-69, PROF PATH, STRITCH SCH MED, LOYOLA UNIV CHICAGO, 69-, CLIN PROF DENT SCH, 70- *Concurrent Pos:* Fel path, Med Sch, Northwestern Univ, 53-55. *Mem:* AAAS; Am Soc Clin Path; AMA; Col Am Path; Asn Am Med Cols. *Res:* Surgical pathology. *Mailing Add:* Lab Serv Vet Admin Hosp Hines IL 60141

RUBOTTOM, GEORGE M, b London, Eng, Mar 19, 40; US citizen; m 67; c 2. ORGANIC CHEMISTRY. *Educ:* Middlebury Col, AB, 62; Mass Inst Technol, PhD(org chem), 67. *Prof Exp:* Fel org chem, Calif Inst Technol, 66-68; instr, Bucknell Univ, 68-71; from asst prof to assoc prof, Univ PR, 70-74; assoc prof, 75-78, PROF ORG CHEM, UNIV IDAHO, 78- *Concurrent Pos:* NIH fel, 67-68. *Mem:* Am Chem Soc. *Res:* Chemistry of organo-silicon compounds; chemistry of small ring compounds; chemistry of natural products. *Mailing Add:* Dept of Chem Univ of Idaho Moscow ID 83843

RUBULIS, ALBERT, b Latvia, May 9, 25; US citizen; m 53; c 2. BIOCHEMISTRY. *Educ:* Syracuse Univ, BS, 55; State Univ NY Upstate Med Ctr, PhD(biochem), 66. *Prof Exp:* Clin lab dir biochem, Adult Clin Ctr, State Univ NY Upstate Med Ctr, 66-68; clin lab dir, Sansum Clin, Santa Barbara, Calif, 68-69; tech coordr clin chem, Leary Lab, Boston, 69-70; lab dir clin chem, Highland Hosp, 70-75; asst prof biochem, Med Sch, Univ Rochester, 70-75; mem staff, Biosci Labs Detroit Br, 75-78; TECH DIR, SMITH K PINE CLIN LABS, 78- *Concurrent Pos:* Consult obstet & gynec, State Univ NY Upstate Med Ctr, 63-66; NIH fel, State Univ NY Upstate Med Ctr, 66-68; KROC Found, Univ Rochester & Highland Hosp, 72- *Mem:* AAAS; Am Asn Clin Chemists; fel Am Inst Chem. *Res:* Mechanism of gallstone formation and dissolution; adenyl cyclase stimulation by aspirin and cholera enterotoxin. *Mailing Add:* Smith K Pine Clin Labs 2800 Winona Ave Burbank CA 91504

RUBY, EDWARD GEORGE, b Rochester, NY, Aug 31, 49; m 75. MICROBIAL SYMBIOSES, MICROBIAL PHYSIOLOGY. *Educ:* Stetson Univ, BS, 71; Scripps Inst Oceanog, PhD(marine biol), 77. *Prof Exp:* Res fel, Harvard Univ, 77-79, Woods Hole Oceanog Inst, 79-81; RES ASSOC, UNIV CALIF, LOS ANGELES, 81- *Concurrent Pos:* Adj asst prof microbial physiol, Boston Univ, 78-79. *Mem:* Am Soc Microbiol; Western Soc Naturalists; Am Soc Limnol & Oceanog; Am Chem Soc. *Res:* Procaryotic cellular differentiation including in the dimorphic growth cycle of the bacterial genus Bdellovibrio; physiological and biochemical studies of their transformation from one cell form to another to understand the processes of development in bacteria. *Mailing Add:* Dept Microbiol Univ Calif Los Angeles CA 90024

RUBY, JOHN L, b Indianapolis, Ind, Mar 1, 12; m 39; c 1. FOREST GENETICS. *Educ:* Purdue Univ, BSF, 34; Mich State Univ, MS, 59, PhD(forest genetics), 64. *Prof Exp:* Instr forestry, 63-64, asst prof natural sci, 65-71, prof, 71-77, EMER PROF NATURAL SCI, MICH STATE UNIV, 77- *Mem:* AAAS; Soc Am Foresters. *Res:* Forest genetics; species variability studies through parental and provenance testing. *Mailing Add:* RR 1 Box 90A Irons MI 49644

RUBY, JOHN ROBERT, b Elida, Ohio, May 26, 35; m 57; c 3. ANATOMY. *Educ:* Baldwin-Wallace Col, BS, 57; St Louis Univ, MS, 59; Univ Pittsburgh, PhD(anat), 63. *Prof Exp:* From instr to asst prof anat, Univ Cincinnati, 63-67; from asst prof to assoc prof, 67-77, PROF ANAT, LA STATE UNIV MED CTR, NEW ORLEANS, 77- *Mem:* Am Asn Anat; Pan-Am Asn Anat; Electron Micros Soc Am. *Res:* Development of female reproductive system; ultrastructure of salivary glands; pancreatic cancer. *Mailing Add:* Dept Anat La State Univ Med Ctr 1100 Florida Ave New Orleans LA 70119

RUBY, LAWRENCE, b Detroit, Mich, July 25, 25; m 51; c 3. NUCLEAR PHYSICS. *Educ:* Univ Calif, Los Angeles, BA, 45, MA, 47, PhD(physics), 51. *Prof Exp:* Physicist, Lawrence Berkeley Lab, 50-, lectr, Univ Calif, Berkeley, 60-61, assoc prof, 61-66, PROF NUCLEAR ENG, UNIV CALIF, BERKELEY, 66- *Mem:* Am Phys Soc; Am Asn Physics Teachers; Am Nuclear Soc. *Res:* Nuclear spectroscopy; accelerators; reactor dynamics; nuclear fusion. *Mailing Add:* 54 Cowper Ave Berkeley CA 94707

RUBY, MICHAEL GORDON, b Muskogee, Okla, May 27, 40. AIR POLLUTION CONTROL, ENVIRONMENTAL ECONOMICS. *Educ:* Univ Okla, BS, 62; Univ Wash, MS, 65, MSE, 78, PhD(civil eng), 81. *Prof Exp:* Environ specialist, City Seattle, 72-76; prin, Environ Res Group, 76-81; ASST PROF CIVIL ENG, UNIV CINCINNATI, 81- *Concurrent Pos:* Consult, World Health Orgn, 79- *Mem:* Air Pollution Control Asn; Am Acad Environ Engrs; Am Indust Hyg Asn; Am Meteorol Asn; Sigma Xi. *Res:* Air pollution measurement and control technology; atmospheric aerosols, particularly with reference to atmospheric visibility; benefit-cost analysis of environmental policies and projects. *Mailing Add:* Dept Civil & Environ Eng (#71) Univ Cincinnati Cincinnati OH 45221

RUBY, PHILIP RANDOLPH, b Aurora, Ill, May 23, 25; m 53; c 1. ORGANIC CHEMISTRY. *Educ:* Univ Ill, BA, 49; Univ Iowa, MS, 51, PhD(org chem), 53. *Prof Exp:* Res chemist, 53-60, GROUP LEADER, PIGMENTS DIV, AM CYANAMID CO, BOUND BROOK, 60- *Mem:* Am Chem Soc. *Res:* Aromatic organic chemistry; organic pigments. *Mailing Add:* 22 Circle Dr Millington NJ 07946

RUBY, RONALD HENRY, b San Francisco, Calif, Dec 1, 32; m 57; c 4. BIOPHYSICS. *Educ:* Univ Calif, Berkeley, AB, 54, PhD(physics), 62. *Prof Exp:* Actg asst prof physics, Univ Calif, Berkeley, 62-64; NSF fel biol, Mass Inst Technol, 64-65; asst prof, 65-70, ASSOC PROF PHYSICS, UNIV CALIF, SANTA CRUZ, 70- *Concurrent Pos:* Sloan Found fel, 66-68. *Mem:* Am Phys Soc. *Res:* Solid state physics; problems of physics in biological systems; energy conversion process in photosynthesis. *Mailing Add:* Natural Sci Div Univ of Calif Santa Cruz CA 95060

RUBY, STANLEY, b Brooklyn, NY, Nov 26, 20; m 46; c 3. PHYSICAL CHEMISTRY, MATERIALS SCIENCE. *Educ:* Cornell Univ, BS, 41; Columbia Univ, PhD(mining, metall), 54. *Prof Exp:* Res assoc Manhattan Proj Sam Labs, 43-46; res assoc, Brookhaven Nat Lab, 50-52; group leader ore concentration, Minerals Beneficiation Lab, Columbia Univ, 52-54; sr engr, Sylvania Elec Prod Inc, 54-56; sect chief reentry mat, Res & Adv Develop Div, Avco Corp, 56-62; sr scientist, Allied Res Assocs, 62-64; prog mgr, Advan Res Proj Agency, Arlington, 64-77; PROG MGR, DEPT ENERGY, WASHINGTON, DC, 78- *Concurrent Pos:* Res assoc, Columbia Univ, 50-51. *Mem:* Am Chem Soc; Am Inst Mining, Metall & Petrol Eng; Sigma Xi; NY Acad Sci; Electrochem Soc. *Res:* Surface chemistry; high temperature chemistry; electrochemistry; ore concentration; winning of metals; radiochemistry. *Mailing Add:* Forestal Bldg Dept Energy Washington DC 20585

RUCH, RICHARD JULIUS, b Perryville, Mo, June 9, 32; m 54; c 4. PHYSICAL CHEMISTRY. *Educ:* Southeast Mo State Col, BS, 54; Iowa State Univ, MS, 56, PhD(chem), 59. *Prof Exp:* Asst prof chem, Univ SDak, 59-62; asst prof, Southern Ill Univ, 62-66; ASSOC PROF CHEM, KENT STATE UNIV, 66-, ASST CHMN DEPT, 72- *Mem:* Sigma Xi; Am Chem Soc. *Res:* Surface and colloid chemistry; the stability of colloidal dispersions is studied with the aid of dielectric measurements and with various interfacial techniques. *Mailing Add:* Dept Chem Kent State Univ Kent OH 44242

RUCH, RODNEY R, b Springfield, Ill, Aug 18, 33; m 56; c 3. ANALYTICAL CHEMISTRY. *Educ:* Univ Ill, BS, 55; Southern Ill Univ, MA, 59; Cornell Univ, PhD(chem), 65. *Prof Exp:* Res asst chem, Gen Atomic Div, Gen Dynamics Corp, 61-63; res chemist, Nat Bur Standards, 65-66; assoc chemist, 66-71, CHEMIST, ILL STATE GEOL SURV, 71-, HEAD ANAL CHEM SECT, 73- *Concurrent Pos:* Prin res officer, Broken Hill Proprietary Co, Australia, 80-81. *Mem:* Am Chem Soc; Am Soc Testing & Mat. *Res:* Radiochemical separations; activation analysis; radiochemistry; trace element analysis; coal analysis. *Mailing Add:* Anal Chem Sect Ill State Geol Surv Urbana IL 61801

RUCHKIN, DANIEL S, b New Haven, Conn, June 29, 35; m 58; c 1. BIOMEDICAL ENGINEERING, ELECTRICAL ENGINEERING. *Educ:* Yale Univ, BE, 56, MEng, 57, DEng, 60. *Prof Exp:* Instr elec eng, Yale Univ, 59-61; asst prof, Univ Rochester, 61-64; res assoc prof psychiat, NY Med Col, 64-70; assoc prof physiol & comput sci, 71-77, PROF PHYSIOL, SCH MED, UNIV MD, BALTIMORE CITY, 77- *Mem:* AAAS; Inst Elec & Electronics Eng; Asn Comput Mach; Am Electroencephalography Soc; Soc Psychophysiol Res. *Res:* Brain research, specifically analysis of evoked and event-related potentials; psychophysiology; signal analysis; mathematical statistics. *Mailing Add:* Dept of Physiol Univ of Md Sch of Med Baltimore MD 21201

RUCHMAN, ISAAC, b New York, NY, July 2, 09; m 40; c 1. MICROBIOLOGY, IMMUNOLOGY. *Educ:* City Col New York, BSc, 37; Univ Cincinnati, MSc, 41, PhD(bact), 44; Am Bd Microbiol, dipl. *Prof Exp:* Tech asst, Rockefeller Inst, 30-39; asst, Children's Hosp Res Found, Cincinnati, Ohio, 39-44, res assoc, 46-52; from instr to asst prof bact, Univ Cincinnati, 44-55; head microbiol, Wm S Merrell Co, 55-63; prof, 63-74, EMER PROF MICROBIOL, UNIV KY, 74- *Concurrent Pos:* USPHS grant in aid; attend bacteriologist, Cincinnati Gen Hosp, 46-55; adj prof, Col Eng, Off Continuing Educ, Univ Ky, 75-; vis prof, Transylvania Univ, 76- *Mem:* Fel Am Acad Microbiol; Soc Exp Biol & Med; Am Asn Immunol; Am Soc Microbiol; NY Acad Sci. *Res:* Toxoplasmosis; tularemia; virology; immunity in virus infections; herpes simplex; neurotropic viruses; antimicrobial screening; upper respiratory infections; chemotherapy. *Mailing Add:* 365 Garden Rd Lexington KY 40502

RUCHTI, RANDAL CHARLES, b Janesville, Wis, Oct 27, 46; m 70; c 2. HIGH ENERGY PHYSICS, ELEMENTARY PARTICLE PHYSICS. *Educ:* Univ Wis-Madison, BS, 68; Univ Ill, Urbana, MS, 70; Mich State Univ, PhD(physics), 73. *Prof Exp:* Res assoc physics, Northwestern Univ, 73-76, asst prof, 76-77; ASST PROF PHYSICS, UNIV NOTRE DAME, 77- *Mem:* Am Inst Physics; Sigma Xi; Am Phys Soc. *Res:* Strong interactions; charm particle production and charm decay processes; new quantum number production. *Mailing Add:* Dept of Physics Univ of Notre Dame Notre Dame IN 46556

RUCKEBUSCH, GUY BERNARD, b Lille, Fr, June 28, 49; m 76; c 1. SYSTEM THEORY, DIGITAL SIGNAL PROCESSING. *Educ:* Ecole des Mines de Paris, Engr, 72; Univ Pierre et Marie Curie, Paris, PhD(probability), 75, Dr es Sci, 80. *Prof Exp:* Res assoc syst theory, Cent di Automatique de Ecole des Mines de Paris, 73-75, Inst Nat de la Recherche en Info et Automatique, 75-78; engr syst sci, 78-80, RES ENGR PETROL SCI, DOLL RES, SCHLUMBERGER, 80- *Concurrent Pos:* Prof probability, Ecole des Mines de Nancy, 75-78. *Res:* Stochastic system theory; develop new signal processing techniques to process schlumberger subsurface measurements. *Mailing Add:* Schlumberger Doll Res PO Box 307 Rodgefield CT 06877

RUCKENSTEIN, ELI, b Botosani, Romania, Aug 13, 25; US citizen; m 48; c 2. CHEMICAL ENGINEERING. *Educ:* Bucharest Polytech Inst, MS, 49, Dr Eng(chem eng), 66. *Prof Exp:* Prof chem eng, Bucharest Polytech Inst, 49-69; NSF sr scientist, Clarkson Col Technol, 69-70; prof, Univ Del, 70-73; fac prof eng, appl sci & chem eng, 73-81, DISTINGUISHED PROF, STATE UNIV NY, BUFFALO, 81- *Honors & Awards:* George Spacu Award, Romanian Acad Sci, 63; Alpha Chi Sigma Award, Am Inst Chem Engrs, 77. *Mem:* Am Inst Chem Engrs; Am Chem Soc; Faraday Soc. *Res:* Transport phenomena in fluids and solids; supported metal catalysts; oxide catalysis; heterogeneous kinetics; thermodynamics and kinetics of interfacial phenomena; micellization; microemulsions and colloids; transport phenomena in colloidal systems; deposition of cells on surfaces; separation processes. *Mailing Add:* Dept Chem Eng State Univ of NY Amherst NY 14260

RUCKER, JAMES BIVIN, b Emporia, Kans, Mar 15, 35; m 57; c 2. GEOLOGY, OCEANOGRAPHY. *Educ:* Univ Mo, BA, 60, MA, 61; La State Univ, PhD(geol), 66. *Prof Exp:* Oceanographer, US Naval Oceanog Off, 63-72; dir, Miss Marine Resources Coun, 72-74; ECOLOGIST, NAT OCEANIC & ATMOSPHERIC ADMIN, 75- *Concurrent Pos:* Prof lectr, George Washington Univ, 66- *Mem:* AAAS; Geol Soc Am; Sigma Xi; Am Soc Limnol & Oceanog. *Res:* Recent marine sediments and benthic biota; environmental impact of deep ocean dumping. *Mailing Add:* Nat Oceanic & Atmospheric Admin Marine Resources 6010 Exec Blvd Rockville MD 20852

RUCKER, ROBERT BLAIN, b Oklahoma City, Okla, Mar 29, 41; m 68; c 2. NUTRITIONAL BIOCHEMISTRY. *Educ:* Oklahoma City Univ, BA, 63; Purdue Univ, MS, 66, PhD(biochem), 69. *Prof Exp:* Fel, Univ Mo-Columbia, 68-70; assoc prof, 70-78, PROF NUTRIT & CHMN DEPT, UNIV CALIF, DAVIS, 78- *Mem:* AAAS; Am Inst Nutrit; Am Chem Soc; Ortho Res Soc; Sigma Xi. *Res:* Connective tissue metabolism; role of trace elements in nutrition; biochemistry of elastin and elastic elements. *Mailing Add:* Dept of Nutrit Univ of Calif Davis CA 95616

RUCKERBAUER, GERDA MARGARETA, b Steyr, Austria, Dec 7, 26; Can citizen. VETERINARY IMMUNOLOGY. *Prof Exp:* Univ Toronto, BA, 51, MA, 55; Ont Vet Col, DVM, 61. *Prof Exp:* Tech asst bot, Univ Toronto, 51-52; cell genetics, 52-53; res fel, Hosp for Sick Children, Toronto, 53-55; res off carcinogens, Ont Vet Col, 55-57; vet, Animal Dis Res Inst, 61-78, RES SCIENTIST SEROL, ANIMAL PATH LABS, CAN DEPT AGR, 68- *Mem:* NY Acad Sci; Genetics Soc Can; Can Vet Med Asn; Can Soc Immunol; Can Micros Soc. *Res:* Methods for diagnosis of animal diseases using serological and fluorescence microscopical techniques. *Mailing Add:* Animal Dis Res Inst Can Dept Agr PO Box 11300 Postal Sta H Nepean ON K2H 8P9 Can

RUCKLE, WILLIAM HENRY, b Neptune, NJ, Oct 29, 36; m 60; c 1. MATHEMATICS. *Educ:* Lincoln Univ, Pa, AB, 60; Fla State Univ, MS, 62, PhD(math), 63. *Prof Exp:* Asst prof math, Lehigh Univ, 63-69; assoc prof, 69-74, PROF MATH SCI, CLEMSON UNIV, 74- *Concurrent Pos:* Vis prof math, Western Washington Univ, 78-79. *Mem:* Am Math Soc; Math Asn Am; Soc Indust Appl Math; Soc Risk Anal. *Res:* Functional analysis, summability theory, game theory and risk analysis. *Mailing Add:* Dept of Math Sci Clemson Univ Clemson SC 29631

RUCKLIDGE, JOHN CHRISTOPHER, b Halifax, Eng, Jan 15, 38; m 62; c 4. MINERALOGY, CRYSTALLOGRAPHY. *Educ:* Cambridge Univ, BS, 59; Univ Manchester, PhD(mineral), 62. *Prof Exp:* Res assoc, Univ Chicago, 62-64; res asst, Oxford Univ, 64-65; from lectr to assoc prof, 65-77, PROF MINERAL, UNIV TORONTO, 77- *Mem:* Mineral Soc Am; Geol Asn Can; Mineral Asn Can; Microbeam Anal Soc; Sigma Xi. *Res:* Electron probe and x-ray crystallographic studies on minerals; ultrasensitive mass spectrometry with tondem accelerators. *Mailing Add:* Dept of Geol Univ of Toronto Toronto ON M5S 1A1 Can

RUCKNAGEL, DONALD LOUIS, b St Louis, Mo, May 30, 28; m 55; c 2. HUMAN GENETICS. *Educ:* Wash Univ, AB, 50, MD, 54; Univ Mich, PhD(human genetics), 64. *Prof Exp:* From intern to jr resident med, Duke Univ Hosp, NC, 54-56; investr human genetics, Nat Inst Dent Res, 57-59; from asst prof to assoc prof, 64-70, PROF HUMAN GENETICS, MED SCH, UNIV MICH, ANN ARBOR, 70- *Concurrent Pos:* Fel, Univ Pittsburgh, 56-57; USPHS sr res fel human genetics, Med Sch, Univ Mich, Ann Arbor, 59-62, res career develop award, 62-69; res assoc internal med, Simpson Mem Inst, 68-77, prof, 77- *Mem:* Am Soc Human Genetics; Am Soc Hemat; Eugenics Soc; Physicians Social Responsibility; Am Fedn Clin Res. *Res:* Internal medicine; hematology; human genetics, especially hemoglobinopathies. *Mailing Add:* Dept of Human Genetics Univ of Mich Med Sch Ann Arbor MI 48109

RUDAK, EDWINA-ANNE, b Derby, Eng, Sept 26, 51. HUMAN CYTOGENETICS. *Educ:* Univ Leicester, BSc, 73; Univ St Andrews, PhD(animal cytol), 77. *Prof Exp:* Asst researcher human cytogenetics, Dept Anat, Sch Med, Univ Hawaii, 76-79; scientist reproductive biol, Med Res Coun, Edinburgh, Scotland, 79-80. *Concurrent Pos:* Vis lectr, Dept Embryol, Sheba Med Ctr, Tel-Hashomer, Israel, 80- *Res:* Reproductive biology; animal cytogenetics. *Mailing Add:* Dept Anat & Reproductive Biol 1960 East-West Rd Honolulu HI 96822

RUDAT, MARTIN AUGUST, b Burbank, Calif, June, 11, 52; m 75. MASS SPECTROMETRY. *Educ:* Harvey Mudd Col, BS, 74; Cornell Univ, MS, 76, PhD(anal chem), 78. *Prof Exp:* RES CHEMIST, CENT RES & DEVELOP DEPT, E I DU PONT DE NEMOURS & CO, INC, WILMINGTON, DEL, 78- *Mem:* Am Chem Soc; Am Soc Mass Spectrometry; Sigma Xi. *Res:* Ionization techniques; mass spectral methods; mass spectral reactions and mechanisms; two dimensional mass spectrometry; linking of mass spectrometry with other techniques; secondary ion mass spectrometry. *Mailing Add:* Du Pont Exp Sta E228/101 Wilmington DE 19898

RUDAVSKY, ALEXANDER BOHDAN, b Poland, Jan 17, 25; US citizen; m 55. CIVIL ENGINEERING. *Educ:* Univ Minn, BS, 53, MS, 55; Hanover Tech Univ, Dr Ing(civil eng), 66. *Prof Exp:* Civil engr, Justin & Courtney, Philadelphia, 56-57 & Iran, 57-58; PROF ENG, SAN JOSE STATE UNIV, 60-; DIR-OWNER, HYDRO RES SCI, 64- *Concurrent Pos:* Vis assoc prof, Stanford Univ, 70. *Mem:* Am Soc Civil Engrs; Am Soc Mech Engrs. *Res:* Hydraulic research, through model studies of engineering problems related to hydraulic structures, rivers, ports and harbors, coastal protection, and sedimentation; development of instrumentation; library documentation system and service; consultative services. *Mailing Add:* Hydro Res Sci 3334 Victor Ct Santa Clara CA 95050

RUDAZ, SERGE, b Verdun, Que, Aug 19, 54. ELEMENTARY PARTICLE PHYSICS. *Educ:* Cornell Univ, MS, 79, PhD(physics), 79. *Prof Exp:* Res fel, European Orgn Nuclear Res, Geneva, 79-81; ASST PROF PHYSICS, UNIV MINN, 81- *Mem:* Inst Particle Physics Can; Am Phys Soc. *Res:* Unified field theories of elementary particle interactions; cosmology and the physics of the early universe; models of high energy processes. *Mailing Add:* Sch Physics & Astron Univ Minn Minneapolis MN 55455

RUDBACH, JON ANTHONY, b Long Beach, Calif, Sept 23, 37; m 59; c 2. MICROBIOLOGY, IMMUNOLOGY. *Educ:* Univ Calif, Berkeley, BA, 59; Univ Mich, MS, 61, PhD(microbiol), 64. *Prof Exp:* Nat Inst Allergy & Infectious Dis fel biophys, Rocky Mountain Lab, USPHS, 64-66; res scientist, 66-67; assoc prof, 70-75, PROF MICROBIOL, UNIV MONT, 75-, DIR, STELLA DINCEN MEM RES INST, 79- *Concurrent Pos:* Lectr, Univ Mont, 67-70; head microbiol lab, Abbott Lab, 77-79. *Mem:* AAAS; Soc Exp Biol & Med; Am Asn Immunol; Am Soc Microbiol. *Res:* Molecular biology of endotoxins from Gram-negative bacteria; relation of structure of endotoxins to biological activity; detoxification of endotoxins by human plasma; immunology of lipopolysaccharides. *Mailing Add:* Dept Microbiol Univ Mont Missoula MT 59812

RUDD, D(ALE) F(REDERICK), b Minneapolis, Minn, Mar 2, 35; m 64; c 2. CHEMICAL ENGINEERING. *Educ:* Univ Minn, BS, 56, PhD(chem eng), 60. *Prof Exp:* Asst prof chem eng, Univ Mich, 60-61; fel, 61-62, from asst prof to prof, 62-68, SLICHTER PROF CHEM ENG, UNIV WIS-MADISON, 80- *Concurrent Pos:* J S Guggenheim fel, 70. *Honors & Awards:* Chem Inst Can Award, 62; Allan P Colburn Award, 71; Am Soc Eng Educ Award, 72. *Mem:* Nat Acad Eng. *Res:* Process Engineering. *Mailing Add:* Dept of Chem Eng Univ of Wis Madison WI 53706

RUDD, DAVID, mathematics, see previous edition

RUDD, DEFOREST PORTER, b Boston, Mass, Aug 17, 23; m 50; c 3. INORGANIC CHEMISTRY. *Educ:* Harvard Univ, BA, 47; Univ Calif, PhD(phys chem), 51. *Prof Exp:* Res assoc, Northwestern Univ, 50-52; PROF CHEM, LINCOLN UNIV, PA, 52- *Concurrent Pos:* NSF sci fac fel, Cornell Univ, 59-60 & Stanford Univ, 66-67. *Mem:* AAAS; Am Chem Soc. *Res:* Solutions and critical phenomena; reactions of transition metal complexes. *Mailing Add:* Dept of Chem Lincoln Univ Lincoln University PA 19352

RUDD, MILLARD EUGENE, b Fargo, NDak, Sept 29, 27; m 53; c 3. ATOMIC PHYSICS. *Educ:* Concordia Col, BA, 50; Univ Buffalo, MA, 55; Univ Nebr, PhD(physics), 62. *Prof Exp:* From asst prof to prof physics, Concordia Col, 54-65; assoc prof physics, 65-68, actg chmn dept, 70-72, PROF PHYSICS, UNIV NEBR, LINCOLN, 68- *Concurrent Pos:* NSF fel, 60-61; mem comn atomic & molecular sci, Nat Acad Sci, 80. *Mem:* Am Asn Physics Teachers; fel Am Phys Soc. *Res:* Atomic collisions; autoionization; ion-atom collisions; electron spectroscopy. *Mailing Add:* Behlen Lab of Physics Univ of Nebr Lincoln NE 68588

RUDD, ROBERT L, b Los Angeles, Calif, Sept 18, 21; m 47; c 2. ZOOLOGY. *Educ:* Univ Calif, PhD(zool), 53. *Prof Exp:* Asst, 47-50, assoc zool, 51-52, asst specialist, 52-56, from asst prof to assoc prof, 56-69, PROF ZOOL, UNIV CALIF, 69- *Mem:* Fel AAAS; Soc Study Evolution; Am Soc Mammal; Am Ornith Union; Ecol Soc Am. *Res:* Pesticides; pollution ecology; vertebrate evolution; population phenomena, chiefly mammals; comparative endocrine structures; tropical ecology; conservation. *Mailing Add:* Dept of Zool Univ of Calif Davis CA 95616

RUDD, VELVA ELAINE, b Fargo, NDak, Sept 6, 10. BOTANY. *Educ:* NDak Agr Col, BS, 31, MS, 32; George Washington Univ, PhD(bot), 53. *Prof Exp:* Asst bot, NDak Agr Col, 31-32 & Univ Cincinnati, 32-33; instr, Sch Hort, Ambler, Pa, 33-34; supvr sci courses, State Dept Supervised Studies, NDak, 35-37; asst bot, Univ Cincinnati, 37-38; asst sci aide, Bur Plant Indust, USDA, 38-42; personnel classification investr, 42-43; agr prog officer, Food Supply Mission, Inst Inter-Am Affairs, Venezuela, 43-45; agr prog analyst, UNRRA, 45-48; from asst cur to cur, Div Phanerogams, Dept Bot, US Nat Mus, Smithsonian Inst, 48-73; SR RES FEL, DEPT BIOL, CALIF STATE UNIV, NORTHRIDGE, 73- *Concurrent Pos:* Res assoc, Div Phanerogams, Dept Bot, Smithsonian Inst, 73- *Mem:* AAAS; Am Soc Plant Taxonomists; Int Bur Plant Taxon; Soc Bot Mexico. *Res:* Systematic botany; plant geography. *Mailing Add:* PO Box 19 Reseda CA 91335

RUDD, WALTER GREYSON, b Teaneck, NJ, Dec 24, 43; m 71; c 1. COMPUTER SCIENCE. *Educ:* Rice Univ, BA, 66, PhD(phys chem), 69. *Prof Exp:* Res assoc phys chem, State Univ NY Albany, 69-70, biophys, 70-71; asst prof, 71-74, assoc prof, 74-81, PROF & CHMN COMPUT SCI, LA STATE UNIV, BATON ROUGE, 81- *Mem:* AAAS; Asn Comput Mach. *Res:* Statistical mechanics and thermodynamics; theoretical biophysics; analog and hybrid computational techniques; computer simulation of biological systems; small computer system development. *Mailing Add:* Dept of Comput Sci La State Univ Baton Rouge LA 70803

RUDDAT, MANFRED, b Insterburg, Ger, Aug 21, 32; m 62; c 2. PLANT PHYSIOLOGY. *Educ:* Univ Tubingen, Dr rer nat(bot), 60. *Prof Exp:* Sci asst bot, Univ Tubingen, 60-61; NSF res fel plant physiol, Calif Inst Technol, 61-64; asst prof bot, 64-68, asst prof biol, 68-70, ASSOC PROF BIOL, UNIV CHICAGO, 70- *Concurrent Pos:* Ed, Bot Gazette, 74- *Mem:* Am Bot Soc; AAAS; Am Soc Plant Physiol; Japanese Soc Plant Physiol. *Res:* Developmental biology of plants; physiology and biochemistry of plant growth regulators and carotenoids; environmental physiology. *Mailing Add:* Dept of Biol Barnes Lab Univ of Chicago 5630 S Ingleside Chicago IL 60637

RUDDICK, JAMES JOHN, b Elmira, NY, June 11, 23. PHYSICS. *Educ:* Woodstock Col, AB, 46, STL, 56; St Louis Univ, MS, 50, PhD(physics), 52. *Prof Exp:* Instr physics, St Peter's Col, 47-48; ASSOC PROF PHYSICS, CANISIUS COL, 57-, DIR, SEISMOG STA, 69- *Mem:* Am Phys Soc; Am Asn Physics Teachers. *Res:* Computer utilization in undergraduate physics instruction; earthquakes of Western New York; integrated circuit electronics. *Mailing Add:* Dept of Physics Canisius Col Buffalo NY 14208

RUDDICK, KEITH, b Haltwhistle, Eng, Dec 2, 39. PHYSICS. *Educ:* Univ Birmingham, BSc, 61, PhD(physics), 64. *Prof Exp:* Res assoc physics, Univ Mich, 64-66; from asst prof to assoc prof, 66-76, PROF PHYSICS, UNIV MINN, MINNEAPOLIS, 76- *Mem:* Inst Physics. *Res:* Experimental high energy physics. *Mailing Add:* Sch of Physics Univ of Minn Minneapolis MN 55455

RUDDLE, FRANCIS HUGH, b West New York, NJ, Aug 19, 29; m 65; c 2. GENETICS, CELL BIOLOGY. *Educ:* Wayne State Univ, BA, 53, MS, 56; Univ Calif, Berkeley, PhD, 60. *Hon Degrees:* MA, Yale Univ. *Prof Exp:* From asst prof zool to assoc prof biol, 61-72, PROF BIOL & HUMAN GENETICS, YALE UNIV, 72-, CHMN DEPT BIOL, 77- *Concurrent Pos:* NIH fel biochem, Univ Glasgow, 60-61; mem cell biol study sect & chmn adv comt human mutant cell strains, NIH, 72- *Honors & Awards:* Dyer lectr, NIH, 78; Conden lectr, Univ Ore, 81; Dickson Prize, Univ Pittsburgh, 81. *Mem:* Nat Acad Sci; AAAS; Soc Develop Biol (pres, 71-72); Am Soc Cell Biol; Am Soc Human Genetics. *Res:* Somatic cell genetics and differentiation. *Mailing Add:* Yale Univ Dept of Biol Kline Biol Tower New Haven CT 06520

RUDDLE, NANCY HARTMAN, b St Louis, Mo, Apr 3, 40; m 64; c 2. IMMUNOLOGY. *Educ:* Mt Holyoke Col, AB, 62; Yale Univ, PhD(microbiol), 68. *Prof Exp:* Asst res develop biol, 62-63, res assoc & lectr tissue typing, Surgery Dept, 68-71, lectr microbiol, 71-74, asst prof, 75-80, ASSOC PROF EPIDEMIOL, YALE UNIV, 80- *Concurrent Pos:* Damon Runyon Mem Found fel, Yale Univ, 72, Am Cancer Soc fel, 73-74, fac res award, 79- *Mem:* Am Soc Microbiol; Sigma Xi; Am Asn Immunol. *Res:* Delayed hypersensitivity in vitro; tumor immunology; leukemia virus-lymphocyte interactions; T cell receptors. *Mailing Add:* Dept of Epidemiol Yale Univ Sch of Med New Haven CT 06510

RUDDON, RAYMOND WALTER, JR, b Detroit, Mich, Dec 23, 36; m 61; c 3. CANCER BIOLOGY, PHARMACOLOGY. *Educ:* Univ Detroit, BS, 58; Univ Mich, PhD(pharmacol), 64, MD, 67. *Prof Exp:* From instr to prof pharmacol, Univ Mich, Ann Arbor, 64-76; dir biol marker prog, Cancer Res Ctr, Md, 76-81; PROF & CHMN, DEPT PHARMACOL, UNIV MICH MED SCH, 81- *Concurrent Pos:* Teaching fel chem, Univ Detroit, 58-59; Am Cancer Soc scholar, 64-67. *Mem:* AAAS; Am Soc Pharmacol & Exp Therapeut; Am Asn Cancer Res. *Res:* Biological markers of neoplasia; differentiation of neoplastic cells; mechanism of action of anticancer agents. *Mailing Add:* Dept Pharmacol Univ Mich Med Sch Ann Arbor MI 48109

RUDDY, ARLO WAYNE, b Humboldt, Nebr, Aug 28, 15; m 43; c 4. ORGANIC CHEMISTRY. *Educ:* Univ Nebr, BSc, 36, MSc, 38; Univ Md, PhD(med chem), 40. *Prof Exp:* Sharp & Dohme res assoc, Northwestern Univ, 40-41; res chemist, Sharples Chem, Inc, Pa Salt Mfg Co, Mich, 41-42; sr res chemist, Sterling-Winthrop Res Inst, 42-51; dir org chem res, Chilcott Labs, 51-52; dir chem develop, Warner-Chilcott Res Labs, 52-57; dir org chem, 57-61; dir chem develop, Warner-Lambert Res Inst, 61-78; RETIRED. *Mem:* Am Chem Soc; Am Pharmaceut Asn; Acad Pharmaceut Sci; fel NY Acad Sci. *Res:* Medicinal chemistry, including mercurials, arsenicals, pressor amines, radiopaques, local anesthetics and antispasmodics. *Mailing Add:* 11 Juniper Dr Morris Plains NJ 07950

RUDE, PAUL A, b Los Angeles, Calif, Nov 4, 30; m 51; c 6. ELECTRONIC ENGINEERING, COMPUTER SCIENCE. *Educ:* Univ Calif, Los Angeles, BS, 55; Univ Pittsburgh, MS, 57, PhD(elec eng), 62. *Prof Exp:* Sr engr, Westinghouse Elec Corp, 55-63; asst prof elec eng, 63-64, ASSOC PROF ELEC ENG & CHMN DEPT, LOYOLA UNIV, LOS ANGELES, 64- *Concurrent Pos:* Lectr, Univ Pittsburgh, 60-61; consult, Space-Gen Corp, 63-64, Pac Tel Co, 64-65 & Hughes Aircraft Co, 66. *Mem:* Am Soc Eng Educ; Inst Elec & Electronics Engrs. *Res:* Medical-optical systems; computer design. *Mailing Add:* Dept of Elec Eng 7101 W 80th St Los Angeles CA 90045

RUDE, THEODORE ALFRED, b Chuquicamata, Chile, Mar 10, 25; US citizen; m 46; c 5. PATHOLOGY, MICROBIOLOGY. *Educ:* Univ Pa, VMD, 52; Am Col Vet Path, dipl. *Prof Exp:* Pvt pract, Wis, 52-59; diagnostician, Cent Animal Health Lab, Wis, 59-61, lab supvr, 61-63; staff vet, Norwich Pharmacal Co, NY, 63-64; staff vet, Salsbury Labs, 64-69, mgr path & toxicol, 69-71, biol devleop mgr, 71-72, gen mgr, Salsbury Labs, 72-80, VPRES & GEN MGR FROMM LABS, INC, 80- *Mem:* Am Vet Med Asn; Am Asn Avian Path. *Res:* Pathology associated with avian, canine and feline diseases; development of diagnostic reagents, vaccines and bacterins for use with canines and felines; toxicology of chemical compounds. *Mailing Add:* Fromm Labs Inc 703 Lakeshore Rd Grafton WI 53024

RUDEE, MERVYN LEA, b Palo Alto, Calif, Oct 4, 35; m 58; c 2. MATERIALS SCIENCE. *Educ:* Stanford Univ, BS, 58, MS, 62, PhD(mat sci), 65. *Prof Exp:* From asst prof to prof mat sci, Rice Univ, 64-74, master, Wiess Col, 69-74; PROF MAT SCI & PROVOST WARREN COL, UNIV CALIF, SAN DIEGO, 74- *Concurrent Pos:* Guggenheim fel, Cavendish Lab, Cambridge Univ, 71-72. *Mem:* Am Phys Soc; Electron Micros Soc Am. *Res:* Defects in crystals, studies primarily by x-ray diffraction and electron microscopy; biomaterials. *Mailing Add:* Warren Col Q022 Univ Calif San Diego La Jolla CA 92093

RUDENBERG, FRANK HERMANN, b Berlin, Ger, Dec 4, 27; nat US; m 79; c 6. NEUROPHYSIOLOGY. *Educ:* Harvard Univ, SB, 49; Univ Chicago, SM, 51, PhD(physiol), 54. *Prof Exp:* Asst physiol, Univ Chicago, 52-53; from instr to asst prof, Mich State Univ, 54-58; asst prof, 58-62, ASSOC PROF PHYSIOL & BIOPHYSICS, UNIV TEX MED BR GALVESTON, 62- *Concurrent Pos:* Consult, Southwest Res Inst, San Antonio, 67-74; vchmn, Sci, Inc, 77-; assoc prof, Sch Allied Health, Univ Tex Med Br, 76. *Mem:* Biophys Soc; Am Inst Biol Sci; Asn Advan Med Instrumentation; Neuroelec Soc; Soc Neurosci. *Res:* Neurophysiology of head injury; cerebral circulation, intracranial pressure and edema; biomechanics; medical instrumentation including microsensors; medical television and education. *Mailing Add:* Dept of Physiol & Biophys Univ of Tex Med Br Galveston TX 77550

RUDENBERG, H(ERMANN) GUNTHER, b Berlin, Ger, Aug 9, 20; nat US; m 52; c 3. PHYSICS, ELECTRONICS. *Educ:* Harvard Univ, SB, 41, AM, 42, PhD, 52. *Prof Exp:* Asst electronics, Harvard Univ, 41-42; asst scientist, Los Alamos Sci Lab, 46; physicist res div, Raytheon Mfg Co, 48-52; dir res, Transitron Electronic Corp, 52-62; SR STAFF MEM, ARTHUR D LITTLE, INC, 62- *Concurrent Pos:* Consult, Spencer-Kennedy Labs, 45-48 & 60-62. *Mem:* Inst Elec & Electronics Engrs. *Res:* Semiconductors; electron ballistics; microwaves; microelectronics; management consulting; technological forecasting; integrated circuits. *Mailing Add:* Res & Develop Dept 25 Acorn Park Rte 2 Cambridge MA 02140

RUDERMAN, IRVING WARREN, b New York, NY, Jan 7, 20; m 45; c 4. ELECTROOPTICS. *Educ:* Columbia Univ, PhD(chem), 49. *Prof Exp:* Res chemist, St Regis Paper Co, NJ, 40-46; asst chem, Columbia Univ, 46-47, lectr, 47-48, res scientist, 48-54; consult, 54-56; pres, Isomet Corp, 56-73; PRES, INTERACTIVE RADIATION, INC, 73- *Mem:* Am Chem Soc; Am Phys Soc; Inst Elec & Electronics Eng; fel NY Acad Sci; fel Am Inst Chem. *Res:* Solid state physics; crystal growth; lasers; active optics. *Mailing Add:* 45 Duane Lane Demarest NJ 07627

RUDERMAN, JOAN V, b Mt Vernon, NY. MOLECULAR BIOLOGY. *Educ:* Barnard Col, Columbia Univ, BA, 69; Mass Inst Technol, PhD(biol), 74. *Prof Exp:* Jane Coffin Childs fel, Mass Inst Technol, 74-76; ASSOC PROF BIOL, HARVARD MED SCH, 76- *Concurrent Pos:* Instr, Marine Biol Lab, 76-, corp mem, 79- *Mem:* Soc Develop Biol. *Res:* Molecular analysis of the levels at which differential gene expression during development is regulated. *Mailing Add:* Dept Anat Harvard Med Sch Boston MA 02115

RUDERMAN, MALVIN AVRAM, b New York, NY, Mar 25, 27; m 53. THEORETICAL PHYSICS. *Educ:* Columbia Univ, AB, 45; Calif Inst Technol, PhD, 51. *Prof Exp:* Physicist, Radiation Lab, Univ Calif, 51-52; NSF fel, Columbia Univ, 52-53; from asst prof to prof physics, Univ Calif, Berkeley, 53-64; prof, NY Univ, 64-69; PROF PHYSICS, COLUMBIA UNIV, 69- *Concurrent Pos:* Guggenheim fel, 57-58. *Mem:* Nat Acad Sci; Am Phys Soc; Am Acad Arts & Sci; Am Astron Soc. *Res:* Elementary particles; astrophysics. *Mailing Add:* Dept of Physics Columbia Univ New York NY 10027

RUDERSDORF, WARD J, b Waupaca, Wis, Sept 1, 23; m 50; c 1. WILDLIFE MANAGEMENT, ECOLOGY. *Educ:* Wis State Univ, Stevens Point, BS, 51; Utah State Univ, MS, 53; Mich State Univ, PhD(wildlife mgt), 62. *Prof Exp:* Instr natural sci, Mich State Univ, 56-63; asst prof zool, Calif State Univ Fullerton, 63-66; assoc prof parasitol, Wis State Univ, Stevens Point, 66-67; assoc prof, 67-74, PROF WILDLIFE MGT, EASTERN KY UNIV, 74- *Mem:* Wildlife Soc; Wilderness Soc; EAfrican Wild Life Soc. *Res:* Moose and beaver management problems in Wyoming; ecological Canada goose studies in Michigan. *Mailing Add:* Dept of Biol Eastern Ky Univ Richmond KY 40475

RUDERSHAUSEN, CHARLES GERALD, b Jersey City, NJ, May 26, 28; m 54; c 4. CHEMICAL ENGINEERING. *Educ:* Univ Va, BChE, 49; Univ Wis, MS, 50, PhD(chem eng), 52. *Prof Exp:* Sr engr, Eastern Lab, 52, res chem engr, 53, group leader, 54, sect head, 55-59, sect asst, 59-60, task coordr, 60-61, res sect head, 61-64, res mgr, Newburgh Res Lab, NY & Poromerics Res Labs, Tenn, 64-69, mgr tech progs, Eastern Lab, NJ, 69-72, LICENSING SPECIALIST, POLYMER INTERMEDIATES DEPT, E I DU PONT DE NEMOURS & CO, INC, WILMINGTON, 72- *Mem:* Am Chem Soc; Am Inst Chem Engrs; Am Inst Chemists; Am Soc Metals. *Res:* Chemical processing; explosives; metallurgy; leather replacement materials; patents; licensing; metal winning. *Mailing Add:* Polymer Intermediates Dept Exp Sta 324/125 Wilmington DE 19898

RUDESILL, JAMES TURNER, b Rapid City, SDak, Nov 26, 23; m 48; c 3. ORGANIC CHEMISTRY. *Educ:* SDak Sch Mines & Tech, BS, 48; Iowa State Col, MS, 50; Purdue Univ, PhD(org chem), 57. *Prof Exp:* Res chemist, Cudahy Packing Co, 50-53; asst, Purdue Univ, 53-57; from asst prof to assoc prof, 57-67, PROF ORG CHEM, NDAK STATE UNIV, 67- *Mem:* Am Chem Soc. *Res:* Determination of configuration in geometrical isomers; additions and substitutions of free radicals; stereochemistry of ring opening processes. *Mailing Add:* Ladd Hall 255 A NDak State Univ Fargo ND 58105

RUDGE, WILLIAM EDWIN, b New Haven, Conn, June 14, 39; m 62; c 3. SOLID STATE PHYSICS. *Educ:* Yale Univ, BS, 60; Mass Inst Technol, PhD(physics), 68. *Prof Exp:* Physicist, Prod Develop Lab, Components Div, Int Bus Mach Corp, 60-63, STAFF MEM, RES LAB, IBM CORP, 68- *Res:* Energy band calculations in solids by relativistic orthogonalized plane wave large scale scientific calculations. *Mailing Add:* IBM Res Lab K03/281 5600 Cottle Rd San Jose CA 95193

RUDGERS, ANTHONY JOSEPH, b Washington, DC, May 23, 38; m 61; c 3. PHYSICS. *Educ:* Univ Md, BS, 61; Cath Univ Am, MSE, 69, PhD(acoust), 77. *Prof Exp:* Res physicist, Acoust Div, Washington, DC, 61-76, RES PHYSICIST ACOUST, UNDERWATER SOUND REF DETACHMENT, NAVAL RES LAB, 76- *Mem:* Acoust Soc Am; Am Asn Physics Teachers; Sigma Xi. *Res:* Acoustics; materials research; radiation, diffraction and scattering theory; random signal theory; elasticity and structural mechanics; linear systems; continuum mechanics. *Mailing Add:* Underwater Sound Ref Detachment Naval Res Lab PO Box 8337 Orlando FL 32856

RUDGERS, LAWRENCE ALTON, b Batavia, NY, May 16, 42. SOIL SCIENCE. *Educ:* Cornell Univ, BSc, 64; Mich State Univ, MSc, 67; Kans State Univ, PhD(soil sci), 69. *Prof Exp:* Exchange scholar, Kans State Univ-Univ Giessen, 69-70; instr soil sci, Dept Land Resource Sci, Univ Guelph, 70-71, Can Dept Agr, fel, 71-73; lectr, 73-75, asst prof, 75-80, ASSOC PROF SOIL SCI, UNIV MAN, 80- *Mem:* Am Soc Agron. *Res:* Soil fertility; plant nutrition; soil chemistry; crop physiology; disposal of animal and human waste. *Mailing Add:* Dept of Soil Sci Univ of Man Winnipeg MB R3T 2N2 Can

RUDIN, ALFRED, b Edmonton, Alta, Feb 5, 24; m 49; c 3. POLYMER SCIENCE. *Educ:* Univ Alta, BSc, 49; Northwestern Univ, Evanston, PhD(org chem), 52. *Prof Exp:* Res chemist, Can Industs, Ltd, 52-60, group leader plastics, 60-64, mgr plastics lab, 64-67; assoc prof, 67-69, PROF CHEM, UNIV WATERLOO, 69-, PROF CHEM ENG, 73- *Res:* Polymer chemistry and engineering. *Mailing Add:* Dept of Chem Univ of Waterloo Waterloo ON N2L 3G1 Can

RUDIN, DONALD OLIVER, b Honolulu, Hawaii, Mar 31, 23; m 62; c 4. RESEARCH ADMINISTRATION, MOLECULAR BIOLOGY. *Educ:* Harvard Med Sch, MD, 48. *Prof Exp:* Res fel, Harvard Univ, 49-51, res assoc, 51-56; dir dept molecular biol, Eastern Pa Psychiat Inst, 56-80; RESEACHER, 80- *Mem:* Am Physiol Soc. *Res:* Synthesis inverse secondary black film (lipid bilayer); hybrid nerve impulse reconstitution; potassium selective bilayer (valinomycin); second level cell membrane concept (basal lamina); substrate beriberi and substrate pellagra; theory of modernization diseases as omega3-essential fatty acid deficiency syndrome. *Mailing Add:* 5450 Wissahickon Ave Apt 1139 Philadelphia PA 19144

RUDIN, MARY ELLEN, b Hillsboro, Tex, Dec 7, 24; m 53; c 4. MATHEMATICS. *Educ:* Univ Tex, PhD(topology), 49. *Prof Exp:* Instr math, Duke Univ, 50-53; asst prof, Univ Rochester, 53-57; LECTR & PROF MATH, UNIV WIS-MADISON, 58- *Honors & Awards:* Hedrick lectr, Math Asn Am, 79. *Mem:* Am Math Soc; Math Asn Am; Am Math Soc (vpres, 80-83); Asn Symbolic Logic. *Res:* Set theoretic topology, particularly the construction of counter examples. *Mailing Add:* Dept of Math Univ of Wis Madison WI 53706

RUDIN, WALTER, b Vienna, Austria, May 2, 21; m 53. MATHEMATICS. *Educ:* Duke Univ, BA & MA, 47, PhD(math), 49. *Prof Exp:* Instr math, Duke Univ, 49-50; Moore instr, Mass Inst Technol, 50-52; from asst prof to assoc prof, Univ Rochester, 52-59; PROF MATH, UNIV WIS-MADISON, 59- *Mem:* Am Math Soc; Math Asn Am. *Res:* Mathematical analysis, especially abstract harmonic analysis, Fourier series and holomorphic functions of one and several variables. *Mailing Add:* Dept of Math Univ of Wis Madison WI 53706

RUDINGER, GEORGE, b Vienna, Austria, May 30, 11; US citizen; m 47, 72; c 4. FLUID MECHANICS, ENGINEERING PHYSICS. *Educ:* Vienna Tech Univ, Ingenieur, 35. *Prof Exp:* Res assoc med radiol, Vienna Gen Hosp, Austria, 35-38; physicist, Sydney Hosp, Australia, 39-46; prin physicist fluid mech, Cornell Aeronaut Lab, 46-70; prin scientist, Textron Bell Aerospace Co, Buffalo, 71-76; CONSULT, 76- *Concurrent Pos:* Proj engr, Royal Australian Air Force & Australian Ministry Munitions, 44-46; teacher physics, Sydney Tech Col, 45-46; physicist, Australian Glass Mgrs Pty, Ltd, Sydney, 45-46; adj prof, Dept Mech & Aero Eng, State Univ NY Buffalo, 75- *Honors & Awards:* Aerospace Pioneer Award, Am Inst Aeronaut & Astronaut, 74; Centennial Medallion, Am Soc Mech Engrs, 80. *Mem:* Fel Am Soc Mech Engrs; fel Am Phys Soc; fel Am Inst Aeronaut & Astronaut; Int Soc Biorheology; fel Brit Inst Physics. *Res:* Gas particle flow, nonsteady duct flow and blood flow. *Mailing Add:* 47 Presidents Walk Buffalo NY 14221

RUDISILL, CARL SIDNEY, b Lincolnton, NC, Mar 21, 29; m 60; c 2. MECHANICAL ENGINEERING. *Educ:* NC State Univ, BME, 54, MS, 61, PhD(mech eng), 66. *Prof Exp:* Instr mech eng, NC State Univ, 60-65; assoc prof, 65-75, NASA res grants, 70-73, 75-76, 77-79, PROF MECH ENG, CLEMSON UNIV, 75- *Mem:* Am Inst Aeronaut & Astronaut; Am Soc Mech Engrs. *Res:* Optimization of aircraft structures. *Mailing Add:* Dept of Mech Eng Clemson Univ Clemson SC 29631

RUDKIN, GEORGE THOMAS, b Bakersfield, Calif, Oct 16, 17; m 46; c 4. GENETICS. *Educ:* Calif Inst Technol, BS, 38, PhD(biol), 42; Stanford Univ, MS, 39. *Prof Exp:* Instr, Calif Inst Technol, 42; Nat Res Coun fel, 46, res assoc genetics, 48-61, assoc mem, 61-78, MEM, INST CANCER RES, 78- *Concurrent Pos:* Vis prof, Cath Univ Nijmegen, 71-73. *Mem:* AAAS; Am Soc Naturalists; Genetics Soc Am; Histochem Soc; Soc Anal Cytol. *Res:* Nutrition, genetics, ovarian development and physiology of Drosophila; genetics of Neurospora; factors influencing growth of interspecific ovary transplants in Drosophila; microspectrophotometry, especially chromosomes; chemistry of gene action. *Mailing Add:* Inst for Cancer Res 7701 Burholme Ave Fox Chase Philadelphia PA 19111

RUDKO, ROBERT I, b New York, NY, Apr 24, 42; m 64; c 2. ELECTRICAL ENGINEERING. *Educ:* Cornell Univ, BEE, 63, MS, 65, PhD, 67. *Prof Exp:* Sr res scientist, 67-77, PRIN RES SCIENTIST, RES DIV, RAYTHEON CO, 77- *Mem:* Inst Elec & Electronics Engrs. *Res:* Laser radars; infrared optics; infrared gas lasers. *Mailing Add:* Res Div Raytheon Co 28 Seyon St Waltham MA 02154

RUDMAN, ALBERT J, b New York, NY, Nov 14, 28; m 51; c 3. GEOPHYSICS. *Educ:* Ind Univ, BS, 52, MA, 54, PhD(geophys), 63. *Prof Exp:* Geophysicist, Carter Oil Co, 54-57 & Ind Geol Surv, 57-65; assoc prof geophysics, 65-77, PROF GEOL, IND UNIV, BLOOMINGTON, 77- *Mem:* Soc Explor Geophys; Am Geophys Union. *Res:* Solid earth geophysics, especially exploration. *Mailing Add:* Dept of Geol Ind Univ Bloomington IN 47401

RUDMAN, DANIEL, b Pittsfield, Mass, Jan 25, 27; m 55; c 2. INTERNAL MEDICINE. *Educ:* Yale Univ, BS, 46, MD, 49; Am Bd Internal Med, dipl, 59. *Prof Exp:* Intern med, New Haven Hosp, 49-50; sr asst surgeon, Nat Cancer Inst, 51-53; resident, Jewish Hosp Brooklyn, 53-54; resident, Columbia Univ Res Serv, Goldwater Mem Hosp, 54-55; assoc med, Col Physicians & Surgeons, Columbia Univ, 57-58, from asst prof to assoc prof, 58-68; PROF MED, EMORY UNIV & DIR CLIN RES CTR, HOSP, 68- *Concurrent Pos:* Res fel, Columbia Univ Res Serv, Goldwater Mem Hosp, 55-68. *Mem:* Harvey Soc; Am Fedn Clin Res; Am Soc Clin Invest; Endocrine Soc; Am Inst Nutrit. *Res:* Cyclic nucleoride metabolism; amino acid metabolism in liver disease; biologically active peptides in animal tissues; cancer related proteins in body fluids; metabolic effects of human growth hormone; melanotropic peptides in the central nervous system; total intravenous hyperalimentation. *Mailing Add:* Dept of Med Emory Univ Sch of Med Atlanta GA 30322

RUDMAN, PETER S, b Passaic, NJ, Apr 30, 29; m 56; c 3. SOLID STATE PHYSICS. *Educ:* Mass Inst Technol, BSc, 51, MSc, 53, DSc, 55. *Prof Exp:* Res engr, Res Lab, Westinghouse Elec Corp, Corp, 55-56; lectr physics, Israel Inst Technol, 56-61; fel, Battelle Mem Inst, 61-66; assoc prof mat sci, Vanderbilt Univ, 67-68; prof physics, Technion-Israel Inst Technol, 68-80; MEM STAFF, INCO RES & DEVELOP INC, 80- *Mem:* Am Phys Soc; Am Soc Metals; Israel Crystallog Soc (secy, 60). *Res:* Metal physics; x-ray diffraction. *Mailing Add:* Inco Res & Develop Inc Suffern NY 10901

RUDMAN, REUBEN, b New York, NY, Jan 18, 37; m 58; c 5. X-RAY CRYSTALLOGRAPHY, STRUCTURAL CHEMISTRY. *Educ:* Yeshiva Univ, BA, 57; Polytech Inst Brooklyn, PhD(chem), 66. *Prof Exp:* Res assoc chem, Brookhaven Nat Lab, 66-67; from asst prof to assoc prof, 67-75, PROF CHEM, ADELPHI UNIV, 75- *Concurrent Pos:* Chmn comn on crystallog apparatus, Int Union Crystallog, 75-78; vis prof, Hebrew Univ, 73-74; ed, Trans Am Crystal Asn, 81; chmn orientational disorder crystals, Gordon Res Conf, 80. *Mem:* Sigma Xi; AAAS; Am Crystallog Asn. *Res:* X-ray structure analysis; x-ray instrumentation and low-temperature apparatus; study of phase transitions and molecular complexes. *Mailing Add:* Dept of Chem Adelphi Univ Garden City NY 11530

RUDMOSE, H WAYNE, b Cisco, Tex, Mar 16, 15; m 40; c 2. PHYSICS. *Educ:* Univ Tex, BA, 35, MA, 36; Harvard Univ, PhD(physics), 46. *Prof Exp:* Asst physics, Univ Tex, 32-35, tutor & chg electronic labs, 35-37; instr, Harvard Univ, 38-39, asst, 39-41, res assoc & group leader, Electro-Acoustic Lab, 41-43; assoc dir, 43-45; from asst prof to prof physics, Southern Methodist Univ, 46-63; group vpres, Sci & Systs Group, Tracor, Inc, 63-80. *Concurrent Pos:* Acoust consult, 46-; mem comt on hearing & bio-acoustics, Nat Acad Sci, 53, chmn, 75-76. *Mem:* Acoust Soc Am; Am Acad Indust Hyg; Am Indust Hyg Asn. *Res:* Audio communication; hearing; architectural acoustics; noise measurement control. *Mailing Add:* 2802 Scenic Dr Austin TX 78703

RUDNER, BERNARD, organic chemistry, deceased

RUDNER, RIVKA, b Ramat-Gan, Israel, Apr 9, 35; m 56; c 3. GENETICS. *Educ:* NY Univ, BA, 57; Columbia Univ, MS, 58, PhD(zool), 61. *Prof Exp:* Res worker biochem, Col Physicians & Surgeons, Columbia Univ, 61-62, res assoc, 62-63, asst prof, 63-68; assoc prof, 68-74, PROF BIOL SCI, HUNTER COL, 74- *Mem:* Fedn Am Biochemists. *Res:* Molecular doning in B subtiles of L and H specific operons; sequence analyis and transcriptioner mapping of promotion regions; variation of nucleotide sequences among related Bacillus genomes in conserved and non conserved regions. *Mailing Add:* Dept of Biol Sci Hunter Col 696 Park Ave New York NY 10021

RUDNEY, HARRY, b Toronto, Ont, Apr 14, 18; nat US; m 46; c 2. BIOCHEMISTRY. *Educ:* Univ Toronto, BA, 47, MA, 48; Western Reserve Univ, PhD(biochem), 52. *Prof Exp:* Res asst biochem, Univ Toronto, 46-48; sr instr, Sch Med, Western Reserve Univ, 51-53, from asst prof to prof, 53-67; PROF BIOL CHEM & DIR DEPT, COL MED, UNIV CINCINNATI, 67- *Concurrent Pos:* Am Cancer Soc scholar, 55-57; NSF sr res fel, 57-58; USPHS res career develop award, 58-63 & res career award, 63-; vis prof, Case Inst Technol, 65-66; ed, Archiv Biochem & Biophys, 65- & J Biochem, 75-80; mem panel metab biol, NSF, 68-71; mem res career award comt, NIH, 69-71; mem biochem test comt, Nat Bd Med Examr, 74; pres, Dept Biochem, Assoc Med Sch, 81-82. *Honors & Awards:* G Rieveschel Jr Award, 77. *Mem:* Am Chem Soc; Am Soc Biol Chemists; Am Soc Microbiol; Brit Biochem Soc. *Res:* Intermediary metabolism and enzyme studies; biosynthesis of isoprenoid precursors of sterols; biosynthesis and function of quinones. *Mailing Add:* Dept of Biol Chem Univ of Cincinnati Col Med Cincinnati OH 45267

RUDNICK, ALBERT, b Manchester, NH, Apr 26, 22. VIROLOGY. *Educ:* Univ NH, BS, 42, MS, 44; Univ Calif, PhD(parasitol), 59. *Prof Exp:* Res asst, Hooper Found, Univ Calif, San Francisco, 47-50; entomologist, State Bur Vector Control, Calif, 52; med entomologist, US Chem Corps, Ft Detrick, Md, 54; res asst, Sch Pub Health, Univ Calif, 55; res assoc, Grad Sch Pub Health, Univ Pittsburgh, 56-60; asst res virologist, Hooper Found, Univ Calif, San Francisco, 60-65, assoc res virologist, 65-71; assoc prog dir, Univ Calif Int Ctr Med Res & Training, 72-74, prog dir, 74-80; PROF VIROL, DEPT EPIDEMIOL & INTERNAL HEALTH, HOOPER FOUND, UNIV CALIF, SAN FRANCISCO, 74- *Concurrent Pos:* Rep, Comn Viral Infections, US Armed Forces Epidemiol Bd, Guam, 48, Tokyo, 49, Manila, 56, assoc mem, 66-72; consult, US Opers Mission, Bangkok, 58; consult to chief surgeon, 13th Air Force, Philippines, 58; actg sr virologist, Inst Med Res, Kuala Lumpur, 62-63; temporary adv, Western Pac Regional Off, WHO, Bangkok, 64; consult, 80- *Mem:* Am Soc Trop Med & Hyg; Wildlife Dis Asn; Am Mosquito Control Asn; Malaysian Soc Parasitol & Trop Med; Pac Sci Asn. *Res:* Ecology of dengue and other arboviruses of southeastern Asia. *Mailing Add:* Dept Epidemiol & Internal Health Univ Calif Med Ctr San Francisco CA 94143

RUDNICK, GARY, b Philadelphia, Pa, Sept 14, 46. BIOCHEMISTRY, PHARMACOLOGY. *Educ:* Antioch Col, BS, 68; Brandeis Univ, PhD(biochem), 74. *Prof Exp:* Fel biochem, Roche Inst Molecular Biol, 73-75; asst prof, 75-80, ASSOC PROF PHARMACOL, SCH MED, YALE UNIV, 80- *Concurrent Pos:* Estab investr, Am Heart Asn, 79-84. *Mem:* Am Soc Biol Chemists. *Res:* Membrane function; mechanisms of solute transport across biological membranes; uptake and storage of neurotransmitters. *Mailing Add:* Dept Pharmacol Yale Univ 333 Cedar St PO Box 3333 New Haven CT 06510

RUDNICK, ISADORE, b New York, NY, May 8, 17; m 39; c 5. ACOUSTICS, LOW TEMPERATURE PHYSICS. *Educ:* Univ Calif, Los Angeles, BA, 38, MA, 40, PhD(physics), 44. *Prof Exp:* Res physicist, Brown Univ, 42; res physicist, Duke Univ, 42-45; from instr to asst prof physics, Pa State Col, 45-48; from asst prof to assoc prof, 48-58, PROF PHYSICS, UNIV CALIF, LOS ANGELES, 59- *Concurrent Pos:* Fulbright fel, 57, 65; vis prof, Royal Inst Technol, Copenhagen, 57-58, Israel Inst Technol, 65 & 73, Univ Paris, 72 & Univ Tokyo, 77; Guggenheim fel, 58; consult, Res & Develop Bd, mem governing bd, Am Inst Physics, 66; fac res lectr, Univ Calif, Los Angeles. *Honors & Awards:* Biennial Award, Acoust Soc Am, 48, Silver Medal, 75; Fritz London Award, Int Conf Low Temp Physics, 81; Gold Medal, Acoust Soc Am, 82. *Mem:* Fel Am Phys Soc; fel Acoust Soc Am (vpres, 62, pres, 69). *Res:* Ultrasonics; high intensity acoustics; cavitation; elastic wave damping in metals; low temperature physics; quantum liquids; non-linear physics. *Mailing Add:* Dept Physics Univ Calif Los Angeles CA 90024

RUDNICK, LAWRENCE, b Philadelphia, Pa, Mar 17, 49; m 70; c 2. RADIO ASTRONOMY, ASTROPHYSICS. *Educ:* Cornell Univ, BA, 70; Princeton Univ, MA, 72, PhD(physics), 74. *Prof Exp:* Res fel radio astron, Nat Radio Astron Observ, 74-76, asst scientist, 76-78, assoc scientist, 78; ASST PROF ASTRON, UNIV MINN, 79- *Mem:* Am Astron Soc; Int Astron Union. *Res:* Extragalactic radio astronomy; radio galaxies; clusters of galaxies; observational cosmology. *Mailing Add:* Sch of Physics & Astron 116 Church St SE Minneapolis MN 55455

RUDNICK, MICHAEL DENNIS, b Huntington, NY, Aug 5, 45; c 2. ANATOMICAL SCIENCES, OTOLOGY. *Educ:* State Univ NY Buffalo, BA, 71, PhD(anat), 78. *Prof Exp:* RESEARCHER OTOL, HEARING FOUND BUFFALO, 69- *Concurrent Pos:* Clin instr, State Univ NY Buffalo, 78- *Res:* Anatomy, physiology and pathology of the inner ear; aminoglycoside antibiotic ototoxicity; cochlear implant and the function of kinocilia in the vestibular system. *Mailing Add:* Hearing Found Bldg B 2211 Main St Buffalo NY 14214

RUDNICK, STANLEY JOHN, b Chicago, Ill, Oct 10, 37; m 58; c 5. INSTRUMENTATION, ELECTRONICS. *Educ:* Northwestern Univ, BS, 59; Univ Ill, MS, 61; Univ Chicago, MBA, 78. *Prof Exp:* Engr electronics, Motorola, Inc, 59-60; engr instrumentation, 61-63, supvr instrumentation, 63-74, DIR ELECTRONICS DIV, ARGONNE NAT LAB, 74- *Concurrent Pos:* Mem, Nat Instrumentation Methods Comt, 64- *Mem:* Inst Elec & Electronics Engrs; Nuclear & Plasma Sci Soc; Eng Mgt Soc. *Res:* Development of instrumentation for energy and environmental research. *Mailing Add:* Argonne Nat Lab Bldg 818 9700 S Cass Ave Argonne IL 60439

RUDO, FRIEDA GALINDO, b New York, NY, Nov 13, 23; m 45; c 2. PHARMACOLOGY. *Educ:* Goucher Col, AB, 44; Univ Md, MS, 60, PhD(pharmacol), 63. *Prof Exp:* From instr exp surg to asst prof pharmacol, Sch Med, 60-68, from asst prof to assoc prof pharmacol, Sch Dent, 68-75, PROF PHARMACOL, SCH DENT, UNIV MD, BALTIMORE, 70- *Concurrent Pos:* Consult, Ohio Chem Co, 60, res grant, 64- *Res:* Cardiovascular research using artificial heart; cardiac output studies on new nitrate compounds; pharmacology and toxicity of new anesthetic agents. *Mailing Add:* Dept of Pharmacol Univ of Md Sch of Dent Baltimore MD 21201

RUDOLF, LESLIE E, b Pelham, NY, Nov 12, 27; m 55; c 4. SURGERY. *Educ:* Union Col, NY, BS, 51; Cornell Univ, MD, 55; Am Bd Surg, dipl, 63. *Prof Exp:* Intern & to resident surg, Peter Bent Brigham Hosp, Boston, 55-59 & 60-61; asst, Harvard Med Sch, 59-60; instr, New York Hosp-Cornell Univ, 61-63; from asst prof to assoc prof, 63-72, PROF SURG, SCH MED, UNIV VA, 72-, VCHMN DEPT SURG, 76- *Concurrent Pos:* Mem, Nat Bd Med Examr; Markle scholar acad med, 66-71. *Mem:* Am Col Surg; Soc Surg Alimentary Tract; Am Soc Nephrology; Am Soc Artificial Internal Organs;

Transplantation Soc. *Res:* Organ and tissue transplantation and preservation; long term organ storage and histocompatibility typing; evaluation of current medical and surgical methods used in treatment of deep thrombophlebitis. *Mailing Add:* Dept of Surg Univ of Va Hosp Charlottesville VA 22901

RUDOLPH, ABRAHAM MORRIS, b Johannesburg, SAfrica, Feb 3, 24; nat US; m 49; c 3. PHYSIOLOGY. *Educ:* Univ Witwatersrand, MB, BCh, 46, MD, 51; Am Bd Pediat, dipl, 53; FRCP(E), 66. *Prof Exp:* Res fel pediat, Harvard Med Sch, 51-53, res fel physiol, 53-54, Am Heart Asn res fel, 54-55, instr pediat, 55-57, assoc, 57-60; assoc prof, Albert Einstein Col Med, 60-63, prof pediat & assoc prof physiol, 63-66; PROF PEDIAT & PHYSIOL, UNIV CALIF, SAN FRANCISCO, 66-, PROF OBSTET & GYNEC, 74- *Concurrent Pos:* Fel, Children's Med Ctr, Boston, 51-53, asst cardiologist in chg cardiopulmonary lab, 55-57, assoc cardiologist in chg, 57-66; Am Heart Asn estab investr, 56-; mem, Nat Adv Heart & Lung Coun. *Honors & Awards:* Mead Johnson Award; Borden Award. *Mem:* Soc Clin Invest; Am Pediat Soc; Am Physiol Soc; Soc Pediat Res; Am Acad Pediat. *Res:* Cardiovascular physiology, particularly physiology of the fetus and newborn; physiology of congenital heart disease; pediatric cardiology. *Mailing Add:* Cardiovasc Res Inst Univ Calif Med Ctr San Francisco CA 94143

RUDOLPH, ARNOLD JACK, b Johannesburg, SAfrica, Mar 28, 18; m 51; c 4. PEDIATRICS. *Educ:* Univ Witwatersrand, MB, BCh, 40. *Prof Exp:* Resident neurol & dermat, Univ Witwatersrand, 41; resident pediat, Transvaal Mem Hosp Children, 41, casualty & outpatient dept officer, 42-46, clin fel med, 47-49, clin asst pediat, 49-56; res fel pediat, Boston-Lying-In Hosp, Children's Med Ctr & Harvard Med Sch, 57-59; from asst prof to assoc prof, 61-70, PROF PEDIAT, OBSTET & GYNEC, BAYLOR COL MED, 70- *Mem:* AMA; Brit Med Asn; Am Pediat Soc. *Res:* Newborn physiology; newborn problems. *Mailing Add:* Dept of Pediat Baylor Col of Med Houston TX 77030

RUDOLPH, EMANUEL DAVID, b Brooklyn, NY, Sept 9, 27; m 62. BOTANY. *Educ:* NY Univ, AB, 50; Wash Univ, PhD(bot), 55. *Prof Exp:* Asst, Hunter Col, 50; docent, Brooklyn Children's Mus, 50-51; asst, cryptogamic herbarium, Mo Bot Garden, 51-55, asst librn, 54-55; from instr to asst prof bot, Wellesley Col, 55-61; from instr to assoc prof, 61-69, res assoc, 61-69, dir inst polar studies, 69-73, dir environ biol prog, 72-78, actg chmn, 78-79, PROF BOT, OHIO STATE UNIV, 69-, CHMN, 79- *Concurrent Pos:* Spec asst, Washington Univ, 53-54; fel mycol, NSF, Univ Wis, 59. *Mem:* AAAS; Bot Soc Am; Am Bryol & Lichenological Soc (vpres, 72-73, pres, 74-75); fel Arctic Inst NAm; fel Linnean Soc London. *Res:* Lichenology; mycology; antarctic and arctic botany; history of botany. *Mailing Add:* Dept Bot Ohio State Univ 1735 Neil Ave Columbus OH 43210

RUDOLPH, GUILFORD GEORGE, b Kiowa, Kans, Jan 2, 18; m 44; c 3. BIOCHEMISTRY. *Educ:* Univ Colo, BA, 40; Wayne State Univ, MS, 42; Univ Utah, PhD(biochem), 48. *Prof Exp:* Teaching fel biochem, Wayne State Univ, 40-42; instr, Univ Utah, 46-48; asst prof, Vanderbilt Univ, 49-57; assoc prof, Univ Md, 57-60; assoc prof, Vanderbilt Univ, 60-67; asst dean basic sci, 67-73, PROF BIOCHEM & HEAD DEPT, SCH MED, LA STATE UNIV, SHREVEPORT, 67- *Concurrent Pos:* Am Cancer Soc res assoc, Univ Chicago, 48-49; prin scientist, Vet Admin Hosp, Nashville, Tenn, 49-57; mem grad fac, Med Ctr, La State Univ, 68-; consult, Vet Admin Hosp, 68. *Mem:* AAAS; Am Physiol Soc; Am Asn Clin Chemistry; Am Chem Soc. *Res:* Effect of androgens on metabolism of secondary sex glands; clinical chemistry. *Mailing Add:* Dept of Biochem & Molecular Biol La State Univ Sch of Med Shreveport LA 71130

RUDOLPH, JEFFREY STEWART, b Chicago, Ill, Oct 30, 42; m 67; c 2. PHARMACY, CHEMISTRY. *Educ:* Univ Ill, Chicago, BS, 66; Purdue Univ, Lafayette, MS, 69, PhD(pharm), 70. *Prof Exp:* Sr res pharmacist, Ciba-Geigy Pharmaceut Corp, 70-72; sr scientist, McNeil Labs Div, Johnson & Johnson, 72-75, group leader pharm, Pilot Plant, 75-76; asst dir, 77-80, DIR PHARMACEUT DEVELOP, STUART PHARMACEUT DIV, ICI AM, INC, 80- *Mem:* Acad Pharmaceut Sci; Am Pharmaceut Asn. *Res:* Optimization of drug delivery systems; development of new dosage forms with emphasis on optimum bioavailability; evaluation of pharmaceutical processing equipment. *Mailing Add:* Stuart Pharmaceut Div Concord Pike & Murphy Rd Wilmington DE 19897

RUDOLPH, JEROME HOWARD, b Minneapolis, Minn, Feb 3, 32; m 54; c 3. OBSTETRICS & GYNECOLOGY. *Educ:* Univ Minn, BA, 52, BS, 53, MD, 56; Am Bd Obstet & Gynec, dipl. *Prof Exp:* Rotating intern, Harbor Gen Hosp, 56-57; asst resident-chief resident, 59-63, from instr to asst prof, 62-68, chief gynec oncol, 68-77, ASSOC PROF OBSTET & GYNEC, SCH MED & DENT, UNIV ROCHESTER, 68- *Concurrent Pos:* Res fel obstet & gynec, Sch Med & Dent, Univ Rochester, 60-61 & 63-64, Food & Drug Admin grant oral contraceptives & urinary tract, 69-77, NIH grant, Gynec Oncol Group, 71- *Mem:* Am Soc Clin Oncol; Am Col Obstet & Gynec. *Res:* Effects of oral contraception on urinary function; gynecologic oncology. *Mailing Add:* Dept of Obstet & Gynec Univ of Rochester Sch Med & Dent Rochester NY 14642

RUDOLPH, LEE, b Cleveland, Ohio, March 28, 48; c 2. KNOT THEORY, COMPLEX PLANE CURVES. *Educ:* Princeton Univ, AB, 69, Mass Inst Technol, PhD(math), 74. *Prof Exp:* Researcher, Proj Logo, Artificial Intelligence Lab, Mass Inst Technol, 74; instr math, Brown Univ, 74-77; asst prof math, Columbia Univ, 77-82; vis researcher, Univ Geneva, Switzerland, 82; VIS ASST PROF, BRANDEIS UNIV, 82- *Mem:* Am Math Soc. *Res:* Relationships between low-dimensional topology and several complex variables; knot theory of complex plane curves; algebraic functions and closed braids. *Mailing Add:* Box 251 Adamsville RI 02801

RUDOLPH, LUTHER DAY, b Cleveland, Ohio, Aug 10, 30; m 54; c 3. INFORMATION SCIENCE. *Educ:* Ohio State Univ, BS, 58; Univ Okla, MEE, 64; Syracuse Univ, PhD(systs & info sci), 68. *Prof Exp:* Engr, Gen Elec Co, 58-64; res engr, Res Corp, 64-68, from asst prof to assoc prof systs & info sci, 68-75, PROF SYSTS & INFO SCI, SCH COMPUT & INFO SCI, SYRACUSE UNIV, 75- *Mem:* Inst Elec & Electronics Engrs; Am Soc Psychical Res; Parapsychol Asn; Am Math Soc. *Res:* Theory and implementation of error-correcting codes; application of combinatorial mathematics to problems in communication and system science; application of information theory to extrasensory communication. *Mailing Add:* 313 Link Hall Syracuse Univ Syracuse NY 13210

RUDOLPH, PHILIP S, b Syracuse, NY, May 10, 12; m 42; c 2. PHYSICAL CHEMISTRY, RADIATION CHEMISTRY. *Educ:* Syracuse Univ, AB, 33, PhD(chem), 51. *Prof Exp:* Instr, Syracuse Univ, 46; chemist, Oak Ridge Nat Lab, 51-73; RETIRED. *Mem:* Am Chem Soc; Radiation Res Soc; NY Acad Sci. *Res:* Mass spectrometric kinetic studies; chemical kinetics and reaction mechanisms; alpha particle induced radiolyses in the mass spectrometer. *Mailing Add:* 106 E Damascus Rd Oak Ridge TN 37830

RUDOLPH, RALPH W, b Erie, Pa, July 14, 40; m 62; c 3. INORGANIC CHEMISTRY. *Educ:* Pa State Univ, BS, 62, Univ Mich, MS, 64, PhD(chem), 66. *Prof Exp:* Res chemist, Frank J Seiler Res Lab, Off Aerospace Res, US Air Force Acad, 66-69; Asst prof, 69-73, assoc prof, 73-78, PROF CHEM, UNIV MICH, ANN ARBOR, 78- *Concurrent Pos:* Vis scholar chem, Stanford Univ, 75-76. *Mem:* Am Chem Soc; Royal Soc Chem. *Res:* Synthesis and characterization of fluorophosphines; mechanistic and synthetic investigations of boron halides and hydrides; correlation of physical properties with chemical properties; catalysis by organometallics. *Mailing Add:* Dept of Chem Univ of Mich Ann Arbor MI 48104

RUDOLPH, RAY RONALD, b Lock Haven, Pa, Feb 6, 27. MATHEMATICS. *Educ:* Johns Hopkins Univ, BE, 50. *Prof Exp:* Instr math, McCoy Col, John Hopkins Univ, 54-59, res asst oper res, Inst Coop Res, 50-53, res staff asst, 53-58, res assoc, 58-63, res scientist, 63-69; sr res analyst, Thor Div, Falcon Res & Develop Co, 69-81; SR RES ANALYST, KETRON, INC, 81- *Mem:* Am Ord Asn. *Res:* Aircraft vulnerability; weapons effectiveness; ballistics; operations research. *Mailing Add:* 219 Quaker Ridge Rd Timonium MD 21093

RUDOLPH, RAYMOND NEIL, b Lansing, Mich, May 19, 46; m 71; c 2. PHYSICAL CHEMISTRY. *Educ:* Univ NMex, BS, 68; Univ Colo, MS, 71, PhD(chem), 77. *Prof Exp:* Lab asst chem, Univ Colo, 68-71; sec teacher physics & math, Koidu Sec Sch, Sierra Leona, Africa, 71-74; ASST PROF CHEM, ADAMS STATE COL, 77- *Mem:* Res Soc NAm; Am Chem Soc. *Res:* Ultraviolet/visual spectrophotometry spectroscopy; photophysics and photochemistry of small molecules. *Mailing Add:* Div of Math Sci & Technol Adams State Col Alamosa CA 81102

RUDOLPH, ROBERT LEWIS, b Taylor's Valley, Va, Feb 12, 21; m 43; c 4. ANALYTICAL CHEMISTRY. *Educ:* Catawba Col, AB, 42. *Prof Exp:* Chemist, Huntsville Arsenal, 42-43; chemist, Tenn Eastman Co, 43-44; chemist, Naval Res Lab, 47-48, chief chem sect, Naval Mine Depot, 48-53, anal chem sect, Rocket Develop Div, Redstone Arsenal, 53-56; chief chemist, Rem-Cru Titanium Corp, 56-58; chemist, Chem Dept, Crucible Alloy & Stainless Steel Div, Colt Industs, Inc, 58-80; RETIRED. *Res:* Spectrography. *Mailing Add:* 332 Pine St MR-9 Beaver PA 15009

RUDOLPH, VICTOR J, b Little Falls, Minn, Sept 26, 16; m 44; c 6. FOREST MANAGEMENT. *Educ:* Utah State Univ, BS, 41; Duke Univ, MF, 43, DFor, 50. *Prof Exp:* Asst forest nursery, Utah State Univ, 39-41; res asst, Duke Univ, 41-42, res assoc, 46-48, asst prof forest mgt & asst dir, Duke Forest, 48-52; from asst prof to assoc prof, 52-66, PROF FORESTRY, MICH STATE UNIV, 66-, FOREST MGR RES, AGR EXP STA, 52-, ASSOC CHMN, 79- *Mem:* Fel Soc Am Foresters. *Res:* Hardwood management; site characteristics and plantation growth; forest plantation management and valuation. *Mailing Add:* Dept of Forestry Mich State Univ East Lansing MI 48824

RUDOLPH, WILLIAM BROWN, b St Paul, Minn, Dec 14, 38; m 61; c 3. MATHEMATICS. *Educ:* Bethany Col, WVa, BA, 60; Purdue Univ, Lafayette, MS, 65, PhD(math educ), 69. *Prof Exp:* Teacher, Shaker Heights Bd Educ, 61-63; instr math, Menlo Col, 63-66; instr, Univ Santa Clara, 64-66; instr & res asst math educ, Purdue Univ, Lafayette, 66-69; asst prof, 69-73; assoc prof, 73-81, PROF MATH & EDUC, IOWA STATE UNIV, 81- *Concurrent Pos:* Consult, Iowa Dept Pub Instr, 71-; consult & res grant evaluator, North Cent Asn, ESEA Title III & State of Iowa, 71- *Mem:* Am Educ Res Asn; Nat Coun Teachers Math. *Res:* Information theory concepts as applied to language analysis; mathematics learning theory; computer assisted instruction. *Mailing Add:* Dept of Math Iowa State Univ Ames IA 50011

RUDOY, WILLIAM, b Pittsburgh, Pa, Oct 31, 23. MECHANICAL ENGINEERING. *Educ:* Univ Pittsburgh, BS, 43; Carnegie Inst Technol, MS, 61; Univ Minn, PhD, 67. *Prof Exp:* Jr engr, Airborne Radar Lab, Philco Corp, 43-45; from instr to asst prof mech eng, Univ Pittsburgh, 45-51; consult engr, Hunting, Larsen & Dunnells, 51; field appln engr, Carrier Corp, 51-54, asst dir training, 54-56; assoc prof mech eng, 56-72, assoc chmn dept, 68-70, ASSOC DEAN, SCH ENG, UNIV PITTSBURGH, 82- *Concurrent Pos:* Training consult, Natural Gas Co Western Pa, 57-59 & Carrier Corp, 57, 59-60; Ford Found fel, Univ Minn, 63-64; NSF sci fac fel, 64-66; Ford Found vis prof, Univ of the Andes, Colombia, 70-71; consult, Peoples Natural Gas Co, 67- *Honors & Awards:* Outstanding Engr Award, Am Soc Mech Engrs, 77; Crosby Field Award, Am Soc Heating, Refrig & Air-Conditioning Engrs, 78. *Mem:* Fel Am Soc Heating, Refrig & Air-Conditioning Engrs; Am Soc Eng Educ; Am Soc Mech Engrs. *Res:* Air conditioning; heating; refrigeration; heat transfer; energy studies; system simulation. *Mailing Add:* Dept of Mech Eng Univ of Pittsburgh Pittsburgh PA 15261

RUDVALIS, ARUNAS, b Bavaria, Ger, June 8, 45; US citizen. ALGEBRA. *Educ:* Harvey Mudd Col, BS, 65; Dartmouth Col, MA, 67, PhD(math), 69. *Prof Exp:* Eng assoc, Gen Atomic Div, Gen Dynamics, 65; vis asst prof math, Dartmouth Col, 69; res assoc, Mich State Univ, 69-70, asst prof, 70-72; asst prof, 72-74, ASSOC PROF MATH, UNIV MASS, 75- *Concurrent Pos:* NSF res grants, 73, 74 & 75. *Mem:* Am Math Soc. *Res:* Finite simple groups; representations of finite groups; finite geometries; coding theory. *Mailing Add:* Dept of Math Univ of Mass Amherst MA 01002

RUDY, BERNARDO, b Mexico City, Mex, March 21, 48. NEUROBIOLOGY, MEMBRANE PHYSIOLOGY. *Educ:* Nat Univ, Mex, MD, 71; Centro Invest Estud Avanzados, Mex, PhD(biochem), 72; Cambridge Univ, UK, PhD(physiol), 76. *Prof Exp:* Res assoc, Univ Pa, 76-78; ASST PROF PHYSIOL & MEMBRANE PHYSIOL, NY UNIV MED CTR, 79- *Mem:* Biophys Soc. *Res:* Molecular understanding of brain function including studies of the structure of the molecules involved in excitation, as well as their metabolism and genetic control. *Mailing Add:* Dept Physiol & Biophysics NY Univ Med Ctr 550 1st Ave New York NY 10016

RUDY, LESTER HOWARD, b Chicago, Ill, Apr 6, 18; m 50; c 1. PSYCHIATRY. *Educ:* Univ Ill, BS, 39; Univ Ill Col Med, MD, 41; Northwestern Univ, MSHA, 57. *Prof Exp:* Resident psychiat, Downey Vet Admin Hosp, Ill, 46-48, chief serv, 48-54; supt, Galesburg State Res Hosp, Ill, 54-58; dir, Ill Ment Health Insts, 72-75; dir, Ill State Psychiat Inst, 58-75; PROF & HEAD, DEPT PSYCHIAT, ABRAHAM LINCOLN SCH MED, UNIV ILL, 75-, DIR, UNIV ILL HOSP, 81- *Concurrent Pos:* Prof, Dept Psychiat, Univ Ill, 59-; comnr, Joint Comn Accreditation Hosps, 67-; chmn, NIMH Res Serv Comt, 72-73; sr consult, Vet Admin; exec dir, Am Bd Psychiat & Neurol, 72- *Mem:* Fel Am Col Psychiat; fel Am Psychiat Asn; Am Asn Social Psychiat. *Res:* Educational standards and evaluation. *Mailing Add:* Univ of Ill 912 So Wood St Chicago IL 60612

RUDY, PAUL PASSMORE, JR, b Santa Rosa, Calif, Aug 29, 33; m 54; c 3. COMPARATIVE PHYSIOLOGY. *Educ:* Univ Calif, Davis, AB, 55, MA, 59, PhD(zool), 66. *Prof Exp:* Res asst pesticides, Univ Calif, Davis, 53-54, isopods, 60, lab technician, Marine Aquaria, 62-65; teacher pub sch, Calif, 56-62; fel salt & water balance in aquatic animals, Univ Birmingham, 66-67; fel, Univ Lancaster, 67-68; asst prof, 68-71, ASSOC PROF BIOL, UNIV ORE, 71-, DIR ORE INST MARINE BIOL, 69- *Concurrent Pos:* Partic, Int Indian Ocean Exped, Stanford Univ, 64; asst dir, Ore Inst Marine Biol, 68-69; NSF grant, 69-71. *Mem:* AAAS; Am Inst Biol Sci; Am Soc Zool. *Res:* Marine biology. *Mailing Add:* Ore Inst of Marine Biol Charleston OR 97403

RUDY, RICHARD L, b Covington, Ohio, Aug 15, 21; m 52; c 5. VETERINARY SURGERY. *Educ:* Ohio State Univ, DVM, 43, MSc, 47. *Prof Exp:* From instr to assoc prof vet surg, 44-57, prof vet surg & radiol, 57-70, assoc dir vet clin, 61, chmn dept vet surg & radiol, 57-70, PROF VET CLIN SCI, OHIO STATE UNIV, 71- *Mem:* Am Asn Vet Clinicians; Am Col Vet Surg; Am Animal Hosp Asn; Am Vet Med Asn; Am Vet Radiol Soc. *Res:* Veterinary surgery, including orthopedics, thoracic and neurologic. *Mailing Add:* Dept of Vet Clin Sci Ohio State Univ Columbus OH 43210

RUDY, THOMAS PHILIP, b Chicago, Ill, Mar 14, 24; m 51. ORGANIC CHEMISTRY. *Educ:* Univ Chicago, MS, 50, PhD(chem), 52. *Prof Exp:* Chemist, Shell Develop Co, 52-56 & 58-62; asst prof chem, Univ Chicago, 56-58; head org chem, 62-67, PRIN SCIENTIST, UNITED TECHNOL CTR, UNITED AIRCRAFT CORP, 67- *Mem:* Am Chem Soc. *Res:* Organic chemistry; lubricants; fuels; antioxidants; polymers; rocket propellants. *Mailing Add:* 21142 Sarahills Dr Saratoga CA 95070

RUDY, YORAM, b Tel-Aviv, Israel, Feb 12, 46. ELECTROCARDIOGRAPHY, CARDIAC ELECTROPHYSIOLOGY. *Educ:* Israel Inst Technol, BSc, 71, MSc, 73; Case Western Reserve Univ, PhD(biomed eng), 78. *Prof Exp:* Res assoc, 78-79, vis asst prof, 79-81, ASST PROF BIOMED ENG, CASE WESTERN RESERVE UNIV, 81- *Concurrent Pos:* Mem, Basic Sci Coun, Am Heart Asn. *Mem:* AAAS; Inst Elec & Electronics Engrs; sr mem Biomed Eng Soc; Cardiat Electrophysiologic Soc; Sigma Xi. *Res:* Model studies of the electrical activity of the heart on the tissue level; body surface mapping of heart potentials; forward and inverse problems in electrocardiography. *Mailing Add:* Dept Biomed Eng Case Western Univ Cleveland OH 44106

RUDZIK, ALLAN D, b Mundare, Alta, Nov 30, 34; m 60; c 2. PHARMACOLOGY. *Educ:* Univ Alta, BSc, 56, MSc, 58; Univ Wis, PhD(pharmacol), 62. *Prof Exp:* Pharmacologist, Ayerst Labs, Que, 62-63; pharmacologist, Pitman-Moore Div, Dow Chem Co, 63-65, sr pharmacologist, 65-66; res scientist cent nerv syst, 66-72, sr scientist, 72-74, res head, 74-79, mgr cent nerv syst res, 79-81, GROUP MGR THERAPEUT, THE UPJOHN CO, 81- *Mem:* AAAS; Am Soc Pharmacol & Exp Therapeut; NY Acad Sci. *Res:* Autonomic pharmacology as applied to smooth muscle, cardiovascular system and the central nervous system. *Mailing Add:* Therapeut I Upjohn Co Kalamazoo MI 49001

RUDZINSKA, MARIA ANNA, b Dabrowa, Poland; nat US; m 30. ZOOLOGY, PROTOZOOLOGY. *Educ:* Jagiellonian Univ, MS & PhD(zool). *Prof Exp:* Res assoc cell physiol, NY Univ, 46-52, instr, 47-49; vis investr electron micros, 52-56, res assoc parasitol, 56-60, from asst prof to assoc prof, 60-75, EMER PROF ROCKEFELLER UNIV, 75- *Honors & Awards:* Alfred Jurzykowski Award for Outstanding Achievements in Biol, in Sci, Alfred Jurzykowski Found, NY, 75. *Mem:* Harvey Soc; Soc Protozool; fel Geront Soc; fel NY Acad Sci. *Res:* Morphogenesis, aging and cell biology of free-living and parasitic protozoa; cell biology; parasitology. *Mailing Add:* Rockefeller Univ New York NY 10021

RUDZITIS, EDGARS, b Riga, Latvia, Sept 8, 25; nat US; m 57. INORGANIC CHEMISTRY, FORENSIC SCIENCE. *Educ:* Univ Tübingen, dipl, 50; Mass Inst Technol, PhD, 57. *Prof Exp:* Asst chem, Mass Inst Technol, 53-57; assoc chemist, Argonne Nat Lab, 57-69; RES ANALYST, ILL BUR IDENTIFICATION, 69- *Mem:* AAAS; Am Chem Soc. *Res:* Inorganic fluorine chemistry; development of fluorine bomb calorimetry; neutron activation analysis; introduction of a computer in crime laboratory operations. *Mailing Add:* Ill Bur of Identification 515 E Woodruff Joliet IL 60432

RUE, EDWARD EVANS, b Harrisburg, Pa, Oct 3, 24; m 44; c 3. EXPLORATION GEOLOGY, RESOURCE MANAGEMENT. *Educ:* Berea Col, AB, 48; Colo Sch Mines, MS, 49. *Prof Exp:* Geologist, Magnolia Petrol Co, 49-53; CONSULT GEOLOGIST, 53- *Mem:* Fel Geol Soc Am; Am Asn Petrol Geol; Soc Petrol Eng; Am Inst Mining, Metall & Petrol Eng; Am Inst Prof Geologists (secy-treas, 66-67, pres, 79). *Res:* Petroleum geology and engineering; evaluations for industry and Governmental agencies; industrial minerals exploration and programming for major producers; geological research coordinated with field work. *Mailing Add:* King City Fed Bldg Mt Vernon IL 62864

RUE, JAMES SANDVIK, b Sheyenne, NDak, Nov 19, 29; m 57; c 2. MATHEMATICS. *Educ:* Mayville State Col, BS, 51; Univ NDak, MS, 55; Iowa State Univ, PhD(math), 65. *Prof Exp:* From instr to asst prof math, Univ NDak, 55-60; mathematician, Boeing Airplane Co, 57-58; instr math, Iowa State Univ, 60-65; asst prof, Univ Wyo, 65-66 & Wash State Univ, 66-70; ASSOC PROF MATH, UNIV N DAK, 70- *Mem:* Am Math Soc; Math Asn Am. *Res:* Functional analysis. *Mailing Add:* Dept of Math Univ of N Dak Grand Forks ND 58201

RUE, ROLLAND R, b Marshfield, Wis, Apr 25, 35; m 58; c 2. PHYSICAL CHEMISTRY. *Educ:* Macalester Col, BA, 57; Iowa State Univ, PhD(phys chem), 62. *Prof Exp:* Asst prof, 62-70, ASSOC PROF CHEM, S DAK STATE UNIV, 70- *Mem:* AAAS; Am Chem Soc. *Res:* Interpretation of molecular wave functions; theoretical chemistry; thermodynamic properties of solutions; electrochemistry. *Mailing Add:* 2043 Elmwood Dr Brookings SD 57006

RUEBNER, BORIS HENRY, b Dusseldorf, Ger, Aug 30, 23; US citizen; m 57. PATHOLOGY. *Educ:* Univ Edinburgh, MB, ChB, 46, MD, 56. *Prof Exp:* Asst prof path, Dalhousie Univ, 57-59; from asst prof to assoc prof, Johns Hopkins Univ, 59-68; PROF PATH, SCH MED, UNIV CALIF, DAVIS, 68- *Mem:* Col Am Path; Int Acad Path; Am Asn Pathologists; Am Asn Study Liver Dis; AMA. *Res:* Liver pathology; hepatic carcinogenesis. *Mailing Add:* Dept of Path Univ of Calif Sch Med Davis CA 95616

RUECKERT, ROLAND R, b Rhinelander, Wis, Nov 24, 31; m 59; c 1. VIROLOGY. *Educ:* Univ Wis, BS, 53, MS, 57, PhD(oncol), 60. *Prof Exp:* Mem res staff, McArdle Mem Lab Cancer Res, Univ Wis, 59-60; asst res virologist, Univ Calif, Berkeley, 61; lectr molecular biol, 64-65; from assoc prof to assoc prof, 65-72, PROF BIOCHEM, UNIV WIS-MADISON, 72- *Concurrent Pos:* Fel, Max Planck Res Inst Biochem, Munich, 60-61; Max Planck Res Inst Virol, Tubingen, 61-62. *Mem:* AAAS; Am Soc Microbiol; Am Soc Biol Chemists. *Res:* Structure of animal viruses; mechanism of virus replication; structure of biological macromolecules. *Mailing Add:* Biophys Lab Univ of Wis 1525 Linden Dr Madison WI 53706

RUEDENBERG, KLAUS, b Bielefeld, Ger, Aug 25, 20; m 48; c 4. THEORETICAL CHEMISTRY, THEORETICAL PHYSICS. *Educ:* Univ Fribourg, Lic rer nat, 44; Univ Zurich, PhD(theoret physics), 50. *Hon Degrees:* PhD Univ Basel, Switz, 75. *Prof Exp:* Asst, Univ Zurich, 46-47; res assoc physics, Univ Chicago, 51-55; from asst prof to assoc prof chem & physics, Iowa State Univ, 55-62; prof chem Johns Hopkins Univ, 62-64; PROF CHEM & PHYSICS, IOWA STATE UNIV, 64-, DISTINGUISHED PROF SCI & HUMANITIES, 78- *Concurrent Pos:* Guggenheim fel, 66-67; vis prof, Swiss Fed Inst Technol, 66-67, Wash State Univ, 71, Univ Calif, Santa Cruz, 73 & Univ Bonn, Ger, 74; adv ed, Int J Quantum Chem & Chem Phys Letters, 67-; assoc ed, Theoretica Chimica Acta, 67- *Mem:* Fel AAAS; Am Chem Soc; Sigma Xi; fel Am Phys Soc; fel Am Inst Chem. *Res:* Atomic and molecular quantum mechanics; chemical binding and reactions; molecular structure and spectra; quantum chemistry; many-body quantum theory. *Mailing Add:* Dept Chem Iowa State Univ Ames IA 50010

RUEDISILI, LON CHESTER, b Madison, Wis, Feb 7, 39; m 65; c 2. HYDROGEOLOGY, ENERGY RESOURCES. *Educ:* Univ Wis, Madison, BS, 61, MS, 65, PhD(geol), 68, MS, 71. *Prof Exp:* Geologist/geophysicist, Standard Oil Co Calif, 67-70; asst prof environ geol, Univ Wis, Parkside, 72-74; assoc prof, 74-79, PROF HYDROGEOL, UNIV TOLEDO, 79- *Concurrent Pos:* Fel water resources specialist, Environ Protection Agency, 71-72. *Mem:* Fel Geol Soc Am; Am Water Resources Asn; Nat Water Well Asn; AAAS. *Res:* Applied water/land/energy resources management; investigating geologic controls to water quality and quantity problems and geologic factors in engineering studies; solid and liquid waste management; environmental impact analysis; petroleum recovery; water law; environmental geology. *Mailing Add:* Dept of Geol Univ of Toledo 2801 W Bancroft Toledo OH 43606

RUEGAMER, WILLIAM RAYMOND, b Huntington, Ind, Dec 15, 22; m 46. BIOCHEMISTRY. *Educ:* Ind Univ, BS, 43; Univ Wis, MS, 44, PhD(biochem), 48. *Prof Exp:* Biochemist, Swift & Co, Ill, 48-49; instr biophys, Univ Colo, 49-51; asst chief radioisotope labs, Vet Admin Hosp, Denver, Colo, 51-54; from assoc prof to prof biochem, State Univ NY Upstate Med Ctr, 54-68, actg chmn dept, 67-68; PROF BIOCHEM & CHMN DEPT, UNIV NEBR MED CTR, OMAHA, 68-, ASSOC DEAN, SCH ALLIED HEALTH PROF, 74- *Mem:* Am Soc Biol Chem; Am Inst Nutrit; Endocrine Soc; Soc Exp Biol & Med; Am Chem Soc. *Res:* Thyroid metabolism and atherosclerosis. *Mailing Add:* Dept of Biochem Univ of Nebr Med Ctr Omaha NE 68105

RUEGER, LAUREN J(OHN), b Archbold, Ohio, Dec 30, 21; m 44; c 4. SPACECRAFT SYSTEM ENGINEERING, PRECISION TIME FREQUENCY TECHNOLOGY. *Educ:* Ohio State Univ, BSc, 43, MSc, 47. *Prof Exp:* Mem staff, Radiation Lab, Mass Inst Technol, 43-45; asst physics, Ohio State Univ, 46-47; res engr, Battelle Mem Inst, 47-49; proj leader, Nat Bur Standards, 49-53; PRIN PROF STAFF MEM, APPL PHYSICS LAB, JOHNS HOPKINS UNIV, 53- *Concurrent Pos:* mem, US Study Group 7, Int Radio Consultive Comt; proceedings ed, Dept Defense Precice Time & Time Interval Appl & Planning Conf. *Mem:* Eng Physics Soc (secy, 41, pres, 42);

Am Phys Soc; sr mem Inst Elec & Electronics Engrs. *Res:* Satellite system engineering and ground station instrumentation; microwave radar system and component design; shipboard satellite navigation equipment design; electronic system reliability engineering; analysis of nuclear radiation effects in electronic systems; hydrogen maser frequency standard design and applications. *Mailing Add:* Appl Physics Lab Johns Hopkins Univ Laurel MD 20707

RUEGGEBERG, WERNER, b Muelheim-Ruhr, Ger, Mar 29, 19; nat US; m 63. ELECTRICAL ENGINEERING. *Educ:* Johns Hopkins Univ, BE, 42, DEng, 49. *Prof Exp:* Asst, Johns Hopkins Univ, 46-49; res engr, Armstrong Cork Co, 49-56; fel engr, Westinghouse Elec Co, 56-57; RES ASSOC, ARMSTRONG CORK CO, 57- *Mem:* Inst Elec & Electronics Engrs. *Res:* Dielectric and induction heating; electronic circuitry; high frequency power generation and transmission; artificial dielectrics, development and applications; micro-wave test methods. *Mailing Add:* Res & Develop Ctr Armstrong Cork Co Lancaster PA 17603

RUEHLE, JOHN LEONARD, b Winter Haven, Fla, Feb 4, 31; m 54; c 4. PLANT PATHOLOGY. *Educ:* Univ Fla, BSA, 53, MS, 57; NC State Col, PhD(plant path), 61. *Prof Exp:* PLANT NEMATOLOGIST, FORESTRY SCI LAB, SOUTHEASTERN FORESTRY EXP STA, US FOREST SERV, 61- *Mem:* Am Phytopath Soc; Soc Nematol. *Res:* Forest nematology, especially host-parasite relationships. *Mailing Add:* Forestry Sci Lab Univ of Ga Carlton St Athens GA 30601

RUEHLI, ALBERT EMIL, b Zurich, Switz, June 22, 37; US citizen. ELECTRICAL ENGINEERING. *Educ:* Zurich Tech Sch, Telecom Engr, 63; Univ Vt, PhD(elec eng), 72. *Prof Exp:* Res staff mem semiconductor circuits & devices, 63-66, eng & math analysit, Develop Lab, 66-71, res staff mem design automation, 71-78, MGR & RES STAFF MEM COMPUT AIDED DESIGN, IBM T J WATSON RES CTR, 78- *Honors & Awards:* Outstanding Contrib Award, IBM, 75, Invention Achievement Awards, 74 & 76, Res Div Outstanding Contrib Award, 78. *Mem:* Sr mem Inst Elec & Electronics Engrs. *Res:* Electrical circuit theory; microwave theory; computer aided design. *Mailing Add:* IBM T J Watson Res Ctr PO Box 218 Yorktown Heights NY 10598

RUEL, MAURICE M J, b Quebec City, Que, Feb 18, 37; m 64; c 2. CHEMICAL ENGINEERING. *Educ:* Laval Univ, BScA, 61, MScA, 65, DSc(chem eng), 68. *Prof Exp:* From asst prof to assoc prof chem eng, Univ Sherbrooke, 68-73; chief res & develop div, environ emergencies, Dept Energy, 73-74; dir renewable resources & environ, 75-77, DIR GEN NORTHERN ENVIRON, DEPT INDIAN & NORTHERN AFFAIRS, 77- *Concurrent Pos:* Mem bd, Mgt Res Ctr, Sherbrooke, Que, 70-73 & Que Comn of Water in Agr, 71-73; mem bd dirs, Ctr Land Use Planning, Univ Sherbrooke, 70-73; mem, Nat Surv & Mapping Comn, 75- *Honors & Awards:* Queen's Silver Jubilee Medal, Govt Can, 77. *Mem:* Fel Chem Inst Can; Chem Eng Soc Can. *Res:* Thermodynamics of liquid solutions; used water treatment; agglomeration. *Mailing Add:* 25 Northview Rd Ottawa ON K2E 6A6 Can

RUELIUS, HANS WINFRIED, b Worms, Ger, Feb 18, 15; nat US; m 46; c 2. DRUG METABOLISM. *Educ:* Univ Geneva, DSc(chem), 42. *Prof Exp:* Res chemist synthesis pharmaceut, Kast & Ehinger, Ger, 44-45; res assoc, Med Res Chem Dept, Max-Planck Inst, 46-51; sr res scientist, Wyeth Inst Med Res, 51-66, mgr drug metab dept, res div, 66-78, ASSOC DIR BIOL RES, DRUG METAB, WYETH LABS, 78- *Concurrent Pos:* Res assoc, Univ Pa, 51-53. *Mem:* AAAS; Am Chem Soc; Am Soc Pharmacol & Exp Therapeut. *Res:* Isolation, characterization and structure proof of natural substances; drug metabolism; chemical carcinogens. *Mailing Add:* Drug Metab Dept Wyeth Labs PO Box 8299 Philadelphia PA 19101

RUELKE, OTTO CHARLES, b Oshkosh, Wis, Feb 18, 23; m 59; c 3. AGRONOMY, PLANT PHYSIOLOGY. *Educ:* Univ Wis, BS, 50, MS, 52, PhD(agron), 55. *Prof Exp:* Instr high sch, 50-51; res asst agron, Univ Wis, 52-55; from asst prof to assoc prof, 55-69, PROF AGRON, UNIV FLA, 69- *Concurrent Pos:* Mem staff crop ecol, Forage & Pasture Sci, 55-; mem exec comt, Southern Pasture & Forage Crop Improv Conf, 63-65, chmn, 64; mem, Am Forage & Grassland Coun. *Mem:* Am Soc Agron; Crop Sci Soc Am. *Res:* Cold injury; plant growth regulation; microclimatology; forage management and quality evaluations. *Mailing Add:* Dept of Agron Univ of Fla 2195 McCarty Hall Gainesville FL 32611

RUENITZ, PETER CARMICHAEL, b Los Angeles, Calif, Nov 10, 43. MEDICINAL CHEMISTRY, ORGANIC CHEMISTRY. *Educ:* Univ Minn, BS, 66; Univ Kans, PhD(med chem), 74. *Prof Exp:* Res assoc med chem, Upjohn Co, 66-68; asst prof, 74-80, ASSOC PROF MED CHEM, SCH PHARM, UNIV GA, 80- *Mem:* Am Chem Soc. *Res:* Chemistry of bicyclic amines; nonsteroidal estrogen/antiestrogen metabolism. *Mailing Add:* Sch of Pharm Univ of Ga Athens GA 30602

RUEPPEL, MELVIN LESLIE, b Rolla, Mo, Sept 18, 45; m 69; c 3. PESTICIDE CHEMISTRY. *Educ:* Univ Mo, BS, 66; Univ Calif, Berkeley, PhD(chem), 70. *Prof Exp:* NIH fel biochem, Cornell Univ, 70-71; sr res chemist metab, 71-75, group leader, 75-77, res mgr environ process, 77-80, RES DIR SYNTHESIS, MONSANTO CO, 80- *Mem:* Am Chem Soc; AAAS; Sigma Xi; Am Soc Mass Spectrometry. *Res:* Environmental fate and safety of pesticides; agricultural and pesticide chemistry; chemical synthetic efforts aimed at the discovery of new herbicides, plant growth regulators and disease control agents. *Mailing Add:* Monsanto Co U3E 800 N Lindbergh Blvd Kirkwood MO 63166

RUESCH, JURGEN, b Naples, Italy, Nov 9, 09; nat; m 37; c 1. PSYCHIATRY. *Educ:* Univ Zurich, MD, 35. *Prof Exp:* Asst neurol, neuroanat & neuropath, Med Sch, Univ Zurich, 36-38; asst psychiat, Univ Basel, 38-39; fel, Rockefeller Found, 39-41; asst, Mass Gen Hosp, 41-43; res fel neuropath, Harvard Med Sch, 41-43; lectr, 43-48, assoc prof, 48-56, PROF PSYCHIAT, SCH MED, UNIV CALIF, SAN FRANCISCO, 56-

Concurrent Pos: Res psychiatrist, Langley Porter Neuropsychiat Inst, 43-58, dir treatment res ctr, 58-64, dir sect social psychiat, 65-75. *Honors & Awards:* Hofheimer Award, Am Psychiat Asn, 51. *Mem:* AAAS; hon mem German Soc Psychiat & Neurol; Am Col Psychiat; fel Am Psychiat Asn; Asn Res Nerv & Ment Dis. *Res:* Social psychiatry; communication; human behavior. *Mailing Add:* Langley Porter Inst Univ of Calif Med Ctr San Francisco CA 94143

RUESINK, ALBERT WILLIAM, b Adrian, Mich, Apr 16, 40; m 63; c 2. PLANT PHYSIOLOGY. *Educ:* Univ Mich, BA, 62; Harvard Univ, MA, 65, PhD(biol), 66. *Prof Exp:* NSF fel bot, Inst Gen Bot, Swiss Fed Inst Technol, 66-67; asst prof, 67-72, assoc prof bot, prof, 72-80, PROF PLANT SCI, IND UNIV, BLOOMINGTON, 80- *Concurrent Pos:* Dir undergrad educ biol sci, Ind Univ, 72-74. *Mem:* AAAS; Am Soc Plant Physiol; Am Inst Biol Sci; Bot Soc Am. *Res:* Relationships between the plant cell plasma membrane and cell wall, especially as related to wall elongation. *Mailing Add:* Dept Biol Ind Univ Bloomington IN 47405

RUETMAN, SVEN HELMUTH, b Rakvere, Estonia, June 14, 27; nat US; m 57; c 2. ORGANIC CHEMISTRY. *Educ:* Millikin Univ, BS, 53; Univ Utah, PhD(chem), 57. *Prof Exp:* Res chemist, Shell Develop Co, 57-61; res chemist, Narmco Res & Develop Telecomput Corp, 61-63; res chemist, 63-70, RES SPECIALIST, WESTERN DIV, DOW CHEM USA, 70- *Mem:* Am Chem Soc. *Res:* Heterocyclic chemistry; polymer chemistry; process development; pesticides. *Mailing Add:* Dow Chem USA 2800 Mitchell Dr Walnut Creek CA 94598

RUEVE, CHARLES RICHARD, b Springfield, Ohio, May 25, 18. MATHEMATICS. *Educ:* St Joseph's Col, Ind, AB, 47; Univ Notre Dame, MS, 49, PhD(math), 63. *Prof Exp:* Chmn dept math & physics, 46-74, PROF MATH, ST JOSEPH'S COL, IND, 46-, CHMN DEPT, 77- *Mem:* AAAS; Math Asn Am; Am Math Soc. *Res:* Modern abstract algebra; number theory; real analysis; algebraic topology. *Mailing Add:* Dept of Math & Physics St Joseph's Col Rensselaer IN 47978

RUF, ROBERT HENRY, JR, b Malden, Mass, Aug 30, 32; m 56. HORTICULTURE. *Educ:* Univ Mass, BS, 55; Cornell Univ, MS, 57, PhD(veg crops), 59. *Prof Exp:* From asst prof to assoc prof hort & from asst horticulturist to assoc horticulturist exp sta, Univ Nev, Reno, 59-75; PRES, GREENHOUSE GARDEN CTR, 74-; VPRES, GEOTHERMAL DEVELOP ASN, 78- *Res:* Greenhouse management; propagation; geothermal-agricultural research. *Mailing Add:* 4201 Palomino Circle Reno NV 89509

RUFENACH, CLIFFORD L, b Ronan, Mont, Nov 16, 36. IONOSPHERIC PHYSICS, PHYSICAL OCEANOGRAPHY. *Educ:* Mont State Univ, BS, 62, MS, 63; Univ Colo, PhD(elec eng), 71. *Prof Exp:* Res engr, Electronics Res Lab, Mont State Univ, 62-67; res physicist, Space Environ Lab, Boulder, Colo, 67-75; res physicist, Ocean Remote Sensing Lab, Miami, 75-76, STAFF MEM, WAVE PROPAGATION LAB, NAT OCEANIC & ATMOSPHERIC ADMIN, BOULDER, 76- *Mem:* Sr mem Inst Elec & Electronics Engrs; Int Sci Radio Union; Am Geophys Union. *Res:* Remote sensing of the atmosphere and ocean. *Mailing Add:* Wave Propagation Lab Nat Oceanic & Atmospheric Admin Boulder CO 80302

RUFF, ARTHUR WILLIAM, JR, b Newark, NJ, Aug 18, 30; m 56; c 3. METAL PHYSICS. *Educ:* Rice Univ, BS, 52; Univ Ariz, MS, 53; Univ Md, PhD(physics), 63. *Prof Exp:* Physicist, Shell Develop Co, 53-54; physicist, Aberdeen Proving Ground, 55-56; PHYSICIST, NAT BUR STANDARDS, 57-, SECT CHIEF MICROSTRUCT CHARACTERIZATION, 63-, CHIEF METAL SCI & STANDARDS DIV, 76- *Honors & Awards:* Dept Commerce Spec Award, 63 & 71, Silver Medal Award, 71. *Mem:* Am Phys Soc; Electron Micros Soc Am; Am Soc Metals; Am Soc Testing & Mat. *Res:* Dislocation; defects in crystals; plastic deformation; electron microscopy; surface physics; thermal evaporation; chemical dissolution; metal physics. *Mailing Add:* Metall Div Nat Bur of Standards Washington DC 20013

RUFF, GEORGE ANTONY, b Bay Shore, NY, May 10, 41; m 66; c 4. PHYSICS. *Educ:* Le Moyne Col, NY, BS, 62; Princeton Univ, MA, 64, PhD(physics), 66. *Prof Exp:* Res assoc physics, Cornell Univ, 66-68; asst prof, 68-75, ASSOC PROF PHYSICS, BATES COL, 75-, CHMN DIV NAT SCI & MATH, 77- *Concurrent Pos:* Vis assoc prof, Univ Ariz, 75-76. *Mem:* Am Phys Soc; Am Asn Physics Teachers; Inst Elec & Electronics Eng. *Res:* Optical and atomic physics; quantum electronics. *Mailing Add:* Dept of Physics Bates Col Lewiston ME 04240

RUFF, GEORGE ELSON, b Wilkes-Barre, Pa, Jan 12, 28; m 51; c 5. PSYCHIATRY. *Educ:* Haverford Col, AB, 48; Univ Pa, MD, 52. *Prof Exp:* Intern, Univ Mich, 52-53, resident psychiat, 53-56; PROF PSYCHIAT, SCH MED, UNIV PA, 56-, V CHMN, 76-, ASSOC DEAN, MED STUDENT PROGS, 76- *Concurrent Pos:* USPHS fel, Inst Neurol Sci, Sch Med, Univ Pa, 56-57; USPHS career investr, 59-64; consult, US Air Force, 60-63, NASA, 62-63 & Vet Admin, 64- *Honors & Awards:* Longacre Award, Aerospace Med Asn, 59. *Mem:* Am Col Psychoanalysts; Am Psychiat Asn; Group Advan Psychiat; Am Col Psychiat; Asn Am Med Cols. *Res:* Psychiatric and psychophysiologic studies of human stress; medical education. *Mailing Add:* 205 Piersol Bldg Univ Pa Hosp Philadelphia PA 19104

RUFF, IRWIN S, b New York, NY, Oct 11, 32; m 59; c 2. METEOROLOGY. *Educ:* City Col New York, BS, 53; NY Univ, MS, 57. *Prof Exp:* Asst res scientist, Dept Meteorol, NY Univ, 55-59; res meteorologist, US Weather Bur, 59-65, RES METEOROLOGIST, NAT EARTH SATELLITE SERV, 65- *Mem:* Am Meteorol Soc; Am Geophys Union; Asn Orthodox Jewish Scientists. *Res:* Reflection properties of the earth and atmosphere in solar wavelengths; satellite determinations of terrestrial radiative properties and influence on climate; climatic change. *Mailing Add:* 5200 Auth Rd Rm 712 Marlow Heights MD 20023

RUFF, JOHN K, b New York, NY, Feb 19, 32; m 54; c 3. INORGANIC CHEMISTRY. *Educ:* Haverford Col, BS, 54; Univ NC, PhD(chem), 59. *Prof Exp:* Asst phys chem, Univ NC, 54-56; chemist, Rohm & Haas Co, 57-68; ASSOC PROF CHEM, UNIV GA, 68- *Mem:* Am Chem Soc; Royal Soc Chem. *Res:* Organometallic chemistry of boron, aluminum and gallium; fluorine chemistry; nitrogen fluorides; hypofluorites; sulfur oxyfluoride derivatives. *Mailing Add:* Dept of Chem Univ of Ga Athens GA 30602

RUFF, MICHAEL DAVID, b Newton, Kans, July 22, 41; m 63; c 2. PARASITOLOGY. *Educ:* Kans State Univ, BS, 64, MS, 66, PhD(parasitol), 68. *Prof Exp:* Instr biol, Marymount Col, 67-68; parasitologist, 406th Med Lab, Japan, 68-71; NIH res fel, Rice Univ, 71-72; from asst prof to assoc prof poultry sci, Univ Ga, 72-77; CHIEF, POULTRY PARASITIC DIS LAB, ANIMAL PARASITOL INST, USDA, 77- *Mem:* Poultry Sci Asn; Am Soc Parasitol; Am Asn Vet Parasitol; Am Micros Soc; Am Asn Avian Pathologists. *Res:* Physiology and biochemistry of parasites; metabolism of larval trematodes; schistosomiasis; avian coccidia, host parasite interactions. *Mailing Add:* Animal Parasitol Inst BARC-East Beltsville MD 20715

RUFF, ROBERT LAVERNE, b Laurel, Mont, Mar 4, 39; m 60; c 2. WILDLIFE ECOLOGY, WILDLIFE MANAGEMENT. *Educ:* Univ Mont, BS, 61, MS, 63; Utah State Univ, PhD(ecol), 71. *Prof Exp:* Furbearer biologist, Mont Fish & Game Dept, 61; NIH res asst parasitol bighorn sheep, Univ Mont, 61-62; res asst magpie predation on pheasant nests, Mont Coop Wildlife Res Unit, 62-63, res assoc ecol grizzly bears & elk, 64-66; NIH res asst behav ground squirrels, Utah State Univ, 66-70; asst prof exten wildlife specialist, 70-74, assoc prof, 74-81, PROF WILDLIFE ECOL & EXTEN WILDLIFE SPECIALIST, UNIV WIS-MADISON, 81- *Mem:* Am Inst Biol Sci; Animal Behav Soc; Ecol Soc Am; Wildlife Soc; Bear Biol Asn. *Res:* Effects of social behavior on the dynamics of animal populations; effects of small watershed projects on fish and wildlife resources; environmental impact assessment; ecology of black bear populations. *Mailing Add:* Dept of Wildlife Ecol Univ of Wis 226 Russell Labs Madison WI 53706

RUFFA, ANTHONY RICHARD, b Pittsburgh, Pa, Dec 12, 33; m 59; c 5. CHEMICAL PHYSICS, SOLID STATE PHYSICS. *Educ:* Carnegie Inst Technol, BS, 55, MS, 57; Catholic Univ, PhD(physics), 60. *Prof Exp:* Theoret solid state physicist, Nat Bur Standards, 60-66; THEORET SOLID STATE PHYSICIST, NAVAL RES LAB, 66- *Concurrent Pos:* Lectr, Am Univ, 59-60 & Georgetown Univ, 63-64. *Mem:* Phys Soc; NY Acad Sci; Sigma Xi. *Res:* Thermal, optical and magnetic properties of crystals; theory of chemical bonding in crystals; quantum theory of atomic and molecular structure. *Mailing Add:* Naval Res Lab Washington DC 20375

RUFFER, DAVID G, b Archbold, Ohio, Aug 25, 37; m 58; c 3. VERTEBRATE ZOOLOGY. *Educ:* Defiance Col, BS, 59; Bowling Green State Univ, MA, 60; Univ Okla, PhD(zool), 64. *Prof Exp:* From instr to assoc prof biol, Defiance Col, 64-73, dean, 69-73; PROVOST, provost, Elmira Col, 73-78; PRES, ALBRIGHT COL, 78- *Mem:* AAAS; Am Soc Mammal; Ecol Soc Am; Animal Behav Soc. *Res:* Ecology and behavior of Cricetid rodents; evolution of behavior in the grasshopper mice. *Mailing Add:* Albright Col Reading PA 19604

RUFFIN, SPAULDING MERRICK, b Emporia, Va, Apr 8, 23; m 58; c 3. BIOLOGICAL CHEMISTRY. *Educ:* Hampton Inst, BS, 43; Mich State Univ, MA, 53, PhD(animal nutrit), 56. *Prof Exp:* Teacher pub schs, NC, 46-52; PROF CHEM, SOUTHERN UNIV, BATON ROUGE, 56- *Mem:* Am Chem Soc. *Res:* Vitamins; amino acids; intermediary metabolism; biochemistry; organic chemistry. *Mailing Add:* Dept of Chem Southern Univ Baton Rouge LA 70813

RUFFINE, RICHARD S, b New York, NY, July 28, 28; m 60; c 3. PHYSICS. *Educ:* Queens Col, NY, BS, 50; Syracuse Univ, MS, 53; NY Univ, PhD(physics), 60. *Prof Exp:* Instr physics, Hunter Col, 54-55; instr, NY Univ, 58-59, res assoc, 59-60; staff scientist, GC Dewey Corp, 60-62; mem tech staff, RCA Labs, 62-67; prog mgr, Advan Res Proj Agency, US Dept Defense, 67-68; asst dir & chief reentry physics div, US Army Advan Ballistic Missile Defense Agency, 68-75; SPECIALIST TECHNOL & ANAL, OFF DIR, DEFENSE RES ENG, 75- *Concurrent Pos:* Adj asst prof, NY Univ, 60-61; consult, Inst Defense Anal, 66-67. *Honors & Awards:* Meritorious Civilian Serv, US Army, 75. *Mem:* AAAS; Am Phys Soc; Am Geophys Union; Am Inst Aeronaut & Astronaut. *Res:* Atomic physics; electromagnetic scattering, re-entry physics. *Mailing Add:* 4050 N 27th Rd Arlington VA 22207

RUFFNER, JAMES ALAN, b Akron, Ohio, Sept 6, 30; m 59; c 2. HISTORY OF SCIENCE, SCIENCE INFORMATION. *Educ:* Ohio State Univ, BSc, 51; Univ Mich, MS, 58; Ind Univ, MA, 63, PhD(hist sci), 66. *Prof Exp:* Physicist, Battelle Mem Inst, 51-52; instr earth sci, ETex State Col, 58-60; from asst prof to assoc prof natural sci, Monteith Col, 64-78, ACAD SERV OFFICER, SCI LIBR, WAYNE STATE UNIV, 78- *Mem:* Soc Hist Technol; Am Libr Asn; Am Meteorol Soc; Hist Sci Soc; Air Pollution Control Asn. *Res:* Air pollution control and fuel technology; communication networks in science. *Mailing Add:* Sci Libr Wayne State Univ Detroit MI 48202

RUFFOLO, JOHN JOSEPH, JR, b Chicago, Ill, Jan 4, 42. CELL BIOLOGY, PROTOZOOLOGY. *Educ:* Loyola Univ Chicago, BS, 66; Univ Iowa, MS, 69, PhD(zool), 72. *Prof Exp:* Fel zool, Univ Wis-Madison, 72-73, res assoc, 73-74; asst prof biol, Va Commonwealth Univ, 74-75, res assoc biophys, Med Col Va, 75-76, asst prof biophys, Med Col Va, 76-80; MEM STAFF, VET ADMIN MED CTR, 80- *Concurrent Pos:* HEW fel, 73-74; prin investr, Nat Eye Inst, 78-81; co-prin investr, US Army Med Res & Develop Command, 78-80; investr, HEW, 78-81, USPHS, 79-82 & Am Cancer Soc, 79-80. *Mem:* Am Micros Soc; Am Soc Cell Biol; Am Soc Zoologists; Biophys Soc; Soc Protozoologists. *Res:* Developmental cell biology of ciliate protozoa; endosymbiosis; intracellular calcification; ocular photopathology and photochemical lesions in mammals. *Mailing Add:* Veterans Admin Med Ctr 3200 Vine St Cincinnati OH 45220

RUFFOLO, ROBERT RICHARD, JR, b Yonkers, NY, Apr 14, 50; m 72. PHARMACOLOGY, NEUROBIOLOGY. *Educ:* Ohio State Univ, BS, 73, PhD(pharmacol), 76. *Prof Exp:* Res assoc, Am Found Pharmaceut Educ, 73-76; res assoc pharmacol, NIH, 77-78; SR PHARMACOLOGIST, LILLY RES LABS, 78- *Concurrent Pos:* Res assoc & fel pharmacol, Nat Inst Gen Med Sci, 77-78. *Mem:* AAAS; Fedn Am Scientists; Am Soc Pharmacol & Exp Therapeut. *Res:* Pharmacology of vascular smooth muscle; adrenergic receptors; hypertension. *Mailing Add:* Dept Cardiovascular Pharmacol MC304 Eli Lilly & Co Indianapolis IN 46285

RUGE, DANIEL, b Murdock, Nebr, May 13, 17; m 42; c 2. NEUROSURGERY. *Educ:* NCent Col, BA, 39; Northwestern Univ, MD, 45, MS, 49, PhD, 61. *Hon Degrees:* DSc, NCent Col, 71. *Prof Exp:* From asst prof to prof surg, Northwestern Univ, Chicago, 61-77; CLIN PROF NEUROSURG, GEORGE WASHINGTON UNIV, 77- *Concurrent Pos:* Dir, Spinal Cord Injury Serv, Vet Admin Cent Off, 76-80; physician to President Ronald Reagan, 81- *Honors & Awards:* Northwestern Univ Serv Award, 67. *Mem:* James IV Asn Surgeons. Am Asn Neurol Surg; Am Col Surgeons. *Mailing Add:* 3318 N St NW Washington DC 20007

RUGGE, HENRY F, b South San Francisco, Calif, Oct 28, 36; m 60. MEDICAL TECHNOLOGY, PLASMA PHYSICS. *Educ:* Univ Calif, Berkeley, AB, 58, PhD(physics), 63. *Prof Exp:* Res asst plasma physics, Lawrence Radiation Lab, Univ Calif, 59-63; staff physicist, Physics Int Co, Calif, 63-69; staff physicist, Arkon Sci Labs, 70-72; vpres, Link Assocs, 72-73; vpres, Norse Systs, Inc, 73-75; vpres & gen mgr, Rasor Assocs Inc, 75-80; pres, Ultra Med Inc, 80-81; PRES, BERLISCAN INC, 81- *Res:* Plasma physics and gaseous electronics; atomic physics; medical and scientific instrumentation development; energy conversion, research and development. *Mailing Add:* 1626 Chestnut Berkeley CA 94702

RUGGE, HUGO R, b San Francisco, Calif, Nov 7, 35; m 69; c 2. PHYSICS. *Educ:* Univ Calif, Berkeley, AB, 57, PhD(physics), 63. *Prof Exp:* Mem tech staff, 62-68, dept head, 68-79, prin dir, Lab Opers, 79-81, DIR, SPACE SCI LAB, AEROSPACE CORP, 81- *Mem:* Int Astron Union; fel Am Phys Soc; Am Geophys Union; Am Astron Soc. *Res:* Space science; solar x-rays; upper atmospheric, Infrared astronomy, high energy physics; satellite instrumentation. *Mailing Add:* Space Sci Lab Aerospace Corp PO Box 92957 Los Angeles CA 90009

RUGGE, RAYMOND A(LBERT), b Netawaka, Kans, Sept 27, 04; m 31. ELECTRICAL ENGINEERING. *Educ:* Univ Kans, BSEE, 29. *Prof Exp:* Engr, Am Tel & Tel Co, 29-32; chief elec design & develop, Curtiss-Wright Corp, 33-49; chief engr & div mgr, Lear, Inc, 49-51; chief engr, Minneapolis-Honeywell Regulator Co, 52-54, asst dir eng, Aeronaut Div, 54-56; vpres & dir corp, Res & Develop Div, W L Maxson Corp, 56-60; dir eng, Kollsman Instrument Corp, 60-62 & Aeronca Mfg Corp, 62-64; STAFF CONSULT, ALTAMIL CORP, 65- *Mem:* AAAS; Am Inst Aeronaut & Astronaut; Inst Elec & Electronics Engrs; NY Acad Sci. *Res:* Automatic control systems engineering on aircraft, missiles, space vehicles and industrial equipment; radar antenna systems; radiation detection equipment; automatic read-out devices. *Mailing Add:* 10651 W Pineaire Sun City AZ 85351

RUGGERI, ROBERT T, US citizen. ELECTROCHEMISTRY, MATHEMATICAL MODELING. *Educ:* Univ Utah, BS, 70; Univ Wash, MS, 72, PhD(chem eng), 78. *Prof Exp:* RES ENG, ELECTROCHEM TECHNOL CORP, 76- *Mem:* Electrochem Soc; Am Inst Chem Engrs; AAAS. *Res:* Electrochemistry; corrosion; transport through polymers; ion-exchange membranes; electrodes for nerve stimulation; mathematical modeling. *Mailing Add:* 14071 117th Ave Northeast Kirkland WA 98033

RUGGERO, MARIO ALFREDO, b Resistencia, Argentina, Nov 7, 43; m 73. NEUROPHYSIOLOGY. *Educ:* Cath Univ Am, BA, 65; Univ Chicago, PhD(physiol), 72. *Prof Exp:* ASST PROF OTOLARYNGOL, UNIV MINN, 75- *Concurrent Pos:* NIH fel, neurophysiol, Univ Wis, 72-75; Fel neurophysiol, Univ Wis-Madison, 72-75. *Mem:* AAAS; Soc Neurosci; Acoust Soc Am. *Res:* Physiology; anatomy of hearing. *Mailing Add:* Dept Otolaryngol Med Sch Univ Minn 2630 University Ave SE Minneapolis MN 55414

RUGGIERI, GEORGE D, b Philadelphia, Pa, Jan 29, 25. MARINE BIOLOGY. *Educ:* St Joseph's Col, Pa, BS, 48; St Louis Univ, PhD(biol), 60. *Hon Degrees:* DSc, St Joseph's Univ, Philadelphia, Pa, 81. *Prof Exp:* Asst micros anat, Sch Med, St Louis Univ, 57; fel & res assoc exp morphogenesis, Dept Marine Biochem & Ecol, New York Aquarium, 64-65; instr biol, St Joseph's Col, Pa, 65-66; res assoc & staff mem, 65-67, coordr res, 67-70, asst dir, 70-72, DIR, OSBORN LABS MARINE SCI, 73-; ASST PROF BIOL, ST JOSEPH'S COL, PA, 66-67; DIR, NY AQUARIUM, 76- *Concurrent Pos:* Mem Bermuda Biol Sta Res, Inc; adj assoc prof, Dept Biol Sci, Grad Sch, Fordham Univ, 67-, mem staff, Louis Calder Conserv & Ecol Ctr, 69-; mem subcomt marine resources, Mayor's Oceanog Adv Comt, NY, 69-73; res assoc, NY Ocean Sci Lab, Montauk, 70-; Diocesan NY Comn Environ & Ecol, LI, 70-72; bd trustees, Univ Scranton, 70-74; res comt, Pharm & Therapeut Comt, Hahnemann Med Col & Hosp of Philadelphia, 72-73; bd dir, St Joseph's Col, Pa, 73-79; assoc dir, NY Aquarium, 73-76; adj assoc prof biol, NY Univ, marine sci adv bd, Coral Reef Soc, bd trustees, Fordham Univ & mem, Int Union Dir Zool Gardens, 78-; mem, Gateway Nat Area Adv Comn, 80. *Mem:* Fel AAAS; fel NY Acad Sci; Am Inst Biol Sci; Am Soc Zoologists; Soc Invert Path. *Res:* Teratology; pharmacotoxicology; marine biology with emphasis on experimental morphogenesis in marine forms and study of pharmacodynamically active substances from the sea. *Mailing Add:* Osborn Labs of Marine Sci Boardwalk & W Eighth St Brooklyn NY 11224

RUGGIERO, ALESSANDRO GABRIELE, b Rome, Italy, Apr 10, 40; m 65; c 2. PARTICLE PHYSICS, ACCELERATOR PHYSICS. *Educ:* Univ Rome, PhD(physics), 64. *Prof Exp:* Physicist, Nat Lab Frascati, Italy, 62-65, Europ Orgn Nuclear Res, Geneva, 66-69 & Nat Lab Frascati, Italy, 69-70; PHYSICIST, FERMI NAT ACCELERATOR LAB, 70- *Mem:* AAAS. *Res:*

Accelerator theory; design of very large proton-proton and electron-positron storage and colliding device for high-energy physics experiment; design of proton-antiproton colliders; study of methods to collect anti-matter. *Mailing Add:* Fermi Nat Accelerator Lab PO Box 500 Batavia IL 60510

RUGGLES, IVAN DALE, b Omaha, Nebr, Dec 7, 27; m 60; c 2. MATHEMATICS. *Educ:* Nebr Wesleyan Univ, AB, 49; Univ Wyo, MA, 51; Iowa State Col, PhD(math), 58. *Prof Exp:* Instr math, Iowa State Col, 57-58; from asst prof to assoc prof, San Jose State Col, 58-65; opers analyst, Stanford Res Inst, 65-66; SCI PROF SPECIALIST APPL MATH, LOCKHEED MISSILES & SPACE CO, 66- *Mem:* AAAS; Am Math Soc; Soc Indust & Appl Math; Math Asn Am; Asn Comput Mach. *Res:* Real variables; elementary number theory; numerical analysis. *Mailing Add:* 127 Belvue Dr Los Gatos CA 95030

RUGH, WILSON J(OHN), II, b Tarentum, Pa, Jan 16, 44. ELECTRICAL ENGINEERING. *Educ:* Pa State Univ, BS, 65; Northwestern Univ, MS, 67, PhD(elec eng), 69. *Prof Exp:* Asst prof, 69-74, ASSOC PROF ELEC ENG, JOHNS HOPKINS UNIV, 74- *Mem:* Inst Elec & Electronics Engrs; Soc Indust & Appl Math. *Res:* Systems and control theory. *Mailing Add:* Dept of Elec Eng Johns Hopkins Univ Baltimore MD 21218

RUGHEIMER, NORMAN MACGREGOR, b Charleston, SC, Feb 10, 30; m 58; c 2. PHYSICS. *Educ:* Col Charleston, BS, 50; Univ NC, PhD(physics), 65. *Prof Exp:* Instr physics, The Citadel, 57-59; asst prof, 64-68, assoc prof, 68-80, PROF PHYSICS, MONT STATE UNIV, 80-, ASST DEAN, COL LETTERS & SCI, 69- *Concurrent Pos:* Adv on energy to comnr higher educ, State of Mont, 75- *Mem:* Am Asn Physics Teachers. *Res:* Transmission and reflection coefficients and properties of thin superconducting films; holography. *Mailing Add:* Col of Letters & Sci Mont State Univ Bozeman MT 59715

RUH, EDWIN, b Westfield, NJ, Apr 22, 24; m 52; c 2. CERAMICS, CHEMISTRY. *Educ:* Rutgers Univ, BSc, 49, MSc, 53, PhD(ceramics, chem), 54. *Prof Exp:* Res engr, Harbison-Walker Refractories Co, 54-57; asst dir res, Garber Res Ctr, 57-70; dir res, 70-73; dir advan technol, 73-74; vpres res, Vesuvius Crucible Co, 74-76; SR LECTR & ASSOC HEAD DEPT METALL & MAT SCI, CARNEGIE-MELLON UNIV, 76- *Concurrent Pos:* Ed, Metall Trans, 78- *Honors & Awards:* Pace Award, Nat Inst Ceramic Engrs, 63. *Mem:* AAAS; fel Am Ceramic Soc; Nat Inst Ceramic Engrs; Am Inst Mining, Metall & Petrol Engrs; Brit Ceramic Soc. *Res:* Refractories and refractory technology; ceramics and refractories. *Mailing Add:* Dept of Metall & Mat Sci Carnegie-Mellon Univ Pittsburgh PA 15213

RUH, MARY FRANCES, b Chicago, Ill, July 18, 41; m 68; c 1. PHYSIOLOGY, ENDOCRINOLOGY. *Educ:* Marquette Univ, BS, 63, MS, 66, PhD(physiol), 69. *Prof Exp:* Instr pub health, Univ Mass, Amherst, 66-67; instr physiol, Univ Ill, Urbana, 69-71; asst prof, 71-76, ASSOC PROF PHYSIOL, SCH MED, ST LOUIS UNIV, 76- *Mem:* Am Soc Cell Biol; Am Physiol Soc; Am Soc Clin Path; Endocrine Soc; Sigma Xi. *Res:* Steroid and terpenoid hormone action; insect endocrinology; mammalian reproductive physiology. *Mailing Add:* Dept of Physiol St Louis Univ Sch of Med St Louis MO 63104

RUH, ROBERT, b Plainfield, NJ, Aug 2, 30; m 52; c 3. CERAMICS, MATERIALS SCIENCE. *Educ:* Rutgers Univ, BS, 52, MS, 53, PhD(ceramics), 60. *Prof Exp:* Res ceramist, Aerospace Res Labs, Wright-Patterson AFB, Ohio, 58-65 & Chem Res Labs, Commonwealth Sci & Indust Res Orgn, Australia, 65-66; res ceramist, Aerospace Res Labs, 66-67, res ceramist, Processing & High Temperature Mat Br, Air Force Mat Lab, 67-70, SR PROJ ENGR, PROCESSING & HIGH TEMPERATURE MAT BR, AIR FORCE MAT LAB, WRIGHT-PATTERSON AFB, 70- *Concurrent Pos:* Ian Potter Found fel, 65-66. *Mem:* Fel Am Ceramic Soc; Nat Inst Ceramic Engrs; Ceramic Educ Coun; fel Am Inst Chem. *Res:* Development of improved ceramic materials through fabrication, characterization and property studies. *Mailing Add:* Processing & High Temperature Mat Br Air Force Mat Lab AFWAL/MLLM Wright-Patterson AFB OH 45433

RUHE, CARL HENRY WILLIAM, b Wilkinsburg, Pa, Dec 1, 15; m 43, 74; c 3. MEDICAL ADMINISTRATION. *Educ:* Univ Pittsburgh, BS, 37, MD, 40. *Prof Exp:* From instr to assoc prof physiol & pharmacol, Sch Med, Univ Pittsburgh, 37-60; from asst dean to assoc dean, 55-60; from asst secy to secy, coun med educ, 60-76, group vpres 76, SR VPRES, AMA, 76- *Mem:* AAAS; Am Physiol Soc. *Res:* Human blood values; blood volume; hypothermia. *Mailing Add:* Am Med Asn 535 N Dearborn St Chicago IL 60610

RUHE, ROBERT VICTORY, b Chicago Heights, Ill, Nov 7, 18; m 43; c 3. GEOLOGY. *Educ:* Carleton Col, BA, 42; Iowa State Col, MS, 48; Univ Iowa, PhD(geol), 50. *Prof Exp:* From instr to asst prof geol, Iowa State Col, 46-51; geomorphologist, Soil Mission, Econ Coop Admin, Belgian Congo, 51-52; res geologist soil surv, Soil Conserv Serv, USDA, 53-70; PROF GEOL & DIR WATER RESOURCES RES CTR, IND UNIV, BLOOMINGTON, 70- *Concurrent Pos:* Geologist, Iowa Geol Surv, 47-51; Nat Res Coun fel, 50-51; vis prof, Cornell Univ, 58; prof, Iowa State Univ, 63-70; vis prof, Johns Hopkins Univ, 66-67; pres comn on paleopedol, Int Union Quaternary Res, 69-73; mem work group on exp basins, Nat Acad Sci, 71-75, mem panel on land burial radioactive wastes, 73- *Honors & Awards:* Kirk Bryan Award, Geol Soc Am, 74. *Mem:* Fel AAAS; fel Geol Soc Am; Soil Sci Soc Am; Int Asn Quaternary Res. *Res:* Geomorphology, quaternary geology; pedology; hydrogeology. *Mailing Add:* Water Resources Res Ctr Ind Univ Bloomington IN 47401

RUHLE, GEORGE CORNELIUS, b Kankakee, Ill, Feb 18, 00. PHYSICAL CHEMISTRY. *Educ:* Univ Ill, BS, 21, Univ Calif, PhD(phys chem), 25. *Prof Exp:* Instr chem, Univ Calif, 25-26; assoc prof, Univ Okla, 26-28; ranger, Yellowstone Nat Park, US Nat Park Serv, Wyo, 28-29; park naturalist, Glacier Nat Park, Mont, 29-40; chief naturalist, Crater Lake Nat Park, 41-42, 46-52 & Hawaii Nat Park, 52-59; chief int coop, 61-64; INT SPECIALIST,

US NAT PARK SERV, 64- *Concurrent Pos:* Ranger-naturalist, Yosemite Nat Park, Calif, 26-27; spec fel, Yale Univ, 40-41; mem asst proj nat parks & conserv, Nat Res Coun, Thailand & Indonesia, 59-60 & 70-77, Micronesia & Vietnam, 60, Guatemala, 70, NZ & Antarctica, 71-72, Siberia & Arctic, 78 & 79; consult nat parks, Int Union Conserv Nature & Natural Resources; mem, Nat Parks & Wildlife, Pac Sci Asn Am Comt for Joint Comn for Rural Reconstruction of Taiwan, 65; wildlife & cultural resources of the Southern Ryukyus for US Civil Admin of Ryukyu Islands, 65; del Sci Mus Ctr Planning Comn, Govt Korea, 66, spec adv, Korean Comn Conserv Nature, 66-; mem, Int Comn Nat Parks, 66-; spec adv, India, 69. *Mem:* Bot Soc S Africa; Wild Life Protection & Conserv Soc S Africa; Siam Soc. *Res:* Natural history; iodide method of separation of radium from carnotite ore; thermodynamic treatment of molten salt solutions; forest cover types; ornithology of Montana; glaciers and glacial recession in Glacier Park; enthnological methods; natural history sciences of the Pacific; volcanoes and volcanism. *Mailing Add:* Div of Int Park Affairs US Nat Park Serv Washington DC 20240

RUHLING, ROBERT OTTO, b Takoma Park, Md, Dec 3, 42; m 64; c 7. EXERCISE PHYSIOLOGY. *Educ:* Univ Md, BS, 64, MA, 66; Mich State Univ, PhD(phys educ), 70. *Prof Exp:* NIH trainee cardiovasc physiol, Inst Environ Stress, Univ Calif, Santa Barbara, 70-71, res physiologist, 71-72; asst prof, 72-78, assoc prof, 72-78, PROF EXERCISE PHYSIOL, COL HEALTH, UNIV UTAH, 78-, DIR HUMAN PERFORMANCE RES LAB, 80- *Concurrent Pos:* Mem Utah Gov's Adv Coun on Phys Fitness. *Mem:* Am Alliance Health, Phys Educ & Recreation; fel Am Col Sports Med; Sigma Xi; NY Acad Sci. *Res:* Investigate the effects of exercise and the environment on the cardiovascular, respiratory, muscular, and nervous systems of the mammalian body. *Mailing Add:* Dir Human Performance Res Lab Col of Health Univ of Utah Salt Lake City UT 84112

RUHMANN-WENNHOLD, ANN GERTRUDE, b Brooklyn, NY, June 12, 32; m 67; c 2. MEDICINE, ENDOCRINOLOGY. *Educ:* Seton Hill Col, BA, 54; State Univ NY Downstate Med Ctr, MD, 58. *Prof Exp:* Res asst radiobiol, 60-61; USPHS res fel, 61-63, from instr to assoc res prof anat, 65-78, res scientist med, 67-81, ASSOC RES PROF MED, UNIV UTAH, 78- *Mem:* Endocrine Soc; Am Fedn Clin Res. *Res:* Pituitary-adrenal physiology; mechanism of steroid action; brain mitochondrial respiration; metabolic effects of hypoxia and hyperoxia; cytochrome P-450; estrogen-androgen effects on corticosteroidogenesis; adrenocorticotropin; effect of steroids on fibroblast growth. *Mailing Add:* Endocrine Res Lab 401 12th Ave Salt Lake City UT 84103

RUHNKE, EDWARD VINCENT, b San Antonio, Tex, May 25, 28; m 49; c 4. PHYSICAL ORGANIC CHEMISTRY. *Educ:* St Mary's Col, Tex, BS, 48; Univ Tex, MA, 51; Tex A&M Univ, PhD(phys org chem), 54. *Prof Exp:* Res chemist, Esso Res Lab, 54-56; asst prof inorg & anal chem, Tex A&I Univ, 56-58, assoc prof inorg & org chem, 58-61, prof phys org chem, 61-81; RETIRED. *Concurrent Pos:* Consult, Nat Asn Standard Med Vocabulary, 62- *Mem:* Am Chem Soc. *Res:* Basic petrochemical research; molecular sieves; effect of structure on reactivity. *Mailing Add:* 508 Shelton Kingsville TX 78363

RUHNKE, LOTHAR HASSO, b Ger, Mar 2, 31; US citizen; m 59; c 2. ATMOSPHERIC PHYSICS. *Educ:* Tech Univ, Munich, MS, 55; Univ Hawaii, PhD(geosci), 69. *Prof Exp:* Res asst, Electrophys Inst, Munich, 54-57; res physicist, Meteorol Div, US Army Res & Develop Lab, Ft Monmouth, 57-61; res scientist, Appl Sci Div, Litton Indust Inc, 61-65; sci dir, Mauna Loa Observ, Nat Oceanic & Atmospheric Admin, Hawaii, 65-68, res physicist, Atmospheric Physics & Chem Lab, Environ Res Lab, 68-72; BR HEAD ATMOSPHERIC PHYSICS, NAVAL RES LAB, 72- *Concurrent Pos:* Mem several subcomns & working groups, Int Comn Atmospheric Elec, 63-, secy, 75- *Honors & Awards:* Outstandin Achievement Award, Nat Oceanic & Atmospheric Admin & NASA, 72. *Mem:* Am Geophys Union; Int Union Geophys & Geodesy. *Res:* Basic and applied research in atmospheric electricity, electrostatics, cloud physics, electrooptics propagation and marine meteorology; research management and administration in atmospheric physics. *Mailing Add:* 11208 Wedge Dr Reston VA 22090

RUIBAL, RODOLFO, b Cuba, Oct 27, 27; nat US; m; c 1. VERTEBRATE ZOOLOGY. *Educ:* Harvard Univ, AB, 50; Columbia Univ, MA, 52, PhD(zool), 55. *Prof Exp:* Instr biol, City Col NY, 52-54; from instr to assoc prof, 54-70, PROF ZOOL, UNIV CALIF, RIVERSIDE, 70- *Concurrent Pos:* Guggenheim fel, 70; res assoc, Smithsonian Inst; vis prof, Univ Chile, 68; vchmn, Nongame Adv Comt, Calif Dept Fish & Game. *Mem:* Soc Study Evolution; Am Soc Zool; Am Soc Ichthyol & Herpet. *Res:* Evolution and ecology. *Mailing Add:* Dept of Biol Univ of Calif Riverside CA 92521

RUINA, J(ACK) P(HILIP), b Rypin, Poland, Aug 19, 23; nat US; m 47; c 3. ELECTRICAL ENGINEERING. *Educ:* City Col, BS, 44; Polytech Inst Brooklyn, MEE, 49, DEE, 51. *Prof Exp:* From instr to assoc prof elec eng, Brown Univ, 50-54; res assoc prof, Control Systs Lab, Univ Ill, 54-59, res prof, Coord Sci Lab & prof elec eng, 59-63; vpres spec labs, 66-70, PROF ELEC ENG, MASS INST TECHNOL, 63- *Concurrent Pos:* Dep for res to Asst Secy Res & Eng, US Air Force, 59-60; asst dir defense res & eng, Off Secy Defense, 60-61; dir adv res projs agency, US Dept Defense, 61-63; pres, Inst Defense Anal, 64-66; mem gen adv comt, Arms Control & Disarmament Agency, 69-73; mem, Int Sci Radio Union; consult, various govt agencies; mem panel on telecommun, Nat Acad Eng; sr consult, Off Sci & Technol Policy, 77- *Honors & Awards:* Fleming Award, 62. *Mem:* Fel AAAS; fel Am Acad Arts & Sci; fel Inst Elec & Electronics Engrs; Inst Strategic Studies. *Res:* Statistical theory of noise; radar systems. *Mailing Add:* Dept Elec Eng Mass Inst Technol Cambridge MA 02139

RUIZ, CARL P, b Santa Barbara, Calif, Feb 1, 34; m 56; c 2. NUCLEAR CHEMISTRY. *Educ:* Univ Calif, Santa Barbara, BA, 56, Univ Calif, Berkeley, PhD(chem), 61. *Prof Exp:* Chemist, 61-69, tech specialist, 69-73, MGR RADIOL & PROCESS ENG, GEN ELEC CO, VALLECITOS

NUCLEAR CTR, 73- *Mem:* Am Chem Soc; Am Nuclear Soc; fel Am Inst Chem; Sigma Xi; AAAS. *Res:* Development of irradiated nuclear fuel measurement methods; Methods and systems for the non-destructive measurement of uranium fuel enrichment; spent nuclear fuel, radioisotope and nuclear reactor decontamination chemical process studies. *Mailing Add:* 38648 Kimbro St Fremont CA 94536

RUIZ-CERETTI, ELENA, b Mendoza, Arg, Nov 19, 33; wid. CARDIAC ELECTROPHYSIOLOGY. *Educ:* Univ Cuyo, MD, 59. *Prof Exp:* Sr instr physiol, Fac Med, Univ Cuyo, 65-68; from asst prof to assoc prof, 68-77, PROF BIOPHYS, FAC MED, UNIV SHERBROOKE, 77-, CHMN DEPT BIOPHYS, 78- *Concurrent Pos:* Res fel heart physiol, Fac Med, Univ Cuyo, 59-63; Arg Nat Coun Sci & Technol Invest fel, 60-62, grant, 66-67, fel heart electrophysiol, Univ Southern Calif, 63-65; Med Res Coun Ottawa grants, 67-; Que Heart Found grant, 69-; Can Heart Found fel, 69-70; Can Heart Found res scholar, 71-75. *Mem:* Int Soc Heart Res; Can Physiol Soc; Am Physiol Soc. *Res:* Electrical activity of the heart and ionic distribution; anoxia and ischemia; atrioventricular conduction; membrane impedance and cytoplasmic resistivity in skeletal and cardiac muscle. *Mailing Add:* Dept of Biophys Univ of Sherbrooke Fac of Med Sherbrooke PQ J1K 2R1 Can

RUKAVINA, NORMAN ANDREW, b Ft William, Ont, June 20, 37; m 60; c 4. SEDIMENTOLOGY. *Educ:* Univ Toronto, BA, 59; Univ Western Ontario, MSc, 61; Univ Rochester, PhD(geol), 65. *Prof Exp:* NSF grant fel & lectr basic mineral, Univ Rochester, 65-66; RES SCIENTIST, CAN CENTRE INLAND WATERS ENVIRON DEPT CAN, 66- *Concurrent Pos:* Ed, Proc Conf Great Lakes Res, 72-75; assoc ed, Geosci Can, 73-76 & J Great Lakes Res, 76- *Mem:* Sigma Xi; fel Geol Soc Am; Soc Econ Paleont & Mineral; Int Asn Gt Lakes Res; fel Geol Asn Can. *Res:* Nearshore sedimentology of the Great Lakes; lakeshore erosion; coastal geomorphology; particle size analysis. *Mailing Add:* Can Centre for Inland Waters PO Box 5050 Burlington ON L7U 4A6 Can

RUKHIN, ANDREW LEO, b Leningrad, USSR, Oct 1, 46; US citizen; m 73; c 2. STATISTICAL DECISION THEORY. *Educ:* Leningrad State Univ, MS, 67; Steklov Math Inst, PhD(math & statist), 70. *Prof Exp:* Res assoc, Steklov Math Inst, Acad Sci USSR, 70-74; assoc prof, 77-80, PROF STATIST, PURDUE UNIV, 82- *Concurrent Pos:* Lectr, Leningrad Technol Inst, 68; vis asst prof, Leningrad State Univ, 72; vis prof, Rome Univ, Italy, 77, Univ Mass, Amherst, 82. *Mem:* Inst Math Statist; Am Statist Asn. *Res:* Description of universal statistical estimaters; adaptive procedures for a finite parameter; characterizations of probability distributions. *Mailing Add:* Dept Statist Purdue Univ West Lafayette IN 47907

RULAND, NORMAN LEE, b Houston, Tex, Feb 26, 38. PHYSICAL CHEMISTRY. *Educ:* Rice Univ, BA, 61; Univ Houston, PhD(chem), 67. *Prof Exp:* Sr chemist prod technol, Monsanto Co, 66-69; SR RES CHEMIST, TENNECO CHEM INC, 69- *Mem:* Am Chem Soc. *Res:* Chemical kinetics; gas-liquid and gas-solid equilibria; organo-metallic pi-complexes; math modeling. *Mailing Add:* 4414 Aztec Pasadena TX 77504

RULE, ALLYN H, b New York, NY, June 18, 34; m 70; c 4. IMMUNOCHEMISTRY, BIOCHEMISTRY. *Educ:* Cent Conn State Col, BSA, 56; Boston Univ, PhD(biol), 65. *Prof Exp:* NIH fel biochem, Brandeis Univ, 65-66; asst prof immunochem & biochem, Boston Col, 66-74; res fel dermat & res assoc med, Sch Med, Tufts Univ, 74-77; ASSOC PROF GRAD DEPT BIOL, BOSTON COL, 77-; ASST PROF OBSTET-GYNEC, TUFTS UNIV SCH MED, 80- *Concurrent Pos:* Aid to Cancer res grant, 67-71; NASA res grant, 70-73; asst res prof, Mt Sinai Med Sch, 70-74. *Mem:* Am Asn Immunologists; AAAS; Path Soc. *Res:* Antigenic purification, characterization and haptenic inhibitions of glycoproteins from blood group substances, lymphocytes, muscle, skin, tumors, carcinoembryonic antigens as well as studies in immune response, suppression and autoimmunity. *Mailing Add:* Grad Dept of Biol Boston Col Chestnut Hill MA 02167

RULFS, CHARLES LESLIE, b St Louis, Mo, Oct 21, 20; m 42; c 5. ANALYTICAL CHEMISTRY, INORGANIC CHEMISTRY. *Educ:* Univ Ill, BS, 42; Purdue Univ, PhD(chem), 49. *Prof Exp:* Res chemist, Res Labs, Linde Air Prods Co Div, Union Carbide Corp, 42-45; from asst prof to assoc prof, 49-61, PROF CHEM, UNIV MICH, ANN ARBOR, 61- *Concurrent Pos:* Consult, Los Alamos Sci Lab, 60- *Mem:* Am Chem Soc. *Res:* Chemistry of technetium and rhenium; polarographic theory and applications; unusual oxidation levels; microanalytical techniques. *Mailing Add:* Dept of Chem Univ of Mich Ann Arbor MI 48109

RULIFFSON, WILLARD SLOAN, b Balaton, Minn, July 19, 18; m 41; c 2. BIOCHEMISTRY. *Educ:* Buena Vista Col, BS, 40; Univ Iowa, MS, 48, PhD(biochem), 53. *Prof Exp:* From asst prof chem to assoc prof biochem, 53-68, PROF BIOCHEM, KANS STATE UNIV, 68- *Mem:* AAAS; Am Chem Soc. *Res:* Radioiron transport; biochemical applications of mass spectrometry; monoamine oxidase enzymes and inhibitors. *Mailing Add:* W-35A Dept of Biochem Kans State Univ Manhattan KS 66502

RULIFSON, JOHNS FREDERICK, b Bellefontaine, Ohio, Aug 20, 41; m 64; c 2. INFORMATION SCIENCE. *Educ:* Univ Wash, BS, 66; Stanford Univ, PhD(comput sci), 73. *Prof Exp:* Res mathematician comput sci, Stanford Res Inst, 66-73; MEM RES STAFF COMPUT SCI, XEROX PALO ALTO RES CTR, 73- *Mem:* Asn Comput Mach. *Res:* Office automation, especially basic research on the role of written communications in managerial and office environments and the design and evaluation of computer systems that impact such communication. *Mailing Add:* Xerox Palo Alto Res Ctr 3333 Coyote Hill Rd Palo Alto CA 94304

RULIFSON, ROGER ALLEN, b Manchester, Iowa, Nov 13, 51; m 81. ANADROMONS FISHES, PENAEID SHRIMPS. *Educ:* Univ Dubuques, BS, 73; NC State Univ, MS, 75, PhD(marine sci eng), 80. *Prof Exp:* Res asst, NC Coop Fishery Res Unit, Dept Zool, NC State Univ, 73-75; leader fish distribution & vulnerability assessment task, Ecol Serv Group, Tex Instruments, Inc, 75-77; res asst, Dept Marine Sci, NC State Univ, 77-80, res assoc, NC Coop Fishery Res Unit, Dept Zool, 80-81; ASST PROF FISHERIES MARINE SCI FISHERIES, CTR ENVIRON SCI, UNITY COL, 81- *Concurrent Pos:* Consult, US Fish & Wildlife Serv, Fishery Resources, Region 4, Atlanta, Ga, 80-82. *Mem:* Am Fisheries Soc; Estuarine Res Fedn; Sigma Xi. *Res:* Behavioral ecologies of penaeid (commercial) shrimps and juvenile estuarine fishes; historical socio-economic importance of anadromous fishes; life history aspects of american shad (alosa sapidissima) and brown trout (solmo trutla). *Mailing Add:* Ctr Environ Sci Unity Col RR #78-Box 1 Unity ME 04988

RULON, KATHLEEN FRIEND, b Paterson, NJ, Mar 1, 49; m 76. IMMUNOLOGY, MICROBIOLOGY. *Educ:* Ohio Wesleyan Univ, BA, 71; Northwestern Univ, PhD(microbiol), 75. *Prof Exp:* Sr fel tumor immunol, Fred Hutchinson Cancer Res Ctr, Univ Wash, 75-76; RES FEL IMMUNOL, WEBB-WARING LUNG INST, UNIV COLO, 76- *Mem:* Sigma Xi; Am Soc Microbiol. *Res:* Tumor immunology; cell biology. *Mailing Add:* Webb-Waring Lung Inst Univ of Colo Med Ctr Denver CO 80220

RULON, RICHARD M, b Babylon, NY, Oct 29, 22; m 43; c 4. PHYSICAL CHEMISTRY, CERAMICS. *Educ:* Alfred Univ, BS, 43; Univ Pittsburgh, PhD(phys chem), 51. *Prof Exp:* Engr, Radio Corp Am, Pa, 43-45; teacher high sch, NY, 45-46; instr physics, Alfred Univ, 46-47; Atomic Energy Comn fel binary metal alloys, Univ Pittsburgh, 50-51; from sr engr to engr-in-charge, Sylvania Elec Prod Inc, Gen Tel & Electronics Corp, Mass, 51-60; res dir glass to metal seals, Hermetite Corp, 60-62; assoc prof, 62-67, PROF CHEM, ALFRED UNIV, 67- *Concurrent Pos:* Lectr & coordr, Northeastern Univ, 55-61; consult, D G O'Brien, Inc, Mass & Tetron, Inc, NY, 62-76 and others. mem comt nomenclature for electron-optical devices, Joint Comt Inst of Elec Eng & Inst Radio Eng, 57-60. *Mem:* Am Ceramic Soc; Electrochem Soc; Nat Inst Ceramic Eng. *Res:* Electroluminescent and electron optical devices; dielectric ceramic materials; glass to metal seals for electronic and hermetic devices. *Mailing Add:* Dept of Chem Alfred Univ Alfred NY 14802

RULON, RUSSELL ROSS, b Apr 26, 36; m 63; c 2. PHYSIOLOGY. *Educ:* Luther Col (Iowa), BA, 58; Univ Iowa, MS, 60, PhD(physiol), 61. *Prof Exp:* Instr physiol, Col Med, Univ Iowa, 61-63; asst prof, 63-72, PROF BIOL, LUTHER COL, IOWA, 72- *Concurrent Pos:* USPHS trainee, Med Sch, Univ Va, 69-70; vis scientist cardiol res, Mayo Clin, 75-76. *Mem:* Am Physiol Soc. *Res:* Muscle physiology; physiological ecology; electrophysiology; comparative physiology of neurogenic and myogenic hearts; environmental physiology; effect of toxic materials on heart metabolism. *Mailing Add:* Dept of Biol Luther Col Decorah IA 52101

RUMBAUGH, MELVIN DALE, b Pella, Iowa, Sept 13, 29; m 53; c 4. CROP BREEDING. *Educ:* Cent Col (Iowa), BS, 51; Univ Nebr, MS, 53, PhD(agron), 58. *Prof Exp:* Asst prof agron, Colo State Univ, 58-59; from asst prof to assoc prof, 59-70, PROF AGRON, S DAK STATE UNIV, 70- *Mem:* Crop Sci Soc Am; Am Soc Agron. *Res:* Biometrical genetics and breeding of plants, especially of Medicago sativa; utilization of legume species for improvement of range. *Mailing Add:* Dept of Plant Sci SDak State Univ Brookings SD 57006

RUMBLE, DOUGLAS, III, b Atlanta, Ga, June, 15, 42; m 67; c 2. METAMORPHIC PETROLOGY, STABLE ISOTOPE GEOCHEMISTRY. *Educ:* Columbia Col, NY, BA, 64; Harvard Univ, PhD(geol), 69. *Prof Exp:* Asst prof geol, Univ Calif, Los Angeles, 71-73; PETROLOGIST, GEOPHYS LAB, CARNEGIE INST WASH, 73- *Mem:* Mineral Soc Am; Am Geophys Union. *Res:* Nature of fluid-rock interaction during metamorphism through chemical thermodynamics and stable isotope geochemistry. *Mailing Add:* Geophys Lab 2801 Upton St NW Washington DC 20008

RUMBLE, EDMUND TAYLOR, III, b Philadelphia, Pa, Oct 26, 42; m 76. NUCLEAR ENGINEERING. *Educ:* US Naval Acad, BS, 65; Univ Calif, Los Angeles, MS, 71, PhD(nuclear eng), 74. *Prof Exp:* Mem staff reactor safety, 74-77, DIV MGR NUCLEAR MAT, SCI APPLNS, INC, 77- *Mem:* Am Nuclear Soc. *Res:* Reactor safety and performance. *Mailing Add:* Sci Applns Inc 5 Palo Alto Sq Suite 200 Palo Alto CA 94304

RUMBURG, CHARLES BUDDY, b Welch, WVa, Dec 12, 31; m 54; c 3. AGRONOMY. *Educ:* Colo State Univ, BS, 54; Rutgers Univ, MS, 56, PhD(farm crops), 58. *Prof Exp:* Res asst farm crops, Rutgers Univ, 54-58; res agronomist, Agr Res Serv, 58-70, supt, Colo Mountain Meadow Res Ctr, 70-77, AGRONOMIST, COOP STATE RES SERV, USDA, 77- *Concurrent Pos:* Fel, Ore State Univ, 65-66; assoc prof agron, Colo State Univ, 70-77. *Mem:* Am Soc Agron. *Res:* Quantity and quality of forage from native meadows; increasing the efficiency of nitrogen fertilizer. *Mailing Add:* Coop State Res Serv US Dept of Agr Washington DC 20250

RUMELY, JOHN HAMILTON, b New York, NY, Jan 14, 26; m 48; c 3. PLANT ECOLOGY, PLANT TAXONOMY. *Educ:* Oberlin Col, AB, 48; Wash State Univ, PhD(bot), 56. *Prof Exp:* Instr biol, Wash State Univ, 55-56; from asst prof to assoc prof, 56-65, PROF BOT, MONT STATE UNIV, 65-, CUR HERBARIUM, 73- *Mem:* AAAS; Bot Soc Am; Ecol Soc Am; Am Inst Biol Sci. *Res:* Flora of Montana; vegetation constitution and succession; plant life histories. *Mailing Add:* Dept of Biol Mont State Univ Bozeman MT 59715

RUMER, RALPH R, JR, b Ocean City, NJ, June 22, 31; m 53; c 4. CIVIL ENGINEERING, HYDRAULIC ENGINEERING. *Educ:* Duke Univ, BS, 53; Rutgers Univ, MS, 59; Mass Inst Technol, ScD(civil eng), 62. *Prof Exp:* Engr, Luken Steel Co, Pa, 53-54; instr civil eng, Rutgers Univ, 56-59; engr, Soil Conserv Serv, USDA, NJ, 57-59, res asst hydraul, Mass Inst Technol, 61-62, asst prof civil eng, 62-63; assoc prof eng, 63-69, actg head dept civil eng, 66-67, chmn dept, 67-74, prof, 69-76, PROF CIVIL ENG, STATE UNIV NY BUFFALO, 78- *Concurrent Pos:* Ford Found fel, 62-63; NIH res grant, 65-69; sr res fel, Calif Inst Technol, 70-71; prin tech consult, Lake Erie Wastewater Mgt Study, Buffalo Dist, US Army Corps Engrs, 73-; prof civil eng & chmn dept, Univ Del, 76-78. *Mem:* Am Soc Civil Engrs; Am Geophys Union; Explorers Club; Int Asn Hydraulic Res; Int Asn Gt Lakes Res. *Res:* Water resources; flow through porous media; sea water intrusion; lake dynamics; hydraulic modelling; hydraulic processes related to water quality control; ice engineering. *Mailing Add:* 821 Eggert Rd Buffalo NY 14226

RUMFELDT, ROBERT CLARK, b Shawinigan Falls, Que, Nov 28, 36; m 59; c 5. PHOTOCHEMISTRY, INORGANIC CHEMISTRY. *Educ:* Loyola Univ, Can, BSc, 59; Univ Alta, PhD(radiation chem), 63. *Prof Exp:* Gen Elec Res Found fel, Univ Leeds, 63-65; asst prof, 65-68, ASSOC PROF CHEM, UNIV WINDSOR, 68- *Mem:* Chem Inst Can. *Res:* Spectroscopy and photochemistry of inorganic systems. *Mailing Add:* Dept of Chem Univ of Windsor Windsor ON N9B 3P4 Can

RUMMEL, ROBERT EDWIN, b Port Carbon, Pa, Sept 1, 11. PHYSICAL CHEMISTRY. *Educ:* Maryville Col, AB, 33; Vanderbilt Univ, MS, 34, PhD(phys chem), 50. *Prof Exp:* Instr chem, Ga Inst Technol, 37-38; head dept sci, Pikeville Col, 38-42; asst prof, 46-63, ASSOC PROF CHEM, VANDERBILT UNIV, 63- *Concurrent Pos:* Mem res staff, Oak Ridge Nat Lab, 51, consult, 51- *Mem:* Am Chem Soc; Royal Soc Chem; Am Soc Mass Spectro; Electrochem Soc. *Res:* Application of mass spectrometric techniques; analytical chemistry procedures including stable isotope dilution techniques; corrosion and passivity; determination of structure; electronic instrumentation. *Mailing Add:* 1008 Milesdale Dr Nashville TN 37204

RUMMEL, ROBERT WILAND, b Dakota, Ill, Aug 4, 15; m 39; c 5. AERONAUTICAL ENGINEERING. *Educ:* Curtiss Wright Tech Inst, Dipl aero eng, 34. *Prof Exp:* Stress analyst, Hughes Aircraft Co, Calif, 35 & Lockheed Aircraft Corp, 36; detail designer, Aero Eng Corp, 36 & Nat Aircraft Co, 37; chief engr, Rearwin Aircraft Co, Mo, Ken Royce Eng Co & Rearwin Aircraft & Engines, 37-43; chief engr, Trans World Airlines, 43-46, vpres eng, 56-59, vpres planning & res, 59-69 & tech develop, 69-77; PRES, ROBERT W RUMMEL ASSOCS, INC, 77- *Concurrent Pos:* Mem comn on aircraft operating probs, NASA, 63-69, mem res comn on aeronaut, 69-70; mem panel on Supersonic Transport environ effects, Commerce Tech adv bd, 71-72; consult, NASA, 72- *Mem:* Nat Acad Eng; fel Am Inst Aeronaut & Astronaut (treas, 71-72); fel Soc Automotive Engrs (vpres, 56). *Res:* Aeronautical research relating to aircraft transport design and operations. *Mailing Add:* Robert W Rummel Assocs Inc PO Box 7330 Mesa AZ 85206

RUMMENS, F H A, b Eindhoven, Netherlands, May 20, 33; m 60; c 3. MOLECULAR SPECTROSCOPY, PHYSICAL CHEMISTRY. *Educ:* Univ Leiden, Drs, 58; Oxford Univ, Brit Coun bursary, 58; Eindhoven Technol Univ, DSc, 63. *Prof Exp:* Sci co-worker, Eindhoven Technol Univ, 59-67; vis prof chem, Univ Colo, 67; assoc prof, 67-72, PROF CHEM, UNIV REGINA, 72- *Concurrent Pos:* Niels Stensen fel, 63-64; Nat Res Coun Can fel, 64-65. *Mem:* Fel Chem Inst Can; Royal Netherlands Chem Soc; Spectros Soc Can; Int Soc Magnetic Resonance. *Res:* Nuclear magnetic resonance, infrared and ultra violet spectroscopy; structure of simple molecules; effects of medium on spectra; analytical spectroscopy. *Mailing Add:* Dept Chem Univ Regina Regina SK S4S 0A2 Can

RUMMERY, TERRANCE EDWARD, b Brockville, Ont, Nov 16, 37; m 67; c 2. SOLID STATE CHEMISTRY. *Educ:* Queen's Univ, Ont, BSc, 61, PhD(chem), 66. *Prof Exp:* Nat Res Coun Can overseas fel, Univ Col, Univ London, 66-67; assoc res scientist mat chem, Ont Res Found, 68-69; scientist phys chem, Airco Speer Res Labs, 69-71; assoc res officer phys chem, 71-76, sr res officer & head, Res Chem Br, 76-79, DIR, WASTE MGT DIV, WHITESHELL NUCLEAR RES ESTAB, ATOMIC ENERGY CAN LTD, 79- *Mem:* Chem Inst Can; Can Nuclear Soc. *Res:* Physical chemistry of power reactor coolant systems; basic science underlying nuclear waste management. *Mailing Add:* Box 418 Pinawa MB R0E 1L0 Can

RUMP, ELLIS SAMUEL, JR, b Hamilton, Ohio, Oct 2, 22; m 46; c 4. PHYSICAL CHEMISTRY. *Educ:* Amherst Col, BA, 46; Univ Del, MS, 53. *Prof Exp:* Anal head, Wyeth Labs Div, Am Home Prod Corp, 46-49; from jr anal chemist to sr anal chemist, 49-55, anal group leader, 55-56, asst mgr res opers, 56-59, admin mgr, 59-67, ASST ADMIN MGR RES, SMITH KLINE & FRENCH LABS, 67- *Mem:* AAAS; Am Chem Soc. *Res:* Structural determination of organic compounds by ultraviolet and infrared spectroscopy. *Mailing Add:* Smith Kline & French Labs 1500 Spring Garden St Philadelphia PA 19101

RUMPEL, MAX LEONARD, b WaKeeney, Kans, Mar 17, 36; m 61; c 2. INORGANIC CHEMISTRY. *Educ:* Ft Hays Kans State Col, AB, 57; Univ Kans, PhD(chem), 62. *Prof Exp:* From instr to assoc prof, 61-68, PROF CHEM, FT HAYS STATE UNIV, 68-, CHMN DEPT, 72- *Concurrent Pos:* Mem, NSF Res Partic Prog Col Teachers, Univ Colo, 65-66 & Wash State Univ, 71. *Mem:* Am Chem Soc; Sigma Xi. *Res:* Unusually low oxidation states of metals; electrochemistry; computer programming for chemistry; instrumentation. *Mailing Add:* Dept of Chem Ft Hays State Univ Hays KS 67601

RUMPF, JOHN L, b Philadelphia, Pa, Feb 21, 21; m 44; c 2. CIVIL ENGINEERING. *Educ:* Drexel Inst Technol, BS, 43; Univ Pa, MS, 54; Lehigh Univ, PhD, 60. *Prof Exp:* From instr to assoc prof civil eng, Drexel Inst Technol, 47-56; res instr, Lehigh Univ, 56-60; prof, Drexel Inst Technol, 60-64, head dept, 64-69; dean col eng technol, 69-76, V PRES ACAD AFFAIRS, TEMPLE UNIV, 76- *Concurrent Pos:* Chmn, Res Coun Riveted & Bolted Struct Joints, 65-71. *Mem:* Am Soc Civil Engrs; Am Soc Eng Educ; Nat Soc Prof Engrs. *Res:* Behavior of steel structures and their component parts and connections. *Mailing Add:* Conwell Hall Temple Univ Philadelphia PA 19122

RUMPF, R(OBERT) J(OHN), b Auburn, NY, July 31, 16; m 40. AERONAUTICAL ENGINEERING. *Educ:* Univ Notre Dame, BS, 39. *Prof Exp:* Design engr, Stinson Aircraft Co, 39-45 & Bendix Aviation Corp, 45-46; res engr, Univ Mich, 46-55; prin res engr, Ford Motor Co, 55-70; DIR

RES & DEVELOP, HAMILL MFG CO DIV, FIRESTONE TIRE & RUBBER CO, 70- *Mem:* Soc Automotive Engrs. *Res:* Aircraft development; guided missile, air defense and highway control systems; automotive safety; automotive restraint systems. *Mailing Add:* 37 Fisher Rd Grosse Pointe MI 48230

RUMSEY, VICTOR HENRY, b Devizes, Eng, Nov 22, 19; m 42; c 3. APPLIED PHYSICS. *Educ:* Cambridge Univ, BA, 41, DSc, 73; Tohoku Univ, Japan, PhD, 62. *Prof Exp:* Asst to sr sci officer, Sci Civil Serv, Gt Brit, 41-45; mem staff theoret physics, Atomic Energy Estab, 45-48; from asst prof to assoc prof elec eng, Ohio State Univ, 48-54; prof, Univ Ill, 54-57 & Univ Calif, Berkeley, 57-69; PROF APPL PHYSICS, UNIV CALIF, SAN DIEGO, 69- *Concurrent Pos:* Head, Antenna Lab, Ohio State Univ, 48-54; Guggenheim fel, 65. *Honors & Awards:* Liebmann Prize, Inst Elec & Electronics Eng, 62. *Mem:* Nat Acad Eng; fel Inst Elec & Electronics Eng; Am Astron Soc; Int Sci Radio Union. *Res:* Theory of electromagnetic waves; antennas; physics of atomic piles; wave propagation in a turbulent medium. *Mailing Add:* Dept Appl Physics & Info Sci Univ Calif San Diego La Jolla CA 92093

RUND, HANNO, b Schwerin, Ger. MATHEMATICS, MATHEMATICAL PHYSICS. *Educ:* Univ Cape Town, BSc, 47, PhD(math), 50; Univ Freiburg, Habil, 52. *Prof Exp:* Lectr appl math, Univ Cape Town, 49-51; docent math, Univ Bonn, 52-54; prof appl math, Univ Toronto, 54-56; prof & head dept math, Univ Natal, 56-60, dean sci, 57-60; res prof math, Univ South Africa, 61-66; prof & head dept pure math, Univ Witwatersrand, 67-69; prof & head dept appl math, Univ Waterloo, 70; head dept, 71-78, PROF MATH, UNIV ARIZ, 71- *Concurrent Pos:* Exhib 1851 scholar, Oxford Univ, 52; mem bd gov, Univ Durban, 60-69; vis prof, Univ Waterloo, 64, adj prof, 70-; vis prof, Univ Toronto, 65, Univ Ariz, 67 & Univ Witwatersrand, 80. *Mem:* Am Math Soc; Can Math Cong; Ger Math Asn; SAfrican Math Asn; SAfrican Acad Arts & Sci. *Res:* Differential geometry; calculus of variations; theory of relativity. *Mailing Add:* Dept of Math Univ of Ariz Tucson AZ 85721

RUND, JOHN VALENTINE, b Champaign, Ill, Mar 9, 38; m 61. INORGANIC CHEMISTRY. *Educ:* Univ Ill, BS, 59; Cornell Univ, PhD(chem), 62. *Prof Exp:* Asst prof, 63-69, ASSOC PROF CHEM, UNIV ARIZ, 69- *Mem:* Am Chem Soc; Royal Soc Chem. *Res:* Reaction mechanisms of coordination complexes; photochemistry; metalloenzyme models. *Mailing Add:* Dept of Chem Univ of Ariz Tucson AZ 85721

RUNDEL, PHILIP WILSON, b Palo Alto, Calif, Aug 7, 43; m 67. PLANT ECOLOGY, LICHENOLOGY. *Educ:* Pomona Col, BA, 65; Duke Univ, AM, 67, PhD(bot), 69. *Prof Exp:* Instr bot, Duke Univ, 68-69; asst prof pop & environ biol, 69-74, ASSOC PROF ECOL & EVOLUTIONARY BIOL, UNIV CALIF, IRVINE, 74- *Concurrent Pos:* Vis prof, Univ Chile, Santiago, 72 & Lehrstuhl Botanik II Univ, Wurzburg, WGer. *Mem:* AAAS; Ecol Soc Am; Am Bryol & Lichenological Soc. *Res:* Physiological plant ecology; lichenology. *Mailing Add:* Dept of Ecol & Evolutionary Biol Univ of Calif Irvine CA 92717

RUNDEL, ROBERT DEAN, b Palo Alto, Calif, Jan 9, 40. PHYSICS. *Educ:* Dartmouth Col, BA, 61; Univ Wash, PhD(physics), 65. *Prof Exp:* Res assoc physics, Culham Lab, Eng, 65-68; sr res assoc space sci, Rice Univ, 68-69, instr physics, 69-70, asst prof, 70-77, adj prof space physics & astron, 77-80; ASSOC PROF PHYSICS, MISS STATE UNIV, 80- *Concurrent Pos:* staff scientist, Johnson Space Ctr, NASA, 74-80. *Mem:* Am Asn Physics Teachers; Am Soc Photobiol; Sigma Xi. *Res:* Atomic collision physics. *Mailing Add:* Dept Physics Mississippi State Univ Mississippi State MS 39762

RUNDELL, CLARK ACE, b Verndale, Minn, Sept 1, 38; m 61; c 2. CLINICAL CHEMISTRY. *Educ:* St Cloud State Col, BS, 61; Univ NDak, MS, 63, PhD(phys chem), 66; Am Bd Clin Chem, dipl, 76. *Prof Exp:* Dept Defense res fel, Purdue Univ, Lafayette, 65-66; res chemist, W R Grace & Co, Clarksville, 66-73; res assoc, Univ Md Hosp, 73-75; CLIN CHEMIST, MAINE MED CTR, 75-, DIR CHEM, 80- *Mem:* Am Chem Soc; Am Asn Clin Chemists. *Res:* Enzymology catalysis; kinetics; data processing. *Mailing Add:* Dept Clin Path Maine Med Ctr Portland ME 04102

RUNDELL, HAROLD LEE, b Hurley, SDak, Dec 1, 22; m 47; c 1. ZOOLOGY. *Educ:* SDak State Col, BS, 52; Univ Iowa, PhD(zool), 57. *Prof Exp:* Assoc prof biol, Parsons Col, 57-59; assoc prof, 59-71, head dept, 59-81, PROF BIOL, MORNINGSIDE COL, 71- *Res:* Fine structure of animal parasites, chiefly tapeworms. *Mailing Add:* Dept of Biol Morningside Col Sioux City IA 51106

RUNDELL, MARY KATHLEEN, b Cleveland, Ohio, Nov 19, 46; m 76. MICROBIOLOGY, VIROLOGY. *Educ:* Univ Rochester, BA, 68; Case Western Reserve Univ, PhD(microbiol), 73. *Prof Exp:* Fel biochem, Univ Calif, Berkeley, 74; fel pharmacol, Case Western Reserve Univ, 74-75; fel microbiol, State Univ NY Stony Brook, 75-76; ASST PROF MICROBIOL, MED CTR, NORTHWESTERN UNIV, 76- *Concurrent Pos:* Nat Cancer Inst fel, 75-76 & res grant, 77-; Am Cancer Soc res grant, 76-77; NSF res grant, 80- *Mem:* Am Soc Microbiol; AAAS. *Res:* Molecular virology and viral genetics; viral transformation. *Mailing Add:* Dept of Microbiol-Immunol 303 E Chicago Ave Chicago IL 60611

RUNDLES, RALPH WAYNE, b Urbana, Ill, Sept 10, 11; m 36; c 4. INTERNAL MEDICINE. *Educ:* DePauw Univ, AB, 33; Cornell Univ, PhD(anat), 37; Duke Univ, MD, 40. *Prof Exp:* Asst & instr anat, Med Col, Cornell Univ, 33-37; intern, Univ Hosp, Univ Mich, 40-41; asst resident internal med, Med Sch, 41-42, resident, 42-43, instr, 43-45; assoc, 45-57, PROF MED, SCH MED, DUKE UNIV, 57-, DIR HEMATOL, 77- *Concurrent Pos:* Consult, NIH, Am Cancer Soc, Am Bur Med Advan China & Burroughs-Wellcome Co. *Mem:* Am Soc Hemat; Am Soc Clin Invest; AMA; Asn Am Physicians; Int Soc Hemat. *Res:* Hematology; cancer chemotherapy. *Mailing Add:* Duke Univ Med Ctr Box 3096 Durham NC 27710

RUNDO, JOHN, b London, Eng, Dec 27, 25; m 53; c 3. RADIOLOGICAL PHYSICS, HUMAN RADIOBIOLOGY. *Educ:* Univ London, BSc, 49, PhD(radiation biophys), 58. *Hon Degrees:* DSc, Univ London, 80. *Prof Exp:* Sci officer, Atomic Energy Res Estab, Harwell, UK, 49-51; sr sci officer, Finsen Lab, Copenhagen, Denmark, 52-54; prin sci officer, Atomic Energy Res Estab, Harwell, UK, 55-69; assoc scientist, 69-74, SR BIOPHYSICIST, ARGONNE NAT LAB, 74-, HEAD, CTR HUMAN RADIOBIOLOGY, 80- *Concurrent Pos:* Task group mem, Int Comn Radiol Units & Measurements, 65-70 & Int Comn Radiol Protection, 69-72; report comt chmn, Int Comn Radiol Units & Measurements, 77-; chmn sci comt, Nat Coun Radiation Protection & Measurements, 60 & 80-, consult, 73 & 81- *Mem:* Brit Inst Radiol; Health Physics Soc; Radiation Res Soc. *Res:* Metabolism and late biological effects of natural and artificial radioactivity in the human body. *Mailing Add:* Argonne Nat Lab 9700 S Cass Ave Argonne IL 60439

RUNECKLES, VICTOR CHARLES, b London, Eng, Sept 2, 30; m 53; c 2. PLANT PHYSIOLOGY. *Educ:* Univ London, BSc, 52, PhD(plant physiol), 55, Imp Col, dipl, 55. *Prof Exp:* Nat Res Coun Can fel plant physiol, Queen's Univ, Ont, 55-57; plant biochemist, Imp Tobacco Co Can Ltd, 57-63, res coordr, 63-65, asst mgr res, 65-66, mgr res & prod design, 66-69; PROF PLANT SCI & CHMN DEPT, UNIV BC, 69- *Concurrent Pos:* Lectr, Sir George Williams Univ. *Mem:* Am Soc Plant Physiol; Phytochem Soc NAm (secy, Plant Phenolics Group NAm, 61-66, vpres, 66, pres, 67, ed-in-chief, 69-); Am Phytopath Soc; Air Pollution Control Asn; AAAS. *Res:* Chemistry and metabolism of secondary plant products; pyrolysis of natural products; effects of air pollution on vegetation, cold hardiness. *Mailing Add:* Dept of Plant Sci Univ of BC Vancouver BC V6T 1W5 Can

RUNEY, GERALD LUTHER, b Charleston, SC, Feb 16, 38; m 69. PHYSIOLOGY. *Educ:* Col Charleston, BS, 60; Univ SC, MS, 63, PhD(physiol), 67. *Prof Exp:* Assoc prof biol, 67-80, PROF BIOL, THE CITADEL, 80- *Res:* Endocrine control of lipid metabolism. *Mailing Add:* Dept of Biol The Citadel Charleston SC 29409

RUNG, DONALD CHARLES, JR, b Rome, NY, Sept 12, 32; m 56; c 6. MATHEMATICAL ANALYSIS. *Educ:* Niagara Univ, BA, 54; Univ Notre Dame, MS, 57, PhD(math), 61. *Prof Exp:* From asst prof to assoc prof, 61-72, PROF MATH, PA STATE UNIV, UNIVERSITY PARK, 72-, HEAD DEPT, 75- *Concurrent Pos:* Sr Fulbright lectr, Nat Tsing Hua Univ, Taiwan, 67-68; vis sr res scientist, Carleton Univ, Ottawa, 74-75. *Mem:* Math Asn Am; Am Math Soc. *Res:* Complex function theory, especially cluster set theory. *Mailing Add:* Dept of Math McAllister Bldg Pa State Univ University Park PA 16802

RUNGE, RICHARD JOHN, b Buffalo, NY, Sept 30, 21; m 57; c 3. GEOPHYSICS. *Educ:* Univ Chicago, BS, 44; Univ NMex, MS, 49, PhD(physics), 52. *Prof Exp:* Asst math biophys, Univ Chicago, 43-45; instr physics, Univ NMex, 46-51, res assoc & asst prof, 51-53; asst prof, Univ Tulsa, 53-54; res engr, Stanolind Oil & Gas Co, 54-56; SR RES ASSOC PHYSICS, CHEVRON OIL FIELD RES CO, 56- *Mem:* Soc Explor Geophys; Soc Prof Well Log Analysts. *Res:* Theoretical geophysics; electromagnetic theory; applied mathematics; well logging; magnetic resonance. *Mailing Add:* Chevron Oil Field Res Co Box 446 La Habra CA 90631

RUNGE, THOMAS MARSCHALL, b Mason, Tex, Jan 24, 24; m 47; c 3. CARDIOVASCULAR DISEASES. *Educ:* Univ Tex Med Br Galveston, MD, 47; Am Bd Internal Med, dipl, 55; Am Bd Cardiovasc Dis, dipl, 67. *Prof Exp:* Intern med, Milwaukee County Gen Hosp, Wis, 47-48; resident, Hosp Univ Pa, 48-51; pvt pract, 53-68; PROF BIOMED ENG, UNIV TEX, AUSTIN, 68- *Concurrent Pos:* Fel, Hosp Univ Pa, 48-51; fel coun clin cardiol, Am Heart Asn, 68-; med dir, Noninvasive Cardiol, Brackenridge Hosp. *Mem:* AMA; Am Heart Asn; fel Am Col Physicians; fel Am Col Cardiol; fel Am Col Chest Physicians. *Res:* Cardiac devices; pulsatile flow cardiopulmonary bypass pumps; contrasting pharmacodynamic action of polar and nonpolar cardiac glycosides as delineated by noninvasive techniques. *Mailing Add:* 1313 Red River Suite 310 Austin TX 78701

RUNION, HOWELL IRWIN, b Ann Arbor, Mich, Oct 26, 33; m 59; c 2. ELECTROPHYSIOLOGY. *Educ:* Col of the Pac, BA, 56; Univ Ore, MS, 63; Univ Glasgow, PhD(electrophysiol), 68. *Prof Exp:* Chmn, Lincoln Unified Sch Dist, Calif, 58-65; res asst electrophysiol, Univ Glasgow, 65-68; res specialist, Univ Calif, Berkeley, 68-69; assoc prof, 69-80, PROF ELECTROPHYSIOL, SCH PHARM, UNIV OF THE PAC, 80- *Concurrent Pos:* Sci adv, Esten Corp, 60-65, Aquatic Res Inst, Port of Stockton, 63-65, & Etec Corp, 72- & Elec Hazards, Underwriters Med-Dent Inst Bd, 75-; mem bd dirs, Alcoholism Coun Calif, 77- & San Joaquin County Alcoholism Adv Bd, 78- *Mem:* Am Inst Biol Sci; Brit Soc Exp Biol. *Res:* Pathological mechanisms involved in atrophy and neuropathy in the chronic and acute alcoholic; neuromuscular mechanism and pathology of delirium tremens. *Mailing Add:* Electrophysiol Unit Sch Pharm Univ of the Pac Stockton CA 95207

RUNK, BENJAMIN FRANKLIN DEWEES, b Germantown, Pa, Apr 10, 06. BOTANY. *Educ:* Univ Va, BS, 29, MS, 30, PhD(biol), 39. *Prof Exp:* Instr sociol, Univ Wis, 30-33; econ analyst, Fed Emergency Relief Admin, 33-34; from asst prof to prof biol, 34-76, registr, 56-59, dean univ, 59-68, EMER PROF BIOL, UNIV VA, 76- *Concurrent Pos:* Instr, Marine Biol Lab, Woods Hole, Mass, 37-41. *Mem:* Fel AAAS; Bot Soc Am; Phycol Soc Am. *Res:* Morphology and taxonomy of the marine algae of the east coast of the United States. *Mailing Add:* Dept of Biol Gilmer Hall Univ of Va Charlottesville VA 22903

RUNK, ROBERT B, b Bridgeton, NJ, Jan 16, 39; m 65; c 1. CERAMICS. *Educ:* Rutgers Univ, BS, 61; State Univ NY Col Ceramics, Alfred Univ, PhD(ceramics), 66. *Prof Exp:* Asst prof metall & mat sci & sr staff mem, Mat Res Ctr, Lehigh Univ, 66-70; MEM RES STAFF, ENG RES CTR, WESTERN ELEC CO, INC, 70- *Mem:* Nat Inst Ceramic Engrs; Am Ceramic Soc. *Res:* Ceramic processing; ferroelectric ceramics; sintering; pressure sintering; oxide films; lattice dynamics; surface chemistry. *Mailing Add:* 58 Jacobs Creek Rd West Trenton NJ 08628

RUNKE, SIDNEY MORRIS, b Greenwood, SDak, Dec 23, 11; m 42; c 2. METALLURGY. *Educ:* Univ Ariz, BS, 35, MS, 36, EMet, 56. *Prof Exp:* Mill foreman, Cia Huanchaca de Bolivia, 36-39 & Coconino Copper Co, Ariz, 40; educ analyst, US Dept Educ, Washington, DC, 42; metall engr, US Bur Mines, Mo, 42-45 & Ark, 45-47, metallurgist, SDak, 47-56; mill supt, Rare Metals Corp Am, Ariz, 57-60, chief metallurgist, Utah, 60-62 & El Paso Natural Gas Co, 62-77; RETIRED. *Mem:* Am Inst Mining, Metall & Petrol Engrs. *Res:* Ore benefication, geology and chemistry. *Mailing Add:* 632 Londonderry Rd El Paso TX 79907

RUNKEL, RICHARD A, b La Crosse, Wis, Aug 21, 32; m 57; c 6. INDUSTRIAL PHARMACY. *Educ:* Univ Wis, BS, 58, PhD(pharm), 67. *Prof Exp:* Lectr, Univ Wis, 66; staff researcher, 67-75, HEAD DEPT DRUG METAB, SYNTEX RES, 75- *Mem:* Am Pharmaceut Asn; Pharmaceut Soc Japan. *Res:* Drug availability, disposition, metabolism, absorption and excretion. *Mailing Add:* Inst of Pharmacol & Drug Metab Syntex Res 3401 Hillview Ave Palo Alto CA 94304

RUNKLES, JACK RALPH, b San Angelo, Tex, Sept 4, 22; m 45; c 4. SOIL PHYSICS. *Educ:* Agr & Mech Col Tex, BS, 50, MS, 52; Iowa State Col, PhD(soil physics), 56. *Prof Exp:* Res assoc, Iowa State Col, 53-55; from asst prof to assoc prof soil physics, SDak State Col, 55-64; PROF SOIL SCI, TEX A&M UNIV, 64-, DIR WATER RESOURCES INST, 74- *Mem:* Soil Sci Soc Am; Am Soc Agron; Am Geophys Union. *Res:* Agronomy; soils; mathematics; physics; physical chemistry; hydrology. *Mailing Add:* Dept of Soil & Crop Sci Tex A&M Univ College Station TX 77843

RUNNALLS, NELVA EARLINE GROSS, b Omaha, Nebr, Feb 28, 30; m 52; c 2. NUCLEAR CHEMISTRY. *Educ:* Nebr State Teachers Col, Kearney, BS, 51; Mankato State Col, MS, 63; Univ Mo, PhD(chem), 66. *Prof Exp:* Asst prof chem, 66-70, chmn dept, 71, chmn fac senate, 71-72, dean grad col, 73-78, PROF CHEM, UNIV WIS-STOUT, 70-, DEAN CURRIC, RES & GRAD STUDIES, 78- *Mem:* Am Chem Soc; Am Phys Soc. *Res:* Radiochemical measurement of independent yields of fission products. *Mailing Add:* Grad Col Univ of Wis-Stout Menomonie WI 54751

RUNNALLS, O(LIVER) JOHN C(LYVE), b Barrie Island, Ont, June 26, 24; m 47; c 2. METALLURGY, CERAMICS. *Educ:* Univ Toronto, BASc, 48, MASc, 49, PhD(extractive metall), 51. *Prof Exp:* Res officer, Atomic Energy Can Ltd, 51-56, head fuel develop br, 56-59, rep to Nat Defence Col, 59-60, head res metall br, 61-67, asst dir chem & mat div, Chalk River Nuclear Labs, 67-69, chief liaison off, Europe, 69-71; sr adv uranium & nuclear energy, Dept Energy, Mines & Res, Can, 71-79; PROF ENERGY STUDIES, UNIV TORONTO, CAN, 79- *Concurrent Pos:* Dir, Ontario Hydro, Uranium Canada Ltd and Uranenz Exp & Mining Ltd. *Honors & Awards:* John McRae Award, Can Nuclear Asn, 80. *Mem:* Can Inst Mining & Metall; Can Nuclear Asn. *Res:* Energy systems with emphasis on uranium resources and nuclear energy development. *Mailing Add:* Fac Appl Sci & Eng Univ Toronto Toronto ON M5S 1A4 Can

RUNNELLS, DONALD DEMAR, b Eureka, Utah, Dec 30, 36; m 58; c 2. GEOCHEMISTRY, HYDROGEOLOGY. *Educ:* Univ Utah, BS, 58; Harvard Univ, MA, 60, PhD(geol), 64. *Prof Exp:* Geochemist, Shell Develop Co, 63-67; asst prof geol, Univ Calif, Santa Barbara, 67-69; assoc prof, 69-75, PROF GEOL SCI, UNIV COLO, BOULDER, 75- *Concurrent Pos:* Regional ed, J Explor Geochem, 71-75; consult, NMex Environ Improv Agency, 74-81, Los Alamos Sci Lab, 75-76 & Argonne Nat Lab, 80- *Mem:* Fel Geol Soc Am; Asn Explor Geochem; Soc Environ Geochem & Health; Soc Econ Paleont & Mineral; Nat Water Well Asn. *Res:* Geochemistry of natural waters; low-temperature geochemistry; water pollution; geochemical exploration; geochemistry of trace substances. *Mailing Add:* Dept of Geol Sci Univ of Colo Boulder CO 80309

RUNNELS, JOHN HUGH, b Mize, Miss, Mar 30, 35; m 60; c 3. ANALYTICAL CHEMISTRY. *Educ:* Univ Denver, BS, 63; Colo State Univ, PhD(chem), 68. *Prof Exp:* Chemist, W P Fuller & Co, 58-60 & Marathon Oil Co, 60-64; SECT SUPVR, ANAL BR, PHILLIPS PETROL CO, 68- *Mem:* Am Chem Soc. *Res:* Analytical methods for determining trace components in natural and synthetic materials. *Mailing Add:* Rm 232 RB-1 Phillips Petrol Co Bartlesville OK 74004

RUNNELS, LYNN KELLY, b Perry, Okla, June 9, 38; m 58; c 4. CHEMICAL PHYSICS, MATHEMATICAL PHYSICS. *Educ:* Rice Univ, BA, 60; Yale Univ, MS, 61, PhD(chem), 63. *Prof Exp:* From asst prof to assoc prof, 63-72, PROF CHEM, LA STATE UNIV, BATON ROUGE, 72- *Concurrent Pos:* Sloan Found fel, 66-70. *Mem:* Am Phys Soc; Am Chem Soc. *Res:* Statistical mechanics of liquids, dense gases and surface-adsorbed phases; theory of phase transitions; theory of liquid crystals; properties of ice. *Mailing Add:* Dept of Chem La State Univ Baton Rouge LA 70803

RUNNELS, ROBERT CLAYTON, b Houston, Tex, Oct 19, 35; m 61; c 3. METEOROLOGY. *Educ:* Univ Houston, BS, 60; Tex A&M Univ, MS, 62, PhD(meteorol), 68. *Prof Exp:* Space scientist planetary atmospheres, Johnson Spacecraft Ctr, NASA, Houston, 65-66; instr, 66-68, ASST PROF METEOROL, TEX A&M UNIV, 68- *Mem:* Sigma Xi; AAAS; Am Geophys Union; Am Meteorol Soc. *Res:* Air pollution; science education; radar and urban meteorology. *Mailing Add:* Dept Meteorol Tex A&M Univ College Station TX 77843

RUNNER, MEREDITH NOFTZGER, b Schenectady, NY, Jan 7, 14; m 41; c 6. EMBRYOLOGY. *Educ:* Ind Univ, AB, 37, PhD(zool), 42. *Prof Exp:* Instr zool, Univ Conn, 42-46; Finney-Howell fel, Jackson Mem Lab, 46-48, res assoc, 48-57, staff scientist, 57-62; chmn dept, 62-63, dir inst develop biol, 66-71, PROF BIOL, UNIV COLO, BOULDER, 62- *Concurrent Pos:* Res biologist, Roswell Park Mem Inst, 55-56; prog dir develop biol, NSF, 59-62, mem panel develop biol, 62-64; mem study sect cell biol, NIH, 64-68, human embryol & develop, 69-73; mem breast cancer task force, 75-78. *Mem:* AAAS; Genetics Soc Am; Am Soc Zool; Am Asn Anat; Teratol Soc (pres,

67). *Res:* Transplantation of embryonic primordia in mammals; transplantation and explantation of the mouse ovum; physiology of reproduction and hormonal balance in the mouse; mechanism of action of teratogenic agents; genetics of development; prenatal development; cause of congenital deformity. *Mailing Add:* Dept of Molecular Univ of Colo Boulder CO 80302

RUNQUIST, OLAF A, b Lohrville, Iowa, Apr 11, 31; m 51; c 4. ORGANIC CHEMISTRY, CHEMICAL EDUCATION. *Educ:* Iowa State Univ, BS, 52; Univ Minn, PhD(chem), 56. *Prof Exp:* From instr to asst prof org chem, Col St Thomas, 55-57; asst prof, 57-73, prof org chem, 73-77, PROF CHEM, HAMLINE UNIV, 77- *Concurrent Pos:* Consult, Minn Mining-Rayette, Inc, 56-57; instr, Exten Div, Univ Minn, 58-59. *Mem:* Am Chem Soc. *Res:* Chemistry of glycosylamines; base strengths of amines. *Mailing Add:* Dept of Chem Hamline Univ St Paul MN 55104

RUNSER, RICHARD HENRY, b Erie, Pa, July 4, 29; m 54; c 5. PHYSIOLOGY, MEDICINE. *Educ:* Gannon Col, AB, 51; Univ Okla, MD, 59; Am Bd Anesthesiol, dipl. *Prof Exp:* Assoc anesthesiologist & asst cardiologist, Mary Imogene Bassett Hosp, Cooperstown, 64-66, asst dir proprietary prod res, Hoffmann-La Roche Inc, NJ, 66-68; staff mem, Wallace Labs Div, Carter-Wallace, Inc, 69-73; asst dir med pharmacol, 73-77, assoc dir clin pharmacol, Hoffmann-La Roche, Inc, 77-80; MED DIR, INT DIV, BRISTOL-MYERS CO, 80- *Concurrent Pos:* Res fel, Cardiopulmonary Lab, Mary Imogene Bassett Hosp, Cooperstown, 63-65; asst physician, Columbia-Presby Med Ctr, 66- *Mem:* Fel Am Col Chest Physicians. *Res:* Clinical pharmacology; pulmonary physiology. *Mailing Add:* Int Div Bristol Myers Co 345 Park Ave New York NY 10022

RUNSTADLER, PETER WILLIAM, JR, b San Francisco, Calif, Jan 19, 34. FLUID DYNAMICS. *Educ:* Stanford Univ, BA, 55, MS, 56, PhD, 61. *Prof Exp:* Teaching asst mech eng, Stanford Univ, 58, res assoc, 60-61; vpres res & develop, 68-75, VPRES & TECH DIR, CREARE PROD INC, 75- *Concurrent Pos:* Adj prof, Thayer Sch Eng, Dartmouth Col, 68- *Mem:* Am Soc Mech Engrs. *Mailing Add:* Creare Inc PO Box 71 Hanover NH 30755

RUNYAN, JOHN WILLIAM, JR, b Memphis, Tenn, Jan 23, 24; m 49; c 2. INTERNAL MEDICINE. *Educ:* Washington & Lee Univ, AB, 44; Johns Hopkins Univ, MD, 47; Am Bd Internal Med, dipl, 55. *Prof Exp:* Intern, Johns Hopkins Hosp, 47-48; resident internal med, Albany Hosp, 48-49, chief resident, 49-50; res assoc & fel metab dis, Thorndike Mem Lab, Harvard Med Sch, 50-53; from instr to asst prof, Albany Med Col, 53-60; from assoc prof to prof med, 60-73, chief sect endocrinol, 64-73, PROF COMMUNITY MED & CHMN DEPT, COL MED, UNIV TENN, MEMPHIS, 73-, DIR, DIV HEALTH CARE SCI, 72-, PROG DIR GERONT, 80- *Concurrent Pos:* Clin dir, Albany Med Ctr Group Clin, 59-60; consult, Memphis Vet Admin Hosp, 62- *Honors & Awards:* John D Rockefeller III Award Pub Serv Health, 77; Rosenthal Award, Am Col Physicians, 80; Upjohn Award, Am Diabetes Asn, 81. *Mem:* Am Diabetes Asn; fel Am Col Physicians; Am Fedn Clin Res. *Res:* Endocrinology and metabolism. *Mailing Add:* Dept Community Med Col Med Univ Tenn Memphis TN 38163

RUNYAN, THORA J, b Lemont Furnace, Pa, Sept 11, 31; m 54; c 2. NUTRITION. *Educ:* Univ Idaho, BS, 61; Harvard Univ, DSc(nutrit), 68. *Prof Exp:* Res assoc nutrit, Sch Pub Health, Harvard Univ, 62-63; asst prof, 68-75, ASSOC PROF FOOD & NUTRIT, IOWA STATE UNIV, 75- *Res:* Effects of age, sex and exercise on nutrient metabolism in experimental animals. *Mailing Add:* Dept Food & Nutrit Iowa State Univ Ames IA 50010

RUNYAN, WILLIAM SCOTTIE, b Merrill, Wis, June 24, 31; m 54; c 2. NUTRITION, CELL BIOLOGY. *Educ:* Univ Idaho, BS, 60, MS, 62; Harvard Univ, DSc(nutrit), 68. *Prof Exp:* Res asst tissue cult, Harvard Univ, 61-63; asst prof food & nutrit, 68-74, Nutrit Found future leader grant, 70-71, ASSOC PROF FOOD & NUTRIT, IOWA STATE UNIV, 74- *Concurrent Pos:* Mem, Am Heart Asn. *Mem:* Tissue Cult Asn; NY Acad Sci. *Res:* Relationships between nutritional status and physical activity; diet and coronary disease. *Mailing Add:* Dept of Food & Nutrit Iowa State Univ Ames IA 50011

RUOF, CLARENCE HERMAN, b Hummelstown, Pa, Sept 6, 19; m 45; c 2. CHEMISTRY. *Educ:* Gettysburg Col, BA, 41; Haverford Col, MS, 42; Pa State Univ, PhD(org chem), 48. *Prof Exp:* Asst chem, Haverford Col, 41-42 & Pa State Univ, 42-48; mem staff, Coal Res Lab, Carnegie Inst Technol, 48-54; sr fel, Mellon Inst, 54-60; staff scientist, 60-69, PRIN STAFF ENGR & SUPVR FUELS & LUBRICANTS, FORD MOTOR CO, 69- *Mem:* Soc Automotive Engrs; Am Soc Testing & Mat; Am Chem Soc; Sigma Xi. *Res:* Steroids; high octane gasoline components; aromatic acids from coal; structure of coals; plastics; automotive lubricants. *Mailing Add:* Eng & Res Staff Ford Motor Co Box 2053 Dearborn MI 48121

RUOFF, ARTHUR LOUIS, b Ft Wayne, Ind, Sept 17, 30; m 54; c 5. PHYSICAL CHEMISTRY. *Educ:* Purdue Univ, BS, 52; Univ Utah, PhD(phys chem), 55. *Prof Exp:* From asst prof to assoc prof eng mat, 55-65, PROF MAT SCI & APPL PHYSICS, CORNELL UNIV, 65 , DIR & CHAIRED PROF, 77- *Concurrent Pos:* NSF sci fac fel & vis assoc prof, Univ Ill, 61-62. *Mem:* Fel Am Phys Soc. *Res:* High pressures; very high pressures; nature of imperfections in solids; transport phenomena in solids; deformation properties of solids; audio-tutorial techniques of instruction. *Mailing Add:* Dept of Mat Sci & Eng Cornell Univ Ithaca NY 14853

RUOFF, WILLIAM (DAVID), b Reading, Pa, Apr 4, 40; m 60; c 3. ORGANIC CHEMISTRY. *Educ:* Albright Col, BS, 62; Univ Del, MS, 65, PhD(chem), 67. *Prof Exp:* From asst prof to assoc prof, 66-74, PROF CHEM, FAIRMONT STATE COL, 74-, CHMN DIV SCI, 68- *Res:* Physical organic and synthetic organic chemistry. *Mailing Add:* Div of Sci Fairmont State Col Fairmont WV 26554

RUOTSALA, ALBERT P, b Morse Twp, Minn, Sept 16, 26; m 50; c 3. MINERALOGY. *Educ:* Univ Minn, BA, 52, MS, 55; Univ Ill, PhD, 62. *Prof Exp:* Jr geologist, Bear Creek Mining Co, 52-54; geologist, C&NW Rwy, 55-56; instr geol, Tex Tech Col, 56-57; asst prof, Tex Western Col, 57-60 & Northern Ill Univ, 62-64; from asst prof to assoc prof, 64-74, PROF MINERAL, MICH TECHNOL UNIV, 74- *Mem:* AAAS; Geochem Soc; Am Geophys Union; Mineral Soc Am; Geol Soc Am. *Res:* Clay mineralogy; igneous and metamorphic petrology; economic geology; mineralogy and chemistry of soils. *Mailing Add:* Dept of Geol Mich Technol Univ Houghton MI 49931

RUPAAL, AJIT S, b Sangrur, Panjab, India, June 25, 33; m 63; c 1. NUCLEAR PHYSICS. *Educ:* Panjab Univ, India, BSc, 54, MSc, 55; Univ BC, PhD(nuclear physics), 63. *Prof Exp:* Sr res scholar physics, Panjab Univ, 56-57; lectr, Ramgarhia Col, Panjab, 55-56; from asst prof to assoc prof, 64-73, PROF PHYSICS, WESTERN WASH UNIV, 74- *Concurrent Pos:* Nat Res Coun Can fel, Chalk River Nuclear Labs, 63-64. *Mem:* Am Asn Physics Teachers; Can Asn Physicists. *Res:* Neutron gamma angular correlations and gamma branching ratios in C; interpretations of Fresnel's equations; neutron time-of-flight spectrometer; positron transmission in thin foils; negative work function of positrons in metals; electrical breakdown of ceramic insulators. *Mailing Add:* Dept of Physics Western Wash Univ Bellingham WA 98225

RUPERT, CLAUD STANLEY, b Porterville, Calif, Feb 24, 19; m 54; c 2. BIOPHYSICS. *Educ:* Calif Inst Technol, BS, 41; Johns Hopkins Univ, PhD(physics), 51. *Prof Exp:* Eng trainee & sr detail draftsman, Lockheed Aircraft Corp, 41-42; jr instr physics, Johns Hopkins Univ, 46-50, res asst to Prof Strong, 50-52, Am Cancer Soc fel biophys, 52-54, asst prof, 54-57, res assoc, Sch Hyg & Pub Health, 57-58, from asst prof to assoc prof, 58-65; dean natural sci & math, 75-80, PROF BIOL, UNIV TEX, DALLAS, 65- *Concurrent Pos:* USPHS sr res fel, 58-65; lab guest, Inst Microbiol, Copenhagen, Denmark, 61-62; mem impact stratospheric change comt, Nat Res Coun, 75-79. *Honors & Awards:* Finsen Medal, Int Comn Photobiol, 64. *Mem:* AAAS; Biophys Soc; Radiation Res Soc; Am Soc Photobiol. *Res:* Infection and transformation of cells by nucleic acids; cell biology; photobiology; photoenzymology; radiation biology. *Mailing Add:* Prog in Biol PO Box 688 Richardson TX 75080

RUPERT, EARLENE ATCHISON, b McCalla, Ala, July 22, 21; m 51; c 3. PLANT GENETICS, TAXONOMY. *Educ:* Huntingdon Col, AB, 41; Univ Ala, Tuscaloosa, MA, 43; Univ Va, PhD(biol), 46. *Prof Exp:* Nat Res Coun fel, Harvard Univ, 46-47; Rockefeller Found fel, Mex Agr Prog, Mexico City, 47-48; from asst prof to assoc prof bot, Univ NC, Chapel Hill, 48-51; res assoc & lectr agron, Univ Calif, Davis, 70-74; assoc prof, 74-78, PROF AGRON & SOILS, CLEMSON UNIV, 78- *Mem:* Am Inst Biol Sci; Bot Soc Am; Genetics Soc Am; Genetics Soc Can; Torrey Bot Club. *Res:* Interspecific hybridization among Leguminosae plant cytogenetics and cytotaxonomy; tissue culture systems for forage legumes. *Mailing Add:* Dept Agron & Soils Clemson Univ Clemson SC 29631

RUPERT, GERALD BRUCE, b Akron, Ohio, Aug 23, 30; m 54; c 2. GEOPHYSICS. *Educ:* Ind Univ, BS, 56, MA, 58; Univ Mo-Rolla, PhD(geophys), 64. *Prof Exp:* Sr seismic computer, Texaco, Inc, 57-60; from asst instr to instr mining engr, Univ Mo-Rolla, 60-64, asst prof geophys, 64-66; res geophysicist, Western Geophys Co, 66-67, mgr, Milano Digital Ctr, Italy, 67-69, sr seismic analyst, 69-74; assoc prof rock mech res & mining eng, 69-74, SR INVESTR ROCK MECH & EXPLOR RES CTR, 74-, PROF GEOPHYSICS & CHMN DEPT GEOL & GEOPHYSICS, UNIV MO-ROLLA, 76- *Mem:* Soc Explor Geophys; Am Geophys Union; Seismol Soc Am; Earthquake Eng Res Inst. *Res:* Exploration geophysics; digital filtering; rock mechanics, particularly wave propagation; earthquake mechanisms; viscoelasticity. *Mailing Add:* Dept Geol & Geophysics Univ Mo Rolla MO 65401

RUPERT, JOHN PAUL, b Delphos, Ohio, Oct 14, 46; m 68; c 2. POLYMER SCIENCE. *Educ:* Heidelberg Col, BS, 68; Akron Univ, PhD(polymer sci), 75. *Prof Exp:* Tech supvr eng, Goodyear Tire & Rubber Co, 68-72; fel chem, Inst Polymer Sci, Akron Univ, 75; chemist polymer physics, Union Carbide Corp, 75-76, sr chemist polyurethane raw mat facia develop, 76-78; SR RES CHEMIST NEW APPLN URETHANE TECHNOL, BASF WYANDOTTE, 78- *Mem:* Am Chem Soc. *Res:* Effect of polymerization variables on anionic polymerizations, polymer characterization and structure-property and rheology-property relationships of engineering thermoplastics; nuclear magnetic resonance of polymers. *Mailing Add:* 22774 Foxcraft Rd Woodhaven MI 48183

RUPERT, JOSEPH PAUL, b Pittsburgh, Pa, Sept 19, 42; m 65; c 2. PHYSICAL CHEMISTRY. *Educ:* Carnegie-Mellon Univ, BS, 64; Univ Pittsburgh, PhD(phys chem), 69. *Prof Exp:* From jr fel to sr fel phys chem, Mellon Inst, 66-74; sr res assoc, 74, MGR MINERAL SYNTHESIS LAB, BAROID DIV, NL INDUSTS, INC, 74- *Mem:* Catalysis Soc. *Res:* Thermodynamic and transport properties of aqueous electrolyte solutions; hydrothermal synthesis of zeolites and clay minerals; colloid chemistry of clay minerals, characterization of rheological control agents; heterogeneous catalysis; electron microscopy. *Mailing Add:* NL Industries Inc PO Box 1675 Houston TX 77001

RUPF, JOHN ALBERT, JR, b Wichita, Kans, Apr 8, 39; m 60; c 3. ELECTRICAL ENGINEERING. *Educ:* Univ Kans, BSEE, 61; Mass Inst Technol, MSEE & EE, 64; Purdue Univ, Lafayette, PhD(elec eng), 69. *Prof Exp:* Instr elec eng, Purdue Univ, Lafayette, 64-69; asst prof, 69-72, ASSOC PROF ELEC ENG & RES ASSOC, BUR CHILD RES, UNIV KANS, 72- *Mem:* Acoust Soc Am; Inst Elec & Electronics Engrs; Inst Noise Control Eng. *Res:* Speech perception, analysis and synthesis; human factors engineering; digital signal processing; noise control. *Mailing Add:* Dept of Elec Eng Univ of Kans Lawrence KS 66045

RUPLEY, JOHN ALLEN, b Brooklyn, NY, July 15, 33; m 60; c 1. PROTEIN CHEMISTRY, ENZYME CHEMISTRY. *Educ:* Princeton Univ, AB, 54; Univ Wash, PhD(biochem), 59. *Prof Exp:* NIH fel, Cornell Univ, 59-61; from asst prof to prof chem, 61-78, PROF BIOCHEM, UNIV ARIZ, 78- *Concurrent Pos:* Consult, Fel Panel, NIH, 68-70 & Biochem Study Sect, 71-75; consult, W R Grace & Co, 68-; NIH spec fel, Oxford Univ, 70; mem biochem chem carc panel, Am Cancer Soc, 72-76; mem pub affairs comt, Fedn Am Soc Exp Biol, 74-77; hon assoc mem, Inst Josef Stefan, Yugoslavia, 74-; co-chmn proteins, Gordon Conf, 83. *Mem:* Am Chem Soc; Am Soc Biol Chemists; AAAS; Am Inst Chemists; NY Acad Sci. *Res:* Correlation of protein structure and properties; mechanism of action of enzymes; thermochemistry. *Mailing Add:* Dept Biochem Univ of Ariz Tucson AZ 85721

RUPP, FRANK ADOLPH, b Syracuse, NY, Apr 16, 23; m 46; c 5. MICROBIOLOGY. *Educ:* Syracuse Univ, BS, 48, MS, 51, PhD, 60. *Prof Exp:* Res scientist microbiol, Bristol Labs, Inc, 52-57 & Biol Res Lab, Colgate-Palmolive Co, 60-66; group leader microbiol, Thomas J Lipton Inc, Englewood Cliffs, 66-78; DIR LABS, WELLS LABS, JERSEY CITY. *Mem:* Am Soc Microbiol; Inst Food Technologists. *Res:* Physiology. *Mailing Add:* Wells Lab 25-27 Lewis Ave Jersey City NJ 07306

RUPP, JOHN JAY, b Archbold, Ohio, Sept 28, 40; m 63; c 2. INORGANIC CHEMISTRY. *Educ:* Ohio Univ, BS, 62; Northwestern Univ, PhD(chem), 67. *Prof Exp:* Asst prof, 66-75, ASSOC PROF CHEM, ST LAWRENCE UNIV, 75- *Concurrent Pos:* NSF instrnl equip prog grant, 69-71. *Mem:* Am Chem Soc. *Res:* Preparative and physical inorganic chemistry, especially unusual Lewis acid-base addition compounds. *Mailing Add:* Dept of Chem St Lawrence Univ Canton NY 13617

RUPP, NELSON WOODWARD, b Springfield, Ohio, Aug 22, 17; m 43; c 2. DENTAL RESEARCH. *Educ:* Denison Univ, BA, 39; Ohio State Univ, DDS, 43; Georgetown Univ, MS, 55. *Prof Exp:* Dent officer, US Navy Dent Corps, 43-69; RES ASSOC DENT MAT, AM DENT ASN HEALTH FOUND RES UNIT, NAT BUR STAND, 69- *Mem:* Am Dent Asn. *Res:* Am Acad Oper Dent; Am Acad Gold Foil Operators. Res: Direct filling materials, especially correlation of laboratory data and clinical, in vivo, experience with emphasis on adaptation of restoration to tooth, wear characteristics, recurrent decay, loss of contour, gingival health and esthetics. *Mailing Add:* Am Dent Asn Health Found Nat Bur of Stand Washington DC 20234

RUPP, RALPH RUSSELL, b Saginaw, Mich, Apr 12, 29; m 55; c 2. AUDIOLOGY, SPEECH PATHOLOGY. *Educ:* Univ Mich, BA, 51, MA, 52; Wayne State Univ, PhD(audiol, speech path), 64. *Prof Exp:* Speech & hearing consult, Detroit Pub Schs, Mich, 52-59; exec dir, Detroit Hearing Ctr, 59-62; assoc audiol, Henry Ford Hosp, 62-65; PROF SPEC EDUC & AUDIOL, SPEECH & HEARING SCI, SCH EDUC, UNIV MICH, ANN ARBOR, 65- *Concurrent Pos:* Consult audiol, C S Mott Children's Health Ctr, Mich, 66-, Ann Arbor Vet Admin Hosp, 67-, St Joseph Mercy Hosp, Ann Arbor, 67 & Dept Hearing Speech & Lang, Kenny-Mich Rehab Found, Pontiac Gen Hosp. *Mem:* Fel Am Speech & Hearing Asn. *Res:* Effect of excessively loud rock 'n roll music on the human hearing mechanisms; improvement of hearing efficiency of the elderly; audiological assessment techniques; language ability of hearing-impaired children; speech audiometry; auditory processing. *Mailing Add:* Communicative Disorders Clin 1111 E Catherine Ann Arbor MI 48109

RUPP, W DEAN, b Archbold, Ohio, Aug 24, 38; m 62; c 1. MOLECULAR GENETICS, GENETIC ENGINEERING. *Educ:* Oberlin Col, AB, 60; Yale Univ, PhD(pharmacol), 65. *Prof Exp:* Res assoc radiobiol, 65-69, asst prof, 69-74, assoc prof, 74-81, PROF THERAPEUT RADIOL, MOECULAR BIOPHYSICS & BIOCHEM, SCH MED, YALE UNIV, 81- *Concurrent Pos:* Res assoc biol chem, Harvard Univ, 67-68. *Mem:* Biophys Soc; Radiation Res Soc; Am Soc Microbiol. *Res:* Cloning of genes and characterization of enzymes involved in DNA repair; expression of proteins from cloned genes. *Mailing Add:* Dept Molecular Biophys & Biochem Yale Univ Sch Med New Haven CT 06510

RUPP, WALTER H(OWARD), b Pittsburgh, Pa, Dec 22, 09; m 37; c 3. CHEMICAL ENGINEERING. *Educ:* Univ Pittsburgh, BS, 30. *Prof Exp:* Jr engr, Standard Oil Co, NJ, 30-36, group head, Esso Res & Eng Co, 36-44, asst div head, 44-49, supv engr, 49-54, tech adv, 54-56, staff engr, 56-62, head tech info ctr, 62-68; PRES, HYLO CO, 68- *Concurrent Pos:* Independent consult, 68- *Mem:* Am Inst Chem Engrs. *Res:* Petroleum refining; design engineering; air pollution; advanced information systems for engineers. *Mailing Add:* 359 Dogwood Way Mountainside NJ 07092

RUPPEL, EARL GEORGE, b Milwaukee, Wis, Nov 10, 32; m 58; c 3. PLANT PATHOLOGY, VIROLOGY. *Educ:* Univ Wis-Milwaukee, BS, 58; Univ Wis-Madison, PhD(plant path), 62. *Prof Exp:* Wis Alumni Res Found-Am Cancer Soc res grant, 62-63; plant pathologist, Tropic & Subarctic Res Br, Crops Res Div, Sci & Educ Admin-Agr Res, 63-65, PLANT PATHOLOGIST, AGR RES SERV, USDA, 65-, MEM AFFIL FAC, 77- *Concurrent Pos:* Fac affil & grad fac, Colo State Univ, 71- *Mem:* Am Phytopath Soc; Mycol Soc Am; Am Soc Sugar Beet Technol; Int Soc Plant Path. *Res:* Epidemiology of sugarbeet diseases; physiological and biochemical nature of disease resistance; physiology and properties of pathogens; breeding for disease resistance in sugarbeet. *Mailing Add:* Crops Res Lab Colo State Univ Ft Collins CO 80523

RUPPEL, EDWARD THOMPSON, b Ft Morgan, Colo, Oct 26, 25; m 56; c 4. GEOLOGY. *Educ:* Univ Mont, BA, 48; Univ Wyo, MA, 50; Yale Univ, PhD(geol), 58. *Prof Exp:* Geologist, 48-71, GEOLOGIST, CENT REGIONAL BR, US GEOL SURV, 71- *Mem:* Geol Soc Am; Soc Econ Geologists. *Res:* Structural geology; economic geology; geomorphology. *Mailing Add:* US Geol Surv M2 913 Box 25046 Fed Ctr Denver CO 80225

RUPPEL, HANS MAX, b Frankfurt, Ger, June 4,34; US citizen; m 56; c 3. THEORETICAL PHYSICS. *Educ:* Harvard Univ, BA, 56; Yale Univ, MS, 60, PhD(physics), 63. *Prof Exp:* STAFF MEM, LOS ALAMOS SCI LAB, 64- *Mem:* Am Phys Soc. *Res:* Nucleon-nucleon and electron-atom scattering. *Mailing Add:* Los Alamos Sci Lab Los Alamos NM 87544

RUPPEL, ROBERT FRANK, b Detroit, Mich, June 2, 25; m 48; c 2. ENTOMOLOGY. *Educ:* Mich State Col, BS, 48; Ohio State Univ, MS, 50, PhD(entom), 52. *Prof Exp:* Res asst, Mich State Col, 48; from asst entomologist to entomologist, Rockefeller Found, Columbia Univ, 52-62; res biologist, Niagara Chem Div, FMC Corp, 62; assoc prof, 63-68, liaison agr proj, 66-67, PROF ENTOM, MICH STATE UNIV, 68- *Concurrent Pos:* Tech dir, Entom Prog, Dept Agr Res, Govt Colombia, 58-62; res assoc, Univ Calif, 60. *Mem:* AAAS; Entom Soc Am; Am Inst Biol Sci. *Res:* Economic entomology; insect ecology; chemical control; taxonomy. *Mailing Add:* Dept of Entomol Mich State Univ East Lansing MI 48823

RUPPEL, THOMAS CONRAD, b Pittsburgh, Pa, June 30, 30; m 57; c 4. PHYSICAL CHEMISTRY. *Educ:* Duquesne Univ, BS, 52; Univ Pittsburgh, BS, 59, MS, 68. *Prof Exp:* Res asst, Heat Insulation Fel, Mellon Inst, 52-53 & Phys Chem Dept, 53-57, res assoc, Food Packaging Fel, 57-58 & Protective Coatings Fel, 58-60; chemist, Res Ctr, Koppers Co, Inc, 60-63; sr res asst water pollution, Grad Sch Pub Health, Univ Pittsburgh, 63-65; res chemist, 65-76, CHEM ENGR, DEPT ENERGY, 76- *Mem:* Am Inst Chemists; Am Chem Soc; Am Inst Chem Engrs; AAAS. *Res:* Thermal diffusion; physical adsorption at elevated pressure; chemistry of gaseous non-disruptive electrical discharges; chemical reaction engineering; thermodynamic coal conversion process calculations; environmental engineering and regulations. *Mailing Add:* US Dept of Energy PO Box 10940 Pittsburgh PA 15236

RUPPRECHT, HANS S, physics, see previous edition

RUPPRECHT, KEVIN ROBERT, b Trenton, NJ, Apr 14, 55; m 79; c 1. MOLECULAR GENETICS, GENETIC ENGINEERING. *Educ:* Cornell Univ, BS, 76; Univ Notre Dame, MS, 80, PhD(microbiol), 81. *Prof Exp:* RES ASSOC, UNIV CHICAGO, 81- *Mem:* Am Soc Microbiol; AAAS. *Res:* Discerning the role of the Ecoli K12 gene lon in capsule production and cell division using recombinant DNA techniques. *Mailing Add:* Dept Microbiol Univ Chicago 920 E 58th St Chicago IL 60637

RUSAY, RONALD JOSEPH, b New Brunswick, NJ, Dec 21, 45; m 67; c 2. ORGANIC CHEMISTRY, BIOLOGICAL CHEMISTRY. *Educ:* Univ NH, BA, 67, MS, 69; Ore State Univ, PhD(org chem, oceanog), 76. *Prof Exp:* Teacher chem, Bridgton Acad, 71-73; Am Chem Soc-Petrol Res Fund res fel, Ore State Univ, 74-76; res chemist synthesis, 76-80, BUS ANALYST, STAUFFER CHEM CO, 81- *Mem:* AAAS; Am Chem Soc; Sigma Xi. *Res:* Development of organic compounds of potential agricultural pharmaceutical importance. *Mailing Add:* 1200 S 47th St Richmond CA 94804

RUSCELLO, DENNIS MICHAEL, b Washington, Pa, Sept 2, 47; m 68; c 2. SPEECH PATHOLOGY. *Educ:* Calif State Col, BS, 69; WVa State Univ, MS, 72; Univ Ariz, PhD(speech path), 77. *Prof Exp:* Speech clinician speech path, Allegheny Intermediate 3, Pittsburgh, Pa, 69-74; res assoc, Univ Ariz, 74-77; asst prof, 77-80, ASSOC PROF SPEECH PATH, WVA UNIV, 80- *Concurrent Pos:* WVa Univ Found, Inc grant, 77-78; abstracter, Cleft Palate J, 77- *Mem:* Am Speech & Hearing Asn; Am Cleft Palate Asn; AAAS. *Res:* Investigation of speech problems exhibited by young children and persons with cranio-facial anomalies. *Mailing Add:* Dept Speech Path & Audiol WVa Univ Morgantown WV 26506

RUSCH, DONALD HAROLD, b Appleton, Wis, Dec 22, 38; m 65; c 1. WILDLIFE ECOLOGY, VERTEBRATE BIOLOGY. *Educ:* Univ Wis-Madison, BS, 62, PhD(wildlife ecol, zool), 70; Utah State Univ, MS, 65. *Prof Exp:* Res specialist birds, Man Dept Natural Resources, 71-72, actg chief wildlife res, 72-73; asst leader, 73-74, LEADER WIS COOP WILDLIFE RES UNIT, US FISH & WILDLIFE SERV, 74- *Concurrent Pos:* Asst prof, Dept Wildlife Ecol, Univ Wis, 73-79, assoc prof, 79- *Mem:* Wildlife Soc; Ecol Soc; Sigma Xi. *Res:* Population ecology; vertebrate predation; waterfowl migration; grouse ecology; population indices; analysis of wildlife habitat. *Mailing Add:* Wis Coop Wildlife Res Unit Univ of Wis Madison WI 53706

RUSCH, HAROLD PAUL, b Merill, Wis, July 15, 08; m 40, 79; c 2. ONCOLOGY. *Educ:* Univ Wis, BA, 31, MD, 33. *Prof Exp:* Intern, Wis Gen Hosp, 33-34; instr physiol, Med Sch, 34-40, Bowman fel, 35-36, res assoc med, 36-37, Bowman fel, 37-41, from asst prof to assoc prof oncol, 41-45, chmn dept, 41-46, prof oncol, 45-79, dir, McArdle Lab Cancer Res, 46-72, EMER PROF ONCOL, UNIV WIS-MADISON, 79- *Concurrent Pos:* Mem nat adv cancer coun, NIH, 45-58, mem adv panel cancer chemother, Nat Serv Ctr, 57-61; mem comt on growth, Nat Res Coun, 49-53; ed-in-chief, Cancer Res, 50-65; mem comn cancer res, Int Union Against Cancer, 58-66; mem, President Kennedy's Comt Heart Dis & Cancer, 61; nat panel consults, Conquest of Cancer, US Senate, 70; mem, Nat Cancer Adv Bd, 72-74; dir, Wis Clin Cancer Ctr, 72-78. *Honors & Awards:* Nat Award, Am Cancer Soc, 72. *Mem:* Hon mem Am Cancer Soc; Am Asn Cancer Res (pres, 54); Soc Exp Biol & Med; Am Soc Cell Biol; fel Am Acad Arts & Sci. *Res:* Carcinogenic action of ultraviolet rays; dietary factors that modify carcinogenesis; effect of caloric restriction on tumor formation; stages in tumor development; growth and differentiation in myxomycetes. *Mailing Add:* McArdle Lab for Cancer Res Univ of Wis Madison WI 53706

RUSCH, WILBERT H, SR, b Chicago, Ill, Feb 19, 13; m 37; c 5. BIOLOGY, GEOLOGY. *Educ:* Ill Inst Technol, BS, 34; Univ Mich, MS, 52; Eastern Mich Univ, ScS, 69. *Hon Degrees:* LLD, Concordia Sem, Mo, 75. *Prof Exp:* Instr music & math, Concordia Teachers Col, Nebr, 32-33; instr physics & math, Concordia Col, Ind, 37-46, assoc prof biol, 46-57; assoc prof, Concordia Teachers Col, Nebr, 57-60, prof biol & geol, 60-63; div chmn, 63-73 & 74-75, actg pres, 73-74, acad dean, 75-77, prof biol & geol, 63-80, EMER PROF BIOL & GEOL, CONCORDIA LUTHERAN COL, MICH, 80- *Concurrent Pos:* Kellogg Found fel, 73. *Mem:* Nat Asn Biol Teachers; Nat Asn Geol Teachers; Nat Sci Teachers Asn; fel Creation Res Soc. *Mailing Add:* Dept of Biol & Geol Concordia Lutheran Col Ann Arbor MI 48104

RUSCHAK, KENNETH JOHN, b Homestead, Pa, March 3, 49; m 78; c 1. CHEMICAL ENGINEERING. *Educ:* Carnegie-Mellon Univ, BS, 71; Univ Minn, PhD(chem eng), 74. *Prof Exp:* RES SCIENTIST, EASTMAN KODAK CO, 74. *Mem:* Am Inst Chem Engrs. *Res:* Capillary hydrodynamics, perturbation methods, and numerical simulation of fluid flow with applications to coating technology. *Mailing Add:* 236 Wimbledon Rd Rochester NY 14617

RUSCHMEYER, ORLANDO R, b Stewart, Minn, Feb 27, 25; m 51; c 2. PUBLIC HEALTH BIOLOGY, AQUATIC BIOLOGY. *Educ:* Univ Minn, Minneapolis, BA, 51, MS, 56, PhD(environ health), 65. *Prof Exp:* Asst microbiol, 52-56, instr pub health biol, 59-65, ASST PROF PUB HEALTH BIOL, UNIV MINN, MINNEAPOLIS, 66- *Concurrent Pos:* Consult biologist, Int Joint Comn Boundary Waters of US & Can, 61-62. *Mem:* AAAS; Am Soc Limnol & Oceanog; Am Soc Microbiol; Int Asn Theoret & Appl Limnol. *Res:* Transformations of organic compounds by soil microflora; limnology of western Lake Superior; water pollution biology; environmental microbiology. *Mailing Add:* 1112 Mayo Mem Bldg Univ Minn Sch Pub Health Minneapolis MN 55455

RUSH, BENJAMIN FRANKLIN, JR, b Honolulu, Hawaii, Jan 14, 24; m 48; c 2. SURGERY. *Educ:* Univ Calif, AB, 44; Yale Univ, MD, 48. *Prof Exp:* Res asst, Sloan-Kettering Div, Med Col, Cornell Univ, 54-57; instr surg, Sch Med, Johns Hopkins Univ, 57-59, asst prof, 59-62; from assoc prof to prof, Col Med, Univ Ky, 62-69; prof, 69-71, JOHNSON & JOHNSON PROF SURG, COL MED & DENT NJ, NEWARK, 71-, CHMN DEPT, 69- *Concurrent Pos:* Resident, Mem Ctr Cancer & Allied Dis, 53-57; asst chief surg, Baltimore City Hosps, 59-62; consult, Nat Cancer Plan, Nat Cancer Inst. *Mem:* Am Fedn Clin Res; fel Am Col Surgeons; Am Cancer Soc; Am Asn Cancer Educ (pres); Am Surg Asn. *Res:* Fluid balance and renal physiology in relation to surgery; surgical oncology. *Mailing Add:* NJ Med Sch 100 Bergen St Newark NJ 07103

RUSH, CECIL ARCHER, b Dillwyn, Va, Apr 14, 17; m 57; c 1. MICROCHEMISTRY. *Educ:* Col William & Mary, BS, 38. *Prof Exp:* Anal chemist, Chem Res Labs, 40-44, microchemist, 44-50, supvr microanal lab, 50-60, CHIEF MICROCHEM LAB, CHEM RES LABS, EDGEWOOD ARSENAL, 60- *Mem:* Am Microchem Soc; Am Chem Soc; Sigma Xi; Am Crystallog Asn. *Res:* Analytical chemistry; crystallography; chemical microscopy; chemical warfare agents. *Mailing Add:* 1410 Northgate Rd Baltimore MD 21218

RUSH, CHARLES KENNETH, b Toronto, Ont, Jan 15, 21; m 46; c 4. MECHANICAL ENGINEERING. *Educ:* Queen's Univ, Ont, BSc, 44; McGill Univ, Dipl, 62; Carleton Univ, Can, MEng, 63. *Prof Exp:* Res engr, Nat Res Coun Can, 44-63; assoc prof mech eng, 63-71, PROF MECH ENG, QUEEN'S UNIV, ONT, 71- *Mem:* Am Soc Eng Educ; assoc fel Can Aeronaut & Space Inst. *Res:* Aircraft icing; aerodynamics of ducted flow; energy utilization. *Mailing Add:* Dept of Mech Eng Queen's Univ Kingston ON K7L 3N6 Can

RUSH, CHARLES MERLE, b Philadelphia, Pa, Oct 10, 42; m 64; c 2. IONOSPHERIC PHYSICS. *Educ:* Temple Univ, BA, 64; Univ Calif, Los Angeles, PhD(meteorol), 67. *Prof Exp:* Staff scientist, Space Systs Div, Avco Corp, Mass, 67-69; res physicist, Air Force Cambridge Res Labs, 69-77; MEM STAFF, NAT OCEANIC & ATMOSPHERIC ADMIN, 77- *Mem:* Am Meteorol Soc; Am Geophys Union. *Res:* Dynamics and structure of the earth's ionized atmosphere. *Mailing Add:* Nat Oceanic & Atmospheric Admin OT/1ts 325 Broadway Boulder CO 80302

RUSH, DAVID EUGENE, b Carthage, Mo, Mar 5, 43; m 66; c 1. MATHEMATICS. *Educ:* Southwest Mo State Col, BSEd, 65; Western Wash State Col, MS, 68; La State Univ, Baton Rouge, PhD(math), 71. *Prof Exp:* High sch teacher, Mo, 65-67; res prof, 71-77, ASSOC PROF MATH, UNIV CALIF, RIVERSIDE, 77- *Mem:* Am Math Soc; Math Asn Am. *Res:* Commutative algebra; algebraic geometry. *Mailing Add:* Dept of Math Univ of Calif Riverside CA 92502

RUSH, FRANCIS EUGENE, b Iowa Co, Iowa, Oct 16, 31; m 54; c 3. GEOLOGY. *Educ:* Iowa State Univ, BS, 55, MS, 57. *Prof Exp:* Geologist, US Geol Surv, 56, Phillips Petrol Co, 57-58, Sinclair Oil & Gas Co, 58-59 & US Geol Surv, 59-63; assoc prof geol, Trenton State Col, 62-63; geologist, 63-67, hydrologist, 67-75, PROJ CHIEF, UTAH GEOTHERMAL EXPLOR, WATER RESOURCES DIV, US GEOL SURV, 75- *Res:* Great Basin hydrology; quantitative hydrologic-budget analysis; ground water recharge-discharge relations; geothermal and hydrothermal exploration. *Mailing Add:* US Geol Surv 8002 Fed Bldg Salt Lake City UT 84138

RUSH, FRANK E(DWARD), JR, b Washington, Pa, July 25, 21; m 44; c 5. CHEMICAL ENGINEERING. *Educ:* Washington & Jefferson Col, BA, 43; Mass Inst Technol, BS, 44; Univ Del, MChE, 53. *Prof Exp:* Res engr, Eng Res Lab, Exp Sta, 46-53, res proj engr, 53-55, res proj supvr, 55-56, res supvr, 56-61, res assoc, 61-63, chem eng consult, Eng Serv Div, 63-68, sr consult, Eng Dept, 68-76, PRIN CONSULT, ENG DEPT, E I DU PONT DE NEMOURS & CO, INC, 76- *Concurrent Pos:* Adj prof, Univ Del, 71-81. *Mem:* Am Chem Soc; Am Inst Chem Engrs. *Res:* Diffusional operations; mass transfer. *Mailing Add:* 8 Briar Lane Newark DE 19711

RUSH, JAMES E, b Warrensburg, Mo, July 18, 35; m 58; c 1. ORGANIC CHEMISTRY. *Educ:* Cent Mo State Univ, BS, 57; Univ Mo, PhD(org chem), 62. *Prof Exp:* Asst ed, Org Index Ed Dept, Chem Abstr Serv, Am Chem Soc, 62-65, asst head chem info procedures dept, 65-68; from asst prof to assoc prof comput & info sci, Ohio State Univ, 68-73; DIR RES & DEVELOP, OCLC, INC, 73- *Concurrent Pos:* Ed, Chem Lit, 70-73; adj prof comput & info sci, Ohio State Univ, 73- *Honors & Awards:* Best Paper Award, Am Soc Info Sci, 71. *Mem:* Sigma Xi; Am Chem Soc; Am Soc Info Sci. *Res:* Organoboron compounds; organometallic and coordination chemistry; stereochemistry; information storage and retrieval. *Mailing Add:* OCLC Inc 1125 Kinnear Rd Columbus OH 43212

RUSH, JOHN EDWIN, JR, b Birmingham, Ala, Aug 11, 37; m 63; c 4. THEORETICAL PHYSICS. *Educ:* Birmingham-Southern Col, BS, 59; Vanderbilt Univ, PhD(physics), 65. *Prof Exp:* From instr to asst prof physics, Univ of the South, 64-67; asst prof, 67-68, chmn dept, 68-72, ASSOC PROF PHYSICS, UNIV ALA, HUNTSVILLE, 68- *Mem:* Am Phys Soc; Am Asn Physics Teachers. *Res:* Molecular collision theory. *Mailing Add:* 804 Ward Ave Huntsville AL 35801

RUSH, JOHN JOSEPH, b Brooklyn, NY, Apr 20, 36; m 61. SOLID STATE PHYSICS, PHYSICAL CHEMISTRY. *Educ:* St Francis Col, NY, BS, 57; Columbia Univ, MA, 58, PhD(phys chem), 62. *Prof Exp:* Asst, Columbia Univ, 57-62; phys chemist, 62-71, CHIEF NEUTRON-SOLID STATE PHYSICS SECT, NAT MEASUREMENTS LAB, NAT BUR STANDARDS, 71- *Concurrent Pos:* Guest scientist, Solid State Sci Div, Argonne Nat Lab, 62-65. *Mem:* AAAS; Am Phys Soc. *Res:* Study of molecular solids and hydrogen in metals by thermal neutron scattering and other spectroscopic techniques; vibrations and rotations in condensed systems; structure; phase transitions. *Mailing Add:* Div 566 0 Nat Measurements Lab Nat Bur of Standards Washington DC 20234

RUSH, KENT RODNEY, b Quakertown, Pa, Sept 5, 38; m 59; c 3. ORGANIC CHEMISTRY. *Educ:* Franklin & Marshall Col, BS, 60; Univ Minn, PhD(org chem), 63. *Prof Exp:* Res chemist, Distillation Prod Indust Div, 63-65, RES ASSOC RES LABS, EASTMAN KODAK CO, 65- *Mem:* Am Chem Soc. *Res:* Chemistry of nitrogen heterocycles, polyenes; carotenoids; photographic chemistry. *Mailing Add:* Res Labs Eastman Kodak Co 1669 Lake Ave Rochester NY 14650

RUSH, MILTON CHARLES, phytopathology, see previous edition

RUSH, RICHARD MARION, b Bristol, Va, Dec 5, 28; m 55; c 2. PHYSICAL CHEMISTRY. *Educ:* Princeton Univ, AB, 49; Univ Va, MS, 52, PhD(chem), 54. *Prof Exp:* Asst chem, Mass Inst Technol, 53-54; asst prof, Haverford Col, 54-56; CHEMIST, OAK RIDGE NAT LAB, 56- *Mem:* AAAS; Am Chem Soc; Am Nuclear Soc. *Res:* Physical chemistry; inorganic solution chemistry; thermodynamics of electrolyte solutions; environmental impact assessment. *Mailing Add:* Energy Div Oak Ridge Nat Lab Oak Ridge TN 37830

RUSH, STANLEY, b New York, NY, June 17, 20; m 52; c 1. ELECTRICAL ENGINEERING. *Educ:* Brooklyn Col, BA, 42; Syracuse Univ, MEE, 58, PhD(elec eng), 62. *Prof Exp:* Design engr, RCA Victor Div, Radio Corp Am, 46-47; supvry electronic scientist, Rome Air Develop Ctr, US Air Force, 47-57; instr elec eng, Syracuse Univ, 57-62; assoc prof, 62-67, PROF ELEC ENG, UNIV VT, 67- *Mem:* Inst Elec & Electronics Engrs; NY Acad Sci. *Res:* Current flow in body from heart and brain generators; interpretation of electrocardiogram on physical basis; electro physiology of the heart; tissue impedance at gross and cellular level; electromagnetic field theory. *Mailing Add:* Dept of Elec Eng Univ of Vt Burlington VT 05401

RUSHFORTH, CRAIG KNEWEL, b Ogden, Utah, Sept 4, 37; m 58; c 5. ELECTRICAL ENGINEERING. *Educ:* Stanford Univ, BS, 58, MS, 60, PhD(elec eng), 62. *Prof Exp:* Res asst radio propagation, Stanford Univ, 58-59; res engr, Stanford Res Inst, 63; asst prof elec eng, Utah State Univ, 62-66; assoc prof, Mont State Univ, 66-72, prof, 72-73; PROF ELEC ENG, UNIV UTAH, 73- *Concurrent Pos:* Lectr, Stanford Univ, 63; consult panel synthetic aperture optics, Nat Acad Sci, 67; mem staff, Int Defense Analyses, 67-68. *Mem:* Inst Elec & Electronics Engrs. *Res:* Communication theory; digital signal processing. *Mailing Add:* Dept Elec Eng Univ Utah Salt Lake City UT 84112

RUSHFORTH, NORMAN B, b Blackpool, Eng, Dec 27, 32; m 56; c 2. ANIMAL BEHAVIOR, EPIDEMIOLOGY. *Educ:* Univ Birmingham, BSc, 54; Cornell Univ, MS, 58, PhD(statist), 61. *Prof Exp:* From instr to assoc prof biol, 61-72, asst prof biostatist, 63-72, ASSOC PROF BIOSTATIST & PROF BIOL, CASE WESTERN RESERVE UNIV, 72-, CHMN DEPT, 71- *Mem:* AAAS; Am Statist Asn. *Res:* Application of quantitative methods in biological research; animal behavior; learning mechanisms in lower invertebrates; mathematical models for biological phenomena. *Mailing Add:* Dept of Biol Case Western Reserve Univ Cleveland OH 44106

RUSHFORTH, SAMUEL ROBERTS, b Salt Lake City, Utah, Nov 24, 45; m 64; c 3. ALGOLOGY. *Educ:* Weber State Col, BS, 66; Brigham Young Univ, MS, 68, PHD(bot), 70. *Prof Exp:* Asst prof, 70-75, ASSOC PROF BOT, BRIGHAM YOUNG UNIV, 75- *Mem:* Bot Soc Am; Int Phycol Soc. *Res:* Taxonomic and ecological investigation of the algae of western America; blue-green algal biology. *Mailing Add:* Dept of Bot & Range Sci Brigham Young Univ Provo UT 84601

RUSHING, ALLEN JOSEPH, b Charlottesville, Va, Oct 23, 44; m 73; c 3. CONTROL SYSTEMS. *Educ:* Univ Denver, BSEE, 66; Univ Mo-Rolla, MSEE, 70, PhD(elec eng), 73. *Prof Exp:* Elec engr instruments, Monsanto Co, 67-70; SR PHYSICIST ELECTROPHOTOG, EASTMAN KODAK CO, 73- *Concurrent Pos:* Mem adj fac, Rochester Inst Technol, 75- *Mem:* Sr mem Inst Elec & Electronics Engrs; Soc Photog Scientists & Engrs; Sigma Xi; Instrument Soc Am. *Res:* Applications of control theory to electrophotography. *Mailing Add:* Eastman Kodak Res Labs 2000 Lake Ave Rochester NY 14650

RUSHING, THOMAS BENNY, b Marshville, NC, Oct 30, 41; m 62; c 2. TOPOLOGY. *Educ:* Wake Forest Univ, BS, 64, MA, 65; Univ Ga, PhD(math), 68. *Prof Exp:* Asst prof math, Univ Ga, 68-69; asst prof, 69-71, assoc prof, 71-77, PROF MATH, UNIV UTAH, 77- *Concurrent Pos:* NSF res grants, Univ Utah, 70-74 & 77-79; Nat Acad Sci exchange visit, 75; exchange scientist, Univ Zagreb, Yugoslavia, 75-76. *Mem:* Am Math Soc. *Res:* Topology of manifolds; embedding problems; piecewise linear topology; shape theory. *Mailing Add:* Dept of Math Univ of Utah Salt Lake City UT 84112

RUSHMER, ROBERT FRAZER, b Ogden, Utah, Nov 30, 14; m 42; c 3. BIOENGINEERING. *Educ:* Univ Chicago, BS, 35; Rush Med Col, MD, 39. *Hon Degrees:* PhD, Univ Linkoping, Sweden, 77. *Prof Exp:* Intern, St Luke's Hosp, San Francisco, 39-40; fel pediat, Mayo Found, Univ Minn, 40-42, asst, 41-42; assoc prof aviation med, Sch Med, Univ Southern Calif, 46-47; from asst prof to prof physiol, Sch Med, 47-68, PROF BIOENG, UNIV WASH, 68-, DIR, CTR ADVANCED STUDIES BIOMEDICAL SCI, 78- *Honors & Awards:* Ida B Gould Award, AAAS, 62; Modern Med Award, 62. *Mem:* Inst Med-Nat Acad Sci; Am Physiol Soc; Am Heart Asn; AAAS; hon fel Am Col Cardiol. *Mailing Add:* 332 Aerospace Lab Ctr Bioeng Univ of Wash Seattle WA 98105

RUSHTON, BRIAN MANDEL, b Sale, Eng, Nov 16, 33; m 58; c 3. CHEMISTRY. *Educ:* Univ Salford, ARIC, 57; Univ Minn, MS, 59; Univ Leicester, PhD(chem), 63. *Prof Exp:* Sr res chemist, Petrolite Corp, Mo, 63-65, group leader corrosion chem, 65-66; group leader polyer chem, Ashland Chem Co, Ohio, 66-69; mgr, Hooker Chem & Plastics Corp, 69-71, dir polymer chem, 71-73, corp dir res, 73-75, vpres res & develop, 75; pres, Celanese Res Corp, 75-80, corp vpres-technol, 80-81; VPRES RES & DEVELOP, AIR PROD & CHEM, INC, 81- *Concurrent Pos:* Mem, Nat Mats Adv Bd, Nat Res Coun, 80- *Mem:* Am Chem Soc; Soc Plastics Engrs; NY Acad Sci; Coun Chem Res; Indust Res Inst. *Res:* Polymer chemistry; general chemistry; electrochemistry administration. *Mailing Add:* Air Prod & Chem Inc PO Box 538 Allentwon PA 18105

RUSHTON, PRISCILLA STRICKLAND, b Clarksdale, Miss, Dec 19, 42; m 66; c 1. RADIOBIOLOGY. *Educ:* Southwestern at Memphis, BA, 63; Emory Univ, MS, 64, PhD(biol), 67. *Prof Exp:* Asst prof, 67-71, ASSOC PROF GENETICS, MEMPHIS STATE UNIV, 71- *Mem:* AAAS; Am Inst Biol Sci; Am Genetic Asn. *Res:* Modification and repair of x-irradiation induced chromosome and chromatid aberrations in plants. *Mailing Add:* Dept of Biol Memphis State Univ Memphis TN 38111

RUSINKO, FRANK, JR, b Nanticoke, Pa, Oct 12, 30; m 57; c 2. FUEL TECHNOLOGY. *Educ:* Pa State Univ, BS, 52, MS, 54, PhD(fuel technol, phys chem), 58. *Prof Exp:* Res assoc, Pa State Univ, 58-59; scientist, Speer Carbon Co, Air Reduction Co, 59-61, mgr develop, Carbon Prod Div, 61-62; mgr develop, IGE Div, Airco, Inc, 62-67, dir develop & technol serv, 67-70, vpres & tech dir, Airco Speer Carbon-Graphite Div, 70-80; WITH ELECTROTOOLS INC, 80- *Mem:* Am Chem Soc; Am Inst Mining, Metall & Petrol Engrs; Am Soc Testing & Mat. *Res:* Carbon and graphite; gas-solid reactions; gas adsorption; coal carbonization; irradiation of coal and graphite; nuclear graphite; catalysis of heterogeneous carbon reactions; fuel cells; surface chemistry; research and development management; high temperature materials technology. *Mailing Add:* Electrotools Inc PO Box 33 Broadview IL 60153

RUSKAI, MARY BETH, b Cleveland, Ohio, Feb 26, 44. MATHEMATICAL PHYSICS, OPERATOR THEORY. *Educ:* Notre Dame Col, Ohio, BS, 65; Univ Wis-Madison, MA, 69, PhD(chem), 69. *Prof Exp:* Battelle fel math physics, Theoret Physics Inst, Univ Geneva, 69-71; res assoc math, Mass Inst Technol, 71-72; res assoc theoret physics, Univ Alta, 72-73; asst prof math, Univ Ore, 73-76; ASST PROF MATH, UNIV LOWELL, 77- *Concurrent Pos:* Consult, Bell Labs, NJ, 72; vis asst prof, Rockefeller Univ, 80-81; guest prof, Univ Vienna, Austria, 81. *Mem:* Am Math Soc; Math Asn Am; Am Phys Soc; Int Asn Math Physics; Asn Women in Math. *Res:* Operator theory; statistical mechanics. *Mailing Add:* 53 Academy St Arlington MA 02174

RUSKIN, ARNOLD M(ILTON), b Bay City, Mich, Jan 4, 37; m 64; c 1. PROJECT MANAGEMENT, TECHNICAL MANAGEMENT. *Educ:* Univ Mich, BSE(chem eng) & BSE(mat eng), 58, MSE, 59, PhD(eng mat), 62; Claremont Grad Sch, MBE, 70. *Prof Exp:* Instr mat eng, Univ Mich, 61-62; lectr appl physics, Rugby Col Eng Technol, Eng, 62-63; from asst prof to prof eng, Harvey Mudd Col, 63-73; eng mgr, Everett/Charles, Inc, 73-74; vpres & prog mgr, Claremont Eng Co, 74-78; MGR, NETWORK STRATEGY DEVELOP, JET PROPULSION LAB, CALIF INST TECHNOL, 80- *Concurrent Pos:* Res engr, E I du Pont de Nemours & Co, Inc, 58; dir joint col & indust libr study, Harvey Mudd Col, 63-65, Union Oil Co fel eng, 66-73, asst dir, Freshman Div Fac, 71-72, dir, 72-73; assoc inst res, Claremont Univ Ctr, 65-67, continuing educ specialist, 74-, lectr, 75-77; from assoc prof to prof econ & bus, Claremont Grad Sch, 70-73; mem tech staff, Jet Propulsion Lab, Calif Inst Technol, 78-; adj prof eng, Univ Calif, Los Angeles, 77-; partner, Claremont Consult Group, 79- *Mem:* Am Soc Metals; Am Mat Asn; Metall Soc; Am Inst Chem Engrs. *Res:* Engineering management; economics of research and development; strategic planning; technology assessment; environmental impact assessment; project management. *Mailing Add:* 545 W Twelfth St Claremont CA 91711

RUSKIN, RICHARD A, b New Rochelle, NY, Oct 1, 24; m 46, 66; c 1. OBSTETRICS & GYNECOLOGY. *Educ:* Duke Univ, BA, 40, MD, 43; Am Bd Obstet & Gynec, dipl, 54. *Prof Exp:* Resident obstet & gynec, New York Lying-In-Hosp, 47-52; from instr to assoc prof, 52-72, PROF OBSTET & GYNEC, MED COL, CORNELL UNIV, 72- *Concurrent Pos:* Resident, Kings County Hosp, New York, 46-47; resident, New York Polyclin Med Sch & Hosp, 47-52, adj prof, 56-65; asst attend obstetrician & gynecologist, New York Lying-In-Hosp, 56-72, attend, 72-, assoc prof, 69-72, prof, 72-; consult, Workmans Compensation Bd; attend obstet & gynec, Roosevelt Hosp, 76-; prof & attend, New York Polyclin Med Sch & Hosp, 65-76. *Mem:* Fel Am Col Obstet & Gynec; fel Am Col Surg; Geriat Soc Am. *Res:* Oxytocin and vasopressin in clinical obstetrics. *Mailing Add:* 850 Park Ave New York NY 10021

RUSKIN, ROBERT EDWARD, b Sioux Falls, SDak, Oct 30, 16; m 42; c 2. ATMOSPHERIC PHYSICS. *Educ:* Kans State Col, AB, 40. *Prof Exp:* Physicist, Uranium Isotope Separation Proj, Naval Res Lab, 42-47, head instrument sect, Atmospheric Physics Br, 47-71, actg head, 71-72, asst head, 72-79; ATMOSPHERIC PHYSICIST, AMAF INDUSTS, 80- *Concurrent Pos:* Vis prof, Colo State Univ, 70. *Honors & Awards:* Meritorious Civilian Serv Award, US Navy, 45, Superior Accomplishment Award, 65. *Mem:* Fel AAAS; Am Phys Soc; Sigma Xi; Am Meteorol Soc; fel Instrument Soc Am. *Res:* Cloud physics; physics of interactions of the atmosphere; aircraft instrumentation; air pollution; marine fog and haze interactions with electrooptical systems; marine salt aerosol in relation to gas turbine ship engines. *Mailing Add:* 1406 Ruffner Rd Alexandria VA 22302

RUSLING, JAMES FRANCIS, b Philadelphia, Pa, Nov 4, 46. ELECTROCHEMISTRY, CHEMOMETRICS. *Educ:* Drexel Univ, BSc, 69; Clarkson Col Technol, PhD(anal chem), 79. *Prof Exp:* Spectroscopist anal chem, Sadtler Res Co, 72-73; anal chemist, Wyeth Labs, 73-76; ASST PROF ANAL CHEM, UNIV CONN, 79- *Concurrent Pos:* Mem, Inst Mat Sci, Univ Conn, 81- *Mem:* Am Chem Soc; Am Asn Univ Professors. *Mailing Add:* Univ Conn Box U 60 Storrs CT 06268

RUSNAK, ROBERT MICHAEL, b New Eagle, Pa, June 4, 38; m 63; c 3. PHYSICAL METALLURGY, MATERIALS SCIENCE. *Educ:* Univ Mich, BS, 61, MS, 62; Univ Notre Dame, PhD(metall eng), 67. *Prof Exp:* Engr, Bettis Atomic Power Lab, Westinghouse Elec Corp, 62-64; proj metallurgist, Bendix Res Labs, 67-73, sr proj engr, 73-76, TECH SUPVR, RES LABS, BENDIX CORP, 76- *Mem:* Am Soc Metals; Soc Advan Mat & Process Eng. *Res:* Powder metallurgy; acoustic emission; nondestructive testing; metal deformation; oxidation; x-ray diffraction; friction and wear; magnetic materials; irradiation effects; advanced composites; materials and processes for sensors; process development. *Mailing Add:* Bendix Res Labs 20800 Civic Center Dr Southfield MI 48076

RUSOFF, IRVING ISADORE, b Newark, NJ, Jan 29, 15; m 41; c 2. NUTRITION. *Educ:* Univ Fla, BS, 37, MS, 39; Univ Minn, PhD(physiol chem), 43. *Prof Exp:* Asst, Nutrit Lab, Exp Sta, Univ Fla, 37-39, asst dairy res, 39-40; fels, Nat Found Infantile Paralysis, Univ Minn, 43-44, Off Sci Res & Develop, 44-45 & US Naval Ord, 45-46; head nutrit lab, Standard Brands, Inc, 46-47; head biochem sect, Res Ctr, Gen Foods Corp, 47-57, head nutrit sect, 57-61, group leader fats & oils, 61-62; mgr res & res serv, DCA Food Industs, 62-63; mgr nutrit & biochem & coordr spec proj res, Beech-Nut Life Savers, Inc, 63-66; head biol sci & asst to res dir, Nat Biscuit Co, 66-67, mgr develop res, 67-68; dir basic studies, 68-70, dir sci, 71-74, sr scientist, 74-78, DIR NUTRIT SCI, NABISCO, 78- *Mem:* Am Chem Soc; Am Inst Nutrit; Inst Food Technologists; NY Acad Sci; Am Pub Health Asn. *Res:* Human and animal nutrition; vitamin and mineral metabolism; trace elements and nutrients; biomedicine. *Mailing Add:* 147 Pascack Rd Park Ridge NJ 07656

RUSOFF, LOUIS LEON, b Newark, NJ, Dec 23, 10; m 45; c 2. ANIMAL NUTRITION, NUTRITION. *Educ:* Rutgers Univ, BS, 31; Pa State Col, MS, 32; Univ Minn, PhD(agr biochem, nutrit), 40. *Prof Exp:* Asst, Nutrit Lab, Exp Sta, Univ Fla, 32-35, lab asst & instr animal nutrit, 35-37, asst & asst prof, 37-42; assoc dairy nutritionist, Exp Sta, La State Univ, Baton Rouge, 42-50, assoc prof dairy nutrit, 48-50, prof dairy nutrit & dairy nutritionist, 50-81; RETIRED. *Honors & Awards:* Charles E Coates Award, Am Chem Soc, 59; Borden Award, Am Dairy Sci Asn, 65, Southern Div Honors Award, 69. *Mem:* AAAS; Am Chem Soc; Am Soc Animal Sci; Am Dairy Sci Asn; Am Inst Nutrit. *Res:* Vitamin assays; minerals and alkaloids; biochemistry of blood; trace elements in animal nutrition; milk analysis; feeding and digestion trials; molasses; urea feeding; antibiotics in food and silage preservation; fluoridation of milk; nutritive value of aquatic plants as foodstuffs for animals and man. *Mailing Add:* Dept Dairy Sci La State Univ Baton Rouge LA 70803

RUSS, CHARLES ROGER, b New London, Wis, July 2, 37; m 61; c 3. INORGANIC CHEMISTRY. *Educ:* Marquette Univ, BS, 59, MS, 61; Univ Pa, PhD(chem), 65. *Prof Exp:* Asst chem, Marquette Univ, 59-61 & Univ Pa, 61-65; asst prof, 65-71, ASSOC PROF CHEM, UNIV MAINE, ORONO, 71- *Mem:* Am Chem Soc. *Res:* Synthesis and properties of silicon or germanium compounds. *Mailing Add:* Dept of Chem Univ of Maine Orono ME 04473

RUSS, DAVID PERRY, b Wilmington, Del, May 7, 45. TECTONIC GEOMORPHOLOGY, QUATERNARY GEOLOGY. *Educ:* Pa State Univ, BS, 67, PhD(geol), 75; WVa Univ, MS, 69. *Prof Exp:* Geologist, Waterways Exp Sta, US Army Corps Engrs, 70-72; GEOLOGIST, US GEOL SURV, 75- *Mem:* Geol Soc Am. *Res:* Geological and geophysical investigations of earthquake hazards; seismotectonics of the New Madrid seismic zone. *Mailing Add:* Stop 966 Box 25046 US Geol Surv Denver Fed Ctr Denver CO 80225

RUSS, GERALD A, b Washington, DC, Oct 17, 36; m 65; c 3. NUCLEAR MEDICINE. *Educ:* Univ Md, BS, 64; Georgetown Univ, PhD(biochem), 74. *Prof Exp:* Res asst physiol, Georgetown Univ, 62-64; res technician cytogenetics, Radiol Health, USPHS, 64; res assoc biochem, Georgetown Univ, 64-72; res assoc biophys, 73-76, ASSOC BIOPHYS, MEM SLOAN-KETTERING CANCER CTR, 76- *Concurrent Pos:* Instr biophys, Sloan-Kettering Div, Grad Sch Med Sci, Cornell Univ, 74-77, asst prof biophys, 77- *Mem:* Am Chem Soc; Soc Nuclear Med. *Res:* Distribution and kinetics of radiolabeled compounds and the physiological interpretations of these; emphasis on short-lived, gamma-emitting compounds. *Mailing Add:* Mem Sloan-Kettering Cancer Ctr 1275 York Ave New York NY 10021

RUSS, GUSTON PRICE, III, b Mobile, Ala, Apr 5, 46. MASS SPECTROMETRY, ISOTOPE GEOCHEMISTRY. *Educ:* Univ of the South, BA, 68; Calif Inst Technol, PhD(chem), 74. *Prof Exp:* Fel, Univ Cailf, San Diego, 74-77; asst prof chem, Univ Hawaii, 77-81; CHEMIST, LAWRENCE LIVERMORE NAT LAB, 81- *Mem:* AAAS; Geochem Soc; Am Geophys Union. *Res:* Nuclear geochemistry; lunar regolith studies; isotopic studies of meteorites; chronology; isotope ratio mass spectrometry. *Mailing Add:* Lawrence Livermore Nat Lab MS L-232 PO Box 808 Livermore CA 94550

RUSS, JAMES STEWART, b Canton, Ohio, Aug 22, 40; m 63, 81; c 2. HIGH ENERGY PHYSICS. *Educ:* Ind Univ, BS, 62; Princeton Univ, MA, 64, PhD(physics), 66. *Prof Exp:* Instr physics, Princeton Univ, 66-67; assoc prof, 67-80, PROF PHYSICS, CARNEGIE-MELLON UNIV, 80- *Mem:* Am Phys Soc; Sigma Xi; Am Asn Physics Teachers. *Res:* Elementary particle physics; experimental using counters and spark chambers; computer-oriented data-handling systems; computer simulation of experimental data. *Mailing Add:* Dept of Physics Carnegie-Mellon Univ Pittsburgh PA 15213

RUSSCHER, GLENN EARL, nuclear & materials engineering, see previous edition

RUSSEK, ARNOLD, b New York, NY, July 13, 26; m 56; c 2. PHYSICS. *Educ:* City Col New York, BS, 47; NY Univ, MS, 48, PhD(physics), 53. *Prof Exp:* Instr physics, Univ Buffalo, 53-55; from asst prof to assoc prof, 55-65, PROF PHYSICS, UNIV CONN, 65- *Mem:* Fel Am Phys Soc. *Res:* Nuclear structure; atomic structure and atomic collisions; electromagnetic diffraction theory. *Mailing Add:* Dept of Physics Univ of Conn Storrs CT 06268

RUSSEK, ESTELLE, b Brooklyn, NY, July 23, 51. MULTIVARIATE METHODS, BIOASSAY METHODS. *Educ:* State Univ NY, Stony Brook, BS, 72; Univ Wash, Seattle, PhD(biomath), 79. *Prof Exp:* Programmer, NY Life Ins, 72-73; res asst biostat, Univ Wash, 73-75, teaching asst, 75-76, instr, 77-78; ASST PROF BIOSTATIST, UNIV MD, 78- *Concurrent Pos:* Consult, Univ Md Sea Grant Prog & Joint Consult Lab, USDA, Univ Md, 81- *Mem:* Am Statist Asn; Biomet Soc; Classification Soc. *Res:* Biostatistics. *Mailing Add:* Dept Dairy Sci Univ Md College Park MD 20704

RUSSEL, DARRELL ARDEN, b McPherson, Kans, May 26, 21; m 49; c 9. AGRONOMY. *Educ:* Kans State Univ, BS, 43; Univ Ill, MS, 47, PhD(soil fertil, anal chem), 55. *Prof Exp:* Spec asst soil fertil, Univ Ill, 46-47, asst soils, 51-55; instr soils, Iowa State Univ, 47-49, dist exten dir, Agr Exten Serv, 49-51; asst prof soil chem, N La Hill Farm Exp Sta, La State Univ, 55-60; agriculturist, Div Agr Develop, 60-78, asst adminr, Int Fertilizer Prog, 78-81, HEAD, EDUC & COMMUN SERV STAFF, DIV AGR DEVELOP, NAT FERTILIZER DEVELOP CTR, TENN VALLEY AUTHORITY, 81- *Concurrent Pos:* AID consult, Morocco, 66, Bolivia, 69, Paraguay, 70, Indonesia, 71, Ghana, 72 & 74, Cent Treaty Orgn, 74, UN Indus Develop Orgn, 76 & Int Fertilizer Develop Ctr, 81. *Mem:* Fel Soil Sci Soc Am; fel Am Soc Agron; Crop Sci Soc Am; Am Chem Soc; Coun Agr Sci & Technol. *Res:* Analytical procedures for soil testing; effect of fertilizers on soil fertility, crop growth and crop quality; fertilizer education. *Mailing Add:* Nat Fertilizer Develop Ctr Tenn Valley Authority Muscle Shoals AL 35660

RUSSEL, MARJORIE ELLEN, b New York, NY, July 16, 44; m 81; c 1. MOLECULAR GENETICS. *Educ:* Oberlin Col, BA, 66; Univ Wis, MS, 68; Univ Colo, PhD(molecular biol), 77. *Prof Exp:* Res asst molecular biol, Dept Genetics, Univ Wash, 68-70 & Dept Molecular Biol, Univ Geneva, 71-73; FEL GENETICS, ROCKEFELLER UNIV, 77- *Concurrent Pos:* Damon Runyon-Walter Winchell Cancer Fund fel, 77-78. *Res:* Control of gene expression in prokaryotes; mechanisms of protein transport into and across bacterial membranes. *Mailing Add:* Rockefeller Univ Dept of Genetics 1230 York Ave New York NY 10021

RUSSEL, WILLIAM, BAILEY, b Corpus Christi, Tex, Nov 17, 45; m 72; c 2. CHEMICAL ENGINEERING. *Educ:* Rice Univ, BA & MChE, 69; Stanford Univ, PhD(chem eng), 73. *Prof Exp:* NATO fel appl math, Dept Appl Math & Theoret Physics, Cambridge Univ, 73-74; ASST PROF CHEM ENG, PRINCETON UNIV, 74- *Concurrent Pos:* Consult, Cities Serv Res & Develop Corp, 75- *Mem:* Am Inst Chem Engrs; Soc Rheology; Soc Petrol Engrs. *Res:* Fluid mechanics; colloidal suspensions; coal conversion; heat and mass transfer. *Mailing Add:* Dept of Chem Eng Princeton Univ Princeton NJ 08540

RUSSELL, ALBERT LEE, b Des Moines, Iowa, Nov 8, 05; m 30; c 4. DENTAL EPIDEMIOLOGY. *Educ:* Creighton Univ, DDS, 29; Univ Mich, MPH, 47; Am Bd Dent Pub Health, dipl, 61. *Prof Exp:* Dir div dent health, State Bd Health, SDak, 46-49; mem staff epidemiol & biomet br, Nat Inst Dent Res, 49-51, chief, 51-66; prof, 67-73, EMER PROF PUB HEALTH DENT, SCH PUB HEALTH & PROF COMMUNITY DENT, SCH DENT, UNIV MICH, ANN ARBOR, 73- *Concurrent Pos:* Chmn expert comt periodont dis, WHO, 60, mem expert adv comt dent health, 60-75; mem bd dirs, Am Bd Dent Pub Health, 63-67, pres, 67. *Honors & Awards:* H Trendley Dean Mem Award, Int Asn Dent Res, 71. *Mem:* Fel AAAS; fel Am Col Dent; Am Dent Asn; Int Asn Dent Res. *Res:* Fluorine and dental caries; epidemiology of dental caries and periodontal disease. *Mailing Add:* 1720 Palomar Dr Ann Arbor MI 48103

RUSSELL, ALLAN MELVIN, b Newark, NJ, Feb 2, 30; m 51; c 5. PHYSICS. *Educ:* Brown Univ, ScB, 51, ScM, 53; Syracuse Univ, PhD(physics), 57. *Prof Exp:* Res assoc physics, Syracuse Univ, 57-58; asst prof, Univ Calif, 58-64; assoc prof, Wesleyan Univ, 64-67; assoc prof, 67-70, assoc provost, 67-68, provost & dean fac, 68-72, PROF PHYSICS, HOBART & WILLIAM SMITH COLS, 70- *Mem:* Am Phys Soc; Am Asn Physics Teachers. *Res:* Low energy electron diffraction; field emission; measurement; molecular beams; paleomagnetism; epistemology; philosophy of science. *Mailing Add:* Dept of Physics Hobart & William Smith Cols Geneva NY 14456

RUSSELL, ALLEN STEVENSON, b Bedford, Pa, May 27, 15; m 41. CHEMISTRY, ENGINEERING. *Educ:* Pa State Univ, BS, 36, MS, 37, PhD(phys chem), 41. *Prof Exp:* Chemist, Bell Tel Labs, 37; asst, Pa State Univ, 37-40; chemist, Aluminum Co Am, 40-44, asst chief phys chem div, 44-53, chief, 53-55, chief process metall div, 55-69, asst dir res, 69-74, assoc dir, 74, vpres, 74-78, vpres sci & technol, 78-81, VPRES & CHIEF SCIENTIST, ALCOA LABS, 81- *Concurrent Pos:* Adj prof, Univ Pittsburgh. *Honors & Awards:* Carl J Bayer Medalist, 81. *Mem:* Nat Acad Eng; Am Chem Soc; fel Am Soc Metals; Sigma Xi; fel Am Inst Mining, Metall & Petrol Engrs. *Res:* Process metallurgy of aluminum. *Mailing Add:* 929 Field Club Rd Pittsburgh PA 15238

RUSSELL, ANTHONY PATRICK, b London, Eng, Sept 10, 47; m 70; c 3. HERPETOLOGY, COMPARATIVE ANATOMY. *Educ:* Univ Exeter, BSc, 69; Univ London, PhD(zool), 72. *Prof Exp:* Lectr zool, Univ Botswana, Lesotho & Swaziland, 73; asst prof, 73-80, ASSOC PROF BIOL, UNIV CALGARY, 80- *Concurrent Pos:* Res assoc, Dept Herpetol, Royal Ont Mus, 80- *Mem:* Am Soc Zoologists; Soc Syst Zool; Linnean Soc London; Zool Soc London; Can Soc Zoologists. *Res:* Investigating into the functional biology and evolutionary history of reptiles and mammals, particularly locomotory and feeding mechanisms. *Mailing Add:* Dept Biol Univ Calgary Calgary AB T2N 1N4 Can

RUSSELL, CATHERINE MARIE, b Tuckahoe, NY, Nov 20, 10. MEDICAL MICROBIOLOGY. *Educ:* Col of Mt St Vincent, BS, 32; Columbia Univ, MA, 48; Univ Va, PhD(biol), 51; Am Bd Med Microbiol, dipl. *Prof Exp:* Technician, Res & Diag Labs, State Dept Health, NY, 39-41; technician, New York Med Col, 41-42, instr bact & parasitol, 42-48; from instr to assoc prof microbiol, 48-77, from assoc prof to prof clin path, 63-77, EMER PROF PATH, MED SCH, UNIV VA, 77- *Mem:* Am Soc Trop Med & Hyg; Am Soc Parasitol; Am Soc Microbiol. *Res:* Trematode infections; development of the egg of Plagitura salamandra; leptospirosis; pathogenesis and identification of the organism; virus-cell relationship. *Mailing Add:* 1622 Mason Lane Charlottesville VA 22901

RUSSELL, CHARLES ADDISON, b Danielson, Conn, Jan 12, 21; m 47; c 3. POLYMER CHEMISTRY, ANALYTICAL CHEMISTRY. *Educ:* Yale Univ, BSc, 42, MSc, 44, PhD(org chem), 49. *Prof Exp:* Assoc prof phys chem, Bucknell Univ, 48-52; chemist, Nat Lead Co, 52-59; mem tech staff, 59-66, SUPVR ATMOSPHERIC EFFECTS, MICROCHEM & CONTACT CHEM GROUP, BELL TEL LABS, 66- *Mem:* AAAS; Am Chem Soc. *Res:* Effects of contamination on telephone equipment; interaction of various materials with environment and each other; behavior of telephone contacts. *Mailing Add:* Bell Tel Labs Rm 4B625 Holmdel NJ 07733

RUSSELL, CHARLES BRADLEY, b Evanston, Ill, Apr 8, 40; m 68. MATHEMATICS, STATISTICS. *Educ:* Univ of the South, BA, 62; Fla State Univ, MS, 63, PhD(statist), 68. *Prof Exp:* Asst prof, 67-72, ASSOC PROF MATH SCI, CLEMSON UNIV, 72- *Mem:* Inst Math Statist; Am Statist Asn; Opers Res Soc Am; Inst Mgt Sci. *Res:* Probability theory; stochastic processes; management science. *Mailing Add:* Dept of Math Sci Clemson Univ Clemson SC 29631

RUSSELL, CHARLES CLAYTON, b Key West, Fla, Oct 9, 37; m 58; c 2. NEMATOLOGY, ENTOMOLOGY. *Educ:* Univ Fla, BSA, 60, MSA, 62, PhD(nematol), 67. *Prof Exp:* NEMATOLOGIST, OKLA STATE UNIV, 67-, ASSOC PROF, DEPT BOT & PLANT PATH, 73- *Mem:* Am Phytopath Soc; Soc Nematol. *Res:* Plant parasitic and insect parasitic nematodes; free living nematodes. *Mailing Add:* Dept of Plant Path Okla State Univ Stillwater OK 74074

RUSSELL, CHARLES DANIEL, JR, b Niagara Falls, NY, Aug 30, 16; m 42; c 3. PHYSICAL CHEMISTRY. *Educ:* Niagara Univ, BS, 38; Calif Inst Technol, MS, 40; Duke Univ, PhD(chem), 41. *Prof Exp:* Res chemist, Tex Co, NY, 41-43; res chemist, Calif Milk Prod Co, 43-46; head recovery methods res sect, Carter Oil Co, 46-57; head reservoir eng res sect, Jersey Prod Res Co, 57-60; chief engr, Cie Francaise des Petroles, 60-69, mgt adv, 69-81; CONSULT PETROL ENG, 82- *Mem:* AAAS; Am Chem Soc; fel Am Inst Chemists; Am Inst Mining, Metall & Petrol Eng. *Res:* Petroleum chemistry; biochemistry; magnetochemical studies on hemoglobin compounds and on complex copper and nickel ions; physiochemical studies on oil deterioration; petroleum reservoir engineering; flow of fluids in porous media; unconventional oil recovery methods. *Mailing Add:* Cie Francaise des Petroles 5 rue Michel-Ange Paris 16 France

RUSSELL, CHARLOTTE SANANES, b Brooklyn, NY, Jan 4, 27; m 47; c 2. BIOCHEMISTRY, ORGANIC CHEMISTRY. *Educ:* Brooklyn Col, AB, 46; Columbia Univ, AM, 47, PhD(org chem), 51. *Prof Exp:* Lectr org chem, Brooklyn Col, 49; res worker biochem, Col Physicians & Surgeons, Columbia Univ, 51-54, res assoc, 54; from instr to assoc prof, 54-72, PROF CHEM, CITY COL NEW YORK, 72- *Concurrent Pos:* Vis asst prof, Col Physicians & Surgeons, Columbia Univ, 63-64. *Mem:* Sigma Xi; AAAS; Am Chem Soc; Am Soc Biol Chemists; Royal Soc Chem. *Res:* Biochemistry of heme compounds; enzymology of heme biosynthesis; invertebrate lectins; solid state reactions in organic chemistry. *Mailing Add:* Dept of Chem City Col of New York New York NY 10031

RUSSELL, CHRISTOPHER THOMAS, b London, Eng, May 9, 43; m 66; c 2. GEOPHYSICS, MAGNETOPHERIC PHYSICS. *Educ:* Univ Toronto, BSc, 64; Univ Calif, Los Angeles, PhD(space physics), 68. *Prof Exp:* RES GEOPHYSICIST, INST GEOPHYS & PLANETARY PHYSICS, UNIV CALIF, LOS ANGELES, 68- *Concurrent Pos:* Prin investr, Int Sun Earth Explorer, 72-; mem, Int Union Radion Sci, 75-81; assoc ed, J Geophys Res, 76-78, Geophys Res Lett, 79-81; ed, Solar Wind Three, 74, Auroral Process, 79. *Mem:* Fel Am Geophys Union; Int Union Radio Sci; fel AAAS; Am Astron Soc. *Res:* Magnetospheric physics; solar-terrestrial relationships; interplanetary physics; lunar physics; planetary physics. *Mailing Add:* Inst Geophys & Planetary Physics Univ of Calif Los Angeles CA 90024

RUSSELL, DALE A, b San Francisco, Calif, Dec 27, 37; m 64; c 3. VERTEBRATE PALEONTOLOGY. *Educ:* Univ Ore, BA, 58; Univ Calif, Berkeley, MA, 60; Columbia Univ, PhD(geol), 64. *Prof Exp:* NSF fel, Yale Univ, 64-65; cur fossil vert, 65-77, CHIEF PALEOBIOL DIV, NAT MUS NATURAL SCI, NAT MUS CAN, 77- *Mem:* Soc Vert Paleont. *Res:* Mesozoic, particularly Cretaceous, reptiles; Cretaceous-Tertiary boundary problems. *Mailing Add:* Nat Mus of Natural Sci Metcalfe & McLeod Sts Ottawa ON K1A 0M8 Can

RUSSELL, DAVID BERNARD, radiation chemistry, physical chemistry, see previous edition

RUSSELL, DAVID L, b Orlando, Fla, May 1, 39; m 60; c 2. MATHEMATICS. *Educ:* Andrews Univ, BA, 60; Univ Minn, PhD(math), 64. *Prof Exp:* Asst prof, 64-69, assoc prof math & comput sci, 69-77, PROF L&S, MATH, UNIV WIS-MADISON, 77- *Concurrent Pos:* Res consult, Honeywell, Inc, 63- *Mem:* Am Math Soc; Soc Indust & Appl Math. *Res:* Control theory of ordinary and partial differential equations; asymptotic theory of ordinary differential equations. *Mailing Add:* Dept of Math Univ of Wis Madison WI 53706

RUSSELL, DENNIS C, b Southampton, Eng, Sept 4, 27; m 51; c 2. MATHEMATICS. *Educ:* Univ Sheffield, BSc, 48; Univ London, MSc, 52, PhD(math anal), 58, DSc, 72. *Prof Exp:* Asst lectr math, Northampton Col Advan Technol, 48-52; demonstr, Univ Col London, 53-55; asst lectr, Keele Univ, 55-57, lectr, 57-60; assoc prof, Mt Allison Univ, 60-62; chmn dept, 62-69, PROF MATH, YORK UNIV, 62- *Concurrent Pos:* Nat Res Coun Can sr res fel, 68; Can Coun leave fel, 69 & 76-77; hon res fel, Birkbeck Col, London, 68-69; Ger Acad Exchange Serv res fel, 71; Nuffield Found res travel award, 73 & Nat Sci Eng Res Coun Can travel grants, 76 & 80, collaborative res grant, 82; consult grad prog, Univ Calgary, 78; vis prof, Tel-Aviv Univ, 81. *Mem:* Am Math Soc; Math Asn Am; Can Math Soc; London Math Soc; fel Inst Math & Applns. *Res:* Mathematical analysis; matrix transformations on sequence spaces, and summability of sequences, series and integrals; approximation theory. *Mailing Add:* Dept Math York Univ Toronto ON M3J 1P3 Can

RUSSELL, DIANE HADDOCK, b Boise, Idaho, Sept 9, 35; c 2. BIOCHEMISTRY, PHARMACOLOGY. *Educ:* Col Idaho, BS, 63; Wash State Univ, PhD(zoophysiol), 67. *Prof Exp:* Fel, Sch Med & Exp Therapeut, Johns Hopkins Univ, 67-69; sr scientist, Baltimore Cancer Res Ctr, Nat Cancer Inst, 69-73; assoc prof, 73-76, PROF PHARMACOL, COL MED, UNIV ARIZ, 76- *Mem:* Soc Develop Biol; Am Soc Pharmacol & Exp Therapeut; Am Asn Cancer Res; Am Soc Biol Chemists; Sigma Xi. *Res:* Induction of ornithine decarboxylase in embryonic and rapid growth systems; physiological and pharmacological roles of polyamines in normal and cancerous growth systems. *Mailing Add:* Dept of Pharmacol Univ of Ariz Col of Med Tucson AZ 85724

RUSSELL, DONALD HAYES, b Peabody, Mass, Aug 26, 13; m 53; c 2. PSYCHIATRY. *Educ:* Tufts Univ, BS, 36; NY Univ, MD, 41. *Prof Exp:* Res psychiat, Med Sch, Boston Univ, 46-48; fel child psychiat, Judge Baker Guid Ctr, 48-50; asst prof psychiat, Med Sch, Boston Univ, 54-60, clin prof legal psychiat, Law-Med Inst, 60-66, Utley prof legal med & dir, Law-Med Inst, 66-69; ASST DIR DIV LEGAL MED, MASS DEPT MENT HEALTH, 69- *Concurrent Pos:* Mem staff, Mass Mem Hosp, 46-69; dir ct clin, Norfolk County Dist Ct, Mass, 49-56; dir child guid clin, Boston City Hosp, 54-56; dir ct clin prog, Mass Dept Ment Health, 56-69; dir child guid clin, Judge Baker Guid Ctr, 60- & Children's Med Ctr, Boston, 61-; instr, Harvard Med Sch, 61-71, asst clin prof psychiat, 71- *Mem:* Am Psychiat Asn. *Res:* Psychoanalysis and child psychiatry. *Mailing Add:* 295 Longwood Ave Boston MA 02115

RUSSELL, DOUGLAS STEWART, b Georgetown, Ont, June 16, 16; m 45; c 3. ANALYTICAL CHEMISTRY, TRACE INORGANIC ANALYSIS. *Educ:* Univ Toronto, BA, 40, MA, 41. *Prof Exp:* Asst chem, Univ Toronto, 40-42; supvr anal chem, Welland Chem Works, Ltd, 42-44; asst res officer radiochem, Can Atomic Energy Proj, 44-46; asst res officer, Nat Res Coun Can, 46-51, sr res officer, 52-70, head anal sect, Div Chem, 52-81, prin res officer, 70-81; RETIRED. *Concurrent Pos:* Secy & vchmn, Colloquium Spectroscopicum Internationale, 67. *Mem:* Am Chem Soc; Chem Inst Can; Spectros Soc Can (vpres, 68-69, pres, 69-70). *Res:* Development of methods for the determination of trace impurities in highly purified metals, ultapure acids, reagents and semiconductor materials; using optical emission spectrometry, spark source mass spectrometry and stable isotope dilution. *Mailing Add:* 44 Tower Rd Nepean ON K2G 2E7 Can

RUSSELL, ELIZABETH SHULL, b Ann Arbor, Mich, May 1, 13; m 36; c 4. GENETICS. *Educ:* Univ Mich, AB, 33; Columbia Univ, MA, 34; Univ Chicago, PhD(zool), 37. *Prof Exp:* Asst zool, Univ Chicago, 35-37; investr, 37-46, Am Asn Univ Women Nourse fel, 39-40, Finney-Howell fel, 47, res assoc, 46-58, staff sci dir, 53-56, SR STAFF SCIENTIST, JACKSON LAB, 58- *Concurrent Pos:* Guggenheim fel, Jackson Lab, 58-59. *Mem:* Nat Acad Sci; Am Acad Arts & Sci; Genetics Soc Am; Am Soc Naturalists; Soc Develop Biol. *Res:* Mammalian physiological genetics; action of deleterious genes; mouse anemias and hemoglobins; coat color; muscular dystrophy; genetic effects on aging. *Mailing Add:* Jackson Lab Bar Harbor ME 04609

RUSSELL, ERNEST EVERETT, b Jackson, Miss, Apr 16, 23; m 49; c 3. GEOLOGY. *Educ:* Miss State Univ, BS, 49, MS, 55; Univ Tenn, PhD(geol), 65. *Prof Exp:* Instr geol, Univ Tenn, 54-55; from asst prof to assoc prof, 55-68, PROF GEOL, MISS STATE UNIV, 68- *Concurrent Pos:* Consult geologist, Tenn Valley Authority, 75-; bd mem, Miss Minerals Resources Inst, 77- *Mem:* Fel Geol Soc Am; Am Asn Petrol Geologists; Paleont Soc; Am Inst Prof Geologists. *Res:* Upper Cretaceous stratigraphy of the eastern Gulf Coastal Plain; facies relations in Mesozoic and Cenozoic sediments. *Mailing Add:* Dept of Geol & Geog Miss State Univ PO Box GG Mississippi State MS 39762

RUSSELL, FINDLAY EWING, b San Francisco, Calif, Sept 1, 19; m 50; c 5. PHYSIOLOGY, TOXINOLOGY. *Educ:* Walla Walla Col, BA, 41; Loma Linda Univ, MD, 50. *Prof Exp:* Intern, White Mem Hosp, Los Angeles, 50-51; res fel biol, Calif Inst Technol, 51-53; physiologist, Inst Med Res, Huntington Mem Hosp, Pasadena, 53-55; res prof neurosurg, Loma Linda Univ, 55-66; PROF NEUROL, PHYSIOL & BIOL, UNIV SOUTHERN CALIF, 66- *Concurrent Pos:* Dir lab neurol res, Los Angeles County Hosp, 55-66; vis physiologist, Lab Marine Biol Asn, Eng, 58; vis prof, Cambridge Univ, 62-63 & 70-71, Ain Shams Univ Cairo, 63 & Univ Ljubljana, 75-76; ed, Toxicon, 62-68. *Mem:* Fel Am Col Physicians; fel Am Col Cardiol; fel NY Acad Sci; Int Soc Toxinology (pres, 62-66); fel Royal Soc Trop Med & Hyg. *Res:* Venoms. *Mailing Add:* Dept Pharmacol & Toxicol Col Pharmacy Univ Ariz Tucson AZ 85721

RUSSELL, FREDERICK A(RTHUR), b New York, NY, Apr 18, 15; m 47; c 2. ELECTRICAL ENGINEERING. *Educ:* Newark Col Eng, BS, 35, EE, 39; Stevens Inst Technol, MS, 41; Columbia Univ, ScD(eng), 53. *Prof Exp:* From instr to asst prof elec eng, Newark Col Eng, 37-44; sr proj engr, Div War Res, Columbia Univ, 44-45; exec assoc, NJ Inst Technol, 45-56, from asst prof to assoc prof elec eng, 45-53, chmn dept, 56-75, prof, 53-80, asst to pres planning, 75-80, ADJ PROF, NJ INST TECHNOL, 80- *Concurrent Pos:* Consult, Franklin Inst, 45-46 & Bell Tel Labs, Inc, 57-70. *Mem:* Am Soc Eng Educ; fel Inst Elec & Electronics Engrs. *Res:* Digital and analog computer simulation; control systems. *Mailing Add:* NJ Inst of Technol 323 High St Newark NJ 07102

RUSSELL, GEORGE A, b Bertrand, Mo, July 12, 21; m 44; c 4. PHYSICS. *Educ:* Mass Inst Technol, BS, 47; Univ Ill, MS, 52, PhD(physics), 55. *Prof Exp:* Physicist, Bur Aeronaut, US Navy, 55-59 & Antisubmarine Warfare Develop Squadron, 59-60; assoc prof physics, Southern Ill Univ, 60-62; assoc prof, 62-65, prof physics & assoc dir mat res lab, 65-74, head dept physics, 68-74, assoc dean grad col, 70-72, assoc vchancellor res & develop, 72-74, DEAN GRAD COL, UNIV ILL, URBANA, 72-, VCHANCELLOR RES, 74- *Concurrent Pos:* Consult, Off Naval Res, 60; chancellor, Univ Mo-Kansas City, 77- *Mem:* Am Phys Soc; Am Asn Physics Teachers. *Res:* Color centers in ionic crystals; infrared radiation; antisubmarine warfare; utilization of educated manpower; university administration. *Mailing Add:* Grad Col 338 Admin Bldg Univ of Ill Urbana IL 61801

RUSSELL, GEORGE ALBERT, b Chicago Heights, Ill, Aug 29, 36; m 57; c 3. AUTOMATIC CONTROL SYSTEMS. *Educ:* Mass Inst Technol, BS, 58; Ariz State Univ, MS, 61; Univ Conn, PhD(elec eng), 67. *Prof Exp:* Develop engr, AiRes Mfg Co Div, Garrett Corp, 58-61, eng specialist, 64-67; asst prof mech eng, 67-70, ASSOC PROF MECH ENG, UNIV MASS, AMHERST, 70- *Concurrent Pos:* Consult, AiRes Mfg Co Div, Garrett Corp, Springfield Wire Inc. *Mem:* Acoust Soc Am; Am Soc Mech Engrs. *Res:* Gas turbine hydromechanical controls. *Mailing Add:* Dept of Mech & Aerospace Eng Univ of Mass Amherst MA 01003

RUSSELL, GEORGE KEITH, b Bronxville, NY, Dec 13, 37; m 70. PLANT PHYSIOLOGY, BIOCHEMISTRY. *Educ:* Princeton Univ, AB, 59; Harvard Univ, PhD(biol), 63. *Prof Exp:* NSF fel biochem, Cornell Univ, 63-64; NSF fel biol, Brandeis Univ, 64-65; asst prof, Princeton Univ, 65-67; from asst prof to assoc prof, 67-77, PROF BIOL, ADELPHI UNIV, 77- *Mem:* Am Soc Plant Physiologists. *Res:* Genetic and biochemical control of photosynthesis; physiology of algae. *Mailing Add:* Dept of Biol Adelphi Univ Garden City NY 11530

RUSSELL, GERALD FREDERICK, b Edmonton, Alta, Feb 29, 44. FOOD CHEMISTRY. *Educ:* Univ Alta, BSc, 64; Univ Calif, PhD(agr chem), 68. *Prof Exp:* ASSOC PROF FOOD SCI, UNIV CALIF, DAVIS, 68- *Concurrent Pos:* Vis assoc prof, Eppley Inst Res in Cancer, Med Col, Univ Nebr, 75-76. *Mem:* Am Chem Soc; Inst Food Technologists; Am Soc Mass Spectrometry. *Res:* Chemistry of food volatiles; natural product chemistry; theories and mechanisms of olfaction; agents and mechanisms of chemical carcinogenesis. *Mailing Add:* Dept of Food Sci & Technol Univ of Calif Davis CA 95616

RUSSELL, GLEN ALLAN, b Rensselaer Co, NY, Aug 23, 25; m 53; c 2. ORGANIC CHEMISTRY. *Educ:* Rensselaer Polytech Inst, BChE, 47, MS, 48; Purdue Univ, PhD(chem), 51. *Prof Exp:* Res assoc, Res Lab, Gen Elec Co, 51-58; assoc prof, 58-62, prof chem, 72-72, DISTINGUISHED PROF, IOWA STATE UNIV, 72- *Concurrent Pos:* Sloan Found fel, 59-62; Am Chem Soc Petrol Res Found award, 64; Fulbright-Hays lectr, Univ Würzburg, 66; Reilly lectr, Univ Notre Dame, 66; vis prof, Univ Wyo, 67; Guggenheim fel, Nuclear Res Ctr, Grenoble, France, 72. *Honors & Awards:* Am Chem Soc Award, 65 & 72. *Mem:* AAAS; Am Chem Soc; The Chem Soc. *Res:* Physical organic chemistry; reactions of free radicals and atoms; chlorination; oxidation; application of electron spin resonance spectroscopy to organic molecules. *Mailing Add:* Dept of Chem Iowa State Univ Ames IA 50010

RUSSELL, GLENN C, b Taber, Alta, June 6, 21; m 47; c 5. SOIL CHEMISTRY. *Educ:* Brigham Young Univ, BS, 43; Univ Mass, MS, 49; Purdue Univ, PhD(soil chem), 52. *Prof Exp:* Instr, Univ Mass, 47-49; fel, Purdue Univ, 49-51; res officer, Agr Res Sta, Lethbridge, 51-54, head soils sect, 54-66, dir exp farm, PEI, 66-70, dir res sta, Ont, 70-75, DIR RES STA, SUMMERLAND, BC, CAN DEPT AGR, 75- *Mem:* Soil Sci Soc Am; Am Soc Agron; Can Soc Soil Sci; Agr Inst Can; Can Soc Agron. *Res:* Effect of fertilizers and soil amendments on chemical changes in the soil and on crop production. *Mailing Add:* Res Sta Can Dept of Agr Summerland Can

RUSSELL, GLENN VINTON, b St Louis, Mo, Dec 30, 22; m 44; c 3. NEUROANATOMY. *Educ:* Cornell Univ, AB, 48, MA, 49, PhD(neuroanat), 51. *Prof Exp:* Asst zool, Cornell Univ, 48-51; instr anat, Univ Tex Med Br Galveston, 51-53, from asst prof to assoc prof neuroanat, 53-64; reader anat, Makerere Univ Col, Uganda, 64-65; assoc prof neuroanat, 66-70, PROF ANAT, UNIV TEX MED BR GALVESTON, 70- *Mem:* AAAS; Sigma Xi; Am Asn Anat; Am Asn Neuropath; Soc Neurosci. *Res:* Anatomy and connections of nuclear locus coeruleus. *Mailing Add:* Ft Crockett Apts B-12 Galveston TX 77550

RUSSELL, GRANT E(DWIN), b Asheville, NC, June 5, 16; m 42; c 6. CHEMICAL ENGINEERING. *Educ:* Wash Univ, BSChE, 38, MSChE, 50. *Prof Exp:* Chemist, Reardon Co, 38-40; anal chemist, Monsanto Co, 40-41, tech asst, 42-45, chem engr, 45-48, supv engr, 48-52, asst eng supt, 52-57, eng mgr, 57-65, sr eng specialist, 65-68, sr res specialist, 68-74; sr chem eng, 75-80, CONSULT PROCESS ECON, SRI INT, 80- *Mem:* Am Inst Chem Engrs. *Res:* Economic evaluation of research projects; preliminary process design; design and economic evaluation of chemical process. *Mailing Add:* SRI Int 333 Ravenswood Ave Menlo Park CA 94025

RUSSELL, HELEN ROSS, b Myerstown, Pa, Feb 21, 15; m 60. BIOLOGY. *Educ:* Lebanon Valley Col, AB, 43; Cornell Univ, MA, 47, PhD(entom, econ bot), 49. *Hon Degrees:* DHL, Lebanon Valley Col, 73. *Prof Exp:* Pub sch teacher, Pa, 34-46; asst, Cornell Univ, 47-49; prof biol, Fitchburg State Col, 49-66, chmn dept sci, 51-56, acad dean, 56-66; CONSULT, WAVE HILL CTR ENVIRON EDUC, NY, 66-; SCI CONSULT, MANHATTAN COUNTRY SCH, 70-; SCI WRITING, 70- *Concurrent Pos:* Sci ed, Jr Encycl Britannica, 55-67; vis lectr, Am Mus Natural Hist, 78-; ed, J Am Nature Study Soc, 80- *Mem:* Fel AAAS; Am Nature Study Soc (secy, 54-58, 1st vpres, 72-74, pres, 74); Conserv Educ Asn. *Res:* Ecology and science education; author of numerous science books. *Mailing Add:* 44 College Dr Jersey City NJ 07305

RUSSELL, HENRY FRANKLIN, b Glenolden, Pa, July 18, 40; m 68; c 1. ORGANIC CHEMISTRY. *Educ:* Univ Del, BS, 63, MS, 65; Univ Va, PhD(org chem), 73. *Prof Exp:* Instr chem, US Naval Acad, 66-68; process & develop chemist, Am Cyanamid Co, 73-80. *Mem:* Am Chem Soc. *Res:* Indole alkaloid precursors; dyes and intermediates; pharmaceuticals, fine chemicals, veterinary chemicals and agricultural chemicals. *Mailing Add:* 3739 Severn Ave Charlotte NC 28210

RUSSELL, HENRY GEORGE, b Eng, June 12, 41. STRUCTURAL ENGINEERING. *Educ:* Univ Sheffield, BEng, 62, PhD(struct eng), 65. *Prof Exp:* Jr res fel struct eng, Bldg Res Sta, Eng, 65-68; struct engr, 68-74, mgr, 74-79, DIR, PORTLAND CEMENT ASN, 79- *Honors & Awards:* Martin P Korn Award, Prestressed Concrete Inst, 80. *Mem:* Fel Am Concrete Inst; Brit Concrete Soc; Prestressed Concrete Inst. *Res:* Shrinkage compensating concretes; time dependent behavior of reinforced concrete columns and posttensioned concrete bridges. *Mailing Add:* Portland Cement Asn 5420 Old Orchard Rd Skokie IL 60077

RUSSELL, IRVING JAMES, b Boston, Mass, June 18, 17; m 58; c 3. NUCLEAR CHEMISTRY, RADIATION BIOPHYSICS. *Educ:* Boston Col, BS, 43; Univ Chicago, MS, 49, PhD(nuclear chem), 56. *Prof Exp:* Weather forecaster, US Air Force, 43-46, lab dir & nuclear chemist, 49-54, tech dir, Nuclear Labs, 57-58, chief biophys res, 59-65; chmn dept, 67-71, ASSOC PROF CHEM, BOSTON COL, 65- *Concurrent Pos:* Consult, Off Civil Defense & Defense Atomic Support Agency, 65- & comt civil defense, Nat Acad Sci. *Mem:* AAAS; Am Chem Soc; Sigma Xi. *Res:* Physical chemistry; radiochemistry; fission phenomenology; fallout formation processes; radioecology; environmental and high-temperature chemistry. *Mailing Add:* Dept of Chem Boston Col Chestnut Hill MA 02167

RUSSELL, JACK UNGER, mathematics, deceased

RUSSELL, JAMES, b Leeds, Eng, Feb 14, 28; m 51; c 2. POLYMER CHEMISTRY, PHYSICAL CHEMISTRY. *Educ:* Univ London, BSc, 50, PhD(polymer chem), 53. *Prof Exp:* Fel, Cornell Univ, 53-55; res chemist, Am Viscose Corp, 55-61; res assoc, St Regis Paper Co, NY, 61-67, mgr res & develop, 67-71, dir corp prod develop, 71-75; VPRES RES & DEVELOP, SYLVACHEM CORP, 75- *Mem:* Am Chem Soc; Tech Asn Pulp & Paper Indust. *Res:* Wood chemistry and its application to pulping and byproducts; polymer chemistry and its application to packaging. *Mailing Add:* Sylvachem Corp 2147 N Sherman Ave Panama City FL 32405

RUSSELL, JAMES A(LVIN), JR, b Lawrenceville, Va, Dec 15, 17; m 43; c 2. ELECTRICAL ENGINEERING. *Educ:* Oberlin Col, AB, 40; Bradley Univ, BS, 41, MS, 50; Univ Md, EdD(indust ed), 67. *Prof Exp:* Instr elec technol, US Naval Training Sch, 42-45 & St Paul's Col, 45-50; assoc prof electronics eng, Hampton Inst, 50-58, div dir technol, 63-68, prof electronics, 67-71; pres, St Paul's Col, Va, 71-81. *Concurrent Pos:* Res engr, Thomas J Watson Res Ctr, IBM Corp, 68-69; chmn dept electronics technol, Hampton Inst, 58-68, chmn dept eng & dir eng & technol div, 68-71. *Mem:* Am Soc Eng Educ; Inst Elec & Electronics Engrs; Tech Educ Asn. *Res:* Industrial education; investigation into changes in critical thinking and achievement in electronics as the result of exposure of subjects to specific techniques of critical thinking. *Mailing Add:* 9800 Channing Circle Richmond VA 23235

RUSSELL, JAMES CHRISTOPHER, b Montreal, Que, Oct 24, 38; m 62; c 1. PHYSIOLOGICAL CHEMISTRY, CLINICAL CHEMISTRY. *Educ:* Dalhousie Univ, BSc, 58; Univ Sask, MSc, 59, PhD(radiation chem), 62. *Prof Exp:* Gen Elec Co fel phys chem, Univ Leeds, 62-64; univ fel chem, 64-67, asst prof biochem in surg & dir biochem lab, Surg-Med Res Inst, 67-72, assoc prof, 72-81, PROF BIOCHEM IN SURG, UNIV ALTA, 81- *Mem:* AAAS; Can Soc Clin Chemists; Can Pysiol Soc. *Res:* Clinical chemistry in both humans and animals; animal models of cardiovascular disease; biochemistry of exercise; physiological chemistry of gastric secretions; renal function and shock. *Mailing Add:* Dept of Surg Clin Sci Bldg Univ of Alta Edmonton AB T6G 2G7 Can

RUSSELL, JAMES E(DWARD), b Rapid City, SDak, May 20, 40; m 63; c 2. ROCK MECHANICS, MINING ENGINEERING. *Educ:* SDak Sch Mines & Technol, BS, 63, MS, 64; Northwestern Univ, Evanston, PhD(theoret & appl mech), 66. *Prof Exp:* Sr res engr, Southwest Res Inst, 66-67; from asst prof to assoc prof civil eng, SDak Sch Mines & Technol, 67-71, from assoc prof to prof civil & mining eng, 71-76; proj mgr rock mech, Off Waste Isolation, Union Carbide Corp, 77-78; PROF PETROL ENG & GEOPHYS, TEX A&M UNIV, 78- *Concurrent Pos:* Vpres struct & mech systs, RE/SPEC, Inc, 69-76. *Mem:* Am Soc Civil Engrs; Am Inst Mining, Metall & Petrol Engrs; Am Acad Mech; Am Geophys Union. *Res:* Rock mechanics; nuclear waste disposal and underground storage; in situ gasification of coal-subsidence. *Mailing Add:* Dept of Petrol Eng Tex A&M Univ College Station TX 77843

RUSSELL, JAMES EDWARD, b Ft Wayne, Ind, Sept 27, 31. PHYSICS. *Educ:* Yale Univ, BS, 53, MS, 54, PhD(physics), 58. *Prof Exp:* Fel, Univ Va, 57-58; res assoc physics, Ind Univ, 58-60; res physicist, Carnegie Inst Technol, 60-62; vis asst prof, Univ Padua, 62-63; sr res officer, Univ Oxford, 63-65; assoc prof, 65-74, PROF PHYSICS, UNIV CINCINNATI, 74- *Res:* Nuclear physics; mesonic atoms. *Mailing Add:* Dept of Physics Univ of Cincinnati Cincinnati OH 45221

RUSSELL, JAMES MADISON, III, b Newport News, Va; m 60; c 3. ATMOSPHERIC SCIENCE, ELECTRICAL ENGINEERING. *Educ:* Va Polytech Inst & State Univ, BS, 62; Univ Va, MEE, 66; Univ Mich, PhD(atmospheric sci), 70. *Prof Exp:* Aerospace engr, NASA Langley Res Ctr, 62-68; res asst, Univ Mich, 68-70; res scientist, 70-75, HEAD ATMOSPHERIC SYSTS BR, ATMOSPHERIC ENVIRON SCI DIV, NASA LANGLEY RES CTR, 76- *Concurrent Pos:* Lectr physics, Christopher Newport Col, 71-73; lectr remote sensing atmosphere, George Washington Univ, 73-; vis scientist spec proj, Nat Ctr Atmospheric Res, Boulder, Colo, 74. *Mem:* Am Meteorol Soc; Sigma Xi. *Res:* Remote sensing of the atmosphere; atmospheric physics including radiation, dynamics, and transport; atmospheric photochemistry; integrity of the ozone layer; tropospheric pollution, stratosphere-troposphere exchange. *Mailing Add:* NASA Langley Res Ctr Mail Stop 401A Hampton VA 23665

RUSSELL, JAMES N(ELSON), b Hereford, Tex, Dec 26, 07; m 39; c 3. CHEMICAL ENGINEERING. *Educ:* Univ Okla, BS, 31. *Prof Exp:* Technician, Oil Refining Lab, Pure Oil Co, Okla, 26-28, anal chemist & chief technician, 32-35, chemist in charge phys dept, Control Lab, Ill, 35-36, refining design engr, 36-42; inspector & pipeline engr, Panhandle Eastern Pipeline Co, Mo, 31-32; process & proj engr, Stone & Webster Eng Corp, Mass, 42-56; supv process engr, Bechtel Corp, Calif, 56-59; sr chem engr, C F Braun & Co, 59-75; consult engr, Fluor, 75-78 & Jacobs Eng Group, 78-80; refinery mgr & consult Huntway Refining Co & planning dir, Edgington Oil Co, 80-81; CONSULT, KINETIC TECHNOL INT, 80- *Mem:* Am Inst Chem Engrs. *Res:* Design, construction and initial operation of refining units; gasoline and chemical plants. *Mailing Add:* 1880 Lorain Rd San Marino CA 91108

RUSSELL, JAMES TORRANCE, b Bremerton, Wash, Feb 23, 31; m 53; c 3. APPLIED PHYSICS, ELECTRONICS. *Educ:* Reed Col, BA, 53. *Prof Exp:* Physicist, Hanford Atomic Prod Oper, Gen Elec Co, 53-60, sr physicist, 60-65; res assoc exp physics, Pac Northwest Labs, Battelle Mem Inst, 65-66, sr res assoc appl physics, 66-80; VPRES & TECH DIR, DIGITAL REC CORP, 80- *Mem:* AAAS; Am Phys Soc; Inst Elec & Electronics Engr; Am Polar Soc; Soc Photo-Optical Instrumentation Engrs. *Res:* Physics of instrumentation; sensor development; digital computer methods; high resolution optical systems; laser devices; development of techniques for experimental physics. *Mailing Add:* Digital Rec Corp 2505 E Parleys Way Salt Lake City UT 84109

RUSSELL, JANE LORENE, b Canton, Ohio, June 16, 49. ASTRONOMY. *Educ:* Mt Union Col, BS, 71; Univ SFla, MA, 73; Univ Pittsburgh, PhD(astron), 76. *Prof Exp:* Res assoc astron, Allegheny Observ, Univ Pittsburgh, 76-80; MEM STAFF, DEPT PHYSICS, IOWA STATE UNIV, 80- *Mem:* Am Astron Soc; Sigma Xi. *Res:* Astrometry; stellar distances and dynamics, double stars, astrometric binaries, the search for extrasolar planetary systems. *Mailing Add:* Physics Bldg Iowa State Univ Ames IA 50010

RUSSELL, JOEL W, b Elkhart, Ind, May 18, 39; m 61; c 5. PHYSICAL CHEMISTRY. *Educ:* Northwestern Univ, BA, 61; Univ Calif, Berkeley, PhD(chem), 65. *Prof Exp:* Res fel, Univ Minn, 65-66; asst prof, 66-70, ASSOC PROF CHEM, OAKLAND UNIV, 70- *Concurrent Pos:* Vis mem staff, Australian Nat Univ, 72-73; res fel, Southampton Univ, 80-81. *Mem:* Am Chem Soc; Am Phys Soc. *Res:* Molecular structure and dynamics; infrared and raman spectroscopy of nitrogen heterocycles and proteins; ultraviolet-visible and infrared modulated specular reflections spectroscopy. *Mailing Add:* Dept Chem Oakland Univ Rochester MI 48063

RUSSELL, JOHN ALBERT, b Ludington, Mich, Mar 23, 13; m 36; c 2. ASTRONOMY. *Educ:* Univ Calif, AB, 35, AM, 37, PhD(astron), 43. *Prof Exp:* Guide, Griffith Observ, 35; asst, Univ Calif, 36-39; instr astron, Pasadena City Col, 39-41, Exten Div, Univ Calif, Los Angeles, 41, Santa Ana Army Air Base, 42 & Pasadena City Col, 46; head dept astron, 46-69, from asst prof to prof, 46-78, chmn div phys sci & math, 59-62, assoc dean natural sci & math, Col Lett, Arts & Sci, 63-68, EMER PROF ASTRON, UNIV SOUTHERN CALIF, 78- *Concurrent Pos:* Fac res lectr, Univ Southern Calif, 57-; mem comn interplanetary dust, Int Astron Union. *Honors & Awards:* Univ Assocs Award, 60. *Mem:* AAAS; Am Astron Soc; Meteoritical Soc (secy, 49-58, pres, 58-62). *Res:* Meteor spectroscopy and statistics. *Mailing Add:* Dept of Astron Univ of Southern Calif Los Angeles CA 90007

RUSSELL, JOHN ALVIN, b San Antonio, Tex, Aug 15, 34; m 58; c 2. TRIBOLOGY. *Educ:* Univ Tex, BS, 57; St Mary's Univ, MS, 64. *Prof Exp:* Assoc engr, Convair Astronaut, San Diego, 57; proj officer nuclear weapons, US Air Force, 57-60; mgr special proj fuels & lubricants, Alcor Inc, 60-71; MGR SYNTHETIC FUELS D DEVELOP, SOUTHWEST RES INST, 71- *Concurrent Pos:* Sr res engr tribology, Southwest Res Inst, 60-66; mem fuels & lubricants comt, Coord Res Coun, 67-; mem tech adv panel, Alternative Fuels, US Dept Energy, 76- *Mem:* Soc Automotive Engrs (pres, 72-73); Am Soc Mech Engrs (vpres, 65-66); Am Soc Lubrication Engrs; Sigma Xi. *Res:* Synthetic fuels and lubricants performance in aviation and automotive power plants; cryogenic tribology; hydrocarbon fuels utilization projection analysis. *Mailing Add:* 7215 Brookside Lane San Antonio TX 78209

RUSSELL, JOHN BLAIR, b Rochester, NY, Dec 13, 29; m 55; c 1. INORGANIC CHEMISTRY. *Educ:* Oberlin Col, AB, 51; Cornell Univ, PhD(chem), 56. *Prof Exp:* Instr & res assoc chem, Cornell Univ, 55-56; from asst prof to assoc prof, 56-65, PROF CHEM, HUMBOLDT STATE UNIV, 65- *Mem:* Am Chem Soc. *Res:* Solutions of metals in liquid ammonia; electrochemistry in aqueous and non-aqueous solvents; complex ions. *Mailing Add:* Dept of Chem Humboldt State Univ Arcata CA 95521

RUSSELL, JOHN GEORGE, b Manila, Philippines, Dec 19, 41; US citizen; m 66. ORGANIC CHEMISTRY. *Educ:* Purdue Univ, BS, 63; Univ Minn, PhD(org chem), 68. *Prof Exp:* Res assoc chem, Ohio State Univ, 68; asst prof, 69-74, ASSOC PROF CHEM, CALIF STATE UNIV, SACRAMENTO, 74-

Mem: Am Chem Soc. *Res:* Nuclear magnetic resonance spectroscopy; conformational analysis; synthesis, rate and equilibria studies of organometallic compounds. *Mailing Add:* Dept of Chem Calif State Univ Sacramento CA 95819

RUSSELL, JOHN HENRY, b Roswell, NMex, Aug 15, 19; m 42; c 4. ENGINEERING. *Educ:* Univ Tex, ChemE, 42. *Prof Exp:* Jr engr, Holston Ord Works, Tenn Eastman Corp, 42-44; sr engr, Manhattan Proj, 44-45; sect leader nuclear weapons res & develop, Manhattan Proj, 45-46, asst group leader, Los Alamos Sci Lab, 46-60, group & assoc div leader, nuclear reactor develop, 60-70, STAFF MEM WEAPON DEVELOP, LOS ALAMOS SCI LAB, UNIV CALIF, 70- *Mem:* Am Chem Soc; Am Inst Chem Engrs; Am Nuclear Soc. *Res:* Ultra high temperature reactor experiment; all aspects of high temperature gas-cooled reactors; classified application of high explosives to nuclear weapons development. *Mailing Add:* 1165-41st St Los Alamos NM 87544

RUSSELL, JOHN LYNN, JR, b Woodsborough, Tex, Aug 5, 30; m 51; c 3. NUCLEAR PHYSICS. *Educ:* Univ Tex, BS, 51; Rice Univ, MA, 54, PhD(physics), 56. *Prof Exp:* Theoret physicist, Vallecitos Atomic Lab, Gen Elec Co, 56-60, mgr exp reactor physics, 60-62; mgr spec projs, Gen Atomic Co, San Diego, Calif, 62-78; PROF, DEPT OF NUCLEAR ENG, GA INST TECHNOL, 78- *Mem:* Am Nuclear Soc; Int Asn Hydrogen Energy; Int Solar Energy Soc; Am Phys Soc. *Res:* Pulsed neutron measurements; fast neutron spectra in bulk media; fast reactors; control of nuclear reactors; solar energy; hydrogen production; charged particle scattering. *Mailing Add:* Dept of Nuclear Eng Ga Inst of Technol Atlanta GA 30332

RUSSELL, JOHN MCCANDLESS, b Drumright, Okla; m 62; c 2. PHYSIOLOGY. *Educ:* Univ NMex, BS, 66; Univ Utah, PhD(pharmacol), 71. *Prof Exp:* NIH fel, Dept Physiol & Biophys, Sch Med, Washington Univ, 72-73; asst prof, 74-78, ASSOC UNIV TEX MED BR, 78- *Mem:* Biophys Soc; Soc Gen Physiologists; AAAS. *Res:* Mechanisms involved in the membrane translocation of ions, especially the chloride anion and its role in introcellular phosphate regulation in biological tissue. *Mailing Add:* Dept of Physiol & Biophys Univ of Tex Med Br Galveston TX 77550

RUSSELL, JOSEPH L, b Independence, Mo, Oct 11, 31; m 52; c 4. CHEMICAL ENGINEERING. *Educ:* Univ Kans, BS, 52; Mass Inst Technol, ScD(chem eng), 55. *Prof Exp:* Proj leader chem eng, Dow Chem Co, 55-58; dir eng res, Sci Design Co Inc, 58-60, dir res, 60-66, vpres res & develop, Halcon Int, Inc, 66-70, SR V PRES RES & DEVELOP, HALCON INT, INC, 70-, CHMN BD, SCI DESIGN CO INC, 70- *Mem:* Am Inst Chem; Am Petrol Inst; Electrochem Soc; Am Chem Soc; Am Inst Chem Engrs. *Res:* New processes for organic and petrochemical fields. *Mailing Add:* Halcon Int Inc 2 Park Ave New York NY 10016

RUSSELL, JOSEPH LOUIS, b Vicksburg, Miss, June 18, 36; m 62; c 1. FLUORINE CHEMISTRY. *Educ:* Alcorn State Univ, BS, 60; Marquette Univ, MS, 71, PhD(inorg chem), 74. *Prof Exp:* Teacher math, Natchez Pub Schs, 60-64; control chemist, Liquid Glaze Chem Co, 65; scientist chem, Battelle-Northwest Lab, 66-69; teaching asst chem, Marquette Univ, 69-74; asst prof, 74-77, ASSOC PROF CHEM, ALCORN STATE UNIV, 77- *Concurrent Pos:* Lab instr chem, Ala State Col, 65. *Mem:* Am Chem Soc. *Res:* Reactions in anhydrous liquid hydrogen fluoride; transition metal bonding to plant harmones; photochemical catalyzed decomposition of volatile Freons. *Mailing Add:* Alcorn State Univ PO Box 1259 Lorman MS 39096

RUSSELL, KENNETH CALVIN, b Greeley, Colo, Feb 4, 36; m 63; c 2. METALLURGY, MATERIALS SCIENCE. *Educ:* Colo Sch Mines, MetE, 59; Carnegie Inst Technol, PhD(metall eng), 64. *Prof Exp:* Asst engr, Westinghouse Elec Corp, 59-61; NSF fel, Oslo, 63-64; from asst prof to assoc prof metall, 64-78, PROF METALL & NUCLEAR ENG, MASS INST TECHNOL, 78- *Concurrent Pos:* Ford Found fel eng, 64-66. *Mem:* Am Inst Mining, Metall & Petrol Engrs; Am Phys Soc; Am Soc Metals; Am Nuclear Soc. *Res:* Phase transformations; lattice defects in solids; radiation damage. *Mailing Add:* 21 Taft Ave Lexington MA 02173

RUSSELL, KENNETH EDWIN, b Barnwell, Eng, Dec 9, 24; m 55; c 3. POLYMER CHEMISTRY. *Educ:* Cambridge Univ, BA, 45, PhD(chem), 48. *Prof Exp:* Vis asst prof, Pa State Col, 48-50; asst lectr, Manchester Univ, 50-52; fel, Princeton Univ, 52-54; lectr, 54-56, from asst prof to assoc prof, 56-66, PROF CHEM, QUEEN'S UNIV, ONT, 66- *Mem:* Am Chem Soc; fel Chem Inst Can; Royal Soc Chem. *Res:* Cationic polymerization; free radical polymerization; hydrogen abstraction reactions in solution; polymer photodegradation; studies of free radical intermediates by electron paramagnetic resonance spectroscopy. *Mailing Add:* Dept of Chem Queen's Univ Kingston ON K7L 3N6 Can

RUSSELL, KENNETH HOMER, b Portland, Ore, June 7, 33; m 54; c 3. PHYSICAL CHEMISTRY. *Educ:* Portland State Col, BS, 58; Washington State Univ, PhD(phys chem), 64. *Prof Exp:* Instr chem, Portland State Col, 58-59; from asst prof to assoc prof, 63-72, PROF CHEM, CALIF STATE UNIV, FRESNO, 72- *Concurrent Pos:* Lectr solar energy; partner, Solar Design & Mfg Co. *Mem:* AAAS; Am Chem Soc; The Chem Soc; Int Solar Energy Soc. *Res:* Molecular structure and infrared spectroscopy of inorganic compounds in the solid state. *Mailing Add:* Dept Chem Calif State Univ Fresno CA 93710

RUSSELL, KENNETH LLOYD, geology, see previous edition

RUSSELL, LEONARD NELSON, b Coldwater, Mich, Jan 15, 22; m 47; c 2. NUCLEAR PHYSICS. *Educ:* Kalamazoo Col, AB, 47; Ohio State Univ, PhD(physics), 52. *Prof Exp:* Res physicist, Mound Lab, 47-54, from asst prof to assoc prof, 54-70, PROF PHYSICS & MATH, OHIO WESLEYAN UNIV, 70- *Res:* Proton capture studies with van de Graaff generator; beta ray spectroscopy. *Mailing Add:* Dept of Physics & Math Ohio Wesleyan Univ Delaware OH 43015

RUSSELL, LEWIS KEITH, b E Liverpool, Ohio, Nov 15, 31; m 57; c 8. PHYSICS, ELECTRONIC ENGINEERING. *Educ:* Univ Calif, Berkeley, BA, 56, MA, 65. *Prof Exp:* Physicist solid-state, Int Bus Mach Corp, Poughkeepsie, 56-58; nuclear physicist, Lawrence Livermore Labs, 58-62; sr engr transistor devices, Raytheon Co, Mountain View, Calif, 62-67; DEPT MGR CIRCUIT RES, SIGNETICS CORP, 67- *Concurrent Pos:* Lectr, Stanford Univ, 79- *Mem:* Sr mem Inst Elec & Electronics Engrs. *Res:* Advanced electronic circuits and systems; computer aided design and simulation; solid state electronic devices; device physics; computer architecture; artificial intelligence. *Mailing Add:* Signetics Corp 811 E Arques Ave Sunnyvale CA 94086

RUSSELL, LIANE BRAUCH, b Vienna, Austria, Aug 27, 23; nat US; m 47; c 2. GENETICS. *Educ:* Hunter Col, AB, 45; Univ Chicago, PhD(zool), 49. *Prof Exp:* Asst, Jackson Mem Lab, 45, 46; asst, Dept Zool, Univ Chicago, 46-47; biologist, 47-75, SECT HEAD MUTAGENESIS & TERATOGENESIS, OAK RIDGE NAT LAB, 75- *Concurrent Pos:* Sci adv to US deleg, First Atoms-for-Peace Conf, 55; mem comt energy & the environ, Nat Acad Sci, 75-77, biological effects of ionizing radiations, 77-; mem sci comt 1 task group, Nat Coun for Radiation Protection & measurements, 75-77; mem comt 1, Int Comn for Protection against Mutagens & Carcinogens, 77- *Honors & Awards:* Int Roentgen Medal, 73. *Mem:* Fel AAAS; Soc Develop Biol; Genetics Soc Am; Environ Mutagen Soc; Teratology Soc. *Res:* Cytogenetics of the mouse; radiation genetics of the mouse; radiation effects of embryonic development; chemical mutagenesis and teratogenesis; genetic activity of the mammalian X chromosome; developmental genetics. *Mailing Add:* Biol Div Oak Ridge Nat Lab PO Box Y Oak Ridge TN 37830

RUSSELL, LORIS SHANO, b Brooklyn, NY, Apr 21, 04; m 38. PALEONTOLOGY. *Educ:* Univ Alta, BSc, 27, LLD, 58; Princeton Univ, AM, 29, PhD(paleont), 30. *Prof Exp:* Field officer, Geol Div, Res Coun, Alta, 28-29; asst paleontologist, Geol Surv Can, 30-37; from asst dir to dir, Royal Ont Mus, 37-50; chief zoologist, Nat Mus Can, 50-56, dir, 56-63; chief biologist, 63-71, EMER CUR, ROYAL ONT MUS, 71- *Concurrent Pos:* From asst prof to prof paleont, Univ Toronto, 37-70, emer prof, 70- *Honors & Awards:* Willet G Miller Medal, Royal Soc Can, 59; Can Jubilee Medal, 78. *Mem:* Geol Soc Am; Paleont Soc; Soc Vert Paleont; Can Mus Asn; Royal Soc Can. *Res:* Vertebrate paleontology; fossil vertebrates and mollusks of western North America; Cretaceous and Tertiary stratigraphy of western North America. *Mailing Add:* Royal Ont Mus 100 Queen's Park Toronto ON M5S 2C6 Can

RUSSELL, MARTIN, b Setauket, NY, June 5, 23; m 47; c 3. PHYSICAL GEOLOGY. *Educ:* City Col New York, BA, 47; Harvard Univ, MA, 49. *Prof Exp:* Geologist, US Geol Surv, 49-58; managing ed tech publ, Am Geol Inst, 58-65; managing ed, Geol Soc Am, 65-68; CHIEF, REPORTS SECT, SUPPORT SERV BR, DEPT TECH COOP FOR DEVELOP, UN, 68- *Mem:* Geosci Info Soc; Soc Tech Commun; Asn Earth Sci Ed; Soc Scholar Publ. *Res:* Scientific and technical documentation; paleontology and stratigraphy; military geology. *Mailing Add:* Reports Sect Dept Tech Coop for Develop UN New York NY 10017

RUSSELL, MARVIN W, b Poole, Ky, Aug 26, 27; m 48; c 4. PHYSICS, APPLIED MATHEMATICS. *Educ:* Western Ky Univ, BS, 50; Univ Fla, MS, 52, PhD(physics), 54. *Prof Exp:* Physicist, Gen Elec Co, 54-61; sr res scientist physics, Kaman Nuclear, 61-62; head dept physics, 62-65, DEAN, OGDEN COL SCI & TECHNOL, WESTERN KY UNIV, 65-, PROF PHYSICS, 74- *Concurrent Pos:* Vis lectr, Ky Wesleyan Col, 56-60. *Mem:* AAAS; Am Phys Soc; Inst Elec & Electronics Eng; Am Vacuum Soc; Am Asn Physics Teachers. *Res:* Electron and heat transfer physics; mass spectrometry; applied mathematics; ion mobility and recombination phenomena; mathematical models; physics applied to the botanical sciences; science education. *Mailing Add:* Ogden Col of Sci & Technol Western Ky Univ Bowling Green KY 42101

RUSSELL, MORLEY EGERTON, b Los Angeles, Calif, June , 29; m 63; c 2. PHYSICAL CHEMISTRY. *Educ:* Col Wooster, AB, 51; Mass Inst Technol, SM, 53; Univ Mich, PhD(chem), 58. *Prof Exp:* Fel phys chem, Nobel Inst Chem, Sweden, 58-59; asst prof, Mich State Univ, 59-64; asst prof, 64-74, ASSOC PROF PHYS CHEM, NORTHERN ILL UNIV, 74- *Mem:* Am Soc Mass Spectrometry; Am Chem Soc. *Res:* Kinetics of homogeneous reactions; mass spectrometry. *Mailing Add:* Dept of Chem Northern Ill Univ DeKalb IL 60115

RUSSELL, NANCY JEANNE, b Virginia, Minn, June 12, 38; m 65. BIOLOGY, PHARMACOLOGY. *Educ:* Univ Minn, BA, 60, MA, 67, PhD(zool), 72. *Prof Exp:* Res assoc develop biol, Reed Col, 67-68; res asst cutaneous biol, Ore Regional Primate Ctr, 68-69; res assoc neuropharmacol, 72-78, res assoc & fel neuropharmacol-morphol, 73-75, res instr pharmacol, 75-78, RES ASST PROF PHARMACOL, SCH MED, UNIV ORE, 78- *Concurrent Pos:* Pharmaceut Mfrs Asn Found fel pharmacol morphol, 73; fel pharmacol, Sch Med, Univ Ore Health Sci Ctr, 73-75. *Mem:* Int Fedn Electron Microscopy Soc; Am Soc Zoologists. *Res:* Neuropharmacology neuroanatomy and neuropathology as related to drug action on sensory system, cochlear and vestibular system, and myenteric plexus of gastro intestinal tract. *Mailing Add:* Dept of Pharmacol Sch Med Univ Ore Health Sci Ctr Portland OR 97201

RUSSELL, ORVILLE EUGENE, b Tiltonville, Ohio, Apr 13, 17; m 41; c 2. ORAL SURGERY. *Educ:* Ohio Univ, AB, 39; Ohio State Univ, DDS, 47. *Prof Exp:* High sch instr, Ohio, 40-42; intern oral surg, 47-48, instr, 48-51, asst prof oral surg & anat, 51-61, assoc prof anat, 61-71, PROF ORAL SURG & ANAT, COL MED & COL DENT, OHIO STATE UNIV, 71-, PROF DENT, 76- *Mem:* Am Dent Asn. *Mailing Add:* Col of Dent Ohio State Univ Columbus OH 43210

RUSSELL, PAUL E(DGAR), b Roswell, NMex, Oct 10, 24; m 43; c 3. ELECTRICAL ENGINEERING. *Educ:* NMex State Univ, BS, 46 & 47; Univ Wis, MS, 50, PhD(elec eng), 51. *Prof Exp:* From instr to asst prof elec eng, Univ Wis, 47-52; sr dynamics engr, Gen Dynamics/Convair, 52-54; prof elec eng, Univ Ariz, 54-63, head dept, 58-63, dir appl res lab, 56-58, 60-63; prof elec eng & dean col eng, Kans State Univ, 63-67; PROF ENG, ARIZ STATE UNIV, 67- *Concurrent Pos:* Consult, NSF, Dynamic Sci, Westinghouse, Motorola, AiResearch & US Army Electronic Proving Grounds. *Mem:* Am Soc Eng Educ; Inst Elec & Electronics Engrs; Nat Soc Prof Engrs. *Res:* Control systems analysis and design; computers; photovoltaic power systems. *Mailing Add:* Col of Eng Sci Ariz State Univ Tempe AZ 85281

RUSSELL, PAUL SNOWDEN, b Chicago, Ill, Jan 22, 25; m 52; c 4. SURGERY, IMMUNOLOGY. *Educ:* Univ Chicago, PhB, 44, BS, 45, MD, 47; Am Bd Surg, dipl, 57; Am Bd Thoracic Surg, dipl, 60. *Hon Degrees:* MA, Harvard Univ, 62. *Prof Exp:* Surg intern, Mass Gen Hosp, 48-49, asst surg resident, 49-51 & 53-55; teaching fel surg, Harvard Med Sch, 56, instr, 57-59; clin assoc surg & tutor med sci, 59-60; assoc prof surg, Col Physicians & Surgeons, Columbia Univ, 60-62; JOHN HOMANS PROF SURG, HARVARD MED SCH, 62- *Concurrent Pos:* USPHS res fel, 54-55; resident, Mass Gen Hosp, 56, asst surg, 57-60; assoc attend surgeon, Presby Hosp & assoc vis surgeon, Francis Delafield Hosp, 60-62; USPHS career develop award, 60-62; chief gen surg serv, Mass Gen Hosp, 62-69, vis surgeon, 69-; mem comts trauma & tissue transplantation, Div Med Sci, Nat Acad Sci-Nat Res Coun, 63; mem allergy & immunol study sect, Div Res Grants, NIH, 63-65, chmn, 65; secy, Depts Surg, Harvard Med Sch, 65-70. *Mem:* Fel Am Col Surg; Am Asn Thoracic Surg; Soc Clin Surg; fel Royal Soc Med; Transplantation Soc (pres, 70-72). *Mailing Add:* Dept of Surg Mass Gen Hosp Boston MA 02114

RUSSELL, PAUL TELFORD, b San Francisco, Calif, June 5, 35; m 59; c 3. BIOCHEMISTRY. *Educ:* Univ Calif, Berkeley, BA, 59; Univ Ore, MS, 61, PhD(biochem), 63. *Prof Exp:* Trainee, Steroid Training Prog, Clark Univ & Worcester Found Exp Biol, 63-64; fel chem, Univ Miss, 64-66; asst prof obstet & gynec, Ohio State Univ, 66-68; asst prof obstet, Gynec & biol chem, 68-76, ASSOC PROF RES OBSTET & GYNEC, MED SCH, UNIV CINCINNATI, 76-, ASSOC PROF PEDIAT, 78- *Res:* Pathways and mechanisms of biosynthesis and metabolism of steroidal compounds; metabolic pathways of prostaglandins. *Mailing Add:* Dept of Obstet & Gynec Univ of Cincinnati Med Sch Cincinnati OH 45229

RUSSELL, PERCY J, b New York, NY, May 29, 26; m 55; c 3. BIOCHEMISTRY. *Educ:* City Col New York, BS, 50; Brooklyn Col, MA, 55; Western Reserve Univ, PhD(biochem), 59. *Prof Exp:* Res fel bact, Harvard Univ, 59-61; from asst prof to assoc prof biochem, Univ Kans, 61-70; ASSOC PROF BIOCHEM, UNIV CALIF, SAN DIEGO, 70- *Res:* Immunochemistry; enzyme mechanisms; phospholipid metabolism. *Mailing Add:* Dept Biol Univ Calif San Diego La Jolla CA 92037

RUSSELL, PETER BYROM, b Manchester, Eng, Oct 24, 18; nat US; m 45; c 2. ORGANIC CHEMISTRY. *Educ:* Univ Manchester, BSc, 40, MSc, 41, PhD, 45, DSc, 54. *Prof Exp:* Sr res chemist, Burroughs Wellcome & Co, Inc, 47-56; dir res, John Wyeth & Brother Ltd, Eng, 56-57; mgr org develop lab, 57-59, DIR RES, WYETH LABS DIV, AM HOME PROD CORP, 59- *Concurrent Pos:* Chmn ad hoc study group med chem, Walter Reed Army Inst Res, 73-75. *Mem:* Am Chem Soc. *Res:* Isolation and synthesis of natural products; synthesis of chemotherapeutically active compounds; medicinal chemistry; pharmaceutical chemistry. *Mailing Add:* Wyeth Labs Inc Box 8299 Philadelphia PA 19101

RUSSELL, PHILIP BOYD, b Buffalo, NY, Mar 15, 44; m 73. REMOTE SENSING. *Educ:* Wesleyan Univ, BA, 65; Stanford Univ, MS, 67, PhD(physics), 71. *Prof Exp:* Fel, Nat Ctr Atmospheric Res, 72-72; physicist, 72-76, SR PHYSICIST, SRI INT, 76- *Concurrent Pos:* Prin investr grants, NSF, NASA & ARO Corp, 74-; mem, Army Basic Res Adv Comn, Nat Res Coun, 79-, Solar Terrestrial Observ Sci Study Group, NASA, 80-82 & Atmospheric Lidar Working Group, 77-79. *Mem:* Am Meteorol Soc; Optical Soc Am; Am Geophys Union; AAAS. *Res:* Atmospheric physics; remote sensing and radiative transfer; radiative and climatic effects of aerosols and gases; satellite measurements; laser and acoustic radar; data validation and error analysis; atmospheric multi-sensor experiment design. *Mailing Add:* EL233 SRI Int 333 Ravenswood Ave Menlo Park CA 94025

RUSSELL, PHILIP KING, b Syracuse, NY, Jan 26, 32; m 55; c 3. INFECTIOUS DISEASES, VIROLOGY. *Educ:* Johns Hopkins Univ, AB, 54; Univ Rochester, MD, 58; Am Bd Internal Med, dipl. *Prof Exp:* Med Corps, US Army, 58-, intern med, NC Mem Hosp, 58-59, lab officer, Walter Reed Army Inst Res, 59-61, resident med, Univ Hosp, Baltimore, 61-63, clin investr infectious dis, Pakistan Med Res Ctr, 63-64, res officer, Walter Reed Army Inst Res, 64-65, mem, Seato Med Res Lab, 65-68, chief dept virus dis, 68-71, dep dir, 76-79, DIR DIV COMMUN DIS & IMMUNOL, WALTER REED ARMY INST RES, US ARMY, 71-, DIR & COMMANDANT, 79- *Concurrent Pos:* Mem bd dir, Gorgas Mem Inst; sci adv comt denque & yellow fever, Pan Am Health Orgn; tech adv comt, Denque haemorrhnqic Fever, WHO, Infectious Dis Comt & Task Force Virology, Nat Inst Allergy & Infectious Dis, NIH; chmn steering comt, Scientific Working Group on Immunology of Malaria, WHO, 80- *Honors & Awards:* Gorgas Medal; Smadel Mem Medal; Paul Siple Medal. *Mem:* Am Soc Trop Med & Hyg; Am Soc Microbiol; Am Asn Immunol; Am Epidemiol Soc; Infectious Dis Soc Am. *Res:* Virus diseases; immunology; pathogenesis of virus diseases; epidemiology of arboviruses. *Mailing Add:* Walter Reed Army Inst Res Washington DC 20012

RUSSELL, R(OBERT) G(RANT), b Baltimore, Md, Dec 11, 11; m 38; c 3. CERAMICS ENGINEERING. *Educ:* Univ Ill, BS, 33. *Prof Exp:* Ceramic engr, Torstenson Glass Co, Ill, 35-42; ceramic engr, Glass Res Dept, 42-50, head, Dept Basic Melting Res, 50-54, proj mgr, 54-72, sr res scientist explor res & new prod develop, 72-75, CONSULT, OWENS-CORNING FIBERGLAS CORP, 75- *Mem:* Am Ceramic Soc. *Res:* Glass melting and enameling; application of high temperature metals to glass work; design of platinum fiber forming units; rotary process research. *Mailing Add:* 2083 Welsh Hills NE Granville OH 43023

RUSSELL, RAYMOND ALVIN, b Buffalo, NY, Jan 16, 17; m 43; c 2. PHYSIOLOGY. *Educ:* Hamilton Col, AB, 38; Univ Rochester, MS, 41, PhD(physiol), 51. *Prof Exp:* Asst agr biochem, Univ Minn, 41-42; asst invest chem, NY Agr Exp Sta, 42-44; from instr to assoc prof, La State Univ Med Ctr, New Orleans, 51-80; RETIRED. *Concurrent Pos:* Consult, Southern Baptist Hosp, New Orleans, La, 59-76. *Mem:* Am Physiol Soc; AAAS. *Res:* Secretion of the small intestine; myocardial metabolism; circulatory shock. *Mailing Add:* Box 507 Kiln MS 39556

RUSSELL, RICHARD DANA, b Pomona, Calif, Nov 15, 06; m 33; c 2. SEDIMENTOLOGY, OCEANOGRAPHY. *Educ:* Pomona Col, BA, 27; Univ Calif, PhD(geol), 32. *Prof Exp:* From instr to assoc prof geol, La State Univ, 31-42; res assoc, Div War Res, Univ Calif, 42-44, oceanogr, 44-45, publ mgr, 45-46; tech ed & head publ dept, US Navy Electronics Lab, 46-47, sr staff geophysicist, 47-50, sr consult geophys & head sci planning bd, 50-55; mgr geol res, Marathon OIl Co, 55-63, assoc dir explor res, 63-70, consult, 70-71. *Concurrent Pos:* With Bikini Sci Resurv, 47; lectr, Calif Inst Technol, 48 & Scripps Inst, Univ Calif, 49-54; mem comt sedimentation, Nat Res Coun, 37-46; hon comt, Ctr Oceanog R Res & Study; vpres, Am Geol Inst, 72, pres, 73. *Mem:* Fel AAAS; fel Geol Soc Am; Soc Econ Paleontologists & Mineralogists (vpres, 43, pres, 48); Am Inst Prof Geologists (pres, 69); Am Asn Petrol Geologists. *Res:* Petrology of recent sediments; oceanography; stratigraphy; field and marine geology; sedimentary petrology and petrography; military oceanography; lake evaporation; petroleum exploration; research administration. *Mailing Add:* 6597 Meadowridge Dr Santa Rosa CA 95405

RUSSELL, RICHARD DONCASTER, b Toronto, Ont, Feb 27, 29; m 51; c 3. GEOPHYSICS. *Educ:* Univ Toronto, BA, 51, MA, 52, PhD(physics, geophys), 54. *Prof Exp:* Lectr physics, Univ Toronto, 54-56, asst prof, 56-58; assoc prof, Univ BC, 58-62; prof, Univ Toronto, 62-63; PROF GEOPHYS, UNIV BC, 63-, HEAD DEPT, 68- *Mem:* Am Geophys Union; fel Royal Soc Can; Can Asn Physicists. *Res:* Mass spectrometry; seismology; electronics. *Mailing Add:* Dept of Geophys & Astron Univ of BC Vancouver BC V6T 1W5 Can

RUSSELL, RICHARD LAWSON, b Bar Harbor, Maine, Nov 24, 40; m 62, 77; c 2. GENETICS, NEUROBIOLOGY. *Educ:* Harvard Col, BA, 62; Calif Inst Technol, PhD(genetics), 67. *Prof Exp:* Asst prof genetics, Cornell Univ, 66-67; mem staff, Lab Molecular Biol, Med Res Coun, Cambridge Univ, 67-70; asst prof biol, Calif Inst Technol, 70-76; ASSOC PROF BIOL SCI, UNIV PITTSBURGH, 76- *Concurrent Pos:* NSF fel, 67-68; NATO fel, 68-69; Am Heart Asn fel, 69-70. *Mem:* AAAS; Fedn Am Scientists. *Res:* Genetic analysis of structure and function in simple nervous systems. *Mailing Add:* Dept of Biol Sci Univ Pittsburgh Pittsburgh PA 15260

RUSSELL, RICHARD OLNEY, JR, b Birmingham, Ala, July 9, 32; m 63; c 4. CARDIOLOGY. *Educ:* Vanderbilt Univ, BA, 53, MD, 56. *Prof Exp:* From instr to assoc prof, 64-73, PROF MED, UNIV ALA, BIRMINGHAM, 73- *Concurrent Pos:* Co-dir myocardial infarction res unit, Univ Ala, Birmingham, 70-75. *Mem:* Am Fedn Clin Res. *Res:* Ischemic heart disease; acute myocardial infrction; hemodynamics of acute and chronic ischemic heart disease. *Mailing Add:* 1320 19th St S Birmingham AL 35205

RUSSELL, ROBERT JOHN, b Ballymena, Northern Ireland, Jan 21, 38; US citizen; m 71; c 1. LABORATORY ANIMAL MEDICINE. *Educ:* Univ Ill, BS, 60, DVM, 62; Tex A&M Univ, MS, 69. *Prof Exp:* Clin pract vet med, Roseland Animal Hosp, Chicago, 62; base vet, US Air Force, Norton AFB, Calif, 62-64 & Royal Air Force, Wethersfield, Eng, 64-67; resident lab animal med, Tex A&M Univ & Brooks AFB, 67-69; dir vet serv, Cam Ranh Bay, AFB, Vietnam, 69-70; MEM C DIV LAB ANIMAL MED, ARMED FORCES INST PATH, 70- *Concurrent Pos:* Consult, Am Asn Accreditation Lab Animal Care, 73-; instr, NatCapital Area Br, Am Asn Lab Animal Sci, 73- & Northern Va Community Col, 75; mem tech merit rev panel, Nat Inst Neurol Dis & Stroke, 74 & proposal & proj rev panel, Nat Cancer Inst, 74-75. *Mem:* Am Col Lab Animal Med; Am Animal Hosp Asn; Am Vet Med Asn; Am Asn Lab Animal Sci. *Res:* Laboratory animal management; infectious disease; animal reproduction; hypobaric medicine. *Mailing Add:* 5432 Donnelly Ct Springfield VA 22151

RUSSELL, ROBERT JULIAN, JR, b Gainesville, Tex, May 2, 26; m 48; c 4. MAMMALOGY. *Educ:* Tex A&M Univ, BS, 50, MS, 51; Univ Kans, PhD(zool), 68. *Prof Exp:* From asst instr to instr zool, Univ Kans, 51-56; asst prof, Univ Mo-Kansas City, 56-65; vis asst prof, Univ Kans, 65-66; assoc prof, 66-70, prof zool, 70-77, PROF BIOL, UNIV MO-KANSAS CITY, 77- *Mem:* Am Soc Mammal. *Res:* Systematics, zoogeography and ecology of mammals; mammals of Mexico, especially Morelos; evolution, phylogeny and classification of geomyid rodents; vertebrate anatomy; mammalian behavior, especially rodents; mammals of Texas and southwestern United States. *Mailing Add:* Dept of Biol Univ of Mo Kansas City MO 64110

RUSSELL, ROBERT LEE, b Independence, Mo, June 27, 27; m 50; c 2. PHYSIOLOGY, PHARMACOLOGY. *Educ:* Univ Mo, PhD(physiol, pharmacol), 54. *Prof Exp:* Asst physiol & pharmacol, 50-53, from asst instr to assoc prof pharmacol, 53-66, PROF PHARMACOL, UNIV MO-COLUMBIA, 66- *Mem:* Fel AAAS; Soc Exp Biol & Med; Am Soc Pharmacol & Exp Therapeut. *Res:* Drugs affecting lipid metabolism. *Mailing Add:* M520 Med Ctr Univ of Mo Columbia MO 65201

RUSSELL, ROBERT RAYMOND, b Beach, Wash, July 3, 20; m 43; c 3. CHEMISTRY. *Educ:* Graceland Col, AB, 43, MA, 46; Univ Kans, PhD(chem), 49. *Prof Exp:* PROF CHEM, UNIV MO-ROLLA, 48- *Mem:* Am Chem Soc. *Res:* Organic chemical reaction mechanisms. *Mailing Add:* Dept of Chem Univ of Mo Rolla MO 65401

RUSSELL, ROSS F, b Auburn, Nebr, May 7, 19; m 44; c 4. CHEMICAL ENGINEERING, POLYMER CHEMISTRY. *Educ:* Peru State Col, BA, 41; Iowa State Univ, PhD(chem eng), 50. *Prof Exp:* Engr, 50-57, process supvr, 57-67, SR RES ENGR, E I DU PONT DE NEMOURS & CO, INC, 67- *Mem:* Am Chem Soc; Am Inst Chem Engrs. *Res:* Plant installations of solvent extraction, distillation and polymerization equipment. *Mailing Add:* 701 Highview Dr Chattanooga TN 37415

RUSSELL, RUTH LOIS, b San Diego, Calif, July 22, 28; m 54; c 1. MICROBIOLOGY. *Educ:* Univ Calif, Los Angeles, BA, 52, PhD(microbiol), 63. *Prof Exp:* Asst bact, Univ Calif, Los Angeles, 52-55; instr biol, Occidental Col, 56-57; med bacteriologist, San Fernando Vet Admin Hosp, Calif, 59-61; res microbiologist, Olive View Hosp, 61-62; med bacteriologist, San Fernando Vet Admin Hosp, Calif, 62-63; from asst prof to assoc prof microbiol, 63-72, prof, 72-73, actg dean, Grad Studies, 74-77, DIR ENVIRON STUDIES, CALIF STATE UNIV, LONG BEACH, 77- *Concurrent Pos:* Consult microbiologist, var clin & biomed labs. *Mem:* AAAS; Am Soc Microbiol; Am Pub Health Asn; NY Acad Sci; Am Soc Qual Control. *Res:* Pub health microbiology; medical bacteriology; environmental microbiology. *Mailing Add:* Dept Microbiol Calif State Univ Long Beach CA 90840

RUSSELL, SCOTT D, b Milwaukee, Wis, Dec 8, 52. CYTOLOGY. *Educ:* Univ Wis, BA, 75; Northern Ariz Univ, MS, 77; Univ Alberta, PhD(bot), 81. *Prof Exp:* ASST PROF STRUCTURAL BOT, UNIV OKLA, 81- *Mem:* Bot Soc Am; AAAS. *Res:* Structural basis of double fertilization and male cytoplasmic transmission in angiosperms; reproductive plant cytology and ultrastructure. *Mailing Add:* Dept Bot & Microbiol Univ Okla Norman OK 73019

RUSSELL, STEPHEN MIMS, b Hot Springs, Ark, Sept 16, 31. ORNITHOLOGY. *Educ:* Va Polytech Inst, BS, 53; La State Univ, PhD(zool), 62. *Prof Exp:* From instr to asst prof biol, La State Univ, 58-64; asst prof, 64-70, ASSOC PROF ZOOL, UNIV ARIZ, 70-, CUR BIRDS, 64- *Mem:* fel Am Ornith Union; Cooper Ornith Soc; Wilson Ornith Soc. *Res:* Biology of desert and neotropical birds, especially behavior, ecology, distribution. *Mailing Add:* Dept of Ecol & Evolutionary Biol Univ of Ariz Tucson AZ 85721

RUSSELL, T(HOMAS) L(EE), b Pomona, Calif, Dec 15, 30; m 55; c 3. MECHANICAL ENGINEERING. *Educ:* Calif Inst Technol, BS, 52, MS, 53, PhD, 58. *Prof Exp:* Lectr metall, Calif Inst Technol, 56-58; res engr, Chevron Res Co Div, Standard Oil Co Calif, 58-60, group supvr, 60-63, supvr res eng, 63-67, staff financial analyst, 67-71, sr adv Mid East, 71-77, pres, Iran Chevron Oil Co, 73-77, MGR ANAL DIV, STANDARD OIL CO CALIF, 77- *Mem:* Am Inst Mining, Metall & Petrol Engrs; Soc Petrol Engrs. *Res:* Metallurgy; oceanography; applied mechanics; reservoir and petroleum engineering; economic analysis. *Mailing Add:* Standard Oil Co of Calif 225 Bush St Rm 1608 San Francisco CA 94104

RUSSELL, T W FRASER, b Moose Jaw, Sask, Aug 5, 34; m 56; c 3. CHEMICAL ENGINEERING. *Educ:* Univ Alta, BSc, 56, MSc, 58; Univ Del, PhD(chem eng), 64. *Prof Exp:* Res chem engr, Res Coun Alta, 56-58; design engr, Union Carbide Can, 58-61; prof chem eng, 64-81, ALLAN P COLBURN PROF CHEM ENG, UNIV DEL, 81-, DIR, INST ENERGY CONVERSION, 79- *Concurrent Pos:* Consult, E I du Pont de Nemours & Co, Inc, 61- *Mem:* Am Inst Chem Engrs; Am Chem Soc; Am Soc Eng Educ. *Res:* Gas-liquid system design; economics of the chemical process industries; development of a continuous process for solar cell manufacture. *Mailing Add:* Inst Energy Conversion One Pike Creek Ctr Wilmington DE 19808

RUSSELL, THOMAS EDWARD, b Tucson, Ariz, May 8, 42; m 65; c 1. PLANT PATHOLOGY. *Educ:* Univ Ariz, BS, 65, MS, 67; Tex A&M Univ, PhD(plant path), 70. *Prof Exp:* Agr specialist pesticide res, Buckman Labs, Tenn, 70-71; asst plant pathologist, 71-76, ASSOC RES SCIENTIST PLANT PATH, UNIV ARIZ, 76- *Mem:* Am Phytopath Soc. *Res:* Diseases of vegetable crops, turf and cotton. *Mailing Add:* Mesa Exp Sta Univ of Ariz Box 1308 Mesa AZ 85201

RUSSELL, THOMAS J, JR, b Dec 1, 31. BIOCHEMISTRY. *Educ:* Rutgers Univ, AB, 57, PhD(biochem), 61. *Prof Exp:* Res assoc biochem, Bur Biol Res & instr, Rutgers Univ, 61-62; FOUNDER & PRES, BIO/DYNAMICS, INC, 62- *Mem:* AAAS; NY Acad Sci; Am Chem Soc. *Res:* Metabolism; toxicology; application of computer technology to biological research. *Mailing Add:* Bio/Dynamics Inc PO Box 43 East Millstone NJ 08873

RUSSELL, THOMAS RANDALL, b Independence, Kans, Dec 7, 40; m 62; c 2. FISHERIES MANAGEMENT. *Educ:* Univ Nebr, BS, 62; Univ Mo, MA, 65. *Prof Exp:* From fisheries biologist I to fisheries biologist II, 65-73, sr fisheries res biologist, 73-75, FISHERIES RES SUPVR STREAM INVESTS, MO DEPT CONSERV, 75- *Mem:* Am Fisheries Soc. *Res:* Coordinator of comprehensive life history investigation of paddlefish; coordinator and supervisor of stream research. *Mailing Add:* Fish & Wildlife Res Ctr 1110 College Ave Columbia MO 65201

RUSSELL, THOMAS SOLON, b Bracey, Va, June 27, 22; m 49; c 4. STATISTICS. *Educ:* Wake Forest Col, BS, 44; Va Polytech Inst, MS, 53, PhD(statist), 56. *Prof Exp:* Instr math, Capitol Radio Engrs Inst, 46-47; instr, Va Polytech Inst, 47-51, asst statistician, Agr Exp Sta, 53-56; from asst statistician to assoc statistician, 56-63, PROF AGR & STATISTICIAN, AGR EXP STA, WASH STATE UNIV, 63- *Mem:* Biomet Soc; Am Statist Asn; Inst Math Statist. *Res:* Mathematical statistics. *Mailing Add:* Statist Serv Wash State Univ Pullman WA 99164

RUSSELL, THOMAS WEBB, b Greenville, Tex, Dec 17, 40; m 64. HETEROGENEOUS CATALYSIS, ORGANIC REDUCTIONS. *Educ:* Tex Col Arts & Indust, BSc, 62; Univ Colo, MSc, 64, PhD(chem), 66. *Prof Exp:* Vis asst prof chem, La State Univ, 66-67; asst prof chem, Eastern NMex Univ, 67-72, assoc prof, 72-79, prof, 79-81; SR RES CHEMIST, EL PASO PETROCHEM CO, 81- *Concurrent Pos:* Am Chem Soc Petrol Res Fund fel, NSF fel. *Mem:* AAAS; Am Chem Soc; NY Acad Sci. *Res:* Heterogeneous hydrogenation and methanation catalysts; organic synthesis; groundwater quality and control. *Mailing Add:* El Paso Prod Res & Develop Ctr PO Box 3986 Odessa TX 79760

RUSSELL, VIRGINIA ANN, b Oneonta, NY, Aug 11, 25. ANALYTICAL CHEMISTRY, INORGANIC CHEMISTRY. *Educ:* Westminster Col, BS, 47; Syracuse Univ, MS, 49, PhD(chem), 53. *Prof Exp:* Fel boron chem, Syracuse Univ, 52-55; CHEMIST, GEN ELEC CO, 55- *Mem:* Am Chem Soc; Soc Appl Spectros; Sigma Xi. *Res:* Instrumental analysis; auger, x-ray diffraction and thermal. *Mailing Add:* 103 Marsh Dr DeWitt NY 13214

RUSSELL, WILBERT AMBRICK, b Lenore, Man, Aug 3, 22; nat US; m 43; c 3. PLANT BREEDING, GENETICS. *Educ:* Univ Man, BSA, 42; Univ Minn, MS, 47, PhD(plant breeding, genetics), 52. *Prof Exp:* Agr res officer, Exp Sta, Can Dept Agr, Morden, 47-52; from asst prof to assoc prof, 52-62, PROF AGRON, COL AGR, IOWA STATE UNIV, 62- *Honors & Awards:* Crop Sci Res Award, Crop Sci Soc Am, 81; Res Award,, Nat Coun Com Plant Breeders, 79. *Mem:* Fel Am Soc Agron; Crop Sci Soc Am. *Res:* Breeding and genetics of field corn. *Mailing Add:* Dept of Agron Iowa State Univ Ames IA 50011

RUSSELL, WILLIAM LAWSON, b Newhaven, Eng, Aug 19, 10; nat US; m 36, 47; c 6. GENETICS. *Educ:* Oxford Univ, BA, 32; Univ Chicago, PhD, 37. *Prof Exp:* Asst zool, Univ Chicago, 34-36; res assoc, Jackson Mem Lab, 37-47; PRIN GENETICIST, OAK RIDGE NAT LAB, 47- *Concurrent Pos:* Adv, US deleg to UN Sci Comt Effects Atomic Radiation, 62-; mem, Nat Acad Sci adv comt to Fed Radiation Coun, 64-; mem, Bd Nat Coun Radiation Protection & Measurements, 65- *Honors & Awards:* Enrico Fermi Award, 77. *Mem:* Nat Acad Sci; Genetics Soc Am (pres, 65); Am Soc Zoologists; Radiation Res Soc. *Res:* Physiological genetics of melanin pigmentation; genetics of the house mouse; relative importance of heredity and pre-natal environment; genetic effects of radiation. *Mailing Add:* Biol Div Oak Ridge Nat Lab PO Box Y Oak Ridge TN 37830

RUSSELL, WILLIAM T(RELOAR), b Medford, Ore, Dec 21, 20; m 46; c 3. MECHANICAL & ELECTRICAL ENGINEERING. *Educ:* Univ Wash, BS, 42; Calif Inst Technol, MS, 47, PhD(eng), 50. *Prof Exp:* Asst gen mgr, Space Vehicles Div, 54-71, vpres & gen mgr, Defense Systs Div, 71-73, V PRES PROD ASSURANCE, TRW DEFENSE & SPACE SYSTS GROUP, REDONDO BEACH, 73- *Mem:* Am Inst Aeronaut & Astronaut; sr mem Inst Elec & Electronics Engrs. *Res:* Systems engineering; spacecraft development; aerospace general management; reliability and quality assurance. *Mailing Add:* 13065 Mindanao Way No 10 Marina del Rey CA 90291

RUSSEY, WILLIAM EDWARD, b Kalamazoo, Mich, Apr 5, 39; m 61; c 2. ORGANIC CHEMISTRY. *Educ:* Kalamazoo Col, AB, 61; Harvard Univ, AM, 64, PhD(chem), 67. *Prof Exp:* From asst prof to assoc prof, 66-75, chmn dept, 68-75, PROF CHEM, JUNIATA COL, 75- *Concurrent Pos:* NSF fac sci fel, Max Planck Inst Coal Res, Mulheim/Ruhr, WGer, 75-76, 80 & 81. *Mem:* AAAS; Am Chem Soc; Royal Soc Chem. *Res:* Steroid biogenesis; olefin cyclization reactions; molecular rearrangements; fossil fuel chemistry. *Mailing Add:* Dept of Chem Juniata Col Huntingdon PA 16652d

RUSSFIELD, AGNES BURT, b Portland, Ore, Jan 9, 17; m 54. PATHOLOGY. *Educ:* Reed Col, BA, 35; Univ Calif, MA, 37; Univ Chicago, PhD(zool), 43; Cornell Univ, MD, 49. *Prof Exp:* Asst zool, Univ Calif, Los Angeles, 35-36; asst, Univ Chicago, 37-39 & 40-41, asst, Off Sci Res & Develop Proj, 42-43; intern, Mass Gen Hosp, 49-50, asst resident, 50-51, fel path, 51-54, asst, 54-57, asst pathologist, 57-58; assoc, Bio-Res Inst Inc, 59-61; res assoc, Children's Cancer Res Found, 61-67; resident, Mallory Inst Path, 67-68, asst pathologist, 68-71; res assoc, Bio-Res Inst, Inc, 72-73; staff pathologist, St Vincent Hosp, 74-75; SCIENTIST, MASON RES INST, 75- *Concurrent Pos:* From instr to assoc clin prof, Harvard Med Sch, 52-68, lectr, 68-; coop scientist, Worcester Found Exp Biol, 65-67 & 68-; assoc prof, Med Sch, Tufts Univ, 68-71 & Med Sch, Univ Mass, 75- *Mem:* Am Asn Cancer Res; Am Soc Exp Path; Endocrine Soc; Am Asn Path & Bact; Am Soc Cytol. *Res:* Endocrine changes in cancer; biology of hypophysis. *Mailing Add:* Mason Res Inst Worcester MA 01608

RUSSI, GARY DEAN, b Canton, Ohio, Apr 23, 46; m 67; c 2. PHARMACOLOGY, TOXICOLOGY. *Educ:* Southwestern Okla State Univ, BS, 69; Kans Univ, PhD(pharmacol, toxicol), 72. *Prof Exp:* Asst pharmacol, Col Pharm, Kans Univ, 69-72; asst prof, 72-75, assoc prof, 75-80, PROF PHARMACOL, COL PHARM, DRAKE UNIV, 80- *Concurrent Pos:* Dir clin externship & dir comput-assisted instr, Col Pharm, Drake Univ, 75-, coordinator prog develop, 79- *Mem:* Am Asn Col Pharm; Sigma Xi. *Res:* Interaction of drugs and autonomic neurotransmitter release; mechanisms of drug-drug interactions; drug utilization review. *Mailing Add:* Col Pharm 25th & University Des Moines IA 50311

RUSSI, SIMON, b Rowne, Poland, Jan 5, 11; nat US; m 38; c 2. ANATOMIC PATHOLOGY. *Educ:* Royal Univ Modena, Italy, MD, 35. *Prof Exp:* Asst path, Wash Univ, 42-46; from instr to asst prof clin path, 46-50, from asst prof to assoc prof path, 50-68, CLIN PROF PATH & CLIN PATH, MED COL VA, 68- *Concurrent Pos:* Chief path sect, Vet Admin Hosp, Richmond, Va, 46-58; consult, US Army Hosp, Ft Lee, 58-; dir labs, Petersburg Gen Hosp, 58-78. *Mem:* Am Soc Clin Path; emer mem Am Asn Path & Bact; emer mem AMA; emer mem Col Am Pathologists; emer mem Int Acad Path. *Res:* Adrenal cortical adenomas; pulmonary hemosiderosis; intestinal lipodystrophy; chemistry of arteriosclerosis. *Mailing Add:* 101 Queen St Alexandria VA 22314

RUSSIN, NICHOLAS CHARLES, b Butler, Pa, Feb 6, 22; m 47; c 3. PHYSICAL CHEMISTRY. *Educ:* Washington & Jefferson Col, AB, 43; Carnegie Inst Technol, MS, 49, DSc, 50. *Prof Exp:* DEVELOP ASSOC, TENN EASTMAN CO, 50- *Mem:* Am Chem Soc; fel Am Inst Chemists; Am Asn Textile Technol. *Res:* Thermodynamic properties of solutions; man-made fibers. *Mailing Add:* 312 McTeer Dr Kingsport TN 37663

RUSSO, DANE MICHAEL, b Houston, Tex, Dec 13, 46. PSYCHOPHARMACOLOGY. *Educ:* Univ Houston, BA, 69; Univ Tex, PhD(psychol), 74. *Prof Exp:* Asst prof psychol, Univ SC, 74-76; ASSOC SCIENTIST BEHAV SCI, SOUTHWEST FOUND RES & EDUC, 76- *Concurrent Pos:* NSF teaching aid grant, 75. *Res:* Behavioral effects of drugs, pollutants and toxic substances; research methodology in fire toxicology. *Mailing Add:* Southwest Found for Res & Educ PO Box 28147 San Antonio TX 78284

RUSSO, EDWIN PRICE, b New Orleans, La, June 4, 38; m 61; c 3. MECHANICAL & ELECTRICAL ENGINEERING. *Educ:* Tulane Univ, BS, 60, MS, 62; La State Univ, PhD(mech eng), 68. *Prof Exp:* Elec engr, Chevron Oil Co, 62-63; res engr, Boeing Co, 63-66; instr eng mech, La State Univ, Baton Rouge, 66-68; assoc prof eng sci, La State Univ, New Orleans, 68-77; PROF MECH ENG, UNIV NEW ORLEANS, 77- *Mem:* Am Soc Mech Engrs; Am Soc Eng Educ. *Res:* Biomedical engineering; fluid mechanics; heat transfer; oceanography. *Mailing Add:* Dept of Mech Eng Lake Front New Orleans LA 70122

RUSSO, EMANUEL JOSEPH, b Philadelphia, Pa, Jan 23, 34; m 65. PHARMACEUTICS. *Educ:* Philadelphia Col Pharm, BSc, 55; Temple Univ, MSc, 57; Univ Wis, PhD(pharm), 60. *Prof Exp:* Chemist, Phys Chem Dept, Schering Corp, NJ, 60-63; group leader pharmaceut develop, 63-78, MGR ORAL & TOPICAL PROD, WYETH LABS, 78- *Mem:* Am Pharmaceut Asn; Acad Pharmaceut Sci. *Res:* Study of physical and chemical properties of drugs, before and after their inclusion into a finished dosage form in order to formulate the most stable and efficacious product. *Mailing Add:* 8 Morris Circle Wayne PA 19087

RUSSO, JOHN A, JR, b New York, NY, June 24, 33; m 59; c 6. METEOROLOGY. *Educ:* City Col New York, BS, 55; Univ Conn, MBA, 68. *Prof Exp:* Weather forecaster, US Weather Bur, 55-56; res asst statist & meteorol, Univ Ariz, 57-60; res assoc radar meteorol, Travelers Res Corp, Conn, 60-63, assoc scientist, 63-66; res scientist, 66-68; dir opers res, 68-71; MGR RES SUPPORT, OPERS RES DEPT, HARTFORD INS GROUP, 71- *Mem:* Am Meteorol Soc. *Res:* Meteorological statistics; design and development of information systems; weather sensitivity analysis; business administration. *Mailing Add:* 311 Cedarwood Lane Newington CT 06111

RUSSO, JOSE, b Mendoza, Argentina, Mar 24, 42; m 69. EXPERIMENTAL PATHOLOGY. *Educ:* A Alvarez Col, Argentina, BA & BS, 59; Sch Med, Univ Cuyo, Argentina, Physician, 67, Med Dr, 68. *Prof Exp:* Instr path, Inst Gen Exp Path, Sch Med, Mendoza, Argentina, 61-66, instr histol & embryol, Inst Histol & Embryol, 66-69, chief instr embryol, 69-71; res fel, Inst Molecular Cell Evolution, Univ Miami, Fla, 71-73; sr res scientist, 73-74, CHIEF EXP PATH LAB, MICH CANCER FOUND, 74- *Concurrent Pos:* Fel, Nat Coun Res, Argentina, 67-69 & 69-71; assoc mem, Mich Cancer Found, 70-; assoc clin prof path, Wayne State Univ, 79. *Mem:* For mem Soc Study Reproduction; Am Soc Cell Biol; Soc Exp Biol & Med; Electron Micros Soc Am; Am Asn Cancer Res. *Res:* Study of the viral etiology and pathogenesis of human breast cancer, and pathogenesis of the same disease in experimental models; chemical carcenogenesis. *Mailing Add:* Exp Path Lab Dept of Biol Mich Cancer Found 110 E Warren Detroit MI 48201

RUSSO, JOSEPH MARTIN, b Middletown, Conn, Feb 6, 49. AGRICULTURAL METEOROLOGY, SYSTEMS SCIENCE. *Educ:* St Louis Univ, BS, 71; McGill Univ, MSc, 74; Cornell Univ, PhD(agrometeorol), 78. *Prof Exp:* Res assoc, Agron Dept, Cornell Univ, 78-79, Dept Entom, NY State Agr Exp Sta, 79-81; ASST PROF, DEPT HORT, PA STATE UNIV, 81- *Concurrent Pos:* Res consult, 78-79; vis fel, Agron Dept, Cornell Univ, 79. *Mem:* Am Meteorol Soc; Am Soc Agron; Soil Sci Soc Am; Am Soc Hort Sci; Int Soc Biometeorol. *Res:* Theory and experimental designs for agricultural production systems. *Mailing Add:* Dept Hort 103 Tyson Bldg Pa State Univ University Park PA 16802

RUSSO, MICHAEL EUGENE, b St Louis, Mo, Aug 5, 39. CHEMISTRY. *Educ:* Wash Univ, AB, 61, PhD(chem), 70. *Prof Exp:* Investr chem res & develop, Mallinckrodt Chem Works, 67-74, RES MGR, MALLINCKRODT, INC, 74- *Concurrent Pos:* Vpres & dir, Parkside Develop Corp; dir, Montecello Corp. *Res:* Physical and inorganic chemistry; molecular spectroscopy. *Mailing Add:* 10 Kingsbury Pl St Louis MO 63112

RUSSO, RALPH P, b New York, NY, Dec, 29, 52; m 76; c 1. MATHEMATICAL STATISTICS. *Educ:* State Univ NY, Binghamton, MA & PhD(math), 80. *Prof Exp:* ASST PROF STATIST, STATE UNIV NY, BUFFALO, 80- *Mem:* Am Statist Asn; Inst Math Statist. *Mailing Add:* Dept Statist State Univ NY Ridge Lea Rd Amherst NY 14022

RUSSO, RAYMOND JOSEPH, b St Louis, Mo, May 30, 44; m 70; c 2. ENTOMOLOGY, ECOLOGY. *Educ:* Southeast Mo State Univ, BS, 66; Northeast Mo State Univ, MA, 71; Univ Notre Dame, PhD(entom), 76. *Prof Exp:* ASST PROF ECOL, IND UNIV-PURDUE UNIV, INDIANAPOLIS, 76- *Concurrent Pos:* Consult, Ind State Bd Health, 78. *Mem:* Entom Soc Am; Am Mosquito Control Asn; Sigma Xi. *Res:* Mosquito ecology; computer applications to biology; medical entomology. *Mailing Add:* Dept Biol 1201 E 38th St Indianapolis IN 46205

RUSSO, RICHARD F, b Somerville, Mass, Apr 22, 27; m 56; c 7. OPERATIONS RESEARCH. *Educ:* Mass Maritime Acad, BS, 47; Boston Col, AB, 51, AM, 53. *Prof Exp:* Develop physicist, Am Optical Co, 52-55; staff mem, Lincoln Lab, Mass Inst Technol, 55-57; sr engr, Shipbldg Div, Bethlehem Steel Co, 57-64; mathematician, Dewey & Almy Chem Div, W R Grace & Co, 64-66; mgr comp mgt sci, Itek Corp, 66-69, sr analyst innovative software, 70-71; sr systs analyst, New Eng Life Inst Co, Mass, 71-73; systs planning specialist, United Illum Co, 73-75; pvt pract, 75-77; sr bus analyst, 77-79, TECH SUPPORT ADMINR, HONEYWELL INFO SYSTS, 79- *Mem:* Opers Res Soc Am. *Res:* Application of advanced mathematical techniques and computer technology to the solution of business and industrial problems. *Mailing Add:* 170 Crosby St Arlington MA 02174

RUSSO, ROY LAWRENCE, b Kelayres, Pa, Nov 6, 35; m 59; c 4. ELECTRICAL ENGINEERING. *Educ:* Pa State Univ, BS, 57, MS, 59, PhD(elec eng), 64. *Prof Exp:* From instr to asst prof elec eng, Pa State Univ, 59-65; res staff mem, 65-68, mgr design automation, 68-78, sr engr, 78-81, MGR DESIGN AUTOMATION STRATEGY, IBM CORP, 81- *Honors & Awards:* Leonard A Doggett Award, 65 & 66; Int Bus Mach Corp Outstanding Contrib Award, 68. *Mem:* Inst Elec & Electronics Engrs (treas, 81, vpres, 82). *Res:* Logic design of computers; computer reliability; design automation. *Mailing Add:* 1793 Blossom Ct Yorktown Heights NY 10598

RUSSO, SALVATORE FRANKLIN, b Hartford, Conn, Feb 6, 38; m 67; c 2. PHYSICAL BIOCHEMISTRY. *Educ:* Wesleyan Univ, BA, 60; Northwestern Univ, PhD(phys chem), 64. *Prof Exp:* Instr, Northwestern Univ, 63-64; res assoc phys biochem, Univ Wash, 64-67; asst prof, 68-72, ASSOC PROF CHEM, WESTERN WASH UNIV, 72- *Concurrent Pos:* NIH fel, 65-67; adjoint prof, Univ Colo, 77-78; vis fac, Wash State Univ, 80; vis scientist, COBE Labs, Inc, 81. *Mem:* Am Chem Soc; Sigma Xi. *Res:* Conformational changes in proteins as they relate to biological functions of enzymes and antibodies; fluorescent probes of protein structure; hydrogen bonds between model peptide groups in solution; blood plasma exchange; biochemistry of blood pressure regulation. *Mailing Add:* Dept Chem Western Wash Univ Bellingham WA 98225

RUSSO, THOMAS JOSEPH, b Brooklyn, NY, Feb 10, 36; div; c 4. ORGANIC CHEMISTRY. *Educ:* Polytech Inst Brooklyn, BSc, 57; Pa State Univ, PhD(org chem), 65. *Prof Exp:* Instr chem, Bucknell Univ, 62 & Juniata Col, 62-64; from instr to asst prof, 64-71, ASSOC PROF CHEM, PA STATE UNIV, ALTOONA, 71- *Mem:* Am Chem Soc. *Res:* Physical organic chemistry. *Mailing Add:* Dept of Chem Pa State Univ Altoona PA 16601

RUSSO, VITO FRANCIS, energy physics, bioengineering, see previous edition

RUSSOCK, HOWARD ISRAEL, b Philadelphia, Pa, Dec 22, 47. ETHOLOGY. *Educ:* Western Md Col, BA, 69; Pa State Univ, MS, 71; WVa Univ, PhD(biol), 75. *Prof Exp:* Eli Lilly Endowment Inc internship, Purdue Univ, 75-76; asst prof, 76-81, ASSOC PROF BIOL, WESTERN CONN STATE COL, 81- *Concurrent Pos:* Investr, NSF fac fel awards, 79-81. *Mem:* AAAS; Am Inst Biol Sci; Am Soc Zoologists; Animal Behav Soc; Sigma Xi. *Res:* Developmental and social behavior; effects and importance of early experience in birds and cichlid fish. *Mailing Add:* Dept of Biol Sci Western Conn State Col Danbury CT 06810

RUSSU, IRINA MARIA, b Bucharest, Romania, Aug 15, 48. BIOPHYSICS. *Educ:* Univ Bucharest, MS, 70; Univ Pittsburgh, PhD(biophys), 79. *Prof Exp:* Res assoc, Univ Pittsburgh, 79-82; RES ASST PROF, CARNEGIE-MELLON UNIV, 82- *Mem:* Am Biophys Soc. *Res:* Structure-function relationships in proteins by means of nuclear magnetic resonance spectroscopy. *Mailing Add:* Dept Biol Sci Carnegie-Mellon Univ Pittsburgh PA 15213

RUST, CHARLES CHAPIN, b Medford, Wis, June 13, 35; m 56; c 3. ZOOLOGY. *Educ:* Wis State Univ, BS, 60; Univ Wis-Madison, MS, 61, PhD(zool), 64. *Prof Exp:* Asst prof zool, Ctr Syst, 64-68, vis scientist, Regional Primate Ctr, 68-69, assoc prof, 69-74, PROF ZOOL, UNIV WIS CTR SYST, 75- *Honors & Awards:* Am Soc Mammalogists Annual Award, 64. *Mem:* AAAS; Am Soc Zoologists; Am Soc Mammalogists. *Res:* Endocrinology of mammalian reproductive and pelage cycles. *Mailing Add:* Dept of Bot & Zool Univ of Wis Ctr Syst Janesville WI 53545

RUST, CHARLES HARRY, b Cincinnati, Ohio, Apr 12, 13. MATHEMATICS, STATISTICS. *Educ:* Loyola Univ, AB, 35; St Louis Univ, MA, 39, PhD(math), 50. *Prof Exp:* Lectr high sch, Ill, 39-40; instr math, John Carroll Univ, 49-51, asst prof & dir dept, 51-55; assoc prof, Xavier Univ, Ohio, 55-58; ASSOC PROF MATH, LOYOLA UNIV CHICAGO, 58- *Mem:* Am Math Soc; Am Soc Eng Educ; Inst Math Statist. *Res:* Mathematical analysis; infinite series. *Mailing Add:* Dept of Math Loyola Univ Chicago IL 60626

RUST, DAVID MAURICE, b Denver, Colo, Dec 9, 39; m 63; c 2. ASTROPHYSICS. *Educ:* Brown Univ, ScB, 62; Univ Colo, PhD(astrophys), 66. *Prof Exp:* Res fel solar physics, Nat Ctr Atmospheric Res, 63-66; Carnegie fel astrophys, Mt Wilson & Palomar Observ, 66-68; astrophysicist, Sacramento Peak Observ, Air Force Cambridge Res Labs, 68-74; SR STAFF SCIENTIST, AM SCI & ENG, INC, 74- *Concurrent Pos:* Consult, Lockheed Calif, 66-70; vis assoc prof, Univ Md, 71; chmn, Working Group Solar Maximum Year, Int Astron Union, 73; vis astronr, Observ of Paris, 78; consult, NASA, 78- *Mem:* Optical Soc Am; Am Geophys Union; Am Astron Soc; Int Astron Union. *Res:* Solar physics and magnetic fields; astronomical instrumentation; solar flares and x-ray emission; satellite-borne telescopes. *Mailing Add:* Am Sci & Eng Inc 955 Massachusetts Ave Cambridge MA 02139

RUST, JAMES HAROLD, b Peoria, Ill, Sept 19, 36. NUCLEAR ENGINEERING. *Educ:* Purdue Univ, BS, 58, PhD(nuclear eng), 65; Mass Inst Technol, SM, 60. *Prof Exp:* Asst prof nuclear eng, Univ Va, 64-67; assoc prof, 67-76, PROF NUCLEAR ENG, GA INST TECHNOL, 76- *Mem:* Am Soc Eng Educ; Am Nuclear Soc; Am Soc Mech Engrs; Nat Soc Prof Engrs. *Res:* Heat transfer and fluid mechanics pertinent to nuclear reactors, especially liquid metals and two phase systems. *Mailing Add:* Sch of Nuclear Eng Ga Inst of Technol Atlanta GA 30332

RUST, JOSEPH WILLIAM, b Butler, Ky, Oct 1, 25. ANIMAL HUSBANDRY, ANIMAL NUTRITION. *Educ:* Univ Ky, BS, 53, MS, 57; Iowa State Univ, PhD(animal nutrit), 63. *Prof Exp:* Instr dairying, Univ Ky, 53-59; res assoc dairy sci, Iowa State Univ, 59-63; asst prof dairy husb, 63-64, from asst prof to assoc prof animal husb, 64-80, PROF ANIMAL HUSB & SUPT, NCENT EXP STA, UNIV MINN, 80- *Mem:* Am Dairy Sci Asn; Am Soc Animal Sci. *Mailing Add:* NCent Exp Sta Univ of Minn Grand Rapids MN 55744

RUST, LAWRENCE WAYNE, JR, b St Paul, Minn, Mar 25, 37; m 64; c 3. MATHEMATICS, STATISTICS. *Educ:* Univ Minn, BS, 59, MS, 61, PhD(aeronaut eng), 64. *Prof Exp:* Sr engr, Ventura Div, Northrop Corp, 64-65 & Appl Sci Div, Litton Industs, 65-66; res engr, NStar Res & Develop Inst, 66-76; PRES, APPL ANAL SERV, 76- *Res:* Mathematical modeling; computer simulation; statistical data analysis; heat and mass transfer; fluid mechanics. *Mailing Add:* 1826 N Alameda St St Paul MN 55113

RUST, MICHAEL KEITH, b Akron, Ohio, Aug 26, 48; m 70; c 2. ENTOMOLOGY. *Educ:* Hiram Col, BA, 70; Univ Kans, MA, 73, PhD(entom), 75. *Prof Exp:* ASST PROF ENTOM, UNIV CALIF, RIVERSIDE, 75- *Mem:* Entom Soc Am; AAAS; Animal Behav Soc; Sigma Xi. *Res:* Urban entomology, especially biology and control of cockroaches, fleas and termites; chemical factors influencing termite feeding. *Mailing Add:* Dept of Entom Univ of Calif Riverside CA 92521

RUST, PHILIP FREDERICK, b Oakland, Calif, 47. BIOSTATISTICS, STATISTICS. *Educ:* Calif Inst Technol, BS, 69; Univ Calif, Berkeley, MA, 71, PhD(biostatist), 76. *Prof Exp:* Lieutenant biostatist, Ctr Dis Control, USPHS, 71-73; asst prof statist, Univ Mo-Columbia, 76-79; ASST PROF BIOMETRY, MED UNIV SC, 79- *Concurrent Pos:* Consult, Med Ctr, Univ Mo, 76-78, consult, Environ Protection Agency grant, 77- *Mem:* Am Statist Asn; Biomet Soc; Sigma Xi. *Res:* Applied stochastic processes; biometry; epidemiology. *Mailing Add:* Dept Biometry Med Univ SC Charleston SC 29425

RUST, RICHARD HENRY, b Bunker Hill, Ill, Oct 12, 21; m 42; c 5. SOIL SCIENCE. *Educ:* Univ Ill, BS, 47, MS, 50, PhD(agron), 55. *Prof Exp:* Asst prof soil physics, Univ Ill, 55-56; asst prof, 56-71, PROF SOILS, UNIV MINN, ST PAUL, 71- *Concurrent Pos:* Consult to indust & govt. *Mem:* Am Soc Agron; Soil Conserv Soc Am. *Res:* Soil genesis, classification and physical chemistry; properties related to clay mineralogy of soils; soil productivity evaluation. *Mailing Add:* Dept of Soil Sci Univ of Minn St Paul MN 55101

RUST, RICHARD W, b Logan, Utah, Oct 11, 42. INSECT ECOLOGY. *Educ:* Utah State Univ, BS, 65, MS, 67; Univ Calif, PhD(entom), 72. *Prof Exp:* Res asst pollination, Wild Bee Pollination Lab, USDA, 65-67; field biologist parasites, Field Mus Nat Hist, Chicago, 69; teaching asst zool, Univ Calif, 72; fac mem entom, Univ Del, 73-78; FAC MEM BIOL, UNIV NEV, 78- *Mem:* Entom Soc Am; Am Entom Soc (rec secy, 74-); Soc Study Evolution; Soc Syst Zoologists; Ecol Soc Am. *Res:* Pollination ecology. *Mailing Add:* Dept of Biol Univ of Nev Reno NV 89557

RUST, VELMA IRENE, b Edmonton, Alta, May 22, 14; m 55. MATHEMATICAL STATISTICS, ECONOMETRICS. *Educ:* Univ Alta, BSc, 34, BEd, 47; Univ Ill, PhD(math, math educ), 59. *Prof Exp:* Teacher math & sci, Alta, 36-44; admin secy fac educ, Univ Alta, 44-52, from lectr to asst prof math educ & dir student teaching prog, 52-56; researcher personnel planning, Royal Can Air Force Hq, Can Dept Nat Defence, Ont, 60-62, chief staff training, Inspection Serv, 62-65; statistician, Origin & Destination Statist, Govt Can, 65-67; sr policy analyst, Can Dept Health & Welfare, 67-79; RETIRED. *Concurrent Pos:* Asst, Univ Ill, 56-59; sessional lectr, Carleton Univ, 59-62. *Mem:* Am Statist Asn; Am Soc Qual Control. *Res:* Social security; aviation; education. *Mailing Add:* 811 Adams Ave Ottawa ON K1G 2Y1 Can

RUST, WALTER DAVID, b Randolph AFB, Tex, Oct 8, 44; m 66; c 2. ATMOSPHERIC PHYSICS. *Educ:* Southwestern Univ, BS, 66; NMex Inst Mining & Technol, MS, 69, PhD(physics), 73. *Prof Exp:* US Nat Res Coun res assoc, 73-75, ATMOSPHERIC PHYSICIST, US DEPT COMMERCE, NAT OCEANIC & ATMOSPHERIC ADMIN, 75- *Mem:* Am Geophys Union; Am Meteorol Soc; Royal Meteorol Soc Eng. *Res:* Cloud electrification; lightning suppression by chaff dispersal within thunderstorms; distribution of electric fields; use of atmospheric electric measurements to assess possibility of triggered lightning by rockets launched near thunderstorms; remote detection of corona; severe storm electricity. *Mailing Add:* Nat Severe Storm Lab 1313 Halley Circle Norman OK 73069

RUSTAD, DOUGLAS SCOTT, b Juneau, Alaska, Sept 25, 40; m 67. INORGANIC CHEMISTRY, PHYSICAL CHEMISTRY. *Educ:* Univ Wash, BS, 62, MS, 64; Univ Calif, Berkeley, PhD(chem), 67. *Prof Exp:* Lectr inorg chem, Univ West Indies, 67-69; asst prof, 69-74, ASSOC PROF INORG CHEM, SONOMA STATE UNIV, 74- *Mem:* Am Chem Soc. *Res:* Reactions and preparations of group IV hydrides and boron hydrides; kinetics of reactions of complex ions and of reactions involving heterogeneous catalysis; high temperature spectroscopic and thermodynamic studies of iron halides. *Mailing Add:* Dept of Chem Sonoma State Univ Rohnert Park CA 94928

RUSTAD, RONALD CAMERON, b Minneapolis, Minn, Jan 18, 33; m 60; c 1. PHYSIOLOGY. *Educ:* Univ Calif, BA, 54, MA, 56, PhD(biophys), 58. *Prof Exp:* Trainee physicist, Nat Bur Standards, 52; asst zool, Univ Calif, 54-57; Nat Cancer Inst fel, Univ Edinburgh, 58; from instr to assoc prof physiol, Fla State Univ, 58-63; asst prof radiol, 64-65, ASSOC PROF BIOL, CASE WESTERN RESERVE UNIV, 64-, ASSOC PROF RADIOL, 65- *Mem:* Am Soc Zool; Biophys Soc; Radiation Res Soc; Soc Protozool; Soc Develop Biol. *Res:* Physical characterization of the cell division cycle; functional anatomy of the mitotic apparatus; nuclear-cytoplasmic relations; mechanism of pinocytosis; radiation embryology. *Mailing Add:* Dept Radiol Case Western Reserve Univ Cleveland OH 44106

RUSTAGI, JAGDISH S, b Sikri, India, Aug 13, 23; m 49; c 3. BIOSTATISTICS. *Educ:* Univ Delhi, BA, 44, MA, 46; Stanford Univ, PhD(statist), 56. *Prof Exp:* Lectr math, Hindu Col, Univ Delhi, 46-52; asst prof, Carnegie Inst Technol, 55-57; asst prof statist, Mich State Univ, 57-58; reader, Aligarh Muslim Univ, 58-60; assoc prof math, Univ Cincinnati, 60-63; from assoc prof to prof math, 63-70, PROF STATIST, OHIO STATE UNIV, 70-, CHMN DEPT, 79- *Concurrent Pos:* NIH res grants, 62-68; consult, Toxic Hazards Unit, Wright-Patterson AFB, Ohio, 64-65; Air Force Off Sci Res grants, 67-; vis scholar, Stanford Univ, 71-72 & Off Naval Res, 78-; adj prof prev med, Col Med, Ohio State Univ, 67-75; mem, Int Statist Inst. *Mem:* Inst Math Statist; Biomet Soc; fel Am Statist Asn; Math Asn Am; Indian Soc Agr Statist. *Res:* Mathematical statistics; medical statistics; operations research; optimizing methods. *Mailing Add:* Dept Statist Ohio State Univ Columbus OH 43210

RUSTAGI, KRISHNA PRASAD, b Khurja, India, Jan 1, 32; m 56; c 2. FOREST BIOMETRICS, LAND USE PLANNING. *Educ:* Agra Univ, India, BSc, 51, MSc, 53; Yale Univ, PhD(forestry), 73. *Prof Exp:* Asst conservator, Forest Dept, India, 55-61, dep conservator, 61-64; lectr, Forest Res Inst & Col, 64-69; asst prof, 73-79, ASSOC PROF FORESTRY, UNIV WASH, 79- *Mem:* Soc Am Foresters. *Res:* Biometric investigations in growth and yield of forest stands and trees; operations research application in land use; forest management planning. *Mailing Add:* Col Forest Resources AR-10 Univ Wash Seattle WA 98195

RUSTED, IAN EDWIN L H, b Nfld, July 12, 21; m 49; c 2. ENDOCRINOLOGY, HEALTH SCIENCES EDUCATION. *Educ:* Univ Toronto, BA, 43; Dalhousie Univ, MD, CM, 48; McGill Univ, MSc, 49; FRCP(C), 53. *Prof Exp:* Med consult, Dept Health, Nfld, 52-67; actg dir postgrad & continuing med educ, 66-67, coordr med sch planning, 66-67, dean med, 67-74, PROF MED, MEM UNIV NFLD, 67-, V PRES HEALTH SCI, 74- *Concurrent Pos:* Physician & dir med educ, St John's Gen Hosp, 53-67, chmn dept med, 67-68; mem coun, Royal Col Physicians & Surgeons Can, 61-70, vpres, 68-70; vis prof, Univ Toronto & Laval Univ, 74-75. *Mem:* Hon mem, Col Family Physicians Can, 59; Asn Can Med Col (vpres, 73-74). *Res:* Thyroid disorders; hypertension, especially epidemiology. *Mailing Add:* Health Sci Ctr Mem Univ St John's NF A1C 5S7 Can

RUSTGI, MOTI LAL, b Delhi, India, Sept 29, 29; m 52; c 2. NUCLEAR PHYSICS. *Educ:* Univ Delhi, India, BSc, 49, MSc, 51; La State Univ, PhD, 57. *Prof Exp:* Instr physics, La State Univ, 57; res assoc, Yale Univ, 57-60, asst prof, 64-66; fel, Nat Res Coun Can, 60-61; reader, Banaras Hindu Univ, 61-63; asst prof, Univ Southern Calif, 63-64; assoc prof, 66-68, PROF PHYSICS, STATE UNIV NY AT BUFFALO, 68- *Concurrent Pos:* Vis prof, State Univ NY Stony Brook, 73; vis scientist, Oak Ridge Nat Lab, 80- *Mem:* Fel Am Phys Soc. *Res:* Electromagnetic interactions with nuclei; nuclear structure; energy losses of high energy particles in matter. *Mailing Add:* Dept Physics State Univ New York Buffalo NY 14260

RUSTGI, OM PRAKASH, b Delhi, India, Aug 1, 31; US citizen; m 63; c 2. SPECTROSCOPY, SOLID STATE PHYSICS. *Educ:* Univ Delhi, BS, 52, MS, 54; Univ Southern Calif, PhD(physics), 60. *Prof Exp:* Head optics div, Proj Celescope, Smithsonian Astrophys Observ, 60-62; physicist ultraviolet radiation, Northrop Corp, 63-67; mem prof staff space res, TRW Systs Inc, 67-71; vis assoc prof physics, Univ Ill, 71-73; asst prof, 73-79, ASSOC PROF PHYSICS, STATE UNIV NY COL BUFFALO, 79- *Concurrent Pos:* Consult, Smithsonian Astrophys Observ, 63-64 & Lawrence Livermore Lab, 74-76; prog mgr, Northrop Corp, 65-67; vis assoc prof physics, Univ Nebr, 81-82. *Mem:* Am Phys Soc; Optical Soc Am; Sigma Xi. *Res:* Optical properties of thin films; photoionization in gases and light elements; lasers and holography; x-rays and crystal structure; laser plasma interaction studies. *Mailing Add:* 362 Sunrise Blvd Williamsville NY 14221

RUSTIGIAN, ROBERT, b Boston, Mass, July 26, 15; m 56; c 2. MEDICAL MICROBIOLOGY. *Educ:* Univ Mass, BS, 38; Brown Univ, MS, 40, PhD, 43. *Prof Exp:* Nat Res Coun fel bact & immunol, Harvard Med Sch, 46-48, instr, 48-49, assoc instr, 49; asst prof microbiol, Univ Chicago, 49-55; asst prof, Sch Med, Tufts Univ, 55-61, assoc prof, 61-67; CHIEF VIROLOGIST, VET ADMIN HOSP, 67-; ASSOC PROF BACT & MOLECULAR GENETICS, SCH DENT MED, 75- *Mem:* Am Soc Microbiol; Am Asn Immunol. *Res:* Virology; immunology. *Mailing Add:* Virol Res Lab Vet Admin Hosp Brockton MA 02401

RUSTIONI, ALDO, b Porto Ceresio, Italy, July 22, 41; m 69; c 2. NEUROBIOLOGY, ANATOMY. *Educ:* Univ Parma, MD, 65. *Prof Exp:* Asst prof neuroanat, Erasmus Univ, Rotterdam, Holland, 68-72, sr asst prof, 72-73; ASSOC PROF ANAT & PHYSIOL, UNIV NC, CHAPEL HILL, 73- *Concurrent Pos:* Vis investr, Nat Inst Health & Med Res, Paris, 72-73; Europ Training Prog Brain & Behav fel, 72-73; grants, Dutch Orgn Fundamental Res Med, 72-73, USPHS, 75-81 & 80-85 & Nat Found March Dimes, 78-80. *Mem:* Europ Neurosci Asn; Am Asn Anatomists; Soc Neurosci; AAAS; Am Acad Neurobiol. *Res:* Neuroanatomy; neurocytology; neurohistochemistry; electron microscopy; neurophysiology; somatosensory system. *Mailing Add:* Dept Anat Rm 111 Swing Building 277 H Univ of NC Chapel Hill NC 27514

RUSTON, HENRY, b Lodz, Poland, July 23, 29; US citizen; m 59; c 3. SOFTWARE ENGINEERING, ELECTRICAL ENGINEERING. *Educ:* Univ Mich, BSE(math) & BSE(elec eng), 52, PhD(elec eng), 60; Columbia Univ, MS, 55. *Prof Exp:* Intermediate test engr, Wright Aeronaut Div, Curtiss-Wright Corp, NJ, 55; elec engr, Reeves Instrument Co, NY, 55-56; res asst, Eng Res Inst, Univ Mich, 56-58, res assoc, 58-60, assoc res engr, 60; asst prof elec eng, Moore Sch Elec Eng, Univ Pa, 60-64; ASSOC PROF, POLYTECH INST NEW YORK, 64- *Concurrent Pos:* Lectr, Univ Mich, 60; indust consult, 61- *Mem:* Sr mem Inst Elec & Electronics Engrs; NY Acad Sci. *Res:* Circuit theory; computer simulation; computer aided circuit design, software engineering. *Mailing Add:* Dept of Elec Eng 333 Jay St Brooklyn NY 11201

RUSY, BEN F, b Sturgeon Bay, Wis, July 12, 27; m 57; c 4. PHARMACOLOGY, ANESTHESIOLOGY. *Educ:* Univ Wis, BS, 52, MD, 56; Temple Univ, MS, 59; Am Bd Anesthesiol, dipl, 62. *Prof Exp:* Asst instr anesthesiol, Med Sch, Temple Univ, 59-60, instr anesthesiol & pharmacol, 60-62, from asst prof to prof anesthesiol & pharmacol, 62-77; PROF, DEPT ANESTHESIOL, UNIV HOSP, UNIV WIS-MADISON, 77- *Concurrent Pos:* NIH fel, 59-61; NIH res grant, 62-; mem coun basic sci & coun circulation, Am Heart Asn, 65-; USPHS spec res fel, Heart & Lung Inst, 71-72; hon res fel, Dept Physiol, Univ Col, Univ London, 71-72. *Mem:* AAAS; Am Soc Anesthesiol; Am Soc Pharmacol & Exp Therapeut. *Res:* Effect of anesthetics and antihypertensive drugs on cardiac function. *Mailing Add:* Dept Anesthesiol 1300 University Ave Madison WI 53706

RUTENBERG, AARON CHARLES, b Chicago, Ill, July 28, 23; m 64; c 2. PHYSICAL CHEMISTRY. *Educ:* Univ Chicago, PhD(chem), 50. *Prof Exp:* Jr inspector, US War Dept, 42; res assoc, Univ Chicago, 50-51; chemist, Oak Ridge Nat Lab, 51-71; DEVELOP CHEMIST, UNION CARBIDE NUCLEAR DIV, Y-12 PLANT, 72- *Mem:* Am Chem Soc. *Res:* nuclear magnetic resonance spectroscopy; mass spectrometry. *Mailing Add:* 101 Monticello Rd Oak Ridge TN 37830

RUTENBERG, ALEXANDER MICHAEL, b Russia, Oct 1, 18; nat US; m 49; c 4. SURGERY, CANCER. *Educ:* Harvard Univ, AB, 40; NY Univ, MD, 43; Am Bd Surg, dipl. *Prof Exp:* Intern surg, Beth Israel Hosp, 44; resident, Montefiore Hosp, Pittsburgh, 44-45; resident urol, Beth Israel Hosp, 45-46, res assoc surg, 47-48, asst resident, 48-50; teaching fel, Harvard Med Sch, 50-51, from asst to asst prof, 55-68; assoc prof surg, Sch Med, Boston Univ, 68-70, prof, 70-80. *Concurrent Pos:* Resident, Beth Israel Hosp, 50-51, res assoc, 54-55, asst dir surg res, 56-58, assoc dir, 59-67, assoc vis surgeon, 56-65, vis surgeon, 65-; lectr, Sch Med, Boston Univ, 64-68, asst clin prof, Harvard Med Sch, 69-72, lectr, 72; dir, Charles River Breeding Labs, Inc & med dir, Charles River Labs. *Mem:* Histochem Soc; Am Asn Cancer Res; Am Cancer Soc; Am Col Surg; Soc Exp Biol & Med. *Res:* Surgical infections; general surgery; shock and trauma; cellular biochemistry; enzymology; histochemistry. *Mailing Add:* 6 Elba St Brookline MA 02146

RUTENBERG, MORTON WOLF, b Philadelphia, Pa, Jan 10, 21; m 42; c 1. ORGANIC CHEMISTRY. *Educ:* Univ Pa, BS, 42, MS, 47, PhD(org chem), 49. *Prof Exp:* Jr chemist, Eastern Regional Res Lab, USDA, 42-43; res group supvr, Nat Starch Prod, Inc, 49-58, res sect leader, 58-75, assoc dir, 75-80, DIR, STARCH RES, NAT STARCH & CHEM CORP, 80- *Mem:* AAAS; Am Chem Soc; fel Am Inst Chem; Royal Soc Chem; Am Asn Cereal Chemists. *Res:* Synthetic organic, carbohydrate and polysaccharide chemistry; starch chemistry and technology; polysaccharides. *Mailing Add:* Nat Starch & Chem Corp 10 Finderne Ave Bridgewater NJ 08807

RUTFORD, ROBERT HOXIE, b Duluth, Minn, Jan 26, 33; m 54; c 3. GEOLOGY. *Educ:* Univ Minn, BA, 54, MA, 63, PhD(geol), 69. *Prof Exp:* Res assoc geol, Univ Minn, 62-67; from asst prof to assoc prof, Univ SDak, 67-72, actg chmn dept geol, 68-69, chmn, 69-71, chmn dept geol & physics, 71-72; co-dir, Ross Ice Shelf Proj, Univ Nebr-Lincoln, 72-73, dir, 75-77, head, Off Polar Progs, NSF, 75-77; interim chancelor, 80-81, VCHANCELLOR RES & GRAD STUDIES, UNIV NEBR-LINCOLN, 77- *Concurrent Pos:* NSF res grant, 68-69; mem panel geol & geophys, Comt Polar Res, Nat Acad Sci, 68-73, mem, Ross Ice Shelf Proj steering group, 72-73, Antarctic adv panel, Deep Earth Sampling Proj, Joint Oceanog Inst; chmn, Interagency Arctic Res Coord Comt, 75-77; mem, Comt Int Relations, Nat Res Ctr, Nat Acad Sci, 77-81 & Polar Res Bd, 80-; mem, Antartic Sect, Ocean Affairs Adv Comt, Dept State, 78- *Honors & Awards:* Antarctic Serv Medal, US Secy Defense, 68; Distinguished Serv Award, NSF, 77. *Mem:* Fel Geol Soc Am; Arctic Inst NAm; Sigma Xi; Nat Coun Univ Res Admin. *Res:* Antarctic geology; geomorphology; glacial geology in eastern South Dakota. *Mailing Add:* Off VChancellor Res & Grad Studies Univ Nebr Lincoln NE 68588

RUTGER, JOHN NEIL, b Noble, Ill, Mar 3, 34; m 58; c 2. GENETICS, PLANT BREEDING. *Educ:* Univ Ill, BS, 60; Univ Calif, Davis, MS, 62, PhD(genetics), 64. *Prof Exp:* Asst prof plant breeding, Cornell Univ, 64-70, assoc prof, 70; RES GENETICIST, AGR RES SERV, USDA & DEPT AGRON & RANGE SCI, UNIV CALIF, DAVIS, 70-, LECTR AGRON, 76- *Mem:* AAAS; fel Am Soc Agron; Crop Sci Soc Am. *Res:* Rice genetics and breeding, especially inheritance of semi-dwarfism, male sterility, cold tolerance and photosynthetic efficiency. *Mailing Add:* USDA Agr Res Serv Univ of Calif Dept Agron Davis CA 95616

RUTGERS, JAY G, b Holland, Mich, Feb 16, 24; m 55; c 1. ANALYTICAL CHEMISTRY. *Educ:* Hope Col, BA, 49; Northwestern Univ, PhD(anal chem), 55. *Prof Exp:* Res assoc, Merck Sharp & Dohme Res Labs, 54-61; RES SCIENTIST, WYETH LABS, INC, 61- *Mem:* Am Chem Soc. *Res:* Analytical method development for pharmaceuticals; purity testing of new drugs. *Mailing Add:* Wyeth Labs PO Box 8299 Philadelphia PA 19101

RUTH, BYRON E, b Chicago, Ill, Mar 25, 31; m 60; c 2. CIVIL ENGINEERING, TRANSPORTATION. *Educ:* Mont State Univ, BSCE, 55; Purdue Univ, MSCE, 59; WVa Univ, PhD(civil eng), 67. *Prof Exp:* Asst dir res & develop, Symons Mfg Co, 60-61; from instr to asst prof civil eng, WVa Univ, 61-70; assoc prof, 70-77, PROF CIVIL ENG, UNIV FLA, 77- *Concurrent Pos:* Mem, Hwy Res Bd, Nat Acad Sci-Nat Res Coun. *Mem:* Am Soc Civil Engrs; Am Soc Testing & Mat; Am Soc Photogram; Asn Asphalt Paving Technol. *Res:* Bituminous materials; concrete and aggregate materials; soil exploration and testing; remote sensing applications to terrain analysis and site selection. *Mailing Add:* Dept of Civil Eng Univ of Fla Gainesville FL 32611

RUTH, JAMES ALLAN, b Wichita, Kans, Dec 24, 46. PHARMACOLOGY, MEDICINAL CHEMISTRY. *Educ:* Univ Kans, BS, 68; Northwestern Univ, Evanston, PhD(org chem), 74. *Prof Exp:* Res assoc med chem, Univ Kans, 74-76, res assoc pharmacol, 76-78; ASST PROF MED CHEM & PHARMACOL, SCH PHARM, UNIV COLO, 78- *Concurrent Pos:* NIH fels med chem, 74-76; Am Heart Asn fels pharmacol, 76-78. *Mem:* Am Chem Soc; Royal Soc Chem. *Res:* Neurochemistry; neuropharmacology. *Mailing Add:* Sch Pharm Univ Colo Boulder CO 80309

RUTH, JOHN MOORE, b Pittsboro, NC, May 26, 24. PHYSICAL CHEMISTRY. *Educ:* Univ NC, BS, 44, PhD(phys chem), 59. *Prof Exp:* Chemist, Dockery Labs, 45-46; jr chemist, Oak Ridge Nat Lab, 47-48, assoc chemist, 48-50, 52; staff mem, Los Alamos Sci Lab, 54-55; staff mem dacron res lab, E I du Pont de Nemours & Co, Inc, 57-59; sr chemist, Res Dept, Liggett & Myers Tobacco Co, 59-66; RES CHEMIST, AGR ENVIRON QUAL INST, AGR RES SERV, USDA, 66- *Concurrent Pos:* Staff mem, Los Alamos Sci Lab, 53, 55 & E I du Pont de Nemours & Co, 56. *Mem:* Fel AAAS; Am Chem Soc; fel Am Inst Chem; Am Soc Mass Spectrometry. *Res:* Mass spectrometry; molecular spectroscopy; identification of organic compounds; determination of molecular structures. *Mailing Add:* Agr Environ Qual Inst Agr Res Serv USDA Beltsville MD 20705

RUTH, ROBERTA JEAN, b Kenton, Ohio, June 17, 49. OPERATIONS RESEARCH, COMPUTER SCIENCE. *Educ:* Univ Mich, BS, 70, MS(appl math), 72, MS(indust & oper eng), 74, PhD(indust oper eng), 79. *Prof Exp:* Asst prof indust eng & operations res, Wayne State Univ, 78-82; ASST PROF QUANTITATIVE METHODS, UNIV WIS-MILWAUKEE, 82- *Concurrent Pos:* Prin investr, Nat Ctr Health Serv Res, 76-77; consult, Transplantation Soc Mich, 80-81; fel, Fac Fel Prog, Am Soc Eng Educ, NASA, 81. *Mem:* Operations Res Soc Am; The Inst Mgt Sci; Inst Indust Engrs; Am Public Health Asn; Am Soc Eng Educ. *Res:* Modelling of health care and production systems, especially the application of operations research to planning and operating such systems. *Mailing Add:* Apt 202 605 Hidden Valley Ann Arbor MI 48104

RUTH, ROYAL FRANCIS, b Des Moines, Iowa, Oct 3, 25; m 50; c 1. EMBRYOLOGY, IMMUNOLOGY. *Educ:* Grinnell Col, AB, 49; Univ Wis, MS, 53, PhD(zool), 54. *Prof Exp:* Fel embryol, Ind Univ, 54-56; staff mem, Carnegie Inst Technol, 56-61; from asst prof to assoc prof, 61-71, PROF ZOOL, UNIV ALTA, 71- *Mem:* Can Soc Zool; Soc Develop Biol; Transplantation Soc. *Res:* Origins and development of lymphoid systems of amniotes; role of the lymphoid system in transplantation immunology. *Mailing Add:* Dept of Zool Univ of Alta Edmonton AB T6G 2G9 Can

RUTH, RUSSELL EDWARD, b Minneapolis, Minn, Sept 30, 48. NEUROBIOLOGY, DEVELOPMENTAL BIOLOGY. *Educ:* Wayne State Univ, BS, 71; Northwestern Univ, MS, 75, PhD(neurobiol), 80. *Prof Exp:* ASST PROF BIOMED RES, ILL INST DEVELOP DISABILITIES, 79- *Concurrent Pos:* Dept affil psychol, Univ Ill, Chicago, 82- *Mem:* Soc Neurosci. *Res:* Rat models of birth defects, emphasizing brain malformation; rat models of epilepsy; development, structure and function of the rat limbic system. *Mailing Add:* Ill Inst Develop Disabilities 1640 W Roosevelt Rd Chicago IL 60608

RUTHERFORD, CHARLES, b Trenton, Mo, May 17, 39; m 63; c 1. CELL BIOLOGY, BIOCHEMISTRY. *Educ:* William Jewell Col, BA, 61; Col William & Mary, MA, 63; Univ Miami, PhD(cell biol), 68. *Prof Exp:* Fel biochem, Med Sch, Washington Univ, 68-69; fel biochem develop, Retina Found, 69-71; asst prof biochem, 72-80, ASSOC PROF ZOOL, VA POLYTECH INST & STATE UNIV, 80- *Concurrent Pos:* Fel, Boston Biomed Res Inst, 69-72. *Res:* Biochemistry of development. *Mailing Add:* Dept Biol Va Polytech Inst & State Univ Blacksburg VA 23215

RUTHERFORD, JAMES CHARLES, b Oakland, Calif, Aug 27, 46. INVERTEBRATE ECOLOGY. *Educ:* Calif State Col, Hayward, BS, 68; Univ Calif, Berkeley, MA, 71, PhD(zool), 75. *Prof Exp:* Asst prof zool, Ore State Univ, 75-76; asst prof biol, Univ Hilo Col, Univ Hawaii, 76-80. *Mem:* Ecol Soc Am; Sigma Xi; AAAS. *Res:* Quantitative invertebrate natural history with emphasis on ecological and evolutionary theory especially as it relates to marine intertidal and benthic invertebrates, echinoderms in particular. *Mailing Add:* PO Box 67 Kamuela HI 96743

RUTHERFORD, JOHN GARVEY, b Baltimore, Md, Sept 25, 42; m 65; c 2. ANATOMY. *Educ:* Cornell Univ, AB, 64; Syracuse Univ, MS, 68; State Univ NY Upstate Med Ctr, PhD(anat), 72. *Prof Exp:* Asst prof, 70-73, ASSOC PROF ANAT, FAC MED, DALHOUSIE UNIV, 73- *Mem:* NY Acad Sci; Am Asn Anatomists; Soc Neurosci. *Res:* Ultrastructure and connections of mammalian brain stem nuclei. *Mailing Add:* Dept of Anat Dalhousie Univ Halifax NS B3H 3J5 Can

RUTHERFORD, JOHN L(OFTUS), b Philadelphia, Pa, Mar 6, 24; m 47; c 2. METALLURGY, MATERIALS SCIENCE. *Educ:* Univ Pa, BA, 52, MS, 61, PhD(metall), 63. *Prof Exp:* Proj engr, Sharples Corp, Pa, 45-52; res physicist, Franklin Inst, 52-60; sr staff scientist, Aerospace Group, Gen Precision, Inc, 63-69; res mgr, 69-80, DIR, MAT & PROCESSES LAB, KEARFOTT DIV, SINGER CO, 80- *Mem:* Am Soc Metals; Am Inst Mining, Metall & Petrol Engrs; Am Inst Aeronaut & Astronaut; Sigma Xi. *Res:* Micro-mechanical properties of metals, polymers, and fiber-reinforced composites; relationships between atomic structure and properties; deformation and mechanisms in materials; surface topology in friction and wear. *Mailing Add:* 161 Pershing Ave Ridgewood NJ 07450

RUTHERFORD, KENNETH GERALD, b Lindsay, Ont, May 10, 24; m 50; c 2. ORGANIC CHEMISTRY. *Educ:* Univ Western Ont, BA, 49; Wayne State Univ, PhD(chem), 54. *Prof Exp:* Res assoc org chem, Ohio State Univ, 54-56; asst prof chem, Univ Tulsa, 56-58; PROF CHEM, UNIV WINDSOR, 58- *Concurrent Pos:* Consult, Howick Chem Co, 70- *Mem:* Chem Inst Can; Am Chem Soc. *Res:* Synthetic organic chemistry; optically active trityl systems; kinetics of hydrolysis of benzhydryl esters; low temperature pyrolitic elimination reactions; potential routes to silicon to carbon compounds. *Mailing Add:* Dept Chem Univ Windsor Windsor ON N9B 3P4 Can

RUTHERFORD, KIM (THOMAS), biology, vertebrate zoology, deceased

RUTHERFORD, MALCOLM JOHN, b Durham, Ont, July 6, 39; m 62; c 2. PETROLOGY. *Educ:* Univ Sask, BScEng, 61, MSc, 63; Johns Hopkins Univ, PhD(geol), 68. *Prof Exp:* Fel, Univ Calif, Los Angeles, 68-69, asst prof geol, 69-70; asst prof, 70-75, ASSOC PROF GEOL, BROWN UNIV, 75- *Mem:* AAAS; Geol Soc Am; Mineral Soc Am; Am Geophys Union; Mineral Soc Can. *Res:* Chemistry variations and origin of igneous and metamorphic rocks in the earth's crust and the lunar crust through a combination of analytical studies and laboratory synthesis; origin and processes involved in formation of economic metal; sulfide deposits in association with igneous rocks. *Mailing Add:* Dept of Geol Brown Univ Providence RI 02912

RUTHERFORD, PAUL HARDING, b Shipley, Eng, Jan 22, 38; m 59; c 2. PLASMA PHYSICS. *Educ:* Cambridge Univ, BA, 59, PhD(plasma physics), 63. *Prof Exp:* Res assoc plasma physics, Princeton Univ, 62-63; res assoc, Culham Lab, UK Atomic Energy Auth, 63-65; mem res staff, 65-68, res physicist, 68-72, head theoret div, 72-79, LECTR PLASMA PHYSICS, PRINCETON UNIV, 68-, SR RES PHYSICIST, PLASMA PHYSICS LAB, 72-, ASSOC DIR, 80- *Mem:* Fel Am Phys Soc. *Res:* Theoretical plasma physics. *Mailing Add:* Plasma Physics Lab Princeton Univ Princeton NJ 08540

RUTHERFORD, WILLIAM, JR, b Locksprings, Mo, Apr 21, 17; m 46; c 3. FORESTRY. *Educ:* Cent Col, Mo, AB, 38; Univ Mich, BSF & MF, 40. *Prof Exp:* Forester, Soil Conserv Serv, USDA, 40-46, res forester, US Forest Serv, 46-50; PROF FORESTRY & HEAD DEPT, PAUL SMITH'S COL, 50-, DEAN FAC, 62- *Mem:* Soc Am Foresters; Am Cong Surv & Mapping; Soc Am Mil Eng. *Res:* Management of forest and wild lands, particularly economic aspects and organization. *Mailing Add:* Paul Smith's Col Paul Smith's NY 12970

RUTHERFORD, WILLIAM M(ORGAN), b Lake Charles, La, Oct 5, 29. CHEMICAL ENGINEERING. *Educ:* Univ Ill, BS, 51, MS, 52, PhD(chem eng), 54. *Prof Exp:* Chemist, Explor & Prod Res Lab, Shell Develop Co, Tex, 54-62; res specialist, 62-66, sr res specialist, 66-69, MONSANTO FEL, MOUND LAB, MONSANTO RES CORP, 69- *Mem:* AAAS; Am Chem Soc; Am Inst Chem Engrs. *Res:* Isotope separation; thermal diffusion; equilibrium and transport properties of fluids; properties of fluids at high pressure. *Mailing Add:* Mound Lab Monsanto Res Corp Miamisburg OH 45342

RUTHVEN, DOUGLAS M, b England, Oct 9, 38; m 68. CHEMICAL ENGINEERING, PHYSICAL CHEMISTRY. *Educ:* Univ Cambridge, BA, 60, MA, 63, PhD(chem eng), 66. *Prof Exp:* Design engr, Power Gas Corp, Eng, 61-63; from asst prof to assoc prof, 66-74, PROF CHEM ENG, UNIV NB, 74- *Mem:* Can Soc Chem Engrs; Am Inst Chem Engrs. *Res:* Catalysis by molten salts; supported metal catalysts; sorption and diffusion in molecular sieve zeolites. *Mailing Add:* Dept of Chem Eng Univ of NB Fredericton BC E3B 5A3 Can

RUTISHAUSER, URS STEPHEN, b Altadena, Calif, Feb 27, 46; m 74. BIOCHEMISTRY, EMBRYOLOGY. *Educ:* Brown Univ, ScB, 67; Rockefeller Univ, PhD(biochem), 73. *Prof Exp:* Jane Coffin Childs fel, Weizmann Inst Sci, Israel, 73-74; asst prof, 74-79, ASSOC PROF BIOCHEM, ROCKEFELLER UNIV, 79- *Res:* Immunology; developmental and cell biology; immunoglobulin structure; cell-cell interactions; neurobiology. *Mailing Add:* Rockefeller Univ York & 66th St New York NY 10021

RUTKIN, PHILIP, b New York, NY, Sept 17, 33; m 57; c 4. ORGANIC CHEMISTRY. *Educ:* City Col New York, BS, 55; NY Univ, PhD(org chem), 60. *Prof Exp:* Res chemist, Faberge, 58-60, dir res, 60-66, vpres res, 66-70; VPRES, ESTEE LAUDER, 75- *Concurrent Pos:* Eve sessions instr, Farleigh Dickinson Univ, 59-; NY Univ, 61 & City Col New York, 62-; gen mgr, Chemspray Div, ATI; vpres, Revlon-Int. *Mem:* Am Chem Soc; Soc Cosmetic Chemists; AAAS; Acad Sci. *Res:* Cosmetic chemistry. *Mailing Add:* 6 Henhawk Rd Great Neck NY 11024

RUTKOWSKI, BEVERLY JEAN, b Benton Harbor, Mich, Oct 28, 24; m 57; c 2. PHYSICAL CHEMISTRY. *Educ:* Western Mich Univ, BS & BA, 47. *Prof Exp:* Chemist, 55-61, res chemist, 62-71, SR RES CHEMIST, WHIRLPOOL CORP, 71- *Mem:* Am Chem Soc; Am Oil Chem Soc; Sci Res Soc Am; Am Asn Textile Chemists & Colorists; Am Soc Test & Mat. *Res:* Physical chemistry of detergency processes; analytical and evaluation procedures for detergents. *Mailing Add:* 137 Eloise Dr Benton Harbor MI 49022

RUTKOWSKI, ROBERT WILLIAM, b Reading, Pa, Apr 29, 41; m 77; c 1. INFORMATION SCIENCE. *Educ:* Drexel Univ, BS, 64; Univ Tenn, Knoxville, PhD(nuclear physics), 71. *Prof Exp:* SCI ANALYST PHYSICS, TECH INFO CTR, US DEPT ENERGY, 70- *Concurrent Pos:* Scientific analyst, US ERDA, 70-; thesaurus specialist, Int Nuclear Info Syst, Int Atomic Energy Agency, Vienna, Austria, 81- *Mem:* Am Phys Soc; Am Asn Physics Teachers. *Res:* Reaction mechanisms of light systems; computerized and manual scientific information storage and retrieval systems. *Mailing Add:* Tech Info Ctr PO Box 62 US Dept Energy Oak Ridge TN 37830

RUTLAND, LEON W, b Commerce, Tex, Aug 24, 19; m 44; c 2. MATHEMATICS. *Educ:* Univ Colo, PhD, 54. *Prof Exp:* From asst prof to assoc prof appl math, Univ Colo, 54-64; chmn dept, 64-70, PROF MATH, VA POLYTECH INST & STATE UNIV, 64- *Mem:* Am Math Soc; Am Soc Eng Educ; Soc Indust & Appl Math; Math Asn Am. *Res:* Applied mathematics. *Mailing Add:* 1391 Locust Ave Blacksburg VA 24060

RUTLEDGE, CARL THOMAS, b Fayetteville, Ark, Sept 17, 44; m 67; c 2. CHEMICAL PHYSICS. *Educ:* Univ Ark, BS, 66, MS, 69, PhD(physics), 71. *Prof Exp:* assoc prof physics, Southern Ark Univ, 70-81; ASSOC PROF PHYSICS, EAST CENT STATE UNIV, 81- *Mem:* Sigma Xi; Am Asn Physics Teachers. *Res:* X-ray diffraction studies of liquids; interferometry and physical optica; improvements in teaching basic astronomy and physics. *Mailing Add:* Box X-4 East Cent State Univ Ada OK 74820

RUTLEDGE, CHARLES O, b Topeka, Kans, Oct 1, 37; m 61; c 4. PHARMACOLOGY. *Educ:* Univ Kans, BS, 59, MS, 61; Harvard Univ, PhD(pharmacol), 66. *Prof Exp:* NATO fel pharmacol, Gothenburg Univ, 66-67; from asst prof to assoc prof, Med Ctr, Univ Colo, Denver, 67-75; PROF PHARMACOL & TOXICOL & CHMN DEPT, SCH PHARM, UNIV KANS, 75- *Mem:* AAAS; Am Soc Pharmacol & Exp Therapeut; Am Soc Neurochem; Soc Neurosci. *Res:* Autonomic, behavioral and biochemical pharmacology; interactions of drugs with the synthesis, storage, uptake, release and metabolism of neurotransmitters in the central nervous system to produce alterations in behavior. *Mailing Add:* Dept Pharmacol & Toxicol Univ Kans Sch Pharm Lawrence KS 66045

RUTLEDGE, DELBERT LEROY, b Mooreland, Okla, July 20, 25; m 47; c 2. THERMAL PHYSICS. *Educ:* Univ NMex, BS, 46; Okla State Univ, MS, 48, EdD, 58. *Prof Exp:* Asst prof physics, Cent State Col, Okla, 47-57; from asst prof to assoc prof, 57-70, PROF PHYSICS, OKLA STATE UNIV, 70- *Concurrent Pos:* Assoc prog dir, NSF Div Undergrad Educ, 65-66. *Mem:* Am Asn Physics Teachers; Am Phys Soc; Am Soc Eng Educ. *Mailing Add:* Dept of Physics Okla State Univ Stillwater OK 74074

RUTLEDGE, DOROTHY STALLWORTH, b Tuscaloosa, Ala, May 3, 30; m 49; c 2. MATHEMATICS. *Educ:* Birmingham-Southern Col, BA, 51; Emory Univ, MS, 60, PhD(math), 66. *Prof Exp:* Asst prof math, Agnes Scott Col, 66-69; asst prof, 69-72, ASSOC PROF MATH, GA STATE UNIV, 72- *Mem:* Am Math Soc; Math Asn Am. *Res:* Analysis; functional analysis. *Mailing Add:* Dept of Math Univ Plaza Atlanta GA 30303

RUTLEDGE, FELIX N, b Anniston, Ala, Nov 20, 17; m 50; c 1. GYNECOLOGIC ONCOLOGY. *Educ:* Univ Ala, BS, 39; Johns Hopkins Univ, MD, 43; Am Bd Obstet & Gynec, dipl, 51. *Prof Exp:* PROF GYNEC, UNIV TEX M D ANDERSON HOSP & TUMOR INST, 54- *Mem:* Am Asn Obstet & Gynec; Am Gynec Soc; Am Radium Soc; Soc Pelvic Surg; Soc Gynec Oncol. *Res:* Diagnosis and treatment of female pelvic malignancies. *Mailing Add:* Dept of Gynec Syst Cancer Ctr Tex Med Ctr Houston TX 77030

RUTLEDGE, GENE PRESTON, b Spartanburg, SC, Dec 3, 25; m 50; c 4. PHYSICAL CHEMISTRY, RESEARCH ADMINISTRATION. *Educ:* Wofford Col, BS, 46; Univ Tenn, MS, 48. *Hon Degrees:* DSc, Wofford Col, 71. *Prof Exp:* Res chemist & proj engr, Lab & Eng Div, Union Carbide Nuclear Co, Tenn, 48-54; supvry engr, Develop Eng Div, Goodyear Atomic Corp, Ohio, 54-56, sr scientist, S5W & Pressurized Water Reactor Projs, Westinghouse Elec Corp, 56-59, supvry scientist physics & appl math, 60-61, mem site manager's staff, 62, supvr S1W anal & test, Naval Reactors Facility, Bettis Atomic Power Lab, 63-67; exec dir, Idaho Nuclear Energy Comn, 67-77; MEM STAFF, DIV ENERGY & POWER DEVELOP, ALASKA, 77- *Concurrent Pos:* Mem bd dirs, Western Interstate Nuclear Compact, 69; mem, Gov Task Force Radioactive Waste Mgt, 71. *Mem:* Am Nuclear Soc; Am Chem Soc; Am Inst Chem Eng. *Res:* Energy development including nuclear, geothermal, solar, geosolar, hydrogen and wind and environmental; forestry, agriculture, mining and research using nuclear methods. *Mailing Add:* Div of Energy & Power Develop Seventh Fl Makay Bldg Anchorage AK 99501

RUTLEDGE, HARLEY DEAN, b Omaha, Nebr, Jan 10, 26; m 54; c 5. SOLID STATE PHYSICS. *Educ:* Tarkio Col, AB, 50; Univ Mo, MS, 56, PhD(photoelec emission), 66. *Prof Exp:* Assoc prof physics, Cent Methodist Col, 57-60; instr, Univ Mo, 60-61; assoc prof, 63-67, PROF PHYSICS, SOUTHEAST MO STATE UNIV, 67-, HEAD DEPT, 64- *Mem:* Am Asn Physics Teachers. *Res:* Experimental study of photoelectric emission from strontium oxide sprayed cathodes; theoretical analysis of photoelectric emission from semiconductors. *Mailing Add:* Dept of Physics Southeast Mo State Univ Cape Girardeau MO 63701

RUTLEDGE, JACKIE JOE, b Woodward, Okla, Dec 20, 41; m 66; c 1. ANIMAL BREEDING. *Educ:* Okla State Univ, BS, 68; NC State Univ, MS, 71, PhD(animal breeding), 73. *Prof Exp:* Res asst animal breeding, NC State Univ, 68-72; res assoc animal breeding, Univ Wis, 72-74; asst prof animal breeding, Univ Vt, 74-75; asst prof, 75-77, assoc prof, 77-80, PROF ANIMAL BREEDING, UNIV WIS, 80- *Mem:* Am Soc Animal Sci; Genetics Soc Am; Sigma Xi; Am Dairy Sci Asn; Am Genetic Asn. *Res:* Dynamics of genetic variances and covariances among and within populations; multivariate statistical theory applications to genetic problems; realized heritability and correlated predictors of fecundity in economic and laboratory animals. *Mailing Add:* Dept Meat & Animal Sci Animal Sci Bldg 1675 Observ Dr Madison WI 53706

RUTLEDGE, JAMES LUTHER, b Woodward, Okla, Oct 1, 37; m 63. SOLID STATE PHYSICS, ELECTRONICS. *Educ:* Okla State Univ, BS, 63, MS, 63, PhD(physics), 68. *Prof Exp:* Sr physicist, Motorola Semiconductor Prod, Inc, 67-74; proj leader res & develop, Fairchild Semiconductor, 74, MGR, ADV PROD RES & DEVELOP LABS, MOTOROLA SEMICONDUCTOR PRODS, 74- *Mem:* Inst Elec & Electronics Engrs; Am Phys Soc. *Res:* Solid state surface physics; electrical properties of semiconductors; physics of semiconductor devices. *Mailing Add:* 4007 S River Dr Tempe AZ 85282

RUTLEDGE, JOSEPH DELA, b Selma, Ala, Aug 9, 28; m 54; c 4. MATHEMATICS, COMPUTER SCIENCES. *Educ:* Swarthmore Col, BA, 50; Cornell Univ, PhD(math), 59. *Prof Exp:* Sr systs engr, Remington Rand Univac div, Sperry Rand Corp, 50-53; asst bact, Univ Hosp, Univ Pa, 53-55; asst math, Cornell Univ, 55-58; STAFF MEM, RES DIV, T J WATSON RES CTR, IBM CORP, 58- *Concurrent Pos:* Vis lectr, Wesleyan Univ, 65-67; lectr, Univ Grenoble, 67-68; adj prof, NY Univ, 69-70; IBM vis prof, Spelman Col, 71-72. *Mem:* Asn Symbolic Logic; Asn Comput Mach; Math Asn Am. *Res:* Theory of automata and computation; computer design and applications, especially man-machine communication and problem specification; programming and programming language. *Mailing Add:* PO Box 218 Yorktown Heights NY 10541

RUTLEDGE, LESTER T, b Big Sandy, Mont, June 12, 24; m 49. PHYSIOLOGY. *Educ:* Univ Utah, MA, 52, PhD(physiol, psychol), 53. *Prof Exp:* Res assoc & res instr physiol, Univ Utah, 53-56; from res assoc to assoc prof, 56-67, PROF PHYSIOL, MED SCH, UNIV MICH, ANN ARBOR, 67-, CHMN, NEUROSCI PROG, 72- *Concurrent Pos:* NIH sr res fel, 58-62, career develop award, 63-68. *Mem:* AAAS; Soc Neurosci; Am Physiol Soc. *Res:* Integrative processes of central nervous systems; electrophysiology of cortical and subcortical relationships; neural basis of learning; spinal and supraspinal reflexes; association cortex; epilepsy; neurological teaching. *Mailing Add:* Dept Physiol-Med Sci Bldg Univ of Mich Med Sch Ann Arbor MI 48109

RUTLEDGE, LEWIS JAMES, b McComb, Miss, Apr 24, 24; m 47; c 3. OTOLARYNGOLOGY, PEDIATRICS. *Educ:* Tulane Univ, MD, 47; Am Bd Pediat, dipl, 55; Am Bd Otolaryngol, dipl, 61. *Prof Exp:* Intern, Charity Hosp, New Orleans, La, 47-48, resident pediat, 48-50, resident otolaryngol, 55-57; instr pediat, Sch Med, Tulane Univ, 53-55; NIH spec trainee otolaryngol, Tulane Univ & Univ Chicago, 57-58; asst prof, 59-62, ASSOC PROF OTOLARYNGOL, SCH MED, TULANE UNIV, 62-, ASST PROF PEDIAT, 59- *Concurrent Pos:* Instr rhinoplasty, Columbia Univ at Mt Sinai Hosp, New York, 59- *Res:* Histopathology of human and animal temporal bones. *Mailing Add:* Dept of Otolaryngol Tulane Univ Med Sch New Orleans LA 70112

RUTLEDGE, ROBERT B, b St Louis, Mo, Dec 9, 35; m 60; c 4. MATHEMATICS, ELECTRICAL ENGINEERING. *Educ:* St Louis Univ, BS, 58, MS, 59, PhD(math), 62. *Prof Exp:* From asst prof to assoc prof math & appl sci, 62-69, assoc prof eng, 69-73, PROF MATH, SOUTHERN ILL UNIV, 73- *Concurrent Pos:* Consult electromagnetic sensor lab, Emerson Elec Co, 62- *Mem:* Math Asn Am; Soc Indust & Appl Math. *Res:* Analysis of advanced radar processing techniques using stochastic models; digital simulation techniques. *Mailing Add:* Div of Sci & Technol Southern Ill Univ Edwardsville IL 62025

RUTLEDGE, ROBERT L, b Pocahontas, Miss, June 23, 30; m 58; c 5. PHYSICAL CHEMISTRY. *Educ:* Miss State Univ, BS, 52; Univ Ill, MS, 53, PhD(phys chem), 58. *Prof Exp:* Sr res chemist, Socony Mobil Oil Co, Tex, 58-60; res chemist, 60-70, res specialist, 70-78, SR RES SPECIALIST, MINN MINING & MFG CO, 78- *Mem:* Soc Photog Sci & Eng. *Res:* Image evaluation of photographic media; novel imaging systems. *Mailing Add:* Minn Mining & Mfg Co 235-BC-01 3M Ctr St Paul MN 55144

RUTLEDGE, THOMAS FRANKLIN, b Cordova, Tenn, June 1, 21; m 43; c 3. ORGANIC CHEMISTRY. *Educ:* Univ Ark, BS, 43; Univ Del, PhD(org chem), 50. *Prof Exp:* Chemist, Res Labs, Socony-Vacuum Oil Co, 43-44, 47-48; sr res chemist, Monsanto Chem Co, 50-51; sect head org div, Res Labs, Air Reduction, Inc, 51-57; SUPVR CHEM & SYNTHETIC RES, CORP RES DEPT, ICI-AMERICAS 57- *Mem:* Am Chem Soc. *Res:* Mechanisms of chemical oxidations via chromic acid; preparation of synthetic lubricants of hydrocarbon type; catalyst preparation; acetylene and hydrocarbon chemistry; urea chemistry; polyurethanes; polymers; catalytic oxidation; polymerization. *Mailing Add:* ICI-Americas Corp Res Dept Chem Res & Develop Labs Wilmington DE 19897

RUTLEDGE, WYMAN COE, b Abrahamsville, Pa, Dec 15, 24; m 45; c 3. APPLIED PHYSICS. *Educ:* Hiram Col, AB, 44; Univ Mich, MS, 48, PhD(physics), 52. *Prof Exp:* Lab instr, Hiram Col, 43-44; res asst, Oceanog Inst, Woods Hole, 46-47; res assoc, Univ Mich, 47-48, res asst, 48-50; jr physicist, Argonne Nat Lab, 50-52; res physicist, Philip Labs, Inc, 52-56; sr res physicist, 56, RES FEL, CENT RES LABS, MEAD CORP, 56-, INST SYST CONSULT, 68- *Concurrent Pos:* Part-time instr, Ohio Univ, 58-68; mem, Simulation Coun, Inc; mem instrumentation comt, Am Inst Paper Res, process systs & controls comt, Tech Asn Pulp & Paper Indust; mem particulate subcomt, Inter Soc Air Sampling Comt, 72-; mem, Environ Res Tech Comt, Instrument Soc Am; vpres, Adv Bd Trustees, Ohico Univ, Chillicothe, 80-; mem, Bd Trustees, Hiram Col, 80- *Mem:* Am Phys Soc; Optical Soc Am; fel Instrument Soc Am; Measurements & Data Soc; Inst Environ Sci. *Res:* Underwater research; upper atmosphere; nuclear spectroscopy; thermionic emission; instrumentation and automation; computer systems application; basic phenomena; air and water quality instrumentation. *Mailing Add:* Cent Res Labs Eighth & Hickory Chillicothe OH 45601

RUTMAN, ROBERT JESSE, b Kingston, NY, June 23, 19; m 41 & 71; c 6. BIOCHEMISTRY. *Educ:* Pa State Univ, BS, 40; Univ Calif, PhD(biochem), 50. *Prof Exp:* Asst prof biochem, Jefferson Med Col, 50-53; res assoc biol, 54-56, chem, 57-64, assoc prof, 64-69, chmn lab biochem, Dept Animal Biol, 71-73, PROF CHEM, SCH VET MED, UNIV PA, 69- *Concurrent Pos:* Prof biochem & chmn dept, Philadelphia Col Osteopath, 59-62; consult, Hartford Found, Presby Hosp, Philadelphia, 63-65; vis prof, Univ Ibadan, Nigeria, 73-74. *Mem:* AAAS; Am Chem Soc; Am Soc Biol Chem; Am Asn Cancer Res. *Res:* Cancer chemotherapy; mechanism of action of chemotherapeutic drugs; nucleic acid metabolism; biochemical thermodynamics; nucleic acid metabolism in embryonic nucleus and mitochondria with particular reference to effect of clinically important anti-cancer drugs. *Mailing Add:* Dept of Animal Biol Sch Vet Med Univ of Pa Philadelphia PA 19174

RUTNER, EMILE, b Budapest, Hungary, Apr 28, 21; nat US. CHEMICAL PHYSICS. *Educ:* Carnegie Inst Technol, BS, 43; Cornell Univ, PhD(chem), 51. *Prof Exp:* Chemist, Control Lab, Koppers Co, 43; anal develop, Publicker Industs, 43-45; asst, Cornell Univ, 47-50; phys chemist, Wright Air Develop Ctr, US Dept Air Force, 51-56; physicist, Lewis Res Ctr, NASA, 56-60; chemist, 60-75, PHYSICIST, US AIR FORCE MAT LAB, WRIGHT PATTERSON AFB, 75- *Concurrent Pos:* Res assoc, Forrestal Res Ctr, Princeton Univ, 51-52. *Mem:* Am Chem Soc; Am Phys Soc. *Res:* Spectra; thermophysics; solid state; radiation effects; kinetics; high energy laser effects. *Mailing Add:* 519 W Norman Ave Dayton OH 45406

RUTOWSKI, RONALD LEE, b Van Nuys, Calif, May 16, 49; m 74. ANIMAL BEHAVIOR. *Educ:* Univ Calif, Santa Cruz, BA, 71; Cornell Univ, PhD(behav), 76. *Prof Exp:* asst prof, 76-80, ASSOC PROF ZOOL, ARIZ STATE UNIV, 80- *Concurrent Pos:* Prin investr, NSF grants, 78-80 & 80-82. *Mem:* Animal Behav Soc; AAAS; Am Soc Naturalists; Lepidopterists Soc. *Res:* Animal communication, especially in invertebrates; reproductive behavior. *Mailing Add:* Dept Zool Ariz State Univ Tempe AZ 85281

RUTSCHKY, CHARLES WILLIAM, b Pottstown, Pa, May 2, 23; m 45; c 4. ENTOMOLOGY. *Educ:* Pa State Univ, BS, 43; Cornell Univ, PhD(entom), 49. *Prof Exp:* Investr fruit insects, NY Agr Exp Sta, 47-49; from asst prof to assoc prof entom, Pa State Univ, 49-62; prof, Univ Hawaii, 62-64; PROF ENTOM, PA STATE UNIV, 65- *Mem:* Entom Soc Am. *Mailing Add:* Dept of Entomol Patterson Bldg Pa State Univ University Park PA 16802

RUTSTEIN, MARTIN S, b Boston, Mass, Apr 1, 40; m 62; c 2. MINERALOGY, GEOCHEMISTRY. *Educ:* Boston Univ, BA, 61, MA, 62; Brown Univ, PhD(mineral), 69. *Prof Exp:* Teaching asst geol, Boston Univ, 60-62; chief geol & soils sect, US Army Eng Sch, 62-64; res asst geol-mineral, Brown Univ, 64-68; asst prof mineral, Juniata Col, 68-70; asst prof, 70-72, chmn dept, 72-74, actg assoc vpres acad affairs, 74-75, ASSOC PROF GEOL SCI, STATE UNIV NY COL NEW PALTZ, 72-, CHMN DEPT, 76- *Concurrent Pos:* Pa Res Found fel, Juniata Col, 69-70; NY Res Found & Geol Soc Am Penrose Fund fels, State Univ NY Col New Paltz, 71-72, NSF fel, 72-73. *Mem:* Mineral Soc Am. *Res:* High temperature-pressure chain silicate phase relations; crystal chemistry of sulphides; environmental geology and human health; petrology. *Mailing Add:* Dept Geol Sci State Univ NY Col New Paltz NY 12561

RUTTENBERG, HERBERT DAVID, b Philadelphia, Pa, June 14, 30; m 55; c 4. PEDIATRICS, CARDIOLOGY. *Educ:* Univ Calif, Los Angeles, BA, 52, MD, 56. *Prof Exp:* Fel pediat, Med Sch, Univ Minn, 57-58 & 60-61, USPHS fel pediat cardiol, 61-63; NIH trainee cardiovasc res technol, Wash Univ, 63-64; asst prof pediat cardiol, Sch Med, Univ Calif, Los Angeles, 64-69; assoc prof pediat cardiol & chmn div, 69-78, PROF PEDIAT & CHMN DIV, COL MED, UNIV UTAH, 78- *Concurrent Pos:* Res assoc cardiovasc path, Charles T Miller Hosp, St Paul, Minn, 62-63; mem coun rheumatic fever & congenital heart dis, Am Heart Asn, 68- *Mem:* Fel Am Acad Pediat; fel Am Col Cardiol; fel NY Acad Sci; Am Fedn Clin Res. *Res:* Neurohumoral control of cardiac function; adreneric receptors; cardiovascular function in clinical and experimental complete heart block; exercise physiology and preventive cardiology. *Mailing Add:* Div of Pediat Cardiol Univ of Utah Col of Med Salt Lake City UT 84132

RUTTENBERG, STANLEY, b St Paul, Minn, Mar 12, 26; m 55; c 2. ATMOSPHERIC PHYSICS, METEOROLOGY. *Educ:* Mass Inst Technol, BS, 46; Univ Calif, Los Angeles, MA, 51. *Prof Exp:* Res asst geophys, Inst Geophys, Univ Calif, Los Angeles, 49-55; prog officer, US Nat Comt, Int Geophys Yr, Nat Acad Sci, 55-56, head prog officer, 57-60; secy, Panel World Magnetic Surv, Spec Comt Int Yrs Quiet Sun, Geophys Res Bd, 61-62, exec secy, US Nat Comt, 62-64; asst to dir, 64-73, mem sr mgt, Nat Ctr Atmospheric Res, 73-79, DIR OFF SCI PROG DEVELOP, UN CORP FOR ATMOSPHERIC RES, 79- *Concurrent Pos:* Consult, US Nat Comt, Spec Comn Int Yrs Quiet Sun, Nat Acad Sci, 64- *Mem:* Int Asn Meteorol & Atmospheric Physics (secy gen, 75-); AAAS; Am Geophys Union. *Res:* Atmospheric physics; space-based observational techniques. *Mailing Add:* UN Corp Atmospheric Res PO Box 3000 Boulder CO 80307

RUTTER, EDGAR A, JR, b Newark, NJ, Feb 3, 37; m 65. MATHEMATICS. *Educ:* Marietta Col, BA, 59; Iowa State Univ, PhD(math), 65. *Prof Exp:* Asst prof math, NMex State Univ, 65-66; asst prof math, Univ Kans, 66-69, assoc prof, 69-76, prof, 76-77; PROF MATH & CHMN DEPT, WRIGHT STATE UNIV, 77- *Mem:* Am Math Soc. *Res:* Ring theory. *Mailing Add:* Dept Math & Statist Wright State Univ Dayton OH 45435

RUTTER, HENRY ALOUIS, JR, b Richmond, Va, Mar 28, 22; m 55; c 1. TOXICOLOGY, BIOCHEMISTRY. *Educ:* Va Polytech Inst, BS, 43; Univ Richmond, MS, 47; Georgetown Univ, PhD(biochem), 52. *Prof Exp:* Chemist, Standard Oil Co, La, 43; chemist, US Naval Ord Lab, 43-45; asst, Univ Tenn, 48-49; instr chem, Am Univ, 49-50; assoc prof org chem, Carson-Newman Col, 50-51; instr phys chem, Georgetown Univ, 51-52; biochemist & mem staff, Biochem Res Found, Franklin Inst, 52-55; chemist, Walter Reed Army Inst Res, 56-59; chief res chemist, Dept Surg, Baltimore City Hosps, 59-60; res coordr chem pharmacol, 60-61, sr chemist, 61-63, sci dir chem dept, 63-64, res coordr pharmacol dept, 64-66, PROJ MGR TOXICOL DEPT, HAZLETON LABS, INC, 66- *Mem:* Am Chem Soc; Soc Cryobiol; Soc Toxicol; Am Inst Chemists. *Res:* Drugs and industrial chemicals; medical application of plastics; environmental sciences. *Mailing Add:* Dept Toxicol Hazleton Labs Inc 9200 Leesburg Turnpike Vienna VA 22180

RUTTER, JERRY L, b Kansas City, Mo, Nov 30, 39; m 60; c 2. ORGANIC CHEMISTRY. *Educ:* Univ Kans City, BS, 62; Univ Mo-Columbia, PhD(org chem), 67. *Prof Exp:* Res technician, Spencer Chem Co, 61-63; res chemist, 67-72, SR RES CHEMIST, GULF RES & DEVELOP CO, 72- *Mem:* Am Chem Soc. *Res:* Synthetic organic chemistry; heterocyclic compounds; thin layer and gas chromatography; interactive computer searching; formulations of pesticides; NMR; tracer synthesis; structure-activity relationships. *Mailing Add:* Gulf Oil Chems Co 9009 W 67th St Merriam KS 66202

RUTTER, NATHANIEL WESTLUND, b Omaha, Nebr, Nov 22, 32; Can citizen; m 61; c 2. QUATERNARY GEOLOGY. *Educ:* Tufts Univ, BS, 55; Univ Alaska, MS, 62; Univ Alta, PhD(geol), 66. *Prof Exp:* Explor geologist, Venezuelan Atlantic Ref Co, 55-58; res scientist, Geol Surv, Can, 65-74, head urban projs, 73-74; environ adv, Nat Energy Bd, 74-75; assoc prof, 75-77, PROF & CHMN GEOL, UNIV ALTA, 77- *Concurrent Pos:* Instr, Dept Archaeol, Univ Calgary, 67-73; consult, R S Peabody Found Archaeol, 70; pres, Westlund Consults Ltd; ed bd, Quaternary Rev; mem subcomt, NAm Stratigraphy; adv bd chmn, Boreal Inst. *Mem:* Fel Geol Soc Am; fel Geol Asn

Can; Soc Econ Paleont & Mineral. *Res:* Pleistocene and recent stratigraphy of the Rocky Mountains, Canada; investigations of surging glaciers; paleosol investigations of glaciated and unglaciated surfaces; terrain analysis and land classification; Mackenzie Valley Transportation Corridor, Canada; amino acid dating methods. *Mailing Add:* Dept of Geol Univ of Alta Edmonton AB T6G 2G7 Can

RUTTER, WILLIAM J, b Malad City, Idaho, Aug 28, 28; m 71; c 2. BIOCHEMISTRY. *Educ:* Harvard Univ, BA, 49; Univ Utah, MS, 50; Univ Ill, PhD(biochem), 52. *Prof Exp:* USPHS fel, Inst Enzyme Res, Univ Wis, 52-54; USPHS fel biochem, Nobel Inst, Sweden, 54-55; from asst prof to prof biochem, Univ Ill, Urbana, 55-65; prof biochem & genetics, Univ Wash, 65-69; HERTZSTEIN PROF BIOCHEM & BIOPHYS & CHMN DEPT, UNIV CALIF, SAN FRANCISCO, 69- *Concurrent Pos:* Consult biochem, Biochem & Nutrit Fel Panel, USPHS, 63-66 & Physiol Chem Study Sect, NIH, 67-71; vis scientist, Guggenheim Mem fel, Stanford Univ, 62-63; assoc ed, J Exp Zool, 68-71; mem exec comn, Div Biol & Agr, Nat Res Coun, 69-72; mem & chmn basic sci adv comn, Nat Cystic Fibrosis Res, 69-74, mem, Pres Adv Coun, 74-75; mem develop biol panel, NSF, 71-73; pres, Pac Slope Biochem Conf, 71-73; mem adv bd, Revista Pan-Am Asn Biochem Soc, 71-; mem biomed adv comt, Los Alamos Sci Lab, 72-75; mem bd sci counrs, Nat Inst Environ Health Sci, 76-, adv comt, Nat Found Basic Res, 76-, bd dirs, Keystone Life Sci Study Ctr, 76- & biol div adv comt, Oak Ridge Nat Labs, 76-; ed, Cell Biol, 76-78 & Arch Biochem & Biophys, 78- *Honors & Awards:* Pfizer Award, Am Chem Soc, 67. *Mem:* Am Soc Cell Biol; Am Chem Soc; Am Soc Biol Chemists (treas, 70-76); Soc Develop Biol (pres-elect, 74-75, pres, 75-76). *Res:* Control of gene expression; mechanisms of cytodifferentiation; regulation of cell proliferation; mechanism of enzyme action; macromolecular variation and evolution. *Mailing Add:* Dept of Biochem & Biophys Univ of Calif San Francisco CA 94143

RUTZ, LENARD O(TTO), b Franklin, Wis, Jan 27, 24; m 53; c 2. CHEMICAL ENGINEERING. *Educ:* Marquette Univ, BChE, 45; Univ Wis, BS, 52, MS, 53; Univ Iowa, PhD(chem eng), 58. *Prof Exp:* Engr, Allis-Chalmers Mfg Co, 45-47, asst engr mining & mineral dressing div, 47-50; res chem engr, E I du Pont de Nemours & Co, 53-54; instr chem eng, Univ Iowa, 56-58, asst prof, 58-61; res engr, Missile & Space Systs Div, Douglas Aircraft Co, Inc, 61, supvr adv space tech, 62-63, chief eng res sect adv biotech, 63-65, sr staff specialist, Astropower Lab, Newport Beach, 65-77; CHEM ENGR, PROCON INC, 77- *Concurrent Pos:* Res fel, Eudora Hull Spalding Lab, Calif Inst Technol, 61-62; consult, Douglas Aircraft Co, Inc, 61-62; adj prof chem eng, Calif Polymer Univ, Univ Southern Calif, 78- *Mem:* Am Inst Aeronaut & Astronaut; Am Chem Soc; Am Inst Chem Eng; Am Soc Eng; Nat Soc Prof Engrs. *Res:* Applied thermodynamics; batteries; bioscience and biotechnology; desalination; fuel cells; heat transfer; membrane separation processes; nuclear engineering; physical and flow porperties of porous media; sorption processes; transport phenomena; ultra-high vacua; petroleum refining processing; synfuels. *Mailing Add:* 2075 Del Mar Ave San Marino CA 91108

RUTZ, RICHARD FREDERICK, b Alton, Ill, Feb 9, 19; m 45; c 3. SEMICONDUCTOR DEVICES & MATERIALS. *Educ:* Shurtleff Col, BA, 41; State Univ Iowa, MS, 46. *Prof Exp:* Staff mem electronics, Sandia Corp, 48-51; mgr semiconductor devices, 51-80, MEM STAFF, T J WATSON RES CTR, IBM CORP, 80- *Mem:* Am Inst Physics; Inst Elec & Electronics Engrs. *Res:* Experimental semiconductor device technology; method of fabrication of crystalline shapes; high speed switching transistors. *Mailing Add:* T J Watson Res Ctr IBM Corp PO Box 218 Yorktown Heights NY 10598

RUUD, CLAYTON OLAF, b Glasgow, Mont, July 31, 34; m 65; c 2. X-RAY DIFFRACTION ANALYSIS, RESIDUAL STRESS ANALYSIS. *Educ:* Wash State Univ, BS, 57; San Jose State Univ, MS, 67; Denver Univ, PhD(mat sci), 70. *Prof Exp:* Asst remelt mat, Kaiser Aluminum & Chem Corp, 57-58; mem staff develop eng, Boeing Aircraft Co, 58-61; res engr, Lockheed Missiles & Space Corp, 62-64, FMC Corp, 64-67; sr res scientist, Denver Univ, 70-79; SR RES ASSOC, PA STATE UNIV, 79- *Concurrent Pos:* Ed, Advances X-Ray Anal, 70-80, X-Ray Spectros, 77-; chmn, Particulates Subcomt, Safe Drinking Water Comt, Nat Acad Sci, 75-77. *Mem:* Am Soc Metals; Am Soc Metall Engrs; Soc Exp Stress Anal; Am Soc Testing Mat. *Res:* Materials characterization using x-ray diffraction; x-ray fluorescence; electron microanalysis; electron microscopy; cause and effect of residual stresses in metallic components, especially measurement methods and instrumentation. *Mailing Add:* 159 Mat Res Lab Pa State Univ University Park PA 16802

RUUS, E(UGEN), b Parnu, Estonia, Aug 19, 17; Can citizen; m 45; c 3. HYDRAULICS. *Educ:* Univ Technol, Tallinn, Estonia, Dipl civil eng, 41; Karlsruhe Tech Univ, DrEng(civil eng), 57. *Prof Exp:* Sr asst & lectr civil eng, Univ Technol, Tallinn, Estonia, 42-43; designer, Dept War, Finland, 44; A B Skanska Cementgjuteriet, Sweden, 45-50 & Wagner & Oliver Consult Engrs, Ont, 50-51; hydraul & sr design engr, B C Eng Co, 51-56; lectr civil eng, 57-58, from asst prof to assoc prof, 58-71, PROF CIVIL ENG, UNIV BC, 71- *Mem:* Am Soc Civil Engrs; Eng Inst Can. *Res:* Water power development; hydraulic transients and turbine governing. *Mailing Add:* Dept of Civil Eng Univ of BC Vancouver BC V6T 1W5 Can

RUVALCABA, ROGELIO H A, b Tepic, Mex, Apr 16, 34; US citizen; m 61; c 3. PEDIATRIC ENDOCRINOLOGY. *Educ:* Univ Guadalajara, MD, 57. *Prof Exp:* Rotating intern med & surg, Hotel Dieu Hosp, New Orleans, 59, resident pediat, 60; resident, Children's Mem Hosp, Omaha, Nebr, 61; resident, Creighton Mem Hosp, 62; trainee pediat endocrinol & metab dis, 62-64, chief trainee, 64-66, from instr to assoc prof pediat endocrinol, 65-77, PROF PEDIAT ENDOCRINOL, UNIV WASH, 77- *Concurrent Pos:* Dir endocrinol clin, Rainier Sch, 66-; mem human res rev bd, Dept Social & Health Serv, 75-78; dir pediat endocrine clin, Mary Bridge Children's Hosp, Tacoma, 75- *Mem:* Endocrine Soc. *Res:* Metabolic and endocrine disorder associated with mental retardation. *Mailing Add:* Dept of Pediat Med Sch Seattle WA 98195

RUVALDS, JOHN, b Jelgava, Latvia, Mar 26, 40; US citizen; m 71. PHYSICS. *Educ:* Grinnell Col, BA, 62; Univ Ore, MA, 65, PhD(physics), 67. *Prof Exp:* Res assoc physics, James Franck Inst, Univ Chicago, 67-69; from asst prof to assoc prof, 69-76, PROF PHYSICS, UNIV VA, 76-, NSF GRANT, 72- *Mem:* Am Phys Soc. *Res:* Theoretical solid state physics. *Mailing Add:* Dept of Physics Univ of Va Charlottesville VA 22901

RUWART, MARY JEAN, b Detroit, Mich, Oct 16, 49. GASTROENTEROLOGY, METABOLISM. *Educ:* Mich State Univ, BS, 70, PhD(biophys), 74. *Prof Exp:* NIH trainee biophys, Mich State Univ, 70-73; res assoc surg, Med Sch, St Louis Univ, 74-75, from instr to asst prof, 75-76; RES SCIENTIST GASTROENTEROL, UPJOHN CO, 76- *Mem:* Am Gastroenterol Asn; Am Fedn Clin Res; Soc Cryobiol; Biophys Soc. *Res:* Intestinal motility; cholesterol metabolism; gallstone disease; organ preservation and function; carbohydrate and lipid metabolism; integration of basic and applied sciences; nutrition; prostaglandins. *Mailing Add:* Exp Biol Upjohn Co Kalamazoo MI 49001

RUYLE, WILLIAM VANCE, b Malcolm, Nebr, Feb 20, 20; m 47; c 6. ORGANIC CHEMISTRY, MEDICINAL CHEMISTRY. *Educ:* Univ Nebr, AB, 42, MS, 43; Univ Ill, PhD(org chem), 49. *Prof Exp:* Res assoc synthetic med chem, Merck & Co, Inc, 49-61, res fel, 61-77, SR RES FEL, MERCK SHARP & DOHME RES LABS, 77- *Mem:* Am Chem Soc. *Res:* Research and development in synthetic organic and medicinal chemistry. *Mailing Add:* 1481 Rahway Rd Scotch Plains NJ 07076

RUZE, JOHN, b New York, NY, May 24, 16; m 56; c 4. ELECTRONIC ENGINEERING. *Educ:* City Col New York, BS, 38; Columbia Univ, MS, 40; Mass Inst Technol, ScD(electronic eng), 52. *Prof Exp:* Sect head antenna design, Signal Corps Radar Labs, 40-46; asst lab head, Air Force Cambridge Res Labs, 46-52; dir, Gabriel Lab, 52-54; pres, Radiation Eng Lab, 54-62; SR STAFF MEM, LINCOLN LABS, MASS INST TECHNOL, 62- *Concurrent Pos:* Ed, Inst Elec & Electronics Engrs Trans Antennas & Propagation, 67-69. *Mem:* Fel Inst Elec & Electronics Engrs; Int Union Radio Sci. *Res:* Microwave optics; large antenna systems; electromagnetic theory. *Mailing Add:* Fitchburg Turnpike Concord MA 01742

RUZICKA, FRANCIS FREDERICK, JR, b Baltimore, Md, June 30, 17; m 41; c 6. RADIOLOGY. *Educ:* Col Holy Cross, AB, 39; Johns Hopkins Univ, MD, 43. *Prof Exp:* Roentgenologist, Cancer Detection Ctr, Univ Minn, 48-49, instr radiol, Univ Hosps, 49-50; chmn dept radiol, St Vincent's Hosp & Med Ctr, New York, 50-73; assoc chmn dept, 73-76, chmn dept, 76-81, PROF RADIOL, MED CTR, UNIV WIS-MADISON, 73- *Concurrent Pos:* Consult radiol, St Elizabeth's Hosp, Elizabeth, NJ, Overlook Hosp, Summit, NJ & Columbus Hosp, New York; assoc clin prof radiol, Sch Med, NY Univ, 50-53, clin prof, 54-73; consult comt Vet Admin health resources, Nat Acad Sci, 75-76. *Mem:* Radiol Soc NAm; AMA; fel Am Col Radiol; NY Acad Sci; Am Roentgen Ray Soc. *Res:* Roentgen aspects of the portal venous system; xeromammagraphy; vascular roentgenology; double contrast techniques in gastrointestinal radiology including the use of drugs; digital video angiography with special reference to renal artery surgery; motility studies of alimentary tract using radiologic techniques. *Mailing Add:* Dept Radiol Univ Wis Med Ctr Madison WI 53706

RYALL, ALAN S, JR, b San Mateo, Calif, July 6, 31; m 57; c 2. SEISMOLOGY. *Educ:* Univ Calif, Berkeley, AB, 56, MA, 59, PhD(geohpys), 62. *Prof Exp:* Res seismologist, Univ Calif, Berkeley, 60-61; geophysicist, US Geol Surv, 62-63; prof seismol, seismologist & dir, Seismol Lab, Mackay Sch Mines, Univ Nev, Reno, 64-76; prog mgr, Defense Adv Res Proj Agency, Washington, DC, 76-78; PROF SEISMOL, SEMISMOLOGIST & DIR, SEISMOL LAB, MACKAY SCH MINES, UNIV NEV, RENO, 78- *Concurrent Pos:* Geophysicist, Defense Adv Res Proj Agency, Washington, DC, 76-78; del, Comprehensive Test Ban Treaty Negotiations, Geneva, 78. *Mem:* AAAS; fel Am Geophys Union; Geol Soc Am; Seismol Soc Am (vpres, 80-81, pres, 81-82); Earthquake Eng Res Inst. *Res:* Earthquake seismology; seismic regionalization; earthquake mechanisms; crust-mantle structure; test ban treaty verification. *Mailing Add:* Mackay Sch of Mines Univ of Nev Reno NV 89507

RYALS, GEORGE LYNWOOD, JR, b Erwin, NC, Nov 14, 41; m 67; c 1. INVERTEBRATE ECOLOGY. *Educ:* Elon Col, AB, 66; Appalachian State Univ, MA, 67; Clemson Univ, PhD(zool), 75. *Prof Exp:* Asst prof biol, Lees-McRae Col, 67-69 & Southeastern Col, 69-70; ASSOC PROF BIOL & CHMN DEPT, ELON COL, 73- *Mem:* Am Inst Biol Sci; AAAS; Am Soc Zoologists; NAm Benthological Soc. *Res:* Structure and function of benthic communities; seasonal regulation in Chironomidae and Odonata. *Mailing Add:* Dept of Biol Elon Col Elon College NC 27244

RYAN, ALLAN JAMES, b Brooklyn, NY, Dec 9, 15; m 42; c 3. MEDICAL EDITING. *Educ:* Yale Univ, BA, 36; Columbia Univ, MD, 40; Am Bd Surg, dipl, 47. *Prof Exp:* From assoc prof to prof rehab med & phys educ, Univ Wis-Madison, 65-76, athletic teams physician, 65-76; ed-in-chief, Postgrad Med, 76-79, ED-IN-CHIEF, THE PHYSICIAN & SPORTS MED, 73- *Res:* Sports medicine; physical education. *Mailing Add:* 4530 W 77th St Edina MN 55435

RYAN, ANNE WEBSTER, b Lowell, Mass, Apr 17, 27; m 55; c 2. ORGANIC CHEMISTRY, INFORMATION SCIENCE. *Educ:* Simmons Col, BS, 49. *Prof Exp:* Asst ed, 49-51 & 52-64, group leader, 64-65, asst dept head, 65-67, MGR, CHEM ABSTRACTS SERV, 67- *Concurrent Pos:* Tech librn res & develop, Lever Bros Co, 51-52. *Mem:* Am Chem Soc; AAAS. *Res:* Chemical information, storage and retrieval. *Mailing Add:* Chem Abstracts Serv Ohio State Univ Columbus OH 43210

RYAN, BILL CHATTEN, b Long Beach, Calif, Oct 2, 28; m 50; c 4. METEOROLOGY. *Educ:* Univ Nev, Reno, BS, 50; Tex A&M Univ, MS, 64; Univ Calif, Riverside, PhD(geog), 74. *Prof Exp:* Officer electronics, US Air Force, 51-58, officer meteorol, 58-65; res meteorologist, Meteorol Res Inc, 65-67; RES METEOROLOGIST, USDA FOREST SERV, 67- *Concurrent*

Pos: Mem, Sci Comt Riverside Air Pollution Control Dist, 69- *Honors & Awards:* Outstanding Meteorologist Award, Riverside-San Bernardino Chap, Am Meteorol Soc, 75. *Mem:* Am Meteorol Soc. *Res:* Development of a mathematical model to diagnose and predict wind in remote areas of mountainous terrain. *Mailing Add:* 2291 Quartz Pl Riverside CA 92507

RYAN, CECIL BENJAMIN, b Runge, Tex, Aug 4, 16; m 41; c 2. POULTRY SCIENCE. *Educ:* Tex Col Arts & Indust, BS, 38; Tex A&M Univ, MS, 47, PhD, 62. *Prof Exp:* Teacher pub sch, 38-42; asst prof, 47-62, assoc prof, 62-81, EMER PROF POULTRY SCI, TEX A&M UNIV, 81- *Concurrent Pos:* Piper Prof, 66. *Mem:* Fel AAAS; Poultry Sci Asn (secy-treas, 54-77, first vpres, 78-79, pres, 79-80); Genetics Soc Am; World Poultry Sci Asn. *Res:* Environmental physiology and management. *Mailing Add:* Dept of Poultry Sci Tex A&M Univ College Station TX 77843

RYAN, CHARLES EDWARD, JR, b Crestline, Ohio, Mar 30, 38; m 62; c 5. ELECTRICAL ENGINEERING. *Educ:* Case Inst Technol, BSc, 60; Ohio State Univ, MSc, 61, PhD(elec eng), 68. *Prof Exp:* Eng asst, North Elec Co, 56-60; res asst, Electrosci Lab, Ohio State Univ, 60-62, res assoc, 62-68, asst supvr, 68-71; SR RES ENGR, ENG EXP STA, GA INST TECHNOL, 71-, PRIN RES ENGR, 76-, CHIEF ELECTROMAGNETIC EFFECTIVENESS DIV, 80- *Mem:* Inst Elec & Electronics Engrs; Sigma Xi. *Res:* Electromagnetic theory applied to antennas and scattering; radar cross section studies; computer analysis. *Mailing Add:* Ga Inst Technol Eng Exp Sta 225 North Ave NW Atlanta GA 30332

RYAN, CHARLES FUTRELL, b Terre Haute, Ind, Dec 30, 41; m 62; c 1. PHARMACOLOGY, TOXICOLOGY. *Educ:* Purdue Univ, BS, 63, MS, 66, PhD(pharmacol), 69. *Prof Exp:* Asst prof pharmacol, Sch Pharm, Univ Wis, 68-73; assoc prof pharmacol & chmn Dept Pharmacodynamics & Toxicol, Col Pharm, Univ Nebr, Lincoln, 73-80; PROF PHARMACOL & DEP DEAN, FAC PHARM, WAYNE STATE UNIV, 80- *Mem:* Am Soc Pharmacol & Exp Therapeut. *Res:* Adrenergic pharmacology; cardiomyopathy; cardiovascular pharmacology. *Mailing Add:* Dept Pharm & Allied Health 103 HSB Wayne State Univ Detroit MI 48202

RYAN, CHARLES LUCE, JR, b Cheverly, Md, May 29, 53; m 75. POLYMER PROCESSING, POLYMER COMPOSITES. *Educ:* Va Polytech Inst & State Univ, BS, 75; Univ Mass, Amherst, 77, PhD(polymer sci), 79. *Prof Exp:* Fel polymer sci, Univ Mass, Amherst, 79-80; RES CHEMIST, PHILLIPS PETROL CO, 80- *Mem:* Am Chem Soc; Am Phys Soc; Soc Plastics Engrs; AAAS. *Res:* Structure and property relationships in polymers, particularly polyolefins. *Mailing Add:* Phillips Res Ctr 328 Pl Bartlesville OK 74004

RYAN, CLARENCE AUGUSTINE, JR, b Butte, Mont, Sept 29, 31; m 54; c 4. CHEMISTRY. *Educ:* Carroll Col, Mont, BA, 53; Mont State Univ, MS, 56, PhD(chem), 59. *Prof Exp:* Fel, Ore State Univ, 59-61; fel, Western Regional Lab, USDA, 61-63, chemist, 63-64; asst agr chemist, 64-68, assoc prof biochem & assoc agr chemist, 68-72, chmn, Dept Agr Chem, 78-80, PROF BIOCHEM & AGR CHEMIST, WASH STATE UNIV, 72- *Concurrent Pos:* USPHS Career Develop Award, 64-74. *Honors & Awards:* Merck Award, 59. *Mem:* AAAS; Am Soc Biol Chemists; Am Chem Soc; Am Soc Plant Phys; fel Inst Biol Chem. *Res:* Protein chemistry; plant proteolytic enzymes, naturally occurring proteinase inhibitors. *Mailing Add:* Dept of Agr Chem Wash State Univ Pullman WA 99163

RYAN, DALE SCOTT, b Pasadena, Calif, Sept 7, 47; m 70; c 1. FOOD SCIENCE. *Educ:* Occidental Col, AB, 69; Univ Calif, Davis, MS, 71, PhD(biochem), 74. *Prof Exp:* Chemist, Agr Res Serv, USDA, 69-70; ASST PROF FOOD CHEM, UNIV WIS-MADISON, 74- *Mem:* Inst Food Technologists. *Res:* Characterization of the biochemical determinants of nutritional value; isolation and characterization of the main proteins of economically important plant protein resources; protein structure and function. *Mailing Add:* Dept of Food Sci Univ of Wis Madison WI 53706

RYAN, DAVID GEORGE, b Quebec, Que, Dec 31, 37. PARTICLE PHYSICS. *Educ:* Queen's Univ, Ont, BSc, 59, MSc, 61; Univ Birmingham, PhD(physics), 65. *Prof Exp:* Res fel physics, Univ Birmingham, 65-66; res assoc, Cornell Univ, 66-67; asst prof, 67-70, assoc prof, 70-81, PROF PHYSICS, MCGILL UNIV, 81- *Mem:* Am Phys Soc. *Res:* Interactions and decays of elementary particles. *Mailing Add:* Dept of Physics McGill Univ 3600 University Montreal PQ H3A 2T8 Can

RYAN, DONALD EDWIN, b San Diego, Calif, July 1, 35. MATHEMATICS, ASTRONOMY. *Educ:* Univ Tex, BA, 57, MA, 61, PhD(math), 64. *Prof Exp:* Aero-engr, Pensacola Naval Air Sta, 55; test engr, Convair Astronaut Div, Gen Dynamics Corp, 57-59; instr math, Univ Tex, 59-63, 63-64; asst prof math, Eastern Mich Univ, 64-65; asst prof, Bowling Green State Univ, 65-68; assoc prof, 68-74, PROF MATH, NORTHWESTERN STATE UNIV, 74- *Concurrent Pos:* NSF consult, India, 67; chmn gifted & talented adv comt, Northwestern State Univ. *Mem:* Am Math Soc; Math Asn Am. *Res:* Functions of a complex variable which are ecart fini and t their topological structures. *Mailing Add:* Dept of Math Northwestern State Univ Natchitoches LA 71457

RYAN, DONALD F, b Syracuse, NY, July 24, 30; m 59; c 4. PHYSICS. *Educ:* LeMoyne Col, NY, BS, 57; Cath Univ Am, MS, 60, PhD(physics), 63. *Prof Exp:* Res fel physics, Cath Univ Am, 63-64, from res asst prof to res assoc prof, 64-66; from asst prof to assoc prof, 66-72, chmn dept physics & earth sci, 70-72, PROF PHYSICS, STATE UNIV NY COL PLATTSBURGH, 72- *Mem:* Am Phys Soc. *Res:* Cosmic ray and elementary particle research. *Mailing Add:* Dept of Physics State Univ of NY Plattsburgh NY 12901

RYAN, DOUGLAS EARL, b Can, Jan 21, 22; m 45; c 3. INORGANIC CHEMISTRY, ANALYTICAL CHEMISTRY. *Educ:* Univ NB, BSc, 44; Univ Toronto, MA, 46; Imp Col, London, dipl & PhD(chem), 51; Univ London, DSc, 65. *Prof Exp:* Asst prof chem, Univ NB, 46-48; from asst prof to assoc prof, 51-63, chmn dept chem, 69-73, MCLEOD PROF CHEM, DALHOUSIE UNIV, 63-, DIR, TRACE ANAL RES CTR, 71-, DIR, SLOWPOKE FACIL, 76- *Concurrent Pos:* Nat Res Coun Can traveling fel, 59-60; exec dir, Ctr Anal Res & Develop, Univ Colombo, Sri Lanka, 80- *Honors & Awards:* Fisher Sci Lect Award, Chem Inst Can, 72. *Mem:* Fel Chem Inst Can. *Res:* Metal chelates; molecular spectroscopy; neutron activation and trace analysis in general. *Mailing Add:* Dept Chem Dalhousie Univ Halifax NS B3H 3J5 Can

RYAN, EDWARD MCNEILL, b St Louis, Mo, May 24, 20; m 76; c 3. GEOLOGY. *Educ:* Miami Univ, BA, 41; Univ Mo-Columbia, MA, 43. *Prof Exp:* Aerial phototopographer, US Army Corp Engrs, 43-46; PROF GEOL, STEPHENS COL, 46- *Mem:* Nat Asn Geol Teachers. *Res:* Geologic travel and color photography in fifty states, most provinces of Canada, Virgin Islands and East Africa. *Mailing Add:* Dept of Geol Box 2072 Stephens Col Columbia MO 65215

RYAN, EDWARD PARSONS, b Trenton, NJ, Oct 3, 22; m 62; c 2. INVERTEBRATE ZOOLOGY, DEVELOPMENTAL BIOLOGY. *Educ:* Ouachita Baptist Univ, BS, 49; Univ Del, MS, 51; Univ Hawaii, PhD(zool), 65. *Prof Exp:* Res aide limnol, Acad Natural Sci, Philadelphia, Pa, 51-52; instr biol, Univ Pittsburgh, 52-53; asst prof, Ark Agr & Mech Col, 53-56; asst zool, Univ Hawaii, 56-58; assoc prof biol, Ark Agr & Mech Col, 59-61; ASSOC PROF BIOL, E CAROLINA UNIV, 65- *Concurrent Pos:* Duke Marine Lab award, 66; NSF res grant, 66-68. *Mem:* Am Inst Biol Sci; Am Soc Zool; Am Soc Cell Biol; Am Soc Limnol & Oceanog; Atlantic Estuarine Res Soc. *Res:* General and reproductive biology of decapod crustaceans; ultrastructure of gametogenesis and fertilization in crabs. *Mailing Add:* Dept of Biol East Carolina Univ Greenville NC 27834

RYAN, FREDERICK MERK, b Pittsburgh, Pa, Jan 20, 32; m 52; c 2. PHYSICS. *Educ:* Carnegie Inst Technol, BS, 54, MS, 56, PhD(physics), 59. *Prof Exp:* Res physicist, 59-61, sr physicist, 61-66, fel scientist, 66-72, ADV SCIENTIST, WESTINGHOUSE ELEC CORP, 72- *Mem:* Am Phys Soc; Electrochem Soc. *Res:* Experimental solid state physics; luminescence; optical physics. *Mailing Add:* Optical Physics Dept Westinghouse Res Labs Pittsburgh PA 15235

RYAN, GEORGE FRISBIE, b Yakima, Wash, July 28, 21; m 47; c 1. HORTICULTURE. *Educ:* State Col Wash, BS, 47; Univ Calif, Los Angeles, PhD(hort sci), 53. *Prof Exp:* Res asst hort, Univ Calif, Los Angeles, 48-52, instr & jr horticulturist, 52-54, asst prof & asst horticulturist, 54-60, assoc specialist, 60-61; asst prof & asst horticulturist, Citrus Exp Sta, Univ Fla, 61-67; assoc horticulturist, 67-79, HORTICULTURIST, WESTERN WASH RES & EXTEN CTR, WASH STATE UNIV, 79- *Mem:* Am Soc Hort Sci; Weed Sci Soc Am; Int Plant Propagation Soc. *Res:* Chemical regulation of plant growth and flowering; nutrition of ornamental plants; chemical weed control. *Mailing Add:* Western Wash Res & Exten Ctr Wash State Univ Puyallup WA 98371

RYAN, JACK A, b Pittsburgh, Pa, Nov 3, 29; m 56; c 2. GEOPHYSICS. *Educ:* Rice Univ, BS, 51; Pa State Univ, PhD(geophys), 59. *Prof Exp:* Res scientist, Douglas Aircraft Co, 59-61, chief lunar & planetary sci sect, 61-63, chief environ sci br, McDonnell Douglas Astronaut Co, Huntington Beach, 69-76, chief lunar & planetary sci br, 73-76; lectr earth sci, 75, team leader, Viking Mars Meteorol Sci, 77-79, PROF EARTH SCI & CHAIR DEPT, CALIF STATE UNIV, FULLERTON, 76- *Concurrent Pos:* Consult, US Army Corps Engrs, 64-69 & McDonnell Douglas Astronaut Co, 78-; mem resources & environ subgroup, Working Group on Extraterrestrial Resources, NASA, 65-71. *Honors & Awards:* Newcombe-Cleveland Award, AAAS, 77. *Mem:* AAAS; Am Geophys Union. *Res:* Planetary physics, Viking 1976 Mars Landers Meteorology Team; atmospheric science, especially Mars atmospheric dynamics; solid earth geophysics. *Mailing Add:* 10182 La Sierra Pl Santa Ana CA 90725

RYAN, JACK LEWIS, b Dallas, Ore, May 14, 33; m 64. INORGANIC CHEMISTRY. *Educ:* Ore State Univ, BS, 53, MS, 56. *Prof Exp:* Chemist, Hanford Lab, Gen Elec Co, 55-60, sr scientist, 60-65; sr res scientist, 65-69, RES ASSOC, PAC NORTHWEST LABS, BATTELLE MEM INST, 69- *Concurrent Pos:* Consult, Lawrence Berkeley Lab, Univ Calif, 74; lectr, Joint Ctr Grad Study, Richland, Wash, 74- *Mem:* AAAS; Am Chem Soc. *Res:* Inorganic and physical chemistry of actinide and lanthanide elements; coordination chemistry; absorption spectroscopy; ion exchange; solvent extraction; non-aqueous solutions; chemical processing of actinide elements. *Mailing Add:* Pac Northwest Lab Battelle Mem Inst Richland WA 99352

RYAN, JAMES ANTHONY, b Cairo, Ill, Mar 16, 43; m 63; c 3. SOIL CHEMISTRY, SOIL BIOCHEMISTRY. *Educ:* Murray State Univ, BS, 66; Univ Ky, MS, 68, PhD(soils), 71. *Prof Exp:* Fel soil sci, Univ Wis-Madison, 71-74; soil scientist, Munic Environ Res Lab, 74-77, MEM STAFF, ULTIMATE DISPOSAL RES PROG, ENVIRON PROTECTION AGENCY, 77- *Mem:* Am Soc Agron; Soil Sci Soc Am; Water Pollution Control Fedn; AAAS; Sigma Xi. *Res:* Nitrogen transformations in soils; sewage sludge disposal on agricultural lands; transformation of heavy metals in soils in relation to their phytotoxic effects. *Mailing Add:* Advan Waste Treat Res Lab Environ Protection Agency Cincinnati OH 45268

RYAN, JAMES M, b Milwaukee, Wis, Feb 20, 32; m 55; c 5. CHEMICAL ENGINEERING. *Educ:* Univ Mich, BS & MS, 55; Mass Inst Technol, ScD(chem eng), 58. *Prof Exp:* Technologist, Shell Chem Co, 58-63, res engr, 63-65; proj leader gas chromatography, Abcor, Inc, 65-66, prog mgr, 66-70, mgr eng, 70-71, mgr commercial plants eng, 71-73, vpres, Abcor Japan, 73-75, dir technol, Abcor, Inc, 75-78; mgr process/prod develop, Helix Process Systs Inc, 78-81; MGR RES & DEVELOP, KOCH PROCESS SYSTS INC, 81- *Mem:* Am Chem Soc; Am Inst Chem Engrs; Soc Petroleum Engrs. *Res:* Chemical process development; membrane process and equipment design, engineering, plants; separation processes; gas chromatography; large scale liquid chromatography; reaction kinetics; chemical manufacturing economics; process simulation; mass transfer; cryogenic gas field separations. *Mailing Add:* 11 King's Grant Rd Weston MA 02193

RYAN, JAMES PATRICK, b Philadelphia, Pa, Jan 10, 47; m 68; c 2. GASTROINTESTINAL PHYSIOLOGY. *Educ:* Villanova Univ, BS, 68, MS, 70; Hahnemann Med Col, PhD(physiol), 74. *Prof Exp:* Fel, Sch Med, Univ Pa, 74-75; asst prof, 75-80, ASSOC PROF, SCH MED, TEMPLE UNIV, 80- *Concurrent Pos:* Lectr, Gwynedd Mercy Col, 76- *Mem:* NY Acad Sci; Sigma Xi. *Res:* Neural and hormonal control of gastrointestinal smooth muscle motility, including how motor patterns are affected during pregnancy. *Mailing Add:* Dept Physiol Sch Med Temple Univ Philadelphia PA 19140

RYAN, JAMES WALTER, b Amarillo, Tex, June 8, 35; m 73; c 4. MEDICINE, BIOCHEMISTRY. *Educ:* Dartmouth Col, AB, 57; Cornell Univ, MD, 61; Oxford Univ, DPhil(biochem), 67. *Prof Exp:* Intern med, Montreal Gen Hosp, Can, 61-62, resident, 62-63; res assoc, NIH, 63-65; hon med officer to Regius prof med, Oxford Univ, 65-67; asst prof biochem, Rockefeller Univ, 67-68; assoc prof, 68-79, PROF MED, SCH MED, UNIV MIAMI, 79- *Concurrent Pos:* USPHS fel, Oxford Univ, 65-67; USPHS spec fel, Rockefeller Univ, 67-68, career develop award, 68; sr scientist, Papanicolaou Cancer Res Inst, 72-77; vis prof, Clin Res Inst Montreal, 74; mem coun cardiopulmonary dis & med adv bd, Coun High Blood Pressure, Am Heart Asn. *Mem:* Am Heart Asn; Am Chem Soc; Am Soc Biol Chemists; Am Inst Chem; Brit Biochem Soc. *Res:* Action and metabolism of the vasoactive polypeptides; bradykinin and angiotensin, and their relation to diseases of high blood pressure. *Mailing Add:* Dept of Med Univ of Miami Sch of Med Miami FL 33101

RYAN, JOHN DONALD, b Norristown, Pa, July 9, 21; m 43; c 3. GEOLOGY. *Educ:* Lehigh Univ, BA, 43, MS, 48; Johns Hopkins Univ, PhD(geol), 52. *Prof Exp:* Asst, Lehigh Univ, 46-48; asst, Johns Hopkins Univ, 49-50; tech expert, State Dept Geol, Md, 50-52; from instr to assoc prof, 52-62, chmn dept, 61-76, PROF GEOL, LEHIGH UNIV, 62- *Concurrent Pos:* Coop geologist, State Topol & Geol Surv, Pa, 47-48, 53; geologist, US Geol Surv, 48-; Fulbright lectr, Cent Univ Ecuador, 71. *Mem:* Geol Soc Am; Am Asn Geol Teachers; Soc Econ Paleont & Mineral; Geol Soc Finland. *Res:* Recent sediments in Chesapeake Bay; studies in the stratigraphic control of uranium deposits; environmental geology; Cretaceous and Tertiary sedimentation in the Wyoming Rockies. *Mailing Add:* Dept of Geol Sci Lehigh Univ Bethlehem PA 18015

RYAN, JOHN F, b Boston, Mass, May 16, 35; m 59; c 3. ANESTHESIOLOGY. *Educ:* Boston Col, AB, 57; Columbia Univ, MD, 61. *Prof Exp:* Asst prof anesthesiol, Col Physicians & Surgeons, Columbia Univ & Columbia-Presby Med Ctr, 68-69; ASST PROF ANESTHESIOL, HARVARD MED SCH & MASS GEN HOSP, 69- *Res:* Pediatric anesthesia; biochemistry of the myoneural junction; hypotensive anesthesia and malignant hyperpyrexia. *Mailing Add:* Dept of Anesthesiol Mass Gen Hosp Boston MA 02114

RYAN, JOHN PETER, b St Paul, Minn, July 28, 21; m 44; c 5. PHYSICAL CHEMISTRY. *Educ:* Col St Thomas, BS, 43; Univ Minn, PhD(phys chem), 52. *Prof Exp:* Instr chem, Col St Thomas, 46-51; res chemist radiochem, 51-61, mgr nuclear prod dept, 61-73, MGR STATIC CONTROL SYSTS DEPT, 3M CO, 73- *Mem:* Am Nuclear Soc; Am Chem Soc. *Res:* Development of commercial and medical products containing radioactive isotopes. *Mailing Add:* 3M Co 3M Ctr St Paul MN 55101

RYAN, JOHN WILLIAM, b La Crosse, Wis, Sept 8, 26; m 52; c 3. ORGANIC CHEMISTRY. *Educ:* Loras Col, BS, 48; Univ Iowa, MS, 51; Univ Ky, PhD(org chem), 57. *Prof Exp:* Proj leader org chem res, 57-65, supvr, 65-68, personnel coordr res, develop & eng, 68-69, mgr tech serv & develop, resins & chem bus, 69-73, MGR RES & DEVELOP SILICONE FLUIDS, DOW CORNING CORP, 73- *Mem:* Sigma Xi. *Res:* Organosilicone and organometallic compounds. *Mailing Add:* 514 Linwood Dr Midland MI 48640

RYAN, JON MICHAEL, b Ottumwa, Iowa, Nov 14, 43; m 65. CELL BIOLOGY. *Educ:* William Penn Col, BA, 65; Univ Nebr, Lincoln, MS, 67; Iowa State Univ, PhD(cell biol), 70. *Prof Exp:* NIH fel, 70-71, res asst, 72-76, res assoc cell biol, Wistar Inst Anat & Biol, 76; res scientist, Res Inst, Ill Inst Technol, 76-78; sr scientist, 78-81; CELL BIOLOGIST, ABBOTT LABS, 81- *Mem:* AAAS; Tissue Cult Asn. *Res:* Control of cellular proliferation in tissue culture; aging; biochemistry of nuclear proteins; hormone-cell interaction; cell differentiation; plasminogen activators. *Mailing Add:* Dept 456 Bldg R1B-6 Abbott Labs North Chicago IL 60064

RYAN, JOSEPH DENNIS, b Lockport, NY, June 13, 04; m 30; c 2. ORGANIC CHEMISTRY. *Educ:* Univ Mich, BSE, 27, MS, 28, PhD(org chem), 31. *Prof Exp:* Lab asst, Carborundum Co, NY, 22-23; lab asst chem, Univ Mich, 24-27, asst, 27-30, instr org chem, 30-31; org res chemist, Libbey-Owens-Ford Glass Co, 31-37, asst dir res, 37-52, assoc dir res, 52-55, dir res, 55-59, gen dir res & develop, 59-63, vpres res & develop, 63-68; CONSULT INDUST, 68- *Concurrent Pos:* Mem, Nat Res Found, Toledo, Ohio. *Mem:* Fel AAAS; Nat Sci Prof Eng; Am Chem Soc; Am Ceramic Soc; Am Soc Test & Mat. *Res:* Refractories; refractory cements; quinoidation polymerization; laminated glass; transparent plastics; coatings for transparent plastics; organic glass substitutes. *Mailing Add:* 3018 Middlesex Dr Toledo OH 43606

RYAN, JULIAN GILBERT, b Metamora, Ill, Oct 6, 13; m 36; c 1. PETROLEUM CHEMISTRY. *Educ:* Univ Ill, BS, 35. *Prof Exp:* Res chemist, Shell Oil Co, 35-42, supvr fuels & lubricants develop, 46-63, tech adv to res dir, 63-70, staff res engr, 70-78; RETIRED. *Concurrent Pos:* Group leader, Coord Res Coun, 53-66, mem diesel div, 66-76. *Mem:* AAAS; Am Chem Soc; Soc Automotive Eng. *Res:* Corrosive wear of engines; gasoline stability; tetraethyl lead antagonism by sulfur compounds; abnormal combustion phenomena; aviation and automotive fuels and lubricants; automotive engines exhaust emission. *Mailing Add:* 664 Halloran Ave Wood River IL 62095

RYAN, KENNETH JOHN, b New York, NY, Aug 26, 26; m 48; c 3. ENDOCRINOLOGY, BIOCHEMISTRY. *Educ:* Harvard Med Sch, MD, 52; Am Bd Obstet & Gynec, dipl, 64. *Prof Exp:* Intern med, Mass Gen Hosp, Boston, 52-53, resident, 53-54, fel biochem, 54-55, Am Cancer Soc fel, 54-56; asst resident, Columbia-Presby Med Ctr, 56-57; resident, Boston Lying-In-Hosp & Free Hosp Women, 57-60; dir, Fearing Lab, Free Hosp Women, 60-61; Arthur H Bill prof obstet & gynec & chmn dept, Sch Med, Case Western Reserve Univ, 61-70, chmn dept reprod biol, 68-70, coordr biol sci, 69-70; prof reprod biol & chmn, Dept Obstet & Gynec, Univ Calif, San Diego, 70-72; KATE MACY LADD PROF OBSTET & GYNEC & CHMN DEPT, HARVARD MED SCH, 73-, DIR LAB HUMAN REPROD & REPROD BIOL, 74-; CHIEF-OF-STAFF, BOSTON HOSP WOMEN, 73- *Concurrent Pos:* Fel med, Harvard Med Sch, 53-54 & 55-56, teaching fel obstet & gynec, 57-60, instr, 60-61; dir, Fearing Res Lab, 60-70; dir dept obstet & gynec, Univ Hosps Cleveland, 61-70; mem nat adv coun, USPHS; mem, Pres Comt Ment Retardation. *Honors & Awards:* Ernst Oppenheimer Award, Endocrine Soc, 64; Weinstein Award United Cerebral Palsy, 71. *Mem:* Inst Med-Nat Acad Sci; Am Soc Biol Chemists; Endocrine Soc; fel Am Col Obstet & Gynec; Soc Gynec Invest. *Mailing Add:* Boston Hosp for Women 221 Longwood Ave Boston MA 02115

RYAN, MICHAEL PATRICK, JR, b Galveston, Tex, Feb 17, 43; m 68. PHYSICS. *Educ:* Mass Inst Technol, SB, 65; Univ Md, PhD(physics), 70. *Prof Exp:* Res assoc physics, Univ Md, 70 & Univ NC, 70; vis scientist, Landau Inst Theoret Physics, Moscow, 71; res assoc, Univ Tex, 71-74; RES PROF PHYSICS, NAT UNIV MEX, 74- *Mem:* Int Soc Gen Relativity & Gravitation. *Res:* General relativity; mathematical physics. *Mailing Add:* Centro De Estudios Nucleares Circuito Exterior CU Mexico 20 DF Mexico

RYAN, MICHAEL T, b Tipperary, Ireland, Sept 29, 25; Irish & Can citizen; m 55; c 3. BIOCHEMISTRY, CHEMISTRY. *Educ:* Univ Col, Dublin, BSc, 46, MSc, 47; McGill Univ, PhD(biochem), 55. *Prof Exp:* Asst chem, Univ Col, Galway, 47-49; from lectr to assoc prof, Fac Med, 49-71, PROF BIOCHEM, FAC MED & SCI, UNIV OTTAWA, 71- *Mem:* Can Biochem Soc. *Res:* Interaction of steroids and proteins. *Mailing Add:* Dept of Biochem Univ of Ottawa Ottawa ON K1N 6N5 Can

RYAN, NORMAN W(ALLACE), b Casper, Wyo, Feb 9, 19; m 42; c 4. CHEMICAL ENGINEERING. *Educ:* Cornell Univ, BChem, 41, ChemE, 42; Mass Inst Technol, ScD, 49. *Prof Exp:* Chem engr, Standard Oil Co, Ind, 42-46; assoc prof chem eng, 48-57, PROF CHEM ENG, UNIV UTAH, 57- *Concurrent Pos:* Consult. *Mem:* Am Chem Soc; Am Inst Aeronaut & Astronaut; Am Inst Chem Engrs. *Res:* Combustion; fluid dynamics. *Mailing Add:* Dept of Chem Eng Univ of Utah Salt Lake City UT 84112

RYAN, PATRICK WALTER, b Chicago, Ill, Nov 14, 33; m 56; c 4. ORGANIC POLYMER CHEMISTRY. *Educ:* Loyola Univ Chicago, BS, 55; Purdue Univ, PhD(chem), 59. *Prof Exp:* From res chemist to sr res chemist, Sinclair Res Inc, 59-65, group leader, 65-68, div dir, 68-69; RES MGR, ARCO CHEM CO, 69- *Mem:* Am Chem Soc; Sigma Xi. *Res:* Syntheses of low molecular weight organic polymers and their applied chemistry; chemicals for tertiary oil recovery and basic petrochemicals. *Mailing Add:* 369 S Ivy Lane Glen Mills PA 19342

RYAN, PETER MICHAEL, b Quincy, Mass, Aug 6, 43; m 68; c 2. MATHEMATICS. *Educ:* Calif Inst Technol, BS, 65; Dartmouth Col, AM, 67, PhD(math), 70. *Prof Exp:* Asst prof math, Gustavus Adolphus Col, 69-76; asst prof math, Moorhead State Univ, 76-78; ASSOC PROF MATH & COMPUT SCI, JACKSONVILLE UNIV, 78- *Mem:* AAAS; Am Math Soc; Math Asn Am; Soc Indust Appl Math. *Res:* Frames; complete Brouwerian lattices. *Mailing Add:* Dept of Math Jacksonville Univ Jacksonville FL 32211

RYAN, RICHARD ALEXANDER, b Detroit, Mich, Feb 27, 25; m 47; c 3. VERTEBRATE ZOOLOGY. *Educ:* Cornell Univ, AB, 48, MS, 49, PhD(zool), 51. *Prof Exp:* From instr to assoc prof, 52-64, chmn dept, 66-69, 74-75, PROF BIOL, HOBART & WILLIAM SMITH COLS, 64- *Mem:* AAAS; Am Soc Ichthyol & Herpet; Am Soc Mammal; Wildlife Soc. *Res:* Life history of vertebrates. *Mailing Add:* Dept Biol Hobart & William Smith Cols Geneva NY 14456

RYAN, RICHARD PATRICK, b Decatur, Ill, May 4, 38; m 60; c 3. PATENT AGENT. *Educ:* Millikin, BA, 60; Univ Ky, PhD(org chem), 68. *Prof Exp:* Chemist, Neisler Labs, Inc, Union Carbide Corp, 60-63; sr scientist, 67-71, group leader, 71-75, sr clin res assoc, Mead Johnson Res Ctr, 75-80, PATENT COORD, BRISTOL MYERS CO, 80- *Concurrent Pos:* Lectr, Univ Evansville, 69-73. *Mem:* Fel Am Geriat Soc; Am Chem Soc; Sigma Xi; Am Heart Asn; Am Col Cardiol. *Res:* Preparation and prosecution of patent applications covering pharmaceutical and nutritional inventions; synthesis of biologically active heterocyclic compounds; correlation of chemical structure with biological activity; drug therapy of cardiovascular, central nervous system, respiratory, neoplastic and nutritional diseases. *Mailing Add:* Mead Johnson & Co Evansville IN 47721

RYAN, ROBERT DEAN, b Upland, Calif, Mar 3, 33; m 61; c 2. MATHEMATICS. *Educ:* Calif Inst Technol, BS, 54, PhD(math), 60; Harvard Univ, MPA, 71. *Prof Exp:* Res assoc math, Calif Inst Technol, 60-61; asst prof, US Army Math Res Ctr, Wis, 61-63, asst prof, Univ, 63-65; mathematician, Math Br, Washington, DC, 65-69; prog dir oper res, 69-71, SPEC ASST RES, OFF NAVAL RES, 71- *Mem:* Am Math Soc; Math Asn Am; Soc Indust & Appl Math. *Res:* Harmonic analysis and measure theory. *Mailing Add:* Dept of the Navy Off of Naval Res Arlington VA 22217

RYAN, ROBERT F, b Hoquiam, Wash, June 23, 22. SURGERY. *Prof Exp:* Resident surg, Emergency Hosp, Washington, DC, 50-51; from instr to asst prof, 56-63, assoc prof plastic surg, 63-67, PROF SURG, MED SCH, TULANE UNIV, 67-, CHIEF SECT PLASTIC SURG, 69- *Mem:* AMA. *Res:* Plastic surgery; tissue transplantation; wound healing; cancer. *Mailing Add:* Sect Plastic Surg Dept Surg Tulane Univ Sch of Med New Orleans LA 70112

RYAN, ROBERT J, b Cincinnati, Ohio, July 18, 27; m 54; c 6. MEDICINE, ENDOCRINOLOGY. *Educ:* Univ Cincinnati, MD, 52. *Prof Exp:* Intern, Henry Ford Hosp, Detroit, 52-53; res fel, Univ Ill Col Med, 53-54, resident med, Res & Educ Hosp, 54-57; Am Col Physicians res fel endocrinol, New Eng Ctr Hosp, 57-58; from instr to assoc prof, Univ Ill Col Med, 58-67; assoc prof, 67-70, PROF MED, MAYO GRAD SCH MED, UNIV MINN, 70-, CHMN DEPT MOLECULAR MED, MAYO CLIN, 73- *Concurrent Pos:* Mem staff molecular med, Mayo Clin, 67-68, consult, 68-70, chmn dept endocrine res, 70-73; mem reproductive biol study sect, NIH; mem pop res comn, Nat Inst Child Health & Human Develop; mem med adv bd, Nat Pituitary Agency. *Mem:* Endocrine Soc; Am Soc Biol Chemists; Soc Study Reprod; Soc Exp Biol & Med; Am Soc Clin Invest. *Res:* Purification, assay and biologic characterization of human gonadotropic hormones. *Mailing Add:* Dept of Molecular Med Mayo Clin Rochester MN 55901

RYAN, ROBERT PAT, b Pensacola, Fla, May 1, 25; m 50; c 2. ULTRASOUND. *Educ:* Rice Univ, BS, 45; Brown Univ, ScM, 59, PhD(physics), 63. *Prof Exp:* Physicist, US Navy Mine Defense Lab, Fla, 47-58; asst prof physics, Univ Ky, 63-65; Nat Acad Sci-Nat Res Coun res assoc solid state physics, Res Dept, Naval Ord Lab, Md, 65-66; physicist, NASA Electronics Res Ctr, 66-70; physicist, mech eng div, 70-82, STAFF ENGR, TRANSP SYSTS CTR, DEPT TRANSP, 82- *Mem:* Acoust Soc Am; Inst Elec & Electronics Eng; Am Soc Nondestructive Test. *Res:* Underwater sound noise measurement; analysis; guided mode and finite-amplitude propagation; ultrasonic relaxations in glasses; second-order optical effects; piezo and ferroelectricity; ultrasonic techniques for nondestructive testing; ultrasonic imaging; signal processing; pattern recognition. *Mailing Add:* Dept Transp-Transp Systs Ctr 55 Broadway Sq Boston MA 02142

RYAN, ROBERT REYNOLDS, b Klamath Falls, Ore, July 29, 36. ACTINIDE CHEMISTRY, ORGANIC EXPLOSIVES. *Educ:* Portland State Univ, BS, 61; Ore State Univ, PhD(chem), 65. *Prof Exp:* Fel x-ray diffraction, Swiss Fed Inst Technol, Zurich, 65-66; fel vibrational spec, 66-67, staff mem, 67-80, DEP GROUP LEADER, LOS ALAMOS NAT LAB, 80- *Mem:* Am Chem Soc; Am Crystallog Asn. *Res:* Transition metal chemistry; actinide chemistry; continuous phase changes; small molecule activation; organic explosives; vibrational spectroscopy; x-ray diffraction; gas phase electron diffraction. *Mailing Add:* Los Alamos Nat Lab Los Alamos NM 87545

RYAN, ROGER BAKER, b Port Chester, NY, May 5, 32; m 55; c 4. INSECT ECOLOGY. *Educ:* State Univ NY Col Forestry, Syracuse, BS, 53; Ore State Univ, MS, 59, PhD(entom, plant path), 61. *Prof Exp:* Entomologist, 61-65, RES ENTOMOLOGIST, FORESTRY SCI LAB, US FOREST SERV, 65- *Mem:* Entom Soc Am; Entom Soc Can; Int Orgn Biol Control. *Res:* Biological control, physiology and behavior of insects. *Mailing Add:* Forestry Sci Lab 3200 Jefferson Way Corvallis OR 97330

RYAN, SIMEON P, b Manhattan, NY, May 30, 22. BIOLOGY. *Educ:* St Francis Col, BS, 51; St Louis Univ, MS, 53, PhD(biol), 57. *Prof Exp:* From instr to assoc prof biol, St Francis Col, NY, 57-70, dir pre-med & pre-dent training, 58-66, actg head dept biol, 66-70; asst prof, 70-74, ASSOC PROF BIOL, NASSAU COMMUNITY COL, 74- *Mem:* AAAS; NY Acad Sci. *Res:* Cytological nutritional effects; cytopathology. *Mailing Add:* Dept of Biol Nassau Community Col Garden City NY 11530

RYAN, STEWART RICHARD, b Schenectady, NY, Jan 26, 42; m 66; c 3. ATOMIC & MOLECULAR PHYSICS. *Educ:* Univ Notre Dame, BS, 64; Univ Mich, MS, 65, PhD(physics), 71. *Prof Exp:* Res staff physicist, Yale Univ, 71-73, instr, 73-74; res assoc, Univ Ariz, 74-76, staff physicist, 76-77; ASST PROF PHYSICS, UNIV OKLA, 77- *Mem:* Am Phys Soc; Am Asn Physics Teachers; Am Asn Eng Educ. *Res:* Molecular dissociation processes; atom-molecule collisions; electron-molecule collisions; low temperature properties of helium 3-helium 4 mixtures; applied physics; instrumentation; energy conservation. *Mailing Add:* Dept of Physics & Astron Univ of Okla Norman OK 73019

RYAN, THOMAS ARTHUR, JR, b Ithaca, NY, June 12, 40; m 66. STATISTICS. *Educ:* Wesleyan Univ, BA, 62; Cornell Univ, PhD(math), 68. *Prof Exp:* Instr math statist, Columbia Univ, 67-68, asst prof, 68-69; asst prof, 69-75, ASSOC PROF STATIST, PA STATE UNIV, UNIVERSITY PARK, 75- *Mem:* Inst Math Statist; fel Am Statist Asn; Asn Comput Mach; Inst Elec & Electronics Engrs Comput Soc. *Res:* Statistical computing. *Mailing Add:* Dept of Statistics 215 Pond Lab Pa State Univ University Park PA 16802

RYAN, THOMAS JOHN, b New York, NY, June 12, 43; m 70; c 3. BIOCHEMISTRY, ORGANIC CHEMISTRY. *Educ:* Manhattan Col, BS, 65; State Univ NY, Stony Brook, PhD(org chem), 70. *Prof Exp:* Res assoc org chem, Johns Hopkins Univ, 69-71; assoc, Rensselaer Polytech Inst, 71-72; fel biochem, 72-74, RES SCIENTIST BIOCHEM, DEPT HEALTH, DIV LABS & RES, ALBANY, NY, 74- *Mem:* Am Chem Soc; AAAS. *Res:* Fibrinolysis; coagulation; enzyme mechanism and structure. *Mailing Add:* Dept of Health Empire State Plaza Albany NY 12201

RYAN, THOMAS WILTON, b San Mateo, Calif, March 20, 46; m 69; c 2. SYSTEMS DESIGN, SYSTEMS SCIENCE. *Educ:* Univ Santa Clara, BS, 68; Univ Ariz, MS, 71, PhD(elec eng), 81. *Prof Exp:* Teacher math & physics, Green Fields Sch, 71-76; res asst, Univ Ariz, 76-79; STAFF SCIENTIST, SCI APPLN, INC, 79- *Mem:* Inst Elec & Electronics Engrs; Soc Photo-Optical Instrumentation Engrs. *Res:* Applications of signal processing in radar signal analysis; image processing. *Mailing Add:* 9115 E Sierra Ave 9115 E Sierra Ave Tucson AZ 85710

RYAN, UNA SCULLY, b Kuala Lumpur, Malaysia, Dec 18, 41; Brit citizen; m 73; c 2. CELL BIOLOGY, PULMONARY DISEASES. *Educ:* Bristol Univ, BSc, 63; Cambridge Univ, PhD(cell biol), 68. *Prof Exp:* From instr to assoc prof, 67-80, PROF MED, SCH MED, UNIV MIAMI, 80- *Concurrent Pos:* Vis investr, Lab Cardiovasc Res, Howard Hughes Med Inst, Miami, 67-

71, dir, Lab Ultrastruct Studies, 70-71; adj asst prof biol, Univ Miami, 68-; sr scientist, Papanicolaou Cancer Res Inst, 72-77; estab investr, Am Heart Asn, 72-77, mem basic sci coun, 77-, mem, Microcirculation Coun, 78-; mem pulmonary dis adv comt, Nat Heart, Lung & Blood Inst, 73-76, mem res rev comt A, 77-81, chmn, 80-81. *Mem:* Royal Entom Soc London; Am Soc Cell Biol; Europ Soc Endocrinol; Tissue Cult Asn; NY Acad Sci. *Res:* Application of advanced techniques of electron microscopy to studies of the endocrine or non-ventilatory functions of the lung, with particular emphasis on correlations of fine structure of endothelial cells with specific metabolic activities. *Mailing Add:* Dept of Med PO Box 016960 Miami FL 33101

RYAN, VICTOR ALBERT, b Laramie, Wyo, Aug 11, 20; m 50; c 4. NUCLEAR CHEMISTRY. *Educ:* Univ Wyo, BS, 42; Univ Minn, PhD(phys chem), 51. *Prof Exp:* Chemist, E I du Pont de Nemours & Co, Tenn, 51-53; chemist, Dow Chem Co, Colo, 53-58; from asst prof to assoc prof chem, 58-80, PROF CHEM ENG, UNIV WYO, 80-, SAFETY DIR, 74- *Mem:* Am Chem Soc; Am Nuclear Soc; Am Asn Univ Profs; Sigma Xi. *Res:* Photochemistry; flash photolysis; industrial chemistry; lanthanide and actinide chemistry; prompt and ordinary activation analysis. *Mailing Add:* Dept Chem Univ Wyo Box 3838 Univ Sta Laramie WY 82070

RYAN, WAYNE L, b Corning, Iowa, June 14, 27; m 48; c 5. BIOCHEMISTRY, IMMUNOLOGY. *Educ:* Creighton Univ, BS, 49, MS, 51; Univ Mo, PhD(biochem), 53. *Prof Exp:* Instr microbiol & asst prof biochem, Sch Med, Creighton Univ, 53-61, assoc prof biochem, 61-64; assoc prof biochem & res assoc prof obstet & gynec, 64-67, PROF BIOCHEM & RES PROF OBSTET & GYNEC, UNIV NEBR MED CTR, OMAHA, 67-, ASST DEAN RES, 73- *Mem:* Am Chem Soc; Am Asn Cancer Res; Soc Exp Biol & Med. *Res:* Asparaginase, mode of action, adenosine 3'5' cyclic monophosphate and cell division; biochemistry of carcinogenesis. *Mailing Add:* Dept of Biochem Univ of Nebr Med Ctr Omaha NE 68105

RYAN, WILLIAM B F, b Troy, NY, Sept 1, 39; m 62; c 2. OCEANOGRAPHY, GEOLOGY. *Educ:* Williams Col, BA, 61; Columbia Univ, PhD(geol), 71. *Prof Exp:* Res asst oceanog, Woods Hole Oceanog Inst, 61-62; res asst geol, 62-74, SR RES ASSOC GEOL, LAMONT-DOHERTY GEOL OBSERV, COLUMBIA UNIV, 74- *Mem:* Am Geophys Union. *Res:* Marine geology and geophysics. *Mailing Add:* Lamont-Doherty Geol Observ Palisades NY 10964

RYANT, CHARLES J(OSEPH), JR, b Chicago, Ill, Apr 1, 20; m 77. ENGINEERING, ENVIRONMENTAL ENGINEERING. *Educ:* Armour Inst Technol, BS, 40; Ill Inst Technol, MS, 41, PhD(chem eng), 47. *Prof Exp:* Instr chem eng, Ill Inst Technol, 40-41, instr chem, 46-47; chem engr, Sinclair Refining Corp, Ind, 41 & Wurster & Sanger, Inc, 41-43; sr proj engr, Standard Oil Co, Ind, 43-59; consult, 59-68; tech consult, Joint Ill House & Senate Air Pollution Study Comt, 68-69; vpres & dir eng, Sparkleen Systs, Inc, 69-70; exec dir, Midwest Legis Coun Environ, Univ Ill, Chicago Circle, 70-80; CONSULT, C J RYANT, JR & ASSOC, 80- *Concurrent Pos:* Civilian with Atomic Energy Comn, 44; instr, Ill Inst Technol, 53-; chmn, Calumet City Environ Control Comn, 74-81. *Mem:* Am Chem Soc; Am Inst Chem Engrs. *Res:* Filtration and sedimentation; heat transfer; conditioning of air; heat transfer in a double exchanger; petroleum refinery furnaces. *Mailing Add:* 504 Ryant Rd Maple City MI 49664

RYASON, PORTER RAYMOND, b Bridgeport, Nebr, Jan 18, 29; m 52; c 4. PHYSICAL CHEMISTRY. *Educ:* Reed Col, BA, 50; Harvard Univ, MA, 52, PhD(chem), 54. *Prof Exp:* Sr res assoc, Chevron Res Co, Stand Oil Co Calif, 53-73; mem tech staff, Jet Propulsion Lab, Calif Inst Technol, 73-78; SR RES ASSOC, CHEVRON RES CO, STANDARD OIL CO OF CALIF, 78- *Concurrent Pos:* Mem, Coop Air Pollution Eng Proj Group, 58-68, 68-; mem, Nat Air Pollution Control Admin Adv Comt Chem & Physics, Dept Health, Educ & Welfare, 68-70; mem, Task Force Hydrocarbon Reactivities, Am Petrol Inst, 69-70, Task Force Aerometric Data Anal, 70- *Mem:* AAAS; Am Chem Soc; Am Phys Soc; Combustion Inst. *Res:* Molecular spectroscopy; gas phase chemical kinetics; fast reactions; combustion and flame; infrared spectra of adsorbed species; air pollution; aerochemistry; solar photochemical conversion. *Mailing Add:* Chevron Res Co 576 Standard Ave Richmond CA 94802

RYBA, EARLE RICHARD, b Elyria, Ohio, June 27, 34; m 54; c 2. PHYSICAL METALLURGY. *Educ:* Mass Inst Technol, BS, 56; Iowa State Univ, PhD(phys metall), 60. *Prof Exp:* Asst prof, 60-65, ASSOC PROF METALL, PA STATE UNIV, UNIVERSITY PARK, 65- *Mem:* Am Crystallog Asn; Am Soc Metals; Am Inst Mining, Metall & Petrol Engrs. *Res:* Crystal structures, properties and theory of bonding in intermetallic compounds. *Mailing Add:* Dept Mat Sci & Eng 304 Steidle Bldg University Park PA 16802

RYBACK, RALPH SIMON, b Detroit, Mich, Oct 17, 40; m 76; c 3. CLINICAL LABORATORY CHEMISTRIES. *Educ:* Wayne State Univ, BA, 63, MD, 66. *Prof Exp:* Res fel, Harvard Med Sch, 67-68, teaching fel psychiat, 70-72, instr, 72-73, asst prof, 73-77; vis scientist, 76-77, MED OFFICER, LAB CLIN STUDIES, NAT INST ALCOHOL ABUSE & ALCOHOLISM, 77- *Concurrent Pos:* Dir, Alcohol & Drug Abuse Serv, McLean Hosp, Div Mass Gen Hosp, 72-76; assoc clin prof, Med Sch, George Washington Univ, 79-80 & Uniform Serv Univ Health Sci, 81- *Mem:* Am Psychiat Asn. *Res:* Interrelationships of commonly order clinical chemistries for the diagnosis of alcoholism and related illness including nonalcoholic liver diseases. *Mailing Add:* 11607 Springridge Rd Potomac MD 20854

RYCHECK, MARK RULE, b Racine, Wis, Dec 30, 37; m 62; c 3. INORGANIC CHEMISTRY. *Educ:* St Francis Col, Pa, BS, 59; Univ Cincinnati, PhD(chem), 67. *Prof Exp:* Res asst spectros, Mellon Inst Sci, 61-62; Ohio State Univ Res Found fel, Ohio State Univ, 66-68; RES CHEMIST, PETROL RES CTR, PHILLIPS PETROL CO, 68- *Mem:* Am Chem Soc. *Res:* Coordination compounds. *Mailing Add:* Petrol Res Ctr Phillips Petrol Co Bartlesville OK 74004

RYCHECK, RUSSELL RULE, b Racine, Wis, June 11, 32; m 62; c 2. MEDICINE, EPIDEMIOLOGY. *Educ:* Univ Pittsburgh, MD, 57, MPH, 59, DrPH, 64; Am Bd Prev Med, dipl, 68. *Prof Exp:* Teaching fel, Children's Hosp, Pittsburgh, 59-61, res fel pediat, 61-62; res fel epidemiol, 62-64, asst prof, 64-67, ASSOC PROF EPIDEMIOL, GRAD SCH PUB HEALTH, UNIV PITTSBURGH, 67-, ASST PROF PEDIAT & MED, 72- *Concurrent Pos:* Consult, Allegheny Co Health Dept, Pa, 64- *Mem:* Am Col Prev Med; Am Pub Health Asn; Soc Epidemiol Res. *Res:* Epidemiology of infectious diseases in hospitals and civilian communities; maternal and child health. *Mailing Add:* Grad Sch of Pub Health Univ of Pittsburgh Pittsburgh PA 15261

RYCKMAN, DEVERE WELLINGTON, b South Boardman, Mich, May 27, 24; m; c 3. ENVIRONMENTAL ENGINEERING, BIOCHEMISTRY. *Educ:* Rensselaer Polytech Inst, BS, 44; Mich State Univ, MS, 49; Mass Inst Technol, ScD, 56; Environ Eng Intersoc, dipl, 78. *Prof Exp:* Instr civil & sanit eng, Mich State Univ, 46-49, asst prof, 49-53; res asst sanit eng, Mass Inst Technol, 53-55; assoc prof environ & sanit eng, Wash Univ, 56-58, prof & dir dept, 58-72; consult, Ryckman, Edgerley, Tomlinson & Assocs, 72-75, CONSULT & PRES, RYCKMAN'S EMERGENCY ACTION & CONSULT TEAM, 75- *Concurrent Pos:* USPHS res & prog grants & consult, 56-; mem eng coun prof develop, Sanit Eng Accreditation Comt, 62; Mo Gov's Sci Adv Comt, 62-; vis lectr, Univ Hawaii, 63 & Vanderbilt Univ, 64; US Air Force Sch Aerospace Med, 64; Mfg Chem Asn res grant, 65-68; mem Nat Sci Traineeship Rev Comt, 65; consult Nat Energy Res & Develop Admin, 77- *Honors & Awards:* Resources Div Award, Am Water Works Asn, 62 & George Warren Fuller Award, 65; Grand Conceptor Award, Am Consult Engrs Coun, 69. *Mem:* Am Water Works Asn; Am Pub Health Asn; Am Soc Civil Engrs; Am Soc Eng Educ; Am Acad Environ Engrs. *Res:* Industrial water; wastewater; solid waste problems; significance of chemical structure in biodegradation of pesticides, synthetic detergents and other organic chemicals; environmental and energy engineering, hazardous substances and environmental crises engineering research. *Mailing Add:* Ryckman's Emergency Action Consult Team PO Box 27310 St Louis MO 63141

RYCKMAN, RAYMOND EDWARD, b Shullsburg, Wis, June 19, 17; m 43; c 3. MEDICAL ENTOMOLOGY, PARASITOLOGY. *Educ:* Univ Calif, BS, 50, MS, 57, PhD, 60. *Prof Exp:* Asst prof entom & head dept, Sch Trop & Prev Med, 50-59, from asst prof to assoc prof, 59-72, PROF MICROBIOL, LOMA LINDA UNIV, 72- *Mem:* Entom Soc Am; Am Soc Trop Med & Hyg. *Res:* Biosystematics; ecology of blood feeding insects and their vertebrate hosts; taxonomy, ecology and vector potential of insects of medical and veterinary importance; world bibliography and literature to the parasitic Hemiptera. *Mailing Add:* Dept of Microbiol Sch of Med Loma Linda Univ Loma Linda CA 92350

RYDELEK, PAUL ANTHONY, b Niagara Falls, NY, June 15, 49. EXPLORATION GEOPHYSICS. *Educ:* Univ Buffalo, BS, 71; Univ Ill, Urbana, MS, 73. *Prof Exp:* RES ASSOC, INST GEOPHYS, UNIV CALIF, 73- *Honors & Awards:* NSF Antarctica Serv Award, 75. *Mem:* Am Geophys Union. *Res:* Analysis of data obtained at South Pole Station; observations of earth tide's and free oscillations. *Mailing Add:* Inst Geophys Univ of Calif Los Angeles CA 90024

RYDEN, FRED WARD, b Boulder, Colo, Dec 20, 19; m 49; c 1. MICROBIOLOGY. *Educ:* Univ Colo, BA, 47; Vanderbilt Univ, MS, 50, PhD(virol), 56, MD, 60. *Prof Exp:* Asst parasitic dis, 47-48, instr, 49-52, microbiol, 52-56, asst prof, 56-60, path, 60-71, dir clin bact & serol lab, Univ Hosp, 60-67, ASST CLIN PROF PATH, SCH MED, VANDERBILT UNIV, 71- *Concurrent Pos:* Dir serol lab, Vanderbilt Univ Hosp, 50-55; consult, Vet Admin Hosp, 60-67; pathologist & dir lab, Nashville Mem Hosp, 67- *Mem:* AAAS; Am Med Asn; fel Am Soc Clin Path; fel Col Am Path. *Res:* Virology; mode of infection and replication of mammalian viruses. *Mailing Add:* Path Lab Nashville Mem Hosp Madison TN 37115

RYDER, BERNARD LEROY, b Morris, Ill, Apr 22, 18; m 41; c 3. ORGANIC CHEMISTRY. *Educ:* Ill State Nor Univ, BEd, 40; Univ Ill, MS, 47, PhD(org chem), 52. *Prof Exp:* Instr high sch, Ill, 40-42 & 45-46; control chemist, E I du Pont de Nemours & Co, 42-44; supvry chemist, US Rubber Co, 44-45; asst prof chem, Ill Wesleyan Univ, 46-50, prof & head dept, 52-56; assoc prof phys sci, 56-60, head dept phys sci, 60-66, dept chem, 66-69, PROF CHEM, ILL STATE UNIV, 60- *Mem:* Am Chem Soc. *Res:* Studies on the steroisomerism of 2, 3-dialkyl-piperidines and pyrrolidines. *Mailing Add:* Dept of Chem Ill State Univ Normal IL 61761

RYDER, D(AVID) F(RANK), b Seekonk, Mass, Aug 22, 19; m 57; c 1. CHEMICAL ENGINEERING. *Educ:* Tufts Univ, BS, 41. *Prof Exp:* Res engr, E I Du Pont de Nemours & Co, Inc, 41-55, sr res engr, 55-75, develop assoc, 75-80; RETIRED. *Mem:* Am Chem Soc; Am Inst Chem Engrs. *Res:* Synthetic and textile fibers; industrial fibers. *Mailing Add:* 101 Watford Rd Wilmington DE 19808

RYDER, EDWARD JONAS, b New York, NY, Oct 6, 29; m 62; c 3. GENETICS, PLANT BREEDING. *Educ:* Cornell Univ, BS, 51; Univ Calif, PhD(genetics), 54. *Prof Exp:* GENETICIST, WESTERN REGION, AGR RES SERV, USDA, 57- *Concurrent Pos:* Instr, Monterey Peninsula Col, 58-64. *Mem:* AAAS; Am Soc Agron; Am Soc Hort Sci; Genetics Soc Am; NY Acad Sci. *Res:* Quantitative genetics; evolution; lettuce and artichoke breeding and genetics. *Mailing Add:* USDA PO Box 5098 Salinas CA 93915

RYDER, ELLIOTT ELKINGTON, JR, b Oakland, Calif, Aug 14, 29; m 54; c 3. ORGANIC CHEMISTRY. *Educ:* Univ Calif, BS, 51; Univ Ill, PhD(org chem), 54. *Prof Exp:* Asst chem, Univ Ill, 51-54; CHEMIST, SHELL DEVELOP CO DIV, SHELL OIL CO, 54- *Res:* Polymers; thermoplastics; rubber; polymeric detergents; pesticides, herbicides and agricultural chemicals; industrial organic chemicals; high energy rocket fuels. *Mailing Add:* PO Box 4248 Modesto CA 95352

RYDER, GERALD H, b Clinton, Mass, Jan 28, 39; m 60; c 2. MATHEMATICAL ANALYSIS. *Educ:* Carnegie Inst Technol, BS, 60, MS, 61, PhD(math). 65. *Prof Exp:* Asst math, Carnegie Inst Technol, 60-64; asst prof, Clarkson Col Technol, 64-67; assoc prof math, Mont State Univ, 67-80; MEM FAC, PA STATE UNIV, 80- *Mem:* Am Math Soc; Math Asn Am. *Res:* Nonlinear differential equations; functional differential equations. *Mailing Add:* Pa State Univ State Hwy Schuylkill Haven PA 17972

RYDER, JOHN C, JR, plant physiology, economic entomology, see previous edition

RYDER, JOHN DOUGLASS, b Columbus, Ohio, May 8, 07; m 33; c 2. ELECTRONICS. *Educ:* Ohio State Univ, BEE, 28, MS, 29; Iowa State Univ, PhD(elec eng), 44; Tri-State Col, DEng, 63. *Prof Exp:* Electronic engr, Gen Elec Co, NY, 29-31; in chg electronic res, Bailey Meter Co, Ohio, 31-41; asst prof elec eng, Iowa State Univ, 41-44, prof, 44-49; prof elec eng & head dept, Univ Ill, 49-54; dean eng, 54-68, prof 68-72, EMER PROF ELEC ENG, MICH STATE UNIV, 72- *Concurrent Pos:* Asst dir, Eng Exp Sta, Iowa State Col, 47-49; ed, Jour, Inst Elec & Electronics Engrs, 58-59, 63-64. *Honors & Awards:* Medal Honor, Nat Electronics Conf, 70; Haraden Pratt Award, Inst Elec & Electronics Engrs, 79. *Mem:* Am Soc Eng Educ; Inst Elec & Electronics Engrs (pres, Inst Radio Eng, 55). *Res:* Vacuum tube and electric circuits; electronic applications. *Mailing Add:* 1839 SE 12th Ave Ocala FL 32670

RYDER, MARTHA, b St Louis, Mo, May 25, 27. PHYSICS. *Educ:* Univ Ill, Urbana, BS, 48; St Louis Univ, MST, 56. *Prof Exp:* Instr, Immaculata High Sch, Chicago, Ill, 51-52; assoc prof physics & chmn dept, Clarke Col, 52-80. *Mem:* Am Asn Physics Teachers. *Res:* Undergraduate and graduate preparation for elementary school science teachers; laboratory materials for elementary and college physics and physical science; astronomy; relations between science and literature; electronic apparatus for psychology teaching. *Mailing Add:* 4165 Flora Pl St Louis MO 63110

RYDER, RICHARD ARMITAGE, b Windsor, Ont, Feb 25, 31; m 56; c 2. FISHERIES ECOLOGY, LIMNOLOGY. *Educ:* Univ Mich, BSc, 53, MSc, 54. *Prof Exp:* Res asst, US Fish & Wildlife Serv, 53-54; dist biologist fisheries, 54-58; biologist-in-chg inventory, 58-61; res scientist, 62-71, COORDR FISHERIES, ONT DEPT LANDS & FORESTS, 61- *Concurrent Pos:* Res scientist, Ont Ministry Natural Resources, 71-81; consult to various int pub & pvt orgn, 71-81; comt mem, Man & Biosphere, 73-76 & Int Joint Comn, 73-81. *Mem:* Am Soc Fishery Res Biologists; Am Fisheries Soc (pres, 80); Int Asn Theoret & Appl Limnol; Am Soc Limnol & Oceanog; Int Asn Great Lakes Res. *Res:* Methods of determining levels of fish production from global waters; defining concepts necessary for a basic understanding of fish communities in fresh water. *Mailing Add:* Box 2089 Thunder Bay ON P7B 5E7 Can

RYDER, RICHARD DANIEL, b Providence, RI, Oct 1, 44. PHYSICS. *Educ:* Univ RI, BS, 66; Brown Univ, ScM, 73, PhD(physics), 74. *Prof Exp:* STAFF MEM PHYSICS, LOS ALAMOS NAT LAB, UNIV CALIF, 77- *Mem:* Am Phys Soc; Inst Elec & Electronics Engrs; Plasma Sci Soc. *Res:* Accelerator physics; particle beam optics; neutron diffraction by time-of-flight methods; underwater acoustics. *Mailing Add:* Los Alamos Nat Lab MS-805 PO Box 1663 Los Alamos NM 87545

RYDER, ROBERT J, b Olean, NY, Apr 19, 31; m 54; c 5. CERAMICS. *Educ:* Alfred Univ, BS, 53; Pa State Univ, MS, 55, PhD(ceramics), 59. *Prof Exp:* Res scientist, 59-62, asst dir res & develop, 62-69, dir res & develop, 69-78, VPRES RES & DEVELOP, BROCKWAY GLASS CO, INC, 78- *Concurrent Pos:* Chmn air & water qual comt, Glass Container Mfrs Inst, 68-75. *Mem:* Fel Am Ceramic Soc; Soc Glass Technol; Am Chem Soc. *Res:* Physical chemistry of glass melting process; colored glasses; physical properties of glasses; reactivity of glass surfaces. *Mailing Add:* Brockway Glass Co Inc McCullough Ave Brockway PA 15824

RYDER, ROBERT THOMAS, b Bowling Green, Ohio, Sept 23, 41; m 68; c 2. STRATIGRAPHY, PETROLEUM GEOLOGY. *Educ:* Mich State Univ, BS, 63; Pa State Univ, PhD(geol), 68. *Prof Exp:* Geologist, Shell Develop Co, Tex, 69-72, Shell Oil Co, 72-74; GEOLOGIST, US GEOL SURV, 74- *Mem:* Geol Soc Am; Am Asn Petrol Geologists; Soc Econ Paleontologists & Mineralogists. *Res:* Seismic detection of stratigraphic traps; sedimentation and tectonics; regional stratigraphy; nonmarine depositional environments. *Mailing Add:* US Geol Surv MS 960 Box 25046 Denver Fed Ctr Denver CO 80225

RYDER, RONALD ARCH, b Kansas City, Kans, Feb 3, 28; m 55; c 2. WILDLIFE MANAGEMENT. *Educ:* Colo Agr & Mech Col, BS, 49; Utah State Univ, PhD(wildlife mgt), 58. *Prof Exp:* Wildlife technician, Dept Game & Fish, Colo, 48-49, 54-55; instr, Wartburg Col, 57-58; from asst prof wildlife mgt to assoc prof wildlife biol, 58-68, chmn wildlife biol majors, Col Forestry & Natural Resources, 69-72, PROF WILDLIFE BIOL, COLO STATE UNIV, 68- *Concurrent Pos:* NSF fel, Univ BC, 65-66; vis prof, Mem Univ Nfld, 72-73. *Mem:* Wildlife Soc; Am Soc Mammal; Cooper Ornith Soc; Wilson Ornith Soc; Am Ornith Union. *Res:* Waterfowl ecology and management; bird banding; distribution of Colorado birds; nongame wildlife management. *Mailing Add:* Dept of Fishery & Wildlife Biol Colo State Univ Ft Collins CO 80523

RYDGREN, A ERIC, b Seattle, Wash. ASTRONOMY. *Educ:* Case Inst Technol, BS, 67; Univ Ariz, MS, 69, PhD(astron), 75. *Prof Exp:* Res assoc astron, Cerro Tololo Inter-Am Observ, 75-77; ASST PROF PHYSICS, RENSSELAER POLYTECH INST, 77- *Mem:* Am Astron Soc; Astron Soc Pac; Int Astron Union. *Res:* Observational stellar astronomy, with emphasis on T Tauri stars and pre-main sequence stellar evolution. *Mailing Add:* Dept of Physics Rensselaer Polytech Inst Troy NY 12181

RYDZ, JOHN S, b Milwaukee, Wis, May 7, 25; m 46; c 2. PHYSICS, ELECTRONICS. *Educ:* Mass Inst Technol, BS, 52; Univ Pa, MS, 56. *Prof Exp:* Proj engr, Radio Corp Am, 52-56, eng group leader, Appl Physics Group, 56-59, mgr new bus develop, 59-61; exec vpres & dir, Nuclear Corp Am, 61-63; mgr new prod develop, 63-66; vpres res & develop, Diebold, Inc, Ohio, 66-71; vpres & tech dir, N Atlantic Consumer Prod Group, NY, 71-74, VPRES ENG, SEWING PROD GROUP, SINGER CO, 74- *Mem:* Inst Elec & Electronics Engrs; Optical Soc Am. *Res:* Spectrophotometry and colorimetry; masers; color electrofax; molecular resonance; zener diodes; nuclear instrumentation; electrostatic printing; closed circuit television techniques; information search and retrieval; consumer products. *Mailing Add:* 29 Ariel Way Avon CT 06001

RYE, DANNY MICHAEL, b Glendale, Calif, Feb 21, 46; m 67; c 2. GEOCHEMISTRY. *Educ:* Occidental Col, AB, 67; Univ Minn, PhD(geol), 72. *Prof Exp:* Fel geol, Purdue Univ, 72; res staff geologist, 72-74, instr, 74-75, asst prof, 75-80, ASSOC PROF GEOL, YALE UNIV, 80- *Honors & Awards:* Lindgren Award, Soc Econ Geologists, 76. *Mem:* Soc Econ Geologists. *Res:* Isotopic composition of carbon, hydrogen, oxygen and sulfur to obtain information about the volatile phases present during hydrothermal ore formation, or during the formation of metamorphic rocks. *Mailing Add:* Dept of Geol & Geophys Yale Univ New Haven CT 06520

RYE, ROBERT O, b Los Angeles, Calif, Nov 29, 38; m 64; c 3. GEOCHEMISTRY. *Educ:* Occidental Col, AB, 60; Princeton Univ, PhD(geol), 65. *Prof Exp:* GEOLOGIST, US GEOL SURV, 64- *Mem:* Geol Soc Am; Geochem Soc. *Res:* Stable isotope studies of ore deposits; sulfur isotope studies. *Mailing Add:* US Geol Surv Fed Ctr Denver CO 80225

RYEBURN, DAVID, b Cincinnati, Ohio, June 19, 35; m 57; c 3. TOPOLOGY. *Educ:* Kenyon Col, AB, 54; Ohio State Univ, PhD(math), 62. *Prof Exp:* Instr math, Kenyon Col, 56-57; asst, Ohio State Univ, 58-61, instr, 61-62; asst prof, Kenyon Col, 62-66; ASST PROF MATH, SIMON FRASER UNIV, 66- *Mem:* AAAS; Am Math Soc; Math Asn Am; Can Math Cong. *Mailing Add:* Dept Math Simon Fraser Univ Burnaby BC V5A 1S6 Can

RYEL, LAWRENCE ATWELL, b Farmington, Mich, Feb 22, 30; m 52; c 2. BIOSTATISTICS, WILDLIFE RESEARCH. *Educ:* Mich State Univ, BS, 51, MS, 53, PhD(zool), 71. *Prof Exp:* Game biologist, Mich Dept Conserv, 53-61, biometrician, 61-64, biomet supvr, Res & Develop Div, 64-72, chief div, 72-73, chief, Off Surv & Statis Serv, 73-78, chief, Surv & Statist Serv, Environ Serv Div, 78-80, HEAD, SURV & STATIST SERV WILDLIFE DIV, MICH DEPT NATURAL RESOURCES, 80- *Concurrent Pos:* Vis prof wildlife sci, Utah State Univ, 77. *Mem:* Biomet Soc; Wildlife Soc; Am Soc Mammal; Wilson Ornith Soc; Sigma Xi. *Res:* Wildlife population dynamics; sample survey design; consultation in design and analysis of fisheries and wildlife research studies. *Mailing Add:* Off of Surv & Statist Serv Box 30028 Lansing MI 48909

RYERSON, GEORGE DOUGLAS, b East Orange, NJ, Apr 29, 34. ORGANIC CHEMISTRY. *Educ:* Lehigh Univ, BS, 55; Mass Inst Technol, PhD(org chem), 60. *Prof Exp:* Chemist, Esso Res & Eng Co, 60-67; sr assoc ed, 67-75, SR ED, CHEM ABSTR SERV, 75- *Mem:* AAAS; Am Chem Soc; Am Soc Info Sci. *Res:* Macromolecular chemistry. *Mailing Add:* 2407 Ravenel Dr Columbus OH 43209

RYFF, JOHN V, b Jersey City, NJ, Oct 18, 32; m 58. MATHEMATICAL ANALYSIS. *Educ:* Syracuse Univ, AB, 57; Stanford Univ, PhD(math), 62. *Prof Exp:* Benjamin Pierce instr math, Harvard Univ, 62-64; Off Naval Res assoc, Univ Wash, 64-65, asst prof, 65-67; asst prof, Inst Advan Study, 67-68 & Inst Defense Anal, 68; prog dir math sci sect, NSF, 69-72; PROF MATH & HEAD DEPT, UNIV CONN, 72- *Concurrent Pos:* Prog dir, Math Sci Sect, NSF, 79-82. *Mem:* Am Math Soc; Math Asn Am. *Res:* Real and complex function theory; functional analysis. *Mailing Add:* Dept Math Univ Conn Storrs CT 06268

RYGE, GUNNAR, b Copenhagen, Denmark, Dec 15, 16; nat US; m 39; c 3. DENTISTRY, PHYSICS. *Educ:* Royal Danish Dent Sch, DDS, 39; Marquette Univ, MS, 57. *Hon Degrees:* Dr, Univ Lund, Sweden, 80. *Prof Exp:* From instr to assoc prof, Royal Danish Dent Sch, 39-47; from instr to assoc prof dent mat, Sch Dent, Marquette Univ, 50-58, coordr res, 53-63, chmn dept, 54-64, coordr grad studies, 57-63, prof, Sch Dent & Grad Sch, 58-64; chief mat & tech br, Div Dent Health, USPHS, 64-69, sci dir, Dent Health Ctr, 69-72; PROF DENT & ASST DEAN RES, SCH DENT, UNIV OF THE PAC, 72- *Concurrent Pos:* Consult, US Vet Admin Ctr, Wood, Wis, 57-64; mem dent study sect, USPHS, 58-62, adv comt adhesive restoration dent mat; lectr, US Naval Training Ctr, 60-63; USPHS liaison rep US tech comt, Int Standards Orgn, vchmn working group filling mat & mem working group dent instruments & equip, 65-67. *Honors & Awards:* Wilmer Souder's Award, Am Col Dent, 66. *Mem:* Fel AAAS; fel Am Col Dent; Am Dent Asn; Int Asn Dent Res (pres, 72-73); Fedn Dent Int. *Res:* Physics, chemistry and metallurgy of dental materials; clinical research on dental materials and procedures. *Mailing Add:* Univ Pac Sch Dent 2155 Webster St San Francisco CA 94115

RYGG, GEORGE LEONARD, b Clifford, NDak, Feb 14, 03; m 35; c 1. PLANT PHYSIOLOGY. *Educ:* NDak Agr Col, BS, 29; Ore State Col, MS, 31; Univ Minn, PhD(plant physiol), 41. *Prof Exp:* Agent small fruit prod, USDA, 30-31, jr pomologist, div fruits & veg crops & dis, Bur Plant Indust, 31-37, asst plant physiologist, 37-43, assoc plant physiologist, Bur Plant Indust, Soils & Agr eng, 43-48, plant physiologist, 48-57, supvy plant physiologist, Agr Mkt Serv, 57-61, prin plant physiologist, 61-63, res plant phsyiologist, Agr Res Serv, 63-70; CONSULT DATE & CITRUS FRUIT HANDLING, TRANSP & STORAGE, 70- *Honors & Awards:* Superior Serv Award, USDA, 58. *Mem:* AAAS; Am Soc Hort Sci; Am Soc Plant Physiol. *Res:* Postharvest physiology of fruits and vegetables, especially citrus and dates. *Mailing Add:* 625 E McKinley Ave Pomona CA 91767

RYGG, PAUL THEODORE, b Grand Forks, NDak, July 23, 23; m 50; c 2. MATHEMATICS. *Educ:* Mont State Univ, BS, 49; Iowa State Univ, MS, 51, PhD(math), 59. *Prof Exp:* Analyst, US Dept Defense, 51-55; asst math, Iowa State Univ, 55-58, instr, 58-59; asst prof, Mont State Univ, 59-61; assoc prof, Univ SDak, 61-62; assoc prof, 62-70, PROF MATH, WESTERN WASH STATE COL, 70- *Mem:* Math Asn Am; Am Math Soc. *Res:* Abstract algebra; geometry. *Mailing Add:* Dept of Math Western Wash Univ Bellingham WA 98225

RYKER, LEE CHESTER, b Indianapolis, Ind, July 1, 40. BIOACOUSTICS, ENTOMOLOGY. *Educ:* Franklin Col, Ind, BA, 63; Univ Mich, MS, 65; Univ Ore, MS, 71; Ore State Univ, PhD(entom), 75. *Prof Exp:* RES ASSOC BIOACOUST, ENTOM DEPT, ORE STATE UNIV, 75- *Mem:* Animal Behav Soc; Coleopterists Soc. *Res:* Chemoacoustic communication research on species of bark beetles destructive to economically important western coniferous trees. *Mailing Add:* Dept of Entom Ore State Univ Corvallis OR 97331

RYKER, NORMAN JENKINS, JR, b Tacoma, Wash, Dec 25, 26; m 47; c 5. STRUCTURAL ENGINEERING. *Educ:* Univ Calif, Berkeley, BS, 49, MS, 51. *Prof Exp:* Stress analyst aerophys lab, NAm Aviation Co, 51-55, supvr struct anal missile div, 55-57, proj engr missile preliminary design, 57-60, prin scientist space systs, Space Div, 60-61, asst chief engr, Apollo Spacecraft, 61-64, dir res & develop, 64-66, asst to prog mgr, Apollo, 66-67, asst chief engr, 67-68, vpres res eng & testing, 68-70, vpres res & eng, MGD Graphic Systs, NAm Rockwell Corp, 70-76; PRES ROCKETDYNE DIV, ROCKWELL INT CORP, 76- *Concurrent Pos:* Proj adminr, Prosthetic Device Res Proj, Univ Calif, 49-51; lectr, Univ Southern Calif, 53-56. *Mem:* fel Am Inst Aeronaut & Astronaut; Sigma Xi; Civil Eng Soc; fel Inst Advan Engrs. *Res:* Stress analysis; space systems. *Mailing Add:* Rocketdyne Div 6633 Canoga Ave Canoga Park CA 91304

RYKER, TRUMAN CLIFTON, b Hutchinson, Kans, May 4, 08; m 33; c 4. PLANT PATHOLOGY. *Educ:* Miss State Univ, BS, 29; La State Univ, MS, 31; Univ Wis, PhD(plant path), 34. *Prof Exp:* Asst plant path, La State Univ, 31, asst plant pathologist, Exp Sta, 36-42, assoc plant pathologist, 46-47; assoc plant pathologist, Univ Wis, 31-34; plant breeder, Wis Cabbage Seed Co, Racine, 34-36; plant pathologist, E I du Pont de Nemours & Co, Inc, 47-66, prod develop mgr, 66-73; CONSULT DIS ORNAMENTALS, TREES & TURF, 73- *Mem:* Am Phytopath Soc; Int Soc Arboricult. *Res:* Sugar cane, fusarium yellows of celery; rice diseases in Louisiana; herbicides; seed treatments; fungicides. *Mailing Add:* 1837 Marsh Rd Wilmington DE 19810

RYLANDER, HENRY GRADY, JR, b Pearsall, Tex, Aug 23, 21; m 43; c 4. MECHANICAL ENGINEERING. *Educ:* Univ Tex, BS, 43, MS, 52; Ga Inst Technol, PhD(mech eng), 65. *Prof Exp:* Design engr, Steam Div, Aviation Gas Turbine Div, Westinghouse Elec Corp, 43-47; from asst prof to assoc prof mech eng, 47-68, res scientist, 50, PROF MECH ENG, UNIV TEX, AUSTIN, 68-, ADJ ASST PROF ELEC & BIOMED ENG, 80- *Concurrent Pos:* Design engr, Fargo Eng Co, 49-50; eng consult, Mobil Oil Corp, 56-70, Tracor, Inc, 60-72 & CMI Corp, 70- *Mem:* Am Soc Mech Engrs; Am Soc Lubrication Engrs. *Res:* Machine design lubrication and bearing performance including the effects of solids in bearing lubrication. *Mailing Add:* 3409 Foothills Terr Austin TX 78731

RYLANDER, MICHAEL KENT, b Hillsboro, Tex, Dec 25, 35; m 58; c 2. ORNITHOLOGY, COMPARATIVE ANATOMY. *Educ:* North Tex State Univ, BA, 56, MS, 62; Tulane Univ, PhD(biol), 65. *Prof Exp:* From asst prof to assoc prof, 65-75, PROF BIOL, TEX TECH UNIV, 75-, CUR BIRDS, MUSEUM, 67-, ADJ PROF, DEPT ANAT, SCH MED, 75- *Res:* Comparative neuroanatomy; comparative anatomy of vertebrates, chiefly birds, in relation to behavior and ecology; bird pests of crops. *Mailing Add:* Dept of Biol Sci Tex Tech Univ Lubbock TX 79409

RYMAL, KENNETH STUART, b Winnepeg, Man, Sept 13, 22; m 49; c 5. FOOD SCIENCE. *Educ:* Mass Inst Technol, BS, 49; Univ Fla, MS, 66; Univ Ga, PhD(food sci), 73. *Prof Exp:* Chemist fish prods, Assoc Fish By-Prods Inc, 49-51; res & develop food mfg, John E Cain Co, Inc, 51-52; owner-mgr, Rymal's Restaurant, 52-64; res assoc, Univ Fla, 64-66; asst prof, 66-68, ASSOC PROF HORT, AUBURN UNIV, 69- *Mem:* Inst Food Technologists; Am Soc Hort Sci. *Res:* Chemistry of horticultural crops; composition, flavor and nutritive content; chemical nature of insect resistance in horticultural crops. *Mailing Add:* Dept of Hort Auburn Univ Auburn AL 36830

RYMER, WILLIAM ZEV, b Melbourne, Australia, June 3, 39; m 77; c 2. NEUROPHYSIOLOGY, NEUROLOGY. *Educ:* Melbourne Univ, Australia, MBBS, 62; Monash Univ, Australia, PhD(neurophysiol), 73. *Prof Exp:* Resident internal med, Dept Med, Monash Univ, Australia, 63-67 & grad scholar neurophysiol, 67-72; Fogarty fel, Lab Neural Control, Nat Inst Neurol & Commun Dis & Stroke, NIH, 72-74; res assoc, Med Sch, Johns Hopkins Univ, 75-76; asst prof neurosurg & physiol, Med Sch, State Univ NY, 77-78; asst prof, 78-81, ASSOC PROF PHYSIOL & NEUROL, MED SCH, NORTHWESTERN UNIV, 81- *Concurrent Pos:* Insti, Cold Spring Harbor Lab, 80-81. *Mem:* Soc Neurosci; AAAS. *Res:* Neural control of movement using animal models, normal and neurologically impaired human subjects; interneuronal circuity of the spinal cord; neurophysiological basis of spasticity. *Mailing Add:* Dept Physiol Med Sch Northwestern Univ Ward 5-150 303 E Chicago Ave Chicago IL 60611

RYMERS, PHILIP CLARK, b Oak Harbor, Ohio, Aug 18, 29; m 51; c 2. ENGINEERING MECHANICS. *Educ:* Gen Motors Inst, BIE, 52; Univ Toledo, MS, 60; Mich State Univ, PhD(mech), 68. *Prof Exp:* Asst prof mech, Univ Toledo, 52-59; asst prof, Ariz State Univ, 59-60; asst prof math & mech, Gen Motors Inst, 60-64; PROF MECH ENG, UNIV NEV, RENO, 66- *Res:* Dynamics; elastic stability; measurement of angular vibrations of uniform bars. *Mailing Add:* Dept of Mech Eng Univ of Nev Reno NV 89507

RYMON, LARRY MARING, b Portland, Pa, Nov 16, 34; m 62; c 2. ANIMAL ECOLOGY, CONSERVATION. *Educ:* East Stroudsburg State Col, BS, 58, MEd, 64; Ore State Univ, PhD(biol), 69. *Prof Exp:* Test dept expediter, Electronics, Electro-Mech Res, Fla, 58; assoc prof, 68-71, PROF BIOL, EAST STROUDSBURG STATE COL, 71-; Cur, East Stroudsburg State Col Natural Hist Mus, 71- *Concurrent Pos:* Danforth Assoc, 70; coordr, Environ Studies Inst, 74- *Mem:* Wildlife Soc; Am Inst Biol Sci; Sigma Xi. *Res:* Life history and ecological study of raccoon; ecological studies in Delaware Water Gap National Recreation Area. *Mailing Add:* Dept of Biol East Stroudsburg State Col East Stroudsburg PA 18301

RYNASIEWICZ, JOSEPH, b Pawtucket, RI, May 22, 17; m 47; c 2. ANALYTICAL CHEMISTRY. *Educ:* Univ RI, BS, 41, MS, 44. *Prof Exp:* Asst agr chem, Exp Sta, Univ RI, 41-45; asst org & anal chem, Northwestern Univ, 45-46; asst anal chem, Knolls Atomic Power Lab, 46-52, res assoc, 52-57, mgr, 57-62, consult anal chem, 62, corrosion engr, 62-64, supvr chem anal, Lamp Metals & Components Dept, 64-71, MGR ANAL CHEM, REFRACTORY METALS PROD DEPT, GEN ELEC CO, 71- *Mem:* Am Chem Soc; Am Soc Test & Mat. *Res:* Soil chemistry; analytical chemistry of nuclear reactor materials; micro separations of uranium and transuranium elements; high temperature thermal analysis; analytical chemistry of tungsten, molybdenum; corrosion of zircaloy and reactor fuels. *Mailing Add:* 5245 E Farnhurst Rd Lyndhurst OH 44124

RYNBRANDT, DONALD JAY, b Jamestown, Mich, Apr 8, 40; m 67. BIOCHEMISTRY, PATHOLOGY. *Educ:* Hope Col, BA, 62; Mich State Univ, PhD(biochem), 67. *Prof Exp:* HEAD, RADIOIMMUNOASSAY/THER DRUG ANAL SECTS, PATH DEPT, ST LUKE'S HOSP, 68- *Concurrent Pos:* Instr, Case Western Reserve Univ, 68-70, adj sr instr, 70-75, adj asst prof, 75-; Ohio Thoracic grant, 72-73. *Mem:* Am Asn Clin Chemists. *Res:* Development of biochemical mechanisms for pulmonary diseases; isolation of lung proteolytic enzymes and proteolytic enzyme inhibitors; development of clinical chemistry tests. *Mailing Add:* Path Dept 11311 Shaker Blvd Cleveland OH 44104

RYND, JAMES ARTHUR, b Chicago, Ill, Nov 8, 42; m 68; c 2. BIOORGANIC CHEMISTRY, PROTEIN STRUCTURE. *Educ:* Univ Ill, BS, 66; Univ Calif, Riverside, PhD(chem), 71. *Prof Exp:* PROF CHEM, BIOLA UNIV, 70- *Concurrent Pos:* Fel, Univ Calif, Riverside, 72 & 73; res assoc, Col Med, Univ Calif, Irvine, 77-78, Calif State Univ, Fullerton, 80. *Mem:* Am Chem Soc; AAAS; Am Sci Affil. *Res:* X-ray crystal structure of organic compound; enzyme model systems involving flavins and prostaglandins. *Mailing Add:* Phys Sci Dept Biola Univ LaMirada CA 90639

RYNN, NATHAN, b New York, NY, Dec 2, 23; m 54; c 3. PLASMA PHYSICS, MICROWAVE TUBES. *Educ:* City Col New York, BEE, 44; Univ Ill, MS, 47; Stanford Univ, PhD(elec eng), 56. *Prof Exp:* Res asst, Univ Ill, 46-47; res engr, RCA Labs, 47-52; res asst, Stanford Univ, 52-56, res assoc, 58; mem tech staff, Ramo Wooldridge Corp, 56-57; supvr, Huggins Labs, 57-58; res staff physicist, Princeton Univ, 58-66; prof elec eng & physics, 66-69, PROF PHYSICS, UNIV CALIF, IRVINE, 69- *Concurrent Pos:* Consult, Curtiss-Wright Corp, 64; vis lectr, Univ Calif, Berkeley, 65-66; consult, Maxwell Labs, 72-73; consult, Lawrence Livermore Labs, 75-80; vis scientist, Fontenay aux Roses Nuclear Res Ctr, France & Ecole Polytech, Paris, 75; consult Hughes Aircraft, Malibu, Calif, 77-78; Fulbright sr res fel, Ecole Polytech, Paliseau, France, 78; consult, TRW, Inc, 80- *Mem:* Fel Am Phys Soc; fel sr mem Inst Elec & Electronics Engrs. *Res:* Physics of plasma generated by the Q-machine; wave interaction in plasmas; plasma turbulence; controlled fusion; plasma diagnostics. *Mailing Add:* Dept of Physics Univ of Calif Irvine CA 92717

RYON, ALLEN DALE, b Republic, Ohio, Mar 18, 20; m 42; c 3. CHEMICAL ENGINEERING, INORGANIC CHEMISTRY. *Educ:* Heidelberg Col, BS, 41. *Prof Exp:* Chemist, Basic Refractories Inc, Ohio, 41-42, Basic Magnesium Inc, Nev, 42-44 & Tenn Eastman Corp, Tenn, 44-48; chem engr, 48-62, ASST SECT CHIEF NUCLEAR FUEL PROCESSING, OAK RIDGE NAT LAB, 62- *Mem:* Am Chem Soc. *Res:* Separation and purification by solvent extraction and chromatography. *Mailing Add:* Oak Ridge Nat Lab PO Box X Oak Ridge TN 37830

RYPKA, EUGENE WESTON, b Owatonna, Minn, May 6, 25; m 67; c 2. BACTERIOLOGY. *Educ:* Stanford Univ, BA, 50, PhD(med microbiol), 58. *Prof Exp:* Asst prof biol, Univ NMex, 57-62; assoc bacteriologist, Leonard Wood Mem Leprosy Res Lab, Johns Hopkins Univ, 62-63; sr scientist, 63-70, HEAD SECT MICROBIOL, LOVELACE MED CTR, 70- *Concurrent Pos:* Vis lectr, Univ NMex, 67-68 & 70-71; adj prof biol, Univ NMex, 72- *Mem:* AAAS; Am Soc Microbiol; Am Soc Cybernet; Inst Elec & Electronics Engrs; Sigma Xi. *Res:* Bacterial physiology; immunology; medical microbiology; systems and cybernetics. *Mailing Add:* Sect of Microbiol 5200 Gibson Blvd SE Albuquerque NM 87108

RYSCHKEWITSCH, GEORGE EUGENE, b Frankfurt, Ger, July 8, 29; nat US; m 50; c 3. INORGANIC CHEMISTRY. *Educ:* Univ Dayton, BS, 52; Ohio State Univ, PhD(chem), 55. *Prof Exp:* Fel, Ohio State Univ, 56; from asst prof to assoc prof, 56-65, PROF CHEM, UNIV FLA, 65- *Mem:* Am Chem Soc. *Res:* Chemistry of Group III elements; boron hydrides; molecular addition compounds; inorganic reaction mechanisms. *Mailing Add:* Dept of Chem Univ of Fla Gainesville FL 32611

RYSER, FRED A, JR, b Albion, Mich, Feb 29, 20; m 45; c 4. ZOOLOGY. *Educ:* Univ Wis, PhD(zool), 52. *Prof Exp:* Res assoc, Univ Wis, 52-53; from asst prof to assoc prof biol, 53-70, PROF BIOL, UNIV NEV, RENO, 70- *Mem:* Am Soc Mammal; Cooper Ornith Soc; Am Ornith Union. *Res:* Temperature regulation and metabolism of mammals; avian and mammalian ecology. *Mailing Add:* Dept of Biol Univ of Nev Reno NV 89557

RYSER, HERBERT JOHN, b Milwaukee, Wis, July 28, 23. MATHEMATICS. *Educ:* Univ Wis, BA, 45, MA, 47, PhD(math), 48. *Prof Exp:* Asst & instr, Univ Wis, 48; fel, Inst Advan Study, 48-49; from asst prof to prof math, Ohio State Univ, 49-62; prof, Syracuse Univ, 62-67; PROF MATH, CALIF INST TECHNOL, 67- *Mem:* Am Math Soc; Math Asn Am. *Res:* Algebra; matrices; combinatorial analysis. *Mailing Add:* Dept Math Calif Inst Technol Pasadena CA 91125

RYSER, HUGUES JEAN-PAUL, b La Chaux-de-Fonds, Switz, June 11, 26; m 61; c 3. CELL BIOLOGY, PHARMACOLOGY. *Educ:* Univ Berne, MD, 53, DrMed(pharmacol), 55. *Prof Exp:* Asst biochem, Med Sch, Univ Berne, 52-55; Swiss Nat Found Sci Res fel med, Univ Med Hosp, Univ Lausanne, 55-56, asst, 56-58; res fel, Harvard Med Sch, 58-60, from instr to asst prof pharmacol, 60-69; assoc prof cell biol & pharmacol, Med Sch, Univ Md, Baltimore, 69-70, prof, 70-72; PROF PATH & PHARMACOL, SCH MED, BOSTON UNIV, 72- *Concurrent Pos:* Clin & res fel med, Mass Gen Hosp, Boston, 58-64; prin investr, Nat Inst Gen Med Sci grant, 61-67; Lederle med fac award, 64-67; consult, George Washington Univ, 67-69; career develop award, Nat Cancer Inst, 68-69, grant, 68-, mem adv group biol & immunol segment carcinogenesis prog, 72- *Mem:* Histochem Soc; Am Asn Cancer Res; Am Soc Cell Biol; Soc Gen Physiol; Am Soc Pharmacol & Exp Therapeut. *Res:* Enzymatic studies on milligram amounts of diseased human liver; penetration and fate of macromolecules into mammalian cells in culture; interaction of basic polymers with cell membranes; molecular mechanisms in chemical carcinogenesis. *Mailing Add:* Dept of Path Boston Univ Med Ctr Boston MA 02118

RYSTEPHANICK, RAYMOND GARY, b Erickson, Man, Aug 24, 40; m 63. THEORETICAL PHYSICS. *Educ:* Univ Man, BSc, 62, MSc, 63; Univ BC, PhD(physics), 65. *Prof Exp:* Fel, McMaster Univ, 65-67; asst prof, 67-71, assoc prof, 71-81, PROF PHYSICS, UNIV REGINA, 81- *Mem:* Am Phys Soc; Can Asn Physicists; AAAS. *Res:* Calculation of soft x-ray emission spectra in metals; gravitational effects in metals. *Mailing Add:* Dept Physics & Astron Univ Regina Regina SK S4S 0A2 Can

RYTTING, JOSEPH HOWARD, b Rexburg, Idaho, June 12, 42; m 65; c 9. PHYSICAL CHEMISTRY, PHARMACEUTICS. *Educ:* Brigham Young Univ, BA, 66, PhD(phys chem), 69. *Prof Exp:* Asst prof, 69-75, assoc prof, 75-80, PROF PHARM, UNIV KANS, 80- *Concurrent Pos:* Prof, The Upjohn Co, 78. *Honors & Awards:* Tensiochimica Int Prize Surfactant Chem, Italian Oil Chemist's Soc, 74. *Mem:* Am Chem Soc; Am Pharmaceut Asn; Acad Pharmaceut Sci; Sigma Xi; Calorimetry Conf. *Res:* Application of solution thermodynamics to drug design and delivery; physical chemistry of biologically active agents; effects of pressure and temperature on biologicals and pharmaceutical products; stability; rectal and intestinal drug absorption; insulin absorption. *Mailing Add:* Pharmaceut Chem Dept Univ of Kans Lawrence KS 66045

RYU, JISOO VINSKY, b Hamhung City, Korea, Mar 11, 41; US citizen; m 71; c 3. EXPLORATION GEOPHYSICS. *Educ:* Univ Utah, BS, 65; Univ Minn, MS, 67; Univ Calif, PhD(eng geosci), 71. *Prof Exp:* Asst res prof geophys, Dept Geol & Geophys Sci, Univ Utah, 71-73; res geophysicist, Space Sci Lab, Univ Calif, Berkeley, 73; res specialist geophys, Exxon Prod Res Co, 73-77; consult, Saratoga, Calif, 77-78; GEOPHYSICIST, CHEVRON OIL FIELD RES CO, LA HABRA, CALIF, 78- *Mem:* Soc Explor Geophys; Europ Asn Explor Geophys. *Res:* Seismic signal processing; forward and inverse modeling and model interpretation for hydrocarbon exploration. *Mailing Add:* Geophys Div Chevron Res PO Box 446 La Habra CA 90631

RYUGO, KAY, b Sacramento, Calif, Apr 10, 20; m 55; c 5. POMOLOGY, PLANT PHYSIOLOGY. *Educ:* Univ Calif, BS, 49, MS, 50, PhD, 54. *Prof Exp:* From asst pomologist to assoc pomologist, 55-69, POMOLOGIST, UNIV CALIF, DAVIS, 69-, LECTR, 76- *Concurrent Pos:* NATO fel, Univ Bologna, 72. *Mem:* Int Soc Hort Sci; Am Soc Hort Sci; Bot Soc Am; Scand Soc Plant Physiol; Am Soc Plant Physiol. *Res:* Physiology and biochemistry; native growth regulators in fruits and trees. *Mailing Add:* Dept of Pomology Univ of Calif Davis CA 95616

RZAD, STEFAN JACEK, b Warsaw, Poland, Mar 15, 38; m 63; c 2. PHYSICAL CHEMISTRY. *Educ:* Univ Louvain, MS, 60, PhD(phys chem), 64. *Prof Exp:* Fel radiation lab, Univ Notre Dame, 64-66 & radiation labs, Mellon Inst, Carnegie-Mellon Univ, 67-74; PHYSICAL CHEMIST, CORP RES & DEVELOP CTR, GEN ELEC CO, 74- *Mem:* Am Chem Soc; Inst Elec & Electronics Engrs; Sigma Xi. *Res:* Reactions of radicals in electron irradiated liquids; gas-phase vacuum ultra-violet photochemistry; ionic processes; conduction and mechanisms of electrical breakdown in liquids, solids and gases; high voltage phenomena. *Mailing Add:* Corp Res & Develop Ctr Gen Elec Co PO Box 8 K1 Schenectady NY 12301

S

SAACKE, RICHARD GEORGE, b Newark, NJ, Oct 31, 31; m 54; c 5. REPRODUCTIVE PHYSIOLOGY, CYTOLOGY. *Educ:* Rutgers Univ, BS, 53; Pa State Univ, MS, 55, PhD(dairy sci), 62. *Prof Exp:* Dairy exten specialist, Univ Md, 57-58; from instr to asst prof dairy physiol, Pa State Univ, 58-65; asst prof, 65-68, PROF DAIRY SCI, VA POLYTECH INST & STATE UNIV, 68- *Concurrent Pos:* Nat Inst Child Health & Human Develop res grant, 65-69. *Mem:* AAAS; Am Dairy Sci Asn; Am Soc Animal Sci. *Res:* Cytology and physiology of bovine spermatozoa; ultrastructural study of the bovine mammary gland with emphasis on milk synthesis and secretion. *Mailing Add:* Saunders Hall Va Polytech Inst & State Univ Blacksburg VA 24061

SAADA, ADEL SELIM, b Heliopolis, Egypt, Oct 24, 34; US citizen; m 60; c 2. SOIL MECHANICS. *Educ:* Ecole Centrale Paris, France, Engr, 58; Univ Grenoble, MS, 59; Princeton Univ, PhD(soil mech), 61. *Prof Exp:* Res assoc civil eng, Princeton Univ, 61-62; asst prof, 62-67, assoc prof, 67-73, PROF CIVIL ENG, CASE WESTERN UNIV, 73-, CHMN DEPT, 78- *Concurrent Pos:* NSF res grant soil mech, 65-81; soils & foundations consult. *Mem:* Am Soc Testing & Mat; Am Soc Civil Engrs; Int Soc Soil Mech. *Res:* Mechanical behavior of soils under different stress systems. *Mailing Add:* Dept Civil Eng University Circle Cleveland OH 44106

SAADE, JOHN MARSHALL, b Atlanta, Ga, Oct 20, 32. MATHEMATICS. *Educ:* Emory Univ, BA, 56, MA, 61, PhD(math), 66. *Prof Exp:* Instr math, Emory Univ, 61-63; ASST PROF MATH, UNIV GA, 66- *Mem:* Am Math Soc; Math Asn Am. *Res:* Algebra. *Mailing Add:* Dept of Math Univ of Ga Athens GA 30602

SAALFELD, FRED ERIC, b Joplin, Mo, Apr 9, 35; m 58; c 1. PHYSICAL CHEMISTRY, INORGANIC CHEMISTRY. *Educ:* Southeast Mo State Col, BS, 57; Iowa State Univ, MS, 59, PhD(chem), 61. *Prof Exp:* Fel, Iowa State Univ, 61-62; sect head mass spectrometry, 62-74, head phys chem br, 74-76, SUPT CHEM DIV, NAVAL RES LAB, 76- *Concurrent Pos:* Chief scientist, Off Naval Res, London Br Off, 80. *Mem:* AAAS; Am Chem Soc; Am Soc Mass Spectrometry (secy, 70-74); fel Chem Soc London; Mass Spectros Soc Japan. *Res:* Application of mass spectrometry to chemical problems; investigation of ion-molecule reaction and the kinetics of chemical reactions occuring in flames and chemical laser; analysis of exceedingly complex mixtures. *Mailing Add:* Naval Res Lab Code 6100 Washington DC 20375

SAALFRANK, CHARLES W, b Pa, Apr 5, 19; m 40. MATHEMATICS. *Educ:* Univ Pa, BS, 41, PhD(math), 48; Univ Nev, MA, 43. *Prof Exp:* Instr math, Univ Pa, 43-47; asst prof, Franklin & Marshall Col, 47-48 & Rutgers Univ, 48-52; PROF & HEAD DEPT MATH, LAFAYETTE COL, 52- *Mem:* Am Math Soc; Math Asn Am. *Res:* Analytic topology. *Mailing Add:* Dept of Math Lafayette Col Easton PA 18042

SAARI, DONALD GENE, b Ironwood, Mich, Mar 9, 40; m 66; c 2. MATHEMATICAL ECONOMICS, CELESTIAL MECHANICS. *Educ:* Mich Technol Univ, BS, 62; Purdue Univ, MS, 64, PhD(math), 67. *Prof Exp:* Res staff astronr, Yale Univ, 67-68; from asst prof to assoc prof, 68-74, PROF MATH, NORTHWESTERN UNIV, 74- *Concurrent Pos:* Consult, Nat Bur Standards, 79- *Mem:* Am Math Soc; Math Asn Am; Soc Indust & Appl Math. *Res:* Qualitative behavior of the N-body problem of celestial mechanics; collisions and singularities; behavior of expanding gravitational systems; differential equations; mathematical economics. *Mailing Add:* Dept of Math Northwestern Univ Evanston IL 60201

SAARI, EUGENE E, b Grand Rapids, Minn, July 17, 36; m 60; c 2. PHYTOPATHOLOGY. *Educ:* Univ Minn, BS, 59, MS, 62, PhD(plant path), 66. *Prof Exp:* Instr plant path, Okla State Univ, 62-65; res asst, Univ Minn, 65-66; res assoc, Mich State Univ, 66-67; plant pathologist, India, 67-73, regional wheat pathologist, Int Maize & Wheat Improv Ctr-Arid Lands Agr Develop Prog, 73-78, REGIONAL PLANT PATHOLOGIST, FORD FOUND, EGYPT, 78- *Mem:* Am Phytopath Soc; Am Soc Agron; Crop Sci Soc Am. *Res:* Wheat diseases, breeding and production. *Mailing Add:* Ford Found PO Box 2344 Cairo Egypt

SAARI, JACK THEODORE, b Virginia, Minn, Jan 1, 43; m 74; c 1. PHYSIOLOGY. *Educ:* Univ Minn, Minneapolis, BChE, 65, PhD(physiol), 70. *Prof Exp:* Instr physiol, Univ Minn, Minneapolis, 70-71; res assoc biophys, Univ Calgary, 71-75; asst prof physiol, Sch Dent, Marquette Univ, 75-78; asst prof, 78-82, ASSOC PROF PHYSIOL, SCH MED, UNIV NDAK, 82- *Concurrent Pos:* William H Davies Mem Res fel, Div Med Biophys, Univ Calgary, 72-74; Med Res Coun Can prof asst, 74-75. *Mem:* Int Soc Biorheology; Am Physiol Soc. *Res:* Study of structure and permeability in erythrocyte membranes; study of calcium kinetics in cardiac muscle. *Mailing Add:* Physiol Dept Sch Med Univ NDak Grand Forks ND 58202

SAARI, WALFRED SPENCER, b Lonsdale, RI, Feb 6, 32; m 53; c 4. ORGANIC CHEMISTRY. *Educ:* Brown Univ, ScB, 53; Mass Inst Technol, PhD(org chem), 57. *Prof Exp:* Res chemist, Shell Develop Co, Calif, 57-59; sr res chemist, 59-75, SR INVESTR, MERCK SHARP & DOHME RES LABS, 75- *Mem:* Am Chem Soc. *Res:* Medicinal chemistry. *Mailing Add:* Merck Sharp & Dohme Res Labs West Point PA 19486

SAARLAS, MAIDO, b Tartu, Estonia, Feb 5, 30; US citizen; m 56; c 2. AERONAUTICAL & MECHANICAL ENGINEERING. *Educ:* Univ Ill, Urbana, BS, 53, MS, 54 & 57; Univ Cincinnati, PhD(mech eng), 66. *Prof Exp:* Res engr, Univ Chicago, 54-56 & Douglas Aircraft Co, 56; sr engr, Autonetics Div, N Am Rockwell Corp, 58-59 & Aeronutronic Div, Ford Motor Co, 59-61; res assoc, Univ Cincinnati, 61-65 & Kinetics Corp, 65-67; sr engr, Gen Elec Co, 67-69; assoc prof, 69-80, PROF AERONAUT ENG, US NAVAL ACAD, 80- *Concurrent Pos:* Lectr, Univ Calif, Los Angeles, 58-61; consult, Douglas Aircraft Co, 65, Gen Elec Co, 65-67, Trident Eng, 69- & Cadcom, Inc, 70- *Mem:* Am Inst Aeronaut & Astronaut; Am Soc Mech Engrs. *Res:* Fluid mechanics and heat transfer; flight mechanics and dynamics; turbo-machinery. *Mailing Add:* Dept Aerospace Eng US Naval Acad Annapolis MD 21402

SAATY, THOMAS L, b Mosul, Iraq, July 18, 26; US citizen; m 48; c 5. MATHEMATICS. *Educ:* Catholic Univ, MS, 49; Yale Univ, MA, 50, PhD, 53. *Prof Exp:* Mathematician, Melpar, Inc, 53-54; mathematician & sci analyst, Mass Inst Technol, 54-57; mathematician, US Dept Navy, 57-58, sci liaison officer, Off Naval Res, Eng, 58-59, dir adv planning, 59-61, head math br, 61-63, mathematician, US Arms Control & Disarmament Agency, Dept State, 63-69; prof statist & oper res, 69-79, UNIV PROF, UNIV PITTSBURGH, 79- *Concurrent Pos:* Lectr, Am Univ & USDA Grad Sch, 54-; prof lectr, Catholic Univ, George Washington Univ & Exten Div, Univ

Calif, Los Angeles; Ford Found lectr, Nat Planning Inst, Cairo, 59 & 64; mathematician, US Dept Air Force & Nat Bur Standards, 51-52; consult var corps, US govt agencies & depts & foreign govts; exec dir, Conf Bd Math Sci, AAAS, 65-67. *Honors & Awards:* Lester R Ford Award, Math Asn Am, 73; Inst Mgt Sci Award, 77. *Mem:* Fel AAAS; Am Math Soc; Math Soc Am; Opers Res Soc Am; Royal Span Acad. *Res:* Optimization; nonlinear processes; graph theory; queueing theory and stochastic processes; operations research, especially in underdeveloped countries; mathematical methods and military uses; models of arms reduction; systems; planning. *Mailing Add:* Grad Sch Bus Univ Pittsburgh Pittsburgh PA 15260

SAAVEDRA, JUAN M, b Buenos Aires, Arg, Oct 5, 41; m 70. PHARMACOLOGY, PSYCHIATRY. *Educ:* Univ Buenos Aires, MD, 65. *Prof Exp:* Vis fel, 71-73, vis scientist pharmacol, 73-79, MED OFFICER, NIH, 79- *Mem:* Int Soc Hypertension; Int Soc Neurochem; Soc Neurosci. *Res:* Psychopharmacology; biological psychiatry; neural regulation of blood pressure; central control of automatic functions; stress and central nervous system. *Mailing Add:* Nat Insts Health Rm 2D-47 Bldg 10 9000 Rockville Pike Bethesda MD 20205

SABA, GEORGE PETER, II, b Wilkes-Barre, Pa, Sept 30, 40; m 67; c 4. RADIOLOGY, BIOPHYSICS. *Educ:* Pa State Univ, BS, 62, MS, 64; State Univ NY Buffalo, MD, 68. *Prof Exp:* Asst physics, Pa State Univ, 62-64; intern med, Buffalo Gen Hosp, 68-69; clin assoc, Nat Heart Inst, 69-71; NIH fel & resident, 71-74, ASST PROF RADIOL, JOHNS HOPKINS HOSP, 74- *Concurrent Pos:* Consult physician radiol, Union Mem Hosp, 73-, Havre de Grace Hosp, 74- & Md Gen Hosp, 74- *Res:* Clinical medicine; pancreatic studies and gastrointestinal radiology. *Mailing Add:* Dept of Radiol Johns Hopkins Hosp Baltimore MD 21205

SABA, THOMAS MARON, b Wilkes Barre, Pa, Mar 8, 41; m 63; c 3. MEDICAL PHYSIOLOGY, BIOPHYSICS. *Educ:* Wilkes Col, BA, 63; Univ Tenn, PhD(physiol, biophys), 67. *Prof Exp:* Lab asst biol, Wilkes Col, 61-62; instr physiol & biophys, Med Units, Univ Tenn, 67-68; from asst prof to assoc prof physiol, Univ Ill Col Med, 68-73; PROF PHYSIOL & CHMN DEPT, ALBANY MED COL, 73- *Concurrent Pos:* Consult physiologist, Vet Admin Hosp, Hines, Ill, 70-73; clinical physiologist, Albany Med Ctr, 73- *Mem:* AAAS; Reticuloendothelial Soc; Soc Exp Biol & Med; Am Asn Study Liver Dis; Am Physiol Soc. *Res:* Cardiovascular and metabolic aspects of the liver; physiology and physiopathology of the reticuloendothelial system; physiological mechanisms of host-defense; lipid metabolism and liver function; liver and spleen scanning; pathophysiology of traumatic shock; lung and peripheral vascular permeability. *Mailing Add:* Dept Physiol Albany Med Col Albany NY 12208

SABA, WILLIAM GEORGE, b Wilkes-Barre, Pa, Aug 15, 32; m 60; c 4. PHYSICAL CHEMISTRY. *Educ:* Wilkes Col, BS, 54; Univ Pittsburgh, PhD(phys chem), 61. *Prof Exp:* Asst chem, Univ Pittsburgh, 54-55, phys chem, 55-61; phys chemist, Heat Div, Nat Bur Stand, 61-69, PATENT EXAM, PATENT OFF, DEPT COMMERCE, 69- *Mem:* Am Chem Soc; Am Phys Soc; AAAS. *Res:* Thermodynamic properties of solid solutions; low-temperature calorimetry; solid state electronics; semiconductor design and processing. *Mailing Add:* 2623 Kinderbrook Lane Bowie MD 20715

SABACKY, M JEROME, b Cedar Rapids, Iowa, June 22, 39; m 67. ORGANIC CHEMISTRY. *Educ:* Coe Col, BA, 61; Univ Ill, MS, 63, PhD(chem), 66. *Prof Exp:* Sr res chemist, Org Chem Div, Monsanto Co, 66-75, res specialist, 75-79, SR RES SPECIALIST, NUTRIT CHEM DIV, MONSANTO INDUST CHEM CO, 79- *Mem:* Am Chem Soc; Brit Chem Soc. *Res:* Magnetic resonance studies of ortho-substituted derivatives of triphenylmethane; homogeneous catalysis; catalytic asymmetric synthesis employing transition metal complexes. *Mailing Add:* Monsanto Co 800 N Lindbergh Blvd St Louis MO 63166

SABADELL, ALBERTO JOSE, b Barcelona, Spain, Oct 31, 29; m 56; c 3. CHEMICAL ENGINEERING. *Educ:* Univ Buenos Aires, Lic chem, 54; Princeton Univ, MSE, 63. *Prof Exp:* Chemist, Invests Inst Sci & Tech Armed Forces, 55-56, chief div explosives and propellants, 57-60; prof theory explosives, Eng Sch Army, Argentinian Army, 60-61; res asst rocket propulsion, Forrestal Res Ctr, Princeton Univ, 62-63; assoc prof combustion, Sch Eng, Univ Buenos Aires, 64-65; res engr, Princeton Chem Res, 66 & Aerochem Res Labs Inc, Sybron Corp, 67-75; TECH STAFF, METREK DIV, MITRE CORP, 76- *Concurrent Pos:* Hon mem space tech comt, Arg Space Nat Comn, 64-65. *Mem:* Am Chem Soc; Am Inst Chem Engrs; Am Soc Testing & Mat. *Res:* author of over 25 publications. *Mailing Add:* 1210 Meadow Green Lane McLean VA 22102

SABATH, LEON DAVID, b Savannah, Ga, July 24, 30; c 3. MEDICINE, MICROBIOLOGY. *Educ:* Harvard Univ, AB, 52; Harvard Med Sch, MD, 56. *Prof Exp:* Intern med, Peter Bent Brigham Hosp, Boston, 56-57; jr resident, Bellevue Hosp, New York, 59-60; res fel, Harvard Med Sch, 60-62; sr resident, Peter Bent Brigham Hosp, 62-63; spec fel, Oxford Univ, 63-65; assoc med, Harvard Med Sch, 65-68; from asst prof to assoc prof, 68-74; PROF MED & HEAD SECT INFECTIOUS DIS, UNIV MINN, MINNEAPOLIS, 74- STAFF PHYSICIAN, UNIV MINN HOSPS, 74- *Concurrent Pos:* Nat Inst Allergy & Infectious Dis career develop award, 68-73; attend physician, Vet Admin Hosp, West Roxbury, 68-74; assoc physician, Boston City Hosp, 69-74. *Mem:* Am Fedn Clin Res; Soc Gen Microbiol; Am Soc Microbiol; Soc Clin Pharmacol & Therapeut; fel Am Col Physicians. *Res:* Antibiotics; infectious diseases; bacterial resistance to antibiotics; antibiotic assays; clinical pharmacology; penicillins, penicillinases; bacterial cell walls. *Mailing Add:* Dept of Med Univ of Minn Minneapolis MN 55455

SABATINI, DAVID DOMINGO, b Buenos Aires, Arg, May 10, 31; m 60; c 2. CELL BIOLOGY, BIOCHEMISTRY. *Educ:* Nat Univ Litoral, MD, 54; Rockefeller Univ, PhD(biochem), 66. *Prof Exp:* Investr cell biol, Inst Gen Anat, Med Sch, Univ Buenos Aires, 56-61, assoc prof & dir admis, Univ,

59-61; Rockefeller Found fel, Med Sch, Yale Univ, 61 & Rockefeller Inst, 61-62; from asst prof to assoc prof cell biol, Rockefeller Univ, 66-72; prof, 72-75, FREDERICK L EHRMAN PROF CELL BIOL, SCH MED, NY UNIV, 75-, CHMN DEPT, 72- Concurrent Pos: Fel, Nat Acad Med, Arg, 56; UNESCO fel, Biophys Inst, Rio de Janeiro, 57. Mem: Am Soc Cell Biol (pres, 78); Am Soc Biol Chemists; Tissue Cult Asn. Res: Electron microscopy; membrane and organelle biogenesis and protein synthesis in free and membrane bound ribosomes; structure of endoplasmic reticulum membrane; mechanisms of cellular aging. Mailing Add: Dept of Cell Biol NY Univ Sch of Med New York NY 10016

SABBADINI, EDRIS RINALDO, b Anzio, Italy, Apr 1, 30; Can citizen; m 60; c 2. IMMUNOBIOLOGY. Educ: Univ Pavia, MD, 54; McGill Univ, PhD(exp biol), 67. Prof Exp: Asst surg, Univ Pavia, 58-63; lectr exp surg, McGill Univ, 68-69; asst prof, 69-72, assoc prof, 72-80, PROF IMMUNOL, UNIV MAN, 80- Mem: Can Soc Immunol; Am Asn Immunologists; Transplantation Soc; NY Acad Sci. Res: Transplantation and tumor immunology; regulation of cell-mediated immunity. Mailing Add: Dept of Immunol Univ of Man Winnipeg MB R3T 2N2 Can

SABBAGH, HAROLD A(BRAHAM), b Lafayette, Ind, Jan 9, 37; m 66; c 2. ELECTRICAL ENGINEERING, PHYSICS. Educ: Purdue Univ, BSEE & MSEE, 58, PhD(elec eng), 64. Prof Exp: Instr elec sci, US Naval Acad, 59-61; asst prof elec eng, Rose-Hulman Inst Technol, 64-67, assoc prof, 67-70, prof elec eng & physics, 70-76; ELECTRONICS ENGR, NAVAL WEAPONS SUPPORT CTR, 76- Concurrent Pos: Consult, Crane Naval Ammunition Dept, Ind. Mem: Inst Elec & Electronics Engrs. Res: Electromagnetic waves; electroacoustic waves. Mailing Add: Naval Weapons Support Ctr Crane IN 47522

SABBAGHIAN, MEHDY, b Tehran, Iran, Nov 22, 35; m 63; c 1. ENGINEERING SCIENCE. Educ: Abadan Inst Technol, Iran, BSc, 58; Case Inst Technol, MSc, 63; Univ Okla, PhD(eng sci), 64. Prof Exp: Proj engr, Iranian Oil Ref Co, 58-60 & Viking Air Prod, 61-62; from asst prof to assoc prof, 64-74, PROF ENG SCI, LA STATE UNIV, BATON ROUGE, 74- Concurrent Pos: Consult, Hydro Vac Inc, 70-71, Gamma Indust, 72- & Nuclear Systs Inc, 73. Mem: Am Soc Mech Engrs; Am Soc Eng Educ. Res: Viscoelastic materials and their physical behaviors; thermoviscoelasticity with time dependent properties. Mailing Add: Dept of Mech Eng La State Univ Baton Rouge LA 70803

SABEL, CLARA ANN, b Louisville, Ky, Aug 19, 32. MATHEMATICS. Educ: Spalding Col, BA, 54; Xavier Univ, Ohio, MA, 61; Syracuse Univ, PhD(math), 70. Prof Exp: Teacher, LaSalette Acad, 57-61 & Nazareth Col & Acad, 61-64; asst prof math, Spalding Col, 69-77, chmn dept, 72-77; PROF, DEPT MATH, NAZARETH COL OF KY, 77- Mem: Math Asn Am; Am Math Soc; Brit Math Asn. Res: Abstract algebra; ring theory; group theory. Mailing Add: Dept of Math Russell Hall Nazareth Col of Ky Nazareth KY 40048

SABELLI, HECTOR C, b Buenos Aires, Arg, July 25, 37; nat US; m 60; c 2. PSYCHIATRY, NEUROPHARMACOLOGY. Educ: Univ Buenos Aires, MD, 59, DrMed, 61. Prof Exp: Res fels, Arg Soc Advan Sci, 59-60 & Arg Coun Res, 60-61; asst prof pharmacol, Chicago Med Sch, 62-64; career investr, Arg Coun Res, 64-66; vis prof pharmacol, Chicago Med Sch, 66-67, actg chmn dept, 70, chmn dept, 71-75; ASST PROF PSYCHIAT, RUSH UNIV, 79- Concurrent Pos: Prof & chmn, Inst Pharmacol, Nat Univ Litoral, 65-66; psychiatrist, Rush-Presby, St Lukes Hosp. Honors & Awards: Soc Biol Psychiat Award, 63. Mem: Soc Biol Psychiat; Am Soc Pharmacol & Exp Therapeut; Soc Neurosci. Res: Biogenic amines psychiatric disorders and drug therapy; psychodynamics and pharmacoltherapy of depression. Mailing Add: Dept Psychiatry Rush-Presby St Luke's Hosp Chicago IL 60612

SABELLI, NORA HOJVAT, b Buenos Aires, Argentina, Dec 22, 36; m 60; c 2. THEORETICAL CHEMISTRY, COMPUTER SCIENCE. Educ: Univ Buenos Aires, MS, 58, PhD(chem), 64. Prof Exp: Res assoc chem, Univ Chicago, 61-63; instr phys chem, Univ Buenos Aires, 64-65; asst prof, Nat Unlv Litoral, 65-66; chemist, Univ Chicago, 67-69; instr comput sci, 69-75, ASSOC PROF COMPUT SCI & CHEM, UNIV ILL CHICAGO CIRCLE, 75- Concurrent Pos: Career investr, Argentine Nat Res Coun, 64-66; vis resident assoc, Argonne Nat Labs, 74- Mem: Am Chem Soc; Int Soc Quantum Biol. Res: Theoretical organic chemistry; molecular orbital and semiempirical methods; computational chemistry; ab initio methods; potential curves. Mailing Add: Comput Ctr Box 4348 Univ of Ill Chicago IL 60680

SABER, AARON JAAN, b London, Eng, Aug 20, 46; Can citizen. COAL PROCESSING, PLASMA ARC TECHNOLOGY. Educ: Eng Univ Toronto, BASc, 69; Princeton Univ, MA, 71, PhD(aerospace), 74. Prof Exp: Mem res staff, Guggenheim Labs, Princeton Univ, 74-75; PROF ENG THERMODYNAMICS, CONCORDIA UNIV, 75- Concurrent Pos: Consult, Govt Can, 76-; pres, Lignasco Resources Ltd, 80- Mem: Am Inst Aeronaut & Astronaut; Eng Inst Can; Can Soc Mech Engrs; Can Inst Mining & Metall. Res: Coal conversion by in-site gasification; flammability limits measurement and prediction; rocket motor instability. Mailing Add: 800 Eglinton Ave W Suite 406 Toronto ON M5N 1G1 Can

SABERSKY, ROLF H(EINRICH), b Berlin, Ger, Oct 20, 20; nat US; m 46; c 2. HEAT TRANSFER, FLUID MECHANICS. Educ: Calif Inst Technol, BS, 42, MS, 43, PhD, 49. Prof Exp: Develop engr, Aerojet-Gen Corp, Gen Tire & Rubber Co, 43-49; from instr to assoc prof, 49-61, PROF MECH ENG, CALIF INST TECHNOL, 61- Concurrent Pos: Consult, Aerojet-Gen Corp, 49-71. Honors & Awards: Heat Transfer Mem Award, Am Soc Mech Engrs, 77. Mem: Am Soc Mech Engrs. Mailing Add: 1060 Fallen Leaf Rd Arcadia CA 91006

SABES, WILLIAM RUBEN, b St Paul, Minn, Jan 18, 31; m 51; c 3. ORAL PATHOLOGY. Educ: Univ Minn, BS & DDS, 59, MSD, 61; Am Bd Oral Path, dipl, 69. Prof Exp: Fel, Univ Minn, 59-61; asst prof oral histopath, Sch Dent, Temple Univ, 61-63; asst prof histol & path & chmn sect, Sch Dent, Univ Detroit, 63-65, from asst prof to assoc prof histopath & diag, 65-68, chmn dept, 66-68; assoc prof, Col Dent, Univ Ky, 68-71, prof oral path & chmn dept, 71-78; PROF PATH DEPT, SCH DENT, UNIV DETROIT, 78- Concurrent Pos: Consult, Vet Admin Hosps, Philadelphia, 61-63, Dearborn, Mich, 65-68, Lexington, Ky, 73-78 & Allen Park, Mich, 78- Honors & Awards: Award, Am Acad Dent Med, 59. Mem: Am Dent Asn; Am Acad Oral Path; Int Asn Dent Res; AAAS; Am Asn Univ Professors. Res: Experimental carcinogenesis. Mailing Add: Dept of Path Sch Dent 2985 E Jefferson Detroit MI 48207

SABESIN, SEYMOUR MARSHALL, b Riga, Latvia, Nov 27, 32; US citizen; m 57; c 3. INTERNAL MEDICINE, GASTROENTEROLOGY. Educ: City Col New York, BS, 54; NY Univ, MD, 58. Prof Exp: Clin fel exp path, Lab Path, Nat Cancer Inst, 59-61; resident internal med, New York Hosp-Cornell Med Ctr, 62-63; instr med, Harvard Med Sch, 63-65, assoc, 65-69; assoc prof med & path & dir electron micros lab, Jefferson Med Col, 69-73; PROF MED & DIR DIV GASTROENTEROL, COL MED, UNIV TENN, MEMPHIS, 73- Concurrent Pos: Nat Inst Arthritis & Metab Dis fel, Mass Gen Hosp & Harvard Med Sch, 62-64, clin & res fel gastroenterol, 63-65; assoc investr, Metab Res Ctr, Mass Gen Hosp, 65-69; consult, Vet Admin Hosp, 69-; NIH & Am Heart Asn grants, Jefferson Med Col, 72-; mem, Gen Med A Study Sect, NIH, 78-; fel Coun Arteriosclerosis, Am Heart Asn. Honors & Awards: Rorer Award, Am Col Gastroenterol, 70 & 71. Mem: Am Soc Clin Nutrit; Am Inst Nutrit; Am Col Physicians; Am Fed Clin Res; Am Heart Asn. Res: Biochemical pathology of the liver; mechanisms of lipid transport in intestine and liver; lipoprotein metabolism; experimental liver injury. Mailing Add: Dept of Med Univ Tenn Ctr Health Sci Memphis TN 38163

SABET, SOHAIR FARID, microbiology, see previous edition

SABET, TAWF!K YOUNIS, b Egypt, Nov 24, 26; nat US; m 53; c 1. IMMUNOBIOLOGY. Educ: Cairo Univ, BSc, 48, MS, 52, PhD(microbiol), 55. Prof Exp: Asst bacteriologist, Cairo Univ, 48-51; instr microbiol, 55-56; res assoc, Univ Ill, 57-64; NIH spec fel, 65 & 66; assoc prof, 67-72, PROF HISTOL, COL DENT, UNIV ILL MED CTR, 72- Concurrent Pos: Guest investr, US Naval Res Unit 3, 55-56; res assoc, Presby-St Luke's Hosp, Chicago, 57-64. Mem: AAAS; Am Soc Microbiol; Am Asn Immunol; Reticuloendothelial Soc. Res: Macrophage activation; macrophage phagocytosis; neutrophil function. Mailing Add: Dept of Histol Univ of Ill Med Ctr Chicago IL 60612

SABEY, BURNS ROY, b Magrath, Alta, May 17, 28; m 48; c 6. SOILS. Educ: Brigham Young Univ, BSc, 53; Iowa State Col, MS, 54, PhD, 58. Prof Exp: Instr soils, Iowa State Col, 54-58; from asst prof to assoc prof soil microbiol, Univ Ill, Urbana, 58-69; PROF SOIL SCI, COLO STATE UNIV, 69- Concurrent Pos: NSF fac fel, 67-68. Mem: Fel Am Soc Agron; fel Soil Sci Soc Am. Res: Soil microbes and their influence on plant nutrient transformations in the soil; nitrification; denitrification; ammonification; organic waste recycling on land; mine land reclamation; revegetation of oil shale retorted. Mailing Add: Dept of Agron Colo State Univ Ft Collins CO 80521

SABHARWAL, CHAMAN LAL, b Ludhiana, India, Aug 15, 37; m 68. MATHEMATICS, COMPUTER SCIENCE. Educ: Panjab Univ, India, BA, 59, MA, 61; Univ Ill, Urbana, MS, 66, PhD(math), 67. Prof Exp: Lectr math, D A V Col, Hoshiarpur, 61-63; teaching asst, Univ Ill, Urbana, 63-67; from asst prof to assoc prof, 67-75, PROF MATH, ST LOUIS UNIV, 75- Concurrent Pos: NSF res grant, McDonnell Douglas Lab, 79. Mem: Am Math Soc; Math Asn Am; Asn Comput Mach. Res: Mathematical physics; functional analysis; software engineering; algorithm development. Mailing Add: Dept Math St Louis Univ St Louis MO 63103

SABHARWAL, KALBIR, b Punjab, India, Jan 5, 43; m 76; c 2. FOOD SCIENCE. Educ: Punjab Agr Univ, India, BSc, 64, MSc, 66; Ohio State Univ, MS, 69, PhD(food sci nutrit), 72. Prof Exp: Res asst, Ohio State Univ, 67-69, res assoc, 69-72; DIR RES & DEVELOP PROD DEVELOP, FISHER CHEESE, AN AMFAC CO, WAPAKONETA, OHIO, 72- Mem: Inst Food Technologists; Am Dairy Sci Asn; Am Cult Dairy Prod Inst; Am Chem Soc; Am Oil Chemists Soc. Res: Development of various cheese substitutes in addition to process cheese and cheese products; functional food ingredients of dairy and non-dairy source. Mailing Add: 3366 Muirfield Place Lima OH 45805

SABHARWAL, PRITAM SINGH, b Jehlum, Punjab, India, Apr 22, 37; US citizen; m 65; c 2. DEVELOPMENTAL BIOLOGY. Educ: Univ Delhi, BSc, 57, MSc, 59, PhD(bot), 63. Prof Exp: Res asst bot, Univ Delhi, 59-63, asst prof, 63-64; NSF fel & res assoc, Univ Pittsburgh, 64-65 & Ind Univ, Bloomington, 65-66; asst prof, 66-71, ASSOC PROF BOT, UNIV KY, 71- Concurrent Pos: USDA contract, 69-72. Mem: AAAS; Tissue Cult Asn; Int Soc Plant Morphol; Bot Soc Am. Res: Control of differentiation in plants. Mailing Add: Dept of Bot Univ of Ky Lexington KY 40506

SABHARWAL, RANJIT SINGH, b Dhudial, Pakistan, Dec 11, 25; m 48; c 3. PURE MATHEMATICS. Educ: Sikh Nat Col, Lahore, BA, 44; Punjab Univ, India, MA, 48; Univ Calif, Berkeley, MA, 62; Wash State Univ, PhD(math), 66. Prof Exp: Lectr math, Khalsa Col, Bombay, 51-58; teaching asst, Univ Calif, 58-62; instr, Portland State Col, 62-63; instr, Wash State Univ, 63-66; asst prof, Kans State Univ, 66-68; assoc prof, 68-74, PROF MATH, CALIF STATE UNIV, HAYWARD, 74- Mem: Am Math Soc; Math Asn Am. Res: Non-Desarguesian planes associated with finite and/or infinite algebraic structures of near-fields. Mailing Add: Dept of Math Calif State Univ Hayward CA 94542

SABIA, RAFFAELE, b Procida, Italy, Aug 27, 33; US citizen; m 68; c 4. POLYMER CHEMISTRY. *Educ:* St Francis Col, BS, 56; Polytech Inst Brooklyn, PhD(polymer chem), 60. *Prof Exp:* Chemist, Polymer Chem Div, W R Grace & Co, 59-60, sect head polymers, 60-63; mem tech staff, 63-67, SUPVR ORGANIC MAT ENG, BELL TEL LABS, NJ, 67- *Mem:* Soc Rheol; Soc Plastics Eng. *Res:* Mechanical and physical properties of polymers and materials in general; materials for wire and cable applications. *Mailing Add:* Bell Tel Labs 2000 Northeast Expressway Norcross GA 30071

SABIDUSSI, GERT OTTO, b Graz, Austria, Oct 28, 29; div; c 1. MATHEMATICS. *Educ:* Univ Vienna, PhD, 52. *Prof Exp:* Mem, Inst Adv Study, NJ, 53-55; instr, Univ Minn, 55-56; res instr math, Tulane Univ, 56-57, asst prof, 57-60; from assoc prof to prof, McMaster Univ, 60-69; dir math res ctr, 71-72, PROF MATH, UNIV MONTREAL, 69- *Concurrent Pos:* Fulbright grant, 53-54. *Mem:* Can Math Soc. *Res:* Graph theory; combinatorics; automata. *Mailing Add:* Dept of Math CP6128 Univ of Montreal Montreal PQ H3C 3J7 Can

SABIN, ALBERT BRUCE, b Russia, Aug 26, 06; nat US; c 2. INFECTIOUS DISEASES, VIROLOGY. *Educ:* NY Univ, BSc, 28, MD, 31. *Hon Degrees:* Numerous from US & foreign univs, 59-75. *Prof Exp:* Res assoc bact, Sch Med, NY Univ, 26-31; house physician, Bellevue Hosp, 32 & 33; Nat Res Coun fel, Lister Inst London, Eng, 34; asst, Rockefeller Inst, 35-37, assoc, 37-39; assoc prof pediat, 39-46, prof res pediat, 46-60, distinguished serv prof, 60-71, EMER DISTINGUISHED SERV PROF RES PEDIAT, COL MED, UNIV CINCINNATI, 71-; EMER DISTINGUISHED RES PROF BIOMED, MED UNIV SC, 82- *Concurrent Pos:* Chief div infectious dis, Children's Hosp Res Found, Cincinnati, 39-69; consult to US Army serving on comn virus & rickettsial dis, Armed Forces Epidemiol Bd & spec mission, Middle East, Italy, Panama, Japan, Korea, China & Ger, 41-62; consult, USPHS, 47-70; mem, Armed Forces Epidemiol Bd, 63-69; mem nat adv coun, Nat Inst Allergy & Infectious Dis, 65-70; mem bd gov, Weizmann Inst Sci & Hebrew Univ, Israel, 65-; trustee, NY Univ, 66-70; Ohio State Regents prof, 68-69; pres, Weizmann Inst Sci, 70-72; mem bd gov, Israel Inst Technol, 70-77 & Tel Aviv Univ, 71-; Fogarty scholar, NIH, 73; mem adv comt med res, Pan-Am Health Orgn, 73-77; expert consult, Nat Cancer Inst, 74; mem, US Army Med Res Develop Adv Panel, 74-80; distinguished res prof, Med Univ SC, 74-82; consult to asst secy health, Dept Health, Educ & Welfare, 75-77. *Honors & Awards:* Mangia d'Oro Medal, City of Siena, Italy, 68; Order of the Sacred Treasure of Japan, 68; Walter Reed Medal, Am Soc Trop Med & Hyg, 69; Gold Medal, Royal Soc Health, 69; Decoration of the Aztec Eagle, Sash First Class, Govt Mex, 70; Ordem do Cruzeiro do Sul, Govt Brazil, 70; US Nat Medal of Sci, 70; Statesman in Med Award, 73; Howland Award, Am Pediat Soc, 74. *Mem:* Nat Acad Sci; fel Am Acad Arts & Sci; fel Am Soc Trop Med & Hyg; Infectious Dis Soc Am (pres, 68-69); fel Royal Soc Health. *Res:* Pneumococcus infection; pleuropneumonia group; experimental arthritis; toxoplasmosis; dengue; sandfly fever; neurotropic viruses; poliomyelitis; live and oral polio vaccine; role of viruses in human cancer. *Mailing Add:* Med Univ SC Charleston SC 29403

SABIN, GERALD ABRODOS, b Tampa, Fla, Jan 24, 24; m 48; c 3. UNDERWATER ACOUSTICS. *Educ:* Univ Tampa, BS, 50; Rollins Col, MS, 65. *Prof Exp:* Physicist, Air Force Missile Test Ctr, 50-52, Underwater Sound Ref Lab, 52-61, Proj Mercury, NASA, Fla, 61-62 & Underwater Sound Ref Div, Naval Res Lab, 62-73; sr engr, Electronics Div, Gen Dynamics, Longwood, Fla, 73-75; analyst, Lear-Siegler Inc, Orlando, Fla, 76-77; engr, Boeing Serv Int, Kennedy Space Ctr, 77-78; CONSULT, 78- *Concurrent Pos:* Instr, Sch Continuing Studies, Rollins Col, 67-68; instr underwater acoust, Fla Inst Technol, Melbourne, 76. *Mem:* Fel Acoust Soc Am. *Res:* Transducer calibration methods; acoustic impedance measurements at high hydrostatic pressures; small-computer applications. *Mailing Add:* 6022 Sage Dr Orlando FL 32807

SABIN, JOHN ROGERS, b Springfield, Mass, Apr 29, 40; div; c 1. QUANTUM MECHANICS. *Educ:* Williams Col, BA, 62; Univ NH, PhD(radiation chem), 66. *Prof Exp:* NIH fel, Quantum Chem Group, Univ Uppsula, 66-67; fel chem, Northwestern Univ, 67-68; asst prof, Univ Mo-Columbia, 68-71; assoc prof, 71-77, prof chem, 77-80, PROF CHEM & PHYSICS, UNIV FLA, 80- *Concurrent Pos:* Assoc ed, Int J Quantum Chem, 73-; consult, Phys Sci Dir, Micom-Redstone Arsenal, 72-; vis prof, Odense Univ, Denmark, 78- *Mem:* Am Chem Soc; fel Am Phys Soc; fel Am Inst Chem; Int Soc Quantum Biol. *Res:* Calculational quantum mechanics of netal films, polymers and small molecules; determination of microscopic and macroscopic properties of materials. *Mailing Add:* Quantum Theory Proj Williamson Hall Univ of Fla Gainesville FL 32611

SABIN, THOMAS DANIEL, b Webster, Mass, Apr 28, 36; m 58; c 3. NEUROLOGY. *Educ:* Tufts Univ, BS, 58, MD, 62. *Prof Exp:* Resident neurol, Boston City Hosp, 64-66; assoc chief rehab, USPHS Hosp, Carville, La, 67-70; assoc dir, 70-75, DIR NEUROL UNIT, BOSTON CITY HOSP, 75- *Concurrent Pos:* Asst prof neurol, Tufts Univ, 70-; assoc prof, Sch Med, Boston Univ, 75-; lectr neurol, Harvard Med Sch, 75-; consult ed, J Phys Ther, 75- *Mem:* AAAS; Am Acad Neurol; Soc Clin Neurologists; Int Leprosy Asn. *Res:* Clinical problems in peripheral nerve disorders; application of computerized tomography of the brain to behavioral disorders and dementia. *Mailing Add:* Neurol Unit Boston City Hosp 818 Harrison Ave Boston MA 02118

SABINA, LESLIE ROBERT, b Fort Erie, Ont, Nov 28, 28; m 55; c 2. VIROLOGY, MICROBIOLOGY. *Educ:* Cornell Univ, AB, 52; Univ Nebr, MS, 56, PhD(microbiol), 60. *Prof Exp:* Bacteriologist, Ont D Dept Health, 52-53; bacteriologist, Mt Sinai Hosp, Toronto, 53-54; asst animal path, Univ Nebr, 56-59, instr vet sci, 59-60; sr res asst virol, Connaught Med Res Labs, Toronto, 60-62, res assoc, 62-63; Upjohn Co, 64-65; asst prof, 65-71, PROF VIROL, UNIV WINDSOR, 71- *Concurrent Pos:* Registered, Nat Registry Microbiol. *Mem:* Am Soc Microbiol; Can Soc Microbiol; Can Col Microbiol. *Res:* Host-virus interactions; viral chemotherapeutics; tissue culture cell nutrition. *Mailing Add:* Dept Biol Univ Windsor Windsor ON N9B 3P4 Can

SABINS, FLOYD F, b Houston, Tex, Jan 5, 31; m 54; c 2. GEOLOGY. *Educ:* Univ Tex, BS, 52; Yale Univ, PhD(geol), 55. *Prof Exp:* Sr res geologist, Chevron Res Co, 55-67, SR RES ASSOC, CHEVRON OIL FIELD RES CO, STANDARD OIL CO, CALIF, 67- *Concurrent Pos:* Asst prof, Calif State Col Fullerton, 65-66; adj prof, Univ Southern Calif, 66-; regents prof, Univ Calif, Los Angeles, 75- *Mem:* Fel Geol Soc Am; Am Soc Photogram; Am Asn Petrol Geologists. *Res:* Remote sensing; sedimentary petrology; stratigraphy; structural geology. *Mailing Add:* Chevron Oil Field Res Co PO Box 446 La Habra CA 90631

SABISKY, EDWARD STEPHEN, b Middleport, Pa, Sept 11, 32; m 55; c 2. SOLID STATE PHYSICS. *Educ:* Pa State Univ, BS, 56; Univ Southern Calif, MS, 59; Univ Pa, PhD(physics), 65. *Prof Exp:* Mem tech staff, Hughes Aircraft Co, 56-59; mem tech staff, RCA Res Labs, 59-80; MEM STAFF, SOLAR ENERGY RES INST, 80- *Mem:* Am Phys Soc; Inst Elec & Electronics Engrs. *Res:* Spin-phonon interaction; liquid helium films; tunable phonon spectrometer; dispersion in sound velocity in liquid helium; masers; double resonance employing optical-microwave techniques; spin memory; circular dichroism in solids; paramagnetic resonance of ions in solids; atomic hydrogen maser. *Mailing Add:* Solar Energy Res Inst 1617 Cole Blvd Golden CO 80406

SABISTON, CHARLES BARKER, JR, b Wake Forest, NC, July 22, 33; m 59; c 2. MICROBIOLOGY, DENTISTRY. *Educ:* Wake Forest Univ, BS, 53; Univ NC, DDS, 57; Va Commonwealth Univ, PhD(microbiol), 68; Univ Iowa, cert periodont, 75. *Prof Exp:* Pvt pract dent, NC, 60-64; Nat Inst Dent Res fel & Dent Res Training Prog fel, Va Commonwealth Univ, 64-67, assoc prof periodont, Med Col Va, 67-72; assoc prof periodont, 72-77, DIR, MICROBIOL RES LAB, COL DENT, UNIV IOWA, 72- & PROF PERIODONT, 77- *Concurrent Pos:* Nat Inst Dent res grants, Va Commonwealth Univ, 71-72 & Col Dent, Univ Iowa, 72-78; consult coun therapeut, Am Dent Asn, 71-; consult J Am Dent Asn, 78- *Mem:* Am Soc Microbiol; Am Dent Asn; Int Asn Dent Res; Am Asn Dent Res. *Res:* Microbial factors in periodontal disease etiology; non-sporing anaerobic bacteria; clinical dental microbiology. *Mailing Add:* Dept of Periodont Univ of Iowa Col of Dent Iowa City IA 52242

SABISTON, DAVID COSTON, JR, b Jacksonville, NC, Oct 4, 24; m 55; c 3. SURGERY. *Educ:* Univ NC, BS, 43; Johns Hopkins Univ, MD, 47. *Prof Exp:* Intern surg, Johns Hopkins Hosp, 47-48, from asst to assoc prof, Univ, 55-64; prof, 64-71, JAMES B DUKE PROF SURG, MED CTR, DUKE UNIV, 71-, CHMN DEPT, 64- *Concurrent Pos:* Asst surg, Johns Hopkins Univ, 48-49, Cushing fel, 49-50; NIH res career award, 62-64; investr, Howard Hughes Med Inst, 55-61; consult, Walter Reed Army Med Ctr, NIH & Womack Army Hosp; chmn, Am Bd Surg, 71-72. *Mem:* Inst Med-Nat Acad Sci; Am Asn Thoracic Surgeons; Am Col Surg; Soc Univ Surg (pres, 68-69); Am Surg Asn (pres, 77-78). *Res:* General and cardiovascular surgery. *Mailing Add:* Dept of Surg Duke Univ Med Ctr Durham NC 27710

SABLATASH, MIKE, b Bienfait, Sask, Sept 30, 35; m 61; c 3. ELECTRICAL ENGINEERING, APPLIED MATHEMATICS. *Educ:* Univ Man, BScEng, 57, MSc, 64; Univ Wis-Madison, PhD(elec eng), 68. *Prof Exp:* Commun engr, Sask Power Corp, 57; mem common sci staff, Res & Develop Labs, Northern Elec Co, 61-65; asst prof elec eng, Univ Toronto, 68-72; statistician V, Energy Bd Can, 72-76; RES SCIENTIST, COMPUT COMMUN IMAGE PROCESSING & INFO TECHNOL, DEPT COMMUN & COMMUN RES CENT, 76- *Concurrent Pos:* Lab demonstr, Univ Man, 57-60, res asst, 58-59; lectr, Univ Ottawa, 64-65; teaching asst, Univ Wis, 65-68; consult, Consociates Ltd, 68-72; Nat Res Coun grant, Univ Toronto, 68-72. *Mem:* AAAS; Inst Elec & Electronics Engrs. *Res:* Communication signals, networks and systems and their optimal design; statistical communication and information theory; mathematical prof programming; functional analysis; computer communications in information systems and technology. *Mailing Add:* 16 Bradgate Dr Ottawa ON K2G 0R6 Can

SABLE, EDWARD GEORGE, b Rockford, Ill, Dec 12, 24; m 54; c 2. GEOLOGY. *Educ:* Univ Minn, BA, 48; Univ Mich, MS, 59, PhD, 65. *Prof Exp:* Geologist petrol explor, 48-56, GEOLOGIST MINERAL EXPLOR, US GEOL SURV, 57- *Honors & Awards:* Case Mem Award, Univ Mich, 59. *Mem:* AAAS; Geol Soc Am; Arctic Inst NAm. *Res:* Mesozoic and Paleozoic stratigraphy and structural and economic geology of Arctic Alaska; tectonics of arctic regions; petroleum exploration of Alaska; granite emplacement; regional Mississippian stratigraphy of Eastern Interior Basin, United States; coordination of Devonian stratigraphic data; petroleum source rock studies; oil and gas appraisal; precambrian of southern Arabian shield. *Mailing Add:* US geol Surv Box 25046 Denver Fed Ctr Lakewood CO 80225

SABLE, HENRY ZODOC, b Toronto, Ont, Apr 1, 18; nat US; m 42; c 2. BIOCHEMISTRY, ORGANIC CHEMISTRY. *Educ:* Univ Toronto, BA, 39, MD, 43; Univ Ill, MS, 47; Wash Univ, PhD(biochem), 50. *Prof Exp:* Instr biochem, Sch Med, Tufts Univ, 50-51, asst prof, 51-53; from asst prof to assoc prof biochem, 53-66, prof chem, 67, co-dir dept biochem, 67-75, actg dir, 66-67 & 75-78, PROF BIOCHEM & CHEM, SCH MED, CASE WESTERN RESERVE UNIV, 66- *Concurrent Pos:* Markle scholar med sci, Sch Med, Case Western Reserve Univ, 56-61; vis prof & NSF fel, Univ Geneva, 59-60. *Mem:* AAAS; Am Chem Soc; Am Soc Biol Chemists; NY Acad Sci. *Res:* Coenzyme mechanisms; analogues of glycerolipids; magnetic resonance spectroscopy; chemistry of cyclitols; conformational analysis; thiamin-polypropylene requiring enzymes; spectroscopy. *Mailing Add:* Sch Med Dept Biochem Case Western Reserve Univ Cleveland OH 44106

SABNIS, ANANT GOVIND, b Chandgad, India, Feb 22, 44; m 73; c 1. ELECTRONICS, SOLID STATE PHYSICS. *Educ:* Univ Bombay, BE, 65; SDak Sch Mines & Technol, MS, 71, PhD(elec eng), 74. *Prof Exp:* Elec engr elec mach, Cropton-Greaves Ltd, Bombay, 65-66; lectr elec eng, Shri Bhagubhai Mafatlal Polytech, Bombay, 66-69; vis asst prof elec eng, Univ Pittsburgh, 74-75, asst prof, 75-80; MEM STAFF, BELL LABS, 80- *Mem:* Inst Elec & Electronics Engrs; Sigma Xi. *Res:* Solid state device physics; thin-films; integrated circuits design and modeling; material characterization. *Mailing Add:* Bell Labs 555 Union Blvd Allentown PA 18103

SABNIS, GAJANAN MAHADEO, b Belgaum, India, June 11, 41; nat US; m 69. STRUCTURAL ENGINEERING. *Educ:* Univ Bombay, BE, 61; Indian Inst Technol, Bombay, MTech, 63; Cornell Univ, PhD(struct eng), 67. *Prof Exp:* Res assoc struct eng, Cornell Univ, 67, fel, Univ Pa, 68; res engr, Am Cement Corp, Calif, 68-69; eng supvr, Bechtel Power Corp, 70-73, sr engr, 73-74; assoc prof, 74-80, PROF CIVIL ENG, HOWARD UNIV, 80- *Concurrent Pos:* Consult engr, Bombay, 63-64; res, McGill Univ; pres, Stride Inc. *Mem:* Fel Am Concrete Inst; Am Soc Civil Engrs; Am Soc Eng Educ; Soc Exp Stress Anal; Inst Engrs India. *Res:* Structural models, shear strength of concrete slabs; deflection of structures; properties of concretes; nuclear power plants; structural failure investigations; ferrocement. *Mailing Add:* 13721 Town Line Rd Silver Spring MD 20906

SABNIS, SUMAN T, b Rajkot, India, Nov 27, 35; US citizen; m 60; c 2. CHEMICAL ENGINEERING, STATISTICS. *Educ:* Christ Church Col, India, BSc, 54; Harcourt Butler Tech Inst, BS, 57; Lehigh Univ, MS, 60, PhD(chem eng), 67; Rutgers Univ, MS, 64. *Prof Exp:* Chem engr, Union Carbide Plastics Co, NJ, 60-63; sr chem engr, Monsanto Co, 66-68, group leader kinetics of polymer systs, 68-74; mgr mat res & develop, Kerite Co, Harvey Hubbell Inc, 74-76, mgr process eng, 76-81; VPRES ENG, LARIBEE WIRE MFG CO INC, 81- *Mem:* Am Inst Chem Engrs; Am Chem Soc; Inst Elec & Electronic Engrs; Soc Plastics Engrs. *Res:* Mixing studies in polymeric systems, kinetics of polymer systems, statistics and process development in area of polymers; compounding of rubber and plastic compounds; vulcanization techniques for insulated wire and cable. *Mailing Add:* 843 Garden Rd Orange CT 06477

SABO, DENNIS JOHN, b Perth Amboy, NJ, Nov 29, 39; m 61; c 2. NUTRITION, BIOCHEMISTRY. *Educ:* Fairleigh Dickinson Univ, BS, 61; Boston Col, MS, 63, PhD(biochem), 67. *Prof Exp:* NIH res fel nutrit, Harvard Univ, 67-68, res assoc, 68-70; asst prof path, Sch Med, Tufts Univ, 70-74; ASST SCIENTIST, DEPT BIOL, WOODS HOLE OCEANOG INST, 74- *Mem:* AAAS. *Res:* Nutritional biochemistry and pathology related to liver disease and vitamin deficiencies. *Mailing Add:* Dept of Biol Woods Hole Oceanog Inst Woods Hole MA 02543

SABO, JULIUS JAY, b Cleveland, Ohio, May 27, 21; m 48; c 2. ENVIRONMENTAL ENGINEERING, POLLUTION CONTROL. *Educ:* Fenn Col, BME, 48; Univ Colo, MPA, 81. *Prof Exp:* Chem engr, Repub Steel Corp, 48-52; consult engr, Reserve Mining Co, 52-55; develop engr, Gen Elec Co, 55-58; chief monitoring, Reactor Testing Sta, US Pub Health Serv, Idaho, 58-60, chief nuclear anal, 60-64, asst chief res grants, Div Radiol Health, 65-67, chief res grants prog & exec secy radiol health study sect, 67-69; dir off grants admin, Environ Control Admin, 69-71; grants info off, Environ Protection Agency, 71-75; mem fac, Colo Tech Col, 78-79; CONSULT ENGR HAZARDOUS WASTE CONTROL, 80- *Concurrent Pos:* Tech chmn, Non Conventional Energy Resources Comt & Conf, 75-77. *Mem:* Am Acad Environ Engrs; fel Royal Soc Health. *Res:* Environmental aspects of developing non-conventional energy resources. *Mailing Add:* 6935 Blackhawk Pl Colorado Springs CO 80919

SABOE, JOSEPH CHARLES, b Bridgeport, Pa, Apr 3, 30; m 52; c 7. PHARMACY. *Educ:* St Joseph's Univ, BS, 69. *Prof Exp:* Lab technician, 57-62, pharmacist, 62-69, res pharmacist, 69-76, SR RES PHARMACIST, MERCK SHARP & DOHME RES LABS, 76- *Mem:* Am Pharmaceut Asn; Acad Pharmaceut Sci. *Res:* Physical-chemical factors which influence the design and utilization of specific pharmaceutical solid dosage forms (capsules, tablets, suppositories and sustained release products). *Mailing Add:* Merck Sharp & Dohme Res Labs West Point PA 19486

SABOL, GEORGE PAUL, b Clairton, Pa, Oct 17, 39; m 63; c 4. NUCLEAR MATERIALS. *Educ:* Pa State Univ, BS, 61; Carnegie Inst Technol, MS, 64, PhD(mat sci), 67. *Prof Exp:* Engr superalloy res & develop, Colwell Res Ctr, TRW Inc, 65-67; sr engr phys metall, 67-72, fel engr, 72-76, adv engr, 76, MGR CORE MAT DEVELOP NUCLEAR MAT, WESTINGHOUSE RES & DEVELOP CTR, 76- *Mem:* Am Soc Metals; Am Inst Mining & Metall Engrs; Am Nuclear Soc. *Res:* Processing, corrosion response and mechanical behavior of zirconium-based alloys; performance of nuclear fuel in light water reactors; physical metallurgy of nickel-based superalloys. *Mailing Add:* Westinghouse Res & Develop Ctr 1310 Beulah Rd Pittsburgh PA 15235

SABOL, STEVEN LAYNE, b Phoenix, Ariz, Sept 21, 44; m 80. BIOCHEMISTRY. *Educ:* Yale Col, BS, 66; NY Univ, MD & PhD(biochem), 73. *Prof Exp:* Intern med, Duke Univ Med Ctr, 73-74; res assoc, 74-77; sr staff fel, 77-79, MED OFFICER RES, LAB BIOCHEM GENETICS, NAT HEART, LUNG & BLOOD INST, NIH, 79- *Mem:* Am Soc Biol Chemists. *Res:* Protein and peptide biosynthesis; cyclic nucleotides and peptides in the nervous system; neurotransmitter receptors. *Mailing Add:* Nat Insts of Health Bldg 36 Rm 1C-06 Bethesda MD 20014

SABOUNGI-BLANDER, MARIE-LOUISE JEAN, b Tripoli, Lebanon, Jan 1, 48; m 76; c 1. PHYSICAL CHEMISTRY, PHYSICS. *Educ:* Univ Aix-Marseille, France, PhD(thermodyn), 73. *Prof Exp:* CHEMIST, CHEM ENG DIV, ARGONNE NAT LAB, 73- *Mem:* Electrochem Soc. *Res:* Molten salt chemistry; alloy thermodynamics; statistical mechanics; electrochemistry. *Mailing Add:* Chem Eng Div 9700 S Cass Ave Argonne IL 60439

SABOURIN, THOMAS DONALD, b Bay City, Mich, May 31, 51; m 74. AQUATIC ENVIRONMENTAL TOXICOLOGY, ENVIRONMENTAL PHYSIOLOGY. *Educ:* Univ Mich, BA, 73; Calif State Univ, MA, 77; La State Univ, PhD(physiol), 81. *Prof Exp:* Anal chemist, Sel Rex Div Occidental Petrol, 73-75; teaching asst physiol, Calif State Univ, Hayward, 75-76; teaching asst biol, physiol & marine, La State Univ, 78-80; FEL, NAT INST ENVIRON HEALTH SCI, ENVIRON HEALTH SCI CTR, ORE STATE UNIV, 81- *Concurrent Pos:* Prin investr, Sigma Xi grant, 80-81 & Lerner Fund Marine Res Grant, 80-82; consult, Browning & Ferris Industs, 80-81. *Mem:* Sigma Xi; AAAS; Am Soc Zoologists. *Res:* Effects of natural and anthropognic stressors on the physiological function of aquatic fishes and invertebrates; salinity, temperature interactions with environmental pollutants (petroleum hydrocarbons and metals) and marine organisms. *Mailing Add:* Ore State Univ Sci Ctr Marine Sci Dr Newport OR 97365

SABOURN, ROBERT JOSEPH EDMOND, b Sturgeon Falls, Ont, July 6, 26; m 53; c 2. GEOLOGY. *Educ:* Univ Ottawa, BSc, 47; Laval Univ, BAppSc, 51, MSc, 52, DSc(geol), 55. *Prof Exp:* From asst prof to assoc prof, 55-67, chmn dept geol & mineral, 65-71, PROF GEOL, LAVAL UNIV, 67- *Concurrent Pos:* Mem, AID Proj, Senegal, WAfrica, 63. *Mem:* Geol Soc Am; fel Geol Asn Can; Can Inst Mining & Metall. *Res:* Engineering, field and areal geology; geomorphology. *Mailing Add:* Fac of Sci Laval Univ Quebec PQ G1K 7P4 Can

SABRAN, IRA BARRY, molecular biology, biochemistry, see previous edition

SABROSKY, CURTIS WILLIAMS, b Sturgis, Mich, Apr 3, 10; m. ENTOMOLOGY, TAXONOMY. *Educ:* Kalamazoo Col, AB, 31; Kans State Univ, MS, 33. *Hon Degrees:* ScD, Kalamazoo Col, 66. *Prof Exp:* From instr to asst prof entom, Mich State Univ, 36-45; entomologist, Entom & Plant Quarantine, 46-53 & Entom Res Br, 53-67, dir syst entom lab, 67-73, res entomologist, 73-80, COOP SCIENTIST, USDA, 80- *Concurrent Pos:* Mem, Int Comn Zool Nomenclature, 63-, pres, 77-; mem permanent comt, Int Cong Entom, 60-80; pres & chmn orgn comt, XV Int Cong Entom, 73-76. *Honors & Awards:* Distinguished Serv Award, Kans State Univ, 65. *Mem:* AAAS; Entom Soc Am (pres, 69); Soc Syst Zool (pres, 62); Am Inst Biol Sci; hon foreign mem Entom Soc USSR. *Res:* Taxonomy of higher flies; problems of zoological nomenclature. *Mailing Add:* USDA Systematic Entom Lab c/o US Nat Mus Natural Hist Washington DC 20560

SABRY, ZAKARIA I, b Tanta, Egypt, Aug 16, 32; Can citizen; m 56; c 2. NUTRITION, BIOCHEMISTRY. *Educ:* Univ Ain Shams, Cairo, BSc, 52; Univ Mass, MSc, 54; Pa State Univ, PhD(biochem), 57. *Prof Exp:* From asst prof to assoc prof food technol & nutrit, Am Univ Beirut, 57-64, head dept, 61-64; from assoc prof to prof nutrit, Univ Toronto, 64-72; pres, Nutrit Res Consults, Inc, 74-79; DIR FOOD POLICY & NUTRIT DIV, FOOD & AGR ORGN, UN, 79- *Concurrent Pos:* Nat Res Coun Can fel, 61-62; nat coordr, Nutrit Can, Health Protect Br, Can Dept Health & Welfare, 69-77; prof appl human nutrit, Univ Guelph, 76-79. *Mem:* Am Inst Nutrit; Int Food Technologists; Nutrit Soc Can; Brit Nutrit Soc. *Res:* Protein metabolism; supplementary effects of dietary proteins vitamin B nutriture; vitamin B and protein interrelationships; nutrition survey; assessment of nutritional status in man. *Mailing Add:* Food & Nutrit Div VIA Delle Termi Caracalla Rome 00100 Italy

SABSHIN, MELVIN, b New York, NY, Oct 28, 25; m 55; c 1. PSYCHIATRY. *Educ:* Univ Fla, BS, 44; Tulane Univ, MD, 48. *Prof Exp:* Resident psychiat, Tulane Univ, 49-52; res psychiatrist, Psychosom & Psychiat Inst, Michael Reese Hosp, 53-55, asst dir, 55-57, assoc dir, 57-61; prof psychiat & head dept, Col Med, Univ Ill, 61-74; MED DIR, AM PSYCHIAT ASN, 74- *Concurrent Pos:* Fel, Ctr Advan Study Behav Sci, 67-68; assoc ed, Am J Psychiat, 71-74; actg dean, Abraham Lincoln Sch Med, Univ Ill, 73-74. *Mem:* AAAS; Am Col Psychiat (pres, 73-74); Am Psychiat Asn; AMA; Am Psychosom Soc; Group Advan Psychiat. *Res:* Social psychiatry; empirical studies of adaptive behavior. *Mailing Add:* 1700 18th St NW Washington DC 20009

SABU, DWARKA DAS, nuclear chemistry, cosmochemistry, see previous edition

SABY, JOHN SANFORD, b Ithaca, NY, Mar 21, 21; m 45; c 4. PHYSICS. *Educ:* Gettysburg Col, AB, 42; Pa State Univ, MS, 44, PhD(physics), 47. *Hon Degrees:* ScD, Gettysburg Col, 69. *Prof Exp:* Lab instr physics, Gettysburg Col, 40-42; asst, Pa State Univ, 42-47; instr, Cornell Univ, 47-50; res physicist, Electronics Lab, 51-52, supvr semiconductor components develop, 52-55, mgr semiconductor & solid state, 55-56, mgr lamp res lab, 56-71, MGR LAMP PHENOMENA RES LAB, GEN ELEC CO, 71- *Mem:* Am Phys Soc; fel Inst Elec & Electronics Eng. *Res:* X-ray liquid diffraction; atmospheric ultrasonics; wave mechanics of interacting particles; x-ray solid state; p-n-p transistor; p-n junction studies; power transistors; luminescence; electroluminescence; gas discharge physics; electron emission. *Mailing Add:* Lighting Res & Tech Serv Oper Gen Elec Co Cleveland OH 44112

SACCO, ANTHONY G, b Utica, NY, Nov 2, 44; m 67; c 2. IMMUNO-REPRODUCTION. *Educ:* Univ Rochester, BA, 66; Univ Tenn, MS, 68, PhD(zool), 71. *Prof Exp:* Res assoc, Inst Cancer Res, 72-74; asst prof, 74-79, ASSOC PROF, DEPTS OBSTET & GYNEC & IMMUNOL & MICROBIOL, SCH MED, WAYNE STATE UNIV, 79- *Concurrent Pos:* Non-clin assoc, Dept Path, Hutzel Hosp, 75- *Mem:* Soc Study Reprod; Sigma Xi. *Res:* Immuno-reproduction: antigenic properties and possible reproductive roles of antigens present in female and male reproductive tissues, tract secretions, and ova and sperm; fertility control: immunocontraception; mammalian reproductive biology: sperm-egg/ova interaction and recognition during the fertilization process. *Mailing Add:* Dept Obstet & Gynec Sch Med Wayne State Univ 275 E Hancock Ave Detroit MI 48201

SACCO, LOUIS JOSEPH, JR, b Chicago, Ill, Mar 24, 24; m 51; c 5. ORGANIC CHEMISTRY. *Educ:* DePaul Univ, ScB, 48, ScM, 50. *Prof Exp:* Res chemist, Baxter Lab, Inc, 50-56 & Nalco Chem Co, 56-57; res & develop chemist, Alkydol Lab, Inc, 57-58; process res chemist & sr res asst, 58-70, tech counr, 70-72, process res chemist & sr res asst, 73-75, supvr, Process Improv Lab, 75-80, SUPVR SAFETY, TRAINING & WASTE MGT, G D SEARLE & CO, 81- *Concurrent Pos:* Lectr, Chicago City Jr Col, 65-70 & DePaul Univ, 69-71 & 78-81. *Mem:* Am Chem Soc. *Res:* Amino acids; carbohydrate chemistry; fatty acids; steroids; prostaglandins. *Mailing Add:* G D Searle & Co PO Box 5110 Chicago IL 60680

SACCOMAN, FRANK (MICHAEL), b Hibbing, Minn, July 31, 31; c 4. ANATOMY, ZOOLOGY. *Educ:* Bemidji State Col, BS, 58; Univ Minn, PhD(anat), 64. *Prof Exp:* Instr anat, Univ Mich, 64-66; from asst prof to prof biol, 66-80, chmn dept, 66-80, DEAN, DIV SCI & MATH, BEMIDJI STATE UNIV, 80- *Concurrent Pos:* NSF fel, Univ Minn, 70. *Res:*

Radioautographic studies of developing extraembryonic membranes in the mouse; cellular migration in developing extraembryonic membranes with the use of radioautography; DNA synthesis in freshwater algae. *Mailing Add:* Dept of Biol Bemidji State Univ Bemidji MN 56601

SACCOMAN, JOHN JOSEPH, b Paterson, NJ, Sept 10, 39; m 63; c 2. MATHEMATICAL ANALYSIS. *Educ:* Seton Hall Univ, BS, 60; NY Univ, MS, 62, PhD(math educ), 74. *Prof Exp:* From instr to asst prof, 61-81, ASSOC PROF MATH, SETON HALL UNIV, 81- *Mem:* Am Math Soc; Math Asn Am. *Res:* Development of a set of normability conditions for topological vector spaces using a generalized Hahn-Banach theorem; applications of non-standard analysis to functional analysis; historical aspects of the Hahn Banach theorem. *Mailing Add:* Dept Math Seton Hall Univ South Orange NJ 07079

SACHAN, DILEEP SINGH, b Makhauli, India, Dec 18, 38; US citizen; m 68; c 3. NUTRITIONAL BIOCHEMISTRY, MICROBIOLOGY. *Educ:* M P Vet Col, India, BVSc, 61, MVSc, 63; Univ Ill, Urbana, MS, 66, PhD(nutrit), 68. *Prof Exp:* Lectr obstet & gynec, M P Vet Col, India, 63-64; res asst nutrit, Univ Ill, Urbana, 64-69; res assoc pharmacol & microbiol, Case Western Reserve Univ, 69-71; asst prof pharmacol, Meharry Med Col, 71-76; res chemist, Vet Admin Hosp, 76-78; fel nutrit & gastroenterol, Vanderbilt Univ Med Ctr, 78-79; ASSOC PROF NUTRIT & BIOCHEM, DEPT NUTRIT & FOOD SCI, UNIV TENN, KNOXVILLE, 79- *Concurrent Pos:* NIH fel, Case Western Reserve Univ, 69-71; consult clin path, Vet Admin Hosp, 78-80; prin investr res grants, NSF, NIH, USDA & AID. *Mem:* Am Inst Nutrit; Biochem, Pharmacol & Nutrit Today Soc; NY Acad Sci. *Res:* Nutrient-nutrient and nutrient-drug interactions; lipid metabolism; role of carnitine in alcoholism; bioavailability of nutrients; nutritional status. *Mailing Add:* Dept Nutrit & Food Sci Col Home Econ Univ Tenn Knoxville TN 37996

SACHDEV, GOVERDHAN PAL, b Lahore, India, July 17, 41; m 68; c 2. BIOCHEMISTRY, BIO-ORGANIC CHEMISTRY. *Educ:* Univ Delhi, BSc, 61, MSc, 63, PhD(chem), 67. *Prof Exp:* Lectr chem, Ramjas Col, Univ Delhi, 63-64; res fel, Univ Delhi, 64-67, sr res fel, 67-68; res assoc biochem, Yale Univ, 68-75; ASST MEM, OKLA MED RES FOUND, 76- *Honors & Awards:* Eason Award, Eason Oil Co/Okla Geol Soc, 78. *Mem:* Am Chem Soc; AAAS; Sigma Xi; Soc Complex Carbohydrates. *Res:* Structure and function of biological membrane-bound enzymes, glycoproteins and proteins; chemical carcinogens. *Mailing Add:* Okla Med Res Found 825 NE 13 St Oklahoma City OK 73104

SACHDEV, SHAM L, b Hoshiarpur, India, Dec 21, 37; m 67; c 2. CHEMISTRY. *Educ:* Panjab Univ, India, BS, 59, MS, 60; La State Univ, PhD(chem), 66; Am Bd Indust Hyg, cert; Int Hazard Control Cert Bd, Hazard Control Mgr. *Prof Exp:* Vis res assoc chem, La State Univ, 65-66, vis asst prof, 66-70; anal specialist, 70-74; mgr methods & develop, Kem-Tech Labs, Inc, 74-78; MEM STAFF, ENV HEALTH SERV, 78- *Concurrent Pos:* USPHS fel, La State Univ, 65-67; Air Pollution Control Admin fel, 66-69, NSF fel, 69-70; mem bd ed, Stand Methods/Water & Waste Water, Am Water Works Asn, 74- *Mem:* AAAS; Am Chem Soc; Air Pollution Control Asn. *Res:* Determination and significance of trace elements in environmental samples such as air, water, food and others; study of trace elements in the environment. *Mailing Add:* Env Health Serv 334 E Woodstone Baton Rouge LA 70808

SACHDEVA, BALDEV KRISHAN, b India, Oct 15, 39; m 78. APPLIED MATHEMATICS. *Educ:* Univ Delhi, India, BSc Hons, 59, MA, 61; Pa State Univ, PhD(math), 73. *Prof Exp:* Lectr math, Univ Delhi, 64-69; res assoc math & elec eng, Carleton Univ, Ottawa & Nat Res Coun, 73-74; lectr math, Univ Wis-Milwaukee, 75-77; vis prof math, Panjab Univ, Chandigarh, India, 77-79; PROF MATH, UNIV NEW HAVEN, CONN, 79-; DIR, ACAD AFFAIRS, 82- *Mem:* Am Math Soc; Soc Indust & Appl Math; Math Asn Am. *Res:* Scattering of acoustic and electromagnetic waves; general applied mathematics; numerical analysis. *Mailing Add:* Dept Math Univ New Haven 300 Orange Ave West Haven CT 06516

SACHER, EDWARD, b New York, NY, June 3, 34; m 62; c 3. PHYSICAL CHEMISTRY. *Educ:* City Col New York, BS, 56; Pa State Univ, PhD(phys chem), 60. *Prof Exp:* Teaching asst chem, Pa State Univ, 56-57; fel, Ohio State Univ, 60-61 & Ottawa Univ, Ont, 61-63; res chemist, E I du Pont de Nemours & Co, Inc, 63-68; staff chemist, 68-70; adv chemist, Mat Lab, Systs Prod Div, 70-80, ADV CHEMIST, MAT LAB, GEN TECHNOL DIV, IBM CORP, 80- *Mem:* Am Chem Soc; Electrochem Soc; Am Phys Soc; Royal Soc Chem. *Res:* Chemical kinetics; AC and DC dielectric properties of polymeric solids; structure and motions of polymeric solids. *Mailing Add:* Mat Lab IBM Gen Technol Div Endicott NY 13760

SACHER, JOSEPH ALBERT, b Irvington, NJ, Dec 27, 18; m 59; c 1. PLANT PHYSIOLOGY. *Educ:* State Univ NY, BS, 41; Univ Calif, PhD(bot), 53. *Prof Exp:* Instr bot, Univ Ill, 53-55; from asst prof to assoc prof, 55-62, PROF BOT, CALIF STATE UNIV, LOS ANGELES, 62- *Concurrent Pos:* NSF res grants, 58-76; NIH res grants, 73- *Mem:* AAAS; Bot Soc Am; Am Soc Plant Physiol; Japanese Soc Plant Physiol. *Res:* Hormone action; enzyme regulation; postharvest physiology of fruits and storage organs; tissue senescence. *Mailing Add:* Dept Biol Calif State Univ Los Angeles CA 90032

SACHER, ROBERT FRANCIS, b Chicago, Ill, July 23, 47; m 73. PLANT PHYSIOLOGY. *Educ:* Univ Ill, BS, 75, MS, 77; Wash State Univ, PhD(hort), 80. *Prof Exp:* Assoc, 80-81, RES ASSOC, BOYCE THOMPSON INST PLANT RES, CORNELL UNIV, 81- *Mem:* Am Soc Plant Physiol; Am Soc Hort Sci; AAAS. *Res:* Plant stress responses and partitioning the contributions of individual systems to overall tolerance; using genetically defined breeding lines with known differences in salt tolerance as model populations for comparative studies. *Mailing Add:* Boyce Thompson Inst Plant Res Cornell Univ Tower Rd Ithaca NY 14853

SACHS, ALLAN MAXWELL, b New York, NY, July 13, 21; m 49; c 3. PHYSICS. *Educ:* Harvard Univ, BA, 42, MA, 47, PhD(physics), 50. *Prof Exp:* Instr, 49-50, assoc, 50-51, from asst prof to assoc prof, chmn dept, 67-71, PROF PHYSICS, COLUMBIA UNIV, 60- *Res:* High energy particle physics; experimental intermediate energy particle physics. *Mailing Add:* Pupin Lab Columbia Univ New York NY 10027

SACHS, BENJAMIN DAVID, b Madrid, Spain, Mar 4, 36; US citizen. BIOLOGICAL PSYCHOLOGY. *Educ:* City Col New York, BA, 57, MSEd, 61; Univ Calif, Berkeley, PhD(comp psychol), 66. *Prof Exp:* From asst prof to assoc prof, 68-76, PROF PSYCHOL, UNIV CONN, 76- *Concurrent Pos:* Nat Inst Child Health & Human Develop fel, Rutgers Univ, Newark, 66-68; mem adv bd, Current Contents/Life Sci, 70- *Mem:* Am Psychol Asn; Animal Behav Soc; Int Soc Psychoneuroendocrinol; Soc Neurosci. *Res:* Reproductive behavior; sexually dimorphic behavior patterns. *Mailing Add:* Dept of Psychol Univ of Conn Storrs CT 06268

SACHS, DAVID, b Chicago, Ill, Aug 18, 33. MATHEMATICS. *Educ:* Ill Inst Technol, BS, 55, MS, 57, PhD(math), 60. *Prof Exp:* Instr math, Ill Inst Technol, 59-60; from instr to asst prof, Univ Ill, Urbana, 60-66; assoc prof, 66-71, PROF MATH, WRIGHT STATE UNIV, 71- *Mem:* Am Math Soc; Math Asn Am. *Res:* Lattice theory; exchange geometries; foundations of geometry. *Mailing Add:* Dept of Math Wright State Univ Dayton OH 45431

SACHS, DONALD CHARLES, b Chicago, Ill, May 19, 22; m 48; c 3. PHYSICS. *Educ:* Univ Chicago, BS, 43; Univ Ill, MS, 46; Univ Calif, Los Angeles, PhD, 51. *Prof Exp:* Asst physics, Metall Lab, Univ Chicago, 44-45; lectr & asst, Univ Ill, 45-46; asst & AEC fel, Univ Calif, Los Angeles, 46-48 & 50-51; sr physicist, Stanford Res Inst, 51-59; sr scientist & supvr, Aeronutronic Div, Ford Motor Co, Calif, 59-62; SR RES SCIENTIST, KAMAN SCIENCES CORP, 62- *Mem:* Am Phys Soc; Sigma Xi; Am Inst Aeronaut & Astronaut; Am Geophys Union; Armed Forces Commun & Electronics Asn. *Res:* Nuclear, plasma, shock wave and re-entry physics; x-ray effects; sensor development; structure dynamics. *Mailing Add:* Kaman Sci Corp 2001 Jefferson Davis Hwy Suite 703 Arlington VA 22202

SACHS, FREDERICK, b New York, NY, Jan 8, 41; m 64; c 2. BIOPHYSICS. *Educ:* Univ Rochester, BA, 62; State Univ NY Upstate Med Ctr, PhD(physiol), 72. *Prof Exp:* Assoc engr electromagnetic compatibility, Douglas Aircraft Co, 62-64; jr researcher biophys, Dept Biochem & Biophys, Univ Hawaii, 69-71; staff fel, Biophys Lab, Nat Inst Neurol Dis & Stroke, 71-75; asst prof pharmacol, 75-80, asst prof biophys, 80-81, ASSOC PROF BIOPHYS, STATE UNIV NY BUFFALO, 81- *Mem:* Biophys Soc; AAAS. *Res:* Mechanisms of ion transport in cells, excitability; single channel, fluctuation and voltage clamp techniques; computer modelling. *Mailing Add:* Dept Biophys Sci State Univ NY 120 Cary Hall Buffalo NY 14214

SACHS, FREDERICK LEE, b Brooklyn, NY, Feb 28, 38; m 60; c 3. INTERNAL MEDICINE. *Educ:* Princeton Univ, AB, 59; Columbia Univ, MD, 63. *Prof Exp:* From intern to chief resident med, Yale-New Haven Hosp, 63-69; instr, 69-70, asst prof med, 70-77, ASSOC CLIN PROF MED, SCH MED, YALE UNIV, 77- *Concurrent Pos:* Winchester fel chest dis, Sch Med, Yale Univ, 69-70; consult, Vet Admin Hosp, West Haven, 69- *Honors & Awards:* Upjohn Award, 68. *Mem:* AAAS; Am Thoracic Soc. *Res:* Alveolar macrophages. *Mailing Add:* Dept of Med Yale Univ Sch of Med New Haven CT 06510

SACHS, GEORGE, b Vienna, Austria, Aug 26, 36; US citizen; m 63; c 4. BIOCHEMISTRY. *Educ:* Univ Edinburgh, BSc, 57, MB, ChB, 60, DSc, 80. *Prof Exp:* Instr biochem, Albert Einstein Col Med, 61-62; asst prof med, 63-65, assoc prof med & physiol, 65-70, assoc prof physiol & biophys, 77-80, PROF MED, SCH MED, UNIV ALA, BIRMINGHAM, 70-, PROF PHYSIOL & BIOPHYS, 80- *Concurrent Pos:* Fel biochem, Albert Einstein Col Med, 61; res fel, Columbia Univ, 62-63. *Mem:* Biophys Soc; Brit Biochem Soc; NY Acad Sci; Soc Exp Biol & Med; Am Physiol Soc. *Res:* Physiology and biochemistry of transport. *Mailing Add:* Dept of Med Univ of Ala Sch of Med Birmingham AL 35233

SACHS, HARVEY MAURICE, b Atlanta, Ga, Dec 10, 44; m 67; c 1. GEOLOGY, ENERGY. *Educ:* Rice Univ, AB, 67; Brown Univ, PhD(geol), 73. *Prof Exp:* Fel oceanog, Ore State Univ, 72-74; asst prof, Case Western Res Univ, 74-76; ASST PROF GEOL, PRINCETON UNIV, 77- *Concurrent Pos:* Prin investr various grants, NSF & Pa Power & Light Co, 81-82. *Mem:* AAAS; Am Geophys Union; Geol Soc Am. *Res:* Engineering and evaluation of energy efficiency modificaitons for dwellings; side effects of conservation; geology of radon distribution. *Mailing Add:* Geol & Geophys Guyot Hall Princeton Univ Princeton NJ 08544

SACHS, HERBERT K(ONRAD), b Chemnitz, Ger, Mar 4, 19; nat US; m 48; c 3. ENGINEERING MECHANICS. *Educ:* Tech Col Zurich, Switz, dipl, 41; Wayne State Univ, MS, 56; Brunswick Tech Inst, DrEng(mech), 63. *Prof Exp:* Designer, St Louis Car Co, Mo, 48-49 & Am Car & Foundry Div, ACF Industs, Inc, 49; design analyst, Int Harvester Co, Ind, 50-53; head, vehicle dynamics, Truck & Coach Div, Gen Motors Corp, Mich, 53-58, assoc prof, 58-75, PROF MECH ENG, WAYNE STATE UNIV, 75- *Concurrent Pos:* Consult, Atomic Power Develop Assocs, Mich, Dana Corp & Rockwell-Standard Corp; chmn & ed proc, Int Conf Vehicle Mech Mich, 68, hon chmn Paris, 71; ed, J Vehicle Systs Dynamics, 71-; res engr, Dept Transp, Nat Hwy Traffic Safety Admin, 71-72; fac fel eng, Dept Transp, Transp Systs Ctr, Mass, 78-79. *Mem:* Indust Math Soc (vpres); Am Soc Mech Engrs; AAUP; Int Asn Vehicle Syst Dynamics (pres, 77-81). *Res:* Nonlinear and vehicle mechanics; general dynamics; vehicle dynamics; theory of controls applied to active suspension design; adaptive controls; stability theory; dynamics and vibration analysis. *Mailing Add:* Dept Mech Eng Wayne State Univ Detroit MI 48202

SACHS, HOWARD, biochemistry, see previous edition

SACHS, HOWARD GEORGE, b New York, NY, Dec 12, 43; m 68; c 2. DEVELOPMENTAL BIOLOGY, ANATOMY. *Educ:* Worcester Polytech Inst, BS, 65; Clark Univ, PhD(biol), 71. *Prof Exp:* Fel develop biol, Carnegie Inst, 70-72; asst prof, 72-78, assoc prof & asst dean, Grad Col, Univ Ill, 78-80; ASSOC PROVOST & ASSOC PROF ANAT, OHIO STATE UNIV, 80- *Mem:* Am Asn Anatomists; NY Acad Sci; AAAS; Sigma Xi; Am Heart Asn. *Res:* Cardiac biology and pathology. *Mailing Add:* Off Acad Affairs Ohio State Univ Columbus OH 43210

SACHS, IRVING BENJAMIN, b Chicago, Ill, Nov 11, 19; m 51; c 3. FORESTRY, WOOD TECHNOLOGY. *Educ:* Univ Ill, BS, 47, MS, 48, PhD(zool), 54. *Prof Exp:* Asst zool, Univ Ill, 47-55; from instr to asst prof biol, Wis State Col, 55-56; proj assoc, Sch Med, Univ Wis, 56-58; forest prod technologist, 58-71, RES SUPVR, FOREST PROD LAB, USDA, 71- *Concurrent Pos:* Woods Hole scholar awarded by grad sch, Univ Wis, 66. *Mem:* Electron Micros Soc Am; Forest Prod Res Soc; Int Asn Wood Anat. *Res:* Wood anatomy and chemistry; submicroscopic-structure and properties in chemical utilization and protection research. *Mailing Add:* Forest Prod Lab USDA Madison WI 53711

SACHS, JOHN RICHARD, b Brooklyn, NY, July 29, 34; m 59; c 3. HEMATOLOGY, PHYSIOLOGY. *Educ:* Manhattan Col, BS, 56; Columbia Univ, MD, 60. *Prof Exp:* Res hematologist, Walter Reed Army Inst Res, 66-69; asst prof physiol, Sch Med, Yale Univ, 69-72, assoc prof, 72-75; assoc prof, 75-77, PROF MED, SCH MED, STATE UNIV NY, STONY BROOK, 77- *Mem:* Am Physiol Soc; Biophys Soc; Soc Gen Physiologists. *Res:* Cation transport, membrane physiology. *Mailing Add:* Dept of Med State Univ NY Stony Brook NY 11794

SACHS, JULES BARRY, b New York, NY, Apr 18, 30; m 55. GEOLOGY. *Educ:* Columbia Univ, BS, 54; NY Univ, MS, 55; Tulane Univ, PhD(geol), 70. *Prof Exp:* Stratigrapher, Gulf Oil Corp, 55-66; assoc prof, 66-75, PROF GEOL, NICHOLS STATE UNIV, 75-, HEAD DEPT EARTH SCI, 66- *Concurrent Pos:* NSF grant, 72-73; consult geologist, 66- *Mem:* AAAS; Geol Soc Am; Am Asn Petrol Geologists. *Res:* Biostratigraphy, stratigraphy, earth science teaching and petroleum geology. *Mailing Add:* Dept of Earth Sci Nicholls State Univ Thibodaux LA 70301

SACHS, LESTER MARVIN, b Chicago, Ill, May 16, 27; m 57; c 1. THEORETICAL PHYSICS, INFORMATION SCIENCE. *Educ:* Ill Inst Technol, BS, 50, MS, 54, PhD(physics), 61. *Prof Exp:* Instr physics, Univ Ill, 55-58; resident assoc, Argonne Nat Lab, 59-60; asst prof physics, Wayne State Univ, 60-64; scientist, Res Inst Advan Studies, 65-69; pres, Comput Prog Assocs, Inc, Md, 69-71; independent consult, 71-72; comput systs analyst, Bur Labor Statist, 72-75; syst develop specialist, 75-80, TECHNICAL ADV, SOCIAL SECURITY ADMIN, 80- *Mem:* Asn Comput Mach; Am Phys Soc; Brit Comput Soc; Sigma Xi. *Res:* Atomic and molecular structure; solid state theory; microcomputers. *Mailing Add:* 8823 Stonehaven Rd Randallstown MD 21133

SACHS, MARTIN WILLIAM, b New Haven, Conn, Sept 30, 37; m 68. COMPUTER SCIENCE. *Educ:* Harvard Univ, AB, 59; Yale Univ, MS, 60, PhD(physics), 64. *Prof Exp:* Dept guest nuclear physics, Weizmann Inst, 64, inst fel, 64, NATO fel, 65, res asst, 66; res assoc, Nuclear Struct Lab, Yale Univ, 67-72, sr res assoc & lectr, 72-76; RES STAFF MEM, DEPT COMPUT SCI, IBM T J WATSON RES CTR, 76- *Concurrent Pos:* Mem panel on-line comput in nuclear res, Nat Res Coun, 68-70. *Mem:* Asn Comput Mach; Am Phys Soc; Sigma Xi; Inst Elec & Electronic Engrs Comput Sci. *Res:* Computer systems and communications; nuclear physics data acquisition with computers. *Mailing Add:* IBM Watson Res Ctr PO Box 218 Yorktown Heights NY 10598

SACHS, MARVIN LEONARD, b Allentown, Pa, Aug 31, 26. INTERNAL MEDICINE. *Educ:* Yale Univ, BA, 46; Harvard Univ, MD, 50; Am Bd Internal Med, dipl, 58. *Hon Degrees:* MA, Univ Pa, 71. *Prof Exp:* Intern surg, obstet & pediat, Allentown Gen Hosp, Pa, 50; intern med, Univ Hosps Cleveland, 51-52, resident, 52-53; instr, 55-61, physician-in-chg, Univ Pa Div Med Clin, Philadelphia Gen Hosp, 60-78, assoc, 61-69, ASST PROF MED, SCH MED, UNIV PA, 69-, MEM CARDIOVASCULAR SECT, DEPT MED, 57- *Concurrent Pos:* Nat Heart Inst fel cardiovasc dis, Hosp Univ Pa, 55-57; consult, Food & Drug Admin, Dept Health, Educ & Welfare, 64; consult, Archit Res Unit, Univ City Sci Ctr, Philadelphia, 65-; lectr, Wharton Sch, 66-; mem res in nursing in patient care rev comt, USPHS, 67-70; attend physician, Vet Admin Hosp, 67-; mem coun arteriosclerosis, coun circulation & mem med adv bd, Am Heart Asn. *Mem:* Fel Am Col Physicians; AMA; Am Fedn Clin Res; Am Thyroid Asn; Am Pub Health Asn. *Res:* Peripheral vascular diseases; patient care research and education; organization and design of health care facilities. *Mailing Add:* Hosp of the Univ of Pa 3400 Spruce St Philadelphia PA 19104

SACHS, MENDEL, b Portland, Ore, Apr 13, 27; m 52; c 4. THEORETICAL PHYSICS, PHILOSOPHY OF PHYSICS. *Educ:* Univ Calif, Los Angeles, AB, 49, MA, 50, PhD(physics), 54. *Prof Exp:* Theoret physicist, Radiation Lab, Univ Calif, 54-56; res scientist, Lockheed Missiles & Space Co, 56-61; res prof, McGill Univ, 61-62; assoc prof physics, Boston Univ, 62-66; PROF PHYSICS, STATE UNIV NY BUFFALO, 66- *Concurrent Pos:* Asst prof, San Jose State Col, 57-61. *Mem:* Brit Soc Philos Sci. *Res:* Relativity; field theory; quantum electrodynamics; elementary particles; philosophy of science; physical applications of group theory; astrophysics and cosmology. *Mailing Add:* Dept of Physics State Univ of NY at Buffalo Amherst NY 14260

SACHS, RAINER KURT, b Frankfurt, Ger, June 13, 32; US citizen; div; c 4. THEORETICAL PHYSICS. *Educ:* Mass Inst Technol, BSc, 53; Syracuse Univ, PhD(physics), 58. *Prof Exp:* Fel physics, Univ Hamburg, 59-60; fel, Univ London, 60-61; asst prof, Stevens Inst Technol, 62-63; from assoc prof to prof, Univ Tex, 63-69; PROF PHYSICS & MATH, UNIV CALIF, BERKELEY, 69- *Mem:* Am Phys Soc; Am Astron Soc. *Res:* General relativity; cosmology. *Mailing Add:* Dept of Math Univ of Calif Berkeley CA 94720

SACHS, ROBERT GREEN, b Hagerstown, Md, May 4, 16; m 41, 50, 68; c 8. RESEARCH ADMINISTRATION, THEORETICAL PHYSICS. *Educ:* Johns Hopkins Univ, PhD(physics), 39. *Hon Degrees:* DSc, Purdue Univ, 67, Univ Ill, 77. *Prof Exp:* Res fel theoret physics, George Washington Univ, 39-41 & Univ Calif, 41; instr physics, Purdue Univ, 41-43; chief air blast sect, Ballistic Res Lab, Aberdeen Proving Ground, 43-46; dir theoret physics div, Argonne Nat Lab, 46-47; from assoc prof to prof physics, Univ Wis, 47-64; dir, Enrico Fermi Inst, 68-73 & Argonne Nat Lab, 73-79; PROF PHYSICS, UNIV CHICAGO, 64- *Concurrent Pos:* Consult, Argonne Nat Lab, 46-52, 60-63; consult, Ballistic Res Lab, Aberdeen Proving Ground, 46-59; Higgins vis prof, Princeton Univ, 55-56; consult, Lawrence Radiation Lab, Univ Calif, 55-59; mem adv panel physics, NSF, 58-61; Guggenheim fel & vis prof, Ecole Normale Superieure, Univ Paris, 59-60; Guggenheim fel, Europ Orgn Nuclear Res, 59-60; assoc lab dir high energy physics, Argonne Nat Lab, 64-68; mem sci policy comt, Stanford Linear Accelerator Ctr, 66-70; high energy physics adv panel, US AEC, 67-69; mem physics surv comt & chmn elem particle physics panel, Physics Surv Comt, Nat Acad Sci, 69-72, chmn physics sect, 77-80. *Mem:* Nat Acad Sci; AAAS; Am Phys Soc; fel Am Acad Arts & Sci (vpres, 79-). *Res:* High energy physics; fundamental particles; nuclear theory; solid state; terminal ballistics; nuclear power reactors. *Mailing Add:* 5490 S Shore Dr Chicago IL 60615

SACHS, ROY M, b New York, NY, Apr 1, 30; m 53; c 5. PLANT PHYSIOLOGY. *Educ:* Mass Inst Technol, BS, 51; Calif Inst Technol, PhD(plant physiol), 55. *Prof Exp:* Fulbright fel, Univ Parma, 55-56; jr res botanist, Univ Calif, Los Angeles, 56-58, asst plant physiologist, 58-61; from asst plant physiologist to assoc plant physiologist, 58-70, PLANT PHYSIOLOGIST & PROF ENVIRON HORT, UNIV CALIF, DAVIS, 70- *Mem:* Am Soc Plant Physiol; Am Soc Hort Sci; Agron Soc Am. *Res:* Vegetative growth; flowering; growth substances. *Mailing Add:* Dept of Environ Hort Univ of Calif Davis CA 95616

SACHS, THOMAS DUDLEY, b St Louis, Mo, Jan 29, 25; m 61; c 3. ULTRASONICS, BIOPHYSICS. *Educ:* Univ Calif, Berkeley, BA, 51; Innsbruck Univ, PhD(physics, math), 60. *Prof Exp:* Pub sch teacher, Calif, 52-53 & high sch & jr col teacher, 53-55; res investr chem, Western Reserve Univ, 60-62; asst prof, 62-77, ASSOC PROF PHYSICS, UNIV VT, 77- *Concurrent Pos:* Consult, Jr High Sch Sci Exp Prog, 62-65, Ladd Res & IBM Corp; pres, Electronic Educator, Inc, 69-79; mem, Vt Regional Cancer Ctr, 80- *Mem:* AAAS; Am Phys Soc; Acoust Soc Am; Inst Elec & Electronics Engrs. *Res:* Perturbed acoustic propagation parameter measurements in liquids, plasmas and biological tissues with applications to liquid structure, cavitation, solar dynamics and mechanics; thermo acoustic sensing of cancers, perfusion and non-invasive temperature measurement by thermo acoustic sensory techniques. *Mailing Add:* Dept of Physics Univ of Vt Burlington VT 05401

SACHSE, WOLFGANG H, b Berlin-Charlottenburg, Ger, Mar 22, 42; US citizen; m 70. PHYSICAL ACOUSTICS. *Educ:* Pa State Univ, University Park, BS, 63; Johns Hopkins Univ, MSE, 66, PhD(mech), 70. *Prof Exp:* Ger acad exchange fel, Inst Metall, Aachen, 69-70; asst prof, 70-76, ASSOC PROF APPL MECH, CORNELL UNIV, 76- *Concurrent Pos:* Consult; Ger acad exchange fel, Nat Bur Standards, 77-78. *Mem:* Acoust Soc Am; Inst Acoust; Inst Elec & Electronics Engrs; Sigma Xi. *Res:* Mechanics of materials; wave propagation in solids; ultrasonics; acoustic emission; non-destructive testing of materials; transducers. *Mailing Add:* Dept of Theoret & Appl Mech Thurston Hall Cornell Univ Ithaca NY 14853

SACHTLEBEN, CLYDE CLINTON, b Lincoln, Nebr, May 4, 36; m 58; c 2. PHYSICS, SCIENCE EDUCATION. *Educ:* Nebr Wesleyan Univ, BA, 57; Univ Nebr, MA, 60; Univ Iowa, PhD(sci educ), 67. *Prof Exp:* From instr to assoc prof, 60-68, PROF PHYSICS, HASTINGS COL, 68-, CHMN DEPT, 62- *Concurrent Pos:* US AEC lectr, Oak Ridge Radioisotope-Mobile Lab, 65-, res assoc, Oak Ridge Assoc Univs, 72; vis prof physics, Univ Nebr, 65-81. *Mem:* Am Asn Physics Teachers. *Res:* Atomic and nuclear physics; development of laboratory program for undergraduate curriculum. *Mailing Add:* Dept of Physics Hastings Col Hastings NE 68901

SACK, E(DGAR) A(LBERT), JR, b Pittsburgh, Pa, Jan 31, 30; m 52; c 2. ELECTRICAL ENGINEERING, SOLID STATE ELECTRONICS. *Educ:* Carnegie Inst Technol, BS, 51, MS, 52, PhD(elec eng), 54. *Prof Exp:* Res engr, Carnegie Inst Technol, 51-54; res engr, Res Labs, Westinghouse Elec Corp, 54-56, proj leader, TV Sect, 56-57, sect mgr, Dielec Devices, 57-60, dept mgr, Electronics, 60-61, dept mgr, Solid State Devices, 61-62, mgr eng, Molecular Electronics Div, 62-65, mgr tech opers, 65-66, asst gen mgr, 66-67, gen mgr, Integrated Circuits Div, 67-69; vpres & gen mgr, Integrated Circuits Div, 69-70, vpres opers, Microelectronics, 70-71, vpres comput prod, 71-73, vpres & gen mgr, Microelectronics, 73-76, SR V PRES, MICROELECTRONICS, GEN INSTRUMENT CORP, 76- *Concurrent Pos:* Dir, Regional Indust Tech Educ Coun, 80- *Mem:* Fel Inst Elec & Electronics Engrs. *Res:* Ferroelectrics; electroluminescence; nonlinear circuits; integrated circuit design and processing; technical and general management; MOS memory device; solid state devices. *Mailing Add:* 57 Margo Lane Huntington NY 11743

SACK, GEORGE H(ENRY), JR, b Baltimore, Md, Apr 17, 43. MEDICAL GENETICS, GENE ORGANIZATION. *Educ:* Johns Hopkins Univ, BA, 65, MD, 68, PhD(molecular biol & microbiol), 75. *Prof Exp:* Intern med, Johns Hopkins Hosp, 68-69, asst resident, 69-70; fel microbiol, Johns Hopkins Univ, 70-73; major med, US Army Med Corps, 73-75; fel med genetics, Johns Hopkins Hosp, 75-76; ASST PROF MED PEDIAT, JOHNS HOPKINS UNIV, 76-, ASST PROF PHYSIOL CHEM, 80- *Mem:* Am Soc Human Genetics; AAAS. *Res:* Molecular biology: human gene structure, organization, expression, polymorphisms; clinical applications of genetic principles and technology. *Mailing Add:* Div Med Genetics Moore Clinic Carnegie 2 Johns Hopkins Univ Baltimore MD 21205

SACK, RICHARD BRADLEY, b Le Sueur, Minn, Oct 25, 35; m 55; c 4. MEDICINE, MICROBIOLOGY. *Educ:* Lewis & Clark Col, BS, 56; Univ Ore, MS & MD, 60; Johns Hopkins Univ, ScD(pathobiol), 68. *Prof Exp:* Johns Hopkins Hosp fel med, Calcutta, 62-64; fel pathobiol, Sch Pub Health, Johns Hopkins Univ, 65-68, from instr to asst prof, Sch Med, 66-70; assoc prof, Sch Med, Univ Ore, 70-72; assoc prof, 72-79, PROF MED, JOHNS HOPKINS UNIV, 79-, HEAD, DIV GEOG MED, 77- *Concurrent Pos:* Consult, WHO. *Mem:* Infectious Dis Soc Am; Am Soc Microbiol; Am Fedn Clin Res; Am Soc Clin Invest. *Res:* Cholera; diarrheal diseases; bacterial enterotoxins. *Mailing Add:* Baltimore City Hosp 4940 Eastern Ave Baltimore MD 21224

SACK, ROBERT A, b Mar 14, 44; US citizen; m 78; c 1. BIOCHEMISTRY, VISUAL SCIENCES. *Educ:* NY Med Col, PhD(biochem), 72. *Prof Exp:* ASSOC PROF BASIC SCI, STATE UNIV NY, 72- *Concurrent Pos:* Guest res assoc, Brookhaven Nat Lab, 71- *Res:* Regeneration of visual pigments; cryobiochemistry; ocular microbiology and immunology. *Mailing Add:* Col of Optom 100 E 25th St New York NY 10010

SACK, RONALD LESLIE, b Minneapolis, Minn, Mar 29, 35; m 58; c 2. SOLID MECHANICS, STRUCTURAL ENGINEERING. *Educ:* Univ Minn, BS, 57, MSCE, 58, PhD(civil eng), 64. *Prof Exp:* Asst prof civil eng, Clemson Univ, 64-65; res engr, Boeing Co, 65-70; assoc prof, 70-81, PROF CIVIL ENG, UNIV IDAHO, 81- *Concurrent Pos:* Vis lectr, Dept Mech Eng, Seattle Univ, 67-68 & Dept Civil Eng, Univ Wash, 68-70; NASA-Am Soc Eng Educ summer fel, Stanford Univ & Moffet Field, 71; Royal Norwegian Coun Sci & Indust Res fel, Trondheim, Norway, 76-77. *Mem:* Am Soc Civil Engrs; Am Soc Eng Educ. *Res:* Application of approximate numerical methods to structural engineering problems; investigation of structural stability problems; seismic design; wind and snow loading on structures. *Mailing Add:* Dept of Civil Eng Univ of Idaho Moscow ID 83843

SACK, WOLFGANG OTTO, b Leipzig, Ger, Mar 17, 28; US citizen; m 55; c 2. ANATOMY, VETERINARY MEDICINE. *Educ:* Univ Toronto, DVM, 57; Univ Edinburgh, PhD(vet anat), 62; Univ Munich, Dr med vet, 72. *Prof Exp:* Asst prof vet anat, Ont Vet Col, Toronto, 58-60, assoc prof, 62-64; assoc prof, 64-73, prof, 73-77, MEM FAC VET ANAT, CORNELL UNIV, 77- *Concurrent Pos:* Mem, Int & Am Comts Vet Anat Nomenclature, 64-; guest prof, Univ Munich, 71-72. *Mem:* Am Asn Vet Anat; Am Asn Anat; Am Vet Med Asn; World Asn Vet Anat; Royal Col Vet Surg. *Res:* Developmental anatomy of domesticated animals; gross anatomy of the horse. *Mailing Add:* Dept of Vet Anat Cornell Univ Ithaca NY 14853

SACKEIM, HAROLD A, b Hackensack, NJ, July 13, 51; m 77. CLINICAL PSYCHOLOGY, NEUROPSYCHOLOGY. *Educ:* Columbia Col, BA, 72; Oxford Univ, BA & MA, 74; Univ Pa, PhD(psychol), 77. *Prof Exp:* Asst prof psychol, Columbia Univ, 77-79; asst prof, NY Univ, 79-81; DEP CHIEF BIOL PSYCHIAT, NY STATE PSYCHIAT INST, 81-; ASSOC PROF PSYCHOL, NY UNIV, 81- *Concurrent Pos:* Lectr psychiat, Col Physicians & Surgeons, Columbia, 80-; consult ed, Imagination, Cobnition & Personality, 80-; assoc ed, J Social & Clin Psychol, 81- *Mem:* Am Psychol Asn; AAAS; Int Neuropsychol Soc; NY Acad Sci. *Res:* The role of functional brain asymmetry in the regulation of emotion; psychobiology of affective disorders; dissociation and consciousness. *Mailing Add:* Dept Psychol NY Univ 4th Floor 6 Wash Pl New York NY 10003

SACKETT, W(ILLIAM) T(ECUMSEH), JR, b Xenia, Ohio, Jan 28, 21; m 46; c 4. ELECTRICAL ENGINEERING. *Educ:* Johns Hopkins Univ, BEE, 41, DrEng(elec eng), 50. *Prof Exp:* Engr, Duquesne Light Co, 41-42; elec engr, US Naval Ord Lab, 42-50; asst chief elec eng div, Battelle Inst, 50-55; mgr res, Kuhlman Elec Co, 55-59; dir res, 60-77, dir, Syst & Res Ctr, 77-80, VPRES, CORP TECHNOL CTR, HONEYWELL INC, 80- *Concurrent Pos:* Instr, Johns Hopkins Univ, 47-48. *Mem:* AAAS; Inst Elec & Electronics Engrs. *Res:* Contact resistance; instrumentation; insulation; research administration; aerospace sciences. *Mailing Add:* 1349 Pikelake Dr St Paul MN 55112

SACKETT, WILLIAM MALCOLM, b St Louis, Mo, Nov 14, 30; m 56; c 2. GEOCHEMISTRY, CHEMISTRY. *Educ:* Washington Univ, BA, 53, PhD(chem), 58. *Prof Exp:* Chemist, Carbide & Carbon Chem Corp, Ky, 53-54; chemist, Mallinckrodt Chem Co, Mo, 54; vis asst res chemist, Scripps Inst Oceanog, Univ Calif, San Diego, 58-59; sr res engr, Pan Am Petrol Corp, 59-61, tech group supvr, 61-62; asst prof geol, Columbia Univ, 62-64; assoc prof chem, Univ Tulsa, 65-68; assoc prof oceanog, Tex A&M Univ, 68-70, prof, 70-79; PROF MARINE SCI & CHMN DEPT, UNIV SOUTH FLA, 79- *Mem:* AAAS; Geochem Soc. *Res:* Isotope geochemistry of carbon and uranium-thorium series of radioactive elements; hydrogeochemistry of aluminum. *Mailing Add:* Dept Marine Sci Univ South Fla St Petersburg FL 33701

SACKMAN, GEORGE LAWRENCE, b Baxley, Ga, Mar 15, 33; m 63; c 2. ELECTRICAL ENGINEERING. *Educ:* Univ Fla, BME, 54, BEE, 57, MSE, 59; Stanford Univ, PhD(elec eng), 64. *Prof Exp:* Res engr, Electron Tube Div, Litton Industs, Inc, 64-65; assoc prof, 65-80, PROF ELEC ENG, NAVAL POSTGRAD SCH, 80- *Concurrent Pos:* Consult, Lansmont Corp, 74- *Mem:* Inst Elec & Electronics Engrs; Acoust Soc Am; Sigma Xi; Res Soc Am. *Res:* Underwater acoustics; ultrasonic image systems; acoustic signal processing. *Mailing Add:* Dept of Elec Eng Naval Postgrad Sch Monterey CA 93940

SACKMAN, JEROME L(EO), b Rockaway Beach, NY, June 16, 29; m 51; c 2. ENGINEERING. *Educ:* Cooper Union, BCE, 51; Columbia Univ, MS, 55, ScD, 59. *Prof Exp:* Civil engr, Eng Res & Develop Labs, US Dept Army, Ft Belvoir, Va, 51-52; asst thermal inelasticity, Inst Flight Struct, Columbia Univ, 56-57, from instr to asst prof appl mech, 57-60; from asst prof to assoc prof, 60-66, PROF CIVIL ENG, UNIV CALIF, BERKELEY, 66-, VCHMN DIV STRUCT ENG & STRUCT MECH, 67- *Concurrent Pos:* Sci consult, Paul Weidlinger, Consult eng, NY, 59-; Math Sci, Wash, 67-; Lockheed Propulsion Co, Calif, 67- & Physics Int Co, 70-; mem at large, US Nat Comt Theoret & Appl Mech, 75-78. *Mem:* AAAS; Am Soc Civil Engrs; Am Soc Mech Engrs; Soc Eng Sci; Soc Exp Stress Anal. *Res:* Mechanics of solids; stress and stability analysis of deformable solids; wave propagation in deformable solids. *Mailing Add:* Dept of Civil Eng Univ of Calif Berkeley CA 94720

SACKMANN, I JULIANA, b Schoenau, EGer, Feb 8, 42; Can citizen; m 73; c 2. ASTROPHYSICS. *Educ:* Univ Toronto, BA, 63, MA, 65, PhD(astrophys), 68. *Prof Exp:* Nat Res Coun Can fel astrophys, Univ Observ, Gottingen, WGer, 68-71; Alexander von Humboldt fel, Max Planck Inst Physics & Astrophys, Munich, WGer, 69-71; res fel, Calif Inst Technol, 71-74; res assoc, Jet Propulsion Lab & vis assoc, Calif Inst Technol, 74-76, SR RES FEL ASTROPHYS, CALIF INST TECHNOL, 76- *Mem:* Am Astron Soc; Can Astron Soc. *Res:* Violent helium shell flashes in stars and their consequences on new element nucleosynthesis explaining carbon stars; new convective breakthroughs in the interior; observable surface variabilities on short timescales; FG Sagittae. *Mailing Add:* Kellogg Radiation Lab 106-38 Calif Inst of Technol Pasadena CA 91125

SACKNER, MARVIN ARTHUR, b Philadelphia, Pa, Feb 16, 32; m 56; c 3. PULMONARY PHYSIOLOGY. *Educ:* Temple Univ, BS, 63; Jefferson Med Col, MD, 57; Am Bd Internal Med, dipl, 65; Am Bd Pulmonary Dis, dipl, 69. *Prof Exp:* Intern med, Philadelphia Gen Hosp, 57-58, resident, 58-61; Am Col Physicians res fel physiol, Grad Sch Med, Univ Pa, 61-64, instr, 63-64; chief div pulmonary dis, 64-78, DIR MED SERV, MT SINAI MED CTR, 74-; PROF MED, UNIV MIAMI, 73- *Concurrent Pos:* Pa Heart Asn fel cardiol, 58-59; Am Col Physicians Brower traveling fel, 66; mem pulmonary dis adv comt, Nat Heart & Lung Inst; mem, Am Bd Pulmonary Dis, 74; mem, Am Bd Internal Med, chmn, Subspecialty Bd Pulmonary Dis, 78-79. *Mem:* Am Fedn Clin Res; fel Am Col Physicians; Am Thoracic Soc (pres, 80-81); Am Physiol Soc. *Res:* Pulmonary circulation; mucociliary clearance; mechanics of breathing, non-invasive respiratory monition. *Mailing Add:* Mt Sinai Med Ctr 4300 Alton Rd Miami Beach FL 33140

SACKOFF, MARTIN M, organic polymer chemistry, see previous edition

SACKS, ALVIN HOWARD, b San Mateo, Calif, May 18, 22; m 49; c 4. MECHANICS, BIOENGINEERING. *Educ:* Univ Wash, BS, 44; Cornell Univ, MAeroE, 49; Stanford Univ, PhD(eng), 57. *Prof Exp:* Aeronaut res scientist, Ames Lab, Nat Adv Comt Aeronaut, 44-57; chief aerophys dept, Adv Res Div, Hiller Aircraft Corp, 57-59; head hemodyn sect, Vidya Div, Itek Corp, 59-66; res assoc, Palo Alto Med Res Found, 66-78; RES ASSOC, INST MED RES, VALLEY MED CTR, 78- *Concurrent Pos:* Mem bd dir, Instranetics, 71-73. *Mem:* Biomed Eng Soc; Microcirculatory Soc; fel Am Col Angiol; Int Soc Biorheol. *Res:* Hemorheology; microcirculation; cardiovascular mechanics. *Mailing Add:* Inst for Med Res 751 S Bascom Ave Bldg H-8 San Jose CA 95128

SACKS, CLIFFORD EUGENE, b Carlisle, Pa, Oct 18, 53; m 77; c 1. ORGANIC CHEMISTRY. *Educ:* Purdue Univ, BS, 75; Calif Inst Technol, PhD(chem), 80. *Prof Exp:* RES CHEMIST PROCESS RES & DEVELOP, UPJOHN CO, 79- *Mem:* Am Chem Soc. *Res:* Process research and development including steroids, heterocycles and insecticidal agents. *Mailing Add:* Upjohn Co 1500-91-1 Kalamazoo MI 49002

SACKS, GERALD ENOCH, b Brooklyn, NY, Mar 22, 33; m 55; c 2. MATHEMATICS. *Educ:* Cornell Univ, BEE & MEE, 58, PhD(math), 61; Harvard Univ, MA, 73. *Prof Exp:* NSF fel math, Inst Advan Study, 61-62; from asst prof to assoc prof, Cornell Univ, 62-67; PROF MATH, MASS INST TECHNOL, 67-; PROF MATH, HARVARD UNIV, 72- *Concurrent Pos:* Guggenheim fel, 66-67. *Mem:* Am Math Soc; Asn Symbolic Logic. *Res:* Mathematical logic; recursive function theory; set theory. *Mailing Add:* Dept Math Room 2-274 Sci Ctr Harvard Univ 1 Oxford St Cambridge MA 02138

SACKS, I SELWYN, b Johannesburg, SAfrica, Mar 20, 34; m 62; c 1. GEOPHYSICS. *Educ:* Univ Witwatersrand, BSc, 54, PhD(geophys), 62. *Prof Exp:* Staff mem seismol & geophys, Bernard Price Inst Geophys Res, Univ Witwatersrand, 55-62; fel seismol, 62-63, STAFF MEM, CARNEGIE INST WASH DEPT TERRESTRIAL MAGNETISM, 64- *Mem:* Am Geophys Union. *Res:* Seismology; attenuation of seismic waves in various regions of the earth; deep structure of continents and oceans; heterogeneity of the lower mantle; strain and earthquakes. *Mailing Add:* Dept of Terrestrial Magnetism Inst of Washington 5241 Broad Branch Rd NW Chevy Chase MD 20015

SACKS, JEROME, b New York, NY, May 8, 31. MATHEMATICS. *Educ:* Cornell Univ, BA, 52, PhD, 56. *Prof Exp:* Instr math, Calif Inst Technol, 56-57; asst prof math statist, Columbia Univ, 57-60; asst prof math, Cornell Univ, 60-61; prof statist, Rutgers Univ, 79-81; assoc prof, 61-66, PROF MATH, NORTHWESTERN UNIV, 66- *Mem:* Am Statist Asn; Inst Math Statist. *Res:* Statistics; calibration; regression analysis; time series; robustness. *Mailing Add:* Dept of Math Northwestern Univ Evanston IL 60201

SACKS, JONATHAN, b Worcester, S Africa, Oct 26, 43; m 69; c 1. GEOMETRY, TOPOLOGY. *Educ:* Univ Cape Town, BSc, 68, MSc, 70; Univ Calif, Berkeley, PhD(math), 75. *Prof Exp:* Vis lectr math, Univ Ill Urbana-Champaign, 75-77; LECTR MATH, UNIV CHICAGO, 77- *Mem:* Am Math Soc. *Res:* Eigenvalues of the Laplacian on Riemannian manifolds; application of the study of the topology of function spaces to variational problems in Riemannian geometry. *Mailing Add:* Dept Math Univ Chicago Chicago IL 60637

SACKS, LAWRENCE EDGAR, b Los Angeles, Calif, Mar 9, 20; m 63; c 2. MICROBIOLOGY. *Educ:* Univ Calif, Los Angeles, AB, 41; Univ Wash, MS, 43; Univ Calif, PhD(microbiol), 48. *Prof Exp:* Asst bacteriologist, Comt Lignin & Cellulose Res, 43-44; bacteriologist, 48-62, prin chemist, 62-72, MICROBIOLOGIST, WESTERN REGIONAL RES CTR, SCI & EDUC ADMIN-AGR RES, USDA, 72- *Mem:* AAAS; Am Soc Microbiol; Am Chem Soc. *Res:* Action of antiobiotics and surface active agents on bacteria; bacterial denitrification; Arthrobacter; spores; Clostridium perfringens; mutagen screening. *Mailing Add:* USDA Western Reg Res Ctr 800 Buchanan St Albany CA 94710

SACKS, LAWRENCE J, b Newark, NJ, June 12, 28; m 55; c 3. INORGANIC CHEMISTRY. *Educ:* Drew Univ, AB, 52; Pa State Univ, MS, 58; Univ Ill, PhD(inorg chem), 64. *Prof Exp:* Instr chem, Pa State, 53-55; res chemist, Monsanto Chem Co, 55-56; asst prof chem, Reed Col, 60-63 & Rose Polytech, 64-65; assoc prof, State Univ NY Col Buffalo, 65-68; prof, Hampton Inst, 68-70; PROF CHEM, CHRISTOPHER NEWPORT COL, 70- *Mem:* AAAS; Am Chem Soc. *Res:* Atmospheric chemistry of trace gases; thermal methods for polymer characterization; theoretical calculations of bond energies, dipole movements and steric effects. *Mailing Add:* Dept Chem Christopher Newport Col Newport News VA 23606

SACKS, MARTIN, b Brooklyn, NY, Aug 30, 24; m 50; c 2. INVERTEBRATE ZOOLOGY. *Educ:* City Col New York, BS, 49; Univ Ill, MS, 50, PhD, 53. *Prof Exp:* Lectr, 53-59, from instr to assoc prof, 59-69, head dept, 69-72, PROF BIOL, CITY COL NEW YORK, 69- *Mem:* AAAS; Am Soc Zoologists; Soc Syst Zool; Am Micros Soc. *Res:* Taxonomy, ecology and embryology of marine and aquatic gastrotricha. *Mailing Add:* Dept of Biol City Col of New York New York NY 10031

SACKS, MARTIN EDWARD, b Bronx, NY, Nov 22, 43; m 67; c 1. CHEMICAL ENGINEERING, COAL SCIENCE. *Educ:* Cooper Union, BChE, 65; Univ Mich, MSE, 66; Stevens Inst Technol, PhD(chem eng), 72. *Prof Exp:* Res engr coal conversion, FMC Corp, 66-70; sr res engr, Cogas Develop Co, 72-78, process design supvr coal gasification, 78-80, eng mgr, 80-81; PRIN PROCESS ENGR, FMC CORP, 81- *Mem:* Am Inst Chem Engrs; Am Chem Soc. *Res:* Coal conversion, especially pyrolysis and gasification. *Mailing Add:* FMC Corp PO Box 8 Princeton NJ 08540

SACKS, WILLIAM, b Toronto, Ont, Jan 30, 26; m 52; c 4. POLYMER CHEMISTRY, POLYMER ENGINEERING. *Educ:* Univ Toronto, BASc, 48, MASc, 49; McGill Univ, PhD(chem), 54. *Prof Exp:* Res officer, Nat Res Coun Can, Ottawa, 49-52, fel, McGill Univ, 52-54; res engr & res sect mgr, Visking Div, Union Carbide Corp, 54-61, group leader, Plastics Div, 61-65; res assoc & res mgr, Gen Chem & Fabricated Prod Div, 66-73, tech dir, Films Dept, 73-79, DIR, ALLIED FIBERS & PLASTICS CO, ALLIED CHEM CORP, 79- *Mem:* Am Chem Soc; Chem Inst Can. *Res:* Physical chemistry of polymers; properties and applications of polymer films; processing behavior of synthetic polymers. *Mailing Add:* 686 Long Hill Rd Gillette NJ 07933

SACKS, WILLIAM, b Philadelphia, Pa, Feb 17, 24; m 54; c 3. BIOCHEMISTRY. *Educ:* Pa State Univ, BS, 47, MS, 48, PhD, 51. *Prof Exp:* Dir chem lab, Southern Div, Einstein Med Ctr, Philadelphia, 51-54, res investr, 54-58; PRIN RES SCIENTIST, ROCKLAND RES INST, 58- *Concurrent Pos:* Res assoc prof psychiat, Sch Med, NY Univ, 79- *Mem:* AAAS; Am Chem Soc; Soc Biol Psychiat; Soc Neurosci; Int Soc Neurochem. *Res:* Cerebral metabolism in vivo in mental disease. *Mailing Add:* Rockland Res Inst Orangeburg NY 10962

SACKSTEDER, RICHARD CARL, b Muncie, Ind, Feb 11, 28; m 52; c 2. MATHEMATICS. *Educ:* Univ Chicago, BS, 48, PhB, 46; Johns Hopkins Univ, PhD, 60. *Prof Exp:* Res mathematician, Ballistics Res Lab, US Dept Army, Aberdeen Proving Ground, Md, 54-59; vis mem, Inst Math Sci, NY Univ, 60-62; asst prof math, Barnard Col & Columbia Univ, 62-65; assoc prof, 65-67, PROF MATH, CITY UNIV NEW YORK, 67- *Concurrent Pos:* Jr instr, Johns Hopkins Univ, 57-59; lectr, Goucher Col, 58. *Mem:* Am Math Soc. *Res:* Differential geometry; analysis in the large; fluid dynamics. *Mailing Add:* Dept of Math City Univ of New York Grad Ctr New York NY 10036

SACKSTON, WALDEMAR ESI, b Manitoba, Jan 4, 18; m 41; c 2. PLANT PATHOLOGY. *Educ:* Univ Manitoba, BSA, 38; McGill Univ, MSc, 40; Univ Minn, PhD(plant path), 49. *Prof Exp:* Asst, Macdonald Col, McGill Univ, 38-40; agr asst, Dom Lab Plant Path, Can Dept Agr, 41-46; from asst plant pathologist to plant pathologist, 46-58, sr plant pathologist & head plant path sect, 58-60; chmn dept plant path, 60-69, PROF PLANT PATH, MACDONALD COL, McGILL UNIV, 60- *Concurrent Pos:* Specialist & consult, Point IV prog, Chile, 54 & Uruguay, 56-57; on leave from McGill Univ to set up res ctr on oilseed crops, Cordoba, Spain, 72-77. *Mem:* AAAS; Am Phytopath Soc; Indian Phytopath Soc; Int Sunflower Asn (pres, 78-80); Can Phytopath Soc (vpres, 58-60, pres, 60-61). *Res:* Diseases of oilseed crops; soilborne and seedborne diseases; epidemiology. *Mailing Add:* Dept of Plant Sci Macdonald Col McGill Univ Ste Anne de Bellevue PQ H0A 1C0 Can

SACKTOR, BERTRAM, b New York, NY, May 11, 22; m 42; c 2. BIOCHEMISTRY, PHYSIOLOGY. *Educ:* Cornell Univ, BS, 43; Rutgers Univ, MS, 47, PhD(biol), 49. *Prof Exp:* Supvry biochemist & chief, Exp Zool Br, Med Res Lab, Edgewood Arsenal, 49-67; CHIEF, LAB MOLECULAR AGING & SECT ON INTERMEDIARY METAB, GERONT RES CTR, NAT INST AGING, NIH, 67- *Concurrent Pos:* NSF travel awards, Int Cong Biochem, Vienna, 58, Moscow, 61 & Tokyo, 67; lectr, Sch Med, Univ Md, 62-64; res assoc path, Sch Hyg & Pub Health, Johns Hopkins Univ, 64-69; vis prof, Mayo Clin, 78. *Mem:* Fel AAAS; Am Soc Physiol; Am Soc Biol Chem; Am Soc Cell Biol; fel Geront Soc. *Res:* Membrane transport mechanisms; hormone action and cyclic nucleotide metabolism; regulation of intermediary metabolism. *Mailing Add:* 6502 Old Pimlico Rd Baltimore MD 21209

SADAGOPAN, VARADACHARI, b Uppiliappan Koil, Madras, India; US citizen; m 62. MATERIALS SCIENCE. *Educ:* Univ Madras, BSc, 53; Annamalai Univ, Madras, MA, 55; Indian Inst Sci, DIISc, 58; Mass Inst Technol, SM, 60, MetE, 61, ScD(metall), 64. *Prof Exp:* Asst econ affairs off, Hq, UN, 62, spec asst to secy-gen & chief liaison off for dels from Asia & Far East, UN Europ Off, Geneva, Switz, 62-63; res assoc mat sci, Mass Inst Technol, 64-67; prin res scientist, Avco Corp, Mass, 67-68; res staff mem phys sci, T J Watson Res Ctr, 68-72, mgr univ relations, 72-76, mgr, tech relations, Off Res & Develop Coord, IBM Europe, 76-79, MGR TECH RELATIONS, IBM RES DIV, IBM CORP, 79- *Concurrent Pos:* Consult, Asian Bank, Manila, 71- *Mem:* Am Phys Soc; Inst Elec & Electronics Engrs. *Res:* Electronic materials. *Mailing Add:* PO Box 218 Yorktown Heights NY 10598

SADANA, YOGINDER NATH, b Peshawar, India, May 15, 31; m 62; c 2. INORGANIC CHEMISTRY. *Educ:* Univ Agra, BSc, 51, MSc, 53; Univ BC, PhD(chem), 63. *Prof Exp:* Sr res fel electrodeposition of metals & alloys, Nat Metall Lab, India, 54-58; res asst, Res Inst Precious Metals & Metall Chem, Ger, 58-59; instr chem, Wash State Univ, 62-63; res engr, Cominco Ltd, Can, 64-66; from asst prof to assoc prof, 66-77, PROF CHEM, LAURENTIAN UNIV, 77- *Concurrent Pos:* Nat Res Coun Can res grants, 66-; fels, Chem Inst Can & Inst Metal Finishing. *Mem:* Am Chem Soc; Chem Inst Can. *Res:* Electrodeposition of metals and alloys; surface finishing techniques; electrodeposition of indium and indium alloys and their x-ray structures. *Mailing Add:* Dept of Chem Laurentian Univ Sudbury ON P3E 2C6 Can

SADANAGA, KIYOSHI, b Onomea, Hawaii, Feb 6, 20; m 66; c 2. GENETICS. *Educ:* Univ Hawaii, BS, 42; Iowa State Univ, MS, 51, PhD(genetics), 55. *Prof Exp:* Asst genetics, Sugar Cane Exp Sta, Hawaii Sugar Planters Asn, 52-53; geneticist, Oat Proj, 56-76, GENETICIST SOYBEAN RES, USDA, 76-; PROF GENETICS, IOWA STATE UNIV, 59- *Concurrent Pos:* Fulbright scholar, Kyoto Univ, 60-61. *Res:* Genetics and cytogenetics of soybeans. *Mailing Add:* Dept of Genetics Iowa State Univ Ames IA 50010

SADAVA, DAVID ERIC, b Ottawa, Ont, Mar 14, 46; m 72. CELL BIOLOGY. *Educ:* Carleton Univ, BSc, 67; Univ Calif, San Diego, PhD(cell biol), 71. *Prof Exp:* Researcher entomol, Can Dept Agr, 65-66; adv sci policy, Sci Secretariat, Can, 67; teaching asst biol, Univ Calif, San Diego, 67-71; researcher marine biol, Scripps Inst Oceanog, 72; asst prof, 72-77, ASSOC PROF BIOL, CLAREMONT COLS, 77-, CHMN JOINT SCI DEPT, 80- *Concurrent Pos:* Woodrow Wilson Found fel, 67. *Res:* Biochemical genetics of thoroughbred horses; isozymes in human development; plant developmental biochemistry. *Mailing Add:* Joint Dept of Sci Claremont Cols Claremont CA 91711

SADEE, WOLFGANG, b Bad Harzburg, WGer, Mar 25, 42; m 74. DRUG METABOLISM, ANALYTICAL BIOCHEMISTRY. *Educ:* Free Univ Berlin, Dr rer nat, 68. *Prof Exp:* NATO fel, Univ Calif, San Francisco, 69; res assoc fel clin pharmacol, Free Univ Berlin, 70-71; asst prof pharm & med, Univ Southern Calif, 71-74; asst prof, 74-75, assoc prof, 76-81, PROF PHARM & PHARMACEUT CHEM, UNIV CALIF, SAN FRANCISCO, 81- *Mem:* Am Chem Soc; AAAS. *Res:* Opiates, pyrimidine and purine antimetabolites. *Mailing Add:* Sch of Pharm Univ of Calif San Francisco CA 94143

SADEH, WILLY ZEEV, b Galatz, Romania, Oct 13, 32; nat US; m 56; c 2. ENGINEERING. *Educ:* Israel Inst Technol, BSc, 58, MSc, 64; Brown Univ, PhD(eng), 68. *Prof Exp:* Res engr, Gen Aero M Dassault, Paris, 58-59, Nat Sci Res Ctr, 59-60 Desalination Plants, Israel, 60-62 & Negev Inst Arid Zone Res, 62; instr mech eng, Israel Inst Technol, 62-64; fel eng, Brown Univ, 64-65, res asst, 65-68; from asst prof to assoc prof, 68-76, PROF CIVIL ENG, COLO STATE UNIV, 76- *Honors & Awards:* Cert appreciation, Technol Utilization Prog, NASA, 71. *Mem:* AAAS; Am Soc Mech Engrs; AAUP; assoc fel Am Inst Aeronaut & Astronaut; Am Soc Eng Educ. *Res:* Fluid mechanics; turbulent flow; instrumentation; structural aerodynamics; atmospheric turbulence; air pollution; turbomachinery; boundary-layer flow. *Mailing Add:* Dept of Civil Eng Colo State Univ Ft Collins CA 80523

SADEK, SALAH ELDINE, b Cairo, Egypt, June 9, 20; m 52; c 3. PATHOLOGY, TOXICOLOGY. *Educ:* Univ Cairo, DVM, 45; Univ Edinburgh, MRCVS, 48; Mich State Univ, MS, 50; Univ Ill, PhD(path), 56; Am Bd Indust Hyg, dipl. *Prof Exp:* Asst prof surg, Univ Cairo, 45-49; res asst path, Univ Ill, 53-55; res pathologist, Dow Chem Co, Mich, 56-67; HEAD PATH, EXP PATH & TOXICOL, HOFFMANN-LA ROCHE, INC, NUTLEY, NJ, 67- *Concurrent Pos:* Clin asst prof, NJ Col Med, 70- *Mem:* Am Vet Med Asn; Soc Toxicol; NY Acad Sci; Am Acad Indust Hyg; Royal Col Vet Surg. *Res:* Pathology and toxicology of chemical and environmental agents. *Mailing Add:* Hoffmann-La Roche Inc 340 Kingsland St Nutley NJ 07110

SADEK, SHAFIK EDWARD, chemical engineering, see previous edition

SADIK, FARID, b Taibeh, Palestine, July 3, 34; US citizen; m 59; c 4. PHARMACEUTICS. *Educ:* Univ Ga, BSPharm, 58; Univ Miss, PhD(pharmaceut), 68. *Prof Exp:* Pharmacist, Kupat Holim, 58-65; instr pharmaceut, Univ Miss, 65-68, asst prof, 68; asst prof, Northeast La Univ, 68-71; assoc prof, Univ Miss, 71-73; assoc prof, 73-76, PROF PHARMACEUT & ASSOC DEAN COL PHARM, UNIV SC, 76- *Mem:* Am Pharmaceut Asn. *Res:* Clinical pharmacy; effect of particle size of drugs on absorption. *Mailing Add:* Col of Pharm Univ of SC Columbia SC 29208

SADIK, SIDKI, b Taibeh, Palestine, June 4, 30; m 55; c 4. PLANT PHYSIOLOGY. *Educ:* Univ Ga, BS, 53; Univ Fla, MS, 55; Univ Calif, Davis, PhD(plant physiol), 62. *Prof Exp:* Teacher, Ministry of Educ, 50-52, asst develop officer, Ministry Agr, 55-57; res asst veg crops, Univ Calif, Davis, 57-62; res specialist, Cornell Univ, 62-65; res assoc, 65-69; plant physiologist, Int Inst Trop Agr, 69-78; HEAD DEPT PHYSIOL, INT POTATO CTR, 78- *Honors & Awards:* Asgrow Seed Co Award, 67. *Mem:* Am Soc Plant Physiol; Scand Plant Physiol Soc; Asn Advan Agr Sci in Africa; Int Root Crop Soc. *Res:* Physiology of root and tuber crops; developmental anatomy; growth and differentiation; physiological studies for the purpose of improvement of tropical root crops. *Mailing Add:* Int Potato Ctr PO Box 5969 Lima Peru

SADLEIR, RICHARD MICHAEL FRANCIS STUART, physiological ecology, see previous edition

SADLER, ARTHUR GRAHAM, b Pontefract, Eng, Oct 20, 25; Can citizen; m 57; c 4. CHEMISTRY, CERAMICS. *Educ:* Univ Leeds, BSc, 51, PhD(ceramics), 56. *Prof Exp:* Mem, Electronic Ceramics, Dept Mines & Tech Surv, Govt Can, 57-59, sr sci staff, 59-62; mem sci staff ferrites, Northern Elec Co Ltd, Ont, 62-63, dept chief magnetic mat, 63-67, mgr phys sci, 67-69; mgr electronic mat & processes, 69-72, MGR STA APPARATUS BR LAB, BELL-NORTHERN RES LTD, 72- *Mem:* Can Ceramic Soc (pres, 69-70); fel Brit Inst Ceramics; fel Chem Inst Can. *Res:* Chemistry of high temperature reactions in inorganic materials; chemistry and physics of electronic ceramics; research management. *Mailing Add:* 3 Greencrest Place Nepean ON K2E 7E9 Can

SADLER, CLARENCE REAGAN, b Hickory, Miss, Sept 18, 36; m 59; c 2. PHYSIOLOGY, PARASITOLOGY. *Educ:* Miss State Univ, BS, 59, MS, 60; Auburn Univ, PhD(poultry path), 65. *Prof Exp:* Asst prof zool, Miss State Univ, 64-67; POULTRY PATHOLOGIST, CENT LAB, 67- *Concurrent Pos:* Consult poultry dis & mgr problems. *Mem:* AAAS; Poultry Sci Asn; World Poultry Sci Asn; Am Asn Avian Path; Am Inst Biol Sci. *Res:* Mechanisms of disease resistance in chickens and quail; immunology studies in quail and chickens; stress in birds; coccidia-species identification and drug evaluation. *Mailing Add:* Cent Lab PO Box 357 Forest MS 39074

SADLER, G(ERALD) W(ESLEY), b Kindersley, Sask, Sept 19, 25; m 55. MECHANICAL ENGINEERING. *Educ:* Univ Sask, BSc, 47; Univ Ill, MS, 51. *Prof Exp:* Lectr & engr for supt bldgs off, 47-50, lectr thermodyn, 51-52, asst prof, 52-55, supt bldgs, 55-59, assoc prof, 60-77, PROF MECH ENG, UNIV ALTA, 77- *Mem:* Am Soc Heating, Refrig & Air-Conditioning Engrs; Eng Inst Can; Can Soc Mech Engrs; Solar Energy Soc. *Res:* Thermodynamic principles in relation to mechanical engineering; heat transfer, power production and fluid flow; heating, air conditioning and solar energy. *Mailing Add:* 11403 48th Ave Edmonton AB T6G 2G8 Can

SADLER, JAMES C, b Silver Point, Tenn, Feb 9, 20; m 41; c 2. METEOROLOGY. *Educ:* Tenn Polytech Inst, BS, 41; Univ Calif, Los Angeles, MA, 47. *Prof Exp:* Mil dir, Sacramento Peak Observ, US Air Force, 51-53, res meteorologist, Air Force Sch Aviation Med, 53-55, dir trop meteorol course, Air Weather Serv, Univ Hawaii, 55-59, chief satellite meteorol br, Air Force Cambridge Res Labs, 59-62, chief satellite utilization, Int Indian Ocean Exped, 62-65; assoc prof, 65-81, PROF METEOROL, UNIV HAWAII, 81- *Concurrent Pos:* Consult, US Air Force, 67- & US Navy, 68- *Mem:* AAAS; Am Meteorol Soc; Am Geophys Union. *Res:* Kinematic description of the general circulation of the tropics and its relation to satellite determined cloud climatology and life history of tropical cyclones. *Mailing Add:* Dept of Meteorol Univ of Hawaii Honolulu HI 96822

SADLER, JOHN, b Edgemont, SDak, Jan 13, 34; m 61; c 4. BIOCHEMISTRY, MOLECULAR BIOLOGY. *Educ:* Reed Col, BA, 56; Oxford Univ, Hons Chem, 59, PhD(biochem), 61. *Prof Exp:* Res assoc molecular genetics, Inst Molecular Biol, Univ Ore, 61-64; asst prof, 64-71, assoc prof, 71-81, PROF BIOPHYS, UNIV COLO, DENVER, 81- *Concurrent Pos:* USPHS career develop awards, 65-75. *Mem:* Biophys Soc; Genetics Soc Am. *Res:* Processes regulating specific enzyme synthesis in cells; molecular mechanisms of genetic recombination; protein-nucleic acid interactions. *Mailing Add:* Dept of Biochem Biophys Univ of Colo Med Ctr Denver CO 80262

SADLER, MONROE SCHARFF, b Natchez, Miss, Oct 2, 20; m 43; c 2. PHYSICAL CHEMISTRY. *Educ:* Mass Inst Technol, SB, 42; Carnegie Inst Technol, MS, 48, DSc(chem), 49. *Prof Exp:* Res chemist, E I Du Pont De Nemours & Co, Inc, 49-53, res supvr, 53-59, lab dir, 59-63, dir mat res, 63-66, asst dir res & develop, 66-68, asst dir, Develop Dept, 68-70, dir develop dept, 70-75, asst dir, Cent Res & Develop Dept, 75-80; MEM STAFF, HERSHEY'S MILL, 80- *Mem:* Am Chem Soc; Am Phys Soc. *Res:* Physics of high pressure; ultrasonics; nuclear magnetic resonance; ferromagnetic materials. *Mailing Add:* Hershey's Mill 228 Chatham Way West Chester PA 19380

SADLER, STANLEY GENE, b Spring Lake, Utah, Mar 6, 38; m 63; c 5. MECHANICAL & AEROSPACE SCIENCES. *Educ:* Univ Utah, BS, 62; Univ Rochester, MS, 64, PhD(mech & aerospace sci), 68. *Prof Exp:* Lab asst, High Velocity Impact Lab, Univ Utah, 62-63; res engr, Rochester Appl Sci Assocs, 67-71, group head aerodyn & hydrodyn res, 71-72; sr proj engr, Homelite Textron, 72-78; dynamic staff specialist, Bell Helicopter Textron, 78-80, group engr aeromechanics, 80-81. *Mem:* Am Soc Mech Engrs; Am Helicopter Soc; Sigma Xi; Am Inst Aeronaut & Astronaut. *Res:* Statics and dynamics of elastic systems; fluid dynamics and stability; helicopter rotor dynamics and noise; shell analysis; rotating system vibration and stability. *Mailing Add:* 1002 Curtis Ct Arlington TX 76012

SADLER, THOMAS WILLIAM, b Portsmouth, Ohio, Feb 25, 49; m 76; c 1. TERATOLOGY, DEVELOPMENTAL BIOLOGY. *Educ:* Wake Forest Univ, BS, 71; Univ Va, PhD(anat), 76. *Prof Exp:* Asst prof anat, Univ Va, 76-79; assoc prof anat, Col Med, Univ Cincinnati, 79-82; ASSOC PROF ANAT, SCH MED, UNIV NC, 82- *Concurrent Pos:* Vis prof, Downing Col, Cambridge Univ, Eng, 76. *Mem:* Teratol Soc; Am Asn Anatomists; AAAS. *Res:* Investigation of normal and abnormal events during embryogenesis; development of techniques for maintaining mammalian embryos in culture during organogenesis. *Mailing Add:* Dept Anat Sch Med Univ NC Med Res Bldg D 331H Chapel Hill NC 27514

SADLER, WILLIAM OTHO, b Chunky, Miss, July 23, 03. LIMNOLOGY. *Educ:* Miss Col, BA, 29, LittD, 69; Cornell Univ, PhD(limnol), 32. *Prof Exp:* Asst prof zool, Miss Col, 29-30; investr, US Bur Fisheries, 30-32; prof zool, 32-72, EMER PROF ZOOL, MISS COL, 72-; CHMN DEPT BIOL SCI, 61- *Mem:* AAAS; Am Fisheries Soc. *Res:* Aquiculture; limnology; vertebrate taxonomy. *Mailing Add:* 213 McRee Dr Clinton MS 39056

SADOCK, BENJAMIN, b New York, NY, Dec 22, 33; m 63; c 2. MEDICINE, PSYCHIATRY. *Educ:* Union Col, NY, AB, 55; New York Med Col, MD, 59; Am Bd Psychiat, dipl, 66. *Prof Exp:* Instr psychiat, Univ Tex Southwestern Med Sch Dallas, 64-65; from instr to assoc prof psychiat, NY Med Col, 65-75, prof, 75-80, co-dir, Sexual Ther Ctr, 72-80, dir continuing educ psychiat, 75-80; PROF PSYCHIAT & DIR STUDENT HEALTH PSYCHIAT, NY UNIV, 80- *Concurrent Pos:* Consult, Wichita Falls State Hosp, Tex, 64-65; chief psychiat consult, Student Health Serv, New York Med Col, 66-; dir div group process, 68-; assoc examr, Am Bd Psychiat, 67-; clin asst prof, Sch Med, NY Univ, 69-73. *Mem:* Am Psychiat Asn; Am Pub Health Asn; Am Orthopsychiat Asn; NY Acad Med; fel Am Col Physicians. *Mailing Add:* 4 E 89th St New York NY 10021

SADOCK, VIRGINIA A, b Bulgaria, Nov 25, 38; US citizen; m 63; c 2. PSYCHIATRY. *Educ:* Bennington Col, AB, 60; New York Med Col, MD, 70. *Prof Exp:* Clin instr psychiat, New York Med Col, 74-80; ASSOC CLIN PROF PSYCHIAT, NEW YORK UNIV MED CTR, 80- *Concurrent Pos:* Dir postgrad prog human sexuality, Dept Psychiat, New York Univ Med Ctr, 80. *Mem:* AMA; Am Psychiat Asn; Am Med Womens Asn; Am Asn Sex Educrs & Counrs. *Mailing Add:* 4 E 89th St New York NY 10028

SADOFF, HAROLD LLOYD, b Minneapolis, Minn, Sept 17, 24; m 46; c 4. MICROBIOLOGY, BIOCHEMISTRY. *Educ:* Univ Minn, BChEng, 47; Univ Ill, MS, 52, PhD(microbiol, biochem), 55. *Prof Exp:* Res assoc chem eng, Univ Ill, 54-55; from asst prof to assoc prof, 55-65, PROF MICROBIOL, MICH STATE UNIV, 65-, PROF PUB HEALTH, 77- *Concurrent Pos:* USPHS fel, Univ Wash, 61-62 & Stanford Univ, 70-71; mem microbiol chem study sect, NIH, 71-73. *Mem:* AAAS; Am Soc Microbiol; Am Soc Biol Chemists; NY Acad Sci; Soc Appl Bact. *Res:* The biochemistry and molecular biology of cell differentiation of microorganisms. *Mailing Add:* Dept Microbiol & Pub Health Mich State Univ East Lansing MI 48824

SADOSKY, THOMAS LEE, b Ft Thomas, Ky, Sept 23, 39; m 64; c 1. INDUSTRIAL ENGINEERING, HUMAN FACTORS. *Educ:* Univ Ohio, BS, 62, MS, 64; Univ Mich, PhD(indust eng), 68. *Prof Exp:* Actg instr eng graphics, Univ Ohio, 62-64; instr, Univ Mich, 64-65; assoc prof indust eng, Ga Inst Technol, 68-80. *Res:* Human performance; operations research. *Mailing Add:* 2793 Atwood Rd NE Atlanta GA 30305

SADOWAY, DONALD ROBERT, b Toronto, Can, Mar 7, 50; m 73; c 2. MOLTEN SALT CHEMISTRY. *Educ:* Univ Toronto, BASc, 72, MASc, 73, PhD(chem metall), 77. *Prof Exp:* NATO fel, 77-78; asst prof, 78-82, ASSOC PROF MAT ENG, MASS INST TECHNOL, 82- *Mem:* Am Inst Metall Engrs; Electrochem Soc; Can Inst Mining & Metall; Int Soc Electrochem. *Res:* Engineering science and electroprocessing of metals in molten salts. *Mailing Add:* 77 Mass Ave Rm 8-109 Cambridge MA 02139

SADOWSKI, ANTHONY JAMES, applied chemistry, see previous edition

SADOWSKI, CHESTER M, b Toronto, Ont, Aug 10, 36; m 79; c 2. PHYSICAL CHEMISTRY. *Educ:* Univ Toronto, BA, 57, PhD(chem kinetics), 61. *Prof Exp:* Res asst high temperature chem kinetics, Cornell Univ, 61-62; defence serv sci officer, Can Armament Res & Develop Estab, 62-67; asst prof natural sci, 67-70, ASSOC PROF CHEM, YORK UNIV, 70- *Concurrent Pos:* Guest worker, Nat Oceanic & Atmospheric Admin, 73-74; sabbaticant, Univ Cambridge, UK, 81-82. *Res:* Laser assisted kinetic studies of free radical reactions. *Mailing Add:* Dept Chem York Univ 4700 Keele St Downsview ON M3J 1P3 Can

SADOWSKI, EDWARD P(ETER), b Bayonne, NJ, July 16, 22; m 49; c 5. METALLURGY. *Educ:* Univ Notre Dame, BS, 50. *Prof Exp:* Staff metallurgist, M W Kellogg Co, Pullman, Inc, 50-53; sr metallurgist, Res Lab, Crucible Steel Co Am, 53-55 & Paul D Merica Res Lab, Int Nickel Co, Inc, 55-78; sr proj eng, 78-79, PRIN METALLURGIST, INCO RES & DEVELOP CTR, 79- *Honors & Awards:* IR 100 Award, 63. *Mem:* Am Soc Metals; Sigma Xi; Am Welding Soc; NY Acad Sci. *Res:* Effects of environment, time and temperature on properties; microstructural changes in high temperature alloys; maraging high strength and stainless steels; hydrospace; nickel base alloys; casting; welding research; materials for coal gasification; underwater welding; platinum metals; welding consumable development; weld overlaying. *Mailing Add:* 57 Walker Dr Ringwood NJ 07456

SADTLER, PHILIP, b Flourtown, Pa, July 19, 09; m 40, 64; c 3. ANALYTICAL CHEMISTRY. *Educ:* Lehigh Univ, BS, 34. *Prof Exp:* Pres, Sadtler Res Labs, Inc, 34-69; PRES, SANDA, INC, 70- *Concurrent Pos:* Consult fluorine damage, infra-red & thermometric titration. *Mem:* Franklin Inst; Am Chem Soc; Am Soc Testing & Mat; Soc Appl Spectros; Am Mgt Asn. *Res:* Molecular studies with infrared spectrophotometry, ultraviolet, nuclear magnetic resonance; analyses, diesel engines; polymers; air pollution; explosion; synthesis of new materials; computerization of analytical instruments; digitization of spectral data. *Mailing Add:* 3555 W School House Lane Philadelphia PA 19144

SADURSKI, EDWARD ALAN, b Detroit, Mich, June 12, 49; m 71. INORGANIC CHEMISTRY, ORGANOMETALLIC CHEMISTRY. *Educ:* Oakland Univ, BS, 71; Wayne State Univ, PhD(inorg chem), 78. *Prof Exp:* Instr chem, Mich Christian Col, 70-72; vis asst prof inorg chem, Miami Univ, 78-82; ASST PROF CHEM, OHIO NORTHERN UNIV, 82- *Mem:* Am Chem Soc. *Res:* Main group organometallics; nuclear magnetic resonance spectroscopy and single crystal X-ray crystallography. *Mailing Add:* Dept of Chem Miami Univ Oxford OH 45056

SAE, ANDY S W, b Hong Kong, China, Jan 5, 41; m; c 1. BIOCHEMISTRY. *Educ:* Kans State Univ, BS, 64, MS, 66, PhD(biochem), 69. *Prof Exp:* Assoc prof, 69-80, PROF CHEM, EASTERN NMEX UNIV, 80-, CHMN DEPT PHYS SCI, 77- *Mem:* Am Chem Soc; NY Acad Sci; Sigma Xi. *Res:* Lipoprotein structures; immobilized-enzyme, enzyme isolation purification; peroxidases. *Mailing Add:* Dept of Phys Sci Eastern NMex Univ Portales NM 88130

SAEGEBARTH, KLAUS ARTHUR, b Berlin, Ger, Jan 5, 29; nat US; m 53; c 3. ORGANIC CHEMISTRY, AGRICULTURAL CHEMISTRY. *Educ:* Univ Calif, BS, 53; Univ Wash, PhD(chem), 57. *Prof Exp:* Chemist, Radiation Lab, Univ Calif, 50; res chemist, Elastomer Chem Dept, 57-65, res & develop supvr, Co, 65-67, res div head, 67-69, lab dir, Fabrics & Finishes Dept, Exp Sta, 69-70, res & develop mgr, Marshall Lab, 71-72, asst nat mgr indust finishes, 72-73, nat mgr trade finishes, 73-74, asst dir, Finishes Div, 74-78, dir res & develop, Fabrics & Finishes Dept, 78-80, DIR, AGRICHEM RES DIV, E I DU PONT DE NEMOURS & CO INC, 80- *Mem:* Am Chem Soc; Sigma Xi. *Res:* Oxidation mechanisms; organometallics; catalysis; elastomers; finishes; agricultural chemicals. *Mailing Add:* 604 Haverhill Rd Wilmington DE 19803

SAEGER, VICTOR WILLIAM, b Kansas City, Mo, May 17, 33; m 62; c 2. ENVIRONMENTAL CHEMISTRY, ANALYTICAL CHEMISTRY. *Educ:* Univ Mo-Kansas City, BA, 53; Iowa State Univ, PhD(phys chem), 60. *Prof Exp:* RES SPECIALIST, MONSANTO CO, ST LOUIS, 60- *Mem:* Am Chem Soc; Am Soc Microbiol. *Res:* Environmental fate testing and assessment. *Mailing Add:* 800 N Lindbergh St Louis MO 63166

SAEKS, RICHARD E, b Chicago, Ill, Nov 30, 41. ELECTRICAL ENGINEERING, APPLIED MATHEMATICS. *Educ:* Northwestern Univ, Evanston, BS, 64; Colo State Univ, MS, 65; Cornell Univ, PhD(elec eng), 67. *Prof Exp:* From asst prof to assoc prof elec eng, Univ Notre Dame, 67-73; assoc prof elec eng & math, 73-77, prof, 77-79, PAUL WHITFIELD PROF ENG, MATH & COMPUT SCI, TEX TECH UNIV, 79- *Concurrent Pos:* NASA fel, Marshall Space Flight Ctr, 69-70; consult, Res Triangle Inst, 78-; ed-at-large, Marcell Dekker Inc, 78-; distinguished fac res award, Tex Tech Univ, 78- *Mem:* Am Soc Eng Educ; fel Inst Elec & Electronics Engrs; Soc Indust & Appl Math; Am Math Soc. *Res:* Fault analysis; large-scale systems; mathematical system theory. *Mailing Add:* Dept Elec Eng Tex Tech Univ Lubbock TX 79409

SAELENS, DAVID ARTHUR, b Camden, NJ, June 10, 43; m 76. AUTONOMIC NERVOUS SYSTEM, DRUG METABOLISM. *Educ:* Albany Col Pharm, BS, 69; Med Univ SC, PhD(pharm), 74. *Prof Exp:* Fel pharm, Med Univ SC, 74-76, instr, 76-77; asst prof pharm, Univ Houston, 77-78; ASST PROF PHARM, EASTERN VA MED SCH, 78- *Concurrent Pos:* Adj asst prof, Old Dominion Univ, 78- *Res:* Factors important in the local control of neurotransmitter release, specifically the role of presynaptic receptors and calcium metabolism, in normal and diseased states and the impact of drug therapy. *Mailing Add:* Dept Pharm Eastern VA Med Sch PO Box 1980 Norfolk VA 23501

SAELENS, JEFFREY K, pharmacology, see previous edition

SAEMAN, W(ALTER) C(ARL), b Norlina, NC, Apr 15, 14; m 40; c 1. CHEMICAL ENGINEERING. *Educ:* Ga Inst Technol, BS, 40. *Prof Exp:* From jr to assoc chem engr, Chem Eng Div, Wilson Dam, Tenn Valley Authority, 40-46, proj leader, 47-52; sr chem engr, Oak Ridge Nat Lab, 46-47; engr, Olin Industs, Inc, 52-58, mgr res dept, Olin Matheison Chem Corp, New Haven, 58-70, asst res dir, 70-77; prin engr, Olin Corp, 77-81; RETIRED. *Mem:* Am Chem Soc; Am Inst Chem Eng; NY Acad Sci. *Res:* Drying; crystallization; ammonium nitrate; process control; nuclear energy development design of experiments; mathematics; natural philosophy. *Mailing Add:* 3635 Hillside Dr NE Cleveland TN 37311

SAEMANN, JESSE C(HARLES), JR, b Adell, Wis, Sept 16, 21; m 58; c 2. ENGINEERING MECHANICS. *Educ:* Univ Wis, BS, 43, MS, 50, PhD(eng mech), 55. *Prof Exp:* From instr to assoc prof, 46-61, PROF ENG MECH, UNIV WIS-MADISON, 61- *Concurrent Pos:* Mem, Hwy Res Bd, Nat Acad Sci-Nat Res Coun. *Mem:* Am Soc Civil Engrs. *Res:* Shrinkage cracking of concrete block; variation of concrete masonry; soil mechanics. *Mailing Add:* Dept Eng Mech Univ Wis Madison WI 53706

SAENGER, EUGENE L, b Cincinnati, Ohio, Mar 5, 17; m 41; c 2. RADIOLOGY, NUCLEAR MEDICINE. *Educ:* Harvard Univ, AB, 38; Univ Cincinnati, MD, 42; Am Bd Radiol, dipl, 46, cert nuclear med, 72. *Prof Exp:* From asst to assoc prof, 43-62, PROF RADIOL, COL MED, UNIV CINCINNATI, 62-, DIR RADIOISOTOPE LAB, 50- *Concurrent Pos:* Radiation therapist, Children's Hosp, Cincinnati, 46-47; pvt pract, 46-62; mem adv comt, Biol Effects Ionizing Radiation, 64-72; mem subcomt sealed gamma sources, Nat Comt Radiation Protection; Am Roentgen Ray Soc rep, Nat Coun Radiation Protection & Measurements, mem bd dirs, chmn sci comt brachyther, 68-; Aubrey Hampton lectr, Mass Gen Hosp, 71; prog dir radiol sci, Nat Inst Gen Med Sci; consult to dir, Bur Radiol Health & to Surgeon Gen, US Air Force. *Mem:* Am Roentgen Ray Soc; fel Am Col Radiol; Health Physics Soc; Soc Nuclear Med; Am Radium Soc. *Res:* Radiobiology; cancer; radiological sciences; public health. *Mailing Add:* Radioisotope Lab Cincinnati Gen Hosp Cincinnati OH 45267

SAENZ, ALBERT WILLIAM, b Medellin, Colombia, Aug 27, 23; nat US; m 57. THEORETICAL PHYSICS. *Educ:* Univ Mich, BS, 44, MA, 45, PhD(physics), 49. *Prof Exp:* Physicist, Naval Res Lab, 50-51; physicist, Inst Appl Math, Ind Univ, 51-52; physicist, Naval Res Lab, 52-64, head anal & theory br, Radiation Div, 64-66, head theory br, Nuclear Sci Div, 66-74, head theory br, Nuclear Tech Div, 74-76, HEAD THEORY CONSULT STAFF, NUCLEAR TECH DIV, NAVAL RES LAB, 76- *Concurrent Pos:* Vis scientist, Mass Inst Technol, 57 & Oak Ridge Nat Lab, 58; vis fel, Johns Hopkins Univ, 64 & Princeton Univ, 76-77; lectr, Univ Md grad prog, Nat Res Lab, 50-51, 54-55 & 63-64; lectr, Cath Univ Am, 55-56 & Univ Md, 62. *Mem:* Fel Am Phys Soc; NY Acad Sci. *Res:* Special and general relativity; symmetry and degeneracy in quantum mechanics; equilibrium and nonequilibrium statistical mechanics; spin-wave theory and inelastic magnetic scattering of neutrons; quantum scattering theory. *Mailing Add:* Code 6603S Nuclear Tech Div Naval Res Lab Washington DC 20375

SAENZ, REYNALDO V, b San Juan, Tex, Sept 29, 30; m 66. PHARMACEUTICAL CHEMISTRY. *Educ:* Univ Tex, BS, 62, MS, 65, PhD(pharmaceut chem), 67. *Prof Exp:* ASSOC PROF PHARMACEUT CHEM, SCH PHARM, NORTHEAST LA UNIV, 66- *Mem:* Am Pharmaceut Asn; Am Chem Soc. *Res:* Synthesis of agents acting on the central nervous system or peripheral nervous system based on known compounds already established as active. *Mailing Add:* Dept of Pharmaceut Chem Northeast La Univ Sch of Pharm Monroe LA 71209

SAETHER, OLE ANTON, b Kristiansand, Norway, Dec 9, 36; m 66; c 3. LIMNOLOGY, ENTOMOLOGY. *Educ:* Univ Oslo, Cand Mag, 60, Cand Real, 63. *Prof Exp:* Sci asst limnol, Univ Oslo, 61-63, lectr hydrobiol, 63-69, Nansen Fund fel, 62-69; res scientist, Freshwater Inst, Fisheries Res Bd Can, 69-77; PROF SYST ZOOL & HEAD DEPT, UNIV BERGEN, 77- *Concurrent Pos:* Vis scientist, Fisheries Res Bd Can, 67-68; consult, Indust Bio-Test Lab, Inc, 71-; adj prof entom, Univ Manitoba, 73-77; adj res scientist, Freshwater Inst, Dept Environ, Man, Can, 78-; ed, Fauna Horvegica Ser B, 79- *Mem:* Int Asn Theoret & Appl Limnol; Am Soc Limnol & Oceanog; Entom Soc Can; Norweg Entom Soc; NAm Benthol Soc. *Res:* Taxonomy, morphology and ecology of Chironomidae, Chaoboridae and Hydracarina; benthic fauna; zooplankton; phytoplankton; systematic zoology. *Mailing Add:* Dept of Syst Zool Univ of Bergen N-5000 Bergen/Univ Norway

SAETTLER, ALFRED WILLIAM, b Peoria, Ill, Mar 8, 40; c 3. PLANT PATHOLOGY. *Educ:* Beloit Col, BA, 62; Univ Wis, PhD(plant path), 66. *Prof Exp:* Res asst plant path, Univ Wis, 62-66; RES PLANT PATHOLOGIST, N CENT REGION, SCI & EDUC ADMIN-AGR RES, USDA, 66- *Mem:* Am Phytopath Soc; Am Inst Biol Sci; Int Soc Plant Pathologists. *Res:* Diseases of field beans; bacterial diseases of beans; breeding disease resistance in beans. *Mailing Add:* Dept of Bot & Plant Path Mich State Univ East Lansing MI 48824

SAEVA, FRANKLIN DONALD, b Rochester, NY, Nov 28, 38; m 63; c 3. CHEMISTRY. *Educ:* Bucknell Univ, BS, 60; State Univ NY Buffalo, PhD(org chem), 68. *Prof Exp:* Sr scientist, Xerox Corp, 68-79; SR SCIENTIST, EASTMAN KODAK CO, 79- *Mem:* Am Chem Soc. *Res:* Organic reaction mechanisms and photochemistry, circular dichroism and nuclear magnetic resonance studies; liquid crystals; organic synthesis; electrochemical behavior of organics. *Mailing Add:* Res Labs Eastman Kodak Co Rochester NY 14650

SAFAIE, BIJAN, b Teheran, Iran, Oct 29, 47; c 1. CIVIL ENGINEERING, HYDRAULICS. *Educ:* Teheran Univ, BS, 70; Univ Calif, Berkeley, MS, 74, PhD(civil eng), 78. *Prof Exp:* Res asst civil eng, Univ Calif, Berkeley, 72-78, ASST PROF CIVIL ENG, STATE UNIV NY BUFFALO, 78- *Mem:* Am Soc Civil Engrs; Am Soc Eng Educ. *Res:* Fate of pollutant, stratified and turbulent flow; coastal engineering; fluid mechanics; hydraulics. *Mailing Add:* Dept of Civil Eng Parker Annex State Univ NY Buffalo NY 14214

SAFANIE, ALVIN H, b Washington, DC, Dec 27, 24; m 50; c 4. ANATOMY, HISTOLOGY. *Educ:* Cornell Univ, DVM, 47; Mich State Univ, MS, 50; Univ Ill, PhD(anat), 62. *Prof Exp:* Instr anat, Col Vet Med, Mich State Univ, 47-51, asst prof, 51-52; instr, 52-62, from asst prof to assoc prof, 62-72, prof anat, 72-77, PROF VET ANAT & HISTOL, COL VET MED, UNIV ILL, URBANA, 77- *Honors & Awards:* Norden distinguished teacher's award, 64 & 68. *Mem:* Am Vet Med Asn; Am Asn Vet Anatomists; Am Soc Zoologists. *Res:* Vagus nerve of pig; embryology of domestic animals. *Mailing Add:* Dept of Vet Anat Univ of Ill Urbana IL 61801

SAFAR, PETER, b Vienna, Austria, Apr 12, 24; nat US; m 50; c 2. ANESTHESIOLOGY, CRITICAL CARE MEDICINE. *Educ:* Univ Vienna, MD, 48; Am Bd Anesthesiol, dipl. *Hon Degrees:* Dr, Univ Mainz, 72. *Prof Exp:* Resident path & surg, Univ Vienna, 48-49; fel surg, Yale Univ, 49-50; resident anesthesiol, Univ Pa, 50-52, chief dept, Nat Cancer Inst, Lima, Peru, 52-53; asst prof, Sch Med, Johns Hopkins Univ, 54-61; prof anethesiol/critical care med & chmn dept, Sch Med, 61-78, DISTINGUISHED PROF RESUSCITATION MED & FOUND DIR, RESUSCITATION RES CTR, UNIV PITTSBURGH, 78- *Concurrent Pos:* Clin assoc prof, Sch Med, Univ Md, 55-61; chief, Baltimore City Hosps, Md, 55-61; res contractor, US Army Res & Develop Div, Off Surgeon Gen, 57-69; vis scientist, Cardiovasc Res Inst, Univ Calif, San Francisco, 69-70; mem comts resuscitation, emergency & critical care, Nat Res Coun, Am Heart Asn & other nat orgns; mem, Interagency White House Comt Emergency Med Serv; Wattie prof, NZ, 81; F S Cheeves prof, Pittsburgh. *Mem:* Am Physiol Soc; Am Soc Anesthesiol; Soc Critical Care Med (pres, 73). *Res:* Resuscitation; neurosciences; author or coauthor of over 500 publications. *Mailing Add:* Dept Anesthesiol/Crit Care Med Sch Med Univ Pittsburgh Pittsburgh PA 15261

SAFDARI, YAHYA BHAI, b Amravati, India, July 25, 30; US citizen; m 62; c 3. ENGINEERING. *Educ:* Aligarh Muslim Univ, India, BSME, 52, BSEE, 53; Univ Wash, MSME, 59; NMex State Univ, DSc(mech eng), 64. *Prof Exp:* Asst engr, Delhi Cloth Mills, India, 54-56; res asst mech engr, Univ Wash, Seattle, 57-58; design engr, Refrig Co, Wash, 58-61; instr mech eng, NMex State Univ, 61-64; assoc prof, Bradley Univ, 64-69, prof, 69-76; pres, Sun Systs Inc, 76-79; PRES, SAF ENERGY CONSULTS, INC, 79- *Mem:* Am Soc Heating, Refrig & Air-Conditioning Engrs; Am Soc Mech Engrs; Int Solar Energy Soc; Int Solar Energy Indust Asn. *Res:* Heat transfer in transparent medii; convection heat transfer in nuclear reactors; solar energy; energy management. *Mailing Add:* Saf Energy Consults Inc PO Box 155 Eureka IL 61530

SAFDY, MAX ERROL, b Brooklyn, NY, Nov 9, 41; m 68; c 1. ORGANIC CHEMISTRY, MEDICINAL CHEMISTRY. *Educ:* Polytech Inst Brooklyn, BS, 63; Univ NC, PhD(org chem), 69. *Prof Exp:* Res scientist, Corp Res Div, 70-76, SR RES SCIENTIST, AMES DIV, MILES LABS, INC, 77- *Mem:* Am Chem Soc; AAAS; Sigma Xi. *Res:* Medical diagnostics, cardiovascular agents, biogenic amines, amino acids and peptides; microencapsulation; medical instrumentation. *Mailing Add:* Miles Labs Inc 1127 Myrtle St Elkhart IN 46514

SAFE, STEPHEN HARVEY, b Belleville, Ont, May 14, 40; m 62; c 2. CHEMISTRY, TOXICOLOGY. *Educ:* Queen's Univ, Ont, BSc, 62, MSc, 63; Oxford Univ, DPhil(chem), 65. *Prof Exp:* Sci Res Coun res asst chem, Oxford Univ, 66-67; NIH res assoc biochem, Harvard Univ, 67-68; assoc res officer microbiol-chem, Nat Res Coun Can, 68-73; prof biochem, Univ Guelph, 73-81; PROF, TEX A&M UNIV, 81- *Res:* Applications of mass spectrometry; biochemistry and toxicology of pollutants. *Mailing Add:* 1207 Charles Ct College Station TX 77840

SAFER, BRIAN, b Brooklyn, NY, Dec 3, 42; m 69. MOLECULAR BIOLOGY, PHARMACOLOGY. *Educ:* Columbia Univ, BA, 64; Baylor Col Med, MS, 67, MD, 69; Univ Pa, PhD(molecular biol), 72. *Prof Exp:* USPHS fel, Univ Pa, 69-71, Pa Plan fel, 71-73; sr staff fel, Nat Heart & Lung Inst, 73-79, CHIEF SECT PROTEIN BIOSYNTHESIS, NAT HEART, LUNG, AND BLOOD INST, NIH, 79- *Honors & Awards:* Louis N Katz Prize, Am Heart Asn, 73. *Mem:* Am Chem Soc; Sigma Xi; Am Heart Asn; Am Soc Biol Chemists. *Res:* Cardiac metabolism; metabolic regulation; amino acid metabolism; myocardial ischemia; regulation of protein synthesis; initiation factor characterization. *Mailing Add:* Nat Heart Lung & Blood Inst NIH Bethesda MD 20014

SAFERSTEIN, LOWELL G, b Newark, NJ, July 25, 40; m 76; c 1. POLYMER CHEMISTRY, ORGANIC CHEMISTRY. *Educ:* Rutgers Univ, BS, 62, MS, 65, PhD(org chem), 67. *Prof Exp:* Res chemist, Celanese Res Co, 67-76; SR RES CHEMIST, ETHICON INC, 76- *Mem:* Am Chem Soc; Am Inst Chemists; Sigma Xi. *Res:* Synthesis of high performance polymers; synthesis of biopolymers. *Mailing Add:* Ethicon Inc Rte 22 Somerville NJ 08876

SAFERSTEIN, RICHARD, b Brooklyn, NY, July 17, 41; m 75; c 2. FORENSIC SCIENCE. *Educ:* City Col New York, BS, 63, MA, 66, PhD(org chem), 70. *Prof Exp:* Chemist, US Treasury Dept, NY, 64-69; chemist, Shell Chem Co, 69-70; CHIEF CHEMIST, FORENSIC SCI BUR, NJ STATE POLICE, 70- *Concurrent Pos:* Instr, Trenton State Col & Ocean County Col, 72- *Mem:* Am Chem Soc; Am Acad Forensic Sci; Forensic Sci Soc; Am Soc Mass Spectrometry; Can Soc Forensic Scientists. *Res:* Application of chemical ionization mass spectroscopy to forensic science. *Mailing Add:* NJ State Police Lab PO Box 7068 West Trenton NJ 08625

SAFF, EDWARD BARRY, b New York, NY, Jan 2, 44; m 66; c 2. MATHEMATICAL ANALYSIS. *Educ:* Ga Inst Technol, BS, 64; Univ Md, College Park, PhD(math), 68. *Prof Exp:* Fulbright grant, Imp Col, Univ London, 68-69; assoc prof, 69-76, PROF MATH, UNIV SOUTH FLA, 76- *Concurrent Pos:* NSF grant, Univ South Fla, 69-72; Air Force res grant, 73-; Guggenheim fel, Oxford Univ, 78. *Mem:* Am Math Soc; Math Asn Am. *Res:* Approximation in complex domain; approximate solutions of differential equations; Pade approximants; geometry of polynomials. *Mailing Add:* Dept of Math Univ of South Fla Tampa FL 33620

SAFFER, ALFRED, b New York, NY, Dec 3, 18; m 42; c 2. PHYSICAL CHEMISTRY. *Educ:* NY Univ, AB, 39, MS, 41, PhD(phys chem), 43. *Prof Exp:* Asst chem, NY Univ, 40-43; res assoc, Princeton Univ, 43-45; sr res chemist, Firestone Tire & Rubber Co, 45-48; sr vpres mfg, Halcon Int Inc, NY, 48-70; pres, Oxirane Int, NJ, 71-78; vchmn, Halcon Int Inc, 78-81; RETIRED. *Concurrent Pos:* Pres, Catalyst Develop Corp, NJ, 57-70. *Honors & Awards:* Chem Pioneer Award, Am Inst Chemists, 82. *Mem:* Nat Acad Eng; Am Chem Soc; Am Inst Chem Eng; Soc Chem Indust. *Res:* Oxidation of hydrocarbons in gas and liquid phases; processes for manufacture of petrochemicals; manufacture of catalysis; mechanisms of organic reactions. *Mailing Add:* Suite 810 2 Park Ave New York NY 10016

SAFFER, CHARLES MARTIN, JR, b Salem, Mass, Dec 15, 14; m 42; c 1. INDUSTRIAL CHEMISTRY. *Educ:* Mass Inst Technol, SB, 36, SM, 37, PhD(chem), 38. *Hon Degrees:* MA, Christ Church, Oxford Univ, 73. *Prof Exp:* Moore traveling fel, Oxford Univ, 39-40; res asst, Harvard Univ, 40-41; res chemist, Aerojet Eng Corp, Calif, 46-48; scientist, Bur Aeronaut, US Dept Navy, 48-51; vpres, Microcard Corp, 51-54; dir res, Nat Fireworks Ord Corp, 53-57; asst mgr nat northern div, Am Potash & Chem Corp, 57-58, head propellant chem res, 58-60; asst dir res planning, Thiokol Chem Corp, 60-65, tech consult, 65-66; tech dir, Sonneborn Div, 66-70, tech dir activated carbon div, 70-75, TECH DIR INORGANIC SPECIALTIES DIV, WITCO CHEM CORP, 75- *Mem:* Am Chem Soc. *Res:* Organo-silicon synthesis; synthetic estrogens; sodium triphenylmethyl; smokeless propellants; explosives. *Mailing Add:* Witco Chem Inorg Specialties Div 277 Park Ave New York NY 10017

SAFFER, HENRY WALKER, b New York, NY, Apr 4, 35; m 63; c 3. PHYSICAL CHEMISTRY, TEXTILE CHEMISTRY. *Educ:* NC State Col, BS, 56, MS, 58; Princeton Univ, MA, 60, PhD(phys chem), 63. *Prof Exp:* Res chemist, 62-66, sr res chemist, 66-72, res supvr, 72-75, mkt develop supvr, 75-76, strategist, Textile Fibers Dept, 76-77, prog mgr, 78-79, DIV MGR, CENT RES & DEVELOP DEPT, E I DU PONT DE NEMOURS & CO, INC, 80- *Res:* Protein chemistry; nuclear magnetic resonance spectroscopy of fibers; textile warp sizing; engineering fibers for special end uses; nonwoven products and processes; business diversification and development. *Mailing Add:* DuPont Bldg E I du Pont de Nemours & Co Inc Wilmington DE 19898

SAFFERMAN, ROBERT S, b Bronx, NY, Dec 19, 32; m 58; c 3. MICROBIOLOGY. *Educ:* Brooklyn Col, BS, 55; Rutgers Univ, PhD(microbiol), 60. *Prof Exp:* Res fel microbiol, Inst Microbiol, Rutgers Univ, 55-59; microbiologist, USPHS, 59-64 & US Dept Interior, 64-70; microbiologist, 70-74, CHIEF VIROL SECT, ENVIRON MONITORING & SUPPORT LAB, US ENVIRON PROTECTION AGENCY, 74- *Mem:* AAAS; Am Soc Microbiologists; Phycol Soc Am; Sigma Xi; fel Am Acad Microbiol. *Res:* Survival and persistence of viruses in water sources; phycoviruses; algal development and control; extracellular products of actinomycetes in natural and wastewater ecology; medical aspects of phycology. *Mailing Add:* US Environ Protection Agency Nat Environ Res Ctr Cincinnati OH 45268

SAFFIOTTI, UMBERTO, b Milan, Italy, Jan 22, 28; US citizen; m 58; c 2. ONCOLOGY. *Educ:* Univ Milan, MD, 51, dipl occup med, 57. *Prof Exp:* Fel, Inst Path Anat, Univ Milan, 51-52; res asst oncol, Chicago Med Sch, 52-54, res assoc, 54-55; chief pathologist, Inst Occup Med & asst occup med, Univ Milan, 56-60; fel, Inst Gen Path, 57-60; from asst prof to prof oncol, Chicago Med Sch, 60-68; assoc sci dir carcinogenesis, Etiol Area, 68-72, assoc dir carcinogenesis, Div Cancer Cause & Prev, 72-76, chief exp path br, 74-78, CHIEF LAB EXP PATH, DIV CANCER CAUSE & PREV, NAT CANCER INST, 78- *Concurrent Pos:* Mem comt young scientists in cancer res, Int Union Against Cancer, 56-58, mem comt cancer prev, 59-66 & mem panel on carcinogenicity, 63-66; NIH career develop award, 64-68; mem path B study sect, NIH, 64-68; partic panel carcinogenesis, Secy's Comn Pesticides & Environ Health, Dept Health, Educ & Welfare, 69, chmn ad hoc comt eval low levels environ carcinogenesis, Surg Gen, 69-70 & mem comt coord toxicol & related prog, 73-76; mem working groups, Eval Carcinogenic Risk of Chem to Man, Int Agency Res Cancer, 70-75; mem adv comt to scholars-in-residence prog, Fogarty Int Ctr, NIH, 73-77; mem bd dirs, Rachel Carson Trust for Living Environ, Inc, 76-79; chmn carcinogenesis contract prog mgt group, Div Cancer Cause & Prev, Nat Cancer Inst, 68-76, mem occup cancer task force & chmn comt carcinogenesis, 78-80; mem, Cancer Prev Task Force, 79-; partic, Work Group on Assessment, Interagency Regulatory Liaison Group, 79-80 & Work Group on Regulation of Carcinogens, US Regulatory Coun, 79-80. *Honors & Awards:* Superior Serv Honor Award, HEW, 71; Pub Interest Sci Award, Environ Defense Fund, 77. *Mem:* AAAS; Am Asn Cancer Res; Europ Asn Cancer Res; Ital Soc Cancerology; fel NY Acad Sci. *Res:* Experimental pathology of chemical carcinogenesis; in-vivo/in-vitro carcinogenesis models, especially for epithelial systems; combined effects of carcinogens; identification and evaluation criteria for carcinogens; occupational and environmental carcinogenesis. *Mailing Add:* Lab Exp Path Nat Cancer Inst Frederick MD 21701

SAFFIR, ARTHUR JOEL, b Chicago, Ill, May 11, 41; m 63; c 2. DENTAL SCIENCE, NUTRITION. *Educ:* Mass Inst Technol, PhD(nutrit), 70; Tufts Univ, DMD, 64. *Prof Exp:* Res assoc, Mass Inst Technol, 64-70; dir res & develop, Mat Analysis, 70; pvt consult, 70-73; DIR ORAL HEALTH RES, COOPER LABS, INC, 73- *Mem:* Int Asn Dent Res. *Res:* Dental research; statistical analysis; electron optics; nutrition clinical research. *Mailing Add:* 2057 Summit Dr Lake Oswego OR 97034

SAFFMAN, PHILIP GEOFFREY, b Leeds, Eng, Mar 19, 31; m 54; c 3. APPLIED MATHEMATICS, FLUID MECHANICS. *Educ:* Cambridge Univ, BA, 53, PhD(appl math), 56. *Prof Exp:* Lectr appl math, Cambridge Univ, 58-60; reader, King's Col, Univ London, 60-64; prof fluid mech, 64-69, PROF APPL MATH, CALIF INST TECHNOL, 69- *Concurrent Pos:* Res fel, Trinity Col, Cambridge Univ, 55-59; vis prof, Mass Inst Technol, 70-71. *Mem:* fel Am Acad Arts & Sci. *Res:* Turbulence; viscous flow; wave interactions; vortex motion. *Mailing Add:* 399 Ninita Pkwy Pasadena CA 91106

SAFFO, MARY BETH, b Inglewood, Calif, Apr 8, 48; m 78. INVERTEBRATE ZOOLOGY, MARINE BIOLOGY. *Educ:* Univ Calif, Santa Cruz, BA, 69; Stanford Univ, PhD(biol), 77. *Prof Exp:* Miller res fel, Dept Bot, Univ Calif, Berkeley, 76-78; ASST PROF BIOL, SWARTHMORE COL, 78- *Concurrent Pos:* Independent investr, Marine Biol Lab, 79-80. *Mem:* Sigma Xi; Am Soc Zoologists; Soc Study Evolution; Mycol Soc Am; fel Am Asn Univ Women. *Res:* Invertebrate biology; functional morphology; physiological ecology; biology of symbiosis; nitrogen excretion; biomineralization; tunicate biology; mycology. *Mailing Add:* Dept Biol Swarthmore Col Swarthmore PA 19081

SAFFORD, EDWARD LAPORTE, b Sycamore, Ill, Jan 28, 36; m 60; c 2. PORK PRODUCTION. *Educ:* Northern Ill Univ, BS, 58; Univ Ill, MS, 60, PhD(inorg chem), 63. *Prof Exp:* Asst prof chem, Thiel Col, 62-66, assoc prof, 67-71, prof, 72-80, chmn dept, 65-80. *Mem:* Am Chem Soc. *Res:* Synthesis and characterization of coordination compounds; amino acid complex compounds and ions. *Mailing Add:* RR 2 Box 51 Sycamore IL 60178

SAFFORD, LAWRENCE OLIVER, b Bremen, Maine, Dec 27, 38; m 58; c 3. FORESTRY, ECOLOGY. *Educ:* Univ Maine, BS, 61, PhD(plant sci), 68; Yale Univ, MFor, 62. *Prof Exp:* Res forester, Maine, 62-68, 69-70, RES FORESTER, NORTHEASTERN FOREST EXP STA, US FOREST SERV, USDA, NH, 70. *Concurrent Pos:* WVa Pulp & Paper Co fel, Yale Univ, 68-69. *Mem:* Soc Am Foresters; AAAS; Am Soc Agron; Sigma Xi. *Res:* Soil-tree relationships; soil moisture and nutrient requirements of forest trees. *Mailing Add:* Forestry Sci Lab PO Box 640 Durham NH 03824

SAFFORD, RICHARD WHILEY, b New York, NY, Sept 1, 24; m 65; c 2. SYSTEMS SCIENCE, OPERATIONS RESEARCH. *Educ:* Union Col, NY, BS, 45; Univ Mich, MS, 46; Mass Inst Technol, PhD(physics), 53. *Prof Exp:* Jr scientist, Brookhaven Nat Lab, 47-48; mem staff, Lab Nuclear Sci, Mass Inst Technol, 48-53; res engr & head adv bomber studies, Boeing Co, 53-56; from sr staff physicist to mgr airborne ltd war systs, Hughes Aircraft Co, 56-62; advan projs mgr solar physics, Space Systs Div & chief space & electronics planning, Repub Aviation Corp, 62-65; MEM TECH STAFF, MITRE CORP, C3 DIV, INTELLIGENCE & NAVAL OPER, BEDFORD, 65- *Concurrent Pos:* Consult & lectr, business admin. *Mem:* Sigma Xi. *Res:* Describing analyzing, evaluating and modelling military command, control and communications systems; computer modelling of air warfare and electronic combat. *Mailing Add:* 12 Meriam St Lexington MA 02173

SAFFRAN, JUDITH, b Montreal, Que, Nov 5, 23; m 47; c 4. BIOCHEMISTRY. *Educ:* McGill Univ, BSc, 44, PhD(biochem), 48. *Prof Exp:* Melville Trust fel biochem, Univ Edinburgh, 58-59; biochemist, Jewish Gen Hosp, Montreal, 55-58; biochemist, Jewish Gen Hosp, Montreal, 61-69; sr res fel, Med Res Inst, Toledo Hosp, 69-74; asst prof, 74-76, assoc prof obstet, gynec & biochem, 76-79, CLIN CHEMIST, MED COL OHIO, 79- *Concurrent Pos:* Adj asst prof, Med Col Ohio, 70-74. *Mem:* Can Biochem Soc; Endocrine Soc; Soc Study Reproduction; Am Soc Biol Chemists. *Res:* Steroid hormones; mechanism of action; reproductive physiology. *Mailing Add:* 2331 Hempstead Rd Toledo OH 43606

SAFFRAN, MURRAY, b Montreal, Que, Oct 30, 24; m 47; c 4. BIOCHEMISTRY. *Educ:* McGill Univ, BSc, 45, MSc, 46, PhD(biochem), 49. *Prof Exp:* Lectr psychiat, McGill Univ, 48-52; Life Ins Med Res Fund fel, Copenhagen Univ, 52-53; asst prof psychiat, McGill Univ, 53-58; Founds Fund Res Psychiat fel, Univ Edinburgh, 58-59; assoc prof biochem & psychiat, McGill Univ, 59-65, bldg dir, McIntyre Med Sci Bldg, 63-65, prof biochem, 65-69; chmn dept, 69-80, PROF BIOCHEM, MED COL OHIO, 69- *Concurrent Pos:* Mem endocrinol study sect, NIH, 64-68, mem neurol A study sect, 77-81; mem biochem test comt, Nat Bd Med Examrs, 65-69, fel, 79; Endocrine Soc Ayerst fel, 67; vis lectr, Ctr Pop Studies, Sch Pub Health, Harvard Univ, 67-68; mem, Int Brain Res Orgn; chmn biochem test comt, Nat Bd Podiatry, 78-; consult, pharmaceut indust; vis prof, Ben Gurion Univ, 81. *Mem:* AAAS; Endocrine Soc; Am Soc Biol Chemists; Am Soc Neurochem; Int Soc Neurochem. *Res:* Neuroendocrinology; peptide hormones; intestinal absorption of peptides. *Mailing Add:* Dept of Biochem Med Col Ohio PO CS 10008 Toledo OH 43699

SAFFREN, MELVIN MICHAEL, b Brooklyn, NY, Sept 13, 29; m 53; c 3. MATHEMATICAL PHYSICS, FLUID DYNAMICS. *Educ:* City Col New York, BS, 51; Mass Inst Technol, PhD(physics), 59. *Prof Exp:* Asst physics, Brookhaven Nat Lab, 52; asst physics, Mass Inst Technol, 52-59; physicist, Res Lab, Gen Elec Co, 59-62; mem tech staff, Jet Propulsion Lab, 62-67, supvr theoret physics group, 67-71, space sci div rep to off res & advan develop, 71-76, STAFF SCIENTIST, JET PROPULSION LAB, CALIF INST TECHNOL, 76- *Concurrent Pos:* Consult & mem vis fac, Univ Southern Calif, 66-68; mem physics subcomt, Bluebook Update Task, NASA, 70-71, mem physics & chem in space working group, 72-, proj scientist, Drop Dynamics Module Proj, 75-; chmn steering comt, Int Colloquium on Drops & Bubbles, 74-, co-ed proceedings, 76; exec secy, Int Symp Relativity Exp Space, 77. *Mem:* Am Phys Soc. *Res:* Theory and computation of energy bands in solids; superconductivity; many body problem; interaction of radiation with matter; low temperature physics; superfluidity; physics and chemistry experiments in earth-orbiting laboratories; tunneling; dynamics of liquid drops and bubbles; theory of theta functions; theory of Hilbert transforms. *Mailing Add:* Jet Propulsion Lab Calif Inst of Technol Pasadena CA 91103

SAFIR, ARAN, medicine, ophthalmology, see previous edition

SAFIR, SIDNEY ROBERT, b Trenton, NJ, June 17, 16; m 42; c 2. MEDICINAL CHEMISTRY. *Educ:* Univ Mich, BS, 37, MS, 38, PhD(org chem), 40. *Prof Exp:* Fuller fel, Univ Mich, 40-41; org chemist, Am Cyanamid Co, 41-46 & Schenley Distillers Co, 46-47; ORG CHEMIST, LEDERLE LABS, AM CYANAMID CO, 47- *Mem:* Am Chem Soc. *Res:* Synthesis of novel antipsychotic, anxiolytic and analgetic agents. *Mailing Add:* 684 Millbrook Rd River Edge NJ 07661

SAFKO, JOHN LOREN, b San Diego, Calif, Oct 29, 38; m 64; c 5. PHYSICS. *Educ:* Case Inst Technol, BS, 60; Univ NC, PhD(physics), 65. *Prof Exp:* Asst prof, 64-74, ASSOC PROF PHYSICS & ASTRON, UNIV SC, 74- *Concurrent Pos:* NSF grants. *Mem:* Am Phys Soc; Am Asn Physics Teachers; Am Astron Soc. *Res:* General relativity and gravitation theory; teaching methods; astrophysical investigations related to relativity; astronomy education. *Mailing Add:* Dept of Physics Univ of SC Columbia SC 29208

SAFLEY, LAWSON MCKINNEY, JR, b Fayetteville, Tenn, Jan 13, 50; m 73; c 2. AGRICULTURAL ENGINEERING. *Educ:* Univ Tenn, BS, 72; Cornell Univ, MS, 74, PhD(agr eng), 77. *Prof Exp:* Res support specialist, Cornell Univ, 76-77; asst prof agr eng, Univ Tenn, 77-81; ASSOC PROF BIO & AGR ENG, NC STATE UNIV, 81- *Mem:* Am Soc Agr Engrs; Sigma Xi. *Res:* Manurial nutrient loss during storage; land application of manure; systems analysis of animal manure systems. *Mailing Add:* Bio & Agr Eng Dept NC State Univ Box 5906 Raleigh NC 27650

SAFONOV, MICHAEL G, b Pasadena, Calif, Nov 1, 48; m 68; c 1. CONTROL THEORY, SIGNAL PROCESSING. *Educ:* Mass Inst Technol, BS & MS, 71, PhD(elec eng), 77. *Prof Exp:* Res & teaching asst, Mass Inst Technol, 75-77; ASST PROF ELEC ENG, UNIV SOUTHERN CALIF, 77- *Concurrent Pos:* Consult, Anal Sci Corp, Systs Control Inc, & Honeywell Inc. *Mem:* Sr mem Inst Elec & Electronics Engrs; Sigma Xi. *Res:* Control and feedback theory; large scale system theory; hierarchical decomposition methods; multivariable control synthesis; stability theory. *Mailing Add:* Dept Elec Eng Systs Univ Southern Calif Los Angeles CA 90007

SAFRANYIK, LASZLO, b Besenyszog, Hungary, Feb 13, 38; Can citizen; m 66; c 2. FOREST ENTOMOLOGY. *Educ:* Univ BC, BSF, 61, MF, 63, PhD(pop dynamics), 69. *Prof Exp:* Res officer forest entom, Can Dept Forestry, 64-69, RES SCIENTIST FOREST ENTOM, CAN FORESTRY SERV, 69- *Mem:* Entom Soc Can; Can Inst Forestry. *Mailing Add:* Pac Forest Res Ctr Can Forestry Serv Victoria BC V8N 2R2 Can

SAFRON, SANFORD ALAN, b Chicago, Ill, July 24, 41. PHYSICAL CHEMISTRY. *Educ:* Univ Calif, Berkeley, BS, 63; Harvard Univ, MA, 65, PhD(chem), 69. *Prof Exp:* Guest researcher, Physics Inst, Univ Bonn, 69-70; asst prof, 70-76, ASSOC PROF CHEM, FLA STATE UNIV, 76- *Concurrent Pos:* Res Corp-Cottrell grant, Fla State Univ, 71, Petrol Res Fund-Am Chem Soc grant, 71-74; Res Corp-Cottrell grant, 76 & NSF-URP grant, 79. *Mem:* AAAS; Am Phys Soc; Am Chem Soc. *Res:* Dynamics of chemical reactions; ion-molecule crossed beam studies of chemical reactions. *Mailing Add:* Dept of Chem Fla State Univ Tallahassee FL 32306

SAGAL, MATTHEW WARREN, b Brooklyn, NY, Nov 23, 36; m 59; c 3. PHYSICAL CHEMISTRY. *Educ:* Cornell Univ, BChE, 58; Mass Inst Technol, PhD(phys chem), 61. *Prof Exp:* Mem tech staff chem, Bell Tel Labs, 61-66; res leader, 66-67, asst dir mat & chem processes, 67-69, dir mat & chem process, 69-76, mgr prod planning, Eng Res Ctr, 76-79, DIR ENG, ALLENTOWN WORKS, WESTERN ELEC CO, 79- *Mem:* Electrochem Soc; sr mem Inst Elec & Electronics Engrs. *Res:* Electronic materials; manufacturing processes; environmental analysis; plastics; ceramics. *Mailing Add:* Western Elec Co 555 Union Blvd Allentown PA 18103

SAGALYN, PAUL LEON, b New York, NY, Mar 21, 21; m 52; c 2. SOLID STATE PHYSICS. *Educ:* Harvard Univ, BS, 42; Mass Inst Technol, PhD(physics), 52. *Prof Exp:* Staff mem, Radiation Lab, Mass Inst Technol, 43-45, res assoc, Dept Physics, 52-56; RES PHYSICIST, US ARMY MAT & MECH RES CTR, 56- *Mem:* Am Phys Soc. *Res:* Use of nuclear magnetic resonance as a tool for studying the electronic structure of solids; ion implantation as a tool for modifying the properties of materials. *Mailing Add:* US Army Mat & Mech Res Ctr Watertown MA 02172

SAGALYN, RITA C, b Lowell, Mass, Nov 24, 24; m 52; c 2. SPACE PHYSICS, IONOSPHERIC PHYSICS. *Educ:* Univ Mich, Ann Arbor, BS, 48; Radcliffe Col, MS, 50. *Prof Exp:* Res physicist, Air Force Cambridge Res Labs, 48-58 & Aeronomy & Ionospheric Physics Labs, 58-69, br chief space physics, Ionospheric Physics Lab, 69-75, RES PHYSICIST, US AIR FORCE GEOPHYS LAB, US AIR FORCE CAMBRIDGE RES LABS, 49-, BR CHIEF ELECTRICAL PROCESSES BR, 75- *Honors & Awards:* Guenther Loeser Award, Air Force Cambridge Res Labs, 58; Patricia Kayes Glass Award, US Air Force, 66. *Mem:* Sigma Xi; Am Geophys Union. *Res:* Upper atmospheric and space research; study experimentally and theoretically of the influence of soft particle fluxes, solar ultraviolet, terrestrial electric and magnetic fields, plasma motions and instabilities on spatial distribution and temporal behavior of environmental plasma. *Mailing Add:* Air Force Geophys Lab Hanscom AFB Bedford MA 01731

SAGAN, CARL, b Brooklyn, NY, Nov 9, 34. PLANETARY SCIENCES. *Educ:* Univ Chicago, AB, 54, BS, 55, MS, 56, PhD(astron, astrophys), 60. *Hon Degrees:* Various from US & foreign univs, cols & insts, 75-80. *Prof Exp:* Miller res fel astron, Inst Basic Res Sci, Univ Calif, Berkeley, 60-62; asst prof, Harvard Univ, 62-68; astrophysicist, Smithsonian Astrophys Observ, 62-68; assoc prof astron, Ctr Radiophysics & Space Res, 68-70, prof, 70-77, assoc dir, Ctr Radiophys & Space Res, 72-81, DAVID DUNCAN PROF ASTRON & SPACE SCI, CORNELL UNIV, 77-, DIR LAB PLANETARY STUDIES, 68- *Concurrent Pos:* Vis asst prof, Sch Med, Stanford Univ, 62-63; Alfred P Sloan Found res fel, 63-67; vchmn working group moon & planets, Comt Space Res, Int Coun Sci Unions, 68-75; lectr, Astronaut Training Prog, NASA, 68-72; ed, Icarus, 68-79; chmn US deleg, Joint Nat Acad Sci-Soviet Acad Sci Conf Commun Extraterrestrial Intel, Armenia, 71; vis assoc, Calif Inst Technol, 71-72 & 76-77, consult, Jet Propulsion Lab; mem bd dir, Coun Advan Sci Writing, 72-75; lectr var US & foreign univs, cols & insts, 59-; judge, Nat Book Awards, 75; mem adv coun, Smithsonian Inst, 75-; mem exobiol comt, Planetary Atmospheres Study Group, mem steering comt exobiol study, space sci bd & panel origins life & astron surv comt, comt sci & pub policy, Nat Acad Sci; mem organizing comt, Comn 16 Phys Study Planets, Int Astron Union; pres, Planetology Sect, Am Geophys Union, 80-82; NSF & Am Astron Soc vis prof; experimenter, Mariner II Venus probe; Mariner IX Mars orbiter, Viking Mars lander; Voyager, outer solar syst probes; pres, Carl Sagan Prods, Inc, 77-, pres, Planetary Soc, 74- *Honors & Awards:* A Calvert Smith Prize, Harvard Univ, 64; Apollo Achievement Award, NASA, 69, Except Sci Achievement Medal, 72; Int Astronaut Prize, Galabert Found, Paris, 73; John W Campbell Mem Award, Best Sci Book of Year, 74; Klumpke-Roberts Prize Popularization Astron, Astron Soc Pac, 74; Golden Plate Award, Am Acad Achievement, 75; Joseph Priestley Award, Dickinson Col, 75; Newcomb Cleveland Prize, 77; Rittenhouse Medal, Franklin Inst/Rittenhouse Astron Soc, 80; Pulitzer Prize, 78; George Foster Peabody Award, Univ Ga, 81; Glenn Seabory Award, Am Platform Asn, 81; Ralph Coats Roe Medal, Am Soc Mech Engrs, 81. *Mem:* Fel AAAS; fel Am Acad Arts & Sci; Am Phys Soc; fel Am Geophys Union; fel Am Inst Aeronaut & Astronaut. *Res:* Physics of planetary atmospheres; planetary surface conditions; production of organic molecules in astronomical environments; origin of life; extraterrestrial biology; space vehicle exploration of the solar system. *Mailing Add:* Lab for Planetary Studies Cornell Univ Ithaca NY 14853

SAGAN, HANS, b Vienna, Austria, Feb 15, 28; nat US; m 54; c 1. MATHEMATICS. *Educ:* Univ Vienna, PhD, 50. *Prof Exp:* Asst prof math, Vienna Tech Univ, 50-54 & Mont State Univ, 54-57; assoc prof, Univ Idaho, 57-61, prof & head dept, 61-63; PROF MATH, NC STATE UNIV, 63- *Concurrent Pos:* Math Asn Am lectr, 63-73, 77-; vis prof, Munich Tech Univ, 64; vis prof, Univ Vienna, 72. *Mem:* Math Asn Am. *Res:* Eigenvalue problems; calculus of variations and optimal control theory; functional analysis; differential equations. *Mailing Add:* Dept of Math NC State Univ Raleigh NC 27650

SAGAN, LEON FRANCIS, b Chicopee Falls, Mass, May 23, 41. MATHEMATICS. *Educ:* Towson State Col, BS, 62; Col William & Mary, MA, 64; Univ Md, College Park, PhD(math educ), 71. *Prof Exp:* PROF MATH, ANNE ARUNDEL COMMUNITY COL, 64- *Mem:* Math Asn Am; Nat Coun Teachers Math; Am Math Asn Two-Year Cols. *Res:* Remedial math; college algebra and trigonometry; calculus. *Mailing Add:* Dept of Math Anne Arundel Community Col Arnold MD 21012

SAGAN, LEONARD A, b San Francisco, Calif, Feb 18, 28; m 54; c 3. INTERNAL MEDICINE, ENVIRONMENTAL MEDICINE. *Educ:* Stanford Univ, AB, 50; Univ Chicago, MD, 55; Harvard Univ, MPH, 65; Am Bd Internal Med, dipl, 64. *Prof Exp:* Intern, Univ Calif Hosp, 55-56, resident internal med, 56-61; physician, Atomic Bomb Casualty Comn, Japan, 61-64; physiciant, US AEC, DC, 65-68; physician, 68-78, assoc dir dept environ med, Palo Alto Med Clin, 71-78; PROG MGR BIOMED STUDIES, ELEC POWER RES INST, 78- *Mem:* Fel Am Col Physicians; Nat Coun Radiation Protection. *Res:* Late effects of radiation. *Mailing Add:* Elec Power Res Inst PO Box 10412 Palo Alto CA 94303

SAGAR, WILLIAM CLAYTON, b Columbus, Ohio, Oct 17, 29; m 53; c 3. SYNTHETIC ORGANIC CHEMISTRY. *Educ:* Capital Univ, BS, 51; Ohio State Univ, MSc, 54, PhD(chem), 58. *Prof Exp:* Res chemist, Ethyl Corp, 58-61; from asst prof to assoc prof chem, 61-70, PROF CHEM, CENTRE COL KY, 70-, CHMN DIV SCI & MATH, 72- *Mem:* Am Chem Soc. *Res:* Synthesis of insecticides; aldol condensations. *Mailing Add:* Div of Sci & Math Centre Col Danville KY 40422

SAGAWA, KIICHI, b Tokyo, Japan, Dec 10, 26; US citizen; m 51; c 2. PHYSIOLOGY, BIOMEDICAL ENGINEERING. *Educ:* Yokohama Med Col, MD, 50; Univ Tokyo, PhD(physiol), 58. *Prof Exp:* Instr physiol, Med Sch, Univ Tokyo, 55-57; from asst prof to assoc prof, Med Sch, Yokohama Univ, 57-64; from asst prof to assoc prof, Med Sch, Univ Miss, 64-68; assoc prof physiol & biomed eng, Med Sch, Case Western Reserve Univ, 68-71; PROF BIOMED ENG, MED SCH, JOHNS HOPKINS UNIV, 71- *Concurrent Pos:* Cardiovasc res trainee, Med Sch, Univ Miss, 59-61. *Mem:* Am Physiol Soc; Biomed Eng Soc; Inst Elec & Electronics Engrs. *Res:* Cardiovascular physiology, particularly its regulation by mechanical and reflex control, mostly from systems analysis viewpoint. *Mailing Add:* Dept of Biomed Eng Johns Hopkins Univ Med Sch Baltimore MD 21205

SAGAWA, YONEO, b Keeau, Hawaii, Oct 11, 26; m 62; c 2. CYTOGENETICS. *Educ:* Washington Univ, AB, 50, MS, 52; Univ Conn, PhD(cytogenetics), 56. *Prof Exp:* Res assoc biol, Brookhaven Nat Lab, 55-57; from asst prof to assoc prof bot, Univ Fla, 57-64; PROF HORT, UNIV HAWAII, 64-, DIR, HAROLD L LYON ARBORETUM, 67- *Concurrent Pos:* Dir undergrad sci educ prog & undergrad res participation & independent study, NSF, Univ Fla, 64. *Mem:* Bot Soc Am; Int Soc Hort Sci; AAAS; Am Soc Hort Sci; Int Asn Plant Tissue Culture. *Res:* Cytogenetics of cultivated plants, especially subtropical plants; morphogenesis; tissue culture. *Mailing Add:* Univ Hawaii H L Lyon Arboretum 3860 Manoa Rd Honolulu HI 96822

SAGE, ANDREW PATRICK, b Charleston, SC, Aug 27, 33; m 62; c 3. DICISION SUPPORT SYSTEMS, INFORMATION PROCESSING. *Educ:* The Citadel, BS, 55; Mass Inst Technol, MS, 56; Purdue Univ, PhD(elec eng), 60. *Prof Exp:* Instr elec eng, Purdue Univ, 56-60; assoc prof, Univ Ariz, 60-63; tech staff mem, Aerospace Corp, Calif, 63-64; prof elec eng, Univ Fla, 64-67, prof nuclear eng, 66-67; prof & dir info & control sci ctr, Inst Technol, Southern Methodist Univ, 67-74, head dept elec eng, 72-74; chmn, Dept Chem Eng, 74-75, assoc dean, 74-80, LAWRENCE R QUARLES PROF ENG & APPL SCI & CHMN, DEPT ENG SCI & SYSTS, UNIV VA, 77- *Concurrent Pos:* Consult var corp & insts, 57-; ed, Trans on Systs, Man & Cybernetics, Inst Elec & Electronics Engrs. *Honors & Awards:* Barry Carlton Award, Inst Elec & Electronics Engrs, 70; Frederick Emmonds Terman Award, Am Soc Eng Educ, 70; Norbert Wiener Award, Inst Elec & Electronics Engrs, 81. *Mem:* AAAS; Inst Mgt Sci; fel Inst Elec & Electronics Engrs; Am Soc Eng Educ; Am Inst Dicision Sci. *Res:* Decision support systems; systems engineering; education; optimization and estimation theory with applications to decision and policy analysis in large-scale systems. *Mailing Add:* Dept Eng Sci & Systs Univ of Va Charlottesville VA 22901

SAGE, GLORIA W, b Brooklyn, NY, Mar 7, 36; m 58; c 1. PHYSICAL CHEMISTRY, ANALYTICAL CHEMISTRY. *Educ:* Cornell Univ, AB, 57; Radcliffe Col, AM, 58; Harvard Univ, PhD(phys chem), 63. *Prof Exp:* Jr chemist, Res & Adv Develop Div, Avco Corp, 57-58; res assoc chem, Univ Ore, 61-63; instr, 63-66, res assoc, 66-67; res assoc, Syracuse Univ, 67-70; res assoc biochem, State Univ NY Upstate Med Ctr, 70-72, asst prof med technol, 72-76, res assoc pediat, 76-77; res assoc chem, Tel Aviv Univ, 77-78; consult, 78-80; RES ASSOC, SYRACUSE RESEARCH CORP, 80- *Mem:* AAAS; Am Chem Soc. *Res:* Phosphorescence; magnetic circular dichroism; ultraviolet and fluorescence spectroscopy of proteins; conformation of proteins; molecular spectroscopy; clinical chemistry method development and lab management evaluation; environmental fate of chemicals; data base development. *Mailing Add:* Syracuse Research Corp Merrill Lane Syracuse NY 13210

SAGE, HARVEY J, b New York, NY, Jan 5, 33; m 68; c 1. IMMUNOCHEMISTRY, BIOCHEMISTRY. *Educ:* Polytech Inst Brooklyn, BS, 54; Yale Univ, PhD(chem), 58. *Prof Exp:* Res assoc hemat, Sch Med, Yale Univ, 58-60; res assoc biochem, St Luke's Hosp, Cleveland, 60-62; res assoc, Brandeis Univ, 62-64; asst prof biochem, 64-71, ASST PROF PATH, DUKE UNIV, 64-, ASSOC PROF BIOCHEM, 71-, ASSOC PROF IMMUNOL, 74- *Mem:* AAAS; Am Soc Biochem; Am Asn Immunologists. *Res:* Specificity of antigen-antibody reactions; in vitro lymphocyte culture and isolation of lymphocyte surface membrane proteins; protein structure; use of synthetic polypeptides as models for protein structure and as immunogens. *Mailing Add:* Dept of Biochem Duke Univ Durham NC 27710

SAGE, JAY PETER, b Pittsburgh, Pa, Nov 8, 43; m 71; c 2. INTEGRATED CIRCUITS. *Educ:* Harvard Univ, BA, 64, MA, 65, PhD(physics), 69. *Prof Exp:* Sr res scientist, Res Div, Raytheon Co, Waltham, Mass, 68-81; MEM TECH STAFF, LINCOLN LAB, MASS INST TECHNOL, 81- *Concurrent Pos:* Raytheon exchange scientist, Toshiba Res & Develop Ctr, Japan, 73-74. *Mem:* Inst Elec & Electronics Engrs. *Res:* Charge-coupled devices and metal oxide semiconductor integrated circuitry for signal processing applications; surface acoustic wave devices. *Mailing Add:* Raytheon Res Div 28 Seyon St Waltham MA 02154

SAGE, JOSEPH D, b Leonardo, NJ, July 14, 31; m 51; c 7. SOIL MECHANICS, ENGINEERING GEOLOGY. *Educ:* Rutgers Univ, BS, 53, MS, 58; Clark Univ, PhD(geog), 74. *Prof Exp:* Pres & mem bd, Geotechnics Inc, 59-65; from instr to assoc prof, 57-77, PROF CIVIL ENG, WORCESTER POLYTECH INST, 77-; PARTNER, SAGE & D'ANDREA, 77- *Mem:* Sigma Xi; Am Soc Civil Engrs; Am Soc Testing & Mat. *Res:* Rock mechanics; frost action in particulate systems; mathematical synthesis of climatological time series. *Mailing Add:* Dept of Civil Eng Worcester Polytech Inst Worcester MA 01609

SAGE, MARTIN, b Torquay, Eng, Dec 6, 35; m 65; c 2. ZOOLOGY, PHYSIOLOGY. *Educ:* Univ Nottingham, BSc, 57, PhD(zool), 60. *Prof Exp:* Demonstr zool, Univ Nottingham, 59-60; from asst lectr to lectr zool, Univ Leicester, 60-66, lectr physiol, 66-69; assoc prof zool, Univ Tex, Austin, 69-74, assoc prof marine studies, 73-74, res scientist, Marine Sci Inst, Port Aransas, 69-74; assoc prof, 74-77, chmn dept, 75-81, PROF BIOL, UNIV MO-ST LOUIS, 77- *Concurrent Pos:* Tutor, Univ Nottingham, 60; resident tutor, Univ Leicester, 60-65; Wellcome Found travel grant & asst zoologist,

Cancer Res Genetics Lab & Bodega Marine Lab, Dept Zool, Univ Calif, Berkeley, 68-69; reader, Marine Biol Lab, Woods Hole, 81-82. *Mem:* AAAS; Europ Soc Comp Endocrinol; Am Inst Biol Sci; Am Soc Zool. *Res:* Comparative endocrinology and physiology; evolution of vertebrate endocrine and neuroendocrine control systems; evolution of biological activity of hormones; endocrine control of osmoregulation; hormones and behavior; biological rhythms. *Mailing Add:* Dept of Biol Univ of Mo St Louis MO 63121

SAGE, MARTIN LEE, b New York, NY, Mar 4, 35; m 58. CHEMICAL PHYSICS. *Educ:* Cornell Univ, AB, 55; Harvard Univ, MA, 48, PhD(chem physics), 59. *Prof Exp:* Fel physics, Brandeis Univ, 59-61; asst prof chem & theoret sci, Univ Ore, 61-67; ASSOC PROF CHEM, SYRACUSE UNIV, 67- *Concurrent Pos:* Vis assoc prof chem, Tel Aviv Univ, Israel, 77-78. *Mem:* AAAS; Am Phys Soc. *Res:* Quantum chemistry; intramolecular dynamics; multiphoton photochemistry; magnetic circular dichroism. *Mailing Add:* Dept of Chem Syracuse Univ Syracuse NY 13210

SAGE, NATHANIEL MCLEAN, JR, b Boston, Mass, Feb 4, 18; m 55, 72; c 5. RESEARCH ADMINISTRATION. *Educ:* Mass Inst Technol, SB, 41, SM, 51, PhD, 53. *Prof Exp:* Teacher high sch, Conn, 46-49; asst to dir admis, Mass Inst Technol, 49-50; from instr to asst prof geol, Amherst Col, 51-55; from asst prof to assoc prof, Univ NH, 55-60, chmn dept, 57-60; assoc dir sponsored res, Mass Inst Technol, 60-68; COORDR RES, UNIV RI, 68- *Mem:* Fel Geol Soc Am; Am Asn Petrol Geologists. *Res:* Invertebrate paleontology; carboniferous of Nova Scotia and Pennsylvania anthracite region. *Mailing Add:* Off of Res Coordr Univ of RI Kingston RI 02881

SAGE, ORRIN GRANT, JR, b Los Angeles, Calif, May 31, 46; m 70. ENVIRONMENTAL GEOLOGY, ENVIRONMENTAL MANAGEMENT. *Educ:* Univ Calif, BA, 69, MA, 71, PhD(geol), 73. *Prof Exp:* Environ scientist environ mgt, Multran Am Corp & Henningson, Durham & Richardson, 72-75; LECTR ENVIRON STUDIES, UNIV CALIF, SANTA BARBARA, 73- *Concurrent Pos:* NSF fel, 70-73; environ resources panel, Santa Barbara County, 74-; environ mgt, Valentine Res, Univ Calif, Santa Barbara & Geopac Corp, Simi, Calif, 74- environ consult, Off Environ Qual, Santa Barbara County, 75-, Santa Barbara City Col, 75, Henningson, Durham & Richardson, 75- & Envicom Corp, 76. *Mem:* Geol Soc Am; Wilderness Soc. *Res:* Tectonic evolution of western California; environmental assessment and land use planning; environmental effects of California agriculture. *Mailing Add:* 1396 Danielson Montecito CA 93108

SAGEBIEL, JOE ALFRED, animal science, see previous edition

SAGER, CLIFFORD J, b New York, NY, Sept 28, 16; c 4. PSYCHIATRY. *Educ:* Pa State Col, BS, 37; NY Univ, MD, 41; Am Bd Psychiat & Neurol, dipl, 48; NY Med Col, cert psychoanal, 49. *Prof Exp:* Consult psychiat, Family Welfare Orgn, Allentown, Pa, 46-47; assoc dean & dir therapeut serv, Postgrad Ctr Ment Health, 48-60; dir clin serv, NY Med Col, 60-63, chief family treatment & study unit, 64-70, prof psychiat & dir partial hosp prog, 66-70; clin prof psychiat, Mt Sinai Sch Med, City Univ New York, 70-80, attend psychiat, Mt Sinai Hosp, 74-80; CLIN PROF PSYCHIAT, NEW YORK HOSP/CORNELL MED CTR, 80-, ATTEND PSYCHIAT, 80- *Concurrent Pos:* Asst adj psychiatrist, Beth Israel Hosp, 48-50; vis psychiatrist, Metrop Hosp, 60-70; attend psychiatrist, Flower & Fifth Ave Hosp, 60-70; chief family treatment & study unit, Beth Israel Med Ctr, 70-74, assoc dir family & group ther, 71-73, chief behav sci serv prog, Ctr & Hosp, 71-73; dir psychiat, Gouverneur Hosp, 70-73; psychiat dir, Jewish Family Serv, New York, 73-; ed, J Sex & Marital Ther, 74-; dir family psychiat, Jewish Bd Family & Children's Serv, New York, 78- *Mem:* Fel Am Psychiat Asn; fel Am Med Asn; fel Am Acad Psychoanal; fel Am Orthopsychiat Asn; fel Am Group Psychother Asn. *Res:* The marital couple and the development of suitable methods of bringing psychiatric treatment to those segments of the population previously not reached by effective psychological and social forms of treatment; new methods of treating the sexual dysfunctions; family process; marital interaction; typography of marriages; problems of remarriage. *Mailing Add:* 65 E 76th St New York NY 10021

SAGER, EARL VINCENT, b Buffalo, NY, Sept 24, 45; m 79. ENGINEERING PHYSICS. *Educ:* State Univ NY, Buffalo, BA, 67, MA, 69; Univ Md, PhD(physics), 79. *Prof Exp:* RES ANALYST, SYST PLANNING CORP, 78- *Mem:* Am Physics Soc. *Res:* Radar digital signal processing. *Mailing Add:* 12941 Lee-Jackson Hwy Fairfax VA 22033

SAGER, JOHN CLUTTON, b New Castle, Pa, Mar 15, 42; m 64; c 2. ENVIRONMENTAL CONTROL. *Educ:* Pa State Univ, BS, 64, MS, 70, PhD(agr eng), 73. *Prof Exp:* AGR RES ENG, RADIATION BIOL LAB, SMITHSONIAN INST, 73- *Concurrent Pos:* instr pilot, Ag Rotors, Inc, 69; res asst, Agr Eng Dept, Pa State Univ, 68-69 & 70-73, instr, 70. *Mem:* Am Soc Agr Eng; Am Soc Photobiol; Int Solar Energy Soc; Hydrogen Energy Soc; AAAS. *Res:* Direct planning and excution of a research program on environmental effects on plants with emphasis on growth and productivity; design new or modified equipment to provide the required management and control of environmental factors critical to the research program. *Mailing Add:* Radiation Biol Lab Smithsonian Inst 12441 Parklawn Dr Rockville MD 20852

SAGER, RAY STUART, b Cuero, Tex, Feb 24, 42; m 62; c 1. INORGANIC CHEMISTRY, PHYSICAL CHEMISTRY. *Educ:* Tex Lutheran Col, BS, 64; Tex Christian Univ, PhD(chem), 68. *Prof Exp:* Asst prof chem, Concordia Col, Moorhead, Minn, 68-69; from asst prof to assoc prof, Capital Univ, 69-74; ASST PROF CHEM, PAN AM UNIV, 75- *Mem:* Am Chem Soc. *Res:* Structure and properties of copper II and zinc II complexes of aromatic N oxides. *Mailing Add:* Dept Chem Pan Am Univ Edinburg TX 78539

SAGER, RUTH, b Chicago, Ill, Feb 7, 18; m 73. GENETICS. *Educ:* Univ Chicago, BS, 38; Rutgers Univ, MS, 44; Columbia Univ, PhD(genetics), 48. *Prof Exp:* Merck fel, Nat Res Coun, 49-51; asst biochem, Rockefeller Inst, 51-55; res assoc zool, Columbia Univ, 55-60, sr res assoc, 61-65; prof biol, Hunter Col, City Univ New York, 66-75; PROF CELLULAR GENETICS, HARVARD MED SCH & CHIEF DIV GENETICS, SIDNEY FARBER CANCER INST, 75- *Concurrent Pos:* Guggenheim res fel, 72-73; nonresident fel, Edinburgh Univ. *Mem:* Nat Acad Sci; Am Soc Cell Biologists; Am Soc Naturalists; Int Soc Cell Biologists; Am Soc Biol Chem. *Res:* Molecular biology; cell and organelle genetics and biogenesis; animal cell genetics; genetic mechanisms of regulation. *Mailing Add:* Sidney Farber Cancer Inst 44 Binney St Boston MA 02115

SAGER, THOMAS WILLIAM, US citizen. STATISTICS. *Educ:* Univ Iowa, BA, 68, MS, 71, PhD(statist), 73. *Prof Exp:* Asst prof statist, Stanford Univ, 73-78; vis asst prof math & bus, 78-79, ASST PROF STATIST, UNIV TEX, AUSTIN, 79- *Mem:* Inst Math Statist; Am Statist Asn; Sigma Xi. *Res:* Spatial patterns; density estimation; isotonic regression; environmental statistics. *Mailing Add:* 2301 Doral Dr Austin TX 78746

SAGER, WILLIAM FREDERICK, b Ill, Jan 22, 18; m 41; c 3. ORGANIC CHEMISTRY. *Educ:* George Washington Univ, BS, 39, MA, 41; Harvard Univ, PhD(chem), 48. *Prof Exp:* Chemist, Tex Co, 41-45; from asst prof to prof chem, George Washington Univ, 48-64; head dept, 65-80, PROF CHEM, UNIV ILL, CHICAGO, 65- *Concurrent Pos:* Guggenheim fel, Oxford Univ, 54-55; consult, Bur Weapons, US Dept Navy, Army Chem Ctr, NIH, W Grace Co & Houdry Process Co. *Mem:* Am Chem Soc. *Res:* Mechanisms of organic reactions; chemistry of high explosives. *Mailing Add:* 2145 Thornwood Wilmette IL 60091

SAGERMAN, ROBERT H, b Kings Co, NY, Jan 23, 30; m 54; c 4. MEDICINE, RADIOLOGY. *Educ:* NY Univ, BA, 51, MD, 55; Am Bd Radiol, dipl, 61. *Prof Exp:* Clin instr radiol, Med Sch, Tulane Univ, 56-57; instr, Sch Med, Stanford Univ, 61-64; asst prof, Columbia-Presby Med Ctr, 64-68; PROF RADIOL & DIR RADIOTHER DIV, STATE UNIV NY UPSTATE MED CTR, 68- *Mem:* AAAS; Am Soc Therapeut Radiol; Radiol Soc NAm; Am Radium Soc; Radiation Res Soc. *Res:* Therapeutic radiology; radiation biology. *Mailing Add:* Radiotherapy Div State Univ NY Upstate Med Ctr Syracuse NY 13210

SAGERS, RICHARD DOUGLAS, b Tooele, Utah, Dec 19, 28; m 50; c 6. MICROBIOLOGY. *Educ:* Brigham Young Univ, BS, 54, MS, 55; Univ Ill, PhD(bact), 58. *Prof Exp:* From asst prof to assoc prof, 58-64, PROF BACT, BRIGHAM YOUNG UNIV, 64- *Honors & Awards:* NIH career development award, 63-68. *Mem:* Am Soc Microbiologists; Am Soc Biol Chemists. *Res:* Metabolic pathways, energy relationships and biosynthetic mechanisms in anaerobic microorganisms; metabolism of natural products. *Mailing Add:* Dept of Microbiol Brigham Young Univ Provo UT 84602

SAGERT, NORMAN HENRY, b Midland, Ont, Mar 31, 36; m 59; c 3. PHYSICAL CHEMISTRY, SURFACE SCIENCE. *Educ:* Queen's Univ, BSc, 59, MSc, 60; Ottawa Univ, PhD(phys chem), 63. *Prof Exp:* Fel phys chem, Cambridge Univ, 63-64; asst res officer, 64-68, assoc res officer, 68-76, SR RES OFFICER, ATOMIC ENERGY CAN LTD, 76- *Mem:* Royal Soc Chem; fel Chem Inst Can. *Res:* Surface and colloid science; interfacial phenomena; thin film stability; adsorption at liquid-liquid and gas-liquid interfaces. *Mailing Add:* Whiteshell Nuclear Res Estab Pinawa MB R0E 1L0 Can

SAGGIOMO, ANDREW JOSEPH, b Philadelphia, Pa, Mar 20, 31; m 53; c 3. MEDICINAL CHEMISTRY, RESEARCH ADMINISTRATION. *Educ:* La Salle Col, BA, 52; Temple Univ, MA, 54. *Prof Exp:* Chemist, Philadelphia Qm Depot, 52; asst, Duquesne Univ, 52-53; res fel, Res Inst, Temple Univ, 53-56; res assoc, Germantown Labs, Inc, 56-61, proj dir, 61-69, financial mgr, 69-72, vpres & treas, 72-80; ADMIN MGR, FRANKLIN RES CTR, 80- *Mem:* Am Chem Soc. *Res:* Organic fluorine chemistry; dyes; polymers; organometallics; medicinals; anticancer and anti-inflammatory agents; psychotropic drugs; antimalarials; polychlorinated biphenyl disposal methods. *Mailing Add:* 1817 Schley St Philadelphia PA 19145

SAGI, CHARLES J(OSEPH), b Phillipsburg, NJ, Mar 10, 35; m 59; c 2. MECHANICAL ENGINEERING. *Educ:* Lehigh Univ, BS, 56; Stanford Univ, MS, 61, PhD(mech eng), 65. *Prof Exp:* Develop engr, Ingersoll-Rand Co, 56-59; asst prof mech eng, Stanford Univ, 64-65; assoc sr res engr, Gen Motors Corp, 65-67; sr res engr, Creare, Inc, 67-68; sr res engr, Spec Progs Dept, 68-77, sr res engr, FLUID DYNAMICS RES DEPT, GEN MOTORS RES LABS, 80- *Mem:* Am Soc Mech Engrs. *Res:* The fluid mechanics of internal flow; aerodynamics of ground vehicles. *Mailing Add:* Fluid Dynamics Dept 216 REB Gen Motors Res Labs Warren MI 48090

SAGIK, BERNARD PHILLIP, b New York, NY, May 8, 25. VIROLOGY. *Educ:* City Col New York, BS, 47; Univ Ill, MS, 48, PhD, 52; Am Bd Med Microbiol, dipl pub health & virol. *Prof Exp:* Asst bact, Univ Ill, 48-52; Nat Found Infantile Paralysis fel & instr biophys, Sch Med, Univ Colo, 52-54; sect head virol, Upjohn Co, 54-62; dir viral chemother, Ciba Pharmaceut Co, 62-66; from assoc prof to prof microbiol, Univ Tex, Austin, 66-73; prof microbiol, Univ Tex Health Sci Ctr, San Antonio, 73-80, prof life sci, 73-80, dean, Col Sci & Math, 73-80; PROF BIOL SCI & VPRES ACAD AFFAIRS, DREXEL UNIV, 80- *Concurrent Pos:* Vis scholar, Univ Ill, 60-61; lectr, City Univ New York, 63-66 & Drew Univ, 66; adj prof environ health eng, Univ Tex, Austin, 73- *Mem:* AAAS; Am Soc Microbiologists. *Res:* Virus-host cell interactions; pathogenesis of virus infections; arbovirus genetics; viruses, sewage and terrestrial waste disposal. *Mailing Add:* Drexel Univ 32nd & Chestnut St Philadelphia PA 19104

SAGLE, ARTHUR A, b Honolulu, Hawaii; m 60. LIE GROUPS, LIE ALGEBRAS. *Educ:* Univ Wash, BS, 56, MS, 57; Univ Calif, Los Angeles, PhD(math), 60. *Prof Exp:* Instr math, Univ Chicago, 60-62; asst prof, Syracuse Univ, 62-64; ONR fel & res instr, Univ Calif, Los Angeles, 64-65; res fel, Yale Univ, 65-66; prof, Univ Minn, 66-72; PROF MATH, UNIV HAWAII, 72- *Concurrent Pos:* NSF grants, 60-72; invit lectr, Am Math Soc, 64; Oberwolfach lectr, Ger Govt, 68. *Mem:* Sigma Xi; Am Math Soc. *Res:* Investigation of the interdependency of differential geometry; H-spaces; lie groups and non-associative algebras; recently computer methods are being attempted in solutions. *Mailing Add:* Dept of Math Univ of Hawaii Hilo HI 96720

SAGURA, JOHN JOSEPH, b Barnesville, Pa, May 10, 22; m 50; c 2. PHOTOGRAPHIC CHEMISTRY. *Educ:* Bradley Univ, BS, 50; Univ Ill, PhD(chem), 53. *Prof Exp:* Res chemist, 53-62, ADMINR, RES LABS, EASTMAN KODAK CO, 62- *Res:* Organic chemistry; heterocyclic compounds; photochemistry of organic compounds; photographic processes; patent liaison. *Mailing Add:* 602 Harvest Dr Rochester NY 14626

SAH, CHIH-HAN, b Peiping, China, Aug 16, 34; US citizen; m 66; c 3. MATHEMATICS. *Educ:* Univ Ill, BS, 54, MS, 56; Princeton Univ, PhD(math), 59. *Prof Exp:* Instr math, Princeton Univ, 59-60; Benjamin Peirce instr, Harvard Univ, 60-63; from asst prof to prof, Univ Pa, 63-70; PROF MATH, STATE UNIV NY STONY BROOK, 70- *Concurrent Pos:* Vis lectr, Harvard Univ, 67-68; vis prof, Univ Calif, Berkeley, 69-70 & 76-77. *Mem:* Am Math Soc. *Res:* Finite groups; algebraic number theory; rings; chohomology of groups. *Mailing Add:* Dept of Math State Univ of NY Stony Brook NY 11794

SAH, CHIH-TANG, b Peiping, China, Nov 10, 32; nat US; m 59; c 2. ENGINEERING PHYSICS, ELECTRICAL ENGINEERING. *Educ:* Univ Ill, BS(eng physics) & BS(elec eng), 53; Stanford Univ, MS, 54, PhD(elec eng), 56. *Hon Degrees:* Dr, Cath Univ Leuven, 75. *Prof Exp:* Res asst, Electronics Lab, Stanford Univ, 54-56, res assoc, 56-57; mem sr staff, Semiconductor Lab, Shockley Transistor Corp, 56-59; sr mem tech staff, Fairchild Semiconductor Corp, 59-61; PROF ELEC ENG & PHYSICS, UNIV ILL, URBANA, 63- *Concurrent Pos:* Mgr & head physics dept, Fairchild Semiconductor Res Lab, 61-65; Honeywell H W Sweatt Eng-Scientist Awards Committeeman, 77; US Nat Acad Sci Committeeman, 75-78; life fel, Franklin Inst of Philadelphia. *Honors & Awards:* Browder J Thompson Award, Inst Radio Eng, Inst Elec & Electronics Engrs, 62; J J Ebers Award, Electron Device Soc, 81. *Mem:* Fel Inst Elec & Electronics Engrs; fel Am Phys Soc. *Res:* Solid state and semiconductor electronics and physics. *Mailing Add:* 403 Pond Ridge Lane Urbana IL 61801

SAHA, ANIL, b Calcutta, India, Mar 1, 30; US citizen. IMMUNOLOGY. *Educ:* Presidency Col, BS, 49; Univ Calcutta, MS, 52, PhD(appl chem), 61. *Prof Exp:* Res asst heme-proteins, Indian Coun Med Res, 53-56; res assoc, Med Col, Cornell Univ, 56-57; res fels, Calif Inst Technol, 60-64; asst prof med & allergy, McGill Univ, 65-69; asst prof, 69-70, ASSOC PROF MICROBIOL, COL MED & DENT NJ, 70-, ASST DEAN GRAD SCH BIOMED SCI, 73- *Mem:* Am Chem Soc; Am Soc Biol Chemists; Am Asn Immunol; Am Soc Microbiol; Transplantation Soc. *Res:* Heme-proteins; immunoglobulins; cellular mediators. *Mailing Add:* Dept of Microbiol Col of Med & Dent of NJ Newark NJ 07103

SAHA, GOPAL BANDHU, b Chittagong, Bangladesh, Apr 30, 38; Can citizen; m 65; c 2. NUCLEAR CHEMISTRY, RADIOPHARMACY. *Educ:* Dacca Univ, Bangladesh, BSc Hons, 59, MSc, 60; McGill Univ, PhD(chem), 65. *Prof Exp:* Asst prof chem, Purdue Univ, 65-66; res assoc nuclear chem, McGill Univ, 66-70; radiopharmacist & assoc scientist nuclear pharm, Royal Victoria Hosp, Montreal, 70-76; assoc prof, 76-80, PROF RADIOPHARMACEUT CHEM, UNIV ARK MED SCI, 80- *Concurrent Pos:* Assoc prof chem, McGill Univ, 70-76. *Mem:* Soc Nuclear Med; Sigma Xi; Am Chem Soc; AAAS; Am Asn Univ Professors. *Res:* Preparation and clinical evaluation of new radiopharmaceuticals; mechanisms of localization of radiopharmaceuticals in cells and tissues. *Mailing Add:* Div of Nuclear Med Univ of Ark for Med Sci Little Rock AR 72201

SAHA, JADU GOPAL, b Bengal, India, Dec 1, 31; Can citizen; m 57; c 1. PESTICIDE CHEMISTRY. *Educ:* Univ Calcutta, BSc, 53, MSc, 56; Univ Sask, PhD(org chem), 62. *Prof Exp:* Sr sci asst, Cent Fuel Res Inst, Dhanbad, India, 56-59; res fel org chem, Radiation Lab, Univ Notre Dame, 62-63; res fel, Univ Sask, 63-64; res officer, 64-66, res scientist, 67-75, DIR, CHEM & BIOL RES INST, CAN DEPT AGR, 75- *Mem:* AAAS; Am Chem Soc; Chem Inst Can; Royal Soc Chem. *Res:* Utilization of coal tar and mechanism of aromatic substitution reactions; persistence, translocation, photodecomposition and metabolism of pesticides. *Mailing Add:* Chem & Biol Res Inst Res Br Can Dept Agr Ottawa ON M7G 1A3 Can

SAHAI, HARDEO, b Bahraich, India, Jan 10, 42; m 73; c 1. STATISTICS. *Educ:* Lucknow Univ, India, BSc, 62; Banaras Hindu Univ, MSc, 64; Univ Chicago, MS, 68; Univ Ky, PhD(statist), 71. *Prof Exp:* Lectr math, Banaras Hindu Univ, 64-65; statist officer, Durgapur Steel Plant, India, 65; statistician, Blue Cross Asn, Chicago, 66; statist programmer, Cleft Palate Ctr, Univ Ill, Chicago, 67 & Chicago Health Res Found, 68; asst statist, Univ Ky, 68-71; mgt scientist, Burroughs Corp, Mich, 72; asst prof, 72-75, assoc prof, 76-80, PROF STATIST, UNIV PR, MAYAGUEZ, 81- *Concurrent Pos:* Statist consult, PR Driving Safety Eval, San Juan, 73; res investr, Water Resources Inst, Mayaguez, 75-; reviewer, Math Rev, 75-79; statist consult, PR Univ Consult Corp, 77-78; vis res prof, Dept Statist & Appl Math, Fed Univ Ceara, Brazil, 78-79. *Mem:* Am Statist Asn; Inst Math Statist; Biomet Soc; Indian Statist Asn. *Res:* Design and analysis for variance components. *Mailing Add:* Dept of Math Univ of PR Mayaguez PR 00708

SAHASRABUDDHE, CHINTAMAN GOPAL, b Shirpur, India, July 18, 36; m 60; c 2. PHYSICS, BIOCHEMISTRY. *Educ:* Agra Univ, India, BSc, 57; Vikram Univ, MSc, 59, MSc, 65; Ore State Univ, MS, 72, PhD(biochem-biophys), 74. *Prof Exp:* Lectr sci, MGGHSS, Mandleshwar, 59-63; lectr physics, Birla Inst Technol & Sci, 65-69; res assoc, 77-78, ASST BIOCHEMIST, M D ANDERSON HOSP & TUMOR INST, UNIV TEX, 78- *Mem:* Biophys Soc; Am Soc Cell Biol; AAAS. *Res:* Structure-function relationship of chromatin, a genetically active complex of DNA, proteins and RNA in eukaryotes. *Mailing Add:* Dept of Biochem M D Anderson Hosp Houston TX 77030

SAHASRABUDHE, MADHU R, b Apr 1, 25; Can citizen; m 50; c 2. FOOD SCIENCE & TECHNOLOGY, ANALYTICAL CHEMISTRY. *Educ:* Agra Univ, BSC, 44; Banaras Hindu Univ, MSc, 46; Univ Bombay, PhD(biochem & nutrit), 52. *Prof Exp:* Res assoc food sci, Univ Ill, 54-57; tech officer, Kraft Foods Ltd, 57-58; head food additives, Nat Health & Welfare, Can, 58-68; mgr res & develop, Salada Foods Ltd, Salada Kelloggs, 69-72; actg dir, 73-74, SR RES SCIENTIST FOOD SCI, FOOD RES INST, AGR CAN, 74- *Mem:* Am Oil Chemists' Soc; Can Inst Food Sci & Technol; Chem Inst Can; Inst Food Technol; Asn Food Scientist & Technologists India. *Res:* Plant lipids; chemistry; nutrition processing; analytical methods; toxic compounds; safety food additives. *Mailing Add:* Cent Exp Farm Food Res Inst Agr Can Ottawa ON K1A 0C6 Can

SAHATJIAN, RONALD ALEXANDER, b Cambridge, Mass, Oct 1, 42; m 66. ORGANOMETALLIC CHEMISTRY, POLYMER SCIENCE. *Educ:* Tufts Univ, BS, 64; Univ Mass, MS, 68, PhD(chem), 69. *Prof Exp:* Res chemist, Film Dept, E I du Pont de Nemours & Co, Inc, 69-71; scientist & supvr positive evaluation group, 71-75, res group leader, 75-80, RES LAB MGR, POLAROID CORP, CAMBRIDGE, 80- *Mem:* AAAS; Soc Photog Scientist & Engr; Am Chem Soc. *Res:* Organometallic carbonium ions; polymeric Schiff bases; dye diffusion processes in photography; non-silver imaging systems; organometallic polymers. *Mailing Add:* 29 Saddle Club Rd Lexington MA 02173

SAHINEN, UUNO MATHIAS, b Mass, Mich, Apr 7, 06; m 30; c 1. ECONOMIC GEOLOGY. *Educ:* Mont Sch Mines, BS, 29, MS, 35. *Hon Degrees:* DE, Mont Col Mineral Sci & Technol, 72. *Prof Exp:* Asst mineral engr & geologist, North Butte Mining Co, Mont, 29-31; geologist & statistician, Mont Bur Mines & Geol, 31-38, from geologist to chief geologist, 45-62, assoc dir, 62-69, dir state geologist, 69-71; RETIRED AS EMER PROF, MONT COL MINERAL SCI & TECHNOL, 71- *Mem:* Soc Econ Geologists; Nat Soc Prof Engrs; Am Inst Prof Geologists; hon mem Asn Am State Geologist. *Res:* Economic geology of metals and nonmetals in Montana; Beltian geology of Montana. *Mailing Add:* 4544 SW Calif St Portland OR 97219

SAHINEN, WINSTON MARTIN, b Butte, Mont, Aug 4, 31; m 57; c 4. MINING ENGINEERING, GEOLOGICAL ENGINEERING. *Educ:* Mont Col Mineral Sci & Technol, BS, 53. *Prof Exp:* Res engr, Zonolite Co, 57-60; mine supt, Werdenhoff Mining Co, 60-61; sr mining engr, Pac Power & Light Co, 61-73; mining & geol engr, John T Boyd Co, 73-76, vpres, 76-80; PRES, SAHINEN MINING & GEOL SERV CO, 80- *Mem:* Am Inst Mining, Metall & Petrol Engrs. *Mailing Add:* 510 Bayou Knoll Dr Houston TX 77079

SAHLI, BRENDA PAYNE, b Richmond, Va, Sept 28, 42; m 67; c 3. OCCUPATIONAL HEALTH, TOXICOLOGY. *Educ:* Richmond Prof Inst, BS, 64; Med Col Va, MS, 67; Va Commonwealth Univ, PhD(pharmaceut chem), 74. *Prof Exp:* Res asst anal res, Am Tobacco Co, 64-65; chemist, Firestone Synthetic Fibers & Textiles Co, 67-69; teaching asst, Health Sci Ctr, Va Commonwealth Univ, 70-73; res chemist polymer res, Textile Fibers Dept, E I du Pont de Nemours & Co, 74-77; TOXICOLOGIST, VA DEPT HEALTH, 77- *Concurrent Pos:* Adj prof, Acad Ctr, Va Commonwealth Univ, 75-77; mem comt D-22, Am Soc Testing & Mat & chmn task force E-34. *Mem:* Am Chem Soc; Sigma Xi; Am Col Toxicol; Am Conf Indust Hygienists. *Res:* Development of analytical test procedures for raw materials and fibers; bovine albumin tryptic hydrolyzate; isothermal compressibility of organic liquids; analytical ultracentrifugation; flame retardants; coatings for spun-bonded products; health hazard evaluation of substances with respect to conditions and circumstances of use. *Mailing Add:* 1950 Camborne Rd Richmond VA 23236

SAHLI, MUHAMMAD S, b Haifa, Palestine, June 8, 35; m 67; c 3. ORGANIC CHEMISTRY, POLYMER CHEMISTRY. *Educ:* Am Univ Beirut, BSc, 60; Univ SC, PhD(org chem), 66. *Prof Exp:* Instr chem, Am Univ Beirut, 60-61; res chemist, Film Res & Develop Lab, E I du Pont de Nemours & Co, Inc, 66-75; SR RES SCIENTIST MONOMER TECHNOL, FIBERS & PLASTICS CO, ALLIED CORP, 75- *Concurrent Pos:* Adj prof, Va Commonwealth Univ, 66- *Mem:* Am Chem Soc; Sigma Xi. *Res:* Organic synthesis; elucidation of structure of alkaloids; mechanism of pyrolysis of sulfoxides; emulsion polymerization and properties of dispersion coatings; formulation of coatings and characterization of polymers; industrial toxicology; Bechman rearrangement by products and mechanisms. *Mailing Add:* 1950 Camborne Rd Richmond VA 23235

SAHNEY, B N, pure & applied mathematics, deceased

SAHNEY, VINOD K, b Amritsar, India, Nov 16, 42; US citizen; m 70, c 2. OPERATIONS MANAGEMENT & PLANNING. *Educ:* Ranchi Univ, BSc, 63; Purdue Univ, MSME, 65; Univ Wis-Madison, PhD(indust eng), 70. *Prof Exp:* Asst prof indust eng, Wayne State Univ, 70-74, assoc prof, 74-77; assoc prof health policy & mgt, Harvard Univ, 77-79; PROF INDUST ENG, WAYNE STATE UNIV, 79- *Concurrent Pos:* Vis lectr, Exec Prog Health Policy & Mgt, Harvard Univ, 79-81; mem, Health Care Technol Study Sect, Dept Health & Human Serv, 80-; consult, Nat Ctr Health Serv Res, 80-; adminr, Henry Ford Hosp, Detroit, 81- *Mem:* Opers Res Soc; Am Inst Indust Engrs. *Res:* Operations management with special emphasis in health services delivery organizations; developing better methods of management control including planning, staffing, and scheduling of operations. *Mailing Add:* 4727 Burnley Dr Bloomfield Hills MI 48013

SAHNI, SARTAJ KUMAR, b Poona, India, July 22, 49; m 75; c 2. ALGORITHMS, DESIGN AUTOMATION. *Educ:* Indian Inst Technol, BTech, 70; Cornell Univ, MS, 72, PhD(comput sci), 73. *Prof Exp:* PROF COMPUT SCI, UNIV MINN, MINNEAPOLIS, 81- *Mem:* Asn Comput Mach; Inst Elec & Electronics Engrs; Soc Indust & Appl Math; Inst Mgt Sci. *Res:* Design and analysis of computer algorithms; parallel computing; design automation of electronic circuits. *Mailing Add:* Dept Comput Sci Univ Minn Minneapolis MN 55455

SAHNI, VIRAHT, b Lahore, India, Dec 31, 44. SOLID STATE PHYSICS, ATOMIC PHYSICS. *Educ:* Indian Inst Technol, India, BTech, 65; Polytech Inst Brooklyn, MS, 68, PhD(physics), 72. *Prof Exp:* Polytech fel elec engr, Polytech Inst Brooklyn, 65-68; instr, Pratt Inst, 68-70; sr res asst physics, Polytech Inst Brooklyn, 70-72; from instr to assoc prof, 72-81, PROF PHYSICS, BROOKLYN COL, 82- *Concurrent Pos:* Instr & fel, Brooklyn Col, 72-74; City Univ New York Res Found fac res grants, 73-74 & 75-82. *Mem:* Am Phys Soc; Sigma Xi. *Res:* Theoretical Studies in surface physics employing variational, statistical and model potential techniques; determination of properties of the inhomogeneous electron gas at metallic surfaces such as densities, work functions and surface energies; application and study of density functional theory to problems in atomic and solid state physics. *Mailing Add:* Dept Physics Brooklyn Col Brooklyn NY 11210

SAHYUN, MELVILLE RICHARD VALDE, b Santa Barbara, Calif, Feb 11, 40; m 66; c 2. PHOTOGRAPHIC CHEMISTRY. *Educ:* Univ Calif, Santa Barbara, AB, 59; Univ Calif, Los Angeles, PhD(chem), 63. *Prof Exp:* Sr asst scientist, Nat Cancer Inst, 62-65; NIH res fel chem, Calif Inst Technol, 65-66; res specialist, Imaging Res Lab, 66-74, sr res specialist, Systs Res Lab, 74-81, STAFF SCIENTIST, CENT RES LAB, 3M C0, 81- *Mem:* Am Chem Soc; Soc Photog Sci & Eng; Chem Soc London. *Res:* Photographic science; photography; reaction kinetics; organic photochemistry; solid state science; computer modelling. *Mailing Add:* Cent Res Lab 3M Co 3M Ctr 201-3E-03 St Paul MN 55144

SAIBEL, EDWARD, b Boston, Mass, Dec 25, 03; m 30; c 2. MATHEMATICS, MECHANICS. *Educ:* Mass Inst Technol, SB, 24, PhD(math), 28. *Prof Exp:* Instr math & mech, Univ Minn, 27-30; from asst prof to prof mech, Carnegie Inst Technol, 30-57; prof, Rensselaer Polytech Inst, 57-67, chmn dept, 60-67; prof appl mech, Carnegie-Mellon Univ, 67-72; assoc dir eng, Durham, NC, 72-76, CHIEF SOLID MECH BR, ARMY RES OFF, RES TRIANGLE PARK, 76- *Concurrent Pos:* Consult, 50-; adj prof, NC State Univ, 73- & Duke Univ, 75- *Honors & Awards:* Mayo Hersey Award, Am Soc Mech Engrs, 78. *Mem:* Am Math Soc; fel Am Soc Mech Engrs; Am Soc Lubrication Engrs; Math Asn Am; Soc Eng Sci (pres, 82). *Res:* Topology; vibrations; stability; structures; mechanical properties, flow and fracture of materials; theory of lubrication; machining of metals. *Mailing Add:* Army Res Off PO Box 12211 Res Triangle Park NC 27709

SAID, SAMI I, b Cairo, Egypt, Mar 25, 28. PULMONARY DISEASE, PEPTIDES. *Educ:* Univ Cairo, MB, BCh, 51. *Prof Exp:* Intern, Univ Hosp, Univ Cairo, 51-52, resident internal med, 53; asst resident, Bellevue & Univ Hosps, Postgrad Med Sch, NY Univ, 53-55, instr med, Sch Med, 55, NY Heart Asn res fel, Bellevue Hosp, 55-57; asst physician & fel, Sch Med, Johns Hopkins Univ & Johns Hopkins Hosp, 57-58; from asst prof to prof, Med Col Va, 58-71; prof internal med & pharmacol, Univ Tex Health Sci Ctr, 71-81; chief, Pulmonary Dis Sect, Vet Admin Hosp, 71-81; PROF MED, UNIV OKLAHOMA HEALTH SCI CTR, 81-; CHIEF, PULMONARY DIS & CRITICAL CARE SECT, VET ADMIN MED CTR, OKLAHOMA CITY, 81- *Concurrent Pos:* Fulbright res fel, Naval Med Res Unit 3, 52-53; Fulbright traveling fel, 53; Nat Heart Inst res career develop award, 62-71; vis scientist, Karolinska Inst, Sweden, 68-70; dir, Pulmonary Specialized Ctr Res, Dallas, 71-81; exchange scientist, Vet Admin-INSERM, France, 73. *Mem:* Am Physiol Soc; Am Soc Clin Invest; Asn Am Physicians; Soc Neurosci. *Res:* Pulmonary physiology and pathophysiology, especially role of humoral mediators; vasoactive intestinal peptide and other biologically active peptides. *Mailing Add:* Univ Okla Health Sci Ctr PO Box 26307 Oklahoma City OK 73126

SAIDAK, WALTER JOHN, b Ottawa, Ont, May 10, 30; m 56; c 2. WEED SCIENCE. *Educ:* Ont Agr Col, BSA, 53; Cornell Univ, MS, 55, PhD(veg crops), 58. *Prof Exp:* Res officer, Plant Res Inst, Can Dept Agr, 58-62, res scientist, Res Sta, 62-73, RES COORDR WEEDS, RES BR, CENT EXP FARM, CAN DEPT AGR, 73- *Mem:* Weed Sci Soc Am; Agr Inst Can. *Res:* Weed control in field and horticultural crops; translocation of herbicides. *Mailing Add:* 50 Kilmory Cr Nepean Ottawa ON K2E 6N1 Can

SAIDE, JUDITH DANA, b Worcester, Mass, Feb 21, 44. MUSCLE STRUCTURE & CHEMISTRY. *Educ:* Vassar Col, AB, 65; Boston Univ, PhD(physiol), 72. *Prof Exp:* Res fel, Dept Med, Mass Gen Hosp, 72-75; asst biochem, 75-77, ASST PROF, DEPT PHYSIOL, SCH MED, BOSTON UNIV, 77- *Concurrent Pos:* Res fel biol chem, Harvard Med Sch, 72-75, instr, Dept Physiol, 75-77; establ investr, Am Heart Asn, 77. *Mem:* AAAS. *Res:* Identification, characterization and assembly of proteins of the two band of striated muscle. *Mailing Add:* L-713 Dept Physiol Sch Med Boston Univ 80 E Concord St Boston MA 02118

SAIDEL, GERALD MAXWELL, b New Haven, Conn, May 27, 38; m 69. PHYSIOLOGICAL SYSTEMS. *Educ:* Rensselaer Polytech Inst, BChE, 60; Johns Hopkins Univ, PhD(chem eng), 65. *Prof Exp:* Asst prof, 67-73, assoc prof, 73-81, PROF BIOMED ENG, CASE WESTERN RESERVE UNIV, 81- *Concurrent Pos:* Res engr, Vet Admin Med Ctr, Cleveland, 70-; sect ed, Annals of Biomed Eng, 79- *Mem:* Am Inst Chem Eng; Soc Math Biol; Biomed Eng Soc; Am Asn Univ Professors. *Res:* Transport processes in lung and kidney; modeling and computer simulation; parameter estimation of dynamic physiological systems; distributed population dynamics of cells and particles. *Mailing Add:* Dept of Biomed Eng Case Western Reserve Univ Cleveland OH 44106

SAIDEL, LEO JAMES, b Lanark, Ill, Aug 22, 16; m 43; c 3. BIOCHEMISTRY. *Educ:* Univ Chicago, BS, 38; Georgetown Univ, MS, 41, PhD(biochem), 46. *Prof Exp:* Lab aide, Food & Drug Admin, USDA, 38 & Bur Dairy Indust, 38-40, jr chemist, 40-42; res assoc, Col Physicians & Surgeons, Columbia Univ, 42-46; chemist, G Barr & Co, Ill, 46-47; assoc, Univ Chicago, 47; from instr to prof biochem, Chicago Med Sch, 47-82, chmn dept, 75-76; RETIRED. *Mem:* Am Chem Soc; Am Soc Biol Chemists. *Res:* Composition, structure and properties of peptides and proteins; ultraviolet absorption spectra of proteins and related materials. *Mailing Add:* 3333 Green Bay Rd North Chicago IL 60064

SAIDUDDIN, SYED, b Kakinada, India, Dec 7, 38; m 67; c 1. ENDOCRINOLOGY, REPRODUCTIVE PHYSIOLOGY. *Educ:* Sri Venkateswara Univ, India, BVSc, 59; Indian Vet Res Inst, NDAG, 62; Univ Nev, Reno, MS, 64; Univ Wis-Madison, PhD(endocrinol), 68. *Prof Exp:* Proj assoc, Univ Wis, 67-69; NIH res fel, Med Sch, Tufts Univ, 69-71; asst prof, 71-76, assoc prof, 76-79, PROF VET PHYSIOL, COL VET MED, OHIO STATE UNIV, 79- *Mem:* Soc Study Reproduction; fel Am Col Vet Pharmacol & Therapeut; Endocrine Soc; Am Physiol Soc. *Res:* Endocrine control of ovarian follicular growth; mechanism of action of estrogen and progesterone. *Mailing Add:* Dept of Vet Physiol Ohio State Univ Col Vet Med Columbus OH 43210

SAIER, MILTON H, JR, b Palo Alto, Calif, July 30, 41; m 61; c 3. MOLECULAR TRANSPORT, CELL REGULATION. *Educ:* Univ Calif, Berkeley, BS, 63, PhD(biochem), 68. *Prof Exp:* Asst prof, 72-76, ASSOC PROF BIOL, UNIV CALIF, SAN DIEGO, 76- *Mem:* Am Soc Microbiol; Am Soc Cell Biol; Am Soc Biol Chemists. *Res:* Mechanism and regulation of sugar transport in bacteria; mechanism and regulation of salt transport in kidney cells. *Mailing Add:* Dept Biol Univ Calif San Diego CA 92093

SAIF, LINDA JEAN, b Columbus, Ohio, June 29, 47; m 70; c 1. MICROBIOLOGY, IMMUNOLOGY. *Educ:* Col Wooster, BA, 69; Ohio State Univ, MS, 71, PhD(microbiol), 76. *Prof Exp:* Res asst, Dept Microbiol, Case Western Reserve Univ, 69-70; instr microbiol, 72-74, res assoc, 75-76, res assoc fel, 77-78, ASST PROF, DEPT VET SCI, OHIO AGR RES & DEVELOP CTR, 79- *Mem:* Am Soc Microbiol. *Res:* Basic mechanisms of the immune response of swine and cattle; mechanisms of protection against enteric viral infections; identification and purification of bovine and porcine enteric viruses and immunoglobulins. *Mailing Add:* Dept of Vet Sci Ohio Agr Res & Develop Ctr Wooster OH 44691

SAIF, YEHIA MOHAMED, b Minia, Egypt, Dec 23, 34; m 70. VETERINARY MICROBIOLOGY. *Educ:* Cairo Univ, DVM, 58; Ohio State Univ, MSc, 64, PhD(vet med), 67; Am Col Vet Microbiol, dipl. *Prof Exp:* Teaching asst vet med, Cairo Univ, 59-62; res asst vet sci, 65-67, fel, 67-68, asst prof, 68-73, assoc prof, 73-77, PROF VET SCI, OHIO AGR RES & DEVELOP CTR, 77- *Mem:* AAAS; Am Soc Microbiol; Poultry Sci Asn; Am Vet Med Asn; NY Acad Sci. *Res:* immune response of domestic animals; poultry diseases. *Mailing Add:* Dept Vet Sci Ohio Agr Res & Develop Ctr Wooster OH 44691

SAIFER, MARK GARY PIERCE, b Philadelphia, Pa, Sept 16, 38; m 61; c 2. BIOPHYSICS, MOLECULAR BIOLOGY. *Educ:* Univ Pa, AB, 60; Univ Calif, Berkeley, PhD(biophys), 67. *Prof Exp:* Actg asst prof zool, Univ Calif, Berkeley, 66; sr cancer res scientist, Roswell Park Mem Inst, 68-70; LAB DIR ENZYM, DIAG DATA, INC, 70- *Concurrent Pos:* Am Cancer Soc fel, Dept Bacteriol & Immunol, Univ Calif, Berkeley, 67-68; fel, Int Lab Genetics & Biophys, Naples, 67; Damon Runyon Mem Fund grant, 68-70; res develop award, Health Res Inc, Buffalo, 68-70. *Mem:* AAAS; NY Acad Sci; Parenteral Drug Asn; Am Soc Photobiol. *Res:* Regulation of synthesis, compartmentalization and secretion of proteins by mammalian cells; biological and medical effects of superoxide dismutase; immunology and pharmacology of enzymes and other proteins. *Mailing Add:* 1561 Hawthorne Terr Berkeley CA 94708

SAIFF, EDWARD IRA, b New Brunswick, NJ, Oct 11, 42; m 67; c 2. ZOOLOGY, ANATOMY. *Educ:* Rutgers Univ, BA, 64, PhD(zool), 73; State Univ NY Buffalo, MA, 68. *Prof Exp:* Instr zool, Rutgers Univ, 70-71, lectr, 71-72; asst prof, 72-75, assoc prof, 75-80, PROF BIOL, RAMAPO COL, NJ, 80- *Mem:* Am Ornith Union; Am Soc Zoologists; Soc Syst Zoology; Linnean Soc London; Sigma Xi. *Res:* Avian anatomy, particularly of the middle ear region with an end of understanding taxonomic relationships above the level of genus; anatomical correlates of hearing in birds; evolutionary theory. *Mailing Add:* Theoret & Appl Sci Ramapo Col 505 Ramapo Valley Rd Mahwah NJ 07430

SAIGER, GEORGE LEWIS, b Burlington, Vt, Dec 5, 22; wid. EPIDEMIOLOGY, MEDICAL STATISTICS. *Educ:* Univ Vt, BS, 45, MD, 48; Columbia Univ, MPH, 51, DrPH(med statist), 55. *Prof Exp:* Intern, US Marine Hosp, Cleveland, Ohio, 48-49; asst county health officer, USPHS, 49-50; instr biostatist, Columbia Univ, 51-52; consult med res, 52-53; chief biometrician, Army Med Res Lab, Ft Knox, Ky, 53-55; asst prof prev med, La State Univ, 55; asst prof biostatist & lectr statist methods in human genetics, Sch Pub Health & Admin Med & Col Physicians & Surgeons, Columbia Univ, 56-59, assoc prof epidemiol, 59-64; dir div res & ref, Food & Drug Admin, DC, 63-64; consult med res, 64-67; OWNER-DIR, GEORGE L SAIGER & ASSOCS, MED RES CONSULTS, 67- *Concurrent Pos:* Lectr, State Univ NY, 52 & Univ Calif, 52; consult, Rand Corp, 55-57 & bur med, Food & Drug Admin, DC, 63; Soc Sci Res Coun travel award, Int Statist Inst, Paris, 61; mem adv comt model prescription recording syst study, Sch Pharm, Univ Pittsburgh, 63-64; expert witness comt on com, US Senate, 65 & comt on interstate & for com, House of Rep, 65 & 69; Rockefeller Found fel & lectr, Univ Aberdeen, 59. *Mem:* Fel AAAS; fel Am Geriat Soc; Asn Teachers Prev Med; fel Am Pub Health Asn; Am Statist Asn. *Res:* Administrative medicine; public health and preventive medicine; biostatistics; biological assay; social statistics; demography; clinical medicine; human genetics; radiobiology; clinical pharmacology; toxicology; biochemistry; biomedical sciences; cancer; chemotherapy; dental research; drug metabolism; experimental medicine; medical research; pharmacology. *Mailing Add:* 28 John St Englewood Cliffs NJ 07632

SAIGO, ROY HIROFUMI, b Sacramento, Calif, Aug 6, 40; m 67. PLANT ANATOMY, PLANT PATHOLOGY. *Educ:* Univ Calif, Davis, BA, 62; Ore State Univ, PhD(plant anat), 69. *Prof Exp:* ASSOC PROF BIOL, UNIV WIS-EAU CLAIRE, 67-, ASST TO THE DEAN ARTS & SCI, 80- *Concurrent Pos:* Fac res grants, Univ Wis-Eau Claire, 68-69 & 71-72, teacher improv assignment, 70; acad affairs intern, Univ Wis Syst, 75-76. *Mem:* AAAS; Bot Soc Am; Am Inst Biol Sci. *Res:* Effect of insects on the bark of coniferous trees; ultrastructural investigation of the phloem of lower vascular plants and protein body development in oats. *Mailing Add:* Dept of Biol Univ of Wis Eau Claire WI 54701

SAI-HALASZ, GEORGE ANTHONY, b Budapest, Hungary, Dec 7, 43; m 70; c 1. SOLID STATE PHYSICS. *Educ:* Eotovos Roland Sci Univ, Budapest, dipl, 66; Case Western Reserve Univ, PhD(physics), 72. *Prof Exp:* Fel, Univ Pa, 72-74; RES STAFF MEM, IBM WATSON RES LAB, 74- *Mem:* Am Phys Soc. *Res:* Low temperature physics; transport in solid helium, nonequilibrium phenomena in superconductivity; semiconductor superlattices; band structure, optical and transport properties; physics of semiconductor devices. *Mailing Add:* IBM T J Watson Res Ctr PO Box 218 Yorktown Heights NY 10598

SAILA, SAUL BERNHARD, b Providence, RI, May 23, 24; m 49; c 3. FISH BIOLOGY. *Educ:* Univ RI, BS, 49; Cornell Univ, MS, 50, PhD(fishery biol), 52. *Prof Exp:* Res assoc zool, Ind Univ, 52-54; fishery biologist, Div Fish & Game, RI Dept Agr & Conserv, 54-56; from asst prof marine biol to assoc prof oceanog, 56-67, coordr comput lab, 59-76, dir marine exp sta, 66-76, PROF OCEANOG, UNIV RI, 67- *Honors & Awards:* Am Fisheries Soc Award, 59. *Mem:* AAAS; Am Fisheries Soc; Am Soc Limnol & Oceanog; Inst Fishery Res Biologists; Int Asn Theoret & Appl Limnol. *Res:* Fish population dynamics. *Mailing Add:* Grad Sch of Oceanog Univ of RI Kingston RI 02881

SAILER, REECE IVAN, b Roseville, Ill, Nov 8, 15; m 39; c 2. ENTOMOLOGY. *Educ:* Univ Kans, AB, 38, PhD(entom), 42. *Prof Exp:* Asst to state entomologist, Kans, 42; assoc entomologist, Bur Entom & Plant Quarantine, USDA, 42-48, entomologist, Entom Res Div, Agr Res Serv, 48-57, asst dir insect identification & parasite introd res br, 57-60, in chg Europ Parasite Lab, 60-66, asst dir insect identification & parasite introd res br, 66-67, chief br, 67-73, chmn, Insect Identification & Beneficial Insect Introd Inst, 72-73; GRAD RES PROF ENTOM & NEMATOL, UNIV FLA, 73- *Concurrent Pos:* Lectr, Univ Md, 51-60; adj prof, Univ NC, 68- *Mem:* AAAS; Entom Soc Am; Ecol Soc Am; Arctic Inst NAm. *Res:* Biological control; taxonomy of Heteroptera; biology of Alaska biting diptera; insect ecology. *Mailing Add:* Dept of Entom & Nematol McCarty Hall Univ of Fla Gainesville FL 32611

SAILLANT, ROGER BARRY, b Philadelphia, Pa, Apr 7, 43; m 66; c 3. INORGANIC CHEMISTRY. *Educ:* Bowdoin Col, AB, 65; Ind Univ, Bloomington, PhD(inorg chem), 69. *Prof Exp:* NSF fel, Univ Calif, Los Angeles, 69-70; inorg chemist, Sci Res Staff, 70-74, SUPVR POWERTRAIN CHASSIS PROD ENG, FORD MOTOR CO, 74- *Mem:* Am Chem Soc. *Res:* Fuels and lubricants; engine designs and octane requirement increase; automotive catalysts. *Mailing Add:* 32 Brookline Dearborn MI 48120

SAILOR, SAMUEL, b Shanghai, China, June 12, 22; US citizen; m 49; c 4. CIVIL ENGINEERING, PHOTOGRAMMETRY. *Educ:* Cornell Univ, BCE, 48, MCE, 52. *Prof Exp:* Rodman, NY, Chicago & St Louis Rwy, 48-50, instrumentman, 50-51; instr civil eng, Rutgers Univ, 52-56, asst prof, 56-65; ASSOC PROF CIVIL ENG, UNIV WYO, 65- *Mem:* Am Soc Photogram; Am Cong Surv & Mapping; Am Soc Civil Engrs; Am Soc Eng Educ; Nat Soc Prof Engrs. *Res:* Structures; surveying; geodesy; computer programming. *Mailing Add:* Dept of Civil Eng Univ of Wyo Laramie WY 82070

SAILOR, VANCE LEWIS, b Springfield, Mo, June 28, 20; m 43; c 3. NUCLEAR SCIENCE. *Educ:* DePauw Univ, AB, 43; Yale Univ, MS, 47, PhD(physics), 49. *Prof Exp:* From assoc physicist to physicist, 49-67, SR PHYSICIST, BROOKHAVEN NAT LAB, UPTON, 67- *Concurrent Pos:* Dir systs anal proj, Int Energy Agency. *Mem:* Am Phys Soc; Am Nuclear Soc; Am Asn Physics Teachers. *Res:* Neutron and reactor physics; charged particle reactions; low temperature physics; nuclear energy; environmental effects of energy production and usage. *Mailing Add:* 100 Durkee Lane East Patchogue NY 11772

SAIMOTO, SHIGEO, physical metallurgy, mechanical metallurgy, see previous edition

SAIN, MICHAEL K(ENT), b St Louis, Mo, Mar 22, 37; m 63; c 5. CONTROL SYSTEMS. *Educ:* St Louis Univ, BS, 59, MS, 62; Univ Ill, PhD(elec eng), 65. *Prof Exp:* From asst prof to assoc prof, 65-72, PROF ELEC ENG, UNIV NOTRE DAME, 72- *Concurrent Pos:* Ed, Inst Elec & Electronics Engrs Transactions on Automatic Control, 79; mem review panel, NSF, 76 & 79; res grants, NASA, 75-81, NSF, 66-71, 73-77 & 81 & Off Naval Res, 79-81. *Mem:* Fel Inst Elec & Electronics Engrs; Soc Indust & Appl Math; Am Soc Eng Educ. *Res:* Algebraic systems theory and applications; multivaniable control systems; engine control. *Mailing Add:* Dept of Elec Eng Univ of Notre Dame Notre Dame IN 46556

SAINI, GIRDHARI LAL, b Hariana, India, Aug 2, 31; m 49; c 3. MATHEMATICS. *Educ:* Panjab Univ, India, BS, 55, MA, 57; Indian Inst Technol, Kharagpur, PhD(math), 61. *Prof Exp:* Assoc lectr math, Indian Inst Technol, Kharagpur, 60, lectr, 60-62; vis asst prof, Math Res Ctr, Univ Wis-Madison, 62-64; asst prof, Indian Inst Technol, New Delhi, 64-67; assoc prof, 67-76, PROF MATH, UNIV SASK, 76- *Concurrent Pos:* Res mem, US Army Res Ctr, Univ Wis-Madison, 62-64. *Mem:* Am Math Soc; Can Math Soc. *Res:* Relativistic fluid mechanics. *Mailing Add:* Dept of Math Univ of Sask Saskatoon SK S7K 2Z1 Can

SAINI, GULSHAN RAI, b Hoshiarpur, India, Oct 1, 24; Can citizen; m 50; c 1. SOIL SCIENCE. *Educ:* Panjab Univ, India, BSc, 45, MSc, 56; Ohio State Univ, PhD(soils), 60. *Prof Exp:* Res asst soils & fertilizers, Govt Agr Col, Ludhiana, India, 45-57, asst prof soils, 60-61; RES SCIENTIST, CAN DEPT AGR, 62- *Concurrent Pos:* Hon lectr, Univ NB, 68- *Mem:* AAAS; Soil Sci Soc Am; Can Soc Soil Sci; Int Soc Soil Sci. *Res:* Effect of soil physical conditions on plant growth; agricultural hydrology. *Mailing Add:* Can Dept of Agr PO Box 20280 Fredericton ON E3B 4Z7 Can

SAINI, RAJINDER S, entomology, see previous edition

SAINI, RAVINDER KUMAR, b Hoshiarpur, India, Jan 28, 46; US citizen; m 71; c 2. CARDIOVASCULAR PHARMACOLOGY, AUTONOMIC PHARMACOLOGY. *Educ:* Col Vet Med, Hissar, India, DVM, 68; Postgrad Med Res Inst, Chandigarh, India, MS, 71; Univ Naples, Italy, PhD(pharmacol), 73. *Prof Exp:* Res assoc pharmacol, Sch Med, Univ Pa, 73-74; res fel pharmacol, Univ Wis, Madison, 74-76; res assoc pharmacol, Sch Med, Univ Miami, Fla, 76-78; res pharmacologist, Merrell Res Ctr, Cincinnati, Ohio, 78-79; SR RES INVESTR PHARMACOL, SQUIBB INST MED RES, 79- *Concurrent Pos:* Res grant investr, Tobacco Inst, 73-74, Am Lung Asn, 74-76 & NIH Cardiovasc Training, 76-78. *Mem:* Am Soc Pharmacol & Exp Therapeut; fel Am Col Angiol; Int Soc Heart Res; Ital Pharmacol Soc. *Res:* Development and design of antianginal, antiarrhythmic and antithrombotic agents in animal models of cardiovascular and occlusive diseases. *Mailing Add:* Dept Pharmacol PO Box 4000 Squibb Inst Med Res Princeton NJ 08540

SAINSBURY, JOHN CHARLES, b London, Eng, Dec 27, 33; m 58; c 2. FISHERIES SCIENCE, NAVAL ARCHITECTURE. *Educ:* Durham Univ, BSc, 57; Univ Southampton, PhD(eng), 66. *Prof Exp:* Systs engr, Blackburn Aircraft Ltd, Eng, 57-59; lectr naval archit, WPark Col, Sunderland, 62-64; sr lectr & head dept, Col Fisheries, Navig, Marine Eng & Electronics, St Johns Univ, Nfld, 64-67; assoc prof fisheries & marine technol, Univ RI, 67-74, chmn dept, 67-76, prof, 75-81, assoc dir, Int Ctr Marine Res & Develop, 79-80; CONSULT, 81- *Mem:* Royal Inst Naval Architects. *Res:* Commercial fishing vessel design; fisheries development; fisheries education and training; fisheries extension. *Mailing Add:* 223 Second Isle S Port Richey FL 33568

SAINSBURY, ROBERT STEPHEN, b Halifax, NS, Apr 16, 43; m 81; c 2. NEUROPSYCHOLOGY. *Educ:* Mt Allison Univ, BA, 63; Dalhousie Univ, MA, 65; McMaster Univ, PhD(psychol), 69. *Prof Exp:* Asst prof, 69-72, assoc prof, 72-80, PROF PSYCHOL, UNIV CALGARY, 80- *Mem:* Can Psychol Asn. *Res:* The effects of brain lesions on species typical behavior in small mammals. *Mailing Add:* Dept of Psychol Univ of Calgary Calgary AB T2N 1N4 Can

ST AMAND, PIERRE, b Tacoma, Wash, Feb 4, 20; m 45; c 4. GEOPHYSICS. *Educ:* Univ Alaska, BS, 48; Calif Inst Technol, MS, 51, PhD(geophys, geol), 53. *Prof Exp:* Magnetic observer, Carnegie Inst, Alaska, 41-42, mem geophys inst, 46-48; physicist, 50-61, head, Earth & Planetary Sci Div & Spec Projs Off, 61-81, CHIEF SCIENTIST, NAVAL WEAPON CTR, US NAVAL ORD TEST STA, 81- *Concurrent Pos:* Asst, Seismol Lab, Calif Inst Technol, 52-54; Fulbright scholar, France, 54-55; Int Coop Admin prof sch geol, Chile, 58-61; consult, UN Chilean & Argentine Govts, 60 & States of Calif, SDak, NDak, Ore & Wash; consult, Orgn Am States, 65-72. *Honors & Awards:* Distinguished Civilian Serv Medal, US Navy, 67; Spec Award, Philippine Air Force; L T E Thompson Award, Naval Weapon Ctr, 74; Distinguished Pub Serv Award, 76; Thunderbird Award, Weather Modification Asn. *Mem:* Fel AAAS; Seismol Soc Am; fel Geol Soc Am; Am Geophys Union; Weather Modification Asn. *Res:* Auroral height measurement; atmospheric refraction; terrestrial magnetism; ionosphere; light of night sky; seismology; earthquakes; structural geology; electronics and instrumentation; circum pacific tectonics; weather modification; oceanography; deep sea research. *Mailing Add:* Earth & Planetary Sci Div Naval Weapon Ctr China Lake CA 93555

ST AMAND, WILBROD, b Old Town, Maine, May 5, 27; m 50. CYTOGENETICS. *Educ:* Univ Maine, BA, 48; Univ Tenn, MS, 49, PhD(zool, entom), 54. *Prof Exp:* Asst zool, Univ Tenn, 48-49, instr, Exten Serv, 50; res assoc radiation biol, Oak Ridge Nat Lab, 54-55, biologist, 55-58; assoc prof biol, 58-61, PROF BIOL, UNIV MISS, 61- *Mem:* AAAS; Am Micros Soc; Am Soc Zoologists; Genetics Soc Am; Am Inst Biol Sci. *Res:* Radiation cytology; radiosensitivity of the stages of mitosis; mouse genetics. *Mailing Add:* Dept of Biol Univ of Miss University MS 38677

ST ANGELO, ALLEN JOSEPH, b New Orleans, La, April 11, 32; m 58; c 3. LIPIDOXIDATION, PROTEIN CHEMISTRY. *Educ:* Southeastern La Univ, BS, 57; Tulane Univ, MS, 65, PhD(biochem), 68. *Prof Exp:* Res chem, 58-79, ACTG RES LEADER, SOUTHERN REGIONAL RES CTR, USDA, 79- *Mem:* Am Chem Soc; Am Oil Chemists Soc; Am Peanut Res & Educ Soc; Sigma Xi. *Res:* Develop methology for assessing overall quality of peanuts, eggs and fish; interaction of lipid oxidation products with proteins. *Mailing Add:* Southern Regional Res Ctr USDA PO Box 19687 New Orleans LA 70179

SAINT-ARNAUD, RAYMOND, b Shawinigan, Que, Sept 23, 35; m 62; c 2. ELECTRICAL ENGINEERING. *Educ:* Laval Univ, BA, 55, BScAppl, 61, Dipl Adm, 72; Univ Strathclyde, PhD(elec eng), 66. *Prof Exp:* Engr, Hydro-Quebec, Montreal, 61-62; res asst eng, Univ Strathclyde, 62-65; asst prof elec eng, 65-70, ASSOC PROF ELEC ENG, LAVAL UNIV, 70- *Concurrent Pos:* Res assoc, Dept Exp Med, Laval Univ, 71- *Mem:* Inst Elec & Electronics Engrs. *Res:* High voltage engineering; ionization phenomena; gas lasers; electrostatics; bioelectricity; biometeorology. *Mailing Add:* Dept of Elec Eng Laval Univ Quebec PQ C1K 7P4 Can

ST ARNAUD, ROLAND JOSEPH, Can citizen. SOILS. *Educ:* Univ Sask, BSA, 48, MSc, 50; Mich State Univ, PhD(soils), 61. *Prof Exp:* Res officer, Sask Soil Surv, Can Dept Agr, 50-56; from asst prof to assoc prof, 56-70, PROF SOIL SCI, UNIV SASK, 70- *Concurrent Pos:* Sci ed, Can Soc Soil Sci, 63-66. *Mem:* fel Can Soc Soil Sci (pres, 74-75); Am Soc Agron; Agr Inst Can. *Res:* Soil classification; mineralogical studies and micropedology. *Mailing Add:* Dept Soil Sci Univ Sask Saskatoon SK S7N 0W0 Can

ST CLAIR, ANNE KING, b Bluefield, WVa, May 31, 47; m 71; c 1. BIOCHEMISTRY. *Educ:* Queens Col, BA, 69; Va Polytech & State Univ, MS, 72. *Prof Exp:* Res assoc, Nat Aeronaut & Space Admin, 72-77; POLYMER RES CHEMIST, LANGLEY RES CTR, NASA, 77- *Concurrent Pos:* Speakers Bur, Soc Advan Mat Process Engrs, 80-; lectr, State Univ NY, 81- *Honors & Awards:* IR-100 Award, 81. *Mem:* Am Chem Soc; Soc Advan Mat Process Engrs; Asn Women Sci. *Res:* Synthesis, characterization and development of high-performance aerospace materials for applications as structural adhesives, advanced composites, films and fibers; author or coauthor of 35 publications. *Mailing Add:* Langley Res Ctr NASA Mail Stop 226 Hampton VA 23665

ST CLAIR, MAURICE W(EBSTER), b Foochow, China, Jan 28, 23; US citizen; m 62; c 1. ELECTRICAL ENGINEERING. *Educ:* Pomona Col, BA, 48; Stanford Univ, Engr, 50. *Prof Exp:* Asst, Microwave Lab, Stanford Univ, 48-50; proj engr, Varian Assocs, 50-52, supvr environ testing, 52-54, proj mgr, 54-57, supvr stable oscillator develop, 57-58, mgr microwave components, 58-62; vpres, Mitek Corp, 62-63; proj mgr, Microwave Electronics Corp, 63-64; assoc prof, 64-74, PROF ENG, FOOTHILL COL, 74- *Mem:* Inst Elec & Electronics Engrs; Am Soc Eng Educ; Sigma Xi. *Res:* High power pulse transformers; electronic industrial process control; microwave tube and component development. *Mailing Add:* 1021 Sierra Dr Menlo Park CA 94025

ST CLAIR, RICHARD WILLIAM, b Sioux Falls, SDak, Oct 10, 40; m 62; c 2. BIOCHEMISTRY, PATHOBIOLOGY. *Educ:* Colo State Univ, BS, 62, PhD(physiol), 65. *Prof Exp:* PROF PATH & PHYSIOL, BOWMAN GRAY SCH MED, WAKE FOREST UNIV, 65- *Concurrent Pos:* NIH fel aging, Bowman Gray Sch Med, 65-67; fel coun arteriosclerosis, Am Heart Asn, estab investr, 70-75. *Mem:* Am Soc Exp Path; Tissue Culture Asn; Soc Exp Biol Med; Sigma Xi; AAAS. *Res:* Atherosclerosis research; arterial metabolism; lipid metabolism in nonhuman primates; bile acid metabolism and gallstone disease. *Mailing Add:* Dept of Path Bowman Gray Sch of Med Winston-Salem NC 27103

ST CLAIR, TERRY LEE, b Roanoke, Va, June 18, 43; m 71. POLYMER CHEMISTRY. *Educ:* Roanoke Col, BS, 65; Va Polytech Inst & State Univ, PhD(org chem), 73. *Prof Exp:* Chemist quality control, E I du Pont, Orlon, 65-67; solid propellants engr, Hercules Inc-Radford Army Ammo Plant, 67-68; chemist adhesives, 72-75, aerospace technologist polymers, 75-80, RES CHEMIST POLYMERS, LANGLEY RES CTR, NASA, 80- *Mem:* Am Chem Soc; Sigma Xi; Soc Aerospaace Mat & Process Engrs. *Res:* Preparation and development of adhesives and composite matrix resins for aerospace applications. *Mailing Add:* 17 Roberts Landing Poquoson VA 23662

ST CYR, LEWIS ALPHA, metallurgical chemistry, see previous edition

SAINTE-MARIE, GUY, b Montreal, Que, May 22, 28; m 55; c 3. HEMATOLOGY, LYMPHOLOGY. *Educ:* Col Ste-Marie, BA, 50; Univ Montreal, MD, 55; McGill Univ, PhD(histol), 62. *Prof Exp:* From asst prof to assoc prof anat, Univ Western Ont, 61-66; assoc prof, 66-69, PROF ANAT, UNIV MONTREAL, 69-, CHMN DEPT, 77- *Concurrent Pos:* Nat Cancer Inst Can fel, 58-60; res fel bact & immunol, Harvard Univ, 60-61; Med Res Coun Can res assoc, 66. *Mem:* Am Soc Anat; Reticuloendothelial Soc; Am Soc Hemat; Int Soc Hemat. *Res:* Studies on structure of blood-forming organs; mode of formation of blood cells; immunological activity of blood cells and blood-forming organs. *Mailing Add:* Dept of Anat Univ of Montreal Montreal PQ H3C 3J7 Can

ST HOYME, LUCILE ELEANOR, b Washington, DC, Sept 8, 24. PHYSICAL ANTHROPOLOGY. *Educ:* George Washington Univ, BSc, 50, MSc, 53; Oxford Univ, DPhil(anthrop), 63. *Prof Exp:* Aide-Technician anthrop, 53-63, ASSOC CUR ANTHROP, SMITHSONIAN INST, 63-; PROF LECTR ORTHODONT, DENT SCH, GEORGETOWN UNIV, 72- *Concurrent Pos:* Prof lectr anthrop, Am Univ, 64-69, adj prof, 69-; assoc prof lectr, George Washington Univ, 65-66 & Univ Pa, 66-67; lay preceptor, Inter-Met, 72-76; sci mgr, Anthropos, 74- *Mem:* Am Anthrop Asn; Am Asn Phys Anthrop; Soc Woman Geographers; Am Inst Biol Sci. *Res:* Physical anthropology including dental and general paleopathology; human osteology; sex differences in skeletal remains; history of physical anthropology. *Mailing Add:* 1805 Monroe St NE Washington DC 20018

ST JEAN, JOSEPH, JR, b Tacoma, Wash, July 24, 23; m 71. MICROPALEONTOLOGY, INVERTEBRATE PALEONTOLOGY. *Educ:* Col Puget Sound, BS, 49; Ind Univ, AM, 53, PhD(geol), 56. *Prof Exp:* Instr geol, Kans State Col, 51-52; from instr to asst prof, Trinity Col, Conn, 55-57; from asst prof to assoc prof, 57-66, PROF GEOL, UNIV NC, CHAPEL HILL, 66- *Concurrent Pos:* Partic, Nat Acad Sci-USSR Acad Sci Exchange Prog, 65. *Mem:* AAAS; Paleont Res Inst; Paleont Soc; Soc Econ Paleont & Mineral; Int Paleont Union. *Res:* Stromatoporoidea and Paleozoic Foraminifera. *Mailing Add:* Dept of Geol Univ of NC Chapel Hill NC 27514

ST JOHN, ANDREW DAVIS, b Kansas City, Mo, Oct, 28, 19; m 54. ANALYTICAL SIMULATION MODELS, HIGHWAY TRAFFIC ENGINEERING. *Educ:* Univ Mo, Columbia, BS, 42, MS, 48. *Prof Exp:* Test engr, Wright Aeronaut Corp, 42-45; instr mech eng, Univ Mo, Columbia, 47-48; SR ADV ENG ANAL, MIDWEST RES INST, 48- *Mem:* Transp Res Bd. *Res:* Development, application and interpretation of analytical models in the areas of economics, engineering and applied technology; computerization and documentation of models. *Mailing Add:* Midwest Res Inst 425 Volker Blvd Kansas City MO 64110

ST JOHN, DANIEL SHELTON, b San Diego, Calif, June 25, 23; m 43; c 4. PHYSICAL CHEMISTRY. *Educ:* Univ Calif, BS, 43; Univ Wis, PhD(chem), 49. *Prof Exp:* Jr technologists, Shell Oil Co, 43-44; engr, Los Alamos Sci Lab, Univ Calif, 44-47; chemist, E I du Pont de Nemours & Co, 49-58, res mgr, 58-64, mem develop dept, 64-66; pres, Holotron Corp, 66-69; res mgr, 70-74, res fel, Polymer Intermediates Dept, 74-80, RES ASSOC, PETROCHEM DEPT, E I DU PONT DE NEMOURS & CO, INC, 80- *Res:* Theoretical reactor physics; physics; physical optics; heterogeneous catalysis. *Mailing Add:* RD 2 Box 371 Hockessin DE 19707

ST JOHN, DOUGLAS FRANCIS, b Toledo, Ohio, May 4, 38; m 60; c 5. MATERIALS SCIENCE, MECHANICS. *Educ:* Univ Toledo, BSME, 60, MSME, 65, MBA, 71; Mich State Univ, PhD(mech), 69. *Prof Exp:* Exp engr, Pratt & Whitney Aircraft, 60; assoc mech engr, 64-65; SR MAT SCIENTIST, OWENS-ILL, INC, 69- *Mem:* Am Phys Soc; Am Inst Physics; Sigma Xi; Tech Asn Graphic Arts. *Res:* Glass melting, refining and homogenizing process analysis and design; solid-to-solid adhesion; motivational research methodology. *Mailing Add:* 2366 Goddard Rd Toledo OH 43606

ST JOHN, FRAZE LEE, b Lebanon, Ohio, May 23, 39; m 62; c 2. ZOOLOGY. *Educ:* Miami Univ, BS, 61; Ind Univ, Bloomington, MA, 63; Ohio State Univ, PhD(zool), 70. *Prof Exp:* Instr zool, Miami Univ, 63-65; naturalist, biol, Wahkeena State Mem, Ohio, 68; res specialist, 69-70, asst prof, 70-79, ASSOC PROF ZOOL, OHIO STATE UNIV, 79- *Res:* Invertebrate ecology. *Mailing Add:* Dept of Zool Ohio State Univ Newark OH 43055

ST JOHN, HAROLD, b Pittsburgh, Pa, July 25, 92; m 22; c 4. BOTANY. *Educ:* Harvard Univ, AB, 14, AM, 15, PhD(biol), 17. *Prof Exp:* Asst bot, Gray Herbarium, Harvard Univ, 13-17, Radcliffe Col, 13-15 & Gray Herbarium, Harvard Univ, 19-20; asst prof, Wash State Univ, 20-23, assoc prof & cur herbarium, 23-29; prof bot, 29-58, EMER PROF BOT, UNIV HAWAII, 58-; ACTG CUR BOT, BISHOP MUS, 58- *Concurrent Pos:* With Geol Surv Can, 15, 17; botanist, Bishop Mus, 29-65; vis prof, Yale Univ, 39-40; botanist, Foreign Econ Admin, Colombia, 43-44; assoc dir, Manoa Arboretum, 53-58; Whitney vis prof, Chatham Col, 58-59; vis prof, Saigon, 59-61. *Honors & Awards:* Named Harold St John Plant Sci Bldg, Univ Hawaii, 71; Garden Club Am Gold Medal of Honor, 75; Am Asn Bot Gardens & Arboeta Award Merit, 75. *Mem:* AAAS; Bot Soc Am; Am Soc Plant Taxon; Torrey Bot Club; Ger Dendrol Soc. *Res:* Taxonomy and phytogeography of vascular plants; ferns and flowering plants; nomenclature of plants; weeds of pineapple fields of the Hawaiian Islands; flora of southeast Washington and adjacent Idaho; revision of genus Pandanus; list of flowering plants of the Hawaiian Islands; nonugraph of Cyrtandra. *Mailing Add:* Bishop Mus Box 6037 Honolulu HI 96818

ST JOHN, JUDITH BROOK, b Memphis, Tenn, Aug 15, 40; m 67; c 2. BIOCHEMISTRY, PLANT PHYSIOLOGY. *Educ:* Millsaps Col, BS, 62; Univ Fla, PhD(bot), 66. *Prof Exp:* Res fel plant physiol, Univ Fla, 66-67; PLANT PHYSIOLOGIST, PLANT INDUST STA, SCI & EDUC ADMIN-AGR RES, USDA, 67- *Mem:* Am Soc Plant Physiologists; Am Inst Biol Sci. *Res:* Mechanisms of herbicide action; plant lipid biochemistry. *Mailing Add:* Agr Res Ctr-W South Bldg Rm 29 AEQT-PAL Agr Res Serv USDA Beltsville MD 20705

ST JOHN, PETER ALAN, b Ashtabula, Ohio, May 11, 41; m 67; c 2. ANALYTICAL CHEMISTRY. *Educ:* Univ Fla, BS, 63, PhD(anal chem), 67. *Prof Exp:* Instrument designer, Southeastern Pesticide Residue Lab, 67; sr res chemist, instrument develop, AMINCO, 67-70; proj mgr, New Prod Develop, 71-79, prog mgr, 79-81, ASST VPRES ENG, INSTRUMENT DIV, BAXTER TRAVENOL LABS, INC, 81- *Mem:* Am Chem Soc; Am Asn Clin Chem; Sigma Xi. *Res:* Atomic and molecular spectroscopy; chromatography; biochemistry; microbiology. *Mailing Add:* 3306 Sellman Rd Adelphi MD 20783

ST JOHN, PHILIP ALAN, b Lexington, Mass, Feb 13, 24; m 51; c 2. CELL PHYSIOLOGY, VERTEBRATE REGENERATION. *Educ:* Univ NH, BS, 49, MS, 51; Harvard Univ, PhD, 56. *Prof Exp:* From instr to asst prof biol, Brandeis Univ, 56-67; PROF BIOL, BUTLER UNIV, 67- *Mem:* AAAS. *Res:* Invertebrate cell culture; physiology of regeneration of Turbellaria and vertebrates parasite chemotherapy. *Mailing Add:* Dept of Zool Butler Univ Indianapolis IN 46208

ST JOHN, RALPH C, b Ft Kent, Maine, Aug 29, 42. STATISTICS. *Educ:* Univ Maine, Orono, BS, 64; Univ Mass, MS, 68; Univ Wis, PhD(statist), 73. *Prof Exp:* Mathematician statist, IBM, 64-66; asst prof, 73-78, ASSOC PROF STATIST, BOWLING GREEN STATE UNIV, 78-, DIR, STATIST CONSULT CTR, 77- *Mem:* Am Statist Asn; Royal Statist Soc; Am Soc Qual Control. *Res:* Regression; design for regression; experiments with mixtures. *Mailing Add:* Dept Appl Statist & Opers Res Bowling Green State Univ Bowling Green OH 43403

ST JOHN, ROBERT MAHARD, b Westmoreland, Kans, Mar 20, 27; m 49; c 2. EXPERIMENTAL ATOMIC PHYSICS. *Educ:* Kans State Univ, BS, 50, MS, 51; Univ Wis, PhD(physics), 54. *Prof Exp:* From asst prof to assoc prof, 54-68, PROF PHYSICS, UNIV OKLA, 68- *Mem:* Fel Am Phys Soc; Am Asn Physics Teachers. *Res:* Gaseous electronics; atomic and electronic collisions; isotope separation by lasers. *Mailing Add:* Dept of Physics & Astron Univ of Okla Norman OK 73019

ST JOHN, WALTER MCCOY, b Providence, RI, Apr 23, 44; m 70; c 1. NEUROPHYSIOLOGY. *Educ:* Brown Univ, AB, 66; Univ NC, Chapel Hill, PhD(physiol), 70. *Prof Exp:* From instr to asst prof physiol, Med Ctr, Univ Ark, Little Rock, 70-74; sr fel & staff assoc, Col Physicians & Surgeons, Columbia Univ, 74-75; res assoc pharmacol, 75-76; Parker B Francis Found fel & res assoc physiol, 76-77, asst prof, 77-79, ASSOC PROF PHYSIOL, DARTMOUTH MED SCH, 79- *Concurrent Pos:* Vis scientist, Fac St Jerome, Manseille, France, 80-81. *Mem:* Am Physiol Soc. *Res:* Neural control of respiration. *Mailing Add:* Dept Physiol Dartmouth Med Sch Hanover NH 03755

ST JOHN, WAYNE LLOYD, b Kankakee, Ill, Sept 7, 25; m 58; c 2. ORGANIC CHEMISTRY, TEXTILES. *Educ:* Univ Ill, BS, 48; Northwestern Univ, MS, 51; Univ Ore, PhD(chem), 54. *Prof Exp:* Chemist, Procter & Gamble Co, 52-72; assoc prof clothing, textiles & interior design, Col Home Econ, Kans State Univ, 72-75; ASSOC PROF CLOTHING & TEXTILES, COL HUMAN RESOURCES, SOUTHERN ILL UNIV, CARBONDALE, 75- *Mem:* Am Asn Textile Chemists & Colorists; Am Chem Soc; Am Soc Testing & Mat; Am Col Prof Textiles & Clothing. *Res:* Fluorescent whitening agents and means of measuring the degree of whiteness the agents produce; triple interaction of detergents, textiles and appliances in the laundry process; performance of textile items. *Mailing Add:* Col of Human Resources Southern Ill Univ Carbondale IL 62901

ST LAWRENCE, PATRICIA, b New York, NY, July 22, 22. GENETICS. *Educ:* Bryn Mawr Col, BA, 44; Columbia Univ, PhD(zool), 52. *Prof Exp:* USPHS fel, Yale Univ, 52-54, res asst microbiol, 55-57; res biologist, Stanford Univ, 57-59; asst prof, 59-65, ASSOC PROF GENETICS, UNIV CALIF, BERKELEY, 65-, ASSOC GENETICIST, AGR EXP STA, 69- *Mem:* AAAS; Genetics Soc Am; Am Soc Naturalists. *Res:* Genetics and cytogenetics of Neurospora. *Mailing Add:* Dept of Genetics Univ of Calif Berkeley CA 94720

ST LAWRENCE, WILLIAM FRANCIS, b Brockton, Mass, Jan 17, 41; m 70; c 2. GLACIOLOGY, MATERIAL SCIENCE. *Educ:* Boston Univ, BS, 65; Pa State Univ, MS, 67; Mont State Univ, MS, 73, PhD(eng mech), 77. *Prof Exp:* Res engr mat sci, Univ Calif, Lawrence Livermore Lab, 67-69; res glaciologist, Dept Earth Sci, Mont State Univ, 72-77; RES GEOPHYSICIST GEOPHYSICS & ICE RHEOLOGY, US ARMY COLD REGIONS RES & ENG LAB, 77- *Mem:* Glaciol Soc. *Res:* Geophysical aspects of snow and ice, glacial seismology, and the rheology of ice and snow. *Mailing Add:* Cold Regions Res & Eng Lab Hanover NH 03755

ST LORANT, STEVE JOSEPH, b Prague, Czech, June 6, 34; m 61; c 2. APPLIED PHYSICS, MATERIALS SCIENCE. *Educ:* Cambridge Univ, BA, 56, MA, 60; Oxford Univ, DPhil(physics), 60. *Prof Exp:* Dept Sci & Indust Res fel physics, Oxford Univ, 60-61; vis fel, Europ Orgn Nuclear Res, 61-64; STAFF PHYSICIST, STANFORD LINEAR ACCELERATOR CTR, 64- *Concurrent Pos:* Consult, 68- *Mem:* Am Phys Soc; Brit Inst Physics; Inst Elec & Electronics Engrs. *Res:* Low temperature solid state physics with emphasis on superconductivity and related phenomena. *Mailing Add:* Stanford Linear Accelerator Ctr PO Box 4349 Stanford CA 94305

ST LOUIS, ROBERT VINCENT, b Los Angeles, Calif, Dec 15, 32; m 60; c 1. PHYSICAL CHEMISTRY. *Educ:* Univ Ca'if, Los Angeles, BS, 54; Univ Minn, PhD(phys chem), 62. *Prof Exp:* Res assoc far-infrared spectros, Johns Hopkins Univ, 62-63; res chemist, US Borax Res Corp, 63-66; res assoc far-infrared spectros, Univ Southern Calif, 66-68; PROF CHEM, UNIV WIS-EAU CLAIRE, 68- *Mem:* Am Chem Soc; Am Phys Soc. *Res:* Chemical infrared spectroscopy; colloid chemistry; solvent effects. *Mailing Add:* Dept of Chem Univ of Wis Eau Claire WI 54701

ST MARY, DONALD FRANK, b Lake Charles, La, July 22, 40. MATHEMATICS, NUMERICAL ANALYSIS. *Educ:* McNeese State Col, BS, 62; Univ Kans, MA, 64; Univ Nebr, Lincoln, PhD(math), 68. *Prof Exp:* Instr math, Univ Nebr, Lincoln, 66-67 & Iowa State Univ, 67-68; asst prof, 68-75, ASSOC PROF MATH, UNIV MASS, AMHERST, 75- *Concurrent Pos:* Danforth assoc. *Mem:* Am Math Soc; Math Asn Am. *Res:* Oscillation and comparison theory of linear differential systems; differential equations. *Mailing Add:* Dept Math Univ Mass Amherst MA 01002

ST MAURICE, JEAN-PIERRE, b Valleyfield, Que, Mar 25, 49; m 72; c 3. IONOSPHERIC PHYSICS. *Educ:* Col Valleyfield, Que, BA, 68; Univ Montreal, BSc, 71; Yale Univ, PhD(geophys), 75. *Prof Exp:* Res asst geophys, Dept Geol & Geophys, Yale Univ, 71-74; scholar ionospheric physics, atmospheric & oceanic sci, Univ Mich, Ann Arbor, 74-76; res asst prof, 77-81, RES ASSOC PROF PHYSICS, UTAH STATE UNIV, 81- *Concurrent Pos:* Vis scientist, Max Plank Inst für Aeromie, WGer, 82. *Mem:* Am Geophys Union. *Res:* Theory and measurement of non-equilibrium ion velocity distributions in the ionosphere; transport properties of the ionosphere; neutral winds near auroral regions; anomalous ionospheric heating. *Mailing Add:* Ctr Atmospheric & Space Sci UMC 34 Utah State Univ Logan UT 84322

ST OMER, VINCENT VICTOR, b Castries, BWI, Nov 16, 34; m 62; c 4. NEUROSCIENCE, VETERINARY PHARMACOLOGY. *Educ:* Univ Guelph, DVM, 62, PhD(pharmacol), 69; Univ Man, MSc, 65. *Prof Exp:* Res assoc bur child res, Univ Kans, 68-71; asst prof vet pharmacol, Col Vet Med, Kans State Univ, 72-74; ASSOC PROF VET ANAT-PHYSIOL, COL VET MED & ASST PROF PHARMACOL, SCH MED, UNIV MO, COLUMBIA, 74-, DIR GRAD STUDIES, 76- *Concurrent Pos:* Adj prof, Univ Kans, 70-73. *Mem:* Sigma Xi; Am Soc Vet Physiologists & Pharmacologists; Can Physiol Soc; Soc Neurosci. *Res:* Neurochemical mechanisms responsible for induced seizures, adverse drug interactions; behavioral and development toxicology and neurotoxicology. *Mailing Add:* Dept Vet Anat-Physiol Univ Mo Col Vet Med Columbia MO 65201

ST PIERRE, GEORGE R(OLAND), b Cambridge, Mass, June 2, 30; m 56; c 4. METALLURGY. *Educ:* Mass Inst Technol, SB, 51, ScD(metall), 54. *Prof Exp:* Sr res metallurgist, Inland Steel Co, 54-56; proj off, US Air Force, 56-57; from asst prof to assoc prof, 57-64, assoc dean, 64-66, PROF METALL ENG, OHIO STATE UNIV, 64- *Concurrent Pos:* Consult, Off Technol Assessment, Mercier Corp, US Environ Protection Agency & others. *Honors & Awards:* Bradley Stoughton Award, Am Soc Metals, 61. *Mem:* Am Soc Metals; fel Am Inst Mining, Metall & Petrol Engrs; Sigma Xi. *Res:* Chemical and process metallurgy; steel making. *Mailing Add:* Dept of Metall 488 Watts Hall 2041 N College Rd Columbus OH 43210

ST PIERRE, JEAN CLAUDE, b St Jean, Que, Aug 21, 42; m 63; c 2. AGRONOMY, PLANT PHYSIOLOGY. *Educ:* Laval Univ, BScA, 64, MSc, 67; Cornell Univ, PhD(agron), 70. *Prof Exp:* res scientist forage crops, 70-81, PROG ANALYST RES MGT, AGR CAN, 81- *Mem:* Am Soc Agron; Can Soc Agron; Crop Sci Soc Am. *Res:* Forage crop production and quality; management and fertilization of grasses; plant physiology applied to breeding. *Mailing Add:* Res Sta Agr Can Sir John Carling Bldg Rm 797 Ottawa ON K1A 0C5 Can

ST PIERRE, LEON EDWARD, b Edmonton, Alta, Sept 1, 24; m 49; c 7. POLYMER CHEMISTRY. *Educ:* Univ Alta, BSc, 51; Notre Dame Univ, PhD, 55. *Prof Exp:* Res chemist, Res Lab, Gen Elec Co, 54-65; PROF POLYMER CHEM, McGILL UNIV, 65-, CHMN DEPT, 72- *Honors & Awards:* Notre Dame Univ Centennial of Sci Award, 65. *Mem:* Chem Inst Can; Soc Plastics Eng; Am Chem Soc. *Res:* Polymers from epoxides; chemorheology and radiation of polymers; surface chemistry on films generated in ultra high vacuum. *Mailing Add:* Dept of Chem McGill Univ PO Box 6070 Sta A Montreal PQ H3A 2A7 Can

ST PIERRE, P(HILIPPE) D(OUGLAS) S, b Liverpool, Eng, Sept 10, 25; nat US; m 48; c 2. CERAMICS, METALLURGY. *Educ:* Royal Sch Mines, BS, 45; Univ London, PhD, 52. *Prof Exp:* Metallurgist, Mines Br, Govt Can, 48-55; metallurgist, Gen Elec Res Lab, 55-67, mgr diamond eng, Gen Elec Co, Mich, 67-68, MGR ENG, SPECIALTY MAT DEPT, GEN ELEC CO, OHIO, 68- *Concurrent Pos:* Nuffield traveling fel, 47. *Mem:* Fel Am Ceramic Soc; sr mem Soc Mfg Engrs. *Res:* Special ceramics; materials processing; education. *Mailing Add:* Specialty Mat Dept Box 568 Worthington OH 43085

ST PIERRE, RONALD LESLIE, b Dayton, Ohio, Feb 2, 38; m 61; c 2. HISTOLOGY, IMMUNOLOGY. *Educ:* Ohio Univ, BS, 61; Ohio State Univ, MSc, 62, PhD(anat), 65. *Prof Exp:* From instr to assoc prof, 65-72, assoc prof, Cancer Ctr, 74-78, PROF ANAT & CHMN DEPT, OHIO STATE UNIV, 72- *Concurrent Pos:* Lederle med fac award, 68-71; vis res assoc, Med Ctr, Duke Univ, 66-67. *Mem:* AAAS; Transplantation Soc; Am Asn Anat; Am Asn Immunologists; Reticuloendothelial Soc. *Res:* Role of lymphoid organs, especially bursa of Fabricius and thymus, in immunity; histocompatibility testing for organ transplantation; clinical and developmental immunology; cancer immunology. *Mailing Add:* Dept of Anat Ohio State Univ Columbus OH 43210

ST PIERRE, THOMAS, b Fall River, Mass, Feb 21, 32; m; c 4. CHEMISTRY. *Educ:* Brown Univ, BS, 54; Polytech Inst Brooklyn, PhD(polymer org chem), 65. *Prof Exp:* Chemist, Pittsburgh Plate Glass Co, Pa, 56-60; jr instr chem, Polytech Inst Brooklyn, 60-65; fel, Brandeis Univ, 65-68; asst prof, 68-73, ASSOC PROF CHEM, UNIV ALA, BIRMINGHAM, 73- *Concurrent Pos:* USPHS res fel, 65-67. *Mem:* Am Chem Soc. *Res:* Synthesis and chemical modification of functional polymers. *Mailing Add:* Dept of Chem Univ of Ala Birmingham AL 35294

ST ROSE, JOHN ELLISTON, immunology, clinical biochemistry, see previous edition

SAITO, THEODORE T, b Poston, Ariz, Sept 9, 42; m 68; c 2. OPTICS. *Educ:* Pa State Univ, PhD(physics), 70. *Prof Exp:* US Air Force, 70-, proj officer optical tech, Air Force Weapons Lab, 70-71, group leader optical eval facil, 71-73, optical coating, 73-74,leader, Energy Res & Develop Admin, Dept Defense, Lawrence Livermore Lab, 74-77, dir, Mfg Tech Transfer Prog, Air Force Mat Lab, Dept Energy, 77-79, tech mgr laser Hardening, Wright Aeronaut Lab, 79-80, DIR AEROSPACE MECH, F J SEILER RES LAB, US AIR FORCE ACAD, 80- *Mem:* Fel Photo Optical Instrumentation Engrs; Optical Soc Am. *Res:* Developing and commercializing diamond turning of optics; laser damage of optical materials; manufacturing technology and technology transfer; optical metrology; lasers; optical fabrication; spectroscopy. *Mailing Add:* Frank J Seiler Res Lab US Air Force Acad Colorado Springs CO 80840

SAJBEN, MIKLOS, b Bekescsaba, Hungary, July 31, 31; US citizen; m 63; c 3. FLUID MECHANICS, AERONAUTICAL & ASTRONAUTICAL ENGINEERING. *Educ:* Budapest Tech Univ, Mech Engr, 53; Univ Pa, MS, 61; Mass Inst Technol, ScD(magnetohydrodyn), 64. *Prof Exp:* Develop engr, Westinghouse Elec Co, Pa, 57-61; res asst magnetohydrodyn, Mass Inst Technol, 61-64; asst prof aeronaut, Calif Inst Technol, 64-70; PRIN SCIENTIST, McDONNELL DOUGLAS RES LABS, 70- *Concurrent Pos:* Consult, Shock Hydrodyn, Inc, 66 & McDonnell Douglas Astronaut Co, 66-70. *Mem:* fel Am Inst Aeronaut & Astronaut. *Res:* Fluid dynamics of plasmas; internal and unsteady flows. *Mailing Add:* Bldg 33 Rm 499 McDonnell Res Labs St Louis MO 63166

SAK, JOSEPH, b Zlin, Czech, Nov 20, 39; m 61; c 1. STATISTICAL MECHANICS. *Educ:* Charles Univ, Prague, MS, 61; Inst Solid State Physics, Prague, PhD(physics), 68. *Prof Exp:* Res assoc physics, Univ Chicago, 69-71; instr, Cornell Univ, 71-73; asst prof, 73-79, ASSOC PROF PHYSICS, RUTGERS UNIV, 79- *Mem:* Am Phys Soc. *Res:* Critical phenomena; renormalization group; kinetic theory; many body theory. *Mailing Add:* Dept of Physics Rutgers Univ New Brunswick NJ 08903

SAKAGAWA, GARY TOSHIO, b Honolulu, Hawaii. FISHERIES. *Educ:* Univ Hawaii, BA, 63; Univ Mich, MSc, 67; Univ Wash, PhD(fisheries), 72. *Prof Exp:* Res assoc, Fisheries Res Inst, Univ Wash, 67-72; fishery biologist, 72-79, CHIEF, OCEANIC FISHERIES RESOURCES DIV, SOUTHWEST FISHERIES CTR, NAT MARINE FISHERIES SERV, 79- *Concurrent Pos:* Sci adv US deleg, Int Comn for Conserv Atlantic Tunas, 72 & 75-81 & Inter-Am Trop Tuna Comn, 73 & 79-81; mem, Billfish Mgt Plan Develop Team, Pac Fishery Mgt Coun, 78-79. *Mem:* Am Fisheries Soc (pres, 81-82); Am Inst Fishery Res Biologists; Sigma Xi. *Res:* Stock assessment and evaluation of tunas and billfishes; biological and stock assessment of marine mammals. *Mailing Add:* Southwest Fisheries Ctr Nat Marine Fisheries Serv La Jolla CA 92038

SAKAGUCHI, DIANNE KOSTER, b Rockville Ctr, NY, Feb 27, 46; m 74. SYSTEM ANALYSIS. *Educ:* Hofstra Univ, BA, 66; Adelphi Univ, MS, 68, PhD(numerical anal), 72. *Prof Exp:* mem tech staff, 72-80, PROJ ENGR, AEROSPACE CORP, 80- *Res:* Air traffic optimization, modelling, software technology, system optimization. *Mailing Add:* Aerospace Corp 2350 E El Segundo Blvd El Segundo CA 90245

SAKAI, ANN K, b Boston, Mass, Jan 15, 51. EVOLUTIONARY ECOLOGY, PLANT ECOLOGY. *Educ:* Oberlin Col, AB, 72; Univ Mich, MS, 73, PhD(bot), 78. *Prof Exp:* ASST PROF BIOL, OAKLAND UNIV, 78- *Mem:* Soc Study Evolution; Ecol Soc Am. *Res:* Ecological and evolutionary relationships of sex expression in plants; biology of woody plants; dynamics of forest succession. *Mailing Add:* Dept of Biol Sci Oakland Univ Rochester MI 48063

SAKAI, SHOICHIRO, b Japan, Jan 2, 28; m 58; c 2. MATHEMATICS. *Educ:* Univ Tohuku, Japan, BS, 53, PhD(math), 61. *Prof Exp:* Asst math, Univ Tohuku, Japan, 53-60; asst prof, Wasedu Univ, Japan, 60-64; vis lectr, Yale Univ, 62-64; assoc prof, 64-69, PROF MATH, UNIV PA, 69- *Concurrent Pos:* Guggenheim fel, 70 & 71; invited speaker, Int Cong Math, Helsinki, 78. *Mem:* Am Math Soc; NY Acad Sci; AAAS; Japan Math Soc. *Res:* Functional analysis. *Mailing Add:* Dept of Math Univ of Pa Philadelphia PA 19104

SAKAI, TED TETSUO, b Newell, Calif, April 12, 45. MEDICINAL CHEMISTRY. *Educ:* Univ Calif, Berkeley, BS, 67; Univ Calif, Santa Barbara, PhD(bioorg chem), 71. *Prof Exp:* Fel biochem & microbiol, Univ Colo Med Ctr, 71-76; ASSOC SCIENTIST, COMPREHENSIVE CANCER CTR, UNIV ALA, 76-, ASST PROF BIOCHEM, 79- *Mem:* Am Chem Soc; AAAS. *Res:* Mechanism of action of chemotherapeutic agents; drug-nucleic acid interactions; polyamines. *Mailing Add:* Comprehensive Cancer Ctr Univ Ala Univ Sta Birmingham AL 35294

SAKAI, WILLIAM SHIGERU, b Cody, Wyo, Sept 9, 42; m 69. BOTANY, ELECTRON MICROSCOPY. *Educ:* Univ Mich, Ann Arbor, BS, 66; Univ Hawaii, PhD(bot), 70. *Prof Exp:* Teaching asst bot, Univ Hawaii, Manoa, 69-70, asst prof, 70-71, asst soil scientist agron & soil sci, 71-74; vpres prod & res, The Flower Cart, Inc, 74-76; asst prof hort, 76-78, ASSOC PROF HORT, UNIV HAWAII, HILO, 78- *Mem:* AAAS; Bot Soc Am; Am Soc Plant Physiol; Sigma Xi. *Res:* Cell biology; plant anatomy and physiology; horticulture. *Mailing Add:* Col Agr Univ Hawaii Hilo HI 96720

SAKAIDA, R(OY) R(YOSUKE), b Los Angeles, Calif, Mar 26, 31; m 57; c 5. CHEMICAL ENGINEERING, ENVIRONMENTAL ENGINEERING. *Educ:* Univ Calif, Los Angeles, BS, 53; Calif Inst Technol, MS, 57, PhD(chem eng), 60. *Prof Exp:* From res engr to group leader, Linde Co, Union Carbide Corp, 60-65; mem tech staff, Rocketdyne, NAm Aviation, Inc, 65-68, mgr autonetics div, NAm Rockwell Corp, 68-70; tech adv to eng dir, RPC Corp/Bausch & Lomb, 70-76; sr engr & actg dir, Pac Environ Servs, Inc, 76-79, dir eng, 79-80; PROJ ENGR, ENERGY GROUP, TRW, 80- *Mem:* Am Inst Chem Engrs; Am Inst Chemists. *Res:* Propellants; biomedical engineering; reaction kinetics; heat transfer; cryobiology; instrumentation; cryogenic preservation of blood; use of bioluminescent bacteria for identification of chemicals. *Mailing Add:* TRW One Space Park R4/1112 Redondo Beach CA 90278

SAKAKURA, ARTHUR YOSHIKAZU, b San Francisco, Calif, May 24, 28; m 56. THEORETICAL PHYSICS. *Educ:* Mass Inst Technol, BS, 49, MS, 50; Univ Colo, PhD(physics), 60. *Prof Exp:* Physicist, US Geol Surv, Colo, 50-58; physicist, Res Ctr, IBM Corp, 60-63; physicist, Joint Inst Lab Astrophys, Univ Colo, 63-65, physicist, Dept Physics, 65-66; physicist, 66-68, ASSOC PROF PHYSICS, COLO SCH MINES, 68- *Mem:* Am Phys Soc. *Res:* Statistical mechanics; quantum mechanical many-body problems. *Mailing Add:* Dept of Physics Colo Sch of Mines Golden CO 80401

SAKALOWSKY, PETER PAUL, JR, b Worcester, Mass, July 29, 42; m 69; c 3. PHYSICAL GEOGRAPHY. *Educ:* Worcester State Col, BSEd, 64; Clark Univ, MA, 66; Ind State Univ, PhD(geog), 72. *Prof Exp:* Instr geog, Bloomsburg State Col, 66; instr, Briarcliff Col, 66-68; assoc prof, 70-80, PROF GEOG, SOUTHERN CONN STATE COL, 80- *Res:* Geomorphology, climatology, coastal processes and beach morphology; historical coastline changes; interrelationship of coastal processes and man, microclimates; regional geography of Anglo-America; meanderina streams; general physical geography. *Mailing Add:* Dept Geog Southern Conn State Col New Haven CT 06515

SAKAMI, WARWICK, b Philadelphia, Pa, Nov 12, 16; m 52. BIOCHEMISTRY. *Educ:* Swarthmore Col, BA, 38; Univ Pa, PhD(physiol chem), 44. *Prof Exp:* Instr physiol chem, Med Sch, Univ Pa, 44-46; res assoc physiol, Univ Minn, 46; from asst prof to assoc prof, 46-63, prof, 63-81, EMER PROF BIOCHEM, CASE WESTERN RESERVE UNIV, 81- *Mem:* AAAS; Am Soc Biol Chem; Am Chem Soc. *Res:* Synthetic organic chemistry; intermediary metabolism; 1-methylhistidine; metabolism of 1-carbon compounds. *Mailing Add:* Dept of Biochem Case Western Reserve Univ Cleveland OH 44106

SAKAMOTO, CLARENCE M, b Lahaina, Hawaii, Nov 1, 31; m 64; c 2. METEOROLOGY, AGRICULTURE. *Educ:* Univ Hawaii, BS, 53; Pa State Univ, BS, 55; Rutgers Univ, MS, 62; Iowa State Univ, PhD(agr climat), 65. *Prof Exp:* Res asst, Rutgers Univ, 60-62 & Iowa State Univ, 62-65; adv agr meteorologist, Rutgers Univ Weather Bur, 65-67; res climatologist, Environ Data Serv, Reno, 67-68; state climatologist, Nat Weather Serv, Nev, 68-73; meteorologist, Environ Study Serv Ctr, Nat Oceanic & Atmospheric Admin, Auburn, Ala, 73-75; meteorologist, 75-77, supv meteorologist, Ctr Climatic & Environ Assessment, Environ Data Serv, 77-78, CHIEF MODELS BR, CTR ENVIRON ASSESSMENT SERV, ENVIRON DATA & INFO SERV, NAT OCEANIC & ATMOSPHERIC ADMIN, COLUMBIA, MO, 78- *Concurrent Pos:* Adj asst prof meteorol, Rutgers Univ, 65-67; adj res assoc, Desert Res Inst, Reno, 67-68; adj assoc prof, Univ Nev, Reno, 68-73;

adj assoc prof, Auburn Univ, 73-75; res assoc, Univ Mo, 77-80, prof, 80-*Honors & Awards:* Unit Citation, Nat Oceanic & Atmospheric Admin, 77; Gold Medal, US Dept Com, 78. *Mem:* Am Statist Asn; Am Meteorol Soc; Am Soc Agron. *Res:* Crop response and environment; climatological analysis; impact of climatic change on food production. *Mailing Add:* NOAA/CEAS Fed Bldg Rm 116 Columbia MO 65201

SAKANO, THEODORE K, b Portland, Ore, Sept 24, 38. PHYSICAL CHEMISTRY. *Educ:* Ore State Col, BS, 60; Univ Wis, PhD(phys chem), 66. *Prof Exp:* From instr to assoc prof, 65-75, PROF CHEM, ROSE-HULMAN INST TECHNOL, 75-, CHMN DEPT, 80- *Mem:* Am Chem Soc; Royal Soc Chem. *Res:* Infrared spectroscopy of inorganic compounds, particularly phosphorus and arsenic oxides. *Mailing Add:* Rose-Hulman Inst Tech Dept Chem 5500 Wabash Ave Terre Haute IN 47803

SAKHARE, VISHWA M, b Belgaum, India, Aug 28, 32; m 56; c 1. MATHEMATICS. *Educ:* Karnatak Univ, India, BS, 51; Cambridge Univ, BA & MA, 54; Univ Tenn, Knoxville, PhD(math), 73. *Prof Exp:* Teaching asst math, Univ Idaho, 59-62, instr, 62-65; assoc prof, 65-76, PROF MATH, EAST TENN STATE UNIV, 76- *Mem:* Math Asn Am; Am Math Soc. *Res:* Applied mathematics. *Mailing Add:* Dept of Math E Tenn State Univ Johnson City TN 37601

SAKHNOVSKY, ALEXANDER ALEXANDROVITCH, b Asheville, NC, July 14, 26; m 53; c 2. PHYSICAL CHEMISTRY. *Educ:* Univ NC, AB, 49, MA, 50. *Prof Exp:* Jr chemist, Erwin Chem Lab, 51-52; res instr, Univ Miami, 52-56, res asst prof, Indust Chem Res Lab & Housing Res Lab, 56-68; DIR, CONSTRUCT RES LAB, 68- *Concurrent Pos:* Asst mgr paint proving grounds, Sun Tests, 50-55. *Honors & Awards:* Charles Martin Hall Award, Architectural Aluminum Mfr Asn, 74. *Mem:* Am Chem Soc; Am Soc Testing & Mat; fel Am Inst Chem. *Res:* Refrigeration chemistry; dehydration of refrigeration systems; desiccants; oil-refrigerant reactions; physical testing of building components; building water leakage. *Mailing Add:* 8220 SW 97th St Miami FL 33156

SAKITA, BUNJI, b Toyama-ken, Japan, June 6, 30; m 59; c 2. THEORETICAL HIGH ENERGY PHYSICS. *Educ:* Kanazawa Univ, Japan, BS, 53; Nagoya Univ, MS, 56; Univ Rochester, PhD(physics), 59. *Prof Exp:* Res assoc physics, Univ Wis, 59-62, asst prof, 62-64; assoc physicist, High Energy Physics Div, Argonne Nat Lab, 64-66; prof physics, Univ Wis-Madison, 66-70; DISTINGUISHED PROF PHYSICS, CITY COL NEW YORK, 70- *Concurrent Pos:* Guggenheim fel, 70; fel, Japan Soc Prom Sci, 75 & 80. *Honors & Awards:* Nishina Mem Medal, 74. *Mem:* Fel Am Phys Soc. *Res:* Elementary particles; symmetries of hadrons; weak interactions; field theories. *Mailing Add:* Dept of Physics City Col of New York New York NY 10031

SAKITT, BARBARA, b New York, NY. VISION. *Educ:* Columbia Univ, PhD(physics), 65. *Prof Exp:* res psychol, Stanford Univ, 76-79; PRIN RES SCIENTIST, MASS INST TECHNOL, 79- *Concurrent Pos:* NIH career develop award, 75- *Mem:* Optical Soc Am; Asn Res Vision & Ophthal; Am Psychol Asn; Psychonomic Soc; Soc Neurosci. *Res:* Vision and visual-motor coordination; visually triggered movements. *Mailing Add:* Bldg E10 Mass Inst Technol Stanford CA 94305

SAKITT, MARK, b Brooklyn, NY, Apr 7, 38; m 63. ELEMENTARY PARTICLE PHYSICS. *Educ:* Polytech Inst Brooklyn, BEE, 58; Univ Md, PhD(physics), 65. *Prof Exp:* Res assoc physics, 64-66; asst physicist, 66, assoc physicist, 67-70, PHYSICIST, BROOKHAVEN NAT LAB, 70- *Mem:* Fel Am Phys Soc; NY Acad Sci. *Res:* High energy experimental physics. *Mailing Add:* Dept of Physics Brookhaven Nat Lab Upton NY 11973

SAKMAR, ISMAIL AYDIN, b Istanbul, Turkey, Sept 29, 25; m 58; c 1. ELEMENTARY PARTICLE PHYSICS, THEORETICAL PHYSICS. *Educ:* Istanbul Univ, MS, 51; Univ Calif, Berkeley, PhD(physics), 63. *Prof Exp:* Lectr physics, Univ Calif, Santa Barbara, 63-64; asst prof, Univ Miami, 64-67; assoc prof appl math, 67-71, PROF APPL MATH, UNIV WESTERN ONT, 71-, NAT RES COUN CAN GRANTS, 68- *Concurrent Pos:* Vis scientist, Int Ctr Theoret Physics, Italy, 65, 69, 70 & 78, Europ Orgn Nuclear Res, Switz, 72 & Lab de Phys Theorique, Univ de Nice, France, 79. *Mem:* Am Phys Soc; Ital Phys Soc; Math Asn Am. *Res:* Elementary particles; S-matrix theory; Regge pole hypothesis; model independent calculations in particle physics. *Mailing Add:* Dept Appl Math Univ Western Ont London ON N6A 5B9 Can

SAKO, KUMAO, b Sebastopol, Calif, Oct 31, 24; m 66. MEDICINE, SURGERY. *Educ:* Univ Ill, BS, 50, MD, 52; Am Bd Surg, dipl, 59. *Prof Exp:* Intern, Cook County Hosp, Chicago, 52-53; resident surg, Augustana Hosp, 53-55; resident, 55-57, sr cancer res surgeon, 57-58, assoc cancer res surgeon, S8-61, ASSOC CHIEF HEAD & NECK SURGEON, ROSWELL PARK MEM INST, 61- *Concurrent Pos:* Asst, Sch Med, Univ Buffalo, 59-60, clin instr, 60-62, clin assoc, 62-65, res assoc, 65-75, res asst clin prof, 75- *Mem:* Fel Am Col Surg; Soc Head & Neck Surgeons; Am Soc Clin Oncol; Soc Surg Oncol; Am Asn Cancer Res. *Res:* Cancer research; head, neck and general surgery. *Mailing Add:* Roswell Park Mem Inst 666 Elm St Buffalo NY 14203

SAKO, YOSHIO, b Forestville, Calif, Jan 25, 18; m 54; c 3. SURGERY. *Educ:* Univ Minn, MD, 47, PhD(surg), 51. *Prof Exp:* Instr, 52, from asst prof to assoc prof, 55-66, PROF SURG, MED SCH, UNIV MINN, MINNEAPOLIS, 66- *Concurrent Pos:* Nat Heart Inst trainee, 51-52; assoc chief surg & chief cardiovasc surg sect, Vet Admin Hosp, Minneapolis, 55- *Mem:* AMA; fel Am Col Surg. *Res:* Cardiovascular surgery. *Mailing Add:* Dept of Surg Vet Admin Hosp Minneapolis MN 55417

SAKODA, WILLIAM JOHN, b Brooklyn, NY, Feb 25, 51; m 77. THEORETICAL COMPUTER SCIENCE, ARTIFICIAL INTELLIGENCE. *Educ:* Harvard Col, AB, 72; Univ Calif, PhD(comput sci), 78. *Prof Exp:* Res asst, Univ Calif, 74-78, instr, 78; asst prof comput sci,

Columbia Univ, 78-80; ASST PROF COMPUT SCI, PA STATE UNIV, 80- *Mem:* Asn Comput Mach; AAAS; Sigma Xi. *Res:* Parallel algorithms for picture analysis. *Mailing Add:* Dept Comput Sci Pa State Univ University Park PA 16802

SAKRISON, DAVID JOHN, b Tucson, Ariz, Aug 26, 33; m 57; c 3. ELECTRICAL ENGINEERING, COMMUNICATIONS. *Educ:* Univ Ariz, BSEE, 56, MSEE, 57; Mass Inst Technol, ScD(elec eng), 61. *Prof Exp:* Asst prof elec eng, Mass Inst Technol, 61-63; from asst prof to assoc prof, 63-70, PROF ELEC ENG, UNIV CALIF, BERKELEY, 70-, CHMN DEPT, 77- *Concurrent Pos:* Whitney fel & Space Technol Labs fel, Mass Inst Technol; NATO fel, Cambridge Univ, 69-70; consult, Lincoln Labs, Mass Inst Technol, 61-63, Mandrel Industs, Ampex Corp, 64- & IBM Corp, 71- *Mem:* Inst Elec & Electronics Engrs. *Res:* Communication and information theory, with particular interest in image processing and source encoding. *Mailing Add:* Dept of Elec Eng Cory Hall Univ of Calif Berkeley CA 94720

SAKS, NORMAN MARTIN, b New York, NY, May 31, 29; m 58; 1. CELL PHYSIOLOGY, PHYSIOLOGICAL ECOLOGY. *Educ:* Brooklyn Col, BS, 51, MA, 56; NY Univ, PhD(biol), 64. *Prof Exp:* From instr to asst prof, 64-72, ASSOC PROF BIOL, CITY COL NEW YORK, 72- *Concurrent Pos:* Res assoc, NY Univ, 64-66; co-prin investr, Ecol Soc Am. *Mem:* Soc Protozool. *Res:* Effects of abiotic factors including light irradiance, salinity and temperature on the growth rates of marine algae; cell metabolism, food web metabolism and dynamics; cryo-preservation of marine microflora and microfauna. *Mailing Add:* Dept of Biol City Col of New York New York NY 10031

SAKSENA, VISHNU P, b Shahjahanpur, India, July 15, 34; m 62. ZOOLOGY, AQUATIC BIOLOGY. *Educ:* Banaras Hindu Univ, BSc, 52, MSc, 54; Univ Okla, PhD(zool), 63. *Prof Exp:* Asst prof biol, Janta Vidyalaya Col, 54-55; res asst animal genetics, Indian Vet Res Inst, 55-57; from asst prof to assoc prof biol, Youngstown State Univ, 63-68; assoc prof, 68-76, PROF BIOL, MUSKINGUM COL, 76-, CHAIRPERSON, 80- *Mem:* Am Inst Fishery Res Biologists; Am Fisheries Soc; Am Inst Biol Sci; World Maricult Soc. *Res:* Physiology of air breathing fishes; ecology of fish larvae; effect of pollution on fishes; fish reproduction and embryology. *Mailing Add:* Dept of Biol Muskingum Col New Concord OH 43762

SAKSHAUG, THOMAS M(AGNUS), b Sherwood, NDak, Feb 10, 21; m 46; c 5. MECHANICAL ENGINEERING. *Educ:* NDak State Univ, BS, 47; Univ Fla, MS, 51. *Prof Exp:* Actg chmn dept mech eng, 65-67, PROF MECH ENG, NDAK STATE UNIV, 47- *Mem:* Nat Soc Prof Engrs; Am Soc Eng Educ; Am Soc Mech Engrs. *Res:* Thermodynamics; heat transfer. *Mailing Add:* Dept of Mech Eng NDak State Univ Fargo ND 58103

SAKURA, JOHN DAVID, b Seattle, Wash, Mar 28, 36. BIOCHEMISTRY. *Educ:* Wheaton Col, BS, 58; Univ Ariz, PhD(biochem), 70. *Prof Exp:* Res asst, Dept Chem, Univ Ore, 61-64; RES ASSOC BIOCHEM, DEPT BIOL CHEM, HARVARD MED SCH, 71- *Concurrent Pos:* Nat Res Coun fel, Dept Biochem, Brandeis Univ, 70-71; asst biochemist, Ralph Lowell Labs, Harvard Med Sch, 71- *Mem:* Am Chem Soc; Am Soc Neurochem; Sigma Xi. *Res:* Structure and function of proteins; lipid-protein interactions; isolation and characterization of proteolipids; proteolipids in membrane transport. *Mailing Add:* 343 Marrett Rd Lexington MA 02178

SAKURAI, JUN JOHN, b Tokyo, Japan, Jan 31, 33; m 61; c 2. THEORETICAL HIGH ENERGY PHYSICS. *Educ:* Harvard Univ, AB, 55; Cornell Univ, PhD(theoret physics), 58. *Prof Exp:* From asst prof to prof physics & nuclear studies, Univ Chicago, 58-70; PROF PHYSICS, UNIV CALIF, LOS ANGELES, 70- *Concurrent Pos:* Mem, Inst Advan Study, 58-59; consult, Argonne Nat Lab, 60-69; Sloan Found fel, 62-66; vis lectr, Univ Tokyo & Nagoya Univ, 63; vis prof Univ Paris, 64, Scuola Normale Superiore, Pisa, Italy, 67 & Univ Calif, Los Angeles, 69-70; John Simon Guggenheim Mem Found fel, 75-76; fel promotion of sci, Japan Soc, 80; sr US scientist award, Alexander Von Humboldt Found, 81-82. *Mem:* Fel Am Phys Soc. *Res:* Elementary particles; quantum field theory; Green's functions in mathematical physics; quantum mechanics. *Mailing Add:* Dept of Physics Univ of Calif Los Angeles CA 90024

SAKURAI, TOSHIO, b Osaka, Japan, Jan 17, 45; m 70; c 2. SURFACE SCIENCE. *Educ:* Univ Tokyo, BS, 67, MS, 69; Pa State Univ, PhD(physics), 74. *Prof Exp:* Mem tech staff, Bell Tel Labs, Murray Hill, 74-76; asst prof physics, Pa State Univ, 77-80; ASSOC PROF, INST SOLID STATE PHYSICS, UNIV TOKYO, 81- *Mem:* Am Phys Soc; Am Vacuum Soc. *Res:* Development of an atom-probe field ion microscope and its applications to surface physics; experimental study of surface electronic structures of semiconductors by ultraviolet photoemission and ion neutralization spectroscopies. *Mailing Add:* Dept of Physics Pa State Univ University Park PA 16802

SALADIN, JURG X, b Solothurn, Switz, July 25, 29; m 63; c 1. NUCLEAR PHYSICS. *Educ:* Swiss Fed Inst Technol, dipl, 54, PhD(nuclear physics), 59. *Prof Exp:* Res asst physics, Swiss Fed Inst Technol, 54-59; res assoc, Univ Wis, 59-61; from asst prof to assoc prof, 61-69, PROF PHYSICS, UNIV PITTSBURGH, 69- *Mem:* Fel Am Phys Soc; Swiss Phys Soc. *Res:* Experimental nuclear physics; nuclear reactions and structure; electromagnetic properties of nuclei; nuclear shapes; collective properties of nuclei; coulomb excitation. *Mailing Add:* Dept of Physics Univ of Pittsburgh Pittsburgh PA 15260

SALADIN, KENNETH S, b Kalamazoo, Mich, May 6, 49; m 79; c 2. ETHOLOGY, PARASITISM, INVERTEBRATE SENSORY PHYSIOLOGY. *Educ:* Mich State Univ, BS, 77; Fla State Univ, PhD(parasitiol), 79. *Prof Exp:* ASST PROF BIOL, GA COL, 77- *Concurrent Pos:* Ed assoc, Humanist Mag, Amherst, NY, 79-; sci columnist, 80- *Mem:* Am Soc Parasitologists; Animal Behav Soc; AAAS. *Res:* Sensory capacities and host-finding behavior of parasitic invertebrates, with emphasis on chemical and photosensory ecology of Digenea, Acarina, Siphonaptera and Hymenoptera. *Mailing Add:* Dept Biol & Environ Sci Ga Col Milledgeville GA 31061

SALAFIA, W(ILLIAM) RONALD, b Baltimore, Md, Dec 28, 38; m 63; c 2. PSYCHOBIOLOGY. *Educ:* Loyola Col, BS, 60; Fordham Univ, MA, 63, PhD(exp psychol), 67. *Prof Exp:* Lectr psychol, Hunter Col City Univ New York, 63-65; from instr to assoc prof, 65-74, chmn, Psychol Dept, 75-77, PROF PSYCHOBIOL, FAIRFIELD UNIV, 74- *Mem:* Psychonomic Soc; Soc Neurosci; AAAS; NY Acad Sci; Am Psychol Asn. *Res:* Neural mechanisms of learning and memory; classical (Pavlovian) conditioning. *Mailing Add:* Dept of Psychol Fairfield Univ Fairfield CT 06430

SALAFSKY, BERNARD P, b Chicago, Ill, Dec 27, 35; m 61; c 2. PHARMACOLOGY. *Educ:* Philadelphia Col Pharm & Sci, BS, 58; Univ Wash, MS, 61, PhD(pharmacol-toxicol), 62. *Prof Exp:* Instr pharmacol, Univ Wash, 62-64; from asst prof to assoc prof, Univ Ill Col Med, 64-70; adj assoc prof, Med Sch, Univ Pa, 70-72; WHO consult, SEARO-Indo 001, 73-75; consult, Biomed Health Consult Inc, H K, 76; PROF & HEAD, DEPT BIOMED SCI, COL MED, UNIV ILL, ROCKFORD, 77- *Concurrent Pos:* Nat Inst Neurol Dis & Stroke res grant, 65-71; Muscular Dystrophy Asn Am spec fel, 72; spec fel, Med Sch, Univ Bristol, 72-74; Fulbright lectr, Malaysia, 68; vis prof, Med Sch, Pahlavi Univ, Iran, 70-72; lectr toxicol, Univ Calif, Berkeley, 78-80; consult indust, 79-81. *Mem:* AAAS; Am Asn Pub Health; Soc Trop Dis Hyg; Am Soc Pharmacol & Exp Therapeut; Am Col Toxicol. *Res:* Neurotrophic control and regulation of skeletal muscle with special interest on regeneration and dystrophic processes; tropical disease pharmacology. *Mailing Add:* Dept of Biomed Sci 1601 Parkview Rockford IL 61101

SALAHUB, DENNIS RUSSELL, b Castor, Alta. THEORETICAL CHEMISTRY, THEORETICAL SOLID STATE PHYSICS. *Educ:* Univ Alta, BSc, 67; Univ Montreal, PhD(chem), 70. *Prof Exp:* Fel chem, Univ Sussex, 70-72; res assoc, Univ Waterloo, 72-74 & Johns Hopkins Univ, 74; chemist, Res & Develop, Gen Elec Co, 75-76; asst prof, 76-79, ASSOC PROF, UNIV MONTREAL, 79- *Mem:* Am Chem Soc; Chem Inst Can; Can Asn Physicists. *Res:* Quantum theoretical studies of the electronic structure and properties of molecules, clusters and solids. *Mailing Add:* Dept of Chem Univ of Montreal Montreal PQ H3C 3V1 Can

SALAMA, CLEMENT ANDRE TEWFIK, b Heliopolis, Egypt, Sept 27, 38; Can citizen; m 74; c 1. ELECTRICAL ENGINEERING. *Educ:* Univ BC, BAS, 61, MAS, 63, PhD(elec eng), 66. *Prof Exp:* Mem sci staff, Bell-Northern Res Labs, Ottawa, 66-67; from asst prof to assoc prof, 67-77, PROF SOLID STATE ELECTRONICS, UNIV TORONTO, 77- *Concurrent Pos:* Nat Res Coun Can grant, Univ Toronto, 67-, Defence Res Bd Can grant, 67-; consult, Elec Eng Consociates, Ltd, 69-, dir, 69-76. *Mem:* Inst Elec & Electronics Engrs; Electrochem Soc. *Res:* Solid state electronics; integrated circuits; electronic circuits. *Mailing Add:* Dept of Elec Eng Univ of Toronto Toronto ON M5S 1A4 Can

SALAMA, GUY, b Cairo, Egypt, Apr 23, 47; US citizen. VOLTAGE-SENSITIVE DYES. *Educ:* City Col New York, BS, 68; Univ Pa, MS, 71, PhD(biophysics), 77. *Prof Exp:* Teaching asst physics, Univ Pa, 70-71, res fel physiol, 73-77, res fel biochem & biophysics, 77-80; ASST PROF PHYSIOL, SCH MED, UNIV PITTSBURGH, 80- *Concurrent Pos:* Lectr physics, Spring Garden Col, Philadelphia, Pa, 69-70; investr, Marine Biol Lab, Woods Hole, Mass, 80-81. *Mem:* Biophys Soc; Soc Gen Physiologists. *Res:* Development and application of voltage-sensitive dyes to measure transmembrane electrical potential in heart muscle and in the sarcoplasmic reticulum; optical recordings of cardiac action potentials, optical voltage-clamps of venticular muscle strips in a surcose-gap chamber and imaging; excitation-contraction coupling. *Mailing Add:* Dept Physiol Sch Med Univ Pittsburgh Pittsburgh PA 15261

SALAMA, KAMEL, b Bahgoura, Egypt, Apr 1, 32; m 65. MATERIALS ENGINEERING, PHYSICAL METALLURGY. *Educ:* Univ Cairo, BSc, 51, MSc, 55, PhD(physics), 59. *Prof Exp:* Res asst physics, Univ Cairo, 51-60, lectr, 60-65; res consult, Ford Sci Lab, 66-68; fel mat sci, Rice Univ, 68-71, sr res scientist, Mat Sci Dept, 71-73; PROF, UNIV HOUSTON, 73- *Concurrent Pos:* Partic, Int Seminar Res & Educ Physics, Uppsala Univ, Sweden, 62-63, fel, 62-64. *Mem:* Am Soc Metals; Am Inst Mining, Metall & Petrol Engrs; Am Phys Soc; Soc Metallurgical Engrs; Am Soc Nondestructive Testing. *Res:* Elastic and mechanical properties of solids by ultrasonic techniques; work hardening in order and disorder alloys; mechanical behavior of metals and alloys; ultrasonic nondestructive testing. *Mailing Add:* Dept Mech Eng Univ of Houston Houston TX 77004

SALAMO, GREGORY JOSEPH, b Brooklyn, NY, Sept 19, 44; m 68; c 2. QUANTUM OPTICS. *Educ:* Brooklyn Col, BS, 66; Purdue Univ, MS, 68; City Univ New York, PhD(physics), 74. *Prof Exp:* Resident visitor physics, Bell Labs-Murray Hill, 71-73; res assoc, Rochester Univ, 73-75; asst prof, 75-80, PROF PHYSICS, UNIV ARK, 80- *Mem:* Sigma Xi; Am Phys Soc. *Res:* Design and use of lasers and related optical systems for coherent optical experiments and spectroscopic experiments with some useful application in mind. *Mailing Add:* Dept of Physics Univ of Ark Fayetteville AR 72701

SALAMON, IVAN ISTVAN, b Budapest, Hungary, Sept 10, 18; nat US; m 50; c 1. BIOCHEMISTRY, ORGANIC CHEMISTRY. *Educ:* Swiss Fed Inst Technol, ChemEng, 41; Univ Basel, PhD(chem), 49. *Prof Exp:* Lab instr & asst, Univ Basel, 42-50; USPHS res fel, Med Col, Cornell Univ, 50-52; res fel biochem, Sloan-Kettering Inst, 52-54, asst, 54-60, assoc, 60-63; asst mem div endocrinol, Res Labs, Albert Einstein Med Ctr, Philadelphia, 63-68; BIOCHEMIST, HEKTOEN INST MED RES, COOK COUNTY HOSP, 68- *Mem:* Am Chem Soc; Swiss Chem Soc; Nat Acad Clin Biochem; Am Asn Clin Chemists. *Res:* Steroid chemistry and biochemistry. *Mailing Add:* Hektoen Inst Med Res Cook Co Hosp 627 S Wood St Chicago IL 60612

SALAMON, KENNETH J, US citizen. TOXICOLOGY, ECOLOGY. *Educ:* Fordham Col, BS, 67, MS, 75, PhD(physiol ecol), 79. *Prof Exp:* Mem staff, Consolidated Edison Co, NY, 76-77, Inst Environ Med, NY Univ, 79-80; PROJ TOXICOLOGIST & ECOLOGIST, WESTON, 80- *Concurrent Pos:* Mem, Advan Study Inst, NATO. *Mem:* Am Fisheries soc; Am Soc Limnol & Oceanog; AAAS. *Res:* Aquatic toxicology; fish physiology; bioassay and ecological investigations; estuarine biology; power plant impact studies; marine and freshwater phytoplankton & zooplankton physiology and ecology. *Mailing Add:* Weston Weston Way West Chester PA 19380

SALAMON, MYRON B, b Pittsburgh, Pa, June 4, 39; m 60; c 2. SOLID STATE PHYSICS. *Educ:* Carnegie Inst Technol, BS, 61; Univ Calif, Berkeley, PhD(physics), 65. *Prof Exp:* NSF fel, 65-66; from asst prof to assoc prof, 66-74, PROF PHYSICS, UNIV ILL, URBANA, 74- *Concurrent Pos:* Vis scientist, Inst Solid State Physics, Univ Tokyo, 71 & Tech Univ Munich, 74-75; Alfred P Sloan Found res fel, 71-72; Inst Laue Langerin & Nat Ctr Sci Res, Grenoble, 81-82. *Honors & Awards:* Humboldt Found Award, 74. *Mem:* Am Phys Soc. *Res:* Experimental studies of phase transitions in magnets, solid electolytes, semiconductors and modulated structures. *Mailing Add:* Dept of Physics Univ of Ill Urbana IL 61801

SALAMON, RICHARD JOSEPH, b Palmer, Mass, Apr 27, 32; m 60; c 1. SCIENCE EDUCATION. *Educ:* Col Holy Cross, BS, 53; Am Int Col, MA, 60; Univ Conn, Prof Dipl Educ, 64, PhD(sci educ), 68. *Prof Exp:* Instr, High Sch, Mass, 59-65; PROF SCI & SCI EDUC, CENT CONN STATE COL, 66- *Mem:* Asn Educ Teachers Sci; Nat Sci Teachers Asn; Nat Asn Res Sci Teaching; Sch Sci & Math Asn. *Res:* Elementary, middle school, high school and college science instruction. *Mailing Add:* Dept of Physics & Earth Sci Cent Conn State Col New Britain CT 06050

SALAMONE, JOSEPH C, b Brooklyn, NY, Dec 27, 39; m 78; c 2. ORGANIC CHEMISTRY, POLYMER CHEMISTRY. *Educ:* Hofstra Univ, BSc, 61; Polytech Inst Brooklyn, PhD(org chem), 66. *Prof Exp:* Res Liverpool, 66-67; res assoc, Univ Mich, Ann Arbor, 67-70, secy, Macromolecular Res Ctr, 68-70; from asst prof to assoc prof, 70-75, chmn dept, 75-78, actg dean, Col Pure & Appl Sci, 78-81, PROF CHEM, UNIV LOWELL, 75-, DEAN, COL PURE & APPL SCI, 81-, CHMN, COUN DEANS, 81- *Mem:* Am Chem Soc (treas div polymer chem, 74-78). *Res:* Syntheses of new monomers and polymers; polyelectrolyte complexes; copolymerization of ionic monomers; catalytically active polyelectorlytes; polyampholytics and ampholytic ionomers. *Mailing Add:* Col of Pure & Appl Sci Univ of Lowell Lowell MA 01854

SALAMUN, PETER JOSEPH, b La Crosse, Wis, June 12, 19; m 46; c 8. BOTANY. *Educ:* Univ Wis, BS, 41, MS, 47, PhD(bot), 50. *Prof Exp:* Asst, Univ Wis, 45-48; instr, 48-55, assoc prof, 55-60, chmn dept, 60-64, PROF BOT, UNIV WIS-MILWAUKEE, 60- *Mem:* AAAS; Am Inst Biol Sci; Bot Soc Am; Am Soc Plant Taxonomists; Soc Study Evolution. *Res:* Floristic and monographic work in plant taxonomy. *Mailing Add:* Dept of Botany Univ of Wis Milwaukee WI 53201

SALANAVE, LEON EDWARD, b San Francisco, Calif, Nov 19, 17; m 49; c 2. ASTRONOMY, ATMOSPHERIC CHEMISTRY. *Educ:* Univ Calif, AB, 40, MA, 47. *Prof Exp:* Assoc astron, Univ Calif, 42-47; instr astron & math, Sacramento Col, 47-52; lectr & consult astron, Morrison Planetarium, 49-53; assoc cur, Calif Acad Sci, 54-56; res assoc site surv, Nat Astron Observ, Asn Univs for Res Astron, 56-58; assoc res engr, Appl Res Lab, Univ Ariz, 58-60; res assoc optics, Inst Atmospheric Physics, 61-71; exec officer & ed jour, Astron Soc Pac, 71-74; prin investr, Lightning Atlas Proj, Off Naval Res, 75-80; INSTR, CITY COL SAN FRANCISCO, 79- *Mem:* Am Geophys Union. *Res:* Atmospheric and astronomical optics; optical spectrum of lightning; science writing and editing. *Mailing Add:* Dept Astron City Col San Francisco 50 Phelan Ave San Francisco CA 94112

SALAND, LINDA C, b New York, NY, Oct 24, 42; m 64; c 2. ANATOMY, CYTOLOGY. *Educ:* City Col New York, BS, 63, PhD(biol), 68; Columbia Univ, MA, 65. *Prof Exp:* Res assoc anat, Col Physicians & Surgeons, Columbia Univ, 68-69; sr res assoc, 71-78, ASST PROF, ANAT, SCH MED, UNIV N MEX, 78- *Concurrent Pos:* Assoc ed, Anat Record. *Mem:* Am Asn Anat; Am Soc Cell Biol; Am Soc Zool; Soc Neurosci. *Res:* Pituitary cytology; electron microscopic autoradiography; hypothalamic cytology; pancreatic islet cell ultrastructure; opiate peptides; neuroendocrine function. *Mailing Add:* Dept Anat Univ NMex Sch of Med Albuquerque NM 87131

SALANECK, WILLIAM R, b Pottstown, Pa, Aug 19, 41; m 67; c 2. SOLID STATE PHYSICS. *Educ:* Albright Col, BS, 63; Univ Pa, MS, 64, PhD(physics), 68. *Prof Exp:* Scientist, Xerox Corp, Rochester, 68-72, mgr mat sci areas, 72-73, mgr photo & insulator physics area, 74, SR SCIENTIST MOLECULAR & ORGANIC MATERIALS AREA, XEROX WEBSTER RES CTR, 74- *Concurrent Pos:* NSF grants, NATO Advan Study Inst, 66 & Army res grant, 67; adj assoc prof physics, Univ Pa, 80- *Mem:* Am Phys Soc; Am Vacuum Soc. *Res:* Electron physics; photoelectron spectroscopy; electronic structure of molecular solids; electronic structure of conducting polymers. *Mailing Add:* Xerox Webster Res Ctr 800 Phillips Rd W-114 Webster NY 14580

SALANITRE, ERNEST, b New York, NY, Feb 3, 15; m 45; c 2. MEDICINE, ANESTHESIOLOGY. *Educ:* City Col New York, BS, 36; Univ Rome, MD, 42. *Prof Exp:* Instr, 53-54, assoc, 55-58, from asst prof to assoc prof, 59-71, PROF ANESTHESIOL, COL PHYSICIANS & SURGEONS, COLUMBIA UNIV, 71- *Concurrent Pos:* From asst attend to assoc attend, Columbia-Presby Med Ctr, 53-71, attend, 71- *Mem:* Am Soc Anesthesiol; AMA; Am Acad Pediat. *Res:* Pediatric anesthesiology; uptake and elimination of inhalational anesthetic agents in man. *Mailing Add:* Dept Anesthesiol Columbia-Presby Med Ctr New York NY 10032

SALANS, LESTER BARRY, b Chicago Heights, Ill, Jan 25, 36; m 58; c 2. MEDICINE, METABOLISM. *Educ:* Univ Mich, Ann Arbor, BA, 57; Univ Ill, Chicago, MD, 61. *Prof Exp:* Intern med, Stanford Med Sch, 61-62, resident, 62-64; asst prof, Rockefeller Univ, 67-68; from asst prof to assoc prof med, Dartmouth Med Sch, 71-78; chief, Lab Cellular Metab & Obesity & assoc dir diabetes, endocrinol & metab dis, 78-81, ACTG DIR, NAT INST ARTHRITIS, DIABETES, DIGESTIVE & KIDNEY DIS, NIH, 81-

Concurrent Pos: Fel, Stanford Med Sch, 63-64; USPHS fel, 64-65; USPHS spec fel, Rockefeller Univ, 65-67, Nat Inst Arthritis & Metab Dis grant, 68-77 & res career develop award, 72-77; adj prof med, Med Sch, Dartmouth Col, 78- *Mem:* Am Soc Clin Nutrit; Am Fedn Clin Res; Endocrine Soc; Am Soc Clin Invest; Am Diabetes Asn. *Res:* Intermediary carbohydrate/lipid metabolism related to diabetes mellitus, obesity and atherosclerosis. *Mailing Add:* Nat Inst Arthritis Diabetes Digestive Kidney Dis Rm 9A52 Bldg 31 Bethesda MD 20205

SALANT, ABNER, b Cincinnati, Ohio, Mar 18, 30; m 52; c 3. FOOD TECHNOLOGY. *Educ:* NY Univ, BA, 50; Rutgers Univ, PhD(food chem & technol), 53. *Prof Exp:* Asst, Rutgers Univ, 52-53; assoc technologist, Gen Foods Corp, 53-56; proj leader, Tenco Div, Coca-Cola Co, 56-62; proj mgr org chem div, 62-68, asst to pres, George Lueders & Co, Inc, NY, 68-69, vpres, Monsanto Flavor/Essence Inc, 69-75; DIR, FOOD ENG LAB, US ARMY NATICK RES & DEVELOP LABS, 76- *Mem:* AAAS; Am Chem Soc; Inst Food Technologists; Am Inst Chemists; fel NY Acad Sci. *Res:* Food chemistry; beverage and dessert products; dehydration; evaporation; extraction; classification; blending; commercial development; flavor and fragrance products; low-calorie foods and beverages; nutrition. *Mailing Add:* Food Eng Lab US Army Natick Res & Develop Command Natick MA 01760

SALANT, RICHARD FRANK, b New York, NY, Sept 4, 41; m 62; c 2. MECHANICAL ENGINEERING. *Educ:* Mass Inst Technol, BS & MS, 63, DSc(mech eng), 67. *Prof Exp:* Asst prof mech eng, Univ Calif, Berkeley, 66-68; from asst prof to assoc prof mech eng, Mass Inst Technol, 68-72; mgr fluid mech res, 72-79, mgr fluid mech & heat transfer, 79-80, MGR FLUID MECH, HEAT TRANSFER & APPL PHYSICS, BORG-WARNER CORP, 80- *Concurrent Pos:* Consult, Veriflo Corp, 67-68 & United Aircraft Res Labs, 69-71. *Mem:* Am Soc Mech Engrs; NY Acad Sci. *Res:* Fluid mechanics; heat transfer; surface physics, lubrication; two-phase flow. *Mailing Add:* Roy C Ingersoll Res Ctr Wolf & Algonquin Rds Des Plaines IL 60018

SALARES, VIRGINIA RAMOS, b Philippines, Dec 16, 46; Can citizen; m 72; c 2. INORGANIC CHEMISTRY, BIOPHYSICAL CHEMISTRY. *Educ:* Univ Philippines, BS, 66; Univ Minn, PhD(chem), 72. *Prof Exp:* Instr chem, Univ Philippines, 66-67; asst, Univ Minn, 67-69; res assoc, Purdue Univ, 69-72; fel, Mem Univ Nfld, 72-74; fel, Nat Res Coun, 74-75, res assoc, 75-78. *Mem:* Can Spectros Soc. *Res:* Resonance Raman spectroscopy; single crystal Raman spectroscopy; carotenoproteins; carotenoids. *Mailing Add:* 25 Ullswater Dr Nepean ON K2H 5H4 Can

SALATI, OCTAVIO M(ARIO), b Philadelphia, Pa, Dec 12, 14; m 51; c 3. ELECTRICAL ENGINEERING. *Educ:* Univ Pa, BS, 36, MS, 39, PhD(elec eng), 63. *Prof Exp:* Trainee, Radio Corp Am, 37-38, develop engr, 39; develop engr, C G Com Ltd, 39-42; sr engr, Hazeltine Electronics Corp, 42-48; from asst prof to assoc prof, 63-75, PROF ELEC ENG, UNIV PA, 75-, PROJ DIR, INST COOP RES, 48-, DIR, TELEVISION SYST, 70- *Concurrent Pos:* Vis prof, Pahlavi Univ, Iran, 69 & People's Repub China, 81; consult, US Air Force & Naval Med Res Inst, 77-; in charge design, construct & oper, Eng Schs Instrnl TV Syst, Univ Pa, dir eng schs, grad TV syst & dir continuing eng educ. *Mem:* AAAS; fel Inst Elec & Electronics Engrs; Sigma Xi. *Res:* Radio interference in communications and radar systems; microwave tubes; biological effects of microwave radiation; studies of out of band performance of antennas and radio propagation studies; BNC electrical connector and microwave absorber. *Mailing Add:* Univ of Pa 103 Moore Sch D-Z Philadelphia PA 19104

SALAZAR, HERNANDO, b Ibague, Colombia, Nov 21, 31; m 56; c 4. PATHOLOGY, PUBLIC HEALTH. *Educ:* Col San Simon, Colombia, BS, 50; Nat Univ Colombia, MD, 58; Univ Pittsburgh, MPH, 71. *Prof Exp:* Instr morphol, Univ Valle, 59-61, asst prof, 63-66; from instr to asst prof, 66-70, ASSOC PROF PATH, UNIV PITTSBURGH, 70- *Concurrent Pos:* Rockefeller Found res fel anat, Wash Univ, 61-63, travel grant, 65; Health Res & Serv Found Pittsburgh grant, 68; NIH res grants, 70-72; Am Cancer Soc grant, 74-76; vis scientist, Sir William Dunn Sch Path, Oxford Univ, 73-74. *Mem:* Am Asn Path & Bact; Am Asn Anat; Soc Study Reproduction; Endocrine Soc; Am Soc Cell Biol. *Res:* Medical education; cancer; endocrinologic and reproductive pathology. *Mailing Add:* Dept Path Magee-Women's Hosp Univ of Pittsburgh Pittsburgh PA 15213

SALBER, EVA JULIET, b Cape Town, SAfrica, Jan 5, 16; US citizen; m 39; c 4. PUBLIC HEALTH, COMMUNITY MEDICINE. *Educ:* Univ Cape Town, MB & ChB, 38, DPH, 45, MD, 55. *Prof Exp:* Staff mem, Inst Family & Community Health, 45-54; med officer, Student Health Serv, Univ Cape Town, 54-55; res assoc epidemiol, Sch Pub Health, Harvard Univ, 59-61, sr res assoc, 61-66, chief Martha M Eliot Family Health Ctr, Med Sch, 67-69, sr assoc eval of health serv, Ctr Community Health & Med Care, 69-70; PROF COMMUNITY & FAMILY MED, DUKE UNIV MED CTR, 72- *Concurrent Pos:* Sr bursar res in infant growth, SAfrican Coun Sci & Indust Res, 49-55; scholar, Radcliffe Inst Advan Study, 66-67; consult, Mass Interagency Coun Smoking & Health, 66-70, Lincoln Community Health Ctr, Durham, NC, 71, Va Health Welfare Recreation Coun, 71-72 & Health Planning Coun for Cent NC, 72-73; lectr, Sch Pub Health, Univ NC, 72-; mem comt tobacco & cancer, Am Cancer Soc, 66-76; sr int fel, Fogarty Int Ctr, NIH, 80. *Mem:* AAAS; Am Col Prev Med; Int Epidemiol Asn; Am Cancer Soc; fel Am Pub Health Asn. *Res:* Epidemiology of smoking in school children; epidemiology of breast cancer; determinants of utilization of medical care services; the lay advisor as a community health resource; rural elderly. *Mailing Add:* Dept of Community & Family Med Duke Univ Med Ctr Durham NC 27710

SALCE, LUDWIG, b New York, NY, Feb 3, 34; m 67; c 1. ORGANIC CHEMISTRY. *Educ:* Fordham Univ, BS, 55, PhD(chem), 67; NY Univ, MS, 61. *Prof Exp:* Chemist, Petrotex Div, Food Mach Chem Corp, 55-56, Burroughs Wellcome & Co, 56-59 & Col Physicians & Surgeons, Columbia Univ, 59-62; sr chemist, Merck & Co, Inc, 66-70; res chemist, Cybertek & Co, 71-72; RES CHEMIST, EVANS CHEMETICS, INC, DARIEN, CONN,

72- *Mem:* Am Chem Soc. *Res:* Purines; pyrimidines; glycosides; amino acids; peptides; aromatic hydrocarbons; steroids; heterocyclics; synthesis of biologically active compounds; synthesis of sulfur compounds. *Mailing Add:* 32 Brynwood Lane Greenwich CT 06830

SALCH, RICHARD K, b Union City, NJ, Sept 10, 40; m 69. PLANT PATHOLOGY. *Educ:* Cent Col, Iowa, BA, 61; Rutgers Univ, MS, 62, PhD(plant biol), 69. *Prof Exp:* Lab technician, Boyce Thompson Inst Plant Res, NY, 63-66; from asst prof to assoc prof, 69-73, PROF BIOL, EAST STROUDSBURG STATE COL, 73- *Res:* Biological methods of plant disease control pollution problems and how they effect agriculture; control of fungus diseases of plants; physiology of fungus. *Mailing Add:* Dept of Biol East Stroudsburg State Col East Stroudsburg PA 18301

SALCMAN, MICHAEL, b Pilsen, Czechoslovakia, Nov 4, 46; US citizen; m 69; c 2. NEUROLOGICAL SURGERY, NEURO-ONCOLOGY. *Educ:* Boston Univ, BA & MD, 69. *Prof Exp:* Intern surg, Univ Hosp, Boston Univ Med Ctr, 69-70; res assoc neurophysiol, Lab Neural Control, Nat Inst Neurol Dis & Stroke, 70-72; resident neurosurg, Neurological Inst NY, Columbia Univ, 72-76; asst prof, 76-79, CHIEF NEURO-ONCOLOGY, SCH MED, UNIV MD, 78-, ASSOC PROF NEUROSURG, 79- *Concurrent Pos:* Co-prin investr cats' visual cortex, Nat Eye Inst, NIH, 72-78 & hyperthermal radiotherapy, Am Cancer Soc, 78-80; assoc ed, Neurosurg, 82- *Mem:* Congress Neurol Surgeons; Am Asn Neurol Surgeons; Asn Advan Med Instrumentation; fel Am Col Surgeons; NY Acad Sci. *Res:* Biology and treatment of brain tumors using microsurgery, laser, microwave hyperthermia, reversal of blood-brain barrier and chemotherapy; chronic microelectrode technology for single unit neurophysiology and neural prosthesis development. *Mailing Add:* Div Neurol Surg Univ Hosp 22 S Greene St Baltimore MD 21201

SALCUDEAN, MARTHA EVA, b Cluj, Romania, Feb 26, 34; m 55; c 1. HEAT TRANSFER, FLUID FLOW. *Educ:* Univ Cluj, BEng, 56, MEng, 62; Inst Polytech, Brasov, Romania, PhD(mech), 69. *Prof Exp:* Engr, Armatura, Cluj, Romania, 56-60; design eng, Nat Ctr Indust Automatics, Bucharest, 60-63; sr res officer, Nat Res Ctr Metall, Bucharest, 63-75; res assoc, McGill Univ, 76-77; assoc prof, 77-80, PROF, UNIV OTTAWA, 80- *Concurrent Pos:* Lectr, Univ Ottawa, 76-77. *Res:* Computational heat transfer and fluid dynamics; convective heat transfer in laminar and turbulent flows; heat transfer in buoyancy affected recirculatory flows; two phase flow in vertical and horizontal channels. *Mailing Add:* Dept Mech Eng 770 King Edward Ave Ottawa ON K1N 6N5 Can

SALDARINI, RONALD JOHN, b Paterson, NJ, Nov 6, 39; m 62; c 3. PHYSIOLOGY, BIOCHEMISTRY. *Educ:* Drew Univ, BA, 61; Univ Kans, PhD(biochem, physiol), 67. *Prof Exp:* Sr res scientist, Metab Dis Ther Res Sect, 69-74; group leader respiratory & skin dis, 74, HEAD, DEPT BIOL, METAB DIS SECT, LEDERLE LABS, 74- *Concurrent Pos:* NIMH training fel biochem & physiol, Brain Res Inst, Sch Med, Univ Calif, Los Angeles, 67-68, NIH fel, 68-69. *Mem:* AAAS; Soc Study Reproduction; Brit Soc Study Fertil; Int Soc Fertil. *Res:* Estrogen and progestin receptors in uterus and corpus luteum; immunological regulation of immediate hypersensitivity disease states; cyclic nucleotide involvement in proliferative skin disease; sperm metabolism in monkeys. *Mailing Add:* Lederle Lab Dept of Biol Metab Dis Sect Pearl River NY 10965

SALDEN, ROBERT WENTWORTH, b Phoenix, Ariz, Aug 11, 36; m 77; c 1. TECHNICAL MANAGEMENT. *Educ:* Pomona Col, Calif, BA, 58, Univ Wis, Madison, MS, 60, PhD(physics), 64. *Prof Exp:* Res asst physics, Univ Wis, 62-64; res assoc appl physics, Lawrence Livermore Lab, 65-67, staff mem, 67-73, group leader, 73-77, asst assoc dir, 78-79; DIV LEADER & APPL THEORET PHYSICS DIV, LOS ALAMOS NAT LAB, 79- *Mem:* Am Phys Soc; AAAS. *Res:* Nuclear weapons; inertial laser fusion; plasma physics; particle beams; strategic weapon technology; nonproliferation and nuclear safeguards. *Mailing Add:* Los Alamos Nat Lab Los Alamos NM 87544

SALDICK, JEROME, b Brooklyn, NY, Mar 24, 21; m 51; c 2. PHYSICAL CHEMISTRY. *Educ:* Brooklyn Col, BA, 40; Columbia Univ, MA, 41, PhD(phys chem, kinetics), 48. *Prof Exp:* Chemist, Kellex Corp, 48-51; assoc chemist, Brookhaven Nat Lab, 51-54; tech engr, Aircraft Nuclear Propulsion Dept, Gen Elec Co, 54-56; assoc, Astra, Inc, 56-58; pres, Gen Radionuclear Co, 58-59; resident scientist, Indust Reactor Labs, Am Mach & Foundry Co, 59-63; group leader, Princeton Chem Res Inc, 64-66; sr res chemist, 66-73, RES ASSOC, FMC CORP, 73- *Mem:* Am Chem Soc. *Res:* Radiation chemistry; heterogeneous catalysis; applied microbiology. *Mailing Add:* 24 Randall Rd Princeton NJ 08540

SALE, JAMES PROWANT, b Stillwater, Okla, Oct 21, 21; m 43; c 4. GEOTECHNICAL ENGINEERING, RESEARCH MANAGEMENT. *Educ:* Okla State Univ, BS, 43. *Prof Exp:* Engr, Ohio River Div Labs, US Army, 46-53, chief, Soils & Found Div, 53-56, chief, Soils Sect, Off Chief Engrs, 56-61, chief, Res Sect, 61-62, spec eng asst to dir, 62-69, CHIEF GEOTECHNICAL LAB, ARMY ENGR WATERWAYS EXP STA, 69- *Concurrent Pos:* Mem rigid pavement design comt, Hwy Res Bd, Nat Acad Sci-Nat Res Coun, 57-64 & chmn, prestressed concrete pavement comt, 60-64; mem bd vis, Okla State Univ, 73-76. *Honors & Awards:* Meritorious Civilian Serv Award, Dept Army, 71. *Mem:* Am Soc Civil Engrs; Am Soc Testing & Mat. *Res:* Engineering research and investigations in soil mechanics and rock mechanics; engineering geology; earthquake engineering; soil dynamics; expedient surfacing development; airfield pavement design. *Mailing Add:* US Army Waterways Exp Sta Geotech Lab GV Vicksburg MS 39180

SALE, PETER FRANCIS, b Jan 12, 41; Can citizen. BEHAVIORAL ECOLOGY, TROPICAL ECOLOGY. *Educ:* Univ Toronto, BSc, 63, MA, 64; Univ Hawaii, PhD(zool), 68. *Prof Exp:* Lectr, 68-74, sr lectr, 75-81, ASSOC PROF BIOL SCI, UNIV SYDNEY, 82- *Concurrent Pos:* Adv Comt

Crown-of-Thorns res grant, Australia, 72-73; Australian Res Grants Comt grant, 74- & 76-79; mem bd, Heron Island Res Sta, 74-; mem consult bd, Lizard Island Res Sta, Australia, 75-; Australian Marine & Sci Technol grant, 80- *Honors & Awards:* Stoye Award, Am Soc Ichthyologists & Herpetologists, 68. *Mem:* Am Soc Naturalists; Soc Animal Behav; Sigma Xi; Ecol Soc Am; Am Soc Ichthyologists & Herpetologists. *Res:* Factors determining the structure and the high diversity characteristic of coral reef fish communities. *Mailing Add:* Sch Biol Sci Univ Sydney Sydney Australia 2006

SALEEB, FOUAD ZAKI, b Toukh, Egypt, Sept 7, 34; m 66; c 3. SURFACE CHEMISTRY, PHYSICAL CHEMISTRY. *Educ:* Univ Alexandria, BS, 56; Univ London, PhD(phys chem) & DIC, 63. *Prof Exp:* Egyptian Govt fel, Imp Col, Univ London, 63-64; res scientist surface chem, Nat Res Ctr, Cairo, Egypt, 64-69; res assoc, Mass Inst Technol, 69-72; sr chemist, 72-80, PRINCIPAL SCIENTIST, TECH CTR, GEN FOODS CORP, 80- *Mem:* Am Chem Soc. *Res:* Surface chemistry of emulsions, foams and suspensions; electrokinetic properties of carbons, minerals and hydroxyapatites; monomolecular films and mass transfer. *Mailing Add:* Technical Ctr T22-1 Gen Foods Corp Tarrytown NY 10602

SALEEBY, JASON BRIAN, b Los Angeles, Calif, Oct 24, 48; m 78; c 1. GEOLOGY. *Educ:* Univ Calif, Santa Barbara, PhD(geol), 75. *Prof Exp:* Asst prof geol, Univ Calif, Berkeley, 75-78; ASSOC PROF GEOL, CALIF INST TECHNOL, 78- *Concurrent Pos:* Mem, US Geol Surv, 75- *Mem:* Geol Soc Am; Am Geophys Union. *Res:* Tectonic and paleogeographic development of western North America; processes of accretion of ocean floor and island areas to continental edges by use of geochronology; field structure and petrology. *Mailing Add:* Div Geol & Planetary Sci Calif Inst Technol Pasadena CA 91125

SALEH, ADEL ABDEL MONEIM, b Alexandria, Egypt, July 8, 42; m 70. ELECTRICAL ENGINEERING. *Educ:* Univ Alexandria, BSc, 63; Mass Inst Technol, SM, 67, PhD(elec eng), 70. *Prof Exp:* Instr elec eng, Univ Alexandria, 63-65; MEM TECH STAFF ELEC ENG, BELL TEL LABS, 70- *Concurrent Pos:* Consult engr, Sylvania Elec Prod, Inc, Mass, 68-70. *Mem:* Sr mem Inst Elec & Electronics Engrs. *Res:* Microwave and millimeter-wave circuits and communication systems research, including power amplifiers, nonlinearities and efficiency power combining networks, mixers and frequency converters, automated microwave measurements, and quasi-optical components. *Mailing Add:* Bell Tel Labs Crawford Hill Lab Holmdel NJ 07733

SALEH, WASFY SELEMAN, b Egypt, Jan 23, 32; Can citizen; m 64; c 3. SURGERY, UROLOGY. *Educ:* Cairo Univ, MB, Bch, 57; McGill Univ, PhD(exp surg), 70. *Prof Exp:* Asst prof surg, Ottawa Univ, 70-73; ASST PROF UROL, UNIV SHERBROOKE, 73- *Mem:* Am Col Surgeons; Int Transplantation Soc; Royal Col Surgeons & Physicians Can; Am Urol Asn. *Res:* Studies in graft versus host reactions. *Mailing Add:* 1081 Carling Ave Suite 502 Ottawa ON K1Y 4G2 Can

SALEHI, HABIB, b Iran, Jan 29, 35; m 62; c 2. MATHEMATICAL ANALYSIS. *Educ:* Univ Tehran, BA, 58; Ind Univ, MA, 62, PhD(math), 65. *Prof Exp:* Instr math, Univ Tehran, 58-60; from asst prof to assoc prof, 65-74, PROF MATH & STATIST, MICH STATE UNIV, 74- *Concurrent Pos:* Nat Inst Gen Med Sci grant, 66-; NSF grants, Mich State Univ, 67-71. *Mem:* Am Math Soc; Inst Math Statist. *Res:* Prediction theory of stochastic processes as initiated by N Wiener and A N Kolmogorov; powerful tools and techniques used in mathematical analysis to solve various problems in prediction and communication theory. *Mailing Add:* Dept of Math Mich State Univ East Lansing MI 48823

SALEM, HARRY, b Windsor, Ont, Mar 21, 29; US citizen; m 57; c 1. PHARMACOLOGY, TOXICOLOGY. *Educ:* Univ Western Ont, BA, 50; Univ Mich, BSc, 53; Univ Toronto, MA, 55, PhD(pharmacol), 58. *Prof Exp:* Res asst, Univ Toronto, 58-59; pharmacologist, Air-Shields Inc, 59-62; sr pharmacologist, Smith Kline & French Labs, 62-65; pharmacologist, Nat Drug Co, 65-70; dir pharmacol & toxicol, Smith, Miller & Patch, New Brunswick, 70-72; dir pharmacol & toxicol, Cooper Labs, Cedar Knolls, NJ, 72-77; pres & chief toxicologist, Cannon Labs, Inc, 77-80; PRES, WHITTAKER TOXIGENICS, INC, DECATUR, ILL, 80- *Concurrent Pos:* From instr to asst prof, Sch Med, Univ Pa, 60-75; assoc prof, 75-; adj prof, Sch Pharm, Temple Univ, 76; Am Acad Clin Toxicol; Am Chem Soc; Am Pharm Asn; Reticulo Endothelial. *Mem:* Am Soc Clin Pharmacol & Therapeut; Pharmacol Soc Can; Am Col Clin Pharmacol. *Res:* Respiratory, cardiovascular and ocular pharmacology, physiology and toxicology. *Mailing Add:* Whittaker ToxiGenics, Inc 1800 E Pershing Rd Decatur IL 19117

SALEM, SEMAAN IBRAHIM, b Bterram, Lebanon, Apr 4, 27; US citizen; m; c 3. PHYSICS. *Educ:* Am Univ, Cairo, BSc, 55; Univ Tex, PhD(physics), 59. *Prof Exp:* Teacher physics & math, Tripoly Col & Tripoly Boys Sch, 55-56; consult radiation, NAm Aviation, Inc, 58-59; asst prof physics, Univ Tex, Arlington, 59-61; from asst prof to assoc prof, 61-68, PROF PHYSICS, CALIF STATE UNIV, LONG BEACH, 68- *Concurrent Pos:* Gen Elec Co educ grant, 64; Res Corp res grants, 64-66. *Honors & Awards:* Lebanon Govt Nat Award for the Best Article of the Year, 63. *Mem:* Am Phys Soc; Nat Asn Physics Teachers; Arab Phys Soc. *Res:* Measurement of x-ray line width, interaction of charged particles with metals; x-ray spectra; channeling; transition probabilities; sets of energy levels in the rare earth and transition elements. *Mailing Add:* Dept Physics Calif State Univ Long Beach CA 90840

SALEMME, ROBERT MICHAEL, b Boston, Mass, June 17, 43; c 1. CHEMICAL ENGINEERING, SYSTEMS ENGINEERING. *Educ:* Tufts Univ, BS, 64, MS, 67, Case Western Reserve Univ, 70. *Prof Exp:* Staff engr, 69-75, tech adminr, 75-77, MGR ENERGY CONVERSION SYSTS, GEN ELEC CORP RES & DEVELOP, 77- *Mem:* Am Inst Chem Engrs. *Res:* Energy conversion systems analysis and development of advanced energy conversion technologies; development and analysis of synthetic fuel processes. *Mailing Add:* Gen Elec Corp Box 43 Schenectady NY 12301

SALERNI, ORESTE LEROY, b Bolivar, Pa, June 11, 34. ORGANIC CHEMISTRY, MEDICINAL CHEMISTRY. *Educ:* Duquesne Univ, BS, 57, MS, 59; Univ Ill, PhD(pharmaceut chem), 63. *Prof Exp:* Assoc chemist, Midwest Res Inst, 62-65; sr chemist, 65-69; assoc prof, 69-77, PROF MED CHEM, COL PHARM, BUTLER UNIV, 77- *Concurrent Pos:* Res grant, 66-67. *Mem:* Am Chem Soc; Royal Soc Chem. *Res:* Synthesis of organic compounds with potential biological activity. *Mailing Add:* Col of Pharm Butler Univ Indianapolis IN 46208

SALERNO, RONALD ANTHONY, b Philadelphia, Pa, Dec 13, 42; m 64; c 4. BIOLOGICAL QUALITY CONTROL, VIROLOGY. *Educ:* St Vincent Col, BA, 64; Villanova Univ, MS, 67; Univ Md, College Park, MS, 70, PhD(zool), 71. *Prof Exp:* Teaching asst biol, Villanova Univ, 64-66; teaching asst zool, Univ Md, College Park, 66-69; sr technologist, Microbiol Assocs, Inc, 69-70, asst scientist, 70-71, asst investr, 71-73; sr virologist, Merck Sharp & Dohme Res Labs, 73-81; SR PROJ DEVELOP BIOLOGIST, BIOL QUAL CONTROL TECH SERV, MERCK SHARP & DOHME, 81- *Concurrent Pos:* Mem fac, Dept Biol, Grad Sch, Villanova Univ, 81- *Mem:* AAAS; NY Acad Sci. *Res:* Biology of the type C RNA tumor and herpes simplex viruses; viral vaccine development; biological assay development. *Mailing Add:* Dept Biol Qual Control Tech Serv Merck Sharp & Dohme West Point PA 19486

SALES, JOHN KEITH, b Syracuse, NY, Jan 4, 34; m 57; c 5. STRUCTURAL GEOLOGY. *Educ:* Syracuse Univ, BS, 56; Univ Nev, Reno, PhD(geol), 66. *Prof Exp:* Explor geologist, Mobil Oil Corp, Wyo, 66-68; asst prof earth sci, State Univ NY Col Oneonta, 68-73, assoc prof, 73-80. *Concurrent Pos:* Lectr, Mobil Oil Corp Explor Sch, 67-; struct consult, 68-; grant, 70-72. *Mem:* Geol Soc Am; Am Asn Petrol Geologists. *Res:* Regional tectonics, plate tectonic scale modeling and glacier dynamics. *Mailing Add:* 106 Woodacre Circle Duneanville TX 75116

SALESIN, EUGENE DENNIS, b Detroit, Mich, Apr 24, 35; m 58; c 3. PHOTOCHEMISTRY. *Educ:* Univ Mich, BS, 58; Case Western Reserve Univ, MS, 60, PhD(anal chem), 62. *Prof Exp:* Anal chemist, Indust Lab, 61-63, sr res chemist, Res Lab, 63-67, TECH ASSOC, FILM EMULSION DIV, EASTMAN KODAK CO, 67- *Res:* Photographic chemistry. *Mailing Add:* Film Emulsion Div Eastman Kodak Co Rochester NY 14650

SALETAN, LEONARD TIMOTHY, b New York, NY, Jan 5, 15; m 37; c 3. CHEMISTRY. *Educ:* Univ Wis, BA, 36, MA, 38. *Prof Exp:* Asst chief chemist & supvr lab, Schwarz Labs, NY, 38-45; brewing technologist, Army Exchange Serv, Europe, 45-46; sect head, Standard Brands, Inc, NY, 47-48; chemist & lab supvr, Wallerstein Co, Staten Island, 48-58; chief brewing lab, 58-66, asst dir res, 66-70, dir brewing lab, 70-72; dir develop hop extracts, Kalamazoo Spice Extraction Co, Mich, 72-75; CONSULT, 75- *Mem:* Am Chem Soc; Am Soc Brewing Chem; Inst Food Technol; Brit Inst Brewing; fel Am Inst Chem. *Res:* Brewing; enzymes; food quality control and analysis. *Mailing Add:* 11 Arbor Ln Roslyn Heights NY 11577

SALEUDDIN, ABU S, b Faridpur, Bangladesh, Jan 14, 37; m 66; c 1. INVERTEBRATE ZOOLOGY. *Educ:* Univ Dacca, BSc, 55, MSc, 57; Univ Reading, PhD(marine ecol), 63. *Prof Exp:* Lectr invert zool, Univ Dacca, 58-60 & 63-64; Nat Res Coun Can fel invert physiol, Univ Alta, 64-66; instr cell physiol, Duke Univ, 66-67; asst prof, 67-70, assoc prof, 70-78, PROF CELL BIOL, YORK UNIV, 78- *Mem:* Am Soc Zoologists; Can Soc Zoologists. *Res:* Physiology of biological calcification with special interest in shell regeneration in molluscs; neurosecretion in invertebrates. *Mailing Add:* Dept of Biol York Univ Downsview ON M3J 2R3 Can

SALGADO, ERNESTO D, b Spain, Nov 16, 23; m 52; c 2. PATHOLOGY. *Educ:* Univ Zaragosa, AB, 40; Univ Madrid, MD, 47; Univ Montreal, PhD, 55. *Prof Exp:* Resident, Univ Madrid Hosp, 47-50; asst, Univ Montreal, 50-52; res assoc, 52-54; sr biologist, Nepera Chem Co, NY, 54-55; dir biol res, 55-57; endocrinologist, Pfizer Therapeut Inst, NJ, 57-58; assoc prof, 61-68, PROF PATH, COL MED & DENT NJ, 68- *Concurrent Pos:* Fel path, Col Med & Dent NJ, 58-61; consult, Pfizer Therapeut Inst, 58-59. *Mem:* AAAS; Am Soc Exp Path; Am Physiol Soc; NY Acad Sci. *Res:* Experimental and clinical pathology. *Mailing Add:* Dept of Path Col of Med & Dent NJ Newark NJ 07103

SALGADO, PETER GORDON, b Amarillo, Tex, June 7, 28; m 50; c 5. CHEMICAL ENGINEERING, PHYSICAL CHEMISTRY. *Educ:* Univ WVa, BS, 51, MS, 56, PhD(chem eng), 58. *Prof Exp:* Chem engr, Union Carbide Chem Corp, 51; STAFF MEM, LOS ALAMOS SCI LAB, UNIV CALIF, 58- *Res:* High temperature materials; chemical kinetics; carbon chemistry; heat and mass transfer; gas analysis; high temperature thermometry; explosives development. *Mailing Add:* 109 Monte Rey Dr N Los Alamos NM 87544

SALHANICK, HILTON AARON, b Fall River, Mass, Sept 17, 24; m 55; c 2. OBSTETRICS & GYNECOLOGY. *Educ:* Harvard Univ, AB, 47, MA, 49, PhD(biol), 50; Univ Utah, MD, 56. *Prof Exp:* Asst endocrinol, Harvard Univ, 47-50; res assoc obstet & gynec, Col Med, Univ Utah, 52-56; intern, St Louis Maternity Hosp, 56-57; from resident to chief resident, Col Med, Univ Nebr, 57-59, from asst prof to assoc prof, 57-62, asst prof biochem, 57-62; head dept pop sci, 71-73, PROF OBSTET & GYNEC, SCH MED, HARVARD UNIV, 62-, FREDERICK LEE HISAW PROF REPRODUCTIVE PHYSIOL, 70-, MEM CTR POP STUDIES, SCH PUB HEALTH, 65- *Concurrent Pos:* Mem endocrinol study sect, NIH, 61-65, chmn, 65-66; obstetrician-gynecologist-in-chief, Beth Israel Hosp, Boston, 62-65. *Mem:* AAAS; Am Chem Soc; fel Am Col Obstet & Gynec; Endocrine Soc; Soc Gynec Invest. *Res:* Endocrinology of reproductive system; conception control. *Mailing Add:* Sch of Pub Health Harvard Univ Boston MA 02115

SALHANY, JIMMY MITCHELL, b Detroit, Mich, Mar 27, 47; m 70. BIOPHYSICS. *Educ:* Univ Fla, BS, 72; Univ Chicago, PhD(biophys), 74. *Prof Exp:* Fel biophys, Bell Tel Labs, 74-75; res asst prof biochem, 75-77, ASSOC PROF DEPT BIOMED CHEM, UNIV NEBR MED CTR, 77-, DIR RES, CARDIOVASC CTR, 75- *Concurrent Pos:* Investr, Am Heart Asn, 80-85. *Mem:* Am Chem Soc; Biophys Soc; Int Soc Oxygen Transp to Tissue. *Res:* Membrane biophysics, ion transport and protein associations; in vivo nuclear magnetic resonance spectroscopy. *Mailing Add:* Dept Biomed Chem Col Pharm Univ of Nebr Med Ctr Omaha NE 68105

SALIHI, JALAL T(AWFIQ), b Sulaymania, Iraq, Dec 6, 25; m 57; c 2. ELECTRICAL ENGINEERING. *Educ:* Univ Leeds, BSc, 48; Univ Calif, Berkeley, MS, 54, PhD(elec eng), 58. *Prof Exp:* Staff engr, Lenkurt Elec Co, Calif, 57-59; asst prof elec eng, Univ Baghdad, 59-61, head dept, 61-63; supvry res engr, Gen Motors Defense Res Labs, Calif, 63-71, supvry res engr elec propulsion dept, Res Labs, Gen Motors Tech Ctr, Mich, 71; chief hybrid & elec systs br, 71-72, ASST DIR, DIV ADVAN AUTOMOTIVE POWER SYSTS DEVELOP, ENVIRON PROTECTION AGENCY, 72- *Mem:* Inst Elec & Electronics Engrs; Soc Automotive Engrs. *Res:* Magnetic amplifiers and other types of nonlinear magnetic circuits; servomechanisms and control; power conversion; electric propulsion. *Mailing Add:* Div of Advan Automotive Power Environ Protection Agency Morristown NJ 07960

SALIK, JULIAN OSWALD, b Czech, Sept 17, 09; nat US; m 39. RADIOLOGY. *Educ:* Jagiellonian Univ, MD, 36; Cambridge Univ, DMRE, 41. *Prof Exp:* Clin clerk radiol, Holzknecht Inst, Vienna, Austria, 37, Panel Hosp, Cracow, Poland, 38 & Middlesex Hosp, London, Eng, 39; resident, Columbia-Presby Med Ctr, New York, 42-44; dir dept radiol, Halloran Vet Admin Hosp, Staten Island, NY, 47-49; asst prof, 56-60, ASSOC PROF RADIOL, SCH MED, JOHNS HOPKINS UNIV, 60-; RADIOLOGIST-IN-CHIEF, SINAI HOSP, 49- *Concurrent Pos:* Asst resident, Col Physicians & Surgeons, Columbia Univ, 42-44; radiologist, Levindale Home for Aged & Chronic Dis Hosp, Baltimore, Md, 51- & Hopkins Hosp, 56- *Mem:* Radiol Soc NAm; AMA; fel Am Col Radiol; fel NY Acad Med; Brit Inst Radiol. *Res:* Diagnostic radiology of gastrointestinal tract, pancreas and lungs; vascular anatomy and pathology; genito-urinary tract. *Mailing Add:* Dept of Radiol Sinai Hosp Belvedere at Greenspring Ave Baltimore MD 21215

SALIN, MARVIN LEONARD, b Brooklyn, NY, July 14, 46; m 72; c 2. BIOCHEMISTRY. *Educ:* Brooklyn Col, City Univ New York, BS, 67; Fla State Univ, MS, 69, PhD(biol sci), 72. *Prof Exp:* Assoc biochem, Univ Ga, 73-74; NIH fel, Duke Univ, 74-76, assoc biochem, 76-78; asst prof, 78-80, ASSOC PROF, MISS STATE UNIV, 80- *Mem:* Am Soc Photobiol; Am Soc Plant Physiologists; Sigma Xi; Am Soc Biol Chemists. *Res:* Plant biochemistry, free radicals of oxygen, leukocyte metabolism, oxidases, oxygenases and peroxidases. *Mailing Add:* Dept of Biochem Miss State Univ Mississippi State MS 39762

SALINAS, DAVID, b New York, NY, Feb 25, 32. ENGINEERING, APPLIED MATHEMATICS. *Educ:* Univ Calif, Los Angeles, BS, 59, MS, 62, PhD(eng), 68. *Prof Exp:* Sr res engr, Space & Info Div, NAm Aviation, Inc, 62-65; scholar eng mech, Univ Calif, Los Angeles, 68-70; ASSOC PROF MECH ENG, US NAVAL POSTGRAD SCH, 70- *Mem:* Am Soc Civil Engrs; Am Soc Mech Engrs; Am Acad Mech; Sigma Xi. *Res:* Optimization of structures; micromechanics of composite materials; finite element methods; inelastic behavior of structures; mechanics of composite materials; optimization of structures; finite element analysis of nonlinear field problems. *Mailing Add:* Code 69ZC US Naval Postgrad Sch Monterey CA 93940

SALINGER, GERHARD LUDWIG, b Berlin, Ger, Aug 25, 34; US citizen; m 58; c 3. LOW TEMPERATURE PHYSICS. *Educ:* Yale Univ, BS, 56; Univ Ill, MS, 58, PhD(physics), 62. *Prof Exp:* Asst physics, Univ Ill, 56-61; vis res prof, Univ Sao Paulo, 61-64; from asst prof to assoc prof, 64-75, PROF PHYSICS, RENSSELAER POLYTECH INST, 75-, CHMN DEPT, 78- *Concurrent Pos:* Vis assoc prof, Iowa State Univ, 74-75. *Mem:* Am Phys Soc; Am Asn Physics Teachers. *Res:* Low temperature thermal properties of amorphous materials. *Mailing Add:* Dept of Physics Rensselaer Polytech Inst Troy NY 12181

SALINGER, RUDOLF MICHAEL, b Berlin, Ger, July 24, 36; US citizen; m 61; c 2. CHEMISTRY, CHEMICAL ENGINEERING. *Educ:* Cooper Union, BChE, 58; Univ Wis, MS, 60; Univ Cincinnati, PhD(org chem), 63. *Prof Exp:* Fel, Stanford Univ, 63-64; res chemist, 64-68, group leader, Res Eng Sect, 68-75, sr res group leader, 75-77, sect mgr anal serv, 77-80, CORP QUAL ASSURANCE MGR, DOW CORNING CORP, 80- *Mem:* Am Inst Chem Engr; Am Chem Soc; Sigma Xi; Am Soc Qual Control. *Res:* Organosilicon chemistry; inorganic chemistry. *Mailing Add:* Dow Corning Corp PO Box 1592 Midland MI 48640

SALINGER, SHELDON NORMAN, electrical engineering, systems analysis, see previous edition

SALIS, ANDREW E, b Boston, Mass, Oct 10, 15; m 41; c 3. ELECTRICAL ENGINEERING. *Educ:* Auburn Univ, BSc, 39, MSc, 40, Prof degree, 48; Tex A&M Univ, PhD(elec eng), 51. *Prof Exp:* From instr to assoc prof elec eng, Tex A&M Univ, 40-51; sr group engr, Gen Dynamics Corp, 51-59; chmn dept elec eng, 59-70, PROF ELEC ENG, UNIV TEX, ARLINGTON, 59-, DEAN ENG, 70- *Concurrent Pos:* Consult, LTV Corp & Gen Dynamics-San Diego Dallas Power & Light Co, 59-71. *Mem:* Inst Elec & Electronics Engrs; Am Soc Eng Educ. *Res:* High frequencies and natural electrical phenomena. *Mailing Add:* Off of the Dean of Eng Univ of Tex Arlington TX 76010

SALISBURY, FRANK BOYER, b Provo, Utah, Aug 3, 26; m 49; c 6. PLANT PHYSIOLOGY. *Educ:* Univ Utah, BS, 51, MA, 52; Calif Inst Technol, PhD, 55. *Prof Exp:* Asst prof bot, Pomona Col, 54-55; asst prof, Colo State Univ, 55-61, prof, 61-66; head dept plant sci, 66-70, PROF PLANT PHYSIOL, UTAH STATE UNIV, 66-, PROF BOT, 70- *Concurrent Pos:* NSF sr fel, Univ Tübingen & Innsbruck Univ, 62-63; plant physiologist, US AEC, 73-74. *Mem:* AAAS; Am Soc Plant Physiol; Ecol Soc Am; Am Inst Biol Sci; Bot Soc Am. *Res:* Physiology of flowering; space biology; physiological ecology. *Mailing Add:* Dept of Plant Sci UMC 48 Utah State Univ Logan UT 84322

SALISBURY, GLENN WADE, b Sheffield, Ohio, June 2, 10; m 32; c 2. DAIRY SCIENCE. *Educ:* Ohio State Univ, BS, 31; Cornell Univ, PhD(animal husb), 34. *Prof Exp:* Asst animal husb, Cornell Univ, 31-34, instr, 34-36, asst prof & asst animal husbandman, Exp Sta, 36-40, assoc prof & assoc animal husbandman, 40-44, prof, 44-47; prof dairy sci & head dept, 47-69, DIR AGR EXP STA, UNIV ILL, URBANA, 69- *Concurrent Pos:* Cornell fel, Iowa State Col, 41; mem bd consults, Milk Mkt Bd Eng & Wales, 48-52; dir, Int Dairy Show, Chicago, 53-70; Fulbright lectr, State Agr Univ, Wageningen, 55-56; mem agr subpanel, President's Sci Adv Comt, 61-63; consult, US Off Sci & Technol, 62- *Honors & Awards:* Borden Award, Am Dairy Sci Asn, 45; Award of Merit, Italian Govt, 64; Morrison Award, Am Soc Animal Sci, 64, Paul A Funk Award, 71; Knight, Order of Merit, Repub Italy, 66. *Mem:* Nat Acad Sci; fel AAAS; Am Dairy Sci Asn; Am Genetic Asn; Am Soc Animal Sci. *Res:* Artificial insemination; reproductive physiology and genetics of dairy cattle. *Mailing Add:* 315 Animal Sci Lab Univ of Ill Urbana IL 61801

SALISBURY, JOHN WILLIAM, JR, b Palm Beach, Fla, Feb 6, 33; m 57; c 2. GEOSCIENCE, REMOTE SENSING. *Educ:* Amherst Col, BA, 55; Yale Univ, MS, 57, PhD(geol), 59. *Prof Exp:* Res scientist, Air Force Cambridge Res Labs, 59-61, chief lunar planetary res br, 61-70, chief spectros studies br, 70-76; chief Geothermal Energy Br, Dept Energy, 76-81; CHIEF, EARTH RESOURCES OBSERVATION SYST OFF, US GEOL SURV, 81- *Concurrent Pos:* Vis prof, Purdue Univ, 61-64; guest lectr, Hayden Planetarium, Am Mus, 64-75. *Honors & Awards:* Outstanding Contribution to Mil Sci Award, US Air Force, 61 & Off of Aerospace Res Sci Achievement Award, 66; Gunter Loeser Award, Air Force Cambridge Res Labs, 69 & Sci Achievement Award, 74. *Mem:* AAAS; Am Geophys Union; fel Geol Soc Am. *Res:* Geology of moon and planets; terrestrial and extraterrestrial geological remote sensing; nature and extent of geothermal resources. *Mailing Add:* 5529 Coltsfoot Ct Columbia MD 21045

SALISBURY, LYNN, b Havana, Ill, Mar 12, 37. ORGANIC CHEMISTRY. *Educ:* Univ Western Mich, BA, 59; Univ Mich, PhD(chem), 66. *Prof Exp:* NIH fel chem, 66-67; asst prof, Univ NDak, 67-70; assoc prof chem & physics, Kean Col, 70-80. *Mem:* Am Chem Soc. *Res:* Carbene chemistry; organic polarography. *Mailing Add:* 547 Page St #5 San Francisco CA 94117

SALISBURY, MATTHEW HAROLD, b Far Rockaway, NY, Mar 17, 43; m 67; c 1. GEOPHYSICS. *Educ:* Mass Inst Technol, BS, 68; Univ Wash, MS, 71, PhD(geol sci), 74. *Prof Exp:* Technician geophys, Woods Hole Oceanog Inst, 64, res asst, 65; res asst seismol, Dept Geol & Geophys, Mass Inst Technol, 66-67; sr observer satellite geodesy, Smithsonian Astrophys Observ, 68-70; asst prof geophys, State Univ NY, Binghamton, 74-76; asst res geol, 76-79, ASSOC CHIEF SCIENTIST, DEEP SEA DRILLING PROJ, SCRIPPS INST OCEANOG, 79- *Concurrent Pos:* Partic scientist, Leg 34 Deep Sea Drilling Proj, Scripps Inst Oceanog, 73-74; asst proj officer, Deep Sea Drilling Proj, NSF, 74-75. *Mem:* Am Geophys Union. *Res:* Determination of the petrology of the lower crust through comparisons of seismic velocity structure determined by refraction and logging with laboratory-determined physical properties of geologic materials at high confining pressures and temperatures. *Mailing Add:* Deep Sea Drilling Proj Scripps Inst Oceanog La Jolla CA 92093

SALISBURY, STANLEY R, b Milwaukee, Wis, Oct 2, 32; m 56; c 4. NUCLEAR PHYSICS. *Educ:* Marquette Univ, BS, 55; Univ Wis, MS, 56, PhD(nuclear physics), 61. *Prof Exp:* Res fel nuclear physics, Univ Wis, 61-62; res scientist, 62-68, staff scientist, 69-74, SR STAFF SCIENTIST, LOCKHEED PALO ALTO RES LAB, 74- *Mem:* Am Phys Soc. *Res:* X-ray phenomenology; Van de Graaff accelerators; neutron induced reactions; neutron cross sections; level parameters; aurora phenomenon; charged particle x-ray and neutron flux measurements from satellites; measurement of x-rays for environmental effects experiments; program management; systems design and fabrication. *Mailing Add:* Lockheed Res Labs Dept 52-11 3251 Hanover St Bldg 203 Palo Alto CA 94302

SALIVAR, CHARLES JOSEPH, b New York, NY, Feb 15, 23; m 45, 75; c 2. ORGANIC CHEMISTRY. *Educ:* Queens Col, NY, BS, 43. *Prof Exp:* Res chemist, Chas Pfitzer & Co, Inc, 45-55, pharmaceut res supvr, 55-62; dir pharm res & develop, Mallinckrodt Chem Works, St Louis, 62-69, dir opers, 69-73; vpres & tech dir, KV Pharmaceut Co, 73-75; dir develop & qual assurance, 75-76, vpres tech, 76-77, mem bd dirs, 76-78, VPRES MFG & TECH OPERS, EMKO CO, 78-; DIR OPERS, SCHERING-PLOUGH CORP, ST LOUIS, 78- *Mem:* Am Pharmaceut Asn; Am Chem Soc. *Res:* Antibiotics; vitamins; medicinals; pharmaceutical dosage forms. *Mailing Add:* 346 Gill Ave Kirkwood MO 63122

SALK, JONAS EDWARD, b New York, NY, Oct 28, 14; m 39, 70; c 3. MEDICINE, IMMUNOLOGY. *Educ:* City Col New York, BS, 34; NY Univ, MD, 39. *Prof Exp:* Intern, Mt Sinai Hosp, NY, 40-42; res assoc, Univ Mich, 44-46, asst prof, 46-47; from assoc res prof bact to res prof bact, Univ Pittsburgh, 47-55, Commonwealth Prof prev med, 55-57, Commonwealth Prof exp med, 57-63, head virus res lab, 47-63; dir, 63-75, FEL, SALK INST BIOL STUDIES, 63-, FOUNDING DIR, 75- *Concurrent Pos:* Fel bact, Col Med, NY Univ, 39-40; Nat Res Coun fel med sci, Sch Pub Health, Univ Mich, 42-43, res fel epidemiol, 43-44; consult, US Secy War, 44-47 & US Secy Army, 47-54; mem comn influenza, Army Epidemiol Bd, 44-54; adj prof, Univ Calif, San Diego, 70-; mem, expert adv panel virus dis, WHO, 51- *Honors & Awards:* Presidential Medal of Freedom, 77. *Mem:* AAAS; Am Epidemiol Soc; Am Soc Clin Invest; Soc Exp Biol & Med; Sigma Xi. *Res:* Immunization and immunological properties of the influenza virus; immunological problems of poliomyelitis; experimental medicine; mechanisms of delayed hypersensitivity; author of over 100 publications. *Mailing Add:* Salk Inst for Biol Studies PO Box 85800 San Diego CA 92138

SALK, MARTHA SCHEER, b Detroit, Mich, Apr 16, 45; m 67; c 2. TERRESTRIAL PLANT ECOLOGY, PHYCOLOGY. *Educ:* Albion Col, BA, 67; Univ Iowa, MS, 69; Univ Louisville, PhD(bot & ecol), 75. *Prof Exp:* Terrestrial ecologist, Gilbert/Commonwealth, Reading, Pa, 74-75; RES ASSOC, OAK RIDGE NAT LAB, 75- *Mem:* Ecol Soc Am; Bot Soc Am. *Res:* Physiological plant ecology. *Mailing Add:* Environ Sci Div Bldg 1505 Oak Ridge Nat Lab PO Box X Oak Ridge TN 37830

SALKELD, ROBERT JOHN, b Glen Rock, NJ, July 26, 32. AEROSPACE ENGINEERING, PHYSICS. *Educ:* Princeton Univ, AB, 54; Harvard Univ, MBA, 56. *Prof Exp:* Admin asst to dir aeronaut res & develop, Ramo Wooldridge Corp, 56-58, asst proj engr, 58-60; proj engr, Aerospace Corp, 60-62, mgr adv manned systs, 62-64; tech dir mil & space systs planning, United Aircraft Corp, 64-67; consult, 67-71; dir planning, Systs Develop Corp, 71-75; CONSULT, 75- *Concurrent Pos:* Mem space panel, Proj Forecast, US Dept Air Force, 63-64; pres, R J Salkeld & Assocs, 67- *Mem:* Fel AAAS; Am Phys Soc; fel Am Inst Aeronaut & Astronaut; fel Brit Interplanetary Soc; sr mem Am Astron Soc. *Res:* Advanced design, planning and analysis of space stations; analysis and evaluation of strategic military systems; rocket combustion theory and analysis. *Mailing Add:* 266 Blood's Ridge Rd Bear Valley CA 95223

SALKFELD, E HELEN, insect physiology, histochemistry, see previous edition

SALKIN, DAVID, b Ukraine, Russia, Aug 8, 06; nat US; m 34; c 2. MEDICINE. *Educ:* Univ Toronto, MD, 29. *Prof Exp:* Intern, St Mary's Hosp, Detroit, Mich, 29-30; pathologist, Mich State Sanitarium, 33-34; demonstr med, Sch Med, WVa Univ, 35-38, from instr to asst prof, 38-48; chief prof serv, San Fernando Vet Admin Hosp, 48-61, chief of staff, 61-71, hosp dir, 67-71; dir res & educ, 71-75, med dir, 75-77, DIR MED RES, LA VINA HOSP, 77- *Concurrent Pos:* Fel path, H Kiefer Hosp, 33; med dir, Hopemont Sanitarium, 34-41, supt, 41-48; assoc clin prof med, Univ Calif, Los Angeles, 51-61; clin prof, Loma Linda Univ, 60- & Univ Southern Calif, 64- *Mem:* Fel Am Soc Clin Pharmacol & Therapeut; fel Am Thoracic Soc; fel AMA; fel Am Col Chest Physicians; fel Am Col Physicians. *Res:* Pneumoperitoneum; intestinal tuberculosis; pulmonary cavities; physiology of pneumothorax; chemotherapy of tuberculosis; bronchiectasis and bronchitis; coccidiodomycosis. *Mailing Add:* La Vina Hosp 3900 N Lincoln Ave Altadena CA 91001

SALKIN, IRA FRED, b Chicago, Ill, Dec 21, 41; m 64; c 1. MEDICAL MYCOLOGY. *Educ:* Northwestern Univ, Evanston, BA, 63, MS, 64; Univ Calif, Berkeley, PhD(bot), 69. *Prof Exp:* Lectr, biol, Univ Calif, Santa Barbara, 69-70; sr res scientist, 70-77, RES SCIENTIST IV MED MYCOL, DIV LABS & RES, NY STATE DEPT HEALTH, 77- *Concurrent Pos:* Mem adj fac, Dept Biol, Russell Sage Col, 77- & Union Col, NY, 78- *Mem:* Med Mycol Soc Am; Int Soc Human & Animal Mycol; Mycol Soc Am; Brit Mycol Soc. *Res:* Development and improvement of diagnostic procedures; taxonomy of zoopathogenic fungi and studies of the physiologic factors associated with pathogenicity in the fungi. *Mailing Add:* Ctr Labs & Res NY State Dept of Health Albany NY 12201

SALKIND, ALVIN J, b New York, NY, June 12, 27; m 65; c 2. ELECTROCHEMICAL ENGINEERING, BIOENGINEERING. *Educ:* Polytech Inst New York, BChE, 49, MChE, 52, DChE, 58. *Prof Exp:* Engr energy res, US Elec Mfg Co, 52-54; sr scientist energy res, Sonotone Corp, 54-56; res assoc, Polytech Inst New York, 56-58; sr scientist energy conversion, ESB Inc, 58-63, head lab electrochem, 63-68, mgr electromed prod, 68-71, vpres technol, 71-79, pres, 77-79; PROF & CHIEF BIOENG SECT, DEPT SURG, COL MED & DENT, RUTGERS MED SCH, 70- *Concurrent Pos:* Adj prof chem eng, Polytech Inst New York, 60-70; consult, Dept Space Sci, Univ Mo, 68-70; consult, Hahnemann Med Sch, 69-71, Nat Res Coun & Dept Energy, 79-; vis prof, Case-Western Reserve Univ, 81-82. *Mem:* Fel AAAS; fel Am Col Cardiol; Asn Advan Med Instrumentation; Am Inst Chem Engrs; Electrochem Soc. *Res:* Energy storage devices; batteries; electromedical devices. *Mailing Add:* 51 Adams Dr Princeton NJ 08540

SALKIND, MICHAEL JAY, b New York, NY, Oct 1, 38; m 59; c 4. MATERIALS & STRUCTURAL ENGINEERING. *Educ:* Rensselaer Polytech Inst, BMetE, 59, PhD(metall), 62. *Prof Exp:* Sr res scientist, United Aircraft Corp Res Labs, East Hartford, 64-65, supvr adv composites res group, 65-67, chief adv metall, 67-68, chief struct & mat, Sikorsky Aircraft Div, United Aircraft Corp, 68-75; dir prod develop, Avco Systs Div, Mass, 75-76; MGR STRUCT & DYNAMICS, NASA HQ, 76- *Concurrent Pos:* Lectr eng mat, Trinity Col Conn, 67-68; chmn Conn Dept Environ Protection Tech Adv Group, 72-75. *Mem:* Am Helicopter Soc; Am Inst Aeronaut & Astronaut; Am Inst Mining, Metall & Petrol Engrs; Am Soc Metals; Am Soc Testing & Mat. *Res:* Composite materials; controlled solidification; composite structures; titanium; fatigue; fracture; structure, dynamics, and design. *Mailing Add:* NASA-RJT Washington DC 20546

SALKOFF, LAWRENCE BENJAMIN, b Brooklyn, NY, Mar 3, 44; m 68; c 1. NEUROGENETICS, NEUROBIOLOGY. *Educ:* Univ Calif, Los Angeles, BA, 67; Univ Calif, Berkeley, PhD(genetics), 79. *Prof Exp:* Teaching assoc genetics, Univ Calif, Berkeley, 76-79, FEL, DEPT BIOL, YALE UNIV, 79- *Honors & Awards:* John Belling Prize, 80. *Mem:* Genetics Soc Am; Soc Neurosci; AAAS. *Res:* Neurogenetics; identification and characterization of genes that affect the function and development of the nervous system. *Mailing Add:* Dept Biol Box 6666 Yale Univ New Haven CT 06511

SALKOVITZ, EDWARD ISAAC, b Braddock, Pa, Sept 3, 17; m 46; c 3. PHYSICS, SCIENCE POLICY. *Educ:* Carnegie Inst Technol, BS, 39, MS & DSc(physics), 50. *Prof Exp:* Physicist, Bacharach Indust Instrument Co, 39-40; psychometric res, Am Soc Heating & Ventilating Engrs, 41; instr physics, Carnegie Inst Technol, 41-42; physicist, US Naval Res Lab, 42-46; asst & instr, Carnegie Inst Technol, 46-50; physicist solid state div, US Naval Res Lab, 50-55, consult metall div, 58-60, head metall br, Off Naval Res, DC, 60-65; prof metall eng & physics, Univ Pittsburgh, 65-74, chmn dept metall & mat eng, 66-70; dir mat sci div, 74-80, DIR RES PROGS, OFF NAVAL RES, 80- *Concurrent Pos:* Instr, Univ Md, 51-53; lectr, Howard Univ, 58-65; chief scientist & sci dir, London Br Off, US Off Naval Res, 70-72; adj prof eng, Univ Pittsburgh, 75- *Honors & Awards:* Meritorious Civilian Award, US Navy, 59. *Mem:* Assoc Inst Mech Engrs; Aerospace Struct Mat; Mat Res Soc; AAAS. *Res:* Brillouin zone investigations of metals and alloys; radiation effects in magnetic materials; single crystal plasticity; x-ray studies of deformed metal and nonmetal crystals; internal friction, liquid state; research and development administration. *Mailing Add:* Off of Naval Res Balliston Tower 800 N Quincy Arlington VA 22217

SALL, MARY ANN, b Portland, Ore, Dec 31, 45; m 78. PLANT PATHOLOGY, EPIDEMIOLOGY. *Educ:* Whittier Col, BA, 67; Ore State Univ, PhD(plant path), 73. *Prof Exp:* ASST PROF PLANT PATH, UNIV CALIF, 75- *Mem:* Am Phytopathological Soc; Am Soc Enologists; Sigma Xi. *Res:* Plant pathology; epidemiology; mathematical modeling; diseases of grapevines. *Mailing Add:* Dept of Plant Path Univ of Calif Davis CA 95616

SALL, THEODORE, b Paterson, NJ, Feb 22, 27; m 53; c 3. MICROBIOLOGY. *Educ:* Univ Louisville, AB, 49, MS, 50; Univ Pa, PhD(microbiol), 55. *Prof Exp:* Biochemist, Vet Admin Hosp, Philadelphia, 55-56; microbiologist & res assoc, Sch Med, Univ Pa, 56-61; staff scientist, RCA Space Ctr, 61-64; chief bact, Pepper Lab, Univ Pa Hosp, 64-68; from asst prof to assoc prof microbiol, NY Med Col, 68-72; PROF LIFE SCI, RAMAPO COL, NJ, 72- *Concurrent Pos:* Consult, Vet Admin Hosp, Philadelphia; chief microbiol serv, Metrop Hosp, New York, 68-71, dir, 71-72; with Ethicon Corp, 76-78. *Mem:* AAAS; Am Chem Soc; Am Soc Microbiol; fel NY Acad Sci. *Res:* Diagnostic bacteriology; microchemical analysis of bacteria; bacterial morphology; electron microscopy; fermentation chemistry; sterilization techniques. *Mailing Add:* 94 Woodcrest Dr Woodcliff Lake NJ 07675

SALLAVANTI, ROBERT ARMANDO, b Scranton, Pa, July 26, 42; m 64; c 3. PHYSICAL CHEMISTRY. *Educ:* Wilkes Col, BS, 63; Univ Pa, PhD(chem), 66. *Prof Exp:* Advan Res Projs Agency fel, Univ Pa, 66-67; USPHS fel, Yale Univ, 67-69; ASSOC PROF CHEM, UNIV SCRANTON, 69- *Concurrent Pos:* Asst prof, Quinnipiac Col, 68-69. *Mem:* Am Chem Soc; fel Am Inst Chemists. *Res:* Molecular orbital theory of organic and biological molecules; intermolecular potentials of the rare gases; transport properties of systems involving critical phenomena. *Mailing Add:* Dept of Chem Univ of Scranton Scranton PA 18510

SALLAY, STEPHEN, b Kiskundorozsma, Hungary, July 1, 20; US citizen; m 61; c 1. ORGANIC CHEMISTRY. *Educ:* Univ Szedeg, BS, 44, MS, 46, PhD(chem), 50. *Prof Exp:* Asst prof org chem, Univ Szeged, 52-55; fel, Harvard Univ, 57-58; res chemist, Wyeth Labs, Am Home Prod Corp, 58-59, group leader, Dept Med Chem, 59-69; PROF CHEM, PURDUE UNIV, FT WAYNE, 70- *Mem:* Am Chem Soc. *Res:* Synthetic organic chemistry, specifically in the alkaloid field. *Mailing Add:* Dept of Chem Purdue Univ Ft Wayne IN 46805

SALLEE, G THOMAS, b Ontario, Ore, Feb 21, 40; m 66; c 3. MATHEMATICS. *Educ:* Calif Inst Technol, BS, 62; Univ Calif, Berkeley, MA, 64; Univ Wash, PhD(math), 66. *Prof Exp:* From asst prof to assoc prof, 66-75, PROF MATH, UNIV CALIF, DAVIS, 75- *Mem:* Math Asn Am; Am Math Soc. *Res:* Geometry, especially geometry of convex sets, sets of constant width and polytopes. *Mailing Add:* Dept of Math Univ of Calif Davis CA 95616

SALLEE, VERNEY LEE, b Amarillo, Tex, June 26, 42; m 64; c 2. MEMBRANES, LIPIDS. *Educ:* Hardin-Simmons Univ, BA, 64; Univ NMex, PhD(med sci, physiol), 70. *Prof Exp:* Fel physiol, Southwestern Med Sch, Univ Tex Health Sci Ctr, 70-72, asst prof, 72-78; asst prof, 78-81, ASSOC PROF PHYSIOL, TEX COL OSTEOP MED, 81- *Concurrent Pos:* mem, Am Heart Asn. *Mem:* Am Physiol Soc. *Res:* Gastrointestinal absorptive physiology; physiology of membrane translocation processes; cholesterol metabolism. *Mailing Add:* Dept of Physiol Tex Col of Osteop Med Ft Worth TX 76107

SALLET, DIRSE WILKIS, b Washington, DC, Aug 10, 36; m 63; c 4. MECHANICAL ENGINEERING, FLUID DYNAMICS. *Educ:* George Washington Univ, BME, 61; Univ Kans, MSME, 63; Univ Stuttgart, Dr Ing, 66. *Prof Exp:* Instr mech eng, Univ Kans, 61-63; sci assoc fluid dynamics, Inst Aero- & Gas Dynamics, Univ Stuttgart, 63-66; res mech engr, US Naval Ord Lab, 66-67; from asst prof to assoc prof, 67-76, PROF MECH ENG, UNIV MD, COLLEGE PARK, 76- *Concurrent Pos:* Consult, US Naval Ord Lab, 67-74 & Gillette Co Res Inst, 71-78; vis scientist, Max Planck Inst & AVA, Gottingen, Ger, 73-74; eng consult, 75-; vis scientist, Ctr Nuclear Res, Kernforschungszentrum Karlsruhe, Inst Reactor Components, Ger, 80-81. *Mem:* AAAS; Am Soc Mech Engrs; Am Phys Soc. *Res:* Thermodynamics and heat transfer; flow induced vibrations; vortex motions; two-phase flow; gas dynamics; hydrodynamics; author or coauthor of various publications. *Mailing Add:* 12440 Old Fletchertown Rd Bowie MD 20715

SALLEY, JOHN JONES, b Richmond, Va, Oct 29, 26; m 50; c 3. ORAL PATHOLOGY. *Educ:* Med Col Va, DDS, 51; Univ Rochester, PhD(path), 54. *Hon Degrees:* DSc, Boston Univ, 75. *Prof Exp:* Instr histol, Eastman Sch Dent Hygienists, 52-54; instr path diag & therapeut, Med Col Va, 54-55, from asst prof to prof path & dent, 55-63; prof path & dent & dean sch dent, Univ Md, Baltimore, 63-74; assoc vpres, 74-80, VPRES RES & GRAD AFFAIRS, VA COMMONWEALTH UNIV, 80- *Concurrent Pos:* Consult, Off Chief Med Examr, Commonwealth of Va, 56, Vet Admin Hosp, 59, NIH, 62-66 & USPHS, 63-74; mem adv comt regional med prog in Md, 66-74; consult, WHO, 68-; hon prof, Univ Peru Cayetano Heredia, 70; pres, Am Asn Dent Sch, 71-72; dent educ rev comt, Bur Health Manpower Educ, 72- *Honors & Awards:* Award, Int Asn Dent Res, 53. *Mem:* Fel AAAS; Am Dent Asn; Am Acad Oral Path; Int Asn Dent Res; Nat Coun Univ Res Adminr. *Res:* Dental school administration; experimental carcinogenesis in oral tissues, including predisposing factors to oral cancer; etiological factors in periodontal diseases; hospital dentistry. *Mailing Add:* Va Commonwealth Univ Box 568 Med Col Va Sta Richmond VA 23298

SALLEY, JOHN JONES, JR, b Rochester, NY, June 2, 54; m 78; c 1. PHARMACEUTICAL CHEMISTRY. *Educ:* Randolph-Macon Col, BS, 76; Med Col Va, PhD(med chem), 80. *Prof Exp:* Fel org chem, Univ Ala, 80-81; RES SCIENTIST, NORWICH-EATON PHARMACEUT, DIV PROCTER & GAMBLE, 81- *Mem:* Am Chem Soc. *Res:* New ethical pharmaceutical products, specifically in the area of cardiovascular agents; development of novel organic chemical methodology and techniques. *Mailing Add:* Org Chem Sect Norwich-Eaton Pharmaceut PO Box 191 Norwich NY 13815

SALLMAN, BENNETT, b New York, NY, Dec 10, 17; m 43; c 3. MICROBIOLOGY. *Educ:* NY Univ, BS, 37; Univ Mich, MS, 39; Ohio State Univ, PhD(bact), 48; Am Bd Microbiol, dipl. *Prof Exp:* Asst prof bact, Hahnemann Med Col & Hosp, Ill, 48-51; chief bacteriologist, Commun Dis Ctr, USPHS, Ga, 51-53; assoc prof bact, 53-58, chmn dept, 61-80, PROF MICROBIOL, SCH MED, UNIV MIAMI, 58- *Mem:* Fel Am Acad Microbiol; fel Geront Soc. *Res:* Biochemical mechanisms of infectious diseases; aging at the cellular level; heart tissue metabolism; metabolic and ecologic interactions of microorganisms in the marine environment. *Mailing Add:* Dept of Microbiol Univ of Miami Sch pf Med Miami FL 33101

SALLOS, JOSEPH, b Budapest, Hungary, Aug 19, 31; Can citizen; m 53; c 2. ELECTRONICS. *Educ:* Budapest Tech Univ, Dip Ing, 55. *Prof Exp:* Engr, Radio Budapest, 49-56 & BC Tel Co, 57-59; RES ELECTRONIC ENGR, UNIV BC, 60-, SUPVR, ELECTRONIC INSTRUMENTATION DIV, 80- *Mem:* Can Coun Prof Engrs. *Res:* Short, middle and long wave broadcasting transmitters; direct distance dialing telephone systems; electron spin resonance spectroscopy; scientific electronic instrumentation; nuclear magnetic resonance spectroscopy. *Mailing Add:* Dept of Chem Univ of BC Vancouver BC V6T 1W5 Can

SALMAN, TALAT, metallurgy, deceased

SALMASSY, OMAR K, b McConnelsville, Ohio, Sept 22, 25; m 54; c 2. MECHANICAL ENGINEERING. *Educ:* Purdue Univ, BSME, 49, MSE, 51. *Prof Exp:* Asst dynamic strain anal, Purdue Univ, 49-50; mech engr, Repub Steel Corp, 50-51; prin mech engr, Mat Res, Battelle Mem Inst, 51-56; sr scientist, Avco Corp, 56-58; group leader, 58-59, from chief mat res, Res & Develop Div to sr consult scientist, Res & Advan Develop Div, 59-61 & 64-67; proj officer, Apollo Spacecraft Struct, Off Manned Space Flight, NASA Hq, Washington, DC, 61-64; br chief, Composites Mat Res & Develop, 67-73, mat specialist, 73-81, SR SCIENTIST, LIQUIFIED NATURAL GAS COMPOSITES, MCDONNELL DOUGLAS ASTRONAUT CO, 81- *Res:* High-modulus fiber reinforced composites; carbon/carbon, graphite and ceramic composites; cryogenic insulations; thermal protection systems; re-entry, antiballistic missile interceptor and space vehicle materials technology; ablation, vulnerability and hardening, inelasticity, dust erosion and fracture phenomenology; liquified natural gas insulation system development. *Mailing Add:* McDonnell Douglas Astronaut Co 5301 Bolsa Ave Huntington Beach CA 92647

SALMI, ERNEST WILLIAM, b Detroit, Mich, Dec 18, 22; m 49; c 4. NUCLEAR PHYSICS. *Educ:* Univ Mich, PhD(physics), 50. *Prof Exp:* MEM STAFF, LOS ALAMOS SCI LAB, 50- *Concurrent Pos:* Consult, Euratom, Italy, 62-63. *Mem:* Am Phys Soc. *Res:* Thermionic conversion reactors. *Mailing Add:* Los Alamos Sci Lab Univ of Calif PO Box 1663 Los Alamos NM 87545

SALMOIRAGHI, GIAN CARLO, b Gorla Minore, Italy, Sept 19, 24; nat US; m 70. PHYSIOLOGY. *Educ:* Univ Rome, MD, 48; McGill Univ, PhD(physiol), 59. *Prof Exp:* From med officer to sr med officer, Int Refugee Orgn, Italy, 49-52; res fel, Cleveland Clin, Ohio, 52-55, res assoc, 55-56; lectr physiol, McGill Univ, 56-58; from neurophysiologist to chief clin neuropharmacol res ctr, NIMH, 59-67, dir div spec ment health res, 67-73; assoc comnr res, NY State Dept Ment Hyg, 73-77; ASSOC DIR RES, NAT INST ALCOHOL ABUSE & ALCOHOLISM, 77- *Concurrent Pos:* Clin prof psychiat, Med Sch, George Washington Univ, 66-73; mem, Int Brain Res Orgn. *Mem:* AAAS; Am Col Neuropsychopharmacol; Am Physiol Soc; Am Soc Pharmacol & Exp Therapeut; Soc Biol Psychiat. *Res:* Neurophysiology and neuropharmacology of mammalian central neurons. *Mailing Add:* 8216 Hamilton Spring Ct Bethesda MD 20817

SALMON, CHARLES G(ERALD), b Detroit, Mich, Oct 28, 30; m 53; c 3. STRUCTURAL & CIVIL ENGINEERING. *Educ:* Univ Mich, BS, 52, MS, 54; Univ Wis, PhD(struct eng), 61. *Prof Exp:* From instr to assoc prof, 56-67, PROF CIVIL ENG, UNIV WIS-MADISON, 67- *Mem:* Am Soc Civil Engrs; Int Asn Bridge & Structural Eng; fel Am Concrete Inst; Am Soc Eng Educ. *Res:* Stability and stresses in edge loaded triangular plates; design methods and behavior of reinforced concrete and steel structures; structural dynamics. *Mailing Add:* 2214 Eng Univ of Wis Madison WI 53706

SALMON, EDWARD DICKINSON, b Montclair, NJ, Mar 1, 44; m 67; c 1. CELL BIOLOGY. *Educ:* Brown Univ, BS, 67; Univ Pa, PhD(biomed eng), 73. *Prof Exp:* Staff scientist cell motility, Marine Biol Lab, Woods Hole, 73-77; ASST PROF ZOOL, UNIV NC, 77- *Concurrent Pos:* Corp mem, Bermuda Biol Sta Res & Marine Biol Lab, Woods Hole. *Mem:* Am Soc Cell Biol. *Res:* Molecular mechanisms of cell motility especially the mitotic mechanisms of motility and the physiological effects of deep-sea cold temperatures and high hydrostatic pressures on cellular processes. *Mailing Add:* Dept of Zool Wilson Hall Univ of NC Chapel Hill NC 27514

SALMON, ELEANOR S(EELY), b Rochester, NY, Feb 16, 10. PETROLEUM TECHNOLOGY. *Educ:* Smith Col, AB, 32; Columbia Univ, MA, 34, PhD(paleont), 42. *Prof Exp:* Jr supvr, Res Proj Foraminifera, Am Mus Natural Hist, 38-42, sci asst micropaleont, 46-51, asst curator, 51-59; chemist, Socony-Vacuum Oil Co, 42-46; abstractor petrol technol, Cent Abstr & Indexing Serv, Am Petrol Inst, 59-66, ed, 66-75; RETIRED. *Concurrent Pos:* Asst ed, Micropaleontol, Am Mus Natural Hist, 55-61; abstractor, Am Petrol Inst, 75-; translator, Bur Res Geol Min, Orleans, France, 81- *Mem:* AAAS; Geol Soc Am; Am Asn Petrol Geol; Am Geol Inst. *Res:* Foraminifera; Ostracoda; taxonomy of middle Ordovician refinesquinids; petroleum technology. *Mailing Add:* 521 W 112th St Apt 42 New York NY 10025

SALMON, ELIAHU J, b Jerusalem, Israel, Dec 15, 28; US citizen; m 56; c 2. ENVIRONMENTAL SCIENCES. *Educ:* Utah State Univ, BSc, 51; Univ Mich, PhD(environ sci), 64. *Prof Exp:* Dir, Soreg Nuclear Res Ctr, 56-69; sr scientist, World Health Orgn, 69-74; Nat Acad Sci, 74-77; sr res assoc, Resources for the Future, 77-78; sr scientist, Med Div, Nat Acad Sci, 78-81; DIR HEALTH, SAFETY & SOCIOECON, FLUOR ENG & CONSTRUCTORS INC, 82- *Concurrent Pos:* Sr lectr, Tech Israel Inst Technol, 64-69; vis prof, Univ Tel Aviv, 64-69; lectr mgt, Univ Md, 78-82; pres, Environ, Health, Energy, Resources Corp, 78-82. *Mem:* Am Health Physics Soc; Am Indust Hyg Asn; Am Pub Health Asn; Am Chem Soc. *Res:* Evaluation of the federal programs and funded research in health and biologic effects of radiation; evaluation of the health, safety, environmental and socioeconomic implication of various energy systems and technologies; evaluation of health and environmental policies and regulations. *Mailing Add:* Fluor Engr & Constructors Inc 2801 Kelvin Ave Irvine CA 92714

SALMON, JAMES HENRY, b Centerville, Pa, Feb 25, 32; m 67; c 2. NEUROSURGERY. *Educ:* Pa State Univ, BS, 53; Hahnemann Med Col, MD, 57; Am Bd Neurol Surg, dipl, 68. *Prof Exp:* Resident neurosurg, Yale Univ, 61-65, instr neurol surg, Sch Med, 64-65; from instr to assoc prof neurosurg, Sch Med, Univ Cincinnati, 66-72; prof neurosurg & chmn div, Sch Med, Southern Ill Univ, 72-77; PVT PRACT NEUROSURG, 77- *Concurrent Pos:* Knight fel neuropath, Sch Med, Yale Univ, 62-63; NIH fel, Univ London, 65; chief neurosurg, Cincinnati Vet Admin Hosp, 66-72; asst dir neurosurg, Children's Hosp, Cincinnati; attend neurosurgeon, Cincinnati Gen Hosp & Christian R Holmes Hosp, Cincinnati; consult neurosurg, Bur Serv Crippled Children, Hamilton County Neuromuscular Diag Clin & Shriners Burns Inst. *Mem:* Cong Neurol Surg; Asn Acad Surg; Int Soc Pediat Neurosurg; fel Am Col Surg; Am Asn Neurol Surg. *Res:* Hydrocephalus, adult and childhood; cerebral blood flow, cortical function; electron microscopy, cerebral capillaries in traumatic encephalopathy; neonatal meningitis, treatment, ultrastructure of brain. *Mailing Add:* 225 W 25th St Erie PA 16502

SALMON, MICHAEL, b New York, NY, Apr 8, 38. ANIMAL BEHAVIOR. *Educ:* Earlham Col, BS, 59; Univ Md, MS, 62, PhD(zool), 64. *Prof Exp:* Asst animal behav, Univ Md, 59-64; NIH fel, Univ Hawaii, 64-65; asst prof biol, DePaul Univ, 65-67; from asst prof to assoc prof zool, 67-77, PROF ECOL, ETHOLOGY & EVOLUTION, UNIV ILL, URBANA-CHAMPAIGN, 77- *Mem:* AAAS; Animal Behav Soc; Am Soc Ichthyologists & Herpetologists; Am Soc Zoologists. *Res:* Marine bioacoustics of crustaceans and fishes; sensory mechanisms; orientation to sound. *Mailing Add:* Dept of Zool Univ of Ill at Urbana-Champaign Champaign IL 61801

SALMON, OLIVER NORTON, b Syracuse, NY, Mar 24, 17; m 45; c 4. PHYSICAL CHEMISTRY. *Educ:* Cornell Univ, AB, 40, PhD(phys chem), 46. *Prof Exp:* Lab asst animal nutrit, Cornell Univ, 40-41; chemist, Corning Glass Works, NY, 41-43; res asst, Off Sci Res & Develop, Cornell Univ, 43-45, res assoc, Off Res & Inventions, US Dept Navy, 46-47; phys chemist, Knowel Atomic Power Lab, Gen Elec Co, 47-56 & Electronics Lab, 56-60; res specialist, 60-62, supvr, 62-64, mgr mat physics res, 64-72, mgr basic & pioneering res, 72-73, sr res specialist, 3M Central Res Labs, 73-81, SR RES SPECIALIST, INDUST & CONSUMER SECTOR RES LAB, 3M CO, 81-; res specialist, 60-62, supvr, 62-64, solids; conversion of ocean wave energy into electricity. mat physics res, 64-72, mgr basic & pioneering res, 72-73, SR RES SPECIALIST, ADVAN RES PROG LAB, MINN MINING & MFG CO, 73- *Mem:* Am Chem Soc; Am Ceramic Soc; Int Solar Energy Soc; Sigma Xi. *Res:* Solar energy; solid state physics and chemistry; chemical thermodynamics; liquid metals; hydrogen isotopes. *Mailing Add:* 201 BE 01 St Paul MN 55144

SALMON, PETER ALEXANDER, b Victoria, BC, Aug 5, 29; US citizen; m 53; c 3. SURGERY. *Educ:* Univ Wash, BS, 51, MD, 55; Univ Minn, Minneapolis, MS & PhD(surg), 61; Am Bd Surg, dipl, 64. *Prof Exp:* Asst prof surg, Med Sch, Univ Minn, Minneapolis, 62-66; assoc prof, 66-72, PROF SURG, UNIV ALTA, 72- *Concurrent Pos:* Hartford Found grant, Mt Sinai Hosp, Minneapolis, 63-67; USPHS res grant, 64-65; Med Res Coun Can grant, Univ Alta, 67-72; dir surg educ & res, Mt Sinai Hosp, Minneapolis, 63-66. *Mem:* AAAS; Soc Exp Biol & Med; fel Am Col Surg; fel Royal Col Surg; Soc Univ Surgeons. *Res:* Gastrointestinal physiology, secretion, motility; gastrointestinal transplantation, especially intestine, pancreas, liver; surgical treatment of obesity. *Mailing Add:* 11-104F Clin Sci Bldg Univ Alta Edmonton AB T6G 2G7 Can

SALMON, RAYMOND EDWARD, b Vancouver, BC, Apr 14, 31; m; c 3. POULTRY NUTRITION. *Educ:* Univ BC, BSA, 54, MSA, 57; Univ Sask, PhD, 72. *Prof Exp:* Nutritionist, Buckerfield's Ltd, 58-67; RES SCIENTIST, CAN AGR RES BR, 67- *Mem:* Poultry Sci Asn; Worlds Poultry Sci Asn. *Res:* Turkey nutrition research; utilization of fats and oils; rapeseed meal research; author of over 30 science publications. *Mailing Add:* Can Agr Res Sta Swift Current Res Sta Swift Current SK S9H 1N5 Can

SALMON, SHIRLEY JOAN, b Kemmerer, Wyo, Nov 8, 34. SPEECH PATHOLOGY. *Educ:* Huron Col, BA, 55; Univ Iowa, MA, 61, PhD(speech path), 65. *Prof Exp:* Teacher first grade, Sioux Falls, SDak, 55-60; speech pathologist, Mayo Clin, 61-62; asst prof speech path, Univ Pittsburgh, 65-67; ASST PROF SPEECH PATH, UNIV KANS MED CTR, KANSAS CITY,

67-; SPEECH PATHOLOGIST, VET ADMIN HOSP, KANSAS CITY, 72- *Concurrent Pos:* Dir speech path, Mercy Hosp, Pittsburgh, Pa, 65-67. *Mem:* Fel Am Speech-Language-Hearing Asn; Int Asn Laryngectomees; Int Asn Logopedics & Phoniatrics. *Res:* Adult speech, language or voice impairments due to organic disorders. *Mailing Add:* Vet Admin Hosp 3801 Linwood Blvd Kansas City MO 64128

SALMON, VINCENT, b Kingston, BWI, Jan 21, 12; nat US; m 37; c 2. ACOUSTICS. *Educ:* Temple Univ, AB, 34, AM, 36; Mass Inst Technol, PhD(physics), 38. *Prof Exp:* Physicist, Jensen Radio Mfg Co, 37, physicist in charge res & develop, Jensen Mfg Co, 38-49; mgr sonics sect, Stanford Res Inst, 49-65, mgr sonics prog, 65-70, staff scientist physics, Sensory Sci Res Ctr, 70-76, CONSULT PROF, STANFORD UNIV, 77- *Concurrent Pos:* Ed, Audio Eng Soc J, 54-55; consult, acoust, 46-, Nat Acad Sci, 65- & Nat Acad Eng, 73-74; pres, Nat Coun Acoust Consults, 69-71; mem, Inst Noise Control Eng & pres, 74; vpres, Indust Noise Serv, 72-77. *Mem:* Fel AAAS; fel Acoust Soc Am (pres, 70-71); fel Audio Eng Soc; Sigma Xi; fel Inst Elec & Electronics Eng. *Res:* Theory of acoustic radiators; electroacoustics; underwater sound; industrial acoustics; audio engineering; sound recording; noise control; architectural acoustics; nondestructive sonic testing. *Mailing Add:* 765 Hobart St Menlo Park CA 94025

SALMOND, WILLIAM GLOVER, b West Wemyss, Scotland, May 29, 41; US citizen; m 68. SYNTHETIC ORGANIC CHEMISTRY, STEROID CHEMISTRY. *Educ:* St Andrews Univ, BSc, 63, PhD(chem), 66. *Prof Exp:* Scientist chem, Sandoz-Wander Inc, 70-72; sr res scientist chem, 72-77, RES MGR, UPJOHN CO, 77- *Res:* Commercially viable synthesis of complex natural products; application of organometallic chemistry to organic synthesis. *Mailing Add:* Upjohn Co Kalamazoo MI 49001

SALMONS, JOHN ROBERT, b Climax Springs, Mo, Sept 12, 32; m 57; c 2. CIVIL ENGINEERING. *Educ:* Univ Mo, BSCE, 60; Univ Ariz, MSCE, 65, PhD(civil eng), 66. *Prof Exp:* Detailer, Bridge Div, Mo State Hwy Dept, 57-59; asst civil eng, Univ Ariz, 61-64; assoc prof, 65-80, PROF CIVIL ENG, UNIV MO-COLUMBIA, 80- *Concurrent Pos:* Res engr, Prestressed Div, United Mat Inc, Ariz; instr, Off Civil Defense, 63-; Am Soc Eng Educ-Ford Found engr in residency with Wilson Concrete Co, Nebr, 69-70; bd dirs & vpres, Wilson Concrete Co, Nebr, 73- *Mem:* Am Soc Civil Engrs; Am Concrete Inst; Prestressed Concrete Inst. *Res:* Evaluation of precast-prestressed composite u-beam bridge slabs; continuity of precast-prestressed bridge members; large panel prefabricated concrete building construction; design of precast-prestressed concrete structures. *Mailing Add:* 1808 Princeton Columbia MO 65201

SALO, ERNEST OLAVI, b Butte, Mont, Dec 31, 19; m 44; c 2. FISHERIES, OCEANOGRAPHY. *Educ:* Univ Wash, BS, 47, PhD(fisheries), 55. *Prof Exp:* Res biologist, Minter Creek Biol Sta, State Dept Fisheries, Wash, 50-54, asst supvr salmon hatcheries, 54-55; from asst prof to prof fisheries, Humboldt State Col, 55-65; assoc prof, 65-67, PROF FISHERIES, UNIV WASH, 67- *Concurrent Pos:* Fels, Ger, Finland & Eng, 64, Chile, 69; consult, var utilities, 64-72; consult, Govt Chile, 69-72 & AEC, 72. *Mem:* Am Fisheries Soc; Am Inst Fishery Res Biologists (past secy). *Res:* Population dynamics; oceanography and marine fisheries; artifical propagation of salmon; biometrics. *Mailing Add:* WH-10 Fish Res Inst Univ of Wash Col of Fisheries Seattle WA 98195

SALO, WILMAR LAWRENCE, b Nichols Twp, Minn, Aug 22, 37; m 60; c 3. BIOCHEMISTRY. *Educ:* Univ Minn, BS, 59, PhD(biochem), 67; Univ Wis, MS, 62. *Prof Exp:* Staff fel, NIH, 67-69; asst prof, Univ, 69-74, ASSOC PROF BIOCHEM, SCH MED, UNIV MINN, DULUTH, 74- *Mem:* Am Soc Biol Chemists; AAAS. *Res:* Biochemistry of complex carbohydrates; enzymology. *Mailing Add:* Dept Biochem Sch Med Univ of Minn Duluth MN 55812

SALOMAN, EDWARD BARRY, b Brooklyn, NY, May 30, 40; m 68. ATOMIC PHYSICS. *Educ:* Columbia Univ, AB, 61, MA, 62, PhD(atomic physics), 65. *Prof Exp:* Res physicist, Columbia Univ, 65-66; asst prof physics, Brown Univ, 66-72; PHYSICIST FAR ULTRAVIOLET PHYSICS, RADIATION PHYSICS DIV, NAT BUR STANDARDS, 72- *Mem:* AAAS; Am Phys Soc; Optical Soc Am. *Res:* Atomic spectroscopy; radiometry; resonance physics; optical resonance studies of stable and radioactive atoms; relaxation of optically oriented atoms; far ultraviolet physics. *Mailing Add:* Far Ultraviolet Physics Nat Bur Stand A251 Physics Bldg Washington DC 20234

SALOMON, LOTHAR L, b Buedingen, Ger, Nov 8, 21; nat US; m; c 3. BIOCHEMISTRY. *Educ:* Columbia Univ, BS, 49, MA, 50, PhD(chem), 52. *Prof Exp:* Asst chem, Columbia Univ, 49-52; instr biochem & nutrit, Univ Tex Med Br, 52-53, from asst prof to assoc prof, 53-64; chief biol div, Dugway Proving Ground, 64-72; dep dir test opers, Deseret Test Ctr, 72-78; dep dir mat test directorate, 78-81, SCI DIR, DUGWAY PROVING GROUND, 81- *Concurrent Pos:* Consult isotopically labelled carbohydrates, 58-62. *Mem:* Fel AAAS; assoc AMA; Am Chem Soc; Soc Exp Biol & Med; fel Am Inst Chem. *Res:* Biosynthesis and metabolism of ascorbic acid and carbohydrates; membrane transport of carbohydrates; aerobiology; research and development administration. *Mailing Add.* 521 A Bonafin Dr Dugway UT 84022

SALOMON, MARK, b Brooklyn, NY, June 2, 35; m 59; c 3. PHYSICAL CHEMISTRY. *Educ:* Hunter Col, BA, 57; Brooklyn Col, MA, 61; Univ Ottawa, PhD(chem), 64. *Prof Exp:* Chemist, Leesona-Moos Labs, 58-61; NSF res assoc chem, Princeton Univ, 64-65; asst prof, Rutgers Univ, 65-67; chemist, NASA, 67-72; CHEMIST, US ARMY ELECTRONIC COMMAND, FT MONMOUTH, 72- *Concurrent Pos:* Res scientist physics, Boston Col, 72-; titular mem comn V8, Int Union Pure & Applied Chem. *Mem:* Electrochem Soc. *Res:* Chemical kinetics; isotope effects; electrochemistry. *Mailing Add:* US Army Electronic Command Mail Code DELET-PR Ft Monmouth NJ 07703

SALOMON, ROBERT EPHRIAM, b Brooklyn, NY, June 8, 33; m 61; c 2. PHYSICAL CHEMISTRY. *Educ:* Brooklyn Col, BA, 54; Univ Ore, PhD(phys chem), 60. *Prof Exp:* Lectr chem, Brooklyn Col, 57; Sloan res fel, 60; from asst prof to assoc prof phys chem, 61-67, chmn dept chem, 68-74, PROF PHYS CHEM, TEMPLE UNIV, 67- *Concurrent Pos:* Consult, Frankford Arsenal, Pa, 61, Gen Elec Co, 66 & Nuclear Regulatory Comn, 79- *Mem:* Am Chem Soc; Am Asn Univ Prof; Sigma Xi; Electrochem Soc. *Res:* Spectroscopic and electrical properties of solids; conversion of ocean wave energy and solar heat into electricity using electrochemical hydrogen concentration cells. *Mailing Add:* 1621 Kenmare Dr Dresher PA 19025

SALOMONE, RAMON ANGELO, b New York, NY, Nov 25, 33. ORGANIC CHEMISTRY. *Educ:* Spring Hill Col, BS, 57; Fordham Univ, PhD(chem), 63; Woodstock Col, Md, BA, 65. *Prof Exp:* Instr chem & math, Fordham Prep Sch, NY, 58-59; fel org chem, Mass Inst Technol, 67-69; asst prof chem, Canisius Col, 69-77, chmn dept, 74-77; ASSOC PROF CHEM, LeMOYNE COL, 77- *Mem:* Am Chem Soc. *Res:* Synthesis and metabolic studies with radioactive pesticides; sequence determmination of amino acids in peptides by mass spectrometry; tandem mass spectrometric-gas chromatographic analysis of amino acid and peptide derivatives. *Mailing Add:* Dept of Chem LeMoyne Col Syracuse NY 13214

SALOMONSON, VINCENT VICTOR, b Longmont, Colo, July 19, 37; m 63; c 3. METEOROLOGY, HYDROLOGY. *Educ:* Colo State Univ, BS, 59, PhD(atmospheric sci), 68; Univ Utah, BS, 60; Cornell Univ, MS, 64. *Prof Exp:* Res hydrologist, Lab Meteorol & Earth Sci, 68-74, head, Hydrospheric Sci Br, Lab Atmospheric Sci, 74-80, CHIEF, EARTH SURV APPL DIV, GODDARD SPACE FLIGHT CTR, NASA, 80- *Concurrent Pos:* Mem working group remote sensing in hydrol, US Int Hydrol Decade-Nat Acad Sci, 71-74; US co-chmn remote sensing subcomt, Int Field Year of Great Lakes, 72-74; proj scientist, Land Sattelite-D, 77- *Honors & Awards:* Cert for Outstanding Performance, Goddard Space Flight Ctr, NASA, 74, 75, 76 & 77, Except Sci Achievement Medal, 76. *Mem:* Am Meterol Soc; Am Geophys Union; Am Water Resources Asn. *Res:* Author of over 40 publications on remote sensing applications and studies in hydrology, atmospheric science and earth resource management. *Mailing Add:* Atmos & Hydrospheric Appl Div NASA Goddard Space Flight Ctr Greenbelt MD 20771

SALOT, STUART EDWIN, b Los Angeles, Calif, Oct 23, 37; m 68; c 2. INORGANIC CHEMISTRY. *Educ:* Univ Calif, Berkeley, AB, 60; Univ Southern Calif, PhD(chem), 69; Am Bd Indust Hyg, cert, 78. *Prof Exp:* Asst prof chem, San Fernando Valley State Col, 68-69; asst prof, Calif State Polytech Col, 69-72; dir tech serv, Daylin Corp, Los Angeles, 72-75; PRES, CERTIFIED TESTING LABS, INC, 75- *Mem:* AAAS; Am Chem Soc; Am Crystallog Asn; Am Acad Indust Hyg; Am Indust Hyg Asn. *Res:* Industrial environment pollution abatement studies; synthetic inorganic chemistry; reactions in non-aqueous solvent systems; non-stoichiometric compounds. *Mailing Add:* 2905 E Century Blvd South Gate CA 90280

SALOTTO, ANTHONY W, b Yonkers, NY, Aug 28, 36; m 63; c 3. PHYSICAL CHEMISTRY. *Educ:* Mass Inst Technol, BS, 58, MS, 59; NY Univ, PhD(chem), 69. *Prof Exp:* Res engr, Calif Res Corp, 59-61; instr chem, Sacramento City Col, 62-63; asst prof, Dutchess Community Col, 63-66; assoc prof, 69-77, asst chmn dept, 75-77, PROF CHEM, PACE UNIV, WESTCHESTER CAMPUS, 77-, CHMN DEPT SCI, 77- *Mem:* AAAS; Am Chem Soc. *Res:* Quantum chemistry; environmental chemistry. *Mailing Add:* Dept of Sci Pace Univ Westchester Campus Pleasantville NY 10570

SALOVEY, RONALD, b New York, July 11, 32; m 54; c 3. PHYSICAL CHEMISTRY, POLYMER CHEMISTRY. *Educ:* Brooklyn Col, BS, 54; Harvard Univ, AM, 58, PhD(phys chem), 59. *Prof Exp:* Res chemist, Interchem Corp, 54-55; mem tech staff, Bell Tel Labs, Inc, 58-70; res supvr, Hooker Res Ctr, Occidental Petrol Corp, Niagara Falls, 70-73, mgr res, 73-75; PROF CHEM ENG & MAT SCI, UNIV SOUTHERN CALIF, 75- *Concurrent Pos:* Dir, Los Angeles Rubber Group Inc Found, 75-; adv bd, Polymer Eng & Sci & J Appl Polymer Sci. *Mem:* Am Chem Soc; Am Phys Soc. *Res:* Physical chemistry of polymers. *Mailing Add:* 6641 Monero Dr Rancho Palos Verdes CA 90274

SALPETER, EDWIN ERNEST, b Vienna, Austria, Dec 3, 24; nat US; m 50; c 2. ASTROPHYSICS. *Educ:* Univ Sydney, MSc, 45; Univ Birmingham, PhD, 48. *Hon Degrees:* DSc, Univ Chicago, 69 & Case Western Reserve Univ, 70. *Prof Exp:* Res fel sci & indust res, Univ Birmingham, 48-49; res assoc, 49-53, assoc prof, 53-56, prof physics & astrophys, 56-72, J G WHITE DISTINGUISHED PROF PHYS SCI, CORNELL UNIV, 72- *Concurrent Pos:* Vis prof, Australian Nat Univ, 53-54; mem, Int Sci Radio Union; H N Russell lectr, 74. *Honors & Awards:* Award, Carnegie Inst, 59; Gold Medal, Royal Astronomical Soc, 63; J. R. Oppenheimer Mem Prize, 74. *Mem:* Nat Acad Sci; Akad Leopoldina; Am Philos Soc; Am Astron Soc (vpres, 71-73); Int Astron Union. *Res:* Quantum theory of atoms; quantum electrodynamics; nuclear theory; energy production stars; theoretical astrophysics. *Mailing Add:* 308 Newman Lab Nuclear Studies Cornell Univ Ithaca NY 14853

SALPETER, MIRIAM MIRL, b Riga, Latvia, Apr 8, 29; US citizen; m 50; c 2. NEUROBIOLOGY, CYTOLOGY. *Educ:* Hunter Col, AB, 50; Cornell Univ, AM, 51, PhD(psychobiol), 53. *Prof Exp:* NIH fel biol, 57-60, res assoc, 60-64, sr res assoc, 64-66, assoc prof neurobiol, 66-73, PROF NEUROBIOL & BEHAVIOR, CORNELL UNIV, 73- *Concurrent Pos:* NIH career develop award, 62- *Mem:* AAAS; Electron Micros Soc Am; Am Soc Cell Biol; Soc Neurosci. *Res:* Cell biology; electron microscopy; regeneration; neurocytology. neurocytology; molecular organization of neuromuscular junctions; neurotropic phenomena. *Mailing Add:* 146 Clark Hal Cornell Univ Ithaca NY 14853

SALSBURY, JASON MELVIN, b Richmond, Va, June 12, 20; m 46; c 2. INDUSTRIAL ORGANIC CHEMISTRY. *Educ:* Univ Richmond, BS, 40; Univ Va, MS, 43, PhD(org chem), 45. *Prof Exp:* Lab asst, Univ Richmond, 38-40; asst, Nat Defense Res Comt, Univ Va, 41-44 & Off Sci Res & Develop,

44-45; chemist, Am Cyanamid Co, 46-53, group leader, 54, mgr textile resin res, 54-57, mgr tech dept, Santa Rosa Plant, 57-61, dir fibers res, Fibers Div, Stamford Labs, 61-63, dir res, 63-64, dir res & commercial develop, 64-65, dir res, 65-66, tech dir, 66-67, vpres res & develop, Formica Corp, 67-72, dir, Chem Res Div, 72-81; PRES, SALJAS MGT & CONSULT, INC, 81- Concurrent Pos: Mem, Indust Res Inst. Mem: Am Chem Soc. Res: Polymer chemistry; synthetic organic chemistry; analysis of organic compounds; B-alkyl aminoalkyl esters of alkozybenzoic acids for local anesthetics; synthetic fibers; textile chemicals; laminates; panels; paper chemistry; polymers; resins; catalysts. Mailing Add: 444 Lakewood Blvd Boca Raton FL 33434

SALSBURY, JOHN GREENSMITH, b Western, Nebr, June 12, 16; m 42; c 5. PHARMACEUTICAL CHEMISTRY. Educ: Iowa State Univ, BS, 38, DVM, 40. Hon Degrees: DSc, Wartburg Col. Prof Exp: Vpres & gen mgr, 40-61, pres, 61-70, CHMN, SALSBURY LABS, 70- Mem: AAAS; Am Vet Med Asn; Am Soc Parasitol. Res: Poultry Protozoa and helminths; biologic manufacturing. Mailing Add: Salsbury Labs Inc 2000 Rockford Rd Charles City IA 50616

SALSBURY, ROBERT LAWRENCE, b Vancouver, BC, July 4, 16; nat US; m 45. RUMINANT NUTRITION, POULTRY NUTRITION. Educ: Univ BC, BA & BSA, 42; Mich State Univ, PhD(animal nutrit), 55. Prof Exp: Jr chemist, Can Dept Pub Works, 42-45; control chemist, E R Squibb & Sons, 45-46; res assoc, NJ Agr Exp Sta, 46-47; bacteriologist, State Dept Health, Mich, 47-49, biochemist, 49-50; agent bur dairy indust, USDA, 52-54; asst prof agr chem, Mich State Univ, 55-61; assoc prof animal sci & agr biochem, 61-73, PROF ANIMAL SCI & AGR BIOCHEM, UNIV DEL, 73- Mem: Am Chem Soc; Am Dairy Sci Asn; Am Soc Animal Sci; Am Soc Microbiol; Poultry Sci Asn. Res: Mineral balance of poultry diets; interactions amoung dietary ingredients; physiological effects of ionophores in poultry. Mailing Add: Dept of Animal Sci & Agr Biochem Univ of Del Newark DE 19711

SALSER, JOSEPHINE SEE, b Manila, Philippines, Sept 7, 24; nat US; m 54. MICROBIOLOGY, BIOCHEMISTRY. Educ: Univ Philippines, BS, 50; Radcliffe Col, MA, 53, PhD(biol), 55. Prof Exp: Res asst bot & biochem, Univ Kans, 55-56, from instr to asst prof biochem, 56-58; asst prof biochem, Med Col, Univ, 59-78, res assoc, 58-61, assoc, div nucleoprotein chem, 61-70 & div cell metab, 70-77, ASSOC MEM, DIV CELL METAB, SLOAN-KETTERING INST CANCER RES, 77-, ASSOC PROF BIOCHEM, SLOAN-KETTERING DIV, GRAD SCH MED SCI, MED COL, CORNELL UNIV, 78- Mem: Am Chem Soc; NY Acad Sci; Am Soc Microbiol; Am Soc Plant Physiol; Am Asn Cancer Res. Res: Enzymes and enzyme systems involved in nucleic acid metabolism of normal and tumor tissues, including thymidine kinase; DNA; control mechanisms in normal and malignant cellular proliferation. Mailing Add: Div of Cell Metab Sloan-Kettering Inst New York NY 10021

SALSER, WINSTON ALBERT, b Wichita, Kans, May 5, 39; m 63; c 3. MOLECULAR BIOLOGY. Educ: Univ Chicago, BS, 63; Mass Inst Technol, PhD(molecular biol), 66. Prof Exp: Helen Hay Whitney fel, Inst Molecular Biol, Geneva, Switz, 65-67 & Inst Biophys & Biochem, Paris, France, 67-68; from asst prof to assoc prof, 68-75, PROF MOLECULAR BIOL, UNIV CALIF, LOS ANGELES, 75- Mem: AAAS. Res: Chromosome structure and gene expression in mammalian genomes; insertion of selected mammalian genes into bacterial plasmids; nucleotide sequence analysis of hemoglobin mRNAs and mammalian satellite DNAs. Mailing Add: Dept of Biol Univ of Calif Los Angeles CA 90024

SALSIG, WILLIAM WINTER, JR, b Medford, Ore, Mar 16, 19; m 44; c 3. MECHANICAL ENGINEERING. Educ: Univ Calif, BS, 43. Prof Exp: Bevatron mech eng, Lawrence Berkeley Lab, Univ Calif, 54-63, 200 Billion Electron Volt Accelerator Study, 63-67, in charge, Electron Ring Accelerator Mech Design, 67-72, in charge, Bevalac Construct, 73-75, design engr, 43-79, adminr, Accelerator & Fusion Res Div, 75-79; RETIRED. Concurrent Pos: Engr, Oak Ridge Nat Lab, 44-45 & Oper Greenhouse-Eniwetok, 50-51. Mem: Life mem Am Soc Mech Engrs. Res: Design of equipment for physical research; cyclotron; synchrotron; calutrons. Mailing Add: 8 Anson Way Kensington CA 94707

SALSTROM, JOHN STUART, molecular biology, biochemistry, see previous edition

SALT, DALE L(AMBOURNE), b Salt Lake City, Utah, July 1, 24; m 50; c 3. CHEMICAL ENGINEERING. Educ: Univ Utah, BS, 48, MS, 49; Univ Del, PhD(chem eng), 59. Prof Exp: Chem engr, Utah Oil Refining Co, 49-51; res fel chem eng, Univ Del, 51-54; from asst prof to assoc prof, 54-70, PROF CHEM ENG, UNIV UTAH, 70- Honors & Awards: A E Marshall Award, Am Inst Chem Engrs, 48. Mem: Am Soc Eng Educ; Am Inst Chem Engrs; Combustion Inst. Res: Gaseous combustion; rheology; accelerated particle dynamics; interphase transfer processes. Mailing Add: Dept of Chem Eng Univ of Utah Salt Lake City UT 84112

SALT, GEORGE WILLIAM, b Spokane, Wash, Oct 9, 19; m 42; c 3. ANIMAL ECOLOGY. Educ: Univ Calif, Los Angeles, BA, 42; Univ Calif, MA, 48, PhD(zool), 51. Prof Exp: Asst zool, Univ Calif, Berkeley, 46-49; assoc, 49-50, lectr, 50-51, instr, 51-53, from asst prof to assoc prof, 53-68, PROF ZOOL, UNIV CALIF, DAVIS, 68- Concurrent Pos: NSF sr fel, 59-60; Rockefeller Found affiliate & vis prof, Univ Valle, Colombia, 71-72; ed, Am Naturalist, 79- Mem: Brit Ecol Soc; Am Soc Limnol Oceanog; Cooper Ornith Soc; Am Ornith Union; Soc Protozool. Res: Faunal analysis and community structure; feeding in Protozoa; predator-prey interactions. Mailing Add: Dept Zool Univ Calif Davis CA 95616

SALT, WALTER RAYMOND, b Eng, Oct 12, 05; m 33; c 1. HISTOLOGY. Educ: Univ Alta, BSc, 40, MSc, 48. Prof Exp: Prof zool, Mt Royal Col, 45-49; from asst prof to prof anat, 49-71, EMER PROF ANAT, UNIV ALTA, 71- Res: Cytology; striated muscle; avian flight. Mailing Add: 8731 117 St Edmonton AB T6G 1R6 Can

SALTER, ELMER GEORGE, anatomy, see previous edition

SALTER, LEWIS SPENCER, b Norman, Okla, Feb 4, 26; m 50; c 4. THEORETICAL PHYSICS. Educ: Univ Okla, BS, 49; Oxford Univ, BA, 51, DPhil, 56. Prof Exp: Instr math, Europ Div, Univ Md, 52-53; from asst prof to prof physics, Wabash Col, 53-68; acad dean, Knox Col, Ill, 68-69, prof physics, 68-78, dean col & vpres acad affairs, 69-78, exec vpres col, 75-78; PROF PHYSICS & PRES COL, WABASH COL, 78- Concurrent Pos: Vis assoc prof, Bandung Tech Inst, 58-60; vis res prof, Nat Res Coun Can, 63-64. Res: Solid state and low temperature physics. Mailing Add: Off of the Pres Wabash Col Crawfordsville IN 47933

SALTER, ROBERT BRUCE, b Stratford, Ont, Dec 15, 24; m 48; c 5. ORTHOPEDIC SURGERY. Educ: Univ Toronto, MD, 47, MS, 60; FRCPS(C), 55; FRACS, 77; FRCS(I), 78. Prof Exp: Clin teacher orthop, Univ Toronto, 55-57; orthop surgeon, Hosp Sick Children, 55-57, chief orthop surg, 57-66; asst prof, 62-66, PROF SURG, UNIV TORONTO, 66-; SURGEON-IN-CHIEF, HOSP SICK CHILDREN, 66- Concurrent Pos: R S McLaughlin traveling fel, London Hosp, Eng, 54-55; consult, Ont Soc Crippled Children, 55-; mem, Med Res Coun Can, 67-69. Honors & Awards: Medal Surg, Royal Col Physicians & Surg Can, 60; Centennial Medal, Govt Can, 67; Gairdner Int Award Med Sci, 69; hon fel, Royal Col Physicians & Surg Glasgow, 70, Royal Col Surgeons Edinburgh, 73, Col Surgeons SAfrica, 73 & Royal Col Surgeons Eng; Sir Arthur Sims Commonwealth Traveling Prof, 73; Nicolas Andry Award, Asn Bone & Joint Surgeons, 74; Charles Mickle Award, Univ Toronto; Officer of Order of Can, 77. Mem: Fel Am Col Surg; Am Orthop Asn; Int Soc Orthop Surg & Traumatol; Can Orthop Res Soc; Royal Col PHysicians & Surgeons Can (vpres, 70-, pres, 78-80). Res: Articular cartilage degeneration; avascular necrosis of epiphyses; epiphyseal injuries, congenital dysplasia and dislocation of the hip; Legg Perthes disease; experimental arthritis. Mailing Add: Dept Surg Hosp Sick Children 555 University Ave Toronto ON M5G 1X8 Can

SALTER, ROBERT MUNKHENK, JR, b Morgantown, WVa, Apr 24, 20; m 77; c 3. ELEMENTARY PARTICLE PHYSICS, APPLIED PHYSICS. Educ: Ohio State Univ, BME, 41; Univ Calif, Los Angeles, MA, 58, PhD(nuclear physics), 65. Prof Exp: Res engr metall & adv eng, Gen Motors Res Lab, 41-42; Lt propulsion, US Navy Aeronaut Exp Sta, Philadelphia & Exp Engines Sect, Bur Aeronaut, Washington, DC, 42-46; res engr, Aerophysics Lab, NAm Aviation, Inc, 46-48; dir proj feedback space systs res, Rand Corp, 48-54; dept mgr satellite br, US Air Force Satellite Prog Develop, Lockheed Missiles & Space Co, 54-58; PHYS SCIENTIST APPL PHYSICS, RAND CORP, 68- Concurrent Pos: Pres & gen mgr, Sigma Corp, 59-60 & Quantatron, 60-62; consult, Lockheed Missiles & Space Co, 59-65 & RCA Labs, 62-65; chmn bd, Telic Corp, 68-71; mem, Nuclear Propulsion Comt, Am Inst Aeronaut & Astronaut, 70-72 & Ad Hoc Comt Early Warning Physics, Adv Res Proj Agency, 72-76; pres, Xerad Inc, 57- & Spectravision Inc, 71- Mem: Sigma Xi. Res: Experimental and theoretical determination of neutron-neutron forces in nucleus through decay of di-neutron formed from pion absorption in deuteron; application of advanced physics in conceptualization of new devices in optics, electronics and aero-space systems. Mailing Add: 1514 Sorrento Dr Pacific Palisades CA 90272

SALTHE, STANLEY NORMAN, b Oct 16, 30; US citizen; m 59; c 2. EVOLUTIONARY BIOLOGY. Educ: Columbia Univ, BS, 59, MA, 60, PhD(zool), 63. Prof Exp: Am Cancer Soc fel, Brandeis Univ, 63-65; from asst prof to assoc prof, 65-72, PROF BIOL, BROOKLYN COL, 72- Concurrent Pos: NSF res grants, 66-71; City Univ New York res grants, 71-72 & 72-73. Mem: NY Acad Sci; Soc Study Evolution; Am Soc Zool; Soc Syst Zool; Am Soc Ichthyol & Herpet. Res: Application of hierarchy theory to evolutionary process; reproductive strategies of cold-blooded vertebrates; macroevolution. Mailing Add: Dept of Biol Brooklyn Col Brooklyn NY 11210

SALTIEL, JACK, b Salonica, Greece, Feb 14, 38; US citizen; m 65. ORGANIC CHEMISTRY. Educ: Rice Univ, BA, 60; Calif Inst Technol, PhD(chem), 64. Prof Exp: NSF fel, Univ Calif, Berkeley, 63-64; from asst prof to assoc prof, 65-75, PROF CHEM, FLA STATE UNIV, 75- Concurrent Pos: Consult, Eli Lilly & Co, 65-67; Alfred P Sloan fel, 71-73. Mem: AAAS; Am Chem Soc; Royal Soc Chem. Res: Photochemistry of organic molecules. Mailing Add: Dept of Chem Fla State Univ Tallahassee FL 32306

SALTMAN, PAUL DAVID, b Los Angeles, Calif, Apr 11, 28; m 49; c 2. BIOCHEMISTRY, NUTRITION. Educ: Calif Inst Technol, BS, 49, PhD(biochem), 53. Prof Exp: From instr to prof biochem, Univ Southern Calif, 53-67; provost, Revelle Col, 67-72, vchancellor acad affairs, 72-80, PROF BIOL, UNIV CALIF, SAN DIEGO, 67- Concurrent Pos: NIH sr fel, 60-; sr Fulbright scholar, Perth, Australia, 81. Mem: Am Chem Soc; Am Soc Plant Physiol; Am Soc Biol Chemists; Am Inst Nutrit. Res: Biological transport mechanisms; trace metal metabolism; photosynthesis; metabolism of higher plants; plant growth hormones; communication of science through films, television and radio. Mailing Add: 105 Matthews Campus Q-001 Univ Calif San Diego La Jolla CA 92093

SALTMAN, ROY GILBERT, b New York, NY, July 15, 32; m 59; c 3. COMPUTER APPLICATIONS, DATA ADMINSTRATION. Educ: Rensselaer Polytech Inst, Troy, NY, BEE, 53; Mass Inst Technol, MSEE, 55; Columbia Univ, EE, 62; Am Univ, MPA, 76. Prof Exp: Res engr, Sperry Gyroscope Co, 55-64; adv systs analyst, IBM Corp, 64-69; COMPUT SCIENTIST, INST COMPUT SCI & TECHNOL, NAT BUR STANDARDS, 69- Concurrent Pos: Intergovt Affairs fel, State Minn/US Civil Serv Comn, 75; exec secy, Comt Automation Opportunities Serv Sector, Fed Coun Sci & Technol, 72-75; com sci fel, US Dept Com/US House Reps, 77-78. Mem: Inst Elec & Electronics Engrs; Am Soc Public Admin. Res: Productivity in federal computer use; policy implications of information systems; data administration, data element standardization. Mailing Add: 7701 Geranium St Bethesda MD 20817

SALTMAN, WILLIAM MOSE, b Perth Amboy, NJ, Nov 19, 17; m 43; c 3. RUBBER CHEMISTRY. *Educ:* Univ Mich, BS(chem eng) & BS(eng math), 38, MS, 39; Univ Chicago, PhD(phys chem), 49. *Prof Exp:* Testing chemist, State Hwy Dept, NJ, 40-42; res assoc, Calif Inst Technol, 45; sr chemist, Shell Chem Co, Colo, 49-54; sr chemist, 55-64, sect head budene & ethylene-propylene rubbers, 64-75, mgr stereo rubbers dept, 75-77, mgr specialty polymers dept, Res Div, 77-80, MGR, POLYMER SERV, GOODYEAR TIRE & RUBBER CO, 80- *Mem:* Am Chem Soc. *Res:* Stereospecific catalysts; rubber technology; polymerization; kinetics; polymer physical properties. *Mailing Add:* Res Div Goodyear Tire & Rubber Co Akron OH 44316

SALTON, GERARD, b Nuremberg, Ger, May 8, 27; nat US; m 50; c 2. APPLIED MATHEMATICS. *Educ:* Brooklyn Col, BA, 50, MA, 52; Harvard Univ, PhD(appl math), 58. *Prof Exp:* From instr to asst prof appl math, Harvard Univ, 58-65; assoc prof comput sci, 66-67, chmn dept, 71-77, PROF COMPUT SCI, CORNELL UNIV, 67- *Concurrent Pos:* Guggenheim fel, 63; consult, Sylvania Elec Prod, Inc & Arthur D Little, Inc; ed-in-chief, Commun J, Asn Comput Mach. *Mem:* Asn Comput Mach; Inst Elec & Electronics Eng; Am Soc Info Sci; Asn Comput Ling. *Res:* Electronic data processing; business applications of computers; mathematical linguistics; theory of information retrieval. *Mailing Add:* Dept of Comput Sci Cornell Univ Upson Hall Ithaca NY 14850

SALTON, MILTON ROBERT JAMES, b NSW, Australia, Apr 29, 21; m 51; c 2. MICROBIOLOGY. *Educ:* Univ Sydney, BSc, 45; Cambridge Univ, PhD(biochem), 51; ScD, Cambridge Univ, 67. *Hon Degrees:* Dr Med, Univ Liege, 67. *Prof Exp:* Res officer microbiol, Commonwealth Sci & Indust Res Orgn, Australia, 45-48; res fel biochem, Cambridge Univ, 48-54, Beit Mem res fel, 50-52, demonstr, 57-61; prof, Univ New South Wales, 62-64; PROF MICROBIOL & CHMN DEPT, SCH MED, NY UNIV, 64- *Concurrent Pos:* Merck Int fel, Univ Calif, 52-53; reader, Manchester Univ, 57-61; lectr, Off Naval Res, 60; Ciba lectr, Rutgers Univ, 60. *Mem:* Am Soc Microbiol; Am Soc Biol Chem; Harvey Soc; Royal Soc Med; Brit Biochem Soc. *Res:* Chemistry and biochemistry of microbial cell surfaces. *Mailing Add:* Dept of Microbiology NY Univ Sch of Med New York NY 10016

SALTONSTALL, CLARENCE WILLIAM, JR, b El Centro, Calif, Jan 26, 25; m 46; c 3. SYNTHETIC MEMBRANE TECHNOLOGY, POLYMER CHEMISTRY. *Educ:* Pomona Col, BA, 48; Columbia Univ, PhD(org chem), 57. *Prof Exp:* Res chemist, Photo Prod Dept, E I du Pont de Nemours & Co, Inc, 53-58; res chemist, Chem Div, Aerojet-Gen Corp, 58-62, asst sr chemist, Solid Rocket Res Div, 62-63, sr chemist, 63-64, sr chemist, Chem & Struct Prod Div, 64-67, mgr res & develop, Phys Processes Dept, Environ Systs Div, 67-70, mgr desalination res, Water Purification Systs Oper, Envirogenics Co, 70-75; dir res & develop, Envirogenics Systs Co, 75-78; CONSULT MEMBRANE TECHNOL, 78- *Mem:* Am Chem Soc; Sigma Xi; AAAS; Water Supply Improvement Asn. *Res:* Synthesis of nomomers, polyelectrolytes, cellulose derivatives, elastomers and novel heterocyclic polymers; solid propellants; membranes for water desalination and the mechanism of reverse osmosis; manufacture of membranes and membrane systems. *Mailing Add:* 1634 Alaska St West Covina CA 91791

SALTSBURG, HOWARD MORTIMER, b New York, NY, Sept 12, 28; m 51; c 2. PHYSICAL CHEMISTRY. *Educ:* City Col New York, 50; Boston Univ, MA, 51, PhD(phys chem), 55. *Prof Exp:* Chemist, Geophys Res Directorate Air Force Cambridge Res Labs, 51-54; Henry & Camille Dreyfus Found fel chem, Univ Rochester, 54-55; chemist, Knolls Atomic Power Lab, Gen Elec Co, 55-57, missiles & space vehicles dept, 57-59; res & develop staff mem, Gen Atomic Div, Gen Dynamics Corp, 59-69; PROF MAT SCI, CHEM ENG & CHEM, UNIV ROCHESTER, 69- *Mem:* Am Phys Soc; Am Chem Soc. *Res:* Nucleation; surface thermodynamics; evaporation; adsorption on oxides; electrical conductivity of oxides; molecular beam scattering from surfaces. *Mailing Add:* Dept of Chem Eng Gavett Hall Univ of Rochester Rochester NY 14627

SALTVEIT, MIKAL ENDRE, JR, b Minneapolis, Minn, Nov 11, 44; m 78. POSTHARVEST PHYSIOLOGY, ETHYLENE PHYSIOLOGY. *Educ:* Univ Minn, BA, 67, MS, 72; Mich State Univ, PhD(hort & bot), 77. *Prof Exp:* Mgr, Biol Labs Antartica, Antartic Res Prog, Nat Sci Found, 68-69 & 70-71; res botanist, NASA Space Prog, Agr Res Serv, US Dept Agr, 72-73; res asst plant physiol, Dept Hort, Mich State Univ, 73-77, res assoc ethylene physiol, Plant Res Lab, 77-78; ASST PROF POSTHARVEST PHYSIOL, HORT DEPT, NC STATE UNIV, 78- *Mem:* Am Soc Hort Sci; Am Soc Plant Physiol; AAAS; Sigma Xi. *Res:* Postharvest physiology of pomological crops (apples) with emphasis on factors controlling ripening; physiology of ethylene produced by ripening and stressed plant tissue. *Mailing Add:* Dept Hort Sci NC State Univ Raleigh NC 27650

SALTZ, DANIEL, b Chicago, Ill, July 25, 32; m 56; c 2. MATHEMATICS. *Educ:* Univ Chicago, BA, 52, BS, 53; Northwestern Univ, MS, 55, PhD(math), 58. *Prof Exp:* Instr math, Northwestern Univ, 58-59; assoc prof, 59-70, PROF MATH, SAN DIEGO STATE UNIV, 70- *Mem:* Am Math Soc; Am Math Asn. *Res:* Fourier analysis; differential equations; generalized function theory. *Mailing Add:* Dept of Math Sant Diego State Univ San Diego CA 92182

SALTZBERG, BERNARD, b Chicago, Ill, Apr 21, 19; m 42; c 5. BIOMATHEMATICS, BIOENGINEERING. *Educ:* Ill Inst Technol, BS, 52, MSEE, 53; Marquette Univ, PhD(biomed & elec eng), 72. *Prof Exp:* Instr eng math, Ill Inst Technol, 53-56; mem sr sci staff, Space Technol Lab, Thompson Ramo-Wooldridge, Inc, 56-60; sr scientist res staff, Bissett-Berman Corp, 60-65; assoc prof psychiat & neurol & dir div med comput sci, Sch Med, Tulane Univ, 65-67, prof psychiat & neurol & dir biomath & neural sci res, 67-75; PROF PSYCHIAT & NEUROL, TEX RES INST MENT SCI, TEX MED CTR HOUSTON, 76- *Concurrent Pos:* Schleider scholar, Tulane Univ, 63, Nat Inst Neurol Dis & Stroke res grant, Sch Med, 71-74; supvry res engr, Res Dept, Am Mach & Foundry Co, 53-56; consult appl math & period anal, Baylor Univ, 56-; instr appl math, Univ Southern Calif & Univ Calif, Los Angeles, 58-61; vis lectr, Tulane Univ, 63-65; mem adv bd, Inst Comprehensive Med, 64; mem adv comt, Comput & Biomath Sci Study Sect, Div Res Grants, NIH, 70-74; consult ed, Soc Psychophysiol Res, 68; prof psychiat, Univ Tex Med Sch Houston; prof, Grad Sch Biomed Sci, Univ Tex; adj prof biomed eng, Rice Univ; adj prof, Univ Houston; head biomath, Epilepsy Res Ctr, Baylor Med Sch & Methodist Hosp. *Mem:* Am EEG Soc; Neuroelec Soc (vpres, 67); Soc Neurosci; Soc Biol Psychiat; Soc Psychophysiol Res. *Res:* Electroencephalographic signal analysis; brain research; pattern recognition; time series analysis. *Mailing Add:* Tex Res Inst of Ment Sci 1300 Moursund Houston TX 77030

SALTZBERG, THEODORE, b Chicago, Ill, Mar 9, 27; m 53; c 3. ELECTRICAL ENGINEERING. *Educ:* Ill Inst Technol, BS, 50, MS, 52, PhD, 63. *Prof Exp:* Develop engr commun systs, Armour Res Found, Ill Inst Technol, 52-54; proj engr control systs, Cook Elec Co, 54-56; group leader digital electronics, Motorola, Inc, 56-59, asst sect head, 59-60, asst chief engr, 60-63, chief engr, 63-66, prod mgr signaling prod, 66-69, MGR INDUST PROD ENG, COMMUN DIV, MOTOROLA, INC, 69- *Mem:* Inst Elec & Electronics Engrs. *Res:* Digital communications, particularly radio systems. *Mailing Add:* 6600 N Mozart Chicago IL 60645

SALTZER, CHARLES, b Cleveland, Ohio, Feb 3, 18; m 40; c 1. MATHEMATICS. *Educ:* Western Reserve Univ, BA, 41; Univ Nebr, MA, 42; Brown Univ, MSc, 45, PhD(math), 49. *Prof Exp:* Instr math, Brown Univ, 44-48; from instr to assoc prof, Case Western Reserve Univ, 48-60; prof appl math, Univ Cincinnati, 60-62; PROF MATH, OHIO STATE UNIV, 62- *Concurrent Pos:* Fulbright award, 50-51; consult, Electronics Lab, Gen Elec Co, 56-58, Thompson-Ramo-Wooldridge, Inc, 58-61 & Bell Tel, 61-63. *Mem:* Am Math Soc; Am Astron Soc; Asn Symbolic Logic; Soc Indust & Appl Math; Math Asn Am. *Res:* Numerical analysis; partial difference equations; conformal mapping; computer theory; network theory; theory of distributions; control and communication theory; automata theory. *Mailing Add:* Dept of Math Ohio State Univ Columbus OH 43210

SALTZER, JEROME H(OWARD), b Nampa, Idaho, Oct 9, 39; m 61; c 3. COMPUTER SYSTEMS. *Educ:* Mass Inst Technol, SB, 61, SM, 63, ScD, 66. *Prof Exp:* From instr to assoc prof elec eng, 63-76, PROF COMPUT SCI, MASS INST TECHNOL, 76- *Concurrent Pos:* Consult, US Dept Defense, 67- & IBM Corp, 70- *Mem:* AAAS; Asn Comput Mach; sr mem Inst Elec & Electronics Engrs. *Res:* Design of computer systems for enterprise support; data communication networks; information protection and privacy; impact of computer systems on society. *Mailing Add:* Mass Inst Technol 545 Technology Square Cambridge MA 02139

SALTZMAN, BARRY, b New York, NY, Feb 26, 31; m 62; c 2. METEOROLOGY. *Educ:* City Col New York, BS, 52; Mass Inst Technol, SM, 54, PhD(meteorol), 57. *Hon Degrees:* MA, Yale Univ, 68. *Prof Exp:* Res asst meteorol, Mass Inst Technol, 52-57, res staff, 57-61; sr res scientist, Travelers Res Ctr, Inc, 61-66, res fel, 66-68; dir grad studies geol & geophys, 71-74, PROF GEOPHYS, YALE UNIV, 68-, CHMN, COMT ATMOSPHERIC SCI & BIOMETEOROL, 74- *Concurrent Pos:* Assoc ed, J Geophys Res, 71-74; ed, Advances Geophys, 77- *Mem:* AAAS; fel Am Meteorol Soc; Am Geophys Union; Sigma Xi. *Res:* Geophysical fluid dynamics; theory of climate and the atmospheric general circulation. *Mailing Add:* Dept Geol & Geophys Yale Univ New Haven CT 06511

SALTZMAN, BERNARD EDWIN, b New York, NY, June 24, 18; m 49; c 3. ENVIRONMENTAL HEALTH, ANALYTICAL CHEMISTRY. *Educ:* City Col New York, BChE, 39; Univ Mich, MS, 40; Univ Cincinnati, PhD(chem eng), 58; Am Bd Indust Hyg, cert. *Prof Exp:* Chem engr, Joseph E Seagram & Sons, Inc, 40-41; jr pub health engr, USPHS, 41-43, from asst engr to sr asst engr, 43-49, from sanit engr to sr sanit engr, 49-61, sanit engr dir & dep chief chem res & develop sect, 61-67; res prof environ health, 67-71, PROF ENVIRON HEALTH, KETTERING LAB, COL MED, UNIV CINCINNATI, 71- *Mem:* Am Chem Soc; Am Indust Hyg Asn; Am Conf Govt Indust Hygienists; Air Pollution Control Asn; Asn Off Anal Chem. *Res:* Air pollution chemistry; administration of research; industrial hygiene. *Mailing Add:* Kettering Lab Univ Cincinnati Col of Med Cincinnati OH 45267

SALTZMAN, HERBERT A, b Philadelphia, Pa, Nov 27, 28; m 54; c 3. MEDICINE. *Educ:* Jefferson Med Col, MD, 52; Am Bd Internal Med, dipl, 60; Am Bd Pulmonary Dis, dipl, 71. *Prof Exp:* Chief pulmonary dis, Vet Admin Hosp, Durham, NC, 58-63; asst dir hyperbaric unit & asst prof med, 63-64, assoc prof, 65-69, dir, F G Hall Lab Environ Res, 64-77, PROF MED, MED CTR, DUKE UNIV, 69- *Concurrent Pos:* Mem comt underwater physiol & med, Nat Res Coun, 72-75. *Mem:* Am Heart Asn; Am Physiol Soc; Am Soc Clin Invest; Undersea Med Soc; Am Thoracic Soc. *Res:* Environmental research; respiratory physiology and chest diseases. *Mailing Add:* Dept of Internal Med Box 3823 Durham NC 27710

SALTZMAN, MARTIN D, b Brooklyn, NY, Mar 20, 41. ORGANIC CHEMISTRY. *Educ:* Brooklyn Col, BS, 61, MA, 64; Univ NH, PhD, 68. *Prof Exp:* Res assoc, Brandeis Univ, 68-69; asst prof chem, 69-74, ASSOC PROF FOUND SCI & SPEC LECTR CHEM, PROVIDENCE COL, 74- *Mem:* AAAS. *Res:* Free radical and photochemistry. *Mailing Add:* Dept of Chem Providence Col Providence RI 02918

SALTZMAN, MAX, b Brooklyn, NY, Apr 17, 17; m 41, 52; c 2. COLOR TECHNOLOGY. *Educ:* City Col New York, BS, 36. *Prof Exp:* Inspector, NY Inspection Div, Chem Warfare Serv, 41-46; res chemist, B F Goodrich Chem Co, 46-52; vpres, Phipps Prod Corp, 52-55; develop supvr, Harmon Colors, Allied Chem Corp, 55-61, tech asst to vpres, Nat Aniline Div, 61-66, sr scientist, Indust Chem Div, 66-69, mgr color technol specialty Chem Div, 69-73; RES SPECIALIST, INST PHYSICS & PLANETARY PHYSICS, UNIV CALIF, LOS ANGELES, 73- *Concurrent Pos:* Adj prof, Rensselaer Polytech, 66-; chmn tech comt, Dry Color Mfrs Assoc, 61-70. *Mem:* Am

Chem Soc; Optical Soc Am; Brit Soc Dyers & Colourists; Fedn Socs Paint Technol; Am Asn Textile Chem & Colorists. *Res:* Color measurement; spectrophotometry; color technology; archaeological chemistry; analytical dyes in ancient textiles. *Mailing Add:* 16428 Sloan Dr Los Angeles CA 90049

SALU, YEHUDA, b Tel-Aviv, Israel, Feb 17, 41; m 64; c 2. MEDICAL PHYSICS. *Educ:* Hebrew Univ, MSc, 64; Tel-Aviv Univ, PhD(physics), 73. *Prof Exp:* Asst scientist, Univ Iowa, 73-78, assoc scientist, 78-80; ASST PROF PHYSICS, HOWARD UNIV, 80- *Concurrent Pos:* Prin investr, NIH, 78- *Res:* Bioelectricity of the human heart, its modeling, measurements and interpretation. *Mailing Add:* Dept Physics & Astron Howard Univ Washington DC 20059

SALUJA, PREET PAL SINGH, b Gonda, India, Nov 7, 44; Can citizen; m 74; c 2. SOLUTIONS & SURFACE CHEMISTRY. *Educ:* Banaras Hindu Univ, India, BSc Hons, 64, MSc, Hons, 66; Univ Pa, PhD(electrochem), 71. *Prof Exp:* NIH res assoc solutions & biophys chem, Cornell Univ, 71-73; Robert A Welch fel solutions & calorimetry, Univ Houston, 75-76; sr res assoc gas phase ion chem, Univ Alta, Can, 76-80; assoc res officer chem processes, Nat Res Coun, Can, 80-81; ASSOC RES OFFICER HIGH TEMP SOLUTIONS & SURFACES, WHITESHELL NUCLEAR RES ESTAB, ATOMIC ENERGY CAN LTD, 81- *Concurrent Pos:* Lectr chem, Banaras Hindu Univ, India, 66, vis fac, 73-75, vis prof, 77. *Mem:* Am Chem Soc; Chem Inst Can. *Res:* High temperature thermochemistry of solutions and interfaces; geochemistry; colloid chemistry and surface microcalorimetry; gas phase ion chemistry and important mass-spectrometry applications; high pressure chemical processes; instrumentation and technique development. *Mailing Add:* Whiteshell Nuclear Res Estab Atomic Energy Can Ltd Pinawa MB R0E 1L0 Can

SALUK, PAUL HOWARD, b Philadelphia, Pa, Dec 12, 41; m 63; c 1. IMMUNOLOGY. *Educ:* Univ Fla, BS, 65, MS, 67, PhD(immunol), 71. *Prof Exp:* Fel immunol, NY Univ Med Ctr, 71-73; ASSOC PROF IMMUNOL, HAHNEMANN MED UNIV, 73- *Concurrent Pos:* Lectr, Pa Col Osteop Med, 81-82. *Mem:* Am Asn Immunologists; Am Soc Microbiol; Soc Exp Biol & Med; Reticuloendothelial Soc; NY Acad Sci. *Res:* Regulation of macrophage activity by T- and B- lymphocytes; relationship between activation signals and macrophage subsets and their state of differentiation. *Mailing Add:* Dept Microbiol & Immunol MS 410 Hahemann Med Univ Philadelphia PA 19102

SALUNKHE, DATTA K, b Kolhapur, India, Nov 7, 25; m 55; c 2. FOOD TECHNOLOGY. *Educ:* Univ Poona, BSc, 49; Mich State Univ, MS, 51, PhD(food technol), 53. *Prof Exp:* From asst prof to assoc prof, 54-65, PROF HORT, UTAH STATE UNIV, 65- *Mem:* Inst Food Technologists. *Res:* Post harvest physiology, pathology and microscopy of fruits and vegetables; horticultural processing; radiation effects on horticultural plants and plant products; food toxicology; nycotoxins and naturally occurring toxicants in plant foods; food and nutrition. *Mailing Add:* Dept of Nutrit & Food Sci Utah State Univ Logan UT 84322

SALUTSKY, MURRELL LEON, b Goodman, Miss, July 16, 23; m 66; c 3. WATER CHEMISTRY. *Educ:* Univ Ky, BS, 44; Mich State Univ, PhD(chem), 50. *Prof Exp:* Asst, Mich State Univ, 46-49; res chemist, Mound Lab, Monsanto Chem Co, 50-52; sr res chemist, 52-55, sr res chemist, Inorg Chem Div, 55-57; supvr chem res, Res Div, 57-65, dir res, Dearborn Chem Div, 65-69, vpres res, 69-71, exec vpres, Dearborn Chem Div, 71-76, GROUP V PRES & CHIEF TECH OFFICER, DEARBORN GROUP, CHEMED CORP, W R GRACE & CO, 76- *Mem:* AAAS; Am Chem Soc; Am Inst Chem; Marine Technol Soc; Int Oceanog Found. *Res:* Inorganic chemical separations; rare earths; radium and rare radioactive elements; phosphorus and phosphates; agricultural chemicals; precipitation from homogenous solution; by-products from the sea; desalination; pretreatment of saline waters; industrial water treatment chemicals; waste water and pollution control chemicals and services. *Mailing Add:* Dearborn Group 300 Genesee St Lake Zurich IL 60047

SALVADOR, RICHARD ANTHONY, b Albany, NY, May 19, 27; m 66; c 2. PHARMACOLOGY. *Educ:* St Bernadine of Siena Col, BS, 51; Boston Univ, AM, 53; George Washington Univ, PhD(pharmacol), 56. *Prof Exp:* Res instr pharmacol, Sch Med, Wash Univ, 58-60; sr pharmacologist, Wellcome Res Labs, 60-69; group chief, 70-75, asst dir, Dept Pharmacol, 75-79, DIR EXP THERAPEUTS, HOFFMAN-LA ROCHE INC, 79- *Concurrent Pos:* Nat Inst Neurol Dis & Blindness fel, 57. *Mem:* AAAS; Am Soc Pharmacol & Exp Therapeut; Am Chem Soc; NY Acad Sci; Fedn Am Socs Exp Biol. *Res:* Lipid metabolism; autonomic drugs; hypolipemic drugs; feasability of altering collagen metabolism with drugs. *Mailing Add:* Hoffmann-La Roche Inc 340 Kingsland St Nutley NJ 07110

SALVADOR, ROMANO LEONARD, b Montreal, Que, Dec 12, 28; m 54; c 3. MEDICINAL CHEMISTRY. *Educ:* St Mary's Col, AB, 50; Univ Montreal, BSc, 54, MSc, 56; Purdue Univ, PhD(pharmaceut chem), 60. *Prof Exp:* From asst prof to assoc prof, 59-70, PROF PHARMACEUT CHEM & V DEAN FAC PHARM, UNIV MONTREAL, 70- *Mem:* Am Chem Soc; Can Soc Chemother; Chem Inst Can. *Res:* Cholinergic-anticholinergic drugs; cholinesterase regenerators; analgesics; central nervous system drugs; acetylenic drugs. *Mailing Add:* Fac of Pharm Univ of Montreal PO Box 6128 Montreal PQ H3C 3J7 Can

SALVADORI, ANTONIO, b Cesena, Italy, Apr 1, 41; m 64; c 3. COMPUTER SCIENCE, SOLID STATE PHYSICS. *Educ:* Nat Univ Ireland, BSc, 62, MSc, 63; McMaster Univ, PhD(physics), 68. *Prof Exp:* Lectr math & physics, Univ Col, Dublin, 62-63; asst prof comput & info sci, 67-73, ASSOC PROF COMPUT & INFO SCI, UNIV GUELPH, 67- *Concurrent Pos:* Vis lectr, Trinity Col, Dublin, 68-69. *Mem:* Asn Comput Mash; Brit Comput Soc; Ital Asn Automatic Calculus. *Res:* Program profiles; programming languages for teaching purposes; biological simulation techniques; ecological modelling. *Mailing Add:* Dept of Comput & Info Sci Univ of Guelph Guelph ON N1G 2W7 Can

SALVADORI, M(ARIO) G(IORGIO), b Rome, Italy, Mar 19, 07; nat US; m 75; c 1. ENGINEERING, APPLIED MATHEMATICS. *Educ:* Univ Rome, DCE, 30, DrMath, 32, Libero Docente, 37. *Hon Degrees:* DrSc, Columbia Univ, 78. *Prof Exp:* Secy, Civil Eng Div, Nat Italian Res Coun, 34-38; lectr civil eng, Columbia Univ, 40-41, from instr to prof, 41-59, chmn, Archit Tech Div, 65-73, prof, Sch Archit, 59-75, EMER PROF CIVIL ENG & ARCHIT, COLUMBIA UNIV, 75- *Concurrent Pos:* Consult, Calculus Applns Inst, Italy, 34-38; asst prof, Univ Rome, 37-38; fel, Int Inst Cult Rels, 38; lectr, Princeton Univ, 55-60; partner, Paul Weidlinger, Consult Eng, 56-; hon prof, Univ Minas Gerais. *Mem:* Fel Am Soc Civil Engrs; fel Am Soc Mech Engrs; fel NY Acad Sci; hon mem Am Inst Architects. *Res:* Theory of structures; applied mathematics and mechanics. *Mailing Add:* 101 E 59th St New York NY 10022

SALVAGGIO, JOHN EDMOND, b New Orleans, La, May 19, 33; m 58; c 5. INTERNAL MEDICINE, IMMUNOLOGY. *Educ:* Loyola Univ, BS, 54; La State Univ, MD, 57; Am Bd Internal Med & Am Bd Allergy, dipl. *Prof Exp:* From instr to assoc prof, 63-72, PROF MED, SCH MED, LA STATE UNIV, 72-; HENDERSON PROF MED, TULANE MED SCH, NEW ORLEANS, 75-; DIR IMMUNOL & CLIN ALLERGY UNIT, CHARITY HOSP, 64- *Concurrent Pos:* NIH res fel immunol & allergy, Dept Med, Mass Gen Hosp & Harvard Med Sch, 61-63; NIH res spec fel, Sch Med, Univ Colo, 72; dir USPHS Training Prog Clin Immunol & Allergy, Tulane Med Sch, 64- *Mem:* AAAS; Am Fedn Clin Res; Am Soc Clin Invest; Am Thoracic Soc; Am Asn Immunol. *Res:* Immediate and delayed hypersensitivity. *Mailing Add:* Dept Med Tulane Sch Med New Orleans LA 70112

SALVESEN, NILS, naval architecture, engineering mechanics, see previous edition

SALVESEN, ROBERT H, b Staten Island, NY, Jan 31, 24; m 48; c 3. ORGANIC CHEMISTRY, POLYMER CHEMISTRY. *Educ:* Wagner Col, BS, 48; Univ Buffalo, MA, 51; Polytech Inst Brooklyn, PhD(org chem), 58. *Prof Exp:* Proj leader petrol specialties, Tech Serv Labs, Socony Mobil Oil Co, NY, 52-59; res assoc, Esso Agr Chem Lab, 59-71, res assoc, Govt Res Lab, 71-79, RES ASSOC, PROD RES DIV, EXXON RES & ENG CO, LINDEN, 79- *Res:* Research and development of agricultural products; wax emulsions and coatings; specialty petroleum products and refinery by-products; new product development activities in polymers; design of oily waste treatment and disposal equipment. *Mailing Add:* Exxon Res & Eng Co PO Box 51 Linden NJ 07036

SALVETER, SHARON CAROLINE, b Pasadena, Calif, June 9, 49. INTELLIGENT SYSTEMS, DATABASE SYSTEMS. *Educ:* Univ Calif, San Diego, BS, 69; Univ Ore, MS, 71; Univ Wis, PhD(comput sci), 78. *Prof Exp:* Instr comput sci, Univ Ore, 71-73; asst prof comput sci, State Univ NY, Stony Brook, 78-82; ASST PROF COMPUT SCI, BOSTON UNIV, 82- *Concurrent Pos:* Prin investr, NSF, 79-81, co prin investr, 81-83; consult, Bell Labs, 80; sabbatical fel comput sci, Int Bus Mach, 81. *Mem:* Sigma Xi; Asn Comput Mach; Asn Comput Linguistics; Inst Elec & Electron Engrs; Cognitive Sci Soc. *Res:* Investigation of computer learning mechanisms; applying artificial intelligence techniques in support of natural language front ends to databases. *Mailing Add:* Math Dept Boston Univ 232 Bay State Rd Boston MA 02215

SALVI, RICHARD J, b Chisholm, Minn, June 30, 46. PHYSIOLOGICAL PSYCHOLOGY. *Educ:* NDak State Univ, BS, 68; Syracuse Univ, PhD(psychol), 75. *Prof Exp:* Asst prof otolaryngol, Upstate Med Ctr, State Univ NY, 75-80; MEM FAC, UNIV TEX, DALLAS, 80- *Mem:* AAAS; Acoust Soc Am. *Res:* Auditory physiology; auditory psychophysics. *Mailing Add:* Univ Tex 1966 Inwood RD Dallas TX 75235

SALVIN, SAMUEL BERNARD, b Boston, Mass, July 10, 15; m; c 3. IMMUNOLOGY, MYCOLOGY. *Educ:* Harvard Univ, AB, 35, EdM, 37, AM, 38, PhD(biol), 41. *Prof Exp:* Asst, Radcliffe Col & Harvard Univ, 37-41; instr, Harvard Univ, 41-43; immunologist & mycologist, Rocky Mountain Lab, Nat Inst Allergy & Infectious Dis, 46-64; head immunol, Res Div, Ciba Pharmaceut Co, 65-67; PROF MICROBIOL & IMMUNOL, SCH MED, UNIV PITTSBURGH, 67- *Mem:* Bot Soc Am; Am Soc Microbiol; Am Asn Immunol; NY Acad Sci; Am Acad Microbiol. *Res:* Hypersensitivity and cellular immunity; antibody formation; immunological tolerance; autoimmune disease; immunology of pathogenic fungi; immunoregulation; lymphokines. *Mailing Add:* Dept of Microbiol Univ of Pittsburgh Sch of Med Pittsburgh PA 15261

SALWEN, HAROLD, b New York, NY, Jan 30, 28; m 50; c 6. THEORETICAL PHYSICS, FLUID DYNAMICS. *Educ:* Mass Inst Technol, SB, 49; Columbia Univ, PhD(physics), 56. *Prof Exp:* Asst physics, Columbia Univ, 50-53; asst, Watson Lab, Int Bus Mach Corp, 53-55; res assoc statist mech, Syracuse Univ, 55-57; res fel solid state physics, Div Eng & Appl Physics, Harvard Univ, 57-59; asst prof, 59-65, assoc prof, 65-81, PROF PHYSICS, STEVENS INST TECHNOL, 81- *Concurrent Pos:* Vis scientist math dept, Imperial Col Sci & Technol, London, 80; adj prof oceanog, Old Dominion Univ, 81-; vis prof math, Reusellaer Polytechnic Inst, 82. *Mem:* AAAS; Am Phys Soc; Sigma Xi. *Res:* Magnetic resonance; molecular structure; statistical mechanics of irreversible processes; kinetic theory; solid state theory; hydrodynamics; quantum-mechanical many-body problem. *Mailing Add:* Dept of Physics Stevens Inst of Technol Hoboken NJ 07030

SALWIN, ARTHUR ELLIOTT, b Chicago, Ill, Feb 18, 48; m; c 1. CHEMICAL PHYSICS, SOFTWARE ENGINEERING. *Educ:* Univ Md, BS, 70; Princeton Univ, PhD(phys chem), 74. *Prof Exp:* Sr analyst comput sci, Xonics Inc, 75-76; sr staff scientist, Appl Physics Lab, Johns Hopkins Univ, 76-78; mem res staff comput anal & simulations, Riverside Res Inst, 78-80; MEM TECH STAFF COMPUT SPEECH EXPERIMENTATION, MITRE CORP, 81- *Res:* Applications of computer technology to scientific problems; studies in state-of-the-art software engineering practices; signal processing applications including computer speech. *Mailing Add:* 1405 Homeric Ct Silver Spring MD 20901

SALWIN, HAROLD, b Kansas City, Mo, Nov 24, 15; m 43; c 2. FOOD CHEMISTRY. *Educ:* Univ Chicago, BS, 41. *Prof Exp:* Chemist, Tenn Valley Authority, 42-43, Explosives Res Lab, US Bur Mines, 43-45 & US Customs Lab, 45-48; res chemist, Armed Forces, Qm Food & Container Inst, 48-58, head food biochem lab, 58-61, actg chief chem br, 61; res chemist, Div Food Chem, 61-64, head decomposition & preservation sect, 64-71, CHIEF PROTEIN & CEREAL PROD BR, FOOD & DRUG ADMIN, 71- *Honors & Awards:* Outstanding Employee Award, Dept Army, 60; Rohland A Isker Award, 62. *Mem:* Am Chem Soc; Inst Food Technol; Am Asn Cereal Chemists; fel Asn Official Anal Chemists. *Res:* Food technology; chemistry of food deterioration; food dehydration; analytical methods. *Mailing Add:* 706 Kerwin Rd Silver Spring MD 20901

SALYER, DARNELL, b Hager Hill, Nov 18, 30; m 56; c 2. ANALYTICAL CHEMISTRY. *Educ:* Eastern Ky State Col, BS, 52; Ohio State Univ, PhD, 56. *Prof Exp:* Prof chem, Shorter Col, 56-59; from asst prof to assoc prof, 59-65; PROF CHEM, EASTERN KY UNIV, 65- *Mem:* Am Chem Soc. *Res:* Radiochemistry; chemistry of cobalt; chemical education; thermogravimetry; analytical methods. *Mailing Add:* Dept of Chem Eastern Ky Univ Richmond KY 40475

SALZANO, FRANCIS J(OHN), b Brooklyn, NY, Mar 23, 33; m 58; c 3. CHEMICAL ENGINEERING. *Educ:* City Univ New York, BChE, 55. *Prof Exp:* Aeronaut res scientist, Lewis Flight Propulsion Lab, Cleveland, 55-57; assoc chem engr, 57-76, prog mgr, 75-76, SR CHEM ENGR & HEAD MAT CHEM & ENERGY DIV, BROOKHAVEN NAT LAB, 76- *Mem:* AAAS. *Res:* Fused salt chemistry; surface adsorption; inorganic carbon chemistry; solid state electrolytes; chemistry of the alkali-metals, especially sodium; atmospheric chemistry; synthetic clean fuels; industrial energy conservation; batteries, fuel cells and advanced materials. *Mailing Add:* 144 Avery Ave Patchoque NY 11772

SALZANO, FRANCISCO MAURO, b Cachoeira, do Sul, Brazil, July 27, 28; m 52; c 2. HUMAN GENETICS. *Educ:* Univ Fed Rio Grande do Sul, Brazil, BS, 50, lic, 52; Univ Sao Paulo, PhD(genetics), 55. *Prof Exp:* From instr to asst prof, 52-66, researcher, Inst Natural Sci, 52-62, head genetics sect, 63-68, dir inst, 68-71, researcher genetics, 71-77, assoc prof, 66-81, PROF GENETICS, INST BIOSCI UNIV FED RIO GRANDE DO SUL, 81- *Concurrent Pos:* Rockefeller Found fel, Univ Mich, 56-57. *Honors & Awards:* Medal, Brazilian Asn Advan Sci, 73. *Mem:* Am Soc Human Genetics; Am Asn Phys Anthrop; Behav Genetics Asn; Int Asn Human Biologists; Brazilian Acad Sci. *Res:* Blood groups, serum proteins, hemoglobin and enzyme types; characteristics of anthropological interest; medical genetics. *Mailing Add:* Univ Fed Rio Grande do Sul Caixa Postal 1953 Dept Genetics 90000 Porto Alegre Brazil

SALZARULO, LEONARD MICHAEL, b Montclair, NJ, Oct 11, 27; m 71; c 1. PHYSICS, CHEMICAL ENGINEERING. *Educ:* Newark Col Eng, BS, 51, MS, 53; Polytech Inst Brooklyn, PhD(chem eng), 66. *Prof Exp:* Head qual control lab, Sun Chem Corp, NJ, 51-53; instr chem, Newark Col Eng, 53-55, chem eng, 55-56; prof engr, S B Penick & Co, NJ, 56-59; asst prof appl mech, Newark Col Eng, 59-60; res assoc chem eng, Polytech Inst Brooklyn, 60-61; asst prof appl mech, 61-63, from asst prof to assoc prof physics, 63-67, asst chmn dept physics, 63-68, assoc chmn dept, 68-74, PROF PHYSICS, NJ INST TECHNOL, 67-, CHMN DEPT, 74- *Concurrent Pos:* Consult, Bendix Corp, NJ, 65-66. *Mem:* NY Acad Sci; Nat Asn Physics Teachers. *Res:* Transport phenomena in ion exchange membranes; electrochemistry, especially ionic transport phenomena; biophysics. *Mailing Add:* Dept of Physics NJ Inst Technol 323 High St Newark NJ 07102

SALZBERG, BERNARD, b New York, NY, July 22, 07; m 41. ELECTRONICS. *Educ:* Polytech Inst Brooklyn, EE, 29, MEE, 33, DEE, 41. *Prof Exp:* Engr res & develop, RCA Commun, Inc, 29-31 & RCA Mfg Co, 31-41; assoc supt, Radio Div, Naval Res Lab, 41-52, assoc supt & consult, Electronics Div, 52-56; chief scientist, AIL Div, Cutler-Hammer, Inc, 56-72; CONSULT, 72- *Honors & Awards:* Mod Pioneer Award, Nat Asn Mfrs, 40; Diamond Award, Inst Radio Engrs, 55; Meritorious Civilian Award, US Navy, 56. *Mem:* Am Phys Soc; fel Inst Elec & Electronics Engrs. *Res:* Semiconductors; microwaves; electrophysics. *Mailing Add:* Ridge Rock Lane East Norwich NY 11732

SALZBERG, BETTY, b Denver, Colo, Jan 19, 44; m 64; c 1. ALGEBRA. *Educ:* Univ Calif, Los Angeles, BA, 64; Univ Mich, MA, 66, PhD(math), 71. *Prof Exp:* Asst prof, 71-77, ASSOC PROF MATH, NORTHEASTERN UNIV, 77- *Mem:* Am Math Soc; Math Asn Am. *Res:* Finite groups of Lie type. *Mailing Add:* Dept of Math Northeastern Univ Boston MA 02115

SALZBERG, BRIAN MATTHEW, b New York, NY, Sept 4, 42. NEUROBIOLOGY, BIOPHYSICS. *Educ:* Yale Univ, BS, 63; Harvard Univ, AM, 65, PhD(physics), 71. *Prof Exp:* Res asst high energy physics, Harvard Univ, 65-71; fel neurobiol, Sch Med, Yale Univ, 71-74, res assoc physiol, 74-75; asst prof, 75-80, ASSOC PROF PHYSIOL, SCH MED & SCH DENT MED, UNIV PA, 80- *Concurrent Pos:* Investr neurobiol, Marine Biol Lab, Woods Hole, 72-, mem corp, 74-, trustee, 80-; mem, Inst Neurol Sci, Univ Pa, 76- *Mem:* Biophys Soc; Soc Neurosci; Am Phys Soc; Soc Gen Physiologists. *Res:* Development of molecular probes of membrane potential and their application to integrative neurophysiology by permitting optical recording of neuronal activity, simultaneously and nondestructively, from many cells in simpler nervous systems. *Mailing Add:* Dept of Physiol & Pharmacol 4010 Locust St Philadelphia PA 19174

SALZBERG, DAVID AARON, b Kansas City, Mo, May 5, 20; m 44; c 4. BIOCHEMISTRY. *Educ:* Univ Chicago, BS, 40; Univ Calif, MS, 48; Stanford Univ, PhD(biochem), 50. *Prof Exp:* Chemist, Ala Ord Works, 42-43 & US Engr Dist, Hawaii, 43-45; USPHS res asst, Stanford Univ, 49-50; biochemist, Palo Alto Med Res Found, 52-62, head, Basic Cancer Res Div, 58-62; asst res prof biochem, Univ San Francisco, 62-64; dir res, Arequipa Found, 63-67; pres, Tahoe Col, 67-68; FEL NEUROBIOL, MED SCH, STANFORD UNIV, 69- *Concurrent Pos:* Am Cancer Soc fel, 50-52 & scholar cancer res, 53-58; mem adv bd, Miramonte Found Ment Health & Great Books Found. *Mem:* Am Asn Cancer Res; Am Chem Soc. *Res:* Diabetes and hormone relationships in cancer; mutagenesis; genetic changes in cancer induction; azo-dye hepatocarcinogenesis; maternal and foster nursing in carcinogenesis; nutritional evaluation of biochemical intermediates; physiology of stress and emotion; brain hormones; nervous system regulation of growth. *Mailing Add:* 4063 Scripps Ave Palo Alto CA 94306

SALZBERG, HUGH WILLIAM, b New York, NY, June 27, 21; m 52. PHYSICAL CHEMISTRY. *Educ:* City Col New York, BS, 42; NY Univ, MS, 47, PhD(phys chem), 50. *Prof Exp:* Res chemist, US Naval Res Lab, 50-53; res chemist, Columbia Univ, 53-54; from instr to assoc prof, 54-70, PROF CHEM, CITY COL NEW YORK, 70- *Mem:* AAAS; Am Chem Soc; Electrochem Soc. *Res:* Electrodeposition and preparative electrochemistry; kinetics. *Mailing Add:* Dept of Chem City Col of New York New York NY 10031

SALZBRENNER, RICHARD JOHN, b Douglas, Ariz, July 25, 48; m 76. MECHANICAL PROPERTIES, ALLOY DEVELOPMENT. *Educ:* Univ Notre Dame, BS, 70; Univ Denver, PhD(mat sci), 73. *Prof Exp:* Res assoc, Mass Inst Technol, 73-78; MEM TECH STAFF, WESTERN ELEC, SANDIA NAT LAB, 78- *Mem:* Am Soc Metals; Am Inst Metall Engrs. *Res:* Mechanical property measurement; structure-property relationships in ferrous and non-ferrous alloys; low alloy steel development; martensitic transformations; corrosion fatigue; formability; fracture toughness; internal friction. *Mailing Add:* Div 5832 Sandia Nat Lab Albuquerque NM 87185

SALZENSTEIN, MARVIN A(BRAHAM), b Chicago, Ill, May 12, 29; m 58; c 2. SAFETY ENGINEERING, MACHINE DESIGN. *Educ:* Ill Inst Technol, BS, 51. *Prof Exp:* Asst res mech engr, Armour Res Found, Ill Inst Technol, 49-51; sales engr, Sci Instruments, W H Kessel & Co, 53-57; assoc engr, Walter C McCrone Assocs, Inc, 57-61; PRES, POLYTECH, INC, 61- *Concurrent Pos:* Res engr, White Sands Proving Grounds. *Mem:* Am Soc Mech Engrs; Am Soc Safety Engrs; Am Gas Asn; Am Soc Planning Off. *Res:* Industrial zoning; combustion. *Mailing Add:* Polytech Inc 3740 W Morse Chicago IL 60645

SALZER, JOHN M(ICHAEL), b Vienna, Austria, Sept 12, 17; nat US; m 44; c 4. ELECTRICAL ENGINEERING. *Educ:* Case Inst Technol, BS, 47, MS, 48; Mass Inst Technol, ScD(elec eng), 51. *Prof Exp:* Instr elec eng, Case Inst Technol, 47-48; res assoc, Digital Comput Lab, Mass Inst Technol, 48-51; mem tech staff, Res & Develop Labs, Hughes Aircraft Co, 51-54; dir systs, Res Labs, Magnavox Co, 54-59; dir intellectronics labs, Thompson Ramo Wooldridge, Inc, 59-63; vpres tech & planning, Librascope Group, Gen Precision, Inc, 63-68; pres, Salzer Technol Enterprises, 68-72; prin, Darling & Alsobrook, 72-75; sr vpres, Darling, Paterson & Salzer, 75-76; PRES, SALZER TECHNOL ENTERPRISES, 76- *Concurrent Pos:* Lectr, Univ Calif, Los Angeles, 52- *Mem:* Int Soc Hybrid Microelectronics; Semiconductor Equip & Mat Inst; Sigma Xi. *Res:* Digital computers and control systems; sampled data systems; information systems; electronic components. *Mailing Add:* 909 Berkeley St Santa Monica CA 90403

SALZMAN, EDWIN WILLIAM, b St Louis, Mo, Dec 11, 28; m 54; c 3. SURGERY. *Educ:* Wash Univ, AB, 50, MD, 53; Harvard Univ, MA, 69. *Prof Exp:* Asst in surg, Mass Gen Hosp, 61-65, asst surgeon, 65-66; instr, 61-65, assoc prof, 69-71, PROF SURG, HARVARD MED SCH, 72-; SURGEON & ASSOC DIR SURG SERV, BETH ISRAEL HOSP, BOSTON, 66-; SR RES ASSOC, MASS INST TECHNOL, 67- *Concurrent Pos:* NIH fel, Radcliffe Infirmary, Oxford Univ, 59; Am Cancer Soc clin fel, Mass Gen Hosp, Boston, 60-61, Med Found, Inc fel, 62-65; Markle scholar acad med, 68; assoc, Univ Seminar Biomat, Columbia Univ, 67-, chmn, 68; consult, Am Nat Res Cross, 68- & thrombosis adv comt, NIH, 70-; mem steering comt, Harvard Univ-Mass Inst Technol Prog Health Sci & Technol, 70-; dep ed, New Eng J Med. *Mem:* Am Physiol Soc; Soc Univ Surg; Soc Vascular Surg; Am Surg Asn; Am Soc Clin Invest. *Res:* Hemostasis and thrombosis; biochemistry of blood platelets; surgical physiology. *Mailing Add:* Dept of Surg Beth Israel Hosp 330 Brookline Ave Boston MA 02215

SALZMAN, GARY CLYDE, b Palo Alto, Calif, May 25, 42; m 65. BIOPHYSICS. *Educ:* Univ Calif, Berkeley, AB, 65; Univ Ore, MS, 68, PhD(nuclear physics), 72. *Prof Exp:* Peace Corps teacher physics & math, Ghana, 65-67; mem staff & presidential intern fel physics, 72-73, STAFF MEM BIOPHYS & INSTRUMENTATION GROUP, LOS ALAMOS SCI LAB, UNIV CALIF, 73- *Mem:* AAAS; Biophys Soc; Am Phys Soc; Optical Soc Am. *Res:* Light scattering from biological cells, automated cytology, instrumentation and techniques for cell identification and cancer diagnosis. *Mailing Add:* Biophys & Instrum Group Los Alamos Sci Lab H-10 MS 888 Los Alamos NM 87545

SALZMAN, GEORGE, b Newark, NJ, Sept 8, 25; m 48; c 2. THEORETICAL PHYSICS. *Educ:* Brooklyn Col, BS, 49; Univ Ill, PhD(physics), 53. *Prof Exp:* Instr physics, Univ Ill, 53-55; res assoc, Univ Rochester, 55-56, asst prof, 55-58, from asst prof to assoc prof, Univ Colo, 58-65; PROF PHYSICS, UNIV MASS, BOSTON, 65- *Concurrent Pos:* Ford Found fel, Theory Group, Europ Orgn Nuclear Res, Switz, 58-59; Fulbright res scholar, Frascati Nat Lab, Italy, 61-62; NSF res grant, 62-; vis assoc prof, Northeastern Univ, 64-65. *Mem:* Sci for the People; Am Phys Soc; AAAS. *Res:* Development of a science for humane survival; theory of elementary particles; high energy scattering theory; electromagnetic structure of nucleons; theory of relativity. *Mailing Add:* Dept of Physics Univ of Mass Boston MA 02125

SALZMAN, LEON, b New York, NY, July 10, 15; m 50; c 4. PSYCHIATRY. *Educ:* City Col New York, BS, 35; Royal Col Physicians & Surgeons, MD, 40. *Prof Exp:* Prof clin psychiat, Med Sch, Georgetown Univ, 45-67; prof psychiat, Med Sch, Tulane Univ, La, 67-69; clin prof psychiat, Albert Einstein Col Med, 69-75; PROF CLIN PSYCHIAT, MED SCH, GEORGETOWN UNIV, 75- *Concurrent Pos:* Dep dir, Bronx State Hosp, 70-75; pvt pract psychiat & psychoanal, 75- *Mem:* Am Acad Psychoanal (pres); Am Psychiat Asn; Am Psychoanal Asn. *Res:* Sex behavior; obsessive and compulsive states. *Mailing Add:* 6625 Braeburn Pkwy Bethesda MD 20014

SALZMAN, LOIS ANN, microbiology, biochemistry, see previous edition

SALZMAN, NORMAN POST, b New York, NY, Aug 14, 26; m 54; c 3. VIROLOGY. *Educ:* City Col New York, BS, 48; Univ Mich, MS, 49; Univ Ill, PhD(biochem), 53. *Prof Exp:* Res asst, Squibb Inst Med Res, 49-50; biochemist, Nat Heart Inst, 53-55; mem, Sect Cell Biol, 61-68, mem, Virol Study Sect, 71-73, BIOCHEMIST, NAT INST ALLERGY & INFECTIOUS DISEASES, 55-, CHIEF LAB BIOL VIRUSES, 68- *Concurrent Pos:* Ed, J Virol, 67-75; vis prof, Univ Geneva, 73-74; prof lectr, Georgetown Univ. *Mem:* Am Soc Cell Biol; Am Soc Biol Chem; Am Asn Immunol; Am Soc Microbiol. *Res:* Virus replication; viral oncology. *Mailing Add:* Lab Biol Viruses Nat Inst Allergy & Infect Dis Bethesda MD 20014

SALZMAN, STEVEN KERRY, b Manhattan, NY, Feb 19, 52; m 74; c 2. NEUROBIOLOGY, NEUROPHYSIOLOGY. *Educ:* Univ Fla, BS, 74; Univ Conn, PhD(neuropharmacol), 79. *Prof Exp:* Fel, 79-82, STAFF SCIENTIST PHYSIOL RES, ALFRED I DU PONT INST NEMOURS FOUND, 82- *Mem:* Soc Neurosci. *Res:* Neurophysiology and neuropharmacology of mammalian thermoregulation and hibernation; neurohumoral control of arousal states; plasma catecholamines and the control of surgical stress; spinal fluid concomitants of movement disorders. *Mailing Add:* Alfred I du Pont Inst Nemours Found Res Dept PO Box 269 Wilmington DE 19899

SALZMAN, WILLIAM RONALD, b Cutbank, Mont, Feb 27, 36; c 2. PHYSICAL CHEMISTRY. *Educ:* Univ Calif, Los Angeles, BS, 59, MS, 64, PhD(chem), 67. *Prof Exp:* Res metallurgist, Southern Res Inst, Ala, 61-62; asst prof, 67-72, actg head dept, 77-78, ASSOC PROF CHEM, UNIV ARIZ, 72-, HEAD DEPT, 78- *Concurrent Pos:* Am Chem Soc-Petrol Res Fund grant, Univ Ariz, 68-70. *Mem:* AAAS; Am Phys Soc; AAAS; Sigma Xi; Am Asn Univ Professors. *Res:* Application of quantum theory to problems of chemical interest; semiclassical and quantum radiation theory. *Mailing Add:* Dept of Chem Univ of Ariz Tucson AZ 85721

SAM, JOSEPH, b Gary, Ind, Aug 15, 23; m 45; c 3. PHARMACEUTICAL CHEMISTRY. *Educ:* Univ SC, BS, 48; Univ Kans, PhD(pharmaceut chem), 51. *Prof Exp:* Instr org chem, Univ SC, 47-48; asst pharmaceut chem, Univ Kans, 48-49; sr res chemist, McNeil Labs, Inc, 51-54, Bristol Labs, 55-57 & E I du Pont de Nemours & Co, 57-59; assoc prof pharmaceut chem, 59-61, chmn dept, 63-69, PROF PHARMACEUT CHEM, UNIV MISS, 61-, DEAN GRAD SCH & DIR UNIV RES, 68-, ASSOC VCHANCELLOR RES, 81- *Concurrent Pos:* Fulbright lectr, Cairo Univ, 65-66; mem pharm rev comt, Bur Health Manpower Educ, Dept Health, Educ & Welfare, 67-71; mem exec comt, Coun Res Policy & Grad Educ, Nat Asn State Univs & Land Grant Cols, 69-71 & 74-76. *Honors & Awards:* Found Res Award Pharmaceut & Med Chem, Am Pharmaceut Asn, 68. *Mem:* Am Chem Soc; Am Pharmaceut Asn; fel Acad Pharmaceut Sci; Am Asn Cols Pharm. *Res:* Medicinal chemistry. *Mailing Add:* Univ Miss University MS 38677

SAMAAN, NAGUIB A, b Girga, Egypt, Apr 2, 25; m 61; c 5. ENDOCRINOLOGY. *Educ:* Univ Alexandria, BA, 46, MB & ChB, 51, DM, 53; Univ London, PhD, 64; FRCP. *Prof Exp:* Intern med, Univ Alexandria, 52-54, resident, 54-56; postgrad training, Chest Inst, Brompton Hosp, London, Eng, 56 & gen med, Postgrad Med Sch London, 56; clin asst endocrinol, Dept Endocrinol & Therapeut, Royal Infirmary, 57; resident med, North Cambridge Hosp Eng, 58; clin asst prof, Postgrad Med Sch London, 60-64; res assoc endocrinol & asst physician, Western Reserve Univ, 64-66; asst prof endocrinol, Univ Iowa, 66-69; assoc prof med & physiol & assoc internist chief, 69-73, PROF MED & PHYSIOL & INTERNIST, SECT ENDOCRINOL, UNIV TEX M D ANDERSON HOSP & TUMOR INST HOUSTON, 73- & PROF MED, UNIV TEX MED SCH, 76- *Concurrent Pos:* Brit Med Res Coun sr res fel, Postgrad Med Sch London, 60-64; physician, Vet Admin Hosp, Iowa City, Iowa, 66-69; mem staff, Univ Tex Grad Sch Biomed Sci Houston, 69; consult, Hermann Gen Hosp, 70. *Mem:* Fedn Am Socs Exp Biol; Am Physiol Soc; Endocrine Soc; Am Diabetes Asn; Am Fedn Clin Res. *Res:* Diagnosis, management and investigation of diabetes and endocrine disorders; investigations of normal and abnormal pregnancy; metabolic and endocrine changes associated with tumors. *Mailing Add:* 14315 Heatherfield St Houston TX 77079

SAMAGH, BAKHSHISH SINGH, b Abohar, India, Oct 1, 38; Can citizen; m 66; c 2. VETERINARY MEDICINE, SEROLOGY. *Educ:* Panjab Univ, BVSc & AH, 60, MSc, 63; Univ Guelph, MSc, 68, PhD(serol), 72, DVM, 75. *Prof Exp:* Dist vet, Panjab Govt, India, 60-61; lectr microbiol, various univs, India, 63-66; fel, Univ Guelph, 66-75; vet scientist, 75-78, HEAD DIAG SEROL, ANIMAL DIS RES INST, AGR CAN, 78- *Mem:* Can Soc Immunol; Can Vet Med Asn; Am Asn Vet Lab Diagnosticians; Am Asn Vet Immunologists. *Res:* Research and development on immune response and sero-diagnosis of bacterial, viral and protozoan diseases of animals. *Mailing Add:* Animal Dis Res Inst 801 Fallowfield Ottawa ON K2H 8P9 Can

SAMANEN, JAMES MARTIN, b Detroit, Mich, June 17, 47. PEPTIDE CHEMISTRY, SYNTHETIC ORGANIC CHEMISTRY. *Educ:* Kalamazoo Col, BA, 69; Univ Mich, PhD(org chem), 75. *Prof Exp:* Res assoc, Mass Inst Technol, 75-77; RES CHEMIST, BIOPRODS DEPT, BECKMAN INSTRUMENTS INC, 77- *Mem:* Am Chem Soc. *Res:* Synthesis and chemistry of peptides, alkaloids, heterocycles, natural products. *Mailing Add:* Beckman Instruments Inc 1117 California Ave Palo Alto CA 94034

SAMARA, GEORGE ALBERT, b Lenanon, Dec 5, 36; US citizen. PHYSICS, CHEMICAL ENGINEERING. *Educ:* Univ Okla, BS, 58; Univ Ill, Urbana, MS, 60, PhD(chem eng, physics), 62. *Prof Exp:* Staff mem phys res, 62-63, div supvr, High Pressure Physics Div, 67-71, DEPT MGR PHYSICS OF SOLIDS RES, SANDOZ LABS, 71- *Mem:* AAAS; Am Phys Soc. *Res:* Effects of high pressure and temperature on the physical properties of solids especially ferroelectric, ferromagnetic and semiconductor properties. *Mailing Add:* Dept 5130 Sandia Labs Albuquerque NM 87115

SAMAROO, WINSTON R, b Trinidad, WI, Feb 24, 34; US citizen; m 62; c 3. ELECTRICAL ENGINEERING, SOLID STATE PHYSICS. *Educ:* McGill Univ, BE, 59; Univ Ottawa, Ont, MS, 61, PhD(elec eng), 65. *Prof Exp:* Lectr physics, Presentation Bros Col, Trinidad, 54-55; engr, Northern Elec Co, Que, 59, assoc mem sci staff, 61; res asst noise in semiconductors, Univ Ottawa, Ont, 59-61, res asst electron & ion optics, 61-65; sr res engr, 65-67, res leader integrated circuits, 67-69, asst dir mat & chem processes, 69-79, RES DIR, WESTERN ELEC ENG RES CTR, 79- *Concurrent Pos:* Res engr, Levy Assocs, Can, 61-62. *Mem:* Inst Elec & Electronics Engrs; Sigma Xi. *Res:* Development of ion implantation systems, components and processes; process development for device fabrication from compound semiconductors, especially gallium phosphide. *Mailing Add:* Western Elec Co PO Box 900 Princeton NJ 08540

SAMBORSKI, DANIEL JAMES, b Hamton, Sask, Aug 9, 21; m 51; c 2. PLANT PATHOLOGY, PLANT PHYSIOLOGY. *Educ:* Univ Sask, BSA, 49, MSc, 51; McGill Univ, PhD(plant path), 55. *Prof Exp:* Res assoc plant physiol, Univ Sask, 53-56; RES SCIENTIST PLANT PATH, AGR CAN RES STA, 56- *Concurrent Pos:* Assoc ed jour, Am Phytopath Soc, 76-79. *Mem:* Fel Royal Soc Can; Can Phytopath Soc; Can Soc Plant Physiologists; Am Phytopath Soc; Sigma Xi. *Res:* Genetics and biochemistry of host-parasite interactions. *Mailing Add:* Agr Can Res Sta 195 Dafoe Rd Winnipeg MB R3T 2M9 Can

SAMEJIMA, FUMIKO, b Tokyo, Japan, Dec 25, 30. PSYCHOMETRICS, MATHEMATICAL STATISTICS. *Educ:* Keio Univ, Tokyo, BA, 53, MA, 56, PhD(psychol), 65. *Prof Exp:* Res psychologist, Educ Testing Serv, 66-67; res fel, Psychometric Labs, Univ NC, 67-68; asst prof psychol, Univ NB, Can, 68-70; assoc prof, Bowling Green State Univ, 70-73; PROF PSYCHOL, UNIV TENN, KNOXVILLE, 73- *Concurrent Pos:* Nat Res Coun Can grant, 69-70; Off Naval Res grant, 77-; consult ed, Appl Psychol Measurement, 75-; assoc ed, Educ Statist, 78- *Mem:* Sigma Xi; Psychometric Soc; Am Statist Soc; Am Educ Res Asn; Am Asn Univ Professors. *Res:* Mathematical statistics and psychometrics; mathematical model buildings in many applied areas. *Mailing Add:* Univ of Tenn Dept of Psychol 312D Austin Peay Hall Knoxville TN 37916

SAMELSON, HANS, b Strassburg, Ger, Mar 3, 16; nat US; m 40, 56; c 3. MATHEMATICS. *Educ:* Swiss Fed Inst Technol, DSc(math), 40. *Prof Exp:* Mem, Inst Advan Study, 41-42; instr math, Univ Wyo, 42-43; asst prof, Syracuse Univ, 43-46; from asst prof to prof, Univ Mich, 46-60; PROF MATH, STANFORD UNIV, 60- *Concurrent Pos:* Mem, Inst Advan Study, 52-54 & 60-61. *Mem:* Am Math Soc; Math Asn Am. *Res:* Topology of group manifolds; differential geometry. *Mailing Add:* Dept Math Stanford Univ Stanford CA 94305

SAMES, GEORGE L, b Upper Black Eddy, Pa, Nov 23, 18. ZOOLOGY. *Educ:* Gettysburg Col, AB, 47; Rutgers Univ, PhD, 52. *Prof Exp:* Jr instr biol, Johns Hopkins Univ, 47-48; asst zool, Rutgers Univ, 48-52; from instr to asst prof biol, 52-62, ASSOC PROF BIOL, TUFTS UNIV, 62- *Mem:* AAAS; Am Soc Zool. *Res:* Physiology of development; effects of adrenal steroid hormones on chick development. *Mailing Add:* Dept of Biol Tufts Univ Medford MA 02155

SAMES, RICHARD WILLIAM, b Louisville, Ky, Apr 13, 28; m 55; c 5. BACTERIOLOGY. *Educ:* Ind Univ, AB, 51, MA, 54, PhD, 56. *Prof Exp:* Assoc prof biol & chmn dept, Bellarmine Col, Ky, 56-66, prof biol & dir sci develop, 66-68; dean col, Benedictine Col, 68-72; dean natural sci, 72-75, asst vpres acad affairs, 75-78, actg vpres acad affairs, 78-79, PROF BIOL, SANGAMON STATE UNIV, 79- *Concurrent Pos:* Dir, Instructional Sci Equip Prog, NSF, 65-66, consult, 66-, consult, Col Sci Improv Prog, 71-74; consult, Developing Insts Prog, US Off Educ, 68-74; gov task force on sci & technol, 79-80. *Mem:* Am Soc Microbiol; AAAS. *Res:* Bacterial viruses for anaerobic bacteria. *Mailing Add:* Sangamon State Univ Springfield IL 62701

SAMET, PHILIP, b New York, NY, Jan 30, 22; m 47; c 3. INTERNAL MEDICINE, CARDIOLOGY. *Educ:* NY Univ, BA, 42, MD, 47. *Prof Exp:* Intern, Mt Sinai Hosp, New York, 47-48; resident internal med, Bronx Vet Hosp, 48-51; from instr to assoc prof, 55-70, PROF MED, SCH MED, UNIV MIAMI, 70- *Concurrent Pos:* Res fel, Cardiopulmonary Lab, Bellevue Hosp, 51-53; chief, Div Cardiol, Mt Sinai Hosp, Miami Beach, Fla, 55- *Mem:* Am Thoracic Soc; Am Physiol Soc; Am Heart Asn; AMA; Am Col Cardiol. *Res:* Cardiac and pulmonary physiology. *Mailing Add:* 4300 Alton Rd Miami Beach FL 33140

SAMFIELD, MAX, b Memphis, Tenn, Apr 20, 18; m 44; c 4. CHEMICAL ENGINEERING. *Educ:* Rice Inst, BS, 40; Univ Tex, MS, 41, PhD(chem eng), 45. *Prof Exp:* Chem engr, Tex, 45-47; unit engr, Servel, Inc, Ind, 47-52; supvr eng res & develop, Liggett & Myers Inc, 52-58, asst to dir res, 58-62, sr asst dir res, 62-73; PROJ OFFICER, US ENVIRON PROTECTION AGENCY, 73- *Concurrent Pos:* Consult, Tabak Jour Int, W Ger, 77- *Honors & Awards:* Merit Awards, US Environ Protection Agency, 75 & 77. *Mem:* AAAS; Sigma Xi. *Res:* Production of acetylene from gaseous hydrocarbons; carbon black; absorption refrigeration; physico-chemical properties of tobacco technology; environmental research; pollution control. *Mailing Add:* 915 W Knox St Durham NC 27701

SAMI, SEDAT, b Istanbul, Turkey, Oct 23, 28; m 58; c 2. FLUID MECHANICS, HYDRAULICS. *Educ:* Tech Univ Istanbul, MSCE, 51; Univ Iowa, MS, 57, PhD(fluid mech), 66. *Prof Exp:* Design engr, Chase T Main, Inc, Turkey, 51-53, asst chief engr, 54-56; chief design engr, Eti Yapi Ltd, Turkey, 58-60, tech dir, 60-62; asst prof civil eng, Middle East Tech Univ, Ankara, 62-63; from asst prof to assoc prof, 66-72, actg chmn, Dept Eng Mech & Mat, 78-79, PROF FLUID MECH & HYDRAUL, SOUTHERN ILL UNIV, 72- *Mem:* AAAS; Am Soc Civil Engrs; Am Soc Eng Educ; Int Asn Hydraul Res; Sigma Xi. *Res:* Turbulence, fluctuating velocities and pressures; turbulent flows; engineering hydrology. *Mailing Add:* Dept of Eng Mech & Mat Southern Ill Univ Carbondale IL 62901

SAMIOS, NICHOLAS PETER, b New York, NY, Mar 15, 32; m 58. PHYSICS. *Educ:* Columbia Univ, AB, 53, PhD(physics), 57. *Prof Exp:* Instr physics, Columbia Univ, 56-59; asst physicist, 59-62, chmn dept physics, 75-81, 59-62, assoc physicist, 62-64, physicist, 64-68, SR PHYSICIST, BROOKHAVEN NAT LAB, 68-, DEP DIR HIGH ENERGY & NUCLEAR PHYSICS, 81- *Honors & Awards:* E O Lawrence Mem Award, 80; Phys & Math Sci Award, NY Acad Sci, 80. *Mem:* Fel Am Phys Soc; fel Am Acad Arts & Sci. *Res:* Particle physics. *Mailing Add:* Dir Off 510F Brookhaven Nat Lab Upton NY 11973

SAMIR, URI, b Tel-Aviv, Israel, Sept 14, 30; m 67. SPACE PHYSICS. *Educ:* Hebrew Univ, Israel, MSc, 60; Univ London, PhD(physics), 67. *Prof Exp:* Teaching asst physics, Israel Inst Technol, 58-60; researcher, Israeli Defence Syst, 60-62; res assoc ionospheric physics, Univ Col, Univ London, 62-67; sci consult Gemini 10 & 11 spacecraft, Electro-Optical Systs, Inc, Calif, 67-68; assoc res physicist, 68-69, RES PHYSICIST, SPACE PHYSICS RES LAB, UNIV MICH, ANN ARBOR, 69- *Concurrent Pos:* Mem, Sci Adv Bd Plasma Physics Exp on Future Space-Shuttles & Space Sta, 72-; mem steering & working group, Atmospheric/Magnetospheric & Plasmas in Space, 73-; assoc prof, Dept of Geophys & Planetary Sci, Tel-Aviv Univ, Israel, 74-; chmn, Plasma Interaction Sect of NASA/Aircraft Multispectral Photog Syst Sci Definition Working Group, 75-76; mem, Subsatellite Sci Definition Team, 77-78. *Mem:* Am Inst Aeronaut & Astronaut; Am Phys Soc; Am Geophys Union; fel Brit Interplanetary Soc. *Res:* Flows of space-plasmas over bodies; ionospheres of the earth and planets; physics of cosmic rays; laboratory simulation of space physics and rarefied plasma physics phenomena and processes. *Mailing Add:* Space Physics Res Lab Univ of Mich Ann Arbor MI 48109

SAMIS, HARVEY VOORHEES, JR, b Easton, Md, July 14, 31; m 56; c 4. BIOCHEMISTRY, PHYSIOLOGY. *Educ:* Wash Col, BS, 56; Brown Univ, PhD(biochem physiol), 63. *Prof Exp:* Instr biol, Washington Col, 55-56; res scientist, Masonic Med Res Lab, 63-75, dir exp geront prog, Utica, NY, 68-75; SR SCIENTIST, MED RES SERV, VET ADMIN MED CTR, BAY PINES, FLA, 75-, COORDR RES & DEVELOP, 77- *Concurrent Pos:* Vis lectr biol, Syracuse Univ, 73-75; vis assoc prof & adj prof chem, Univ SFla, Tampa, 77- *Mem:* AAAS; Soc Gen Physiol; fel Geront Soc; Soc Develop Biol; fel Am Inst Chemists. *Res:* Chelation chemistry of biomolecules; alcoholism effect of aging on properties of biological macromolecules and their functions; effects of age on the temporal organization of biological systems; molecular genetics and neoplasia; nucleic acid metabolism. *Mailing Add:* Off Coordr Res & Develop Med Res-151 Vet Admin Ctr Bay Pines FL 33504

SAMITZ, M H, b Philadelphia, Pa, Dec 18, 09; m 45; c 2. DERMATOLOGY. *Educ:* Temple Univ, MD, 33; Univ Pa, MSc, 45. *Prof Exp:* From instr to asst prof dermat, Grad Sch Med, 40-53, from asst prof to assoc prof, Sch Med, 49-67, prof dermat & dir grad dermat, 67-75, EMER PROF DERMAT, SCH MED, UNIV PA, 75- *Concurrent Pos:* Med dir, Skin & Cancer Hosp, Philadelphia, 53-54; prin investr, USPHS res grants, 58-75; consult, US Naval Hosp, 65-; consult & vis prof, Pa Col Podiat Med, 65-75, emer prof dermat, 75-; vis prof, Hahnemann Med Col, 67-, Univ Dar es Salaam, 75-; chief dept dermat, Grad Hosp, Univ Pa, 67-; mem comt, Div Educ, Nat Prog Dermat, 71-; mem comt on nickel, Nat Res Coun; consult, Food & Drug Admin, Dermat Adv Comt, 77-78; US-Poland health scientist exchange fel, 80; bd dirs, Found Int Dermatol Educ, 75-, pres, 79- *Mem:* AAAS; Am Acad Dermat; Am Col Physicians; Am Col Allergists; Soc Invest Dermat. *Res:* Industrial dermatology, particularly effects of chromium salts and nickel on the skin; clinical investigations in various aspects of clinical dermatology. *Mailing Add:* Duhring Labs Hosp of the Univ of Pa Philadelphia PA 19104

SAMLOFF, I MICHAEL, b Rochester, NY, Jan 24, 32; m 54; c 2. MEDICINE, GASTROENTEROLOGY. *Educ:* State Univ NY, MD, 56. *Prof Exp:* Instr med, Sch Med & Dent, Univ Rochester, 62-64, sr instr med & psychiat, 64-65, asst prof, 65-68; assoc prof, 68-72, PROF MED, SCH MED, UNIV CALIF, LOS ANGELES, 72-; ASSOC CHIEF STAFF & RES, VET ADMIN MED CTR, 80- *Concurrent Pos:* USPHS fel med, Strong Mem Hosp, 58-59, fel psychiat, 61-62 & trainee med, 61-63; Am Cancer Soc advan clin fel, 63-66; chief, Gastroenterol Div, Harbor Hosp, Univ Calif, Los Angeles Med Ctr, 68-80. *Mem:* Am Fedn Clin Res; Am Psychosom Soc; Am Gastroenterol Asn; Am Soc Clin Invest; fel Am Col Physicians. *Res:* Gastritis; ulcer. *Mailing Add:* Vet Admin Med Ctr 16111 Plummer St Sepulveda CA 91343

SAMMAK, EMIL GEORGE, b Brooklyn, NY, Apr 3, 27; m 50; c 3. EMULSION POLYMERIZATION. *Educ:* Polytech Inst Brooklyn, BS, 49, PhD(chem), 58. *Prof Exp:* Sr res chemist, Chem Div, Int Latex & Chem Corp, 55-60, mgr basic polymer res, 60-68; mgr basic res, Standard Brands Chem Industs, Inc, 68-76; MGR POLYMER & ANAL RES, EMULSION POLYMERS DIV, REICHHOLD CHEM, INC, 76- *Mem:* AAAS; Am Chem Soc. *Res:* Synthesis, characterization and mechanical properties of butadiene latex, polyelectrolytes, polyacrylates, polyurethanes, allyl and formaldehyde resins; ionic polymerization; grafting olefin copolymers; starch utilization; rheology, computer applications, pollution control, analytical research. *Mailing Add:* Reichhold Chem Inc PO Drawer K Dover DE 19901

SAMMARCO, PAUL WILLIAM, marine biology, ecology, see previous edition

SAMMELWITZ, PAUL H, b Buffalo, NY, Mar 13, 33; m 62; c 3. REPRODUCTIVE PHYSIOLOGY. *Educ:* Cornell Univ, BS, 55; Univ Ill, MS, 57, PhD(reprod physiol), 59. *Prof Exp:* Asst prof, 59-68, ASSOC PROF AVIAN & MAMMALIAN PHYSIOL & GENETICS, UNIV DEL, 68- *Concurrent Pos:* AAAS; Am Soc Animal Sci; Poultry Sci Asn; Soc Study Reproduction. *Res:* Mammalian and avian reproductive physiology; avian heat stress physiology; endocrine factors influenced by moderate dietary vitamin A deficiency; genetic resistance to Marek's disease. *Mailing Add:* Dept Animal Sci & Agr Biochem Univ of Del Newark DE 19711

SAMMET, JEAN E, b New York, NY, Mar 23, 28. COMPUTER SCIENCE. *Educ:* Mt Holyoke Col, BA, 48; Univ Ill, MA, 49. *Hon Degrees:* DSc, Mt Holyoke Col, 78. *Prof Exp:* Asst math, Univ Ill, 48-51; dividend technician, Metrop Life Ins Co, 51-52; asst math, Barnard Col, Columbia Univ, 52-53; engr, Sperry Gyroscope Co, 53-58; sect head, Mobidic Programming, Sylvania Elec Prod, 58-59, staff consult prog res, 59-61; Boston adv prog mgr, 61-65, prog lang tech mgr, 65-68, prog technol planning mgr, 68-74, MGR PROG LANG TECHNOL, IBM CORP, 74- *Concurrent Pos:* Lectr, Adelphi Col, 56-58, Northeastern Univ, 67 & Mt Holyoke Col, 74. *Mem:* Nat Acad Eng; Asn Comput Mach (vpres, 72-74, pres, 74-76); Math Asn Am. *Res:* Higher level programming languages; use of computers for non-numerical mathematics; formula manipulation systems; programming systems; language measurement; practical uses of artificial intelligence; use of natural language on a computer; history of computing. *Mailing Add:* IBM Corp 545 Technology Sq Cambridge MA 02139

SAMMONS, DAVID JAMES, b Columbus, Ohio, Sept 2, 46; m 70; c 2. AGRONOMY, PLANT BREEDING. *Educ:* Tufts Univ, BS, 68; Harvard Univ, AM, 72; Univ Ill, PhD(agron), 78. *Prof Exp:* Vol, Peace Corps, Philippines, 68-70; asst biol, Harvard Univ, 70-72; assoc dir natural hist, Norwalk Mus & Zoo, Conn, 72; teacher-naturalist, Nat Audubon Soc; 72-75; res asst, Univ Ill, 75-78; ASST PROF AGRON, UNIV MD, 78- *Concurrent Pos:* Mem fac adv comt, Univ Ill, 75-76; curriculum consult, Sinclair Community Col, Dayton, Ohio, 73-74; mem environ qual bd, Dept Urban Develop, New Towns Prog, 73-74; mem curric develop, Govt Philippines, 68-70; fac adv & partic, Study Abroad Prog, Univ Md, Asia, 79 & Caribbean, 81; fac mem, Grad Sch, USDA, Washington, DC, 80-; vis prof, Berkeley Col, Yale Univ, 81. *Mem:* Crop Sci Soc Am; Am Soc Agron; Asn Asian Studies-Middle Atlantic Region. *Res:* Applied breeding research designed to improve barley and wheat cultivars for producers in Maryland and the Mid-Atlantic region; small grain production, breeding and physiology. *Mailing Add:* Dept Agron Univ Md College Park MD 20742

SAMN, SHERWOOD, b Los Angeles, Calif, Apr 20, 41; m 68; c 1. MATHEMATICS. *Educ:* Univ Calif, Berkeley, BA, 63, PhD(math), 68. *Prof Exp:* Asst prof math, Ind Univ-Purdue Univ, Indianapolis, 68-74; MATHEMATICIAN, BROOKS AFB, US AIR FORCE, SAN ANTONIO, TEX, 74- *Mem:* Am Math Soc. *Res:* Ordinary differential equations; basis in Banach spaces. *Mailing Add:* 12418 Magnifico Dr San Antonio TX 78233

SAMOILOV, SERGEY MICHAEL, b Baku, USSR, Dec 17, 25. POLYMER CHEMISTRY, CATALYSIS. *Educ:* Moscow Inst Fine Chem Technol, MS, 49; USSR Acad Sci, PhD(chem), 58. *Prof Exp:* Engr catalysis, USSR Nat Res Inst Artificial Fuel, 49-51, USSR Petrochem Plant No 16, 51-55; res assoc, USSR Acad Sci, 58-61; sr res assoc polymers, USSR Nat Res Inst Petrochem, 62-76; res assoc, Columbia Univ, 77-78; RES ASSOC POLYMERS, CELANESE RES CO, 78- *Concurrent Pos:* Abstractor, Chem Abstracts J, Inst Sci Info, USSR Acad Sci, 56-76. *Mem:* Am Chem Soc. *Res:* Synthesis and investigation of polyolefins; radical pressure copolymerization of lower olefins; polymer emulsions; metalorganic polymers; structural and relaxational properties of polymers. *Mailing Add:* Apt 2-F 501 Lindsley Dr Morristown NJ 07960

SAMOLLOW, PAUL B, b San Francisco, Calif, Mar 20, 48; m 68. ECOLOGICAL GENETICS, EVOLUTIONARY BIOLOGY. *Educ:* Univ Calif, BA, 71; Ore State Univ, PhD(zool), 78. *Prof Exp:* Lectr genetics & evolution, Humboldt State Univ, 78; asst prof, Univ Mont, 79; fel, Hawaii Inst Marine Biol, 79-81; FEL BIOMED, BIOCHEM & GENETICS, SOUTHWEST FOUND RES, SAN ANTONIO, TEX, 81- *Mem:* Genetics Soc Am; Soc Study Evolution; AAAS. *Res:* Genetic dynamics of populations in varying environments; population structure and maintenance of genetic diversity in nature; biochemical genetics of New World marsupials; linkage and functional relationships among genes in or near the major histocompatibility complex in the house mouse. *Mailing Add:* Dept Genetics Southwest Found Res & Educ PO Box 28147 San Antonio TX 78284

SAMOLS, DAVID R, b Washington, DC, Aug 31, 45; m 76; c 2. RECOMBINANT DNA. *Educ:* Earlham Col, Bs, 67; Univ Chicago, PhD(biol), 75. *Prof Exp:* Fel, Roche Inst Molecular Biol, 76-79; res assoc, Inst Molecular Biol, Univ Ore, 79; ASST PROF BIOCHEM, MED SCH, CASE WESTERN RESERVE UNIV, 80- *Mem:* Am Soc Cell Biol. *Res:* Signal and mechanism by which tissue injury and infection induce the liver to secrete c-reactive protien; types of genetic rearrangements and alterations caused by chemical carcinogenesis. *Mailing Add:* Dept Biochem Sch Med Case Western Reserve Univ Cleveland OH 44106

SAMORAJSKI, THADDEUS, b Shelburne, Mass, Oct 29, 23; m 52; c 2. ANATOMY. *Educ:* Univ Mich, BS, 48; Univ Chicago, PhD(anat), 56. *Prof Exp:* Asst & instr, Univ Chicago, 55-56; instr anat, Ohio State Univ, 56-60; dir lab neurochem, Cleveland Psychiat Inst, 60-74; MEM STAFF, TEX RES INST MENT SCI, 74- *Concurrent Pos:* Adj prof, Dept Biol, Tex Women's Univ, 78- & Dept Neurobiol & Anat, Sch Med, Univ Tex, 80- *Honors & Awards:* Cralow Medal, Polish Acad Sci. *Mem:* Soc Neurosci; Geront Soc. *Res:* Neurochemistry, particularly in relation to neurobiology of aging; environmental modification of life span; radiation neuropathology; myelin formation and degeneration; catecholamine metabolism. *Mailing Add:* Tex Res Inst Ment Sci 1300 Moursund Ave Houston TX 77025

SAMPATH, ANGUS C, medical microbiology, see previous edition

SAMPLE, HOWARD H, b Dallas, Tex, Sept 20, 38; m 58; c 3. SOLID STATE PHYSICS. *Educ:* Iowa State Univ, BS, 60, PhD(physics), 66. *Prof Exp:* NATO fel sci, Clarendon Lab, Oxford Univ, 66-67; asst prof, 67-73, ASSOC PROF PHYSICS, TUFTS UNIV, 73- *Concurrent Pos:* Vis scientist, Francis Bitter Nat Magnet Lab, 68- *Res:* Low temperature physics, superconductivity, thermal properties of disordered solids, low temperature thermometry in high magnetic fields. *Mailing Add:* Dept of Physics Tufts Univ Medford MA 02155

SAMPLE, JAMES HALVERSON, b Cicero, Ill, Feb 27, 14; m 40; c 3. ORGANIC POLYMER CHEMISTRY. *Educ:* Elmhurst Col, BS, 35; Univ Ill, MS, 36, PhD(org chem), 39. *Prof Exp:* Asst chem, Univ Ill, 36-39; prof, Ind Cent Col, 39-42; prof, Franklin Col, 42-44; res chemist, Sherwin Williams Co, 55-57, chem res supvr, 47-58, asst dir resin res dept, 58-65, dir, 66-73, dir polymer & mat res-coating, 74-79; CONSULT, 80- *Mem:* AAAS; Am Chem Soc. *Res:* Resins for surface coatings; alkyds. *Mailing Add:* 1206 E 165th Pl South Holland IL 60473

SAMPLE, JOHN THOMAS, b Kerrobert, Sask, May 4, 27; m 53; c 5. NUCLEAR PHYSICS. *Educ:* Univ BC, BA, 48, MA, 50, PhD, 55. *Prof Exp:* Sci officer, Defence Res Bd, Can, 55-58; from asst prof to assoc prof, 58-66, chmn dept physics, 67-76, PROF NUCLEAR PHYSICS, UNIV ALTA, 66-; dir, TRIUMF, 76-81, DIR RES SECRETARIAT, UNIV BC, 81- *Concurrent Pos:* Vis scientist, Brookhaven Nat Lab, 65-66. *Mem:* Am Inst Physics; Am Asn Physics Teachers; Am Phys Soc; Can Asn Physicists. *Res:* Reactions of low and intermediate energy nuclear physics. *Mailing Add:* Dir TRIUMF Univ of BC Vancouver BC V6T 1W5 Can

SAMPLE, PAUL E(DWARD), b Chicago, Ill, Nov 24, 28; m 53; c 5. CHEMICAL ENGINEERING. *Educ:* Ill Inst Technol, BS, 51; Univ WVa, MS, 55, PhD(chem eng), 57. *Prof Exp:* Asst, Exp Sta, Univ WVa, 54, 55-57; res engr, Film Dept, 57-59, group leader, Chem Develop, 59-60, supvr, Mfg Div, 60-62, tech rep, Mkt Div, 62-66, res supvr, Res & Develop Div, 66-69, group mgr, 69-72, TECH CONSULT, RES & DEVELOP DIV, E I DU PONT DE NEMOURS & CO, INC, 72- *Mem:* Am Chem Soc; Am Soc Metals; Am Inst Chem Engrs. *Res:* Process automation and instrumentation; packaging systems and packaging materials. *Mailing Add:* 308 Walden Rd Wilmington DE 19803

SAMPLE, STEVEN BROWING, b St Louis, Mo, Nov 29, 40; m 61; c 2. ELECTROHYDRODYNAMICS. *Educ:* Univ Ill, Urbana, BS, 62, MS, 63, PhD(elec eng), 65. *Prof Exp:* Scientist, Melpar, Inc, 65-66; asst prof elec eng, Purdue Univ, 66-70, assoc prof, 70-73; prof elec eng & exec vpres, Univ Nebr, 74-82, dean, Grad Col, 77-82; PRES & PROF ELEC ENG, STATE UNIV NY, BUFFALO, 82- *Concurrent Pos:* Dep dir, Ill Bd Higher Educ, 71-74; bd dir, Design & Mfr Corp, Connersville, Ill, 77- *Mem:* Sigma Xi; Inst Elec & Electronics Engrs. *Res:* Electrohydrodynamic instability of liquid drops in electric fields; harmonic electrical spraying of liquids from capillaries; solid-state digital control systems for appliances. *Mailing Add:* Capen Hall State Univ NY Buffalo NY 14260

SAMPLE, THOMAS EARL, JR, b Magnolia Park, Tex, Dec 17, 24; m 53, 62; c 3. PHYSICAL ORGANIC CHEMISTRY. *Educ:* Rice Inst, BA, 48; Univ Tex, MA, 54, PhD(chem), 59. *Prof Exp:* Chemist, Magnet Cove Barium Corp, Tex, 48-49; teaching fel chem, Univ Tex, 50-51; US Air Force res scientist, 51-53; res chemist explor org group, Plastics Div, Monsanto Chem Co, 54-56; res group supvr, Magnet Cove Barium Corp, 57-61; res proj leader, Champion Chem, Inc, 61-63; Robert A Welch res fel chem, Univ Tex, 63-66; sr res chemist, Bellaire Res Labs, Texaco Inc, 66-71; tech adv, Oilfield Prod Div, 71-78, SR RES SCIENTIST, MAGCOBAR GP, DRESSER INDUSTS, INC, HOUSTON, 78- *Mem:* Am Inst Chemists; Royal Soc Chem; Am Chem Soc; Am Phys Soc; Gesellschaft Deutscher Chem; petroleum treating chemicals; diene reactions; organic sulfur chemistry; emulsion and surfactant theory. *Res:* Organic modification of mineral surfaces; oilwell and geothermal drilling fluids; lubrication; chemistry and physics of clay colloids; organo-sulfur chemistry. *Mailing Add:* 8015 Windswept Lane Houston TX 77063

SAMPLES, WILLIAM R(EAD), b Whipple, WVa, Oct 17, 31; m 53; c 4. SANITARY ENGINEERING, ENVIRONMENTAL ENGINEERING. *Educ:* Univ WVa, BS, 53; Harvard Univ, MS, 55, PhD(eng), 59. *Prof Exp:* Asst prof civil eng, Calif Inst Technol, 59-65; fel water resources, Mellon Inst, 65-68, sr fel & head water resources, 68-71; coordr, 71-78, MGR, ENVIRON CONTROL, WHEELING-PITTSBURGH STEEL CORP, WHEELING, W VA, 78- *Concurrent Pos:* Mem, Nat Air Pollution Control Techniques Adv Comt, Environ Protection Agency. *Mem:* Am Soc Civil Engrs; Water Pollution Control Fedn; Am Inst Chem Engrs; Air Pollution Control Asn; Am Iron & Steel Inst. *Res:* Industrial waste water control; air pollution; industrial hygiene; water quality; water and sewage treatment. *Mailing Add:* 2293 Weston Dr Pittsburgh PA 15241

SAMPLEY, MARILYN YVONNE, b Ala. NUTRITION. *Educ:* Auburn Univ, BS, 57; Univ Ala, MS, 61; Tex Woman's Univ, PhD(nutrit, biochem & foods), 69. *Prof Exp:* Instr nutrit & chief dietician, Sacred Heart Dominican Col, St Joseph Hosp, Houston, 57-58; teacher, K J Clark Jr High Sch, Mobile Ala, 59-60; res asst, Univ Ala, 60-61; instr nutrit & chief dietician, Sacred Heart Dominican Col, St Joseph Hosp, Houston, 62; dir food serv, Dickinson Sch Dist, Dickenson, Tex, 63-67; res asst, Tex Woman's Univ, 67-69; ASSOC PROF & CHMN, DEPT HOME ECON, TEX A&I UNIV, 72- *Mem:* Am Pub Health Asn; AAAS; Soc Nutrit Educ; Nat Coun Admin Home Econ; Nat Educ Asn. *Res:* Eating and food buying habits. *Mailing Add:* Dept of Home Econ Tex A&I Univ Kingsville TX 78363

SAMPSON, CALVIN COOLIDGE, b Cambridge, Md, Feb 1, 28; m 53; c 2. MEDICINE, PATHOLOGY. *Educ:* Hampton Inst, BS, 47; Meharry Med Col, MD, 51. *Prof Exp:* From asst prof to assoc prof, 58-69, PROF PATH, COL MED, HOWARD UNIV, 69- *Concurrent Pos:* Asst ed, J Nat Med Asn, 65-77, ed, 78- *Mem:* Nat Med Asn; Int Acad Path; fel Col Am Path. *Mailing Add:* Dept Path Howard Univ Col of Med Washington DC 20059

SAMPSON, CHARLES BERLIN, b Iowa Falls, Iowa, Dec 15, 39; m 65; c 3. STATISTICS, MATHEMATICS. *Educ:* Univ Iowa, BS, 61, MS, 63; Iowa State Univ, PhD(statist), 68. *Prof Exp:* Sr statistician, 68-73, res scientist, 73-74, head, Statist & Math Serv, 74-81, HEAD, SCI INFO SERV, ELI LILLY & CO, 81- *Mem:* Am Statist Asn; Biometric Soc. *Res:* Application of statistical and mathematical models to biological, medical, and chemical research; design of experiments; pharmaceutical quality control. *Mailing Add:* Eli Lilly & Co 307 E McCarty St Indianapolis IN 46206

SAMPSON, DEXTER REID, b New Glasgow, NS, Can, Sept 9, 30. GENETICS, PLANT BREEDING. *Educ:* Acadia Univ, BSc, 51; Harvard Univ, AM, 54, PhD, 56. *Prof Exp:* Res officer hort crops, 55-66, RES SCIENTIST CEREAL CROPS, CAN DEPT AGR, 66- *Mem:* Genetics Soc Can; Can Bot Asn; Sigma Xi; Can Soc Agron; Agr Inst Can. *Res:* Genetics of self-incompatability in angiosperms; genetics of Brassica and oats; wheat breeding. *Mailing Add:* Ottawa Res Sta Can Dept Agr Cent Exp Farm Ottawa ON K1A 0C6 Can

SAMPSON, DOUGLAS HOWARD, b Devils Lake, NDak, May 19, 25; m 56; c 4. ASTROPHYSICS. *Educ:* Concordia Col, Moorhead, Minn, BA, 51; Yale Univ, MA, 53, PhD(theoret physics), 56. *Prof Exp:* Staff mem, Theoret Div, Los Alamos Sci Lab, NMex, 56-61; theoret physicist, Space Sci Lab, Gen Elec Co, Pa, 61-64; group leader atomic & radiation physics, 64-65; assoc prof, 65-70, PROF ASTROPHYS, PA STATE UNIV, 70- *Concurrent Pos:* Consult, Gen Atomic Div, Gen Dynamics Corp. *Mem:* Am Phys Soc; Am Astron Soc. *Res:* Theoretical astrophysics; statistical mechanics and kinetic theory; atomic physics; radiative transport. *Mailing Add:* Dept of Astron Pa State Univ University Park PA 16802

SAMPSON, GARY ROBERT, veterinary medicine, see previous edition

SAMPSON, HENRY T, b Jackson, Miss, Apr 22, 34; m 61; c 2. NUCLEAR ENGINEERING. *Educ:* Purdue Univ, BS, 56; Univ Calif, Los Angeles, MS, 61; Univ Ill, PhD(nuclear eng), 67. *Prof Exp:* Res engr, US Naval Weapons Ctr, 56-62; mem tech staff, 67-81, DIR PLANNING & OPERS, SPACE TEXT PROG, AEROSPACE CORP, 81- *Mem:* AAAS; Am Nuclear Soc; Am Inst Aeronaut & Astronaut. *Res:* Research and development of rocket propellants and plastic bonded explosives; direct conversion of nuclear energy to electrical energy; analysis of space electrical power systems. *Mailing Add:* Aerospace Corp PO Box 95085 Los Angeles CA 90045

SAMPSON, JEFFREY ROBERT, b Washington, DC, Nov 4, 42; div; c 2. COMPUTER SCIENCE, INFORMATION SCIENCE. *Educ:* Northwestern Univ, BA, 63; Univ Mich, Ann Arbor, MA, 65, PhD(comput & commun sci), 69. *Prof Exp:* Asst prof, 68-72, assoc prof, 72-78, PROF COMPUT SCI, UNIV ALTA, 78- *Concurrent Pos:* Nat lectr, Asn Comput Mach, 78-80. *Mem:* AAAS; Asn Comput Mach. *Res:* Adaptive systems; simulation; artificial intelligence; biological information processing. *Mailing Add:* Dept of Comput Sci Univ of Alta Edmonton AB T6G 2G7 Can

SAMPSON, JOHN LAURENCE, b Lynn, Mass, Dec 14, 29; m 52; c 3. PHYSICS. *Educ:* Mass Inst Technol, BS, 51; Tufts Univ, MS, 54, PhD, 62. *Prof Exp:* Physicist, Air Force Cambridge Res Labs, 51 & 55-59; instr physics, Tufts Univ, 54-55, asst, 59-61; physicist, Arthur D Little, Inc, 61-62; PHYSICIST, AIR FORCE ROME AIR DEVELOP CTR, BEDFORD, 62- *Mem:* Am Phys Soc; Sigma Xi. *Res:* Radiation effects on integrated circuits. *Mailing Add:* 8 Bedford St Lexington MA 02173

SAMPSON, JOSEPH HAROLD, b Spokane, Wash, Sept 14, 25. MATHEMATICS. *Educ:* Princeton Univ, MA, 49, PhD(math), 51. *Prof Exp:* Res grant, Off Naval Res, 51-52; C L E Moore instr math, Mass Inst Technol, 52; asst prof, Johns Hopkins Univ, 52-64; prof assoc, Univ Strasbourg, 64-65, Univ Grenoble, 74-75; chmn dept, 70-80, PROF MATH, JOHNS HOPKINS UNIV, 65- *Concurrent Pos:* Prof assoc, Univ Strasbourg, 68-69; ed, Am J Math, 78- *Mem:* Am Math Soc; Math Soc France. *Res:* Algebraic geometry; geometry of manifolds. *Mailing Add:* Dept of Math Johns Hopkins Univ Baltimore MD 21218

SAMPSON, PHYLLIS MARIE, b New York, NY, Sept 13, 28; m 74. BIOCHEMISTRY. *Educ:* Hunter Col, BA, 50; Columbia Univ, PhD(biochem), 72. *Prof Exp:* Res assoc chem, Yeshiva Univ, 72-73; res assoc biochem, Columbia Univ, 73-76; RES ASSOC MED, UNIV PA, 76- *Mem:* Sigma Xi; Soc Complex Carbohydrates; AAAS; NY Acad Sci. *Res:* Proteoglycan and glycosaminoglycan distribution in normal and pathological lung tissue and production by lung cells in tissue and organ culture; biochemistry and chemistry of carbohydrates. *Mailing Add:* Hosp of Univ Pa 36th & Spruce St Philadelphia PA 19104

SAMPSON, RICHARD LEON, mechanical engineering, see previous edition

SAMPSON, RONALD N, b Pittsburgh, Pa, Sept 16, 30; m 53; c 4. CHEMICAL ENGINEERING. *Educ:* Carnegie-Mellon Univ, BS, 52 & 57. *Prof Exp:* Engr, Mat Eng Dept, 52-57, supvry engr, Chem Appln Sect, 57-62, mgr insulation, 62-80, MGR, CHEM SCI DIV, RES LABS, WESTINGHOUSE ELEC CORP, 80- *Mem:* Am Chem Soc; Soc Plastics Engrs; AAAS; Inst Elec & Electronics Engrs. *Res:* Research and development of polymers and plastics in areas of electrical insulation, laminates, molding materials, adhesives and films. *Mailing Add:* Westinghouse Elec Corp Res & Develop Ct Pittsburgh PA 15325

SAMPSON, SANFORD ROBERT, b Los Angeles, Calif, Feb 27, 37; m 59; c 2. PHYSIOLOGY, PHARMACOLOGY. *Educ:* Univ Calif, Berkeley, BA, 59; Univ Utah, PhD(pharmacol), 64. *Prof Exp:* Lectr, 68-69, asst prof pharmacol, 69-71, asst prof physiol, 71-74, ASSOC PROF PHYSIOL, MED CTR, UNIV CALIF, SAN FRANCISCO, 74- *Concurrent Pos:* Fel pharmacol, Albert Einstein Col Med, 64-66; res fel, Cardiovasc Res Inst, Med Ctr, Univ Calif, San Francisco, 64-69, Nat Heart Inst spec fel, 69-71; Macy fac scholar, 78-79; vis scientist, Weizmann Inst Sci, 78-79. *Mem:* Am Physiol Soc; Soc Neurosci; Am Soc Pharmacol & Exp Therapeut. *Res:* Physiology of arterial chemoreceptors; regulation of respiration and airways; electrophysiological and pharmacological properties of nerve and smooth muscle cells. *Mailing Add:* Dept of Physiol Univ of Calif Med Ctr San Francisco CA 94143

SAMPSON, THOMAS EDWARD, b Garrettsville, Ohio, June 8, 41; m 64; c 3. NUCLEAR SCIENCE. *Educ:* Case Inst Technol, BS, 63; Univ Mich, MS, 64, PhD(nuclear sci), 69. *Prof Exp:* Staff mem, Los Alamos Sci Lab, 69-77; DEVELOP STAFF MEM, UNION CARBIDE CORP, NUCLEAR DIV, OAK RIDGE Y-12 PLANT, 77- *Res:* Gamma ray spectroscopy; radiation detection; nuclear safeguards; non-destructive testing. *Mailing Add:* Union Carbide Corp PO Box Y Oak Ridge TN 37830

SAMPSON, WILLIAM B, b Toronto, Ont, Aug 31, 34; m 55; c 2. PHYSICS. *Educ:* Univ Toronto, BA, 58, MA, 59, PhD(physics), 62. *Prof Exp:* PHYSICIST, ACCELERATION DEPT, BROOKHAVEN NAT LAB, 62- *Mem:* Am Phys Soc. *Res:* Superconductivity and applications to high energy physics. *Mailing Add:* 7 Bayview St Bellport NY 11713

SAMPSON, WILLIAM WILSON, b Barstow, Calif, Feb 5, 13; m 49; c 3. ENTOMOLOGY. *Educ:* Univ Calif, PhD(entom), 41. *Prof Exp:* Assoc sanitarian, Student Health Serv, Univ Calif, 41-43 & 46, lectr, pub health, 47-55; consult, Alameda County Health Care Serv Agency, 56-78; RETIRED. *Concurrent Pos:* Historian, Nat Environ Health Asn, 61- *Honors & Awards:* Cavaliere, Order of the Crown, Italy, 46. *Mem:* Entom Soc Am. *Res:* Control of animal vectors of human diseases; urban ecology; taxonomy of aleyrodidae. *Mailing Add:* 64 Leo Lane Antioch CA 94509

SAMPUGNA, JOSEPH, b Sept 27, 31; US citizen; m 57; c 2. BIOCHEMISTRY, NEUROCHEMISTRY. *Educ:* Univ Conn, BA, 59, MA, 62, PhD(biochem), 68. *Prof Exp:* Res asst biochem, Univ Conn, 62-68; asst prof, 68-72, ASSOC PROF BIOCHEM, UNIV MD, COLLEGE PARK, 72- *Concurrent Pos:* Vpres, Chem Assocs Md, 73- *Mem:* AAAS; Am Chem Soc; Am Oil Chem Soc; Am Soc Neurochem; NY Acad Sci. *Res:* Lipid biochemistry; lipids in the nervous system, especially lipid biochemistry of brain during development; membrane structure and function. *Mailing Add:* Dept of Chem Univ of Md College Park MD 20742

SAMS, BURNETT HENRY, III, b Seattle, Wash, Apr 30, 31; m 56; c 2. DATABASES, MULTIPROCESSING. *Educ:* Univ Wash, BS, 51; Univ Ill, MS, 53, PhD(math), 58. *Prof Exp:* Res assoc, Control Systs Lab, Univ Ill, 57-58 & Comput Ctr, Mass Inst Technol, 58-59; proj engr, Astro-Electronics Prods Div, Radio Corp Am, 59-61, mgr, Prog Sci Sect, Data Systs Ctr, RCA Labs, 62-64, mgr systs res lab, 64-76, leader comput aided mfg, Solid State Technol Ctr, 76-81, MGR ENG AUTOMATION, NAT BROADCASTING CO, 81- *Concurrent Pos:* Instr, Dartmouth Col, 58-59; prof, Dept Elec Eng & Comput Sci, Stevens Inst Technol, 72- *Mem:* AAAS; Asn Comput Mach; Math Asn Am; Am Math Soc; Inst Elec & Electronics Engrs. *Res:* Computer system architecture; distributed systems; multiprocessing; information storage and retrieval; data communications; process control; software engineering; integrated circuit manufacturing; television switching systems. *Mailing Add:* 513 Prospect Ave Princeton NJ 08540

SAMS, CARL EARNEST, b Knoxville, Tenn, Dec 8, 51; m 71; c 2. POST-HARVEST PHYSIOLOGY. *Educ:* Univ Tenn, BS, 74, MS, 76; Mich State Univ, PhD(hort), 80. *Prof Exp:* RES PLANT PHYSIOLOGIST, USDA, 80- *Mem:* Am Soc Hort Sci; Int Soc Hort Sci; Am Soc Plant Physiologists. *Res:* Post-harvest physiology of horticultural crops: ripening, senescence, and physiological disorders of fruits and berries and methods of extending storage. *Mailing Add:* Hort Crops Qual Lab Bldg 002 Rm 220 Agr Res Ctr-W Beltsville MD 20705

SAMS, EMMETT SPRINKLE, b Burnsville, NC, July 17, 20; m 46; c 2. MATHEMATICS EDUCATION. *Educ:* Western Carolina Univ, BS, 41; George Peabody Col, MA, 49. *Prof Exp:* Teacher math, Yancey County Bd Educ, 41-45; teacher, Madison County Bd Educ, 45-47; from instr to assoc prof, 47-57, PROF MATH, MARS HILL COL, 57- *Mem:* Math Asn Am; Nat Coun Teachers Math. *Res:* Serial correlation. *Mailing Add:* Dept of Math Mars Hill Col Mars Hill NC 28754

SAMS, JOHN ROBERT, JR, b Kinston, NC, Feb 16, 36; m 63; c 2. CHEMICAL PHYSICS, ORGANOMETALLIC CHEMISTRY. *Educ:* Amherst Col, BA, 58; Univ Wash, PhD(phys chem), 62. *Prof Exp:* NATO fel, Imp Col, Univ London, 62-63; from asst prof to assoc prof, 63-72, PROF CHEM, UNIV BC, 72- *Mem:* NY Acad Sci. *Res:* Mössbauer spectroscopy; theoretical chemistry; physical adsorption. *Mailing Add:* Dept of Chem Univ of BC Vancouver BC V6T 1W5 Can

SAMS, LEWIS CALHOUN, JR, b Dallas, Tex, Sept 13, 28; m 52; c 2. SPECTROSCOPY, INORGANIC CHEMISTRY. *Educ:* Midwestern Univ, BS, 50; Tex A&M Univ, MS, 54, PhD(inorg chem), 61. *Prof Exp:* Microanalyst, Ft Worth Gen Depot, US Army, 54-56; chemist, Celanese Chem Corp, 56-57; instr chem, ETex State Univ, 57-59; asst prof chem, Trinity Col, Tex, 61-63; asst prof, 63-70, assoc prof inorg chem, 70-81, PROF CHEM, TEX WOMAN'S UNIV, 81- *Mem:* Am Chem Soc. *Res:* Microwave spectroscopy; inorganic fluorine synthesis. *Mailing Add:* Dept of Chem Tex Woman's Univ Denton TX 76204

SAMS, RICHARD ALVIN, b Lebanon, Ohio, Aug 28, 46. ANALYTICAL CHEMISTRY. *Educ:* Ohio State Univ, BS, 69, PhD(pharm), 75. *Prof Exp:* Sr scientist anal res, Pharmaceut Div, Ciba-Geigy Corp, 74-75; ASST PROF PHARMACOL & VET CLIN SCI, COL VET MED, OHIO STATE UNIV, 76- *Mem:* Am Chem Soc. *Res:* Investigation of high-pressure liquid chromatography and gas liquid chromatography separation mechanisms; investigation of comparative pharmacokinetics in various animal species. *Mailing Add:* 1935 Coffey Rd Columbus OH 43210

SAMS, WILEY MITCHELL, JR, b Ann Arbor, Mich, Apr 15, 33; m 59; c 2. DERMATOLOGY. *Educ:* Univ Mich, BS, 55; Emory Univ, MD, 59; Am Bd Dermat, dipl. *Prof Exp:* Intern, Emory Univ Hosp, 59-60; asst resident & resident dermat, Duke Univ Hosp, 60-62, assoc, Med Ctr, 63-64; asst clin prof, Med Ctr, Univ Calif, San Francisco, 65-66; from asst prof to assoc prof, Mayo Grad Sch Med, Univ Minn, 66-72; prof dermat & head div, Univ Colo

Med Ctr, Denver, 72-76; PROF DERMAT, UNIV NC, CHAPEL HILL, 76- *Concurrent Pos:* Nat Cancer Inst fel, 62-64. *Mem:* Am Acad Dermat; Soc Invest Dermat; Am Fedn Clin Res. *Res:* Immunology of skin diseases. *Mailing Add:* Dept of Dermat Univ of NC Chapel Hill NC 27514

SAMSON, CHARLES HAROLD, JR, b Portsmouth, Ohio, July 12, 24; m 47; c 2. SYSTEMS ENGINEERING, STRUCTURAL ENGINEERING. *Educ:* Univ Notre Dame, BS, 47, MS, 48; Univ Mo, PhD(struct eng), 53. *Prof Exp:* Asst to field rep, Loebl, Schlossman & Bennett, Ill, 48-49; struct engr, Gen Dynamics/Convair, Tex, 51-52, sr struct engr, 52-53; asst prof civil eng, Univ Notre Dame, 53-56; proj aerodyn engr, Gen Dynamics/Ft Worth, 56-58, proj struct engr, 58-60; head, Civil Eng Dept, 64-79, actg pres, 80-81, PROF AEROSPACE & CIVIL ENG, TEX A&M UNIV, 60-, VPRES PLANNING, 81- *Concurrent Pos:* Lectr, Southern Methodist Univ, 52-53 & 56-80. *Mem:* Am Soc Civil Engrs; Am Soc Eng Educ; Nat Soc Prof Engrs (vpres, 81-); Am Pub Works Asn. *Res:* Systems engineering; structural mechanics; engineering education. *Mailing Add:* Dept of Civil Eng Tex A&M Univ College Station TX 77843

SAMSON, EUCHARISTE, b Quebec, Que, Aug 17, 10; m; c 4. MEDICINE. *Educ:* Laval Univ, MD, 37. *Prof Exp:* Resident surg, Hotel-Dieu, Quebec, 38, Laennec Hosp, Paris, France, 39, Peter Bent Brigham Hosp, Boston, Mass, 40 & Mayo Clin, 41; asst prof surg, Laval Univ, 49-63, prof, 63-78; RETIRED. *Concurrent Pos:* Head dept surg, Hotel-Dieu Quebec, 63-78. *Honors & Awards:* Royal Col Medal, 49. *Mem:* Am Col Surgeons; Can Med Asn; Int Soc Surgeons. *Res:* Surgery. *Mailing Add:* 250 Grande Allee Quest Apt 402 Quebec PQ G1R 2H4 Can

SAMSON, FRED BURTON, b West Lafayette, Ind, Dec 10, 40; m 66. WILDLIFE ECOLOGY. *Educ:* Ind Univ, Bloomington, BS, 62, MA, 66; Utah State Univ, PhD(biol), 74. *Prof Exp:* Wildlife biologist, Bur Sport Fisheries & Wildlife, US Dept Interior, 68-69, res biologist, 69-70; asst prof wildlife ecol, Pa State Univ, University Park, 74-76; biologist & asst unit leader, 76-81, BIOLOGIST & UNIT LEADER, MO COOP WILDLIFE RES UNIT, US FISH & WILDLIFE SERV, 81- *Mem:* Am Ornithologists Union; Cooper Ornith Soc; Wilson Ornith Soc; Wildlife Soc; Am Soc Mammalogists. *Res:* Avian and mammalian population ecology; endangered species. *Mailing Add:* 112 Stephens Hall Univ Mo Columbia MO 65211

SAMSON, FREDERICK EUGENE, JR, b Medford, Mass, Aug 16, 18; m 45; c 3. PHYSIOLOGY, NEUROBIOLOGY. *Educ:* Univ Chicago, PhD(physiol), 52. *Prof Exp:* From asst prof to prof physiol, 52-73, actg chmn dept biochem & physiol, 61-62, chmn dept physiol & cell biol, 62-73, DIR, R L SMITH RES CTR, MED CTR, UNIV KANS, 73- *Concurrent Pos:* Resident scientist, Neurosci Res Prog, Mass Inst Technol, 65- *Mem:* Am Physiol Soc; NY Acad Sci; Soc Neurosci; Am Soc Neurochem; Am Soc Cell Biol. *Res:* Physiological chemistry; metabolism; microtubular systems; axoplasmic transport; brain regional functional mapping. *Mailing Add:* R L Smith Res Ctr Univ Kans Med Ctr Kansas City KS 66103

SAMSON, JAMES ALEXANDER ROSS, b Scotland, Sept 9, 28; nat US; m 54; c 2. ATOMIC PHYSICS. *Educ:* Univ Glasgow, BSc, 52, DSc, 70; Univ Southern Calif, MS, 55, PhD(physics), 58. *Prof Exp:* Asst physics, Univ Southern Calif, 53-58, res assoc, 58-60; res physicist, Univ Mich & Harvard Univ, 60-61, GCA Corp, Mass, 61-70; prof, 70-81, REGENTS PROF PHYSICS, UNIV NEBR-LINCOLN, 81- *Concurrent Pos:* Assoc ed, J of the Optical Soc Am, 70-81; mem adv screening comt physics, Coun for Int Exchange of Scholars, 78-81; vis prof, Univ Southampton, Eng, 72, Bonn Univ, W Ger, 76, Daresbury Synchrotron Lab, Eng, 76-77, Phys Res Lab, Ahmedabad, India, 77 & Univ Hawaii, Honolulu, 80; mem, Comt Line Spectra Elements-Atomic Spectros, Nat Res Coun, 81- *Mem:* AAAS; Fel Am Phys Soc; fel Optical Soc Am. *Res:* Vacuum ultraviolet spectroscopy; atomic and molecular physics; photoelectron spectroscopy. *Mailing Add:* Dept Physics Univ Nebr Lincoln NE 68588

SAMSON, STEN, b Stockholm, Sweden, Mar 25, 16; m 48; c 2. CHEMISTRY. *Educ:* Univ Stockholm, Fil Kand, 53, Fil Lic, 56, Fil Dr, 68. *Prof Exp:* Res fel chem, Univ Stockholm, 48-53; res fel, 53-61, sr res fel, 61-73, res assoc, 73-80, SR RES ASSOC CHEM, CALIF INST TECHNOL, 80- *Concurrent Pos:* Consult, Comn Crystal Data, Int Union Crystal, 67-73; Syst Anal Instruments, 69-71 & Advan Res & Applications Corp, 80-; mem, US Panel Joint US Brazil Study Group Grad Training & Res Brazil, 75-76. *Mem:* Am Crystallog Asn. *Res:* Crystal structures of very complex intermetallic compounds; crystallographic transformations associated with changes in physical properties, parallectric and ferroelectrin, conductors and insulator transitions especially in one-dimensional conductors. *Mailing Add:* Chem Dept Calif St Calif Inst Technol Pasadena CA 91125

SAMSON, WILLIS KENDRICK, b Syracuse, NY, May 15, 47. NEUROENDOCRINOLOGY, PEPTIDE NEUROCHEMISTRY. *Educ:* Duke Univ, AB, 68; Univ Tex Health Sci Ctr Dallas, PhD(physiol), 79. *Prof Exp:* ASST PROF PHYSIOL, UNIV TEX HEALTH SCI CTR DALLAS, 81- *Mem:* Endocrine Soc. *Res:* Neuroendocrinology; brain and gut peptides; control of anterior pituitary function. *Mailing Add:* Dept Physiol Univ Tex Health Sci Ctr 5323 Harry Hines Blvd Dallas TX 75218

SAMTER, MAX, b Berlin, Ger, Mar 3, 08; nat US; m 47; c 1. CLINICAL MEDICINE, EXPERIMENTAL MEDICINE. *Educ:* Univ Berlin, MD, 33; Univ Ill, MS, 47; Am Bd Internal Med, dipl. *Prof Exp:* Asst dispensary physician, Sch Med, Johns Hopkins Univ, 37-38; asst biochem, 46, from instr to assoc prof, 46-60, head sect allergy & clin immunol, 47-75, assoc dean clin affairs, 74-75, chief of staff, Univ Hosp, 74-75, prof, 60-80, EMER PROF MED, ABRAHAM LINCOLN SCH MED, UNIV ILL MED CTR, 80-; DIR, INST ALLERGY & CLIN IMMUNOL, GRANT HOSP, CHICAGO, 75- *Concurrent Pos:* Consult, Chicago West Side & Hines Vet Admin Hosps. *Mem:* AMA; fel Am Col Physicians; Am Acad Allergy (treas, 54, pres, 58); Int Asn Allergol (past pres); hon mem Int Asn Allergology. *Res:* Function of eosinophils; mechanism of drug reactions; pathogenesis of bronchial asthma. *Mailing Add:* 645 Sheridan Rd Evanston IL 60202

SAMUEL, ALBERT, b Tanjore, India, Feb 27, 37; US citizen; m 69; c 2. MOLECULAR BIOLOGY. *Educ:* Univ Madras, India, BA, 59, MSc, 61; Oberlin Col, Ohio, MA, 65; Mich State Univ, PhD(entomol), 71. *Prof Exp:* Demonstr zool, Am Col, Madurai, India, 61-63; fel entom, Mich State Univ, 71-73; ASSOC PROF BIOL & CHMN DEPT SCI & MATH, ST PAUL'S COL, VA, 73- *Concurrent Pos:* Activities coordr, 16 Insts Health Sci Consortium & Health Serv Consortium, St Paul's Col, 73-, dir, Biomed Res Activities, 73-; NIH fac fel, 77-79; res biologist, Lawrence Livermore Lab. *Mem:* Tissue Culture Asn; AAAS; Cell Kinetic Soc; Soc Analytical Cytol. *Res:* Comparative study of chemically induced aging and natural aging in cells in vitro; Kinetics of tumor cells and its application in chemotherapy; aging and non-aging mammalian cells are used; changes at the molecular level studied and compared; correlation studies of the expression of cell surface antigens and specific cell cycle phases of in vitro T cell line. *Mailing Add:* Dept of Sci & Math St Paul's Col Lawrenceville VA 23868

SAMUEL, ARYEH HERMANN, b Hildesheim, Ger, Feb 19, 24; US citizen; m 54; c 1. OPERATIONS RESEARCH. *Educ:* Univ Ill, BS, 43; Northwestern Univ, MS, 46; Univ Notre Dame, PhD(chem), 53. *Prof Exp:* Scientist, Broadview Res, 56-60; scientist, Stanford Res Inst, 60-65; res leader phys chem, Gen Precision, 65-67; sr scientist, Stanford Res Inst, 67-72; criminalist, County Santa Clara, Calif, 72-74; sr scientist, Vector Res Inc, 74-77; PRIN RES SCIENTIST, BATTELLE MEM INST, 77- *Honors & Awards:* Lanchester Prize, Oper Res Soc Am, 62. *Mem:* Oper Res Soc Am. *Res:* Operations research-public systems, especially military and postal; remote sensing; chemical effects of radiations. *Mailing Add:* Battelle Mem Inst 2030 M St NW Washington DC 20036

SAMUEL, CHARLES EDWARD, b Portland, Ore, Nov 28, 45; m 68; c 2. VIROLOGY, INTERFERON. *Educ:* Mont State Univ, BS, 68; Univ Calif, Berkeley, PhD(biochem), 72. *Prof Exp:* Damon Runyon Scholar, Duke Univ Med Ctr, 72-74; asst prof, 74-79, ASSOC PROF BIOL, UNIV CALIF, SANTA BARBARA, 79- *Concurrent Pos:* Fel, Damon Runyon-Walter Winchell Cancer Fund, 72-74; prin investr, Nat Inst Allergy & Infectious Dis & Am Cancer Soc, 75-; Res Career Develop Award, NIH, 79-84; assoc ed, Virol, 80-; consult, NIH, 80- *Mem:* Am Soc Biol Chemists; Am Soc Microbiol; Am Soc Virol. *Res:* Biochemistry of animal virus-cell interactions; mechanism of interferon action; molecular biology of reovirus. *Mailing Add:* Sect Biochem Molecular Biol Dept Biol Sci Univ Calif Santa Barbara CA 93106

SAMUEL, DAVID EVAN, b Johnstown, Pa, July 28, 40; m 66. WILDLIFE BIOLOGY, ORNITHOLOGY. *Educ:* Juniata Col, BS, 62; Pa State Univ, MS, 64; Univ WVa, PhD(zool), 69. *Prof Exp:* Instr biol, Bethany Col, 64-66; instr zool, 68-69, ASSOC PROF WILDLIFE BIOL, WVA UNIV, 69-, ASSOC WILDLIFE BIOLOGIST, 76- *Concurrent Pos:* USDA grant. *Mem:* Am Ornith Union; Wildlife Soc; Wilson Ornith Soc; Nat Audubon Soc. *Res:* Behavior. *Mailing Add:* Div of Forestry WVa Univ Morgantown WV 26505

SAMUEL, EDMUND WILLIAM, b Canton, Ohio, Sept 17, 24; m 63. DEVELOPMENTAL BIOLOGY. *Educ:* Case Western Reserve Univ, BSEE, 45, MS, 49; Princeton Univ, MS, 59, PhD(biol), 60. *Prof Exp:* Res investr theoret physics, Sperry Gyroscope Corp, 49-50; res asst med physics, Mass Gen Hosp, Boston, 52-53; from asst prof to assoc prof biol, 60-71, PROF BIOL, ANTIOCH COL, 72- *Concurrent Pos:* NSF instrumentation grant, 62-64, undergrad res partic grant, 65-66. *Res:* Biophysics; theoretical and molecular biology; history and philosophy of science; East Asian science such as Japanese medicine; bioethics. *Mailing Add:* Dept of Biol Antioch Col Yellow Springs OH 45387

SAMUEL, JAY MORRIS, b Stuttgart, WGer, Jan 24, 46. WELDING METALLURGY, WELDING PROCESSES. *Educ:* Rensselaer Polytech Inst,BS, 67, PhD(mat eng), 79. *Prof Exp:* Adj prof mech tech, Hudson Valley Community Col, 77-79; ASST PROF MECH ENG, UNIV WIS, MADISON, 79- *Honors & Awards:* Clyde Sanders Award, Foundry Educ Found & Am Colloid Co, 82. *Mem:* Am Welding Soc; Am Soc Metals. *Res:* Solidification mechanics; physical metallurgy of weldments; control of welding processes; structure; properties of engineering materials. *Mailing Add:* Dept Mech Eng Univ Wis 1513 Univ Ave Madison WI 53706

SAMUEL, MARK AARON, b Montreal, Que, Jan 26, 44; m 65; c 2. THEORETICAL HIGH ENERGY PHYSICS. *Educ:* McGill Univ, BSc, 64, MSc, 66; Univ Rochester, PhD(physics), 69. *Prof Exp:* Asst prof, 69-75, assoc prof, 75-81, PROF PHYSICS, OKLA STATE UNIV, 81- *Concurrent Pos:* Consult, NSF Educ Res Grant, Okla State Univ, 72-75; vis scientist, Stanford Linear Accelerator Ctr, 73 & 75; res grant, US Energy Res & Develop Admin, Dept Energy, 76-; vis scientist, Niels Bohr Inst, Copenhagen, Denmark, 77; vis scientist, Aspen Ctr Physics, 81. *Mem:* Am Phys Soc; Am Asn Physics Teachers; Can Asn Physicists. *Res:* Field theory; particle physics; atomic physics; tests of quantum electrodynamics and quantum chromodynamics; applied mathematical techniques. *Mailing Add:* Dept of Physics Okla State Univ Stillwater OK 74074

SAMUEL, WILLIAM MORRIS, b Windber, Pa, July 28, 40; m 70; c 2. PARASITOLOGY. *Educ:* Juniata Col, BSc, 62; Pa State Univ, MSc, 65; Univ Wis, PhD(vet sci, zool), 69. *Prof Exp:* Fel parasitol, 69-71, asst prof zool, 71-75, assoc prof, 75-78, PROF ZOOL, UNIV ALTA, 81- *Concurrent Pos:* Assoc ed, J Wildlife Dis, 81- *Mem:* Am Soc Parasitol; Wildlife Dis Asn; Am Soc Mammal; Wildlife Soc; Can Soc Zoologists. *Res:* Epizootiology of wildlife parasites; importance for host populations; emphasis on big game. *Mailing Add:* Dept of Zool Univ of Alta Edmonton AB T6G 2E9 Can

SAMUEL-CAHN, ESTER, Oslo, Norway, May 16, 33; Israeli citizen; m 70; c 4. DECISION THEORY, SEQUENTIAL ANALYSIS. *Educ:* Hebrew Univ, BA, 58; Columbia Univ, NY, MA, 59, PhD(statist), 61. *Prof Exp:* PROF STATIST, HEBREW UNIV, 62- *Concurrent Pos:* Vis prof, Columbia Univ, 80 & Rutgers Univ, 81. *Mem:* Fel Inst Math Statist; Am Statist Asn; Int Statist Inst; Israel Statist Asn (vpres); Israel Soc Oper Res. *Mailing Add:* Dept Statist Hebrew Univ Jerusalem 91905 Israel

SAMUELS, GEORGE, b Philadelphia, Pa, July 7, 22; m 45; c 2. SOIL FERTILITY, PLANT PHYSIOLOGY. *Educ:* Univ Del, BSc, 46; Rutgers Univ, PhD(soils), 49. *Prof Exp:* Plant physiologist, 49-55, agronomist, Exp Sta, Univ PR, Rio Piedras, 56-77. *Concurrent Pos:* Res consult, Agr Res Assocs, 60-81; fertilizer consult, Consejo Estatal del Azucar, Dominican Repub, 71-75 & Copersucar, Brazil, 76-78; consult biomass energy, Dept Energy, Univ PR, 79-81. *Mem:* Am Soc Agron; Soil Sci Soc Am; Caribbean Food Crops Soc (secy-treas, 64-75). *Res:* Foliar diagnosis and soil analyses of tropical soils and crops to determine their fertilizer requirements; use of sugarcane for energy crop via alcohol and fiber and use of distillery wastes for fertilizer. *Mailing Add:* 826 Carvell Dr Winter Park FL 32792

SAMUELS, J(OHN) CLIFTON, engineering, see previous edition

SAMUELS, MARTIN E(LMER), b Dayton, Ohio, Apr 24, 18; m 43; c 2. CHEMICAL ENGINEERING. *Educ:* Univ Dayton, BChE, 39. *Prof Exp:* Chemist, Dayton Tire & Rubber Co, 39-43; chemist, 43-45, develop supvr, 45-47, develop mgr, 57-61, prod qual mgr, 61-67, MGR TECH SERV, COPOLYMER RUBBER & CHEM CORP, 67- *Mem:* Am Chem Soc. *Res:* Development, evaluation, quality control, end uses and utilization of synthetic latexes and elastomers. *Mailing Add:* Copolymer Rubber & Chem Corp PO Box 2591 Baton Rouge LA 70821

SAMUELS, MICHAEL R(OBERT), chemical engineering, see previous edition

SAMUELS, MYRA LEE, b Chicago, Ill, Mar 23, 40; m 67; c 2. STATISTICS. *Educ:* Swarthmore Col, BA, 61; Univ Calif, Berkeley, PhD(statist), 69. *Prof Exp:* Mathematician, US Naval Res Lab, 61-63; res asst statist & biostatist, Univ Calif, Berkeley, 66-68; instr statist, 68-69, asst prof, 70-71, VIS ASST PROF STATIST, PURDUE UNIV, LAFAYETTE, 72- *Mem:* Am Statist Asn; Biomet Soc. *Res:* Biostatistics; stochastic models for biological processes; branching processes. *Mailing Add:* Dept Statist Purdue Univ West Lafayette IN 47907

SAMUELS, ROBERT, b Philadelphia, Pa, June 12, 18; m 48; c 3. BIOLOGY. *Educ:* Univ Pa, AB, 38, MA, 40; Univ Calif, PhD(zool), 52. *Prof Exp:* Jr entomologist, USPHS, 41-43; teaching asst zool, Univ Calif, 46-49, assoc, 49-52; instr biol, Calif State Polytech Col, 53; from instr to asst prof microbiol, Sch Med, Univ Colo, 53-63, vis prof, 63; prof, Merharry Med Col, 63-67; prof biol, Purdue Univ, Indianapolis, 67-70; prof biol, Ind Univ-Purdue Univ, Indianapolis, 70-78, chmn dept, 72-76; PROF BIOL & CHMN DEPT, E TENN STATE UNIV, 79- *Concurrent Pos:* Sect rep, Purdue Univ, 69-70; lectr, Univ Calif, 50-52; lectr, Sch Med, Univ Colo; consult, Indian Health Surv, Wyo State Bd Health, USPHS, Wetherill Mesa Archaeol Proj, Nat Park Serv & Nat Geog Surv. *Mem:* Soc Protozool (asst treas, 58-60, treas, 60-66, pres, 72-73); Am Soc Microbiol; Am Micros Soc; Soc Exp Biol & Med; Am Soc Parasitol. *Res:* Protozoology; cytology; nutrition; morphogenesis. *Mailing Add:* Dept of Biol Sci E Tenn State Univ Johnson City TN 37601

SAMUELS, ROBERT BIRELEY, b Palo Alto, Calif, Feb 27, 40; m 60; c 3. FOOD CHEMISTRY. *Educ:* Calif State Polytech Col, BS, 62; Univ Ill, PhD(food sci), 65. *Prof Exp:* USPHS trainee fel, 65-66; res chemist, 66-67, sr res chemist, 67, group supvr chromatography res, 67-68, group supvr chromatog res & appln, 68-71, prog coordr bioprod, 71-72, biochem prog mgr, 72-73, MGR BIOPROD, SPINCO DIV, BECKMAN INSTRUMENTS, INC, PALO ALTO, 73- *Mem:* AAAS; Am Chem Soc; Inst Food Technologists. *Res:* Lipid chemistry; lipoprotein structure; peptide synthesis and purification; instrumentation. *Mailing Add:* Beckman Instruments Inc 1117 California Ave Palo Alto CA 94304

SAMUELS, ROBERT JOEL, b Brooklyn, NY, Jan 8, 31; m 54; c 2. PHYSICAL CHEMISTRY, POLYMER CHEMISTRY. *Educ:* Brooklyn Col, BS, 52; Stevens Inst Technol, MS, 55; Univ Akron, PhD(polymer chem), 61. *Prof Exp:* Res chemist, Picatinny Arsenal, 52-55, Res Ctr, Goodyear Tire & Rubber Co, 57-59 & Inst Rubber Res, Akron, 59-60; res chemist, Res Ctr, Hercules Inc, 60-67, sr res chemist, 67-70, res scientist, 70-80; MEM FAC, GA INST TECHNOL, 80- *Concurrent Pos:* Adj prof, Dept Chem Eng, Univ Del, 72-; affil prof, Dept of Chem Eng, Univ Wash, 78- *Honors & Awards:* Am Chem Soc Award, 71. *Mem:* Am Chem Soc; Am Phys Soc; Am Crystallog Asn; Soc Rheol. *Res:* Polymer morphology and mechanics; x-ray diffraction; infrared; birefringence; small-angle light scattering, sonic and mechanical properties of polymers; chemical stress relaxation of polymers; polymer chromatography; physical chemistry of stress relaxation of polmers; polymer chromatography; physical chemistry of dilute solutions. *Mailing Add:* Sch Chem Eng Ga Inst Technol Atlanta GA 30332

SAMUELS, ROBERT LYNN, b Goldfield, Iowa, Oct 20, 30; m 52; c 3. ELECTRICAL ENGINEERING. *Educ:* Iowa State Univ, BS, 59, MS, 60, PhD, 63. *Prof Exp:* Adv res engr, Sylvania Electronic Systs-West, 63; asst prof elec eng, 63-70, ASSOC PROF ELEC ENG, IOWA STATE UNIV, 70- *Res:* Thin ferromagnetic film materials. *Mailing Add:* Dept of Elec Eng Iowa State Univ Ames IA 50011

SAMUELS, STANLEY, b New York, NY, Oct 13, 29; m 51; c 3. NEUROCHEMISTRY. *Educ:* Syracuse Univ, AB, 51, MS, 54, PhD(biochem), 58. *Prof Exp:* Asst instr zool, Syracuse Univ, 52-54, asst, 55-57; asst biochem, Col Med, Univ Ill, 54-55; instr ophthalmic res, Col Med, Western Reserve Univ, 57-59; instr, Albert Einstein Col Med, 61-63; asst prof, 64-69, ASSOC PROF EXP NEUROL, SCH MED, NY UNIV, 69- *Concurrent Pos:* Nat Inst Neurol Dis & Blindness fel neurol, Albert Einstein Col Med, 59-61; Nat Multiple Sclerosis Soc fel, 61-63; consult, NY Eye & Ear Infirmary, 61-63. *Mem:* AAAS; Harvey Soc; Asn Res Nerv & Ment Dis; Int Soc Neurochem; Am Soc Neurochem. *Res:* Amino acid transport; thin-layer chromatography; inborn metabolic errors; brain biochemistry. *Mailing Add:* Dept of Neurol NY Univ Med Ctr New York NY 10016

SAMUELSON, DONALD JAMES, b Warren, Pa, May 15, 40; m 65; c 2. MATHEMATICS. *Educ:* Cornell Col, BA, 62; Univ Calif Berkeley, MA, 65; Univ Calif, Santa Barbara, PhD(math), 69. *Prof Exp:* Asst prof math, Cornell Col, 65-67, Univ Hawaii, 69-71 & Pa State Univ, McKeesport, 71-75; asst prof, 75-77, ASSOC PROF MATH, PA STATE UNIV, UNIVERSITY PARK, 77- *Mem:* Am Math Soc. *Res:* Universal algebra. *Mailing Add:* Dept of Math University Dr McKeesport PA 15132

SAMULON, HENRY A, b Graudenz, Ger, Dec 26, 15; nat US; m 43; c 2. ELECTRONICS. *Educ:* Swiss Fed Inst Technol, MS, 39. *Prof Exp:* Res engr & instr acoust lab, Swiss Fed Inst Technol, 43-44, assoc, Inst Commun Technol, 44-47; mem staff, Electronics Lab, Gen Elec Co, 47-51, mgr eng anal subsect, 51-55; gen mgr electronic systs div, TRW Systs, 55-71, vpres, 64-71, vpres electronics equip, TRW Electronics, 71-74; vpres & mgr, Electronics Div, Xerox Corp, 74-81; PRES, H A SAMULON CONSULT, INC, 81- *Mem:* Fel Inst Elec & Electronics Engrs. *Res:* Circuitry; color television; space and missile guidance and communication systems; microelectronics; general management. *Mailing Add:* 575 Muskingum Ave Pacific Palisades CA 90272

SAMULSKI, EDWARD THADDEUS, b Augusta, Ga, May 23, 43. PHYSICAL CHEMISTRY, POLYMER CHEMISTRY. *Educ:* Clemson Univ, BS, 65; Princeton Univ, PhD(chem), 69. *Prof Exp:* NIH fel, State Univ Groningen, 69-70; univ fel, Univ Tex, Austin, 71-72; asst prof, 72-75, assoc prof, 75-81, PROF CHEM, UNIV CONN, 81-, MEM STAFF, INST MAT SCI, 72- *Mem:* AAAS; Am Chem Soc. *Res:* Liquid crystals; biological macromolecules and synthetic polymers; application of magnetic resonance techniques to study molecular dynamics of polymer solutions and liquid crystal phases. *Mailing Add:* Dept of Chem Univ of Conn Storrs CT 06268

SAMWORTH, ELEANOR A, b Wilmington, Del, May 10, 36. PHYSICAL CHEMISTRY. *Educ:* Wilson Col, AB, 58; Johns Hopkins Univ, MA, 60, PhD(phys chem), 63. *Prof Exp:* Nat Cancer Inst fel phys chem, Harvard Univ, 63-64; asst prof, 64-70, ASSOC PROF CHEM, SKIDMORE COL, 70- *Mem:* AAAS; Am Inst Chemists; Am Phys Soc. *Res:* Molecular structure; vibrational spectroscopy; inorganic synthesis. *Mailing Add:* Dept of Chemistry & Physics Skidmore Col Saratoga Springs NY 12866

SANABOR, LOUIS JOHN, b Cleveland, Ohio, Dec 2, 20; m 45; c 1. CHEMICAL ENGINEERING. *Educ:* Case Inst Technol, BS, 42; Carnegie Inst Technol, MS, 54. *Prof Exp:* Asst shift foreman, Butadiene Div, 43-45, from pilot plant group leader to sr chem engr, Res Dept, 45-58, staff asst to mgr explor res sect, 58-65, pilot plant group leader, Cost Anal & Design Group, 65-81, SR CHEM ENGR, ENG EVAL GROUP, RES DEPT, KOPPERS CO, INC, 70- *Mem:* Am Inst Chem Engrs; Am Chem Soc. *Mailing Add:* Res Dept Koppers Co Inc 440 College Park Dr Monroeville PA 15146

SANADI, D RAO, b India, July 8, 20; nat US; m 50; c 2. BIOCHEMISTRY. *Educ:* Univ Calif, PhD(biochem), 49. *Prof Exp:* Fel, Nat Cancer Inst, 49-52, res assoc, 52-53; asst prof biochem, Univ Wis, 53-55; asst prof, Univ Calif, 55-58; chief sect comp biochem, NIH, 58-66; exec dir, 69-71 & 75-77, DIR DEPT CELL PHYSIOL, BOSTON BIOMED RES INST, 66- *Concurrent Pos:* Estab investr, Am Heart Asn, 54-58; chmn, Gordon Res Conf Energy Coupling Mechanisms, 69-72 & 74; chmn, Gordon Res Conf Biol of Aging, 74; mem adult develop & aging res & training comt, Nat Inst Child Health & Human Develop, 70-73; mem adv panel metab biol, NSF, 71-74; assoc prof, Dept Biol Chem, Harvard Med Sch, 75-; ed, J Bioenergelis Biomembrane, 75- *Mem:* AAAS; Am Chem Soc; Am Soc Biol Chem; fel Geront Soc. *Res:* Intermediary metabolism; bioenergetics; enzymology; isotopes; aging. *Mailing Add:* Dept Cell Physiol Boston Biomed Res Inst 20 Staniford St Boston MA 02114

SAN ANTONIO, JAMES PATRICK, b New York, NY, June 4, 25; m 51; c 3. HORTICULTURE, PHYSIOLOGY. *Educ:* Univ Chicago, SB, 48, PhD(physiol), 51. *Prof Exp:* Res assoc mycol physiol, Univ Chicago, 51-53; plant physiologist, Sect Cotton & Other Fiber Crops & Dis, Agr Res Serv, 53-55, Veg & Ornamentals Res Br, Crops Res Div, 55-72, HORTICULTURIST, PLANT GENETICS & GERMPLASM INST, SCI & EDUC ADMIN-AGR RES, USDA, 72- *Mem:* Am Soc Plant Physiol; Bot Soc Am; Am Soc Hort Sci; Scand Soc Plant Physiologists. *Res:* Cultivation of edible fungi; physiology and genetics. *Mailing Add:* Hort Sci Inst Agr Res Sect USDA Beltsville Agr Res Ctr Beltsville MD 20705

SANATHANAN, C(HATHILINGATH) K, b Kerala, India, Feb 17, 36; m 63. ENGINEERING, APPLIED MATHEMATICS. *Educ:* Univ Madras, BS, 59; Case Inst Technol, MS, 62, PhD(eng), 64. *Prof Exp:* Asst nuclear engr, Argonne Nat Lab, Ill, 63-68; assoc prof info eng, 68-71, PROF INFO ENG, UNIV ILL, CHICAGO CIRCLE, 71- *Mem:* Am Nuclear Soc. *Res:* Boiling water reactor dynamics; high performance fast reactor dynamics; hybrid computer applications to systems analysis; control and simulation; urban mass transportation. *Mailing Add:* Dept of Info Eng Univ of Ill at Chicago Circle Chicago IL 60680

SANATHANAN, LALITHA P, b Sandakan, NBorneo, Jan 21, 43; nat US; m 63; c 1. APPLIED STATISTICS, MATHEMATICAL STATISTICS. *Educ:* Univ Mysore, BSc, 60, MSc, 62; Univ Chicago, PhD(statist), 69. *Prof Exp:* Res asst, Nat Opinion Res Ctr, 67-68; asst prof, 68-72, ASSOC PROF STATIST, UNIV ILL, CHICAGO CIRCLE, 72- *Concurrent Pos:* Consult, Presby St Lukes Hosp, 69-70; vis mathematician, Argonne Nat Lab, 78-79. *Mem:* Am Statist Asn. *Res:* Multinomial analysis; regression; multivariate statistics; decision theory; optimal allocation of resources. *Mailing Add:* 10 S-261 Argonne Ridge Rd Hinsdale IL 60521

SANAZARO, PAUL JOSEPH, b Sanger, Calif, Sept 27, 22; m 74. MEDICINE. *Educ:* Univ Calif, AB, 44, MD, 46; Am Bd Internal Med, dipl, recert, 77. *Prof Exp:* From asst prof to assoc prof med, Sch Med, Univ Calif, San Francisco, 53-62; dir div educ, Asn Am Med Cols, Ill, 62-68; dir nat ctr

health serv, Res & Develop, 68-72; assoc dep adminr develop, Health Serv & Ment Health Admin, US Dept Health, Educ & Welfare, 72-73; dir pvt initiative, 73-77, DIR, PVT INITIATIVE QUAL ASSURANCE & PROF STANDARDS REV ORGN, BERKELEY, CALIF, 78-; CLIN PROF MED, SCH MED, UNIV CALIF, SAN FRANCISCO, 75- *Concurrent Pos:* Clin assoc prof, Univ Ill Col Med, 62-67; clin prof, 67-68; consult, NIH. *Mem:* Fel Am Col Physicians; fel Am Pub Health Asn. *Res:* Health services research and development, especially quality of medical care. *Mailing Add:* 1126 Grizzly Peak Blvd Berkeley CA 94708

SANBORN, ALBERT FRANCIS, b Calif, June 21, 13; m 36, 71; c 2. GEOLOGY. *Educ:* Fresno State Col, AB, 48; Stanford Univ, MS, 50, PhD(geol), 52. *Prof Exp:* Div stratigrapher, Western Opers, Standard Oil Co, Calif, 55-63, sr geologist, Western Div, Calif Oil Co, 63-66, sr explor geologist, Western Div, Chevron Oil Co, Denver, 66-78; GEOL CONSULT, 78- *Mem:* Asn Prof Geol Scientists; Am Asn Petrol Geologists. *Res:* Petroleum geology; stratigraphy. *Mailing Add:* 3759 E Nobles Rd Littleton CO 80122

SANBORN, CHARLES E(VAN), b Mankato, Minn, July 11, 19; m 41, 80; c 4. CHEMICAL ENGINEERING, MATHEMATICS. *Educ:* Univ Minn, BChE, 41, PhD(chem eng), 49. *Prof Exp:* Engr, Shell Develop Co, Calif, 49-72, Shell Oil Co, 72-73, STAFF RES ENGR, SHELL DEVELOP CO, 73- *Mem:* Am Inst Chem Engrs; AAAS. *Res:* Process development; industrial chemicals. *Mailing Add:* Shell Develop Co PO Box 1380 Houston TX 77001

SANBORN, DAVID MICHAEL, b Detroit, Mich, Dec 6, 42; m 66; c 2. MECHANICAL ENGINEERING. *Educ:* Univ Mich, BSE, 65, MSE, 67, PhD(mech eng), 69. *Prof Exp:* Asst prof mech eng, Ga Inst Technol, 69-77; STAFF CONSULT, CADRE CORP, 77- *Concurrent Pos:* Consult, Whirlpool Corp, 71- & Sci Atlanta, Inc, 72- *Mem:* Am Soc Mech Engrs. *Res:* Lubrication; lubricant rheology; dynamics of machinery; design. *Mailing Add:* Cadre Corp PO Box 47837 Atlanta GA 30362

SANBORN, I B, b Pepperell, Mass, Apr 29, 32; m 53; c 6. AUTOMATIC CONTROL SYSTEMS. *Educ:* Rensselaer Polytech Inst, BChE, 54; Inst Paper Chem, MCh, 56, PhD, 61. *Prof Exp:* Proj engr, 61-65, process engr, 65-67, mgr process control, 67-68, mgr process develop & control, 68-76, ASSOC DIR PROD DEVELOP, CONSOL PAPERS, INC, 76- *Mem:* Tech Asn Pulp & Paper Indust; Instrument Soc Am. *Res:* Application of automatic control principles to the control of the paper making process. *Mailing Add:* Consol Papers Inc PO Box 50 Wisconsin Rapids WI 54494

SANBORN, MARK ROBERT, b Mason City, Iowa, Mar 17, 46; m 68; c 2. VIROLOGY, IMMUNOLOGY. *Educ:* Univ Northern Iowa, BA, 68, MA, 71; Iowa State Univ, PhD(bacteriol), 76. *Prof Exp:* ASST PROF VIROL & IMMUNOL, OKLA STATE UNIV, 76- *Mem:* Am Soc Microbiol; Sigma Xi; NY Acad Sci; AAAS. *Res:* Early events in paramyxovirus infection; induction of neurological autoimmune disease; immunological assay for gene expression. *Mailing Add:* 407 Life Sci E Okla State Univ Stillwater OK 74074

SANBORN, RUSSELL HOBART, b Laconia, NH, Mar 31, 30; m 64. PHYSICAL CHEMISTRY. *Educ:* Wesleyan Univ, BA, 52; Univ Calif, PhD(chem), 56. *Prof Exp:* CHEMIST, LAWRENCE LIVERMORE LAB, UNIV CALIF, 56- *Mem:* Am Chem Soc. *Res:* Infrared spectroscopy; molecular structure and spectra; numerical analysis; data processing; computer simulation. *Mailing Add:* Dept of Chem Lawrence Livermore Nat Lab Livermore CA 94550

SANBORN, WARREN GORDON, medical physiology, see previous edition

SANCES, ANTHONY, JR, b Chicago, Ill, July 13, 32; m 65; c 3. BIOMEDICAL ENGINEERING. *Educ:* Am Inst Technol, BSEE, 53; DePaul Univ, MS, 59; Northwestern Univ, PhD(biomed eng), 63. *Prof Exp:* Res engr, Mech Res Dept, Am Mach & Foundry Co, 53-59; mgr, Advan Res Dept, Sunbeam Corp, 59-60; asst prof, Am Inst Technol, 60-61; consult numerous firms, 61-64; PROF ELEC ENG & NEUROSURG & DIR BIOMED ENG, MARQUETTE UNIV, 64-; PROF BIOMED ENG & CHMN PROG, MED COL WIS, 64- *Concurrent Pos:* Walter Murphy fel, 62-63; NIH fel, 63-64; staff, Wood Vet Admin Hosp, 64-, Milwaukee County Gen Hosp, 64- & Deaconness Hosp, Milwaukee, 72- *Mem:* Biophys Soc; sr mem Inst Elec & Electronics Engrs; Instrument Soc Am; Neuroelec Soc (pres); Alliance Eng Med & Biol (past pres). *Res:* Nervous system research related to biomedical engineering and biomechanics. *Mailing Add:* Milwaukee County Gen Hosp 8700 W Wisconsin Ave Milwaukee WI 53226

SANCETTA, CONSTANCE ANTONINA, b Richmond, Va, Apr 17, 49; div. MARINE GEOLOGY, MICROPALEONTOLOGY. *Educ:* Brown Univ, BA, 71, MS, 73; Ore State Univ, PhD(oceanog), 76. *Prof Exp:* Res assoc geol, Stanford Univ, 76-78; RES ASSOC GEOL, LAMONT-DOHERTY GEOL OBSERV, COLUMBIA UNIV, 79- *Concurrent Pos:* NSF Ocean Sci Exec Adv Comt, 81- *Mem:* Geol Soc Am; Am Geophys Union; AAAS. *Res:* Cenozoic paleoceanography; fossil marine diatoms, biostratigraphy and paleoecology. *Mailing Add:* Lamont-Doherty Geol Observ Palisades NY 10964

SANCHEZ, ALBERT, b Solomonsville, Ariz, Feb 10, 36; m 62; c 4. NUTRITION, BIOCHEMISTRY. *Educ:* Loma Linda Univ, BA, 59, MS, 62; Univ Calif, Los Angeles, DrPH, 68. *Prof Exp:* Biochemist, Int Nutrit Res Found, 61-65; from asst prof to prof nutrit, Loma Linda Univ, 68-74; prof biochem & nutrit, Sch Med, Montemorelos Univ, Mex, 74-80; PROF NUTRIT, LOMA LINDA UNIV, 80- *Mem:* AAAS; Am Dietetic Asn; Latin Am Nutrit Soc. *Res:* Protein and amino acid nutrition; role of nutritional factors as they relate to public health problems. *Mailing Add:* Dept Nutrit Sch Health Loma Linda Univ Loma Linda CA

SANCHEZ, DAVID A, b San Francisco, Calif, Jan 13, 33; m 58; c 2. MATHEMATICS. *Educ:* Univ NMex, BS, 55; Univ Mich, MA, 60, PhD(math), 64. *Prof Exp:* Res asst, Radar Lab, Inst Sci & Technol, Univ Mich, 59-63; instr math, Univ Chicago, 63-65; from asst prof to prof math, Univ Calif, Los Angeles, 65-77; PROF MATH, UNIV NMEX, 77- *Concurrent Pos:* Vis lectr, Univ Manchester, 65-66. *Mem:* Am Math Soc; Math Asn Am; Soc Indust & Appl Math. *Res:* Direct methods in the calculus of variations; nonlinear ordinary differential equations. *Mailing Add:* Dept Math Univ NMex Albuquerque NM 87131

SANCHEZ, GILBERT, microbiology, parasitology, see previous edition

SANCHEZ, ISAAC CORNELIUS, b San Antonio, Tex, Aug 11, 41; m 76; c 2. POLYMER PHYSICS. *Educ:* St Mary's Univ, Tex, BS, 63; Univ Del, PhD(phys chem), 69. *Prof Exp:* Nat Res Coun-Nat Acad Sci assoc, Nat Bur Stand, Washington, DC, 69-71; assoc scientist polymer sci, Xerox Corp, 71-72; asst prof polymer sci & eng, Univ Mass, Amherst, 72-77; RES CHEMIST, CTR MAT SCI, NAT BUR STANDARDS, 77- *Concurrent Pos:* Adj assoc prof, Polymer Sci & Eng, Univ Mass, 77- *Mem:* Am Chem Soc; Am Phys Soc. *Res:* Application of statistical mechanics to problems in polymer science. *Mailing Add:* Ctr Mat Sci Nat Bur Standards Washington DC 20234

SANCHEZ, JOSE, b Suffern, NY, June 30, 36:; m 62; c 2. ORGANIC CHEMISTRY. *Educ:* Univ Rochester, BS, 58; Brown Univ, PhD(org chem), 66. *Prof Exp:* Res chemist, F & F Dept, E I du Pont de Nemours, 65-67; GROUP LEADER, PEROXIDES, LUCIDOL DIV PENNWALT CORP, 67- *Mem:* Am Chem Soc. *Res:* Synthesis, evaluation, process development and production troubleshooting in the areas of organic peroxides and organic specialty compounds. *Mailing Add:* Lucidol Div Pennwalt Corp 1740 Military Rd Buffalo NY 14240

SANCHEZ, PEDRO ANTONIO, b Havana, Cuba, Oct 7, 40; US citizen; m 65; c 3. AGRONOMY, SOIL FERTILITY. *Educ:* Cornell Univ, BS, 62, MS, 64, PhD(soil sci), 68. *Prof Exp:* Asst soil sci, Philippine Prog, Cornell Univ, 65-68; asst prof soil sci & co-leader, Nat Rice Res Prog Mission to Peru, NC State Univ, 68-71, assoc prof, 71-77; coordr, Trop Pastures Prog, Cent Int Agr Trop, 77-79; PROF SOIL SCI & LEADER TROP SOILS PROG, NC STATE UNIV, 79- *Mem:* Am Soc Agron; Soil Sci Soc Am; Int Soc Soil Sci; Brazilian Soc Soil Sci; Colombian Soc Soil Sci. *Res:* Fertility and management of tropical soils; fertility and management of rice soils and tropical pastures. *Mailing Add:* Dept of Soil Sci NC State Univ Raleigh NC 27650

SANCHEZ, ROBERT A, b Colombia, SAm, Feb 4, 38; US citizen; m 60; c 4. BIO-ORGANIC CHEMISTRY, ORGANIC CHEMISTRY. *Educ:* Pomona Col, BA, 58; Kans State Univ, PhD(org chem), 62. *Prof Exp:* Fel org chem, Univ Colo, 62-64, asst prof, 63-64; asst prof, Haverford Col, 64-65; sr res assoc, Salk Inst Biol Studies, 65-72; dir res, Terra-Marine Bioresearch, Inc, 72-74; DIR BIO-ORG RES & DEVELOP, CALBIOCHEM-BEHRING CORP, 74- *Mem:* AAAS; NY Acad Sci; Am Chem Soc; Intra-sci Res Found; Sigma Xi. *Res:* Fundamental and developmental research; pharmaceuticals and biochemicals; pre-biological chemistry and origins of life; bio-organic chemistry and natural products; cancer chemotherapy. *Mailing Add:* Calbiochem-Behring Corp 10933 N Torrey Pines Rd La Jolla CA 92037

SANCIER, KENNETH MARTIN, b New York, NY, June 21, 20. PHYSICAL CHEMISTRY. *Educ:* Polytech Inst Brooklyn, BS, 42; Johns Hopkins Univ, MA, 47, PhD(chem), 49. *Prof Exp:* Phys chemist gas chem, Linde Air Prod Co, Union Carbide & Carbon Corp, 42-46; lab instr, Johns Hopkins Univ, 46-49; phys chemist low temperature chem, Brookhaven Nat Lab, 49-53; PHYS CHEMIST, SRI INT, 54- *Concurrent Pos:* Vis instr chem, Conn Col, 48; fel, Standard Oil Ind, 48-49; NSF vis scientist, Univ Tokyo, 66-67. *Mem:* Am Chem Soc; Sigma Xi; NY Acad Sci; AAAS. *Res:* Photochemistry related to solar energy conversion; energy transfer processes in solution and between gases and solids; hydrogen bonding; absorption spectroscopy, particularly at low temperature; heterogeneous catalysis; electron spin resonance of gaseous atoms, gas-solid interactions, and biochemical systems. *Mailing Add:* Stanford Res Inst Menlo Park CA 94025

SANCILIO, FREDERICK DOMINICK, b Hoboken, NJ, Mar 15, 50; m 76; c 2. PHARMACEUTICAL CHEMISTRY, ANALYTICAL CHEMISTRY. *Educ:* Rutgers Univ, BS, 71, MS, 74, PhD(chem), 75. *Prof Exp:* Scientist, Hoffman-LaRoche, Inc, 71-75; sect leader, Schering Res Co, 76-77; ASST DIR QUAL ASSURANCE, BURROUGHS WELLCOME CO, 77- *Mem:* Am Chem Soc; Sigma Xi; Am Crystallog Asn. *Res:* Complete automation of routine analytical functions; application of new technology to routine analysis. *Mailing Add:* Burroughs Wellcome Co PO Box 1887 Greenville NC 27834

SANCILIO, LAWRENCE F, b Brooklyn, NY, Dec 13, 32; m 60; c 5. PHARMACOLOGY. *Educ:* St John's Univ, NY, BS, 54; Georgetown Univ, PhD(pharmacol), 60. *Prof Exp:* Teaching asst pharmacol, Georgetow Univ, 58-59; res pharmacologist, Miles Labs, Inc, Ind, 60-68; assoc res pharmacologist, 68-71, group mgr pharmacol res sect, 71-81, DIR PHARMACOL, A H ROBINS, INC, 81- *Mem:* Soc Exp Biol & Med; Am Soc Pharmacol & Exp Therapeut. *Res:* Analgesia; mechanism of inflammation and the evaluation of systemic nonsteroidal and topical steroidal anti-inflammatory agents; immediate hypersensitivity. *Mailing Add:* A H Robins Inc 1211 Sherwood Ave Richmond VA 23220

SAN CLEMENTE, CHARLES LEONARD, b Milford, Mass, May 27, 14; m 44; c 2. MICROBIOLOGY. *Educ:* Univ Mass, BS, 37; Mich State Univ, MS, 40, PhD(bact), 42. *Prof Exp:* Asst biochem, Mich State Univ, 37-39, bact, 39-42; res immunologist, Sch Med, Western Reserve Univ, 42-43; assoc prof chem & bact, Mich Tech Univ, 46-51; assoc prof, 51-61, PROF MICROBIOL, MICH STATE UNIV, 61- *Mem:* AAAS; Am Chem Soc; Am Soc Microbiol; Soc Indust Microbiol; Am Inst Biol Sci. *Res:* Complement; brucellosis; antibiotics; pesticides; enzymology; characterization of Staphylococci; environmental studies. *Mailing Add:* Dept of Microbiol & Pub Health Mich State Univ East Lansing MI 48824

SAND, LEONARD B, b Eveleth, Minn, Oct 5, 22; m 47; c 3. MINERALOGY. *Educ:* Univ Minn, BA, 48, MA, 50; Pa State Col, PhD(mineral), 52. *Prof Exp:* Res assoc geochem, Pa State Col, 52-53; proj engr, Stand Oil Co, Ind, 53-55; asst prof mineral, Univ Utah, 55-58; res dir, Tem-Pres, Inc, 58-59; chief zeolon unit, Norton Co, Mass, 59-67; PROF CHEM ENG, WORCESTER POLYTECH INST, 67- *Mem:* Fel Mineral Soc Am; Geochem Soc; Geol Soc Am; Am Inst Chem Eng; Clay Minerals Soc. *Res:* Geochemistry; hydrothermal phase chemistry; molecular sieve zeolites; catalysts, sorbents; ion exchangers. *Mailing Add:* Dept of Chem Eng Worcester Polytech Inst Worcester MA 01609

SAND, RALPH E, b Stamford, Conn, May 16, 21; c 2. PHYSICAL ORGANIC CHEMISTRY. *Educ:* Univ Conn, BS, 42; Polytech Inst Brooklyn, MS, 48, PhD(org chem), 50. *Prof Exp:* proj leader, Lab Advan Res, Remington Rand, Inc, 50-53; group leader, Res Ctr, Gen Foods, Inc, 53-61; sr chemist, Pratt & Whitney Div, United Aircraft Corp, 61-66; mgr pioneering res, Nat Biscuit Co, 66-70; dir tech develop, CPC Int, 70-71; SR CHEMIST ANAL METHODS DEVELOP, ANDERSON CLAYTON RES CTR, 71- *Mem:* Am Chem Soc; Sigma Xi; Inst Food Technologists; Am Asn Cereal Chemists. *Res:* Enzyme models; organic, photographic, lithographic, food, natural polymers, carbohydrates and proteins. *Mailing Add:* Anderson Clayton Foods W L Clayton Res Ctr Richardson TX 75080

SAND, SEAWARD ALWYN, b Lockport, NY, Sept 20, 22; m 48; c 6. GENETICS, PROTOPLAST FUSION. *Educ:* Cornell Univ, AB, 47, MS, 48, PhD(genetics), 55. *Prof Exp:* Instr high sch, NY, 48-50; asst plant breeding, Cornell Univ, 50-54; geneticist, Conn Agr Exp Sta, 54-64; GENETICIST, ROSWELL PARK MEM INST, 64- *Concurrent Pos:* Vis assoc prof, State Univ NY Long Island Ctr, 62; guest assoc geneticist, Brookhaven Nat Lab, 62-; Fulbright lectr, Trinity Col, Dublin, 63. *Mem:* Fel AAAS; Am Genetic Asn; Am Soc Naturalists; Genetics Soc Am; Am Inst Biol Sci. *Res:* Plant cytogenetics and radiation genetics; interspecific hybridization and evolution; biometrics and quantitative inheritance; gene mutation and action; gene-environmental interaction; genus Nicotiana; theoretical biology; cytoplasmic inheritance; plant cell and tissue culture. *Mailing Add:* Roswell Park Mem Inst Orchard Park Lab Orchard Park NY 14127

SANDA, ANTHONY ICHIRO, physics, see previous edition

SANDAGE, ALLAN REX, b Iowa City, Iowa, June 18, 26; m 59; c 2. ASTRONOMY. *Educ:* Univ Ill, AB, 48, Dsc, 67; Calif Inst Technol, PhD(astron), 53. *Hon Degrees:* DSc, Yale Univ, 66, Univ Chicago, 67; LLD, Univ Southern Calif, 71; ScD, Miami Univ, 74. *Prof Exp:* Asst astronr, 52-56, ASTRONR, MOUNT WILSON OBSERV, 56- *Concurrent Pos:* Rouse Ball lectr, Cambridge Univ, 57; lectr, Harvard Univ, 57 & Haverford Col, 58 & 66; consult, NSF, 62-63; mem vis comt, Nat Radio Astron Observ, 63-64, chmn, 65; mem comt astron facil, Nat Acad Sci, 64-65 & comt sci & pub policy, 65; fels, Australian Nat Univ, 68-69 & 72; Fulbright-Hays scholar, Australia, 72-73. *Honors & Awards:* Warner Prize, Am Astron Soc, 58; Eddington Medal, Royal Astron Soc, 63, Gold Medal, 70; Pope Pius XI Gold Medal, Pontifical Acad Sci, 66; Nat Medal of Sci, 71; Cresson Medal, Franklin Inst, 73; Russell Prize, Am Astron Soc, 73; Bruce Gold Medal, Astron Soc Pac, 75. *Mem:* Nat Acad Sci; AAAS; Am Astron Soc; Am Acad Arts & Sci; Royal Astron Soc. *Res:* Stellar evolution; photoelectric photometry; observational cosmology; galaxies; stellar kinematics; quasi-stellar radio sources; extragalactic distance scale; age and evolution of the universe. *Mailing Add:* 8319 Josard Rd San Gabriel CA 91775

SANDALL, ORVILLE CECIL, b Cupar, Sask, July 4, 39; m 61. CHEMICAL ENGINEERING. *Educ:* Univ Alta, BS, 61, MS, 63; Univ Calif, Berkeley, PhD(chem eng), 66. *Prof Exp:* Assoc prof, 66-81, PROF CHEM ENG, UNIV CALIF, SANTA BARBARA, 81- *Concurrent Pos:* Am Chem Soc fel, 67-70. *Mem:* Am Inst Chem Engrs; Am Chem Soc. *Res:* Gas absorption, heat and mass transfer in turbulent flow; heat transfer in non-Newtonian fluids; separation processes; freeze-drying of food stuffs. *Mailing Add:* Dept of Chem & Nuclear Eng Univ of Calif Santa Barbara CA 93106

SANDBERG, ANN LINNEA, b Denver, Colo. IMMUNOLOGY. *Educ:* Mont State Univ, BS, 60; Univ Chicago, PhD(pharmacol), 64. *Prof Exp:* USPHS training grant, Med Sch, Tufts Univ, 65-67; assoc immunol, Pub Health Res Inst, New York, 68-72; res biologist, 72-76, CHIEF HUMORAL IMMUNOL SECT LAB, NAT INST DENT RES, 76- *Concurrent Pos:* Res assoc prof, Med Sch, NY Univ, 71-72. *Mem:* AAAS; Am Asn Immunol. *Res:* Alternate pathway of complement activation; definition of system and its biological consequences. *Mailing Add:* Humoral Immunol Sect Lab Nat Inst of Dent Res Bethesda MD 20014

SANDBERG, AVERY ABA, b Poland, Jan 29, 21; nat US; m 43; c 4. INTERNAL MEDICINE. *Educ:* Wayne Univ, BS, 44, MD, 46; Am Bd Internal Med, dipl, 48. *Prof Exp:* Intern, Receiving Hosp, Detroit, Mich, 46-47; resident cardiol, Mt Sinai Hosp, New York, 49-50; resident med, Vet Admin Hosp, Salt Lake City, Utah, 50-51; resident instr med, Col Med, Univ Utah, 52-53, instr med, 53-54; assoc chief med, 54-57, CHIEF MED, ROSWELL PARK MEM INST, 57- *Concurrent Pos:* Dazian Found Med Res fel, 50; univ fel med & NIH res fel, Col Med, Univ Utah, 51-52, Dazian Found Med Res fel, 52-53, Am Cancer Soc scholar, 53-56; asst prof, Med Sch, Univ Buffalo, 54-, asst res prof, Grad Sch, 56-57, res prof, 57-; res prof, Canisius Col, 69- & Niagara Univ, 69-; consult, Med Found Buffalo, NY. *Mem:* Am Soc Clin Invest; Endocrine Soc; Am Soc Hemat; Am Asn Cancer Res; Am Fedn Clin Res. *Res:* Metabolism of steroids; metabolic changes in leukemia; cytogenetics of human leukemia and cancer. *Mailing Add:* Roswell Park Mem Inst 666 Elm St Buffalo NY 14203

SANDBERG, CARL LORENS, b Aniwa, Wis, July 24, 22; m 51; c 4. POLYMER CHEMISTRY. *Educ:* Univ Wis, BS, 48, MS, 49. *Prof Exp:* Chemist, Minn Mining & Mfg Co, 50-54, res chemist, 54-67, res specialist, 67-76, SR RES SPECIALIST, 3M CO, 76- *Mem:* Am Chem Soc. *Res:* Synthesis and characterization of organic and fluoro-organic polymers. *Mailing Add:* Cent Res Lab 3M Co St Paul MN 55133

SANDBERG, EUGENE CARL, b Ashtabula, Ohio, Jan 4, 24; m 53; c 2. OBSTETRICS & GYNECOLOGY. *Educ:* Univ Calif, AB, 45, MD, 48; Am Bd Obstet & Gynec, dipl, 59. *Prof Exp:* Intern, San Francisco City & County Hosp, 48-49; intern, Vanderbilt Univ Hosp, 49-50, asst resident, 50-51 & 53-54, resident, 54-55; from instr to asst prof, 55-64, ASSOC PROF OBSTET & GYNEC, SCH MED, STANFORD UNIV, 64- *Concurrent Pos:* Trainee steroid biochem, Worcester Found Exp Biol, 61-62; Macy Found fel, Col Physicians & Surgeons, Columbia Univ, 62-63. *Mem:* Am Col Obstet & Gynec; Soc Gynec Invest; Endocrine Soc. *Mailing Add:* Dept of Obstet & Gynec Stanford Univ Sch of Med Stanford CA 94305

SANDBERG, I(RWIN) W(ALTER), b New York, NY, Jan 23, 34; m 58; c 1. MATHEMATICS, ELECTRICAL ENGINEERING. *Educ:* Polytech Inst Brooklyn, BEE, 55, MEE, 56, DEE, 58. *Prof Exp:* Mem tech staff, 56 & 58-67, head, Systs Theory Res Dept, 67-72, MEM STAFF, MATH & STATISTICS RES CTR, BELL LABS, 72- *Mem:* Nat Acad Eng; fel Inst Elec & Electronic Engrs; AAAS; Sigma Xi. *Res:* Nonlinear analysis: network theory; theory of feedback systems; communication systems; differential equations; integral equations; functional analysis; numerical analysis; economics. *Mailing Add:* Bell Labs 600 Mountain Ave Murray Hill NJ 07974

SANDBERG, PHILIP A, b Cincinnati, Ohio, Mar 29, 37; c 2. GEOLOGY, PALEONTOLOGY. *Educ:* La State Univ, BS, 60, MS, 61; Univ Stockholm, Fil Lic, 64, Fil Dr(geol, paleont), 65. *Prof Exp:* From asst prof to assoc prof geol, 65-75, actg dept head, 77-78, PROF GEOL, UNIV ILL, URBANA, 75- *Concurrent Pos:* Vis assoc prof, Univ Minn, 70; NATO fel, Brit Mus Natural Hist, London, 72-73; vis assoc, Calif Inst Technol, 73; vis lectr, Philipps Univ, Marburg, WGer, 82. *Mem:* Int Paleont Union; Soc Econ Paleont & Mineral (vpres, 80-81); Paleont Soc; Int Asn Sedimentol. *Res:* Ultrastructure and chemistry of fossil and modern invertebrate skeletons; diagenesis of skeletal carbonates; scanning electro microscopy; Cenozoic microfossils; modern marine and estuarine microfaunas. *Mailing Add:* Dept Geol Univ Ill Urbana IL 61801

SANDBERG, ROBERT GUSTAVE, b Minneapolis, Minn, Mar 20, 39; m 59; c 3. CLINICAL BIOCHEMISTRY. *Educ:* Hamline Univ, BS, 61; Ohio State Univ, MS, 63. *Prof Exp:* Group leader polymers, Cargill Inc, 63-66; sr chemist, Hoerner-Waldorf Inc, 66-69; clin chemist, St Johns Hosp, 69-71; mkt planning mgr automatic clin anal, 75-80, PROD SUPVR CLIN CHEM, E I DU PONT DE NEMOURS & CO, INC, 71-, TECH MGR MKT, 80- *Mem:* Am Asn Clin Chem; Biomed Mkt Asn (pres, 79); Am Chem Soc. *Res:* Standards and control materials for clinical chemistry; development and marketing; automated clinical chemistry analyzers; preparation of stable enzyme solutions for verification of standard methods; evaluation of automated clinical chemistry and immunoassay methods. *Mailing Add:* Clin Systs Div Concord Plaza E I du Pont de Nemours & Co Inc Wilmington DE 19898

SANDBERG, VERNON DEAN, physics, see previous edition

SANDBORN, VIRGIL A, b Conway Springs, Kans, Apr 30, 28; m 55; c 2. AERONAUTICAL ENGINEERING. *Educ:* Univ Kans, BS, 50; Univ Mich, MS, 54. *Prof Exp:* Aeronaut res scientist, Nat Adv Comt Aeronaut, 51-58; aerospace res scientist, NASA, 58-61; consult scientist, Avco Corp, 61-62; prof aerodyn & fluid mech, 62-77, PROF CIVIL ENG, COLO STATE UNIV, 77- *Concurrent Pos:* Vis prof, Purdue Univ, 66- *Mem:* Am Inst Aeronaut & Astronaut. *Res:* Turbulent air flow; turbulent boundary layer flow; separation of boundary layers from surfaces. *Mailing Add:* Dept of Civil Eng Colo State Univ Ft Collins CO 80523

SANDE, RONALD DEAN, b Twin Falls, Idaho, July 3, 42; m 64; c 3. VETERINARY RADIOLOGY. *Educ:* Wash State Univ, DVM, 66, MS, 71, PhD(vet sci), 75. *Prof Exp:* Res vet radionuclides, Univ Utah, 66-67; resident vet med & surg, 68-69, instr, 69-70, from asst prof vet radiol to assoc prof, 71-77, assoc prof, 77-79, PROF VET CLIN MED & SURG, WASH STATE UNIV, 77- *Mem:* Am Col Vet Radiologists; Am Vet Radiol Soc; Am Vet Med Asn. *Res:* Inherited metabolic bone disorders in animals; animal models. *Mailing Add:* McCoy Hall Wash State Univ Pullman WA 99163

SANDEFUR, KERMIT LORAIN, b Arkansas City, Kans, Sept 1, 25; m 46; c 2. OPTICS. *Educ:* Univ Kans, BS, 50 & 51. *Prof Exp:* Assoc physicist, Midwest Res Inst, 51-56; sr res scientist, Hycon Mfg Co, Calif, 56-69; RES & DEVELOP ENG, LOCKHEED-CALIF CO, 69- *Res:* Photographic reconnaissance and infrared systems; supersonic flow; ballistics; optical systems analysis. *Mailing Add:* 3635 Landfair Rd Pasadena CA 91107

SANDEL, BILL ROY, b Brady, Tex, Nov 19, 45. SPACE PHYSICS. *Educ:* Rice Univ, BA, 68, MS, 71, PhD(space sci), 72. *Prof Exp:* Sr assoc-in-res, Kitt Peak Nat Observ, 73-78; res assoc planetary atmospheres, Lunar & Planetary Lab, Univ Ariz, 78-79; RES SCIENTIST, EARTH & SPACE SCI INST, UNIV SOUTHERN CALIF, 79- *Concurrent Pos:* Co-investr Voyager ultraviolet spectrometer exp. *Mem:* Am Geophys Union; Am Astron Soc. *Res:* Atmospheric and space physics of the outer planets; ultraviolet spectroscopy; development of ultraviolet imaging detectors. *Mailing Add:* Earth & Space Sci Inst Univ Southern Calif Los Angeles CA 90007

SANDEL, THOMAS THEODORE, b Dallas, Tex, Jan 2, 24; m 47; c 4. PHYSIOLOGICAL PSYCHOLOGY. *Educ:* Univ Tex, Austin, BA, 48, MA, 50, PhD(psychol), 54. *Prof Exp:* Res scientist, Defense Res Lab, Univ Tex, 51-54; mem staff, Res Lab Electronics, Mass Inst Technol, 55-59, Lincoln Lab, 59-63, Ctr Develop Off, 63-64; PROF PSYCHOL, WASHINGTON UNIV, 64-, CHMN DEPT PSYCHOL, 69- *Concurrent Pos:* Nat Inst Neurol Dis & Blindness fel, 55-57; consult, Adv Comt Comput Res, NIH, 63. *Mem:*

Fel Acoust Soc Am; Psychonomic Soc. *Res:* Biological communication: coding and transmission of information in nervous systems; embryonic development of behavior. *Mailing Add:* Dept of Psychol Washington Univ St Louis MO 63130

SANDEL, VERNON RALPH, b Marquette, Mich, June 4, 33; m 59; c 2. PHYSICAL ORGANIC CHEMISTRY. *Educ:* Mich Tech Univ, BS, 55; Northwestern Univ, PhD(org photochem), 62. *Prof Exp:* Chemist, Ethyl Corp, 55-57; spec proj chemist, Dow Chem Co, Mich, 61-62; res chemist, Eastern Res Lab, Mass, 63-67; ASSOC PROF CHEM, MICH TECHNOL UNIV, 67- *Mem:* Am Chem Soc; Sigma Xi. *Res:* Nuclear magnetic resonance of carbanions; carbanion chemistry; organic reaction mechanisms. *Mailing Add:* Dept Chem Mich Technol Univ Houghton MI 49931

SANDELL, DEWEY JAY, physical chemistry, deceased

SANDELL, ERNEST BIRGER, b Minneapolis, Minn, Feb 20, 06. CHEMISTRY. *Educ:* Univ Minn, BS, 28, MS, 29, PhD(anal chem), 32. *Prof Exp:* Asst, 28-31, from instr to assoc prof, 32-46, PROF ANAL CHEM, UNIV MINN, MINNEAPOLIS, 46- *Concurrent Pos:* Vis prof, Cairo Univ, 60; adv, US Geol Surv. *Mem:* AAAS; Am Chem Soc; Geol Soc Am; fel Royal Chem Soc; Geochem Soc. *Res:* Inorganic and photometric trace analysis; microanalysis; geochemistry. *Mailing Add:* 4424 Victory Ave Minneapolis MN 55412

SANDELL, LIONEL SAMUEL, b Montreal, Que, May 29, 45; m 71. WATER GEL EXPLOSIVES, OPACIFYING PIGMENTS. *Educ:* McGill Univ, BSc, 66, PhD(phys chem), 70. *Prof Exp:* From postdoctoral assoc to res assoc, State Univ NY Col Environ Sci & Forestry, 70-73; res chemist colloid chem, Pigments Dept, 73-78, res chemist, 78-80, SR CHEMIST WATER GEL EXPLOSIVES, PETROCHEM DEPT, E I DU PONT DE NEMOURS & CO, INC, 80- *Mem:* Am Chem Soc; Sigma Xi; AAAS. *Res:* Developed method to prevent gel breakdown in water gel explosives; developed novel opacifying pigments for paint, paper, and other items; flexibility of glycosidic linkage in sugars from monolayer studies. *Mailing Add:* Petrochem Dept Dupont Co Inc Drawer 863 Martinsburg WV 25401

SANDENAW, THOMAS ARTHUR, b Helena, Mont, Apr 20, 10; m 33; c 3. METAL PHYSICS. *Educ:* Mont State Col, BS, 34; Carnegie Inst Technol, MS, 39. *Prof Exp:* Jr chemist anal, US Navy Dept, Munhall, Pa, 39-41; asst chem & assoc engr mat tests, Panama Canal, Diablo Heights, CZ, 41-43; assoc engr concrete res, Cincinnati Testing Lab, Ohio, 43-44; engr res & develop, RCA Corp, Pa, 44-48; staff mem res, 48-74, CONSULT, LOS ALAMOS NAT LAB, 74- *Mem:* Am Forestry Asn; Am Chem Soc; fel Am Inst Chemists. *Res:* Consequences of martensitic transformations in actinide materials: two-phase systems, valence fluctuations, charge-density waves, incommensurate structures, discommensurations, solitons and shape memory. *Mailing Add:* 762-A 45th St Los Alamos NM 87544

SANDER, CHARLES H, b Lansing, Mich, Mar 2, 33. MEDICINE, PATHOLOGY. *Educ:* Mich State Univ, BS, 55; Univ Mich, MD, 58; Univ London, dipl clin path, 64; Am Bd Path, dipl, 66. *Prof Exp:* From instr to assoc prof, 65-76, PROF PATH, COL HUMAN MED, MICH STATE UNIV, 76- *Res:* Comparative pathology, particularly oncology; pathology of the placenta; pulmonary pathology. *Mailing Add:* Dept of Path Mich State Univ East Lansing MI 48824

SANDER, DONALD HENRY, b Creston, Nebr, Apr 21, 33; m 53; c 2. AGRONOMY. *Educ:* Univ Nebr, BS, 54, MS, 58, PhD(agron, soils), 67. *Prof Exp:* Soil scientist, US Forest Serv, 58-64; asst prof agron, Exten, Kans State Univ, 64-67; assoc prof, 67-80, PROF AGRON, EXTEN, UNIV NEBR, LINCOLN, 80- *Mem:* Am Soc Agron; Soil Sci Soc Am. *Res:* Influence soil properties, especially nutrients and nutrient interactions on plant growth and composition. *Mailing Add:* 1616 Devoe Dr Lincoln NE 68506

SANDER, DUANE E, b Sioux Falls, SDak, Feb 14, 38; m 60; c 4. ELECTRICAL ENGINEERING. *Educ:* SDak Sch Mines & Technol, BS, 60; Iowa State Univ, MS, 62, PhD(elec eng), 64. *Prof Exp:* Instr elec eng, Iowa State Univ, 60-63; res asst, 63-64; intel analyst, US Army Foreign Sci & Technol Ctr, Washington, DC, 65-67; assoc prof elec eng, 67-75, PROF ELEC ENG, S DAK STATE UNIV, 75- *Concurrent Pos:* Consult, Med Eng Serv Asn, 77- *Mem:* Inst Elec & Electronics Engrs; Int Soc Hybrid Microelectronics. *Res:* Bioengineering and data acquisition; clinical engineering. *Mailing Add:* Dept of Elec Eng SDak State Univ Brookings SD 57006

SANDER, EUGENE GEORGE, b Fargo, NDak, Sept 17, 35; m 79; c 2. ENZYMOLOGY. *Educ:* Univ Minn, BS, 57; Cornell Univ, MS, 59, PhD(biochem), 65. *Prof Exp:* NIH fel biochem, Brandeis Univ, 65-67; asst prof, Dept Biochem, Univ Fla, 67-70, assoc prof, 70-75, prof, 75-76; prof & chmn dept, WVa Univ, 76-80; PROF & IIEAD, DEPT BIOCHEM & BIOPHYSICS, TEX A&M UNIV, 80- *Mem:* Am Chem Soc; Am Soc Biol Chemists; Sigma Xi; Biophys Soc; Am Inst Nutrit. *Res:* Mechanism of action of enzymes involved in dihydropyrimidine synthesis and degradation along with related organic model systems. *Mailing Add:* Dept Biochem & Biophysics Tex A&M Univ College Station TX 77843

SANDER, LEONARD MICHAEL, b St Louis, Mo, Aug 17, 41; m 64; c 1. PHYSICS. *Educ:* Washington Univ, BS, 63; Univ Calif, Berkeley, MA, 66, PhD, 68. *Prof Exp:* NSF fel physics, Univ Calif, San Diego, 68-69; asst prof, 69-74, ASSOC PROF PHYSICS, UNIV MICH, ANN ARBOR, 74- *Mem:* Am Phys Soc. *Res:* Theoretical solid state physics. *Mailing Add:* 1206 Henry St Ann Arbor MI 48109

SANDER, LINDA DIAN, b Harrisburg, Pa, Sept 2, 47; m 70; c 3. MEDICAL PHYSIOLOGY, GASTROINTESTINAL ENDOCRINOLOGY. *Educ:* Ariz State Univ, BS, 69; Univ Okla, PhD(physiol), 73. *Prof Exp:* Fel, Dept Physiol, Med Sch, Univ Tex, Houston, 73-76; ASST PROF, DEPT PHYSIOL, MED CTR, LA STATE UNIV, NEW ORLEANS, 76- *Mem:* Am Physiol Soc; Soc Exp Biol & Med. *Res:* The role of gastrointestinal hormones and brain-gut polypeptides on pituitary adrenal hormonal secretion and circadian rhythms; influence of stress on gastrointestinal function. *Mailing Add:* Dept Physiol Med Ctr La State Univ 1901 Perdido New Orleans LA 70112

SANDER, LOUIS FRANK, b Rockville Centre, NY, Aug 1, 33; m 56; c 3. METALLURGY, MATERIALS SCIENCE. *Educ:* Marquette Univ, BSME, 55, MS, 61; Pa State Univ, PhD(metall), 66. *Prof Exp:* Engr, Refining Div, Mobil Oil Co, 58-59; instr eng, Marquette Univ, 59-61; from asst prof to assoc prof, 61-72, PROF ENG, VILLANOVA UNIV, 72-, CHMN DEPT MECH ENG, 70- *Concurrent Pos:* NSF grant, 63-65; consult, Pitman-Dunn Labs, US Army, Frankford Arsenal, 62, 68, E W Bliss Co, 63, Titanium Metals Corp, 67-68 & Naval Air Eng Ctr, 71- *Mem:* AAAS; Am Soc Metals; Am Inst Mining, Metall & Petrol Engrs; Am Soc Eng Educ; fel Am Inst Chem. *Res:* Solid lubricants; metal sulfide-metal oxide equilibria; high temperature plasticity of titanium alloys; heat capacity of solids; sulfidation of metals; fracture toughness; mechanical engineering; failure analysis. *Mailing Add:* Dept of Mech Eng Villanova Univ Villanova PA 19085

SANDER, LOUIS W, b San Francisco, Calif, July 31, 18; m 53; c 3. PSYCHIATRY. *Educ:* Univ Calif, AB, 39, MD, 42; Boston Psychoanal Inst, grad, 61; Am Bd Psychiat & Neurol, dipl, 51. *Prof Exp:* Asst psychiat, Sch Med, Boston Univ, 47-51, instr, 51-57, asst prof, 54-58, res psychiatrist, Univ Med Ctr, 54-78, from asst res prof to assoc res prof, 58-68, prof psychiat, 68-78; PROF PSYCHIAT, SCH MED, UNIV COLO, 78- *Concurrent Pos:* Asst, Mass Mem Hosps, 48-55, asst vis physician, 55-59, assoc vis physician, 59-78; mem staff, James Jackson Putnam Children's Ctr, 50-53; jr vis physician, Boston City Hosp, 53-57, assoc vis physician, Pediat Serv, 57-78, USPHS grants, 54-78, career develop award, 63-68; consult, Bd Missions, Methodist Church, 54-60; res scientist award, Nat Inst Ment Health, 68 & 73-78. *Mem:* Am Psychiat Asn; Am Acad Child Psychiat; Soc Res Child Develop; Am Col Psychoanalysts; AAAS. *Res:* Early personality development, especially in relation to the influence of maternal personality on mother-child interactions; investigation of neonatal state regulation in the caretaking systems by non-intrusive bassinet monitoring; twenty-five year longitudinal study of personality development. *Mailing Add:* 4200 E 9th Ave Container C249 Denver CO 80262

SANDER, NESTOR JOHN, b Oakland, Calif, Dec 5, 14; m 46. GEOLOGY, PALEONTOLOGY. *Educ:* Univ Calif, Berkeley, BA, 36, MA, 38; Univ Paris, DSc(geol), 52. *Prof Exp:* Paleontologist, Stand Oil Co Calif, 38; geologist, Calif Arabian Stand Oil Co, 38-41; geologist, Stand Oil Co Calif, 41-42; sr geologist & asst chief geologist, Arabian Am Oil Co, 46-55; sr staff geologist, Conorada Petrol Corp, 55-63; sr staff geologist, Amoco Int Oil Co, 63-68, chief res geologist, 68-77; RETIRED. *Mem:* Am Asn Petrol Geologists. *Res:* Regional stratigraphy and structure with emphasis on evaluation of petroleum potential; larger Foraminifera of the Tertiary of the Middle East. *Mailing Add:* Casa Hesperis Travesia de Munoz Grandes 11 Matalpino Madrid Spain

SANDER, WILLIAM AUGUST, III, b Charleston, SC, May 11, 42; m 67; c 2. ELECTRONICS. *Educ:* Clemson Univ, BS, 64; Duke Univ, MS, 67, PhD(elec eng), 73. *Prof Exp:* Res asst, Duke Univ, 67-70; engr, Commun & Electronics Bd, US Army Airborne, 70-75; STAFF SCIENTIST RES MGT, US ARMY RES OFF, 75- *Concurrent Pos:* Instr, Fayetteville State Univ, 74-75. *Mem:* Inst Elec & Electronics Engrs; Sigma Xi. *Res:* Signal processing; electronic circuit design. *Mailing Add:* US Army Res Off PO Box 12211 Research Triangle Park NC 27709

SANDERFER, PAUL OTIS, b Union City, Tenn, Mar 1, 37; m 59; c 1. ORGANIC CHEMISTRY. *Educ:* Union Univ, BS, 59; Univ Fla, PhD(org chem), 65. *Prof Exp:* Asst prof chem, 65-71, ASSOC PROF CHEM & PHYSICS, WINTHROP COL, 71-, ACTG CHMN DEPT CHEM & PHYSICS, 81- *Mem:* Am Chem Soc. *Res:* Kinetic studies of reaction mechanisms; organic synthesis. *Mailing Add:* Dept of Chem & Physics Winthrop Col Rock Hill SC 29733

SANDERS, AARON PERRY, b Phoenix, Ariz, Jan 12, 24; m 44; c 3. CELL PHYSIOLOGY, RADIOBIOLOGY. *Educ:* Tex Western Col, BS, 50; Univ Rochester, MS, 52; Univ NC, PhD(physiol, biochem), 64. *Prof Exp:* Assoc health physicist, Brookhaven Nat Lab, 51-53; instr physics & radiol safety officer, NC State Col, 53; asst prof physiol, 67-75, dir radiobiol lab, 53-65, from instr to assoc prof radiobiol, 53-70, PROF RADIOBIOL, MED CTR, DUKE UNIV, 70-, DIR DIV RADIOBIOL, 65- *Concurrent Pos:* Fulbright lectr, Arg, 58-59. *Mem:* AAAS; Am Asn Physicists in Med; Health Physics Soc; Soc Nuclear Med; Soc Exp Biol & Med. *Res:* Biophysics; effects of radiation and hyperbaric oxygen on cell functions; methods of protection of central nervous system and facilitation of post-ischemia central nervous system recovery; metabolic alterations in malignant tissues. *Mailing Add:* Div Radiobiol Med Ctr Duke Univ Durham NC 27710

SANDERS, BENJAMIN ELBERT, b Bowersville, Ga, Oct 19, 18; m 46; c 2. BIOCHEMISTRY. *Educ:* Wofford Col, BS, 39; Univ Ga, MS, 42; Purdue Univ, PhD(chem), 49; Am Bd Clin Chemists, dipl. *Prof Exp:* Asst chem, Univ Ga, 39-42; res biochemist, Dept Labs, Henry Ford Hosp, 49-51; res assoc immunichem, Merck, Sharp & Dohme, 51-53, protein chem, Merck Inst Therapeut Res, 53-58, dir, 58-61; assoc prof, 61-67, PROF BIOCHEM, STATE UNIV NY BUFFALO, 67- *Mem:* Fel AAAS; Am Soc Biol Chem; Am Chem Soc; NY Acad Sci. *Res:* Isolation and characterization plasma proteins; biochemistry schizophrenia; clinical chemistry; immunoglobulins. *Mailing Add:* Dept of Biochem State Univ of NY Buffalo NY 14214

SANDERS, BOBBY GENE, b Rhodell, WVa, Apr 16, 32; m 51; c 4. IMMUNOGENETICS. *Educ:* Concord Col, BS, 54; Pa State Univ, MEd, 58, PhD(genetics), 61. *Prof Exp:* Asst prof biol, Lafayette Col, 61-64; fel immunogenetics, Calif Inst Technol, 64-66, asst prof biol, 66-68; assoc prof, 68-74, PROF ZOOL, UNIV TEX, AUSTIN, 74- *Mem:* AAAS; Genetics Soc Am; Am Genetic Asn. *Res:* Genetic mechanism resulting in the synthesis of immunoglobulin molecules. *Mailing Add:* Dept of Zool Univ of Tex at Austin Austin TX 78712

SANDERS, BOBBY LEE, b Ben Wheeler, Tex, Jan 12, 35; m 54; c 2. APPLIED MATHEMATICS. *Educ:* ETex State Univ, BS, 56; Fla State Univ, MS, 58, PhD(math), 62; Southern Methodist Univ, JD, 77. *Prof Exp:* Instr math, Fla State Univ, 57-58; from asst prof to prof math, Tex Christian Univ, 62-77; PARTNER, SANDERS & SANDERS, 77- *Mem:* Am Math Soc; Math Asn Am. *Res:* Structure theory of Banach spaces; functional analysis; categorical applications; applications of finite mathematical structures; quantitative and qualitative applications of mathematics to judicial problems and processes. *Mailing Add:* Sanders & Sanders PO Box 416 Canton TX 75103

SANDERS, CHARLES ADDISON, b Dallas, Tex, Feb 10, 32; m 56; c 4. CARDIOLOGY. *Educ:* Univ Tex Southwestern Med Sch Dallas, MD, 55. *Prof Exp:* Intern & asst resident med serv, Boston City Hosp, Mass, 55-57, chief resident, 57-58; clin & res fel cardiol, Mass Gen Hosp, 58-60, prog dir myocardial infarction res unit, 67-72, prog dir medlab systs, 69-73, assoc physician, 70-73, chief cardiac catheter unit, 62-72, gen dir, 72-81, physician, 73-81; EXEC VPRES, E R SQUIBB & SONS INC, 81- *Concurrent Pos:* Instr, Harvard Med Sch, 64-66, assoc, 66-68, asst prof, 69, assoc prof, 69-80. *Mem:* Am Fedn Clin Res; Am Heart Asn; Am Col Physicians; Asn Univ Cardiol; Am Soc Clin Invest. *Mailing Add:* E R Squibb & Sons PO Box 4000 Princeton NJ 08540

SANDERS, CHARLES F(RANKLIN), JR, b Louisville, Ky, Dec 22, 31; m 56; c 3. CHEMICAL ENGINEERING, MECHANICAL ENGINEERING. *Educ:* Univ Louisville, BChE, 54, MChE, 58; Univ Southern Calif, PhD(chem eng), 70. *Prof Exp:* Engr, Esso Res & Eng Co, 55-62; from asst prof to assoc prof eng, 62-71, chmn dept thermal-fluid systs, 69-72, dean, Sch Eng & Comput Sci, 72-81, PROF ENG, CALIF STATE UNIV, NORTHRIDGE, 71- *Concurrent Pos:* Consult, KVB Eng Co, 70- *Mem:* Am Inst Chem Engrs; Am Soc Eng Educ; Combustion Inst; Nat Soc Prof Engrs. *Res:* Combustion; pollution from combustion; radiative transfer through particulate clouds; combustion modelling. *Mailing Add:* 11164 Bertrand Ave Granada Hills CA 91344

SANDERS, CHARLES IRVINE, b Baltimore, Md, Feb 18, 36; m 57; c 3. CHEMISTRY. *Educ:* Clemson Univ, BS, 56; Iowa State Univ, MS, 59, PhD(phys chem), 61. *Prof Exp:* Asst chem, Iowa State Univ, 56-61; res chemist, 61-68, res supvr, 68-70, sr res scientist, Res & Develop Ctr, 70-77, mgr physics res, Anal Dept, Armstrong Cork Co, 77-80, MGR TECH SERV, ANAL DEPT, ARMSTRONG WORLD INDUST INC, 80- *Concurrent Pos:* Resident indust scientist, Pa Tech Assistance Prog, Pa State Univ, 69. *Mem:* Am Chem Soc. *Res:* Physical chemistry of polymers; analytical chemistry; scanning electron microscopy; radiochemistry. *Mailing Add:* Res & Develop Ctr Armstrong World Indust Inc PO Box 3511 Lancaster PA 17604

SANDERS, CHARLES LEONARD, JR, b Chicago, Ill, Dec 27, 38; m 63; c 3. RADIOBIOLOGY. *Educ:* Col William & Mary, BS, 60; Tex A&M Univ, MS, 63; Univ Rochester, PhD(radiobiol), 66. *Prof Exp:* AEC fel, 66-68, res assoc, 68-78, STAFF SCIENTIST INHALATION TOXICOL, LIFE SCI DEPT, PAC NORTHWEST LABS, BATTELLE MEM INST, 78- *Concurrent Pos:* Affil asst prof, Univ Wash, 75-80, affil prof, 80-; mem, Nat Coun Radiation Protection & Measurements. *Res:* Inhalation toxicology and carcinogenesis of plutonium and other transuranic elements, and of beryllium, lead, mercury, cadmium, asbestos, silica and volcanic ash. *Mailing Add:* Baftelle Mem Inst Batelle Blvd Richland WA 99352

SANDERS, CHRISTINE CULP, b Tampa, Fla, Sept 3, 48; m 74. MEDICAL MICROBIOLOGY, INFECTIOUS DISEASES. *Educ:* Univ Fla, BS, 70, PhD(med microbiol), 73. *Prof Exp:* Technician microbiol, Shands Teaching Hosp & Clin, 69-70; chief technologist, Alachua Gen Hosp, 70; asst prof, 73-79, ASSOC PROF MICROBIOL, SCH MED, CREIGHTON UNIV, 79- *Concurrent Pos:* Res award, Sigma Xi, 74. *Mem:* Am Soc Microbiol; Am Fedn Clin Res; Infectious Dis Soc Am; NY Acad Sci. *Res:* Bacterial interference; evaluation of new antimicrobial agents; cell wall deficient bacteria; antimicrobial antagonisms. *Mailing Add:* Dept Med Microbiol Sch Med Creighton Univ Omaha NE 68178

SANDERS, COREY LEROY, b Hillier, Ont, Apr 27, 24; m 46; c 3. PHOTOMETRY. *Educ:* Univ Toronto, BA, 50; Univ London, PhD(physics), 55. *Prof Exp:* Assoc res officer photom, Nat Res Coun Can, 50-69, sr res officer, 69-79; RETIRED. *Concurrent Pos:* Mem, Can Nat Comt, Int Comn Illum, 60-79, pres, 63-67, chmn, Photom Comt, 71-; mem, Photom Comt, Int Comn Weights & Measures, 61-79. *Mem:* Fel Optical Soc Am. *Res:* Spectroradiometry; primary standard of light. *Mailing Add:* 2060 Beaverhill Dr Ottawa ON K1J 6P1 Can

SANDERS, DARRYL PAUL, b Arch, NMex, Feb 11, 36; m 62; c 2. ENTOMOLOGY. *Educ:* Tex Tech Col, BS, 59; Purdue Univ, MS, 64, PhD(entom), 67. *Prof Exp:* Exten entomologist, Purdue Univ, 65-67; teaching & res entomologist, Tex A&M Univ, 67-70; teaching & exten entomologist, Purdue Univ, West Lafayette, 70-75; PROF ENTOM & CHMN DEPT, TEX TECH UNIV, 76- *Mem:* Entom Soc Am; Am Mosquito Control Asn; Am Registry Prof Entomologists. *Res:* Insects affecting man and livestock. *Mailing Add:* Dept of Entom Tex Tech Univ Lubbock TX 79409

SANDERS, DAVID MICHAEL, b Hershey, Pa, May 30, 47; m 68; c 2. MATERIALS SCIENCE, THIN FILMS. *Educ:* Alfred Univ, BS, 69; Univ Fla, PhD(mat), 73. *Prof Exp:* Res chemist glass vaporization, 73-77, GEN PHYSICAL SCIENTIST THIN FILMS, NAT BUR STANDARDS, 77-*Mem:* Am Ceramic Soc; Soc Appl Spectros; Am Vacuum Soc. *Res:* Glass; vaporization; surface science; fracture mechanics; solar energy; corrosion. *Mailing Add:* Rm B328 Bldg 223 Nat Bur of Standards Washington DC 20234

SANDERS, DOUGLAS CHARLES, b Lansing, Mich, May 21, 42; m 65. HORTICULTURE, PLANT PHYSIOLOGY. *Educ:* Mich State Univ, BS, 65; Univ Minn, MS, 69, PhD(hort), 70. *Prof Exp:* Res fel hort, Univ Minn, 69-70; exten asst prof, 70-75, EXTEN ASSOC PROF HORT, NC STATE UNIV, 75- *Mem:* Am Soc Hort Sci; Am Soc Agron; Crop Sci Soc Am; Sigma Xi; Potato Asn Am. *Res:* Vegetable crop cultural practices; crop microclimate modification; influence of climate on plant physiology. *Mailing Add:* 230 Kilgore Hall NC State Univ Raleigh NC 27650

SANDERS, FRANK CLARENCE, JR, b Tiquisate, Guatemala, Dec 26, 40; US citizen; m 63; c 2. ATOMIC PHYSICS, MOLECULAR PHYSICS. *Educ:* Univ Tex, Austin, BS, 63, PhD(physics), 68. *Prof Exp:* Asst prof physics, Univ Tex, Austin, 68-69; asst prof, 69-77, ASSOC PROF PHYSICS, UNIV SOUTHERN ILL, CARBONDALE, 77- *Mem:* Am Phys Soc; Am Asn Physics Teachers. *Res:* Theoretical atomic and molecular physics; perturbation theory and its application to simple atomic and molecular systems. *Mailing Add:* Dept Physics Southern Ill Univ Carbondale IL 62901

SANDERS, FREDERICK, b Detroit, Mich, May 17, 23; m 46; c 3. METEOROLOGY. *Educ:* Amherst Col, BA, 44; Mass Inst Technol, ScD, 54. *Prof Exp:* Aviation forecaster, US Weather Bur, 47-49; asst, 49-52, from instr to assoc prof, 52-69, PROF METEOROL, MASS INST TECHNOL, 69-*Mem:* Fel Am Meteorol Soc; Royal Meteorol Soc. *Res:* Application of approach, methods and results of theoretical meteorology to prediction; forecasting in probabilistic terms; synthesis of observations in theoretically meaningful terms. *Mailing Add:* Rm 54-1612 Mass Inst of Technol Cambridge MA 02139

SANDERS, GARY HILTON, b New York, NY, Aug 27, 46; m 73; c 2. PARTICLE PHYSICS. *Educ:* Columbia Univ, AB, 67; Mass Inst Technol, PhD(physics), 71. *Prof Exp:* Res asst high energy physics, Mass Inst Technol, 67-71; res assoc physics, Princeton Univ, 71-73, asst prof, 73-78; STAFF MEM, LOS ALAMOS SCI LAB, 78- *Concurrent Pos:* Vis scientist, Deutsches Elektronen Synchrotron, Hamburg, 68-71; NSF fel, 71-72; vis scientist, Brookhaven Nat Lab, 71-74 & Fermi Nat Accelerator Lab, Ill, 75-*Mem:* Am Phys Soc; Sigma Xi. *Res:* Experimental studies of elementary particles including quantum electrodynamics, photoproduction of vector mesons, hyperon beta decay, hadronic production of dimuons, new particles and hypernuclear physics, rare decays of muons; particle beam physics. *Mailing Add:* Los Alamos Sci Lab PO Box 1663 Los Alamos NM 87545

SANDERS, HARVEY DAVID, b Winnipeg, Man, June 22, 25; m 59; c 4. PHARMACOLOGY, PHYSIOLOGY. *Educ:* Univ BC, BSP, 59, MSP, 61, MD, 72; Univ Man, PhD(pharmacol), 63; FRCP(C), 77. *Prof Exp:* Lectr pharmacog, 59-60, lectr chem, 61- from instr to asst prof pharmacol, 64-69, ASSOC PROF PHARMACOL & MED, UNIV BC, 69- *Concurrent Pos:* Ford fel, 63-64; McEachern fel, 64-66. *Mem:* Am Soc Pharmacol & Exp Therapeut; Am Fedn Clin Res; NY Acad Sci; Can Med Asn; Am Col Physicians. *Res:* Effects of centrally active drugs on responses of the cerebral cortex to electrical stimulation; intracellular and extracellular recordings; cardiovascular effects of local anesthetics; pharmacology of the human urinary bladder. *Mailing Add:* Dept of Pharmacol Univ of BC Vancouver BC V6T 1W5 Can

SANDERS, HOWARD L(AWRENCE), b Newark, NJ, Mar 17, 21; m 49; c 2. ZOOLOGY. *Educ:* Univ BC, BA, 49; Univ RI, MS, 51; Yale Univ, PhD(zool), 55. *Prof Exp:* From res assoc marine biol to assoc scientist, 55-66, SR SCIENTIST, WOODS HOLE OCEANOG INST, 66- *Concurrent Pos:* Instr, Marine Biol Lab, Woods Hole, 58-66. *Mem:* Fel AAAS; Am Soc Limnol & Oceanog. *Res:* Deep sea benthic ecology; marine pollution biology; invertebrate zoology. *Mailing Add:* Woods Hole Oceanog Inst Woods Hole MA 02543

SANDERS, J(OHN) LYELL, JR, b Highland, Wis, Sept 11, 24; m 60; c 3. STRUCTURAL MECHANICS. *Educ:* Purdue Univ, BSc, 45; Mass Inst Technol, ScM, 50; Brown Univ, PhD(appl math), 54. *Hon Degrees:* MA, Harvard Univ, 60. *Prof Exp:* Res engr, Nat Adv Comt Aeronaut, 54-57; vis lectr struct mech, 57-58, lectr, 58-60, assoc prof, 60-64, GORDON McKAY PROF STRUCT MECH, HARVARD UNIV, 64- *Concurrent Pos:* NSF sr fel, Delft Technol Univ, 67-68. *Mem:* Am Soc Mech Engrs; fel Am Acad Arts & Sci. *Res:* Theory of thin shells; theory of plasticity and fracture mechanics. *Mailing Add:* Pierce Hall Harvard Univ Cambridge MA 02138

SANDERS, JAMES GRADY, b Norfolk, Va, June 10, 51; m 72. TRACE METAL BIOGEOCHEMISTRY, PHYTOPLANKTON ECOLOGY. *Educ:* Duke Univ, BS, 73; Univ NC, Chapel Hill, MS, 75, PhD(marine sci), 78. *Prof Exp:* Fel, Woods Hole Oceanog Inst, 78-80; vis asst prof, Chesapeake Biol Lab, Ctr Environ & Estuarine studies, Univ Md, 80-81; ASST CURATOR, BENEDICT ESTUARINE RES LAB, DIV ENVIRON RES, ACAD NATURAL SCI, 81- *Concurrent Pos:* vis lectr, Dept Earth Sci, Bridgewater State Col, 80; vis prof, Chesapeake Biol Lab, Ctr Environ Estuarine Studies, Univ Md, 82- *Mem:* AAAS; Am Soc Limnol & Oceanog; Estuarine & Brackish Water Sci Asn; Estuarine Res Fedn; Psycholog Soc Am. *Res:* Impact of marine phytoplankton on trace metal transfer in food webs; biogeochemical cycling of metals and metalloids; effects of sublethal concentrations of toxic substances on the morphology growth, and community structure of marine phytoplankton and zooplankton. *Mailing Add:* Benedict Estuarine Lab Div Environ Res Acad Natural Sci Benedict MD 20612

SANDERS, JAMES VINCENT, b Twinsburg, Ohio, July 24, 32; m 55; c 4. UNDERWATER ACOUSTICS, FLUID DYNAMICS. *Educ:* Kent State Univ, BS, 54; Cornell Univ, PhD(physics), 61. *Prof Exp:* Asst prof, 61-68, ASSOC PROF PHYSICS, NAVAL POSTGRAD SCH, 68- *Res:* Fluid mechanics of non-Newtonian fluids; large amplitude standing acoustic waves; interaction of acoustic waves with fluid flow; acoustic properties of the ocean. *Mailing Add:* Dept of Physics Naval Postgrad Sch Monterey CA 93940

SANDERS, JAY W, b Baltimore, Md, July 26, 24; m 50; c 3. AUDIOLOGY. *Educ:* Univ NC, AB, 50; Columbia Univ, MA, 51; Univ Mo, PhD(speech path), 57. *Prof Exp:* Instr speech, Univ Mo, 52-57; from asst prof to assoc prof, Trenton State Col, 57-62; PROF AUDIOL, VANDERBILT UNIV, 70-; MEM STAFF, BILL WILKERSON HEARING & SPEECH CTR, 64-*Concurrent Pos:* Nat Inst Neurol Dis & Blindness fel audiol, Northwestern Univ, 62-64; consult, St Francis Hosp, Hearing & Speech Ctr, Trenton, NJ, 61-62; asst prof, Vanderbilt Univ, 64-65, assoc prof, 65-70. *Mem:* Am Speech & Hearing Asn. *Res:* Audition; disorders of audition and diagnostic audiology. *Mailing Add:* Wilkerson Hearing & Speech Ctr 1114 19th Ave S Nashville TN 37212

SANDERS, JOHN CLAYTOR, b Roanoke, Va, Oct 29, 14; m 54; c 2. MECHANICAL ENGINEERING, AERONAUTICS. *Educ:* Va Polytech Inst, BS, 36, MS, 37. *Prof Exp:* Indust engr, Aluminum Co Am, 37-39; aeronaut res scientist, NASA, 39-58, asst chief advan systs div, Lewis Res Ctr, 58-77; RETIRED. *Concurrent Pos:* Mem subcomt internal flow, Nat Adv Comt Aeronaut, 47-48, subcomt power plant controls, NASA, 53-58 & subcomt struct dynamics, 63-64; consult indust automation & control. *Mem:* Fel Am Soc Mech Engrs. *Res:* Dynamics and control of aircraft and missile propulsion systems, including propeller engines, jet engines, chemical rockets and nuclear rockets. *Mailing Add:* 15305 Forest Park Ave Strongsville OH 44136

SANDERS, JOHN D, b Louisville, Ky, Aug 2, 38; m 67; c 1. ELECTRICAL ENGINEERING. *Educ:* Univ Louisville, BEE, 61; Carnegie-Mellon Univ, MS, 62, PhD(elec eng), 65. *Prof Exp:* Develop engr, Receiving Tube Dept, Gen Elec Co, Ky, 61; mem tech staff, Radio Corp Am Labs, NJ, 62; instr elec eng, Carnegie-Mellon Univ, 62-64; proj officer, US Cent Intel Agency, 64-68; V PRES, WACHTEL & CO, INC, 68- *Concurrent Pos:* Asst prof lectr, George Washington Univ, 67-68; financial adv, Indust Training Corp, Radiation Systs, Inc, Tork, Inc, Fla Glass Indust & Temporaries, Inc. *Mem:* Inst Elec & Electronics Engrs; Financial Analysts Fedn; Nat Security Traders Asn. *Res:* Aiding management of small technical companies, primarily in communications and electronics. *Mailing Add:* Wachtel & Co Inc 1000 Vermont Ave NW Washington DC 20005

SANDERS, JOHN ESSINGTON, b Des Moines, Iowa, May 5, 26; m 52; c 3. GEOLOGY. *Educ:* Ohio Wesleyan Univ, BA, 48; Yale Univ, PhD(geol), 53. *Hon Degrees:* DSc, Ohio Wesleyan, 68. *Prof Exp:* Nat Res Coun fel, geol surv, Smithsonian Inst, 52-53 & Brit Mus Natural Hist, Neth, 53-54; instr geol, Yale Univ, 54-56, asst prof, 56-64; sr res assoc, Hudson Labs, 64-69, vis prof, 68-69, PROF GEOL, BARNARD COL, COLUMBIA UNIV, 69-*Concurrent Pos:* NSF fac fel sci, Yale Univ & Mass Inst Technol, 62-63; assoc ed, J Sedimentary Petrol, 62-76; mem, Bd Dirs, Mutual Oil Am, Inc, 69-75; mem NY State Dept Environ Conserv Hudson River PCB Settlement Adv Comt, 76-, chmn, 77; mem Nat Res Coun Comt Assess PCB's in Environ, 78. *Mem:* Fel AAAS; fel Geol Soc Am; Soc Econ Paleontologists & Mineralogists; Am Asn Petrol Geologists; NY Acad Sci. *Res:* sedimentology; stratigraphy; paleogeography; primary structures in sedimentary deposits; Mississippian of southern Appalachians; Mississippian Brachiopoda; Triassic-Jurassic of Connecticut, New York and New Jersey; nearshore marine sediments; geological applications of side-looking sonar; origin and occurrence of petroleum. *Mailing Add:* Dept Geol Barnard Col Columbia Univ New York NY 10027

SANDERS, JOHN P(AUL), SR, b Hope, Ark, July 4, 26; m 57; c 2. CHEMICAL & NUCLEAR ENGINEERING. *Educ:* Univ Ark, BSChE, 50, MS, 52; Ga Inst Technol, PhD(chem eng), 63. *Prof Exp:* Instr chem eng, Univ Ark, 50-52; engr, Oak Ridge Nat Lab, 52-55; assoc prof chem eng, Univ Ark, 57-65; res staff mem, 65-80, SR RES STAFF MEM, OAK RIDGE NAT LAB, 80- *Concurrent Pos:* Lectr, Oak Ridge Assoc Univ. *Mem:* Am Inst Chem Engrs; Sigma Xi. *Res:* Heat removal from nuclear reactor cores; transfer of heat through outer wall of annuli as a function of the system parameters; evaluation of the performance of the cores of nuclear reactors; computational procedures for systems analysis. *Mailing Add:* Bldg 9102-2 PO Box Y Oak Ridge Nat Lab Oak Ridge TN 37830

SANDERS, JOHN STEPHEN, b Phoenix, Ariz, Apr 10, 50; m 73; c 2. AIR POLLUTION EFFECTS, SOIL-BORNE DISEASES. *Educ:* Univ Ariz, BS, 72, MS, 74; NC State Univ, PhD(plant path), 81. *Prof Exp:* Res asst, Environ Res Lab, 74-77; grad res asst, NC State Univ, 77-80; AIR POLLUTION RES SPECIALIST, CALIF AIR RESOURCES BD, 80- *Mem:* Am Phytopath Soc. *Res:* Effects of ozone, sulfur dioxide and nitrogen dioxide on horticultural plants. *Mailing Add:* 9481 Roseport Way Sacramento CA 95826

SANDERS, LOUIS LEE, b Little Rock, Ark, May 18, 29; m 58; c 4. INTERNAL MEDICINE, BIOCHEMISTRY. *Educ:* Univ Ark, BS, 51, MD, 55; MS, 61. *Prof Exp:* From instr to asst prof, 62-69, assoc prof, 69-80, PROF INTERNAL MED, SCH MED, UNIV ARK, LITTLE ROCK, 80-; CHIEF METAB SECT, LITTLE ROCK VET ADMIN HOSP, 69-, ASST CHIEF MED SERV, 75- *Concurrent Pos:* Asst dir clin res ctr, Univ Ark, Little Rock, 62-65; attend physician, Little Rock Vet Admin Hosp, 62-65; staff physician, 66-69. *Mem:* Fel Am Col Physicians; Am Rheumatism Asn; Am Fedn Clin Res. *Res:* Diabetes mellitus; insulin metabolism in adult-onset diabetes; effect of oral hypoglycemic agents on insulin metabolism. *Mailing Add:* Little Rock Vet Admin Hosp 300 E Roosevelt Rd Little Rock AR 72206

SANDERS, MARILYN MAGDANZ, b Norfolk, Nebr, Aug 12, 42; div. BIOCHEMISTRY, MOLECULAR BIOLOGY. *Educ:* Stanford Univ, BSc, 64; Univ Wash, PhD(biochem), 69. *Prof Exp:* From instr to res assoc biochem sci, Princeton Univ, 71-73; instr, 73-74, asst prof, 74-79, ASSOC PROF PHARMACOL, COL MED & DENT NJ, RUTGERS MED SCH, 79- *Concurrent Pos:* Med Res Coun Can grant, Univ BC, 69-71. *Mem:* AAAS; Am Soc Cell Biol; Genetics Soc Am; Am Soc Biol Chemists. *Res:* Molecular aspects of eukaryote chromosome structure; gene regulation in heat shock in Drosophilia melanogaster; regulation of development and gene expression in eukaryotic organisms. *Mailing Add:* Col of Med & Dent of NJ Rutgers Med Sch Piscataway NJ 08854

SANDERS, MARY ELIZABETH, b Kobe, Japan, Mar 1, 17; US citizen. GENETICS. *Educ:* Mt Holyoke Col, AB, 38; Cornell Univ, MS, 40; Smith Col, PhD(genetics), 47. *Prof Exp:* Asst, Dept Genetics, Carnegie Inst, 40-41; teacher sch, SDak, 41-42; asst bot, Conn Col, 42-43; asst genetics, Exp Sta, Smith Col, 43-46; instr bot, Mt Holyoke Col, 46-47; asst, Yale Univ, 47-48; instr & res assoc integrated lib studies & bot, Univ Wis, 48-54; instr biol sci, Northwestern Univ, 54-55; res assoc agron, SDak State Col, 55-62; res assoc, Arnold Arboretum, Harvard Univ, 62-65; Am Asn Univ Women fel, 64-65; from asst prof to prof bot, Mont Alto Campus, Pa State Univ, 65-77; PROF BOT, MONT ALTO CAMPUS, PA RETIRED. *Mem:* Am Genetic Asn; Am Inst Biol Sci. *Res:* Genetics and embryo culture of Datura; origin of colchicine-induced diploid sorghum mutants with multiple changed characters, many mutants immediately true-breeding; investigations of tomato for responses to colchicine, similar to those found in sorghum. *Mailing Add:* Dept of Biol 202 Buckhout Lab University Park PA 16802

SANDERS, OLIVER PAUL, b Caney, Okla, Dec 26, 24; m 45; c 2. MATHEMATICS. *Educ:* Southeastern State Col, BA, 47; Okla State Univ, MS, 49, PhD, 56. *Prof Exp:* Asst prof math, Arlington State Col, 49-51 & Southeastern State Col, 51-54; instr, Okla State Univ, 54-56; asst prof, Univ Ark, 56-57; assoc prof, La Polytech Univ, 57-59; prof & head dept, Hardin-Simmons Univ, 59-62; prof & head dept, 62-65; acad dean, 65-68; provost, 68-70, vpres acad affairs, 70-74, PROF MATH APPALACHIAN STATE UNIV, 74- *Mem:* Math Asn Am. *Res:* Partial differential equations. *Mailing Add:* Dept of Math Appalachian State Univ Boone NC 28608

SANDERS, OTTYS E, b Hubbard, Tex, Apr 25, 03; m 30. HERPETOLOGY. *Educ:* Southern Methodist Univ, AB, 24. *Prof Exp:* Mgr, Southwestern Biol Supply Co, 27-80; RETIRED. *Concurrent Pos:* Res assoc, Strecker Mus, Baylor Univ, 66- *Mem:* Am Soc Ichthyol & Herpet; Soc Syst Zool; Herpetologists' League; Soc Study Amphibians & Reptiles. *Res:* Amphibia; Planaria. *Mailing Add:* 5712 W Ledbetter Dr Dallas TX 75236

SANDERS, R(AY) W, physics, electrical engineering, see previous edition

SANDERS, RAYMOND THOMAS, b Ogden, Utah, June 23, 23; m 47; c 1. PHYSIOLOGY. *Educ:* Univ Utah, BS, 49, MS, 50; Stanford Univ, PhD(biol), 56. *Prof Exp:* Nat Found Infantile Paralysis fel, Physiol Inst, Univ Uppsala, 56-58; from asst prof to prof physiol, 58-70, prof zool, 70-77, PROF BIOL, UTAH STATE UNIV, 77- *Concurrent Pos:* Dir, Hons Prog, Utah State Univ, 74- *Mem:* Am Soc Zoologists; Soc Gen Physiol. *Res:* Permeability phenomena in cells and model systems; role of salts in metabolism; sensory physiology of invertebrates. *Mailing Add:* Dept of Biol Utah State Univ Logan UT 84321

SANDERS, RICHARD MARK, b Waterloo, Iowa, June 20, 26. DATA PROCESSING. *Educ:* Iowa State Univ, BS, 50; Univ Wis, MS, 53, PhD(physics), 56. *Prof Exp:* PRIN PROGRAMMER, SPERRY UNIVAC COMPUT SYSTS, 56- *Mailing Add:* Univac Park PO Box 3525 St Paul MN 55165

SANDERS, RICHARD PAT, b Chicago, Ill, Mar 18, 43; m 67. GEOLOGY. *Educ:* Northern Ill Univ, BS, 65, MS, 68; Univ Ill, PhD(geol), 71. *Prof Exp:* Asst prof geol, Univ Wis-Stevens Point, 71-74; ASST PROF GEOL, W GA COL, 74- *Mem:* Am Geophys Union; Geol Soc Am. *Res:* Igneous and metamorphic petrology; mode of implacement of igneous plutons and volcanics. *Mailing Add:* Dept of Geol WGa Col Carrollton GA 30117

SANDERS, ROBERT ALAN, physical chemistry, analytical chemistry, see previous edition

SANDERS, ROBERT B, b Augusta, Ga, Dec 9, 38; m 61; c 2. BIOLOGICAL CHEMISTRY. *Educ:* Paine Col, BS, 59; Univ Mich, MS, 61, PhD(biochem), 64. *Prof Exp:* Am Cancer Soc fel biochem, Univ Wis, 64-66; asst prof, 66-72, ASSOC PROF BIOCHEM, UNIV KANS, 72- *Concurrent Pos:* Battelle Mem Inst fel, 70 & 71; consult, Interex Res Corp, 72-80; NIH & NSF; vis assoc prof, Dept Pharmacol, Sch Med, Univ Tex, Houston, 74-75; NIH fel, 74-75; prog dir, Regulatory Biol Prog, NSF, Washington, DC, 78-79. *Mem:* Sigma Xi; Am Soc Biol Chemists; Am Soc Pharmacol & Exp Therapeut. *Res:* Active and amino acide transport; biochemistry of hormone action; cyclic nucleotides. *Mailing Add:* Dept of Biochem Univ of Kans Lawrence KS 66045

SANDERS, ROBERT CHARLES, b Anaconda, Mont, Dec 17, 42; m 70. NUCLEAR ENGINEERING, THERMAL HYDRAULICS. *Educ:* Ore State Univ, BS, 66; Mass Inst Technol, ScD(nuclear eng), 70. *Prof Exp:* Nuclear engr, Div Naval Reactors, US Dept Energy, 70-75; asst prof, Univ Mo, 75-79; ENGR CONSULT, MPR ASSOCS, 79- *Concurrent Pos:* Consult, Consumers Power Co, 77. *Mem:* Am Nuclear Soc; Nat Soc Prof Engrs; Sigma Xi. *Res:* Nuclear power plant thermal-hydraulics, safety, and reliability; waste heat utilization; neutron activation analysis. *Mailing Add:* MPR Assocs 1140 Connecticut Ave NW Washington DC 20036

SANDERS, ROBERT HUGH, astrophysics, see previous edition

SANDERS, ROBERT N, b Carlinville, Ill, Feb 2, 35; m 57; c 2. PHYSICAL CHEMISTRY, INORGANIC CHEMISTRY. *Educ:* Shurtleff Col, BS, 57; Washington Univ, MA, 60; La State Univ, PhD(chem), 66. *Prof Exp:* Res asst chem, Shell Oil Co, 56-57; instr, MacMurray Col, 59-63; scientist, Lockheed Missiles & Space Co, 63-64; res chemist, 65-73, SR RES CHEMIST, ETHYL CORP, 73- *Res:* Flotation; mineral benefication; metallurgy of alluminum; high temperature processes. *Mailing Add:* Ethyl Corp Box 341 Baton Rouge LA 70821

SANDERS, RONALD L, b Greenway, Ark, June 19, 47. BIOCHEMISTRY. *Educ:* Wash Univ, AB, 70; St Louis Univ, PhD(biochem), 75. *Prof Exp:* Res assoc, Dept Biochem, Univ Colo Med Ctr, 75-76; fel, W Alton Jones Cell Sci Ctr, 76-78; res assoc, 78-79, ASST RES PROF, SCH MED, TUFTS UNIV, 79-, LECTR BIOCHEM, 80- *Concurrent Pos:* Am Lung Asn grant, 77-79. *Mem:* Am Chem Soc; Am Oil Chemists Soc; AAAS; Am Phys Soc. *Res:* Pulmonary biochemistry, phospholipid and surfactant metabolism, type II culture. *Mailing Add:* Dept of Anat 136 Harrison St Boston MA 02111

SANDERS, RUTH EVELYN, b Coolodge, Tex, Oct 15, 18. MEDICAL MICROBIOLOGY. *Educ:* Tex Christian Univ, BA, 39; Mich State Col, MS, 43, PhD(bact), 47. *Prof Exp:* Bacteriologist, Globe Labs, Tex, 39-42; asst, Exp Sta, 42-43, asst prof, 43-50, ASSOC PROF MICROBIOL & PUB HEALTH, MICH STATE UNIV, 50- *Mem:* AAAS; Am Chem Soc; Am Soc Microbiol. *Res:* Electrophoretic analyses of serum, plasma and colostrum in immunization studies; nutritional requirement metabolism and dissociation of Brucella; enzymes in Brucella cells; sensitins from atypical mycobacteria. *Mailing Add:* Dept of Microbiol & Pub Health Mich State Univ East Lansing MI 48823

SANDERS, SAMUEL MARSHALL, JR, b Charleston, SC, July 26, 28; m 49; c 2. HEALTH PHYSICS, RADIOBIOLOGY. *Educ:* The Citadel, BS, 49; La State Univ, Baton Rouge, MS, 52; Am Bd Health Physics, dipl, 61; Med Col Ga, PhD(radiobiol), 74. *Prof Exp:* Sr supvr, Bio-Assay Lab, Savannah River Plant, 52-55, chemist, Health Physics Sect, 55-60 & 62-64, SR RES CHEMIST, ENVIRON SCI SECT, SAVANNAH RIVER LAB, E I DU PONT DE NEMOURS & CO, INC, 64- *Concurrent Pos:* Partic traveling lect prog, Oak Ridge Asn Univs, 63-67; consult, Dept Radiol, Med Col Ga, 68- *Honors & Awards:* Elda E Anderson Mem Award, Health Physics Soc, 66. *Mem:* Am Chem Soc; Health Physics Soc; Microbeam Anal Soc. *Res:* Metabolism of water with the fixing of hydrogen in non-labile positions in macromolecules of plants and animals; microbeam analysis of plutonium-bearing microaerosols from fuel reprocessing facilities. *Mailing Add:* 1220 Fernwood Ct Aiken SC 29801

SANDERS, T H, JR, b Philadelphia, Pa, July 23, 43. PHYSICAL METALLURGY. *Educ:* Ga Inst Technol, BS, 66, MS, 69, PhD(metall), 74. *Prof Exp:* Res scientist, Aluminum Co Am, Alcoa Ctr, Pa, 74-79, Fracture & Fatigue Res Lab, Metall Prog, Ga Inst Technol, 79-81; ASSOC PROF PHYS METALL, PURDUE UNIV, 81- *Mem:* Am Inst Mining, Metall & Petrol Engrs; Am Soc Metals; Am Soc Eng Educ. *Res:* Aluminum alloy development for aerospace applications; microstructural mechanisms of fracture and fatigue, solidification and microstructure, and primary processing to improve properties. *Mailing Add:* Rm #209 CMET Bldg Purdue Univ West Lafayette IN 47907

SANDERS, THEODORE MICHAEL, JR, b New York, NY, Sept 14, 27; wid; c 2. PHYSICS. *Educ:* Harvard Univ, AB, 48; Columbia Univ, MS, 51, PhD(physics), 54. *Prof Exp:* Asst physics, Columbia Univ, 49-51; res assoc, Stanford Univ, 53-55; from asst prof to prof, Univ Minn, 55-63; vis prof, 63-64, PROF PHYSICS, UNIV MICH, ANN ARBOR, 64- *Concurrent Pos:* Sloan fel, 58-62. *Mem:* Fel Am Phys Soc. *Res:* Physics of atoms, molecules and solids; radio frequency spectroscopy; low temperature physics. *Mailing Add:* H M Randall Physics Lab Univ of Mich Ann Arbor MI 48109

SANDERS, THOMAS GARRISON, b St Louis, Mo, Nov 18, 40; m 68. BIOCHEMISTRY, GENETICS. *Educ:* Williams Col, BA; Univ Ill, Urbana, MS, 65, PhD(biochem), 70. *Prof Exp:* Res fel, Univ BC, 69-71; asst prof biol, Princeton Univ, 71-78; ASST PROF BIOL, LAKE FOREST COL, 78- *Mem:* Am Chem Soc; NY Acad Sci; Soc Develop Biol; Genetics Soc Am. *Res:* Biochemical and developmental genetics of Drosophila; gene regulation in eukaryotic organisms; behavior genetics of olfaction and gustation. *Mailing Add:* Dept of Biol Lake Forest Col Lake Forest IL 60045

SANDERS, TIMOTHY D, b Laramie, Wyo, Apr 1, 35; m 57; c 2. PHYSICS. *Educ:* Stanford Univ, BS, 57, MSc, 59, PhD(physics), 62. *Prof Exp:* Res assoc theoret physics, Washington Univ, 62-64; asst prof physics & math, 64-69, asst dean fac, 68-70, assoc prof, 69-77, PROF PHYSICS, OCCIDENTAL COL, 77- *Concurrent Pos:* NSF sci fac fel, Stanford Linear Accelerator Ctr, 71-72. *Mem:* AAAS; Am Phys Soc; Am Math Soc. *Res:* Elementary particles; hyper-nuclei and light nuclei; group theory and its applications to quantum theory. *Mailing Add:* Dept of Physics Occidental Col Los Angeles CA 90041

SANDERS, W EUGENE, JR, b Frederick, Md, June 25, 34; m 56; c 4. MEDICINE, MICROBIOLOGY. *Educ:* Cornell Univ, AB, 56, MD, 60; Am Bd Internal Med, dipl, 68. *Prof Exp:* Intern med, Johns Hopkins Hosp, 60-61, resident, 61-62; epidemic intel serv officer, Commun Dis Ctr, USPHS, 62-64; chief resident med, Teaching Hosps, Col Med, Univ Fla, 64-65, from asst prof to assoc prof med & microbiol, 65-72; PROF MED & MED MICROBIOL & CHMN DEPT MED MICROBIOL, SCH MED, CREIGHTON UNIV, 72- *Concurrent Pos:* Am Soc Pharmacol & Exp Therapeut travel award, 67; NIH res career develop award, 68-; Markle scholar acad med, 68-; instr, Sch Med, Emory Univ, 62-64; consult, W T Edwards Hosp, Tampa, Fla. *Mem:* AAAS; Am Pub Health Asn; Am Fedn Clin Res; Am Soc Microbiol. *Res:* Internal medicine; infectious diseases and epidemiology; bacterial interference; antimicrobial agents and chemotherapy; bacterial carrier states. *Mailing Add:* Dept of Med Microbiol Creighton Univ Sch of Med Omaha NE 68178

SANDERS, W(ILLIAM) THOMAS, b Owensboro, Ky, June 13, 33; m 54; c 2. SOLID MECHANICS, MECHANICAL ENGINEERING. *Educ:* Purdue Univ, BS, 54; NY Univ, MS, 57; Columbia Univ, ScD(mech eng), 62. *Prof Exp:* Engr, Dow Chem Co, 54; engr-trainee, Oak Ridge Nat Lab, 54-55; engr, Combustion Eng, Inc, 55-57 & Am Mach & Foundry Co, 57-60; asst prof mech eng, 62-66, ASSOC PROF MECH ENG, COLUMBIA UNIV, 66- *Concurrent Pos:* Consult, Am Mach & Foundry Co, Avion Corp & Columbia Broadcasting Syst Labs. *Mem:* Am Phys Soc; Am Soc Mech Engrs; Sigma Xi. *Res:* Solid state engineering; dislocations in crystals; solar energy applications. *Mailing Add:* Dept of Mech Eng Columbia Univ Sch of Eng & Appl Sci New York NY 10027

SANDERS, W(ALLACE) W(OLFRED), JR, b Louisville, Ky, June 24, 33; m 56; c 2. CIVIL ENGINEERING. *Educ:* Univ Louisville, BCE, 55, MEng, 73; Univ Ill, MS, 57, PhD(civil eng), 60. *Prof Exp:* Asst civil eng, Univ Ill, 55-59, res assoc, 59-60, asst prof, 60-64; assoc prof, 64-70, PROF CIVIL ENG, IOWA STATE UNIV, 70-, ASST DIR, ENG RES INST, 80- *Honors & Awards:* Adams Memorial Membership Award, Am Welding Soc, 70; R C Reese Res Prize, Am Soc Civil Engrs, 78. *Mem:* Am Soc Civil Engrs; Am Welding Soc; Am Rwy Eng Asn; Am Soc Eng Educ; Nat Soc Prof Engrs. *Res:* Fatigue of welded joints in structural metals; behavior of timber, steel and concrete bridges. *Mailing Add:* Dept of Civil Eng Iowa State Univ Ames IA 50011

SANDERS, WALTER L, b Evansville, Ind, Aug 21, 37; m 60; c 1. SCIENCE TEACHING, COMPUTER PROGRAMMING. *Educ:* Univ Gottigen, DR, 70. *Prof Exp:* Res assoc astron, Yerkes Observ, Univ Chicago, 70-71; assoc, Kitt Peak Nat Observ, 71-72; ASSOC PROF ASTRON, NMEX STATE UNIV, 72- *Concurrent Pos:* Vis astronomer, Univ Munster, 80, Kitt Peak Nat Observ, Cerro Tolo Nat Observ, Mt Wilson & Paloman Observ, Europ Southern Observ, Chili & Los Campanos Observ. *Mem:* Am Astron Soc; Royal Astron Soc; Int Astron Union; Astron Soc Pac; Astron Ges. *Res:* Galactic structure studies, including galactic cluster, spiral structure, and galactic distance scale; extragalactic distance scale. *Mailing Add:* Dept Astron NMex State Univ PO Box 4500 Las Cruces NM 80003

SANDERS, WALTER MACDONALD, (III), b Bluefield, WVa, Dec 5, 30; m 56; c 4. CIVIL & SANITARY ENGINEERING. *Educ:* Va Mil Inst, BS, 53; Johns Hopkins Univ, MS, 56, PhD(sanit eng), 64. *Prof Exp:* Eng asst, WVa Water Serv Co, 47-52; sanit engr, Greeley & Hansen Engrs, 53; asst, dept sanit eng, Johns Hopkins Univ, 55-56; sanit eng consult, USPHS, Div Int Health, 56-58, asst chief, Water Supply Sect, Dept Water Supply & Pollution Control, 58-60, res sanit engr, Southeast Region, Clemson Univ, 62-64; chief, Freshwater Ecosysts Br, 64-76, ASSOC DIR, WATER QUAL RES, ATHENS ENVIRON RES LAB, US ENVIRON PROTECTION AGENCY, 76- *Concurrent Pos:* Adj prof, Div Interdisciplinary Studies, Clemson Univ, 62-75; res assoc & prof, Ecol Inst, Univ Ga, 67- & adj res assoc, Dept Microbiol, 72- *Mem:* Am Soc Civil Engrs; AAAS; Sigma Xi. *Res:* Aquatic ecosystem studies and use of controlled environmental chamber-stream ecosystem complex to develop predictive models for future water quality and stream conditions; environmental pollution; ecological engineering; sanitary engineering; water quality management; control of toxic chemicals. *Mailing Add:* Athens Environ Res Lab US Environ Protection Agency Athens GA 30605

SANDERS, WILLIAM ALBERT, b Lafayette, Ind, Apr 28, 33; m 56; c 4. THEORETICAL CHEMISTRY, CHEMICAL DYNAMICS. *Educ:* Purdue Univ, BSChE, 55, PhD(phys chem), 63; Georgetown Univ, MS, 61. *Prof Exp:* Instr chem, US Naval Acad, 57-60; NSF fel theoret chem, Univ Wis, 63-65, res assoc, 65; asst prof, 65-69, ASSOC PROF CHEM, CATH UNIV AM, 69-, CHMN DEPT, 81- *Concurrent Pos:* Consult, Phys Res Labs, Edgewood Arsenal, 68-70 & Naval Res Lab, 78- *Mem:* Sigma Xi; Am Phys Soc. *Res:* Gas phase kinetics; theory of molecular beam scattering; applications of perturbation theory; theory of inter- and intramolecular forces; chemical dynamics. *Mailing Add:* Dept of Chem Cath Univ of Am Washington DC 20064

SANDERS, WILLIAM MACK, b West Point, Ark, June 12, 26; m 49; c 3. MATHEMATICS. *Educ:* Ark State Teachers Col, BS, 49; Univ Ark, MA, 52; Univ Ill, Urbana, PhD(math), 65. *Prof Exp:* Instr math, Southern Miss Univ, 52-55, assoc prof, 58-64; assoc prof, Lawrence Univ, 64-69; PROF MATH & HEAD DEPT, JAMES MADISON UNIV, 69- *Mem:* Math Asn Am; Am Math Soc. *Res:* Foundations of geometry, especially abstract models of geometries. *Mailing Add:* Dept of Math James Madison Univ Harrisonburg VA 22807

SANDERS-BUSH, ELAINE, b Russellville, Ky, Apr 27, 40; m 67; c 1. PHARMACOLOGY. *Educ:* Western Ky Univ, BS, 62; Vanderbilt Univ, PhD(pharmacol), 67. *Prof Exp:* NIMH grant, 67-69, from instr to assoc prof, 68-80, PROF PHARMACOL, SCH MED, VANDERBILT UNIV, 80- *Concurrent Pos:* NIMH res scientist develop award, 74. *Mem:* Am Soc Pharmacol & Exp Therapeut; Am Col Neuropsychopharmacol; Neurosci Soc. *Res:* Psychopharmacology; serotonic receptor subtypes; biogenic amines; neurotoxic agents; amphetamine derivatives. *Mailing Add:* Dept of Pharmacol Vanderbilt Univ Sch of Med Nashville TN 37203

SANDERS-LOEHR, JOANN, b New York, NY, Sept 2, 42; m 65. BIOCHEMISTRY. *Educ:* Cornell Univ, BS, 64, PhD(biochem), 69. *Prof Exp:* Fel biochem, Ore Health Sci Univ, 69-71; asst prof, 71-76, assoc prof, 76, PROF CHEM, PORTLAND STATE UNIV, 80- *Concurrent Pos:* NIH fel, 70-71; Cottrell res grant, 72-74; NIH grant, 75-; vis assoc chem, Calif Inst Technol, Pasadena, 78-79. *Mem:* Am Soc Microbiol. *Res:* Role of metal ions in biological systems including metal ion transport and metalloprotein structure and function. *Mailing Add:* Dept of Chem Portland State Univ Portland OR 92707

SANDERSON, ARTHUR CLARK, b Providence, RI, Oct 23, 40; m 71. SIGNAL PROCESSING, ROBOTICS. *Educ:* Brown Univ, BS, 68; Carnegie-Mellon Univ, MS, 70, PhD(elec eng), 72. *Prof Exp:* Res engr, Res & Develop Lab, Westinghouse, 68-71; fel, Delft Univ Technol, 72-73; asst prof elec eng, Carnegie-Mellon Univ, 73-75; vis prof biomed eng, Univ Iberoamericana, Mex, 76-77; assoc prof, 77-81, PROF ELEC ENG & ROBOTICS INST, CARNEGIE-MELLON UNIV, 81- *Concurrent Pos:* Vis scientist, Inst Politech Nat, Mex, 76-77; adj prof, Med Sch, Univ Pittsburgh, 80- *Mem:* Inst Elec & Electronics Engrs; AAAS; Soc Neurosci; Sigma Xi. *Res:* Signal processing and pattern recognition applied to robotics and biomedicine; sensor based control of robots. *Mailing Add:* Dept Elec Eng Carnegie-Mellon Univ Pittsburgh PA 15213

SANDERSON, BENJAMIN S, b Buffalo, NY, Mar 18, 22; m 52; c 4. PHYSICAL CHEMISTRY. *Educ:* Hobart Col, BS, 42; Ohio State Univ, PhD(phys chem), 55. *Prof Exp:* Tech supvr, Holston Ord Works, Tenn Eastman Corp, 43-44; res chemist, 55-58, group leader, 58-68, sect mgr anal sect, 68-72, PROCESS SUPT, RES LAB, NL INDUSTS, INC, 72- *Concurrent Pos:* Lectr, Rutgers Univ, 62-71. *Mem:* Am Chem Soc; Am Statist Asn; fel Am Inst Chemists. *Res:* X-ray diffraction and spectroscopy; statistics; use of computers in research; infrared spectroscopy; quality control. *Mailing Add:* 32 Sherwood Cir Little Silver NJ 07739

SANDERSON, DONALD EUGENE, b Oskaloosa, Iowa, Feb 4, 26; m 49; c 3. TOPOLOGY. *Educ:* Cornell Col, BA, 49; Calif Inst Technol, MS, 51; Univ Wis, PhD(math), 53. *Prof Exp:* Asst instr math, Calif Inst Technol, 49-51; from instr to assoc prof, 53-64, PROF MATH, IOWA STATE UNIV, 64- *Concurrent Pos:* Vis assoc prof, Mich State Univ, 62-63. *Honors & Awards:* Allendoerfer Award, Math Asn Am, 80. *Mem:* AAAS; Am Math Soc; Math Asn Am. *Res:* Topology of manifolds; general topology; infinite dimensional topology. *Mailing Add:* Dept of Math Iowa State Univ Ames IA 50011

SANDERSON, EDWIN S, b Mannville, Alta, Aug 19, 20; m 42; c 4. ORGANIC CHEMISTRY, POLYMER CHEMISTRY. *Educ:* Univ Alta, BSc, 50; McGill Univ, PhD(cellulose & wood chem), 53. *Prof Exp:* Res chemist, Visking Corp, 53-54; mgr cellulose & casing res, 54-57; plant mgr, Visking Div, Union Carbide Can, Ltd, 57-60, admin mgr, 60-62, dir res & develop plastic prod, 62-66; DIR TECHNOL BR, DEPT INDUST, TRADE & COM, 66- *Mem:* Chem Inst Can; Am Chem Soc; Can Inst Food Technol. *Res:* Cellulose and high polymer chemistry; food packaging and preservation. *Mailing Add:* Dept Indust Trade & Com Technol Br 240 Sparks Ottawa ON K2H 7C9 Can

SANDERSON, GARY WARNER, b Thermal, Calif, Dec 17, 34; m 53; c 4. FOOD CHEMISTRY. *Educ:* Univ Calif, Davis, BS, 56; Univ Nottingham, PhD(bot), 61. *Prof Exp:* Biochemist & head biochem div, Tea Res Inst, Ceylon, 62-66; mgr tea res, Thomas J Lipton, Inc, 66-71, asst dir tea res & develop, 71-75, dir beverage prod res, 76-78; V PRES RES, UNIVERSAL FOODS CORP, 78- *Concurrent Pos:* Adj prof, Col New Rochelle, 75. *Mem:* NY Acad Sci; Inst Food Technologists; Am Asn Cereal Chemists; Am Chem Soc; Brit Biochem Soc. *Res:* Plant biochemistry and physiology; food chemistry; tea chemistry and biochemistry; fermentation science and microbiology. *Mailing Add:* Universal Foods Corp 6143 N 60th St Milwaukee WI 53218

SANDERSON, GEORGE ALBERT, b New Haven, Conn, Aug 22, 26; m 61; c 3. GEOLOGY, PALEONTOLOGY. *Educ:* Trinity Col, Conn, BS, 49; Univ Wis, PhD(geol), 54. *Prof Exp:* Asst geol, Univ Wis, 50-54; geologist, Shell Develop Co, Tex, 54-55, jr stratigrapher, Shell Oil Co, 55, paleontologist, 55-64; sr res scientist, Pan Am Petrol Corp, 64-65, staff res scientist, 65-69, res group supvr, 69-77, SPEC RES ASSOC, AMOCO PROD CO, 77- *Mem:* Paleont Soc; Soc Econ Paleont & Mineral; Paleont Asn. *Res:* Paleozoic micropaleontology; paleoecology and biostratigraphy, especially Fusulinidae and small Foraminifera; biometrics; detailed biostratigraphy, especially Pennsylvanian and Permian. *Mailing Add:* Res Ctr Amoco Prod Co Box 591 Tulsa OK 74102

SANDERSON, GLEN CHARLES, b Wayne Co, Mo, Jan 21, 23; m 47; c 2. ZOOLOGY, PHYSIOLOGY. *Educ:* Univ Mo, BS, 47, MA, 49; Univ Ill, PhD, 61. *Prof Exp:* Game biologist, Iowa State Conserv Comn, 49-55; game biologist, Ill Dept Conserv & Ill Natural Hist Surv, 55-60, assoc wildlife specialist, Ill Natural Hist Surv, 60-63, wildlife specialist, 63-64, actg head, Sect Wildlife Res, 63-64, HEAD SECT WILDLIFE RES, ILL NATURAL HIST SURV, 64- *Concurrent Pos:* Prof, Univ Ill, 65-; adj res prof, Southern Ill Univ, 64, adj prof, 64-; ed, J Wildlife Mgt, 71-72. *Honors & Awards:* Oak Leaf Award, Nature Conservancy, 75. *Mem:* Am Soc Mammal; Wildlife Soc; AAAS; Am Inst Biol Sci. *Res:* Population dynamics of wild animals, especially furbearers; physiological factors of reproductive and survival rates; lead poisoning in waterfowl. *Mailing Add:* Ill Natural Hist Surv 607 E Peabody Champaign IL 61820

SANDERSON, HENRY PRESTON, b Midgell, PEI, Aug 28, 25; m 51; c 2. CHEMISTRY, ENVIRONMENTAL HEALTH. *Educ:* Dalhousie Univ, BSc, 49; Univ Minn, Minneapolis, MPH, 62, PhD(environ health), 69. *Prof Exp:* Plant chemist, Can Packers Ltd, 49; chemist sci serv, Can Dept Agr, NS, 49-51, chemist plant prod serv, Ont, 51-54; chemist, Int Joint Comn, 54-56; res scientist occup health div, Dept Nat Health & Welfare, 56-70; Res Coun Off environ secretariat, Div Biol, Nat Res Coun Can, 70-77; CHIEF, ATMOSPHERIC CHEM CRITERIA & STANDARDS, ATMOSPHERIC EVAL SERV, 77- *Mem:* Can Standards Asn; Am Indust Hyg Asn; Air Pollution Control Asn. *Res:* Compilation of scientific data related to cause and effects of pollutants on receptors; air pollution; atmospheric chemistry; acidification of precipitation; toxic chemicals; oxidants and photochemical reaction; effects of pollutants on vegetation. *Mailing Add:* Atmospheric Eval Serv 4905 Dufferin Downsview ON M3H 5T4 Can

SANDERSON, JAMES GEORGE, b Somerset, NJ, Oct 10, 49. NUMERICAL ANALYSIS. *Educ:* Lafayette Col, BS, 71; Univ NMex, MA, 73, PhD(math), 76. *Prof Exp:* STAFF MEM, THEORET DESIGN DIV, LOS ALAMOS SCI LAB, 76- *Mem:* Soc Indust & Appl Math. *Res:* Numerical solutions to coupled nonlinear differential equations; eigenvalue problems; fully 3-D tomography; floating point correctness proofs; integral equations. *Mailing Add:* MS 232 Los Alamos Sci Lab Los Alamos NM 87545

SANDERSON, JUDSON, b Orrick, Mo, July 15, 21; m 54; c 3. MATHEMATICS. *Educ:* Univ Ill, BS, 47, MS, 48, PhD(math), 50. *Prof Exp:* Asst math, Univ Ill, 47-48; asst prof, Tulane Univ, 50-51; assoc prof, US Air Force Inst Technol, 51-56; assoc prof, 56-75, PROF MATH, UNIV REDLANDS, 75- *Concurrent Pos:* Lectr, Ohio State Grad Ctr, Wright-Patterson AFB, 53-56; consult, San Bernadino County Sch Syst, 63-66. *Mem:* Am Math Soc; Math Asn Am. *Res:* Real variable measure theory and foundations of mathematics. *Mailing Add:* Dept of Math Univ of Redlands Redlands CA 92373

SANDERSON, KENNETH CHAPMAN, b Woodbury, NJ, Jan 9, 33; m 61; c 2. FLORICULTURE. *Educ:* Cornell Univ, BS, 55; Univ Md, MS, 58, PhD(hort), 65. *Prof Exp:* Teaching asst hort, Univ Md, 55-57; retail florist, C J Sanderson Florist, 58-60; greenhouse mgr, Univ Md, 60-65; asst prof floricult, La State Univ, 65-66; from asst prof to assoc prof, 66-76, PROF FLORICULT, AUBURN UNIV, 77- *Concurrent Pos:* Vis lectr, Calif Polytech State Univ, 76-77; assoc ed, Hortsci & J Am Soc Hort Sci, 77-81. *Mem:* Sigma Xi; Am Hort Soc; Am Soc Hort Sci. *Res:* Greenhouse management, florist crop production, pest control; floral design, retail flower shop management; plant propagation; environmental control, pollution; waste utilization. *Mailing Add:* 222 Green St Auburn AL 36830

SANDERSON, KENNETH EDWIN, b Holland, Man, Sept 14, 34; m 62; c 4. MICROBIAL GENETICS. *Educ:* Univ Man, BSA, 56, MSc, 57; Cornell Univ, PhD(genetics), 62. *Prof Exp:* Res assoc genetics, Cornell Univ, 61-62; AEC res assoc, Brookhaven Nat Lab, 62-64, vis biologist, 64-65; Wellcome Trust fel genetics, Lister Inst Prev Med, London, 65, microbial genetics res unit, Hammersmith Hosp, London, 65-66; from asst prof to assoc prof, 66-73, PROF BIOL, UNIV CALGARY, 73- *Concurrent Pos:* Nat Res Coun Can grants, 66-80; NSF grant, 68-76; Humboldt fel, Max Planck Inst, Freiburg, Ger, 72-73; vis scientist, Stanford Univ, 79-80. *Mem:* Genetics Soc Am; Am Soc Microbiol; Genetics Soc Can; Can Soc Microbiol. *Res:* Mechanisms of parasexual recombination in fungi; genetic structure of the chromosome of Salmonella typhimurium; genetic basis of cell wall synthesis in Salmonella typhimurium; recombinant DNA methods. *Mailing Add:* Dept of Biol Univ of Calgary Calgary AB T2N 1N4 Can

SANDERSON, MARIE ELIZABETH, b Chesley, Ont, Nov 16, 21; m 46; c 3. PHYSICAL GEOGRAPHY. *Educ:* Univ Toronto, BA, 44; Univ Md, MA, 46; Univ Mich, PhD(geog), 65. *Prof Exp:* Res scientist, Ont Res Found, 46-50; res assoc climat, C W Thornwaite Asn Lab Climat, NJ, 50-51; from asst prof to assoc prof, 65-74, PROF GEOG, UNIV WINDSOR, 74-, DIR GREAT LAKES INST, 81- *Concurrent Pos:* Vis prof, Univ Hawaii, 79. *Mem:* Can Asn Geogrs (pres, 80-81); Asn Am Geogrs; Am Water Resources Asn; Can Meteorol Soc; Am Geophys Union. *Res:* Urban climatology; water balance of the Great Lakes. *Mailing Add:* Dept of Geog Univ of Windsor Windsor ON N9B 3P4 Can

SANDERSON, RICHARD BLODGETT, b Waltham, Mass, July 20, 35. PHYSICS. *Educ:* Mass Inst Technol, BS, 57; Syracuse Univ, PhD(physics), 63. *Prof Exp:* Res assoc physics, Ohio State Univ, 62-64, vis asst prof, 65, asst prof, 65-71; PHYSICIST, US AIR FORCE AVIONICS LAB, 72- *Mem:* Optical Soc Am. *Res:* Infrared spectroscopy; optical properties of materials; infrared sensors. *Mailing Add:* USAF Avionics Lab/WRP Wright-Patterson AFB OH 45433

SANDERSON, RICHARD JAMES, b Sydney, Australia, Aug 4, 33; m 58; c 1. BIOPHYSICS, CELL BIOLOGY. *Educ:* Univ Sydney, BE, 54; Univ Denver, MS, 71, PhD(appl physics), 74. *Prof Exp:* Aerodynamicist, English Elec Aviation, Eng, 55-61; sect chief, Stanley Aviation, Denver, 61-63; sr res scientist, Martin Marietta Corp, Denver, 63-72; STAFF INVESTR MICROBIOL, WEBB-WARING LUNG INST, SCH MED, UNIV COLO, 72- *Res:* Function of human peripheral cells in the immune response and their isolation into pure populations; red cell aging; biophysics of lung surfactant. *Mailing Add:* Webb-Waring Lung Inst 4200 E Ninth Ave Denver CO 80262

SANDERSON, ROBERT THOMAS, b Bryson City, NC, Dec 25, 12; m 39, 78; c 3. INORGANIC CHEMISTRY. *Educ:* Yale Univ, BS, 34; Univ Chicago, PhD(chem), 39. *Prof Exp:* Chemist, Grasselli Chem Div, E I du Pont de Nemours & Co, 34-35; asst, Univ Chicago, 36-39; chief chemist, Western Geophys Co, 39-40; res chemist & proj leader, Tex Co, 40-49; assoc prof chem, Univ Fla, 49-50; prof inorg chem, Univ Iowa, 50-63; prof chem, 63-78, EMER PROF CHEM, ARIZ STATE UNIV, 78- *Mem:* Fel AAAS; Am Chem Soc; Sigma Xi. *Res:* Aluminum borohydride; geochemical exploration for petroleum; synthetic fuels and lubricants; volatile hydrides and derivatives; organometallic chemistry; electronegativity; bond energies; interpretations of inorganic chemistry; theory of polar convalence. *Mailing Add:* 4725 Player Dr Ft Collins CO 80525

SANDFORD, MAXWELL TENBROOK, II, b Kansas City, Mo, Nov 7, 44; m 71; c 1. ASTROPHYSICS, MATHEMATICAL PHYSICS. *Educ:* Univ Kans, AB(math), AB(physics) & AB(astron), 66, MA, 68; Univ Ind, Bloomington, PhD(astrophys), 71. *Prof Exp:* STAFF MEM, LOS ALAMOS SCI LAB, 71- *Mem:* Sigma Xi; Royal Astron Soc; Am Astron Soc. *Res:* Radiative transfer; hydrodynamics of dusty objects; digital vidicon observations. *Mailing Add:* 160 Monte Rey S Los Alamos NM 87545

SANDFORT, ROBERT MELVIN, b St Charles, Mo, Apr 4, 42; m 64; c 3. ELECTRICAL ENGINEERING, SOLID STATE PHYSICS. *Educ:* Univ Mo-Columbia, BS, 64, MS, 66, PhD(elec eng), 71. *Prof Exp:* Sr res engr, Monsanto Commercial Prod Co, 71-76, RES MGR, MONSANTO CO, 76- *Mem:* Inst Elec & Electronics Engrs. *Res:* Garnets; III-IV materials; silicon. *Mailing Add:* Monsanto Co PO Box 8 St Peters MO 63376

SANDHAM, HERBERT JAMES, b Lethbridge, Alta, Sept 30, 32; m 55; c 4. ORAL BIOLOGY, MICROBIOLOGY. *Educ:* Univ Alta, DDS, 57; Univ Man, MSc, 63, PhD(oral biol), 67. *Prof Exp:* Asst prof med microbiol, Univ Man, 66-68; asst prof microbiol & dent, Univ Ala, Birmingham & investr microbiol, Inst Dent Res, 68-71; assoc prof prev dent, 71-77, PROF MICROBIOL, FAC DENT, UNIV TORONTO, 77- *Mem:* Int Asn Dent Res. *Res:* Dental caries etiology and prevention; oral microbiology; dental plaque composition, metabolism and prevention. *Mailing Add:* Fac of Dent Univ of Toronto Toronto ON M5G 1G6 Can

SANDHU, HARBHAJAN SINGH, b Sarih, India, May 1, 32; m 62; c 2. PHYSICS. *Educ:* Punjab Univ, India, BSc, 54, MSc, 55; Pa State Univ, PhD(physics), 61. *Prof Exp:* Asst prof physics, Col William & Mary, 61-62 & Univ Southern Calif, 62-64; asst prof, 64-68, PROF PHYSICS, CALIF STATE UNIV NORTHRIDGE, 68- *Mem:* Am Phys Soc. *Res:* Pair and multiplet production by 5-90 million electron volt x-rays; charged particle nuclear reaction cross sections. *Mailing Add:* Dept of Physics Calif State Univ Northridge CA 91330

SANDHU, MOHAMMAD AKRAM, b Baddomahli, Pakistan, Mar 26, 36; m 62; c 3. ORGANIC POLYMER CHEMISTRY. *Educ:* Univ Punjab, Pakistan, BSc, 58, MSc, 61; Univ Strathclyde, PhD(chem), 67. *Prof Exp:* Res chemist, Pakistan Coun Sci & Indust Res, 61-64; res specialist, Univ Minn, Minneapolis, 67-70; sr res chemist, 70-77, SR STAFF, EASTMAN KODAK CO, 77- *Concurrent Pos:* Assoc, Royal Inst Chem, 66; Walter Reed Army Inst Res fel, Univ Minn, Minneapolis, 67-69, NIH fel, 69-70. *Honors & Awards:* Hamilton Barrett Res Prize, Univ Strathclyde, 65. *Mem:* Royal Soc Chem; Am Chem Soc; Sigma Xi. *Res:* Organic syntheses, polymer for photographic, electrographic and electronic imaging systems; aromatic, heterocyclic and natural products; organic chemistry of Ferrocene. *Mailing Add:* Eastman Kodak Co Res Labs Rochester NY 14650

SANDHU, RANBIR SINGH, b Lyallpur, Pakistan, Jan 19, 28; US citizen; m 57; c 3. CIVIL ENGINEERING, STRUCTURAL MECHANICS. *Educ:* Univ Punjab, Pakistan, BA, 46; E Panjab Univ, India, BSc, 49; Univ Sheffield, MEng, 62; Univ Calif, Berkeley, PhD(civil eng), 68. *Prof Exp:* Asst engr to dep dir designs, Irrig Dept, Govt of Punjab, India, 50-63; assoc prof civil eng, Punjab Eng Col, India, 63-65; sr engr, Harza Eng Co, Ill, 68-69; assoc prof, 69-73, PROF CIVIL ENG, OHIO STATE UNIV, 73- *Concurrent Pos:* Consult applications finite element method, var agencies, 66-; vis scientist, Univ Dayton, 79; guest prof, Univ Stuttgart, WGer, 80. *Mem:* Am Soc Civil Engrs; Am Acad Mech; Soc Eng Sci. *Res:* Soil and structural mechanics; mathematical, numerical and variational methods; approximate solution of boundary value problems; theoretical and applied mechanics; mechanics of continua; finite element methods. *Mailing Add:* Dept Civil Eng Ohio State Univ 2070 Neil Ave Columbus OH 43210

SANDHU, SHINGARA SINGH, b Pauhowind, India, Oct 10, 32; m 60; c 4. SOIL CHEMISTRY. *Educ:* Panjab Univ, BS, 52, MS, 54; Utah State Univ, PhD(soil chem), 70. *Prof Exp:* Asst prof chem, Punjab Agr Univ, India, 55-65; assoc prof, Alcorn Agr & Mech Col, 68-69; PROF CHEM, CLAFLIN COL, 70- *Concurrent Pos:* Res affil, Punjab Agr Univ, India, 72. *Mem:* AAAS; Am Chem Soc; Soil Sci Soc Am. *Res:* Pollutants in rural drinking water supplies. *Mailing Add:* Dept of Chem Claflin Col Orangeburg SC 29115

SANDI, EMIL, b Drohobycz, Poland, Jan 2, 19; Can citizen; m 49; c 2. ANALYTICAL CHEMISTRY, TOXICOLOGY. *Educ:* Univ Bologna, DrChem, 42; Hungarian Acad Sci, Cand Chem Sci, 61. *Prof Exp:* Res officer nutrit, NIH, Budapest, 47-49; sr res officer anal chem & toxicol, Inst Nutrit, Budapest, 49-64; prin res officer toxicol & anal chem, NIH & Med Res, Accra, Ghana, 64-68; HEAD FOOD CONTAMINANTS SECT, DIV TOXICOL EVAL, HEALTH PROTECTION BR, DEPT NAT HEALTH & WELFARE, 68- *Mem:* Soc Toxicol; Asn Off Anal Chemists; Can Soc Chem Eng; Chem Inst Can. *Res:* Development of analytical methods for trace element determination in foods; electrochemical methods; polarography. *Mailing Add:* Food Contam Sec Div Toxicol Eval Health Protec Br Tunneys Pasture Ottawa ON K1A 0L2 Can

SANDIFER, JAMES ROY, b Blakely, Ga, May 21, 45; m 68. ELECTROCHEMISTRY. *Educ:* Miss Col, BS, 67; Univ NC, Chapel Hill, PhD(anal chem), 73. *Prof Exp:* RES CHEMIST, EASTMAN KODAK CO, 73- *Mem:* Am Chem Soc. *Res:* Mass transport properties of membranes, their electrical characteristics and their use in the fabrication of ion selective electrodes. *Mailing Add:* 231 Pearson Ln Rochester NY 14612

SANDIFER, MYRON GUY, JR, b Lowrys, SC, Sept 4, 22; m; c 2. PSYCHIATRY. *Educ:* Davidson Col, BS, 43; Harvard Med Sch, MD, 47; Am Bd Psychiatry, dipl, 54; Am Bd Internal Med, dipl, 74. *Prof Exp:* Instr psychiat, Sch Med, Univ NC, 55-58, asst prof, 58-59, from clin asst prof to clin assoc prof, 59-65; clin prof, Columbia Univ, 65-66; assoc dean acad affairs, 69-75, PROF PSYCHIAT, UNIV KY, 66-, PROF FAMILY PRACT, 74- *Concurrent Pos:* Dir res, NC Dept Ment Health, 59-65. *Mem:* AMA; Am Psychiat Asn. *Res:* Psychiatric diagnosis. *Mailing Add:* Univ of Ky Med Ctr Lexington KY 40506

SANDIFER, PAUL ALAN, b Cincinnati, Ohio, Jan 3, 47; m 66; c 4. MARINE ZOOLOGY. *Educ:* Col Charleston, BS, 68; Univ Va, PhD(marine sci), 72. *Prof Exp:* Asst marine scientist, 72-74, assoc marine scientist, 74-76, ASST DIR, DEPT WILDLIFE & MARINE RESOURCES, MARINE RESOURCES RES INST, SC, 76- *Mem:* Am Soc Zoologists, SE Estuarine Res Soc; World Mariculture Soc (secy-treas, 75, pres, 79). *Res:* Culture, ecology and taxonomy of decapod crustacean larvae; mariculture of crustaceans; biology of commercially important crustaceans; ecosystem analysis; research management. *Mailing Add:* Marine Resources Res Inst PO Box 12559 Charleston SC 29412

SANDIFER, RONDA MARGARET, b Barnwell, SC, May 31, 54. ORGANIC CHEMISTRY. *Educ:* Newberry Col, BS, 76; Vanderbilt Univ, PhD(chem), 80. *Prof Exp:* NIH FEL, UNIV UTAH, 80- *Mem:* Am Chem Soc. *Res:* Mechanisms of the enzymatic synthesis of terpenes, in particular inhibition of squalene synthetase. *Mailing Add:* 135 K St Salt Lake City UT 84103

SANDIFER, SAMUEL HOPE, b Walterboro, SC, May 27, 16. MEDICINE. *Educ:* The Citadel, BS, 37; Med Univ SC, MD, 41. *Prof Exp:* Prof mil sci, Med Col Va, 47-49; asst clin prof med, Univ Ga, 55-56; assoc clin prof pediat cardiol, Sch Med, Univ Louisville, 64-65; prof, 68-81, EMER PROF PREV MED, MED UNIV SC, 81- *Mem:* AAAS; fel Am Col Cardiol; fel Am Col Prev Med; fel Am Col Physicians. *Res:* Preventive medicine; pesticide study. *Mailing Add:* Dept of Family Med & Prev Med Div Med Univ SC Charleston SC 29425

SANDIN, THOMAS ROBERT, b Beloit, Wis, July 19, 39; m 60; c 5. SOLID STATE PHYSICS. *Educ:* Univ Santa Clara, BS, 60; Purdue Univ, Lafayette, MS, 62, PhD(physics), 68. *Prof Exp:* Instr physics, Purdue Univ, Indianapolis, 62-65; assoc prof, 68-77, PROF PHYSICS, NC A&T STATE UNIV, 77- *Concurrent Pos:* Lectr, Ind Univ, Kokomo Campus, 62-64. *Mem:* Am Asn Physics Teachers; Fedn Am Scientists. *Res:* Low temperature solid state; Mossbauer effect. *Mailing Add:* Dept of Physics NC A&T State Univ Greensboro NC 27411

SANDINE, WILLIAM EWALD, b Des Moines, Iowa, June 6, 28; m 55; c 1. BACTERIOLOGY, MICROBIOLOGY. *Educ:* Iowa State Univ, BS, 50; NC State Univ, MS, 55; Ore State Univ, PhD(bact), 58. *Prof Exp:* Instr bact, Ore State Col, 58-59; res assoc dairy biochem, Univ Ill, 59-60; from asst prof to assoc prof, 60-66, PROF MICROBIOL, ORE STATE UNIV, 66- *Honors & Awards:* Pfizer Paul Lewis Award, 64. *Mem:* Am Soc Microbiol; Am Dairy Sci Asn. *Res:* Lactic acid bacteria, especially bacteriophage, growth, taxonomy, metabolism and genetics; Staphylococci in food; microbiology of cheese; ecology of lactic acid bacteria including their role in human and animal nutrition. *Mailing Add:* Dept of Microbiol Ore State Univ Corvallis OR 97331

SANDLER, HAROLD, b Cincinnati, Ohio, Nov 24, 29; m 61; c 2. MEDICINE, PHYSIOLOGY. *Educ:* Univ Cincinnati, BS, 51, MD, 55. *Prof Exp:* Intern med, Univ Chicago, 55-56; asst med, Univ Wash, 56-58, res fel cardiol, 58-61, from instr to asst prof med, 63-65; clin investr cardiol, Vet Admin Hosp, Seattle, Wash, 63-65; res med officer cardiovasc physiol, Biomed Res Div, 65-69, actg chief div, 69-72, CHIEF BIOMED RES DIV, NASA-AMES RES CTR, MOFFETT FIELD, 72- *Concurrent Pos:* Wash State Heart Asn fel, 58-59; NIH fel, 59-61; asst clin prof, Sch Med, Standford Univ, 66-71, assoc clin prof, 71-78, clin prof med, 78- *Mem:* AMA; Am Fedn Clin Res; Aerospace Med Asn; Am Col Cardiol. *Res:* Internal medicine; cardiology; angiocardiography and cineangiocardiography; cardiovascular physiology; aerospace medicine; space bioscience; biophysics; bioengineering. *Mailing Add:* Biomed Res Div NASA-Ames Res Ctr N-239-8 Moffett Field CA 94035

SANDLER, LAURENCE MARVIN, b Brooklyn, NY, Dec 3, 29; m 54; c 2. GENETICS. *Educ:* Cornell Univ, BS, 52; Univ Mo, MA, 54, PhD(genetics), 56. *Prof Exp:* Res assoc, Biol Div, Oak Ridge Nat Lab, 56-57; fel genetics, Am Cancer Soc, Univ Wis, 57-59, asst prof, 59-61; assoc prof, 62-66, PROF GENETICS, UNIV WASH, 66- *Concurrent Pos:* NSF sr fel, Inst Genetics, Univ Rome, 65-66. *Mem:* AAAS; Genetics Soc Am; Am Soc Naturalists. *Res:* Chromosome behavior in Drosophila. *Mailing Add:* Dept of Genetics Univ of Wash Seattle WA 98105

SANDLER, MELVIN, b Brooklyn, NY, July 1, 37; m 61; c 3. ELECTRICAL ENGINEERING, ENERGY CONVERSION. *Educ:* Polytech Inst Brooklyn, BEE, 58, MEE, 60, PhD(electrophysics), 65. *Prof Exp:* Instr elec eng, Polytech Inst Brooklyn, 59-60; res asst comput sci, Microwave Res Inst, 60-62; sr res assoc, Farmingdale Grad Ctr, 62-64; group leader, Airborne Instruments Lab, Div, Cutter-Hammer, 64-68; sr venture specialist, W R Grace & Co, 68-69; chmn admis comt, 71-77, chmn, Dept Elec Eng, 75-77, assoc prof, 69-77, PROF ELEC ENG, COOPER UNION, 77- *Mem:* Inst Elec & Electronics Engrs; Sigma Xi. *Res:* Communication theory; application of phase and injection lock techniques to signal processing and communication systems; power electronics. *Mailing Add:* Dept of Elec Eng Cooper Union Cooper Sq New York NY 10003

SANDLER, RIVKA BLACK, b Warsaw, Poland, Feb 20, 18; US citizen; m 47; c 2. GERONTOLOGY. *Educ:* Hebrew Univ, MSc, 42, PhD(endocrinol), 50. *Prof Exp:* Instr, Hebrew Univ, 47-50; lectr pharmacol, Sch Med, Univ Ottawa, 50-52; asst prof pharmacol, Med Sch, 64-70, assoc prof, 70-78, PROF SCI, SCH HEALTH RELATED PROFESSIONS, INTERDISCIPLINARY PROGS, UNIV PITTSBURGH, 78- *Res:* Gerontolog; osteoporosis. *Mailing Add:* 114 Pa Hall Univ of Pittsburgh Sch of Health Rel Professions Pittsburgh PA 15261

SANDLER, SAMUEL, b Lipivitz, USSR, Jan 1, 21; Can citizen; m 48; c 3. CHEMICAL ENGINEERING, ANALYTICAL CHEMISTRY. *Educ:* Univ Toronto, BASc, 44, MASc, 48. *Prof Exp:* Lab supvr, Defence Indusrs Ltd, 44-45; instr chem eng, Univ Toronto, 46-48; prin sci res officer, Defence Res Bd Can, 48-58; from asst prof to assoc prof chem eng, 58-69, PROF CHEM ENG, UNIV TORONTO, 69- *Concurrent Pos:* Instr, Can Voc Training Inst, 46-48; consult, Chem Eng Res Consult, Ltd, 62- *Mem:* Fel Chem Inst Can. *Res:* Kinetics and mechanisms of oxidation, decomposition, ignition and detonation of fuel vapors and gases; associated instrumental methods of chemical analysis. *Mailing Add:* 5 Evanston Dr Downsview ON M3H 5N9 Can

SANDLER, SHELDON SAMUEL, b Cleveland, Ohio, Dec 17, 32; m 58; c 1. BIOPHYSICS, APPLIED PHYSICS. *Educ:* Case Western Reserve Univ, BSEE, 54; Yale Univ, MEng, 55; Harvard Univ, MS, 58, PhD(appl physics), 62. *Prof Exp:* Res assoc, Horizons, Inc, 56-57; mem staff, Lincoln Lab, Mass Inst Technol, 58-59; sr engr, Electronic Commun, Inc, 59-60; from asst prof to assoc prof, 62-81, PROF ELEC ENG, NORTHEASTERN UNIV, 81- *Concurrent Pos:* Consult, Harvard Col Observ, 62-63; res fel appl physics, Harvard Univ, 63-; consult, Raytheon Corp, 63-64; guest prof, Swiss Fed Inst Technol, 64-65; consult, US Naval Res Lab, 65-69; vis scholar, Med Res Coun Lab Molecular Biol, Eng, 69-70; consult, Geosci Surv, 70-72, Block Eng, 73-74 & Am Sci & Eng, 74-75 & Geo-Ctr Inc; mem, Comt VI, Int Union Radio Sci; vis prof, Univ Zurich, 76-77. *Mem:* Sigma Xi. *Res:* Bioengineering; picture processing and reconstruction, radiation effects on biological tissue; electromagnetics; geophysical exploration. *Mailing Add:* Dept of Elec Eng Northeastern Univ Boston MA 02115

SANDLER, STANLEY I, b New York, NY, June 10, 40; m 62; c 3. THERMODYNAMICS, CHEMICAL ENGINEERING. *Educ:* City Col New York, BChE, 62; Univ Minn, PhD(chem eng), 66. *Prof Exp:* NSF fel, Inst Molecular Physics, Univ Md, 66-67; from asst prof to assoc prof chem eng, 67-73, PROF CHEM ENG, UNIV DEL, 73- *Concurrent Pos:* Camille & Henry Dreyfus Fac Scholar, 71; consult, Mobil Res & Develop Corp, 77-; vis prof, Imperial Col, London, 73-74 & Tech Univ, Berlin, 81. *Mem:* Am Phys Soc; Am Inst Chem Engrs. *Res:* Relate properties of liquids to their structural characteristics; predict properties of fluids under extreme conditions; thermodynamic and transport properties prediction and measurement; computer-aided design. *Mailing Add:* Dept of Chem Eng Univ of Del Newark DE 19711

SANDLIN, BILLY JOE, b Hunt Co, Tex, Jan 10, 27; m 49; c 2. PHYSICS. *Educ:* ETex State Univ, BS, 48, MS, 49; Univ Tex, PhD, 60. *Prof Exp:* Instr physics, ETex State Teachers Col, 46-49; instr, LeTourneau Tech Inst, 49; instr physics, geol & math, Odessa Col, 49-53; asst prof physics, Tex Tech Col, 55-57; instr math, Univ Tex, 57-58; ASSOC PROF PHYSICS, TEX TECH UNIV, 59- *Mem:* Am Phys Soc; Am Asn Physics Teachers. *Res:* Measurements of high accuracy and precision involving electrical and electronic techniques; temperature and temperature-difference measurements; properties of solids at low temperatures; electronic circuit development. *Mailing Add:* Dept of Physics Tex Tech Univ Lubbock TX 79409

SANDMAN, ROBERT PAUL, b St Louis, Mo, July 5, 23. BIOCHEMISTRY. *Educ:* St Louis Univ, BS, 47; Univ Tex, MA, 52, PhD(biochem), 54. *Prof Exp:* Instr biochem, Tulane Univ, 54-57; Jane Coffin Childs Mem Fund Med Res fel, Rome & Paris, 57-60; asst res biochemist, Rice Univ, 60-62; asst res scientist, Kaiser Found Res Inst, 62-64; asst res biochemist, Univ Calif, Berkeley, 64-69; asst res biochemist, Dept Pediat, 69-76, ASST RES BIOCHEMIST, DEPT OPHTHAL, MED CTR, UNIV CALIF, SAN FRANCISCO, 76- *Mem:* Am Chem Soc. *Res:* Amino acid metabolism in gyrate atrophy of the choroid and retina; analytical biochemistry and methodology; isolation and purification of enzymes; studies of lysosomal enzymes in relation to kidney transplant rejection and genetic deficiency diseases. *Mailing Add:* Dept of Pediat Univ of Calif Med Ctr San Francisco CA 94122

SANDMANN, WILLIAM HENRY, b Yakima, Wash, Jan 15, 28; m 53; c 3. ASTRONOMY, EXPERIMENTAL PHYSICS. *Educ:* Reed Col, BA, 53; Univ Utah, PhD, 60. *Prof Exp:* Asst prof physics, Grinnell Col, 59-63; assoc prof, 63-72, PROF PHYSICS, HARVEY MUDD COL, 73- *Concurrent Pos:* Vis scholar, Univ Tex, Austin, 72-73 & 76-77; vis prof, Univ Capetown & Sutherland Observ, 76-77. *Mem:* Am Astron Soc. *Res:* Observational astronomy; astronomical instrumentation. *Mailing Add:* Dept of Physics Harvey Mudd Col Claremont CA 91711

SANDMEIER, HENRY ARMIN, b Antwerp, Belg, Mar 17, 20; nat US; m 61; c 2. NUCLEAR PHYSICS. *Educ:* Swiss Fed Inst Technol, dipl, 49, DSc(elec eng), 54, PhD(physics), 59; Mass Inst Technol, SM, 52, EE, 54. *Prof Exp:* Mem res staff, Mass Inst Technol, 51-54; assoc physicist, Argonne Nat Lab, 56-61; liaison scientist, London Br, US Off Naval Res, London Embassy, UK, 61-63; PHYSICIST, NAT SECURITY PROG, LOS ALAMOS NAT LAB, 63- *Concurrent Pos:* Vis prof nuclear eng, Purdue Univ, 66; consult, US Naval Weapons Eval Facility, 66-, Army Res Off, 70-; vis prof, Univ Stuttgart, 68-69; consult, Defense Depts, Switz, Norway, Sweden & Ger, 68- *Mem:* Am Phys Soc; Am Nuclear Soc. *Res:* Reactor physics and engineering; engineering education; assay techniques of fissionable materials; vulnerability of nuclear weapons and nuclear weapons effects; international scientific liaison and consulting. *Mailing Add:* Nat Security Prog Los Alamos Nat Lab PO Box 1663 Los Alamos NM 87545

SANDMEYER, ESTHER E, b Winterthur, Switz, Aug 9, 29; US citizen. PHARMACOLOGY, TOXICOLOGY. *Educ:* Winterthur Tech Univ, Switz, BSc, 51; Ohio State Univ, MSc, 60, PhD(biochem), 65. *Prof Exp:* Lab asst clin anal, Gen Hosp, Winterthur, 45-47; chemist, Nuffield Lab, Univ Birmingham, 52-53, Feldmühle, Rorschach, Switz, 53-55; Bell Tel Labs, Inc, NJ, 55-57 & Chem Abstr, Ohio, 58-60; asst prof chem, Friends Univ, 65 & biochem, Univ Nev, Reno, 65-70; trainee physiol & biophys, Hahnemann Med Col, 70-71 & toxicol, Sch Med, Univ Calif, San Francisco, 71-72; biochemist-toxicologist, Gulf Oil Corp, 72-75, toxicologist & dir biochem lab, 75; INDUST CONSULT, 75- *Concurrent Pos:* Desert Res Inst grant, 66-67. *Mem:* AAAS; Am Chem Soc. *Res:* Biochemistry, chemical engineering; feasibility studies; literature surveys; training of toxicologists and toxicology managers. *Mailing Add:* 610 Foxhurst Rd Pittsburgh PA 15238

SANDO, KENNETH MARTIN, b Oglivie, Minn, May 15, 41; m 66. THEORETICAL CHEMISTRY. *Educ:* Univ Minn, BCh, 62; Univ Wis, PhD(chem), 68. *Prof Exp:* Physicist, Smithsonian Astrophys Observ, 68-69; asst prof chem, 69-73, ASSOC PROF CHEM, UNIV IOWA, 73- *Concurrent Pos:* Guest worker, Nat Bur Standards, 75-76. *Mem:* Am Phys Soc; Am Chem Soc. *Res:* Quantum chemistry; atomic and molecular processes. *Mailing Add:* Dept of Chem Univ of Iowa Iowa City IA 52242

SANDO, WILLIAM JASPER, b Washington, DC, Apr 23, 27; c 2. STRATIGRAPHY, PALEONTOLOGY. *Educ:* Johns Hopkins Univ, BA, 50, MA, 51, PhD(geol), 53. *Prof Exp:* Fel, Johns Hopkins Univ, 53-54; GEOLOGIST, US NAT MUS, US GEOL SURV, 54- *Mem:* Geol Soc Am; Paleont Soc; Am Asn Petrol Geologists. *Res:* Lower Ordovician paleontology and stratigraphy; Mississippian stratigraphy and coral faunas; lexicon of geologic names of North America. *Mailing Add:* Room E-318 US National Museum Natural Hist Washington DC 20560

SANDOK, PAUL LOUIS, b Rice Lake, Wis, Aug 18, 43; m 69; c 5. INFECTIOUS DISEASES, BIOCHEMISTRY. *Educ:* Univ Wis, Madison, BS, 68, MS, 71, PhD(bact), 74. *Prof Exp:* Proj asst, Med Sch, Univ Wis-Madison, 68-69, res asst, Dept Bact, 69-74; Hormel fel, Hormel Inst, Univ Minn, 74-77, res assoc, 77-78; ASST PROF MICROBIOL, UNIV NC, CHARLOTTE, 78- *Mem:* Sigma Xi; Am Soc Microbiol; Am Soc Zoologists; AAAS; Am Inst Biol Sci. *Res:* Host-parasite interaction, at the cellular and molecular levels, including cell mediated immunity in brucellosis; bacterial physiology in syphilis and surface interaction in disease caused by anaerobes. *Mailing Add:* Dept Biol Univ NC Charlotte NC 28223

SANDOR, GEORGE N(ASON), b Budapest, Hungary, Feb 24, 12; US citizen; m 64. MECHANICAL ENGINEERING, DESIGN ENGINEERING. *Educ:* Univ Polytech, Budapest, Dipl Ing, 34; Columbia Univ, DEngSc, 59. *Prof Exp:* Asst chief engr, Hungarian Rubber Co, Dunlop Ltd, 35-37, head mfg dept, 37-38; design engr, Babcock Printing Press Corp, Conn, 39-44; vpres & chief engr, Harry W Faeber Corp, NY, 44-50; chief engr, Graphic Arts Res Lab, Time Inc, Conn, 50-61 & Huck Design Co, NY, 61; assoc prof mech eng, Yale Univ, 61-66; Alcoa Found prof mech design, Rensselaer Polytech Inst, 66-75, chmn, Div Machines & Struct, Sch Eng, 67-74, dir, Ctr Eng Design, 74-75; RES PROF MECH ENG & DIR, MECH ENG DESIGN & ROTORDYNAMICS LABS, UNIV FLA, GAINESVILLE, 76- *Concurrent Pos:* Instr, Univ Conn, 41-44; lectr, Columbia Univ, 61-62; consult, Graphic Arts Res Lab, Time Inc, 61-63, McCall's Corp, 61-62 & Huck Design Co, 61-67; mem bd dirs, Huck Co, Inc, 67-71; consult, Xerox Corp, 71- & Instituto Politecnico Olivetti, Ivrea, Italy; consult engr, 71-; NSF, NASA & Army Res Off grants. *Honors & Awards:* Machine Design & Applied Mechanisms Awards, Am Soc Mech Engrs, 75. *Mem:* Fel Am Soc Mech Engrs; Am Soc Eng Educ; Nat Soc Prof Engrs; NY Acad Sci; Am Acad Mech. *Res:* Methodology and philosophy of engineering design; design and development of automatic machinery; printing, paper processing and allied machine design; kinematic and kineto-elastodynamic synthesis of planar and spatial mechanisms; mechanisation of natural locomotion. *Mailing Add:* 220 MEB Univ of Fla Gainesville FL 32611

SANDOR, THOMAS, b Budapest, Hungary, Nov 3, 24; Can citizen; m 49; c 1. BIOCHEMISTRY, ENDOCRINOLOGY. *Educ:* Pazmany Peter Univ, Budapest, dipl chem, 48; Univ Toronto, PhD(path chem), 60. *Prof Exp:* Res biochemist, Clin Res Dept, Hotel-Dieu Hosp, 56-59; from res asst prof to res assoc prof, 61-70, RES PROF MED, UNIV MONTREAL, 70-; SR RES SCIENTIST, LAB ENDOCRINOL, HOPITAL NOTRE DAME, 59- *Concurrent Pos:* Career investr, Med Res Coun Can, 62-; Nuffield Found traveling fel, 64; Sci Res Coun sr vis res fel, 66 & 79-80; Schering traveling fel, 66; Endocrine Soc traveling fel, 68; vis prof zool, Univ Sheffield, 70-71 & 79-80; hon vis prof, Dept Biol Chem, Fac Exact & Natural Sci, Univ Buenos Aires, 74; assoc mem exp med, McGill Univ, 69-; corresp ed, J Steroid Biochem, 70-79; mem ed bd, Gen & Comp Endocrinol. *Mem:* Endocrine Soc; Can Biochem Soc; Can Soc Clin Invest; Royal Soc Med; Brit Soc Endocrinol. *Res:* Steroid biochemistry; comparative steroid endocrinology; mechanism of steroid hormone action. *Mailing Add:* Lab of Endocrinol Hopital Notre Dame PO Box 1560 Sta C Montreal PQ H2L 4K8 Can

SANDORFF, PAUL E(DWIN), b Perth Amboy, NJ, Oct 1, 16; m 55; c 2. MATERIALS SCIENCE. *Educ:* Mass Inst Technol, SB, 39. *Prof Exp:* Group engr struct res, Lockheed Aircraft Corp, 39-52; from assoc prof to prof aeronaut & astronaut, Mass Inst Technol, 52-64, vis prof, 65-68; SR RES & DEVELOP ENGR, RYE CANYON RES LAB, LOCKHEED CALIF CO, 68- *Concurrent Pos:* Indust consult, 53-; consult, NASA, 59-, mem res adv comt missile & space vehicle struct, 59-; consult scientist, Sr Mem Res Lab, Lockheed Missiles & Space Co, 61-68. *Mem:* Am Inst Aeronaut & Astronaut; AAAS. *Res:* Solid mechanics; structural dynamics; shock and stress wave propagation; hypervelocity impact; materials and structures testing; fatigue and fracture; flight mechanics; vehicle systems engineering; structures design and analysis. *Mailing Add:* Rye Canyon Res Labs Lockheed Calif Co Burbank CA 91520

SANDOVAL, HOWARD KENNETH, b New York, NY, Aug 15, 31; m 51. MICROBIOLOGY. *Educ:* City Col New York, BS, 53; Columbia Univ, AM, 56; Cornell Univ, PhD(microbiol), 64. *Prof Exp:* Teacher high sch, NY, 56-58; res asst, Sloan-Kettering Inst Cancer Res, NY, 58-59; Sloan fel, 64-65; instr biol, Brooklyn Col, 65-67; microbiologist, Lederle Labs, NY, 67-69; asst prof, 69-72, ASSOC PROF BIOL, MIAMI-DADE COMMUNITY COL NORTH, 72- *Mem:* Am Soc Microbiol. *Res:* Colicins; lysogeny; microbial genetics; electron microscopy of bacterial viruses. *Mailing Add:* Dept of Biol Miami-Dade Comm Col Miami FL 33167

SANDOW, ALEXANDER, biophysics, deceased

SANDOW, BRUCE ARNOLD, b Los Angeles, Calif, Jan 26, 45; m 71. REPRODUCTIVE BIOLOGY, ELECTRON MICROSCOPY. *Educ:* Univ Calif, Berkeley, BA, 67, MA, 70, PhD(endocrinol), 78. *Prof Exp:* Res fel, Ore Regional Primate Res Ctr, 76-81; ASST PROF ANAT, EASTERN VA MED SCH, 81- *Mem:* Sigma Xi. *Res:* Hormonal regulation of female reproductive tract secretions; electron microscopy of oocyte maturation and fertilization. *Mailing Add:* Dept Anat PO Box 1980 Eastern Va Med Sch Norfolk VA 23501

SANDOZ, GEORGE, b Toledo, Ohio, Jan 24, 21; m 61; c 3. METALLURGICAL ENGINEERING. *Educ:* Wayne State Univ, BS, 43; Univ Mich, MS, 45; Univ Md, PhD(metall), 59. *Prof Exp:* Metallurgist, Chevrolet Motor Co, 43-44 & US Naval Res Lab, 46-72; metallurgist, Chicago Br Off, 72-77, DIR SCI, OFF NAVAL RES, CHICAGO, 77- *Concurrent Pos:* Mem malleable iron comt, Welding Res Coun, 56-57. *Mem:* Am Soc Metals; Am Inst Mining, Metall & Petrol Engrs; Am Soc Testing & Mat; Nat Asn Corrosion Engrs. *Res:* Reaction kinetics; mechanical properties; fracture and corrosion of steel and cast iron; protective coatings for refractory metals; mechanical properties of intermediate phases; electric and magnetic alloys; stress corrosion and hydrogen embrittlement. *Mailing Add:* 2030 Glencoe Wheaton IL 60187

SANDQUIST, GARY MARLIN, b Salt Lake City, Utah, Apr 19, 36; m 60; c 5. NUCLEAR & MECHANICAL ENGINEERING. *Educ:* Univ Utah, BSME, 60, PhD(mech eng), 64; Univ Calif, Berkeley, MS, 61. *Prof Exp:* Teaching asst mech eng, 59 & 61-62, instr, 62-63 & 64-65, from asst prof to assoc prof, 65-75, PROF MECH ENG, UNIV UTAH, 75-, RES ASSOC PROF SURG, 78- *Concurrent Pos:* Vis scientist, Mass Inst Technol, 69-70. *Mem:* Am Nuclear Soc; Am Soc Eng Educ; Am Soc Mech Engrs. *Res:* Safety and environment aspects of nuclear energy; nuclear fusion; biomedical engineering; applied mathematics; system analysis. *Mailing Add:* Dept of Mech & Indust Eng Univ of Utah Salt Lake City UT 84112

SANDRI, JOSEPH MARIO, b Chicago, Ill, Mar 9, 29; m 59; c 4. ORGANIC CHEMISTRY. *Educ:* Ill Inst Technol, BS, 52; Mich State Univ, PhD(chem), 56. *Prof Exp:* Res proj chemist, Am Oil Co, 56-61, sr proj chemist, 61-62; sr group leader, Nalco Chem Co, Ill, 62-70; dir res & develop, Ott Chem Co, 71-72, Story Chem Co, 72-80. *Mem:* AAAS; Am Chem Soc; Royal Soc Chem; Am Asn Textile Chemists & Colorists. *Res:* Isocyanates; phosgene and medicinal chemistry; amino acids; agricultural and paper chemicals; chemicals, latices and resins for textiles; surfactants; macrocyclic chemistry; fragrance chemicals; polymers; reaction mechanisms. *Mailing Add:* 632 Magothy Veiw Dr Arnold MD 21017

SANDRIDGE, ROBERT LEE, b Junior, WVa, June 12, 32; m 53; c 5. ANALYTICAL CHEMISTRY, ORGANIC POLYMER CHEMISTRY. *Educ:* WLiberty State Col, BS, 54; WVa Univ, MS, 58, PhD(org chem), 69. *Prof Exp:* Chemist, NC State Univ, 54; group leader anal chem, 58-73, mgr anal group, Process Res Dept, 73-78, MGR ANALYTICAL & ENVIRON RES, MOBAY CHEM CORP, 78- *Concurrent Pos:* Chmn, NAm Analytical Comt, Int Isocyanate Inst. *Mem:* Am Chem Soc; Am Soc Testing & Mat; Soc Plastics Indust; AAAS. *Res:* Isocyanates; urethanes; polycarbonates; amines. *Mailing Add:* Process Res Dept Mobay Chem Corp New Martinsville WV 26155

SANDRIK, JAMES LESLIE, b Chicago, Ill, July 7, 38; m 67; c 2. DENTAL MATERIALS. *Educ:* Northwestern Univ, PhB, 67, MS, 68, PhD(biol mat), 72. *Prof Exp:* from asst professor to assoc prof, 72-81, PROF DENT MAT & CHMN DEPT, SCH DENT, LOYOLA UNIV CHICAGO, 82- *Concurrent Pos:* NIH fel, Northwestern Univ, 72. *Mem:* Am Dent Asn; Am Soc Metals; Int Asn Dent Res. *Res:* Polymeric restorative and reconstructive materials; non-precious casting alloys. *Mailing Add:* Dept of Dent Mat Loyola Univ Sch of Dent Maywood IL 60153

SANDS, DAVID CHANDLER, b Los Angeles, Calif, Aug 30, 41; m 69; c 1. PLANT PATHOLOGY, BACTERIOLOGY. *Educ:* Pomona Col, AB, 63; Univ Calif, Berkeley, PhD(plant path), 69. *Prof Exp:* NSF fel soil microbiol, Div Soils, Commonwealth Sci & Indust Res Orgn, Australia, 69-70; asst plant pathologist, Conn Agr Exp Sta, 70-77; ASST PROF PLANT PATH, MONT STATE UNIV, 77- *Concurrent Pos:* Adj asst prof microbiol, Mont State Univ, 81- *Mem:* AAAS; Am Phytopath Soc; Am Soc Microbiol; Brit Soc Gen Microbiol; Am Inst Biol Sci. *Res:* Physiology, taxonomy and ecology of bacterial plant pathogens, especially Pseudomonas; ecology and general physiological differences between plant pathogenic pseudomonads and saprophytes; bacterial diseases of cereal crops; selection of high lysine lines of bacteria for food fermentation and high lysine lines of cereal crops. *Mailing Add:* Dept of Plant Path Mont State Univ Bozeman MT 59717

SANDS, DONALD EDGAR, b Leominster, Mass, Feb 25, 29; m 56; c 2. PHYSICAL CHEMISTRY. *Educ:* Worcester Polytech Inst, BS, 51; Cornell Univ, PhD, 55. *Prof Exp:* Res assoc, Cornell Univ, 55-56; crystallographer, Lawrence Radiation Lab, 56-62; from asst prof to assoc prof, 62-65, dir gen chem, 74-75, assoc dean advan studies, Col Arts & Sci, 75-80, actg dean, 80-81, PROF CHEM, UNIV KY, 68-, ASSOC VPRES ACAD AFFAIRS, 81- *Mem:* Sigma Xi; AAAS; Am Chem Soc; Am Crystallog Asn. *Res:* Crystallography. *Mailing Add:* Dept Chem Univ Ky Lexington KY 40506

SANDS, ELAINE S, b Brooklyn, NY, Jan 25, 40; m 64; c 2. SPEECH PATHOLOGY. *Educ:* Brooklyn Col, AB, 60; Univ Mich, MS, 61; NY Univ, PhD(speech path, audiol), 77. *Prof Exp:* Speech pathologist, Med Ctr, NY Univ, 61-70; ASST PROF SPEECH PATH & AUDIOL, ADELPHI UNIV, 70- *Concurrent Pos:* Consult, New York Vet Admin Hosp, 76- *Mem:* Acad Aphasia; NY Acad Sci; fel Am Speech, Hearing & Language Asn. *Res:* Neurological aspects of language; aphasia in adults; recovery from aphasia. *Mailing Add:* Dept Speech Path Adelphi Univ Garden City NY 11530

SANDS, GEORGE DEWEY, b Norfolk, Va, June 16, 19; m 42; c 3. PHYSICAL CHEMISTRY. *Educ:* Col William & Mary, BS, 39; Univ Richmond, MS, 41; Univ Ill, PhD(phys chem), 45. *Prof Exp:* Sr res chemist, Firestone Tire & Rubber Co, 45-48; assoc prof chem, Col William & Mary, 48-56; chief, Nuclear Br, Transportation Res Command, US Dept Army, 56-59; dir sci requirements, Martin Co, 59-60; aerospace polymer chemist, 60-70, assoc proj scientist, Proj Viking, 70-76, CHIEF, SCI & TECH INFO PROGS DIV, LANGLEY RES CTR, NASA, 70-76. *Mem:* Am Chem Soc. *Res:* Physical chemistry of high polymers. *Mailing Add:* Viking Proj 180A NASA Langley Res Ctr Hampton VA 23665

SANDS, HOWARD, b New York, NY, Aug 20, 42; m 68. PHARMACOLOGY, BIOCHEMISTRY. *Educ:* Rutgers Univ, New Brunswick, BA, 64; Case Western Reserve Univ, PhD(pharmacol), 69. *Prof Exp:* NIH training grant renal dis, Northwestern Univ, 69-71; pharmacologist, Nat Jewish Hosp & Res Ctr, 71-81; GROUP LEADER, PHAMACOL/TOXICOL, NEW ENGLAND NUCLEAR, 81- *Concurrent Pos:* Pharmacologist, Vet Admin Res Hosp, 70-71; asst prof, Dept Oral Biol, Sch Dent, Univ Colo, 75-77. *Mem:* AAAS; Soc Exp Biol & Med. *Res:* Biochemical aspects of drug actions; radio pharmaceutical research and related immunology. *Mailing Add:* New England Nuclear 601 Treble Cove Rd North Billerica MA 01862

SANDS, JEFFREY ALAN, b Kingston, Pa, Jan 16, 48; m 73. BIOPHYSICS. *Educ:* Univ Del, BS, 69; Pa State Univ, MS, 71, PhD(biophys), 73. *Prof Exp:* Asst prof, 73-77, ASSOC PROF PHYSICS, LEHIGH UNIV, 77- *Mem:* Biophys Soc; Am Soc Microbiol. *Res:* Molecular virology, antiviral agents, amphiphile-virus interactions. *Mailing Add:* Dept of Physics Bldg 16 Lehigh Univ Bethlehem PA 18015

SANDS, MATTHEW, b Oxford, Mass, Oct 20, 19; m; c 3. PHYSICS. *Educ:* Clark Univ, BA, 40; Rice Inst, MA, 41; Mass Inst Technol, PhD(physics), 48. *Prof Exp:* Physicist, US Naval Ord Lab, 41-43 & Los Alamos Sci Lab, 43-46; res assoc, Mass Inst Technol, 46-48, asst prof physics, 48-50; sr res fel, Calif Inst Technol, 50-52, from assoc prof to prof, 52-63; prof & dep dir, Linear Accelerator Ctr, Stanford Univ, 63-69; vchancellor sci, 69-72, PROF PHYSICS, UNIV CALIF, SANTA CRUZ, 69- *Concurrent Pos:* Fulbright scholar, Italy, 52-53; consult, Inst Defense Anal, 60-68, Off Sci & Technol, 61-66 & Arms Control & Disarmament Agency, 62-66; mem, Comn Col Physics, 60-66, chmn, 64-66; mem, Pugwash Conf Sci & World Affairs, 61-62. *Mem:* Fel Am Phys Soc; Am Asn Physics Teachers; Fedn Am Sci. *Res:* Electronic instrumentation; cosmic rays; accelerators; high-energy physics; education; science and public affairs. *Mailing Add:* Physics/NS-2 Univ of Calif Santa Cruz CA 95064

SANDS, RICHARD DAYTON, b Skaneateles, NY, Nov 18, 29; m 53; c 3. ORGANIC CHEMISTRY. *Educ:* Oberlin Col, AB, 51; Syracuse Univ, MS, 54, PhD(org chem), 59. *Prof Exp:* Asst instr chem, Syracuse Univ, 52-56; from asst prof to prof, 56-70, chmn div math & sci, 74-76, Ferro prof, 70-80, chmn div phys sci, 76-80, PROF CHEM & CHMN DEPT, ALFRED UNIV, 80- *Mem:* Am Chem Soc. *Res:* Ring size in the pinacol rearrangement of alicyclic glycols; synthesis and cleavage of aliphatic bicyclic compounds. *Mailing Add:* Dept of Chem Alfred Univ Alfred NY 14802

SANDS, RICHARD HAMILTON, b San Diego, Calif, Sept 28, 29; m 51; c 4. BIOPHYSICS, ATOMIC PHYSICS. *Educ:* Univ Redlands, BS, 50; Washington Univ, PhD(physics), 54. *Prof Exp:* Res assoc & instr physics, Stanford Univ, 54-57; from asst prof to assoc prof, 57-65, chmn, Dept Physics, 77-82, PROF PHYSICS & RES BIOPHYSICIST, UNIV MICH, ANN ARBOR, 65- *Mem:* AAAS; Am Asn Physics Teachers; Am Phys Soc; Biophys Soc. *Res:* Magnetic and optical resonance fluorescence in atomic and solid state physics; biophysical applications of electron paramagnetic resonance spectrometry; Mossbauer spectroscopy and electron-nuclear double resonance spectrometry. *Mailing Add:* 1049 Randall Lab Univ of Mich Ann Arbor MI 48104

SANDS, SEYMOUR, b New York, NY, Mar 16, 18. TEXTILE CHEMISTRY. *Educ:* City Col, BS, 39; NY Univ, MS, 48; Polytech Inst Brooklyn, PhD(chem), 53. *Prof Exp:* Org chemist, Fleischmann Distilling Co, 46-49; res chemist, 53-82, DEVELOP ASSOC, TEXTILE FIBERS DEPT, E I DU PONT DE NEMOURS & CO, INC, 68- *Mem:* Am Chem Soc. *Res:* Polymer chemistry pertaining to fiber technology. *Mailing Add:* Christina Lab E I du Pont de Nemours & Co Inc Wilmington DE 19898

SANDSON, JOHN I, b Jeannette, Pa, Sept 20, 27; m 57; c 2. MEDICINE. *Educ:* Wash Univ, MD, 53; Am Bd Internal Med, dipl, 60. *Prof Exp:* From intern to asst resident med serv, Presby Hosp, New York, 53-56; chief resident, Bronx Munic Hosp Ctr, 56-57; instr, Albert Einstein Col Med, 57-59, assoc, 59-61, from asst prof to prof med, 61-74, from assoc dir med to dir, Hosp, 66-74, actg chmn dept, 70-72, med dir, 70-74; PROF MED & DEAN, SCH MED, BOSTON UNIV, 74- *Concurrent Pos:* Nat Inst Arthritis & Metab Dis trainee, Albert Einstein Col Med, 57-59, Arthritis & Rheumatism Found fel, 59-61; asst vis physician, Bronx Munic Hosp Ctr, 57-66, vis physician, 66-; attend physician, Bronx Vet Admin Hosp, 57-66; investr health res coun, City New York, 61-71; head, Arthritis Group, Albert Einstein Col Med-Bronx Munic Hosp Ctr, 68-72; consult, Study Sect, NIH, 71-74. *Mem:* AAAS; Am Soc Clin Invest; Harvey Soc; Am Rheumatism Asn; Royal Soc Med. *Res:* Rheumatology. *Mailing Add:* Boston Univ Sch of Med 80 E Concord St Boston MA 02118

SANDSTEAD, HAROLD HILTON, b Omaha, Nebr, May 25, 32; m 58; c 3. INTERNAL MEDICINE, NUTRITION. *Educ:* Ohio Wesleyan Univ, BA, 54; Vanderbilt Univ, MD, 58; Am Bd Internal Med, dipl, 67. *Prof Exp:* From intern to asst resident med, Barnes Hosp, St Louis, Mo, 58-60; asst resident path, Vanderbilt Hosp, Nashville, Tenn, 60-61; first asst resident med, Vet Admin & Vanderbilt Hosps, 63-64, Hugh J Morgan resident, Vanderbilt Hosp, 64-65; from instr to asst prof med, Sch Med, Vanderbilt Univ, 65-67, asst prof biochem, 65-67, asst prof med & nutrit, 67-70, assoc prof nutrit, 70-71; res prof biochem & med, 71-75, ADJ PROF BIOCHEM & CLIN PROF MED, SCH MED, UNIV N DAK, 75-; DIR, GRAND FORKS HUMAN NUTRIT RES CTR, AGR RES SERV, USDA, 71- *Concurrent Pos:* Nutrit Found Future leader, 68-71. *Honors & Awards:* Hull Gold Medal Award, AMA, 70; Meade Johnson Award, Am Inst Nutrit, 72. *Mem:* Fel Am Col Physicians; Am Inst Nutrit; Am Soc Clin Nutrit; Soc Exp Biol & Med; Cent Soc Clin Res. *Res:* Clinical nutrition; zinc metabolism; essential and toxic trace elements; nutrition, brain development and function. *Mailing Add:* USDA Agr Res Serv Grand Forks Human Nutrit Res Ctr PO Box D Univ Sta Grand Forks ND 58202

SANDSTED, ROGER FRANCE, b Holdrege, Nebr, Aug 5, 18; m 49; c 3. VEGETABLE CROPS. *Educ:* Univ Nebr, BS, 48; Univ Minn, PhD, 54. *Prof Exp:* Asst hort, Univ Nebr, 48-50 & Univ Minn, 52-54; asst horticulturist, Parma Br Exp Sta, Idaho, 54-57; from asst prof to assoc prof, 57-77, PROF VEG CROPS, EXTEN, CORNELL UNIV, 77-, DEPT EXTEN LEADER, 77- *Mem:* Am Soc Hort Sci. *Res:* Legume vegetables; dry beans; cultural problems. *Mailing Add:* 22 Dutcher Rd Freeville NY 13068

SANDSTROM, DONALD RICHARD, b Spokane, Wash, May 9, 40; m 63; c 1. PHYSICS. *Educ:* Wash State Univ, BS, 63, PhD(physics), 67. *Prof Exp:* NSF fel, Univ Bonn, 67; NSF & UK Atomic Energy Authority fel, Univ Liverpool, 67-69; from asst prof to assoc prof, 69-81, PROF PHYSICS & CHEM PHYSICS, WASH STATE UNIV, 81- *Concurrent Pos:* Guest worker, Nat Bur Standards, 74-75. *Mem:* Am Phys Soc; AAAS. *Res:* X-ray absorption spectroscopy; determination of local structure in condensed matter by analysis of the extended x-ray absorption fine structure. *Mailing Add:* Dept of Physics Wash State Univ Pullman WA 99164

SANDSTROM, WAYNE MARK, b Seattle, Wash, Feb 17, 27; m 53; c 3. UNDERWATER ACOUSTICS, ORDNANCE. *Educ:* Univ Wash, BS, 48, PhD(physics), 53. *Prof Exp:* From assoc physicist to sr physicist, Appl Physics Lab, Univ Wash, 52-59, asst dir, 59-64, dep dir, 64-70; PRES, HENDERSON TECH CORP, 70- *Concurrent Pos:* Consult, US Naval Torpedo Sta, Wash, 70- *Mem:* Am Phys Soc. *Res:* Electromagnetics. *Mailing Add:* Henderson Tech Corp 1107 NE 45th St Rm 210 Seattle WA 98105

SANDULEAK, NICHOLAS, b Lackawanna, NY, June 22, 33. ASTRONOMY. *Educ:* Case Inst Technol, BS, 56, MS, 61, PhD(astron), 65. *Prof Exp:* Staff astronr, Cerro Tololo Inter-Am Observ, 65-67; SR RES ASSOC, CASE WESTERN RESERVE UNIV, 67- *Mem:* Int Astron Union; Am Astron Soc. *Res:* Astronomical spectroscopy applied to studies of galactic structure and the Magellanic Clouds. *Mailing Add:* Warner & Swasey Observ 1975 Taylor Rd East Cleveland OH 44112

SANDUS, OSCAR, b New York, NY, July 29, 24; m 46; c 3. PHYSICAL CHEMISTRY. *Educ:* Univ Ky, BS, 49; Univ Chicago, MS, 50; Ill Inst Technol, PhD(chem), 55. *Prof Exp:* Asst chemist, Argonne Nat Lab, 55-58; res assoc phys chem, Radiation Lab, Univ Mich, 58-60, assoc res phys chemist, 60-61; res phys chemist, Conductron Corp, 62-63; sr chemist, Chemotronics, Inc, 63-64; assoc res chemist, Infrared Physics Lab, Univ Mich, Ann Arbor, 64-67; RES CHEMIST, ENERGETIC MAT DIV, ARMY ARMAMENT RES & DEVELOP COMMAND, US ARMY, 68- *Mem:* AAAS; Am Chem Soc; Sigma Xi. *Res:* Thermodynamics and properties of nonelectrolytic solutions; uranium fuel and feed materials process development; dielectric relaxation; electromagnetic materials; electroplating process and plastic foam process development; fundamental aspects of physics and chemistry relating to missile reentry; photochemistry; spectroscopy; explosives. *Mailing Add:* Energetic Mat Div Command Bldg 3024 US Army Armament Res & Develop Command Dover NJ 07801

SANDUSKY, HAROLD WILLIAM, b Baltimore, Md, Sept 12, 49; m 78. COMBUSTION, DETONATION PHYSICS. *Educ:* Georgia Tech, BAE, 71; Princeton Univ, MSE, 73, MA, 74, PhD(aerospace & mech sci), 76. *Prof Exp:* MECH ENGR, NAVAL SURFACE WEAPONS CTR, 76- *Res:* Nitric oxide emissions from turbojet combustors and cigarette burning; deflagration to detonation transition for explosives and propellants. *Mailing Add:* 9307 Scaggsville Rd Laurel MD 20707

SANDVIG, ROBERT L(EROY), b Lead, SDak, Sept 11, 23; m 57; c 3. CHEMICAL ENGINEERING. *Educ:* SDak Sch Mines & Technol, BS, 44; Univ Cincinnati, MS, 48; Univ Colo, PhD(chem eng), 53. *Prof Exp:* Mech engr, Nat Adv Comt Aeronaut, Va, 44; instr chem, SDak Sch Mines & Technol, 46-47; chem engr, Darling & Co, Ohio, 48-49; instr chem, 49-50, asst prof chem & chem eng, 51-55, assoc prof chem eng, 56-63, PROF CHEM ENG, S DAK SCH MINES & TECHNOL, 63-, HEAD DEPT, 73- *Concurrent Pos:* Instr, Univ Colo, 52-53; consult, Rocky Flats Plant, Dow Chem Co, 69-75 & Rocky Flats Plant, Rockwell Int, 75- *Mem:* Am Chem Soc; Am Soc Eng Educ; Am Inst Chem Engrs; Sigma Xi. *Res:* Rheology of non-Newtonian fluids; vapor liquid equilibria of binary and ternary systems; pyrochemistry of actinides. *Mailing Add:* Dept of Chem Eng SDak Sch of Mines & Technol Rapid City SD 57701

SANDVIK, PETER OLAF, b Moose Lake, Minn, Sept 24, 27; m 53; c 7. GEOLOGY. *Educ:* Univ Alaska, BS, 50, BME, 51; Stanford Univ, MS, 61, PhD(geol), 64. *Prof Exp:* Mining engr-assayer, Alaska Territorial Dept Mines, 50-52 & 54-56; instr geol, Univ Alaska, 57-60; CHIEF GEOLOGIST & DIR MINERAL DEVELOP, INT MINERALS & CHEM CORP, 64- *Mem:* Am Inst Mining, Metall & Petrol Engrs; Geol Soc Am; Soc Econ Geologists; Can Inst Mining & Metall. *Res:* Trace and minor element content of sulphide ore minerals; application of economic geology in mineral exploration. *Mailing Add:* Int Minerals & Chem Corp Resource Develop Group IMC Plaza Libertyville IL 60048

SANDWEISS, JACK, b Chicago, Ill, Aug 19, 30; m 56; c 3. PHYSICS. *Educ:* Univ Calif, BS, 52, PhD(physics), 56. *Prof Exp:* Physicist, Radiation Lab, Univ Calif, 56-57; instr, 57-59, from asst prof to assoc prof, 59-64, prof, 64-80, chmn dept, 77-80, DONNER PROF PHYSICS, YALE UNIV, 80- *Concurrent Pos:* Consult, Lab Marine Physics, Yale Univ, 57-60, Brookhaven Nat Lab, 61-, Argonne Nat Lab & Nat Accelerator Lab. *Mem:* Am Phys Soc. *Res:* High energy physics; bubble chamber technique; physics of strange particles; counter and spark chamber techniques. *Mailing Add:* Sloane Physics Lab Yale Univ New Haven CT 06520

SANDWITH, COLIN JOHN, b Friday Harbor, Wash, Nov 9, 36; m 57; c 4. MECHANICAL ENGINEERING. *Educ:* Univ Wash, BSME, 61; Ore State Univ, PhD(mat sci), 67. *Prof Exp:* Draftsman, Commercial Airplane Div, Boeing Airplane Co, 57-58 & Duffy, Lawver & Kumpf Eng Consult Co, 59; mech engr, Hanford Atomic Prod Opers, Gen Elec Co, 61-62; mech engr,

Albany Res Ctr, US Bur Mines, 63-66; asst prof mech engr, 66-74, RES ASSOC PROF MECH ENG, UNIV WASH, 74- *Concurrent Pos:* NIH grant, Univ Wash, 67-69, NASA grant, 68-70. *Honors & Awards:* Gold Medal Valor Award, US Dept Interior, 66; Ralf Teetor Award, Soc Automotive Engrs, 72. *Mem:* Am Soc Metals; Am Soc Mech Engrs; Nat Asn Corrosion Engrs; Am Soc Eng Educ; Soc Mfg Engrs. *Res:* Corrosion, failure analysis, design, materials, ceramic coatings; structural failures; biomedical instrumentation; fiberoptic cardiovascular catheters; marine and industrial corrosion; mechanical behavior of materials; manufacturing processes. *Mailing Add:* Dept Mech Eng Univ Wash Seattle WA 98195

SANDZA, JOSEPH GERARD, b New York, NY, Feb 4, 17; m 42; c 5. BIOCHEMISTRY. *Educ:* Polytech Inst Brooklyn, BS, 37; Fordham Univ, MS, 40, PhD(biochem), 42. *Prof Exp:* Asst & instr, Fordham Univ, 37-42; Rockefeller Found res assoc, Northwestern Univ, 42; mem, Comt Med Res, Off Sci Res & Develop, 43-44; from res chemist to group leader, Lederle Labs, Am Cyanamid Corp, 44-46, head penicillin develop dept, 46-47; sr chemist, Hoffmann-La Roche, Inc, 48; asst mgr, Fermentation Dept, Stauffer Chem Co, 48-50, Biochem Sect, Eastern Res Div, 50-55, asst to dir, Eastern Res Lab, 55-62; vpres, Com-Dev Inc, 62-63; PRES, CARIBBEAN TECH ASSOCS, 63- *Concurrent Pos:* Consult, 63-; prof chem & chmn div sci & technol, World Univ, 66- *Mem:* Am Chem Soc; Am Inst Chem Eng. *Res:* Nutrition; organic and fermentation chemistry; industrial biochemistry; bioengineering; research administration; process development; process and plant economics and feasibility; management; pollution control. *Mailing Add:* Caribbean Tech Assocs GPO Box 2242 San Juan PR 00936

SANES, JOSHUA RICHARD, b Buffalo, NY, Sept 5, 49. DEVELOPMENTAL NEUROBIOLOGY. *Educ:* Yale Univ, BA, 70; Harvard Univ, MA & PhD(neurobiol), 76. *Prof Exp:* ASST PROF PHYSIOL, WASHINGTON UNIV, 80- *Mem:* AAAS; Soc Neurosci. *Res:* Investigation of structures and molecules that account for specificity in the formation of synaptic connections, especially in the neuromuscular system. *Mailing Add:* Dept Physiol Med Ctr Washington Univ St Louis MO 63110

SAN FILIPPO, JOSEPH, JR, b Chicago, Ill, Feb 3, 44. ORGANIC CHEMISTRY, ORGANOMETALLIC CHEMISTRY. *Educ:* DePaul Univ, BS, 65; Mass Inst Technol, PhD(chem), 70. *Prof Exp:* NIH fel, Stanford Univ, 70-71; ASST PROF CHEM, RUTGERS UNIV, NEW BRUNSWICK, 71- *Mem:* Am Chem Soc. *Res:* Transition and main group metal hydrides and organometallic compounds; reactive organic intermediates. *Mailing Add:* Dept of Chem Wright Lab Rutgers Univ New Brunswick NJ 08903

SANFORD, ALLAN ROBERT, b Pasadena, Calif, Apr 25, 27; m 56; c 2. GEOPHYSICS. *Educ:* Pomona Col, BA, 49; Calif Inst Technol, MS, 54, PhD(geophys), 58. *Prof Exp:* PROF GEOPHYS, NMEX INST MINING & TECHNOL, 57-, COORDR GEOPHYS, 78- *Mem:* AAAS; Soc Explor Geophysicists; Seismol Soc Am; Am Geophys Union; Sigma Xi. *Res:* Seismology and seismicity; crustal exploration; tectonophysics; gravity. *Mailing Add:* Dept of Geosci NMex Inst of Mining & Technol Socorro NM 87801

SANFORD, BARBARA ANN, b Beaumont, Tex, Aug 5, 41. MICROBIOLOGY, IMMUNOLOGY. *Educ:* Hardin-Simmons Univ, BA, 62; Baylor Univ, MS, 65, PhD(microbiol), 68. *Prof Exp:* From res asst to res assoc immunol, Med Ctr, Baylor Univ, 63-68; from instr to asst prof, 68-77, ASSOC PROF MICROBIOL, UNIV TEX MED SCH SAN ANTONIO, 77- *Mem:* Am Soc Microbiol. *Res:* Development of in vitro models of delayed hypersensitivity to chemical carcinogens in humans and experimental animal models. *Mailing Add:* Dept of Microbiol Univ of Tex Med Sch San Antonio TX 78229

SANFORD, BARBARA HENDRICK, b Brockton, Mass, Oct 17, 27. GENETICS, IMMUNOLOGY. *Educ:* Boston Univ, BS, 49; Brown Univ, MA, 60, PhD(biol), 63. *Prof Exp:* Health info specialist, Mass Dept Pub Health, 49-51; from cancer res scientist to sr cancer res scientist, Roswell Park Mem Inst, 61-63; res fel, Mass Gen Hosp & Harvard Med Sch, 63-65; fel, Harvard Med Sch, 65-66, from res assoc to prin res assoc path, 69-73; biologist, NIH, 73-75, prog dir for immunol, DCRRC, Nat Cancer Inst, 75-78; dir res, Sidney Farber Cancer Inst, 78-81; assoc prof path, Harvard Med Sch, 78-81; DIR, JACKSON LAB, 81- *Concurrent Pos:* USPHS fel, Mass Gen Hosp, 63-64 & grants, 67-; Am Cancer Soc res grant, 65-67; asst biologist, Mass Gen Hosp, 65-73; asst mem, Inst Health Sci, Brown Univ, 71-75; mem animal resources adv comt, NIH, 72- *Mem:* Am Genetic Asn; Genetics Soc Am; Am Asn Immunol; Transplantation Soc; Am Asn Cancer Res. *Res:* Immunogenetics; transplantation; cancer research; human genetics. *Mailing Add:* Jackson Lab Bar Harbor ME 04609

SANFORD, EDWARD RICHARD, b Clifton, NJ, Feb 15, 28; m 57; c 1. PHYSICS. *Educ:* Iowa State Univ, BS, 49, MS, 50, PhD(physics), 59. *Prof Exp:* Sr scientist, Bettis Atomic Power Lab, Westinghouse Elec Corp, 53-61; assoc prof physics, 61-66, PROF PHYSICS, OHIO UNIV, 66-, CHMN DEPT, 78- *Mem:* Am Phys Soc; Am Nuclear Soc; Inst Elec & Electronics Eng; Am Asn Physics Teachers. *Res:* Solid state physics; nuclear reactor physics and engineering. *Mailing Add:* Dept of Physics Ohio Univ Athens OH 45701

SANFORD, JAMES R, b Zanesville, Ohio, Jan 29, 33; m 56; c 2. PHYSICS. *Educ:* Oberlin Col, AB, 55; Yale Univ, MS, 57, PhD(physics), 61. *Prof Exp:* Fel, Yale Univ, 61-62; physicist, Brookhaven Nat Lab, 62-69; head exp facil sect, Nat Accelerator Lab, 69-72, assoc dir, Fermi Nat Accelerator Lab, 72-76; ASSOC DIR, BROOKHAVEN NAT LAB, 76-, HEAD ISABELLE PROJ, 76- *Concurrent Pos:* Mem high energy physics adv panel, Dept of Energy; consult, Stanford Linear Accelerator Ctr, 74- *Mem:* Am Phys Soc. *Res:* High energy particle physics and the use of accelerators. *Mailing Add:* Bldg 902 Brookhaven Nat Lab Upton NY 11713

SANFORD, JAMES WALKER, economic entomology, see previous edition

SANFORD, JAY PHILIP, b Madison, Wis, May 27, 28; m 50; c 5. INFECTIOUS DISEASES. *Educ:* Univ Mich, MD, 52; Am Bd Internal Med, dipl, 62; Am Bd Microbiol, dipl & cert med microbiol, 64. *Prof Exp:* Res assoc med, Univ Mich, 50-52; med house officer, Peter Bent Brigham Hosp, 52-53, asst med, 53-54; sr asst resident med, Duke Univ Hosp, 56-57; from asst prof to prof internal med, Univ Tex Health Sci Ctr Dallas, 57-75; PROF INTERNAL MED & DEAN, SCH MED, UNIFORMED SERV UNIV HEALTH SCI, 75-, PRES, 81- *Concurrent Pos:* Consult, Vet Admin Hosp, Dallas, 57-75, Vet Admin Ctr, Temple, 62-75, Wilford Hall US Air Force Hosp, Lackland Air Force Base, 63-, Div Health Mobilization, USPHS, 64-72, Brooke Gen Hosp, Ft Sam Houston, 64- & Clin Ctr, NIH, 75-; mem bd trustees, Dallas Health & Sci Mus, 61-70; mem bact & mycol study sect, Div Res Grants, NIH, 62-66; district dir, Disaster Med Care, Tex District 1A, 63-75; bd dir, Dallas County Chapter, Am Red Cross, 65-71, chmn disaster med nursing comt, 65-71; mem training grant comt, Nat Inst Allergy & Infectious Dis, 69-73, chmn, 71-73; mem, Am Bd Internal Med, 72-80, chmn, 79-80. *Honors & Awards:* Bristol Award, Infectious Dis Soc Am, 81. *Mem:* Am Fedn Clin Res; Soc Exp Biol & Med; Am Soc Clin Invest; Asn Am Physicians; fel Am Acad Microbiol. *Res:* Bacteriology; immunology. *Mailing Add:* Uniformed Serv Univ 4301 Jones Bridge Rd Bethesda MD 20814

SANFORD, JOHN THERON, geology, deceased

SANFORD, KARL JOHN, b New York, NY, Mar 10, 47; m 75; c 2. CLINICAL BIOCHEMISTRY, BIOTECHNOLOGY. *Educ:* Rutgers Univ, AB, 69; Univ Fla, PhD(chem), 72. *Prof Exp:* Res assoc biochem, Mass Inst Technol, 73-74; res chemist clin biochem, 75-80, RES ASSOC & LAB HEAD BIOCHEM, EASTMAN KODAK CO, 80- *Res:* Management responsibilities for directing research in clinical biochemistry, immunology and biotechnology areas. *Mailing Add:* Eastman Kodak Co 82C 1669 Lake Ave Rochester NY 14650

SANFORD, KATHERINE KOONTZ, b Chicago, Ill, July 19, 15; m 71. ZOOLOGY. *Educ:* Wellesley Col, BA, 37; Brown Univ, MA, 39, PhD(zool), 42. *Hon Degrees:* DSc, Med Col Pa, Philadelphia, 74. *Prof Exp:* Asst biol, Brown Univ, 37-41; instr, Western Col, 41-42 & Allegheny Col, 42-43; asst dir sch nursing, Johns Hopkins Univ Hosp, 43-47; res biologist, 47-73, CHIEF IN VITRO CARCINOGENESIS SECT, CANCER CAUSE & PREV DIV, LAB CELLULAR & MOLECULAR BIOL, NAT CANCER INST, 73- *Concurrent Pos:* With USPHS, 47; mem cell cult collection adv comt, Am Type Cult Collection, 60- *Mem:* Tissue Cult Asn; Am Soc Cell Biol; Am Asn Cancer Res; Int Soc Cell Biol. *Res:* Physiological genetics of Cladocera; nutrition of tissue cells grown in culture; characteristics of malignant cells in vitro; carcinogenesis studies in vitro. *Mailing Add:* In Vitro Carcinogenesis Sect Nat Cancer Inst Bethesda MD 20014

SANFORD, L G, b Parrish, Ala, Sept 16, 30; m 55; c 2. ENTOMOLOGY, VERTEBRATE ZOOLOGY. *Educ:* Florence State Col, BS, 57; Auburn Univ, MS, 63, PhD(entom), 66. *Prof Exp:* Biol aide fisheries dept, Tenn Valley Authority, 56-58; teacher high sch, Ala, 58-60; instr zool, Auburn Univ, 60-63, res asst entom, 63-65; assoc prof biol, 65-69, PROF BIOL, JACKSONVILLE STATE UNIV, 69- *Mem:* Am Inst Biol Sci. *Res:* Mammalogy and Siphonaptera. *Mailing Add:* Dept of Biol Jacksonville State Univ Jacksonville AL 36265

SANFORD, MALCOLM THOMAS, b Miami Beach, Fla, Oct 23, 42; m 70. APICULTURE. *Educ:* Univ Tex, BA, 64; Thunderbird Grad Sch Int Mgt, Ariz, BFT, 67; Univ Ga, MA, 73, PhD, 77. *Prof Exp:* Res assoc geog, Univ Ga, 70-73, res asst apicult, 74-77, lectr, 77; asst prof apicult, Ohio State Univ, 78-81; ASSOC PROF & EXTEN APICULTURIST, UNIV FLA, 81- *Mem:* Am Beekeeping Fedn; Int Bee Res Asn. *Res:* Transmission and scanning electron microscopy to study abdominal glands of queen honey bee; honey bee management in tropical and temperate lands; beekeeping industry of Yucatan. *Mailing Add:* Inst Food & Agr Sci 202 Newell Hall Univ Fla Gainesville FL 32601

SANFORD, PAUL EVERETT, b Milford, Kans, Jan 14, 17; m 42; c 3. POULTRY NUTRITION. *Educ:* Kans State Univ, BS, 41; Iowa State Univ, MS, 42, PhD(poultry nutrit), 49. *Prof Exp:* Student asst poultry husb, Kans State Univ, 37-41; grad asst, Iowa State Univ, 46-49; assoc prof poultry nutrit, 49-60, PROF POULTRY NUTRIT & NUTRITIONIST, KANS STATE UNIV, 60- *Concurrent Pos:* Guest lectr, Univ PR, 57; lectr, US Feed Grain Coun, Tokyo, 63; mem, Animal Nutrit Res Coun, 73-; state coordr, Nat Asn Col & Teachers Agr, 76- *Honors & Awards:* Sr Fac Award Merit, Kans State Univ Chapter, Gamma Sigma Delta, 73; E Walter Morrison Award, Kans State Univ, 76. *Mem:* Fel AAAS; Poultry Sci Asn; hon mem Broiler Soc Japan; Sigma Xi (secy, 73-75, pres-elect, 75-76, pres, 76-77); Am Poultry Hist Soc (secy, 67-70). *Res:* Nutrition; growth and nutritional requirements of chicks; effects of feeding protein supplement; antibiotics; vitamin A; sorghum grain and wheat utilization; calcium and other mineral requirements for layers; feed additives for growth, feed efficiency and egg production. *Mailing Add:* Dept of Animal Sci & Indust Kans State Univ Manhattan KS 66506

SANFORD, RICHARD FREDERICK, b Bronxville, NY, July 29, 50. KINETICS, ORE DEPOSITS. *Educ:* Johns Hopkins Univ, BA & MA, 73; Harvard Univ, PhD(geol), 78. *Prof Exp:* GEOLOGIST, US GEOL SURV, 78- *Mem:* Geol Soc Am; Mineral Soc Am; Am Geophys Union. *Res:* Kinetics and mass transport in sedimentary, hydrothermal, and metamorphic ore deposits; mathematical and computer applications; igneous and metamorphic petrology; fluid inclusions; uranium ore formation; lunar impact phenomena; metamorphism of ultramafic and impure carbonate rocks. *Mailing Add:* Mail Stop 916 US Geol Surv Denver Fed Ctr Denver CO 80225

SANFORD, RICHARD SELDEN, b Mass; c 6. ELECTRICAL ENGINEERING, CONTROL SYSTEMS. *Educ:* Yale Univ, BEE, 49, MEE, 51; Worcester Polytech Inst, PhD(elec eng), 69. *Prof Exp:* Sr engr, Wayland Labs, Raytheon Mfg Co, 53-56; ASSOC PROF ELEC ENG, CLARKSON COL TECHNOL, 56- *Mem:* AAAS; Inst Elec & Electronics Engrs. *Res:* Electrical, mechanical and hydraulic control systems; acoustic networks; circuits and systems. *Mailing Add:* Dept Elec Eng Clarkson Col Technol Potsdam NY 13676

SANFORD, ROBERT ALOIS, b East St Louis, Ill, Mar 1, 22; m 46; c 4. ORGANIC CHEMISTRY. *Educ:* St Louis Univ, BS, 43; Purdue Univ, PhD(chem eng & chem), 49. *Prof Exp:* Asst org chem, Univ Pittsburgh, 43-44; res chemist, Manhattan Proj, Univ Rochester, 44-46; res chemist, Catalysis Res Div, Sinclair Res Labs, Inc, Ill, 49-52, res chemist, Petrochem Div, 52-53, group leader, 53-57, asst dir, Res Div, 57-60, dir, Explor Div, 60-66; dir 66-79, VPRES RES & DEVELOP, BROWN & WILLIAMSON TOBACCO CO, 79- *Res:* Chemical engineering; heterogeneous catalysis; petrochemicals. *Mailing Add:* 1600 W Hill St Louisville KY 40201

SANFORD, ROBERT JOSEPH, b Washington, DC, Sept 2, 39; m 61; c 3. ENGINEERING MECHANICS, FRACTURE MECHANICS. *Educ:* George Washington Univ, BME, 62, MSE, 65; Cath Univ Am, PhD(solid mech), 71. *Prof Exp:* Res mech engr, Mech Div, 62-69, head stress anal sect, 69-75, HEAD, STRUCT RELIABILITY SECT, MARINE TECHNOL DIV, NAVAL RES LAB, 75- *Concurrent Pos:* Vis prof, Mech Eng Dept, Univ Md, 79- *Honors & Awards:* Hetenyi Award, Soc Exp Stress Anal, 74. *Mem:* Am Soc Mech Engrs; fel Soc Exp Stress Anal; Am Acad Mech. *Res:* New methods for experimental stress analysis utilizing holographic interferometry, photoelasticity and/or moire; fracture mechanics of metals and composites; matrix theory of stress-optics. *Mailing Add:* Code 8431 Naval Res Lab Washington DC 20375

SANFORD, THOMAS BAYES, b Toledo, Ohio, Apr 22, 40; m 62; c 3. PHYSICAL OCEANOGRAPHY, MARINE GEOPHYSICS. *Educ:* Oberlin Col, AB, 62; Mass Inst Technol, PhD(oceanog), 67. *Prof Exp:* Physicist, NASA, 62-63; instr oceanog, Mass Inst Technol, 66-67; asst scientist, Woods Hole Oceanog Inst, 67-71, assoc scientist, 71-79; PRIN OCEANOGR, APPL PHYSICS LAB & RES PROF, SCH OCEANOG, UNIV WASH, SEATTLE, 79- *Concurrent Pos:* Consult, Sippican Ocean Systs Inc, 79- *Honors & Awards:* A F Bulgin Premium, Inst Electronic & Radio Engrs, UK, 72. *Mem:* AAAS; Am Geophys Union; Sigma Xi; Am Meteorol Soc. *Res:* Motionally induced electromagnetic fields in the sea; marine magneto-tellurics; ocean circulation; internal waves; eddy motion; marine acoustics. *Mailing Add:* Appl Physics Lab Univ Wash 1013 NE 40th St Seattle WA 98105

SANFORD, WALLACE GORDON, b Pasadena, Calif, Aug 1, 23; m 57; c 3. PLANT PHYSIOLOGY. *Educ:* Pomona Col, BA, 47; Univ Md, MS, 49; Univ Calif, Los Angeles, PhD(plant sci), 52. *Prof Exp:* Asst gen bot & plant physiol, Univ Md, 47-49 & Univ Calif, Los Angeles, 49-52; assoc plant physiologist, Pineapple Res Inst, Hawaii, 52-54, plant physiologist, 54-65, head dept agron, 55-65, dir res, 65-67; PROF AGRON & SOIL SCI & CHMN DEPT, UNIV HAWAII, 67- *Mem:* AAAS; Bot Soc Am; Am Soc Plant Physiol. *Res:* Administration; plant nutrition. *Mailing Add:* Dept of Agron & Soil Sci Univ of Hawaii Honolulu HI 96822

SANFORD, WILLIAM WARREN, plant physiology, see previous edition

SANGER, ALAN RODNEY, b Southampton, Eng, Apr 23, 43; Can citizen. INORGANIC CHEMISTRY, ORGANOMETALLIC CHEMISTRY. *Educ:* Univ Sussex, BSc, 65, MSc, 66, DPhil(inorg chem), 69. *Prof Exp:* Teaching fel chem, Univ Alta, 69-72 & Simon Fraser Univ, 73; RES OFFICER CHEM, ALTA RES COUN, 73- *Mem:* Royal Soc Chem; Chem Inst Can. *Res:* Preparation, characterization and evaluation of inorganic and organometallic materials of use as catalysts. *Mailing Add:* Alta Res Coun 11315 87th Ave Edmonton AB T6G 2C2 Can

SANGER, GREGORY MARSHALL, b Spokane, Wash, Feb 2, 46; m 72; c 1. OPTICAL ENGINEERING, MATERIALS SCIENCE. *Educ:* Calif State Univ, BS, 68; Univ Ariz, MS, 71, PhD(optics), 76. *Prof Exp:* Res assoc, Optical Sci Ctr, Univ Ariz, 71-72, proj engr, 72-76; GROUP LEADER, LAWRENCE LIVERMORE LAB, 76- *Mem:* Optical Soc Am; fel Soc Photo-Optical Instrumentation Engrs; Sigma Xi. *Res:* Physics, engineering, manufacturing and metrology of high precision optical surfaces as applied to advanced aerospace, astronomical and energy related applications. *Mailing Add:* Lawrence Livermore Lab PO Box 808 L-332 Livermore CA 94550

SANGER, JON EDWARD, b Minneapolis, Minn, May 31, 39. AQUATIC ECOLOGY. *Educ:* Univ Minn, Minneapolis, BS, 61, MS, 64, PhD(plant ecol), 68. *Prof Exp:* Asst prof bot, Univ Minn, 68-69; asst prof, 69-74, assoc prof, 74-78, PROF BOT & BACT & CHMN DEPT, OHIO WESLEYAN UNIV, 78- *Concurrent Pos:* Prin co-investr, NSF Grant, Ohio Wesleyan Univ & Univ Minn, 70-72. *Mem:* AAAS; Sigma Xi; Int Asn Pure & Appl Limnol; Ecol Soc Am; Am Soc Limnol & Oceanog. *Res:* Geochemical studies on lakes, with special emphasis on productivity indices; historical aspects of lake eutrophication; landscape erosion and soil weathering. *Mailing Add:* Dept of Bot & Bact Ohio Wesleyan Univ Delaware OH 43015

SANGER, JOSEPH WILLIAM, b New York, NY, Feb 25, 41; m 64; c 2. MOLECULAR BIOLOGY, DEVELOPMENTAL BIOLOGY. *Educ:* Manhattan Col, BS, 62; Dartmouth Col, PhD(molecular biol), 68. *Prof Exp:* Trainee physiol, Dartmouth Med Sch, 67-68; trainee cell differentiation, 68-71, assoc anat, 71-72, asst prof, 72-76, ASSOC PROF ANAT, SCH MED, UNIV PA, 76- *Concurrent Pos:* Mem, Corp Bermuda Biol Sta, trustee, 77- Pa Plan scholar, 71-74. *Mem:* Am Soc Cell Biol; Am Asn Anatomists. *Res:* Cell differentiation; cytology; muscle structure and function; motility embryology. *Mailing Add:* Dept Anat Sch Med Univ Pa Philadelphia PA 19104

SANGER, VANCE L, b WVa, Aug 11, 17; m. VETERINARY PATHOLOGY, PATHOLOGY. *Educ:* Manchester Col, AB, 43; Ohio State Univ, DVM, 49, MSc, 53. *Prof Exp:* Instr vet path, Ohio State Univ, 52-53, asst prof, 53-55, prof vet sci & vet pathologist, Ohio Agr Exp Sta, Wooster, 55-65; assoc prof vet path, 65-72, PROF VET PATH, MICH STATE UNIV, 72- *Mem:* Am Vet Med Asn; Am Col Vet Path; Int Acad Path; Electron Micros Soc Am. *Res:* Infectious, nutritional and neoplastic diseases of animals and poultry. *Mailing Add:* Dept Path Fee Hall Mich State Univ Col Vet Med East Lansing MI 48824

SANGER, WARREN GLENN, b Minden, Nebr, Oct 6, 45; m 69; c 1. MEDICAL GENETICS. *Educ:* Kearney State Col, BS, 67; Univ Nebr-Lincoln, MS, 69, PhD(genetics), 74. *Prof Exp:* Res assoc cytogenetics, 73-74, ASST PROF HUMAN GENETICS, UNIV NEBR MED CTR, OMAHA, 75-, ASSOC PROF PEDIAT, 79- *Concurrent Pos:* Coordr, Nebr Tay-Sachs Screening Prog, Univ Nebr Med Ctr, Omaha, 73-, asst dir, Ctr Human Genetics, 75-79, lab dir, Genetic Semen Bank, 75-79, dir, Ctr Human Genetics & Cytogenetics & Semen Bank, 79- *Mem:* Sigma Xi; Am Soc Human Genetics; Am Genetics Asn; Tissue Cult Asn. *Res:* Prenatal diagnosis of genetic defects and the cytogenetics of infertility. *Mailing Add:* Ctr for Human Genetics Univ Nebr Med Ctr Omaha NE 68105

SANGREE, JOHN BREWSTER, JR, geology, geophysics, see previous edition

SANGREN, WARD CONRAD, b Kalamazoo, Mich, Apr 20, 23; m 44; c 3. APPLIED MATHEMATICS. *Educ:* Princeton Univ, AB, 43; Univ Mich, MA, 47, PhD(math), 50. *Prof Exp:* Asst prof math, Miami Univ, 49-51; sr mathematician, Oak Ridge Nat Lab, 51-55; chief math & comput res div, Curtiss-Wright Corp, 55-56, chief gen atomic div, Gen Dynamics Corp, 56-62; vpres, Comput Applns Inc, Calif, 62-70; coordr comput activities, Univ Calif, Berkeley, 70-76; DIR INFO SYST & ANAL, SAN FRANCISCO STATE UNIV, 76- *Mem:* Am Math Soc; Soc Indust & Appl Math; Math Asn Am; Asn Comput Mach. *Res:* Boundary value and eigenvalue problems; high speed calculation of reactors; nonlinear differential equations. *Mailing Add:* 121 Bates Ct Orindo CA 94563

SANGREY, DWIGHT A, civil & geotechnical engineering, see previous edition

SANGSTER, RAYMOND CHARLES, b Lyons, Kans, Mar 15, 28; m 55; c 2. INORGANIC CHEMISTRY. *Educ:* Univ Chicago, PhB, 46, BS, 47; Mass Inst Technol, PhD(chem), 51. *Prof Exp:* Asst chem, Mass Inst Technol, 48-49, res assoc, 51-52; mem tech staff, Semiconductor Res & Develop Dept, Hughes Aircraft Co, 52-54; mem tech staff, Cent Res Lab, Tex Instruments, Inc, 54-57, dir, Mat Res Dept, 57-58, res assoc, 58-62, dir, Semiconductor Exp Lab, 62-65; dir res, Bayside Lab, Gen Tel & Electronics Labs, Inc, NY, 65-68; chief electormagnetics div, Inst Basic Standards, Nat Bur Standards, 69-74, prog mgr strategic planning, 74-78, sr scientist, 78-80; GUEST SCIENTIST, GMELIN INST, FRANKFURT, WGER, 80- *Concurrent Pos:* Chmn, Gordon Conf Chem & Metall Semiconductors, 67; chmn, NASA Working Group Electronic Mat, 68-70; US chmn, Marine Commun & Electronics Panel, US-Japan Natural Resources Comn, 69-71. *Honors & Awards:* President's Mgt Improv Cert, 71. *Mem:* Fel AAAS; Am Chem Soc; Am Phys Soc; Inst Elec & Electronics Engrs; fel Am Inst Chemists. *Res:* Research management; semiconductor materials and devices; organic scintillators; science and technology for development. *Mailing Add:* Gmelin Inst Varrentrapp Strasse 40142 D-6000 Frankfurt 90 West Germany

SANGSTER, WILLIAM M(CCOY), b Austin, Minn, Dec 9, 25; m 46; c 3. HYDRAULIC ENGINEERING, ENGINEERING MECHANICS. *Educ:* Univ Iowa, BS, 47, MS, 48, PhD, 64. *Prof Exp:* Asst instr, Univ Iowa, 48; from asst prof to prof civil eng, Univ Mo-Columbia, 48-67, assoc dean col eng & assoc dir eng exp sta, 64-67; prof civil eng & dir sch civil eng, 67-74, DEAN, COL ENG, GA INST TECHNOL, 74- *Mem:* Am Soc Civil Engrs (pres, 74-75); Am Soc Eng Educ; Eng Joint Coun; Engrs Coun Prof Develop. *Res:* Hydrodynamic stability of stratified flows; orbital mechanics; general hydraulics. *Mailing Add:* Col of Eng Ga Inst of Technol Atlanta GA 30332

SANI, BRAHMA PORINCHU, b Trichur, India, Sept 13, 37; m 67; c 2. BIOCHEMISTRY, CANCER. *Educ:* Univ Kerala, BS, 60; Vikram Univ, MS, 62; Indian Inst Sci, Bangalore, PhD(biochem), 67. *Prof Exp:* Res scholar biochem, Indian Inst Sci, Bangalore, 62-65, Univ Grants Comn India jr res fel, 65-67, Coun Sci & Indust Res India sr res fel, 67-68; staff fel, Boston Biomed Res Inst, 68-71; res assoc, Inst Cancer Res, Philadelphia, 71-74; sr biochemist, 74-78, HEAD, PROTEIN BIOCHEM SECT, SOUTHERN RES INST, 79- *Concurrent Pos:* Res consult, Cornea Res Dept, Retina Found, Boston, 68-70. *Mem:* AAAS; Am Asn Cancer Res; Am Soc Biol Chemists. *Res:* Molecular mechanism of chemical carcinogenesis and anticarcinogenesis; carcinogen-protein interactions; specific interactions of vitamins and hormones with proteins; characterization of a retinoic acid-binding protein which may be involved in epithelial differentiation and carcinogenesis. *Mailing Add:* Southern Res Inst 2000 9th Ave S Birmingham AL 35205

SANI, ROBERT L(E ROY), b Antioch, Calif, Apr 20, 35; m 66; c 3. CHEMICAL ENGINEERING. *Educ:* Univ Calif, Berkeley, BS, 58, MS, 60; Univ Minn, PhD(chem eng), 63. *Prof Exp:* Instr math, Rensselaer Polytech Inst, 63-64; from asst prof to assoc prof chem eng, Univ Ill, Urbana, 64-76; PROF CHEM ENG, UNIV COLO, BOULDER, 76- *Concurrent Pos:* Guggenheim fel, 70-71; consult, Atomic Sci Div, Lawrence Livermore Labs, 71- *Mem:* Am Inst Chem Engrs; Soc Appl & Indust Math. *Res:* Nonlinear aspects of the dynamics of physical systems exhibiting transport and transformation processes that are coupled at the macroscopic level; computational fluid dynamics. *Mailing Add:* Dept of Chem Eng Campus Box 449 RL2-221 Univ Colo Boulder CO 80309

SANIK, JOHN, JR, b Stamford, Conn, Oct 2, 19; m 44; c 4. ANALYTICAL CHEMISTRY. *Educ:* Univ RI, BS, 42, MS, 48; Kans State Univ, PhD(chem), 51. *Prof Exp:* Instr chem, Univ RI, 43-44 & 46-48; res chemist, Standard Oil Co, Ind, 51-57; res chemist, Amoco Chem Corp, 57-63; prof chem, 63-69, dean grad studies, 69-76, PROF CHEM, STATE UNIV NY COL ONEONTA, 76- *Mem:* Am Chem Soc. *Res:* Inorganic analytical chemistry; polymer properties. *Mailing Add:* 51 Union St Oneonta NY 13820

SANK, DIANE, b New York, NY, Dec 22, 27; div; c 3. BIOLOGICAL ANTHROPOLOGY, MEDICAL GENETICS. *Educ:* Long Island Univ, BS, 49; Univ Ill, MS, 51; Columbia Univ, PhD(human variations), 63. *Prof Exp:* Sr res scientist, NY State Psychiat Inst, 52-67; CHIEF INVESTR, HUMAN GENETICS LAB, ROCKLAND RES INST, ORANGEBURG, 67-; PROF ANTHROP, CITY COL NEW YORK, 67- *Concurrent Pos:* Res assoc psychiat, Col Physicians & Surgeons, Columbia Univ, 53-67, lectr, 67-71, assoc, Univ Sem Genetics & Evolution of Man, 67-; prof doctoral prog, Grad Ctr, City Col New York, 67-71; mem, Nat & Int Conf Dermatologlyphics. *Mem:* Fel Int Soc Twin Studies; Am Soc Human Genetics; Soc Study Human Biol; Am Soc Primatologists; Soc Anthrop Visual Commun. *Res:* Hereditary and bio-social studies of mental illness, mental retardation, deafness, learning diability and normal human behavior; primate behavior. *Mailing Add:* Dept Anthrop City Col New York Convent Ave & W 138th St New York NY 10031

SANK, VICTOR J, b Washington, DC, Sept 17, 44; m 65; c 2. ENGINEERING PHYSICS. *Educ:* Polytech Inst Brooklyn, BS, 66, PhD(physics), 71. *Prof Exp:* Instr physics, Polytech Inst Brooklyn, 68-71; res asst, 70-71; asst prof, Quinnipiac Col, 71-75; asst prof, San Antonio Col, 75-79; RES PHYSICIST NEURORADIOL & COMPUT TOMOGRAPHY, NIH, 79- *Concurrent Pos:* Electronic engr, Schulz Controls, 74-75; res assoc, Dept Radiol, Univ Tex Health Sci Ctr, San Antonio, 75- *Res:* Mathematics and computer interfacing for computed axial tomography for diagnostic medical use. *Mailing Add:* Bldg 10 Rm 11N242 NIH Bethesda MD 20014

SANKAR, D V SIVA, b Vizianagram, India, Apr 7, 27; nat US; m 59; c 3. BIOCHEMISTRY, CHEMICAL PATHOLOGY. *Educ:* Univ Madras, MSc, 49, PhD(biochem), 51; Am Bd Clin Chemists, dipl. *Prof Exp:* Fulbright scholar, Mass Inst Technol, 53-55; NSF fel, Johns Hopkins Univ, 56; asst prof biochem, Adelphi Col, 56-58; sr res scientist & head biochem res lab, Children's Unit, Creedmoor State Hosp, 58-63, assoc res scientist, 63-69; chief lab res, Queen's Children's Hosp, 69-81; PRES, AM HEALTH SCI SYSTS CORP, 81- *Concurrent Pos:* Adj prof, Long Island Univ, 64-, Fordham Univ, 70- & St Johns Univ, 71-; adj assoc prof psychiat, NY Univ Med Ctr, 78-; ed, J Med. *Honors & Awards:* Indian Chem Soc Gold Medal, 53. *Mem:* AAAS; Am Chem Soc; Am Soc Microbiol; Am Asn Clin Chemists; Am Soc Pharmacol & Exp Therapeut. *Res:* Molecular mechanisms of metabolism; drug actions and pathogenesis. *Mailing Add:* PO Box 966 Westbury NY 11426

SANKAR, RAMAN, US citizen. NEUROPHARMACOLOGY, AGING. *Educ:* Univ Bombay, BSc, 65 & 68; Univ Wash, PhD(pharm sci), 74. *Prof Exp:* Asst prof, 74-81, ASSOC PROF MED CHEM, COL PHARM, XAVIER UNIV, 81- *Concurrent Pos:* Adj asst prof pharmacol, Sch Med, Tulane Univ, 79- *Mem:* Am Chem Soc; Am Asn Col Pharm; AAAS; NY Acad Sci; Soc Neurosci. *Res:* Effect of hypertension, aging and vasoactive drugs on the blood-brain barrier; neuropeptides and the blood-brain barrier; effect of antineoplastic agents on the blood-brain barrier-possible role in cerebral metastasis. *Mailing Add:* Col Pharm Xavier Univ New Orleans LA 70125

SANKAR, SESHADRI, b Udamalpet, India; Can citizen. COMPUTER AIDED DESIGN, VIBRATION CONTROL. *Educ:* Univ Madras, BEng, 70; Sir George Williams Univ, MEng, 71, DEng, 73. *Prof Exp:* Dynamics analyst, res & develop, United Aircraft Can Ltd, 73-74; sr proj engr, Naval Eng Test Estab, Ville LaSalle, 74-75; asst prof, 75-78, ASSOC PROF MECH ENG, CONCORDIA UNIV, 78- *Concurrent Pos:* Assoc ed, Simulation, Soc Comput Simulation, 79-; consult, Naval Eng Test Estab, 75-77, Recreational Vehicle Div, Bombardier Ltd, 79- & VIA Rail, Montreal, 81-; mem, Comn Educ, Can Rep, Int Fedn Theory Mach & Mech, 79- *Mem:* Can Coun Theory Mach & Mech; Am Soc Mech Engrs; Soc Comput Simulation; Int Soc Math & Comput Simulation; Corp Engrs Que. *Res:* Computer aided optimal design of mechanical and hydromechanical systems using digital, analog and hybrid computation; vibration control using passive, semi-active and active devices for off-road, on-road and rail vehicles; use of interactive graphics in computer aided design. *Mailing Add:* Dept Mech Eng H-929-21 Concordia Univ 1455 de Maisonneuve Blvd W Montreal PQ H3G 1M8 Can

SANKAR, SURYANARAYAN G, b Madras, India, July 1, 42; m 74; c 2. SOLID STATE CHEMISTRY. *Educ:* Andhra Univ, BSc, 62, MSc, 63; Poona Univ, PhD(solid state chem), 68. *Prof Exp:* Fel chem, Tex Tech Univ, 70; fel, Univ Pittsburgh, 70-73, from res asst prof to res assoc prof, 73-78; SR RES CHEMIST, MAT RES CTR, ALLIED CORP, 78- *Res:* Study of structural and magnetic properties of permanent magnets; study of the influence of paramagnetic impurities in superconductors; heterogeneous catalysis; metal hydrides. *Mailing Add:* Mat Res Ctr PO Box 1021-R Allied Corp Morristown NJ 07960

SANKAR, THIAGAS SRIRAM, b Udamalpet, India, Feb 18, 40; m 67; c 2. MECHANICAL ENGINEERING. *Educ:* Univ Madras, BE, 61; Indian Inst Sci, ME, 63; Univ Waterloo, PhD(solid mech), 67. *Prof Exp:* Sect officer, Neyveli Lignite Corp, Madras, 61-62; teaching asst & res fel civil eng, Univ Waterloo, 63-65, lectr, 65-67; res engr, United Aircraft Can, 67-68; from asst prof to assoc prof mech eng, 68-77, PROF MECH ENG & CHMN DEPT, CONCORDIA UNIV, 77-, MEM, BD GOV, 78- *Concurrent Pos:* Res fel solid mech, Nat Res Coun Can, 65-67; grants, Nat Res Coun Can, Concordia Univ, 68-, Defence Res Bd Can, 72-76 & Govt Que, 71-; treas, Can Coun Theory Mach & Mech, 71- *Mem:* Am Acad Mech; Can Soc Mech Engrs (vpres, 79-); Am Soc Mech Engrs. *Res:* Stochastic dynamics of mechanical systems; surface mechanics; machine tool dynamics. *Mailing Add:* Dept Mech Eng H929 1455 de Maisonneuve Montreal PQ H3G 1M8 Can

SANKOFF, DAVID, b Montreal, Quebec, Can, Dec 31, 42. MATHEMATICS. *Educ:* McGill Univ, PhD(math), 69. *Prof Exp:* RES, CTR RECH MATH APPLIQUEES, UNIV MONT, 69- *Honors & Awards:* Prix Vincent, Asn Can Fr Pour L'auancement Sci, 77. *Mem:* Soc Indust & Appl Math; Linguistics Soc Am. *Res:* Statistical procedures for the analysis of sociolinguistic data; algorithms for the study of macromolecular structure and evolution; mathematics applied to natural and social science and the humanities. *Mailing Add:* Ctr Rech Math Appliquees Univ Montreal cp 6128 Montreal PQ H3C 3J7 Can

SANMANN, EVERETT EUGENE, b Geronimo, Okla, Nov 10, 37; m 65. OPTICAL PHYSICS. *Educ:* Univ Okla, BS, 59, MS, 62, PhD(physics), 74. *Prof Exp:* Res physicist, Brown Eng Co, 66-68; gen engr optics, Ballistic Missile Defense Advan Technol Ctr, 68-79; DIR SYSTS ANAL, NICHOLS RES CTR, 79- *Mem:* Am Phys Soc; Sigma Xi; Optical Soc Am. *Res:* Remote sensing using infrared receivers in space environments; scattering of coherent radiation from dielectric materials with varying reflectivity and surface roughness; theoretical and experimental nature of backscatter statistics. *Mailing Add:* 11207 Mountaincrest Dr Huntsville AL 35803

SANN, KLAUS HEINRICH, b Driesen, Ger, Aug 6, 19; m 44; c 2. ELECTRONICS, RADAR SYSTEMS. *Educ:* Technische Universitat Berlin, Diplom-Ingenieur, 51. *Prof Exp:* Electronics engr, Telefunken GmbH, Berlin, 51-53, asst lab mgr, 53-56, lab mgr, 56-58; electronics engr, 59-69, CHIEF, ADVAN RES BR, HARRY DIAMOND LABS, 69- *Concurrent Pos:* Mem working group on Radar Minimum Performance, Radio Adv Comt, 67. *Honors & Awards:* Hinman Award, Harry Diamond Labs, 76. *Mem:* Sr mem Inst Elec & Electronics Engrs; affil Nat Soc Prof Engrs. *Res:* Advanced development of fuzzing systems and solid state microwave sources; conceives and coordinates research programs of substantial importance to installation. *Mailing Add:* Harry Diamond Labs Br 11100 2800 Powder Mill Rd Adelphi MD 20783

SANNELLA, JOSEPH L, b Boston, Mass, July 27, 33; m 59; c 3. RESEARCH ADMINISTRATION. *Educ:* Harvard Univ, AB, 55; Univ Mass, MS, 58; Purdue Univ, PhD(biochem), 63; Univ Del, MBA, 69. *Prof Exp:* Res chemist, Am Viscose Div, FMC Corp, Pa, 62-67; supvr chem res, 67-74, DIR RES, RES DEVELOP & ENG, BALL CORP, 74- *Mem:* Am Chem Soc; Soc Plastics Engrs; Nat Metal Decorators Asn. *Res:* Process chemistry; analytical chemistry; plastics; packaging; glass; coatings; materials. *Mailing Add:* Ball Corp Res Develop & Eng 1509 S Macedonia Ave Muncie IN 47302

SANNER, FERN RUSTEBERG, b Chicago, Ill, Sept 8, 21; m 49; c 4. ANESTHESIOLOGY. *Educ:* Cent YMCA Col, BS, 45; Univ Ill, MD, 48. *Prof Exp:* Intern med, Cook County Hosp, Chicago, 48-50; resident anesthesia, Res Hosp, Univ Ill, 50-51; instr, 67-69, PROF ANESTHESIA, SCH DENT, LOYOLA UNIV CHICAGO, 69- *Concurrent Pos:* Head dept anesthesia, Franklin Blvd Community Hosp, Chicago, 56- & Cent Community Hosp, 72-; instr, Ill Col Podiat Med, 70-; dept chairperson anesthesia, Franklin Blvd Community Hosp, Cent Community Hosp & Glendale Heights Community Hosp; prof anesthesia, Ill Col Pediat Med. *Mem:* AMA; Am Soc Anesthesia; Am Asn Dent Schs. *Res:* Clinical research in pain control and sedation in dentistry. *Mailing Add:* 6139 N Tripp Ave Chicago IL 60646

SANNER, FREDERICK CHARLES, astronomy, see previous edition

SANNER, JOHN HARPER, b Anamosa, Iowa, Apr 29, 31; m 58; c 2. PHARMACOLOGY. *Educ:* Univ Iowa, BS, 54, MS, 61, PhD(pharmacol), 64. *Prof Exp:* From res investr to sr res investr, 63-75, RES FEL PHARMACOL, G D SEARLE & CO, 75- *Concurrent Pos:* Dir, Educ Media Co. *Mem:* Soc Pharmacol & Exp Therapeut; AAAS; NY Acad Sci. *Res:* Pharmacological antagonists; pharmacology of vasoactive peptides and prostaglandins; pharmacological mechanisms of smooth muscle; anti-inflammatory mechanisms. *Mailing Add:* Dept of Biol Res G D Searle & Co PO Box 5110 Chicago IL 60680

SANNES, FELIX RUDOLPH, b Zaporozhe, Ukraine, Nov 20, 40; Can citizen; m 69; c 2. ELEMENTARY PARTICLE PHYSICS. *Educ:* Univ BC, BS, 63; McGill Univ, PhD(physics), 68. *Prof Exp:* Res asst physics, Atomic Energy Can, 63-64; fel, 69-71, asst prof, 71-76, assoc prof, 76-81, PROF PHYSICS, RUTGERS UNIV, 81- *Mem:* Am Phys Soc. *Res:* Studied energy dependence of proton-proton elastic and inelastic scattering and proton-antiproton annihilation. *Mailing Add:* Dept of Physics Rutgers Univ New Brunswick NJ 08903

SANNES, PHILIP LOREN, b Canton, Ohio, Mar 10, 48; m 73; c 1. ENVIRONMENTAL HEALTH, CELL BIOLOGY. *Educ:* Ohio State Univ, BA, 70, MSc, 73, PhD(anat), 75. *Prof Exp:* Instr path, Med Univ SC, 75-77, asst prof, 77-78; ASST PROF ENVIRON HEALTH SCI, JOHNS HOPKINS UNIV, 78-, ASST PROF CELL BIOL & ANAT, 79- *Concurrent Pos:* NIH fel, Inst Gen Health Sci, 77-78. *Mem:* Am Asn Anatomists; Histochem Soc; Soc Cell Biol; Electrophoresis Soc. *Res:* Cell biology: ultrastructure and cytochemistry; alteration of lung structure and function relationships by environmental agents. *Mailing Add:* Dept Environ Health Sci 615 N Wolfe St Baltimore MD 21205

SANNUTI, PEDDAPULLAIAH, b Rajupalem, India, Apr 2, 41; m 65; c 1. CONTROL SYSTEMS, INFORMATION SCIENCE. *Educ:* Eng Col, Anantapur, India, BE, 63; Indian Inst Technol, Kharagpur, MTech, 65; Univ Ill, Urbana, PhD(elec eng), 68. *Prof Exp:* PROF ELEC ENG, RUTGERS UNIV, NEW BRUNSWICK, 68- *Mem:* Inst Elec & Electronics Engrs. *Res:* Singular perturbation method in the theory of optimal control; communication systems; filtering. *Mailing Add:* Dept of Elec Eng Rutgers Univ New Brunswick NJ 08903

SANSING, GERALD ALLEN, b Champaign, Ill, Oct 25, 45. MICROBIAL BIOCHEMISTRY. *Educ:* Huntingdon Col, BA, 68; Auburn Univ, MS, 70, PhD(microbial biochem), 72. *Prof Exp:* Nat Res Coun-Agr Res Serv res assoc, Northern Regional Res Lab, Agr Res Serv, USDA, Peoria, 72-73; res assoc, Peoria Sch Med, Univ Ill Col Med, 73-74; RES BIOCHEMIST MICROBIAL BIOCHEM, COM SOLVENTS CORP, 74- *Mem:* Am Soc Microbiol; Sigma Xi. *Res:* Fermentation processes involving the microbiology, production, isolation, purification, structural determination, toxicology and pharmacology of microbial metabolites. *Mailing Add:* Res & Develop Div Com Solvents Corp Terre Haute IN 47808

SANSING, NORMAN GLENN, b Woodstock, Ala, Aug 17, 32; m 55; c 3. BIOCHEMISTRY, PLANT PHYSIOLOGY. *Educ:* Auburn Univ, BS, 54, MS, 59; Iowa State Univ, PhD(plant physiol), 62. *Prof Exp:* Res assoc nucleic acid enzym, Biol Div, Oak Ridge Nat Lab, 62-64; asst prof biochem & bot, 64-72, ASSOC PROF BIOCHEM, UNIV GA, 72- *Mem:* AAAS; Am Soc Plant Physiologists. *Res:* Nucleic acid enzymology; isolation and characterization of plant nucleases. *Mailing Add:* Dept Biochem Univ Ga Athens GA 30602

SANSING, RAYMOND CLAYTON, b North Little Rock, Ark, May 6, 40; m 62. STATISTICS, MATHEMATICS. *Educ:* Southern Methodist Univ, BS, 67, MS, 69, PhD(statist), 71. *Prof Exp:* Nat Bur Stand & Nat Res Coun-Nat Acad Sci res assoc, Nat Bur Standards, 71-72; asst prof math sci, Va Commonwealth Univ, 72-77; MATH STATISTICIAN, OFF POLICY & ANAL, INTERSTATE COM COMN, 77- *Mem:* Inst Math Statist; Am Math Soc; Am Statist Asn; Math Asn Am. *Res:* Statistical inference; robustness of statistical procedures; distribution theory; functions of order statistics. *Mailing Add:* Off of Policy & Anal Interstate Com Comn Washington DC 20423

SANSLONE, WILLIAM ROBERT, b Vineland, NJ, Feb 16, 31; m 60; c 1. NUTRITIONAL BIOCHEMISTRY. *Educ:* Rutgers Univ, BS, 53, PhD(biochem), 61; Univ NH, MS, 55. *Prof Exp:* Asst, Univ NH, 53-55; asst, Rutgers Univ, 58-61; instr biochem, State Univ NY Downstate Med Ctr, 61-64, from asst prof to assoc prof, 64-71; sr proj scientist, 71-73, exec secy biochem study sect, Div Res Grants, 73-75, PROG DIR REVIEW, DIV EXTRAMURAL ACTIVITIES, NAT CANCER INST, NIH, 75- *Concurrent Pos:* Vis assoc prof, Med Col Pa, 70-71. *Mem:* AAAS; Am Inst Nutrit; Soc Exp Biol & Med; Sigma Xi. *Res:* Muscle and nutritional biochemistry; health-science administration. *Mailing Add:* Rm 805 Westwood Bldg NIH Bethesda MD 20205

SANSONE, ERIC BRANDFON, b New York, NY, Mar 26, 39; c 2. INDUSTRIAL HYGIENE, SAFETY. *Educ:* City Col New York, BChE, 60; Univ Mich, MPH, 62, PhD(indust health), 67. *Prof Exp:* From asst prof to assoc prof, Indust Hyg & Air Eng, Univ Pittsburgh, 67-74; MEM STAFF, FREDERICK CANCER RES FACIL, NAT CANCER INST, 74-, CHIEF ENVIRON CONTROL & RES LAB, 79- *Mem:* AAAS; Am Indust Hyg Asn; NY Acad Sci; Brit Occup Hyg Soc; Soc Occup Environ Health. *Res:* Risk assessment and environmental monitoring. *Mailing Add:* Nat Cancer Inst Frederick Cancer Res Facil PO Box B Bldg 538 Frederick MD 21701

SANSONE, FRANCES MARIE, b Birmingham, Ala, June 30, 31. HUMAN ANATOMY. *Educ:* Cath Univ Am, AB, 52; Marquette Univ, MS, 56; Univ Tex, PhD(anat), 65. *Prof Exp:* Teaching asst histol & neuroanat, Dent Br, Univ Tex, 57-60; instr, 64-68, asst prof histol & neuroanat, 68-76, clin asst prof, 76-81, ASSOC PROF ANAT SCI, SCH MED, STATE UNIV NY BUFFALO, 81- *Res:* Extra pyramidal motor system, particularly the nucleus substantia nigra; electrophysiological work in cats; ultrastructural and histochemical study in rats. *Mailing Add:* Dept of Neuroanat State Univ of NY Buffalo NY 14214

SANSONE, FRED J, b New York, NY, Apr 7, 34; m 57. MATHEMATICS. *Educ:* Univ Mich, BSE, 56, MSE, 59; Rutgers Univ, MS, 62, PhD(math), 64. *Prof Exp:* Mathematician, Melpar, Inc, 56-57; systs analyst, Bendix Corp, 59-60; asst prof math, Case Univ Technol, 63-65; asst prof, 65-75, ASSOC PROF MATH, ARIZ STATE UNIV, 75- *Mem:* Am Math Soc; Asn Symbolic Logic. *Res:* Recursive function theory; mathematical logic. *Mailing Add:* Dept of Math Ariz State Univ Tempe AZ 85281

SAN SOUCIE, ROBERT LOUIS, b Adams, Mass, Apr 30, 27; m 53. MATHEMATICS, RESEARCH ADMINISTRATION. *Educ:* Univ Mass, BA, 49; Univ Wis, MA, 50, PhD(math), 53. *Prof Exp:* Wis Alumni Res Found asst math, Univ Wis, 49-51; univ asst, 51-52; instr, Univ Ore, 53-55, asst prof, 55-57; head math sect, Sylvania Electronic Systs Div, Gen Tel & Electronics Corp, 57-59, mgr adv commun, 59-61, mgr systs projs, 61-62; vpres eng electronics & space div, Emerson Elec Co, 62-64, pres & gen mgr, 64-67, exec vpres, 67-71; pres, DLJ Capital Corp, Subsidiary of Donaldson, Lufkin & Jenrette, Inc, 71-75; MANAGING DIR, MILL RIVER VENTURES, LTD, 75- *Mem:* Am Math Soc; Am Mgt Asn; Am Astronaut Soc; Sigma Xi. *Res:* Right alternative rings; additive and multiplicative systems; error correcting codes. *Mailing Add:* 35 Cayuga Way Shore Hills NJ 07078

SANTACANA-NUET, FRANCISCO, b Barcelona, Spain, Jan 16, 31; US citizen; m 59; c 4. ANALYTICAL CHEMISTRY. *Educ:* Barcelona Indust Col, BSc, 51; Purdue Univ, MS, 59. *Prof Exp:* Chemist, S A Rovira, Bachs & Macia, 50-53, chief anal sect, 53-56, consult dye chem, 59-60; res chemist org chem div, 60-70, group leader anal res & develop, 70-71, group head chem res div, Bound Brook, NJ, 71-80, MGR ANAL SERV, CHEM RES DIV, AM CYANAMID CO, STAMFORD, CONN, 80- *Mem:* Am Chem Soc. *Res:* chromatography; automation and instrumentation; spectrophotometry; identification of organic structures; nuclear magnetic resonance; mass spectrometry; management. *Mailing Add:* 112 Haverford St New Brunswick NJ 08902

SANT'AMBROGIO, GUISEPPE, b Milano, Italy, Nov 28, 31; m 58; c 3. RESPIRATORY PHYSIOLOGY, NEUROPHYSIOLOGY. *Educ:* Univ Milan, MD, 56. *Prof Exp:* Asst prof physiol, Med Sch, Univ Milan, 57-63, assoc prof, 63-75; assoc prof, 75-77, PROF, DEPT PHYSIOL, UNIV TEX MED BR, GALVESTON, 77- *Concurrent Pos:* Res fel, Dept Physiol, Univ Ky, 58-59 & 60-61, Univ Oxford, 63-64; vis prof, Dept Physiol, McGill Univ, 73. *Mem:* Italian Soc Physiol; Brit Physiol Soc; Europ Soc Respiratory Pathophysiol; Am Physiol Soc; Soc Exp Biol & Med. *Res:* Neural control of breathing in mammals. *Mailing Add:* Dept Physiol & Biophysics Univ Tex Med Br Galveston TX 77550

SANTAMOUR, FRANK SHALVEY, JR, b Lowell, Mass, Mar 7, 32; m 52; c 1. PLANT GENETICS, BIOCHEMISTRY. *Educ:* Univ Mass, BS, 53; Yale Univ, MF, 54; Harvard Univ, AM, 57; Univ Minn, PhD(forestry, plant genetics), 60. *Prof Exp:* Geneticist northeast forest exp sta, US Forest Serv, 57-64; geneticist, Morris Arboretum, Univ Pa, 64-67; RES GENETICIST, AGR RES SERV, USDA, 67- *Concurrent Pos:* Am Philos Soc grants, 66-; Holly Soc Am grant, 71. *Mem:* Soc Am Foresters; Bot Soc Am; Am Hort Soc; Int Soc Arboriculture. *Res:* Genetics and breeding of shade trees and wood ornamentals for urban areas; biochemistry of incompatabilities and pest resistance; biochemical systematics; cytology. *Mailing Add:* US Nat Arboretum Washington DC 20002

SANTE, DANIEL P(AUL), b Lackawanna, NY, Nov 16, 19; m 58. ELECTRONICS. *Educ:* Tri-State Col, BS, 41. *Prof Exp:* Jr engr, Colonial Radio Corp, 41-42; sr design engr, Sylvania Electric Prod Co, 43-48; assoc electronics engr, Cornell Aeronaut Lab, Inc, 48-52, res engr, 52-59; sect head, Sylvania Elec Prod Inc Div, Gen Tel & Electronics Corp, 59-63; asst prof elec eng, 64-72, ASSOC PROF ELEC ENG, ERIE COMMUNITY COL, 72- *Res:* Radio telemetry; communications systems; missile systems; establishment of reliability techniques in a circuit sense for electronics equipment. *Mailing Add:* 4530 Greenbriar Rd Williamsville NY 14221

SANTELMANN, PAUL WILLIAM, b Ann Arbor, Mich, Oct 18, 26; m 50; c 4. AGRONOMY, WEED SCIENCE. *Educ:* Univ Md, BS, 50; Mich State Col, MS, 52; Ohio State Univ, PhD(agron), 54. *Prof Exp:* Asst prof agron, Univ Md, 54-61, assoc prof, 61-62; from assoc prof to prof, 62-74, regents prof, 74-78, PROF AGRON & HEAD DEPT, OKLA STATE UNIV, 78- *Concurrent Pos:* Mem adv group pest mgt & res, President's Coun Environ Qual; mem herbicide study group, Environ Protection Agency; mem study probs pest control team, Nat Acad Sci; mem bd dirs, Coun Agr Sci & Technol, 75-78; ed, newslett, Weed Sci Soc Am; res award, Sigma Xi. *Mem:* Am Inst Biol Sci; AAAS; fel Weed Sci Soc Am (pres, 78); fel Am Soc Agron; Weed Sci Soc. *Res:* Crop and weed management and ecology; herbicide persistence and activity. *Mailing Add:* Dept of Agron Okla State Univ Stillwater OK 74074

SANTER, JAMES OWEN, b Benenden, Eng, May 3, 31; m 57; c 4. ORGANIC CHEMISTRY. *Educ:* Univ London, BSc, 55; Ill Inst Technol, PhD(chem), 61. *Prof Exp:* Res chemist, Shawinigan Resins Corp, 61-65; SR RES SPECIALIST, MONSANTO POLYMERS & RESINS CO, 65- *Mem:* Am Chem Soc. *Res:* Chemistry and technology of aminoplast resins in surface coatings. *Mailing Add:* Monsanto Polymers & Resins Co 730 Worcester St Indian Orchard MA 01151

SANTER, MELVIN, b Boston, Mass, Aug 23, 26; m 55; c 3. MICROBIOLOGY. *Educ:* St John's Univ, NY, BS, 49; Univ Mass, MS, 51; George Washington Univ, PhD(bact), 54. *Prof Exp:* Nat Found Infantile Paralysis fel, Yale Univ, 54-55, NIH fel, 55-56; from asst prof to assoc prof biol, 56-68, PROF BIOL, HAVERFORD COL, 68- *Concurrent Pos:* Lalor fac award, 58; NSF sr fel, 62-63; Weizmann Inst Sci fel, 69-70. *Mem:* AAAS; Am Soc Microbiol; Am Soc Biol Chemists. *Res:* Biochemistry of autotrophic bacteria; ribosome structure and RNA sequence work. *Mailing Add:* Dept Biol Haverford Col Haverford PA 19041

SANTERRE, ROBERT FRANK, b Hanover, NH, June 28, 40; m 58; c 4. CELL CULTURE, MICROBIOLOGY. *Educ:* Southern Conn State Col, BS, 65; Univ NH, MS, 67, PhD(zool), 70. *Prof Exp:* Fel biol, Mass Inst Technol, 70-73 & Univ Calif, San Diego, 73-75; RES SCIENTIST MOLECULAR BIOL, LILLY RES LABS, 75- *Mem:* Sigma Xi; AAAS; Am Soc Cell Biol; NY Acad Sci. *Res:* Oxidative phosphorylation and lipid metabolism; biochemical characterization of non-muscle actins; in vitro studies of insulin biosynthesis; development of cloning vectors for gene analysis and expression in higher eukaryotic cells. *Mailing Add:* Div Molecular & Cell Biol Lilly Res Labs 307 E McCarty St Indianapolis IN 46285

SANTI, DANIEL V, b Buffalo, NY, Feb 6, 42. ORGANIC CHEMISTRY, BIOCHEMISTRY. *Educ:* State Univ NY Buffalo, BS, 63, PhD(med chem), 67. *Prof Exp:* Asst prof chem, Univ Calif, Santa Barbara, 66-70; assoc prof pharmaceut chem & biochem, 70-76, PROF PHARMACEUT CHEM & BIOCHEM, UNIV CALIF, SAN FRANCISCO, 76- *Mem:* Am Chem Soc. *Res:* Enzyme mechanisms; protein biosynthesis; design of enzyme inhibitors; model enzyme reactions; nucleic acids; heterocyclic chemistry. *Mailing Add:* Dept of Biochem & Biophysics Univ of Calif San Francisco CA 94143

SANTIAGO-MELENDEZ, MIGUEL, b Corozal, PR, Sept 28, 30; m 54; c 4. STRUCTURAL ENGINEERING. *Educ:* Univ PR, Mayagüez, BSCE, 54; Tex A&M Univ, MCE, 60, PhD(struct eng), 62. *Prof Exp:* Instr mech, Univ PR, Mayagüez, 54-59, prof struct eng, 62-69; exec dir, Commonwealth of PR, 69-73; CHMN DEPT CIVIL ENG, UNIV PR, 77- *Concurrent Pos:* Consult, PR Planning Bd, 63-69; vis scholar, Univ Calif, Berkeley, 76-77. *Mem:* Am Concrete Inst; Am Soc Civil Engrs; Am Soc Eng Educ; Earthquake Eng Res Inst. *Res:* Shear and diagonal tension in reinforced concrete members, especially beams. *Mailing Add:* H-12-A Terrace Mayaguez PR 00708

SANTILLI, ARTHUR A, b Everett, Mass, July 25, 29; m 64; c 1. ORGANIC CHEMISTRY, PHARMACEUTICAL CHEMISTRY. *Educ:* Boston Univ, AB, 51; Tufts Col, MS, 52; Univ Mass, PhD(chem), 58. *Prof Exp:* Asst chem, Univ Mass, 54-57; fel, Tufts Univ, 58-60; sr res scientist, 60-65, GROUP LEADER, WYETH LABS, INC, 65- *Mem:* Am Chem Soc. *Res:* Synthesis of heterocyclic compounds of possible medicinal interest. *Mailing Add:* Res Dept Wyeth Labs Inc Box 8299 Philadelphia PA 19087

SANTILLI, RUGGERO MARIA, b Capracotta, Italy, Sept 8, 35; m 65; c 2. THEORETICAL PHYSICS. *Educ:* Univ Naples, BA, 58; Univ Turin, PhD(theoret physics), 66. *Prof Exp:* Asst prof physics, Inst A Avogadro, Turin, Italy, 65-67; vis scientist, Ctr Theoret Studies, Univ Miami, 66-68; sr res assoc, Univ Boston, 68-70, asst prof, 70-75; vis scientist, Ctr Theoret Physics, Mass Inst Technol, 76-77; res scientist, Sci Ctr, 77-80, PROF

PHYSICS & PRES, INST BASIC RES, HARVARD UNIV, 80- *Concurrent Pos:* Founder & ed-in-cheif, Hadronic J. *Mem:* Am Phys Soc; Italian Phys Soc; Sigma Xi. *Res:* Methodological foundations for theoretical physics. *Mailing Add:* Inst Basic Res Harvard Univ Cambridge MA 02138

SANTINI, WILLIAM A(NDREW JOHN), JR, b New York, NY, Feb 1, 31; m 55; c 6. CHEMICAL ENGINEERING. *Educ:* Univ Notre Dame, BS, 52; NY Univ, MChE, 56. *Prof Exp:* Ord engr, Picatinny Arsenal, US Dept Army, 52-53; asst, NY Univ, 54-55; chem engr, Westinghouse Elec Corp, 56-58; res chem engr, Tex Instruments, Inc, 58-60, sect mgr cent res, 60-62, eng mgr mat dept, 62-64; pres, S & D Assocs, 64; pres, Pittsburgh Mat & Chem Corp, 64-68; PRES, PHOENIX MAT CORP, 68-, BD CHMN & CHIEF EXEC OFF, 80- *Concurrent Pos:* Consult engr, Europe, USA, 66-; bd chmn, chief exec off & pres, Pensilco Corp, 78-; bd chmn, Continental Indust Corp & Topsoil A/S, Denmark. *Mem:* Am Inst Chem Engrs; Electrochem Soc. *Res:* Preparation and purification of elements and compounds and design and manufacture of chemical vapor deposition equipment for the semiconductor industry; semiconductor and refractory materials chemistry and metallurgy. *Mailing Add:* Phoenix Mat Corp 833 Butler Rd Kittanning PA 16201

SANTISTEBAN, GEORGE ANTHONY, b Mex, Apr 12, 18; nat US; m 42; c 3. NEUROENDOCRINOLOGY, CARDIOVASCULAR DISEASES. *Educ:* Univ Mont, BA, 45; Univ Utah, MA, 49, PhD(human anat), 51. *Prof Exp:* Asst zool, Univ Mont, 47-48; lectr anat, Univ Utah, 49-51, res instr anat & radiobiol, 51-53; asst prof anat, Med Col Va, 53-54; asst prof sch med, Univ Southern Calif, 54-59, asst prof physiol, 59-64; head dept biol, 64-68, assoc prof, 68-75, PROF BIOL, SEATTLE UNIV, 75- *Concurrent Pos:* Sr biologist, Pac Northwest Res Found, 68-; USPHS spec fel, Gothenburg Univ, 66-67; affil investr, Fred Hutchinson Cancer Ctr, 73- *Mem:* AAAS; Am Asn Cancer Res; NY Acad Sci; Am Asn Anat. *Res:* Effects of early experience as a modifying influence upon the function of the hypothalamus; psychosocial stress and development of hypertension, cardiovascular disease and malignancy; interrelationship between stress imprinting and intraneuronal RNA. *Mailing Add:* 2308 NE 108th Seattle WA 98125

SANTNER, JOSEPH FRANK, b Chicago, Ill, Aug 19, 19; m 46; c 5. MATHEMATICAL STATISTICS, OPERATIONS RESEARCH. *Educ:* St Louis Univ, BS, 50, MS, 52. *Prof Exp:* Mathematician, McDonnell Aircraft Corp, 52-54; opers res analyst, NAm Aviation, Inc, 54-55; lectr, Xavier Univ, Ohio, 55-58, asst prof, 58-62; math statistician, Robert A Taft Sanit Eng Ctr, US Dept Health, Educ & Welfare, 62-65, head math sci, 65-70; HEAD MATH SCI, ENVIRON PROTECTION AGENCY, 70- *Mem:* Am Statist Asn. *Res:* Mathematical logic; non-parametric statistical methods; design and analysis of experiments; applied mathematics. *Mailing Add:* Nat Training Ctr US Environ Protection Agency Cincinnati OH 45268

SANTNER, THOMAS JOSEPH, b St Louis, Mo, Aug 29, 47; m 70; c 2. MATHEMATICAL STATISTICS. *Educ:* Univ Dayton, BS, 69; Purdue Univ, MS, 71, PhD(math statist), 73. *Prof Exp:* Asst prof statist, Sch Opers Res & Indust Eng, Cornell Univ, 73-78; VIS SCIENTIST, BIOMETRY BR, NAT CANCER INST, 78- *Concurrent Pos:* Vis scientist & prin investr, NSF grant, 75-77, vis scientist & co-prin investr, 77-79. *Mem:* Inst Math Statist; Am Statist Asn; Biometric Soc. *Res:* Selection and ranking theory; reliability and survivorship analysis; contingency table analysis; applied statistics. *Mailing Add:* Sch Opers Res/Indust Eng Cornell Univ Ithaca NY 14850

SANTO, GERALD SUNAO, b Olaa, Hawaii, Dec 22, 44; m 68; c 3. PLANT NEMATOLOGY. *Educ:* Univ Hawaii, BS, 67, MS, 69; Univ Calif, Davis, PhD(plant path), 74. *Prof Exp:* NEMATOLOGIST, WASH STATE UNIV, 74- *Concurrent Pos:* Mem, Coun Agr & Sci Technol. *Mem:* Soc Nematologists; Am Phytopath Soc; Sigma Xi; Orgn Trop Am Nematologists; Potato Asn Am. *Res:* Study of biology, pathogenicity and control of plant-parasitic nematodes. *Mailing Add:* Irrigated Agr Res & Exten Ctr Wash State Univ Prosser WA 99350

SANTORA, NORMAN JULIAN, b Camden, NJ, Sept 17, 35; m 62; c 3. CHEMICAL INFORMATION, QUANTITATIVE DRUG DESIGN. *Educ:* Temple Univ, AB, 57, AM, 60, PhD(org chem), 65. *Prof Exp:* Asst chem, Temple Univ, 57-60 & 61-65; fel, Univ Pa, 65-68; res assoc med chem, Wm H Rorer, Inc, 68-81; CHEMICAL INFORMATION SPECIALIST, 81- *Mem:* Am Chem Soc; Am Pharmaceut Asn. *Res:* Pyrimidine chemistry; synthesis and characterization of analogs of sulfonamides and nucleosides; quantitative structure-activity relationship studies, with special emphasis on non-computer approaches to drug design. *Mailing Add:* 1323 Partridge Rd Roslyn PA 19001

SANTORO, THOMAS, b Brooklyn, NY, Oct 22, 28; m 64; c 2. MICROBIOLOGY. *Educ:* Brooklyn Col, BS, 54; Univ Kans, MA, 57; Pa State Univ, PhD(microbiol), 61. *Prof Exp:* Res asst bact, Univ Kans, 54-57; soil microbiologist, Pa State Univ, 57-61, res assoc, 61-63; res asst, Brooklyn Bot Garden, 63-69; ASST PROF BIOL, STATE UNIV NY COL NEW PALTZ, 69- *Mem:* Am Soc Microbiol; Mycol Soc Am; Brit Soc Gen Microbiol. *Res:* Antibiotics by Mycorrhizal fungi; effect of pesticides and insecticides on the ecology of soil microorganisms; interactions between clay minerals and microbial cells. *Mailing Add:* Dept of Microbiol State Univ of NY Col New Paltz NY 12561

SANTOS, EUGENE (SY), b Manila, Philippines, Feb 15, 41; m 67; c 2. MATHEMATICS, COMPUTER SCIENCE. *Educ:* Mapua Inst Technol, BSME, 61; Univ Philippines, MSc, 63; Ohio State Univ, PhD(math), 65. *Prof Exp:* Instr math, Mapua Inst Technol, 62-63; teaching asst, Ohio State Univ, 63-65, asst prof, 65-68; assoc prof, 68-74, PROF MATH, YOUNGSTOWN STATE UNIV, 74- *Mem:* Asn Comput Mach; Am Math Soc; Soc Indust & Appl Math. *Res:* Theory of automata, computability and formal languages; general applied mathematics; theory of elasticity and thin shells. *Mailing Add:* Dept of Math 410 Wick Ave Youngstown OH 44503

SANTOS, GEORGE WESLEY, b Oak Park, Ill, Feb 3, 28; m 52; c 4. ONCOLOGY, IMMUNOLOGY. *Educ:* Mass Inst Technol, BS & MS, 51; Johns Hopkins Univ, MD, 55; Am Bd Internal Med, dipl, 62. *Prof Exp:* Intern med, Johns Hopkins Hosp, 55-56, asst resident, 58-60, fel, 60-62; from instr to assoc prof med, 62-75, prof oncol, 73-75, PROF ONCOL & MED, SCH MED, JOHNS HOPKINS UNIV, 75-; PHYSICIAN, JOHNS HOPKINS HOSP, 62- *Concurrent Pos:* Leukemia Soc scholar, 61-66; asst dir med oncol unit, Baltimore City Hosps, 62-, asst physician-in-chief, 63-; mem, Cancer Clin Investigative Rev Comt & Immunol-Epidemiol Spec Virus-Cancer Prog, NIH, 69 & Cell Biol-Immunol-Genetics Res Evaluations Comt, Vet Admin, 69; chmn, Bone Marrow Transplant Registry & mem, Int Comt Organ Transplant Registry, Am Col Surgeons-NIH, 69; mem bd dir, Leukemia Soc Am, 73. *Mem:* Am Soc Hemat; Transplantation Soc; Am Asn Immunologists; Am Asn Cancer Res. *Res:* Transplantation immunology. *Mailing Add:* Johns Hopkins Univ Dept of Oncol Baltimore MD 21205

SANTOS-BUCH, CHARLES A, b Santiago, Cuba, Mar 20, 32; US citizen; m 56; c 3. EXPERIMENTAL PATHOLOGY. *Educ:* Harvard Univ, BA, 53; Cornell Univ, MD, 57. *Prof Exp:* Asst path, Med Col, Cornell Univ, 58-61, instr neuropath, 61-62; from asst prof to prof path, Sch Med, Emory Univ, 62-68; assoc prof, 68-76, assoc dean, 70-74, PROF PATH, MED COL, CORNELL UNIV, 76-; DIR, PAPANICOLAOU CYTOL LAB, NEW YORK HOSP, 79- *Concurrent Pos:* USPHS res training fel, 59-62; Markle scholar acad med, 64. *Mem:* Am Soc Exp Path; Am Asn Path & Bact; NY Acad Sci; Pan-Am Med Asn; Am Soc Cytol. *Res:* Diseases of small arteries; high resolution enzyme histochemistry; immunology of hypersensitivity diseases; immunology of parasitic diseases. *Mailing Add:* Dept of Path Cornell Univ Med Col New York NY 10021

SANTOS-MARTINEZ, JESUS, b Vieques, PR, Mar 5, 24; m 55; c 4. PHYSIOLOGY, PHARMACOLOGY. *Educ:* Univ PR, BS, 46; Univ Ill, MS, 48; Purdue Univ, PhD(pharmacol), 54. *Prof Exp:* Asst instr pharm, Col Pharm, Univ PR, San Juan, 46-47, instr, 47-51, asst prof pharmacol, 51-55, from asst prof to prof physiol, Sch Med, 55-72, lectr pharmacol, Sch Pharm, 58, prof basic sci & chmn dept, Sch Dent, 72-76, prof pharmacol, Sch Med, 76-80; MEM FAC, DEPT PHYSIOL & PHARMACOL, SCH MED, UNIV CARIBE, 80- *Concurrent Pos:* Nat Inst Arthritis & Metab Dis fel, Med Ctr, Ind Univ, 66-67; vis prof, Sch Med, Univ Nicaragua, 62. *Mem:* AAAS; Am Physiol Soc; Am Soc Nephrology; Int Soc Nephrology; Tissue Cult Soc. *Res:* Renal physiology; electrolyte distribution. *Mailing Add:* Dept Physiol & Pharmacol Univ Caribe Sch Med Cayey PR 00634

SANTRY, D C, b Charlottetown, PEI, Apr 21, 31; m 51; c 3. NUCLEAR CHEMISTRY, SOLID STATE SCIENCE. *Educ:* Dalhousie Univ, BS, 53, MS, 55; McGill Univ, PhD(radiochem), 58. *Prof Exp:* Nat Res Coun Can fel, Cambridge Univ, 58-59; assoc res officer chem, 59-75, SR RES OFFICER CHEM, ATOMIC ENERGY CAN, LTD, 75- *Mem:* Can Asn Physicists; Chem Inst Can; Am Chem Soc. *Res:* Fast-neutron cross section measurements and calculations; isotope production and decay scheme determinations; ion implantation studies; range, retention and stopping cross sections of heavy ions in solids. *Mailing Add:* 1 Laurier Ave Deep River ON K0J 1P0 Can

SANTULLI, THOMAS V, b New York, NY, Mar 16, 15; m 43; c 2. SURGERY. *Educ:* Columbia Univ, BS, 35; Georgetown Univ, MD, 39; Am Bd Surg, dipl, 47, cert spec competence pediat surg, 75. *Prof Exp:* Assoc prof, 55-67, PROF SURG, COL PHYSICIANS & SURGEONS, COLUMBIA UNIV, 67-, CHIEF PEDIAT SURG, 55- *Concurrent Pos:* Consult, Monmouth Mem & Fitkin Mem Hosps, NJ, 50-, St Joseph's Hosp, Yonkers, NY, 53- & St Joseph's Hosp, Stamford, Conn, 59-; attend surgeon, Presby Hosp, New York, 60- *Mem:* Fel Am Col Surg; fel Am Acad Pediat; Am Surg Asn; Am Pediat Surg Asn (pres, 80-81); Brit Asn Pediat Surg. *Res:* Pediatric surgery. *Mailing Add:* Babies Hosp 3959 Broadway New York NY 10032

SANUI, HISASHI, b Orosi, Calif, Jan 7, 24; m 54; c 2. BIOPHYSICS, CELL PHYSIOLOGY. *Educ:* Univ Calif, AB, 51, PhD(biophys), 58. *Prof Exp:* Jr res physiologist, 57-59, lectr physiol, 60-61, asst res physiologist, 61-67, ASSOC RES PHYSIOLOGIST, UNIV CALIF, BERKELEY, 67- *Mem:* AAAS; Am Physiol Soc; Biophys Soc; NY Acad Sci; Sigma Xi. *Res:* Active ion transport by living cells; subcellular morphology and biochemistry; ion binding by biological materials; atomic absorption spectrophotometry; role of cell membrane and ions in cell transformation; role of inorganic actions in cell growth regulation; mechanisms of heavy metal action on cells. *Mailing Add:* Dept Molecular Biol Univ Calif Berkeley CA 94720

SANYER, NECMI, b Konya, Turkey, Oct 5, 19; nat US; m 53; c 2. WOOD CHEMISTRY. *Educ:* Inst Agr, Ankara, Turkey, BS, 41; State Univ NY, MS, 50, PhD, 53. *Prof Exp:* Hibbert Mem fel, McGill Univ, 53-54; res chemist, Mead Corp, 54-59; supvry chemist, 59-73, SUPVR RES CHEM, FOREST PRODS LAB, US FOREST SERV, 73- *Mem:* Fel Am Inst Chemists; Am Chem Soc. *Res:* Lignin, cellulose and pulping chemistry. *Mailing Add:* Forest Prods Lab PO Box 5130 Madison WI 53705

SANZONE, GEORGE, b Brooklyn, NY, Jan 13, 34; m 56; c 3. CHEMICAL PHYSICS, CHEMICAL KINETICS. *Educ:* Univ Ill, Urbana, BS, 65, MS, 67, PhD(chem), 69. *Prof Exp:* Designer, Burton Rodgers, Inc, Ohio, 59-60; proj engr, Bendix Corp, 60-63; engr dept chem, Univ Ill, Urbana, 63-65; asst prof, 69-81, ASSOC PROF CHEM, VA POLYTECH INST & STATE UNIV, 81- *Mem:* Am Chem Soc; Am Phys Soc; Am Soc Mass Spectros. *Res:* High temperature, fast chemical reaction studies employing shock tubes with mass spectrometric and optical detection techniques; molecular beam fluorescence; reactions in high-velocity flows. *Mailing Add:* Dept of Chem Va Polytech Inst & State Univ Blacksburg VA 24061

SAPAKIE, SIDNEY FREIDIN, b Port Chester, NY, May 10, 45; m 72; c 2. CHEMICAL ENGINEERING, FOOD ENGINEERING. *Educ:* Univ Mich, BSChEng, 67; Univ Minn, MBA, 72. *Prof Exp:* Res engr, Gen Mills, Inc, 67-70; group leader, Betty Crocker Div, 70-73, asst prod mgr mkt,

Protein Div, 73-74, develop leader, Spec Technol Activ, 74-77, dir res, Gorton Group, 77-78, dir, Subsidiary Res & Develop, 78-80, DIR, APPL ENG & NEW PROCESS DEVELOP, GEN MILLS INC, 80- *Mem:* Am Inst Chem Engrs; Inst Food Technologists. *Res:* Food sterilization, especially thermal processing, aseptic processing and microwave processing; food extrusion, especially math modeling and development; engineering economics. *Mailing Add:* Gen Mills Inc 9000 Plymouth Ave N Minneapolis MN 55427

SAPEGA, A(UGUST) E(DWARD), b Bridgeport, Conn, Dec 10, 25; m 55; c 2. ELECTRICAL ENGINEERING. *Educ:* Columbia Univ, BS, 46, MS, 51; Worcester Polytech Inst, PhD, 72. *Prof Exp:* From instr to assoc prof, 51-67, chmn dept, 71-81, PROF ENG, TRINITY COL, CONN, 67- *Mem:* Am Soc Mech Engrs; Inst Elec & Electronics Engrs. *Res:* Electrical engineering circuits and devices; semiconductor physics and circuits; computer applications. *Mailing Add:* Dept of Eng Trinity Col Hartford CT 06106

SAPERS, GERALD M, b Brookline, Mass, Jan 17, 35; m 60; c 2. FOOD SCIENCE. *Educ:* Mass Inst Technol, SB & SM, 59, PhD(food technol), 61. *Prof Exp:* Food scientist, Pioneering Res Div, US Army Natick Labs, 61-63; sr res assoc, Lever Bros Co, NJ, 63-64; unit leader food res, Corn Prod Food Technol Inst, Mass, 64-68; res chemist, 68-80, RES LEADER, EASTERN REGIONAL RES CTR, NE REGION, AGR RES SERV, USDA, 80- *Mem:* AAAS; Inst Food Technologists; Am Chem Soc. *Res:* Flavor chemistry and stability of dehydrated potato products and other dehydrated foods; quality of fruit and vegetable products; fruit and vegetable processing; natural pigments; home canning safety. *Mailing Add:* Eastern Regional Res Ctr USDA 600 E Mermaid Lane Philadelphia PA 19118

SAPERSTEIN, ALVIN MARTIN, b Bronx, NY, June 3, 30; m 56; c 2. THEORETICAL NUCLEAR PHYSICS, ENVIRONMENTAL EDUCATION. *Educ:* NY Univ, BA, 51; Yale Univ, MS, 52, PhD(physics), 56. *Prof Exp:* Asst physics, Yale Univ, 52, res asst, 52-56; res physicist, Eng Res Inst, Univ Mich, 56-57; res assoc, Brown Univ, 57-59; asst prof physics, Univ Buffalo, 59-62; res assoc, Argonne Nat Lab, 62-63; assoc prof, 63-68, dir, Prog Environ Studies, 78-80, PROF PHYSICS, WAYNE STATE UNIV, 68- *Concurrent Pos:* NSF res grant, 65-67 & 67-71; hon res assoc, Univ Col, Univ London, 69-70 & 76-77; prof sci & technol, Weekend Col, Wayne State Univ, 74-75; vis prof, Open Univ, Eng, 76-77; mem, Mayor's Energy Comn, City of Detroit; mem exec bd, Ctr Peace & Conflict Studies, Wayne State Univ. *Mem:* Fel AAAS; fel Am Phys Soc; Fedn Am Sci; Union Concerned Scientists. *Res:* Scattering of nucleons from nucleons and nuclei; general theory of nuclear reactions; elementary particle reactions; general scattering theory; interaction between science and society. *Mailing Add:* Dept of Physics Wayne State Univ Detroit MI 48202

SAPERSTEIN, DAVID DORN, b New York, NY, June 30, 46; m 76; c 1. PHYSICAL CHEMISTRY. *Educ:* Johns Hopkins Univ, BA, 67; NY Univ, PhD(chem), 73. *Prof Exp:* Sr res chemist, Merck Sharp & Dohme Res Labs, 73-77, res fel, 77-81; ADV SCIENTIST, IBM INSTRUMENTS, 81- *Mem:* Am Chem Soc; AAAS. *Res:* Molecular investigations of organic substances using physical, spectroscopic, analytic and quantum chemical methods; application of vibrational spectroscopy to chemistry and biology. *Mailing Add:* IBM Instruments 40 W Brokaw Rd San Jose CA 95110

SAPERSTEIN, LEE W(ALDO), b New York, NY, July 14, 43; m 67; c 2. MINING ENGINEERING. *Educ:* Mont Sch Mines, BS, 64; Oxford Univ, DPhil(eng sci), 67. *Prof Exp:* From asst prof to assoc prof, 67-78, PROF MINING ENG & SECT CHMN, PA STATE UNIV, 78- *Concurrent Pos:* Mem comt mineral technol, Nat Res Coun, 76-78, comt on surface mining & reclamation, 78-79 & visitor, accreditation bd eng & technol, 79- *Mem:* Am Inst Mining, Metall & Petrol Engrs. *Res:* Materials handling in mines and tunnels; rapid excavation; noise in underground mines; rock fragmentation; mined-land reclamation; surface mining for coal; quarries; pre-mining planning; advances in mining sciences. *Mailing Add:* 118 Mineral Sci Bldg Pa State Univ University Park PA 16802

SAPERSTEIN, RICHARD, b Brooklyn, NY, June 6, 40. BIOCHEMICAL ENDOCRINOLOGY. *Educ:* Queen's Col, BS, 62; Brown Univ, MS, 66, PhD(biol), 69. *Prof Exp:* Res fel endocrinol, Tufts New Eng Med Ctr Hosp, 69-72, neuroendocrinol, 72-74; res fel biochem endocrinol, Merck Inst Therapeut Res, 74-80; MEM FAC, DEPT ENDOCRINOL, TUFTS UNIV, 80- *Res:* Biochemical endocrinology; neuroendocrinology; pituitary, hypothalmic and pancreatic physiology. *Mailing Add:* Dept Endocrinol 171 Harrison Ave Boston MA 02111

SAPERSTEIN, SIDNEY, b Brooklyn, NY, Apr 2, 23; m 47; c 3. NUTRITION. *Educ:* Brooklyn Col, AB, 47; Univ Calif, Los Angeles, MA, 48; Univ Calif, PhD(microbiol), 53. *Prof Exp:* Asst bact, Univ Calif, 49-53; res assoc antileukemics, Col Dent, NY Univ, 53-54; bacteriologist, Borden Co, 54-56, supvr microbiol res & develop, Borden Spec Prod Co, 56-65, res assoc, 65-66, dir res pharmaceut div, Borden Foods Co, 67-71; asst dir nutrit sci, Syntex Labs, Inc, 71-73, prin scientist, Nutrit Prod Div, 73-78, clin trials mgr, 78-81, MGR, SCI AFFAIRS, SYNTEX RES LABS, SYNTEX CORP, 81- *Concurrent Pos:* Mem tech adv group, Comn Nutrit, Am Acad Pediat, 75-81. *Mem:* Am Chem Soc; Am Inst Nutrit; Am Soc Clin Nutrit; Inst Food Technol; AAAS. *Res:* Bacteriology; biochemistry; allergy; nutrition. *Mailing Add:* Syntex Labs 3401 Hillview Ave Palo Alto CA 94304

SAPINO, CHESTER, JR, b Troy, NY, Jan 28, 41; m 60; c 2. ORGANIC CHEMISTRY. *Educ:* Rensselaer Polytech Inst, BSc, 65, PhD(org chem), 69. *Prof Exp:* Res asst org chem, Sterling Winthrop Res Inst, 59; lab technician anal chem, B T Babbit & Co, Inc, 59-60; org chemist silicone prod develop ctr, Gen Elec Co, 65; assoc prof org chem, Hudson Valley Community Col, 68-69; SR DEVELOP CHEMIST, BRISTOL LABS INC, 69- *Mem:* Am Chem Soc. *Res:* Penicillin and cephalosporin chemistry; natural product chemistry; antibiotic research and development; spectroscopy; computer applications to chemical problems. *Mailing Add:* Bristol Labs Inc PO Box 657 Syracuse NY 13201

SAPIR, DANIEL GUSTAVE, b Brussels, Belgium, May 21, 35; US citizen; m 62; c 2. MEDICINE. *Educ:* Brown Univ, AB, 56; Johns Hopkins Univ, MD, 60. *Prof Exp:* Fel nephrol, Tufts New Eng Med Ctr, 64-66; instr, 66-68, asst prof, 68-73, ASSOC PROF, SCH MED, JOHNS HOPKINS UNIV, 73- *Concurrent Pos:* Consult to various pvt & pub orgn, 67-; Irvine-Blum scholar, Sch Med, Johns Hopkins Univ, 77. *Mem:* Am Fedn Clin Res; Am Soc Nephrol; Sigma Xi. *Res:* Renal metabolism; nutrition. *Mailing Add:* Johns Hopkins Hosp Baltimore MD 21205

SAPIRIE, S(AMUEL) R(ALPH), b Indianapolis, Ind, June 25, 09; m 36; c 1. CIVIL ENGINEERING. *Educ:* Purdue Univ, BS, 30, CE, 42. *Hon Degrees:* DEng, Purdue Univ, 58. *Prof Exp:* Field engr, State Dept Conserv, Ind, 30-33; construct engr camps, Emergency Conserv Work, 33-35; regional engr & chief land develop div, USDA, 35-42, engr in charge design projs, Soil Conserv Serv, 45-46; civil engr, Milwaukee Dist, US War Dept, 42-43, chief construct br, Northwest Div, 43-44, asst dir opers, Manhattan Dist, 46; dir prod & eng div, Oak Ridge Opers, Atomic Energy Comn, 47-49, dep mgr, 49-51, mgr, 51-72; ENG CONSULT, 72- *Concurrent Pos:* Sr consult, Bechtel Corp, 73-77. *Honors & Awards:* Nat Civil Serv League Career Serv Award, US Atomic Energy Comn, 55; Distinguished Serv Award, Nat Res Coun, 57. *Mem:* Am Nuclear Soc; Am Soc Civil Engrs. *Res:* Design of large dams; management responsibility for design, construction, process improvement and development and operation of facilities for production of uranium-235; processing of source materials as feed for production of fissionable and special materials; management of research, development and analytical control laboratories. *Mailing Add:* 100 Ogden Circle Oak Ridge TN 37830

SAPONARA, ARTHUR G, b Newark, NJ, Nov 27, 36; m 59; c 2. BIOCHEMISTRY. *Educ:* Rutgers Univ, AB, 58; Univ Wis, MS, 61, PhD(biochem), 64. *Prof Exp:* BIOCHEMIST, LOS ALAMOS NAT LAB, UNIV CALIF, 64- *Mem:* AAAS; Am Chem Soc. *Res:* Amino acid activation in protein biosynthesis; ribonucleic acid biosynthesis and modification in mammalian cells. *Mailing Add:* Los Alamos Nat Lab Los Alamos NM 87545

SAPOROSCHENKO, MYKOLA, b Ukraine, May 19, 24; nat US; m 60; c 2. PHYSICS. *Educ:* Ursinus Col, BS, 52; Washington Univ, AM, 54, PhD(physics), 58. *Prof Exp:* Asst prof physics, Univ Ark, 58-59 & Ill Inst Technol, 59-60; res assoc, Washington Univ, 60-62, asst prof, 62-65; asst prof, 65-70, ASSOC PROF PHYSICS & ASTRON, SOUTHERN ILL UNIV, CARBONDALE, 70- *Mem:* Am Phys Soc. *Res:* Gaseous electronics; ion-molecule reactions; mass spectrometry. *Mailing Add:* Dept of Physics Southern Ill Univ Carbondale IL 62901

SAPORTA, SAMUEL, b Athens, Greece, Mar 30, 46; m 70. NEUROANATOMY, NEUROBIOLOGY. *Educ:* Univ Calif, Davis, BA, 67; Univ Southern Calif, PhD(physiol psychol), 73. *Prof Exp:* Instr anat, Univ Calif, Los Angeles, 76, res asst, 76-77; ASST PROF ANAT, UNIV S FLA, 77- *Concurrent Pos:* NIMH fel, 70-73, NIH fel, 74-76. *Mem:* Am Asn Anatomists; Soc Neurosci; Sigma Xi; AAAS. *Res:* Neuroanatomical and physiological organization of the somatosensory system; functional interrelationships of neurons which produce coding and decoding of information. *Mailing Add:* Dept Anat Col Med 12901 N 30th St Box 6 Tampa FL 33612

SAPP, RICHARD CASSELL, b Kokomo, Ind, Sept 8, 28; m 57; c 2. PHYSICS. *Educ:* Wilmington Col, BSc, 49; Ohio State Univ, PhD(physics), 55. *Prof Exp:* Res assoc physics, Ohio State Univ, 55; Welch Found fel, Rice Univ, 55-57; from asst prof to assoc prof, 57-67, PROF PHYSICS, UNIV KANS, 67- *Concurrent Pos:* Sloan Found fel, 62-64; Am Phys Soc fel, 69. *Mem:* Am Phys Soc; Am Asn Physics Teachers. *Res:* Low temperature physics, especially magnetic cooling and nuclear orientation; magnetic relaxation. *Mailing Add:* Dept of Physics Univ of Kans Lawrence KS 66045

SAPP, WALTER J, b Shreveport, La, Feb 16, 34; m 62; c 3. CELL BIOLOGY. *Educ:* Wiley Col, BS, 61; Univ Wis-Madison, MS, 64, PhD(zool), 66. *Prof Exp:* From asst prof to assoc prof, 66-76, head dept, 68-76, res assoc, 73-76, PROF BIOL & DEAN STUDENTS, TUSKEGEE INST, 76- *Mem:* AAAS; Am Soc Cell Biol. *Res:* Ultrastructure of genetic systems; ultrastructure and cytogenetics of tumor systems. *Mailing Add:* Dept of Biol Tuskegee Institute AL 36088

SAPPENFIELD, DALE S, b Miami, Fla, Dec 14, 33; m 60; c 4. PHYSICAL CHEMISTRY. *Educ:* Northwestern Univ, BA, 55; Univ Minn, PhD(phys chem), 62. *Prof Exp:* Mem staff, Los Alamos Sci Lab, Univ Calif, 62-70; SR SCIENTIST, MISSION RES CORP, 71- *Res:* Upper atmosphere chemistry and physics; nuclear weapon effects. *Mailing Add:* PO Drawer 719 Santa Barbara CA 93102

SAPPENFIELD, ROBERT W, b Bedford, Ind, Oct 2, 24; m 48; c 3. MEDICINE. *Educ:* Ind Univ, MD, 47. *Prof Exp:* Intern, Med Ctr, Ind Univ, 47-48 & 49, resident pediat, 49-51; resident, Chicago Contagious Dis Hosp, 48; resident, La Rabida Sanitarium Rheumatic Fever, 48-49; epidemiologist, State Bd Health, La, 51-52; from instr to assoc prof pub health & pediat, 53-63, prof prev med, pub health & pediat & head dept pub health & prev med, 63-72, assoc dean, 72-79, PROF PREV MED & PUB HEALTH, SCH MED, LA STATE UNIV MED CTR, NEW ORLEANS, 79- *Concurrent Pos:* Res fel, Children's Hosp, 52-53; proj dir, Collab Child Develop Prog, Charity Hosp New Orleans, 60-62. *Mem:* Am Col Prev Med; Asn Teachers Prev Med; Am Acad Pediat. *Res:* Preventive medicine; pediatrics; epidemiology, especially communicable disease and perinatal problems. *Mailing Add:* Dept Prev Med & Pub Health La State Univ Med Ctr New Orleans LA 70112

SAPPENFIELD, WILLIAM PAUL, b Lee's Summit, Mo, Apr 10, 23; m 56; c 4. AGRONOMY, PLANT BREEDING. *Educ:* Univ Mo, BS, 48, PhD(plant breeding), 52. *Prof Exp:* Instr agron, Univ Mo, 48-51; agronomist, NMex Col, 51-54; agronomist, Univ Calif, Davis, USDA, 54-56; assoc prof, 56-70, PROF AGRON, UNIV MO-COLUMBIA, 70- *Concurrent Pos:* Mem, Nat Cotton Testing Comt & Crop Variety Regist Comt; mem, Nat Cotton Res

Task Force Comt; chmn, Miss Delta Cotton Variety Testing Comt; rep comt cotton quality, State Agr Exp Sta, USDA; res grants, Cotton Inc. *Mem:* Am Soc Agron; Crop Sci Soc Am. *Res:* Cotton breeding, host plant resistance, and fiber technology. *Mailing Add:* 607 Holly Hill Dr Sikeston MO 63801

SAPRA, VAL T, b Beawar, India, Nov 15, 42; m 73. PLANT BREEDING, PLANT CYTOGENETICS. *Educ:* Kans State Univ, PhD(plant breeding, genetics), 72. *Prof Exp:* Res asst plant breeding, Govt of Rajastham, India, 65-68; res asst, Kans State Univ, 68-72; fel, 72-73, assoc prof plant breeding & plant cytogenetics, 73-80, PROF AGRON, ALA A&M UNIV, 80- *Concurrent Pos:* Consult, Somdiaa, Paris, France; agronomist, WCent Africa. *Mem:* Crop Sci Soc Am; Am Soc Agron; Can Soc Genetics; Can Soc Agron. *Res:* Triticale breeding and cytogenetics; development of new triticale strains through conventional and mutation breeding procedures. *Mailing Add:* PO Box 67 Ala A&M Univ Normal AL 35762

SAR, MADHABANANDA, b Palchakada, India, Dec 31, 33; m 56; c 3. VETERINARY MEDICINE, PHYSIOLOGY. *Educ:* Bihar Univ, BVSc & AH, 56; Mich State Univ, MS, 63, PhD(physiol), 68. *Prof Exp:* Vet asst surg, Dept Vet Serv & Animal Husbandry, India, 56-59; instr parasitol, Orissa Col Vet Sci & Animal Husbandry, 59-61; res assoc neuroendocrinol, Univ Chicago, 68-69, res assoc, 69-70, instr & res assoc pharmacol, 69; res assoc neuroendocrinol, Labs Reprod Biol, 69-77, res asst prof, 77-78, RES ASSOC PROF ANAT, SCH MED, UNIV NC, CHAPEL HILL, 78- *Mem:* AAAS; Endocrine Soc; Soc Study Reprod; Int Brain Res Orgn; Am Physiol Soc. *Res:* Neuroendocrinology; endocrinology; reproductive physiology; hormone localization in brain and peripheral target tissues by autoradiography and immunohistochemistry. *Mailing Add:* Labs for Reprod Biol Univ of NC Chapel Hill NC 27514

SARA, RAYMOND VINCENT, b Carbondale, Pa, Jan 24, 27; m 52; c 4. MATERIALS SCIENCE. *Educ:* Pa State Univ, BS, 50, MS, 52. *Prof Exp:* SR RES SCIENTIST MAT SCI, UNION CARBIDE CORP, 52- *Mem:* Am Ceramic Soc. *Res:* Phase equilibria and reaction mechanisms of refractory materials, mechanical and thermal properties of metal/non-metal fiber and particulate composite systems, oxidation and diffusion phenomenon, graphitization and intercalation; abradable seals. *Mailing Add:* Parma Tech Ctr Union Carbide Corp Box 6116 Cleveland OH 44101

SARACENO, ANTHONY JOSEPH, b Reggio, Italy, June 20, 33; nat US; m 70. INORGANIC CHEMISTRY. *Educ:* St Vincent Col, BS, 55; Univ Notre Dame, PhD(chem), 58. *Prof Exp:* Res assoc, Univ Notre Dame, 56-58; res chemist, Gulf Res & Develop Co, 58-61; sr chemist, 61-64, prof leader, Pennwalt Corp, 65-67; group leader, 67-73, SECT HEAD, GOODYEAR ATOMIC CORP, 73- *Mem:* AAAS; Am Chem Soc. *Res:* Coordination compounds; solid state inorganic chemistry; inorganic polymers; infrared spectroscopy; organometallic compounds; lubricants; coatings; process development; air-water pollution control; halogen chemistry; metal corrosion. *Mailing Add:* Goodyear Atomic Corp PO Box 628 Piketon OH 45661

SARACHEK, ALVIN, b Pittsburgh, Pa, July 29, 27; m 56, 76. MICROBIOLOGY. *Educ:* Univ Mo-Kansas City, BA, 48, MA, 50; Kans State Univ, PhD(microbiol genetics), 58. *Prof Exp:* Instr biol, Univ Mo-Kansas City, 50-51; res assoc biol res lab, Univ Southern Ill, 51-54; fel microbial biochem, Inst Microbiol, Rutgers Univ, 57-58; asst prof biol, 58-59, from assoc prof to prof, 59-72, DISTINGUISHED PROF NATURAL SCI, WICHITA STATE UNIV, 72-, CHMN DEPT BIOL, 61- *Concurrent Pos:* Microbial geneticist, US AEC, 65-66, mem adv comt prog in food irradiation, 67-72; chmn panel student oriented prog, NSF, 71-75; chmn grants & awards comt, Am Cancer Soc, Kans Div, 70-76, mem exec comt, 70-78; prof assoc, Sci Educ Directorate, NSF, 77-78; mem, Dept Energy adv coun life sci prog, Argonne Nat Lab, 78-80 & NSF adv panel, 81-; NATO sci fel, 81- *Mem:* Am Cancer Soc; Am Soc Microbiol; Genetics Soc Am; Bot Soc Am; fel Am Acad Microbiol. *Res:* Genetics and physiology of microorganisms; radiobiology; radiation genetics and chemical mutagenesis in fungi. *Mailing Add:* Dept of Biol Wichita State Univ Wichita KS 67208

SARACHIK, EDWARD S, b New York, NY, Apr 22, 41; m 68. DYNAMIC METEOROLOGY, OCEANOGRAPHY. *Educ:* Queens Col, NY, BS, 60; Brandeis Univ, MS, 63, PhD(physics), 66. *Prof Exp:* Res assoc Linear Acceleration Ctr, Stanford Univ, 65-67; staff physicist, Electronics Res Ctr, NASA, 67-70; staff mathematician Transport Systs Ctr, Dept Transport, 70-71; NSF fel & res assoc meteorol, Mass Inst Technol, 71-73; res fel & lectr atmospheric physics, 73-78, RES ASSOC & PROJ MGR, CTR EARTH & PLANETARY PHYSICS, HARVARD UNIV, 78- *Mem:* Am Phys Soc; Am Meteorol Soc. *Mailing Add:* Ctr for Earth & Planetary Physics Harvard Univ Cambridge MA 02138

SARACHIK, MYRIAM PAULA, b Antwerp, Belgium, Aug 8, 33; US citizen; m 54; c 1. SOLID STATE PHYSICS. *Educ:* Barnard Col, Columbia Univ, BA, 54, Columbia Univ, MS, 57, PhD(physics), 60. *Prof Exp:* From res asst to res assoc exp solid state physics, Watson Lab, Columbia Univ, 55-61; mem tech staff, Bell Tel Labs, NJ, 62-64; from asst prof to assoc prof physics, 64-71, PROF PHYSICS, CITY COL NEW YORK, 71- *Concurrent Pos:* Prin investr, US Air Force Res Grant, 65-72; NSF grant, 72-74, Phys Sci Ctr, City New York grant, 71-72, 75-76 & 80-81. *Mem:* Fel Am Phys Soc. *Res:* Properties of superconducting materials; magnetic and transport properties of alloys; disordered systems. *Mailing Add:* Dept Physics City Col New York Convent Ave at 138th St New York NY 10031

SARACHIK, PHILIP E(UGENE), b New York, NY, Dec 3, 31; m 64; c 1. CONTROL SYSTEMS. *Educ:* Columbia Univ, AB, 53, BS, 54, MS, 55, PhD(elec eng), 58. *Prof Exp:* Staff engr, Int Bus Mach Res Lab, NY, 58-60; from asst prof to assoc prof elec eng, Columbia Univ, 60-64; assoc prof, NY Univ, 64-67, prof elec eng, 67-73; PROF ELEC ENG, POLYTECH INST NY, 73- *Concurrent Pos:* Consult, Aerospace Group, Gen Precision, Inc, 63-68; vis prof control & comput syts, Dept Com, Tel Aviv Univ, 79-80. *Mem:* Inst Elec & Electronics Engrs; Soc Indust & Appl Math. *Res:* Applications of computers to real time control systems; problems in optimal and adaptive control systems; application of control theory to transportation problems. *Mailing Add:* 225 W 86th St Apt 305 New York NY 10024

SARACHMAN, THEODORE N, b West Warwick, RI, Feb 26, 32; m 65; c 2. MOLECULAR PHYSICS. *Educ:* Univ Chicago, AB, 51, MS, 54; Harvard Univ, PhD(phys chem), 61. *Prof Exp:* Nat Bur Standards-Nat Res Coun fel, 61-63; asst prof physics, State Univ NY Buffalo, 63-70; ASSOC PROF PHYSICS & CHMN DEPT, WHITTIER COL, 70- *Mem:* AAAS; Am Phys Soc; Am Asn Physics Teachers. *Res:* Microwave and radio frequency spectroscopy; atomic and molecular structure; biophysics. *Mailing Add:* Dept Physics Whittier Col Whittier CA 90608

SARADA, THYAGARAJA, b Madras, India, Apr 19, 29. PHYSICAL & INORGANIC CHEMISTRY. *Educ:* Annamalai Univ, Madras, BSc, 51; Am Univ, MS, 70, PhD(phys chem), 72. *Prof Exp:* Lectr & head, Dept Chem, St Mary's Col, Madras, 51-52, SPW Col, Tirupati, India, 52-63; prof, 63-67, head, Dept Chem, 52-67, fel phys chem, 73-74, res asst, 75-78, ASST PROF, AM UNIV, WASHINGTON, 78- *Concurrent Pos:* Dreyfus & Camille Found fel, Am Univ, 73-74; res asst, ERDA, 75-76 & US Defense, 76-78; sci pool officer, CLRI, Madras, 74-75. *Res:* Optical properties of liquid crystals; physico-chemical, electrical properties and characterization of fuel cell electrolytes and electrodes; electrochemical corrosion, complex ion theory. *Mailing Add:* Am Univ Washington DC 20016

SARAKWASH, MICHAEL, b South River, NJ, Feb 20, 25; m 72. STATISTICS, QUALITY CONTROL. *Educ:* Columbia Univ, BS, 50; Stevens Inst Technol, MS, 58, PE, 78. *Prof Exp:* Mathematician, Evans Signal Lab, 50-53; sr qual control engr propeller div, Curtiss-Wright Corp, 53-58; sr mathematician reaction motors div, Thiokol Chem Corp, Denville, 58-63, statist mathematician, 63-67; consult statist & exp design, MS Assocs, 67-74; sr reliability engr, Res-Cottrell, NJ, 74-77; consult statist, reliability, qual control & exp design, M S Assocs, 77-80; SUPVRY STATISTICIAN, MIL SEALIFT COMMAND, MOTBY, BAYONNE, NJ, 80- *Mem:* Am Statist Asn; Am Soc Qual Control; NY Acad Sci. *Res:* Quality control; marketing; statistics in finance; reliability. *Mailing Add:* 377 Colfax Ave Clifton NJ 07013

SARAN, CHITARANJAN, b Lucknow, India, Sept 22, 39; US citizen; m 69; c 1. SAFETY CONTROL, BIOMECHANICS. *Educ:* Indian Inst Technol, BTech, 62, MTech, 63; NC State Univ, PhD(bioeng, agr eng), 67. *Prof Exp:* Asst, NC State Univ, 63-67; asst agr engr, Univ PR, 67-68, from instr to asst prof math, 68-71; US Pub Health Serv Trainee, Med Ctr & Ctr Safety, NY Univ, 71-73, asst prof safety, Ctr Safety, 73-75; coordr, St Louis Degree Prog, 75-78, assoc prof, 75-80, PROF INDUST SAFETY & HYG, CENT MO STATE UNIV, WARRENSBURG, 80- *Mem:* Am Soc Agr Engrs; Inst Eng, India; Am Soc Safety Engrs; Human Factors Soc; Sigma Xi. *Res:* Human engineering and safety aspects of agriculture and industry. *Mailing Add:* Cent Mo State Univ Warrensburg MO 64093

SARANTAKIS, DIMITRIOS, b Nafplion, Greece, May 20, 36; m 65; c 2. MEDICINAL CHEMISTRY. *Educ:* Nat Univ Athens, BSc, 59; Imp Col, dipl, 65, Univ London, PhD(org chem), 65. *Prof Exp:* Res fel org chem, Univ Leicester, 65-66; res assoc, Royal Res Estab, Greece, 66-67; res assoc, Univ Wash, 67-71; chief chemist, Fox Chem Co, 71; GROUP LEADER ORG CHEM, WYETH LABS INC, PHILADELPHIA, PA, 71- *Mem:* Am Chem Soc. *Res:* Synthesis of biologically active polypeptides; synthesis of behavior inducing compounds. *Mailing Add:* 1524 High Meadow Lane West Chester PA 19380

SARANTITES, DEMETRIOS GEORGE, b Athens, Greece, May 5, 33; m 65; c 1. NUCLEAR CHEMISTRY, NUCLEAR PHYSICS. *Educ:* Mass Inst Technol, PhD(nuclear chem), 63. *Prof Exp:* Radiochemist, Cyclotron Lab, Mass Inst Technol, 60-63; res assoc nuclear chem, Washington Univ, 63-65, from asst prof to assoc prof, 65-74; vis prof, Res Inst Physics, Stockholm, 74-75; assoc prof, 75-76, PROF NUCLEAR CHEM, WASHINGTON UNIV, 76- *Mem:* Am Phys Soc; Sigma Xi. *Res:* Investigations of nuclear reaction mechanisms and of nuclear structure with emphasis on the electromagnetic and nuclear properties of the high spin states. *Mailing Add:* Dept of Chem Washington Univ St Louis MO 63130

SARASOHN, ILYA M, physical organic chemistry, see previous edition

SARASON, DONALD ERIK, b Detroit, Mich, Jan 26, 33. MATHEMATICS. *Educ:* Univ Mich, BS, 55, AM, 57, PhD(math), 63. *Prof Exp:* Mem math, Inst Adv Study, 63-64; from asst prof to assoc prof, 64-70, PROF MATH, UNIV CALIF, BERKELEY, 70- *Concurrent Pos:* NSF fel, 63-64; Sloan fel, 69-71. *Mem:* Am Math Soc; Math Asn Am. *Res:* Functional analysis. *Mailing Add:* Dept of Math Univ of Calif Evans Hall Berkeley CA 94720

SARASON, LEONARD, b Brooklyn, NY, May 29, 25; m 62. MATHEMATICS. *Educ:* Yale Univ, BS, 45, BMus, 48, MusM, 49; NY Univ, PhD(math), 61. *Prof Exp:* Res asst math, Courant Inst Math Sci, NY Univ, 60-63; actg asst prof, Stanford Univ, 63-65; from asst prof to assoc prof, 65-74, PROF MATH, UNIV WASH, 74- *Mem:* Am Math Soc. *Res:* Partial differential equations. *Mailing Add:* Dept of Math GN-50 Univ of Wash Seattle WA 98195

SARAVANAMUTTOO, HERBERT IAN H, b Monkton, Scotland, June 20, 33; Can citizen; m 60; c 3. MECHANICAL ENGINEERING. *Educ:* Glasgow Univ, BSc, 55; Bristol Univ, PhD(mech), 68. *Prof Exp:* Engr, Orenda Engines, 55-59; analyst, KCS Ltd, Toronto, 59; engr, Orenda Engines, 59-64; lectr mech eng, Bristol Univ, 64-70; assoc prof aerothermodyn, Carleton Univ, 70-75, prof mech & aeronaut eng & chmn dept, 75-80. *Concurrent Pos:* Consult, Rolls Royce Ltd, 66-70, Brit Aircraft Corp, 75 & Avionics Div, Smith's Indust, 75-76; vis res fel, Royal Naval Eng Col, 80-81; dir, Gas Tops Ltd, Ottawa, 80- *Mem:* Fel Can Aeronaut & Space Inst (vpres, 78-79, pres 79-80); fel Brit Inst Mech Engrs; Am Soc Mech Engrs. *Res:* Dynamic response of gas turbines; improvement of part load performance; engine health monitoring. *Mailing Add:* Dept of Mech & Aeronaut Eng Carleton Univ Ottawa ON K1S 5B6 Can

SARAVIS, CALVIN, b Englewood, NJ, Feb 27, 30; m 54; c 4. IMMUNOLOGY. *Educ:* Syracuse Univ, AB, 51; WVa Univ, MS, 55; Rutgers Univ, PhD(zool), 58. *Prof Exp:* Asst physiol, serol & immunol, Rutgers Univ, 55-58; head antiserum prod & develop, Blood Grouping Lab, Mass, 58-59; dir immunochem lab, Blood Res Inst, Inc, 59-72; PRIN ASSOC SURG & MEM FAC MED, HARVARD MED SCH, 71-; RES ASSOC PATH, SCH MED, BOSTON UNIV, 74- *Concurrent Pos:* Assoc med, Peter Bent Brigham Hosp, 61-69; res assoc, Harvard Med Sch, 62-71; chief immunol div, Harvard Surg Unit, Boston City Hosp, 66-68; sr res assoc & asst dir, Gastrointestinal Res Lab, Mallory Inst Path Found, 74-; mem spec sci staff, Boston City Hosp & Mallory Inst Path, 78-; sr res assoc, Cancer Res Inst, New Eng Deaconess Hosp, Boston, 79- *Mem:* Transplantation Soc; Am Asn Immunologists. *Res:* Transplantation immunology; cancer immunology; isolation and identification of antibodies and antigens; hepatitis; detection, isolation and characterization of human cancer markers. *Mailing Add:* Mallory Inst Path Boston City Hosp Boston MA 02118

SARAZIN, CRAIG L, b Milwaukee, Wis, Aug 11, 50; m 71; c 2. THEORETICAL ASTROPHYSICS. *Educ:* Calif Inst Technol, BS, 72; Princeton Univ, MA, 74, PhD(physics), 75. *Prof Exp:* Millikan fel physics, Calif Inst Technol, 75; mem physics, Inst Advan Study, 75-77; asst prof, 77-80, ASSOC PROF ASTRON, UNIV VA, 80- *Concurrent Pos:* Vis fel, Inst Astron, Cambridge Univ, 76; vis asst scientist, Nat Radio Astron Observ, 77-78 & 79-81; vis asst prof, Astron Dept, Univ Calif, Berkeley, 79; vis mem, Inst Advan Study, 80-82. *Mem:* Am Astron Soc; Int Astron Union. *Res:* Interstellar medium; clusters of galaxies; x-ray emission; extragalactic astronomy. *Mailing Add:* Dept Astron Univ Va PO Box 3818 Univ Sta Charlottesville VA 22903

SARBACH, DONALD VICTOR, b Lincoln, Nebr, Nov 3, 11; m 34; c 3. ORGANIC CHEMISTRY. *Educ:* Univ Nebr, BSc, 34. *Prof Exp:* From mem tech staff to mgr new prod develop, B F Goodrich Co, Ohio, 37-55; dir res, Hewitt-Robins, Inc, Conn, 55-58; dir rubber tech, Goodrich-Gulf Chem, Inc, 58-69; prod mgr, 69-73, elastomer specialist, BF Goodrich Chem Co, 73-77; RETIRED. *Mem:* AAAS; Am Chem Soc; fel Am Inst Chem. *Res:* Rubber; synthetic rubber and plastics technology; product development and applications. *Mailing Add:* 242 River Rd Hinckley OH 44233

SARBER, RAYMOND WILLIAM, b Hammond, Ind, Apr 15, 16; m 37; c 2. MEDICAL BACTERIOLOGY. *Educ:* Western Mich Univ, AB, 38; Univ Cincinnati, MS, 41. *Prof Exp:* Asst bact, Univ Mich, 40; asst prof col pharm, Univ Cincinnati, 40-42; res bacteriologist, Parke, Davis & Co, 42-59; exec secy, Am Acad Microbiol, 68-78; EXEC SECY, AM SOC MICROBIOL, 59- *Concurrent Pos:* Consult, Clopay Corp, 41-43; registrar, Nat Registry Microbiol, 68-74. *Mem:* Am Soc Microbiol; Sigma Xi. *Res:* Tuberculosis antigens; tuberculins; pertussis, biological and chemical tuberculosis antigens; germicide testing methods; tissue culture. *Mailing Add:* 1913 I St NW Washington DC 20006

SARCHET, BERNARD REGINALD, b Byesville, Ohio, June 13, 17; m 41; c 3. ENGINEERING MANAGEMENT. *Educ:* Ohio State Univ, BChE, 39; Univ Del, MChE, 41. *Prof Exp:* Asst, Univ Del, 39-41; operator, Eng & Construct Div, Koppers Co, Inc, Pa, 41-42, gen foreman, Butadiene Div, 42-45, supv chem engr, Res Div, 45-46, supvr, Eng & Construct Div, 46-47, mgr, Oil City Plant, 47-50, mgr, Kobuta Plant, 50-53, asst mgr sales, Chem Div, 54-56, mgr develop dept, 56-58, mgr prod develop, Plastics Div, 58-61, mgr panel dept, 61-64, dir commercial develop, 64-67; chmn dept eng mgt, 67-81, exec dir, External Affairs, 75-79, PROF ENG MGT, UNIV MO-ROLLA, 67- *Mem:* Am Chem Soc; Am Soc Eng Educ; Am Inst Chem Engrs; Am Soc Eng Mgt. *Res:* Absorption distillation; robotics and impact on management; housing construction panels. *Mailing Add:* Dept Eng Mgt Harris Hall Univ Mo Rolla MO 65401

SARCIONE, EDWARD JAMES, b Lawrence, Mass, Dec 3, 25; m 53; c 3. BIOCHEMISTRY. *Educ:* St Michael's Col, BS, 48; Univ Kans, PhD(biochem), 57. *Prof Exp:* Biochemist, Dept Pub Health, Mass, 49-50; asst instr biochem, Sch Med, Univ Kans, 50-55; assoc cancer res scientist, 55-72, PRIN CANCER RES SCIENTIST & PROF & CHMN PHYSIOL PROG, ROSWELL PARK MEM INST, 72- *Mem:* AAAS; Am Soc Biol Chemists; Am Chem Soc; Am Asn Cancer Res; Soc Exp Biol & Med. *Res:* Biosynthesis of glycoproteins and fetal proteins; molecular diseases. *Mailing Add:* Dept Med Roswell Park Mem Inst 666 Elm St Buffalo NY 14203

SARD, RICHARD, b Brooklyn, NY, Apr 19, 41; m 63; c 2. SURFACE CHEMISTRY, SCIENCE MANAGEMENT. *Educ:* Stevens Inst Technol, BE, 62, MS, 63, PhD(phys metall), 68. *Prof Exp:* Electron microscopist, Cent Res Labs, Air Reduction Corp, 63-64; mem tech staff, Bell Tel Labs, 68-73, supvr plated film properties & interface studies, 73-78, supvr mat develop & comput applns, 78-79; DIR TECHNOL, PLATING SYSTS DIV, OCCIDENTAL PETROL CORP, 79- *Mem:* AAAS; Electrochem Soc; Am Electroplaters Soc. *Res:* Structure and properties of electrodeposits and other coatings in relation to process conditions; electrodeposition; surface characterization; physical properties; device phenomena; process control sensors; microprocessor applications. *Mailing Add:* 21441 Hoover Rd Warren MI 48089

SARD, ROBERT DANIEL, b New York, NY, Aug 23, 15; wid; c 3. EXPERIMENTAL HIGH ENERGY PHYSICS. *Educ:* Harvard Univ, SB, 35, AM, 40, PhD(physics), 42. *Prof Exp:* Asst, Kamerlingh Onnes Lab, Leiden, Neth, 36-38; instr physics, Harvard Univ, 38-42, res assoc radio res lab, 42-45; res assoc, Mass Inst Technol, 45-46; asst prof physics, Wash Univ, St Louis, 46-48, from assoc prof to prof, 48-61; PROF PHYSICS, UNIV ILL, URBANA, 61- *Concurrent Pos:* Fulbright adv res scholar, Univ Manchester, 51-52 & Lawrence Radiation Lab, Univ Calif, 59-60; consult particle accelerator div, Argonne Nat Lab, 58-60; vis scientist, Europ Orgn Nuclear Res, Serpukhov, USSR & Geneva, Switz, 70-71. *Mem:* Fel Am Phys Soc. *Res:* Elementary particles; cosmic rays; experimental particle physics. *Mailing Add:* Dept Physics Univ Ill Urbana IL 61801

SARDELLA, DENNIS JOSEPH, b Lawrence, Mass, July 3, 41; m 66; c 4. CHEMISTRY. *Educ:* Boston Col, BS, 62; Ill Inst Technol, PhD(phys org chem), 67. *Prof Exp:* Nat Res Coun Can fel, Univ Western Ont, 66-67; asst prof chem, 67-71, ASSOC PROF CHEM, BOSTON COL, 71- *Concurrent Pos:* Vis lectr biol chem, Sch Med, Harvard Univ, 73-75. *Mem:* Am Chem Soc; Sigma Xi. *Res:* Nuclear magnetic resonance spectroscopy; structural chemistry; theoretical organic chemistry. *Mailing Add:* Dept Chem Boston Col Chestnut Hill MA 02167

SARDESAI, VISHWANATH M, b Goa, India, Nov 17, 32; m 66. BIOCHEMISTRY, CLINICAL CHEMISTRY. *Educ:* Univ Bombay, BS, 54, MS, 57; Wayne State Univ, PhD(physiol chem), 62. *Prof Exp:* Instr chem, Univ Bombay, 54-57; res chemist, Zandu Pharmaceut Works Ltd, India, 57-59; teaching asst biochem, Wayne State Univ, 59-60; instr, Sch Med, Tulane Univ, 62-63; asst prof, 63-69, ASSOC PROF BIOCHEM, SCH MED, WAYNE STATE UNIV, 69- *Mem:* AAAS; Am Physiol Soc; Am Inst Nutrit; Am Chem Soc; NY Acad Sci. *Res:* Porphyrin biosynthesis and metabolism; oxidative phosphorylation; alcohol metabolism; metabolism in shock; clinical methods. *Mailing Add:* Dept of Surg Wayne State Univ Sch of Med Detroit MI 48201

SARDINAS, AUGUST A, b Bronx, NY, June 19, 22; m 44; c 3. MATHEMATICAL ANALYSIS. *Educ:* Brooklyn Col, BA, 43; Harvard Univ, MA, 47; Univ Pa, PhD(math), 62. *Prof Exp:* Res asst info theory, Univ Pa, 49-50; staff engr, Burroughs Corp, 50-63; ASSOC PROF MATH, VILLANOVA UNIV, 63- *Concurrent Pos:* Logical design consult, Burroughs Corp, 65- *Mem:* Math Asn Am. *Res:* Information theory; logical design; analysis. *Mailing Add:* Dept of Math Villanova Univ Villanova PA 19085

SARDINAS, JOSEPH LOUIS, b Havana, Cuba, Aug 1, 19; US citizen; m 42; c 2. MICROBIOLOGY, BIOCHEMISTRY. *Educ:* Brooklyn Col, AB, 48, MA, 52; St John's Univ, NY, PhD(microbiol), 61. *Prof Exp:* Res asst, Merck Sharp & Dohme, NY, 48; MICROBIOLOGIST, PFIZER INC, 48- *Mem:* Am Soc Microbiol; Am Soc Indust Microbiol; Am Chem Soc. *Res:* Industrial fermentations; microbiological transformations; isolation and purification of fermentation products. *Mailing Add:* Pfizer Inc Eastern Point Rd Groton CT 06340

SARDISCO, JOHN BAPTIST, b Shreveport, La, July 27, 34; m 59; c 1. PHYSICAL CHEMISTRY. *Educ:* Spring Hill Col, BS, 56; La State Univ, MS, 58, PhD(phys chem), 60. *Prof Exp:* Sect supvr phys chem sect, Res Eng & Develop Dept, Pennzoil United, Inc, 61-75, DIV MGR INORGANIC RES, RES & DEVELOP DEPT, PENNZOIL CO, 75- *Mem:* Am Chem Soc; NY Acad Sci; Electrochem Soc; Smithsonian Inst. *Res:* Corrosion research and control; inorganic process development; hydrometallurgical refining of metals; instrumental inorganic analysis; water pollution control and water purification. *Mailing Add:* Pennzoil Co PO Box 6199 Shreveport LA 71106

SAREM, AMIR M SAM, b Teheran, Iran, Sept 5, 30; US citizen; m 57; c 3. CHEMICAL & PETROLEUM ENGINEERING. *Educ:* Univ Tulsa, BSPE, 54, MSPE, 56; Univ Okla, PhD(eng sci), 64. *Prof Exp:* Jr engr, Sinclair Res Inc, Okla, 54-55, intermediate res engr, 55-59, res engr, 59-61; teaching asst petrol eng, Univ Okla, 61-64; res engr, 64-66, sr res engr, 66-77, RES ASSOC, UNION RES CTR, UNION OIL CO CALIF, 77- *Concurrent Pos:* Lectr, Sinclair Res Lab, Inc, 59-61 & 64; lectr exten sch, Univ Calif, Los Angeles, 65- *Mem:* Am Inst Mining, Metall & Petrol Engrs; Am Chem Soc; Am Inst Chem Engrs; Soc Rheol. *Res:* Petroleum reservoir engineering; P-V-T properties of hydrocarbon systems; fluid flow mechanics in porous media; viscous and surfactant water flood of oil fields; rheological properties of polymer solutions; pipeline flow drag reduction. *Mailing Add:* Union Res Ctr PO Box 76 Brea CA 92621

SARETT, HERBERT PAUL, b Brooklyn, NY, Feb 5, 16; m 48; c 3. NUTRITION, BIOCHEMISTRY. *Educ:* Brooklyn Col, BA, 36; Cornell Univ, MS, 37; Duke Univ, PhD(biochem), 42; Am Bd Nutrit, dipl, 52. *Prof Exp:* Instr biochem, Sch Med, Duke Univ, 42-43; asst prof & res assoc, Ore State Col, 43-45; res assoc med div, Chem Warfare Serv, US Dept Army, Md, 45; asst prof biochem & med, Sch Med, Tulane Univ, 46-51, assoc prof, 51-52; dir nutrit res, Mead Johnson Res Ctr, 52-67, dir nutrit & biochem res, 58-62, vpres nutrit sci, 67-71, vpres nutrit sci resources, 71-81; CONSULT NUTRIT SCI, 81- *Concurrent Pos:* Mem tech adv group comt nutrit, Am Acad Pediat, 61-67, 69-81, chmn, 71-74; mem panel new foods, White House Conf Foods, Nutrit & Health, 69; mem food standards & fortification policy, Food & Nutrit Bd, Nat Acad Sci, 70-72; chmn nutrit sci comt, Infant Formula Coun, 71-81; indust adv to US deleg comt foods for spec dietary uses, Codex Alimentarius Comn, 71-81. *Mem:* Am Inst Nutrit; Soc Exp Biol & Med; Am Soc Clin Nutrit; Am Chem Soc; Am Soc Biol Chem. *Res:* Foods for special dietary uses; protein evaluation; infant nutrition; milk substitute formulas; formulas for infants with metabolic disorders; formula diets; meal replacements; medium chain triglycerides; cholestyramine; nutrition regulations. *Mailing Add:* 451 Audubon Dr Evansville IN 47715

SARETT, LEWIS HASTINGS, b Champaign, Ill, Dec 22, 17; m 44, 69; c 4. ORGANIC CHEMISTRY, RESEARCH ADMINISTRATION. *Educ:* Northwestern Univ, BS, 39; Princeton Univ, PhD(chem), 42. *Hon Degrees:* DSc, Northwestern Univ, 72, Bucknell Univ, 77. *Prof Exp:* Res chemist, Merck & Co, Inc, 42-48, asst dir dept org chem & biochem res, 48-52, dir dept med chem, 52-56, dir dept synthetic org chem, 56-62, exec dir fundamental res, 62-66, vpres basic res, 66-69, pres, Merck Sharp & Dohme Res Labs, 69-76, SR V PRES, SCI & TECHNOL, MERCK & CO, INC, 76- *Concurrent Pos:* Consult med chem sect, USPHS, 64-67; mem res & eval comt, Nat Cystic Fibrosis Res Found, 64-69; trustee, Cold Spring Harbor Lab Quant Biol, 68-70; rep, Indust Res Inst, 68-, dir, 74-77; rep, Pharmaceut Mfrs Asn, 69-; mem vis comt div biol, Calif Inst Technol, 69-76, chmn, 72-76; mem, Dirs Indust Res, 70-, secy, 71-72, chmn, 72-73; mem indust adv comt, Univ Calif, San Diego, 71-; mem adv panel develop res develop & eng in developing countries, Nat Acad Sci, 71-72; mem, bd trustees, Med Ctr, Princeton Univ, 77-79; mem, Sci & Technol Panel, Reagan Transition Team, 80-81, Drugs for

Rare Dis, Pharmaceut Mfrs Asn Comn, 81- *Honors & Awards:* Julius W Sturmer Mem Lectr, 59; Sci Award, Bd Dirs, Merck & Co, Inc, 51; Baekeland Award, Am Chem Soc, 51, Award, 64; Medal, Synthetic Org Chem Mfrs Asn, 64; William Scheele Lectr, Royal Pharmaceut Inst, Stockholm, Sweden, 64; Chem Pioneer Award, Am Inst Chem, 72; Nat Medal Sci, 75; Perkin Medal Award, Soc Chem Indust, 76; Gold Medal, Am Inst Chemists, 81. *Mem:* Nat Acad Sci; Inst Med-Nat Acad Sci; Am Inst Chem; fel NY Acad Sci; Brit Soc Chem Indust. *Res:* Biomedical research organization. *Mailing Add:* Merck & Co Inc Rahway NJ 07065

SARGE, THEODORE WILLIAM, b Taunton, Mass, Feb 4, 18; m 44; c 5. PHYSICAL ORGANIC CHEMISTRY. *Educ:* Col Holy Cross, BS, 40, MS, 41. *Prof Exp:* Chemist, 41-44, chemist, Saran Develop Lab, 44-56, res admin asst petrochem & gen res, Saginaw Bay Res Dept, 56-67, res admin asst new prod, 67-69, res admin asst pilot plant & process develop & eng admin, 69-74, MEM STAFF, PATENT DEPT, DOW CHEM CO, 74- *Mem:* AAAS; Am Chem Soc; Sigma Xi. *Res:* Vinyl polymerizations; polymer properties; polymeric film applications and properties, especially water vapor and gas transmissions; petrochemicals-hydrocarbons processing and extraction; research administration, especially research and development, patents, safety and training. *Mailing Add:* Dow Chem Co Midland MI 48640

SARGEANT, PETER BARRY, b Cedar Rapids, Iowa, Jan 18, 36; m 56; c 3. TEXTILE CHEMISTRY, RESEARCH ADMINISTRATION. *Educ:* Iowa State Univ, BS, 58; Ohio State Univ, PhD, 62. *Prof Exp:* Res asst, Ohio State Univ, 58-59; res chemist cent res dept, 62-66, sr res chemist, Textile Fibers Dept, Va, 66-69, res supvr, Dacron Res Lab, NC, 69-71, res supvr textile res lab, 71-73, sr supvr process, 73-75, SR SUPVR DACRON TECH, TEXTILE FIBERS DEPT, E I DU PONT DE NEMOURS & CO, INC, NC, 75- *Mem:* Am Chem Soc. *Res:* Polymer chemistry; fiber technology. *Mailing Add:* Textile Fibers Dept Dacron Res & Develop Ctr E I du Pont de Nemours & Co Inc Kinston NC 28501

SARGEANT, WALTER JAMES, b Strathroy, Ont, Apr 7, 44; m 67; c 2. PHYSICS, ELECTRICAL ENGINEERING. *Educ:* Univ Western Ont, BSc, 66, MSc, 67, PhD(physics), 71. *Prof Exp:* Asst dir res & develop, Gen-Tec Inc, 71-73; scientist, Lumonics Res Ltd, 73-75; scientist, Nat Res Coun Can, 75-78; scientist, Los Alamos Sci Labs, 79-81; PROF DEPT ELEC ENG, STATE UNIV NY, BUFFALO, 81- *Concurrent Pos:* Indust fel, Gen-Tec Inc, 71-73; consult, Dept Nat Defence, 71-73, Atomic Energy Can Ltd, 75-; adj prof elec eng, Tex Tech Univ, 77-; adj prof physics, Univ Ill, 79-; scientific adv, DARDA, 81-; consult, Los Alamos Nat Lab, 81- *Mem:* Inst Elec & Electronics Engrs; Optical Soc Am; Can Asn Physicists; Asn Prof Engrs. *Res:* High repetition rate power conditioning systems; gas discharge laser physics and chemical kinetics; generation and measurement of picosecond electrical impulses; electrical insulation and breakdown processes. *Mailing Add:* 4232 Ridge Lea Rd Dept Eng State Univ NY, Buffalo Amherst NY 14226

SARGENT, BERNICE WELDON, b Williamsburg, Ont, Sept 24, 06; m 40. NUCLEAR PHYSICS. *Educ:* Queen's Univ, Ont, BA, 26, MA, 27; Cambridge Univ, PhD(physics), 32. *Prof Exp:* Lectr physics, Queen's Univ, Ont, 30-36, asst prof, 36-43; res physicist, Atomic Energy Proj, Nat Res Coun Can, 43-49, prin res physicist, 49-51, asst dir, 51; prof physics & head dept, 51-67, R Samuel McLaughlin res prof, 54-72, EMER PROF PHYSICS, QUEEN'S UNIV, ONT, 72- *Concurrent Pos:* Mem, Nat Res Coun Can, 56-62. *Honors & Awards:* Order British Empire, 46; Gold Medal, Can Asn Physicists, 59. *Mem:* Fel Am Phys Soc; fel Royal Soc Can; Can Asn Physicists (vpres, 54-55, pres, 55-56). *Res:* Radioactivity; neutron physics; nuclear reactors; photonuclear reactions; nuclear structure; history of physics. *Mailing Add:* Dept Physics Queen's Univ Kingston ON K7L 3N6 Can

SARGENT, CHARLES, b Mitchell, Nebr, May 24, 13; m 38; c 1. CIVIL ENGINEERING. *Educ:* Univ Idaho, BS, 48, CE, 52; Stanford Univ, MS, 58. *Prof Exp:* Asst prof civil eng, Univ Idaho, 48-53; from asst prof to prof, 53-61, dean math phys sci & eng, 61-67, EMER DEAN MATH, PHYS SCI & ENG, UNIV ALASKA, COLLEGE, 70- *Concurrent Pos:* Consult engr, 48-; exec dir planning & opers, Univ Alaska, 67-70; prof construct mgt, NDak State Univ, 70-75. *Mem:* Am Soc Civil Engrs; Am Soc Eng Educ. *Res:* Economic problems in engineering construction, particularly concrete aggregates. *Mailing Add:* 609 Dollar St Coeur d'Alene ID 83814

SARGENT, CHARLES P, b Beaver, Pa, Aug 3, 25; m 57; c 3. NUCLEAR PHYSICS. *Educ:* Dartmouth Col, AB, 49; Columbia Univ, PhD(physics), 54. *Prof Exp:* Staff physicist, 53-60, lectr physics, 60-70, res physicist, 60-74, SR RES SCIENTIST, MASS INST TECHNOL, 74- *Mem:* Am Phys Soc. *Res:* Experimental nuclear physics, specializing in photon and electron induced reactions; linear electron accelerator science and technology. *Mailing Add:* Dept of Physics Mass Inst of Technol Cambridge MA 02139

SARGENT, DAVID FISHER, b Victoria, BC, June 29, 45; m 67; c 1. MEMBRANE BIOLOGY, ELECTRICAL PROPERTIES. *Educ:* Univ BC, BSc, 66; Univ Western Ont, PhD(biophys), 71. *Prof Exp:* Fel biochem, Univ Sydney, 74-75; fel biophys, 71-74, RES ASST BIOPHYS, FED TECH UNIV, ZURICH, 75- *Concurrent Pos:* Med Res Coun Can fel, 71-74. *Mem:* Biophys Soc; Union Swiss Soc Exp Biol. *Res:* Use of electrical properties of artificial lipid membranes for study of membrane dynamics; interactions with membrane-active substances, reconstitution. *Mailing Add:* Inst Molecular Biol & Biophys ETH-Hönggerberg 8093 Zürich Switzerland

SARGENT, FRANK DORRANCE, b Concord, NH, July 9, 35; m 59; c 2. QUANTITATIVE GENETICS, REPRODUCTIVE PHYSIOLOGY. *Educ:* Univ NH, BS, 57; NC State Univ, MS, 60, PhD(animal sci), 65. *Prof Exp:* Res asst animal breeding, 57-63, instr dairy husb, 63-65, asst prof exten dairy husb, 65-70, assoc prof, 70-76, prof exten dairy husb, 76-81, PROF ANIMAL SCI, NC STATE UNIV, 81- *Mem:* Am Dairy Sci Asn. *Res:* Dairy cattle breeding; dairy herd management; production record systems. *Mailing Add:* Dept of Animal Sci NC State Univ PO Box 5126 Raleigh NC 27607

SARGENT, FREDERICK, II, human ecology, nutrition, deceased

SARGENT, FREDERICK PETER, b Plymouth, UK, July 26, 40; m 67; c 2. NUCLEAR WASTE DISPOSAL. *Educ:* Univ Exeter, BS, 61; Univ Leeds, MS, 63, PhD(chem), 65. *Prof Exp:* Nat Res Coun Can fel, Univ Sask, 65-67; Sci Res Coun UK fel, Univ Leeds, 67-69; res officer chem, 69-77, mem plutonium chem group, 77-78, sect leader exp pathways anal radionuclide migration in geologic formations, 78-81, HEAD, GEOCHEM & APPL CHEM BR, ATOMIC ENERGY CAN LTD, 81- *Mem:* Chem Inst Can; Am Chem Soc; Sigma Xi; Can Nuclear Soc. *Res:* Fundamental processes in radiation chemistry; electron spin resonance; leaching; nuclide sorption; ion exchange; geochemical and geophysical aspects of nuclear waste disposal; product and process development for immobilization of nuclear waste. *Mailing Add:* Atomic Energy of Can Ltd Pinawa MB R0E 1L0 Can

SARGENT, GORDON ALFRED, b Winterton, Eng, Apr 8, 38; m 66; c 7. MATERIALS SCIENCE. *Educ:* Univ London, BSc, 60, DIC, 63, PhD(metall), 64; Royal Sch Mines, ARSM, 60. *Prof Exp:* Res fel, Mellon Inst, 63-67; from asst prof to assoc prof mat sci, 67-77, PROF METALL ENG & MAT SCI, UNIV KY, 77-, CHMN DEPT, 81- *Mem:* Am Soc Metals; Am Inst Mining, Metall & Petrol Engrs. *Res:* Deformation and physical properties of materials under high pressures; properties of materials subjected to irradiation damage. *Mailing Add:* Dept of Metall Univ of Ky Lexington KY 40506

SARGENT, HOWARD HARROP, III, b Hartford, Conn, June 12, 36; m 68; c 2. SOLAR-TERRESTRIAL PHYSICS. *Educ:* Univ Conn, BS, 63; Univ Colo, MS, 72. *Prof Exp:* Engr-in-charge ionospheric physics, Nat Bur Standards, S Pole Sta, Antarctica, 63-64; res asst, Stanford Univ, 65-66; instrumentation engr, Environ Sci Serv Admin, 68-71; instrumentation engr solar radio astron, 71-73, gen phys scientist solar physics, 73-77, SPACE SCIENTIST SOLAR PHYSICS, NAT OCEANIC & ATMOSPHERIC ADMIN, 77- *Honors & Awards:* NOAA Spec Achievement Award, Nat Oceanic & Atmospheric Admin, 75. *Mem:* AAAS; Am Geophys Union; Am Meteorol Soc. *Res:* Geophysical, including weather, effects of solar activity; intra-cycle changes in solar behavior; solar and geomagnetic activity prediction techniques; long-term solar variability; time series analysis. *Mailing Add:* Space Environ Lab 325 S Broadway Boulder CO 80303

SARGENT, KENNETH ALBERT, b Ellsworth, Maine, Aug 16, 32; m 54; c 3. GEOLOGY. *Educ:* Bates Col, BS, 54; Univ Iowa, MS, 57, PhD(geol), 60. *Prof Exp:* Instr field geol, Univ Iowa, 60; petrol geologist, Texaco, Inc, 60-62; geologist Spec Proj Br, 62-72, supvr Tech Reports Unit, 72-75, GEOLOGIST CENT ENVIRON BR, US GEOL SURV, 75- *Mem:* Fel Geol Soc Am. *Res:* Volcanic rock petrography and petrology; geology of south central Utah. *Mailing Add:* US Geol Surv Mail Stop 913 Bldg 25 Fed Ctr Denver CO 80225

SARGENT, LOWRIE BARNETT, JR, physical chemistry, tribology, deceased

SARGENT, MALCOLM LEE, b Grayling, Mich, Sept 14, 37; c 3. BIOCHEMICAL GENETICS: BIOLOGICAL RHYTHMS. *Educ:* Univ Mich, BS, 60; Stanford Univ, PhD(biol), 66. *Prof Exp:* NIH fel bot, Univ Mich, 66-68; asst prof bot, 68-73, ASSOC PROF GENETICS & DEVELOP, UNIV ILL, URBANA, 73- *Mem:* Am Bryolog & Lichenological Soc; Am Soc Plant Physiol; Genetics Soc Am. *Res:* Biochemical-genetics of circadian rhythms and development in Neurospora and other fungi; reproductive and developmental physiology of bryophytes. *Mailing Add:* Dept of Genetics & Develop Univ of Ill Urbana IL 61801

SARGENT, MURRAY, III, b New York, NY, Aug 18, 41; m 67; c 2. QUANTUM OPTICS, COMPUTER SCIENCE. *Educ:* Yale Univ, BS, 63, MS, 64, PhD(physics), 67. *Prof Exp:* Fel physics, Yale Univ, 67; mem tech staff, Bell Tel Labs, 67-69; asst prof optical sci, 69-72, assoc prof optical sci & comput sci, 72-74, assoc prof, 74-77, PROF OPTICAL SCI, UNIV ARIZ, 77- *Concurrent Pos:* Gast prof, Univ Stuttgart & Max Planck Inst, 75-76. *Honors & Awards:* Humboldt Award, Fed Repub Ger, 75. *Mem:* Am Phys Soc; fel Optical Soc Am. *Res:* Laser physics and applications; micro computer systems; technical word processing systems. *Mailing Add:* Dept of Optical Sci Univ of Ariz Tucson AZ 85721

SARGENT, NICHOLAS E, b New York, NY, Dec 13, 16; m 43; c 3. RADIOLOGY. *Educ:* NY Univ, BS, 36, MD, 40; Am Bd Radiol, dipl, 47. *Prof Exp:* Intern, Los Angeles County-Univ Southern Calif Med Ctr, 40-41; resident, Kings County Hosp, New York, 41-42, Bellevue Hosp, 42, St Louis City Hosp, Army Sch Roentgenol & Mayo Clin, 42-47; assoc radiologist, Orange County Med Ctr, Calif, 58-60, dir radiol, 63-67; assoc prof, 67-70, PROF RADIOL, SCH MED, UNIV SOUTHERN CALIF, 70- *Concurrent Pos:* Consult, various private & naval hosps & Long Beach, Calif, 64-, Barlow Chest Sanitarium, Los Angeles, 67-, Lavina Hosp, Los Angeles, 67-, Los Alamitos Naval Hosp, Long Beach, 67-, Pneumoconiosis Prog, USPHS Panel, 71- & US Naval Hosp, Bethesda, Md, 77-; instr, US Navy Asbestos Prog. *Mem:* Fel Am Col Radiol; AMA; Am Roentgen Ray Soc; NY Acad Sci; Asn Univ Radiol. *Res:* Radiology of chest diseases; gastrointestinal diseases. *Mailing Add:* LAC/USC Med Ctr 1200 N State St Box 677 Los Angeles CA 90033

SARGENT, ROBERT GEORGE, b Port Huron, Mich, June 14, 37; m 70; c 1. OPERATIONS RESEARCH, INDUSTRIAL ENGINEERING. *Educ:* Univ Mich, BSE, 59, MS, 63, PhD(indust eng), 66. *Prof Exp:* Electronics engr, Hughes Aircraft Co, 59-61; grad asst & lectr eng, Univ Mich, 62-66; asst prof, 66-70, assoc prof, 70-82, PROF INDUST ENG & OPERS RES, SYRACUSE UNIV, 82- *Concurrent Pos:* Vis assoc prof, Cornell Univ, 81-82. *Mem:* Opers Res Soc Am; Inst Mgt Sci; Am Inst Indust Engrs; Assoc Comput Mach; Inst Elec & Electronics Engrs. *Res:* Digital simulation; modelling and performance evaluation of computer systems; scheduling; production and inventory control; model validation. *Mailing Add:* Dept Indust Eng & Opers Res Syracuse Univ Syracuse NY 13210

SARGENT, ROGER GARY, b Sandborn, Ind, Mar 7, 39; m 62; c 2. PARASITOLOGY. *Educ:* Ind State Univ, BS, 62, MS, 64; Univ SC, PhD(parasitol), 71. *Prof Exp:* Off Econ Opportunity fel malnutrit & parasitism, 70-71, dir fac res develop & lectr biol, 71-74, asst dean, Col Health & Phys Educ, 74-81, ASSOC PROF BIOL, UNIV SC, 74-, ASSOC DEAN COL HEALTH, 81- *Concurrent Pos:* Jannsen Pharmaceut fel clin drug eval, 71-72, res grant, 75; mem, Nat Coun Univ Res Adminr. *Mem:* Am Soc Parasitol; Am Zool Soc; Am Asn Health, Phys Educ & Recreation; Sigma Xi. *Res:* Intestinal parasites Ascaris lumbricoides and Trichuris trichura with emphasis in drug regimens and ovicidal effects of various compounds; comparative drug studies establishing efficacy of current drugs of choice for Ascaris lumbricoides to investigational drugs. *Mailing Add:* Col of Health & Phys Educ Univ of SC Columbia SC 29208

SARGENT, ROGER N, b Stelton, NJ, June 3, 28; m 52; c 2. ANALYTICAL CHEMISTRY, PHYSICAL CHEMISTRY. *Educ:* Lafayette Col, BS, 51; Rutgers Univ, PhD(anal chem), 56. *Prof Exp:* Shift supvr styrene control lab, Koppers Co, 51-52; asst chem, Rutgers Univ, 52-56, res fel, 56-57; sr res chemist ion exchange div, Dow Chem CO, Mich, 57-68, group leader anal chem, 68-76, sr res specialist, Human Health Res & Develop Lab, 76-80; MEM FAC, COL HEALTH PHYS EDUC, UNIV SC, 80- *Mem:* Am Chem Soc; Sigma Xi. *Res:* Chromotographic separation and purification of organic compounds with ion exchange resins; ion-exchange chromatography and exclusion; salting-out chromatography. *Mailing Add:* Col Health Phys Educ Univ SC Columbia SC 29208

SARGENT, THEODORE DAVID, b Peabody, Mass, Oct 25, 36; m 67; c 2. ZOOLOGY. *Educ:* Univ Mass, BS, 58; Univ Wis, MS, 60, PhD(zool), 63. *Prof Exp:* Instr zool, 63-64, from asst prof to assoc prof, 64-75, PROF ZOOL, UNIV MASS, AMHERST, 75- *Concurrent Pos:* Ed, J. Lepidop Soc, 72-74. *Mem:* Am Ornith Union; Animal Behav Soc; Soc Study Evolution; Lepidop Soc (pres, 79). *Res:* Cryptic moths, behavior, ecology, genetics; melanism in North American moths; bird behavior; moths of the genus catocala. *Mailing Add:* Dept of Zool Univ of Mass Amherst MA 01003

SARGENT, THORNTON WILLIAM, III, b St Louis, Mo, June 25, 28; m 52; c 2. NUCLEAR MEDICINE, BIOCHEMICAL PHARMACOLOGY. *Educ:* Reed Col, BA, 51; Univ Calif, Berkeley, PhD(radiobiol), 59. *Prof Exp:* Physicist, Michelson Lab, US Naval Ord Test Sta, Calif, 51-52; res biophysicist, 59-77, STAFF SR SCIENTIST, DONNER LAB, LAWRENCE BERKELEY LAB, UNIV CALIF, BERKELEY, 77- *Mem:* Soc Nuclear Med; Soc Biol Psychiat; Sigma Xi. *Res:* Whole-body counting of in vivo radionuclides in medical research; chromium metabolism in diabetes; iron absorption in henatologic disorders and iron storage diseases; metabolism of schizophrenia and manic depressive illness by in vivo positron emission tomography and respiration analysis of radioisotope labelled bioamine metabolites. *Mailing Add:* Donner Lab Univ of Calif Berkeley CA 94720

SARGENT, WALLACE LESLIE WILLIAM, b Elsham, Eng, Feb 15, 35; m 64; c 2. ASTROPHYSICS. *Educ:* Univ Manchester, BSc, 56, MSc, 57, PhD(astron), 59. *Prof Exp:* Res fel astron, Calif Inst Technol, 59-62; sr res fel, Royal Greenwich Observ, Eng, 62-64; asst prof physics, Univ Calif, San Diego, 64-66; from asst prof to prof astron, 66-81, exec officer, 75-81, IRA S BOWEN PROF ASTRON, CALIF INST TECHNOL, 81- *Concurrent Pos:* Hon vis fel, Australian Nat Univ, 65 & 67; vis fel, Cambridge Univ, 68-72, 74-75 & 79, Oxford Univ, 73, Univ Groningen, 78 & Univ Florence, 81; Alfred P Sloan Found fel, 68-70; mem staff, Owens Valley Radio Observ, 78- *Honors & Awards:* Helen B Warner Prize, Am Astron Soc, 69. *Mem:* Am Astron Soc; fel Am Acad Arts & Sci; fel Royal Astron Soc; Int Astron Union. *Res:* Stellar and extragalactic spectroscopy; evolution of galaxies; clusters of galaxies; quasars. *Mailing Add:* Dept of Astron Calif Inst of Technol Pasadena CA 91125

SARGENT, WILLIAM QUIRK, b Bell, Calif, Jan 26, 45; m 69; c 3. FLUID METABOLISM, ELECTROLYTE METABOLISM. *Educ:* Johns Hopkins Univ, BA, 67; Univ Tenn, PhD(physiol), 73. *Prof Exp:* USPHS trainee, Col Basic Med Sci, Univ Tenn, 69-71, teaching fel, 71-73; fel, Alcohol & Drug Res Ctr, Tenn Psychol Hosp, 73-75; ASST PROF PHYSIOL & PSYCHIAT, UNIV TENN CTR HEALTH SCI MEMPHIS, 75- *Mem:* Am Physiol Soc. *Res:* Renal and gastrointestinal electrolyte metabolism during long term drug administrations (ie, ethanol). *Mailing Add:* Alcohol & Drug Res Ctr 865 Poplar Ave PO Box 4966 Memphis TN 38104

SARGES, REINHARD, b Siegen, Ger, July 25, 35; US citizen; m 80; c 2. ORGANIC CHEMISTRY. *Educ:* Univ Frankfurt, dipl, 60, PhD(peptide chem), 62. *Prof Exp:* Vis fel chem, NIH, 62-64, vis assoc, 64-65; res chemist, 65-75, proj leader, 75-81, PRIN INVESTR, PFIZER INC, 81- *Mem:* Am Chem Soc. *Res:* Peptide and medicinal chemistry; biochemistry. *Mailing Add:* Pfizer Inc Eastern Point Rd Groton CT 06340

SARI, JAMES WILLIAM, b Buffalo, NY, Oct 13, 42; m 71. SPACE SCIENCE, PLASMA PHYSICS. *Educ:* Oberlin Col, BA, 64; Univ Md, PhD(physics), 72. *Prof Exp:* Physicist plasma physics, Cornell Aeronaut Lab, 72-77; SR PHYSICIST, APPL PHYSICS LAB, JOHNS HOPKINS UNIV, 77- *Mem:* Am Geophys Union. *Res:* Interplanetary magnetic fields; cosmic-ray propagation; geomagnetic micropulsations; ocean magnetic fields. *Mailing Add:* Appl Physics Lab Johns Hopkins Rd Laurel MD 20810

SARI, SEPPO OLIVER, b Helsinki, Finland, Mar 13, 45; m 67; c 2. ELECTROOPTICS. *Educ:* Univ Wash, Seattle, BS, 67; Princeton Univ, MS, 68, PhD(physics), 71. *Prof Exp:* Res assoc, Mass Inst Technol, 71-72, instr, 72-75; asst prof optics, Univ Ariz, 75-79; assoc prof, Ore State Univ, 79-80; MEM TECH STAFF ELECTROOPTICS, ROCKWELL SCI CTR, 80- *Concurrent Pos:* Prin investr, Div Mat, Dept Energy, 75-80, Avionics Div, Wright Patterson Aerunaut Lab, 81- *Mem:* Optical Soc Am; Am Phys Soc; Soc Photo-Optical Instrumentation Engrs. *Res:* Thin films; electro and magneto optics; laser detectors; non-linear optics; author or coauthor of over 30 publications. *Mailing Add:* Rockwell Sci Ctr 1049 Camino dos Rios Thousand Oaks CA 91360

SARIAN, EDWARD, mathematics, computer science, see previous edition

SARIC, WILLIAM SAMUEL, b Chicago, Ill, Sept 28, 40; m 62; c 1. HYDRODYNAMIC STABILITY. *Educ:* Ill Inst Technol, Bs, 63, PhD(mech), 68; Univ NMex, MS, 65. *Prof Exp:* Staff mem environ testing, Sandia Labs, 63-66; instr, Ill Inst Technol, 66-68; staff mem, Sandia Labs, 68-75; assoc prof, 75-79, PROF MECH ENG, VA POLYTECH INST & STATE UNIV, 79- *Concurrent Pos:* Adj prof, Univ NMex, 72 & Va Polytech Inst & State Univ, 74-75; mem, Nat Tech Comt Fluid Dynamics, Am Inst Aeronaut & Astronaut, 75-78; consult, Sanda Labs, 75-81, Ecodynamics Corp, 76, Ballistic Res Labs, 76 & Lockheed-Ga, 77-; invited guest & researcher, USSR Acad Sci, 76 & 81. *Mem:* Assoc fel Am Inst Aeronaut & Astronaut; Am Phys Soc; Am Soc Mech Engrs; Am Soc Eng Educ. *Res:* Hydrodynamic stability; boundary-layer transition; nonlinear waves; nonlinear dynamics; transpiration cooling; boundary-layer flows; laminar flow control; electron-beam induced nuclear fusion; stability of stratified flows. *Mailing Add:* Eng Sci & Mech Dept Va Polytech Inst & State Univ Blacksburg VA 24061

SARICH, VINCENT M, b Chicago, Ill, Dec 13, 34; m 61; c 2. PHYSICAL ANTHROPOLOGY. *Educ:* Ill Inst Technol, BS, 55; Univ Calif, Berkeley, PhD(anthrop), 67. *Prof Exp:* Instr anthrop, Stanford Univ, 65; asst prof, 67-70, assoc prof, 70-81, PROF ANTHROP, UNIV CALIF, BERKELEY, 81- *Mem:* AAAS; Am Asn Phys Anthrop; Am Soc Mammal. *Res:* Construction of quantitative phylogenies by the use of comparative molecular data; evolutionary and selective bases of human variation. *Mailing Add:* Dept of Anthrop Univ of Calif Berkeley CA 94720

SARID, DROR, b Haifa, Israel, Dec 13, 38; US citizen; m 63; c 2. NONLINEAR GUIDED WAVE OPTICS. *Educ:* Hebrew Univ, Jerusalem, BSc, 66, MSc, 68, PhD(physics), 72. *Prof Exp:* Fel physics, Univ Calif, Santa Barbara, 72-74; scientist, Xerox Webster Res Ctr, 74-78; sr lectr, Hebrew Univ, Jerusalem, 78-80; PROF PHYSICS, OPTICAL SCI CTR, UNIV ARIZ, 80- *Concurrent Pos:* Consult, EG&G, Santa Barbara, 74; vis scholar, Univ Calif, Santa Barbara, 75; consult, Xerox Webster Res Ctr, 78-81, US Army, 81-82. *Mem:* Optical Soc Am; Soc Photo-Optical Instrumentation Engrs. *Res:* Surface plasma waves; laser light scattering and critical phenomena, surface acoustic waves, nonlinear optics and surface plasma waves. *Mailing Add:* Optical Sci Ctr Univ Ariz Tucson AZ 85721

SARIDIS, GEORGE N, b Athens, Greece, Nov 17, 31. ELECTRICAL ENGINEERING. *Educ:* Athens Tech Univ, Dipl, 55; Purdue Univ, MSEE, 62, PhD(optimal control), 65. *Prof Exp:* Instr elec mach, Athens Tech Univ, 55-63; from instr to prof elec eng, Purdue Univ, West Lafayette, 63-81; PROF ELEC, CIVIL & SYSTS ENG & DIR, ROBOTICS & AUTOMATION LAB, RENSSELAER POLYTECH INST, 81- *Concurrent Pos:* Mem, Technol Chamber of Greece, 55; engr, Telecommun Orgn Greece, 55-56 & Pub Power Corp Greece, 57-63. *Mem:* Fel Inst Elec & Electronics Engrs; NY Acad Sci. *Res:* Optimal control theory and applications; adaptive and learning systems; self-organizing control systems; bioengineering systems; prosthetics and robotics; intelligent systems. *Mailing Add:* Dept Elec Civil & Systs Eng Rensselaer Polytech Inst Troy NY 12181

SARIN, PREM S, b Sohana, India; m 65; c 2. BIOCHEMISTRY, MOLECULAR BIOLOGY. *Educ:* Univ Delhi, BSc, 54, MSc, 56, PhD(chem), 59; Cambridge Univ, PhD(chem), 62. *Prof Exp:* Lectr chem, Univ Delhi, 57-60; res fel, Harvard Univ, 63-65; biochemist, Univ Toronto, 65-67; head sect nucleic acids, Merck Inst, NJ, 67-70; dir molecular biol, Litton Bionetics, Md, 71-72; vis scientist, 72-74, ASSOC CHIEF LAB TUMOR CELL BIOL, NAT CANCER INST, 74- *Mem:* Am Soc Cell Biol; Am Chem Soc; Am Soc Microbiol; Am Soc Biol Chem; Am Asn Cancer Res. *Res:* Nucleic acids and enzymes of nucleic acids metabolism; oncogenic viruses; cancer chemotherapy; etiology of cancer, especially human leukemia. *Mailing Add:* Lab of Tumor Cell Biol Nat Cancer Inst Bethesda MD 20014

SARIN, VIRENDER KUMAR, b Kanpur, India, Mar 11, 52. PEPTIDES, PROTEINS. *Educ:* Delhi Univ, BS, 72, MS, 74; City Univ NY, PhD(org chem), 78. *Prof Exp:* Fel, 78-79, RES ASSOC ORG CHEM, ROCKEFELLER UNIV, 79- *Mem:* Am Chem Soc; Sigma Xi. *Res:* Synthesis of peptides and proteins using solid phase peptide synthesis; synthesizing peptide-protein conjugates which are eventually used to raise antibodies against the synthetic peptide. *Mailing Add:* Rockefeller Univ 1230 York Ave New York NY 10021

SARIO, LEO REINO, b Finland, May 18, 16; nat US; m 41; c 3. MATHEMATICS. *Educ:* Univ Helsinki, AM, 41, PhD(math), 48. *Prof Exp:* Lectr math, Univ Helsinki, 45-48; res fel, Finland Acad, 48-50; vis mem, Inst Advan Study, 50-52; res fel, Harvard Univ, 52-54; assoc prof, 54-58, PROF MATH, UNIV CALIF, LOS ANGELES, 58- *Concurrent Pos:* Vis assoc prof, Mass Inst Technol, 54-; Guggenheim fel, 57-58. *Honors & Awards:* Cross of Comdr of Order of Finland's Knighthood, 58. *Mem:* Am Math Soc; Math Asn Am; Math Soc France. *Res:* Theory of Riemann surfaces and Riemannian spaces. *Mailing Add:* Dept of Math Univ of Calif Los Angeles CA 90024

SARJEANT, PETER THOMSON, b Orillia, Ont, June 24, 29; m 56; c 2. PAPER CHEMISTRY, ENGINEERING. *Educ:* Queens Univ, BSc, 53, MSc, 56; Pa State Univ, PhD(mat sci), 67. *Prof Exp:* Prod supvr pharmaceut, Merck Sharpe & Dohme, 54-57; res engr wood prod, 57-60, prod develop supvr lignin prod, 60-63, res chemist electrocopy, 63-64, res chemist paper coatings, 67-69, group leader, 69-70, assoc res dir, 70-71, res dir, 71-78, SECT LEADER WOOD CHEM PROD, WESTVACO CORP, 78- *Mem:* Tech Asn Pulp & Paper Indust; Am Chem Soc. *Res:* Process control of papermaking and chemical recovery processing; wood pulping processes; refining; cleaning; fourdrinier optimization; converting equipment for paper and board; history of papermaking; wood by-product chemicals. *Mailing Add:* Res Ctr Westvaco Corp Charleston SC 29406

SARJEANT, WILLIAM ANTONY SWITHIN, b Sheffield, Eng, July 15, 35; m 66; c 3. PALEONTOLOGY, HISTORY OF GEOLOGY. *Educ:* Univ Sheffield, BSc Hons, 56, PhD(geol), 59; Univ Nottingham, DSc(geol), 72. *Prof Exp:* Demonstr temp lectr geol, Univ Col N Staffordshire, Eng, 60-61; res fel, Univ Reading, 61-62; from asst lectr to lectr, Univ Nottingham, 63-72; assoc prof, 72-80, PROF GEOL SCI, UNIV SASK, 80- *Concurrent Pos:* Vis prof geol & geophys, Univ Okla, 68-69. *Mem:* Fel Geol Soc London; fel Linnean Soc London; Geol Soc France; Paleont Asn; Am Asn Stratigraphical Palynologists. *Res:* Dinoflagellate cysts and acritarchs of the Jurassic and Cretaceous, Great Britain, France, Greenland, Algeria, Iran and Canada; fossil vertebrate footprints and trace-fossil classification; history and bibliography of the geological sciences; history of science. *Mailing Add:* Univ of Sask Dept of Geol Sci Gen Purpose Bldg Rm 108/2 Saskatoon SK S7N 0W0 Can

SARKANEN, KYOSTI VILHO, b Helsinki, Finland, Sept 25, 21; US citizen; m 45; c 2. WOOD CHEMISTRY, PULP CHEMISTRY. *Educ:* Univ Helsinki, BSc, 47; Syracuse Univ, MSc, 52, PhD(org chem), 56. *Prof Exp:* Res asst org chem cent lab, Finnish P&P Industs, 47-53; lab dir process control, Kajaani Ltd, Finland, 53-54; fel chem, Syracuse Univ, 56-57; assoc prof wood chem, State Univ NY Col Forestry, Syracuse, 57-61; PROF CHEM ENG, UNIV WASH, 61- *Mem:* Am Chem Soc; Tech Asn Pulp & Paper Indust. *Res:* General lignin chemistry; alkaline degradation of polysaccharides; environmental emissions from pulp mills; delignification by oxygen. *Mailing Add:* Col of Forest Resources Univ of Wash Seattle WA 98195

SARKAR, BIBUDHENDRA, b Kushtia, India, Aug 2, 35; m 65; c 2. BIOCHEMISTRY, Physical CHEMISTRY. *Educ:* Banares Univ, India, BPharm, 56, MPharm, 57; Univ Southern Calif, PhD(biochem), 64. *Prof Exp:* Vis prof, Inst Phys Chem Biol, Univ Paris, 76-77 & Cambridge, 77; PROF, UNIV TORONTO, 78- *Concurrent Pos:* Med Res Coun Can res scholar, 65-Concurrent. *Mem:* AAAS; Can Biochem Soc; Am Chem Soc; NY Acad Sci; Am Soc Biol Chemists. *Res:* Chemical and physico chemical studies related to coordination compounds of metals with proteins, peptides, amino acids, sugars and nucleic acids conducted for understanding their biochemical role in physiological systems and pathological conditions; molecular design to mimic functional sites of biomolecules. *Mailing Add:* Res Inst Hosp for Sick Children 555 University Ave Toronto ON M5G 1X8 Can

SARKAR, KAMALAKSHA, b Calcutta, India, Sept 27, 47; m 78; c 1. COMPUTER-AIDED DESIGN. *Educ:* Bengal Eng Col, Sibpur, India, BE, 68; Indian Inst Technol, Kanpur, MTech, 74; Univ Tenn, Knoxville, PhD(eng sci), 80. *Prof Exp:* Structural engr, Indian Space Res Orgn, Trivandrum, 69-74; DEVELOP ENGR, ALLIED CORP, MORRISTOWN, NJ, 80- *Mem:* Am Inst Aeronaut & Astronaut; Am Soc Mech Engrs. *Res:* Computer-aided design to develop materials and components using an interdisciplinary approach (mechanical, structural, metallurgical and materials); composite material; fracture mechanics; robotics. *Mailing Add:* L 31 Gateways 44 Center Grove Rd Randolph NJ 07869

SARKAR, NILIMA, b India, June 2, 35; US citizen; m 61; c 2. MOLECULAR BIOLOGY. *Educ:* Univ Calcutta, India, BS, 53, MS, 55; Northwestern Univ, PhD(biochem), 61. *Prof Exp:* Fel, Dept Biochem, Univ Chicago, 61-63; fel, Dept Microbiol, Tufts Univ, 63-64; res fel, 64-67, res assoc, 67-69, assoc, 69-75, LECTR, DEPT BIOL CHEM, HARVARD MED SCH, 75-; STAFF SCIENTIST, DEPT METABOLIC REGULATION, BOSTON BIOMED RES INST, 76- *Mem:* Am Soc Biol Chemists; Am Soc Cell Biol; Am Chem Soc; AAAS. *Res:* Mechanisms of replication of the chromosome, especially in relation to the involvement of RNA primers; poly(A) RNA in bacteria with respect to structure, function and biosynthesis, using the technique of cloning of DNA. *Mailing Add:* Dept Metabolic Regulation Boston Biomed Res Inst 20 Stanford St Boston MA 02114

SARKAR, NITIS, b Gauhati, India, Dec 1, 38; m 70; c 2. WATER SOLUBLE POLYMERS, MINERAL ENGINEERING. *Educ:* Gauhati Univ, India, BS, 57; Univ Calcutta, MS, 60; Mass Inst Technol, ScD(mineral eng), 65. *Prof Exp:* Res trainee, Fuel Res Inst, India, 60-61; lectr, Barasat Govt Col, 61-62; res asst, Mass Inst Technol, 62-65; res chemist chem lab, Dow Chem Co, 65-68 & Betz Labs, Inc, 68; RES SPECIALIST, DESIGNED POLYMERS & CHEM RES, DOW CHEM CO, 68- *Mem:* Am Chem Soc. *Res:* Flocculation; water treatment; characterization of water soluble polymers; rheology of polymer solutions; detergency; dispersion; adhesion; paints; latexes; thickeners; enhanced oil recovery, cellulosic polymers, surface and colloid chemistry flotation; use of polymer in food; suspension polymerization. *Mailing Add:* 1604 Bldg Dow Chem USA Midland MI 48640

SARKAR, NURUL HAQUE, b Naroshingapur, WBengal, India, Aug 5, 37; m 65; c 2. BIOPHYSICS, ONCOLOGY. *Educ:* Univ Calcutta, BSc, 57, MSc, 60, PhD(biophysics), 66. *Prof Exp:* Lectr physics, Grad Sch, Univ Calcutta, 61-67; res fel biophys, Inst Med Res, 67-68, res assoc, 68-69, assoc mem, 71-73; ASSOC MEM, SLOAN-KETTERING INST CANCER RES, 73-, ASSOC PROF BIOL, SLOAN-KETTERING DIV, CORNELL UNIV, 75-, MEM, CORNELL DIV, 81- *Concurrent Pos:* Res scholar, Biophys Div, Saha Inst Nuclear Physics, Calcutta, 61-67; vis asst prof, Univ Pa, 69-72, asst prof, 72-75; mem, Exp Biol Comt, Breast Cancer Task Force, NIH, 76-79; chmn biol unit, Sloan-Kettering Div, Cornell Univ, 77-78. *Mem:* Electron Micros Soc Am; Am Soc Microbiol. *Res:* Ultrastructure, biochemical and immunological studies of the oncogenic RNA tumor viruses; search for the causative agent(s) responsible for breast cancer in humans and the characterization of such an agent or agents. *Mailing Add:* Sloan-Kettering Inst Cancer Res 1275 York Ave New York NY 10021

SARKAR, PRIYABRATA, b Comilla, India, May 1, 29; Can citizen; m 55; c 3. PLANT CYTOGENETICS. *Educ:* Univ Calcutta, BSc, 49, MSc, 51; Univ Man, PhD(plant cytogenetics), 55. *Prof Exp:* Res assoc plant cytogenetics, Univ Man, 55-56 & Univ Montreal, 56-57; asst cytogeneticist, Indian Agr Res Inst, 58-59; sr res officer, Forest Res Inst, India, 59; lectr bot, 60-62, asst prof, 62-68, grad secy, 66-69, ASSOC PROF BOT, UNIV TORONTO, 68- *Mem:* Genetics Soc Can. *Res:* Cytogenetics and cytotaxonomy of species in Triticeae; karyotype analysis in species of pine and some species in Liliaceae. *Mailing Add:* Dept of Bot Univ of Toronto Toronto ON M5S 2R8 Can

SARKES, LOUIS A(NTHONY), b New Bedford, Mass, June 15, 25; m 55; c 3. NUCLEAR PHYSICS, GAS ENERGY. *Educ:* Boston Col, BS, 51, MS, 54. *Prof Exp:* Radio isotope physicist gamma spectros, Boston Vet Admin Hosp, 51-54; mgr qual assurance nuclear eng, M & C Nuclear, Inc, 55-65; dir res & eng natural gas res, 65-78, VPRES ENG, AM GAS ASN, 78- *Concurrent Pos:* Res assoc, Boston Col, 51-52 & Brown Univ, 53-55; corp assoc, Am Inst Physics, 66-76; panelist, NSF, 74 & Nat Bur Standards, 77-78. *Mem:* Am Inst Physics; Am Soc Testing & Mat; Am Nuclear Soc; Soc Nondestructive Testing. *Res:* Gamma ray spectroscopy; particle reactions; nuclear reactor design and engineering; natural gas research, primarily combustion and cryogenics. *Mailing Add:* Am Gas Asn 1515 Wilson Blvd Arlington VA 22209

SARKO, ANATOLE, b Tallinn, Estonia, May 27, 30; m 55; c 1. POLYMER CHEMISTRY, POLYMER PHYSICS. *Educ:* Upsala Col, BS, 52; NY Univ, MS, 60; State Univ NY Col Forestry, Syracuse, PhD(phys chem), 66. *Prof Exp:* Mem biochem staff, Gen Foods Corp, NY, 52-60, sr chemist, 60-63; res assoc chem, 66-67, from asst prof to assoc prof, 67-76, PROF CHEM, STATE UNIV NY COL ENVIRON & FORESTRY, 76- *Mem:* AAAS; Am Chem Soc; Am Phys Soc. *Res:* Physical chemistry of polymers; conformation of polysaccharides in solid and solution states and their structure-function relationships; x-ray techniques of polymers; computer techniques in chemistry. *Mailing Add:* Dept of Chem State Univ of NY Col of Environ Sci & Forestry Syracuse NY 13210

SARLES, F(REDERICK) WILLIAMS, JR, b Cincinnati, Ohio, Sept 27, 31; m 60; c 2. ELECTRICAL ENGINEERING. *Educ:* Duke Univ, BSEE, 53; Mass Inst Technol, MS, 55, ScD(elec eng), 61. *Prof Exp:* Res asst comput components & systs group, 53-61, mem staff div sponsored res, 61, mem staff space commun, Lincoln Lab, 61-69, asst group leader, 69-71, GROUP LEADER SPACE COMMUN, LINCOLN LAB, MASS INST TECHNOL, 71- *Concurrent Pos:* Lectr, Northeastern Univ, 67-71. *Mem:* Sr mem Inst Elec & Electronics Engrs; Am Inst Aeronaut & Astronaut. *Res:* Design of control and communication systems; telemetry systems; design of space experiments. *Mailing Add:* Lincoln Lab Mass Inst of Technol 244 Wood St Lexington MA 02173

SARLES, LYNN REDMON, b Grand Forks, NDak, Jan 22, 30; m 51; c 4. PHYSICS, RESEARCH ADMINISTRATION. *Educ:* Stanford Univ, PhD(physics), 57. *Prof Exp:* Sloan fel physics, Univ Calif, 57-58; res physicist, Varian Assocs, 58-62; mgr phys optics, Interphase Corp, 62-63; mgr geophys res, Varian Assocs, 63-67; dir admin, Ore Grad Ctr, 67-68, vpres, 68-72; VPRES RES, SYSTS MGT ASSOCS, INC, 72- *Mem:* Fel AAAS; Am Phys Soc. *Res:* Magnetic resonance; optical pumping; geomagnetism; lasers; instrumentation; technological forecasting. *Mailing Add:* 2855 W 107th Ave Portland OR 97225

SARLES, WILLIAM BOWEN, b Viroqua, Wis, Oct 1, 06; m 27; c 2. MICROBIOLOGY. *Educ:* Univ Wis, BS, 26, MS, 27, PhD(agr bact), 31. *Prof Exp:* Asst, Univ Wis, 26; instr bact, Kans State Col, 27-29; instr dairy bact, Iowa State Col, 30-32; from asst prof to assoc prof agr bact, 32-43, prof, 45-72, asst to pres, 45-46, coordr lake invests, 47-54, chmn dept bact, 54-68, EMER PROF AGR BACT, UNIV WIS-MADISON, 72- *Concurrent Pos:* Carnegie vis prof, Univ Hawaii, 59; consult, US Dept Defense; Soc Am Bact rep, Nat Res Coun, 45-49; ed, J Bact, Am Soc Microbiol, 61-65. *Honors & Awards:* Officer, Order British Empire. *Mem:* Fel AAAS; Am Soc Microbiol (vpres, 65-66, pres, 66-67, secy-treas, Soc Bact, 42-43); fel Am Acad Microbiol. *Res:* Intestinal microorganisms; disinfectants; ecology of microorganisms. *Mailing Add:* 5505 Barton Rd Madison WI 53711

SARMA, DITTAKAVI S R, b Tenali, India, June 15, 36; m 72. BIOCHEMISTRY, EXPERIMENTAL PATHOLOGY. *Educ:* Andhra Univ, India, BSc, 54; Univ Nagpur, MSc, 57; Univ Madras, PhD(biochem), 62. *Prof Exp:* Coun Sci & Indust Res sr res fel, Dept Biochem, Indian Inst Sci, Bangalore, 62-65; res assoc exp path, Sch Med, Univ Pittsburgh, 65-70, asst res prof, 70-71; asst res prof chem carcinogenesis, Fels Res Inst, Med Sch, Temple Univ, 71-77; ASSOC PROF PATH, UNIV TORONTO, 77- *Mem:* Am Soc Exp Path; Am Asn Cancer Res; Environ Mutagen Soc; NY Acad Sci. *Res:* Chemical carcinogenesis; DNA repair. *Mailing Add:* Dept Path Med Sci Bldg Univ Toronto Toronto ON M5S 2R8 Can

SARMA, PADMAN S, b India, Dec 3, 31; US citizen. VIROLOGY, VETERINARY MEDICINE. *Educ:* Madras Vet Col, India, DVM, 53; Univ Minn, MS, 57, PhD(virol), 59. *Prof Exp:* Asst lectr animal husb & microbiol, Madras Vet Col, 53-55; res officer, Pasteur Inst, India, 59-61; asst prof microbiol, Univ Ky, 61-62; vis scientist, NIH, 62-64; proj dir viral carcinogenesis, Microbiol Assoc Inc, 64-68; res microbiologist & head ecol & epizool sect, 68-73, chief sect ecol & epizool, Viral Carcinogenesis Br, 73-77, CHIEF ANIMAL VIROL & FIELD STUDIES SECT, LAB CELLULAR & MOLECULAR BIOL, NIH, 77- *Mem:* AAAS; Am Vet Med Asn; Am Soc Exp Path; Soc Exp Biol & Med. *Mailing Add:* Bldg 7 Rm 313 Nat Inst of Health Bethesda MD 20014

SARMA, PRAMOD LAL, b Gandhia, India, Sept 1, 16; nat US; m 47; c 3. ANALYTICAL CHEMISTRY. *Educ:* Univ Calcutta, BSc, 39; Bernares Hindu Univ, MSc, 46; La State Univ, MS, 50, PhD(chem eng), 51. *Prof Exp:* Res assoc chem, La State Univ, 51, fel chem, 54-55; technician, Indust Air Control, Ltd, India, 53-54; asst prof chem, Tex A&M Univ, 55-58 & Eastern Wash State Col, 58-59; from asst prof to assoc prof, Univ NDak, 59-67; PROF CHEM, EDINBORO STATE COL, 67- *Res:* Microanalysis, especially with visible and x-ray spectroscopy and electronic chemical instrumentation. *Mailing Add:* Dept of Chem Edinboro State Col Edinboro PA 16444

SARMA, RAGHUPATHY, b Udipi, India, Feb 18, 37; m 63; c 2. MOLECULAR BIOLOGY, BIOCHEMISTRY. *Educ:* Presidency Col, Madras, BSc, 57; Univ Madras, MSc, 58, PhD(physics), 63. *Prof Exp:* Fel & res assoc, Royal Inst, London, 63-66 & Oxford Univ, 66-68; vis assoc, NIH, 68-71; asst prof, 71-77, assoc prof, 78-80, PROF BIOCHEM, STATE UNIV

NY STONY BROOK, 80- *Mem:* Am Crystallog Asn. *Res:* Structure and function of biological macromolecules; x-ray crystallography; crystallographic computing. *Mailing Add:* Dept of Biochem State Univ of New York Stony Brook NY 11794

SARMA, RAMASWAMY HARIHARA, b Perumbavoor, India, May 10, 39; m 63. BIOCHEMISTRY. *Educ:* Univ Kerala, BSc, 59, MS, 61; Brown Univ, PhD(chem), 67. *Prof Exp:* Fel biochem, Brandeis Univ, 67-69; fel, Univ Calif, San Diego, 69-70; asst prof, 70-75, assoc prof, 75-77, PROF CHEM, STATE UNIV NY ALBANY, 77-, DIR, INST BIOMOLECULAR STEREODYNAMICS, 77-, DIR, CTR BIOL MACROMOLECULES, 81- *Mem:* AAAS; Am Inst Chem; NY Acad Sci; Am Soc Biol Chemists. *Res:* nucleic acid structures and their complexes with anticancer agents. *Mailing Add:* Inst Biomolecular Stereodynamics State Univ of NY at Albany Albany NY 12222

SARNAT, BERNARD GEORGE, b Chicago, Ill, Sept 1, 12; m 41; c 2. PLASTIC SURGERY, CRANIOFACIAL BIOLOGY. *Educ:* Univ Chicago, BS, 33, MD, 37; Univ Ill, MS, 40; Am Bd Plastic Surg, dipl, 47. *Prof Exp:* Asst, Dept Surg, Sch Med, Wash Univ, 44-46; prof & dir, Dept Oral & Plastic Surg, Sch Dent, St Louis Univ, 45-46; private practice, Chicago, 46-56; prof & Head, Dept Oral & Maxillofacial Surg, Col Dent, Univ Ill, Chicago, 46-56, dir grad prog, 48-56, clin asst prof plastic surg, Col Med, 49-56; chief plastic surg, Cedars Div, 64-71, Sinai Div, 71-75, mem, Med Exec Comt, 72-74; chief plastic surg, Med Ctr, 75-81, SR RES SCIENTIST, CEDARS-SINAI MED RES INST, LOS ANGELES, 71- *Concurrent Pos:* Mem attend staff, Barnes Hosp & Children; s Hosp, St Louis, 44-46; mem attend staff, Univ Ill Hosp, Cook Co Hosp, Univ Hosp & Michael Reese Hosp, Chicago, 46-56; adj prof oral biol, Sch Dent, 68-; adj prof & attend plastic surgeon, Dept Surg, Sch Med & Hosp, Univ Calif, Los Angeles, 74- *Honors & Awards:* J A Capps Prize, Inst Med, Chicago, 40; Jr Res Award, Found Am Soc Plastic & Reconstructive Surg, 50, Sr Res Award, 58; Award, Am Rhinologic Soc, 80. *Mem:* Sigma Xi; AAAS; Plastic Surg Res Coun; Am Asn Plastic Surg; Int Asn Dent Res. *Res:* Normal and abnormal postnatal craniofacial growth: sites, patterns, rates and amount. *Mailing Add:* 435 Roxbury Dr Beverly Hills CA 90210

SARNA-WOJCICKI, ANDREI M, b Gdynia, Poland, May 30, 37; US citizen; m 79; c 2. TEPHROCHRONOLOGY, NEOTECTONICS. *Educ:* Columbia Col, NY, BA, 59; Univ Calif, Berkeley, PhD(geol), 71. *Prof Exp:* GEOLOGIST, US GEOL SURV, 71- *Concurrent Pos:* Instr geol, Univ Calif, Berkeley, 71-73. *Res:* Correlation of volcanic ash layers (tephrochronology) in the western United States; assessment of volcanic and seismic hazards in the western United States; volcanic ash dispersal from Mount St Helens, Washington. *Mailing Add:* Br Western Regional Geol MS 75 US Geol Surv Menlo Park CA 94025

SARNER, STANLEY FREDERICK, b New York, NY, Oct 15, 31; m 67; c 2. PHYSICAL CHEMISTRY. *Educ:* City Col New York, BSc, 52; Univ Cincinnati, MSc, 61; Univ Del, PhD, 70. *Prof Exp:* Chemist, Picatinny Arsenal, NJ, 52-54; res chemist flight propulsion units, Gen Elec Co, Ohio, 56-61; sr chemist, Thiokol Chem Corp, Md, 61-66, staff chemist, 66-67; res chemist, F&M Sci Div, Hewlett-Packard Co, Pa, 67-68; res chemist exp sta, E I du Pont de Nemours & Co, Inc, 68-70; res chemist, Chem Data Systs, 70-71; RES CHEMIST, REACTION INSTRUMENTS, 71- *Concurrent Pos:* Sr res assoc & instr chem, Univ Del, 71-; Archmere Acad, 74- *Honors & Awards:* Bendix Aviation Corp Award, 57; Del Award, Am Chem Soc, 70. *Mem:* Am Chem Soc; Am Inst Aeronaut & Astronaut; Brit Interplanetary Soc. *Res:* High temperature reactions; thermodynamics and kinetics; rocket propellants; pyrolysis; gas chromatography; instrument research. *Mailing Add:* 140 Possum Hollow Rd Newark DE 19711

SARNESKI, JOSEPH EDWARD, b East Orange, NJ, Oct 27, 44; m 75. ANALYTICAL CHEMISTRY, INORGANIC CHEMISTRY. *Educ:* Kings Col, BS, 66; Case Western Reserve Univ, PhD(chem), 71. *Prof Exp:* Res assoc, Univ NC, Chapel Hill, 72-75; vis asst prof anal chem, Duke Univ, 75-78; asst prof, 78-80, ASSOC PROF CHEM, FAIRFIELD UNIV, 80- *Mem:* Am Chem Soc. *Res:* Nuclear magnetic resonance; analytical and structural applications; chelate chemistry; conformation analysis; chromatography. *Mailing Add:* Dept of Chem Fairfield Univ Fairfield CT 06430

SAROFF, HARRY ARTHUR, b New York, NY, Mar 8, 14; m 50; c 3. ORGANIC CHEMISTRY. *Educ:* Rensselaer Polytech Inst, BS, 36, MS, 37, PhD(org chem), 40. *Prof Exp:* Res exec chem, US Naval Med Res Inst, 47-50; from chemist to chief sect, 50-74, CHIEF SECT MACROMOLECULES, LAB BIOPHYS CHEM, NAT INST ARTHRITIS & METAB DIS, 74- *Mem:* AAAS; Am Soc Biol Chemists; Biophys Soc; Am Chem Soc. *Res:* Physical chemistry of proteins; protein modification reactions; binding of ions and small molecules to proteins; action of hemoglobin. *Mailing Add:* Lab of Biophys Chem Nat Inst Arthritis & Metab Dis Bethesda MD 20014

SAROFF, JACK, b Chicago, Ill, Nov 19, 25; m 56; c 2. BIOCHEMISTRY, ENDOCRINOLOGY. *Educ:* Univ Vt, BS, 52; Rutgers Univ, MS, 54; Univ Mo, PhD(endocrinol), 57. *Prof Exp:* USPHS trainee, Training Inst Steroid Biochem, Univ Utah, 57-59; res assoc, Med Found Buffalo, 59-66; biochemist, May Inst Med Res, Jewish Hosp, 66-75, BIOCHEMIST, ROSWELL PARK MEM INST, 75- *Concurrent Pos:* Consult, United Health Found Western NY, 64-65; prin & co-investr, NIH, 65-75. *Mem:* AAAS; Endocrine Soc; Am Chem Soc; NY Acad Sci. *Res:* Phyiology of reproduction; steroid metabolism in endocrine disorders; investigation of steroid biochemistry in cardiovascular disease and related endocrine subjects. *Mailing Add:* Roswell Park Mem Inst 666 Elm St Buffalo NY 14263

SAROFIM, ADEL FARES, b Cairo, Egypt, Oct 21, 34; US citizen; m 67. CHEMICAL ENGINEERING. *Educ:* Oxford Univ, BA, 55; Mass Inst Technol, SM, 57, ScD(chem eng), 62. *Prof Exp:* From asst prof to assoc prof chem eng, 61-72, PROF CHEM ENG, MASS INST TECHNOL, 72-, JOSPEH R MARES PROF, 81- *Concurrent Pos:* Chevron vis prof, Calif Inst Technol, 78; comt hazardous wastes in lab, Nat Acad Sci, 81- *Mem:* Am Chem Soc; Am Inst Chem Engrs; Combustion Inst; Solar Energy Soc. *Res:* Radiative heat transfer, combustion, fluidization, gas-solid reactions, aerosol formation. *Mailing Add:* Dept Chem Eng Mass Inst Technol Cambridge MA 02139

SARPHIE, THEODORE G, b Hattiesburg, Miss, July 18, 44; m 73; c 2. HISTOCHEMISTRY. *Educ:* Univ Southern Miss, BS, 66, MS, 68; Univ Miss, PhD(anat & path), 72. *Prof Exp:* Asst prof anat, Univ South Ala, 72-79; ASST PROF ANAT, HAHNEMANN MED COL, 79- *Mem:* Am Soc Cell Biol; Histochem Soc; Am Asn Anatmists. *Res:* Macromolecular response of endothelial cell surfaces to hemodynamic forces and pathological conditions; using transmission and scanning electron microscopy and histo/cytochemistry. *Mailing Add:* Dept Anat 230 N Broad St Hahnemann Med Col & Hosp Philadelphia PA 19102

SARPKAYA, TURGUT, b Turkey, May 7, 28; US citizen; m 62. MECHANICAL ENGINEERING, MATHEMATICS. *Educ:* Tech Univ Istanbul, BS & MS, 50; Univ Iowa, PhD(eng mech), 54. *Prof Exp:* Res engr, Hydrodyn Lab, Mass Inst Technol, 54-55; lectr hydrodyn, Univ Paris, 55-56; from asst prof to prof eng mech, Univ Nebr, Lincoln, 57-64, Fawick prof, 64-66, prof mech eng, 66-67; prof, 67-76, chmn dept, 67-71, DISTINGUISHED PROF MECH ENG, NAVAL POSTGRAD SCH, 76- *Concurrent Pos:* Res vis prof, Univ Manchester; aerodyn res inst, Univ Gottingen, 71-72; Sigma Xi res award, 71. *Honors & Awards:* L F Moody Award, Am Soc Mech Engrs, 67; Collingwood Prize, Am Soc Civil Engrs, 57. *Mem:* Int Asn Hydraulics Res; Am Soc Mech Engrs; Am Soc Civil Engrs; Am Inst Aeronaut & Astronaut; Sigma Xi. *Res:* Hydrodynamics; heat transfer; unsteady fluid motions; turbulence; biomedical engineering; vortex motion; stability of flows; fluidics; pulsating flows in rigid and elastic systems. *Mailing Add:* Dept of Mech Eng Naval Postgrad Sch Monterey CA 93940

SARRIF, AWNI M, b Acre, Palestine, Sept 2, 42; US citizen; m 71; c 1. PHARMACOLOGY, ONCOLOGY. *Educ:* Am Univ Beirut, BS, 65; Univ Wis, 69, PhD(pharmacol), 72. *Prof Exp:* Proj assoc oncol, Univ Wis-Madison, 72-74, res assoc, 74-76; ASST PROF PHARMACOL & PATH, UNIV ALA, 76- *Mem:* Am Asn Cancer. *Res:* Am Soc Pharmacol & Exp Therapeut; Soc Toxicol; Am Chem Soc. *Res:* Chemical carcinogens and environmental pharmacology. *Mailing Add:* Dept of Pharmacol Univ of Ala Birmingham AL 35294

SARTAIN, CARL CLINTON, b Coker, Ala, Jan 16, 13; m 41; c 2. METALS PHYSICS. *Educ:* Univ Ala, BS, 35, MA, 37; Univ Va, PhD(physics), 49. *Prof Exp:* Instr physics, Univ Ala, 39-41, asst prof, 46-47, assoc prof, 49-54; sr physicist, Oak Ridge Nat Lab, 54-58; physicist, Lawrence Radiation Lab, Univ Calif, 58-62; sr res specialist, Bourns, Inc, 62-68; pres, Tech Consult & Mfg Co, 68-69; PROF PHYSICS, IND STATE UNIV, TERRE HAUTE, 69- *Concurrent Pos:* Res partic, Oak Ridge Nat Lab, 51-52 & 75, consult, 51-54; fac res partic, Argonne Nat Lab, 73 & 74. *Mem:* AAAS; Hist Sci Soc; Brit Soc Hist Sci; Am Vacuum Soc; Brit Soc Glass Technol. *Res:* Experiments at liquid helium and incandescent temperatures; beta activities; neutron spectrum and cross sections; reactor irradiation; nuclear explosive testing and design; semiconducting materials; biophysics; alloy design by computer simulation; history of physics in Great Britain; plasma physics. *Mailing Add:* Dept Physics Ind State Univ Terre Haute IN 47809

SARTAIN, JERRY BURTON, b Walnut, Miss, May 29, 45; m 65; c 1. SOIL SCIENCE, STATISTICS. *Educ:* Miss State Univ, BS, 67, MS, 70; NC State Univ, PhD(soil sci), 74. *Prof Exp:* Asst prof, 74-80, ASSOC PROF, DEPT SOIL SCI, UNIV FLA, 80- *Mem:* Am Soc Agron; Soil Sci Soc Am; Soil & Crop Sci Soc Fla. *Res:* Turf and ornamental soil fertility. *Mailing Add:* Dept of Soil Sci 106 Newell Hall Univ of Fla Gainesville FL 32611

SARTELL, JACK A(LBERT), b St Cloud, Minn, June 18, 24; m 51; c 1. METALLURGY. *Educ:* Univ Minn, BS, 49, MS, 51; Univ Wis, PhD(metall), 56. *Prof Exp:* Res engr, Res Lab, Aluminum Co Am, 51-52; instr, Univ Wis, 52-56; sr res scientist, 56-63, staff scientist, 63-64, head res sect, 64-67, MGR APPL PHYSICS DEPT, HONEYWELL RES CTR, 67- *Mem:* Fel Am Soc Metals; Am Inst Mining, Metall & Petrol Engrs; Brit Inst Metals. *Res:* Oxidation of metals and alloys; magnetics, computer memories and process control. *Mailing Add:* Appl Physics Dept 10701 Lyndale Ave S Bloomington MN 55420

SARTOR, ALBIN FRANCIS, JR, b Bartlett, Tex, Oct 14, 19; m 50; c 1. PETROLEUM CHEMISTRY. *Educ:* Rice Inst, BA, 41. *Prof Exp:* Jr res chemist, Shell Oil Co, 41-44, from res chemist to sr res chemist, 44-56, supvr, 56-63, sr res chemist, 63-72, SR RES CHEMIST, SHELL DEVELOP CO, 72- *Mem:* Am Chem Soc. *Res:* Process and catalyst development; hydrogenation; technical information. *Mailing Add:* 10902 Valley Hills Dr Houston TX 77071

SARTOR, ANTHONY, b Englewood, NJ, Mar 28, 43; m 64; c 3. CHEMICAL ENGINEERING. *Educ:* Manhattan Col, BChE, 64; Univ Mich, Ann Arbor, MSE, 65, PhD(chem eng), 68. *Prof Exp:* Develop engr, Celanese Plastics Co, 68-70; sr water qual engr, Consol Edison of New York, Inc, 70-72; dir environ affairs, New York Power Pool, 72-77; pres, Sartor Assocs, 77-78, EXEC VPRES, PAUCUS, SOLCOLOWSKI & SARTOR, 78- *Mem:* Am Inst Chem Eng; Am Chem Soc. *Res:* Effects of power plant discharges on the environment. *Mailing Add:* Paucus Solcolowski & Sartor 61 Mountain Blvd Ext Warren NJ 07060

SARTOR, CLYDE FLAKE, entomology, see previous edition

SARTOR, JAMES DOYNE, meteorology, deceased

SARTORELLI, ALAN CLAYTON, b Chelsea, Mass, Dec 18, 31. BIOCHEMICAL PHARMACOLOGY. *Educ:* Northeastern Univ, BS, 53; Middlebury Col, MS, 55; Univ Wis, PhD(oncol), 58. *Hon Degrees:* MA, Yale Univ, 67. *Prof Exp:* Asst chem, Middlebury Col, 53-55; asst oncol, Univ Wis, 55-58; from res chemist to sr res chemist, Biomed Div, Samuel Roberts Noble Found, 58-61; from asst prof to assoc prof, 61-67, PROF PHARMACOL, SCH MED, YALE UNIV, 67-, CHMN DEPT, 77-, HEAD DEVELOP THERAPEUT PROG, DIV ONCOL, 74- *Concurrent Pos:* Mem cancer clin invest rev comt, NIH, 68-72, consult psoriasis topical chemother planning comt, 72; consult biochem, Univ Tex M D Anderson Hosp & Tumor Inst, Houston, 70-75; mem adv comt, Cancer Res Ctr, Mallinckrodt Inst Radiol, Sch Med, Wash Univ, 71 & inst res grants comt, Am Cancer Soc, 71-75; mem bd dirs, Am Asn Cancer Res, 75-78; mgt consult, Off Dir, Div Cancer Treat, Nat Cancer Inst, 75-76, mem, Bd Sci Counr, 78-82; consult, Nat Inst Arthritis, Metab & Digestive Dis prog on develop of iron chelators for clin use, 75-76; regional ed, Am Continent, Biochem Pharmacol; assoc ed, Cancer Res; exec ed, Pharmacol & Therapeut; mem exp therapeut study sect, USPHS, 73-77; Charles B Smith vis res prof, Mem Sloan Kettering Cancer Ctr, 79; mem, Nat Prog Comt, 13th Int Cancer Cong, 79-, Publ Comt, Am Asn Cancer Res, 79-82, chmn comt, 81-82; mem adv bd, Univ Iowa Cancer Ctr, 79-, Drug & Vaccine Develop Corp, Ctr Pub Resources, 80-, Clin Cancer Res Ctr, Brown Univ, 80- & Specialized Cancer Ctr, Mt Sinai Med Ctr, 81- *Mem:* Am Asn Cancer Res; Am Soc Cell Biol; Am Soc Pharmacol & Exp Therapeut; Am Soc Biol Chemists; fel NY Acad Sci. *Res:* Biochemistry; molecular pharmacology; action of growth-inhibitory agents; nucleotide and polynucleotide metabolism; mechanisms of cell death; cell membranes; oncology; mechanisms of differentiation. *Mailing Add:* Dept of Pharmacol Yale Univ Sch of Med New Haven CT 06510

SARTORI, LEO, b Milan, Italy, Dec 9, 29; nat US; m 61; c 2. THEORETICAL ASTROPHYSICS, DEFENSE POLICY. *Educ:* Mass Inst Technol, SB, 50. PhD(physics), 56. *Prof Exp:* Physicist, Brookhaven Nat Lab, 55-56; instr physics, Princeton Univ, 56-59; asst prof, Rutgers Univ, 59-63; mem res staff sci teaching ctr, Mass Inst Technol, 63-66, lectr, 66-68, assoc prof, 68-72; chmn dept, 72-78, PROF PHYSICS, UNIV NEBR-LINCOLN, 72- *Concurrent Pos:* Consult, Lockheed Aircraft Corp, 58-63; on leave, Arms Control & Disarmament Agency, 78-81. *Mem:* Fel Am Phys Soc; Arms Control Asn; Am Asn Physics Teachers; Fedn Am Sci; Int Astron Union. *Res:* High-energy astrophysics; supernovas; radio and x-ray sources; defense policy and arms control; theory of synchrotron radiation. *Mailing Add:* Behlen Lab Physics Univ Nebr Lincoln NE 68588

SARTORIS, NELSON EDWARD, b Auburn, Ill, Aug 2, 41; m 64; c 2. ORGANIC CHEMISTRY. *Educ:* MacMurray Col, AB, 63; Northwestern Univ, PhD(org chem), 68. *Prof Exp:* Asst prof, 68-73, assoc prof, 73-80, PROF CHEM, WITTENBERG UNIV, 80- *Concurrent Pos:* Vis prof chem, Rice Univ, 81-82. *Mem:* Am Chem Soc; AAAS. *Res:* Base catalyzed reactions; addition of ketenes to olefins; stereochemistry. *Mailing Add:* Dept Chem Wittenberg Univ Springfield OH 45501

SARTWELL, PHILIP EARL, b Salem, Mass, Sept 11, 08; m 36; c 2. EPIDEMIOLOGY. *Educ:* Boston Univ, MD, 32; Harvard Univ, MPH, 38. *Prof Exp:* From asst prof to prof, 47-73, EMER PROF EPIDEMIOL, SCH HYG & PUB HEALTH, JOHNS HOPKINS UNIV, 73- *Concurrent Pos:* Consult, WHO, NIH & USPHS. *Honors & Awards:* John Snow Award, Am Pub Health Asn. *Mem:* Am Epidemiol Soc; hon mem Royal Soc Med. *Res:* Epidemiology of acute and chronic conditions, including adverse effects of oral contraceptives. *Mailing Add:* 38 Cloutman Lane Marblehead MA 01945

SARUP, RAM, b Delhi, India, Aug 7, 28; m 59; c 1. SOLID STATE PHYSICS, SPECTROSCOPY. *Educ:* Univ Delhi, MSc, 51; Johns Hopkins Univ, PhD(physics), 59. *Prof Exp:* Lectr physics, D J Col, Baraut, India, 51-53; lectr, Vaish Col, Bhiwani, 53-54; jr instr, Johns Hopkins Univ, 54-58, res asst, 58-59; asst prof, Valparaiso Univ, 59-60; sci officer, Atomic Energy Estab, Bombay, India, 60-61; from asst prof to assoc prof physics, 61-69, PROF PHYSICS, COL OF THE HOLY CROSS, 69- *Concurrent Pos:* Vis prof, Univ Paris & Nat Ctr Sci Res, Paris, France, 66-67; consult scientist, Argonne Nat Lab, 67-; guest scientist, Coun Sci & Indust Res, New Delhi, India, 69-70. *Mem:* Am Asn Physics Teachers. *Res:* Solid state spectroscopy. *Mailing Add:* Dept of Physics Col of the Holy Cross Worcester MA 01610

SARVER, EMORY WILLIAM, b Bluefield, WVa, Oct 1, 42; m 63; c 2. ANALYTICAL CHEMISTRY. *Educ:* WVa Univ, AB, 64; Marshall Univ, MS, 66; Lehigh Univ, PhD(chem), 69. *Prof Exp:* CHEMIST, PHYS RES DIV, CHEM SYST LAB, ABERDEEN PROVING GROUND, 71- *Mem:* Am Chem Soc; Sigma Xi. *Res:* Kinetic and product isolation studies of amines, sulfides and arsines; development of methods for analysis of these reactants in dilute aqueous and nonaqueous systems. *Mailing Add:* Phys Res Div DRDARR-CLB-R Chem Syst Lab Aberdeen Proving Ground MD 21010

SARVEY, JOHN MICHAEL, b North Tonawanda, NY, Dec 31, 46; m 80. NEUROPHARMACOLOGY, ELECTROPHYSIOLOGY. *Educ:* Williams Col, BA, 69; State Univ NY, Buffalo, PhD(pharmacol), 76. *Prof Exp:* Vis scientist, Max Planck Inst Brain Res, Ger, 76-79; ASST PROF PHARMACOL, UNIFORMED SERV UNIV HEALTH SCI, 79- *Mem:* Soc Neurosci. *Res:* Electrophysiological investigation of synaptic pharmacology neurotransmitter function, and neuronal plasticity in the rat hippocampus in situ and in thin hippocampal slices in vitro; multidisciplinary studies of recovery of neuronal function. *Mailing Add:* Dept Pharmacol Uniformed Serv Univ Health Sci 4301 Jones Bridge Rd Bethesda MD 20814

SARWATE, DILIP VISHWANATH, b Nagpur, India, Dec 25, 45. ELECTRICAL ENGINEERING, COMPUTER SCIENCE. *Educ:* Univ Jabalpur, BSc, 65; Indian Inst Sci, Bangalore, India, BE, 68; Princeton Univ, PhD(elec eng), 73. *Prof Exp:* Res assoc, 73-74, asst prof, 74-80, ASSOC PROF ELEC ENG, UNIV ILL, 80- *Concurrent Pos:* Sr investr, Joint Serv Electronics Prog, 73-85; fac investr, NSF grant, 73-76, co-prin investr, 76-80; co-prin investr, Army Res Off grant, 78-84. *Mem:* Inst Elec & Electronics Engrs; Asn Comput Mach. *Res:* Multiple-access communications; spread-spectrum communication; information theory; coding theory; computational complexity; analysis of algorithms; parallel processing. *Mailing Add:* Dept of Elec Eng Univ of Ill Urbana IL 61801

SARWER-FONER, GERALD, b Poland, Dec 6, 24; nat Can; m 50; c 5. PSYCHIATRY. *Educ:* Univ Montreal, BA, 45, MD, 51; Royal Col Physicians Can, cert psychiat, 55; Am Bd Psychiat & Neurol, dipl, 57; FRCP(C), 71. *Prof Exp:* Intern, Univ Montreal Hosps, 50-51, clin lectr psychiat, Fac Med, 53-55; sr asst resident, Western Reserve Univ Hosps, 52-53; clin demonstr, Fac Med, McGill Univ, 54-55, demonstr, 55-58, lectr, 58-62, asst prof, 62-66, assoc prof psychiat, 66-71; dir dept psychiat & psychiatrist-in-chief, Queen Elizabeth Hosp, 66-71; PROF PSYCHIAT, FAC MED, UNIV OTTAWA, 71-, CHMN DEPT, 74-; DIR DEPT PSYCHIAT, OTTAWA GEN HOSP, 71- *Concurrent Pos:* Fel, Butler Hosp, Providence, RI, 51-52; asst resident, Queen Mary Vet Hosp, 53-54, chief resident, 54-55, dir psychiat res, 55-60; dir psychiat res, Jewish Gen Hosp, 55-65, assoc psychiatrist, 55-71; mem adv bd psychiat, Defence Res Bd Can, 58-62; vis prof, Fac Med, Laval Univ, 64-; consult, Notre Dame Hosp, 64-71; vis prof, Chicago Med Sch, 68-76; consult, Ottawa Civic Hosp, 71-, Pierre Janet Hosp, 72- & Nat Defence Med Ctr, 74- *Mem:* Fel Royal Col Psychiatrists; fel Am Col Psychiat; fel Am Col Psychoanalysts; fel Int Col Psychom Med (secy, 79-81); Am Acad Psychiat & Law (pres, 75-77). *Res:* Dynamics of psychiatric drug therapy; adaptive difficulties of immigrant groups; psychoanalytic psychotherapy of marital problems; object relationship classification of depressive illnesses; human territoriality and instinct theory; anal object relationships. *Mailing Add:* 501 Smyth Rd Ottawa ON K1H 8L6 Can

SARWINSKI, RAYMOND EDMUND, b La Salle, Ill, Jan 11, 36; m 65; c 2. PHYSICS. *Educ:* Univ Ill, Urbana, BS, 60, MS, 61, PhD(physics), 66. *Prof Exp:* Fel physics, Ohio State Univ, 66-67, asst prof, 67-72; MGR ADVAN DEVELOP, S H E CORP, 72- *Concurrent Pos:* Consult, Gardner Cryogenics Corp, 68-70. *Mem:* Am Phys Soc. *Res:* Cryogenic research on helium three, helium four and mixtures of helium three and helium four at very low temperatures; design of cryogenic instrument systems. *Mailing Add:* S H E Corp 4174 Sorrento Valley Blvd San Diego CA 92121

SASAKI, CLARENCE TAKASHI, b Honolulu, Hawaii, Jan 24, 41; m 67; c 2. OTORHINOLARYNGOLOGY, NEUROPHYSIOLOGY. *Educ:* Pomona Col, BA, 62; Yale Univ, MD, 66. *Prof Exp:* Intern, Univ Calif, San Francisco, 66-67; resident surg, Dartmouth Med Ctr, 67-68 & Yale-New Haven Med Ctr, 70-73; from instr to asst prof, 73-77, ASSOC PROF SURG, YALE SCH MED, 77- *Concurrent Pos:* Attend surg, Yale-New Haven Hosp; attend surg, West Haven Vet Admin Hosp, 73-76, consult, 73-, Windham Community Hosp, 80- & Backas Hosp, 81-; mem, Commmun Sci Study Sect, NIH, 80-; prin investr, NIH grant. *Honors & Awards:* First Prize Clin Res, Am Acad Ophthalmol & Otolaryngol, 72. *Mem:* Sigma Xi; Am Col Surgeons; Am Soc Head & Neck Surg; Triol Soc; Am Laryngol Soc. *Res:* Neurophysiology of the larynx; postnatal development as related to the sudden infant death syndrome; tinnitus, especially development of a neurophysiologic correlate. *Mailing Add:* Dept of Surg Yale Sch Med PO Box 3333 New Haven CT 06510

SASAKI, GORDON HIROSHI, b Honolulu, Hawaii, July 27, 42; m 69; c 1. PLASTIC SURGERY, GENERAL SURGERY. *Educ:* Pomona Col, BA, 64; Yale Univ, MD, 68. *Prof Exp:* Intern, Health Sci Ctr, Univ Ore, 68-69, surg resident, 69-70, surg res fel, 72-74, gen surg, 74-77; chief res plastic surg, Med Sch, Yale Univ, 77-79; ASST PROF PLASTIC SURG, SOUTHWESTERN MED SCH, UNIV TEX, 79- *Concurrent Pos:* Instr gen surg & res assoc, Med Sch, Yale Univ, 78-79. *Mem:* AMA; Am Col Surg; Asn Acad Surg; Am Asn Plastic Surg; Am Asn Hand Surg. *Res:* Steroid and peptide hormones in breast cancer and other target tissues; microcirculation in skin; prostaglandins and microcirculation; macrophage-myofitonblast and wound contraction. *Mailing Add:* 5323 Harry Hines Blvd Div Plastic Surg Southwestern Med Sch Dallas TX 75235

SASAKI, YOSHI KAZU, b Akita, Japan, Jan 2, 27; m 54; c 4. DYNAMIC METEOROLOGY. *Educ:* Univ Tokyo, BS, 50, PhD, 55. *Prof Exp:* Res scientist meteorol res found, Agr & Mech Col, Tex, 56-60, prin investr, 58-60, mem fac, 59-60; res scientist, 60-62, adj assoc prof, 61-64, assoc prof, 64-67, PROF METEOROL, UNIV OKLA, 67-, GEORGE LYNN CROSS RES PROF, 74- *Concurrent Pos:* Res dir, Naval Environ Prediction Res Fac, 74-75; dir, Coop Inst Mesoscale Meteorol Studies, 80- *Honors & Awards:* Prize, Meteorol Soc Japan, 55. *Mem:* Fel Am Meteorol Soc; Meteorol Soc Japan. *Res:* Mesometeorology; numerical weather prediction; variational methods. *Mailing Add:* Sch of Meteorol Univ of Okla Norman OK 73019

SASAMORI, TAKASHI, b Tokyo, Japan, Feb 1, 30; m 58; c 3. METEOROLOGY. *Educ:* Tohoku Univ, Japan, BSc, 53, MSc, 55, DrSc(meteorol), 58. *Prof Exp:* Res assoc meteorol, Geophys Inst, Tohoku Univ, Japan, 58-60; staff scientist, Tech Inst, Japan Defense Agency, 60-64; res assoc dept astron & geophys, Univ Colo, 64-65; staff scientist, Japan Defense Agency, 65-66; staff scientist, Nat Ctr Atmospheric Res, 67-78; PROF METEOROL, UNIV ILL, URBANA-CHAMPAIGN, 78- *Concurrent Pos:* Fel, Univ Colo, 64-65. *Mem:* Am Geophys Union; Am Meteorol Soc; Meteorol Soc Japan. *Res:* Radiation transfer in planetary atmosphere; numerical modelling of planetary boundary layer. *Mailing Add:* Lab Atmospheric Res Univ Ill Urbana IL 61801

SASHIHARA, THOMAS F(UJIO), b Los Angeles, Calif, May 7, 29; m 57; c 3. CHEMICAL ENGINEERING. *Educ:* Ohio State Univ, BChE & MSc, 53, PhD(chem eng), 57. *Prof Exp:* Instr chem eng, Ohio State Univ, 55-56; chem engr, Polychem Dept, 56-63, sr res engr, Plastics Dept, 63-71, SUPT RES LAB, PLASTICS DEPT, E I DU PONT DE NEMOURS & CO, INC, 71- *Mem:* Am Chem Soc; Am Inst Chem Engrs. *Res:* Chemical processes. *Mailing Add:* 3 Roan Ct Wilmington DE 19803

SASHIN, DONALD, b New York, NY, Dec 11, 37; m 67; c 2. RADIOLOGICAL PHYSICS, HEALTH PHYSICS. *Educ:* Mass Inst Technol, BS, 60; Carnegie Inst Technol, MS, 62; Carnegie-Mellon Univ, PhD(medium energy physics), 68. *Prof Exp:* Proj physicist, Carnegie Inst Technol, 62-67; from instr to asst prof radiol & radiation health, 67-74, res assoc prof radiol, 74-75, ASSOC PROF RADIOL, SCH MED, UNIV PITTSBURGH, 75-, DIR RADIOL IMAGING, 75- *Concurrent Pos:* Pa Lions Sight Conserv & Eye Res Found grants, 71; Nat Cancer Inst contract, 73-74; Am Cancer Inst grant, 77-79; Nat Heart, Lung & Blood Inst contracts, 77-79 & 80-83. *Mem:* AAAS; Optical Soc Am; Soc Photo-Optical Instrumentation Eng; Health Physics Soc; Am Asn Physicists in Med. *Res:* Development of an electronic radiographic imaging system to improve diagnostic radiography to reduce exposure, reduce procedure time and improving image quality; clinical evaluation of the system performance in neurosurgery, gastro-intestinal fluoroscopy, angiography, mammography, pelvimetry, intra-uterine fetal transfusions and intravenous angiography. *Mailing Add:* RC 406 Scaife Hall Univ of Pittsburgh Pittsburgh PA 15261

SASHITAL, SANAT RAMANATH, b Bagalkot, India; US citizen. SOLID STATE PHYSICS, MATERIALS SCIENCE. *Educ:* Univ Bombay, BSc, 59, MSc, 61; Pa State Univ, PhD(solid state sci), 67. *Prof Exp:* Physicist, Res Labs, Zenith Radio Corp, 69-74; vis scholar, Dept Mat Sci, Northwestern Univ, 74-76; MEM TECH STAFF, RES LABS, HUGHES AIRCRAFT CO, 76- *Mem:* Am Asn Crystal Growth; Am Vacuum Soc. *Res:* Crystal growth; epitaxial growth; thin films, structure and properties; electro-optic materials. *Mailing Add:* Hughes Res Labs 3011 Malibu Canyon Rd Mailbu CA 90265

SASHKIN, LAWRENCE, b New York, NY, Dec 27, 29; m 48; c 3. SYSTEM SIMULATION, DATA MANAGEMENT. *Educ:* Univ Calif, Los Angeles, BS, 52. *Prof Exp:* Math analyst, Lockheed Aircraft Corp, 52-55; struct engr radioplane div, Northrop Corp, 55-57; sr scientist aeronutronic div, Ford Motor Co, 57-60, mgr appl anal & prog, 60-63, mgr appl math, 63-64; asst dir math & comput ctr, Aerospace Corp, San Bernardino, 64-67, assoc dir, 67-69, dir, 69-72, DIR DATA PROCESSING SUBDIVISION, INFO PROCESSING DIV, AEROSPACE CORP, EL SEGUNDO, 72- *Mem:* Soc Comput Simulation. *Res:* Computer systems applications; interactive computing; data systems management. *Mailing Add:* 17962 Fiesta Way Tustin CA 92680

SASIELA, RICHARD, b Brooklyn, NY, June 1, 40; m 62; c 2. LASERS. *Educ:* Polytech Inst Brooklyn, BEE, 61, MS, 62, PhD(electrophys), 67. *Prof Exp:* Res engr, Microwave Assocs, Inc, 67-69; MEM STAFF, LINCOLN LAB, MASS INST TECHNOL, 69- *Mem:* Inst Elec & Electronics Engrs. *Res:* Design and development and analysis of data of radar systems. *Mailing Add:* Lincoln Lab PO Box 73 Lexington MA 02173

SASIN, RICHARD, b Warsaw, Poland, Nov 16, 22; nat US; m 57; c 1. ORGANIC CHEMISTRY. *Educ:* Drexel Inst, BS, 47; Temple Univ, MA, 49, PhD(chem), 54. *Prof Exp:* Asst chem, Temple Univ, 47-51; instr, Drexel Inst, 51-53, asst prof, 53-57, assoc prof, 57-60, prof, 60-68; PROF CHEM & DEAN DIV SCI & MATH, MILLERSVILLE STATE COL, 68- *Concurrent Pos:* Consult, Hardesty Industs, 55-57; Fatty Acid Producers Coun fel, Eastern Regional Res Lab, USDA, 57-58. *Mem:* AAAS; Am Chem Soc; Am Oil Chem Soc. *Res:* Nitrogen heterocyclics; organotin compounds; derivatives of long-chain fatty acids; sulfur compounds and phosphorus derivatives of fatty acids. *Mailing Add:* Div Sci & Math Millersville State Col Millersville PA 17551

SASKI, WITOLD, b Poland, Dec 4, 09; nat US; wid. PHARMACEUTICS. *Educ:* Batory Univ, Poland, MPharm, 33; Univ Bologna, DPharm, 46; Inst Optical Sci, London, Eng, dipl, 50; Univ Nebr, BSc, 54. *Prof Exp:* Practicing pharmacist, Poland, 33-36; pharmaceut inspector, Polish Ministry Labor & Soc Welfare, 37-39; chief pharmacist med clin, Eng, 47-48; sr pharmacist supplies div, Brit Ministry Health, 48-51; asst prof pharm, Mont State Univ, 51-52; asst prof, 52-55, from assoc prof to prof, 55-75, EMER PROF PHARM, COL PHARM, UNIV NEBR, MED CTR, 75- *Concurrent Pos:* Vis assoc prof sch pharm, Univ Calif, San Francisco, 59-60; Fulbright scholar, Univ Pisa, 67-68; Nat Acad Sci exchange scientist, Poland, 70. *Honors & Awards:* Lederle Pharm fac awards, 62, 64 & 66. *Mem:* Fel Am Acad Pharmaceut Sci; Am Asn Cols Pharm. *Res:* Surface-active agents and drug absorption mechanisms; medicinal product formulation; experimental pharmaceutical technology. *Mailing Add:* 2600 S 46th St Lincoln NE 68506

SASLAW, LEONARD DAVID, b Brooklyn, NY, Aug 27, 27. BIOCHEMISTRY. *Educ:* City Col New York, BS, 49; George Washington Univ, MS, 54; Georgetown Univ, PhD(chem), 63. *Prof Exp:* Chemist, Nat Cancer Inst, NIH, 51-57; chemist, Div Biophys, Sloan-Kettering Inst, 57-58; chemist, Biochem Br, Armed Forces Inst Path, 58-65; dir div biochem pharmacol, Cancer Chemother Dept, Microbiol Assocs, Inc, 65-68; sr biochemist, Nat Drug Co, 68-69; chief, Lab Cellular Biochem, Albert Einstein Med Ctr, 69-70; clin lab dir, Med Diag Ctrs, Inc, 70-71; lab dir & res assoc, Renal Lab, New York Med Col, 71-73; mgr biochem invests, Bio/dynamics Inc, NJ, 73-74; prof assoc, Smithsonian Sci Info Exchange, 75-77; PHYSIOLOGIST, DIV TOXICOL, BUR FOODS, FOOD & DRUG ADMIN, 78- *Mem:* AAAS; Am Chem Soc; Am Soc Pharmacol & Exp Therapeut; Clin Ligand Assay Soc; Am Asn Cancer Res. *Res:* Drug metabolism; analytical biochemistry; cancer research; oxidation of unsaturated fatty acids; clinical chemistry. *Mailing Add:* 425 G St SW Washington DC 20024

SASLOW, WAYNE MARK, b Philadelphia, Pa, Aug 11, 42; m 71; c 2. LOW TEMPERATURE PHYSICS, SOLID STATE SCIENCE. *Educ:* Univ Pa, BA, 64; Univ Calif, Berkeley, MA, 67; Univ Calif, Irvine, PhD(physics), 68. *Prof Exp:* Res assoc, Univ Pittsburgh, 69-71; asst prof, 71-77, ASSOC PROF PHYSICS, TEX A&M UNIV, 77- *Concurrent Pos:* Joliot-Curie fel & vis prof, Univ Paris, 80-81. *Mem:* Am Phys Soc. *Res:* Theory of liquid helium, solid state theory; surface physics; spin glasses; hydrodynamics of condensed matter systems. *Mailing Add:* Dept of Physics Tex A&M Univ College Station TX 77843

SASMOR, DANIEL JOSEPH, b New York, NY, July 24, 21; m 50; c 4. PHYSICAL CHEMISTRY, MATERIALS SCIENCE. *Educ:* Univ Richmond, BS, 43; Western Reserve Univ, PhD(phys chem), 51. *Prof Exp:* Sr chemist, Oak Ridge Nat Lab, 51-56; sr opers analyst, Combat Opers Res Group, 56-57; sr mil proj specialist, Olin Mathieson Chem Corp, 57-60; MEM STAFF, MAT SCI RES & DEVELOP, SANDIA LABS, 60- *Mem:* Am Chem Soc. *Res:* Thermodynamics; thermochemistry; calorimetry; high resolution nuclear magnetic resonance; materials research and development. *Mailing Add:* Sandia Labs Div 4453 Albuquerque NM 87115

SASNER, JOHN JOSEPH, JR, b Lawrence, Mass, June 15, 36; m 58; c 3. COMPARATIVE PHYSIOLOGY, INVERTEBRATE ZOOLOGY. *Educ:* Univ NH, BA, 57, MS, 59; Univ Calif, Los Angeles, PhD(comp physiol), 65. *Prof Exp:* Res assoc physiol & biophys, Univ Ill, 62-63; res & develop off, US Air Force Sch Aerospace Med, 63-65; asst prof zool, 65-69, assoc prof, 69-81, PROF ZOOL, UNIV NH, 81- *Res:* Effects of naturally occurring microorganism toxins on excitable membranes. *Mailing Add:* Dept of Zool Univ of NH Durham NH 03824

SASS, DANIEL B, b Rochester, NY, Mar 28, 19; m 59; c 2. PALEONTOLOGY, ENVIRONMENTAL SCENCES. *Educ:* Univ Rochester, BA & MS, 51; Univ Cincinnati, PhD, 59. *Prof Exp:* From asst prof to assoc prof geol, 52-63, chmn dept, 52-74, PROF GEOL, ALFRED UNIV, 63-, COORDR ENVIRON STUDIES PROG, 74- *Concurrent Pos:* Scholes Sigma Xi lectr, 65. *Mem:* AAAS; fel Geol Soc Am; Paleont Soc. *Res:* Devonian stratigraphy and paleontology; electron microscopy; ultrastructure of bivalve shells; biomedical research. *Mailing Add:* 27 High St Alfred NY 14802

SASS, JOHN HARVEY, b Chatham, Ont, July 20, 37; m 61. GEOPHYSICS. *Educ:* Univ Western Ont, BS, 59, MS, 61; Australian Nat Univ, PhD(geophys), 65. *Prof Exp:* GEOPHYSICIST, US GEOL SURV, 67- *Concurrent Pos:* Nat Res Coun Can fel, Univ Western Ont, 64-66; vis fel, Australian Nat Univ, 71-72 & Stanford Univ, 72. *Mem:* AAAS; Am Geophys Union; Can Geophys Union. *Res:* Earth's heat and internal temperatures. *Mailing Add:* US Geol Surv 2255 N Gemini Dr Flagstaff AZ 86001

SASS, NEIL LESLIE, b Baltimore, Md, Oct 24, 44; m 69; c 2. NUTRITIONAL BIOCHEMISTRY, TOXICOLOGY. *Educ:* Wake Forest Col, BS, 66; WVa Univ, MS, 69, PhD(biochem), 71. *Prof Exp:* Res toxicologist, Chem-Toxicol, Biomed Lab, US Army Edgewood Arsenal, 71-73, res anal chemist explosives, Chem Lab, 73-74; chief lab serv, Med Res & Develop, William Beaumont Army Med Ctr, 74-77; TOXICOLOGIST, BUR FOODS, FOOD & DRUG ADMIN, 77- *Concurrent Pos:* Fel, Appl Behav Sci/Orgn Develop, Johns Hopkins Univ. *Mem:* Sigma Xi; Soc Appl Spectroscopy; Am Chem Soc; Soc Armed Forces Med Lab Scientists; Am Col Toxicol. *Res:* Biochemical mechanisms of the chemical pain response; mechanisms of idiopathic respiratory distress syndrome; reptilian venoms as presynaptic acetylcholine inhibitors; radioimmunoassay development for thyroid hormone precursors; thyroid hormone actions; biochemical toxicology. *Mailing Add:* DHHS PHS FDA 200 C St SW Washington DC 20204

SASS, RONALD L, b Davenport, Iowa, May 26, 32; m 52; c 4. BIOPHYSICAL CHEMISTRY. *Educ:* Augustana Col, BA, 54; Univ Southern Calif, PhD, 57. *Prof Exp:* Res fel chem, Brookhaven Nat Lab, 57-58; from asst prof to assoc prof, 58-66, PROF CHEM & BIOL, RICE UNIV, 66- *Concurrent Pos:* Guggenheim fel, Cambridge Univ, 65; adj prof, Baylor Col Med, 70- *Honors & Awards:* Salgo-Noren Distinguished Prof Award, 66. *Mem:* Am Chem Soc; Am Soc Cell Biol; Am Crystallog Asn; Biophys Soc. *Res:* X-ray diffraction; crystal and molecular structure of biologically active molecules; structure and function of fibrous proteins and lipoprotein systems; biological calcification. *Mailing Add:* Dept of Biol Rice Univ Houston TX 77001

SASS, SAMUEL, b Baltimore, Md, Nov 21, 15; m 42; c 2. ANALYTICAL CHEMISTRY. *Educ:* Johns Hopkins Univ, BS, 40. *Prof Exp:* Anal chemist chem & radiol labs, US Army Chem Ctr, 45-49, sect chief, 49-53, asst br chief, 53-57, chief anal res br chem res div, Chem Res & Develop Labs, 57-66, chief anal chem dept, Res Labs, Edgewood Arsenal, 66-71, chief anal chem br, Chem Lab, 71-76; RES ADV & CONSULT, RES DIV, CHEM SYSTS LAB, ABERDEEN PROVING GROUND, 77- *Concurrent Pos:* Res assoc dept surg, Sinai Hosp, Baltimore, Md. *Honors & Awards:* Civilian Meritorious Serv Medal Sci Achievement, US Army, 74. *Mem:* AAAS; Am Chem Soc; Sigma Xi. *Res:* Colorimetric methods of analysis; chemical process control and applications; insecticide analysis; analysis of chemical warfare agents; ultraviolet and atomic absorption; spectrophotometry; gas-liquid chromatography; thermogravimetry and differential thermal analysis; bioanalysis; thin layer and paper chromatography; chemotherapeutics; environmental pollution, identification and measurement; infrared and mass spectrometry; electrochemistry. *Mailing Add:* 17 N Reed St Bel Air MD 21014

SASS, STEPHEN L, b New York, NY, Mar 11, 40; m 66; c 2. MATERIALS SCIENCE. *Educ:* City Col New York, BChE, 61; Northwestern Univ, PhD(mat sci), 66. *Prof Exp:* Res asst mat sci, Northwestern Univ, 61-66; Fulbright scholar, Delft Univ, 66; asst prof, 67-73, assoc prof, 73-79, PROF MAT SCI, CORNELL UNIV, 79- *Concurrent Pos:* Max-Planck fel, 80-81. *Mem:* Am Inst Metall Engrs; Am Ceramic Soc; Environ Mutagen Soc Am. *Res:* Phase transformations in solids; electron microscopy; electron diffraction; x-ray diffraction; diffraction from crystalline imperfections; grain boundaries. *Mailing Add:* Dept of Mat Sci & Eng Cornell Univ Ithaca NY 14850

SASSA, SHIGERU, b Tokyo, Japan, Mar 3, 35; m 63; c 2. HEMATOLOGY, BIOCHEMISTRY. *Educ:* Univ Tokyo, MD, 61, DrMedSci, 66. *Prof Exp:* Res assoc med, Fac Med, Univ Tokyo, 68; res assoc, 68-71, asst prof hemat & biochem, 71-75, ASSOC PROF HEMAT & BIOCHEM & PHYSICIAN, ROCKEFELLER UNIV, 75- *Mem:* Am Soc Biol Chem. *Res:* Heme biosynthesis; the regulatory mechanism of enzyme induction. *Mailing Add:* Rockefeller Univ New York NY 10021

SASSAMAN, CLAY ALAN, b Washington, DC, Dec 27, 48. POPULATION BIOLOGY, COMPARATIVE PHYSIOLOGY. *Educ:* Col William & Mary, BS, 70; Stanford Univ, PhD(biol), 76. *Prof Exp:* Scholar, Woods Hole Oceanog Inst, 75-76; ASST PROF BIOL, UNIV CALIF, RIVERSIDE, 76- *Mem:* Genetics Soc Am; AAAS; Am Genetic Asn. *Res:* Population genetics; population ecology; comparative physiology of invertebrates and lower vertebrates. *Mailing Add:* Dept of Biol Univ of Calif Riverside CA 92521

SASSCER, DONALD S(TUART), b Washington, DC, June 30, 29; m 58; c 3. NUCLEAR ENGINEERING. *Educ:* Univ Utah, BS, 53; Iowa State Univ, MS, 59, PhD(nuclear eng), 64. *Prof Exp:* Instr mech, Iowa State Univ, 56-59, asst prof nuclear eng, 61-64; chief scientist & head div nuclear eng, PR Nuclear Ctr, Atomic Energy Comn, 64-76, PROF & HEAD DEPT, UNIV PR, MAYAGUEZ, 64-, ACTING ASSOC DIR, CTR ENERGY & ENVIRON RES & HEAD, OTEC PROG, 77- *Mem:* Am Nuclear Soc; Am Soc Eng Educ. *Res:* Radiation shielding; heat transfer transport of neutrons and gamma rays; system analysis. *Mailing Add:* Div of Nuclear Eng PR Nuclear Ctr Atomic Energy Comn College Sta Mayaguez PR 00708

SASSE, EDWARD ALEXANDER, b Amarillo, Tex, July 10, 38; m 60; c 2. CLINICAL CHEMISTRY, CLINICAL PATHOLOGY. *Educ:* Arlington State Col, BS, 63; Univ Tenn, Memphis, PhD(biochem), 68; Am Bd Clin Chem, dipl, 73. *Prof Exp:* From instr to asst prof clin path, Sch Med, Univ Ala, Birmingham, 68-70; asst prof, 70-74, ASSOC PROF PATH, MED COL WIS, 74- *Concurrent Pos:* Consult scientist, Univ Ala Hosps & Clins, 68-70; co-dir clin chem sect, Dept Path & Labs, Milwaukee County Gen Hosp, 70- *Mem:* AAAS; Am Chem Soc; Am Asn Clin Chem. *Res:* Clinical chemistry methodology; toxicology; endocrinology; physical and chemical properties of proteins; enzyme immunoassay. *Mailing Add:* Dept Path Med Col Wis 8700 W Wisconsin Ave Milwaukee WI 53226

SASSEEN, J(OHN) H(OWARD), b San Antonio, Tex, Nov 21, 21; m 48. ELECTRICAL ENGINEERING. *Educ:* Rice Univ, BS, 44. *Prof Exp:* Explor geophysicist, Humble Oil & Refining Co, 46-51, sr explor geophysicist, 51-66, proj eng geophys res, 55-66, sect head geophys eng, Esso Prod Res Co, 66-67; mgr geophys res & serv, Imperial Oil Ltd, 67-69; sect head geophys eng, Esso Prod Res Co, 69-72, mgr admin, 72-76, SR RES ASSOC GEOPHYS, EXXON PROD RES, 76- *Mem:* Soc Explor Geophys; Am Geophys Union; sr mem Inst Elec & Electronics Engrs; Marine Technol Soc. *Res:* Electronics for geophysical instrumentation; electronic computers and data processors for geophysical data; geophysics instrumentation and computer data processing. *Mailing Add:* Exxon Prod Res Geophys Strat Div PO Box 2189 Houston TX 77001

SASSENRATH, ETHELDA NORBERG, b Dubuque, Iowa, Feb 21, 21; m 51; c 2. BEHAVIORAL PHYSIOLOGY, PSYCHOPHARMACOLOGY. *Educ:* Dubuque Univ, AB, 42; Iowa State Univ, PhD(chem), 49. *Prof Exp:* Asst res biochemist sch med, Univ Calif, 49-59; res assoc psychopharmacol, Ind Univ, 59-64; res specialist, Nat Ctr Primate Biol, 64-68; lectr behav biol, Sch Med, 68-73, res behav biologist, Calif Primate Res Ctr, 73-76, ASSOC PROF BEHAV BIOL, SCH MED, UNIV CALIF, DAVIS, 76-, PROF PSYCHIAT, 80- *Mem:* AAAS; Soc Neurosci; Soc Exp Biol & Med; West Pharmacol Soc. *Res:* Mechanisms of psychoactive drug action; endocrine correlates of behavior; psycho endocrine correlates of stress and aging. *Mailing Add:* Dept Psychiat Univ of Calif Sch of Med Davis CA 95616

SASSER, JOSEPH NEAL, b Goldsboro, NC, May 19, 21; m 45; c 4. NEMATOLOGY. *Educ:* NC State Col, BS, 43, MS, 50; Univ Md, PhD, 53. *Prof Exp:* Asst nematologist, USDA, 51-53; from asst prof to assoc prof plant path, 53-64, PROF PLANT PATH, NC STATE UNIV, 64- *Concurrent Pos:* Tech consult, Rockefeller Found, Chile, 63-64; ed, Am Phytopath Soc, 63-65. *Mem:* Soc Nematol (vpres, 61-63, pres, 63-64); Am Phytopath Soc; Orgn Trop Am Nematol. *Res:* Nematode diseases of plants. *Mailing Add:* Dept of Plant Path NC State Univ Raleigh NC 27607

SASSER, LYLE BLAINE, b Tremonton, Utah, Feb 20, 39; m 63; c 4. ANIMAL NUTRITION. *Educ:* Univ Idaho, BS, 61; Colo State Univ, MS, 65, PhD(nutrit), 68. *Prof Exp:* Asst prof animal sci, Fresno State Col, 67; asst scientist, Univ Tenn-AEC Agr Res Lab, 68-72, asst prof, 73-77, ASSOC PROF NUTRIT, COMP ANIMAL RES LAB, UNIV TENN-OAK RIDGE, 78- *Mem:* Am Asn Veterinary Nutritionists; Am Inst Nutrit; Am Asn Nutrit Today; Soc Exp Biol & Med; Soc Environ Geochem & Health. *Res:* Metabolism of trace elements in animal nutrition; radioisotope tracers; trace element absorption studies; toxicity of heavy metals; interaction of heavy metals and dietary nutrients; body composition; effects of radiation on domestic animals; prenatal nutrition. *Mailing Add:* Comp Animal Res Lab 1299 Bethel Valley Rd Oak Ridge TN 37830

SASS-KORTSAK, ANDREW, b Debrecen, Hungary, Aug 1, 16; Can citizen; m 44; c 3. BIOCHEMICAL GENETICS, GASTROENTEROLOGY. *Educ:* Univ Budapest, MD, 40. *Prof Exp:* Res assoc path, 62-74, assoc prof pediat, 63-66, prof biochem, 69-73, PROF PEDIAT, UNIV TORONTO, 66- *Concurrent Pos:* Physician, Hosp Sick Children, 62-, sr scientist, Res Inst, 65- *Mem:* Am Pediat Soc; Soc Pediat Res; Can Pediat Soc; Can Soc Clin Invest; Can Biochem Soc. *Res:* Liver diseases in children; copper metabolism; Wilson's disease and Menkes' disease; genetics. *Mailing Add:* Hosp for Sick Children Res Inst 555 University Ave Toronto ON M5G 1X8 Can

SASSOON, HUMPHREY FREDERICK, nutrition, see previous edition

SASSOUNI, VIKEN, b Beirut, Lebanon, Jan 25, 22; m 54; c 3. DENTISTRY, ORTHODONTICS. *Educ:* Univ Paris, dipl, 51; Univ Pa, MSc, 56, DSc(dent), 58, DDS, 60. *Prof Exp:* Teacher French, St Nechan Col, Lebanon, 40-42; dent extern, Univ Paris Hosp, 50-51; res assoc orthod, Growth Ctr, Grad Sch Med, Univ Pa, 55-58, asst prof, 58-60; prof orthod & chmn dept, Sch Dent, Univ WVa, 60-63; PROF ORTHOD & CHMN DEPT, SCH DENT, UNIV PITTSBURGH, 63- *Concurrent Pos:* Res assoc, Children's Hosp, Philadelphia, 56-60; lectr, Post-Grad Dept, Dent Sch, Univ Pa, 59-66; lectr,

Dent Sch, Univ Southern Calif, 62-67; pres, Dento-Facial Abnormalities Asn. *Mem:* Am Dent Asn; Am Asn Phys Anthrop. *Res:* Growth and development; computerized orthodontic diagnosis and treatment planning; cephalometry; identification; treatment of dento-facial abnormalities. *Mailing Add:* Dept of Orthod Univ of Pittsburgh Sch of Dent Pittsburgh PA 15213

SASTRE, ANTONIO, b Los Angeles, Calif, June 14, 50. NEUROTRANSMITTER RECEPTORS. *Educ:* Cornell Univ, BA, 70, MS, 73, PhD(appl math), 74. *Prof Exp:* Lectr, Cornell Univ, 74-76; instr, pharmacol, Cornell Med Col, 76-77; ASST PROF PHYSIOL, SCH MED, JOHNS HOPKINS UNIV, 77-, ASST PROF NEUROSCI, 80- *Concurrent Pos:* Adj asst prof pharmacol, Cornell Med Col, 79-; mem, Basic Sci Coun, Am Heart Asn. *Mem:* Soc Neurosci. *Res:* Cholinergic and adrenergic receptors in the heart and vascular smooth muscle; synaptogenesis in and properties of neurons and cardiocytes in tissue-culture. *Mailing Add:* Dept Physiol Sch Med Johns Hopkins Univ Baltimore MD 21209

SASTRI, SURI A, b Tanjore, SIndia, Dec 26, 39; m 69. PHYSICAL METALLURGY, MATERIALS SCIENCE. *Educ:* Banaras Hindu Univ, BSc, 60; Univ London, PhD(eng) & DIC, 64. *Prof Exp:* Australian Inst Nuclear Sci & Eng fel mat physics, Australian Atomic Energy Comn Res Labs, Sydney, 64-66; AEC res assoc metall, Ames Inst Atomic Res, Iowa State Univ, 67-68; res & develop scientist, Microphys Div, Gillette Safety Razor Co, 68-69, chief res & develop scientist, 69-71, group mgr mat res, 71-76, DIR, CHEM & MAT RES, BOSTON RES & DEVELOP LABS, GILLETTE CO, 76- *Mem:* Electron Micros Soc Am; Am Soc Metals; Am Inst Mining, Metall & Petrol Engrs; Brit Iron & Steel Inst. *Res:* Application of electron microscopy to the understanding of the relationship between microstructure and mechanical properties of materials; phase transformations and strengthening mechanisms in materials. *Mailing Add:* Gillette Co Gillette Park Boston MA 02106

SASTRY, AKELLA N, b Kakinada, India, Sept 21, 34; m 64; c 1. BIOLOGICAL OCEANOGRAPHY. *Educ:* Andhra Univ, India, BSc Hons, 54, MSc, 55; Fla State Univ, PhD(biol oceanog), 61. *Prof Exp:* Instr zool, Adnhra Univ, India, 55-56; asst marine biol oceanog inst, Fla State Univ, 56-61; res assoc marine lab, Duke Univ, 61-62; asst prof oceanog, Cent Inst Fisheries Educ, 63; prin investr marine biol & res assoc, Marine Lab, Duke Univ, 64-66; from asst prof to assoc prof oceanog, 66-77, PROF OCEANOG, NARRAGANSETT MARINE LAB, UNIV RI, 77- *Concurrent Pos:* NSF grant, 64-66; vis prof, Univ Chile, 81. *Mem:* Fel AAAS; Am Soc Zoologists; Am Soc Limnol & Oceanog; Marine Biol Asn UK; Marine Biol Asn India. *Res:* Environmental ecology; effects of environmental factors in reproduction and larval development of marine animals; physiological adaptation of marine organisms; aquaculture; energetics and environmental adaptations. *Mailing Add:* Grad Sch of Oceanog Narragansett Marine Lab Univ RI Kingston RI 02881

SASTRY, BHAMIDIPATY VENKATA RAMA, b Andhra, India, Oct 21, 27; nat US; m 68; c 1. PHARMACOLOGY, MEDICINAL CHEMISTRY. *Educ:* Andhra Univ, India, BSc, 49, MSc, 50, DSc(med chem), 56; Emory Univ, MS, 59; Vanderbilt Univ, PhD(pharmacol), 62. *Prof Exp:* Demonstr pharmaceut chem, Andhra Univ, India, 51-52, lectr, 52-56; res asst pharmacol, Emory Univ, 56-59; res assoc, 59-60, from instr to assoc prof, 60-71, PROF PHARMACOL, VANDERBILT UNIV, 71- *Mem:* AAAS; Soc Exp Biol & Med; fel Am Inst Chem; Soc Toxicol; Am Soc Pharmacol & Exp Therapeut. *Res:* Physiology, pharmacology and toxicology of radionuclides and insecticides; synthesis and screening of psychotherapeutic agents; pharmacology and structure-activity drugs active on autonomic nervous system. *Mailing Add:* Dept of Pharmacol Vanderbilt Univ Sch of Med Nashville TN 37232

SASTRY, CHERLA BHASKARA RAMA, b Andhra Pradesh, India, Oct 15, 36; Can citizen; m 59; c 2. FOREST PRODUCTS. *Educ:* Andhra Univ, MSc, 58; Univ BC, MS, 67, PhD(wood & pulp sci), 71. *Prof Exp:* Lectr bot, Andhra Univ, 58-62; asst foreman forest prod, Ministry of Defense, 62-65; sales & tech consult, Western India Plywoods Ltd, 70-71; res fel, Univ BC, 71-72; fel, Univ NB, 72-73; res fel, Univ BC, 73-74; adv & vis prof forestry & forest prod, Agr Univ Malaysia, Can Int Develop Agency, 74-77; assoc prof, Univ Toronto, 77-79; RES SCIENTIST, FORINTEK CAN CORP, 79- *Concurrent Pos:* Adj prof, Univ Toronto, 79- *Mem:* Forest Prod Res Soc; Tech Asn Pulp & Paper Indust; Int Asn Wood Anatomists; fel Inst Wood Sci. *Res:* Forestry education and curriculum development; research on tropical woods; manufacture of forest products and new product development; basic research in wood science; wood quality studies; wood deterioration and protection. *Mailing Add:* Forintek Can Corp 800 Montreal Rd Ottawa ON K1G 3Z5 Can

SASTRY, SHANKARA M L, b India, June 11, 46; m 74; c 3. METALLURGY. *Educ:* Bangalore Univ, BS, 65; Indian Inst Sci, BEng, 68, MEng, 70; Univ Toronto, PhD(metall & mat sci), 74. *Prof Exp:* Vis scientist metall, Air Force Mat Lab, Wright Patterson AFB, 74-76; res scientist, 77-78, scientist, 78-81, SR SCIENTIST PHYS METALL, MCDONNEL DOUGLAS RES LABS, 82- *Concurrent Pos:* Prin investr, various res contracts, 78- *Mem:* Metall Soc Am; Am Soc Metals; Electron Micros Soc Am. *Res:* Rapid solidification processing of titanium and aluminum alloys; novel consolidation techniques (explosive and dynamic compaction) of rapidly solidified powders; advanced titanium fabrication techniques; laser processing of materials. *Mailing Add:* 14872 Rutland Circle Chesterfield MO 63017

SATAS, DONATAS, b Lithuania, Apr 7, 29; US citizen; m 53; c 3. CHEMICAL ENGINEERING. *Educ:* Ill Inst Technol, BS, 53. *Prof Exp:* Res engr, Armour Res Found, 55-57; group leader, Kendall Co, 57-69; tech dir, Whitman Prod Ltd, 69-75; CONSULT, SATAS & ASSOCS, 75-; PRES, POLYHESIVE CO, 75- *Concurrent Pos:* Abstractor, Chem Abstr, 62-; reviewer, Appl Mech Rev, 65- *Mem:* Am Inst Chem Engrs; Soc Plastics Engrs; Asn Consult Chemists & Chem Engrs; Am Lithuanian Engrs &

Architects Asn. *Res:* Adhesives and coating technology; pressure sensitive adhesives; emulsion and solution polymerization; paper coating and saturation; coating and lamination equipment. *Mailing Add:* 99 Shenandoah Rd Warwick RI 02886

SATCHELL, DONALD PRENTICE, b Bridgeport, Mich, Mar 23, 23; m 45; c 2. SOIL CHEMISTRY. *Educ:* Mich State Col, BS, 46, MS, 47; NC State Col, PhD(soil chem), 51. *Prof Exp:* Asst prof soil tech, Pa State Univ, 51-59; mgr agron serv div, Am Agr Chem Co, 59-66; supv res scientist plant foods res div, Continental Oil Co, 66-69; vis lectr, Southern Ill Univ, Carbondale, 69-71, assoc prof plant & soil sci, 71-78; environ scientist, Ill Pollution Control Bd, 78-81. *Concurrent Pos:* Chmn, Coun Fertilizer Appln, 67; US mem agr adv comn & agr comt, Int Superphosphate Mfrs Asn, 66-67; mem, Ill Pollution Control Bd, 76-81. *Mem:* Fel AAAS; Am Soc Agron; Soil Sci Soc Am; Am Chem Soc; Int Soc Soil Sci. *Res:* Plant nutrition and soil management; soil chemistry of applied phosphates; interaction of plant nutrients. *Mailing Add:* 608 Glenview Dr Carbondale IL 62901

SATCHELL, FRED E(UGENE), b Saginaw, Mich, Aug 9, 21; m 46; c 4. CHEMICAL ENGINEERING. *Educ:* Mich State Univ, BS, 44, MS, 47. *Prof Exp:* Chem engr, Dow Chem Co, Mich, 45-46; asst agr chem, Purdue Univ, 47-49; phys chemist food res, Am Meat Inst Found, Ill, 49-51; sr chemist, Brunswick Corp, 51-53, asst chief chemist, 53-56, chief chemist, 56-60, dir chem res & develop, 61-66, vpres res & prod develop, MacGregor/Brunswick, 66-68; DIR PROD RES & DEVELOP, SHERWOOD MED INDUSTS, INC, 68- *Mem:* Am Chem Soc; Am Soc Testing & Mat; Asn Advan Med Instrumentation. *Res:* Plastics; finishes; medical instrumentation; medical devices; sutures. *Mailing Add:* 3 Conway Springs Dr Chesterfield MO 63017

SATCHER, ROBERT LEE, radiation chemistry, photochemistry, see previous edition

SATCHLER, GEORGE RAYMOND, b London, Eng, June 14, 26; m 48; c 2. THEORETICAL PHYSICS. *Educ:* Oxford Univ, BA & MA, 51, DPhil(physics), 55. *Prof Exp:* Sr studentship, Clarendon Lab, Oxford Univ, 51-56, Imp Chem Industs res fel, 56-59; PHYSICIST, OAK RIDGE NAT LAB, 59- *Concurrent Pos:* Res assoc, Univ Mich, 56-57. *Honors & Awards:* Tom W Bonner Prize, Am Phys Soc, 77. *Mem:* Fel Am Phys Soc. *Res:* Theory of nuclear structure and nuclear reactions. *Mailing Add:* Physics Div PO Box X Oak Ridge TN 37830

SATER, VERNON E(UGENE), b Rock Rapids, Iowa, Apr 10, 35; m 57; c 3. CHEMICAL ENGINEERING. *Educ:* Ill Inst Technol, BS, 57, MS, 59, PhD(chem eng), 63. *Prof Exp:* Instr chem eng, Ill Inst Technol, 62; from asst prof to assoc prof, 62-74, PROF CHEM ENG & ACTG CHMN, ARIZ STATE UNIV, 74- *Mem:* Am Chem Soc; Am Inst Chem Engrs. *Res:* Process control; process simulation; microcomputer. *Mailing Add:* Sch of Eng Ariz State Univ Tempe AZ 85281

SATHE, SHARAD SOMNATH, b Bombay, India, Oct 10, 40; m 66; c 2. ORGANIC & MEDICINAL CHEMISTRY. *Educ:* Bombay Univ, BSc, 60; Banaras Hindu Univ, BPharm, 63; Ind Univ, PhD(org chem), 71. *Prof Exp:* Anal chemist, Hoffman-La Roche Co, India, 63-65; res asst chem, CIBA Res Ctr, India, 65-67; assoc, Res Triangle Inst, 71-73; res investr, 75-79, tech supvr, 79-81, GROUP LEADER RES & DEVELOP, MALLINCKRODT INC, 81- *Mem:* Am Chem Soc. *Res:* Research and development in organic chemistry related to drug products, drug intermediates and fine organic chemicals. *Mailing Add:* Mallinckrodt Inc PO Box 5439 St Louis MO 63147

SATHER, BRYANT THOMAS, b Wallace, Idaho, Feb 8, 35; m 63. PHYSIOLOGY, ECOLOGY. *Educ:* Univ Idaho, BS, 57; Univ Hawaii, PhD(zool), 65. *Prof Exp:* Asst physiologist, Pac Biomed Res Ctr, Univ Hawaii, 64-66; asst prof zool NC State Univ, 66-67; asst prof, 67-69, ASSOC PROF PHYSIOL, RUTGERS UNIV, NEWARK, 69- *Mem:* AAAS; Am Soc Zoologists; Am Physiol Soc. *Res:* Comparative and ecological physiology; osmoregulation and electrolyte balance; mineral metabolism; renal physiology. *Mailing Add:* Dept Physiol Rutgers Univ Newark NJ 07102

SATHER, DUANE PAUL, b Minneapolis, Minn, Sept 19, 33; m 55; c 3. MATHEMATICS. *Educ:* Univ Minn, BPhys, 59, MS, 60, PhD(math), 63. *Prof Exp:* Instr math, Univ Minn, 63-64; res assoc, Univ Md, 64-65; asst prof, Cornell Univ, 65-68; assoc prof math, Math Res Ctr, US Army, Univ Wis-Madison, 68-70; assoc prof, 70-74, PROF MATH, UNIV COLO, BOULDER, 74- *Mem:* Am Math Soc; Soc Natural Philos. *Res:* Partial differential equations; applied mathematics. *Mailing Add:* Dept of Math Univ of Colo Boulder CO 80309

SATHER, GLENN A(RTHUR), b Franklin, Minn, Jan 18, 28; m 52; c 1. CHEMICAL ENGINEERING, SOLUTION THERMODYNAMICS. *Educ:* Univ Minn, BCE & BBA, 52, PhD(chem eng), 59. *Prof Exp:* From asst prof to assoc prof, 59-70, PROF CHEM ENG, UNIV WIS-MADISON, 70- *Concurrent Pos:* NSF sci fac fel, Imp Col, Univ London, 66-67; year-in-indust prof, E I du Pont de Nemours & Co, 73-74 *Mem:* Am Inst Chem Engrs, Am Chem Soc; Am Soc Eng Educ. *Res:* Cryogenics; thermodynamics. *Mailing Add:* Dept Chem Eng Univ Wis Madison WI 53706

SATHER, JOHN HENRY, b Presho, SDak, July 12, 21; m 48; c 2. ZOOLOGY. *Educ:* Univ Nebr, BSc, 43, PhD(zool), 53; Univ Mo, AM, 48. *Prof Exp:* Sr biologist fur invests, Game, Forestation & Parks Comn, Nebr, 48-53, leader game res, 53-55; prof biol & dean grad sch, 55-80, EMER DEAN GRAD SCH & PROF BIOL SCI, WESTERN ILL UNIV, 80- *Concurrent Pos:* Mem, Nat Wetlands Tech Coun, 76-; adv to proj leader, Nat Wetland Inventory, 76-; mem environ adv bd to chief engrs, 79- *Mem:* AAAS; Ecol Soc Am. *Res:* Mammals, upland game birds and wetlands. *Mailing Add:* Grad Off Western Ill Univ Macomb IL 61455

SATHER, NORMAN F(REDERICK), b Elmhurst, Ill, Sept 17, 36; m 57; c 3. THERMODYNAMICS. *Educ:* Univ Ill, BS, 58; Univ Minn, PhD(chem eng), 62. *Prof Exp:* Asst prof chem eng, Univ Wash, 62-68, assoc prof, 68-74, prof, 74; chem engr energy & environ systs, 74-79, ASSOC DIV DIR, ARGONNE NAT LAB, 79- *Concurrent Pos:* Fel, Univ Cambridge, Eng, 71-72; consult, Ocean Thermal Energy Conversion to Ministry, Int Trade & Indust, Japan, 79. *Mem:* Am Inst Chem Eng. *Res:* Development of ocean thermal energy converison power systems components and designs; thermochemical and biological processes for conversion of biomass to fuels and chemicals, and environmental control technology for coal combustion and gasification. *Mailing Add:* Energy Environ Systs Argonne Nat Lab Argonne IL 60439

SATHER, ROY O(SCAR), b New York, NY, July 17, 17; m 45; c 4. ELECTRICAL ENGINEERING. *Educ:* Wayne State Univ, BSEE, 40; Univ Ill, MS, 51, PhD(elec eng), 60. *Prof Exp:* Asst prof elec eng, US Air Force Inst Technol, 51-54; assoc prof, 57-63, PROF ELEC ENG, WAYNE STATE UNIV, 63- *Mem:* Sr mem Inst Elec & Electronics Engrs. *Res:* Electronic circuits; servomechanisms; analog and digital computers. *Mailing Add:* Dept of Elec Eng Wayne State Univ Detroit MI 48202

SATHOFF, H JOHN, b Peoria, Ill, Sept 21, 31; m 54; c 2. CHEMICAL PHYSICS. *Educ:* Bradley Univ, BS, 53; Ohio State Univ, MS, 55, PhD(nuclear physics), 60. *Prof Exp:* Res assoc physics, Ohio State Univ, 61; asst prof physics & chem, 61-64, assoc prof physics, 64-69, chmn dept, 64-81, PROF PHYSICS, BRADLEY UNIV, 69- *Mem:* Am Asn Physics Teachers; Am Chem Soc. *Res:* Nuclear beta and gamma ray spectroscopy; nuclear decay scheme. *Mailing Add:* Dept of Physics Bradley Univ Peoria IL 61625

SATIJA, KANWAR (KEN) SAIN, b Bhakkar, Pakistan, July 1, 42; m 67; c 3. MECHANICAL & CIVIL ENGINEERING. *Educ:* Panjab Univ, India, ME, 62, MS, 64; Univ Iowa, PhD(eng), 71. *Prof Exp:* Assoc prof mech eng, Punjab Eng Col, India, 62-67; res asst, Univ Iowa, 68-70; designer, Powers Willis & Assoc, Iowa City, 68-69; design supvr, Pioneer Serv & Eng Co, Chicago, 70-72; sr engr, Sargent & Lundy Engrs, Chicago, 72-73; sr nuclear engr, 73-80, PROJ ENG MGR, UNITED ENGRS & CONSTRUCTORS, 80- *Concurrent Pos:* Adj asst prof, Drexel Univ, 75- *Mem:* Am Soc Mech Engrs; Am Soc Civil Engrs; Am Water Res Asn; Am Water Works Asn; Nat Soc Prof Engrs. *Res:* Fluids engineering including heat and mass transfer and potential flow; nuclear power plant engineering; hydraulics including hydrology and oceanography. *Mailing Add:* United Engrs & Constructors 30 S 17th St Philadelphia PA 19101

SATIR, PETER, b New York, NY, July 28, 36; m 62; c 2. ZOOLOGY. *Educ:* Columbia Col, AB, 56; Rockefeller Inst, PhD, 61. *Prof Exp:* Instr biol & zool, Univ Chicago, 61-63, asst prof, 63-67; assoc prof anat, Univ Calif, Berkeley, 67-73, dir, Electron Micros Lab, 69-76, prof physiol-anat, 73-77; PROF ANAT & CHMN DEPT, ALBERT EINSTEIN COL MED, 77- *Mem:* AAAS; Am Soc Cell Biol; Soc Protozool; Am Asn Anatomists. *Res:* Cell biology, ciliary motility. *Mailing Add:* Dept of Anat Albert Einstein Col of Med Bronx NY 10461

SATKIEWICZ, FRANK GEORGE, b Cambridge, Mass, Mar 6, 27; m 51; c 4. PHYSICAL CHEMISTRY. *Educ:* Northeastern Univ, BS, 47; Wesleyan Univ, MA, 49; Mass Inst Technol, PhD(phys chem), 58. *Prof Exp:* Radiochemist, Tracerlab, Inc, 49-52; head high sch math dept, 52-54; res assoc, Norton Co, 58-63; staff scientist, GCA Corp, 63-69, prin scientist, 69-73; SR STAFF, APPL PHYSICS LAB, JOHNS HOPKINS UNIV, 73- *Mem:* Am Chem Soc; Am Soc Mass Spectrometry. *Res:* Solid state chemistry and physics; sputter-ion source mass spectrometry of solids. *Mailing Add:* Appl Physics Lab Johns Hopkins Univ Laurel MD 20707

SATO, CLIFFORD SHINICHI, b Hawaii, June 9, 25; m 56; c 1. MOLECULAR PATHOLOGY, BIOCHEMISTRY. *Educ:* Univ Hawaii, BS, 51; Mich State Univ, PhD(chem), 55. *Prof Exp:* Head radiobiochem, Calif Corp Biochem Res, 61-62; dir radiobiochem, Int Chem & Nuclear Corp, 62-63; dir res, US Nuclear Corp, 63; sr investr, Inst Med Res, Huntington Mem Hosp, Pasadena, Calif, 63-67; asst prof biochem, Baylor Col Med, 67-71; res biochemist, Dept Path, 67-79, DIR MOLECULAR PATHOL RES, VET ADMIN MED CTR, 79- *Concurrent Pos:* Res fel, Argonne Nat Lab, 54; res fel biol, Calif Inst Technol, 55-61. *Mem:* AAAS; Am Chem Soc; Tissue Cult Asn; Sigma Xi. *Res:* Specific marker-macromolecules unique for carcinomatous, hyperplastic, and normal human prostates for development of diagnostic methods and for clear understanding of both disease processes. *Mailing Add:* Dept of Path Vet Admin Hosp 2002 Holcombe Blvd Houston TX 77211

SATO, DAIHACHIRO, b Fujinomiya-Shi, Japan, June 1, 32; m 56; c 3. MATHEMATICS. *Educ:* Tokyo Univ Educ, BS, 55; Univ Calif, Los Angeles, MA, 57, PhD(math), 63. *Prof Exp:* Reader math, Univ Calif, Los Angeles, 57-58, from asst to assoc, 58-61; asst prof, San Fernando Valley State Col, 61; instr, Tokai Univ, Japan, 61-62; instr, 63, lectr, 63, from asst prof to assoc prof, 63-71, PROF MATH, UNIV REGINA, 71- *Concurrent Pos:* Vis asst prof & NSF fel, Univ Calif, Los Angeles, 64; Can Math Cong res fel, Queen's Univ, Ont, 65; Univ Alta, 66 & 71, Univ BC, 67, Univ Man, 68 & 69, Carlton Univ, 73, Univ Calgary, 74 & 75 & Res Inst Math Sci, Kyoto Univ, 76. *Honors & Awards:* Lester R Ford Award, Math Asn Am, 77. *Mem:* Am Math Soc; Math Asn Am; Soc Indust & Appl Math; Can Math Cong; Math Soc Japan. *Res:* Integer valued entire functions; generalized interpolations by analytic functions; prime representing functions; function theory; number theory; padic analysis; transcendentality problems; mathematics education; computer sciences; operations research. *Mailing Add:* 10 Wesson Bay Regina SK S4S 6J5 Can

SATO, GORDON HISASHI, b Los Angeles, Calif, Dec 17, 27; m 52; c 6. BIOLOGY. *Educ:* Univ Southern Calif, BA, 50; Calif Inst Technol, PhD(biol), 55. *Prof Exp:* Teaching asst microbiol, Calif Inst Technol, 53-55; fel virol & jr asst virologist, Univ Calif, Berkeley, 55-56; fel & instr biophys, Med Sch, Univ Colo, 56-58; from asst prof to prof biochem, Brandeis Univ,

58-69; PROF BIOL, UNIV CALIF, SAN DIEGO, 69- *Concurrent Pos:* Mem panel molecular biol study sect, NIH; mem breast cancer task force, Nat Cancer Inst. *Mem:* AAAS; Am Asn Immunologists; Endocrine Soc; Asn Biol Chem. *Res:* Animal cell culture; endocrinology; bacteriophage. *Mailing Add:* Dept of Biol Q-058 Univ of Calif San Diego La Jolla CA 92037

SATO, HIROSHI, b Matsuzaka, Japan, Aug 31, 18; m 47; c 3. SOLID STATE PHYSICS. *Educ:* Hokkaido Univ, MSc, 41; Univ Tokyo, DSc, 51. *Prof Exp:* Res assoc physics, Hokkaido Univ, 42, asst prof, Inst Low Temperature Res, 42-43; res physicist, Inst Phys Chem Res, Tokyo, 43-45; prof metal physics, Res Inst Iron, Steel & Other Metals, Tohoku Univ, Japan, 45-57; prin res physicist, Sci Lab, Ford Motor Co, Mich, 56-74; PROF, SCH MAT ENG, PURDUE UNIV, WEST LAFAYETTE, 74- *Concurrent Pos:* Res physicist, Res Lab, Westinghouse Elec Corp, 54-56; Guggenheim Mem fel, 66-67; consult, Solid State Div, Oak Ridge Nat Lab, 78-80; Alexander von Humboldt US sr scientist award, 80. *Honors & Awards:* Prize, Japan Inst Metals, 51. *Mem:* Fel Am Phys Soc; Phys Soc Japan; Am Ceramic Soc; Metall Soc; NY Acad Sci. *Res:* Metal physics; magnetism; diffusion and ion transport phenomena; high temperature ceramic materials; super ionic conductors; composite sic materials; kinetics of phase transitions; crystal growth. *Mailing Add:* Sch of Mat Eng Purdue Univ West Lafayette IN 47907

SATO, MAKIKO, b Nishinomiya, Hyogo, Japan, May 29, 47; m 69. PLANETARY ATMOSPHERES. *Educ:* Osaka Univ, BS, 70; Yeshiva Univ, MA, 72, PhD(physics), 78. *Prof Exp:* Res scientist, Columbia, Univ, 78; res assoc, State Univ NY, Stony Brook, 78-79; SCI ANALYST PLANETARY SCI, SIGMA DATA SERV CORP, 80- *Concurrent Pos:* Co-investr, Voyager Spacecraft Mission, 80- *Mem:* Am Astron Soc. *Res:* Determination of the chemical compositions, cloud-haze structure and temperature profiles of the atmospheres of the outer planets by analyzing visible and infrared spectra. *Mailing Add:* Goddard Inst Space Studies 2880 Broadway New York NY 10025

SATO, MOTOAKI, b Tokyo, Japan, Oct 11, 29; m 61, 78; c 3. GEOCHEMISTRY, ECONOMIC GEOLOGY. *Educ:* Univ Tokyo, BS, 53, MS, 55; Univ Minn, Minneapolis, PhD(geol), 59. *Prof Exp:* Res fel geophys, Harvard Univ, 58-61; asst prof geol, Inst Thermal Springs Res, Okayama Univ, 61-63; res geologist, 63-65, PROJ LEADER, US GEOL SURV, 65- *Concurrent Pos:* Apollo 12-17 prin investr oxygen fugacity studies lunar basalts, NASA. *Mem:* Am Geophys Union; Geochem Soc Japan. *Res:* Electrochemistry of minerals; mineral reaction mechanisms; origin of sulfide self-potentials; volatile components of magma, rocks and ores; electrochemical sensors for volcanic gas monitoring; oxidation-reduction reactions in planets; thermochemistry of fossil fuels. *Mailing Add:* Mail Stop 959 Nat Ctr US Geol Surv Reston VA 22092

SATOH, PAUL SHIGEMI, b Osaka, Japan, Nov 6, 36; US citizen; m; c 2. BIOCHEMISTRY. *Educ:* St Paul's Univ, Tokyo, BA, 59; Wayne State Univ, PhD(biochem), 64. *Prof Exp:* Res assoc immunochem, Wayne State Univ, 64-66; res staff tumor immunol, Aichi Cancer Ctr, Nagoya, Japan, 66-68; sr res assoc protein chem, Med Sch, Tufts Univ, 68-72; sr res scientist III immunol, 72-79, MGR RES & DEVELOP, UPJOHN DIAG, THE UPJOHN CO, 79- *Mem:* Sigma Xi; NY Acad Sci; Am Chem Soc. *Res:* Immunological diagnosis of human cancer; enzyme-immunoassay; immunology of mediaters; lymphocytemembrane; cell mediated immunology of cancer patients, and immunosuppressive drugs; radioimmunoassay; bioluminescence. *Mailing Add:* Upjohn Diag The Upjohn Co Kalamazoo MI 49001

SATRAN, RICHARD, b New York, NY, Oct 3, 28; m 51; c 2. NEUROLOGY. *Educ:* Univ Louisville, BA, 49, MD, 56; NY Univ, MA, 51. *Prof Exp:* Instr neurol & EEG, 62-63, dir, EEG Lab, 62-70, sr instr neurol, 63-64, from asst prof to assoc prof, 64-75, actg chmn div, 66, PROF NEUROL, UNIV ROCHESTER MED CTR, 75-, VCHMN DEPT, 79- *Mem:* AAAS; fel Am Col Physicians; fel Am Acad Neurol; Sigma Xi. *Res:* Electroencephalography; cerebrovascular disease; medical history. *Mailing Add:* Dept of Neurol Univ of Rochester Med Ctr Rochester NY 14642

SATTAR, SYED ABDUS, b Hyderrabad, India, Mar 23, 38; m 70; c 2. ANIMAL VIROLOGY, WATER POLLUTION. *Educ:* Univ Karachi, BSc, 58, MSc, 60; Univ Toronto, dipl bact, 62, MA, 64; Univ Ottawa, PhD(microbiol), 67. *Prof Exp:* Asst lectr microbiol, Univ Karachi, 60-61; res fel, Univ Ottawa, 64-67; lectr, Univ Karachi, 68-70; ASSOC PROF MICROBIOL, UNIV OTTAWA, 70- *Mem:* Can Soc Microbiologists; Am Soc Microbiol. *Res:* Study of human pathogenic viruses in liquid and solid wastes and the water environment. *Mailing Add:* Dept Microbiol Sch Med Univ Ottawa Ottawa ON K1N 9A9 Can

SATTEN, ROBERT A, b Chicago, Ill, Aug 4, 22; m 46; c 2. SOLID STATE SPECTROSCOPY. *Educ:* Univ Chicago, BS, 44; Univ Calif, Los Angeles, MA, 47, PhD(physics), 51. *Prof Exp:* Instr physics, Univ Calif, Los Angeles, 51-52; asst prof, Mass Inst Technol, 52-53; from asst prof to assoc prof, 53-63, vchmn dept, 68-69 & 70-73, PROF PHYSICS, UNIV CALIF, LOS ANGELES, 63- *Concurrent Pos:* Consult, Argonne Nat Lab, 59-72, Hughes Res Lab, 59-67 & Lockheed Res Lab, 63-65; Fulbright res fel, France, 61-62; Fulbright res fel, Ger, 69-70; vis Erskine fel, Univ Canterbury, 71. *Mem:* Fel Am Phys Soc; Am Asn Physics Teachers. *Res:* Rare earth and actinide spectra in solids, vibronic spectra in crystals; optical detection of spin-lattice relaxation. *Mailing Add:* 1358 Woodruff Ave Los Angeles CA 90024

SATTER, LARRY DEAN, b Madelia, Minn, July 30, 37; m 66; c 1. ANIMAL NUTRITION. *Educ:* SDak State Univ, BS, 60; Univ Wis, MS, 62, PhD(biochem, dairy sci), 64. *Prof Exp:* From asst prof to assoc prof dairy sci, Univ Wis-Madison, 64-73, prof, 73-81; MEM STAFF, DAIRY FORAGE RES CTR, UNIV WIS, USDA, 81- *Honors & Awards:* Am Feed Mfgrs Award, 77. *Mem:* Am Dairy Sci Asn; Am Soc Animal Sci; Am Inst Nutrit; Brit Nutrit Soc. *Res:* Digestive phenomena occurring in the rumen and quantitative aspects of the rumen fermentation. *Mailing Add:* Dairy Forage Res Ctr USDA Univ Wis 1925 W Linden Dr Madison WI 53706

SATTER, RUTH, b New York, NY, Mar 8, 23; m 46; c 4. CHRONOBIOLOGY, PLANT PHYSIOLOGY. *Educ:* Barnard Col, Columbia Univ, AB, 44; Univ Conn, PhD(bot), 68. *Prof Exp:* Res fel biol, Yale Univ, 67-73, res assoc biol, 73-78, sr res assoc, 78-81; PROF-IN-RESIDENCE, UNIV CONN, 81- *Concurrent Pos:* Counr, Am Soc Photobiol, 74-77; vis assoc prof bot, Conn Col, 77; mem gov bd, Am Inst Biol Sci, 78-81, exec comt, 81-83; vis prof bot, Cornell Univ, 79; mem metab biol panel, NSF, 81. *Mem:* AAAS; Am Soc Plant Physiologists; Am Inst Biol Sci; Int Soc Chronobiol; Am Soc Photobiol. *Res:* Time measurement in higher plants with emphasis on the role of fluxes and membrane changes in the clock mechanism. *Mailing Add:* Biol Sci U-82 Univ Conn Storrs CT 06268

SATTERFIELD, CHARLES N(ELSON), b Dexter, Mo, Sept 5, 21; m 46; c 2. CHEMICAL ENGINEERING. *Educ:* Harvard Univ, SB, 42; Mass Inst Technol, SM, 43, ScD(chem eng), 46. *Prof Exp:* Res engr, 43-45, from asst prof to assoc prof chem eng, 46-59, PROF CHEM ENG, MASS INST TECHNOL, 59- *Concurrent Pos:* Vis lectr, Harvard Univ, 48-57; consult, 48-; consult, US Res & Develop Bd, 52-53 & US Dir Defense Res & Eng, 53-60; mem comt chem kinetics, Nat Acad Sci-Nat Res Coun, 60-66; mem adv bd, Indust & Eng Chem, 66-68 & comt air qual mgt & chmn ad hoc panel abatement nitrogen oxides emissions from stationary sources, Nat Acad Eng, 70-72. *Honors & Awards:* Wilhelm Award, Am Inst Chem Engrs. *Mem:* Am Chem Soc; Am Inst Chem Engrs; fel Am Acad Arts & Sci. *Res:* Applied chemical kinetics and heterogeneous catalysis; mass transfer in chemical reactors. *Mailing Add:* 66-572 Mass Inst of Technol Cambridge MA 02139

SATTERLEE, JAMES DONALD, b Seattle, Wash, Feb 16, 48. BIOINORGANIC & PHYSICAL CHEMISTRY. *Educ:* Cent Wash Univ, BA, 70, MS, 71; Univ Calif, Davis, PhD(chem), 75. *Prof Exp:* Res fel chem biol, Dept Chem, Calif Inst Technol, 75-78; asst prof, Dept Chem, Northern Ill Univ, 78-81; ASST PROF, DEPT CHEM, UNIV NMEX, 81- *Res:* Chemistry; metal ions in biology; nuclear magnetic resonance spectroscopy in diamagnetic and paramagnetic systems; transition metal chemistry. *Mailing Add:* Dept of Chem Univ NMex Albuquerque NM 87131

SATTERLEE, LOWELL DUGGAN, b Duluth, Minn, July 30, 43; m 63; c 2. FOOD CHEMISTRY, BIOCHEMISTRY. *Educ:* SDak State Univ, BS, 65; Iowa State Univ, MS, 66, PhD(biochem), 68. *Prof Exp:* Asst prof food technol, Iowa State Univ, 68-69; from asst prof to assoc prof, 69-75, PROF FOOD SCI, UNIV NEBR-LINCOLN, 75- *Concurrent Pos:* Viobin Labs indust grant, 69-73; Nebr Agr Asn grants, 72-79; NSF grant, 74-79 & 79-82. *Mem:* AAAS; Inst Food Technologists; Am Meat Sci Asn. *Res:* Isolation, characterization and utilization of human food proteins. *Mailing Add:* Dept of Food Sci & Technol Univ of Nebr Lincoln NE 68583

SATTERLUND, DONALD ROBERT, b Polk Co, Wis, Apr 10, 28; m 55; c 3. FORESTRY. *Educ:* Univ Mich, BSF, 51, MF, 55, PhD(forestry), 60. *Prof Exp:* Asst forestry, Univ Mich, 53-58; instr forest influences, State Univ NY Col Forestry, Syracuse, 58-60, asst prof, 60-64; from asst prof to assoc prof forestry & range mgt, 64-71, PROF FORESTRY & RANGE MGT, WASH STATE UNIV, 71- *Mem:* Soc Am Foresters; Soil Conserv Soc Am; Am Geophys Union. *Res:* Watershed management; forest influences and ecology. *Mailing Add:* Dept of Forestry & Range Mgt Wash State Univ Pullman WA 99164

SATTERLY, GILBERT T(HOMPSON), b Detroit, Mich, Sept 27, 29; m 52; c 4. CIVIL ENGINEERING. *Educ:* Wayne State Univ, BS, 52, MS, 61; Northwestern Univ, PhD(transp eng), 65. *Prof Exp:* Detailer struct design, Giffels & Vallet, Inc, 53-54; asst civil engr, Bur Hwy & Expressways, City of Detroit, 54-56; struct engr, Stran-Steel Corp, 56-57; instr transp & struct eng, Wayne State Univ, 57-59; sr asst engr, Bur Hwy & Expressways, City of Detroit, 59-60; lectr transp & traffic eng, Northwestern Univ, 63-65, asst prof, 65-66; assoc prof, Univ Mich, Ann Arbor, 66-68; assoc prof, Wayne State Univ, 68-70; assoc prof, 70-76, PROF CIVIL ENG, PURDUE UNIV, 76- *Concurrent Pos:* Mem, Hwy Res Bd, Nat Acad Sci-Nat Res Coun. *Mem:* Am Soc Civil Engrs; Am Soc Eng Educ; Inst Traffic Engrs. *Res:* Transportation and traffic engineering. *Mailing Add:* Sch of Civil Eng Purdue Univ West Lafayette IN 47907

SATTERTHWAIT, ARNOLD CHASE, JR, enzyme mechanism, see previous edition

SATTERTHWAITE, CAMERON B, b Salem, Ohio, July 26, 20; m 50; c 5. PHYSICAL CHEMISTRY, PHYSICS. *Educ:* Col Wooster, BA, 42; Univ Pittsburgh, PhD(phys chem), 51. *Prof Exp:* Res assoc cryogenics res found, Ohio State Univ, 44-45; res chemist, Mound Lab, 45-46, group leader, 46-47; res chemist, E I du Pont de Nemours & Co, 50-53; res physicist, Westinghouse Elec Co, 53-61; assoc prof physics, Dept Physics & Mat Res Lab, Univ Ill, Urbana, 61-64, prof physics, 64-80; MEM FAC DEPT PHYS, VA COMMONWEALTH UNIV, 80- *Concurrent Pos:* On leave, Ohio State Univ, 70-71; prog dir, NSF, 75-76. *Mem:* AAAS; Am Phys Soc. *Res:* Low temperature properties of metals, particularly superconductors; properties of metal hydrides. *Mailing Add:* Dept Phys Va Commonwealth Univ Richmond VA 23284

SATTERTHWAITE, FRANKLIN EVES, b New York, NY, July 22, 14; m 39; c 3. STATISTICS. *Educ:* Swarthmore Col, BS, 36; Univ Iowa, PhD(statist), 41. *Prof Exp:* With Aetna Life Ins Co, Conn, 41-46; statist engr, Gen Elec Co, 46-52; OWNER, STATIST ENG INST, 58- *Concurrent Pos:* Statist consult, Rath & Strong, Inc, 52-60; assoc prof, Merrimack Col, 56-62. *Mem:* AAAS; fel Am Soc Qual Control; Am Statist Asn; Inst Math Statist. *Res:* Statistical engineering and thinking. *Mailing Add:* 8 Fuller Rd Wellesley Hills MA 02181

SATTERWHITE, RAMON S(TEWART), b Little Rock, Ark, Feb 9, 40; m 62; c 1. ELECTRICAL ENGINEERING. *Educ:* Univ Ark, BSEE, 62; Univ NMex, MS, 64; Ohio State Univ, PhD(elec eng), 69. *Prof Exp:* Staff mem, Sandia Corp, 62-66; from asst prof to assoc prof elec eng, Lamar Univ, 69-76; V PRES, SOUTHERN AVIONICS CO, 76- *Mem:* Inst Elec & Electronics Engrs; Sigma Xi. *Res:* Electromagnetic field theory. *Mailing Add:* 5210 Gail Dr Beaumont TX 77708

SATTINGER, IRVIN J(ACK), b Indianapolis, Ind, Nov 1, 12; m 37; c 2. ELECTRICAL ENGINEERING. *Educ:* Univ Mich, BSE, 33, MS, 35. *Prof Exp:* Jr engr, Cent Ohio Light & Power Co, 36-37; elec draftsman, Commonwealth & Southern Corp, Mich, 37-38 & Loup River Pub Power Dist, Nebr, 38-39; asst engr, Ind Serv Corp, 39-41; elec designer, Basic Magnesium, Inc, Nev, 41-43; design engr, Lear, Inc, Mich, 43-48; res engr, Willow Run Labs, Inst Sci & Technol, Univ Mich, Ann Arbor, 48-73; RES ENGR, ENVIRON RES INST MICH, ANN ARBOR, 73- *Mem:* Sr mem Inst Elec & Electronics Engrs. *Res:* Application of computers to scientific problems; electronic measurement and control systems, particularly for aerospace and ground vehicles; applications of airborne and spacecraft remote sensing systems; energy studies; infrared technology. *Mailing Add:* Environ Res Inst of Mich PO Box 8618 Ann Arbor MI 48107

SATTIZAHN, JAMES EDWARD, JR, b Moline, Ill, June 16, 20; m 43; c 2. PHYSICAL CHEMISTRY. *Educ:* Lawrence Col, BA, 42; Univ NMex, PhD(chem), 57. *Prof Exp:* Chemist, E I du Pont de Nemours & Co, 42-46; MEM STAFF, LOS ALAMOS NAT LAB, 46- *Mem:* Am Chem Soc. *Res:* Fission product behavior in various matrices. *Mailing Add:* 1422 44th St Los Alamos NM 87544

SATTLER, ALLAN R, b Los Angeles, Calif, June 28, 32; m 59; c 1. ATOMIC PHYSICS, NUCLEAR PHYSICS. *Educ:* Univ Calif, Los Angeles, BA, 54; Pa State Univ, MS, 59, PhD(physics), 62. *Prof Exp:* Eng aide, Univ Calif, Los Angeles, 53-54; jr engr, Douglas Aircraft Co, Inc, 54; physicist atomic power equip dept, Gen Elec Co, 56-57; STAFF MEM, SANDIA CORP, 63- *Concurrent Pos:* Fulbright travel grant, 62-63; mem staff, Asse Nuclear Waste Repository, 77. *Mem:* Am Phys Soc. *Res:* Atomic particle energy; channelling; radiation effect; neutron cross section measurements; nuclear waste technology; earth sciences; fuel technology and petroleum engineering. *Mailing Add:* Sandia Corp Div 4512 Kirtland AFB Albuquerque NM 87185

SATTLER, CAROL ANN, b DuBois, Pa, Sept 23, 46; m 71; c 2. BIOLOGICAL STRUCTURE. *Educ:* Thiel Col, BA, 68; Univ Colo, PhD(biol), 74. *Prof Exp:* Res assoc path, Med Sch, 74-75, proj assoc oncol, McArdle Lab Cancer Res, 75-77, ASST SCIENTIST, MCARDLE LAB CANCER RES, UNIV WIS-MADISON, 77- *Mem:* Am Soc Cell Biol; AAAS; Electron Micros Soc Am. *Res:* Ultrastructural characterization of membrane specializations in cilia and the oral cavity of Tetrahymena pyriformis, and rat liver cells cultured on floating collagen gels. *Mailing Add:* McArdle Lab Cancer Res Univ Wis 450 N Randall Madison WI 53706

SATTLER, FRANK A(NTON), b New England, NDak, July 5, 20; m 45; c 9. CHEMICAL ENGINEERING. *Educ:* Univ NDak, BS, 42. *Prof Exp:* Res engr, Res Labs, Westinghouse Elec Corp, 42-54, supv chemist, 54-73, mgr wire, 73-78, ADV SCIENTIST, WESTINGHOUSE RES & DEVELOP CTR, 78- *Mem:* Am Chem Soc. *Res:* Development of electrical insulating materials. *Mailing Add:* Westinghouse Res & Develop Ctr Pittsburgh PA 15235

SATTLER, JOSEPH PETER, b New York, NY, Oct 19, 40; m 68. LASERS. *Educ:* Iona Col, BS, 62; Georgetown Univ, MS, 66, PhD(physics), 69. *Prof Exp:* PHYSICIST, HARRY DIAMOND LABS, 66- *Honors & Awards:* Res & Develop Achievement Award, US Army, 75; Hinman Tech Achievement Award, Harry Diamond Labs, 78. *Mem:* Am Phys Soc; Inst Elec & Electronics Engrs. *Res:* High resolution infrared and submillimeter wave spectroscopy; solid state physics; quantum electronics; electron paramagnetic resonance. *Mailing Add:* Harry Diamond Labs Br 13200 2800 Powder Mill Rd Adelphi MD 20783

SATTLER, ROBERT E(DWARD), b St Louis, Mo, Mar 31, 25; m 50; c 2. CHEMICAL ENGINEERING, MATHEMATICS. *Educ:* Wash Univ, St Louis, BS, 49; Univ Mo, MS, 52. *Prof Exp:* Process engr, Lago Oil & Transport Co, Ltd, 49-51; process design engr, 52-57, planning & correlation engr, 57-61, theoret develop engr, 61-63, mgr process fundamentals sect, 63-66, rate processes sect, 66-69, sr engr kinetics & mass transfer sect, 69-73, res & develop engr, Hydrocarbon Processes Br, 73-77, RES & DEVELOP ENGR, COAL PROCESSES SECT, ALT ENERGY BR, RES & DEVELOP DEPT, PHILLIPS PETROL CO, 77- *Mem:* AAAS; Am Inst Chem Eng; Am Chem Soc. *Res:* Heat transfer; reaction kinetics; reactor design. *Mailing Add:* Phillips Petrol Co Bldg 92-E PRC Bartlesville OK 74004

SATTLER, ROLF, b Göppingen, Ger, Mar 8, 36. PLANT MORPHOLOGY. *Educ:* Univ Munich, PhD(taxon), 61. *Prof Exp:* NATO fel, 62-64; from asst prof to assoc prof, 64-77, PROF BOT, McGILL UNIV, 77- *Honors & Awards:* Lawson Medal, Can Bot Asn, 74. *Mem:* Bot Soc Am; Hist Sci Soc; Can Bot Asn; Int Soc Plant Morphol; Linnean Soc London. *Res:* Philosophy of biology; developmental and theoretical plant morphology. *Mailing Add:* Dept of Biol McGill Univ Montreal Can

SATTSANGI, PREM DAS, b Ghazipur City, India, May 2, 39; m 68; c 2. *Educ:* Univ Allahabad, India, BS, 58, MS, 60, PhD(chem), 64. *Prof Exp:* Res assoc chem, Univ Ill, Urbana, 65-68; pool officer, 68-70, asst prof chem, 70-73, res assoc, 73-77, ASST PROF CHEM, PA STATE UNIV, 77- *Mem:* Am Chem Soc; The Chem Soc; Sigma Xi. *Res:* Synthesis of fluorescent probes; fluorescent modification of polypeptides of physiological interest; synthesis of heterocyclic compounds of biological interest. *Mailing Add:* Pa State Univ Fayette Campus Rte 119 N Uniontown PA 15401

SATTUR, THEODORE W, b Passaic, NJ, Oct 20, 20; m 41; c 3. ANALYTICAL CHEMISTRY. *Educ:* Rutgers Univ, BS, 42. *Prof Exp:* Chemist, Raritan Copper Works, 42-43; res chemist, Metal & Thermit Corp, 43-47; res chemist, Cent Res Labs, Am Smelting & Refining Co, NJ, 47-60, asst chief chemist, 60-73, sr res chemist, 73-76, RES ASSOC CENT RES LABS, ASARCO INC, 76- *Mem:* Am Chem Soc; Sigma Xi; Soc Appl Spectros; fel Am Inst Chemists. *Res:* Methods for trace determination of halogens, sulfur and arsenic; application of atomic absorption spectroscopy. *Mailing Add:* Cent Res Labs Asarco Inc South Plainfield NJ 07080

SATURNO, ANTONY FIDELAS, b Rochester, NY, Apr 7, 31; m 56; c 4. CHEMICAL PHYSICS. *Educ:* Univ Rochester, BS, 54; Carnegie Inst Technol, MS, 57, PhD(chem), 59. *Prof Exp:* Instr chem, Carnegie Inst Technol, 58-59; from asst prof to assoc prof, Univ Tenn, 59-66; assoc prof, 66-71, PROF CHEM, STATE UNIV NY ALBANY, 71-, CHMN DEPT, 74- *Concurrent Pos:* Consult, Metal & Ceramics Div, Oak Ridge Nat Lab, 63-66. *Mem:* AAAS; Am Chem Soc; Am Phys Soc. *Res:* Quantum chemistry, especially the application of high speed computers to chemical problems concerning the electronic structure of small molecules and atoms. *Mailing Add:* Dept of Chem State Univ of NY Albany NY 12203

SATYA, AKELLA V S, b Madras, India, Nov 21, 39; m 64; c 2. MATERIALS SCIENCE, PHYSICAL METALLURGY. *Educ:* Indian Inst Technol, Kharagpur, BTech, 60, MTech, 62; Mich State Univ, PhD(mat sci), 69. *Prof Exp:* Assoc lectr phys metall, Indian Inst Technol, Kharagpur, 60-62; chief metallurgist, Midwest Mach Co Ind, Inc, Mich, 64-66, consult, 66-67; adv engr, 69-80, MGR, DIAG DEVELOP, IBM CORP, 80- *Concurrent Pos:* Hon lectr, Indian Inst Sci, Bangalore, 62; consult, Nat Aeronaut Labs, Bangalore, 62. *Mem:* Am Phys Soc; Electrochem Soc; Am Soc Metals; Indian Inst Metals (treas-secy, 60-62). *Res:* Microelectronic device design and processing; metal/SC contacts, ion implantation, thin films; low-temperature specific heats, electronic energy bands, metal and semiconductor physics; charge coupled devices; system reliability; semiconductor device diagnostics methodologies, yield modeling/forecasting and test structures; solid state physics; electronics engineering. *Mailing Add:* IBM Corp E Fishkill Facility Hopewell Junction NY 12533

SATYANARAYANA, MOTUPALLI, b Masulipatam, India, Feb 24, 28; m 55; c 3. ALGEBRA. *Educ:* Andhra Univ, BA, 47, MA, 49; Univ Wis, PhD(math), 66. *Prof Exp:* Asst prof math, Govt Cols, Andhra, India, 50-56; sr lectr, Sri Venkateswara Univ, 56-63; from asst prof to assoc prof, 66-71, PROF MATH, BOWLING GREEN STATE UNIV, 71- *Concurrent Pos:* Reviewer, Zentralbalatt Für Mathematik, 71- *Mem:* Am Math Soc. *Res:* Semigroups; rings and ordered structures; topological algebra. *Mailing Add:* 512 N Main Bowling Green OH 43402

SATZ, RONALD WAYNE, b Seattle, Wash, May 24, 51. OPERATIONS RESEARCH. *Educ:* Rensselaer Polytech Inst, BSc & MEng, 74. *Prof Exp:* Design engr, Int Harvester Co, 73; res engr, Caterpillar Tractor Co, 75; chief prod engr, Transpower Corp, 76-77; advan proj engr, 3M Co, 77-78; prod res engr, Budd Co, 78-80; SR SYST ENGR, GEN ELEC CO, 80- *Mem:* Am Soc Mech Engrs; Soc Automotive Engrs; Operations Res Soc Am; Int Soc Unified Sci. *Res:* Computer simulation of complex machines and processes, including system dynamics, structural analysis, and operations research; mathematical details of the reciprocal system of theoretical science. *Mailing Add:* PO Box 622 King of Prussia PA 19406

SAUBERLICH, HOWERDE EDWIN, b Ellington, Wis, Jan 23, 19; m 45; c 2. BIOCHEMISTRY, MICROBIOLOGY. *Educ:* Lawrence Univ, BA, 44; Univ Wis, MS, 46, PhD(biochem), 48. *Prof Exp:* Assoc animal nutritionist, Exp Sta, Auburn Univ, 48-50, prof & animal nutritionist, 50-58; assoc prof animal husb, Iowa State Univ, 59; chief chem div, Med Res & Nutrit Lab, Fitzsimons Gen Hosp, US Dept Army, Denver, 59-74; chief dept nutrit, 74-80, CHIEF, WESTERN HUMAN NUTRIT RES CTR, USDA, LETTERMAN ARMY INST RES, PRESIDIO OF SAN FRANCISCO, 80- *Concurrent Pos:* Res fel, Univ Tenn, 51; prof, Univ Indonesia, 57-59; prof, Colo State Univ, 64-74; vis prof, Vanderbilt Univ, 70-71; Dept Army res & study fel award, 70; adj prof, Univ Calif, Berkeley. *Honors & Awards:* Johnson Award, 52 & Borden Award, 71, Am Inst Nutrit; Meritorious Civilian Serv Award, US Army, 64; McLester Award, 65. *Mem:* Soc Exp Biol & Med; Am Soc Biol Chemists; Am Soc Animal Sci; Am Soc Microbiol; Am Soc Clin Nutrit. *Res:* Protein, amino acid, vitamin and mineral metabolism in the human, rat, monkey and mouse; nutrition of microorganisms; nutritional assessment and surveillance; vitamin metabolism; human nutrition; mineral and lipid metabolism. *Mailing Add:* Western Human Nutrit Res Ctr USDA Letterman Army Inst of Res Presidio of San Francisco CA 94129

SAUCIER, ROGER THOMAS, b New Orleans, La, Aug 30, 35; m 57; c 2. PHYSICAL GEOGRAPHY, ENVIRONMENTAL GEOLOGY. *Educ:* La State Univ, BA, 57, MA, 58, PhD, 68. *Prof Exp:* Res asst geol, Coastal Studies Inst, La State Univ, 59-61; geogr, Geol Br, Soils Div, 59-61, SPEC ASST, ENVIRON LAB, US ARMY ENGR WATERWAYS EXP STA, 74- *Mem:* Am Quaternary Asn; Soc Am Archaeol; fel Geol Soc Am; Asn Eng Geologists; Coastal Soc. *Res:* Applied research in geomorphology; alluvial and coastal morphology; sedimentology and areal geographic and geologic mapping as related to engineering design and construction activities; anthropology; quaternary and environmental geology; earth sciences. *Mailing Add:* Environ Lab PO Box 631 US Army Engr Waterways Exp Sta Vicksburg MS 39180

SAUCIER, WALTER JOSEPH, b Moncla, La, Oct 5, 21; m 43; c 7. METEOROLOGY. *Educ:* Univ Southwestern La, BA, 42; Univ Chicago, SM, 47, PhD(meteorol), 51. *Prof Exp:* Asst meteorol, Univ Chicago, 46-48, instr, 48-52; from asst prof to prof, Tex A&M Univ, 52-60; prof, Univ Okla, 60-69; PROF METEOROL, NC STATE UNIV, 69- *Concurrent Pos:* Bd trustees, Univ Corp Atmospheric Res, 67-69; mem bd cert consult meteorologists, Am Meteorol Soc, 70-75, chmn, 71-75; consult, Nat Acad Sci-Nat Res Coun, 71-77; mem bd dirs, Triangle Univs Consortium on Air Pollution, 72- *Mem:* Fel AAAS; Sigma Xi; fel Am Meteorol Soc; Am Geophys Union. *Res:* Atmospheric circulations and weather analysis. *Mailing Add:* Dept of Geosci NC State Univ Raleigh NC 27650

SAUDEK, CHRISTOPHER D, b Bronxville, NY, Oct 8, 41; m 66; c 3. DIABETES, LIPID METABOLISM. *Educ:* Harvard Univ, BA, 63; Cornell Univ, MD, 67. *Prof Exp:* Intern med, Presby-St Luke's Hosp, 67-68, resident, 68-69; resident, Harvard Med Serv, Boston City Hosp, 69-70; fel metab, Thorndike Mem Lab, 70-72; instr med, Harvard Med Sch, 72-73; ASST PROF, SCH MED, CORNELL UNIV, 73- *Concurrent Pos:* Dir, Metab Lab,

Sch Med, Cornell Univ, 73-, dir, Clin Res Ctr, 74-; adj asst prof, Rockefeller Univ, 74-; mem, Coun Arteriosclerosis, Am Heart Asn. *Mem:* Am Fedn Clin Res; Am Heart Asn; NY Acad Sci. *Res:* Choresteral metabolism in diabetes; diabetic pregnancy. *Mailing Add:* Cornell Sch Med 1300 York Ave New York NY 10021

SAUDER, WILLIAM CONRAD, b Wheeling, WVa, Jan 3, 34; m 55; c 2. PHYSICS, X-RAY SPECTROSCOPY. *Educ:* Va Mil Inst, BS, 55; Johns Hopkins Univ, PhD(physics), 63. *Prof Exp:* From instr to assoc prof, 55-68, PROF PHYSICS, VA MIL INST, 68- *Concurrent Pos:* Consult, Nat Bur Standards, 65-81. *Mem:* Am Phys Soc; Am Asn Physics Teachers. *Res:* Atomic constants; x-ray and gamma ray spectroscopy; ultrasonic interferometry. *Mailing Add:* Dept of Physics Va Mil Inst Lexington VA 24450

SAUER, CHARLES WILLIAM, b Louisville, Ky, Oct 5, 19; m 61. ORGANIC CHEMISTRY, BIOCHEMISTRY. *Educ:* Mass Inst Technol, SB, 41, PhD(chem), 49. *Prof Exp:* Sr chemist, Arthur D Little Inc, 49-62, bus mgr, Energy & Mat Div, 60-62; asst to mgr plans & liaison, Res & Develop, Missile & Space Systs Div, Douglas Aircraft Co, 62-65; dir res admin, Res Dept, Bell Aerosysts Co, 66, dir future systs res, 66-69; dir technol surv, Am Can Co, 69-72; prin scientist planning, Calspan Corp, 72-73; CONSULT, 74-; ADJ PROF, FUTURE STUDIES ACAD, STATE UNIV NY COL BUFFALO, 77- *Mem:* Fel AAAS; Am Chem Soc; Sigma Xi; Am Inst Aeronaut & Astronaut; World Future Soc. *Res:* Application of systems approach to analysis and synthesis of how and why man developes science and technology, technology enters society and influences the future; strategic and longer range planning; high temperature metallurgy; aliphatic nitro compounds and nitramines; research management. *Mailing Add:* 4421 Chestnut Ridge Rd Tonawanda NY 14150

SAUER, DAVID BRUCE, b Akron, Ohio, Sept 20, 39; m 61; c 5. PLANT PATHOLOGY. *Educ:* Kent State Univ, BA, 61; Univ Minn, MS, 64, PhD(plant path), 67. *Prof Exp:* RES PLANT PATHOLOGIST, US GRAIN MKT RES CTR, AGR RES SERV, USDA, 67- *Mem:* Am Phytopath Soc; Am Soc Microbiol. *Res:* Ecology and control of microorganisms in stored grain, including grain quality surveys, grain drying, mycotoxin studies and testing of chemical grain preservatives. *Mailing Add:* US Grain Mkt Res Ctr 1515 College Ave Manhattan KS 66502

SAUER, DENNIS THEODORE, b Lamont, Wash, Oct 26, 44; m 69. INORGANIC CHEMISTRY. *Educ:* Whitworth Col, BS, 66; Cent Wash State Col, MS, 68; Univ Idaho, PhD(inorg chem), 72. *Prof Exp:* Asst chem, Cent Wash State Col, 66-68; res fel, Univ Idaho, 68-71; fac intern chem, Univ Utah, 71-72; STAFF SCIENTIST, HERCULES, INC, 72- *Mem:* Am Chem Soc. *Res:* Fluorine chemistry; phosphorus and boron chemistry. *Mailing Add:* 7854 Deer Creek Rd Salt Lake City UT 84121

SAUER, HARRY JOHN, JR, b St Joseph, Mo, Jan 27, 35; m 56; c 9. MECHANICAL & AEROSPACE ENGINEERING. *Educ:* Mo Sch Mines, BS, 56, MS, 58; Kans State Univ, PhD(heat transfer), 63. *Prof Exp:* From instr to asst prof mech eng, Mo Sch Mines, 57-60; instr, Kans State Univ, 60-62; assoc prof, 62-66, PROF MECH & AERO ENG, UNIV MO-ROLLA, 66- *Concurrent Pos:* Sr eng & consult, Midwest Res Inst, 63-70. *Honors & Awards:* Hermann F Spoehrer Mem Award, Am Soc Heat, Refrig & Air-Conditioning Engrs, 79. *Mem:* Am Soc Mech Engrs; fel Am Soc Heat, Refrig & Air-Conditioning Engrs; Soc Automotive Engrs. *Res:* Heat transfer; thermophysical properties; environmental control; photographic science; author or co author of 60 technical publications. *Mailing Add:* Dept of Mech & Aerospace Eng Univ of Mo Rolla MO 65401

SAUER, HELMUT WILHELM, b Kassel, WGer, Aug 12, 36; m 68; c 2. DEVELOPMENTAL BIOLOGY. *Educ:* Univ Marburg, WGer, Dr rer nat, 65. *Prof Exp:* Asst prof, Univ Heidelberg, 65-73; assoc prof, Univ Konstanz, 73-76; prof, Univ Wurzburg, 76-81; PROF & HEAD DEVELOP BIOL, DEPT BIOL, TEX A&M UNIV, 81- *Concurrent Pos:* Fel cell biol, McArdle Lab Cancer Res, Univ Wis, Madison, 67-69. *Mem:* Ger Soc Zool; Ger Soc Biol Chemists; Ger Soc Entwicklungsbiol; Am Soc Zoologists; Soc Develop Biol. *Res:* Control of cellular growth and differentiation, employing a simple eukaryotic model Physarum and analyzing the mechanism of genome expression. *Mailing Add:* 1105 Austin College Station TX 77840

SAUER, HERBERT H, b Newark, NJ, Dec 9, 29; m 57; c 4. PHYSICS. *Educ:* Rutgers Univ, BSc, 53; Univ Iowa, PhD(physics), 62. *Prof Exp:* Vacuum tube engr, Fed Telecommun Labs, NJ, 53-54; physicist inst telecommun & aeronomy, Environ Sci Serv Admin, 63-70, PHYSICIST SPACE ENVIRON LAB, NAT OCEANIC & ATMOSPHERIC ADMIN, 70- *Concurrent Pos:* Vis lectr, Univ Colo, 65; vis prof, Univ Calgary, 69. *Mem:* Am Phys Soc; Am Geophys Union. *Res:* Magnetospheric and cosmic ray physics. *Mailing Add:* Space Environ Lab Nat Oceanic & Atmospheric Admin Boulder CO 80303

SAUER, JOHN ROBERT, b Aberdeen, SDak, Aug 1, 36; m 62; c 3. ENTOMOLOGY. *Educ:* St John's Univ, Minn, BS, 59; NMex Highlands Univ, MS, 64; Tulane Univ, PhD(biol), 69. *Prof Exp:* From asst to assoc prof, 69-77, PROF INSECT PHYSIOL, OKLA STATE UNIV, 77- *Concurrent Pos:* Sigma Xi grant-in-aid res, 68; NSF res grant, 72-; NIH res grant, 78- *Mem:* Sigma Xi; Entom Soc Am. *Res:* Insect physiology; osmoregulation; tick physiology. *Mailing Add:* 1304 W Osage Stillwater OK 74074

SAUER, JON ROBERT, b Schenectady, NY, Nov 24, 40; m 72; c 1. HIGH ENERGY PHYSICS, ACCELERATOR PHYSICS. *Educ:* Stanford Univ, BS, 62; Tufts Univ, PhD(physics), 70. *Prof Exp:* Staff physicist accelerator physics, Stanford Linear Accelerator Ctr, 62-64; Cambridge Electron Accelerator, 69-70 & Fermilab, 70-77; sr res assoc high energy physics, Ind Univ, 77-78; ASST PHYSICIST HIGH ENERGY PHYSICS, ARGONNE NAT LAB, 78- *Mailing Add:* Argonne Nat Lab 9700 S Cass Ave Argonne IL 60439

SAUER, JONATHAN DEININGER, b Ann Arbor, Mich, July 5, 18; m 46; c 1. BIOGEOGRAPHY. *Educ:* Univ Calif, AB, 39; Washington Univ, MA, 48, PhD(genetics), 50. *Prof Exp:* From instr to assoc prof bot, Univ Wis-Madison, 50-59, from assoc prof to prof bot & geog, 59-67; vis prof geog, La State Univ, 67- *Concurrent Pos:* Vis assoc cur, Herbarium, Univ Mich, 55-56; dir bot gardens & herbarium, Univ Calif, Los Angeles, 74- *Mem:* Am Geog Soc; Ecol Soc Am; Am Soc Plant Taxon; Org Trop Studies; Soc Econ Bot. *Res:* Recent plant migration and evolution; systematics of Amaranthus, Canavalia and Stenotaphrum; dynamics of seacoast and riverbank pioneer vegetation. *Mailing Add:* 659 Erskine Dr Pacific Palisades CA 90272

SAUER, KENNETH, b Cleveland, Ohio, June 19, 31; m 58; c 4. BIOPHYSICAL CHEMISTRY. *Educ:* Oberlin Col, AB, 53; Harvard Univ, MA, 54, PhD(chem), 58. *Prof Exp:* From instr to asst prof chem, Am Univ Beirut, 57-60; NIH res fel, 60-63, from asst prof to assoc prof, 63-72, PROF CHEM, UNIV CALIF, BERKELEY, 72-, MEM SR STAFF, LAB CHEM BIODYN, 62- *Concurrent Pos:* Guggenheim fel, 76-77. *Mem:* Fel AAAS; Am Chem Soc; Biophys Soc; Am Soc Plant Physiologists; Am Soc Photobiol. *Res:* Photosynthetic energy conversion; biological molecular structure; molecular spectroscopy; fluorescence liftimes; excitation transfer. *Mailing Add:* Dept of Chem Univ of Calif Berkeley CA 94720

SAUER, LEONARD A, b Schenectady, NY, Aug 20, 29; m 56; c 3. CELL BIOLOGY, BIOCHEMISTRY. *Educ:* Cornell Univ, BS, 56; Univ Rochester, MD, 60; Rockefeller Univ, PhD(cell biol), 66. *Prof Exp:* From instr to assoc prof med, Sch Med, Yale Univ, 67-73; RES PHYSICIAN PATH, MARY IMOGENE BASSETT HOSP, 73- *Concurrent Pos:* USPHS spec fel, Univ Marburg, 66-67. *Mem:* Am Soc Biol Chemists; Am Soc Cell Biol; Endocrine Soc; Soc Exp Biol & Med. *Res:* Cell regulatory processes; mitochondrial physiology; adrenal steroidogenesis; tumor biology. *Mailing Add:* Dept of Path Mary Imogene Bassett Hosp Cooperstown NY 13326

SAUER, MYRAN CHARLES, JR, b Pittsburgh, Pa, Nov 30, 33; m 59; c 3. RADIATION CHEMISTRY. *Educ:* Carnegie Inst Technol, BS, 55; Univ Wis, PhD(chem), 58. *Prof Exp:* Resident res assoc, 59-61, asst chemist, 61-63, ASSOC CHEMIST, ARGONNE NAT LAB, 63- *Mem:* Am Chem Soc; Radiation Res Soc. *Res:* Kinetics and mechanisms of reactions initiated by ionizing radiation and light. *Mailing Add:* Chem Div Argonne Nat Lab Argonne IL 60439

SAUER, PETER WILLIAM, b Winona, Minn, Sept 20, 46; m 69; c 2. ELECTRICAL ENGINEERING. *Educ:* Univ Mo-Rolla, BS, 69; Purdue Univ, MS, 74, PhD(elec eng), 77. *Prof Exp:* Design engr, US Air Force Tactical Air Command, 69-73; res asst, Elec Eng Dept, Purdue Univ, 73-77; ASST PROF ELEC ENG, UNIV ILL, URBANA, 77- *Concurrent Pos:* Elec power consult, US Army Corps Eng Res Lab, 75-; prin investr, NSF grant, 78-; res dir, Ill Power Affil Prog, 78- *Mem:* Sigma Xi; Inst Elec & Electronics Engrs. *Res:* Electrical power system simulation and analysis; electric power system operation and planning methods; electric power system operation and planning methods; electric power system dynamics and control. *Mailing Add:* 155 Elec Eng Bldg Univ Ill 1406 W Green St Urbana IL 61801

SAUER, RICHARD JOHN, b Walker, Minn, Nov 15, 39; m 62; c 4. ENTOMOLOGY. *Educ:* St John's Univ, Minn, BS, 62; Univ Mich, Ann Arbor, MS, 64; NDak State Univ, PhD(entom), 67. *Prof Exp:* Teaching asst zool, Univ Mich, Ann Arbor, 62-64; asst prof biol, St Cloud State Col, 67-68; asst prof biol & entom, Mich State Univ, 68-70, exten entom, 70-72, assoc prof exten entom & exten pesticide coordr, 72-76; prof entom & head dept, Kans State Univ, 76-80; DIR, MINN AGR EXP STA, UNIV MINN, ST PAUL, 80- *Concurrent Pos:* Entom consult, Coop State Res Serv, USDA, 74-75. *Mem:* Entom Soc Am; Sigma Xi. *Res:* Taxonomy and biology of spiders; clearance of minor use pesticides; pesticide usage and safety. *Mailing Add:* Minn Agr Exp Sta 1420 Eckles Ave 220 Coffey Hall St Paul MN 55108

SAUER, THEODOR CHARLES, JR, b New Brunswick, NJ, Jan 23, 47; m 71. GEOCHEMISTRY, MARINE CHEMISTRY. *Educ:* Lehigh Univ, BS, 70; Old Dominion Univ, MS, 74; Tex A&M Univ, MEng, 77, PhD(chem oceanog), 78. *Prof Exp:* Res asst, Dept Chem, Woods Hole Oceanog Inst, 75; res asst, Dept Oceanog, Tex A&M Univ, 75-77, res assoc, 77-78; RES CHEMIST, EXXON PROD RES CO, 78- *Mem:* Am Geophys Union; Am Inst Chem Engrs. *Res:* Volatile organics in marine and natural waters; natural and petroleum hydrocarbon geochemistry; trace metal hydrocarbon pollution; computer modelling of pollutant discharges into the marine environment. *Mailing Add:* Exxon Prod Res Co PO Box 2189 Houston TX 77001

SAUER, WILLIAM GEORGE, medicine, deceased

SAUERBRUNN, ROBERT DEWEY, b Jonesboro, Ill, Dec 27, 22; m 47; c 2. ANALYTICAL CHEMISTRY, POLYMER CHEMISTRY. *Educ:* Southern Ill Univ, BS, 47; Univ Minn, PhD(anal chem), 53. *Prof Exp:* Develop assoc res & develop, 53-62, sr res chemist polymer chem, 62-63, SUPVR RES & DEVELOP, E I DU PONT DE NEMOURS & CO, INC, 63- *Mem:* Am Chem Soc. *Res:* Electrochemical and spectrophotometric analyses; chemical kinetics and polymer chemistry. *Mailing Add:* 904 Robin Dr Seaford DE 19973

SAUERLAND, EBERHARDT KARL, b Ger, Dec 17, 33; US citizen. ANATOMY. *Educ:* Univ Kiel, MD, 60. *Prof Exp:* From intern to resident, St John Gen Hosp, NB, 60-62; res scientist aerospace med, Lockheed-Calif Co, Burbank, 62-64; asst prof anat, Sch Med, Univ Calif, Los Angeles, 64-70, assoc prof anat & oral med, 70-71; prof anat, Univ Tex Med Br Galveston, 71-80; DIR, CLIN INVEST FAC, WILFORD HALL, US AIR FORCE MED CTR, LACKLAND AIR FORCE BASE, TEX, 80-, RESIDENT DIAG RADIOL, 80- *Concurrent Pos:* Adj prof anat, Univ Tex Med Br Galveston, 80-; vis prof anat, USUHS, 80. *Mem:* Am Asn Anat. *Res:* Interaction of brain and reflex mechanisms; electromyography. *Mailing Add:* Wilford Hall US Air Force Med Ctr Lackland Air Force Base TX 78236

SAUERMANN, GERHARD OTTO, electrooptics, see previous edition

SAUERS, CAROL KILBOURNE, b Boston, Mass, Apr 12, 33; div; c 2. ORGANIC CHEMISTRY. *Educ:* Pembroke Col, AB, 54; Univ Ill, PhD(org chem), 57. *Prof Exp:* Res chemist, Union Carbide Plastics Co, 57-59; res assoc, Inst Microbiol, Rutgers Univ, 61-64; asst prof chem, Georgian Court Col, 65-67; from instr to asst prof, 67-71, ASSOC PROF CHEM, DOUGLASS COL, RUTGERS UNIV, NEW BRUNSWICK, 71- *Concurrent Pos:* NIH spec fel & vis assoc prof, Brandeis Univ, 72-73. *Mem:* Am Chem Soc; The Chem Soc. *Res:* Hydrolysis of isoimides; dehydration of amic acids; carbon dioxide, carbonyl sulfide and carbon disulfide-alcohol interactions; general acid catalysis. *Mailing Add:* Dept of Chem Douglass Col Rutgers Univ New Brunswick NJ 08904

SAUERS, RICHARD FRANK, b Philadelphia, Pa, Apr 4, 39; m 66; c 4. ORGANIC CHEMISTRY. *Educ:* LaSalle Col, BA, 65; Univ Minn, PhD(org chem), 69. *Prof Exp:* Chemist, Smith Kline & French Labs, 63-65; sr res chemist, 69-80, RES SUPVR, E I DU PONT DE NEMOURS & CO, INC, 80- *Mem:* Am Chem Soc. *Res:* Biologically active materials. *Mailing Add:* Biochem Dept Exp Sta E I du Pont de Nemours & Co Inc Wilmington DE 19898

SAUERS, RONALD RAYMOND, b Pittsburgh, Pa, June 19, 32; c 2. ORGANIC CHEMISTRY. *Educ:* Pa State Univ, BS, 53; Univ Ill, PhD(chem), 56. *Prof Exp:* USPHS fel, Univ Ill, 56-57; from instr to assoc prof, 57-70, PROF CHEM, RUTGERS UNIV, NEW BRUNSWICK, 70- *Concurrent Pos:* Vis fel, Princeton Univ, 66-67; USPHS spec fel, Brandeis Univ, 72-73. *Mem:* Am Chem Soc. *Res:* Stereochemistry of organic reactions; polycyclic hydrocarbon systems; organic photochemistry. *Mailing Add:* Dept of Chem Rutgers Univ New Brunswick NJ 08903

SAUL, FRANK PHILIP, b New York, NY, Oct 31, 30; m 64; c 2. BIOLOGICAL ANTHROPOLOGY, ANATOMY. *Educ:* Brooklyn Col, AB, 52; Harvard Univ, AM, 59, PhD, 72; Am Bd Forensic Anthrop, dipl, 78. *Prof Exp:* Field asst, archaeol exped to SDak, Univ Mus, Kans, 50; asst phys anthrop, Am Mus Natural Hist, 51-52; phys anthropologist, Aero Med Lab, Wright Air Develop Ctr, US Dept Air Force, 53-58 & Natick Qm Res & Eng Ctr, US Dept Army, 58-59; field study Hutterite morphol, Harvard Univ, 59, teaching fel anthrop, 59-62; instr, Pa State Univ, 62-67, asst prof anthrop & phys anthropologist, Eastern Pa Archaeol Projs, 67-69; asst prof anat, 69-71, ASSOC PROF ANAT, MED COL OHIO, 72- *Concurrent Pos:* Human factors consult, 59-; res assoc, Boston Mus Sci, 60-62; phys anthropologist Maya area projs, Peabody Mus, Harvard Univ, 62-; biol anthropologist Maya area projs, Cambridge Univ, 70-; Sigma Xi-Sci Res Soc Am regional lectr, 71-; hon cur biomed anthrop, Toledo Mus Health & Natural History, 77; vis prof phys anthrop, Univ Cambridge, 78. *Mem:* Fel Am Anthrop Asn; Am Asn Phys Anthrop; fel Royal Anthrop Inst; Am Soc Human Genetics; Int Asn Human Biol. *Res:* Osteology; human factors; origin and evolution of the Maya; biomedical anthropology; paleopathology; paleoepidemiology. *Mailing Add:* Dept Anat Med Col Ohio C S 10008 Toledo OH 43699

SAUL, GEORGE BRANDON, II, b Hartford, Conn, Aug 8, 28; m 53. GENETICS. *Educ:* Univ Pa, AB, 49, AM, 50, PhD(zool), 54. *Prof Exp:* Asst instr zool, Univ Pa, 50-52; from instr to assoc prof, Dartmouth Col, 54-67; chmn dept, 68-76, acad vpres, 76-79, PROF BIOL, MIDDLEBURY COL, 67- *Concurrent Pos:* NSF sci fac fel, Univ Zurich, 59-60; res fel biol, Calif Inst Technol, 64-65; vis scientist, Boyce Thompson Inst Plant Res, 72-73. *Mem:* Fel AAAS; Radiation Res Soc; Genetics Soc Am; Am Genetic Asn; Sigma Xi. *Res:* Cytogenetics; biochemical genetics; embryological genetics of Mormoniella vitripennis; extranuclear genetics. *Mailing Add:* Dept of Biol Middlebury Col Middlebury VT 05753

SAUL, LEON JOSEPH, b New York, NY, Apr 26, 01; m 34; c 3. PSYCHIATRY. *Educ:* Columbia Univ, AB, 21, MA, 23; Harvard Med Sch, MD, 28; Am Bd Psychiat & Neurol, dipl, 37. *Prof Exp:* Commonwealth fel, Boston Psychopath Hosp & Harvard Med Sch, 30-32; clin assoc, Inst Psychoanal, Chicago, 32-42; assoc prof psychiat, Sch Med, Temple Univ, 46-48; prof clin psychiat, 48-60, prof psychiat, 60-69, EMER PROF PSYCHIAT, SCH MED, UNIV PA, 69- *Concurrent Pos:* Assoc attend physician, Cook County Psychopath Hosp, 36-42; consult, Vet Admin Hosp, Pa, 46-54; staff & training analyst, Philadelphia Psychoanal Inst, 46-70, emer analyst, 70-; lectr, Bryn Mawr Col, 46-50; chief psychiat consult, Swarthmore Col, 48-71, emer psychiat consult, 71-; mem staff, Inst of Pa Hosp, 56-70, hon consult, 70- *Mem:* Am Physiol Soc; Am Psychosom Soc (pres, 48-49); fel Am Acad Psychoanal; fel Am Col Psychoanal; fel Am Col Psychiat. *Res:* Cerebral action potentials; emotional factors in essential hypertension asthma and urticaria; psychodynamics role of hostility in neuroses and social relations. *Mailing Add:* 275 Highland Ave Media PA 19063

SAUL, ROBERT H, b New York, NY, Apr 4, 40; m 66; c 2. MATERIALS SCIENCE, SOLID STATE PHYSICS. *Educ:* Carnegie-Mellon Univ, BS, 63, MS, 65, PhD(mat sci), 67. *Prof Exp:* GROUP SUPVR, BELL LABS, 67- *Mem:* Electrochem Soc; Am Phys Soc. *Res:* Electro-optic materials and devices; reliability of electroluminescent devices and optical interfaces. *Mailing Add:* Bell Labs 600 Mountain Ave Murray Hill NJ 07974

SAUL, WILLIAM EDWARD, b New York, NY, May 15, 34. STRUCTURAL ENGINEERING, STRUCTURAL DYNAMICS. *Educ:* Mich Technol Univ, BS, 55, MS, 61; Northwestern Univ, PhD(civil eng), 64. *Prof Exp:* Mech engr, Shell Oil Co, 55-59; teaching asst, Mich Technol Univ, 59-60, instr eng mech, 60-62; from asst prof to assoc prof, 64-72, chmn dept, 76-80, PROF CIVIL ENG, UNIV WIS-MADISON, 72- *Concurrent Pos:* Indust consult, 64-; vis prof, Inst Static & Dynamic Aerospace Eng, Univ Stuttgart, 70-71, Fulbright travel grant, Alexander von Humboldt stipendium & Univ Wis Alumni Res Found grant. *Mem:* Fel Am Soc Civil Engrs; Int Asn Bridge & Struct Engrs; Sigma Xi; Am Soc Eng Educ. *Res:* Dynamic response of structures; computer methods in structural analysis; theory of structures; reinforced concrete structures; applications in the response of structures due to high intensity forces such as earthquake, blast or storm; foundations; pite foundations. *Mailing Add:* 2817 Regent St Madison WI 53705

SAULL, VINCENT ALEXANDER, b Montreal, Que, June 25, 27; m 54; c 5. GEOPHYSICS. *Educ:* McGill Univ, BSc, 48; Mass Inst Technol, PhD(theoret geophys), 52. *Prof Exp:* Res asst geophys, Mass Inst Technol, 48-49, teaching fel, 49-51; from asst prof to assoc prof, 52-67, PROF GEOL SCI, McGILL UNIV, 67- *Concurrent Pos:* Sr res fel, Nat Res Coun Can, 67-68, mem subcomt seismol & physics of earth's interior, Nat Assoc Comt Geod & Geophys, 71-75; indust consult seismicity & seismic hazard, 75- *Mem:* Am Geophys Union; Can Inst Mining & Metall; Can Soc Study Hist & Philos Sci. *Res:* Role of chemical energy in tectonics and in the energy economy of the earth's crust; earthquake hazard and earthquake prediction; paleoclimate calculations from borehole temperature measurements; design of electronic systems to monitor seismic and other geophysical activity. *Mailing Add:* Dept of Geol Sci McGill Univ 3450 Univ St Montreal PQ H3A 2A7 Can

SAUNDERS, ALLEN PERRY, microbiology, deceased

SAUNDERS, B DAVID, b Bryan, Tex, April 12, 44; m 68; c 3. COMPUTER ALGEBRA. *Educ:* Univ Wis, BA, 70, PhD(math), 75. *Prof Exp:* PROF MATH & COMPUT SCI, RENSSELAER POLYTECH INST, 75- *Mem:* Asn Comput Mach; Am Math Soc; AAAS. *Res:* Systems and algorithms for symbolic mathematical computation, particularly integration in finite terms. *Mailing Add:* Math Sci Dept Rensselaer Polytech Inst Troy NY 12181

SAUNDERS, BARBARA GAIL BREIDENBACH, chemical kinetics, see previous edition

SAUNDERS, DONALD FREDERICK, b Utica, NY, Nov 9, 24; m 50; c 3. EXPLORATION GEOLOGY. *Educ:* St Lawrence Univ, BS, 46; Univ Wis, PhD(chem), 50. *Prof Exp:* Proj assoc, Univ Wis, 50-53; sr engr, Tex Instruments, Inc, 53-57; chief res geochemist, Geophys Serv, Inc, 57-62; mem tech staff, 62-67, mgr radiation sci, 67-70, mgr new prog develop, 70-73, SR GEOSCIENTIST, TEX INSTRUMENTS INC, 73- *Mem:* AAAS; Asn Explor Geochemists. *Res:* Thermoluminescence of rocks and minerals; geochemistry of the origin of uranium deposits; geochemical prospecting; nuclear arms control studies; remote sensing of natural resources; geological interpretation of satellite imagery; environmental studies. *Mailing Add:* 4057 Northaven Rd Dallas TX 75229

SAUNDERS, DONALD ROY, b Chicago, Ill, June 2, 40; m 79. TOXICOLOGY, ENVIRONMENTAL SCIENCES. *Educ:* Leland Stanford Jr Univ, AB, 63; Purdue Univ, MS, 70, PhD(pharmacol, toxicol), 73; Am Bd Toxicol, dipl, 81. *Prof Exp:* Sr toxicologist, Riker Labs Inc, 73-76; res toxicologist, 76-77, sr toxicologist, 77-78, toxicol contract admin, 78-82, MGR TOXICOL PLANNING & CONTRACTS, STAUFFER CHEM CO, 82- *Mem:* AAAS; Soc Environ Toxicol & Chem. *Res:* Safety evaluation of new drugs; effects of aging on responses to drugs. *Mailing Add:* 400 Farmington Ave Stauffer Chem Co Farmington CT 06032

SAUNDERS, EDWARD A, b Manilla, Iowa, Mar 30, 25; m 46; c 4. SOLID STATE ELECTRONICS, NUCLEAR SCIENCE. *Educ:* US Mil Acad, BSMSE, 46; Purdue Univ, MS, 51; Rensselaer Polytech Inst, PhD(nuclear sci), 65. *Prof Exp:* Instr electronics, 51-54, prof elec, 61-65, PROF PHYSICS & HEAD DEPT, US MIL ACAD, 65- *Mem:* Am Asn Physics Teachers; Am Soc Eng Educ. *Res:* Radiation damage on semiconductor materials. *Mailing Add:* Dept of Physics US Mil Acad West Point NY 10996

SAUNDERS, FRANK AUSTIN, b Suffolk, Va, Dec 4, 40; m 63; c 2. REHABILITATINN ENGINEERING, PSYCHOLOGY. *Educ:* Juilliard Sch, BS, 61; Ind Univ, Bloomington, PhD(psychol), 65. *Prof Exp:* Res psychologist, Langley Porter Neuropsychiat Inst, 66-68; RES ASSOC & SR SCIENTIST, SMITH-KETTLEWELL INST VISUAL SCI, 68- *Concurrent Pos:* Fel med psychol, Langley Porter Neuropsychiat Inst, San Francisco, 65-66; clin instr med psychol, Sch Med, Univ Calif, San Francisco, 68-; lectr psychol, San Francisco State Col, 68- *Honors & Awards:* Hektoen Award, Am Med Asn, 72 & 77. *Mem:* Am Psychol Asn; Acoust Soc Am; Inst Elec & Electronics Eng; Biomed Eng Soc. *Res:* Development of electrotactile displays and sensory aids for deaf and blind persons. *Mailing Add:* 2232 Webster St San Francisco CA 94115

SAUNDERS, FRANK LINWOOD, b Moline, Ill, July 26, 26; m 49; c 2. PHYSICAL CHEMISTRY. *Educ:* Augustana Col, AB, 50; Case Western Reserve Univ, MS, 52, PhD(chem), 53. *Prof Exp:* Proj leader, 56-66, group leader, 66-75, sr res specialist, 75-80, RES ASSOC, DOW CHEM CO, 80- *Mem:* Am Chem Soc; Sigma Xi. *Res:* Polymer and colloid chemistry; latexes; stereospecific polymers. *Mailing Add:* Cent Res Dow Chem Co 1712 Bldg Midland MI 48640

SAUNDERS, FRANK WENDELL, b Reidsville, NC, Sept 27, 22; m 51; c 3. MATHEMATICS. *Educ:* Univ NC, AB, 45, MA, 47. *Prof Exp:* Instr math, Univ NC, 47-49; prof, Coker Col, 49-61; dir grad studies in math, 70-76, actg chmn dept, 76-78, PROF MATH, EAST CAROLINA UNIV, 61- *Res:* Number theory. *Mailing Add:* Dept of Math E Carolina Univ Greenville NC 27834

SAUNDERS, FRED MICHAEL, b Lawton, Okla. WATER & WASTEWATER TREATMENT. *Educ:* Va Polytech Inst, BS, 67, MS, 69; Univ Ill, Urbana-Champaign, PhD(civil eng), 75. *Prof Exp:* Design engr, Wiley & Wilson Consults, Inc, 74; asst prof, 74-80, ASSOC PROF CIVIL ENG, GEORGIA INST TECHNOL, 80- *Concurrent Pos:* Vchmn, Water Pollution Control Fedn Res Comt, 80-82; mem, Sessions Progs Comt, Am Soc Civil Engrs, 80-82, Nat Environ Eng Abstract Review Comt, 81-82, Distinguished Lectr Comt, Asn Environ Eng Profs, 77-82, Water Pollution Control Fedn Standard Methods Comt, 75-82, & Toxic Substances Comt, Water Pollution Control Fedn, 77-82; ed, Am Soc Chem Engrs Nat Conf Environ Eng, 81. *Mem:* Am Soc Civil Engrs; Int Asn Water Pollution Res; Water Pollution Control Fedn; Am Chem Soc; Asn Environ Eng Professors. *Res:* Investigation of unit operations and processes used in treatment, reclamation and disposal of industrial and domestic waters, wastewaters and residues including biological wastewater treatment; thickening, dewatering and reclamation of aluminum-finishing and metal-plating wastewaters and sludges; ozonation of wastewaters. *Mailing Add:* Environ Eng Daniel Lab Georgia Inst Technol Atlanta GA 30332

SAUNDERS, GEORGE CHERDRON, b Flushing, NY, Jan 4, 40; m 67; c 2. IMMUNOLOGY, IMMUNOCHEMISTRY. *Educ:* Univ Pa, VMD, 64. *Prof Exp:* Fel immunopath, Univ Colo Med Ctr, Denver, 64-66, from instr to asst prof, 66-72; STAFF MEM DIAG IMMUNOL, LOS ALAMOS SCI LAB, UNIV CALIF, 73- *Concurrent Pos:* Adj asst prof path, Sch Med, Univ NMex, 73-77, adj assoc prof, 78- *Mem:* Soc Anal Cytol; Am Asn Path. *Res:* Design, development and implementation of rapid automated antibody screening tests; indirect enzyme labeled antibody concept as a major tool in this research; clinical applications of flow cytometry. *Mailing Add:* Exp Path Group Mail Stop 888 Los Alamos Nat Lab PO Box 1663 Los Alamos NM 87545

SAUNDERS, GRADY FRANKLIN, b Bakersfield, Calif, July 11, 38; m 59; c 1. MOLECULAR BIOLOGY. *Educ:* Ore State Univ, BS, 60, MS, 62; Univ Ill, Urbana, PhD(microbiol), 65. *Prof Exp:* USPHS fel, Inst Physicochem Biol, Univ Paris, 65-66; from asst prof to assoc prof, 66-78, PROF BIOCHEM, UNIV TEX SYST CANCER CTR, M D ANDERSON HOSP & TUMOR INST, 78- *Concurrent Pos:* US-USSR exchange scientist, Inst Molecular Biol, USSR Acad Sci, Moscow, 72. *Mem:* Am Chem Soc; Biophys Soc; Am Soc Biol Chemists; Am Soc Cell Biol. *Res:* Regulation of gene activity; chromosome anatomy. *Mailing Add:* Univ of Tex Syst Cancer Ctr M D Anderson Hosp & Tumor Inst Houston TX 77030

SAUNDERS, HARRY LINK, b Orange, NJ, Aug 10, 25; m 53; c 4. MAMMALIAN PHYSIOLOGY. *Educ:* Rutgers Univ, BSc, 50, MSc, 52; Cornell Univ, PhD, 55. *Prof Exp:* Sr biochemist, 55-59, group leader biochem, 59-64, asst sect head endocrinol, 64-67, assoc dir biochem, 67-78, assoc dir res & develop regulatory affairs, 78-80, DIR REGULATORY COORD, SMITH KLINE & FRENCH LABS, 80- *Mem:* AAAS; Endocrine Soc; Am Physiol Soc; Am Diabetes Asn; NY Acad Sci. *Res:* Diabetes and endocrine aspects of intermediary metabolism. *Mailing Add:* Smith Kline & French Labs 1500 Spring Garden St Philadelphia PA 19101

SAUNDERS, JACK K, JR, mammalian ecology, wildlife biology, see previous edition

SAUNDERS, JACK PALMER, b London, Eng, Sept 11, 15; nat US; m 42; c 2. PHARMACOLOGY. *Educ:* City Col New York, BS, 36; Univ Md, MS, 49, PhD(biochem), 53. *Prof Exp:* Chemist, R H Macy & Co, NY, 39-41; pharmacologist, Pharmacol Br, Chem Corps Med Labs, US Army Chem Ctr, Md, 46-48, 50-56, dep chief, 54-56; biochemist, USPHS Nutrit Unit, State Dept Health, Md, 48-50; exec secy, Pharmacol Exp Therapeut Study Sect, NIH, 56-57, asst chief extramural progs, Nat Inst Allergy & Infectious Dis, 57, exec secy, Cancer Chemotherapy Study Sect, 57-59, exec secy, Metab Study Sect, 59, asst chief biol sci, Res Grants Rev Br, Div Res Grants, 59-60, exec secy biochem, Biophys Sci, 60-61, chief, 61-64, assoc chief, Div Res Grants, 64-65, dep sci dir chemother, Nat Cancer Inst, 65-67, assoc dir extramural activities, 67-72, dir div cancer grants, 72-73, dir div cancer res resources & ctr, 73-74; PROF PHARMACOL & TOXICOL & DEAN GRAD SCH BIOMED SCI, UNIV TEX MED BR GALVESTON, 74- *Concurrent Pos:* Consult, Nat Cancer Inst, 74-; co-chmn, Int Symp Immunol Cancer, Univ Tex Med Br/Montpellier Univ, France, 80. *Mem:* AAAS; Am Soc Pharmacol & Exp Therapeut; Am Chem Soc; fel Am Inst Chem; Soc Toxicol. *Res:* Toxicology; pharmacology of pesticides; nutrition. *Mailing Add:* 164 San Fernando Dr Galveston TX 77550

SAUNDERS, JAMES ALLEN, b Cleveland, Ohio, Oct 4, 49; m 75; c 1. PLANT BIOCHEMISTRY, PLANT PHYSIOLOGY. *Educ:* Univ SFla, BA, 71; Miami Univ Ohio, PhD(bot), 75. *Prof Exp:* Teaching assoc, Miami Univ Ohio, 71-75; res biochemist, Univ Calif, Davis, 75-77; RES BIOCHEMIST, TOBACCO LAB, BARC-WEST, USDA, 77-; PRES, NATIVE SEEDS, INC, 80- *Mem:* Sigma Xi; Am Soc Plant Physiologists; Phytochem Soc NAm; AAAS. *Res:* Subcellular localization of secondary natural products in plants and their biosynthetic enzyme complexes including flavonoids, cyanogenic glucosides, alkaloids, and phenolics; health related poblems from tobacco use. *Mailing Add:* Tobacco Lab USDA SEA BARC-West Beltsville MD 20705

SAUNDERS, JAMES CHARLES, b Elizabeth, NJ, May 8, 41; m 67; c 2. PHYSIOLOGICAL PSYCHOLOGY, NEUROBIOLOGY. *Educ:* Ohio Wesleyan Univ, BA, 63; Conn Col, MA, 65; Princeton Univ, PhD(psychol), 68. *Hon Degrees:* MA, Univ Pa, 80. *Prof Exp:* Asst prof psychol, Monash Univ, Australia, 69-72; res assoc, Cent Inst Deaf, St Louis, 72-73; asst prof, 73-79, ASSOC PROF OTORHINOLARYNGOL, SCH MED, UNIV PA, 79- *Concurrent Pos:* Fel, Auditory Labs, Princeton Univ, 68; res fel, Dept Physiol, Univ Western Australia, 70; med assoc, Philadelphia Gen Hosp, 75-77; res assoc, Philadelphia Vet Hosp, 77-78; actg dir, Inst Neurol Sci, Univ Pa, 81-82. *Mem:* Acoust Soc Am; Asn Res Otolaryngol; AAAS; Neurosci Soc. *Res:* Communicative science; communicative disorders; audition; auditory neurobiology; animal psychoacoustics; physiological acoustics; developmental neurobiology; auditory psychology. *Mailing Add:* Dept Otorhinolaryngol & Human Commun 5 Silverstein OTO 3400 Spruce St Philadelphia PA 19104

SAUNDERS, JAMES HENRY, b Ames, Iowa, May 3, 23; m 46; c 4. POLYMER CHEMISTRY, ORGANIC CHEMISTRY. *Educ:* Univ Ky, BS, 44; Univ Ill, PhD(org chem), 46. *Prof Exp:* Spec asst rubber res, Univ Ill, 44-47, group leader, 46-47; chemist, Monsanto Chem Co, 47-50, group leader, 50-54; group leader, Mobay Chem Co, Pa, 54-55, asst dir res, 55-59, dir res, 59-67; mgr nylon res, 68-69, dir nylon & polyester res, 69-75, dir res, Tech Ctr, 76-78, dir polyester res & develop, 79-80, GEN MGR TECHNOL, MONSANTO TEXTILES CO, 80- *Mem:* AAAS; Am Inst Chemists; NY Acad Sci; Am Chem Soc; Fiber Soc. *Res:* Emulsion polymerization; synthesis of substituted styrenes and butadienes; biphenyl and phosgene chemistry; preparation, reactions and applications of isocyanates; polyesters; polycarbonates; polyethers; polyurethanes; polyamides; synthetic foams; elastomers; coatings; adhesives; thermoplastics; synthetic fibers. *Mailing Add:* Monsanto Textiles Co 800 N Lindbergh Blvd St Louis MO 63166

SAUNDERS, JAMES ROBERT, b Simcoe, Ont, Oct 6, 31; m 55; c 4. VETERINARY PATHOLOGY, VETERINARY MICROBIOLOGY. *Educ:* Ont Vet Col, Univ Guelph, DVM, 54; Univ Toronto, dipl vet pub health, 57; Univ Wis, PhD(vet sci, cell physiol), 61. *Prof Exp:* Vet practitioner, Sask, 54-56; res asst microbiol vet sci, Univ Wis, 57-60; vet pathologist, Sask Dept Agr, 60-61; asst prof vet path & microbiol, Purdue Univ, 61-65; assoc prof vet microbiol, 65-70, PROF VET MICROBIOL, UNIV SASK, 70-, CHMN DEPT, 74- *Concurrent Pos:* NIH gen res grant, 63-65; Nat Res Coun Can grant, 66-67. *Mem:* Am Asn Avian Path; Am Col Vet Path; Conf Res Workers Animal Dis; Am Vet Med Asn; Can Vet Med Asn. *Res:* Role of viruses in pneumonias of cattle; pathology of encephalitic diseases; pseudorabies in swine; toxoplasmosis and Marek's disease in chickens; etio-pathogenesis of clostridial infections in birds and animals; ocular diseases of animals; congenital disorders of central nervous system of swine. *Mailing Add:* Dept of Vet Microbiol Univ of Sask Saskatoon SK S7N 0W0 Can

SAUNDERS, JEFFREY JOHN, b Minneapolis, Minn, Dec 12, 43. PALEONTOLOGY. *Educ:* Univ Minn, Minneapolis, BA, 66; Univ Ariz, MS, 70, PhD(geosci), 75. *Prof Exp:* res assoc vert paleont, Ill State Mus Soc, 75-78, CUR VERT PALEONT, ILL STATE MUS, 78- *Mem:* Soc Vert Paleont; Am Quaternary Asn. *Res:* Taphonomy of spring deposits and the paleoecology of fossil Proboscidea. *Mailing Add:* Dept Geol Ill State Mus Springfield IL 62706

SAUNDERS, JOHN BERTRAND DE CUSANCE MORANT, b Grahamstown, SAfrica, July 2, 03; m 30, 77; c 2. HISTORY OF MEDICINE, HUMAN ANATOMY. *Educ:* Univ Edinburgh, MB, ChB, 25; Royal Col Surgeons Eng, FRCS; Royal Col Surgeons Edinburgh, FRCSE; Academia Sinica, PhD, 81. *Hon Degrees:* LLD, Univ Calif; DSc, Univ Edinburgh, 72; HLD, Univ San Francisco, 75. *Prof Exp:* Demonstr physiol, Univ Edinburgh, 23, demonstr anat, 25-30, lectr, 28-30; surgeon, Settler's Hosp, SAfrica, 30-31; from asst prof to prof anat, Sch Med, 31-71, librn, Med Ctr, 43-71, dean sch med, 56-63, provost, Univ, 58-64, chancellor, 64-66, LECTR HIST HEALTH SCI, SCH MED, UNIV CALIF, SAN FRANCISCO, 33-, CHMN DEPT, 37-, REGENTS PROF MED HIST, 66-, EMER PROF ANAT, SCH MED & EMER UNIV LIBRN, MED CTR, 71-, EMER CHANCELLOR, 77- *Concurrent Pos:* Lectr, Dunfermline Col Phys Educ & Hyg, 25-30; clin asst, Royal Infirmary, Edinburgh, Scotland, 25-28, hon clin asst, 28-30; res surgeon, Royal Hosp Sick Children, 28-29; pvt pract, Scotland, 29-30. *Mem:* AAAS; Soc Exp Biol & Med; Hist Sci Soc; Am Asn Hist Med; Am Asn Phys Anthrop. *Res:* Surgical anatomy; embryology; bone histology and growth; locomotion and muscle physiology; medical history. *Mailing Add:* Dept Hist Health Sci Univ Calif Hosp Bldg U-406 San Francisco CA 94143

SAUNDERS, JOHN WARREN, JR, b Muskogee, Okla, Nov 12, 19; m 42; c 5. EMBRYOLOGY. *Educ:* Univ Okla, BS, 40; Johns Hopkins Univ, PhD(embryol), 48. *Prof Exp:* Instr zool, Univ Chicago, 48-49; from asst prof to prof, Marquette Univ, 49-66, chmn dept, 57-65; prof anat, Univ Pa, 66-67; PROF BIOL SCI, STATE UNIV NY ALBANY, 67- *Concurrent Pos:* Consult develop biol prog, NSF, 62-66, div biol & med sci, 69-71, chmn, 71. *Mem:* Am Soc Zoologists (secy, 64-66); Soc Develop Biol (pres, 67-68); Am Asn Anatomists; Soc Exp Biol & Med; NY Acad Sci. *Res:* Experimental morphogenesis; chick limb bud and feather tracts; cellular death in embryogenesis. *Mailing Add:* Dept of Biol Sci State Univ of NY Albany NY 12222

SAUNDERS, JOSEPH FRANCIS, b Mt Pleasant, Pa, Apr 2, 27; m 50; c 2. BIOCHEMISTRY. *Educ:* Duquesne Univ, BS, 50; Georgetown Univ, MS, 55, PhD(chem), 60. *Prof Exp:* Tissue technologist, Pittsburgh Hosp, Pa, 50-51; asst head med & dent br, Off Naval Res, US Dept Navy, Washington, DC, 52-60, head, 60-64; chief environ biol & biosatellite prog & scientist, Off Space Sci & Appln, Nasa Hq, 64-70, chief biol prog, Off Life Sci, Off Manned Space Flight, 71-73; PROG MGR US-USSR, US-CHINA & US-HUNGARY CANCER PROGS, NAT CANCER INST, 73-, DEP DIR INT AFFAIRS, 74- *Concurrent Pos:* Instr, Bus Training Col, 50-51; guest scientist, Naval Med Res Inst, Bethesda, Md, 58-60; mem adv panel biochem, Off Naval Res, 64-65; exec secy space biol subcomt, NASA, 66-70; mem US nat comt, Int Inst Refrig, 69-71; foreign affairs ed, Biosci Commun, 75-77; coord ed, J Soviet Oncol, 79- *Honors & Awards:* Arthur S Flemming Award, 62; Group Achievement Award, NASA, 74. *Mem:* Am Chem Soc; Am Physiol Soc. *Res:* Cholesterol metabolism in atherosclerosis and nerve tissue; space biology and medicine; radiation biology; molecular biology of cancer. *Mailing Add:* Off Int Affairs Nat Cancer Inst NIH Bethesda MD 20014

SAUNDERS, JOSEPH LLOYD, b Elk City, Okla, Oct 26, 35; m 63; c 2. ENTOMOLOGY, NEMATOLOGY. *Educ:* Colo State Univ, BS, 59; Univ Wis, MS, 60, PhD(entom), 63. *Prof Exp:* Proj assoc entom, Univ Wis, 64-66; asst entomologist, Wash State Univ, 66-69, assoc prof entom, 69-71; assoc prof entom & int agr develop, Cornell Univ, 71-76; ENTOMOLOGIST, CROPPING SYSTS PROG, TROP AGRON CTR RES & EDUC, COSTA RICA, 76- *Mem:* Entom Soc Am. *Res:* Pest management. *Mailing Add:* CATIE Turrialba Costa Rica

SAUNDERS, KENNETH V(AR), JR, systems engineering, see previous edition

SAUNDERS, KIM DAVID, b Chicago, Ill, Jan 21, 45; m 68. PHYSICAL OCEANOGRAPHY. *Educ:* Rose Polytech Inst, BSc, 66; Mass Inst Technol, PhD(oceanog), 71. *Prof Exp:* Res assoc oceanog, Mass Inst Technol, 71-72; NATO fel, Inst Geophys, Univ Bergen, 72-73, Royal Norwegian Coun Sci & Indust Res fel, 73-74; asst environ scientist, Environ & Energy Systs Div, Argonne Nat Lab, 74-78; OCEANOGRAPHER, NAVAL OCEAN RES &

DEVELOP ACTIVITY, NAT SPACE TECHNOL LABS, 78- *Concurrent Pos:* Consult, Underwater Explosion Damage Prev, 80- *Mem:* AAAS; Am Geophys Union; Sigma Xi; Asn Comput Mach; Int Asn Gt Lakes Res. *Res:* Near shore circulations; high frequency internal waves; oceanographic instrumentation; geophysical fluid dynamics; numerical analysis and data quality control. *Mailing Add:* Naval Ocean Res & Develop Activity Nat Space Technol Labs Station MI 39529

SAUNDERS, LEON Z, b Winnipeg, Man, Dec 16, 19; nat US; m 65; c 1. VETERINARY PATHOLOGY, HISTORY OF PATHOLOGY. *Educ:* Univ Toronto, VS & DVM, 43; Iowa State Col, MS, 46; Cornell Univ, PhD(vet path), 51. *Hon Degrees:* Dr Med Vet, Vet Col Vienna, 68. *Prof Exp:* Instr vet path, Iowa State Col, 46-48; asst, Cornell Univ, 48-51; pathologist, Chem Corps Med Labs, US Army Chem Ctr, Md, 51-52; assoc vet, Brookhaven Nat Lab, 52-54, vet, 55-58; head path & toxicol sect, 58-68, dir path & toxicol, 68-80, VPRES DRUG SAFETY EVAL, SMITH KLINE & FRENCH LABS, 80- *Concurrent Pos:* Vis asst prof, Univ Pa, 58-62, vis assoc prof, 62-63, adj prof, 64-; vpres, World Fedn Vet Path, 59-67, pres, 67-71; ed, Pathologia Veterinaria, 63-67. *Honors & Awards:* Schofield Mem Medal, 73. *Mem:* Am Vet Med Asn; Am Col Vet Path (vpres, 67-, pres, 68); Conf Res Workers Animal Dis; Int Acad Path; Am Asn Pathologists. *Res:* Animal ophthalmic pathology; history of veterinary pathology. *Mailing Add:* Smith Kline & French Labs 1500 Spring Garden St Philadelphia PA 19101

SAUNDERS, MARTIN, b Brooklyn, NY, Jan 10, 31; m 63; c 2. ORGANIC CHEMISTRY. *Educ:* City Col, BS, 52; Harvard Univ, PhD(org chem), 56. *Prof Exp:* From instr to assoc prof chem, 55-70, PROF CHEM, YALE UNIV, 70-, FEL, BRANFORD COL, 70- *Concurrent Pos:* Yale Univ jr fac fel sci, 62-63; spec award, von Humboldt Found, 77-78; Kharasch award, Univ Chicago, 82-83. *Res:* Applications of nuclear magnetic resonance spectroscopy to organic chemistry; measurement of fast reaction rates; study of stable carbonium ion solutions. *Mailing Add:* Dept of Chem Yale Univ New Haven CT 06520

SAUNDERS, MORTON JEFFERSON, b Norfolk, Va, Nov 19, 25; m 50; c 2. OPTICS. *Educ:* Univ Va, BS, 50, MS, 52; Univ Fla, PhD(physics), 56. *Prof Exp:* Lab asst physics, Univ Va, 50-51, res asst, 51-52; optical engr, Farrand Optical Co, NY, 52-53; res asst physics, US Air Force Contract, Univ Fla, 55-56 & US Army Ord Contract, 56; MEM TECH STAFF, BELL TEL LABS, 56- *Mem:* AAAS; Optical Soc Am; NY Acad Sci. *Res:* Phase contrast studies of turbulent media; visibility through the atmosphere; electromagnetic scattering from microscopic water droplets and dielectric cylinders; fiber optic structures, losses in fiber optic structures; fiber optic index of refraction measurement. *Mailing Add:* Div 54 Bell Tel Labs 2000 Northeast Expwy Norcross GA 30071

SAUNDERS, PETER REGINALD, b Wokingham, Eng, Aug 21, 28; m 57; c 4. PHYSICAL CHEMISTRY, PHYSICS. *Educ:* Univ London, BSc, 51. *Prof Exp:* Res officer, Brit Gelatin & Glue Res Asn, 51-55, sr res officer, 55-57; res assoc concentrated polymer solutions, Univ Wis, 57-58; res physicist, Chemstrand Res Ctr, Inc, 58-64, sr res physicist, 64-67; prin scientist, Brit Food Res Asn, 67-68; SR SCIENTIST & RES SUPVR, FIBERS DIV, TECH CTR, ALLIED CHEM CORP, 68- *Mem:* Am Chem Soc; Soc Rheol; Am Asn Textile Chemists & Colorists. *Res:* Molecular characterization of macromolecules; rheological properties of solutions and gels of macromolecules; physics of fiber formation; relation of fiber structure to mechanical properties; dye diffusion in fibers. *Mailing Add:* 6618 Philbrook Rd Richmond VA 23234

SAUNDERS, PRISCILLA PRINCE, b Monterey, Calif, Apr 21, 38; m 59; c 1. BIOCHEMICAL PHARMACOLOGY. *Educ:* Ore State Univ, BS, 60, MS, 61; Univ Ill, PhD(biochem), 65. *Prof Exp:* USPHS fel, Enzym Lab, Nat Ctr Sci Res, France, 65-66; res assoc, 66-75, asst prof, 75-80, ASSOC PROF BIOCHEM, UNIV TEX M D ANDERSON HOSP & TUMOR INST, 80- *Mem:* Am Asn Cancer Res; Am Soc Pharmacol & Exp Therapeut; Am Soc Cell Biol. *Res:* Mechanism of action of antitumor agents in bacteria and cultured mammalian cells. *Mailing Add:* Univ of Tex M D Anderson Hosp & Tumor Inst Houston TX 77025

SAUNDERS, RICHARD HENRY, JR, b Holland, Va, Feb 13, 19; m 44; c 2. GERONTOLOGY. *Educ:* Univ Richmond, BA, 39; Univ Rochester, MD, 43; Am Bd Internal Med, dipl, 52. *Prof Exp:* Instr med, Sch Med, Yale Univ, 49; from asst prof clin path & med to assoc prof med, Col Med, Univ Vt, 50-57; clin asst prof, Sch Med, Univ Rochester, 57-60; asst prof med & assoc dean, Med Col, Cornell Univ, 60-65; assoc dir Nat Bd Med Examr, 65-69; assoc prof med & assoc dean, 69-74, dir ambulatory care, 74-78, PROF MED, MED SCH, UNIV MASS, WORCESTER, 74-, ASSOC DIR, UNIT STUDY AGING, 78- *Concurrent Pos:* Runyon clin res fel, New Eng Ctr Hosp, 49-50; Markle scholar, 54-57; assoc attend physician, Mary Fletcher Hosp, Burlington, Vt, 50-57; attend physician, Highland Hosp, 57-60; assoc physician, Strong Mem Hosp, 57-60; asst attend, New York Hosp, 60-65. *Mem:* Geront Soc; fel Am Col Physicians; Am Fedn Clin Res; Am Geriat Soc. *Mailing Add:* Univ of Mass Med Sch 55 Lake Ave N Worcester MA 01605

SAUNDERS, RICHARD L DE C II, b Grahamstown, SAfrica, May 29, 08; m 36; c 1. NEUROANATOMY, RADIOLOGY. *Educ:* Univ Edinburgh, MB, 32; MD, 40. *Hon Degrees:* Dipl radiol, Univ Lisbon, 65. *Prof Exp:* Vis physician, Settlers Hosp, SAfrica, 32; house surgeon, Bradford Royal Infirmary, Eng, 33; lectr anat, Univ Edinburgh, 33-37; from asst prof to assoc prof anat, 38-48, prof path & dir med mus, 48-49, prof anat & head dept, 49-73, EMER PROF ANAT, DALHOUSIE UNIV, 74- *Concurrent Pos:* Res prof neuroanat, Radcliffe Infirmary, Oxford, Eng, 74-79. *Mem:* Fel Royal Micros Soc; Am Asn Anatomists. *Res:* Microfocal radiography in experimental and clinical medicine, with special emphasis on cerebral microcirculation and neural structure. *Mailing Add:* West Jeddore Halifax County NS B0J 1P0 Can

SAUNDERS, RICHARD LEE, b Lynn, Mass, June 24, 28; m 55; c 3. PHYSIOLOGY. *Educ:* Univ Mass, BS, 51; Univ Toronto, MA, 53, PhD(zool), 60. *Prof Exp:* RES SCIENTIST, FISHERIES RES BD CAN, 60- *Mem:* Am Fisheries Soc; Can Soc Zoologists; Int Asn Theoret & Appl Limnol; Brit Soc Exp Biol. *Res:* Environmental physiology; fish respiration and metabolism; osmotic and ionic changes resulting from stress; endocrinological control of salmon smolting and growth; Atlantic salmon biology; salmonid genetics; salmonid aquaculture. *Mailing Add:* Biol Sta Fisheries Res Bd of Can St Andrews NB E0Q 2X0 Can

SAUNDERS, ROBERT M(ALLOUGH), b Winnipeg, Man, Sept 12, 15; nat US; m 43. ELECTRICAL ENGINEERING. *Educ:* Univ Minn, BEE, 38, MS, 42; Tokyo Inst Technol, DEng, 71. *Prof Exp:* Instr elec eng, Univ Minn, 42-44; from lectr to assoc prof, Univ Calif, Berkeley, 47-55, prof elec eng, 56-65, chmn dept, 59-63; asst to chancellor, 64-65, dean sch eng, 64-73, PROF ELEC ENG, UNIV CALIF, IRVINE, 65- *Concurrent Pos:* Vis assoc prof, Mass Inst Technol, 54-55; mem eng educ & accreditation comt, Eng Coun Prof Develop, 65-71, chmn, 69-70, mem bd dirs, 71-75; mem eng adv comt, NSF, 68-71; mem bd visitors, Army Transp Sch, Ft Eustis, Va, 70-73; consult, Aerospace Corp, El Segundo, 71-, Gen Motors Corp, Apollo Support Dept, Gen Elec Co, Rohr Corp, Chula Vista & Hughes Aircraft Co, Fullerton; secy, Nat Comn Eng Films. *Mem:* Am Soc Eng Educ; fel Inst Elec & Electronics Engrs. *Res:* Electrical machinery theory; feedback control systems; applications of digital computers to electrical machine design; theory of electromechanical energy converters; system simulation and optimization. *Mailing Add:* Univ of Calif Elec Eng Irvine CA 92664

SAUNDERS, ROBERT MONTGOMERY, b North Shields, Eng, Nov 25, 39. FOOD SCIENCE. *Educ:* Univ Birmingham, BSc, 60; Univ Newcastle, PhD(chem), 63. *Prof Exp:* Fel biochem, Univ Calif, Berkeley, 63-65; sr res biochemist, Philadelphia Gen Hosp, 65-66; prin res chemist, 66-75, RES LEADER, USDA, 75- *Mem:* Am Chem Soc; Am Asn Cereal Chemists; Am Inst Nutrit; Inst Food Technol. *Res:* Influence of processing on nutrient availability in grains; cereal fortification, wheat, rice, human nutrition. *Mailing Add:* USDA Albany CA 94710

SAUNDERS, RONALD STEPHEN, b Parsons, Kans, Oct 8, 40; m 65; c 3. GEOLOGY, PLANETOLOGY. *Educ:* Univ Wis-Madison, BS, 63; Brown Univ, MSc, 68, PhD(geol), 70. *Prof Exp:* Sr scientist, 69-74, MEM TECH STAFF, JET PROPULSION LAB, 74- *Mem:* Sigma Xi; Am Geophys Union; Soc Econ Paleontologists & Mineralogists; AAAS. *Res:* Planetary geology of the moon, Mars, and Venus. *Mailing Add:* Jet Propulsion Lab 4800 Oak Grove Dr Pasadena CA 91103

SAUNDERS, SAM CUNDIFF, b Richland, Ore, Feb 24, 31; m 54; c 3. MATHEMATICAL STATISTICS. *Educ:* Univ Ore, BS, 52; Univ Wash, PhD(math statist), 56. *Prof Exp:* Mathematician, Math Serv Unit, Boeing Airplane Co, 56-58 & Math Res Lab, 58-60; asst prof math, Math Res Ctr, Univ Wis, 60-61; staff mem, Math Res Lab, Boeing Sci Res Labs, Wash, 61-72; PROF PURE & APPL MATH, WASH STATE UNIV, 72- *Mem:* Am Math Soc; Soc Indust & Appl Math; Math Asn Am; Am Statist Asn; Inst Math Statist. *Res:* Non-parametric methods; reliability theory; statistical inference. *Mailing Add:* Dept of Math Wash State Univ Pullman WA 99164

SAUNDERS, SHELLEY RAE, b Toronto, Can, Feb 28, 50; m 71; c 2. EVOLUTIONARY THEORY. *Educ:* Univ Toronto, BA, 72, MA, 73, PhD(phys anthrop), 77. *Prof Exp:* Lectr & sr demonstrater, McGill Univ, 76-79; asst prof, Univ Toronto, 79-81; ASST PROF ANTHROP, MCMASTER UNIV, 81- *Concurrent Pos:* Ed, J Can Asn Phys Anthropologists, 78-81. *Mem:* Am Asn Phys Anthropologists; AAAS; Human Biol Coun; Can Asn Phys Anthropologists; Acad Med Toronto. *Res:* Investigation of bone remodeling of human infracranial bone, using SEM studies of surface changes; morphological variation of human bone; evolutionary changes of past human populations. *Mailing Add:* Dept Anthrop McMaster Univ 1280 Main St W Hamilton ON L8S 4L9 Can

SAUNDERS, VERNON IRVING, b Southampton, Ont, Nov 13, 23; US citizen; m 49; c 2. SOLID STATE CHEMISTRY. *Educ:* Western Ont Univ, BS, 45, MS, 46. *Prof Exp:* Chemist, B F Goodrich Co, 46-48; res chemist, 48-57, sr res chemist, 57-60, RES ASSOC, EASTMAN KODAK CO, 60- *Honors & Awards:* Jour Award, Soc Photog Scientists & Engrs, 60 & 66. *Mem:* Soc Photog Scientists & Engrs. *Res:* Latent image formation in and spectral sensitization of silver halides. *Mailing Add:* Eastman Kodak Co Res Labs Kodak Park Works Rochester NY 14650

SAUNDERS, VIRGINIA FOX, b Roanoke, Va, May 31, 38; m 63; c 2. NEUROPSYCHOLOGY, NEUROSCIENCES. *Educ:* Univ Mich, BA, 60; Ind Univ, PhD(psychol & neurophysiol), 66. *Prof Exp:* Fel, Interdisciplinary Training Prog, Univ Calif Med Ctr, 65-67; from asst prof to assoc prof, 67-76, PROF PSYCHOL, SAN FRANCISCO STATE UNIV, 76- *Concurrent Pos:* Spec progs coordr, Kentfield Sch Dist, Calif, 74-76; mem, Res & Eval Comt, Redwood High Sch, Calif, 75-77. *Res:* Physiological and pharmacological factors in sensation, perception, learning and memory. *Mailing Add:* Dept of Psychol San Francisco State Univ San Francisco CA 94132

SAUNDERS, WILLIAM BRUCE, b Tuscaloosa, Ala, Nov 12, 42; m 64; c 1. INVERTEBRATE PALEONTOLOGY, GEOLOGY. *Educ:* Univ Ark, BSc, 66, MSc, 68; Univ Iowa, PhD(geol), 71. *Prof Exp:* Asst prof, 70-76, chmn geol, 80-81, ASSOC PROF GEOL, BRYN MAWR COL, 76- *Concurrent Pos:* Exchange scientist, Nat Acad Sci-USSR Acad Sci, 74-75; prin investr, NSF grants marine biol, paleobiol, 75-77, 77-79, 80-84 & RV Alpha Helix, Philippines, 79. *Mem:* Int Union Geol Sci; fel Geol Soc Am; Int Paleont Asn; Paleont Soc; fel Explorers Club. *Res:* Evolution and paleobiology of fossil cephalopods, cephalopod biostratigraphy and biology of cephalopods; particularly living nautilus. *Mailing Add:* Dept of Geol Bryn Mawr Col Bryn Mawr PA 19010

SAUNDERS, WILLIAM H, b Omaha, Nebr, Jan 7, 20; m; c 4. OTOLARYNGOLOGY. *Educ:* Univ Omaha, AB, 39; Univ Iowa, MD, 43. *Prof Exp:* From asst prof to assoc prof, 54-60, actg chmn dept, 61-63, PROF OTOLARYNGOL, COL MED, OHIO STATE UNIV, 60-, CHMN DEPT, 63- *Concurrent Pos:* Dir, Am Bd Otolaryngol, 74. *Mem:* AMA; Am Acad Ophthal & Otolaryngol; Am Laryngol, Rhinol & Otol Soc; Am Laryngol Asn; Am Otol Soc. *Res:* Otology. *Mailing Add:* Dept of Otolaryngol Ohio State Univ Hosp Columbus OH 43210

SAUNDERS, WILLIAM HUNDLEY, JR, b Pulaski, Va, Jan 12, 26; m 60; c 2. PHYSICAL ORGANIC CHEMISTRY. *Educ:* Col William & Mary, BS, 48; Northwestern Univ, PhD(chem), 52. *Prof Exp:* Res assoc chem, Mass Inst Technol, 51-53; from instr to assoc prof, 53-64, PROF CHEM, UNIV ROCHESTER, 64- *Concurrent Pos:* Guggenheim fel & hon res assoc, Univ Col, Univ London, 60-61; Sloan Found fel, 61-64; NSF sr fel & guest researcher, Univ Gothenburg, 70-71. *Mem:* Am Chem Soc. *Res:* Rearrangements; elimination reactions; isotope effects and isotopic tracers. *Mailing Add:* Dept of Chem Univ of Rochester Rochester NY 14627

SAUPE, ALFRED (OTTO), b Badenweiler, WGer, Feb 14, 25; m 63; c 3. PHYSICS, PHYSICAL CHEMISTRY. *Educ:* Univ Freiburg, MS, 55, Dr rer nat(physics), 58. *Prof Exp:* Ger Res Asn fel, Univ Freiburg, 58-61; res assoc physics, Electronics Inst, Freiburg, 61-62; sci asst, Univ Freiburg, 62-67, docent phys chem, 67-68; vis prof, 68-70, PROF PHYSICS, KENT STATE UNIV, 70- *Mem:* AAAS. *Res:* Physics of liquid crystals, particularly molecular theories and elastic and optical properties; nuclear magnetic resonance on oriented molecules. *Mailing Add:* Liquid Crystal Inst Kent State Univ Kent OH 44242

SAUR, JESSE FRANCIS THEODORE, b Fairfield, Iowa, Aug 11, 21; m 45; c 2. PHYSICAL OCEANOGRAPHY, UNDERWATER ACOUSTICS. *Educ:* Parsons Col, BS, 42; Univ Calif, San Diego, MS, 48. *Prof Exp:* Asst phys oceanog, Scripps Inst, Univ Calif, 46-48; oceanogr, US Navy Electronics Lab, 48-57; asst lab dir, Biol Lab, US Bur Commercial Fisheries, Stanford Univ, 57-70; res oceanogr, Southwest Fisheries Ctr, US Nat Marine Fisheries Serv, Calif, 70-75; OCEANOG SPECIALIST, SCRIPPS INST OCEANOG, UNIV CALIF, SAN DIEGO, 75- *Concurrent Pos:* Vis assoc prof, Agr & Mech Col, Tex, 54; res assoc, Stanford Univ, 63-70; actg lab dir tuna resources lab, US Bur Commercial Fisheries, Calif, 66-67. *Mem:* Am Meteorol Soc; Am Soc Limnol & Oceanog; Am Geophys Union; Marine Technol Soc. *Res:* Descriptive physical oceanography; fisheries oceanography. *Mailing Add:* Scripps Inst Oceanog A-003 La Jolla CA 92093

SAURO, JOSEPH PIO, b New Rochelle, NY, Apr 4, 27; m 48; c 3. PHYSICS. *Educ:* Polytech Inst Brooklyn, BS, 55, MS, 58, PhD(physics), 66. *Prof Exp:* Instr physics, Polytech Inst Brooklyn, 56-65; ASSOC PROF PHYSICS, SOUTHEASTERN MASS UNIV, 65-, DEAN COL ARTS & SCI, 69- *Mem:* Am Phys Soc. *Res:* Scattering of x-rays by thin films; dielectric properties of phosphors. *Mailing Add:* Dept Physics Southeastern Mass Univ North Dartmouth MA 02742

SAUSE, H WILLIAM, b Baltimore, Md, Sept 29, 20; m 44; c 3. ORGANIC CHEMISTRY. *Educ:* Johns Hopkins Univ, AB, 48, MA, 50, PhD(chem), 53. *Prof Exp:* Jr instr chem, Johns Hopkins Univ, 48-52; res assoc, Northwestern Univ, 52-54; res chemist, 54-77, CLIN PHARM ASSOC, SEARLE LABS, CHICAGO, 77- *Mem:* AAAS; Am Chem Soc. *Res:* Natural products; pharmaceutical chemistry; heterocyclic chemistry. *Mailing Add:* 1061 Springfield Ave Deerfield IL 60015

SAUSEN, GEORGE NEIL, b St Paul, Minn, Aug 14, 27; m 51; c 5. ORGANIC CHEMISTRY. *Educ:* Col St Thomas, BS, 49; Univ Wis, PhD(chem), 53. *Prof Exp:* Res chemist, 53-63, supvr, 64-67, sr res chemist, 68-71, PATENT LIAISON, CENT RES & DEVELOP DEPT, E I DU PONT DE NEMOURS & CO, INC, 71- *Mem:* Am Chem Soc. *Res:* Angular methylation studies of steroid intermediates; cyanocarbons; fluorine chemistry; polymer intermediates. *Mailing Add:* Cent Res & Develop Dept E I du Pont de Nemours & Co Inc Wilmington DE 19898

SAUSVILLE, JOSEPH WINSTON, b Brooklyn, NY, Oct 17, 18; m 45; c 3. HIGH TEMPERATURE CHEMISTRY, ENGINEERING MANAGEMENT. *Educ:* Polytech Inst Brooklyn, BS, 41; Univ Iowa, PhD(phys chem), 48. *Prof Exp:* Chemist, Tenn Eastman Corp, 44-46 & Nuclear Energy Propulsion Aircraft Div, Fairchild Eng & Airplane Corp, 47-48; from asst prof to assoc prof phys chem, Univ Cincinnati, 48-56, chmn grad studies, 51-56; mgr nuclear mat, Res Div, Curtiss-Wright Corp, Pa, 56-61, eng head advan develop metall, Wright Aero Div, NJ, 62-67; mgr phosphor advan develop, 67-70, MGR PHOSPHOR DEVELOP, FLUORESCENT & VAPOR LAMP DIV, WESTINGHOUSE ELEC CORP, 70- *Mem:* Am Chem Soc; Am Inst Chemists; Illum Eng Soc; Am Soc Photobiol. *Res:* Fundamental properties of matter; high temperature materials fabrication and evaluation; effects of ionizing radiations. *Mailing Add:* Fluorescent & Vapor Lamp Div Westinghouse Elec Corp Bloomfield NJ 07003

SAUTE, ROBERT E, b West Warwick, RI, Aug 18, 29; m 57; c 3. PHARMACY, PHARMACOLOGY. *Educ:* RI Col Pharm, BS, 50; Purdue Univ, MS, 52, PhD(pharm), 53. *Prof Exp:* Tech asst to gen mgr, Lafayette Pharmacol Co, 55-56; res chemist, H K Wampole Co, 56-58; plant supt, Strong Cobb Arner Co, 58-60; res chemist, Avon Prod Inc, NY, 60-64; dir prod & process develop & dir res & develop admin, 64-68; res dir, Toiletries Div, Gillette Co, 68-71; group vpres, Dart Industs Inc, 71-74; OWNER, SAUTE CONSULTS, 74- *Mem:* AAAS; Soc Invest Dermat; Am Pharmaceut Asn; Acad Pharmaceut Sci; NY Acad Sci. *Res:* Consulting in the cosmetic, drug, toiletries and fragrance industries. *Mailing Add:* 10236 Mossy Rock Circle Los Angeles CA 90024

SAUTER, ERWIN ANDREW, b The Dalles, Ore, Feb 4, 19; m 55; c 3. FOOD SCIENCE, MICROBIOLOGY. *Educ:* Wash State Univ, BS, 50, MS, 52, PhD(animal sci), 66. *Prof Exp:* Asst poultry sci, Wash State Univ, 55-56; asst prof poultry sci prod, 56-66, assoc res prof poultry & food sci, 67-73, RES PROF, POULTRY SCI, UNIV IDAHO, 73- *Mem:* Am Soc Animal Sci; Am Meat Sci Asn; Poultry Sci Asn; World Poultry Sci Asn; Inst Food Technologists. *Res:* Food quality, acceptability and spoilage problems; microbiology of poultry and meat products; physical, functional and microbiological properties of eggs and egg products. *Mailing Add:* Dept Animal Sci Univ Idaho Moscow ID 83843

SAUTER, FREDERICK JOSEPH, b Pittsburgh, Pa, Dec 12, 43; m 66; c 3. ORGANIC CHEMISTRY. *Educ:* Duquesne Univ, BS, 65; Mass Inst Technol, PhD(org chem), 69. *Prof Exp:* sr res chemist, 69-76, RES ASSOC EASTMAN KODAK CO, 76- *Mem:* AAAS; Am Chem Soc. *Res:* Organic syntheses and reaction mechanisms as applied to conventional and unconventional imaging systems. *Mailing Add:* Res Labs Eastman Kodak Co 1669 Lake Ave Rochester NY 14650

SAUTHOFF, NED ROBERT, b Belleville, Ill, Apr 14, 49; m 75. PLASMA PHYSICS. *Educ:* Mass Inst Technol, SB & SM, 72; Princeton Univ, PhD(astrophys), 75. *Prof Exp:* RES PHYSICIST, PLASMA PHYSICS LAB, PRINCETON UNIV, 75-, HEAD, TFTR EXP COMPUT BR, 80- *Mem:* Am Phys Soc; Sigma Xi; Am Nuclear Soc. *Res:* Plasma physics in general; x-ray techniques; magnetohydrodynamics in tokamaks by x-ray imaging. *Mailing Add:* Princeton Univ Plasma Physics Lab PO Box 451 Princeton NJ 08540

SAUTTER, CHESTER A, b Scotia, Nebr, Nov 16, 33; m 59; c 4. EXPERIMENTAL ATOMIC PHYSICS, ENVIRONMENTAL PHYSICS. *Educ:* Nebr Wesleyan Univ, AB, 55; Univ Nebr, MA, 58, PhD(physics), 63. *Prof Exp:* Fulbright travel grant & guest physicist, Inst Physics, Aarhus, Denmark, 63-64; ASSOC PROF PHYSICS, CONCORDIA COL, MOORHEAD, MINN, 65- *Concurrent Pos:* Consult & vis prof, Wash State Univ, 74-75; consult, Lutheran Coun, USA & Lutheran World Ministries, 81-82. *Mem:* Am Asn Physics Teachers; Am Phys Soc; Int Solar Energy Soc; Hist Sci Soc; Sigma Xi. *Res:* Charge exchange of slow atoms and ions in gases; stopping power of ions and atoms in carbon and hydrocarbon films; ion channelling in single crystals and neutron activation analysis; residual environmental effects of Church Rock, New Mexico 1979 uranium mill tailings spill. *Mailing Add:* Dept Physics Concordia Col Moorhead MN 56560

SAUTTER, JAY HOWARD, b Waynesburg, Ohio, Nov 11, 12; m 37; c 3. VETERINARY PATHOLOGY. *Educ:* Ohio State Univ, DVM, 44; Univ Minn, PhD(path), 48. *Prof Exp:* Instr vet med, 47-48, assoc prof vet path, 48-52, PROF VET PATH, UNIV MINN, ST PAUL, 52- *Concurrent Pos:* AID consult, Peru, 65; tech asst, Nebr Proj, Columbia Univ, 70-71; tech asst, Food & Agr Orgn, Dom Repub, 72; prof & head dept path & microbiol, Ahmadu Bella Univ, Nigeria, 74-76; tech asst, Kans AID Proj, Ahmadu Bella Univ, 74- *Mem:* Am Asn Avian Pathologists; Am Vet Med Asn; Am Col Vet Pathologists; Nigerian Vet Med Asn; Am Asn Pathologists. *Mailing Add:* 1550 Fulham St St Paul MN 55108

SAUVE, JAMES WILLARD, mathematics, see previous edition

SAVAGE, ALBERT B, b Minneapolis, Minn, Dec 22, 12; m 41, 57; c 2. CHEMICAL ENGINEERING. *Educ:* Univ Minn, BChE & BA, 35, MS, 37. *Prof Exp:* Sr res specialist, Cellulose Res, Designed Polymers Res Lab, Dow Chem Co, 37-76; RETIRED. *Mem:* Sigma Xi. *Res:* Etherification; cellulose; soluble polymers; plastics. *Mailing Add:* 122 Varner Ct Midland MI 48640

SAVAGE, BLAIR DEWILLIS, b Mt Vernon, NY, June 7, 41; m 66; c 1. ASTRONOMY. *Educ:* Cornell Univ, BEngrPhysics, 64; Princeton Univ, PhD(astron), 67. *Prof Exp:* Res assoc astron, Princeton Univ, 67-68; from asst prof to assoc prof, 68-78, PROF ASTRON, UNIV WIS-MADISON, 78- *Concurrent Pos:* vis fel, Joint Inst Lab Astrophys, Colo, 74-75. *Mem:* Am Astron Soc; Int Astron Union. *Res:* Ultraviolet space astronomy; interstellar matter. *Mailing Add:* Washburn Observ Univ of Wis Madison WI 53706

SAVAGE, CARL RICHARD, JR, b Bloomsburg, Pa, Dec 1, 42; m 65; c 2. BIOCHEMISTRY, ENDOCRINOLOGY. *Educ:* Gettysburg Col, BA, 64; State Univ NY Buffalo, PhD(biochem), 71. *Prof Exp:* Dir res biochem, Vet Admin Hosp, Albany, NY, 73-75; ASST PROF BIOCHEM, SCH MED, TEMPLE UNIV, 75- *Concurrent Pos:* Damon Runyon fel, 71-73; Dermatol Found grant, Temple Univ, 75-76, Inst grant, 75-76, Am Cancer Soc Inst grant, 76-77 & NIH Diabetes grant, 78-81. *Mem:* Am Soc Biol Chemists; Tissue Cult Asn. *Res:* Mechanism of action of polypeptide hormones; metabololic regulation; control of growth and differentiation; primary cultures of liver parenchymal cells; tissue culture. *Mailing Add:* Dept of Biochem Temple Univ Sch of Med Philadelphia PA 19140

SAVAGE, CHARLES, b Berlin, Conn, Sept 25, 18; m 40; c 2. PSYCHIATRY. *Educ:* Yale Univ, BA, 39; Univ Chicago, MD, 44; Am Bd Psychiat & Neurol, dipl, 51. *Prof Exp:* Intern, Univ Chicago, 45; asst resident psychiatry, Yale Univ, 46; resident psychiatrist, US Naval Hosp, Md, 47-48, chief psychiatrist, SC, 48-49; res psychiatrist, Naval Med Res Inst, Nat Naval Med Ctr, 49-52; actg chief adult psychiatrist, Nat Inst Mental Health, 53-58; fel, Ctr Advan Study in Behavioral Sci, 57-58; psychiatrist, Livermore Sanitarium, 58-60; psychiatrist, Stanford Vet Admin Hosp, 61-62; med dir, Int Found Advan Study, 62-64; psychiatrist, County of Santa Clara, 64-65; dir res, Spring Grove State Hosp, 65-68; from clin asst prof to assoc prof, 65-80, PROF PSYCHIAT, INST PSYCHIAT & HUMAN BEHAVIOR, UNIV MD, 72-; CHIEF PSYCHIATRIC SERV & DRUG TREATMENT CTR, VET ADMIN HOSP, 72- *Concurrent Pos:* David C Wilson Soc lectr, Univ Va, 67; prin investr, Nat Inst Mental Health grant, Studies of Selected Narcotic Agonists & Antagonists, 72-75; chief, Psychiatric Serv & Drug Treatment Ctr, Vet Admin Hosp, 72-82. *Mem:* Fel Am Psychiat Asn; Am Psychoanal Asn; Am EEG Soc; AAAS. *Mailing Add:* Coral Bay St John VI 00830

SAVAGE, DENNIS JEFFREY, b Warren, Ohio, Oct 13, 42; m 68; c 1. ORGANIC CHEMISTRY. *Educ:* Univ Colo, Boulder, BA, 65; Univ Ariz, PhD(chem), 71. *Prof Exp:* SR ANAL CHEMIST, EASTMAN KODAK CO, 70- *Res:* Organometallic chemistry; organic polymer synthesis. *Mailing Add:* Eastman Kodak Co 343 State St Rochester NY 14630

SAVAGE, DONALD ELVIN, b Floydada, Tex, May 28, 17; m 42; c 4. PALEONTOLOGY. *Educ:* WTex State Col, BS, 37; Univ Okla, MS, 39; Univ Calif, PhD(paleont), 49. *Prof Exp:* From asst prof to assoc prof paleont, 49-62, PROF PALEONT, UNIV CALIF, BERKELEY, 62-, CUR MUS, 49- *Mem:* Geol Soc Am; Soc Vert Paleont. *Res:* Late Cenozoic mammals; nonmarine stratigraphy of western United States. *Mailing Add:* Dept of Paleont Univ of Calif Berkeley CA 94720

SAVAGE, DWAYNE CECIL, b Arco, Idaho, Aug 8, 34; m 57; c 2. MEDICAL MICROBIOLOGY. *Educ:* Univ Idaho, BS, 56; Univ Calif, Berkeley, MA, 61, PhD(bact), 65. *Prof Exp:* Guest investr & fel, Rockefeller Univ, 65-67; from asst prof to assoc prof, Univ Tex, Austin, 67-73; assoc prof, Univ & Sch Basic Med Sci, 73-75, PROF MICROBIOL, UNIV ILL & SCH BASIC MED SCI, COL MED, 75- *Concurrent Pos:* Nat Inst Allergy & Infectious Dis res proj grant, 68-; vis assoc prof, Sch Med, Univ Colo, Denver, 70, consult, Div Gastroenterol, 70-73; Am Soc Microbiol Found Lectr, 72-73. *Mem:* Am Acad Microbiol; Am Soc Microbiol; NY Acad Sci; Sigma Xi; Asn Gnotobiotics. *Res:* Gastrointestinal microflora and its influence on animals. *Mailing Add:* Dept of Microbiol Univ of Ill Urbana IL 61801

SAVAGE, E LYNN, b New York, NY. SEDIMENTOLOGY, MEDICAL GEOLOGY. *Educ:* Brooklyn Col, BS; NY Univ, MS; Rutgers Univ, PhD(sedimentation, stratig), 67. *Prof Exp:* Part-time lectr, 54-56, annual lectr, 66-67, from instr to asst prof, 67-73, ASSOC PROF GEOL, BROOKLYN COL, CITY UNIV NEW YORK, 73- *Concurrent Pos:* Instr, Hunter Col, 54-55, adj assoc prof, 78- *Mem:* Fel Geol Soc Am; Soc Econ Paleontologists & Mineralogists; NY Acad Sci; Sigma Xi; Int Soc Sedimentologists. *Res:* Triassic sedimentation, including petrology, paleodirections, and provenance of the Newark-Gettysburg Basin; sedimentology of sandstones; application of geology to disease patterns. *Mailing Add:* Dept Geol Brooklyn Col City Univ New York Brooklyn NY 11210

SAVAGE, EARL JOHN, b Uniontown, Pa, Feb 28, 31; m 61. PLANT PATHOLOGY, MYCOLOGY. *Educ:* Waynesburg Col, BS, 57; WVa Univ, MS, 60, PhD(plant path), 63. *Prof Exp:* Res asst plant path, WVa Univ, 57-62; instr biol & head dept, Lewis Col, 62-63; asst prof, Univ Notre Dame, 63-68; asst prof bot, 68-70, ASSOC PROF BOT, IND UNIV, SOUTH BEND, 71-, CHMN DEPT BIOL SCI, 69- *Concurrent Pos:* NSF res grant, 64-66; consult ball band div, US Rubber Co, Ind, 64-; consult, Bendix Corp, 64-65. *Mem:* AAAS; Am Inst Biol Sci; Mycol Soc Am. *Res:* Sexuality in genus Phytophthora which includes homothallism, heterothallism and inter and intraspecific matings; effects of various environmental factors upon the production and germination of oospores of Phytophthora species. *Mailing Add:* Dept of Biol Sci Ind Univ Northside Blvd at Greenlaw South Bend IN 46615

SAVAGE, ELDON P, b Bedford, Iowa, Apr 4, 26; m 48; c 2. PUBLIC HEALTH. *Educ:* Univ Kans, BA, 50; Tulane Univ, MPH, 57; Univ Okla, PhD(prev med, pub health), 67. *Prof Exp:* Entomologist, Tech Br, Nat Commun Dis Ctr, Kans, 50-51, WVa, 51-52, Ga, 53-54, proj entomologist, Kans, 54-55, demonstration entomologist, Iowa, 56-57, proj dir environ control, 57-58, dir commun dis control demonstration, Pa, 58-64, asst chief state aids sect, 64-66, chief state serv pesticides prog, Ga, 67-70; PROF ENVIRON HEALTH & TOXICOL, CHIEF CHEM EPIDEMIOL SECT & DEP DIR, INST RURAL ENVIRON HEALTH, COLO STATE UNIV, 70- *Mem:* Sigma Xi; Res Soc Am; Nat Environ Health Asn; Am Mosquito Control Asn; Am Acad Sanitarians. *Res:* Ecology of flies; environmental sanitation; human ecology; environmental toxicology; chemical pesticides; chemical pollutants in mother's milk; epidemiology. *Mailing Add:* Spruce Hall Colo State Univ Ft Collins CO 80523

SAVAGE, GEORGE ROLAND, b Ft Worth, Tex, Apr 2, 29; m 55; c 4. MICROBIOLOGY. *Educ:* N Tex State Univ, BS, 49; Univ Tex, MA, 50; Nat Registry Microbiol, cert, 66. *Prof Exp:* Res technician, Samuel Roberts Noble Res Found, Okla, 50-51; bacteriologist & serologist, NMex Dept Pub Health, 51-52; chief clin lab, Carlsbad Mem Hosp, NMex, 52-55; asst dir admin, Carnegie Inst, Ohio, 55-58; microbiologist, Directorate Biol Opers, Dept Army, 59-62, chief bact & fungal develop sect, 62-64, chief viral & rickettsial labs, 64-67; sr microbiologist, Biol Sci Div, Midwest Res Inst, Mo, 67-73; ENVIRON SCIENTIST, BLACK & VEATCH CONSULT ENGRS, 73- *Mem:* Am Soc Microbiol; NY Acad Sci; Sigma Xi. *Res:* Environmental studies related to the establishment and operation of energy production facilities; physiological and genetic problems associated with large-scale growth of pathogenic bacteria, viruses and rickettsia. *Mailing Add:* Black & Veatch 1500 Meadow Lake Parkway Kansas City MO 64114

SAVAGE, GODFREY H, b Niagara Falls, NY, June 13, 27; m 60; c 3. MECHANICAL ENGINEERING, OCEAN ENGINEERING. *Educ:* Princeton Univ, BSE, 50; Stanford Univ, MS, 51, PhD(earth sci), 70; Harvard Univ, MBA, 54. *Prof Exp:* Petrol engr, Standard Oil Co Calif, 51-52; staff mem, Arthur D Little, Inc, 54-55, assoc & proj leader, 55-58; asst to dean grad sch bus, Harvard Univ, 58-59; asst vpres overseas opers, Leesona Holt Ltd, Eng & Leesona Corp, RI, 59-60; staff engr, Nat Acad Sci, 60-61; res engr, Woods Hole Oceanog Inst, 63-65; PROF MECH ENG & DIR ENG DESIGN LAB, UNIV NH, 65- *Concurrent Pos:* Vis engr, Mass Inst Technol, 63-66; founding co-chmn, Maine-NH Bi-State Comn Oceanog, 66-68; chmn, NH State Port Authority & Tidelands Conserv Authority, 67-69; pres, Ocean Technol Explor Co, 73-; Fulbright fel & vis prof, Heriot Watt Univ, 75-76; chief eng adv, Ocean Margin Drill Prog, JOI Inc, 79-81. *Mem:* Marine Technol Soc; Inst Offshore Eng, Scotland. *Res:* Invention and development of structural and mechanical-electrical systems for ocean exploration and defense: in buoy systems, deep diving systems and vehicles; wave energy measurement and analysis. *Mailing Add:* Kingsbury Hall Univ of NH Durham NH 03824

SAVAGE, H(ARRY) C(LIFTON), b Easley, SC, Dec 26, 20; m 43; c 4. CHEMICAL ENGINEERING. *Educ:* Ga Inst Technol, BS, 42. *Prof Exp:* Develop engr, Tenn Corp, 42-43; group leader in chg mat testing lab, Bell Aircraft Corp, Ga, 43-45; DEVELOP ENGR, MAT EXP ENG SECT, OAK RIDGE NAT LAB, UNION CARBIDE NUCLEAR CO DIV, UNION CARBIDE CORP, 46- *Mem:* Am Nuclear Soc; AAAS; Nat Soc Prof Engrs. *Res:* Nuclear reactor field. *Mailing Add:* 105 Wiltshire Dr Oak Ridge TN 37830

SAVAGE, HOWARD EDSON, b Hyannis, Mass, Feb 1, 42; m 66; c 1. CELL BIOLOGY. *Educ:* Univ Vt, BA, 64, MS, 66; Rutgers Univ, PhD(microbiol), 71. *Prof Exp:* USPHS fel pharmacol, 71-73, INSTR PHARMACOL, BAYLOR COL MED, 73- *Mem:* Am Soc Microbiol. *Res:* Tumor antigens, oncology, biochemical pharmacology of cancer cells. *Mailing Add:* Dept of Pharmacol Baylor Col of Med Houston TX 77030

SAVAGE, I RICHARD, b Detroit, Mich, Oct 26, 25; m 50; c 2. STATISTICS. *Educ:* Univ Chicago, BS, 44; Univ Mich, MS, 45; Columbia Univ, PhD(statist), 54. *Prof Exp:* Statistician, Nat Bur Standards, 51-54; actg asst prof statist, Stanford Univ, 54-57; from assoc prof to prof, Univ Minn, 57-63; prof, Fla State Univ, 63-74; PROF STATIST, YALE UNIV, 74- *Concurrent Pos:* Consult, Ctr Advan Study Behav Sci, 56, NSF sr fel, 70-71; vis assoc prof, Sch Bus, Harvard Univ, 60-61; vis prof, Yale Univ, 67-68; ed, Ann of Statist, 74-77. *Mem:* Fel Am Statist Asn; Am Math Soc; fel Inst Math Statist; Int Statist Inst. *Res:* Government statistics; non-parametric techniques; control theory. *Mailing Add:* Dept Statist Yale Univ New Haven CT 06520

SAVAGE, JAMES CRAMPTON, b Dallas, Tex, Sept 18, 26. GEOPHYSICS. *Educ:* Univ Ariz, BS, 50; Calif Inst Technol, PhD(geophys), 57. *Prof Exp:* Lectr geophys, Mass Inst Technol, 57-58; asst prof physics, Univ BC, 58-61; NSF fel, 61-62; asst prof physics, Univ BC, 62-63, assoc prof geophys, 63-64; assoc prof, Univ Minn, 64-65; assoc prof physics, Univ Toronto, 65-69; GEOPHYSICIST, NAT CTR EARTHQUAKE RES, US GEOL SURV, 69- *Mem:* Am Geophys Union; Seismol Soc Am. *Res:* Earthquake source mechanism; attenuation of elastic waves; glaciology. *Mailing Add:* US Geol Surv 345 Middlefield Rd Menlo Park CA 94025

SAVAGE, JANE RAMSDELL, b Boston, Mass, Sept 23, 25. NUTRITION, BIOCHEMISTRY. *Educ:* Simmons Col, BS, 46, MS, 49; Univ Wis, PhD(nutrit, biochem), 63. *Prof Exp:* Asst chem, Simmons Col, 46-49; asst prof nutrit & chem, Univ Tenn, 49-59; res asst nutrit, Univ Wis, 59-62; from asst prof to assoc prof, 62-73, PROF NUTRIT, UNIV TENN, KNOXVILLE, 73- *Mem:* AAAS; Am Chem Soc; Am Home Econ Asn; NY Acad Sci; Soc Nutrit Educ. *Res:* Tryptophan metabolism; niacin containing co-enzymes; amino acid imbalance. *Mailing Add:* Dept Nutrit & Food Sci Food Syst Admin Univ of Tenn Knoxville TN 37996

SAVAGE, JAY MATHERS, b Santa Monica, Calif, Aug 26, 28; c 2. HERPETOLOGY. *Educ:* Stanford Univ, AB, 50, MA, 54, PhD(biol sci), 55. *Prof Exp:* Asst gen biol, Stanford Univ, 50-53, asst comp vert anat & embryol, 54; asst prof zool, Pomona Col, 54-56; from instr to assoc prof biol, 56-64, vchmn, Nat Oceanog Lab Syst, 71-74, PROF BIOL & ASSOC DIR, ALLAN HANCOCK FOUND, UNIV SOUTHERN CALIF, 64- *Concurrent Pos:* Mem, Stanford field exped, Mex, 50; herpetologist, Sefton Found-Stanford Exped, Gulf of Calif & Mex, 52; actg asst cur herpet, Philadelphia Acad Natural Sci, 54; Guggenheim Found fel, 63-64; dir advan sci sem trop biol, Univ Costa Rica, 61-63, prof & tech adv to dept biol, 63-66; res assoc, Los Angeles County Mus; mem bd dirs, Orgn Trop Studies, Inc, 63-, exec secy, 63-65, pres, 74-80; chmn comt select biol problems in the humid tropics, NAtlantic Coun/Nat Res Coun, 80-81. *Mem:* AAAS; Soc Study Evolution; Am Soc Ichthyologists & Herpetologists (treas, 60-63); Soc Study Amphibians & Reptiles. *Res:* Ecology and evolution of amphibians and reptiles; ecology of midwater fishes; herpetofauna of tropical America; biosystematics frog genus Eleutherodactylus; ecological dynamics and evolution in the tropics; encounter groups in higher education; evolution of consciousness. *Mailing Add:* Allan Hancock Found Univ of Southern Calif Los Angeles CA 90007

SAVAGE, JIMMIE EUEL, b Calico Rock, Ark, Feb 15, 20; m 48; c 2. POULTRY NUTRITION. *Educ:* Univ Ark, BSA, 43; Univ Mo, MA, 48, PhD(agr chem), 55. *Prof Exp:* Nutritionist, Farm Bur Mills, Ark, 50-54; from asst prof to assoc prof, 55-64, PROF POULTRY NUTRIT, UNIV MO-COLUMBIA, 64-, CHMN DEPT, 66- *Mem:* AAAS; Am Inst Nutrit; Poultry Sci Asn (pres, 73-74). *Res:* Amino acid; trace mineral and unrecognized vitamin requirements of poultry. *Mailing Add:* Dept of Poultry Husbandry Univ of Mo Columbia MO 65211

SAVAGE, JOHN EDMUND, b Lynn, Mass, Sept 19, 39; m 66; c 2. ELECTRICAL ENGINEERING, COMPUTER SCIENCE. *Educ:* Mass Inst Technol, SB & SM, 62, PhD(elec eng), 65. *Prof Exp:* Res asst elec eng, Mass Inst Technol, 62-65; mem tech staff, Bell Tel Labs, NJ, 65-67; from asst prof to prof eng, 67-78, PROF COMPUT SCI & ENG, BROWN UNIV, 78- *Concurrent Pos:* Consult, Codex Corp, Mass, 67-68, Fed Systs Div, IBM Corp, Md, 68-69, Jet Propulsion Lab, 70-73, Lincoln Lab, Mass Inst Technol, 72-73 & Battelle Inst, 77-; Guggenheim fel & Fulbright-Hays fel, 73; assoc ed, Inst Elec & Electronics Engrs Transactions on Comput, 76-78. *Mem:* Inst Elec & Electronics Engrs Comput Soc; Asn Comput Mach; Sigma Xi. *Res:* Computer science; analysis of algorithms; computational complexity; information theory and coding. *Mailing Add:* Dept Comput Sci Brown Univ Providence RI 02912

SAVAGE, JOHN EDWARD, b Philadelphia, Pa, June 11, 07; m 33; c 2. MEDICINE. *Educ:* Univ Md, BS, 28, MD, 32; Am Bd Obstet & Gynec, dipl, 40. *Prof Exp:* Asst clin prof obstet & gynec, Sch Med, Univ Md, 46-61; chief of staff, Greater Baltimore Med Ctr, 65-68, chief obstet, 65-73. *Concurrent Pos:* Lectr, Johns Hopkins Univ, 58-73, emer lectr, 73- *Mem:* Fel Am Asn Obstet & Gynec; fel Am Col Obstet & Gynec; fel Am Col Surgeons. *Mailing Add:* 7424 Catamaran II 2400 S Ocean Dr Fort Pierce FL 33450

SAVAGE, MICHAEL, b Yonkers, NY, Sept 6, 41; m 66; c 2. MECHANICAL ENGINEERING. *Educ:* Manhattan Col, BME, 63; Purdue Univ, Lafayette, MSME, 65, PhD(mech eng), 69. *Prof Exp:* Consult engr, Res Div, United Shoe Mach Co, Mass, 65-66; asst prof, Wash State Univ, 69-70; asst prof eng, Case Western Reserve Univ, 70-76; chief engr, Erickson Tool Co, 76-77; assoc prof mech eng, Purdue Univ, Calumet Campus, 77-79; ASSOC PROF MECH ENG, UNIV AKRON, 79- *Honors & Awards:* Tech Achievement Award, Cleveland Tech Soc Coun, 77. *Mem:* Am Soc Mech Engrs; Am Soc Eng Educ; Soc Exp Stress Anal. *Res:* Kinematic analysis and synthesis of linkages and other machine components; applications of analysis to the design of machinery; dynamics of machinery; mechanical design; kinematics. *Mailing Add:* Dept Mech Eng Univ Akron Akron OH 44325

SAVAGE, NEVIN WILLIAM, b Berwick, Pa, Feb 17, 28; m; c 2. MATHEMATICS. *Educ:* Pa State Univ, BS, 50, MA, 52; Univ Calif, Los Angeles, PhD(math), 56. *Prof Exp:* Asst prof math, Polytech Inst Brooklyn, 55-59; assoc prof, 59-66, PROF MATH, ARIZ STATE UNIV, 66-, CHMN DEPT, 69- *Concurrent Pos:* NSF fac fel, 64-65. *Mem:* Am Math Soc; Math Asn Am. *Res:* Riemann surface theory and functional analysis. *Mailing Add:* Dept of Math Ariz State Univ Tempe AZ 85281

SAVAGE, NORMAN MICHAEL, b Dover, Eng, Aug 23, 36; m 64; c 3. PALEONTOLOGY, STRATIGRAPHY. *Educ:* Bristol Univ, BS, 59; Univ Sydney, PhD(geol), 68. *Prof Exp:* Teaching fel geol, Univ Sydney, 62-66; res fel, Univ Col Swansea, Wales, 66-68; lectr, Univ Natal, 68-71; assoc prof, 71-79, PROF GEOL & HEAD DEPT, UNIV ORE, 79- *Concurrent Pos:* Consult, US Geol Surv, 74-76. *Mem:* Fel Geol Soc London; fel Geol Soc Am; Brit Palaeont Asn; Paleont Soc. *Res:* Lower Paleozoic Brachiopods and conondonts. *Mailing Add:* Dept of Geol Univ of Ore Eugene OR 97403

SAVAGE, RICHARD LOUIS, b South Portland, Maine, Nov 3, 27; m 50; c 3. CIVIL ENGINEERING. *Educ:* Univ Maine, BSCE, 50; Northeastern Univ, MSCE, 55. *Prof Exp:* ASSOC PROF CIVIL ENG, TUFTS UNIV, 50- *Concurrent Pos:* Consult, Congdon, Guerney & Towle, Mass, 64-66 & Charles A Maguire & Assoc, 66- *Mem:* Am Soc Civil Engrs; Am Concrete Inst; Am Soc Eng Educ. *Res:* Design criteria for concentrically and eccentrically loaded prestressed concrete columns. *Mailing Add:* Dept of Civil Eng Tufts Univ Medford MA 02155

SAVAGE, ROBERT E, b Middlebury, Vt, Dec 8, 32; m 64; c 2. CELL BIOLOGY. *Educ:* Oberlin Col, BA, 54; Univ Wis, MS, 58, PhD(bot), 63. *Prof Exp:* Lectr biol, Queens Col, NY, 62-63; from instr to asst prof, 63-67; from asst prof to assoc prof, 71-76, chmn dept, 76-81, PROF BIOL, SWARTHMORE COL, 76- *Concurrent Pos:* Vis researcher, Inst Cell Res, Karolinska Inst, Sweden, 70-71, 74 & Inst Physiol Bot, Univ Uppsala, Sweden, 79. *Mem:* AAAS; Am Soc Cell Biol; Am Soc Zoologists; Tissue Culture Asn. *Res:* Chromosomal chemistry and structure; somatic cell hybridization. *Mailing Add:* Dept of Biol Swarthmore Col Swarthmore PA 19081

SAVAGE, STEVEN PAUL, b Topeka, Kans, Apr 8, 50; m 71; c 2. PHYSICAL ANTHROPOLOGY. *Educ:* Univ Kans, BA, 71; Univ Colo, MA, 73, PhD(anthrop), 78. *Prof Exp:* Asst prof, 75-81, ASSOC PROF ANTHROP, EASTERN KY UNIV, 81- *Concurrent Pos:* Proj dir, NSF grant, 78-81. *Mem:* Am Asn Phys Anthropologists; Soc Med Anthrop; Paleopath Asn. *Res:* Photobiology; growth; osteology. *Mailing Add:* Dept Anthrop Sociol & Social Work Eastern Ky Univ Richmond KY 40475

SAVAGE, STUART B, b Far Rockaway, NY, Oct 18, 32; m 68. APPLIED MECHANICS, FLUID MECHANICS. *Educ:* McGill Univ, BEng, 60, PhD(eng mech), 67; Calif Inst Technol, MSc, 61, AeroE, 62. *Prof Exp:* Prin aerodyn engr, Appl Res & Develop Lab, Repub Aviation Corp, NY, 62-64; lectr civil eng, 64-67, from asst prof to assoc prof, 67-77, PROF CIVIL ENG, McGILL UNIV, 77- *Concurrent Pos:* Acad visitor, Imp Col, Univ London, 71-72 & Cambridge Univ, 77-80. *Mem:* Am Soc Civil Engrs; Am Soc Mech Engrs; Am Acad Mech; Int Asn Hydraul Res; Sigma Xi. *Res:* Storage and flow of bulk solids; pneumatic transport; incompressible fluid mechanics. *Mailing Add:* Dept of Civil Eng & Appl Mech McGill Univ Montreal PQ H3A 2K6 Can

SAVAGE, WARREN F(AIRBANK), b Harvard, Mass, Mar 10, 22; m 43; c 2. PHYSICAL METALLURGY. *Educ:* Rensselaer Polytech Inst, BChE, 43, MMetE, 49, PhD(metall), 54. *Prof Exp:* Metall engr, Adirondack Foundries & Steel, Inc, 42-44; res assoc metall eng, 45-49, from asst prof to assoc prof, 49-58, PROF METALL ENG, RENSSELAER POLYTECH INST, 58-, DIR WELDING RES, 61- *Concurrent Pos:* Consult, Asn Am Railroads, Escoa Fintube, Gen Elec Co & US Dept Transp; pres, Duffers Assocs, Inc, 57-64. *Mem:* Nat Acad Eng; fel Brit Inst Welding; hon mem Am Welding Soc; Am Inst Mining, Metall & Petrol Engrs; fel Am Soc Metals. *Res:* Application of physical metallurgical principles to problems in welding and joining; resistance and fusion welding problems. *Mailing Add:* Mat Div MRC Bldg Rensselaer Polytech Inst Troy NY 12181

SAVAGE, WILLIAM F(REDERICK), b Anchorage, Alaska, May 23, 23; m 49; c 2. NUCLEAR ENGINEERING, MECHANICAL ENGINEERING. *Educ:* Rensselaer Polytech Inst, BAeroE, 43; Purdue Univ, MAeroE, 49. *Prof Exp:* Aerodynamicist, Consol Aircraft Co, Tex, 44-46; instr mech & aeronaut eng, Univ Ky, 46-49, assoc prof, 49-52; chief engr, Kett Corp, 53-55; prin engr, Aircraft Nuclear Propulsion Dept, Gen Elec Co, 55-58, supvr preliminary design, 58, mgr applns tech anal, 59-60; dir nuclear prod area, Adv Progs, Martin Co, 61-64; mgr resources planning, 65-67; asst dir eng & develop, Off Saline Water, US Dept Interior, 67-74, chief advan systs eval, 74-81, DIR UTILITY COORD, US DEPT ENERGY, 81- *Mem:* Am Soc Mech Engrs; Am Nuclear Soc. *Res:* Advanced nuclear systems technology, power plant technology, desalting technology. *Mailing Add:* 8025 Garlot Dr Annandale VA 22003

SAVAGE, WILLIAM RALPH, b Cedar Rapids, Iowa, Sept 12, 26; m 52; c 2. PHYSICS. *Educ:* Iowa State Univ, BS, 51, PhD(physics), 56. *Prof Exp:* Draftsman, Allis-Chalmers Mfg Co, Iowa, 44-49; asst physics, Iowa State Univ, 50-56, res assoc, 56; sr res scientist, Honeywell Res Ctr, Minneapolis-Honeywell Regulator Co, Minn, 56-58; mem tech staff, Cent Res Labs, Tex Instruments, Inc, 58-63; assoc prof, 63-79, PROF PHYSICS, UNIV IOWA, 80- *Mem:* AAAS; Am Phys Soc; Acoust Soc Am; Sigma Xi; Am Asn Physics Teachers. *Res:* Solid state physics; magnetic, optical electronic and thermal properties of solids; physical electronics; high field electron emission; ultra-high vacuum; musical acoustics; analytic methods in experimental physics. *Mailing Add:* Dept of Physics & Astron Univ of Iowa Iowa City IA 52242

SAVAGEAU, MICHAEL ANTONIO, b Fargo, NDak, Dec 3, 40; m 67; c 2. MATHEMATICAL MODELING OF GENETIC CIRCUITS. *Educ:* Univ Minn, BS, 62; Univ Iowa, MS, 63; Stanford Univ, PhD(cell physiol, syst sci), 67. *Prof Exp:* Res asst bioeng, Univ Iowa, 62-63; res asst, Stanford Univ, 63-64, lectr, 69-70; from asst prof to assoc prof, 70-78, actg chmn, 79-80, PROF MICROBIOL, UNIV MICH, ANN ARBOR, 78- *Concurrent Pos:* NIH fel, Univ Calif, Los Angeles, 67-68 & Stanford Univ, 68-70; NSF grants, Univ Mich, Ann Arbor, 71-; Guggenheim fel & Fulbright sr res fel, Max Planck Inst Biophys Chem, Gottingen, Ger, 76-77. *Mem:* AAAS; Am Soc Microbiol; Biophys Soc; Inst Elec & Electronics Engrs; Soc Indust & Appl Math. *Res:* Microbial physiology and ecology; function, design and evolution of molecular control mechanisms; biochemical systems analysis and computer simulation; nonlinear systems analysis. *Mailing Add:* Dept of Microbiol Univ of Mich Ann Arbor MI 48109

SAVAIANO, DENNIS ALAN, b Pomona, Calif, Dec 28, 53; m 75; c 1. AGING, INTESTINAL METABOLISM. *Educ:* Claremont Men's Col, BA, 75; Univ Calif, Davis, MS, 77, PhD(nutrit), 80. *Prof Exp:* ASST PROF NUTRIT, UNIV MINN, 80- *Mem:* Geront Soc Am; assoc Am Inst Nutrit. *Res:* Intestinal purine metabolism; intestinal cell and tissue aging. *Mailing Add:* Dept Food Sci & Nutrit Univ Minn 1334 Eckles Ave St Paul MN 55108

SAVAN, MILTON, b Manchester, NH, June 24, 20; m 55; c 3. VETERINARY MEDICINE, VIROLOGY. *Educ:* Univ NH, BS, 41; Ont Vet Col, DVM, 45; Univ Wis, MS, 49, PhD, 56. *Prof Exp:* Pvt pract, Farmington, Maine, 45-47; res vet, Europ Mission on Foot & Mouth Dis, USDA, Denmark, 51-54 & Plum Island Animal Dis Lab, 56-58; ASSOC PROF VIROL, ONT VET COL, UNIV GUELPH, 58- *Mem:* Sigma Xi; Wildlife Dis Asn; Can Wildlife Fedn. *Res:* Veterinary virology; virus diseases of fish; viruses of veterinary importance. *Mailing Add:* 471 Stevenson St N Guelph ON N1E 5C6 Can

SAVANICK, GEORGE ADRIAN, b Crucible, Pa, Jan 10, 38; m 63; c 4. MINING, SOLID STATE SCIENCE. *Educ:* Pa State Univ, BS, 59, MS, 61, PhD(solid state sci), 70. *Prof Exp:* Phys sci asst biol, US Army Biol Res Lab, Ft Detrick, 61-63; electron microscopist, Tex Instruments, Inc, 63-66; PHYSICIST, TWIN CITIES MINING RES LAB, BUR MINES, DEPT INTERIOR, 70- *Res:* Elucidation of the adhesive forces acting at grain boundaries to hold a rock together; development of a practical system of remotely controlled hydraulic mining through boreholes. *Mailing Add:* Twin Cities Mining Res Lab PO Box 1660 Twin Cities MN 55111

SAVARA, BHIM SEN, b Sialkote, India, Dec 4, 24; nat US; m 68; c 3. DENTISTRY. *Educ:* Forman Christian Col, Lahore, India, FSc, 42; Punjab Univ, India, BDS, 46; Univ London, LDS, 47; Univ Ill, MS, 50; Univ Ore, DMD, 57. *Prof Exp:* Asst prof & in-chg div pedodontics, Col Dent, Howard Univ, 49-50; from asst prof to assoc prof, 50-59, clin instr dent med, 50-62, clin assoc, 62-67, clin prof dent, 67-71, dir child study clin, 51-57, PROF DENT, DENT SCH, UNIV ORE, 59-, CHMN CHILD STUDY CLIN, 57-, PROF DENT, MED SCH, 71- *Concurrent Pos:* Consult to Surgeon Gen. *Mem:* AAAS; Am Dent Asn; Int Asn Dent Res; Brit Soc Study Human Biol. *Res:* Face and physical child growth and development; public health dentistry; biophysics; radiology; electroanesthesia; neutron radiography; physical anthropology. *Mailing Add:* Dept of Dent Univ of Ore Portland OR 97201

SAVARD, EDWARD VICTOR, b Tupper Lake, NY, Oct 25, 39; m 70. MICROBIOLOGY, PARASITOLOGY. *Educ:* McGill Univ, BSc, 63; State Univ Iowa, MS, 68, PhD(microbiol), 70. *Prof Exp:* Res microbiologist, Vet Admin Hosp, Baltimore, 64-65; sr bacteriologist, Gtr Baltimore Med Ctr, 65-66; instr med microbiol, State Univ Iowa, 69-70; asst prof, Univ Minn, Minneapolis, 70-73; chief res group, 73-77, SECT HEAD, HOFFMANN-LA ROCHE, INC, 78- *Mem:* Am Soc Microbiol; Am Acad Microbiol; Tissue Cult Asn. *Res:* Medical microbiology; mechanisms of pathogenesis; effect of parasites on host metabolism; gonococcal research; diagnostic medical microbiology and immunology; and numerical taxonomy; vertebrate cell culture; hybridoma technology. *Mailing Add:* Hoffmann-La Roche Inc Bldg 58T 340 Kingsland St Nutley NJ 07110

SAVARD, FRANCIS GERALD KENNETH, b Quebec City, Que, Feb 26, 18; m; c 2. BIOCHEMISTRY, ENDOCRINOLOGY. *Educ:* Laval Univ, BSc, 39, DSc, 46; McGill Univ, MSc, 43. *Prof Exp:* Analyst, Ayerst, McKenna Harrison Co, 40-43; researcher pharmaceut chem, 43-46; mem staff hypertension, Res Div, Cleveland Clin, 48-52; mem staff hormones, Worcester Found Exp Biol, 52-57; prof biochem & med & chief endocrine lab, Sch Med, Univ Miami, 57-73; vis scientist, Ctr for Pop Res, NIH, 72-75; dir grant prog, KROC Found, Santa Ynez, 75-77; PROF BIOCHEM & CHMN DEPT, FAC MED, UNIV MONTREAL, 77- *Concurrent Pos:* Res fel endocrinol, Univ Exp Med, Univ Montreal, 46-47; res fel cancer, Sloan-Kettering Inst, 47-48; investr, Howard Hughes Med Inst, 57-69. *Mem:* Am Soc Biol Chemists; Endocrine Soc; Am Chem Soc; Can Physiol Soc; Royal Soc Med. *Res:* Analysis of natural products; steroid hormones biosynthesis; metabolism, chromatographic separation, mechanism of hormone action. *Mailing Add:* Dept of Biochem Fac Med Box 6128 Br A Montreal PQ H3C 3S7 Can

SAVARD, JEAN YVES, b Quebec, Que, Jan 25, 35; m 58; c 2. SOLID STATE PHYSICS. *Educ:* Laval Univ, BASc, 57; Univ London, PhD(microwaves), 61. *Prof Exp:* Asst prof elec eng, 61-67, ASSOC PROF ELEC ENG, LAVAL UNIV, 67- *Mem:* Am Phys Soc. *Res:* Paramagnetic resonance in solids. *Mailing Add:* Dept of Elec Eng Laval Univ Quebec PQ C1K 7P4 Can

SAVAS, ÖMER, b Bayburt, Turkey, Oct 30, 52. AERONAUTICAL ENGINEERING, ASTRONAUTICAL ENGINEERING. *Educ:* Middle East Tech Univ, Turkey, BS, 74; Calif Inst Technol, Pasadena, MS, 75, PhD(aeronaut), 79. *Prof Exp:* Instr boundary layer theory, Middle East Tech Univ, Turkey, 81; ASST PROF FLUID MECH, UNIV OKLA, 81- *Mem:* Am Inst Aeronaut & Astronaut; Am Phys Soc. *Res:* Turbulent boundary layers; rotating flows; vortex flows. *Mailing Add:* 865 Asp Ave Rm 212 Norman OK 73019

SAVEDOFF, LYDIA GOODMAN, b New York, NY, Dec 23, 20. CHEMISTRY. *Educ:* Hunter Col, BA, 41; Columbia Univ, MA, 44, PhD(chem), 47. *Prof Exp:* Technician, Manhattan Proj, SAM Labs, Columbia Univ, 42-43, asst univ, 43-47; assoc supvr, Ohio State Univ, 47-49; res assoc, Sch Med, Univ Wash, 49-52; instr chem, Gonzaga Univ, 52-54, asst prof, 54-59; NSF fac fel, Univ Calif, Los Angeles, 59-60; from asst prof to assoc prof, 60-67, PROF CHEM, CALIF STATE UNIV, NORTHRIDGE, 67- *Mem:* AAAS; Am Chem Soc; Am Phys Soc. *Res:* Physical properties and conductance of electrolyte and polyelectrolyte solutions. *Mailing Add:* Dept of Chem Calif State Univ Northridge CA 91324

SAVEDOFF, MALCOLM PAUL, b New York, NY, July 4, 28; m 48; c 3. ASTROPHYSICS. *Educ:* Harvard Univ, AB, 48; Princeton Univ, MA, 50, PhD(astron), 51. *Prof Exp:* Nat Res Coun fel, Mt Wilson & Palomar Observs, Calif Inst Technol, 51-52; NSF fel, Leiden Observ, 52-53; res assoc & asst prof physics, 53-56, asst prof optics, 56-59, Sloan Found res fel, 56-60, from asst prof to assoc prof physics & astron, 57-64, PROF PHYSICS & ASTRON, UNIV ROCHESTER, 64- *Concurrent Pos:* Dir, C E Kenneth Mees Observ, 64; NSF fel, Univ Leiden, 64-65; Nat Res Coun sr assoc, Goddard Space Flight Ctr, NASA, 79-80. *Mem:* Am Phys Soc; Am Astron Soc; Int Astron Union. *Res:* Interstellar material; stellar interiors. *Mailing Add:* Dept of Physics & Astron Univ of Rochester Rochester NY 14627

SAVEREIDE, THOMAS J, b Rockford, Ill, Nov 18, 32; m 57; c 3. INDUSTRIAL ORGANIC CHEMISTRY. *Educ:* St Olaf Col, BA, 57; Northwestern Univ, PhD(org chem), 61. *Prof Exp:* Sr res chemist, St Paul, Minn, 61-64, supvr org res, 64-69, tech mgr chem div, 69-73, tech dir, Chem Resources Div, 73-80, TECH DIR, SUMITOMO DIV 3M CO, TOKYO, JAPAN, 81- *Mem:* Am Chem Soc. *Res:* Organic synthesis; polymer chemistry. *Mailing Add:* Chem Resources Div 3M Co St Paul MN 55101

SAVERY, CLYDE WILLIAM, b White Plains, NY, Jan 3, 35; m 58; c 2. MECHANICAL ENGINEERING. *Educ:* Univ Ill, Urbana, BS, 57; Univ Wash, MS, 60; Univ Wis-Madison, PhD(mech eng), 69. *Prof Exp:* Res & develop assoc, Gen Atomic Div, Gen Dynamics, 60-66; asst prof mech eng, 69-74, ASSOC PROF MECH ENG, DREXEL UNIV, 74- *Concurrent Pos:* Consult, Choice Mag, 69- & Gilbert Assoc, Inc, 72-77; res grants, NSF, US Dept Energy, HUD & Elec Power Res Inst, 73- *Honors & Awards:* Ralph Teetor Award, Soc Automotive Engrs, 71. *Mem:* Soc Automotive Engrs; Am Soc Mech Engrs; Am Nuclear Soc; Sigma Xi. *Res:* Thermodynamics and heat and mass transfer with applications to vaporization, combustion, air pollution, cooling towers and nuclear power reactor safety. *Mailing Add:* Dept of Mech Eng & Mech Drexel Univ Philadelphia PA 19104

SAVERY, HARRY P, b Coffeyville, Kans, Jan 4, 20; m 50; c 4. PHYSIOLOGY, ENDOCRINOLOGY. *Educ:* Colo Agr & Mech Col, BS, 49; Univ Wyo, MS, 50; Tex A&M Univ, PhD(reprod of physiol), 54. *Prof Exp:* Assoc prof biol, 60-71, PROF BIOL & HEAD DEPT, CENT MO STATE UNIV, 71- *Mem:* AAAS; Am Soc Animal Sci; Am Soc Zoologists; Am Inst Biol Sci. *Res:* Cytological studies of normal and superovulated ova. *Mailing Add:* Dept of Biol Cent Mo State Univ Warrensburg MO 64093

SAVICKAS, DAVID FRANCIS, b Chicago, Ill, Nov 9, 40. THEORETICAL PHYSICS. *Educ:* St Mary's Col, BA, 62; Mich State Univ, MS, 64, PhD(physics), 66. *Prof Exp:* Asst prof, Bucknell Univ, 66-69; ASSOC PROF PHYSICS, WESTERN NEW ENG COL, 69- *Mem:* Am Phys Soc; Am Asn Physics Teachers. *Res:* Radiation pressure on interstellar particles; relativity theory; astrophysical kinematics. *Mailing Add:* Dept of Physics Western New Eng Col Springfield MA 01119

SAVILE, DOUGLAS BARTON OSBORNE, b Dublin, Ireland, July 19, 09; m 39; c 2. BOTANY. *Educ:* McGill Univ, BSA, 33, MSc, 34; Univ Mich, PhD(bot), 39. *Hon Degrees:* DSc, McGill Univ, 78. *Prof Exp:* Agr asst, 36-39, agr scientist, 39-53, sr mycologist, 53-57, prin mycologist, 57-75, EMER RES ASSOC, BIOSYST RES INST, AGR CAN, OTTAWA, 75- *Mem:* AAAS; Mycol Soc Am; Am Soc Plant Taxon; fel Arctic Inst NAm; fel Royal Soc Can. *Res:* Mycology; taxonomy of parasitic fungi; biology of rusts; co-evolution of rusts and host plants; arctic biology; avian aerodynamics. *Mailing Add:* Biosyst Res Inst Res Br Cent Exp Farm Ottawa ON K1A 0C6 Can

SAVILLE, D(UDLEY) A(LBERT), b Lincoln, Nebr, Feb 25, 33; m 59; c 2. CHEMICAL ENGINEERING, FLUID MECHANICS. *Educ:* Univ Nebr, Lincoln, BS, 54, MS, 59; Univ Mich, Ann Arbor, PhD(chem eng), 66. *Prof Exp:* Engr chem eng, Union Carbide Corp, 54-55; res engr, Calif Res Corp, 59-61 & Shell Develop Co, 66-68; from asst prof to assoc prof chem eng, 68-71, PROF CHEM ENG, PRINCETON UNIV, 77- *Mem:* Am Inst Chem Engrs; Am Chem Soc. *Res:* Interfacial phenomena; electrohydrodynamics; hydrodynamic stability; coal pyrolysis and hydropyrolysis; heat and mass transfer in particulate suspensions. *Mailing Add:* Dept of Chem Eng Princeton Univ Princeton NJ 08540

SAVILLE, THORNDIKE, JR, b Baltimore, Md, Aug 1, 25; m 50; c 3. CIVIL ENGINEERING. *Educ:* Harvard Univ, AB, 47; Univ Calif, MS, 49. *Prof Exp:* Res asst, Univ Calif, 47-49; hydraul engr, Beach Erosion Bd & Coastal Eng Res Ctr, Corps Engrs, 49-53, asst chief res div, 53-64, chief gen proj br, 54-64, chief res div, Coastal Eng Res Ctr, 64-71, TECH DIR, COASTAL ENG RES CTR, CORPS ENGRS, US ARMY, 71- *Concurrent Pos:* Mem coun wave res, Eng Found, 54-64; mem, Permanent Int Asn Navig Cong, 56-, secy, US Deleg, Sect II, London, 57 & Baltimore, Md, 61, liaison officer, Int Comn Force of Waves & chmn, Am Sect Subcomt, 64-72; US mem, Permanent Int Comn, 71-78; mem comt tidal hydraul, US Army Corps Engrs, 64-; mem adv bd, Nat Oceanog Data Ctr, 64-72; gen chmn, Specialty Conf Coastal Engrs, Santa Barbara, 65 & Washington, DC, 71; liaison rep, Panel Coastal Eng & Inland Waters, Comt Earthquake Eng Res, Nat Acad Eng, 66-70. *Honors & Awards:* Am Soc Civil Engrs Res Award, 63. *Mem:* Nat Acad Eng; AAAS; Am Soc Civil Engrs; Am Geophys Union; Int Asn Hydraul Res. *Res:* Basic laws governing wave and surge action on beaches and shore structures and application of these to engineering design; coastal erosion processes and littoral tranpost; hydraulic model studies. *Mailing Add:* 5601 Albia Rd Washington DC 20016

SAVIN, SAMUEL MARVIN, b Boston, Mass, Aug 31, 40. GEOCHEMISTRY, GEOLOGY. *Educ:* Colgate Univ, BA, 61; Calif Inst Technol, PhD(geochem), 67. *Prof Exp:* From asst prof to assoc prof, 67-76, PROF GEOL SCI, CASE WESTERN RESERVE UNIV, 76-, CHMN DEPT, 77- *Concurrent Pos:* Assoc ed, Geuchimica et Cosmochimica Acta, 76-79; mem, Earth Sci Adv Panel, NSF, 78-81; ed, Marine Micropaleontol, 79- *Mem:* Geol Soc Am; Geochem Soc; fel AAAS; Am Geophys Union; Clay Minerals Soc. *Res:* Stable isotope geochemistry; low temperature geochemistry; oceanography; stable isotopes in medicine. *Mailing Add:* Dept Earth Sci Case Western Reserve Univ Cleveland OH 44106

SAVINELLI, EMILIO A, b New York, NY, May 7, 30; c 8. CHEMISTRY. *Educ:* Manhattan Col, BCE, 50; Univ Fla, MSE, 51, PhD(chem), 55. *Prof Exp:* Engr, Du Pont Co, 56-60; res dir, 60-62, div mgr, 62-68, dir mkt, 64-68, vpres, 68-71, PRES, DREW CHEM CORP, 71- *Mem:* Nat Acad Sci; Am Chem Soc; Am Soc Mech Engrs. *Mailing Add:* Drew Chem Corp One Drew Chemical Plaza Boonton NJ 07005

SAVIT, CARL HERTZ, b New York, NY, July 19, 22; m 46; c 3. GEOPHYSICS. *Educ:* Calif Inst Technol, BS, 42, MS, 43. *Prof Exp:* Chief mathematician, Western Geophys Co Am, Calif, 48-60, dir systs res, 60-65, vpres res & develop, Tex, 65-70; asst to President's Sci Adv & chmn, US Interagency Comt Atmospheric Sci, 70-71; SR VPRES TECHNOL, WESTERN GEOPHYS CO AM, 71- *Concurrent Pos:* Assoc prof, San Fernando Valley State Col, 59-60; mem panel on-site inspection unidentified seismic events, US Govt, 61, select panel initiatives transp, 71; mem, President's Panel Disposition Oil Leasing Santa Barbara Channel & Offshore Pollution, 69; mem comt seismol, Nat Acad Sci-Nat Res Coun, 71-75, chmn, 72-74, mem US nat comt tunneling technol, 72-76, chmn geophys data panel, Geophys Res Bd, 75-76, mem, Panel on Earthquake Prediction & Assembly Math & Phys Sci, 77; US deleg to USSR in explor geophys, 71; consult panel, President's Sci Adv, 71-74; mem nat adv comt, Univ Tex Marine Biomed Inst, 73-; mem, US Coastal Zone Mgt Comt, 75-78; mem nat offshore opers indust adv comt, US Coast Guard, 75-77; mem sea-bottom surv panel, US-Japan Coop Prog Natural Resources, US Dept Com, 75-78. *Honors & Awards:* Compass Award, Marine Technol Soc, 79; Kauffman Gold Medal, Soc Explor Geophysicists, 79. *Mem:* Soc Explor Geophys (pres, 71-72); Asn Earth Sci Eds; Mex Asn Geophys Explor; Marine Technol Soc; fel Geol Soc Am. *Res:* Signal detection; data processing systems; crustal studies; oceanography; seismic exploration. *Mailing Add:* PO Box 2469 Houston TX 77001

SAVIT, JOSEPH, b Chicago, Ill, Oct 23, 21; m 42; c 4. REPROGRAPHY, INFORMOGRAPHY. *Educ:* Univ Chicago, BS, 42. *Prof Exp:* Res assoc gas warfare, Univ Chicago, 42-46; pres & mgr, Travelers Hotel Co, Calif, 47-51; plant chemist, Reproduction Prod Co, 52-53; staff chemist, A B Dick & Co, 53-56; chief chemist, Huey Co, 56-57; mgr res & develop, Eugene Dietzgen Co, 58-63 & Colonial Carbon Co, 63-64; mgr, Microstatics Div, SCM Corp, 64-66; dir res & asst vpres, Apeco Corp, 66-73; PRES, SAVIT ENTERPRISES, INC, 73- *Mem:* Tech Asn Pulp & Paper Indust; Am Chem Soc; Soc Photog Sci & Eng; Nat Microfilm Asn; fel Am Inst Chem. *Res:* Reprography, especially electrography and electrophotography; office print out; non-impact computer print-out systems; paper and film coatings; offset printing systems; ink-jet printing systems. *Mailing Add:* 751 Vernon Ave Glencoe IL 60022

SAVIT, ROBERT STEVEN, b Chicago, Ill, Aug 21, 47. HIGH ENERGY PHYSICS, THEORETICAL PHYSICS. *Educ:* Univ Chicago, BA, 69; Stanford Univ, MS, 70, PhD(physics), 73. *Prof Exp:* Res assoc theoret physics, Stanford Linear Accelerator Ctr, 73 & Fermi Nat Accelerator Lab, 73-74; vis scientist, Europ Orgn Nuclear Res, 74-75; physicist, Fermi Nat Accelerator Lab, 75-78; ASSOC RES SCIENTIST & LECTR, PHYSICS DEPT, UNIV MICH, ANN ARBOR, 78- *Concurrent Pos:* NATO fel, NSF, 74-75; grant recipient, Am-Swiss Found Sci Exchange, 74-75; assoc ed, Nuclear Phys Bull Field Theory & Statist Systs, 80-; res fel, Sloan Found, 81-; assoc vis scientist, Inst Theoret Physics, Santa Barbara, 81-82. *Mem:* Am Phys Soc. *Res:* High energy scattering; field theory; critical phenomena; statistical mechanics. *Mailing Add:* Physics Dept Univ Mich Ann Arbor MI 48104

SAVITCH, WALTER JOHN, b Brooklyn, NY, Feb 21, 43. COMPUTER SCIENCE, MATHEMATICS. *Educ:* Univ NH, BS, 64; Univ Calif, Berkeley, MA & PhD(math), 69. *Prof Exp:* Assoc prof info & comput sci, 69-80, PROF ELEC ENG & COMPUT SCI, UNIV CALIF, SAN DIEGO, 80- *Concurrent Pos:* NSF res grant, 70-76. *Mem:* Am Math Soc; Asn Comput Mach; Asn Symbolic Logic; Soc Indust & Appl Math. *Res:* Theoretical computer science; complexity of algorithms; formal languages; automata theory; mathematical logic. *Mailing Add:* Dept of Appl Physics & Info Sci Univ of Calif San Diego La Jolla CA 92037

SAVITSKY, DANIEL, b New York, NY, Sept 26, 21; m 62; c 3. NAVAL ARCHITECTURE. *Educ:* City Col New York, BCE, 42; Stevens Inst Technol, MSc, 52; NY Univ, PhD, 71. *Prof Exp:* Struct engr, Edo Corp, 42-44; aeronaut res scientist, Nat Adv Comt Aeronaut, 44-47; DEP DIR, DAVIDSON LAB, STEVENS INST TECHNOL, 47-, PROF OCEAN ENG, 67- *Concurrent Pos:* Ottens res award, Stevens Inst Technol, 68; consult, indust & US Navy. *Honors & Awards:* Adm Cochrane Award, Soc Naval Archit & Marine Eng, 67. *Mem:* Soc Naval Archit & Marine Eng. *Res:* Hydrodynamics; ocean science and engineering. *Mailing Add:* 597 Delcina Dr River Vale NJ 07675

SAVITSKY, GEORGE BORIS, b Harbin, China, Mar 10, 25; nat US; m 48; c 3. PHYSICAL CHEMISTRY. *Educ:* Aurora Univ, China, BS, 47; Univ Fla, PhD(chem), 59. *Prof Exp:* Res assoc chem, Princeton Univ, 59-61; asst prof, Univ Calif, Davis, 61-65; assoc prof, 65-71, PROF CHEM, CLEMSON UNIV, 71- *Mem:* AAAS; fel Am Inst Chem; Am Chem Soc. *Res:* Spectroscopy; nuclear magnetic resonance spectroscopy. *Mailing Add:* Dept of Chem & Geol Clemson Univ Clemson SC 29631

SAVITSKY, HELEN, b Poltava, Russia, Feb 17, 01; nat US; m 26. GENETICS. *Educ:* Univ Moscow, MS, 37; Univ Leningrad, PhD(cytogenetics), 40. *Prof Exp:* Jr specialist, Breeding Sta Belaja Zerkov, Russia, 27-28, sr specialist, 29-30; prof chief cytol lab, Res Inst Sugar Indust, Russia, 30-41; chief cytol lab & lab oil crops, Ukrainian Inst Plant Breeding, Russia, 41-43; cytologist, Univ Posen, Poland, 43-45; cytogeneticist, Univ Halle, Ger, 45; res collabr, Sugar Beet Breeding Co, Ger, 46; prof anat & cytol, Ukrainian Tech Inst, Ger, 47; cytogeneticist, Beet Sugar Develop Found, Utah, 47-61; geneticist, 61-71, EMER COLLABR, USDA, 71- *Mem:* Genetics Soc Am; Genetics Soc Can; Am Soc Sugar Beet Technologists. *Res:* Cytogenetics; embryology; polyploidy; momogerm beet; interspecific hybridization in genus Beta. *Mailing Add:* USDA PO Box 5098 Salinas CA 93901

SAVITZ, JAN, b Sellersville, Pa, Apr 8, 41; m 68. LIMNOLOGY. *Educ:* Pa State Univ, BS, 63; Ind Univ, PhD(limnol), 67. *Prof Exp:* Asst prof biol, Rockford Col, 67-69; asst prof, 69-74, ASSOC PROF BIOL, LOYOLA UNIV CHICAGO, 74- *Honors & Awards:* Mary Ashby Cheek Award, 68. *Mem:* AAAS; Am Fisheries Soc; Am Inst Biol Sci; Am Soc Limnol & Oceanog; Ecol Soc Am. *Res:* Protein metabolism of fish; fish predation on benthic organisms. *Mailing Add:* Dept of Biol Loyola Univ of Chicago Chicago IL 60626

SAVITZ, MAXINE LAZARUS, b Baltimore, Md, Feb 13, 37; m 61; c 2. ORGANIC CHEMISTRY, ELECTROCHEMISTRY. *Educ:* Bryn Mawr Col, AB, 58; Mass Inst Technol, PhD(org chem), 61. *Prof Exp:* NSF fel, Univ Calif, Berkeley, 61-62; instr chem, Hunter Col, 62-63; res chemist, Elec Power Div, US Army Eng Res & Develop Lab, Ft Belvoir, 63-68; assoc prof chem, Fed City Col, 68-71, prof, 71-72; prof mgr, Res Appl to Nat Needs, NSF, 72-73; chief bldgs conserv policy res, Fed Energy Admin, 73-75; div dir bldgs & indust conserv, Energy Res & Develop Admin, 75-76, div dir bldgs & community systs, 76-79, DEP ASST SECY CONSERV, DEPT OF ENERGY, 79- *Mem:* AAAS; Am Chem Soc; Am Soc Heating, Refrig & Air-Conditioning Engrs. *Res:* Free radical mechanisms; anodic hydrocarbon oxidation; fuel cells; more efficient use of energy in buildings; community systems; applianes; agriculture and industrial processes; transportation; batteries and other storage systems. *Mailing Add:* 5019 Lowell St NW Washington DC 20016

SAVITZKY, ABRAHAM, b New York, NY, May 29, 19; m 42; c 2. PHYSICAL CHEMISTRY, COMPUTER SCIENCE. *Educ:* State Univ NY, BA, 41; Columbia Univ, MA, 47, PhD(phys chem), 49. *Prof Exp:* Res assoc electron micros, Columbia Univ, 49-50; staff scientist, 50-71, SR STAFF SCIENTIST CORP COMPUT FACIL, PERKIN-ELMER CORP, 71- *Concurrent Pos:* Mem, Nat Acad Sci-Nat Res Coun Eval Panel Atomic & Molecular Physics, Nat Bur Standards, 70-72; dir, Time Share Peripherals Corp, 70-77; Sci Apparatus Makers Asn rep, Am Nat Standards Comt X-3 Comput & Data Processing, 72- *Mem:* Am Chem Soc; Am Phys Soc; Optical Soc Am; Soc Appl Spectros; Asn Comput Mach. *Res:* Development of laboratory and process analytical instrumentation; infrared spectroscopy; computer aided experimentation and data reduction; time sharing systems and languages; computer plotting. *Mailing Add:* 3 Mail Coach Ct Wilton CT 06897

SAVITZKY, ALAN HOWARD, b Danbury, Conn, June 23, 50; m 72; c 2. HERPETOLOGY, EVOLUTIONARY BIOLOGY. *Educ:* Univ Colo, BA, 72; Univ Kans, MA, 74, PhD(biol), 79. *Prof Exp:* Fel, Nat Mus Natural Hist, Smithsonian Inst, 76-78; MEM STAFF, SECT ECOL & SYSTEMETICS, CORNELL UNIV, 78- *Mem:* Am Soc Ichthyologists & Herpetologists; Am Soc Zoologists; Herpetologists League; Soc Study Amphibians & Reptiles; Soc Systematic Zool. *Res:* Relationship between phylogeny and adaptation, especially among snakes; morphological correlates of specialized feeding habits; parallel evolution of complex adaptations. *Mailing Add:* Sect Ecol & Systematics Biol Sci Bldg Tower Rd Cornell Univ Ithaca NY 14853

SAVKAR, SUDHIR DATTATRAYA, b Poona, India, Sept 27, 39; US citizen; m 64; c 2. FLUID MECHANICS, ACOUSTICS. *Educ:* Catholic Univ Am, BS, 61; Univ Mich, MS, 63, PhD(mech eng), 66. *Prof Exp:* Res engr, 66-78, MGR ENG MECH, GEN ELEC CORP RES & DEVELOP, 78- *Concurrent Pos:* Adj assoc prof, Nuclear Eng Dept, Rensselaer Polytech Inst, 77- *Mem:* Assoc fel Am Inst Aeronaut & Astronaut; Sigma Xi. *Res:* Unsteady flow and structural interaction; acoustics; combustion instability; electro-hydrodynamics. *Mailing Add:* Gen Elec Corp Res & Develop Bldg K-1 Rm 5B29 Schenectady NY 12345

SAVOIE, RODRIGUE, b Carleton, Que, Oct 1, 36; m 60; c 3. PHYSICAL CHEMISTRY. *Educ:* Univ of the Sacred Heart, BA, 56; Laval Univ, BSc, 60, PhD(chem), 63. *Prof Exp:* From asst prof to assoc prof, 65-75, PROF CHEM, LAVAL UNIV, 75- *Mem:* Chem Inst Can. *Res:* Infrared and Raman spectroscopy; molecular and crystal structures. *Mailing Add:* Dept of Chem Laval Univ Quebec PQ G1K 7P4 Can

SAVOL, ANDREJ MARTIN, b Slovakia, Feb 4, 40; US citizen; m 69. ELECTRICAL ENGINEERING, COMPUTER SCIENCE. *Educ:* Carnegie-Mellon Univ, BS, 67; Univ Pittsburgh, MS, 75, PhD(elec eng), 79. *Prof Exp:* Comput programmer, Westinghouse Indust Systs Div, 67-69; head, comput servs, Mellon Inst, 69-72; SR SPECIALIST ENGR, BOEING AEROSPACE CO, 77- *Honors & Awards:* Outstanding Tech Achievement Award, Pac Northwest Sect, Am Inst Aeronaut & Astronaut, 78. *Mem:* Inst Elec & Electronics Engrs. *Res:* Applications of computerized pattern recognition; computer analysis of images in two areas: medical, black lung chest X-rays; military, guidance and target recognition. *Mailing Add:* Boeing Aerospace Co M|S 86-18 Box 3999 Seattle WA 98124

SAVORY, JOHN, b Lancashire, Eng, Apr 4, 36; US citizen; m 77; c 2. CLINICAL CHEMISTRY, PATHOLOGY. *Educ:* Univ Durham, BSc, 58, PhD(chem), 61. *Prof Exp:* Res chemist, Chemstrand Res Ctr, NC, 63-64; dir clin chem & instr path, Univ Fla, 66-67, asst dir clin labs & asst prof path, 67-72; assoc prof med & dir clin chem, Univ NC, Chapel Hill, 72-77; med & dir clin chem, Univ NC, Chapel Hill, 72-77; MEM FAC, DEPT PATH CLIN LABS, MED CTR, UNIV VA, 77- *Concurrent Pos:* Res fel chem, Univ Fla, 61-63; sr fel biochem, Univ Wash, 64-66; dir exp & clin path grad prog, Col Med, Univ Fla, 66-72; consult, Vet Admin Hosp, Gainesville, Fla, 67-72. *Mem:* Am Asn Clin Chemists; Am Chem Soc; Asn Clin Sci; The Chem Soc. *Res:* Organic fluorine chemistry; biochemistry. *Mailing Add:* Dept of Path Clin Labs Med Ctr Univ of Va Charlottesville VA 22908

SAVORY, LEONARD E(RWIN), b Denver, Colo, Jan 11, 20; m 47; c 3. CHEMICAL ENGINEERING. *Educ:* Univ Denver, BSChE, 42; Ill Inst Technol, MSChE, 44. *Prof Exp:* Asst, Manhattan Proj, SAM Labs, Columbia Univ, 44-45; res technologist, Tenn Eastman Corp, 45-46; asst prof chem eng, Univ Denver, 46-50; mem staff, Los Alamos Sci Lab, NMex, 50-53; res proj supvr, Res Dept, United Gas Corp, 53-60, asst dir res, 60-66, mgr admin div, Res, Eng & Develop Dept, Pennzoil United, Inc, 67-73, sr tech adv, Environ, Safety & Health Affairs Dept, Pennzoil Co, 73-81; RETIRED. *Mem:* AAAS; Am Chem Soc; Am Inst Chem Engrs; Air Pollution Control Asn. *Res:* Nuclear energy; natural gas technology; pollution control. *Mailing Add:* PO Box 1675 Estes Park CO 80517

SAVOS, MILTON GEORGE, b Nashua, NH, July 14, 27; m 62; c 1. ENTOMOLOGY. *Educ:* Am Int Col, BA, 52; Univ Mass, MS, 54; Ore State Univ, PhD, 58. *Prof Exp:* Res entomologist, Inst Zool, Nancy Univ, France, 58-59; exten PROF ENTOM, COL AGR & NATURAL RESOURCES, UNIV CONN, 72-, EXTEN ENTOMOLOGIST, 60- *Mem:* Entom Soc Am; AAAS; Sigma Xi. *Res:* Biology and taxonomy of Symphyla; bionomics of garden symphylid; taxonomy; economic entomology. *Mailing Add:* Col of Agr & Natural Resources Univ of Conn Storrs CT 06268

SAWAN, SAMUEL PAUL, b Akron, Ohio, Apr 18, 50. POLYMER CHEMISTRY, BIOPOLYMERS. *Educ:* Univ Akron, BS, 72, PhD(polymer sci), 76. *Prof Exp:* Data analyst, Akron Regional Air Pollution Control Agency, 73-74; scholar, Dept Pharmaceut Chem, Univ Calif, San Francisco, 76-78; ASST PROF, DEPT CHEM, UNIV LOWELL, 78- *Concurrent Pos:* Prin investr, Am Chem Soc Petrol Res Fund, 78-80; co-investr, Xerox Corp grant, 80-82; lectr radiol, Harvard Med Sch, 80- *Mem:* Am Chem Soc; Sigma Xi; AAAS. *Res:* Synthesis and characterization of macromolecules that exhibit catalytic activity; biocompatible polymeric materials; nmr investigations of polymer conformations and enzyme active sites; new radiological imaging agents. *Mailing Add:* Dept Chem Univ Lowell One Univ Ave Lowell MA 01854

SAWARD, ERNEST WELTON, b New York, NY, Oct 19, 14; m 38; c 3. INTERNAL MEDICINE. *Educ:* Colgate Univ, AB, 36; Univ Rochester, MD, 39; Am Bd Internal Med, dipl, 46. *Prof Exp:* House officer, Barnes Hosp, St Louis, Mo, 39-41; resident, Peter Bent Brigham Hosp, Boston, 41-42; chief med, Hanford Eng Works, Atomic Energy Proj, 42-45; med dir, Permanente Clin, Kaiser Found Hosp, Portland, Ore, 45-70; PROF MED & SOCIAL MED & ASSOC DEAN EXTRAMURAL AFFAIRS, SCH MED & DENT, UNIV ROCHESTER, 70- *Concurrent Pos:* Tech adv, Community Health Proj, Cordoba, Arg, 62-; proj dir, Off Econ Opportunity Health Proj, Ore, 66-70; mem & chmn, Health Ins Benefits Adv Coun, 70-74 & Nat Prof Standards Coun, 73-76; chmn bd dirs, Monroe Community Hosp, Rochester, NY, 74-; chmn vis comt health serv, Harvard Univ, 75-; mem & co-chmn, Gov Health Adv Coun, NY, 75-76; vchmn, Finger Lakes Health Systs Agency, 75-78; mem, NY State Hosp Planning & Rev Coun, 76-; fel Ctr Advan Study Behav Sci, Stanford, Calif, 78-79; vis prof med & family, community & prev med, Med Sch, Stanford Univ, 78-79; chmn, Secy's Ad Hoc Comt Rev US Pub Health Serv Hosps, 78; mem panel on health status of disadvantaged, Nat Acad Sci; mem med coun, Nat Inst Med; mem bd, Prev Heart Reconditioning Found, Vt. *Mem:* Nat Inst Med; Am Heart Asn; Am Col Chest Physicians; Am Fedn Clin Res; Am Pub Health Asn. *Res:* Social medicine; organization and delivery of health services. *Mailing Add:* Off of the Dean Univ of Rochester Sch Med & Dent Rochester NY 14620

SAWARDEKER, JAWAHAR SAZRO, b Goa, India, Nov 22, 37; m 66; c 1. PHYSICAL PHARMACY, ANALYTICAL CHEMISTRY. *Educ:* Univ Bombay, BS, 57; Univ Iowa, MS, 61, PhD(pharm), 64. *Prof Exp:* Res chemist, USDA, Ill, 64-66; assoc scientist, Ortho Pharmaceut Corp, 67-69, group leader scientist, 69-73; group mgr, Whitehall Labs, 73-77, dir qual control, 77-81; DIR QUAL CONTROL, GLAXO INC, 81- *Mem:* Am Pharmaceut Asn; Am Chem Soc; Am Soc Qual Control. *Res:* Gas chromatography application to pharmaceutical systems and carbohydrate chemistry; exploration of analytical techniques and development of procedures; preformulation research; bioavailability studies. *Maili. g Add:* Glaxo Inc 302 S Broadway St Louis MO 63102

SAWATZKY, ERICH, b Cholm, Poland, Apr 21, 34; US citizen; m 61; c 3. PHYSICS. *Educ:* Univ BC, BSc, 58, MSc, 60, PhD(physics), 62. *Prof Exp:* RES STAFF SCIENTIST, SAN JOSE RES LAB, IBM CORP, 62- *Mem:* Am Phys Soc; Inst Elec & Electronics Engrs. *Res:* Magnetism in solid state materials; nuclear magnetic resonance, preparation and characterization of physical properties of thin films; magnetic and magneto-optic properties of thin films. *Mailing Add:* IBM Corp E41/013 5600 Cottle Rd San Jose CA 95193

SAWCHUK, ALEXANDER ANDREW, b Washington, DC, Feb 20, 45; m 71. ELECTRICAL ENGINEERING, OPTICS. *Educ:* Mass Inst Technol, SB, 66; Stanford Univ, MS, 68, PhD(elec eng), 72. *Prof Exp:* Elec engr, Goddard Space Flight Ctr, NASA, Md, 66 & Commun Satellite Corp, Washington, DC, 67; asst prof elec eng, 71-77, ASSOC PROF ELEC ENG, UNIV SOUTHERN CALIF, 77- *Concurrent Pos:* Consult, TRW Defense & Space Systs Group, 77- *Mem:* Inst Elec & Electronics Engrs; Optical Soc Am; Soc Photo-Optical Instrumentation Engrs; Soc Info Display. *Res:* Digital image processing; statistical optics; optical information processing; multidimensional signal processing and system theory. *Mailing Add:* Dept of Elec Eng Univ of Southern Calif Los Angeles CA 90007

SAWCHUK, RONALD JOHN, b Toronto, Ont, May 29, 40; m 67; c 3. PHARMACOKINETICS, MEDICAL RESEARCH. *Educ:* Univ Toronto, BScPhm, 63, MScPhm, 66; Univ Calif, San Francisco, PhD(pharmaceut), 72. *Prof Exp:* asst prof, 72-77, ASSOC PROF PHARMACEUT, COL PHARM, UNIV MINN, MINNEAPOLIS, 77- *Mem:* Am Pharmaceut Asn; Am Asn Cols Pharm. *Res:* Pharmacokinetics and kinetic modeling; drug distribution, metabolism and excretion; drug-drug interactions; quantitative analysis of foreign compounds in biological tissues. *Mailing Add:* Dept of Pharmaceut Univ of Minn Col of Pharm Minneapolis MN 55455

SAWERS, JAMES RICHARD, JR, b Memphis, Tenn, Feb 4, 40; m 61; c 2. ENGINEERING PHYSICS. *Educ:* Duke Univ, BS, 62, PhD(nuclear physics), 66. *Prof Exp:* Res physicist, Du Pont Instruments, Del, 66-71, sr scientist, 71-73; tech supvr, Du Pont Biomed, 74-75, mgr microtomy prod, 76-77, mgr clin prod, 77-78, MGR INSTRUMENT PROD ADMIN, E I DU PONT DE NEMOURS & CO, INC, 78- *Mem:* Soc Magnetism & Magnetic Mat; Electron Micros Soc Am; Am Phys Soc; Sigma Xi; Soc Photog Scientists & Engrs. *Res:* Neutron polarization; magnetism; photochemistry; electroluminescence; electron imaging; submicron particle size analysis; diamond knives; computer analysis; biomedical instrumentation; process and pollution control instrumentation. *Mailing Add:* Snug Hill Rd 2 Box 378 Hockessin DE 19707

SAWHILL, ROY BOND, b Tacoma, Wash, June 1, 22; m 43; c 3. TRANSPORTATION, CIVIL ENGINEERING. *Educ:* Univ Wash, BS, 50; Univ Calif, MEng, 52. *Prof Exp:* Jr hwy engr, State Hwy Dept, Wash, 50-51; jr res engr, Inst Transp & Traffic Eng, Univ Calif, 51-52; jr traffic engr, City Eng Dept, Seattle, 52, asst traffic engr, 52-53, assoc traffic engr, 53-56; from asst prof to assoc prof civil eng, 56-69, PROF CIVIL ENG, UNIV WASH, 69- *Concurrent Pos:* Mem, Hwy Res Bd, Nat Acad Sci-Nat Res Coun. *Res:* Traffic engineering; operation characteristics, including fuel and travel time, of commercial vehicles and relation to highway design and economic determination of highway improvements. *Mailing Add:* Dept of Civil Eng Univ of Wash Seattle WA 98105

SAWHNEY, VIPEN KUMAR, b India. BOTANY, PLANT PHYSIOLOGY. *Educ:* Univ Punjab, BSc, 65, MSc, 67; Univ Western Ont, PhD(plant sci), 72. *Prof Exp:* Fel plant sci, Univ Western Ont, 67-72; fel biol, Simon Fraser Univ, 72-74; asst prof, 75-80, ASSOC PROF BIOL, UNIV SASK, 81- *Mem:* Am Soc Plant Physiologists; Can Soc Plant Physiologists; Can Bot Asn; Am Bot Asn. *Res:* Growth regulation of vegetation and floral species of normal and mutant plants; physiological and ultrastructural studies on plant cell elongation. *Mailing Add:* Dept of Biol Univ of Sask Saskatoon SK S7H 0W0 Can

SAWICKI, JOHN EDWARD, b Philadelphia, Pa, March 10, 44; m 71; c 2. EXPERIMENTALIST, REACTION KINETICS. *Educ:* Drexel Univ, BS, 67, MS, 68; Univ Va, PhD(chem eng), 72. *Prof Exp:* Sr res officer, Chem Eng Group, SAfrica Coun Sci & Indust Res, 72-74; res engr & group leader, Joseph Schlitz Brewing Co, 74-78; SR PRIN RES ENGR, AIR PROD & CHEMICALS, INC, 78- *Mem:* Am Inst Chem Engrs. *Res:* Applied and basic research in aromatic nitgration processes and chemistry; unit operations and plant optimization; process development. *Mailing Add:* RD 2 Breinigsville PA 18031

SAWICKI, STANLEY GEORGE, b Oklahoma City, Okla, Feb 23, 42; m 69. VIROLOGY, TISSUE CULTURE. *Educ:* Georgetown Univ, BS, 64; Columbia Univ, MA & PhD(pathobiol), 74. *Prof Exp:* Fel molecular cell biol, Rockefeller Univ, 74-77; ASST PROF MICROBIOL, MED COL OHIO, 77- *Mem:* AAAS; Am Soc Microbiol; Sigma Xi. *Res:* RNA and protein synthesis in eukaryotic cells; control of the replication cycle in alphaviruses and adenoviruses. *Mailing Add:* Caller Serv No 10008 Med Col Ohio Toledo OH 43699

SAWITSKY, ARTHUR, b Jersey City, NJ, Jan 31, 16; m; c 2. HEMATOLOGY, ONCOLOGY. *Educ:* NY Univ, BA, 36, MD, 40; Am Bd Internal Med, dipl, 48, cert hemat, 72. *Prof Exp:* Intern, Kings County Hosp, 40-42; fel hemat, Dept Therapeut, Col Med, NY Univ, 46-47; asst resident med, Goldwater Mem Hosp, NY Univ Div, 47-48; assoc med, NY Med Col, 50-54; CHIEF DIV HEMAT, LONG ISLAND JEWISH-HILLSIDE MED CTR, 55-; PROF MED & CLIN PATH, STATE UNIV NY STONY BROOK, 71- *Concurrent Pos:* Asst vis physician, Goldwater Mem Hosp, NY Univ Div, 48-52; assoc vis physician hemat & physician-in-chg blood bank, Queens Hosp Ctr, 48-64; assoc vis physician hemat, Jamaica Hosp, 49-54; asst vis physician hemat, Flushing Hosp, 50-55; attend hematologist, North Shore Hosp, Manhasset, NY, 54-67; attend physician-in-chg, Long Island Jewish Hosp-Queens Hosp Ctr Affil, 64-; clin assoc prof, State Univ NY Downstate Med Ctr, 69-73; NIH grants, 61-; fels, NY Leukemia Soc & United Leukemia Soc, 64-, Zelda Grossberg Found, 65-72 & Dennis Klar Mem Fund, 69-; res collabr, Brookhaven Nat Lab; sr immuno hematologist, Bur Labs, New York City Dept Health, 74-; consult hematologist, North

Shore Hosp, Manhasset, Huntington Hosp, St Francis Hosp, Roslyn, Flushing Hosp & Peninsula Gen Hosp, Edgemere, NY. *Mem:* Am Soc Hemat; Soc Exp Biol & Med; Am Fedn Clin Res; Am Asn Cancer Res; Am Soc Clin Oncol. *Res:* Biology and classification of sub-populations of patients in the chronic leukemias; basic understanding of the defect in the syndrome of the sea-blue histiocyte. *Mailing Add:* Long Island Jewish Hillside Med Ctr New Hyde Park NY 11040

SAWITZ, PETER H, b Rostock, Ger, Sept 8, 16; nat US; m 42; c 3. COMMUNICATIONS, SYSTEMS ANALYSIS. *Educ:* Va Polytech Inst, BS, 43; Ohio State Univ, MS, 46. *Prof Exp:* Jr engr, Pilotless Plane Div, Fairchild Engine & Aircraft Corp, 47; asst prof physics & elec eng, Champlain Col, 47-48; asst prof elec eng, Univ Buffalo, 48-51; res scientist, Frederick Res Corp, 51-53; electronic engr, Thieblot Aircraft Co, 53-56; chief electronic engr, Am Res & Mfg Co, 56-58; staff physicist, Radiation, Inc, 58-59; assoc prof appl sci, George Washington Univ, 59-70; PRIN SCIENTIST, ORI, INC, 70- *Concurrent Pos:* Mem staff, Inst Defense Anal, 59-65. *Mem:* Inst Elec & Electronics Engrs. *Res:* Electromagnetic theory; communications; atmospheric physics; radio interference; nonlinear and systems analysis. *Mailing Add:* 6434 Kenhowe Dr Bethesda MD 20034

SAWLE, DAVID RICHARD, engineering science, see previous edition

SAWOROTNOW, PARFENY PAVOLICH, b Ust-Medveditskaya, Russia, Feb 20, 24; nat US. PURE MATHEMATICS. *Educ:* Harvard Univ, MA, 51, PhD, 54. *Prof Exp:* From instr to assoc prof, 54-67, PROF MATH, CATH UNIV AM, 67- *Concurrent Pos:* NSF grants, 67 & 70. *Mem:* Sigma Xi; Am Asn Univ Profs; Am Math Soc; Math Asn Am; NY Acad Sci. *Res:* Functional analysis; Hilbert spaces; Banach algebras; vector measures. *Mailing Add:* 6 Avon Pl Avondale MD 20018

SAWYER, BALDWIN, b Naragansett Pier, RI, July 21, 22; m 47; c 4. PHYSICS. *Educ:* Yale Univ, BS, 43; Carnegie Inst Technol, DSc(physics), 52. *Prof Exp:* Jr metallurgist, Manhattan Proj, Univ Chicago, 43-46; instr & res assoc, Carnegie Inst Technol, 48-51; mem tech staff, Bell Tel Labs, Inc, 51-53, group supvr, 53-57; treas & chief engr, Sawyer Res Prods, Inc, 57-60, vpres eng, 60-64, exec vpres, 64-74; PRES, BALDWIN SAWYER CRYSTALS INC. *Mem:* AAAS; Am Phys Soc; Electrochem Soc; Inst Elec & Electronic Engrs; Sigma Xi. *Res:* Physics of solids, especially crystals, including quartz and semiconductor crystals, their growth, characterization and applications. *Mailing Add:* Berkshire Rd Box 96 Gates Mills OH 44040

SAWYER, C GLENN, b New Bern, NC, Feb 27, 22; m; c 4. CARDIOLOGY. *Educ:* Bowman Gray Sch Med, MD, 44; Am Bd Internal Med, dipl, 52. *Prof Exp:* From intern to chief med resident, Peter Bent Brigham Hosp, Boston, Mass, 44-50; instr med, Harvard Med Sch, 50-51; from instr to assoc prof med, 51-63, chief cardiol, 63-81, PROF MED, BOWMAN GRAY SCH MED, 63- *Concurrent Pos:* Fel clin coun cardiol, Am Heart Asn. *Mem:* Am Heart Asn; AMA; fel Am Col Physicians; fel Am Col Cardiol; Asn Univ Cardiol. *Mailing Add:* Dept Med Bowman Gray Sch Med Winston-Salem NC 27103

SAWYER, CHARLES HENRY, b Ludlow, Vt, Jan 24, 15; m 41; c 1. ANATOMY, NEUROENDOCRINOLOGY. *Educ:* Middlebury Col, AB, 37; Yale Univ, PhD(zool), 41. *Hon Degrees:* ScD, Middlebury Col, 75. *Prof Exp:* Instr anat, Stanford Univ, 41-44; assoc, Duke Univ, 44-45, from asst prof to prof, 45-51; PROF ANAT, SCH MED, UNIV CALIF, LOS ANGELES, 51- *Concurrent Pos:* Commonwealth Found fel, 58-59; consult, Vet Admin Hosp, Long Beach, Calif, 52-74; chmn dept anat, Univ Calif, Los Angeles, 55-63, res lectr, 66-67; mem adv panel, Nat Bd Med Examr, 60-64, chmn, 64; mem fel rev bd pharmacol & endocrinol, USPHS, 61-63, 68-70; mem neuroendocrine panel, Int Brain Res Orgn, 61-, mem cent coun, 64-67; mem neurol study sect, NIH, 63-67. *Honors & Awards:* Koch Res Medal, Endocrine Soc, 73. *Hartman Award, Soc Study Reprod, 77. *Mem:* Nat Acad Sci; hon mem Hungarian Soc Endocrinol & Metab; Am Asn Anatomists (vpres, 68-70); Soc Study Reprod; fel Am Acad Arts & Sci. *Res:* Physiology of reproduction; nervous control of pituitary secretion; function, distribution, ontogenesis and properties of cholinesterases; effects of hormones on brain function. *Mailing Add:* Dept of Anat Univ of Calif Los Angeles CA 90024

SAWYER, CONSTANCE B, b Lewiston, Maine, June 3, 26; div; c 4. ASTROPHYSICS, OCEANOGRAPHY. *Educ:* Smith Col, AB, 47; Harvard Univ, AM, 48, PhD, 52. *Prof Exp:* Res asst, Sacramento Peak Observ, 53-55; mem res staff, High Altitude Observ, Univ Colo, 55-58; astronr, Space Environ Lab, 58-75, phys scientist, Atlantic Oceanog Meterol Labs, 75-76, PHYS SCIENTIST, PAC MARINE ENVIRON LAB, NAT OCEANIC & ATMOSPHERIC ADMIN, 76- *Concurrent Pos:* Staff scientist, High Altitude Observ, 79-; satellite oper, NASA, 80. *Mem:* Int Astron Union; Int Union Geod & Geophys; AAAS; Am Geophys Union; Am Astron Soc. *Res:* Solar physics and solar-terrestrial relations; ocean remote sensing; internal waves. *Mailing Add:* High Altitude Observ PO Box 3000 Boulder CO 80307

SAWYER, DAVID ERICKSON, b Boston, Mass, Feb 6, 27; div; c 3. SOLID STATE ELECTRONICS. *Educ:* Clark Univ, BA, 53; Univ Ill, MS, 55; Worcester Polytech Inst, PhD, 76. *Prof Exp:* Res staff mem, Lincoln Lab, Mass Inst Technol, 55-59; develop staff mem, Int Bus Mach Corp, NY, 59-61; res staff mem, Sperry Rand Res Ctr, Mass, 61-66; sect head & sr scientist semiconductor device res, Electronics Res Ctr, NASA, 66-70; group leader, Electron Device Div, Nat Bur Standards, 70-75, sr staff mem, 75-79; SR RES ENGR, CHEVRON RES CO, 79- *Honors & Awards:* Indust Res 100 Award, 76. *Mem:* Am Phys Soc; Inst Elec & Electronics Engrs. *Res:* Solid-state physics and devices; energy conversion; exploratory measurement techniques. *Mailing Add:* Solar Energy Div Chevron Res Co 576 Standard Ave Richmond CA 94802

SAWYER, DAVID W(ILLIAM), b Pittsburgh, Pa, Feb 1, 10; m 38; c 1. PETROLEUM, ORGANIC CHEMISTRY. *Educ:* Univ Pittsburgh, BS, 33. *Prof Exp:* Asst civil engr, City Planning Comn, Pittsburgh, Pa, 33-34; fel petrol, Mellon Inst, 34-35; res chemist, Gulf Res & Develop Co, 34-43; res engr, Alcoa Res Labs, Aluminum Co Am, 43-53, sr res engr, Lubricants Div, Alcoa Tech Ctr Pittsburgh, 53-75; CONSULT, 75- *Concurrent Pos:* Mem interim subcomt turbine-gear oils, US Dept Navy, 53- *Mem:* Am Chem Soc; fel Am Inst Chemists; Am Soc Lubrication Engrs; Sigma Xi. *Res:* Lubricants; lubrication; petroleum refining; corrosion. *Mailing Add:* 620 Twelfth St Oakmont PA 15139

SAWYER, DONALD C, b New York, NY, Aug 23, 36; m 62; c 3. ANESTHESIOLOGY. *Educ:* Mich State Univ, BS, 59, DVM, 61, MS, 62; Colo State Univ, PhD(vet anesthesiol), 69; Am Col Vet Anesthesiologists, dipl. *Prof Exp:* Asst instr vet med, Mich State Univ, 61-62; pvt pract, 62-63; NIH spec fel, Colo State Univ & Univ Calif, 65-70; assoc prof, 70-77, assoc dean, 74-75, prof vet med, 77-80, PROF ANESTHESIA & HEAD ANESTHESIOL SECT, MICH STATE UNIV, 77- *Concurrent Pos:* Support grant, 70-72. *Mem:* Am Vet Med Asn; Am Soc Vet Anesthesiol (pres 72); Am Soc Anesthesiol; Am Col Vet Anesthesia; Am Bd Vet Practitioners (pres, 79-82). *Res:* Cardiovascular effects of anesthetics; metabolism of inhalation anesthetics; malignant hyperthermia. *Mailing Add:* Dept Small Animal Clin Serv Vet Clin Ctr Mich State Univ East Lansing MI 48824

SAWYER, DONALD TURNER, JR, b Pomona, Calif, Jan 10, 31; m 52; c 3. ANALYTICAL CHEMISTRY, BIOINORGANIC CHEMISTRY. *Educ:* Univ Calif, Los Angeles, BS, 53, PhD(chem), 56. *Prof Exp:* Guggenheim fel, Cambridge 75- 62-63; vis res fel, Merton Col, Oxford Univ, 70; chmn, Gordon Res Conf Anal Chem, 71; mem adv comt, Res Corp, 78-; fac res lectr, Univ Calif, Riverside, 79; sci adv, US Food & Drug Admin, Calif, 75-82. *Mem:* Fel AAAS. *Res:* Electroanalytical chemistry; physical chemical studies of metal chelates; chemical instrumentation; optical, nuclear magnetic resonance and electron spin resonance spectroscopy; model studies of metalloenzymes; nuclear magnetic resonance studies of coordination complexes; oxygen activation by metalloproteins and transistion metal complexes. *Mailing Add:* Dept of Chem Univ of Calif Riverside CA 92521

SAWYER, FREDERICK GEORGE, b Brooklyn, NY, Mar 14, 18; m 50; c 2. CHEMICAL ENGINEERING. *Educ:* Polytech Inst Brooklyn, BChE, 39, MChE, 41, DChE, 43. *Prof Exp:* Res chem engr, Eastman Kodak Co, 41; instr chem eng, Polytech Inst Brooklyn, 42-43; chem engr, Am Cyanamid Co, Conn, 43-45; tech serv, NY, 45-46; assoc ed, Indust & Eng Chem & Chem & Eng News, Am Chem Soc, 46-50; adminr air pollution res, Stanford Res Inst, 50-51, asst to dir res, 51-53; dir info, Ralph M Parsons Co, 53-57; vpres, Jacobs Eng Co, 57-63; consult corp commun & mkt, 63-72; vpres, Reynolds Environ Group, 72-78; CONSULT, FREDERICK G SAWYER & ASSOCS, 78- *Concurrent Pos:* Lectr, Stanford Univ, 52-53, Univ Southern Calif, 67-69, Univ Calif, Los Angeles, 68, Saddleback Col, 77-, Calif State Univ, Pomona, 79- & Univ Calif, Irvine, 82-; pres, Vita-Cell Prod, 64; dir, Econ Int, Inc, 65-; mem, Advan Technol Consults Corp. *Mem:* AAAS; Am Inst Chem Engrs; Chem Mkt Res Asn; Asn Mgt Consults; Am Chem Soc. *Res:* Corporate and scientific communications; technical public relations; business development; lexical research; environmental planning and assessment; handmade paper. *Mailing Add:* 12922 Keith Pl Tustin CA 92680

SAWYER, FREDERICK MILES, b Brockton, Mass, Nov 30, 24; m 48. FOOD TECHNOLOGY, NUTRITION. *Educ:* Mass Inst Technol, SB, 48; Univ Calif, MS, 51, PhD(nutrit), 58. *Prof Exp:* Food technologist seafoods div, Gen Foods Corp, 48-49; sr lab technician, Univ Calif, 50-57; from asst prof food technol to ASSOC PROF RES FOOD TECHNOL, UNIV MASS, AMHERST, 57- *Mem:* AAAS; Am Chem Soc; Inst Food Technologists. *Res:* Flavor chemistry; biochemistry of food spoilage; frozen foods; sensory analysis of foods. *Mailing Add:* Dept of Food Sci & Nutrit Univ of Mass Amherst MA 01003

SAWYER, GEORGE ALANSON, b Chicago, Ill, July 20, 22; m 47; c 2. PLASMA PHYSICS. *Educ:* Univ Mich, BSE, 44, MS, 48, PhD(physics), 50. *Prof Exp:* Mem staff, 50-72, group leader, 72-74, alt div leader, 74-79, ASSOC DIV LEADER, LOS ALAMOS NAT LAB, 79- *Concurrent Pos:* Vis scientist, Royal Inst Technol, Sweden, 59-60. *Mem:* Fe; Am Phys Soc. *Res:* Plasma physics; nuclear reactions; radioactivity; x-ray and visible spectroscopy; controlled thermonuclear research; particle accelerators. *Mailing Add:* Los Alamos Nat Lab Los Alamos NM 87545

SAWYER, JAMES W, b Malone, NY, June 30, 33; m 66. MANAGEMENT SCIENCE, SYSTEMS ENGINEERING. *Educ:* Clarkson Col Technol, BChE, 54; Univ Pa, MS, 70, PhD(systs eng), 73. *Prof Exp:* Res chem eng, E I du Pont de Nemours & Co Inc, 54-68; res assoc, Resources for the Future, 73-75, sr res assoc, Qual Environ Prog, 75-76, fel & asst dir, 76-78; prin analyst, Congressional Budget Off, 78-81; SR SCIENTIST, ERCO, 81- *Concurrent Pos:* Sr energy specialist, Nat Transp Policy Studies Comn 77-78. *Mem:* Inst Elec & Electronic Eng; Am Inst Chem Engrs; Inst Mgt Sci; Am Inst Chem Engrs; Am Econ Asn. *Res:* Environmental quality policy; water resources; secondary materials (scrap) studies; mathematical modeling of water, secondary materials, fossil fuel and synfuel studies with emphasis on environmental quality; policy aspects. *Mailing Add:* ERCO 8290 Old Courthouse Rd Vienna VA 22180

SAWYER, JANE ORROCK, b Richmond, Va, June 15, 44; div; c 2. MATHEMATICS. *Educ:* Va Polytech Inst & State Univ, BS, 66, MS, 68, PhD(math), 75. *Prof Exp:* Instr, 69-73, asst prof, 73-80, ASSOC PROF MATH, MARY BALDWIN COL, 80- *Concurrent Pos:* Coordr & researcher, NASA, 75-76, prin investr, 76-77. *Mem:* Am Math Soc; Math Asn Am; Asn Women Math. *Res:* Rings of continuous functions, specifically pseudocompact topological spaces and pseudocompactifications. *Mailing Add:* Mary Baldwin Col Staunton VA 24401

SAWYER, JOHN ORVEL, JR, b Chico, Calif, Nov 22, 39; m 60; c 2. PLANT ECOLOGY. *Educ:* Chico State Col, AB, 61; Purdue Univ, MS, 63, PhD(plant ecol), 66. *Prof Exp:* Ecologist, Wilson Nuttall Raimond Engrs, Inc, 64-66; from asst prof to assoc prof ecol, 66-75, PROF BOT, HUMBOLDT STATE UNIV, 75- *Mem:* Ecol Soc Am. *Res:* Vegetation of northern California. *Mailing Add:* Dept of Biol Humboldt State Univ Arcata CA 95521

SAWYER, JOHN WESLEY, b Raleigh, NC, Nov 2, 16; m 39; c 1. GEOMETRY. *Educ:* Wake Forest Col, AB, 38, AM, 43; Univ Mo, AM, 48, PhD(math), 51. *Prof Exp:* Instr high sch math, NC, 38-46 & Mo, 46-50; from asst prof to assoc prof math, Univ Ga, 50-53; assoc prof, Univ Richmond, 53-56; assoc prof, 56-61, PROF MATH, WAKE FOREST UNIV, 61- *Concurrent Pos:* Consult, R J Reynolds Industs, 58- *Mem:* Math Asn Am; Opers Res Soc Am; fel AAAS. *Res:* Differential and distance geometry; operations research; computer science. *Mailing Add:* Dept of Math Box 7401 Wake Forest Univ Winston-Salem NC 27109

SAWYER, LOUANNE BROWN, b Toledo, Ohio, Apr 21, 41; m 66. COMPUT SCI, MATHEMATICS. *Educ:* Bowling Green State Univ, BS, 63; George Washington Univ, MS, 78. *Prof Exp:* Mathematician, E I du Pont de Nemours & Co Inc, 63-73; CHIEF, COMPUT SERVS, RESOURCES FOR THE FUTURE, 73- *Mem:* Asn Comput Mach. *Res:* Linear programming models for environmental quality management. *Mailing Add:* Resources for the Future 1755 Mass Ave NW Washington DC 20036

SAWYER, PAUL THOMPSON, b Hanover, NH, Aug 7, 40. PLANT TAXONOMY. *Educ:* Univ Vt, BS, 65; Mont State Univ, MS, 67, PhD(bot), 70. *Prof Exp:* Asst prof, 69-76, ASSOC PROF BIOL, MONT COL MINERAL SCI & TECHNOL, 76- *Mem:* Bot Soc Am; Am Soc Plant Taxon; Int Asn Plant Taxon. *Res:* Systematic investigations of the genera Delphinium and Ledum using chromatographic procedures; investigations of environmental changes occurring when grassland-shrub communities influenced by mining activities are reforested. *Mailing Add:* Dept of Biol Sci Mont Col Mineral Sci & Technol Butte MT 59701

SAWYER, PHILIP JOHN, b Concord, NH, May 24, 18; m 42; c 1. ZOOLOGY. *Educ:* Univ NH, BS, 40, MS, 49; Univ Mich, PhD(zool), 57. *Prof Exp:* Inspector precision tools, Gen Elec Co, 41-44; supt mill work, D'Arcy Co, 44-47; from instr to assoc prof, 52-69, chmn dept, 73-78, PROF ZOOL, UNIV NH, 69- *Mem:* Am Soc Ichthyol & Herpet; Am Fisheries Soc; World Mariculture Soc; Am Soc Limnol & Oceanog; AAAS. *Res:* Ecology of intertidally occurring, estuarine and freshwater fishes; aquaculture. *Mailing Add:* Dept of Zool Univ of NH Durham NH 03824

SAWYER, PHILIP NICHOLAS, b Bangor, Maine, Oct 25, 25; m 53; c 4. THORACIC SURGERY. *Educ:* Univ Pa, MD, 49; Am Bd Surg, dipl, 58; Am Bd Thoracic Surg, dipl, 60. *Prof Exp:* Asst, Harrison Dept Surg Res, Univ Pa, 47-49, intern, Hosp Univ Pa, 49-50; staff mem, Naval Med Res Inst, 51-53; chief resident, St Luke's Hosp, New York, 56-57; from instr to assoc prof surg, 57-66, PROF SURG, STATE UNIV NY DOWNSTATE MED CTR, 66-, HEAD VASCULAR SURG SERV & BIOPHYS & ELECTROCHEM LABS, 64- *Concurrent Pos:* Fel surg, Univ Pa, 53-56, Nat Cancer Inst res fel biophys, Johnson Found Med Physics, 50; fel path, St Luke's Hosp, New York, 57; Markle scholar, 59-64; vis surgeon, Kings County Hosp & univ hosp, State Univ NY; assoc attend surgeon, St John's Episcopal Hosp & Methodist Hosp, Brooklyn; consult vascular surg, USPHS Hosp, Staten Island, NY, 66. *Mem:* AAAS; Am Chem Soc; Am Heart Asn; Am Physiol Soc; Am Soc Artificial Internal Organs. *Res:* Tissue electrical potential differences and metabolism; ionic movement across cellular membranes; etiology of vascular thrombosis; preservation of tissues; homotransplantation techniques; cardiovascular surgery. *Mailing Add:* State Univ NY Downstate Med Ctr 450 Clarkson Ave Brooklyn NY 11203

SAWYER, RALPH STANLEY, b Gray, Maine, Jan 9, 21; m 51; c 2. PHYSICS, ENGINEERING. *Educ:* Tufts Univ, BS, 44. *Prof Exp:* Res & lab instr piezo elec, Tufts Univ, 46-47; res engr instrumentation, Nat Adv Comt Aeronaut Labs, Langley Field, Va, 47-48; electronic engr, Indust Instrument Div, Minneapolis-Honeywell Regulator Co, 50; electronics engr commun, Hastings Instrument Co, Hampton, Va, 50-51; supvry electronic control engr, US Naval Weapons Sta, Yorktown, Va, 51-53; head, Range Data & Homing Test Sect, US Naval Underwater Ordnance Sta, Newport, RI, 53-54; head Ballistic Instrumentation Br, & consult, Missile Br, Spec Projs Off, US Naval Bur Weapons Labs, Dahlgren, Va, 54-59; res engr & head, commun sect, Space Task Group, Nat Aeronaut & Space Admin, Langley Field, Va, 59-61; head, elec systs br, 61-62, chief, Instrumentation & Electronic Systs Div, 62-69, CHIEF, TRACKING & COMMUN DEVELOP DIV, JOHNSON SPACE CTR, HOUSTON, 69- *Honors & Awards:* Exceptional Serv Medals, Nat Aeronaut & Space Admin, 69. *Mem:* Inst Elec & Electronics Engrs; Am Inst Aeronaut & Astronaut; Nat Telecommunications Conf (chmn, 72); Aerospace & Electronic Systs Soc. *Res:* Responsible for the research, development, and test of all tracking, television, telemetry and communications systems used on all current and past manned space flight programs sponsored by the United States. *Mailing Add:* Box 630 Friendswood TX 77546

SAWYER, RAYMOND FRANCIS, b Northfield, Minn, Aug 30, 32; m 56; c 2. THEORETICAL PHYSICS. *Educ:* Swarthmore Col, AB, 53; Harvard Univ, MA, 55, PhD, 58. *Prof Exp:* NSF fel physics, Europ Orgn Nuclear Res, Geneva, 58-59; Wis Alumni Res Found fel, Univ Wis, 59-60, from asst prof to prof, 60-65; PROF PHYSICS, UNIV CALIF, SANTA BARBARA, 65- *Mem:* Am Phys Soc. *Res:* High energy physics; fundamental particle theory. *Mailing Add:* Dept of Physics Univ of Calif Santa Barbara CA 93106

SAWYER, RICHARD LEANDER, b New Sharon, Maine, Mar 17, 21; m 46; c 2. PHYSIOLOGY. *Educ:* Cornell Univ, PhD(veg crops), 53. *Hon Degrees:* DSc, Univ Maine, 79. *Prof Exp:* From asst prof to prof veg crops, Cornell Univ, 53-67; mem NC State Mission to Peru, US AID, 67-71; DIR GEN, INT POTATO CTR, 71- *Mem:* Am Soc Hort Sci; Am Soc Plant Physiol; Potato Asn Am. *Res:* Vegetable physiology; potato research; sprout inhibition; weed control; fertilizer studies. *Mailing Add:* Dir Gen El Centro Int de la Pappa Apartado 5969 Lima Peru

SAWYER, RICHARD TREVOR, b Washington, DC, Sept 14, 48; m 72. MONONUCLEAR PHAGOCYTE BIOLOGY, CELL KINETICS. *Educ:* Colo State Univ, BS, 71; Eastern Mich Univ, MS, 74; Mich State Univ, PhD(mycol), 78. *Prof Exp:* Fel microbiol, Dept Microbiol & Pub Health, Mich State Univ, 78; res assoc cell kinetics, Dept Path & Lab Med, Sch Med, E Carolina Univ, 78-80; res scientist IV immunol, Norwich-Eaton Pharmaceut, 80-82; ASST PROF MICROBIOL & IMMUNOL, SCH MED, MERCER UNIV, 82- *Concurrent Pos:* Sigma Xi res award, Mich State Univ, 75. *Mem:* Reticuloendothelial Soc. *Res:* Functional activities and cell kinetics of mononuclear phagocytes, in particular resident macrophages. *Mailing Add:* Div Basic Med Sci Sch Med Mercer Univ Macon GA 31207

SAWYER, ROBERT FENNELL, b Santa Barbara, Calif, May 19, 35; m 57; c 2. MECHANICAL ENGINEERING. *Educ:* Stanford Univ, BS, 57, MS, 58; Princeton Univ, MA, 63, PhD(aerospace & mech sci), 66. *Prof Exp:* Instr physics, Antelope Valley Col, 58-61; mem res staff, Princeton Univ, 65-66; from asst prof to assoc prof mech eng, 66-75, PROF MECH ENG, UNIV CALIF, BERKELEY, 75- *Concurrent Pos:* Res engr, US Air Force Rocket Propulsion Lab, 58-61, chief liquid systs anal, 61; consult to various co & govt agencies, 64-; mem, Calif Air Resources Bd, 75-76. *Mem:* Am Inst Aeronaut & Astronaut; Am Soc Mech Engrs; Am Chem Soc; Am Soc Eng Educ; Soc Automotive Engrs. *Res:* Propulsion; combustion; air pollution; chemical kinetics; fire science. *Mailing Add:* Dept Mech Eng Univ Calif Berkeley CA 94720

SAWYER, ROGER HOLMES, b Portland, Maine, Sept 5, 42; m 61; c 3. DEVELOPMENTAL BIOLOGY. *Educ:* Univ Maine, BA, 65; Univ Mass, PhD(zool), 70. *Prof Exp:* NIH fel, Univ Calif, Davis, 70-71, NSF res assoc genetics, 71-72; asst res anatomist develop biol, Calif Primate Res Ctr, 73-74; asst prof, 75-79, ASSOC PROF BIOL, UNIV SC, 79- *Mem:* Sigma Xi; Soc Develop Biol; Am Soc Zoologists. *Res:* Control of biochemical and morphological differentiation by epithelialmesenchymal interactions during skin organogenesis and the action of mutant genes and teratogens on these interactions. *Mailing Add:* Dept of Biol Univ of SC Columbia SC 29208

SAWYER, STANLEY ARTHUR, b Juneau, Alaska, Mar 19, 40. MATHEMATICS. *Educ:* Calif Inst Technol, BS, 60, PhD(math), 64. *Hon Degrees:* AM, Brown Univ, 69. *Prof Exp:* Courant instr math, Courant Inst, NY Univ, 65-67; from asst prof to assoc prof, Brown Univ, 67-69; from asst prof to prof math, Yeshiva Univ, 69-77; prof, Univ Wash, 77-78; PROF MATH & STATIST, PURDUE UNIV, 78- *Mem:* Am Math Soc. *Res:* Probability; population genetics. *Mailing Add:* Dept Math Math Sci Bldg Purdue Univ West Lafayette IN 47907

SAWYER, WEBSTER MORRILL, JR, surface chemistry, see previous edition

SAWYER, WILBUR HENDERSON, b Brisbane, Australia, Mar 23, 21; US citizen; m 42; c 4. PHYSIOLOGY, PHARMACOLOGY. *Educ:* Harvard Univ, AB, 42, MD, 45, PhD(biol), 50. *Prof Exp:* Instr biol, Harvard Univ, 50-53; asst prof physiol, Col Med, NY Univ, 53-57; from assoc prof to prof, 57-78, GUSTAVUS A PFEIFFER PROF PHARMACOL, COL PHYSICIANS & SURGEONS, COLUMBIA UNIV, 78- *Concurrent Pos:* Lederle med fac award, 55-57; mem adv panel regulatory biol, NSF, 59-62; mem gen med B study sect, Div Res Grants, NIH, 70-74; sr res scholar, Australian-Am Educ Found, 74; vis res fel, Howard Florey Inst Exp Biol & Med, Univ Melbourne, Australia, 74. *Mem:* Endocrine Soc; Am Soc Pharmacol & Exp Therapeut; Soc Endocrinol; Am Soc Zool; Soc Gen Physiol. *Res:* Comparative endocrinology; renal physiology; pharmacology of neurohypophysial hormones. *Mailing Add:* Dept of Pharmacol Columbia Univ Col Phys & Surg New York NY 10032

SAWYER, WILLIAM D, b Roodhouse, Ill, Dec 28, 29; m 51; c 2. MICROBIOLOGY, INTERNAL MEDICINE. *Educ:* Univ Ill, 47-50; Wash Univ, MD, 54. *Prof Exp:* Asst prof microbiol, Sch Med, Johns Hopkins Univ, 64-67; mem staff, Rockefeller Found, 67-73; prof microbiol & immunol & chmn dept, Sch Med, Ind Univ, Indianapolis, 73-80; PROF, DEPT MED, MICROBIOL & IMMUNOL, WRIGHT STATE UNIV, OHIO, 81-, DEAN, SCH MED, 81- *Concurrent Pos:* Fel med, Sch Med, Wash Univ, 58-60; consult, Army Med Res & Develop Command, 65-67, Armed Forces Inst Pathol, 79- & Lobund Adv Bd, Notre Dame Univ, 79-; vis prof & chmn, Dept Microbiol, Mahidol Univ, Thailand, 67-73; consult, WHO Immunol Res & Training Ctr, Singapore, 69-73. *Mem:* Am Soc Microbiol; Am Col Physicians; Am Acad Microbiol; Soc Exp Biol & Med; Am Asn Pathologists. *Res:* Bacterial infection, genetics and physiology. *Mailing Add:* Sch Med Wright State Univ PO Box 927 Dayton OH 45401

SAWYER, WILLIAM T(HOMAS), b Nantucket, Mass, Apr 13, 18; m 41; c 2. MECHANICAL ENGINEERING. *Educ:* US Naval Acad, BS, 39; Mass Inst Technol, SM, 44; Swiss Fed Inst Technol, DrSc(aerodyn), 49. *Prof Exp:* Gas turbine develop officer, Bur Ships, US Navy, 48-51, design supt, San Francisco Naval Shipyard, 53-55, tech aide, power plants, Off Naval Res, 56-61, dir naval appln & dep asst chief res, 61-63; head dept mech eng, Cath Univ Am, 63-68; dean, Chesapeake Col, 68-71; asst to pres, Washington Col, 71-77; CONSULT ENG, 77- *Concurrent Pos:* Consult, Franklin Inst, 64-65 & Southwest Res Inst, 65-66. *Mem:* Am Soc Mech Engrs; Am Asn Naval Engrs. *Res:* Power plant engineering; gas turbine engine development and application, especially marine; ocean engineering; mechanical failure prevention; power plant siting. *Mailing Add:* PO Box 11 Oxford MD 21654

SAWYERS, JOHN LAZELLE, b Centerville, Iowa, July 26, 25; m 57; c 3. SURGERY. *Educ:* Univ Rochester, BA, 46; Johns Hopkins Univ, MD, 49. *Prof Exp:* From asst prof to assoc prof, 60-69, PROF SURG, VANDERBILT UNIV, 69- *Mem:* Soc Univ Surg; Am Asn Thoracic Surg; Am Col Surg; Am Surg Asn; Int Cardiovasc Soc. *Res:* Surgery of the alimentary tract. *Mailing Add:* Dept of Surg Vanderbilt Univ Nashville TN 37203

SAWYERS, KENNETH NORMAN, b Chicago, Ill, May 19, 36; m 62. APPLIED MATHEMATICS. *Educ:* Ill Inst Technol, BS, 62; Brown Univ, PhD(appl math), 67. *Prof Exp:* Math physicist, Stanford Res Inst, 66-69; asst prof, 69-75, ASSOC PROF APPL MATH, CTR APPLN MATH, LEHIGH UNIV, 75- *Mem:* Am Acad Mechs; Soc Rheol. *Res:* Theoretical seismology; mechanics of fluids and solids; stability theory. *Mailing Add:* Ctr Appln of Math Lehigh Univ Bethlehem PA 18015

SAX, KARL JOLIVETTE, b Ancon, CZ, Sept 7, 18; US citizen; m 42; c 2. CHEMISTRY. *Educ:* Harvard Univ, BS, 40; Yale Univ, MS, 53, PhD(org chem), 55. *Prof Exp:* Asst, Harvard Univ, 40; chemist, E I du Pont de Nemours & Co, NJ, 40-41, control chemist, Ind, 41-42, Okla, 42-43, res chemist, Ill, 43; res chemist, Clinton Lab, Tenn, 43-45 & Lederle Labs, Am Cyanamid Co, NY, 45-51; asst, Yale Univ, 51-53; chemist, Shell Develop Co, 54-60; chemist, Lederle Labs, Am Cyanamid Co, 60-82; RETIRED. *Mem:* Assoc Am Chem Soc. *Res:* Natural products; lipids of coelenterates; synthetic lubricants; isolation and identification of steroids; isolation and identification of antibiotics; process and preparations research. *Mailing Add:* 55 Wax Myrtle Ct Hilton Head Island SC 29928

SAX, ROBERT LOUIS, b Wheeling, WVa, Apr 7, 28; m 58; c 2. GEOPHYSICS. *Educ:* Mass Inst Technol, BS, 52, PhD(geophys), 60. *Prof Exp:* Geologist-geophysicist, Standard Oil Co Calif, 52-56; mem tech staff, Ramo-Wooldridge Labs, 59-60 & Hughes Aircraft Corp, 60-62; sr geophysicist, United Earth Sci Div, Teledyne Indust, 62-68; SR SCIENTIST, TELEDYNE INC, GEOTECH CORP, 68- *Mem:* AAAS; Am Geophys Union; Soc Explor Geophys; Seismol Soc Am; Inst Elec & Electronics Engrs. *Res:* Interpretation of earth gravity measurements; design of systems for probing and analyzing planetary atmospheres; wave propagation and source mechanisms in a solid earth; theory of seismic noise. *Mailing Add:* Teledyne Inc Geotech Corp 3707 Cameron Mills Rd Alexandria VA 22305

SAX, SYLVAN MAURICE, b Wheeling, WVa, Feb 8, 23; m 57; c 3. CLINICAL CHEMISTRY. *Educ:* Univ Pittsburgh, BS, 44, PhD(org chem), 53; Am Bd Clin Chem, Dipl, 60. *Prof Exp:* Group leader res, Glyco Prods Co, 53-55; CLIN BIOCHEMIST, WESTERN PA HOSP, 55- *Concurrent Pos:* Instr & adj asst prof, Sch Med, Univ Pittsburgh, 57- *Mem:* Am Chem Soc; Am Asn Clin Chem. *Res:* Clinical chemistry methodology and control. *Mailing Add:* Western Pa Hosp 4800 Friendship Ave Pittsburgh PA 15224

SAXE, HARRY CHARLES, b Long Island City, NY, Mar 18, 20; m 45; c 2. CIVIL & STRUCTURAL ENGINEERING. *Educ:* City Col New York, BCE, 42; Univ Fla, MSE, 49; Mass Inst Technol, ScD, 52. *Prof Exp:* Asst civil eng, Univ Fla, 48-49, instr, 49-50; res asst, Mass Inst Technol, 50-52; assoc prof, Ga Inst Technol, 52-56; engr, Praeger-Kavanagh & Assocs, NY, 56-57; assoc prof civil eng, Polytech Inst Brooklyn, 57 & Univ Cincinnati, 57-59; prof & head dept, Univ Notre Dame, 59-60 & 61-65, actg dean col eng, 60-61 & 66-67, chmn dept civil eng, 67-69; DEAN SPEED SCI SCH, UNIV LOUISVILLE, 69-, PROF CIVIL ENG, 76- *Concurrent Pos:* NSF sci fac fel & vis prof, Imp Col, Univ London, 65-66; pres, Univ Louisville Inst Indust Res, 69-; mem, Ky Sci & Technol Adv Coun, 70-; Ky Bd Registr for Prof Engrs & Land Surveyors, 72- *Mem:* Fel Am Soc Civil Engrs; Am Soc Eng Educ; Nat Soc Prof Engrs; Soc Am Mil Engrs; Am Soc Testing & Mat. *Res:* Structural mechanics including computer applications. *Mailing Add:* Off of the Dean Speed Sci Sch Univ of Louisville Louisville KY 40208

SAXE, RAYMOND FREDERICK, b London, Eng, May 26, 20; m 52; c 2. NUCLEAR & ELECTRICAL ENGINEERING. *Educ:* Univ London, BSc, 40; Univ Liverpool, PhD(elec eng), 48. *Prof Exp:* Res asst, Nat Phys Lab, Eng, 37-41; sr sci officer, Atomic Weapons Res Estab, 48-52; Imp Chem Industs res fel, London, 52-55; lectr elec eng, 55-58; reader nuclear eng, 58-64; PROF NUCLEAR ENG, NC STATE UNIV, 64- *Concurrent Pos:* Secy & nat del, Brit Nat Comt High Speed Photog, 59-64; consult, Oak Ridge Nat Lab, Union Carbide Co, 65- *Mem:* Am Nuclear Soc. *Res:* Electrical discharge phenomena; high speed photography; nuclear reactor kinetics, control and safety. *Mailing Add:* Dept of Nuclear Eng NC State Univ Raleigh NC 27607

SAXE, STANLEY RICHARD, b Chelsea, Mass, Feb 1, 32; m 58; c 3. PERIODONTOLOGY, DENTISTRY. *Educ:* Boston Univ, AB, 53; Harvard Univ, DMD, 58; Univ Wash, MSD, 60. *Prof Exp:* Instr periodont, Sch Dent, Univ Wash, 60-62; from asst prof to assoc prof, 62-77, chmn dept, 66-69, PROF PERIODONT, COL DENT, UNIV KY, 77- *Concurrent Pos:* Consult, Vet Admin Hosp, Am Lake, Wash, 61-62, Lexington, Ky, 62- & USPHS Hosp, 62-76; vis prof, Hadassah Sch Dent Med, Hebrew Univ Jerusalem, 70. *Mem:* Am Dent Asn; Am Acad Periodont; Int Asn Dent Res. *Res:* Etiology and treatment of periodontal disease. *Mailing Add:* Dept Periodont Col Dent Univ Ky Lexington KY 40536

SAXENA, ANJALI, neuroendocrinology, animal behavior, see previous edition

SAXENA, BRIJ B, b India, July 6, 30. BIOCHEMISTRY, ENDOCRINOLOGY. *Educ:* Agra Univ, BSc, 49; Lucknow Univ, MSc, 51, PhD(biochem), 54; Univ Munster, Dr rer nat(physiol), 57; Univ Wis, PhD(biochem, endocrinol), 61. *Prof Exp:* Lectr biol, Lucknow Univ, 54-55; res assoc endocrinol, Univ Wis, 57-62; from asst prof to assoc prof biochem, NJ Col Med, 62-66; assoc prof biochem, Dept Med, 66-72, assoc prof endocrinol, Dept Obstet & Gynec, 70-72, PROF BIOCHEM, DEPT MED & PROF ENDOCRINOL, DEPT OBSTET & GYNEC, MED COL, CORNELL UNIV, 72-, DIR, DIV REPRODUCTIVE ENDOCRINOL, DEPT OBSTET & GYNEC, 80- *Concurrent Pos:* Career sci award, Health Res Coun, New York, 69. *Mem:* AAAS; Endocrine Soc; NY Acad Sci; fel Royal Soc Med; Harvey Soc. *Res:* Physiology and biochemistry of pituitary hormones. *Mailing Add:* NY Hosp-Cornell Med Ctr 525 E 68th St New York NY 10021

SAXENA, NARENDRA K, b Agra, India, Oct 15, 36; US citizen; m 70; c 2. MARINE SURVEYS, GEODESY. *Educ:* Agra Univ, BSc, 55; Hannover Tech Univ, dipl Ing, 65; Graz Tech Univ, Dr tech (satellite geod), 72. *Prof Exp:* Proj-in-charge satellite geod, Space Sci & Technol Ctr, India, 69; res assoc geod, Ohio State Univ, 69-74; asst prof geod eng, Univ Ill, Urbana, 74-78; asst prof surv, 78-80, ASSOC PROF CIVIL ENG, UNIV HAWAII, MANOA, 80- *Concurrent Pos:* Mem, Spec Study Group, Int Asn Geod, 73-; ed-in-chief, Marine Geod J Int J Ocean Surv Mapping & Sensing, 77- *Mem:* Marine Technol Soc; Am Geophys Union; Inst Navig; Am Soc Civil Engrs. *Res:* Ocean survey and navigation; computational methods to solve large systems; engineering survey. *Mailing Add:* Dept Civil Eng Univ Hawaii Honolulu HI 96822

SAXENA, SATISH CHANDRA, b Lucknow, India, June 24, 34; US citizen; m 61; c 4. ENERGY ENGINEERING. *Educ:* Lucknow Univ, BSc, 51; MSc, 53; Calcutta Univ, PhD(physics), 56. *Prof Exp:* Res assoc, Univ Md, 56-58 & Columbia Univ, 58-59; res assoc physics, Yale Univ, 61; engr, Bhabha Atomic Res Ctr, India, 59-61; reader & head, Dept Physics, Rajasthan Univ, India, 61-66; assoc prof, Purdue Univ, 66-68; PROF ENG ENERGY, UNIV ILL, 68- *Concurrent Pos:* Sr res assoc, Ames Res Ctr, NASA, 69 & 70; sr res assoc, Argonne Nat Lab, 77; consult, Purdue Univ, Argonne Nat Lab, E I du Pont de Nemours & Co Inc, Oak Ridge Nat Lab & Gen Elec Co, Morgantown Energy Technol Ctr, WVa, Inst Gas Technol, Chicago, Ortho Inc, Chicago & Maremac Corp. *Mem:* Am Inst Chem Engrs. *Res:* Transport properties of gases and gaseous mixtures; modeling of fluidied bed operations, coal combustion and coal gasification. *Mailing Add:* Dept of Energy Eng Univ of Ill Chicago IL 60680

SAXENA, SURENDRA K, b Bundi, India. GEOTECHNICAL ENGINEERING, CIVIL ENGINEERING. *Educ:* Aligarh Univ, BSc, 55; Duke Univ, MS, 65, PhD(geotech eng), 71. *Prof Exp:* Dist engr, state govt Rajasthan, India, 55-62; soils engr, Port Authority NY & NJ, 69-74; sr engr, Dames & Moore, Cranford, NJ, 74-76; assoc prof, 76-80, PROF CIVIL ENG & CHMN DEPT, ILL INST TECHNOL, 80- *Concurrent Pos:* Res assoc, Mass Inst Technol, 73-74; consult, Argonne Nat Lab, 78-, Nat Hwy Res Prog, Transp Res Bd, 77- *Honors & Awards:* Hwy Res Bd Award, 70. *Mem:* Am Soc Civil Engrs; Am Soc Testing & Mat; Earthquake Eng Res Inst; Sigma Xi; Int Soc Soil Mech & Found Eng. *Res:* Geotechnical engineering; earthquake engineering; soil-structure interaction; geo-energy. *Mailing Add:* Dept of Civil Eng Ill Inst Technol Chicago IL 60616

SAXENA, UMESH, b Pilibhit, India; m 62; c 2. INDUSTRIAL ENGINEERING. *Educ:* Univ Roorkee, BS, 60; Univ Wis-Madison, MS, 65, PhD, 68. *Prof Exp:* Lectr mech eng, Indian Inst Technol, Delhi, 62-64; ASSOC PROF INDUST ENG, UNIV WIS-MILWAUKEE, 68- *Mem:* Am Soc Qual Control; Am Inst Indust Engrs. *Res:* Health care systems and delivery; application of quantitative methods in analysis and control of industrial and service systems. *Mailing Add:* Dept of Systs-Design Univ of Wis Col Appl Sci & Eng Milwaukee WI 53201

SAXENA, VINOD KUMAR, b Agra, India, May 23, 44. METEOROLOGY, CLOUD PHYSICS. *Educ:* Agra Univ, BS, 61, MS, 63; Univ Rajasthan, PhD(physics), 67. *Prof Exp:* Lectr physics, Agra Col, 63-64; asst prof pharmaceut sci, Univ Saugar, 67-68; Off Naval Res fel, Univ Mo-Rolla, 68-71; res assoc cloud physics, Univ Denver, 71-73, cloud physicist & lectr physics, Denver Res Inst, 73-77; res assoc prof meteorol, Univ Utah, 77-79; ASSOC PROF METEOROL, NC STATE UNIV, 79- *Mem:* Am Meteorol Soc; Am Geophys Union. *Res:* Cloud and aerosol physics; air pollution meteorology; condensation and nucleation phenomena; cloud-aerosol interactions; instrumentation for simulating atmospheric environment and monitoring Aitken; cloud and ice-forming nuclei. *Mailing Add:* Dept of Geosci PO Box 5068 Raleigh NC 27650

SAXENA, VISHV PRAKASH, b Sirsa, India, Mar 7, 33; m 67; c 1. PHYSICAL BIOCHEMISTRY, MEDICAL RESEARCH. *Educ:* Univ Delhi, BSc, 52, MSc, 55; Clark Univ, PhD(chem), 65. *Prof Exp:* Sci asst polymers res, Nat Chem Lab, 59-61; USPHS fel proteins res, Univ Minn, Minneapolis, 66-70 & Univ Conn, 70-73; BIOMED ED, COUN TOBACCO RES, 73- *Mem:* Am Chem Soc. *Res:* Physical chemistry of macromolecules, natural and synthetic, especially the proteins and the enzymes. *Mailing Add:* Coun Tobacco Res 110 E 59th St Suite 808 New York NY 11203

SAXON, DAVID STEPHEN, b St Paul, Minn, Feb 8, 20; m 40; c 6. THEORETICAL NUCLEAR PHYSICS. *Educ:* Mass Inst Technol, BS, 41, PhD(physics), 44. *Hon Degrees:* LHD, Hebrew Union Col, 76, Univ Judaism, 77; LLD, Univ S Calif, 78. *Prof Exp:* Mem staff, Radiation Lab, Mass Inst Technol, 42-46; assoc physicist, Philips Lab, Inc, NY, 46-47; asst prof physics, Univ Calif, Los Angeles, 47-50; physicist, Inst Numerical Anal, Nat Bur Stand, Calif, 50-53; assoc prof physics, 53-58, chmn dept, 63-66, dean phys sci, 66-70, exec vchancellor, 72-75, PRES, UNIV CALIF, LOS ANGELES, 75-, PROF PHYSICS, 58- *Concurrent Pos:* Guggenheim Mem fel, 56-57 & 61-62; Fulbright lectr, 61-62; consult, Systs Corp Am, 58-63, Convair Div, Gen Dynamics Corp, 60-63 & E H Plessit Assoc, 61-63. *Mem:* Fel Am Phys Soc; Am Asn Physics Teachers. *Res:* Electromagnetic theory; quantum theory; nuclear physics. *Mailing Add:* Pres Off Systemwide Admin Univ of Calif Berkeley CA 94720

SAXON, JAMES GLENN, b Marlin, Tex, July 16, 41; m 68; c 2. ANATOMY. *Educ:* Baylor Univ, BS, 63, MS, 66; Tex A&M Univ, PhD(wildlife sci), 70. *Prof Exp:* Asst prof biol, Memphis State Univ, 69-70; asst prof & chmn dept, Erskine Col, 70-74; asst prof, 74-77, asst prof II, 77-80, ASSOC PROF ANAT, SOUTHERN COL OPTOM, 80- *Mem:* Am Inst Biol Sci; AAAS. *Res:* Anatomy and reproductive physiology of amphibians and reptiles. *Mailing Add:* Dept Bioptics Southern Col Optom Memphis TN 38104

SAXON, ROBERT, b Brooklyn, NY, June 3, 24; m 60; c 2. POLYMER CHEMISTRY. *Educ:* Northwestern Univ, PhD(chem), 52. *Prof Exp:* Res chemist, US Indust Chem Co, 43-49; asst chem, Northwestern Univ, 50-52; res assoc, Harris Res Labs, 52-56; res chemist, 56-72, PROJ LEADER, AM CYANAMID CO, 72- *Mem:* AAAS; Am Chem Soc; Am Soc Testing & Mat. *Res:* Organic synthesis and mechanisms; urethane chemistry and technology; surface coatings; laminated plastics; elastomer synthesis and technology. *Mailing Add:* Am Cyanamid Co Chem Res Div Bound Brook NJ 08805

SAXTON, HARRY JAMES, b Bell, Calif, July 2, 39; m 61; c 2. MATERIALS SCIENCE. *Educ:* Stanford Univ, MS, 62, PhD(mat sci), 69. *Prof Exp:* Systs analyst, Ctr Naval Anal, 69-71; mem tech staff, 71-74, div supvr, 74-76, DEPT MGR, SANDIA NAT LABS, 76- *Concurrent Pos:* Consult, Lawrence Livermore Lab, 66-71. *Mem:* Am Soc Metals; Am Ceramic Soc. *Res:* Relation of materials microstructure to macroscopic properties; battery research and development. *Mailing Add:* Sandia Nat Labs Dept 2520 Albuquerque NM 87185

SAXTON, KEITH E, b Crawford, Nebr, Dec 22, 37; m 57; c 2. AGRICULTURAL ENGINEERING. *Educ:* Univ Nebr, BS, 61; Univ Wis, MS, 65; Iowa State Univ, PhD, 72. *Prof Exp:* HYDRAUL ENGR, FED RES, SCI & EDUC ADMIN, USDA, 61- *Mem:* Am Soc Agr Engrs; Am Soc Civil Engrs. *Res:* Hydrologic research on small agricultural watersheds. *Mailing Add:* USDA-SEA-FR Smith Agr Eng Wash State Univ Pullman WA 99164

SAXTON, ROMAINE EDWARD, virology, see previous edition

SAXTON, RONALD L(UTHER), b US, May 15, 27; m 81; c 1. CHEMICAL ENGINEERING. *Educ:* Pa State Univ, BSc, 50; Univ Ill, PhD(chem eng), 54. *Prof Exp:* Res engr, 53-59, res assoc, Plastics Dept, 59-80, RES REL, POLYMER DEPT, E I DU PONT DE NEMOURS & CO, INC, 80- *Mem:* Am Inst Chem Engrs. *Res:* Plastics processing, mixing and reactions in viscous systems. *Mailing Add:* Plastic Prod & Resins Res Lab E I du Pont de Nemours & Co Inc Wilmington DE 19898

SAXTON, WILLIAM REGINALD, b Montreal, Que, May 3, 28; m 53; c 2. PULP CHEMISTRY. *Educ:* McGill Univ, BSc Hons, 49. *Prof Exp:* Mgr rayon res, Indust Cellulose Res Ltd, 58-62, mgr res planning, 62-65; mgr new prod develop, Int Cellulose Res Ltd, 65-68; asst to vpres res & develop, Int Paper Co, 68-71; PRES, CIP RES LTD, 71- *Mem:* Can Pulp & Paper Asn; Can Res Mgt Asn; Tech Asn Pulp & Paper Indust. *Res:* Chemical and mechanical wood pulps for printing and industrial papers, paper board packaging, tissue products, conversion to rayon, cellophane and other cellulosic products. *Mailing Add:* CIP Res Ltd 179 Main St W Hawkesbury ON K6A 2H4 Can

SAYEG, JOSEPH A, b Fresno, Calif, Sept 22, 25; m 56; c 2. BIOPHYSICS. *Educ:* Univ Calif, Berkeley, AB, 47, PhD(biophys), 54; Am Bd Health Physics, dipl, 66; Am Bd Radiol, dipl, 69. *Prof Exp:* Res asst biophys, Donner Lab Med Physics & Biophys, Univ Calif, Berkeley, 49-54; biophysicist, Los Alamos Sci Lab, 54-61; sci specialist, Santa Barbara Labs, Edgerton, Germeshausen & Grier Inc, 61-66; assoc prof health physics, Univ Pittsburgh, 66-67; ASSOC PROF RADIATION MED, COL MED, UNIV KY, 67-, CHMN DEPT HEALTH RADIATION SCI, COL ALLIED HEALTH PROF, 68- *Concurrent Pos:* Consult, Nat Comt Radiation Protection, 58-70, Armed Forces Radiobiol Res Inst, 63-64, Walter Reed Army Inst Res, 65-67 & Mercy Hosp, Pittsburgh, Pa, 66-67; lectr, Univ Calif, Santa Barbara, 62-65. *Mem:* Am Asn Physicists in Med; Soc Nuclear Med; Health Physics Soc; Radiation Res Soc. *Res:* Radiation dosimetry, including x-rays, neutrons and heavy charge particles; health physics; neutron dosimetry for personnel dose evaluation; radiobiology; effect of radiation on unicellular organisms. *Mailing Add:* Dept of Radiation Med Univ of Ky Med Ctr Lexington KY 40506

SAYEGH, FAYEZ S, b Jordan, Feb 25, 27; US citizen; m 55; c 3. MICROSCOPIC ANATOMY. *Educ:* Manila Cent Univ, DMD, 61; Univ Rochester, MS, 66; Colo State Univ, PhD(anat), 72. *Prof Exp:* Instr microbiol, South Chicago Community Hosp, 56-58; chmn histol dept, Eastman Dent Ctr, 61-69; NIH fel anat, Colo State Univ, 69-72; PROF HISTOL & CHMN DEPT, DENT SCH, UNIV MO, 72-, PROF MED & ANAT, MED SCH, 75- *Concurrent Pos:* Consult, Kerr Mfg Co, 64-71 & Lee Pharmaceut, 72- *Mem:* Am Asn Anatomists; Am Dent Asn; Int Asn Dent Res. *Res:* Oral biology; skeletal tissue mineralization; tooth germ formation and calcification. *Mailing Add:* Univ of Mo Dent Col 650 E 25th St Kansas City MO 64108

SAYEGH, JOSEPH FRIEH, b Rmeimeen, Jordan, Mar 5, 28; m 55; c 4. BIOCHEMISTRY, BIOLOGY. *Educ:* NY Univ, BA, 54, MS, 65, PhD(biol), 69. *Prof Exp:* Teacher, Al-Ahlyah Col, Jordan, 54-56, St George Col, 56-60; res scientist, Res Ctr, Rockland State Hosp, 60-69; sr res scientist, 70-78, SCIENTIST IV, ROCKLAND RES INST, 78- *Res:* Psychopharmacology; biochemical endocrinology; automated chromatography; computerized analytical systems; immunology; radio and enzyme immunoassays. *Mailing Add:* Rockland Res Inst Orangeburg Rd Orangeburg NY 10962

SAYEGH, SALEM F, b Mosul, Iraq, May 17, 21; US citizen; m 58; c 3. THORACIC SURGERY, CARDIOVASCULAR SURGERY. *Educ:* Royal Col Med, Baghdad, MB, ChB, 46. *Prof Exp:* From instr to assoc prof surg, Sch Med, Tulane Univ, 54-68; assoc prof clin surg, 68-71, PROF SURG, LA STATE UNIV SCH MED, NEW ORLEANS, 71- *Concurrent Pos:* NIH fel surg, Tulane Univ, 56-57; asst chief surg serv, Vet Admin Hosp, New Orleans, 60-, chief sect thoracic & cardiovasc surg, 68- *Mem:* Am Heart Asn; AMA; Am Col Surgeons; Am Col Chest Physicians. *Res:* Organ transplantations. *Mailing Add:* Vet Admin Hosp 1601 Perdido St New Orleans LA 70146

SAYEKI, HIDEMITSU, b Yokohama, Japan, July 2, 33; m 59; c 1. MATHEMATICS. *Educ:* Univ Tokyo, BSc, 56; Univ Warsaw, MA, 61, PhD, 65. *Prof Exp:* Nat Res Coun Can fel, Univ Montreal, 66-67, asst prof, 67-70, ASSOC PROF MATH, UNIV MONTREAL, 70- *Mem:* Asn Symbolic Logic; Math Soc Japan; Can Math Cong; Am Math Soc. *Res:* Mathematical logic; set theory. *Mailing Add:* Dept of Math Univ of Montreal Box 6128 Montreal PQ H3C 3J7 Can

SAYER, JANE M, b Keene, NH, Mar 7, 42. BIO-ORGANIC CHEMISTRY. *Educ:* Middlebury Col, BA, 63; Yale Univ, PhD(biochem), 67. *Prof Exp:* NIH fel biochem, Brandeis Univ, 67-69, sr res assoc, 69-74; RES ASST PROF CHEM, UNIV VT, 74- *Concurrent Pos:* Sabbatical leave, Nat Inst Arthritis, Diabetes, Digestive Dis & Kidney, NIH, 79- *Mem:* Sigma Xi; Am Chem Soc. *Res:* Mechanisms of catalysis in enzymatic and related non-enzymatic reactions; organic oxidation-reduction reactions of biochemical interest. *Mailing Add:* Nat Inst Arthritis Diabetes Digestive Dis & Kidney NIH Bldg 4 Rm 220-LBC Bethesda MD 20205

SAYER, JOHN SAMUEL, b St Paul, Minn, July 27, 17; m 40; c 4. INFORMATION SCIENCE, SYSTEMS ENGINEERING. *Educ:* Univ Minn, BSME, 40. *Prof Exp:* Supvr plant develop, E I du Pont de Nemours & Co, 47-52, eng planning, 52-54, sect mgr plant eng, 54-56, mgt sci, 56-60; exec vpres, Documentation Inc, 60-62; vpres mgt sci, Auerbach Corp, 62-65; vpres, Info Dynamics Corp, 65-66; pvt consult info sci, Mass, 66-69; exec vpres, Leasco Systs & Res, Md, 69; pvt consult, 70-71; exec vpres, Leasco Info Prod, 72; pres, REMAC Infor Corp, 73-81; PRES, DAKOTA MGT CORP, 82- *Mem:* Am Mgt Asn; Am Soc Info Sci; Am Soc Mech Engrs. *Res:* Large scale information systems concepts and designs, users needs, value functions and use patterns, in management and in scientific and engineering fields. *Mailing Add:* 13209 Colton Lane Gaithersburg MD 20760

SAYER, MICHAEL, b Newport, Eng, Nov 6, 35; m 60; c 4. PHYSICS. *Educ:* Univ Birmingham, BSc, 57; Univ Hull, PhD(physics), 61, PEng, 80. *Prof Exp:* Nat Res Coun Can fel, 60-62; assoc prof physics, 62-75, PROF PHYSICS, HEAD OF DEPT, QUEEN'S UNIV, ONT, 75- *Concurrent Pos:* Vis asst prof, Univ Trent, 65-66; vis fel physics, Univ Sheffield, 72-73. *Mem:* Can Asn Physicists; Can Ceramic Soc; Am Ceramic Soc. *Res:* Superionic conductors; amorphous and vitreous semiconductors; metal-semiconductor transitions; dielectric, infrared and electron spin resonance behavior of transition metal compounds; thin film devices; piezoelectric devices and materials; industrial instrumentation. *Mailing Add:* Dept Physics Queen's Univ Kingston ON K7L 3N6 Can

SAYER, ROYCE ORLANDO, b Toccoa, Ga, Apr 29, 41; m 64; c 2. NUCLEAR PHYSICS. *Educ:* Furman Univ, BS, 62; Univ Tenn, PhD(physics), 68. *Prof Exp:* Physicist, US Army Nuclear Effects Lab, 68-70; asst prof physics, Furman Univ, 70-73; res assoc, Vanderbilt Univ, 73-74; comput appln specialist, 74-80, COMPUT CONSULT, OAK RIDGE NAT LAB, 80- *Concurrent Pos:* Oak Ridge Assoc Univs fac res partic, Oak Ridge Nat Lab, 71; consult, Union Carbide Corp, 72- *Mem:* Am Phys Soc; Am Chem Soc. *Res:* Coulomb excitation of nuclear levels; gamma ray angular correlations; accelerator ion optics; heavy-ion physics; MHD stability; graphical display systems. *Mailing Add:* Bldg 6000 Oak Ridge Nat Lab Oak Ridge TN 37830

SAYERS, DALE EDWARD, b Seattle, Wash, Nov 29, 43; m 64; c 2. SOLID STATE PHYSICS. *Educ:* Univ Calif, Berkeley, BA, 66; Univ Wash, MS, 68, PhD(physics), 71. *Prof Exp:* Res engr physics, Boeing Aerospace Co, 72-73; sr res assoc physics, Univ Wash, 74-76; ASST PROF PHYSICS, NC STATE UNIV, 76- *Honors & Awards:* Sidhu Award, Pittsburgh X-ray Diffraction Conf, 73. *Mem:* AAAS; Am Phys Soc. *Res:* Development of the extended x-ray absorption fine structure technique and its application to structural studies of amorphous materials, biological systems, catalysts and other systems. *Mailing Add:* Dept of Physics NC State Univ Raleigh NC 27650

SAYERS, EARL ROGER, b Sterling, Ill, July 20, 36; m 58; c 3. GENETICS, PLANT BREEDING. *Educ:* Univ Ill, BS, 58; Cornell Univ, MS, 61, PhD(plant breeding), 64. *Prof Exp:* Asst prof genetics, 63-66, asst acad vpres, 71-76, dean acad develop, 72-76, assoc acad vpres, 76-80, ASSOC PROF GENETICS, UNIV ALA, 66-, ACAD VPRES, 80- *Concurrent Pos:* Dir arboretum, Univ Ala, 64-66; actg head dept biol, 66-68, asst dean col arts & sci, 68-70, spec asst off acad affairs, 70-71, dean spec progs, 71-72; fel, Am Coun on Educ, mem acad admin internship prog. *Mem:* Genetics Soc Am. *Res:* Self and cross incompatibility in cultivated alfalfa; genetics of the colonial green alga Volvox aureus. *Mailing Add:* Off for Acad Affairs Univ of Ala PO Box 1933 University AL 35486

SAYERS, GEORGE, b Glasgow, Scotland, June 10, 14; nat US; m 66; c 4. ENDOCRINOLOGY. *Educ:* Wayne Univ, BS, 34, MS, 41; Univ Mich, MS, 36; Yale Univ, PhD(biochem), 43. *Prof Exp:* Asst & instr biochem, Sch Med, Yale Univ, 43-45; from asst prof to assoc prof pharmacol, Sch Med, Univ Utah, 45-52; chmn dept, 52-76, PROF PHYSIOL, DEPT, SCH MED, CASE WESTERN RESERVE UNIV, 52- *Honors & Awards:* Abel Award, Am Soc Pharmacol & Exp Therapeut, 47; Ciba Award, Endocrine Soc, 49. *Mem:* AAAS; Endocrine Soc; Soc Exp Biol & Med; Am Soc Pharmacol & Exp Therapeut; Am Physiol Soc. *Res:* Pituitary and adrenocortical physiology. *Mailing Add:* Dept of Physiol Case West Res Univ Sch of Med Cleveland OH 44106

SAYERS, ROSS, clinical pharmacology, see previous edition

SAYETTA, THOMAS C, b Williamsport, Pa, Apr 12, 37; m 68; c 1. MAGNETIC RESONANCE. *Educ:* Univ SC, BS, 59, PhD(physics), 64. *Prof Exp:* Engr, Radio Corp Am, NJ, 59-60; ASSOC PROF PHYSICS, E CAROLINA UNIV, 64- *Concurrent Pos:* Asst ed, Int J Math & Math Sci. *Mem:* Am Asn Physics Teachers; Sigma Xi. *Res:* Quantum chemistry and electron spin resonance. *Mailing Add:* Dept Physics ECarolina Univ Greenville NC 27834

SAYLE, WILLIAM ERVEN, II, b Baytown, Tex, Sept 30, 41; c 1. PHYSICAL ELECTRONICS, ELECTRONIC ENGINEERING. *Educ:* Univ Tex, Austin, BSEE, 63, MSEE, 64; Univ Wash, PhD(elec eng), 70. *Prof Exp:* Res engr, Boeing Co, 65-67, sr engr, 70; asst prof elec eng, 70-76, ASSOC PROF ELEC ENG, GA INST TECHNOL, 76- *Concurrent Pos:* Consult prof, UNESCO, Venezuela, 73-74; consult, Hughes Aircraft, 78-80 & Hewlett-Packard, 81. *Mem:* Sr mem Inst Elec & Electronics Engrs. *Res:* Solid-state power electronics; computer-aided electronic circuit design. *Mailing Add:* Sch of Elec Eng Ga Inst of Technol Atlanta GA 30332

SAYLES, DAVID CYRIL, b Scollard, Alta, Mar 23, 17; nat US; m 51; c 2. ORGANIC CHEMISTRY, EXPLOSIVES. *Educ:* Univ Alta, BSc, 39; Univ Chicago, MS, 41; Purdue Univ, PhD(chem), 46. *Prof Exp:* Asst, Univ Alta, 38-39, Univ Chicago, 40-41 & Purdue Univ, 43-44; instr gen eng chem, 45-46; prof org chem & head dept chem, Ferris Inst, 46-47; dep dir res, Lowe Bros Co, 47-52; chief chem prod & equip unit, Wright Air Develop Ctr, Wright-Patterson AFB, Ohio, 52-53; chief high explosives & propellants unit, 53-54, chief ammunition sect, Gun & Rocket Br, 54-56; from asst chief to chief, Gun & Ammunition Br, Munitions Develop Labs, Armament Ctr, Eglin AFB, Fla, 56-57, tech adv, Tech Planning Group, 57-58; chief, Res Plans Br, Ord Missile Command, US Dept Army, Redstone Arsenal, 58-60, actg dep chief, Res Plans Div, 61-63, group leader propellants & mat, Propulsion Lab, US Army Missile Command, 63-66, res phys scientist, Propulsion Technol & Mgt Ctr, 66-70, gen engr, Missile Develop Div, Advan Ballistic Missile Defense Agency, 70-75, GEN ENGR, INTERCEPTOR DIRECTORATE, BALLISTIC MISSILE DEFENSE ADVAN TECHNOL CTR, US ARMY MISSILE COMMAND, 75- *Concurrent Pos:* Consult, C C Letroy & Co, 46-47, Harrow Enterprises, 46-49, Sayles Chem Consults, 46-49 & Glo-Rnz, Inc, 54-58. *Honors & Awards:* Hon Scroll, Am Inst Chemists, 65, 67 & 68; Res Achievement Award, Chem Inst Can, 70. *Mem:* Am Chem Soc; Am Inst Chemists; Am Ord Asn. *Res:* Reactions of organometallic compounds; diethylstilbesterol analogs; lysine; alkyd resins; silicones; epichlorohydrin-bisphenol A resins; surface coatings; synthetic drying oils; lacquers; linoleum; laminates; high explosives; liquid propellants; solid and hybrid materials and propellants; ammunition development; missile, rocket and interceptor propulsion subsystems, materials and propulsion technology. *Mailing Add:* 9616 Dortmond Dr SE Huntsville AL 35803

SAYLES, EVERETT DUANE, b Hillsdale, Mich, July 27, 03; m 30; c 4. ZOOLOGY. *Educ:* Kalamazoo Col, AB, 27; Kans State Col, MS, 28; Univ Chicago, PhD(zool), 42. *Hon Degrees:* LLD, Eastern Col, 75. *Prof Exp:* Instr biol, Va Jr Col, Minn, 30-45; prof, Thiel Col, 45-54; prof, 54-74, chmn biol dept & sci div, 61-74, EMER PROF BIOL, EASTERN COL, 74- *Concurrent Pos:* Vis prof, Fla Mem Col, 61-62. *Mem:* Fel AAAS; Am Inst Biol Sci; emer mem Sigma Xi; emer mem Sci Res Soc NAm. *Res:* Biology of male in mammals; castration of male guinea pig; male guinea pig post natal sexual differentiation; identification and culturing of Archiannelid worms (Dinophilus) and other microscopic Annelid worms. *Mailing Add:* 2247 Sandrala Dr Sarasota FL 33581

SAYLES, FREDERICK LIVERMORE, geochemistry, marine chemistry, see previous edition

SAYLOR, CHARLES (HAMILTON) PROFFER, b Camden, NJ, June 14, 01; m 30; c 1. PHYSICAL CHEMISTRY, CHEMICAL MICROSCOPY. *Educ:* Cornell Univ, BChem, 23, PhD(phys chem), 28. *Prof Exp:* Chemist, Pub Serv Comn NY, 23-24; asst chem, Cornell Univ, 24-28, chem microscopist, City Div Trade Waste, Cleveland, Ohio, 28-30; chem microscopist, 31-50, chief sect pure substances, 50-60, consult, Anal Chem Div, 60-72, GUEST WORKER, INST MAT RES, NAT BUR STAND, 72- *Concurrent Pos:* Mem, Comn Physicochem data & stand, Int Union Pure & Appl Chem & Subcomt Physicochem Stand Div Chem & Chem Tech, Nat Res Coun, 59-63. *Mem:* AAAS; Am Chem Soc; Optical Soc Am. *Res:* Conditions affecting formation of crystalline phases; crystalline rubber; ultrapurification; purity determination; optical properties of crystals; refractive index of micro quantities of chemicals; migration of boundaries and surface forms of metals. *Mailing Add:* 10001 Riggs Rd Adelphi MD 20783

SAYLOR, LEROY C, b Cedar Rapids, Iowa, July 17, 31; m 55; c 3. FORESTRY, GENETICS. *Educ:* Iowa State Univ, BS, 58; NC State Univ, MS, 60, PhD(genetics), 62. *Prof Exp:* Asst geneticist, 61-62, from asst prof to prof genetics & forestry, 62-69, asst dean, Sch Forest Resources, 69-74, ASSOC DEAN, SCH FOREST RESOURCES, NC STATE UNIV, 74-, PROF GENETICS & FORESTRY, 69- *Concurrent Pos:* NSF res grants, 61-66; McIntire-Stennis res grants, 64-72. *Honors & Awards:* NC State Col Chap Res Award, Sigma Xi, 67. *Mem:* Genetics Soc Am; Soc Am Foresters; AAAS; Am Forestry Asn; Sigma Xi. *Res:* Cytogenetics of forest tree species; speciation and introgression in forest tree species. *Mailing Add:* Sch of Forest Resources Biltmore Hall NC State Univ Raleigh NC 27650

SAYLOR, PAUL EDWARD, b Dallas, Tex, Mar 19, 39; m 64; c 2. NUMERICAL ANALYSIS. *Educ:* Stanford Univ, BS, 61; Univ Tex, MA, 63; Rice Univ, PhD(math), 68. *Prof Exp:* Asst prof, 67-73, ASSOC PROF COMPUT SCI, UNIV ILL, URBANA, 73- *Concurrent Pos:* Vis prof, Inst Fluid Dynamics & Appl Math, Univ Md, College Park, 73-74; hydrologist, US Geol Surv, Reston, Va, 75- *Mem:* Am Math Soc; Soc Indust & Appl Math. *Res:* Solution of linear systems arising from partial differential equations. *Mailing Add:* Dept of Comput Sci Univ of Ill Urbana IL 61801

SAYRE, CLIFFORD L(EROY), JR, b Pittsburgh, Pa, June 14, 27; m 53; c 2. MECHANICAL ENGINEERING. *Educ:* Duke Univ, BSME, 47; Stevens Inst Technol, MS, 50; Univ Md, PhD(mech eng), 61. *Prof Exp:* Proj engr, Stevens Inst Technol, 50-51; from instr to assoc prof, 51-55, assoc dean, Col of Eng, 76-79, PROF MECH ENG, UNIV MD, COLLEGE PARK, 55- *Concurrent Pos:* Engr, Bur Aeronaut, US Navy Dept, 55-56, physicist, David Taylor Model Basin, 56-60; partner, Sayre & Sayre Eng Assocs, 65-; educ consult, Univ Philippines, 67-68. *Mem:* Assoc Am Soc Mech Engrs; assoc Soc Naval Archit & Marine Eng; Marine Technol Soc; Soc Naval Eng. *Res:* Aerodynamics; hydrodynamics. *Mailing Add:* Dept of Mech Eng Univ of Md College Park MD 20742

SAYRE, CLIFFORD M(ORRILL), JR, b Springfield, Mass, Dec 17, 30; m 59; c 2. CHEMICAL ENGINEERING. *Educ:* Mass Inst Technol, SB, 52. *Prof Exp:* Develop engr, Tech Sect, Polychem Dept, 52-56, engr, Plants Tech Mgrs Off, 56-57, asst tech supt, 57-58, res supvr, 58-59, res supvr, Indust & Biochem Dept, 59-63, sr res engr, Plastics Dept, 63-66, sr res supvr, 66, div supt process res, Victoria Plant, 66-69, tech supt, Pontchartrain Works, 69-72, mgr financial & bus anal, Polymer Intermediates, 72-73, intermediates studies mgr, 73-74, mat & distrib mgr, 74-76, planning mgr, Nylon Intermediates, 76-77, DIV MGR, TRANSP & DISTRIB, E I DU PONT DE NEMOURS & CO, INC, 77- *Concurrent Pos:* Mem, Maritime Trans Res Bd, Nat Res Coun; vchmn, Sea Trans Comt, US Coun for Int Bus. *Mem:* Fel AAAS; fel Am Inst Chemists; Am Chem Soc; Am Inst Chem Engrs. *Res:* Nylon and polymer intermediates; industrial chemicals; plastics and environmental control; business and financial analysis; petrochemicals; transportation and distribution of chemicals; maritime research. *Mailing Add:* Transp & Distrib Dept E I du Pont de Nemours & Co Wilmington DE 19898

SAYRE, DAVID, b New York, NY, Mar 2, 24; m 47. X-RAY CRYSTALLOGRAPHY. *Educ:* Yale Univ, BS, 43; Ala Polytech Inst, MS, 49; Oxford Univ, DPhil(chem crystallog), 51. *Prof Exp:* Mem staff radiation lab, Mass Inst Technol, 43-46; consult, US Off Naval Res, 51; assoc biophys, Johnson Res Found, Univ Pa, 51-55; mathematician, 55-60, dir prog, 60-62, mgr mach reasoning, 62-64, mgr exp prog, 64-69, RES STAFF MEM, IBM CORP, 69- *Concurrent Pos:* Mem nat comt crystallog, Nat Res Coun, 57-59 & 81-; vis fel, All Souls Col, Oxford Univ, 72-73; fac mem, Int Sch of Crystallogr, Erice, 74, 76, 78, Prague, 75, Ottawa, 81; guest scientist physics, State Univ NY, Stony Brook, 78- *Mem:* Am Crystallog Asn (treas, 53-55, pres, 81). *Res:* Direct methods for determination of large structures; x-ray microscopy. *Mailing Add:* Math Sci Dept IBM Res Ctr Yorktown Heights NY 10598

SAYRE, EDWARD VALE, b Des Moines, Iowa, Sept 8, 19; m 43. PHYSICAL CHEMISTRY. *Educ:* Iowa State Col, BS, 41; Columbia Univ, AM, 43, PhD(chem), 49. *Prof Exp:* Chemist, Manhattan Dist Proj, SAM Labs, Columbia Univ, 42-45 & Eastman Kodak Co, 49-52; SR CHEMIST, BROOKHAVEN NAT LAB, 52- *Concurrent Pos:* Vis lectr, Stevens Inst, 55-63; consult fel, Conserv Ctr, Inst Fine Arts, NY Univ, 60-67, adj prof, 65-74; Guggenheim fel, 69; distinguished vis prof, Am Univ Cairo, 69-70; regents prof, Univ Calif, Irvine, 72; head res lab, Mus Fine Arts, Boston, 75-78, sr scientist, 78-; Alexander von Humboldt US sr scientist award, Berlin, 80. *Mem:* Fel Int Inst Conserv Hist & Artistic Works; Am Chem Soc; fel Am Inst Conserv. *Res:* Technical study of fine art and archaeological materials; single crystal spectra, cryogenic measurements; catalyst exchange and surface chemistry studies. *Mailing Add:* Dept of Chem Brookhaven Nat Lab Upton NY 11973

SAYRE, FRANCIS WARREN, b Larchwood, Iowa, Nov 20, 24; m 54. BIOCHEMISTRY. *Educ:* Univ Calif, AB, 49, PhD(biochem), 55; Col Pacific, MA, 51. *Prof Exp:* Chemist, Aluminum Co Am, 43-44; asst chem, Modesto Jr Col, 45-46 & Col Pacific, 50-51; chemist, Agr Lab, Shell Develop Co, 51; res scientist, Clayton Found Biochem Inst, Univ Tex, 51-52; asst biochem, Univ Calif, 52-55; res assoc, City of Hope Med Ctr, 55-58; assoc res scientist, Kaiser Found Res Inst, 59-68; PROF BIOCHEM, UNIV OF THE PAC, 68- *Concurrent Pos:* Mem biochem subsect, Am Chem Soc Exam Comt, 74- *Mem:* Am Chem Soc; Brit Biochem Soc; AAAS; NY Acad Sci; Sigma Xi. *Res:* Growth and metabolic regulation; specific recognition sites in proteins; cellular aging; carcinogenesis; specific growth factors; enzyme synthesis; nutrition; nutrient interrelationships. *Mailing Add:* Sch of Pharm Univ of the Pac 751 Brookside Rd Stockton CA 95207

SAYRE, GENEVA, b Guthrie, Iowa, June 12, 11. BOTANY. *Educ:* Grinnell Col, BA, 33; Univ Wyo, MA, 35; Univ Colo, PhD(bot), 38. *Prof Exp:* Asst biol, Univ Colo, 35-38, instr, 39-40; from instr to prof, 40-72, chmn dept biol, 46-69, EMER PROF BIOL, RUSSELL SAGE COL, 72- *Concurrent Pos:* Am Asn Univ Women fel, 49-50, NSF grants, 57-58, 63-66, 69-70; res assoc, Farlow Herbarium, Harvard Univ, 72- *Mem:* Am Bryol Soc (pres, 51-53); Brit Bryol Soc; Int Asn Taxon. *Res:* Taxonomy of mosses; history of botanical publication. *Mailing Add:* South St Chesterfield MA 01012

SAYRE, RICHARD MARTIN, b Hillsboro, Ore, Mar 25, 28; m 62; c 1. PLANT PATHOLOGY. *Educ:* Ore State Univ, BS, 51, MS, 54; Univ Nebr, PhD(plant nematol), 58. *Prof Exp:* Nematologist, Harrow Res St, Can Dept Agr, 58-65; NEMATOLOGIST, USDA, 65- *Mem:* Am Phytopath Soc; Soc Nematol. *Res:* Biological control of plant parasitic nematodes. *Mailing Add:* Nematol Lab Biosci Bldg Agr Res Ctr-West Beltsville MD 20705

SAYRE, ROBERT NEWTON, b Cottonwood Falls, Kans, July 25, 32; m 54; c 4. AGRICULTURAL CHEMISTRY, HISTOLOGY. *Educ:* Kans State Univ, BS, 54; Univ Wis, MS, 61, PhD(biochem, meat sci), 62. *Prof Exp:* Asst county agr agent, Kans Agr Exten Serv, USDA, 56-58; res asst muscle biochem, Univ Wis, 58-62; food technologist, Am Meat Inst Found, Ill, 62-64; res chemist poultry meat invests, 64-70, freeze damage reduction in plant tissue, 70-71, res chemist food technol-potato invests, 72-79, RES CHEMIST, CEREALS RES UNIT-GRAIN COMPOS, WESTERN REGIONAL RES CTR, USDA, 79- *Mem:* AAAS; Inst Food Technol; Am Chem Soc; Am Asn Cereal Chemists. *Res:* Investigation of cereal grains and plants related to water and salt stress. *Mailing Add:* Western Regional Res Lab USDA 800 Buchanan St Albany CA 94710

SAYRE, WILLIAM WHITAKER, b New York, NY, Aug 31, 27; m 51; c 3. CIVIL ENGINEERING, HYDRAULICS. *Educ:* Princeton Univ, BSE, 49; Colo State Univ, MS, 57, PhD(civil eng, hydraul), 67. *Prof Exp:* Eng draftsman, US Bur Reclamation, 52, civil engr, 52-53, hydraul engr, 56-58; civil engr, US Bur Indian Affairs, 53-54; res asst hydraul, Colo State Univ, 54-55; irrigation engr, Agr Res Serv, US Dept Agr, 56; asst civil engr, Colo State Univ, 58-62; res hydraul engr, US Geol Surv, 62-68; assoc prof hydraul & res engr, 68-71, prof mech & hydraul, 71-77, PROF ENERGY ENG, UNIV IOWA, 77- *Honors & Awards:* Huber Prize, Am Soc Civil Engrs, 66 & J C Stevens Awards, 70; Univ Minn Straub Award, 67. *Mem:* Am Water Resources Asn; Am Geophys Union; Am Soc Civil Engrs; Soc Social Responsibility in Sci. *Res:* Dispersion processes in open channel flow; mixing of heated effluents; sediment transport; tracer techniques; resistance to flow in rigid and alluvial boundary channels; general hydraulics. *Mailing Add:* Inst of Hydraul Res Univ of Iowa Iowa City IA 52242

SAYRES, ALDEN R, b New York, NY, Mar 7, 32; m 72. NUCLEAR PHYSICS. *Educ:* Dartmouth Col, AB, 53; Columbia Univ, PhD(physics), 60. *Prof Exp:* Res assoc physics, Columbia Univ, 60-65; from asst prof to assoc prof, 65-72, PROF PHYSICS, BROOKLYN COL, 72- *Mem:* NY Acad Sci; Am Phys Soc; Am Asn Physics Teachers. *Res:* Nuclear particle detection and nuclear spectroscopy. *Mailing Add:* Dept Physics Brooklyn Col Bedford Ave & Ave H Brooklyn NY 11210

SAZ, ARTHUR KENNETH, b New York, NY, Dec 2, 17; m 45; c 1. MICROBIOLOGY. *Educ:* City Col New York BS, 38; Univ Mo, MA, 39; Duke Univ, PhD(bact), 43; Am Bd Microbiol, dipl. *Prof Exp:* Asst pharmacol, Sch Med, Duke Univ, 40-42, instr bact, 42-43; instr, New York Med Col, 46-47; asst prof, Iowa State Col, 48-49; bacteriologist, Nat Inst Allergy & Infectious Dis, 48-57, chief med & physiol bact sect, 57-64; PROF MICROBIOL & CHMN DEPT, SCHS MED & DENT, GEORGETOWN UNIV, 64- *Concurrent Pos:* Fel, Rockefeller Inst, 47-49. *Mem:* AAAS; Am Soc Microbiol; Am Acad Microbiol. *Res:* Microbial biochemistry; bacterial physiology and mode of action of antibiotics; penicillinase induction; resistance to penicillin in staphylococcus and gonococcus; bacteriophages of Bacillus cereus. *Mailing Add:* Dept of Microbiol Georgetown Univ Sch of Med & Dent Washington DC 20007

SAZ, HOWARD JAY, b New York, NY, Sept 29, 23; m 46; c 3. BIOCHEMISTRY, PARASITE BIOCHEMISTRY. *Educ:* City Col, BS, 48; Western Reserve Univ, PhD(microbiol), 52. *Prof Exp:* Res assoc microbiol, Western Reserve Univ, 52-53, Nat Found Infantile Paralysis fel biochem & microbiol, Univ Sheffield, 53-54; res assoc pharmacol, La State Univ, 54-55, from asst prof to assoc prof, 55-60; assoc prof pathobiol, Sch Hyg & Pub Health, Johns Hopkins Univ, 60-69; PROF BIOL, UNIV NOTRE DAME, 69- *Concurrent Pos:* Mem trop med & parasitol study sect, USPHS, 65-69, chmn, 69-70. *Mem:* Am Soc Microbiol; Sigma Xi; Am Soc Biol Chem; Brit Biochem Soc; Am Soc Parasitol. *Res:* Bacterial and helminth biochemistry; comparative biochemistry employing isotopic tracers and enzyme purification techniques. *Mailing Add:* Dept of Biol Col of Sci Univ of Notre Dame Notre Dame IN 46556

SBAR, MARC LEWIS, b Philadelphia, Pa, Oct 7, 44; m 68; c 3. SEISMOLOGY, TECTONICS. *Educ:* Lafayette Col, Easton, Pa, BS, 66; Columbia Univ, PhD(geophys), 72. *Prof Exp:* Res scientist, 72-73, res assoc, Lamont-Doherty Geol Observ, Columbia Univ, 73-77; ASST PROF SEISMOL, UNIV ARIZ, 77- *Concurrent Pos:* Consult earthquake seismol. *Mem:* Seismol Soc Am; Am Geophys Union; Geol Soc Am; Royal Astron Soc (Eng); Soc Explor Geophys. *Res:* Earthquake hazard evaluation; earthquake prediction; regional and global earth movements and causes (tectonics); measurement and interpretation of stress in the earth. *Mailing Add:* Dept Geosci Univ Ariz Tucson AZ 85721

SBARRA, ANTHONY J, b Victor, NY, Sept 3, 22; m 56; c 3. BACTERIOLOGY. *Educ:* Siena Col, BS, 48; Ind Univ, BA, 51; Univ Ky, MS, 51; Univ Tenn, PhD(bact), 54; Am Bd Microbiol, dipl. *Prof Exp:* Assoc biologist, Oak Ridge Nat Lab, 53-56; res assoc, Harvard Med Sch, 58-60, instr, 60; asst prof bact, 59-65, assoc prof obstet & gynec, 65-73, PROF OBSTET & GYNEC, MED SCH, TUFTS UNIV, 73- *Concurrent Pos:* Res fel bact & immunol, Harvard Med Sch, 56-58; lectr, Univ Tenn, 54-55; assoc dir dept path & med res, St Margaret's Hosp, 59-74, dir dept, 74-; biochem sect ed, RES, 66-73, mem adv bd, 74-; ed, J Infection & Immunol, 73- & Proc Soc Exp Biol & Med, 74. *Mem:* Am Soc Microbiol; Am Soc Exp Path; Reticuloendothelial Soc; affil AMA. *Res:* Biological and biochemical approach to the host-parasite relationships. *Mailing Add:* St Margaret's Hosp 90 Cushing Ave Boston MA 02125

SCADRON, MICHAEL DAVID, b Chicago, Ill, Feb 12, 38; m 60; c 2. THEORETICAL PHYSICS, HIGH ENERGY PHYSICS. *Educ:* Univ Mich, BS, 59; Univ Calif, Berkeley, PhD(physics), 64. *Prof Exp:* Fel physics, Lawrence Radiation Lab, 64-66; NSF fel, Imp Col, Univ London, 66-68; asst prof, Northwestern Univ, 68-70; vis prof, 70-71, PROF PHYSICS, UNIV ARIZ, 71- *Concurrent Pos:* Sr res fel, Imp Col, Univ London, 72 & 78, Univ Durham, 78; Fulbright Scholar to Pakistan, 79; Australian fel, NSF, Univ Tasmania & Melbourne, 79. *Mem:* Am Phys Soc; Fedn Am Sci. *Res:* elementary particle theory; strong, electromagnetic and weak interactions. *Mailing Add:* Dept of Physics Univ of Ariz Tucson AZ 85721

SCAFE, DONALD WILLIAM, b Highgate, Ont, Nov 30, 37; m 62. GEOLOGY, OCEANOGRAPHY. *Educ:* Univ Western Ont, BSc, 60; Univ Kans, MS, 63; Tex A&M Univ, PhD(oceanog), 68. *Prof Exp:* WITH RES OFF, ALTA RES COUN, 67- *Mem:* Clay Minerals Soc. *Res:* Bentonite; ceramic clays; volcanic ash; industrial minerals. *Mailing Add:* Alta Res Coun 4445 Calgary Trail S Edmonton AB T6H 5R7 Can

SCAGLIONE, PETER ROBERT, b Tampa, Fla, Oct 9, 25; m 56; c 4. PEDIATRICS. *Educ:* City Col New York, BS, 48; Columbia Univ, MD, 52. *Prof Exp:* Asst pediat, Columbia Univ, 54-57, instr, 57-61, assoc, 61-65; pediatrician-in-chief, Brooklyn-Cumberland Med Ctr, 65-74; DIR PEDIAT, ST VINCENT'S HOSP & MED CTR, 74-; PROF CLIN PEDIAT, MED CTR, NY UNIV, 74- *Concurrent Pos:* From clin asst prof to clin assoc prof pediat, State Univ NY Downstate Med Ctr, 65-74; mem coun kidney in cardiovasc dis, Am Heart Asn, 73- *Mem:* Am Soc Nephrology; Int Soc Nephrology; Am Soc Pediat Nephrology. *Res:* Pediatric renal and acid-base disorders. *Mailing Add:* St Vincent's Hosp & Med Ctr 130 W 12th St New York NY 10011

SCAIFE, CHARLES WALTER JOHN, b Williamsport, Pa, Jan 27, 38; m 64; c 2. INORGANIC CHEMISTRY, SCIENCE EDUCATION. *Educ:* Cornell Univ, BA, 59, PhD(inorg chem), 66. *Prof Exp:* NSF fel, York, Eng, 66-67; asst prof chem, Middlebury Col, 67-72; chmn dept, 72-78, ASSOC PROF CHEM, UNION COL, NY, 72- *Concurrent Pos:* Vis prof, NMex State Univ, 78-79. *Mem:* Am Chem Soc; Brit Chem Soc. *Res:* Synthesis and characterization of new borazine derivatives; rates and mechanisms of inorganic and bioinorganic reactions; study of ion-ion and ion-solvent interactions in aqueous and nonaqueous solutions. *Mailing Add:* Dept Chem Union Col Schenectady NY 12308

SCALA, ALFRED ANTHONY, b Brooklyn, NY, Apr 29, 36; m 57; c 3. PHOTOCHEMISTRY. *Educ:* Brooklyn Col, BS, 57, MA, 61; Polytech Inst Brooklyn, PhD(org chem), 65. *Prof Exp:* Res chemist, Pfister Chem Works, 57-61; res assoc, Nat Res Coun, Nat Bur Stand, 64-66; asst prof org chem, 66-70, assoc prof, 70-75, PROF ORG CHEM, WORCESTER POLYTECH INST, 75-, HEAD DEPT OF CHEM, 77- *Mem:* Am Chem Soc. *Res:* Radiation chemistry. *Mailing Add:* Dept of Chem Worcester Polytech Inst Worcester MA 01609

SCALA, E(RALDUS), b Trieste, Italy, June 22, 22; nat US; m 48; c 4. METALLURGY. *Educ:* City Col New York, BS, 43; Columbia Univ, MS, 48; Yale Univ, DEng(metall), 53. *Prof Exp:* Metall chemist, Ledoux & Co, 43; res assoc, AEC Proj, Columbia Univ, 47-48; res metallurgist, Chase Brass & Copper Co, 48-52, training dir, 52-53, head phys metall sect, 53-55; mgr, Mat Dept, Res & Adv Develop Div, Avco Corp, 55-61; prof metall & mat sci, Cornell Univ, 61-68; dir, US Army Mat & Mech Res Ctr, Mass, 68-70; prof mat sci & eng, Cornell Univ, 70-74; dir, Cortland Line Co, 74-81, PRES, CORTLAND CABLE CO, 81- *Concurrent Pos:* Guggenheim fel, Delft Technol Univ, 67-68; consult, Aerospace Corp, Man Labs & Air Force Ballistic Missile Re-entry Systs, Battelle Mem Inst; mem adv bd mat, NASA, mem res adv comt mat; mem mat adv bd, Nat Acad Sci; consult eng, Scola & Co, 78- *Mem:* Am Inst Aeronaut & Astronaut; Am Soc Metals; Am Inst Mining, Metall & Petrol Engrs; Marine Technol Soc. *Res:* Physical metallurgy; high strength fibers and composites; cables and ropes; marine cable technology. *Mailing Add:* Cortland Line Co PO Box 1362 Cortland NY 13045

SCALA, JAMES, b Ramsey, NJ, Sept 16, 34; m 57; c 4. BIOCHEMISTRY. *Educ:* Columbia Col, AB, 60; Cornell Univ, PhD(biochem), 64. *Prof Exp:* Biochemist, Miami Valley Labs, Procter & Gamble Co, 64-66; sr res scientist, Owens-Ill Glass Inc, 66-68, chief life sci, Tech Ctr, 68-69, dir fundamental res, 69-71; dir appl nutrit, Tech Res, Thomas J Lipton, Inc, 71-75; dir nutrit & health sci, Gen Foods Corp, Tarrytown, NY, 75-78; VPRES RES & DEVELOP, SHAKLEE CORP, 78- *Concurrent Pos:* Lectr & adj prof, Med Col, Ohio Univ; lect prof, Georgetown Univ Sch Med, 73- *Mem:* Am Chem Soc; Am Soc Cell Biol; Inst Food Technol; Am Inst Nutrit. *Res:* Selenium metabolism in microorganisms and mammalian systems; percutaneous absorption; control mechanisms in protein biosynthesis; intermediary metabolism, especially the interrelationship of carbohydrate and lipid metabolism; relationship between metabolism and exercise physiology with emphasis on stress; interrelationship between nutrition and dental health. *Mailing Add:* 1992 Alpine Way Shaklee Corp Hayward CA 94545

SCALA, LUCIANO CARLO, b Rome, Italy, July 24, 23; nat US; m 51; c 7. ORGANIC CHEMISTRY. *Educ:* Univ Bologna, DSc(chem), 48. *Prof Exp:* Instr chem, Univ Bologna, 47-49; res assoc, Mass Inst Technol, 50-51; res chemist, Conn Hard Rubber Co, 51-53; MGR RES LABS, WESTINGHOUSE ELEC CORP, 53- *Concurrent Pos:* Fulbright fel, 50. *Mem:* Sr mem Am Chem Soc. *Res:* Organic synthesis; high temperature insulation; thermal degradation mechanisms; organic monolayers; photoresists; electrophoretic processes; liquid crystals; radiation chemistry; reverse osmotic membranes. *Mailing Add:* Westinghouse Res Lab Bldg 501 1310 Beulah Rd Pittsburgh PA 15235

SCALA, ROBERT ANDREW, b Utica, NY, Nov 14, 31; m 57; c 4. TOXICOLOGY. *Educ:* Hamilton Col, AB, 53; Univ Rochester, MS, 56, PhD(physiol), 58. *Prof Exp:* Res asst toxicol, Nat Acad Sci-Nat Res Coun, 58-60; sect supvr toxicol-pharmacol dept, Hazleton Labs, Inc, 60-61, asst chief, 62, dir lab opers, 62-65; toxicologist, Med Res Div, Esso Res & Eng Co, 65-74, dir toxicol, 74-81, SR SCI ADV, RES & ENVIRON HEALTH DIV, MED & ENVIRON HEALTH DEPT, EXXON CORP, 81- *Concurrent Pos:* Adj asst prof environ med, NY Univ, 70-; adj assoc prof pharmacol, Med Col Va. *Mem:* Am Chem Soc; Am Physiol Soc; Soc Toxicol; Am Indust Hyg Asn; Europ Soc Toxicol. *Res:* Relation of chemical structure to biological function or activity; toxicology of chemicals used in foods, drugs, pesticides, cosmetics, industry and military chemicals. *Mailing Add:* Exxon Corp Res & Environ Health Div PO Box 235 E Millstone NJ 08873

SCALA, SINCLAIRE M(AXIMILIAN), b Charleston, SC, June 27, 29; m 51; c 3. AERONAUTICAL SCIENCE, SPACE SCIENCE. *Educ:* City Col New York, BME, 50; Univ Del, MME, 53; Princeton Univ, MA, 55, PhD, 57; Univ Pa, MBA, 78. *Prof Exp:* Design engr, Aviation Gas Turbine Div, Westinghouse Elec Corp, 51-53; res engr, Missile & Space Div, Space Sci Lab, 56-58, consult res engr, 58-59, mgr high altitude aerodyn, 60-64, mgr theoret fluid physics, 64-68, mgr fluid physics projs, 68-69, mgr environ sci lab, 69-73, chief scientist, 73-74, sr consult scientist, 74-80, MGR ADV WEAPONS CONCEPTS, GEN ELEC CO, 80- *Concurrent Pos:* Consult, Princeton Univ, 56-58; mem NASA res & technol adv subcomt fluid mech, 65-70. *Mem:* AAAS; Am Phys Soc; Am Inst Aeronaut & Astronaut; NY Acad Sci; Sigma Xi. *Res:* Gas dynamics; aerodynamics; hypersonics; viscous flow; applied mathematics; multicomponent fluid processes; ablation; nonequilibrium flow; shock waves; transport phenomena; radiative energy transfer; systems analysis; solar energy; biomedical science; computer science; heat transfer. *Mailing Add:* Gen Elec Co R&E Systs Div 3198 Chestnut St Philadelphia PA 19101

SCALAPINO, DOUGLAS J, b San Francisco, Calif, Dec 10, 33; m 55; c 5. PHYSICS. *Educ:* Yale Univ, BS, 55; Stanford Univ, PhD(physics), 61. *Prof Exp:* Res assoc physics, Wash Univ, 61-62; res assoc, Univ Pa, 62-64, from asst prof to prof, 64-69; PROF PHYSICS, UNIV CALIF, SANTA BARBARA, 69- *Concurrent Pos:* Consult, E I du Pont de Nemours & Co, Inc, 64- *Res:* Many-body problems; superconductivity; magnetism; surfaces; statistical mechanics; phase transitions. *Mailing Add:* Dept Physics Univ Calif Santa Barbara CA 93106

SCALES, ROY WILLIAM, b Jackson, Miss, July 24, 43; m 69. IMMUNOLOGY. *Educ:* Miss Col, BS, 65; Univ Miss, MS, 67, PhD(immunol), 70. *Prof Exp:* Asst physiol Univ Miss, 65-69, asst immunol, 69-70; USPHS fel, Univ Fla, 70-71; STAFF FEL IMMUNOL, NAT CTR DIS CONTROL, 72- *Res:* Immunology of gonorrhea. *Mailing Add:* Venereal Dis Res Lab Nat Ctr for Dis Control Atlanta GA 30333

SCALES, WILLIAM WEBB, b Shreveport, La, Aug 20, 32; m 61; c 2. UNDERWATER ACOUSTICS. *Educ:* Columbia Univ, AB, 54; Rice Univ, MA, 56, PhD(physics), 58. *Prof Exp:* MEM TECH STAFF, BELL LABS, 58- *Mem:* AAAS; Acoust Soc Am; Sigma Xi. *Res:* Low temperature specific heats of crystals; underwater transmission of sound; underwater acoustic systems. *Mailing Add:* Ocean Systs Studies Ctr Whippany Rd Whippany NJ 07981

SCALET, CHARLES GEORGE, b Chicago, Ill, Sept 9, 42; m 66; c 3. FISH BIOLOGY, ICHTHYOLOGY. *Educ:* Southern Ill Univ, Carbondale, BA, 64, MA, 67; Univ Okla, PhD(zool), 71. *Prof Exp:* Asst prof zool, Cent State Univ, 71-72; instr, Iowa State Univ, 72-73; asst prof, 73-76, assoc prof, 76-82, PROF WILDLIFE & FISHERIES SCI, SDAK STATE UNIV, 82-, DEPT HEAD, 76- *Mem:* Am Fisheries Soc; Am Soc Ichthyologists & Herpetologists; Wildlife Soc. *Res:* Management of South Dakota waters for fish production; culture of fishes; description of the life histories and ranges of South Dakota fishes. *Mailing Add:* 1715 Santee Terr SDak State Univ Brookings SD 57006

SCALETTAR, RICHARD, b New York, NY, Dec 9, 21; m 58; c 2. THEORETICAL PHYSICS. *Educ:* City Col NY, BS, 41; Univ Wis, MA, 43; Cornell Univ, PhD(physics), 59. *Prof Exp:* Physicist, Metall Lab, Univ Chicago, 43-44 & Clinton Labs, Oak Ridge, Tenn, 44-46; asst prof physics, Univ Rochester, 49-51; physicist, Curtiss-Wright Corp, 52-53; asst prof physics, Univ Southern Calif, 53-59; sr theoret physicist, John Jay Hopkins Lab Pure & Appl Sci, Gen Atomic, 60-68; PROF PHYSICS & CHMN DEPT PHYSICS-ASTRON, CALIF STATE UNIV, LONG BEACH, 68- *Concurrent Pos:* Consult, Aerojet Gen Corp, 56; lectr, Edwards Air Force Base, 57; consult, Atomics Int, 58-59. *Mem:* Am Phys Soc. *Res:* Electron and gamma ray transport; interaction of electromagnetic radiation with plasmas; statistical mechanics and transport theory; reactor kinetics; particle and field theory. *Mailing Add:* Dept of Physics-Astron Calif State Univ Long Beach CA 90801

SCALETTI, JOSEPH VICTOR, b New London, Conn, July 22, 26; m 51; c 2. BACTERIOLOGY. *Educ:* Univ Conn, BA, 50, MS, 53; Cornell Univ, PhD(bact), 57. *Prof Exp:* Instr bact, Univ Conn, 52-53; asst, Cornell Univ, 53-56; bacteriologist, Am Cyanamid Co, 56-57; res assoc pub health, Univ Minn, St Paul, 57-58, asst prof animal husb, 58-64; assoc prof microbiol, 64-70, PROF MICROBIOL, UNIV NMEX, 70-, CHMN DEPT, 76- *Mem:* Am Soc Microbiol; Am Pub Health Asn; Am Acad Microbiol. *Res:* Nucleic acid metabolism as related to bacteriophage-bacterial systems; growth characteristics of psychorophilic microorganism. *Mailing Add:* Dept of Microbiol Univ of NMex Albuquerque NM 87106

SCALFAROTTO, ROBERT EMIL, b Alexandria, Egypt, June 4, 20; US citizen; m 46; c 1. PIGMENTS CHEMISTRY, PAPER CHEMISTRY. *Educ:* Univ Genoa, DSc(indust chem), 48. *Prof Exp:* Chemist, Lechner & Muratori Co, 46-50, tech dir pigments, 50-57; tech mgr gen chem, Mercantile Develop, Inc, 57-58; appl res chemist, Pigments Div, Am Cyanamid Co, 58-63; asst mgr pigments div, Ciba Chem & Dye Co, NJ, 63-67, promotion coordr, 67-70, mgr tech develop, Pigments Dept, Ciba-Geigy Corp, NY, 70-76; mgr int indust chems res & develop, 76-78, MGR NEW PROD TESTING, AM CYANAMID CO, 78- *Concurrent Pos:* Consult, Shell Ital Chem Serv, 50-54. *Mem:* Am Chem Soc; Am Asn Textile Chemists & Colorists; Tech Asn Pulp & Paper Indust. *Res:* Paper chemicals; pigments chemistry. *Mailing Add:* One Conrad Ct Montvale NJ 07645

SCALIA, FRANK, b Brooklyn, NY, Mar 18, 39; m 60; c 2. NEUROBIOLOGY. *Educ:* NY Univ, BA, 59; State Univ NY, PhD(anat), 64. *Prof Exp:* From instr to assoc prof, 63-77, PROF ANAT, STATE UNIV NY DOWNSTATE MED CTR, 77- *Mem:* AAAS; Am Asn Anat; Soc Neurosci. *Res:* Experimental neuroanatomy; neuroembryology; vision; olfaction. *Mailing Add:* State Univ NY Downstate Med Ctr 450 Clarkson Ave Brooklyn NY 11203

SCALLAN, ANTHONY MICHAEL, b Blackpool, Eng, Apr 12, 36; m 61; c 5. PAPER CHEMISTRY. *Educ:* Univ Liverpool, BSc, 57, PhD(polymer chem), 63. *Prof Exp:* Chemist, Roan Antelope Copper Mines, Zambia, 57-59; SR SCIENTIST & HEAD FIBER CHEM SECT, PULP & PAPER RES INST CAN, 63- *Mem:* Can Pulp & Paper Asn; Tech Asn Pulp & Paper Indust. *Res:* Physical chemistry of pulping and papermaking with emphasis on aspects related to the porous structure of wood and paper. *Mailing Add:* Pulp & Paper Res Inst Can 570 St Johns Rd Pointe Claire PQ H9R 3J9 Can

SCALLEN, TERENCE, b Minneapolis, Minn, Jan 16, 35; m 57; c 4. BIOCHEMISTRY. *Educ:* Col St Thomas, BS, 57; Univ Minn, Minneapolis, MD, 61, PhD(biochem, org chem), 65. *Prof Exp:* From asst prof to assoc prof, 65-76, PROF BIOCHEM, SCH MED, UNIV NMEX, 76- *Concurrent Pos:* Am Col Cardiol young investr award, 69. *Mem:* Am Chem Soc; Am Soc Biol Chemists; Am Soc Cell Biol. *Res:* Mechanisms of sterol and lipid biosynthesis; application of physical techniques to problems of steroid structure; sterol carrier protein. *Mailing Add:* Dept of Biochem Univ of NMex Sch of Med Albuquerque NM 87106

SCALLET, BARRETT LERNER, b St Louis, Mo, May 13, 16; m 43; c 3. FOOD CHEMISTRY, GRAIN PRODUCTS CHEMISTRY. *Educ:* Wash Univ, BS, 37, MS, 43, PhD(org chem), 46. *Prof Exp:* Control chemist, Anheuser-Busch, Inc, 37-38, res chemist, 38-46, res group leader, 46-47, res proj leader, 47-48, sect dir, 48-52, dir corn prod sect, Cent Res Dept, 52-55, assoc dir, 55-75, dir corn prod res, 75-80; PRES, CENTRAL RESEARCH, INC, 80- *Mem:* AAAS; Am Chem Soc; Am Asn Cereal Chem; Tech Asn Pulp & Paper Indust; Am Ceramic Soc. *Res:* Physical study of proteins and starches; electrophoresis; ultracentrifugation; chemistry of zein; beer proteins; corn syrups and starches; industrial utilization of corn products; food products; consumer products; new corn genetic varieties. *Mailing Add:* Cent Res Inc PO Box 11841 Clayton MO 63105

SCALORA, FRANK SALVATORE, b New York, NY, June 16, 27. MATHEMATICS. *Educ:* Harvard Univ, AB, 49; Univ Ill, AM, 51, PhD(math), 58. *Prof Exp:* Asst math, Univ Ill, 49-54; mathematician, Repub Aviation Corp, 54; mathematician, Int Bus Mach Corp, 56-63, info planning mgr, IBM World Trade Corp, 63-67, data mgt mgr, 67-71, sr analyst, 71-74, SR ANALYST, IBM DATA PROCESSING DIV, 74- *Concurrent Pos:* Adj prof, Polytech Inst Brooklyn, 60-61; adj asst prof, Courant Inst Math Sci, NY Univ, 61-63. *Mem:* Am Math Soc; Inst Math Statist. *Res:* Probability theory and stochastic processes; measure theory; statistics; operations research; bank asset and liability management. *Mailing Add:* 225 E 57th St Apt 10-S New York NY 10022

SCALZI, FRANCIS VINCENT, b Reading, Pa, Dec 4, 33; m 63; c 2. ORGANIC CHEMISTRY. *Educ:* Gettysburg Col, BA, 55; Univ Del, MS, 60, PhD(chem), 63. *Prof Exp:* Res chemist, Firestone Tire & Rubber Co, Pa, 56-58; lectr chem, Rutgers Univ, 63-64; PROF CHEM, HIRAM COL, 64- *Concurrent Pos:* NSF res participation col teachers grant, 64-66; vis assoc prof, Univ Wis-Milwaukee, 70-71; NSF spec proj grant, 70-72; prof, Univ Akron, 76- *Mem:* Am Chem Soc. *Res:* N-halamine chemistry; aromatic substitution; thermal degradation of organic compounds. *Mailing Add:* Dept of Chem Hiran Col Hiram OH 44234

SCALZI, JOHN BAPTIST, b Milford, Mass, Nov 13, 15; m 40; c 2. STRUCTURAL ENGINEERING, CIVIL ENGINEERING. *Educ:* Worcester Polytech Inst, BS, 38; Mass Inst Technol, MS, 40, ScD(civil eng), 51. *Prof Exp:* Field engr, Metcalf & Eddy, Mass, 39; struct engr, Curtiss-Wright Corp, NY, 40-45; engr, Eng Div, Nat Aniline Div, 45-46; prof struct eng, Case Inst Technol, 46-60; mem staff, Mkt Develop Div, US Steel Corp, 60-64, dir mkt tech serv, 64-67, gen mgr, 67-71; mem staff res & technol, HUD, 71-73; PROG MGR, NSF, WASHINGTON, DC, 73- *Concurrent Pos:* Lectr, Exten Eng Sci & Mgt War Training Prog, Cornell Univ, 42-45 & Univ Buffalo, 45; prof lectr, Western Reserve Univ, 46-60; lectr, Carnegie-Mellon Univ, 65-71 & George Washington Univ, 72-; struct consult, Cleveland eng firms. *Mem:* Am Soc Civil Engrs; Earthquake Eng Res Inst. *Res:* Earthquake engineering. *Mailing Add:* 2111 Jefferson Davis Hwy Arlington VA 22202

SCAMEHORN, RICHARD GUY, b Elkhart, Ind, June 20, 42; m 64; c 2. ORGANIC CHEMISTRY. *Educ:* Hanover Col, BA, 64; Northwestern Univ, PhD(org chem), 68. *Prof Exp:* Asst prof, 68-74, ASSOC PROF CHEM, RIPON COL, 74- *Concurrent Pos:* Res Corp res grants, 69-72 & 80-81; res assoc, Univ Calif, Santa Cruz, 75-76. *Mem:* Am Chem Soc. *Res:* Organic reaction mechanisms; carbanion rearrangement reactions; kinetics; aromatic substitutions. *Mailing Add:* Dept of Chem Ripon Col Ripon WI 54971

SCANDALIOS, JOHN GEORGE, b Nysiros, Greece, Nov 1, 34; US citizen; m 61; c 3. GENETICS. *Educ:* Univ Va, BA, 57; Adelphi Univ, MS, 60; Univ Hawaii, PhD(genetics), 65. *Prof Exp:* Instr biol, Hunter Col, 59-60; res assoc bact genetics, Cold Spring Harbor Lab, 60-63; NIH res fel molecular genetics, Univ Hawaii, 65; asst prof res genetics, AEC Plant Res Lab, Mich State Univ, 65-70, assoc prof, 70-72; prof genetics & head dept biol, Univ SC, 72-75; PROF GENETICS & HEAD DEPT, NC STATE UNIV, 75- *Concurrent Pos:* Instr radiation biol & biol & genetics, Adelphi Univ, 60-62; vis prof, Univ Calif, Davis, 68; Orgn Am States vis prof, Arg, 72. *Mem:* AAAS; Genetics Soc Am (pres, 81-82); Soc Develop Biol; Am Genetic Asn; Int Soc Differentiation. *Res:* Developmental-molecular genetics of eukaryotes; genetics, structure and function of isozymes; genetic regulation. *Mailing Add:* Dept Genetics NC State Univ Raleigh NC 27650

SCANDRETT, JOHN HARVEY, b Liberal, Kans, July 7, 33; m 54; c 3. PHYSICS. *Educ:* La State Univ, BS, 54; Univ Wis, MS, 56, PhD(physics), 63. *Prof Exp:* Lectr physics, Mich State Univ, 60-62; lectr, Ind Univ, 62-63, asst prof, 63-66; assoc prof, 66-81, PROF PHYSICS, WASHINGTON UNIV, 81- *Mem:* Am Phys Soc. *Res:* Medical physics; image processing. *Mailing Add:* Dept of Physics Washington Univ St Louis MO 63130

SCANDURA, JOSEPH M, b Bay Shore, NY, Apr 29, 32; m 60; c 3. MATHEMATICS. *Educ:* Univ Mich, BA, 53, MA, 55; Syracuse Univ, PhD(math educ), 62. *Prof Exp:* Teacher, White Plains & Bay Shore Sch Systs, NY, 53-55; asst prof math, State Univ NY Col Oswego, 55-56; instr, Syracuse Univ, 56-63, asst prof math & educ, State Univ NY Buffalo, 63-64; asst prof math educ, Fla State Univ, 64-66; PROF & DIR, INTERDISCIPLINARY STUDIES IN STRUCT LEARNING & INSTRNL SCI, UNIV PA, 66- *Concurrent Pos:* Consult, Merge Res Inst; Pres, Instrnl Micro Systs. *Mem:* AAAS; Am Psychol Asn; Am Educ Res Asn. *Res:* Theory and research in structural learning, cognitive psychology, instructional systems design and computer-based instruction. *Mailing Add:* Grad Sch of Educ Univ of Pa Philadelphia PA 19104

SCANES, COLIN G, b London, Eng, July 11, 47; m 76; c 1. ENDOCRINOLOGY, OVARIAN PHYSIOLOGY. *Educ:* Univ Hull, UK, BS, 69; Univ Wales, PhD(zool), 72. *Prof Exp:* Lectr animal physiol & nutrit, Univ Leeds, UK, 72-78; ASSOC PROF PHYSIOL, RUTGERS UNIV, 78-, CHMN DEPT ANIMAL SCI, 81- *Mem:* Am Physiol Soc; Poultry Sci Asn; Am Soc Zoologists; Endocrine Soc; Soc Endocrinol. *Res:* Hormonal control of growth and reproduction, particularly in the domestic fowl and other farm animals. *Mailing Add:* Dept Animal Sci Cook Col Rutgers Univ New Brunswick NJ 08903

SCANIO, CHARLES JOHN VINCENT, b Ann Arbor, Mich, June 23, 40; m 65. ORGANIC CHEMISTRY. *Educ:* Univ Mich, BS, 62; Northwestern Univ, PhD(org chem), 66. *Prof Exp:* From instr to asst prof chem, Iowa State Univ, 66-72; staff chemist, Pfizer, Inc, 72-77; HEAD PROCESS RES, UPJOHN, INC, 77- *Mem:* Am Chem Soc; Brit Chem Soc. *Res:* Processes to manufacture fine chemicals. *Mailing Add:* Upjohn Inc 410 Sackett Point Rd North Haven CT 06473

SCANLAN, J(ACK) A(DDISON), JR, b Chicago, Ill, Sept 25, 17; m 40; c 3. MECHANICAL ENGINEERING. *Educ:* Univ Tex, BS, 40, MS, 52; Northwestern Univ, PhD(eng), 57. *Prof Exp:* Asst proj engr, Wright Aeronaut Corp, 40-47; asst prof mech eng, Univ Tex, 47-52; vis lectr, Northwestern Univ, 52-54; assoc prof, Univ Tex, 54-67; PROF MECH ENG, MONT STATE UNIV, 67- *Concurrent Pos:* Consult, Union Carbide Nuclear Co Div, Union Carbide Corp; vis prof, Mont State Univ, 66-67. *Mem:* AAAS; Am Inst Aeronaut & Astronaut; Am Soc Eng Educ; Soc Automotive Engrs; Am Soc Mech Engrs. *Res:* Heat transfer; nuclear power; thermodynamics; alternative energy sources. *Mailing Add:* Dept of Mech Eng Mont State Univ Bozeman MT 59717

SCANLAN, MARY ELLEN, b New York, NY, Sept 20, 42. ORGANIC CHEMISTRY. *Educ:* Chestnut Hill Col, BS, 64; Univ RI, PhD(org chem), 70. *Prof Exp:* SR ASSOC ED, DEPT ORG CHEM, CHEM ABSTR SERV, 70- *Mem:* Am Chem Soc; AAAS; Am Women Sci. *Mailing Add:* Chem Abstr Serv Dept 51 PO Box 3012 Columbus OH 43210

SCANLAN, RICHARD ANTHONY, b Syracuse, NY, Dec 13, 37; m 59; c 5. FOOD SCIENCE. *Educ:* Cornell Univ, BS, 60, MS, 62; Ore State Univ, PhD, 67. *Prof Exp:* Res & develop coordr, US Army Natick Labs, Mass, 62-64; asst food sci, 64-67, from asst prof to assoc prof, 67-78, PROF FOOD SCI, ORE STATE UNIV, 78- *Concurrent Pos:* Prin investr, res grants. *Mem:* AAAS; Am Chem Soc; Sigma Xi; Inst Food Technologists. *Res:* Food toxicology; chemistry of formation and inhibition of N-nitrosamines; development of analytical methodology for nitrosamines; biological effects of N-nitrosamines; food chemistry; flavor chemistry. *Mailing Add:* Dept of Food Sci & Technol Ore State Univ Corvallis OR 97331

SCANLAN, ROBERT HARRIS, b Chicago, Ill, Aug 15, 14; m 39; c 4. STRUCTURAL DYNAMICS. *Educ:* Univ Chicago, SB, 36, SM, 39; Mass Inst Technol, PhD(math), 43; Univ Paris, Dr es Sci(mech), 56. *Prof Exp:* Assoc prof aeronaut, Rensselaer Polytech Inst, 46-51; Nat Res Coun-Nat Adv Comt Aeronaut fel, France, 51-52; res fel aeronaut, Nat Sci Res Ctr, France, 52-55; res engr, Nat Off Aeronaut Studies & Res, France, 55-57; Schlumberger Corp, Tex, 58-60; prof mech, Case Inst Technol, 60-66; PROF CIVIL ENG, PRINCETON UNIV, 66- *Concurrent Pos:* Sloan vis prof, Princeton Univ, 66-67. *Honors & Awards:* State-of-the Art in Civil Eng Award, Am Soc Civil Engrs, 69. *Mem:* Am Inst Aeronaut & Astronaut; Acoust Soc Am; Am Soc Mech Engrs; Am Soc Civil Engrs. *Res:* Acoustics; aeroelasticity; vibrations; applied mechanics; wind engineering; bridge aerodynamics. *Mailing Add:* Dept of Civil & Geol Eng Princeton Univ Princeton NJ 08540

SCANLEY, CLYDE STEPHEN, b Milwaukee, Wis, June 16, 21; div; c 3. WATER SOLUBLE POLYMERS. *Educ:* Univ Wis, BS, 43, PhD(org chem), 49. *Prof Exp:* Chemist, Standard Oil Co, Ind, 49-53; group leader, Am Cyanamid Co, 53-73; MGR RES, DREW CHEM CORP, 74- *Mem:* Am Chem Soc; Tech Asn Pulp & Paper Indust. *Res:* Vinyl polymers, especially polyelectrolyte flocculants, polycrylamides, surfactants, organic synthesis and process development. *Mailing Add:* 330 Speedwell Ave Morristown NJ 07960

SCANLON, CHARLES HARRIS, b Austin, Tex, Oct 13, 37; m 65; c 5. MATHEMATICAL ANALYSIS. *Educ:* Univ Tex, BA, 61, MA, 63, PhD(math), 67. *Prof Exp:* Asst prof math, Univ Okla, 67-70; ASSOC PROF MATH, ARK STATE UNIV, 70- *Mem:* Am Math Soc; Math Asn Am. *Res:* Analysis in metric spaces; generalized Riemann and Stieltjes integration. *Mailing Add:* Div of Math Ark State Univ State University AR 72467

SCANLON, JACK M, b Binghampton, NY, Jan 3, 42; m 63; c 4. COMPUTER SCIENCE, ELECTRICAL ENGINEERING. *Educ:* Univ Toronto, BASc, 64; Cornell Univ, MS, 65. *Prof Exp:* Mem staff elec eng, 65-68; supvr comput sci, 68-74, dept head electronic switching syst design, 74-77, dir software & syst design lab, 77-79, EXEC DIR PROCESSOR & COMMON SOFTWARE SYSTEMS DIV, BELL LABS, 79- *Concurrent Pos:* NSF fel, 64-65; comput sci & technol bd, Nat Res Coun-Nat Acad Sci. *Mem:* Inst Elec & Electronics Engrs. *Res:* Computer science; communications science; physics mathematics. *Mailing Add:* Bell Labs 1100 E Warrenville Rd Naperville IL 60566

SCANLON, JOHN EARL, b New York, NY, Nov 29, 25; m 47; c 2. MEDICAL ENTOMOLOGY. *Educ:* Fordham Univ, BS, 50; Cornell Univ, MS, 55; Univ Md, PhD, 60. *Prof Exp:* Med entomologist, Far East Med Res Unit, US Army, Tokyo, 50-53; Med Field Serv Sch, San Antonio, 55-56, Walter Reed Army Inst, 56-58, SEATO, Bangkok, 60-64 & Walter Reed Army Inst, 64-69; prof med zool, 69-75, ASSOC DEAN, SCH PUB HEALTH, UNIV TEX, HOUSTON, 75- *Mem:* AAAS; Am Soc Trop Med & Hyg (sect-tres, 80-). *Res:* Epidemiology of malaria and arbovirus; taxonomy and ecology of mosquitoes. *Mailing Add:* Sch of Pub Health Univ Tex San Antonio TX 78284

SCANLON, PATRICK FRANCIS, b Athlone, Ireland, Sept 16, 41; m 67; c 4. REPRODUCTIVE PHYSIOLOGY, WILDLIFE RESEARCH. *Educ:* Nat Univ Ireland, BAgrSci, 65, MAgrSci, 66, PhD(animal physiol), 70. *Prof Exp:* Res demonstr animal physiol, Fac Agr, Univ Col, Dublin, 65-66, res scholar, 66-69; res assoc appl physiol, Univ Guelph, 69-71; from asst prof to assoc prof wildlife physiol, 71-78, PROF, DEPT FISHERIES & WILDLIFE SCI, VA POLYTECH INST & STATE UNIV, 78- *Mem:* Am Soc Animal Sci; Wildlife Soc; Am Soc Mammal; Wildlife Dis Asn. *Res:* Reproductive physiology of wild animals; influences of environmental containments on wild animals; vertebrate pest control; control of reproduction in wild and domestic animals. *Mailing Add:* Dept Fisheries & Wildlife Sci Va Polytech Inst & State Univ Blacksburg VA 24061

SCANNELL, JAMES PARNELL, b Oak Park, Ill, Jan 16, 31; m 56; c 4. BIOCHEMISTRY. *Educ:* Univ Ill, BA, 51; Univ Calif, Berkeley, PhD(biochem), 60. *Prof Exp:* Fel biochem, Univ Calif, San Francisco, 60; lectr chem, Southern Ill Univ, 60-61; sr chemist, Papst Res Biochem, Pabst Brewing Co, 61-63 & Burroughs Wellcome & Co, 64-65; sr chemist, 66-75, res fel, 75-81, SR RES FEL,, HOFFMANN LA ROCHE & CO, 81- *Mem:* Am Chem Soc. *Res:* Isolation and characterization of natural products; chemistry and metabolism of nucleosides, amino acids and antibiotics. *Mailing Add:* 4 Canterbury Dr North Caldwell NJ 07006

SCANU, ANGELO M, b Bonnanaro, Italy, Dec 16, 24; m 58; c 2. MEDICINE, BIOCHEMISTRY. *Educ:* Univ Sassari, MD, 49. *Prof Exp:* From intern to resident, Med Sch, Univ Sassari, 49-52; asst prof internal med, Med Sch, Univ Naples, 53-55; res assoc, Cleveland Clin, 58, staff asst, 59-62; asst prof, 63-66, res assoc biochem, 65-66, assoc prof internal med & biochem, 66-70, PROF INTERNAL MED & BIOCHEM, MED SCH, UNIV CHICAGO, 70-, DIR, LIPOPROTEIN RES LAB, 73- *Concurrent Pos:* Res fel, Med Sch, Univ Barcelona, 52 & Med Sch, Univ Lund, 53; Fulbright scholar & res fel, Res Div, Cleveland Clin, 55-57; Fulbright scholar, Univ Nice, 80. *Mem:* Am Soc Biol Chemists; Am Chem Soc; Am Physiol Soc; Biophys Soc; Am Soc Clin Invest. *Res:* Structure and function of serum lipoproteins in normal and disease states; lipoprotein cell interactions. *Mailing Add:* Dept Med Box 231 Univ Chicago 950 E 59th St Chicago IL 60637

SCAPINO, ROBERT PETER, b Chicago, Ill, July 20, 36; m 58; c 3. ANATOMY, DENTISTRY. *Educ:* Univ Ill, BS, 59, DDS, 62, MS, 63, PhD(anat), 68. *Prof Exp:* From instr to assoc prof, 65-75, PROF ORAL ANAT, COL DENT, COL MED, UNIV ILL, 75- *Concurrent Pos:* Nat Inst Dent Res fel anat, 62-65. *Mem:* AAAS; Sigma Xi; Am Dent Asn. *Res:* Biomechanics of feeding in carnivores; comparative and human anatomy; function and pathology of jaw joints. *Mailing Add:* Dept of Oral Anat Univ of Ill Col of Dent Chicago IL 60612

SCARBOROUGH, CHARLES SPURGEON, b Goodman, Miss, May 20, 33; m 70. INVERTEBRATE ZOOLOGY, ACAROLOGY. *Educ:* Rust Col, BA, 55; Northwestern Univ, Evanston, MS, 58; Mich State Univ, PhD(zool), 69. *Prof Exp:* Instr bot & zool, Alcorn Agr & Mech Col, 57-59; asst zool, 59-63, from instr to assoc prof natural sci, 63-77, from asst dir resident instr to dir resident instr, 71-77, from asst dean to actg dean, 77-81, PROF NATURAL SCI, MICH STATE UNIV, 77-, DIR, LYMAN BRIGGS SCH, 81- *Mem:* AAAS. *Res:* Free-living mites associated with bracket fungi, their taxonomy and biology. *Mailing Add:* E-28 Holmes Hall Lyman Briggs Sch Mich State Univ East Lansing MI 48823

SCARBOROUGH, CHARLES T, JR, b Dunn, NC, Aug 2, 35; m 59; c 1. MATHEMATICS. *Educ:* Tulane Univ, BS, 59, PhD(math), 64. *Prof Exp:* Asst prof math, Wayne State Univ, 64-66; ASSOC PROF MATH, MISS STATE UNIV, 66- *Mem:* Am Math Soc. *Res:* Minimal topologies and compactifications. *Mailing Add:* Dept of Math Miss State Univ State College MS 39762

SCARBOROUGH, ERNEST N, b Annapolis, Md, May 21, 22; m 44; c 4. AGRICULTURAL ENGINEERING, AUTOMOTIVE ENGINEERING. *Educ:* Iowa State Col, BS, 43, MS, 47. *Prof Exp:* Asst prof agr eng, NC State Col, 48-52; assoc prof, Tenn Polytech Inst, 52-53; sr test engr, Thompson Prod Co, 53-54; prod analyst, 54-55; assoc prof agr eng, 55-70, chmn dept, 68-81, PROF AGR ENG, UNIV DEL, 70- *Honors & Awards:* Award, Christian R & Mary H Lindbach Found, 64. *Mem:* Am Soc Agr Engrs. *Res:* Farm machinery and power; crop processing; environmental control; soil and water conservation. *Mailing Add:* Dept of Agr Eng Univ of Del Newark DE 19711

SCARBOROUGH, GENE ALLEN, b Hugo, Colo, Oct 8, 40; m 66. BIOCHEMISTRY. *Educ:* Univ Ariz, BS, 63; Univ Calif, Los Angeles, PhD(biochem), 66. *Prof Exp:* from asst to assoc prof biochem, Sch Med, Univ Colo, 76-77; ASSOC PROF PHARMACOL, UNIV NC, CHAPEL HILL, 77- *Concurrent Pos:* Whitney fel, Harvard Med Sch, 67-68. *Mem:* AAAS; Am Soc Biol Chemists. *Res:* Phospholipid biosynthesis; structure and function of biomembranes. *Mailing Add:* Dept of Pharmacol Univ NC Chapel Hill NC 27514

SCARDERA, MICHAEL, b Providence, RI, May 11, 35; m 62; c 4. INDUSTRIAL ORGANIC CHEMISTRY. *Educ:* Brown Univ, BS, 57; Univ Bridgeport, MBA, 63. *Prof Exp:* Res chemist fuels res, 57-63, sr res chemist, 64-75, SR RES ASSOC SURFACE ACTIVE AGENTS, OLIN CORP, 76- *Concurrent Pos:* Instr, Southern Conn State Col, 65-75. *Mem:* Sigma Xi; Am Oil Chem Soc; Am Chem Soc. *Res:* Synthesis and application of surface active agents. *Mailing Add:* Olin Corp 275 Winchester Ave New Haven CT 06511

SCARF, FREDERICK LEONARD, b Philadelphia, Pa, July 25, 30; m 53; c 3. THEORETICAL PHYSICS. *Educ:* Temple Univ, AB, 51; Mass Inst Technol, PhD(physics), 55. *Prof Exp:* Res assoc physics, Lab Insulation Res, Mass Inst Technol, 54-56; from asst prof to assoc prof, Univ Wash, 56-62; mgr space physics anal dept, 65-75, physicist, 62-77, mgr space sci dept, 77-81, CHIEF SCIENTIST SPACE RES & TECHNOL, TRW SYSTS, 81- *Concurrent Pos:* NSF fel, Europ Orgn Nuclear Res, Switz, 58-59; consult, Space Tech Labs, Inc, Calif, 60-62; chmn, Nat Acad Sci Panel Int Magnetospheric Study, 73-79; mem bd, Nat Acad Space Sci. *Mem:* Int Sci Radio Union; fel Am Geophys Union. *Res:* Space and plasma physics; principal investigation of wave experiments on NASA missions Voyager 1 & 2, Pioneer Venus, etc.). *Mailing Add:* Bldg R-1 Rm 1176 TRW Systs Redondo Beach CA 90278

SCARFE, COLIN DAVID, b Danbury, Eng, Dec 17, 40; m 67; c 2. ASTRONOMY. *Educ:* Univ BC, BSc, 60, MSc, 61; Cambridge Univ, PhD(astron), 65. *Prof Exp:* Asst prof, 65-71, assoc prof, 71-81, PROF ASTRON, UNIV VICTORIA, BC, 81- *Concurrent Pos:* Sabbatical, Observs, Cambridge, Eng, 71-72, Mt Stromlo Observ, Australia & Mt John Observ, New Zealand, 78-79; vis fel, Mt Stromlo Observ, Australia, 78-79. *Mem:* Am Astron Soc; Royal Astron Soc Can; fel Royal Astron Soc; Can Astron Soc; Astron Soc Pac. *Res:* Spectroscopy and photometry of binary and multiple stars and cepheids. *Mailing Add:* Dept Physics Univ Victoria Victoria BC V8W 2Y2 Can

SCARFONE, LEONARD MICHAEL, b North Adams, Mass, Oct 5, 29; m 55; c 3. PHYSICS. *Educ:* Williams Col, BA, 53, MA, 55; Rensselaer Polytech Inst, PhD(physics), 60. *Prof Exp:* Instr physics, Rensselaer Polytech Inst, 60-61; fel, Fla State Univ, 61-62, asst prof, 62-63; from asst prof to assoc prof, 63-70, PROF PHYSICS, UNIV VT, 70- *Mem:* Am Phys Soc; Am Asn Physics Teachers. *Res:* Quantum field theory; quantum theory of scattering; mathematical physics; elementary particles; theoretical solid state. *Mailing Add:* Cook Phys Sci Univ of Vt Burlington VT 05401

SCARGLE, JEFFREY D, b Evanston, Ill, Nov 24, 41; div; c 2. ASTRONOMY. *Educ:* Pomona Col, BA, 63; Calif Inst Technol, PhD(astron), 68. *Prof Exp:* Fel astron, Univ Calif, Berkeley, 68; instr astron & jr astronr, Univ Calif, Santa Cruz, 68-69, asst prof astron & astrophys, 69-74; RES SCIENTIST, AMES RES CTR, NASA, 75- *Mem:* Am Astron Soc; Int Astron Union. *Res:* Plasma astrophysics; quasars; The Crab Nebula; radiative transfer; statistical analysis of random processes; infrared astronomy; time series analysis; planetary detection astrometry. *Mailing Add:* MS 245-3 NASA Ames Res Ctr Moffett Field CA 94035

SCARINGE, RAYMOND PETER, b Albany, NY, July 31, 50. PHYSICAL INORGANIC CHEMISTRY, X-RAY DIFFRACTION. *Educ:* State Univ NY, Plattsburgh, BA, 72; Univ NC, PhD(inorg chem), 76. *Prof Exp:* Fel chem, Northwestern Univ, 76-78; RES CHEMIST, EASTMAN KODAK CO, 78- *Mem:* Am Chem Soc; Am Crystallog Asn. *Res:* Structural, electrical and magnetic properties in the solid state. *Mailing Add:* Eastman Kodak Co Res Lab Rochester NY 14650

SCARL, DONALD B, b Easton, Pa, Sept 17, 35. PHYSICS. *Educ:* Lehigh Univ, BA, 57; Princeton Univ, PhD(physics), 62. *Prof Exp:* Res assoc physics, NY Univ, 62-63; instr, Cornell Univ, 63-65, instr elec eng, 65-66; from asst prof to assoc prof physics, Polytech Inst Brooklyn, 66-74; ASSOC PROF, POLYTECH INST NY, 74- *Mem:* Am Phys Soc; Optical Soc Am; AAAS. *Res:* Quantum optics, particularly photon correlations and temporal coherence. *Mailing Add:* Dept of Physics Polytech Inst of New York Farmingdale NY 11735

SCARPA, ANTONIO, b Padua, Italy, July 3, 42. BIOCHEMISTRY, BIOPHYSICS. *Educ:* Univ Padua, MD, 66, PhD(gen path), 70. *Prof Exp:* Asst prof gen path, Univ Padua, 69-71; assoc prof biophys, Johnson Found, 73-79, PROF BIOPHYS & BIOCHEM, SCH MED, UNIV PA, 79- *Concurrent Pos:* Nat Res Coun Italy exchange fel biochem, Univ Bristol, 68; Dutch Orgn Advan Pure Res fel biochem, Univ Utrecht, 70; NATO fel, Johnson Found, Univ Pa, 71; estab investr, Am Heart Asn, 73-78; prog chmn, US Bioenergetics Group, Biophys Soc, 74-75; assoc ed, Biophys J; adv bd, Biophys Soc Coun, 79-83. *Mem:* Am Phys Soc; Brit Biochem Soc; Biophys Soc; Am Soc Biol Chem; Soc Gen Physiol. *Res:* Structure and function of biological membranes; ion transport; regulation of contraction of heart muscle; mechanisms secretion. *Mailing Add:* Johnson Res Found & Dept Biophys Univ Pa Sch Med Philadelphia PA 19174

SCARPELLI, DANTE GIOVANNI, b Padua, Italy, Feb 5, 27; nat US; m 51; c 3. EXPERIMENTAL PATHOLOGY. *Educ:* Baldwin-Wallace Col, BS, 50; Ohio State Univ, MS, 53, MD, 54, PhD, 60. *Hon Degrees:* DSc, Baldwin-Wallace Col, 66. *Prof Exp:* From instr to prof path, Ohio State Univ, 58-66; dean fac & acad affairs, Univ Kans Med Ctr, Kansas City, 72-73, prof path & oncol & chmn dept, 66-76; PROF PATH & CHMN DEPT, NORTHWESTERN UNIV MED SCH, CHICAGO, 76- *Honors & Awards:* Silver Medal, Am Soc Clin Path, 56. *Mem:* AAAS; Am Soc Clin Path; Am Asn Path; Histochem Soc; Soc Exp Biol & Med. *Res:* Ultrastructural cytochemistry; carcinogenesis; comparative pathology. *Mailing Add:* 303 E Chicago Ave Chicago IL 60611

SCARPELLI, EMILE MICHAEL, b New York, NY, July 24, 31; m 52; c 7. PEDIATRICS, CARDIOPULMONARY PHYSIOLOGY. *Educ:* Fordham Univ, BS, 51; Duke Univ, MD, 60, PhD(physiol), 62. *Prof Exp:* Instr pediat & physiol, 62-64, res asst prof pediat, 64-66, assoc prof, 68-72, asst prof physiol, 64-71, ASSOC PROF PHYSIOL, ALBERT EINSTEIN COL MED, 71-, PROF PEDIAT, 73-, DIR PEDIAT PULMONARY DIV, 64- *Concurrent Pos:* Res grants, New York Heart Asn, 63-76, John Polachek Found Med Res, 65-66 & NIH career develop award, 66-76; mem, Int Med Comt, Lourdes; Nat Heart & Lung Inst, NIH Prog-Proj, 73-78 & training grant, 75-80. *Mem:* AAAS; Am Physiol Soc; Soc Pediat Res; NY Acad Sci; Am Heart Asn. *Res:* Cardiovascular physiology and disease, including dynamics of cardiac arrhythmias and circulatory shunts; pulmonary physiology and disease, including airway dynamics and the physiology, chemistry and morphology of lung surfactant. *Mailing Add:* Dept of Pediat Albert Einstein Col of Med New York NY 10461

SCARPINO, PASQUALE VALENTINE, b Utica, NY, Feb 13, 32; c 1. ENVIRONMENTAL. *Educ:* Syracuse Univ, BA, 55; Rutgers Univ, MS, 58, PhD(microbiol), 61. *Prof Exp:* USPHS res asst microbiol, Rutgers Univ, 58-61; asst prof biol sci, Fairleigh Dickinson Univ, 61-63; from asst prof to assoc prof environ eng, 63-71, PROF ENVIRON ENG, UNIV CINCINNATI, 71- *Concurrent Pos:* Water pollution control admin, USPHS res award, 65-68; NASA Space Inst grant, Univ Cincinnati, 67-69; Fed Water Pollution Control Admin res contract, 69-71; US Environ Protection Agency grants, 72-82; chmn, Water Subcomt, Environ Task Force, City of Cincinnati, 72-73, Citizen-Scientist Comt Drinking Water Qual & Water Comt Environ Adv Coun, 75-76. *Mem:* Am Water Works Asn; Int Asn Water Pollution Res; Am Soc Microbiol; Sigma Xi; fel Am Soc Microbiol. *Res:* Environmental microbiology; halogen inactivation of viruses in water and waste water; microbial food production; microbial survival in water, landfills and landfill leachates; dissemination of microbes in sewage treatment plant aerosols. *Mailing Add:* Dept of Civil & Environ Eng 721 Rhodes Hall Univ Cincinnati Cincinnati OH 45221

SCARPONE, ANTHONY JOHN, b Newark, NJ, May 10, 31; m 57; c 3. PHARMACY. *Educ:* Rutgers Univ, BS, 53, MS, 64, PhD(pharmaceut chem), 69. *Prof Exp:* Pharmacist in charge, Jennis Drugs, Union, NJ, 57-68; res pharmacist, 68-72, group leader res & develop, Lederle Labs, Div Am Cyanamid Co, 72-78; SECT HEAD PHARMACEUT TECHNOL, SQUIBB INST MED RES, NEW BRUNSWICK, 78- *Mem:* Am Pharmaceut Asn; Acad Pharmaceut Sci; Sigma Xi. *Res:* Development of new pharmaceutical products, specifically tablet dosage forms involving new drug delivery systems and tabletting techniques; air suspension tablet film coating and development of new all aqueous film coating systems. *Mailing Add:* 76 Cannonball Rd Wanaque NJ 07465

SCARRATT, DAVID JOHNSON, b Liverpool, Eng, Dec 21, 35; m 62. MARINE BIOLOGY. *Educ:* Univ Wales, BSc, 58, PhD(marine zool), 61. *Prof Exp:* SCIENTIST, FISHERIES & MARINE SERV, DEPT FISHERIES & OCEANS, 61- *Mem:* Marine Biol Asn UK; Can Soc Zoologists. *Res:* The ecology and behavior of larval, juvenile and adult stages of North American lobster; effects of pollutants; industrial developments and fishing practices on commercial fisheries. *Mailing Add:* Dept Fisheries & Oceans Biol Sta Fisheries & Marine Serv St Andrews NB E0G 2Y0 Can

SCATLIFF, JAMES HOWARD, b Chicago, Ill, July 9, 27; m 61; c 2. RADIOLOGY. *Educ:* Northwestern Univ, BS, 49, MD, 52. *Prof Exp:* Intern, Cook County Hosp, Chicago, 52-53; resident radiol, Michael Reese Hosp, Chicago, 53-56; from instr to assoc prof, Sch Med, Yale Univ, 57-66; PROF RADIOL & CHMN DEPT, SCH MED, UNIV NC, CHAPEL HILL, 66- *Concurrent Pos:* NIH fel neuroradiol, St George's Hosp, London, Eng, 62-63; consult radiologist, Watts Hosp, Durham, NC, 66- *Mem:* AMA; Asn Univ Radiol (pres, 71-72); fel Am Col Radiol; Radiol Soc NAm; Am Soc Neuroradiol. *Res:* Microvasculature, neuroradiology and cardiac radiology. *Mailing Add:* Dept of Radiol Univ of NC Sch of Med Chapel Hill NC 27514

SCATTERDAY, JAMES WARE, b Westerville, Ohio, Dec 10, 35; m 59. GEOLOGY. *Educ:* Denison Univ, BS, 57; Ohio State Univ, PhD(geol), 63. *Prof Exp:* From asst prof to assoc prof geol, 63-70, chmn dept geol sci, 69-77, PROF GEOL, COL ARTS & SCI, STATE UNIV NY COL GENESEO, 70- *Mem:* AAAS; Geol Soc Am; Paleont Soc; Int Palaeont Asn. *Res:* Study of ecology and sediments of recent coral reefs; stratigraphic and conodont biostratigraphic study of the Mississippian System of Ohio; stratigraphic and paleontologic studies of the Silurian and Devonian Systems of New York. *Mailing Add:* Dept of Geol Sci State Univ of NY Col Arts & Sci Geneseo NY 14454

SCATTERGOOD, EDGAR MORRIS, b Philadelphia, Pa, Mar 2, 36; m 65; c 2. CHEMICAL ENGINEERING, BIOCHEMICAL ENGINEERING. *Educ:* Mass Inst Technol, BS, 58; Univ Wis-Madison, PhD(chem eng), 66. *Prof Exp:* Design engr, Standard Oil Co of Calif, 59-61; res asst transport properties ion-exchange membranes, Univ Wis, 62-66; res engr, Gen Mills, Inc, 66-69 & North Star Res & Develop Inst, 69-70; res fel, St Olaf Col, 70-72; chem engr, Calgon Havens Systs, 72-73; RES FEL, MERCK SHARP & DOHME RES LABS, 73- *Mem:* Am Chem Soc; Am Inst Chem Engrs. *Res:* Transport properties of ion-exchange membranes; food processing; membrane processes; artificial biological membranes; mass tissue culture, virology, bacterial fermentation and vaccines. *Mailing Add:* 1375 Steven Lane Lansdale PA 19446

SCATTERGOOD, LESLIE WAYNE, b Seattle, Wash, May 22, 14; m 40; c 4. FISH BIOLOGY. *Educ:* Univ Wash, BS, 36. *Prof Exp:* Aquatic biologist, US Fish & Wildlife Serv, 39-49, fisheries res biologist, 49-58, dir fisheries biol lab, 58-61, chief br of reports, 61-68, chief div publ, 68-70; chief ed br, Nat Oceanic & Atmospheric Admin, 70-71, chief, Sci & Tech Publ Div, 71-80; FISHERY CONSULT, 81- *Concurrent Pos:* Sci asst, Int Pac Salmon Comn, Can, 38; biologist, Wash State Dept Fisheries, 39; local coordr, Off Coord Fisheries, Washington, DC, 43-45; fishery off, Panama, 52-53; Fulbright scholar, Univ Bergen, Norway, 53-54; mem res comt, Int Passamaquoddy Fisheries Bd, 56-59. *Mem:* AAAS; Am Fisheries Soc; Wildlife Soc; Coun Biol Ed; Inst Fishery Res Biol. *Res:* Life history of marine animals; science information. *Mailing Add:* 2514 N 24th St Arlington VA 22207

SCATTERGOOD, RONALD O, b Philadelphia, Pa, June 27, 37; m 66; c 1. METALLURGY. *Educ:* Lehigh Univ, SB, 60; Mass Inst Technol, SM, 63, ScD(metall), 68. *Prof Exp:* Assoc metallurgist, Argonne Nat Lab, 68-81; PROF MAT ENG, NC STATE UNIV, 81- *Mem:* Am Inst Mining, Metall & Petrol Engrs; Am Soc Metals. *Res:* Deformation of metals; dislocation theory; radiation effects. *Mailing Add:* Dept Mat Eng NC State Univ Raleigh NC 27650

SCATURRO, LOUIS S, plasma physics, nuclear fusion, see previous edition

SCAVIA, DONALD, b Schenectady, NY. LIMNOLOGY, MODELING. *Educ:* Rensselaer Polytech Inst, BS, 73, MS, 74; Univ Mich, PhD, 80. *Prof Exp:* Res assoc aquatic modeling, Freshwater Inst, Rensselaer Polytech Inst, 74-75; RES SCIENTIST NUTRIENTS & ECOSYST DYNAMICS, GREAT LAKES ENVIRON RES LAB, NAT OCEANIC & ATMOSPHERIC ADMIN, 75- *Concurrent Pos:* Adj asst prof, Div Biol Sci, Univ Mich, 81- *Mem:* Am Soc Limnol & Oceanog; Int Asn Great Lakes Res; AAAS; Int Soc Ecol Modelling; Soc Int Limnol. *Res:* Investigation of biological, chemical and physical controls of nutrient cycles in the aquatic environment with particular emphasis on the use of models in the analysis; experimental analysis of ecological aspects of phytoplankton and zooplankton interactions in the control of primary production and nutrient cycling. *Mailing Add:* Great Lakes Environ Res Lab 2300 Washtenaw Ave Ann Arbor MI 48104

SCAVUZZO, RUDOLPH J, JR, b Plainfield, NJ, Jan 21, 34; m 55; c 10. MECHANICAL ENGINEERING. *Educ:* Lehigh Univ, BSME, 55; Univ Pittsburgh, MSME, 59, PhD(mech eng), 62. *Prof Exp:* Sr engr, Bettis Atomic Power Lab, Westinghouse Elec Corp, 55-64; asst prof mech eng, Univ Toledo, 64-67, assoc prof, 67-70; assoc prof mech eng, Hartford Grad Ctr, Rensselaer Polytech Inst Conn, Inc, 70-73; PROF MECH ENG & HEAD DEPT, UNIV AKRON, 73- *Concurrent Pos:* Adj instr, Univ Pittsburgh, 63-64. *Mem:* Am Soc Mech Engrs; Am Soc Eng Educ. *Res:* Solid mechanics; mechanical vibrations; dynamic shock analysis. *Mailing Add:* 4366 Shaw Rd Akron OH 44313

SCHAAD, LAWRENCE JOSEPH, b Columbus, Ohio, Sept 23, 30; m 54. PHYSICAL CHEMISTRY. *Educ:* Harvard Univ, AB, 52; Mass Inst Technol, PhD, 57. *Prof Exp:* Res assoc & NIH fel, Math Inst, Oxford Univ, 56-58; res assoc chem, Univ Ind, 59-61; from asst prof to assoc prof, 61-72, PROF CHEM, VANDERBILT UNIV, 72- *Mem:* Am Chem Soc; Am Phys Soc. *Res:* Quantum chemistry. *Mailing Add:* Box 1575 Dept Chem Vanderbilt Univ Nashville TN 37235

SCHAAD, NORMAN W, b Myrtle Point, Ore, Nov 9, 40; m 66; c 2. PLANT PATHOLOGY. *Educ:* Univ Calif, Davis, BS, 64, MS, 66, PhD(plant path), 69. *Prof Exp:* Fel plant path, Univ Calif, Davis, 69-71; asst prof, 71-80, ASSOC PROF PHYTOBACTERIA, TAXON & ECOL, GA EXP STA, UNIV GA, 80- *Mem:* Am Soc Microbiol; Am Phytopath Soc; Int Seed Testing Asn; Int Soc Plant Path. *Res:* Serology of phytobacteria; ecology of phytobacteria; seed pathology. *Mailing Add:* Dept Plant Path Ga Exp Sta Univ Ga Experiment GA 30212

SCHAAF, HERBERT MARTIN, b Deerfield, Kans, June 29, 21; m 51; c 4. AGRONOMY. *Educ:* Kans State Univ, BS, 49; Pa State Univ, MS, 52, PhD(agron), 54. *Prof Exp:* Asst corn breeding, Pa State Univ, 49-54; asst agronomist-in-chg forage grass breeding, Univ Idaho, 54-55; res agronomist, Northern Great Plains Field Sta, Agr Res Serv, USDA, 55-69; res agronomist, 69-71, PROF PLANT BREEDING, NY STATE COL AGR & LIFE SCI, 71- *Mem:* Soc Range Mgt; Am Soc Agron. *Res:* Application of genetic and cytogenetic principles to plant breeding; design, direction and analysis of field, greenhouse and laboratory experiments with perennial range grasses. *Mailing Add:* Dept of Plant Breeding & Biomet Cornell Univ Ithaca NY 14850

SCHAAF, NORMAN GEORGE, b Buffalo, NY, May 29, 36; m 59; c 3. MAXILLOFACIAL PROSTHETICS, PROSTHODONTICS. *Educ:* Univ Buffalo, DDS, 60; Am Bd Prosthodontics, dipl, 71. *Prof Exp:* Resident, Sch Dent, 63-64, instr prosthodontics, 64-65, asst prof, 65-67, assoc prof, 67-74, PROF MAXILLOFACIAL PROSTHETICS, STATE UNIV NY BUFFALO, 74- DIR REGIONAL CTR MAXILLOFACIAL PROSTHETICS, 67-; CHIEF DENT SERV, ROSWELL PARK MEM INST, 68- *Concurrent Pos:* Prosthodontic consult, J Sutton Regan Cleft Palate Found, Children's Hosp, Buffalo, 63-, asst attend, hosp, 65-; prosthodontic consult, Erie County Health Dept, NY State Medicaid Prog, 67-70; univ assoc, Buffalo Gen Hosp, 73-; maxillofacial prosthodontic consult, Buffalo Vet Hosp, 74- *Mem:* Am Cleft Palate Asn. *Res:* Anatomic, functional and cosmetic reconstruction, by the use of non-living substitutes, of those regions of the head and neck that are missing or defective whether from congenital anomaly, injury or disease. *Mailing Add:* Dept Dent Maxillofacial Prosthet Roswell Park Mem Inst Buffalo NY 14263

SCHAAF, ROBERT LESTER, b Baptistown, NJ, June 17, 29. ORGANIC CHEMISTRY. *Educ:* Rutgers Univ, BS, 50; Univ Mich, MS, 52, PhD(pharmaceut chem), 55. *Prof Exp:* From res chemist to sr res chemist, 55-67; res assoc, 67-77, SR RES STAFF MEM, BASF WYANDOTTE CORP, 77- *Mem:* Am Chem Soc. *Mailing Add:* BASF Wyandotte Corp Wyandotte MI 48192

SCHAAF, SAMUEL A(LBERT), b Ft Wayne, Ind, Jan 26, 18; m 43; c 1. MATHEMATICS, ENGINEERING. *Educ:* Univ Calif, AB, 39, PhD(math), 44. *Prof Exp:* Instr math, Univ Calif, 44-45; res mathematician, NY Univ, 45-47; lectr math, 46-47; asst prof mech eng, 47-51, assoc prof eng sci, 51-57; res engr, 47-51, chmn div aeronaut sci, 57-60, chmn dept mech eng, 60-65, chmn econ opportunity orgn, 64-65, prof exp col prog letters & sci, 65-67, chmn eng sci prog, 71-78, assoc dean, Col Eng, 76-78, prof eng sci, 57-80, dir low pressure proj, 51-80, PROF MECH ENG, UNIV CALIF, BERKELEY, 80-, PRES BD EDUC, 64- *Concurrent Pos:* Consult mem, Comt Reentry, Nat Adv Comt Aeronaut, 58 & adv comt fluid mech, NASA, 59-64; mem sci adv panel, Vidya Corp, 59-65; mem hypersonics adv comt, Aeronaut Res Lab, Wright Air Develop Ctr, 60-64. *Mem:* Am Math Soc; fel Am Phys Soc. *Res:* Rarefied gas dynamics; fluid mechanics; heat conduction; mechanics of combustion; mathematical analysis. *Mailing Add:* Col of Eng Univ of Calif Berkeley CA 94720

SCHAAF, THOMAS KEN, b Louisville, Ky, July 17, 43; m 67; c 3. MEDICINAL CHEMISTRY. *Educ:* Kalamazoo Col, BA, 65; Stanford Univ, PhD(chem), 69. *Prof Exp:* Res fel, Harvard Univ, 69-70; res chemist, 70-74, proj leader, 74-76, mgr, 76-81, ASST DIR, MED CHEM LAB, PFIZER INC, 81- *Mem:* NY Acad Sci; Am Chem Soc. *Res:* Synthesis of prostaglandins and agents for treatment of pulmonary, inflammatory and gastrointestinal diseases, cancer and diabetes. *Mailing Add:* Med Res Lab Pfizer Inc Groton CT 06340

SCHAAF, WILLIAM EDWARD, b Martins Ferry, Ohio, Aug 9, 38; m 61; c 3. FISHERIES RESOURCE MODELING. *Educ:* Duke Univ, BS, 61; Univ NC, MS, 63; Univ Mich, PhD(fisheries), 72. *Prof Exp:* Biostatistician, NIH, 63-66; biometrician, Inst Fisheries Res, Mich Dept Natural Resources, 66-69; BIOMETRICIAN, NAT MARINE FISHERIES SERV, DEPT COMMMERCE, 69- *Mem:* Am Statist Asn; Am Fisheries Soc. *Res:* Modeling the population dynamics of exploited marine fishes, emphasizing optimal management strategies; developing ecosystem models of multi-species fisheries; investigation impacts of environmental variability, and life history strategies on expected yields. *Mailing Add:* PO Box 54 Gloucester NC 28528

SCHAAL, BARBARA ANNA, b Berlin, Ger, Sept 17, 47; US citizen. POPULATION BIOLOGY. *Educ:* Univ Ill, Chicago, BS, 69; Yale Univ, MPhil, 71, PhD(pop biol), 74. *Prof Exp:* asst prof, Univ Houston, 74-76; ASST PROF BOTANY, OHIO STATE UNIV, 76- *Mem:* AAAS; Genetics Soc Am; Am Soc Plant Taxonomists; Brit Ecol Soc; Ecol Soc. *Res:* Genetic structure of outbreeding plant population; plant demographic genetics. *Mailing Add:* Dept of Botany Ohio State Univ Columbus OH 43210

SCHAAP, ARTHUR PAUL, b Scottsburg, Ind, June 4, 45. ORGANIC CHEMISTRY. *Educ:* Hope Col, AB, 67; Harvard Univ, PhD(org chem), 70. *Prof Exp:* Asst prof, 70-74, ASSOC PROF CHEM, WAYNE STATE UNIV, 74- *Concurrent Pos:* Alfred P Sloan Res Fel, 74-76. *Mem:* Am Chem Soc; Royal Soc Chem. *Res:* Photo-oxidation; chemistry of singlet oxygen; chemiluminescence; photochemistry. *Mailing Add:* Dept of Chem Wayne State Univ Detroit MI 48202

SCHAAP, LUKE ANTHONY, b South Holland, Ill, Nov 11, 31; m 59; c 4. ORGANIC CHEMISTRY. *Educ:* Calvin Col, AB, 53; Northwestern Univ, PhD(org chem), 57. *Prof Exp:* Asst, Northwestern Univ, 53-54; res chemist, Am Oil Co, Whiting, Ind, 57-74; RES CHEMIST, RES CTR, AMOCO OIL CO, 74- *Concurrent Pos:* Instr, Trinity Christian Col, 64-65. *Mem:* Am Chem Soc; Am Sci Affiliation; Am Soc Lubrication Engrs; Soc Automotive Engrs. *Res:* Base catalyzed reactions of hydrocarbons; high pressure and petroleum chemistry; olefin hydration; chemistry of nitrogen fluorides; lubricant research and development. *Mailing Add:* 463 E 163rd St South Holland IL 60473

SCHAAP, WARD BEECHER, b Holland, Mich, Sept 15, 23; m 44; c 3. INORGANIC CHEMISTRY, ANALYTICAL CHEMISTRY. *Educ:* Wheaton Col, Ill, BS, 44; Univ Ill, MS, 48, PhD(inorg chem), 50. *Prof Exp:* Anal chemist, Metall Lab, Univ Chicago, 44; res chemist, Manhattan Proj, Oak Ridge Nat Lab, 44-47; from instr to assoc prof chem, 50-63, assoc dean, Col Arts & Sci, 66-71, assoc dean, Res & Develop, 71-73, actg vchancellor admin & budgetary planning, 73-76, PROF CHEM, IND UNIV, BLOOMINGTON, 63-, DEAN ADMIN & BUDGETARY PLANNING, 76- *Concurrent Pos:* Consult, Union Carbide Nuclear Corp, 56- & E I du Pont de Nemours & Co, 58-60; NSF fel, Univ Calif, 60-61. *Mem:* Am Chem Soc. *Res:* Metal chelate compounds; polarography; electrochemistry in nonaqueous solvents; kinetics of inorganic reactions. *Mailing Add:* Dept of Chem Ind Univ Bloomington IN 47401

SCHABEL, FRANK MILTON, JR, b Great Falls, Mont, June 22, 18; m 42; c 2. CHEMOTHERAPY. *Educ:* Univ Wash, BS, 39; Univ Chicago, PhD(bact), 50; Am Bd Microbiol, dipl. *Prof Exp:* Virologist, Poliomyelitis Proj, Univ Chicago & Chicago Health Dept, 46-50; PROF MICROBIOL, SCH MED, UNIV ALA, BIRMINGHAM, 50-, ASSOC PROF EXP PATH, 68-, CLIN PROF MED, 72-; DIR CHEMOTHER RES, SOUTHERN RES INST, 51- *Concurrent Pos:* Microbiologist, Baptist Hosps, Birmingham, Ala, 50-71; mem drug eval panel, Cancer Chemother Nat Serv Ctr, Nat Cancer Inst, 60-62, mem acute leukemia task force, 67-69 & bd sci counrs, Div Cancer Treatment, 74-78; assoc ed, Cancer Res, 74-81; consult tumor therapy, Dept Develop Therapeut, Univ Tex M D Anderson Hosp & Tumor Inst, Houston, 76-; Fulbright-Hays sr lectr, Inst Jules Bordet, Brussels, 81. *Mem:* Fel AAAS; fel Am Pub Health Asn; fel Am Acad Microbiol; fel NY Acad Sci; Am Asn Cancer Res. *Res:* Experimental cancer chemotherapy; virus and bacterial chemotherapy; tumor biology; neurotropic viruses. *Mailing Add:* Southern Res Inst 2000 Ninth Ave S Birmingham AL 35205

SCHABER, GERALD GENE, b Covington, Ky, May 29, 38; m 61; c 3. GEOLOGY, ASTROGEOLOGY. *Educ:* Univ Ky, BS; Univ Cincinnati, MS, 62, PhD(geol), 65. *Prof Exp:* GEOLOGIST LUNAR & PLANETARY EXPLOR RES, FLAGSTAFF FIELD CTR, US GEOL SURV, 65- *Honors & Awards:* Spec Commendation for Apollo Astronaut Training, Geol Soc Am, 73; Group Achievement Award for Apollo Traverse Planning, NASA, 71. *Res:* Lunar and planetary geologic mapping; terrestrial, lunar and planetary remote sensing; geochemistry; terrestrial and planetary radar research. *Mailing Add:* Ctr of Astrogeol US Geol Surv 2255 N Gemini Drive Ave Flagstaff AZ 86001

SCHACHER, GORDON EVERETT, b Portland, Ore, Aug 24, 35; m 79; c 6. ATMOSPHERIC SCIENCES, SOLID STATE PHYSICS. *Educ:* Reed Col, AB, 56; Rutgers Univ, PhD(physics), 61. *Prof Exp:* Instr physics, Rutgers Univ, 60-61; fel, Argonne Nat Lab, Ill, 61-64; asst prof, 64-74, assoc prof, 77-80, PROF PHYSICS, NAVAL POSTGRAD SCH, 80- *Mem:* Am Phys Soc; Am Asn Physics Teachers; Sigma Xi; Soc Photo-optical Instrumentation Engrs. *Res:* Marine atmospheric boundary layer processes; electromagnetic propagation in the atmosphere; transport and dispersion. *Mailing Add:* Dept of Physics Naval Postgrad Sch Monterey CA 93940

SCHACHER, JOHN FREDRICK, b Jamestown, NDak, July 17, 28; m 52; c 3. PARASITOLOGY, INFECTIOUS DISEASES. *Educ:* NDak State Univ, BS, 53; Tulane Univ, MS, 56, PhD(parasitol), 61. *Prof Exp:* Tulane Univ prof asst parasitol, Univ Malaya, Singapore, 56-58; from asst prof to assoc prof trop dis, Am Univ Beirut, 60-69; assoc prof, 69-72, PROF INFECTIOUS TROP DIS & EPIDEMIOL, UNIV CALIF, LOS ANGELES, 72-, ASST DEAN ACAD AFFAIRS, 80- *Concurrent Pos:* NIH res grant, Am Univ Beirut & Univ Calif, Los Angeles, 63-76; Interam fel trop med, La State Univ, 66; consult, La Fisheries & Wildlife Comn, 54-55; mem expert comt filariasis, WHO, 73-, mem sci tech comt onchocerciasis control, 74- *Mem:* Int Filariasis Asn; Am Soc Parasitol; Am Soc Trop Med & Hyg; Royal Soc Trop Med & Hyg; Malaysian Soc Parasitol Trop Med. *Res:* Parasitology, especially helminthology, filariasis; host-parasite relations and pathology, taxonomy and identification of parasites in tissue. *Mailing Add:* Dept of Pub Health Univ of Calif Los Angeles CA 90024

SCHACHMAN, HOWARD KAPNEK, b Philadelphia, Pa, Dec 5, 18; m 45; c 2. MOLECULAR BIOLOGY, BIOCHEMISTRY. *Educ:* Mass Inst Technol, BS, 39; Princeton Univ, PhD(phys chem). *Hon Degrees:* DSc, Northwestern Univ, 74. 48. *Prof Exp:* Chem engr, Continental Distilling Corp, Pa, 39-40; tech asst, Rockefeller Inst, 41-44; from instr to assoc prof biochem, 48-59, PROF BIOCHEM & MOLECULAR BIOL, UNIV CALIF, BERKELEY, 59-, CHMN, DEPT MOLECULAR BIOL & DIR, VIRUS LAB, 69- *Concurrent Pos:* Guggenheim fel, 57-58; Fogarty Int Sch, NIH, 77-78. *Honors & Awards:* E H Sargent & Co Award, Am Chem Soc, 62; Warren prize, Mass Gen Hosp, 65. *Mem:* Nat Acad Sci; Sigma Xi; Am Chem Soc; Am Soc Biol Chem; Am Acad Arts & Sci. *Res:* Physical chemistry of macromolecules of biological interest; structure, function and interactions of proteins, nucleic acids and viruses; development and application of the ultracentrifuge. *Mailing Add:* Dept of Molecular Biol & Virus Lab Stanley Hall Univ of Calif Berkeley CA 94720

SCHACHT, JOCHEN (HEINRICH), b Konigsberg, Ger, July 2, 39; m 67; c 2. NEUROCHEMISTRY. *Educ:* Univ Bonn, BS, 62; Univ Heidelberg, MS, 65, PhD(biochem), 68. *Prof Exp:* Asst res biochemist, 69-72, asst prof, 73-78, ASSOC PROF BIOL CHEM OTORHINOL, KRESGE HEARING RES INST, UNIV MICH, 78- *Concurrent Pos:* Fogarty Int fel, 79-80; vis prof, Dept Otolaryngol, Karolinska Inst, Stockholm, Sweden, 79- *Mem:* Ger Soc Biol Chem; Am Soc Biol Chemists; Soc Neurosci; Asn Res Otolaryngol; Int Soc Neurochem. *Res:* Biochemistry of hearing and deafness; metabolism and function of phospholipids. *Mailing Add:* Kresge Hearing Res Inst Univ Mich Ann Arbor MI 48109

SCHACHT, LEE EASTMAN, b Detroit, Mich, Sept 13, 30. HUMAN GENETICS. *Educ:* Dartmouth Col, AB, 52; Univ NC, MA, 55, PhD(zool), 57. *Prof Exp:* Instr human genetics, Univ Mich, 57-60; SUPVR HUMAN GENETICS UNIT, STATE DEPT HEALTH, MINN, 60- *Concurrent Pos:* Lectr, Sch Pub Health, Univ Minn, 64-74; adj asst prof, 74-76; adj assoc prof, 76- *Mem:* Am Soc Human Genetics. *Res:* Genetics in public health; genetic counseling. *Mailing Add:* Minn Dept Health 717 Delaware SE Mineapolis MN 55440

SCHACHTELE, CHARLES FRANCIS, b Kearny, NJ, May 3, 42. DENTAL RESEARCH, MICROBIOLOGY. *Educ:* Macalester Col, BA, 63; Univ Minn, Minneapolis, MS, 65, PhD(microbiol), 68. *Prof Exp:* Asst prof, 68-72, assoc prof, 72-78, assoc prof microbiol, 74-78, PROF DENT, SCH DENT, UNIV MINN, MINNEAPOLIS, 78- PROF MICROBIOL, 78- *Concurrent Pos:* USPHS res career develop award, 71. *Mem:* AAAS; Am Soc Microbiol; Int Asn Dent Res. *Res:* Dental caries and periodontal disease. *Mailing Add:* Sch of Dent Univ of Minn Minneapolis MN 55455

SCHACHTER, DAVID, b New York, NY, Oct 29, 27; m 56. MEDICINE. *Educ:* NY Univ, BS, 46, MD, 49; Am Bd Internal Med, dipl, 55. *Prof Exp:* From asst prof to assoc prof med, 57-69, PROF PHYSIOL, COL PHYSICIANS & SURGEONS, COLUMBIA UNIV, 69- *Mem:* AAAS; Soc Exp Biol & Med; Am Soc Clin Invest; Am Gastroenterol Asn; Am Physiol Soc. *Res:* Calcium transport and metabolism; membrane function and organization; active transport mechanisms. *Mailing Add:* Col of Physicians & Surgeons Columbia Univ New York NY 10032

SCHACHTER, H, b Vienna, Austria, Feb 25, 33; Can citizen; m 58; c 2. BIOCHEMISTRY. *Educ:* Univ Toronto, BA, 55, MD, 59, PhD(biochem), 64. *Prof Exp:* From asst prof to assoc prof, 64-70, PROF BIOCHEM, UNIV TORONTO, 70- *Concurrent Pos:* Cystic Fibrosis Res Found fel, 66-68; head res div, Dept Biochem, Hosp Sick Children. *Mem:* Am Soc Biol Chem; Can Biochem Soc; UK Biochem Soc; Soc Complex Carbohydrates. *Res:* Glycoprotein biosynthesis and metabolism; differentiation. *Mailing Add:* 555 University Ave Toronto ON 5MG 1X8 Can

SCHACHTER, JOSEPH, b New York, NY, Aug 26, 25; m 49; c 1. PSYCHIATRY. *Educ:* Dartmouth Col, AB, 46; Harvard Univ, PhD, 55; NY Univ, MD, 52. *Prof Exp:* Res assoc psychiat, Col Physicians & Surgeons, Columbia Univ, 56-60, asst clin prof, Univ & Columbia Psychoanal Clin Training & Res, 60-68, dir postdoctoral res training prog, 65-68; dir res child psychiat, 68-74, assoc prof, 68-76, RES ASSOC PROF PSYCHIAT, SCH MED, UNIV PITTSBURGH, 76-, RES ASSOC PROF EPIDEMIOL, GRAD SCH PUB HEALTH, 78- *Concurrent Pos:* Found Fund Res Psychiat fel, Columbia Univ & NY State Psychiat Inst, 55-56; pres, Pittsburgh Psychoanal Ctr, 78-80. *Mem:* Am Psychosom Soc; Am Psychiat Asn; Am Psychoanal Asn; Soc Psychophysiol Res; Am Fedn Clin Res. *Res:* Schizophrenic disorders; infant and child development; hypertension; cardiovascular development. *Mailing Add:* 5400 Darlington Rd Pittsburgh PA 15217

SCHACHTER, JULIUS, b New York, NY, June 1, 36; m 62; c 2. BACTERIOLOGY. *Educ:* Columbia Col, BA, 57; Hunter Col, MA, 60; Univ Calif, PhD(bact), 65. *Prof Exp:* Grad res microbiol, 60-65, asst res microbiologist, 65-68, from asst prof to assoc prof epidemiol & med, 68-75, asst dir, G W Hooper Found, 72-76, actg dir, 77-81, PROF EPIDEMIOL, UNIV CALIF, SAN FRANCISCO, 75-, PROF LAB MED, 80- *Concurrent Pos:* Mem viral & rickettsial registry comt, Am Type Cult Collection; co-dir, Collab Centre Reference & Res on Trachoma & Other Chlamydial Infections, WHO, 72-77, dir, 77- *Mem:* Infectious Dis Soc Am; Am Soc Microbiol; Soc Exp Biol & Med; Am Venereal Dis Asn. *Res:* Chlamydial infections, including psittacosis, trachoma, inclusion conjunctivitis, lymphogranuloma venereum, venereal diseases and perinatal infection; microbiology; epidemiology; host-parasite relationships. *Mailing Add:* Dept Lab Med Univ of Calif San Francisco CA 94143

SCHACHTER, MELVILLE, b Sept 22, 20; Can citizen; m 44; c 3. PHYSIOLOGY. *Educ:* McGill Univ, BSc, 41, MSc, 42, MD, 46. *Prof Exp:* Asst prof physiol, Dalhousie Univ, 47-50; staff mem, Nat Inst Med Res, London, 50-53; reader, Univ Col, Univ London, 53-65; PROF PHYSIOL & HEAD DEPT, UNIV ALTA, 65- *Concurrent Pos:* Consult, Parke, Davis &

Co, 60-65; vis prof, Stanford Univ, 71. *Mem:* Brit Physiol Soc; Brit Pharmacol Soc; Brit Soc Immunol; Can Physiol Soc; Can Pharmacol Soc. *Res:* Autopharmacology. *Mailing Add:* Dept of Physiol Univ of Alberta Edmonton AB T6G 2N7 Can

SCHACH VON WITTENAU, MANFRED, b Pennekow, Ger, June 19, 30; m 55; c 3. ORGANIC CHEMISTRY, DRUG METABOLISM. *Educ:* Univ Heidelberg, BS, 52, MS, 55, PhD(org chem), 57. *Prof Exp:* Fel, Mass Inst Technol, 57-58; res chemist, 58-64, group supvr drug metab, 64-67, mgr drug metab, 67-71, from asst dir to dir, Dept Drug Metab, 71-74, exec dir, Safety Eval & Drug Metab, 74-81, VPRES SAFETY EVAL, PFIZER, INC, 81- *Mem:* Am Chem Soc; Soc Ger Chem; Am Soc Pharmacol & Exp Therapeut. *Res:* Medicinal chemistry; analytical chemistry; toxicology. *Mailing Add:* Pfizer Inc Cent Res Eastern Point Rd Groton CT 06340

SCHACK, CARL J, b St Louis, Mo, Dec 26, 36; m 59; c 2. INORGANIC CHEMISTRY. *Educ:* St Louis Univ, BSChem, 58; Polytech Inst Brooklyn, PhD(inorg chem), 64. *Prof Exp:* Sr res engr, 64-68, MEM TECH STAFF, ROCKETDYNE DIV, N AM ROCKWELL CORP, 68- *Mem:* Am Chem Soc; The Chem Soc. *Res:* Fluorine chemistry; synthesis and material characterization of inorganic oxidizers, fluorine compounds including fluorocarbons and boron-nitrogen species. *Mailing Add:* Rocketdyne Div Rockwell Int Corp 6633 Canoga Ave Canoga Park CA 91304

SCHACTER, BERNICE ZELDIN, b Philadelphia, Pa, June 20, 43; m 68; c 2. IMMUNOGENETICS. *Educ:* Bryn Mawr Col, AB, 65; Brandeis Univ, PhD(biol), 70. *Prof Exp:* Charles F Kettering fel photosynthetic membrane, Lawrence Berkeley Lab, 70-71, res chemist, 71; Fla Heart Asn fel, Sch Med, Univ Miami, 72, instr pharmacol of cell membranes, 72-73; fel tumor cell membrane immunol, Oncol Ctr, Johns Hopkins Univ, 73-74, instr med & oncol, Sch Med, 74-76; mem staff, Dept Immunopath, Cleveland Clin, 76-77; ASST PROF EXP PATH, CASE WESTERN RESERVE UNIV, 77- *Mem:* Am Asn Immunologists; Am Soc Human Genetics; Am Asn Clin Histocompatibility Testing. *Res:* Human immunogenetics of transplantation antigens, tumor specific antigens of human leukemia. *Mailing Add:* Inst of Path Case Western Reserve Univ Cleveland OH 44106

SCHACTER, BRENT ALLAN, b Winnipeg, Man, June 1, 42; m 81; c 2. MEDICAL RESEARCH, HEMATOLOGY. *Educ:* Univ Man, BSc & MD, 65; FRCP(C), 71. *Prof Exp:* asst prof, 72-77, ASSOC PROF INTERNAL MED, UNIV MAN, 77- *Concurrent Pos:* Fel, Med Res Coun Can, 70-72, scholar, 75-80. *Mem:* Am Soc Clin Oncol; Am Fedn Clin Res; Can Soc Clin Invest; Am Soc Hemat; Am Asn Study Liver Dis. *Res:* Investigation of the mechanism of action of heme oxygenase and the nature of the regulation of heme catabolism by this enzyme. *Mailing Add:* Dept of Internal Med Univ of Man Winnipeg MB R3T 2N2 Can

SCHAD, GERHARD ADAM, b Brooklyn, NY, Apr 2, 28; m 53; c 2. PARASITOLOGY. *Educ:* Cornell Univ, BS, 50; McGill Univ, MSc, 52, PhD(parasitol), 55. *Hon Degrees:* Dr sci, Univ Pa, 75. *Prof Exp:* Scripps res fel, Biol Res Inst, San Diego Zool Soc, 53; parasitologist, USDA, 55-58; asst prof parasitol, Inst Parasitol, Macdonald Col, McGill Univ, 58-64; from asst prof to assoc prof pathobiol, Johns Hopkins Univ, 64-73; prin investr parasitol, 72-79, assoc prof, 73-77, PROF PATHOBIOL, SCH VET MED, UNIV PA, 77-, HEAD, LAB PARASITOL, 74-, CHMN, GRAD GROUP PARASITOL, 78- *Concurrent Pos:* Prin investr parasitol, Johns Hopkins Univ Ctr Med Res & Training, Calcutta, 64-66 & 68-70, NIH, 79-81, WHO, 79-81 & USDA, 81-; mem, Nat Selection Comt, US Educ Found, India, 68-69. *Mem:* AAAS; Am Soc Nat; Am Soc Trop Med & Hyg; Royal Soc Trop Med & Hyg; Am Soc Parasitol. *Res:* Population ecology of parasitic helminths; systematics; evolution and biology of parasitic helminths. *Mailing Add:* Dept Pathobiol Sch Vet Med Univ Pa Philadelphia PA 19104

SCHAD, THEODORE M(ACNEEVE), b Baltimore, Md, Aug 25, 18; m 44; c 2. CIVIL ENGINEERING, HYDROLOGY. *Educ:* Johns Hopkins Univ, BE, 39. *Prof Exp:* Eng aide, US Army Corps Engrs, Md, 39-40, chief specifications sect, Wash, 42-45, engr, 45-46; jr engr, US Bur Reclamation, Colo, 40-42, engr, 46-49, chief coord plans sect, 50-51, asst chief prog coord div, 51-54; budget exam, US Bur Budget, 54-58; sr specialist eng & pub works, Legis Ref Serv, Libr Cong, 58-68, actg chief sci policy res div, 66-67, dep dir, 67-68; exec dir, US Nat Water Comn, 69-73; exec secy, Environ Studies Bd, 73-77, DEP EXEC DIR, COMN NATURAL RESOURCES, NAT RES COUN, 77- *Concurrent Pos:* Staff dir, Select Comt Nat Water Resources, US Senate, 59-61; consult, Comt Interior & Insular Affairs, 63, Comt Water Resources Res, Fed Coun Sci & Tech, 62, Comt Sci & Astron, House of Rep, 63-64, Off Saline Water, 64-67 & A T Kearney, Inc, 79-80; mem US comt large dams, Int Comn Large Dams, 64-; mem permanent int comn, Permanent Int Asn Navig Cong, 63-70; vis fel, Woodrow Wilson Nat Fel Found, 78-81. *Honors & Awards:* Icko Iben Award, Am Water Resources Asn. *Mem:* Fel Am Soc Civil Engrs; Am Geophys Union; Nat Speleol Soc; hon mem Am Water Works Asn; Am Acad Environ Engrs. *Res:* Water resources policy; federal policies and programs; water resources research; environmental policy. *Mailing Add:* 4138 26th Rd N Arlington VA 22207

SCHADE, HENRY A(DRIAN), b St Paul, Minn, Dec 3, 00; m 25; c 2. NAVAL ARCHITECTURE. *Educ:* US Naval Acad, BS, 23; Mass Inst Technol, SM, 28; Tech Univ Berlin, Dr Ing, 37. *Hon Degrees:* Dr Ing, Tech Univ Berlin, 72. *Prof Exp:* Chief tech mission, US Navy, Europe, 45, dir, Naval Res Lab, 46-49; prof naval archit, 49-69, EMER PROF NAVAL ARCHIT, UNIV CALIF, BERKELEY, 69- *Honors & Awards:* David Taylor Gold Medal, Soc Naval Archit & Marine Engrs, 64; Gibbs Bros Medal, Nat Acad Sci, 71. *Mem:* Soc Naval Archit & Marine Engrs (vpres, 65). *Res:* Ship structure design. *Mailing Add:* Col of Eng Univ of Calif Berkeley CA 94704

SCHADLER, DANIEL LEO, b Dayton, Ky, Apr 5, 48. PLANT PATHOLOGY, BIOCHEMISTRY. *Educ:* Thomas More Col, AB, 70; Cornell Univ, MS, 72, PhD(plant path), 74. *Prof Exp:* Res assoc, Univ Wis, 74-75; asst prof, 75-79, ASSOC PROF BIOL, OGLETHORPE UNIV, 79- *Mem:* Am Phytopath Soc; Int Soc Plant Path; Am Chem Soc. *Res:* Physiology and biochemistry of plant disease and of plant pathogens, especially phytotoxins. *Mailing Add:* Dept of Biol 4484 Peachtree Rd NE Atlanta GA 30319

SCHADLER, HARVEY W(ALTER), b Cincinnati, Ohio, Jan 4, 31; m 54; c 3. METALLURGY. *Educ:* Cornell Univ, BMetE, 54; Purdue Univ, PhD, 57. *Prof Exp:* Metallurgist, Res Labs, 57-69, mgr surfaces & reactions br, 69-71, mgr phys metall br, 71-73, MGR, METALL LAB, GEN ELEC CO, 73- *Honors & Awards:* Geisler Award, Am Soc Metals. *Mem:* Fel Am Soc Metals; Am Inst Mining, Metall & Petrol Engrs. *Res:* Physical metallurgy; brittle fracture; diffusion; crystall perfection; plastic deformation; superconductivity. *Mailing Add:* Gen Elec Co R&D Ctr Metall Lab PO Box 8 Schenectady NY 12301

SCHADT, FRANK LEONARD, III, b Syracuse, NY, Feb 3, 47. ORGANIC CHEMISTRY. *Educ:* Le Moyne Col, BS, 68; Princeton Univ, MA, 71, PhD(chem), 74. *Prof Exp:* Res chemist, 74-80, SR RES CHEMIST, PHOTOPROD DEPT, E I DU PONT DE NEMOURS & CO INC, 80- *Mem:* Am Chem Soc; Sigma Xi. *Res:* Mechanistic organic chemistry; factors affecting substitution reactions at carbon; photochemically induced polymerization and rearrangement; photographic chemistry; organic synthesis; synthesis of specialized polymers; electrically conductive coatings. *Mailing Add:* 7 Rockford Rd F22 Wilmington DE 19806

SCHAECHTER, MOSELIO, b Milan, Italy, Apr 26, 28; US citizen; m 53; c 2. MICROBIOLOGY, MOLECULAR BIOLOGY. *Educ:* Univ Kans, MA, 51; Univ Pa, PhD(microbiol), 54. *Prof Exp:* From instr to assoc prof microbiol, Univ Fla, 58-62; assoc prof, 62-65, PROF MICROBIOL, TUFTS UNIV, 65-, CHMN DEPT, 70- *Concurrent Pos:* Am Cancer Soc grant, State Serum Inc, Copenhagen, Denmark, 56-58; mem bact & mycol study sect, NIH, 75-79, chmn, 78-79. *Mem:* Am Soc Microbiol. *Res:* Regulatory aspects of structural organization in bacteria and bacteriophages. *Mailing Add:* Dept of Molecular Biol Tufts Univ Med Sch Boston MA 02111

SCHAEDLE, MICHAIL, b Tallinn, Estonia, Dec 27, 27; US citizen; m 66. PLANT PHYSIOLOGY. *Educ:* Univ BC, BSA, 57, MSA, 59; Univ Calif, Berkeley, PhD(plant physiol), 64. *Prof Exp:* Fel, Univ Calif, Berkeley, 64-65; asst prof, 65-71, assoc prof, 71-81, PROF BOT, STATE UNIV NY COL ENVIRON SCI & FORESTRY, 81- *Mem:* AAAS; Am Inst Biol Sci; Am Soc Plant Physiol. *Res:* Ion transport and cell permeability; photosynthesis in tissues of perennial plants; plant nutrition; calcium and aluminum problems. *Mailing Add:* 111 Warwick Rd Dewitt NY 13214

SCHAEDLER, RUSSELL WILLIAM, b Hatfield, Pa, Dec 17, 27. MEDICINE, MICROBIOLOGY. *Educ:* Ursinus Col, BS, 49; Jefferson Med Col, MD, 53. *Prof Exp:* Intern hosp, Jefferson Med Col, 53-54; asst & asst physician med & microbiol, Rockefeller Univ, 54-57, asst prof & resident assoc physician, 57-61, assoc prof & physician, 61-68; PROF MICROBIOL & CHMN DEPT, JEFFERSON MED COL, 68- *Mem:* Harvey Soc; Am Soc Microbiol; Am Gastroenterol Asn; Infectious Dis Soc Am; Am Asn Immunol. *Res:* Influence of environmental factors and nutrition on host resistance; ecology of the flora of the digestive tract and diarrheal diseases. *Mailing Add:* Dept of Microbiol Jefferson Med Col Philadelphia PA 19107

SCHAEFER, ALBERT RUSSELL, b Oklahoma City, Okla, Oct 13, 44; m 68. RADIOMETRIC PHYSICS, OPTICAL DETECTORS. *Educ:* Univ Okla, BS, 66, PhD(physics), 70. *Prof Exp:* PHYSICIST, OPTICAL RADIATION SECT, NAT BUR STAND, 70- *Concurrent Pos:* Instr, Montgomery Col, 74-77, adj prof, 78- *Honors & Awards:* Bronze Medal, Dept Com, 81. *Mem:* Am Phys Soc; Optical Soc Am. *Res:* Transition probabilities; radiometric physics; electro-optic devices; lifetimes; radiometry; photometry; spectroscopy; silicon detectors. astrophysics. *Mailing Add:* B-306-MET Nat Bur of Stand Washington DC 20234

SCHAEFER, ARNOLD EDWARD, b Tripp, SDak, Dec 8, 17; m 42; c 3. NUTRITION. *Educ:* SDak State Col, BS, 39; Univ Wis, MS, 41, PhD(biochem), 47. *Prof Exp:* Asst, Exp Sta, SDak State Col, 39-40; asst biochem, Univ Wis, 40-41, asst animal nutrit, 46-47, instr, 47; assoc animal nutrit, Ala Polytech Inst, 47-51; head nutrit res dept, E R Squibb & Sons, 51-55; biochemist, Interdept Comt Nutrit for Nat Defense, NIH, 55-56, exec dir, 56-64, Off Int Res, 64-67, chief nutrit prog, Health Serv & Ment Health Admin, 67-71; consult nutrit surveillance, Pan Am Health Orgn, 71-73; DIR, SWANSON CTR NUTRIT, UNIV NEBR MED CTR, OMAHA, 73- *Concurrent Pos:* Mem interdept ad hoc adv group res & develop food for shelters, Off Civil & Defense Mobilization, UN; mem interdept group freedom from hunger, Food & Agr Orgn; mem US comt, Int Union Nutrit Sci; pres, Fedn Am Socs Exp Biol, 67. *Honors & Awards:* Conrad Elvehjem Award, Am Inst Nutrit, 70. *Mem:* AAAS; Am Cancer Soc; fel Am Pub Health Asn; Am Inst Nutrit (secy, 60-63, pres, 67); Animal Nutrit Res Coun. *Res:* Biochemistry; nutritional requirements and metabolism in animals; nutritional appraisal of man. *Mailing Add:* Swanson Ctr for Nutrit 502 S 44 St Rm 3007 Omaha NE 68105

SCHAEFER, CARL FRANCIS, b Schenectady, NY, Mar 20, 41; m 75; c 2. PHYSIOLOGICAL PSYCHOLOGY, ANESTHESIOLOGY. *Educ:* Univ Toronto, BA; Univ Rochester, PhD(physiol psychol), 72. *Prof Exp:* Asst prof psychol, Wilkes Col, 70-71; fel psychosom med, 71-74, asst prof res med, 74-76, asst prof res anesthesiol, 76-80, ASSOC PROF ANESTHESIOL, UNIV OKLA HEALTH SCI CTR, 80- *Concurrent Pos:* NIMH res grant, 77-78. *Mem:* Am Psychol Asn; Sigma Xi; NY Acad Sci; Am Soc Anesthesiol; Am Physiol Soc. *Res:* Behavioral correlates of hypertension in the spontaneously hypertensive rat; neural mechanisms underlying hypertensive disease; cardiovascular effects of anesthetic agents; endotoxin shock; effects of active and passive marihuana smoking. *Mailing Add:* Dept of Anesthesiol PO Box 26901 Oklahoma City OK 73190

SCHAEFER, CARL W, II, b New Haven, Conn, Sept 6, 34; div; c 2. ENTOMOLOGY. *Educ:* Oberlin Col, BA, 56; Univ Conn, PhD(entom), 64. *Prof Exp:* From instr to asst prof biol, Brooklyn Col, 63-66; asst prof, 66-69, assoc prof, 69-75, PROF BIOL, UNIV CONN, 76- *Concurrent Pos:* Grant, City Univ NY Grad Div, 64-66, Univ Conn Res Found, 66-67 & NSF, 67-69, 79-81; co-ed, Annals Entom Soc Am, 73- *Mem:* Entom Soc Am; Soc Syst Zool; Soc Study Evolution; Indian Entom Soc; Am Soc Naturalist. *Res:* Comparative morphology and phylogeny of the terrestrial Heteroptera. *Mailing Add:* Biol Sci Group Univ of Conn Storrs CT 06268

SCHAEFER, CHARLES HERBERT, b Albany, Calif, Sept 24, 35; m 57; c 2. ENTOMOLOGY, AGRICULTURAL CHEMISTRY. *Educ:* Univ Calif, Berkeley, BS, 58, PhD(entom), 62. *Prof Exp:* Insect physiologist, US Forest Serv, Md, 62-64 & Shell Develop Co, Calif, 64-67; DIR MOSQUITO CONTROL RES LAB, UNIV CALIF, 67- *Mem:* AAAS; Entom Soc Am; Entom Soc Can; Mosquito Control Asn Am. *Res:* New approaches to insect control; biochemical relationships between insects and their respective plant hosts; mechanisms of insecticide degradation by target insects and by the environment. *Mailing Add:* 1514 E Calimyrna Ave Fresno CA 93710

SCHAEFER, DALE WESLEY, b Willoughby, Ohio, May 17, 41; m 62; c 2. CHEMICAL PHYSICS. *Educ:* Wheaton Col, BS, 63; Mass Inst Technol, PhD(phys chem), 68. *Prof Exp:* Fel physics, Mass Inst Technol, 68-70 & T J Watson Res Ctr, IBM Corp, 70-72; STAFF MEM, SANDIA LABS, 72- *Mem:* Am Phys Soc; Biophys Soc. *Res:* Polymer physics light scattering, motility, colloid physics and structure of fluids; small angle x-ray scattering; corrosion. *Mailing Add:* Div 5152 Sandia Labs Albuquerque NM 87185

SCHAEFER, DONALD JOHN, b Sioux Falls, SDak, Dec 9, 32; m 55; c 2. COMPUTER SCIENCE, MATHEMATICS. *Educ:* San Jose State Col, AB, 57; Ohio State Univ, MA, 58, PhD(math), 63. *Prof Exp:* Res engr, Lockheed Aircraft Corp, 60-61, 62; instr math, Ohio State Univ, 63-64; assoc prof math, 64-77, PROF COMPUT SCI & MATH, WRIGHT STATE UNIV, 77-, DIR RES & INSTR COMPUT CTR, 69- *Mem:* Am Math Soc; Mat Asn Am; Asn Comput Mach. *Res:* Numerical analysis and computer applications. *Mailing Add:* Res & Inst Comput Ctr Wright State Univ Dayton OH 45431

SCHAEFER, FRANCIS T, b Hamilton, Mont, Mar 11, 13; m 37; c 2. CIVIL ENGINEERING, HYDROLOGY. *Educ:* Univ Minn, BCE, 34. *Prof Exp:* Observer, US Coast & Geod Surv, 34-35; surveyman, Corps Engrs, New Orleans, La, 35-36; engr, Gulf Res & Develop Co, 36-37; hydraul engr, Surface Water Br, Ark, Tenn & Okla, 37-42, off engr, Nebr, asst dist engr, Ky, 49-54, dist engr, Wis, 54-60, br area chief, 60-64, ASST REGIONAL HYDROLOGIST, WATER RESOURCES DIV, US GEOL SURV, 64- *Concurrent Pos:* Delaware River Master, US Geol Surv, 75- *Mem:* Fel Am Soc Civil Engrs. *Res:* Science administration. *Mailing Add:* US Geol Surv Nat Ctr Stop 433 Reston VA 22092

SCHAEFER, FRANK WILLIAM, III, b Dayton, Ohio, Sept 1, 42. ANIMAL PARASITOLOGY. *Educ:* Miami Univ, BA, 64; Univ Cincinnati, MS, 70, PhD(biol), 73. *Prof Exp:* res assoc parasitol, Univ Notre Dame, 73-78; MICROBIOLOGIST, US ENVIRON PROTECTION AGENCY, 78- *Mem:* AAAS; Sigma Xi; Am Soc Parasitol; Am Soc Microbiol; Soc Protozoologists. *Res:* In vitro cultivation of helminth and protozoan parasites; physiological studies relating to these parasites. *Mailing Add:* Health Effects Res Lab 26 West St Clair Cincinnati OH 45268

SCHAEFER, FREDERIC CHARLES, b Syracuse, NY, Nov 28, 17; m 45; c 3. ORGANIC CHEMISTRY. *Educ:* Syracuse Univ, BS, 39; Univ Akron, MS, 40; Mass Inst Technol, PhD(org chem), 43. *Prof Exp:* Res chemist, Goodyear Tire & Rubber Co, Ohio, 40-41; res chemist, 43-56, RES ASSOC, AM CYANAMID CO, 56-, PROJ LEADER, 74- *Concurrent Pos:* Am Cyanamid Co fel, Inst Org Chem, Univ Munich, 62-63. *Mem:* Am Chem Soc. *Res:* Organic nitrogen chemistry; heterocycles; s-triazines; reactive polymerizable materials; synthetic resin intermediates; keratin chemistry; hair care science. *Mailing Add:* Am Cyanamid Co Stamford CT 06904

SCHAEFER, FREDERICK VAIL, b Fort Dix, NJ, May 25, 49; m 69. CELL BIOLOGY, DEVELOPMENTAL BIOLOGY. *Educ:* Univ Md, BS, 71; NC State Univ, PhD(biochem), 79. *Prof Exp:* Res technician, Electronucleonics Lab, 71-73; fel res, 79-81, RES ASSOC, INST CANCER RES, 81- *Concurrent Pos:* Res fel, NIH, 80-81. *Mem:* Sigma Xi; Am Breast Cancer Res; Am Chem Soc; AAAS. *Res:* Regulation of the differentiation of ferritin by iron in maturing red cells; regulation of different pathways of mammary gland development and the induction of squamous metaplasia in various epithelia by cyclic adenosine monophosphate and prostglandins. *Mailing Add:* Inst Cancer Res Fox Chase Cancer Inst 7701 Burholme Ave Philadelphia PA 19111

SCHAEFER, GEORGE, b New York, NY, May 30, 13; m 44; c 2. OBSTETRICS & GYNECOLOGY. *Educ:* NY Univ, BS, 33; Cornell Univ, MD, 37; Am Bd Obstet & Gynec, dipl, 48. *Prof Exp:* Attend obstetrician & gynecologist, Sea View Hosp, 40-48; from asst prof to prof, 51-78, EMER PROF OBSTET & GYNEC, MED COL, CORNELL UNIV, 78-; DIR OBSTET & GYNEC RESIDENCY TRAINING PROG, MERCY HOSP & MED CTR, SAN DIEGO, 80- *Concurrent Pos:* Consult, Booth Mem Hosp, 63-; attend, NY Hosp, 62- *Mem:* Fel Am Col Surg; fel Am Col Obstet & Gynec; hon fel Span Gynec Soc. *Res:* Tuberculosis in obstetrics and gynecology; expectant father. *Mailing Add:* Mercy Hosp & Med Ctr 4077 Fifth Ave San Diego CA 92103

SCHAEFER, HENRY FREDERICK, III, b Grand Rapids, Mich, June 8, 44; m 66. THEORETICAL CHEMISTRY. *Educ:* Mass Inst Technol, SB, 66; Stanford Univ, PhD(chem), 69. *Prof Exp:* From asst prof to assoc prof, 69-78, staff mem, Nuclear Chem Div, Lawrence Berkeley Lab, 71-75, PROF CHEM, UNIV CALIF, BERKELEY, 78-, STAFF MEM, MOLECULAR & MAT RES DIV, LAWRENCE BERKELEY LAB, 75- *Concurrent Pos:* Consult, Lawrence Livermore Lab, 68- & Eastman Kodak, 74-; joint study

proj, Univ Calif-IBM Res Lab, 72-; J S Guggenheim fel, 76-77; Alfred P Sloan Found fel. *Honors & Awards:* Am Chem Soc Pure Chem Award, 79. *Mem:* Fel Am Phys Soc. *Res:* Rigorous quantum mechanical studies of the electronic structure of atoms and molecules. *Mailing Add:* Dept of Chem Univ of Calif Berkeley CA 94720

SCHAEFER, HUGH FERDINAND, chemistry, see previous edition

SCHAEFER, JACOB FRANKLIN, b San Francisco, Calif, Aug 13, 38; m 62; c 2. PHYSICAL CHEMISTRY. *Educ:* Carnegie Inst Technol, BS, 60; Univ Minn, PhD(phys chem), 64. *Prof Exp:* Res chemist phys chem, 64-74, SCI FEL, DEPT NUCLEAR MAGNETIC RESONANCE, MONSANTO CO, 74- *Mem:* Am Chem Soc. *Res:* Nuclear magnetic resonance spectroscopy of polymers. *Mailing Add:* Dept of Nuclear Magnetic Resonance Monsanto Co St Louis MO 63166

SCHAEFER, JACOB W, b Paullina, Iowa, June 27, 19; m 41; c 3. COMMUNICATIONS, SYSTEMS ENGINEERING. *Educ:* Ohio State Univ, BME, 41. *Hon Degrees:* DSc, Ohio State Univ, 66. *Prof Exp:* Engr, Bell Tel Labs, 41-42, 46-50, supvr Nike Ajax & Hercules syst design, 50-57, dept head Nike Zeus res, 57-61, asst dir Nike Zeus proj, 61-63, dir Kwajalien Field Sta, 63-65, dir data commun lab, 65-68, exec dir data & PBX div, 68-70, exec dir customer switching servs, 70-81, EXEC DIR, MIL SYSTS DIV, BELL LABS, 81- *Concurrent Pos:* Mem subcomt, Air Force Sci Adv Bd, 61-63. *Mem:* Am Ord Asn. *Res:* Servomechanisms for missile control surfaces; missile guidance and air defense missile systems; design of data communication terminals. *Mailing Add:* 115 Century Lane Watchung NJ 07060

SCHAEFER, JOSEPH ALBERT, b Bellevue, Iowa, Dec 24, 40; m 65; c 2. SOLID STATE PHYSICS. *Educ:* Loras Col, BS, 62; Univ Toledo, MS, 64; Northwestern Univ, Evanston, PhD(physics), 72. *Prof Exp:* Instr, 64-67, asst prof, 71-75, assoc prof 75-80, PROF PHYSICS, LORAS COL, 80- *Concurrent Pos:* Res fel, Northwestern Univ, Evanston, 74; consult, John Deere Co, 80; NSF sci fac prof develop fel, Iowa State Univ, 81-82. *Mem:* Am Phys Soc; Am Asn Physics Teachers; Am Soc Eng Educ. *Res:* Magnetoresistance of potassium; transport properties of metals. *Mailing Add:* Dept of Physics Loras Col 1450 Alta Vista Dubuque IA 52001

SCHAEFER, JOSEPH THOMAS, b Milwaukee, Wis, Oct 23, 43; m 68; c 3. METEOROLOGY, WIND ENGINEERING. *Educ:* St Louis Univ, BS, 65, PhD(meteorol), 73. *Prof Exp:* Meteorologist, Nat Weather Serv, St Louis, Mo, 66-69; res meteorologist, US Navy Weather Res Facil, 69-71; res meteorologist, Nat Severe Storms Lab, 71-76, CHIEF TECH DEVELOP UNIT, NAT SEVERE STORMS FORECAST CTR, NAT OCEANIC & ATMOSPHERIC ADMIN, 76- *Mem:* Am Meteorol Soc; Am Geophys Union. *Res:* Severe thunderstorm forecast; tornado climatology; severe thunderstorm environment; severe thunderstorm dynamics and structure; atmospheric boundary layer structure; mesoscale numerical atmospheric modelling; cumulus dynamics. *Mailing Add:* Nat Severe Storms Forecast Ctr Rm 1728 601 E 12th St Kansas City MO 64106

SCHAEFER, KARL ERNST, physiology, deceased

SCHAEFER, PAUL THEODORE, b Rochester, NY, Mar 7, 30; m 51. MATHEMATICS. *Educ:* Univ Rochester, AB, 51, MA, 56; Univ Pittsburgh, PhD(infinite series), 63. *Prof Exp:* Instr math, Rochester Inst Tech, 55-56; from asst prof to prof, State Univ NY Albany, 56-67; PROF MATH, STATE UNIV NY COL GENESEO, 67- *Concurrent Pos:* First vchmn seaway sect, Math Asn Am, 76-77, chmn, 77-78; vis prof, Calif State Univ, Los Angeles, 78-79. *Mem:* Am Math Soc; Math Asn Am. *Res:* Series; summability; real and complex analysis. *Mailing Add:* Dept of Math State Univ Col of Arts & Sci Geneseo NY 14454

SCHAEFER, PHILIP WILLIAM, b Baltimore, Md, Feb 16, 35; m 58; c 4. APPLIED MATHEMATICS. *Educ:* John Carroll Univ, BS, 56, MS, 57; Univ Md, PhD(math), 64. *Prof Exp:* Instr math, Loyola Col, Md, 59-60; asst prof, Univ SFla, 64-67; assoc prof, 67-77, PROF MATH, UNIV TENN, KNOXVILLE, 77- *Mem:* Am Math Soc; Soc Indust & Appl Math. *Res:* Elliptic partial differential equations; improperly posed problems and maximum principles. *Mailing Add:* Dept of Math Univ of Tenn Knoxville TN 37916

SCHAEFER, ROBERT J(AMES), physical metallurgy, see previous edition

SCHAEFER, ROBERT L(EO), b Cleveland, Ohio, Oct 23, 22; m 51; c 4. CHEMICAL ENGINEERING. *Educ:* Case Inst Technol, BS, 47, MS, 48, PhD(chem eng), 54. *Prof Exp:* Process engr, Harshaw Chem Co, 48; mat engr, Gen Elec Co, 48-52; instr chem eng, Case Inst Technol, 52-53; proj leader, Dow Chem Co, 53-58; supt adv design dept, Allegany Ballistics Lab, Hercules Powder Co, 58-63, MGR RES & DEVELOP, BACCHUS PLANT LAB, HERCULES INC, 63- *Concurrent Pos:* Vpres, Treathewey-Schaefer Co, Inc, 49-53. *Mem:* Am Inst Chem Engrs; Am Ord Asn; Am Soc Metals; Am Mgt Asn. *Res:* Chemical propulsion rocket systems; propellant chemistry; structural mechanics; fluid mechanics and heat transfer; magnetohydrodynamics and plasma physics; high temperature materials; continuous glass filament structure; polymerization and plastics fabrication; synthetic fibers. *Mailing Add:* PO Box 98 Bacchus Plant Lab Hercules Res Ctr Magma UT 84044

SCHAEFER, ROBERT WILLIAM, b Schenectady, NY, Dec 5, 27; m 54; c 3. ANALYTICAL CHEMISTRY. *Educ:* Siena Col, BS, 49; Union Col, NY, MS, 51. *Prof Exp:* Asst, 49-51, from asst prof to assoc prof, 52-81, PROF & CHAIRPERSON ANAL CHEM, UNION COL, NY, 81- *Concurrent Pos:* Develop chemist, Willsboro Mining Co, 50; asst, Univ Ky, 51; sr sanit chemist, State Dept Health, NY, 54-60; lectr, Bard Col, 55; consult, Power Technol Inc, Schenectady, NY, 80- *Mem:* Am Chem Soc. *Res:* Instrumental analytical chemistry; sanitary chemistry; methods for trace metals in streams receiving industrial wastes. *Mailing Add:* Dept of Chem Union Col Schenectady NY 12308

SCHAEFER, SETH CLARENCE, b Tripp, SDak, Feb 15, 23. METALLURGY, THERMODYNAMICS. *Educ:* SDak Sch Mines, BS, 47; Univ Mo-Rolla, MS, 63. *Prof Exp:* Jr metallurgist, Am Smelting & Refining Co, Nebr, 47-49, actg smelter supt, 50-55, asst lead refinery supt, 56, smelter supt, 57-59, asst lead refinery supt, NJ, 59-61; metallurgist, 63-66, proj leader chem processes, 67-69, METALLURGIST, ALBANY METALL RES CTR, US BUR MINES, 69- *Mem:* Sigma Xi; Am Inst Mining, Metall & Petrol Engrs; Am Soc Metals. *Res:* Metallurgical thermodynamics. *Mailing Add:* Albany Metall Res Ctr US Bur Mines PO Box 70 Albany OR 97321

SCHAEFER, THEODORE PETER, b Winnipeg, Man, July 22, 33; m 60; c 3. PHYSICAL CHEMISTRY. *Educ:* Univ Man, BSc, 54, MSc, 55; Oxford Univ, DPhil(chem), 58. *Prof Exp:* From asst prof to assoc prof, 58-70, PROF CHEM, UNIV MAN, 70- *Concurrent Pos:* Nat Res Coun Can sr res fel, 64-65; mem, Chem Grants Comt, Nat Res Coun Can, 75-77; mem, Natural Sci & Eng Res Coun, Can, 80-83. *Honors & Awards:* Noranda Award, Chem Inst Can, 73; Herzberg Award, Spectroscopy Soc Can, 75. *Mem:* Fel Royal Soc Can; fel Chem Inst Can; Int Soc Magnetic Resonance. *Res:* Nuclear magnetic resonance spectroscopy in chemistry. *Mailing Add:* Dept of Chem Univ of Man Winnipeg MB R3T 2N2 Can

SCHAEFER, WILBUR CARLS, b Beardstown, Ill, Sept 18, 25; m 49; c 2. AGRICULTURAL CHEMISTRY. *Educ:* Bradley Univ, BS, 49, MS, 50. *Prof Exp:* Res chemist, 50-61, ASST TO DIR, NORTHERN REGIONAL RES CTR, AGR RES SERV, USDA, 61- *Mem:* AAAS; Am Asn Cereal Chem (treas, 72-74); Am Chem Soc. *Res:* Utilization of cereal grains and oilseeds; starch and dextran structure; starch derivatives; wheat gluten properties; histochemistry of wheat endosperm; chemical research administration; carbohydrate and protein chemistry. *Mailing Add:* Northern Regional Res Lab USDA 1815 N University St Peoria IL 61604

SCHAEFER, WILLIAM PALZER, b Bisbee, Ariz, Jan 13, 31; m 54; c 2. SYNTHETIC INORGANIC & ORGANOMETALLIC CHEMISTRY. *Educ:* Stanford Univ, BS, 52; Univ Calif, Los Angeles, MS, 54, PhD(anal chem), 60. *Prof Exp:* From instr to asst prof chem, Calif Inst Technol, 60-66; asst prof, Univ Calif, Davis, 66-68; sr res fel chem, 68-77, registrar, 71-77, dir financial aid, 72-77, res assoc, 77-81, SR RES ASSOC, CALIF INST TECHNOL, 81- *Mem:* Am Chem Soc; Am Crystallog Asn; AAAS. *Res:* Structure and stability of complexes of the transition metals; x-ray crystallography; structural chemistry. *Mailing Add:* A A Noyes Lab of Chem Physics Calif Inst of Technol Pasadena CA 91125

SCHAEFERS, GEORGE ALBERT, b Erie, Pa, Mar 19, 29; m 60; c 3. ENTOMOLOGY. *Educ:* Univ Calif, BS, 55, PhD, 58. *Prof Exp:* From asst prof to assoc prof, 58-74, PROF ENTOM, NY STATE COL AGR, CORNELL UNIV, 74- *Concurrent Pos:* Vis scientist, Int Inst Trop Agr, 74-75. *Mem:* Entom Soc Am. *Res:* Economic entomology; small fruit insects; insect vectors plant diseases; Aphid biology. *Mailing Add:* NY State Col Agr Exp Sta Geneva NY 14456

SCHAEFFER, BOBB, b New Haven, Conn, Sept 27, 13; m 41; c 2. VERTEBRATE PALEONTOLOGY. *Educ:* Cornell Univ, BA, 36; Columbia Univ, MA, 37, PhD(zool), 41. *Prof Exp:* Demonstr histol & embryol, Jefferson Med Col, 41-42; asst cur vert paleont, Am Mus Natural Hist, 46-49, assoc cur fossil fishes, 49-55, chmn dept, 66-76; vis assoc prof zool, Columbia Univ, 55-57, adj prof, 57-59, prof, 59-78; EMER CUR VERT PALEONT, AM MUS NATURAL HIST, 76- *Concurrent Pos:* Cur vert paleont, Am Mus Natural Hist, 55-76. *Mem:* Soc Vert Paleont (actg secy, 52-53, pres, 53); Soc Syst Zool; Soc Study Evolution; fel Geol Soc Am. *Res:* Systematics; morphology and embryology of fishes; systematic theory. *Mailing Add:* Am Mus of Natural Hist Cent Park W 79th St New York NY 10024

SCHAEFFER, CHARLES DAVID, b Allentown, Pa, June 14, 48. INORGANIC CHEMISTRY. *Educ:* Franklin & Marshall Col, BA, 70; State Univ NY, Albany, PhD(chem), 74. *Prof Exp:* Fel inorg chem, Yale Univ, 74-76; asst prof, 76-81, ASSOC PROF CHEM, ELIZABETHTOWN COL, 81- *Concurrent Pos:* Res grant, Cottrell Col, 77-78; Petrol Res Fund, Am Chem Soc grant, 78-80; res grant, Cottrell Col, 82-84. *Mem:* Am Chem Soc; Chem Soc London. *Res:* Main group organometallic chemistry; nuclear magnetic resonance spectroscopy. *Mailing Add:* Dept Chem Elizabethtown Col Elizabethtown PA 17022

SCHAEFFER, DAVID GEORGE, b Cincinnati, Ohio, Oct 6, 42; m 70. MATHEMATICS. *Educ:* Univ Ill, Urbana, BS, 63; Mass Inst Technol, PhD(math), 68. *Prof Exp:* Instr math, Brandeis Univ, 68-70; asst prof, 70-75, ASSOC PROF MATH, MASS INST TECHNOL, 75- *Mem:* Am Math Soc. *Res:* Partial differential equations; approximations by finite differences; functional analysis. *Mailing Add:* Dept of Math Mass Inst of Technol Cambridge MA 02139

SCHAEFFER, DAVID JOSEPH, b Brooklyn, NY, Feb 7, 43; m 70; c 2. ENVIRONMENTAL MANAGEMENT. *Educ:* Brooklyn Col, BS, 63; Northwestern Univ, MS, 65; City Univ New York, PhD(org chem), 69. *Prof Exp:* Res asst chem, Brooklyn Col, 60-63, lectr, 65-69; res assoc, State Univ NY Binghamton, 69-70; asst prof, Sangamon State Univ, 70-72; ADV ENVIRON SCI, ILL ENVIRON PROTECTION AGENCY, 72- *Concurrent Pos:* Adj assoc prof toxicol, Southern Ill Univ, 79-; adj asst prof health serv, Sangamon State Univ, 80. *Mem:* Am Chem Soc; NY Acad Sci; Int Asn Gt Lakes Res; Am Statist Asn; Nat Speleol Soc. *Res:* Environmental chemistry of water pollutants; statistical properties, chance mechanisms and quality control of environmental data. *Mailing Add:* 1716 Walnut St Chatham IL 62629

SCHAEFFER, GENE THOMAS, b Reading, Pa, Jan 15, 32; m 57; c 3. METALLURGY. *Educ:* Albright Col, BS, 56; Syracuse Univ, MS, 61, PhD(solid state sci & technol), 65. *Prof Exp:* Process engr, Western Elec Co, Inc, 56-57; ADVAN DEVELOP ENGR, CHEM & METALL DIV, GTE SYLVANIA INC, 65- *Mem:* Am Inst Mining, Metall & Petrol Engrs; Am Soc Metals. *Res:* Heavy metals; mechanical properties of materials; properties and processing of incandescent lamp metals. *Mailing Add:* 16 Thomas St Towanda PA 18848

SCHAEFFER, GIDEON W, b Menno, SDak, Nov 5, 29; m 53. TISSUE CULTURE, BIOCHEMICAL GENETICS. *Educ:* Yankton Col, BA, 52; Univ Nebr, MSc, 57, PhD(physiol genetics), 60. *Prof Exp:* AEC & USPHS fels & res assoc cellular biol, Brookhaven Nat Lab, 60-62; fel, Phytotron Lab, Gif-sur-Yvette, France, 62-63; chief lab, 77, RES SCIENTIST, BELTSVILLE AGR RES CTR, SCI & EDUC ADMIN-AGR RES, USDA, 63- *Mem:* Am Soc Plant Physiol; AAAS; Tissue Cult Asn; Scand Soc Plant Physiol; Am Soc Agron. *Res:* Tissue culture research in cellular physiology and genetic control of development; nucleic acid methylation and biochemistry of methionine in dormant and cytokinin-activated auxiliary buds in plants; phospholipid changes during bud activation; anther culture and protoplast isolation from crop plants; biochemical selection using inhibitors and analogs; interspecies somatic hybridization. *Mailing Add:* Cell Cult & (N) Fixation Lab USDA Beltsville Agr Res Ctr Beltsville MD 20705

SCHAEFFER, HAROLD FRANKLIN, b Philadelphia, Pa, Sept 21, 99; m 32. CHEMICAL MICROSCOPY, PHYSICAL CHEMISTRY. *Educ:* Muhlenberg Col, BSc, 22; Univ NH, MSc, 26. *Prof Exp:* High sch teacher, Pa, 22-24; asst agr chem, Univ NH, 24-26; prof chem, Waynesburg Col, 26-42, head dept, 40-42; instr, Univ Mo, 42-43; prof, Col Our Lady of the Elms, 43-44; res assoc in chg sulfur-org res lab, Univ Ala, 44-48; asst prof chem, Valparaiso, 48-52; res scientist, US Army Ord, Rensselaer Polytech, 52-53; prof chem, Grove City Col, 53-55; prof & head dept, Col of Emporia, 55-59; prof, Westminster Col, 59-68, res prof chem, 68-76; CONSULT, SCHAEFFER RES ASSOC, 76- *Concurrent Pos:* Abstractor, Chem Abstracts, 48-76; Res Corp grants, 54, 57 & 60. *Mem:* AAAS; Am Chem Soc; fel Am Inst Chemists; Am Microchem Soc. *Res:* Direct sulfuration of organic compounds; microscopic methods in chemistry; chemical microscopy of platinum metals; quantitative microscopy; thermal microscopy; reaction of organic squarates. *Mailing Add:* 15 E Chestnut St Fulton MO 65251

SCHAEFFER, HARRY GEORGE, engineering mechanics, see previous edition

SCHAEFFER, HOWARD JOHN, b Rochester, NY, Mar 14, 27; m 50; c 4. MEDICINAL CHEMISTRY. *Educ:* Univ Fla, PhD(pharmaceut chem), 55. *Prof Exp:* Sr scientist, Southern Res Inst, 55-57, head pharmaceut chem sect, 57-59; assoc prof med chem & actg chmn dept, State Univ NY Buffalo, 59-63, prof, 63-70, chmn dept, 65-70; dept head org chem, Wellcome Res Labs, Burroughs Wellcome Co, 70-74; mem fac, Med Col Va, Va Commonwealth Univ, 74-77; MEM STAFF, BURROUGHS WELLCOME CO, 77- *Honors & Awards:* Ebert Prize, Am Pharmaceut Asn. *Mem:* Am Chem Soc; Acad Pharmaceut Sci. *Res:* Enzyme inhibition; kinetics; stereochemistry. *Mailing Add:* Burroughs Wellcome Co 3030 Cornwallis Rd Research Triangle Park NC 27709

SCHAEFFER, JAMES ROBERT, b Rochester, NY, Aug 2, 33; m 67; c 4. ORGANIC CHEMISTRY, MICROBIOLOGY. *Educ:* Univ Notre Dame, BS, 55; Univ Pa, PhD(org chem), 59. *Prof Exp:* Res chemist, Synthetic Chem Div, 60-62, from res chemist to sr res chemist, Chem Div, 62-69, RES ASSOC, CHEM DIV, RES LABS, EASTMAN KODAK CO, 69- *Concurrent Pos:* US Army Off Ord Res fel, Northwestern Univ, 59-60. *Mem:* Am Chem Soc. *Res:* Chelate, dye and microbiological chemistry; organic sulfur compounds; development laboratory studies in organic synthesis; application of fermentation techniques to the synthesis of organic compounds. *Mailing Add:* 49 Jackson Rd Exten Penfield NY 14526

SCHAEFFER, JURGEN RICHARD, b Marburg-Lahn, Ger, June 22, 27; US citizen; m 58; c 4. PLANT BREEDING, CYTOGENETICS. *Educ:* Univ Giessen, dipl, 53, Dr Agr, 55. *Prof Exp:* Ger Res Found fel cytogenetics, Wash State Univ, 56-57; from asst prof to assoc prof agron, 57-65, PROF AGRON & GENETICS, DEPT PLANT & SOIL SCI, COL AGR, MONT STATE UNIV, 65- *Concurrent Pos:* NSF grants, 61-67; agronomist, Food & Agr Orgn, UN, Govt Turkey, 66-68. *Mem:* Fel AAAS; Am Soc Agron; Crop Sci Soc Am; Bot Soc Am. *Res:* Cytology of Bromus, Agropyron, Triticum and Hordeum; origin of B-chromosomes; wheat monosomics; crossing techniques; cytotaxonomy; biosystematics; hybridization between Triticum and Agropyron; cytoplasmic male sterility in Agropyron intermedium, A desertorum, and Bromus inermis; plant exploration; phytogeography. *Mailing Add:* Dept Plant & Soil Sci Mont State Univ Col Agr Bozeman MT 59717

SCHAEFFER, LEE ALLEN, b Allentown, Pa, June 20, 43; m 70. ORGANIC CHEMISTRY. *Educ:* Lehigh Univ, BS, 65, MS, 69, PhD(org chem), 72. *Prof Exp:* Chemist, Lubrizol Corp, Cleveland, Ohio, 65-67; RES ASSOC, CROMPTON & KNOWLES CORP, 73- *Mem:* Am Chem Soc; Am Asn Textile Chemists & Colorists. *Res:* Preparation of dyes and related chemicals. *Mailing Add:* PO Box 341 500 Pear St Crompton & Knowles Corp Reading PA 19603

SCHAEFFER, MORRIS, b Berdichev, Ukraine, Russia, Dec 31, 07; US citizen; m 43; c 4. MEDICINE, MICROBIOLOGY. *Educ:* Univ Ala, AB & MA, 30; NY Univ, PhD(microbiol), 35, MD, 44; Am Bd Prev Med, dipl, 50. *Prof Exp:* Asst instr, Univ Ala, 28-30; asst, Res Labs, Dept Health, New York, 30-31, bacteriologist, 35-36; res assoc, 36-41, mem, Pub Health Res Inst, 41-42; house officer, City Hosp, Boston, Mass, 44-45; asst prof microbiol & pediat, Sch Med, Western Reserve Univ, 46-49; med dir, Virus & Rickettsia Sect, Commun Dis Ctr, USPHS, 49-59; mem, Pub Health Res Inst & dir, Bur Labs, Dept Health, New York, 59-71; consult, Pan-Am Health Orgn, 71-72; DIR OFF EFFICACY REV, BUR BIOLOGICS, FOOD & DRUG ADMIN, 72- *Concurrent Pos:* Instr, Sch Med, NY Univ, 33-36, lectr, 36-37, adj prof, 59-; lectr, Sch Pub Health, Columbia Univ, 63-73; resident contagious div, City & Babies & Childrens Hosps, Cleveland, 45-48; dir contagious pavillion, City Hosp & librn, lectr & consult, Nursing Sch, 48-49; assoc prof, Sch Med, Emory Univ, 51-59; vis lectr, Sch Med, Tulane Univ, 52-59; vis prof, Univ Havana, 52, Univ Hawaii, 59 & Univ Wash, 72; consult to Surgeon Gen, US Air Force, 59-64 & Surgeon Gen comt influenza res, USPHS, 59-63; mem expert panel on viruses, WHO, 60-; assoc mem, Armed Forces Epidemiol Bd, Comn Respiratory Dis, 61-70; mem adv comt, Ctr Dis Control, USPHS, 62-

71, bd sci counsr, Div Biol Standards, 63-67; panel on virus dis, US-Japan Comt Biomed Res, NIH, 65-69; vis prof microbiol, Univ Wash, 72- *Mem:* Am Col Prev Med; Am Soc Microbiol; Soc Exp Biol & Med; Am Pub Health Asn; Am Asn Immunol. *Res:* Virology; public health; infectious diseases; pediatrics; epidemiology; public health and epidemiology. *Mailing Add:* 8930 Bradmoor Dr Bethesda MD 20817

SCHAEFFER, OLIVER ADAM, cosmochemistry, deceased

SCHAEFFER, RILEY, b Michigan City, Ind, July 3, 27; m 50; c 4. INORGANIC CHEMISTRY. *Educ:* Univ Chicago, BS, 46, PhD(chem), 49. *Prof Exp:* Res chemist, Univ Chicago, 49-52; from asst prof to assoc prof chem, Iowa State Univ, 52-58; from assoc prof to prof, Ind Univ, Bloomington, 58-75, chmn dept, 67-72; dean arts & sci, Univ Wyo, 76-77, prof chem, 76-81; PROF & CHMN, DEPT CHEM, UNIV NMEX, 81- *Concurrent Pos:* NSF sr fel, 61-62; Guggenheim fel, 65-66; bd mem, Petrol Res Found, 70-72; vis comt inorg mat, Nat Bur Stand, 73-79; mem adv comt, NSF, 77- *Mem:* Am Chem Soc; AAAS; Am Asn Univ Professors; Sigma Xi; Royal Soc Chem. *Res:* Inorganic and physical inorganic chemistry of hydrides; chemistry of covalent inorganic compounds; archaeology; metal-oxygen clusters; structural inorganic chemistry; x-ray diffraction. *Mailing Add:* Dept Chem Univ NMex Albuquerque NM 87131

SCHAEFFER, ROBERT L, JR, b Allentown, Pa, Oct 31, 17. PLANT TAXONOMY. *Educ:* Haverford Col, BS, 40; Univ Pa, PhD(bot), 48. *Prof Exp:* Asst bot, Univ Pa, 42-44, instr, 46-47; from asst prof to assoc prof biol, Upsala Col, 48-52; from asst prof to assoc prof, 52-58, PROF BIOL, MUHLENBERG COL, 59- *Mem:* AAAS; Am Fern Soc; Bot Soc Am; Torrey Bot Club. *Res:* Floristics of eastern Pennsylvania and northern New Jersey; floristic, taxonomic and evolutionary botany. *Mailing Add:* Dept of Biol Muhlenburg Col Allentown PA 18104

SCHAEFFER, WARREN IRA, b Newark, NJ, Aug 13, 38. BACTERIOLOGY, CELL BIOLOGY. *Educ:* Rutgers Univ, BS, 60, MS, 62, PhD(bact), 64. *Prof Exp:* Res assoc cell biol, Mass Inst Technol, 64-66; asst prof med microbiol, Univ Calif-Calif Col Med, 66-67; assoc prof, 67-77, PROF & ACTG CHMN, MED MICROBIOL, COL MED, UNIV VT, 77- *Mem:* AAAS; Am Soc Microbiol; Soc Exp Biol & Med; Tissue Cult Asn; Am Soc Cell Biol. *Res:* Tissue culture; effects of biologically active agents in cell cultures; mode of action of carcinogenic mycotoxins in cell culture; in vitro aging of epithelial cells. *Mailing Add:* Dept of Med Microbiol Univ of Vt Col of Med Burlington VT 05401

SCHAEFFER, WILLIAM DWIGHT, b Reading, Pa, Dec 4, 21; m 46; c 3. COLLOID CHEMISTRY. *Educ:* Lehigh Univ, BS, 43, MS, 47, PhD(chem), 67. *Prof Exp:* Asst instr chem, Lehigh Univ, 46-47; chemist & group leader, Res & Develop Dept, Godfrey L Cabot, Inc, 47-55; assoc res dir, Nat Printing Ink Res Inst, Lehigh Univ, 55-69; RES DIR, GRAPHIC ARTS TECH FOUND, 69- *Concurrent Pos:* Vchmn, Int Asn Res Insts Graphic Arts Indust, 71-77. *Mem:* Am Chem Soc; Tech Asn Pulp & Paper Indust; NY Acad Sci; Tech Asn Graphic Arts (pres, 69-70); Inter-Soc Color Coun (pres, 81-82). *Res:* Physical colloid and surface chemistry; carbon blacks; printing and printing inks; dispersions of pigments; environmental science. *Mailing Add:* Graphic Arts Tech Found 4615 Forbes Ave Pittsburgh PA 15213

SCHAEFGEN, JOHN RAYMOND, b Wilmette, Ill, Apr 9, 18; m 45; c 9. POLYMER CHEMISTRY. *Educ:* Northwestern Univ, Ill, BS, 40; Ohio State Univ, PhD(phys org chem), 44. *Prof Exp:* Sr chemist, Res Lab, Goodyear Tire & Rubber Co, 44-51; jr res assoc, 51-58, res assoc, 58-77, RES FEL, TEXTILE FIBERS DEPT, PIONEERING RES, E I DU PONT DE NEMOURS & CO, INC, 77- *Mem:* Am Chem Soc. *Res:* Physical organic chemistry; mechanisms of organic reactions; synthesis and study of properties of high polymers; fiber technology. *Mailing Add:* Exp Sta E I du Pont de Nemours & Co Inc Wilmington DE 19898

SCHAEFLER, SAM, b Cernauti, Romania, Jan 15, 20; m 47; c 2. MICROBIOLOGY. *Educ:* Univ Bucharest, Lic biol, 47; NY Univ, PhD(microbiol), 66. *Prof Exp:* Lab chief microbiol, Inst Cantacuzino, Bucharest, Romania & biochemist, Alexandrescu Hosp, 49-61; asst prof microbiol, NY Univ, 66-69; SR RES SCIENTIST, BUR LABS, CITY OF NEW YORK & ASSOC MICROBIOL, PUB HEALTH RES INST, CITY OF NEW YORK, INC, 69- *Concurrent Pos:* NIH grant, 68- *Mem:* Am Soc Microbiol; Genetics Soc Am. *Res:* Biochemical genetics; metabolism of beta glucosides; antibiotic resistance; bacterial evolution. *Mailing Add:* Pub Health Res Inst 455 First Ave New York NY 10016

SCHAEPPI, ULRICH HANS, b Brugg, Switz, Sept 1, 25; US citizen; m 56; c 4. NEUROTOXICOLOGY, NEUROPHARMACOLOGY. *Educ:* Univ Bern, MD, 51. *Prof Exp:* Resident, Aarau State Hosp, Switz, 51-54; pharmacologist, Univ Zurich, 55-57 & J R Geigy Chem Corp, Switz, 57-60; staff scientist, Worcester Found Exp Biol, Mass, 60-67; dir pharmacol, Mason Res Inst, 67-69, vpres, 69-76; mem staff, 76-81, SCIENTIST, CIBA-GEIGY LTD, SWITZ, 81- *Mem:* Am Soc Pharmacol & Exp Therapeut; Soc Toxicol. *Res:* Preclinical pharmacological evaluation of drugs; mode and site of action of drugs and chemicals upon the central nervous system; mechanisms of neurotoxicity. *Mailing Add:* Ciba-Geigy Ltd CH-4002 Basel Switzerland

SCHAER, JONATHAN, b Bern, Switz, Oct 1, 29; m 63; c 2. MATHEMATICS. *Educ:* Univ Bern, dipl educ, 52 & 57, Dr Phil(theoret physics), 62. *Prof Exp:* Pub sch teacher, Bern, Switz, 55-56; asst physics, Univ Bern, 56-57; asst math, Swiss Fed Inst Technol, 57-58; asst physics, Univ Bern, 58-62; asst prof math, Univ Alta, 62-67; ASSOC PROF MATH, UNIV CALGARY, 67- *Mem:* Can Math Soc; Am Math Soc; Math Asn Am. *Res:* Geometry; convexity; combinatorics; theory of relativity. *Mailing Add:* Dept of Math Univ of Calgary Calgary AB T2N 1N4 Can

SCHAERF, HENRY MAXIMILIAN, b Rohatyn, Poland, Mar 17, 07; nat US. MEASURE THEORY, INTEGRATION THEORY. *Educ:* Univ Lwow, MA, 29; Univ Göttingen, actuary's cert, 31; Swiss Fed Inst Technol, ScD(math), 43, Habilitated(math), 45. *Prof Exp:* Head actuarial dept, Der Anker Ins Co, Poland, 31-37; chief actuary, Vita-Kotwica Life Ins Co, 37-39; lectr math, Polish mil internees, Switz, 41-44; privat docent, Swiss Fed Inst Technol, 45-48; instr, Mont State Col, 46-47; from asst prof to assoc prof, 47-75, EMER ASSOC PROF MATH, WASHINGTON UNIV, 75- *Concurrent Pos:* Ford Found fel, Inst Advan Study, NJ & Denmark, 53-54; mem, US Army Math Res Ctr, Univ Wis, 58 & 61, vis prof, Ctr, 62-64; assoc prof, McGill Univ, 64-72. *Mem:* Am Math Soc; Swiss Math Soc; Swiss Asn Actuaries; Polish Math Soc. *Res:* Actuarial theory; real variables; measure and integration theory; structure and cardinality of bases; topological properties of maps; invariant measures; mathematical foundations of actuarial theory. *Mailing Add:* Dept of Math Washington Univ St Louis MO 63130

SCHAETTI, HENRY JOACHIM, b Kodaikanal, India, Aug 10, 21; nat US; m 50; c 3. PETROLEUM EXPLORATION. *Educ:* Univ Bern, PhD(geol), 49. *Prof Exp:* Asst to dir geol, Univ Bern, 45-49; Rotary Found fel, Stanford Univ, 49-50; field geologist, Brit Am Oil Co, Ltd, Can, 51-52; res geologist, Res Lab, Carter Oil Co, 52-56, sect head, Jersey Prod Res Co, 56-60; regional geologist, Esso Argentina, Inc, 60-61, chief geologist, Esso Sahara, Inc, 61-66, explor mgr, Esso Atlantic Study Group, 66-67, gen mgr, Esso Explor, Inc, Senegal, 67-69, Morocco, 69-70 & Malaysia, 70-71, vpres & dir, Houston, 71-74, Singapore, 75-77, REGIONAL VPRES & DIR, ESSO EXPLOR, INC, ENGLAND, 77- *Mem:* AAAS; Am Asn Petrol Geologists; Am Geophys Union; NY Acad Sci; Geol Soc London. *Res:* Structural and petroleum geology; geochemistry. *Mailing Add:* Esso Explor Inc Walton-on-Thames Surrey England KT12 2QL United Kingdom

SCHAETZLE, WALTER J(ACOB), b Pittsburgh, Pa, Feb 17, 34; m 65; c 2. MECHANICAL ENGINEERING. *Educ:* Carnegie Inst Technol, BS, 57, MS, 58; Wash Univ, DSc(mech eng), 62. *Prof Exp:* Propulsion engr, McDonnell Aircraft Corp, 58-62; from asst prof to assoc prof, 62-66, PROF MECH ENG, UNIV ALA, TUSCALOOSA, 66- *Concurrent Pos:* Mem staff, Col Petrol, Saudi Arabia, 69-71. *Mem:* Am Soc Mech Engrs; Am Soc Heating, Refrig & Air Conditioning Engrs; Am Soc Eng Educ; Int Solar Energy Soc. *Res:* Rarefied gas flow; experiments in molecule surface interactions; thermal energy storage; community energy systems; man produced energy tornado correlations; heating and cooling systems; heat pump systems; home energy conservation; solar energy. *Mailing Add:* Col Eng Drawer ME Univ of Ala in Tuscaloosa University AL 35486

SCHAFER, ALICE TURNER, b Richmond, Va, June 18, 15; m 42; c 2. ALGEBRA. *Educ:* Univ Richmond, BA, 36; Univ Chicago, MS, 40, PhD(math), 42. *Hon Degrees:* DSc, Univ Richmond, 64. *Prof Exp:* High sch teacher, Va, 36-39; instr math, Conn Col, 42-44; mathematician, Off Sci Res & Develop, Appl Physics Lab, Johns Hopkins Univ, 45; instr math, Univ Mich, 45-46; lectr, NJ Col Women, Rutgers Univ, 46-48; asst prof, Swarthmore Col, 48-51 & Drexel Inst Technol, 51-53; from asst prof to prof, Conn Col, 54-62; prof, 62-69, Helen Day Gould prof math, Wellesley Col, 69-80; RETIRED. *Concurrent Pos:* NSF sci fac fel, 58-59; mem, Inst Advan Study, 58-59; co-ed, Asn Women Math Newslett, 75-76; lectr, Simmons Col, 80- *Mem:* Asn Women Math (pres, 73-75, co-treas, 75-76); Am Math Soc; Am Asn Univ Prof; Math Asn Am. *Res:* Group theory. *Mailing Add:* 60 Spring Valley Rd Belmont MA 02178

SCHAFER, DAVID EDWARD, b Wichita, Kans, Mar 8, 31; m 49; c 2. MEDICAL RESEARCH. *Educ:* Friends Univ, AB, 48; Univ Minn, PhD, 59. *Prof Exp:* Asst English, Univ Minn, 48-51, asst physiol, 53-56, instr, 57-58; from instr to asst prof, Sch Med, NY Univ, 58-63; asst prof pathobiol, Johns Hopkins Univ Ctr Med Res & Training, Calcutta, India, 64-66; mem field staff, Rockefeller Found, 66-68; res physiologist, Exp Surg Lab, Vet Admin Hosp, Minneapolis, 68-73; RES PHYSIOLOGIST, VET ADMIN HOSP, WEST HAVEN, 73-; LECTR PHYSIOL, SCH MED, YALE UNIV, 73- *Concurrent Pos:* Fulbright lectr, Sci Col, Calcutta Univ, 63-64; vis prof physiol & actg head dept, Fac Med Sci, Bangkok, 66-68; asst prof physiol, Med Sch, Univ Minn, Minneapolis, 68-73. *Mem:* AAAS; Biophys Soc; Soc Math Biol. *Res:* Cell physiology; perfusion; membrane permeability; gastrointestinal physiology; cholera. *Mailing Add:* Med Serv Vet Admin Hosp West Haven CT 06516

SCHAFER, GEORGE EDWARD, b Lincoln, Nebr, Apr 27, 22; m 43; c 2. PHYSICS. *Educ:* Macalester Col, BA, 43; Univ Minn, MA, 49; Univ Colo, PhD(physics), 58. *Prof Exp:* Instr physics, Southern Methodist Univ, 48-49; asst prof, Chadron State Col, 49-50; phys sci aide, Nat Bur Stand, 51-52, physicist, 52-56, supvry physicist, 56-62, chief radio stand eng div, 62-66, asst to dep dir radio stand, 66-69, chief microwave stand sect, 69-70; chief scientist & tech dir, US Army Electronics Proving Ground, 70-80; MEM STAFF, UNIT HANDLING SYSTS, LITTON INDUST, INC, 80- *Concurrent Pos:* Vis prof, NC State Col, 61-62; US Dept Com sci & tech fel, 64-65. *Mem:* Am Phys Soc; Sigma Xi; Inst Elec & Electronics Eng. *Res:* Microwave measurements and standards; molecular spectrosopy; electronics testing and evaluation. *Mailing Add:* Unit Handling Systs Litton Indust Inc 7100 Indust Rd Florence KY 41042

SCHAFER, IRWIN ARNOLD, b Pittsburgh, Pa, Mar 22, 28; m 48; c 3. PEDIATRICS, GENETICS. *Educ:* Univ Pittsburgh, BS, 48, MD, 53; Am Bd Pediat, dipl, 59. *Prof Exp:* Intern, Montefiore Hosp, Pittsburgh, 53-54; epidemic intel off & chief hepatitis invest unit, Commun Dis Ctr, USPHS, 54-56; jr asst resident, Children's Hosp Med Ctr, Boston, 56-58; from instr to asst prof pediat, Stanford Univ, 61-67; assoc prof, 67-74, PROF PEDIAT, SCH MED, CASE WESTERN RESERVE UNIV, 74- *Concurrent Pos:* Res fel med, Children's Hosp Med Ctr, Boston, 58-61; res fel prev med, Harvard Med Sch, 58-61; dir premature infant res ctr, USPHS, 63-64, dir birth defects study ctr, 64-69; pediatrician, Case Western Univ Hosp & Cleveland Metrop Gen Hosp. *Mem:* Am Pediat Soc; Am Soc Pediat Res; Am Soc Human Genetics; Am Soc Cell Biol; Tissue Cult Asn. *Res:* Metabolism of cells in culture; cell differentiation and biology; embryonic organogenesis; biochemical genetics. *Mailing Add:* Rm 346 Research Bldg Cleveland Metrop Gen Hosp Cleveland OH 44109

SCHAFER, JAMES A, b Rochester, NY, Dec 11, 39; m 61; c 2. MATHEMATICS. *Educ:* Univ Rochester, BA, 61; Univ Chicago, MS, 62, PhD(math), 65. *Prof Exp:* Asst prof math, Univ Mich, Ann Arbor, 65-70; ASSOC PROF MATH, UNIV MD, COLLEGE PARK, 70- *Concurrent Pos:* Vis lectr, Aarhus Univ, 69-71 & 78-79. *Mem:* Am Math Soc. *Res:* Algebraic topology; homological algebra. *Mailing Add:* Dept of Math Univ of Md College Park MD 20742

SCHAFER, JAMES ARTHUR, b Buffalo, NY, Oct 10, 41; m 64; c 2. PHYSIOLOGY, NEPHROLOGY. *Educ:* Univ Mich, BS, 63, PhD(physiol), 68. *Prof Exp:* Fel biochem, Gustav-Embden Ctr, W Ger, 68-69; fel physiol, Duke Univ, 69-70; from asst prof to assoc prof physiol, 70-76, asst prof med, 70-78, PROF PHYSIOL, UNIV ALA, 76-, ASSOC PROF MED, 78-, SR SCIENTIST, NEPHROLOGY RES & TRAINING CTR, 77- *Honors & Awards:* Estab Investr Award, Am Heart Asn, 71. *Mem:* Am Physiol Soc; Am Soc Nephrol; Biophys Soc; Am Fedn Clin Res; Am Heart Asn. *Res:* Membrane transport process as related to renal tubules and Ehrlich ascites tumor cells. *Mailing Add:* Dept of Physiol & Biophys Univ of Ala Birmingham AL 35294

SCHAFER, JOHN FRANCIS, b Pullman, Wash, Feb 17, 21; m 47; c 3. PLANT PATHOLOGY. *Educ:* State Col Wash, BS, 42; Univ Wis, PhD(plant path, agron), 50. *Prof Exp:* Agt, Bur Plant Indust, USDA, 39-42; asst plant path, Univ Wis, 46-49; from asst prof to prof plant path, Purdue Univ, 49-68; prof & head dept, Kans State Univ, 68-72; prof & chmn dept, Wash State Univ, 72-80; integrated pest mgt coordr, Sci & Educ Admin, 80-81, actg nat res prog leader path & nemotol, Agr Res Serv, 81-82, DIR, CEREAL RUST LAB, AGR RES SERV, UNIV MINN, USDA, 82- *Concurrent Pos:* Vis res prof, Duquesne Univ, 65-66; adj prof, Univ Minn, 82- *Mem:* Fel AAAS; Am Phytopath Soc (pres, 78-79); Am Soc Agron. *Res:* Diseases of cereal crops; cereal breeding; plant disease resistance. *Mailing Add:* Cereal Rust Lab Univ Minn 1551 Lindig St St Paul MN 55108

SCHAFER, JOHN WILLIAM, JR, b Mt Pleasant, Mich, May 18, 37; m 67; c 3. SOIL SCIENCE, SOIL GEOGRAPHY. *Educ:* Mich State Univ, BS, 59, PhD(soil sci), 68; Kans State Univ, MS, 60. *Prof Exp:* Assoc prof, 68-80, PROF AGRON, IOWA STATE UNIV, 80- *Concurrent Pos:* Vis prof, Shenyang Agr Col, People's Repub China. *Mem:* Am Soc Agron; Soil Sci Soc Am; fel Nat Asn Cols & Teachers Agr; Soil Conserv Soc Am. *Res:* Relationships of soils to landscapes and their influence on land use and food production; new methods for effective teaching of undergraduate soil science. *Mailing Add:* Dept of Agron Iowa State Univ Ames IA 50011

SCHAFER, LOTHAR, b Dusseldorf, WGer, May 5, 39; m 65; c 2. PHYSICAL CHEMISTRY, INORGANIC CHEMISTRY. *Educ:* Univ Munich, dipl, 62, PhD(inorg chem), 65. *Prof Exp:* NATO fel chem, Oslo, 65-67; res assoc, Ind Univ, Bloomington, 67-68; from asst prof to assoc prof phys chem, 68-75, PROF PHYS CHEM, UNIV ARK, FAYETTEVILLE, 75- *Concurrent Pos:* Teacher-scholar grant, Dreyfus Found, 71; vis prof, Yukawa Hall, Univ Kyoto, Japan, 76. *Mem:* Am Chem Soc; Royal Soc Chem. *Res:* Structural studies by abinitio calculations. electron diffraction and spectroscopy; theoretical investigations of biophysical phenomena. *Mailing Add:* Dept of Chem Univ of Ark Fayetteville AR 72701

SCHAFER, MARY LOUISE, b Shelburn, Ind, Nov 4, 15. FOOD CHEMISTRY. *Educ:* Purdue Univ, BS, 38, PhD(chem), 55; Columbia Univ, MS, 49. *Prof Exp:* Intern, Univ Hosp, Western Reserve Univ, 39, dietitian, 40-42; asst nutrit, Teachers Col, Columbia Univ, 47-51; asst chem, Purdue Univ, 51-54; chemist, USPHS, Ohio, 55-69; CHEMIST, CINCINNATI RES LABS, FOOD & DRUG ADMIN, 69- *Mem:* Am Chem Soc; Am Dietetic Asn. *Res:* Detection and assay methods for organomercury compounds in the environment; gas chromatographic methods for microbiological assessment of canned foods. *Mailing Add:* Food & Drug Admin Res Labs DM 1090 Tusculum Ave Cincinnati OH 45226

SCHAFER, RICHARD DONALD, b Buffalo, NY, Feb 25, 18; m 42; c 2. MATHEMATICS. *Educ:* Univ Buffalo, BA, 38, MA, 40; Univ Chicago, PhD(math), 42. *Prof Exp:* Instr math, Univ Mich, 45-46; mem, Inst Advan Study, 46-48; asst prof math, Univ Pa, 48-53; prof & head dept, Univ Conn, 53-59; dep head dept, 59-68, PROF MATH, MASS INST TECHNOL, 59- *Concurrent Pos:* NSF sr fel, Inst Advan Study, 58-59; mem, Sci Manpower Comn, 59-63. *Mem:* Am Math Soc (assoc secy, 54-58); Math Asn Am. *Res:* Nonassociative and Lie algebras. *Mailing Add:* Rm 2-243 Dept of Math Mass Inst of Technol Cambridge MA 02139

SCHAFER, ROBERT JOSEPH, metallurgy, chemistry, see previous edition

SCHAFER, ROBERT LOUIS, b Burlington, Iowa, Aug 1, 37; m 59; c 1. AGRICULTURAL ENGINEERING, ENGINEERING MECHANICS. *Educ:* Iowa State Univ, BS, 59, MS, 61, PhD(agr eng, eng mech), 65. *Prof Exp:* Agr engr, Agr Res Serv, Ames, Iowa, 59-64, AGR ENGR, NAT TILLAGE MACH LAB, AGR RES SERV, USDA, 64- *Concurrent Pos:* Res lectr, Auburn Univ, 70- *Mem:* Am Soc Agr Engrs; Instrument Soc Am; Asn Comput Mach; Int Soc Terrain Vehicle Systs. *Res:* Soil dynamics as a mechanics of the actions of tillage tools and traction devices in soil. *Mailing Add:* Nat Tillage Mach Lab PO Box 792 Auburn AL 36830

SCHAFER, ROLLIE R, b Denver, Colo, Feb 17, 42; m 64; c 2. NEUROBIOLOGY. *Educ:* Univ Colo, Boulder, BA, 64, MA, 67, PhD(zool), 69. *Prof Exp:* Asst prof biol, Metrop State Col Colo, 68-69 & NMex Inst Mining & Technol, 69-73; asst prof biol sci, Div Biol Sci, Univ Mich, Ann Arbor, 73-76; ASSOC PROF BIOL SCI & ASST DEAN GRAD SCH, NORTH TEX STATE UNIV, 78- *Concurrent Pos:* NSF res grants, 72-73, 74-76 & 81-83. *Mem:* AAAS; Am Soc Zoologists; NY Acad Sci; Am Soc Neurochem; Soc Neurosci. *Res:* Sensory mechanisms; microtubule function in neurons. *Mailing Add:* Dept Biol Sci North Tex State Univ Denton TX 76203

SCHAFER, RONALD W, b Tecumseh, Nebr, Feb 17, 38; m 60; c 3. ELECTRICAL ENGINEERING. *Educ:* Univ Nebr, Lincoln, BSc, 61, MSc, 62; Mass Inst Technol, PhD(elec eng), 68. *Prof Exp:* Instr elec eng, Univ Nebr, Lincoln, 62-63 & Mass Inst Technol, 64-68; mem tech staff, Bell Tel Labs, 68-74; PROF SCH ELEC ENG, GA INST TECHNOL, 74- *Mem:* Fel Inst Elec & Electronics Engrs; fel Acoust Soc Am; Acoust, Speech & Signal Processing Soc (pres, 77-79); Optical Soc Am. *Res:* Digital signal processing for speech analysis/synthesis, waveform coding, and deconvolution. *Mailing Add:* Sch of Elec Eng Ga Inst of Technol Atlanta GA 30332

SCHAFER, THOMAS WAYNE, b Fresno, Calif, Oct 21, 38; m 62; c 3. MICROBIOLOGY, BIOCHEMISTRY. *Educ:* Univ Calif, Santa Barbara, BA, 61; Fresno State Col, MA, 62; Univ Kans, PhD(microbiol), 67. *Prof Exp:* Fel viron, E I du Pont de Nemours & Co, 67-69; sr scientist, 69-73, dept head, 75-77, PRIN SCIENTIST, SCHERING CORP, 73-, MGR ANTIBIOTIC CHEMOTHER, 77- *Mem:* AAAS; Am Soc Microbiologists; Sigma Xi; Brit Soc Gen Microbiol. *Res:* Inhibition of viral replication; interferon; antiviral drugs; modes of action at cellular and molecular levels; structure and replication of animal viruses in vitro and in vivo evaluation of novel antibiotics. *Mailing Add:* Virol Dept Schering Corp 86 Orange St Bloomfield NJ 07003

SCHAFFEL, GERSON SAMUEL, b Braddock, Pa, Mar 17, 18; m 43; c 3. CHEMISTRY, RESEARCH ADMINISTRATION. *Educ:* Carnegie Inst Technol, BS, 39, MS, 40, DSc(org chem), 42. *Prof Exp:* Fel, Westinghouse Res Lab, 42-43, group leader, Plastics Sect, 43-46; instr chem, Carnegie Inst Technol, 45-46; dir plastics res & develop, Gen Tire & Rubber Co, 46-50, mgr mfg & develop, Chem Div, 50-54, dir res, Brea Chem, Inc, 54-56; dir res, Sci Design Co, Inc, 56-60, asst vpres, 60-63, vpres, New York, 63-73; MGR NEW TECHNOL, BADGER CO, INC, CAMBRIDGE, 73- *Mem:* Am Chem Soc; fel Am Inst Chemists; NY Acad Sci. *Res:* Kinetics and mechanisms of organic reactions; mechanism of formation of condensation polymers; polymerization of vinyl compounds; new polyesters; petrochemicals; research administration; process licensing. *Mailing Add:* Badger Co Inc One Broadway Cambridge MA 02142

SCHAFFER, ARNOLD MARTIN, b New York, NY, Sept 24, 42; m 63; c 3. PHYSICAL CHEMISTRY, SURFACE SCIENCE. *Educ:* Polytech Inst Brooklyn, BS, 63; Univ Wash, PhD(chem), 70. *Prof Exp:* Fel chem, Univ Houston, 71-74; SR RES CHEMIST, PHILLIPS PETROL CO, 74-, MGR CATALYTIC CRACKING, 81- *Concurrent Pos:* Instr, Univ Houston, 73-74. *Mem:* Am Chem Soc; Am Phys Soc. *Res:* Properties of heterogeneous catalysts; development of spectroscopic techniques; molecular spectroscopy; molecular orbital calculations. *Mailing Add:* Phillips Petrol Co 85G PRC Bartlesville OK 74004

SCHAFFER, ERWIN LAMBERT, b Milwaukee, Wis, Nov 26, 36; m 60; c 1. ENGINEERING MECHANICS, CHEMICAL ENGINEERING. *Educ:* Univ Wis, BS, 59, MS, 61, PhD(eng mech), 71. *Prof Exp:* Struct engr, US Bur Reclamation, 61-63; res engr, 63-73, supvry res engr, Forest Prod Lab, 73-82, NAT WOOD CONSTRUCTION SPECIALIST, STATE & PVT FORESTRY, US FOREST SERV, 82- *Concurrent Pos:* Consult, Am Soc Testing & Mat, 68-; res assoc, Nat Bur Standards, 76-77. *Mem:* Soc Wood Sci & Technol (exec secy, 66-77, pres, 77-78); Forest Prod Res Soc; Am Soc Civil Engrs; Nat Soc Prof Engrs; Nat Inst Bldg Sci. *Res:* Effects of elevated temperature and fire on material and structural performance. *Mailing Add:* Forest Prod Lab US Forest Serv PO Box 5130 Madison WI 53705

SCHAFFER, ERWIN MICHAEL, b Dumont, Minn, July 9, 22; m 47; c 4. PERIODONTOLOGY. *Educ:* Univ Minn, DDS, 45, MSD, 51. *Prof Exp:* Clin prof & chmn div, 57-64, dean, 64-80, PROF PERIODONTICS, SCH DENT, UNIV MINN, MINNEAPOLIS, 64- *Honors & Awards:* William J Gies Award Periodont, 74. *Mem:* Am Dent Asn; fel Am Col Dent; Am Acad Periodont; Am Acad Oral Med; Int Asn Dent Res. *Res:* Bone regeneration in periodontal disease; cartilage or cementum and dentine grafts; etiology of periodontal disease; root curettage; circadian periodicity. *Mailing Add:* Univ of Minn Sch of Dent Minneapolis MN 55455

SCHAFFER, FREDERICK LELAND, b Kingsburg, Calif, July 5, 21; m 45; c 6. VIROLOGY, BIOCHEMISTRY. *Educ:* Univ Calif, Berkeley, BA, 43, PhD(biochem), 50. *Prof Exp:* Asst, 47-50, from asst res biochemist to assoc res biochemist, 54-63, RES BIOCHEMIST, UNIV CALIF, BERKELEY, 63- *Concurrent Pos:* Res fel, Univ Calif, Berkeley, 50-53, lectr med microbiol, 64-77; mem, Int Comt Taxon Viruses, 81- *Mem:* AAAS; Am Soc Microbiol; Tissue Cult Asn; Am Soc Virol. *Res:* Tissue culture; microanalysis; purification, properties and molecular biology of viruses. *Mailing Add:* Naval Biosci Lab Warren Hall Univ of Calif Berkeley CA 94720

SCHAFFER, HENRY ELKIN, b New York, NY, May 4, 38; m 64; c 2. GENETICS. *Educ:* Cornell Univ, BS, 59; NC State Univ, MS, 62, PhD(genetics), 64. *Prof Exp:* NIH fel gen med studies, Cornell Univ, 64-65; asst prof biol, Brandeis Univ, 65-66; from asst prof to assoc prof, 66-80, PROF GENETICS, NC STATE UNIV, 74-, PROF BIOMATH, 80- *Mem:* AAAS; Biomet Soc; Genetics Soc Am; Soc Study Evolution; Am Soc Naturalists. *Res:* Population and mathematical genetics; biometrics; computing and bioinstrumentation. *Mailing Add:* Dept of Genetics NC State Univ PO Box 5487 Raleigh NC 27650

SCHAFFER, MARVIN BAKER, b New York, NY, July 14, 26; m 48; c 3. CHEMICAL ENGINEERING, OPERATIONS RESEARCH. *Educ:* Cooper Union, BChE, 50; Newark Col Eng, MSChE, 56. *Prof Exp:* Engr, Heparin, Inc, NJ, 50-51, Nord & Co, 51-52 & Picatinny Arsenal, 52-60; mem prof staff opers res, Lockheed Electronics Co, 60-61 & Rand Corp, 61-71; mem prof staff opers res, R & D Assocs, 72-76; mem staff, 76-80, SR SCIENTIST, SCI APPLN INC, 80- *Concurrent Pos:* Instr, Newark Col Eng, 56-61. *Mem:* Am Chem Soc; Am Inst Chem Engrs; Opers Res Soc Am; Am Inst Aeronaut & Astronaut; Am Ord Asn. *Res:* Physical phenomenology of weapons; design, effectiveness and employment of military weaponry; mathematical modeling of military and sociological phenomena for purposes of analysis. *Mailing Add:* Sci Appln Inc 1801 Ave of Stars Los Angeles CA 90067

SCHAFFER, MICHAEL IRVING, b Chicago, Ill, Mar 21, 45; m 68; c 2. TOXICOLOGY, PHARMACOLOGY. *Educ:* Univ Ill, BS, 66 & 69, MS, 70; Univ Chicago, PhD(toxicol), 74. *Prof Exp:* RES ASSOC TOXICOL, UNIV CHICAGO, 74- *Mem:* AAAS; Sigma Xi. *Res:* Drug interactions involving the induction of microsomal enzymes and the effect in vivo on metabolism of organophosphate and organochlorine compounds; determinations of cholinesterase, aliesterase, Cytochrome P-450 and b5 are measured. *Mailing Add:* Univ of Chicago 1116 E 59th St Chicago IL 60637

SCHAFFER, PRISCILLA ANN, b St Louis, Mo, Dec 28, 41. VIROLOGY. *Educ:* Hobart & William Smith Cols, BA, 64; Cornell Univ, PhD(microbiol), 69. *Prof Exp:* asst prof virol, Dept Virol & Epidemiol, Baylor Col Med, 71-76; assoc prof, 76-81, PROF MICROBIOL, DEPT MICROBIOL & MOLECULAR GENETICS, HARVARD MED SCH, 81- *Concurrent Pos:* Fel, Baylor Col Med, 69-71; Found lectr, Am Soc Microbiol, 81-82. *Mem:* AAAS; Am Soc Microbiol; Am Soc Trop Med & Hyg; Brit Soc Gen Microbiol. *Res:* Genetics of DNA tumor viruses, especially herpesviruses. *Mailing Add:* Sidney Farber Cancer Inst Harvard Med Sch Boston MA 02115

SCHAFFER, ROBERT, b New York, NY, Mar 8, 20; m 42; c 3. ANALYTICAL CHEMISTRY, BIO-ORGANIC CHEMISTRY. *Educ:* Brooklyn Col, AB, 43; Washington Univ, PhD(chem), 50. *Prof Exp:* Chemist, Int Hormones, Inc, NY, 41-44; chemist, Los Alamos Sci Lab, Univ Calif, 44-46; org chemist, Washington Univ, 46-50; org chemist, 50-66, chief org chem sect, 66-73, chief bio-org standards sect, 73-78, SUPVRY RES CHEMIST, ANAL CHEM CTR, NAT BUR STANDARDS, 78- *Concurrent Pos:* Lectr, Georgetown Univ, 59-61; fel, Cambridge Univ, 61-62; consult diag prod comt, Food & Drug Admin, 74-76; mem coun, Nat Ref Syst Clin Chem, 81- *Mem:* AAAS; Am Chem Soc; Am Asn Clin Chem. *Res:* Reaction mechanisms; radiochemical applications; position labeled carbohydrates; organic chemical analysis and characterization; purity; chemical and clinical chemical standards. *Mailing Add:* Bio-org Standards Sect Nat Bur Stand Anal Chem Div Washington DC 20234

SCHAFFER, SHELDON ARTHUR, b Salt Lake City, Utah, June 12, 43; m 66; c 3. BIOLOGICAL CHEMISTRY. *Educ:* Univ Calif, Berkeley, BS, 65; Univ Ill, Urbana, PhD(chem), 70. *Prof Exp:* NIH res fel biol chem, Med Sch, Harvard Univ, 70-72; teaching fel biochem, 72-73; res biochemist immunol, 73-74, group leader atherosclerosis res, 74-81, HEAD, DEPT METAB & ENDOCRINOL RES, MED RES DIV, AM CYANAMID CO, 81- *Mem:* Am Chem Soc; Am Heart Asn; The Chem Soc. *Res:* Lipids chemistry and metabolism; atherosclerosis; platelet structure and function; membrane biochemistry. *Mailing Add:* Med Res Div N Middletown Rd Pearl River NY 10965

SCHAFFER, STEPHEN WARD, b San Diego, Calif, Oct 15, 44; m 67; c 2. BIOCHEMISTRY. *Educ:* Buena Vista Col, BS, 66; Univ Minn, PhD(biochem), 70. *Prof Exp:* Vis prof biochem, Univ El Salvador, 70-71; fel, Johnson Found, Univ Pa, 71-73; from asst prof to assoc prof chem, LeHigh Univ, 73-80; res assoc prof physiol, Hahnemann Med Col, 78-80; ASSOC PROF PHARMACOL, UNIV SOUTH ALA, 80- *Mem:* Am Chem Soc; Int Study Group Study Cardiac Metab. *Res:* Examination of several aspects of cardiac metabolism, including effects of taurine and tolbutamide, the role of calcium in cardiac ischemia, and diabetic cardiomyopathy. *Mailing Add:* Dept Pharmacol Col Med Univ South Ala Mobile AL 36688

SCHAFFER, WILLIAM JOSEPH, b St Louis, Mo, Feb 8, 49. SURFACE SCIENCE, CRYSTAL GROWTH. *Educ:* Univ Tex, Austin, BS, 70, MS, 73, PhD(elec eng & physics), 77. *Prof Exp:* Develop engr, Off Prods Div, IBM, 71-75; MEM TECH STAFF, SCI CTR, ROCKWELL INT, 78- *Mem:* Am Phys Soc; Am Vacuum Soc. *Res:* Growth of tailored III-V ternary and quaternary semiconductors thin film compounds by molecular beam epitaxy; surface properties of these compounds. *Mailing Add:* Sci Ctr Rockwell Int 1049 Camino Dos Rios Thousand Oaks CA 91360

SCHAFFER, WILLIAM MORRIS, b Elizabeth, NJ, May 11, 45; m 70. ECOLOGY, EVOLUTIONARY BIOLOGY. *Educ:* Yale Univ, BS, 67; Princeton Univ, MS, 71, PhD(biol), 72. *Prof Exp:* Asst prof biol, Univ Utah, 72-75; asst prof, 75-77, assoc prof biol, 77-80, ASSOC PROF ECOL & EVOLUTIONARY BIOL, UNIV ARIZ, 80- *Mem:* AAAS; Sigma Xi; Soc Study Evolution; Ecol Soc Am; Am Soc Naturalists. *Res:* Evolutionary and ecological aspects of reproductive strategies; plant-pollinator interactions. *Mailing Add:* Dept Ecol & Evolutionary Biol Univ of Ariz Tucson AZ 87521

SCHAFFERS, WILHELMUS J, b Haarlem, Neth, Dec 6, 27; US citizen; m 54; c 5. APPLIED MATHEMATICS, MECHANICAL ENGINEERING. *Educ:* Delft Univ Technol, MS, 50; Univ Del, PhD(appl sci), 67. *Prof Exp:* Res engr, Dutch State Mines, 51-57; engr, Indust Prod Res Lab, Textile Fibers Dept, 57-59, res engr, 59-61, eng res div, 61-63, tech serv engr, Math & Statist Sect, 63-64, sr engr, 64-65, SUPVR ENG RES DIV, MATH & STATIST SECT, E I DU PONT DE NEMOURS & CO, 65- *Concurrent Pos:* Lectr, Inst Tech, Heerlen, Neth, 53-57; asst prof, Univ Del exten div, 67- *Res:* Aerodynamics; solid mechanics; numerical analysis. *Mailing Add:* 2408 Dorval Rd Chalfonte Wilmington DE 19810

SCHAFFNER, CARL PAUL, b Bayonne, NJ, Feb 13, 28. BIOCHEMISTRY. *Educ:* Columbia Univ, AB, 50; Univ Ill, PhD, 53. *Prof Exp:* Fel microbiol, Univ, 53-54, from instr to assoc prof, Inst, 54-72, PROF MICROBIOL, WAKSMAN INST MICROBIOL, RUTGERS UNIV, 72-, PROF BIOCHEM, 80- *Honors & Awards:* Pres Medal Honor, Repub Philippines, 73. *Mem:* AAAS; Am Soc Microbiol; Am Soc Biol Chemists; Am Chem Soc; Royal Soc Chem. *Res:* Antibiotic chemistry; chemotherapy mechanism of action; biosynthesis. *Mailing Add:* 10 Youngs Rd Trenton NJ 08619

SCHAFFNER, FENTON, b Chicago, Ill, Dec 8, 20; m 43, 78; c 4. MEDICINE, LIVER DISEASES. *Educ:* Univ Chicago, BS, 41, MD, 43; Northwestern Univ, MS, 49; Am Bd Internal Med, dipl, 52 & 77; Am Bd Gastroenterol, dipl, 59. *Prof Exp:* Asst path, Med Sch, Northwestern Univ,

48-53, instr med, 55-57; assoc med, Col Physicians & Surgeons, Columbia Univ, 58-61, assoc prof path, 61-66; from assoc prof to prof, 66-73, actg chmn dept, 72-74, GEORGE BAEHR PROF MED, MT SINAI SCH MED, 73-, PROF PATH, 66- *Concurrent Pos:* chmn dept med, Woodlawn Hosp, Chicago, 50-57; from asst attend physician to attend physician, Mt Sinai Hosp, 58- *Mem:* Am Asn Path; Am Gastroenterol Asn; fel Am Col Physicians; Am Asn Study Liver Dis (secy, 58-72, vpres, 75-76, pres, 76-77); Int Asn Study Liver. *Res:* Liver disease, especially electron microscopy of liver, drug induced liver disease. *Mailing Add:* 1176 Fifth Ave New York NY 10029

SCHAFFNER, GERALD, b Chicago, Ill, May 14, 27; m 52; c 3. ELECTRICAL ENGINEERING. *Educ:* Purdue Univ, BS, 49, MS, 50; Northwestern Univ, PhD(electronics), 56. *Prof Exp:* Asst, Purdue Univ, 49-50; design engr, Thordarson Elec Co, 50-51; proj engr, Stewart-Warner Corp, 51-57 & Motorola, Inc, 57-66; opers mgr microwave semiconductor devices, 66-69; ENG MGR MICROWAVES & MICROELECTRONICS, TELEDYNE RYAN ELECTRON CO, 69- *Mem:* Inst Elec & Electronics Engrs. *Res:* Microwave applications of solid state devices; microwave radar systems; impatt diodes. *Mailing Add:* 10325 Caminito Cuervo Apt 193 San Diego CA 92108

SCHAFFNER, JOSEPH CLARENCE, b Paducah, Ky, Mar 20, 30; m 60; c 2. ENTOMOLOGY. *Educ:* Iowa Wesleyan Col, BS, 51; Iowa State Univ, MS, 53, PhD(entom), 64. *Prof Exp:* Instr entom, Univ, 61 & Iowa State Univ, 61-62; asst prof, 63-68, assoc prof, 68-80, PROF ENTOM, TEX A&M UNIV, 80- *Mem:* Entom Soc Am; Soc Syst Zool; Royal Entom Soc London. *Res:* Systematic entomology; insect taxonomy. *Mailing Add:* Dept of Entom Tex A&M Univ College Station TX 77843

SCHAFFNER, ROBERT M(ICHAEL), b Brooklyn, NY, Jan 30, 15; m 40; c 3. CHEMICAL ENGINEERING. *Educ:* Polytech Inst Brooklyn, BChE, 36; WVa Univ, MS, 39; Univ Pittsburgh, PhD(chem eng), 41. *Prof Exp:* Chem engr, A Hess & Co, NY, 36-37; asst chem eng, WVa Univ, 37-39; instr, Univ Pittsburgh, 39-41; chem engr, Res Dept, Standard Oil Co, Ind, 41-43; chem engr & head food dehydration, Miner Labs, 43-44; chem engr, Libby, McNeill & Libby, 45-48, asst to vpres prod, 49-53, asst gen supt, Eastern Div, 53-57, vpres res & qual standards, 57-70; ASSOC DIR TECHNOL, BUR FOODS, FOOD & DRUG ADMIN, 71- *Mem:* Am Chem Soc; Am Inst Chem Engrs; fel Inst Food Technol. *Res:* Drying; vacuum distillation; food dehydration; food canning; food freezing. *Mailing Add:* Bur Foods BF400 200 C St SW Washington DC 20204

SCHAFFNER, WILLIAM ROBERT, b Winthrop, Mass, Feb 29, 36; m 59; c 2. AQUATIC ECOLOGY. *Educ:* Univ Hartford, BS, 64; Cornell Univ, MS, 66, PhD(aquatic ecol), 71. *Prof Exp:* RES ASSOC AQUATIC SCI, CORNELL UNIV, 71- *Concurrent Pos:* Lectr, Cornell Univ, 79- *Mem:* Am Soc Limnol & Oceanog; Ecol Soc Am; Sigma Xi. *Res:* Marine and freshwater phytoplankton ecology; nutrient sources for lakes and streams. *Mailing Add:* Dept of Natural Resources Cornell Univ Ithaca NY 14853

SCHAFFRATH, ROBERT EBEN, b Syracuse, NY, Feb 19, 22; m 61; c 3. ORGANIC CHEMISTRY. *Educ:* Bates Col, BS, 44; Syracuse Univ, MS, 48, PhD(chem), 58. *Prof Exp:* Instr chem, New Eng Col, 48-51; instr org chem, Univ Mass, 51-54; vis lectr chem, State Univ NY Teachers Col, New Paltz, 58-59, assoc prof, 59-60; chmn dept, 60-65, assoc prof, 60-75, PROF CHEM, C W POST COL, LONG ISLAND UNIV, 75- *Mem:* AAAS; Am Chem Soc; NY Acad Sci. *Res:* Mannich reaction; hindered rotation in organic compounds; nitrogen-sulfur heterocycles; hydrazines; organic synthesis. *Mailing Add:* Dept of Chem C W Post Col Greenvale NY 11548

SCHAFFT, HARRY ARTHUR, b New York, NY, May 21, 32; m 62; c 2. ELECTRONICS. *Educ:* NY Univ, BS, 54; Univ Md, MS, 58. *Prof Exp:* PHYSICIST, NAT BUR STANDARDS, 58- *Mem:* Inst Elec & Electronics Engrs; Am Phys Soc. *Res:* Materials, process, assembly, and device characterization and measurement for power transistors, integrated circuits, solar cells; technology transfer and information dissemination. *Mailing Add:* Nat Bur Standards Washington DC 20234

SCHAFROTH, DON W, b Enid, Okla, Apr 18, 28; m 58; c 2. STRUCTURAL GEOLOGY, STRATIGRAPHY. *Educ:* Colo Col, BS, 57; Univ Ariz, PhD(geol), 65. *Prof Exp:* Asst prof geol, Portland State Col, 62-71, admin asst to pres, 64-71; dean undergrad studies, 71-80, PROF PHYSICS & EARTH SCI, CALIF STATE POLYTECH UNIV, POMONA, 71- *Mem:* Geol Soc Am; Am Inst Prof Geologists. *Res:* Structural geology and Cretaceous stratigraphy of the Empire Mountains, Arizona; engineering geologic problems of the West Portland metropolitan area. *Mailing Add:* Calif State Polytech Univ 3801 W Temple Ave Pomona CA 91768

SCHAIBERGER, GEORGE ELMER, b Saginaw, Mich, Oct 27, 28; m 50; c 2. ECOLOGY. *Educ:* Univ Fla, BS, 50, MS, 51; Univ Tex, PhD(microbiol), 55. *Prof Exp:* Asst, Univ Fla, 50-51 & Univ Tex, 51-52; instr microbiol, Univ Ark, 55-57; sr res scientist, Merck & Co, 57-61; from instr to asst prof, 62-69, assoc prof, 69-77, PROF MICROBIOL, SCH MED, UNIV MIAMI, 77- *Concurrent Pos:* Del, Int Cong Microbiol, 61; NASA & NIH grants, 66-67; res career develop award, USPHS, 67-72. *Honors & Awards:* Outstanding Res Award, Merck & Co, 61. *Mem:* Am Soc Microbiol; fel Geront Soc. *Res:* Microbial ecology; radiation biology; nucleic acid and protein synthesis; metabolic changes associated with aging; environmental effects on cells; environmental virology. *Mailing Add:* Dept Microbiol Univ Miami Miami FL 33101

SCHAIBLE, ROBERT HILTON, b Horton, Kans, Apr 30, 31; m 73; c 2. COMPARATIVE MEDICAL GENETICS. *Educ:* Colo State Univ, BS, 53; Iowa State Univ, MS, 59, PhD(genetics, embryol), 63. *Prof Exp:* Res assoc, Hall Lab Mammalian Genetics, Univ Kans, 62-63; fel, Biol Dept, Yale Univ, 63-64; asst prof genetics, NC State Univ, 64-68; USPHS spec res fel, Dept Zool, Ind Univ, Bloomington, 68-70; asst prof biol, Ind Univ-Purdue Univ,

Indianapolis, 70-73; ASST PROF, DEPT MED GENETICS, SCH MED, IND UNIV, 73- *Concurrent Pos:* Adj asst prof, Sch Vet Med, Purdue Univ, 77- *Mem:* AAAS; Am Genetic Asn; Int Pigment Cell Soc; Am Asn Univ Prof; Am Soc Human Genetics. *Res:* Comparative genetics of vertebrates; genetic control of morphogenesis; proliferation, migration, mutation and differentiation of pigment cells in the clonal development of the pigmentation of the integument. *Mailing Add:* Dept Med Genetics Ind Univ Sch Med 1100 W Michigan St Indianapolis IN 46223

SCHAICH, KAREN MARIE, b Hamilton, Ohio, Nov 21, 47. FOOD SCIENCE, BIOCHEMISTRY. *Educ:* Purdue Univ, BS, 69; Mass Inst Technol, ScD(food sci), 74. *Prof Exp:* Res assoc, 74-76, asst scientist, 76-78, assoc scientist, 78-80, SCIENTIST, MED DEPT, BROOKHAVEN NAT LAB, 80- *Mem:* Am Chem Soc; Inst Food Technologists; AAAS; NY Acad Sci; Sigma Xi. *Res:* Electron spin resonance studies; free radicals in biological systems; oxidizing lipids: especially, free radical reactions, interactions with proteins and toxicology; biochemistry of food deterioration; diet and nutrition effects of toxicological sensitivities and mechanisms. *Mailing Add:* Med Dept Brookhaven Nat Lab Upton NY 11973

SCHAICH, WILLIAM LEE, b Springfield, Mass, Oct 15, 44; m 66; c 2. THEORETICAL SOLID STATE PHYSICS. *Educ:* Denison Univ, BS, 66; Cornell Univ, MS, 68, PhD(theoret physics), 70. *Prof Exp:* Fel physics, Air Force Off Sci Res, 70-71; res assoc, Univ Calif, San Diego, 71-73; asst prof, 73-76, assoc prof, 76-80, PROF PHYSICS, IND UNIV, BLOOMINGTON, 80- *Mem:* Am Phys Soc. *Res:* Fundamental problems in theory of electronic structure and processes. *Mailing Add:* Dept of Physics Swain Hall Ind Univ Bloomington IN 47401

SCHAIN, RICHARD J, b New York, NY, Oct 16, 32; m 52; c 2. PEDIATRIC NEUROLOGY. *Educ:* NY Univ, AB, 50, MD, 54. *Prof Exp:* Resident pediat, Sch Med, Yale Univ, 57-59; from asst prof to assoc prof neurol & psychiat, Univ Nebr, 62-66; assoc prof pediat, Univ Calif, Los Angeles, 67-77, prof pediat, neurol & psychiat, 77-80. *Concurrent Pos:* Spec fel neurol, 59-60 & 61-62; spec fel physiol & pharmacol, Nat Inst Med Res, London, 60-61; adj prof pediat, neurol & psychiat, Univ Calif, Los Angeles, 80- *Mem:* Am Acad Neurol; Am Acad Pediat; Soc Res Child Develop; Soc Pediat Res; Am Asn Ment Deficiency. *Res:* Early nutrition and brain development; factors affecting postnatal brain protein metabolism; epilepsy; minimal brain dysfunction in childhood. *Mailing Add:* Dept of Pediat Univ of Calif Los Angeles CA 90024

SCHAIRER, G(EORGE) S(WIFT), b Wilkinsburg, Pa, May 19, 13; m 35; c 4. AERONAUTICAL ENGINEERING. *Educ:* Swarthmore Col, BS, 34; Mass Inst Technol, MS, 35. *Hon Degrees:* DEng, Swarthmore Col, 58. 58. *Prof Exp:* Aeronaut engr, Bendix Prod Corp, 35-37 & Consol Aircraft Corp, 37-39; from aerodynamicist to dir res, Boeing Co, 39-59, vpres & develop, 59-71, vpres, 71-78; CONSULT, 78- *Concurrent Pos:* Mem sci adv group, US Air Force, 44-45; sci adv bd, 56-59; mem aerodyn comt, Power Plant Comt & chmn subcomt propellers for aircraft, Nat Adv Comt Aeronaut; mem steering comt, Adv Panel Aeronaut, US Dept Defense, 57-61; mem comt aircraft operating prog, NASA, 59-60; mem panel on sci & tech manpower, President's Sci Adv Comt, 63-64; mem sci adv comt, Defense Intel Agency, 65-71; trustee, Univ Res Asn, 66-76; mem aeronaut & space eng bd, Nat Res Coun. *Honors & Awards:* Reed Award, Am Inst Aeronaut & Astronaut, 49; Am Soc Mech Engrs Medal, 58; Daniel Guggenheim Medal. *Mem:* Nat Acad Sci; Nat Acad Eng; Int Acad Astronaut; fel Am Inst Aeronaut & Astronaut. *Res:* Aerodynamic design of large aircraft. *Mailing Add:* 4242 Hunts Point Rd Bellevue WA 98004

SCHAIRER, ROBERT S(ORG), b Plum Twp, Pa, Sept 7, 15; m 47; c 6. AERONAUTICS. *Educ:* Swarthmore Col, BS, 36; Calif Inst Technol, MS, 37, PhD(aeronaut), 39. *Prof Exp:* Aerodynamicist & asst chief airborne vehicles sect, Proj Rand, Douglas Aircraft Co, 39-48; asst chief aircraft div, Rand Corp, 48-53, chief, 53-56; tech asst to corp dir develop planning, Lockheed Aircraft Corp, 56-60, asst dir, 60-61; chief scientist, Pac Missile Range, Dept Navy, Calif, 61-62; asst corp dir develop planning, Lockheed Aircraft Corp, 62-63, corp dir, 63-67, assoc dir corp plan, 76-81; RETIRED. *Mem:* Am Inst Aeronaut & Astronaut. *Res:* Unsymmetrical lift distribution on a stalled monoplane wing; stability and control in flight testing; airplane performance. *Mailing Add:* Develop Planning PO Box 551 Lockheed Aircraft Corp Burbank CA 91503

SCHAKE, LOWELL MARTIN, b Marthasville, Mo, 39; m; c 2. ANIMAL SCIENCE. *Educ:* Univ Mo, BS, 60, MS, 62; Tex A&M Univ, PhD(animal nutrit), 67. *Prof Exp:* Asst prof, 65-72, area livestock specialist, 67-69, mem grad fac, 67-80, assoc prof, 72-80, PROF ANIMAL SCI, TEX A&M UNIV, 80- *Concurrent Pos:* Prof consult, Feed Co, Oil Co & Feedlots. *Mem:* Am Soc Animal Sci. *Res:* Feedlot management; cow body weight and compositional changes; beef cattle behavior and shipping fever complex. *Mailing Add:* Dept of Animal Sci Tex A&M Univ College Station TX 77843

SCHALEGER, LARRY L, b Milwaukee, Wis, Nov 24, 34; m 58, 78; c 3. ORGANIC CHEMISTRY. *Educ:* Grinnell Col, BA, 57; Univ Minn, PhD(org chem), 61. *Prof Exp:* Res assoc phys chem, Cornell Univ, 61-62, vis asst prof, 62-63; asst prof, Univ Hawaii, 63-75, assoc prof org chem, 67-75; vis assoc prof chem, Calif State Univ, Long Beach, 75-76; NSF fac fel, 76-77, specialist wood chem, Forest Prod Lab, Univ Calif, 77-78, STAFF SCIENTIST, LAWRENCE BERKELEY LAB, UNIV CALIF, 78- *Concurrent Pos:* Res assoc, Univ Pittsburgh, 70-71. *Mem:* Am Chem Soc; AAAS; The Chem Soc. *Res:* Development of technologies for production of liquid fuels and chemicals from biomass and the development of analytical methods for their characterization. *Mailing Add:* Bldg 934 Lawrence Berkeley Lab Berkeley CA 94720

SCHALES, OTTO, b Frankfurt, Ger, Dec 27, 10; nat US; m 40. CHEMISTRY. *Educ:* Univ Frankfurt, BSc, 29, DSc(chem), 35; Am Bd Clin Chem, dipl, 51. *Prof Exp:* Asst org chem, Univ Frankfurt, 35; assoc pharmacol, Dorpat Univ, Estonia, 36-38; assoc biochem, Univ Copenhagen, 38; fel med, Harvard Univ, 39-41, res assoc med & tutor biochem sci, 41-44; dir chem res, Alton Ochsner Med Found, 44-62; sci dir, Intersci Labs, Inc, 63-66; sci chem, North Central Labs, 68-75, dir, Dept Chem, 66-80, pres, 75-80; CONSULT CLIN CHEM, 80- *Concurrent Pos:* Chemist, Peter Bent Brigham Hosp, 39-44; dir clin chem lab, Ochsner Clin, 44-57, dir clin chem lab, Ochsner Med Found Hosp, 47-52, consult, 52-62; from asst prof to assoc prof biochem, Tulane Univ, 47-52, prof, 52-64. *Mem:* Fel AAAS; fel Am Asn Clin Chemists (pres, 55-56); Am Chem Soc; Am Soc Biol Chemists; Soc Exp Biol & Med. *Res:* Enzymes; chemotherapeutics; blood pigments and preservation; chemiluminescence; iron metabolism; microanalytical methods; biochemistry of hypertension; organic and clinical chemistry. *Mailing Add:* 544 S Fourth St Columbus OH 43206

SCHALGE, ALVIN LAVERNE, b Akron, NY, Nov 23, 30; m 53; c 2. ANALYTICAL CHEMISTRY. *Educ:* Eastern Mich Univ, AB, 54; Univ Ill, MS, 56; PhD(chem), 59. *Prof Exp:* Res chemist, Ohio Oil Co, 59-63, spectros suprv, Denver Res Ctr, Marathon Oil Co, 63-66, chem sect suprv, 66-72, advan res chemist, 72-76, SR RES CHEMIST, DENVER RES CTR, MARATHON OIL CO, 76- *Mem:* Am Chem Soc; Soc Appl Spectros; Sigma Xi. *Res:* Emission spectroscopy; x-ray diffraction and fluorescence analysis; infrared and ultraviolet spectrometric analysis; nuclear magnetic resonance spectroscopy; ion selective electrodes; chemical stimulation of oil wells. *Mailing Add:* Denver Res Ctr Marathon Oil Co Littleton CO 80160

SCHALIT, LEWIS MARTIN, chemical physics, research administration, see previous edition

SCHALK, JAMES MAXIMILLIAN, b New York, NY, Dec 19, 32; m 61; c 4. ENTOMOLOGY. *Educ:* Univ Ga, BSA, 60; Cornell Univ, MS, 63; Univ Nebr, PhD(entom), 70. *Prof Exp:* Res asst entom, Cornell Univ, 61-63; res entomologist, Birds Eye Div, Gen Foods Corp, 63-65; res entomologist, Grain & Forage Div, 65-71, res entomologist, Plant Genetics & Germplasm Inst, Sci & Educ Admin-Agr Res, USDA, 71-78; RES LEADER, US VEG BREEDING LAB, 78- *Concurrent Pos:* Res entomologist, US AID, 71 & Int Prog Div, USDA, 71-76. *Mem:* Entom Soc Am; Am Soc Hort Sci; Sigma Xi. *Res:* Developing vegetable germplasm with resistance to insects and mites and investigating the nature of arthropod resistance in these plants. *Mailing Add:* US Veg Breeding Lab 2875 Savannah Hwy Charleston SC 29407

SCHALK, MARSHALL, b Boston, Mass, Apr 25, 07; m 33; c 4. GEOLOGY. *Educ:* Harvard Univ, AB, 29, AM, 31, PhD(geol), 36. *Prof Exp:* From asst prof to prof, 41-72, EMER PROF GEOL, SMITH COL, 72- *Mem:* Fel Geol Soc Am; Nat Asn Geol Teachers; Am Geophys Union. *Res:* Beach sedimentation; arctic shoreline of Alaska. *Mailing Add:* Clark Sci Ctr Smith Col Northampton MA 01063

SCHALK, TERRY LEROY, b Eldora, Iowa, Aug 3, 43; m 65; c 2. HIGH ENERGY PHYSICS. *Educ:* Iowa State Univ, BS, 65, PhD(high energy physics), 69. *Prof Exp:* Res assoc, Univ Calif, Riverside, 69-72; Stanford Linear Accelerator Ctr, 72-75; RES PHYSICIST, UNIV CALIF, SANTA CRUZ, 75- *Mem:* Am Phys Soc. *Res:* Computer science. *Mailing Add:* 717 Hickory Way San Jose CA 95129

SCHALL, ELWYN DELAUREL, b Montpelier, Ohio, May 6, 18; m 42; c 4. ANALYTICAL CHEMISTRY. *Educ:* Ohio State Univ, BS, 40, Purdue Univ, MS, 42, PhD(biochem), 49. *Prof Exp:* From asst prof to assoc prof, 49-61, PROF BIOCHEM, PURDUE UNIV, WEST LAFAYETTE, 61- *Concurrent Pos:* State chemist & seed comnr, Ind, 65- *Mem:* Am Chem Soc. *Res:* Analytical methods. *Mailing Add:* Dept of Biochem Purdue Univ West Lafayette IN 47907

SCHALL, JOSEPH JULIAN, b Philadelphia, Pa, June 18, 46; m 72. EVOLUTIONARY ECOLOGY, PARASITE-HOST ECOLOGY. *Educ:* Pa State Univ, BS, 68; Univ RI, MS, 72; Univ Tex, Austin, PhD(zool), 76. *Prof Exp:* NIH res serv award, Univ Calif, Berkeley, 77-80; ASST PROF ZOOL, UNIV VT, 80- *Mem:* AAAS; Soc Study Evolution; Ecol Soc Am. *Res:* Interface between evolutionary theory and ecology, behavior and physiology; interspecific associations such as the parasite-host and plant-herbavore relationships; ecology of lizard malaria. *Mailing Add:* Dept Zool Univ Vt Burlington VT 05405

SCHALL, ROY FRANKLIN, JR, b Pittsburgh, Pa, June 4, 39. RADIOIMMUNOLOGY. *Educ:* Va Mil Inst, BS, 61; Carnegie Inst Technol, MS, 65; Carnegie-Mellon Univ, PhD(nuclear chem), 69. *Prof Exp:* Chief, health phys, Walter Reed Army Med Ctr, 68-71; mem staff radioimmunoassay chem, Mt Sinai Med Ctr, Miami Beach, 71-74; group leader radioimmunol, Corning Glass Works, Medfield, Mass, 74-76; sr scientist enzyme immunol, 76-81; TECH DIR, ORGANON DIAG, 81- *Mem:* Am Asn Clin Chemists; Am Chem Soc; Clin Radioassay Soc. *Res:* Development of new immunoassay systems using enzymes as labeling entitles. *Mailing Add:* 2208 E Linfield Glenrdora CA 91740

SCHALLAU, CON H, forest economics, see previous edition

SCHALLEK, WILLIAM BARRETT, b New York, NY, May 29, 17; m 52. PHARMACOLOGY. *Educ:* Harvard Univ, AB, 41, MA, 42, PhD(biol), 45. *Prof Exp:* Asst prof biol, Univ Ore, 48-49; from physiologist to sr physiologist, 50-67, RES FEL, DEPT PHARMACOL, RES DIV, HOFFMANN-LA ROCHE, INC, 67- *Concurrent Pos:* Res fel neurophysiol, Wash Univ, 45-46; res fel biol, Calif Inst Technol, 46-48; vis investr, Woods Hole Oceanog Inst, 42-43. *Mem:* Fel AAAS; Am Physiol Soc; Am Soc Pharmacol & Exp Therapeut; Soc Neurosci; NY Acad Sci. *Res:* Cellular and comparative physiology; neurophysiology; neuropharmacology; psychopharmacology. *Mailing Add:* Dept Pharmacol Hoffmann-La Roche Inc Res Div Nutley NJ 07110

SCHALLENBERG, ELMER EDWARD, b Rome, NY, Dec 30, 29; m 57; c 2. PETROLEUM CHEMISTRY, RESEARCH ADMINISTRATION. *Educ:* Cornell Univ, AB, 51; Univ Calif, PhD(chem), 54. *Prof Exp:* Mem staff lubricants res & develop, Texaco Res Ctr, Texaco Inc, Beacon, NY, 54-80, sci planning, 80-81, SR COORDR RES, TEXACO SERV EUROP-LONDON, 81- *Mem:* AAAS; Am Chem Soc; Sigma Xi. *Res:* Lubricant additives and product development. *Mailing Add:* Texaco Serv Europe 1 Knights Bridge Green London SW-1X 7QJ England

SCHALLER, CHARLES WILLIAM, b Holmen, Wis, June 8, 20; m 42; c 3. AGRONOMY. *Educ:* Univ Wis, BS, 41, MS, 43, PhD(agron), 46. *Prof Exp:* Asst agron, Univ Wis, 41-46; from jr agronomist to assoc agronomist, Exp Sta, 46-61, from instr to assoc prof agron, Univ, 46-61, PROF AGRON, UNIV CALIF, DAVIS, 61-, AGRONOMIST, EXP STA, 61- *Mem:* Am Phytopath Soc; Am Soc Agron; Genetics Soc Am. *Res:* Genetics of disease resistance in wheat and barley; production of disease resistant varieties of of barley. *Mailing Add:* 213 Hunt Hall Univ of Calif Davis CA 95616

SCHALLER, DARYL RICHARD, b Milwaukee, Wis, Oct 21, 43; m 66; c 2. FOOD SCIENCE. *Educ:* Univ Wis, BS, 64, MS, 66, PhD(food sci), 69. *Prof Exp:* Res fel, Dept Food Sci, Univ BC, 69-72; group leader cereal chem, 72-77, dir res serv, 77-79, dir res, 79-81, VPRES, KELLOGG CO, 81- *Mem:* Am Chem Soc; Am Asn Cereal Chemists. *Res:* Ultrastructural changes in meat; chemistry of plant polyphenols, pigments; chemistry and analysis of dietary fiber; food chemistry. *Mailing Add:* Res Dept Kellogg Co Battle Creek MI 49016

SCHALLER, EDWARD JAMES, b Philadelphia, Pa, Mar 28, 39; m 68. COATINGS CHEMISTRY, COLLOID CHEMISTRY. *Educ:* Villanova Univ, BE, 61; Univ Pa, PhD(chem eng), 65. *Prof Exp:* Sr chemist, 65-73, proj leader, 73-80, SECT MGR TRADE SALES COATINGS, ROHM AND HAAS CO, SPRING HOUSE, 80- *Mem:* Am Chem Soc. *Res:* Trade sales coatings; adhesives; sealants. *Mailing Add:* 640 Runnymede Ave Jenkintown PA 19046

SCHALLER, ROBIN EDWARD, b St Paul, Minn, July 10, 37; m 66; c 2. FLUID AND PARTICLE TECHNOLOGY. *Educ:* Univ Minn, BS, 59, MSAeroEngr, 63, PhD(environ health eng), 75. *Prof Exp:* Develop engr, Ord & Aerospace Div, Honeywell Inc, 63-65; prod engr, Res Ctr, 3M Co, St Paul, Minn, 65-66; MANAGING ENGR, RES & DEVELOP DIV, DONALDSON CO INC, 66- *Concurrent Pos:* Chmn, Am Inst Chem Engrs Classifier Equip Testing & Eval Procedure Comt, 76- *Mem:* Am Soc Mech Engrs; Am Inst Chem Engrs; Air Pollution Control Asn; Am Indust Hygiene Asn. *Res:* Fluid and particle mechanics pertaining to the behavior, production, sampling and characterization of particles; recognition, evaluation and engineering control of environmental pollutants. *Mailing Add:* Donaldson Co Inc PO Box 1299 Minneapolis MN 55440

SCHALLERT, WILLIAM FRANCIS, b Maplewood, Mo, Sept 3, 27; m 54; c 2. ENGINEERING. *Educ:* Washington Univ, St Louis, BS, 53; St Louis Univ, MS, 55, MBA, 60, PhD, 76. *Prof Exp:* Asst prof aeronaut eng & head elec prog, Parks Col Aeronaut Technol, St Louis, 53-61, asst prof basic eng, St Louis Univ, 61-64; assoc prof eng, Florissant Valley Community Col, 64-67, chmn div eng & eng technol, 64-78, prof eng, 67-82; DEAN ACAD AFFAIRS, PARKS COL, ST LOUIS UNIV, 82- *Concurrent Pos:* Consult, Emerson Elec Mfg Co, 55-64, Electro-Core, Inc 69- & Sch Eng, Univ Mo-Columbia, 72-76; comnr higher educ, NCent Asn, 71-76; co-dir, NSF grant, 72-76. *Mem:* Inst Elec & Electronics Engrs; Am Soc Eng Educ; Nat Soc Prof Engrs; Am Soc Cert Eng Technicians. *Res:* Avionics and systems engineering; behavioral and educational systems. *Mailing Add:* Parks Col St Louis Univ Cahokia IL 62206

SCHALLES, ROBERT R, b Durango, Colo, Mar 25, 35; m 56; c 4. ANIMAL BREEDING, POPULATION GENETICS. *Educ:* Colo State Univ, BS, 63; Va Polytech Inst, MS, 66, PhD(animal breeding), 67. *Prof Exp:* Mgr, Feedlot Serv, Inc, Colo, 61-62; asst prof animal husbandry & asst animal husbandman, 66-70, assoc prof, 70-80, PROF ANIMAL SCI & ASSOC, AGR EXP STA, KANS STATE UNIV, 80- *Mem:* Am Soc Animal Sci; Am Genetic Asn. *Res:* Genetic and environmental influences on growth and development of animals. *Mailing Add:* Dept of Animal Sci & Indust Kans State Univ Manhattan KS 66502

SCHALLHORN, CHARLES H, b Saginaw, Mich, Mar 26, 44; m 73; c 1. PHOTOGRAPHIC CHEMISTRY. *Educ:* Univ Mich, Ann Arbor, BS, 66; Univ Calif, Berkeley, PhD(chem), 70. *Prof Exp:* Sr res chemist, 70-79, RES ASSOC, EASTMAN KODAK CO, 79- *Concurrent Pos:* Lectr chem, Univ Rochester, 73- *Res:* Synthetic organic chemistry; organic photochemistry. *Mailing Add:* Res Labs Eastman Kodak Co Rochester NY 14650

SCHALLIOL, WILLIS LEE, b Elkhart, Ind, Dec 20, 19; m 42; c 3. MATERIALS SCIENCE, ELECTRICAL ENGINEERING. *Educ:* Purdue Univ, BS, 42; Stanford Univ, PhD(metall eng), 50. *Prof Exp:* Mat engr, Westinghouse Elec Corp, Calif, 48-50; actg instr x-ray tech, Stanford Univ, 49-50; supvr pile fuels, Hanford Works, Gen Elec Co, 50-53; mgr br, Nibco Inc, 53-54, dir eng, 55-59; dir res aerospace div, Bendix Corp, 59-63, proj engr, CTS Corp, 63-64; dir res, CTS Res, Inc, 64-69; mem staff, 69-75, asst coordr coop eng educ, 76-80, assoc prof mat eng, 76-80, ASSOC COORDR COOP ENG EDUC & MGR INDUST RELS, SCH ELEC ENG, PURDUE UNIV, WEST LAFAYETTE, 80- *Concurrent Pos:* Dir critical needs prog, Purdue Univ, 76-80. *Mem:* Am Soc Eng Educ. *Res:* Microtranspiration for protection of rocket nozzle throats; chromium-magnesia composites; high-power precision cermet resistor modules; thermoset polymers for mechanical applications; computer-aided cooperative engineering education administration; profile of graduates from the engineering co-op program. *Mailing Add:* Sch Elec Eng Purdue Univ West Lafayette IN 47907

SCHALLY, ANDREW VICTOR, b Wilno, Poland, Nov 30, 26; US citizen; m 56, 76; c 2. ENDOCRINOLOGY. *Educ:* McGill Univ, BSc, 55, PhD(biochem), 57. *Hon Degrees:* Twelve from various foreign & Can Univs. *Prof Exp:* Asst protein chem, Nat Inst Med Res, Eng, 49-52; assoc endocrinol, Allan Mem Inst Psychiat, Can, 52-57; asst prof & res assoc protein chem & endocrinol, Col Med, Baylor Univ, 57-62; assoc prof med, 62-66, PROF MED, SCH MED, TULANE UNIV, 66-; CHIEF, ENDOCRINOL & POLYPEPTIDE LABS, VET ADMIN HOSP, 62-, SR MED INVESTR, 73- *Concurrent Pos:* NIH fel, 60-62; consult indust, 62-; consult, Vet Admin Hosp, Houston, 60-62. *Honors & Awards:* Nobel Prize in Med, 77; Award, Am Thyroid Asn, 69; US Middleton Award, Vet Admin, 70; Ayerst Squibb Endocrine Soc Award; Charles Mickle Award, Univ Toronto, 74; Gardner Found Award, 74; Edward T Tyler Award, 75; Borden Award, 75; Albert Lasker Award, 75. *Mem:* Nat Acad Sci; Am Soc Biol Chem; Am Physiol Soc; AAAS; Endocrine Soc. *Res:* Chemistry and biology of protein and peptide hormones; control of release; determination of structure and synthesis of thyrotropin releasing hormone, luteinizing hormone and follicle-stimulating hormone-releasing hormone; pro-somato statin; endocrine dependent cancer. *Mailing Add:* Vet Admin Hosp 1601 Perdido St New Orleans LA 70146

SCHALM, OSCAR WILLIAM, b Sturgis, Mich, Aug 28, 09; m 30; c 2. VETERINARY SCIENCE. *Educ:* Mich State Col, DVM, 32; Univ Calif, MS, 33, PhD(comp path), 35. *Prof Exp:* From instr to asst prof vet sci, 32-44, assoc dean sch vet med, 54-63, chmn dept clin path, 60-67, prof vet sci, 44-76, EMER PROF VET SCI, UNIV CALIF, DAVIS, 76- *Concurrent Pos:* Fulbright res scholar, Univ Munich, 59-60; sabbatical res mastitis, State of Israel, 66-67. *Honors & Awards:* Borden Award, Am Vet Med Asn, 64; Am Animal Hosp Asn Vet of Year Award, 65 & 72. *Mem:* Am Vet Med Asn; hon mem Israel Vet Med Asn. *Res:* Veterinary clinical pathology. *Mailing Add:* 321 W Eighth St Davis CA 95616

SCHAMBERG, RICHARD, b Frankfurt, Ger, Dec 18, 20; nat US; m 47, 69; c 3. AERODYNAMICS, SYSTEMS ANALYSIS. *Educ:* Calif Inst Technol, BS, 43, MS, 44, PhD(aeronaut), 47. *Prof Exp:* Asst, Calif Inst Technol, 43-47, asst aerodyn, 46-47; aerodyn engr, Proj Rand, Douglas Aircraft Co, 47-48; assoc engr, Rand Corp, Calif, 48-50, tech asst to chief, Aircraft Div, 50-55, assoc head, Aero-astronaut Dept, 56-63, head, 63-68; mem sr tech staff-engr, 68-71, CORP DIR TECHNOL APPLNS, NORTHROP CORP, 71- *Concurrent Pos:* Consult tech adv panel on aeronaut, Off Asst Secy Defense Res & Eng, 57-63; mem advan technol panel, Defense Advan Res Proj Agency, 73-75. *Mem:* Opers Res Soc Am; Am Inst Aeronaut & Astronaut; Unmanned Vehicles Soc. *Res:* Aerodynamics of rarefied gases; research and development planning operations research. *Mailing Add:* 10630 Bradbury Rd Los Angeles CA 90064

SCHAMBERGER, ROBERT D, nuclear physics, deceased

SCHAMBRA, PHILIP ELLIS, b Saginaw, Mich, Nov 8, 34; m 67; c 3. BIOPHYSICS. *Educ:* Rice Univ, BA, 56; Yale Univ, PhD(biophys), 61. *Prof Exp:* Grants assoc, NIH, 67-68; budget examr, Off Mgt & Budget, Exec Off of the President, 68-71; staff mem, Coun Environ Qual, 71-74; ASSOC DIR INTERAGENCY PROGS, NAT INST ENVIRON HEALTH SCI, NIH, 74- *Mailing Add:* Nat Inst of Environ Health Sci NIH PO Box 12233 Research Triangle Park NC 27709

SCHAMP, HOMER WARD, JR, b St Marys, Ohio, June 23, 23; m; c 2. HIGH PRESSURE PHYSICS. *Educ:* Miami Univ, AB, 44; Univ Mich, PhD(physics), 52. *Prof Exp:* Physicist, Mound Lab, Monsanto Chem Co, 51-52; from assoc prof to prof, Inst Molecular Physics, 52-71, dir, Inst, 64-65, dean fac, 65-71, RES PROF EDUC, UNIV MD, BALTIMORE COUNTY, 71- *Mem:* Fel Am Phys Soc. *Res:* Self-diffusion and ionic conductivity in alkali halides; experiments in high pressure physics; thermodynamics. *Mailing Add:* 5401 Wilkins Ave Catonsville MD 21228

SCHANBACHER, FLOYD LEON, b Cherokee, Okla, Dec 19, 41; m 64; c 1. BIOCHEMISTRY, DIFFERENTIATION. *Educ:* Northwestern State Col, BS, 64; Okla State Univ, MS, 67, PhD(biochem), 70. *Prof Exp:* Res assoc biochem & entom, Okla State Univ, 70; asst prof dairy sci, 70-75, ASSOC PROF DAIRY SCI, OHIO AGR RES & DEVELOP CTR, 75- *Mem:* Am Dairy Sci Asn. *Res:* Milk protein characterization, biosynthesis and function; control and initiation of mammary differentiation; immunobiology of mammary differentiation; immunotoxicology; biochemical responses to toxic agents. *Mailing Add:* Dept of Dairy Sci Ohio Agr Res & Develop Ctr Wooster OH 44691

SCHANBERG, SAUL M, b Clinton, Mass, Mar 22, 33; m 55; c 2. NEUROPHARMACOLOGY. *Educ:* Clark Univ, BA, 54, MA, 56; Yale Univ, PhD(pharmacol), 61, MD, 64. *Prof Exp:* Teaching asst bot & zool, Clark Univ, 54-55 & physiol, 55-56; res assoc pharmacol, Yale Univ, 61-62, univ scholar, 61-64; intern pediat, Albert Einstein Col Med, 64-65; res assoc pharmacol, Lab Clin Sci, NIMH, 65-67; asst prof clin pharmacol, 67-69, PROF PHARMACOL, ASST PROF NEUROL & CHIEF SECT NEUROPHARMACOL, SCH MED, DUKE UNIV, 69- *Concurrent Pos:* Res consult psychoneuropharmacol, Inst Behav Res, Silver Spring, Md, 65-68; Neurosci Res Prog award, Cent Nerv Syst Intensive Study Unit, 66; NIMH res scientist award, 68. *Honors & Awards:* Rehme-Anna Monika Prize, Ger, 67. *Mem:* Am Fedn Clin Res; Am Soc Pharmacol & Exp Therapeut; Int Soc Biochem Pharmacol; Am Col Neuropsychopharmacol; Am Soc Neurochem. *Res:* Pharmacologic and toxic effects of drugs, hormones and environmental influences on the metabolism of biogenic amines in the central nervous system; the role biogenic amines play in controlling cell metabolism and in mediating the effects of drugs and hormones on brain metabolism and development in normal and disease states. *Mailing Add:* Dept of Pharmacol Duke Univ Sch of Med Durham NC 27710

SCHANEFELT, ROBERT VON, b Abilene, Kans, Sept 21, 42; m 63; c 2. FOOD SCIENCE, CEREAL CHEMISTRY. *Educ:* Kans State Univ, BS, 66, MS, 67, PhD(food sci), 70. *Prof Exp:* Food technologist, 70-73, group leader, 73-76, DIR FOOD & AGR PROD RES & DEVELOP, A E STALEY MFG CO, 76- *Mem:* Am Asn Cereal Chem; Inst Food Technologists. *Res:* Research and applications development of modified food starches and corn sweetness. *Mailing Add:* A E Staley Mfg Co Decatur IL 62525

SCHANFIELD, MOSES SAMUEL, b Minneapolis, Minn, Sept 7, 44. IMMUNOGENETICS, PATERNITY TESTING. *Educ:* Univ Minn, Minneapolis, BA, 66; Harvard Univ, MA, 69; Univ Mich, Ann Arbor, PhD(human genetics), 71. *Prof Exp:* Res fel genetics, Univ Calif, San Francisco, 71-72, NIH fel, 72-74, asst res geneticist, 74-75; dir transfusion serv & ref lab, Milwaukee Blood Ctr, 75-78; asst sci dir, 78-80, ASST DIR, AM RED CROSS BLOOD SERV, 80- *Honors & Awards:* Gold Medal, 1st Latin Am Cong Hemotherapy & Immunohemat. *Mem:* Am Soc Human Genetics; Am Asn Phys Anthropologists; Soc Study Human Biol; Am Asn Immunologists; Am Asn Blood Banks. *Res:* Determination of the biological significance, or properties, of the genetic markers on antibodies and the evolutionary forces which act on them. *Mailing Add:* Am Red Cross 4915 Auburn Ave Bethesda MD 20814

SCHANIEL, CARL L, b San Diego, Calif, Oct 21, 26; m 50; c 6. OPERATIONS RESEARCH. *Educ:* San Diego State Col, BA, 50, MS, 58. *Prof Exp:* Physicist, US Navy Electronics Lab, 51-56, physicist & opers res analyst, 56-62, assoc for opers anal, Naval Ord Test Sta, 62-65, head weapons planning group & asst tech dir plans, 65-78, ASST TECH DIR DEVELOP ORD SYSTS & HEAD ORD SYSTS DEPT, NAVAL WEAPONS CTR, 78- *Concurrent Pos:* Mem, Joint Serv Adv Group for Res in Appl Statist, 63-70, chmn, Dir Navy Labs, Adv Tech Objectives Working Group for Amphibious Opers, 66-69. *Honors & Awards:* L T E Thompson Award, Naval Weapons Ctr, 73; Meritorious Civilian Serv Award, 78. *Mem:* Opers Res Soc Am; Sigma Xi. *Res:* Physics; underwater acoustics; antisubmarine warfare; methods of operations research; weapons systems analysis; long range corporate planning; research administration; training for analysts. *Mailing Add:* 1901 Blue Ridge Rd Ridgecrest CA 93555

SCHANK, STANLEY COX, b Fallon, Nev, Oct 31, 32; m 54; c 5. CYTOGENETICS, PLANT BREEDING. *Educ:* Utah State Univ, BS, 54; Univ Calif, PhD(genetics), 61. *Prof Exp:* From asst prof to assoc prof, 61-72, PROF GENETICS, UNIV FLA, 72- *Concurrent Pos:* Consult, IRI Res Inst, Brazil, 66; vis res prof, Brazil-Fla Contract, 73. *Mem:* Am Soc Agron; Genetics Soc Am; Bot Soc Am; Genetics Soc Can. *Res:* General genetics; forage grass cytogenetics and breeding, primarily Digitarias, Brachiarias and Hemarthrias; biological nitrogen fixation on tropical grass bacterial systems. *Mailing Add:* 2199 McCarty Hall Univ Fla Gainesville FL 32601

SCHANKER, LEWIS STANLEY, b Kansas City, Mo, Sept 23, 30; c 2. PHARMACOLOGY. *Educ:* Univ Mo-Kansas City, BS, 51, MS, 53; Univ Wis, PhD(pharmacol), 55. *Prof Exp:* Asst scientist, USPHS, 55-56, sr asst scientist, 56-57, pharmacologist, Nat Heart Inst, 57-59, head sect cellular pharmacol & sect biochem drug action lab chem pharmacol, 59-66; TRUSTEE PROF PHARMACOL, SCH PHARM, PROF DENT & CHMN DEPT PHARMACOL, SCH DENT & PROF MED, SCH MED, UNIV MO-KANSAS CITY, 66- *Concurrent Pos:* Mem pharmacol panel, US Bd Civil Serv Examr, 59-66; consult, Nat Conf Cardiovasc Dis, 64. *Honors & Awards:* Lehn-Fink Medal Award, 51; John J Abel Prize, Am Soc Pharmacol & Exp Therapeut, 66. *Mem:* AAAS; Am Soc Pharmacol & Exp Therapeut; Am Physiol Soc; Soc Exp Biol & Med; Sigma Xi. *Res:* Pulmonary and gastrointestinal absorption of drugs and nutrients, drug penetration into central nervous system, liver, heart, red cells, platelets and other tissues; biliary excretion of drugs; drug binding, distribution and metabolism. *Mailing Add:* Pharmacy Bldg Univ of Mo Kansas City MO 64110

SCHANNE, OTTO F, b Stuttgart, Ger, Feb 21, 32; m 56; c 2. BIOPHYSICS, CARDIAC ELECTROPHYSIOLOGY. *Educ:* Univ Heidelberg, Dr med, 60; Univ Paris, Dr Etat, 79. *Prof Exp:* Res asst physiol, Univ Heidelberg, 58-60, instr, 60-64; assoc prof pharmacol, Univ Southern Calif, 64-65; asst prof biophys, Univ Montreal, 65-66; from asst prof to assoc prof, 66-71, chmn dept, 70-78, PROF BIOPHYS, UNIV SHERBROOKE, 71- *Concurrent Pos:* Med Res Coun Can scholar, 66-70, mem comt physiol & pharmacol, 73-76, mem core comt heart res develop grants, 77-; mem assoc comt biophys, Nat Res Coun Can, 68-69, mem nat comt biophys, 77-81. *Mem:* Biophys Soc; Am Physiol Soc; Can Soc Cell Biol; Can Physiol Soc; Inst Elec & Electronics Engrs. *Res:* Antiarrhythmic drugs and cellular cardiac electrophysiology; membrane properties of cultured cardiac cells. *Mailing Add:* Dept of Biophys Univ of Sherbrooke Fac of Med Sherbrooke PQ J1H 5N4 Can

SCHANO, EDWARD ARTHUR, b Buffalo, NY, Oct 8, 18; m 42; c 4; m 67; c 10. POULTRY HUSBANDRY. *Educ:* Cornell Univ, BS, 51; Mich State Univ, MS, 58. *Prof Exp:* PROF POULTRY HUSB & EXTEN SPECIALIST, CORNELL UNIV, 52- *Mem:* Poultry Sci Asn; World Poultry Sci Asn. *Res:* Youth poultry science projects. *Mailing Add:* 105 Rice Hall Cornell Univ Ithaca NY 14850

SCHANTZ, EDWARD JOSEPH, b Hartford, Wis, Aug 27, 08; m 40; c 5. BIOCHEMISTRY. *Educ:* Univ Wis, BS, 31, PhD(biochem), 39; Iowa State Col, MS, 33. *Prof Exp:* Res asst, Wis Agr Exp Sta, 36-40; biochemist, Res Labs, Carnation Milk Co, 40-42; res chemist, US Army Biol Ctr, 46-72; prof, 72-80, EMER PROF BIOCHEM, FOOD RES INST, UNIV WIS-MADISON, 80- *Concurrent Pos:* Consult, USPHS, 54- *Mem:* Fel AAAS; Am Chem Soc; Am Soc Biol Chem; fel NY Acad Sci. *Res:* Isolation and characterization of toxins and poisons produced by microorganisms; diffusion of substances in gels and various biological systems; studies on poisons produced by certain dinoflagellates and other algae. *Mailing Add:* Food Res Inst Univ of Wis-Madison Madison WI 53706

SCHANTZ, ILENE SUE COTTLER, reproductive biology, cytochemistry, see previous edition

SCHANTZ, PETER MULLINEAUX, b Camden, NJ, Oct 22, 39; c 2. VETERINARY PUBLIC HEALTH, PARASITOLOGY. *Educ:* Univ Pa, AB, 61, VMD, 65; Univ Calif, Davis, PhD(comp path), 71. *Prof Exp:* Epidemiologist, Pan-Am Zoonosis Ctr, Pan-Am Health Orgn-WHO, Arg, 69-74; VET EPIDEMIOLOGIST, CTR DIS CONTROL, USPHS, 74- *Mem:* Am Vet Med Asn; Am Soc Parasitol; Am Soc Trop Med & Hyg. *Res:* Epidemiology, immunodiagnosis and pathology of parasitic zoonoses. *Mailing Add:* USPHS Ctr for Dis Control Atlanta GA 30333

SCHANUEL, STEPHEN HOEL, b St Louis, Mo, July 14, 33; m 58; c 2. MATHEMATICS. *Educ:* Princeton Univ, AB, 55; Univ Chicago, MS, 56; Columbia Univ, PhD(math), 63. *Prof Exp:* Instr math, Ill Inst Technol, 59-61; instr, Columbia Univ, 61-63; instr, Johns Hopkins Univ, 63-65; asst prof, Cornell Univ, 65-69; assoc prof, State Univ NY Stony Brook, 69-72; ASSOC PROF MATH, STATE UNIV NY BUFFALO, 72- *Concurrent Pos:* Mem, Inst Advan Study, 65-66. *Mem:* Am Math Soc. *Res:* Algebra and number theory, especially transcendental numbers. *Mailing Add:* Dept of Math State Univ of NY Buffalo NY 14214

SCHAPERY, RICHARD ALLAN, b Duluth, Minn, Mar 3, 35; m 57; c 1. SOLID MECHANICS, MATERIALS ENGINEERING. *Educ:* Wayne State Univ, BS, 57; Calif Inst Technol, MS, 58, PhD(aeronaut), 62. *Prof Exp:* From asst prof to prof aeronaut & eng sci, Purdue Univ, 62-69; dir mech & mat res ctr, 71-77, prof, 69-80, ALUMNI PROF & DISTINGUISHED PROF AEROSPACE ENG & CIVIL ENG, TEX A&M UNIV, 80- *Concurrent Pos:* Indust consult, Struct Anal & Mat Characterization, 60-; mem solid propellant struct integrity comt & chmn subcomt theoret characterization & anal, Interagency Chem Rocket Propulsion Group, 66- *Mem:* Am Inst Aeronaut & Astronaut. *Res:* Elasticity; viscoelasticity; fracture mechanics; thermodynamics; composite materials. *Mailing Add:* Dept of Civil Eng Tex A&M Univ College Station TX 77843

SCHAPIRO, HARRIETTE CHARLOTTE, b New York, NY, Feb 9, 35. BIOCHEMISTRY. *Educ:* Univ Miami, BS, 56, PhD(biochem), 62; Brandeis Univ, MA, 59. *Prof Exp:* Sr lab asst, Howard Hughes Med Inst, 59-60; res instr biochem, Univ Miami, 62-63; res fel, Scripps Clin & Res Found, 63-66; from asst prof to assoc prof, 66-77, PROF BIOL, SAN DIEGO STATE UNIV, 77- *Mem:* AAAS; Am Chem Soc. *Res:* Molecular interactions utilizing fluorescence polarization measurements; immunochemistry. *Mailing Add:* Dept of Biol San Diego State Univ San Diego CA 92182

SCHAPIRO, HERBERT, b New York, NY, Sept 17, 25; m 49; c 2. ANATOMY, PHYSIOLOGY. *Educ:* NY Univ, AB, 48; Univ Southern Calif, MS, 49; Univ Fla, PhD(anat), 64. *Prof Exp:* Res assoc, Univ Calif, Los Angeles, 51-58 & Univ Fla, 58-61; from asst prof anat to assoc prof anat & surg res, Univ Tenn, Memphis, 64-73; PROF ANAT, EASTERN VA MED SCH, 73- *Concurrent Pos:* Consult, Vet Admin Hosp, 69- *Mem:* AAAS; Am Asn Anat; Am Physiol Soc; Am Gastroenterol Asn. *Res:* Neural and hormonal regulation of gastrointestinal activities. *Mailing Add:* Dept of Anat Eastern Va Med Sch Norfolk VA 23501

SCHAPPELL, FREDERICK GEORGE, b Pottsville, Pa, Dec 20, 38; m 62; c 2. ORGANIC CHEMISTRY. *Educ:* Franklin & Marshall Col, BS, 60; Northwestern Univ, PhD(chem), 64. *Prof Exp:* From res chemist to sr res chemist, 64-74, res supvr chem, 74-76, mgr acquisitions & planning org dept, 76-77, mgr corp mkt develop polypropylene new bus, 78-81, MGR COM DEVELOP RESINS, HERCULES, INC, 78- *Mem:* Am Chem Soc. *Res:* Chemistry of reactive intermediates; free radicals-peroxide synthesis and reaction mechanism; nitrenes-synthesis and applications of nitrene precursors-azidoformates, sulfonylazides, azides; 1-3 dipoles-synthesis and application; toner resins and toner technology; printing ink vehicles and ink resin technology. *Mailing Add:* Res Ctr Hercules Inc Wilmington DE 19899

SCHAPPERT, GOTTFRIED T, b Mannheim, Ger, Sep 10, 34, US citizen; c 1. LASER PHYSICS, MATTER. *Educ:* Mass Inst Technol, BS, 56, MS, 58, PhD(physics), 61. *Prof Exp:* Fel, Max Planck Inst Astrophysics, 61-62; instr, Dept physics, Mass Inst Technol, 62-63; consult, Cambridge Res Labs, US Air Force, 63-65; res assoc, Brandeis Univ, 65-67; physicist, Electronics Res Ctr, NASA, 67-71; MEM STAFF & GROUP LEADER, LOS ALAMOS NAT LAB, 71- *Mem:* Am Phys Soc; AAAS; Sigma Xi. *Res:* Laser fusion physics; laser physics and engineering; laser matter interaction physics. *Mailing Add:* 145 San Juan St Los Alamos NM 87544

SCHAR, RAYMOND DEWITT, b Butler, Pa, Apr 9, 23; m 43; c 3. POULTRY SCIENCE. *Educ:* Pa State Univ, BS, 50. *Prof Exp:* Instr voc agr, Pub Schs, Pa, 45-49; sr poultry inspector, Pa Dept Agr, 50-59; poultry coordr, 59-71, PROJ LEADER RANDOM SAMPLE POULTRY TESTING, ANIMAL IMPROV PROGS LAB, ANIMAL PHYSIOL & GENETICS INST, SCI & EDUC ADMIN-AGR RES, USDA, 60-, SR POULTRY COORDR, 71- *Concurrent Pos:* Adv mem & secy, Nat Comt Random Sample Poultry Testing, 60- *Mem:* Poultry Sci Asn; World Poultry Sci Asn. *Res:* Poultry production and diseases; study trends; measures to combat diseases through blood testing of breeder flocks. *Mailing Add:* Nat Poultry Improv Plan Animal & Plant Health Inspection Serv-Vet Sci Beltsville MD 20705

SCHARBER, SAMUEL ROBERT, JR, b Winchester, Tenn, Mar 23, 33; m 54, 77; c 3. PHYSICAL CHEMISTRY. *Educ:* Univ Notre Dame, BS, 55; Harvard Univ, EdM, 63; Univ Tex, Austin, PhD(chem), 70. *Prof Exp:* High sch teacher, Ill, 56-59; PROF CHEM, SAN DIEGO COMMUNITY COLS, 60-; consult & res, Bud Toye Co, El Cajon, 71-80; CONSULT & RES, 80- *Mem:* Am Chem Soc; Optical Soc Am. *Res:* Solid waste recycle, chiefly plastics, metals and rubber; air pollution. *Mailing Add:* Dept of Chem San Diego Mesa College San Diego CA 92111

SCHARDT, ALOIS WOLFGANG, b Ger, Sept 15, 23; m 53; c 5. NUCLEAR PHYSICS, ASTROPHYSICS. *Educ:* Calif Inst Technol, BS, 44, PhD(physics), 51. *Prof Exp:* Asst, Calif Inst Technol, 48-50; assoc physicist, Brookhaven Nat Lab, 50-54; mem staff, Los Alamos Sci Lab, 54-61; spec asst, nuclear test detection off, Adv Res Proj Agency, 61-63; chief particles & fields, 63-70, from dep dir to dir physics & astron, 70-75, dir astrophys prog, 75-76, STAFF SCIENTIST, GODDARD SPACE FLIGHT CTR, NASA, 76- *Concurrent Pos:* Mem Fed Exec Inst. *Mem:* AAAS; Am Phys Soc; Am Astron Soc; Am Geophys Union. *Res:* Space physics; nuclear reactions induced by particles accelerated by a Van de Graaff generator; scintillation spectroscopy and decay schemes of radioisotopes. *Mailing Add:* 926 Wodburn Ct McLean VA 22102

SCHAREN, ALBERT LOIS, b Greybull, Wyo, Aug 9, 27; m 64; c 3. PLANT PATHOLOGY. *Educ:* Univ Wyo, BS, 52; Univ Nebr, MS, 56, PhD, 60. *Prof Exp:* PLANT PATHOLOGIST, AGR RES SERV, USDA, 60- *Mem:* Am Phytopath Soc; Australian Plant Path Soc; AAAS. *Res:* Diseases of cereal grains; physiology of host-parasite relationships; disease resistance genetics and breeding. *Mailing Add:* USDA Agr Res Serv Mont State Univ Dept Plant Path Bozeman MT 59717

SCHARENBERG, ROLF PAUL, b Hamburg, Ger, Mar 11, 27; m 55; c 2. NUCLEAR PHYSICS. *Educ:* Univ Mich, Ann Arbor, BS, 49, MS, 50, PhD(physics), 55. *Prof Exp:* From instr to asst prof physics, Mass Inst Technol, 55-60; assoc prof, Case Inst Technol, 61-65; assoc prof, 65-70, PROF PHYSICS, PURDUE UNIV, WEST LAFAYETTE, 71- *Mem:* Fel Am Phys Soc. *Res:* Magnetic and electric structure of nuclei. *Mailing Add:* 144 E Navajo West Lafayette IN 47906

SCHARER, JOHN EDWARD, b Monroe, Wis, Oct 11, 39; m 65; c 2. ELECTRICAL ENGINEERING, APPLIED PHYSICS. *Educ:* Univ Calif, Berkeley, BS, 61, MS, 63, PhD(elec eng), 66. *Prof Exp:* From asst prof to assoc prof, 66-78, PROF ELEC ENG, UNIV WIS-MADISON, 78-, ASSOC CHMN GRAD STUDIES, 80- *Concurrent Pos:* NSF grant, Univ Wis-Madison, 67-, Dept Energy res contract, 67-; Fr Atomic Energy Comn vis scientist, Ctr Nuclear Studies, Fontenay-aux-Roses, France, 69-70. *Mem:* Am Phys Soc; Inst Elec & Electronics Engrs. *Res:* Plasma physics, particularly linear and nonlinear wave propagation and instabilities; microwave heating of plasmas; lasers. *Mailing Add:* Dept of Elec Eng Univ of Wis Madison WI 53706

SCHARF, ARTHUR ALFRED, b Chicago, Ill, July 27, 27; m 56; c 4. BIOLOGY, BIOPHYSICS. *Educ:* Northwestern Univ, BS, 48, MS, 50, PhD(bot), 53. *Prof Exp:* Bacteriologist, NShore Sanit Dist, Ill, 48; res asst, Arctic Res Lab, Alaska, 52; instr biol & bot, Ill Teachers Col Chicago-North, 53-56; asst prof biol, Elmhurst Col, 56-57; from asst prof to assoc prof biol & bot, 57-65, chmn natural sci div, 62-63, chmn dept biol, 63-65, prof bot, 65-80, PROF BIOL, NORTHEASTERN ILL UNIV, 65- *Mem:* AAAS. *Res:* History of science. *Mailing Add:* Dept of Biol Northeastern Ill Univ Chicago IL 60625

SCHARF, BERTRAM, b New York, NY, Mar 3, 31; m 78; c 2. PSYCHOACOUSTICS. *Educ:* City Col New York, BA, 53; Univ Paris, dipl, 55; Harvard Univ, PhD(exp psychol), 58. *Prof Exp:* PROF PSYCHOL, NORTHEASTERN UNIV, 58- *Concurrent Pos:* Res assoc, Tech Hochschule Stuttgart, 61; vis res assoc, Sensory Res Lab, Syracuse Univ, 66; vis scientist, Med Sch, Helsinki Univ, 71-72; chmn, Working Group, US Standards Inst, 71-78; assoc ed, J Acoust Soc Am, 77-80; vis prof, Univ Provence, Marseille, 78-79; vis scientist, Nat Ctr Sci Res, France, 82-83. *Honors & Awards:* Distinguished Serv Award, Mass Speech & Hearing Asn, 77. *Mem:* Fel Acoust Soc Am; fel AAAS; Psychonomics Soc; Am Psychol Asn; Int Audiol Soc. *Res:* Effects of noise on people; sensory psychology; psychophysics; psychoacoustics; loudness; frequency analysis; sound localization; normal and pathological hearing. *Mailing Add:* 30 Griggs Rd Brookline MA 02146

SCHARF, WALTER, b Vienna, Austria, July 19, 29; nat US. GEMOLOGY. *Educ:* City Col New York, BS, 52; Columbia Univ, MA, 54, PhD(chem), 57. *Prof Exp:* Asst chem, Columbia Univ, 52-53; lectr, City Col New York, 53-58, from instr to asst prof, 58-68; ASSOC PROF CHEM & CHMN DEPT NATURAL SCI, BARUCH COL, 68- *Concurrent Pos:* Proj leader, Evans Res & Develop Corp, 57-58; vis lectr, Columbia Univ, 65. *Mem:* Royal Soc Chem; Am Chem Soc; Sigma Xi; fel Gemol Asn Gt Brit. *Res:* Isolation, purification and mechanism of action of polyphenol oxidases and flavorese enzymes; effects of gamma radiation on proteins; biodegradation of ascorbic acid; contraceptive plant estrogens; crystal growth from melts and solutions. *Mailing Add:* Dept Natural Sci Baruch Col New York NY 10010

SCHARFETTER, D(ONALD) L, b Pittsburgh, Pa, Feb 21, 34; m 55; c 3. ELECTRICAL ENGINEERING. *Educ:* Carnegie Inst Technol, BS, 60, MS, 61, PhD(elec eng), 62. *Prof Exp:* Mem tech staff, Bell Labs, 62-76; prof elec eng, Carnegie-Mellon Univ, 76-80; MEM STAFF, PALO ALTO RES CTR, XEROX CORP, 80- *Mem:* Inst Elec & Electronics Engrs. *Res:* Analysis of device characteristics; device physics as applied to semiconductors. *Mailing Add:* Palo Alto Res Ctr Xerox Corp 3333 Coyote Hill Palo Alto CA 94304

SCHARFF, MATTHEW DANIEL, b New York, NY, Aug 28, 32; m 54; c 3. CELL BIOLOGY, IMMUNOLOGY. *Educ:* Brown Univ, AB, NY Univ, MD, 59. *Prof Exp:* Intern & resident, Boston City Hosp, Mass, 59-61; res assoc, Nat Inst Allergy & Infectious Dis, 61-63; assoc cell biol, 63-64, from asst prof to assoc prof, 64-71, PROF CELL BIOL & CHMN DEPT, ALBERT EINSTEIN COL MED, 71-, DIR DIV BIOL SCI, 74- *Honors & Awards:* Harvey lectr, 74; Dyer lectr, NIH, 80. *Mem:* Harvey Soc; Am Asn Immunol; Am Soc Clin Invest. *Res:* Immunobiology. *Mailing Add:* Dept of Cell Biol Albert Einstein Col of Med Bronx NY 10461

SCHARFF, RAYMOND, b New York, NY, Mar 6, 34; m 58; c 3. PHYSIOLOGY, BIOCHEMISTRY. *Educ:* City Col New York, BS, 56; Univ Chicago, PhD(physiol), 64. *Prof Exp:* Fel physiol, Univ Chicago, 65; staff fel, Sect Cellular Physiol, Nat Heart & Lung Inst, 65-67; PHYSIOLOGIST, LAB CELL BIOL, NAT HEART, LUNG & BLOOD INST, 67- *Res:* Role of cellular organization in general and membranes in particular in regulating biosynthetic processes; enzyme complexes involved in DNA synthesis. *Mailing Add:* Lab of Cell Biol Bldg 3 Rm B1 06 Nat Heart Lung & Blood Inst NIH Bethesda MD 20014

SCHARFF, THOMAS G, b Paterson, NJ, Mar 9, 23; m 46; c 5. PHARMACOLOGY. *Educ:* Trinity Col, Conn, BS, 48, MS, 51; Univ Rochester, PhD(pharmacol), 56. *Prof Exp:* Lab supvr, Bigelow-Sanford Carpet Co, 48-49; res assoc, US AEC Proj, Trinity Col, Conn, 51-52; from instr to assoc prof pharmacol, 56-70, PROF PHARMACOL, SCHS MED & DENT, UNIV LOUISVILLE, 70- *Concurrent Pos:* Prin investr, Am Heart Asn, 63-68. *Mem:* AAAS; Am Soc Pharmacol & Exp Therapeut; Soc Exp Biol & Med; Soc Toxicol; Am Chem Soc. *Res:* Cellular pharmacology and biochemistry; cell metabolism and transport. *Mailing Add:* Dept of Pharmacol Univ Louisville Sch Med & Dent Louisville KY 40208

SCHARFSTEIN, LAWRENCE ROBERT, b New York, NY, July 21, 27; m 55; c 3. CHEMICAL METALLURGY. *Educ:* Pa State Univ, BS, 46; NY Univ, PhD(phys chem), 53. *Prof Exp:* Supvr phys chem res, Goodyear Atomic Corp, 53-55; lead engr, Bettis Plant, Westinghouse Elec Corp, 55-59; supvr corrosion res, Carpenter Steel Corp, 59-65, asst mgr chem res, 65-68, mgr chem technol res, Carpenter Technol Corp, 68-71, dir nuclear mat, Carpenter Technol Corp, 71-76; GROUP LEADER, MAT ENG, MOBIL RES & DEVELOP CORP, 76- *Mem:* Am Soc Metals; Am Soc Testing & Mat; Nat Asn Corrosion Engrs; Am Chem Soc; Am Nuclear Soc. *Res:* Corrosion; chemistry of metals and surfaces; electrochemistry; plating; nuclear chemistry; physical metallurgy of stainless steels; gas-metal reactions; heat treating. *Mailing Add:* 40 Clover Lane Princeton NJ 08540

SCHARN, HERMAN OTTO FRIEDRICH, b Ger, July 20, 11; US citizen; m 40; c 4. MATHEMATICS, PHYSICS. *Educ:* Univ Gottingen, MS, 48; Darmstadt Tech Univ, Dr rer nat(math, physics), 66. *Prof Exp:* Aeronaut engr, Aeronaut Res Inst, Ger, 40-45; high sch teacher, Hanover, 48-57; astronaut engr, Holloman AFB, US Air Force, 57-71 & Kirtland AFB, 71-73; RETIRED. *Honors & Awards:* US Air Force Systs Command Tech Achievement Award, 70; Dept Air Force Award Meritorious Civilian Serv, 73. *Res:* Theory of optimal trajectories in space navigation. *Mailing Add:* 8100 Connecticut St NE Albuquerque NM 87110

SCHARNHORST, KURT PETER, b Hamburg, Ger, Apr 19, 36; US citizen; m 62; c 2. SOLID STATE PHYSICS. *Educ:* City Col New York, BS, 61; Univ Md, PhD(physics), 69. *Prof Exp:* Physicist electromagnetics, 60-70, RES PHYSICIST SOLID STATE PHYSICS, NAVAL SURFACE WEAPONS CTR, 70- *Mem:* Am Phys Soc. *Res:* Electrooptics; superconductivity; wave propagation phenomena; solid state device physics. *Mailing Add:* Naval Surface Weapons Ctr White Oak Silver Spring MD 20910

SCHARPEN, LEROY HENRY, b Red Wing, Minn, Oct 15, 35; m 63; c 1. PHYSICAL CHEMISTRY, SURFACE SCIENCE. *Educ:* Harvard Univ, AB, 61; Stanford Univ, PhD(chem), 66. *Prof Exp:* Res scientist, McDonnell Douglas Corp, 66-68; appln chemist, Sci Instruments Div, Hewlett Packard Co, 68-73, mgr electron spectros, Chem Anal Appln Lab, 73-76; EXEC VPRES, SURFACE SCI LABS, INC, 76- *Mem:* AAAS; Am Chem Soc. *Res:* Application of surface analysis techniques to industrial research; materials and process problem solving. *Mailing Add:* 10145 McLaren Pl Cupertino CA 95014

SCHARPF, LEWIS GEORGE, JR, b Springfield, Mo, Sept 15, 40; m 65; c 2. ENZYMOLOGY, FOOD SAFETY. *Educ:* Southwest Mo State Col, BS, 61; Iowa State Univ, MS, 63, PhD(biochem), 65. *Prof Exp:* Res chemist, Monsanto Co, 65-70, res specialist, Monsanto Indust Chem Co, 70-74, mgr res & develop, 74-77; dir develop & toxicol & vpres res & develop, 77-80, VPRES TECH DIR, INT FLAVORS & FRAGRANCES, 80- *Mem:* Flavor & Extract Mfrs Asn; Environ Mutagen Soc; Inst Food Technol; Sigma Xi. *Res:* Muscle biochemistry; food and fermentation chemistry; food ingredient development; flavor chemistry; product safety assurance and environmental science. *Mailing Add:* 35 Lewis Point Rd Fair Haven NJ 07701

SCHARPF, ROBERT F, b St Louis, Mo, June 22, 31; m 57; c 2. PLANT PATHOLOGY. *Educ:* Univ Mo, BS, 54; Univ Calif, Berkeley, MS, 57, PhD(plant path), 63. *Prof Exp:* PLANT PATHOLOGIST, PAC SOUTHWEST FOREST & RANGE EXP STA, US FOREST SERV, 60- *Mem:* Am Phytopath Soc. *Res:* Forest diseases; epidemiology; hyperparasites. *Mailing Add:* Pac SW Forest & Range Exp Sta PO Box 245 Berkeley CA 94701

SCHARPF, WILLIAM GEORGE, b Baltimore, Md, Aug 24, 25; m 57; c 2. ORGANIC CHEMISTRY, PESTICIDE CHEMISTRY. *Educ:* Univ Md, BS, 50; Rider Col, MBA, 81. *Prof Exp:* Res chemist pesticides, US Indust Chem, 43-52; res chemist med, Johnson & Johnson, 53-56; plant chemist, Gen Elec Co, 57-58; sr process chemist boron fuels, Thiokol, 58-59; sr res chemist pesticides, 59-78, RES ASSOC, FMC CORP, 78- *Mem:* Am Chem Soc; Org Reactions Catalysis Soc. *Res:* Structure biological activity correlations; process research related to organic pesticides, particularly carbamate and pyrethroid insecticides. *Mailing Add:* FMC Corp PO Box 8 Princeton NJ 08540

SCHARRER, BERTA VOGEL, b Munich, Ger, Dec 1, 06; nat US; m 34. ANATOMY. *Educ:* Univ Munich, PhD(zool), 30. *Hon Degrees:* Dr, Univ Giessen, WGer, 76; DSc, Northwestern Univ, 77, Univ NC, 78. *Prof Exp:* Asst, Res Inst Psychiat, Munich, 32-34; guest investr, Neurol Inst, Frankfurt, 34-37; guest investr, Dept Anat, Univ Chicago, 37-38 & Rockefeller Inst, 38-40; sr instr, Western Reserve Univ, 40-46; instr & asst prof res, Univ Colo,

46-54; prof, 55-78, EMER PROF ANAT, ALBERT EINSTEIN COL MED, 78- *Concurrent Pos:* Fel, Western Reserve Univ, 40-46; Guggenheim fel, 47-48; USPHS fel, 48-50; NSF grant, 78-80. *Honors & Awards:* Kraepelin Gold Medal Award, 78. *Mem:* Nat Acad Sci; Am Soc Zoologists; Am Asn Anat (pres, 78-79); Am Acad Arts & Sci; hon mem Europ Soc Comp Endocrinol. *Res:* Comparative neuroendocrinology and neurosecretion; comparative endocrinology; ultrastructure. *Mailing Add:* Dept of Anat Albert Einstein Col of Med Bronx NY 10461

SCHARTON, TERRY DON, b York, Nebr, May 12, 39; m 64; c 3. ACOUSTICS, VIBRATIONS. *Educ:* Mass Inst Technol, BS, 62, MS, 64, ScD(mech eng), 66. *Prof Exp:* Regional mgr acoust, Bolt, Beranck & Newman, 66-77; PRIN SCIENTIST VIBRATIONS, ANCO ENGRS INC, 77- *Mem:* Acoust Soc Am; Am Inst Aeronaut & Astronaut; Am Inst Automotive Engrs. *Res:* Offshore tower vibration testing for nondestructive evaluation; tube bundle heat exchange vibration diagnosis. *Mailing Add:* Anco Engr Inc 9937 Jefferson Blvd Culver City CA 90230

SCHARVER, JEFFREY DOUGLAS, b Massillon, Ohio, Nov 3, 47; m 70; c 2. ORGANIC CHEMISTRY. *Educ:* Bowling Green State Univ, BS, 69; Duke Univ, PhD(chem), 75. *Prof Exp:* Res chemist, 74-81, GROUP LEADER, CHEM DEVELOP LABS, BURROUGHS WELLCOME CO, USA, 81- *Res:* The development of new organic processes and their application to pharmaceutical research. *Mailing Add:* 5202 Autumn Dr Durham NC 27712

SCHASCHL, E(DWARD), b Chicago, Ill, May 9, 24; m 53; c 2. CHEMICAL ENGINEERING. *Educ:* Ill Inst Technol, BS, 45. *Prof Exp:* Operator prod, Calverts Distillery, 45-46; asst metall, Ill Inst Technol, 46-47, corrosion lab, 47-48; jr res engr, Pilot Plant Sect, Res Ctr, Pure Oil Co, Ill, 48-55, sr res engr, 55-66; SR RES ENGR, UNION OIL CO, 66- *Honors & Awards:* Nat Asn Corrosion Engrs Award, 57. *Mem:* Nat Asn Corrosion Engrs. *Res:* Corrosion and metallurgy, especially in the petroleum industry. *Mailing Add:* Res Dept Union Oil Co PO Box 76 Brea CA 92621

SCHATTEN, GERALD PHILLIP, b New York, NY, Nov 1, 49; m 77. CELL BIOLOGY, DEVELOPMENTAL BIOLOGY. *Educ:* Univ Calif, Berkeley, BS, 71, PhD(cell biol), 75. *Prof Exp:* Instr zool, Univ Calif, Berkeley, 75; fels reproduction, Rockefeller Found, NY, 76 & 77; guest researcher, Ger Cancer Res Ctr, Heidelberg, 76-77; asst prof, 77-81, ASSOC PROF BIOL SCI, FLA STATE UNIV, 81-, DIR ELECTRON MICROS LAB, INST MOLECULAR BIOPHYS, 81- *Concurrent Pos:* Prin investr res grants, fertil, NSF, 78, 79 & 81, NIH, 79 & 81, Am Cancer Soc, 80, Environ Protection Agency, 81 & Fla State Univ Found; NIH career development award, 80. *Honors & Awards:* Micrograph Award, Exp Cell Res, Stockholm, 76. *Mem:* AAAS; Am Soc Cell Biol; Soc Develop Biol; Soc Study Reproduction; Am Soc Zoologists. *Res:* Fertilization; cancer; egg activation; cell transformation; movement of sperm; pronuclear movements and fusion; intracellular calcium localization; mitosis; cytokinesis; mitotic apparatus; nuclear envelope; membranes; electron microscopy; video microscopy; ion localization. *Mailing Add:* Dept Biol Sci Fla State Univ Tallahassee FL 32306

SCHATTEN, HEIDE, b Niederweidbach, WGer, Sept 24, 46; m 77. CELL BIOLOGY, CANCER. *Educ:* Ger Cancer Res Ctr, Inst Cell Res, diplom, 74, Dr rer nat, 77. *Prof Exp:* Fel cell biol, Univ Calif, Berkeley, 77; fac res assoc cell biol, 77-81, ASST RES SCIENTIST CELL BIOL, FLA STATE UNIV, 81- *Concurrent Pos:* Co prin investr, NSF grant, 79; sr investr res grants, NIH, 80-, Environ Protection Agency, 81-; travel grant, Am Soc Cell Biol, 81. *Mem:* Am Soc Cell Biol; Ger Soc Cell Biol. *Res:* Fertilization; pronuclear movements; mitotic apparatus; cell division; microtubules; protein chemistry; mitosis; synchronization; cell culture; transformation; activation; cancer drugs; reproduction; electron microscopy. *Mailing Add:* Dept of Biol Sci Fla State Univ Unit I Tallahassee FL 32306

SCHATTEN, KENNETH HOWARD, b New York, NY, Feb 1, 44; m 70. SOLAR PHYSICS. *Educ:* Mass Inst Technol, SB, 64; Univ Calif, Berkeley, PhD(physics), 68. *Prof Exp:* Researcher space physics, Univ Calif, Berkeley, 68-69; Nat Acad Sci fel, Goddard Space Flight Ctr, NASA, 69-70, researcher, 70-72; SR LECTR PHYSICS, VICTORIA UNIV, WELLINGTON, 72- *Res:* Solar terrestrial relationships; sun, solar corona, interplanetary space, geophysics; planetary physics; electric and magnetic fields; plasma physics. *Mailing Add:* Victoria Univ Dept of Physics Private Bag Wellington New Zealand

SCHATTNER, ROBERT I, b New York, NY, June 4, 25; c 2. PHARMACEUTICAL CHEMISTRY, PESTICIDE CHEMISTRY. *Educ:* Univ Pa, DDS, 48; City Univ New York, BS, 49. *Prof Exp:* Dent surgeon, USPHS, 48-49; pvt pract, 49-59; RES DIR, R SCHATTNER CO, 63-; OFFICER & DIR, R SCHATTNER FOUND MED RES, 64-; OFFICER & RES DIR, SPORICIDIN CO, WASHINGTON, DC, 77- *Concurrent Pos:* Res dir, Chloraseptic Co, 52-63; consult, Norwich Pharmacal Co, 63-65. *Mem:* Am Soc Microbiol; Royal Soc Health; Int Dent Fedn; Am Dent Asn. *Res:* Chemical development and microbiological testing of new sterilizing solution; aerosol disinfectant spray; antimicrobial additive and preservative; antiseptic and analgesic pharmaceutical preparation for skin, lips and vagina. *Mailing Add:* 4000 Massachusetts Ave NW Washington DC 20016

SCHATZ, EDWARD R(ALPH), b St Mary's, Pa, Nov 28, 21; m 48; c 2. ELECTRICAL ENGINEERING. *Educ:* Carnegie Inst Technol, BS, 42, MS, 43, DSc, 49. *Prof Exp:* Asst engr, Metall Lab, Univ Chicago, 44 & Los Alamos Sci Lab, Univ Calif, 44-46; instr elec eng, 46-49, asst prof elec eng & indust admin, 49-52, assoc prof elec eng, 53-61, head dept, 53-57, asst dean col eng & sci, 57-60, assoc dean, 60-61, dean res, 61-64, PROF ELEC ENG, CARNEGIE-MELLON UNIV, 61-, VPRES ACAD AFFAIRS, 64-, PROVOST, 73- *Mem:* Am Soc Eng Educ; sr mem Inst Elec & Electronics Engrs. *Res:* Skin effect in wires; atomic bomb; transients in tapered transmission lines; communications. *Mailing Add:* Carnegie-Mellon Univ 5000 Forbes Ave Pittsburgh PA 15213

SCHATZ, IRWIN JACOB, b St Boniface, Man, Oct 16, 31; m 67; c 4. INTERNAL MEDICINE, CARDIOVASCULAR DISEASES. *Educ:* Univ Man, MD, 56. *Prof Exp:* Fel, Mayo Clin, 58-61; chief sect peripheral vascular dis, Henry Ford Hosp, Detroit, 61-68; chief sect cardiovasc dis, Sch Med, Wayne State Univ, 68-72; assoc prof cardiol, Med Ctr, Univ Mich, Ann Arbor, 72-75, assoc dir div cardiol, 72-75, prof med, 73-75; PROF MED & CHMN DEPT, JOHN A BURNS SCH MED, UNIV HAWAII, HONOLULU, 75- *Concurrent Pos:* Fel coun circulation & clin cardiol, Am Heart Asn; spec consult health manpower, Dept Health, Educ & Welfare, 68-69. *Mem:* Fel Am Col Physicians; fel Am Col Cardiol. *Res:* Ischemic heart disease; platelet morphology; atherosclerosis. *Mailing Add:* Dept Med 1356 Lusitana St Honolulu HI 96813

SCHATZ, JOSEPH ARTHUR, b US, June 23, 24; m 48; c 4. MATHEMATICS. *Educ:* Va Polytech Inst, BS, 47; Brown Univ, PhD(math), 52. *Prof Exp:* Draftsman, E I du Pont de Nemours & Co, Inc, 41-42; inspector, Signal Corps, US Dept Army, 42-43, engr, Manhattan Proj, 46; ed asst, Math Rev, Am Math Soc, 48-52; instr math, Lehigh Univ, 52-55 & Univ Conn, 55-57; mem staff, Sandia Corp, 57-72; ASSOC PROF MATH & COMPUT SCI, UNIV HOUSTON, 72- *Mem:* Am Math Soc; Math Asn Am; Asn Comput Mach; Asn Symbolic Logic. *Res:* Applied mathematics; computer sciences; logic. *Mailing Add:* 6035 Wigton Houston TX 77096

SCHATZ, LEO, anatomy, histology, see previous edition

SCHATZ, PAUL NAMON, b Philadelphia, Pa, Oct 20, 28; m 54; c 3. PHYSICAL CHEMISTRY. *Educ:* Univ Pa, BS, 49; Brown Univ, PhD(chem), 52. *Prof Exp:* Jewett fel, Calif Inst Technol, 52-53; res assoc chem, Brown Univ, 53-54; from asst prof to assoc prof, 56-65, PROF CHEM, UNIV VA, 65- *Concurrent Pos:* NSF sr fel, Oxford Univ, 63-64, Guggenheim fel, 74-75. *Mem:* Am Chem Soc; Am Phys Soc. *Res:* Molecular structure, especially spectroscopy and quantum mechanics. *Mailing Add:* Dept of Chem Univ of Va Charlottesville VA 22901

SCHATZKI, THOMAS FERDINANT, b Berlin, Ger, Oct 20, 27; nat US; m 52; c 2. CHEMICAL PHYSICS. *Educ:* Univ Mich, BS, 49; Mass Inst Technol, PhD(chem), 54. *Prof Exp:* Res assoc, Univ Wis, 54-55 & Univ Ill, 55-57; chemist, Shell Develop Co, Calif, 57-72; RES CHEMIST, WESTERN REGIONAL LAB, USDA, 72- *Mem:* Am Phys Soc; Inst Elec & Electronics Engrs; Am Chem Soc. *Res:* Image analysis; polymer physics. *Mailing Add:* USDA Western Regional Lab Albany CA 94710

SCHATZLEIN, FRANK CHARLES, b Oceanside, NY, July 6, 29; m 52; c 2. INVERTEBRATE PHYSIOLOGY. *Educ:* Colgate Univ, BA, 51; Ind Univ, PhD(zool), 62. *Prof Exp:* From asst prof to assoc prof, 59-73, prof physiol, 73-80, PROF BIOL, CALIF STATE UNIV, LONG BEACH, 80- *Concurrent Pos:* USPHS trainee endocrinol, 62-63. *Mem:* AAAS; Am Soc Zoologists. *Res:* Hormonal regulation of metabolism in crustacean larvae and adults. *Mailing Add:* Dept of Biol Calif State Univ Long Beach CA 90804

SCHAUB, JAMES H(AMILTON), b Moundsville, WVa, Jan 27, 25; m 48. CIVIL ENGINEERING. *Educ:* Va Polytech Inst, BS, 48; Harvard Univ, SM, 49; Purdue Univ, PhD(civil eng), 60. *Prof Exp:* Soils engr, State Hwy Dept, Ore, 49-50 & 51-52; lab dir, Palmer & Baker, Inc, Ala, 52-55; asst prof civil eng, Va Polytech Inst, 55-58; instr & res engr, Purdue Univ, 58-60; prof & chmn dept, Univ WVa, 60-67, assoc dean eng, 67-69; PROF CIVIL ENG & CHMN DEPT, UNIV FLA, 69- *Mem:* Fel Am Soc Civil Engrs; Am Soc Eng Educ; Nat Soc Prof Engrs; Am Pub Works Asn. *Res:* Soil mechanics; highway engineering. *Mailing Add:* Dept Civil Eng Univ Fla Gainesville FL 32611

SCHAUB, STEPHEN ALEXANDER, b Walla Walla, Wash, Sept 29, 40; m 65; c 2. VIROLOGY, ENVIRONMENTAL HEALTH. *Educ:* Wash State Univ, BS, 64; Univ Tex, Austin, MA, 70, PhD(microbiol), 72. *Prof Exp:* Asst health serv officer, USPHS, 64-66; res microbiologist, 72-73, SUPVRY MICROBIOLOGIST, US ARMY MED BIOENG RES & DEVELOP LAB, 74- *Mem:* Am Soc Microbiol; Sigma Xi; Am Pub Health Asn; AAAS. *Res:* Virus concentration and enumeration from water and wastewater; aerobiology of spray irrigation of wastewater; infiltration of viruses in land systems by wastewater application; mechanisms of microbial disinfection by chlorine and ozone. *Mailing Add:* US Army Med Bioeng R&D Lab Environ Prot Res Div Ft Detrick Frederick MD 21701

SCHAUBLE, J HERMAN, b Macomb, Ill, Jan 18, 32; m 58; c 2. ORGANIC CHEMISTRY. *Educ:* Western Ill Univ, BS, 54, MS, 56; Univ Ill, PhD(org chem), 64. *Prof Exp:* Instr chem, Springfield Jr Col, 56-59; res assoc, Mass Inst Technol, 63-65; assoc prof org chem, 65-80, PROF CHEM, VILLANOVA UNIV, 80- *Mem:* Am Chem Soc; Royal Soc Chem. *Res:* Synthesis and conformational analysis of four and five membered ring heterocycles; organosulfur and selenium chemistry; synthetic photochemistry in the crystal state and in solution; complex metal hydride reduction of carbon-carbon multiple bonds. *Mailing Add:* Dept of Chem Villanova Univ Villanova PA 19085

SCHAUER, JOHN JOSEPH, b Dayton, Ohio, Aug 5, 36; m 70; c 4. MECHANICAL ENGINEERING. *Educ:* Univ Dayton, BME, 58; Carnegie-Mellon Univ, MS, 59; Stanford Univ, PhD(mech eng), 64. *Prof Exp:* Assoc prin res engr, Technol, Inc, Ohio, 65-67; PROF MECH ENG, UNIV DAYTON, 68- *Res:* Convective heat and mass transfer; acoustics. *Mailing Add:* Dept of Mech Eng Univ of Dayton Dayton OH 45469

SCHAUER, RICHARD C, b Pittsburgh, Pa, July 21, 37; m 69. PHYSIOLOGY. *Educ:* Univ Pittsburgh, BS, 60; NC State Univ, MS, 68, PhD(physiol zool), 72. *Prof Exp:* From instr to asst prof physiol, Univ NC, Greensboro, 71-78; ASSOC PROF, GANNON UNIV, ERIE, 78- *Mem:* AAAS; NY Acad Sci. *Res:* Estrogen stimulation of RNA synthesis in the rat uterus; molecular endocrinology. *Mailing Add:* Dept Biol Gannon Univ Erie PA 16541

SCHAUF, CHARLES LAWRENCE, b Chicago, Ill, Sept 16, 43; m 77; c 2. PHYSIOLOGY, BIOPHYSICS. *Educ:* Univ Chicago, SB, 65, PhD(physiol), 69. *Prof Exp:* Asst prof, 72-75, assoc prof, 75-78, PROF NEUROL SCI & PHYSIOL, RUSH UNIV, 78- *Concurrent Pos:* NIH fel, Univ Md, 70-72; NIH res career develop award, 75-80. *Mem:* AAAS; Biophys Soc; Soc Gen Physiol; Soc Neurosci. *Res:* Biophysics of excitable membranes; demyelinating diseases; neuropharmacology. *Mailing Add:* Physiol Rush Univ 1753 W Congress Chicago IL 60612

SCHAUF, VICTORIA, b New York, NY, Feb 17, 43; c 1. INFECTIOUS DISEASES, IMMUNOLOGY. *Educ:* Univ Chicago, BS, 65, MD, 69. *Prof Exp:* ASSOC PROF PEDIAT, COL MED, UNIV ILL, 77- *Concurrent Pos:* Head, Sect Pediat Infectious Dis & Immunol, Univ Ill, 74-, dir, Chiang Mai-Ill Leprosy Res Proj, 79- *Mem:* Soc Pediat Res; Infectious Dis Soc Am; Cent Soc Clin Res. *Res:* Clinical and laboratory research in immunology, virology, and bacteriology; clinical trials with antimicrobial agents; leprosy, immunology and epidemiology. *Mailing Add:* Dept Pediat Univ Ill 840 S Wood St Chicago IL 60612

SCHAUFELE, RONALD A, b Calgary, Alta, Oct 5, 30; m 53. MATHEMATICAL STATISTICS. *Educ:* Univ Alta, BEd, 56; Univ Wash, BSc, 57, MSc, 62, PhD(math), 63. *Prof Exp:* Asst prof statist, Stanford Univ, 63-64 & Columbia Univ, 64-66; asst prof, 66-68, ASSOC PROF MATH, YORK UNIV, 68- *Concurrent Pos:* Can Nat Res Coun grant, 68-69. *Mem:* Am Math Soc; Math Asn Am; Inst Math Statist. *Res:* Probability; stochastic processes. *Mailing Add:* Dept of Math York Univ Downsview ON M3J 1P3 Can

SCHAUMANN, ROLF, b Nuremberg, Ger, July 29, 41; m 69. FILTER DESIGN, INTEGRATED CIRCUITS. *Educ:* Univ Stuttgart, DiplIng, 67; Univ Minn, Minneapolis, PhD(elec eng), 70. *Prof Exp:* ASSOC PROF ELEC ENG, UNIV MINN, MINNEAPOLIS, 70- *Mem:* Inst Elec & Electronics Engrs. *Res:* Theory of active and passive networks; distributed networks; linear integrated circuits; digital filters. *Mailing Add:* Dept Elec Eng Univ Minn Minneapolis MN 55455

SCHAUMBERG, GENE DAVID, b Rochester, Minn, Oct 3, 39; m 61; c 2. ORGANOMETALLIC CHEMISTRY. *Educ:* Pac Lutheran Univ, BS, 61; Wash State Univ, PhD(chem), 65. *Prof Exp:* Teaching asst chem, Wash State Univ, 61-65; from asst prof to assoc prof, 65-72, chmn div natural sci, 69-78, PROF ORG CHEM, SONOMA STATE UNIV, 72- *Concurrent Pos:* Fulbright lectr, 71-72; Scientists & Engrs in Econ Develop & NSF grant, 75. *Mem:* Am Chem Soc. *Res:* Synthesis of new organoboron compounds of possible biological interest; soil and environmental chemistry. *Mailing Add:* Dept of Chem Sonoma State Univ Rohnert Park CA 94928

SCHAUMBERGER, NORMAN, b Brooklyn, NY, May 2 8, 29; m 54; c 2. MATHEMATICS. *Educ:* City Col New York, BS, 51, MA, 52; Brooklyn Col, MA, 58; Columbia Univ, EdD(math educ), 62. *Prof Exp:* Teacher, NY Pub Schs, 51-57; instr math, Cooper Union, 57; PROF MATH, BRONX COMMUNITY COL, 59- *Concurrent Pos:* Lectr, City Col New York, 55-63; instr, Teachers Col, Columbia Univ, 63; NSF acad year inst sec math teachers, Dominican Col, NY, 66-67. *Mem:* Math Asn Am; Am Math Soc. *Res:* Problems in number theory and complex variables. *Mailing Add:* Dept of Math Bronx Community Col Bronx NY 10468

SCHAUMBURG, FRANK DAVID, b Watseka, Ill, Jan 15, 38; m 60; c 2. ENVIRONMENTAL ENGINEERING. *Educ:* Ariz State Univ, BSCE, 61; Purdue Univ, West Lafayette, MSCE, 64, PhD(sanit eng), 66. *Prof Exp:* Res engr, BC Res Coun, 66; asst prof environ eng, 67-69, assoc prof, 69-80, PROF CIVIL ENG, ORE STATE UNIV, 80-, HEAD DEPT, 72- *Concurrent Pos:* Consult, Govt Acct Off, 75- & UNESCO, 77-78. *Mem:* Am Soc Civil Engrs; Water Pollution Control Fedn; Am Soc Eng Educ. *Res:* Biological waste treatment; environmental tradeoffs and interactions. *Mailing Add:* Dept of Civil Eng Ore State Univ Corvallis OR 97331

SCHAUMBURG, HERBERT HOWARD, b Houston, Tex, Nov 6, 32; m 66; c 2. NEUROLOGY, EXPERIMENTAL NEUROPATHOLOGY. *Educ:* Harvard Univ, AB, 56; Wash Univ, MD, 60. *Prof Exp:* Fel neurol, Albert Einstein Col Med, 67-69; instr path, Harvard Med Sch, 69-71; assoc prof, 72-76, PROF NEUROL, ALBERT EINSTEIN COL MED, 77-, VCHMN DEPT, 78- *Honors & Awards:* Moore Award, Am Asn Neuropath, 77. *Mem:* Am Soc Neurol; Am Neurol Asn; Am Asn Neuropathologists. *Res:* Experimental neuropathology of myelin disease and effects of toxic chemicals on nervous system. *Mailing Add:* Dept Neurol Albert Einstein Col Med Bronx NY 10461

SCHAWLOW, ARTHUR LEONARD, b Mt Vernon, NY, May 5, 21; m 51; c 3. LASERS. *Educ:* Univ Toronto, BA, 41, MA, 42, PhD, 49. *Hon Degrees:* DSc, State Univ Ghent, 68 & Univ Bradford, 70; LLD, Univ Toronto, 70. *Prof Exp:* Demonstr physics, Univ Toronto, 41-44; demonstr microwave develop, Res Enterprises, Ltd, 44-45; demonstr physics, Univ Toronto, 45-49; fel & res assoc, Columbia Univ, 49-51; res physicist, Bell Tel Labs, Inc, 51-61; chmn dept physics, 66-70 & 73-74, prof physics, 61-78, J G JACKSON-C J WOOD PROF PHYSICS, STANFORD UNIV, 78- *Concurrent Pos:* Vls assoc prof, Columbia Univ, 60; Marconi int fel, 77. *Honors & Awards:* Ballantine Medal, Franklin Inst, 62; Thomas Young Medal & Prize, Brit Inst Physics, 63; Liebmann Mem Prize, Inst Elec & Electronics Engrs, 64; Frederick Ives Medal, Optical Soc Am, 76; Nobel Prize Physics, 81. *Mem:* Nat Acad Sci; fel AAAS; fel Am Phys Soc (pres, 81); fel Optical Soc Am (pres, 75); fel Inst Elec & Electronics Engrs. *Res:* Radio frequency, optical and microwave spectroscopy; lasers and quantum electronics. *Mailing Add:* Dept of Physics Stanford Univ Stanford CA 94305

SCHAY, GEZA, b Budapest, Hungary, June 22, 34; US citizen. MATHEMATICAL PHYSICS. *Educ:* Eotvos Lorand Univ, Budapest, BA, 56; Princeton Univ, PhD(math physics), 61. *Prof Exp:* Instr physics, Tufts Univ, 58-59; staff mathematician, Int Bus Mach Corp, 60-63; from asst prof to assoc prof math, George Washington Univ, 63-66; assoc prof, 66-70, PROF MATH, UNIV MASS, BOSTON, 70- *Mem:* Am Math Soc; Inst Math Statist. *Res:* Stochastic processes; diffusion theory; relativistic mechanics. *Mailing Add:* 298 Waltham St Newton MA 02165

SCHAYE, ALVIN ALBERT, b New York, NY, Nov 19, 04; m 39; c 1. MEDICINE. *Educ:* Columbia Univ, BA, 25; Yale Univ, MD, 28; Am Bd Internal Med, dipl, 42. *Prof Exp:* Assoc attend physician, New York City Hosp, 36-55; CLIN PROF INTERNAL MED, NEW YORK POLYCLIN MED SCH, 55-; ASSOC PROF, NEW YORK MED COL, 56- *Concurrent Pos:* Vis physician, Sydenham Hosp, 35- & Bird S Coler & Metrop Hosps, 56-; consult physician, Sydenham Hosp. *Mem:* AMA; fel Am Col Physicians; fel NY Acad Med. *Res:* Internal medicine. *Mailing Add:* 255 Central Park W New York NY 10024

SCHAYER, RICHARD WILLIAM, b Sydney, Australia, Feb 3, 15; US citizen; m 39; c 2. BIOCHEMICAL PHARMACOLOGY. *Educ:* George Washington Univ, BS, 40; Columbia Univ, PhD(biochem), 49. *Hon Degrees:* MD, Univ Lund, 75. *Prof Exp:* Chemist, USPHS, 36-42; asst, Columbia Univ, 46-49; res assoc, Rheumatic Fever Res Inst, Med Sch, Northwestern Univ, 49-57; Merck Inst Therapeut Res, 57-64; USPHS spec fel, 64-65; PRIN RES SCIENTIST, ROCKLAND RES INST, 65- *Mem:* Am Soc Biol Chemists; Am Soc Pharmacol & Exp Therapeut; Am Physiol Soc; Soc Exp Biol & Med; Brit Pharmacol Soc. *Res:* Histamine; metabolism; physiological and pathological significance; mechanism of action of glucocorticoids. *Mailing Add:* Rockland Res Inst Orangeburg NY 10962

SCHEAFFER, RICHARD LEWIS, b Williamsport, Pa, July 13, 40; m 63; c 2. STATISTICS. *Educ:* Lycoming Col, AB, 62; Bucknell Univ, MA, 64; Fla State Univ, PhD(statist), 68. *Prof Exp:* From asst prof to assoc prof statist, 67-77, PROF STATIST & CHMN DEPT, UNIV FLA, 77- *Mem:* Am Statist Asn; Inst Math Statist; Biomet Soc. *Res:* Sampling theory; applied probability, especially in the areas of reliability and two and three dimensional sampling problems. *Mailing Add:* Dept of Statist Univ of Fla Gainesville FL 32601

SCHEARER, LAIRD D, b Allentown, Pa, Nov 26, 31; m 50; c 4. ATOMIC PHYSICS. *Educ:* Muhlenberg Col, BS, 54; Lehigh Univ, MS, 58; Rice Univ, PhD(physics), 66; Muhlenberg Col, DSc, 80. *Prof Exp:* Instr physics, Lafayette Col, 55-59; sr scientist, Tex Instruments, Inc, 59-71; chmn, Dept Physics, 71-77, PROF PHYSICS, UNIV MO-ROLLA, 77- *Concurrent Pos:* Vis fel, Joint Inst Lab Astrophys, 77-78; prog assoc, NSF, 79-80. *Mem:* AAAS; Am Phys Soc; Sigma Xi. *Res:* Optical pumping; magnetometers; line shapes and line broadening, stark shifts; penning ionization; magnetic resonance; atomic beams; gas lasers. *Mailing Add:* Dept Physics Univ Mo Rolla MO 65401

SCHEARER, SHERWOOD BRUCE, b Reading, Pa, Jan 27, 42; m 63; c 2. POPULATION STUDIES, SCIENCE ADMINISTRATION. *Educ:* Lafayette Col, AB, 63; Columbia Univ, PhD(biochem), 71. *Prof Exp:* From res assoc to staff scientist, 71-74, asst dir, Biomed Div, 71-76, from assoc to sr assoc, Int Progs Div, Pop Coun, 76-81, PRES, POP RESOURCE CTR, 81- *Concurrent Pos:* Mem, bd dir, Western Hemisphere Region, Int Planned Parenthood Fedn, 77-81, Planned Parenthood of New York, Pop Resource Ctr, adv bd, Margaret Sanger Ctr, chmn, Western Hemisphere Reserve/Int Planned Fedn Info & Educ Panel, 79-81. *Mem:* AAAS. *Res:* Development, transfer, absorption, implementation and monitoring of contraceptive technology; design and evaluation of epidemiological studies of drugs and devices; social science research into attitudes and practices of populations; analysis and development of population policy. *Mailing Add:* Pop Resource Ctr 622 Third Ave New York NY 10017

SCHEARER, WILLIAM RICHARD, b Kutztown, Pa, July 19, 35; m 58; c 3. ORGANIC CHEMISTRY. *Educ:* Ursinus Col, BS, 57; Princeton Univ, MA, 59, PhD(org chem), 63. *Prof Exp:* From asst prof to assoc prof chem, Hartwick Col, 61-65; sr chemist, Ciba Pharmaceut Co, 65-68; ASSOC PROF CHEM, DICKINSON COL, 68- *Mem:* Am Chem Soc. *Res:* Natural products; chemical education; organic synthesis; applied chemistry. *Mailing Add:* Dept of Chem Dickinson Col Carlisle PA 17013

SCHECHTER, ALAN NEIL, b New York, NY, June 28, 39; m 65; c 2. MEDICAL RESEARCH, PROTEIN CHEMISTRY. *Educ:* Cornell Univ, AB, 59; Columbia Univ, MD, 63. *Prof Exp:* Intern med, Bronx Munic Hosp Ctr, 63-64, asst resident, 64-65; res assoc, 65-67, USPHS vis fel, 67-68, med officer, 68-72, CHIEF, SECT MACROMOLECULAR BIOL, LAB CHEM BIOL, NAT INST ARTHRITIS, METAB & DIGESTIVE DIS, 72- *Concurrent Pos:* Sr asst surgeon, USPHS, 65-67. *Mem:* AAAS; Am Fedn Clin Res; Am Soc Biol Chemists; Am Soc Clin Invest; Biophys Soc. *Res:* Structure-function relations in proteins; protein folding; biophysical and immunochemical techniques; hemoglobin chemistry; genetic disease. *Mailing Add:* Lab of Chem Biol Nat Inst of Arthritis Metab & Digestive Dis Bethesda MD 20014

SCHECHTER, DANIEL, b Brooklyn, NY, Sept 18, 31; m 62; c 2. PHYSICS. *Educ:* Univ Calif, Los Angeles, AB, 53; Carnegie Inst Technol, MS, 56, PhD(physics), 58. *Prof Exp:* Sr engr, Gen Tel & Electronics Labs, Inc; asst prof electrophys, Polytech Inst Brooklyn, 62-65; staff scientist, TRW Systs, Inc, 65-69; assoc prof, 69-80, PROF PHYSICS, CALIF STATE UNIV, LONG BEACH, 80- *Concurrent Pos:* Consult, Bell Tel Labs, Inc, 55-56, Autonetics, 75-79 & Hughes Aircraft Co, 80- *Mem:* Am Phys Soc. *Res:* Electronic properties of semiconductors; shallow impurities; surface impurities; electrostatics of charge-coupled devices; charge transfer dynamics of charge-coupled devices; properties of semiconductor visible and infrared detector materials. *Mailing Add:* Dept of Physics Calif State Univ Long Beach CA 90840

SCHECHTER, GERALDINE POPPA, b New York, NY, Jan 16, 38; m 65; c 2. HEMATOLOGY. *Educ:* Vassar Col, AB, 59; Columbia Univ, MD, 63. *Prof Exp:* Intern & asst resident med, Columbia-Presby Hosp, 63-65; resident med & hemat, 65-67, res assoc hemat, 68-69, asst chief, 70-74, CHIEF HEMAT, VET ADMIN HOSP, WASHINGTON, DC, 74- *Concurrent Pos:* From instr to asst prof med, George Washington Univ, 70-74, assoc prof, 74-81, prof, 81- *Mem:* Am Fedn Clin Res; Am Soc Hemat; Am Soc Clin Oncol; Am Asn Immunol. *Res:* Lymphocyte biology; immunological response to blood transfusion; hematological malignancies. *Mailing Add:* Hemat Sect Vet Admin Med Ctr 50 Irving St NW Washington DC 20422

SCHECHTER, JOEL ERNEST, b Detroit, Mich, Apr 18, 39; div; c 2. CELL BIOLOGY, ELECTRON MICROSCOPY. *Educ:* Wayne State Univ, BA, 61; Johns Hopkins Univ, MA, 63; Univ Calif, Los Angeles, PhD(anat), 68. *Prof Exp:* Instr med art, Sch Med, Johns Hopkins Univ, 63-64; asst prof, 69-73, assoc prof histol, 73-80, ASSOC PROF ANAT, SCH MED, UNIV SOUTHERN CALIF, 73- *Concurrent Pos:* Univ Calif, Los Angeles ment health trainee & fel, Brain Res Inst, Los Angeles, 68-69; instr exten art prog, Univ Calif, Los Angeles, 69- *Mem:* AAAS; Am Soc Cell Biol; Tissue Cult Asn; Am Asn Anatomists. *Res:* Developmental cell biology; ultrastructural histochemical studies of human pituitary tumors. *Mailing Add:* Dept of Anat Univ of Southern Calif Med Sch Los Angeles CA 90033

SCHECHTER, JOSEPH M, b New York, NY, Sept 28, 38. PHYSICS. *Educ:* Cooper Union, BEE, 59; Univ Rochester, PhD(physics), 65. *Prof Exp:* Res assoc physics, Fermi Inst, Univ Chicago, 65-67; asst prof, 67-70, assoc prof, 70-77, PROF PHYSICS, SYRACUSE UNIV, 78- *Mem:* Am Phys Soc. *Res:* Theoretical elementary particle physics. *Mailing Add:* Dept of Physics Syracuse Univ Syracuse NY 13210

SCHECHTER, MANNIE M, b Johannesburg, SAfrica, Oct 2, 23; US citizen; m 58. RADIOLOGY. *Educ:* Univ Witwatersrand, MB, ChB, 46, dipl med radiol diagnostic, 55. *Prof Exp:* Mid grade registr neuroradiol, Nat Hosp, London, Eng, 55-56, sr registr, 56-58; assoc prof radiol, 59-64, PROF RADIOL, ALBERT EINSTEIN COL MED, 64- *Concurrent Pos:* Consult, Nat Inst Neurol Dis & Blindness, 60-; secy-gen, Int Cong Neuroradiol, 61-64; ed, J Neuroradiol; chief neuroradiologist, St Vincent's Hosp, New York, 58-76. *Mem:* AMA; Am Soc Neuroradiol (vpres, 63-64, pres, 64-65); Radiol Soc NAm; Asn Univ Radiol; Brit Inst Radiol. *Res:* Neuroradiology. *Mailing Add:* Dept of Radiol Albert Einstein Col of Med Bronx NY 10461

SCHECHTER, MARSHALL DAVID, b Sept 4, 21; US citizen; div; c 4. CHILD PSYCHIATRY. *Educ:* Univ Wis, BS, 42; Univ Cincinnati, MD, 44. *Hon Degrees:* MA, Univ Pa, 77. *Prof Exp:* Pvt pract, 49-64; clin instr psychiat, Sch Med, Univ Calif, Los Angeles, 53, asst clin prof, 57, assoc clin prof, 63-64; prof psychiat, vchmn & head div child psychiat, Health Sci Ctr, Univ Okla, 69-73, consult prof pediat, 64-73, prof biol psychol, 66-73; prof & dir div child & adolescent psychiat, State Univ NY Upstate Med Ctr, 73-76; PROF PSYCHIAT & DIR DIV CHILD & ADOLESCENT PSYCHIAT, SCH MED, UNIV PA, PHILADELPHIA, 76- *Concurrent Pos:* Consult, Vet Admin Hosp, Oklahoma City, 64-73, Children's Med Ctr, Tulsa, 64-73, Okla State Dept Pub Health, 64-73, Okla State Dept Ment Health, 64-73, Wilford Hall, Lackland AFB, 66-, Head Start, Off Econ Opportunity, Hutchings Psychiat Ctr, 73-, Vet Admin Hosp, NY, 74-76, Off Child Develop, 75, Nat Inst Ment Hyg, 75-76 & Vet Admin Hosp, Philadelphia, 76-; distinguished vis prof, Wilford Hall Lackland Air Force Base, 72- *Mem:* Am Psychiat Asn; Am Psychoanal Asn; Soc Res & Child Develop. *Res:* Adoption; adolescence; autism; learning disabilities. *Mailing Add:* 1142 Morris Rd Wynnewood PA 19096

SCHECHTER, MARTIN, b Philadelphia, Pa, Mar 10, 30; m 57; c 4. PARTIAL DIFFERENTIAL EQUATIONS. *Educ:* City Col New York, BS, 53; NY Univ, MS, 55, PhD(math), 57. *Prof Exp:* Assoc res scientist, NY Univ, 57-58, from instr to asst prof math, 58-61; vis assoc prof, Univ Chicago, 61-62; from assoc prof to prof, NY Univ, 62-66; chmn dept, 66-69, PROF MATH, YESHIVA UNIV, 65- *Concurrent Pos:* NSF sr fel, 65-66; mem, Inst Advan Study, 65-66, mem, Asn, 74-; vis prof math, Hebrew Univ, 73 & Univ Mex, 79. *Mem:* Am Math Soc; Inst Adv Studies. *Res:* Partial differential equations; functional analysis; operator theory; quantum mechanics; scattering theory; spectral theory. *Mailing Add:* Dept Math Belfer Grad Sch Yeshiva Univ New York NY 10033

SCHECHTER, MARTIN DAVID, b Brooklyn, NY, Feb 28, 45; m 68; c 1. PHARMACOLOGY. *Educ:* Brooklyn Col, BS, 65; State Univ NY Buffalo, PhD(pharmacol), 70. *Prof Exp:* Res assoc pharmacol, Med Col Va, 70-72; sr res fel, Univ Melbourne, 72-74; from asst prof to assoc prof pharmacol, Eastern Va Med Sch, 76-78; ASSOC PROF PHARMACOL, COL MED, NORTHEASTERN OHIO UNIV, 78- *Concurrent Pos:* Fel, NIMH, 68-70; fel, AMA Educ & Res Found, 70-72, sr res fel, 72-74. *Mem:* Sigma Xi; Soc Neurosci; Behav Pharmacol Soc; Am Soc Pharmacol & Exp Therapeut; Am Chem Soc. *Res:* Psychopharmacology with special interest in correlations between behavioral and biochemical events associated with centrally-active drugs; operant conditioning; stimulus properties of drugs; drug abuse; hyperactive and aggressive behavior; drug self-administration. *Mailing Add:* Dept of Pharmacol Northeastern Ohio Univ Col Med Rootstown OH 44272

SCHECHTER, MILTON SEYMOUR, b Brooklyn, NY, Aug 9, 15; m 46; c 2. ORGANIC CHEMISTRY, AGRICULTURAL CHEMISTRY. *Educ:* Brooklyn Col, BS, 35. *Prof Exp:* Chemist, Insecticide Div, Bur Entom & Plant Quarantine, 37-53 & Pesticide Chem Res Br, Entom Res Div, 53-72, chief chem & biophys control lab, Agr Environ Qual Inst, Beltsville Agr Res Ctr, 72-75, CONSULT, CHEM & BIOPHYS CONTROL LAB, BELTSVILLE, AGR RES CTR, SCI & EDUC ADMIN-AGR RES, USDA, NORTHEASTERN REGION, 75- *Concurrent Pos:* Chmn pesticide monitoring subcomt, Fed Comt Pest Control, 66-67, mem fed working group pest mgt, Monitoring Panel; US mem, Collab Int Pesticide Anal Coun. *Honors & Awards:* Harvey W Wiley Award, Asn Off Agr Chem, 62; Burdick & Jackson Int Award, Am Chem Soc, 80. *Mem:* Fel AAAS; Am Chem Soc; NY Acad Sci; Entom Soc Am. *Res:* Synthesis of organic insecticides; pyrethrin-type esters and allethrin; methods of analysis for traces of organic pesticides; disinsection of aircraft; insecticide formulation; photoperiodism; biological rhythms; diapause; effects of light on insects; analytical chemistry. *Mailing Add:* 10909 Hannes Ct Silver Spring MD 20901

SCHECHTER, MURRAY, b New York, NY, Dec 6, 35; m 59; c 2. MATHEMATICS. *Educ:* Brooklyn Col, BA, 57; NY Univ, PhD(math), 63. *Prof Exp:* Staff mathematician, Kollsman Instrument Corp, 62-63; asst prof, 63-68, assoc prof, 68-80, PROF MATH, LEHIGH UNIV, 80- *Mem:* Am Math Soc; Soc Indust & Appl Math. *Res:* Convexity and its applications to optimization problems. *Mailing Add:* Dept of Math Lehigh Univ Bethlehem PA 18015

SCHECHTER, NISSON, b Detroit, Mich, May 11, 40. BIOCHEMISTRY. *Educ:* Western Mich Univ, BA, 63, MS, 67, PhD(biochem), 71. *Prof Exp:* Fel biochem, Col Med, Univ Cincinnati, 71-73 & Weizmann Inst Sci, 73-75; RES ASST BIOCHEM, STATE UNIV NY, STONY BROOK, 75- *Concurrent Pos:* Weizmann fel, Weizmann Inst Sci, 73-74, Ahron Katzir fel, 74-75. *Mem:* Am Chem Soc; AAAS; The Chem Soc. *Res:* Protein synthesis in brain and neural tissue. *Mailing Add:* Dept of Psychiat State Univ of NY Stony Brook NY 11794

SCHECHTER, ROBERT SAMUEL, b Houston, Tex, Feb 26, 29; m 53; c 3. CHEMICAL ENGINEERING. *Educ:* Agr & Mech Col, Tex, BS, 50; Univ Minn, PhD(chem eng), 56. *Prof Exp:* From asst prof to prof chem eng, 56-75, Cockrell prof chem & petrol eng, 75-81, DULA & ERNEST COCKRELL SR CHAIR IN ENG, UNIV TEX, AUSTIN, 81- *Concurrent Pos:* Vis prof, Univ Edinburgh, 65-66. *Honors & Awards:* D P Katz Lectureship Award, Chevalier Order Palmes Academique. *Mem:* Nat Acad Eng; Am Inst Chem Engrs; Soc Petrol Engrs; Am Inst Mining Engrs; Am Chem Soc. *Res:* Surface phenomena; applied mathematics. *Mailing Add:* Dept of Chem Eng Univ of Tex Austin TX 78712

SCHECHTER, SAMUEL, b Rozwadow, Poland, Mar 28, 23; nat US; m 46; c 3. NUMERICAL ANALYSIS, APPLIED MATHEMATICS. *Educ:* Brooklyn Col, AB, 44; Syracuse Univ, PhD(math), 52. *Prof Exp:* Asst math, Brown Univ, 45 & Univ Wis, 46-47; asst & instr, Syracuse Univ, 47-50; instr, Lehigh Univ, 50-54; res scientist, Courant Inst Math Sci, NY Univ, 54-60, sr res scientist & adj assoc prof math, 60-65; actg assoc prof comput sci, Stanford Univ, 65-66; SR RES MATHEMATICIAN, SRI INT, 66- *Mem:* Sigma Xi; Am Math Soc; Soc Indust & Appl Math. *Res:* Partial differential equations; automatic digital computers; matrix analysis; mathematical programming; computer science. *Mailing Add:* 12734 Alto Verde Lane Los Altos Hills CA 94022

SCHECHTMAN, BARRY H, b New York, NY, Jan 23, 43; m 63; c 2. SOLID STATE PHYSICS, ENGINEERING. *Educ:* Cooper Union, BEE, 63; Stanford Univ, MS, 64, PhD(elec eng), 69. *Prof Exp:* mem tech staff & chief scientist, 75-76, mgr org solids, 76-79, MEM RES STAFF, SAN JOSE RES LAB, IBM CORP, 68-, MGR APPL SCI, 79- *Mem:* Am Phys Soc; Sigma Xi. *Res:* Electronic properties of organic solids; materials and device research for semiconductor fabrication, optical technologies, computer printing, display and data storage; electronic states of molecular solids; charge generation and transport in insulators. *Mailing Add:* IBM Res Lab 5600 Cottle Rd San Jose CA 95193

SCHECKLER, STEPHEN EDWARD, b Irvington, NJ, Mar 17, 44; m 68; c 3. MORPHOLOGY, PALEOBOTANY. *Educ:* Cornell Univ, BSc, 68, MSc, 70, PhD(bot), 73. *Prof Exp:* Asst prof, Univ Alta, 75-76; ASST PROF BOT, VA POLYTECH INST & STATE UNIV, 77- *Concurrent Pos:* Nat Res Coun Can fel, Dept Bot, Univ Alta, 73-75 & 76-77; prin investr, Nat Geog Soc & Sigma Xi grants. *Honors & Awards:* Diamond Fund Award, Bot Soc Am. *Mem:* Bot Soc Am; Can Bot Asn; Int Asn Plant Taxon; Int Org Paleobot; Sigma Xi. *Res:* Structure and patterns of organization, phylogenies of biocharacters and paleoecology of early land plants, especially early ferns, progymnosperms and gymnosperms. *Mailing Add:* Dept of Biol Va Polytech Inst & State Univ Blacksburg VA 24061

SCHECTER, LARRY, b Montreal, Que, Nov 21, 20; US citizen; m 51; c 2. NUCLEAR PHYSICS. *Educ:* Univ Calif, AB, 48, MA, 51, PhD, 53. *Prof Exp:* Res physicist, Radiation Lab, Univ Calif, 52, Calif Res & Develop Co, Stand Oil Co, Calif, 53-54 & Radiation Lab, Univ Calif, 54-55; from asst prof to assoc prof physics, 55-64, chmn dept, 71-77, PROF PHYSICS, ORE STATE UNIV, 64- *Mem:* Am Phys Soc; Am Asn Physics Teachers. *Res:* Particle scattering; intermediate energy nuclear physics. *Mailing Add:* Dept of Physics Ore State Univ Corvallis OR 97331

SCHECTMAN, RICHARD MILTON, b Wilkes-Barre, Pa, Apr 9, 32; m 60; c 1. ATOMIC PHYSICS. *Educ:* Lehigh Univ, BS, 54; Pa State Univ, MS, 56; Cornell Univ, PhD(physics), 62. *Prof Exp:* Asst prof eng physics, 61-64, assoc prof physics & astron, 64-71, PROF PHYSICS & ENG PHYSICS, UNIV TOLEDO, 71- *Concurrent Pos:* Consult, Lawrence Radiation Lab, Univ Calif, 63-65; vis assoc prof, Univ Ariz, 68 & Hebrew Univ, 69; vis scientist, Argonne Nat Lab, 72 & 75. *Mem:* Am Phys Soc. *Res:* Particle accelerators; atomic transition probability measurements; beam foil spectroscopy. *Mailing Add:* Dept of Physics & Astron Univ of Toledo Toledo OH 43606

SCHEDL, HAROLD PAUL, b St Paul, Minn, Sept 17, 20; m 45; c 3. MEDICINE. *Educ:* Yale Univ, BS, 42, MS, 44, PhD(chem), 46; Univ Iowa, MD, 55. *Prof Exp:* Res chemist, J T Baker Chem Co, 45-46 & Calco Chem Co, 46-49; intern, Res & Educ Hosp, Univ Ill, 55-56; responsible investr, Nat Heart Inst, 56-59; from res asst prof to res assoc prof med, 59-67, PROF MED, COL MED, UNIV IOWA, 67- *Concurrent Pos:* Commonwealth Found overseas fel, Churchill Col, Cambridge, 65; mem clin res fel panel, NIH, 67-70; ed, J Lab Clin Med, 70-74; Macy fac scholar, Westminster Hosp Med Sch, London, 77-78. *Mem:* AAAS; Am Chem Soc; Am Physiol Soc; Am Gastroenterol Asn; Endocrine Soc. *Res:* Small intestinal transport mechanisms for hexose, amino acids and peptides and their regulation through gene expression in the gastrointestinal tract; gastroenterology; calcium metabolism and vitamin D, diabetes and the gastrointestinal tract. *Mailing Add:* Dept of Internal Med Univ of Iowa Hosp Iowa City IA 52242

SCHEEL, CARL ALFRED, b LaCrosse, Wis, May 4, 23; m 46; c 4. ENTOMOLOGY. *Educ:* Wis State Univ, LaCrosse, BS, 48; Univ Wis, MS, 49, PhD(entom), 56. *Prof Exp:* Instr biol, Wis State Univ, Platteville, 50; asst prof, Cent Mich Univ, 51-52 & Mt Union Col, 52-54; asst entom, Univ Wis, 54-56; from asst prof to assoc prof biol, 56-64, PROF BIOL, CENT MICH UNIV, 64- *Mem:* Entom Soc Am; Am Inst Biol Sci; Nat Asn Biol Teachers. *Res:* Nutritional physiology of insects. *Mailing Add:* Dept of Biol Cent Mich Univ Mt Pleasant MI 48859

SCHEEL, KONRAD WOLFGANG, b Mougden, China, Dec 26, 32; US citizen; m 59; c 2. CARDIOVASCULAR PHYSIOLOGY. *Educ:* Tulane Univ, BS, 62; Univ Miss, PhD(physiol), 68. *Prof Exp:* Res instr physiol, Med Ctr, Univ Miss, 63-64, res assoc surg, 67-68, asst prof physiol & med, 68-72; asst prof, Univ Tenn, Memphis, 72-75, assoc prof physiol, biophys & med, Ctr Health Sci, 75-80; PROF & CHMN PHYSIOL, KIRKSVILLE COL OSTEOPATH MED, 81- *Concurrent Pos:* Volkswagen grant, Univ Kiel, 70-71; Tenn Heart investr, Ctr Health Sci, Univ Tenn, Memphis, 72-74 & USPHS grant, 72-75; guest lectr cardiol, Univ Kiel, 70-71; consult, Vet Admin, 73-75 & NIH, 74. *Mem:* Am Physiol Soc; Am Heart Asn; Biomed Eng Soc. *Res:* Coronary and coronary collateral hemodynamics; computer simulations; mechanisms of coronary collateral formation. *Mailing Add:* Kirksville Col Osteopath Med 800 W Jefferson St Kirksville MO 63501

SCHEELE, GEORGE F(REDERICK), b Yonkers, NY, May 23, 35; m 70. CHEMICAL ENGINEERING. *Educ:* Princeton Univ, BSE, 57; Univ Ill, MS, 59, PhD(chem eng), 62. *Prof Exp:* Asst prof, 62-68, ASSOC PROF CHEM ENG, CORNELL UNIV, 68- *Concurrent Pos:* Year-in-Indust Prof, E I du Pont de Nemours & Co, Inc, 70-71, consult, 73-; vis prof, Univ Calif, Berkeley, 77-78. *Mem:* Am Inst Chem Engrs. *Res:* Fluid mechanics of immiscible liquid-liquid systems; drop coalescence. *Mailing Add:* Cornell Univ Sch of Chem Eng Olin Hall Ithaca NY 14853

SCHEELE, LEONARD ANDREW, b Ft Wayne, Ind, July 25, 07; m 81; c 3. PUBLIC HEALTH, MEDICINE. *Educ:* Univ Mich, AB, 31, Wayne State Univ, BS, 33, MD, 34; Am Bd Prev Med, dipl, 49. *Prof Exp:* Intern, US Marine Hosp, Chicago, 33-34; asst quarantine officer, USPHS, Calif, 34-35 & Hawaii, 35-36, health officer, Queen Anne County, Md, 36-37, spec cancer fel, Mem Hosp, New York, 37-39, officer in chg nat cancer control prog, Nat Cancer Inst, 39-42, chief field casualty sect, Med Div, Off Civilian Defense, 42-43, asst chief, Nat Cancer Inst, 46-47, asst surgeon gen, NIH & dir, Nat Cancer Inst, 47-48, surgeon gen, USPHS, 48-56; pres, Warner-Chilcott Labs, Warner-Lambert Pharmaceut Co, 56-60, mem bd dirs, 57-62 & 63-68, sr vpres, 60-68, pres, Warner-Lambert Res Inst, 65-68; RETIRED. *Concurrent Pos:* Head nutrit mission, US Dept Army, Ger, 48; pres, Int Cong Trop Dis & Malaria, Wash, 48; chmn US deleg, World Health Assembly, Rome, 49, Geneva, 50-53, deleg, 54, pres assembly, 51. *Honors & Awards:* Order of S S Maurizio Lazzo, Italy; Grand Officer Order of Carlos Finaly, Cuba; Carix de Guerre, France; Legion of Merit & Typhus Medal, US. *Mem:* Fel Am Col Surg; Am Pub Health Asn; Am Med Asn; Asn Mil Surg US (pres, 54); fel Am Col Physicians. *Res:* Cancer therapy end results; epidemiology; public health administrative techniques; business management; pharmaceutical development, manufacturing and marketing. *Mailing Add:* 700 New Hampshire Ave NW Washington DC 20037

SCHEELE, ROBERT BLAIN, b New York, NY, Dec 23, 40; m 63; c 2. BIOPHYSICS, MOLECULAR BIOLOGY. *Educ:* Yale Univ, BS, 62; Univ Pittsburgh, PhD(biophys), 68. *Prof Exp:* NIH fel biophys, State Univ NY Buffalo, 68-70; res assoc biophys, Univ Conn, 70-75; res assoc molecular biol, 75-77, ASST SCIENTIST MOLECULAR BIOL, LAB MOLECULAR BIOL, UNIV WIS-MADISON, 77- *Mem:* Biophys Soc. *Res:* Protein-protein interactions, self-assembly of protein polymers, virus self-assembly and molecular aspects of motility. *Mailing Add:* Lab of Molecular Biol Univ of Wis Madison WI 53706

SCHEELINE, ALEXANDER, b Altoona, Pa, June 6, 52. EMISSION SPECTROSCOPY, ANALYTICAL PHYSICS. *Educ:* Mich State Univ, BS, 74; Univ Wis, Madison, PhD(chem), 78. *Prof Exp:* Nat Res Coun fel anal chem, Nat Bur Standards, 78-79; asst prof chem, Univ Iowa, 79-81; ASST PROF CHEM, UNIV ILL, 81- *Concurrent Pos:* Consult, Nat Bur Standards, 82- *Honors & Awards:* W F Meggers Award, Soc Appl Spectros, 79. *Mem:* Am Chem Soc; Soc Appl Spectros; Optical Soc Am; Am Soc Testing & Mat. *Res:* Plasma physics technology for elemental analysis of solid materials; sparks and pinches are studied through spectroscopy and simulation; particulate characterization via light scattering. *Mailing Add:* 68 Roger Adams Lab Box 48 1209 W Calif Ave Urbana IL 61801

SCHEER, ALFRED C(ARL), b Center, Nebr, Feb 1, 26; m 46; c 4. CIVIL ENGINEERING. *Educ:* Iowa State Univ, BS, 48, MS, 50. *Prof Exp:* Instr civil eng, Iowa State Univ, 48-50; from asst prof to assoc prof, SDak Sch Mines & Technol, 50-58; assoc prof, 58-72, PROF CIVIL ENG, MONT STATE UNIV, 72- *Concurrent Pos:* Mem, Hwy Res Bd, Nat Acad Sci-Nat Res Coun. *Mem:* Am Soc Eng Educ; Am Soc Civil Engrs. *Res:* Soil mechanics; highway engineering. *Mailing Add:* Dept of Civil Eng Mont State Univ Bozeman MT 59717

SCHEER, BRADLEY TITUS, b Los Angeles, Calif, Dec 17, 14; m 36. PHYSIOLOGY. *Educ:* Calif Inst Technol, BS, 36; Univ Calif, PhD(comp physiol), 40. *Prof Exp:* Asst physiol, Scripps Inst, Univ Calif, 36-37, Med Sch, 37-38 & Inst, 38-40; instr zool, WVa Univ, 40-42; asst biochem, Col Physicians & Surgeons, Columbia Univ, 42-43; instr biol, Calif Inst Technol, 43-45; asst prof biochem, Univ Southern Calif, 45-48, lectr zool, 46-48; assoc prof, Univ Hawaii, 48-50; assoc prof biol, 50-53, head dept, 58-64, prof, 54-77, EMER PROF BIOL, UNIV ORE, 77-; INSTR BIOL, WESTMONT COL, 78- *Concurrent Pos:* Vis asst prof, Hopkins Marine Sta, Stanford, 47; vis prof, Univ Calif, 52; Fulbright fel, Italy, 53-54; Guggenheim fel, France, 57-58. *Mem:* AAAS; Am Physiol Soc; Soc Gen Physiol; Am Soc Zoologists. *Res:* Comparative biochemistry of carotenoids; isolation of enzymes; blood proteins of invertebrates; ecology of marine fouling organisms; physiology of fertilization; hormones of crustaceans; ion transports; thermodynamics in biology; systems analysis of salt and water balance; science and religion. *Mailing Add:* 1905 Mission Ridge Rd Santa Barbara CA 93103

SCHEER, DONALD JORDAN, b Louisville, Ky, July 25, 34; m 66. ELECTRICAL ENGINEERING. *Educ:* Univ Louisville, BEE, 57, MEE, 58, MEng, 72; Ohio State Univ, PhD(elec eng), 66. *Prof Exp:* From instr to assoc prof, 59-72, PROF ELEC ENG, UNIV LOUISVILLE, 72-, CHMN DEPT, 80- *Mem:* Inst Elec & Electronics Engrs; Am Astron Soc. *Res:* Antennas; microwave engineering; radio astronomy. *Mailing Add:* Dept of Elec Eng Univ of Louisville Louisville KY 40208

SCHEER, MILTON DAVID, b New York, Dec 22, 22; m 45; c 3. PHYSICAL CHEMISTRY. *Educ:* City Col New York, BS, 43; NY Univ, MS, 47, PhD, 51. *Prof Exp:* Chemist, US Bd Econ Warfare, Guatemala, 43-44; res asst, NY Univ, 47-50; phys chemist, US Naval Air Rocket Test Sta, 51-52, US Bur Mines, 52-55 & Gen Elec Co, 55-58; phys chemist, 58-68, chief photochem sect, 68-70, chief, Phys Chem Div, 70-77, dir, Ctr Thermodyn & Molecular Sci, 77-80, CHEM PHYSICIST, CHEM KINETICS DIV, NAT BUR STANDARDS, 81- *Concurrent Pos:* Vis prof, Chem Dept, Univ Md, 80-81. *Mem:* Fel AAAS; Am Chem Soc; Am Phys Soc. *Res:* Reaction kinetics and photochemistry; surface chemistry and physics; low temperature chemistry; high temperature thermodynamics; excited state chemistry. *Mailing Add:* Chem Kinetics Div Nat Bur of Stand Washington DC 20234

SCHEERER, ANNE ELIZABETH, b Philadelphia, Pa, Aug 7, 24. MATHEMATICS. *Educ:* Univ Pa, BS, 46, MS, 47, PhD(math), 53. *Prof Exp:* Instr math, Temple Univ, 47-50 & Washington Univ, 53-55; assoc prof, Georgetown Univ, 55-66; asst dean, Col Eng, Boston Univ, 66-67; specialist higher educ, Md Coun Higher Educ, 67-69; DEAN SUMMER SESSIONS & LIFELONG EDUC, CREIGHTON UNIV, 69- *Mem:* Am Math Soc; Math Asn Am; Sigma Xi. *Res:* Complex variable; probability; information theory. *Mailing Add:* Creighton Univ 2500 California St Omaha NE 68178

SCHEETZ, HOWARD A(NSEL), b Sturgis, Mich, Mar 20, 27; m 52; c 2. MATERIALS SCIENCE, ENGINEERING MECHANICS. *Educ:* Mich State Univ, BS, 50; Pa State Univ, MS, 59. *Prof Exp:* Process engr, pilot plant, Corning Glass Works, 50-52, sr engr, Res & Develop Lab, 52-56; res assoc shock & vibration, Pa State Univ, 57-58; res engr, Physics Dept, Cornell Aeronaut Lab, 58-60, Mat Dept, 60-62 & Physics Dept, Armstrong Cork Co, 62-69; res assoc, Packaging Prod Div, Kerr Glass Mfg Corp, 69-80; SR ENGR, TECH CTR, POLYMER CORP, 80- *Concurrent Pos:* Lectr grad fac, Pa State Univ, 66-67; corp rep, Am Ceramic Soc. *Mem:* AAAS; Inst Elec & Electronics Engrs; Acoust Soc Am. *Res:* Analytical modeling and computer-aided studies of composite physical properties of glass, ceramic, polymeric and mixed composite material systems; applications of ultrasonic techniques to materials research and glass technology. *Mailing Add:* Tech Ctr Polymer Corp 501 Crescent Ave Reading PA 19603

SCHEFER, ROBERT WILFRED, b San Francisco, CA, July 7, 46; m 74. MECHANICAL ENGINEERING. *Educ:* Univ Calif, Berkeley, BS, 68, MS, 70, PhD(mech eng), 76. *Prof Exp:* RES ENGR COMBUSTION, LAWRENCE BERKELEY LAB, 76- *Concurrent Pos:* NSF energy fel, 76-77. *Mem:* Combustion Inst; Sigma Xi. *Res:* Combustion; combustion generated air pollution; chemistry (chemical kinetics); fire research; high temperature catalysis; coal utilization. *Mailing Add:* Lawrence Berkeley Lab One Cyclotron Rd Berkeley CA 94720

SCHEFF, BENSON H(OFFMAN), b New York, NY, May 16, 31; m 53; c 4. SOFTWARE ENGINEERING, SYSTEM ARCHITECTOR. *Educ:* Oberlin Col, BA, 51; Columbia Univ, MA, 52. *Prof Exp:* Training instr electronic data processing mach, Nat Security Agency, 52-55; res engr, Servomechanisms Lab, Mass Inst Technol, 55-59; head adv comput control systs implementation, Group Data Systs Eng, Radio Corp Am, Mass, 59-66; mgr comput anal & appln, Software Dept, Missile Systs Div, Bedford, 66-73, MGR DATA PROCESSING, EQUIP DIV, RAYTHEON CO, WAYLAND, MASS, 73- *Mem:* Asn Comput Mach; Am Mgt Asn. *Res:* Digital system architecture; digital computer systems design (hardware/software), software engineering methodology implementation and research; software research and development. *Mailing Add:* Concord Rd Box 577 Lincoln MA 01773

SCHEFF, GEORGE JULIUS, b Budapest, Hungary, June 6, 97; nat US; m 24. MICROBIOLOGY. *Educ:* Budapest Univ, MD, 22, cert chem, 25; Inst Pub Health, Hungary, cert pub health, 35; Yale Univ, PhD, 43. *Prof Exp:* Instr physiol chem, Budapest, 22-26; from asst prof to assoc prof bact & pub health, Univ Pecs, 26-38; asst prof med, Ohio State Univ, 44-47, Am Tuberc Asn fel, 46-47; from asst prof to prof microbiol & pub health, 74-77, EMER PROF MICROBIOL, CHICAGO MED SCH, 77- *Mem:* AAAS; Soc Exp Biol & Med; Am Acad Microbiologists. *Res:* Biochemistry of microorganisms; metabolism of infectious diseases; epidemiology; immunology; virology; experimental leukemia. *Mailing Add:* 246 Hill Ave Glen Ellyn IL 60137

SCHEFFER, JOHN R, b Missoula, Mont, Feb 28, 39; m 63; c 2. ORGANIC CHEMISTRY. *Educ:* Univ Chicago, BS, 62. Univ Wis, PhD(chem), 67. *Prof Exp:* ASSOC PROF CHEM, UNIV BC, 67- *Concurrent Pos:* Nat Res Coun Can grant, 67-; Res Corp grant, 68-; Petrol Res Fund grant, 70-73 & 75-77; Guggenheim fel, 73-74. *Mem:* Am Chem Soc; Royal Soc Chem; Chem Inst Can. *Res:* Organic photochemistry, including new sources and reactions of singlet oxygen. *Mailing Add:* Dept of Chem Univ of BC Vancouver BC V6T 1W5 Can

SCHEFFER, ROBERT PAUL, b Newton, NC, Jan 26, 20; m 51; c 2. PLANT PATHOLOGY. *Educ:* NC State Col, BS, 47, MS, 49; Univ Wis, PhD(plant path), 52. *Prof Exp:* Asst plant path, NC State Col, 47-49; asst, Univ Wis, 49-52, proj assoc, 52-53; from asst prof to assoc prof bot & plant path, 53-63, PROF BOT & PLANT PATH, MICH STATE UNIV, 63- *Concurrent Pos:* NIH fel & guest investr, Rockefeller Inst, 60-61; NSF consult, Panel Regulatory Biol, 65-68. *Mem:* Fel Am Phytopath Soc; Am Soc Plant Physiol. *Res:* Physiology of disease development and and disease resistance; toxins in plant disease. *Mailing Add:* Dept of Bot & Plant Path Mich State Univ East Lansing MI 48824

SCHEFFER, THEODORE COMSTOCK, b Manhattan, Kans, Feb 10, 04; m 27; c 2. FOREST PRODUCTS. *Educ:* Univ Wash, BS, 26, MS, 29; Univ Wis, PhD(forest path), 34. *Prof Exp:* Nat Res Coun fel, Johns Hopkins Univ, 34-35; pathologist, Forest Prod Lab, US Forest Serv, 35-65, in chg fungus & insect invests, 65-69; RES ASSOC, FOREST RES LAB, ORE STATE UNIV, 69- *Mem:* Forest Prod Res Soc; Soc Am Foresters. *Res:* Fundamental and applied control of fungus damage to wood and wood products; effects of fungi on physical-chemical properties; testing fungus resistance; preservation of wood with volatile fungicides; bioassay techniques for appraising quality of preservative treatment. *Mailing Add:* Forest Res Lab Ore State Univ Corvallis OR 97331

SCHEFFLAN, RALPH, b Berlin, Ger, Dec 25, 34; US citizen; m 58. CHEMICAL ENGINEERING. *Educ:* City Col New York, BChE, 57; Pratt Inst, MChE, 62; Columbia Univ, DEngS(chem eng), 71. *Prof Exp:* Develop engr, Mearl Chem Co, 58-60; group leader, Am Agr Chem Co, 60-63; sr engr, Leesona Moos Labs, 63-64 & Mobil Oil Co, 67-69; mgr develop, Petro Chem Serv Div, Mauchly Assocs, 69-70; mgt sci specialist, Comput Serv Div, Caltex Petrol, 71-72; SR ENGR, HOFFMANN-LA ROCHE INC, 72- *Concurrent Pos:* Indust consult, Chem Systs, Alcorn Combustion Co, Realtime Systs & Davis Comput Systs, 65-69; asst prof, Pratt Inst, 70-71. *Mem:* Am Inst Chem Engrs. *Res:* Thermodynamics; process simulation; separation processes; optimization; applied mathematics; computer applications in chemical engineering. *Mailing Add:* 8 Peter Cooper Rd New York NY 10010

SCHEFFLER, IMMO ERICH, b Dresden, Ger, Dec 17, 40; Can citizen; m 65; c 1. MOLECULAR BIOLOGY, SOMATIC CELL GENETICS. *Educ:* Univ Manitoba, BSc, 63, MSc, 64; Stanford Univ, PhD(biochem), 69. *Prof Exp:* Helen Hay Whitney fel, Harvard Med Sch, 68-70; fel, Pasteur Inst, Paris, 70-71; asst prof, 71-77, ASSOC PROF BIOL, UNIV CALIF, SAN DIEGO, 77- *Concurrent Pos:* NIH 71-74, 74-77 & 77-82; 74-77; Am Cancer Soc grant, 74-76 & 76-78; NSF grants, 78-81 & 81-84, mem adv panel genetic biol, 77-80; mem adv panel personnel res, Am Cancer Soc. *Mem:* AAAS; Am Soc Cell Biol; fel Am Soc Exp Biol. *Res:* Selection of mutants of mammalian cells grown in tissue culture; study of control of the cell cycle; mammalian cell genetics; biogenesis of mitochondrion. *Mailing Add:* Dept of Biol B-022 Univ of Calif La Jolla CA 92093

SCHEIB, RICHARD, JR, b New York, NY, May 24, 14; m 42; c 1. PHYSICS. *Educ:* Columbia Univ, AB, 36, MA, 39. *Prof Exp:* Asst physics, Columbia Univ, 36-41, lectr, 37-41; engr & sr engr, Sperry Gyroscope Co, 41-49, eng dept head, 49-62, planning mgr, 62-64, prog mgr, 64-69; ASSOC PROF BASIC SCI, ACAD AERONAUT, NY, 70-, CHMN DEPT, 73- *Mem:* Am Phys Soc. *Res:* Development of servomechanisms. *Mailing Add:* 29 Crest Rd New Hyde Park NY 11040

SCHEIBE, JOSEPH E, b San Francisco, Calif, Apr 22, 32. PLANT PHYSIOLOGY. *Educ:* Univ Calif, Berkeley, AB, 60; Calif Inst Technol, PhD(biol), 66. *Prof Exp:* Nat Acad Sci res fel plant physiol, Agr Res Serv, USDA, Md, 65-67; asst prof bot & molecular biophys, 67-72, ASSOC PROF BOT & MOLECULAR BIOPHYS, WASH STATE UNIV, 72- *Mem:* Am Soc Photobiol; AAAS; Am Soc Plant Physiol. *Res:* Plant and microbial photobiology. *Mailing Add:* Dept of Bot Wash State Univ Pullman WA 99163

SCHEIBE, MURRAY, b Bronx, NY, Feb 28, 32; m 55; c 3. PHYSICS. *Educ:* Brooklyn Col, BS, 53; Univ Md, College Park, PhD(physics), 59. *Prof Exp:* Staff scientist, Lockheed Palo Alto Res Lab, Lockheed Aircraft Co, 58-71; STAFF MEM, MISSION RES CORP, 71- *Mem:* Am Phys Soc. *Res:* Atmospheric physics and chemistry; high temperature gas dynamics; optical radiation phenomena. *Mailing Add:* 1133 Palomino Rd Santa Barbara CA 93105

SCHEIBE, PAUL OTTO, b Marion, NDak, Apr 7, 34; m 54; c 3. ELECTRICAL ENGINEERING. *Educ:* Univ NDak, BS, 58, MS, 59; Stanford Univ, PhD(elec eng), 62. *Prof Exp:* Instr, NDak State Sch Sci, 53-56; from instr to asst prof elec eng, Univ NDak, 58-60; mem eng staff, Sylvania Electronic Defense Labs, 62-64; mem sr eng staff & dir technol, ESL, Inc, Calif, 64-70; V PRES & TECH DIR, ADAC LABS, 70- *Concurrent Pos:* Lectr, Univ Santa Clara, 62- *Mem:* Inst Elec & Electronics Engrs; Soc Nuclear Med; Asn Comput Mach. *Res:* Characterization and bounds on the performance of time-variant systems; automatic design and analysis of electrical networks; statistical parameter estimation; mathematical modeling of physiological systems. *Mailing Add:* 11 Yerba Buena Ave Los Altos CA 94022

SCHEIBEL, ARNOLD BERNARD, b New York, NY, Jan 18, 23; m 50. NEUROPHYSIOLOGY, PSYCHOPHYSIOLOGY. *Educ:* Columbia Univ, BA, 44, MD, 46; Univ Ill, MS, 53; Am Bd Psychiat & Neurol, dipl, 52. *Prof Exp:* Intern, Mt Sinai Hosp, New York, 46-47; resident psychiat, Barnes Hosp, St Louis, 47-48; from asst prof to assoc prof psychiat & anat, Sch Med, Univ Tenn, 51-55; from asst prof to assoc prof, 55-68, PROF PSYCHIAT & ANAT, SCH MED, UNIV CALIF, LOS ANGELES, 68- *Concurrent Pos:* Guggenheim fel, Inst Physiol, Italy, 53-54 & 60-61; consult physician, Brentwood Vet Admin Hosp, Calif & Sepulveda Vet Admin Hosp. *Mem:* AAAS; fel Am Psychiat Asn; Am Acad Neurol; Am Neurol Asn; fel Am Acad Arts & Sci. *Res:* Distortions of perception and memory in psychoses; experimental study of structural patterns of neuropil in the central nervous system and its relation to functional activity; aging in human brain; neuropsychiatry; neuroscience. *Mailing Add:* Dept Anat & Psychiat Univ Calif Med Ctr Los Angeles CA 90024

SCHEIBEL, EDWARD G(EORGE), b Ridgewood, NY, Jan 15, 17; m 45; c 4. CHEMICAL ENGINEERING. *Educ:* Cooper Union, BS, 37; Polytech Inst Brooklyn, MChE, 40, DChE, 43. *Prof Exp:* From asst chemist to plant supt, H C Bugbird Co, NJ, 37-42; chem engr, M W Kellogg Co, NY, 42-43; res assoc, Polytech Inst Brooklyn, 43-44; chem engr, Hydrocarbon Res, Inc, 44-45 & Hoffmann-LaRoche, Inc, 45-55; dir eng, York Process Equip Corp, 55-63; prof chem eng & head dept, Cooper Union, 63-70; mgr process technol, Iglehart Oper, Gen Elec Co, Mt Vernon, Ind, 70-77; res engr, Suntech Inc, 77-81; MEM STAFF, E G SCHEIBEL, INC, 81- *Concurrent Pos:* Instr & adj prof, Polytech Inst Brooklyn, 42-52; adj prof, Newark Col Eng, 53-63. *Mem:* Am Chem Soc; Am Inst Chem Eng. *Res:* Distillation, absorption and liquid extraction; liquid oxygen production; fractional liquid extraction; extractive distillation of petroleum; heavy and fine chemicals. *Mailing Add:* E G Scheibel Inc 410 Notson Terr Port Charlotte FL 33951

SCHEIBER, DAVID HITZ, b Cleveland, Ohio, Aug 16, 31; m 56; c 5. POLYMER CHEMISTRY. *Educ:* Univ Notre Dame, BS, 53, PhD, 56. *Prof Exp:* Res chemist, Electrochem Dept, 56-61, staff scientist, 61-62, res assoc, 62-64, res supvr, 64-68, RES ASSOC, PHOTO PROD DEPT, E I DU PONT DE NEMOURS & CO, INC, 68- *Mem:* Am Chem Soc. *Res:* Electronic materials. *Mailing Add:* Photo Prod Dept E I du Pont Exp Sta Bldg 352 Rm 252 Wilmington DE 19898

SCHEIBER, DONALD JOSEPH, b Ft Wayne, Ind, Jan 24, 32; m 54; c 8. UNDERWATER ACOUSTICS. *Educ:* St Procopius Col, 53; Univ Notre Dame, 53-57, PhD(physics), 57. *Prof Exp:* Nat Res Coun res assoc, Nat Bur Stand, 57-58, physicist, 58-62; SR STAFF ENGR, MAGNAVOX CO, 62- *Mem:* Nat Security Indust Asn. *Res:* Underwater sound; directional sensors; dynamics of buoy systems; oceanographic sensors. *Mailing Add:* Magnavox Govt & Indust Group 4624 Executive Blvd Dept 529 Ft Wayne IN 46808

SCHEIBNER, RUDOLPH A, b Escanaba, Mich, Oct 22, 26; m 61; c 3. ENTOMOLOGY. *Educ:* Mich State Univ, BS, 51, MS, 58, PhD(entom), 63. *Prof Exp:* Instr natural sci, Mich State Univ, 63-65; asst prof, 65-69, assoc prof, 69-77, EXTEN PROF ENTOM, UNIV KY, 78- *Mem:* Am Entom Soc. *Res:* Taxonomy and ecology of insects. *Mailing Add:* Dept of Entom Univ of Ky Lexington KY 40506

SCHEID, FRANCIS, b Plymouth, Mass, Sept 24, 20; m 44; c 3. MATHEMATICS. *Educ:* Boston Univ, BS, 42, AM, 43; Mass Inst Technol, PhD(math), 48. *Prof Exp:* From instr to assoc prof, 48-59, chmn dept, 56-69, PROF MATH, BOSTON UNIV, 59- *Concurrent Pos:* Consult, Instrumentation Lab, Mass Inst Technol, 54- & Sch Math Study Group, 63; Fulbright lectr, Univ Rangoon, 61-62; TV lectr, 61-66. *Mem:* Am Math Soc; Soc Indust & Appl Math; Math Asn Am. *Res:* Numerical analysis; problems of measuring golfing ability and golf course difficulty and golf related problems. *Mailing Add:* Dept of Math Boston Univ Boston MA 02215

SCHEID, STEPHAN ANDREAS, b Munich, Ger, May 22, 41. VIROLOGY. *Educ:* Univ Cologne, DrMed, 69. *Prof Exp:* Intern, Inst Physiol Chem, Univ Cologne, 67-68 & Univ Hosp, Cologne, 68-69; fel, 69-73, asst prof, 73-76, ASSOC PROF VIROL, ROCKEFELLER UNIV, 76- *Concurrent Pos:* USPHS Int fel, 69-71; res fel, Ger Res Asn, 71-73. *Mem:* Am Soc Microbiol; Am Asn Immunologists; Soc Gen Microbiol. *Res:* Animal virology; myxoviruses; paramyxoviruses; structure and replication of enveloped viruses. *Mailing Add:* Rockefeller Univ 1230 York Ave New York NY 10021

SCHEID, VERNON EDWARD, b Baltimore, Md, Sept 5, 06; m 34; c 2. ECONOMIC GEOLOGY, MINERAL ECONOMICS. *Educ:* Johns Hopkins Univ, AB, 28, PhD(econ geol), 46; Univ Idaho, MS, 40. *Prof Exp:* Instr geol, Johns Hopkins Univ, 31-34; from instr to asst prof, Univ Idaho, 34-42, prof & head dept, 47-51; geologist, US Geol Surv, 42-47; prof mineral sci & dean, Mackay Sch Mines, 51-72, PROF MINERAL ECON, MACKAY SCH MINES, UNIV NEV, RENO, 72- *Concurrent Pos:* Mineralogist, Idaho Bur Mines & Geol, 38-39; seismol collabr, US Coast & Geod Surv, 39-42 & 47-51; dir, Nev Bur Mines, Geol & Mining Anal Lab, 51-72; pvt consult, 72-; mining eng consult, UN, 73-; app geologist mem, Nat Adv Comt on Oceans & Atmosphere, 81- *Honors & Awards:* Robert Earll McConnell Award, Am Inst Mining, Metall & Petrol Engrs, 80. *Mem:* Fel AAAS; fel Geol Soc Am; Soc Econ Geologists; Asn Am State Geologists; Am Inst Mining, Metall & Petrol Engrs. *Res:* Economic and engineering geology; mineral resources; industrial minerals. *Mailing Add:* Mackay Sch of Mines Univ of Nev Reno NV 89557

SCHEIDT, FRANCIS MATTHEW, b Streator, Ill, Mar 2, 22; m 52. ORGANIC CHEMISTRY. *Educ:* Univ Ill, BS, 50, MS, 54, PhD(org chem), 56. *Prof Exp:* Res asst chem, State Geol Surv, Ill, 50-54; chemist, 56-66, sr res chemist, 66-72, res specialist, 72-77, sr res specialist, Britton Res Lab, 77-80, RES ASSOC, DOW CHEM CO, 80- *Concurrent Pos:* Sect ed, Chem Abstr, 68- *Mem:* Fel Am Inst Chemists; Am Chem Soc; Sigma Xi; NY Acad Sci; Royal Soc Chem. *Res:* Synthetic organic chemistry; heterogeneous catalysis. *Mailing Add:* 1906 Norwood Dr Midland MI 48640

SCHEIDT, WALTER ROBERT, b Richmond Heights, Mo, Nov 13, 42; m 64. CHEMISTRY, X-RAY CRYSTALLOGRAPHY. *Educ:* Univ Mo-Columbia, BS, 64; Univ Mich, Ann Arbor, MS, 66, PhD(chem), 68. *Prof Exp:* Res fel, Cornell Univ, 68-70; assoc prof, 70-80, PROF CHEM, UNIV NOTRE DAME, 80- *Mem:* AAAS; Am Chem Soc; Am Crystallog Asn. *Res:* Structure and chemistry of metalloporphyrins; structure of inorganic complexes. *Mailing Add:* Dept of Chem Univ of Notre Dame Notre Dame IN 46556

SCHEIDY, SAMUEL F, b Shartlesville, Pa, Mar 13, 07; m 32. VETERINARY MEDICINE. *Educ:* Univ Pa, VMD, 29. *Prof Exp:* Res vet, Univ Pa, 29-31, res assoc, 37-38, instr vet med & res vet, 38-43; field vet med dir, Merck Sharp & Dohme Div, 43-57 & Smith, Kline & French Corp, 57-72, adj asst prof, Clin Studies, Vet Med Univ Pa, 60, & VET CONSULT, SMITH KLINE CORP, 72- *Concurrent Pos:* Vet consult, Harcum Jr Col, 72. *Mem:* Am Vet Med Asn; US Animal Health Asn. *Res:* Clinical veterinary medicine. *Mailing Add:* 28 Brennan Dr Bryn Mawr PA 19010

SCHEIE, CARL EDWARD, b Fosston, Minn, July 14, 38; m 59; c 3. ENGINEERING PHYSICS. *Educ:* Concordia Col, Moorhead, Minn, BA, 60; Univ NMex, MS, 62, PhD, 65. *Prof Exp:* Res assoc physics, Univ NMex, 62-65; res aide, Inst Paper Chem, 65-68; from asst prof to assoc prof physics, Concordia Col, Moorhead, Minn, 68-73; PROD EVAL ENGR, MACGREGOR DIV, BRUNSWICK CORP, 73- *Concurrent Pos:* Vis scientist, Argonne Nat Lab, 72-73. *Mem:* AAAS; Am Asn Physics Teachers. *Res:* Molecular motion in solids using nuclear magnetic resonance techniques. *Mailing Add:* 1113 Dawes Libertyville IL 60048

SCHEIE, HAROLD GLENDON, b Brookings, SDak, Mar 24, 09; m 51; c 2. OPHTHALMOLOGY. *Educ:* Univ Minn, BS, 31, MB & MD, 35; Univ Pa, DSc(med ophthal), 40; Am Bd Ophthal, dipl, 40. *Prof Exp:* From intern to resident, Hosp Univ Pa, 35-40, from instr to prof, Grad Sch Med, 46-60, chmn dept ophthal, 60-75, William F Norris & George E Deschweinitz prof ophthal, Sch Med, Grad Sch Med, Univ Pa, 60-75, dir, Scheie Eye Inst, 72-75, EMER WILLIAM F NORRIS & GEORGE E DE SCHWEINITZ PROF OPHTHAL, UNIV PA & FOUNDING DIR, SCHEIE EYE INST, 75- *Concurrent Pos:* From instr to prof, Med Sch, Univ Pa, 40-60, prof & chmn dept, Div Grad Med, 64; ophthal consult to many hosps, labs & govt agencies, 44-; lectr, US Naval Hosp, Philadelphia; chief ophthal serv, Philadelphia Gen Hosp & Children's Hosp, 49-70; chief ophthal serv & consult, Vet Admin Hosp; numerous name lectureships, 52-74; mem adv coun reserve affairs, Surgeon Gen, US Army, 44; mem nat adv comt, Eye-Bank Sight Restoration, Inc & Nat Coun Combat Blindness; mem bd examr, Am Bd Ophthal, 59-66; mem med adv comt, Medic Alert Found Int, 66. *Honors & Awards:* Hon mem, Order of the Brit Empire; Brit Minister Defense Medal, 64; Howe Award, AMA, 64; Am Acad Ophthal & Otolaryngol Honor Award; Distinguished Serv Award for Excellence in Ophthal, Am Soc Contemporary Ophthal, 74; Distinguished Serv Award, Pa Acad Ophthal & Otolaryngol, 74; Horatio Alger Award, Am Schs & Cols Asn, 74; Golden Plate Award, Am Acad Achievement, 75. *Mem:* AAAS; Am Acad Ophthal & Otolaryngol (vpres, 60-61); Am Asn Ophthal (3rd vpres, 70); fel Am Col Surg (vpres, 61-62); AMA. *Res:* Infantile glaucoma; anesthesia in ophthalmic surgery; ACTH and cortisone; arteriosclerosis; retrolental fibroplasia. *Mailing Add:* Scheie Eye Inst 51 N 39th St Philadelphia PA 19104

SCHEIE, PAUL OLAF, b Minn, June 24, 33; m 63; c 2. PHYSICS, BIOPHYSICS. *Educ:* St Olaf Col, BA, 55; Univ NMex, MS, 57; Pa State Univ, PhD(biophys), 65. *Prof Exp:* Asst prof physics, Oklahoma City Univ, 58-63, chmn dept, 58-61; asst prof biophys, Pa State Univ, 66-73; assoc prof, 73-80, PROF PHYSICS & CHMN DEPT, TEX LUTHERAN COL, 80- *Concurrent Pos:* Vis prof, Med Fac, Univ Bergen, Norway, 80-81. *Mem:* AAAS; Am Asn Physics Teachers; Biophys Soc. *Res:* Electrophysiology; physical properties of bacteria. *Mailing Add:* Dept of Physics Tex Lutheran Col Seguin TX 78155

SCHEIER, ARTHUR, b Flushing, NY, May 16, 27; m 53; c 3. OPTOMETRY. *Educ:* NY Univ, BA, 49; Pa Col Optom, OD, 53. *Prof Exp:* Biologist, 53-61, CHIEF BIOASSAY LAB, ACAD NATURAL SCI, 61- *Concurrent Pos:* Co-investr, USPHS grant, 61-65, chief investr, 66- *Mem:* AAAS; Am Fisheries Soc. *Res:* Basic physiological changes in an organism as the result of exposure to toxic materials. *Mailing Add:* Limnol Dept Acad of Natural Sci 19th & Parkway Philadelphia PA 19103

SCHEIG, ROBERT L, b Warren, Ohio, Mar 16, 31; m 52; c 1. INTERNAL MEDICINE, GASTROENTEROLOGY. *Educ:* Yale Univ, MD, 56. *Prof Exp:* From intern to sr asst resident med, Grace-New Haven Hosp, Conn, 56-61; from instr to assoc prof med, Sch Med, Yale Univ, 63-73, assoc dir liver study unit, 63-73, assoc dean regional affairs, 71-73; prof med & head, Div Gastroenterol, Sch Med, Univ Conn, Farmington, 73-81, actg chmn, Dept Med, 78-79; PROF MED, STATE UNIV NY BUFFALO, 81-; HEAD, DEPT MED, BUFFALO GEN HOSP, 81- *Concurrent Pos:* Fel, Sch Med, Yale Univ, 61-62; res fel, Harvard Med Sch, 62-63; from assoc physician to attend physician, Yale-New Haven Med Ctr, 63-73, dir adult clin res ctr, 69-71; attend physician, West Haven Vet Admin Hosp, Conn, 66-73, John Dempsey Hosp, Conn, 73-81 & Buffalo Gen Hosp, Erie County Med Ctr, Buffalo & Buffalo Vet Admin Med Ctr, 81-; consult, Hosp of St Raphael, New Haven, 69-73 & Waterbury Hosp, 72-73; attend physician & chief med, Newington Vet Admin Med Ctr, 73-81. *Mem:* Fel Am Col Physicians; Am Gastroenterol Asn; Am Asn Study Liver Dis; Am Fedn Clin Res. *Res:* Toxic liver injury; effect of ethanol on lipid metabolism and biochemical and histopathological correlation with clinical disease. *Mailing Add:* Dept Med Buffalo Gen Hosp 100 High St Buffalo NY 14203

SCHEIN, ARNOLD HAROLD, b New York, NY, June 10, 16; m 40; c 2. BIOCHEMISTRY. *Educ:* City Col, BS, 36; Univ Iowa, PhD(biochem), 43; Am Bd Clin Chem, dipl. *Prof Exp:* Instr biochem, NY Med Col, 43-46; dir res, Mouton Processors of Can, Ltd, 46-47; from asst prof to assoc prof biol chem, Col Med, Univ Vt, 47-69; chmn dept, 69-73, PROF CHEM, CALIF STATE UNIV, SAN JOSE, 69- *Concurrent Pos:* Exchange sr lectr, Dept Biochem, St Bartholomew's Hosp Col Med, Eng, 56-57; Commonwealth fel, Virus Res Labs, Cambridge, 63-64; vis prof chem, Dept Microbiol, Sch Med Hebrew Univ Jerusalem, 77. *Mem:* Fel Am Soc Clin Chem; Am Soc Biol Chem; Brit Biochem Soc. *Res:* RNA and DNA structure and metabolism. *Mailing Add:* Dept of Chem Calif State Univ San Jose CA 95192

SCHEIN, CLARENCE JACOB, b New York, NY, Jan 15, 18; m 60. SURGERY. *Educ:* NY Univ, BS, 38, MD, 42; Am Bd Surg, dipl, 50; Am Bd Thoracic Surg, dipl, 52. *Prof Exp:* Asst clin prof, 58-68, assoc prof, 68-71, PROF SURG, ALBERT EINSTEIN COL MED, 71- *Concurrent Pos:* From assoc surgeon to surgeon, Montefiore Hosp, New York, 56-; attend surgeon, Bronx Munic Hosp. *Mem:* Fel Am Col Surg; Am Col Gastroenterol; fel NY Acad Med. *Res:* General and thoracic surgery. *Mailing Add:* Montefiore Hosp 111 E 210th St Bronx NY 10467

SCHEIN, LAWRENCE BRIAN, b Brooklyn, NY, Jan 31, 44; m 69. EXPERIMENTAL SOLID STATE PHYSICS. *Educ:* Pa State Univ, BS, 65; Columbia Univ, MA, 67; Univ Ill, PhD(physics), 70. *Prof Exp:* Mem tech staff solid state res, RCA Corp, 65-67; David Sarnoff res fel, 67-69; asst, Univ Ill, 69-70; mem tech staff, 70-79, MGR, EXPLOR MAKING AREA, XEROX RES LABS, XEROX CORP, 79- *Mem:* Am Phys Soc; Electrostatic Soc Am. *Res:* Metal-semiconductor tunneling; xerographic sciences; transport properties of molecular crystals. *Mailing Add:* Xerox Corp 800 Phillips Rd Bldg 114 Rochester NY 14526

SCHEIN, LONNIE GREG, b Iowa City, Iowa, Nov 22, 46; m 74; c 1. PHARMACOLOGY, PHYSIOLOGY. *Educ:* Pa State Univ, BS, 68; Univ NC, MSPH, 72, WVa Univ, PhD(pharmacol), 78. *Prof Exp:* Res assoc, WVa Univ, 78; fel nutrit, Sch Pub Health, Harvard Univ, 78-82; ASST PROF PHARMACOL, RUSH PRESBYTARIAN UNIV, 82- *Concurrent Pos:* Lectr, Loyola Hines, Va. *Res:* Blood substitutes; growth factors; male endocrinology. *Mailing Add:* 29 Sammett Ave Roslindale MA 02131

SCHEIN, MARTIN WARREN, b Brooklyn, NY, Dec 23, 25; m 61; c 3. ETHOLOGY, EDUCATIONAL ADMINISTRATION. *Educ:* Univ Iowa, AB, 49; Johns Hopkins Univ, ScD(vert ecol), 54. *Prof Exp:* Biol aide, USPHS, 47-48; animal climatologist, Exp Sta, La State Univ & USDA, 51-55; from asst prof to assoc prof animal behav, Pa State Univ, 55-65, prof zool, 65-68; CENTENNIAL PROF BIOL, WVA UNIV, 68-, CLIN PROF BEHAV MED & PSYCHIAT, 73-, CHMN, DEPT BIOL, 80- *Concurrent Pos:* Comnr undergrad educ in biol sci, George Washington Univ, 62-64, vchmn comn, 64-65, dir, 65-68, vis prof biol, univ, 65-68; vis lectr, Univ Southern Ill, 64. *Mem:* AAAS; Am Soc Zoologists; Animal Behav Soc (secy, 56-62, pres-elect, 66, pres, 67); Nat Asn Biol Teachers; Am Inst Biol Sci. *Res:* Behavior of domestic animals; sexual, social and feeding behavior; education in biology. *Mailing Add:* Dept of Biol WVa Univ Morgantown WV 26506

SCHEIN, PHILIP SAMUEL, b Asbury Park, NJ, May 10, 39; m 67. PHARMACOLOGY, ONCOLOGY. *Educ:* Rutgers Univ, AB, 61; State Univ NY Upstate Med Ctr, MD, 65; Am Bd Internal Med, dipl, 72, 73; FRCPS(G), 81. *Hon Degrees:* Dr, Nat Univ Rosario, Argentina, 80. *Prof Exp:* Intern med, Beth Israel Hosp, Boston, Mass, 65-66; res assoc pharmacol, Nat Cancer Inst, 66-68; asst resident med, Beth Israel Hosp, Boston, 68-69; res physician Radcliffe Infirmary, Oxford, 69-70; instr, Harvard Med Sch, 70-71; sr investr oncol, Nat Cancer Inst, 71-74, head clin pharmacol, 73-74; CHIEF MED ONCOL, GEORGETOWN UNIV HOSP & LOMBARDI CANCER RES CTR, 74- *Concurrent Pos:* Chief resident med, Beth Israel Hosp, Boston, 70-71; clin asst prof, 71-74, assoc prof med & pharmacol, 74-77, prof med & pharmacol, Med Sch, Georgetown Univ, 77-; consult, Walter Reed Army Hosp, 71 & Clin Ctr, NIH, 74; chmn, Gastrointestinal Tumor Study Group, 74-, Oncol Comt Adv Comt, Food & Drug Admin, 78-81, Med Oncol Comt, Am Bd Int Med, 80- *Mem:* Am Asn Cancer Res; Am Soc Clin Oncol; fel Am Col Physicians; Am Soc Hemat; fel Royal Soc Med. *Res:* Laboratory and clinical investigations in cancer chemotherapy and endocrinology. *Mailing Add:* Div Med Oncol Georgetown Univ Hosp Washington DC 20007

SCHEIN, RICHARD DAVID, b East St Louis, Ill, Nov 18, 27; m 55; c 3. PLANT PATHOLOGY, ECOLOGY. *Educ:* DePauw Univ, BA, 48; Univ Calif, PhD(plant path), 52. *Prof Exp:* Asst, Univ Calif, 48-52; asst plant pathologist, Ill Natural Hist Surv, 52-53; from asst prof to assoc prof plant path, 55-63, assoc prof bot, 63-66, asst dean col sci, 64, assoc dean, 65-71, dir off environ qual progs, 71-75, prof bot, 66-76, PROF PLANT PATHOL, PA STATE UNIV, 76- *Concurrent Pos:* Sr res fel, Agr Univ Neth, 75-76. *Mem:* AAAS; Am Inst Biol Sci; Am Phytopath Soc. *Res:* Plant disease epidemiology; parasitic ecology; influences of physical environment on plant disease development; instrumentation for plant disease study; research and education; economic botany. *Mailing Add:* 108 Buckhout Lab University Park PA 16802

SCHEINBERG, ELIYAHU, b Tel Aviv, Israel, Mar 30, 34. POPULATION GENETICS, APPLIED STATISTICS. *Educ:* Univ Calif, Davis, BS, 61, MS, 62; Purdue Univ, PhD(pop genetics, appl statist), 66. *Prof Exp:* Res assoc, NC State Univ, 65-66; res scientist, Animal Genetics Sect, Animal Res Inst, Cent Exp Farm, Univ Ottawa, 66-68; assoc prof, 68-74, PROF BIOL, UNIV CALGARY, 74- *Concurrent Pos:* Vis prof, Tel Aviv Univ, 71; Nat Res Coun Can traveling fel, 71-72. *Mem:* AAAS; Genetics Soc Can; Am Inst Biol Sci. *Res:* Computer simulation of genetic systems and testing biometrical and population genetics models using Tribolium and Drosophila. *Mailing Add:* Dept of Biol Univ of Calgary Calgary AB T2N 1N4 Can

SCHEINBERG, ISRAEL HERBERT, b New York, NY, Aug 16, 19; m 52, 57; c 3. MEDICINE. *Educ:* Harvard Univ, AB, 40, MD, 43; Am Bd Internal Med, dipl. *Prof Exp:* Intern & asst resident med, Peter Bent Brigham Hosp, 43-44; res assoc chem, Mass Inst Technol, 47-51; instr med, Harvard Med Sch, 51-53, assoc, 53; asst prof, Columbia Univ, 53-55; assoc prof, 55-57, PROF MED, ALBERT EINSTEIN COL MED, 58-, HEAD DIV GENETIC MED, 73- *Concurrent Pos:* Commonwealth Fund fel, 63-64; jr fel, Soc Fellows, Harvard Univ, 47-50; consult, WHO, 52, 67; prin res scientist, NY State Psychiat Inst, 53-55; vis physician, Bronx Munic Hosp Ctr, 55-; res collabr, Med Dept, Brookhaven Nat Lab, 58-; Miller lectr, Dartmouth Med Sch, 61; vis prof physics, Univ Calif, San Diego, 63-64; chmn subcomt copper, Comn Biol & Med Effects Atmospheric Pollutants, Nat Res Coun, 72-77; vis prof, Children's Hosp, Harvard Med Sch, 77- *Honors & Awards:* Asn Res Nerv & Ment Dis Award, 59. *Mem:* Am Soc Clin Invest (vpres, 64-65); Asn Am Physicians. *Res:* Protein chemistry; chemistry and genetics of copper metabolism. *Mailing Add:* Dept of Med Albert Einstein Col of Med Bronx NY 10461

SCHEINBERG, LABE CHARLES, b Memphis, Tenn, Dec 11, 25; m 52; c 4. NEUROLOGY. *Educ:* Univ NC, AB, 45; Univ Tenn, MD, 48. *Prof Exp:* Asst neurol, Columbia Univ, 52-56; from asst prof to assoc prof, 56-64, co-chmn dept neurol, 64-68, dir neurol serv, Hosp, 64-74, from assoc dean to dean clin affairs, 68-72, from asst dean to dean med sch, 68-72, PROF NEUROL,

ALBERT EINSTEIN COL MED, 64-; DIR NEUROL & PSYCHIAT, ST BARNABAS HOSP, BRONX, 74- *Concurrent Pos:* Jacobs Found fel, Albert Einstein Col Med, 56-61; Kenny Found scholar, 59-64; mem adv bd, Epilepsy Found; med adv bd, Nat Multiple Sclerosis Soc. *Mem:* Am Psychiat Asn; Tissue Cult Asn; Asn Res Nerv & Ment Dis; Am Acad Neurol. *Res:* Myelination and the demyelination diseases; experimental and clinical brain tumors. *Mailing Add:* Dir Neurol & Psychiat St Barnabas Hosp Bronx NY 10457

SCHEINBERG, PERITZ, b Miami, Fla, Dec 21, 20; m 42; c 2. NEUROLOGY. *Educ:* Emory Univ, AB, 41, MD, 44; Am Bd Internal Med, dipl, 51; Am Bd Psychiat & Neurol, dipl, 54. *Prof Exp:* Instr med neurol, Duke Univ, 49-50; res assoc, Med Res Univ, 50-51, res asst prof physiol, Sch Med, 51-55, assoc prof neurol & chief div, 55-59, PROF NEUROL, SCH MED, UNIV MIAMI, 59-, CHMN DEPT, 61- *Concurrent Pos:* Res fel med neurol, Am Col Physicians, Med Sch, Duke Univ, 48-49; Am Heart Asn res fel, 49-50; consult, Vet Admin Hosp; med adv bd, Nat Multiple Sclerosis Soc & Myasthenia Gravis Found; consult, Surgeon Gen US; examr, Am Bd Psychiat & Neurol; trustee, Asn Univ Prof Neurol; mem stroke coun, Am Heart Asn. *Mem:* Asn Res Nerv & Ment Dis; Am Neurol Asn (pres); fel Am Col Physicians; fel Am Acad Neurol; Am Fedn Clin Res. *Res:* Medical neurology; blood flow and metabolism of the brain. *Mailing Add:* Dept of Neurol Univ of Miami Sch of Med Miami FL 33124

SCHEINBERG, SAM LOUIS, b New York, NY, June 15, 22; m 45; c 3. GENETICS. *Educ:* Cornell Univ, BS, 49; Iowa State Univ, MS, Univ Wis, PhD(genetics, poultry husb & zool), 54. *Prof Exp:* Fel immunogenetics, NIH, Univ Wis, 54-56; res biologist immunogenetics & immunochem, Oak Ridge Nat Lab, 56-58; geneticist & group leader, USDA, 58-70; LEADER, PIONEERING RES LAB, 70- *Res:* Immunogenetics; cellular and serum antigens in birds and mammals; somatic variation in birds and man; immunochemistry. *Mailing Add:* Pioneering Res Lab 7409 Wellesley Dr College Park MD 20740

SCHEINDLIN, STANLEY, b Philadelphia, Pa, July 18, 26; m 54; c 3. PHARMACEUTICAL CHEMISTRY. *Educ:* Temple Univ, BS, 45; Philadelphia Col Pharm, MS, 47, DSc(pharmaceut chem), 55. *Prof Exp:* Res fel, Philadelphia Col Pharm, 47-48, asst pharm, 48-49, instr, 49-55; res assoc labs, Nat Drug Co, 55-64, dir pharmaceut res labs, 64-70 & pharmaceut res & develop, 70-71; independent pharmaceut consult, 71-72; dir res, 72-77, DIR TECH AFFAIRS, LEMMON PHARMACAL CO, 78- *Concurrent Pos:* Lectr, Philadelphia Col Pharm, 68-69 & Spring Garden Col, 79- *Mem:* Am Soc Pharmacog; Am Pharmaceut Asn; Acad Pharmaceut Sci; Parenteral Drug Asn. *Res:* Plant constituents; interactions of vitamins; stability; compatibility and incompatibility of drugs; formulation of parenterals; cancer chemotherapy. *Mailing Add:* 3011 Nesper St Philadelphia PA 19152

SCHEINER, BERNARD JAMES, b Atlantic City, NJ, Mar 12, 38; m 59; c 2. METALLURGY, CHEMISTRY. *Educ:* Univ Nev, Reno, BS, 61, PhD(org chem), 69. *Prof Exp:* Proj leader & res chemist, Reno Metall Res Sta, 66-79, SUPV METALLURGIST, FINE PARTICLE TECHNOL GROUP, TUSCALOOSA RES CTR, US BUR MINES, 79- *Mem:* Am Inst Mining, Metall & Petrol Engrs. *Res:* Development of processes for the recovery of metals from low-grade, refractory, and sulfide ores by means of innovative hydrometallurgical techniques. *Mailing Add:* US Bur Mines Univ Ala PO Box L Tuscaloosa AL 35486

SCHEINER, DONALD M, b New York, NY, Mar 12, 32; m 54; c 2. BIOCHEMISTRY, MICROBIOLOGY. *Educ:* Cornell Univ, BS, 53, MFS, 54, PhD(biochem), 60. *Prof Exp:* Res chemist, Rohm and Haas Co, 60-63; asst prof, 63-71, ASSOC PROF CHEM, RUTGERS UNIV, 71- *Mem:* AAAS; Am Chem Soc; NY Acad Sci. *Res:* Analytical biochemistry; microbial metabolism; plant pigments; immunology. *Mailing Add:* Dept of Chem 311 N 5th St Camden NJ 08102

SCHEINER, PETER, b Brooklyn, NY, Mar 13, 35; m 60; c 2. ORGANIC CHEMISTRY. *Educ:* Cornell Univ, AB, 57; Univ Mich, MS, 60, PhD(chem), 61. *Prof Exp:* NIH fel, Mass Inst Technol, 61-62; asst prof chem, Carleton Col, 62-64; from res chemist to sr res chemist, Mobil Oil Corp, 64-69; assoc prof, 69-73, PROF CHEM & CHMN DEPT NATURAL SCI, YORK COL, NY, 73- *Concurrent Pos:* NIH res grant, Carleton Col, 62-64; NY Col, 79-82; consult, Dept Air Resources, New York, 71-; Am Chem Soc-Petrol Res Fund res grant, York Col, NY, 71-73. *Mem:* Am Chem Soc; Sigma Xi. *Res:* Organic photochemistry; heterocycles; air pollution; atmospheric chemistry. *Mailing Add:* Dept of Chem York Col Jamaica NY 11451

SCHEINER, STEVE, b New York, NY, Feb 27, 51. PHYSICAL CHEMISTRY, QUANTUM CHEMISTRY. *Educ:* City Col New York, BS, 72; Harvard Univ, AM, 74, PhD(chem physics), 76. *Prof Exp:* Weizmann Found fel chem, Ohio State Univ, 76-78; ASST PROF CHEM, SOUTHERN ILL UNIV, CARBONDALE, 78- *Concurrent Pos:* Prin investr, Res Corp grant, 79-; NIH grant, 81- *Mem:* Int Soc Quantum Biol. *Res:* Proton transfer; hydrogen bonding; protein structure; opiate activity; biomembranes; hydration. *Mailing Add:* Dept of Chem & Biochem Southern Ill Univ Carbondale IL 62901

SCHEINOK, PERRY AARON, b The Hague, Neth, Sept 21, 31; nat US; m 53, 71; c 2. RESEARCH ADMINISTRATION, MATHEMATICS. *Educ:* City Col New York, BS, 57; Ind Univ, PhD(math, statist), 60. *Prof Exp:* Asst math, Ind Univ, 52-54 & 56-59; mathematician, Burroughs Corp, 56; vis res assoc, Brookhaven Nat Lab, 59; instr comput & math, Wayne State Univ, 59-60, asst prof math, 60-62; sr systs analyst, Radio Corp Am, 62-64; res asst prof pharmacol, Hahnemann Med Col, 64-68, res assoc prof, 68-70, res prof physiol & biophys, 70-72, dir comput ctr, 64-72, div biomet & comput, 70-72; exec dir, Del Health Serv Authority, 72-74; proj dir, University City Sci Ctr, 74-77; SR DIR MED DATA CONTROL, CIBA-GEIGY CORP, 77- *Concurrent Pos:* Consult, Henry Ford Hosp, 61-62; consult, Pa Hosp, 65-66; prin investr, NIH grant biomed res, Comput Ctr, 65-72. *Mem:* Inst Math Statist; Am Statist Asn; Math Asn Am. *Res:* Application of probabilistic models to medical diagnosis; computerization of clinical hospital functions; electrocardiogram; clinical labs; time series analysis; large scale biological data bases; health services research. *Mailing Add:* 376 Timber Dr Berkeley Heights NJ 07922

SCHEIRER, DANIEL CHARLES, b Lebanon, Pa, Dec 10, 46; m 67; c 1. BOTANY, ELECTRON MICROSCOPY. *Educ:* Wheaton Col, Ill, BS, 68; Pa State Univ, MS, 71, PhD(bot), 74. *Prof Exp:* asst prof, 74-80, ASSOC PROF BIOL, NORTHEASTERN UNIV, 80-, DIR, ELECTRON MICROSCOPY CTR, 78- *Concurrent Pos:* Vis scholar, Harvard Univ, 81-82. *Mem:* AAAS; Am Bryological & Lichenological Soc; Bot Soc Am; Electron Microscopy Soc Am; Sigma Xi. *Res:* Ultrastructure of conducting tissue in lower plants; anatomy and ultrastructure of polytrichaceae; anatomy and ultrastructure of Taro. *Mailing Add:* Dept of Biol Northeastern Univ Boston MA 02115

SCHEIRING, JOSEPH FRANK, b Puchbach, Austria, Apr 18, 45; m 69; c 1. ENTOMOLOGY, ECOLOGY. *Educ:* Kent State Univ, BS, 68, MA, 70; Univ Kans, PhD(entom), 75. *Prof Exp:* Res assoc, Dept Entom, Mich State Univ, 75-76; ASST PROF, DEPT BIOL, UNIV ALA, 76- *Concurrent Pos:* Prin investr, Geol Surv Ala, 78-79 & Res Grants Comt, Univ Ala, 77 & 78. *Honors & Awards:* R H Beamer Award, Dept Entom, Univ Kans, 74. *Mem:* Ecol Soc Am; Entom Soc Am; NAm Benthological Soc; Sigma Xi. *Res:* Ecology of aquatic and semi-aquatic insects; niche relations in insects; applications of multivariate statistical methods to biology. *Mailing Add:* Ecol and Systs Sect Dept of Biol Univ of Ala University AL 35486

SCHEKEL, KURT ANTHONY, b Colorado Springs, Colo, Jan 3, 43; m 68; c 1. ORNAMENTAL HORTICULTURE, FLORICULTURE. *Educ:* Colo State Univ, BS, 65, PhD(floricult), 71; Univ Nebr, Lincoln, MS, 68. *Prof Exp:* Assoc prof ornamental hort, 71-80, ASSOC PROF DEPT HORT & LANDSCAPE ARCHIT, WASH STATE UNIV, 80- *Mem:* Am Soc Hort Sci. *Res:* Nutrition and growing temperatures of greenhouse crops. *Mailing Add:* Dept of Hort and Landscape Archit Wash State Univ Pullman WA 99164

SCHEKMAN, RANDY W, b St Paul, Minn, Dec 30, 48; m 73; c 1. CELL BIOLOGY. *Educ:* Univ Calif, Los Angeles, BA, 70; Stanford Univ, PhD(biochem), 75. *Prof Exp:* Fel, Univ Calif, San Diego, 74-76; asst prof, 76-81, ASSOC PROF, UNIV CALIF, BERKELEY, 81- *Concurrent Pos:* Fel, Cystic Fibrosis Found, 74; sabbatical fel, John S Guggenheim Found, 82. *Mem:* Am Soc Microbiol; Am Soc Biol Chemists. *Res:* Molecular mechanism of secretion and membrane assembly in eucaryotic cells. *Mailing Add:* Dept Biochem Univ Calif Berkeley CA 94720

SCHELAR, VIRGINIA MAE, b Kenosha, Wis, Nov 26, 24. ANALYTICAL CHEMISTRY. *Educ:* Univ Wis, BS, 47, MS, 53; Harvard Univ, EdM, 62; Univ Wis, PhD, 69. *Prof Exp:* Instr chem, Univ Wis-Milwaukee, 47-51; lit chemist, Abbott Labs, Ill, 53-56; instr phys sci, Wright Jr Col, 57-58; asst prof chem, Northern Ill Univ, 58-65; prof, St Petersburg Jr Col; prof chem, Grossmont Col, 68-80; CONSULT, 80- *Mem:* Am Chem Soc; fel Am Inst Chem. *Res:* Analytical instrumentation computers. *Mailing Add:* 5702 Baltimore Dr 282 LaMesa CA 92041

SCHELBERG, ARTHUR DANIEL, physics, see previous edition

SCHELDORF, JAY J(OHN), b Camden, NJ, Jan 22, 32; m 53; c 2. CHEMICAL ENGINEERING. *Educ:* Univ Ill, BS, 53; Kans State Univ, MS, 54; Univ Colo, PhD(chem eng), 58. *Prof Exp:* Res chemist, Chem Div, Corn Prod Refining Co, 54-55; instr chem eng, Univ Colo, 55-58, asst prof, 58-66; assoc prof, 66-74, PROF CHEM ENG & ENG SCI, UNIV IDAHO, 74- *Mem:* Am Inst Chem Engrs; Am Chem Soc; Am Soc Eng Educ. *Res:* Fluid dynamics and heat transfer; physical chemistry; thermodynamics. *Mailing Add:* Dept of Chem Eng Univ of Idaho Moscow ID 83843

SCHELL, ALLAN CARTER, b New Bedford, Mass, Apr 14, 34; m 57; c 2. ELECTRICAL ENGINEERING. *Educ:* Mass Inst Technol, SB, 56, SM, 58 & ScD(elec eng), 61. *Prof Exp:* Res physicist, Microwave Physics Lab, Air Force Cambridge Res Labs, 56-76; CHIEF, ELECTROMAGNETIC SCI DIV, ROME AIR DEVELOP CTR, 76- *Concurrent Pos:* Guenter Loeser Mem lectr, 65; vis assoc prof, Mass Inst Technol, 74; ed press, Inst Elec & Electronics Engrs, 76-79. *Mem:* Fel Inst Elec & Electronics Engrs; Int Union Radio Sci; Nat Soc Prof Engrs. *Res:* Electromagnetic theory; antennas; angular resolution enhancement. *Mailing Add:* Electromagnetic Sci Div RADC/EE Hanscom AFB MA 01731

SCHELL, ANNE MCCALL, b Waco, Tex, Apr 23, 42; m 1. PSYCHO-PHYSIOLOGY. *Educ:* Baylor Univ, BS, 63; Univ Southern Calif, MA, 68, PhD(psychol), 70. *Prof Exp:* Vis asst prof psychol, Univ Southern Calif, 70-71; asst prof, 71-78, ASSOC PROF PSYCHOL, OCCIDENTAL COL, 78- *Concurrent Pos:* Statist consult, Pasadena Unified Sch Dist, 73-75; res consult, Gateways Hosp, 75- *Mem:* Am Psychol Asn; Soc Psychophysiol Res. *Res:* Study of physiological components and concommitants of cognitive and affective processes in humans; physiological aspects of psychopathology. *Mailing Add:* Occidental Col Dept of Psychol 1600 Campus Rd Los Angeles CA 90041

SCHELL, FRED MARTIN, b Cincinnati, Ohio, Oct 6, 43; m 74; c 2. SYNTHETIC ORGANIC CHEMISTRY. *Educ:* Univ Cincinnati, BS, 66, MS, 68; Ind Univ, PhD(chem), 72. *Prof Exp:* ASST PROF CHEM, UNIV TENN, KNOXVILLE, 72- *Mem:* Am Chem Soc; AAAS. *Res:* Development of new carbon-carbon bond-forming reactions and their application to the synthesis of natural products. *Mailing Add:* Dept of Chem Univ of Tenn Knoxville TN 37916

SCHELL, GEORGE W(ASHINGTON), b Easton, Pa, June 25, 21; m 46; c 2. CHEMICAL ENGINEERING. *Educ:* Lafayette Col, BS, 43. *Prof Exp:* Jr chem engr, Atlantic Refining Co, Pa, 44; asst chem, Univ Southern Calif, 44-45; jr chem engr, Atlantic Refining Co, Philadelphia, 45-46, asst chemist, 46-47, asst prod foreman, 47-57, foreman, 57-66, prod technologist, Atlantic Richfield Co, Pa, 66-71; supv chemist, Qual Control Lab, Pennzoil United, Inc, 71-73, chief chemist, Pennzoil Co, 73-77, supt oil movements, 77-79, MGR PACKAGING, PENNZOIL CO, 79- *Mem:* Am Chem Soc. *Res:* Petroleum technology. *Mailing Add:* Qual Control Lab Pennzoil Co Rouseville PA 16344

SCHELL, JOSEPH FRANCIS, b Miamisburg, Ohio, Dec 24, 28; m 54; c 7. GEOMETRY. *Educ:* Univ Dayton, BS, 50; Ind Univ, MA, 52, PhD(math), 57. *Prof Exp:* Asst, Ind Univ, 50-54; instr math, Univ Dayton, 54-56; res mathematician, Wright-Patterson AFB, Ohio, 56-61; asst prof math, Fla State Univ, 61-64; assoc prof, 64-68, chmn dept, 68-80, PROF MATH, UNIV NC, CHARLOTTE, 68- *Concurrent Pos:* Resident dir, Eglin Grad Ctr, Eglin AFB, 63-64. *Mem:* Am Math Soc; Math Asn Am; Soc Indust & Appl Math. *Res:* Differential geometry; relativity theory; topology. *Mailing Add:* Dept of Math Univ of NC Charlotte NC 28223

SCHELL, ROBERT RAY, b Perry, Iowa, Sept 12, 37; m 61; c 2. ELECTRICAL ENGINEERING. *Educ:* Univ Ariz, BS, 59, MS, 61, PhD(elec eng), 67. *Prof Exp:* Jr engr, Melabs, Calif, 61-62; instr elec eng, Univ Ariz, 62-67; assoc engr, Collins Radio Co, 67-72; assoc engr, 72-76, ENG ANALYST, ELECTROSPACE SYSTS, INC, 76- *Mem:* AAAS; Inst Elec & Electronics Engrs. *Res:* Electromagnetic theory; wave propagation; antenna theory diffraction; numerical methods. *Mailing Add:* Electrospace Systs Inc Box 1359 Richardson TX 75080

SCHELL, STEWART CLAUDE, b Reading, Pa, Feb 4, 12; m 41; c 2. PARASITOLOGY. *Educ:* Kans State Univ, BS, 39; NC State Col, MS, 41; Univ Ill, PhD(zool, parasitol), 50. *Prof Exp:* From asst prof to assoc prof, 49-63, chmn dept, 74-78, prof, 64-78, EMER PROF ZOOL, UNIV IDAHO, 78- *Mem:* Am Soc Parasitologists. *Res:* Life histories and development of parasitic helminths. *Mailing Add:* Dept Biol Sci Univ Idaho Moscow ID 83843

SCHELL, WILLIAM JOHN, b Buffalo, NY, Oct 19, 40; m 76. POLYMER CHEMISTRY. *Educ:* State Univ NY Col Forestry, Syracuse Univ, BS, 64, MS, 66; Univ Southern Calif, PhD(polymer chem), 69. *Prof Exp:* Mgr spec membrane prod, Envirogenics Systs Co, 69-78; partner, KS&W Consult, 78-79; PRES, SPECTRUM SEPARATIONS INC, 79- *Mem:* Am Chem Soc. *Res:* Membrane systems for fluid separations; pollution control processes; polymer characterization; relaxation behavior of polymers. *Mailing Add:* 5375 E Eighth St Long Beach CA 90804

SCHELL, WILLIAM R, b Portland, Ore, Apr 17, 32; m 59; c 1. NUCLEAR CHEMISTRY, AGRICULTURAL CHEMISTRY. *Educ:* Ore State Univ, BS, 54; Univ Idaho, MS, 56; Univ Wash, PhD(inorg chem, nuclear chem), 63. *Prof Exp:* Res technician soils chem, Univ Idaho, 54-56; independent investr, US Naval Radiol Defense Lab, 56-59; res asst chem, Univ Wash, 60-63; sr radiochemist, Hazleton-Nuclear Sci Corp, Isotopes, Inc, Calif, 64-65, head div atmospheric & oceanog sci, 65-68; vis scientist, Radiochem Div, Lawrence Radiation Lab, Univ Calif, 68; with div res & labs, Int Atomic Energy Agency, 68-71; res assoc prof with lab radiation ecol, 71-77, assoc prof, 78-79, PROF FISHERIES, COL FISHERIES, UNIV WASH, 79- *Concurrent Pos:* Guest lectr, Colo State Col, 66; adj prof oceanog, Dept Oceanog & radiol scientist, Dept Environ Health, Univ Wash, 79-82; vis scientist, Gas & Particulate Sci Div, Ctr Anal Chem, Nat Bureau Standards, 81-82. *Mem:* AAAS; Am Chem Soc. *Res:* Environmental radiochemistry; colloidal chemistry; fallout studies; radiotracer techniques; chemical and radiochemical instrumentation; gas technology; carbon-14 dating; geophysics; nuclear debris in meteorology; oceanography and air pollution; radiation ecology. *Mailing Add:* Univ of Wash Col of Fisheries Seattle WA 98195

SCHELLENBERG, KARL A, b Hillsboro, Kans, July 13, 31; m 55; c 4. BIOCHEMISTRY. *Educ:* Col William & Mary, BS, 53; Johns Hopkins Univ, MD, 57; Harvard Univ, PhD(biochem), 64. *Prof Exp:* Intern med, Grace-New Haven Community Hosp, Conn, 57-58; biochemist, NIH, 58-60; from asst prof to assoc prof physiol chem, Johns Hopkins Univ, 63-73; PROF BIOCHEM & CHMN DEPT, EASTERN VA MED SCH, 73- *Concurrent Pos:* Markle Found scholar med sci, 65-70. *Mem:* Am Chem Soc; Am Soc Biol Chem; NY Acad Sci. *Res:* Biochemical reaction mechanisms. *Mailing Add:* Dept Biochem Eastern Va Med Sch Norfolk VA 23507

SCHELLENBERG, PAUL JACOB, b Leamington, Ont, Dec 31, 42; m 66. MATHEMATICS. *Educ:* Univ Waterloo, BSc, 65, MA, 66, PhD(math), 71. *Prof Exp:* Lectr math, Univ Waterloo, 66-67; systs programmer, Comput Ctr, Indian Inst Technol, Kanpur, 67-69; lectr, 71, asst prof, 71-79, ASSOC PROF MATH, UNIV WATERLOO, 79- *Res:* Combinatorial mathematics and designs; room squares; balanced room squares; Hadamard matrices and (r, lambda)-systems. *Mailing Add:* Dept Combinatorics & Optimization Univ Waterloo Waterloo ON N2L 3G1 Can

SCHELLENG, JOHN H, b Neptune, NJ, Mar 16, 33; m 67; c 2. SOLID STATE PHYSICS. *Educ:* Lehigh Univ, BS, 55; Carnegie Inst, MS, 58, PhD(physics), 63. *Prof Exp:* RES PHYSICIST, US NAVAL RES LAB, 63- *Mem:* Am Phys Soc. *Res:* Magnetic properties of materials through measurement of such basic properties as susceptibility and anisotropy; study of magnetic phase transitions by thermal measurements. *Mailing Add:* Naval Res Lab 4555 Overlook Ave SW Washington DC 20375

SCHELLENG, R(OBERT) D(OUGLAS), b Fulton, NY, Aug 1, 25; m 53; c 3. METALLURGICAL ENGINEERING. *Educ:* Univ Mich, BS, 50, MS, 51. *Prof Exp:* Res metallurgist, Res Lab, Int Nickel Co, Inc, 51-56, supvr ferrous castings res, 57-66, mem staff, P D Merica Res Lab, 66-70, supvr

copper, aluminum & ceramics res, 70-78, SR DEVELOP ENGR ALUMINUM & COPPER ALLOYS, INCO RES & DEVELOP CTR, 78- *Mem:* Am Soc Metals; Am Foundrymen's Soc. *Res:* Uses of nickel in copper alloys, aluminum alloys and ceramics. *Mailing Add:* Inco Res & Develop Ctr Sterling Forest Suffern NY 10901

SCHELLER, W(ILLIAM) A(LFRED), b Milwaukee, Wis, June 6, 29; m 51; c 2. CHEMICAL ENGINEERING. *Educ:* Northwestern Univ, BS, 51, PhD(chem eng), 55. *Prof Exp:* Res engr, Calif Res Corp, Standard Oil Co, Calif, 55-60, group supvr, 60-63; assoc prof, 63-69, chmn dept, 71-78, PROF CHEM ENG, UNIV NEBR, LINCOLN, 69- *Concurrent Pos:* Du Pont fac fel, 64; Univ Res Coun fac fel, 65; Off Water Resources res grant, Univ Nebr, Lincoln, 66-69; guest prof, Univ Erlangen, 69-70, Ger Res Asn grant, 70; consult, Northern Natural Gas Co & Brunswick Corp; consult, IRAS Develop Corp, NY, 76- *Mem:* Am Chem Soc; Am Inst Chem Engrs; Am Soc Eng Educ. *Res:* Phase equilibrium; direct energy conversion; reaction kinetics; thermodynamics; computer aided design; process economics; alcohol blended fuels, gasohol. *Mailing Add:* Dept of Chem Eng Univ of Nebr Lincoln NE 68588

SCHELLING, GERALD THOMAS, b Sterling, Ill, Mar 24, 41; m 63; c 2. NUTRITION. *Educ:* Univ Ill, BS, 63, MS, 64, PhD(nutrit), 68. *Prof Exp:* Res assoc nutrit, Univ Ill, 68; nutritionist, Smith, Kline & French Labs, 68-70; prof nutrit, Univ Ky, 70-79; PROF NUTRIT, TEX A&M UNIV, 79- *Mem:* Am Soc Animal Sci. *Res:* Ruminant and nonruminant nutrition, with emphasis on nitrogen metabolism. *Mailing Add:* Tex A&M Univ College Station TX 77843

SCHELLMAN, JOHN ANTHONY, b Philadelphia, Pa, Oct 24, 24; m 54; c 2. PHYSICAL CHEMISTRY. *Educ:* Temple Univ, AB, 48; Princeton Univ, MA, 49, PhD(phys chem), 51. *Prof Exp:* USPHS fel, Univ Utah, 51, res assoc, 52; USPHS fel, Carlsberg Lab, Denmark, 53-55; Du Pont fel, Univ Minn, 55-56, asst prof chem, 56-58; assoc prof, 58-62, PROF CHEM, UNIV ORE, 62- *Concurrent Pos:* Sloan fel, 59-64; mem NIH study sect biophys & biophys chem, 62-67; sr fel, USPHS, Lab des Hautes Pressions, Bellevue, France, 63-64; Guggenheim fel, Weizmann Inst, 69-70. *Mem:* Am Chem Soc; Am Soc Biol Chemists. *Res:* Optical rotation and thermodynamics of biochemical molecules. *Mailing Add:* Dept of Chem Univ of Ore Eugene OR 97403

SCHELLY, ZOLTAN ANDREW, b Budapest, Hungary, Feb 15, 38; m 67; c 3. PHYSICAL CHEMISTRY. *Educ:* Vienna Tech Univ, BS, 62, DSc(phys chem), 67. *Prof Exp:* AEC fel, Lab Surface Studies, Univ Wis-Milwaukee, 68; Air Force Off Sci Res fel, Univ Utah, 69-70; asst prof phys chem, Univ Ga, 70-76; ASSOC PROF PHYS CHEM, UNIV TEX, ARLINGTON, 77- *Concurrent Pos:* Alexander von Humboldt lectr fel, Max-Planck Inst Biophys Chem, 74. *Mem:* Sigma Xi; Am Chem Soc; Austrian Chem Soc; Royal Soc Chem. *Res:* Reaction kinetics; dynamics of fast rate processes; relaxation spectrometry; diffusion; laser techniques; dynamics of agneous and reversed micelles; chemical instabilities and bifurcations. *Mailing Add:* Dept of Chem Univ Tex Arlington TX 76019

SCHELP, RICHARD HERBERT, b Kansas City, Mo, Apr 21, 36; m 58; c 2. MATHEMATICS. *Educ:* Cent Mo Univ, BS, 59; Kans State Univ, MS, 61, PhD(math), 70. *Prof Exp:* Assoc math missile scientist, Appl Physics Lab, Johns-Hopkins, 61-66; instr math, Kans State Univ, 66-70; asst prof, 70-74, assoc prof, 74-79, PROF MATH, MEMPHIS STATE UNIV, 79- *Concurrent Pos:* Managing ed, J Graph Theory, 81-83. *Mem:* Am Math Soc; Math Asn Am. *Res:* Graph theory and lattice theory; Ramsey theory and Hamiltonian graph theory. *Mailing Add:* Memphis State Univ Memphis TN 38152

SCHELSKE, CLAIRE L, b Fayetteville, Ark, Apr 1, 32; m 57; c 3. AQUATIC ECOLOGY, LIMNOLOGY. *Educ:* Kans State Teachers Col, AB, 55, MS, 56; Univ Mich, PhD(zool), 61. *Prof Exp:* Res assoc, Univ Ga Marine Inst, 60-62; fishery biologist, Radiobiol Lab, Bur Com Fisheries, 62-63; supvry fishery biologist, 63; chief estuarine ecol prog, 63-66; tech asst, Off Sci & Technol, Exec Off President, 66-67; from asst res limnologist to assoc res limnologist, Univ Mich, Ann Arbor, 67-71; asst prof radiol health, Sch Pub Health, 67-68, lectr, Biol Sta, 70, from asst dir to actg dir, Great Lakes Res Div, 70-76, res limnologist, Great Lakes Res Div, 71-77, ASSOC PROF LIMNOL, DEPT ATMOSPHERIC & OCEANIC SCI & ASSOC PROF NATURAL RESOURCES, SCH NATURAL RESOURCES, UNIV MICH, ANN ARBOR, 76- *Concurrent Pos:* Adj asst prof, NC State Univ, 64-66; consult to Ill Atty Gen, WAPORA Inc, US Dept Justice. *Mem:* Fel AAAS; Am Soc Limnol & Oceanog (secy, 76); Ecol Soc Am; Int Asn Great Lakes Res; fel Am Inst Fishery Res Biologists. *Res:* Eutrophication and limnology of the Great Lakes, fresh-water ecosystem ecology; relationships among silica, nitrogen, phosphorus and phytoplankton production; nutrients and other factors limiting primary productivity. *Mailing Add:* Great Lakes Res Div Univ Mich Ann Arbor MI 48109

SCHELTEMA, RUDOLF S, b Madison, Wis, May 27, 26; m 55; c 2. MARINE BIOLOGY, BIOGEOGRAPHY. *Educ:* George Washington Univ, BS, 51, MS, 54; Univ NC, PhD(zool), 60. *Prof Exp:* Marine biologist, Chesapeake Biol Lab, Md, 51-54; res assoc, Oyster Res Lab, Rutgers Univ, 59-60; res assoc marine biol, 60-63, asst scientist, 63-67, ASSOC SCIENTIST, WOODS HOLE OCEANOG INST, 67- *Concurrent Pos:* Fac mem, Cape Cod Community Col, 61-62; sr Fulbright-Hays Scholar, James Cook Univ, NQueensland, Australia, 77-78. *Mem:* Am Soc Zool; Am Soc Limnol & Oceanog; Soc Syst Zool; Am Soc Naturalists. *Res:* Invertebrate zoology; morphology, ecology and comparative physiology of larval marine benthic invertebrate organisms; zoogeography and evolution; reproduction of deep-sea benthos; life history and settlement of fouling organisms. *Mailing Add:* Woods Hole Oceanog Inst Woods Hole MA 02543

SCHELTGEN, ELMER, b Limerick, Sask, Feb 5, 30; m 53; c 2. BIOPHYSICS, MOLECULAR GENETICS. *Educ:* Univ BC, BA, 55; Ind Univ, Bloomington, AM, 65; Univ Tex, Houston, PhD(biomed sci), 68. *Prof Exp:* Lectr & instr physics, Univ BC, 54-60; NASA grant, Univ Houston,

68-69; USPHS fel, Univ Tex M D Anderson Hosp & Tumor Inst Houston, 69; asst prof cancer res, 69-71, res assoc bact, 71-77, RES ASSOC MICROBIOL, UNIV SASK, 78- *Mem:* Am Chem Soc; Am Inst Biol Sci. *Mailing Add:* Dept of Bact Univ of Sask Col of Med Saskatoon SK S7H 0W0 Can

SCHEMAN, PAUL, b New York, NY, Feb 1, 16; m 41; c 3. DENTISTRY, ORAL MEDICINE. *Educ:* City Col New York, BS, 37; NY Univ, DDS, 41; Am Bd Oral Surg, dipl, 59. *Prof Exp:* Dir dent, 60-75, DIR MED-DENT AFFAIRS, KINGSBROOK JEWISH MED CTR, 75- *Concurrent Pos:* Stomatol res, Isaac Albert Res Inst Kingsbrook. *Mem:* Am Dent Asn; NY Acad Sci; Int Asn Dent Res. *Res:* Oral surgery and dysfunctions and diseases of the temporomandibular joint; cytodiagnosis of oral cancer and early detection. *Mailing Add:* Dir Med/Dent Affairs Rutland Rd & E 49th St Brooklyn NY 11203

SCHEMENAUER, ROBERT STUART, b Prince Albert, Sask, Nov 3, 46; m 70. CLOUD PHYSICS. *Educ:* Univ Sask, BA, 67; Univ Toronto, MSc, 69, PhD(meteorol), 72. *Prof Exp:* Meteorologist, 67-69, RES SCIENTIST CLOUD PHYSICS, ATMOSPHERIC ENVIRON SERV, ENVIRON CAN, 72- *Mem:* Can Meteorol Soc; Am Meteorol Soc. *Res:* Laboratory and airborne studies of the microphysical processes responsible for precipitation formation; weather modification to increase and target rainfall; ice fog; precipitation chemistry. *Mailing Add:* Atmospheric Environ Serv 4905 Dufferin St Downsview ON M3H 5T4 Can

SCHEMM, CHARLES EDWARD, b Baltimore, Md, Oct 30, 47; m 77. DYNAMIC METEOROLOGY, FLUIDS. *Educ:* Loyola Col, Md, BS, 69; Princeton Univ, PhD(geophys fluid dynamics), 74. *Prof Exp:* Res assoc, Inst Phys Sci & Technol, Univ Md, 74-77; SR PHYSICIST, APPL PHYSICS LAB, JOHNS HOPKINS UNIV, 77- *Concurrent Pos:* Vis lectr, Dept Meteorol, Univ Md, 76-81. *Mem:* Am Meteorol Soc; Sigma Xi; AAAS; Am Phys Soc. *Res:* At-sea experiments; analysis of ocean turbulence data; numerical modeling of small-scale ocean processes. *Mailing Add:* Appl Phys Lab Johns Hopkins Univ Laurel MD 20707

SCHEMMEL, RACHEL A, b Farley, Iowa, Nov 23, 29. NUTRITION. *Educ:* Clarke Col, BA, 51; State Univ Iowa, MS, 52; Mich State Univ, PhD(nutrit), 67. *Prof Exp:* Dietitian, Childrens Hosp Soc, Calif, 52-54; adminstr, St Joseph's Hosp, Calif, 54-55; instr food & nutrit, 55-63, asst prof nutrit, 68-70, assoc prof nutrit, 71-76, PROF NUTRIT, MICH STATE UNIV, 77- *Concurrent Pos:* Res fel, Dunn Nutrit Lab, Cambridge, 68. *Mem:* AAAS; Am Inst Nutrit; Soc Exp Biol & Med; Brit Nutrit Soc; Am Dietetic Asn. *Res:* Obesity and lipid and carbohydrate metabolism; hypertension; nutritional status of human subjects; dental caries and taste acuity. *Mailing Add:* Dept of Food Sci & Human Nutrit Mich State Univ East Lansing MI 48824

SCHEMNITZ, SANFORD DAVID, b Cleveland, Ohio, Mar 10, 30; m 58; c 3. WILDLIFE RESEARCH, WILDLIFE ECOLOGY. *Educ:* Univ Mich, BS, 52; Univ Fla, MS, 53; Okla State Univ, PhD(wildlife zool), 54. *Prof Exp:* Res game biologist, Bur Res & Planning, State Dept Conserv, Minn, 57-59; asst prof wildlife, Univ Maine, 59-60; from instr to asst prof, Pa State Univ, 60-62; from asst prof to prof wildlife, Sch Forest Resources, Univ Maine, Orono, 63-75; HEAD DEPT FISHERY & WILDLIFE & PROF SCI, NMEX STATE UNIV, 75- *Concurrent Pos:* With sub group 108-wildlife habitat mgt, Int Union Forest Res Orgn. *Mem:* Ecol Soc Am; Wildlife Soc; Am Soc Mammalogists. *Res:* Wildlife conservation; ecology of birds and mammals; forest zoology and ecology; effects of off-road vehicles on environment. *Mailing Add:* Dept of Fish & Wildlife Sci NMex State Univ Las Cruces NM 88003

SCHEMPP, ELLORY, b Philadelphia, Pa. CHEMICAL PHYSICS. *Educ:* Tufts Univ, BS, 62; Brown Univ, PhD(physics), 68. *Prof Exp:* Fel physics, Brown Univ, 67-68; res physicist, Bell Tel Labs, NJ, 68-70; asst prof crystallog & res asst prof physics, Univ Pittsburgh, 70-77; vis prof physics, Univ Ill, Champaign-Urbana, 77-78; VIS PROF, UNIVERSITE DE GENEVA, 77- *Mem:* Am Phys Soc. *Res:* Nuclear quadrupole resonance studies of chemical bonds; molecular and ionic field gradients in crystals; hydrogen bonding and lattice dynamics; ferroelectrics. *Mailing Add:* Am Col Switzerland 1854 Leysin Geneva Switzerland

SCHEMSKE, DOUGLAS WILLIAM, b Chicago, Ill, Sept 8, 48. POPULATION BIOLOGY. *Educ:* Univ Ill, BS, 70, PhD(ecol), 77. *Prof Exp:* Fel, Smithsonian Trop Res Inst, 77-78; asst prof evolution & ecol, Amherst Col, 78-79; ASST PROF EVOLUTION & ECOL, UNIV CHICAGO, 79- *Concurrent Pos:* Vis instr, Field Sta, Univ Minn, 79-80. *Mem:* AAAS; Am Soc Naturalists; Asn Trop Biol; Ecol Soc Am; Soc Study Evolution. *Res:* Evolutionary processes in plant populations, with particular emphasis on breeding systems, population structure, gene flow and the assessment of selection intensities. *Mailing Add:* Dept Biol Univ Chicago 1103 E 57th St Chicago IL 60637

SCHENCK, HARRY ALLEN, b San Diego, Calif, May 29, 38; m 59; c 4. ACOUSTICS. *Educ:* Pomona Col, BA, 59; Harvard Univ, SM, 60, PhD(appl physics), 64. *Prof Exp:* Lectr & res fel acoust, Harvard Univ, 64; res physicist, US Navy Electronics Lab, 64-69; surveillance systs prog mgr, Naval Undersea Ctr, 69-75; HEAD UNDERSEA SURVEILLANCE DEPT, NAVAL OCEAN SYSTS CTR, 75- *Mem:* Acoust Soc Am. *Res:* Electroacoustic transducers; acoustic radiation theory. *Mailing Add:* Undersea Surveillance Dept Code 71 Naval Ocean Systs Ctr San Diego CA 92152

SCHENCK, HILBERT VAN NYDECK, JR, b Boston, Mass, Feb 12, 26; m 50; c 4. PHYSICS, MECHANICAL ENGINEERING. *Educ:* Williams Col, BA, 50; Stanford Univ, MS, 52. *Prof Exp:* Test engr, Pratt & Whitney Aircraft Div, United Aircraft Corp, Conn, 52-56, from asst prof to prof mech eng, Clarkson Col Technol, 56-67; PROF MECH ENG & APPL MECH & OCEAN ENG, UNIV RI, 67-, DIR SCUBA SAFETY PROJ, 71- *Concurrent Pos:* NSF grant, 63-64, res grant, 65-; Food & Drug Admin res grant scuba

safety, 69-71; US Coast Guard grant scuba safety, 71-72; Manned Undersea Sci & Technol grants, 72- *Mem:* Am Phys Soc. *Res:* Engineering heat transfer; statistics of experimentation; instrumentation; underwater photography and oceanographic optics; diving technology and safety; scuba tank corrosion. *Mailing Add:* Dept of Mech Eng Univ of RI Wales Hall Kingston RI 02881

SCHENCK, JAY RUFFNER, b Geneva, Ill, Jan 10, 15; m 48; c 2. BIOCHEMISTRY. *Educ:* Univ Ill, BS, 36, MS, 37; Cornell Univ, PhD(biochem), 41. *Prof Exp:* Sci asst, Soybean Res Lab, USDA, 36-37; asst biochem, Sch Med, George Washington Univ, 37-38 & Cornell Univ, 38-40; RES BIOCHEMIST, ABBOTT LABS, 41- *Mem:* Am Chem Soc; Am Soc Biol Chem. *Res:* Microbiological assay; intermediary metabolism; isolation and chemistry of antibiotics; immunochemistry. *Mailing Add:* 90C Abbott Labs North Chicago IL 60064

SCHENCK, JOHN FREDERIC, b Decatur, Ind, June 7, 39; c 3. MEDICAL RESEARCH, SOLID STATE PHYSICS. *Educ:* Rensselaer Polytech Inst, BS, 61; Albany Med Col, MD, 77. *Prof Exp:* Assoc prof elec eng, Syracuse Univ, 70-73; consult scientist, Electronics Lab, 65-70, scientist, 73-80, MEM TECH STAFF, CORP RES & DEVELOP CTR, GEN ELEC CO, 80- *Mem:* Am Med Asn; Am Phys Soc; Inst Elec & Electronics Engrs; Biophys Soc; Sigma Xi. *Res:* Electrical and electronic technology applied to clinical medicine; nuclear magnetic resonance and solid state devices in medical diagnosis; electric potentials at biological interfaces; social implications of technology. *Mailing Add:* Gen Elec Corp Res & Develop Ctr Schenectady NY 12301

SCHENCK, NORMAN CARL, b Oak Park, Ill, July 8, 28; m 51; c 4. PLANT PATHOLOGY. *Educ:* Univ Ill, BS, 51, PhD(plant path), 55. *Prof Exp:* Asst plant pathologist, 56-63, assoc plant pathologist, 63-69, PLANT PATHOLOGIST, AGR RES CTR & PROF PLANT PATH, UNIV FLA, 69- *Mem:* Am Phytopath Soc; Mycol Soc Am. *Res:* Soil-borne plant disease; endomycorrhizal fungi; fungal plant pathogens. *Mailing Add:* Dept of Plant Path Univ of Fla Gainesville FL 32611

SCHENGRUND, CARA-LYNNE, b New York, NY, Feb 18, 41; m 61; c 2. BIOCHEMISTRY. *Educ:* Upsala Col, BS, 62; Seton Hall Univ, MS, 65, PhD(biochem), 66. *Prof Exp:* Part-time instr, Upsala Col, 67; res worker, Col Physicians & Surgeons, Columbia Univ, 67-68, res assoc biochem, 68-69; res assoc, 69-72, asst prof, 72-79, ASSOC PROF BIOCHEM, HERSHEY MED CTR, PA STATE UNIV, 79- *Mem:* Am Soc Biol Chemists; Am Chem Soc; Am Soc Neurochem. *Res:* Subcellular fractionation isolation and characterization of plasma membranes of normal and transformed cells; neural cell differentiation; neurochemistry. *Mailing Add:* Milton S Hershey Med Ctr Pa State Univ Hershey PA 17033

SCHENK, H(AROLD) L(OUIS), JR, b Columbus, Ohio, Jan 27, 29; c 2. ELECTROMAGNETIC ANALYSIS, APPLIED MAGNETICS. *Educ:* Ohio State Univ, BSc, 51, MSc, 52. *Prof Exp:* Res physicist, Gen Motors Corp, 52-55; SR ENGR, WESTINGHOUSE RES & DEVELOP CTR, 57- *Mem:* Am Phys Soc; Inst Elec & Electronics Engrs. *Res:* Magnetic phenomena and technology. *Mailing Add:* Westinghouse R&D Ctr MS 401-4X9D 1310 Beulah Rd Churchill Borough Pittsburgh PA 15235

SCHENK, JOHN ALBRIGHT, b Stevens Point, Wis, Oct 22, 24; m 55; c 2. FOREST ENTOMOLOGY. *Educ:* Univ Mich, BS, 50; Univ Wis, MS, 56, PhD(entom), 61. *Prof Exp:* Relief model aid cartog, Relief Model Div, Army Map Serv, 51-53; forester, US Forest Serv, 53-54; res fel forest entom, Univ Wis, 54-59 & Wis Conserv Dept, 59-61; from asst prof to assoc prof, 61-66, PROF FOREST ENTOM, UNIV IDAHO, 71- *Mem:* Entom Soc Am; Entom Soc Can; Smithsonian Inst; Soc Am Foresters. *Res:* Forest entomological research with emphasis on biology and ecology of forest pests and their control by silvicultural and biological methods; cone and seed insects; bark beetles. *Mailing Add:* Col Forestry Univ Idaho Moscow ID 83843

SCHENK, PAUL EDWARD, b Stratford, Ont, Feb 26, 37; m 60; c 2. PETROLOGY, STRATIGRAPHY. *Educ:* Univ Western Ont, BSc, 59; Univ Wis, MS, 61, PhD(geol), 63. *Prof Exp:* From asst prof to assoc prof, 63-75, PROF GEOL, DALHOUSIE UNIV, 75-, CHMN DEPT, 81- *Concurrent Pos:* Can leader, IGCP Proj Caledonian Orogeny, 74-82; Comnr, NAm Comn Stratig Nomenclature, 75-78. *Mem:* Geol Soc Am; Am Asn Petrol Geol; Soc Econ Paleont & Mineral; fel Geol Asn Can; Int Asn Sedimentologists. *Res:* Petrology and stratigraphy of evaporites; paleoecology and petrology of carbonate sediments; paleocurrent study of flysch; sedimentology in Paleozoic Atlantic of southeastern Atlantic Canada and northwestern Africa. *Mailing Add:* Dept of Geol Dalhousie Univ Halifax NS B3H 3J5 Can

SCHENK, ROY URBAN, b Evansville, Ind, Nov 18, 29. BIOCHEMISTRY. *Educ:* Purdue Univ, BS, 51; Cornell Univ, MS, 53, PhD(chem), 54. *Prof Exp:* Instr chem, Evansville Col, 54-55; chemist, Northern Regional Res Lab, Ill, 55-57; asst chemist, Univ Ga Exp Sta, 57-60; asst prof chem, Univ Ky, 60-62; mem staff org chem, Mat Lab, Wright-Patterson AFB, Ohio, 62-64; sr res chemist, Drackett Co, Ohio, 64-65; assoc prof pharmaceut chem, Univ Cincinnati, 65-67; res assoc, Univ Wis-Madison, 67-70, BIOCHEMIST, BJORKSTEN RES LABS, 70- & PRES, BIOENERGETICS, INC, 73- *Mem:* Am Chem Soc; Inst Food Technologists; Sigma Xi. *Res:* Biochemistry; nutritional aspects of health and disease; heavy metal extraction from industrial waste waters; road de-icing alternatives; chemistry related testing for insurance claims. *Mailing Add:* Bioenergetics Inc PO Box 9141 Madison WI 53715

SCHENK, STEVEN PAUL, microbiology, see previous edition

SCHENK, WORTHINGTON G, JR, b Buffalo, NY, Feb 10, 22; m 46; c 7. SURGERY. *Educ:* Williams Col, BA, 42; Harvard Med Sch, MD, 45; Am Bd Surg, dipl, 54. *Prof Exp:* Assoc, 54-56, from asst prof to assoc prof, 56-66, actg chmn dept, 69-72, PROF SURG, SCH MED, STATE UNIV NY BUFFALO,

66-, CHMN DEPT, 72- *Concurrent Pos:* Buswell fel surg res, State Univ NY Buffalo, 56-60; attend surgeon, E J Meyer Hosp, 54-66, from assoc dir to dir surg res labs & dir surg, 54-; mem surg study sect, NIH, 69-73. *Mem:* Soc Vascular Surg (treas, pres); Soc Surg Alimentary Tract; Soc Univ Surg; Soc Clin Surg (secy); Am Surg Asn. *Res:* Biophysics of surgical problems in hemodynamics. *Mailing Add:* Dept of Surg State Univ of NY Buffalo NY 14215

SCHENKEIN, ISAAC, b Antwerp, Belg, Mar 12, 23; US citizen. BIOLOGICAL CHEMISTRY. *Educ:* City Col New York, BS, 62; NY Univ, PhD(biochem), 65. *Prof Exp:* Asst res scientist, NY Univ, 59-66; res scientist, Inst Biophys & Biochem, Paris, France, 66-67; from assoc res scientist to res scientist, NY Univ, 67-74, assoc prof microbiol, 74-76, RES ASSOC PROF MICROBIOL, SCH MED, NY UNIV, 77- *Concurrent Pos:* Consult, Col Dent, NY Univ, 67-68. *Res:* Proteolytic enzymes and nerve growth stimulating factors from mouse submaxillary glands; chemistry of immunoglobulins. *Mailing Add:* Dept of Microbiol NY Univ Sch of Med New York NY 10016

SCHENKEL, ROBERT H, b New York, NY, June 12, 44; m 71; c 1. PARASITOLOGY, IMMUNOBIOLOGY. *Educ:* Lafayette Col, BS, 65; Adelphi Univ, MS, 67; Univ Ill, PhD(zool), 71. *Prof Exp:* Res assoc immunoparasitol, Univ Ill, Urbana, 71-72; res scientist, Univ NMex, 72-75; sr res parasitologist, 75-77, group leader parasitol res, 77-80, GROUP LEADER CHEMOTHER & IMMUNOL, AM CYANAMID CO, 80- *Mem:* Am Soc Parasitologists; AAAS. *Res:* Development of new drugs for use in treating parasitic infections; development of new host-parasite systems for testing drugs; monoclonal antibodies for antigen identification. *Mailing Add:* Am Cyanamid Co PO Box 400 Princeton NJ 08540

SCHENKEN, JOHN RUDOLPH, pathology, bacteriology, deceased

SCHENKENBERG, THOMAS, b St Louis, Mo, Nov 3, 43; m 69. NEUROPSYCHOLOGY. *Educ:* Rockhurst Col, AB, 65; Univ Utah, MA, 69, PhD(clin psychol), 70. *Prof Exp:* Asst prof, 73-80, ASSOC PROF, DEPT NEUROL, UNIV UTAH, 80-, RES ASSOC PROF, DEPT PSYCHOL, 73-; CLIN PSYCHOLOGIST, VET ADMIN HOSP, 70- *Concurrent Pos:* Asst prof, Dept Neurol, Univ Utah, 73-, res assoc prof, Dept Psychol, 73-, adj asst prof, Dept Psychiat, 77-; Nat Inst Aging grant, 77; adj assoc prof, Dept Psychol, Brigham Young Univ, 73; adj asst prof, Dept Psychiat, Univ Utah, 77- *Mem:* Sigma Xi; AAAS; Am Psychol Asn; Nat Register Health Serv Providers Psychol. *Res:* Clinical neuropsychology; electrophysiology; medical psychology. *Mailing Add:* Vet Admin Hosp 500 Foothill Dr Salt Lake City UT 84148

SCHENKER, HENRY HANS, b Vienna, Austria, June 19, 26; nat US; m 55; c 3. TEXTILE CHEMISTRY. *Educ:* City Col, BS, 49; Rutgers Univ, PhD(chem), 53. *Prof Exp:* Asst, Rutgers Univ, 51-52; res chemist, 52-56, supvr, Anal Lab, 56-61, SR RES CHEMIST, E I DU PONT DE NEMOURS & CO, 61- *Mem:* Am Chem Soc; NY Acad Sci. *Res:* Ion-exchange; textile chemistry; polymer chemistry. *Mailing Add:* Christina Lab E I du Pont de Nemours & Co Wilmington DE 19898

SCHENKER, STEVEN, b Krakow, Poland, Oct 5, 29; US citizen; m; c 5. INTERNAL MEDICINE, GASTROENTEROLOGY. *Educ:* Cornell Univ, BA, 51, MD, 55. *Prof Exp:* From intern to sr resident, Harvard Med Serv, Boston City Hosp, 55-57; clin assoc gastroenterol, Nat Inst Allergy & Infectious Dis, 59-61; asst prof, Col Med, Univ Cincinnati, 63-64; from asst prof to assoc prof internal med, Univ Tex Southwestern Med Sch, 64-69; PROF MED BIOCHEM & HEAD DIV GASTROENTEROL, SCH MED, VANDERBILT UNIV, 69- *Concurrent Pos:* Fel gastroenterol, Col Med, Univ Cincinnati, 58-59; res fel med, Thorndike Mem Lab, Harvard Med Sch, 61-63; Markle scholar acad med, 63-68; USPHS res career develop award, 68; mem alcoholism & alcohol probs rev comt, NIMH, 67-71, chmn, 80-81. *Mem:* Am Asn Study Liver Dis (pres, 80); Am Fedn Clin Res; Am Soc Clin Invest; Am Gastroenterol Asn; Am Acad Neurol. *Res:* Liver disease, especially bilirubin metabolism in maturation; metabolic encephalopathies, especially hepatic coma, drug metabolism in liver disease and thiamine deficiency. *Mailing Add:* 403 S Wilson Blvd Nashville TN 37205

SCHENKMAN, JOHN BORIS, b New York, NY, Feb 10, 36; m 60. BIOCHEMISTRY, PHARMACOLOGY. *Educ:* Brooklyn Col, BS, 60; State Univ NY, PhD(biochem), 64. *Prof Exp:* Phys biochemist, Johnson Res Found, Sch Med, Univ Pa, 64-66; NSF vis scientist, Osaka Univ, 67-68; assoc prof pharmacol, Sch Med, Yale Univ, 68-78; PROF & HEAD PHARMACOL, SCH MED, UNIV CONN, FARMINGTON, 78- *Concurrent Pos:* NIH fel, Sch Med, Univ Pa, 64-67; res assoc, Inst Toxicol, Univ Tubingen, Ger, 68, pharmacol study sect, 74-78; ed, Int Encyclopedia Pharmacol Therapeut; assoc ed Biochem Pharmacol. *Mem:* Am Soc Biol Chem; Am Soc Pharmacol & Exp Therapeut; Brit Biochem Soc; Ger Pharmacol Soc. *Res:* Biological oxidations; microsomal mixed function oxidations; hemoprotein oxidases. *Mailing Add:* Dept of Pharmacol Univ Conn Sch Med Farmington CT 06032

SCHENLER, W(ILLIAM) W(ALTER), b Decatur, Ill, Sept 1, 23; m 51; c 2. CIVIL ENGINEERING. *Educ:* Purdue Univ, BSCE, 47, MSCE, 50, PhD(hwy transp), 61. *Prof Exp:* Instr civil eng, Purdue Univ, 47-51; asst prof, Univ Wash, 54-62; from asst prof to assoc prof, 62-71, chmn dept, 70-74, prof civil eng, 71-80, PROF ENVIRON RESOURCES ENG, HUMBOLDT STATE UNIV, 80- *Concurrent Pos:* Asst, Purdue Univ, 59-60. *Mem:* Am Soc Eng Educ. *Res:* Priority rating system for major urban street intersections. *Mailing Add:* Dept of Eng Humboldt State Univ Arcata CA 95521

SCHENNUM, WAYNE EDWARD, b Elgin, Ill, Aug 23, 49. ECOLOGY, POPULATION BIOLOGY. *Educ:* Univ Ill, Chicago Circle, BS, 71, PhD(biol), 75. *Prof Exp:* Teaching asst, Univ Ill, Chicago Circle, 74-75, asst prof biol, 76; asst prof biol, Judson Col, 76-77; asst prof biol, Wheaton Col, 77-78; environ consult, The Nature Conservancy & Ill Natural Land Inst,

78-81. *Concurrent Pos:* Vis asst prof, Judson Col, 76 & 78-79, Concordia Teacher's Col, 76, Wheaton Col, 79 & Barat Col, 80-81. *Mem:* Soc Study Evolution; Ecol Soc Am; Lepidopteritsts Soc; Natural Areas Asn; Xerces Soc. *Res:* Application of multivariate techniques to ecological and systematic problems; study of ecological relationships and taxonomy of insects and plants in prairies. *Mailing Add:* 3234 N Arlington Heights Rd Arlington Heights IL 60004

SCHENTER, ROBERT EARL, b St Louis, Mo, Jan 4, 37; m S9; c 4. NUCLEAR PHYSICS. *Educ:* Calif Inst Technol, BS, 58; Univ Colo, Boulder, PhD(physics), 63. *Prof Exp:* Res assoc nuclear physics, Case Inst Technol, 63-65; sr res scientist, Nuclear Physics & Fast Reactor Cross Sections, Batelle Mem Inst Pac Northwest Labs, 65-70; res assoc, 70-76, MGR NUCLEAR ANAL, WESTINGHOUSE HANFORD CO, 76-78. *Concurrent Pos:* Lectr, Joint Ctr Grad Study, 66- *Mem:* Am Phys Soc. *Res:* Theoretical calculations of the nucleon-nucleus optical model potential in terms of the nucleon-nucleus interaction; calculation of neutron reaction cross sections for reactor analyses. *Mailing Add:* Westinghouse Hanford Co PO Box 1970 Richland WA 99352

SCHENZ, ANNE FILER, b Sharon, Pa, Sept 16, 45; m 68. PHYSICAL CHEMISTRY. *Educ:* Westminster Col, Pa, BS, 67; Kent State Univ, PhD(phys chem), 74. *Prof Exp:* Teacher chem, Springfield Sch Dist, Akron, Ohio, 67-68; vis prof anal chem, King's Col, NY, 75-76; prin develop chemist laundry detergents, Lever Bros Co, NJ, 76-78; proj specialist, 78-81, GROUP LEADER LIQUID TEXTURE, GEN FOODS CORP, 81- *Concurrent Pos:* Vis prof phys chem, King's Col, NY, 79. *Res:* Liquid crystals; surfactant and bleach chemistry; texture of liquid foods; surface rheology. *Mailing Add:* Gen Foods Corp 555 S Broadway Tarrytown NY 07641

SCHENZ, TIMOTHY WILLIAM, b Washington, DC, Jan 2, 46; m 68. PHYSICAL CHEMISTRY. *Educ:* Westminster Col, Pa, BS, 68; Kent State Univ, PhD(phys chem), 73. *Prof Exp:* Sr chemist, 74-76, proj specialist, 76-79, RES SPECIALIST PHYS CHEM, GEN FOODS CORP, 79- *Mem:* Am Chem Soc; Sigma Xi. *Res:* Physical adsorption from solution; interactions with proteins in disperse systems; instrumentation and automation; foams and emulsions; thermal analysis. *Mailing Add:* 369 Orchard Pl Haworth NJ 07641

SCHEP, RAYMOND ALBERT, b Pretoria, SAfrica, Apr 11, 46; m 75, 81. POLYMER CHEMISTRY, COAL CHEMISTRY. *Educ:* Univ Pretoria, BSc, 69, MSc, 71, DSc(chem), 74. *Prof Exp:* Res chemist fuel chem, Fuel Res Inst, SAfrica, 69-75; res chemist fuel chem, Occidental Res Corp, 75-81; CONSULT COAL CONVERSION, 81- *Mem:* Assoc mem Am Inst Chem engrs; Am Chem Soc. *Res:* Coal conversion; chemicals from coal; fuels processes invention and development. *Mailing Add:* 3470 Adina Dr Hollywood Hills CA 90068

SCHEPARTZ, ABNER IRWIN, b New York, NY, July 29, 22; m 49; c 2. BIOCHEMISTRY. *Educ:* Purdue Univ, BS, 43; Univ Pittsburgh, PhD(chem), 50. *Prof Exp:* Asst chem, Univ Pittsburgh, 43-44; res assoc, Manhattan proj, Univ Rochester, 44-46; Nat Heart Inst fel, Univ Wis, 50-51; res biochemist, Vet Hosp, Pittsburgh, Pa, 51-56; sr res fel, USDA, Pa, 56-60; res assoc in charge biochem & biophys, Merck Inst Therapeut Res, 60-62; res chemist, 62-65, RES LEADER LEAF RES, TOBACCO LAB, USDA, 65- *Concurrent Pos:* Asst chem, Univ Pittsburgh, 46-49, instr, 54-55; consult, Children's Hosp, Pittsburgh, 56. *Mem:* Am Chem Soc; Am Soc Biol Chem; AAAS. *Res:* Uranium toxicology; fat chemistry; isolation of natural products; allergens; electrophoresis of proteins; chemistry of tobacco smoke; biochemistry and biophysics of viruses; electron microscopy; enzymology; tobacco biochemistry. *Mailing Add:* Tobacco Lab Russell Res Ctr USDA Athens GA 30604

SCHEPARTZ, BERNARD, b New York, NY, Nov 9, 18; m 44. BIOCHEMISTRY, BIOMATHEMATICS. *Educ:* Ohio Wesleyan, BA, 41; Univ Mich, MS, 42; Univ Pa, PhD(biochem), 49. *Prof Exp:* Asst, Comt Med Res War Proj, Dept Surg Res, Univ Pa, 42-44, chemist, Nat Defense Res Comt War Proj, Towne Sci Sch, 44-46; from instr to assoc prof biochem, 48-65, prof, 65-80, EMER PROF BIOCHEM, JEFFERSON MED COL, 80- *Mem:* AAAS; Am Soc Biol Chem; Am Chem Soc; Sigma Xi. *Res:* Intermediary metabolism of amino acids; dimensional analysis. *Mailing Add:* Dept of Biochem Jefferson Med Col Philadelphia PA 19107

SCHEPARTZ, SAUL ALEXANDER, b Nutley, NJ, Mar 18, 29; m 56; c 3. BIOCHEMISTRY. *Educ:* Ind Univ, AB, 51; Univ Wis, MS, 53, PhD(biochem), 55. *Prof Exp:* Res assoc, Wistar Inst, Univ Pa, 55-57; biochemist, Microbiol Assocs, Inc, 57-58; biochemist, Sect on Screening, Cancer Chemother, Nat Serv Ctr, 58-61, head biochem sect, Drug Eval Br, 61-64, asst chief drug eval br, 64, asst chief cancer chemother, Nat Serv Ctr, 64-66, chief, 66-72, assoc sci dir, Drug Res & Develop Chemother, 72-73, assoc dir drug res & develop, 73-76, actg dep dir, 76-78, actg dir, 80-81, DEP DIR, DIV CANCER TREAT, NAT CANCER INST, 78- *Mem:* AAAS; Am Chem Soc; Am Soc Microbiol; NY Acad Sci; Am Asn Cancer Res. *Res:* Cancer chemotherapy; fermentation biochemistry; tissue culture; mode of action of antibiotics; microbial polysaccharides. *Mailing Add:* Div Cancer Treatment Nat Cancer Inst Bldg 31 Rm 3A-51 Bethesda MD 20205

SCHEPLER, KENNETH LEE, b Clinton, Iowa, Apr 1, 49; m 72; c 2. LASER PHYSICS, BIOPHYSICS. *Educ:* Mich State Univ, BS, 71; Univ Mich, MS, 73; PhD(physics), 75. *Prof Exp:* Res biophysicist, Laser Effects Br, Sch Aerospace Med, 75-79, nuclear physicist, McClellan AFB, 79-81, LASER PHYSICIST, AVIONICS LAB, WRIGHT-PATTERSON AFB, US AIR FORCE, 81- *Mem:* Am Biophys Soc; Am Phys Soc. *Res:* Optical spectroscopy of laser crystals; tunable lasing of solid state materials; excited state absorption of transition metal doped crystals; computer modeling of laser performance and laser damage; mechanisms of biological interactions with laser radiation, cataractogenesis. *Mailing Add:* AFWAL/AADO-1 Wright-Patterson AFB OH 45433

SCHEPPERS, GERALD J, b North Bend, Nebr, Apr 11, 33; m 60; c 5. ANALYTICAL CHEMISTRY. *Educ:* Nebr State Teachers Col, Wayne, BA, 62; Iowa State Univ, MS, 65, PhD(anal chem), 67. *Prof Exp:* Asst prof, 66-67, assoc prof, 67-77, PROF CHEM, UNIV WIS-PLATTEVILLE, 78-, CHMN DEPT, 80- *Mem:* Am Chem Soc. *Res:* Fluorescent indicators; complex formation in non-aqueous solvents. *Mailing Add:* Dept of Chem Univ of Wis Platteville WI 53818

SCHER, ALLEN MYRON, b Boston, Mass, Apr 17, 21; m 52; c 2. PHYSIOLOGY. *Educ:* Yale Univ, BA, 42, PhD, 50. *Prof Exp:* From instr to assoc prof, 50-62, PROF PHYSIOL, UNIV WASH, 62- *Concurrent Pos:* Mem comput study sect, NIH, 63-67 & cardiovasc A study sect, 67-71. *Mem:* AAAS; Am Physiol Soc; Biophys Soc. *Res:* Cardiovascular control systems; cardiac electrophysiology. *Mailing Add:* Dept Physiol & Biophysics SJ-40 Univ of Wash Seattle WA 98195

SCHER, CHARLES D, b Newark, NJ, July 25, 39; m 64; c 2. GROWTH CONTROL, REGULATION. *Educ:* Brandeis Univ, BA, 61; Univ Pa, MD, 65. *Prof Exp:* Intern, Bronx Munic Hosp, 65-66, asst resident, 66-67; res assoc, Nat Cancer Inst, 67-71; asst resident, Children's Hosp Med Ctr, 71-72, fel hemat, 72-74; asst prof, Med Sch, Harvard Univ, 74-78, assoc prof, 78-82; PROF, CHILDREN'S HOSP PHILADELPHIA, MED SCH, UNIV PA, 82- *Concurrent Pos:* Spec fel, NIH, 72-74; scholar, Leukemia Soc Am, 77-82; mem staff, Sidney Farber Cancer Inst, 77-82. *Mem:* Tissue Cult Asn; NY Acad Sci; Am Soc Cell Biol. *Res:* Control of cell replication by growth factors. *Mailing Add:* Sidney Farber Cancer Inst 44 Binney St Boston MA 02115

SCHER, HERBERT BENSON, b New York, NY, Dec 11, 37; m 59; c 2. PHYSICAL CHEMISTRY, COLLOID CHEMISTRY. *Educ:* Cornell Univ, BChEng, 60; Univ Minn, MS, 62, PhD(phys chem), 64. *Prof Exp:* Res chemist rheology, Chem Res & Develop Lab, US Army, Edgewood Arsenal, 64-66; sr res chemist, Res Lab, Eastman Kodak Co, 66-68; SR RES ASSOC CONTROLLED RELEASE PESTICIDES & PESTICIDE DISPERSIONS, STAUFFER CHEM CO, 68- *Concurrent Pos:* Exten Div Instr, Univ Calif, Berkeley, 71-77; adj assoc prof, Dept Chem, Univ San Francisco, 78-80, vis lectr, 81- *Mem:* Am Chem Soc. *Res:* Controlled release pesticides; microencapsulation; interfacial polymerization; coating technology; diffusion of organic molecules through polymers; pesticide formulations; emulsions and dispersions; rheology; organic molecule-clay interactions; kinetics of pesticide degradation; stabilization of pesticides. *Mailing Add:* Stauffer Chem Co 1200 S 47th St Richmond CA 94804

SCHER, JORDAN MAYER, psychiatry, see previous edition

SCHER, MARYONDA E, b Oakland, Calif, Feb 26, 31; m 52; c 2. PSYCHIATRY. *Educ:* Univ Wash, BS, 50, MD, 54. *Prof Exp:* Clin asst, 55-59, clin instr, 59-65, clin asst prof, 65-69, clin assoc prof, 69-76, ASSOC PROF PSYCHIAT, UNIV WASH SCH MED, 76- *Concurrent Pos:* Staff psychiatrist, Vet Admin Hosp, Seattle, 59-80; active mem med staff, Harborview Hosp, Seattle, 65- *Mem:* Fel Am Psychiat Asn; Asn Acad Psychiat. *Res:* Education; women. *Mailing Add:* Dept Psychiat and Behav Sci Sch of Med Univ of Wash Seattle WA 98195

SCHER, ROBERT BANGEL, b Newport, Va, Apr 30, 49. ELECTRICAL ENGINEERING. *Educ:* Harvard Univ, BA, 71; Univ Va, MS, 75, PhD(elec eng), 77. *Prof Exp:* Res asst elec eng, Res Labs Eng Sci, Univ Va, 73-76; sr engr, Booz, Allen & Hamilton, 76-78; SR SCIENTIST ELEC ENG, AMECOM DIV, LITTON INDUSTS, 78- *Mem:* Inst Elec & Electronics Engrs; Comput Soc. *Res:* Communications and radar systems; imdge processing and pattern recognition; applications of charge transfer devices. *Mailing Add:* Amecom Div Litton Industs 5115 Calvert Rd College Park MD 20740

SCHER, ROBERT SANDER, b Cincinnati, Ohio, May 24, 34; m 61; c 3. MECHANICAL ENGINEERING. *Educ:* Mass Inst Technol, SB, 56, SM, 58, Mech Eng, 60, ScD(mech eng), 63. *Prof Exp:* Engr aerospace, Astro Electronics Div, RCA Corp, 63-65; dept mgr optical encoders, Sequential Info Syst, 65-70; VPRES ENG, TELEDYNE GURLEY, 70- *Mem:* Am Soc Mech Engrs; Optical Soc Am. *Res:* Design and development of precision measuring instruments, particularly optical encoders. *Mailing Add:* Two Laurel Oak Ln Clifton Park NY 12065

SCHERAGA, HAROLD ABRAHAM, b Brooklyn, NY, Oct 18, 21; m 43; c 3. BIOPHYSICAL CHEMISTRY. *Educ:* City Col New York, BS, 41; Duke Univ, AM, 42, PhD(chem), 46. *Hon Degrees:* ScD, Duke Univ, 61. *Prof Exp:* Am Chem Soc fel, Harvard Med Sch, 46-47; from instr to prof, 47-65, chmn dept, 60-67, TODD PROF CHEM, CORNELL UNIV, 65- *Concurrent Pos:* Guggenheim fel & Fulbright scholar, Carlsberg Lab, Denmark, 56-57; vis lectr, Div Protein Chem, Wool Res Lab, Commonwealth Sci & Indust Res Orgn, Australia, 59; mem adv panel molecular biol, NSF, 60-62; co-ed, Molecular Biol, 61-; Welch Found lectr, Univ Tex, 62; co-chmn, Gordon Res Conf Proteins, 63; mem biochem training comt, NIH, 63-65 & career develop comt, 67-71; Guggenheim fel & Fulbright scholar, Weizmann Inst Sci, 63, NIH spec fel, 70, mem bd gov, 70-; mem adv bd, Biopolymers, 63- & Biochemistry, 69-74; Harvey lectr, 68; Gallagher lectr, 68-69; mem-at-large coun, Gordon Res Conf, 69-71, Lemieux lectr, 73; mem tech adv panel, Xerox Corp, 69-71 & 74-79; Hill lectr, 76; vis prof, Japan Soc Promotion Sci, 77; distinguished invited lectr, Univ Calgary, 79. *Honors & Awards:* Lilly Award, Am Chem Soc, 57, Nichols Medal, 74; Townsend Harris Medal, City Col New York, 70; Kendall Award, Am Chem Soc, 78. *Mem:* Nat Acad Sci; AAAS; Am Acad Arts & Sci; Am Chem Soc; Am Soc Biol Chem. *Res:* Physical chemistry of proteins and other macromolecules; structure of water and dilute aqueous solutions; blood clotting. *Mailing Add:* Dept of Chem Cornell Univ Ithaca NY 14853

SCHERB, FRANK, b Union City, NJ, Sept 17, 30; m 64; c 4. SPACE PHYSICS. *Educ:* Mass Inst Technol, SB, 53, PhD(physics), 58. *Prof Exp:* Res staff assoc space physics, Mass Inst Technol, 58-61, from asst prof to assoc prof physics, 61-65; assoc prof, 65-69, PROF PHYSICS, UNIV WIS-MADISON, 69- *Mem:* Am Phys Soc; Am Geophys Union; Am Astron Soc. *Res:* Cosmic rays; physics of interplanetary medium, especially the solar wind. *Mailing Add:* Dept of Physics Univ of Wis Madison WI 53706

SCHERBA, GERALD MARRON, b Chicago, Ill, Feb 9, 27; m 51; c 3. ZOOLOGY. *Educ:* Univ Chicago, BS, 50, MS, 52, PhD(zool), 55. *Prof Exp:* From instr to assoc prof biol, Chico State Col, 55-62; prof & chmn natural sci div, 62-66, dean acad affairs, 66-68, VPRES, CALIF STATE COL, SAN BERNARDINO, 68- *Concurrent Pos:* Res grants, NY Zool Soc, 55-56 & 59, Am Acad Arts & Sci, 57 & NSF, 62-64. *Res:* Animal ecology; animal behavior; biology of social insects, especially ants. *Mailing Add:* Calif State Col 5500 State College Pkwy San Bernardino CA 92407

SCHERBENSKE, M JAMES, b Jamestown, NDak, Jan 13, 37; m 59; c 4. PHYSIOLOGY, BIOCHEMISTRY. *Educ:* Jamestown Col, BS, 59; Univ SDak, MA, 64, PhD(physiol), 66. *Prof Exp:* Fel renal physiol, Med Ctr, Kans Univ, 66-68; health scientist adminr, Nat Heart Inst, 68-69, HEALTH SCIENTIST ADMINR KIDNEY & UROL, NAT INST ARTHRITIS, METAB & DIGESTIVE DIS, NIH, 69- *Concurrent Pos:* Consult, Coordr Coun Urol, Am Urol Asn, 71- *Mem:* Am Soc Nephrology; Soc Univ Urologists. *Res:* Renal physiology and transport. *Mailing Add:* Kidney Dis & Urol Prog & Digestive Dis NIH Bethesda MD 20205

SCHERBERG, NEAL HARVEY, b Minneapolis, Minn, Nov 10, 39. MOLECULAR BIOLOGY, BIOCHEMISTRY. *Educ:* Oberlin Col, AB, 61; Tufts Univ, PhD(biochem), 66. *Prof Exp:* Asst prof, 71-76, ASSOC PROF MED, UNIV CHICAGO, 76-, RES ASSOC, 71- *Concurrent Pos:* Fel molecular biol, Univ Chicago, 66-71, Am Cancer Soc fel, 66-68. *Mem:* Am Soc Biochem. *Res:* Protein synthesis and the mechanism of hormone action. *Mailing Add:* Univ Chicago Thyroid Study Unit 950 E 59th St Chicago IL 60637

SCHERER, GEORGE ALLEN, b Kokomo, Ind, Apr 3, 07; m 29; c 3. CHEMISTRY. *Educ:* Earlham Col, BS, 27; Cornell Univ, MS, 28; Purdue Univ, PhD(chem), 33. *Prof Exp:* Asst chem, Cornell Univ, 27-28 & Purdue Univ, 28-33; prof, Pac Col, 33-34 & McKendree Col, 34-36; from instr to prof, Earlham Col, 36-57; admin secy, Am Friends Bd Missions, 57-60; prof chem & head dept, Western Col, 60-72; adj prof chem, Ind Univ East, 72-77; CHEM TECHNICIAN, EARLHAM COL, 72- *Concurrent Pos:* Vis prof, Univ Col Women, Hyderabad, India, 65-66. *Mem:* Am Chem Soc. *Res:* Electrode potentials; free energy measurements. *Mailing Add:* 510 College Ave Richmond IN 47374

SCHERER, GEORGE WALTER, b Teaneck, NJ, Apr 27, 49; m 71. MATERIALS SCIENCE. *Educ:* Mass Inst Technol, SB, 72, SM, 72, PhD(mat sci), 74. *Prof Exp:* SR CERAMIST, CORNING GLASS WORKS, 74- *Mem:* Am Ceramic Soc; NY Acad Sci. *Res:* Kinetics of crystallization and glass formation; viscous sintering; thermal stress analysis; optical waveguide fabrication. *Mailing Add:* Tech Staffs Div Corning Glass Works Corning NY 14830

SCHERER, JAMES R, b Kansas City, Mo, Dec 31, 31; div; c 5. PHYSICAL CHEMISTRY, VIBRATIONAL SPECTROSCOPY. *Educ:* St Mary's Col, Calif, BS, 53; Univ Minn, PhD(phys chem), 58. *Prof Exp:* Res chemist, Chem Physics Res Lab, Dow Chem Co, Mich, 58-63; RES CHEMIST, WESTERN REGIONAL RES LAB, SCI & EDUC ADMIN-AGR RES, USDA, 63- *Mem:* AAAS; Am Chem Soc; Am Phys Soc; Coblentz Soc (pres, 71-72); Am Optical Soc. *Res:* Molecular infrared and Raman spectroscopy; vibrational assignments; force constant calculations and application of normal coordinate calculations to group frequencies; laboratory data acquisition with digital computers. *Mailing Add:* 1309 Arch St Berkeley CA 94708

SCHERER, KIRBY VAUGHN, JR, b Evansville, Ind, Feb 7, 36; m 61; c 3. ORGANIC CHEMISTRY. *Educ:* Harvard Univ, AB, 57, AM, 59, PhD(chem), 63. *Prof Exp:* Asst prof chem, Univ Calif, Berkeley, 62-67; ASSOC PROF CHEM, UNIV SOUTHERN CALIF, 67- *Concurrent Pos:* Sr scientist, Jet Propulsion Lab, 75- *Mem:* AAAS; Am Chem Soc; Royal Soc Chem. *Res:* Organofluorine chemistry; synthesis and properties of strained ring systems; chlorocarbon derivatives; organic chemistry of nitrogen. *Mailing Add:* Dept of Chem Univ of Southern Calif Los Angeles CA 90007

SCHERER, LEE RICHARD, JR, aeronautical engineering, see previous edition

SCHERER, ROBERT C, b Jersey Shore, Pa, Apr 26, 31; m 54; c 3. ANIMAL ECOLOGY. *Educ:* Haverford Col, BS, 53; Pa State Univ, MS, 63, PhD(zool), 65. *Prof Exp:* Assoc prof, 65-71, PROF ZOOL, LOCK HAVEN STATE COL, 71- *Mem:* Am Fisheries Soc; Ecol Soc Am. *Res:* Population dynamics as applied to fish populations. *Mailing Add:* Div of Natural Sci Lock Haven State Col Lock Haven PA 17745

SCHERER, WILLIAM FRANKLIN, b Buffalo, NY, Aug 2, 25; m 46; c 3. MEDICINE, MICROBIOLOGY. *Educ:* Univ Rochester, MD, 47. *Prof Exp:* Intern internal med, Barnes Hosp, St Louis, 47-48; intern path, Strong Mem Hosp, Rochester, NY, 48-49; asst resident internal med, Univ Hosp, Vanderbilt Univ, 49-50; from instr to prof microbiol, Univ Minn, 50-62; chmn, Dept Microbiol, 62-82, PROF MICROBIOL MED COL, CORNELL UNIV, 62- *Concurrent Pos:* Nat Res Coun fel microbiol, Univ Minn, 50-51; Markle scholar, 53-55 & 57-60. *Mem:* Soc Exp Biol & Med; Am Soc Trop Med & Hyg; Am Asn Path & Bact; Am Asn Immunol; Am Acad Microbiol. *Res:* Virology; animal cell culture. *Mailing Add:* Dept Microbiol Cornell Univ Med Col New York NY 10021

SCHERFIG, JAN W, b Copenhagen, Denmark, Apr 24, 36. ENVIRONMENTAL & CHEMICAL ENGINEERING. *Educ:* Danish Tech Univ, MS, 59; Univ Calif, Berkeley, PhD(sanit eng), 68. *Prof Exp:* Res engr, Danish Defense Res Bd, 60-61; prod engr, Danish Mineral Oil Refinery, 61-63; teacher chem, Technol Inst, Copenhagen, 62-63; res engr, Eng Sci, Inc, Calif, 63-66; res asst, Univ Calif, Berkeley, 66-67; from asst prof to assoc prof, 67-77, chmn environ & resources eng, 70-77, PROF CIVIL & ENVIRON ENG, UNIV CALIF, IRVINE, 77- *Concurrent Pos:* Consult, City of Calexico, Calif, Irvine Ranch Water Dist, Lowry Eng-Sci, Santa Ana, Encibra, Rio de Janeiro & Lowry & Assocs, Santa Ana, 67, City of Laguna Beach, 71. *Mem:* Am Soc Civil Engrs; Am Inst Chem Engrs. *Res:* Eutrophication; marine waste disposal, planning and optimization of water and waste. *Mailing Add:* Sch of Eng Univ of Calif Irvine CA 92664

SCHERGER, DALE ALBERT, b Toledo, Ohio, Aug 22, 49. ENVIRONMENTAL ENGINEERING. *Educ:* Univ Mich, BSE, 71, MSE, 72. *Prof Exp:* Engr, 71-73, sr engr, 73-75, chief engr, 75-77, DIR ENG, ENVIRON CONTROL TECHNOL CORP, 77- *Mem:* Water Pollution Control Fedn; Am Water Resources Asn; Nat Prof Eng Soc. *Res:* Advanced waste treatment technology for industrial and municipal wastes; methods development and implementation for control, cleanup and disposal of hazardous substances; development of techniques for controlling urban non-point source runoff. *Mailing Add:* 3965 Research Park Dr Ann Arbor MI 48104

SCHERK, PETER, b Berlin, Ger, Sept 2, 10; Can citizen; m 46; c 3. GEOMETRY. *Educ:* Univ Göttingen, PhD(geom), 35. *Prof Exp:* From instr to prof math, Univ Sask, 43-59; prof, 59-80, EMER PROF MATH, UNIV TORONTO, 80- *Concurrent Pos:* Ed, Can Math Cong Newsletter, 54-57; ed-in-chief, Can Math Bull, 58-61, managing ed, 61-62; ed-in-chief, Can J Math, 62-67. *Mem:* Fel Royal Soc Can; Am Math Soc; Can Math Cong. *Res:* Projects in the geometry of orders and in the foundations of geometry. *Mailing Add:* Dept of Math Univ of Toronto Toronto ON M5S 1A1 Can

SCHERLAG, BENJAMIN J, b Brooklyn, NY, Oct 31, 32; m 60; c 4. CARDIOVASCULAR PHYSIOLOGY. *Educ:* City Col New York, BS, 54; Brooklyn Col, MA, 61; State Univ NY, PhD(physiol), 63. *Prof Exp:* Asst physiol, State Univ NY Downstate Med Ctr, 56-63; res physiologist, Cardiopulmonary Lab, USPHS Hosp, NY, 65-68; res physiologist, Sect Cardiovasc Dis, Mt Sinai Hosp Greater Miami, 68-74; PROF MED & ADJ PROF PHYSIOL, UNIV OKLA HEALTH SCI CTR, 78-, CARDIOVASC PHYSIOLOGIST, VET ADMIN HOSP, OKLAHOMA CITY, 78- *Concurrent Pos:* NIH fel pharmacol, Col Physicians & Surgeons, Columbia Univ, 63-65; lectr, Brooklyn Col, 60-67; res assoc, Columbia Univ, 65-67; prof med, Med Sch, Univ Miami, 74-78; res physiologist, Vet Admin Hosp, Miami, 74-78. *Mem:* Am Physiol Soc; Am Fedn Clin Res; fel Am Col Cardiol. *Res:* Cardiac electrophysiology; pharmacology. *Mailing Add:* 151F Med Ctr Vet Admin 921 NE 13th St Oklahoma City OK 73104

SCHERLIS, SIDNEY, b Philadelphia, Pa, Dec 14, 14; m 42; c 2. CARDIOVASCULAR DISEASES. *Educ:* Univ Pa, AB, 34; Univ Md, MD, 38; Am Bd Internal Med & Am Bd Cardiovasc Dis, dipl. *Prof Exp:* Intern, Sinai Hosp, 38-39, resident, 39-40; asst cardiol, Johns Hopkins Hosp, 40-42; res asst, Nat Res Coun, 42-69; asst prof med & pediat, 47-70, PROF CARDIOL IN PEDIAT, SCH MED, UNIV MD, BALTIMORE CITY, 70-, ASSOC CLIN PROF ANAT, DENTAL SCH, 80- *Concurrent Pos:* Attend physician, Univ Hosp, 47-; adj attend physician, Sinai Hosp, 47-; consult, US Dept Army, 55-65; chmn, Mayor's Comt Study Heart Dis Among City Employees, Baltimore, 60-62; chmn comt stress, strain & heart dis, Am Heart Asn, 73-77; mem, Am Heart Asn. *Mem:* Am Soc Internal Med; fel AMA; Am Soc Law & Med (pres, 81-); sr mem Am Fedn Clin Res; fel Am Col Physicians. *Res:* Coronary artery disease, especially the role of coronary spasm and neurogenic factors in coronary disease. *Mailing Add:* Ruxton Towers 8415 Bellona Lane Towson MD 21204

SCHERMER, EUGENE DEWAYNE, b Spokane, Wash, June 21, 34; m 58; c 2. ENVIRONMENTAL CHEMISTRY. *Educ:* Eastern Wash State Col, BA, 58; Ore State Univ, MS, 62; La State Univ, PhD(chem), 71. *Prof Exp:* Teacher high schs, Wash, 58-61; INSTR CHEM, GRAYS HARBOR COL, 62- *Concurrent Pos:* Investr, Wash State Dept Ecol, 74-76, co-investr with US Corps Engrs, 75, 79-80. *Mem:* Am Chem Soc. *Res:* The effects of woodwaste leachate on quality of ground and surface waters; effects of dredging on the Grays Harbor Estuary; water quality effects of ocean disposal of dredge spoils. *Mailing Add:* Grays Harbor Col Aberdeen WA 98520

SCHERMER, ROBERT IRA, b Brooklyn, NY, Sept 10, 34; m 58; c 4. NUCLEAR PHYSICS, CRYOGENICS. *Educ:* Cornell Univ, BEngPhys, 56; Mass Inst Technol, PhD(nuclear eng), 61. *Prof Exp:* Res assoc nuclear cryogenics, Brookhaven Nat Lab, 60-62, assoc physicist, 62-65, physicist, 65-70; chmn dept physics, Springfield Tech Community Col, 70-74; mem staff, 74-80, ASST GROUP LEADER, LOS ALAMOS NAT LAB, 80- *Mem:* Am Phys Soc. *Res:* Low temperature physics; experiments with polarized neutrons and nuclear targets; design of superconducting magnets. *Mailing Add:* MS 840 Los Alamos Nat Lab Los Alamos NM 87545

SCHERMERHORN, JOHN W, b NJ, Sept 1, 20; m 45; c 4. PHARMACY, BIONUCLEONICS. *Educ:* Rutgers Univ, BS, 42; Univ Minn, PhD(pharmaceut chem), 49. *Prof Exp:* Assoc prof pharmaceut chem, George Washington Univ, 49-53; prof pharm & chmn dept, Mass Col Pharm, 53-66; prof, Col Pharm, Northeastern Univ, 66-71; dean div health sci, 69-71; PROF HEALTH CARE SCI & DEAN SCH ALLIED HEALTH SCI, HEALTH SCI CTR, UNIV TEX, 71-, INSTR CHMN DEPT HEALTH CARE SCI, 74- *Concurrent Pos:* Consult, 53- *Mem:* AAAS; Am Pharmaceut Asn. *Res:* Pharmaceutical product development. *Mailing Add:* Sch of Allied Health Sci Health Sci Ctr Univ Tex Dallas TX 75235

SCHERPEREEL, DONALD E, b South Bend, Ind, Dec 21, 37; m 60; c 2. METALLURGY, MATERIALS SCIENCE. *Educ:* Univ Notre Dame, BS, 59, MS, 61, PhD(metall, mat sci), 64. *Prof Exp:* Instr metall, Univ Notre Dame, 60-62; asst prof metall & mat sci, Mich State Univ, 64-69; sr res mat scientist, 69-76, DIR MECH SYST RES, RES & ENG CTR, WHIRLPOOL CORP, 76- *Mem:* Am Soc Metals; Am Soc Mech Engrs; Sigma Xi. *Res:* X-ray diffraction; electron microscopy; research management; product simulation; automated design; structural analysis. *Mailing Add:* Whirlpool Res & Eng Ctr Monte Rd Benton Harbor MI 49022

SCHERR, CHARLES W, b Philadelphia, Pa, Mar 19, 26; m 52, 70; c 2. PHYSICS. *Educ:* Univ Pa, BS, 49; Univ Chicago, MS, 51, PhD(chem physics), 54. *Prof Exp:* Res assoc physics, Univ Chicago, 54-56; from asst prof to assoc prof, 56-66, PROF PHYSICS, UNIV TEX, AUSTIN, 66- *Mem:* Am Phys Soc. *Res:* Quantum mechanical investigation of atomic and molecular structure. *Mailing Add:* Dept Physics Univ Tex Austin TX 78712

SCHERR, DAVID DELANO, b Columbia, Mo, Oct 15, 34; m 58; c 3. ORTHOPEDIC SURGERY, MICROBIOLOGY. *Educ:* Univ Mo-Columbia, BA, 56, MD, 59; Univ Iowa, MS, 63, PhD(microbiol), 66; Am Bd Orthop Surg, dipl, 69. *Prof Exp:* Staff orthop surg, David Grant Med Ctr, Travis AFB, Calif, 67-69; asst prof orthop surg & microbiol, Sch Med, Univ Mo-Columbia, 69-73, assoc prof, 73-75. *Mem:* Am Soc Microbiol; Am Acad Orthop Surg; Orthop Res Soc; Asn Acad Surg; AMA. *Res:* Activity of antibiotics in clinical uses; role of autoimmune mechanisms in rheumatic diseases. *Mailing Add:* 1111 Madison St Jefferson City MO 65101

SCHERR, GEORGE HARRY, b New York, NY, Dec 30, 20; m 44; c 3. MICROBIOLOGY. *Educ:* Queens Col, NY, BS, 41; Univ Ky, MS, 49, PhD(bact), 51. *Prof Exp:* Bacteriologist, City Dept Health, New York, 41-42; chemist, Calco Chem Div, Am Cyanamid Co, 43-44 & 45-48; asst prof microbiol, Sch Med, Creighton Univ, 51-54; asst prof bact, Col Med, Univ Ill, 54-59; vpres & dir res, Consol Labs, Inc, Ill, 59-69; dir, Colab Labs, Inc, Ill, 69-71; pres, Mat & Technol Syst, Inc, 71-72; PRES, TECHNAM, INC, 72- *Concurrent Pos:* Community prof environ sci, Governors State Univ, 73- *Mem:* AAAS; Am Soc Microbiol; Soc Indust Microbiol; Genetics Soc Am; Mycol Soc Am. *Res:* Immunology and infectious disease; effect of carcinogens on microorganisms; effect of hormones on infectious diseases; microbial genetics. *Mailing Add:* Technam Inc 2405 Bond St Park Forest IL 60466

SCHERR, HARVEY MURRAY, b Pittsburgh, Pa, Aug 6, 32; m 54; c 3. ELECTRONIC ENGINEERING, MECHANICAL ENGINEERING. *Educ:* NY Univ, BME, 57, BEE, 62. *Prof Exp:* Prin engr analog comput design, Ford Instrument Co, 56-64; dept dep weapon syst eng, 64-74, dir testing & eval, 74-76, TECH DIR, NAVAL SHIP WEAPONS ENG STA, 76- *Concurrent Pos:* Chmn, Prof Coun Scientists & Engrs, 75-77. *Mem:* Am Preparedness Asn. *Mailing Add:* 1406 Feather Ave Thousand Oaks CA 91360

SCHERR, LAWRENCE, b New York, NY, Nov 6, 28; m 54; c 2. INTERNAL MEDICINE, CARDIOLOGY. *Educ:* Cornell Univ, AB, 50, MD, 57. *Prof Exp:* From asst to assoc prof, 58-71, PROF MED, MED COL, CORNELL UNIV, 71-, ASSOC DEAN, 70-; DIR DEPT MED, NORTH SHORE UNIV HOSP, 67- *Concurrent Pos:* NY Heart Asn fel, Med Col, Cornell Univ, 59-60; Am Heart Asn teaching scholar, 66-67; from intern to chief resident, Cornell Med Div, Bellevue Hosp & Mem Ctr, 57-61, co-dir cardiorenal lab & asst vis physician, 61-63, assoc vis physician, 63-65, vis physician, 66-67, dir cardiol & renal unit, 63-67; physician to outpatients, NY Hosp, 61-63, from asst attend to attend, 63-; attend, Manhattan Vet Admin Hosp, 64-69; asst attend, Mem Hosp, 66-69, consult, 69-; career scientist, Health Res Coun New York, 62-66; fel coun clin cardiol, Am Heart Asn; chmn, NY State Bd Med, 73-75; trustee, Nassau Acad Med, 74-; chmn, Res Reveiw Comt, Int Med, 80-82. *Mem:* Fel Am Col Physicians; Am Fedn Clin Res; AMA. *Res:* Internal medicine, including cardiovascular and renal disease and fluid and electrolyte problems. *Mailing Add:* North Shore Univ Hosp Manhasset NY 11030

SCHERRER, JOSEPH HENRY, b Chicago, Ill, Sept 5, 31; m 60; c 3. POLYMER CHEMISTRY. *Educ:* DePaul Univ, BS, 53; Univ Kans, PhD(org chem), 57. *Prof Exp:* Res chemist, Spencer Chem Co, 57-64; RES CHEMIST, COOK PAINT & VARNISH CO, 64- *Mem:* Am Chem Soc; Royal Soc Chem. *Res:* Synthesis of organic nitrogen compounds. *Mailing Add:* Cook Paint & Varnish Co PO Box 389 Kansas City MO 64141

SCHERRER, RENE, b Boulogne, France, June 15, 32. MICROBIOLOGY. *Educ:* Univ Lausanne, dipl med, 58; Univ Basel, Dr Med, 61. *Prof Exp:* Third asst, Inst Microbiol, Univ Basel, 59-60, second asst, 60-63; res assoc microbiol, Univ Mich, 63-65; from instr to asst prof, Mich State Univ, 65-72; CONTRIB SCIENTIST, WESTERN REGIONAL RES CTR, AGR RES SERV, USDA, BERKELEY, 72- *Concurrent Pos:* Supvr clin diag lab, Inst Microbiol, Univ Basel, 59-63. *Mem:* AAAS; Am Soc Microbiol; Am Soc Cell Biol; Electron Micros Soc Am; Brit Soc Gen Microbiol. *Res:* Chemical, morphological and molecular ultrastructures of bacteria; biophysical cytology; scanning and transmission; electron microscopy; x-ray microanalysis of microbial substances; resistance of bacterial spores; cell wall structure. *Mailing Add:* Western Regional Res Ctr USDA Berkeley CA 94710

SCHERRER, ROBERT ALLAN, b Sacramento, Calif, Nov 21, 32; m 54; c 4. ORGANIC CHEMISTRY. *Educ:* Univ Calif, BS, 54; Univ Ill, PhD(chem), 58. *Prof Exp:* Assoc res chemist, Parke, Davis & Co, 58-61, res chemist, 61-66; sr med chemist, Minn Mining & Mfg Co, 66-69, res specialist, 69-72, SR RES SPECIALIST, RIKER LABS DIV, 3M CO, 72- *Mem:* Am Chem Soc. *Res:* Synthetic medicinal chemistry; antiarthritic agents; regression analysis. *Mailing Add:* Riker Labs 3M Co 3M Ctr 270-25 St Paul MN 55144

SCHERTZ, CLETUS E, b El Paso, Ill, Apr 12, 30; m 58; c 5. AGRICULTURAL ENGINEERING. *Educ:* Univ Ill, Urbana, BS(agr sci) & BS(agr eng), 54; Iowa State Univ, PhD(agr eng & theoret & appl mech), 62. *Prof Exp:* Asst prof agr eng, Univ Calif, Davis, 62-67; assoc prof, 67-71, PROF AGR ENG, UNIV MINN, ST PAUL, 71- *Mem:* Am Soc Agr Engrs. *Res:* Machines for harvest of food and fiber crops. *Mailing Add:* Dept of Agr Eng Univ of Minn St Paul MN 55101

SCHERTZ, KEITH FRANCIS, b El Paso, Ill, Feb 25, 27; m 54; c 6. CYTOGENETICS. *Educ:* Univ Ill, BS, 49, MS, 50; Cornell Univ, PhD(plant breeding), 57. *Prof Exp:* Geneticist, Fed Exp Sta, Agr Res Serv, PR, 57-59, GENETICIST, DEPT SOIL & CROP SCI, TEX A&M UNIV, USDA, 60- *Mem:* AAAS; Genetics Soc Am; Am Soc Agron; Crop Sci Soc. *Res:* Genetics and cytogenetics of sorghum, apomixis, reproductive behavior and sterility systems. *Mailing Add:* Dept of Soil & Crop Sci Tex A&M Univ College Station TX 77843

SCHERY, ROBERT WALTER, b St Louis, Mo, Mar 12, 17; m 41; c 2. BOTANY. *Educ:* Wash Univ, AB, 38, MS, 40, PhD(bot), 42. *Prof Exp:* Asst bot, Wash Univ, 40-42, from instr to asst prof, 42-51; botanist, Monsanto Chem Co, 51-54 & Scott Co, 54-58; DIR, LAWN INST, 58- *Concurrent Pos:* Asst, Mo Bot Garden, 38-46, res assoc, 46-51; assoc field technician, Rubber Develop Corp, Brazil, 43-44; sr field technician, 45-46. *Mem:* AAAS; Am Soc Econ Bot; Am Soc Agron; Am Soc Hort Sci; Ecol Soc Am. *Res:* Taxonomy of Malvaviscus; flora of Panama; economic botany textbooks and horticultural books and encyclopedias. *Mailing Add:* 1005 W Fifth St Marysville OH 43040

SCHERY, STEPHEN DALE, b Rio de Janeiro, Brazil, July 1, 45; US citizen. NUCLEAR PHYSICS, NATURAL RADIOACTIVITY. *Educ:* Ohio State Univ, BS, 67; Univ Ark, MS, 70; Univ Colo, PhD(physics), 73. *Prof Exp:* Asst prof physics, Kenyon Col, 73-74, marine sci, Tex A&M Univ Galveston, 74-79; ASST PROF PHYSICS & RES PHYSICIST, NMEX INST MINING & TECHNOL, 79- *Concurrent Pos:* Vis prof & consult, Cyclotron Lab, Mich State Univ, 75-78; prin investr, NSF, 77-79. *Mem:* Am Phys Soc; Am Geophys Union. *Res:* Experimental nuclear physics with specialty in neutron time-of-flight measurements; natural radioactivity in Earth and atmospheric science applications. *Mailing Add:* Dept Physics NMex Inst Mining & Technol Socorro NM 87801

SCHERZ, JAMES PHILLIP, b Rice Lake, Wis, May 12, 37; m 62; c 1. CIVIL ENGINEERING. *Educ:* Univ Wis, BS, 59, MS, 61, PhD(civil eng), 67. *Prof Exp:* Instr civil eng, 65-66, res asst, 66-67, from asst prof to assoc prof, 67-77, PROF CIVIL & ENVIRON ENG, INST ENVIRON STUDIES, UNIV WIS-MADISON, 77- *Concurrent Pos:* Aerial monitoring systs consult, 71- *Res:* Remote sensing to include water quality analysis, especially with special photography; surveying of prehistoric calendon sites. *Mailing Add:* Dept of Civil Eng Univ of Wis Madison WI 53706

SCHETKY, L(AURENCE) M(CDONALD), b Baguio, Philippines, July 15, 22; m 68; c 1. METALLURGY, CHEMICAL ENGINEERING. *Educ:* Rensselaer Polytech Inst, BChE, 43, MMetE, 48, PhD(metall), 53. *Prof Exp:* Instr metall, Rensselaer Polytech Inst, 46-53; mem res staff, Mass Inst Technol, 53-56, dir mat res, Instrumentation Lab, 56-59; vpres & tech dir, Alloyd Electronics Corp, Mass, 59-63; TECH DIR METALL, INT COPPER RES ASN, INC, 63- *Concurrent Pos:* Lectr, Rensselaer Polytech Inst & Mass Inst Technol; US rep, Int Metall Cong, 53; World Exchange Lectr, Am Foundrymen's Soc, 67. *Mem:* Am Soc Metals; Am Inst Mining, Metall & Petrol Engrs; Am Phys Soc; Soc Naval Archit & Marine Engrs; Am Welding Soc. *Res:* Physical metallurgy; materials problems in instrumentation; metrology; vapor phase theory; welding and joining; copper research technology. *Mailing Add:* Int Copper Res Asn Inc 708 Third Ave New York NY 10017

SCHETTLER, PAUL DAVIS, JR, b Salt Lake City, Utah, Mar 31, 37; m 66; c 2. PHYSICAL CHEMISTRY. *Educ:* Univ Utah, BS, 58; Yale Univ, PhD(phys chem), 64. *Prof Exp:* Fel, Univ Utah, 63-66; teaching intern chem, Antioch Col, 66-67; assoc prof, 67-78, chmn dept, 75-78, PROF CHEM, JUNIATA COL, 76- *Mem:* Am Chem Soc. *Res:* Metal ammonia solutions; particularly liquid phase separation and electrical properties; theory of gas chromatography; gas bearing shales. *Mailing Add:* Dept Chem Juniata Col Huntingdon PA 16652

SCHETZ, JOSEPH A, b Orange, NJ, Oct 19, 36; m 59; c 4. AEROSPACE & OCEAN ENGINEERING. *Educ:* Webb Inst Naval Archit, BS, 58; Princeton Univ, MSE, 60, MA, 61, PhD(mech eng), 62. *Prof Exp:* Sr scientist, Gen Appl Sci Lab, NY, 61-64; assoc prof aerospace eng, Univ Md, College Park, 64-69; PROF AEROSPACE & OCEAN ENG & CHMN DEPT, VA POLYTECH INST & STATE UNIV, 69- *Concurrent Pos:* Consult, Appl Physics Lab, Johns Hopkins Univ, 64- *Mem:* Am Inst Aeronaut & Astronaut; Am Soc Mech Engrs; fel Am Soc Mech Engrs; Soc Naval Architects & Marine Engrs. *Res:* Fluid dynamics; ocean engineering; combustion; wind energy. *Mailing Add:* Dept Aerospace & Ocean Eng Va Polytech Inst & State Univ Blacksburgh VA 24061

SCHETZEN, MARTIN, b New York, NY, Feb 10, 28. ELECTRICAL ENGINEERING. *Educ:* NY Univ, BEE, 51; Mass Inst Technol, SM, 54, ScD(elec eng), 61. *Prof Exp:* Electronic scientist, Nat Bur Standards, 51-52; asst microwaves, Res Lab Electronics, Mass Inst Technol, 52-54; engr, Appl Physics Lab, Johns Hopkins Univ, 54-56; asst elec eng, Mass Inst Technol, 56-58, commun & nonlinear theory, Res Lab Electronics, 58-60, instr elec eng, 60-61, asst prof elec eng & staff mem, Res Lab Electronics, 61-65; assoc prof, 65-69, PROF ELEC ENG, NORTHEASTERN UNIV, 69- *Concurrent Pos:* Consult, Atlantic Refining Co, Tex, 61-66, Instrumentation Lab, Mass Inst Technol, 64-71 & Radio Corp Am, Mass, 68-72; vis prof elec eng, Univ Calif, Berkeley, 77-78. *Honors & Awards:* Apollo Achievement Award & Apollo Cert of Commendation, NASA, 70. *Mem:* AAAS; Inst Elec & Electronics Engrs; Sigma Xi. *Res:* Nonlinear and communication theory; analysis and synthesis of nonlinear systems; determination of optimum nonlinear systems. *Mailing Add:* 328 Dana Research Bldg Northeastern Univ Boston MA 02115

SCHETZINA, JAN FREDERICK, b Moundsville, WVa, Nov 29, 40; m 68; c 1. PHYSICS. *Educ:* Gannon Col, BA, 63; Pa State Univ, MS, 65, PhD(physics), 69. *Prof Exp:* Res assoc solid state physics, Pa State Univ, 69-70; asst prof, 70-75, ASSOC PROF PHYSICS, NC STATE UNIV, 75- *Mem:* Am Phys Soc; Am Vacuum Soc. *Res:* Optical and electrical properties of semiconductors. *Mailing Add:* Dept of Physics NC State Univ Raleigh NC 27607

SCHEUCH, DON RALPH, b Seattle, Wash, Sept 12, 18; m 50; c 3. ELECTRICAL ENGINEERING. *Educ:* Univ Calif, BS, 43; Stanford Univ, MA, 46, PhD(elec eng), 49. *Prof Exp:* Res assoc, Radio Res Lab, Harvard Univ, 43-45; sr res engr, SRI Int, 49-51, supvr, 51-53, group head, 53-55, lab mgr, 55-59, asst dir eng, 59-60, exec dir electronics & radio sci, 60-68, vpres eng, 68-69, vpres & chmn, Off Res Opers, 77-80, sr vpres, 77-80; PVT CONSULT, 80- *Concurrent Pos:* Spec consult, US Air Force, 42-45. *Mem:* Sigma Xi; Inst Elec & Electronics Engrs. *Res:* Weapons systems evaluation; lasers; antennas; communications. *Mailing Add:* 430 Golden Oak Dr Portola Valley CA 94025

SCHEUCHENZUBER, H JOSEPH, b Lancaster, Pa, June 4, 44; m 68. BIOMECHANICS, PHYSICAL EDUCATION. *Educ:* West Chester State Col, BS, 68; Pa State Univ, MS, 70; Ind Univ, PhD(human performance), 74. *Prof Exp:* Phys dir, York YMCA, Pa, 68; instr scuba, Pa State Univ, 69-70; instr aquatics, York Col, Pa, 70-72; asst prof biochem, 74-80, ASSOC PROF PHYS EDUC, SPRINGFIELD COL, 80- *Concurrent Pos:* Spec consult acad appln comput sci, Springfield Col, 74- *Mem:* Am Asn Health Phys Educ & Recreation; Am Col Sports Med. *Res:* Biomechanical study of kinetic and kinematic factors present during normal human locomotive movements, and modification of similar abnormal motions based on that information. *Mailing Add:* Springfield Col Box 1726 Springfield MA 01109

SCHEUER, ERNEST MARTIN, b Ger, July 28, 30; US citizen; m 53, 72; c 2. STATISTICS, OPERATIONS RESEARCH. *Educ:* Reed Col, BA, 51; Univ Wash, MS, 54; Univ Calif, Los Angeles, PhD(math), 60. *Prof Exp:* Math statistician, Control Data Corp, Rand Corp, Space Technol Labs & US Naval Ord Test Sta, 51-70; assoc prof, 70-72, PROF MGT SCI, CALIF STATE UNIV, NORTHRIDGE, 72-, PROF MATH, 76- *Mem:* Fel Am Statist Asn; Math Asn Am; Inst Math Statist; Inst Mgt Sci; Int Statist Inst. *Res:* Reliability, theory and applications; statistical distributions; generating random variables for simulations; testing goodness-of-fit; statistical and economic analysis of warranties. *Mailing Add:* Dept of Mgt Sci Calif State Univ Northridge CA 91330

SCHEUER, JAMES, b New York, NY, Feb 21, 31. PHYSIOLOGY, BIOCHEMISTRY. *Educ:* Univ Rochester, BA, 55; Yale Univ, MD, 56. *Prof Exp:* Res assoc, Res Inst Muscle Dis, New York, 62-63; trainee metab & nutrit, Grad Sch Pub Health, Univ Pittsburgh, 63-64, from instr to assoc prof med, Sch Med, 64-72, assoc prof biochem, Fac Arts & Sci, 70-72; assoc prof physiol, 72-78, PROF MED, ALBERT EINSTEIN COL MED, 72-, PROF PHYSIOL, 78-, VCHMN MED, 80-; CHIEF CARDIOL, MONTEFIORE HOSP & MED CTR, 72- *Concurrent Pos:* USPHS fel cardiol, Mt Sinai Hosp, New York, 59; USPHS fel myocardial metab, Cornell Univ, 62-63; USPHS fel biochem, Univ Pittsburgh, 64-65, career develop award myocardial metab, 68-; mem coun circulation, Am Heart Asn; mem, Int Study Group Res Cardiac Metab. *Mem:* Am Soc Clin Invest; Am Physiol Soc; Soc Exp Biol & Med. *Res:* Correlation of biochemistry, metabolism and mechanical function of the heart, with emphasis on myocardial hypoxia, the effects of physical conditioning and the effects of diabetes and uremia. *Mailing Add:* Div Cardiol Montefiore Hosp & Med Ctr New York NY 10467

SCHEUER, PAUL JOSEF, b Heilbronn, Ger, May 25, 15; nat US; m 50; c 4. ORGANIC CHEMISTRY. *Educ:* Northeastern Univ, BS, 43; Harvard Univ, MA, 47, PhD(chem), 50. *Prof Exp:* From asst prof to assoc prof, 50-61, chmn dept, 59-62, PROF CHEM, UNIV HAWAII, 61- *Concurrent Pos:* Vis prof, Univ Copenhagen, 77; J F Toole lectr, Univ New Brunswick, 77; ed, Marine Natural Prod, 78- *Mem:* AAAS; Am Chem Soc; Royal Soc Chem; Swiss Chem Soc. *Res:* Structure of natural products; secondary metabolites of terrestrial plants and marine organisms; marine toxins. *Mailing Add:* Dept of Chem Univ of Hawaii 2545 The Mall Honolulu HI 96822

SCHEUING, RICHARD A(LBERT), b Lynbrook, NY, Aug 19, 27; m 50; c 3. AERONAUTICAL ENGINEERING. *Educ:* Mass Inst Technol, SB & SM, 48; NY Univ, PhD, 71. *Prof Exp:* Aerodyn res engr, 48-52, aerodyn res group leader, 52-56, head fluid mech sect, 56-70, dep dir, Res Dept, 61-77, DIR RES DEPT, GRUMMAN AEROSPACE CORP, 77- *Mem:* AAAS; assoc fel Am Inst Aeronaut & Astronaut. *Res:* Fluid dynamics; hypersonics; shock tunnels; magnetohydrodynamics. *Mailing Add:* Res Dept Grumman Aerospace Corp Bethpage NY 11714

SCHEULE, HAROLD J(OSEPH), b Havertown, Pa, Dec 7, 21; m 45; c 3. CHEMICAL ENGINEERING. *Educ:* Bucknell Univ, BS, 43. *Prof Exp:* Process engr, Phillips Petrol Co, 43-46; group supvr, E I du Pont de Nemours & Co, Inc, 46-64, tech mgr, Mid-Continent Region, Okla, 64-67, head chem div, NJ, 67-70, ASST MKT MGR, E I DU PONT DE NEMOURS & CO, INC, 70- *Mem:* Am Chem Soc; Am Inst Chem Eng. *Res:* Additives for improvement of gasoline quality; gasoline treating technology; factors affecting automotive engine performance. *Mailing Add:* 11 Kresswold Lane Woodstown NJ 08098

SCHEUPLEIN, ROBERT J, b May 9, 32; US citizen. PHYSICAL CHEMISTRY, BIOPHYSICS. *Educ:* Univ Miami, BS, 55, MS, 56; Univ Utah, PhD(phys chem), 61. *Prof Exp:* Res assoc dermat, 62-68, assoc biophys, 68-71, PRIN ASSOC DERMAT, HARVARD MED SCH, 71-; ASST PHYS CHEMIST, MASS GEN HOSP, 62- *Honors & Awards:* Ross Coffin Purdy Award, Am Ceramic Soc, 60-61; Lit Award, Soc Cosmetic Chem, 68. *Mem:* Am Ceramic Soc. *Res:* Solid state physics; mechanical properties of corundum; membrane permeability; transport across skin and cellular membranes; theoretical kinetics; structure of hydrated biological membranes. *Mailing Add:* Mass Gen Hospital Fruit St Boston MA 02114

SCHEUSNER, DALE LEE, b Watertown, SDak, Feb 10, 44; m 71; c 2. MICROBIOLOGY, FOOD SCIENCE. *Educ:* SDak State Univ, BS, 66; NC State Univ, MS, 68; Mich State Univ, PhD(food sci), 72. *Prof Exp:* RES MICROBIOLOGIST, S C JOHNSON & SON INC, 72- *Mem:* Am Soc Microbiol; Inst Food Technologists; Soc Indust Microbiol. *Res:* Methods development and application of environmental microbiology and microbial decontamination, especially as applied to health care and food processing facilities. *Mailing Add:* 4625 N Green Bay Rd Racine WI 53404

SCHEVE, BERNARD JOSEPH, b Cincinnati, Ohio, July 2, 45; m 69; c 2. PHOTOCHEMISTRY, RADIATION CHEMISTRY. *Educ:* Xaiver Univ, Ohio, BS, 67, MS, 68; Mich State Univ, PhD(photochem), 74. *Prof Exp:* Asst chemist drug chem, Merrell Nat Labs, Richardson Merrell Inc, 71-73; res chemist, 74-80, SR RES CHEMISTS, HERCULES INC, 80- *Mem:* Am Chem Soc; AAAS; NY Acad Sci. *Res:* Polymer modification; free radical chemistry; photo- polymers; polysaccharides; polyole fins; terpenes. *Mailing Add:* Hercules Res Ctr Lancaster Pike Wilmington DE 19899

SCHEVE, LARRY GERARD, b Palo Alto, Calif, Mar 1, 50. BIOCHEMISTRY, CELL BIOLOGY. *Educ:* Seattle Pac Univ, BS, 72; Univ Calif, Riverside, PhD(biochem), 76. *Prof Exp:* Res asst biochem, Dept Surg, Vet Admin Hosp, Martinez, Calif, 77; lectr, Dept Chem, 77-79, asst prof, 79-81, ASSOC PROF CHEM, CALIF STATE UNIV, 81- *Mem:* Am Chem Soc; Sigma Xi; NY Acad Sci; Am Sci Affil. *Res:* Biochemistry of peroxidases (thyroid peroxidase and myeloperoxidase of the leukocyte); isolation and purification of membrane-bound proteins. *Mailing Add:* Dept of Chem Calif State Univ Hayward CA 94542

SCHEVING, LAWRENCE EINAR, b Hensel, NDak, Oct 20, 20; m 49; c 4. ANATOMY, BIOLOGY. *Educ:* DePaul Univ, BS, 49, MS, 50; Loyola Univ Ill, PhD(anat), 57. *Prof Exp:* Asst embryol, DePaul Univ, 49-50; from instr biol sci to assoc prof & chmn dept, Lewis Col, 50-57; from instr to prof anat, Chicago Med Sch, 57-66; prof, Sch Med, La State Univ, New Orleans, 67-70; REBSAMEN PROF ANAT SCI, COL MED, UNIV ARK, LITTLE ROCK, 70- *Concurrent Pos:* Instr, Sch Nursing, Garfield Park Hosp, 49-50. *Honors & Awards:* Von Humboldt Sr Scientist Award, 73. *Mem:* Int Soc Chronobiol (secy-treas); Am Asn Anat. *Res:* Chronobiology. *Mailing Add:* Dept of Anat Univ of Ark Col of Med Little Rock AR 72201

SCHEWE, PHILLIP FRANK, b Evanston, Ill, July 7, 50. HIGH ENERGY PHYSICS. *Educ:* Univ Ill, BS & MS, 72; Mich State Univ, BA, 77, PhD(physics), 78. *Prof Exp:* Asst physicist, Brookhaven Nat Lab, 78-80; WITH AM INST PHYSICS, 80- *Mem:* Am Phys Soc. *Res:* Deep inelastic lepton scattering; development of superconducting magnets. *Mailing Add:* Am Inst Physics 335 E 45th St New York NY 10071

SCHEXNAYDER, MARY ANNE, b La, Nov 6, 48. ORGANIC CHEMISTRY, PHOTOCHEMISTRY. *Educ:* La State Univ, BS, 70; Rice Univ, PhD(chem), 74. *Prof Exp:* NIH trainee, Inst Lipid Res, Baylor Col Med, 75; RES CHEMIST, HERCULES INC, 75- *Mem:* Am Chem Soc. *Res:* Free radical chemistry; organic and inorganic photochemistry. *Mailing Add:* Res Ctr Hercules Inc Wilmington DE 19899

SCHEY, HARRY MORITZ, b Chicago, Ill, Feb 20, 30. BIOSTATISTICS. *Educ:* Northwestern Univ, BS, 50; Harvard Univ, AM, 51; Univ Ill, PhD, 54. *Prof Exp:* Asst physics, Univ Ill, 52-54; sr physicist, Theoret Physics Div, Lawrence Livermore Lab, Univ Calif, 54-66; physicist, Educ Res Ctr, Mass Inst Technol, 66-73, co-dir, Proj, CALC, 73-75; fel, Dept Biostatist, Univ NC, Chapel Hill, 75-77; ASST PROF BIOSTATIST, BOWMAN GRAY SCH MED, WAKE FOREST UNIV, 78- *Mem:* Am Statist Asn; Biomet Soc. *Res:* Kolmogorov-Smirnov goodness-of-fit tests; clinical studies; renal disease epidemiology; statistical methods in psychiatric diagnosis; obesity in children; leukemia clustering; blood pressure measurement techniques; statistical computing. *Mailing Add:* Dept Family & Comt Med Bowman Gray Sch of Med Winston-Salem NC 27103

SCHEY, JOHN ANTHONY, b Sopron, Hungary, Dec 19, 22; US citizen; m 48; c 1. METAL DEFORMATION PROCESSES, TRIBOLOGY OF METALWORKING. *Educ:* Jozsef Nador Tech Univ, Hungary, dipl, 46; Acad Sci, Budapest, Hungary, PhD(metall), 53. *Prof Exp:* Supt metal works, Steel & Metal Works, Csepel, Budapest, 47-51; reader metals technol, Tech Univ, Miskolic, Hungary, 51-56; supvr fabrication, Res Lab, Brit Aluminum Co, 56-62; metall adv metal working, IIT Res Inst, Chicago, 62-68; prof metall eng, Univ Ill, Chicago Circle, 68-74; PROF MECH ENG, UNIV WATERLOO, ONT, 74- *Concurrent Pos:* Mem, Metalworking Processes Comt, Mat Adv Bd/Nat Acad Sci, 67-70; consult, 16 indust orgns, 68-; NAm ed, J Mech Working Technol, 77-; course dir, Forging Indust Asn, Die Design Inst, 78-; assoc ed, J Lubrication Technol, Am Soc Mech Engrs, 81- *Honors & Awards:* W H A Robertson Medal, Inst Metals, London, Eng, 66; Gold Medal Award, Soc Mfg Engrs, 74. *Mem:* Nat Acad Eng; Am Soc Metals; Soc Mfg Engrs; Sigma Xi. *Res:* Interactions between material properties and process conditions in metalworking processes, friction, lubrication and wear; development of new manufacturing processes; application of theory to realistic conditions. *Mailing Add:* Dept Mech Eng Univ Waterloo Waterloo ON N2L 3G1 Can

SCHIAFFINO, SILVIO STEPHEN, b Brooklyn, NY, Nov 1, 27; m 54; c 2. BIOCHEMISTRY, RESEARCH ADMINISTRATION. *Educ:* Georgetown Univ, BS, 47, MS, 48, PhD(biochem), 56. *Prof Exp:* Lab instr chem, Georgetown Univ, 46-48; biochemist, Div Nutrit, US Food & Drug Admin, Wash, DC, 48-50 & 54-60 & Chem Sect, Hazleton Labs, Inc, 60-61; scientist adminr, Nat Cancer Inst, 61-64, asst chief, Res Grants Rev Br, 64-69, chief, 69-72, assoc dir sci rev, 72-78, DEP DIR, DIV RES GRANTS, NIH, 78- *Mem:* AAAS; Soc Exp Biol & Med; Am Inst Nutrit. *Res:* Biochemistry and microbiology of nutritionally important substances, especially vitamins, amino acids and proteins; stability of vitamins; clinical chemistry; food additives. *Mailing Add:* Div Res Grants NIH Bethesda MD 20014

SCHIAGER, KEITH JEROME, b Hot Springs, SDak, Mar 29, 30; m 51; c 4. ENVIRONMENTAL HEALTH, HEALTH PHYSICS. *Educ:* Colo Agr & Mech Col, BS, 56; Univ Mich, MPH, 62, PhD(environ health), 64. *Prof Exp:* Health physicist, Argonne Nat Lab, 57-61; assoc prof radiation biol, Colo State Univ, 64-73; alt group leader environ studies, Los Alamos Sci Lab, 73-75; prof health physics, Univ Pittsburgh, 75-78; PRES, ALARA, INC, 78- *Mem:* AAAS; Am Nuclear Soc; Sigma Xi; Health Physics Soc; Am Indust Hyg Asn. *Res:* Radiological health; environmental radiation; inhalation exposure from radon progeny. *Mailing Add:* Alara Inc PO Box 590 Ft Collins CO 80522

SCHIAVELLI, MELVYN DAVID, b Chicago, Ill, Aug 8, 42; m 66. PHYSICAL ORGANIC CHEMISTRY. *Educ:* DePaul Univ, BS, 64; Univ Calif, Berkeley, PhD(chem), 67. *Prof Exp:* Res assoc chem, Mich State Univ, 67-68; asst prof, 68-71, assoc prof, 71-80, PROF CHEM, COL WILLIAM & MARY, 80-, CHMN DEPT, 78- *Mem:* Am Chem Soc; Royal Soc Chem. *Res:* Secondary isotope effects; acid-catalysis; vinyl cations. *Mailing Add:* Dept Chem Col William & Mary Williamsburg VA 23185

SCHICK, JEROME DAVID, b Pontiac, Mich, Jan 23, 38; m 66; c 2. CHEMISTRY, PHYSICS. *Educ:* Wheaton Col, BS, 60; Wayne State Univ, MS, 65, PhD(phys chem), 68. *Prof Exp:* Res chemist, Henry Ford Hosp, Detroit, Mich, 60-63; proj chemist, Bendix Res Labs, 66-68; res chemist, Air Force Avionics Lab, Wright-Patterson AFB, 68-69; ADV ENGR SEMICONDUCTOR DEVICES, IBM CORP, HOPEWELL JUNCTION, 69- *Mem:* Am Chem Soc; Electrochem Soc; Creation Res Soc. *Res:* Semiconductor devices and materials; electron spectroscopy; scanning electron microscopy; auger spectrometry; integrated circuits processing and failure studies; electron beam induced current; transistor and junction charaterization. *Mailing Add:* Kuchler Dr La Grangeville NY 12540

SCHICK, KENNETH LEONARD, b New York, NY, Feb 20, 30; m 57; c 3. SOLID STATE PHYSICS, BIOPHYSICS. *Educ:* Columbia Univ, BA, 51; Rutgers Univ, PhD(physics), 59. *Prof Exp:* Physicist, US Naval Air Missile Test Ctr, 51-52; from asst prof to assoc prof, 59-74, chmn dept, 71-77, PROF PHYSICS, UNION COL, NY, 74- *Concurrent Pos:* Vis res prof, State Univ Leiden, 65-66 & 72-73; NATO & NSF sr fel, 67; fel, Weizmann Inst, Israel, 79-80. *Mem:* Am Asn Physics Teachers. *Res:* Magnetic resonance; membrane structure in living systems. *Mailing Add:* Dept of Physics Union Col Schenectady NY 12308

SCHICK, LEE HENRY, b Philadelphia, Pa, Nov 23, 35; m 61; c 3. THEORETICAL NUCLEAR PHYSICS. *Educ:* Univ Pa, BS, 56; Univ Colo, MA, 58, PhD(theoret nuclear physics), 61. *Prof Exp:* Lectr math, Univ Birmingham, 61-63; res assoc, Univ Minn, 63-65; asst prof, Univ Southern Calif, 65-70; assoc prof, 70-74, PROF PHYSICS, UNIV WYO, 74- *Mem:* Am Phys Soc. *Res:* Application of information-theory and scattering theory to geophysical problems. *Mailing Add:* Dept of Physics & Astron Univ of Wyo Laramie WY 82070

SCHICK, LLOYD ALAN, b Bluffton, Ohio, Mar 7, 45; m 75; c 2. BIOCHEMISTRY, CHEMISTRY. *Educ:* Ohio Northern Univ, BA, 66; Purdue Univ, MS, 68; Univ Notre Dame, PhD(biochem), 74. *Prof Exp:* Anal chemist, Ind State Chemist's Lab, 66-68; asst res scientist, 68-71, assoc res scientist, 71-74, res scientist, 74-77, SR RES SCIENTIST, AMES DIV MILES LABS, 77- *Concurrent Pos:* Res Award, Ohio Heart Asn, 65-66. *Mem:* Am Chem Soc; Am Soc Microbiol; Am Asn Blood Banks. *Res:* Medical diagnostics; immunoassay; protein purification techniques; thyroid diagnostics; enzymology; hemolytic and fibrinolytic pathways. *Mailing Add:* Ames Div Miles Labs PO Box 70 Elkhart IN 46515

SCHICK, MARTIN J, b Prague, Czech, Oct 20, 18; nat US; div; c 2. COLLOID CHEMISTRY. *Educ:* Carnegie Inst Technol, BS, 42; Polytech Inst Brooklyn, PhD(chem), 48. *Prof Exp:* Res chemist, Shell Develop Co, 42-45 & 48-58; sr res assoc, Res & Develop Ctr, Lever Bros Co, 58-66; prin scientist, Cent Res Lab, Interchem Corp, Clifton, 66-69; res mgr, Surfactant & Org Chem Lab, 69-78, SR SCIENTIST, PROCESS CHEM DIV, DIAMOND SHAMROCK CORP, 78- *Mem:* Am Chem Soc. *Res:* Surface and polymer chemistry; nonionic surfactants; surfactant synthesis; friction and lubrication of synthetic fibers. *Mailing Add:* Process Chem Div Shamrock Corp 350 Mt Kemble Ave Morristown NJ 07960

SCHICK, PAUL KENNETH, b Czech, Oct 12, 32; US citizen; m 62; c 2. HEMATOLOGY, ONCOLOGY. *Educ:* Boston Univ, MD, 61. *Prof Exp:* Intern & resident med, Kings County Hosp, Brooklyn, NY, 61-63; resident med, New York Med Col, 63-65; pvt pract, 65-69; hemat trainee, Montefiore Hosp, Bronx, 69-71; asst prof, 71-76, assoc prof med, 76-79, ASSOC PROF BIOCHEM, MED COL PA, 79-; PROF MED, SCH MED, TEMPLE UNIV, 82- *Concurrent Pos:* Assoc prof med, Sch Med, Temple Univ, 79-82. *Mem:* Int Soc Thrombosis & Hemostasis; fel Am Col Physicians; Am Soc Hemat; Sigma Xi; Am Fedn Clin Res. *Res:* Understanding the structure and function of platelet membranes in order to define the role of platelets in hemostasis and to develop anti-platelet drugs for the prevention of thrombosis; investigation of Megakaryocyte maturation and biochemistry. *Mailing Add:* Temple Univ Health Sci Ctr 3400 N Broad St Philadelphia PA 19140

SCHICKEDANTZ, PAUL DAVID, b Columbus, Ohio, Aug 20, 31; m 57; c 4. ORGANIC CHEMISTRY, ANALYTICAL BIOCHEMISTRY. *Educ:* Oberlin Col, AB, 53; Ohio State Univ, PhD(org chem), 59. *Prof Exp:* Res chemist, Am Cyanamid Co, 59-61; res chemist, Consumer Prod Div, Union Carbide Co, WVa, 61-63 & Chem & Plastics Div, 63-67; SR RES CHEMIST, LORILLARD DIV, LOEW'S THEATERS, INC, 67- *Mem:* Am Chem Soc; Sigma Xi. *Res:* Synthesis and properties of bridgehead nitrogen compounds; stain repellant and wash and wear textile finishes; synthesis of S-triazines, insect repellents, and condensation polymers; liquid chromatographic analysis of polycyclic aromatic hydrocarbons in tobacco smoke; analysis of urinary drug metabolites; cigarette flavor chemistry. *Mailing Add:* 2809 Watauga Dr Greensboro NC 27401

SCHIDLOVSKY, GEORGE, b Kenitra, French Morocco, Jan 27, 27; nat US; m 53; c 6. ELECTRON MICROSCOPY. *Educ:* NY Univ, BS, 53. *Prof Exp:* Asst cytol, Brookhaven Nat Lab, NY, 54-55; asst electron micros, Rockefeller Inst, 55-58; scientist photosynthetic apparatus, Res Inst Advan Study, 58-63; head electron micros, Pfizer, Inc, 63-75; sr scientist electron micros, Frederick Cancer Res Ctr, 75-77; staff scientist & head electron microscopist, 77-80, SR SCI ASSOC, MED DEPT, BROOKHAVEN NAT LAB, 80- *Concurrent Pos:* Assoc ed, Bull Electron Micros Soc Am, 79- *Mem:* Am Asn Cancer Res; Electron Micros Soc Am; Microbeam Anal Soc. *Res:* RNA virus-cancer etiology; inhalation toxicology; electron probe elemental analysis. *Mailing Add:* Brookhaven Nat Lab Med Dept Upton NY 11973

SCHIEBEL, HERMAN MAX, b Baltimore, Md, Jan 18, 09; m 69; c 1. SURGERY. *Educ:* Johns Hopkins Univ, BA, 29, MD, 33; Am Bd Surg, dipl, 41. *Prof Exp:* From instr to asst prof, 41-60, assoc clin prof, 60-75, CLIN PROF SURG, SCH MED, UNIV NC, 75- *Concurrent Pos:* Attend surgeon, Duke Hosp, 39-; chief surg, Lincoln Hosp, 44-74; sr attend surgeon, Watts Hosp, 45-, chief surg, 47-52; chief surg, John Umstead State Hosp, 52-67; mem nat bd dirs, Am Cancer Soc, 56-68; instr surg, Sch Med, Duke Univ, 34-50, assoc surg, 50-76, assoc clin prof surg, 76- attend surgeon, Dorothea Dix Hosp, Raleigh, NC, 68- *Mem:* Am Col Surg. *Res:* Peripheral vascular diseases; cancer; extension of cancer surgery; combination of cancer surgery with drug and radiation therapy. *Mailing Add:* 1202 Broad St Durham NC 27705

SCHIEBLE, JACK H, b Ionia, Mich, Apr 3, 25; m 47; c 2. VIROLOGY. *Educ:* Mich State Univ, BS, 49; Univ Mich, PhD(virol), 62. *Prof Exp:* RES VIROLOGIST, VIRAL & RICKETTSIAL DIS LAB, CALIF STATE DEPT PUB HEALTH, 62- *Concurrent Pos:* Consult, Cutter Labs, Calif, 64- *Mem:* Am Soc Microbiol. *Res:* Cell virus relationships of oncogenic viruses; biosynthesis of sub-viral components of respiratory syncytial virus and their biological, biochemical and biophysical properties. *Mailing Add:* Viral & Rickettsial Dis Lab Calif State Dept Pub Health Berkeley CA 94704

SCHIEBLER, GEROLD LUDWIG, b Hamburg, Pa, June 20, 28; m 54; c 6. MEDICINE, PEDIATRIC CARDIOLOGY. *Educ:* Franklin & Marshall Col, BS, 50; Harvard Med Sch, MD, 54. *Prof Exp:* Asst prof, 60-63, assoc prof, 63-66, PROF PEDIAT, COL MED, UNIV FLA, 66-, CHMN DEPT, 68- *Concurrent Pos:* Teaching fel med, Harvard Med Sch, 55-56; med fel pediat, Univ Minn Hosps, 56-57; med fel specialist, Med Ctr, Univ Minn, 57-59, med fel, Mayo Clin & Found, 59-60; Nat Heart Inst res fel, 59-60; mem study sect, Coun Rheumatic Fever & Congenital Heart Dis, Am Heart Asn, 61-64. *Mem:* AAAS; Am Acad Pediat; Am Col Cardiol; Am Heart Asn. *Res:* Heart disease in infants and children; cardiovascular physiology. *Mailing Add:* Dept of Pediat Univ of Fla Col of Med Gainesville FL 32610

SCHIEBOUT, JUDITH ANN, b Tampa, Fla, Oct 16, 46. VERTEBRATE PALEONTOLOGY, PALEOECOLOGY. *Educ:* Univ Tex, Austin, BA, 68, MA, 70, PhD(geol), 73. *Prof Exp:* Lectr, San Diego State Univ, 74-76; ASST PROF GEOL, LA STATE UNIV, 76- *Mem:* Soc Vertebrate Paleont; Geol Soc Am; Sigma Xi; Paleont Soc; Soc Econ Paleontologists & Mineralogists. *Res:* Analysis of early Tertiary mammal distribution and paleogeography; relationship between vertebrate taphonomy and fluvial sedimentation; paleoclimatic interpretation of ancient soils. *Mailing Add:* Dept of Geol La State Univ Baton Rouge LA 70803

SCHIEFELBEIN, BENEDICT, inorganic chemistry, electron microscopy, see previous edition

SCHIEFER, H BRUNO, b Cologne, Ger, Aug 25, 29; m 57; c 4. VETERINARY PATHOLOGY. *Educ:* Univ Munich, DVM, 58, PhD(vet path), 65. *Prof Exp:* Res asst vet path, Univ Munich, 58-64, asst prof, 64-66; res assoc prof animal dis, Univ Ct, 66-67; asst prof vet path, Univ Munich, 67-69; assoc prof, 69-71, head dept, 74-77, PROF VET PATH, UNIV SASK, 71-, RES COORDR TOXICOL, 77-, CHMN TOXICOL GROUP, 78- *Concurrent Pos:* Fulbright scholar, 66-67. *Mem:* Europ Soc Vet Path; Soc Toxicol Can; Can Vet Med Asn. *Res:* Pulmonary pathology; mycoses; cardiovascular diseases; neuropathology; diseases of swine; feline leprosy; toxico pathology; mycotoxicoses. *Mailing Add:* Dept of Vet Path Univ of Sask Saskatoon SK S7N 0W0 Can

SCHIEFERSTEIN, GEORGE JACOB, b Buffalo, NY, July 22, 42; m 73; c 1. PHARMACOLOGY. *Educ:* LeMoyne Col, BS, 64; Univ Buffalo, PhD(pharmacol), 70. *Prof Exp:* Pharmacologist, G D Searle, Inc, 68-71 & Wm H Rorer, Inc, 71-72; PHARMACOLOGIST, NAT CTR TOXICOL RES, FOOD & DRUG ADMIN, 72- *Mem:* Soc Toxicol. *Res:* Subchronic and chronic testing of chemical carcinogens in laboratory animals; design, execution and evaluation of results and presentation of test results; preparation of final reports and manuscripts. *Mailing Add:* Div Chem Toxicol Nat Ctr for Toxicol Res Jefferson AR 72079

SCHIEFERSTEIN, ROBERT HAROLD, b Klamath Falls, Ore, May 18, 31; m 50; c 5. PLANT PHYSIOLOGY. *Educ:* Ore State Univ, BS, 54; Iowa State Univ, MS, 55, PhD(plant physiol), 57. *Prof Exp:* Asst plant physiol, Iowa State Univ, 54-56; res assoc, 56-57; tech rep agr chem, Chipman Chem Co, Inc, 57-61, tech mgr, 61-62; plant physiologist, Shell Develop Co, 62-65, supvr herbicides res, 65-67, chief plant physiologist, 67-68, dept head plant physiol, 68-70, supvr pesticide develop, 71, res & develop proj mgr agron prods, 71-72, prod rep, 72-73, tech support rep, 73-77, staff tech serv rep, Shell Chem Co, 77-79, FIELD DEVELOP & TECH SERV REP, SHELL DEVELOP CO, 79- *Mem:* Am Soc Plant Physiol; Weed Sci Soc Am. *Res:* Herbicides; defoliants; plant growth regulators; plant surface wax and cuticle; research and development administration with agricultural chemicals. *Mailing Add:* Shell Develop Co 7846 S Centaur Dr Evergreen CO 80439

SCHIENLE, JAN HOOPS, b Washington, DC, June 20, 45; c 3. ENVIRONMENTAL TOXICOLOGY, INDUSTRIAL TOXICOLOGY. *Educ:* Calif State Univ, Northridge, BS, 74, MS, 76. *Prof Exp:* BIOL SAFETY OFFICER & INDUST HYGIENIST, UNIV CALIF, SANTA BARBARA,

76-; ASST PROF ENVIRON OCCUPATIONAL HEALTH, CALIF STATE UNIV, NORTHRIDGE, 81- *Concurrent Pos:* Environ sound consult, Santa Barbara Coun Bowl Orgn & Pvt developers, 76-; fac, Calif Spec Training Inst, 79-81; mem, Santa Barbara Count Hazardous Mat task Force, 81-, Health Adv Comt, Santa Barbara Coun, 82- *Mem:* Am Indust Hygiene Asn; Am Conf Govt Hygienists; Nat Environ Health Asn. *Mailing Add:* Environ Health & Safety Univ Calif Santa Barbara CA 93106

SCHIERMAN, LOUIS W, b Carlyle, Ill, Feb 16, 26; m 57; c 2. IMMUNOGENETICS. *Educ:* Univ Ill, BS, 51; Iowa State Univ, MS, 61, PhD(genetics, immunol), 62. *Prof Exp:* Res assoc immunogenetics, Iowa State Univ, 62-64; asst prof, 64-65; res assoc, Mt Sinai Hosp, New York, 65-66, asst prof, Mt Sinai Sch Med, 66-68; assoc prof path, New York Med Col, 68-77; PROF, UNIV GA, 77- *Mem:* AAAS; Genetics Soc Am; Am Asn Immunol. *Res:* Relationships of blood groups to histocompatibility; tumor immunology; genetic control of immune responses. *Mailing Add:* Dept Avian Med Univ Ga Athens GA 30605

SCHIESSER, ROBERT H, b Niagara Falls, NY, Jan 12, 37; m 65; c 3. PHYSICAL CHEMISTRY, SURFACE CHEMISTRY. *Educ:* Clarkson Tech, BChE, 58, MChE, 60; Lehigh Univ, PhD(phys chem), 66. *Prof Exp:* Sr res chemist, Rohm and Haas Co, 65-68; SR RES CHEMIST, BETZ LABS, INC, 68- *Mem:* Am Chem Soc. *Res:* Adsorption at solid-liquid interface; polymer solution properties; stability of lyophobic colloids; structure and properties of polyelectrolytes. *Mailing Add:* 1834 Mare Rd Warrington PA 18976

SCHIESSER, W(ILLIAM) E(DWARD), b Willow Grove, Pa, Jan 9, 34; m 58; c 2. CHEMICAL ENGINEERING. *Educ:* Lehigh Univ, BS, 55; Princeton Univ, MA, 58, PhD(chem eng), 60. *Prof Exp:* From asst prof to prof, 60-76, McCANN PROF CHEM ENG, LEHIGH UNIV, 76-, MGR USER SERV, COMPUT CTR, 69- *Concurrent Pos:* Consult, Indust & Govt; mem, Am Automatic Control Coun. *Mem:* Am Inst Chem Engrs; Inst Elec & Electronics Engrs. *Res:* Applied mathematics; systems analysis. *Mailing Add:* Dept of Chem Eng Lehigh Univ Bethlehem PA 18015

SCHIESSL, H(ENRY) W(ILLIAM), b Ingolstadt, Ger, Dec 1, 24; nat US. INORGANIC CHEMISTRY, CHEMICAL ENGINEERING. *Educ:* Cornell Univ, BChE, 50; Univ Heidelberg, DSc, 64. *Prof Exp:* Process design engr, 50-56, asst to dir res & develop, 56-61, res assoc, 64-70, RES MGR, OLIN CORP, 70- *Concurrent Pos:* Mem fac, Univ New Haven. *Mem:* Am Chem Soc; Nat Asn Corrosion Engrs. *Res:* Inorganic chemistry; heavy chemicals; statistical analysis of experimental data; thermochemistry; kinetics; hydrazine chemistry. *Mailing Add:* 79 Parsonage Hill Rd Northford CT 06472

SCHIEVE, JAMES FERDINAND, b Hancock, Mich, Mar 12, 18; m 43; c 5. INTERNAL MEDICINE. *Educ:* Mich State Univ, DVM, 40; Univ Cincinnati, MD, 43. *Prof Exp:* Instr med, Duke Univ, 50-52; from asst to prof, Ohio State Univ, 52-67; asst dean & dir continuing med educ, 67-71, assoc dean & dir continuing med educ, Col Med, Univ Cincinnati, 71-75; assoc dean for hosp affairs, Wright State Univ, 75-76; V PRES MED AFFAIRS, GOOD SAMARITAN HOSP & HEALTH CTR, 76- *Mem:* AMA; fel Am Col Physicians. *Mailing Add:* Good Samaritan Hosp & Health Ctr 2222 Philadelphia Dr Dayton OH 45406

SCHIEVE, WILLIAM, b Portland, Ore, Apr 28, 29; m 52; c 2. THEORETICAL PHYSICS, STATISTICAL MECHANICS. *Educ:* Reed Col, AB, 51; Lehigh Univ, MS, 57, PhD(physics), 59. *Prof Exp:* Asst physics, Lehigh Univ, 51-57; res fel, Bartol Res Found, 57-60; res physicist, US Naval Radiol Defense Lab, 61-67; actg dir statist mech & thermodyn, 69-77; ASSOC PROF PHYSICS, UNIV TEX, AUSTIN, 67- *Concurrent Pos:* Study fel with Prof Prigogine, Free Univ Brussels, 64-65. *Honors & Awards:* Silver Medal, US Naval Radiol Defense Lab, 64. *Mem:* Am Phys Soc. *Res:* Thermal conductivity of insulating crystals; statistical mechanics of phonons; fundamental theory of statistical mechanics; perturbation theory; reversibility; molecular dynamics. *Mailing Add:* Dept of Physics Univ of Tex Austin TX 78712

SCHIEWETZ, D(ON) B(OYD), b Dayton, Ohio, Nov 15, 27; m 56; c 1. CHEMICAL ENGINEERING. *Educ:* Northwestern Univ, BS, 50; Univ Cincinnati, MS, 52, PhD(chem eng), 54. *Prof Exp:* Res engr, 54-59, tech supvr, , 59-63, area supvr, 63-65, plant supt, 66-70, tech supt, 70-73, mfg supt, 73-75, capacity mgr, 75-76, MFG & RES MGR, PLASTICS PROD DIV, PLASTIC PROD & RESINS DEPT, E I DU PONT DE NEMOURS & CO, INC, 76- *Mem:* Am Inst Chem Engrs. *Res:* Polymer science and processing technology; chemical kinetics; process economics; venture analysis. *Mailing Add:* Permasep Prod Plastics Prod Div E I du Pont de Nemours & Co Inc Wilmington DE 19898

SCHIFERL, DAVID, b US citizen. HIGH PRESSURE PHYSICS, SOLID STATE PHYSICS. *Educ:* Univ Chicago, BS, 66, MS, 69, PhD(physics), 75. *Prof Exp:* Res physicist, Dept Geophys Sci, Univ Chicago, 74-75, x-ray consult, 77; vis scientist, Max-Planck Inst Solid Body Res, Stuttgart, W Ger, 75-77; STAFF SCIENTIST, UNIV CALIF, LOS ALAMOS SCI LAB, 77- *Concurrent Pos:* NATO fel, Max Planck Inst Solid Body Res, Stuttgart, 75-76 & Ger Acad Exchange Serv, 76-77. *Res:* Experimental high pressure physics primarily with diamond-anvil cells; theoretical and experimental studies on crystal structure stability; materials, non-destructive testing. *Mailing Add:* Los Alamos Sci Lab PO Box 1663 Los Alamos NM 87545

SCHIFF, ANSHEL J, b Chicago, Ill, Sept 24, 36. EARTHQUAKE ENGINEERING. *Educ:* Purdue Univ, Lafayette, BSME, 58, MSESc, 61, PhD(eng sci), 67. *Prof Exp:* Res asst aeronaut, astronaut & eng sci, 59-67, from asst prof to assoc prof, 67-78, PROF MECH ENG, PURDUE UNIV, WEST LAFAYETTE, 78- *Concurrent Pos:* Consult, Goddard Space Flight Ctr, NASA, 68-; Midwest Appl Sci Corp, 65-; Fed Elec Co, Int Tel & Tel Corp, 71- & precision measurement industs and other indust companies, 75-;

instr indust courses instrumentation & measurements, 74- *Mem:* Instrument Soc Am; Am Soc Eng Educ; Am Soc Mech Engrs; Am Soc Civil Engrs; Earthquake Eng Res Inst. *Res:* Design of instumentation for structural dynamics; experimental and analytical studies of dynamic systems; system identification; evaluation of the impact of natural disasters on community services. *Mailing Add:* Sch of Mech Eng Purdue Univ West Lafayette IN 47907

SCHIFF, ERIC ALLAN, b Los Angeles, Calif, Aug 29, 50; m 73; c 1. SEMICONDUCTOR PHYSICS, FAR-INFRARED SPECTROSCOPY. *Educ:* Calif Inst Technol, BS, 71; Cornell Univ, PhD(physics), 79. *Prof Exp:* Res assoc, James Franck Inst, Univ Chicago, 78-81; ASST PROF, DEPT PHYSICS, SYRACUSE UNIV, 81- *Mem:* Am Phys Soc. *Res:* Electron transport and photocarrier recombination in amorphous semiconductors, especially hydrogenated amorphous silicon; optical and photoconductive characterization of semiconductors. *Mailing Add:* Dept Physics Syracuse Univ Syracuse NY 13210

SCHIFF, GILBERT MARTIN, b Cincinnati, Ohio, Oct 21, 31; m 55; c 2. INFECTIOUS DISEASES, VIROLOGY. *Educ:* Univ Cincinnati, BS, 53, MD, 57. *Prof Exp:* Intern, Univ Hosp, Iowa City, 57-58, resident internal med, 58-59; med officer, Lab Br, Commun Dis Ctr, Ga, 59-61; head tissue cult invest unit, Sect Virol, Perinatal Res Br, Nat Inst Neurol Dis & Blindness, 61-64; asst prof med & microbiol, 64-70, assoc prof med, 70-73, ASST PROF MICROBIOL, COL MED, UNIV CINCINNATI, 70-, PROF MED, 73-, DIR CLIN VIROL LAB, 64- *Concurrent Pos:* Nat Inst Child Health & Human Develop career res develop award, 64-69; prin investr, USPHS grant, 64-67 & Nat Found res grant, 65-67. *Mem:* AAAS; Am Soc Microbiol; Sigma Xi; Am Fedn Clin Res; Am Pub Health Asn. *Res:* Clinical virology. *Mailing Add:* 520 Chisholm Trail Cincinnati OH 45215

SCHIFF, HAROLD IRVIN, b Kitchener, Ont, June 24, 23; m 48; c 2. PHYSICAL CHEMISTRY. *Educ:* Univ Toronto, BA, 45, MA, 46, PhD(chem), 48. *Prof Exp:* Asst chem, Univ Toronto, 45-48; fel, Nat Res Coun Can, 48-50; from asst prof to prof, McGill Univ, 50-65, dir upper atmosphere chem group, 59-65; prof & chmn dept chem & dir nat sci, 64-66, dean sci, 66-72, PROF CHEM, YORK UNIV, 72-, UNIV PROF, 80- *Concurrent Pos:* Nuffield fel, Cambridge Univ, 59-60; Eskine prof, Univ Canterbury, NZ, 73-74; Collisions; reporter, Working Group VII-Lab Data, Int Asn Geomagnetism & Aeronomy; mem comt stratospheric pollution, Govt Can; mem bd dirs, Scintrex, Ltd; chmn panel atmospheric chem & transport, US Acad Sci, 78-80; adv panel, Fed Aviation Admin High Altitude Pollution Prog; pres, Unisearch Assoc, Inc. *Mem:* Am Meteorol Soc; fel Chem Inst Can; fel Royal Soc Can. *Res:* Mass spectrometry; chemical kinetics; atomic physics; upper atmosphere; excitation processes; ion-molecule reactions; interstellar molecules. *Mailing Add:* Dept of Chem York Univ 4700 Keele St Downsview ON M3J 2R3 Can

SCHIFF, HARRY, b Boryslaw, Poland, May 17, 22; Can citizen; m 52; c 1. THEORETICAL PHYSICS. *Educ:* McGill Univ, BSc, 49, MSc, 50, PhD(physics), 53. *Prof Exp:* Lectr, 53-54, from asst prof to assoc prof, 54-64, chmn dept, 64-67, PROF PHYSICS, UNIV ALTA, 64-, DIR THEORET PHYS INST, 80- *Mem:* Am Phys Soc; Can Asn Physicists. *Res:* Unitary field theories, particularly modified Maxwell fields with application to elementary particle structure; solitons with virial constraints. *Mailing Add:* Dept of Physics Univ of Alta Edmonton AB T6G 2J1 Can

SCHIFF, JEROME A, b Brooklyn, NY, Feb 20, 31. PLANT PHYSIOLOGY. *Educ:* Brooklyn Col, BA, 52; Univ Pa, PhD(bot, biochem), 56. *Prof Exp:* Res assoc microbiol, 56-57, from instr to prof biol, 57-74, ABRAHAM & ETTA GOODMAN PROF BIOL, BRANDEIS UNIV, 74-, DIR, INST PHOTOBIOL CELLS & ORGANELLES, 75- *Concurrent Pos:* Carnegie fel, Dept Plant Biol, 62-63; asst ed, Plant Physiol, 64-79; mem develop biol grant rev panel, NSF, 65-68; dir exp marine bot prog, Marine Biol Lab, Woods Hole 74-79; mem, Grad Fel Prog Panel, NSF-Nat Res Coun, 74; mem, Biol Grant Rev Panel, US-Israel Binational Sci Found, 74-; consult grant applns, Dept Army, 74-77. *Mem:* Fel AAAS; Soc Develop Biol (secy, 64-66); Am Soc Cell Biol; Phycol Soc Am; Am Soc Plant Physiol. *Res:* Inorganic metabolism, particularly sulfur metabolism; pigment formation in plants; physiology of algae and other Protista, particularly Euglena; development and inheritance of chloroplasts and other cell organelles. *Mailing Add:* Inst Photobiol Cells & Org Brandeis Univ Waltham MA 02254

SCHIFF, LEON, b Riga, Latvia, May 1, 01; nat US; m 25; c 3. INTERNAL MEDICINE. *Educ:* Univ Cincinnati, BS, 22, MD, 24, MS, 27, PhD(med), 29. *Prof Exp:* Asst bact, 22-23, asst med, 25-26, from instr to assoc prof, 26-55, prof clin med, 55-58, prof med, 58-70, EMER PROF MED, COL MED, UNIV CINCINNATI, 70- *Concurrent Pos:* Prof med, Sch Med, Univ Miami, 70-72, clin prof, 73-; attend physician, Med Serv, Cincinnati Gen Hosp; consult, US Vet Hosp. *Honors & Awards:* Friedenwald Medal, Am Gastroenterol Asn, 73; Nat Comn Digestive Dis Award, 77; Leon Schiff Ann lectr, Univ Cincinnati, 81. *Mem:* Am Soc Clin Invest; Am Gastroenterol Asn; Am Col Physicians; Am Asn Study Liver Dis. *Res:* Diseases of the digestive tract; liver disease and jaundice; clinical research. *Mailing Add:* Dept of Med Sch of Med Univ of Miami Miami FL 33101

SCHIFF, LEONARD NORMAN, b New York, NY, Dec 7, 38; m 62; c 2. COMMUNICATIONS ENGINEERING. *Educ:* City Col New York, BEE, 60; NY Univ, MSc, 62; Polytech Inst Brooklyn, PhD(elec eng), 68. *Prof Exp:* Mem tech staff, Bell Tel Labs, Inc, 60-67; mem tech staff, 67-78, HEAD COMMUN ANAL RES, RCA LABS, 78- *Honors & Awards:* David Sarnoff Award, 81. *Mem:* Inst Elec & Electronics Engrs. *Res:* Communications theory; systems science; satellite communications. *Mailing Add:* RCA Labs Princeton NJ 08540

SCHIFF, PAUL L, JR, b Columbus, Ohio, Feb 3, 40; m 61; c 2. PHARMACOGNOSY, NATURAL PRODUCTS CHEMISTRY. *Educ:* Ohio State Univ, BSc, 62, MSc, PhD(pharmacog). *Prof Exp:* Asst prof pharmacog, Col Pharm, Butler Univ, 67-69, Dept Pharmacog, Sch Pharm, Univ Miss, 70; assoc prof, 70-74, PROF PHARMACOG, SCH PHARM, UNIV PITTSBURGH, 74-, CHMN DEPT, 70- *Mem:* Am Soc Pharmacog; Acad Pharmaceut Sci; Am Pharmaceut Asn; Am Chem Soc; Phytochem Soc Am. *Res:* Isolation and identification of plant metabolites with potential pharmacological activity and in particular with the isolation and identification of benzylisoquinoline-derived alkaloids. *Mailing Add:* Dept Pharmacog 512 Salk Hall Sch Med Univ Pittsburgh Pittsburgh PA 15261

SCHIFF, ROBERT, b New York, NY, Jan 7, 42; m 64; c 2. MEDICAL RESEARCH. *Educ:* City Univ New York, BS, 64; Iowa State Univ, MS, 66; Univ Calif, Davis, PhD(genetics), 68. *Prof Exp:* Trainee, USPHS, 69; asst prof anat, Sch Med, Tufts Univ, 69-72; mgr serology res, Hyland Div, Travenol Labs, 72-74; dir res & develop, J T Baker Diagnostics, 74-77; DIR DEPT DIAG RES & PROD DEVELOP, HOFFMANN-LA ROCHE, INC, 77- *Mem:* Genetics Soc Am; NY Acad Sci; Histochem Soc; Am Asn Anatomists; Am Soc Clin Pathologists. *Res:* Research and development of tests and reagents for clinical laboratory medicine. *Mailing Add:* Dept of Diag Res & Prod Develop Hoffmann- La Roche Inc Nutley NJ 07110

SCHIFF, SIDNEY, b Chicago, Ill, June 9, 29; m 54; c 2. ORGANIC CHEMISTRY. *Educ:* Ill Inst Technol, BS, 51; Ohio State Univ, MS, 54, PhD(chem), 58. *Prof Exp:* Res chemist, 58-77; SUPVR, PHILLIPS PETROL CO, 77- *Mem:* Soc Automotive Engrs; Am Chem Soc. *Res:* Lubricating oil additives; fuels and lubricants; synthetic lubricants; catalytic cracking catalysts; metals passivation. *Mailing Add:* 1122 Swan Dr Bartlesville OK 74003

SCHIFF, STEFAN OTTO, b Braunschweig, Ger, July 22, 30; US citizen; m 57; c 2. RADIATION BIOLOGY. *Educ:* Roanoke Col, BS, 52; Univ Tenn, PhD(radiation biol), 64. *Prof Exp:* Instr zool, Univ Tenn, 63-64; asst prof zool, 64-71, assoc prof, 71-77, chmn, Dept Biol Sci, 77, PROF ZOOL, GEORGE WASHINGTON UNIV, 77-, CHMN GRAD PROG GENETICS, 71- *Mem:* Radiation Res Soc; Sigma Xi; AAAS. *Res:* Effects of microwave radiation on mammalian sensory structures. *Mailing Add:* Dept of Biol George Washington Univ Washington DC 20052

SCHIFFER, JOHN PAUL, b Budapest, Hungary, Nov 22, 30; nat US; m 60; c 2. NUCLEAR PHYSICS. *Educ:* Oberlin Col, BA, 51; Yale Univ, MS, 52, PhD(physics), 54. *Prof Exp:* Asst physics, Yale Univ, 51-54; res assoc, Rice Inst, 54-56; asst physicist, 56-59, assoc physicist, 59-65, assoc dir, Physics Div, 64-79, SR PHYSICIST, ARGONNE NAT LAB, 65-, DIR, PHYSICS DIV, 79-; PROF PHYSICS, UNIV CHICAGO, 69- *Concurrent Pos:* Guggenheim fel, 59-60; vis assoc prof, Princeton Univ, 64; vis prof, Univ Rochester, 67-68; ed, Comments on Nuclear & Particle Physics, 72-75; assoc ed, Revs Modern Physics, 72-77 vis prof, Tech Univ Munich, 73-74; Alexander von Humboldt Found sr US scientist award, 73-74; mem panel future nuclear sci, Nat Acad Sci-Nat Res Coun, 75-76; ed, Physics Letters, 78- *Honors & Awards:* Tom W Bonner Prize, Am Phys Soc, 76. *Mem:* Fel Am Phys Soc. *Res:* Experimental nuclear physics; nuclear reactions and structure; heavy ion reactions, pion reactions in nuclei. *Mailing Add:* Argonne Nat Lab 9700 SCass Ave Argonne IL 60439

SCHIFFER, LEWIS MARTIN, b New York, NY, July 10, 30; m 55; c 2. HEMATOLOGY, ONCOLOGY. *Educ:* NY Univ, AB, 51; State Univ NY, MD, 55. *Prof Exp:* Intern med, Grace-New Haven Community Hosp, 55-56; resident, State Univ NY Col Med, 58-61; from res assoc exp path to scientist, Brookhaven Nat Lab, 61-68; sr scientist & head sect hemat, Cell & Radiation Biol Lab, 68-80, DIR CANCER RES LABS, ALLEGHENY GEN HOSP, 80- *Concurrent Pos:* Nat Cancer Inst fel, Col Med, State Univ NY, 60-61; clin asst prof, Sch Med, Univ Pittsburgh, 68-, adj assoc prof, Grad Sch Pub Health, 70-79. *Mem:* AAAS; Am Soc Clin Oncol; Int Soc Hemat; Radiation Res Soc; Am Asn Cancer Res. *Res:* Cell kinetics of normal and abnormal hematopoeitic cells; cell kinetics of animal and human solid tumors; radiation biology as related to cell kinetics. *Mailing Add:* Cancer Res Labs Allegheny Gen Hosp Pittsburgh PA 15212

SCHIFFER, MARIANNE TSUK, b Budapest, Hungary, June 28, 35; US citizen; m 60; c 2. X-RAY CRYSTALLOGRAPHY. *Educ:* Petrik Lajos Chem Indust Tech Sch, Hungary, BS, 55; Smith Col, MA, 58; Columbia Univ, PhD(biochem), 65. *Prof Exp:* Res assoc biochem, Biol & Med Res Div, 65-67, asst biochemist, 68-74, BIOPHYSICIST, BIOL & MED RES DIV, ARGONNE NAT LAB, 74- *Concurrent Pos:* Vis scientist, Max Planck Inst Biochem, 73-74. *Mem:* Am Crystallog Asn; Am Asn Immunologists. *Res:* Determination of immunoglobulin structure by x-ray diffraction; correlation of amino acid sequence and conformation of protein molecules. *Mailing Add:* Biol & Med Res Div Argonne Nat Lab Argonne IL 60439

SCHIFFER, MENAHEM MAX, b Berlin, Ger, Sept 24, 11; nat US; m 37; c 1. MATHEMATICAL ANALYSIS. *Educ:* Hebrew Univ, Israel, MA, 34, PhD(math), 38. *Hon Degrees:* DS, Israel Inst Technol, 73. *Prof Exp:* Instr, Hebrew Univ, Israel, 34-38, sr asst, 38-43, lectr, 43-46, prof, 50-51; res lectr, Harvard Univ, 46-49; vis prof, Princeton Univ, 49-50; chmn dept, 53-60, PROF MATH STANFORD UNIV, 51- *Concurrent Pos:* Fulbright fel, 65-66. *Mem:* Nat Acad Sci; Am Math Soc; Am Acad Arts & Sci; foreign mem Finnish Acad Sci; Am Math Asn. *Res:* Theory of functions; partial differential equations; calculus of variations; applied mathematics. *Mailing Add:* 3748 Laguna Ave Palo Alto CA 94306

SCHIFFMACHER, E(DWARD) R(OBERT), b Lawrence, NY, July 8, 24; m 56; c 2. ELECTRICAL ENGINEERING. *Educ:* Union Col, NY, BS, 45; Cornell Univ, MS, 52. *Prof Exp:* Instr elec eng, Union Col, NY, 46-47; instr, Cornell Univ, 48-52, res assoc, 52-57; electronic scientist, Nat Bur Standards, 57-60, supvry electronic engr, 60-65; supvry electronic engr, Environ Sci Serv Admin, 65-70, supvry electronic engr, 70-80, ELECTRONIC ENG, NAT

OCEANIC & ATMOSPHERIC ADMIN, 80- *Mem:* Am Astron Soc; Inst Elec & Electronics Engrs. *Res:* Ionospheric studies using radio astronomy techniques and several earth satellite experiments; solar radio astronomy; ground-based ionospheric sounding. *Mailing Add:* Environ Res Lab Nat Oceanic & Atmospheric Admin Boulder CO 80303

SCHIFFMAN, LOUIS F, b Poland, July 15, 27; nat US; m 63; c 2. PHYSICAL CHEMISTRY. *Educ:* NY Univ, BChE, 48, MS, 52, PhD(phys chem), 55. *Prof Exp:* Res chem engr, Pa Grade Crude Oil Asn, 48-50; teaching fel chem, NY Univ, 50-54; res chemist, E I du Pont de Nemours & Co, Inc, 54-56 & Atlantic Refining Co, 56-59; res chemist, Amchem Prods Inc, 59-67, head corrosion group, 67-70; PRES & CONSULT, TECHNI RES ASSOCS, INC, WILLOW GROVE, 70- *Concurrent Pos:* Publ & ed, Patent Licensing Gazette. *Mem:* Am Chem Soc; Am Inst Chem; NY Acad Sci; Am Electroplaters Soc. *Res:* Combustion; radiochemistry; barrier separations; corrosion; surface treatment of metals; electroplating; industrial chemistry. *Mailing Add:* 1837 Merritt Rd Abington PA 19001

SCHIFFMAN, ROBERT L, b New York, NY, Oct 27, 23; m 47; c 2. SOIL MECHANICS, COMPUTER SCIENCE. *Educ:* Cornell Univ, BCE, 47; Columbia Univ, MS, 51; Rensselaer Polytech Inst, PhD(soil mech), 60. *Prof Exp:* Asst civil engr, New York Dept Hosps, 47-49; res assoc, Columbia Univ, 49-54, instr civil eng, 54-55; asst prof, Lehigh Univ, 55-57 & Rensselaer Polytech Inst, 57-60, assoc prof, 60-63, prof, 63-66 & theoret soil mech, Univ Ill, Chicago Circle, 66-70; lectr civil eng & fac res assoc, Comput Ctr, 69-70, assoc dir res, 70-77, PROF CIVIL ENG, UNIV COLO, BOULDER, 70- *Concurrent Pos:* Prin investr, Res Projs, Am Iron & Steel Inst-Pa State Hwy Dept, 55-57, Off Naval Res, 58-66, land locomotion lab, Army Mat Command, 59-65, NSF, 61-, US Geol Surv, 61-64 & US Bur Pub Rds, 64-66; mem comt stress distrib in earth masses, Hwy Res Bd, Nat Acad Sci-Nat Res Coun, 56-63, dept soils, found & geol, comt composite pavements & res needs comt, 64-70, mem comt on mech of earth masses & layered systs, 64-, chmn, 64-70, mem comt theories of pavement design, 65-, comt design of composite pavements & struct overlays & task force on comt interaction on pavement design, 70-; vis assoc prof civil eng, Mass Inst Technol, 62-63, lectr, 63-65, vis prof, 65-66; ed, newsletter, Inst Soc Terrain-Vehicle Systs, 65-67; ed, Soil Mech & found div newsletter, 66-68; lectr, Northwestern Univ, 67-68; indust consult; lectr. *Honors & Awards:* Hogentogler Award, Am Soc Testing & Mat, 60. *Mem:* Am Soc Civil Engrs; Int Soc Terrain-Vehicle Systs; Am Soc Cybernetics; Asn Comput Mach; Am Soc Testing & Mat. *Res:* Theoretical soil mechanics; theory of consolidation; elasticity; computer science. *Mailing Add:* Dept of Civil Eng Univ of Colo Boulder CO 80309

SCHIFFMAN, SANDRA, b Minneapolis, Minn, Feb 26, 37; m 57; c 2. BIOCHEMISTRY. *Educ:* Univ Calif, Berkeley, AB, 58; Univ Southern Calif, PhD(biochem, blood clotting), 61. *Prof Exp:* From instr to asst prof biochem, 61-75, ASSOC PROF MED & BIOCHEM, SCH MED, UNIV SOUTHERN CALIF, 75- *Concurrent Pos:* Estab investr, Am Heart Asn, 71-76. mem, Thrombosis Coun, Am Heart Asn. *Mem:* Am Soc Biol Chemists; Am Soc Hemat; Am Heart Asn; NY Acad Sci; AAAS. *Res:* Chemistry of proteins of blood coagulation. *Mailing Add:* Univ of Southern Calif Sch of Med 2025 Zonal Ave Los Angeles CA 90033

SCHIFFMAN, SUSAN S, b Chicago, Ill, Aug 24, 40; div; c 1. PSYCHOPHYSICS, CHEMORECEPTIONS. *Educ:* Syracuse Univ, BA, 65; Duke Univ, PhD(psychol), 70. *Prof Exp:* Fel aging & obesity, 70-72, asst prof, 72-77, DIR, WEIGHT CONTROL UNIT, DEPT PSYCHIAT, DUKE MED CTR, 76-, ASSOC PROF PSYCHIAT, 78- *Concurrent Pos:* mem, Salt & Water Subgroup, Nat Hypertension Task Force, 76; Comt Sodium Restricted Diets, Food & Nutrit Bd, 74-79; vis scientist biochem, Oxford, 80-81. *Mem:* Sigma Xi; Asn Chemorecption Sci; Am Chem Soc; Europ Chemorecption Sci. *Res:* Physicochemical properties that relate to perception of taste and smell; changes of taste and smell with age, obesity and disease state. *Mailing Add:* Dept Psychol Duke Univ Durham NC 27706

SCHIFFMANN, ELLIOT, b Newark, NJ, Apr 23, 27; m 60. BIOCHEMISTRY, ORGANIC CHEMISTRY. *Educ:* Yale Univ, BA, 49; Columbia Univ, PhD(biochem), 55. *Prof Exp:* Scientist, Nat Heart Inst, 55-61; scientist, 61-64, BIOCHEMIST, NAT INST DENT RES, 64- *Concurrent Pos:* Lectr, Grad Biochem Lab, Georgetown Univ, 57-58. *Res:* Antimetabolites and cholesterol biosynthesis; mechanisms of calcification in non osseous tissue; chemotaxis in leucocytes; biosynthesis of connective tissue components; recognition processes in cells. *Mailing Add:* Lab Develop Biol & Anomalies Nat Inst of Dent Res Bethesda MD 20014

SCHIFFMANN, ROBERT F, b New York, NY, Feb 11, 35; m 56; c 3. FOOD SCIENCE, MICROWAVE ENGINEERING. *Educ:* Columbia Univ, BS, 55; Purdue Univ, BS, 59. *Prof Exp:* Anal develop chemist, DCA Food Industs, Inc, 59-60, res proj leader, 60-61; dir lab radiochem, Nucleonics Corp Am, Inc, 61-62, vpres & tech dir radiochem & health physics, 62-63; res scientist microwave processing & foods, DCA Food Industs, Inc, 63-68, sr proj mgr, 68-71; partner new prod res & develop consult, Bedrosian & Assocs, 71-78; PRES, R F SCHIFFMANN ASSOC, CONSULT MICROWAVE, 78- *Concurrent Pos:* Secy & mem exec directorate, Int Microwave Power Inst, 69-71, mem bd gov, 69-, pres, 73-81, chmn, 81-; assoc ed foods, J Microwave Power, 70-; vpres, Natural Pak Systs, 77- *Honors & Awards:* Putman Award, Putman Publ Co, 72. *Mem:* Inst Food Technologists; Sigma Xi; Int Microwave Inst. *Res:* New product and process research and development; microwave processing applications; food processing; extrusion technology; physical chemistry of food systems; fruit and vegetable storage; bakery and dairy production. *Mailing Add:* R F Schiffmann Assoc 149 W 88 St New York NY 10024

SCHIFREEN, RICHARD STEVEN, b Trenton, NJ, Mar 17, 52. CLINICAL CHEMISTRY, ANALYTICAL CHEMISTRY. *Educ:* Muhlenberg Col, BS, 74; Univ Ga, PhD(chem), 78. *Prof Exp:* Fel clin chem, Hartford Hosp, 78-80; MEM STAFF, E I DU PONT DE NEMOURS & CO, INC, 80- *Concurrent Pos:* Mem area comt clin chem, Nat Comt Clin Lab Standards. *Mem:* Am Chem Soc; Am Asn Clin Chem; Sigma Xi. *Res:* Measurement of glycosylated hemoglobins and the use of liquid chromatography in separating proteins. *Mailing Add:* Clin Systs Div E I du Pont de Nemours & Co Inc Wilmington DE 19898

SCHILB, THEODORE PAUL, b St Louis, Mo, May 13, 33; m 65; c 1. BIOPHYSICS, PHYSIOLOGY. *Educ:* Univ Louisville, BS, 55, MS, 57, PhD(biophys), 65. *Prof Exp:* Instr physiol, Univ Louisville, 65-67, instr biophys, 67-68; asst prof, Mt Sinai Sch Med, 68-74; ASST PROF PHYSIOL, LA STATE UNIV SCH MED, NEW ORLEANS, 74- *Concurrent Pos:* Career develop award, 69. *Mem:* Biophys Soc; Am Physiol Soc. *Res:* Active transport of inorganic ions across cell membranes; secretory physiology. *Mailing Add:* Dept of Physiol La State Univ Sch of Med New Orleans LA 70112

SCHILD, ALBERT, b Hessdorf, Mar 3, 20; nat US; m 46; c 7. MATHEMATICS. *Educ:* Univ Toronto, BA, 46; Univ Pa, MA, 48, PhD(math), 51. *Prof Exp:* Asst instr math, Univ Pa, 46-50; from instr to assoc prof, 50-62, chmn dept, 63-79, PROF MATH, TEMPLE UNIV, 62- *Mem:* Am Math Soc; Math Asn Am; Inst Math Statist; Nat Coun Teachers Math. *Res:* Theory of functions; complex variables; operations research. *Mailing Add:* Dept of Math Temple Univ Philadelphia PA 19122

SCHILD, RUDOLPH ERNEST, b Chicago, Ill, Jan 10, 40. ASTRONOMY, PHYSICS. *Educ:* Univ Chicago, BS, 62, MS, 63, PhD(astrophys), 66. *Prof Exp:* Res assoc, Calif Inst Technol, 66-69; ASTROPHYSICIST, SMITHSONIAN ASTROPHYS OBSERV, 69-; LECTR ASTRON, HARVARD UNIV, 73- *Concurrent Pos:* Res consult, Mass Inst Technol, 73-74. *Mem:* Am Astron Soc; Int Astron Union. *Res:* Spectroscopy and spectrometry of hot normal and peculiar stars; extragalactic studies of the history and evolution of galaxies and clusters of galaxies. *Mailing Add:* Ctr for Astrophys 60 Garden St Cambridge MA 02138

SCHILDCROUT, STEVEN MICHAEL, b Grand Rapids, Mich, July 18, 43; m 64; c 2. PHYSICAL INORGANIC CHEMISTRY. *Educ:* Univ Chicago, BS, 64; Northwestern Univ, PhD(chem), 68. *Prof Exp:* Res fel chem, Rice Univ, 68-69; asst prof, 69-74, assoc prof, 74-81, PROF CHEM, YOUNGSTOWN STATE UNIV, 81- *Mem:* Am Chem Soc; Am Soc Mass Spectrometry; Sigma Xi. *Res:* Mass spectrometry and ion-neutral reactions; inorganic and organometallic kinetics. *Mailing Add:* Dept Chem Youngstown State Univ Youngstown OH 44555

SCHILDKNECHT, EUGENE GEORGE, b Newark, NJ, Apr 26, 37; m 62; c 4. POULTRY SCIENCE. *Educ:* Seton Hall Univ, AB, 59; Fairleigh Dickinson Univ, MA, 68; Rutgers Univ, PhD(animal sci), 76; Kean Col, MA, 80. *Prof Exp:* Asst bacteriologist, Animal Health Res Dept, Schering Corp, 59-63; SR SCIENTIST, ANIMAL HEALTH RES DEPT, HOFFMANN-LA ROCHE INC, 63- *Mem:* Poultry Sci Asn; World's Poultry Sci Asn; Am Soc Parasitologists; Soc Protozoologists. *Res:* Protozoan and bacterial diseases of poultry, specifically avian coccidiosis; nutrition and disease interrelationships; chemotherapy of avian diseases. *Mailing Add:* Animal Health Res Dept Hoffmann-La Roche Inc Nutley NJ 07110

SCHILDKRAUT, CARL LOUIS, b Brooklyn, NY, June 20, 37. BIOLOGICAL CHEMISTRY. *Educ:* Cornell Univ, AB, 58; Harvard Univ, AM, 59, PhD(chem), 61. *Prof Exp:* NSF fel, 61-63; asst prof, 64-70, assoc prof, 71-76, PROF CELL BIOL, ALBERT EINSTEIN COL MED, 76- *Concurrent Pos:* Kennedy scholar, 66-69; NIH career develop award, 69-74; mem molecular biol adv panel, NSF, 70-73. *Honors & Awards:* Hirschl Career Scientist Award, 75. *Mem:* AAAS; Am Chem Soc; Am Soc Cell Biol; Am Soc Biol Chem. *Res:* Physical chemistry and enzymology of DNA; analysis of the organization and replication of the DNA of mammalian cells; regulatory mechanisms in mammalian cells. *Mailing Add:* Dept of Cell Biol Albert Einstein Col of Med Bronx NY 10461

SCHILDKRAUT, JOSEPH JACOB, b Brooklyn, NY, Jan 21, 34; m 66; c 2. PSYCHIATRY, NEUROPSYCHOPHARMACOLOGY. *Educ:* Harvard Col, AB, 55; Harvard Med Sch, MD, 59. *Prof Exp:* Intern med, Univ Calif Hosp, San Francisco, 59-60; teaching fel, Harvard Med Sch, 60-63; clin assoc, Lab Clin Sci, NIMH, 63-65, spec fel, 65-66, res psychiatrist, 66-67; asst prof, Harvard Med Sch, 67-70, assoc prof, 70-74; resident psychiat, 60-63, chief resident res unit, 61-63, SR PSYCHIATRIST & DIR NEUROPSYCHOPHARMACOL LAB, MASS MENT HEALTH CTR, 67-; PROF PSYCHIAT, HARVARD MED SCH, 74- *Concurrent Pos:* Prin investr numerous grants; consult comts & orgns. *Honors & Awards:* Anna-Monika Found Prize, Dortmund, Ger, 67; McCurdy-Rinkel Prize, Am Psychiat Asn, 69, Hofheimer Prize, 71; William C Menninger Mem Award, Am Col Physicians, 78. *Mem:* Am Psychiat Asn; Am Col Psychiatrists; World Psychiat Asn; Am Col Neuropsychopharmacol; Am Soc Pharmacol & Exp Therapeut. *Res:* Neuropsychopharmacology, biochemistry, and biology of psychiatric disorders, particularly the affective disorders (depressions and manias) and the schizophrenic disorders. *Mailing Add:* Mass Ment Health Ctr 74 Fenwood Rd Boston MA 02115

SCHILE, RICHARD DOUGLAS, b New Haven, Conn, Apr 3, 31; m 53; c 3. ENGINEERING MECHANICS, MATERIALS ENGINEERING. *Educ:* Rensselaer Polytech Inst, BAeroE, 53, MS, 57, PhD(mech), 67. *Prof Exp:* Res engr, Res Labs, United Aircraft, 57-59, group supvr, 59-62, sr mat scientist, 62-69; assoc prof eng, Dartmouth Col, 69-76; ENG RES DIR, CIBA-GEIGY CORP, 76- *Mem:* Am Acad Mech; Am Soc Mech Engrs. *Res:* Technical management of engineering research and development of high strength, light weight components; materials for aircraft and aerospace structures. *Mailing Add:* 22 Bloomer Rd Ridgefield CT 06877

SCHILLACI, MARIO EDWARD, b Philadelphia, Pa, Feb 18, 40; m 62; c 3. RADIATION PHYSICS, PARTICLE PHYSICS. *Educ:* Drexel Univ, BS, 62; Brandeis Univ, MA, 64, PhD(physics), 68. *Prof Exp:* Fel, 67-69, STAFF SCIENTIST, MEDIUM-ENERGY PHYSICS DIV, LOS ALAMOS SCI

LAB, UNIV CALIF, 67- *Mem:* Am Phys Soc; Am Asn Physicists Med. *Res:* Medium energy particle physics; medical radiation physics; chemical effects in meson capture processes. *Mailing Add:* Medium-Energy Physics Div Los Alamos Sci Lab Univ of Calif Los Alamos NM 87545

SCHILLER, ALFRED GEORGE, b Irma, Wis, Dec 5, 18; m 44; c 2. VETERINARY MEDICINE. *Educ:* Mich State Univ, DVM, 43, MS, 56; Am Col Vet Surg, dipl, 66. *Prof Exp:* Practr small animal med, Minneapolis, Minn, 47-52; from instr to assoc prof, 52-63, acting head Dept Vet Clin Med, 76-78, acting assoc dean acad affairs, 78, PROF VET CLIN MED, SMALL ANIMAL CLIN, UNIV ILL, URBANA, 63- *Honors & Awards:* Ill Vet Serv Award, 72. *Mem:* Am Col Vet Surg (pres, 72, exec secy, 75-). *Res:* Veterinary surgery. *Mailing Add:* Small Animal Clin Univ of Ill Urbana IL 61801

SCHILLER, CAROL MASTERS, b St Augustine, Fla, Dec 31, 40; m 64; c 2. BIOCHEMICAL TOXICOLOGY, DEVELOPMENTAL GASTROENTEROLOGY. *Educ:* State Univ NY, Cortland, BSc, 62; Univ NC, MAT, 63; Univ Tex, Dallas, PhD(biochem), 70. *Prof Exp:* Instr chem & physics, Barlow High Sch, Redding, Conn & Jordan High Sch, Durham, NC, 63-65; fel med & tutor chem, Univ Toronto, 71-73; res assoc biochem, Univ NC, 73-75; sr staff fel, 75-78, RES CHEMIST, NIH, 79- *Concurrent Pos:* Alt mem, Nutrit Coord Comt, NIH, 75-, coordr, Fed Women's Prog, 77-78, mem, Digestive Dis Coord Comt, 78-; adj asst prof biochem, Univ NC, 76-80, adj assoc prof, 80-, mem fac, Med Sch, 78-, mem grad fac toxicol, 80-; mem fac, W A Jones Cell Sci Ctr, 77-78, chmn, In Vitro Res & Human Values Comt, Tissue Cult Asn, 74-78. *Mem:* Tissue Cult Asn; AAAS; Asn Women Sci; Soc Toxicol; NY Acad Sci. *Res:* Development of intestinal function in normal and stressed animals; in vivo and in vitro techniques with isolated cells and subcellular organelles. *Mailing Add:* Nat Inst Environ Health Sci NIH Research Triangle Park NC 27709

SCHILLER, EVERETT L, b Marshfield, Wis, Aug 31, 17; m 45; c 1. MEDICAL PARASITOLOGY. *Educ:* Univ Wis, BS, 49, MS, 50; Johns Hopkins Univ, ScD(parasitol), 58. *Prof Exp:* Asst parasitol, Univ Wis, 49-50; parasitologist, Arctic Health Res Ctr, USPHS, Alaska, 50-55; instr zool, Anchorage Community Col, 55; res assoc, 57-58, from asst prof to assoc prof, 58-65, PROF PATHOBIOL, SCH HYG & PUB HEALTH, JOHNS HOPKINS UNIV, 65- *Concurrent Pos:* Supvr & instr, Diag Parasitol Lab, Johns Hopkins Hosp, 56-61; mem bd dirs, Gorgas Mem Inst Trop & Prev Med, 72-77; consult, US Army Med Res & Develop Command, 74-76; mem expert adv panel, WHO, Geneva, 75-80. *Honors & Awards:* Henry Baldwin Ward Award, Am Soc Parasitol, 64; J N Chowdhuri Award, Sch Trop Med, Calcutta, India, 69. *Mem:* Am Soc Parasitol; Am Micros Soc; Am Inst Biol Sci; Am Soc Trop Med & Hyg. *Res:* Helminthology; experimental parasitology; tropical diseases. *Mailing Add:* Sch of Hyg & Pub Health Johns Hopkins Univ 615 NWolfe St Baltimore MD 21205

SCHILLER, JOHN JOSEPH, b Philadelphia, Pa, Dec 10, 35; m 57; c 3. MATHEMATICS. *Educ:* La Salle Col, BA, 57; Temple Univ, MA, 60; Univ Pa, PhD(math), 66. *Prof Exp:* Physicist, US Naval Res & Develop Ctr, 57-59; from instr to asst prof, 59-71, ASSOC PROF MATH, 71- & RES ASSOC PROF PHYSIOL & BIOPHYS, TEMPLE UNIV, 78- *Concurrent Pos:* Mathematician, John D Kettelle Corp, 69. *Mem:* Am Math Soc. *Res:* Riemann surfaces; artificial intelligence. *Mailing Add:* Dept of Math Temple Univ Philadelphia PA 19122

SCHILLER, NEAL LEANDER, b Lowell, Mass, Nov 5, 49; m 73; c 3. MEDICAL MICROBIOLOGY, INFECTIOUS DISEASES. *Educ:* Boston Col, BS, 71; Univ Mass, Amherst, PhD(microbiol), 76. *Prof Exp:* Res fel, Div Infectious Dis, Cornell Med Ctr, New York Hosp, 76-78, clin lab tech trainee, Diag Microbiol Lab, 77-78; ASST PROF MED MICROBIOL, DIV BIOMED SCI, UNIV CALIF, RIVERSIDE, 79- *Mem:* Am Soc Microbiol; AAAS. *Res:* The interaction of pathogenic bacteria with host defense mechanisms; characterization of bacterial virulence factors; examination of host defenses including chemotaxis, serum killing, opsonization, complement activation, phagocytic uptake and intracellular killing; identifying ways to enhance the host defense mechanisms. *Mailing Add:* Div Biomed Sci Univ Calif Riverside CA 92521

SCHILLER, RALPH, b New York, NY, July 8, 26; m 50; c 3. THEORETICAL PHYSICS. *Educ:* Brooklyn Col, BA, 48; Syracuse Univ, MS, 50, PhD(physics), 52. *Prof Exp:* Asst physics, Syracuse Univ, 48-52; asst prof, Univ Sao Paulo, 52-54; from asst prof to assoc prof, 54-63, PROF PHYSICS, STEVENS INST TECHNOL, 63-, HEAD DEPT, 75- *Concurrent Pos:* Res assoc, Syracuse Univ, 60-61; vis prof, Weizmann Inst, 80. *Mem:* Am Phys Soc. *Res:* Physical biology. *Mailing Add:* Dept of Physics Stevens Inst of Technol Hoboken NJ 07030

SCHILLETTER, JULIAN CLAUDE, b Clemson University, SC, Nov 1, 01. HORTICULTURE. *Educ:* Clemson Univ, BS, 22; Iowa State Univ, MS, 23, PhD, 30. *Prof Exp:* From instr to assoc prof, 22-45, prof hort & dir residence, 45-67, residence analyst, 67-72, EMER PROF HORT, IOWA STATE UNIV, 72- *Concurrent Pos:* Mem, Int Hort Cong, 30; horticulturist, Nat Res Proj, Works Progress Admin, 38. *Res:* Differentiation of flower bud in Dunlap strawberries; growth of Dunlap strawberries; textbook of general horticulture. *Mailing Add:* 111 Lynn Ames IA 50010

SCHILLING, CHARLES H(ENRY), b Louisville, Ky, June 3, 18; m 45; c 5. CIVIL ENGINEERING. *Educ:* US Mil Acad, BS, 41; Univ Calif, MS, 47; Rensselaer Polytech Inst, PhD(civil eng), 59. *Prof Exp:* US Army, 41-80, engr combat battalion, France & Ger, 44-45, engr aviation battalion, Ger, 47-50, instr mil art & eng, US Mil Acad, 51-52, assoc prof, 52-55, area engr, Eastern Ocean Dist, Corps Engrs, 55-56, prof mil art & eng, US Mil Acad, 56-69, head dept, 63-69, prof eng & head dept, US Mil Acad, 69-80; CIVIL ENGR, ALLEN & HOSHALL INC, 81- *Concurrent Pos:* Vis prof, Univ Mich, 65 & Univ Stuttgart, 68-69. *Mem:* Am Soc Eng Educ; Soc Am Mil Engrs; Am Soc Civil Engrs; Nat Soc Prof Engrs. *Res:* Structural engineering; vibrations in suspension bridges; application of computers in engineering and education. *Mailing Add:* 4 Trahern Terr Clarksville TN 37040

SCHILLING, CURTIS LOUIS, JR, b Goshen, NY, May 19, 40; m 61; c 2. POLYMER CHEMISTRY, ORGANOSILICON CHEMISTRY. *Educ:* Syracuse Univ, BS, 61, MS, 64; Univ Ariz, PhD(org chem), 67. *Prof Exp:* US Army Res Off grantee, Univ Iowa, 67-68; RES CHEMIST, CHEM & PLASTICS DIV, UNION CARBIDE CORP, 68- *Mem:* Am Chem Soc; Am Ceramic Soc. *Res:* Organosilicon chemistry; silicone surfactant stabilization of polyurethane foams; organosilicon routes tosilicon carbide. *Mailing Add:* Silicones 220 Silicon-Urethane Div Union Carbide Corp PO Box 65 Tarrytown NY 10591

SCHILLING, EDWARD EUGENE, b Los Angeles, Calif, Sept 23, 53. PLANT SYSTEMATICS, CHEMOTAXONOMY. *Educ:* Mich State Univ, BS, 74; Ind Univ, PhD(biol), 78. *Prof Exp:* Instr bot, Univ Tex, 78-79; ASST PROF BOT, UNIV TENN, 79- *Mem:* AAAS; Am Soc Plant Taxonomists; Bot Soc Am; Sigma Xi. *Res:* Systematics and evolution of weeds; cytoplasmic genetics; flavonoid chemistry. *Mailing Add:* Dept Bot Univ Tenn Knoxville TN 37996

SCHILLING, EDWARD GEORGE, b Lancaster, NY, Nov 9, 31; m 59; c 2. STATISTICS. *Educ:* Univ Buffalo, BA, 53, MBA, 54; Rutgers Univ, MS, 62, PhD(statist), 67. *Prof Exp:* Instr statist, Univ Buffalo, 57-59; engr, Radio Corp Am, 59-61; teaching asst statist, Rutgers Univ, 61-62; sr engr, Carborundum Corp, 62-64; instr statist, Rutgers Univ, 64-67; assoc prof, Rochester Inst Technol, 67-69; consult, 68-69, consult statistician, Lamp Bus Div, Lighting Res Lab, 69-74, mgr statist & qual systs oper, 75-80, MGR LIGHTING QUALITY OPER, LIGHTING BUS GROUP, GEN ELEC CO, 80- *Honors & Awards:* Brumbaugh Award, Am Soc Qual Control, 74, 78 & 79. *Mem:* Fel Am Statist Asn; fel Am Soc Qual Control; Inst Math Statist; Am Soc Testing & Mat; Am Econ Asn. *Res:* Mathematical statistics with applications in the physical and engineering sciences, quality control, business and economics. *Mailing Add:* Lighting Bus Group Gen Elec Co Nela Park Cleveland OH 44112

SCHILLING, FREDERICK P(AUL), b Missoula, Mont, Dec 3, 28; m 59; c 3. CHEMICAL ENGINEERING. *Educ:* Mont State Univ, BS, 51, PhD(chem eng), 59. *Prof Exp:* Engr, Phillips Petrol, Co, 54-55; GROUP LEADER, LOS ALAMOS NAT LAB, UNIV CALIF, 59- *Mem:* Am Inst Chem Engrs; Am Nuclear Soc. *Mailing Add:* 775 Camino Encantado Los Alamos NM 87544

SCHILLING, GERD, b Hannover, Ger, Oct 6, 39; m 69; c 2. PLASMA HEATING. *Educ:* Mass Inst Technol, BS, 61; Case Inst Technol, MS, 63, PhD(physics), 67. *Prof Exp:* Res assoc, Notre Dame Univ, 68-70; res physicist, Max-Planck Inst für Plasma-physik, WGerm, 70-74 & Oak Ridge Nat Lab, Fusion Energy Div, 74-77; RES PHYSICIST, PLASMA PHYSICS LAB, PRINCETON UNIV, 77- *Res:* Controlled thermonuclear fusion and plasma physics. *Mailing Add:* Princeton Univ Plasma Physics Lab C-Site RF 245 Princeton NJ 08544

SCHILLING, GERHARD FRIEDRICH, b Vienna, Austria, Sept 9, 25; nat US; m 51; c 3. GEOPHYSICS, ATMOSPHERIC SCIENCES. *Educ:* Univ Vienna, PhD(geophys), 48. *Prof Exp:* Res asst physics, Univ Vienna, 48-49; res asst geophys, Univ Calif, Los Angeles, 49-50; intel res analyst, US Air Force, 50-51; res assoc geophys, Univ Calif, Los Angeles, 51-54; prog officer, Int Geophys Year, Nat Acad Sci, 54-56; exec asst to dir, Smithsonian Astrophys Observ, 57-58; chief, Astron & Astrophys Prog, NASA, 59-60; assoc head, Planetary Sci Dept, 60-62, sr staff mem, 63-74, consult, Rand Corp, 75-78; RETIRED. *Concurrent Pos:* Tech adv, Metro-Goldwyn-Mayer, 52-54; secy, Tech Panel on Rocketry, Int Geophys Year, 55-56; res assoc, Harvard Univ, 57-58; mem sci adv bd, US Air Force, 59-62; consult, Planetary & Interplanetary Sci Comt, NASA, 60-62; liaison officer, Hq, Air Force Systs Command, 69-71; commun support coordr, Calif Dept Forestry, 80-82. *Mem:* Am Astron Soc; Am Meteorol Soc; Am Geophys Union; Austrian Meteorol Soc; Am Radio Relay League. *Res:* Atmospheric electricity; stratospheric meteorology; satellite and space probe tracking; planetary physics; systems analysis; radio wave propagation. *Mailing Add:* Star Rte Box 299 Hemet CA 92343

SCHILLING, JESSE WILLIAM, b Huntingdon, Pa, Nov 11, 39; m 62. CRYSTALLOGRAPHY. *Educ:* Juniata Col, BS, 60; Yale Univ, MS, 63; Univ Mich, PhD(chem), 68. *Prof Exp:* Res assoc crystallog, Univ Mich, 68-70 & Yale Univ, 70-72; asst prof, 72-76; ASSOC PROF CHEM, TRINITY UNIV, TEX, 77- *Mem:* Am Crystallog Asn; Am Chem Soc. *Res:* Growth and structure of protein crystals; crystallographic computing; structures of biological molecules, especially proteins; computer graphics. *Mailing Add:* Dept of Chem Trinity Univ San Antonio TX 78284

SCHILLING, JOHN ALBERT, b Kansas City, Mo, Nov 5, 17; m 43; c 4. SURGERY. *Educ:* Dartmouth Col, AB, 37; Harvard Univ, MD, 41; Am Bd Surg, dipl, 48. *Prof Exp:* Resident, Roosevelt Hosp, Columbia Univ, 44; instr surg, Univ Rochester, 44-48, asst prof surg & surg anat, Sch Med & Dent, 48-56; prof surg & head dept, Med Ctr, Univ Okla, 56-74; PROF SURG, MED SCH, UNIV WASH, 74-, CHMN DEPT, 75- *Concurrent Pos:* Mem, Boyd-Bartlett Exped, Arctic, 41; mem adv bd, Am J Surg, 58-; mem surg study sect, Div Res Grants, NIH, 60-64, mem bd sci counr, Nat Cancer Inst, 66-71, chmn, 69-71, mem diag subcomt, Breast Cancer Task Force, 71-; mem, Am Bd Surg, Inc, 63-69, chmn, 68-69; mem comt metab in trauma, Surgeon Gen, US Army, 63-71, chmn, 67-71; consult, Div Hosp & Med Facil, Dept Health, Educ & Welfare, 66-; mem comt trauma, Div Med Sci, Nat Res Coun, 69-72; consult, Off Surgeon Gen, US Dept Air Force. *Mem:* Am Soc Exp Path; Am Surg Asn; Soc Exp Biol & Med; Am Cancer Soc; Soc Univ Surg. *Res:* Intestinal obstruction; circulation of liver; transplantation of cancer; paper chromatography; peptic ulcer; visualization of biliary tract; wound healing; respiratory physiology; shock. *Mailing Add:* Dept Surg RF-25 Univ Wash Health Sci Ctr Seattle WA 98195

SCHILLING, JOHN H(AROLD), b Lincoln, Nebr, Sept 7, 27; m 53; c 2. GEOLOGY, MINING. *Educ:* Pa State Univ, BS, 51; NMex Inst Mining & Technol, MS, 52. *Prof Exp:* Geol technician, NMex Bur Mines, 51, geologist, 53-56 & 59-60; geologist, Cerro de Pasco Corp, Peru, 56-58; mining geologist, Nev Bur Mines & Geol, 60-70, assoc dir, 70-73, DIR, NEV BUR MINES & GEOL, 73- *Concurrent Pos:* Mem adv bd, Ctr Water Res, 51-79; secy, Nev Oil & Gas Conserv Comn, 66-70, comnr, 70-76; ed, Isochron/West, 69-; mem Gov's Mapping Comt, 70-; consult various companies & govt agencies; mem bd trustees, Nev Hist Press, 71- *Mem:* Am Inst Mining, Metall & Petrol Engrs; Soc Econ Geol; Am Asn State Geologists. *Res:* Economic geology; metallogenics; molybdenum deposits; isotopic age of intrusive rocks. *Mailing Add:* 1301 Royal Dr Reno NV 89503

SCHILLING, PRENTISS EDWIN, b Magnolia, Miss, Oct 16, 41. EXPERIMENTAL STATISTICS. *Educ:* Miss State Univ, BS, 62; La State Univ, MS, 64; Ore State Univ, PhD(genetics & statist), 66. *Prof Exp:* From asst prof to prof, 66-77, PROF & HEAD EXP STATIST, LA STATE UNIV, BATON ROUGE, 77- *Concurrent Pos:* Consult, Inst Nutrit Cent Am & Panama, US Agency Int Develop & Exten Proj, Sierra Leone. *Mem:* Biomet Soc; Am Soc Animal Sci; Am Dairy Sci Asn; Am Statist Asn. *Res:* Experimental designs; consulting to researchers in all areas of the university community doing experimental work; administration. *Mailing Add:* Dept of Exp Statist La State Univ Baton Rouge LA 70803

SCHILLING, ROBERT FREDERICK, b Adell, Wis, Jan 19, 19; m 46; c 5. MEDICINE. *Educ:* Univ Wis, BS, 40, MD, 43; Am Bd Nutrit, dipl; Am Bd Internal Med, dipl, 51. *Prof Exp:* Asst med, Harvard Med Sch, 49-51; from asst prof to assoc prof, 51-62, PROF MED, UNIV WIS-MADISON, 62- *Concurrent Pos:* Commonwealth Fund res fel, London Hosp, Eng, 59; consult, NIH & Food & Drug Admin. *Mem:* Am Soc Clin Invest; Soc Exp Biol & Med; Am Fedn Clin Res; Asn Am Physicians. *Res:* Hematology; nutrition. *Mailing Add:* Dept of Med Univ of Wis Madison WI 53706

SCHILLING, WILLIAM FREDERICK, b Toledo, Ohio, Aug 21, 42; m 69; c 1. PHYSICAL METALLURGY. *Educ:* Case Inst Technol, BS, 64; Mass Inst Technol, ScD, 69. *Prof Exp:* Res engr phys metall, Alcoa Res Labs, 64-65; res asst, Mass Inst Technol, 65-69, staff mem, Div Sponsored Res, 69-71; sr res assoc, Lab Phys Sci, PR Mallory Co, 71-72; engr process develop, Mat & Processes Lab, 72-76, mgr mat develop, 76-79, MGR ADVAN MAT SYSTS, GAS TURBINE DIV, GEN ELEC CO, 79- *Mem:* Am Soc Metals; Am Powder Metall Inst. *Res:* Materials and process development of high temperature materials for advanced industrial gas turbines, including superalloy development, directional solidification, hot corrosion resistant coatings, coating processes and hot isostatic pressing applications; plasma spray processing, especially vacuum plasma spraying deposition. *Mailing Add:* Bldg 53 Rm 316 Gen Elec Co Schenectady NY 12345

SCHILLINGER, EDWIN JOSEPH, b Chicago, Ill, July 14, 23; m 49; c 6. PHYSICS, SCIENCE EDUCATION. *Educ:* DePaul Univ, BS, 44; Univ Notre Dame, MS, 48, PhD(physics), 50. *Prof Exp:* From instr to assoc prof, 50-63, chmn dept, 52-68 & 76-79, dean, Col Lib Arts & Sci, 66-70 & 80-81, PROF PHYSICS, DEPAUL UNIV, 63- *Concurrent Pos:* Consult, NSF, 62-67 & Off Supt Pub Instr, State of Ill, 69-72. *Mem:* AAAS; fel Am Phys Soc; Am Asn Physics Teachers. *Res:* Development of courses and curricula in physics and interdisciplinary science for general students, with emphasis on history, philosophy and methodology of science and its interaction with society and public policy. *Mailing Add:* Dept of Physics 2219 N Kenmore Ave Chicago IL 60614

SCHILLINGER, JOHN ANDREW, JR, b Severn, Md, June 17, 38; m 59; c 2. AGRONOMY, CROP BREEDING. *Educ:* Univ Md, College Park, BS, 60, MS, 62; Mich State Univ, PhD(plant breeding), 65. *Prof Exp:* Assoc instr plant breeding, Mich State Univ, 63-65; res entomologist, Entom Res Div, USDA & Mich State Univ, 65-67; from asst prof to assoc prof plant breeding, Univ Md, College Park, 67-73; SOYBEAN & ALFALFA PROJ LEADER, ASGROW SEED CO, 73- *Mem:* Am Soc Agron; Entom Soc Am. *Res:* Development of improved varieties of alfalfa and soybeans with resistance to pests and with high yield potential. *Mailing Add:* RR4 Ames IA 50010

SCHILSON, ROBERT E(ARL), b Keokuk, Iowa, May 25, 27; m 52; c 1. CHEMICAL ENGINEERING. *Educ:* Univ Ill, BS, 50; Univ Minn, PhD(chem eng), 58. *Prof Exp:* Chem engr, Hanford Works, Gen Elec Co, Wash, 50-53; res engr, Marathon Oil Co, 58-61, adv res engr, 61-65, sr res engr, Denver Res Ctr, 65-73, mgr, Eng Dept, 73-77, ADV SR REFINING ENGR, LA REFINING DIV, MARATHON OIL CO, 77- *Mem:* Am Inst Mining, Metall & Petrol Engrs; Am Inst Chem Eng. *Res:* Thermal methods of oil recovery; catalysis and chemical kinetics; refining and petrochemicals; coke and carbon technology. *Mailing Add:* 135 Somerset St La Place LA 70068

SCHILT, ALFRED AYARS, b Haigler, Nebr, Aug 30, 27; m 49; c 4. ANALYTICAL CHEMISTRY. *Educ:* Univ Colo, BA, 50, MA, 52; Univ Ill, PhD(chem), 56. *Prof Exp:* Anal chemist, Eastman Kodak Co, 51-53; asst, Univ Ill, 53-56; from instr to asst prof chem, Univ Mich, 56-62; assoc prof, 62-64, PROF CHEM, NORTHERN ILL UNIV, 64- *Concurrent Pos:* Vis res prof, Ind Univ, 70-71. *Mem:* Am Chem Soc. *Res:* Coordination compounds and their application in chemical analysis; analytical separations; spectroscopy; general analytical methods. *Mailing Add:* Dept of Chem Northern Ill Univ De Kalb IL 60115

SCHIMA, FRANCIS JOSEPH, b Chicago, Ill, Apr 15, 35; m 67; c 2. NUCLEAR PHYSICS, RADIOACTIVITY METROLOGY. *Educ:* Ill Benedictine Col, BS, 57; Univ Notre Dame, PhD(physics), 64. *Prof Exp:* Res assoc, Ind Univ, 64-66; PHYSICIST, NAT BUR STANDARDS, 66- *Concurrent Pos:* Consult, Nat Coun Radiation Protection & Measurements, 75- *Mem:* Am Phys Soc; Sigma Xi. *Res:* Study nuclear structure through measurement of radioactive decay; prepare standards of radioactivity. *Mailing Add:* US Dept Com Nat Bur Standards Washington DC 20234

SCHIMEK, ROBERT ALFRED, b Beaver Falls, Pa, May 1, 26; m 50; c 2. MEDICINE. *Educ:* Franklin & Marshall Col, BS, 45; Johns Hopkins Univ, MD, 50. *Prof Exp:* Asst instr, Johns Hopkins Univ & house officer & resident, Hosp, 50-53; staff ophthalmologist, Henry Ford Hosp, Mich, 53-57; head dept ophthal, Ochsner Clin & Found Hosp, 57-77; assoc prof, 57-76, CLIN PROF OPHTHAL, SCH MED, TULANE UNIV, 76- *Concurrent Pos:* Clin prof, Sch Med, La State Univ, 78; mem vis staff, Eye, & Ear Inst, Charity, Touro & E Jefferson Hosp, 57- *Mem:* AMA; Asn Res Vision & Ophthal; Am Col Surgeons; Am Acad Ophthal. *Res:* Ophthalmology. *Mailing Add:* Ochsner Clin 1514 Jefferson Hwy New Orleans LA 70121

SCHIMELPFENIG, CLARENCE WILLIAM, b Dallas, Tex, Apr 8, 30; m 56; c 3. ORGANIC CHEMISTRY. *Educ:* NTex State Col, BS, 53, MS, 54; Univ Ill, PhD, 57. *Prof Exp:* Asst prof chem, George Washington Univ, 57-59 & NTex State Univ, 59-62; res chemist, E I du Pont de Nemours & Co, Inc, 62-73; asst prof chem, State Univ NY Buffalo, 73-75 & Erskine Col, 75-76; asst prof chem, Tex Wesleyan Col, 76-79, assoc prof, 79-81; ASSOC PROF CHEM, NTEX STATE UNIV, 81- *Concurrent Pos:* Robert A Welch Found grantee, 60-62, 77- *Mem:* Am Chem Soc; Royal Soc Chem. *Res:* Organic and polymer chemistry. *Mailing Add:* Dept Chem NTex State Univ Fort Worth TX 76203

SCHIMERT, GEORGE, b Raemismuehle-Zell, Switz, Feb 19, 18; US citizen; m 56; c 8. CARDIOVASCULAR SURGERY. *Educ:* Univ Bonn, MD, 42; Pazmany Peter Univ, Budapest, MD, 43; Univ Minn, MSc, 60; Am Bd Surg, dipl, 61; Am Bd Thoracic Surg, dipl, 62. *Prof Exp:* Asst surg, Univ Md, 54-55; adv surg & chief thoracic surg, Med Col, Seoul Univ, 58-59; from instr to asst prof surg, Univ Minn, 60; asst prof, 60-65, assoc prof, 66-75, PROF SURG, STATE UNIV NY, BUFFALO, 75-; CHIEF CARDIOVASC SURG, BUFFALO GEN HOSP, 65-, SURGEON, 68- *Concurrent Pos:* Fel cardiovasc surg, Univ Md, 55-56; fel med, Hosps, Univ Minn, 56-58; attend thoracic surgeon, Vet Hosp, Buffalo, 61-; assoc surg, Buffalo Gen Hosp, 65-68; assoc attend cardiovasc surgeon, Children's Hosp, 67-; assoc prof, Sch Med, NY Univ, 69- *Mem:* AMA; fel Am Col Chest Physicians; fel Am Col Surg; fel Soc Thoracic Surg; fel Soc Vascular Surg. *Res:* Development of cardiopulmonary bypass equipment; design of prosthetic heart valves; multivalvular replacement; determination of myocardial sodium potassium ratios; correction of overwhelming heart failure by cardiac surgical procedures. *Mailing Add:* Dept of Surg State Univ NY Buffalo NY 14214

SCHIMITSCHEK, ERHARD JOSEF, b Neutitschein, Czech, Dec 8, 31; m 56; c 2. PHYSICAL CHEMISTRY, PHYSICS. *Educ:* Univ Munich, Dr rer nat, 57. *Prof Exp:* Sr res engr, Convair Gen Dynamics Corp, 58-60, staff scientist, 60-62; PHYSICIST, NAVAL OCEAN SYSTS CTR, 62- *Mem:* Am Phys Soc. *Res:* Electrooptics; quantum electronics; liquid and gas discharge lasers. *Mailing Add:* Naval Ocean Syst Ctr Code 811 San Diego CA 92152

SCHIMKE, ROBERT T, b Spokane, Wash, Oct 25, 32; m 75; c 4. BIOCHEMISTRY, MOLECULAR BIOLOGY. *Educ:* Stanford Univ, AB, 54, MD, 58. *Prof Exp:* Biochemist, NIH, 60-65, chief sect biochem regulation, 65-66; chmn dept pharmacol, 70-73, chmn dept biol, 78-82, PROF BIOL, STANFORD UNIV, 66- *Honors & Awards:* Outstanding Scientist, Md Acad Sci, 64; Charles Pfizer Award Enzyme Chem, Am Chem Soc, 69; Boris Pregal Award Res Biol, NY Acad Sci, 74. *Mem:* Nat Acad Sci; Am Soc Biol Chemists; Am Acad Arts & Sci. *Res:* Mechanisms of actions of hormones in metabolic regulation and development; significance and control mechanisms of protein turnover in animals; gene amplification and resistance phenomena. *Mailing Add:* Dept of Biol Sci Stanford Univ Stanford CA 94305

SCHIMMEL, ELIHU MYRON, b Bayonne, NJ, Dec 14, 29; m 55; c 2. MEDICINE. *Educ:* Univ Ill, Urbana, AB, 50; Yale Univ, MD, 54. *Prof Exp:* Instr med, Sch Med, Yale Univ, 60-64; ASSOC PROF MED, SCH MED, BOSTON UNIV, 64- *Concurrent Pos:* USPHS res fel, Mass Gen Hosp, Harvard Univ, 58-60; lectr med, Sch Med, Tufts Univ. *Mem:* Am Fedn Clin Res. *Res:* Gastroenterology. *Mailing Add:* Dept of Med Boston Univ Sch of Med Boston MA 02118

SCHIMMEL, HERBERT, b New York, NY, Sept 12, 09; m 34, 71; c 6. BIOMATHEMATICS, BIOPHYSICS. *Educ:* Univ Pa, BA, 30, MS, 32, PhD(physics), 36. *Prof Exp:* Engr-economist, US Nat Res Proj, Philadelphia, 36-41; staff dir & consult, US Cong, Washington, DC, 41-47; sr officer sci, technol & econ, UN, 48-52; independent consult, 53-63; assoc math & physics, 64-70, organizer & dir, Sci Comput Ctr, 67-71, assoc prof, 71-78, EMER PROF NEUROL, ALBERT EINSTEIN COL MED, 78-; CONSULT, 79- *Mem:* Inst Elec & Electronics Eng. *Res:* Applications of math and physics to medicine and biology, especially stochastic processes to brain research and use of time series to estimate adverse effects of air pollution; relations of science to economic and social development. *Mailing Add:* 26 Usonia Rd Pleasantville NY 10570

SCHIMMEL, KARL FRANCIS, b Allentown, Pa, Mar 24, 36; m 61; c 4. POLYMER SYNTHESIS, ORGANIC SYNTHESIS. *Educ:* Muhlenberg Col, BS, 57; Duquesne Univ, PhD(org chem), 61. *Prof Exp:* Res chemist, E I du Pont de Nemours & Co, Inc, 62-64; SR RES ASSOC, PPG INDUSTS, 64- *Mem:* Am Chem Soc. *Res:* Coating and resins end uses. *Mailing Add:* PPG Industs Res Ctr Allison Park PA 15101

SCHIMMEL, PAUL REINHARD, b Hartford, Conn, Aug 4, 40; m 61; c 2. BIOPHYSICS, BIOCHEMISTRY. *Educ:* Ohio Wesleyan Univ, AB, 62; Mass Inst Technol, PhD(phys biochem), 66. *Prof Exp:* Res assoc chem, Stanford Univ, 66-67; asst prof, 67-71, assoc prof, 71-76, PROF BIOL & CHEM, MASS INST TECHNOL, 76- *Concurrent Pos:* Alfred P Sloan fel, 70-72; consult, NIH, 75-79. *Honors & Awards:* Pfizer Award, Am Chem Soc, 78. *Mem:* Am Soc Biol Chem; Am Chem Soc; NY Acad Sci. *Res:* Gene, protein structure and function; aminoacyl transfer ribonucleic acid synthetases; cloning, sequecins, and regulation of genes from yewt; directed mutagenesis approach to structure-function relationships. *Mailing Add:* Dept of Biol Mass Inst of Technol Cambridge MA 02139

SCHIMMEL, ROBERT L, b Fairmont, WVa, Dec 10, 23; m 50; c 2. ELECTRICAL ENGINEERING. *Educ:* Univ WVa, BSEE, 50. *Prof Exp:* Jr engr, Monongahela Power Co, 50-53; engr, Cent Ill Pub Serv Co, 53-55 & Shippingport atomic power plant proj, Bettis Plant, Westinghouse Elec Corp, 55-60; supvr control elec & instrumentation sect, Nuclear Eng & Res Dept, Martin Co, 60-64, supvr radiation physics sect, Nuclear Develop Dept, 64-65, mgr, Nuclear Develop Dept, Martin Marietta Corp, 65-69; MGR, ENGINEERED PROD DEPT, MONSANTO RES CORP, 69- *Mem:* Am Nuclear Soc. *Res:* Instrumentation and control, particularly nuclear reactor control; radiation damage mechanism as related to electronic devices and materials; thermoelectric materials and devices; radioisotope sources. *Mailing Add:* Engineered Prod Dept Monsanto Res Corp Dayton OH 45407

SCHIMMEL, STEVEN DAVID, b New York, NY, Aug 31, 44; m 65; c 2. BIOCHEMISTRY. *Educ:* Columbia Col, BA, 66; Albert Einstein Col Med, PhD(molecular biol), 69. *Prof Exp:* Asst prof biochem, Col Med, Univ SFla, 74-81; MEM STAFF, DEPT INTERNAL MED, JAMES A HALEY VET ADMIN HOSP, 81- *Concurrent Pos:* NY Heart Asn fel, Albert Einstein Col Med, 70; Am Cancer Soc fel, Sch Med, Wash Univ, 71-73. *Mem:* AAAS; Am Chem Soc. *Res:* Enzymology of membranes and lipids; membrane structure and function; muscle development; thyroid hormone metabolism; tumor promoter mechanisms; insulin receptor structure and metabolism. *Mailing Add:* James A Haley Vet Admin Med Ctr 13000 N 30th St Tampa FL 33612

SCHIMMER, BERNARD PAUL, b Newark, NJ, June 14, 41; m 65; c 2. ENDOCRINOLOGY, MEDICAL RESEARCH. *Educ:* Rutgers Univ, BS, 62; Tufts Univ, PhD(pharmacol), 67. *Prof Exp:* Fel endocrinol & biochem, Brandeis Univ, 67-69; asst prof, 69-74, assoc prof, 74-80, PROF ENDOCRINOL & MED RES, UNIV TORONTO, 80- *Mem:* Am Soc Biol Chemists; Can Soc Biol Chemists; Can Endocrine Soc; AAAS. *Res:* Studies concerned with regulation of differentiated functions in mammalian somatic cell cultures, with principal emphasis on mechanism of hormone action, specifically ACTH action in adrenal cortex; hormone action studied through use of biochemistry and genetics in cell culture systems. *Mailing Add:* Banting & Best Dept Med Res Univ of Toronto 112 College St Toronto ON M5G 1L6 Can

SCHIMMERLING, WALTER, b Milan, Italy, Mar 10, 37; m 61; c 3. PHYSICS, BIOPHYSICS. *Educ:* Univ Buenos Aires, MS, 62; Rutgers Univ, PhD(radiation sci), 71. *Prof Exp:* Instr physics & Ger, Univ Buenos Aires, 59-62; res assoc physics, Atomic Energy Comn, Arg, 62-65; health physicist, Princeton Univ, 65-66, mem prof staff, Princeton-Pa Accelerator, 66-68, head, radiation measurements, 68-71, asst dir, 71-72; RES SR SCIENTIST, LAWRENCE BERKELEY LAB, UNIV CALIF, BERKELEY, 72- *Concurrent Pos:* Prin invest, NASA, 75- & Nat Cancer Inst, 78-; lectr, Univ Calif Exten, 78- *Mem:* Am Phys Soc; Radiation Res Soc. *Res:* High energy heavy ions. *Mailing Add:* Lawrence Berekely Lab Bldg 29 Rm 215C One Cyclotron Rd Berkeley CA 94720

SCHINDLER, ALBERT ISADORE, b Pittsburgh, Pa, June 24, 27; m 51; c 3. PHYSICS. *Educ:* Carnegie Inst Technol, BS, 47, MS, 48, DSc(physics), 50. *Prof Exp:* Asst physics, Carnegie Inst Technol, 47-50, res physicist, 50-51; physicist, 51-60, head metal physics br, Metall Div, 60-75, ASSOC DIR RES FOR MAT AND GEN SCI, US NAVAL RES LAB, 75- *Honors & Awards:* Hulburt Award, 56; Nat Capital Award, 62; Washington Acad Sci Award, 65; Naval Res Lab-Sci Res Soc Am Award, 65; Distinguished Achievement Sci, Dept of Navy, 75. *Mem:* Fel Am Phys Soc; Sigma Xi. *Res:* Solid state physics; physics of metals; ferromagnetism; low temperature properties; effects of alloying on physical properties. *Mailing Add:* Code 6000 Naval Res Lab 4555 Overlook Ave SW Washington DC 20375

SCHINDLER, CHARLES ALVIN, b Boston, Mass, Dec 27, 24; m 55; c 3. MICROBIOLOGY, BIOCHEMISTRY. *Educ:* Rensselaer Polytech Inst, BS, S0; Univ Tex, MA, 56, PhD(microbiol), 61. *Prof Exp:* Res & develop officer, Radiobiol Lab, Atomic Warfare Div, US Air Force, 52, asst prog dir, Armed Forces Spec Weapons Proj, 52-53, res scientist microbiol, Army Biol Warfare Lab, 56-58, Univ Tex, 61 & Armed Forces Inst Path, 62-68; asst prof microbiol, Univ Okla, 68-72; prof natural sci, Flagler Col, 72-73; SCI TEACHER, NORMAN PUB SCHS, 74- *Mem:* Am Soc Microbiol; Am Chem Soc; Brit Soc Gen Microbiol; NY Acad Sci. *Res:* Antibiotics and bacteriolytic enzymes, especially their production and mode of action on the bacterial cell; relationship of action of bacteriolytic enzymes to structure of microorganisms. *Mailing Add:* 2000 Morgan Dr Norman OK 73069

SCHINDLER, DAVID WILLIAM, b Fargo, NDak, Aug 3, 40; m 64, 79; c 3. LIMNOLOGY. *Educ:* NDak State Univ, BS, 62; Oxford Univ, DPhil(ecol), 66. *Hon Degrees:* DSc, NDak State Univ, 78. *Prof Exp:* Asst prof biol, Trent Univ, 66-68; RES SCIENTIST, FRESHWATER INST, CAN DEPT FISHERIES & OCEANS, 68-, DIR EXP LAKES AREA PROJ, 70- *Concurrent Pos:* Res grants, Can Nat Res Coun, Ont Dept Univ Affairs, 66-68 & NSF, 67-68; adj prof zool, Univ Man, 72-, adj prof bot, 81-; vis sr res assoc, Lamont-Doherty Geol Observ, Columbia Univ, 76-; chmn, US Nat Acad Sci Comt Atmosphere & Biosphere, 79-81. *Mem:* Am Soc Limnol & Oceanog (vpres, 81, 82); Brit Ecol Soc; Int Asn Theoret & Appl Limnol. *Mailing Add:* Freshwater Inst 501 University Crescent Winnipeg MB R3T 2N6 Can

SCHINDLER, GUENTER MARTIN, b Ebersdorf, Ger, Sept 15, 28; nat US; m 57; c 2. MATHEMATICS. *Educ:* Univ Gottingen, dipl, 53, Dr rer nat, 56. *Prof Exp:* Assoc math, Univ Gottingen, 53-56, res mathematician, Kernreactor, Karlsruhe, 56-57; res mathematician, Kernreactor, Karlsruhe, 56-57; sr mathematician, US Air Force Missile Develop Ctr, NMex, 57-58; sr scientist, Aerophys Develop Corp, Calif, 58-59; chief mathematician, Adv Tech Corp, 59-61; proj mgr, Gen Elec Co, 61-65; sr tech specialist, NAm Rockwell Corp, 65-68; prin scientist, Douglas Aircraft Co, Long Beach, Calif, 68-74; vis prof, Univ Southern Calif, 74-75; indep consult, 75-77; MEM TECH STAFF, ROCKWELL INT-ROCKETDYNE, CANOGA PARK, 77- *Concurrent Pos:* Lectr, Univ NMex, 58; assoc prof, Univ Calif, 58-59; consult, Avco-Crosley Corp, 59, Astro-Res Corp, 61-65 & US Navy Marine Eng Lab, 65. *Mem:* Am Math Soc; NY Acad Sci. *Res:* Pure and applied mathematics; theoretical physics. *Mailing Add:* 28026 Beechgate Dr Rancho Palos Verdes CA 90274

SCHINDLER, HANS, b Vienna, Austria, Sept 2, 11; nat US; m 39. PETROLEUM CHEMISTRY. *Educ:* Prague Ger Univ, DSc(org chem), 34. *Prof Exp:* Asst chief chemist, Julius Schindler Oil Works, Ger, 35-38; sr res chemist, Pure Oil Co, 38-46; sr res chemist, 46-52, mgr Petrolia Ref, 53-60, vpres, Sonneborn Div, Witco Chem Corp, 60-76; CONSULT, 76- *Concurrent Pos:* Mem, Tech Oil Mission, 45. *Mem:* NY Acad Sci; Am Inst Chem; Am Chem Soc. *Mailing Add:* 1 Washington Square Village New York NY 10012

SCHINDLER, JAMES EDWARD, b Fargo, NDak, Apr 20, 44; m 67; c 2. ZOOLOGY. *Educ:* NDak State Univ, BS, 66; Queen's Col, Oxford Univ, DPhil(zool), 69. *Prof Exp:* Asst prof Univ Ga, 69-76, ASSOC PROF ZOOL, CLEMSON UNIV, 76- *Mem:* Am Soc Limnol & Oceanog. *Res:* Aquatic ecology; limnology. *Mailing Add:* Dept of Zool Clemson Univ Clemson NC 29631

SCHINDLER, JOEL MARVIN, b New York, NY, Oct 27, 50; m 74; c 1. DEVELOPMENTAL BIOLOGY, CELL BIOLOGY. *Educ:* Hebrew Univ Jerusalem, BSc, 73, MSc, 75; Univ Pittsburgh, PhD(biol), 78. *Prof Exp:* Teaching & res asst, develop biol, Hebrew Univ Jerusalem, 73-75; teaching fel biol, Univ Pittsburgh, 76-77, researcher, 77-78; fel develop biol, Roche Inst Molecular Biol, 78-81; ASST PROF, DEPT ANAT, COL MED, UNIV CINCINNATI, 81- *Mem:* Sigma Xi; Soc Develop Biol. *Res:* Molecular aspects of development and differentiation; cell-cell interaction; interaction between differentiating cells and their environment; changes in the expression of active gene sequences during differentiation. *Mailing Add:* Dept Anat Col Med Univ Cincinnati Cincinnati OH 45267

SCHINDLER, JOHN FREDERICK, b Chicago, Ill, Aug 23, 31; m 55; c 2. FRESH WATER BIOLOGY. *Educ:* Mich State Univ, BS, 53, MS, 60. *Prof Exp:* Res asst phycol, Mich State Univ, 53, 54, 59-60; test design aide & off biol warfare, US Army, Dugway Proving Ground, Utah, 56-57; chief foreman mining, Minnas Cerro Colo, Mex, 58; asst dir, Naval Arctic Res Lab, Univ Alaska-Off Naval Res, 60-71, dir, 71-73; chief scientist & environ eng, Alaskan Resource Sci Corp, 73-76; DIR ENVIRON AFFAIRS, HUSKY OIL NPR OPERS INC, 76- *Concurrent Pos:* Mem, NSF Chihuahua Biol Exped, 55; mem, Scott Polar Res; arctic consult & vpres, Pac Alaska Assoc Ltd, 73-, environ consult, Pipeline Coordr Off, State Alaska, 75-76. *Mem:* AAAS; Phycol Soc Am; Soc Am Mil Eng; fel Arctic Inst NAm; Explorers Club. *Res:* Arctic logistics and science support in the Arctic; Arctic oceanography; freshwater algae of the Flathead Basin, Montana; genus Staurastrum. *Mailing Add:* 2473 Captain Cook Dr Anchorage AK 99503

SCHINDLER, MAX J, b Warnsdorf, Czech, June 21, 22; US citizen; m 55; c 3. COMPUTER SCIENCE, MICROWAVES. *Educ:* Vienna Tech Univ, Dipl Ing, 51, Dr Tech Sc, 53. *Prof Exp:* Asst sound recording & magnetics res, Vienna Tech Univ, 51-54; engr, Tungsram-Watt, Austria, 54-57; res scientist, Aeronaut Res Lab, Wright Air Develop Ctr, Ohio, 57-58; engr, Phys & Chem Lab, RCA Microwave, NJ, 58-61, lead engr, 62-67, mem tech staff, RCA Labs, David Sarnoff Res Ctr, 67-69, sr engr solid state & TWT subsysts eng, RCA Microwave, Harrison, 69-75; comput consult, 76; comput ed, Electronic Design, 76-79; PRES, PRIME TECHNOL INC, 80- *Concurrent Pos:* Eng physics consult, Nat Corp Sci, NY, 77-; Microwave consult, Photovolt, NY, 78- *Honors & Awards:* Award, Inst Elec & Electronics Engrs, 76. *Mem:* Inst Elec & Electronics Engrs. *Res:* Magnetic materials and measurements; magnetic focusing structures; high-efficiency traveling-wave tubes; microwave solid state amplifiers; electronic delay devices; computer-aided design; computer system design. *Mailing Add:* RD 3 Box 77 Rockaway Dr Boonton NJ 07005

SCHINDLER, STEPHEN MICHAEL, b New York, NY, Apr 9, 40; m 61; c 2. ASTROPHYSICS. *Educ:* Long Island Univ, BS, 68; Colo State Univ, PhD(physics), 74. *Prof Exp:* Sr scientist physics, Bettis Atomic Power Lab, 73-74; res assoc physics, Case Western Reserve Univ, 74-78; SR SCIENTIST & MEM PROF STAFF PHYSICS, CALIF INST TECHNOL, 79- *Mem:* Am Phys Soc. *Res:* High energy astrophysics, with emphasis in gamma-ray astronomy, cosmic ray origin theory, and solar particle production. *Mailing Add:* 220-47 Downs Lab Calif Inst Technol Pasadena CA 91125

SCHINDLER, SUSAN, b Brooklyn, NY, June 4, 42. MATHEMATICS. *Educ:* Mt Holyoke Col, AB, 63; Univ Wis, MA, 65, PhD(math), 69. *Prof Exp:* Asst prof math, Long Island Univ, 69-70; asst prof, 70-77; PROF MATH, BARUCH COL, 77- *Mem:* Am Math Soc; Math Asn Am; Soc Indust & Appl Math. *Res:* Decompositions of group representations. *Mailing Add:* Baruch Col 17 Lexington Ave New York NY 10016

SCHINDLER, WILLIAM JOSEPH, b Cleveland, Ohio, Dec 11, 31; m 72; c 3. ENDOCRINOLOGY. *Educ:* Univ Calif, Los Angeles, BA, 55, PhD(anat), 59; Baylor Col Med, MD, 74. *Prof Exp:* Asst physiol, Sch Med, Univ Calif, Los Angeles, 55-56, asst anat, 56-57, interdisciplinary trainee neurol sci, 58-59; instr, 59-60, asst prof, 62-67, ASSOC PROF PHYSIOL, BAYLOR COL MED, 67- *Concurrent Pos:* NSF fel neuroendocrinol, Maudsley Hosp, London, 60-61, Found Fund for Res in Psychiat fel, 61-62; Nat Inst Arthritis & Metab Dis res career develop award, 66- *Mem:* AAAS; Endocrine Soc; Am Physiol Soc; Soc Exp Biol & Med; NY Acad Sci. *Res:* Neuroendocrinology; developmental endocrinology, especially pituitary-thyroid maturation and function; human infertility; growth hormone secretion and control. *Mailing Add:* Dept of Physiol Baylor Col Med Houston TX 77030

SCHINGOETHE, DAVID JOHN, b Aurora, Ill, Feb 15, 42; m 64; c 2. DAIRY NUTRITION. *Educ:* Univ Ill, Urbana, BS, 64, MS, 65; Mich State Univ, PhD(nutrit), 68. *Prof Exp:* Assoc prof, 69-80, PROF DAIRY SCI & NUTRIT, SOUTH DAK STATE UNIV, 80- *Concurrent Pos:* NSF res grants, 70- *Mem:* Am Dairy Sci Asn; Am Soc Animal Sci; Am Inst Nutrit. *Res:* Nutritional biochemistry of rumen metabolism; gastrointestinal digestion and absorption; milk synthesis; isolation of naturally occurring animal growth inhibitors; protein and vitamin E nutrition of dairy cattle; whey utilization. *Mailing Add:* Dept of Dairy Sci SDak Univ Brookings SD 57007

SCHINK, CHESTER ALBERT, b Portland, Ore, Feb 17, 20; m 47; c 2. ORGANIC CHEMISTRY. *Educ:* Reed Col, BA, 41; Ore State Col, MA, 43, PhD(org chem), 47. *Prof Exp:* Chemist, Exp Sta, Hercules Powder Co, Del, 43-44, Radford Ord Works, Va, 44-45; asst, Ore State Col, 45-47; res chemist, E I du Pont de Nemours & Co, Inc, 47-51; mgr, Krishell Labs, Inc, 51-56; mgr, Chem Support Lab, 56-70, sr chemist, 70-71, CORP CHEMIST, TEKTRONIX, INC, 71- *Mem:* Pollution Control Asn; Am Indust Hyg Asn; Am Chem Soc. *Res:* Identification of constituents of natural products; biologically active compounds; synthetic resins and plastics primarily of the vinyl type; research chemicals, especially purines, pyrimidines and enzymes; air and water quality; water pollution control, industrial hygiene and safety. *Mailing Add:* 3943 SE Cooper St Portland OR 97202

SCHINK, DAVID R, b Los Angeles, Calif, Aug 3, 31; m 51; c 4. CHEMICAL OCEANOGRAPHY. *Educ:* Pomona Col, BA, 52; Univ Calif-Los Angeles, MS, 53; Univ Calif-San Diego, PhD(oceanog), 62; Stanford Univ, MS, 58. *Prof Exp:* Res geochemist, Scripps Inst, Calif, 60-62; asst prof oceanog, Narragansett Marine Lab, Univ RI, 62-66; mgr air-ocean studies, Palo Alto Labs, Teledyne-Isotopes, 66-71; assoc prof, 72-76, PROF OCEANOG, TEX A&M UNIV, 76- *Concurrent Pos:* Mem, Atomic Safety & Licensing Bd Panel, Nuclear Regulatory Comn, 74- *Mem:* AAAS; Am Geophys Union. *Res:* Oceanic silicon budgets and behavior; air-ocean gas exchange; hydrocarbons in sea water. *Mailing Add:* Dept of Oceanog Tex A&M Univ College Station TX 77843

SCHINZINGER, ROLAND, b Osaka, Japan, Nov 22, 26; nat US; m 52; c 3. ELECTRICAL ENGINEERING. *Educ:* Univ Calif, BS, 53, MS, 54, PhD, 66. *Prof Exp:* Engr, Westinghouse Elec Corp, Pa, 54-58; prof elec eng, Robert Col, Istanbul, 58-63; assoc prof, 66-80, PROF ELEC ENG, UNIV CALIF, IRVINE, 80- *Mem:* AAAS; Inst Elec & Electronics Engrs; Opers Res Soc Am. *Res:* Power systems; utility networks; operations research. *Mailing Add:* Sch Eng Univ Calif Irvine CA 92717

SCHIOLER, LISELOTTE JENSEN, b Copenhagen, Denmark, May 8, 50; US citizen. CRYSTAL CHEMISTRY. *Educ:* Ohio State Univ, BFA, 74, BS, 77; Mass Technol ScD, 82. *Prof Exp:* CERAMIC RES ENGR, ARMY MAT MECH RES CTR, DEPT DEFENSE, 79- *Mem:* Am Ceramic Soc; Am Crystallog Asn. *Res:* Processing/properties relationships. *Mailing Add:* Bldg 313N Arsenal St Watertown MA 02172

SCHIPMA, PETER B, b Chicago, Ill, Oct 24, 41; m 62; c 3. INFORMATION SCIENCE. *Educ:* Ill Inst Technol, BS, 65, MS, 67. *Prof Exp:* Res asst physics, R R Donnelley & Sons Co, 62-66; from asst scientist to assoc scientist info sci, 67-70, res scientist, 70-72, MGR INFO SCI, IIT RES INST, 72- *Concurrent Pos:* Adj assoc prof, Ill Inst Technol, 67-74; consult, WHO, 77-, Sandia Arabia, 81; instr, Trinity Christian Col, 77-; chmn finance comt, Asn Info & Dissemination Ctrs, 78-79. *Mem:* Am Soc Info Sci; Asn Info & Dissemination Ctrs (secy-treas, 77). *Res:* Machine-readable data base design; application of video technology to information retrieval; artificial intelligence. *Mailing Add:* IIT Res Inst 10 W 35th St Chicago IL 60616

SCHIPPER, ARTHUR LOUIS, JR, b Bryan, Tex, Apr 8, 40; m 64; c 2. PLANT PATHOLOGY, PLANT PHYSIOLOGY. *Educ:* Univ of the South, BS, 62; Univ Minn, St Paul, MS, 65, PhD(plant path), 68. *Prof Exp:* Plant physiologist, NCent Forest Exp Sta, 68-78, STAFF RES PLANT PATHOLOGIST, WASHINGTON OFF, FOREST SERV, USDA, 79- *Concurrent Pos:* Adj asst prof, Dept Plant Path, Univ Minn, 68-75; adj assoc prof, 75-78. *Mem:* Am Phytopath Soc; AAAS; Sigma Xi. *Res:* Biochemical and physiological changes in plants infected with plant parasitic fungi. *Mailing Add:* FIDR 605 RP-E Forest Serv USDA PO Box 2417 Washington DC 20013

SCHIPPER, EDGAR, b Vienna, Austria, Sept 12, 20; nat US; m 51; c 2. ORGANIC CHEMISTRY. *Educ:* City Col New York, BS, 47; Univ Pa, MS, 48, PhD(chem), 51. *Prof Exp:* Pharmaceut chemist, Gold Leaf Pharmaceut Co, 41-42; assoc chemist, Ethicon, Inc, 51-61; mgr org & med chem, Shulton, Inc, 61-65; GROUP LEADER, ETHICON INC, 65- *Mem:* Am Chem Soc. *Res:* Medicinal organic chemistry; biomedical devices research. *Mailing Add:* 44 Nomahegan Ct Cranford NJ 07016

SCHIPPER, ITHEL ARIE, b Pelican Rapids, Minn, June 17, 19; m 41; c 1. VETERINARY VIROLOGY, VETERINARY PHARMACOLOGY. *Educ:* Univ Minn, BS, 46, MS, 47, DVM, 51; NDak State Univ, MS, 71. From asst prof to assoc prof, 54-69, PROF VET SCI, N DAK STATE UNIV, 69- *Concurrent Pos:* NIH fel virol, Colo State Univ, 65-66; postdoctoral fel, Dept Vet Med, Colo St Univ, 65-66. *Mem:* Am Vet Med Asn; Am Col Vet Toxicol; Am Soc Microbiol; NY Acad Sci; Royal Soc Health. *Res:* Bovine mastitis; antibiotics; Herpes virus; bovine virus diarrhea. *Mailing Add:* Dept of Vet Med NDak State Univ Fargo ND 58102

SCHIPPER, LEE (LEON JAY), b Santa Monica, Calif, Apr 7, 47; m 71; c 2. ENERGY ANALYSIS, ENERGY POLICY. *Educ:* Univ Calif, Berkeley, AB, 68, MA, 71, PhD(physics), 82. *Prof Exp:* LECTR ACOUST, SAN FRANCISCO CONSERV MUSIC, 71-; STAFF SCIENTIST ENERGY ANAL, LAWRENCE BERKELEY LAB, UNIV CALIF, 77- *Concurrent Pos:* Specialist energy anal, Energy & Resources Group, Univ Calif, 74-77; mem Demand Panel, Study Nuclear & Alternative Energy Syst, Nat Acad Sci, 76-78; energy consult to various int orgn, 76-; guest researcher, Beijer Inst, Royal Swed Acad Sci, 77- *Honors & Awards:* Royal Medal, HM King Karl 16th Gustav, Sweden, 78. *Mem:* Soc Heating & Air Conditioning Engrs, Sweden; AAAS; Int Asn Energy Economists. *Res:* Conservation; policy; economics of energy systems; energy use in developing countries; structure of clusters of galaxies; life and recordings of Wilhelm Furtwaengler, conductor; acoustics. *Mailing Add:* Lawrence Berkeley Lab Univ of Calif Berkeley CA 94720

SCHIRALDI, MICHAEL THOMAS, physical chemistry, polymer physics, see previous edition

SCHIRBER, JAMES E, b Eureka, SDak, June 9, 31; m 55; c 7. SOLID STATE PHYSICS. *Educ:* St John's Univ, 53; Mass Inst Technol, 53-54; Iowa State Univ, PhD(physics), 60. *Prof Exp:* Nat Acad Sci-Nat Res Coun fel, Bristol, 61-62; staff mem, 62-64, div supvr solid state physics, 64-68, MGR SOLID STATE RES DEPT, SANDIA LABS, 68- *Mem:* Fel Am Phys Soc. *Res:* Low temperature high pressure metal physics; Fermi surface of metals under hydrostatic pressure; magnetism and superconductivity studies under pressure. *Mailing Add:* Dept 5150 Sandia Labs Albuquerque NM 87185

SCHIRCH, LAVERNE GENE, b Chenoa, Ill, Aug 9, 36; m 58; c 3. BIOCHEMISTRY, ORGANIC CHEMISTRY. *Educ:* Bluffton Col, BS, 58; Univ Mich, PhD(biochem), 63. *Prof Exp:* From asst prof to prof chem, Bluffton Col, 63-78; ASSOC PROF BIOCHEM, MED COL VA, VA COMMONWEALTH UNIV, 78- *Concurrent Pos:* Res consult, Ente Nazionale Idrocarburi, Rome, 69-70. *Mem:* Am Chem Soc; Am Soc Biol Chemists. *Res:* Mechanism of action of serine and threonine aldolases, especially the role of pyridoxal phosphate in these enzymes. *Mailing Add:* Dept of Biochem Va Commonwealth Univ Richmond VA 23298

SCHIRMER, HELGA H, b Chemnitz, Ger, Oct 18, 27. MATHEMATICS. *Educ:* Univ Frankfurt, MSc, 53; Dr rer nat(math), 54. *Prof Exp:* Brit Coun res scholar math, Univ Oxford, 54-56; asst lectr, Univ Wales, 56-59; from asst prof to assoc prof, Univ NB, 59-66; assoc prof, 66-74, PROF MATH, CARLETON UNIV, 74- *Mem:* Am Math Soc; Can Math Cong. *Res:* General and algebraic topology; theory of fixed points and coincidences; multifunctions. *Mailing Add:* Dept of Math Carleton Univ Ottawa ON K1S 5B6 Can

SCHIRMER, JOSEPH P, JR, b Rochester, NY, Feb 22, 38; m 60; c 2. ORGANIC CHEMISTRY. *Educ:* St John Fisher Col, BS, 59; State Univ NY Buffalo, PhD(org chem), 65. *Prof Exp:* MEM STAFF, FIBER TECH CTR, GOODYEAR TIRE & RUBBER CO, 65- *Res:* Synthesis, characterization, evaluation and applications of copolyesters for use as hot melt adhesives; solution adhesives and powder coatings chemistry; properties and uses for block copolymer elastomers. *Mailing Add:* 3318 Helmsdale Dr Akron OH 44312

SCHISLA, ROBERT M, b Indianapolis, Ind, Mar 30, 30; m 53; c 5. ORGANIC CHEMISTRY. *Educ:* Purdue Univ, BS, 52, MS, 54, PhD(org chem), 57. *Prof Exp:* Asst, Purdue Univ, 52-54; res chemist, Monsanto Co, 57-61, sr res chemist, 61-65, res specialist, 65, group leader, 66-71, RES SPECIALIST FINE CHEM, MONSANTO INDUST CHEM CO, 71- *Res:* Synthetic organic chemistry related to functional fluids and fine chemicals; process development for fine chemicals. *Mailing Add:* 1333 Woodgate St Louis MO 63122

SCHISLER, LEE CHARLES, b Northampton, Pa, June 25, 28; m 51; c 2. MYCOLOGY. *Educ:* Pa State Univ, BS, 50, MS, 52, PhD(bot), 57. *Prof Exp:* Dir res, Butler Co Mushroom Farm, Inc, 57-64; PROF PLANT PATH, PA STATE UNIV, 64- *Mem:* Am Soc Plant Physiol; Mycol Soc Am; Am Phytopathological Soc. *Res:* Physiology and pathology of cultivated mushrooms; fungus physiology and mycology. *Mailing Add:* 116 Buckhout Lab Pa State Univ University Park PA 16802

SCHISSLER, DONALD OWEN, b Spangler, Pa, May 1, 23; m 45, 75; c 3. PHYSICAL CHEMISTRY. *Educ:* Pa State Univ, BS, 42; Princeton Univ, MA, 50, PhD(chem), 51. *Prof Exp:* Asst res chemist, Houdry Process Corp, 43-44, assoc res chemist, 46-48; asst, Princeton Univ, 48-50; res chemist, Shell Develop Co, 51-65, mgr, Chem & Chem Eng Dept, 65-67, dir indust chem, Res & Develop Lab, Shell Chem Co, 67-71, tech mgr, Indust Chem Div Mfg, 71-72, mgr mat sci & eng, 72-74, tech supt, 74-77, mgr qual assurance, 77-80, MGR MEASUREMENT & LOSS CONTROL, SHELL OIL CO, 80- *Mem:* Am Chem Soc. *Res:* Mass spectrometry; catalysis; radiation chemistry; optical spectroscopy. *Mailing Add:* Shell Oil Co PO Box 2099 Houston TX 77001

SCHIVELL, JOHN FRANCIS, b Cleveland, Ohio, Sept 5, 42; m 66. PLASMA PHYSICS. *Educ:* Harvard Univ, AB, 63, AM, 64, PhD(physics), 68. *Prof Exp:* Physicist, Nat Accelerator Lab, 68-73; MEM TECH STAFF, PRINCETON PLASMA PHYSICS LAB, 73- *Mem:* Am Phys Soc. *Res:* Photoproduction of elementary particles; design and development of particle accelerators; design, construction, and basic measurements on tokamak plasma confinement devices; software systems for experiment control and analysis. *Mailing Add:* Princeton Plasma Physics Lab PO Box 451 Princeton NJ 08540

SCHJEIDE, OLE ARNE, b Heroy, Norway, Nov 15, 21; US citizen; c 2. CELL BIOLOGY, RADIOBIOLOGY. *Educ:* Univ Calif, Los Angeles, AB, 48, MA, 50, PhD(zool), 52. *Prof Exp:* Asst res biologist, Atomic Energy Proj, Univ Calif, Los Angeles, 53-59, assoc res biologist radiobiol & biophys, Lab Nuclear Med & Radiation Biol, 59-65, res biologist & lectr biophys, 65-69; PROF BIOL SCI & CELL BIOL, NORTHERN ILL UNIV, 69- *Concurrent Pos:* Asst prof radiobiol, Univ Calif, Los Angeles, 54-63, asst prof biophys, 61-63; Nat Acad Sci travel award, Int Cong Radiobiol, Cortina, 64; consult, Inst Arteriosclerosis Res, 65-; vis lectr, Pepperdine Univ, 66-69; vis prof, Univ Marburg, WGer, 74, 75, 76 & 77. *Mem:* Radiation Res Soc; Soc Develop Biol; Am Soc Cell Biol; Soc Study Reprod; Am Aging Asn. *Res:* Biochemical, metabolic and morphological parameters of cell and organelle growth; effects of ionizing radiations on differentiation and aging. *Mailing Add:* Dept of Biol Sci Northern Ill Univ De Kalb IL 60115

SCHJELDERUP, HASSEL CHARLES, b Vernon, BC, June 18, 26; US citizen; m 53; c 7. ENGINEERING MECHANICS. *Educ:* Univ BC, BASc, 49; Stanford Univ, MSc, 50, PhD(eng mech), 53. *Prof Exp:* Asst, Stanford Univ, 49-52; group leader struct eng, Northrop Aircraft Corp, 53-55; tech asst strength & dynamics, Douglas Aircraft Corp, 55-59; assoc dir eng, Nat Eng Sci Co, 59-64; dir eng, Dynamic Sci Corp, 64-65; mgr advan technol, 65-67, asst dir res, 67-68, dir res, 68-72, dep dir mat & process eng, 72-79, DIR MAT

& PROCESS ENG, DOUGLAS AIRCRAFT CORP, LONG BEACH, 79- *Concurrent Pos:* Instr, Exten, Univ Calif, Los Angeles, 53-58; struct & dynamics consult, 53- *Mem:* Am Inst Aeronaut & Astronaut; Soc Advan Mat & Process Engrs. *Res:* Random vibrations; structural vibration and fatigue caused by jet engine noise; advanced composite materials. *Mailing Add:* Douglas Aircraft Corp 3855 Lakewood Blvd Long Beach CA 90846

SCHLABACH, T(OM) D(ANIEL), b Cleveland, Ohio, July 4, 24; m 48; c 2. METALLURGY, PHYSICAL CHEMISTRY. *Educ:* Baldwin-Wallace Col, BS, 48; Mich State Col, PhD(chem), 52. *Prof Exp:* Asst, Mich State Col, 48-49 & 51-52; mem tech staff & res chemist, 52-59, supvr, 59-65, DEPT HEAD METALL ENG, BELL TEL LABS, INC, 65- *Mem:* AAAS; Am Chem Soc; Am Soc Testing & Mat; Am Soc Metals; Am Inst Mining, Metall & Petrol Engrs. *Res:* Alloy development; mechanical properties; composites; surface chemistry. *Mailing Add:* Bell Tel Labs Rm 1A-160 Murray Hill NJ 07971

SCHLACHTER, ALFRED SIMON, b Cedar City, Utah, Feb 18, 42. ATOMIC PHYSICS. *Educ:* Univ Calif, Berkeley, AB, 63; Univ Wis, Madison, MA, 65, PhD(physics), 69. *Prof Exp:* Asst physics, Univ Wis, 63-68; prin res scientist, Honeywell Corp Res Ctr, 68-70; res assoc, Faculty Sci, Inst Fundamental Electronics, Univ Paris & Researcher, Saclay Nuclear Res Ctr, 71-75; PHYSICIST, LAWRENCE BERKELEY LAB, UNIV CALIF, 75- *Concurrent Pos:* Nat Ctr Sci Res fel, Univ Paris, 71-72; Joliot-Curie Fel, Saclay Nuclear Res Ctr, 72-73; vis scientist, Justus-Liebig Univ, Giessen, WGer, 80-81. *Mem:* Am Phys Soc. *Res:* Atomic collisions for fusion energy; sources of metastable atoms and negative ions; intense sources of neutral atomic beams; multicharged ion-atom collisions. *Mailing Add:* Lawrence Berkeley Lab Univ Calif Berkeley CA 94720

SCHLAEGER, ALBERT JOSEPH, industrial chemistry, see previous edition

SCHLAEGER, RALPH, b Milwaukee, Wis, Nov 24, 21. RADIOLOGY. *Educ:* Univ Wis, BS, 42, MD, 45; Univ Pa, 48-49. *Prof Exp:* Asst instr radiol, Temple Univ, 50-52, instr, 52-54; from instr to assoc prof, 54-71, PROF CLIN RADIOL, COLUMBIA UNIV, 71- *Mem:* Radiol Soc NAm; fel Am Col Radiol; Soc Gastrointestinal Radiol; Am Asn Hist Med. *Res:* Radiology, especially the gastrointestinal tract. *Mailing Add:* Presby Hosp 622 W 168th St New York NY 10032

SCHLAG, EDWARD WILLIAM, b Los Angeles, Calif, Jan 12, 32; m 55; c 3. PHYSICAL CHEMISTRY. *Educ:* Occidental Col, BA, 53; Univ Wash, PhD(phys chem), 58. *Prof Exp:* Res asst, Univ Wash, 54-58; Wissenschaftlicher asst, Inst Phys Chem, Univ Bonn, 58-59; res chemist, Yerkes Lab, E I du Pont de Nemours & Co, NY, 59-60; from asst prof to prof phys chem, Northwestern Univ, Evanston, 60-71; PROF PHYS CHEM, MUNICH TECH UNIV, 71- *Concurrent Pos:* Alfred P Sloan res fel, 65-67. *Mem:* Am Phys Soc; Bavarian Acad Sci. *Res:* Energy transfer; gas phase reaction kinetics; photochemistry of the vacuum and near ultraviolet; laser chemistry; laser spectroscopy; radiationless processes. *Mailing Add:* Inst for Phys Chem 8046 Garching Lichtenbergstr 4 Germany, Federal Republic of

SCHLAG, JOHN, b Liege, Belg, Feb 13, 27; US citizen; m 53; c 2. NEUROPHYSIOLOGY. *Educ:* Univ Liege, MD, 52. *Prof Exp:* Asst exp therapeut, Univ Liege, 53-61, lectr psychophysiol, 60-61; asst res anatomist, 61-63, from asst prof to assoc prof, 63-69, PROF ANAT, UNIV CALIF, LOS ANGELES, 69- *Concurrent Pos:* Fulbright grant, Univ Wash, 53-54; NIH res career develop award, 64-; secy, Belg Nat Ctr Anesthesiol, 59-61. *Honors & Awards:* Theophile Gluge Prize, Royal Acad Belg, 61. *Mem:* Am Physiol Soc; Fr Asn Physiol; Belg Asn Physiol; Int Brain Res Orgn; corresp mem Royal Acad Med Belg. *Res:* Cerebral control of motor functions; spontaneous activity of cerebral neurons; mechanisms of cortical evoked potentials. *Mailing Add:* Dept of Anat Univ of Calif Los Angeles CA 90024

SCHLAGEL, CARL ALVIN, b Meridian, Pa, Dec 14, 23; m 48; c 2. PHARMACOLOGY. *Educ:* Univ Pittsburgh, BS, 52; Ohio State Univ, MS, 54, PhD(pharmacol), 55. *Prof Exp:* Res assoc prod develop, 55-58, sect head pharmacol, 59-61, CLIN INVESTR, UPJOHN CO, 61- *Mem:* AAAS; Am Pharmaceut Asn; Acad Pharmaceut Sci; Am Acad Dermat; Am Fedn Clin Res. *Res:* Clinical drug evaluation methodology; mental disease drugs, anti-inflammatory drugs and topical therapeutic agents; electronic medical instrumentation. *Mailing Add:* 3411 Pinegrove Lane Kalamazoo MI 49008

SCHLAGENHAUFF, REINHOLD EUGENE, b Amsterdam, Neth, Aug 14, 23; US citizen; m 55; c 2. NEUROLOGY. *Educ:* Univ Würzburg, MD, 51. *Prof Exp:* dir, EEG, Electromyography & Echoencephalography Dept, Meyer Mem Hosp, Buffalo, 63-81, assoc dir, Dept Neurol, 69-81; ASSOC PROF NEUROL, STATE UNIV NY BUFFALO, 72-; DIR, DEPT NEUROL, ERIE COUNTY MED CTR, 81- *Concurrent Pos:* Consult neurol & EEG, Vet Admin Hosp, Buffalo, Buffalo Psychiat Ctr & Gowanda Psychiat Ctr, 68- & West Seneca Develop Ctr, 70- *Mem:* Acad Neurol; Am Med EEG Asn; Am Inst Ultrasonics in Med; AMA; Am Psychiat Asn. *Res:* Clinical neurology, electroencephalography, electromyography and ultrasound (Doppler flow). *Mailing Add:* 41 Chaumont Dr Williamsville NY 14221

SCHLAGER, GUNTHER, b New York, NY, Jan 14, 33; m 56; c 3. GENETICS. *Educ:* Univ Denver, BA, 56; Univ Kans, MA, 59, PhD(entom), 62. *Prof Exp:* USPHS fel, Hall Lab, Mammalian Genetics, Univ Kans, 61-62; assoc staff scientist, Jackson Lab, 62-65, staff scientist, 65-69; assoc prof, 69-72, chmn dept, 72-79, PROF SYSTS & ECOL, UNIV KANS, 72-, CHMN, DIV BIOL SCI, 79- *Concurrent Pos:* Lectr, Univ Maine, 64-69; vis prof genetics, Sch Med, Univ Hawaii, 75; mem genetic subgroup Hypertension Task Force, Nat Heart Lung & Blood Inst, NIH, 76-78; consult, Med Dept, Brookhaven Nat Lab, 77- *Mem:* Genetics Soc Am; AAAS; Environ Mutagen Soc; Biometric Soc. *Res:* Quantitative genetics; genetics of blood pressure in mice. *Mailing Add:* Dept of Systs & Ecol Univ of Kans Lawrence KS 66045

SCHLAGER, SEYMOUR I, b Hanover, Ger, April 20, 49; US citizen; m 71; c 2. TUMOR IMMUNOLOGY, MOLECULAR & CELLULAR IMMUNOLOGY. *Educ:* Univ Ill, BS, 69, Med Ctr, MS, 73, PhD(microbiol & immunol), 75. *Prof Exp:* Proj chemist, H B Taylor Co, 69-70; sr chemist, DeSoto, Inc, 70-71; grad res assoc med immunol, Univ Ill Med Ctr, 71-75; staff fel, Nat Cancer Inst, NIH, 75-78, sr staff fel, 78-80, cancer expert, 80; ASSOC PROF IMMUNOL, UNIV NOTRE DAME, 80- *Concurrent Pos:* Assoc prof & lectr, George Washington Univ, 78-80; consult, Waters Assocs, 77-; sci adviser, NIH, 80- & WHO, 82-; vis prof, Ponce Med Sch, 81- *Mem:* Am Asn Immunologists; Am Asn Cancer Res; NY Acad Sci; AAAS; Found Advan Educ Sci. *Res:* Molecular interactions between tumor cell membranes and humoral and cellular components of the immune system; mechanisms of tumor cell killing by lymphocytes and macrophages; the role of tumor cell metabolism in resisting immune killing. *Mailing Add:* Dept Microbiol Univ Notre Dame Notre Dame IN 46556

SCHLAIKJER, CARL ROGER, b Boston, Mass, Mar 3, 40; m 70. ELECTROCHEMISTRY. *Educ:* Harvard Univ, AB, 61; Mass Inst Technol, PhD(inorg nuclear chem), 66. *Prof Exp:* Mem res staff, Arthur D Little, Inc, 65-67; mem staff, Lab Phys Sci, P R Mallory & Co, 68-75, staff scientist, 75-78, MGR RES, POWER SOURCES CTR, GTE LABS, INC, 78- *Mem:* Am Chem Soc; Electrochem Soc; AAAS; Sigma Xi. *Res:* Solid state electrolyte cells and systems; organic and inorganic electrolyte primary and secondary batteries; interaction of alkali and alkaline earth metals with organic and inorganic systems. *Mailing Add:* GTE Labs Inc 40 Sylvan Rd Waltham MA 02254

SCHLAIN, DAVID, b Philadelphia, Pa, July 21, 10. CHEMICAL ENGINEERING. *Educ:* Univ Pa, BS, 32, MS, 37; Univ Md, PhD(chem eng), 51. *Prof Exp:* Metallurgist & chemist, 37-48, electrochemist, 48-52, chief galvanic corrosion sect, 52-55, supvry chem res engr, 55-58, proj coordr, 58-70, res supvr, 70-74, RES CHEM ENGR, US BUR MINES, 74- *Mem:* Electrochem Soc; Am Inst Mining, Metall & Petrol Engrs; Nat Asn Corrosion Engrs; fel Am Inst Chemists; Am Inst Chem Engrs. *Res:* Electrowinning and electrorefining of metals; metallic corrosion; electrodeposition of coatings from molten salts and aqueous baths; effects of ultrasonics on metallurgical processes; electrometallurgy; crystallization. *Mailing Add:* 2A Gardenway Greenbelt MD 20770

SCHLAM, ELLIOTT, b New York, NY, Oct 7, 40; m 66; c 2. ELECTRONICS, PHYSICS. *Educ:* NY Univ, BEE, 61, MEE, 64, PhD(elec eng), 66; Fairleigh Dickinson Univ, MS, 74. *Prof Exp:* Mem tech staff electroluminescence, RCA Corp, 64, design engr digital design, 61-62; TEAM LEADER DISPLAYS, US ARMY, 66-; INSTR, GEORGE WASHINGTON UNIV, 76- *Concurrent Pos:* Dep army mem, Adv Group Electron Devices, 75-; assoc ed, Transactions on Electron Devices, Inst Elec & Electronics Engrs, 78- *Mem:* Inst Elec & Electronics Engrs; Soc Info Display. *Res:* Display devices; rare earth activate phosphors and DC excited rare earth activated zinc sulphide electroluminescent devices; thin film electroluminescent displays; thin film transistor addressed displays. *Mailing Add:* USAERADCOM DELET-BD Ft Monmouth NJ 07703

SCHLAMEUS, HERMAN WADE, b Blanco, Tex, Nov 27, 37; m 61. ORGANIC CHEMISTRY. *Educ:* Southwest Tex State Univ, BS, 60. *Prof Exp:* Technician chem, 60-62, res chemist, 62-70, SR RES CHEMIST, SOUTHWEST RES INST, 70- *Mem:* Sigma Xi. *Res:* Mainly concerned in research and development in the field of microencapsulation. *Mailing Add:* Southwest Res Inst 6220 Culebra Rd San Antonio TX 78238

SCHLAMOWITZ, MAX, b New York, NY, Nov 13, 19; m 44; c 1. BIOCHEMISTRY, IMMUNOCHEMISTRY. *Educ:* City Col New York, BS, 40; Univ Mich, MS, 41, PhD(biochem), 46. *Prof Exp:* Res assoc, Manhattan Dist, Rochester Univ, 44-45; instr biochem, Univ Calif, 47-50; asst, Sloan-Kettering Inst Cancer Res, 51-54; assoc cancer res scientist, Roswell Park Mem Inst, 54-62; assoc prof microbiol, Baylor Col Med, 62-64; assoc biologist, 64-67, assoc biochemist, 67-71, chief sect immunochem & immunol, 67-81, BIOCHEMIST, SYST CANCER CTR, UNIV TEX M D ANDERSON HOSP & TUMOR INST, HOUSTON, 71-, ASSOC PROF BIOCHEM, GRAD SCH BIOMED SCI, UNIV TEX, HOUSTON, 79- *Concurrent Pos:* Markle Found fel, Univ Calif, 46-47; USPHS & Du Pont fels, Ohio State Univ, 50-51. *Mem:* AAAS; Am Soc Biol Chemists; Am Asn Immunol; NY Acad Sci; Reticuloendothelial Soc. *Res:* Carbohydrate chemistry; enzymes; ribonuclease; immunoglobulin chemistry and membrane transport; hormone receptors; phospho-glucomutase-phosphatase; pepsin; glycoproteins; Fc receptors. *Mailing Add:* Dept of Biochem Univ Tex Syst Cancer Ctr Houston TX 77030

SCHLANGER, SEYMOUR OSCAR, b New York, NY, Sept 17, 27. GEOLOGY. *Educ:* Rutgers Univ, BSc, 50, MSc, 51; Johns Hopkins Univ, PhD(geol), 59. *Prof Exp:* Res asst, Rutgers Univ, 50-51; geologist, US Geol Surv, 51-59; prof, Petroleo Brasileiro, Brazil, 59-61; geologist, US Geol Surv, 61-62; from assoc prof to prof geol sci, Univ Calif, Riverside, 62-75; prof geol, State Univ Leiden & State Univ Utrecht, Netherlands, 75-77; prof marine geol, Univ Hawaii, 78-81; PROF GEOL, NORTHWESTERN UNIV, 81- *Concurrent Pos:* Vis prof, Tohuku Univ, Japan, 65-66; Guggenheim fel, Swiss Fed Inst Technol, 69-70. *Mem:* Fel Geol Soc Am; Int Asn Sedimentologists (treas, 75-77); Soc Econ Paleontologists & Mineralogists; Am Asn Petrol Geologists; fel Explorers Club. *Res:* Geology of Pacific basin and coral reefs; geology of Europe; stratigraphy and sedimentary petrology; petroleum geology. *Mailing Add:* Dept Geol Northwestern Univ Evanston IL 60201

SCHLANT, ROBERT C, b El Paso, Tex, Apr 16, 29; m 80; c 3. INTERNAL MEDICINE, CARDIOLOGY. *Educ:* Vanderbilt Univ, BA, 48, MD, 51; Am Bd Internal Med, dipl, 58; Am Bd Cardiovasc Dis, dipl, 62. *Prof Exp:* House officer, Peter Bent Brigham Hosp, Mass, 51-52, from jr asst resident med to asst, 52-58; from asst prof to assoc prof, 58-67, PROF MED, SCH MED, EMORY UNIV, 67- *Concurrent Pos:* Res fel med, Harvard Med Sch, 56-58; mem, Subspecialty Bd Cardiovasc Dis, 71-; fel coun clin cardiol, Am Heart Asn. *Mem:* Fel Am Col Physicians; fel Am Col Cardiol; Am Fedn Clin Res; Asn Univ Cardiol. *Res:* Cardiovascular physiology. *Mailing Add:* Dept Med Emory Univ Sch Med Atlanta GA 30303

SCHLAPFER, WERNER T, b Zurich, Switz, July 19, 35; US citizen; m 65; c 3. NEUROBIOLOGY. *Educ:* Univ Calif, Berkeley, BA, 63, PhD(biophys), 69. *Prof Exp:* Instr med physics, Univ Calif, Berkeley, 69-70; asst res physiologist, Dept Psychiat, Univ Calif, San Diego, 70-72; RES PHYSIOLOGIST, PSYCHIAT SERV, VET ADMIN HOSP, SAN DIEGO, 72- *Concurrent Pos:* Lectr psychiat, Univ Calif, San Diego, 74-78, asst prof in residence, 78- *Mem:* AAAS; Soc Neurosci. *Res:* Mechanisms of the modulation of synaptic transmission, depression, facilitation, post-tetanic potentiation, heterosynaptic facilitation and heterosynaptic inhibition; presynaptic pharmacological regulation of neurotransmitter economics and release in molluscan central nervous systems. *Mailing Add:* Psychiat Res Vet Admin Hosp La Jolla Village Rd San Diego CA 92161

SCHLATTER, JAMES CAMERON, b Madison, Wis, Feb 5, 45; m 67; c 2. CHEMICAL ENGINEERING, CHEMISTRY. *Educ:* Univ Wis, Madison, BS, 67; Stanford Univ, MS & PhD(chem eng), 71. *Prof Exp:* Sr res engr, Gen Motors Res Labs, 71-80; RES ASSOC, CATALYTICA ASSOCS, 80- *Mem:* Am Chem Soc; Am Inst Chem Engrs; Catalysis Soc. *Res:* Heterogeneous catalysis; automotive emission control. *Mailing Add:* Catalytica Assocs Inc 3255 Scott Blvd St 7E Santa Clara CA 95051

SCHLATTER, RUDOLPH, b Schaffhausen, Switz, Nov 16, 24; nat US; m 56. CHEMISTRY. *Educ:* Swiss Fed Inst Technol, MS, 48, DrScTech, 52. *Prof Exp:* Res engr, 52-60, res scientist, 60-63, eng assoc, 63-65, res supvr, 65-79, PROJ MGR, EXP STA, E I DU PONT DE NEMOURS & CO, INC, 79- *Mem:* Am Chem Soc. *Res:* Organic synthesis; catalysis; process development; process and plant design. *Mailing Add:* du Pont Exp Sta Bldg 324 E I du Pont de Nemours & Co Wilmington DE 19898

SCHLATTER, THOMAS WILLARD, meteorology, see previous edition

SCHLAUDECKER, GEORGE F(REDERICK), b Erie, Pa, Feb 10, 17; m 80; c 2. CHEMICAL ENGINEERING. *Educ:* Univ Notre Dame, BS, 38; Mass Inst Technol, MS, 39. *Prof Exp:* Develop engr, Am Locomotive Co, NY, 39; jr engr, E I du Pont de Nemours & Co, Del, 39-41, eng group leader, 41-45; secy-treas, Maumee Develop Co, 46-50, pres, 50-53, pres, Maumee Chem Co, 53-69; gen mgr, Sherwin-Williams Chem, 69-70, dir & group vpres, Sherwin-Williams Co, Cleveland, 70-78; PRES, ERIE ISLES ASSOCS INC, PORT CLINTON, OHIO, 79- *Concurrent Pos:* Asst prof, Univ Toledo, 47-49; dir, Indust Nucleonics Corp, 75-80, Energy Utilization Systs, 79- & Accuray Corp, 80- *Mem:* Am Inst Chem Engrs; Am Chem Soc. *Res:* Diffusional operations; organometallic reactions; organic chemical reaction rates; sublimation; precipitation and filtration; drying. *Mailing Add:* 2208 N Carriage Lane Port Clinton OH 43452

SCHLAUG, ROBERT NOEL, b Jamaica, NY, Dec 21, 39; m 60; c 2. NUCLEAR ENGINEERING. *Educ:* Case Inst Technol, BS, 61; Univ Calif, Berkeley, PhD(nuclear eng), 65. *Prof Exp:* Staff mem high energy fluid dynamics, Gen Atomic Div, Gen Dynamics Corp, 65-68; staff mem radiation hydrodynamics, Systs, Sci & Software, Inc, 68-72; STAFF SCIENTIST RADIATION HYDRODYNAMICS, SCI APPLNS, INC, 72- *Mem:* Am Nuclear Soc; Sigma Xi. *Res:* Interactions of radiation and atomic particles with materials and development of computer methods for describing those interactions. *Mailing Add:* Sci Applns Inc PO Box 2351 La Jolla CA 92037

SCHLAX, T(IMOTHY) ROTH, b Kenosha, Wis, Mar 19, 38; m 65; c 4. ELECTRICAL ENGINEERING, COMPUTER TECHNOLOGY. *Educ:* Marquette Univ, BSEE, 60, MSEE, 63; Mass Inst Technol, PhD(solid state electronics), 68. *Prof Exp:* Develop engr, 72-75, PROJ MGR ENG STAFF, GEN MOTORS CORP, 75- *Honors & Awards:* 1975 SAE Vincent Bendix Automotive Electronics Award, Soc Automotive Engrs, 76. *Mem:* Inst Elec & Electronics Engrs; Soc Automotive Engrs. *Res:* Automotive control computer applications; custom computer approaches for fuel, ignition, and other engine control functions; advanced aids for refining control algorithms. *Mailing Add:* 4150 Chapman Rochester MI 48063

SCHLECH, BARRY ARTHUR, b Bayonne, NJ, June 7, 44; m 63; c 4. MICROBIOLOGY. *Educ:* Univ Tex, Austin, BA, 65, MA, 68, PhD(microbiol), 70. *Prof Exp:* Sr scientist, 70, head microbiol res sect, 70-72, head microbiol develop, 72-74, head ophthalmic microbiol, 74-76, CORP MICROBIOLOGIST, ALCON LABS, INC, 76- *Mem:* Am Soc Microbiol; Soc Appl Bact; Soc Indust Microbiol; Ocular Microbiol & Immunol Group; Pharmaceut Mfrs Asn Biol Sect. *Res:* Pharmaceutical microbiology; microbial limit testing; antibiotics; sterilization procedures; microbiological control; ocular infections; contact lens disinfection; ophthalmic and cosmetic preservatives. *Mailing Add:* Alcon Labs Inc PO Box 1959 Ft Worth TX 76101

SCHLECHTEN, ALBERT WILBUR, b Bozeman, Mont, Nov 28, 14; m 41; c 5. METALLURGICAL ENGINEERING. *Educ:* Mont Sch Mines, BS, 37; Mass Inst Technol, DSc(mineral dressing), 40. *Prof Exp:* Instr metall, Univ Minn, 40-41, asst prof nonferrous metall, 41-42; assoc prof mining & metall, Ore State Col, 42-44; metallurgist, US Bur Mines, Ore, 44-46; prof metall eng, Mo Sch Mines, 46-63; DIR INST EXTRACTIVE METALL & PROF METALL ENG, COLO SCH MINES, 63- *Concurrent Pos:* Ed, Dept Mining & Metall, Encycl Britannica, 55-60; Fulbright lectr, Univ Melbourne, 66. *Honors & Awards:* James Douglas Gold Medal, Am Inst Mining Engrs, 78; Kroll Medal, Metals Soc London, 81. *Mem:* Am Soc Metals; Am Soc Eng Educ; Am Inst Mining, Metall & Petrol Engrs (vpres, 66). *Res:* Production of zirconium and titanium metal; vacuum metallurgy. *Mailing Add:* Dept Metall Eng Colo Sch Mines Golden CO 80401

SCHLEE, FRANK HERMAN, b New York, NY, Apr 22, 35; m 58; c 3. NAVIGATION. *Educ:* Polytech Inst Brooklyn, BS, 56; Univ Mich, MS, 49, PhD(instrumentation eng), 63. *Prof Exp:* Engr, Sperry Gyroscope Co, 56-58; res assoc navig, Inst Sci & Technol, Univ Mich, 62-63; sr engr, 63-66, ADVAN ENGR, FED SYSTS DIV, IBM CORP, 66- *Mem:* Am Inst Navig; Am Inst Aeronaut & Astronaut. *Res:* Space guidance; space and aircraft navigation, particularly using optimal filtering techniques. *Mailing Add:* 96 Ivory Foster Rd Owego NY 13827

SCHLEE, JOHN STEVENS, b Detroit, Mich, Sept 27, 28; m 69; c 1. GEOLOGY. *Educ:* Univ Mich, BS, 50; Univ Calif, Los Angeles, MA, 53; Johns Hopkins Univ, PhD(geol), 56. *Prof Exp:* Geologist, US Geol Surv, 56-58; asst prof geol, Univ Ga, 58-62; RES GEOLOGIST, US GEOL SURV, 62- *Concurrent Pos:* NSF grant, 60-62. *Mem:* AAAS; fel Geol Soc Am; Soc Econ Paleont & Mineral; Am Asn Petrol Geol. *Res:* Texture, composition and structures in sediments and sedimentary rocks; structure and stratigraphy of continental margins. *Mailing Add:* US Geol Surv Woods Hole MA 02543

SCHLEEF, DANIEL J, b Norfolk, Nebr, Sept 29, 27; m 56; c 2. MECHANICAL ENGINEERING. *Educ:* Univ Ark, BSME, 50; Kans State Univ, MS, 52; Purdue Univ, PhD(mech eng), 60. *Prof Exp:* Instr mech eng, Kans State Univ, 52-53; asst prof, Univ Cincinnati, 53-56; instr, Purdue Univ, 56-58; assoc prof, 59-61, head dept, 61-70, PROF MECH ENG, UNIV CINCINNATI, 61- *Concurrent Pos:* Mem, Year-in-Indust prog, E I du Pont de Nemours & Co, Del, 67-68. *Mem:* Am Soc Mech Engrs; Am Soc Eng Educ. *Res:* Thermodynamics; heat transfer; fluid mechanics; thermodynamic and transport properties of matter. *Mailing Add:* Dept of Mech Eng Univ of Cincinnati Cincinnati OH 45221

SCHLEGEL, DAVID EDWARD, b Fresno, Calif, Sept 3, 27; m 48; c 4. PLANT PATHOLOGY. *Educ:* Ore State Univ, BS, 50; Univ Calif, PhD(plant path), 54. *Prof Exp:* Jr specialist, 53-54, instr plant path & jr plant pathologist, 54-56, asst prof & asst plant pathologist, 56-62, assoc prof & assoc plant pathologist, 62-69, Miller prof, 66-67, chmn dept plant path, 70-76, actg dean, Col Natural Resources, 77-78, PROF PLANT PATH, UNIV CALIF, BERKELEY, 69-, ASSOC DEAN RES, 76-, DEAN, COL NAT RESOURCES, 78- *Mem:* AAAS; Am Phytopath Soc; Soc Gen Microbiol. *Res:* Plant virology; plant pathology; comparative virology; international crop protection. *Mailing Add:* Col Natural Resources Univ of Calif Berkeley CA 94720

SCHLEGEL, EARL S, b Bechtelsville, Pa, May 28, 28; m 50; c 2. PHYSICS. *Educ:* Lehigh Univ, BS, 51; Drexel Inst Technol, MS, 60. *Prof Exp:* Engr, Philco-Ford Corp, 51-71; ENGR, WESTINGHOUSE ELEC CORP, 71- *Mem:* Electrochem Soc; Inst Elec & Electronics Engrs. *Res:* Semiconductor devices, processes and materials. *Mailing Add:* Advance Tech Labs Washington Electric Corp Baltimore MD 21203

SCHLEGEL, JAMES M, b Ogden, Utah, Aug 24, 37; m 62; c 1. PHYSICAL CHEMISTRY. *Educ:* Univ of the Pac, BS, 59; Iowa State Univ, PhD(phys chem), 62. *Prof Exp:* Res asst phys chem, Iowa State Univ, 59-62; asst prof, 62-69, assoc prof, 69-76, PROF PHYS CHEM, RUTGERS UNIV, NEWARK, 76- *Mem:* Am Chem Soc. *Res:* Stoichiometry and kinetics of reactions in fused salt media. *Mailing Add:* Dept Chem Newark Col Arts & Sci Rutgers Univ Newark NJ 07102

SCHLEGEL, JORGEN ULRIK, b Copenhagen, Denmark, July 18, 18; nat US; m 43; c 2. MEDICINE. *Educ:* Copenhagen Univ, MD, 45, PhD, 48; Tulane Univ, MD, 59. *Prof Exp:* Instr micros anat, Copenhagen Univ, 42-43, asst prof histol, 45-49; asst prof urol res & dir urol res lab, Univ Rochester, 49-57, asst prof urol surg, 57-59; assoc dean admin & clin affairs, 75-76, PROF UROL & HEAD DEPT, SCH MED, TULANE UNIV, 59-, CHIEF STAFF, UNIV HOSP, 77- *Concurrent Pos:* Rockefeller fel, Carnegie Inst, 48-49; asst resident, County Hosp, Copenhagen, Denmark, 44-45; asst resident, Strong Mem Hosp, Rochester, NY, 54-56, resident, 56-57; urologist in chief, Tulane Serv Charity Hosp, New Orleans, 59-; consult, Ochsner Found Hosp, 59-, Vet Admin Hosp, 60-, Touro Infirmary, 60-, Vet Admin Hosp, Alexandria, 61 & Lallie Kemp Charity Hosp, Independence, 63-; dir dept urol, Huey P Long Charity Hosp, Pineville, 64-; mem comt urol, Nat Acad Sci-Nat Res Coun, chmn ad hoc comt urol. *Mem:* Am Physiol Soc; Soc Exp Biol & Med; Am Asn Anat; Danish Med Asn. *Res:* Renal physiology. *Mailing Add:* Tulane Univ Sch of Med 1430 Tulane Ave New Orleans LA 70112

SCHLEGEL, RICHARD, b Davenport, Iowa, Aug 29, 13; m 46; c 2. THEORETICAL PHYSICS, PHILOSOPHY OF SCIENCE. *Educ:* Univ Chicago, AB, 35; Univ Iowa, MA, 36; Univ Ill, PhD(phys chem), 43. *Prof Exp:* Lectr & demonstr, Mus Sci & Indust, Univ Ill, 38-40; assoc physicist, Manhattan Dist, Univ Chicago, 43-45; instr physics, Princeton Univ, 45-48; from asst prof to assoc prof, 48-57, actg head dept, 55-56, PROF PHYSICS, MICH STATE UNIV, 57- *Mem:* Fel Am Phys Soc; Am Asn Physics Teachers; Philos Sci Asn. *Res:* Theoretical physics; philosophical problems in physics. *Mailing Add:* Dept of Physics Mich State Univ East Lansing MI 48824

SCHLEGEL, ROBERT ALLEN, b Chicago, Ill, Feb 17, 45; m 68. CELL BIOLOGY, BIOMEMBRANES. *Educ:* Univ Iowa, BS, 67; Harvard Univ, AM, 68, PhD(biochem & molecular biol), 71. *Prof Exp:* Fel, Walter & Eliza Hall Inst Med Res, Melbourne, 71-74; res asst prof immunol, Univ Utah, 74-76; ASST PROF MOLECULAR & CELL BIOL, PA STATE UNIV, 76- *Concurrent Pos:* Prin investr res grants, NIH, Nat Cancer Inst, & Am Chem Soc, 76- *Mem:* Am Soc Cell Biol; Int Cell Cycle Soc. *Res:* Introduction of macromolecules into eukaryotic cells; cell fusion; cell cycle regulation; membrane structure and function; hematopoietic cell surfaces; chromatin and chromosome structure and function. *Mailing Add:* Molecular & Cell Biol Prog Pa State Univ 101 S Frear University Park PA 16802

SCHLEGEL, ROBERT JOHN, b Ft Wayne, Ind, Dec 31, 27; m 49; c 3. PEDIATRICS, GENETICS. *Educ:* Univ Chicago, PhB, 49, MD, 55; Am Bd Pediat, dipl, 60. *Prof Exp:* From intern to chief resident, State Univ NY Upstate Med Ctr, 55-58; chief pediat serv, Walson Army Hosp, 59-60; asst chief pediat serv, Tripler Gen Hosp, 60-62, chief, 62-63; asst chief pediat serv, Walter Reed Gen Hosp & cytopathologist, Div Med, Walter Reed Army Inst Res, 66-69; assoc prof pediat, Sch Med, Stanford Univ, 69-71; PROF PEDIAT, SCH MED, UNIV CALIF, LOS ANGELES & PROF & CHAIRPERSON PEDIAT, CHARLES R DREW POSTGRAD MED SCH, 71- *Concurrent Pos:* Res fel human genetics & endocrinol, State Univ NY

Upstate Med Ctr, 63-65 & Univ Georgetown, 66-67, clin prof, 67-; dir clin serv, Dept Pediat, Martin Luther King Gen Hosp, Los Angeles, 71- *Mem:* fel Am Acad Pediat; Endocrine Soc; Soc Pediat Res; Am Pediat Soc. *Res:* Peritoneal dialysis; human cytogenetics; cytogenetics of the embryo; embryogenesis of the gonads; sexual differentiation; biochemistry of phagocytosis, leucocyte chemotaxis and cell mediated immune responses; gene content and mode of action of genes of the x chromosome; gonadal proteins; dermatoglyphics; effects of infections on chromosomes. *Mailing Add:* Dept of Pediat Charles R Drew Postgrad Med Sch Los Angeles CA 90059

SCHLEICH, THOMAS W, b Staten Island, NY, May 29, 38; m 62. BIOCHEMISTRY, MOLECULAR BIOLOGY. *Educ:* Cornell Univ, BS, 60; Rockefeller Univ, PhD(biochem), 66. *Prof Exp:* Res assoc biochem, Dartmouth Col, 66-67; res assoc chem, Univ Ore, 67-69; asst prof, 69-74, assoc prof, 74-79, PROF CHEM, UNIV CALIF, SANTA CRUZ, 79- *Concurrent Pos:* Helen Hay Whitney Found fel, 68-69. *Mem:* AAAS; Am Chem Soc; Biophys Soc; Am Soc Biol Chemists. *Res:* Protein and nucleic acid conformation; biophysical chemistry; eye lens metabolism (cataractogenesis); whole tissue nuclear magnetic resonance. *Mailing Add:* Div of Natural Sci Univ of Calif Santa Cruz CA 95064

SCHLEICHER, DAVID LAWRENCE, b Palmerton, Pa, July 22, 37; m 61. ENVIRONMENTAL IMPACT STATEMENTS, TECHNICAL WRITING. *Educ:* Pa State Univ, BS, 59, PhD(geol), 65; Calif Inst Technol, MS, 62. *Prof Exp:* GEOLOGIST, US GEOL SURV, 65-, CENT REGION COORDR, ENVIRON AFFAIRS OFF, 77- *Mem:* Geol Soc Am. *Res:* Mechanics of tuffisite intrusion; seismicity induced by reservoirs in grabens; preparation of environmental impact statements. *Mailing Add:* US Geol Surv Mail Stop 701 Box 25046 Fed Ctr Denver CO 80225

SCHLEICHER, JOHN ANTHONY, b Kansas City, Mo, Nov 25, 25; m 72; c 6. ANALYTICAL CHEMISTRY. *Educ:* Univ Kans, BS, 49. *Prof Exp:* Asst chemist, Kans State Geol Surv, 49-51, chemist & spectographer, 51-56; chief chemist, Okla Geol Surv, 56-64; assoc prof scientist, Ill State Geol Surv, 64-79; SR SCIENTIST, DATABASE ADMIN, INST MINING & MINERALS RES, LEXINGTON, KY, 79- *Concurrent Pos:* Consult, US Dept Justice, 59- *Mem:* Geochem Soc; Soc Appl Spectros. *Res:* Classical, instrumental, ultraviolet emission analysis of rocks and minerals; geochemistry of sediments; forensic analysis; computer data handling and statistical analysis. *Mailing Add:* 1301 Personality Ct Lexington KY 40502

SCHLEICHER, JOSEPH BERNARD, b Nanticoke, Pa, Apr 4, 29; m 58; c 4. CELL BIOLOGY, VIROLOGY. *Educ:* Wilkes Col, BS, 51; Miami Univ, MS, 55; Kans State Univ, PhD(microbiol), 61. *Prof Exp:* Res asst immunol, Kans State Univ, 56-58; sr scientist, Develop Dept, Pitman-Moore Co, Ind, 58-62; head virus res sect, Alcon Labs, Inc, Tex, 62-63, head virus & microbiol res sect, 63-64; virologist, Virus Res Dept, 64-69, head antiviral tissue cult screening prog, 67-69, head res of biochem prod from tissue cult cells, Molecular Biol Dept, 69-71, SR RES SCIENTIST, BIOCHEM DEVELOP DEPT, ABBOTT LABS, INC, 71- *Mem:* AAAS; Am Soc Microbiol; Sigma Xi; NY Acad Sci; Tissue Cult Asn. *Res:* Research and development in virus vaccines for humans and animals, primarily in the area of respiratory diseases; antiviral chemotherapy and prophalaxis; interferon; tissue culture mass scale methodology and physiology; production of biochemicals by tissue culture cells; immunology. *Mailing Add:* Biochem Develop Dept 456 Abbott Labs Inc North Chicago IL 60064

SCHLEIDT, WOLFGANG MATTHIAS, b Vienna, Austria, Dec 18, 27; m 65; c 3. ETHOLOGY, BIOACOUSTICS. *Educ:* Univ Vienna, DrPhil(zool), 51. *Prof Exp:* Asst ethol, Max Planck Inst Physiol of Behav, 51-64; res assoc, Duke Univ, 64-65; PROF ZOOL, UNIV MD, COLLEGE PARK, 65- *Concurrent Pos:* Ger Res Asn grants, 52-64; mem, Int Ethol Comt, 71-77. *Mem:* AAAS; Animal Behav Soc; Ger Soc Scientists & Doctors; fel Animal Behav Soc. *Res:* Behavior of animals and man, especially stereotyped behavior and releasing mechanisms; animal communication; ontogeny and phylogeny of behavior; temporal patterning; physiological basis of behavior. *Mailing Add:* Dept of Zool Univ of Md College Park MD 20742

SCHLEIF, FERBER ROBERT, b Oroville, Wash, Mar 6, 13; m 37; c 2. ELECTRICAL ENGINEERING. *Educ:* Wash State Univ, BS, 35. *Prof Exp:* Mem staff construct & oper eng, Coulee Dam, Wash, US Bur Reclamation, 36-48, syst planning work, Mo River Basin Proj, 48-50, oper & maintenance eng, 50-62, chief elec power br, 62-74; CONSULT ELEC POWER, 74- *Concurrent Pos:* Mem, NAm Power Systs Interconnection comt, Colo, 65, mem spec sessions, North-South Intertie Task Force, 65. *Mem:* Fel Inst Elec & Electronics Engrs. *Res:* Power system stabilization; hydraulic turbine governing; excitation control for stability; generator insulation test techniques; power system tests. *Mailing Add:* 800 S Fillmore St Denver CO 80209

SCHLEIF, ROBERT FERBER, b Wenatchee, Wash, Nov 22, 40; m 67. MOLECULAR BIOLOGY, BIOCHEMISTRY. *Educ:* Tufts Univ, BS, 63; Univ Calif, Berkeley, PhD(biophys), 67. *Prof Exp:* Helen Hay Whitney fel, Harvard Univ, 67-71; asst prof, 71-74, assoc prof, 74-81, PROF BIOCHEM, BRANDEIS UNIV, 81- *Concurrent Pos:* USPHS res grant, 71. *Mem:* Am Soc Biol Chemists. *Res:* Regulatory mechanisms governing gene activity in microorganisms and their viruses; genetic, physical and physiological studies; structure of proteins and nucleic acids. *Mailing Add:* Dept of Biochem Brandeis Univ Waltham MA 02154

SCHLEIF, ROBERT H, b Watertown, Wis, Apr 20, 23; m 48; c 3. INDUSTRIAL PHARMACY. *Educ:* Univ Wis, BS, 47, PhD(pharm), 50. *Prof Exp:* Asst prof pharm, St Louis Col Pharm, 50-54, from assoc prof to prof, 54-62; res pharmacist, 62-65, mgr prof specifications & stability, 65-70, dir qual assurance, Consumer Div, Abbott Labs, 70-79, MGR QUAL ASSURANCE, NUTRIT ABBOTT INT, NORTH CHICAGO, 79- *Concurrent Pos:* Consult, Vet Admin Hosp. *Mem:* AAAS; Am Pharmaceut Asn; Am Soc Qual Control. *Res:* Arabic acid; ophthalmic solutions; antacids. *Mailing Add:* 2330 Grove Ave Waukegan IL 60085

SCHLEIGH, WILLIAM ROBERT, b Olean, NY, Feb 26, 41; m 62; c 2. ORGANIC CHEMISTRY. *Educ:* Clarkson Col Technol, BS, 62, PhD(org chem), 66. *Prof Exp:* Fel, Univ Wis, Madison, 65-67; RES CHEMIST, EASTMAN KODAK CO, 67- *Mem:* Am Chem Soc; Royal Soc Chem. *Res:* Heterocyclic chemistry; synthesis and reactions of heterocyclic compounds; organic reaction mechanisms; photochemistry of heterocyclic compounds. *Mailing Add:* Eastman Kodak Co Bldg 82 Rochester NY 14650

SCHLEIN, HERBERT, b New Haven, Conn, Nov 7, 27; m 52; c 2. ORGANIC CHEMISTRY. *Educ:* Harvard Univ, BS, 50; Boston Univ, PhD, 54. *Prof Exp:* Chemist, Children's Cancer Res Found, Boston, Mass, 53-58; chemist, Chem & Plastics div, Qm Res & Eng Command, US Dept Army, 58-60: head, Org Chem Sect, Explor Chem & Physics Div, Itek Corp, 60-63; vpres & dir res, Rahn Labs, 63-66; RES GROUP LEADER, POLAROID CORP, 66- *Mem:* Am Chem Soc. *Res:* Diffusion transfer processes; product design; image-forming systems; electrophotography; photoconductors. *Mailing Add:* Dept 882 Polaroid Corp 784 Mem Dr Cambridge MA 02139

SCHLEIN, PETER ELI, b New York, NY, Nov 18, 32; m 62; c 2. PHYSICS. *Educ:* Union Col, NY, BS, 54; Northwestern Univ, PhD, 59. *Prof Exp:* Res assoc physics, Johns Hopkins Univ, 59-61; res assoc, 61-62, from asst prof to assoc prof, 61-68, PROF PHYSICS, UNIV CALIF, LOS ANGELES, 68- *Concurrent Pos:* Vis physicist, Saclay, France, 63-64 & European Orgn Nuclear Res, 63-64 & 69-74; J S Guggenheim fel, 69-70; consult, Space Tech Labs, 66. *Mem:* Fel Am Phys Soc. *Res:* Experimental particle physics; properties of elementary particle interactions using electronic techniques. *Mailing Add:* Dept of Physics Univ of Calif Los Angeles CA 90024

SCHLEMMER, FREDERICK CHARLES, II, b Watts Bar Dam, Tenn, Aug 10, 43; m 67; c 1. PHYSICAL OCEANOGRAPHY. *Educ:* US Naval Acad, BS, 65; Univ SFla, MA, 71; Tex A&M Univ, PhD(oceanog), 78. *Prof Exp:* asst prof marine sci & asst to pres, Moody Col, 78-80; ASST PROF, MARINE SCI, TEX A&M UNIV, GALVESTON, 80- *Concurrent Pos:* Consult, Encyclopedia Britannical Film Rev Bd. *Mem:* Am Meteorol Soc; Am Geophys Union; Nat Geosci Hon Soc. *Res:* Assessment of circulation patterns and hydrographic property distributions to evaluate pathways for water movement over large areas. *Mailing Add:* Moody Col PO Box 1675 Galveston TX 77553

SCHLEMPER, ELMER OTTO, b Pacific, Mo, Apr 13, 39; m 59; c 4. INORGANIC CHEMISTRY. *Educ:* Wash Univ, AB, 61, Univ Minn, PhD(inorg chem), 65. *Prof Exp:* Res assoc chem, Brookhaven Nat Lab, 64-66; from asst prof to assoc prof, 66-76, PROF INORG CHEM, UNIV MO-COLUMBIA, 76- *Mem:* Am Chem Soc; Am Crystallog Asn; The Chem Soc. *Res:* Structure of inorganic metal complexes and organometallics; hydrogen bonding; chemical bonding. *Mailing Add:* Dept of Chem Univ of Mo Columbia MO 65201

SCHLENDER, KEITH K, b Newton, Kans, Oct 3, 39; m 63; c 2. BIOCHEMISTRY, PHARMACOLOGY. *Educ:* Westmar Col, BA, 61; Mich State Univ, MS, 63, PhD(biochem), 66. *Prof Exp:* Asst prof, 69-74, assoc prof, 74-81, PROF PHARMACOL & THERAPEUT, MED COL OHIO, 81- *Concurrent Pos:* Res fel biochem, Univ Minn, Minneapolis, 66-69. *Mem:* Am Chem Soc; NY Acad Sci; Am Soc Pharmacol & Exp Therapeut; Am Soc Biol Chemists; Sigma Xi. *Res:* Hormonal and non-hormonal control of glycogen synthesis; protein phosphorylation. *Mailing Add:* Dept Pharmacol & Therapeut Med Col Ohio CS 10008 Toledo OH 43699

SCHLENK, FRITZ, b Munich, Ger, 1909; nat US; m 40; c 2. BIOCHEMISTRY, MICROBIOLOGY. *Educ:* Univ Berlin, PhD(chem), 34. *Prof Exp:* Asst, Univ Stockholm, 34-37, res assoc, 37-40; asst prof biochem, Sch Med, Univ Tex, 40-43; assoc prof nutrit, Sch Med, prof biochem, Sch Dent & biochemist in charge, M D Anderson Hosp & Tumor Inst, 43-47; prof bact, Iowa State Col, 47-54; sr biochemist, Argonne Nat Lab, 54-74; RES PROF BIOL, UNIV ILL, CHICAGO CIRCLE, 75- *Mem:* Am Soc Biol Chem; Am Soc Microbiol; Am Acad Microbiol. *Res:* Enzymes, coenzymes; transmethylation; yeast cytology. *Mailing Add:* Biol Sci Div Box 4348 Univ Ill Chicago IL 60680

SCHLENK, HERMANN, b Jena, Ger, July 28, 14; nat US; m 46; c 1. ORGANIC CHEMISTRY, BIOCHEMISTRY. *Educ:* Univ Berlin, dipl, 36; Univ Munich, Dr rer nat(chem), 39. *Prof Exp:* Res chemist, Baden Anilin & Soda Works, Ger, 39-42; res assoc org chem, Univ Munich, 44-46; teaching asst & lectr, Univ Würzburg, 46-49; asst prof biochem, Agr & Mech Col Tex, 49-52, assoc prof, 52; from asst prof org chem to assoc prof biochem, 53-56, asst dir, Inst, 67-75, PROF BIOCHEM, HORMEL INST, UNIV MINN, 56- *Mem:* Am Chem Soc; Am Soc Biol Chem; Am Oil Chem Soc. *Res:* Chemistry and biochemistry of lipids. *Mailing Add:* Hormel Inst 801 NE 16th Ave Austin MN 55912

SCHLENKER, EVELYN HEYMANN, b La Paz, Bolivia, May 30, 48; US citizen. RESPIRATORY PHYSIOLOGY. *Educ:* City Col New York, BS, 70; State Univ NY, Buffalo, MA, 73, PhD(biol), 76. *Prof Exp:* Vis asst physiol, Rochester Inst Technol, 76-77; fel respiration physiol, Univ Fla, 78-80; ASST PROF PHYSIOL, UNIV SDAK, 80- *Mem:* Am Soc Zoologist; Sigma Xi; Am Physiol Soc. *Res:* Control of respiration in animal models of respiratory-muscular diseases; factors affecting airway reactivity in human subjects, including air pollution, smoking and industrial pollution. *Mailing Add:* Physiol Sect Med Sch Univ SDak Vermillion SD 57069

SCHLENKER, ROBERT ALISON, b Rochester, NY, Oct 25, 40; m 68; c 2. RADIATION PHYSICS. *Educ:* Mass Inst Technol, SB, 62, PhD(nuclear physics), 68. *Prof Exp:* Appointee radium poisoning, Radioactivity Ctr, Mass Inst Technol, 68-69; asst physicist, 70-75, BIOPHYSICIST RADIATION DOSIMETRY, ARGONNE NAT LAB, 75- *Concurrent Pos:* Math instr, Col DuPage, 75-78; mem Sci Comt, Nat Coun Radiation Protection and Measurements, 57 & 78-, mem Task Group Prob Bone, 78- *Mem:* Am Asn Physicists Med; Health Physics Soc; Radiation Res Soc; AAAS. *Res:*

Autoradiography, microradiography, radiation dosimetry and alpha, beta and gamma-ray spectrometry as applied to the study of the concentrations and effects of radioisotope in human and animal tissues, especially skeletal tissue. *Mailing Add:* Argonne Nat Lab 9700 S Cass Ave Argonne IL 60439

SCHLEPPNIK, ALFRED ADOLF, b Mar 2, 22; US citizen; m 49; c 1. SYNTHETIC ORGANIC CHEMISTRY, CHEMORECEPTION. *Educ:* Univ Vienna, DPhil(chem), 57. *Prof Exp:* Instr org chem, Univ Vienna, 56-57; res assoc, Wash Univ, 57-58; res chemist, 58-59, sr res chem, 59-63, from res specialist to sr res specialist, 63-76, SCI FEL, MONSANTO CO, 76- *Mem:* Am Chem Soc; Europ Chemoreception Res Orgn; Soc Ger Chemists; AAAS; NY Acad Sci. *Res:* Synthesis of flavor and fragrance aroma chemicals; molecular biochemistry of gustation and olfaction primarily at the level of peripheral stimulus/receptor interactions; induced selective reversible anosmia. *Mailing Add:* Monsanto Co 800 N Lindbergh Blvd St Louis MO 63166

SCHLESINGER, ALLEN BRIAN, b New York, NY, Feb 18, 24; m 47; c 4. EMBRYOLOGY, ENVIRONMENTAL BIOLOGY. *Educ:* Univ Minn, BA, 49, MS, 51, PhD(zool), 57. *Prof Exp:* Instr, 52-54, from asst prof to assoc prof, 54-61, dir dept, 58-72, PROF BIOL, CREIGHTON UNIV, 61-, CHMN DEPT, 77- *Concurrent Pos:* Mem bd dirs, Omaha Zoo; consult, Omaha Pub Power Dist. *Mem:* Soc Develop Biol; Am Soc Zool; Am Chem Soc; Am Asn Anat; Soc Nuclear Med. *Res:* Embryonic growth control; morphogenetic movement; environmental influences on development; effects of discharges of generating plants on river biota. *Mailing Add:* Dept of Biol Creighton Univ 2500 California St Omaha NE 68178

SCHLESINGER, DAVID HARVEY, b New York, NY, Apr 28, 39; m 70; c 2. PROTEIN BIOCHEMISTRY. *Educ:* Columbia Col, BA, 62; Albany Med Col, MS, 65; Mt Sinai Med Sch, PhD(med & cell biol), 72. *Prof Exp:* Fel med res, Mass Gen Hosp, Harvard Med Sch, Harvard Univ, 72-75, instr med res & asst biochem, 75-77; assoc prof physiol & biophy, Univ Ill Med Ctr, 77-81; PROF MED, NY UNIV MED CTR, 81- *Concurrent Pos:* Consult, Ortho Pharamaceut Corp, 78- *Mem:* NY Acad Sci; Am Physiol Soc; Am Soc Biol Chemists; Am Chem Soc. *Res:* Primary structure determination and peptide synthesis of biologically active peptide hormones and other biologically active polypeptides, such as ubiquitin, thymoprotein, neurophysin, statherin, corticotrophin releasing peptide, somatostatin. *Mailing Add:* Dept Med NY Univ Med Ctr 550 First Ave New York NY 10016

SCHLESINGER, EDWARD BRUCE, b Pittsburgh, Pa, Sept 6, 13; m 41; c 4. NEUROSURGERY. *Educ:* Univ Pa, BA, 34, MD, 38; Am Bd Neurol Surg, dipl, 49. *Prof Exp:* Res asst neurol, 46-47, res assoc neurol surg, 47-49, assoc, 49-52, asst prof clin neurol surg, 52-64, prof clin neurol surg, 64-73, chmn dept, 73-80, BYRON STOOKEY PROF NEUROL SURG, COL PHYSICIANS & SURGEONS, COLUMBIA UNIV, 73- *Concurrent Pos:* Teagle fel, Col Physicians & Surgeons, Columbia Univ, 46-47; jr asst neurologist, Pres Hosp, New York, 45-47, from asst attend neurol surgeon to attend, 47-73; consult, Monmouth Mem Hosp, NJ, 47-49, Walter Reed Army Hosp, DC, 47-50 & Knickerbocker Hosp, New York, 47-49; attend neurol surgeon, Inst Crippled & Disabled, New York, 47-58 & White Plains Hosp, NY, 54-73; pres, Med Bd, Presbyterian Hosp, 76-79. *Mem:* AAAS; Neurosurg Soc Am (vpres, 59-70, pres, 70-71); Am Asn Neurol Surg; Harvey Soc; fel NY Acad Sci. *Res:* Use of radioisotopes in neurology; pharmacology and biogenetics of tumors of the central nervous system. *Mailing Add:* 710 W 168th St New York NY 10032

SCHLESINGER, ERNEST CARL, b Hildesheim, Ger, Nov 25, 25; nat US; m 58; c 2. MATHEMATICAL ANALYSIS. *Educ:* Univ Wash, BS, 47, MA, 50; Harvard Univ, PhD, 55. *Prof Exp:* Instr philos, Univ Wash, 49-50; instr math, Yale Univ, 55-58; asst prof, Wesleyan Univ, 58-62; from asst prof to assoc prof, 62-73, PROF MATH, CONN COL, 73- *Concurrent Pos:* Fulbright lectr, Univ Col, Dublin, 68-69. *Mem:* Am Math Soc; Math Asn Am. *Res:* Functions of a complex variable. *Mailing Add:* Dept Math Box 1566 Conn Col New London CT 06320

SCHLESINGER, JAMES WILLIAM, b Salina, Kans, June 20, 31; m 52; c 4. MATHEMATICS. *Educ:* Mass Inst Technol, BS, 55, PhD(math), 64. *Prof Exp:* From instr to asst prof, 60-67, chmn dept, 69-73, ASSOC PROF MATH, TUFTS UNIV, 67- *Mem:* Am Math Soc. *Res:* Homotopy groups of spheres; semi-simplicial topology; homotopy theory. *Mailing Add:* Bromfield-Pearson Bldg Tufts Univ Medford MA 02155

SCHLESINGER, KURT, behavioral genetics, deceased

SCHLESINGER, LEE, b Chicago, Ill, July 4, 26; m 54; c 3. ENGINEERING, SOILS. *Educ:* Ill Inst Technol, BS, 49, MS, 50. *Prof Exp:* Mat engr, Corps Eng, US Dept Army, 50; found & soils engr, Soil Testing Servs, Inc, 51-54; chief soils engr, Alfred Benesch & Assocs, 53-56; chief struct engr, Western-Knapp Eng Co, 56-60; proj mgr, Meissner Engrs, Inc, 60-63; PRES & DIR CONSTRUCT DIV, HOYER-SCHLESINGER-TURNER, INC, CHICAGO, 63- *Concurrent Pos:* Mem, Int Conf Soil Mech & Found Eng, 52; environ comnr, Village Morton Grove, Ill, 70- *Mem:* AAAS; Soc Am Mil Engrs; Am Soc Civil Engrs; Iron & Steel Asn; Am Concrete Inst. *Res:* Application of soil mechanics to civil engineering design; management concept of design-construction in heavy process industry. *Mailing Add:* 6417 Hoffman Terr Morton Grove IL 60053

SCHLESINGER, MARTIN D(AVID), b New York, NY, Aug 9, 14; m 45; c 3. CHEMICAL ENGINEERING. *Educ:* Univ Okla, BS, 41; NY Univ, MChE, 44. *Prof Exp:* Chem engr, M W Kellogg Co, 41-48; asst chief, Gas Synthesis Sect, US Bur Mines, 48-56, asst chief, Coal Hydrogenation Sect, 56-62, res coordr, 62-67, proj coordr process technol, 67-71, staff coordr, 71-74; dep res dir, Pittsburgh Energy Res Ctr, ERDA, 74-77; PRES, WALLINGFORD GROUP LTD, 77- *Concurrent Pos:* Consult coal conversion, UN & US Agency Int Develop. *Mem:* Am Chem Soc; Am Inst Chem Engrs; AAAS. *Res:* Conversion of coal to synthetic fuels and chemicals; utilization of waste materials; research management. *Mailing Add:* Wallingford Group Ltd 4766 Wallingford St Pittsburgh PA 15213

SCHLESINGER, MILTON J, b Wheeling, WVa, Nov 26, 27; m 55. BIOCHEMISTRY, MICROBIOLOGY. *Educ:* Yale Univ, BS, 51; Univ Rochester, MS, 53; Univ Mich, PhD(biochem), 59. *Prof Exp:* Res assoc, Univ Mich, 53-56 & 59-60; vis scientist, Int Ctr Chem Microbiol, Superior Inst Health, Italy, 60-61; res assoc biol, Mass Inst Technol, 61-64; from asst prof to assoc prof, 64-72, PROF MICROBIOL & IMMUNOL, SCH MED, WASHINGTON UNIV, 72- *Concurrent Pos:* Vis scientist, Imp Can Res Fund, London, 74-75. *Mem:* Am Soc Biol Chemists; Am Chem Soc; Am Soc Microbiol. *Res:* Protein structure and function; molecular biology of animal viruses; protein-lipid interactions. *Mailing Add:* Dept Microbiol & Immunol Sch Med Washington Univ St Louis MO 63110

SCHLESINGER, MORDECHAY, b Budapest, Hungary, Sept 2, 31; m 57; c 2. CONDENSED MATTER, PHYSICS. *Educ:* Hebrew Univ, Israel, MSc, 59, PhD(physics), 63. *Prof Exp:* NASA fel physics, Univ Pittsburgh, 63-65; asst prof, Univ Western Ont, 65-66, assoc prof, 66-68; PROF PHYSICS, UNIV WINDSOR, 68- *Concurrent Pos:* Div ed, J Electrochem Soc, 79- *Mem:* Am Phys Soc; Can Asn Physicists; Electrochem Soc. *Res:* Crystal field studies; angular momentum algebra; thin films; magneto-optical and electrical properties of ionic crystals; electron microscopy. *Mailing Add:* Dept of Physics Univ of Windsor Windsor ON N9B 3P4 Can

SCHLESINGER, RICHARD CARY, b Oberlin, Ohio, Apr 27, 40; m 61; c 2. SILVICULTURE. *Educ:* Middlebury Col, BA, 63; Yale Univ, MF, 65; State Univ NY Col Forestry, PhD(forest micrometeorol), 70. *Prof Exp:* Forester, Nat Forest Admin, 65-66, RES FORESTER, N CENT FOREST EXP STA, US FOREST SERV, 69- *Concurrent Pos:* Adj asst prof, Southern Ill Univ, 70- *Mem:* Am Meteorol Soc; Soc Am Foresters; Sigma Xi. *Res:* Culture of black walnut with emphasis on the microenvironmental requirements; modeling of tree growth and of microenvironments. *Mailing Add:* Forestry Sci Lab Southern Ill Univ Carbondale IL 62901

SCHLESINGER, S PERRY, b New York, NY, Oct 9, 18; m 43; c 2. ELECTRICAL ENGINEERING, PLASMA PHYSICS. *Educ:* Mich State Univ, BA, 41; Union Col NY, MS, 50; Johns Hopkins Univ, DEng(elec eng), 57. *Prof Exp:* Engr, Res Sect, Turban Generator Div, Gen Elec Co, 46-47; asst prof elec eng, Union Col NY, 47-50 & US Naval Acad, 50-53; res assoc microwaves, Radiation Lab, Johns Hopkins Univ, 53-56; from asst prof to assoc prof, 56-66, PROF ELEC ENG, COLUMBIA UNIV, 66- *Concurrent Pos:* Vis res assoc, Plasma Physics Lab, Princeton Univ, 62-63, consult, 63-64; pres, Faculties Assoc Consults Inc, 63-69; mem fac, Israel Inst Technol, 69-70; indust consult. *Mem:* Sr mem Inst Elec & Electronics Engrs; Am Phys Soc. *Res:* Plasma waves and instabilities; microwaves; antennas; electromagnetic theory. *Mailing Add:* Dept of Elec Eng Columbia Univ New York NY 10027

SCHLESINGER, SONDRA, b Long Branch, NJ, July 10, 34; m 55. VIROLOGY, MICROBIOLOGY. *Educ:* Univ Mich, BS, 56, PhD(biochem), 60. *Prof Exp:* Res assoc microbiol, Mass Inst Technol, 61-64; from asst prof to assoc prof microbiol, 64-76, PROF MICROBIOL & IMMUNOL, SCH MED, WASHINGTON UNIV, 76- *Concurrent Pos:* Nat Found fel, Inst Superiore Sanita, Italy, 60-61; Am Cancer Soc grant, 64-65; USPHS grant, 65- *Mem:* Fedn Am Scientists Exp Biol; Am Soc Microbiol. *Res:* Synthesis and structure of enveloped RNA viruses. *Mailing Add:* Dept of Microbiol Wash Univ Sch of Med St Louis MO 63110

SCHLESINGER, STEWART IRWIN, b Chicago, Ill, Apr 22, 29; m 51; c 2. COMPUTER SCIENCE, MATHEMATICS. *Educ:* Ill Inst Technol, BS, 49, MS, 51, PhD(math), 55. *Prof Exp:* Staff mem, Los Alamos Sci Lab, 51-56; mgr math & comput, Aeronutronic Div, Ford Motor Co, 56-63; dir, Math & Comput Ctr, 63-69, gen mgr, Info Processing Div, 69-80, gen mgr, Mission Info Systs Div, 80-81, GEN MGR, SATELLITE CONTROL DIV, AEROSPACE CORP, 81- *Mem:* Soc Indust & Appl Math; Asn Comput Mach; Soc Comput Simulation (vpres, 78-79, pres, 79-82). *Res:* Real-time computing systems; applied mathematics, numerical analysis, data reduction, simulation, interactive computing, and management of software development, particularly involving large scale digital computers. *Mailing Add:* Info Processing Div Aerospace Corp PO Box 92957 Los Angeles CA 90009

SCHLESINGER, WILLIAM HARRISON, b Cleveland, Ohio, Apr 30, 50. PLANT ECOLOGY. *Educ:* Dartmouth Col, BA, 72; Cornell Univ, PhD(biol), 76. *Prof Exp:* Asst prof ecol, Univ Calif, Santa Barbara, 76-80; ASST PROF BOT, DUKE UNIV, 80- *Mem:* Ecol Soc Am; Bot Soc Am; AAAS; Sigma Xi. *Res:* Ecosystem ecology including nutrient cycling in natural systems and global geochemical cycles; plant community structure. *Mailing Add:* Dept Bot Duke Univ Durham NC 27706

SCHLESSINGER, BERNARD S, b Mar 19, 30; m 52; c 3. INFORMATION SCIENCE. *Educ:* Roosevelt Univ, BS, 50; Miami Univ, Ohio, MS, 52; Univ Wis, PhD(phys chem), 55; Univ RI, MSLS, 75. *Prof Exp:* Res chemist, Am Can Co, 55-56; res supvr, US Air Force Sch Aviation Med, 56-58; indexer & dept head indexing, Chem Abstracts, 58-66; info scientist, Olin-Mathieson Chem Corp, 66-68; prof libr sci & asst dir div, Southern Conn State Col, 68-75; prof librarianship, Univ SC, 75-77; DEAN, GRAD LIBR SCH, UNIV RI, 77- *Mem:* Am Chem Soc; Am Libr Asn; Spec Libr Asn. *Res:* Electrophoresis; cardiovascular disease diagnosis; indexing; abstracting; search strategy; library statistical data. *Mailing Add:* Grad Libr Sch Univ of RI Kingston RI 02881

SCHLESSINGER, DAVID, b Toronto, Ont, Sept 20, 36; US citizen; m 60; c 2. MOLECULAR BIOLOGY, MICROBIOLOGY. *Educ:* Univ Chicago, BA, 55, BS, 57; Harvard Univ, PhD(biochem), 60. *Prof Exp:* NSF fel, Pasteur Inst, Paris, France, 60-62; from instr to assoc prof, 62-72, PROF MICROBIOL, SCH MED, WASH UNIV, 72- *Concurrent Pos:* Macy fel, 81. *Mem:* Am Chem Soc; Am Soc Microbiol. *Res:* Cell physiology; biochemistry. *Mailing Add:* Dept of Microbiol Wash Univ Sch of Med St Louis MO 63110

SCHLESSINGER, GERT GUSTAV, b Karlsruhe, Ger, Mar 20, 33; nat US; m 59; c 2. WATER CHEMISTRY. *Educ:* City Col New York, BS, 53; Case Inst Technol, MS, 55; Univ Pa, PhD, 57. *Prof Exp:* Asst, Case Inst Technol, 53-55; asst instr chem, Univ Pa, 55-57; res assoc inorg chem, Univ Fla, 58-59; asst prof chem, Pace Col, 59-60; sr res chemist, Evans Res & Develop Corp, 60-61; assoc prof chem, Gannon Col, 61-66, Newark Col Eng, 66-68 & US Coast Guard Acad, 68-71; chief clin chemist, Fairfield Hills State Hosp, Conn, 71-73; SR ENVIRON CHEMIST, STATE OF CONN, HARTFORD, 73- *Mem:* Am Chem Soc; Am Inst Chemists; Royal Soc Chem; Water Pollution Control Fedn. *Res:* Coordination complexes; kinetics; application of inorganic reagents to organic syntheses; wastewater analysis. *Mailing Add:* 8 Norton Ct Norwich CT 06360

SCHLESSINGER, MICHAEL, b July 2, 37; m 58; c 3. ALGEBRA. *Educ:* Johns Hopkins Univ, BA, 59; Harvard Univ, PhD(math), 64. *Prof Exp:* Lectr math, Princeton Univ, 64-66; asst prof, Univ Calif, Berkeley, 66-73; assoc prof, 73-79, PROF MATH, UNIV NC, CHAPEL HILL, 79- *Concurrent Pos:* Res assoc, Inst Math, Pisa, 69 & Harvard Univ, 72; NSF res grants, 73-81. *Res:* Deformation theory in algebraic geometry, singularities. *Mailing Add:* Dept of Math Univ of NC Chapel Hill NC 27514

SCHLESSINGER, RICHARD H, b Greeley, Colo, Sept 20, 35. ORGANIC CHEMISTRY. *Educ:* Edinboro State Col, BSEd, 57; Ohio State Univ, PhD(org chem), 64. *Prof Exp:* Fel org chem, Harvard Univ, 64-65 & Columbia Univ, 65-66; from asst prof to assoc prof, 66-74, PROF ORG CHEM, UNIV ROCHESTER, 74- *Res:* Total synthesis of natural products; synthetic methods. *Mailing Add:* Dept of Chem Univ of Rochester Rochester NY 14627

SCHLEUSENER, PAUL E(DWARD), b Oxford, Nebr, May 26, 22; m 52; c 4. AGRICULTURAL ENGINEERING. *Educ:* Univ Nebr, BSc, 44; Mich State Univ, MSc, 49, PhD(agr eng), 57. *Prof Exp:* Instr agr eng, Mich State Univ, 48-51; from asst prof to assoc prof, Univ Nebr, 53-63; res mgt specialist agr engr, Coop State Res Serv, Washington, DC, 63-64, res mgt specialist engr res prog develop & eval staff, 64-66, agr engr, 66-68, actg asst dir, Agr Exp Sta, Cornell Univ, 68-69, agr engr, 69-77, AGR ENGR, COOP STATE RES SERV, USDA, 77- *Honors & Awards:* Award, Am Soc Agr Engrs, 64; Superior Serv Award, USDA, 67. *Mem:* Am Soc Agr Engrs; AAAS. *Res:* Administration of agricultural engineering research; management of animal wastes; enhancing and protecting environmental quality; energy in agriculture. *Mailing Add:* USDA Coop State Res Serv Washington DC 20250

SCHLEUSENER, RICHARD A, b Oxford, Nebr, May 6, 26; m 49; c 5. METEOROLOGY, ENGINEERING. *Educ:* Univ Nebr, BS, 49; Kans State Univ, MS, 56; Colo State Univ, PhD(irrig eng), 58. *Prof Exp:* Instr agr eng, Kans State Univ, 49-50; assoc prof civil eng, Colo State Univ, 58-64; dir inst atmospheric sci, 65-74, vpres & dean eng, 74-75, actg pres, 75-76, PRES, SDAK SCH MINES & TECHNOL, 76- *Mem:* Am Soc Civil Eng; Am Meteorol Soc; Am Soc Agr Eng; Am Geophys Union. *Res:* Development in weather modification. *Mailing Add:* 315 S Berry Pine Rd Rapid City SD 57701

SCHLEUSNER, JOHN WILLIAM, b Birmingham, Ala, Jan 16, 43; m 71. MATHEMATICS. *Educ:* Univ Ala, BS, 65, MA, 66, PhD(math), 69. *Prof Exp:* Asst prof, 69-74, ASSOC PROF MATH, WVA UNIV, 74- *Mem:* Am Math Soc. *Res:* Special functions; analysis. *Mailing Add:* Dept of Math WVa Univ Morgantown WV 26505

SCHLEYER, HEINZ, b Pforzheim, Ger, Oct 29, 27; m 63; c 1. BIOPHYSICS, ENZYMOLOGY. *Educ:* Karlsruhe Tech Univ, Diplom chem, 54, Dr rer nat(chem), 60. *Prof Exp:* Fel biophys, 61-64, res assoc, 64-69, ASST PROF BIOPHYS & BIOPHYS IN SURG, JOHNSON RES FOUND, SCH MED, UNIV PA, 69- *Mem:* Biophys Soc; Soc Ger Chem; Am Soc Biol Chem; AAAS. *Res:* Electron transfer systems of photosynthesis; photochemistry of bacteriochlorophyll; structure and function of the hemeprotein P-450 in steroid metabolism; chemical carcinogenesis; application of magnetic resonance and spectroscopic techniques to biologically important compounds. *Mailing Add:* 5014 Ravdin Courtyard Univ of Pa Hosp Philadelphia PA 19104

SCHLEYER, PAUL VON RAGUE, b Cleveland, Ohio, Feb 27, 30. PHYSICAL ORGANIC CHEMISTRY. *Educ:* Princeton Univ, AB, 51; Harvard Univ, MA, 56, PhD(chem), 57. *Hon Degrees:* Dr, Univ Lyon, 71. *Prof Exp:* From instr to prof, Princeton Univ, 54-69, Eugene Higgins prof org chem, 69-76; INST CO-DIR & PROF, UNIV ERLANGEN-NURNBERG, WGER, 76- *Concurrent Pos:* A P Sloan res fel, 62-66; Guggenheim fel, 65-66; Fulbright res fel, Univ Munich, 65-66; vis & guest prof, Univ Colo, 63, Univ Wurzburg, 67, Univ Mich, 69, Univ Munich, 69 & 74-75, Carnegie-Mellon Univ, 69, Kyoto Univ, 70, Univ Munster, 71, Iowa State Univ, 72, Univ Geneva, 72, Univ Groningen, Neth, 72-73, Hebrew Univ Jerusalem, 73, Univ Paris-Sud, 73, Univ Lausanne, Switz, 74, Univ Louvain, Belg, 74, Univ Liege, 74, Univ Western Ont, 78, Univ Copenhagen, 79-80 & Univ Utrecht, 82; consult, Hoffmann-La Roche, 71-72 & Hoechst AG, 80-; DuPont lectr, Clemson Univ, 71; Alexander von Humboldt Found sr US scientist award, 74-75; adj prof, Case Western Reserve Univ, 76-77 & Carnegie-Mellon Univ, 77-78; sr fel, Hydrocarbon Inst, Univ Southern Calif, 78-; co-ed, J Comput Chem, 80- *Mem:* Fel AAAS; Am Chem Soc; The Chem Soc; fel NY Acad Sci; fel Am Inst Chemists. *Res:* Bridged ring systems; adamantane and diamondoid molecules; structure, stability and rearrangements of carbonium ions; spectroscopy and hydrogen bonding; conformational analysis; theoretical calculations applied to organic intermediates and the exploration of new molecular structures; lithium and other electron deficient compounds. *Mailing Add:* Inst of Org Chem Henkestrasse 42 8520 Erlangen Germany, Federal Republic of

SCHLEYER, WALTER LEO, b Berlin, Ger, June 4, 19; nat US; m 51; c 2. BIOPHYSICAL CHEMISTRY. *Educ:* Rutgers Univ, AB, 48; Columbia Univ, AM, 50, PhD(phys chem), 52. *Prof Exp:* Res assoc, Col Physicians & Surgeons, Columbia Univ, 52-54; chemist, Res & Develop Dept, 54-63, tech field serv mgr, 63-66, mkt develop mgr, 66-67, commercial develop mgr, 67-69, tech serv mgr, 69-71, GOVT & INDUST RELS MGR, PQ CO, 71- *Mem:* Am Chem Soc. *Res:* Physical chemistry of biological processes; fundamental properties and industrial applications of alkali silicates; effects of silica and silicates on health and environment; predictive biomedical testing for regulatory purposes. *Mailing Add:* 410 Harvard Ave Swarthmore PA 19081

SCHLEZINGER, NATHAN STANLEY, b Columbus, Ohio, June 2, 08; m 40; c 3. NEUROLOGY, PSYCHIATRY. *Educ:* Ohio State Univ, BA, 30; Jefferson Med Col, MD, 32; Columbia Univ, ScD(med), 38. *Prof Exp:* PROF CLIN NEUROL, JEFFERSON MED COL, 52- *Concurrent Pos:* Dir neuro-ophthal clin, Wills Eye Hosp, 39-; dir myasthenia gravis clin, Jefferson Hosp, 45-; consult, Vet Admin Hosp, Coatesville & Grandview Hosp, Sellersville. *Mem:* Am Neurol Asn; fel Am Acad Neurol; Asn Res Nerv & Ment Dis; Am Psychoanal Asn; fel Am Psychiat Asn. *Mailing Add:* Dept Clin Neurol Jefferson Med Col Philadelphia PA 19107

SCHLICHT, RAYMOND CHARLES, b North Bergen, NJ, Oct 13, 27; m 48; c 5. SYNTHETIC ORGANIC CHEMISTRY. *Educ:* Cent Col, Iowa, BS, 48; Univ Maine, MS, 50; Ohio State Univ, PhD(org chem), 52. *Prof Exp:* Chemist, 52-62, res chemist, 62-70, SR RES CHEMIST, TEXACO INC, 70- *Mem:* Am Chem Soc. *Res:* Reaction chemistry of higher olefins; phosphorus chemistry; nitrogen chemistry; synthesis of lubricating oil additives and fluids. *Mailing Add:* Lyndon Rd RD 2 Fishkill NY 12524

SCHLICHTING, DAVID ARTHUR, b Ann Arbor, Mich, Nov 21, 19; m 43; c 4. CLINICAL MEDICINE. *Educ:* Univ Mich, BS, 42; Purdue Univ, MS, 48, PhD(pharmaceut chem), 50. *Prof Exp:* Res pharmacist, William S Merrell Co, 49-52, Armour & Co, 52-54 & McNeil Labs, 54-66; assoc dir res, Carter-Wallace Labs, 66-68, dir proprietary drug res, 68-75, dir med affairs, Carter Prod Div, 75-76, DIR SCI & REGULATORY AFFAIRS, VICK DIV, RICHARDSON-VICKS, INC, 76- *Mem:* Am Chem Soc; Am Pharmaceut Asn. *Res:* Local anesthetics; synthetic cardiac aglycons; pharmaceutical dosage forms; ion exchange resins; clinical medicine; pesticides; biopharmaceutics; drug safety and efficacy; dental research. *Mailing Add:* Vick Div Richardson-Vicks Inc One Bedford Rd Mt Vernon NY 10553

SCHLICHTING, HAROLD EUGENE, JR, b Detroit, Mich, Mar 19, 26; m 49; c 6. PHYCOLOGY. *Educ:* Univ Mich, BS, 51; Mich State Univ, MS, 52, PhD(bot), 58. *Prof Exp:* Instr natural sci & bot, Mich State Univ, 52-54; fishery res biologist, US Fish & Wildlife Serv, 54-62; asst bot, Mich State Univ, 56-57; asst prof biol, Cent Mich Univ, 57-59; pvt res biologist, 59-60; assoc prof biol, NTex State Univ, 60-68; Fulbright-Hayes lectr, Univ Col Cork, 68-69; assoc prof bot, NC State Univ, 69-73; PRES, BIOCONTROL CO, INC, 73- *Concurrent Pos:* Res grants, NIH, 59-68 & Sigma Xi, 63-64; vis prof, Univ Okla Biol Sta, 64, 66, 68, 70 & 72; NSF fel, Marine Lab, Duke Univ, 66; State of Tex res grant, 66-68; sea grant, 70-72; vis prof bot, Univ Minn Biol Sta, 73, 75, 76 & 77. *Mem:* Int Asn Aerobiol; Sigma Xi; Phycol Soc Am; Int Phycological Soc. *Res:* Dispersal of algae and protozoa; algal ecology; mass culturing of algae; biological monitoring; organic waste handling. *Mailing Add:* Box 43 Port Sanilac MI 48469

SCHLICKE, HEINZ M, b Dresden, Ger, Dec 13, 12; US citizen; m 39; c 2. ELECTRONIC ENGINEERING, APPLIED PHYSICS. *Educ:* Dresden Tech Univ, BS, 35, MS, 37, DSc(elec eng), 39. *Prof Exp:* Res engr, Telefunken, Ger, 38-40; dept head submarine warfare, Naval Test Fields, 40-43, naval coun, High Command of Navy, 43-44, proj engr & spec consult, Spec Devices Ctr, Off Naval Res, NY, 46-50; mgr, Electronics Labs, Allen-Bradley Co, 50-68, chief scientist, 68-75; CONSULT ENGR, 75- *Mem:* Fel AAAS; fel Inst Elec & Electronics Engrs. *Res:* Electromagnetic interference and hazard control in civilian systems. *Mailing Add:* 8220 N Poplar Dr Milwaukee WI 53217

SCHLIESSMANN, D(ONALD) J(OSEPH), b Colome, SDak, Aug 15, 17; m 44; c 5. PUBLIC HEALTH ENGINEERING, ENVIRONMENTAL HEALTH. *Educ:* Univ Ill, BS, 41; Harvard Univ, MS, 49; Environ Eng Intersoc Bd, dipl, 70. *Prof Exp:* Mem staff malaria & typhus control, USPHS, 41-46, training off environ sanit & vector control, 47-48, engr & epidemiologist, 49-53, chief, Cumberland Field Sta, 54-57, dir & chief sanit eng, State Aids Sect, 57-61, dept chief, Tech Br, 61-63, chief aedes aegypti eradication br, 63-66, chief malaria eradication prog, Ga, 66-67; sanit engr, Pan Am Health Orgn, Washington, DC, 67-77; CONSULT ENGR, 77- *Concurrent Pos:* Consult comn enteric disease, US Armed Forces Epidemiol Bd, 51, mem comn environ sanit, 60-63, comn environ hyg, 63-72; consult, WHO, 58-63, mem expert comt control enteric diseases, 63-68. *Mem:* Am Pub Health Asn; Am Mosquito Control Asn; Water Pollution Control Fedn; Am Acad Environ Eng. *Res:* Public health engineering; epidemiology and control of diarrheal diseases; control of vectors and reservoirs of communicable diseases. *Mailing Add:* 707 Baycliff Rd Gulf Breeze FL 32561

SCHLIMM, GERARD HENRY, b Baltimore, Md, May 26, 29; m 56; c 3. CIVIL ENGINEERING, STRUCTURES. *Educ:* Univ Md, BS, 57, PhD(structures), 70; NJ Inst Technol, MS, 60. *Prof Exp:* Mech engr compressors, Exxon Res & Eng Co, 57-60; instr civil eng, Univ Md, 60-62; asst prof mech eng, US Naval Acad, 62-66; DIR DIV ENG & PHYS SCI, EVE COL, JOHNS HOPKINS UNIV, 66- *Concurrent Pos:* Consult, Trident Eng Asn, 62-68 & Ellicott City Eng Co, 71-73; mem bd dirs continuing eng studies div, Am Soc Eng Educ, 72-75, mem eng manpower comt, 77-; mem, Gov's Sci Adv Coun, State Md, 75- *Mem:* Am Soc Civil Engrs; Am Soc Eng Educ (secy, 71-72); Nat Soc Prof Engrs; Sigma Xi. *Res:* Engineering manpower; continuing education for engineers. *Mailing Add:* Dept of Eng & Phys Sci Johns Hopkins Univ Baltimore MD 21218

SCHLIMME, DONALD VINCENT, food science, see previous edition

SCHLINGER, EVERT IRVING, b Los Angeles, Calif, Apr 17, 28; m 57; c 4. ENTOMOLOGY, SYSTEMATICS. *Educ:* Univ Calif, Berkeley, BS, 50; Univ Calif, Davis, PhD(insect taxon), 57. *Prof Exp:* Lab asst entom, Univ Calif, 46-50, asst, 50-54 & 55-56; prof collector, Calif Acad Sci, 54-55; jr entomologist, Univ Calif, Riverside, 56-57, asst entomologist, 57-61, assoc prof entom & assoc entomologist, 61-68, chmn dept, 68-69, chmn div entomol & parasitol, 75-76, chmn dept entom sci, 76-79, PROF ENTOM, UNIV CALIF, BERKELEY, 69- *Concurrent Pos:* Prof collector, Assocs Trop Biogeog, 53, 54; Guggenheim fel, 66-67. *Honors & Awards:* Nat Sci Found award, 63-68. *Mem:* Fel AAAS; Entom Soc Am; Ecol Soc Am; Am Entom Soc; Assoc Syst Collections. *Res:* Insect (diptera) biosystematics; biogeography; insect ecosystems and land use management; biogeography; spider ecology; arthropod non-target studies. *Mailing Add:* Div of Entomol and Parasitol Univ of Calif Berkeley CA 94720

SCHLINGER, W(ARREN) G(LEASON), b Los Angeles, Calif, May 29, 23; m 47; c 3. CHEMICAL ENGINEERING. *Educ:* Calif Inst Technol, BS, 44, MS, 46, PhD(chem & mech eng), 49. *Prof Exp:* Res fel, Calif Inst Technol, 49-53; chem engr, 53-57, sr chem engr, 57-60, supvr res, 60-68, dir, 68-70, mgr, Montebello Res Lab, 70-81, ASSOC DIR GASIFICATION, TEXACO INC, 81- *Honors & Awards:* Tech Achievement Award, Am Inst Chem Engrs, 76; Chem Eng Pract Award, Am Inst Chem Engrs, 81. *Mem:* AAAS; Am Chem Soc; fel Am Inst Chem Engrs. *Res:* Fluid flow; heat transfer; coal gasification; hydrogen production and hydrogenation reactions; hydrocarbon gasification. *Mailing Add:* 3835 Shadow Grove Pasadena CA 91107

SCHLINK, F(REDERICK) J(OHN), b Peoria, Ill, Oct 16, 91; m 32. PHYSICS, MECHANICAL ENGINEERING. *Educ:* Univ Ill, BS, 12, ME, 17. *Prof Exp:* Mech engr & physicist, Nat Bur Standards, 12-13, from lab asst to tech asst to the dir, 13-19; physicist in charge, Instruments-Control Dept, Firestone Tire & Rubber Co, Ohio, 19-20; mech engr & physicist, Western Elec Co, 20-22; asst secy, Am Standards Asn, 22-31; TECH DIR & ED IN CHARGE OPERS, CONSUMERS' RES, INC, 29- *Concurrent Pos:* Lectr, Univ Tenn, 47-49, vis prof, 50; mem consumer adv coun, Underwriters' Labs. *Honors & Awards:* Longstreth Medal, Franklin Inst, 19. *Mem:* Fel Am Phys Soc; fel Am Soc Mech Engrs; Sigma Xi; Inst Elec & Electronics Engrs; Am Nat Standards Inst. *Res:* Measuring instruments and variant and hysteretic types of error; standards and specifications for products manufactured for ultimate consumer use; economics and technology of consumption goods; methods of test of appliances, materials and consumer-use products in general. *Mailing Add:* Consumers Res Inc Washington NJ 07882

SCHLIPF, JOHN STEWART, b Fargo, NDak, Oct 29, 48; m 70. MATHEMATICAL LOGIC. *Educ:* Carleton Col, BA, 70; Univ Wis-Madison, MA, 72, PhD(math), 75. *Prof Exp:* Instr math, Calif Inst Technol, 75-77; vis lectr math, Univ Ill, 77-80; MEM STAFF, ENVIRON CONTROL INC, 80- *Mem:* Asn Symbolic Logic; Am Math Soc; Math Asn Am. *Res:* Mathematical logic; specifically, infinitary model theory, generalized recursion theory and relative constructability. *Mailing Add:* 103 Poplar Lane Lexington Park MD 20653

SCHLISELFELD, LOUIS HAROLD, b Chicago, Ill, Sept 15, 31. BIOCHEMISTRY. *Educ:* Univ Ill, Urbana, BS, 53, MS, 55; Vanderbilt Univ, PhD(biochem), 64. *Prof Exp:* Res assoc contractile proteins, Inst Muscle Dis, Inc, 66-74; ASST RES PROF, DEPT BIOL CHEM, UNIV ILL MED CTR, 74- *Concurrent Pos:* USPHS fel biochem, Univ Wash, 64-66. *Mem:* Am Chem Soc; Am Soc Biol Chemists; Biophys Soc. *Res:* Enzymes and diseases involved in muscle glycogen breakdown; interaction of myosin and actin with adenosine triphosphate; mechanism of muscle contraction. *Mailing Add:* Dept of Biol Chem Univ Ill at the Med Ctr Chicago IL 60612

SCHLISSEL, ARTHUR, b Austria, July 7, 31; US citizen; m 63; c 2. MATHEMATICS. *Educ:* Brooklyn Col, BS, 54; NY Univ, MS, 58, PhD(math), 74. *Prof Exp:* Lectr math, Brooklyn Col, 57-60, Hunter Col, 60-63 & NY Univ, 63-64; asst prof, Fairleigh Dickinson Univ, 64-67 & Manhattan Col, 67-70; from instr to asst prof, 70-75, assoc prof, 75-80, PROF MATH & CHMN DEPT, JOHN JAY COL CRIMINAL JUSTICE, CITY UNIV NEW YORK, 80- *Concurrent Pos:* Vis prof math, King-Kennedy Prog, Albert Einstein Med Sch, 68-69. *Mem:* Am Math Soc; Math Asn Am; Sigma Xi. *Res:* Asymptotic behavior of the solutions of ordinary and partial differential equations; development of analysis in the 19th and 20th century, with special reference to differential equations. *Mailing Add:* 1364 E 27th St Brooklyn NY 11210

SCHLISSEL, HARVEY JOEL, microbiology, see previous edition

SCHLITT, DAN WEBB, b Lincoln, Nebr, Nov 2, 35; m 57; c 4. THEORETICAL HIGH ENERGY PHYSICS, MATHEMATICAL PHYSICS. *Educ:* Mass Inst Technol, BS, 57; Univ Wash, PhD(physics), 63. *Prof Exp:* Vis asst prof physics, Univ Md, 63-64; from asst prof to assoc prof, 64-77, PROF PHYSICS, UNIV NEBR, LINCOLN, 77- *Concurrent Pos:* NSF grant, 65-69; vis scientist, Inst Theoret Physics, State Univ Utrecht, 72-73. *Mem:* Am Phys Soc; Am Asn Physics Teachers; Soc Indust & Appl Math; Asn Comput Mach; Am Asn Univ Professors. *Res:* Elementary particle theory; mathematical physics; foundations of statistical mechanics; numerical analysis and computation. *Mailing Add:* 2600 C St Lincoln NE 68502

SCHLITT, WILLIAM JOSEPH, III, b Columbus, Ohio, June 12, 42. HYDROMETALLURGY, SOLUTION MINING. *Educ:* Carnegie Inst Technol, BS, 64; Pa State Univ, PhD(metall), 68. *Prof Exp:* Scientist, 68-75, sr scientist, 75-76, mgr, Hydrometall Dept, 77-81, PRIN PROG MGR, PROCESS TECHNOL GROUP, KENNECOTT MINERALS CO, 81- *Concurrent Pos:* mem, Oversight Comt Solution Mining Grant, NSF, 77-79, Oversight Comt Treatment Smelter Flue Dust Grant, Environ Protection Agency, 78-79; 2nd Int Solution Mining Symposium, 80-82. *Mem:* Sigma Xi; Can Inst Mining & Metall; Soc Mining Engrs. *Res:* Processes for extraction and refining of metal values contained in ores and other source materials including approaches involving hydrometallurgy and solution mining. *Mailing Add:* Process Technol Group Kennecott Minerals Co PO Box 11248 Salt Lake City UT 84147

SCHLITTER, DUANE A, b Monona, Iowa, Apr 2, 42; m 63; c 2. MAMMALOGY. *Educ:* Wartburg Col, BA, 65; Univ Kans, MA, 69; Univ Md, PhD, 76. *Prof Exp:* Res & curatorial asst mammal, African Mammal Proj, Smithsonian Inst, 67-72; ASSOC CUR MAMMAL, CARNEGIE MUS NATURAL HIST, 73- *Mem:* Am Soc Mammal (secy-treas, 77-); Soc Syst Zool; Sigma Xi; AAAS; Zool Soc SAfrica. *Res:* Systematics, evolution, biogeography and ecology of mammals of Africa and Southwest Asia; relationship of diseases, ectoparasite vectors and mammal host in old world medical zoological problems. *Mailing Add:* Carnegie Mus of Natural Hist 4400 Forbes Ave Pittsburgh PA 15213

SCHLOEMANN, ERNST, b Borgholzhausen, Ger, Dec 13, 26; nat US; m 55; c 3. MAGNETIC MATERIALS, MAGNETIC DEVICES. *Educ:* Univ Gottingen, BS, 51, MS, 53, PhD(theoret physics), 54. *Prof Exp:* Asst, Inst Theoret Physics, Univ Gottingen, 52-53; Fulbright fel solid state physics, Mass Inst Technol, 54-55; mem res staff, 55-60, proj dir, 60-64, SCI FEL, RAYTHEON CO, 64- *Concurrent Pos:* Vis assoc prof, Stanford Univ, 61-62 & Univ Hamburg, 66. *Mem:* Fel Am Phys Soc; fel Inst Elec & Electronics Engrs. *Res:* Solid state physics; magnetic phenomena; ferromagnetic resonance; lattice dynamics; thermal conductivity of solids; microwave physics and technology; statistical mechanics; environmental science; resource recovery from waste. *Mailing Add:* 38 Brook Rd Weston MA 02193

SCHLOEMER, ROBERT HENRY, b New York, NY, July 3, 46; m 69; c 2. VIROLOGY. *Educ:* Boston Col, BS, 68; Univ Va, MS, 72, PhD(biol), 73. *Prof Exp:* Fel, Sch Med, Univ Va, 73-75; ASST PROF MICROBIOL, SCH MED, IND UNIV, 75- *Mem:* Am Soc Microbiol; Sigma Xi. *Res:* Biochemical and biological analysis of viral membrane proteins; structure and assembly of viruses; mechanisms of virus persistence. *Mailing Add:* Dept of Microbiol Ind Univ Sch of Med Indianapolis IN 46202

SCHLOER, GERTRUDE M, b Milwaukee, Wis, May 16, 26. MICROBIOLOGY, GENETICS. *Educ:* Marquette Univ, BS, 48, MS, 53; Univ Wis-Madison, PhD(virol), 65. *Prof Exp:* Res assoc virol, Univ Wis-Madison, 66-67; NIH fel, Inst Virol, Univ Giessen, 67-69; instr microbiol, Mt Sinai Sch Med, 69-70, assoc, 70-71, asst prof, 71-73; MEM STAFF, PLUM ISLAND ANIMAL DIS LAB, USDA, 73- *Mem:* AAAS; Am Soc Microbiol. *Res:* Structure, function and genetics of influenza virus proteins; factors associated with virulence and transmission of Newcastle Disease virus. *Mailing Add:* Little Neck Rd Cutchoque NY 11935

SCHLOERB, PAUL RICHARD, b Buffalo, NY, Oct 22, 19; m 49; c 5. SURGERY. *Educ:* Harvard Univ, AB, 41; Univ Rochester, MD, 44; Am Bd Surg, dipl, 52. *Prof Exp:* Asst surg, Peter Bent Brigham Hosp, Boston, 51; instr, Sch Med, Univ Rochester, 52; from asst prof to assoc prof, Med Ctr, Univ Kans, 52-64, res prof, 64-72, asst dean res, 70-72, dean res, 72-78, prof surg, 72-79; PROF SURG, SCH MED & DENT, UNIV ROCHESTER, 79-; SURGEON, STRONG MEM HOSP, ROCHESTER, 79- *Concurrent Pos:* AEC fel med sci, Nat Res Coun, 48-49; USPHS career develop award, 62-67; consult, Vet Admin Hosps, Wichita, Kans, 55- & Kansas City, Mo, 59-79. *Mem:* AAAS; Am Physiol Soc; Soc Univ Surg; Am Heart Asn; fel Am Col Surgeons. *Res:* Postoperative care; surgical physiology; renal disorders; shock; water and electrolytes; transplantation. *Mailing Add:* Univ Rochester Med Ctr Dept Surg 601 Elmwood Ave Rochester NY 14642

SCHLOM, JEFFREY, b New York, NY, June 22, 42. MICROBIOLOGY, BIOCHEMISTRY. *Educ:* Ohio State Univ, BS, 64; Adelphi Univ, MS, 66; Rutgers Univ, PhD(microbiol), 69. *Prof Exp:* Guest worker oncol, Nat Cancer Inst, 67-69; from instr to asst prof virol, Col Physicians & Surgeons, Columbia Univ, 69-73; chmn breast cancer virus segment, 73-77, head, Tumor Virus Detection Sect, 77-80, CHIEF, EXP ONCOL SECT, NAT CANCER INST, 80- *Concurrent Pos:* Adj prof, Grad Fac, George Washington Univ. *Mem:* AAAS; Harvey Soc; NY Acad Sci. *Res:* Viral oncology; tumor immunology; molecular biology. *Mailing Add:* Nat Cancer Inst Nat Inst of Health Bethesda MD 20205

SCHLOMIUK, DANA, b Burcharest, Romania, Jan 5, 37; m 58. MATHEMATICS. *Educ:* Univ Bucharest, dipl math, 58; McGill Univ, PhD, 67. *Prof Exp:* Fel, 67-68, res assoc, 69, asst prof, 69-75, ASSOC PROF MATH, UNIV MONTREAL, 75- *Mem:* Am Math Soc. *Res:* Applied mathematics. *Mailing Add:* Dept of Math Box 6128 Univ of Montreal Montreal PQ H3C 3J7 Can

SCHLOMIUK, NORBERT, b Cernauti, Rumania, Apr 23, 32; Can citizen; m 58. MATHEMATICS. *Educ:* Univ Bucharest, MA, 55; McGill Univ, PhD(math), 66. *Prof Exp:* Instr math, Univ Bucharest, 54-58; lectr, Dalhousie Univ, 61-62, asst prof, 62-63; res asst, Univ Calif, Berkeley, 63-64; lectr, McGill Univ, 64-66, asst prof, 66-68; asst prof, 68-72, ASSOC PROF MATH, UNIV MONTREAL, 72- *Concurrent Pos:* Vis prof, Math Inst, Univ Perugia, 71-72 & Math Res Inst, Swiss Fed Inst Technol, 71-72. *Mem:* Am Math Soc; Math Soc France; Ital Math Union. *Res:* Algebraic topology and homotopy theory. *Mailing Add:* Dept of Math Univ of Montreal Montreal PQ H3C 3J7 Can

SCHLOSBERG, RICHARD HENRY, b New York, NY, May 23, 42; m 67; c 3. FUEL TECHNOLOGY, ORGANIC CHEMISTRY. *Educ:* City Univ New York, BS, 63; Mich State Univ, PhD(chem), 67. *Prof Exp:* Fel org chem, Case Western Reserve Univ, 67-69; asst prof chem, Univ Wis-Whitewater, 69-73; sr staff chemist coal sci, 73-80, RES ASSOC FUELS SCI, EXXON RES & ENG CO, 80- *Concurrent Pos:* Ed, Chem of Coal Conversion & assoc ed, Liquid Fuels Technol, 82. *Mem:* Am Chem Soc; Am Inst Chem Engrs. *Res:* Chemistry of synthetic fuels; coal science; shale science; heavy oil science; thermal hydrocarbon chemistry; strong acid chemistry; friedel crafts chemistry. *Mailing Add:* Exxon Res & Eng Co PO Box 45 Linden NJ 07036

SCHLOSSER, HERBERT, b Brooklyn, NY, Nov 18, 29; m 60; c 2. SOLID STATE THEORY, MOLECULAR BIOPHYSICS. *Educ:* Brooklyn Col, BS, 50; Polytech Inst Brooklyn, MS, 52; Carnegie Inst Technol, PhD(physics), 60. *Prof Exp:* Proj supvr res lab, Horizons Inc, 53-55; proj physicist, Carnegie Inst Technol, 59-60; sr physicist, Bayside Res Lab, Gen Tel & Electronics, 60-62; specialist physicist, Repub Aviation Corp, 62-63; asst prof, Polytech Inst Brooklyn, 63-68; assoc prof, 68-72, PROF PHYSICS, CLEVELAND STATE UNIV, 72- *Concurrent Pos:* Consult, Repub Aviation Co, 63; Fulbright-Hays lectr, Univ Sao Paulo, 66-67; Sr Weizmann Res Fel, Weizmann Inst Sci, Israel, 73-74; res assoc & vis prof, Dept Macromolecular Sci, Case Western Reserve Univ, 78-79. *Mem:* Am Phys Soc. *Res:* Surface physics; localized orbital theory; localized states in molecules and solids; electronic structure of macromolecules; molecular biophysics. *Mailing Add:* Dept Physics Cleveland State Univ Cleveland OH 44115

SCHLOSSER, JON A, b Houston, Tex, July 26, 37; m 64; c 2. MATHEMATICS, PHYSICS. *Educ:* Univ Tex, PhD(physics), 63. *Prof Exp:* Res assoc relativity theory, Univ Tex, 63-64; instr appl math, Univ Chicago, 64-66; asst prof math, La State Univ, Baton Rouge, 66-70; assoc prof, 72-78, PROF MATH, NMEX HIGHLANDS UNIV, 78- *Mem:* Opers Res Soc Am; Am Math Soc; Math Asn Am. *Res:* Functional analysis; relativity theory; operations research. *Mailing Add:* Dept of Sci & Math NMex Highlands Univ Las Vegas NM 87701

SCHLOSSER, PHILIP A, b Plymouth, Ind, Apr 14, 42; m 66; c 2. NUCLEAR ENGINEERING, RADIATION PHYSICS. *Educ:* Ohio State Univ, BSc, 65, MSc, 67, PhD(nuclear eng), 72. *Prof Exp:* Asst prof, 73-78, ASSOC PROF NUCLEAR ENG, OHIO STATE UNIV, 78- *Mem:* Inst Elec & Electronics Engrs; Am Nuclear Soc; Am Soc Eng Educ. *Res:* Nuclear instrumentation; semiconductor detectors; nuclear medicine imaging systems. *Mailing Add:* Dept of Nuclear Eng 206 W 18th Ave Columbus OH 43210

SCHLOSSER, WALTER, JR, b Philadelphia, Pa, Sept 15, 33. PHARMACOLOGY. *Educ:* St Joseph's Col, BS, 55; Univ Notre Dame, MS, 57; Jefferson Med Col, PhD(pharmacol), 64. *Prof Exp:* Instr pharmacol, Jefferson Med Col, 63-66; sr pharmacologist, 66-77, ASST RES GROUP CHIEF, HOFFMAN-LA ROCHE, INC, 77- *Concurrent Pos:* Co-investr, Subcontract US Army Chem Ctr, 64-65. *Res:* Investigation of drug effect on spinal and supraspinal somatic and sympathetic reflex activity. *Mailing Add:* Dept of Pharmacol Hoffmann-La Roche Inc Nutley NJ 07110

SCHLOSSMACHER, EDWARD JOHN, chemical engineering, see previous edition

SCHLOSSMAN, IRWIN S, b New York, NY, July 2, 30; m 51; c 2. ORGANIC CHEMISTRY. *Educ:* City Col New York, BS, 51; Polytech Inst Brooklyn, MS, 59; Xavier Univ, Ohio, MBA, 71. *Prof Exp:* Chemist, Nopco Chem Co, NJ, 51-54; Gallowhur Chem Co, NY, 54-55; proj leader res & develop, Halcon Int, Inc, NJ, 55-66; GROUP LEADER RES, EMERY INDUSTS, INC, 66- *Mem:* Am Chem Soc. *Res:* Liquid and vapor phase oxidation; catalysis; free radical chemistry; hydrogenation; polymer intermediates. *Mailing Add:* 8922 Cherry Blossom Lane Cincinnati OH 45231

SCHLOSSMAN, MITCHELL LLOYD, b Brooklyn, NY, Dec 30, 35; m 56; c 3. COSMETIC CHEMISTRY. *Educ:* NY Univ, BS, 56. *Prof Exp:* Group leader skin treat prod, Revlon Inc, 57-63; mgr res & develop, Leeming/Pacquin Div, Pfizer & Co, 64-69; dir tech opers, Paris Cosmetics Inc, 69-70; vpres res & develop, Prince Indust Ltd, 70-74; vpres mkt & res, Malmstrom Chem Div, Emery Indust Inc, 74-78; PRES, TEVCO INC, 78- *Honors & Awards:* Merit Award, Soc Cosmetic Chemists, 71. *Mem:* Fel Soc Cosmetic Chemists; Am Chem Soc; Am Pharmaceut Asn. *Res:* Lanolin and cosmetic ester research; cosmetic product development; nail lacquers. *Mailing Add:* 20 Lake Shore Dr Rockaway NJ 07866

SCHLOSSMAN, STUART FRANKLIN, b New York, NY, Apr 18, 35; m 58; c 2. IMMUNOLOGY, HEMATOLOGY. *Educ:* NY Univ, BA, 55, MD, 58. *Prof Exp:* Intern med, Ill Med Div, Bellevue Hosp, 58-59, asst resident, 59-60; res assoc, Lab Biochem, Nat Cancer Inst, 63-65; from instr to assoc prof, 65-77, PROF MED, HARVARD MED SCH, 77-, CHIEF DIV TUMOR IMMUNOL, SIDNEY FARBER INST, 73- *Concurrent Pos:* Nat Found fel microbiol, Col Physicians & Surgeons, Columbia, 60-62; Ward hemat fel internal med, Sch Med, Wash Univ, 62-63; Guggenheim fel, 71; asst physician, Med Serv, Vanderbilt Clin, Presby Hosp, 60-62; clin instr med, Sch Med, George Washington Univ, 64-65; dir blood bank, Beth Israel Hosp, Mass, 65-66, assoc med, 65-67, from asst physician to assoc physician, 67-73; chief clin immunol, Beth Israel Hosp, Mass, 71-73; sr assoc med, Peter Bent Brigham Hosp, Mass, 76- *Mem:* Am Soc Hemat; Am Asn Immunol; Am Soc Clin Invest. *Res:* Internal medicine. *Mailing Add:* Dept of Med Harvard Med Sch Sidney Farber Cancer Inst Boston MA 02115

SCHLOTTHAUER, JOHN CARL, b Rochester, Minn, Oct 6, 30; m 64; c 2. VETERINARY PARASITOLOGY. *Educ:* Univ Minn, BS, 52, DVM, 54, PhD(vet parasitol), 65. *Prof Exp:* Gen practitioner, 54-55; scientist, Arctic Aeromed Lab, US Air Force, 55-57; instr vet diag, 57-58, instr vet parasitol, 59-65, asst prof, 65-71, head microbiol-parasitol sect, 74-75, actg head chmn dept vet biol, 75-76, ASSOC PROF, COL VET MED, UNIV MINN, ST PAUL, 71- *Concurrent Pos:* Short term adv, Midwest Univs Consortium Int Activ/USAID Indonesian Agr Higher Educ Proj, 72. *Mem:* Am Vet Med Asn; Am Soc Parasitol; Am Asn Vet Parasitol; Wildlife Dis Asn. *Res:* Pathogenesis of canine dirofilariasis; biological control of helminths of veterinary importance; parasites of food producing animals; diseases and parasites of wildlife. *Mailing Add:* Col of Vet Med Univ of Minn St Paul MN 55108

SCHLOUGH, JAMES SHERWYN, b Wheeler, Wis, Sept 14, 31; m 63; c 2. ANIMAL PHYSIOLOGY, ENDOCRINOLOGY. *Educ:* Wis State Univ-River Falls, BS, 60; Univ Wis, MS, 63, PhD(zool), 66. *Prof Exp:* Instr, 65-66, asst prof, 66-68, from asst dean to assoc dean, Col Letters & Sci, 69-74, assoc prof, 68-76, PROF BIOL, UNIV WIS-WHITEWATER, 76- *Concurrent Pos:* Consult, Nasco, Inc, Wis, 67- *Mem:* AAAS; Soc Study Reproduction; Am Soc Mammal. *Res:* Early embryonic development in mammals; estrogen antagonism. *Mailing Add:* Dept of Biol Univ of Wis Whitewater WI 53190

SCHLUB, ROBERT LOUIS, b Springfield, Ohio, Jan 22, 51. SUGARCANE PATHOLOGY. *Educ:* Ohio State Univ, BS, 73, MS, 75; Mich State Univ, PhD(plant path), 79. *Prof Exp:* Asst, Plant Dis Clinic, Ohio State Univ, 74; asst slide-tape teaching aids gen path, Mich State Univ, 76-78; fel, Soilborne Dis Lab, USDA, Beltsville, Md, 79-80; ASST PROF SUGARCANE DIS, DEPT PLANT PATH & CROP PHYSIOL, LA STATE UNIV, 80- *Mem:* Am Phytopath Soc. *Res:* Diseases of sugarcane with major responsibilities in the area of varietal selection and yield loss estimation; etiology; epidemiology; environmental stress. *Mailing Add:* Dept Plant Path & Crop Physiol La State Univ Baton Rouge LA 70810

SCHLUEDERBERG, ANN ELIZABETH SNIDER, b Detroit, Mich, May 31, 29; m 51; c 5. VIROLOGY, IMMUNOLOGY. *Educ:* Ohio State Univ, BS, 50; Johns Hopkins Univ, ScM, 54, ScD(microbiol), 59. *Prof Exp:* Instr med, Sch Med, Univ Md, 59-61; res assoc, Sch Med, Yale Univ, 62-69, sr res assoc epidemiol, 69-76; assoc prof epidemiol, Sch Hyg & Pub Health, Johns Hopkins Univ, 76-78; EXEC SECY, EPIDEMIOL DIS CONTROL STUDY SECTION, DIV RES GRANTS, NIH, 78- *Concurrent Pos:* USPHS fel, 61-62, USPHS grants, 61-78; Mem, Scholars Adv Panel, Fogarty Int Ctr, NIH, 80- *Mem:* Soc Epidemiol Res; Infectious Dis Soc Am; fel Am Asn Immunol. *Res:* Measles and rubella virus characterization; evaluation of measles and rubella vaccines and vaccine regimens; viral immunity. *Mailing Add:* NIH Westwood Bldg Rm 203 Bethesda MD 20205

SCHLUETER, DONALD JEROME, b Oak Park, Ill, Nov 14, 31. NUCLEAR PHYSICS. *Educ:* Northwestern Univ, BS, 53, MS, 57; Univ Kans, PhD(physics), 64. *Prof Exp:* From instr to asst prof, 62-68, ASSOC PROF PHYSICS, PURDUE UNIV, WEST, 68- *Concurrent Pos:* NSF consult, AID, India, 67. *Mem:* AAAS; Am Asn Physics Teachers. *Res:* Optical interferometry; nuclear structure. *Mailing Add:* Dept of Physics Purdue Univ Lafayette IN 47907

SCHLUETER, DONALD PAUL, b Milwaukee, Wis, July 24, 27; m 53; c 1. INTERNAL MEDICINE. *Educ:* Marquette Univ, BS, 51, MD, 59; Ga Inst Technol, MS, 56. *Prof Exp:* Chemist, E I du Pont de Nemours & Co, 51-52; instr internal med, Ga Inst Technol, 53-55; intern med, Milwaukee County Hosp, Wis, 59-60, resident, 60-63; from instr to assoc prof, 64-75, PROF MED, MED COL WIS, 75-; CHIEF MED CHEST SERV, MILWAUKEE COUNTY HOSP, 68- *Concurrent Pos:* NIH res fel, 62-63; NIH res fel pulmonary physiol, Med Col Wis, 63-64; consult, Vet Admin Hosp, Wood, Wis, 63-; staff physician, Muirdale Sanatorium, 64-66, clin dir pulmonary dis, 66-68. *Mem:* Am Fedn Clin Res; Am Thoracic Soc; Am Col Chest Physicians; Am Med Asn; Am Occup Med Asn. *Res:* Inorganic paper chromatography; flame spectroscopy; pulmonary physiology-respiratory mechanics; hypersensitivity lung disease. *Mailing Add:* Milwaukee County Hosp Milwaukee WI 53226

SCHLUETER, EDGAR ALBERT, b Milwaukee, Wis, Sept 23, 18; m 57; c 3. ZOOLOGY, PARASITOLOGY. *Educ:* NTex State Univ, BS, 42; Univ Wis, MS, 49, PhD, 62. *Prof Exp:* Instr biol & natural sci, Mich State Univ, 49-55, 57-59; asst prof, Wis State Univ-Superior, 59-62; from asst prof to assoc prof, 62-69, PROF, NTEX STATE UNIV, 69- *Mem:* Am Soc Parasitol; Am Micros Soc. *Res:* Host-parasite relationships; parasitology; biochemistry of diseases of parasitic origin. *Mailing Add:* Dept Biol Sci NTex State Univ Denton TX 76203

SCHLUETER, ROBERT J, b Chicago, Ill, Feb 28, 29; m 59; c 3. BIOCHEMISTRY, PHARMACEUTICAL. *Educ:* Valparaiso Tech Inst, BA. 51; Northwestern Univ, PhD(biochem), 63. *Prof Exp:* Technician, Res & Develop Biol Control, Armour & Co, 48-51, anal chemist, Res Control Lab, 51, biochemist, Pharmaceut Res Dept, 51-52, biochemist, Res Div, 54-60, sr res biochemist, 63-68, assoc res scientist, 68-76, prin scientist, 76-78, MGR BIOCHEM PROCESSES, ARMOUR PHARMACEUTICAL CO, KANKAKEE, 78- *Mem:* Am Soc Pharmacol & Exp Therapeut; Am Soc Biol Chem; Soc Exp Biol & Med; Am Chem Soc; Endocrine Soc. *Res:* Isolation, purification and characterization of biologically active natural products and synthetic polypeptides; analytical and physical biochemistry; enzymology; collagen chemistry; bioassay development; calcitonin; insulin; insulin-like growth factor; carrier proteins; ACTH. *Mailing Add:* Armour Pharmaceut Co Box 511 Kankakee IL 60901

SCHLUTER, MICHAEL ANDREAS, b Straubing, WGer, Feb 23, 45; m 72; c 1. SOLID STATE PHYSICS. *Educ:* Univ Karlsruhe, WGer, dipl, 69; Fed Polytech Sch, Lausanne, Switz, PhD(physics), 72. *Prof Exp:* Asst physics, Fed Polytech Sch, 72-73; fel physics, Univ Calif, Berkeley, 73-75; MEM TECH STAFF, BELL LABS, 75- *Mem:* Am Phys Soc. *Res:* Solid state theory; bandstructures; surfaces; defects. *Mailing Add:* Bell Labs Murray Hill NJ 07974

SCHLUTER, ROBERT ARVEL, b Salt Lake City, Utah, Aug 27, 24; m 65; c 1. ELEMENTARY PARTICLE PHYSICS, EXPERIMENTAL HIGH ENERGY PHYSICS. *Educ:* Univ Chicago, BS, 47, PhD(physics), 54. *Prof Exp:* Res assoc physics, Enrico Fermi Inst Nuclear Studies, Chicago, 54-55; from instr to asst prof, Mass Inst Technol, 55-60; PROF PHYSICS, NORTHWESTERN UNIV, 61- *Concurrent Pos:* Guest scientist, Brookhaven Nat Lab, 57-; vis physicist, Lawrence Radiation Lab, Univ Calif, 58-; assoc scientist, Argonne Nat Lab, 60-72. *Mem:* AAAS; Am Phys Soc. *Res:* Interactions of fundamental particles; high energy and elementary particle physics. *Mailing Add:* Dept of Physics Northwestern Univ Evanston IL 60201

SCHMALBERGER, DONALD C, b Union City, NJ, Oct 24, 26; m 47. ASTROPHYSICS. *Educ:* Okla State Univ, BS, 58; Ind Univ, MA, 59, PhD(astrophys), 62. *Prof Exp:* From instr to asst prof astron, Univ Rochester, 62-67; asst prof astron, 67-70, asst prof astron & space sci, 70-72, ASSOC PROF ASTRON & SPACE SCI, STATE UNIV NY ALBANY, 72- *Mem:* AAAS; Am Astron Soc; fel Royal Astron Soc; NY Acad Sci; Int Astron Union. *Res:* Solar physics; theory of stellar atmospheres; physical structure of variable stars; turbulent energy transport in astrophysical media. *Mailing Add:* 75 Lenox Ave Albany NY 12203

SCHMALE, ARTHUR H, JR, b Lincoln, Nebr, Mar 14, 24; m 54; c 3. MEDICINE, PSYCHIATRY. *Educ:* Pa State Col, 45; Univ Md, MD, 51. *Prof Exp:* Med intern, Univ Hosp, Baltimore, Md, 51-52, asst resident med & psychiat, 52-53, asst resident psychiat, 53-54; asst resident med & psychiat, Strong Mem Hosp, 54-56; from instr to assoc prof med & psychiat, 56-73, PROF PSYCHIAT, SCH MED & DENT, UNIV ROCHESTER, 73- *Concurrent Pos:* NIMH Teaching fel psychiat, Sch Med, Univ Md, 53-54; Hochstetter fel med & psychiat, Sch Med & Dent, Univ Rochester, 54-55, USPHS res fel, 55-57, Markle scholar med sci, 57-62, Buswell fac fel, 60-; Found Fund Res Psychiat fel psychoanal training, 59-63. *Mem:* AAAS; Am Psychosom Soc; Am Asn Univ Prof. *Res:* Psychosomatic medicine; emotions; cancer. *Mailing Add:* Dept of Psychiat Univ of Rochester Sch of Med & Dent Rochester NY 14642

SCHMALTZ, LLOYD JOHN, b Chicago, Ill, Apr 10, 29; m 52; c 4. GEOMORPHOLOGY, GLACIAL GEOLOGY. *Educ:* Augustana Col, AB, 53; Univ Mo, AM, 56, PhD(geol), 59. *Prof Exp:* Instr geol, Augustana Col, 54-55 & Univ Mo, 56-59; from asst prof to assoc prof, 59-66, head dept, 65-71, PROF GEOL, WESTERN MICH UNIV, 66-, CHMN, DEPT GEOL,74- *Mem:* Fel Geol Soc Am; Nat Asn Geol Teachers; Am Quaternary Asn. *Res:* Pediments in central Arizona; Pleistocene geology in southwestern Michigan. *Mailing Add:* Dept of Geol Western Mich Univ Kalamazoo MI 49008

SCHMALZ, ALFRED CHANDLER, b Dedham, Mass, June 30, 24; m 47; c 2. ORGANIC CHEMISTRY. *Educ:* Bowdoin Col, AB, 47; Middlebury Col, MS, 51; UVa, PhD(org chem), 54. *Prof Exp:* Res chemist, Hercules Inc, Del, 54-61, Va, 61-62, group leader fiber develop, 62-63, res supvr fibers & film, 63-71, mgr, Prod Develop, 71-73, mgr, appl res, polymers-fibers, 73-78; RES SCIENTIST DEVELOP & FIBERS, HERCULES INC, 78- *Mem:* Am Chem Soc; Sigma Xi; Am Asn Textile Chem & Colorists. *Res:* Synthetic organic chemistry; paper chemicals; wet strength resins; water soluble polymers; antioxidants; light stabilizers; polyolefin fiber development; dyeing mechanisms. *Mailing Add:* 2594 Harvest Dr Conyers GA 30208

SCHMALZ, ROBERT FOWLER, b Ann Arbor, Mich, May 29, 29; m 64; c 2. MARINE GEOLOGY. *Educ:* Harvard Univ, AB, 51, MA, 54, PhD(geol), 59. *Prof Exp:* Asst marine sedimentation, Oceanog Inst, Woods Hole, 57-58; from asst prof to assoc prof, 58-69. chmn geol sect, Dept Geosciences, 71-74, PROF GEOL, PA STATE UNIV, 69- *Concurrent Pos:* Trustee, Bermuda Biol Sta, 67-79. *Mem:* Am Asn Petrol Geol; fel Geol Soc Am; Geochem Soc; Am Geophys Union; Soc Econ Paleont & Mineral. *Res:* Geochemistry petrology of marine sediments; surface chemistry; nucleation and reaction kinetics as related to sedimentary petrology; marine evaporite deposition; petroleum geology; nuclear waste management. *Mailing Add:* 536 Deike Bldg Dept of Geosci Pa State Univ University Park PA 16802

SCHMALZER, DAVID KEITH, b Baltimore, Md, Aug 20, 42; m 65. CHEMICAL ENGINEERING. *Educ:* Johns Hopkins Univ, BES, 64, MS, 65; Univ Pittsburgh, PhD(chem eng), 69. *Prof Exp:* Assoc engr, Com Atomic Power Div, Westinghouse Elec Co, 67; proj engr, Gulf Res & Develop Co, Pa, 68-77; res mgr, Pittsburg & Midway Coal Mining Corp, 77-80; MEM STAFF, GULF MINERAL RESOURCES CO, 80- *Mem:* Am Chem Soc; Am Inst Chem Engrs. *Res:* Hydrocarbon pyrolysis ranging from fundamental experimental work in small equipment at severe conditions to applied research and optimization of operating large scale industrial pyrolysis plants. *Mailing Add:* Gulf Mineral Resources Co 1700 Bellaire Denver CO 80222

SCHMARS, WILLIAM THOMAS, b Lockport, Ill, Jan 10, 38. ELECTRON OPTICS, ELECTRICAL ENGINEERING. *Educ:* Univ Ill, BS, 61. *Prof Exp:* Res engr, 61-66, sr res engr, 66-68, SR ENGR, AUTONETICS DIV, ROCKWELL INT, 68- *Mem:* Nat Soc Prof Engrs. *Res:* Navigation instruments, especially photoelectric autocollimators, precision shaft angle encoders and vibrating string gyro and accelerometer; the electrochemical tiltmeter. *Mailing Add:* Rockwell Int Autonetics Div 3370 Mira Loma Anaheim CA 92805

SCHMECKENBECHER, ARNOLD F, b Allendorf, Ger, Feb 15, 20; US citizen; m 53; c 1. INORGANIC CHEMISTRY. *Educ:* Univ Heidelberg, dipl, 50; Univ Kiel, PhD(chem), 53. *Prof Exp:* Instr inorg chem, Univ Kiel, 53-54; chemist, Gen Aniline & Film Corp, NJ, 55-58; sr chemist, Remington Rand Univac, Pa, 58-60; assoc chemist, 60-61, staff chemist, 61-64, adv chemist, 64-69, SR CHEMIST, COMPONENTS DIV, IBM CORP, 69- *Concurrent Pos:* Ger Res Asn scholar, 53-54. *Mem:* Am Chem Soc. *Res:* Magnetics materials, particularly materials for use in computer memories and phase locked oscillators; multilayered ceramic substitutes for integrated circuit chips. *Mailing Add:* 228 Wilbur Blvd Poughkeepsie NY 12603

SCHMEDTJE, JOHN FREDERICK, b St Louis, Mo, July 9, 19; m 56; c 3. ANATOMY. *Educ:* Columbia Univ, AB, 41; Rutgers Univ, PhD(zool), 51. *Prof Exp:* Instr anat, Sch Med, St Louis Univ, 51-53, asst prof, 53-56; instr, Harvard Med Sch, 56-58; asst prof, Sch Med, Tufts Univ, 58-66; ASSOC PROF ANAT, SCH MED, IND UNIV, INDIANAPOLIS, 66- *Mem:* AAAS; Am Asn Anat; Electron Micros Soc Am; Histochem Soc; Soc Cell Biologists. *Res:* Immunocytochemistry; electron microscopy; identification of intracellular immunoglobulins and enzymes; cellular aspects of immune reactions in lymphatic tissue and epithelium. *Mailing Add:* Dept of Anat Ind Univ Sch of Med Indianapolis IN 46202

SCHMEE, JOSEF, b Grieskirchen, Austria, Feb 13, 45; m 67. STATISTICS. *Educ:* Univ Comm, Vienna, Magister, 68; Union Col, NY, MSc, 70, PhD(statist), 74. *Prof Exp:* Res asst sociol, Col Com, Vienna, 67-68; analyst finance, Gen Elec Co, 69; asst prof mgt, 72-78, assoc prof, 78-80, PROF MGT & DIR, INST ADMIN, UNION COL, NY, 80- *Concurrent Pos:* Asst prof mgt, Univ Munich, 75; dir, Bur Health Mgt Standards, New York Dept Health, 78-79; Fulbright-Hays res scholar, Ger, 80-81. *Honors & Awards:* Wilcoxon Award, Am Soc Qual Control, 80, Brumbaugh Award, 81. *Mem:* Sigma Xi; Inst Math Statist; Am Statist Asn; Biomet Soc; Am Soc Qual Control. *Res:* Exact confidence intervals on mean, variance, percentiles and range of normal distribution with single censoring; sequential analysis t-test and estimation; semi-Markov models in health care systems; statistics in dentistry; censored data regression analysis. *Mailing Add:* Bailey Hall Inst of Admin & Mgt Union Col Schenectady NY 12308

SCHMEELK, JOHN FRANK, b Newark, NJ, July 19, 39; m 67. APPLIED MATHEMATICS. *Educ:* Seton Hall Univ, BS, 62; NY Univ, MS, 65; George Washington Univ, PhD(math), 76. *Prof Exp:* Instr math, Seton Hall Univ, 63-65 & NC State Univ, 65-66; teaching asst math, George Washington Univ, 71-73; instr math, Middlesex County Col, 74-75; ASST PROF MATH, VA COMMONWEALTH UNIV, 75- *Mem:* Am Math Soc; Math Asn Am; Soc Indust & Appl Math; Am Asn Univ Professors. *Res:* Development of an infinite-dimensional generalized function, for example, continuous linear functionals on test functions that are infinitely differentiable on an infinite dimensional vector space. *Mailing Add:* Dept Math Va Commonwealth Univ 901 W Franklin St Richmond VA 23284

SCHMEER, ARLINE CATHERINE, b Rochester, NY, Nov 14, 29. CELL BIOLOGY. *Educ:* Col St Mary, Ohio, BA, 51; Univ Notre Dame, MS, 61; Univ Colo, Denver, PhD(cell biol), 69. *Hon Degrees:* DSc, Albertus Magnus Col, 74. *Prof Exp:* Chmn high sch sci dept, Ohio, 54-59 & NY, 59-63; asst prof biol & co-dir med res lab, Ohio Dom Col, 63, chmn dept, 63-68, assoc prof biol & dir med res lab, 64-72, dir, Inst Divi Thomae Res Lab, 69-72; res scientist, Cancer Res Ctr & Hosp, Am Med Ctr, Denver, 72-73, dir med res fel prog & anticancer agents of marine origin, 72-82; DIR, MERCENENE MED RES INST, HOSP ST RAPHAEL, NEW HAVEN, CONN, 82- *Concurrent Pos:* NSF res fels, 59-64; Ohio Sertoma award, 66; USPHS Nat Cancer Inst & Am Cancer Soc grants; Nat Cancer Inst spec res fel; chmn biol educ sec schs, Archdiocese of New York, 61-63; partic, NSF High Sch Biol Sci Curric Study & Comn Undergrad Educ Biol Sci Comt Col Biol Teacher Training, DC, 62-63; sr investr & mem cell biol specialty panel, Marine Biol Lab, Woods Hole, 62-, corp mem, 65-; partic, Int Cancer Cong, Tokyo, Japan, 66 & Houston, Tex, 70, Buenas Aires, Argentina, 78, Seattle, Wash, 82; res scientist, Inst Med Biophys, Univ Wurzburg, 69-70; vis scientist, Am Med Ctr Cancer Res; consult, Sch Trop Med, Univ Sydney. *Mem:* Am Soc Cell Biol; NY Acad Sci; Electron Micros Soc Am; Am Physiol Soc; fel Royal Micros Soc. *Res:* Cellular biology; developmental drugs cancer; pharmacology and experimental therapeutics in use of growth inhibitors from naturally occurring products and effects of these products on abnormal growth such as cancer. *Mailing Add:* Hosp St Raphael Cancer Res Dir New Haven CT 06511

SCHMEHL, WILLARD REED, b Arlington, Nebr, Apr 16, 18; m 43; c 2. SOILS. *Educ:* Colo State Univ, BS, 40; Cornell Univ, PhD(soil sci), 48. *Prof Exp:* Asst, Cornell Univ, 40-42; supvr, Hercules Powder Co, 42-43; assoc prof & assoc agronomist, 48-56, PROF AGRON & AGRONOMIST, COLO STATE UNIV, 56- *Concurrent Pos:* Proj assoc, Univ Wis, 54-55. *Mem:* Soil Sci Soc Am; Am Soc Agron; Clay Minerals Soc; Int Soc Soil Sci. *Res:* Soil acidity and fertility; availability of phosphates to plants; radioactive tracers in soil and fertilizer research; sugar beet nutrition. *Mailing Add:* Dept of Agron Colo State Univ Ft Collins CO 80521

SCHMEISSER, GERHARD, JR, b Baltimore, Md, Mar 27, 26; m 57. ORTHOPEDIC SURGERY. *Educ:* Princeton Univ, AB, 49; Johns Hopkins Univ, MD, 53. *Prof Exp:* From instr to assoc prof, 57-61, PROF ORTHOP SURG, SCH MED, JOHNS HOPKINS UNIV, 71- *Concurrent Pos:* Vis surgeon, Children's Hosp, 58-; orthop surgeon, Johns Hopkins Hosp, 58-; chief orthop surg, Baltimore City Hosps, 59-; consult, USPHS Hosp, 64-65. *Honors & Awards:* IR 100 Award, 71. *Mem:* Fel Am Acad Orthop Surg. *Res:* External power and control of limb prostheses and braces. *Mailing Add:* Johns Hopkins Hosp 600 N Wolfe St Baltimore MD 21205

SCHMELING, SHEILA KAY, b Brookings, SDak, May 5, 49. WILDLIFE DISEASE. *Educ:* Univ Mass, Amherst, BS, 71; Colo State Univ, MS & DVM, 77. *Prof Exp:* WILDLIFE VET, NAT WILDLIFE HEALTH LAB, 79- *Mem:* Wildlife Disease Asn; Am Asn Wildlife Vets; Am Vet Med Asn; Sigma Xi. *Res:* Determination of the causes of mortality in free-flying raptors, especially the bald and golden eagle. *Mailing Add:* Nat Wildlife Health Lab 6006 Schroeder Rd Madison WI 53711

SCHMELTEKOPF, ARTHUR L, JR, b Kyle, Tex, Feb 24, 32; m 55; c 1. SPECTROSCOPY. *Educ:* Univ Tex, PhD(physics), 62. *Prof Exp:* PHYSICIST, AERONOMY LAB, ENVIRON RES LABS, NAT OCEANIC & ATMOSPHERIC ADMIN, 62- *Mem:* Am Phys Soc; Sigma Xi. *Res:* Ion-molecule collision processes; plasma physics in the excitation of the metastable states of helium and cataphoresis measurements of rare mixtures; molecular physics. *Mailing Add:* Environ Res Lab/Nat Oceanic & Atmospheric Admin 325 Broadway 24-2107 R448 Boulder CO 80302

SCHMELTZ, IRWIN, b New York, NY, Feb 26, 32; m 62; c 4. BIO-ORGANIC CHEMISTRY, ANALYTICAL CHEMISTRY. *Educ:* City Col New York, BS, 53; Univ Utah, PhD(org biochem), 59. *Prof Exp:* Teaching fel chem, Univ Utah, 55-59, fel biochem, 59-60; Cigar Mfrs Asn sr res fel, Eastern Regional Lab, USDA, 60-62, res chemist tobacco invests, 62-65, head pyrolysis invests, tobacco lab, 65-70, head smoke invests, 70-71, lubricant invests, Animal Fat Prod Lab, 71-73; head bio-org chem, Div Environ Carcinogensis, Naylor-Dana Inst Dis Prev, Am Health Found, 73-79; TECH FEL, HOFFMANN-LAROCHE, NUTLEY, NJ, 79- *Concurrent Pos:* Consult, Nat Cancer Inst, 73- & Princeton Univ, 74- *Mem:* Am Oil Chemists

Soc; Soc Environ Geochem & Health; AAAS; Am Chem Soc; Am Asn Cancer Res. *Res:* Chemical carcinogenesis, environmental chemistry; organic synthesis; biosynthesis of pteridines; chemical composition of tobacco and tobacco smoke; pyrolysis of organic compounds; products from animal fats; analytical organic chemistry. *Mailing Add:* 340 Kingsland St Nutley NJ 07110

SCHMELZ, DAMIAN VINCENT, b Georgetown, Ind, May 7, 32. ECOLOGY. *Educ:* St Meinrad Col, BA, 58; Purdue Univ, Lafayette, MS, 64, PhD(ecol), 69. *Prof Exp:* Teacher high sch, Ind, 59-67; instr, 65-70, from asst prof to assoc prof, 70-75, PROF & ACAD DEAN, ST MEINRAD COL. 75- *Concurrent Pos:* Mem, Ind Natural Areas Surv, Purdue Univ, 67-69; mem, Ind Natural Resources Comn, 75- *Mem:* Ecol Soc Am; Sigma Xi. *Res:* Forest ecology. *Mailing Add:* Dept of Biol St Meinrad Col St Meinrad IN 47577

SCHMERLING, ERWIN ROBERT, b Vienna, Austria, July 28. 29; m 57; c 2. SPACE PHYSICS, DATA SYSTEMS. *Educ:* Cambridge Univ, BA, 50, MA, 54, PhD(radio physics), 58. *Prof Exp:* Vis asst prof elec eng, Pa State Univ. 55-57, from asst prof to assoc prof, 57-64; prog chief magnetospheric physics, 64-76, CHIEF SPACE PLASMA PHYSICS, OFF SPACE SCI, NASA HQ, 76- *Concurrent Pos:* Mem comns G & H, Int Sci Radio Union, 58, secy, US Comn III, 66-69, chmn, 69-72. *Mem:* AAAS; fel Inst Elec & Electronics Eng; Am Geophys Union; fel Brit Phys Soc. *Res:* Ionospheric and radio physics; physics of the ionosphere; radio wave propagation; electron densities and sounding of ionized regions from the ground and from space vehicles; atmospheric and space physics, environment of earth, planets and interplanetary space; scientific data systems. *Mailing Add:* SC-7 Off Space Sci NASA Hq Washington DC 20546

SCHMERR, MARY JO F, b Dubuque, Iowa, Nov 4, 45; m 72; c 2. IMMUNOCHEMISTRY, MOLECULAR BIOLOGY. *Educ:* Clarke Col, Iowa, BA, 68; Iowa State Univ, PhD(biochem), 75. *Prof Exp:* RES CHEMIST BIOCHEM ANIMAL DIS, NAT ANIMAL DIS CTR, USDA, 75- *Mem:* Am Soc Microbiol; Am Chem Soc; Sigma Xi. *Res:* Biochemistry and immunochemistry of animal diseases caused by viruses; study of the function of viral proteins. *Mailing Add:* Nat Animal Dis Ctr PO Box 70 Dayton Rd Ames IA 50010

SCHMERTMANN, JOHN H(ENRY), b New York, NY, Dec 2, 28; m 56; c 4. CIVIL ENGINEERING. *Educ:* Mass Inst Technol, BSCE, 50; Northwestern Univ, MS, 54, PhD(civil eng), 62. *Prof Exp:* Soils engr, Moran, Proctor, Mueser & Rutledge, NY, 51-54; from asst prof to assoc prof, 56-65, PROF CIVIL ENG, UNIV FLA, 65- *Concurrent Pos:* Prin investr, NSF res grants, 56-; NSF fel, Norweg Geotech Inst, Oslo, 62-63; Nat Res Coun Cross-Can lectr, 71; vis scientist, Nat Res Coun Can, 71-72; partner, Schmertmann & Crapps, Inc, Consult Geotech Engrs, 78- *Honors & Awards:* Collingwood Prize, Am Soc Civil Engrs, 56, Norman Medal, 71, State-of-the-Art Award, 77. *Mem:* Am Soc Civil Engrs; Am Soc Testing & Mat. *Res:* Soil mechanics and foundation engineering; consolidation and shear strength; methods for field exploration; special soil mechanics problems. *Mailing Add:* Dept Civil Eng Univ Fla Gainesville FL 32611

SCHMICKEL, ROY DAVID, b Millville, NJ, Feb 9, 36; m 60; c 4. PEDIATRICS, GENETICS. *Educ:* Oberlin Col, BA, 57; Duke Univ, MD, 61. *Prof Exp:* Instr genetics & pediat, Med Sch, Johns Hopkins Univ, 66-68; asst prof pediat, Univ Mich, Ann Arbor, 68-70, assoc prof, 70-75, prof, 75-81, assoc prof human genetics, 71-81; PROF PEDIAT, UNIV PA, 81-, PROF & CHMN HUMAN GENETICS, 81- *Concurrent Pos:* Larry Silver res award; 57; fel, Dept Microbiol, Johns Hopkins Univ, 66-68; spec adv, President's Coun Ment Retardation, 76-; investr, NIH grant, 77-82; adv, NIH, Genetics Study Sect, 78-; assoc ed, Am J Human Genetics, 81- *Honors & Awards:* Pub Health Serv Res Award, US Pub Health Serv, 64. *Mem:* Soc Pediat Res; Am Pediat Soc; Am Soc Human Genetics; Am Acad Pediat. *Res:* Chromosomal diseases and characterization of human DNA; human DNA and human chromosomes; genetics; isolation of human ribosomal genes. *Mailing Add:* Med Sch G3 Univ Pa 37th & Hamilton Walk Philadelphia PA 19104

SCHMID, CARL WILLIAM, b Philadelphia, Pa. BIOPHYSICAL CHEMISTRY. *Educ:* Drexel Inst Technol, BS, 67; Univ Calif, Berkeley, PhD(chem), 71. *Prof Exp:* Chemist, Eastern Regional Res Labs, 63-67; res asst biophys chem, Univ Calif, Berkeley, 67-71; res fel, Calif Inst Technol, 71-73; ASSOC PROF CHEM, UNIV CALIF, DAVIS, 73- *Concurrent Pos:* Jane Coffin Childs Found fel, 71-73. *Mem:* AAAS. *Res:* Determining the biological function of different DNA sequence classes which comprise the eukaryotic genome. *Mailing Add:* Dept of Chem Univ of Calif Davis CA 95616

SCHMID, FRANK RICHARD, b New York, NY, June 25, 24; m 54; c 9. MEDICINE. *Educ:* NY Univ, MD, 49. *Prof Exp:* From asst to resident to chief resident, Bellevue Hosp, New York, 50-51 & 52-54; asst med, Col Med, NY Univ, 54-57; from assoc to assoc prof, 57-69, PROF MED, MED SCH, NORTHWESTERN UNIV, CHICAGO, 69- *Concurrent Pos:* Fel, Arthritis & Rheumatism Found, 56-59; Markle scholar med sci, 60-65; trainee, Med Div, NIH, 54-56; asst vis physician, Bellevue Hosp, 54-57; attend physician, Vet Admin Res Hosp, 57-, Northwestern Mem Hosp, 61- & Cook County Hosp, 66-69, consult, Rehab Inst Chicago, 67-; consult, Children's Mem Hosp, Chicago. *Mem:* Am Rheumatism Asn; Am Fedn Clin Res; Cent Soc Clin Res. *Res:* Immunological considerations in rheumatic diseases. *Mailing Add:* Dept of Med Northwestern Univ Med Sch Chicago IL 60611

SCHMID, FRANZ ANTON, b Hermersdorf, Czech, Sept 21, 22; US citizen; m 55. CANCER. *Educ:* Univ Munich, DVM, 51; Fordham Univ, MS, 54. *Prof Exp:* Res asst surg physiol, Sloan-Kettering Inst Cancer Res, 54-56; vet meat inspector, USDA, 56-58; res assoc, 58-66, ASSOC EXP CANCER CHEMOTHER, WALKER LAB, SLOAN-KETTERING INST CANCER RES, 66- *Mem:* AAAS; Am Asn Cancer Res; Am Vet Med Asn. *Res:* Experimental chemotherapy of cancer; chemical cancerigenesis; mouse genetics. *Mailing Add:* Sloan-Kettering Inst for Cancer Res Rye NY 10580

SCHMID, GEORGE HENRY, b Madison, Wis, Aug 6, 31; m 57; c 2. ORGANIC CHEMISTRY. *Educ:* Univ Southern Calif, BS, 53, PhD(org chem), 61. *Prof Exp:* Fel, Harvard Univ, 61-63; from asst prof to assoc prof, 63-75, PROF CHEM, UNIV TORONTO, 75- *Mem:* Am Chem Soc; Can Inst Chem; Royal Soc Chem. *Res:* The elucidation of the mechanism of electrophilic additions to unsaturated carbon-carbon bonds. *Mailing Add:* Dept of Chem Univ of Toronto Toronto ON M5S 1A1 Can

SCHMID, GERHARD MARTIN, b Ravensburg, Ger, Oct 26, 29; m 58; c 2. ELECTROCHEMISTRY. *Educ:* Innsbruck Univ, PhD(phys chem), 58. *Prof Exp:* Fel, Univ Tex, 58-62; temp asst prof, Univ Alta, 62-64; asst prof, 64-70, ASSOC PROF CHEM, UNIV FLA, 70- *Concurrent Pos:* Sr res chemist, Tracor, Inc, 60-62. *Mem:* Am Chem Soc; Electrochem Soc. *Res:* Structure of the electrical double layer; adsorption on solid electrodes; passivity of metals; corrosion and corrosion inhibition. *Mailing Add:* Dept of Chem Univ of Fla Gainesville FL 32611

SCHMID, HARALD HEINRICH OTTO, b Graz, Austria, Dec 10, 35. BIOCHEMISTRY. *Educ:* Graz Univ, MS, 58, PhD, 64. *Prof Exp:* From res fel biochem to res assoc, 62-66, from asst prof to assoc prof, 66-74, PROF BIOCHEM, HORMEL INST, UNIV MINN, 74- *Mem:* Am Chem Soc; Am Oil Chem Soc; Am Soc Biol Chem. *Res:* Structure and biochemistry of natural products; metabolism of complex lipids in biomembranes; lipid neurochemistry; lipid metabolism in ischemia and myocardial infarct. *Mailing Add:* Hormel Inst Univ of Minn Austin MN 55912

SCHMID, JACK ROBERT, b Chicago, Ill, Oct 3, 24; m 48; c 4. PHARMACOLOGY, PHYSIOLOGY. *Educ:* Mich State Univ, BS, 52, MS, 54; Univ Ark, Little Rock, PhD(pharmacol), 67. *Prof Exp:* Assoc pharmacologist, Mead Johnson Res Ctr, Ind, 54-58; high sch teacher, Mich, 59-62; sr pharmacologist, 66-73, PHARMACOLOGIST SPECIALIST, RIKER RES LABS, 3M CO, 73- *Mem:* Int Soc Heart Res; NY Acad Sci; Am Chem Soc. *Res:* Cardiopulmonary effects of drugs. *Mailing Add:* Riker Labs Inc 3M Co 3M Ctr Bldg 218-2 St Paul MN 55101

SCHMID, JOHN, b Milwaukee, Wis, Apr 17, 20; m 48; c 3. APPLIED STATISTICS, EDUCATIONAL PSYCHOLOGY. *Educ:* Univ Wis, BS, 45, MS, 46, PhD(educ, statist), 49. *Prof Exp:* Instr math, Univ Wis Exten Div, 46-47; asst prof res, Mich State Univ, 49-52; res psychologist, Air Force Personnel & Training Res Ctr, 52-57; prof statist, Univ Ark, 57-66; PROF RES, UNIV NORTHERN COLO, 66- *Concurrent Pos:* Ed, J Exp Educ, 63- *Mailing Add:* Dept Res & Statist Methodology Univ of Northern Colo Greeley CO 80631

SCHMID, KARL, b Erlinsbach, Switz, July 23, 20; nat US; m 47; c 2. BIOCHEMISTRY. *Educ:* Swiss Fed Inst Technol, dipl rer nat, 43; Univ Basel, MA & PhD(chem), 46. *Prof Exp:* Res assoc, Harvard Med Sch, 48-52; assoc biochemist, Lovett Mem Lab, Mass Gen Hosp, 52-63; assoc prof, 63-66, PROF BIOCHEM, SCH MED, BOSTON UNIV, 66- *Concurrent Pos:* Zurich Univ fel chem, Cambridge Univ, 47-48. *Mem:* Am Chem Soc; Am Soc Biol Chemists; Soc Complex Carbohydrates (pres, 80). *Res:* Isolation, purification, characterization, chemical structure and biological importance of human plasma proteins, especially glycoproteins. *Mailing Add:* Dept Biochem Sch Med Boston Univ Boston MA 02118

SCHMID, LAWRENCE ALFRED, b Philadelphia, Pa, Mar 11, 28; m 62. THEORETICAL PHYSICS. *Educ:* Univ Pa, BS, 49; Princeton Univ, MA, 51, PhD(physics), 53. *Prof Exp:* Asst prof physics, Mich State Univ, 53-59; physicist, Goddard Space Flight Ctr, NASA, 59-80; PHYSICIST, NAT BUR STANDARDS, 80- *Mem:* AAAS; Am Phys Soc; Am Asn Physics Teachers. *Res:* Fluid dynamics; thermodynamics; meteorology; relativity; variational formalism; group theory. *Mailing Add:* 12 Maplewood Ct Greenbelt MD 20770

SCHMID, LOREN CLARK, b Ypsilanti, Mich, Feb 1, 31; m 54; c 3. ENERGY CONVERSION. *Educ:* Univ Mich, BS, 53, MS, 54, PhD(physics), 58. *Prof Exp:* Asst, Eng Res Inst, Univ Mich, 53-56; res assoc, Argonne Nat Lab, 56-58; physicist, Gen Elec Co, 58-65; res mgr, 65-68, mgr reactor physics dept, 68-73, dir energy prog, 73-75, fusion technol prog mgr, 73-76, energy mission dir, 75-79, MGR, OFF PLANNING, BATTELLE MEM INST, 79- *Concurrent Pos:* Actg assoc prof nuclear eng, Univ Wash, 68-74; coordr plutonium recycle short course, Joint Ctr Grad Study, Univ Wash, 73-77, affiliated prof, prog adv & coordr, Nuclear Eng, 74- *Mem:* Fel Am Nuclear Soc; NY Acad Sci. *Res:* Fusion reactor technology; nuclear and reactor physics; analysis of radioactive-decay schemes; energy production and conservation. *Mailing Add:* Mgr Off Planning Pac Northwest Labs Battelle Mem Inst Richland WA 99352

SCHMID, PETER, b Signau, Switz, Sept 5, 27; US citizen; m 54; c 2. MEDICAL SCIENCES, BIOCHEMISTRY. *Educ:* Winterthur Tech. Switz, BS, 52; Univ Calif, Berkeley, MS, 59; Univ Calif, San Francisco, PhD(biochem, pharmaceut chem), 64. *Prof Exp:* Investr org chem, Ciba Pharmaceut Co, Switz, 52-55; res assoc biochem, State Univ NY Upstate Med Ctr, 55-56; fel, Med Ctr, Univ Calif, San Francisco, 63; sr investr radiobiol, US Naval Radiol Defense Lab, 64-67; SR INVESTR RADIOBIOL & GROUP LEADER CUTANEOUS HAZARDS, LETTERMAN ARMY INST RES, 67- *Mem:* AAAS; Am Chem Soc; NY Acad Sci; Am Soc Microbiol; Sigma Xi. *Res:* Mechanism of cell replication and cell growth; biophysics of skin; medical research in dermatology to include biochemical, biophysical, morphometrics, biostatistics aspects, cosmethology and cell biology; contract review; budget and program development and management. *Mailing Add:* Letterman Army Inst of Res San Francisco CA 94129

SCHMID, RUDI, b Glarus, Switz, May 2, 22; nat US; m 49; c 2. INTERNAL MEDICINE, BIOCHEMISTRY. *Educ:* Univ Zurich, MD, 47; Univ Minn, PhD, 54; Am Bd Internal Med, dipl, 57. *Prof Exp:* Intern, Univ Hosp, Univ Calif, 48-49; resident, Univ Hosp, Univ Minn, 49-51; instr med, Sch Med, 52-54; sr hematologist, Nat Inst Arthritis & Metab Dis, 55-57; assoc med,

Harvard Med Sch, 57-59, asst prof, 59-62; prof, Univ Chicago, 62-66; PROF MED, UNIV CALIF, SAN FRANCISCO, 66- Concurrent Pos: USPHS spec res fel biochem, Columbia Univ, 54-55; asst physician, Thorndike Mem Lab, Boston City Hosp, 57-; consult, US Army Surgeon Gen & San Francisco Vet Admin Hosp. Mem: Nat Acad Sci; Am Soc Clin Invest; Am Soc Exp Path; Am Soc Hemat; Am Soc Biol Chemists. Res: Liver physiology and pathophysiology; hepatic enzymes and metabolism; porphyrins; bile pigments; jaundice; porphyria; liver diseases. Mailing Add: Dept of Med Univ of Calif San Francisco CA 94143

SCHMID, WALTER EGID, b Philadelphia, Pa, Nov 24, 33; m 59; c 1. BOTANY. Educ: Univ Pa, AB, 55; Univ Wis, MS, 58, PhD(bot), 61. Prof Exp: Asst bot, Univ Wis, 55-61; jr res plant physiologist, Univ Calif, Davis, 61-62; from asst prof to assoc prof bot, 62-72, assoc dean grad sch, 70-72, PROF BOT, SOUTHERN ILL UNIV, CARBONDALE, 72- Mem: AAAS; Am Soc Plant Physiol; Bot Soc Am; Japanese Soc Plant Physiol. Res: Inorganic nutrition of plants. Mailing Add: Dept of Bot Southern Ill Univ Carbondale IL 62901

SCHMID, WERNER E(DUARD), b Waldershof, Ger, Feb 15, 27; nat US; m 63; c 2. CIVIL ENGINEERING. Educ: Munich Tech Univ, Dipl Ing, 53; Lehigh Univ, MSc, 55; Univ Vienna, Dr Techn Sc, 65. Prof Exp: Asst soil mech, Munich Tech Univ, 53; instr civil eng, Lafayette Col, 54-55, asst prof, 55-56; asst prof, 56-59, ASSOC PROF CIVIL ENG, PRINCETON UNIV, 59- Concurrent Pos: Pres, Technotron, Inc; dir, Geos S A. Honors & Awards: Hogentogler Award, Am Soc Testing & Mat, 59. Mem: Am Soc Civil Engrs; Am Soc Testing & Mat; Am Soc Eng Educ; Ger Soc Soil Mech & Found Engrs. Res: Soil mechanics; foundation engineering; construction technology and environmental impact. Mailing Add: Dept of Civil Eng Princeton Univ Princeton NJ 08540

SCHMID, WILFRIED, b Hamburg, Ger, May 28, 43. MATHEMATICS. Educ: Princeton Univ, BA, 64; Univ Calif, Berkeley, PhD(math), 67. Prof Exp: Asst prof math, Univ Calif, Berkeley, 67-70; Sloan fel & vis assoc prof, Columbia Univ, 68-69; vis mem, Inst Advan Study, 69-70; prof math, Columbia Univ, 70-78; PROF MATH, HARVARD UNIV, 78- Concurrent Pos: Vis prof, Univ Bonn, 73-74; John Simon Guggenheim Mem Fel, 75-76; vis, Inst Advan Study, Princeton Univ, 75-76. Res: Representations of Lie groups; complex manifolds. Mailing Add: Dept of Math Harvard Univ Cambridge MA 02138

SCHMID, WILLIAM DALE, b Santa Ana, Calif, Apr 21, 37; div; c 2. ANIMAL ECOLOGY, COMPARATIVE ANIMAL PHYSIOLOGY. Educ: Uni Minn, St Paul, BS, 59; Univ Minn, Minneapolis, PhD(zool), 62. Prof Exp: Asst prof biol, Univ NDak, 62-66; from asst prof to assoc prof, 66-74, PROF ZOOL, UNIV MINN, MINNEAPOLIS, 74-, DIR INST HERMONOGRAPHY, 70- Mem: AAAS; Ecol Soc Am; Am Soc Zoologists; Am Soc Mammalogists; Wildlife Dis Asn. Res: Amphibian water balance; vertebrate physiology. Mailing Add: Dept of Ecol & Behav Biol Univ of Minn Minneapolis MN 55455

SCHMIDL, MARY KATHERINE, b Marysville, Calif, Aug 11, 51. PARENTERAL NUTRITION, SENSORY SCIENCE. Educ: Univ Calif, Davis, BS, 73; Cornell Univ, MS, 76, PhD(food chem), 78. Prof Exp: Res chemist, 78-81, SR RES CHEMIST, CUTTER LABS, 81- Mem: Inst Food Technologists; Am Soc Parenteral & Enteral Nutrit; Am Oil Chem Soc; Nat Nutrit Consortium. Res: Enzymatic and chemical modification of food proteins; functional and nutritional properties and micro and macromolecules in food and intravenous systems; nutritional status and sensory abnormalities; nutrition and ethology of cancer. Mailing Add: 4th & Parker Sts Berkeley CA 94710

SCHMIDLE, CLAUDE JOSEPH, b Buffalo, NJ, June 14, 20; m 45; c 2. COATINGS TECHNOLOGY, RADIATION CURING. Educ: Univ Notre Dame, BS, 41, MS, 42, PhD(chem), 48. Prof Exp: Sr res scientist, Rohm and Haas Co, 48-62; sect head org & polymers, J T Baker Chem Co, 62-64; sect head coatings res, Gen Tire & Rubber Co, 64-73; supvr radiation curable coatings, Thiokol Corp, 74-78; mgr res, 79-81, PRIN SCIENTIST, CONGOLEUM CORP, 81- Mem: Am Chem Soc; Soc Plastics Engrs; Nat Asn Corrosion Engrs; Soc Mfg Engrs. Res: Aqueous and high solids coatings; radiation curable coatings and inks; acrylic monomers; acrylated urethanes; polyurethane and polyvinyl chloride coatings and foams. Mailing Add: 95 Jacobs Creek Rd West Trenton NJ 08628

SCHMIDLIN, ALBERTUS ERNEST, b Paterson, NJ, Apr 9, 17; m 43; c 3. MECHANICAL ENGINEERING. Educ: Stevens Inst Technol, ME, 39, MS, 41, ScD(mech eng), 62. Prof Exp: Instr mech eng lab, Stevens Inst Technol, 39-41; develop engr, Walter Kidde & Co, Inc, 41-47, proj engr, 47-51, chief proj engr, 51-54, asst mgr develop dept, 54-56, mgr res dept, 56-62, assoc tech dir, 62-63; prin staff scientist & mgr fluidics dept, Singer-Gen Precision Inc, 63-69; indust consult, 69; sr res scientist, Concepts & Effectiveness Div, Nuclear Develop & Eng Dir, US Army Picatinny Arsenal, 70-77, SR RES SCIENTIST, LARGE CALIBER WEAPON SYSTS LAB, CONCEPTS & ANAL BR, US ARMY ARMAMENT RES & DEVELOP COMMAND, 77- Mem: Am Soc Mech Engrs; Soc Automotive Engrs; Am Ord Asn. Res: Fluid mechanics and heat transfer as related to navigation, guidance and control of aerospace vehicles; internal fluid flow in fluid amplifiers; fluidics; gas dynamics; transient flow phenomena; fluid power transmission. Mailing Add: US Army DRDAR-LCN-F Bldg 65 Dover NJ 07801

SCHMIDLIN, FREDERICK W, b Maumee, Ohio, Aug 28, 25; m 59; c 3. SOLID STATE PHYSICS. Educ: Univ Toledo, BEEP, 50; Cornell Univ, PhD(physics), 56. Prof Exp: Asst, Cornell Univ, 50-54; mem tech staff, Ramo-Wooldridge Corp, 56-58; sr mem tech staff, Space Technol Labs, 58-60; sr scientist, Gen Technol Corp, 60-63; PRIN SCIENTIST, XEROX CORP, 63- Mem: AAAS; Soc Photog Scientists & Engrs; Am Phys Soc; Inst Elec & Electronics Engrs. Res: Theory of electrophotography; solid state theory; superconductivity; semiconductivity; photoconductivity; thin film devices. Mailing Add: Wilson Ctr for Technol Xerox Corp Webster NY 14580

SCHMIDLING, DAVID (GILBERT), organometallic chemistry, theoretical chemistry, see previous edition

SCHMIDLY, DAVID JAMES, b Lubbock, Tex, Dec 20, 43; m 66; c 2. MAMMALLIAN SYSTEMATICS, NON-GAME WILDLIFE. Educ: Tex Tech Univ, BS, 66, MS, 68; Univ Ill, PhD(zool), 71. Prof Exp: Asst prof, 71-76, ASSOC PROF WILDLIFE & FISHERIES SCI, TEX A&M UNIV, 76- Concurrent Pos: Consult, Environomics Ecol Firm, 72- Mem: Am Soc Mammalogists; Soc Syst Zool; Sigma Xi; Southwestern Asn Naturalists. Res: Mammalian systematics, natural history and management with special emphasis on non-game mammals from the southwestern United States and northern Mexico. Mailing Add: Dept Wildlife & Fisheries Sci Tex A&M Univ College Station TX 77843

SCHMID-SCHOENBEIN, GEERT W, b Ebingen, WGer, Jan 1, 48; m 76; c 1. MICROCIRCULATION, BIOMECHANICS. Educ: Univ Calif, San Diego, MS, 73, PhD(bioeng), 76. Prof Exp: Sr staff assoc physiol, Columbia Univ, 76-79; ASST PROF BIOENG, UNIV CALIF, SAN DIEGO, 79- Honors & Awards: Malphigi Award, Europ Soc Microcirculation, 80. Mem: Am Physiol Soc; Am Microcirculatory Soc; Biomed Eng Soc. Mailing Add: Dept Appl Mech & Eng Sci Univ Calif San Diego La Jolla CA 92093

SCHMIDT, ALEXANDER MACKAY, b Jamestown, NDak, Jan 26, 30; m 52; c 2. INTERNAL MEDICINE. Educ: Northwestern Univ, BS, 51; Univ Utah, MD, 55. Prof Exp: Intern med, Affil Hosps, Univ Utah, 55-56, resident, 58-60, instr med, Col Med, 62-64, asst prof, 64-67, instr physiol, 66-67, dir cardiovasc lab, 62-67; chief educ & training, Regional Med Progs Serv, Dept Health, Educ & Welfare, 67-68; prof med & dean Abraham Lincoln Sch Med, Univ Ill Med Ctr, 69-73; comnr food & drugs, FDA, USPHS, 73-76; vchancellor health serv, 77-80, VCHANCELLOR ACAD AFFAIRS, UNIV ILL MED CTR, 80- Concurrent Pos: Res fel cardiol, Col Med, Univ Utah, 60-62; Markle scholar med, 66; mem rev comt, Regional Med Progs Serv, Dept Health, Educ & Welfare; dir, Am Cyanamid Co, 79. Mem: AAAS; Am Fedn Clin Res; Am Thoracic Soc; AMA; Am Soc Internal Med. Res: Cardiac and pulmonary hemodynamics. Mailing Add: Univ of Ill Med Ctr 1737 W Polk St Chicago IL 60612

SCHMIDT, ALFRED OTTO, b Mogilno, Ger, May 12, 06; nat US; m 41; c 2. MACHINE & TOOL DESIGN. Educ: Ilmenau Sch Eng, ME, 28; Univ Mich, MSE, 40, DSc(metal processing), 43. Prof Exp: Mech engr, Carl Zeiss Optical Works, 29-38; from instr to asst prof mech eng, Colo State Col, 40-42; assoc, Univ Ill, 42-43; res engr, Kearney & Trecker Corp, 43-61; res prof mech eng, Marquette Univ, 58-63; prof mach tool tech, Univ Roorkee, 64 & 81; prof, 64-71, EMER PROF INDUST ENG, PA STATE UNIV, 71- Concurrent Pos: Adv, UN Indust Develop Orgn, Israel, 67, Pakistan, 71, Kenya, 71, Brazil, 72, Srilanka, 77 & Argentina, 78 & 79; vis prof, Univ RI, 74-75 & Univ Wis-Milwaukee, 75-76, Korean Advan Inst Sci, 79, Univ Busan, Korea, 80. Honors & Awards: Gold Medal, Soc Mfg Eng, 59. Mem: Am Soc Mech Engrs; Soc Mfg Engrs. Res: Metal processing; machine tool design and utilization; production; metal cutting calorimeter; carbide milling cutter; research surveys; laser applications. Mailing Add: 634 W Prospect Ave State College PA 16801

SCHMIDT, ANTHONY JOHN, b Winnipeg, Man, May 11, 27; m 55; c 4. EMBRYOLOGY. Educ: Univ Wash, BA, 52, MSc, 54; Princeton Univ, PhD(biol), 57. Prof Exp: Instr biol, Princeton Univ, 57-58; from asst prof to prof anat, Univ Ill Med Ctr, 58-74; PROF ANAT & CHMN DEPT, PRESBY-ST LUKE'S MED CTR, RUSH MED COL, 75- Mem: AAAS; Soc Develop Biol; Am Soc Cell Biol; Am Soc Zool; Soc Exp Biol & Med. Res: Chemistry of the cellular progression in organ development and regeneration; limb regeneration in amphibia; comparative anatomy; histology; neuroanatomy; experimental embryology; human gross anatomy. Mailing Add: Dept of Anat Rush Med Col Chicago IL 60612

SCHMIDT, BERLIE LOUIS, b Treynor, Iowa, Oct 2, 32; m 54; c 5. AGRONOMY, SOIL CONSERVATION. Educ: Iowa State Univ, BS, 54, MS, 59, PhD(agron), 62. Prof Exp: Soil scientist, Soil Conserv Serv, USDA, 54, 56-57; res assoc soil mgt, Iowa State Univ, 59-62; from asst prof to assoc prof agron, Ohio State Univ & Ohio Agr Res & Develop Ctr, 62-70, assoc chmn agron, Ohio Agr Res & Develop Ctr, 69-75, PROF AGRON, OHIO STATE UNIV, 70-, CHMN DEPT, 75- Mem: Am Soc Agron; Soil Sci Soc Am; Soil Conserv Soc Am; Int Soil Sci Soc. Res: Soil and water pollution from erosion and runoff; soil and water conservation; wind erosion control; water infiltration into soils; agronomic research administration. Mailing Add: Dept of Agron Ohio State Univ Columbus OH 43210

SCHMIDT, BRUNO (FRANCIS), b Strawberry Point, Iowa, June 10, 42; m 64; c 2. PHYSICS. Educ: Cornell Col, BA, 64; Iowa State Univ, PhD(physics), 69. Prof Exp: Asst prof, 69-75, assoc prof, 75-81, PROF PHYSICS, SOUTHWEST MO STATE UNIV, 81- Mem: Am Asn Physics Teachers. Res: Optical properties of solids. Mailing Add: Dept of Phys Southwest Mo State Univ Springfield MO 65802

SCHMIDT, CARL FREDERIC, b Lebanon, Pa, July 29, 93; m 20; c 2. PHYSIOLOGY, PHARMACOLOGY. Educ: Lebanon Valley Col, AB, 14; Univ Pa, MD, 18. Hon Degrees: ScD, Lebanon Valley Col, 55 & Univ Pa, 65; DmedSci, Charles Univ, Prague, 63. Prof Exp: Instr pharmacol, Univ Pa, 19-22; assoc, Peking Union Med Col, 22-24; from asst prof to assoc, 24-59, EMER PROF PHARMACOL, SCH MED, UNIV PA, 59-; CLIN PROF PHARMACOL, UNIV S FLA, 71- Concurrent Pos: Res dir, US Naval Air Develop Ctr, 62-69; hon pres, Int Union Pharmacol, 66- Honors & Awards: Medal, Am Heart Asn, 62; Schmiedeberg Plaquette, Ger Pharmacol Soc, 63. Mem: Nat Acad Sci; AAAS; Am Physiol Soc; Am Soc Pharmacol & Exp Therapeut (vpres, 40-42, pres, 48-50); Soc Exp Biol & Med. Res: Physiology and pharmacology of respiration and of circulation in brain, kidney and heart; aerospace physiology and pharmacology; Chinese drugs; drug evaluation and control. Mailing Add: 15462 Gulf Blvd Madeira Beach FL 33708

SCHMIDT, CHARLES WILLIAM, b St Petersburg, Fla, Aug 11, 42; m 71; c 2. PHYSICS, ACCELERATOR TECHNOLOGY. *Educ:* Fla State Univ, BS, 64. *Prof Exp:* Sci asst physics, Argonne Nat Lab, 64-69; PHYSICIST ACCELERATOR PHYSICS, FERMI NAT ACCELERATOR LAB, 69- *Mem:* Am Phys Soc; Sigma Xi. *Res:* Accelerator physics especially ion source development, magnetic measurements and operation. *Mailing Add:* 60 Oakwood Dr Naperville IL 60540

SCHMIDT, CLAUDE HENRI, b Geneva, Switz, May 6, 24; nat US; m 53; c 2. ENTOMOLOGY. *Educ:* Stanford Univ, BA, 48, MA, 50; Iowa State Univ, PhD(entom), 56. *Prof Exp:* Instr zool, Iowa State Univ, 55-56; med entomologist, USDA, 56-62; entomologist, Div Isotopes, Int Atomic Energy Agency, Vienna, Austria, 62-64; proj leader insect physiol & metab sect, Metab & Radiation Res Lab, 64-67, chief insects affecting man & animal res br, Entom Res Div, 67-72, dir, Dakotas-Alaska Area, 72-81, DIR, DAKOTAS AREA, NORTH CENT REGION, AGR RES SERV, USDA, 81- *Concurrent Pos:* Res consult, USAID, 68; consult, US Army Med Res & Develop Cmnd, 73-77. *Mem:* Fel AAAS; Am Mosquito Control Asn (pres, 81); Am Entom Soc; Am Inst Biol Sci; Am Chem Soc. *Res:* Application of radioisotopes and radiation in entomology; application of the sterile male technique. *Mailing Add:* Agr Res Serv Sci & Educ Admin USDA Room 419 Fed Bldg PO Fargo ND 58102

SCHMIDT, CLIFFORD LEROY, b Los Angeles, Calif, Mar 27, 26; m 49; c 1. BOTANY, ECOLOGY. *Educ:* San Jose State Col, AB, 55, MA, 58; Stanford Univ, PhD(pop biol), 67. *Prof Exp:* Teacher, San Jose Unified Sch Dist, 56-60; asst prof natural sci, 60-65, from asst prof to assoc prof biol, 65-71, PROF BIOL, SAN JOSE STATE UNIV, 71- *Mem:* AAAS; Am Inst Biol Sci; Soc Study Evolution; Am Soc Plant Taxonomists; Bot Soc Am. *Res:* Biosystematic studies involving chromosomal analysis of Ludwigia sect Dantia; human impact studies on alpine vegetation; ecological studies on Ceanothus; revegetation of disturbed sites. *Mailing Add:* Dept of Biol San Jose State Univ San Jose CA 95192

SCHMIDT, DAVID KELSO, b Lafayette, Ind, Mar 4, 43; c 3. AEROSPACE ENGINEERING, SYSTEMS ENGINEERING. *Educ:* Purdue Univ, BS, 65, PhD(eng), 72; Univ Southern Calif, MS, 68. *Prof Exp:* Engr & scientist missile design, McDonnell-Douglas Astronaut Corp, 65-69; vis asst prof aerospace eng, Purdue Univ, 72-73; res engr transp eng, Stanford Res Inst, 73-74; asst prof, 74-79, ASSOC PROF AEROSPACE ENG, PURDUE UNIV, 79- *Mem:* Am Inst Aeronaut & Astronaut; Opers Res Soc Am; Am Soc Eng Educ. *Res:* Systems analysis; optimization; control theory and applications; manual control; operations research; flight vehicle dynamics and control. *Mailing Add:* Sch of Aeronaut & Astronaut Purdue Univ Grissom Hall West Lafayette IN 47907

SCHMIDT, DENNIS EARL, b Plymouth, Wis, Jan 23, 40; m 71; c 3. PSYCHOPHARMACOLOGY. *Educ:* Lakeland Col, BS, 62; Kans State Univ, PhD(biochem), 68. *Prof Exp:* Instr pharmacol, Mt Sinai Sch Med, 69-70; instr, 70-71, asst prof, 71-78, ASSOC PROF PHARMACOL, VANDERBILT UNIV, 79- *Concurrent Pos:* NIH fels, Cornell Med Col, 68 & Mt Sinai Sch Med, 68-69; Smith Kline & French fel, Vanderbilt Univ, 70-72. *Mem:* Am Soc Pharmacol & Exp Therapeut; Soc Neurosci; Neurochem Soc. *Res:* Investigation of central cholinergic mechanisms. *Mailing Add:* Dept of Pharmacol Vanderbilt Univ Nashville TN 37203

SCHMIDT, DONALD ARTHUR, b Wis, Jan 29, 22; m 51; c 3. VETERINARY PATHOLOGY, CLINICAL PATHOLOGY. *Educ:* Univ Wis, BS, 44; Mich State Univ, DVM, 47, PhD, 61; Univ Minn, MS, 50. *Prof Exp:* Veterinarian, Chicago Zool Park, Ill, 50-53; instr vet path, Mich State Univ, 53-63, assoc prof path, 63-67, PROF VET PATH, UNIV MO-COLUMBIA, 67- *Mem:* Am Vet Med Asn; Am Col Vet Path. *Res:* Food producing animals. *Mailing Add:* Dept of Vet Path Univ of Mo Columbia MO 65201

SCHMIDT, DONALD DEAN, b Highland. Ill, Dec 21, 42; m 64; c 2. PHYSICAL INORGANIC CHEMISTRY. *Educ:* Wabash Col, AB, 65; Ore State Univ, PhD(chem), 70. *Prof Exp:* RES CHEMIST, DOW CHEM CO, 70- *Mem:* Am Chem Soc. *Res:* Polymer chemistry; elemental carbon; catalysis by transition metals; coordination chemistry; surface chemistry; industrial chemistry; drilling fluids. *Mailing Add:* 7108 S Redbud Ave Broken Arrow OK 74012

SCHMIDT, DONALD EMIL, JR, bio-organic chemistry, see previous edition

SCHMIDT, DONALD HENRY, b Rhinelander, Wis, July 20, 35; m 65; c 4. CARDIOVASCULAR DISEASE, INTERNAL MEDICINE. *Educ:* Univ Wis, BS, 57, MD, 60. *Prof Exp:* Assoc prof, 74-77, PROF MED, UNIV WIS, MILWAUKEE, 77-; HEAD CARDIOVASCULAR SECT, MT SINAI MED CTR, 74- *Concurrent Pos:* Asst med, Col Physicians & Surgeon, Columbia Univ, 66-67, instr, 67-68, asst prof clin med, 69-70, asst prof, 70-74; asst vis prof, Harlem Hosp Ctr, 68; dir EKG, 70; asst dir, Cardiovascular Lab, Presby Hosp, New York, 70; asst attending physician, 71-; dir, Adult Cardiovascular Lab, Columbia Presby Med Ctr, 73-; attending physician, Mt Sinai Med Ctr, 74-; mem, Am Heart Asn. *Mem:* Nuclear Med Soc; Harvey Soc; Am Fedn Clin Res; Cent Soc Clin Res. *Res:* Physiology of the coronary circulation; nuclear cardiology. *Mailing Add:* 7135 N Barnett Lane Milwaukee WI 53217

SCHMIDT, DONALD L, b Park Falls, Wis, Jan 29, 30; m 62; c 3. MATERIALS SCIENCE, CHEMISTRY. *Educ:* Wis State Univ, Superior, BSc, 52; Okla State Univ, MSc, 54. *Prof Exp:* Proj engr, Mat Lab, 54-57, mat engr, 57, aeronaut struct mat engr, 57-59, aeronaut struct mat res engr, 59-60, res mat engr mat cent, 60, supvry mat res engr directorate mat, 60-61, TECH MGR, THERMAL PROJ MAT, AIR FORCE WRIGHT AERONAUT LABS, WRIGHT-PATTERSON AFB, 61- *Concurrent Pos:* Mem, Advan Missile Mat Res Coun, US Dept Defense, 70- *Honors & Awards:* Award,

Sigma Xi, 66. *Mem:* Sigma Xi; Soc Aerospace Mat & Process Engrs. *Res:* Thermal protection materials; high temperature materials sciences, including composites, plastics and glass. *Mailing Add:* 1092 Lipton Lane Dayton OH 45430

SCHMIDT, DONALD L, b Sept 10, 31; US citizen; m 63; c 3. ORGANIC POLYMER CHEMISTRY. *Educ:* Univ Utah, BS, 56, PhD(org chem), 62. *Prof Exp:* Res chemist, ARPA Lab, Bow Chem Co, 61-63, proj leader aluminum chem, 63-67, sr res chemist, SPL Lab, 67-68, sr res chemist, 68-78, RES ASSOC, PHYS RES LAB, DOW CHEM CO, 78- *Honors & Awards:* IR 100 Awards, Indust Res Mag, 69 & 72; A K Doolittle Award, Am Chem Soc, 75. *Mem:* AAAS; Am Chem Soc; Sigma Xi. *Res:* Metal hydride chemistry; inorganic polymer containing Al-O-P bonds; condensation polymerization involving cyclic sulfonium compounds; theory of surfactants and foams. *Mailing Add:* Phys Res Lab 1712 Dow Chem Co Midland MI 48640

SCHMIDT, DWIGHT LYMAN, b Fond du Lac, Wis, May 30, 26; m 58; c 2. GEOLOGY. *Educ:* Univ Wash, BS, 54, MS, 57, PhD(geol), 61. *Prof Exp:* GEOLOGIST, US GEOL SURV, 61- *Concurrent Pos:* Mem comt polar res, Nat Acad Sci. 68-70. *Mem:* AAAS; Geol Soc Am; Mineral Soc Am; Soc Econ Geol; Am Geophys Union. *Res:* Radioactive placer deposits and petrography of the Idaho batholith; geology of Pensacola and Lassiter Coast Mountains, Antarctica; Precambrian and Cenozoic geology of Saudi Arabia; geologic history of the Red Sea. *Mailing Add:* US Geol Surv Box 25046 Mail Stop 913 Denver CO 80225

SCHMIDT, ECKART W, b Essen, West Germany, Apr 16, 35; m 62; c 2. INDUSTRIAL CHEMISTRY, FUEL SCIENCE. *Educ:* Univ Marburg, BS, 58; Univ Tübingen, Dr rer nat(org chem, astron), 64. *Prof Exp:* Res chemist, German Res Inst Aero & Astronaut, 64-66; mgr chem res, 66-78, SR STAFF SCIENTIST, ROCKET RES CO, 66- *Mem:* Am Inst Aeronaut & Astronaut; Soc Automotive Engrs. *Res:* High energy rocket propellants; explosives; fuel technology; astronautics; safety systems; extraterrestrial preparation of rocket propellants; planeto chemistry; energy storage and conversion. *Mailing Add:* Rocket Res Co York Ctr Redmond WA 98052

SCHMIDT, EDWARD GEORGE, b Cut Bank, Mont, Dec 13, 42; m 63; c 3. ASTRONOMY. *Educ:* Univ Chicago, BS, 65; Australian Nat Univ, PhD(astron), 70. *Prof Exp:* Res assoc astron, Univ Ariz, 70-72; sr res fel, Royal Greenwich Observ, 72-74; asst prof, 74-77, ASSOC PROF ASTRON, UNIV NEBR, 77- *Mem:* Am Astron Soc; INT ASTRON UNION; Royal Astron Soc. *Res:* Cepheid variable stars; nonvariable yellow supergiants; interstellar medium; star clusters; instrumentation. *Mailing Add:* Dept of Physics & Astron Univ of Nebr Lincoln NE 68588

SCHMIDT, EDWARD MATTHEWS, b Elgin, Ill, Mar 24, 33; m 59; c 2. BIOENGINEERING. *Educ:* Northwestern Univ, BSEE, 56; Purdue Univ, MSEE, 57, PhD, 65. *Prof Exp:* Asst, Argonne Nat Lab, 53-55; sr res engr, Borg-Warner Res Ctr, 57-61; from instr to assoc elec eng & vet anat, bioeng, Purdue Univ, West Lafayette, 61-72; RES BIOENGR, LAB NEURAL CONTROL, NAT INST NEUROL DIS, COMMUN DIS & STROKE, 72- *Concurrent Pos:* Spec fel, Lab Neurol Control, NIH, Bethesda, 69-71, mem adv comt, NIH, 72-73. *Mem:* AAAS; Inst Elec & Electronics Engrs; Soc Neurosci. *Res:* Biological control systems; neurophysiology; microelectrode study of cells in the motor cortex of the monkey and their relationship to limb movements. *Mailing Add:* Lab of Neural Control Nat Inst of Neurol Dis Commun Dis & Stroke Bethesda MD 20205

SCHMIDT, FRANCIS HENRY, b Cincinnati, Ohio, Aug 6, 41; m 68; c 1. PHYSICAL ORGANIC CHEMISTRY. *Educ:* Xavier Univ, BS, 63, MS, 65; Ind Univ, Bloomington, PhD(org chem), 74. *Prof Exp:* res chemist, 69-80, SR RES CHEMIST, E I DU PONT DE NEMOURS & CO, 80- *Mem:* Am Chem Soc. *Res:* The process development of finishes for natural and synthetic fibers and components for photo-sensitive systems. *Mailing Add:* E I du Pont de Nemours & Co Chem & Pigments Dept Jackson Lab Wilmington DE 19898

SCHMIDT, FRANK W(ILLIAM), b Madison, Wis, Mar 16, 29; m 54; c 4. MECHANICAL ENGINEERING. *Educ:* Univ Wis, BS, 50, PhD(mech eng), 59; Pa State Univ, MS, 52. *Prof Exp:* Engr, Kuchler-Huhn Corp, Philadelphia, 52-54; from instr to asst prof mech eng, Univ Wis, 56-62; from asst prof to assoc prof, 62-70, PROF MECH ENG, PA STATE UNIV, UNIVERSITY PARK, 70- *Concurrent Pos:* Nat Sci fel, Imp Col, Univ London, 65-66. *Mem:* Am Soc Mech Engrs. *Res:* Fluid mechanics; heat and mass transfer. *Mailing Add:* Dept of Mech Eng Pa State Univ University Park PA 16802

SCHMIDT, FRED HENRY, b Detroit, Mich, Sept 12, 15; m 39; c 2. PHYSICS. *Educ:* Univ Mich, BSE, 37; Univ Buffalo, MA. 40; Univ Calif, PhD(physics), 45. *Prof Exp:* Engr, Am Tel & Tel Co, 37-39; res assoc, Manhattan proj, Los Alamos Sci Lab, Calif & Oak Ridge Nat Lab, 42-46; from asst prof to assoc prof, 46-56, PROF PHYSICS, UNIV WASH, 56- *Concurrent Pos:* Guggenheim fel, 55-56; NSF sr fel, 63-64. *Mem:* Fel Am Phys Soc. *Res:* Nuclear and elementary particle research; energy crisis problems. *Mailing Add:* Dept of Physics Univ of Wash Seattle WA 98105

SCHMIDT, FREDERICK ALLEN, b Cincinnati, Ohio, Dec 26, 30; m 51; c 4. MATERIAL SCIENCE, METALLURGY. *Educ:* Xavier Univ, BS, 51. *Prof Exp:* Jr chemist, 51-54, jr res assoc, 54-56, assoc, 56-59, assoc metallurgist, 59-71, metallurgist, 71-76, SR METALLURGIST, AMES LAB, IOWA STATE UNIV, 76- *Mem:* Am Soc Metals; Am Inst Mining, Metall & Petrol Engrs; Am Inst Aeronaut & Astronaut. *Res:* Methods for preparing high purity refractory metals and thin film solar cells; electrotransport, thermotransport and diffusion of solutes in metals; characterization of refractory metals and alloys. *Mailing Add:* 121 Metals Develop Iowa State Univ Ames IA 50010

SCHMIDT, GEORGE, b Budapest, Hungary, Aug 1, 26; US citizen; m 55; c 2. PHYSICS. *Educ:* Budapest Tech Univ, dipl eng, 50; Hungarian Acad Sci, PhD(physics), 56. *Hon Degrees:* MEng, Stevens Inst Technol, 66. *Prof Exp:* Res assoc physics, Cent Res Inst Physics, Hungary, 55-56; sr lectr, Israel Inst Technol, 57-58; res assoc, 58-59, from asst prof to assoc prof, 59-65, PROF PHYSICS, STEVENS INST TECHNOL, 65- *Concurrent Pos:* Consult, Grumman Aircraft Eng Co, 62; UK Atomic Energy Auth, 65-66 & Fr Atomic Energy Comn, 66; vis prof, Univ Wis, 65, Univ Calif, Los Angeles, 72-73; consult, Exxon Corp, 71, Cornell Univ, 78-79 & Appl Sci Inc, 81. *Mem:* NY Acad Sci; fel Am Phys Soc. *Res:* Plasma physics; stochasticity theory. *Mailing Add:* Dept of Physics Stevens Inst of Technol Hoboken NJ 07030

SCHMIDT, GEORGE THOMAS, b Jersey City, NJ. SYSTEMS ENGINEERING. *Educ:* Mass Inst Technol, BS, 64, MS, 65, ScD(instrumentation), 70. *Prof Exp:* DIV LEADER, ADVAN SYSTS DEPT, DRAPER LAB, 62- *Concurrent Pos:* Adj assoc prof systs elec & comput eng, Boston Univ, 65-80, adj prof, 80- *Mem:* Am Inst Aeronaut & Astronaut; Inst Elec & Electronics Engrs; Am Soc Eng Educ. *Res:* Control and estimation theory; guidance and navigation systems; guidance, navigation and control of systems engineering. *Mailing Add:* Div Leader MS #70 Draper Lab Cambridge MA 02139

SCHMIDT, GERALD D, b Greeley, Colo, Mar 12, 34; m 58; c 2. ZOOLOGY, PARASITOLOGY. *Educ:* Colo State Col, AB, 60; Colo State Univ, MS, 62, PhD(zool), 64. *Prof Exp:* Instr zool, Univ Mont, 63-64; from asst prof to assoc prof, 64-72, PROF PARASITOL, UNIV NORTHERN COLO, 72-, PROF ZOOL, 74- *Concurrent Pos:* NATO sr fel sci, South Australian Mus, Adelaide, 70-71. *Mem:* Am Soc Parasitologists; Am Micros Soc; Wildlife Dis Asn; Am Soc Trop Med & Hyg; Int Filariasis Asn. *Res:* Morphology, biology and taxonomy of parasitic helminths. *Mailing Add:* Dept of Biol Univ of Northern Colo Greeley CO 80631

SCHMIDT, GERHARD, biochemistry, deceased

SCHMIDT, GILBERT CARL, b Cincinnati, Ohio, Apr 15, 21; m 66; c 3. BIOCHEMISTRY. *Educ:* Univ Cincinnati, BS, 46, MS, 49, PhD(biochem), 51. *Prof Exp:* Res assoc, Sperti, Inc, 46-48; asst prof chem, Col Pharm, Univ Cincinnati, 51-52, assoc prof, 52-53, prof pharmacog, 53-56, prof biol sci, 56-66, asst prof biol chem, Col Med, 59-66; assoc prof biochem & asst prof pediat, Med Col, Univ Ala, 66-68; prof biochem, Northeast La State Univ, 68-70; prof pharmacog & biol, 70-81, PROF PHARMACUET SCI & DIR GRAD STUDIES & RES, COL PHARM, MED UNIV SC, 81- *Concurrent Pos:* USPHS fel chem, Col Pharm, Univ Cincinnati, 51-52, NSF fel, 52-53; dir res labs, Children's Hosp, Birmingham, Ala, 66-68. *Mem:* AAAS; Am Chem Soc; Am Soc Microbiol; Am Pharmaceut Asn. *Res:* Drug metabolism; biochemical pharmacology; azolesterases; synthesis isotopically labeled drugs; pineal gland metabolism; drug abuse; isolation and properties of natural products. *Mailing Add:* Col Pharm Med Univ SC Charleston SC 29401

SCHMIDT, GLEN HENRY, b Manning, Iowa, Jan 25, 31; m 52; c 5. DAIRY HUSBANDRY. *Educ:* Iowa State Univ, BS, 52; Cornell Univ, MS, 56, PhD(dairy sci), 58. *Prof Exp:* Asst animal sci, NY State Col Agr, Cornell Univ, 54-57, from instr to assoc prof, 57-72, prof, 72-74, PROF DAIRY SCI & CHMN DEPT, OHIO STATE UNIV, 74- *Mem:* Am Dairy Sci Asn; fel AAAS. *Res:* Biochemistry and physiology of milk secretion; factors affecting yield and composition of milk; mastitis. *Mailing Add:* Ohio State Univ 2027 Coffey Rd Columbus OH 43210

SCHMIDT, GLENN ROY, b Two Rivers, Wis, Feb 26, 43; m 66; c 1. MEAT SCIENCES. *Educ:* Univ Wis, BSc, 65, MSc, 68, PhD(animal sci), 69. *Prof Exp:* Vis scientist meat technol, Meat Indust Res Inst NZ, 69-70; vis scientist animal sci, Res Inst Animal Husb, Zeist, The Neth, 70-71; from asst prof to assoc prof, Univ Ill, Urbana, 71-79; PROF ANIMAL SCI, COLO STATE UNIV, 79- *Mem:* Am Soc Animal Sci; Am Meat Sci Asn; Inst Food Technol. *Res:* Processed meat technology; swine physiology; muscle biochemistry. *Mailing Add:* Dept of Animal Sci Colo State Univ Ft Collins CO 80523

SCHMIDT, HARTLAND H, b St Paul, Minn, Nov 22, 29; m 57; c 2. PHYSICAL CHEMISTRY. *Educ:* Univ Minn, BA, 51; Univ Calif, Berkeley, PhD(chem), 54. *Prof Exp:* From instr to assoc prof, Univ Calif, Davis & Univ Calif, Riverside, 54-68, PROF CHEM, UNIV CALIF, RIVERSIDE, 68- *Mem:* Am Chem Soc; Am Phys Soc. *Res:* Thermodynamics; statistical mechanics; critical phenomena. *Mailing Add:* Dept of Chem Univ of Calif Riverside CA 92502

SCHMIDT, HARVEY JOHN, JR, b Spokane, Wash, June 20, 41; m 69; c 1. MATHEMATICS. *Educ:* Lewis & Clark Col, BA, 63; Univ Ore, MA, 65, PhD(math), 69. *Prof Exp:* Asst prof, Ill State Univ, 69-74; asst prof, 74-76, ASSOC PROF MATH, LEWIS & CLARK COL, 76- *Concurrent Pos:* Vis fel math, Univ Warwick, 70-71. *Mem:* Am Math Soc; Math Asn Am. *Res:* Finite group theory; representation theory of finite groups. *Mailing Add:* Dept of Math LC Box 111 Lewis & Clark Col Portland OR 97219

SCHMIDT, HELMUT, b Danzig, Ger, Feb 21, 28; m 55; c 3. PHYSICS, PARAPSYCHOLOGY. *Educ:* Univ Gottingen, MA, 53; Univ Cologne, PhD(physics), 54. *Prof Exp:* Asst prof physics, Univ Cologne. 54-55 & 58-59, docent, 60-63; vis lectr, Univ BC, 64-65; sr res physicist, Boeing Sci Res Lab, 66-69; res assoc, Inst Parapsychol, 69-70, dir, 70-73; RES ASSOC, MIND SCI FOUND, 74- *Concurrent Pos:* Nat Acad Sci fel, Univ Calif, Berkeley, 56-57; NATO exchange prof, Southern Methodist Univ, 62. *Mem:* Am Phys Soc; Parapsychol Asn. *Res:* Quantum physics; cosmology; solid state physics; study of parapsychological effects with modern electronic equipment. *Mailing Add:* Mind Sci Found 102 W Rector St San Antonio TX 78216

SCHMIDT, JACK RUSSELL, b Milwaukee, Wis, July 23, 26; m 58. RESEARCH ADMINISTRATION. *Educ:* Univ Wis, BS, 48, MS, 50, PhD(med microbiol), 52. *Prof Exp:* Asst microbiol & immunol, Med Sch, Univ Wis, 49-52; virologist, Walter Reed Army Inst Res, 52-56; head viral immunol lab, Walter Reed Army Inst Res & Vet Admin Cent Lab Clin Path & Res, 56-57; head dept virol, US Naval Med Res Unit 3, 58-66, tech dir field facil, Ethiopia, 66-72, tech dir res & sci adv, Bur Med & Surg, Navy Dept, 72-74, DIR PROGS & SCI ADV, NAVAL MED RES DEVELOP COMMAND, 74- *Mem:* Am Soc Trop Med & Hyg; Royal Soc Trop Med & Hyg; Ethiopian Med Asn. *Res:* Ecology and epidemiology of arboviral infections; viral immunology; medical entomology and parasitology; tropical diseases. *Mailing Add:* Naval Med Res & Develop Command Nat Naval Med Ctr Bethesda MD 20014

SCHMIDT, JAMES L, b Clarksburg, WVa, July 26, 35; m 57; c 2. PHARMACOLOGY, INDUSTRIAL MEDICINE. *Educ:* Univ WVa, AB, 58, MS, 61, PhD(pharmacol), 62, MD, 64. *Prof Exp:* Asst pharmacol, Med Ctr, Univ WVa, 60-62, res assoc, 62, instr, 62-64; intern med, Charleston Mem Hosp, WVa, 64-65; INSTR SUBMARINE MED, US NAVAL SUBMARINE MED CTR, NEW LONDON, CONN, 67- *Concurrent Pos:* Attend physician, Westerly Hosp, RI; med dir, Edward Weck Corp, Div Squibb Corp & Mystic Div, Cerro Wire & Cable Co. *Mem:* AAAS; Indust Med Asn; Am Acad Clin Toxicol. *Res:* Industrial toxicology; atmosphere control and its biodynamics; sensitivity changes to drugs in the ileum of animals. *Mailing Add:* US Naval Submarine Med Ctr New London CT 06320

SCHMIDT, JAMES ROBERT, b Linton, NDak, May 31, 29; m 57; c 5. PROSTHODONTICS. *Educ:* Mont State Col, BS, 54 & 59; St Louis Univ, DDS, 61, MSD, 67. *Prof Exp:* Dent intern, Westfield State Sanatorium, Mass, 61-62; asst prof crown & bridge dent, Sch Dent, St Louis Univ, 67-68; asst prof, Med Univ SC, 68-69, assoc prof, 69; assoc prof fixed prosthodont & chmn dept, NJ Dent Sch, Col Med & Dent NJ, 69-73; PROF RESTORATIVE DENT & CHMN DEPT, SCH DENT MED, SOUTHERN ILL UNIV, EDWARDSVILLE, 73- *Concurrent Pos:* Consult, Dento Dynamic Systs, Inc, 71-; mem, Am Asn Dent Schs. *Mem:* Am Dent Asn. *Res:* Oro-facial physiology; biomedical products and instrumentation; fixed prosthodontics; clinical and educational research. *Mailing Add:* Dept of Restorative Dent Southern Ill Univ Sch Dent Med Edwardsville IL 62025

SCHMIDT, JANE ANN, b Minneapolis, Minn, May 25, 51. ENZYMOLOGY, PROTEIN CHEMISTRY. *Educ:* Macalester Col, BA, 73; Iowa State Univ, PhD(biochem), 80. *Prof Exp:* Assoc, Dept Chem, Univ Iowa, 78-81; FEL, DEPT CHEM, UNIV DEL, 81- *Mem:* Am Chem Soc; AAAS. *Res:* Modification of apo asparate aminotransferase with pyridoxal sulfate; modification of glutamate dehydrogenase with nucleotide affinity labels; kinetics and stereochemistry of decarboxylation reactions of serine hydroxymethylase. *Mailing Add:* Dept Chem Univ Del Newark DE 19711

SCHMIDT, JEAN M, b Waterloo, Iowa, June 5, 38. MICROBIOLOGY. *Educ:* Univ Iowa, BA, 59, MS, 61; Univ Calif, Berkeley, PhD(bact), 65. *Prof Exp:* NIH fel, Univ Edinburgh, 65-66; from asst prof to assoc prof, 66-79, PROF MICROBIOL, ARIZ STATE UNIV, 79- *Concurrent Pos:* NIH res grants, 67-70, 71-74; NSF res grant, 79-82. *Mem:* AAAS; Am Soc Microbiol; Brit Soc Gen Microbiol. *Res:* Virology; animal cell culture; differentiation in stalk-forming bacteria. *Mailing Add:* Dept of Bot & Microbiol Ariz State Univ Tempe AZ 85281

SCHMIDT, JERÒME P, b Nortonville, Kans, Feb 1, 28; m 58. MEDICAL MICROBIOLOGY. *Educ:* St Benedict's Col, Kans, BS, 49; Univ Kans. MA, 52; Univ NH, PhD(microbiol), 63. *Prof Exp:* Bacteriologist, Arctic Aeromed Lab, Fairbanks, Alaska, 56-61; chief infectious processes unit, 63-68, CHIEF IMMUNOL, US AIR FORCE SCH AEROSPACE MED, 68- *Concurrent Pos:* Instr, Univ Alaska, 60-61; vis prof, Tex A&M Univ, 65- & NTex State Univ, 68-; mem Hibernation Info Exchange. *Mem:* AAAS; Am Soc Microbiol; Aerospace Med Asn; Soc Exp Biol & Med; fel Am Acad Microbiol. *Res:* Epidemiology and etiology of acute upper respiratory diseases; microbiological aspects of mammalian hibernation; effect of environmental factors on infectious processes. *Mailing Add:* Epidemiol Div USAF Sch Aerospace Med Brooks AFB TX 78235

SCHMIDT, JOHN ALLEN, b Aberdeen. SDak, Dec 31, 40; m 68. PLASMA PHYSICS. *Educ:* SDak State Univ, BS. 62; Univ Wis, MS, 64, PhD(physics), 69. *Prof Exp:* Res assoc, Univ Wis, 69; res assoc physics, 69-78, co-head, Tokamac Fusion Test Reactor, 78-80, SR RES PHYSIST, PRINCETON UNIV, 78-, HEAD APPLIED PHYSICS DIV, PLASMA PHYSICS LAB, 80- *Res:* Use of low plasma pressure toroidal magnetic field geometries to confine plasmas for thermonuclear energy sources. *Mailing Add:* Plasma Lab Princeton Univ Princeton NJ 08540

SCHMIDT, JOHN EDWARD, mechanical & nuclear engineering, see previous edition

SCHMIDT, JOHN LANCASTER, b McPherson, Kans, Sept 19, 43; m 68; c 2. WILDLIFE ECOLOGY, WILDLIFE MANAGEMENT. *Educ:* Ottawa Univ, BA, 66; Colo State Univ, MS, 68, PhD(wildlife biol), 70. *Prof Exp:* Exten specialist wildlife, SDak State Univ, 70-72; exten prog leader, 72-75, asst dean natural resources, 75-78, ASSOC PROF WILDLIFE, COLO STATE UNIV, 78- *Concurrent Pos:* Consult, City Littleton, Colo, 73, Rogers Nagel Langhart Inc, 74-, Thorne Ecol Inst, 75-, Rocky Mountain Energy Co, Int Environ Consults & Dept Army. *Mem:* Wildlife Soc; Nat Wildlife Fedn; Nat Geog Soc. *Res:* Reintroduction of desert bighorn sheep in Colorado National Monument; feeding ecology at Cape Buffalo in Kruger National Park. *Mailing Add:* Dept Fishery & Wildlife Biol 233 Wagar Bldg Colo State Univ Ft Collins CO 80523

SCHMIDT, JOHN P, b Northhampton, Mass, Apr 17, 33; m 63; c 3. CHEMICAL ENGINEERING. *Educ:* Rensselaer Polytech Inst, BChE, 55; Mass Inst Technol, ScD(chem eng), 63. *Prof Exp:* Mem staff, Eng Dept, E I du Pont de Nemours & Co, Inc, 55-58; vpres res & develop, Halcon Int, Inc, 63-73; exec vpres, Oxirane Int, 73-80; SR VPRES, ARCOCHEM, 80- *Mem:* Soc Chem Indust; Am Inst Chem Engrs. *Res:* Organic and petrochemical processing. *Mailing Add:* 11 Honey Lake Dr RD 2 Princeton NJ 08540

SCHMIDT, JOHN RICHARD, b Madison, Wis, July 3, 29; m 51; c 3. AGRICULTURAL ECONOMICS, OPERATIONS RESEARCH. *Educ:* Univ Wis, BS, 51, MS, 53; Univ Minn, PhD(agr econ), 60. *Prof Exp:* Asst prof agr econ, Univ Wis, 56-61, assoc prof, 61-65, chmn dept, 66-70, PROF AGR ECON, UNIV WIS-MADISON, 65-; DIR, NORTH CENT COMPUT INST, 81- *Concurrent Pos:* Consult, Am Farm Bur Fedn, 62, Bank Mex, 72-, World Bank, 73-77 & Agr Develop Bank Iran, 74-75. *Mem:* Am Asn Agr Econ. *Res:* Economics of soil conservation; electronic farm records; computerized decision aids. *Mailing Add:* North Cent Comput Inst 666 WARF Off Bldg 610 Walnut St Madison WI 53706

SCHMIDT, JOHN THOMAS, b Louisville, Ky, Sept 25, 49; m 79; c 1. NEUROBIOLOGY, DEVELOPMENT OF NEURAL CONNECTIONS. *Educ:* Univ Detroit, BS, 71; Univ Mich, PhD(biophysics & neurosci), 76. *Prof Exp:* Fel, Nat Inst Med Res, London, Eng, 76-77; fel, Anat Dept, Vanderbilt Univ, 77-80; ASST PROF BIOL SCI, STATE UNIV NY, ALBANY, 80- *Mem:* Soc Neurosci; Asn Res Vision & Opthal. *Res:* Developmental and regeneration of retinotopic projections in the nervous system; role of activity in the stabilization of synaptic connections. *Mailing Add:* Dept Biol Sci State Univ NY 1400 Washington Ave Albany NY 12222

SCHMIDT, JOHN WESLEY, b Moundridge, Kans, Mar 13, 17; m 43; c 5. AGRONOMY. *Educ:* Tabor Col, BA, 47; Kans State Univ, MSc, 49; Univ Nebr, PhD(agron), 52. *Prof Exp:* Assoc prof agron, Kans State Univ, 51-54; assoc agronomist, 54-62, PROF AGRON, UNIV NEBR, LINCOLN, 62- *Concurrent Pos:* NSF-US-Japan Coop Sci Prog vis scientist, Japan, 66. *Honors & Awards:* Int Award Distinguished Serv Agr, Gamma Sigma Delta. 69; Crop Sci Award, Crop Sci Soc Am, 75. *Mem:* Fel Am Soc Agron; Crop Sci Soc Am; Am Genetic Asn. *Res:* Breeding, genetics and cytogenetics of wheat and related species and genera. *Mailing Add:* Dept of Agron Univ of Nebr Lincoln NE 68503

SCHMIDT, JUSTIN ORVEL, b Rhinelander, Wis, Mar 23, 47; m 71. ENTOMOLOGY, BIOLOGY. *Educ:* Pa State Univ, BS, 69; Univ BC, BSc, 72; Univ Ga, PhD(entom), 77. *Prof Exp:* Fel biol, Univ NB, 77-78; res scientist, Univ Ga, 78-80; ENTOMOLOGIST & TOXINOLOGIST, BEE RES LAB, TUCSON, 80- *Mem:* Entom Soc Am; Int Soc Toxicol; Am Chem Soc; AAAS; Sigma Xi. *Res:* Pheromones; insect venoms; chemical ecology; insect physiology and biochemistry. *Mailing Add:* Bee Res Lab 2000 E Allen Rd Tucson AZ 85719

SCHMIDT, KLAUS H, b Stuttgart, Ger, Oct 9, 28; m 55; c 1. RADIATION CHEMISTRY, PHYSICAL CHEMISTRY. *Educ:* Univ Tübingen, Dipl physics, 54; Univ Frankfurt, Dr phil nat(biophys), 60. *Prof Exp:* Res assoc biophys & radiation chem, Max Planck Inst Biophys, 60-63; resident res assoc radiation chem, 63-66, assoc physicist, 66-76, PHYSICIST, CHEM DIV, ARGONNE NAT LAB, 76- *Mem:* AAAS; Radiation Res Soc. *Res:* Kinetics of radiation-induced chemical reactions with optical and electrical methods; developing techniques and equipment for radiation chemistry research; using radiation chemical techniques to study chemical mechanisms or structures. *Mailing Add:* Chem Div Argonne Nat Lab Argonne IL 60439

SCHMIDT, KURT, b Geiss-Nidda, Ger, July 28, 29; m 58; c 3. EXPERIMENTAL PHYSICS. *Educ:* Univ Giessen, dipl, 54, Dr rer nat, 56. *Prof Exp:* Ger Res Asn fel, Univ Giessen, 56-57; tech leader gaseous discharges, Gen Elec Co, 57-69; tech dir, ITT Lamp Div, Int Tel & Tel Corp, 69-73; DIR RES & ENG, N AM PHILIPS LIGHTING CORP, 75- *Mem:* Illum Eng Soc. *Res:* Plasma physics; low and high pressure discharges; high temperature plasmas; parapsychology. *Mailing Add:* N Am Phillips Lighting Corp Bank St Hightstown NJ 08520

SCHMIDT, KURT F, b New York, NY, Feb 25, 26; m 55; c 3. ANESTHESIOLOGY. *Educ:* Univ Munich, MD, 51. *Prof Exp:* Instr anesthesiol, Harvard Med Sch, 55; instr, Sch Med Yale Univ, 55-61, asst prof anesthesiol, 63-68; prof anesthesiol & chmn dept, Albany Med Col, 68-73; assoc prof anaesthesiol, Harvard Med Sch, 73-75; PROF ANESTHESIOL & CHMN DEPT, TUFTS-NEW ENG MED CTR, 75- *Concurrent Pos:* NIH spec fel neuropharmacol, 61-63. *Mem:* Am Soc Anesthesiol, AMA; NY Acad Sci; Int Anesthesia Res Soc; Asn Univ Anesthetists. *Res:* Neuropharmacology. *Mailing Add:* Dept Anesthesia Tufts-New Eng Med Ctr Boston MA 02111

SCHMIDT, LANNY D, b Waukegan, Ill, May 6, 38; m 62; c 2. PHYSICAL CHEMISTRY, CHEMICAL ENGINEERING. *Educ:* Wheaton Col, BS, 60; Univ Chicago, PhD(phys chem), 64. *Prof Exp:* Res assoc phys chem, Univ Chicago, 64-65; assoc prof, 65-69, PROF CHEM ENG, UNIV MINN, MINNEAPOLIS, 69- *Mem:* Am Phys Soc; Am Chem Soc; Am Vacuum Soc. *Res:* Surface chemistry and physics; adsorption; catalysis; field emission microscopy; charge transport in liquids; auger electron spectrometry; kinetics. *Mailing Add:* Dept of Chem Eng Univ of Minn Minneapolis MN 55455

SCHMIDT, LEON HERBERT, b Huron, Ohio, June 28, 09; m 31; c 2. EXPERIMENTAL MEDICINE. *Educ:* DePauw Univ, BA, 29; Univ Cincinnati, MS, 30, PhD(biol chem), 32. *Hon Degrees:* DSc, DePauw Univ, 68. *Prof Exp:* From instr to res prof biol chem, Col Med, Univ Cincinnati, 35-63; dir nat ctr primate biol & prof comp pharmacol, Sch Vet Med, Univ Calif, Davis & Sch Med, Univ San Francisco, 63-68; prof pharmacol, Sch Med, Univ Calif, Davis, 68-69; PROF PHARMACOL, COL MED, UNIV ALA, BIRMINGHAM, 69- *Concurrent Pos:* Res fel biol chem, Col Med, Univ Cincinnati, 32-34; res assoc, Christ Hosp, Inst Med Res, Cincinnati, 32-35, dir, 36-63; Craig lectr, 56; Barnwell lectr, 71; consult, USPHS; mem comts, Nat Res Coun; mem adv panel on malaria chemother, WHO; assoc dir chemother res, Southern Res Inst, 69-76; ed-in-chief, Antimicrob Agents Chemother. *Honors & Awards:* Trudeau Medal, Nat Tuberc & Respiratory Dis Asn, 67. *Mem:* AAAS; Am Chem Soc; Am Soc Biol Chem; Am Soc Microbiol; Am Soc Pharm Exp Ther. *Res:* Metabolism of bile acids; sterols and phospholipids; physiology of the thyroid; bacterial chemotherapy; sulfonamides; biology and chemotherapy of malaria, tuberculosis and cancer; pharmacology of chemotherapeutic agents; comparative primatology. *Mailing Add:* Dept Pharmacol Univ Ala Box 191 Univ Sta Birmingham AL 35294

SCHMIDT, LOUIS VINCENT, b Chicago, Ill, May 26, 26; m 49; c 1. AERONAUTICAL ENGINEERING, SOLID MECHANICS. *Educ:* Calif Inst Technol, BS, 46, MS, 48, PhD(aeronaut), 63. *Prof Exp:* Wind tunnel engr, Calif Inst Technol, 45-50; aerodynamicist, Boeing Airplane Co, 50-56; design specialist, Gen Dynamics/Convair, 56-59; res fel aeronaut, Calif Inst Technol, 63-64; assoc prof, Naval Postgrad Sch, 64-71, prof aeronaut, 71-81; Eng res & develop adminr, Off Asst Secy Navy, Res, Eng & Systems, Washington, DC, 80- *Mem:* Am Soc Mech Engrs; assoc fel Am Inst Aeronaut & Astronaut. *Res:* Aircraft stability and control; aeroelasticity; unsteady aerodynamics about bluff bodies; structural mechanics. *Mailing Add:* Res Eng & Systs Off Asst Secy Navy Washington DC 20350

SCHMIDT, MAARTEN, b Groningen, Netherlands, Dec 28, 29; m 55; c 3. ASTRONOMY. *Educ:* Groningen, BSc, 49; Univ Leiden, PhD, 56. *Hon Degrees:* ScD, Yale Univ, 66. *Prof Exp:* Sci off, Leiden Observ, Netherlands, 53-59; assoc prof, 59-64, exec officer, 72-75, chmn div physics, math & astron, 75-78, mem staff, Owens Valley Radio Observ, 70-78, PROF ASTRON, CALIF INST TECHNOL, 64-, MEM STAFF, HALE OBSERV, 59-, DIR, 78- *Concurrent Pos:* Carnegie fel, 56-58. *Honors & Awards:* Helen B Warner Prize, Am Astron Soc, 64; Rumford Award, Am Acad Arts & Sci, 68. *Mem:* Foreign assoc Nat Acad Sci; Am Astron Soc; fel Am Acad Arts & Sci; Assoc Royal Astron Soc (London). *Res:* Structure, dynamics and evolution of the galaxy; radio astronomy; redshifts and cosmic distribution of quasars. *Mailing Add:* Hale Observ 813 Santa Barbara St Pasadena CA 91109

SCHMIDT, NATHALIE JOAN, b Flagstaff, Ariz, Sept 24, 28. VIROLOGY. *Educ:* Univ Ariz, BA, 50; Northwestern Univ, MS, 52, PhD(bact, immunol), 53. *Prof Exp:* Asst instr med bact, Northwestern Univ, 50-53; bacteriologist, Evanston Hosp Asn, Ill, 53-54; RES SPECIALIST, VIRAL & RICKETTSIAL DIS LAB, STATE DEPT PUB HEALTH, CALIF, 54- *Concurrent Pos:* Consult, NIH, 63-; ed, J Clin Microbiol, 75- *Honors & Awards:* Kimble Award Lab Methodology, 77. *Mem:* Am Soc Microbiol; Am Acad Microbiol; Am Asn Immunol; Soc Exp Biol & Med; Am Soc Microbiol. *Res:* Immunology; etiology and epidemiology of viral infections; development of reagents for the laboratory diagnosis of viral infections; characterization of viral antigens and antibodies. *Mailing Add:* 2151 Berkeley Way Berkeley CA 94704

SCHMIDT, NORBERT OTTO, b Highland Park, Mich, Nov 15, 25; m 53; c 5. CIVIL ENGINEERING, SOILS. *Educ:* US Mil Acad, BS, 49; Harvard Univ, MS, 55; Univ Ill, PhD(civil eng), 65. *Prof Exp:* From asst prof to assoc prof mil sci, Mo Sch Mines, 59-62; asst civil eng, Univ Ill, 63-65, from instr to asst prof, 65-66; from asst prof to assoc prof, 66-75, PROF CIVIL ENG, UNIV MO-ROLLA, 75- *Mem:* Am Soc Civil Engrs; Am Soc Testing & Mat; Nat Soc Prof Engrs; Am Soc Eng Educ. *Res:* Geotechnical engineering; dams; foundations; testing, dewatering and instrumentation. *Mailing Add:* Dept of Civil Eng Univ of Mo-Rolla Rolla MO 65401

SCHMIDT, OTTO ERNEST LINCOLN, dermatology, deceased

SCHMIDT, P(HILIP) S(TEPHEN), b Houston, Tex, Feb 26, 41; m 66; c 2. MECHANICAL ENGINEERING, HEAT TRANSFER. *Educ:* Mass Inst Technol, SB, 62; Stanford Univ, MS, 65, PhD(mech eng), 69. *Prof Exp:* Res engr, Bell Helicopter Co, 62-64; Woodrow Wilson teaching intern & assoc prof mech eng, Prairie View Agr & Mech Col, 68-70; asst prof, 70-77, assoc prof, 77-81, PROF MECH ENG, UNIV TEX, AUSTIN, 81- *Honors & Awards:* Ralph R Teetor Award, Soc Automotive Engrs, 72. *Mem:* Am Soc Eng Educ; Am Soc Mech Engrs; Soc Automotive Engrs. *Res:* Fluid mechanics; thermodynamics and industrial energy conservation. *Mailing Add:* Dept of Mech Eng Univ of Tex Austin TX 78712

SCHMIDT, PARBURY POLLEN, b Norwalk, Conn, Sept 4, 39; m 61; c 2. CHEMICAL PHYSICS. *Educ:* Kalamazoo Col, BA, 61; Wake Forest Col, MA, 64; Univ Mich, Ann Arbor, PhD(chem), 66. *Prof Exp:* NSF fel, Univ Col, Univ London, 66-67; NSF fel & vis res fel, Australian Nat Univ, 67-68; asst prof chem, Univ Ga, 68-70; asst prof, 70-75, ASSOC PROF CHEM, OAKLAND UNIV, 75- *Concurrent Pos:* Spec lectr gen studies sch, Australian Nat Univ, 68; Fulbright res scholar & vis prof, Southampton Univ, UK. *Res:* Theory of electron transfer reactions; theory of nerve impulse conduction; theory of nonradiative transitions in molecules. *Mailing Add:* Dept of Chem Oakland Univ Rochester MI 48063

SCHMIDT, PAUL F, b Narva, Esthonia, Aug 20, 16; US citizen; m 44; c 2. SEMICONDUCTORS, SURFACE PHYSICS. *Educ:* Inst Tech, Tallinn, Esthonia, BA, 38; Univ Koenigsberg, MA, 44; Univ Heidelberg, PhD, 51. *Prof Exp:* Res assoc, Max-Planck Inst, Ger, 52; res assoc, Res Inst, Temple Univ, 52-54; res assoc, Philco Corp, 54-59, res sect mgr, Res Labs, Westinghouse Elec Corp, 59-64; MEM TECH STAFF, BELL LABS, 64- *Mem:* Electrochem Soc; Inst Elec & Electronics Engrs. *Res:* Physics and chemistry of surfaces; anodic oxide films; dielectrics; radiation effects in dielectrics; radiation effects; semiconductors; neutron activation analysis; gamma-ray spectrometry. *Mailing Add:* Dept 2133 Bell Labs Allentown PA 18103

SCHMIDT, PAUL GARDNER, b Pasadena, Calif, June 9, 44; m 66; c 2. BIOPHYSICAL CHEMISTRY. *Educ:* Pomona Col, BA, 66; Stanford Univ, PhD(chem), 70. *Prof Exp:* Asst prof chem & biochem, Univ Ill, Urbana, 70-77; ASSOC MEM, OKLA MED RES FOUND & ASSOC PROF, DEPT BIOCHEM, HEALTH SCI CTR, UNIV OKLA, OKLAHOMA CITY, 77- *Concurrent Pos:* USPHS res grant, 70-; res career develop award, USPHS, 79-84. *Mem:* AAAS; Am Chem Soc; Biophys Soc; Am Soc Biol Chem. *Res:* Nuclear magnetic resonance; enzyme structure and function; transfer RNA structure. *Mailing Add:* Okla Med Res Found 825 NE 13th St Oklahoma City OK 73104

SCHMIDT, PAUL J, b Cincinnati, Ohio, May 26, 43; m 69; c 2. ORGANIC CHEMISTRY. *Educ:* Xavier Univ, BS, 65; Univ Cincinnati, PhD(chem), 69. *Prof Exp:* Res chemist, 69-74, asst dir chem res, 74-75, dir chem res, 75-80, VPRES RES & DEVELOP, HILTON-DAVIS DIV, STERLING DRUG, INC, 80- *Mem:* Am Chem Soc. *Res:* Platinium complexes; organic synthetics. *Mailing Add:* Hilton-Davis Chem Co 2235 Langdon Farm Rd Cincinnati OH 45237

SCHMIDT, PAUL JOSEPH, b New York, NY, Oct 22, 25; m 53; c 3. MEDICINE, CLINICAL PATHOLOGY. *Educ:* Fordham Univ, BS, 48; St Louis Univ, MS, 52; NY Univ, MD, 53; Am Bd Path, cert clin path, 64, cert blood banking, 73. *Prof Exp:* Intern, St Elizabeth's Hosp, Boston, 53-54; physician, Clin Ctr Blood Bank & chief blood bank sect, NIH, 55-60, resident, Clin Path Dept, 61-62, asst chief, 62-64, chief blood bank dept, 65-74; DIR, SOUTHWEST FLA BLOOD BANK, INC, 75-; PROF PATH, COL MED, UNIV SOUTH FLA, 75- *Concurrent Pos:* From clin assoc prof to clin prof path, Sch Med, Georgetown Univ, 65-74. *Honors & Awards:* Silver Medal, Red Cross Spain; Emily Cooley Mem Award, Am Asn Blood Banks, 74. *Mem:* Col Am Path; Am Soc Clin Path; Int Soc Blood Transfusion. *Res:* Immunohematology; physiology of the formed elements of blood and the effects of storage on their viability; hepatitis; administration and education in blood banking and clinical pathology. *Mailing Add:* 598 Riviera Dr Tampa FL 33606

SCHMIDT, PAUL WOODWARD, b Madison, Wis, May 8, 26; m 50; c 5. PHYSICS. *Educ:* Carleton Col, BA, 49; Univ Wis, MS, 50, PhD(physics), 53. *Prof Exp:* From asst prof to assoc prof, 53-66, PROF PHYSICS, UNIV MO-COLUMBIA, 66- *Mem:* Fel Am Phys Soc; Am Crystallog Soc; Clay Minerals Soc. *Res:* Small angle x-ray scattering, both theory and experiment; chemical physics; liquids; biophysics; colloids. *Mailing Add:* Dept of Physics Univ of Mo Columbia MO 65211

SCHMIDT, RAYMOND LEROY, b Tiffin, Ohio, July 7, 42; m 65; c 2. PHYSICAL CHEMISTRY. *Educ:* Fla Presby Col, BS, 64; Emory Univ, PhD(phys chem), 67. *Prof Exp:* Instr chem, Emory Univ, 67-68; res fel chem eng, Calif Inst Technol, 68-70; from asst prof to assoc prof chem, Univ New Orleans, 70-78; SR RES CHEMIST, CHEVRON OIL FIELD RES CO, 78- *Concurrent Pos:* Fel Emory Univ, 67-68; vis assoc, Calif Inst Technol, 77-80. *Mem:* Am Chem Soc; Soc Petrol Engrs. *Res:* Laser scattering spectroscopy from fluid media; adsorption phenomena; surface chemistry of geologic materials; high pressure physical property measurements. *Mailing Add:* Chevron Oil Field Res Co PO Box 446 La Habra CA 90631

SCHMIDT, REESE BOISE, b Knoxville, Iowa, May 16, 13; m 49; c 5. ANALYTICAL CHEMISTRY. *Educ:* Cent Col, Iowa, BS, 34. *Prof Exp:* Technician exp canning, Calif Packing Corp, Ill, 39-40, foreman, 40-43; chemist, US Rubber Co, Iowa, 44-45; teacher pub sch, Iowa, 45-46; chemist, 46-62, mgr appl res, 62-69, mgr process & test, W A Sheaffer Pen Co, 70-78, CONSULT, SHEAFFER EATON, DIV TEXTRON INC, 78- *Mem:* Am Chem Soc. *Mailing Add:* Prod Develop Dept Sheaffer-Eaton Ft Madison IA 52627

SCHMIDT, RICHARD ARTHUR, b Elizabeth, NJ, Mar 18, 35; m 55; c 2. ECONOMIC GEOLOGY. *Educ:* Franklin & Marshall Col, BS, 57; Univ Wis-Madison, MS, 59, PhD(geol), 63. *Prof Exp:* Nat Acad Sci resident res assoc, NASA-Ames Res Ctr, 63-65; proj scientist, Aerospace Systs Div, Bendix Corp, 65-67; sr geologist, Stanford Res Inst, 67-74; TECH MGR FOSSIL FUEL RESOURCES, ELEC POWER RES INST, 74- *Mem:* Am Inst Mining, Metall & Petrol Engrs; fel Geol Soc Am. *Res:* Coal; surface mining; environmental assessment; resources management and planning. *Mailing Add:* 22205 Rac Lane Cupertino CA 95014

SCHMIDT, RICHARD EDWARD, b Detroit, Mich, Sept 3, 31; m 56; c 1. AGRONOMY. *Educ:* Pa State Univ, BS, 54, MS, 58; Va Polytech Inst, PhD(agron), 65. *Prof Exp:* Asst agron, Pa State Univ, 56-58; from instr to asst prof, 58-66, ASSOC PROF AGRON, VA POLYTECH INST & STATE UNIV, 66- *Concurrent Pos:* Consult, Weblite Corp, Va, 65- & US Mkt Group, 81- *Mem:* Am Soc Agron. *Res:* Turfgrass ecology, particularly environmental influences on the physiological affects of grasses. *Mailing Add:* 406 Hearthstone Dr Blacksburg VA 24060

SCHMIDT, RICHARD RALPH, b Milwaukee, Wis, Mar 28, 44; m 65; c 2. TERATOLOGY. *Educ:* Univ Wis-Madison, BA, 68; Med Col Wis, PhD(anat), 74. *Prof Exp:* INSTR GROSS ANAT, DANIEL BAUGH INST ANAT, JEFFERSON MED COL, 74- *Res:* Biochemical alterations in fetuses with multiple congenital skeletal malformations. *Mailing Add:* Daniel Baugh Inst of Anat Jefferson Med Col Philadelphia PA 19107

SCHMIDT, ROBERT, b Chomci, Ukraine, May 18, 27; US citizen. MECHANICS, ENGINEERING. *Educ:* Univ Colo, BS, 51, MS, 53; Univ Ill, PhD(civil eng), 56. *Prof Exp:* Asst prof mech, Univ Ill, 56-59; assoc prof, Univ Ariz, 59-63; chmn, Civil Eng Dept, 78-80, PROF ENG MECH, UNIV DETROIT, 63- *Concurrent Pos:* NSF res grants, 60-63, 64-67, 70-72 & 76-78; ed, Indust Math, Indust Math Soc. *Mem:* Am Soc Civil Engrs; Am Soc Mech Engrs; Am Soc Eng Educ; Indust Math Soc (pres, 66-67 & 81-82); Am Acad Mech. *Res:* Theories of plates and shells, sandwich plates and shells and multilaminate plates and shells; nonlinear theories of arches and rods; biosophy. *Mailing Add:* Col of Eng Univ of Detroit 4001 W McNichols Rd Detroit MI 48221

SCHMIDT, ROBERT GEORGE, b New York, NY, May 31, 21; m 59; c 4. GEOLOGY, FIELD GEOLOGY. *Educ:* Univ Colo, AB, 43; Harvard Univ, AM, 48, PhD(geol), 53. *Prof Exp:* Geologist, 48-49, GEOLOGIST, US GEOL SURV, 51- *Mem:* Fel Geol Soc Am. *Res:* Igneous petrology; geology of western Pacific islands and western Montana; earthquake hazard studies Helena area, Montana; mineral resource appraisal; geologic mapping. *Mailing Add:* US Geol Surv Nat Ctr MS 928 Reston VA 22092

SCHMIDT, ROBERT REINHART, b St Louis, Mo, Feb 18, 33; m 56; c 4. BIOCHEMISTRY. *Educ:* Va Polytech Inst, BS, 55, PhD(biochem), 61; Univ Md, MS, 57. *Prof Exp:* From asst prof to assoc prof, Va Polytech Inst & State Univ, 61-67, prof biochem, 67-80; MEM FAC, UNIV FLA, 80- *Concurrent Pos:* Res grants, NIH & NSF, 61- *Mem:* Am Soc Microbiol; Am Soc Biol Chemists; Am Soc Plant Physiol. *Res:* Use of synchronized cultures of microorganisms, plant and animal cells to study operation and control of metabolic pathways and enzymes located therein during cellular growth and division. *Mailing Add:* Univ Fla 1059 McCarty Hall Gainsville FL 32611

SCHMIDT, ROBERT SHERWOOD, b Des Moines, Iowa, May 16, 28; m 51; c 3. BEHAVIORAL PHYSIOLOGY. *Educ:* Ball State Teachers Col, BS, 50; Univ Mich, MS, 51; Univ Chicago, PhD(zool), 54. *Prof Exp:* From asst prof to assoc prof biol sci, Ill State Norm Univ, 54-61; asst prof otolaryngol, Univ Chicago, 62-65; ASSOC PROF PHARMACOL, INST STUDY MIND, DRUGS & BEHAV, STRITCH SCH MED, LOYOLA UNIV CHICAGO, 65- *Concurrent Pos:* Nat Inst Neurol Dis & Blindness career develop award, Univ Chicago, 63-65 & Stritch Sch Med, Univ Loyola Chicago, 66-70. *Mem:* AAAS; Animal Behav Soc; Am Soc Zool; Soc Neurosci. *Res:* Anuran acoustic neuroethology. *Mailing Add:* Inst Study Mind Drugs & Behav Loyola Univ Stritch Sch Med Maywood IL 60153

SCHMIDT, ROBERT W, b Enid, Okla, Feb 16, 30; m 53; c 4. BIOCHEMISTRY. *Educ:* Bethel Col, AB, 52; Univ Okla, MSc, 55, PhD(chem), 60. *Prof Exp:* Instr math & sci high sch, Kans, 52-53; asst prof chem, Simpson Col, 58-61; assoc prof, 61-67, PROF CHEM, BETHEL COL, KANS, 67- *Concurrent Pos:* Assoc marine scientist, Va Inst Marine Sci, 69-70. *Mem:* AAAS; Am Chem Soc; NY Acad Sci. *Res:* Comparative biochemistry of marine invertebrates; natural products of plants; organic chemistry. *Mailing Add:* Dept of Chem Bethel Co North Newton KS 67117

SCHMIDT, ROBERT W, b Toledo, Ohio, July 22, 26; m 63; c 2. PATHOLOGY. *Educ:* Univ Toledo, BS, 50; Ohio State Univ, MD, 54. *Prof Exp:* Intern, 54-55, resident path, 55-59, from instr to assoc prof, 59-69, PROF PATH, UNIV HOSP, UNIV MICH, ANN ARBOR, 69- *Concurrent Pos:* Dir path, Wayne County Gen Hosp, Eloise, Mich. *Mem:* Am Soc Clin Path. *Res:* Clinical and anatomical pathology; pathology of the thyroid gland; exfoliative cytology. *Mailing Add:* Dept of Path Univ of Mich Hosp Ann Arbor MI 48104

SCHMIDT, ROGER PAUL, b Abilene, Kans, Jan 16, 44; m 74. PARASITOLOGY, BIOLOGY. *Educ:* Univ Kans, BA, 66, MA, 72; Kans State Univ, PhD(parasitol), 78. *Prof Exp:* Instr biol, Univ SC, 77-79, asst prof, 79-82. *Mem:* Sigma Xi; AAAS; Am Inst Biol Sci. *Res:* Effects and interactions between pesticides and parasites in poultry. *Mailing Add:* Col of Gen Studies Univ of SC Columbia SC 29208

SCHMIDT, RONALD GROVER, b Bloomfield, NJ, Oct 13, 31; m 55; c 2. HYDROGEOLOGY. *Educ:* Columbia Univ, AB, 53, MA, 55; Univ Cincinnati, PhD(geol), 57; Am Inst Prof Geol & Calif Bd Regist, cert & regist geol. *Prof Exp:* Geologist, USAEC Contr NMex, 52; tech officer, Geol Sur Can, 53-54; asst geol, Columbia Univ, 54; instr Hunter Col, 55; asst, Univ Cincinnati, 55-57; geologist, Standard Oil Co, Tex, 56; asst prof, Univ Cincinnati, 57-63; pres & geol consult, Earth Sci Labs, Inc, 60-70; dir, Off Environ Studies, 70-74, Dir, Brehm Lab, 72-75, PROF GEOL & ENG, WRIGHT STATE UNIV, 70-, CHMN DEPT GEOL, 74- *Mem:* AAAS; Am Geophys Union; Amer Water Res Asn; Geol Soc Am; Water Pollution Control Fed. *Mailing Add:* Dept of Geol Wright State Univ Dayton OH 45435

SCHMIDT, RUTH A M, b Brooklyn, NY, Apr 22, 16. GEOLOGY. *Educ:* NY Univ, AB, 36; Columbia Univ, AM, 39, PhD(geol), 48. *Prof Exp:* X-ray technician, L I Col Hosp, 36-38; asst paleont, Columbia Univ, 39-42; geologist, US Geol Surv, 43-56, dist geologist, 56-63; CONSULT GEOLOGIST & MICROPALEONTOLOGIST, 64- *Concurrent Pos:* Environ consult, Off Pipeline Coordr, Off of Gov, Alaska, 75-77; chmn geol dept, Anchorage Community Col, Univ Alaska, 70- *Mem:* Fel AAAS; Fedn Am Sci; fel Geol Soc Am; Am Inst Prof Geol; Soc Econ Paleont & Mineral. *Res:* Cretaceous and Tertiary micropaleontology; geomorphology; engineering and military geology; general geology of Alaska. *Mailing Add:* 1040 C St Anchorage AK 99501

SCHMIDT, THOMAS JOHN, b Mt Holly, NJ, Dec 13, 46. ENDOCRINOLOGY, CELLULAR PHYSIOLOGY. *Educ:* Univ Del, BA, 69; Cornell Univ, MS, 73, PhD(physiol), 76. *Prof Exp:* Fel biochem & endocrinol, Nat Cancer Inst, 76-79; SR FEL, FELS RES INST, 79- *Mem:* Sigma Xi; Endocrine Soc; NY Acad Sci. *Res:* Mode of action of steroid hormones; function of receptors, particularly for glucocorticoids, in normal and neoplastic cells. *Mailing Add:* Fels Res Inst Temple Univ Sch Med Philadelphia PA 19140

SCHMIDT, THOMAS WILLIAM, b Evansville, Ind, Aug 9, 38; m 61; c 2. CHEMICAL PHYSICS. *Educ:* Univ Evansville, BA, 60; Univ Fla, MS, 63; Univ Tenn, PhD(chem), 67. *Prof Exp:* Sr res chem physicist, 67-77, SECT SUPVR, ENG DATA, PHILLIPS PETROL CO, 77- *Mem:* Am Phys Soc. *Res:* Molecular beams; mass spectroscopy; chemical kinetics; ultra high vacuum; vapor-liquid equilibrium. *Mailing Add:* Phillips Petrol Co Phillips Res Ctr 182 PL Bartlesville OK 74003

SCHMIDT, VICTOR ADOLF, b Brooklyn, NY, Nov 9, 36; m 68. GEOPHYSICS, PALEOMAGNETISM. *Educ:* Carnegie-Mellon Univ, BS, 58, MS, 60, PhD(physics), 66. *Prof Exp:* Instr physics, Carnegie-Mellon Univ, 66-67; NASA fel, 67-68; asst prof, 68-75, ASSOC PROF GEOPHYS, UNIV PITTSBURGH, 75- *Mem:* Am Geophys Union; fel Nat Speleol Soc. *Res:* Rock magnetism and paleomagnetism; geology and hydrology of caves in the Appalachians; mechanisms of thermoremanence. *Mailing Add:* Dept Earth & Planetary Sci Univ Pittsburgh EH 321 Pittsburgh PA 15260

SCHMIDT, VICTOR HUGO, b Portland, Ore, July 10, 30; m 58; c 4. SOLID STATE PHYSICS. *Educ:* Wash State Univ, BS, 51; Univ Wash, PhD(physics), 61. *Prof Exp:* Mech design engr, Gilfillan Bros, Inc, 53-54; assoc res engr, Boeing Airplane Co, 55-57; asst prof physics, Valparaiso Univ, 61-64; assoc prof, 64-73, PROF PHYSICS, MONT STATE UNIV, 73- *Mem:* Fel Am Phys Soc; Am Asn Physics Teachers; Sigma Xi; Fedn Am Scientists. *Res:* Nuclear magnetic resonance, light scattering, dielectric and high pressure studies of ferroelectric phase transitions; physical properties of materials used in fuel cells and coal-fired MHD generators; wind generation of electric power. *Mailing Add:* Dept of Physics Mont State Univ Bozeman MT 59717

SCHMIDT, VOLKMAR, b Heidelberg, Ger, Aug 27, 32. MARINE GEOLOGY. *Educ:* Univ Heidelberg, BS, 56; Univ Kiel, PhD(geol), 61. *Prof Exp:* Sr res geologist, Mobil Oil Corp, Tex, 61-69, head, Geol Lab, Mobil Oil Can, Ltd, 68-76; MGR GEOL RES, PETRO CAN, CALGARY, 76- *Mem:* Am Asn Petrol Geologists; Soc Econ Paleontologists & Mineralogists. *Res:* Sedimentology; carbonate petrography; recent carbonate sediments; diagenesis of sediments; petroleum reservoir petrography; evaporite facies and petrography; facies and paleoenvironmental studies; sandstone petrography. *Mailing Add:* Petro Can PO Box 2844 Calgary AB T2P 3E3 Can

SCHMIDT, WALTER HAROLD, b Gordon, Nebr, Sept 19, 35; m 59; c 4. AGRONOMY. *Educ:* Univ Nebr, Lincoln, BS, 57, MS, 60, PhD(crop prod), 65. *Prof Exp:* Asst county exten agent, Nebr Coop Exten Serv, fall 57; from asst prof to assoc prof, 65-76, PROF AGRON, OHIO COOP EXTEN SERV, OHIO STATE UNIV, 76- *Mem:* Am Soc Agron; Nat Asn Coop Agr Agents; Am Soc Sugar Beet Technol; Sigma Xi. *Res:* Crop production techniques for corn, forages, grain, soybeans, sugar beets and sunflowers. *Mailing Add:* 1708 Oak Dr Fremont OH 43420

SCHMIDT, WERNER H(ANS), b Frankfurt, Ger, Sept 24, 14; nat US; m 41; c 2. CHEMICAL ENGINEERING. *Educ:* Tufts Univ, BS, 36. *Prof Exp:* Chemist foods, Johnson-Salisbury Co, 36; chemist edible oils, Lever Bros Co, 36-39, res chemist, 39-45, res supvr foods, 45-52, chief foods processing sect, 52-60, develop mgr, 60-64, develop mgr foods & toiletries, 64-73, dir develop foods, Foods Div, 73-78; RETIRED. *Concurrent Pos:* Consult, Lever Bros Foods Div, 78- *Mem:* Am Chem Soc; Am Oil Chem Soc; Am Inst Chem Engrs. *Res:* Edible oil processing; shortening and margarine formulation and manufacture; catalytic hydrogenation; esterification. *Mailing Add:* 42 Liverpool Dr Yarmouth Port MA 02675

SCHMIDT, WILLFRED G, b Chicago, Ill, Aug 17, 30; m 53; c 3. CHEMICAL KINETICS. *Educ:* Univ Chicago, AB, 50, MS, 61, PhD(complex ion chem), 62. *Prof Exp:* RES SPECIALIST COMBUSTION, AEROJET-GEN CORP, 62- *Mem:* Am Chem Soc; Combustion Inst; Am Inst Aeronaut & Astronaut. *Res:* Reaction kinetics of complexes and chelates of transition metal ions; combustion kinetics of solid propellants and metals. *Mailing Add:* 4816 Nile Court Sacramento CA 95841

SCHMIDT, WILLIAM EDWARD, b Pittsburgh, Pa, Sept 7, 20; m 47; c 5. ANALYTICAL CHEMISTRY. *Educ:* George Washington Univ, BS, 43, MS, 50; Princeton Univ, MA & PhD(chem), 53. *Prof Exp:* Asst chem, George Washington Univ, 41-43, res assoc, Nat Defense Res Comt, 43-44, assoc, 46-50; asst anal chem, Princeton Univ, 50-53; from asst prof to assoc prof, 53-61, PROF CHEM, GEORGE WASHINGTON UNIV, 61- *Concurrent Pos:* Consult, US Vet Admin, 57-59; ed consult, Am Chem Soc, 65- *Mem:* AAAS; Am Chem Soc; Electrochem Soc. *Res:* Measurement of electrode potentials; mercury cathode electrolysis; electroanalysis; overvoltage; electroplating; radio tracers; reagent chemicals. *Mailing Add:* Dept of Chem George Washington Univ Washington DC 20006

SCHMIDT, WOLFGANG M, b Vienna, Austria, Oct 3, 33; m 60; c 3. MATHEMATICS. *Educ:* Univ Vienna, PhD(math), 55. *Prof Exp:* Asst docent math, Univ Vienna, 55-56; instr, Univ Mont, 56-57; asst docent, Univ Vienna, 57-58; asst prof, Univ Mont, 58-59; asst docent, Univ Vienna, 59-60; asst prof, Univ Colo, 60-61; res assoc, Columbia Univ, 61-62; docent, Univ Vienna, 62-64; assoc prof, 64-65, PROF MATH, UNIV COLO, BOULDER, 65- *Concurrent Pos:* Univ Colo, Boulder fac fel, Univ Cambridge, 66-67; grant & invited address, Int Cong Mathematicians, Nice, 70; mem, Inst Advan Study, 70-71. *Honors & Awards:* Cole Prize Number Theory, Am Math Soc, 72. *Mem:* Am Math Soc; Austrian Math Soc. *Res:* Number theory, especially geometry of numbers and diophantine approximations. *Mailing Add:* Dept of Math Univ of Colo Boulder CO 80309

SCHMIDT, WYMAN CARL, b Ocheyedan, Iowa, Sept 9, 29; m 53; c 5. SILVICULTURE. *Educ:* Univ Mont, BS, 58, MS, 61, PhD, 80. *Prof Exp:* Forester, Black Hills Nat Forest, 59-60; from res forester to res silviculturist, 60-75, RES UNIT LEADER, INTERMOUNTAIN FOREST & RANGE EXP STA, FORESTRY SCI LAB, MONTANA STATE UNIV, 75- *Mem:* Soc Am Foresters; Ecol Soc Am. *Res:* Autecological, synecological and silvicultural research in the coniferous forests of the northern Rocky Mountains, including forest regeneration, stand development, cone production, soil moisture, phenology and tree growth relationships; silviculture and forest ecology of subalpine forest ecosystems. *Mailing Add:* Forestry Sci Lab Mont State Univ Bozeman MT 59717

SCHMIDTKE, JON ROBERT, b Detroit, Mich, Mar 27, 43. IMMUNOLOGY. *Educ:* Mich State Univ, BS, 65; Univ Mich, MS, 67, PhD(immunol), 69. *Prof Exp:* Asst prof microbiol & surg, Univ Minn, Minneapolis, 72-76, assoc prof, 76-79; HEAD, DEPT IMMUNOL, ELI LILLY & CO, 79- *Concurrent Pos:* USPHS training grant, Scripps Clin & Res Found, La Jolla, Calif, 69-72. *Mem:* Am Asn Immunol; Am Soc Microbiol; Transplantation Soc; Am Soc Exp Path; Reticuloendothelial Soc. *Res:* Cellular immunology of human lymphocytes; macrophage function; modification of immunogenicity. *Mailing Add:* Dept Immunol Eli Lilly & Co 307 E McCarty St Indianapolis IN 46285

SCHMIDTKE, R(ICHARD) A(LLEN), b Benton Harbor, Mich, July 27, 25; m 48; c 2. MECHANICAL ENGINEERING. *Educ:* Univ Mich, BS, 48, MS, 49; Ill Inst Technol, PhD(mech eng), 53. *Prof Exp:* Instr mech eng, Ill Inst Technol, 49-53, asst prof, 53; mem tech staff, Melpar, Inc, Westinghouse Air Brake Co, 53, sr mem tech staff, 53-54, sr engr, 54-55, proj engr, 55-57, res br leader, 57-58, asst to vpres res & eng, 58-60, spec asst adv develop, 60; dir appl res, 60-70, sr prog mgr, 70-76, vpres laser progs, 76-80, VPRES ENG, GOV PROD DIV, PRATT & WHITNES AIR CRAFT DIV, UNITED TECHNOLOGISTS CORP WEST PALM BEACH, 80- *Mem:* Am Soc Mech Engrs; Am Astronaut Soc; Am Inst Aeronaut & Astronaut. *Res:* Free-piston, turbojet, ramjet and rocket engines; heat transfer; aerodynamics; thermodynamics, applied mathematics; marine propulsion; high energy lasers. *Mailing Add:* 372 Fairway N Tequesta FL 33458

SCHMIDT-KOENIG, KLAUS, b Heidelberg, Ger, Jan 21, 30; m 59; c 3. ZOOLOGY. *Educ:* Univ Freiburgh, PhD(zool), 58. *Prof Exp:* Fel, Max Planck Inst Physiol of Behav, Ger, 55-57, mem staff, 58-63; zool, 59-71, adj assoc prof, 71-75, PROF ZOOL, DUKE UNIV, 75- *Concurrent Pos:* Pvt docent, Univ Gottingen, 63-71, appl prof, 71-75; prof zool, Univ Tubingen, 75- *Res:* Animal orientation; biological rhythms; sensory physiology; biostatistics. *Mailing Add:* Dept of Zool Duke Univ Durham NC 27706

SCHMIDT-NIELSEN, BODIL MIMI, b Copenhagen, Denmark, Nov 3, 18; nat US; m 39, 68; c 3. PHYSIOLOGY. *Educ:* Copenhagen Univ, DDS, 41, DOdont, 46, PhD, 55. *Prof Exp:* Instr, Copenhagen Univ, 41-44, secy & res assoc, 44-46; res assoc, Swarthmore Col, 46-48; res assoc, Stanford Univ, 48-49; res assoc, Col Med, Univ Cincinnati, 49-52, asst prof, 52; res assoc zool, Duke Univ, 52-54, sr res assoc, 54-57, assoc res prof, 57-64; prof biol, Case Western Reserve Univ, 64-71; RES SCIENTIST, MT DESERT ISLAND BIOL LAB, 71- *Concurrent Pos:* Guggenheim fel, 52-53; established investr, Am Heart Asn, 54-62; trustee, Mt Desert Island Biol Lab, 55-69 & 76-, vpres, 79-81, dep dir, 79-, pres, 81; Bowditch lectr, 58; mem physiol training grant comt, Nat Inst Gen Med Sci, 67-71; chmn dept biol, Case Western Reserve Univ, 70-71, adj prof, 71-; adj prof, Brown Univ, 71-; assoc ed, Am J Physiol: Regulatory, Integrative & Comp Physiol, 76-81. *Honors & Awards:* NIH Career Award, 62-64. *Mem:* Fel AAAS; Am Physiol Soc (pres, 75-76); Soc Exp Biol & Med; Am Soc Nephrology; Am Soc Zoologists. *Res:* Biochemistry of saliva; water metabolism of desert animals; osmoregulation; comparative physiology of cellular volume and ion regulation; comparative renal physiology; physiology of the mammalian renal pelvis. *Mailing Add:* Mt Desert Island Biol Lab Salisbury Cove ME 04672

SCHMIDT-NIELSEN, KNUT, b Trondheim, Norway, Sept 24, 15; m 39; c 3. PHYSIOLOGY. *Educ:* Copenhagen Univ, Mag Sc, 41, Dr Phil(zoophysiol), 46. *Prof Exp:* Res assoc, Swarthmore Col, 46-48; res assoc, Stanford Univ, 48-49; asst prof, Col Med, Univ Cincinnati, 49-52; prof, 52-63, JAMES B DUKE PROF PHYSIOL, DUKE UNIV, 63- *Concurrent Pos:* Docent, Univ Oslo, 47-49; Guggenheim fel, Univ Algeria, 53-54; consult, NSF, 57-61; trustee, Mt Desert Island Biol Lab, 58-61; Brody Mem lectr, Univ Mo, 62; regent's lectr, Univ Calif, 63; USPHS res career award, 64-; Hans Gadow lectr, Cambridge Univ, 71; mem sci adv comt, New Eng Regional Primate Res Ctr, Harvard Med Sch, 62-66; nat adv bd, Physiol Res Lab, Scripps Inst, Univ Calif, 63-69, chmn, 68-69; mem subcomt environ physiol, US Nat Comt Int Biol Prog, 65-67; US Nat Comt Int Union Physiol Sci, 66-78, vchmn, 69-78; mem comt res utilization uncommon animals, Div Biol & Agr, Nat Acad Sci, 66-68; animal resources adv comt, NIH, 68; biomed eng adv comt, Duke Univ, 68-; sect ed, Am J Physiol & J Appl Physiol, 61-64; pres, Int Union Physiol Soc, 80- *Mem:* Nat Acad Sci; fel AAAS; Am Acad Arts & Sci; Am Physiol Soc; fel NY Acad Sci. *Res:* Comparative physiology, respiration and oxygen supply; water metabolism and excretion; temperature regulation, physiology of desert animals. *Mailing Add:* Dept Zool Duke Univ Durham NC 27706

SCHMIEDER, ROBERT W, b Phoenix, Ariz, July 10, 41; m 63; c 3. ATOMIC PHYSICS. *Educ:* Occidental Col, AB, 63; Calif Inst Technol, BS, 63; Columbia Univ, MA, 65, PhD(physics), 68. *Prof Exp:* Physicist, Lawrence Berkeley Lab, 69-73; MEM TECH STAFF, SANDIA NAT LABS, 73- *Mem:* Am Phys Soc; Optical Soc Am. *Res:* Combustion physics, including spectroscopy, laser plasmas and chemical physics. *Mailing Add:* Sandia Nat Labs Livermore CA 94550

SCHMIEDESHOFF, FREDERICK WILLIAM, b Brooklyn, NY, Mar 28, 25; wid; c 3. RESEARCH ADMINISTRATION, APPLIED MECHANICS. *Educ:* Rensselear Polytech Inst, BS, 48, MS, 53, PhD(mech), 66. *Prof Exp:* Engr chg physics, Beers & Heroy Co, NY, 48-52; physicist, W & L E Gurley Co, 52; res scientist, Rensselaer Polytech Inst, 52-56, asst prof mech, 56-59; chief theoret & exp labs, Watervliet Arsenal, 59-63, dir res, 63-77; CHIEF MECH OF MAT BR, ARMY RES OFF, 77- *Concurrent Pos:* NATO consult, Adv Group Aeronaut, Res & Develop, London, 63; mem interface comt, Mat Adv Bd, Nat Acad Sci, 63-65, micromech comt, 64-65, designing with composites comt, 66-67; mem adv bd, Army Mat & Mech Res Ctr, Watertown, Mass, 70-75. *Mem:* AAAS; Sigma Xi. *Res:* Nonlinear heat conduction, thermal stresses, composite materials. *Mailing Add:* Rte 1 Box 308C Hillsborough NC 27278

SCHMIEG, GLENN MELWOOD, b Detroit, Mich, Aug 25, 38. PHYSICS. *Educ:* Univ Mich, BSE, 60, MS, 62; Univ NC, PhD(physics), 67. *Prof Exp:* ASSOC PROF PHYSICS, UNIV WIS-MILWAUKEE, 67- *Mem:* Am Asn Physics Teachers; Electrostatics Soc Am. *Res:* Classical field theory; electrostatics; mathematical physics. *Mailing Add:* Dept of Physics Univ of Wis Milwaukee WI 53201

SCHMIEGE, DONALD CHARLES, b Antigo, Wis, June 22, 27; m 52; c 3. FOREST ENTOMOLOGY. *Educ:* Univ Minnesota, BS, 52, MS, 58, PhD(entom), 62. *Prof Exp:* Forest ranger, Wis Conserv Dept, 52-54, forest entomologist, 54-57; Lake States Forest Exp Sta, US Forest Serv, 57-62, proj leader forest insect res, Northern Forest Expa Sta, 62-67, prin entomologist, Inst Northern Forestry, 67-72, PROG LEADER FORESTRY SCI LAB, PAC NORTHWEST STA, ALASKA, US FOREST SERV, 72- *Concurrent Pos:* Vis prof entom, Univ Wis-Madison, 66-67; proj leader, Insecticide Eval, Univ Calif, Berkeley, 70-72. *Mem:* Soc Am Foresters; AAAS. *Res:* Forest biology. *Mailing Add:* Box 909 Juneau AK 99802

SCHMIEGEL, WALTER WERNER, b Chemnitz, Ger, Jan 13, 41; US citizen; m 71. RUBBER CHEMISTRY. *Educ:* Univ Mich, Ann Arbor, BS, 63; Dartmouth Col, AM, 65; Johns Hopkins Univ, PhD(chem), 70. *Prof Exp:* Res chemist, 69-80, RES ASSOC, E I DU PONT DE NEMOURS & CO, INC, 80- *Mem:* Am Chem Soc; Sigma Xi. *Res:* Synthetic elastomers; Ziegler catalysis; fluoroelastomer synthesis and reactivity; vulcanization chemistry; polymer nuclear magnetic resonance. *Mailing Add:* Polymer Prod Dept DuPont Exp Sta Wilmington DE 19898

SCHMIR, GASTON L, b Metz, France, June 8, 33; US citizen; m 60; c 3. BIOCHEMISTRY, ORGANIC CHEMISTRY. *Educ:* Harvard Univ, AB, 54; PhD(biochem), Yale Univ, 58. *Prof Exp:* Asst scientist, USPHS, 58-60; from instr to assoc prof biochem, 60-69, ASSOC PROF MOLECULAR BIOPHYS, YALE UNIV, 69- *Mem:* Am Chem Soc; Am Soc Biol Chemists. *Res:* Bio-organic reaction mechanisms; enzyme models. *Mailing Add:* Dept Molecular Biophys & Biochem Yale Univ New Haven CT 06510

SCHMISSEUR, WILSON EDWARD, b East St Louis, Ill, July 17, 42; m 69; c 2. FARM MANAGEMENT, PRODUCTION ECONOMICS. *Educ:* Univ Ill, BS, 64; Purdue Univ, MS, 66, PhD(agr econ), 73. *Prof Exp:* Res assoc, 71-79, asst prof, 79-81, ASSOC PROF AGR ECON, ORE STATE UNIV, 81- *Concurrent Pos:* Consult, Ethanol Int, Inc, 79. *Res:* Economics of livestock production; range management issues in the high desert region of the western United States. *Mailing Add:* Dept Agr & Resource Econ Ore State Univ Corvallis OR 97330

SCHMIT, JOSEPH LAWRENCE, b Cold Springs, Minn, July 22, 33; m 56; c 6. PHYSICS, CRYSTAL GROWTH. *Educ:* St John's Univ, BA, 57. *Prof Exp:* RES SCIENTIST PHYSICS, HONEYWELL MAT SCI CTR, HONEYWELL INC, 59- *Mem:* Am Phys Soc; AAAS; Fedn Am Scientists. *Res:* Growth and evaluation of HgCdTe suitable for infrared detectors; growth by Bridgman and by open-tube slider LPE; developed technique to measure composition, measurement of the band gap and calculation of the intrinsic carrier concentration of HgCdTe. *Mailing Add:* Honeywell Inc 10701 Lyndale Ave S Bloomington MN 55420

SCHMIT, LUCIEN A(NDRE), JR, b New York, NY, May 5, 28; m 51; c 1. STRUCTURAL MECHANICS. *Educ:* Mass Inst Technol, SB, 49, SM, 50. *Prof Exp:* Struct engr, Grumman Aircraft Eng Corp, 51-53; res engr, Aeroelastic & Struct Res Lab, Mass Inst Technol, 54-58; from asst prof to prof struct, Case Western Reserve Univ, 58-69, Wilbert J Austin distinguished prof eng, 69-70, head div solid mech, struct & mech design, 66-70; chmn, Dept Mech & Struct, 76-79, PROF ENG & APPL SCI, UNIV CALIF, LOS ANGELES, 70- *Concurrent Pos:* Mem, Sci Adv Bd, USAF, 77-, struct & mat panel, Adv Group Aerospace Res & Develop, NATO, 81- *Honors & Awards:* Walter L Huber Civil Eng Res Prize, 70; AIAA Struct Design Lect Award, 77; Struct Dynamics & Mat Award, Am Inst Aeronaut & Astronaut Struct, 79. *Mem:* Fel Am Soc Civil Engrs; assoc fel Am Inst Aeronaut & Astronaut; Am Soc Mech Engrs. *Res:* Analysis and synthesis of structural systems; design optimization; finite element methods; nonlinear analysis; design methods for fiber composite structures. *Mailing Add:* 6731K Boelter Hall Univ of Calif Los Angeles CA 90024

SCHMITENDORF, WILLIAM E, b Oak Park, Ill, Aug 6, 41; m 64; c 2. ENGINEERING. *Educ:* Purdue Univ, BS, 63, MS, 65, PhD(optimization tech), 68. *Prof Exp:* From asst prof to assoc prof, 67-78, PROF MECH ENG, NORTHWESTERN UNIV, 78- *Concurrent Pos:* Assoc ed, Inst Elec & Electronics Engrs, Transactions Automatic Control, 80- & J Optimization Theory, 80- *Mem:* Inst Elec & Electronics Engrs. *Res:* Optimal control problems; zero-sum and nonzero-sum differential games; optimization problems with vector-valued criteria; controllability problems; minmox problems. *Mailing Add:* Technol Inst Dept of Mech Eng Northwestern Univ Evanston IL 60201

SCHMITT, ANTHONY PAUL, inorganic chemistry, electrochemistry, see previous edition

SCHMITT, CHARLES RUDOLPH, b New York, NY Mar 31, 20; m 45; c 2. APPLIED CHEMISTRY. *Educ:* Queens Col, NY, BS, 42. *Prof Exp:* Supvr, Plum Brook Ord Works, Sandusky, Ohio, 42-43; pross mech, Spec Eng Detachment, US Army, Oak Ridge, Tenn, 44-45; tech engr, K-25 Plant, Union Carbide Corp, Oak Ridge, Tenn, 46-49, develop engr & specialist, 50-75, supvr develop, Y-12 Plant, 75-80; SR SCIENTIST, BECHTEL CORP, OAK RIDGE, TENN, 81- *Concurrent Pos:* Consult, Rust Eng Co, 70-75. *Mem:* Am Chem Soc; Nat Soc Prof Engrs. *Res:* Polymerization of polyfurfuryl alcohol resins; dezincification of brass in sea water; metallurgy studies of high purity tungsten; uranium solubility and corrosion studies; water treatment for scale and corrosion control. *Mailing Add:* 110 Adelphi Rd Oak Ridge TN 27830

SCHMITT, DONALD PETER, b New Hampton, Iowa, Oct 29, 41; m 67; c 4. PLANT NEMATOLOGY, PLANT PATHOLOGY. *Educ:* Iowa State Univ, BS, 67, MS, 69, PhD(plant path), 71. *Prof Exp:* Plant pathologist & nematologist plant disease, Div Plant Industs, Tenn Dept Agr, 71-75; PLANT PATHOLOGIST & NEMATOLOGIST SOYBEANS, DEPT PLANT PATH, N C STATE UNIV, 75- *Mem:* Am Phytopath Soc; Soc Nematologists; Sigma Xi. *Res:* Ecology of nematodes on soybean; epidemiology of soybean diseases caused by nematodes. *Mailing Add:* Dept of Plant Path NC State Univ Box 5397 Raleigh NC 27607

SCHMITT, ERICH, b Sandhausen, Ger, Jan 7, 28; m 56; c 1. COMPUTER SCIENCE. *Educ:* Univ Karlsruhe, Dipl Ing, 60, Dr Ing(elec eng), 64, Venia legendi, 67. *Prof Exp:* Dir res dept, Inst Info Processing, Univ Karlsruhe, 64-67; chief adv avionics, Bell Aerosysts Co, 67-68; ASSOC PROF COMPUT SCI, STATE UNIV NY BUFFALO, 68- *Mem:* Asn Comput Mach; Inst Elec & Electronics Engrs. *Res:* Adaptive computing methods; pattern recognition; automatic design; theory on adaptive automata; information theory and coding. *Mailing Add:* Dept of Elec Eng State Univ of NY Buffalo NY 14201

SCHMITT, FRANCIS OTTO, b St Louis, Mo, Nov 23, 03; m 27; c 3. BIOLOGY. *Educ:* Wash Univ, AB, 24, PhD(physiol), 27. *Hon Degrees:* Numerous from US & foreign univs, 50-81. *Prof Exp:* Nat Res Coun fel chem, Univ Calif, Berkeley, 27-28, Univ London, 28-29 & Kaiser Wilhelm Inst, 29; from asst prof to prof zool, Wash Univ, 29-40, head dept, 40-41; prof biol, 41-55, head dept, 42-55, inst prof, 55-69, EMER INST PROF BIOL, MASS INST TECHNOL, 69-, FOUND SCIENTIST, NEUROSCI RES, 77-

Concurrent Pos: Trustee, Mass Gen Hosp, 47-; mem, study sect morphol & genetics, NIH, 49-53, chmn, study sect biophys & biophys chem, 54-58; mem, Nat Adv Health Coun, 59-62; Gen Med Sci Coun, 69-71; bd sci consults, Sloan-Kettering Inst Cancer Res, 63-72; chmn neurosci res prog, 62-74, chmn res found, 62- *Honors & Awards:* Alsop Award, Am Leather Chem Asn, 47; Lasker Award, Am Pub Health Asn, 56; T Duckett Jones Award, Helen Hay Whitney Found, 63. *Mem:* Nat Acad Sci; Soc Develop Biol (treas, Soc Growth & Develop, 45-56, pres, 47); Electron Micros Soc Am (pres, 49); NY Acad Sci; Soc Neurosci. *Res:* Molecular biology; investigation of molecular organization of tissues, particularly of nerve, connective tissue and muscle, by biophysical and physical-chemical means; integration of all disciplinary levels in study of physical basis of brain function. *Mailing Add:* Neurosci Res Prog 165 Allandale St Boston MA 02130

SCHMITT, GEORGE JOSEPH, b Farmingdale, NY, June 21, 28; m 52; c 4. POLYMER CHEMISTRY. *Educ:* Polytech Inst Brooklyn, BS, 50; State Univ NY Col Forestry, Syracuse Univ, PhD(chem), 60. *Prof Exp:* Develop chemist, Am Cyanamid Co, 53-57; sr res chemist, cent res lab, Allied Chem Corp, 60-61; res supvr polymer chem, 61-62, dir lab res, 62-64, asst dir cent res lab, 64-68, mgr polymer sci, Corp Res Lab, 68-80, DIR CORP POLYMER LAB, ALLIED CORP, 80- *Concurrent Pos:* mem bd dirs, Res & Develop Coun, NJ, 81- *Mem:* Am Chem Soc; Sigma Xi. *Res:* Free radical, ionic and condensation polymerization; fibers; polymer composites; membranes. *Mailing Add:* Chem Res Ctr Allied Chem Corp Box 1021R Morristown NJ 07960

SCHMITT, HAROLD WILLIAM, b Sequin, Tex, Aug 11, 28; m 52; c 3. NUCLEAR PHYSICS. *Educ:* Univ Tex, BA, 48, MA, 52, PhD(physics), 54. *Prof Exp:* Asst physics, Los Alamos Sci Lab, 52-54; physicist, Oak Ridge Nat Lab, 58-80, group leader, Physics of Fission Group, 60-80; MEM STAFF, ATOM SCI INC, 80- *Concurrent Pos:* Founding pres & chmn bd dirs, Ortec, Inc, 60-64; guest scientist, Nuclear Res Ctr, Karlsruhe, Ger, 66-67; guest prof, Munich Tech Univ, 69 & Univ Frankfurt, 70; on leave, pres, Environ Systs Corp, Knoxville, Tenn, 73- *Mem:* AAAS; fel Am Phys Soc; Sigma Xi; Am Chem Soc; Am Soc Testing & Mat. *Res:* Fission physics; neutron physics; nuclear reactions; accelerators; reactors; detectors; instrumentation; energy and environmental sciences. *Mailing Add:* Atom Sci Inc 114 Ridgeway Ctr Oak Ridge TN 37830

SCHMITT, JOHN ALOYSIUS, b Grand Rapids, Mich, Mar 9, 21; m 51; c 11. PHYSICAL CHEMISTRY. *Educ:* Univ Detroit, BS, 43, MS, 48; Univ Wis, PhD(chem), 53. *Prof Exp:* Res chemist, Upjohn Co, 48-50; res dept, Standard Oil Co (Ind), 50-56; res chemist, 56-76, SR RES SPECIALIST, DOW CHEM CO, 76- *Res:* Nutrition; antimetabolites; relative reaction ratio of carbon isotopes; asphalt aging; emulsion polymerization; polymer synthesis and properties; paper coating structure and properties. *Mailing Add:* Designed Latexes & Resins Bldg 1604 Dow Chemical Co Midland MI 48640

SCHMITT, JOHN ARVID, JR, b Buffalo, NY, July 30, 25; m 47; c 2. MEDICAL MYCOLOGY. *Educ:* Univ Mich, BS, 49, MS, 50, PhD(mycol), 54. *Prof Exp:* Prof biol & head dept, Findlay Col, 53-54; asst prof, Univ Miss, 54-55; instr bot & plant path, 55-57, from asst prof to assoc prof, 57-69, assoc prof med microbiol, 66-71, chmn dept bot, 69-74, adj assoc prof med, Col Med, 67-74, PROF BOT, OHIO STATE UNIV, 69- *Concurrent Pos:* Consult mycol, Merrell-Nat Labs & Allergy Labs Ohio, Inc, 65- & Philips Roxane Labs, 74- *Mem:* Mycol Soc Am; Am Soc Microbiol; Bot Soc Am; Med Mycol Soc of the Americas; Fedn Socs for Coating Technol. *Res:* Medical mycology; zoopathogenic fungi, especially Candida albicans; paint mildew fungi; microbial succession in the establishment of paint mildew. *Mailing Add:* Dept of Botany Ohio State Univ Columbus OH 43210

SCHMITT, JOHN LEIGH, b Newberry, Mich, July 30, 41; m 66; c 1. INSTRUMENTATION, ASTRONOMY. *Educ:* Mich Col Mining & Technol, BS, 63; Univ Mich, MS, 64, PhD(astron), 68. *Prof Exp:* Fel & part-time lectr astron, Univ Toronto, 68-69; asst prof physics, Southwestern at Memphis, 69-74; vis asst prof, 74-76, RES ASST PROF PHYSICS, UNIV MO-ROLLA, 76- *Mem:* Am Astron Soc; Am Optic Soc. *Res:* Vapor to liquid nucleation, instrumentation and astronomical spectroscopy. *Mailing Add:* Ctr for Cloud Physics Univ of Mo Rolla MO 65401

SCHMITT, JOSEPH LAWRENCE, JR, b Cumberland, Md, Sept 22, 41; m 63; c 2. PHYSICAL CHEMISTRY. *Educ:* Shippensburg State Col, BS, 63; Bowling Green State Univ, MA, 67; Pa State Univ, PhD(fuel sci), 70. *Prof Exp:* Teacher pub sch, Pa, 63-67; res chemist, 70-74, sr res chemist, 74-77, PROJ LEADER, AM CYANAMID CO, 77- *Mem:* Am Chem Soc; Catalysis Soc; AAAS. *Res:* Heterogeneous catalysis; surface chemistry; carbon chemistry. *Mailing Add:* Chem Res Div Am Cyanamid Co Stamford CT 06904

SCHMITT, JOSEPH MICHAEL, b Louisville, Ky, Feb 9, 30; m 52; c 6. POLYMER CHEMISTRY. *Educ:* Univ Louisville, BS, 51, PhD(chem), 57. *Prof Exp:* Res chemist, 57-62, SR RES CHEMIST, AM CYANAMID CO, 62- *Mem:* Am Chem Soc. *Res:* Plastics; homopolymers, copolymers, multipolymer blends and properties; flocculants; polymers for water treatment. *Mailing Add:* Chem Res Div Am Cyanamid Co 1937 W Main St Stamford CT 06904

SCHMITT, KLAUS, b Rimbach, Ger, May 14, 40; US citizen; m 62; c 2. MATHEMATICS. *Educ:* St Olaf Col, BA, 62; Univ Nebr, MA, 64, PhD(math), 67. *Prof Exp:* Asst prof math, Nebr Wesleyan Univ, 66-67; from asst prof to assoc prof, 67-75, PROF MATH, UNIV UTAH, 75- *Concurrent Pos:* Res grants, NASA, 67, NSF, 69-71 & US Army, 71-; vis prof, Univ Wurzburg & Univ Karlsruhe, Ger, 73-74; Alexander von Humboldt sr US scientist award, 78-79. *Mem:* AAAS; Math Asn Am; Am Math Soc. *Res:* Differential equations; nonlinear analysis; functional differential equations. *Mailing Add:* Dept of Math Univ of Utah Salt Lake City UT 84112

SCHMITT, NEIL MARTIN, b Pekin, Ill, Oct 25, 40; m 63; c 2. BIOMEDICAL ENGINEERING. *Educ:* Univ Ark, Fayetteville, BSEE, 63, MSEE, 64; Southern Methodist Univ, PhD(elec eng), 69. *Prof Exp:* Systs engr, IBM Corp, 66-67; engr, Tex Instruments, Inc, 67-70; assoc prof, 70-80, PROF ELEC ENG, UNIV ARK, FAYETTEVILLE, 80- *Concurrent Pos:* NSF res grant elec eng, Univ Ark, Fayetteville, 71-72. *Mem:* Inst Elec & Electronics Engrs; Biomed Eng Soc; Asn Advan Med Instrumentation; Am Soc Eng Educ. *Res:* Health care delivery systems; early detection of heart disease. *Mailing Add:* E204 Col Eng Univ Ark Fayetteville AR 72701

SCHMITT, OTTO HERBERT, b St Louis, Mo, Apr 6, 13; m 37. BIOPHYSICS, BIOMEDICAL ENGINEERING. *Educ:* Washington Univ, AB, 34, PhD(physics, zool), 37. *Prof Exp:* Nat Res Coun fel, Univ Col, London, 38, Sir Halley Stewart fel, 39; from instr to prof zool & physics, 39-80, prof biophys, 49-80, prof elec eng, 68-80, PROF BIOMED ENG, UNIV MINN, MINNEAPOLIS, 73- *Concurrent Pos:* Off investr, Nat Defense Res Comt Contract, 40-42; res engr, Columbia Univ, 42-43; supvr engr, Spec Devices Div, Airborne Instruments Lab, NY, 43-47; consult, USPHS & Inst Defense Anal; mem adv panel, Space Sci Bd Biol & Psychol, 58-61; chmn exec coun bioastronaut, Joint Armed Forces-Nat Acad Sci, 58-61. *Honors & Awards:* Lovelace Award, 60; Morlock Award, Inst Elec & Electronics Engrs, 63; Wetherill Medal, Franklin Inst, 72. *Mem:* Nat Acad Eng; fel Am Phys Soc; Biophys Soc; Am Physiol Soc; Am Inst Aeronaut & Astronaut. *Res:* Nerve impulse mechanisms; tridimensional oscilloscopic displays; bivalent computers; biological tissue impedance analyses; direct current transformers; trigger circuits; electronic plethysmography; antenna radiation pattern measurements; stereovectorelectrocardiography; phase space displays; bioastronautics; biomimetics; electromagneto biology; technical optimization of biomedical communication and control systems. *Mailing Add:* Biophys Group 200 TNCE Dept Elec Eng Univ of Minn Minneapolis MN 55455

SCHMITT, RAYMOND W, JR, b Pittsburgh, Pa, Mar 18, 50; m 81. PHYSICAL OCEANOGRAPHY. *Educ:* Carnegie-Mellon Univ, BS, 72; Univ RI, PhD(oceanog), 78. *Prof Exp:* Res assoc, Grad Sch Oceanog, Univ RI, 77-78; fel, 78-79, investr, 79-80, ASST SCIENTIST, WOODS HOLE OCEANOG INST, 80- *Mem:* Am Geophys Union; AAAS. *Res:* Oceanic mixing and microstructure; double-diffusive convection (salt fingers); geophysical fluid dynamics. *Mailing Add:* Woods Hole Oceanog Inst Woods Hole MA 02543

SCHMITT, ROLAND WALTER, b Seguin, Tex, July 24, 23; m 51, 57; c 4. SOLID STATE PHYSICS. *Educ:* Univ Tex, BA & BS, 47, MA, 48; Rice Inst, PhD(physics), 51. *Prof Exp:* Res assoc physics, Res Lab, Gen Elec Co, 51-57, mgr mat studies sect, 57-65; res assoc, Div Eng & Appl Physics, Grad Sch Pub Admin, Harvard Univ, 65; mgr, Metall & Ceramics Lab, 66-67, res & develop mgr phys sci & eng, 67-74, res & develop mgr, Energy Sci & Eng, 74-78, VPRES CORP RES & DEVELOP GEN ELEC RES & DEVELOP CTR, 78- *Concurrent Pos:* Mem, Liaison Subcomt Mgt & Technol, Nat Acad Sci Adv Comt IIASA, Panel Condensed Matter, Physics Surv Comt & Comt on Surv Mat Sci & Eng; mem, Energy Adv Bd, Walt Disney Enterprises; mem vis comt, Elec Eng Dept, Univ Tex; chmn eval panel, Inst Basic Standards, Nat Bur Standards; mem, Nat Res Coun Solid State Sci Comt & Comt Nat Progs, Numerical Data Adv Bd. *Mem:* Nat Acad Eng; fel Am Phys Soc; sr mem Inst Elec & Electronics Engrs; AAAS; Am Nuclear Soc. *Mailing Add:* Gen Elec Res & Develop Ctr Bldg K-1 PO Box 8 Schenectady NY 12301

SCHMITT, ROMAN A, b Johnsburg, Ill, Nov 13, 25; m 54; c 4. PHYSICAL CHEMISTRY. *Educ:* Univ Chicago, MS, 50, PhD(nuclear chem), 53. *Prof Exp:* Instr nuclear chem, Univ Ill, 53-54, res assoc, 54-56; res scientist chem, Gen Atomic Div, Gen Dynamics Corp, 56-66; assoc prof, 66-69, PROF CHEM, ORE STATE UNIV, 69- *Concurrent Pos:* Consult, NASA, 71-75. *Honors & Awards:* George P Merrill Award, Nat Acad Sci, 72. *Mem:* Fel AAAS; Am Chem Soc; Geochem Soc; fel Meteoritical Soc. *Res:* Neutron activation analysis of rare earth elements and other elements in meteorites; terrestrial and lunar matter; cosmochemistry. *Mailing Add:* Dept of Chem Ore State Univ Corvallis OR 97331

SCHMITT, WALTER R, b Ludwigshafen, Ger, Oct 6, 25; m 56; c 3. OCEANOGRAPHY. *Educ:* Karlsruhe Tech Univ, Vordiplom, 49; Munich Tech Univ, Diplom, 53. *Prof Exp:* Aeronaut engr, Canadair, Ltd, 52-53; electronic engr, Can Aviation Electronics, 53-54; explor geophysicist, Shell Oil Co Can, 54-61; OCEANOGR, SCRIPPS INST OCEANOG, UNIV CALIF, SAN DIEGO, 61- *Concurrent Pos:* Mem coun on energy & & adv comt on appropriate technol, Univ Calif. *Mem:* World Acad Art & Sci. *Res:* Marine resources; food and water resources; energy resources of the oceans, their potentials and environmental effects. *Mailing Add:* Scripps Inst of Oceanog Mail Code A-027 La Jolla CA 92093

SCHMITTER, RUTH ELIZABETH, b Detroit, Mich. CELL BIOLOGY, PHYCOLOGY. *Educ:* Mich State Univ, BS, 64; Univ Edinburgh, MSc, 66; Harvard Univ, PhD(biol), 73. *Prof Exp:* Sr technician electron micros, AEC Plant Res Lab, Mich State Univ, 66-67; res fel biol, Harvard Univ, 73-74; Brown fel bot, Yale Univ, 74-75; ASST PROF BIOL, UNIV MASS, BOSTON, 75- *Concurrent Pos:* Fulbright scholar, Int Inst Educ, 64-66. *Mem:* Am Soc Cell Biol; Am Phycol Soc; Electron Micros Soc Am; Brit Phycol Soc. *Res:* Cell ultrastructure, especially functional correlates of dinoflagellate fine structure, and organelle development; algal physiology, including algal nutriton; biochemistry of bioluminescence. *Mailing Add:* Biol Dept Univ Mass Boston MA 02125

SCHMITTHENNER, AUGUST FREDRICK, b Kotagiri, SIndia, Apr 16, 26; US citizen; m 54; c 2. PLANT PATHOLOGY. *Educ:* Gettysburg Col, BA, 49; Ohio State Univ, MSc, 51, PhD(bot), 53. *Prof Exp:* From instr to assoc prof, 52-66, PROF PLANT PATH, OHIO AGR RES & DEVELOP CTR & OHIO STATE UNIV, 66- *Mem:* Am Phytopath Soc. *Res:* Forage crop, soybean and root rot diseases; physiology of oomycetes and parasitism; photobiology; bean diseases. *Mailing Add:* Dept of Plant Path Ohio Agr Res & Develop Ctr Wooster OH 44691

SCHMITTLE, SAMUEL CONRAD, b Altoona, Pa, Apr 9, 25; m 47; c 2. VETERINARY PATHOLOGY. *Educ:* Ohio State Univ, DVM, 47; Univ Ill, MS, 49, PhD(vet path), 52. *Prof Exp:* Asst vet path & hyg, Univ Ill, 47-49, instr, 49-52; asst prof poultry path, Univ Ga, 52-53; assoc prof, Mich State Univ, 53-57; prof poultry path & dir poultry dis res ctr, Univ Ga, 57-69; res pathologist, Vantress Farms, Inc, Ga, 69-72; exec vpres & gen mgr, Vantress Biologics, Inc, 72-73; prof vet sci, Miss State Univ, 74-76; STAFF MEM, STERWIN LAB, 76- *Concurrent Pos:* Consult, Bur Vet Med, Food & Drug Admin, Dept HEW, 68-71 & Poultry Inspection Br, Consumer & Mkt Serv, USDA. *Mem:* Am Vet Med Asn; Poultry Sci Asn. *Res:* Serology of Newcastle disease of poultry; chronic respiratory disease; toxic fat disorder; crotalaria seed poisoning; diseases of the avian leukosis complex and control of poultry diseases. *Mailing Add:* Sterwin Lab PO Box 537 Millsboro DE 19966

SCHMITZ, EUGENE H, b Wamego, Kans, Aug 13, 34; m 60; c 2. INVERTEBRATE ZOOLOGY, LIMNOLOGY. *Educ:* Univ Kans, AB, 56; Univ Colo, MA, 58, PhD(zool), 61. *Prof Exp:* Instr biol, Univ Colo, 59-60; from asst prof to assoc prof zool, La State Univ, 61-65; from asst prof to assoc prof, 65-74, PROF ZOOL, UNIV ARK, FAYETTEVILLE, 74- *Mem:* Am Soc Zool; Am Micros Soc; Am Soc Limnol & Oceanog; Sigma Xi. *Res:* Invertebrate morphology; plankton limnology. *Mailing Add:* Dept of Zool Univ of Ark Fayetteville AR 72701

SCHMITZ, FRANCIS JOHN, b Raymond, Iowa, Jan 18, 32; m 61; c 3. NATURAL PRODUCTS CHEMISTRY, MARINE CHEMISTRY. *Educ:* Maryknoll Sem, BA, 54; Loras Col, BS, 58; Univ Calif, Berkeley, PhD, 61. *Prof Exp:* NIH fel, Stanford Univ, 61-62, NSF fel, 62-63; from asst prof to assoc prof, 63-71, PROF CHEM, UNIV OKLA, 71- *Mem:* Am Chem Soc; The Chem Soc; Marine Technol Soc; Int Oceanog Found. *Res:* Structure determination of natural products, emphasis on marine natural products; synthesis of natural products; chemistry of sulfur compounds. *Mailing Add:* Dept of Chem Univ of Okla 620 Parrington Oval Norman OK 73069

SCHMITZ, GEORGE WILLIAM, b Minneapolis, Minn, Dec 15, 19. AGRONOMY. *Educ:* Univ Ariz, BS, 48; Ohio State Univ, MS, 50, PhD(soils), 52. *Prof Exp:* Sr agronomist, Zonolite Res Lab, 52-56; res agronomist, Calif Spray Chem Corp Div, Standard Oil Co, Calif, 56-60; asst prof agron, Fresno State Col, 60-66; assoc prof, 66-72, prof agron, 72-77, PROF PLANT & SOIL SCI, CALIF STATE POLYTECH UNIV, POMONA, 77- *Res:* Soil fertility; plant physiology. *Mailing Add:* Dept of Plant & Soil Sci Calif State Polytech Univ Pomona CA 91768

SCHMITZ, HAROLD GREGORY, b Helena, Mont, Aug 31, 43; m 66; c 4. ELECTRICAL ENGINEERING. *Educ:* Carroll Col, Mont, BA, 65; Mont State Univ, BS, 66, MS, 67, PhD(elec eng), 70. *Prof Exp:* Res engr, Mont State Univ, 69-70; prin investr comput technol, Honeywell Systs & Res Ctr, 70-76, SECT CHIEF, COMPUT SYSTS TECHNOL, HONEYWELL INC, 76- *Mem:* Inst Elec & Electronics Engrs. *Res:* Research and advanced development in the area of computer architecture and organization. *Mailing Add:* Comput Systs Technol 2600 Ridgeway Pkwy Minneapolis MN 55413

SCHMITZ, HENRY, b Vienna, Austria, Oct 2, 17; nat US; m 40; c 2. ORGANIC CHEMISTRY. *Educ:* NY Univ, BA, 47; Rutgers Univ, MS & PhD(org chem), 50. *Prof Exp:* Res chemist, J T Baker Chem Co, Vick Chem Co, 50-55; sr res scientist, Bristol Labs Div, Bristol-Myers Co, 55-81. *Concurrent Pos:* Adj prof, Onondaga Community Col, Syracuse, 80- *Mem:* Am Chem Soc. *Res:* Steroids; antibiotics; natural products. *Mailing Add:* 323 DeForest Rd Syracuse NY 13214

SCHMITZ, JOHN ALBERT, b Silverton, Ore, Oct 21, 40; m 71. VETERINARY PATHOLOGY & MICROBIOLOGY. *Educ:* Colo State Univ, DVM, 64; Univ Mo-Columbia, PhD(path), 71. *Prof Exp:* Res assoc vet path, Univ Mo-Columbia, 68-71; asst prof vet sci, Univ Nebr, 71-72; assoc prof, 72-78, PROF VET MED, ORE STATE UNIV, 78-, DIR VET DIAG LAB, 78- *Mem:* Am Col Vet Pathologists; Int Acad Path; Am Vet Med Asn. *Res:* Infectious diseases of food-producing animals. *Mailing Add:* Sch of Vet Med Ore State Univ Corvallis OR 97331

SCHMITZ, JOHN VINCENT, b Dubuque, Iowa, Nov 15, 22; m 46; c 6. ORGANIC CHEMISTRY. *Educ:* Loras Col, BS, 44; Ohio State Univ, PhD(chem), 49; Harvard Bus Sch, AMP, 70. *Prof Exp:* Asst, Ohio State Univ, 47-49; res assoc, Res Lab, Gen Elec Co, 49-54, prod engr chem div, 54-57, tech leader chem lab, Major Appliance Div, 57-58, mgr chem res, Major Appliance Chem Lab, 58-64; mgr tech ctr, Celanese Chem Co, 64-66, tech dir, 66-68, vpres & tech dir, 68-71, tech dir chem, Celanese Corp, 71-73; vpres tech div, Loctite Corp, 73-75; mgr spec projs, Air Prods & Chem, 75-76; vpres phys & life sci, Franklin Res Ctr, 76-81; CHMN, TECHNOL HELP, INC, 81- *Mem:* Am Chem Soc; fel Am Inst Chemists; Am Acad Advan Sci; Soc Plastics Engrs; Am Inst Chem Engrs. *Res:* Petrochemicals; polymerization and properties of plastics; synthetic organic and radiation chemistry; environmental sciences; synthetic fuels; biotechnology; new ventures. *Mailing Add:* 2024 Mt Vernon St Philadelphia PA 19130

SCHMITZ, KENNETH STANLEY, b St Louis, Mo, Sept 6, 43; m 75; c 2. BIOPHYSICAL CHEMISTRY. *Educ:* Greenville Col, BA, 66; Univ Wash, PhD(chem), 72. *Prof Exp:* NIH fel, Univ Wash, 72 & Stanford Univ, 72-73; asst prof chem, Fla Atlantic Univ, 73-75; asst prof, 75-79, ASSOC PROF CHEM, UNIV MO-KANSAS CITY, 79- *Mem:* AAAS; Am Chem Soc; Biophys Soc; Sigma Xi. *Res:* Conformational changes in biopolymers determined by quasielastic light scattering; theory of diffusion-controlled reactions; effect of cooperativity on binding isotherms; nonequilibrium thermodynamics. *Mailing Add:* Dept of Chem Univ of Mo Kansas City MO 64110

SCHMITZ, NORBERT LEWIS, b Green Bay, Wis, May 18, 21; m 50; c 4. ELECTRICAL ENGINEERING. *Educ:* Univ Wis, BS, 42, MS, 47, PhD, 51. *Prof Exp:* Instr, Eve Tech Div, Milwaukee Voc Sch, 44-45; instr elec eng, Marquette Univ, 45-46; from instr to assoc prof, 47-60, PROF ELEC ENG,

UNIV WIS-MADISON, 60- *Concurrent Pos:* Elec engr, Cutler Hammer Inc, 42-46, consult, 46-47; consult, Gisholt Mach Co, 51, John Oster Mfg Co, 55-57, Sundstrand Aviation Co, 57-, Caterpillar Tractor Co, 61-70 & Marathon Elec Mfg Corp, 64-72. *Mem:* AAAS; Am Soc Eng Educ; Inst Elec & Electronics Engrs; fel NY Acad Sci. *Res:* Electric machine theory and control; industrial control; power semiconductor applications. *Mailing Add:* Dept of Elec Eng Univ of Wis-Madison Madison WI 53706

SCHMITZ, ROBERT L, b Chicago, Ill, Mar 10, 14; m; c 5. CANCER. *Educ:* Univ Chicago, BS, 36, MD, 38; Am Bd Surg, dipl, 48. *Prof Exp:* From assoc clin prof to clin prof surg, Stritch Sch Med, Loyola Univ Chicago, 46-72; PROF SURG, UNIV ILL, 72- *Concurrent Pos:* Assoc attend surgeon, Mercy Hosp, Chicago, 46-58, sr attend surgeon, 58- *Mem:* Am Cancer Soc; AMA; fel Am Col Surg. *Res:* Surgical oncology. *Mailing Add:* Dept Surg Mercy Hosp & Med Ctr Stevenson Expressway & King Dr Chicago IL 60616

SCHMITZ, ROGER A(NTHONY), b Carlyle, Ill, Oct 22, 34; m 57; c 3. CHEMICAL ENGINEERING. *Educ:* Univ Ill, BS, 59; Univ Minn, PhD(chem eng), 62. *Prof Exp:* Instr chem eng, Univ Minn, 60-62; from asst prof to assoc prof chem eng, Univ Ill, 62-71, prof, 71-79; chmn, 79-81, KEATING-CRAWFORD PROF CHEM ENG, UNIV NOTRE DAME, 79-, DEAN ENG, 81- *Concurrent Pos:* Guggenheim fel, 68-69. *Honors & Awards:* Colburn Award, Am Inst Chem Engrs, 70; Westinghouse Award, Am Soc Eng Educ, 77; Wilhelm Award, Am Inst Chem Engrs, 81. *Mem:* Am Inst Chem Engrs; Combustion Inst; Am Chem Soc; Am Soc Eng Educ. *Res:* Dynamics of chemical reaction systems. *Mailing Add:* Col Eng Univ Notre Dame Notre Dame IN 46556

SCHMITZ, WILLIAM JOSEPH, JR, b Houston, Tex, Dec 20, 37; m 59; c 4. PHYSICAL OCEANOGRAPHY. *Educ:* Univ Miami, ScB, 61, PhD(phys oceanog), 66. *Prof Exp:* Res aide, Univ Miami, 59-61; instr, Univ Miami, 64-66; fel, Nova Univ, 66-67; asst scientist, 67-71, assoc scientist, 71-79, SR SCIENTIST, WOODS HOLE OCEANOG INST, 79- *Mem:* Am Geophys Union. *Res:* Low-frequency ocean circulation. *Mailing Add:* Woods Hole Oceanog Inst Woods Hole MA 02543

SCHMITZ, WILLIAM ROBERT, b Wauwatosa, Wis, Jan 24, 24; m 51; c 2. LIMNOLOGY, FISH BIOLOGY. *Educ:* Univ Wis, BS, 51, MS, 53, PhD(zool), 58. *Prof Exp:* Asst zool, Univ Wis, 52-54, proj asst, 54-58, proj assoc, 58-59, instr biol, Ctr Syst, 59-60, asst prof, 60-66, chmn dept bot & zool, Ctr Syst, 67-70, assoc prof, 66-76, asst dir, Trout Lake Res Sta, 67-77, PROF ZOOL, UNIV WIS, 76- *Mem:* Am Fisheries Soc; Am Soc Limnol & Oceanog; Soc Int Limnol. *Res:* Hydrobiology; limnology, especially of ice-bound lakes; fisheries biology. *Mailing Add:* Univ of Wis 518 S Seventh Ave Wausau WI 54401

SCHMUCKER, DOUGLAS LEES, b McKeesport, Pa, Jan 22, 44. CELLULAR BIOLOGY, ANATOMY. *Educ:* Kenyon Col, AB, 65; Clark Univ, MA, 68, PhD(biol), 72. *Prof Exp:* asst prof, 75-80, ASSOC PROF ANAT, UNIV CALIF, SAN FRANCISCO, 80-; RES BIOLOGIST, VET ADMIN MED CTR, SAN FRANCISCO, 73-, ASST CHIEF, CELL BIOL & AGING SECT, 80- *Concurrent Pos:* NIH grant, 72-73; fel anat, Nat Inst Aging grant, 77-81; Sigma Xi lectr, 81. *Mem:* Soc Exp Biol & Med; Am Soc Cell Biol; fel Geront Soc; Am Asn Anatomists; Am Aging Asn. *Res:* Age-related changes in cellular structure and function; mechanisms of hepatic bile secretion; mechanisms of drug actions; liver pathology; lipid metabolism; lipoprotein synthesis and secretion; drug metabolism. *Mailing Add:* Cell Biol Sect 151-E 4150 Clement St San Francisco CA 94121

SCHMUCKLER, JOSEPH S, b Philadelphia, Pa, Feb 15, 27; m 50; c 4. SCIENCE EDUCATION. *Educ:* Univ Pa, BS, 52, MS, 54, EdD(chem educ), 68. *Prof Exp:* Instr sci educ, Univ Pa, 64-67; assoc prof sci, 68-73, PROF CHEM & SCI, TEMPLE UNIV, 73-, CHMN DEPT SCI EDUC, 69- *Concurrent Pos:* Teacher, Pa High Sch, 53-68; partic, Chem Educ Mat Study Prog; consult, Sadtler Res Lab, 54-62; mem bd gov, Chem Bd Proj Corp, 64-67; pres, Chem Proj Corp, 80-81; prof chem educ, Tianjin Normal Univ, Repub China, 80- *Honors & Awards:* Serv Award, Am Chem Soc, 67, James Bryant Conant Award, 68; Benjamin Rush Medal, Chem Indust Coun, 68. *Mem:* Am Chem Soc; Nat Sci Teachers Asn; Franklin Inst; fel Am Inst Chemists. *Res:* Chemistry; organic synthesis; science education at the secondary school level; chemistry education. *Mailing Add:* Dept of Sec Educ Temple Univ Philadelphia PA 19122

SCHMUDDE, THEODORE HENRY, physical geography, resource geography, see previous edition

SCHMUDE, KEITH E, b Rockford, Ill, Feb 10, 34; m 55; c 2. PHYSICAL CHEMISTRY. *Educ:* Carroll Col, BS, 55; Univ Rochester, PhD(chem), 59. *Prof Exp:* Assoc physicist, Armour Res Found, 59-61; from asst prof to assoc prof chem, Parsons Col, 61-64; res chemist, Dacron Res Lab, 64-68, SR RES CHEMIST, TEXTILE RES LAB, E I DU PONT DE NEMOURS & CO, INC, 68- *Mem:* AAAS. *Res:* Synthetic fibers; kinetics; radiation and nuclear chemistry. *Mailing Add:* Textile Res Lab E I du Pont de Nemours & Co Inc Wilmington DE 19898

SCHMUGGE, THOMAS JOSEPH, b Chicago, Ill, Oct 18, 37; m 61; c 4. REMOTE SENSING, EVAPOTRANSPIRATION. *Educ:* Ill Inst Technol, BS, 59; Univ Calif, Berkeley, PhD(physics), 65. *Prof Exp:* Asst prof physics, Trinity Col, Conn, 64-70; Nat Acad Sci sr res assoc, 70-71, PHYSICIST, NASA-GODDARD SPACE FLIGHT CTR, 71- *Concurrent Pos:* Assoc ed, J Geophys Res, 79- *Mem:* AAAS; Am Geophys Union. *Res:* Magnetic resonance of rare earth ions; low temperature physics; remote sensing of the environment and interaction of electromagnetic waves with natural materials; microwave emission from natural surfaces; soil moisture; soil physics; snow; hydrology; evapotranspiration and the atmospheric boundary layer. *Mailing Add:* Hydrological Sci Br Code 924 Goddard Space Flight Ctr NASA Greenbelt MD 20771

SCHMUKLER, MORTON, hematology, biochemistry, see previous edition

SCHMUKLER, SEYMOUR, b Baltimore, Md, Oct 27, 25; m 57; c 2. ORGANIC CHEMISTRY. *Educ:* Johns Hopkins Univ, AB, 48; Columbia Univ, AM, 50, PhD(chem), 54. *Prof Exp:* Asst, Col Physicians & Surg, Columbia Univ, 53; res chemist, E I du Pont de Nemours & Co, 53-54; res chemist, Colgate-Palmolive Co, 54-57; develop chemist, Merck & Co, Inc, 57-59; res & develop chemist, Nopco Chem Co, 59-63; develop chemist, Gen Elec Co, Mass, 63-67; SR RES CHEMIST, CHEMPLEX CO, 67- *Mem:* Am Chem Soc; Royal Soc Chem. *Res:* Molecular rearrangements; synthetic organic and polymer chemistry; polymer modification, evaluation and process development. *Mailing Add:* Chemplex Co 3100 Golf Rd Rolling Meadows IL 60008

SCHMULBACH, CHARLES DAVID, b Belleville, Ill, Feb 2, 29; m 55; c 3. INORGANIC CHEMISTRY. *Educ:* Univ Ill, PhD, 58. *Prof Exp:* Asst prof chem, Pa State Univ, 58-65; assoc prof, 65-70, PROF CHEM & BIOCHEM, SOUTHERN ILL UNIV-CARBONDALE, 70-, CHMN DEPT, 75- *Mem:* Am Chem Soc; Chem Soc London. *Res:* Stabilization of uncommon oxidation states; electrochemical synthesis of inorganic compounds; homogeneous catalysis by transition metal complexes. *Mailing Add:* Dept of Chem & Biochem Southern Ill Univ Carbondale IL 62903

SCHMULBACH, JAMES C, b New Athens, Ill, July 5, 31; m; c 2. FISH BIOLOGY. *Educ:* Southern Ill Univ, BA, 53, MA, 57; Iowa State Univ, PhD(fisheries biol), 59. *Prof Exp:* Asst, Southern Ill Univ, 55-57; asst, Iowa State Univ, 57-59; asst prof, 59-65, PROF BIOL, UNIV SDAK, 65- *Concurrent Pos:* Fel, Marine Lab, Miami, 63. *Mem:* AAAS; Am Fisheries Soc; Am Inst Biol Sci. *Res:* Limnology; bionomics of fishes; macrobenthos of lotic environments. *Mailing Add:* Dept of Biol Univ of SDak Vermillion SD 57069

SCHMUTZ, ERVIN MARCELL, b St George, Utah, Oct 26, 15; m 36; c 1. RANGE MANAGEMENT, ECOLOGY. *Educ:* Utah State Univ, BS, 39, MS, 41; Univ Ariz, PhD(plant sci), 63. *Prof Exp:* Range exam, Agr Adjust Admin, 37, 39-40 & 41; sr fire guard, US Forest Serv, 38; range exam, Bur Animal Indust, 40; range conservationist, Soil Conserv Serv, USDA, 41-48 & 50-52, dist conservationist, 48-50, work unit conservationist, 52-55; res asst weed control, Univ Ariz, 55-56, from instr to prof range mgt, 56-81, EMER PROF RANGE MGT, UNIV ARIZ, 82- *Concurrent Pos:* Res scientist, Ariz Agr Exp Sta; mem, Range Mgt Educ Coun; consult, range mgt. *Honors & Awards:* Commendation Award, Soil Conserv Soc Am, 74. *Mem:* Fel Soc Range Mgt; fel Soil Conserv Soc Am; Sigma Xi. *Res:* Range ecology, evaluation, conservation and management; reseeding poisonous plants. *Mailing Add:* Sch Renewable Natural Resources Univ of Ariz Tucson AZ 85721

SCHNAARE, ROGER L, b Staunton, Ill, June 24, 38; m 60; c 3. PHARMACEUTICS, QUANTUM CHEMISTRY. *Educ:* St Louis Col Pharm, BS, 60; Purdue Univ, MS, 63, PhD(pharm), 65. *Prof Exp:* Asst prof pharm, St Louis Col Pharm, 65-68; assoc prof pharm, Philadelphia Col Pharm & Sci, 68-74, assoc prof, 74-77, prof, 77-80. *Mem:* Acad Pharmaceut Sci; Sigma Xi. *Res:* Rheological evaluation of structure in disperse system; suspension and emulsion technology. *Mailing Add:* 804 Liberty Lane Turnersville NJ 08012

SCHNABEL, TRUMAN GROSS, JR, b Philadelphia, Pa, Jan 5, 19; m 47; c 4. INTERNAL MEDICINE. *Educ:* Yale Univ, BS, 40; Univ Pa, MD, 43; Am Bd Internal Med, dipl, 52, recert, 74. *Prof Exp:* Intern med, Hosp Univ Pa, 44; asst resident, Mass Gen Hosp, 47-48; asst resident, Hosp Univ Pa, 48; instr physiol, 48-49, from asst instr to prof med, 49-73, vchmn dept med, 73-77, C MAHLON PROF MED, SCH MED, UNIV PA, 77-, STAFF PHYSICIAN CARDIOVASC SERV, 77- *Concurrent Pos:* Am Heart Asn fel, Sch Med, Univ Pa, 49-52, Markle scholar, 52-57; mem staff, Hosp Univ Pa, 52-; with Prof Lars Werko, St Erick's Hosp, Stockholm, Sweden, 55-56; asst ward chief, Philadelphia Gen Hosp, 56-59, ward chief, 59-73, coordr, Univ Pa Med Serv, 65-71, chief, 66-72; consult, Walston Gen Hosp, Ft Dix, NJ, 60-65; mem, Am Bd Internal Med, 63-72, secy-treas, 71-72; mem med educ adv comt, Rehab Serv Admin, HEW, Washington, DC, 68-71; mem clin res fel rev comt, Career Develop Rev Br, Div Res Grants, NIH, 68-71; D V Mattia lectr, Rutgers Med Sch, 75; Neuton Stern lectr & vis prof, Univ Tenn, 77. *Honors & Awards:* Alfred E Stengel Mem Award, Am Col Physicians, 78. *Mem:* Am Soc Clin Invest; Am Physiol Soc; AMA; Am Clin & Climat Asn (vpres, 68-69 & 76-77); Am Col Physicians (pres-elect, 73-74, pres, 74-75). *Res:* Cardiovascular physiology. *Mailing Add:* 191 Gibson Bldg Univ of Pa Hosp Philadelphia PA 19104

SCHNABLE, GEORGE LUTHER, b Reading, Pa, Nov 26, 27; m 57; c 2. INORGANIC CHEMISTRY, MICROELECTRONICS. *Educ:* Albright Col, BS, 50; Univ Pa, MS, 51, PhD(chem), 53. *Prof Exp:* Asst chem, Univ Pa, 53; proj engr, Microelectronics Div, Philco Corp, 53-57, eng specialist, 57-59, eng group supvr, 59-62, head mat & processes develop group, 62-68, mgr advan mat & processes dept, 68-71; head process res group, 71-79, HEAD DEVICE PHYSICS & RELIABILITY GROUP, RCA LABS, 79- *Concurrent Pos:* Div ed, J Electrochem Soc, 79- *Mem:* AAAS; Am Chem Soc; Electrochem Soc; fel Am Inst Chem; sr mem Inst Elec & Electronics Engrs. *Res:* Semiconductor devices; materials and processes for fabrication of transistors and integrated circuits; silicon chemistry and metallurgy. *Mailing Add:* RCA Labs Princeton NJ 08540

SCHNACK, LARRY G, b Harlan, Iowa, Mar 19, 37; m 55; c 4. ORGANIC CHEMISTRY. *Educ:* Iowa State Univ, BS, 58, PhD(org chem), 65. *Prof Exp:* Teacher, Minn High Sch, 58-61; asst prof, 65-69, assoc prof, 69-81, asst to vchancellor, 70-75, PROF ORG CHEM, UNIV WIS-EAU CLAIRE, 81-, ASST VCHANCELLOR ACAD AFFAIRS, 76- *Mem:* Am Chem Soc. *Res:* Stereochemistry and rearrangements. *Mailing Add:* Dept of Chem Univ of Wis Eau Claire WI 54701

SCHNAIBLE, H(AROLD) W(ILLIAM), b Lafayette, Ind, Apr 5, 25. CHEMICAL ENGINEERING. *Educ:* Purdue Univ, BS, 50, MS, 53, PhD(chem eng), 55. *Prof Exp:* Res engr, Gulf Res & Develop Co, 55-58; technologist, 59-63, SR RES ENGR, APPL RES LAB, US STEEL CORP, 63- *Mem:* Am Chem Soc; Am Inst Chem Engrs; Am Inst Mining, Metall & Petrol Engrs; Iron & Steel Soc. *Res:* Thermodynamics; kinetics, particularly hydrocarbon reactions; heat transfer; ingot solidification; computer simulation of processes. *Mailing Add:* US Steel Corp 125 Jamison Lane Monroeville PA 15146

SCHNAITMAN, CARL A, b Dayton, Ohio, Dec 16, 36; m 65. MICROBIOLOGY, BIOCHEMISTRY. *Educ:* Syracuse Univ, BS, 60, MS, 63, PhD(microbiol), 65. *Prof Exp:* From asst prof to assoc prof, 67-73, PROF MICROBIOL, SCH MED, UNIV VA, 73- *Concurrent Pos:* Fel biochem, Sch Med, Johns Hopkins Univ, 65-67; fel Am Cancer Soc, 66-67; ed, J Bact, 74-; mem study sect microbiol chem, NIH, 75- *Mem:* AAAS; Am Soc Cell Biol; Am Soc Microbiol; Am Soc Biol Chemists. *Res:* Structure, function and biosynthesis of membrane proteins of bacterial cells, animal cells and viruses. *Mailing Add:* Dept of Microbiol Univ of Va Sch of Med Charlottesville VA 22901

SCHNAPER, HAROLD WARREN, b Boston, Mass, Nov 11, 23; m 51; c 5. MEDICINE, CARDIOVASCULAR PHYSIOLOGY. *Educ:* Harvard Univ, AB, 45; La State Univ, cert, 44; Duke Univ, MD, 49. *Prof Exp:* Intern med, Boston City Hosps, 49-50; chief med, US Army 7th Evacuation Hosp, Ger, 51-53; resident, Mt Sinai Hosp, New York, 53-54; asst chief med serv, Vet Admin Hosp, DC, 54-60, chief internal med res, Vet Admin Cent Off, 60-64, assoc dir res serv, 64-66, actg dir, 66-67; exec vchmn dept med, 69-72, PROF MED & SR SCIENTIST, CARDIOVASC RES & TRAINING CTR, MED CTR, UNIV ALA, BIRMINGHAM, 69-, PROF PUB HEALTH & EPIDEMIOL & DIR DIV GERONT & GERIAT MED, 72-, DIR ALL UNIV CTR AGING, 76- *Concurrent Pos:* Fel neurol & dermat, Sch Med, Duke Univ, 49; fel cardiovasc dis, Sch Med, Georgetown Univ, 50-51; fel path, Mt Sinai Hosp, New York, 53; instr, Sch Med, Georgetown Univ, 54-58, asst prof, 58-66; attend physician, DC Gen Hosp, 54-66; vis prof, Mercy Hosp, Buffalo, NY, 59-66; co-dir cardiovasc res & training ctr, Med Ctr, Univ Ala, Birmingham, 66-70; assoc dir for heart & stroke, Ala Regional Med Prog, 69-76; chief, Vet Admin Cardiovasc Res Prog, 69-80. *Mem:* AAAS; AMA; fel Am Col Physicians; Am Fedn Clin Res; fel Geront Soc. *Res:* Clinical hypertension; aging mechanisms; multicenter clinical trials. *Mailing Add:* Ctr for Aging Univ Ala Birmingham AL 35294

SCHNAPF, ABRAHAM, b New York, NY, Aug 1, 21; m 43; c 2. MECHANICAL ENGINEERING, SPACECRAFT SYSTEMS TECHNOLOGY. *Educ:* City Col New York, BSME, 48; Drexel Univ, MSME, 53. *Prof Exp:* Develop engr aeronaut eng, Goodyear Aircraft Corp, Ohio, 48-50; leader develop eng, Airborne-Navig Systs, Defense Electronic Prod, Radio Corp Am, Camden, 50-55; mgr airborne weapon systs, 55-58, proj mgr Tiros, Astro-Electronics Div, 58-70, mgr prog mgt, 70-76, mgr satellite prog, 77-79, PRIN SCIENTIST, ASTRO-ELECTRONICS DIV, RCA CORP, 79- *Honors & Awards:* Annual Award, Am Soc Qual Control, 68. *Mem:* AAAS; NY Acad Sci; fel Am Inst Aeronaut & Astronaut; Am Meteorol Soc. *Res:* Development, design and testing of spacecraft, ground stations and field operations; management of satellite programs. *Mailing Add:* Astro-Electronics Div RCA Corp PO Box 800 Princeton NJ 08540

SCHNAPPINGER, MELVIN GERHARDT, JR, b Baltimore, Md, Oct 29, 42; m 67; c 1. AGRONOMY. *Educ:* Univ Md, College Park, BS, 65, MS, 68; Va Polytech Inst & State Univ, PhD(agron), 70. *Prof Exp:* RES REP FIELD RES & DEVELOP, AGR DIV, CIBA-GEIGY CORP, 70- *Mem:* Am Soc Agron; Soil Sci Soc Am; Weed Sci Soc Am. *Res:* Field testing of herbicides, insecticides and micronutrient fertilizers. *Mailing Add:* Rte 3 Box 39 Centreville MD 21617

SCHNARE, PAUL STEWART, b Berlin, NH, Oct 16, 36; m 60; c 2. COMPUTER SCIENCE. *Educ:* Univ NH, BA, 60, MS, 61; Tulane Univ, La, PhD(math), 67. *Prof Exp:* Instr math, La State Univ, New Orleans, 61-66; asst prof, Univ Fla, 67-74; asst prof, Colby Col, 74-75 & Fordham Univ, 75-76; asst prof math, Univ Petrol & Minerals, Dhahran, Saudi Arabia, 76-80; ASSOC PROF MATH, EASTERN KY UNIV, 80- *Concurrent Pos:* NSF sci fac fel, Tulane Univ, 66-67. *Mem:* AAAS; London Math Soc; Math Asn Am; Am Math Soc. *Res:* Applied and computational mathematics; numerical methods; analytic inequalities; operations research. *Mailing Add:* Eastern Ky Univ Richmond KY 40475

SCHNATHORST, WILLIAM CHARLES, b Ft Dodge, Iowa, May 8, 29; m 51; c 3. PLANT PATHOLOGY. *Educ:* Univ Wyo, BS, 52, MS, 53; Univ Calif, PhD(plant path), 57. *Prof Exp:* Asst & lab instr plant physiol & bot, Univ Wyo, 52-53; asst plant path, Univ Calif, 54-56, lectr, 70, ASSOC PLANT PATH, EXP STA, UNIV CALIF, DAVIS & PLANT PATHOLOGIST, SCI & EDUC ADMIN-AGR RES, USDA, 56- *Mem:* Bot Soc Am; Mycol Soc Am; Am Phytopath Soc. *Res:* Nature of disease resistance of plants; physiology of fungi; verticillium wilt; ecology of plant pathogens; diseases of field and tree crops. *Mailing Add:* Dept of Plant Path Univ of Calif Davis CA 95616

SCHNATTERLY, STEPHEN EUGENE, b Topeka, Kans, Oct 2, 38; m 63; c 2. SOLID STATE PHYSICS. *Educ:* Univ Wash, BS, 60, MS, 61; Univ Ill, PhD(physics), 65. *Prof Exp:* Instr physics, Princeton Univ, 65-67, asst prof, 67-70, assoc prof, 70-74, prof, 74-77; PROF PHYSICS, UNIV VA, 77- *Concurrent Pos:* Res Corp res grant, 66-67; prin investr, NSF grant, Univ Va, 77- *Mem:* Am Phys Soc. *Res:* Optical properties of solids; inelastic electron scattering spectroscopy; soft x-ray emission spectroscopy. *Mailing Add:* Physics Dept Univ Va Charlottesville VA 22901

SCHNECK, LARRY, b New York, NY, May 15, 26; m 59; c 3. PEDIATRIC NEUROLOGY, NEUROCHEMISTRY. *Educ:* NY Univ, BS, 49; Chicago Med Sch, MD, 53. *Prof Exp:* Resident pediat, Brooklyn Jewish Hosp, 54-56 & neurol, Bronx Munic Hosp, 57-60; asst prof neurol, 60-73, PROF NEUROL, STATE UNIV NY DOWNSTATE MED CTR, 74- *Concurrent Pos:* NIH fel, Albert Einstein Col Med, 67-70; dir neurol, Kingsbrook Jewish Med Ctr, 70-; dir, Albert Isaac Res Inst, 70-; attend physician, Vet Admin Hosp, Brooklyn, 71- *Mem:* Am Acad Pediat; Am Acad Neurol; Am Soc Neurochem; Int Soc Neurochem. *Res:* Neurochemistry and sphingolipidosis. *Mailing Add:* Kingsbrook Jewish Med Ctr 86 E 49th St Brooklyn NY 11203

SCHNECKLOTH, ROLAND EDMUNDS, b Iowa, Oct 11, 22. INTERNAL MEDICINE. *Educ:* Univ Nebr, AB, 43, MD, 45. *Prof Exp:* Intern, Charles T Miller Hosp, St Paul, Minn, 45-46; asst, Res Div, Cleveland Clin, Ohio, 54-59; res assoc med, Am Heart Asn, 59-62, from assoc dir to dir res, 62-72, vpres res, 72-73; CLIN ASSOC DEAN RES, MED COL, CORNELL UNIV, 73- *Concurrent Pos:* Fel internal med, Cleveland Clin, Ohio, 48-51; fel med, Harvard Med Sch & Beth Israel Hosp, Boston, 51-52; USPHS fel, Karolinska Inst, Sweden, 53-54. *Mem:* Am Fedn Clin Res; Am Heart Asn; NY Acad Sci. *Res:* Cardiovascular-renal disease; hypertension; medical administration. *Mailing Add:* Cornell Univ Med Col 1300 York Ave New York NY 10021

SCHNEEBERGER, TIMOTHY JAMES, astronomy, see previous edition

SCHNEEMAN, BARBARA OLDS, b Seattle, Wash, Oct 3, 48; m 74; c 1. NUTRITION, FOOD SCIENCE. *Educ:* Univ Calif, Davis, BS, 70; Univ Calif, Berkeley, PhD(nutrit), 74. *Prof Exp:* Fel gastroenterol, Bruce Lyon Mem Res Lab, Children's Hosp, 74-76; ASST PROF, UNIV CALIF, DAVIS, 76- *Concurrent Pos:* NIH fel, 74-76, 77. *Mem:* Am Inst Nutrit; Am Physiol Soc; Soc Exp Biol & Med; AAAS; Inst Food Technologists. *Res:* Dietary regulation of digestion; impact of processed foods on nutrition and digestion. *Mailing Add:* Dept of Nutrit Univ of Calif Davis CA 95616

SCHNEER, CECIL JACK, b Far Rockaway, NY, Jan 7, 23; m 43; c 2. GEOLOGY. *Educ:* Harvard Univ, AB, 43, AM, 50; Cornell Univ, PhD(geol), 54. *Prof Exp:* Mining geologist, Cerro de Pasco Co, SAm, 43-44; instr geol, Univ NH, 50; instr, Hamilton Col, 50-52; asst mineral, Cornell Univ, 52-54; from asst prof to assoc prof, 54-63, PROF GEOL & HIST SCI, UNIV NH, 63- *Concurrent Pos:* Pres, US Nat Comt on Hist Geol, 75-79. *Mem:* Fel Geol Soc Am; Mineral Soc Am; Hist Sci Soc; Nat Asn Geol Teachers; London Geol Soc. *Res:* Crystal morphology, growth and structure; Neoplatonic background to Renaissance science; history of science. *Mailing Add:* Dept Earth Sci James Hall Univ NH Durham NH 03824

SCHNEID, EDWARD JOSEPH, b Syracuse, NY, Apr 1, 40; m 67; c 1. NUCLEAR PHYSICS. *Educ:* LeMoyne Col, BS, 61; Univ Pittsburgh, PhD(physics), 66. *Prof Exp:* NSF res fel nuclear physics, Rutgers Univ, New Brunswick, 66-68; res scientist, 68-76, br head, 76-78, LAB HEAD, GRUMMAN AEROSPACE CORP, 78- *Mem:* Am Nuclear Soc; Int Elec & Electronic Engrs; Am Phys Soc. *Res:* Ion beam analysis; advanced nuclear sensor development; gamma ray astronomy. *Mailing Add:* Res Dept PLT 26 Grumman Aerospace Corp Bethpage NY 11714

SCHNEIDAU, JOHN DONALD, JR, b New Orleans, La, May 14, 13; m 43; c 3. MEDICAL MYCOLOGY. *Educ:* Loyola Univ, BS, 38; Tulane Univ, MS, 40, PhD(microbiol), 56. *Prof Exp:* From instr to assoc prof biol, Loyola Univ, 45-54; res assoc, 54-56, from asst prof to assoc prof, 56-73, PROF MICROBIOL, TULANE UNIV, 73-, PROF IMMUNOL, 76- *Concurrent Pos:* Consult mycologist, Ochsner Found Hosp, New Orleans, La, 50-; lectr, ICA Prog Med Educ, Tulane-Colombia, 58-60. *Mem:* Am Soc Microbiol; Int Soc Human & Animal Mycol; Med Microbiol Soc Am. *Res:* Skin hypersensitivity to fungal antigens in systemic mycotic disease with particular emphasis on cross-reactivity among fungal skin-test antigens; taxonomy and biology of Nocardia and related Actinomycetales. *Mailing Add:* Dept of Microbiol & Immunol Tulane Univ Sch of Med New Orleans LA 70112

SCHNEIDER, ALAN M(ICHAEL), b Milwaukee, Wis, Feb 28, 25; m 48; c 4. SYSTEMS ENGINEERING, INSTRUMENTATION. *Educ:* Villanova Univ, BEE, 45; Univ Wis, MS, 48; Mass Inst Technol, ScD(instrumentation), 57. *Prof Exp:* Res engr, Hughes Aircraft Co, 48-49; engr, AC Spark Plug Div, Gen Motors Corp, 50-53; res engr, Instrumentation Lab, Mass Inst Technol, 53-55; eng scientist, Airborne Systs Lab, Radio Corp Am, 57-59, sr eng scientist, Missile Electronics & Control Div, 59-61, mgr systs anal, Aerospace Systs Div, 61-65; assoc prof aerospace & mech eng sci, 65-68, PROF APPL MECH & ENG SCI, UNIV CALIF, SAN DIEGO, 68- *Concurrent Pos:* Consult, Gen Dynamics, Convair, 65, Aerospace Systs Div, Radio Corp Am, 65, Aerospace Corp, 65-68, Gen Micro-Electronics Div, Philco Corp, 66, TRW Systs, 67-70, Teledyne Ryan, 69, Air Pollution Technol Inc, 77 & Linkabit Corp, 77-; vis assoc, Environ Qual Lab, Calif Inst Technol, 73. *Honors & Awards:* Best Paper Award, Inst Radio Engrs Fifth East Coast Conf on Aeronaut & Navig Electronics, 58; Samuel M Burka Award, 62. *Mem:* Assoc fel Am Inst Aeronaut & Astronaut; Am Inst Navig. *Res:* Space vehicle guidance; automatic and manual rendezvous guidance; inertial systems; systems theory and applications; physiological systems; urban systems and problems; air pollution; energy. *Mailing Add:* Dept Appl Mech & Eng Sci B-010 Univ of Calif San Diego La Jolla CA 92093

SCHNEIDER, ALFRED, b Ger, Dec 17, 26; nat US; m 50; c 3. NUCLEAR ENGINEERING, CHEMICAL ENGINEERING. *Educ:* Cooper Union, BChE, 51; Polytech Inst New York, PhD(chem eng), 58. *Prof Exp:* Chemist, US Testing Co, 51-52; develop proj mgr, Celanese Corp Am, 52-56; assoc chem engr, Argonne Nat Lab, 56-61; mgr nuclear res & develop, Martin Co, 61-64; mgr mat & processes, Nuclear Utility Serv, Washington, DC, 64-65; res assoc to dir nuclear technol, Allied Chem Corp, NJ, 65-71, dir nuclear technol, Allied-Gen Nuclear Serv, SC, 71-75; PROF NUCLEAR ENG, GA INST TECHNOL, 75- *Concurrent Pos:* Consult, Allied-Gen Nuclear Serv, 75- & NY State Energy Res & Develop Authority, 76- *Mem:* Am Chem Soc;

Am Inst Chem Engrs; Am Nuclear Soc. *Res:* Reprocessing of nuclear fuels; nuclear materials; radioactive waste management; nuclear power reactors; nuclear fuel cycles; isotope separation; energy systems. *Mailing Add:* Sch of Nuclear Eng & Health Physics Ga Inst of Technol Atlanta GA 30332

SCHNEIDER, ALFRED MARCEL, b Vienna, Austria, Nov 7, 25; nat US; m 53; c 2. MATHEMATICAL STATISTICS, OPERATIONS RESEARCH. *Educ:* Univ London, BSc, 48. *Prof Exp:* Res chemist, Vitamins, Ltd, Eng, 48-52; chem engr, Cyanamid Can, 53-55, exp statistician, Am Cyanamid Co, 55-57, leader math anal group, 58-61; mgr math anal dept, Dewey & Almy Chem Div, 61-66, dir math sci, Tech Group, 66-71, DIR OPERS RES, W R GRACE & CO, 71- *Mem:* Am Statist Asn; Opers Res Soc Am; Royal Inst Chem. *Res:* Experimental design; computer applications to chemistry and chemical engineering; simulation. *Mailing Add:* W R Grace & Co 1114 Ave of the Americas New York NY 10036

SCHNEIDER, ALLAN FRANK, b Chicago, Ill, Feb 7, 26; m 50; c 3. GLACIAL GEOLOGY. *Educ:* Beloit Col, BS, 48; Pa State Univ, MS, 51; Univ Minn, PhD(geol), 57. *Prof Exp:* Asst geol, Pa State Univ, 48-50, instr, 50-51; instr, Univ Minn, 51-54; from instr to asst prof, Wash State Univ, 54-59; geologist, Ind Geol Surv, 59-70, assoc map ed, 60-61, map & illus ed, 61-65; assoc prof, 70-80, PROF EARTH SCI, UNIV WIS-PARKSIDE, 80- *Concurrent Pos:* Geologist, US Geol Surv, 49, Minn Geol Surv, 51-54 & Wis Geol Surv, 76; coordr earth sci prog, Univ Wis-Parkside, 73-75, 80- *Mem:* Fel Geol Soc Am; Nat Asn Geol Teachers; Arctic Inst NAm; Int Glaciol Soc; Am Quaternary Asn. *Res:* Geomorphology; glacial geology; sedimentary petrography; Pleistocene geology of Minnesota, Indiana and Wisconsin. *Mailing Add:* Div of Sci Univ of Wis-Parkside Box 2000 Kenosha WI 53141

SCHNEIDER, ALLAN STANFORD, b New York, NY, Sept 26, 40; m 68; c 2. PHYSICAL CHEMISTRY, BIOCHEMISTRY. *Educ:* Rensselaer Polytech Inst, BChemE, 61; Pa State Univ, MS, 63; Univ Calif, Berkeley, PhD(chem), 68. *Prof Exp:* ASST PROF BIOCHEM, GRAD SCH MED SCI, CORNELL UNIV, 73-, staff, SLOAN-KETTERING INST CANCER RES, 73- *Concurrent Pos:* Weizmann Inst fel, Weizmann Inst Sci, Rehovot, Israel, 69-71; staff fel, NIH, 71-73; established investr, Am Heart Asn, 77. *Mem:* Am Soc Biol Chemists; Biophys Soc; NY Acad Sci; AAAS. *Res:* Biophysical chemistry; biological membrane structure and function; hormone and neurotransmitter secretion and action at cell surface receptors. *Mailing Add:* Sloan-Kettering Inst 410 E 68th St New York NY 10021

SCHNEIDER, ARTHUR LEE, b St Louis, Mo, Feb 11, 39; m 64; c 2. PROTEIN CHEMISTRY. *Educ:* Univ Mo, Columbia, BS, 61, PhD(biochem), 66. *Prof Exp:* Res assoc biochem, Albert Einstein Col Med, Yeshiva Univ, 66-68; res assoc, Col Physicians & Surgeons, Columbia Univ, 69-70; assoc med, Albert Einstein Col Med, 71-73; GROUP LEADER CLIN CHEM, DADE, DIV AM HOSP SUPPLY CORP, 73- *Concurrent Pos:* USPHS fel, NIH, 67-69. *Mem:* Am Chem Soc; Am Asn Clin Chemists; AAAS. *Res:* Use of plasma proteins for clinical chemistry control materials; development of clinical chemistry control materials. *Mailing Add:* 1851 Delaware Pkwy Miami FL 33152

SCHNEIDER, ARTHUR SANFORD, b Los Angeles, Calif, Mar 24, 29; m 50; c 3. PATHOLOGY, HEMATOLOGY. *Educ:* Univ Calif, BS, 51; Chicago Med Sch, MD, 55. *Prof Exp:* Intern & resident, Vet Admin Hosp, Los Angeles, 55-59; chief med serv, US Air Force Hosp, Mather Air Force Base, Calif, 59-61; instr med, Univ Calif Med Sch, 61-64, asst prof med & path, 65-68; chief clin path, Vet Admin Hosp, Los Angeles, 62-68; dir clin path, City of Hope Med Ctr, 68-70, chmn clin path, 70-75; ACTG CHIEF LAB SERV, VET ADMIN MED CTR, 75-; PROF & CHMN PATH, UNIV HEALTH SCI & CHICAGO MED SCH, 75- *Concurrent Pos:* Hemat trainee, Univ Calif Sch Med, 61-62; res assoc, 62-66, asst clin prof med & path, 68-72, assoc clin prof, 72-75; attend specialist, Wadsworth Vet Admin Ctr, Los Angeles, 68-75. *Mem:* Asn Path Chmn; Am Soc Hemat; Am Soc Clin Pathologists; Acad Clin Lab Physicians & Scientists; Am Fedn Clin Res. *Res:* Inherited erythrocyte biochemical abnormalities; computer applications in laboratory medicine. *Mailing Add:* Dept of Path Chicago Med Sch North Chicago IL 60064

SCHNEIDER, BARRY I, b Brooklyn, NY, Nov 16, 40; m 62; c 2. MOLECULAR PHYSICS, THEORETICAL CHEMISTRY. *Educ:* Brooklyn Col, BS, 62; Yale Univ, MS, 64; Univ Chicago, PhD(theoret chem), 68. *Prof Exp:* Fel chem, Univ Southern Calif, 68-69; mem tech staff, Gen Tel & Electronics Lab, 69-72; MEM TECH STAFF PHYSICS, LOS ALAMOS SCI LAB, 72- *Mem:* Am Phys Soc. *Res:* Scattering theory, photoionization; many-body theory; structure of molecules. *Mailing Add:* Theoret Div Los Alamos Sci Lab Los Alamos NM 87545

SCHNEIDER, BERNARD ARNOLD, b Washington, DC, June 8, 44; m 68; c 1. PLANT PHYSIOLOGY, AGRONOMY. *Educ:* Univ Md, College Park, BS, 66, MS, 68, PhD(forage physiol, biochem), 71. *Prof Exp:* Asst agron, Univ Md, 66-71; plant physiologist, Plant Biol Lab, 72-74, radioisotope safety officer, 74-77, supvry plant physiologist, 77-79, PLANT PHYSIOLOGIST, ENVIRON PROTECTION AGENCY, 79- *Concurrent Pos:* Rep, Plant Growth Regulator Soc Nomenclature Comt, Am Nat Stnadards Inst-K62, 74-; leader pesticide prod performance guidelines, Terminol Subcomt, Environ Protection Agency. *Mem:* Am Soc Agron; Weed Sci Soc Am; Am Soc Hort Sci; Am Soc Testing & Mat; Am Chem Soc. *Res:* Develop methods for determining the biological effectiveness of algaecides, herbicides and plant regulators for public protection; determine the fate of pesticides in the environment using radioisotopes of pesticides. *Mailing Add:* Plant Sci Br BFSD 401 MST SW Washington DC 20460

SCHNEIDER, BRUCE ALTON, b Detroit, Mich, July 17, 41; m 67; c 2. AUDITORY PSYCHOPHYSICS, AUDITORY DEVELOPMENT. *Educ:* Univ Mich, Ann Arbor, BA, 63; Harvard Univ, PhD(psychol), 68. *Prof Exp:* Lectr psychol, Columbia Univ, 67-68; asst prof, 68-72, assoc prof, 72-74; assoc prof, 74-81, PROF PSYCHOL, UNIV TORONTO, 81- *Concurrent Pos:* Distinguished vis prof, Univ Alberta, 81. *Mem:* Soc Math Psychologists. *Res:* Infant and adult auditory perception; how the ear processes sound and how the nature of this auditory processing system changes from infancy to adulthood. *Mailing Add:* Dept Psychol Erindale Col Univ Toronto Mississauga ON L5L 1C6

SCHNEIDER, BRUCE E, b Sacramento, Calif, July 4, 50; m 75; c 1. BIOSTATISTICS. *Educ:* Brown Univ, BSc, 72; Villanova Univ, MS, 73; Temple Univ, PhD(appl statist), 77. *Prof Exp:* Group leader, 72-75, supvr, 76-77, MGR BIOSTATIST, WYETH LABS, 77- *Mem:* Am Statist Asn; Biometrics Soc. *Res:* Nonparametrics; statistical computing; pharmacokinetics. *Mailing Add:* Wyeth Labs PO Box 8299 Philadelphia PA 19101

SCHNEIDER, CARL STANLEY, b Baltimore, Md, Dec 20, 42; m 71. SOLID STATE PHYSICS. *Educ:* Johns Hopkins Univ, BA, 63; Mass Inst Technol, SM, 65, PhD(physics), 68. *Prof Exp:* From asst prof to assoc prof, 68-81, PROF PHYSICS, US NAVAL ACAD-NAT BUR STANDARDS, 81- *Concurrent Pos:* Naval Acad Res Coun grant, US Naval Acad-Nat Bur Standards, 69-75, NSF res grants neutron diffraction, 74-76; affil, Naval Ship Res & Develop Ctr, 77- *Mem:* Am Phys Soc; Sigma Xi (pres, 80-81); Am Asn Physics Teachers; AAAS. *Res:* Neutron diffraction; prism refraction of thermal neutron for the determination of scattering amplitudes; nonlinear theory of magnetoelasticity. *Mailing Add:* Dept of Physics US Naval Acad Annapolis MD 21402

SCHNEIDER, CHARLES ALOYSIUS, b Covington, Ky, Oct 20, 36; m 59; c 5. ORGANIC CHEMISTRY. *Educ:* Thomas Moore Col, AB, 58; Loyola Univ Chicago, MS, 61, PhD(chem), 64. *Prof Exp:* Chemist, Addressograph-Multigraph Corp, 62-64; from asst lab dir to lab dir, 64-74, PROD MGR, SHERWIN WILLIAMS CHEM, 74- *Mem:* Am Chem Soc. *Res:* Organic process research. *Mailing Add:* Chem Div Sherwin Williams Chem 501 Murray St Bernard OH 45217

SCHNEIDER, CRAIG WILLIAM, b Manchester, NH, Oct 23, 48; m 72. PHYCOLOGY. *Educ:* Gettysburg Col, BA, 70; Duke Univ, PhD(bot), 75. *Prof Exp:* asst prof, 75-81, ASSOC PROF BIOL, TRINITY COL, 81- *Mem:* Phycol Soc Am; Int Phycol Soc; Brit Phycol Soc. *Res:* Benthic algal studies on the North Carolina and Southeastern United States continental shelf; benthic algal ecology in Connecticut; life-history cultural studies; red-algal morphological studies. *Mailing Add:* Dept of Biol Trinity Col Hartford CT 06106

SCHNEIDER, DAVID EDWIN, b Philadelphia, Pa, Mar 16, 37. PHYSIOLOGICAL ECOLOGY, MARINE ECOLOGY. *Educ:* Bates Col, BS, 59; Duke Univ, PhD(zool), 67. *Prof Exp:* From instr to asst prof, 66-71, ASSOC PROF BIOL, WESTERN WASH UNIV, 71- *Mem:* AAAS; Am Soc Zoologists; Am Soc Limnol & Oceanog; Ecol Soc Am. Sci. *Res:* Temperature adaptations of poikilotherm animals; adaptation to hydrostatic pressure in deep sea fish; trophic relationships and physiological responses of Arctic marine species. *Mailing Add:* Dept Biol Western Wash Univ Bellingham WA 98225

SCHNEIDER, DONALD LEONARD, b Muskegon, Mich, Jan 15, 41. BIOCHEMISTRY. *Educ:* Kalamazoo Col, BA, 63; Mich State Univ, PhD(biochem), 69. *Prof Exp:* Fel biochem, Cornell Univ, 69-71; res assoc biochem cytol, Rockefeller Univ, 71-72, asst prof, 72-73; asst prof biochem, Univ Mass, 73-76; ASST PROF BIOCHEM, DARTMOUTH MED SCH, 76- *Mem:* Am Soc Cell Biol; Am Chem Soc; Sigma Xi; AAAS; Am Soc Biol Chemists. *Res:* Transport in lysosomes; mechanism and regulation of protein degradation; structure and function of the inner mitochondrial membrane. *Mailing Add:* Dept of Biochem Dartmouth Med Sch Hanover NH 03755

SCHNEIDER, DONALD LOUIS, b Ft Wayne, Ind, Apr 9, 19; m 41; c 2. BIOCHEMISTRY, NUTRITION. *Educ:* Evansville Col, BA, 52; Univ Ariz, MS, 60, PhD(biochem), 63. *Prof Exp:* Chemist, Mead Johnson Res Ctr, 52-58; res assoc biochem & nutrit, Ariz Agr Exp Sta, 58-62; sr scientist, 62-63, group leader, 63-68, prin investr, 68-73, sect leader nutrit, 73-76, PRIN RES ASSOC, MEAD JOHNSON RES CTR, 76- *Mem:* AAAS; Am Inst Nutrit; NY Acad Sci; Am Inst Biol Sci; Am Inst Chemists. *Res:* Cyclopropenoid fatty acids, biochemical and physiological effects; lipid, cholesterol and bile salt metabolism; baby pig and infant nutrition. *Mailing Add:* Dept of Nutrit Res Mead Johnson Res Ctr Evansville IN 47721

SCHNEIDER, EDWARD GREYER, b Indianapolis, Ind, Sept 2, 41; m 63; c 2. PHYSIOLOGY. *Educ:* DePauw Univ, BA, 63; Ind Univ, Indianapolis, PhD(physiol), 67. *Prof Exp:* Fel physiol, Univ Mo, 67-70, asst prof, 70-71; asst prof, Mayo Grad Sch Med, Univ Minn, 71-73; ASSOC PROF PHYSIOL, UNIV TENN CTR HEALTH SCI MEMPHIS, 73- *Concurrent Pos:* Estab investr, Am Heart Asn, 72-77. *Mem:* Am Physiol Soc; Am Fedn Clin Res; Am Soc Nephrology; Sigma Xi; Int Soc Nephrology. *Res:* Examination of the control of renal sodium excretion and the effects of alteration in fluid balance on the excretion of electrolytes by the kidney and the secretron of aldosterone by the adrenal. *Mailing Add:* Dept of Physiol & Biophys Univ Tenn Ctr Health Sci Memphis TN 38163

SCHNEIDER, EDWARD LEE, b Portland, Ore, Sept 14, 47. PLANT MORPHOLOGY, PLANT ANATOMY. *Educ:* Cent Wash Univ, BA, 69, MS, 71; Univ Calif, Santa Barbara, PhD(bot), 74. *Prof Exp:* asst prof, 74-79, ASSOC PROF BOT, SOUTHWEST TEX STATE UNIV, 79- *Concurrent Pos:* Mem, Int Comn Bee Bot, 77- *Mem:* Bot Soc Am; Sigma Xi. *Res:* Descriptive plant anatomy-morphology; evolution of flowering plants; influence of beetle pollination on the evolution of angiosperms; reproductive biology of aquatic plants. *Mailing Add:* Dept of Biol Southwest Tex State Univ San Marcos TX 78666

SCHNEIDER, EDWARD LEWIS, b New York, NY, June 22, 40. GERIATRICS, HUMAN GENETICS. *Educ:* Rensselaer Polytech Inst, BS, 61; Boston Univ, MD, 66. *Prof Exp:* Intern med, Cornell Univ-New York Hosp, 66-67, resident med, 67-68; res assoc, Lab Biol Viruses, Nat Inst Allergy & Infectious Dis, NIH, 68-70; res fel human genetics, Univ Calif Med Ctr, San Francisco, 70-73; PROG COORDR, LCCP RES CTR, NAT INST AGING, 73- *Concurrent Pos:* Asst prof human genetics, Johns Hopkins Univ Sch Med, 73- *Mem:* Am Soc Cell Biol; Geront Soc; Am Soc Human Genetics; Tissue Cult Asn. *Res:* Studies on cellular aging utilizing human diploid cell cultures in vitro and animal systems to examine cell replication, nucleic acid metabolism and repair of DNA damage. *Mailing Add:* Geront Res Ctr Nat Inst on Aging Baltimore MD 21224

SCHNEIDER, EDWIN KAHN, b Philadelphia, Pa, May 6, 48. METEOROLOGY. *Educ:* Harvard Col, AB, 70; Harvard Univ, MS, 73, PhD(appl physics), 76. *Prof Exp:* Res assoc, Mass Inst Technol, 74-77; NATO fel, Reading Univ, Eng, 77-78; RES FEL, HARVARD UNIV, 78- *Res:* Atmospheric general circulation and climate modelling; tropical meteorology. *Mailing Add:* Pierce Hall 109 Harvard Univ Cambridge MA 02138

SCHNEIDER, ERIC DAVIS, b Wilmington, Del, Nov 21, 40; c 2. MARINE GEOLOGY, MARINE POLLUTION. *Educ:* Univ Del, BA, 62; Columbia Univ, MS, 65, PhD, 69. *Prof Exp:* Comdr, US Naval Oceanog Off, 67-69, dir, Global Ocean Floor & Anal Res Ctr, 68-71; dir, Off Spec Projs, 71-72, DIR ENVIRON RES LAB, ENVIRON PROTECTION AGENCY, 72- *Concurrent Pos:* Adj prof, Grad Sch Oceanog, Univ RI, 72-; chmn, Working Group Effect Pollutants on Marine Organisms, US/USSR Joint Comt Coop Environ Protection, 72-76; mem, Joint Group Experts Sci Aspects Marine Pollution, 74-; chmn, Int Coun Explor Seas, 74- *Mem:* AAAS; Nat Wildlife Fedn. *Res:* Marine pollution; marine geology; oceanography. *Mailing Add:* Environ Res Lab Narragansett S Ferry Rd Narragansett RI 02882

SCHNEIDER, ERIC WEST, b Wilkes-Barre, Pa, Sept 1, 52; m 74; c 2. NUCLEAR CHEMISTRY. *Educ:* Rensselaer Polytech Inst, BS, 74; Univ Md, PhD(nuclear chem), 78. *Prof Exp:* Assoc res scientist, 78-81, sr res scientist, 81, STAFF RES SCIENTIST, RES LABS, GEN MOTORS CORP, 81- *Mem:* Am Chem Soc; Am Phys Soc. *Res:* Development of radioisotopic methods for industrial applications including, radiotracer methods for measuring wear, radioisotopic gauging and radiographic inspection of materials, and neutron activation and x-ray fluorescence elemental analysis. *Mailing Add:* Res Labs RCEL-215 Gen Motors Corp Warren MI 48090

SCHNEIDER, FRANK L, b New York, NY, May 26, 06; m 45; c 1. ANALYTICAL CHEMISTRY. *Educ:* Polytech Inst Brooklyn, BS, 28; NY Univ, MS, 30; Rutgers Univ, PhD(chem), 36. *Prof Exp:* Asst, Rutgers Univ, 33-34, instr, 34-37, exten div, 36-37; instr chem, Trinity Col, Conn, 37-39; from asst to prof, 39-72, EMER PROF CHEM, QUEENS COL (NY), 72- *Honors & Awards:* Benedetti-Pichler Award. *Mem:* Am Chem Soc; fel Am Inst Chemists; Sigma Xi; hon mem Austrian Microchem Soc. *Res:* Microchemistry; organic analysis; air and water pollution control. *Mailing Add:* Round Hill Lane Port Washington NY 11050

SCHNEIDER, FRED BARRY, b NY, Dec 7, 53. COMPUTER SCIENCE. *Educ:* Cornell Univ, BS, 75; State Univ NY, Stony Brook, MS, 77, PhD(comput sci), 78. *Prof Exp:* ASST PROF COMPUT SCI, CORNELL UNIV, 78- *Mem:* Am Asn Comput Mach; Inst Elec & Electronics Engrs. *Res:* Operating systems; programming languages; concurrency; software engineering. *Mailing Add:* Dept of Comput Sci Cornell Univ Ithaca NY 14850

SCHNEIDER, FREDERICK HOWARD, b Detroit, Mich, Nov 19, 38; m 61; c 2. PHARMACOLOGY. *Educ:* Ariz State Univ, BS, 60, MS, 61; Yale Univ, PhD(autonomic pharmacol), 66. *Prof Exp:* Jr chemist, Merck Sharp & Dohme Res Labs, 61-62; asst prof pharmacol, Sch Med, Univ Colo, Denver, 67-73; assoc prof, Sch Med, Emory Univ, 73-75; PRES, BIOASSAY SYSTS CORP, CAMBRIDGE, MASS, 75- *Concurrent Pos:* NSF fel pharmacol, Oxford Univ, 66-67; estab investr, Am Heart Asn, 69-74. *Mem:* AAAS; Am Soc Pharmacol & Exp Therapeut; Tissue Cult Asn. *Res:* Effects of drugs on responses to sympathetic nerve stimulation; neurotransmitter secretion; lysosomal secretion mechanisms; nerve cells in tissue culture; toxicology; in vitro cytotoxicity. *Mailing Add:* Bioassay Systs Corp 100 Inman St Cambridge MA 02139

SCHNEIDER, G MICHAEL, b Detroit, Mich, May 28, 45. SOFTWARE ENGINEERING. *Educ:* Univ Mich, BS, 66; Univ Wis, MSc, 68, PhD(comput sci), 74. *Prof Exp:* ASST PROF COMPUT SCI, UNIV MINN, 74- *Concurrent Pos:* Vis prof, Univ Calif, Berkeley, 79 & Imperial Col, Univ London, 80. *Mem:* Asn Comput Mach; Inst Elec & Electronics Engrs. *Res:* Interface between the user and the computer system. *Mailing Add:* Comput Sci Dept 136 Lind Hall Univ Minn Minneapolis MN 55455

SCHNEIDER, GEORGE RONALD, b Chicago, Ill, Mar 6, 32. CHEMICAL ENGINEERING, CHEMISTRY. *Educ:* Ill Inst Technol, BS, 53; Mass Inst Technol, SM, 56, ScD(chem eng), 61. *Prof Exp:* Chem engr, Gen Elec Co, 53-54; MEM TECH STAFF, ADVAN PROGS DEPT, ROCKETDYNE DIV, N AM ROCKWELL CORP, 61- *Mem:* Am Chem Soc; Am Inst Chem Engrs; Combustion Inst. *Res:* Freeze desalination; chemical kinetics of combustion; environmental chemistry, especially pollution control. *Mailing Add:* 6110 Nevada Ave Woodland Hills CA 91367

SCHNEIDER, GEORGE WILLIAM, b East Canton, Ohio, Apr 4, 16; m 38; c 2. POMOLOGY. *Educ:* Ohio State Univ, BSc, 38, MS, 39; Rutgers Univ, PhD, 50. *Prof Exp:* Asst pomol, NMex Col, 39-46; res assoc, NJ Exp Sta, 46-50; from res assoc prof to res prof hort, NC State Col, 50-58; res prof & head dept, 58-60, assoc dir agr exten, 60-69, PROF HORT, UNIV KY, 69- *Mem:* Fel AAAS; fel Am Soc Hort Sci; Am Soc Plant Physiol. *Res:* Peach breeding; mechanism of abscission; dwarfing by apple stocks. *Mailing Add:* Dept of Hort Univ of KY Lexington KY 40506

SCHNEIDER, GERALD EDWARD, b Libertyville, Ill, Aug 20, 40; m 77; c 3. NEUROSCIENCE. *Educ:* Wheaton Col, BSc, 63; Mass Inst Technol, PhD(psychol), 66. *Prof Exp:* Res assoc, 66-67, from asst prof to assoc prof, 67-78, PROF PSYCHOL, MASS INST TECHNOL, 78- *Concurrent Pos:* Prin investr, Nat Eye Inst, NIH, 70-, co-investr, Nat Inst Neurological Dis & Stroke, 75-78 & Nat Eye Inst, 78, mem, Biopsychol Study Sect, 78-82, Basic Sci Task Force & Panel Behavior, Comt Long-term Res Strategies, NINCDS, 78. *Honors & Awards:* Young Psychologist Award, Am Psychol Asn, 66. *Mem:* Am Asn Anatomists; Soc Neurosci. *Res:* Neuroanatomical changes following early brain damage; behavioral alterations and recovery of function after neonatal or adult brain lesions in small mammals; development and organization of the visual system. *Mailing Add:* Dept of Psychol Mass Inst Technol Cambridge MA 02139

SCHNEIDER, GERHARDT, b Milwaukee, Wis, Feb 6, 34; m 56; c 2. FOREST ECOLOGY. *Educ:* Univ Mich, BS, 56, MF, 57; Mich State Univ, PhD(forest ecol), 63. *Prof Exp:* Asst dist ranger forest admin, US Forest Serv, 57; res asst forestry, Mich State Univ, 59-62; asst prof, Stephen F Austin State Col, 62-65; from asst prof to prof forestry fisheries & wildlife, Mich State Univ, 65-77; PROF & HEAD DEPT FORESTRY, WILDLIFE & FISHERIES, UNIV TENN, 77- *Concurrent Pos:* Consult, AEC-Oak Ridge Assoc Univs, 66-72; US Forest Serv and various forest industries, 66- *Mem:* AAAS; Soc Am Foresters; Soil Sci Soc Am; Am Forestry Asn; Ecol Soc Am. *Res:* Production ecology; biomass and nutrient analysis of tree species; environmental factors influencing tree growth and development; nutrient cycle in the forest ecosystem; forest soil moisture relations. *Mailing Add:* Dept of Forestry Univ of Tenn Knoxville TN 37901

SCHNEIDER, HAROLD O, b Cincinnati, Ohio, Apr 8, 30; m 60; c 2. PHYSICS, MATHEMATICS. *Educ:* Univ Cincinnati, BS, 51, MS, 52, PhD(physics), 56. *Prof Exp:* Aeronaut res scientist, Lewis Res Ctr, NASA, 51-61; mathematician, Rand Develop Corp, Ohio, 61-62; staff mem, Lincoln Lab, Mass Inst Technol, 62-72; sr systs analyst, Dynamics Res Corp, Wilmington, Mass, 72-78; MEM STAFF, LOCKHEED CORP, SUNNYVALE, CALIF, 78- *Mem:* Am Inst Aeronaut & Astronaut; Sigma Xi. *Res:* Spline methods for nonlinear parameter estimation; radar data processing and analyses of flight test data; optimal control, nonlinear state and parameter estimation; mathematical modeling and simulation; spline methods for time series modelling, real time estimation, identification, optical control and guidance. *Mailing Add:* 789 Coastland Dr Palo Alto CA 94303

SCHNEIDER, HAROLD WILLIAM, b Rochester, NY, Oct 8, 43; m 69; c 2. TOPOLOGY. *Educ:* Univ Rochester, AB, 65; Univ Chicago, MS, 66, PhD(math), 72. *Prof Exp:* Teaching asst math, Univ Chicago, 66-69; instr, 69-72, asst prof, 72-77, ASSOC PROF MATH, ROOSEVELT UNIV, 77- *Mem:* Am Math Soc; Math Asn Am. *Res:* Differential topology; algebraic topology. *Mailing Add:* Dept of Math Roosevelt Univ 430 S Michigan Ave Chicago IL 60605

SCHNEIDER, HENRY, b Los Angeles, Calif, July 25, 15; m 42; c 3. PLANT PATHOLOGY & ANATOMY. *Educ:* Univ Calif, Los Angeles, AB, 38; Univ Calif, Berkeley, MS, 39, PhD(plant path), 43. *Prof Exp:* Asst pathologist, Guayule Res Proj, USDA, 43-44, pathologist, Emergency Plant Dis Prev Proj, 44-45; assoc, Citrus Exp Sta, 45-47, from asst plant pathologist to assoc plant pathologist, 47-60, PLANT PATHOLOGIST, UNIV CALIF, RIVERSIDE, 60-, LECTR PLANT PATH, 59- *Concurrent Pos:* Sabbatical leave, Univ Pretoria, 64. *Mem:* Am Phytopath Soc; Bot Soc Am; Biol Stain Comn. *Res:* Pathological plant anatomy; graft transmissible diseases of trees. *Mailing Add:* Dept of Plant Path Univ of Calif Riverside CA 92521

SCHNEIDER, HENRY, b Montreal, Que, Dec 5, 33; m 62; c 3. BIOCHEMISTRY, GENETICS. *Educ:* Sir George Williams Univ, BSc, 55; Univ Western Ontario, MSc, 57; McGill Univ, PhD(phys chem), 63. *Prof Exp:* Res assoc, Cornell Univ, 62-64; res chemist, Miami Valley Labs, Procter & Gamble Co, 64-66; asst res officer, 66-69, assoc res officer, 70-78, SR RES OFFICER, NAT RES COUN CAN, 78- *Mem:* Chem Inst Can; Can Biochem Soc; Am Chem Soc. *Res:* Yeast fermentations; pentose fermentation; molecular genetics; genetic engineering. *Mailing Add:* Nat Res Coun Can Ottawa ON K1A 0R6 Can

SCHNEIDER, HENRY C, SR, b Philadelphia, Pa, Aug 17, 07; m 37; c 2. MEDICINE. *Educ:* Ind Univ, BS, 30; Franklin & Marshall Col, BS, 32; Temple Univ, MD, 36; Am Bd Colon & Rectal Surgeons, dipl, 54. *Prof Exp:* High sch fac, Philadelphia, 28-30; chief serv proctol, Frankford Hosp, Philadelphia, 42, med dir, 50-57; asst prof, 57-62, CLIN ASSOC PROF SURG, SCH MED, TEMPLE UNIV, 62- *Concurrent Pos:* emer attend surgeon, Abington Mem Hosp, Pa & Holy Redeemer Hosp, Meadowbrook, Pa; emer chief serv proctol, Frankford Hosp, Philadelphia. *Mem:* Fel Am Proctol Soc; fel AMA; fel Am Col Surgeons; fel Int Col Surgeons; hon fel Arg Soc Proctol. *Res:* Colon and rectal surgery; anesthesia; therapeutics. *Mailing Add:* 1637 Paper Mill Rd Meadowbrook PA 19046

SCHNEIDER, HENRY JOSEPH, b York, Pa, Dec 21, 20; m 44; c 5. ORGANIC CHEMISTRY. *Educ:* La Salle Col, BA, 42; Temple Univ, MA, 48; Univ Wis, PhD(org chem), 51. *Prof Exp:* Chemist, Ugite Sales Corp, 42-43; res chemist, Rohm & Haas Co, 46-48; asst, Univ Wis, 48-51; res chemist, 51-56, mem staff sales develop, 56-60, mgr sales develop spec prod, 60-63, asst mgr, 63-68, asst mgr, indust chem, 68-69, mgr, 69-71, mkt develop mgr, Chem Div, 71-75, CORP DIR RES & DEVELOP, INDUST CHEM GROUP, ROHM & HAAS CO, PHILADELPHIA, 76- *Concurrent Pos:* Instr, La Salle Col, 52-56. *Mem:* Am Chem Soc; London Chem Soc; Com Develop Asn; Chem Mkt Res Asn. *Res:* Acetylene; hydrogen; high pressure reactions; ion exchange; acrylic monomers and polymers; petroleum additives; direction of broad scope. *Mailing Add:* Rohm & Haas Co Springhouse PA 19477

SCHNEIDER, HENRY PETER, b Philadelphia, Pa, Apr 4, 12. LABORATORY ANIMAL SCIENCE, MEDICAL RESEARCH. *Educ:* Univ Pa, VMD, 34. *Prof Exp:* Pvt pract vet med, 34-59; res assoc anat, 58-60, prof vet med & head div, 59-63, dir, Biol Res Lab, 63-72, res prof anat, 64-73, prof anat, Grad Sch, 71, CHMN DEPT BIO-MED SUPPORTING SERV, HAHNEMANN MED COL & HOSP, 72-, PROF ANAT, 75-, PROF PHYSIOL & BIOPHYS, 75- *Concurrent Pos:* Vet consult, Albert Einstein Med Ctr, Philadelphia, Pa, 63-67, Nat Drug Co Div, Richards & Merrill Co, 63-70 & US Vet Admin, 66-; actg dir, Federated Med Resources, 66-67, mem bd dirs, 66-, vpres, 73-79, pres, 79-; adj fel, Franklin Inst Res Labs, 78. *Mem:* Am Asn Anatomists; Am Vet Med Asn; Asn Neuroanatomists; Am Asn Lab Animal Sci; Nat Soc Med Res. *Res:* All phases of laboratory animal medicine contributing to abstracting physiological data from animal models, particularly comparative anatomy and physiology; expertise in animal anesthesia and surgical procedures, especially cardiovascular. *Mailing Add:* Hahnemann Med Col & Hosp 230 N Broad St Philadelphia PA 19102

SCHNEIDER, HOWARD ALBERT, b Milwaukee, Wis, Dec 25, 12; m 37; c 2. NUTRITION, BIOCHEMISTRY. *Educ:* Univ Wis, BS, 34, MS, 36, PhD(biochem), 38. *Prof Exp:* Asst biochem, Univ Wis, 36-39; Rockefeller Found fel natural sci, Hosp, Rockefeller Inst, 39-40, from asst to assoc, 40-57, assoc prof nutrit & microbiol, 58-65; mem, Inst Biomed Res, AMA, 65-70, actg dir, 67-68, dep dir, 69-70; prof & dir inst nutrit, 70-78, EMER PROF NUTRIT & BIOCHEM, SCH MED, UNIV NC, CHAPEL HILL, 78- *Concurrent Pos:* Chmn, Inst Lab Animal Resources, Nat Acad Sci-Nat Res Coun, 66-69; mem pub affairs comt, Fedn Am Socs Exp Biol, 68-74, chmn, 70-72; prof, NC State Univ, 70-78 & Univ NC, Greensboro, 70-78; mem, President's Comn World Hunger, 78-80; chief ed, Nutrit Support Med Practice, 77- *Mem:* fel AAAS; fel Am Inst Chemists; Am Pub Health Asn; Am Inst Nutrit; Am Inst Biol Sci. *Res:* Nutrition; resistance to infection. *Mailing Add:* 228 Marrham Dr Chapel Hill NC 27514

SCHNEIDER, HUBERT H, b Coesfeld, Ger, July 3, 26; US citizen; m 58. MATHEMATICAL LOGIC. *Educ:* Univ Münster, Dr rer nat(math), 54. *Prof Exp:* Res asst math logic, Inst Math Logic & Res Found Math, Univ Münster, 54-57; asst prof math, Univ Nebr, Lincoln, 57-61, assoc prof, 61-80. *Concurrent Pos:* Res fel, Univ Nebr, Lincoln. *Mem:* Am Math Soc; Math Asn Am; Asn Symbolic Logic. *Res:* Mathematical logic; foundations of mathematics; lattice theory. *Mailing Add:* 3451 M Lincoln NE 68510

SCHNEIDER, IMOGENE PAULINE, b Milwaukee, Wis, June 6, 34. PARASITOLOGY. *Educ:* Ohio State Univ, BS, 56, MS, 58; Univ Chicago, PhD(genetics), 61. *Prof Exp:* NSF fel, Univ Zurich, 61-62; res biologist, Yale Univ, 62-65; RES BIOLOGIST, WALTER REED ARMY INST RES, 65- *Mem:* AAAS; Am Soc Trop Med & Hyg; Am Soc Parasitol; Tissue Cult Asn. *Res:* Developmental genetics of Drosophila; insect tissue culture; nutritional requirements of malarial parasites in vitro. *Mailing Add:* Dept of Entom Walter Reed Army Inst of Res Washington DC 20012

SCHNEIDER, IRVING ROBERT, b San Francisco, Calif, Feb 7, 15; m 50; c 1. PLANT PATHOLOGY. *Educ:* Univ Calif, BS, 49, PhD(plant path), 53. *Prof Exp:* Asst plant path, Univ Calif, 49-54; asst plant pathologist, Natural Hist Surv, Univ Ill, 54-56; pathologist, Plant Virol Lab, USDA, 56-79; VIS VIROLOGIST, DEPT BIOCHEM & BIOPHYS, UNIV CALIF, DAVIS, 80- *Concurrent Pos:* NSF sr fel, John Innes Inst, Norwich, Eng, 68-69. *Mem:* AAAS; Am Phytopath Soc; Am Inst Biol Sci. *Res:* Chemotherapy of plant diseases; physiology of plant virus diseases; satellite viruses. *Mailing Add:* Dept Biochem & Biophys Univ Calif Davis CA 95616

SCHNEIDER, IRWIN, b New York, NY, Aug 17, 32; m 59; c 2. SOLID STATE PHYSICS, OPTICS. *Educ:* Univ Ill, BS, 54, MS, 56; Univ Pa, PhD(physics), 63. *Prof Exp:* Fel physics, Lab Insulation Res, Mass Inst Technol, 63-64; RES PHYSICIST, US NAVAL RES LAB, 64- *Concurrent Pos:* Nat Acad Sci-Nat Res Coun fel, 64-65, US Naval Res Lab. *Mem:* Fel Am Phys Soc; fel Sigma Xi. *Res:* Color centers in alkali halide crystals; holography. *Mailing Add:* Code 6551 US Naval Res Lab Washington DC 20375

SCHNEIDER, JACOB DAVID, b St Louis, Mo, Apr 14, 46; m 72. EXPERIMENTAL ATOMIC PHYSICS, ENGINEERING DESIGN. *Educ:* Univ Mo-Rolla, BS, 68; Kans State Univ, MS, 70. *Prof Exp:* Res asst, Los Alamos Sci Lab, 68-69; assoc physicist, Appl Physics Lab, Johns Hopkins Univ, 70-74; PHYSICIST, LOS ALAMOS SCI LAB, 74- *Mem:* Am Inst Physics. *Res:* The development of an intense one-ampere tritium ion source for use on the intense neutron source facility; development of a 125mA, 100 KV deuteron injector. *Mailing Add:* MS 459 Box 1663 Los Alamos Sci Lab Los Alamos NM 87545

SCHNEIDER, JAMES ROY, b Bellevue, Ky, Nov 28, 34; m 56; c 4. PHYSICS. *Educ:* Villa Madonna Col, AB, 56; Univ Cincinnati, MS, 59, PhD(physics), 65. *Prof Exp:* Instr physics, Villa Madonna Col, 59-63, asst prof, 63-64; from asst prof to assoc prof, 64-74, PROF PHYSICS, UNIV DAYTON, 74-, CHMN DEPT, 75- *Mem:* Am Phys Soc; Am Asn Physics Teachers. *Res:* Single crystals; x-ray techniques; optical properties of solids; laser interactions; visible and infrared radiation. *Mailing Add:* Dept of Physics Univ of Dayton Dayton OH 45469

SCHNEIDER, JOHN ARTHUR, b Saginaw, Mich, Feb 27, 40; m 63; c 2. ORGANIC CHEMISTRY, POLYMER CHEMISTRY. *Educ:* Albion Col, AB, 62; Mass Inst Technol, PhD(org chem), 66. *Prof Exp:* Res chemist, 66-69, proj leader latex res, 69-72, develop specialist org chem, 72-73, group leader org chem develop, 73-77, NY dist sales mgr, 77-79, CHEM & METALS DEPT MGR FOR BRAZIL, DOW CHEM CO, 79- *Concurrent Pos:* Instr, Delta Col, 67-69 & Cent Mich Univ, 74-77; vis indust scientist, Univ Wis-Superior, 67. *Mem:* Am Chem Soc (secy, 62-); Sigma Xi. *Res:* Cephalosporin C synthesis; bromine chloride; styrene-butadiene latexes; unsaturated polyesters; oxonium chemistry; polyamines; fire retardancy; peptide synthesis. *Mailing Add:* Dow Chem Co Park 80 Plaza E Saddle Brook NJ 07862

SCHNEIDER, JOHN H, b Eau Claire, Wis, Sept 29, 31. INFORMATION SCIENCE, BIOCHEMISTRY. *Educ:* Univ Wis, BS, 53, MS, 55, PhD(exp oncol), 58. *Prof Exp:* Asst prof biochem, Am Univ Beirut, 58-61 & Vanderbilt Univ, 61-62; ed-in-chief, Biol Abstr, 62-63; mem staff scientist-adminr training prog, NIH, 63-64, sci & prog info specialist, 64-67, sci & tech info officer, 67-73, DIR INT CANCER RES DATA BANK PROG, NAT CANCER INST, 73- *Mem:* AAAS; Am Soc Info Sci. *Res:* Development of large automated data bank for collection, processing and dissemination of all technical documents dealing with cancer and descriptions of all current cancer research projects; decimal classifications of biomedicine for use in program analysis; information retrieval and selective dissemination of information; design and development of computer systems for using hierarchical classifications in information systems. *Mailing Add:* Westwood Bldg Rm 10A18 Nat Cancer Inst Bethesda MD 20205

SCHNEIDER, JOHN MATTHEW, b Coulterville, Ill, Apr 27, 35; m 60; c 3. ELECTROHYDRODYNAMICS, PHYSICAL ELECTRONICS. *Educ:* Univ Ill, BS, 59, MS, 60, PhD(elec eng), 64. *Prof Exp:* Instr elec eng, Univ Ill, 60-64, asst prof, 64-66; prof scientist res lab, Xerox Corp, 66-68, mgr res lab, 69-81; DIR, ADV TECHNOL LABS, MEAD DIGITAL SYSTS, DAYTON, OHIO, 81- *Res:* Electrostatics research dealing with the interaction of fields and liquids. *Mailing Add:* 9421 Tanglewyck Pl Spring Valley OH 45370

SCHNEIDER, JOSEPH, b Jersey City, NJ, June 25, 18. CHEMISTRY. *Educ:* Columbia Univ, BS, 39; NY Univ, MS, 47; Polytech Inst Brooklyn, PhD(org chem), 62. *Prof Exp:* From instr to asst prof chem, Long Island Univ, 46-55; lectr, Polytech Inst Brooklyn, 56-62; assoc prof, 63-70, PROF CHEM, ST FRANCIS COL, NY, 70- *Concurrent Pos:* Adj prof, Polytech Inst Brooklyn, 64-69; adj prof, Hunter Col, 70-71; US Off Educ fel, NY Univ, 71-72. *Mem:* AAAS; Am Chem Soc; Royal Soc Chem. *Res:* Enzyme model systems; decarboxylase models; reaction mechanisms; Diels-Alder reaction and its catalysis; formation of carbohydrates from formaldehyde; catalysis by metal ions. *Mailing Add:* Dept of Chem St Francis Col 180 Remsen St Brooklyn NY 11201

SCHNEIDER, JULIUS EDWARD, JR, biochemical genetics, see previous edition

SCHNEIDER, JURG ADOLF, b Basle, Switz, May 27, 20; nat US; m 46; c 4. PHYSIOLOGY, PHARMACOLOGY. *Educ:* Univ Basle, MD, 45. *Prof Exp:* Resident surg, Hosp, Basle, Switz, 46-47; resident, Univ Hosp, Univ Basle, 48-51; res assoc cardiol, Sch Med, Univ Calif, 47-48; sr pharmacologist, Ciba Pharmaceut Prod, Inc, 52-54, dir physiol res, 54-57; dir macrobiol res dept, Chas Pfizer & Co, Inc, 57-62; dir pharmaceut res, 62-72, DIR PROD LIC, E I DU PONT DE NEMOURS & CO, INC, 72- *Concurrent Pos:* Res fel, Res Lab, Ciba, Ltd, 45-46; lectr, Col Physicians & Surgeons, Columbia Univ, 57-65, adj prof, 70- *Mem:* Am Physiol Soc; Am Soc Pharmacol & Exp Therapeut; fel Am Col Clin Pharmacol & Chemother; fel Am Col Neuropsychopharmacol; NY Acad Sci. *Res:* Central nervous system and cardiovascular pharmacology; research administration. *Mailing Add:* 520 Rothbury Rd Wilmington DE 19803

SCHNEIDER, KATHRYN CLAIRE (JOHNSON), b Wiltshire, Eng, March 5, 53; US citizen; m 75; c 1. ORNITHOLOGY, BEHAVIORAL ECOLOGY. *Educ:* Cornell Univ, BA, 75; Princeton Univ, MS, 77, PhD(biol), 79. *Prof Exp:* ASST PROF BIOL, UNIV RICHMOND, 79- *Concurrent Pos:* Marcy Brady Tucker Travel Award, Am Ornithologists Union, 79. *Mem:* AAAS; Am Ornithologists Union; Ecol Soc Am; Sigma Xi; Nat Audubon Soc. *Res:* Optimal foraging theory and its relationship to dominance hierarchies and predation in winter foraging flocks of birds. *Mailing Add:* Dept Biol Univ Richmond Richmond VA 23175

SCHNEIDER, KENNETH JOHN, b Denver, Colo, Nov 5, 26; m 55; c 3. CHEMICAL ENGINEERING. *Educ:* Colo Sch Mines, PRE, 50. *Prof Exp:* Process engr, Gen Elec Co, 50-58, develop engr, 58-61, sr engr, 61-65; Pac Northwest Lab, Battelle Mem Inst, 65-67, res assoc process develop & prog planning, 67-71; eng assoc, Process Develop & Prog Planning, Westinghouse-Hanford Co, 71-72; mgr process evalutions, 72-78, STAFF ENGR, PAC NORTHWEST LAB, BATTELLE MEM INST, 78- *Concurrent Pos:* Prin engr, Int Atomic Energy Agency, Vienna, Austria, 78-80. *Mem:* Am Inst Chem Engrs; Am Nuclear Soc. *Res:* Process and equipment development in reprocessing of spent nuclear fuels; development of methods for solidification of highly radioactive wastes for safe storage; project engineering; development program planning and management; evaluation of nuclear fuel cycles. *Mailing Add:* 1507 Alder Ave Richland WA 99352

SCHNEIDER, LAWRENCE KRUSE, b Portland, Ore, Dec 17, 36; m 61; c 3. ANATOMY. *Educ:* Univ Wash, BA, 60, PhD(cytochem), 66. *Prof Exp:* Instr biol struct, Univ Wash, 65-66; asst prof anat, Univ NDak, 66-68; asst prof anat & dir grad training, Dept Anat, Col Med, Univ Ariz, 68-73; assoc prof anat & head dept, 73-75, dir div biomed sci, 75-76, dir med admis & asst dean basic sci, 76-77, asst dean acad affairs, 77-78, PROF ANAT & HEAD DEPT, SCH MED SCI, UNIV NEV, RENO, 76- *Concurrent Pos:* Instnl res grant, Univ NDak, 66-68; Gen Res Support, NASA & Am Cancer Soc instnl res grants, Col Med, Univ Ariz, 68-72. *Mem:* Am Asn Anat; Am Soc Cell Biol; Sigma Xi. *Res:* Radioautography of DNA and RNA synthesis in chromosomes of mammalian lymphocytes in vitro; cell kinetics; effects of various agents on cell growth in tissue culture; cytogenetics. *Mailing Add:* Dept Anat Sch Med Sci Univ Nev Reno NV 89557

SCHNEIDER, MARC H, b Rochester, NY. WOOD SCIENCE & TECHNOLOGY. *Educ:* State Univ NY, BS, 65, MS, 67, PhD(wood & polymer sci), 78. *Prof Exp:* Fel wood coating, Paint Res Inst, 65-67; asst prof, 67-74, ASSOC PROF WOOD SCI & TECHNOL, UNIV NB, 74- *Mem:* Soc Wood Sci & Technol; Forest Prods Res Soc; Inst Asn Wood Anatomists. *Res:* Wood-chemical interactions such as sorption, adhesion and interdiffusion; wood as fuel. *Mailing Add:* Dept of Forest Resources Univ of NB Fredericton NB E3B 5A3 Can

SCHNEIDER, MARK JOSEPH, b Minneapolis, Minn, Nov 22, 42; m 65; c 2. PHYSIOLOGICAL ECOLOGY. *Educ:* Univ Minn, BA, 64; Univ Ore, MA, 66, PhD(biol), 69. *Prof Exp:* Res scientist, aquatic ecol, 69-71, sect mgr, aquatic physiol, 71-78, SR RES SCIENTIST, FRESHWATER SCI, BATTELLE NORTHWEST, 78- *Res:* Thermal effects; fish toxology; physiology and ecology of aquatic biota. *Mailing Add:* Ecosysts Dept Battelle Northwest Richland WA 99352

SCHNEIDER, MARTIN V, b Bern, Switz, Oct 20, 30; m 55. PHYSICS. *Educ:* Swiss Fed Inst Technol, MS, 55, PhD(physics), 59. *Prof Exp:* Res assoc microwave res lab, Swiss Fed Inst Technol, 60-62; mem tech staff radio res, 63-68, SUPVR RADIO RES DEPT, BELL LABS, 68- *Mem:* Am Phys Soc; Am Vacuum Soc; Inst Elec & Electronics Engrs. *Res:* Microwave active and passive devices and circuits; optical and thin film active devices; photodetectors. *Mailing Add:* 46 Line Rd Holmdel NJ 07733

SCHNEIDER, MAXYNE DOROTHY, b North Adams, Mass, Nov 4, 42. PHYSICAL CHEMISTRY. *Educ:* Col Our Lady of the Elms, AB, 65; Boston Col, PhD(chem), 75. *Prof Exp:* Teacher chem, Cathedral High Sch, Springfield, Mass, 65-69; instr, 73-81, ASST PROF CHEM, COL OUR LADY OF THE ELMS, 81- *Res:* Hydrocarbon combustion kinetics; instrumentation in analytical chemistry. *Mailing Add:* Col of Our Lady of the Elms Chicopee MA 01013

SCHNEIDER, MICHAEL CHARLES, b Chicago, Ill, May 7, 29; m 54; c 2. GEOLOGY. *Educ:* Cornell Col, BA, 52; Miami Univ, MS, 56; Brigham Young Univ, PhD(geol), 67. *Prof Exp:* From instr to assoc prof geol, DePauw Univ, 59-68; prof geol, 68-76, PROF EARTH SCI, EDINBORO STATE COL, 76- *Mem:* AAAS; Geol Soc Am; Soc Econ Paleontologists & Mineralogists; Nat Asn Geol Teachers. *Res:* Water pollution; acid mine drainage; stratigraphic correlation and age dating; science education. *Mailing Add:* Dept of Earth Sci Edinboro State Col Edinboro PA 16444

SCHNEIDER, MICHAEL J, b Saginaw, Mich, Apr 21, 38; m 67. PLANT PHYSIOLOGY, PHOTOBIOLOGY. *Educ:* Univ Mich, BS, 60; Univ Tenn, MS, 62; Univ Chicago, PhD(bot), 65. *Prof Exp:* Nat Acad Sci-Nat Res Coun fel, Plant Physiol Lab, USDA, Beltsville, Md, 65-67; USPHS fel bot, Univ Wis-Madison, 67-68; asst prof biol sci, Columbia Univ, 68-73; assoc prof, 73-77, PROF BIOL, UNIV MICH-DEARBORN, 77- CHMN DEPT NATURAL SCI, 75- *Concurrent Pos:* Dept Energy vis prof, Plant Res Lab, Mich State Univ, 80-81. *Mem:* AAAS; Am Soc Plant Physiol; Bot Soc Am; Am Soc Photobiol. *Res:* Physiology and biochemistry of plant growth and development. *Mailing Add:* Dept of Natural Sci Univ of Mich Dearborn MI 48128

SCHNEIDER, MORRIS HENRY, b Sutton, Nebr, Nov 26, 23; m 52; c 1. INDUSTRIAL ENGINEERING. *Educ:* Univ Nebr, BS, 51 & 59; Kans State Univ, MS, 61; Okla State Univ, PhD(indust eng), 66. *Prof Exp:* Instr mech eng, Univ Nebr, 54-60; asst prof indust eng, Kans State Univ, 60-62 & Tex Tech Col, 62-64; assoc prof mech eng, 65-70, PROF INDUST ENG & CHMN DEPT, UNIV NEBR, LINCOLN, 70- *Concurrent Pos:* Am Soc Tool & Mfg Eng res grant, 66-67; NSF sci equip prog grant, 66-68. *Mem:* Am Soc Eng Educ; Am Inst Indust Engrs; Nat Soc Prof Engrs. *Res:* Production design and processes. *Mailing Add:* Dept of Indust Eng 175 Nebraska Hall Univ of Nebr Lincoln NE 68508

SCHNEIDER, PAUL, b New York, NY, May 3, 34; m 57; c 2. CLINICAL CHEMISTRY. *Educ:* City Col New York, BS, 56; Yale Univ, MS, 58; NY Univ, PhD(org chem), 61. *Prof Exp:* Res chemist, IIT Res Inst, 61-62; res scientist, Res Div, NY Univ, 62-64, asst prof chem, 64-65; res scientist, Diag Div, Chas Pfizer & Co, 65-68; dir tech develop & eval, Technicon Instrument Corp, 69-75; dir sci rel, Bio-Dynamics/BMC, 75-81; DIR, REAGENT OPER MCTPATH, INC, 81- *Mem:* Fel Am Inst Chemists; NY Acad Sci; Am Chem Soc; Nat Registry Clin Chemists; Am Asn Clin Chemists. *Res:* Hemolytic disease of the newborn; bilirubin metabolism; causes of hypertension and their detection; chemical basis of mental disease; hyperlipidemea, automated analysis and calibration materials. *Mailing Add:* 548 Stevens Ave Ridgewood NJ 07450

SCHNEIDER, PHILIP ALLEN DAVID, b St Louis, Mo, Oct 26, 38; m 63; c 6. INFORMATION SCIENCE, APPLIED STATISTICS. *Educ:* Cornell Univ, AB, 61; Duke Univ, PhD(methodology sci), 68. *Prof Exp:* Mathematician, Abbott Labs, 61-62; plans officer info sci, US Army Security Agency, 62-64; group leader, Defense Commun Agency, 64; consult, Dept Math, Duke Univ, 64-68; dir sci serv, US Army Syst Anal Group, 68-73; chief, Manpower Statist Div, 73-75, assoc dir workforce info, Bur Personnel Mgt Info Systs, 75-80, ASST DIR WORKFORCE INFO, US OFF PERSONNEL MGT, US CIVIL SERV COMN, 80- *Concurrent Pos:* NSF fel, 67; assoc prof, Sch Gen Studies, Univ Va, 68-73; lectr, Northern Va Community Col, 73- *Mem:* Am Statist Asn; Am Philol Asn; Asn Comput Mach; Opers Res Soc Am; Soc Mgt Info Systs. *Mailing Add:* 8511 Browning Ct Annandale VA 22003

SCHNEIDER, PHILLIP WILLIAM, JR, b Corvallis, Ore, Sept 2, 44; m 69; c 2. FISHERIES, TOXICOLOGY. *Educ:* Ore State Univ, BS, 66, PhD(fisheries, pharmacol), 74; Univ Maine, MS, 71. *Prof Exp:* Fisheries biologist, US Environ Protection Agency, 68-71; fish & wildlife biologist, River Basins Studies, US Fish & Wildlife Serv, res toxicologist, 75-78, CHIEF, CHRONIC INVEST, TOXICOLOGIST, HASKELL LAB, E I DU PONT DE NEMOURS & CO, 78- *Mem:* Am Soc Testing & Mat; Am Fisheries Soc; AAAS. *Res:* Neuromuscular physiology, pharmacology and detoxification mechanisms in fish as compared with other vertebrates. *Mailing Add:* Haskell Lab Elkton Rd E I du Pont de Nemours & Co Newark DE 19711

SCHNEIDER, RALPH JACOB, b Oxford, Ohio, Sept 2, 22; m 45; c 3. ELECTRONICS, ELECTRICAL ENGINEERING. *Educ:* Clarkson Col Technol, BEE, 49. *Prof Exp:* Instrumentation engr, Bell Aircraft Corp, 49-54, preliminary design engr, 54-57; engr, Melpar Div, Westinghouse Air Brake Co, 57-58, proj engr, 58-60; ELECTRONICS ENGR, ANAL SERV, INC, 60- *Mem:* Sr mem Inst Elec & Electronics Engrs. *Res:* Evaluation of research aircraft and missile components such as storage batteries, critical mechanical components, and radar subsystems; analysis of airborne radar, communications and electronic penetration aids and fire control systems. *Mailing Add:* 718 N Overlook Dr Alexandria VA 22305

SCHNEIDER, RICHARD COY, b Newark, NJ, May 29, 13; m 43. NEUROSURGERY. *Educ:* Dartmouth Col, BS, 35; Univ Pa, MD, 39; Univ Mich, MS, 48; Am Bd Neurol Surg, dipl, 50. *Prof Exp:* From asst prof to assoc prof, 50-62, head sect, 69-79, PROF NEUROSURG, MED SCH & HOSP, UNIV MICH, ANN ARBOR, 62- *Concurrent Pos:* Consult, US Vet Hosp, 50-; mem comt med aspects sports, AMA, 63-72; mem, Am Bd Neurol Surg, 66-72, vchmn, 70-72; mem coun med specialty socs; rep, World Fedn Neurosurg Soc, 69-81, second vpres, 77-81. *Honors & Awards:* Teachenor Mem lectr, Med Sch, Univ Kans, 59; Odeku Mem lectr, Med Sch, Univ Ibedon, Nigeria, 76; Yendell Mem lectr, Med Sch, Univ Louisville, 79. *Mem:* Soc Neurol Surgeons; Neurosurg Soc Am (vpres, 61); Am Asn Neurol Surgeons (vpres, 72, pres, 74); AMA; Acad Neurol Surg. *Res:* Spinal cord injuries; alteration of muscular tonus and movement; traumatic cerebrovascular and spinovascular insufficiency; surgical treatment of epilepsy; central vestibular disease and spatial orientation; theory of space sickness. *Mailing Add:* Sect of Neurosurg Univ of Mich Hosp Ann Arbor MI 48104

SCHNEIDER, RICHARD S, b Los Angeles, Calif, Jan 30, 41; m 63; c 2. CLINICAL BIOCHEMISTRY. *Educ:* Univ Calif, Berkeley, BS, 62; Univ Wis, PdD(org chem), 66. *Prof Exp:* Res fel, Univ Wis, 66, NIH fel, Mass Inst Technol, 66-67; sr res chemist & sect mgr, 67-73, asst dir develop, 73-75, VPRES & DIR DEVELOP, SYVA CO, 75- *Mem:* Am Chem Soc; Am Asn Clin Chem. *Res:* Synthesis of natural products and pharmaceuticals; polycyclic aromati heterocarbons; enzymology; clinical toxicology; design and development of non radio chemical immuno assay techniques; enzymology and immuno chemistry; synthesis of haptens and immuno chemical premisors. *Mailing Add:* Syva Res Inst 3181 Porter Dr Palo Alto CA 94304

SCHNEIDER, RICHARD THEODORE, b Munich, Ger, July 29, 27; m 50; c 2. PLASMA PHYSICS, SPECTROSCOPY. *Educ:* Univ Stuttgart, dipl, 58, PhD(physics), 61. *Prof Exp:* Res asst plasma physics, Inst High Temperature Res, Stuttgart, Ger, 59-61; sec chief, Allison Div, Gen Motors Corp, 61-65; assoc prof, 65-68, PROF NUCLEAR ENG, UNIV FLA, 68- *Concurrent Pos:* Liason scientist br off, London, UK, Off of US Naval Res, 74-75. *Mem:* Optical Soc Am; Soc Appl Spectros; Am Inst Aeronaut & Astronaut; Am Nuclear Soc. *Res:* Plasma diagnostics using spectroscopic techniques; nuclear pumped lasers; infra red spectroscopy; uranium plasmas. *Mailing Add:* Dept of Nuclear Eng Sci Univ of Fla Gainesville FL 32601

SCHNEIDER, ROBERT, b Brooklyn, NY, Apr 7, 21; m 46; c 3. GROUNDWATER GEOLOGY, HYDROLOGY. *Educ:* Brooklyn Col, AB, 41. *Prof Exp:* Photogrammetrist, US Geol Surv, 41-43, geologist, 43-44, groundwater geologist, Tenn, 45-50, dist geologist, Minn, 50-60, asst to chief res sec, Groundwater Br, 60-62, actg chief res sect, 62-64, staff geologist, Gen Hydrol Br, 64-65, res geologist, 65-67, chief off radiohydrol, 67-71; water res scientist, Off Water Resources Res, US Dept Interior, 71-75; STAFF HYDROLOGIST, US GEOL SURV, 75- *Concurrent Pos:* Consult, Govt Brazil, 60 & Govt Israel, 62. *Mem:* Geol Soc Am; Am Geophys Union; Nat Water Well Asn. *Res:* Thermal characteristics of aquifers; subsurface disposal of radioactive waste; geohydrology of glacial deposits. *Mailing Add:* US Geol Surv Mail Stop 410 Reston VA 22092

SCHNEIDER, ROBERT FOURNIER, b New York, NY, Feb 24, 33; div; c 3. CHEMICAL PHYSICS. *Educ:* Columbia Univ, AB, 54, MA, 56, PhD(chem), 59. *Prof Exp:* Res assoc chem, Brookhaven Nat Lab, 59-60; asst prof, 60-68, ASSOC PROF CHEM, STATE UNIV NY STONY BROOK, 68-, ASSOC DEAN RES, 73- *Mem:* AAAS. *Res:* Nuclear quadrupole resonance; vibrational spectroscopy of solids; inorganic complexes. *Mailing Add:* Off of Res Admin State Univ NY Stony Brook NY 11794

SCHNEIDER, ROBERT JULIUS, b Troy, NY, Mar 9, 39; m 61; c 2. ACCELERATOR PHYSICS, RADIATION PHYSICS. *Educ:* Oberlin Col, BA, 60; Wesleyan Univ, MA, 63; Tufts Univ, PhD(physics), 68. *Prof Exp:* Staff assoc physics, Columbia Univ, 68-73; res fel physics, Harvard Univ, 73-80; PHYSICIST, GEN INDEX CORP, 80- *Concurrent Pos:* Lectr physics, Harvard Univ, 79-80. *Mem:* Am Phys Soc; Am Asn Physicists Med. *Res:* Radiation applied to cancer therapy; accelerators; isotopes; nuclear physics. *Mailing Add:* 8 Braebrook Rd Acton MA 01720

SCHNEIDER, ROBERT W(ILLIAM), b Staten Island, NY, Dec 30, 25; m 46; c 3. CHEMICAL ENGINEERING. *Educ:* Lehigh Univ, BS, 48, MS, 49. *Prof Exp:* Design engr, Linde Co Div, Union Carbide Corp, 49-52, asst design & metall engr, 52-54; asst supv engr, Travelers Indemnity Co, 54-56, in chg boiler & pressure vessel design, 56-60; stress analyst, Oak Ridge Nat Lab, 60-62, asst supt, Inspection Eng Dept, 62-68; mgr eng, Energy Prod Group, Gulf & Western MFG Co, 68-82; CONSULT ENG, R W SCHNEIDER ASSOC, 82- *Mem:* Am Soc Mech Engrs. *Res:* Pressure vessel design, especially evaluation of secondary or discontinuity stresses; plastic behavior of engineering materials; development of theory and design rules for analysis of flat faced flanges in metal-to-metal contact; theoretical and experimental work on behavior of nozzles subjected to pressure and external loads. *Mailing Add:* 3918 Lincoln Parkway W Cedar & Meadow Sts Allentown PA 18104

SCHNEIDER, RONALD ALAN, b Berkeley, Calif, May 29, 39. ORGANIC CHEMISTRY. *Educ:* Stanford Univ, BS, 62; Cornell Univ, PhD(org chem), 66. *Prof Exp:* Asst prof chem, Oberlin Col, 66-67; SR RES CHEMIST, CHEVRON RES CO, STANDARD OIL CO CALIF, 68- *Res:* Petrochemical processes; synthetic organic chemistry; heterogenous catalytic oxidation; thin-film photoroltaic devices. *Mailing Add:* Chevron Res Co 576 Standard Ave Richmond CA 94802

SCHNEIDER, RONALD E, b Akron, Ohio, Sept 14, 28; m 53; c 4. THEORETICAL PHYSICS, NUCLEAR PHYSICS. *Educ:* Univ Akron, BS, 51; Va Polytech Inst, MS, 53; John Carroll Univ, MS, 58; Case Inst Technol, PhD(physics), 64. *Prof Exp:* Engr, Goodrich Tire & Rubber Co, 53-54; sr engr, Goodyear Aerospace Corp, 56-58; instr math, John Carroll Univ, 58-60; asst prof, 62-64, ASSOC PROF PHYSICS, UNIV AKRON, 64- *Res:* Nuclear forces. *Mailing Add:* Dept of Physics Univ of Akron Akron OH 44304

SCHNEIDER, ROSE G, b Minsk, Russia, July 19, 08; US citizen; m 41; c 3. MEDICINE. *Educ:* Barnard Col, Columbia Univ, AB, 29; Harvard Med Sch, MA, 32; Cornell Med Col, PhD, 37. *Prof Exp:* Instr path, Univ Tex Med Br Galveston, 42-43; asst pathologist, Robert B Green Hosp, San Antonio, 44-45; res assoc, Tissue Cult Lab & Tissue Metab Res Lab, 48-62, asst res prof surg, 62-63, asst res prof pediat, 63-65, assoc res prof, 65-69, RES PROF PEDIAT & PROF HUMAN BIOL CHEM & GENETICS, UNIV TEX MED BR GALVESTON, 69- *Mem:* Int Soc Hematol; Soc Exp Biol & Med; Am Soc Human Genetics; Am Soc Hemat; Sigma Xi. *Res:* Abnormal hemaglobins. *Mailing Add:* Dept of Pediat Univ of Tex Med Br Galveston TX 77550

SCHNEIDER, SANDRA LEE, b Pueblo, Colo, July 10, 44; m 73. IMMUNOHEMATOLOGY, IMMUNOLOGY. *Educ:* Southern Colo State Col, BS & Univ Colo, MT, 66. *Prof Exp:* Med technologist immunohemat, Belle Bonfils Mem Blood Band, 66-68; supvr blood bank, East Tenn Baptist Hosp, 68-69; med technologist II hemat, Med Ctr, Univ Kans, 69-70; med technologist immunol, Knoxville Blood Bank & Reagents, 70-71; RES SCIENTIST IMMUNOL & IMMUNOHEMAT, SOUTHWEST FOUND RES & EDUC, 73- *Concurrent Pos:* Tech transfusion consult, ETenn Baptist Hosp, Knoxville, Tenn, 68-69 & Knoxville Blood Ctr, 70-71. *Mem:* AAAS; Am Soc Primatologists; Am Soc Clin Pathologists; Am Asn Blood Banks; Am Soc Microbiol. *Res:* Design and development of techniques to determine alveolar macrophage and lymphocyte interactions, particularly in the baboon exposed to anti-cancer drugs, cigarette derived smoke and chemically defined environmental agents. *Mailing Add:* Southwest Found for Res & Educ PO Box 28147 San Antonio TX 78284

SCHNEIDER, SOL, b New York, NY, Feb 24, 24; m 57. ELECTRONICS. *Educ:* Brooklyn Col, BA, 46; NY Univ, MS, 49. *Prof Exp:* Chief res unit power & gas tube sect, Electronics Technol & Devices Lab, US Army, 48-55, asst sec chief, 55-56, chief, Plasma & Pulse Power Br, Electronics Technol & Devices Lab, 56-81; adj prof, Southeastern Ctr Elec Eng Educ, 81-; CONSULT, 81- *Concurrent Pos:* Chmn, Pulse Power Modulator Symp, Int Elec & Electronics Engrs, 58- *Honors & Awards:* Res & Develop Achievement Awards, 63 & 78, US Army & Secy Army Spec Act Award, 63; Bronze Medallion, Army Sci Conf, 78. *Mem:* Am Phys Soc; fel Inst Elec & Electronics Engrs; NY Acad Sci. *Res:* Modulators; pulse power; physicaland gaseous electronics; plasma physics; electron tubes; lasers; modulators. *Mailing Add:* 37 Northvale Ave Little Silver NJ 07739

SCHNEIDER, STEPHEN HENRY, b New York, NY, Feb 11, 45; m 78. CLIMATOLOGY. *Educ:* Columbia Univ, BS, 66, MS, 67, PhD(mech eng), 71. *Prof Exp:* Nat Acad Sci-Nat Res Coun grant & res assoc, Goddard Inst Space Studies, NASA, NY, 71-72; advan study prog fel, 72-73, sci & dep head, climate proj, 73-78, actg leader, Climate Sensitivity Group, 78-80, HEAD, VIS PROGS & DEP DIR, ADVANCED STUDY PROG, NAT CTR ATMOSPHERIC RES, 80- *Concurrent Pos:* mem, Comt Paleoclimatol & Climatic Change, Am Meteorol Soc, 73, mem global atmospheric res prog working group for numerical experimentation, 74-78; ed, Climatic Change, 75-; mem climate dynamics panel, Nat Acad Sci, 76-81; mem, Carter-Mondale Task Force on Sci Policy & Coun Sci & Technol for Develop, 76; Univ Corp Atmospheric Res Affil Prof, Lamont-Doherty Geol Observ, Columbia Univ, 76-; mem, Nat Acad Sci, Subcomt Resources & Environ, Int Inst Appl Systs Analysis, 78-80, Adv & Planning Comt, Social Indicators, Social Sci Res Coun, 79-, US Nat Climate Prog Adv Comt, 80-, Comt Pub Understanding Sci, Nat Sci Found, 80-81, Sci Adv Comt, World Climate Studies Prog, United Nations Enviorn Prog, 80-; co-ed, Food-Climate Interactions, 81, Social Sci Res, An Interdisciplinary Appraisal, 82. *Mem:* AAAS; fel Scientists Inst Pub Info; US Asn Club Rome; Am Meteorol Soc; Am Geophys Union. *Res:* Theoretical investigations of climatic changes arising from both natural and possible man-made causes; impact of human activities on climate; impact of climatic change on society; science policy; science popnairization. *Mailing Add:* Nat Ctr Atmospheric Res Boulder CO 80307

SCHNEIDER, WALTER CARL, b Cedarburg, Wis, Sept 26, 19; m 42; c 3. CHEMISTRY. *Educ:* Univ Wis, BS, 41, PhD(physiol chem), 45. *Prof Exp:* Asst, Univ Wis, 41-45, Childs fel, 45-47; Rockefeller Inst, 46-47; instr oncol, Univ Wis, 47-48; CHEMIST, USPHS, 48- *Mem:* Am Soc Biol Chem; Am Chem Soc; Am Asn Cancer Res. *Res:* Distribution of enzymes and nucleic acids within normal and cancer cells. *Mailing Add:* Nat Cancer Inst Bethesda MD 20014

SCHNEIDER, WILLIAM AEPPLI, b St Paul, Minn, Jan 24, 33; m 55; c 2. GEOPHYSICS. *Educ:* Univ Wis, BS, 55; Mass Inst Technol, PhD(geophys), 61. *Prof Exp:* Res geophysicist, 61-62, sect leader, 64-69, SR RES GEOPHYSICIST, RES DEPT, SCI SERV DIV, TEX INSTRUMENTS, INC, 63-, MGR GEOPHYS RES BR, 69- *Mem:* Soc Explor Geophys; Europ Asn Explor Geophys. *Res:* Petroleum exploration; seismology; underwater acoustics; data processing; statistical communications theory; geophysical data processing; time series analysis. *Mailing Add:* Tex Instruments Inc PO Box 5621 MS 965 Dallas TX 75222

SCHNEIDER, WILLIAM CHARLES, b New Orleans, La, Jan 22, 40; m 68; c 3. SOLID MECHANICS, ENGINEERING MECHANICS. *Educ:* La State Univ, BS, 62; Univ Houston, MS, 68; Rice Univ, PhD(mech eng), 72. *Prof Exp:* AEROSPACE ENGR, NASA, 62- *Concurrent Pos:* Consult mech, 77-; eng consult, DiCaro & Assocs, 77-78; eng consult & vpres, Accident Anal Consult Engrs, 78- *Mem:* Sigma Xi. *Res:* Thermoelasticity; elasticity; fluid-filled porous elastic solids. *Mailing Add:* Johnson Space Ctr NASA Rd One Houston TX 77058

SCHNEIDER, WILLIAM GEORGE, b Wolseley, Sask, June 1, 15; m 40; c 2. PHYSICAL CHEMISTRY. *Educ:* Univ Sask, BSc, 37, MS, 39; McGill Univ, PhD(phys chem), 41. *Hon Degrees:* DSc, York Univ, 66, Mem Univ Newf, 68, Univ Moncton, 69, Univ Sask, 69, McMaster Univ, 69, Laval Univ, 69, Univ NB, 70, Univ Montreal, 70, McGill Univ, 70; LLD, Univ Alta, 68, Laurentian Univ, 68; DSc, Ottawa Univ, 78. *Prof Exp:* Royal Soc Can traveling fel, Harvard Univ, 41-43; res physicist, Woods Hole Oceanog Inst, 43-46; head gen phys chem sect, Div Pure Chem, Nat Res Coun Can, 43-63, dir div pure chem, 63-65, vpres sci, 65-67, PRES, 67-80; RES CONSULT, 80- *Honors & Awards:* Medal, Chem Inst Can, 61; Henry Marshall Tory Medal, Royal Soc Can, 69; Montreal Medal, Chem Inst Can, 73; Order of Can, 77. *Mem:* Am Chem Soc; Am Phys Soc; fel Chem Inst Can; fel Royal Soc Can; fel Royal Soc London. *Res:* Intermolecular forces; critical phenomena; ultrasonics; nuclear magnetic resonance; organic semiconductors. *Mailing Add:* Admin Bldg Nat Res Coun of Can Ottawa ON K1A 0R6 Can

SCHNEIDER, WILLIAM PAUL, b Marietta, Ohio, Mar 25, 21; m 44; c 4. ORGANIC CHEMISTRY. *Educ:* Marietta Col, AB, 44; Univ Wis, MS, 46, PhD(chem), 50. *Prof Exp:* Instr chem, Marietta Col, 46-47, fel, Harvard Univ, 50-51; CHEMIST, UPJOHN CO, 51- *Mem:* Am Chem Soc. *Res:* Synthetic organic chemistry; steroids; prostaglandins; natural products. *Mailing Add:* Dept Chem Upjohn Co Kalamazoo MI 49001

SCHNEIDER, WOLFGANG, b Oberhausen, Ger, Mar 25, 35; m 63; c 2. ORGANIC CHEMISTRY, INORGANIC CHEMISTRY. *Educ:* Aachen Tech Univ, BS, 57, MS, 59; Max Planck Inst Coal Res, PhD(org chem), 62. *Prof Exp:* Asst metal-organics, Max Planck Inst Coal Res, 59-61, fel org chem, 61-62; res chemist, 63-65, sr res & develop chemist, 65-78, res & develop assoc, 78-80, SR RES & DEVELOP ASSOC, B F GOODRICH CO, 80- *Res:* Heterogeneous and homogenous catalysis via transition metal pi complex; organic chemistry; polymerization; chemical engineering. *Mailing Add:* B F Goodrich Co 9921 Brecksville Rd Brecksville OH 44141

SCHNEIDERMAN, HOWARD ALLEN, b New York, NY, Feb 9, 27; m 51; c 2. DEVELOPMENTAL BIOLOGY, DEVELOPMENTAL GENETICS. *Educ:* Swarthmore Col, AB, 48; Harvard Univ, MA, 49, PhD(physiol), 52. *Hon Degrees:* DSc, La Salle Col, 75. *Prof Exp:* Res fel zool, Harvard Univ, 52-53; from asst prof to assoc prof, Cornell Univ, 53-61; prof biol & chmn dept, Western Reserve Univ, 61-66, Jared Potter Kirtland distinguished prof, 66-69, co-dir develop biol ctr, 61-69; prof biol sci, 69-77, PROF DEVELOP BIOL & INSECT PHYSIOL, UNIV CALIF, IRVINE, 77-, DIR CTR PATH, CHMN DEPT DEVELOP & CELL BIOL & DEAN SCH, 69- *Concurrent Pos:* NSF sr fel, Cambridge Univ; trustee, Marine Biol Lab, Woods Hole, 66-72; dir, NIH training prog develop biol, 62-, chmn, Pop Res Training Comt, Nat Inst Child Health & Human Develop, 69-70 perinatal biol & infant mortality training comt, 71-72, mem, Maternal & Child Health Res Comt, NIH, 75- *Mem:* Nat Acad Sci; Am Acad Arts & Sci; Am Soc Cell Biol; AAAS; Am Soc Zoologists. *Res:* Insect physiology and endocrinology; genetics. *Mailing Add:* Sch of Biol Sci Univ of Calif Irvine CA 92664

SCHNEIDERMAN, LAWRENCE J, b New York, NY, Mar 24, 32; m 56; c 4. INTERNAL MEDICINE. *Educ:* Yale Univ, BA, 53; Harvard Med Sch, MD, 57. *Prof Exp:* Intern path, Boston City Hosp, Mass, 57-58, intern med, Strong Mem Hosp, Rochester, NY, 58-59; clin assoc, Sect Human Genetics, Nat Inst Dent Res, 59-61; med resident, Sch Med, Stanford Univ, 62-64, from instr to asst prof med, 64-70; ASSOC PROF COMMUNITY MED, SCH MED, UNIV CALIF, SAN DIEGO, 70- *Concurrent Pos:* Nat Heart Inst sr fel, Galton Lab, London, 61-62. *Mem:* AAAS; Am Soc Human Genetics; AMA; Am Soc Health & Human Values. *Res:* Genetic diseases and primary medical care. *Mailing Add:* Dept of Community Med Sch Med Univ Calif San Diego La Jolla CA 92093

SCHNEIDERMAN, MARTIN HOWARD, b Brooklyn, NY, Dec 24, 41; m 72. RADIATION BIOLOGY, CELL BIOLOGY. *Educ:* Cornell Univ, BS, 63; Colo State Univ, MS, 67, PhD(physiol & biophys), 70. *Prof Exp:* Picker Found fel, Univ Fla, 70-72; res scientist, Battelle Mem Inst, 72-75; asst prof, 75-79, ASSOC PROF RADIATION BIOL, THOMAS JEFFERSON UNIV, 79- *Concurrent Pos:* Mem exp combined modalities study group, Nat Cancer Inst, 76- *Mem:* Radiation Res Soc; Biophys Soc; Cell Kinetics Soc; Am Soc Cell Biol; AAAS. *Res:* Effects of radiation, drugs and other challenges on the kinetics and survival of mammalian cells in culture; mechanisms related to observed changes. *Mailing Add:* Dept of Radiation Therapy & Nuclear Med 10th & Walnut St Philadelphia PA 19107

SCHNEIDERMAN, MARVIN ARTHUR, b New York, NY, Dec 25, 18; m 41; c 3. STATISTICS. *Educ:* City Col New York, BS, 39; Am Univ, MA, 53, PhD(math statist), 61. *Prof Exp:* Jr statistician, Bur Census, US Dept Commerce, DC, 40-41; statistician, US War Dept, 41-43, Wright-Patterson AFB, Ohio, 46-48; statistician, 48-60, assoc chief biomet br, 60-70, ASSOC DIR FIELD STUDIES & STATIST, NAT CANCER INST, 70- *Concurrent Pos:* Adj prof, Georgetown Univ; adj prof, Grad Sch Pub Health, Univ Pittsburgh. *Mem:* Fel AAAS; hon fel Am Statist Asn; Am Asn Cancer Res; fel Royal Statist Soc; Int Statist Inst. *Res:* Design of experiments; mathematical biology; sequential analysis. *Mailing Add:* Nat Cancer Inst Room 4C03 Landow Bldg Bethesda MD 20014

SCHNEIDERMAN, NEIL, b Brooklyn, NY, Feb 24, 37; m 60; c 3. PSYCHOPHYSIOLOGY. *Educ:* Brooklyn Col, BA, 60; Ind Univ, PhD(psychol), 64. *Prof Exp:* From asst prof to assoc prof, 65-74, PROF PSYCHOL, UNIV MIAMI, 74-, MEM STAFF, LAB QUANT BIOL, 65- *Concurrent Pos:* Asst, Physiol Inst, Univ Basel, 64-65; NSF res grant, 66-72; NIH training grant, 67- *Mem:* Psychonomic Soc; Am Psychol Asn. *Res:* Physiological psychology; psychopharmacology; conditioning; role of central nervous system in autonomic conditioning and cardiovascular regulation. *Mailing Add:* Dept of Psychol Univ of Miami Coral Gables FL 33124

SCHNEIDERWENT, MYRON OTTO, b Milwaukee, Wis, Jan 8, 35; m 54; c2. PHYSICS, SCIENCE EDUCATION. *Educ:* Univ Wis-Stevens Point, 60; Western Mich Univ, MA, 63; Univ Miss, MSCS, 64; Univ Northern Colo, DEd(sci educ), 70. *Prof Exp:* Teacher, Muskegon Pub Schs, 60-63; instr physics, Interlochen Arts Acad, 64-67; ASSOC PROF PHYSICS, UNIV WIS-SUPERIOR, 67- *Concurrent Pos:* Field consult, Harvard Proj Physics, 65-67, mgr, 67; dir proj AWARE, Univ Wis-Superior, 74-76. *Mem:* Am Asn Physics Teachers; Nat Sci Teachers Asn. *Res:* Classroom use of behavioral objectives; heavy metal uptake in aquatic flora due to coal leachate. *Mailing Add:* Dept of Physics Univ of Wis Superior WI 54880

SCHNEIR, MICHAEL LEWIS, b Chicago, Ill, Nov 17, 37; m 65; c 2. COLLAGEN METABOLISM, DIABETES COMPLICATIONS. *Educ:* Univ Ill, Urbana, BS, 59, Chicago, MS, 62, PhD(biochem), 66. *Prof Exp:* Fel, Dept Biochem, Tufts Sch Med, 65-66; fel, Dept Biochem, Univ Pittsburgh Sch Med, 66-67; asst prof, 67-70, ASSOC PROF BIOCHEM, UNIV SOUTHERN CALIF SCH DENT, 70- *Concurrent Pos:* Sabbatical leave, Univ Ala Dent Res Inst, 75. *Mem:* Int Asn Dent Res; Am Diabetes Asn; Am Chem Soc; Sigma Xi. *Res:* The effect of streptozotocin-induced diabetes on tissue collagen catabolism with emphasis on procollagen catabolism in rat skin and gingiva. *Mailing Add:* ACB 440 Univ Southern Calif Los Angeles CA 90089

SCHNEIWEISS, JEANNETTE W, b Corona, NY, Apr 14, 20; m 41; c 3. PHYSIOLOGY, BIOMETRICS. *Educ:* Brooklyn Col, BS, 58; NY Univ, MA, 61, PhD(biol), 63. *Prof Exp:* NY State Regents col teaching scholar, 59-61; teaching fel sci, NY Univ, 61-63; instr biol, Nassau Community Col, 63-64; asst prof, Adelphi Univ, 64-68; asst prof, 68-73, ASSOC PROF BIOL & PHYSIOL, HOFSTRA UNIV, 73- *Honors & Awards:* Founders Day Award, NY Univ, 62. *Mem:* Fel AAAS; Nat Asn Biol Teachers; Nat Sci Teachers Asn. *Res:* Determination of endocrinological effects of high fat diets in weanling, female and albino rats. *Mailing Add:* Dept of Biol Hofstra Univ Hempstead NY 11550

SCHNELL, GARY DEAN, b Lyons, Kans, July 30, 42; m 65; c 2. ZOOLOGY. *Educ:* Cent Mich Univ, BS, 64; Northern Ill Univ, MS, 66; Univ Kans, PhD(zool), 69. *Prof Exp:* Coordr biol, Origin & Struct of Ecosysts Integrated Res Prog, US Partic Int Biol Prog, 69-70; res assoc zool, Univ Tex, Austin, 69-70; asst prof zool, Univ Okla, 70-75, head cur zool, Stovall Mus Sci & Hist, 72-74, interim dir, 79-80, ASSOC PROF ZOOL, UNIV OKLA, 75-, CURATOR BIRDS, STOVALL MUS SCI & HIST, 71-, HEAD CUR LIFE SCI, 74-, DIR OKLA BIOL SURV, 78- *Concurrent Pos:* Vis res assoc, Dept Biol & Ctr Evolution & Paleobiol, Univ Rochester, 77-78. *Mem:* AAAS; Am Ornith Union; Cooper Ornith Soc; Soc Study Evolution; Soc Syst Zool; Wilson Ornith Soc. *Res:* Systematic biology and ornithology; application of numerical techniques to the classification of organisms; evolutionary biology. *Mailing Add:* Dept of Zool Univ of Okla Norman OK 73019

SCHNELL, GENE WHEELER, b Wapakoneta, Ohio, Jan 27, 24; m 46; c 3. MICROBIOLOGY, BIOCHEMISTRY. *Educ:* Ohio State Univ, BSc, 47, MSc, 48, PhD(microbiol), 57. *Prof Exp:* Microbiologist, Ft Detrick, Md, 49-57; microbiologist, Res Ctr, Mead Johnson & Co, 57-70, prin investr, 70-73; MGR MICROBIOL DEPT, KRAFT RES & DEVELOP, 73- *Mem:* AAAS; Am Soc Microbiol; Am Chem Soc; NY Acad Sci. *Res:* Microbial physiology; fermentations; microbial genetics; antibiotics; nutritional biochemistry; food microbiology; nutritional and pharmaceutical quality control; immobilized enzymes, continuous fermentations, dairy starter cultures, protein hydrolysates, single cell protein, food safety. *Mailing Add:* Kraft Res & Develop 801 Waukegan Rd Glenview IL 60025

SCHNELL, JAY HEIST, b Philadelphia, Pa, Nov 21, • 32. RAPTORS, REMOTE SENSING INSTRUMENT DESIGN. *Educ:* Earlham Col, AB, 55; Univ Calif, Berkeley, MA, 57; Univ Ga, PhD(zool), 64. *Prof Exp:* Res asst ecol, Savannah River Plant, Univ Ga, 62-63, fel pop ecol, 64-65; fel radio tracking tech, Cedar Creek Radio-Tracking Sta, Univ Minn, Minneapolis, 65-69; res biologist, Tall Timbers Res Sta, Fla, 69-72; wildlife telemetry consult, Ill, 72-73; dir, Res Ranch, 73-74; dir, George Whittell Wildlife Preserve, Ariz, 74-76; CONSULT BIOL, 76- *Mem:* Am Asn Mammal. *Res:* Population ecology of small mammals; behavior and ecology of birds of prey; radio-tracking techniques aiding studies in animal and bird behavior; black hawks nesting in Aravaipa Canyon, Arizona. *Mailing Add:* Box 54 Klondyke Rural Sta Wilcox AZ 85643

SCHNELL, JEROME VINCENT, b Aitkin, Minn, July 19, 34. BIOCHEMISTRY. *Educ:* Col St Thomas, BS, 56; Univ Nebr, MS, 59, PhD(chem), 63. *Prof Exp:* Res assoc enzymol, Biol Div, Oak Ridge Nat Lab, 63-64; res assoc protozool, Med Ctr, Stanford Univ, 65-69; asst prof med microbiol & trop med, Univ Hawaii, Leahi, 70-75; res chemist, Nat Marine Fisheries Serv, Nat Oceanic & Atmospheric Admin, 75-81, ASSOC PROF, SEATTLE UNIV, 80-, EXEC DIR, ALCOHOL STUDIES PROG, 80- *Concurrent Pos:* USPHS fel, Oak Ridge Nat Lab, 64-65; instr, Alcohol Studies Prog, Seattle Univ, 78- *Res:* Biochemistry of malarial parasites; enzymology of amino acid and protein metabolism; xenobiotic metabolism in fish. *Mailing Add:* 533 Harvard Ave E Apt 204 Seattle WA 98102

SCHNELL, LORNE ALBERT, b Saskatoon, Sask, Jan 3, 33; m 60; c 4. PHARMACY. *Educ:* Univ Sask, BSP, 56; Univ Fla, PhD(pharm), 60. *Prof Exp:* Sr scientist, Mead Johnson Co, 60-66; dir tech servs, Mead Johnson Can, 66-73; asst dir qual control, 74-75, DIR QUAL CONTROL, AYERST LABS, 75- *Mailing Add:* Ayerst Labs Rouses Pt NY 12979

SCHNELLE, K(ARL) B(ENJAMIN), JR, b Canton, Ohio, Dec 8, 30; m 54; c 2. CHEMICAL ENGINEERING, ENVIRONMENTAL ENGINEERING. *Educ:* Carnegie Inst Technol, BS, 52, MS, 57, PhD(chem eng), 59. *Prof Exp:* Chem engr, Columbia-Southern Chem Corp, 52-54; from asst prof to assoc prof chem eng, Vanderbilt Univ, 58-64; mgr ed & res, Instrument Soc Am, 64-66; assoc prof air resources eng, 66-70, prof environ & air resources eng, 70-80, chmn, Dept Environ Eng & Policy Mgt & dir environ & water resources eng prog, 76-80, PROF CHEM & ENVIRON ENG & CHMN DEPT, VANDERBILT UNIV, 80- *Concurrent Pos:* Fulbright Chair, Univ of Liege, Belgium, Comn Int Exchange Scholars, 77. *Mem:* Am Soc Eng Educ; Instrument Soc Am; fel Am Inst Chem Engrs; Air Pollution Control Asn; Am Soc Environ Engrs. *Res:* Process dynamics and control; dynamic testing; instrumentation for pollution control; air pollution control; atmospheric diffusion modeling; mechanism of coagulation and fluctuation of heavy metals. *Mailing Add:* Vanderbilt Univ Box 1683 Nashville TN 37235

SCHNELLER, STEWART WRIGHT, b Louisville, Ky, Feb 27, 42; m 66. ORGANIC CHEMISTRY. *Educ:* Univ Louisville, BS, 64, MS, 65; Ind Univ, Bloomington, PhD(org chem), 68. *Prof Exp:* NIH fel, Stanford Univ, 68-69, res assoc org chem, 69-70; res assoc, Univ Mass, 70-71; asst prof, 71-75, asst chmn dept, 72-74, actg chmn dept 74-75, assoc prof, 75-78, PROF ORG CHEM, UNIV S FLA, 78- *Concurrent Pos:* Petrol Res Fund-Am Chem Soc fel, Univ S Fla, 71-74; Nat Insts Health & Dept Army Support. *Mem:* AAAS; Am Chem Soc; Royal Soc Chem; Int Soc Heterocyclic Chem (vpres). *Res:* Heterocyclic synthetic methods; synthetic medicinal chemistry. *Mailing Add:* Dept of Chem Univ of SFla Tampa FL 33620

SCHNEPFE, MARIAN MOELLER, b San Pedro de Macoris, Dominican Repub, Nov 15, 23; US citizen; m 54. INORGANIC CHEMISTRY, ANALYTICAL CHEMISTRY. *Educ:* George Washington Univ, BS, 53, MS, 60, PhD(chem), 66. *Prof Exp:* ANAL CHEMIST, US GEOL SURV, 54- *Mem:* Am Chem Soc. *Res:* Testing of natural materials with a view to their potential for fixation of some of the problem radio-nuclides; development of various analytical procedures; development of spectrophotometric and atomic absorption procedures for the determination of platinum, palladium, rhodium iridium and spectrophotometric procedures for the determination of antimony, arsenic, bromine, germanium, iodine, selenium and thallium in sub-microgram quantities. *Mailing Add:* US Geol Surv Nat Ctr Stop 973 Reston VA 22092

SCHNEPP, OTTO, b Vienna, Austria, July 7, 25; m 50; c 2. PHYSICAL CHEMISTRY, CHEMICAL PHYSICS. *Educ:* St John's Univ, China, BS, 47; Univ Calif, Berkeley, AB, 48, PhD(chem), 51. *Prof Exp:* Res asst chem, Univ Calif, Berkeley, 51-52; from lectr to sr lectr, Israel Inst Technol, 52-59, from assoc prof to prof, 59-65; PROF CHEM, UNIV SOUTHERN CALIF, 65- *Concurrent Pos:* Res assoc, Duke Univ, 57-58; res physicist, Nat Bur Stand, DC, 58-59. *Honors & Awards:* Assocs Award Creative Scholar & Res, Univ Southern Calif, 78; Outstanding Educr Am, 73. *Mem:* Am Phys Soc; Am Chem Soc. *Res:* Molecular and solid state spectroscopy; coherent raman spectroscopy; lattice vibrations of molecular solids; circular dichroism and magnetic circular dichroism spectroscopy; vacuum ultraviolet spectroscopy. *Mailing Add:* Dept Chem Univ Southern Calif Los Angeles CA 90007

SCHNEPPER, DONALD H(ERMAN), b Beardstown, Ill, Feb 10, 22; m 59; c 1. CIVIL ENGINEERING, HYDRAULICS. *Educ:* Carthage Col, BA, 43; Univ Ill, BS, 51, MS, 54. *Prof Exp:* Res asst, Univ Ill, 52-54; assoc prof scientist, 54-71, PROF SCIENTIST, WATER QUAL SECT, ILL STATE WATER SURV, 71- *Mem:* Am Water Works Asn; Water Pollution Control Fedn; Int Asn Hydraul Res. *Res:* Artificial recharge of groundwater; industrial water use; thermal pollution of surface water; self-purification of streams. *Mailing Add:* Water Qual Sect Box 697 State Water Surv Peoria IL 61652

SCHNEPS, JACK, b New York, NY, Aug 18, 29; m 60; c 3. PHYSICS. *Educ:* NY Univ, BA, 51; Univ Wis, MS, 53, PhD(physics), 56. *Prof Exp:* From asst prof to assoc prof, 56-63, PROF PHYSICS, TUFTS UNIV, 63-, DEPT CHMN, 80- *Concurrent Pos:* NSF fel, 58-59; vis scientist, Europ Orgn Nuclear Res, 65-66; vis res fel, Univ Col, Univ London, 73-74. *Mem:* NY Acad Sci; Europ Phys Soc; fel Am Phys Soc; Sigma Xi. *Res:* Elementary particles. *Mailing Add:* Dept of Physics Tufts Univ Medford MA 02155

SCHNETTLER, RICHARD ANSELM, b St Nazianz, Wis, May 3, 37; m 65. MEDICINAL CHEMISTRY, ORGANIC CHEMISTRY. *Educ:* Univ Wis, BS, 61; Univ Kans, PhD(med chem), 65. *Prof Exp:* Sr res chemist, Lakeside Labs Inc, 65-75; SR DEVELOP CHEMIST, MERRELL-NAT LABS, 75- *Mem:* Am Chem Soc. *Res:* Reaction mechanisms; natural product synthesis; biogenesis of natural products; cardiovascular and psychopharmacologic agents. *Mailing Add:* Merrell Nat Labs 10 Westport Rd Wilton CT 06897

SCHNEYER, CHARLOTTE A, b St Louis, Mo, Nov 21, 23; m 45. PHYSIOLOGY. *Educ:* Wash Univ, AB, 45; NY Univ, MS, 47, PhD(physiol), 52. *Prof Exp:* Asst zool, Wash Univ, 43-45; res assoc, 53-55, from asst prof to assoc prof dent, 55-64, asst prof physiol, 62-65, assoc prof physiol & biophys, 65-67, PROF DENT, SCH DENT, UNIV ALA, BIRMINGHAM, 64-, PROF PHYSIOL & BIOPHYS, MED CTR, 67- *Concurrent Pos:* Teaching fel biol, NY Univ, 45-52 (fel res) & histol, Sch Dent, Univ Ala, Birmingham, 42-43; mem adv coun gen med sci, NIH, 72-76; mem special grants review comt, Nat Inst Dental Res, 79-82. *Mem:* AAAS; Am Physiol Soc; Soc Exp Biol & Med. *Res:* Secretion of electrolytes and proteins by salivary glands; autonomic regulation of growth and development of salivary glands. *Mailing Add:* Lab Exocrine Physiol Dept Physiol Univ Ala Med Ctr Birmingham AL 35294

SCHNIEWIND, ARNO PETER, b Cologne, Ger, June 1, 29; US citizen. FOREST PRODUCTS. *Educ:* Univ Mich, BS, 53, MWT, 55, PhD(wood technol), 59. *Prof Exp:* Sr lab technician, 56, asst specialist wood sci & technol, 56-59, lectr forestry, 59-65, assoc prof, 66, PROF FORESTRY, UNIV CALIF, BERKELEY, 66- *Concurrent Pos:* NSF fel, 63-64. *Honors &*

Awards: Wood Award, 59. *Mem:* Soc Wood Sci & Technol (pres, 73-74); Int Acad Wood Sci; Forest Prod Res Soc; Am Soc Testing & Mat. *Res:* Mechanical behavior and physical properties of wood. *Mailing Add:* Forest Prod Lab Univ Calif 47th & Hoffman Blvd Richmond CA 94804

SCHNIPELSKY, PAUL NICHOLAS, analytical chemistry, see previous edition

SCHNITKER, DETMAR, b Wilhelmshaven, Ger, July 5, 37; m 64; c 2. MICROPALEONTOLOGY, PALEOCEANOGRAPHY. *Educ:* Univ NC, Chapel Hill, MS, 66; Univ Ill, Urbana, PhD(geol), 67. *Prof Exp:* Geologist, Soc Nat Petrol Aquitaine, 67-69; asst prof, 69-72, assoc prof, 72-79, PROF OCEANOG & GEOL SCI, UNIV MAINE, ORONO, 79- *Concurrent Pos:* Fulbright exchange scholar, 60-61; assoc dir, Submarine Geol & Geophys Prog, NSF, 80-81. *Mem:* Paleont Soc; Paleont Res Inst; Paleontologische Ges; Int Paleont Asn; Am Geophys Union. *Res:* Foraminiferal ecology; paleoecology; paleoceanography. *Mailing Add:* Dept of Oceanog Univ Maine at Orono Walpole ME 04573

SCHNITZER, HOWARD J, b Newark, NJ, Nov 12, 34; m 66; c 1. THEORETICAL HIGH ENERGY PHYSICS. *Educ:* Newark Col Eng, BS, 55; Univ Rochester, PhD(physics), 60. *Prof Exp:* Res assoc physics, Univ Rochester, 60-61; res assoc, 61-62, from asst prof to assoc prof, 62-68, PROF PHYSICS, BRANDEIS UNIV, 68- *Concurrent Pos:* Alfred P Sloan Found fel, 64-66; vis prof, Rockefeller Univ, 69-70; vis res assoc, Harvard Univ, 74-81; assoc ed, Phys Review Lett, 78-80, chmn, 81-83. *Mem:* Fel Am Phys Soc. *Res:* Elementary particle theory; quantum field theory. *Mailing Add:* Dept Physics Brandeis Univ Waltham MA 02154

SCHNITZER, MORRIS, b Bochum, WGer, Feb 4, 22; Can citizen; m 48; c 1. SOIL CHEMISTRY, ORGANIC CHEMISTRY. *Educ:* McGill Univ, BSc, 51, MSc, 52, PhD(agr chem), 55. *Prof Exp:* Res scientist, Aluminum Labs Ltd, 55-56; PRIN RES SCIENTIST, CHEM & BIOL RES INST, CAN DEPT AGR, 56- *Concurrent Pos:* Sabbatical fel, Imp Col, Univ London, 61-62. *Mem:* Fel Can Soc Soil Sci; Int Soc Soil Sci; fel Soil Sci Soc Am. *Res:* Chemical structure and reactions of humic substances in soils and waters. *Mailing Add:* Chem & Biol Res Inst Can Dept of Agr Ottawa ON K1A 0C6 Can

SCHNITZLEIN, HAROLD NORMAN, b Hannibal, Mo, Aug 29, 27; m 49; c 4. NEUROANATOMY. *Educ:* Westminster Col, Mo, AB, 50; St Louis Univ, MS, 52, PhD, 54. *Prof Exp:* From instr to prof anat, Sch Med, Univ Ala, Birmingham, 54-73; chmn dept, 73-78, PROF ANAT, COL MED, UNIV S FLA, 73- *Concurrent Pos:* USPHS spec fel, 60-61. *Res:* Autonomic nervous system; comparative vertebrate neuroanatomy. *Mailing Add:* Dept of Anat Univ of S Fla Col of Med Tampa FL 33612

SCHNITZLER, RONALD MICHAEL, b Providence, RI, Jan 13, 39; m 68; c 2. PHYSIOLOGY. *Educ:* Brown Univ, AB & ScB, 62; Univ Vt, MS, 64, PhD(physiol), 69. *Prof Exp:* Instr physiol, Med Col, Univ Vt, 69-70; Alexander von Humboldt scholar & res assoc, Microbiol Labs, Luisenhosp, Aachen, WGer, 70-71; res assoc physiol, Med Col, Univ Vt, 71-75; asst prof, 75-77, assoc prof, 77-81, PROF BIOL, SCI DEPT, BAY PATH JR COL, 81- *Concurrent Pos:* NIH spec fel, 71-74. *Mem:* AAAS. *Res:* Physiology and pharmacology of neuromuscular transmission, especially mechanism of drug desensitization at the motor end plate; effects of ultrasound on biological tissue. *Mailing Add:* Dept Sci Bay Path Jr Col Longmeadow MA 01106

SCHNIZER, ARTHUR WALLACE, b Des Plaines, Ill, Jan 16, 23; m 47; c 3. ORGANIC CHEMISTRY. *Educ:* Baylor Univ, BS, 43; Northwestern Univ, PhD(chem), 51. *Prof Exp:* Develop chemist, Columbia Chem Div, Pittsburgh Plate Glass Co, 43-46; asst, Northwestern Univ, 47-50; res chemist, Celanese Corp, 50-52, res group leader, 52-55, res sect head, 55-61, dir chem res, 61-66, dir eng res, 66, mgr tech ctr, Celanese Chem Co, Tex, 66-69, dir chem & polymer res, Celanese Res Co, NJ, 69-71; tech dir, Day & Zimmermann, Inc, Philadelphia, 71-76; VPRES RES & DEVELOP, BIRD & SON, INC, 76- *Mem:* Am Chem Soc; AAAS; Am Inst Chem Engr; Soc Chem Indust. *Res:* Reactions of alkyl sodiums, lithiums, magnesium bromides with methoxyl groups; reactions and synthesis of ketene; derivatives of oxygenated petrochemicals; asphalt roofing and plastics extrusion; organic synthesis and process development. *Mailing Add:* Four Onondaga Lane Medfield MA 02052

SCHNIZLEIN, JOHN GLENN, b Chicago, Ill, Feb 4, 22; m 49, 74; c 8. PHYSICAL INORGANIC CHEMISTRY. *Educ:* Univ Ill, BS, 46; Univ Minn, MS, 49. *Prof Exp:* Asst, Univ Minn, 46-49, fel, 49-51; res assoc, Res Inst, Temple Univ, 51-52; assoc chemist, Off Indust Coop, 66-69, chemist, Chem Eng Div, 69-73, assoc scientist, Prog Mgt Support Off, 74-80, SCIENTIST, INT ENERGY PROG, ARGONNE NAT LAB, 80- *Mem:* AAAS; Am Chem Soc; Sigma Xi. *Res:* computer utilization and data base administration; industrial utilization of technology; information transfer; x-ray fluorescence analysis; nuclear energy; oxidation and ignition of uranium, plutonium and other metals; fluorine chemistry. *Mailing Add:* 606 S Wehrli Dr Naperville IL 60540

SCHNOBRICH, WILLIAM COURTNEY, b St Paul, Minn, Nov 26, 30; m 56. ENGINEERING MECHANICS, STRUCTURAL ENGINEERING. *Educ:* Univ Ill, Urbana, BS, 53, MS, 55, PhD(thin shells), 62. *Prof Exp:* Res asst, 53-55, 58-62, from asst prof to assoc prof, 62-68, PROF CIVIL ENG, UNIV ILL, URBANA, 68- *Concurrent Pos:* Summer res engr, Space Technol Labs, Calif, 62 & 63; consult, John R Gullaksen, Struct Engr, Ill, 64-; Schappert Eng, 66, Assoc Eng Serv, 74 & Greeley & Hansen Engrs, 76. *Honors & Awards:* Humboldt Sr US Scientist Award, Alexander Von Humboldt-Stiftung, 77. *Mem:* Am Soc Civil Engrs; Am Soc Mech Engrs; Am Inst Aeronaut & Astronaut; Am Concrete Inst; Int Asn Shell Struct. *Res:* Structural mechanics, particularly thin shell structures; nuclear reactor vessels; earthquake resistant design; cooling towers. *Mailing Add:* 1419 Mayfair Rd Champaign IL 61820

SCHNOES, HEINRICH KONSTANTIN, b Knetzgau, Ger, July 12, 39; m 69. ORGANIC CHEMISTRY, BIOCHEMISTRY. *Educ:* Long Island Univ, BS, 61; Mass Inst Technol, PhD(org chem), 65. *Prof Exp:* Asst res chemist, Space Sci Lab, Univ Calif, Berkeley, 65-67; from asst prof to assoc prof, 67-74, PROF BIOCHEM, UNIV WIS-MADISON, 74- *Concurrent Pos:* Consult & mem lunar sample anal planning team, NASA, 70-73, mem lunar sample rev panel, 74-75; mem exobiol adv panel, Am Inst Biol Sci-NASA, 74-79. *Mem:* AAAS; Am Chem Soc; Am Soc Biol Chemists; Royal Soc Chem. *Res:* Natural products chemistry and biochemistry; mass spectrometry and its application to structural and biochemical problems. *Mailing Add:* Dept Biochem Univ Wis Madison WI 53706

SCHNOPPER, HERBERT WILLIAM, b Brooklyn, NY, Mar 13, 33; m 69; c 2. ASTROPHYSICS, X-RAY ASTRONOMY. *Educ:* Rensselaer Polytech Inst, 54; Cornell Univ, MS, 58, PhD(physics), 62. *Prof Exp:* Sr scientist, Jet Propulsion Lab, 62-63; instr & res assoc physics, Cornell Univ, 63-66; from asst prof to assoc prof physics, Mass Inst Technol, 66-73, physicist, 73-74; physicist, Smithsonian Astrophys Observ & lectr, Dept Astron, Harvard Univ, 74-80; WITH DANISH SPACE RES INST, 80- *Concurrent Pos:* Consult, Jet Propulsion Lab, 63- & Am Sci & Eng, 69-; vis prof, Steward Observ, Univ Ariz, 70-73; guest physicist, Brookhaven Nat Lab, 71-; consult, Quartz et Silice, Paris, 72- *Mem:* AAAS; Int Astron Union; Am Phys Soc; Am Astron Soc; NY Acad Sci. *Res:* Astrophysics; x-ray astronomy; diagnostics of high temperature plasmas; x-rays from heavy ion collisions; x-ray spectroscopy; x-ray optics. *Mailing Add:* Danish Space Res Inst Lundtoftevej 7 DK 2800 Lyngby Denmark

SCHNUELLE, GARY WAYNE, applied physics, deceased

SCHNUR, JOEL MARTIN, b Washington, DC, Feb 5, 45; m 71; c 1. CHEMICAL PHYSICS. *Educ:* Rutgers Univ, BS, 66; Georgetown Univ, PhD(phys chem), 71. *Prof Exp:* Head, molecular optics sect, 73-79, DEPT HEAD, OPTIC PROBES BR, NAVAL RES LAB, 79-, HEAD, PICOSECOND SPECTROSCOPY SECT, 79-, DEP COORDR, ENERGETIC MAT PROGS, 80- *Concurrent Pos:* VPres, Concepts Unlimited, 71-; fel, Nat Res Coun, Naval Res Lab, 71-72; fel, Nat Acad Sci, 73. *Mem:* Sigma Xi. *Res:* Picosecond spectroscopic techniques are applies to the elucidation of the kinetics of important ultra fast energetic materials reactions; time resolved techniques are also utilized to study electrohydrodynamics phemonmena at high pressures in lubricants as well as polymer morphology. *Mailing Add:* Code 6504 Naval Res Lab Washington DC 20375

SCHNUR, RODNEY CAUGHREN, b Evanston, Ill, Dec 25, 45. MEDICINAL CHEMISTRY, SYNTHETIC ORGANIC CHEMISTRY. *Educ:* Williams Col, AB, 67; Pa State Univ, PhD(chem), 73. *Prof Exp:* NIH res fel chem, Stanford Univ, 73-74; RES SCIENTIST MED CHEM, PFIZER INC, 74- *Mem:* Am Chem Soc. *Res:* Design and synthesis of human pharmaceuticals for treatment of diabetes mellitus. *Mailing Add:* Pfizer Inc Eastern Point Rd Groton CT 06340

SCHNUR, SIDNEY, b New York, NY, June 23, 10; m 44; c 1. MEDICINE. *Educ:* City Col New York, BS, 30, MS, 31; NY Univ, MD, 35; Am Bd Internal Med & Am Bd Cardiovasc Dis, dipl, 44. *Prof Exp:* Intern, Morrisania City Hosp, New York, 35-37; resident internal med, Kings County Hosp, 37-38; resident path, Jefferson Davis Hosp, Houston, 38-39; from clin asst prof to clin assoc prof med, Baylor Col Med, 46-62; coordr cardiol courses, Postgrad Sch Med, Univ Tex Grad Sch Biomed Sci, Houston, 53-75; clin prof, 62-76, EMER CLIN PROF MED, BAYLOR COL MED, 76-; EMER CLIN PROF MED, POSTGRAD SCH MED, UNIV TEX GRAD SCH BIOMED SCI, HOUSTON, 75-, EMER CLIN PROF MED, MED SCH, 76- *Concurrent Pos:* Pvt pract internal med, Houston, 39-; assoc physician, Jefferson Davis Hosp, 40-, chief dept electrocardiol, 45-50, chief cardiac clin, 45-51, chief 4th div med, 58-60; consult, USPHS, 46-50, St Luke's Hosp, 54- & Polly Ryan Mem Hosp, Richmond, 57-59; assoc physician, Methodist Hosp, 46-53, attend physician, 54-66, consult cardiologist, 66-; attend specialist, Vet Admin Regional Off & Hosp, 46-61; clin asst prof med, Univ Tex Grad Sch Biomed Sci Houston, 50-52, clin assoc prof, 52-57; ed consult, Heart Bull, 51-70; contrib ed, Med Rec & Ann, 52-62; consult cardiologist, San Jacinto Mem Hosp, Baytown, 54-58; consult cardiologist & electrocardiologist, South Pac Hosp, 54-61; chief med & electrocardiol dept, St Joseph Hosp, Houston, 54-, pres med staff, 62-65; chief electrocardiol, Med Arts Hosp, 58-60, chief med, 63, pres staff, 62-63; mem coun clin cardiol, Am Heart Asn, 63; attend physician, Ben Taub Hosp, 64-; trustee, Houston Mus Natural Sci; clin prof med, Sch Med, Univ Tex Biomed Sci, Houston, 57-76. *Mem:* Am Heart Asn (vpres, 77); fel Am Col Physicians; emer fel Am Col Chest Physicians; emer fel Am Col Cardiol; sr mem Am Fedn Clin Res. *Res:* Clinical cardiology; internal medicine. *Mailing Add:* 2139 Sunset Blvd Houston TX 77005

SCHNURR, NORMAN M, mechanical engineering, see previous edition

SCHNURRENBERGER, PAUL ROBERT, b Youngstown, Ohio, Aug 19, 29; m 68; c 2. VETERINARY PUBLIC HEALTH. *Educ:* Ohio State Univ, DVM, 53; Univ Pittsburgh, MPH, 58. *Prof Exp:* Pvt pract, 53; chief pub health vet, Dept Health, Ohio, 56-63 & Dept Pub Health, Ill, 63-72; prof pub health, Sch Vet Med, Auburn Univ, 72-74; prof & head fac vet med, Ahmadu Bello Univ, Zaria, Nigeria, 74-76; PROF PUB HEALTH, SCH VET MED, AUBURN UNIV, 76- *Mem:* Am Vet Med Asn; US Animal Health Asn; Am Col Vet Prev Med; Wildlife Dis Asn. *Res:* Control of zoonosis; health maintenance. *Mailing Add:* Dept of Microbiol Auburn Univ Sch of Vet Med Auburn AL 36830

SCHOBER, CHARLES COLEMAN, b Shreveport, La, Nov 30, 24; m 47, 72; c 3. PSYCHIATRY, PSYCHOANALYSIS. *Educ:* La State Univ, Baton Rouge, BS, 46; La State Univ, New Orleans, MD, 49. *Prof Exp:* Intern, Philadelphia Gen Hosp, 49-51; resident psychiat & Nat Inst Ment Health residency training grant, Norristown State Hosp, Pa, 53-56, staff physician, 56-57; assoc clin dir, Pa Hosp Ment & Nerv Dis, 57-59; instr psychiat, Med

Sch, Univ Pa, 58-62, assoc, 62-70, asst prof clin psychiat, 65-71; prof psychiat & head dept, Sch Med, La State Univ, Shreveport, 71-73; prof psychiat, Sch Med, St Louis Univ & mem fac, St Louis Psychoanal Inst, 73-78; PROF PSYCHIAT, LA STATE UNIV MED SCH, 78- Concurrent Pos: Attend psychiatrist, Pa Hosp Inst, 63-68, sr attend psychiatrist, 68-71; chief psychiat serv, Vet Admin Hosp, Shreveport, La & Confederate Mem Hosp, 71-73; consult, Brentwood Neuropsychiat Hosp, 71-73; consult, Vet Admin Hosps, St Louis, Mo, 73-78; staff, Brentwood Psychiat Hosp, Schumpert Med Ctr & La State Univ Med Ctr Hosp, 78- Mem: Fel Am Col Psychiat; fel Am Psychiat Asn; Am Psychoanal Asn; AMA. Res: Follow-up studies in psychotherapy of schizophrenia; evaluation of effectiveness of clinical teaching methods in psychiatric training of medical students and residents. Mailing Add: 1513 Line Ave Suite 216 Shreveport LA 71101

SCHOBER, DONALD LINCOLN, organic polymer chemistry, see previous edition

SCHOBER, GLENN E, b Minneapolis, Minn, July 1, 38; m 66; c 2. MATHEMATICS. Educ: Univ Minn, BS, 60, PhD(math, 65. Prof Exp: Asst prof math, Univ Calif, San Diego, 65-66; from asst prof to assoc prof, 66-76, PROF MATH, IND UNIV, BLOOMINGTON, 76- Mem: Am Math Soc. Res: Complex function and potential theories. Mailing Add: Dept of Math Ind Univ Bloomington IN 47405

SCHOBERT, HAROLD HARRIS, b Wilkes-Barre, Pa, Nov 13, 43; m 68; c 2. COAL CHEMISTRY. Educ: Bucknell Univ, BS, 65; Iowa State Univ, PhD(chem), 70. Prof Exp: Instr chem, Iowa State Univ, 70-72; res chemist, Deepsea Ventures Inc, 72-76; res chemist, 76-78, supvr anal chem, 78, MGR ANAL RES, GRAND FORKS ENERGY TECH CTR, US DEPT ENERGY, 78- Mem: Am Chem Soc; Sigma Xi. Res: Studies of the chemistry and analysis of coal tar; studies of the structure of coal as it influences coal conversion processes; studies of the viscosity of coal ash slags. Mailing Add: Grand Forks Energy Tech Ctr Box 8213 Univ Sta Grand Forks ND 58202

SCHOCHET, CLAUDE LEWIS, b Minneapolis, Minn, Aug 5, 44; m 67; c 3. MATHEMATICS. Educ: Univ Minn, BA, 65; Univ Chicago, MS, 67, PhD(math), 69. Prof Exp: Asst prof math, Roosevelt Univ, 69-70; amanuensis, Aarhus Univ, Denmark, 70-71; fel, Hebrew Univ, Jerusalem, 71-72; asst prof math, Ind Univ, Bloomington, 72-76; assoc prof, 76-80, PROF MATH, WAYNE STATE UNIV, 80- Concurrent Pos: Vis assoc prof, Univ Calif, Los Angeles, 79-80. Mem: Am Math Soc; Math Asn Am; Asn Women Math; London Math Soc. Res: Functional analysis; algebraic and differential topology. Mailing Add: Dept Math Wayne State Univ Detroit MI 48202

SCHOCHET, MELVIN LEO, b New York, NY, June 16, 24; m 51; c 3. PHYSICAL CHEMISTRY. Educ: City Col New York, BS, 44; NY Univ, PhD(chem), 54. Prof Exp: Instr chem, Brooklyn Col, 51-53; asst prof, Miss State Univ, 54-57; from asst prof to assoc prof, 57-70, PROF CHEM, BALDWIN-WALLACE COL, 70-, HEAD DEPT, 74- Mem: AAAS; Am Chem Soc. Res: Kinetics of reactions in solutions; acid-base catalysis; corrosion. Mailing Add: Dept of Chem Baldwin-Wallace Col Berea OH 44017

SCHOCHET, SYDNEY SIGFRIED, JR, b Chicago, Ill, Feb 7, 37; m 61; c 1. PATHOLOGY, NEUROPATHOLOGY. Educ: Tulane Univ, BS, 58, MD, 61, MS, 65. Prof Exp: Assoc prof pathol, Univ Tex Med Br, 73-79, prof, 79-81; PROF PATHOL, COL MED, WVA UNIV, 81- Concurrent Pos: Nat Inst Neurol Dis & Blindness spec fel, Armed Forces Inst Path, 66-67; prof path, Univ Okla, 79-81. Mem: Am Asn Neuropath; Am Asn Path & Bact; Am Asn Pathologists; Soc Exp Biol & Med; Int Acad Path. Res: Reactions of the neuron to injury; ultrastructural neuropathology; neuromuscular diseases. Mailing Add: Dept Path Med Ctr WVa Univ Morgantown WV 26506

SCHOCK, ROBERT NORMAN, b Monticello, NY, May 25, 39; m 59; c 3. GEOPHYSICS. Educ: Colo Col, BSc, 61; Rensselaer Polytech Inst, MSc, 63, PhD(geophys), 66. Prof Exp: Res assoc, Univ Chicago, 66-68; res scientist high pressure physics, 68-72, group leader, 72-74, geosci sect leader, 74-76, EARTH SCI DIV LEADER, LAWRENCE LIVERMORE LAB, UNIV CALIF, 76- Concurrent Pos: Instr, Univ Chicago, 68 & Chabot Col, 69-; sr Fulbright fel, Univ Bonn, 73; assoc ed, J Geophys Res, 78-80; vis res fel, Australian Nat Univ, 80-81. Mem: AAAS; The Chem Soc; Am Geophys Union; Sigma Xi. Res: High pressure physics; solid state processes; equation of state of solids; rock deformation. Mailing Add: Lawrence Livermore Lab Univ Calif, Box 808 Livermore CA 94550

SCHODT, KATHLEEN PATRICIA, b Erie, Pa, Jan 27, 50. POLYMER SCIENCE. Educ: Case Western Reserve Univ, BS, 72, MS, 74, PhD(macromolecular sci), 77. Prof Exp: RES CHEMIST, E I DU PONT DE NEMOURS & CO, INC, 77- Mem: Am Chem Soc. Res: Physical and mechanical properties of polymers, especially elastomers; polymer blends. Mailing Add: Elastomer Chem Dept E I du Pont de Nemours & Co Inc Wilmington DE 19898

SCHOEBERLE, DANIEL F, b Shipman, Ill, Aug 14, 31; m 65; c 2. ENGINEERING MECHANICS, MECHANICAL ENGINEERING. Educ: Univ Ill, Urbana, BS, 53, MS, 57, PhD(eng mech), 61. Prof Exp: Teaching fel mech eng, Univ Notre Dame, 56; asst mech engr, Argonne Nat Lab, 57-61; asst prof, 64-70, ASSOC PROF MAT ENG, UNIV ILL, CHICAGO CIRCLE, 70- Res: Nuclear reactor heat transfer; elastic wave propagation in solid bodies; thermoelasticity. Mailing Add: Dept of Mat Eng Box 4348 Chicago IL 60680

SCHOEFER, ERNEST A(LEXANDER), b Brooklyn, NY, Sept 15, 08; m 37; c 3. METALLURGICAL ENGINEERING. Educ: Rensselaer Polytech Inst, CE, 32; Polytech Inst Brooklyn, MMetE, 57. Prof Exp: Statistician, Equity Corp, NY, 32-34; res engr, Repub Steel Corp, Ohio, 35-36; field engr, Distributors Group, Inc, NY, 36-37; secy, Alloy Casting Res Inst, 38-40, exec vpres, 40-70; METALL CONSULT, 70- Concurrent Pos: Mem, Tech Adv Comt High Alloy Castings, War Prod Bd, 42-45 & Nickel Conserv Panel, Metall Adv Bd, Nat Acad Sci, 52-53, High Alloys Comt, Welding Res Coun, 56- & Int Coun Alloy Phase Diagrams, 79- Mem: Am Soc Metals; Am Soc Testing & Mat; Am Foundrymen's Soc; Am Inst Mining, Metall & Petrol Engrs; Nat Asn Corrosion Engrs. Res: Metallurgy of stainless steels and other heat and corrosion resistant casting alloys. Mailing Add: 77 Wyatt Rd Garden City NY 11530

SCHOELLER, DALE ALAN, analytical chemistry, biochemistry, see previous edition

SCHOELLMANN, GUENTHER, b Stuttgart, Ger, Nov 17, 28; m 58; c 4. BIOCHEMISTRY, ORGANIC CHEMISTRY. Educ: Stuttgart Tech Univ, dipl, 55, PhD(org chem), 57. Prof Exp: Res assoc, 59-61, from instr to asst prof, 61-67, ASSOC PROF BIOCHEM, SCH MED, TULANE UNIV, 67-, ASSOC PROF OPHTHAL, 76- Mem: Am Chem Soc; NY Acad Sci; Ger Chem Soc; Ger Biol Soc. Res: Chemistry and function of proteins and amino acids; active site of enzymes; enzyme mechanism; peptide synthesis. Mailing Add: Sch of Med Tulane Univ New Orleans LA 70112

SCHOEMPERLEN, CLARENCE BENJAMIN, b Strathclair, Man, Mar 13, 13; m 39; c 3. MEDICINE. Educ: Univ Man, MD, 37, Royal Col Physicians & Surgeons Can, cert internal med, 46, FRCPS(C), 72. Prof Exp: Demonstr, 46-49, lectr, 49-53, ASSOC PROF MED, UNIV MAN, 53-; ASST MED DIR, GREAT WEST LIFE ASSURANCE CO, 77- Concurrent Pos: Consult & endoscopist, Deer Lodge Vet Admin Hosp, 45-; assoc physician & bronchoesophagologist, Winnipeg Gen Hosp, 46-81, Children's Hosp, Winnipeg, 50-81 & Respiratory Dis Hosp; hon attend staff & consult, Health Sci Ctr, 81. Mem: Am Thoracic Soc; fel Am Col Physicians; sr & fel Am Col Chest Physicians; sr mem Am Broncho-Esophagol Asn; Can Med Asn. Res: Diseases of the chest; bronchoesophagology. Mailing Add: 351 Yale Ave Winnipeg MB R3M 0L5 Can

SCHOEN, HERBERT M, b Long Island, NY, Oct 2, 28; m 51; c 4. CHEMICAL ENGINEERING. Educ: Syracuse Univ, BS, 52, MS, 53, PhD(chem eng), 57. Prof Exp: Res engr, Am Cyanamid Co, 57-60; dir res, Radiation Applns Inc, 60-62; dir contracts, Quantum Inc, 62-64; dir contracts, 64-66, group leader, 66-68, sr group leader, 68-69, res mgr, Birds Eye Div, 69-72, dir, Basic Sci, 72-78, dir fundamental res & phys sci, 78-79, CORP SCIENTIST, GEN FOODS CORP, 79- Concurrent Pos: Ed, Intersci Libr Chem Eng & Processing, 61-; vis prof, Univ Tex, 67 & Cornell Univ, 68-69. Mem: Fel Am Inst Chem Engrs; Am Chem Soc; NY Acad Sci. Res: Crystallization, concentration and separation techniques; foam separation; food research. Mailing Add: 73 Clay Hill Rd Stamford CT 06905

SCHOEN, JOHN WARREN, b Anacortes, Wash, Apr 17, 47; m 70; c 1. FOREST WILDLIFE ECOLOGY. Educ: Whitman Col, BA, 69; Univ Puget Sound, MS, 72; Univ Wash, PhD(wildlife ecol), 77. Prof Exp: Game biologist II, 76-77, GAME BIOLOGIST III, ALASKA DEPT FISH & GAME, 77- Mem: Wildlife Soc; Ecol Soc Am; Am Soc Mammalogists. Res: Wildlife habitat relationships principally black-tailed deer, mountain goats and brown bear; home range patterns and habitat selection to understand the value of old-growth forests as wildlife habitats. Mailing Add: Alaska Dept Fish & Game 230 S Franklin Juneau AK 99801

SCHOEN, KENNETH, b Bronxville, NY, Jan 18, 32; m 54; c 5. MATHEMATICS. Educ: Univ Conn, BA, 54; Yale Univ, AM, 55; Rensselaer Polytech Inst, 61; Univ Pittsburgh, PhD(math), 68. Prof Exp: Anal engr, Hamilton Stand Div, United Aircraft Corp, 55-62; prof math, Wheeling Col, 62-66; instr, Univ Pittsburgh, 67-68; prof, Worcester Polytech Inst, 68-71; PROF MATH, WORCESTER STATE COL, 71- Concurrent Pos: Lectr, Univ Conn, 55-62; prof, W Liberty State Col, 63-66 & Clark Univ, 71-72. Mem: Soc Indust & Appl Math; Math Asn Am. Res: Numerical analysis. Mailing Add: Dept of Math Worcester State Col Worcester MA 01602

SCHOEN, KURT L, b Dec 14, 27; US citizen; m 56; c 3. CHEMISTRY. Educ: City Col New York, BS, 49; Polytech Inst Brooklyn, MS, 56. Prof Exp: Chemist, Felton Chem Co, 49-52; flavor chemist, H Kohnstamm & Co, Inc, 52-55; flavor chemist, 56-61, vpres & tech dir, 61-80, EXEC VPRES & TECH DIR, DAVID MICHAEL & CO, INC, 80- Mem: Am Chem Soc; Inst Food Technol; Soc Flavor Chemists. Res: Synthetic and natural flavorings; development and production of flavorings and synthetic food adjuncts to be used in comestibles. Mailing Add: 9222 Burbank Rd Philadelphia PA 19115

SCHOEN, MAX H, b New York, NY, Feb 4, 22; m 50; c 2. PUBLIC HEALTH. Educ: Univ Southern Calif, BS, 43, DDS, 43; Univ Calif, Los Angeles, MPH, 62, DrPH, 69. Prof Exp: Vis prof, Sch Dent Med, Univ Conn, 72; prof dent health serv, Sch Dent Med, Health Sci Ctr, State Univ NY Stony Brook, 73-76, actg dean, 74-75, assoc dean clin affairs, 75-76; asst dean acad affairs, 77-79, PROF PREV DENT & PUB HEALTH & CHMN SECT, SCH DENT, UNIV CALIF, LOS ANGELES, 76- Concurrent Pos: Consult, Prov Man & BC, 74-75, Kaiser Found Health Plan, Southern Calif, 74-75, Blue Cross Southern Calif, 77- & Group Health Plan, Inc, St Paul, Minn, 78- Mem: Inst Med-Nat Acad Sci; fel Am Pub Health Asn; Am Dent Asn; Int Dent Fedn; Fedn Am Scientists. Res: Delivery of dental care, especially organization, economics and quality evaluation. Mailing Add: Sch of Dent Univ of Calif Ctr for Health Sci Los Angeles CA 90024

SCHOEN, RICHARD ISAAC, b New Rochelle, NY, Aug 13, 27; m 51; c 2. SCIENCE ADMINISTRATION, MOLECULAR PHYSICS. Educ: Calif Inst Technol, BS, 49; Univ Southern Calif, MS, 54, PhD(physics) 60. Prof Exp: Asst prof physics, Mo Sch Mines, 55-59; asst, Univ Southern Calif, 59-60, res assoc, 60-61; staff mem, Boeing Sci Res Labs, 61-71; prog dir aeronomy, 71-73, prog mgr energy, 73-75, dep div dir energy & resources res, 75-78, SECT HEAD, APPL PHYS, MATH, BIOL SCI & ENG, DIV APPL RES, NAT SCI FOUND-RES APPLN NAT NEEDS, 78- Mem: AAAS; Am Phys Soc; Am Geophys Union. Mailing Add: Nat Sci Found 1800 G St NW Washington DC 20550

SCHOENBERG, BRUCE STUART, b New Brunswick, NJ, Nov 2, 42; m 73; c 2. NEUROLOGY, EPIDEMIOLOGY. *Educ:* Univ Pa, BA, 64; Yale Univ, MD, 68; Johns Hopkins Univ, MPH, 73; Univ Minn, MS, 76; Am Bd Psychiat & Neurol, cert neurol, 77. *Prof Exp:* Staff assoc cancer epidemiol, Nat Cancer Inst, 68-70; intern internal med, Mayo Grad Sch Med, 70-71; spec fel, Nat Inst Neurol Dis & Stroke at Mayo Clin & Johns Hopkins Univ, 71-74; HEAD SECT EPIDEMIOL, NAT INST NEUROL & COMMUN DIS & STROKE, 75- *Concurrent Pos:* Abstractor enzymol, Chem Abstr, 65-; lectr, Dept Epidemiol & Pub Health, Sch Med, Yale Univ, 68-; consult, Epidemiol Br, Nat Cancer Inst, 71-; clin instr neurol, Sch Med, Georgetown Univ, 72-75; instr neurol, med statist & epidemiol, Mayo Med Sch, Univ Minn, 74-; clin asst prof neurol, Sch Med, Georgetown Univ, 75-; vis scientist neurol, Mayo Clinic, 75-; mem biomet & epidemiol contract review comt, Nat Cancer Inst, 75-78; adv ed, J Neurol Sci, 77-; secy-gen, World Fedn Neurol Res Comt on Neuroepidemiol, 77- *Honors & Awards:* Roche Labs Award, 72; William C Menninger Award Res Neurol, 72; Award Res Hist Med, Mayo Found Hist Med Soc, 74; Mary Rooney Weigel Award, Int Acad Proctol Res Epidemiol, 74; Richmond Award, Am Acad Cerebral Palsy & Develop Med, 77. *Mem:* Fel AAAS; Am Acad Neurol; fel Royal Soc Med; Am Fedn Clin Res; Int Epidemiol Asn. *Res:* Chronic disease epidemiology, particularly the epidemiology of stroke and cancer; computer applications in medicine; medical history of the late nineteenth century. *Mailing Add:* Head Sect Epidemiol Dis & 19 Stroke NIH Bethesda MD 20014

SCHOENBERG, DANIEL ROBERT, b Chicago, Ill, Aug 14, 49; m 74. MOLECULAR ENDOCRINOLOGY. *Educ:* Univ Ill, Urbana, BS, 71; Univ Wis-Madison, PHD(oncol), 77. *Prof Exp:* Fel cell biol, Baylor Col Med, 78-80, instr, 80-81; ASST PROF PHARMACOL, UNIFORMED SERV UNIV HEALTH SCI, 81- *Mem:* AAAS; Am Soc Cell Biol; Sigma Xi; Edocrine Soc. *Res:* Mechanisms by which small molecules, such as steroid hormones and drugs, repress the expression of specific genes; effects of estrogen on albumin synthesis in Xenopus laevis as a model system. *Mailing Add:* Dept Pharmacol Uniformed Serv Univ Health Sci 4301 Jones Bridge Rd Bethesda MD 20814

SCHOENBERG, LEONARD NORMAN, b Erie, Pa, Nov 29, 40; m 67; c 2. ELECTROCHEMISTRY, ELECTRONIC PACKAGING. *Educ:* Univ Rochester, BS, 62; Univ Mich, MS, 64, PhD(chem), 66. *Prof Exp:* MEM TECH STAFF, BELL LABS, 66- *Mem:* Electrochem Soc; Am Chem Soc; Am Electroplaters Soc. *Res:* Coordination chemistry; printed circuit board fabrication; electrodeposition; electroless copper and nickel deposition; electroplating of nickel, copper, and gold; electropolishing of copper; characterization of plated metal deposits; advanced electronic packaging technology. *Mailing Add:* Bell Labs Whippany NJ 07981

SCHOENBERG, MARK, b New York, NY, Sept 3, 43. PHYSIOLOGY. *Educ:* Mass Inst Technol, SB, 64; NY Univ, MD, 68. *Prof Exp:* Intracurricular res fel, Mass Inst Technol-NY Univ, 66-67; intern pediat, Cleveland Metrop Gen Hosp, 68-69; resident internal med, Univ Chicago Hosps & Clins, 69-70; res assoc, NIH, 70-72, sr staff fel, 72-75, MED OFFICER RES, NAT INST ARTHRITIS, METAB & DIGESTIVE DIS, 75- *Concurrent Pos:* Res assoc, Dept Med, Univ Chicago, 69-70. *Honors & Awards:* Res Award in Med, Borden Inc, 68. *Mem:* AAAS; Biophys Soc; NY Acad Sci. *Res:* Muscle physiology. *Mailing Add:* Bldg 6 Rm 101 NIH Bethesda MD 20205

SCHOENBERG, THEODORE, b Brooklyn, NY, Aug 11, 39. CHEMICAL ENGINEERING. *Educ:* City Col New York, BChE, 60; Mass Inst Technol, SM, 62, ScD(chem eng), 65. *Prof Exp:* DIR OPERS, AVCO SPEC METALS DIV, AVCO CORP, 65- *Mem:* Am Inst Chem Engrs; Am Chem Soc; Nat Soc Prof Engrs. *Res:* Composite materials; high temperature chemical processes. *Mailing Add:* 120 Park Ave Medford MA 02155

SCHOENBERGER, JAMES A, b Cleveland, Ohio, July 16, 19; m 43; c 3. CLINICAL MEDICINE. *Educ:* Univ Chicago, BS, 42, MD, 43. *Prof Exp:* Asst med, Univ Chicago, 46; fel med, 49-50, from instr to asst prof, 50-60, assoc clin prof, 60-68, clin prof med, Univ Ill Med Ctr, 68-71; PROF PREV MED, RUSH MED COL, 71-, CHMN DEPT, 74-; PROF PREV MED & CHMN DEPT, RUSH-PRESBY-ST LUKES MED CTR, 75- *Concurrent Pos:* Pres, Chicago Heart Asn, 74-76; vpres, Am Heart Asn, 76-77. *Mem:* Fel Am Col Physicians; Am Fedn Clin Res. *Res:* Renal function; capillary permeability; body water and electrolytes; therapy of hypertension; epidemiology and prevention of coronary heart disease; systems management of hypertension. *Mailing Add:* Rush-Presby-St Lukes Med Ctr 1753 W Congress Pkwy Chicago IL 60612

SCHOENBERGER, MICHAEL, b McKeesport, Pa, Jan 5, 40; m 64; c 3. GEOPHYSICS. *Educ:* Carnegie Inst Technol, BS, 61; Univ Ill, MS, 63, PhD(elec eng), 66. *Prof Exp:* From teaching asst to instr & res assoc elec eng & control theory, Univ Ill, 61-66; sr engr, Surface Div, Westinghouse Elec Corp, 66-67; sr res engr, 67-71, sr res specialist, 71-76, res assoc, 76-81, SR RES ASSOC, EXPLOR SYSTS DIV, EXXON PROD RES CO, 81- *Mem:* Inst Elec & Electronics Eng; Europ Asn Explor Geophysicists; Soc Explor Geophys. *Res:* Seismic data analysis; optimization and implementation of system parameters; seismic data enhancement. *Mailing Add:* Stratig Explor Div Exxon Prod Res Co Box 2189 Houston TX 77001

SCHOENBERGER, ROBERT J(OSEPH), b Weissport, Pa, Mar 12, 38; m 61; c 2. ENVIRONMENTAL ENGINEERING. *Educ:* Drexel Univ, BSCE, 62, MS, 64, PhD(environ), 69. *Prof Exp:* Jr engr, Pa Power & Light Co, 57-60; sanit engr I, Pa Dept of Health, 62-63, engr-in-charge facil, 63-64; res assoc, Drexel Univ, 65-69, asst prof, 69-72, assoc dir, Environ Studies Inst, 75-76, assoc prof environ eng, 72-78; MEM STAFF, ROY F WESTON, CO, 78- *Concurrent Pos:* Pres, Imagineering Assocs, 75-78; consult, Roy F Weston, Inc, 78- *Mem:* Am Soc Civil Engrs; Am Soc Mech Engrs; Water Pollution Control Fedn. *Res:* Theoretical combustion of domestic solid wastes; biological and chemical treatment; thermal processing of wastes; resource recovery; hazardous waste management and control. *Mailing Add:* Weston Weston Way West Chester PA 19380

SCHOENBORN, BENNO P, b Basel, Switz, May 2, 36; m 62. MOLECULAR BIOLOGY, BIOPHYSICS. *Educ:* Univ Calif, Los Angeles, BA, 58; Univ New South Wales, PhD(physics), 62. *Prof Exp:* NIH fel molecular biol, Med Ctr, Univ Calif, San Francisco, 62-63, asst physicist, 63-64; res fel molecular biol, Cambridge Univ, 64-66; assoc prof biophysics, Univ Calif, San Francisco, 66-67; from assoc biophysicist to biophysicist, 67-72, SR BIOPHYSICIST, BROOKHAVEN NAT LAB, 72-; ADJ PROF BIOCHEM, COLUMBIA UNIV MED SCH, 78- *Honors & Awards:* E O Lawrence Award, 80. *Mem:* Biophys Soc; assoc Australian Inst Physics; Am Crystallog Asn. *Res:* Molecular mechanism of anesthesia; x-ray and neutron scattering of biological structures. *Mailing Add:* Dept of Biol Brookhaven Nat Lab Upton NY 11973

SCHOENBRUNN, ERWIN F(REDERICK), b Newark, NJ, July 15, 21; m 48; c 4. CHEMICAL ENGINEERING. *Educ:* Princeton Univ, BS, 47; Univ Pa, MS, 49. *Prof Exp:* Res engr, Sharples Corp, 47-51; proj mgr, Petrochem Dept, Nat Res Corp, 51-58; proj mgr, Res Labs, Escambia Chem Corp, Conn, 58-61; group leader, 61-66, head explor res & process develop, 66-68, SR CHEM ENGR, AM CYANAMID CO, STAMFORD, 68- *Mem:* Am Chem Soc; Am Inst Chem Engrs. *Res:* Ion exchange; hydrocarbon oxidation; process development; polymerization kinetics; catalysis. *Mailing Add:* 22 Christopher Rd Ridgefield CT 06877

SCHOENDORF, WILLIAM H(ARRIS), b New York, NY, Jan 21, 36; m 58; c 3. ELECTRICAL ENGINEERING. *Educ:* Mass Inst Technol, BSEE, 57; Univ Pa, MSEE, 58; Purdue Univ, PhD(elec eng), 63. *Prof Exp:* Instr elec eng, Purdue Univ, 58-62; assoc res engr, Conductron Corp, 63-65; radio astron observ, Univ Mich, Ann Arbor, 65-70; ASST GROUP LEADER, LINCOLN LAB, MASS INST TECHNOL, 70- *Mem:* Inst Elec & Electronics Engrs. *Res:* Scattering of electromagnetic waves by conductors, dielectrics, plasmas and random objects; wave propagation in plasmas and other random media; antenna theory; astrophysical processes; pattern recognition. *Mailing Add:* 16 Ledgewood Dr Bedford MA 01730

SCHOENE, NORBERTA WACHTER, b Pittsburg, Kans, July 9, 43. BIOCHEMISTRY, NUTRITION. *Educ:* Pittsburg State Univ, BA, 65; George Washington Univ, PhD(biochem), 71. *Prof Exp:* RES CHEMIST, LIPID NUTRIT LAB, NUTRIT INST, SCI & EDUC ADMIN-AGR RES, USDA, 71- *Mem:* Sigma Xi; AAAS. *Res:* Essential fatty acid and prostaglandin metabolism; phospholipases; effect of dietary essential fatty acids on platelet function and development of hypertension. *Mailing Add:* Nutrit Inst B-308 BARC-E Beltsville MD 20705

SCHOENER, AMY, b New York, NY, Oct 18, 43; m 66. BIOLOGICAL OCEANOGRAPHY, BIOGEOGRAPHY. *Educ:* Queens Col, NY, BS, 64; Harvard Univ, MA, 65, PhD(biol), 69. *Prof Exp:* Res scholar zool, Radcliffe Inst, 69-71, vis res scholar, 71-75; RES ASST PROF BIOL OCEANOG, UNIV WASH, 75- *Mem:* Am Soc Limnol & Oceanog; Ecol Soc Am. *Res:* Benthic marine invertebrates; substrate colonization; marine fouling; island biogeography. *Mailing Add:* Dept of Oceanog Univ of Wash Seattle WA 98195

SCHOENER, EUGENE PAUL, b New York, NY, Oct 22, 43; m 65; c 2. NEUROPHARMACOLOGY, NEUROPHYSIOLOGY. *Educ:* City Col New York, BS, 64; Rutgers Univ, MS, 65, PhD(physiol), 70. *Prof Exp:* Res assoc neuropharmacol, Col Physicians & Surgeons, Columbia Univ, 73-74; asst prof, 74-78, ASSOC PROF PHARMACOL, SCH MED, WAYNE STATE UNIV, 78- *Concurrent Pos:* NIH training grant, Col Physicians & Surgeons, Columbia Univ, 70-73; vis asst prof, State Univ NY Col Purchase, 72-73. *Honors & Awards:* Award, Pharmaceut Mfg Asn Found, 75. *Mem:* Am Phys Soc; Soc Neurosci. *Res:* Control systems, especially body temperature, respiration and vestibular system; pain and analgesia; drug abuse, tolerance and dependence. *Mailing Add:* Dept Pharmacol Sch Med Wayne State Univ Detroit MI 48201

SCHOENER, THOMAS WILLIAM, b Lancaster, Pa, Aug 9, 43; m 66. ECOLOGY. *Educ:* Harvard Univ, BA, 65, PhD(biol), 69. *Prof Exp:* Jr fel, Harvard Univ, 69-71, from asst prof to assoc prof biol, 72-74; assoc prof, 75-76, PROF ZOOL, UNIV WASH, 76- *Concurrent Pos:* Ed, Theoret Pop Biol, 75-80. *Mem:* Am Soc Ichthyologists & Herpetologists; Am Soc Naturalists; Soc Study Evolution; Ecol Soc Am; Soc Study Reptiles & Amphibians. *Res:* Feeding strategies; resource partitioning and the diversity of ecological communities; population dynamics; island ecology; biogeography; theoretical ecology; biology of lizards. *Mailing Add:* Dept of Zool Univ of Wash Seattle WA 98195

SCHOENEWALDT, ERWIN FREDERICK, b Brooklyn, NY, Aug 11, 21; m 47; c 3. SYNTHETIC ORGANIC CHEMISTRY. *Educ:* Brooklyn Col, BA, 42; NY Univ, BS, 45; Columbia Univ, MA, 46, PhD(chem), 48. *Prof Exp:* Res assoc cancer & hormones, Col Physicians & Surgeons, Columbia Univ, 48-51; sr chemist process res, 51-60, sect head, 60-63, res assoc protein chem explor res, 63-66, mgr process res, 66-75, sr investr, 75-77, DIR, PHYS CHEM & SPECTROS, MERCK & CO, INC, 77- *Res:* Heterogenous reactions; spectroscopy. *Mailing Add:* Merck Sharp & Dohme Res Labs Merck & Co PO Box 2000 Rahway NJ 07065

SCHOENEWEISS, DONALD F, b Columbus, Ohio, July 27, 29; m 64; c 2. PLANT PATHOLOGY. *Educ:* Ohio State Univ, BA, 51, MSc, 53, PhD(bot), 58. *Prof Exp:* Asst plant path, Ohio Agr Exp Sta, 55-58; inspector plant parasitic nematodes, USDA, 58; from asst plant pathologist to assoc plant pathologist, 58-72, PLANT PATHOLOGIST, STATE NATURAL HIST SURV, ILL, 72- *Mem:* Am Soc Hort Sci; Soc Nematol; Am Phytopath Soc. *Res:* Diseases of shade and ornamental trees and shrubs, especially nursery plants; influence of environmental stresses on disease susceptibility. *Mailing Add:* Ill State Natural Hist Surv Natural Resources Bldg Rm 172 Urbana IL 61801

SCHOENFELD, ALAN HENRY, b New York, NY, July 9, 47; m 70. PROBLEM SOLVING. *Educ:* Queens Col, NY, BA, 68; Stanford Univ, MS, 69, PhD(math), 73. *Prof Exp:* Lectr math, Univ Calif, Davis, 73-75, lectr sci educ, Berkeley, 75-78; asst & assoc prof, Hamilton Col, 78-81; ASSOC PROF MATH & EDUC, UNIV ROCHESTER, 81- *Concurrent Pos:* Consult, Xerox Corp, 79; prin investr res grants, NSF, 79-; vis lectr, Math Asn Am, 81- *Honors & Awards:* Lester R Ford Award, Math Asn Am, 80. *Mem:* Math Asn Am; Am Math Soc; Am Educ Res Asn; Cognitive Sci Soc; AAAS. *Res:* Psychology of mathematical problem solving. *Mailing Add:* Educ & Math Univ Rochester Rochester NY 14627

SCHOENFELD, DAVID ALAN, b Ft Monmouth, NJ, Apr 19, 45. BIOSTATISTICS. *Educ:* Reed Col, BA, 67; Univ Ore, MA, 68, PhD(math statist), 74. *Prof Exp:* Statistician, Sch Med, Univ Ore, 71-72; fel, Dept Statist, Stanford Univ, 74-75; res asst prof statist sci, State Univ NY Buffalo, 75-78; asst prof, 78-81, ASSOC PROF BIOSTATIST, HARVARD SCH PUB HEALTH, 81- *Mem:* Biomet Soc; Am Statist Asn; Inst Math Statist. *Res:* Clinical trials of cancer therapies with the Eastern Cooperative Oncology Group; development and application of statistical methodologies for clinical data. *Mailing Add:* Dept of Biostatist 44 Binney St Boston MA 02115

SCHOENFELD, ROBERT GEORGE, b Topeka, Kans, Nov 29, 26; m 46; c 5. BIOCHEMISTRY. *Educ:* Univ Okla, BS, 49, MS, 56, PhD(biochem), 58; Am Bd Clin Chemists, dipl; Am Asn Clin Chemists, cert toxicol chem, 72. *Prof Exp:* Asst chemist, State Hwy Res Lab, Okla, 45-48; asst chief chemist, Wilson & Co, 49-51; clin biochemist, Vet Admin Hosp, 58-65; DIR SCHOENFELD CLIN LAB, INC, 61- *Mem:* Am Chem Soc; fel Am Asn Clin Chemists; Am Acad Forensic Sci; fel Asn Off Racing Chemists (pres, 74-75 & 77-79). *Res:* Clinical chemistry, toxicology and methodology; drug and narcotic assays; GC-MS analyses. *Mailing Add:* Schoenfeld Clin Lab Inc 8100 Constitution Pl NE Albuquerque NM 87110

SCHOENFELD, ROBERT LOUIS, b New York, NY, Apr 1, 20; m 65; c 5. ELECTRONICS, COMPUTER SCIENCE. *Educ:* NY Univ, BA, 42; Columbia Univ, BS, 44; Polytech Inst NY, MEE, 49, DEE, 56. *Prof Exp:* Electronic engr, Allied Lab Instrument Co, NY, 46-47; res assoc neurol, Col Physicians & Surg, Columbia Univ, 47-51; sr physicist, New York Dept Hosps, 51-52; res fel physics, Sloan-Kettering Inst, 52-57; asst prof electronics & comput sci, 57-63, ASSOC PROF ELECTRONICS & COMPUT SCI, ROCKEFELLER UNIV, 63-, HEAD ELECTRONICS & COMPUT LAB, 71- *Concurrent Pos:* From instr to assoc prof, Polytech Inst Brooklyn, 47-59, adj prof, 59-68, 77- *Mem:* Fel Inst Elec & Electronics Engrs; Asn Comput Mach. *Res:* Electronic instrumentation for biophysics and neurophysiology; bioelectric signals; application of network and communication theory to physical systems; application of computer techniques in biology; microprocessor based instruments; laboratory applications of computer languages. *Mailing Add:* 500 E 63rd St New York NY 10021

SCHOENFIELD, LESLIE JACK, b Bronx, NY, Feb 20, 32; m; c 6. GASTROENTEROLOGY, INTERNAL MEDICINE. *Educ:* Temple Univ, BA, 52, MD, 56; Univ Minn, Minneapolis, PhD(med physiol), 64. *Prof Exp:* From instr to assoc prof internal med, Mayo Grad Sch Med, Univ Minn, 63-70; assoc prof, 71-72, PROF MED, UNIV CALIF, LOS ANGELES, 72-; DIR DEPT GASTROENTEROL, CEDARS-SINAI MED CTR, LOS ANGELES, 71- *Concurrent Pos:* NIH spec fel, Karolinska Inst, Stockholm, 65; res grant, Mayo Clin & Cedars-Sinai Med Ctr, 66-; res assoc, Fells Inst Gastrointestinal Res, Temple Univ, 63; consult internal med & gastroenterol, Mayo Clin, 63-70, assoc dir res unit & gastrointestinal training prog, 66-70; rev, Gen Med Study Sect, NIH, 70; mem res eval comt, Vet Admin, 70 & merit rev bd, 72; dir, Nat Coop Gallstone Study, 73-; vchmn, Nat Sci Adv Comt, Nat Found Ileitis & Colitis, Inc, 78-; chmn, AASLD Res Comt, 75- *Mem:* AAAS; AMA; Am Gastroenterol Asn; Am Asn Study Liver Dis; Int Asn Study Liver. *Res:* Bile flow and composition; hepatic conjugation and secretion; cholestasis biliary lipids and cholelithiasis; acute and chronic hepatitis. *Mailing Add:* Cedars-Sinai Med Ctr 8700 Beverly Blvd Los Angeles CA 90048

SCHOENHALS, ROBERT JAMES, b Petoskey, Mich, Apr 29, 33; m 56; c 2. MECHANICAL ENGINEERING. *Educ:* Univ Mich, BSE, 56, MSE, 57, PhD(mech eng), 61. *Prof Exp:* Lab asst bearings, Res Labs Div, Gen Motors Co, 54, engr, AC Sparkplug Div, 55; teaching fel mech eng, Univ Mich, 56, res asst, 57-60; from asst prof to assoc prof, 60-68, PROF MECH ENG, PURDUE UNIV, WEST LAFAYETTE, 68- *Concurrent Pos:* Consult, Bendix Energy Controls Div, 63-69; vis prof, Ariz State Univ, 69-70; dir heat transfer prog, Eng Div, NSF, 73-74, energy res coordr, 74-75. *Mem:* AAAS; Am Soc Mech Engrs; Am Soc Eng Educ; Am Soc Heating, Refrig & Air-Conditioning Engrs. *Res:* Heat and mass transfer; fluid mechanics; dynamics and automatic control. *Mailing Add:* Sch of Mech Eng Purdue Univ West Lafayette IN 47907

SCHOENHARD, DELBERT E, b Scales Mound, Ill, Sept 7, 19; m 43; c 2. MICROBIAL GENETICS. *Educ:* Univ Dubuque, BA, 41; Kans State Teachers Col Pittsburg, MS, 42; Mich State Univ, PhD(bact), 51. *Prof Exp:* From instr to asst prof natural sci, 46-55, from asst prof to assoc prof microbiol & pub health, 55-64, assoc chmn dept, 68-75, PROF MICROBIOL & PUB HEALTH, MICH STATE UNIV, 64- *Mem:* Am Soc Microbiol. *Res:* Nature of plasmids in procaryotes. *Mailing Add:* Dept of Microbiol & Pub Health Mich State Univ East Lansing MI 48824

SCHOENHERR, ROMAN UHRICH, b St Henry, Ohio, Jan 2, 34; m 65; c 3. CHEMICAL ENGINEERING, PHYSICAL CHEMISTRY. *Educ:* Univ Dayton, BS, 56; Iowa State Univ, PhD(chem eng), 59. *Prof Exp:* Sr engr, 59-68, eng specialist, 68-72, sr eng specialist, 72-75, CORP ENG SCIENTIST, 3M CO, 75- *Mem:* Am Inst Chem Engrs. *Res:* Research and development in heat, mass and momentum transfer with emphasis on mathematical modeling. *Mailing Add:* 3M Co Eng Systs & Technol St Paul MN 55101

SCHOENHOLZ, WALTER KURT, b Recklinghausen, Ger, Jan 23, 23; US citizen; m 52; c 3. IMMUNOLOGY. *Educ:* Univ Calif, Berkeley, BSc, 56, MA, 59, PhD(med microbiol), 62. *Prof Exp:* Res assoc med microbiol, Med Ctr, Univ Calif, 60-62; asst prof microbiol, Univ NMex, 62-64; vis asst prof virol, Univ Ill, 64-65; assoc prof, 65-69, PROF MED MICROBIOL, CALIF STATE UNIV, HAYWARD, 70- *Concurrent Pos:* Consult clin microbiol & NASA. *Res:* Immune mechanisms in infectious diseases; microbial latency. *Mailing Add:* Dept Biol Sci Calif State Univ Hayward CA 94542

SCHOENIKE, ROLAND ERNEST, b Watertown, Wis, May 9, 25. FOREST GENETICS, AGRICULTURE. *Educ:* Univ Minn, BS, 51, MS, 53, PhD(forest genetics), 62. *Prof Exp:* Forester, US Forest Serv, Ark, 52-56; res asst forestry, Univ Minn, 57-62, asst prof, 63; assoc prof, 63-77, PROF FORESTRY, CLEMSON UNIV, 77- *Concurrent Pos:* Vis fel, Australian Nat Univ, 77. *Mem:* Soc Am Foresters; Am Forestry Asn; Sigma Xi. *Res:* Forest genetics and tree improvement; dendrology, forestry arboretum, tree distribution and variation. *Mailing Add:* Dept of Forestry Clemson Univ Clemson SC 29631

SCHOENSTADT, ARTHUR LORING, b New York, NY, Nov 8, 42; m 64; c 2. APPLIED MATHEMATICS. *Educ:* Rensselaer Polytech Inst, BS, 64, MS, 65, PhD(math), 68. *Prof Exp:* ASSOC PROF MATH, NAVAL POSTGRAD SCH, 70- *Honors & Awards:* Army Commendation Medal with Oak Leaf. *Mem:* Soc Indust & Appl Math. *Res:* Ordinary and partial differential equations; numerical methods. *Mailing Add:* Code 53ZH Naval Postgrad Sch Monterey CA 93940

SCHOENTHALER, ARNOLD CHARLES, organic chemistry, see previous edition

SCHOENWOLF, GARY CHARLES, b Chicago, Ill, Nov 22, 49; m 71; c 2. MORPHOGENESIS, DEVELOPMENTAL BIOLOGY. *Educ:* Elmhurst Col, BA, 71; Univ Ill, Urbana Champaign, MS, 73, PhD(zool), 76. *Prof Exp:* Vis lectr embryol, Univ Ill, 76-77; fel anat, Sch Med, Univ NMex, 77-79; ASST PROF ANAT & EMBRYOL, SCH MED, UNIV UTAH, 79- *Concurrent Pos:* Assoc ed, The Anat Record, 81- *Mem:* Am Soc Zoologists; Am Asn Anatomists; Soc Development Biol; Electron Micros Soc Am; Am Soc Cell Biol. *Res:* Analysis of the mechanisms of morphogenesis, especially those mechanisms involved in the formation of the early rudiments of the central nervous system. *Mailing Add:* Dept Anat Sch Med Univ Utah Salt Lake City UT 84132

SCHOEPFER, ARTHUR E(RIC), b Chicago, Ill, Apr 28, 31; m 53; c 3. CHEMICAL ENGINEERING, CHEMISTRY. *Educ:* Univ Ill, BS, 52. *Prof Exp:* Process engr, Olin-Mathieson Chem Corp, 52-55, asst proj supvr, High Energy Fuel Div, 55-57, proj supvr, 57-59; develop engr, 59-61, sr develop engr, 61-65, group leader eng res, 65-77, prod mgr, 77-79, PLANT MGR, A E STALEY MFG CO, 79- *Mem:* Am Inst Chem Engrs. *Res:* High energy fuels; fused salt electrolysis; solvent extraction; economic evaluation; crystallization; fermentation; ion exchange; process development and design. *Mailing Add:* 4332 Leslie Lane Decatur IL 62526

SCHOEPFLE, GORDON MARCUS, b Louisville, Ky, June 11, 15; m 42; c 4. PHYSIOLOGY. *Educ:* DePauw Univ, AB, 37; Princeton Univ, AM, 39, PhD(biol), 40. *Prof Exp:* Asst physiol, Princeton Univ, 39-40; from instr to prof, Sch Med, Wash Univ, 41-69; PROF NEUROBIOL IN PSYCHIAT, PHYSIOL & BIOPHYS, SCH MED, UNIV ALA, BIRMINGHAM, 69- *Mem:* AAAS; Am Neurosci; Am Physiol Soc; Biophys Soc; Soc Exp Biol & Med. *Res:* Neurophysiology; muscle physiology; interfacial tensions; bioluminescence; mathematics of excitation. *Mailing Add:* Neurosci Prog Sch Med Univ Ala Birmingham AL 35294

SCHOEPKE, HOLLIS GEORGE, b Kenosha, Wis, Feb 22, 29; m 54; c 2. PHARMACOLOGY. *Educ:* Univ Wis, BS, 51, PhD(pharmacol), 60. *Prof Exp:* Res asst, Univ Wis, 56-60; res pharmacologist, Abbott Labs, 60-65, head dept pharmacol, 65-69, dir div exp pharmacol, 69-71, dir prod planning & develop div, 71-73, vpres res & develop, Hosp Prod Div, 73-78; dir res & develop, Pharmaceut Div, E I Du Pont De Nemours & Co, 78-80; PRES PRECLIN RES & DEVELOP, G D SEARLE & CO, 80- *Mem:* Am Soc Pharmacol & Exp Therapeut; Am Heart Asn. *Res:* Cardiovascular and autonomic pharmacology; cardiotonic drugs. *Mailing Add:* G D Searle & Co Chicago IL 60680

SCHOESSLER, JOHN PAUL, b Denver, Colo, May 9, 42; m 64; c 3. OPTOMETRY, VISUAL PHYSIOLOGY. *Educ:* Ohio State Univ, BScOpt, 65, OD, 66, MSc, 68, PhD(physiol optics), 71. *Prof Exp:* From instr to assoc prof optom & physiol optics, 68-75, ASST DEAN, COL OPTOM, OHIO STATE UNIV, 73- *Concurrent Pos:* Mem continuing educ comt, Am Optom Asn, 74- *Mem:* Am Acad Optom; Am Optom Asn. *Res:* Corneal physiology; contact lenses; glaucoma detection; human electroretinogram; visual field defects. *Mailing Add:* Ohio State Univ Col Optom 338 W Tenth Ave Columbus OH 43210

SCHOETTGER, RICHARD A, b Arlington, Nebr, Oct 24, 32; m 54; c 2. FISH BIOLOGY, ENVIRONMENTAL BIOLOGY. *Educ:* Colo State Univ, BS, 54, MS, 59, PhD(zool), 66. *Prof Exp:* Physiologist, Fish Control Lab, 62-67, asst dir lab, 67-69, dir, Fish-Pesticide Res Lab, 69-80, DIR, COLUMBIA NAT FISHERIES RES LAB, US FISH & WILDLIFE SERV, 80- *Concurrent Pos:* Res assoc, Dept Forestry, Fish & Wildlife, Univ Mo-Columbia, 71-; adv comt water qual criteria, Nat Acad Sci, 71-72; co-proj leader, Effects of Pollutants on Aquatic Organisms & Ecosysts, Develop Water Qual Criteria, US/USSR Environ Exchange Agreement, 79- *Mem:* Am Fisheries Soc; Sigma Xi; Soc Environ Toxicol & Chem. *Res:* Toxicity, physiology and ecological effects of pesticides and other contaminants in aquatic organisms. *Mailing Add:* Fish-Pesticide Res Lab US Fish & Wildlife Serv Rte 1 Columbia MO 65201

SCHOETTLER, JAMES ROBERT, b Appleton, Wis, Mar 23, 25; m 48; c 3. PULP & PAPER TECHNOLOGY. *Educ:* Purdue Univ, BS, 46; Inst Paper Chem, MS, 49, PhD(pulp & paper technol), 52. *Prof Exp:* Res chemist, Kimberly-Clark Corp, 53-55; tech supt, Consol Papers, Inc, 56-59; tech dir, Great Northern Paper Co, Maine, 59-64, dir prod develop, 64-66; mgr new prod res, 67-76, MGR PROCESSING & PULP & PAPER RES, NEKOOSA-EDWARDS PAPER CO, 76- *Res:* Product development of business communications papers and chemical carbonless paper systems; statistical quality control and design of experiments in the paper industry; research and development and product development management. *Mailing Add:* Res Dept Nekoosa-Edwards Paper Co Port Edwards WI 54469

SCHOFELD, RICHARD ALAN, b Royersford, Pa, June 30, 24; m 49; c 2. MEDICINE. *Educ:* Jefferson Med Col, MD, 48. *Prof Exp:* Instr path, Med Col & resident, Univ Hosp, Univ Ala, 50-51; instr & resident, Sch Med & Univ Hosp, Duke Univ, 53-55; ASST PROF PATH, HAHNEMANN MED COL, 56-; PATHOLOGIST & DIR LAB, POTTSTOWN MEM MED CTR, 57- *Mem:* Am Soc Clin Path; AMA; Col Am Path. *Res:* Mycology; hemoglobinopathies. *Mailing Add:* Pottstown Mem Med Ctr 1600 High St Pottstown PA 19464

SCHOFFSTALL, ALLEN M, b Harrisburg, Pa, Mar 20, 39; m 61; c 2. ORGANIC CHEMISTRY. *Educ:* Franklin & Marshall Col, BS, 60; State Univ NY Buffalo, PhD(org chem), 66. *Prof Exp:* NIH fel, Univ Ill, 66-67; from asst prof to assoc prof, 67-77, PROF CHEM, UNIV COLO, COLORADO SPRINGS, 77- *Concurrent Pos:* Consult, Kaman Sci Corp, Colo. *Mem:* AAAS; Am Chem Soc. *Res:* Nitrogen heterocyclic and organophosphorus chemistry; chemical evolution. *Mailing Add:* Dept of Chem Univ of Colo Colorado Springs CO 80907

SCHOFIELD, BRIAN, b Manchester, Eng, Feb 26, 20; m 44; c 3. PHYSIOLOGY, GASTROENTEROLOGY. *Educ:* Cambridge Univ, BA, 41, MA, MB & BChir, 44, MD, 54. *Prof Exp:* Lectr physiol, Royal Col Surg, 48-50; reader, Univ Newcastle, 51-67; prof, Univ West Indies, 67-68; vis prof, Univ Toronto, 68-69; PROF PHYSIOL, UNIV CALGARY, 69- *Mem:* Can Physiol Soc; Brit Physiol Soc; Brit Soc Gastroenterol; Brit Med Asn; Brit Asn Study Med Educ. *Res:* Neurohormonal integration in the gastrointestinal tract, particularly in relation to the intramural plexuses and gastrin; medical education. *Mailing Add:* Div of Med Physiol Univ of Calgary Calgary AB T2N 1N4 Can

SCHOFIELD, DEREK, b Oldham, Eng, Feb 14, 28; m 55; c 3. PHYSICS. *Educ:* Univ Sheffield, BSc, 49, PhD(physics), 52. *Prof Exp:* Sci off, H M Underwater Detection Estab, Royal Navy, 52-55; sci off, Underwater Physics Sect, Naval Res Estab, 55-56, group leader transducer group, 56-58, head, Elec Sect, 59-61, head, Physics & Math Sect, 61-64, supt physics wing, 64-68, sci adv to vchief Defence Staff, Can Forces Hq, 68-72, chief, Defence Res Estab Atlantic, 72-77; DEP CHIEF RES & DEVELOP LABS, DEPT NAT DEFENCE, 77- *Mem:* Am Phys Soc. *Res:* Underwater acoustics; electroacoustics. *Mailing Add:* 101 Colonel By Dr 19NT Ottawa ON K1A 0K2 Can

SCHOFIELD, EDMUND ACTON, JR, b Worcester, Mass, Nov 26, 38. ENVIRONMENTAL SCIENCES, CONSERVATION. *Educ:* Clark Univ, BA, 62, MA, 64; Ohio State Univ, PhD(bot), 72. *Prof Exp:* Tech ed, Battelle Mem Inst, 65-67; res asst, Dept Bot, Ohio State Univ, 67-71, res assoc plant ecol, 67-72, asst to dir, Inst Polar Studies, 72; NASA Nat Res Coun resident res assoc biol, Calif Inst Technol, 72-73; environ scientist, Ohio Dept Natural Resources, 73-76; dir res, Sierra Club, 76-77; staff ecologist, Inst Ecol, Butler Univ, 77-80; AUTHOR & CONSULT, 80- *Concurrent Pos:* Partic, US Antarctic Res Prog, Cape Hallett, Ross Island and southern Victoria Land, Antarctica, Clark Univ, 63-64 & Ohio State Univ, 67-68 & 68-69; res assoc, Inst Polar Studies, Ohio State Univ, 73-76; adj asst prof bot, Butler Univ, 78-80. *Mem:* AAAS; Sigma Xi; Am Inst Biol Sci. *Res:* Ecology of Antarctic and Arctic lichens and blue-green algae; effects of soluble salts on plants and acidic precipitation; nitrogen metabolism, including nitrogen fixation and the role of molybdenum in plants; history of ecology; history of conservation movement; environmental consequences of national energy policy. *Mailing Add:* Ohio State Univ PO Box 3106 Columbus OH 43210

SCHOFIELD, JAMES ROY, b Spring, Tex, July 12, 23. ACADEMIC ADMINISTRATION. *Educ:* Baylor Univ, BS, 45, MD, 47. *Prof Exp:* From instr to asst prof anat, Baylor Col Med, 47-53, assoc prof admin med, 59-66, prof anat, 66-71, from asst dean to acad dean, 53-71; DIR DIV ACCREDITATION, ASN AM MED COLS, 71-, SECY, LIAISON COMT MED EDUC, 74- *Concurrent Pos:* Trustee, Baylor Med Found, 52-62, exec vpres, 52-56; Nat coordr, Med Educ Nat Defense, 55-58; consult, Surgeon Gen, US Army, 60 & Div Gen Med Sci, NIH, 61. *Mem:* Assoc Soc Exp Biol & Med; Asn Am Med Cols (asst secy, 59-66); AMA. *Res:* Medical education. *Mailing Add:* Dept Inst Develop Asn Am Med Col One Dupont Circle NW Suite 200 Washington DC 20036

SCHOFIELD, WILFRED BORDEN, b NS, July 19, 27; m 56; c 3. BOTANY. *Educ:* Acadia Univ, BA, 50; Stanford Univ, MA, 56; Duke Univ, PhD, 60. *Prof Exp:* Instr bot, Duke Univ, 58-60; from instr to assoc prof, 60-71, PROF BOT, UNIV BC, 71- *Mem:* Am Bryol & Lichenological Soc (vpres, 65-67, pres, 67-69); Can Bot Asn. *Res:* Taxonomy, ecology, phytogeography and evolution of vascular plants and bryophytes. *Mailing Add:* Dept of Bot Univ of BC Vancouver BC V6T 1W5 Can

SCHOKNECHT, JEAN DONZE, b Urbana, Ill. MYCOLOGY, ULTRASTRUCTURE. *Educ:* Univ Ill, Urbana-Champaign, BS, 65, MS, 67, PhD(bot), 72. *Prof Exp:* Res assoc life sci, Univ Ill, 72-73; vis asst prof electron micros, 73-74, asst prof, 74-78, ASSOC PROF MYCOL & MICROBIOL, IND STATE UNIV, 78- *Mem:* Mycol Soc Am; Brit Mycol Soc; Brit Lichen Soc; Bot Soc Am; Sigma Xi. *Res:* Cytology and development and systematics of the fungi; primarily the Ascomycetes and their imperfect stages and the Myxomycetes; Mycorrhizae; mineral translocation in cell develoment and between symbionts. *Mailing Add:* Dept of Life Sci Ind State Univ Terre Haute IN 47809

SCHOLANDER, PER FREDRIK, physiology, deceased

SCHOLAR, ERIC M, b New York, NY, Aug 28, 39; m 65; c 2. PHARMACOLOGY, BIOCHEMISTRY. *Educ:* Rutgers Univ, BS, 61; Univ Ill, PhD(pharmacol), 68. *Prof Exp:* Res assoc biomed sci, 67-70, instr, 70-72, asst prof biochem pharmacol, Brown Univ, 72-75; ASST PROF PHARMACOL, MED SCH, UNIV OF NEBR, 75- *Mem:* Am Soc Exp Pharmacol & Therapeut; Am Asn Cancer Res; AAAS. *Res:* Nucleotide metabolism in human leukemia cells; mechanism of action of anti-neoplastic and immunosuppressive drugs; effect of purine and pyrimidines on vascular responsiveness. *Mailing Add:* Dept of Pharmacol Med Sch Univ of Nebr Omaha NE 68105

SCHOLBERG, HAROLD MILTON, b Minot, NDak, July 6, 10; m 35; c 2. CHEMISTRY. *Educ:* Univ NDak, BChE, 32, MChE, 33; Univ Chicago, PhD(phys chem), 38. *Prof Exp:* Chemist, Hendricks Res Corp, 34-36, Sherwin-Williams Co, Ohio, 38-41 & Am Can Co, NY, 41-44; chemist, Minn Mining & Mfg Co, 44-48, sect leader, 48-51, from asst dir to assoc dir cent res, 51-55, res assoc, 55-58; group leader, Monsanto Chem Co, 58-59, consult, 59-60; tech dir, Photek, Inc, 60-62, consult, 62-65; vpres & tech dir, Moleculon Res Corp, 65-68; CONSULT, 68- *Mem:* Am Chem Soc; The Chem Soc; Electrochem Soc. *Res:* Office duplication methods; combustion of gasoline in motors; surface chemistry; insoluble films; electrochemistry; fluorine; prevention of knock in motors with metal organics other than lead; adhesion and adhesives; radiation damage effects. *Mailing Add:* 5 Old Causeway Rd Bedford MA 01730

SCHOLER, CHARLES FREY, b Manhattan, Kans, May 31, 34; m 57; c 3. CIVIL ENGINEERING. *Educ:* Kans State Univ, BS, 56; Purdue Univ, MS, 57, PhD(civil eng mat), 65. *Prof Exp:* Engr, Burgwin & Martin Consult Engrs, 57-58; asst hwy engr, Riley County, Kans, 60; from instr to asst prof, 60-69, ASSOC PROF CIVIL ENG, PURDUE UNIV, WEST LAFAYETTE, 69- *Concurrent Pos:* Mem comt mech properties concrete, Hwy Res Bd; assoc dir, Highway Exten Res Project, Indiana Cities & Counties, Purdue Univ, West Lafayette. *Mem:* Am Soc Civil Engrs; Am Concrete Inst; Am Soc Testing & Mat; Am Soc Eng Educ. *Res:* Construction materials, especially portland cement; concrete durability, physical and mechanical properties and its applications; nondestructive testing; aggregates, soils, bituminous materials and plastics. *Mailing Add:* Sch of Civil Eng Purdue Univ West Lafayette IN 47907

SCHOLES, CHARLES PATTERSON, b Auburn, NY, Oct 31, 42; m 66; c 2. BIOPHYSICS. *Educ:* Cornell Univ, AB, 64; Yale Univ, PhD(biophys), 69. *Prof Exp:* NSF fel, Oxford Univ, 69-70; NIH fel, Univ Calif, San Diego, 70-73; asst prof, 73-78, ASSOC PROF PHYSICS, STATE UNIV NY ALBANY, 78- *Concurrent Pos:* NIH fel, 76-81. *Mem:* Biophys Soc; Am Phys Soc. *Res:* Study of biological molecules by techniques of electron paramagnetic resonance and electron nuclear double resonance. *Mailing Add:* Dept of Physics State Univ of NY Albany NY 12222

SCHOLES, NORMAN W, b Ogden, Utah, June 9, 30; m 50; c 1. PHARMACOLOGY, PHYSIOLOGY. *Educ:* Univ Utah, BS, 53; Univ Calif, Los Angeles, MS, 56, PhD(pharmacol), 59. *Prof Exp:* Res chemist, Wasatch Chem Corp, Utah, 53-54; res neuropharmacologist, City of Hope Med Ctr, Duarte, Calif, 60-64; asst prof pharmacol, Univ Calif, Davis, 64-68; PROF PHARMACOL, SCH MED, CREIGHTON UNIV, 68- *Concurrent Pos:* Giannini-Bank of Am fel, 59-61. *Mem:* AAAS; Soc Exp Biol & Med; Am Soc Pharmacol & Exp Therapeut; NY Acad Sci. *Res:* Synaptic mechanisms in the central nervous system and their physiological significance; mode and site of action of drugs acting upon the central nervous system; neurochemical and electrophysiological correlates of learning. *Mailing Add:* Dept of Physiol & Pharmacol Creighton Univ Sch of Med Omaha NE 68131

SCHOLES, SAMUEL RAY, JR, b Pittsburgh, Pa; m 44; c 2. CHEMISTRY. *Educ:* Alfred Univ, BS, 37; Yale Univ, PhD(phys chem), 40. *Prof Exp:* Asst quant anal, Yale Univ, 37-40; instr chem, Alfred Univ, 40-41 & phys chem, Tufts Col, 41-46; assoc prof, 46-55, chmn dept, 55-70, prof, 55-80, EMER PROF CHEM, ALFRED UNIV, 80- *Mem:* Am Chem Soc; Sigma Xi. *Res:* Properties of solutions of electrolytes; analysis of microgram quantities of fluorine; analysis of water in transformer oils. *Mailing Add:* 45 W Universtiy St Alfred NY 14802

SCHOLES, VERNON EUGENE, medical microbiology, infectious diseases, see previous edition

SCHOLFIELD, CHARLES REXEL, b Morgan Co, Ill, Nov 9, 14. ANALYTICAL CHEMISTRY, ORGANIC CHEMISTRY. *Educ:* Ill Col, AB, 36; Univ Ill, AM, 41. *Prof Exp:* Sci aide chem, Regional Soybean Prod Lab, Northern Regional Res Ctr, USDA, 37-41, chemist, 41-42, res chemist, 42-81; RETIRED. *Mem:* Am Chem Soc; Am Oil Chemists Soc. *Res:* Chemistry and hydrogenation of fats and oils; liquid and gas chromatography. *Mailing Add:* 1116 W Moss Apt 7-B Peoria IL 61606

SCHOLL, DAVID WILLIAM, b Antioch, Calif, June 3, 34; m 61; c 2. GEOLOGY. *Educ:* Univ Southern Calif, BS, 56, MS, 59; Stanford Univ, PhD(geol), 62. *Prof Exp:* Marine geologist, US Geol Surv, 58-59; oceanogr, US Navy Electronics Lab, 62-69; OCEANOGR, US GEOL SURV, 69- *Concurrent Pos:* Nat Acad Sci-Nat Res Coun resident res assoc, 62-63. *Mem:* AAAS; Am Asn Petrol Geologists; Geol Soc Am; Soc Econ Paleontologists & Mineralogists. *Res:* Marine geology; sedimentology; geophysics. *Mailing Add:* US Geol Surv 345 Middlefield Rd Menlo Park CA 94025

SCHOLL, MARIJA STROJNIK, b Ljubljana, Yugoslavia; US citizen. LASERS, INFRARED OPTICS. *Educ:* Ariz State Univ, BS, 72, MS, 74; Univ Ariz, Tuscon, MS, 77, PhD(optical sci), 79; Univ Calif, Los Angeles, MEngr, 81. *Prof Exp:* Teaching asst physics, Ariz State Univ, 72-75; res assoc optical sci, Univ Ariz, 75-78; sr staff mem optics, Rockwell Int, 78-79, mgr optics technol, 79-81; STAFF ENGR PHOSPHOR RES, SPERRY CORP, 81- *Mem:* Sigma Xi; Am Phys Soc; Optical Soc Am; AAAS; Inst Elec & Electronics Engrs. *Res:* Infrared target activation, as manifested by the target response to the laser irradiation; development of coatings for high energy laser mirrors; fabrication of phosphors for color displays. *Mailing Add:* 721 E Chilton Dr Tempe AZ 85283

SCHOLL, PHILIP JON, b Madison, Wis, Jan 25, 45; m 75. LIVESTOCK ENTOMOLOGY, LIVESTOCK PARASITOLOGY. *Educ:* Univ Wis, Madison, BS, 70, MS, 73, PhD(entom), 78. *Prof Exp:* Res asst parasitol & entom, Univ Wis, 71-78, res assoc med entom, 78; RES ENTOMOLOGIST LIVESTOCK INSECTS, AGR RES SERV, USDA, 79- *Concurrent Pos:* Consult med entom, Univ Federal Rural do Rio de Janeiro, Brazil, 78; grad fac, Univ Nebr Syst, 79-; asst prof, Univ Nebr, Lincoln, 79- *Mem:* Sigma Xi; Entom Soc Am; Am Registry Prof Entomologists. *Res:* Ecology and population parameters of blood-feeding diptera of veterinary and medical importance, especially livestock pests including gongtrophic age-grading, population sampling, seasonal distribution, and the effects of control strategies on population characteristics. *Mailing Add:* Biting Fly-Cattle Grub Livestock Unit Insects Lab USDA PO Box 232 Kerrville TX 78028

SCHOLLE, PETER ALLEN, b New York, NY, Sept 12, 44; m 67; c 2. SEDIMENTOLOGY, PETROGRAPHY. *Educ:* Yale Univ, BS, 65; Princeton Univ, MA, 69, PhD(geol), 70. *Prof Exp:* Res geologist, Explor & Prod Res Lab, Cities Serv Oil Co, 70-71; asst prof sedimentol, Univ Tex, Dallas, 71-74; GEOLOGIST, US GEOL SURV, 74- *Concurrent Pos:* Geologist, US Geol Surv, 74-; distinguished lectr, Am Asn Petrol Geologists, 75-76. *Mem:* Am Asn Petrol Geologists; Soc Econ Paleontologists & Mineralogists. *Res:* Petrology and trace element geochemistry of chalks and other micritic carbonate rocks; sedimentology of deep water sediments; diagenesis and petroleum potential of deep-sea fans. *Mailing Add:* US Geol Surv MS 934 Federal Ctr Denver CO 80225

SCHOLLENBERGER, CHARLES SUNDY, b Wooster, Ohio, Aug 8, 22; m 49; c 2. POLYMER CHEMISTRY, ORGANIC CHEMISTRY. *Educ:* Col Wooster, AB, 43; Cornell Univ, PhD(org chem), 47. *Prof Exp:* Lab asst, Col Wooster, 42-43; lab asst, Cornell Univ, 44, asst org chem, 44-47; res chemist & sect leader, 47-75, RES & DEVELOP FEL, B F GOODRICH RES & DEVELOP CTR, 75- *Concurrent Pos:* Chem analyst, Ohio Exp Sta, 42-44. *Mem:* Am Chem Soc. *Res:* Polyurethanes; stereo rubbers; polymers; environmental resistance. *Mailing Add:* B F Goodrich Res & Develop Ctr Brecksville OH 44141

SCHOLLER, JEAN, b Boston, Mass, Apr 14, 19. PHARMACOLOGY. *Educ:* Carnegie Inst Technol, BS, 41; Georgetown Univ, PhD, 52. *Prof Exp:* Res assoc path, Sch Med, Georgetown Univ, 48-52; assoc pharmacol, Sloan-Kettering Inst Cancer Res, 52-58, actg head dept, 55-56; asst prof, Sloan-Kettering Div, Med Col, Cornell Univ, 56-58; assoc cancer res, Christ Hosp Inst Med Res, Cincinnati, Ohio, 58-59; head dept pharmacol, John L Smith Mem Lab Cancer Res, Chas Pfizer & Co, Inc, 59-61; chmn dept exp therapeut, Stanford Res Inst, 61-68; prof pharmacol, Univ Tex, Austin, 68-77, dir lab comp pharmacol, 69-77; sr res toxicologist, Richmond Res Ctr, Stauffer Chem Co, 77-80; WITH SCHOLLER ASSOCS, 80- *Mem:* AAAS; Am Soc Pharmacol & Exp Therapeut; Soc Exp Biol & Med; Am Asn Cancer Res; Soc Toxicol. *Res:* Pharmacology and toxicology; cancer chemotherapy and virology; drug metabolism. *Mailing Add:* Scholler Assocs 1146 Lea Dr Novato CA 94947

SCHOLNICK, FRANK, b Philadelphia, Pa, Apr 17, 25; m 57; c 2. ORGANIC CHEMISTRY. *Educ:* Temple Univ, BA, 46, MA, 48; Univ Pa, PhD(chem), 55. *Prof Exp:* Org chemist, E F Houghton & Co, 48-49 & Plastics & Coal Chems Div, Allied Chem Corp, 55-59; ORG RES CHEMIST, EASTERN REGIONAL RES LAB, USDA, 59- *Mem:* Am Chem Soc; Am Oil Chem Soc; Am Leather Chem Asn. *Res:* Polymers; coal tar chemistry; organic synthesis; detergents; coatings. *Mailing Add:* 2345 Pine Ridge Dr Lafayette Hill PA 19444

SCHOLTEN, PAUL DAVID, b Grand Haven, Mich, Apr 17, 49. SOLID STATE PHYSICS. *Educ:* Kalamazoo Col, BA, 71; Fla State Univ, PhD(physics), 76. *Prof Exp:* res assoc, Tex A&M Univ, 76-77, vis asst prof, 77-78; ASST PROF PHYSICS, MIAMI UNIV, 78- *Mem:* Am Phys Soc. *Res:* Superconductivity; thermal properties of solids; thin films; ion implantation; magnetism. *Mailing Add:* Dept of Physics Miami Univ Oxford OH 45056

SCHOLTEN, ROBERT, geology, tectonics, see previous edition

SCHOLTENS, ROBERT GEORGE, b Grand Rapids, Mich, Feb 11, 29; m 52; c 3. EPIDEMIOLOGY, PARASITOLOGY. *Educ:* Mich State Univ, BS, 57, DVM, 59; Univ Ill, MS, 61; London Sch Hyg & Trop Med, dipl, 66. *Prof Exp:* Dir animal care, Biochem Res Found, 60-61; asst chief rabies, Nat Rabies Lab, Commun Dis Ctr, USPHS, 61-62; vet epidemiologist, 63-66, chief parasitic dis br, Ctr for Dis Control, 66-67; dep dir malaria prog, 67-73, dir vector biol & control div, Ctr Dis Control, 72-76; assoc prof, 76-80, PROF, DEPT PATHOBIOL, COL VET MED, UNIV TENN, 80- *Concurrent Pos:* Mem subcomt animal dis surveillance, Animal Health Comt, Nat Acad Sci-Nat Res Coun, 64-; epidemiologist, London Sch Hyg & Trop Med, 65-66. *Mem:* Am Soc Trop Med & Hyg; Royal Soc Trop Med & Hyg; Am Soc Parasitol. *Res:* Epidemiology of parasitic diseases. *Mailing Add:* Univ of Tenn PO Box 1071 Knoxville TN 37901

SCHOLTES, WAYNE HENRY, b Clinton, Iowa, Dec 3, 17; m 41; c 3. SOIL SCIENCE. *Educ:* Iowa State Col, BS, 39, PhD(soil classification), 51; Duke Univ, MS, 40. *Prof Exp:* Jr soil scientist, Soil Conserv Serv, USDA, 41-45, assoc soil scientist, 45-46, soil scientist, Bur Plant Indust, 46-51; from asst prof to assoc prof, 51-55, PROF SOILS, IOWA STATE UNIV, 55-, PROF FORESTRY & DISTINGUISHED PROF AGR, 77- *Concurrent Pos:* Vis prof, Univ Ill, 58; Univ Ariz, 66 & 69 & San Carlos Univ Guatemala, 68 & 69; soils specialist, Fac Agron, Univ of the Repub, Uruguay, 63-65. *Mem:* Soil Sci Soc Am; Am Soc Agron; Soil Conserv Soc Am. *Res:* Soil classification and genesis. *Mailing Add:* 135 Agron Bldg Iowa State Univ Ames IA 50010

SCHOLTZ, ROBERT A, b Lebanon, Ohio, Jan 26, 36; m 62; c 2. ELECTRICAL ENGINEERING. *Educ:* Univ Cincinnati, EE, 58; Univ Southern Calif, MSEE, 60; Stanford Univ, PhD(elec eng), 64. *Prof Exp:* Mem tech staff, Hughes Aircraft Co, 58-63, staff engr, 63-68, sr staff engr, 68-78;

res assoc, 63-65, from asst prof to assoc prof, 65-74, PROF ELEC ENG, UNIV SOUTHERN CALIF, 74- *Concurrent Pos:* Consult, Lincom, 76- & Aniomatix, Inc, 79-; vis colleague, Univ Hawaii, 78. *Mem:* Fel Inst Elec & Electronics Engrs. *Res:* Communication and information theory; synchronization techniques; transmitter optimization and signal design. *Mailing Add:* Dept Elec Eng Univ Southern Calif Los Angeles CA 90007

SCHOLZ, CHRISTOPHER HENRY, b Pasadena, Calif, Feb 25, 43; m 62; c 2. GEOPHYSICS. *Educ:* Univ Nev, BS, 64; Mass Inst Technol, PhD(geol), 67. *Prof Exp:* Res fel, Seismol Lab, Calif Inst Technol, 67-68; res assoc, 68-71, assoc prof, Univ, 73-76, SR RES ASSOC GEOPHYS, LAMONT-DOHERTY GEOL OBSERV, COLUMBIA UNIV, 71-, PROF, UNIV, 76- *Concurrent Pos:* Mem Nat Acad Sci Comn rock mech, 75-78 & Comn seismol; Sloan fel, 75-77 & Green fel, 80-81. *Mem:* Am Geophys Union; Seismol Soc Am. *Res:* Mechanics of rock fracture and flow; earthquake mechanism and seismicity. *Mailing Add:* Lamont-Doherty Geol Observ Palisades NY 10964

SCHOLZ, DAN ROBERT, b Marysville, Kans, Sept 17, 20; m 34; c 1. MATHEMATICS. *Educ:* Southwest Tex State Teachers Col, BS, 41, MA, 42; Calif Inst Technol, MS, 43; Washington Univ, PhD(math), 51. *Prof Exp:* Asst math, Washington Univ, 48-50; asst prof, Southwestern La Inst, 51-52; from instr to assoc prof, 46-63, PROF MATH, LA STATE UNIV, BATON ROUGE, 63-, PROF MECH ENG, 77- *Mem:* Am Math Soc; Math Asn Am; Soc Indust & Appl Math. *Res:* Functions of a complex variable; numerical analysis. *Mailing Add:* Dept of Math La State Univ Baton Rouge LA 70803

SCHOLZ, EARL WALTER, b Marysville, Kans, Sept 24, 25; m 47; c 5. HORTICULTURE, PLANT PHYSIOLOGY. *Educ:* Kans State Col, BS, 50; Iowa State Univ, MS, 55, PhD(hort, plant physiol), 57. *Prof Exp:* Horticulturist, Agr Mkt Serv, USDA, 57-63; horticulturist, 63-80, ASSOC PROF HORTICULTURE & FORESTRY, NDAK STATE UNIV, 80- *Mem:* Am Soc Hort Sci. *Res:* Vegetable and strawberry culture. *Mailing Add:* Dept of Hort NDak State Univ Fargo ND 58102

SCHOLZ, JOHN JOSEPH, JR, b Parshall, NDak, June 11, 26; m 50; c 2. PHYSICAL CHEMISTRY. *Educ:* Univ NDak, BS, 48; Univ Ill, PhD, 55. *Prof Exp:* Res chemist, Minn Mining & Mfg Co, 53-55; res assoc, Univ Ill, 55-57; from asst prof to assoc prof, 57-68, PROF CHEM, UNIV NEBR-LINCOLN, 68-, VCHMN DEPT, 74- *Mem:* Am Chem Soc; Am Phys Soc. *Res:* Physical absorption; intermolecular forces; physical biochemistry; properties of macromolecules. *Mailing Add:* Dept of Chem Univ of Nebr Lincoln NE 68588

SCHOLZ, LAWRENCE CHARLES, b New York, NY, Aug 8, 33; m 54; c 2. SOFTWARE ENGINEERING, SYSTEMS ENGINEERING. *Educ:* City Col New York, BEE, 54. *Prof Exp:* Engr electron tube design, Tube Div, RCA Corp, 54-60; res physicist plasma physics, IIT Res Inst, 60-65; group leader nuclear effects, Vitro Labs, 65-69; dir advan syst simulations, Mantech, 69-70; mgr software eng, 70-80, MGR MISSION OPERS, SATCOM SATELLITE PROJ, ASTRO ELECTRONICS DIV, RCA CORP, 80- *Mem:* Sr mem Inst Elec & Electronics Engrs; Soc Comput Simulation; AAAS. *Res:* Software reliability; the relation between specification, implementation and testability; software organization for critical applications, for example, on board satellite control. *Mailing Add:* 28 Old Salem Rd West Orange NJ 07052

SCHOLZ, PAUL DRUMMOND, b Sedro Woolley, Wash, Nov 11, 36; m 60; c 2. MECHANICAL ENGINEERING. *Educ:* Univ Wash, BS, 60; Northwestern Univ, MS, 65, PhD(mech eng, astronaut sci), 67. *Prof Exp:* Mech engr, Pasadena Annex, US Naval Ord Test Sta, 60-62; from asst prof to assoc prof, 67-78, PROF ENERGY ENG, UNIV IOWA, 78-, ASSOC DEAN, 79- *Mem:* AAAS; Am Soc Mech Eng; Am Soc Eng Educ. *Res:* Coagulation enhancement in aerosols; plasma non-equilibrium and spectroscopy; kinetic theory of aerosols; thermodynamics. *Mailing Add:* Eng Admin Univ Iowa Iowa City IA 52242

SCHOLZ, RICHARD W, b Ft Riley, Kans, Apr 1, 42. NUTRITIONAL BIOCHEMISTRY. *Educ:* Cornell Univ, BS; Purdue Univ, MS, 66, PhD(nutrit), 68. *Prof Exp:* Res asst nutrit, Purdue Univ, 64-65; asst prof, 68-75, assoc prof, 75-81, PROF VET SCI, PA STATE UNIV, UNIVERSITY PARK, 81- *Mem:* Am Inst Nutrit. *Res:* Lung metabolism; metabolic adaptation to alterations in diet and other environmental factors. *Mailing Add:* Dept of Vet Sci Pa State Univ Col Agr University Park PA 16802

SCHOLZ, ROBERT GEORGE, b Chicago, Ill, July 3, 30; m 54; c 3. ANALYTICAL CHEMISTRY. *Educ:* Univ Ill, BS, 54; Purdue Univ, PhD(anal chem), 61. *Prof Exp:* Res chemist, Continental Can Co, 61-64 & IIT Res Inst, 64-71; MGR, ANAL CHEM, BEATRICE FOODS, CHICAGO, 71- *Concurrent Pos:* Lectr, Roosevelt Univ, 68-72. *Mem:* Am Chem Soc. *Res:* Analysis of food and food products using gas chromatography; atomic absorption; liquid chromatography. *Mailing Add:* 422 Hudson Ave Clarendon Hills IL 60514

SCHOLZ, WILFRIED, b Landau, Ger, Sept 14, 36; US citizen; m 66; c 2. PARTICLE SOLID INTERACTIONS, NUCLEAR & ATOMIC PHYSICS. *Educ:* Univ Freiburg, dipl physics, 60, PhD(physics), 62. *Prof Exp:* Asst nuclear physics, Univ Freiburg, 61-64; res assoc, Yale Univ, 64-67; asst prof physics, Univ Pa, 67-70; from asst prof to assoc prof, 70-82, PROF PHYSICS, STATE UNIV NY ALBANY, 82- *Concurrent Pos:* Consult ed, Atomic Data & Nuclear Data Tables, 82- *Mem:* Am Phys Soc. *Res:* Nuclear spectroscopy and reactions; theory of nuclear structure; electron atom collisions; superconductivity. *Mailing Add:* Dept of Physics State Univ NY Albany NY 12222

SCHOM, CHARLES BENJAMIN, b Saskatoon, Sask, Jan 5, 44; m 67; c 2. QUANTITATIVE GENETICS, POPULATION GENETICS. *Educ:* Univ BC, BSA, 67; Tex A&M Univ, MSc, 71; Univ Calif, PhD(genetics), 76. *Prof Exp:* Instr genetics, Dalhousie Univ, 74-76; asst prof, Univ NB, 76-77, Brock

Univ, 77-78 & Univ Winnepeg, 78-80; asst prof, 80-81, ASSOC PROF GENETICS, UNIV NB, ST JOHN, 80-, IBM MARINE SCI CHAIR, 80- *Mem:* Am Genetics Asn; Can Genetics Soc. *Res:* Genetic components controlling resistance and the possibility of selecting for more resistant strains in salmonids exposed to environmental disturbances such as acid rain. *Mailing Add:* Dept Biol Univ NB St John NB E2L 4L5

SCHOMAKER, VERNER, b Nehawka, Nebr, June 22, 14; m 44; c 3. PHYSICAL CHEMISTRY, STRUCTURAL CHEMISTRY. *Educ:* Univ Nebr, BSc, 34, MSc, 35; Calif Inst Technol, PhD(chem), 38. *Prof Exp:* Hale fel chem, Calif Inst Technol, 38-40, sr fel, 40-45, from asst prof to prof, 45-58; chemist, Union Carbide Res Inst, 58-59, from asst dir to assoc dir, 59-65; chmn dept, 65-70, PROF CHEM, UNIV WASH, 65- *Concurrent Pos:* Guggenheim Mem Found fel, 47-48; consult, Chem Div, Brookhaven Nat Lab, 48-49, Oak Ridge Nat Lab, 52-55, US Naval Ord Testing Sta, Calif, 55-58 & Union Carbide Corp, 57-58 & 65-80; mem ad hoc comt comput, Int Union Crystallog, 57, Nat Comt Crystallog, 61-64 & 71-74, subcomt molecular struct, Nat Acad Sci-Nat Res Coun, 61-63, adv comt math & phys sci, NSF, 67-69 & eval panel, Reactor Radiation Div, Nat Bur Stand, 74-77. *Honors & Awards:* Award, Am Chem Soc, 50. *Mem:* Fel AAAS; Am Crystallog Asn (pres, 62); fel NY Acad Sci. *Res:* Structural chemistry; determination of crystal and molecular structures by x-ray and electron diffraction; crystallographic computations; zeolite catalysis. *Mailing Add:* Dept of Chem Univ of Wash Seattle WA 98195

SCHOMAN, CHARLES M, JR, b Rochester, NY, Dec 24, 24; m 46. RESEARCH & DEVELOPMENT. *Educ:* US Naval Acad, BS, 46; Rutgers Univ, MS, 57, PhD(sci), 60. *Prof Exp:* Equip engr, US Naval Supply Res & Develop Facil, 54, asst to tech dir, Res Div, 54-55, head Planning, Surv & Coordr Br, 55-57, asst tech dir, 57-58, asst tech dir & head eng planning & surv team, 58-59, sr staff tech consult & asst to officer in chg, 59-61, chief scientist, 61-64, tech dir, 64-66, head advan planning & systs anal, US Naval Ord Lab, 66-73; head advan planning, Naval Surface Weapons Ctr, 73-76; DIR PLANS & PROGS, DAVID W TAYLOR NAVAL SHIPS RES & DEVELOP CTR, 76- *Concurrent Pos:* sr exec assoc, Nat Conf Advan Res Conf Comt, 80-84. *Honors & Awards:* Jump Award, 58 & Isker Award, US Navy, 62. *Mem:* Inst Food Technol; Fed Prof Asn (nat pres, 76); Am Asn Avionic & Astronaut; Sigma Xi. *Res:* Scientific and engineering research management; technology transfer; food science. *Mailing Add:* 3600 Pimlico Pl Silver Spring MD 20906

SCHONBAUM, EDUARD, b Vienna, Austria, Sept 18, 23; m 55. PHARMACOLOGY, PHYSIOLOGY. *Educ:* Univ Amsterdam, ChemCand, 50; McGill Univ, PhD(biochem), 55. *Prof Exp:* Res assoc physiol, 55-57, asst prof med res, 57-60, asst prof pharmacol, 60-63, ASSOC PROF PHARMACOL, UNIV TORONTO, 63-; head central nervous system pharmacol, 73-81, head gen pharmacol, 79-81, INT COORDR PHARMACOL RES, RES & DEVELOP LABS, ORGANON INT BV, OSS, NETHERLANDS, 81- *Concurrent Pos:* Assoc med dir pharmacol, Ciba-Geigy Can Ltd, 68-73. *Mem:* AAAS; Can Physiol Soc; Can Pharmacol Soc; Am Physiol Soc; Dutch Soc Pharmacol. *Res:* Temperature regulation; cardiovascular pharmacology; autonomic pharmacology. *Mailing Add:* Peelkensweg 4 Venhorst 5428 NM Netherlands

SCHONBECK, NIELS DANIEL, b Baltimore, Md, Nov 1, 45; m 77; c 1. BIOENERGETICS, ENZYMOLOGY. *Educ:* Swarthmore Col, BA, 67; Univ Mich, Ann Arbor, PhD(biochem), 73. *Prof Exp:* Res technician biochem, Univ Mich, Ann Arbor, 69-71, fel, 73-74; Nat Cancer Inst fel, Univ Calif, Berkely, 74-75, lectr biochem, 75-78; asst prof, 78-80, ASSOC PROF CHEM, METROPOLITAN STATE COL, DENVER, 80- *Concurrent Pos:* Lectr health & med sci prog, Univ Calif, Berkeley, 75-; lectr, Div Natural Sci II, Univ Calif, Santa Cruz, 76. *Mem:* AAAS; Sigma Xi. *Res:* Development of undergraduate research programs in: chloroplast bioenergetics, hemoglobin-ligand interactions, glycosylated hemoglobins, enzyme kinetics, antioxidants and secondary metabolites; mutagenesis and plant metabolism. *Mailing Add:* Dept Chem 1006 11th St Denver CO 80204

SCHONBERG, RUSSELL GEORGE, b Minneapolis, Minn, Sept 15, 26; m 48; c 6. ENGINEERING, RESEARCH MANAGEMENT. *Educ:* Calif State Polytech Col, BS, 50. *Prof Exp:* Engr, US Air Force, McClellan Field, Calif, 50-51, Calif Res & Develop Co, 51-53 & Radiation Lab, Univ Calif, 53-55; engr, Varian Assocs, 55-58, proj engr, 58-60, mgr elec eng, 60-64, mgr lab opers, 64-68; vpres opers, SHM Nuclear Corp, 68-70; FOUNDER & PRES, SCHONBERG RADIATION CORP, 70- *Mem:* Sr mem Inst Elec & Electronics Engrs; Am Nuclear Soc; Am Soc Non-Destructive Testing. *Res:* Radiation research on polymerization; free radical chemistry and process techniques; development of new and improved radiation sources; design and development of miniature 3.5 million electron volts electron linear accelerator; development of real time x-ray imaging systems, automatic inspection devices and microprocessor controlled remote handling devices. *Mailing Add:* 12386 Melody Lane Los Altos Hills CA 94022

SCHONBRUNN, AGNES, b Budapest, Hungary, Oct 29, 48; Can citizen; m 74. RECEPTOR MECHANISMS, NEUROPEPTIDE ACTION. *Educ:* McGill Univ, BSc, 70; Brandeis Univ, PhD(biochem), 75. *Prof Exp:* Fel pharmacol, Harvard Sch Dent Med, 75-79; ASST PROF PHYSIOL, HARVARD SCH PUBLIC HEALTH, 79- *Mem:* Am Soc Cell Biol; Endocrine Soc. *Res:* Structure, function and regulation of membrane receptors in eukaryotic cells; mechanisms involved in neuropeptide regulation of hormone secretion and synthesis in target endocrine cells. *Mailing Add:* Dept Physiol Harvard Sch Public Health 665 Huntington Ave Boston MA 02115

SCHONE, HARLAN EUGENE, b Bluffs, Ill, Feb 14, 32; m 56; c 3. PHYSICS. *Educ:* Univ Calif, PhD(physics), 61. *Prof Exp:* Physicist, Sci Res Lab, Boeing Airplane Co, 60-65; from asst prof to assoc prof, 65-74, actg grad dean, 70-71, PROF PHYSICS, COL WILLIAM & MARY, 74- *Mem:* Am Phys Soc. *Res:* Nuclear magnetic resonance; metal physics. *Mailing Add:* Dept of Physics Col of William & Mary Williamsburg VA 23185

SCHONFELD, EDWARD, b New York, NY, Oct 23, 30; m 76; c 1. POLYMER CHEMISTRY, ORGANIC CHEMISTRY. *Educ:* Brooklyn Col, BS, 52; Syracuse Univ, MS, 55, PhD(polymer & org chem), 57. *Prof Exp:* Chemist, Thiokol Chem Corp, 57-59; chemist & group leader, Nopco Chem Co, 59-64; chemist & lab mgr, Adhesives Prods Div, PPG Industs, 64-68; SR RES SCIENTIST, JOHNSON & JOHNSON, 68- *Concurrent Pos:* Instr, Brooklyn Col, 61-62, Bloomfield Col, 78-; co-adj asst prof, Rutgers Univ, 72-73. *Mem:* Am Chem Soc. *Res:* Medical and surgical adhesives; pressure sensitive adhesives; sealants; urethane polymers; polymerization and characterization of polymers; bactericidal polymers; synthesis of quaternaries; UV and EB curing of polymers. *Mailing Add:* Johnson & Johnson Res Ctr New Brunswick NY 08903

SCHONFELD, GUSTAV, b Mukacevo, Czech, May 8, 34; m 61; c 3. INTERNAL MEDICINE, METABOLISM. *Educ:* Wash Univ, BA, 56, MD, 60. *Prof Exp:* Asst prof internal med, Sch Med, Wash Univ, 68-70; assoc prof metab & human nutrit, Mass Inst Technol, 70-72; assoc prof prev med & med, 72-77, PROF PREV MED & MED, SCH MED, WASH UNIV, 77- *Concurrent Pos:* Asst dir, Mass Inst Technol Clin Res Ctr, 70-72; dir, Lipid Res Ctr, Sch Med, Wash Univ, 72-; NIH grants; guest speaker, Asn Am Physicians & Am Soc Biochem Chemists. *Mem:* Endocrine Soc; Am Soc Clin Invest; Am Physiol Soc; Am Diabetes Asn; Am Heart Asn. *Res:* Lipoproteins; hyperlipidemia; atherosclerosis; diabetes mellitus. *Mailing Add:* Lipid Res Ctr 4566 Scott Ave St Louis MO 63110

SCHONFELD, HYMAN KOLMAN, b New York, NY, Aug 5, 19; m 44; c 2. PUBLIC HEALTH. *Educ:* Brooklyn Col, BA, 40; NY Univ, DDS, 43; Univ NC, MPH, 60, DrPH(epidemiol), 62. *Prof Exp:* Pvt dent pract, 47-56; dentist, Cent State Hosp, Petersburg, Va, 57-59; clin res assoc, Warner Lambert Res Inst, 62-64, biometrician, 64; sr res assoc med care, Dept Epidemiol & Pub Health, Sch Med, Yale Univ, 64-69, assoc prof pub health, Health Serv Admin, 69-74; sr staff officer, Nat Res Coun, Nat Acad Sci, 74-76; private consult, 76-81; STAFF MEM, DEPT MED & SURG, VET ADMIN, 77- *Concurrent Pos:* Staff mem, Dept Med & Surg, Vet Admin, 77- *Res:* Quality of medical and dental health care; evaluation of dental care systems. *Mailing Add:* 1116 Caddington Ave Silver Spring MD 20901

SCHONFELD, JONATHAN FURTH, b New York, NY, June 7, 51; m 81. QUANTUM FIELD THEORY, ACCELERATOR PHYSICS. *Educ:* Yale Col, BS, 72; Princeton Univ, PhD(physics), 75. *Prof Exp:* Res fel, Calif Inst Technol, 76-78; res assoc, Univ Minn, 78-79; chercheur associe, Ecole Normale Supereure, Paris, 79-80; ASSOC SCIENTIST, FERMI NAT ACCELERATOR LAB, 80- *Res:* Nonlinear effects in classical and quantized fields. *Mailing Add:* Theory Dept Fermi Lab PO Box 500 Batavia IL 60510

SCHONFELD, STEVEN EMANUEL, b New York, NY, Sept 3, 47; m 72; c 2. PERIODONTAL IMMUNOLOGY. *Educ:* State Univ NY Stony Brook, BS, 69; NY Univ, DDS, 73; Univ Southern Calif, PhD(cell & molecular biol), 76. *Prof Exp:* Asst prof, 76-82, ASSOC PROF MICROBIOL & IMMUNOL, SCH DENT, UNIV SOUTHERN CALIF, 82- *Concurrent Pos:* Chmn, Dept Microbiol & Immunol, Sch Dent, Univ Southern Calif, 78-; consult dentist, Long Beach Vet Admin Hosp, 78- *Honors & Awards:* E H Hatton Award, Int Asn Dent Res, 75. *Mem:* AAAS; Int Asn Dent Res; Am Acad Periodontol; Sigma Xi; Western Soc Periodontol. *Res:* Host humoral immune responses in chronic oral disease; antigenic specificity of plasma cells in diseased human gingiva. *Mailing Add:* Sch Dent Univ Southern Calif PO Box 77951 Los Angeles CA 90007

SCHONHOFF, THOMAS ARTHUR, b Quincy, Ill, July 11, 47; m 69; c 3. COMMUNICATIONS THEORY. *Educ:* Mass Inst Technol, BSEE, 69; Johns Hopkins Univ, MSEE, 72; Northeastern Univ, PhD(elec eng), 80. *Prof Exp:* Engr, Johns Hopkins Appl Physics Lab, 69-73; advan res engr, Gen Tel & Electron Sylvania, Inc, 73-78; mem tech staff, MITRE Corp, 78-80; MEM TECH STAFF, SPERRY RES CTR, 80- *Concurrent Pos:* Adj prof, Worcester Polytech Inst, 82- *Mem:* AAAS; Inst Elec & Electron Engrs; Sigma Xi; Planetary Soc. *Res:* Using communication theory and principles to improve the performance of radio communications systems and digital magnetic recording systems. *Mailing Add:* 13 Heatherwood Dr Shrewsbury MA 01545

SCHONHORN, HAROLD, b New York, NY, Apr 2, 28; m 54; c 2. PHYSICAL CHEMISTRY, SURFACE CHEMISTRY. *Educ:* Brooklyn Col, BS, 50; Polytech Inst Brooklyn, PhD(phys chem), 59. *Prof Exp:* USAEC fel, Polytech Inst Brooklyn, 59-60; res scientist phys chem, Am Cyanamid Co, 60-61; mem tech staff surface chem, 61-67, SUPVR SURFACE CHEM, BELL LABS, INC, 67- *Honors & Awards:* Union Carbide Chem Prize, Am Chem Soc, 66. *Mem:* Am Chem Soc. *Res:* Surface chemistry and adhesion. *Mailing Add:* Bell Labs Inc Murray Hill NJ 07974

SCHONHORST, MELVIN HERMAN, b Slater, Iowa, Jan 21, 19; m 49; c 4. AGRONOMY, PLANT BREEDING. *Educ:* Iowa State Univ, BS, 51, MS, 53; Purdue Univ, PhD(agron, plant breeding), 58. *Prof Exp:* From asst agronomist to assoc agronomist, 56-64, AGRONOMIST PLANT BREEDER ALFALFA IMPROV, UNIV ARIZ, 56- *Concurrent Pos:* Sabbatical leave, Mex Fed Alfalfa Breeding Prog, 76-77. *Honors & Awards:* Pac Seedsmen Award, 72. *Mem:* Am Soc Agron; Crop Sci Soc Am. *Res:* Hybrid alfalfa; development of insect, nematode, and disease resistant varieties of alfalfa; pest resistance and tolerance to environmental stresses in alfalfa; aslo tolerance to high chloride concentration, high temperatures, increased nodulation and association with mycorrhizal fungi. *Mailing Add:* Plant Sci Dept Univ of Ariz Tucson AZ 85721

SCHONING, ROBERT WHITNEY, b Seattle, Wash, Sept 29, 23; m 52; c 4. FISHERIES. *Educ:* Univ Wash, BS, 44. *Prof Exp:* Res biologist, Ore Fish Comn, 47-52, in-chg Columbia River invests, 52-54, from asst dir to dir res, 54-58, from asst state fisheries dir to state fisheries dir, 58-71; dep dir, Nat Marine Fisheries Serv, US Dept Commerce, 71-73, dir, 73-78; VIS PROF, DEPT FISHERIES & WILDLIFE, ORE STATE UNIV, 78- *Concurrent Pos:*

Mem fishing indust adv comt, US Dept State; comnr, Int Pac Halibut Comn, 72- *Honors & Awards:* Bronze Star Medal. *Mem:* Fel Am Fisheries Soc; Am Inst Fishery Res Biol. *Res:* Research and management of fish and shellfish in Oregon. *Mailing Add:* Dept of Fisheries & Wildlife Ore State Univ Corvallis OR 97331

SCHONSTEDT, ERICK O(SCAR), b Minneapolis, Minn, Sept 2, 17; m 57. MECHANICAL ENGINEERING. *Educ:* Univ Minn, BME & BBA, 41. *Prof Exp:* Mech engr, US Naval Ord Lab, 41-48, chief airborne magnetometer sect, 48-53; owner, Schonstedt Eng Co, 53-61; PRES, SCHONSTEDT INSTRUMENT CO, 61- *Concurrent Pos:* Dir, Augustana Col, Rock Island, Ill, 78- *Mem:* Am Geophys Union. *Res:* Invention of helical core magnetic field sensing element for use in rocket, satellite and laboratory magnetometers. *Mailing Add:* 1604 Greenbrier Ct Reston VA 22090

SCHOOLAR, JOSEPH CLAYTON, b Marks, Miss, Feb 28; m 60; c 5. PSYCHIATRY, PHARMACOLOGY. *Educ:* Univ Tenn, AB, 50, MS, 52; Univ Chicago, PhD, 57, MD, 60. *Prof Exp:* Asst zool, Univ Tenn, 50-52, instr biochem, Univ Tenn-AEC Lab, Oak Ridge, 53-54; res asst pharmacol, Univ Chicago, 54-57, res assoc, 57-60; resident & asst in psychiat, Baylor Col Med, 61-64, assoc prof psychiat & pharmacol, 63-74; asst dir, 68-72, DIR, TEX RES INST MENT SCI, 74-; PROF PHARMACOL, BAYLOR COL MED, 74-, PROF PSYCHIAT, 75-; ASSOC PROF MENT SCI, UNIV TEX GRAD SCH BIOL SCI, HOUSTON, 68- *Mem:* AAAS; Am Psychiat Soc; AMA. *Res:* Psychopharmacology; drug abuse and addiction; effects of drugs on metabolic topography of the central nervous system; passage of drugs across the blood-brain barrier; physiological effects of ionizing radiation on mammals. *Mailing Add:* Tex Res Inst of Ment Sci 1300 Moursund Houston TX 77030

SCHOOLER, JAMES M, JR, biochemistry, physiology, see previous edition

SCHOOLEY, ALLEN H, electronics engineering, deceased

SCHOOLEY, ARTHUR THOMAS, b Plymouth, Pa, July 4, 32; m 55; c 3. CHEMICAL ENGINEERING, POLYMER CHEMISTRY. *Educ:* Carnegie Mellon Univ, BS, 54; Univ Akron, MS, 59. *Prof Exp:* Mat engr, 54-56, res engr, 56-66, sr res engr, 66-68, res assoc, 68-79, SR RES ASSOC, RES CTR, B F GOODRICH CO, 79- *Mem:* Am Inst Chem Engrs. *Res:* Process modeling and simulation; microplants; process economics; process research. *Mailing Add:* 2015 Burlington Rd Akron OH 44313

SCHOOLEY, DAVID ALLAN, b Denver, Colo, Apr 17, 43; m 68; c 3. BIOLOGICAL CHEMISTRY, ANALYTICAL CHEMISTRY. *Educ:* NMex Highlands Univ, BSc, 63; Stanford Univ, PhD(org chem), 68. *Prof Exp:* Fel bio-inorg chem, Univ Fla, 68-69; fel bio-org chem, Columbia Univ, 69-71; sr biochemist, 71-74, DIR BIOCHEM RES, ZOECON CORP, 74- *Concurrent Pos:* NIH fel, Columbia Univ, 69-70. *Mem:* Am Chem Soc; Royal Soc Chem. *Res:* Biosynthesis and identification of insect juvenile hormones; isolation and identification of neuropeptides in insects; analysis for hormones at physiological levels; intermediary metabolism and environmental chemistry; pesticide biochemistry. *Mailing Add:* Zoecon Corp 975 California Ave Palo Alto CA 94304

SCHOOLEY, JAMES FREDERICK, b Auburn, Ind, Aug 24, 31; m 53; c 7. THERMAL PHYSICS. *Educ:* Ind Univ, AB, 53, Univ Calif, Berkeley, MS, 55, PhD(nuclear chem), 61. *Prof Exp:* Physicist, Cryogenic Physics Sect, 60-74, CHIEF, TEMPERATURE DIV, NAT BUR STANDARDS, 74- *Concurrent Pos:* Nat Acad Sci-Nat Res Coun fel, 60-62. *Mem:* Am Phys Soc; Instrument Soc Am; Sigma Xi. *Res:* Cryogenic physics; energy transport at low temperatures; superconductivity. *Mailing Add:* Temperature Div B128 Physics Nat Bur of Standards Washington DC 20234

SCHOOLEY, JOHN C, b Chicago, Ill, Apr 24, 28; m 53; c 3. PHYSIOLOGY. *Educ:* Univ Calif, AB, 51, PhD, 57. *Prof Exp:* Physiologist, Donner Lab, PHYSIOLOGIST, LAWRENCE BERKELEY LAB, UNIV CALIF, BERKELEY, 71- *Mem:* AAAS; Am Physiol Soc; Soc Exp Biol & Med; Int Soc Hemat; Am Asn Immunologists. *Res:* Physiology of lymphoid tissue and bone; experimental hematology. *Mailing Add:* Bldg 74 Lawrence Berkeley Lab Univ of Calif Berkeley CA 94720

SCHOOLEY, ROBERT, anatomy, see previous edition

SCHOOLMAN, HAROLD M, b Chicago, Ill, Jan 14, 24; m 59; c 2. MEDICINE. *Educ:* Univ Ill, MD, 50; Am Bd Internal Med, dipl, 57. *Prof Exp:* Resident med, Cook County Hosp, Ill, 51-53; assoc prof med, Cook County Grad Sch Med, 54-59; instr, Univ Ill, 57-59, clin asst prof, 59-65, assoc prof, 65-67; dir educ serv, Vet Admin Cent Off, Washington, DC, 67-70; spec asst to dir med prog develop & eval, 70-72, asst dep dir, Nat Libr Med, 72-77, DEP DIR RES & EDUC NAT LIBR MED, 77- *Concurrent Pos:* Fel hemat, Cook County Hosp, Ill, 53-54; NIH spec res fel, Div Med Sci, London Sch Trop Med, 59-60; assoc attend physician, Res & Educ Hosp & Cook County Hosp, 54-57; med educ, Cook County Hosp, 57-59, attend physician, 59, res assoc, Hektoen Inst Med Res, 54-59; chief, Hemat Res Labs, Vet Admin Hosp, Hines, Ill, 61-67 & biostatist res support ctr, 63-67; clin prof, Sch Med, Georgetown Univ, 70- *Mem:* AMA; fel Am Col Physicians; assoc Royal Soc Med. *Res:* Hematology; biostatistics. *Mailing Add:* Nat Lib Med 8600 Rockville Pike Bethesda MD 20014

SCHOON, DAVID JACOB, b Luverne, Minn, May 6, 43; m 69. CHEMICAL ENGINEERING, ELECTRONICS. *Educ:* Univ Minn, Minneapolis, BS, 65, PhD(chem eng), 69. *Prof Exp:* SR CHEM ENGR, 3M CO, 69- *Res:* Electrooptical object detection and counting systems; biomedical electronics. *Mailing Add:* 219-1 3M Co St Paul MN 55101

SCHOONMAKER, GEORGE RUSSELL, b Chicago, Ill, Dec 1, 16; m 44; c 2. GEOLOGY. *Educ:* Univ Chicago, BS, 38. *Prof Exp:* Asst inspector core drilling, Corps Engrs, US Dept Army, 39-40; geologist, Marathon Oil Co, 40-53, dist mgr, Can, 53-55, from asst mgr to explor mgr foreign dept, 55-60, explor mgr & vpres, Marathon Int Oil Co, 61-62, explor mgr, Marathon Oil Co, 62-80, vpres, 64-80; RETIRED. *Mem:* Am Asn Petrol Geol; Soc Explor Geophys. *Res:* General oil exploration. *Mailing Add:* 119 E Edgar Findlay OH 45840

SCHOONMAKER, RICHARD CLINTON, b Schenectady, NY, Dec 21, 30; m 56; c 4. THERMODYNAMICS, MATERIAL PROPERTIES. *Educ:* Yale Univ, ChEng, 52; Cornell Univ, PhD(chem), 60. *Prof Exp:* Asst phys chem, Cornell Univ, 56-58; res physicist, Columbia Univ, 59-60; from asst prof to assoc prof, 60-69, chmn dept, 67-73 & 78-79, PROF CHEM, OBERLIN COL, 69- *Concurrent Pos:* NSF sci fac fel, Math Inst, Oxford Univ, 66-67; vis sr res fel, Dept Physics, Univ York, York Eng, 73-74; NSF prof develop fel; vis prof, Dept Chem, Univ Calif, Berkeley, 80-81. *Mem:* Am Phys Soc; Am Chem Soc; Sigma Xi. *Res:* Thermochemistry; thermochemical properties of gaseous molecules; phase equilibria; high temperature chemistry; mass spectrometry; thermodynamics and kinetics of vaporization and condensation processes; surface physics; molecular beams. *Mailing Add:* Dept of Chem Kettering Lab Oberlin Col Oberlin OH 44074

SCHOONOVER, CARROLL OWEN, b Buffalo, Wyo, July 28, 16. ANIMAL BREEDING. *Educ:* Univ Wyo, BS, 52, MS, 54, PhD, 57. *Prof Exp:* From instr to assoc prof, 54-64, prof, 64-81, agr exten livestock specialist, 70-81, EMER PROF ANIMAL SCI, UNIV WYO, 81- *Mem:* Am Soc Animal Sci; Am Meat Sci Asn. *Res:* Beef cattle; carcass evaluation of sheep and beef. *Mailing Add:* Animal Sci Div Univ of Wyo Box 3354 Univ Sta Laramie WY 82070

SCHOONOVER, JOHN LODGE, nuclear physics, history of science, see previous edition

SCHOOR, W PETER, b Frankfurt, WGer, June 4, 36; US citizen; m 70. BIOPHYSICAL CHEMISTRY, COMPARATIVE BIOCHEMISTRY. *Educ:* Auburn Univ, PhD(biochem), 66. *Prof Exp:* Fel, Inst Molecular Biophys, Fla State Univ, 66-68; asst prof pharmacol, Sch Med, La State Univ, 68-70; br chief, 70-80, MEM STAFF BIOCHEM, GULF BREEZE ENVIRON RES LAB, ENVIRON PROTECTION AGENCY, 80- *Mem:* Am Chem Soc; Sigma Xi. *Res:* Biochemical molecular mechanisms; metabolism of chemical carcinogens by aquatic organisms; mechanism of osmoregulation and membrane transport. *Mailing Add:* Gulf Breeze Environ Res Lab Environ Protection Agency Gulf Breeze FL 32561

SCHOPF, JAMES WILLIAM, b Urbana, Ill, Sept 27, 41; m 65; c 1. PALEOBIOLOGY, ORGANIC GEOCHEMISTRY. *Educ:* Oberlin Col, AB, 63; Harvard Univ, AM, 65, PhD(biol), 68. *Prof Exp:* From asst prof to assoc prof, 68-73, PROF PALEOBIOL, UNIV CALIF, LOS ANGELES, 73- *Concurrent Pos:* Vis res chemist, Ames Res Ctr, NASA, 67; mem lunar sample preliminary exam team, NASA, 68-71, prin investr lunar samples, 69-74; mem, Inst Evolutionary & Environ Biol, 70-73 & Inst Geophysics & Planetary Physics, 73- Guggenheim fel, 73; assoc ed, Origins of Life, 73- & Paleobiol, 74-; Nat Acad Sci vis scientist, Soviet Union, 75; mem working groups Cambrian-Precambrian boundary, UNESCO Int Geol Correlation Prog, 75- & Precambrian biostratigraphy, 76-; mem terrestrial bodies sci working group, NASA, 75-76 & life sci comt, Space Prog Adv Coun, 76-; vis scientist, Bot Soc Am, China, 78- *Honors & Awards:* NY Bot Garden Award, Bot Soc Am, 66; NASA Group Achievement Award, 69; Outstanding Paper Award, Soc Econ Paleontologists & Mineralogists, 71; Schuchert Award, Paleont Soc, 74; Alan T Waterman Award & Medal, NSF, 77. *Mem:* Paleont Soc; Geol Soc Am; Bot Soc Am; Int Soc Study Origin Life (treas, 77-); Phycol Soc Am. *Res:* Precambrian paleobiology; optical and electron microscopy of fossil and modern microorganisms; origin of life; paleobotany; organic geochemistry of ancient sediments; interrelationships of atmospheric and biotic evolution. *Mailing Add:* Dept of Geol Univ of Calif Los Angeles CA 90024

SCHOPF, THOMAS JOSEPH MORTON, b Urbana, Ill, Aug 26, 39; m 63; c 3. PALEOBIOLOGY. *Educ:* Oberlin Col, AB, 60; Ohio State Univ, PhD(paleont), 64. *Prof Exp:* Teaching asst geol, Ohio State Univ, 60-62, asst, Orton Mus, 62-64; fel systs-ecol prog, Marine Biol Lab, Woods Hole, Mass, 64-67; asst prof paleont & oceanog, Lehigh Univ, 67-69; from asst prof to assoc prof, 69-78, PROF PALEOBIOL, UNIV CHICAGO, 78- *Concurrent Pos:* NSF grants, 68-; fac assoc, Ctr Grad Studies, Field Mus Natural Hist, 69-, res assoc, 80-, mem corp, Bermuda Biol Sta; mem corp, Marine Biol Lab, Woods Hole, instr, 72-76; co-ed, Paleobiol, v.1, 75; Guggenheim fel, 81-82; vis res assoc, Dept Biol, Calif Inst Technol, 81-82; mem, Comt Evolutionary Biol, Morris Fishbein Ctr Study Hist Sci & Med, 69- *Honors & Awards:* Schuchert Award, Paleontol Soc Am, 76. *Mem:* AAAS; Geol Soc Am; Paleont Soc; Soc Syst Zool; Int Bryozool Asn. *Res:* Evolution; population genetics; bryozoa. *Mailing Add:* Dept Geophys Sci Univ Chicago 5734 S Ellis Ave Chicago IL 60637

SCHOPFER, LAWRENCE MARTIN, US citizen. ENZYME KINETICS. *Educ:* Univ Mich, PhD(biochem), 79. *Prof Exp:* FEL BIOCHEM, UNIV MICH, 79- *Res:* Mechanistic and structural studies on flauoproteins. *Mailing Add:* Dept Biol Chem Box 034 Univ Mich Ann Arbor MI 48109

SCHOPP, JOHN DAVID, b St Joseph, Mo, Oct 18, 27; m 57; c 2. ASTRONOMY. *Educ:* Northwestern Univ, BS, 49; Princeton Univ, PhD(astron), 54. *Prof Exp:* Asst, Princeton Univ, 49-53; res assoc, Northwestern Univ, 55; asst prof astron, Univ Mo, 55-62; from asst prof to assoc prof, 62-68, PROF ASTRON, SAN DIEGO STATE UNIV, 68- *Mem:* AAAS; Am Astron Soc. *Res:* Stellar spectroscopy and structure; photoelectric and photographic photometry; astronomy of binary stars. *Mailing Add:* Dept of Astron San Diego State Univ San Diego CA 92182

SCHOPP, ROBERT THOMAS, b Pontiac, Ill, Nov 5, 23; m 50; c 4. PHYSIOLOGY. *Educ:* Univ Ill, BS, 50, MS, 51; Univ Wis, PhD(physiol), 56. *Prof Exp:* Instr biol, St Norbert Col, 51-52; asst physiol, Univ Wis, 52-55, instr, 55-56; from instr to asst prof, Sch Med, Univ Colo, 56-67; assoc prof, Kirksville Col Osteop & Surg, 67-69; PROF PHYSIOL & CHMN DEPT, SCH DENT MED, SOUTHERN ILL UNIV, EDWARDSVILLE, 69- *Mem:* AAAS; Am Physiol Soc; Am Soc Pharmacol & Exp Therapeut; Am Inst Biol Sci; Am Soc Zoologists. *Res:* Neuromuscular research; autonomic nervous systems; reflex regulation of circulation and respiration. *Mailing Add:* Dept of Physiol Sch Dent Med Southern Ill Univ Edwardsville IL 62026

SCHOR, JOSEPH MARTIN, b New York, NY, Jan 10, 29; m 53; c 3. BIOCHEMISTRY. *Educ:* City Col New York, BS, 51; Fla State Univ, PhD(chem), 57. *Prof Exp:* Sr res chemist, Armour Pharmaceut Co, 57-59; res chemist, Lederle Labs, Am Cyanamid Co, 59-64; dir biochem, Endo Labs, E I du Pont de Nemours & Co, Inc, 64-77; V PRES SCI AFFAIRS, FOREST LABS, 77- *Mem:* Am Chem Soc; fel Am Inst Chemists; Int Soc Thrombosis & Hemostasis; Int Soc Hemat; AAAS. *Res:* Absorption, metabolism and disposition of drugs; blood clot lysis; blood coagulation; isolation and characterization of proteins; immunology; cardiovascular drugs. *Mailing Add:* Forest Labs Inc 919 Third Ave New York NY 10022

SCHOR, NORBERTO AARON, b Cordoba, Arg, Dec 24, 29; m 58; c 2. PATHOLOGY. *Educ:* Nat Univ Litoral, Arg, MD, 55; Am Bd Path, dipl & cert anat path, 72. *Prof Exp:* Vis pathologist, Hosp Ramos Mejia, Buenos Aires, 55; asst prof histol, Nat Univ Litoral, 56-58; Brit Coun res fel, Postgrad Med Sch, Univ London, 58-59; Nat Res Coun Arg res fel, Dept Histol, Gothenburg Univ, Sweden, 59-60; from asst prof to assoc prof cell biol, Nat Univ Cordoba, 60-63; Guggenheim res assoc path, Stanford Univ, 64-67 & res fel, Univ Wis, 67-70; asst prof, 70-74, assoc prof, 74-79, PROF PATH, SCH MED, TULANE UNIV, 79- *Mem:* AAAS; Am Asn Pathologists & Bacteriologists; Histochem Soc; Int Acad Path. *Res:* Metabolic pathways of neoplastic cells; transfer of reducing equivalents in neoplastic cells; early activation and transformation of chemical carcinogens by lung and liver; response of lymphoid organs to the action of carcinogens. *Mailing Add:* Dept of Path Tulane Univ Sch of Med New Orleans LA 70112

SCHOR, ROBERT, b New York, NY, Oct 25, 29; m 49; c 2. BIOPHYSICS, SOLID STATE PHYSICS. *Educ:* Mass Inst Technol, BS, 50; Univ Mich, MS, 52, PhD(physics), 58. *Prof Exp:* Asst, Univ Mich, 54-58; instr, 58-63, asst prof, 63-69, assoc prof, 69-80, PROF PHYSICS, UNIV CONN, 80- *Concurrent Pos:* Res fel, Inst Chemico-Phys Biol, Sorbonne, France, 66-67; vis scientist, Mass Inst Technol, 77-78. *Mem:* Am Phys Soc; Biophys Soc; Am Asn Physics Teachers; NY Acad Sci. *Res:* Structure and physical properties of fibrous proteins; chemical thermodynamics; crystal physics; phase transformations in magnetic systems; theory of diffusion coefficient of charged spherical macromolecules in solution. *Mailing Add:* Dept of Physics Univ of Conn Storrs CT 06268

SCHOR, ROBERT HYLLEL, b Visalia, Calif, Oct 29, 45. NEUROPHYSIOLOGY. *Educ:* Calif Inst Technol, BS, 67; Rockefeller Univ, PhD, 73. *Prof Exp:* Res assoc neurophysiol, Univ Chicago, 73-75 & Eye & Ear Hosp Pittsburgh, 75-76; res assoc, Inst Brain Res, Univ Tokyo, 76-78; ASST PROF NEUROPHYSIOL, ROCKEFELLER UNIV, 78- *Concurrent Pos:* NIH fel, Univ Chicago, 74-75. *Mem:* AAAS; Soc Neurosci; Asn Comput Mach; Barany Soc. *Res:* Information processing in the vestibular system. *Mailing Add:* Rockefeller Univ 1230 York Ave New York NY 10021

SCHOR, STANLEY, b Philadelphia, Pa, Mar 3, 22; m 49; c 3. BIOSTATISTICS. *Educ:* Univ Pa, AB, 43, AM, 50, PhD(econ statist), 52. *Prof Exp:* Res assoc statist, Wharton Sch Com & Finance, Univ Pa, 50-55, from instr to assoc prof, 51-64, asst prof, Sch Med, 58-64, USPHS grant & dir nat periodic health exam res prog, 61-64; dir dept biostatist, AMA, 64-66; prof biomet & chmn dept, Med Sch, Temple Univ, 66-75; EXEC DIR CLIN BIOSTATIST & RES DATA SYST, MERCK & CO, 75- *Concurrent Pos:* Prof, Chicago Med Sch, 64-66; mem comt standard cert, USPHS, 64-66; mem task force on prescription drugs, US Dept Health, Educ & Welfare, 67-; vis prof, Med Sch, Tel-Aviv Univ, 73-74; clin prof, Hahnemann Med Col, 74-; adj prof, Med Sch, Temple Univ, 75- *Mem:* Fel Am Statist Asn; fel Am Pub Health Asn. *Res:* Application of biostatistics to solving of medical problems. *Mailing Add:* Merck Sharp & Dohme Res Labs West Point PA 19486

SCHORE, NEIL ERIC, b Newark, NJ, Mar 6, 48; m 78. ORGANIC CHEMISTRY, ORGANOMETALLIC CHEMISTRY. *Educ:* Univ Pa, BA, 69; Columbia Univ, PhD(org chem), 73. *Prof Exp:* Fel chem, Calif Inst Technol, 74-76; ASST PROF CHEM, UNIV CALIF, DAVIS, 76- *Mem:* Am Chem Soc; NY Acad Sci; Sigma Xi. *Res:* Preparation and organic synthesis applications of new organometallic compounds; properties of compounds possessing intramolecular metal-metal interactions. *Mailing Add:* Dept Chem Univ Calif Davis CA 95616

SCHORER, CALVIN E, b Sauk City, Wis, June 29, 19; m 61; c 4. PSYCHIATRY. *Educ:* Univ Wis, BA, 39, MD, 55; Univ Chicago, MA, 42, PhD(eng), 48. *Prof Exp:* Intern, Detroit Receiving Hosp, 55-56; resident psychiat, 56-59, staff psychiatrist, 59-67, DIR TRAINING PSYCHIAT, LAFAYETTE CLIN, 67-; PROF PSYCHIAT, SCH MED, WAYNE STATE UNIV, 68- *Mem:* Am Psychiat Asn; AMA. *Res:* Hypnosis; psychotherapy; teaching of psychiatry; psychopharmacology. *Mailing Add:* Lafayette Clin 951 E Lafayette Detroit MI 48207

SCHORI, RICHARD M, b Tiskilwa, Ill, Oct 30, 38. TOPOLOGY. *Educ:* Kenyon Col, BA, 60; Univ Iowa, MS, 62, PhD(math), 64. *Prof Exp:* From asst prof to prof math, La State Univ, Baton Rouge, 64-78; PROF MATH & CHMN DEPT, ORE STATE UNIV, 78- *Concurrent Pos:* NSF res grant math, 68-75. *Mem:* Math Asn Am; Am Math Soc. *Res:* Inverse limits; hyperspaces and infinite dimensional topology. *Mailing Add:* Dept of Math Ore State Univ Corvallis OR 97331

SCHORK, MICHAEL ANTHONY, b Elyria, Ohio, June 11, 36; m 58; c 7. BIOSTATISTICS. *Educ:* Univ Notre Dame, BA, 58, MS, 60; Univ Mich, MPH, 61, PhD(biostatist), 63. *Prof Exp:* From instr to assoc prof, 62-72, PROF BIOSTATIST, UNIV MICH, ANN ARBOR, 72- *Concurrent Pos:* Visitor, Inst Human Genetics, Univ Heidelberg, 69-70; consult, Col Am Pathologists, 74- *Mem:* Am Statist Asn; Biomet Soc. *Res:* Applications of biostatistical design and analysis techniques to biomedical problems. *Mailing Add:* Dept of Biostatist Univ of Mich Sch of Pub Health Ann Arbor MI 48104

SCHORNO, KARL STANLEY, b Berkeley, Calif, Nov 28, 39; m; c 2. ORGANIC GEOCHEMISTRY. *Educ:* Univ Calif, Berkeley, BA, 62, Okla State Univ, PhD(chem), 67. *Prof Exp:* Res chemist org chem, Univ Calif, 62; teaching asst, Okla State Univ, 62-67, fel, 67; teaching asst med chem, Univ Kans, 67-68; RES CHEMIST, PHILLIPS PETROL CO, 68- *Mem:* Europ Geochem Soc; NY Acad Sci; Am Chem Soc; Sigma Xi. *Res:* Medicinal chemistry in the study of drug design; physical organic chemistry, the study of mechanism of several reactions; organic geochemistry, the genesis of petroleum. *Mailing Add:* Phillips Petrol Co Res Lab No 1 Bartlesville OK 74004

SCHORR, HERBERT, b New York, NY, Jan 20, 36; m 62; c 3. ELECTRICAL ENGINEERING. *Educ:* City Col New York, BEE, 57; Princeton Univ, MA, 60, MS, 61, PhD(elec eng), 62. *Prof Exp:* Instr elec eng, Princeton Univ, 61-62; NSF fel math, Cambridge Univ, 62-63; asst prof elec eng, Columbia Univ, 63-64; mgr archit & prog, IBM Corp, Calif, 64-68, dir comput sci, NY, 68-72, vpres prod & serv planning, Advan Systs Develop Div, 73-75, mgr subsysts anal, Systs Prod Div, 75, mem corp tech comt, CHQ, 75-77, MGR SYSTS TECHNOL, RES DIV, IBM CORP, 77- *Concurrent Pos:* Adj asst prof, Columbia Univ, 64-65; lectr, Univ Calif, Berkeley, 65-70. *Mem:* Asn Comput Mach; Inst Elec & Electronics Engrs. *Res:* Computer architecture and systems software. *Mailing Add:* IBM Corp PO Box 218 Yorktown Heights NY 10598

SCHORR, MARVIN GERALD, b New York, NY, Mar 10, 25; m 57; c 2. PHYSICS. *Educ:* Yale Univ, BS, 44, MS, 47, PhD(electromagnetics), 49. *Prof Exp:* Physicist, Tracerlab, Inc, 49-51; assoc tech dir, 51-57, exec vpres & treas, 57-62, PRES, TECH OPERS, INC, 62- *Concurrent Pos:* Mem nuclear adv comt, Univ Lowell & AEC adv comt isotope & radiation develop, 64-66; chmn, Mass Technol Develop Corp, 74- *Mem:* Fel AAAS; Am Phys Soc; Opers Res Soc Am; Inst Elec & Electronics Eng. *Res:* Wound ballistics; electromagnetic radiation; radioactivity and nuclear measurement; electronics; operations research. *Mailing Add:* 330 Beacon St Boston MA 02116

SCHOTLAND, RICHARD MORTON, b Irvington, NJ, Feb 11, 27; m 52; c 2. METEOROLOGY. *Educ:* Mass Inst Technol, SB, 48, SM, 50, ScD(meteorol), 52. *Prof Exp:* Asst, Mass Inst Technol, 50-52; res assoc, Oceanog Inst, Woods Hole, Mass, 52; from asst prof to prof meteorol, NY Univ, 52-73; PROF ATMOSPHERIC PHYSICS, UNIV ARIZ, 73- *Concurrent Pos:* Consult, Brookhaven Nat Lab, chmn, Group Laser Atmospheric Probing; mem, Army Basic Res Comt, Nat Res Coun, 74-, Adv Panel, Nat Ctr Atmospheric Res, 75- & adv panel, Wave Propagation Lab, Nat Oceanic & Atmospheric Admin, 78- *Mem:* Am Meteorol Soc; Am Geophys Union; Royal Meteorol Soc; Optical Soc Am. *Res:* Meteorological instrumentation; atmospheric physics; radiowave propagation; atmospheric radiation; remote sensing laser radar. *Mailing Add:* Dept of Atmospheric Sci Univ of Ariz Tucson AZ 85721

SCHOTT, FREDERICK W(ILLIAM), b Phoenix, Ariz, Oct 2, 19; m 46; c 1. ELECTRICAL ENGINEERING. *Educ:* San Diego State Col, AB, 40; Stanford Univ, EE, 43, PhD(elec eng), 48. *Prof Exp:* Jr engr, San Diego Gas & Elec Co, 43-44; instr physics, San Diego State Col, 46-47; from asst prof to assoc prof, 48-69, PROF ENG, UNIV CALIF, LOS ANGELES, 69- *Concurrent Pos:* Physicist, US Naval Electronics Lab, 49-50; res physicist, Hughes Aircraft Co, 56; consult, 78- *Mem:* Inst Elec & Electronics Engrs; Am Soc Eng Educ. *Res:* Rotating electric machines; applied electromagnetics. *Mailing Add:* Rm 7732 Boelter Hall Univ of Calif Los Angeles CA 90024

SCHOTT, GARRY LEE, b Detroit, Mich, Dec 20, 31; m 60; c 2. PHYSICAL CHEMISTRY. *Educ:* Univ Mich, BS, 52; Calif Inst Technol, PhD(chem), 56. *Prof Exp:* STAFF MEM, LOS ALAMOS SCI LAB, 56- *Mem:* Am Chem Soc; Am Phys Soc; Combustion Inst. *Res:* Shock wave processes; chemical kinetics; gaseous combustion; detonation; chemical lasers; fossil fuel extraction. *Mailing Add:* 120 Monte Vista Los Alamos NM 87544

SCHOTT, HANS, b Ger, Oct 25, 22; nat US; m 58. PHYSICAL CHEMISTRY, PHARMACEUTICS. *Educ:* Univ Sao Paulo, 43; Univ Southern Calif, MS, 51; Univ Del, PhD(phys chem), 58. *Prof Exp:* Res chemist, Cent Lab, Matarazzo Industs, Brazil, 43-44, head chem lab, Viscose Rayon Plant, 44-47, plant adminstr, 49; res chemist, Thiokol Chem Corp, 47-48 & Textile Fibers Dept, Pioneering Res Div, E I du Pont de Nemours & Co, 51-56; res assoc, Film Div, Olin Mathieson Chem Corp, 58-60; sr res assoc phys chem sect, Res Ctr, Lever Bros Co, 61-67; res chemist, US Forest Prod Lab, 67-68; assoc prof, 69-72, PROF PHYS & COLLOID CHEM, SCH PHARM, TEMPLE UNIV, 72- *Mem:* Am Chem Soc; fel Am Inst Chemists; fel Acad Pharmaceut Sci; Am Asn Cols Pharm. *Res:* Solubilization; micelles; hydrophile-lipophile balance and effect of electrolytes on nonionic surfactants; colloidal properties and rheology of aqueous dispersions of drugs, bacteria and clays; surface and bulk properties of polymers and skin; phase rule; colloid and polymer chemistry. *Mailing Add:* Temple Univ Sch Pharm 3307 N Broad St Philadelphia PA 19140

SCHOTTE, WILLIAM, b Burlington, Iowa, July 3, 27; m 50; c 3. CHEMICAL ENGINEERING. *Educ:* Columbia Univ, BS, 50, MS, 51, EngScD, 55. *Prof Exp:* Res assoc, Columbia Univ, 51-54; res engr, 54-58, res proj engr, 58-61, sr res engr, 61-69, sr res specialist, 69-78, SR RES ASSOC, ENG TECH LAB, EXP STA, E I DU PONT DE NEMOURS & CO, INC, 78- *Mem:* Am Chem Soc; Am Inst Chem Engrs. *Res:* Pollution abatement; chemical reactors; separation technology. *Mailing Add:* Eng Technol Lab Eng Dept E I du Pont de Nemours & Co Inc Wilmington DE 19898

SCHOTTELIUS, BYRON ARTHUR, b Phoenix, Ariz, Dec 16, 22; m 49. PHYSIOLOGY. Educ: Univ Iowa, BA, 49; Wash State Univ, MS, 51; Univ Iowa, PhD(physiol), 54. Prof Exp: From instr to asst prof physiol, Univ NC, 54-57; from asst prof to assoc prof, 57-67, PROF PHYSIOL, UNIV IOWA, 67- Mem: Am Physiol Soc; Soc Exp Biol & Med; Soc Gen Physiol; Biophys Soc. Res: Muscle chemistry, subcellular fractions, mechanics, potentials and heat; myopathies; active transport. Mailing Add: Dept Physiol & Biophys 5450 BSB Univ of Iowa Iowa City IA 52242

SCHOTTELIUS, DOROTHY DICKEY, b Lohrville, Iowa, Oct 9, 27; m 49. BIOCHEMISTRY. Educ: Univ Iowa, BA, 49; State Col Wash, MS, 51; Univ NC, PhD, 57. Prof Exp: Res asst biochem, Univ Iowa, 52-54; res asst, Univ NC, 54-57; res assoc radiation, 59-71, res assoc neurol & physiol, 71-75, ASST PROF NEUROL, UNIV IOWA, 75- Mem: Am Physiol Soc; Am Epilepsy Soc; Biophys Soc; Am Asn Clin Chem. Res: Neurochemistry; biochemistry of normal and diseased muscle; pharmacology of anticonvulsant drugs; protein and nucleic acid chemistry. Mailing Add: Dept Neurol Univ Hosp Iowa City IA 52242

SCHOTTMILLER, JOHN CHARLES, b Rochester, NY, Aug 6, 30; m 56; c 2. IMAGING MATERIALS, TECHNICAL MANAGEMENT. Educ: Univ Rochester, BA, 53; Syracuse Univ, PhD(chem), 58. Prof Exp: Asst, AEC, Syracuse Univ, 57-58; res chemist, Union Carbide Metals Co, 58-61; staff chemist, Components Div, Int Bus Mach Corp, 61-62; sr scientist, 62-71, mgr photoreceptor develop & eng, 71-77, mgr proces eng, Europ Opers, Res Labs, 77-79, MGR TECH SERV, SPECIAL MAT MFG, XEROX CORP, 79- Mem: Am Chem Soc; Sigma Xi. Res: Photoconductivity; solid state and metallurgical chemistry; vacuum deposition; electrophotography; x-rays; microcircuitry; thermodynamics; phase diagrams; reactive metals; metal-metal oxide equilibria. Mailing Add: Xerox Corp Xerox Sq 103 Rochester NY 14603

SCHOTTSTAEDT, MARY GARDNER, b Lafayette, Ind, Dec 29, 23; m 47; c 4. PSYCHIATRY. Educ: Univ Calif, Berkeley, AB, 45; Univ Calif, San Francisco, MD, 48. Prof Exp: From intern to resident med, Univ Calif Hosp, 48-51; physician, NY Tel Co, 52-53; resident psychiat, Sch Med, Univ Okla, 64-67, from instr to asst prof, 68-71, assoc prof psychiat & med, 71-74; ASSOC PROF PSYCHIAT, UNIV TEX MED BR GALVESTON, 74- Concurrent Pos: NIH fel neurocardiol, Sch Med, Univ Okla, 62-63. Res: Hypertension; depression. Mailing Add: 118 Graves Galveston TX 77550

SCHOTTSTAEDT, WILLIAM WALTER, b Fresno, Calif, Mar 28, 17; m 47; c 4. MEDICINE, PUBLIC HEALTH. Educ: Univ Calif, BA, 47, MD, 48; Univ Mich, BMus, 40, MMus, 41. Prof Exp: From asst prof to assoc prof med, prev med & pub health, Univ Okla, 53-60, assoc prof psychiat, 56-60, prof prev med & pub health & chmn dept & consult prof psychiat, neurol & behav sci, 60-68, dean, Col Health, 68-73; dir Health Educ Ctr, 76-79, PROF PREV MED & COMMUNITY HEALTH, UNIV TEX MED BR, GALVESTON, 74-, ASSOC DEAN, CONTINUING EDUC, 79- Concurrent Pos: Commonwealth fel psychosom med, NY Hosp, 51-53. Mem: Am Psychosom Soc; AMA; Am Pub Health Asn. Res: Renal excretion. Mailing Add: 123 Keiller Bldg Univ of Tex Med Br Galveston TX 77550

SCHOTZ, MICHAEL C, b New York, NY, June 30, 28; m 51; c 2. BIOCHEMISTRY. Educ: Marietta Col, BS, 47; Univ Southern Calif, MS, 50, PhD(biochem), 53. Prof Exp: Harvard Univ res fel cholesterol metab, Huntington Res Labs, Mass Gen Hosp, 53-54; USPHS officer, Res Div, Cleveland Clin Ohio, 55-57, asst staff mem, 57-60; BIOCHEMIST, LIPID RES LAB, VET ADMIN WADSWORTH MED CTR, 60-; PROF MED, UNIV CALIF, LOS ANGELES, 74- Concurrent Pos: Asst prof, Ctr Health Sci, Univ Calif, Los Angeles, 60-68, assoc prof, 68-72, adj assoc prof, 72-74; USPHS grant, 60. Mem: AAAS; Am Heart Soc; Am Chem Soc; Am Soc Biol Chem. Res: Role of lipoprotein lipase in the deposition of lipids in adipose tissue and heart tissue; determination of antibiotics using high-pressure liquid chromatography; the role of endotoxin in gram-negative septicemia. Mailing Add: Vet Admin Wadsworth Med Ctr 691/151R Wilshire & Sawtelle Blvds Los Angeles CA 90073

SCHOULTIES, CALVIN LEE, b Dayton, Ky, Nov 18, 43. PLANT PATHOLOGY. Educ: Univ Ky, BS, 65, PhD(plant path), 71. Prof Exp: Staff res assoc plant path, Univ Calif, Berkeley, 71-75; PLANT PATHOLOGIST, FLA DEPT AGR & CONSUMER SERV, 75- Mem: Sigma Xi; Am Phytopath Soc. Res: Soil microbiology and ecology; biological control of plant pathogens. Mailing Add: Div Plant Indust Fla Dept Agr & Consumer Serv PO Box 1269 Gainesville FL 32602

SCHOULTZ, TURE WILLIAM, b Alhambra, Calif, June 6, 40; m 59; c 3. NEUROSCIENCES. Educ: Colo State Univ, BS, 65; Univ Colo, Boulder, MA, 67; Univ Colo Med Ctr, Denver, PhD(anat), 71. Prof Exp: Instr physiol, Med Sch, NY Univ, 71-72; asst mem neurobiol, Pub Health Res Inst, City of New York, 71-72; ASST PROF ANAT, COL MED, UNIV ARK, LITTLE ROCK, 72-, ASST DEAN COL MED, 77- Mem: Soc Neurosci; Am Asn Anatomists. Res: The acute phase of mammalian spinal cord injury; determination of the role of catecholamines in trauma-induced progressive spinal cord destruction and determination of changes in dissolved oxygen concentration after injury. Mailing Add: Col Med Univ Ark Little Rock AR 72201

SCHOWALTER, KENNETH ARTHUR, b St Louis, Mo, Nov 5, 19; m 47; c 2. FUEL SCIENCE. Educ: Univ Mo, Rolla, BS, 42; Univ Ill, MS, 49, PhD(org chem), 51. Prof Exp: Chem engr, Org Res Div, Mallinckrodt Chem Works, 46-48; coal chem fel, Mellon Inst, 51-52, sr fel, 52-54; sect leader coal chem div, Appl Res Lab, 54-56, sect leader to asst div chief, 56-60, div chief, Chem Div, 60-69, chief staff engr, 69-75, chief res engr, 75-78, SR RES CONSULT CHEM, RES LAB, US STEEL CORP, 78- Mem: Am Chem Soc; Am Inst Chem Engrs. Res: Chemicals from coal carbonization; ammonia; cyanide derivatives; plastics; resins; coal utilization to include liquefaction, gasification, carbonization and recovery of chemicals from coal processing. Mailing Add: 1261 Catalina Dr Monroeville PA 15146

SCHOWALTER, WILLIAM RAYMOND, b Milwaukee, Wis, Dec 15, 29; m 53; c 3. CHEMICAL ENGINEERING. Educ: Univ Wis, BS, 51; Univ Ill, MS, 53, PhD(chem eng), 57. Prof Exp: From asst prof to assoc prof, 57-66, actg chmn dept chem eng, 71, assoc dean sch eng & appl sci, 72-77, PROF CHEM ENG, PRINCETON UNIV, 66-, CHMN DEPT, 78- Concurrent Pos: Mem adv bd for chem eng series, McGraw-Hill Book Co; vis sr fel, Brit Sci Res Coun, Cambridge, 70; mem, US Nat Comt Theoret & Appl Mech, 72-81; Sherman Fairchild Distinguished Scholar, Calif Inst Technol, 77-78. Honors & Awards: Lectureship Award, Am Soc Eng Educ, 71. Mem: Am Chem Soc; Am Inst Chem Engrs; Soc Rheol (pres, 81-). Res: Fluid mechanics; non-Newtonian flow; rheology. Mailing Add: Dept of Chem Eng Princeton Univ Princeton NJ 08544

SCHOWEN, RICHARD LYLE, b Nitro, WVa, Aug 29, 34; m 63; c 2. MECHANISM CHEMISTRY. Educ: Univ Calif, Berkeley, BS, 58; Mass Inst Technol, PhD(org chem), 62. Prof Exp: Res assoc, Mass Inst Technol, 62-63; from asst prof to assoc prof, 63-71, PROF CHEM, UNIV KANS, 71- Concurrent Pos: NIH res career develop award, 68-73; Summerfield prof chem, 77- Mem: AAAS; fel Am Inst Chemists; Chem Soc Japan; Am Chem Soc. Res: Reaction mechanisms; biodynamics; isotope effects; enzyme mechanisms. Mailing Add: Dept of Chem Univ of Kans Lawrence KS 66045

SCHOWENGERDT, FRANKLIN DEAN, b Bellflower, Mo, Mar 8, 36; m 62; c 2. ATOMIC PHYSICS. Educ: Univ Mo-Rolla, BS, 66, MS, 67, PhD(physics), 69. Prof Exp: Res assoc physics, Univ Nebr, 69-71, vis asst prof, 71-73; assoc prof, 73-80, PROF PHYSICS, COLO SCH MINES, 80-, HEAD DEPT, 73- Mem: Sigma Xi; Am Phys Soc. Res: Electron and ion collisions; ion energy loss spectroscopy; low energy electron spectroscopy; cloud physics applied to control of respirable coal dust. Mailing Add: Dept of Physics Colo Sch of Mines Golden CO 80401

SCHOWENGERDT, GEORGE CARL, b Kansas City, Mo, Jan 14, 01; m 25; c 2. AGRICULTURE. Educ: Univ Mo, BSA, 28, AM, 29, PhD(hort), 44. Prof Exp: Asst prof agr, Northwest Mo State Teachers Col, 29-34; county supvr, Rural Resettlement Admin, Mo, 34-36; farm mgr, Union Cent Life Ins Co, 36-37; prof agr & head dept, 39-71, chmn div practical arts, 60-71, EMER PROF AGR, SOUTHEAST MO STATE UNIV, 71- Res: Mineral nutrition of the strawberry. Mailing Add: Rte 4 Box 133A Columbia MO 65201

SCHOWENGERDT, ROBERT ALAN, b St Charles, Mo, Oct 10, 46; m 74; c 2. DIGITAL IMAGE PROCESSING, REMOTE SENSING. Educ: Univ Mo, BS, 68; Univ Ariz, PhD(optical sci), 75. Prof Exp: Res assoc, Optical Sci Ctr, 72-77, ASST PROF REMOTE SENSING, OFF ARID LANDS & ELEC ENG, UNIV ARIZ, 77- Concurrent Pos: Physical scientist, Earth Resources Observation Syst, US Geol Surv, Va, 75-80. Mem: Optical Soc Am; Am Soc Photogrammetry; Inst Elec & Electronics Engrs Comput Soc. Res: Computer image enhancement; pattern recognition of satelite and aerial remote sensing images; sensor design and performance analysis; image texture; multiresolution image analysis. Mailing Add: Off Arid Lands 845 N Park Ave Univ Ariz Tucson AZ 85719

SCHRACK, ROALD AMUNDSEN, b Ft Meade, Fla, Aug 26, 26; m 54; c 2. PHYSICS. Educ: Univ Calif, Los Angeles, BS, 49, MS, 50; Univ Md, PhD, 61. Prof Exp: Physicist, 49-56, NUCLEAR PHYSICIST, NAT BUR STANDARDS, 56- Mem: Am Phys Soc; Inst Elec & Electronics Engrs. Res: Measurement of nuclear matter distribution by neutral meson photoproduction; nuclear structure physics; neutron cross sections; isotopic assy and distribution by resonance neutron radiography. Mailing Add: Div 532 Nat Bur of Standards Washington DC 20234

SCHRADER, DAVID HAWLEY, b Syracuse, NY, Dec 9, 25; m 68; c 4. ELECTRICAL ENGINEERING. Educ: Univ Kans, BS, 51; Univ Wash, MS, 59, PhD(fading of radio waves), 63. Prof Exp: Assoc engr, Hazeltine Electronics Corp, 51-55; instr, Univ Wash, 55-63; PROF ELEC ENG, WASH STATE UNIV, 63- Mem: AAAS; Inst Elec & Electronics Engrs; Am Geophys Union. Res: Physics of the magnetosphere and the ionosphere-propagation of radio waves. Mailing Add: Dept of Elec Eng Wash State Univ Pullman WA 99164

SCHRADER, DAVID MARTIN, b Minneapolis, Minn, Sept 24, 32; m 55; c 3. PHYSICAL CHEMISTRY. Educ: Iowa State Univ, BS, 54; Univ Minn, Minneapolis, PhD(theoret chem), 62. Prof Exp: Res fel theoret chem, Columbia Univ, 61-62 & IBM Watson Lab, 62-63; asst prof phys chem, Univ Iowa, 63-67; asst prof chem, Univ Minn, Minneapolis, 67-68; PROF CHEM, MARQUETTE UNIV, 68- Mem: AAAS; Am Phys Soc; Am Chem Soc; Phys Soc London. Res: Atomic and molecular quantum mechanics. Mailing Add: Dept of Chem Marquette Univ Milwaukee WI 53233

SCHRADER, DOROTHY VIRGINIA, b Boston, Mass, Jan 2, 21. MATHEMATICS. Educ: Mass State Col Bridgewater, BS, 42; Boston Col, MA, 46; Univ Wis, PhD(math, hist sci), 61. Prof Exp: Instr math, Col St Teresa, Minn, 46-52; asst prof, Dominican Col, Wis, 52-61; assoc prof, 61-64, chmn dept, 69-76, PROF MATH, SOUTHERN CONN STATE COL, 64- Mem: Math Asn Am; Hist Sci Soc; Sigma Xi. Res: History of medieval mathematics; mathematics education. Mailing Add: Dept of Math Southern Conn State Col New Haven CT 06515

SCHRADER, GEORGE FREDERICK, b Mattoon, Ill, July 21, 20; m 43; c 2. INDUSTRIAL ENGINEERING, RESEARCH ADMINISTRATION. Educ: Univ Ill, BS, 47, MS, 51, PhD(indust eng), 60. Prof Exp: Instr mech eng, Univ Ill, 47-51, asst prof indust eng, 53-61; prof, Okla State Univ, 61-62; prof & head dept, Kans State Univ, 62-66; dir tech serv, Univ Nebr, Lincoln, 66-67, dir indust res, 67-69; chmn dept indust eng & mgt systs, actg chmn dept eng math & comput systs, 69-77, PROF INDUST ENG & MGT SYSTS, UNIV CENT FLA, 69-, ASSOC DEAN, COL ENG, 77- Concurrent Pos: Consult, Joliet Ord & Ammunition Corp, 53, Caterpillar Tractor Co, 54, Champion Paper & Fibre Co, 56-57, Ill Bell Tel Co, 59-60, Bayer & McElrath, Inc, 64-66 & Air Force Oper Anal Group,

63-71. *Mem:* Am Inst Indust Engrs; Am Soc Qual Control; Am Soc Eng Educ. *Res:* Productivity analysis; management systems; research and development administration. *Mailing Add:* Univ Cent Fla Col Eng Box 25000 Orlando FL 32816

SCHRADER, KEITH WILLIAM, b Apr 22, 38; US citizen; m 60; c 2. MATHEMATICS. *Educ:* Univ Nebr, BS, 59, MS, 61, PhD(math), 66. *Prof Exp:* Engr electronic warfare, Sylvania Electronic Defense Lab, Gen Tel & Electronics Corp, 63-64; from asst prof to assoc prof, 66-78, PROF MATH, UNIV MO-COLUMBIA, 78- *Concurrent Pos:* NASA study grant, 66-68; NSF study grant, 68- *Mem:* Am Math Soc; Math Asn Am; Soc Indust & Appl Math. *Res:* Differential equations; boundary value problems; oscillation; convergence theorems. *Mailing Add:* Dept of Math Univ of Mo Columbia MO 65201

SCHRADER, LAWRENCE EDWIN, b Lancaster, Kans, Oct 22, 41; m 63; c 3. PLANT BIOCHEMISTRY, PLANT PHYSIOLOGY. *Educ:* Kans State Univ, BS, 63; Univ Ill, Urbana, PhD(agron), 67. *Prof Exp:* Biochemist, US Army Med Res & Nutrit Lab, Fitzsimons Gen Hosp, 67-69; asst prof, 69-72, assoc prof, 72-76, PROF AGRON, UNIV WIS-MADISON, 76- *Concurrent Pos:* Chief, Competitive Res Grants Off, USDA, Washington, DC, 80-81. *Mem:* Am Chem Soc; Am Soc Agron; Crop Sci Soc Am; Am Soc Plant Physiol; AAAS. *Res:* Nitrate uptake and assimilation in higher plants; enzyme regulation; photosynthesis; translocation; carbon-nitrogen interactions. *Mailing Add:* Dept of Agron Univ of Wis Madison WI 53706

SCHRADER, MALCOLM ELLIOT, b Brooklyn, NY, Aug 13, 25; m 52; c 3. PHYSICAL CHEMISTRY, SURFACE CHEMISTRY. *Educ:* Brooklyn Col, BS, 47; Syracuse Univ, MS, 49; Polytech Inst Brooklyn, PhD(phys chem), 56. *Prof Exp:* Chemist mat lab, Bur Ships, 56-57, supvry chemist, 57-60; res phys scientist, US Electronic Res & Develop Lab, 60-62; res chemist, Naval Appl Sci Lab, 63-70; RES CHEMIST, MAT DEPT, DAVID TAYLOR NAVAL SHIP RES & DEVELOP CTR, 70- *Concurrent Pos:* Lectr, City Univ New York, 64-67. *Mem:* NY Acad Sci; Am Chem Soc; Sigma Xi; Mat Res Soc; Am Vacuum Soc. *Res:* Surface chemistry of glass; adhesion promoters; contact angles in vacuum; wettability of ultra-clean solid surfaces; molecular processes at solid surfaces; adhesion of biological materials to solid surfaces. *Mailing Add:* Mat Dept David Taylor Naval Ship R&D Ctr Annapolis MD 21402

SCHRADER, R(OBERT) J, b South Bend, Ind, Oct 27, 18; m 42; c 3. CHEMICAL ENGINEERING. *Educ:* Purdue Univ, BS & MS, 40; Mass Inst Technol, ScD(chem eng), 43. *Prof Exp:* Instr chem eng, Mass Inst Technol, 42-43; asst supt chem prod plant, Clinton Eng Works, 43-45, head dept chem eng, 45-46; sr engr, Tenn Eastman Corp, 46-52, in chg develop & process improv dept, 52-53, supt polyethylene dept, 53-60, from asst supt to gen supt, Plastics Div, 60-75, WORKS MGR, TEX EASTMAN CO, DIV EASTMAN KODAK CO, 75-, VPRES, 81- *Mem:* Am Chem Soc; Am Inst Chem Engrs; Soc Plastics Engrs. *Res:* Development and pilot plant work on new chemical processes; effect of pressure on enthalpy of hydrocarbons and their mixtures; synthetic resins and plastics; petroleum; natural gas and textile products. *Mailing Add:* Tex Eastman Co Longview TX 75603

SCHRADER, WILLIAM THURBER, b Mineola, NY, Oct 12, 43; m 67. ENDOCRINOLOGY, MOLECULAR BIOLOGY. *Educ:* Johns Hopkins Univ, BA, 64, PhD(biol), 69. *Prof Exp:* Res assoc obstet & gynec, Med Sch, Vanderbilt Univ, 71, asst prof, 71-72; asst prof, 72-75, ASSOC PROF CELL BIOL, BAYLOR COL MED, 76- *Mem:* Endocrine Soc. *Res:* Molecular mechanisms of hormone action; gene regulation in eukaryotic cells. *Mailing Add:* Dept of Cell Biol Baylor Col of Med Houston TX 77030

SCHRADIE, JOSEPH, b Los Angeles, Calif, July 19, 33; m 60; c 3. PHARMACOGNOSY. *Educ:* Univ Southern Calif, PharmD, 57, MS, 61, PhD(pharmaceut chem, pharmacog), 66. *Prof Exp:* Asst prof, 66-70, ASSOC PROF PHARMACOG, COL PHARM, UNIV TOLEDO, 70-, CHMN, DEPT MED CHEM & PHARMACOG, 81- *Mem:* Am Pharmaceut Asn; Acad Pharmaceut Sci; NY Acad Sci; Am Soc Pharmacog. *Res:* Isolation of natural products from marine organisms, also their cultivation; biosynthesis and intermediary metabolism of carbohydrates in lower and higher plants; isolation of antibiotics; biological and phytochemical screens of higher plants. *Mailing Add:* 3323 Gallatin Toledo OH 43606

SCHRADY, DAVID ALAN, b Akron, Ohio, Nov 11, 39; m 62; c 3. OPERATIONS RESEARCH. *Educ:* Case Inst Technol, BS, 61, MS, 63, PhD(opers res), 65. *Prof Exp:* Assoc dir, Off Naval Res, 70-71; asst prof opers res, 65-70, assoc prof, 71-74, chmn, Dept Opers Res & Admin Sci, 74-76, dean info & policy sci, 76-80, ACTG PROVOST & ACAD DEAN, NAVAL POSTGRAD SCH, 80- *Concurrent Pos:* Consult, Decision Studies Group, 67-69; Litton-Mellonics, 67-70 & Naval Supply Systs Command, 70-73. *Mem:* Opers Res Soc Am (treas, 76-79); Mil Opers Res Soc (pres, 78-79); Inst Mgt Sci. *Res:* Inventory control; command and control. *Mailing Add:* Naval Postgrad Sch Monterey CA 93940

SCHRAER, HARALD, b Boston, Mass, June 10, 20; m 52; c 1. CELL BIOLOGY. *Educ:* Syracuse Univ, AB, 48, MA, 49; Cornell Univ, PhD(biol), 54. *Prof Exp:* Res assoc radiol, Albert Einstein Med Ctr, Pa, 52-56; res assoc physics, 56-58, sr res assoc biophys, 58-61, assoc prof, 61-67, PROF BIOPHYS, PA STATE UNIV, UNIVERSITY PARK, 67- *Concurrent Pos:* Vis scientist, NIH, 61. *Mem:* AAAS; Am Physiol Soc; Soc Exp Biol & Med; Am Soc Cell Biol. *Res:* Structural-functional aspects of metal transport; electron microscopy; skeletal physiology; mineral physiology. *Mailing Add:* Dept Biochem & Biophys Pa State Univ University Park PA 16802

SCHRAER, ROSEMARY, b Ilion, NY, Aug 1, 24; m 52; c 1. BIOCHEMISTRY, CELL BIOLOGY. *Educ:* Syracuse Univ, AB, 46, MS, 49, PhD(biochem), 53. *Prof Exp:* Res assoc biochem, Albert Einstein Med Ctr, 53-56; res asst biophys, 56-59, lectr, 59-60, asst prof, 61-69, assoc prof, 69-75, assoc dean res, Col Sci, 72-78, univ asst provost, 78-81, PROF BIOCHEM,

PA STATE UNIV, UNIVERSITY PARK, 75-, UNIV ASSOC PROVOST, 81- *Mem:* Fel AAAS; Am Chem Soc; Am Soc Cell Biol; Am Physiol Soc; Biophys Soc. *Res:* Cellular ultrastructure; calcium transport in cells and tissues; mechanisms of steroid hormone action. *Mailing Add:* Dept Biochem Pa State Univ University Park PA 16802

SCHRAG, JOHN L, b Siloam Springs, Ark, Apr 14, 37; m 60; c 1. POLYMER CHEMISTRY. *Educ:* Univ Omaha, BA, 59; Okla State Univ, MS, 61, PhD(physics), 67. *Prof Exp:* Proj assoc chem, 67-70, asst prof chem & eng, 70-71, asst prof chem, 71-75, ASSOC PROF CHEM, UNIV WIS-MADISON, 75- *Concurrent Pos:* Alfred P Sloan Found res fel, 73-74. *Mem:* Am Chem Soc; Am Phys Soc; Sigma Xi; AAAS; NY Acad Sci. *Res:* Optical and mechanical properties of macromolecules. *Mailing Add:* Dept of Chem Univ of Wis Madison WI 53706

SCHRAG, ROBERT L(EROY), b Moundridge, Kans, Nov 10, 24; m 66; c 1. PHYSICAL ELECTRONICS. *Educ:* Kans State Univ, BSEE, 45; Calif Inst Technol, MSEE, 46; Pa State Univ, PhD(ionosphere res), 54. *Prof Exp:* Res analyst, Douglas Aircraft Co, 46-48; instr elec eng, Pa State Univ, 48-53; mem tech staff, Bell Tel Labs, 54-57; PROF ELEC ENG, WICHITA STATE UNIV, 57- *Concurrent Pos:* NSF res grants, 62-64. *Mem:* Inst Elec & Electronics Engrs. *Res:* Electromagnetic wave propagation; physics of electron beams. *Mailing Add:* Dept of Elec Eng Wichita State Univ Wichita KS 67208

SCHRAGE, ROBERT W, b Brooklyn, NY, July 1, 25; m 65. CHEMICAL ENGINEERING. *Educ:* Columbia Univ, BA, 46, BS & MS, 48, PhD(chem eng), 50. *Prof Exp:* Engr, East Coast Tech Serv Div, Esso Standard Oil Co, 50-58, sect head tech div, Mfg Dept, 58-61, sect head econ, Coord Dept, Esso Standard Eastern Inc, 62-66, mgr econ & planning, Esso Eastern Chem Inc, 66-71, mgr corp affairs, Essochem Eastern Ltd, Hong Kong, 71-73, ECON RES ADVISOR, EXXON CHEM AM, 73- *Mem:* Am Chem Soc. *Res:* Petroleum and chemical industry economics. *Mailing Add:* 1752 S Gessner Houston TX 77063

SCHRAGE, SAMUEL, b Vienna, Austria, Feb 1, 20; nat US; m 53; c 2. PHYSICAL CHEMISTRY, HISTORY OF SCIENCE. *Educ:* Dalhousie Univ, BSc, 44, MSc, 46; McGill Univ, PhD(phys chem), 51. *Prof Exp:* Instr phys chem, Dalhousie Univ, 45-46, lectr, 46-48; demonstr, McGill Univ, 48-51; res assoc, Univ Notre Dame, 51-52; from instr to asst prof, 52-59, ASSOC PROF PHYS CHEM, UNIV ILL, CHICAGO CIRCLE, 59-, DIR, UNIV HONS PROGS, 70- *Res:* Radiation chemistry; science education. *Mailing Add:* Dept Chem Univ Ill Chicago IL 60680

SCHRAM, ALFRED C, b Brussels, Belg, Sept 17, 30; US citizen; m 57; c 2. BIOCHEMISTRY. *Educ:* Polytech Inst Brooklyn, BS, 54; Univ Tex, Austin, MA, 56, PhD(chem), 58. *Prof Exp:* Res biochemist, St Barnabas Hosp, Minneapolis, Minn, 58-59; clin instr biochem, Southwestern Med Sch, Univ Tex, 59-62, clin asst prof, 62-65; assoc prof chem, 65-70, PROF CHEM, WTEX STATE UNIV, 70- *Concurrent Pos:* Res biochemist, Vet Admin Hosp, Dallas, 59-65; NIH grant cancer res, 63-65; abstractor, Chem Abstr, 63-; Welch Found res grant, 67-69. *Mem:* AAAS; Am Chem Soc; affil AMA. *Res:* Immunochemistry of synthetic antigens. *Mailing Add:* Dept of Chem W Tex State Univ Canyon TX 79016

SCHRAM, ALFRED FRANCIS, b Lawton, Okla, July 9, 19; m 43; c 4. PHYSICAL CHEMISTRY. *Educ:* Univ Okla, BA, 41, MS, 43, PhD(chem), 48. *Prof Exp:* Chemist, Continental Oil Co, 43-45 & Skelly Oil Co, 45-46; prof chem, Southwestern State Col, 48-51; prof & head dept, Midwestern Univ, 51-53; from asst prof to assoc prof, Agr & Mech Col Tex, 53-61; assoc prof chem, Univ Dallas, 61-80. *Mem:* AAAS; Am Chem Soc. *Res:* Corrosion inhibition; electrochemical electrode phenomena. *Mailing Add:* 407 King Richard Irving TX 75061

SCHRAM, EUGENE P, b Milwaukee, Wis, Apr 19, 34; m 56; c 1. INORGANIC CHEMISTRY. *Educ:* Carroll Col, BS, 56; Purdue Univ, PhD(inorg chem), 62. *Prof Exp:* Res technician, Allis Chalmers Mfg Co, 54-55, res chemist, 56-58; res chemist, Carbon Prod Div, Union Carbide Corp, 62-64; asst prof, 64-69, ASSOC PROF CHEM, OHIO STATE UNIV, 69- *Mem:* AAAS; Am Chem Soc. *Res:* Chemistry of aluminum heterocycles and molecular compounds containing metal-metal bonds. *Mailing Add:* Dept of Chem Ohio State Univ Columbus OH 43210

SCHRAM, FREDERICK R, b Chicago, Ill, Aug 11, 43. INVERTEBRATE PALEOBIOLOGY, CARCINOLOGY. *Educ:* Loyola Univ, Ill, BS, 65; Univ Chicago, PhD(paleozool), 68. *Prof Exp:* Asst prof, 68-73, assoc prof zool, Eastern Ill Univ, 73-78; CUR PALEONT & CHMN GEOL, NATURAL HIST MUS, SAN DIEGO, 78- *Concurrent Pos:* Res assoc, Field Mus Natural Hist. *Mem:* Crustacean Soc; Paleont Soc; fel Linnean Soc London; Am Soc Zool; Int Paleont Asn. *Res:* Late Paleozoic history of the Malacostraca; comparative anatomy of the skeleto-musculature of crustaceans and pycnogonids; arthropod relationships and evolution. *Mailing Add:* Dept of Paleont Nat Hist Mus San Diego CA 92112

SCHRAMEL, ROBERT JOSEPH, b St Louis, Mo, Sept 6, 24; m 47; c 5. SURGERY. *Educ:* Tulane Univ, BS, 45, MD, 48. *Prof Exp:* From instr to assoc prof, 55-70, prof surg, 70-76, CLIN PROF SURG, SCH MED, TULANE UNIV, 76- *Concurrent Pos:* Prin investr, NIH, 57- *Mem:* AAAS; Am Asn Thoracic Surg; NY Acad Sci; Asn Hosp Med Educ; Asn Am Med Cols. *Res:* Pulmonary function in disease states; trauma; extracorporeal circulation; shock; hyperbaric oxygenation; surgical treatment of cardiovascular disease. *Mailing Add:* Dept of Surg Tulane Med Ctr Sch of Med New Orleans LA 70112

SCHRAMM, CHARLES H, organic chemistry, see previous edition

SCHRAMM, DAVID N, b St Louis, Mo, Oct 25, 45; div; c 2. THEORETICAL ASTROPHYSICS, NUCLEAR PHYSICS. *Educ:* Mass Inst Technol, BS, 67; Calif Inst Technol, PhD(physics), 71. *Prof Exp:* Res fel physics, Calif Inst Technol, 71-72; asst prof astron & physics, Univ Tex-Austin, 72-74; assoc prof astrophys, 74-76, actg chmn dept, 77, PROF ASTRON & ASTROPHYS, ENRICO FERMI INST & COL, UNIV CHICAGO, 77-, PROF PHYSICS, UNIV CHICAGO, 77-, CHMN DEPT ASTRON & ASTROPHYS, 78- *Concurrent Pos:* Consult, NSF Astrophys Curruculum, 74, Aerospace Corp, 74- & Lawrence Livermore Lab, 75-; lectr Adler Planetarium, 76-; assoc ed Am J Physics, 78-; mem, Mayor Jane Byrne's Adv Comt High Technol, 81-; mem sci adv comt, Demystifying Sci, Mus Sci & Indust, Chicago, Ill, 81-; astrophys ed, Physics Reports, 81- *Honors & Awards:* Robert J Trumpler Award, Astron Soc Pac, 74; Am Astron Soc Helen B Warner Prize, 78; Gunnar Kullen Mem Lectr, Lund, Sweden, 81. *Mem:* Fel Am Phys Soc; Am Astron Soc; Int Astron Union; Sigma Xi; Meteoritical Soc. *Res:* Theoretical studies of astrophysics with particular emphasis on: cosmology, the origin of the elements, cosmic rays, stellar evolution and supernova, neutrino astrophysics; nucleochronology, the early solar system and black holes; particle physics. *Mailing Add:* Enrico Fermi Inst Univ Chicago Chicago IL 60637

SCHRAMM, LEE CLYDE, b Portsmouth, Ohio, July 20, 34; m 64; c 3. PHARMACOGNOSY. *Educ:* Ohio State Univ, BSc, 57; Univ Conn, MS, 59, PhD(pharmacog), 62. *Prof Exp:* Asst prof, Col Pharm, Univ Minn, Minneapolis, 61-67; assoc prof pharmacog & head dept, Sch Pharm, Univ Ga, 67-81; REGIONAL MED ASSOC, SMITH KLINE & FRENCH LABS, 81- *Concurrent Pos:* Chmn pharmacog & natural prod sect, Acad Pharmaceut Sci, 79-80; chmn sect teachers biol sci, Am Asn Cols Pharm, 75-76. *Honors & Awards:* Kilmer Prize, Am Pharmaceut Asn, 57. *Mem:* Am Pharmaceut Asn; Soc Econ Bot; Ger Soc Drug Plant Res; Am Soc Pharmacognosy (treas, 75-81). *Res:* Phytochemistry, particularly plants and fungi with potential medicinal or toxic activity. *Mailing Add:* 290 Kings Rd Athens GA 30606

SCHRAMM, MARTIN WILLIAM, JR, b Pittsburgh, Pa, Apr 21, 27; m 53; c 4. GEOLOGY. *Educ:* Univ Pittsburgh, BS, 54, MS, 55; Univ Okla, PhD(geol), 63. *Prof Exp:* Explor geologist, Gulf Oil Corp, 55-57; consult petrol, A W McCoy Assocs, 57-59; proj supvr explor res, Cities Serv Oil Co, Okla, 59-69; mgr foreign div, White Shield Explor Corp, 69-70, mgr explor/exploitation, White Shield Oil & Gas Corp, 70-72, consult geologist, 72-74; MEM, GEOQUEST INTERNAT INC, 74- *Mem:* Am Asn Petrol Geologists; Am Inst Prof Geologists; fel Geol Soc Am. *Res:* Middle Ordovician stratigraphy and paleogeology; basin analysis; environments of deposition. *Mailing Add:* Geoquest Internat Inc 4605 Post Oak Pl Suite 330 Houston TX 77027

SCHRAMM, RAYMOND EUGENE, b St Charles, Mo, Aug 11, 41. MATERIALS SCIENCE, PHYSICS. *Educ:* Regis Col, Colo, BS, 64; Mich Technol Univ, MS, 65. *Prof Exp:* Jr physicist nuclear physics, Ames Lab, Iowa State Univ, 65-66; PHYSICIST MAT, FRACTURE & DEFORMATION DIV, NAT BUR STANDARDS, 67- *Mem:* Am Asn Physics Teachers; AAAS. *Res:* Microstructural properties of deformed metals; cryogenic mechanical properties of composites; ultrasonic non-destructive evaluation of welds using long-wavelength electromagnetic transducers. *Mailing Add:* Fracture & Deformation Div Nat Bur of Standards Boulder CO 80303

SCHRAMM, ROBERT FREDERICK, b Philadelphia, Pa, Feb 23, 42; m 68; c 2. CHEMISTRY. *Educ:* St Joseph's Col, Pa, BS, 64; Univ Pa, PhD(chem), 69. *Prof Exp:* Advan Res Projs Agency fel, Univ Pa, 69-70; asst prof to assoc prof, 70-75, PROF CHEM, EAST STROUDSBURG STATE COL, 75- *Concurrent Pos:* Lectr, St Joseph's Col, Pa, 70. *Mem:* AAAS; Am Chem Soc; Sigma Xi. *Res:* Synthesis and characterization of coordination complexes of palladium, platinum and gold; molecular orbital calculations; application of computers to scientific instruction. *Mailing Add:* Dept of Chem East Stroudsburg State Col East Stroudsburg PA 18301

SCHRAMM, ROBERT JOHNSON, JR, b Bellaire, Ohio, Aug 29, 18; m 43. PLANT NUTRITION. *Educ:* Hiram Col, AB, 49; Duke Univ, MA, 50, PhD(plant physiol), 54. *Prof Exp:* Instr bot, Sch Pharm, Univ Tenn, 50-52; instr bot, NC State Col, 54-55, res asst prof hort, 55-62; Diamond Alkali Co fel, Boyce Thompson Inst Plant Res, 62-64; researcher agr & biol chem, Diamond Alkali Co, 64-68; ASSOC PROF ORNAMENTAL HORT, UNIV CONN, 68-, STATE EXTEN NURSERYMAN, 68- *Mem:* Weed Sci Soc Am; Torrey Bot Club; Am Soc Hort Sci. *Res:* Ornamental plant nutrition; chemical weed control in horticulture and agronomic crops; plant pathology; basic biological chemicals screening; soil-herbicide mode of action; adsorption. *Mailing Add:* Dept of Plant Sci Univ of Conn Storrs CT 06268

SCHRAMM, ROBERT WILLIAM, b Wheeling, WVa, Nov 13, 34; m 67. PHYSICS. *Educ:* Liberty State Col, BS, 58; Univ WVa, MS, 59. *Prof Exp:* From instr to asst prof, 58-65, head dept, 66-71, ASSOC PROF PHYSICS, WEST LIBERTY STATE COL, 65- *Concurrent Pos:* Dir, Regional Sci Fair, 58-; archivist, West Liberty State Col, 77- *Mem:* Am Asn Physics Teachers; Am Phys Soc. *Res:* Nuclear spectroscopy. *Mailing Add:* Box 102 108 Walnut St West Liberty WV 26074

SCHRAMM, VERN LEE, b Howard, SDak, Nov 9, 41; m 64; c 2. BIOCHEMISTRY. *Educ:* SDak State Col, BS, 63; Harvard Univ, SM, 65; Australian Nat Univ, PhD(biochem), 69. *Prof Exp:* Nat Res Coun-NSF res assoc, NASA Ames Res Ctr, 69-71; asst prof, 71-76, assoc prof, 76-81, PROF BIOCHEM, SCH MED, TEMPLE UNIV, 81- *Concurrent Pos:* Mem biochem study sect, NIH, 81- *Mem:* AAAS; Am Chem Soc; Am Soc Biol Chem. *Res:* Regulation and mechanism of enzymes of nucleotide degradation and gluconeogenesis; nucleotide biosynthesis and degradation; metabolic controls. *Mailing Add:* Dept of Biochem Temple Univ Sch of Med Philadelphia PA 19140

SCHRANK, AULINE RAYMOND, b Hamilton, Tex, Aug 15, 15; m 42; c 2. PHYSIOLOGY, BIOPHYSICS. *Educ:* Tarleton Agr Col, AS, 37; Southwest Tex State Col, AB, 37; Univ Tex, PhD(physiol, biophys), 42. *Prof Exp:* From instr to assoc prof, 39-58, chmn dept zool, 63-70, actg dean, 72-74, assoc dean, 74-78, PROF PHYSIOL, UNIV TEX, AUSTIN, 58-, DEAN, COL NATURAL SCI, 78- *Mem:* AAAS; Am Soc Plant Physiol; Soc Gen Physiol; Biophys Soc; Scand Soc Plant Physiol. *Res:* Bioelectrical fields in relation to growth phenomena and cell correlation; tropisms, regeneration and active transport. *Mailing Add:* Dept of Zool Univ of Texas Austin TX 78712

SCHRANK, GLEN EDWARD, b Omaha, Nebr, Aug 6, 26; m 47. PHYSICS. *Educ:* Univ Calif, Los Angeles, BA, 47, MA, 50, PhD, 53. *Prof Exp:* Res assoc physics, Univ Calif, Los Angeles, 53; from instr to asst prof, Princeton Univ, 53-61; res physicist, Lawrence Radiation Lab, Univ Calif, 61-63; ASSOC PROF PHYSICS, UNIV CALIF, SANTA BARBARA, 63- *Concurrent Pos:* Guest physicist, Brookhaven Nat Lab, 59-; consult, AEC; consult, Giannini Sci Corp, 59. *Mem:* Am Phys Soc; Ital Phys Soc. *Res:* Nuclear and elementary particle physics. *Mailing Add:* Dept of Physics Univ of Calif Santa Barbara CA 93106

SCHRANK, GORDON DABNEY, b San Angelo, Tex, Aug 11, 48; m 75. MICROBIOLOGY. *Educ:* Angelo State Univ, BS, 70; Univ Tex Med Br Galveston, PhD(microbiol), 74. *Prof Exp:* Med technologist bact & serol, Univ Tex Med Br Galveston, 74-75; instr microbiol, Ctr Health Sci, Univ Tenn, Memphis, 75-77, asst prof, 77-81; ASST PROF BIOL, ST CLOUD STATE UNIV, 81- *Concurrent Pos:* USDA Res Agreement Grant, Immunity to Brucellosis at Mucosal Surfaces, 78- *Mem:* Am Soc Microbiol; AAAS; Sigma Xi. *Res:* Area of host-parasite relationships in infectious diseases and how immunity may alter these relationships. *Mailing Add:* Dept Biol Sci St Cloud State Univ St Cloud MN 56301

SCHRANKEL, KENNETH REINHOLD, b Rice Lake, Wis, Mar 26, 45; m 70; c 2. TOXICOLOGY, ENVIRONMENTAL HEALTH. *Educ:* Wartburg Col, BS, 67; Ill State Univ, MS, 73, PhD(biol), 78. *Prof Exp:* Vis asst prof biol, Tex A&M Univ, 78-79; fel trainee, Univ Wis, 79-81; RES TOXICOLOGIST, INT FLAVORS & FRAGRANCES, 81- *Mem:* AAAS; Sigma Xi; Am Soc Zoologists; Electron Micros Soc Am; Am Col Toxicol. *Res:* Mammalian toxicology; biochemical aspects of insect oogenesis; ultrastructural aspects of insect reproduction; dermatoxicology and phototoxicology of fragrance materials; safety assessment of chemicals. *Mailing Add:* Int Flavors & Fragrances 1515 Highway 36 Union Branch NJ 07735

SCHRAUT, KENNETH CHARLES, b Hillsboro, Ill, May 19, 13; m 52; c 1. MATHEMATICS. *Educ:* Univ Ill, AB, 36; Univ Cincinnati, AM, 38, PhD(math), 40. *Prof Exp:* From instr to prof, 40-72, head dept math, 54-72, DISTINGUISHED SERV PROF MATH, UNIV DAYTON, 72- *Concurrent Pos:* Lectr, Wright Field Grad Ctr, Ohio State Univ, 48-52; dir, US Air Force Proj, Univ Dayton, 52-54; actg prof, Grad Sch, Univ Cincinnati, 58-60; pres, Honor Sem Metrop Dayton, Inc, 65-67. *Mem:* Am Math Soc; Am Soc Eng Educ; Math Asn Am. *Res:* Infinite series; mathematical analysis. *Mailing Add:* Dept of Math Univ of Dayton Dayton OH 45469

SCHRAUZER, GERHARD N, b Franzensbad, Czech, Mar 26, 32; m 57; c 4. INORGANIC CHEMISTRY. *Educ:* Univ Munich, BS, 53, MS, 54, PhD(chem), 56. *Prof Exp:* Res asst chem, Univ Munich, 55-57; res assoc, Monsanto Chem Co, 57-59; res asst chem, Univ Munich, 59-63, lectr inorg chem, 63-64; res supvr, Shell Develop Co, 64-66; PROF CHEM, UNIV CALIF, SAN DIEGO, 66- *Concurrent Pos:* Ed & Founder, Bioinorg Chem J, 70-; pres & founder, Int Asn Bioinorg Scientists, Inc. *Mem:* Am Chem Soc; NY Acad Sci; Soc Ger Chem. *Res:* Organometallic coordination and enzyme chemistry; homogeneous catalysis; trace element, vitamin and cancer research. *Mailing Add:* Dept of Chem Univ of Calif San Diego La Jolla CA 92093

SCHRAY, KEITH JAMES, b Portland, Ore, Nov 25, 43; m 63; c 7. BIO-ORGANIC CHEMISTRY, IMMUNOASSAYS. *Educ:* Univ Portland, BS, 65; Pa State Univ, PhD(phys org chem), 70. *Prof Exp:* NIH fel, Inst Cancer Res, Philadelphia, 70-72; assoc prof, 72-80, PROF CHEM, LEHIGH UNIV, 80- *Mem:* Am Chem Soc. *Res:* Model and enzyme reaction mechanisms; phosphoryl transfer; anomerases; enzyme immunoassays. *Mailing Add:* Dept Chem Lehigh Univ Bethlehem PA 18015

SCHRAYER, GROVER J, JR, b Fountain Hill, Pa, July 14, 29; m 52; c 3. ORGANIC GEOCHEMISTRY. *Educ:* Lehigh Univ, BS, 50, MS, 52. *Prof Exp:* From chemist to res chemist, 52-68, SR RES CHEMIST, EXPLOR DIV, GULF RES & DEVELOP CO, 68- *Mem:* AAAS; Am Chem Soc; Geochem Soc. *Res:* Analysis, composition, origin and natural alteration of natural gases, petroleum, coal and other naturally occurring organic materials; isotope geochemistry; geochemical exploration methods. *Mailing Add:* Gulf Res & Develop Co Explor Div PO Drawer 2038 Pittsburgh PA 15230

SCHRECK, CARL BERNHARD, b San Francisco, Calif, May 18, 44; m 66; c 2. FISH BIOLOGY. *Educ:* Univ Calif, Berkeley, AB, 66; Colo State Univ, MS, 69, PhD(fish physiol), 72. *Prof Exp:* Asst prof, Va Polytech Inst & State Univ, 72-75; asst unit leader, 75-78, asst prof fisheries, 75-78, LEADER ORE COOP & ASSOC PROF FISHERIES, FISHERIES RES UNIT, 78- *Mem:* AAAS; Am Fisheries Soc; Am Inst Fishery Res Biologists; Am Soc Zoologists; Sigma Xi. *Res:* Biology of freshwater and anadromous fish with special emphasis on physiology, endocrinology, genetics and organism-environment interactions. *Mailing Add:* Ore Coop Fisheries Res Unit Ore State Univ Corvallis OR 97331

SCHRECK, JAMES OTTO, b Houston, Tex, Nov 6, 37; m 66. ORGANIC CHEMISTRY. *Educ:* St Thomas Univ, Tex, BA, 59; Tex A&M Univ MS, 62, PhD(chem), 64. *Prof Exp:* Res assoc chem, Ga Inst Technol, 64-65; vis asst prof & fel, La State Univ, 65-66; from asst prof to assoc prof, 66-74, chmn dept, 75-81, PROF CHEM, UNIV NORTHERN COLO, 74- *Mem:* Am Chem Soc. *Res:* Synthesis, characterization, and reactions of new organic compounds. *Mailing Add:* Dept of Chem Univ of Northern Colo Greeley CO 80639

SCHRECKENBERG, GERVASIA MARY, b Paderborn, Ger, Jan 4, 16; US citizen. NEUROBIOLOGY, DEVELOPMENTAL BIOLOGY. *Educ:* Cath Univ Am, BS, 52, MS, 54, PhD(zool), 57. *Prof Exp:* Pres & dean, Tombrock Col, Paterson, NJ, 56-62; prof mod biol, Cheng Kung Nat Univ, Tainan, Taiwan, 63-70; PROF NEUROBIOL, FAIRLEIGH DICKINSON UNIV, 74- *Concurrent Pos:* Trustee, Tombrock Col, 72-74; fel, Columbia Univ, 70; NSF res grant, Univ Tex, Austin, 71. *Mem:* Soc Neurosci; Soc Develop Biol; Soc Am Zoologists; Sigma Xi; AAAS. *Res:* Problems dealing with developmental neurobiology; brain opiates, especially the endorphins. *Mailing Add:* Dept of Biol Montross Ave Rutherford NJ 07070

SCHREIBEIS, LEE J, JR, b Pittsburgh, Pa, Sept 26, 24; m 49; c 1. INDUSTRIAL HYGIENE. *Educ:* Univ Pittsburgh, BS, 44; Univ Mich, MPH, 48. *Prof Exp:* Pub health engr, Calhoon County Dept Health, Mich, 48-49; indust hyg engr, City of Pittsburgh, 49-51 & Indust Hyg Found, Inc, Mellon Inst, 51-57; chief, Bur Air Pollution Control, Allegheny County Health Dept, Pa, 57-60; indust hyg engr, Lackawanna, 60-68, asst fuel engr, Buffalo, 68-72, ASST MGR, POLLUTION ABATEMENT, BETHLEHEM STEEL CO, 72- *Res:* Direction of corporate pollution abatement activities in air, water and solid waste. *Mailing Add:* 270 Flagstone Dr Bethlehem PA 18017

SCHREIBEIS, WILLIAM J, b Pittsburgh, Pa, Oct 28, 29; m 80; c 4. INDUSTRIAL HYGIENE. *Educ:* Univ Pittsburgh, BS, 51, MPH, 56. *Prof Exp:* Sanit engr, USPHS, 51-54; pub health engr, City of Pittsburgh Dept Pub Health, 54-56; indust hyg engr, Indust Health Found, Mellon Inst, 56-65; INDUST HYG ENGR, BELL LABS, 65- *Concurrent Pos:* Eng comt, Indust Health Found. *Mem:* Am Indust Hyg Asn; Air Pollution Control Asn; Brit Occup Hyg Soc. *Res:* Evaluation of environmental health and safety hazards. *Mailing Add:* Bell Labs Rm 3A-209 Murray Hill NJ 07974

SCHREIBER, B CHARLOTTE, b Brooklyn, NY, June 27, 31; m 50; c 2. SEDIMENTARY PETROLOGY, STRATIGRAPHY. *Educ:* Wash Univ, AB, 53; Rutgers Univ, New Brunswick, MS, 66; Rensselaer Polytech Inst, PhD(geol), 74. *Prof Exp:* Sedimentologist & oceanogr, Alpine Geophys Assoc, 66-68; instr geol, Lehman Col, City Univ New York, 68-69; instr, Barnard Col, Columbia Univ, 69-71; instr, Rensselaer Polytech Inst, 71-72, res asst, 72-74; asst prof, 74-77, ASSOC PROF GEOL, QUEENS COL, NY, 78- *Concurrent Pos:* Teaching fel, Rutgers Univ, 63-66; consult sedimentologist, Johnson Soils Inc, 68-70; teaching fel, Rensselaer Polytech Inst, 71-72; NSF res fel, 72-74; NSF energy related res, Imperial Col, London, 76-77; assoc ed, Soc Econ & Petrol Geologists J, 77-; res assoc, Lamont-Doherty Geol Observ, Columbia Univ, 78-81, sr res assoc, 81. *Honors & Awards:* Levorsen Award, Am Asn Petrol & Geologists, 75. *Mem:* Geol Soc Am; Soc Econ & Petrol Geologists; Can Soc Petrol Geologists; Paleont Res Found; fel Geol Soc London. *Res:* Origin and diagenesis of evaporites and associated carbonates; sedimentologic and stratigraphic sequences as developed on continental margins. *Mailing Add:* Dept of Earth & Environ Sci Queens Col NY Flushing NY 11367

SCHREIBER, DAVID LAURENCE, b Klamath Falls, Ore, Nov 15, 41; m 63; c 3. HYDRAULIC ENGINEERING, HYDROLOGIC ENGINEERING. *Educ:* Ore State Univ, BS, 63; Wash State Univ, MS, 65, PhD(eng sci), 70. *Prof Exp:* Res asst agr & civil eng, Wash State Univ, 63-67; asst prof civil eng, Univ Wyo, 67-68; instr, Wash State Univ, 68-69; res hydraul engr, Northwest Watershed Res Ctr, Agr Res Serv, USDA, 69-72; sr res engr, Water & Land Resources Dept, Pac Northwest Lab, Battelle Mem Inst, 72-74; hydraul engr, Hydrol-Meteorol Br, Off Nuclear Reactor Regulation, US Nuclear Regulatory Comn, 74-78; consult hydrol engr, 78-80; PRES, SCHREIBER CONSULT, INC, 80- *Concurrent Pos:* Groundwater dispersion honorarium, Argonne Nat Lab, 81. *Honors & Awards:* Robert E Horton Award, Am Geophys Union, 75. *Mem:* Am Geophys Union; Am Soc Agr Engrs; Am Soc Civil Engrs; Nat Soc Prof Engrs; Nat Water Well Asn. *Res:* Hydraulics and hydrology of surface water and ground water; water resources planning and environmental impact analyses; radionuclide and pollutant dispersion in surface water and ground water; radioactive and hazardous waste management. *Mailing Add:* PO Box 1087 Schreiber Consult Inc Coeur d'Alene ID 83814

SCHREIBER, DAVID SEYFARTH, b Wilmington, Del, Apr 3, 36; m 65; c 2. SOLID STATE PHYSICS. *Educ:* Wabash Col, BA, 57; Cornell Univ, PhD(physics), 62. *Prof Exp:* NSF fel physics, Univ Calif, Berkeley, 62-63; asst prof, Northwestern Univ, 63-68; ASSOC PROF PHYSICS, UNIV ILL, CHICAGO CIRCLE, 68- *Concurrent Pos:* NSF res grant, 65-67. *Mem:* Am Phys Soc. *Res:* Study of magnetic properties, superconductivity and electronic band structure by means of nuclear magnetic resonance; alternative energy systems such as solar, wind and water. *Mailing Add:* Dept of Physics Univ of Ill at Chicago Circle Chicago IL 60680

SCHREIBER, EDWARD, b Brooklyn, NY, Sept 11, 30; m 50; c 2. CERAMICS, GEOPHYSICS. *Educ:* State Univ NY Col Ceramics, Alfred, BS, 56, PhD(ceramic sci), 63. *Prof Exp:* Res scientist, Am Standard Corp, 62-63; res scientist, Lamont Geol Observ, Columbia Univ, 63-65, res assoc, 65-68; assoc prof earth & environ sci, 68-71, PROF EARTH & ENVIRON SCI, QUEENS COL, NY, 72- *Concurrent Pos:* Lectr, Queens Col, NY, 65-66, adj asst prof, 66-67; vis res assoc, Lamont-Doherty Geol Observ, 68-71, vis sr res assoc, 72-; mem lunar sample rev panel, 71-74 & lunar sample anal planning team, 74-77. *Mem:* AAAS; Am Ceramic Soc; Mineral Soc Am; Am Geophys Union; Geochem Soc. *Res:* Study of physical properties of solids, equation of state, elastic properties and experimental mineralogy; inorganic materials at high pressures and temperatures; tectonophysics; submarine geology. *Mailing Add:* Dept of Earth & Environ Sci Queens Col Flushing NY 11367

SCHREIBER, ERIC CHRISTIAN, b Frankfurt, Ger, Aug 16, 21; US citizen; m 74; c 4. PHARMACOLOGY, ORGANIC CHEMISTRY. *Educ:* Polytech Inst Brooklyn, BS, 51, MS, 53; Univ Conn, PhD(pharmacol), 63. *Prof Exp:* Chemist, Nat Dairy Res Lab, 49-51; chemist, Chas Pfizer & Co, NY, 51-58,

head radioisotope lab, Conn, 58-63; dept head drug metab, Wm S Merrell Co, 63-66; dir biopharmaceut res, E R Squibb & Sons, Inc, 66-67, dir drug metab, 67-75, assoc dir, Squibb Inst, 75-77, dir Squibb Int Res Ctr, Regensburg, W Ger, 75-77; PROF PHARMACOL & DIR TOXICOL & DRUG METAB, UNIV TENN CTR HEALTH SCI, 77- *Mem:* Fel Am Inst Chem; Am Pharmaceut Asn; Am Soc Pharmacol & Exp Therapeut; fel Acad Pharmaceut Sci. *Res:* Metabolism of drugs; pharmacokinetics; transfer of chemicals from mother to offspring, central nervous system deficits. *Mailing Add:* Dir Toxicol & Drug Metab 874 Union Ave CR200 Memphis TN 38163

SCHREIBER, HANS, b Quedlinberg, Ger, Feb 5, 44; m 69; c 3. IMMUNOLOGY OF CANCER, BIOLOGY OF CANCER. *Educ:* Univ Freiburg, MD, 69; Univ Chicago, PhD, 77. *Prof Exp:* Staff mem oncol, Oak Ridge Nat Lab, 70-74; res assoc oncol, 74-77, ASST PROF PATH, UNIV CHICAGO, 77- *Concurrent Pos:* Prin investr, 77- *Mem:* Am Asn Cancer Res; Am Asn Path; Am Soc Cytol; Am Asn Immunol. *Res:* Selective regulation of immune responses to antigens, particularly to transplants and cancer cells; biologic and immunologic analysis of antigenic changes detected on the surface of malignant cells; cancer immunology. *Mailing Add:* La Rabida Univ Chicago Inst E 65th St at Lake Mich Chicago IL 60649

SCHREIBER, HENRY DALE, b Lebanon, Pa, Nov 13, 48. PHYSICAL CHEMISTRY, MATERIALS SCIENCE. *Educ:* Lebanon Valley Col, BS, 70; Univ Wis-Madison, PhD(phys chem), 76. *Prof Exp:* Asst prof, 76-80, ASSOC PROF CHEM, VA MIL INST, 80- *Concurrent Pos:* Res asst, NASA Johnson Space Ctr, 73-76. *Mem:* AAAS; Am Chem Soc; Am Ceramic Soc; Am Geophys Union; Geochem Soc. *Res:* Oxidation-reduction equilibria of multivalent elements in silicate melts which simulate basaltic magmas as well as simple glass-forming systems. *Mailing Add:* Dept of Chem Va Mil Inst Lexington VA 24450

SCHREIBER, HENRY PETER, b Brunn, Czech, Nov 3, 26; nat Can; m 54; c 4. PHYSICAL CHEMISTRY. *Educ:* Univ Manitoba, BSc, 49, MSc, 50; Univ Toronto, PhD(phys chem), 53. *Prof Exp:* Fel phys chem, Nat Res Coun Can, 53-55; res chemist high polymer systs, Can Industs, Ltd, 55-74; PROF CHEM ENG, POLYTECH SCH MONTREAL, 74- *Honors & Awards:* Protective Coatings Award, Chem Inst Can, 77; Medaille Archambault & Alcan Prize, Asn Can-Francaise pour L'Advan Sci, 80. *Mem:* Soc Rheology; Chem Inst Can; Soc Plastics Eng. *Res:* Rheology of high polymer melts; properties of solutions of macromolecules; thermodynamics of liquids; structure of macromolecules. *Mailing Add:* Dept Chem Eng Polytech Sch Montreal Montreal PQ H3C 3A7 Can

SCHREIBER, JOSEPH FREDERICK, JR, b Baltimore, Md, June 2, 25; m 51; c 2. GEOLOGY. *Educ:* Johns Hopkins Univ, AB, 48, MA, 50; Univ Utah, PhD, 58. *Prof Exp:* Asst geol, Johns Hopkins Univ, 48-49; jr instr, 49-50; geologist, Chesapeake Bay Inst, Md, 51 & Calif Co, La, 54-55; asst prof geol, Okla State Univ, 55-59; assoc prof, 59-66, PROF GEOL, UNIV ARIZ, 66- *Concurrent Pos:* Jr geologist, Atlantic Refining Co, Tex, 49-50 & Shell Oil Co, Wyo, 52. *Mem:* Soc Econ Paleontologists & Mineralogists; Am Asn Petrol Geol; Geol Soc Am. *Res:* Sedimentology; stratigraphy; marine geology. *Mailing Add:* Dept of Geosci Univ of Ariz Tucson AZ 85721

SCHREIBER, KURT CLARK, b Vienna, Austria, Feb 23, 22; nat US; m 51; c 3. PHYSICAL ORGANIC CHEMISTRY. *Educ:* City Col New York, BS, 44; Columbia Univ, AM, 47, PhD(chem), 49. *Prof Exp:* Asst, Columbia Univ, 46-49; res assoc chem, Univ Calif, Los Angeles, 49-51; from asst prof to assoc prof, 51-58, head dept, 58-72, assoc dean, Col Arts & Sci, 62-66, PROF CHEM, DUQUESNE UNIV, 58-, ACTG DEAN, GRAD SCH, 81- *Concurrent Pos:* Ed, Pa Acad Sci Newsletter, 79- *Mem:* Am Chem Soc; Soc Appl Spectros; NY Acad Sci; Am Inst Chemists. *Res:* Mechanism of organic reactions. *Mailing Add:* 1812 Wightman St Pittsburgh PA 15217

SCHREIBER, LAWRENCE, b Chicago, Ill, June 15, 31. PLANT PATHOLOGY. *Educ:* Northwestern Univ, BS, 53; Purdue Univ, MS, 59, PhD, 61. *Prof Exp:* PLANT PATHOLOGIST, SCI & EDUC ADMIN-AGR RES, USDA, 61- *Res:* Soil microbiology; vascular wilt diseases; general diseases of shade trees and ornamental plants. *Mailing Add:* Nursery Crops Res Lab USDA 359 Main Rd Delaware OH 43015

SCHREIBER, MANUEL, b Rochester, NY, July 20, 22; m 57; c 1. TOXICOLOGY, PHYSIOLOGY. *Educ:* Ohio State Univ, BSc, 49; Univ Wis, MSc, 52, PhD(biochem & nutrit), 55. *Prof Exp:* Res asst nutrit, Dept Agr Biochem, Univ Wis, 50-55; res & clin biochemist, Dept Surg, Sch Med, Univ Buffalo, 57-60; res & clin biochemist, Dept Hemat & Path, Millard Fillmore Res Inst & Hosp, Buffalo, NY, 60-61; res biochemist, Food & Drug Admin, 61-62, res pharmacologist, Div Pharmacol, 62-81. *Concurrent Pos:* Fel physiol, Sch Med & Dent, Univ Rochester, 55-57. *Mem:* AAAS; Am Chem Soc; Am Asn Clin Chem; Soc Toxicol; fel Am Inst Chem. *Res:* Arsenical and heavy metal metabolism and toxicity; nutritional and environmental stresses, changes in homeostatic regulation; clinical, chemical, hematological and toxicological changes in disease processes; intermediary metabolism with hormonal imbalances; nutrition; broad spectrum studies on life-enhancing to life-threatening effects produced in experiments on heavy metal interactions in viable sub-cellular to whole animal systems using the various techniques of bio-medical disciplines. *Mailing Add:* 7032 Basswood Rd Frederick MS 22701

SCHREIBER, MARVIN MANDEL, b Springfield, Mass, Oct 17, 25; m 49; c 1. AGRONOMY, PLANT PHYSIOLOGY. *Educ:* Univ Mass, BS, 50; Univ Ariz, MS, 51; Cornell Univ, PhD(agron, plant physiol), 54. *Prof Exp:* Asst prof agron, Cornell Univ, 54-59; assoc prof, 59-73; PROF PLANT PHYSIOL, PURDUE UNIV, 73- *Concurrent Pos:* Res agronomist, Sci & Educ, Agr Res Serv, USDA, 56- *Mem:* AAAS; Am Soc Agron; Weed Sci Soc Am; Int Weed Sci Soc (pres, 79-81). *Res:* Phenology of weed species; integrated weed management; weed control in field crops; weed competition in field crops; microenvironment of weed competition. *Mailing Add:* Dept Bot & Plant Path Purdue Univ West Lafayette IN 47907

SCHREIBER, MELVYN HIRSH, b Galveston, Tex, May 28, 31; m 77; c 4. RADIOLOGY. *Educ:* Univ Tex, BA, 53, MD, 55. *Prof Exp:* From instr to assoc prof, 59-67, PROF RADIOL, UNIV TEX MED BR GALVESTON, 67- & CHMN RADIOL, 76- *Concurrent Pos:* Markle Found scholar, 63-68. *Mem:* Asn Univ Radiol; fel Am Col Physicians; fel Am Col Radiol; Am Fedn Clin Res; Radiol Soc NAm. *Res:* Cardiovascular and renal disease. *Mailing Add:* Dept of Radiol Univ of Tex Med Br Galveston TX 77550

SCHREIBER, PAUL J, b Buffalo, NY, June 23, 40; m 62; c 2. MOMENTUM SPACE WAVE FUNCTION. *Educ:* Univ Rochester, BS, 62; Univ Dayton, MS, 69; State Univ NY, Buffalo, PhD(physiol), 79. *Prof Exp:* PHYSICIST INFRARED DETECTORS & ELECTRO-OPTICS, AVIONICS LAB, ELECTRONICS TECHNOL DIV, AIR FORCE WRIGHT AERONAUT LAB, 62- *Mem:* Am Phys Soc. *Res:* Atomic structure of multi-electron atoms in momentum space; developing helium atom mometum space wave function; infrared heterodyne dectors and special properties of infrared detectors; helium compton profile; electro optics. *Mailing Add:* Wright Aeronaut Lab AADO-3 Wright Patterson AFB OH 45433

SCHREIBER, RALPH WALTER, b Wooster, Ohio, July 6, 42; m 72. ORNITHOLOGY, MARINE ECOLOGY. *Educ:* Col Wooster, BA, 64; Univ Maine, MS, 66; Univ SFla, PhD(marine biol), 74. *Prof Exp:* Res biologist, Smithsonian Inst, 66-69; GRANT ORNITH, NAT AUDUBON SOC, 74- *Concurrent Pos:* Pres, Seabird Res, Inc, 72-; adj res position, Univ SFla, 74-; mem, Brown Pelican Recovery Team, US Dept Interior, 75- *Mem:* Am Ornithologists Union; Wilson Ornith Soc; Cooper Ornith Soc. *Res:* Studies of the breeding biology of marine birds, primarily tropical species within the Pelecaniformes, Charadriiformes and Procellariiformes; specifically interested in controls on breeding cycles and population stability. *Mailing Add:* Dept of Biol Univ of SFla Tampa FL 33620

SCHREIBER, RICHARD KENT, vertebrate ecology, environmental science, see previous edition

SCHREIBER, RICHARD WILLIAM, b Lawrence, Mass, Apr 4, 17; m 47; c 1. BOTANY, CELL BIOLOGY. *Educ:* Univ NH, BS, 51, MS, 52; Univ Wis, PhD(bot), 56. *Prof Exp:* Instr biol, Exten Ctr, Univ Wis-Green Bay, 55-57; from asst prof to assoc prof, 57-67, PROF BOT, UNIV NH, 67- *Mem:* AAAS; Sigma Xi; NY Acad Sci; Am Soc Cell Biol. *Res:* Metabolic autonomy and evolution of chloroplasts; structure and function of the kinnetochore. *Mailing Add:* Dept of Bot Nesmith Hall Univ of NH Durham NH 03824

SCHREIBER, ROBERT ALAN, b Brooklyn, NY, Feb 11, 40; m 67; c 2. BIOLOGICAL PSYCHOLOGY, BEHAVIORAL GENETICS. *Educ:* Univ NC, Chapel Hill, BA, 65; Univ Colo, Boulder, MA, 69, PhD(psychol), 70. *Prof Exp:* Fel dept biochem, Med Univ SC, 70-74; asst prof, 74-80, ASSOC PROF BIOCHEM, UNIV TENN CTR HEALTH SCI, 80- *Concurrent Pos:* NIMH fel, Med Univ SC, 72-73. *Mem:* Soc Neurosci; Behavior Genetics Asn; Int Soc Develop Psychobiol. *Res:* Central nervous system hyperreactivity, using mice susceptible to sound-induced seizures; brain energy reserves which are immediately available; physical dependence on ethanol. *Mailing Add:* Dept of Biochem 800 Madison Ave Memphis TN 38163

SCHREIBER, SIDNEY S, b NY, May 1, 21; m 45; c 2. PHYSIOLOGY, NUCLEAR MEDICINE. *Educ:* City Col New York, BS, 41; NY Univ, MS, 45, MD, 49. *Prof Exp:* Instr physics, Townsend Harris, 41-42; instr biol, City Col New York, 42 & NY Univ, 45; instr histol, Hunter Col, 50; instr clin med, 59-64, from asst prof to assoc prof med, 64-74, PROF CLIN MED, SCH MED, NY UNIV, 74- *Concurrent Pos:* Clin asst, Mt Sinai Hosp, 52-58, sr clin asst, 58-; consult, internist, Radioisotope Unit, sr consult, Dept Nuclear Med, Vet Admin Hosp, Bronx, 52- & New York, 56-; instr, Hunter Col, 60-61. Metab; assoc ed, Alcoholism J. *Mem:* AAAS; fel Am Col Physicians; NY Acad Sci; Int Study Group Res Cardiac Metab; Int Soc Heart Res. *Res:* Nerve regeneration; endocrinology; effect of hormones on tissue growth; effect of anti-folic acid substance on tissue growth; electrolyte metabolism of heart muscle; use of radioactive isotopes in physiology; cation exchange of heart muscle; protein metabolism in heart muscle in stress, hypertension, alcohol and ischemia. *Mailing Add:* 122 E 36th St New York NY 10016

SCHREIBER, THOMAS PAUL, b Detroit, Mich, Mar 5, 24; m 53; c 4. ELECTRON MICROSCOPY. *Educ:* Univ Notre Dame, BS, 46; Univ Mich, MS, 48. *Prof Exp:* Qual control engr, US Rubber Co, 46; jr physicist, Physics & Instrumentation Dept, 47-49, from res physicist to sr res physicist, 49-59, STAFF RES SCIENTIST, ANAL CHEM DEPT, GEN MOTORS CORP, 59- *Mem:* AAAS; Am Vacuum Soc; Microbeam Anal Soc. *Res:* Electron probe microanalysis; scanning electron microscopy; surface analysis by electron spectroscopy; analytical electron microscopy. *Mailing Add:* Res Lab Anal Chem Gen Motors Tech Ctr Warren MI 48090

SCHREIBER, WILLIAM F(RANCIS), b New York, NY, Sept 18, 25. ELECTRONICS. *Educ:* Columbia Univ, BS, 45, MS, 47; Harvard Univ, PhD(appl physics), 53. *Prof Exp:* Jr engr, Sylvania Elec Prod, Inc, 47-49; res assoc, Harvard Univ, 53; res physicist, Technicolor Corp, 53-59; assoc prof, 59-68, prof, 68-79, BERNARD GORDON PROF ELEC ENG, MASS INST TECHNOL, 79- *Concurrent Pos:* Vis prof, Indian Inst Technol, Kanpur, 64-66; consult, Sylvania Elec Prod, Inc, 53, 60, Technicolor Corp, 59-62, Smithsonian Astrophys Observ, 61-64, Raytheon Corp, 62-64, ECRM, Inc, 68-78 & Addressograph-Multigraph, 78-; dir, Shintron Corp, 62- & ECRM, Inc, 68-78; vis prof, Univ Que, 80-81. *Mem:* Fel Inst Elec & Electronics Engrs. *Res:* Application of information theory to image transmission systems; image processing for the graphic arts; laser scanners. *Mailing Add:* 36-677 Dept of Elec Eng Mass Inst of Technol Cambridge MA 02139

SCHREIBER, WILLIAM LEWIS, b New York, NY, Aug 10, 43; m 66; c 2. ORGANIC CHEMISTRY. *Educ:* Mass Inst Technol, BS, 65; Univ Rochester, PhD(chem), 70. *Prof Exp:* Res assoc org chem, Rockefeller Univ, 69-71; PROJ CHEMIST ORG SYNTHESIS, INT FLAVORS & FRAGRANCES INC, 71- *Mem:* Am Chem Soc. *Res:* Fragrance chemical synthesis; terpene chemistry. *Mailing Add:* Int Flavors & Fragrances Inc 1515 Hwy 36 Union Beach NJ 07735

SCHREIBMAN, MARTIN PAUL, b New York, NY, Sept 18, 35; m 60; c 1. ZOOLOGY, COMPARATIVE ENDOCRINOLOGY. *Educ:* Brooklyn Col, BS, 56; NY Univ, MS, 59, PhD(biol), 62. *Prof Exp:* From instr to assoc prof, 62-72, PROF BIOL, BROOKLYN COL, 72-; RES ASSOC FISH ENDOCRINOL, NEW YORK AQUARIUM, NY ZOOL SOC, 66- *Concurrent Pos:* City Univ New York res grant, 77-81; NSF res grants, 65-70 & 77-80; res collabr, Brookhaven Nat Lab, 77-; NIH grants, 80- *Mem:* AAAS; Am Soc Zoologists; Endocrine Soc. *Res:* Comparative endocrinology of lower vertebrates, especially teleosts and relating to pituitary cytology and function; osmoregulation; melanogenesis; effects of hypophysectomy on endocrine functions; genetic control of sexual maturation and aging; hypothalamic-pituitary-gonadal axis. *Mailing Add:* Dept Biol Brooklyn Col Brooklyn NY 11210

SCHREIDER, BRUCE DAVID, b Denver, Colo, Mar 8, 46. CLINICAL PHARMACOLOGY, PHYSIOLOGY. *Educ:* Univ Chicago, BS, 68, MD & PhD(pharmacol & physiol), 75. *Prof Exp:* RES ASSOC TOXICOL, DEPT PHARMACOL & PHYSIOL SCI, UNIV CHICAGO, 75- *Mem:* AAAS; Sigma Xi. *Res:* Hepatic microsomal enzyme induction and inhibition by various therapeutic and environmental agents and the interactions between these agents. *Mailing Add:* 3630 N Bosworth Ave Chicago IL 60613

SCHREIER, ETHAN JOSHUA, b New York, NY, Sept 22, 43. ASTROPHYSICS, ASTRONOMY. *Educ:* City Univ New York, BS, 64; Mass Inst Technol, PhD(physics), 70. *Prof Exp:* Sr scientist, Am Sci & Eng, 70-73; physicist, Smithsonian Astrophys Observ, 73-81; CHIEF DATA & OPER SCIENTIST, SPACE TELESCOPE SCI INST, 81- *Mem:* Am Astron Soc. *Res:* X-ray astronomy. *Mailing Add:* Space Telescope Sci Inst Homewood Campus Baltimore MD 21218

SCHREIER, HANSPETER, b Basel, Switzerland, Nov 3, 41; Can citizen; m 70; c 1. SOIL & WATER CHEMISTRY. *Educ:* Univ Colo, BA, 70; Univ Sheffield, MSc, 73; Univ BC, PhD(geomorphol), 76. *Prof Exp:* Res asst chem, Sandoz Pharmaceut, 61-64; fel terrain sci, 77-79, ASST PROF, DEPT SOIL SCI, UNIV BC, 79- *Mem:* Am Soc Photogrammetry; Int Soc Soil Sci. *Res:* Water chemistry and sediments in river systems; terrain analysis, classification, and evaluation (numerical methods); remote sensing: soils and terrain emphasizing chemical properties. *Mailing Add:* Dept Soil Sci 2357 Main Hall Univ BC Vancouver BC V6T 2A2 Can

SCHREIER, STEFAN, b Vienna, Austria, July 21, 31; US citizen. GAS DYNAMICS, MECHANICAL ENGINEERING. *Educ:* Pa State Univ, BA, 53; Princeton Univ, MSE, 56; Univ Md, College Park, PhD(aerospace eng), 67. *Prof Exp:* Instr aeronaut eng, Univ Md, College Park, 56-59, instr math, 61-63; spec auditor, Harvard Univ, 66-67; ASSOC PROF MECH ENG, UNIV CONN, 67- *Concurrent Pos:* Assoc prof lectr, George Washington Univ, 63-64; consult, Systs Div, Avco Corp, 67-71; sci info adminr, NSF, 72. *Res:* Theoretical research in the area of compressible viscous flows; compressible unsteady, two and three dimensional laminar boundary layers; computation methods in gas dynamics; boundary layer theory. *Mailing Add:* Dept Mech Eng Univ Conn Storrs CT 06268

SCHREINER, ALBERT WILLIAM, b Cincinnati, Ohio, Feb 15, 26; m 53; c 1. INTERNAL MEDICINE, HEMATOLOGY. *Educ:* Univ Cincinnati, BS, 47, MD, 49. *Prof Exp:* Instr internal med, 55-59, asst clin prof, 59-62, assoc prof, 62-68, PROF MED, COL MED, UNIV CINCINNATI, 68-; DIR DEPT INTERNAL MED, CHRIST HOSP, 68- *Concurrent Pos:* Fel hemat, Cincinnati Gen Hosp, Ohio, 61-62, attend physician, 57-, clinician, Outpatient Dept, 57-62, chief clinician, 62-65; clin investr leukemia res, Vet Admin Hosp, Cincinnati, 57-59, chief med serv, 59-71, consult, 71-; consult to med dir, Ohio Nat Life. *Mem:* Am Col Physicians; Am Fedn Clin Res; NY Acad Sci. *Res:* Experimental viral oncogenesis in rodents. *Mailing Add:* 8525 Gwen Rd Cincinnati OH 45243

SCHREINER, ANTON FRANZ, b Apr 29, 37; US citizen; m 66; c 1. INORGANIC CHEMISTRY. *Educ:* Univ Detroit, BS, 61, MS, 63; Univ Ill, PhD(inorg chem), 67. *Prof Exp:* Res assoc, Univ Ill, 67-68; from asst prof to assoc prof, 68-76, grad adminr, 74-77, PROF CHEM, NC STATE UNIV, 76-, CHMN ANAL-INORG CHEM, 78- *Honors & Awards:* Outstanding Young Scientist Award, Sigma Xi, 73. *Mem:* Am Chem Soc; Sigma Xi; Royal Soc Chem. *Res:* Chemistry and magnetic circular dichroism of transition metals; magnetic circular luminescence; luminescence; crystal field, linear combination of atomic orbitals-molecular orbital, and normal coordinate theory applications; spectroscopy of inorganic materials; laser-optical semiconductor; 4d and 5d metal chemistry. *Mailing Add:* Dept of Chem NC State Univ Raleigh NC 27607

SCHREINER, CEINWEN ANN, b Philadelphia, Pa, May 27, 43. GENETICS, REPRODUCTION & TERATOLOGY. *Educ:* Muhlenberg Col, BS, 65; Univ NH, MS, 67, PhD(genetics), 72. *Prof Exp:* Res assoc teratol, E R Squibb & Sons, Inc, 67-69; prin scientist mutagenicity, McNeil Labs, Inc, 72-79; SUPVR GENETIC TOXICOL, MOBIL OIL CORP, 79- *Concurrent Pos:* Vchmn, Gordon Conf Genetic Toxicol, 81, chmn, 83. *Mem:* Environ Mutagen Soc; Genetics Soc Am; Teratol Soc; Am Col Toxicol; Genetic Toxicol Asn (treas). *Res:* Development of testing and research program in genetic toxicology to assess mutagenic and carcinogenic potential of petroleum products and to monitor environmental materials: techniques include bacterial invitro mammalian cell culture and animal testing; cytogenetics. *Mailing Add:* Toxicol Div Mobil Oil Corp PO Box 1029 Princeton NJ 18940

SCHREINER, ERIK ANDREW, b Hammonton, NJ, Dec 7, 35; m 60; c 3. MATHEMATICS. *Educ:* Wayne State Univ, BA, 58, MA, 60, PhD(math), 64. *Prof Exp:* Asst prof, 63-68, assoc prof, 68-79, PROF MATH, WESTERN MICH UNIV, 79- *Concurrent Pos:* Vis asst prof, Univ Mass, 67-68. *Mem:* Am Math Soc; Math Asn Am. *Res:* Lattice theory. *Mailing Add:* Dept Math Western Mich Univ Kalamazoo MI 49008

SCHREINER, FELIX, b Hamburg, Ger, Sept 28, 31; m 60, 69; c 2. PHYSICAL CHEMISTRY, INORGANIC CHEMISTRY. *Educ:* Univ Hamburg, Vordiplom, 54, dipl, 57, PhD(chem), 59. *Prof Exp:* Asst prof phys chem, Univ Kiel, 59-61; resident res assoc & fel, 61-63, asst chemist, 63-65, ASSOC CHEMIST, ARGONNE NAT LAB, 65- *Mem:* Am Chem Soc. *Res:* Thermodynamics; low-temperature calorimetry; noble gas chemistry; inorganic fluorine chemistry; energy research. *Mailing Add:* Chem Div Argonne Nat Lab Argonne IL 60439

SCHREINER, GEORGE E, b Buffalo, NY, Apr 26, 22; m 48; c 8. MEDICINE, PHYSIOLOGY. *Educ:* Canisius Col, AB, 43; Georgetown Univ, MD, 46; Am Bd Internal Med, dipl, 55. *Prof Exp:* Intern, Med Serv, Boston City Hosp, 46-47; asst physiol, Sch Med, NY Univ-Bellevue Med Ctr, 47-48, instr, 48-50; sr resident med, Mt Alto Hosp, 50-51; clin instr, 51-52, from instr to assoc prof, 52-61, PROF MED, GEORGETOWN UNIV, 61- *Concurrent Pos:* Fel physiol, NY Univ-Bellevue Med Ctr, 49-50; dir renal clin, Georgetown Univ Hosp, 52-59, nephrol div, 59-72 & clin study unit, 61-72; mem, Nat Res Coun, 60-63; chmn, Nat Drug Res Bd Comt for Armed Forces Inst Path Registry Adverse Reactions, 63, mem subcomt drug efficacy, 66; Secy-Gen, Int Cong Nephrology, 63-66; mem, Nat Kidney Found Sci Adv Bd & chmn, DC Chap, 63-68, pres, 68-70, chmn, Nat Adv Bd, 70-; mem, Nat Coun Regional Med Progs, Dept Health, Educ & Welfare; chmn comn res in nephrol, Vet Admin, 72-, mem merit rev bd, nephrol; consult, NIH, Walter Reed Army Med Ctr, Vet Admin Hosp & Nat Naval Med Ctr; ed-in-chief, Trans, Soc Artificial Internal Organs, 55- & Nephron, Int Soc Nephrology, 63-72; nephrol registry, 78- *Mem:* Am Fedn Clin Res (secy-treas, 58-61, pres elect, 61-62, pres, 62-63); Soc Artificial Internal Organs (secy-treas, 56-58, pres elect, 58-59, pres, 59-60); Am Soc Nephrology (secy, 66, pres, 71); AAAS; Int Soc Nephrology (pres-elect, 75, pres, 78-81). *Res:* Clinical nephrology; internal medicine; renal physiology; hemodialysis; dialysis of poisons; renal homotransplantation, biopsy and pathology; pyelonephritis; nephrotic syndrome. *Mailing Add:* Georgetown Univ Sch of Med Washington DC 20007

SCHREINER, PHILIP ALLEN, b Duluth, Minn, Sept 29, 43. EXPERIMENTAL HIGH ENERGY PHYSICS. *Educ:* Univ Calif, Los Angeles, BS, 65, MS, 66, PhD(physics), 70. *Prof Exp:* Fel, Argonne Nat Lab, 71-73, asst physicist high energy physics, 73-77, physicist, 77-81; MEM TECH STAFF, BELL LABS, 81- *Mem:* Am Phys Soc. *Res:* Neutrino interactions. *Mailing Add:* Bell Labs Naperville IL 60540

SCHREIWEIS, DONALD OTTO, b Tacoma, Wash, July 27, 41. COMPARATIVE ANATOMY, VERTEBRATE EMBRYOLOGY. *Educ:* Univ Puget Sound, AB, 63, MS, 66; Wash State Univ, PhD(zool), 72. *Prof Exp:* Asst prof biol, Univ Puget Sound, 71-72; asst prof biol, Univ Nev, Las Vegas, 72-77; chairperson & assoc prof biol, Gonzaga Univ, 77-81; DIR PREPROFESSIONAL HEALTH STUDIES, ST LOUIS UNIV, 81- *Mem:* Am Soc Zoologists; Soc Syst Zool; Am Ornith Union; Am Soc Mammal; Am Soc Ichthyologists & Herpetologists. *Res:* Comparative myological studies of birds and bats using numerical methods; comparative vertebrate morphology; teratogenic effects of herbicides, pesticides and heavy metals on vertebrate development. *Mailing Add:* Preprofessional Health Studies St Louis Univ St Louis MO 63103

SCHREMP, FREDERIC WILLIAM, b Utica, NY, Aug 14, 16; m 48, 58; c 4. PHYSICAL CHEMISTRY. *Educ:* Rensselaer Polytech Inst, BS, 42; Univ Wis, PhD(phys chem), 50. *Prof Exp:* Res elec engr, Am Steel & Wire Co, 42-44; res chemist, Oak Ridge Nat Lab, 44-45; sr res assoc, Chevron Oil Field Res Co, Standard Oil Co, Calif, 50-81; CONSULT. *Mem:* Am Chem Soc. *Res:* Rheology of high polymers; oil field drilling fluid; corrosion. *Mailing Add:* Chevron Res Co Box 446 La Habra CA 90631

SCHRENK, GEORGE L, b Seymour, Ind, Nov 28, 37; m 59. ENGINEERING. *Educ:* Ind Univ, BS, 58, MS, 59, PhD(theoret physics), 63. *Hon Degrees:* MA, Univ Pa, 71. *Prof Exp:* Sr res assoc, Inst Direct Energy Conversion, Univ Pa, 63-65, chief plasma eng br, 64-66, asst prof, 65-68, assoc dir comput ctr, 66-69, assoc prof eng, Towne Sch Civil & Mech Eng, 68-80, assoc prof, Moore Sch Elec Eng, 70-80; ENG CONSULT, 60- *Concurrent Pos:* Adj assoc prof mech eng & appl mech, Univ Pa, 80- *Mem:* Am Phys Soc; Am Soc Mech Engrs; Inst Elec & Electronics Engrs; Asn Comput Mach. *Res:* Computational engineering physics; computer applications in engineering: radio engineering; optical analysis procedures and simulation of solar-thermal energy conversion systems; mathematical modeling and simulation; direct energy conversion; thermal engineering; solar-thermal energy conversion; surface physics. *Mailing Add:* Dept of Mech Eng & Appl Mech Univ of Pa Philadelphia PA 19174

SCHRENK, WILLIAM GEORGE, b Hiawatha, Kans, July 13, 10; m 32; c 2. CHEMISTRY. *Educ:* Western Union Col, AB, 32; Kans State Col, MS, 36, PhD(chem), 45. *Prof Exp:* Teacher, High Schs, Iowa, 32-38; from instr to assoc prof, Univ, 38-51, asst chemist, Exp Sta, 43-51, PROF CHEM, KANS STATE UNIV & CHEMIST, EXP STA, 51- *Mem:* AAAS; Am Chem Soc; Soc Appl Spectros. *Res:* Minor elements in plants; physical methods in chemical analysis; spectroscopy for analytical purposes; instrumental techniques in analysis; atomic absorption spectroscopy; flame emission spectroscopy. *Mailing Add:* Dept of Chem Kans State Univ Manhattan KS 66506

SCHREUDER, GERARD FRITZ, b Modan, Indonesia, Apr 4, 37; Dutch citizen; m 61; c 2. FOREST ECONOMICS. *Educ:* State Agr Univ Wageningen, MS, 60; NC State Univ, MS, 67; Yale Univ, PhD(econ), 68. *Prof Exp:* Asst expert aerial photos, Orgn Am States, 61-64; asst prof opers res, Yale Univ, 67-70; assoc prof, 71-75, prof forestry, 75-77, PROF FORESTRY RESOURCES & DIR FOREST RESOURCES MGT STUDIES, UNIV WASH, 77- *Concurrent Pos:* Dir res, Univ Wash, 72-; mem comt renewable resources for indust mat, Nat Acad Sci, 75-76. *Mem:* AAAS; Neth Inst Agr Engrs. *Res:* Forest resource modelling; aerial photo interpretation as related to environmental impacts and animal damage; forest resource economics. *Mailing Add:* Col of Forest Resources Univ of Wash Seattle WA 98195

SCHREURS, JAN W H, b Winterswijk, Netherlands, Feb 10, 32; m 56; c 5. PHYSICAL CHEMISTRY, MAGNETIC RESONANCE. *Educ:* Free Univ, Amsterdam, BSc, 53, MSc, 57, PhD(phys chem), 62. *Prof Exp:* Res assoc chem, Columbia Univ, 57-59; res fel, Nat Res Coun Can, 60-62; RES ASSOC PHYS PROPERTIES RES DEPT, CORNING GLASS WORKS, 62- *Mem:* NY ACAD SCI; Am Phys Soc. *Res:* Electron spin resonance and magnetic susceptibility of glasses and glass ceramics. *Mailing Add:* Phys Properties Res Dept Corning Glass Works Corning NY 14831

SCHREYER, JAMES MARLIN, b Asheville, NC, Dec 26, 15; m 51; c 3. CHEMISTRY. *Educ:* Univ NC, AB, 38; Ore State Col, PhD(inorg chem), 48. *Prof Exp:* Teacher, High Sch, NC, 38-41; inspector powder & explosives, Radford Ord Works, Va, 41-42; chem engr & area chief inspector, Badger Ord Works, Wis, 42-43; process engr, US Rubber Co, NC, 43-44; res engr, Sulphonics, Inc, Md, 44-45; asst, Ore State Col, 45-47; asst prof chem, Univ Ky, 48-50, prof, 50-51; sr chemist, Oak Ridge Nat Lab, 51-53; sr chemist, Union Carbide Nuclear Co, 53-78, head, Develop Dept, 78-80, sr tech adv, Union Carbide Corp, 80-82; SR MEM STAFF, OAK RIDGE NAT LAB, 82- *Res:* Properties of ferrates; preparation and analysis of potassium ferrate; ferrate oxidimetry; spectrophotometric studies cobalt-2 in alkaline solution; solubility of uranium-6 and -4 phosphates in phosphate solution; clean room technology; cleaned moon box and associated hardware for Apollo moon landings; solar energy technology; installation of solar water heaters. *Mailing Add:* Y-12 Plant Union Carbide Nuclear Co Oak Ridge TN 37830

SCHREYER, RALPH COURTENAY, b Washington, DC, July 27, 19; m 44; c 2. ORGANIC POLYMER CHEMISTRY. *Educ:* Cath Univ Am, BA, 41; Purdue Univ, PhD(chem), 46. *Prof Exp:* Res chemist, Polychem Dept, Exp Sta, DE, 46-60, tech assoc, Eastern Lab, Explosives Dept, NJ, 60-68, sr res chemist, Polymer Intermediates Dept, 68-73, staff chemist, 73-76, patent assoc, 76-78, PATENT ASSOC, PETROCHEM DEPT, E I DU PONT DE NEMOURS & CO, INC, 78- *Mem:* Am Chem Soc. *Res:* Synthesis of flurocarbons; reactions of carbon monoxide and carbon monoxide and hydrogen with organic compounds; synthesis of nylon intermediates; polymerization of ethylene and fluoro-olefins. *Mailing Add:* Petrochem Dept Exp Sta E I du Pont de Nemours & Co Inc Wilmington DE 19898

SCHRIBER, STANLEY OWEN, b St Boniface, Man, July 20, 40; m 62; c 2. ACCELERATOR PHYSICS. *Educ:* Univ Man, BSc, 62, MSc, 63; McMaster Univ, PhD(physics), 67. *Prof Exp:* Asst res off, 66-70, assoc res off, 71-75, SR RES OFF, CHALK RIVER NUCLEAR LABS, ATOMIC ENERGY CAN LTD, 76- *Concurrent Pos:* Guest scientist, Los Alamos Nat Lab, 77 & 78-79 & Kek Lab High Energy Physics, Japan, 81; consult, Argonne Nat Lab, 80, Inst Fur Kernphysik, Karlspruhe, Ger, 80. *Mem:* Can Asn Physicists; Am Phys Soc. *Res:* Design, construction and testing of pulsed and continuous wave linear accelerations; charged particle beam dynamics; beam diagnostics; radio frequency systems and beam dynamics; practical uses of accelerator beams. *Mailing Add:* Accelerator Physics Br Chalk River Nuclear Labs Chalk River ON K0J 1J0 Can

SCHRIBER, THOMAS J, b Flint, Mich, Oct 28, 35; m 67. COMPUTER SCIENCE, MATHEMATICS. *Educ:* Univ Notre Dame, BS, 57; Univ Mich, MSE, 58, AM, 59, PhD(chem eng), 64. *Prof Exp:* Asst prof math, Eastern Mich Univ, 63-66; from asst prof to assoc prof mgt sci, 66-72, chmn dept statist & mgt sci, 70-72 & 75-78, PROF MGT SCI, UNIV MICH, ANN ARBOR, 72- *Concurrent Pos:* Consult, Ford Motor Co, 66, 71 & 74, Stanford Res Inst, 73, Int Tel & Tel, 74 & CPC Int, 77. *Mem:* Inst Mgt Sci; Am Inst Decision Sci; Soc Comput Simulation; Asn Comput Mach; fel Am Inst Decision Sci. *Res:* Computer applications in management science, information systems and data processing, especially discrete-event simulation, numerical methods and optimization. *Mailing Add:* 2116 Dorset Rd Ann Arbor MI 48104

SCHRICKER, ROBERT LEE, b Davenport, Iowa, June 28, 28; m 56; c 3. VETERINARY MEDICINE, MICROBIOLOGY. *Educ:* Iowa State Univ, DVM, 52; Univ Ill, Urbana, MS, 58, PhD(vet sci), 61; Am Col Vet Microbiol, dipl. *Prof Exp:* Pvt pract, 52-54; res vet, US Army Biol Labs, 61-71; MEM VET BIOL STAFF, USDA, 71- *Mem:* Am Vet Med Asn; Conf Res Workers Animal Dis; Sigma Xi; Am Soc Microbiol. *Res:* Precipitating antigens of leptospires; pathogenesis of zoonotic infectious diseases in primates; pathology and clinical biochemistry; veterinary biologics. *Mailing Add:* USDA-APHS-VS-VB Fed Ctr Bldg Hyattsville MD 20782

SCHRIEFFER, JOHN ROBERT, b Oak Park, Ill, May 31, 31; m 60; c 3. PHYSICS. *Educ:* Mass Inst Technol, BS, 53; Univ Ill, MS, 54, PhD(physics), 57. *Hon Degrees:* Dr rer nat, Munich Tech Univ, 68; Dr es Sci, Univ Geneva, 68; DSc, Univ Pa, 73, Univ Ill, 74 & Univ Cincinnati, 77. *Prof Exp:* NSF fel, Univ Birmingham & Inst Theoret Physics, Univ Copenhagen, 57-58; asst prof physics, Univ Chicago, 57-60; from asst prof to assoc prof, Univ Ill, 59-62; prof, 62-64, MARY AMANDA WOOD PROF PHYSICS, UNIV PA, 64-; PROF UNIV CALIF-SANTA BARBARA, 80-, MEM, INST THEORET PHYSICS, 81- *Concurrent Pos:* Guggenheim fel, 66-67; Andrew D White prof-at-lg, Cornell Univ, 67-73; Exxon fac fel, 79- *Honors & Awards:* Nobel Prize in Physics, 72; Comstock Prize, Nat Acad Sci, 68; Oliver E Buckley Solid State Physics Prize, Am Phys Soc, 68. *Mem:* Nat Acad Sci; Am Acad Arts & Sci; Am Philos Soc; fel Am Phys Soc. *Res:* Theoretical solid state physics, especially superconductivity; surface physics; general theory of many body problem; magnetism; low dimensional conductors; nonlinear phenomena. *Mailing Add:* Dept of Physics Univ of Pa Philadelphia PA 19104

SCHRIEMPF, JOHN THOMAS, b Sandusky, Ohio, July 6, 34; m 57. SOLID STATE PHYSICS. *Educ:* Carnegie Inst Technol, BS, 56, MS, 60, PhD(physics), 64. *Prof Exp:* Instr physics, Carnegie Inst Technol, 60-63; res physicist, 63-81, SUPVR, CONDENSED MATTER & RADIATION SCI DIV, US NAVAL RES LAB, 81- *Concurrent Pos:* Vis res scholar, Univ Calif, Irvine, 68-69. *Mem:* AAAS; Sigma Xi; Am Phys Soc; Am Asn Physics Teachers. *Res:* Transport properties, especially thermal conductivity of metals and alloys; transport properties of metals at high temperatures, especially in the liquid state; interaction between laser radiation and metallic systems. *Mailing Add:* US Naval Res Lab Code 6600 Washington DC 20375

SCHRIER, EUGENE EDWIN, b New York, NY, May 24, 34; m 70. PHYSICAL BIOCHEMISTRY. *Educ:* Kenyon Col, AB, 55; Rensselaer Polytech Inst, PhD(phys chem), 61. *Prof Exp:* Vis instr chem, Kenyon Col, 60-61; res assoc, Cornell Univ, 61-63; from asst prof to assoc prof, State Univ NY Binghamton, 63-74, prof chem, 74-80, chmn dept, 78-80. *Concurrent Pos:* NIH fel, 62-63; Mayo Found fel, 77-78; adj prof chem, State Univ NY Binghamton, 80- *Mem:* Am Soc Biol Chemists; Am Chem Soc. *Res:* Structure and thermodynamic properties of water and aqueous solutions; ion-nonelectrolyte interactions in solution; protein denaturation; biological calcification. *Mailing Add:* Dept of Chem State Univ of NY Binghamton NY 13901

SCHRIER, MELVIN HENRY, b Brooklyn, NY, Dec 13, 27; m 50; c 2. CHEMISTRY. *Educ:* Brooklyn Col, BS, 51. *Prof Exp:* Chemist, Pittsburg Testing Lab, 51-53; chemist, Otto B May Inc, Newark, NJ, 53-59, head chemist, Anal Sect, 59-70, mgr, Anal Dept, 70-79; GROUP LEADER, US TESTING CO, HOBOKEN, NJ, 80- *Mem:* Am Chem Soc. *Res:* Analytical research in dyestuff and intermediates. *Mailing Add:* 64 Barbara St Staten Island NY 10306

SCHRIER, STANLEY LEONARD, b New York, NY, Jan 2, 29; m 53; c 3. MEDICINE. *Educ:* Univ Colo, AB, 49; Johns Hopkins Univ, MD, 54; Am Bd Internal Med, dipl. *Prof Exp:* From instr to assoc prof, 59-72, PROF MED, MED CTR, STANFORD UNIV, 72-, HEAD DIV HEMAT, 68- *Concurrent Pos:* Markel scholar acad med, 61-66; consult, Palo Alto Vet Admin Hosp. *Mem:* Am Fedn Clin Res; Am Soc Hemat; Int Soc Hemat; Am Soc Clin Invest. *Res:* Metabolism and transport of red cell membranes; properties of erythrocyte membranes in health, disease and aging. *Mailing Add:* Stanford Univ Med Ctr 300 Pasteur Dr Stanford CA 94305

SCHRIESHEIM, ALAN, b NY, Mar 8, 30; m 53; c 2. ORGANIC CHEMISTRY. *Educ:* Polytech Inst Brooklyn, BS, 51; Pa State Univ, PhD(org chem), 54. *Prof Exp:* Res chemist, Nat Bur Standards, 54-56; res chemist, Exxon Res & Eng Co, 56-58, sr chemist, 58-59, res assoc, 59-63, sect head, 63-65, asst dir, 65-66, asst mgr, 66-69, dir chem sci lab, 69-75, dir corp res labs, 75-78, GEN MGR TECHNOL DEPT, EXXON RES & ENG CO, 78- *Concurrent Pos:* Mem adv bd, Corp Vis Comt for Dept Chem, Mass Inst Technol, CHEMTECH & Stanford Energy Inst; co-chmn, Assembly Math & Phys Sci Comt on Chem Sci, Nat Res Coun, Indust Adv Comt-Rutgers Univ, Solid State Sci Adv Panel & Pure & Appl Chem Deleg to the People's Republic of China, Nat Acad Sci, 78. *Honors & Awards:* Petrol Chem Award, Am Chem Soc, 69; Karcher Silver Medalist Lectr. *Mem:* AAAS; Am Chem Soc (secy, Div Petrol Chem, 72-75); Sigma Xi; fel NY Acad Sci; fel Am Inst Chemists. *Res:* Kinetics and mechanism of acid and base catalyzed organic reactions including alkylation, isomerization, hydrogenation and polymerization. *Mailing Add:* Exxon Res & Eng Co PO Box 45 Linden NJ 07036

SCHRIEVER, BERNARD ADOLF, b Ger, Sept 14, 10; nat US; m 38; c 3. AERONAUTICAL ENGINEERING. *Educ:* Agr & Mech Col, Tex, BS, 31; Stanford Univ, MA, 42. *Hon Degrees:* DSc, Rider Col & Creighton Univ, 58, Adelphi Col, 59, Rollins Col, 61; LLD, Loyola Univ, Calif, 62, C W Post Col, Long Island, 65; DrAeroSci, Univ Mich, 62; DrEng, Polytech Inst Brooklyn, 62, PMC Cols, 66. *Prof Exp:* US Air Force, 32-66, chief staff, Far East Air Serv Command, 43-44, comdr adv echelon, 44-45, chief plans & policy div, Res & Develop, 45-49, asst opers, Develop Planning, 50-54, asst to comdr, Air Res & Develop Command, 54-59, comdr, 59-61, Air Force Systs Command, 61-66; indust consult, 66-71; CHMN BD, SCHRIEVER & McKEE INC, 71- *Mem:* Nat Acad Eng. *Res:* Advanced technology in aerospace missions. *Mailing Add:* Schriever & McKee Inc 1899 L St NW Ste 405 Washington DC 20036

SCHRIEVER, RICHARD L, b Salt Lake City, Utah, Nov 22, 40; m 61; c 3. PHYSICS. *Educ:* Univ Utah, BS, 63, PhD(elec eng), 67. *Prof Exp:* Res engr, Lawrence Livermore Lab, 67-74; br chief, Laser Fusion Br, US Am Eng Comn, 74-76; dep dir, Off Inertial Fusion, Energy Res & Develop Admin, 76-77; dep dir, 77-81, DIR, OFF INERTIAL FUSION, US DEPT ENERGY, 81- *Mem:* Inst Elec & Electronics Engrs; Am Phys Soc. *Res:* Physics of laser and particle beam driven inertial fusion; application of inertial fusion to nuclear explosives and fusion power. *Mailing Add:* US Dept Energy Washington DC 20545

SCHRILS, RUDOLPH, nuclear physics, deceased

SCHRIRO, GEORGE R, b New York, NY, Sept 3, 21; m 48; c 4. APPLIED MATHEMATICS, AERODYNAMICS. *Educ:* NY Univ, BS, 47, MA, 50. *Prof Exp:* Night mgr, Western Union Tel Co, NY, 36-42; instr math, Wash Univ, St Louis, 48-49; teacher high sch, NJ, 49-51; chmn math dept, NY, 51-56; STRUCTURAL ANALYST, DYNAMICIST & SR ENGR, GRUMMAN AEROSPACE CORP, 56- *Concurrent Pos:* Adj asst prof math, C W Post Col, Long Island Univ, 62-80, adj assoc prof, 80- *Mem:* Math Asn Am; Am Inst Aeronaut & Astronaut. *Res:* Stability and control; aeroelastic effects; dynamic analysis; stress and fatigue. *Mailing Add:* 121 Prospect St Farmingdale NY 11735

SCHROCK, GOULD FREDERICK, b Rockwood, Pa, Apr 23, 36; m 57; c 2. BOTANY, MYCOLOGY. *Educ:* Indiana Univ Pa, BS, 57, MEd, 61; Univ Chicago, PhD(bot), 64. *Prof Exp:* Joint high sch teacher, Ind, 58-61; assoc prof bot, Kutztown State Col, 64-68; PROF BOT, INDIANA UNIV PA, 68- *Mem:* Mycol Soc Am; Bot Soc Am; Int Soc Human & Animal Mycol; Am Inst Biol Sci; Am Hort Soc. *Res:* Factors influencing growth and development of human pathogenic fungi; succession of fungi in selected natural environments. *Mailing Add:* Dept Biol Indiana Univ Pa Indiana PA 15705

SCHROCK, RICHARD ROYCE, b Berne, Ind, Jan 4, 45. ORGANOMETALLIC CHEMISTRY. *Educ:* Univ Calif, Riverside, AB, 67; Harvard Univ, PhD(chem), 71. *Prof Exp:* NSF fel, Cambridge Univ, 71-72; res chemist, Cent Res & Develop Dept, E I du Pont de Nemours & Co, Inc, 72-75; asst prof chem, 75-78, assoc prof, 78-80, PROF CHEM, MASS INST TECHNOL, 80- *Concurrent Pos:* A P Sloan fel, 76-80; Dreyfus teacher-scholar, 78-83. *Mem:* Am Chem Soc. *Res:* Synthetic and mechanistic organo-transition metal chemistry; homogeneous catalysis; early transition metal chemistry; metal-alkyl, metal-carbene and metal-carbyne complexes; reduction of carbon monoxide; olefin metathesis; olefin polymerization; acetylene metathesis. *Mailing Add:* Mass Inst of Technol 6-331 77 Massachusetts Ave Cambridge MA 02139

SCHROCK, VIRGIL E(DWIN), b San Diego, Calif, Jan 22, 26; m 46; c 2. NUCLEAR ENGINEERING. *Educ:* Univ Wis, BS, 46, MS, 48; Univ Calif, ME, 52. *Prof Exp:* Instr mech eng, Univ Wis, 46-48; lectr mech eng, 48-51, asst prof, 54-58, from asst prof to assoc prof nuclear eng, 58-68, asst dean res, 68-74, PROF NUCLEAR ENG, UNIV CALIF, BERKELEY, 68- *Concurrent Pos:* Vis res fel, Ctr Info, Studies & Exp, Milan, Italy, 62-63 & 74-75; consult to indust & govt; tech ed, J Heat Transfer, Am Soc Mech Engrs, chmn, Heat Transfer Div, 78-, chmn, Nat Heat Transfer Conf Coord Comn, 80-81; vchmn & chmn elect, Thermal Hydraulics Div, Am Nuclear Soc, 81-82. *Mem:* Fel Am Nuclear Soc; fel Am Soc Mech Engrs. *Res:* Thermodynamic and transport properties of fluids; heat transfer and fluid dynamics; boiling and two-phase flow; thermal design of nuclear power plants; environmental aspects of nuclear power; safety analysis of nuclear systems; resources conservation and planning. *Mailing Add:* Dept Nuclear Eng Univ Calif Berkeley CA 94720

SCHRODER, GENE DAVID, b Atascadero, Calif, Oct 25, 44. ECOLOGY. *Educ:* Rice Univ, BA, 67, MA, 70; Univ NMex, PhD(ecol), 74. *Prof Exp:* Asst prof, 74-80, ASSOC PROF ECOL, SCH PUB HEALTH, UNIV TEX, HOUSTON, 80- *Concurrent Pos:* Adj assoc prof ecol, Rice Univ, Houston, 79- *Mem:* Ecol Soc Am; Am Soc Mammalogists. *Res:* Dynamics of species interactions with particular interests in competition among desert rodents and factors regulating urban rodent populations. *Mailing Add:* Sch of Pub Health Univ of Tex PO Box 20186 Houston TX 77025

SCHRODER, JACK SPALDING, b Atlanta, Ga, Jan 17, 17; m 38; c 5. INTERNAL MEDICINE. *Educ:* Georgetown Univ, AB, 37; Emory Univ, MD, 41; Am Bd Internal Med & Am Bd Gastroenterol, dipl. *Prof Exp:* Assoc prof, 58-67, PROF MED, SCH MED, EMORY UNIV, 67- *Concurrent Pos:* Consult, Atlanta Vet Admin Hosp & Third Army Sr Surgeon; civilian consult. *Mem:* Am Gastroenterol Asn; fel Am Col Physicians. *Res:* Gastroenterology; clinical medicine. *Mailing Add:* Emory Univ Clin Atlanta GA 30322

SCHRODER, KLAUS, b Celle, Ger, Nov 1, 28; m 57; c 2. SOLID STATE PHYSICS, MATERIALS SCIENCE. *Educ:* Univ Marburg, Vordiplom, 51; Univ Gottingen, Dr rer nat, 54- *Prof Exp:* Res officer, Commonwealth Sci & Indust Res Orgn, Univ Melbourne, 55-58; res assoc mining & metall eng, Univ Ill, 58-60, res asst prof, 60-61; assoc prof metall eng, 61-68, PROF METALL, SYRACUSE UNIV, 68- *Mem:* Am Soc Metals; Am Phys Soc; Am Asn Univ Prof; Sigma Xi. *Res:* Magnetic memory; plastic properties of metals; specific heat; Hall and Seebeck effects of transition element alloys; optical properties of alloys; crack studies. *Mailing Add:* Dept of Mat Sci Syracuse Univ Syracuse NY 13210

SCHRODER, VINCENT NILS, b Chicago, Ill, Dec 8, 20; m 59; c 4. PLANT PHYSIOLOGY. *Educ:* Univ Ga, BSA, 48; Duke Univ, PhD(plant physiol), 56. *Prof Exp:* Asst prof, 55-69, ASSOC PROF AGRON, UNIV FLA, 69- *Mem:* Am Soc Agron; Am Soc Plant Physiologists. *Res:* Plant mineral nutrition; effects of environment on photosynthesis; soil temperature effects on plant growth. *Mailing Add:* Dept of Agron Univ Fla Inst Food & Agr Sci Gainesville FL 32611

SCHRODT, JAMES THOMAS, b Louisville, Ky, Oct 7, 37; m; c 2. CHEMICAL ENGINEERING, MATHEMATICS. *Educ:* Univ Louisville, BChE, 60, PhD(chem eng), 66; Villanova Univ, MChE, 62. *Prof Exp:* Jr engr, Tenn Eastman Co, 60; instr chem eng, Univ Louisville, 62-65; sr res engr, Tenn Eastman Co, 65-66; asst prof, 66-72, ASSOC PROF CHEM ENG, UNIV KY, 72- *Mem:* Am Chem Soc; Am Inst Chem Engrs. *Res:* Simultaneous heat and mass transfer; thermodynamics; electrodialysis. *Mailing Add:* Dept of Chem Eng Univ of Ky Lexington KY 40506

SCHRODT, VERLE N(EWTON), b Muscatine, Iowa, Apr 26, 33; m 55; c 8. CHEMICAL ENGINEERING. *Educ:* Univ Ill, Urbana, BS, 55; Pa State Univ, MS, 58, PhD(chem eng), 61. *Prof Exp:* Supvr, Appl Sci Labs, Inc, 56-61; sr res engr, 61-67, eng fel, 67-77, SR ENG FEL, MONSANTO CO, ST LOUIS, 77- *Mem:* Am Inst Chem Engrs. *Res:* Mathematical modeling of chemical and biological systems; design of agricultural growth facilities; image processing; x-ray analysis. *Mailing Add:* 1565 Zurich Dr Florissant MO 63031

SCHROEDER, ALFRED C(HRISTIAN), b West New Brighton, NY, Feb 28, 15; wid; c 1. ELECTRICAL ENGINEERING, COLORIMETRY. *Educ:* Mass Inst Technol, BS & MS, 37. *Prof Exp:* Mem tech staff, David Sarnoff Res Ctr, RCA Corp, 37-80. *Honors & Awards:* David Sarnoff Gold Medal Award, Soc Motion Picture & TV Engrs, 65; Vladimir K Zworykin Award, Inst Elec & Electronics Engrs, 71. *Mem:* AAAS; fel Inst Elec & Electronics Engrs; Soc Motion Picture & TV Engrs; Optical Soc Am; Sigma Xi. *Res:* Sequential, simultaneous, and simultaneous subcarrier color television systems; tri-color tubes; mechanism of color vision. *Mailing Add:* Apt I 114 Pennswood Village Newtown PA 18940

SCHROEDER, ALICE LOUISE, b Knoxville, Tenn, June 22, 41; m 66. GENETICS. *Educ:* Univ Colo, Boulder, BA, 63; Stanford Univ, PhD(biol, genetics), 70. *Prof Exp:* NIH fel, 69-70; lectr genetics, 71, asst prof, 71-78, ASSOC PROF GENETICS, WASH STATE UNIV, 78- *Concurrent Pos:* NIH res grants, 71-74, 78-80 & 79-82. *Mem:* AAAS; Genetics Soc Am; Am Women Sci. *Res:* DNA maintenance systems; recombination; genetics of radiation sensitivity; fungal, bacterial and viral genetics. *Mailing Add:* Genetics Prog Wash State Univ Pullman WA 99163

SCHROEDER, ALLEN C, b Cincinnati, Ohio, Oct 30, 41; m 65; c 3. ANIMAL PHYSIOLOGY, COMPARATIVE ENDOCRINOLOGY. *Educ:* Loyola Col, Md, BS, 63; Cath Univ Am, MS & PhD(physiol), 68. *Prof Exp:* Asst prof, 67-74, ASSOC PROF BIOL, GETTYSBURG COL, 74- *Mem:* AAAS; Am Soc Zoologists; Am Micros Soc; Am Inst Biol Sci. *Res:* Neuroendocrinology of poikilotherms. *Mailing Add:* Dept of Biol Gettysburg Col Gettysburg PA 17325

SCHROEDER, ANITA GAYLE, b Wichita, Kans. APPLIED STATISTICS. *Educ:* Baker Univ, BS, 66; Kans State Univ, MS, 68; Ore State Univ, PhD(statist), 72. *Prof Exp:* Proj dir, Ark Health Statist Ctr, 72-73; dir, Emergency Med Serv Data & Eval, Ark Health Systs Found, 73-74; pres, Schroeder & Assocs, 74-75; STATISTICIAN, WESTAT, INC, 75-, DIR, SOCIAL SCI SERV, 79- *Concurrent Pos:* Asst prof biomet, Univ Ark Med Ctr, 72-74. *Mem:* Sigma Xi; Am Statist Asn; Biomet Soc. *Res:* Surveys in social services and health; evaluation. *Mailing Add:* Westat Inc 1650 Res Blvd Rockville MD 20850

SCHROEDER, CHARLES ARTHUR, b St Paul, Minn, Jan 25, 13; m 43; c 2. BOTANY. *Educ:* Univ Calif, Los Angeles, BA, 35, MA, 36, PhD(hort sci), 43. *Prof Exp:* Asst, Col Agr, 39-43, from instr to assoc prof subtrop hort, 43-59, prof bot, 43-80, EMER PROF BOT, UNIV CALIF, LOS ANGELES, 80- *Concurrent Pos:* Plant explor, Mex, 47, 48, 50, 52-58 & 62. *Mem:* Soc Econ Bot; Am Inst Biol Sci; Asn Trop Biol. *Res:* Plant morphology and physiology; economic botany; horticulture. *Mailing Add:* Dept of Biol Univ of Calif Los Angeles CA 90024

SCHROEDER, DANIEL JOHN, b Manitowoc, Wis, Sept 23, 33; m 55; c 2. ASTRONOMY, OPTICS. *Educ:* Beloit Col, BS, 55; Univ Wis, MS, 57, PhD(physics), 60. *Prof Exp:* Res assoc astron, Univ Wis, 60-63; asst prof physics, 63-68, assoc prof physics & astron, 68-74, PROF PHYSICS & ASTRON, BELOIT COL, 74- *Concurrent Pos:* Telescope scientist, Space Telescope Proj, NASA. *Mem:* Am Astron Soc; Am Asn Physics Teachers; Optical Soc Am; Int Astron Union. *Res:* Optical spectroscopy and instrumentation; astronomical optics and space astronomy. *Mailing Add:* Dept of Physics Beloit Col Beloit WI 53511

SCHROEDER, DAVID HENRY, b Indianapolis, Ind, Feb 16, 40; m 62; c 2. BIOCHEMICAL PHARMACOLOGY. *Educ:* Purdue Univ, West Lafayette, BS, 62, MS, 66, PhD(biochem), 68. *Prof Exp:* Res assoc chem pharmacol, NIH, 68-70; RES BIOCHEMIST, WELLCOME RES LABS, 70- *Mem:* Am Chem Soc. *Res:* Distribution and metabolism of drugs; effects of various chemicals and conditions upon drug metabolism; development of analytical methods for detection and quantitation of drugs and metabolites. *Mailing Add:* Wellcome Res Lab-Med Biochem 3030 Cornwallis Rd Research Triangle Park NC 27709

SCHROEDER, DOLORES MARGARET, b New York, NY, July 30, 37. NEUROANATOMY. *Educ:* Notre Dame Col, BS, 58; John Carroll Univ, MS, 63; Case Western Reserve Univ, PhD(anat), 70. *Prof Exp:* Fel neurosurg, Med Sch, Univ Va, 70-72; from instr to asst prof, 72-75; assoc prof, 75-80, TENURED ASSOC PROF MED SCI, SCH MED, IND UNIV, BLOOMINGTON, 80- *Mem:* Soc Neurosci; Am Asn Anat; AAAS; Int Brain Res Orgn. *Res:* Comparative neuroanatomy; development and organization of mesencephalon, diencephalon and telecephalon. *Mailing Add:* Dept of Med Sci Myers Hall Ind Univ Bloomington IN 47401

SCHROEDER, DUANE DAVID, b Newton, Kans, Nov 4, 40; m 61; c 3. BIOCHEMISTRY. *Educ:* Bethel Col, AB, 62; Tulane Univ, PhD(biochem), 67. *Prof Exp:* Damon Runyon fel, Mass Inst Technol, 67-69; sr res biochemist, 69-71, biochem res supvr, 71-73, mgr biochem res, 73-80, ASSOC DIR, BIOCHEM RES & DEVELOP, CUTTER LABS, INC, 80- *Concurrent Pos:* Res fel, Bayer AG, Ger, 75. *Mem:* AAAS. *Res:* Enzyme active sites and structure/function relationships; plasma proteins for use in replacement therapy; hepatitis transmission. *Mailing Add:* Cutter Labs Inc Biochem Res & Develop Dept 4th & Parker Sts PO Box 1986 Berkeley CA 94710

SCHROEDER, FRANK, JR, b Bartlesville, Okla, Sept 8, 27; m 49; c 2. NUCLEAR REACTOR SAFETY, REACTOR REGULATION. *Educ:* Univ Ill, BS, 49, MS, 51. *Prof Exp:* Asst physics, Univ Ill, 49-51; physicist, Atomic Energy Div, Phillips Petrol Co, 51-57, supvr Spert-3 reactor exps, 57-60, mgr, Spert Proj, 60-66, reactor safety prog officer, 66-68; dep dir div reactor licensing, US AEC, 68-72, asst dep tech rev directorate of licensing, 72-75; dep dir, Div Tech Rev, 75-76, dep dir, Div Systs Safety, 76-80, ASST DIR, GENERIC PROJS, DIV SAFETY TECHNOL OFF NUCLEAR REACTOR REGULATION, US NUCLEAR REGULATORY COMN, 80- *Mem:* Fel Am Nuclear Soc. *Res:* Nuclear reactor safety and kinetics; reactor physics; nuclear engineering. *Mailing Add:* 802 S Belgrade Rd Silver Spring MD 20902

SCHROEDER, FRIEDHELM, b Kastorf, Ger, July 16, 47; US citizen; m 79. MEMBRANE LIPID ASYMMETRY, ATHEROSCLEROSIS. *Educ:* Univ Pittsburgh, BS, 70; Mich State Univ, PhD(biochem), 74. *Prof Exp:* NSF fel biochem, Mich State Univ, 70-74; Am Cancer Soc fel biol chem, Med Sch, Washington Univ, 74-76; ASST PROF PHARMACOL, SCH MED, UNIV MO, 76- *Concurrent Pos:* Prin investr grants, Am Heart Asn, 77-, Nat Cancer Inst, 78-, Pharmaceut Mfg Asn, 78-80, & Hereditary Dis Found, 80-; consult, Miles Res Labs, 76, Hemotropic Dis Group, 80-, & Hormel Inst, 81; mem, Am Heart Asn Arteriosclerosis Coun, 78- *Mem:* Am Soc Pharmacol & Exp Therapeut; Am Soc Biol Chemists; Soc Neurosci; Am Oil Chemists Soc. *Res:* Structure and function of lipids in membranous particles (plasma membranes and lipoproteins) from cancer cell, blood, brain, liver and skin fibroblasts; biochemical, biophysical (fluorescence and differential scanning calorimetry), and pharmacological methods. *Mailing Add:* Dept Pharmacol Sch Med Univ Mo Columbia MO 65212

SCHROEDER, HANSJUERGEN ALFRED, b Lautawerk, Ger, Jan 21, 26; nat US; m 53. ORGANIC CHEMISTRY. *Educ:* Univ Berlin, BS, 49, MS, 50; Univ Freiburg, PhD(chem), 53. *Prof Exp:* Asst chem, Univ Berlin, 48-50, instr, 51; res assoc, 52-56, sr res chemist, 57-58, res specialist, 59-63, sect mgr, 64-69, venture mgr, 70-72, mgr res & develop, 73-74, DIR PROD RES, OLIN CORP, 75- *Mem:* Am Chem Soc; Ger Chem Soc. *Res:* Organic synthetic chemistry; nitrogen heterocycles; fluorine, boron and phosphorous compounds; pesticides; lubricants; high temperature polymers, biocides; pool chemicals; product development. *Mailing Add:* Apt A3 609 Mix Ave Hamden CT 06514

SCHROEDER, HARTMUT RICHARD, b Hitzdorf, Ger, Aug 29, 42; US citizen; m 72. BIOCHEMISTRY. *Educ:* Youngstown Univ, BS, 66; Pa State Univ, MS, 70, PhD(biochem), 72. *Prof Exp:* Res assoc biochem, Mich State Univ, 72-74; res scientist, 74-80, SR RES SCIENTIST BIOCHEM, AMES DIV, MILES LABS, INC, 80- *Mem:* Am Chem Soc; Am Soc Photobiol. *Res:* Bioluminescence, chemiluminescence and fluorescence, competitive protein binding reactions, enzyme assays and immunochemistry. *Mailing Add:* Immunochem Sect Ames Div Miles Labs 1127 Myrtle St Elkhart IN 46514

SCHROEDER, HERBERT AUGUST, b Cleveland, Ohio, Feb 26, 30; m 63; c 3. ORGANIC CHEMISTRY. *Educ:* Univ Idaho, BS, 52, MS, 54; Univ Hamburg, DSc(org chem), 60. *Prof Exp:* Res chemist, Forest Prod Lab, US Forest Serv, 61-63; asst prof forest prod chem, Forest Res Lab, Ore State Univ, 63-68; assoc prof, 68-69, PROF WOOD CHEM, FOREST & WOOD SCI, COLO STATE UNIV, 79- *Mem:* Am Chem Soc; Soc Wood Sci & Technol; Tech Asn Pulp & Paper Indust. *Res:* Chemistry of wood carbohydrates, wood polyphenolics and pulping processes; chemical treatment of wood; wood adhesives; biomass conversion to energy and chemicals. *Mailing Add:* Dept of Forest & Wood Sci Colo State Univ Ft Collins CO 80523

SCHROEDER, HERMAN ELBERT, b Brooklyn, NY, July 6, 15; m 38; c 4. ORGANIC CHEMISTRY, POLYMER CHEMISTRY. *Educ:* Harvard Univ, AB, 36, AM, 37, PhD(chem), 39. *Prof Exp:* Res chemist, Exp Sta, E I du Pont de Nemours & Co, Inc, 38-45, res chemist, Jackson Lab, 45-46, group leader, 46-49, head miscellaneous dyes div, 49-51, asst dir lab, 51-57, asst dir res, Elastomer Chem Dept, 57-63, res dir, 63-65, dir res & develop, 65-80; PRES, SCHROEDER SCI SERV INC, 80- *Concurrent Pos:* Chmn res comt & trustee, Univ Del Res Found; sci consult, Metropolitan Mus Art, 80- *Mem:* AAAS; Am Chem Soc; Soc Chem Indust; Royal Soc Chem; AAAS. *Res:* Catalysis; resins; adhesives; polymers; rubber chemicals; color photography; vat dyes; pigments; application of dyes; fluorine chemicals; textile chemicals; elastomers; discovery and development of new elastomeric polymers and intermediates. *Mailing Add:* Rte 2 Box 122 Hockessin DE 19707

SCHROEDER, JOHN, b Pardan, Yugoslavia, Aug 31, 38; US citizen; m 64; c 2. HIGH PRESSURE PHYSICS. *Educ:* Univ Rochester, BS, 62, MS, 64; Catholic Univ Am, PhD(physics), 74. *Prof Exp:* Res & develop officer, Atmospheric Effects Div, Defense Atomic Support Agency, 67-70; res asst, Catholic Univ Am, 70-74; physicist, Acoustics Div, Naval Res Lab, 74-75; res assoc, dept chem, Univ Ill, 75-78; physicist, Corp Res & Develop, Gen Elec Co, 78-81; ASSOC PROF PHYSICS, RENSSELAER POLYTECH INST, 82- *Concurrent Pos:* Sr staff mem, Mats Res Lab, Univ Ill, 76-78. *Mem:* Am Phys Soc; Optical Soc Am. *Res:* Brillouin, raman and rayleigh spectroscopy with emphasis on amorphous solids (glasses) and liquids; high pressure research; behavior of materials under extreme conditions of pressure and temperature; optical properties of glasses, fiber optics. *Mailing Add:* Dept Physics Rensselaer Polytech Inst Troy NY 12181

SCHROEDER, JOHN SPEER, b South Bend, Ind, May 6, 37. CARDIOLOGY. *Educ:* Univ Mich, MD, 62; Am Bd Internal Med, dipl, 69; Am Bd Cardiovasc Dis, dipl, 73. *Prof Exp:* Intern, 62-63, resident internal med, 65-67, asst prof med & cardiol, 70-77, ASSOC PROF MED & CARDIOL, MED CTR, STANFORD UNIV, 77-, DIR INTENSIVE CARDIAC CARE UNIT, 73- *Concurrent Pos:* Fel cardiol, Med Ctr, Stanford Univ, 67-69. *Mem:* Am Fedn Clin Res; fel Am Col Cardiol; NY Acad Sci; fel Am Col Physicians. *Res:* Cardiac transplantation; coronary artery spasm; calcium antagonists; coronary artery disease. *Mailing Add:* Cardiol Div Stanford Univ Hosp Stanford CA 94305

SCHROEDER, JUEL PIERRE, b New England, NDak, Jan 23, 20; m 43, 77. ORGANIC CHEMISTRY. *Educ:* Univ NDak, BS, 41; Univ Wis, PhD(chem), 48. *Prof Exp:* Anal chemist, Org Chem Div, Monsanto Co, 42-43, res chemist, Plastics Div, 43-46; res chemist, Union Carbide, 48-58, asst dir res & develop, Plastics Div, 58-63; Robert A Welch fel, Univ Tex, 63-65; assoc prof chem, Univ NC, Greensboro, 65-68, prof, 68-80. *Mem:* Fel AAAS; Am Chem Soc. *Res:* Liquid crystals; polymer chemistry; imidates and orthoesters. *Mailing Add:* 1435 Sylvan Ridge Rd Indianapolis IN 46240

SCHROEDER, KLAUS GERHARD, radar systems, communication systems, see previous edition

SCHROEDER, LAUREN ALFRED, b Long Prairie, Minn, Feb 24, 37; m 60; c 2. ECOLOGY. *Educ:* St Cloud State Col, BS, 60; Univ SDak, MA, 65, PhD(zool), 68. *Prof Exp:* From asst prof to assoc prof, 68-76, PROF BIOL, YOUNGSTOWN STATE UNIV, 76- *Mem:* AAAS; Am Inst Biol Sci; Ecol Soc Am; Entom Soc Am. *Res:* Ecological energetics of Lepidoptera especially as related to plant defense mechanisms and growth performance of larvae; population dynamics; ecosystem structure. *Mailing Add:* Dept Biol Youngstown State Univ Youngstown OH 44503

SCHROEDER, LEE S, b Braddock, Pa, Apr 11, 38; m 57; c 4. ELEMENTARY PARTICLE PHYSICS, HIGH ENERGY NUCLEAR COLLISIONS. *Educ:* Drexel Inst, 61; Ind Univ, Bloomington, MS, 63, PhD(physics), 66. *Prof Exp:* Assoc physics, Iowa State Univ, 65-67, asst prof, 67-71; res physicist, 71-76, STAFF SCIENTIST, LAWRENCE BERKELEY

LAB, 76- *Concurrent Pos:* Assoc, Ames Lab, AEC, 65-67, assoc physicist, 67-71. *Mem:* Am Phys Soc. *Res:* Experimental elementary particle physics, particularly the use of bubble chamber, counters, and spark chambers to study the strong interactions of the elementary particles; high energy ions. *Mailing Add:* 1135 Juanita Dr Walnut Creek CA 94595

SCHROEDER, LELAND ROY, b Caledonia, Minn, June 26, 38; m 60; c 2. ORGANIC CHEMISTRY. *Educ:* Ripon Col, AB, 60; Inst Paper Chem, MS, 62, PhD(org chem), 65. *Prof Exp:* From asst prof to assoc prof, 65-77, PROF ORG CHEM, INST PAPER CHEM, 77-, ASSOC DEAN, 80- *Concurrent Pos:* Instr, George Washington Univ, 65-66. *Mem:* Am Chem Soc; The Chem Soc. *Res:* Reaction mechanisms, syntheses and analyses of carbohydrates. *Mailing Add:* Inst of Paper Chem PO Box 1039 Appleton WI 54911

SCHROEDER, LEON WILLIAM, b Guthrie, Okla, Jan 25, 21; m 42; c 2. ASTROPHYSICS, ASTRONOMY EDUCATION. *Educ:* Okla State Univ, BS, 47, MS, 48; Ind Univ, PhD(astrophys), 58. *Prof Exp:* From instr to assoc prof, 47-69, PROF PHYSICS, OKLA STATE UNIV, 69- *Concurrent Pos:* Guest investr, Dominion Astrophys Observ, 60; vis assoc prof, Northwestern Univ, 61-62; guest observer, Dyer Observ, 64; vis astronr, Kitt Peak Nat Observ, 71. *Mem:* Am Astron Soc. *Res:* Stellar spectrophotometry and photoelectric photometry; scanner energy distributions; education. *Mailing Add:* Dept Physics Okla State Univ Stillwater OK 74078

SCHROEDER, LEROY WILLIAM, b Watertown, Wis, July 18, 43; m 67; c 1. PHYSICAL CHEMISTRY, BIOPHYSICS. *Educ:* Wartburg Col, BA, 64; Northwestern Univ, Evanston, PhD(phys chem), 69. *Prof Exp:* Nat Res Coun-Nat Bur Standards assoc, 69-71, res assoc, Am Dent Asn Res Div, 71-74, head dent crystallog, Am Dent Asn Health Found, Nat Bur Standards, 74-77; proj scientist, Div Chem & Physics, 77-80, RES CHEMIST, BUR RADIOL HEALTH, FOOD & DRUG ADMIN, 80- *Mem:* Am Chem Soc; Am Crystallog Asn. *Res:* Molecular structure and dynamics; thermodynamics; chemical processes; hydrogen bonding; diffusion in solids. *Mailing Add:* Bur Radiol Health HFX-120 5600 Fishers Lane Rockville MD 20857

SCHROEDER, MANFRED ROBERT, b Ahlen, Ger, July 12, 26; nat US; m 56; c 3. PHYSICS. *Educ:* Univ Goettingen, dipl, 51, Dr rer nat(physics), 54. *Hon Degrees:* Dr, Univ Maine, Le Mans, France, 82. *Prof Exp:* Sci asst microwaves & acoustics, Univ Goettingen, 52-54; mem tech staff, Bell Tel Labs, Inc, 54-58, head acoustics res, 58-63, dir, Acoustics & Speech Res Lab, 63-64, dir, Acoust, Speech & Mech Res Lab, 64-69; PROF PHYSICS & DIR THIRD PHYSICS INST, UNIV GOETTINGEN, 69- *Honors & Awards:* Gold Medal, Audio Eng Soc, 72; W R G Baker Prize Award, Inst Elec & Electronics Engrs, 75; Sr Award Speech & Signal Processing, Inst Elec & Electronics Engrs, 79. *Mem:* Fel Acoust Soc Am; fel Audio Eng Soc; fel Inst Elec & Electronics Engrs; Ger Phys Soc; foreign sci mem Max Planck Soc. *Res:* Speech communication; room acoustics; psycho-acoustics; electro-acoustics; coherent optics; spatial stochastic processes; digital signal processing. *Mailing Add:* Univ Goettingen Third Physics Inst Buergerstrasse 42/44 34 Goettingen Germany, Federal Republic of

SCHROEDER, MARK EDWIN, b Cincinnati, Ohio, July 31, 46; m 68; c 1. INSECT PHYSIOLOGY. *Educ:* Loyola Col, BS, 68; Purdue Univ, PhD(entom), 74. *Prof Exp:* Res fel insect physiol, Univ Calif, Riverside, 74-75; RES ENTOMOLOGIST, SHELL DEVELOP CO, 75- *Mem:* AAAS; Entom Soc Am; Am Soc Zoologists. *Res:* Design and execution of experiments to investigate, on a suborgan level, the mode of action of selected neurotoxins on the insect central nervous system. *Mailing Add:* Shell Develop Co PO Box 4248 Modesto CA 95352

SCHROEDER, MELVIN CARROLL, b Saskatoon, Sask, July 19, 17; nat US; m 42; c 2. GEOLOGY. *Educ:* Wash State Univ, BS, 42, MS, 47, PhD(geol), 53. *Prof Exp:* Geologist, US Geol Surv, 49-54; from asst prof to assoc prof, 54-63, PROF GEOL, TEX A&M UNIV, 63- *Mem:* Fel Geol Soc Am; Nat Asn Geol Teachers; Am Asn Petrol Geologists. *Res:* Ground water; radiohydrology; water contamination. *Mailing Add:* Dept Geol Tex A&M Univ College Station TX 77843

SCHROEDER, MICHAEL ALLAN, b Little Falls, NY, Nov 13, 38. ORGANIC CHEMISTRY, PHYSICAL CHEMISTRY. *Educ:* Union Col, NY, BS, 61; Johns Hopkins Univ, PhD(chem), 68. *Prof Exp:* Res chemist, Naval Weapons Ctr, 67-68; RES CHEMIST, US ARMY BALLISTIC RES LABS, 68- *Concurrent Pos:* Resident res assoc, Nat Res Coun, 67-68. *Mem:* AAAS; Am Chem Soc; Am Defense Preparedness Asn. *Res:* Organic mechanisms; chemistry of organic nitro and nitroso compounds; heteroaromatic chemistry; explosive and propellant chemistry; laser spectroscopy; chemistry of high-nitrogen compounds; deamination chemistry. *Mailing Add:* US Army Ballistic Res Labs Aberdeen Proving Ground MD 21005

SCHROEDER, PAUL CLEMENS, b Brooklyn, NY, Aug 13, 38; m 66. EXPERIMENTAL ZOOLOGY. *Educ:* St Peter's Col, NJ, BS, 60; Stanford Univ, PhD(biol sci), 66. *Prof Exp:* NSF fel zool, Univ Calif, Berkeley, 66-67, USPHS fel, 67-68; asst prof, 68-73, ASSOC PROF ZOOL, WASH STATE UNIV, 73- *Concurrent Pos:* Alexander Von Humboldt Found fel, Zool Inst, Univ Cologne, 74-75. *Mem:* AAAS; Am Soc Cell Biol; Am Soc Zool; Am Inst Biol Sci. *Res:* Hormonal control of developmental and reproductive processes primarily in polychaete worms, echinoderms and amphibians. *Mailing Add:* Dept Zool Wash State Univ Pullman WA 99164

SCHROEDER, PETER A, b Dunedin, NZ, Dec 6, 28; m 53; c 2. PHYSICS. *Educ:* Univ Canterbury, MSc, 50; Bristol Univ, PhD(physics), 55. *Prof Exp:* Asst lectr physics, Univ Canterbury, 54-56, lectr, 56-59; fel, Nat Res Coun Can, 59-60, asst res officer, 60-61; from asst prof to assoc prof, 61-69, PROF PHYSICS, MICH STATE UNIV, 69- *Mem:* Brit Inst Physics; Am Phys Soc. *Res:* Electron transport properties of metals and alloys, especially thermopower and high field galvanomagnetic effects. *Mailing Add:* Dept of Physics Mich State Univ East Lansing MI 48824

SCHROEDER, ROBERT SAMUEL, b Chicago, Ill, July 9, 43; m 65; c 2. PESTICIDE CHEMISTRY, ORGANIC BIOCHEMISTRY. *Educ:* Iowa State Univ, BS, 64; Ind Univ, Bloomington, PhD(chem), 70. *Prof Exp:* Res chemist, 69-75, actg sect supvr, 74-75, SECT SUPVR, GULF OIL CHEM CO, 76- *Mem:* Am Chem Soc; Plant Growth Regulator Working Group; Sigma Xi; Coun Agr Sci & Technol; Royal Soc Chem. *Res:* Pesticide metabolism and disposition in plants, animals, soil and water; development of residue methods for pesticides; application of instrumental analysis for structure determinations; direction of analytical biochemistry and environmental research. *Mailing Add:* Gulf Oil Chem Co 9009 W 67th St Merriam KS 66201

SCHROEDER, ROY ALLEN, b Hutchinson, Kans, July 12, 42. OCEANOGRAPHY, ORGANIC GEOCHEMISTRY. *Educ:* Bethel Col, BS, 64; Univ Calif, Berkeley, MS, 66, San Diego, PhD(oceanog), 74. *Prof Exp:* Instr geol, Yale Univ, 74-76; asst prof, Univ Utah, 76-78; hydrologist water quality, US Geol Surv, 78-82; ADJ PROF ENG, UNIV CALIF, IRVINE, 82- *Res:* Dating of sediments and fossils; hydrology research including water quality problems associated with contamination by organic chemicals and acid rain. *Mailing Add:* Dept Civil Eng Univ Calif Irvine CA 92717

SCHROEDER, RUDOLPH ALRUD, b Evansville, Minn, Oct 11, 23; m 66. PHYSICAL CHEMISTRY. *Educ:* NDak Agr Col, BS, 52, MS, 53; Univ Md, PhD(chem), 57. *Prof Exp:* Asst prof chem, Univ Ky, 57-58; from asst prof to assoc prof, 58-74, PROF CHEM, UNIV SOUTHWESTERN LA, 74- *Mem:* Am Chem Soc. *Res:* Infrared and Raman spectroscopy; hydrogen and interatomic bonding; bond energies; metal chelates; quantum mechanics. *Mailing Add:* 805 Myrtle Pl Blvd Lafayette LA 70506

SCHROEDER, THOMAS DEAN, b Reedsburg, Wis, May 2, 39; m 63; c 2. ANALYTICAL CHEMISTRY. *Educ:* Univ Wis-Platteville, BS, 65; Univ Iowa, MS, 68, PhD(anal chem), 69. *Prof Exp:* ASSOC PROF CHEM, SHIPPENSBURG STATE COL, 69- *Concurrent Pos:* Pa teaching fel, 81. *Mem:* Am Chem Soc; Sigma Xi. *Res:* Chemical instrumentation; gas chromatographic-mass spectrometry of biochemicals; construction of specific electrodes; flameless atomic absorption. *Mailing Add:* Dept Chem Box F305 Shippensburg State Col Shippensburg PA 17257

SCHROEDER, W(ILBURN) CARROLL, b Tell City, Ind, Mar 22, 06; m 45; c 2. CHEMICAL ENGINEERING. *Educ:* Univ Mich, BS, 30, MSE, 31, PhD, 33. *Prof Exp:* From chem engr to chief officer synthetic liquid fuels, US Bur Mines, 33-50, asst dir, 50-52; PROF CHEM ENG, UNIV MD, COLLEGE PARK, 52- *Concurrent Pos:* Consult, 52- *Mem:* Am Chem Soc; Am Inst Chem Engrs. *Res:* Combustion and utilization of fuels; chemicals from gas, oil, and coal; conversion of solid fuels to gaseous and liquid fuels; gasification; evaluation of experimental programs on fuels. *Mailing Add:* Dept of Chem Eng Univ of Md College Park MD 20740

SCHROEDER, WALTER ADOLPH, b Kansas City, Mo, Apr 30, 17; m 49; c 2. PROTEIN CHEMISTRY. *Educ:* Univ Nebr, BSc, 39, MA, 40; Calif Inst Technol, PhD(chem), 43. *Prof Exp:* Res fel, 42-46, sr res fel, 45-56, res assoc, 56-81, SR RES ASSOC CHEM, CALIF INST TECHNOL, 81- *Concurrent Pos:* Guggenheim fel, 59-60. *Res:* Carotenoids in plants; chromatographic separation of amino acids, peptides and proteins; propellants; organic chemistry; proteins; structure and function of hemoglobin and heme proteins. *Mailing Add:* Div of Chem & Chem Eng Calif Inst of Technol Pasadena CA 91125

SCHROEDER, WALTER ARTHUR, b Wheaton, Ill, Aug 14, 27; m 52; c 2. POLYMER CHEMISTRY, ORGANIC CHEMISTRY. *Educ:* Bradley Univ, BS, 51; Univ Notre Dame, MS, 55; Univ Pa, PhD(org chem), 59. *Prof Exp:* Res chemist res & develop, E I du Pont de Nemours & Co, Inc, 57-61; proj leader, Nalco Chem Co, 61-65; MGR, FIRESTONE & TEXTILES FIBERS CO, FIRESTONE TIRE & RUBBER CO, HOPEWELL, VA, 65- *Mem:* Sigma Xi. *Res:* Polymer and fibers research managment. *Mailing Add:* 12633 Percival St Chester VA 23831

SCHROEDER, WARREN LEE, b Longview, Wash, Jan 3, 39; m 61; c 3. SOILS, CIVIL ENGINEERING. *Educ:* Wash State Univ, BS, 62, MS, 63; Univ Colo, Boulder, PhD(civil eng), 67. *Prof Exp:* From asst prof to assoc prof, 67-77, PROF CIVIL ENG, ORE STATE UNIV, 77-, ASST DEAN ENG, 71- *Concurrent Pos:* Staff engr, McDowell & Assocs, Consult Engrs, 66-67 &CH2M/Hill, Consult Engrs, 67-70; pres, Willamette Geotechnical, Inc, 78- *Mem:* Am Soc Civil Engrs; Int Soc Soil Mech & Found Engr. *Res:* Deep foundations; retaining structures; behavior of submerged cohesionless soils; cofferdams and docks. *Mailing Add:* Dept of Civil Eng Ore State Univ Corvallis OR 97331

SCHROEDER, WILLIAM, JR, b New York, NY, Apr 9, 27; m 58; c 3. ORGANIC CHEMISTRY. *Educ:* Purdue Univ, BS, 55, PhD(chem), 58. *Prof Exp:* Res assoc org chem, Upjohn Co, 58-65; dir res, 65-66, vpres res, 66-75, secy, 68-75, vpres, 75-78, DIR, BURDICK & JACKSON LABS, MUSKEGON, MI, 75-, PRES, 78- *Mem:* Am Chem Soc. *Res:* Structures; natural products; carbohydrates; organic synthesis. *Mailing Add:* 667 Lake Forest Lane North Muskegon MI 49441

SCHROEDER, WILLIAM HENRY, b Breslau, Ger, Apr 27, 44; Can citizen; m 75; c 1. ATMOSPHERIC CHEMISTRY. *Educ:* Univ Alta, Calgary, BSc, 66; Univ Colo, PhD(chem), 71. *Prof Exp:* Res fel, Fresenius Inst, Wiesbaden, Fed Repub Ger, 71-72; head, Abstracting Sect, Environ Sci, Air Pollution Control Directorate, Ottawa, 73-75; phys scientist, Technol Develop & Demonstr, Water Pollution Control Directorate, Burlington, 75-77; RES SCIENTIST ATMOSPHERIC CHEM, ATMOSPHERIC ENVIRON SERV, ENVIRON CAN, DOWNSVIEW, ONT, 77- *Concurrent Pos:* Sci liaison officer, Energy Recovery Demonstration Proj, Environ Can contract, St Lawrence Cement Co, Mississauga, Ont, 76-77; sci authority, Environ Can Contract, Barringer Res Inc, 80-82. *Mem:* Am Chem Soc; Chem Inst Can; Air Pollution Control Asn; Am Soc Testing & Mat. *Res:* Atmospheric pathways (sources, transport, transformation and fate); characteristics (physics-chemical, toxicological) of toxic trace elements and organic substances; environmental analytical chemistry. *Mailing Add:* Environ Can Atmospheric Environ Serv 4905 Dufferin St Downsview ON M3H 5T4 Can

SCHROEER, DIETRICH, b Berlin, Ger, Jan 24, 38; US citizen; m 64; c 2. PHYSICS. *Educ:* Ohio State Univ, BSc, 60, PhD(physics), 65. *Prof Exp:* NATO fel, Munich Tech Univ, 65-66; asst prof, 66-73, assoc prof, 73-79, PROF PHYSICS, UNIV NC, CHAPEL HILL, 79- *Concurrent Pos:* Fulbright fel & Nat Endowment for Humanities fel, Munich, Ger, 72-73. *Honors & Awards:* Am Inst Physics-US Steel Sci Writing Award, 72. *Mem:* AAAS; Am Asn Physics Teachers; Am Phys Soc; Soc for Social Studies of Sci. *Res:* Low energy nuclear spectroscopy; crystal-defect and radiation-damage studies by Mossbauer effect; science and policy. *Mailing Add:* Dept of Physics Univ of NC Chapel Hill NC 27514

SCHROEER, JUERGEN MAX, b Berlin, Ger, Oct 2, 33; US citizen; m 64; c 4. SOLID STATE PHYSICS, MASS SPECTROMETRY. *Educ:* Ohio State Univ, BS & MS, 58; Cornell Univ, PhD(physics), 64. *Prof Exp:* Res assoc quantum electronics, Sch Elec Eng, Cornell Univ, 64-65; asst prof physics, Univ Wyo, 65-69; assoc prof, 69-74, PROF PHYSICS, ILL STATE UNIV, 74- *Concurrent Pos:* Vis prof & Fulbright travel grant, Univ Münster, 75. *Mem:* Am Phys Soc; Am Vacuum Soc; Am Soc Mass Spectrometry; Am Asn Physics Teachers; AAAS. *Res:* Surface physics; secondary ion mass spectrometry. *Mailing Add:* Dept of Physics Ill State Univ Normal IL 61761

SCHROEN, WALTER, b Munich, Ger, June 3, 30; m 67; c 2. SOLID STATE PHYSICS. *Educ:* Univ Munich, BS, 52, MS, 56; Clausthal Tech Univ, PhD(atomic physics), 62. *Prof Exp:* Physicist, Cent Res Labs, Siemens Corp, 53-55 & Semiconductor Div, 56-58; res asst physics, Clausthal Tech Univ, 58-62; sr scientist semiconductor res, Int Tel & Tel Semiconductors, Calif, 62-65; sect head semiconductor res & develop labs, 65-75, MGR SEMICONDUCTOR GROUP PROCESS CONTROL, TEX INSTRUMENTS INC, 75- *Concurrent Pos:* Ger co-rep, Int Seminar Nucelar Sci, Saclay, France, 59. *Mem:* Am Phys Soc; Ger Phys Soc; Electrochem Soc. *Res:* Semiconductor and surface physics; physics of failure in electronics; analysis and modeling; thin films physics; superconductivity; physics of ionization; bipolar and metal-oxide semiconductor devices; semiconductor process control. *Mailing Add:* Semiconductor Qual & Tex Instruments PO Box 225012 Dallas TX 75265

SCHROEPFER, GEORGE JOHN, JR, b St Paul, Minn, June 15, 32. BIOCHEMISTRY, CHEMISTRY. *Educ:* Univ Minn, BS, 55, MD, 57, PhD, 61. *Prof Exp:* Intern med, Univ Minn, 57-58, Nat Heart Inst res fel, 58-61; res assoc, Univ Minn, 61-63, asst prof biochem, 63-64; asst prof, Univ Ill, Urbana, 64-67, from assoc prof to prof biochem & org chem, 67-72, dir sch basic med sci, 68-70; PROF BIOCHEM & CHEM & CHMN DEPT BIOCHEM, RICE UNIV, 72- *Concurrent Pos:* USPHS res career develop award, 62-64; fel, Harvard Univ, 62-63; fel, Coun Arteriosclerosis, Am Heart Asn, 64-; mem panel biochem nomenclature, Nat Acad Sci, 65-; assoc ed, Lipids, 69-78; mem biochem training comt, NIH, 70-73. *Mem:* NY Acad Sci; fel AAAS; Am Chem Soc; Am Soc Biol Chem. *Res:* Sterol biosynthesis and metabolism; intermediary metabolism of lipids; stereochemistry and mechanism of enzymatic reactions. *Mailing Add:* Dept of Biochem Rice Univ Houston TX 77001

SCHROER, RICHARD ALLEN, b Celina, Ohio, July 10, 44; m 72; c 2. CLINICAL PATHOLOGY. *Educ:* Kent State Univ, BS, 66, PhD(chem), 70. *Prof Exp:* Res assoc biochem, Univ Calif, Irvine-Calif Col Med, 71-73; dir biol, Nelson Res & Develop, 73-75; sr res biologist, 75-76, GROUP LEADER CLIN CHEM/HEMAT, LEDERLE LABS, 76- *Concurrent Pos:* NIH fel, Univ Calif, Irvine-Calif Col Med, 71-73. *Mem:* AAAS; Am Asn Clin Chemists. *Res:* Toxicology; clinical pathology of laboratory animals. *Mailing Add:* Lederle Labs Pearl River NY 10965

SCHROETER, GILBERT LOREN, b Reedley, Calif, May 24, 36; m 63; c 1. GENETICS, CYTOGENETICS. *Educ:* Fresno State Col, BA, 63; Univ Calif, Davis, PhD(genetics), 68. *Prof Exp:* asst prof, 68-77, ASSOC PROF BIOL, TEX A&M UNIV, 77- *Mem:* AAAS; Genetics Soc Am. *Res:* Population cytology; chromosome evolution; cytotaxonomy of orthopteroid insects. *Mailing Add:* Dept of Biol Tex A&M Univ College Station TX 77843

SCHROETER, SIEGFRIED HERMANN, b Schweidnitz, Ger, Apr 20, 34; m 62. CHEMISTRY. *Educ:* Darmstadt Tech Univ, BSc, 56; Univ Gottingen, MSc, 59, PhD(chem), 62. *Prof Exp:* Chemist, Max Planck Inst, Muelheim-Ruhr, Ger, 59-63; res assoc, Univ Notre Dame, 63-65 & Yale Univ, 65-66; chemist, 66-73, MGR, GEN ELEC CORP RES & DEVELOP CTR, 73- *Mem:* Am Chem Soc; AAAS; Soc Adv Mat & Processing Engr. *Res:* Photochemistry; organic synthesis; engineering polymers; silicones; insulating materials; polymers for microelectronics; coatings; chemical synthesis and engineering. *Mailing Add:* Gen Elec Res & Develop Ctr Schenectady NY 12301

SCHROF, WILLIAM ERNST JOHN, b Cincinnati, Ohio, June 5, 31; m 58; c 5. ORGANIC POLYMER CHEMISTRY. *Educ:* Univ Cincinnati, AB, 58, PhD(org chem), 64. *Prof Exp:* Res chemist, 63-71, SR RES CHEMIST, E I DU PONT DE NEMOURS & CO, INC, 71- *Mem:* Am Chem Soc; Am Inst Chem. *Res:* Synthesis of anticancer compounds such as coumarins and furoquinolines; polymerization of polyamides for textile and industrial end uses; product development of textile and industrial yarns. *Mailing Add:* 954 Wawaset Rd Kennett Square PA 19348

SCHROGIE, JOHN JOSEPH, internal medicine, clinical pharmacology, see previous edition

SCHROHENLOHER, RALPH EDWARD, b Cincinnati, Ohio, Aug 6, 33; m 60; c 2. PROTEIN CHEMISTRY, IMMUNOCHEMISTRY. *Educ:* Univ Cincinnati, BS, 55, PhD(biochem), 59. *Prof Exp:* Res chemist, Nat Cancer Inst, 58-60; asst prof arthritis res, Med Col Ala, 61-63; guest investr, Rockefeller Inst, 63-64; asst prof, 64-69, ASSOC PROF MED & PATH, SCH MED, UNIV ALA, BIRMINGHAM, 73- *Concurrent Pos:* Nat Inst Arthritis & Metab Dis grants, 65-78; Nat Cancer Inst res contract, 75-78. *Mem:* Am Rheumatism Asn; AAAS; Am Chem Soc; Am Asn Immunol. *Res:* Immunoglobulin structure and function; autoantibodies and immune complexes in connective tissue diseases; structure of collagen. *Mailing Add:* Dept of Med Univ of Ala Sch of Med Birmingham AL 35294

SCHROLL, GENE E, b North Manchester, Ind, June 29, 28; m 49; c 3. ORGANIC CHEMISTRY. *Educ:* Manchester Col, BA, 51; Purdue Univ, PhD(chem), 55. *Prof Exp:* Res chemist, Ethyl Corp, 55-61; res assoc, Celanese Coatings Co, 62-67; res assoc, 68-80, SUPVR, APPL SCI RES & DEVELOP DEPT, CINCINNATI MILACRON CO, 80- *Mem:* Am Chem Soc; Royal Soc Chem. *Res:* Protective coatings; plastics; organometallics; reaction mechanisms. *Mailing Add:* 10451 Londonderry Ct Cincinnati OH 45242

SCHROTER, STANISLAW GUSTAW, b Katowice, Poland, May 8, 17; US citizen; m 46; c 5. CHEMICAL ENGINEERING, INORGANIC CHEMISTRY. *Educ:* Polish Univ Col, Eng, Dipl Eng, 49. *Prof Exp:* Tech officer, Steatite & Porcelain Prod Ltd, Eng, 49-52; engr, Can Radio Mfg Corp, Can, 52-56; sr engr, Quincy, 56-61, SR ENGR, RAYTHEON CO, 61- *Concurrent Pos:* Consult, Georgetown Porcelain Ltd, 53-54. *Res:* Electron emissive materials; high temperature electrical insulation; ferromagnetic porcelains; potting and encapsulation; microelectronics. *Mailing Add:* 103 High St Newton MA 02164

SCHROTH, MILTON NEIL, b Fullerton, Calif, June 25, 33; m 59; c 3. PLANT PATHOLOGY. *Educ:* Pomona Col, BA, 55; Univ Calif, Berkeley, PhD(plant path), 61. *Prof Exp:* From instr to assoc prof plant path, 61-71, asst dean res, Col Agr Sci, 68-73, assoc dean res, Col Natural Resources & actg asst to vpres agr sci, 73-76, PROF PLANT PATH, UNIV CALIF, BERKELEY, 71-, ASST DIR, DIV AGR SCI, 76- *Honors & Awards:* Campbell Award, Am Inst Biol Sci, 64. *Mem:* Am Soc Microbiol; Am Phytopath Soc. *Res:* Root disease research, especially plant bacterial diseases. *Mailing Add:* Dept of Plant Path Univ of Calif Berkeley CA 94720

SCHRUBEN, JOHANNA STENZEL, b Flushing, NY. MATHEMATICS, OPTICS. *Educ:* Queens Col, City Univ New York, BS, 64; Univ Mich, AM, 66, PhD(math), 68. *Prof Exp:* Instr math, Univ Minn, 68-69; SR SCIENTIST, WESTINGHOUSE RES & DEVELOP CTR, 69- *Concurrent Pos:* NSF fel, Univ Mich, 65-67; mem nat comt, Int Comn Illum, 76-78. *Mem:* Am Math Soc; Soc Indust & Appl Math; Optical Soc Am; Illum Eng Soc NAm. *Res:* Partial differential equations; illumination design; thermal stresses in single-crystal silicon ribbon being grown for photovoltaic cells. *Mailing Add:* Westinghouse Res & Develop Ctr 1310 Beulah Rd Pittsburgh PA 15235

SCHRUM, MARY IRENE KNOLLER, b New York, NY, Apr 18, 26; m 69. BIOCHEMISTRY, INFORMATION SCIENCE. *Educ:* Col Notre Dame, Md, AB, 48; Georgetown Univ, MS, 56. *Prof Exp:* Sr org chemist, Crown Cork & Seal Co, 48-50; chemist, Dept Med, Johns Hopkins Univ, 50-52; biochemist cellular physiol & metab, Nat Heart Inst, 52-55, supvr metab, 55-59, biochemist, Nat Inst Arthritis & Metab Dis, 59-62, sci reference analyst, Div Res Grants, NIH, 62-63; chemist, 63-66, head, Cent Retrieval Index Group, Sci Info Facility, 66-68, SR SYSTS ANALYST, TECH OPERS STAFF, FOOD & DRUG ADMIN, WASHINGTON, DC, 68- *Mem:* Am Chem Soc; Am Soc Info Sci. *Res:* Arteriosclerosis; physical-chemical studies of proteins; amino acid chemistry; information storage and retrieval of scientific information and data; research and development; chemical notations; automatic and electronic data processing. *Mailing Add:* 5528 Warwick Pl Chevy Chase MD 20015

SCHRUM, ROBERT WALLACE, b Hammond, Ind, Oct 19, 30; m 52; c 2. PETROLEUM CHEMISTRY. *Educ:* Univ Ill, BS, 52. *Prof Exp:* Chemist, Sinclair Res Labs, Inc, 52-55, asst sect leader engine oils, 55-59, asst sect leader fuels, 59-63, sect leader engine oils, 63-66; sect leader engine oils, Res Div, 66-74, PROJ LEADER, RES DIV, ROHM AND HAAS CO, 74- *Mem:* Soc Automotive Engr. *Res:* Fuel and lubricant additive research and development. *Mailing Add:* 1560 Temple Dr Maple Glen PA 19002

SCHRUMPF, BARRY JAMES, b San Francisco, Calif, July 13, 43; m 72; c 1. RANGE ECOLOGY, REMOTE SENSING. *Educ:* Willamette Univ, BA, 66; Ore State Univ, MS, 68, PhD(rangeland resources), 73. *Prof Exp:* Actg dir, 73-75, DIR, ENVIRON REMOTE SENSING APPLN LAB, ORE STATE UNIV, 75-, ASST PROF, 80- *Mem:* Soc Range Mgt; Am Soc Photogram. *Res:* Multispectral, multiseasonal and multistage remote sensing for natural vegetation inventory and analysis. *Mailing Add:* Environ Remote Sensing Appln Lab Ore State Univ Corvallis OR 97331

SCHRYER, NORMAN LOREN, b Detroit, Mich, Jan 16, 43; m 65. APPLIED MATHEMATICS. *Educ:* Univ Mich, BS, 65, MS, 66, PhD(math), 69. *Prof Exp:* MEM TECH STAFF APPL MATH, BELL TEL LABS, 69- *Mem:* Asn Comput Mach; Soc Indust & Appl Math. *Res:* Numerical solution of elliptic and parabolic partial differential equations. *Mailing Add:* 122 Sulfram New Providence NJ 07974

SCHRYVER, HERBERT FRANCIS, b New York, NY, Oct 15, 27; m 64. VETERINARY PHYSIOLOGY, VETERINARY PATHOLOGY. *Educ:* Cornell Univ, DVM, 54; Univ Pa, MS, 60, PhD(path), 64; Hofstra Col, BA, 61. *Prof Exp:* From instr to asst prof path, Univ Pa, 58-66; ASSOC PROF PATH, NY STATE VET COL, CORNELL UNIV, 66- *Concurrent Pos:* Arthritis Found fel, 64-65. *Mem:* AAAS; Am Soc Cell Biol; Am Vet Med Asn; Int Acad Path; Am Inst Nutrit. *Res:* Mineral nutrition and metabolism; connective tissue physiology and pathology; bone diseases; diseases of domestic animals and wildlife. *Mailing Add:* Equine Res Prog NY State Vet Col Cornell Univ Ithaca NY 14850

SCHTEINGART, DAVID E, b Buenos Aires, Arg, Oct 17, 30; m 60; c 3. INTERNAL MEDICINE. *Educ:* Nat Col 6, Buenos Aires, BA, 47; Univ Buenos Aires, MD, 54. *Prof Exp:* Resident med, Hosp Nat Clin, Buenos Aires, 56-57; resident, 59-60, instr, 60-61 & 62-63, asst prof, 63-67, assoc prof, 67-73, PROF MED, UNIV HOSP, UNIV MICH, ANN ARBOR, 73- *Concurrent Pos:* Fel med, Mt Sinai Hosp, New York, 57-58; fel endocrinol, Maimonides Hosp, Brooklyn, 58-59 & Univ Hosp, Univ Mich, Ann Arbor, 61-62. *Mem:* Am Fedn Clin Res; NY Acad Sci; Endocrine Soc. *Res:* Endocrinology; clinical abnormalities of adrenal cortical steroids; secretion and metabolism; obesity. *Mailing Add:* S3452 Univ Hosp Univ of Mich Ann Arbor MI 48104

SCHUBACK, PHILIP, b New York, NY, June 19, 25; m 57; c 2. PERIODONTICS, ORAL PATHOLOGY. *Educ:* NY Univ, BA, 48, DDS, 53. *Prof Exp:* Res fel periodont & oral path, Beth Israel Hosp, Boston, 53-55; instr periodont, Grad Sch Med, Univ Pa, 56-60; asst prof periodont & oral path, Sch Grad Dent, Boston Univ, 59-66; assoc prof periodont, 66-77, PROF PERIODONT, COL MED & DENT NJ, NJ DENT SCH, 77- *Concurrent Pos:* Vis lectr periodont & oral path, Dept Dent Hyg, Univ RI, 62-66; consult periodont, East Orange Vet Admin Hosp, 74-; Fel, Int Col Dent, 78- *Mem:* Am Acad Periodont; AAAS; Am Asn Univ Prof; Am Asn Dent Schs. *Res:* Behavior of bone in periodontal disease; chemical mediators that stimulate osteogenesis. *Mailing Add:* 29 Carteret St West Orange NJ 07052

SCHUBEL, JERRY ROBERT, b Bad Axe, Mich, Jan 26, 36; m 58; c 2. MARINE GEOLOGY. *Educ:* Alma Col, BS, 57; Harvard Univ, MAT, 59; Johns Hopkins Univ, PhD(oceanog), 68. *Prof Exp:* From asst res scientist to res scientist, Chesapeake Bay Inst, Johns Hopkins Univ, 67-74, adj res prof & assoc dir, 73-74; PROF MARINE SCI & DIR MARINE SCI RES CTR, STATE UNIV NY STONY BROOK, 74- *Concurrent Pos:* Vis assoc prof, Univ Del, 69, lect prof, Univ Md, 69-71; vis prof, Franklin & Marshall Col, 70-71; sci dir & vpres, Hydrocon Inc, 71-74; mem, Univ-Nat Oceanog Lab Syst Adv Coun, 77-80, vchmn, 80; partic workshop, Sci Comt Ocean Res, Intergovt Oceanog Comn, 79, chmn, 80; panel chmn & partic workshop, Eng Found Conf Offshore Indust, Nat Oceanic & Atmospheric Admin, 79; mem oversight review team, Off Oceanog Facil, NSF, 80; mem bd trustees, Stony Brook Found, State Univ NY, 78-; sr ed, Coastal Ocean Pollution Assessment, 80-; mem sci work group, Nat Oceanic Satellite Syst, NASA, 80- *Mem:* Am Soc Limnol & Oceanog; AAAS; Nat Asn Geol Teachers; NY Acad Sci; Estuarine Res Fedn (vpres, 81-). *Res:* Estuarine and shallow water sedimentation; suspended sediment transport; interactions of sediment and organisms; pollution; continental shelf sedimentation; marine geophysics; thermal ecology. *Mailing Add:* Marine Sci Res Ctr State Univ NY Stony Brook NY 11794

SCHUBERT, BERNICE GIDUZ, b Boston, Mass, Oct 6, 13. PLANT TAXONOMY. *Educ:* Univ Mass, BS, 35; Radcliffe Col, MS, 37, PhD, 41. *Prof Exp:* Tech asst taxon bot, Gray Herbarium, Harvard Univ, 41-50; Guggenheim fel, 50-51; consult plant taxon, Pedobot Proj, Econ Coop Admin, Brussels, Belg, 51-52; plant taxonomist, New Crops Res Br, Agr Res Serv, USDA, 52-61; assoc curator, 62-69, lectr biol, 71, CURATOR, ARNOLD ARBORETUM, HARVARD UNIV, 69-, SR LECTR BIOL, 75- *Concurrent Pos:* Ed, J Arnold Arboretum, 63-78. *Mem:* Am Soc Plant Taxon; Soc Econ Bot; Bot Soc Am; Am Inst Biol Sci; hon mem Soc Bot Mex. *Res:* Desmodium; American species of Dioscorea and Begonia. *Mailing Add:* Harvard Univ Arnold Arboretum 22 Divinity Ave Cambridge MA 02138

SCHUBERT, CEDRIC F, b Murray Bridge, Australia, Oct 20, 35; wid; c 2. MATHEMATICS. *Educ:* Univ Adelaide, BSc, 57, Hons, 58, MSc, 60; Univ Toronto, PhD(math), 62. *Prof Exp:* Lectr math, Univ Toronto, 61-62; asst prof, Univ Calif, Los Angeles, 62-69; assoc prof, 69-77, PROF MATH, QUEEN'S UNIV, ONT, 77- *Mem:* Can Math Soc; AAAS; Am Math Soc. *Res:* Operator and function theoretic properties of linear elliptic partial differential equations. *Mailing Add:* Dept of Math & Statist Queen's Univ Kingston ON K7L 3N6 Can

SCHUBERT, CLARENCE, b Buffalo, NY, Sept 25, 20. SOLID STATE CHEMISTRY. *Educ:* Spring Hill Col, BS, 43; Canisius Col, MS, 46; Princeton Univ, PhD, 56. *Prof Exp:* Instr phys chem, Canisius Col, 43-45; instr anal & phys chem, St Peter's Col, 46-47; asst phys chem, Princeton Univ, 52-55; asst prof, Fordham, 56-62; from assoc prof to prof, Le Moyne Col, NY, 62-73; vis prof, 73-75, assoc chmn dept chem, 75-77, LECTR CHEM, BOSTON COL, 77- *Concurrent Pos:* Vis fel, St Edmund's House, Cambridge Univ, 70-71; sr vis res metall, Cambridge Univ, 70-71. *Mem:* Am Chem Soc; Am Asn Jesuit Sci; Combustion Inst. *Res:* Ozone in combustion processes; electron emission microscopy, organic phosphors and free radicals; gas phase kinetics and infrared spectroscopy; ion emission microscopy; silicon thin film solar cell development. *Mailing Add:* Dept of Chem Boston Col Chestnut Hill MA 02167

SCHUBERT, DANIEL SVEN PAUL, b Buffalo, NY, Sept 28, 35; m 69. PSYCHIATRY, PSYCHOLOGY. *Educ:* State Univ Buffalo, BA, 55, MD, 65; Univ Chicago, PhD(psychol), 69. *Prof Exp:* Resident psychiat, Yale Univ, 69-72; asst prof, 72-77, ASSOC PROF PSYCHIAT, CASE WESTERN RESERVE UNIV, 77- *Concurrent Pos:* Consult ed, J Creative Behav, 71-, Int J Psychiat Med, 79, J Psychiat Treat Eval, 79. *Mem:* Am Psychol Asn; fel Am Psychiat Asn; Sigma Xi. *Res:* Psychobiology; psychosomatic medicine; variants of normal personality; measurement of personality. *Mailing Add:* Metrop Gen Hosp-Psychiat 3395 Scranton Rd Cleveland OH 44109

SCHUBERT, DAVID CRAWFORD, b Shillington, Pa, Jan 8, 25; m 49; c 3. LASERS. *Educ:* Lehigh Univ, BS, 49, MS, 50; Univ Md, PhD(physics), 61. *Prof Exp:* Asst physics, Lehigh Univ, 49-50; res physicist, Nat Bur Standards, 50-66; RES PHYSICIST, WESTINGHOUSE ELEC CORP, 66- *Mem:* Am Phys Soc. *Res:* Physics of the free electron; electron optical study of gas flow at extremely low pressures; plasma physics; quantum optics. *Mailing Add:* Aerospace Div Box 1521 Westinghouse Elec Corp Baltimore MD 21203

SCHUBERT, EDWARD THOMAS, b Brooklyn, NY, Apr 24, 27; m 53; c 3. BIOCHEMISTRY. *Educ:* Fordham Univ, BS, 49, MS, 52, PhD(biochem), 59. *Prof Exp:* Lectr biochem, Fordham Univ, 56-59; res assoc, 59-60, instr, 60-65, ASST PROF BIOCHEM, MED COL, CORNELL UNIV, 65- *Concurrent Pos:* Dir biochem, Pediat Ultramicro Chem Labs, New York Hosp, 66- *Mem:* AAAS; Am Chem Soc; Am Asn Clin Chem. *Res:* Biochemistry of growth and development; clinical chemistry; enzymic changes in renal diseases. *Mailing Add:* Dept of Clin Biochem Cornell Univ Med Col New York NY 10021

SCHUBERT, GERALD, b New York, NY, Mar 2, 39; m 60; c 3. GEOPHYSICS, PLANETARY SCIENCES. *Educ:* Cornell Univ, BEngPhys & MAE, 61; Univ Calif, Berkeley, PhD(eng), 64. *Prof Exp:* Nat Acad Sci-Nat Res Coun res fel, Dept Appl Math & Theoret Physics, Univ Cambridge, 65-66; from asst prof planetary & space sci to assoc prof planetary physics, 66-74, PROF GEOPHYS & PLANETARY PHYSICS, UNIV CALIF, LOS ANGELES, 74- *Concurrent Pos:* Alexander von Humboldt fel & Fulbright grant, 69; John Simon Guggenheim Mem Found fel, 72. *Honors & Awards:* James B Macelwane Award, Am Geophys Union, 75. *Mem:* AAAS; Am Geophys Union. *Res:* Geophysical and astrophysical fluid dynamics; planetary physics. *Mailing Add:* Dept Earth & Space Sci Univ Calif Los Angeles CA 90024

SCHUBERT, JOHN ROCKWELL, b East Orange, NJ, Aug 1, 25; m 48; c 4. NUTRITIONAL BIOCHEMISTRY. *Educ:* Pa State Univ, BS, 48; Ore State Univ, MS, 51, PhD(nutrit), 56. *Prof Exp:* Res asst agr chem, Ore State Univ, 50; mem prod staff, Cutter Labs, Calif, 51; res asst, agr chem, Ore State Univ, 51-57, asst prof, 57-63; EXEC SECY NUTRIT STUDY SECT, RES GRANTS REV BR, DIV RES GRANTS, NIH, 63-, REFERRAL OFFICER, 67- *Concurrent Pos:* Spec res fel, Exp Liver Dis Sect, Nat Inst Arthritis & Metab Dis, 60-61. *Mem:* AAAS; Am Chem Soc; Am Inst Nutrit; Am Soc Clin Nutrit. *Res:* Agricultural chemistry; animal nutrition; bacterial physiology; metabolic diseases of nutritional origin; science administration. *Mailing Add:* Res Grant Rev Br Div Res Grants Nat Inst Health Bethesda MD 20014

SCHUBERT, KAREL RALPH, b Urbana, Ill, Oct 12, 49; m 57. PLANT BIOCHEMISTRY. *Educ:* WVa Univ, BS, 71; Univ Ill, MS, 73, PhD(biochem), 75. *Prof Exp:* Fel bot & plant path, Ore State Univ, 75-76; asst prof, 76-81, ASSOC PROF BIOCHEM, MICH STATE UNIV, 81- *Mem:* Am Soc Plant Physiologists; Am Chem Soc; Sigma Xi; Am Soc Biol Chem. *Res:* Biochemical, physiological and molecular factors involved in the establishment of effective symbiotic association between leguminous and actinoriza plants and nitrogen-fixing bacteria including Rhizobium and Frankia. *Mailing Add:* Dept Biochem Mich State Univ East Lansing MI 48824

SCHUBERT, OSCAR EDMUND, b Flushing, Ohio, Aug 10, 21; m 42; c 4. HORTICULTURE. *Educ:* WVa Univ, BS, 42; Univ Ill, MS, 47, PhD(hort), 49. *Prof Exp:* Asst hort, WVa Univ, 42-43, instr, 46; asst floricult, Univ Ill, 46-47, asst pomol, 47-48, asst res & exten tree fruits, 49; from asst prof to assoc prof, 49-61, PROF HORT & HORTICULTURIST, WVA UNIV, 61- *Mem:* Am Soc Hort Sci; Weed Sci Soc Am. *Res:* Nutrition of apple and peach trees; effect of sprays on apple color; blending of apple juices; weed control in apples, peaches, strawberries, tomatoes and ornamentals; production of greenhouse plants. *Mailing Add:* Div of Plant Sci WVa Univ Morgantown WV 26506

SCHUBERT, RUDOLF, b New York, NY, Sept 28, 40; m 63; c 2. MASS SPECTROMETRY, SURFACE PHYSICS. *Educ:* Fairleigh Dickinson Univ, BS, 62, MS, 64; Univ Del, PhD(physics), 69. *Prof Exp:* MEM TECH RES STAFF, BELL LABS, 69- *Concurrent Pos:* Instr, Am Vacuum Soc. *Mem:* Am Phys Soc; Am Vacuum Soc. *Res:* Mass spectrometry of micro volumes; secondary ion mass spectrometry. *Mailing Add:* Bell Labs 6200 E Broad St Columbus OH 43213

SCHUBERT, THOMAS HERMAN, forestry, see previous edition

SCHUBERT, WILLIAM K, b Cincinnati, Ohio, July 12, 26; m 48; c 4. PEDIATRICS. *Educ:* Univ Cincinnati, BS, 49, MD, 52; Am Bd Pediat, dipl, 57. *Prof Exp:* Intern, Med Ctr, Ind Univ, 52-53; resident pediat, Cincinnati Children's Hosp, 53-55; instr pediat, Med Ctr, Univ Cincinnati, 56-59, sr res assoc, 59-63, assoc prof, 63-69; dir clin res ctr, 63-72, assoc dir hosp, 72-73, DIR DIV GASTROENTEROL & GASTROENTEROL CLIN, CHILDREN'S HOSP, 72-, CHIEF OF STAFF, MED CTR, 73-, PHYSICIAN EXEC DIR, 79-; PROF PEDIAT, UNIV CINCINNATI, 69-, CHMN DEPT, 79- *Mem:* Soc Pediat Res; Am Fedn Clin Res; Am Asn Study Liver Dis; Am Gastroenterol Asn; Am Pediat Soc. *Res:* Gastroenterology; metabolism. *Mailing Add:* Children's Hosp 240 Elland Ave Cincinnati OH 45229

SCHUBERT, WOLFGANG MANFRED, b Hanover, Ger, Feb 16, 20; nat US; m 41, 64; c 2. ORGANIC CHEMISTRY. *Educ:* Univ Ill, BS, 41; Univ Minn, PhD(org chem), 47. *Prof Exp:* Res chemist, Am Cyanamid Co, Conn, 44-46; from instr to assoc prof, 47-58, PROF ORG CHEM, UNIV WASH, 58- *Concurrent Pos:* Guggenheim fel & Fulbright res scholar, 60-61. *Mem:* Am Chem Soc; Royal Soc Chem. *Res:* Mechanisms of organic chemical reactions; solvent effects; substituent effects; acid base catalysis. *Mailing Add:* Dept of Chem Univ of Wash Seattle WA 98195

SCHUBRING, NORMAN W(ILLIAM), b Port Hope, Mich, June 1, 24; m 48; c 1. MICROWAVES, ANTENNAS. *Educ:* Wayne State Univ, BSEE, 52, MSEE, 59. *Prof Exp:* Res asst, Willow Run Res Ctr, Univ Mich, 52; STAFF RES ENGR, GEN MOTORS RES LABS, 52- *Honors & Awards:* Sr Award, Inst Elec & Electronics Engrs, 58-59; Charles L McCuen Spec Achievement Award, Gen Motors Res Labs, 78. *Mem:* Inst Elec & Electronics Engrs; Soc Automotive Engrs. *Res:* Electronics; microwaves; automobile radar; antennas; guided missile countermeasures; instrumentation; ultrasonics; sonics; nondestructive testing; piezoelectrics and ferroelectrics; microwave sintering of cermaics. *Mailing Add:* Gen Motors Res Labs 12 Mile & Mound Rds Warren MI 48090

SCHUCANY, WILLIAM ROGER, b Dallas, Tex, Sept 7, 40; m 61; c 3. MATHEMATICAL STATISTICS, APPLIED STATISTICS. *Educ:* Univ Tex, BA, 63, MA, 65; Southern Methodist Univ, PhD(statist). 70. *Prof Exp:* Engr-scientist, Tracor, Inc, Tex, 63-66; sr engr, LTV Electrosysts, Inc, 66-68; lab mgr statist consult, 68-70, asst prof math statist, 70-74, assoc prof, 74-80, PROF STATIST, SOUTHERN METHODIST UNIV, 80- *Concurrent Pos:* Assoc ed, Commun Statist, 71-; consult, Medicus Corp, 72-, Louis, Bowles & Grace, Inc, 70- & Grove & Assocs, 77- *Mem:* Am Statist Asn; Inst Math Statist. *Res:* Extensions and applications of techniques for improvement of estimators and the construction of approximate statistical tests and interval estimation; nonparametric ranking statistics; computer simulation variance reductions. *Mailing Add:* Dept of Statist Southern Methodist Univ Dallas TX 75275

SCHUCHARD, ALFRED, b San Francisco, Calif, Sept 30, 21; m 45; c 3. DENTISTRY. *Educ:* Univ Calif, DDS, 44. *Prof Exp:* Demonstr, 48-58, from asst prof to assoc prof, 58-67, prof oper dent, 67-80, PROF RESTORATIVE DENT, UNIV CALIF, SAN FRANCISCO, 80-, CHMN DIV, 62- *Concurrent Pos:* Mem, Coun on Dent Mats & Devices, Am Dent Asn. *Mem:* Am Inst Oral Biol; fel Am Col Dent; Am Acad Restorative Dent. *Res:* Pulpal, thermal and histologic response to high speed and ultrahigh speed cutting in tooth structure, using dry and wet field. *Mailing Add:* Dept of Oper Dent Univ Calif Sch Dent San Francisco Med Ctr San Francisco CA 94143

SCHUCHARDT, LEE FRANK, b Lansdowne, Pa, June 30, 23; m 47; c 3. BACTERIOLOGY, VIROLOGY. *Educ:* Temple Univ, BA, 55, MA, 59; Hahnemann Med Col, PhD(microbiol), 65. *Prof Exp:* Lab asst, Sharp & Dohme Div, 41-43 & 46-47, res asst bact, 47-50, res assoc, Merck Sharp & Dohme Div, 50-57, assoc biol develop, 57-62, microbiologist, 62-76, SR PROJ MICROBIOLOGIST, MERCK SHARP & DOHME DIV, MERCK & CO, INC, 76- *Mem:* AAAS; Am Soc Microbiol. *Res:* Development of agents for immunization against bacterial and viral infectious diseases of animals and man; computer controlled manufacture of sterile pharmaceuticals. *Mailing Add:* Merck Sharp & Dohme West Point PA 19486

SCHUCHER, REUBEN, b Zhitomir, Russia, June 11, 22; Can citizen; m 56; c 2. CLINICAL CHEMISTRY, BIOCHEMISTRY. *Educ:* McGill Univ, BSc, 49, PhD(biochem), 54; Univ Sask, MSc, 51. *Prof Exp:* Res asst biochem, McGill Univ, 51-55; biochemist & res assoc, Dept Med, 55-68, DIR DEPT CLIN CHEM, JEWISH GEN HOSP, 68- *Concurrent Pos:* Cancer Res Soc fel, Res Inst, Montreal Gen Hosp, 54-55; lectr, Dept Invest Med, McGill Univ, 59; treas & bd mem, Que Hosp Biochem Corp, 63-68; consult, Maimonides Hosp & Home for Aged, 66-, Jewish Convalescent Hosp, 67- & Med Data Sci Labs, 70-; proj dir, Lady Davis Inst Med Res, Jewish Gen Hosp, 68- *Mem:* NY Acad Sci; Chem Inst Can; Can Soc Clin Chemists (vpres, 67, pres, 68); Can Biochem Soc; Can Physiol Soc. *Res:* Synthesis of enzyme proteins by pancreas slices in vitro; metabolism of insulin by pancreas, especially synthesis and breakdown by pancreatic insulinase; insulin secretion in vivo; thyroid function tests in clinical laboratory. *Mailing Add:* Dept of Clin Chem Jewish Gen Hosp 3755 Cote St Catherine Rd Montreal PQ H3T 1E2 Can

SCHUCK, JAMES MICHAEL, b Chicago, Ill, Nov 5, 34; m 56; c 5. BIO-ORGANIC CHEMISTRY, PROTEIN CHEMISTRY. *Educ:* Univ Wis, BS, 56; Mass Inst Technol, PhD(org chem), 60. *Prof Exp:* Teaching asst, Mass Inst Technol, 57; res chemist, Res & Eng Div, Monsanto Chem Co, 60-61, sr res chemist, 61-64 & Cent Res Dept, 64-66, res group leader, Cent Res Dept, 66-68 & New Enterprise Div, 68-69, sr res group leader, New Enterprise Div, 69-77 & Corp Res & Develop, 77-78, res mgr biosynthesis, Corp Res Develop, 78-81, MGR EXPLOR RES & DEVELOP, ENVIRON POLICY STAFF, MONSANTO CO, 81- *Res:* Protein and synthetic organic chemistry; study of structure and function of mammalian growth hormones and analogs; blood protein fractionation; mammalian cell culture; structure and function of proteolytic enzymes; tumor angiogenesis and antiangiogenesis. *Mailing Add:* Dept Bio-Med Monsanto Co St Louis MO 63167

SCHUCKER, GERALD D, b McConnellstown, Pa, Oct 29, 36. ANALYTICAL CHEMISTRY. *Educ:* Juniata Col, BS, 58; Univ Mo-Rolla, MS, 67. *Prof Exp:* Chemist, Pa RR Test Dept, 58-62; res technician anal chem, Cornell Univ, 63-65; SR RES CHEMIST, CORNING GLASS WORKS, 68- *Mem:* Am Chem Soc; Soc Appl Spectros; Am Inst Chemists. *Res:* Separation and preconcentration of trace amounts of elements and their determination by spectrophotometry; emission spectroscopy; atomic absorption; flame emission spectroscopy. *Mailing Add:* Corning Glass Works Science Park Corning NY 14830

SCHUCKER, ROBERT CHARLES, b Altoona, Pa, Jan 10, 45; m 68; c 2. PETROLEUM CHEMISTRY, CATALYSIS. *Educ:* Univ SC, BS, 68, MS, 70; Ga Inst Technol, PhD(chem eng), 74. *Prof Exp:* Res engr, Procter & Gamble Co, 74-77; Corp Res Lab, 77-80, STAFF ENGR, EXXON RES & DEVELOP LABS, EXXON CO, 80- *Mem:* Am Chem Soc. *Res:* Chemistry of heavy petroleum feedstocks with focus on macromolecular structure and reactivity; enhance yield of desirable product via catalytic reactions. *Mailing Add:* Exxon Res & Develop Labs PO Box 2226 Baton Rouge LA 70821

SCHUDER, CHARLES BERNHARD, b Olney, Ill, Mar 17, 23; m 45; c 4. MECHANICAL ENGINEERING. *Educ:* Univ Ill, BSME, 50; US Merchant Marine Acad, BS, 50; Purdue Univ, MSME, 58. *Prof Exp:* Test engr, Cent Ill Pub Serv Co, 50-52; chief mech engr, Elec Energy, Inc, 52-55; instr mech eng, Purdue Univ, 55-58; mech engr, Fisher Controls Co, 58-62, res dir mech eng, 62-78; MECH ENGR, SOUTHWELL ENG CO, 78- *Mem:* Am Soc Mech Engrs; Instrument Soc Am. *Res:* Heat-power; fluid flow; automatic control. *Mailing Add:* Southwell Eng Co Wilkesboro NC 28697

SCHUDER, DONALD LLOYD, b Bartholomew Co, Ind, Mar 4, 22; m 45; c 2. ENTOMOLOGY. *Educ:* Purdue Univ, BSA, 48, MS, 49, PhD, 57. *Prof Exp:* Assoc prof, 49-62, PROF ENTOM, PURDUE UNIV, WEST LAFAYETTE, 62- *Concurrent Pos:* Ed, Ind Nursery News, 54- *Mem:* Entom Soc Am; Int Soc Arboriculture; Am Asn Nurserymen. *Res:* Coccidae; insect pests of ornamental trees, shrubs and Christmas trees. *Mailing Add:* Dept of Entom Entom Hall Purdue Univ West Lafayette IN 47907

SCHUDER, JOHN CLAUDE, b Olney, Ill, Mar 2, 22; m 46; c 3. BIOENGINEERING, BIOPHYSICS. *Educ:* Univ Ill, BSEE, 43; Purdue Univ, MSEE, 51, PhD(elec eng), 54. *Prof Exp:* Instr elec eng, Purdue Univ, 49-54, asst prof, 54-56; assoc prof physics, Doane Col, 56-57; asst prof eng in surg res, Univ Pa, 59-60; assoc prof, 60-64, PROF SURG, UNIV MO-COLUMBIA, 64- *Concurrent Pos:* Fel eng in surg res, Univ Pa, 57-59; res engr, Hosp Univ Pa, 57-60; estab investr, Am Heart Asn, 65-70. *Mem:* Inst Elec & Electronics Eng; Am Soc Artificial Internal Organs; Inst Elec & Electronic Engrs Eng in Med & Biol Soc. *Res:* Application of physics to medical problems, in particular, cardiac pacing, cardiac defibrillation, artificial hearts, electromagnetic energy transport through biological tissue. *Mailing Add:* Dept Surg Univ Mo Columbia MO 65212

SCHUE, JOHN R, b Gaylord, Minn, Feb 6, 32; m 57; c 4. ALGEBRA. *Educ:* Macalester Col, AB, 53; Mass Inst Technol, PhD(math), 59. *Prof Exp:* Instr math, Mass Inst Technol, 58-59; asst prof, Oberlin Col, 59-62; assoc prof, 62-69, PROF MATH, MACALESTER COL, 69- *Concurrent Pos:* NSF sci faculty fel, 68-69. *Mem:* Am Math Soc; Math Asn Am. *Res:* Lie algebras and functional analysis. *Mailing Add:* Dept of Math Macalester Col St Paul MN 55105

SCHUEL, HERBERT, b New York, NY, Apr 8, 35; m 62; c 2. CELL BIOLOGY, DEVELOPMENTAL BIOLOGY. *Educ:* NY Univ, BA, 56; Univ Pa, PhD(zool), 60. *Prof Exp:* Res assoc develop biol, Oceanog Inst, Fla State Univ, 60-61; res assoc chem, Northwestern Univ, 63-65; asst prof biol, Oakland Univ, 65-68; asst prof anat, Mt Sinai Sch Med, 68-72, assoc res prof, 72-73; assoc prof biochem, State Univ Downstate Med Ctr, 73-77; ASSOC PROF ANAT, STATE UNIV NY, BUFFALO, 77- *Concurrent Pos:* NIH fel, Oak Ridge Nat Lab, 61-63; NIH res career develop award, Oakland Univ & Mt Sinai Sch Med, 68-73; mem, Corp Marine Biol Labs. *Mem:* AAAS; Am Physiol Soc; Am Asn Anat; Am Soc Cell Biol; Biophys Soc. *Res:* Sub-cellular biochemistry; isolation and molecular characterization of sub-cellular organelles; elucidation of role in cellular functions; fertilization, prevention of polyspermy secretion and cell division. *Mailing Add:* Dept of Anat Sci State Univ NY at Buffalo Buffalo NY 14214

SCHUELE, DONALD EDWARD, b Cleveland, Ohio, June 16, 34; m 56; c 6. SOLID STATE PHYSICS. *Educ:* John Carroll Univ, BS, 56, MS, 57; Case Inst Technol, PhD(physics), 63. *Prof Exp:* Instr math & physics, John Carroll Univ, 56-57, instr physics, 57-59; from instr to assoc prof, 62-74, actg dean, 72-73, dean, 73-80, PROF PHYSICS, CASE WESTERN RESERVE UNIV, 74-, CHMN DEPT, 76- *Concurrent Pos:* On leave, Bell Tel Labs, 70-; Univ rep, Argonne Univ Assocs; mem bd overseers, St Mary Sem. *Mem:* Am Inst Physics; Am Asn Physics Teachers. *Res:* Low frequency dielectric constant of ionic crystals, their pressure and temperature dependence; lattice dynamics; thermal expansion at low temperatures; elastic constants of single crystals; equation of state of solids; high pressure physics; polymer physics. *Mailing Add:* Dept of Physics Case Western Reserve Univ Cleveland OH 44106

SCHUELE, WILLIAM JOHN, b Philadelphia, Pa, Apr 27, 23; m 52; c 2. INORGANIC CHEMISTRY. *Educ:* Univ Pa, PhD(chem), 56. *Prof Exp:* Sr res chemist, Res Lab, Franklin Inst, 55-65; ADV CHEMIST, IBM CORP, 65- *Mem:* AAAS; Sigma Xi; Am Chem Soc; NY Acad Sci. *Res:* Fine particles; ferromagnetism; photolithography; semiconductor chemistry; chemical conservation. *Mailing Add:* 33 Clover St South Burlington VT 05401

SCHUELER, ARNOLD P(AUL), chemical engineering, see previous edition

SCHUELER, BRUNO OTTO GOTTFRIED, b Estcourt, SAfrica, Apr 21, 32; m 60; c 2. ORGANIC CHEMISTRY, CHEMICAL ENGINEERING. *Educ:* Univ Natal, BSc, 53, Hons, 54, MSc, 55, PhD(org chem), 57; Cambridge Univ, PhD(chem eng), 60. *Prof Exp:* Res engr process develop, Exp Sta, Del, 60-66, sr res engr, 66-69, asst div supt, Plastics Dept, Tex, 69-73, staff engr, 73-81, TECH FEL, PLASTICS DEPT, E I DU PONT DE NEMOURS & CO, INC, 81- *Res:* Indole alkaloids, especially voacangine and ibogaine; bubble formation at submerged orifices; effect of chemical structure on distribution coefficients; polymer manufacturing. *Mailing Add:* Plastics Prod Dept E I du Pont de Nemours & Co Inc Orange TX 77630

SCHUELER, DONALD G(EORGE), b Harvard, Nebr, Oct 22, 40. ELECTRICAL ENGINEERING. *Educ:* Univ Nebr, Lincoln, BS, 62, MS, 63, PhD(elec eng), 69. *Prof Exp:* Staff mem electronics, Sandia Labs, 63-67; instr elec eng, Univ Nebr, 67-68; staff mem electronics, 69-70, supvr, Solid State Electronics Res, 70-75, supvr Photovoltaic Projs, 75-81, MGR SOLAR ENERGY DEPT, SANDIA LABS, 81- *Mem:* Inst Elec & Electronics Engrs; Int Solar Energy Soc. *Res:* Solid state microwave devices; ferroelectric ceramic optical devices. *Mailing Add:* 13200 Mountain Shadows Rd NE Albuquerque NM 87111

SCHUELER, PAUL EDGAR, b New York, NY, Apr 18, 45; m 72. PHYSICAL ORGANIC CHEMISTRY. *Educ:* Univ Rochester, BS, 65; NY Univ, PhD(chem), 73. *Prof Exp:* Fel org chem, Rutgers Univ, 72-73; res assoc hot-atom chem, Brookhaven Nat Lab, 73-75; lectr chem, Rutgers Univ, New Brunswick, 75-77; mem staff dept chem, 77-80, ASSOC PROF CHEM, SOMERSET CITY COL, 80- *Concurrent Pos:* Res collabr, Brookhaven Nat Lab, 75- *Mem:* Am Chem Soc. *Res:* Mechanistic physical organic chemistry, with emphasis on reactive intermediates in polar aprotic solvents. *Mailing Add:* Dept of Chem PO Box 3300 Somerset NJ 08876

SCHUELLEIN, ROBERT, b NY, Feb 22, 20. GENETICS. *Educ:* Univ Dayton, BS, 43; Univ Pittsburgh, MS, 48, PhD(genetics), 56. *Prof Exp:* Teacher parochial high sch, Pa, 43-49; teacher, Ohio Univ, 49-53; instr, Univ Dayton, 53, assoc prof biol, 59-64; mem staff, training grants & awards br, Nat Heart Inst, 64-65, exec secy grants assoc prog, Div Res Grants, NIH, 65-68, chief periodont dis & soft tissue prog, 68-70, chief soft tissue stomatol prog, 70-74, SPEC ASST RES MANPOWER, NAT INST DENT RES, 74- *Mem:* Genetics Soc Am; Am Soc Human Genetics; Am Genetic Asn. *Res:* Genetics of Drosophila; population and human genetics; evolution and biometrical analysis. *Mailing Add:* 5626 Larmar Rd Bethesda MD 20816

SCHUERCH, CONRAD, b Boston, Mass, Aug 2, 18; m 48; c 4. ORGANIC CHEMISTRY. *Educ:* Mass Inst Technol, BS, 40, PhD(org chem), 47. *Prof Exp:* Res assoc inorg war res, Mass Inst Technol, 42-43; chemist, Res Lab, Nat Adv Comt Aeronaut, Ohio, 45; sessional lectr, McGill Univ, 47-48, 48-49; from asst prof to prof chem, 49-78, chmn dept, 56-72, DISTINGUISHED PROF CHEM, STATE UNIV NY COL ENVIRON SCI & FORESTRY, 78- *Concurrent Pos:* Guggenheim fel, 60-61. *Honors & Awards:* Anselme Payen Award, Am Chem Soc, 72. *Mem:* AAAS; Am Chem Soc; Tech Asn Pulp & Paper Indust. *Res:* Chemistry of lignin; carbohydrates; vinyl polymers; polysaccharides; wood. *Mailing Add:* Dept Chem State Univ NY Col of Environ Sci & Forestry Syracuse NY 13210

SCHUERCH, HANS, applied mechanics, deceased

SCHUERGER, T(HOMAS) R(OBERT), b Cleveland, Ohio, Nov 1, 25; m 52; c 4. SYSTEMS RESEARCH, INDUSTRIAL CONTROLS. *Educ:* Case Inst Technol, BS, 50; Carnegie Inst Technol, MS, 52. *Prof Exp:* Asst, Carnegie Inst Technol, 50-52; res engr, Preston Labs, Inc, 52-54; sect mgr, Electromech Eng Div, 54-60, supv technologist systs eng, 60-66, chief, Elec Systs Div, 66-79, CHIEF MATH & SYSTS RES DIV, RES LAB, US STEEL CORP, 79- *Mem:* Asn Iron & Steel Engrs; Am Soc Mech Engrs; Instrument Soc Am. *Res:* Systems research; automatic control and process computer systems; process instrumentation; nondestructive inspection; process analysis; data processing and computing. *Mailing Add:* Elec Systs Div MS 67 125 Jamison Lane Monroeville PA 15146

SCHUERMAN, DONALD WILLIAM, b Cincinnati, Ohio, July 13, 43; c 2. ASTROPHYSICS, SPACE SCIENCE. *Educ:* Univ Cincinnati, BS, 65; Univ Rochester, PhD(physics & astron), 70. *Prof Exp:* Nat Res Coun res assoc, Johnson Spacecraft Ctr, NASA, 70-72; res assoc, Dudley Observ, Albany, 72-75; sr res assoc, Space Astron Lab, State Univ NY Albany, 75-80; ASSOC RES SCIENTIST, SPACE ASTRON LAB, UNIV FLA, 80- *Concurrent Pos:* Mgr, UV Rocket Prog, Johnson Spacecraft Ctr, NASA, 71-72, co-investr & sci mgr, Skylab coronagraph Exp T025, 72-75 & Solar Polar Mission Zodiacal Light|Starlight Exp, 78-89, secy, Sci Airlock Working Group, Skylab, 73-75, co-investr, Pioneer 10 & 11 Zodiacal Light Exp, 75-77 & Characteristics of Shuttle|Spacelab Induced Atmosphere Exp, OFT-4, 78-81, prin investr, Study Contaminant Particles Around Skylab, 76-77; co-investr background sky brightness measurements, US Air Force, 77-78; prin investr, US Army, 77-83, chmn, Int Workshop Light Scattering by Irregularly Shaped Particles, 78-79; co-investr, ESA's Giotto Mission Halley's Comet, 81-86. *Mem:* Am Astron Soc; Royal Astron Soc; Int Astron Union. *Res:* Space observations and interpretation of zodiacal light, background starlight and interplanetary dust; experimental and theoretical physics of light-scattering by small particles. *Mailing Add:* Space Astron Lab Executive Park E Albany NY 12203

SCHUERMANN, ALLEN CLARK, JR, b Denver, Colo, Sept 28, 43; m 65; c 2. INDUSTRIAL ENGINEERING. *Educ:* Univ Kans, BA, 65; Wichita State Univ, MS, 68; Univ Ark, PhD(indust eng), 71. *Prof Exp:* Oper res analyst, Boeing Co, 65-69; sr oper res analyst, Boeing Comput Serv, 71; asst prof, 71-78, ASSOC PROF INDUST ENG, WICHITA STATE UNIV, 78-, CHMN DEPT, 79- *Concurrent Pos:* Prin investr, Rehab Serv Admin, 76-81; consult, Boeing Co, 72-73, Kans Gas & Elec Co, 78- & Kans Power & Light Co, 79- *Mem:* Am Inst Indust Engrs; Inst Mgt Sci; Oper Res Soc Am; Am Soc Eng Educ. *Res:* Modeling of the economic factors, incentives and disincentives which have an impact on the successful rehabilitation and employment of the severely physically disabled. *Mailing Add:* Dept Indust Eng Wichita State Univ Wichita KS 67208

SCHUESSLER, CARLOS FRANCIS, b Mexico City, Mex, June 20, 06; m 30; c 1. DENTISTRY. *Educ:* Univ Southern Calif, BS & DDS, 31; Univ Ala, Birmingham, BA, 80. *Prof Exp:* Chief, Dept Dent Sci, Sch Aviation Med, US Air Force, 46-49 & 60-62; prof dent, Dent Sch, Univ Ala, Med Ctr, Birmingham, 62-76. *Mem:* Am Dent Asn; fel Am Col Dent; Int Asn Dent Res. *Res:* Dental equipment and materials. *Mailing Add:* 2213 Vesthaven Way E Birmingham AL 35216

SCHUESSLER, HANS ACHIM, b Mannheim, Ger, June 25, 33. ATOMIC PHYSICS. *Educ:* Univ Heidelberg, MS, 61, PhD(physics), 64. *Prof Exp:* Asst prof physics, Tech Univ, Berlin, 63-66; from res asst prof to res assoc prof, Univ Wash, 66-69; ASSOC PROF PHYSICS, TEX A&M UNIV, 69-, WELCH FOUND GRANT, 71- *Concurrent Pos:* Res Corp Gardner-Cottrell grant, Tex A&m Univ, 69-73; Nat Bur Standards grant, 72- *Mem:* Am Phys Soc; Europ Phys Soc; Ger Phys Soc. *Res:* Radio frequency spectroscopy; optical pumping; ion storage; atomic clocks; lasers; photodissociation of ion molecules; polarized atomic beams; nuclear moments; level crossing; laser generated plasmas; magnetic resonance in dilute plasmas. *Mailing Add:* Dept of Physics Tex A&M Univ College Station TX 77843

SCHUESSLER, RICHARD BRUCE, b St Louis, Mo, Jan 24, 51; m 74. BIOMEDICAL ENGINEERING, CARDIOVASCULAR PHYSIOLOGY. *Educ:* Univ Mo-Rolla, BS, 72, MS, 74; Clemson Univ, PhD(biomed eng), 77. *Prof Exp:* Res asst, Univ Mo-Rolla, 73-74; res asst, Clemson Univ, 74-77; BIOMED ENGR, VET ADMIN HOSP, 77-; INSTR, MED COL GA, 78- *Concurrent Pos:* Fel Nat Blood, Lung & Heart Inst. *Honors & Awards:* Austin Moore Award, Clemson Univ, 78. *Res:* Cardiac electrophysiology; cardiac mechanics; computer applications in medicine; numerical analysis; pattern recognition. *Mailing Add:* Vet Admin Hosp Eng Serv 138L Augusta GA 30904

SCHUETTE, EVAN H(ENRY), b Rock Springs, Wis, Dec 12, 18; m 43; c 3. ENGINEERING MECHANICS. *Educ:* Univ Wis, BS, 40. *Prof Exp:* Aeronaut res scientist, Nat Adv Comt Aeronaut, 42-46; chief design res, Dow Metal Prods Co Div, Dow Chem Co, 46-61; staff engr, Lockheed Missiles & Space Co, 61-71; ENGR, COMBUSTION POWER CO, INC, 72- *Res:* Fatigue; minimum weight design; metals application development. *Mailing Add:* Combustion Power Co Inc 1346 Willow Rd Menlo Park CA 94025

SCHUETTE, OSWALD FRANCIS, JR, b Washington, DC, Aug 20, 21; m 47; c 3. PHYSICS. *Educ:* Georgetown Univ, BS, 43; Yale Univ, MA, PhD(physics), 49. *Prof Exp:* Instr physics, Yale Univ, 43-44, asst instr, 46-48; assoc prof, Col of William & Mary, 48-53; Fulbright scholar, Ger, 53; sci liaison officer, Sci & Tech Unit, US Dept Navy, Ger, 54-58; mem staff, Nat Acad Sci, 59-60; dep spec asst space, Off Secy Defense, 60-63; head dept, 63-80, PROF PHYSICS, UNIV SC, 63- *Concurrent Pos:* Guest prof, Univ Vienna, Austria, 80. *Mem:* Am Phys Soc; Am Asn Physics Teachers. *Res:* Separation of isotopes; underwater sound; mass spectroscopy. *Mailing Add:* Dept of Physics Univ of SC Columbia SC 29208

SCHUETZ, ALLEN W, b Monroe, Wis, July 8, 36; m 65. ENDOCRINOLOGY, CELL BIOLOGY. *Educ:* Univ Wis, BS, 58, PhD(endocrinol), 65. *Prof Exp:* From instr to assoc prof pop dynamics, obstet & gynec, 66-75, PROF POPULATION DYNAMICS, SCH HYG & PUB HEALTH, JOHNS HOPKINS UNIV, 75- *Concurrent Pos:* Fels steroid biochem, Univ Minn, 64-65, 65-66; fel, Marine Biol Lab, Woods Hole, 65, corp mem, 80; Fogarty Found sr int fel, Cambridge Univ. *Mem:* Endocrine Soc; Cell Biol Soc; Soc Study Reprod; Am Soc Zoologists. *Res:* Mechanisms and factors controlling pituitary gland hormone secretions and the means by which these hormones act on their target organs; specific role of gonadotrophic hormones in regulating gametogenesis and follicular maturation; control mechanisms in oocyte growth and meiotic maturation; nuclear-cytoplasmic interactions in fertilization and early development. *Mailing Add:* Sch of Hyg & Pub Health Johns Hopkins Univ Baltimore MD 21205

SCHUETZE, CLARKE E, b San Antonio, Tex, May 4, 21; m 48; c 1. ORGANIC CHEMISTRY. *Educ:* Trinity Univ, BS, 57. *Prof Exp:* Chemist, 56-75, SR RES CHEMIST, SOUTHWEST RES INST, 75- *Mem:* Sigma Xi. *Res:* Microencapsulation research and process development, particularly mechanical extrusion processes; controlled release-pesticides, nutrients, reactants; coating and film formulation and application to small particles, seed. *Mailing Add:* Southwest Res Inst 6220 Culebra Rd San Antonio TX 78228

SCHUETZLE, DENNIS, b Sacramento, Calif, July 21, 42; m 68; c 2. ANALYTICAL CHEMISTRY. *Educ:* Calif State Univ, San Jose, BS, 65; Univ Wash, MS, 70, PhD(chem & eng), 72. *Prof Exp:* Technician, Stoner Labs, 64-65; res chemist, Stanford Res Inst, 65-68; res assoc, Univ Wash, 68-72, res assoc prof anal chem, 72-73; SR STAFF SCIENTIST ENG & RES, FORD MOTOR CO, 73- *Concurrent Pos:* Consult, Calif Dept Health & Environ Protection Agency, 70-75. *Mem:* Am Chem Soc; Air Pollution Control Asn; Sigma Xi. *Res:* New analytical techniques for environmental monitoring, process monitoring, quality control and materials properties (adhesion). *Mailing Add:* Sci Res Lab-53016 Ford Motor Co Box 2053 Dearborn MI 48121

SCHUFLE, JOSEPH ALBERT, b Akron, Ohio, Dec 21, 17; m 42; c 2. PHYSICAL CHEMISTRY, HISTORY OF SCIENCE. *Educ:* Univ Akron, BS, 38, MS, 42; Western Reserve Univ, PhD(chem), 48. *Prof Exp:* Chemist, Akron, Ohio, 39-42; instr math, Western Reserve Univ, 46-47; from asst prof to prof chem, N Mex Inst Mining & Technol, 48-64; head dept chem & dir inst sci res, 64-70, PROF CHEM, NMEX HIGHLANDS UNIV, 64- *Concurrent Pos:* Vis prof, Univ Col, Dublin, 61-62; vis scholar, Univ Uppsala, Sweden, 77. *Mem:* Fel AAAS; fel Am Inst Chemists; Am Chem Soc; Inst Chem Ireland; Hist Sci Soc. *Res:* Structure of water; dating arid zone sediments; 18th century science. *Mailing Add:* 1301 Eighth St Las Vegas NM 87701

SCHUG, JOHN CHARLES, b New York, NY, Mar 31, 36; m 58; c 3. PHYSICAL CHEMISTRY. *Educ:* Cooper Union, BChE, 57; Univ Ill, MS, 58, PhD(chem), 60. *Prof Exp:* Res chemist, Gulf Res & Develop Co, 60-64; from asst prof to assoc prof, 64-73, PROF CHEM, VA POLYTECH INST & STATE UNIV, 73- *Concurrent Pos:* Consult, Philip Morris Res Ctr, 66- *Mem:* Am Chem Soc. *Res:* Quantum chemistry; high-resolution nuclear magnetic resonance; mass spectrometry. *Mailing Add:* Dept Chem Va Polytech Inst & State Univ Blacksburg VA 24061

SCHUG, KENNETH, b Easton, Pa, Aug 27, 24; m 48; c 3. INORGANIC CHEMISTRY. *Educ:* Stanford Univ, AB, 45; Univ Southern Calif, PhD, 55. *Prof Exp:* Res assoc chem, Univ Wis, 54-56; from instr to assoc prof, 56-75, PROF CHEM, ILL INST TECHNOL, 75-, CHMN DEPT, 76- *Concurrent Pos:* Consult, Argonne Nat Lab, 61-63; Fulbright res fel, Kyushu Univ, 64-65. *Mem:* AAAS; Am Chem Soc. *Res:* Inorganic, coordination and solution chemistry; inorganic mechanisms. *Mailing Add:* Dept of Chem Ill Inst of Technol Chicago IL 60616

SCHUGAR, HARVEY, b Pittsburgh, Pa, Dec 2, 36; m 63. INORGANIC CHEMISTRY, BIOINORGANIC CHEMISTRY. *Educ:* Carnegie Inst Technol, BS, 58; Columbia Univ, MA, 59, PhD(chem), 61. *Prof Exp:* Res chemist, Esso Res & Eng Co, 61-63; res chemist, Sci Design Co, 63-65; res assoc & lectr chem, Columbia Univ, 65-67; res assoc, Calif Inst Technol, 67-68; asst prof, 68-73, ASSOC PROF CHEM, RUTGERS UNIV, NEW BRUNSWICK, 73- *Mem:* Am Chem Soc. *Res:* Aquo chemistry of ferric complexes; metal ions in biological systems. *Mailing Add:* Sch of Chem Rutgers Univ New Brunswick NJ 08903

SCHUH, JAMES DONALD, b Chicago, Ill, Oct 9, 28; m 54; c 5. ANIMAL NUTRITION. *Educ:* Kans State Univ, BS, 53; Okla State Univ, MS, 57, PhD(animal nutrit), 60. *Prof Exp:* Exten dairy specialist, Univ Nev, 60-64; assoc prof dairy sci, 64-72, PROF DAIRY SCI, UNIV ARIZ, 72- *Mem:* Am Dairy Sci Asn. *Res:* Dairy herd management; calf nutrition and immunity; water quality for dairy cattle; dairy heifer management. *Mailing Add:* Dept of Animal Sci Univ of Ariz Tucson AZ 85721

SCHUH, JOSEPH EDWARD, b Brooklyn, NY, Mar 26, 14. CYTOLOGY. *Educ:* Georgetown Univ, AB, 38; Woodstock Col, PhL, 39; Fordham Univ, MS, 41, PhD(biol), 51; Weston Col, STL, 46. *Prof Exp:* Instr biol, St Joseph's Col, Pa, 41-42; from asst prof to assoc prof, St Peters Col, NJ, 51-62, head dept, 51-62; sr lectr, Univ Lagos, 62-65; assoc prof, 65-67, head dept, 67-77, PROF BIOL, ST PETERS COL, NJ, 67- *Concurrent Pos:* Vis res assoc, LeMoyne Col, 77-78. *Mem:* AAAS; Soc Protozool; Am Soc Zool; Am Asn Jesuit Sci; NY Acad Sci. *Res:* Development in Sciara, mosquitoes and Chaoborus; effects of colchicine on metamorphosis; use of tritiated thymidine in developmental and regeneration studies; limnoria, cytology and development. *Mailing Add:* Dept Biol St Peters Col Jersey City NJ 07306

SCHUH, MERLYN DUANE, b Avon, SDak, Feb 21, 45; m 69. PHYSICAL CHEMISTRY. *Educ:* Univ SDak, BA, 67; Ind Univ, Bloomington, PhD(phys chem), 71. *Prof Exp:* Asst prof phys chem & biochem, Middlebury Col, 71-75; asst prof, 75-80, ASSOC PROF PHYS CHEM & BIOCHEM, DAVIDSON COL, 80- *Mem:* Inter-Am Photochem Soc; Am Chem Soc; Sigma Xi. *Res:* Energy transfer phenomena in vapor phase organic triplet state molecules; physical properties of rhodopsin in the process of vision. *Mailing Add:* Dept of Chem Davidson Col Davidson NC 28036

SCHUH, RANDALL TOBIAS, b Corvallis, Ore, May 11, 43; div. SYSTEMATIC ENTOMOLOGY. *Educ:* Ore State Univ, BS, 65; Mich State Univ, MS, 67; Univ Conn, PhD(entom), 71. *Prof Exp:* Res grant recipient, Bache Fund, Nat Acad Sci, 71-72; prof biol, Fed Univ Para, Brazil, 73-74; asst cur, 74-80, ASSOC CUR ENTOM & CHMN DEPT, AM MUS NATURAL HIST, 74- *Concurrent Pos:* Adj prof biol, City Univ New York, 78-; ed, Systematic Zool, 71-79. *Mem:* Entom Soc Am; AAAS; Soc Syst Zool. *Res:* Taxonomy, phylogeny and biogeography of Hemiptera of the class Insecta, especially Miridae and semiaquatic families. *Mailing Add:* Dept Entom Am Mus Natural Hist Central Park W at 79th St New York NY 10024

SCHUHMANN, R(EINHARDT), JR, b Corpus Christi, Tex, Dec 16, 14; m 37; c 2. METALLURGICAL ENGINEERING. *Educ:* Univ Mo, BS, 33; Mont Sch Mines, MS, 35; Mass Inst Technol, ScD, 38. *Prof Exp:* From instr to assoc prof metall, Mass Inst Technol, 37-54; chmn div, 54-59, head sch metall eng, 59-64, ROSS PROF ENG, PURDUE UNIV, WEST LAFAYETTE, 54- *Concurrent Pos:* Battelle vis prof, Ohio State Univ, 66-67. *Honors & Awards:* James Douglas Gold Medal, Am Inst Mining, Metall & Petrol Engrs, 70. *Mem:* Nat Acad Eng; Am Soc Metals; Am Chem Soc; Am Inst Mining, Metall & Petrol Engrs; fel Metall Soc. *Res:* Applications of physical chemistry to metallurgical systems; thermodynamics of high temperature multicomponent systems; nonferrous extractive metallurgy. *Mailing Add:* Sch Mat Eng Purdue Univ West Lafayette IN 47907

SCHUHMANN, ROBERT EWALD, b El Paso, Tex, Sept 27, 24; m 53; c 1. PHYSIOLOGY, ENGINEERING. *Educ:* Univ Tex, Austin, BS, 49, MS, 52; Baylor Col Med, PhD(physiol), 69. *Prof Exp:* Instr eng, Univ Tex, Austin, 50-51; engr, Tenn Gas Transmission Co, 51-54; supvry engr, Trunkline Gas Co, 54-62; asst to chief engr, Bovay Engrs, Inc, 62-63, mgr dept mech eng, 63-64; sr res physiologist, Southwest Res Inst, 69-74; prof & dean, 74-78, PROF PHYSIOL, SCH SCI & TECHNOL, UNIV HOUSTON, CLEAR LAKE, 74- *Concurrent Pos:* Asst prof, Univ Tex Health Sci Ctr, San Antonio, 72-74; vis prof biomed eng, Baylor Col Med, 80- *Mem:* Am Physiol Soc; Sigma Xi; Asn Advan Med Instrumentation. *Res:* Cardiovascular and respiratory physiology and central nervous system control of respiration; transvalvular heart assist, bypass during fibrillation without thoracotomy by ventricular catheterization; bioinstrumentation; biological control system theory; physiology of human stress; physiology of human aging. *Mailing Add:* Univ of Houston Clear Lake 2700 Bay Area Blvd Houston TX 77058

SCHUIT, KENNETH EDWARD, b Ticonderoga, NY, Aug 28, 42; m 64; c 3. ANATOMY, CELL BIOLOGY. *Educ:* Wheaton Col, BS, 64; Univ Ill, MS, 66, PhD(cell biol), 69; Univ Va, MD, 74. *Prof Exp:* From instr to asst prof anat, Sch Med, Univ Va, 69-72, resident pediat, 74-76; fel pediat infectious dis, Univ NC, 76-78; ASST PROF PEDIAT, UNIV PITTSBURGH, 78- *Mem:* Am Soc Cell Biol; Am Soc Microbiol; Am Asn Anat. *Mailing Add:* Children's Hosp of Pittsburgh 125 DeSoto St Pittsburgh PA 15213

SCHUKNECHT, HAROLD FREDERICK, b Chancellor, SDak, Feb 10, 17; m 41; c 2. OTOLARYNGOLOGY. *Educ:* Univ SDak, SB, 38; Rush Med Col, MD, 40; Am Bd Otolaryngol, dipl, 49; FRCS(G). *Hon Degrees:* MA, Harvard Univ, 61; DSc, Univ SDak, 73. *Prof Exp:* Resident otolaryngol, Univ Chicago, 46-49, asst prof, 49-53; assoc surgeon, Div Otolaryngol, Henry Ford Hosp, 53-60; PROF OTOL & OTOLARYNGOL, HARVARD MED SCH, 60-; CHIEF OTOLARYNGOL, MASS EYE & EAR INFIRMARY, 61- *Mem:* Am Otol Soc; Am Laryngol, Rhinol & Otol Soc; Am Acad Opthal & Otolaryngol; fel Acoust Soc Am; AMA. *Res:* Physiology of hearing; otological surgery; ear pathology. *Mailing Add:* 263 Highland St Weston MA 02193

SCHULDINER, SIGMUND, b Chicago, Ill, June 12, 13; m 46; c 3. PHYSICAL CHEMISTRY. *Educ:* NY Univ, BA, 38; Columbia Univ, MA, 39. *Prof Exp:* Phys sci aide, Glass Sect, Nat Bur Standards, 40-41; asst head metals sect, Norfolk Naval Shipyard, 41-45, head indust probs sect, 45-46; phys chemist, Corrosion Br, US Naval Res Lab, 46-48, head electrode mech sect, Electrochem Br, 48-71, head, Electrochem Br, 71-75; CONSULT. *Honors & Awards:* William Blum Award, Electrochem Soc, 60; Pure Sci Award, Sci Res Soc Am, 66. *Mem:* Am Chem Soc; Sigma Xi; Electrochem Soc. *Res:* Electrochemistry; kinetics of electrode processes; adsorption; gases in metals; catalysis; corrosion. *Mailing Add:* 12705 Prestwick Dr Oxon Hill MD 20744

SCHULDT, ERICH HENRY, b Newark, NJ, July 11, 25; m 54; c 2. MICROBIOLOGY, FOOD TECHNOLOGY. *Educ:* Brown Univ, BA, 46; Univ Ill, MS, 48; Rutgers Univ, PhD(food technol), 63. *Prof Exp:* Microbiologist, Nat Yeast Corp, 52-63; DIR MICROBIOL RES CENT RES DEPT, ANHEUSER-BUSCH, INC, 63- *Mem:* AAAS; Am Soc Microbiol; Inst Food Technol; Am Asn Cereal Chem. *Res:* Research and development of bakers yeast, bakery products, industrial enzymes, proteins and microbial products. *Mailing Add:* Anheuser-Busch Cent Res Dept 721 Pestalozzi St St Louis MO 63118

SCHULDT, MARCUS DALE, b Geneva, Ill, Aug 31, 30; m 50; c 2. COMPUTER SCIENCE. *Educ:* Aurora Col, BS, 60. *Prof Exp:* Draftsman, Geneva Kitchens, 46-51; engr, Burgess Norton Mfg Co, 55-60; oceanogr, US Coast & Geod Surv, 60-65 & Inst Oceanog, Environ Sci Serv Admin, 65-66; supvry res phys scientist, 66-76, ENVIRON SCIENTIST, ENVIRON PROTECTION AGENCY, 76- *Res:* Application of automation; limnology; oceanography. *Mailing Add:* USEPA-CERL 200 SW 35th St Corvallis OR 97333

SCHULDT, SPENCER BURT, b St Paul, Minn, July 1, 30; m 57, 72; c 5. THEORETICAL PHYSICS, APPLIED MATHEMATICS. *Educ:* Univ Minn, BA, 51, MS, 57. *Prof Exp:* STAFF SCIENTIST, HONEYWELL CORP RES CTR, 57- *Mem:* Am Phys Soc. *Res:* Submicron physics; heat transfer; process control; mathematical programming methods. *Mailing Add:* Honeywell Res Ctr Bloomington MN 55420

SCHULENBERG, JOHN WILLIAM, b Passaic, NJ, Sept 7, 30; m 52, 82; c 4. ORGANIC CHEMISTRY. *Educ:* Queens Col, NY, BS, 51; Columbia Univ, MA, 52, PhD(org chem), 56. *Prof Exp:* Res assoc, 56-60, SR RES CHEMIST ORG CHEM, STERLING-WINTHROP RES INST, 60- *Mem:* Am Chem Soc. *Res:* Heterocyclic synthesis; medicinal chemistry. *Mailing Add:* 187 Adams St Delmar NY 12054

SCHULER, ALAN NORMAN, b Arlington, Mass, Dec 8, 49; m 71; c 2. POLYMER SCIENCE. *Educ:* Univ Mass, BS, 71, MS, 74, PhD(polymer sci & eng), 76. *Prof Exp:* Sr chemist emulsion polymer, Union Carbide Corp, 75-78; scientist polymerization, 78-79, sr scientist, 79-81, RES GROUP LEADER, POLAROID CORP, 81- *Mem:* Am Chem Soc. *Res:* Emulsion polymerization and polymer colloid characterization structure; properties correlations. *Mailing Add:* Polaroid Corp Dept 707 730 Main St Cambridge MA 02139

SCHULER, GEORGE ALBERT, b Altoona, Pa, Sept 21, 33; m 61; c 3. FOOD SCIENCE, MICROBIOLOGY. *Educ:* Pa State Univ, BS, 59; Univ Tenn, MS, 66; Va Polytech Inst & State Univ, PhD(food sci), 70. *Prof Exp:* Mem staff sales & serv, Pa Farm Bur, 59-61; poultry expert, Windsor Poultry Serv Ltd, Australia, 61-63; mem staff sales & serv, Swift & Co, 63-64; teacher, Monroe County Sch Bd, 64-66; FOOD SCIENTIST, COOP EXTEN SERV, UNIV GA, 70- *Mem:* Inst Food Technologists; World Poultry Sci Asn; Poultry Sci Asn. *Res:* Sanitation in and bacteriological surveys of food processing plants and food handling facilities; plans for food processing facilities; rabbit programs processing. *Mailing Add:* Dept of Exten Food Sci Coop Exten Serv Univ of Ga Athens GA 30602

SCHULER, MARTIN N, b Kansas City, Mo, Dec 9, 21; m 46; c 5. BIOCHEMISTRY. *Educ:* Univ Kansas City, BA, 42, MA, 52. *Prof Exp:* Sect head indust chem, 45-61, asst to pres, 61-62, mgr inst rel, 62-65, CORP SECY, MIDWEST RES INST, 63-, MGR STAFF DEVELOP, 65- *Mem:* Am Chem Soc. *Res:* Bacteriology; research administration; industrial chemistry. *Mailing Add:* Midwest Res Inst 425 Volker Blvd Kansas City MO 64110

SCHULER, MATHIAS JOHN, b New York, NY, Apr 29, 18; m 42; c 4. DYEING TECHNOLOGY, COLOR SCIENCE. *Educ:* Brooklyn Col, BA, 38. *Prof Exp:* Asst, Mem Hosp, New York, 38-39; chemist, Continental Baking Co, 39-40; res chemist, Ansbacher Siegle Corp, 40-41; instr, Bd Educ, New York, 41-44; supvr, Kellex Corp, 44-45; res chemist, 45-59, sr res chemist, 59-65, res assoc, 65-70, div head, 70-79, ENVIRON MGR, E I DU PONT DE NEMOURS & CO, INC, 79- *Mem:* Am Asn Textile Chemists & Colorists; Am Chem Soc. *Res:* X-rays and chemical reactions; instrumentation; mass spectrometry; physics of interaction of light on dyes and pigments; color and color specification; mechanisms of dyeing hydrophobic fibers; organometallic compounds. *Mailing Add:* 102 Cyrus Ave Pitman NJ 08071

SCHULER, NORMAN WILLIAM, b Boston, Mass, Aug 23, 28; m 48; c 4. POLYMER CHEMISTRY. *Educ:* Norwich Univ, BS, 50. *Prof Exp:* Asst scientist, 52-58, scientist, 58-66, instr, 65, sr lab supvr, 66-69, res group leader, 69-70, MGR RES & DEVELOP DEPT, POLAROID CORP, 70- *Concurrent Pos:* Consult modern plastics. *Mem:* Optical Soc Am; Soc Photo Optical Instrument Engrs; Soc Info Displays. *Res:* Synthesis of novel polymers; polarizer research. *Mailing Add:* Polaroid Corp Res & Develop Dept 20 Ames St Cambridge MA 02139

SCHULER, ROBERT FREDERICK, b New York, NY, Mar 17, 07; m 29; c 2. ORGANIC CHEMISTRY. *Educ:* Mass Inst Technol, BS, 28, MS, 29. *Hon Degrees:* ScD, St Andrews Univ, 58. *Prof Exp:* Jr res assoc, Am Petrol Inst, 28-29; res chemist, Standard Oil Co, NJ, 29-37; chief chemist & asst plant mgr, Jacqueline Cochran Cosmetics, Inc, 37-42, plant mgr, 42-45, dir res & mgr, J. C. Labs, NJ, 43-45; dir res & prod mgr, Cosmetic Div, Int Latex Corp, 45-50; tech dir, Prince Matchabelli, Inc, 50-58; sect head, Chesebrough-Pond's, Inc, 58-60; sr scientist, Lever Bros Co, 60-61; group mgr res & develop, Toiletries Div, Gillette Co, 61-72; CONSULT, 72- *Mem:* Am Chem Soc; Soc Cosmetic Chem. *Res:* Reactions of olefins to form alcohols; preparation of alkyl phenols from olefins for use as germicides; development and utilization of byproducts of petroleum industry; rubber and plastic products development; development and manufacture of antiseptic baby cosmetics; men's and women's cosmetics and toiletries. *Mailing Add:* 15 Trinity Terr Newton Center MA 02159

SCHULER, ROBERT HUGO, b Buffalo, NY, Jan 4, 26; m 52; c 5. PHYSICAL CHEMISTRY, PHOTOCHEMISTRY. *Educ:* Canisius Col, BS, 46; Univ Notre Dame, PhD(phys chem), 49. *Prof Exp:* Asst prof chem, Canisius Col, 49-53; from assoc chemist to chemist, Brookhaven Nat Lab, 53-56; staff fel & dir radiation res labs, Mellon Inst Sci, Carnegie-Mellon Univ, 56-76, prof chem, 67-76; PROF CHEM & DIR RADIATION LAB, UNIV NOTRE DAME, 76- *Concurrent Pos:* Mem adv comt, Mellon Inst Sci, 62-; mem adv comt, Radiation Chem Data Ctr, 65-76, chmn, 73-75. *Honors & Awards:* Notre Dame Centennial Award, 65. *Mem:* AAAS; Am Chem Soc; Am Phys Soc; Radiation Res Soc (pres, 75-76); Royal Soc Chem. *Res:* Radiation chemistry; kinetics of ionic reactions in the radiolysis of hydrocarbons; electron spin resonance and pulse radiolysis methods to study the nature and reaction kinetics of radiation produced radicals heavy particle radiation chemistry. *Mailing Add:* Radiation Lab Univ of Notre Dame Notre Dame IN 46556

SCHULER, RONALD THEODORE, b Manitowoc, Wis, Dec 26, 40; m 67. AGRICULTURAL ENGINEERING. *Educ:* Univ Wis-Madison, BS(agr) & BS(mech eng), 63, MS, 67, PhD(agr eng), 72. *Prof Exp:* Res asst agr eng, Univ Wis-Madison, 65-69, instr, 69-70; from asst prof to assoc prof, NDak State Univ, 70-76; assoc prof agr eng, Univ Minn, St Paul,76-81; PROF AGR ENG & CHMN DEPT, UNIV WIS-PLATTEVILLE, 81- *Mem:* Am Soc Agr Engrs; Soil Conserv Soc Am. *Res:* Agricultural engineering instrumentation; reduced tillage for soil, water and energy conservation, sunflower seed drying; cattail harvesting. *Mailing Add:* Dept of Agr Eng Univ Wis Platteville WI 53818

SCHULER, RUDOLPH WILLIAM, b Stuttgart, Ger, Sept 2, 19; US citizen; m 44; c 2. CHEMICAL ENGINEERING. *Educ:* Purdue Univ, BS, 48, PhD, 51. *Prof Exp:* Res engr, Colgate-Palmolive-Peet Co, 50-51; res engr, Monsanto Co, 51-55, res group leader, 55-57, asst dir res, 57-64, dir eng & mat res, 64-70, dir technol, New Enterprise Div, 70-76, RES DIR, NEW ENTERPRISE DIV, MONSANTO RES CTR, MONSANTO CO, 76- *Mem:* Am Chem Soc; Am Inst Chem Engrs. *Res:* Reaction kinetics; reactor design; mass transfer. *Mailing Add:* New Enterprises Div 800 N Lindbergh Blvd St Louis MO 63166

SCHULER, VICTOR JOSEPH, b New York, NY, Mar 9, 33; m 56. FISHERIES. *Educ:* Cornell Univ, BS, 66, MS, 69. *Prof Exp:* Lab instr, Ithaca Col, 64-65; res asst, Cornell Univ, 66-68; sr res biologist, 67-68, V PRES PROJ DIR, ICHTHYOLOGICAL ASSOC INC, 75-, SR V PRES, 78- *Mem:* Am Fisheries Soc; Am Inst Fishery Res Biologists. *Res:* Fisheries population studies; environmental impact studies; fish screening studies; ecological consultant in research program initiation and administration. *Mailing Add:* 100 S Cass St Middletown DE 19709

SCHULERT, ARTHUR ROBERT, b Gladwin, Mich, Feb 26, 22; m 49; c 7. CHEMISTRY. *Educ:* Wheaton Col, BS, 43; Princeton Univ, MA, 47; Univ Mich, PhD(biol chem), 51; Am Bd Health Physics, dipl, 63; Am Bd Clin Chem, dipl, 64. *Prof Exp:* Res asst, Manhattan Proj, Princeton Univ, 43-46, teaching asst chem, Univ, 46-47; instr chem & physics, Taylor Univ, 47-48; res asst, Dept Biol Chem, Univ Mich, 48-49, teaching asst, 49-51; New York City Pub Health Res Inst fel biol chem, Goldwater Mem Hosp, 51-53, Columbia Univ Res Serv res fel, 53-55, res assoc, Lamont Geol Observ, 55-61, actg dir geochem lab, 58-59; from asst prof to assoc prof biochem, Sch Med, Vanderbilt Univ, 61-70; PRES, ENVIRON SCI & ENG CORP, 70- *Concurrent Pos:* Consult, Isotopes Inc, NJ, 57-61 & Interdept Comt for Nutrit for Nat Develop, 59-64; dir biochem div, US Naval Med Res Unit, Cairo, 61-64, head biochem dept, 64-66; mem sci adv comt, 2, 4, 5-T, Environ Protection Agency, 71. *Mem:* Fel Am Inst Chemists; Am Chem Soc; Am Inst Nutrit; Health Physics Soc; fel Am Asn Clin Chemists. *Res:* Role of trace elements in nutrition and disease; mineral metabolism; microanalytical techniques including low level radiochemistry; nuclear fallout, particularly the disposition of fission radioisotopes in the environment and man; drug metabolism and mechanism of action. *Mailing Add:* Environ Sci & Eng Corp Mt Juliet TN 37122

SCHULKE, HERBERT ARDIS, JR, b New Ulm, Minn, Nov 12, 23; m 49; c 2. ELECTRONICS, COMMUNICATIONS. *Educ:* US Mil Acad, BS, 46; Univ Ill, Urbana, MS, 52, PhD(electronics), 54. *Prof Exp:* Assigned adv develop long range radio, Signal Res & Develop Labs, Signal Corps, US Army, Ft Monmouth, NJ, 54-56 & Signal Sch Regiment, 57-58, assoc prof elec eng, US Mil Acad, 58-61, chief of staff, Signal Res & Develop Labs, 61-63, commun-electronics proj officer, Adv Res Projs Agency, Vietnam, 64-65, mil asst tactical warfare, Off Dir Defense Res & Eng, Off Secy Defense, Washington, DC, 66-69, commanding officer, 29th signal group, US Army Strategic Commun Command, Thailand, 69-70, dep dir plans, Defense Commun Agency, Washington, DC, 70-76; gen mgr & exec dir, Inst Elec & Electronics Engrs, 75-77; DIR TELECOMMUN, CHASE MANHATTAN BANK, 77- *Mem:* fel Inst Elec & Electronics Engrs. *Res:* Military electronics equipment research and development; management of all types of military research and development efforts. *Mailing Add:* 138 Borden Rd Middletown NJ 07748

SCHULKE, JAMES DARRELL, b Aurelia, Iowa, June 25, 32; m 56; c 3. PLANT GENETICS, AGRONOMY. *Educ:* Iowa State Univ, BS, 58; Univ Calif, MS, 60, PhD(genetics), 63. *Prof Exp:* GENETICIST, SPRECKELS SUGAR DIV, AMSTAR CORP, 63- *Mem:* Am Soc Sugar Beet Technol; Crop Sci Soc Am; Am Inst Biol Sci. *Res:* Genetics and plant breeding of sugar beets. *Mailing Add:* Spreckels Sugar Div Amstar Corp Spreckels CA 93962

SCHULKIN, MORRIS, b Brooklyn, NY, Feb 6, 19; m 40, 64, 70; c 2. ACOUSTICS. *Educ:* Brooklyn Col, BA, 39; George Washington Univ, MS, 48; Cath Univ Am, PhD, 69. *Prof Exp:* Sci aide, US Weather Bur, 40-41; physicist & engr, Nat Bur Standards, 41-47; physicist, Naval Res Lab, US Dept Navy, 47-48; physicist & engr, Nat Bur Standards, 48-50; physicist, Underwater Sound Lab, 50-56; chief engr, Martin Co, 56-59; chief scientist, Marine Electronics Off, Avco Corp, 59-63; adv engr, Underseas Div, Westinghouse Elec Corp, 63-66; dir performance anal, Antisubmarine Warfare, Spec Proj Off, 66-67; res physicist, Naval Res Lab, 68; consult physicist, Naval Underwater Systs Ctr, 68-72; assoc sci & tech dir, Naval Oceanographic Off, 72-75; vpres, Mar Assoc, Inc, 75-76; ASSOC TO DIR & PRIN PHYSICIST, APPL PHYSICS LAB, UNIV WASH, 76- *Concurrent Pos:* Assoc, George Washington Univ & asst, Univ Md, 47-48; lectr, Drexel Inst, 59; instr, USDA Grad Sch, 61-65; consult, US Off Naval Res, 61 & 73-75; lectr ocean acoustics & eng, Cath Univ Am, 73-77. *Mem:* Am Geophys Union; fel Acoust Soc Am; Inst Elec & Electronics Eng. *Res:* Operations research; underwater sound; oceanography; wave propagation; theory of underwater explosions; oceanic variabilities. *Mailing Add:* 9325 Orchard Brook Dr Potomac MD 20854

SCHULKIND, MARTIN LEWIS, b New York, NY, Feb 22, 36; m 63; c 3. PEDIATRICS, IMMUNOLOGY. *Educ:* NY Univ, AB, 56; Chicago Med Sch, MD, 60. *Prof Exp:* From instr to asst prof, 67-72, ASSOC PROF PEDIAT & COMMUNITY HEALTH & FAMILY MED, COL MED, UNIV FLA, 72- *Concurrent Pos:* NIH spec trainee acad pediat, Univ Fla, 65-67; res grants, Nat Found March of Dimes, 70-72, Fla Med Found, 70-71 & Fla Heart Asn, 71-72. *Mem:* AAAS; Am Fedn Clin Res; Soc Pediat Res; Am Asn Immunol. *Res:* Developmental immunology; restoration of cell-mediated immunity; cell-mediated immunity in rheumatic diseases; immunological deficiency disorders; rural health care delivery. *Mailing Add:* Dept of Pediat Univ of Fla Col of Med Gainesville FL 32610

SCHULL, WILLIAM JACKSON, b Louisiana, Mo, Mar 17, 22; m 46. HUMAN GENETICS. *Educ:* Marquette Univ, BS, 46, MS, 47; Ohio State Univ, PhD(genetics), 49. *Prof Exp:* Head dept genetics, Atomic Bomb Casualty Comn, Japan, 49-51; jr geneticist, Inst Human Biol, Univ Mich, 51-53, asst geneticist, 53-56, from asst prof to prof human genetics, Med Sch, 56-72, prof anthrop, 69-72; PROF HUMAN GENETICS, UNIV TEX GRAD SCH BIOMED SCI, HOUSTON, 72- *Concurrent Pos:* Vis fel, Australian Nat Univ, 69; consult, Atomic Bomb Casualty Comn, Japan, 54 & 56; consult, NIH, 56-, chmn genetics study sect, 69-72; dir, Child Health Surv, Japan, 59-60; vis prof, Univ Chicago, 63; Ger Res Asn guest prof, Univ Heidelberg, 70; vis prof, Univ Chile, 75; mem comt atomic casualties, Nat Res Coun, 51 & subcomt biol, Comt Dent, 51-55; mem comt on collab proj, Nat Inst Neurol Dis & Stroke, 57-; mem panel in genetic effects of radiation, WHO, 58- & panel of experts human heredity, 61-; mem nat adv comt radiation, USPHS, 60-64 & bd sci counsrs, Nat Inst Dent Res, 66-69; dir, Radiation Effects Res Found & head dept epidemiol & Japan, 78-80; adv, Nat Heart & Lung Inst; mem subcomt biol & med, AEC; mem human biol coun, Soc Study Human Biol. *Honors & Awards:* Centennial Award, Ohio State Univ, 70. *Mem:* AAAS; USMex Border Health Asn; hon mem Japanese Soc Human Genetics; hon mem, Peruvian Soc Human Genetics; hon mem Genetic Soc Chile. *Res:* Biometry. *Mailing Add:* Ctr Demographic & Pop Genetics PO Box 20334 Houston TX 77025

SCHULLER, IVAN KOHN, b Cluj, Rumania, June 8, 46; Chile citizen; m 74; c 2. PHYSICS. *Educ:* Univ Chile, Licenciado, 70; Northwestern Univ, MS, 72, PhD(physics), 76. *Prof Exp:* Res asst physics, Univ Chile, 66-70; res asst, Northwestern Univ, 70-74; sr res aide, Argonne Nat Lab, 74-76; adj asst prof, Univ Calif, Los Angeles, 76-78; PHYSICIST, ARGONNE NAT LAB, 78- *Mem:* Am Phys Soc; Sigma Xi; Inst Elec & Electronic Engrs; Soc Explor Geophysicists. *Res:* Low temperature physics; solid state physics; prospecting geophysics; superconducting electronics. *Mailing Add:* Solid State Sci Div Argonne Nat Lab Argonne IL 60439

SCHULLERY, STEPHEN EDMUND, b Harrisonburg, Va, June 8, 43; m 69; c 1. PHYSICAL BIOCHEMISTRY. *Educ:* Eastern Mich Univ, BA, 65; Cornell Univ, PhD(phys chem), 70. *Prof Exp:* From asst prof to assoc prof, 70-80, PROF CHEM, EASTERN MICH UNIV, 80- *Mem:* AAAS; Am Chem Soc; Biophys Soc. *Res:* Physical chemistry of biological macromolecules; structure and function of model biological cell membranes. *Mailing Add:* Dept of Chem Eastern Mich Univ Ypsilanti MI 48197

SCHULMAN, HAROLD, b Newark, NJ, Oct 26, 30; m 54; c 3. OBSTETRICS & GYNECOLOGY. *Educ:* Univ Fla, BS, 51; Emory Univ, MD, 55; Bd Maternal Fetal Med, cert, 75. *Prof Exp:* From instr to asst prof obstet & gynec, Temple Univ, 61-65; from asst prof to assoc prof, 65-71, PROF OBSTET & GYNEC, ALBERT EINSTEIN COL MED, 71- *Concurrent Pos:* Am Cancer Soc fel, 59-60; USPHS fel, 68. *Mem:* AAAS; Am Col Obstet & Gynec; Soc Gynec Invest. *Res:* Obstetric physiology. *Mailing Add:* Dept Obstet & Gynec Jacobi Hosp Pelham Pkwy S & Gastchester Rd Bronx NY 10461

SCHULMAN, HERBERT MICHAEL, b New York, NY, Feb 7, 32. CELL BIOLOGY, BIOCHEMISTRY. *Educ:* Bard Col, BA, 55; Yale Univ, PhD(microbiol), 62. *Prof Exp:* Asst prof biol, Univ Calif, San Diego, 63-69; STAFF INVESTR EXP HEMAT, LADY DAVIS INST, JEWISH GEN HOSP, 69- *Concurrent Pos:* NIH fel, Univ Calif, San Diego, 62-63 & res grant, 63-69; Med Res Coun & Nat Res Coun grants, Lady Davis Inst, Jewish Gen Hosp, 69-; vis prof, Univ Helsinki, 68-69; asst prof, McGill Univ, 69-72; Can Dept Agr grants; vis scientist, John Innes Inst, Norwich, Eng, 77-78; Nujfield Found Travel Grant, 77-78; consult nitrogen fixation res, Can Dept Agr, 76- *Mem:* Can Soc Cell Biol; Int Soc Develop Biol. *Res:* Control of hemoglobin synthesis and development of erythrocytes; biochemistry of iron metabolism; synthesis of leg-hemoglobin; differentiation of root nodules. *Mailing Add:* Lady Davis Inst Jewish Gen Hosp 3755 Cote St Catherine Rd Montreal PQ H3T 1E2 Can

SCHULMAN, HOWARD, b Holon, Israel, Feb 5, 49. NEUROPHARMACOLOGY, BIOCHEMISTRY. *Educ:* Univ Calif, Los Angeles, BS, 71; Harvard Univ, PhD(biochem), 76. *Prof Exp:* Fel, Med Sch, Yale Univ, 76-78; ASST PROF PHARMACOL, SCH MED, STANFORD UNIV, 78- *Res:* Calcium and cyclic adenosine monophosphate-dependent protein phosphorylation in brain function; mechanism of action of psychotropic drugs. *Mailing Add:* Dept of Pharmacol Stanford Univ Sch of Med Stanford CA 94305

SCHULMAN, IRVING, b New York, NY, Feb 17, 22; m 50; c 2. MEDICINE, PEDIATRICS. *Educ:* NY Univ, BA, 42, MD, 45. *Prof Exp:* Instr pediat, Sch Med, NY Univ, 49-50; from instr to assoc prof, Cornell Univ, 52-58; prof, Med Sch, Northwestern Univ, 58-61; prof & head dept, Univ Ill Col Med, 61-72; PROF PEDIAT & CHMN DEPT, SCH MED, STANFORD UNIV, 72- *Concurrent Pos:* USPHS res fel, Med Col, Cornell Univ, 50-52; consult, Nat Inst Child Health & Human Develop, 64-; ed-in-chief, Advances in Pediat. *Honors & Awards:* Mead-Johnson Award, 60. *Mem:* Soc Pediat Res (pres, 66); Am Pediat Soc; Am Soc Clin Invest; Am Acad Pediat; Am Soc Hemat. *Res:* Pediatric hematology; coagulation physiology. *Mailing Add:* Dept of Pediat Stanford Univ Med Ctr Stanford CA 94305

SCHULMAN, JAMES HERBERT, b Chicago, Ill, Nov 15, 15; m 40; c 3. SOLID STATE PHYSICS, OPTICAL PHYSICS. *Educ:* Mass Inst Technol, SB, 39, PhD(inorg chem), 42. *Prof Exp:* Instr, Suffolk Univ, 40-41; asst, Div Indust Coop, Mass Inst Technol, 41-44; sr engr, Sylvania Elec Prod, 46-53; head dielectrics br, US Naval Res Lab, 53-60, dep sci dir, Off Naval Res, London, 60-61, head dielectrics br, US Naval Res Lab, 62-64, chair mat sci, US Naval Res Lab, 64-65, supt optical physics div, 65-67, assoc dir res, 67-74, sci dir & chief scientist, London Br Off, 74-77, chair mat sci, US Naval Res Lab & actg tech dir, US Off Naval Res, 77-79; RES PROF & STAFF SCIENTIST, GEORGE WASHINGTON UNIV, 79- *Concurrent Pos:* Nat Mat Adv Bd, Nat Acad Sci/Nat Res Coun, 80-; US mem, Res Grants Prog Panel, NATO, 79-81; assoc ed, J Opt Soc Am, 71-80; consult, sci & tech mgt, 79- *Honors & Awards:* Sigma Xi Award, 57. *Mem:* Fel AAAS; fel Am Phys Soc; fel Optical Soc Am; Am Chem Soc. *Res:* Luminescent materials; radiation sensitive solids; dosimetry; crystal chemistry and physics; glass; lasers; color centers. *Mailing Add:* 5628 Massachusetts Ave Bethesda MD 20816

SCHULMAN, JEROME LEWIS, b New York, NY, Nov 15, 25; m 49; c 3. PSYCHIATRY. *Educ:* Univ Rochester, BA, 46; Long Island Col Med, MD, 49. *Prof Exp:* Intern med, Jewish Hosp, Brooklyn, 49-50, resident pediat, 50-51 & 53-54; resident psychiat, Johns Hopkins Hosp, 54-57; asst prof pediat, psychiat & neurol, 57-65, PROF PEDIAT & PSYCHIAT & CHIEF PSYCHIAT, MED SCH, NORTHWESTERN UNIV, CHICAGO, 65- *Concurrent Pos:* Dir child guid & develop clins & attend pediatrician & psychiatrist, Children's Mem Hosp, 57-; consult, Joseph P Kennedy Jr Found, 58-; asst prof, Med Col, Cornell Univ, 68-69. *Mem:* Am Psychiat Asn; Am Asn Ment Deficiency; Am Pediat Soc; Soc Biol Psychiat; Am Acad Pediat. *Res:* Child psychiatry and development; mental retardation; child psychotherapy. *Mailing Add:* Dept of Pediat Northwestern Univ Chicago IL 60611

SCHULMAN, JEROME M, b New York, NY, Oct 21, 38; m 65. CHEMICAL PHYSICS. *Educ:* Rensselaer Polytech Inst, BChE, 60; Columbia Univ, MA, 61, PhD(chem), 64. *Prof Exp:* Res assoc theoret chem, NY Univ, 64-66, asst prof chem, 66-67; sr res assoc, Yeshiva Univ, 67-68; from asst prof to assoc prof chem physics, Polytech Inst Brooklyn, 68-71; assoc prof chem, 71-74, PROF CHEM, QUEENS COL, NY, 74- *Concurrent Pos:* Alfred P Sloan fel, Polytech Inst Brooklyn & Queens Col, NY, 71-73. *Mem:* Am Chem Soc; Am Phys Soc. *Res:* Quantum theory of atoms and molecules; perturbation theory; electromagnetic properties of atoms and molecules; theoretical organic chemistry. *Mailing Add:* Dept of Chem Queens Col Flushing NY 11367

SCHULMAN, JOSEPH DANIEL, b Brooklyn, NY, Dec 20, 41; m 64; c 2. HUMAN GENETICS, OBSTETRICS. *Educ:* Brooklyn Col, BA, 61; Harvard Univ, MD, 66. *Prof Exp:* Intern & resident pediat, Mass Gen Hosp, 66-68; clin assoc genetics, NIH, 68-70; resident obstet, Cornell Med Ctr, 70-73; fel develop biochem, Cambridge Univ, Eng, 73-74; head human genetics sect, 74-79, DIR, INTERINST GENETICS TRAINING PROG, NIH, 79- *Concurrent Pos:* Prof obstet & gynec, George Washington Univ, Sch Med, 75- *Mem:* Soc Pediat Res; Soc Gynec Invest; Am Soc Human Genetics; Am Soc Clin Invest. *Res:* Human biochemistry, genetics and development; human genetic diseases. *Mailing Add:* Bldg 10 Rm 13N-260 NIH Bethesda MD 20205

SCHULMAN, LADONNE HEATON, b Jacksonville, Fla, May 13, 36; m 65. MOLECULAR BIOLOGY, BIOCHEMISTRY. *Educ:* Wheaton Col, Mass, BA, 57; Columbia Univ, MA, 60, PhD(chem), 64. *Prof Exp:* Res assoc biochem, Med Ctr, NY Univ, 66-68; from asst prof to assoc prof, 68-78, PROF DEVELOP BIOL & CANCER, ALBERT EINSTEIN COL MED, 78- *Concurrent Pos:* NIH fel biochem, Med Ctr, NY Univ, 64-66; NIH career develop award, 69-74; Am Cancer Soc fac res award, 74-77. *Mem:* Am Chem Soc; Am Soc Biol Chem. *Res:* Protein-nucleic acid interactions; structure and function of transfer RNA; protein synthesis. *Mailing Add:* Dept Develop Biol & Cancer Albert Einstein Col of Med Bronx NY 10461

SCHULMAN, LAWRENCE S, b Newark, NJ, Nov 21, 41; c 3. PHYSICS, STATISTICAL MECHANICS. *Educ:* Yeshiva Univ, BA, 63; Princeton Univ, PhD(physics), 67. *Prof Exp:* From asst prof to prof physics, Ind Univ, Bloomington, 67-78; assoc prof, 72-77, PROF PHYSICS, ISRAEL INST TECHNOL, 77- *Concurrent Pos:* consult, Los Alamos Sci Labs, 64, Lawrence Radiation Lab, Livermore, 65 & 68 & IBM Corp, 75-81; Vis scientist, Israel Inst Technol, 70-71; NATO fel, 70-71. *Mem:* Am Phys Soc; Israel Phys Soc. *Res:* Mathematical physics; phase transitions; elementary particles; quantum mechanics. *Mailing Add:* Dept of Physics Israel Inst Technol Haifa Israel

SCHULMAN, MARTIN PHILLIP, b New York, NY, Apr 4, 25; div; c 2. BIOCHEMICAL PHARMACOLOGY. *Educ:* City Col New York, BS, 44; Univ Calif, PhD(biochem), 49. *Prof Exp:* Sr chemist, Fleischmann Labs, 44-45; res assoc physiol chem, Sch Med, Univ Pa, 50-51; from instr to asst prof biochem, Med Sch, State Univ NY Upstate Med Ctr, 51-60; assoc prof pharmacol, 60-65, PROF PHARMACOL, UNIV ILL COL MED, 65- *Concurrent Pos:* Nat Res Coun fel, Sch Med, Univ Pa, 49-50; Lalor fel, Marine Biol Lab, Woods Hole, 51; Swedish Med Res Coun fel, Karolinska Inst, Stockholm, 75-76; mem, Minority Access Res Career Review Comt, Nat Inst Gen Med Sci, 76-79. *Mem:* Am Soc Biol Chem; Am Soc Pharmacol & Exp Therapeut. *Res:* Ethanol and drug metabolism. *Mailing Add:* Dept Pharmacol Univ Ill Col Med Chicago IL 60612

SCHULMAN, MARVIN, b Brooklyn, NY, Nov 13, 27; m 54; c 4. ENGINEERING. *Educ:* Brooklyn Col, BA, 53. *Prof Exp:* Electronic scientist, Mat Lab, 50-54, SUPVRY GEN ENGR, AIRCRAFT & CREW SYSTS TECHNOL DIRECTORATE, NAVAL AIR DEVELOP CTR, US DEPT NAVY, 54- *Concurrent Pos:* Mem occupant restraint systs comt, Soc Automotive Engrs; Survival & Flight Equip Asn. *Mem:* Instrument Soc Am; SAFE. *Res:* Design and development of aircraft escape and fixed seating systems; restraint, occupant protective devices and energy absorption on impact and high acceleration exposure. *Mailing Add:* Aircraft & Crew Syst Technol Directorate Code 6034 NADC Warminster PA 18974

SCHULMAN, SIDNEY, b Chicago, Ill, Mar 1, 23; m 45; c 3. NEUROLOGY. *Educ:* Univ Chicago, BS, 44, MD, 46. *Prof Exp:* From asst prof to assoc prof, 52-65, PROF NEUROL, UNIV CHICAGO, 65- *Mem:* Am Acad Neurol; Am Neurol Asn. *Res:* Neuropathology; clinical neurology; behavioral effects of experimental lesions in the thalamus. *Mailing Add:* Univ of Chicago Culver Hall 1025 E 57th St Chicago IL 60637

SCHULMAN, STEPHEN GREGORY, b Brooklyn, NY, June 11, 40; m 68; c 3. ANALYTICAL CHEMISTRY, PHOTOCHEMISTRY. *Educ:* City Col New York, BS, 61; Univ Ariz, PhD(chem), 67. *Prof Exp:* Asst chemist, Boyce Thompson Inst Plant Res, 62-64, phys chemist, 67-68; mem tech staff, Bellcomm Inc, 68-69; from asst prof to assoc prof, 70-77, PROF PHARMACEUT CHEM, COL PHARM, UNIV FLA, 77- *Concurrent Pos:* Fel, Dept Chem, Univ Fla, 69-70. *Mem:* Am Soc Photobiol; Am Chem Soc; The Chem Soc; Acad Pharmaceut Sci; NY Acad Sci. *Res:* Molecular electronic spectroscopy, mixed ligand chelates; analytical chemistry in biological fluids and living tissues; binding of drugs to proteins and nucleic acids. *Mailing Add:* Col of Pharm Univ of Fla Gainesville FL 32610

SCHULSON, ERLAND MAXWELL, b Ladysmith, BC, May 28, 41; m 64; c 4. MATERIALS ENGINEERING, PHYSICAL METALLUGY. *Educ:* Univ BC, BASc, 64, PhD(metall eng), 68. *Prof Exp:* Sr res fel, Univ Oxford, 68-69; res officer, Chalk River Nuclear Labs, Atomic Energy Can Ltd, 69-78; ASSOC PROF ENG, THAYER SCH ENG, DARTMOUTH COL, 78- *Mem:* Am Inst Mining, Metall & Petrol Engrs. *Res:* Materials science; relationship between the microstructure and the plastic flow and fracture of materials; scanning electron microscopy. *Mailing Add:* Thayer Sch Eng Dartmouth Col Hanover NH 03755

SCHULT, ROY LOUIS, b Brooklyn, NY, Aug 31, 34; m 58, 77; c 3. THEORETICAL PHYSICS. *Educ:* Univ Rochester, BS, 56; Cornell Univ, PhD(theoret physics), 61. *Prof Exp:* Res assoc, 61-63, res asst prof, 63-64, asst prof, 64-69, ASSOC PROF PHYSICS, UNIV ILL, URBANA, 69- *Concurrent Pos:* Vis assoc physicist, Brookhaven Nat Labs, 69-70. *Mem:* Am Phys Soc. *Res:* Weak interactions; theory of elementary particles; nonlinear systems. *Mailing Add:* Dept of Physics Univ of Ill Urbana IL 61801

SCHULTE, DANIEL HERMAN, b Osceola, Iowa, Aug 3, 29; m 55; c 3. ASTRONOMY, OPTICS. *Educ:* Phillips Univ, AB, 51; Univ Chicago, PhD(astron), 58. *Prof Exp:* Asst, Yerkes Observ, Univ Chicago, 51-56; optical engr, Perkin-Elmer Corp, 56-59; asst astronomer, Kitt Peak Observ, Ariz, Asn Univs Res in Astron, 59-65; staff physicist, Optical Design Dept, Itek Corp, 65-81; RES SCIENTIST, LOCKHEED PALO ALTO RES LABS, 81- *Concurrent Pos:* Consult, Haneman Assocs, Tex, 61 & Tropel, Inc, NY, 62-63. *Mem:* Am Astron Soc; Optical Soc Am; Int Astron Union. *Res:* Observational astronomy; astronomical spectroscopy and photometry; optical design; computer applications to astronomical problems. *Mailing Add:* Lockheed Palo Alto Res Labs Bldg 201 3251 Hanover St Palo Alto CA 94304

SCHULTE, HARRY FRANK, b St Louis, Mo, Jan 1, 14; m 35; c 3. INDUSTRIAL HYGIENE. *Educ:* Wash Univ, BS, 34; Harvard Univ, MS, 46. *Prof Exp:* Res chemist, Shell Oil Co, 35-41; indust hyg engr, State Bd Health, Mo, 41-48; leader indust hyg group, 48-74, prog coordr, Biomed & Environ Prog, Energy Off, 74-75, sci adv indust hyg group, Los Alamos Sci Lab, 75-78, CONSULT INDUST HYG, 78- *Concurrent Pos:* Lectr, Sch Med, Univ Kans, 42-48 & Harvard Sch Pub Health, 63-77; mem, Nat Coun Radiation Protection & measurements. *Honors & Awards:* Cummings Award in Indust Hyg, 72. *Mem:* Health Phys Soc; Am Indust Hyg Asn (pres, 63-64); Am Conf Govt Indust Hygienists; Am Acad Indust Hyg (pres, 72); Brit Occup Hyg Soc. *Res:* Evaluation and control of health hazards in industrial environment; dust; toxic chemicals; noise; air pollution. *Mailing Add:* 861 43rd St Los Alamos NM 87544

SCHULTE, HARRY JOHN, JR, b Newark, NJ, July 1, 25; m 49; c 3. EXPERIMENTAL PHYSICS. *Educ:* Rensselaer Polytech Inst, BS, 48; Univ Rochester, PhD(physics), 53. *Prof Exp:* Jr physicist, Univ Rochester, 48, asst, 48-52, instr, 52-53; res assoc physics, Univ Minn, 53-55; mem tech staff, Bell Tel Labs, Inc, 55-62 & Bellcomm, 62-64, PHYSICIST, BELL LABS, INC, 64- *Res:* Particle accelerators; instrumentation; digital, radio and optical communication techniques. *Mailing Add:* 10 Rustic Terr Fair Haven NJ 07701

SCHULTE, WILLIAM JOHN, JR, b Stryker, Ohio, Nov 6, 28; m 61; c 7. SURGERY. *Educ:* Univ Toledo, BS, 52; Ohio State Univ, MD, 56; Am Bd Surg, dipl, 64. *Prof Exp:* Asst clin instr, 59-63, from instr to assoc prof, 63-77, PROF SURG, MED COL WIS, 77-; asst chief surg serv, 78-80, CHIEF SURG INTENSIVE CARE UNIT, VET ADMIN CTR, 70-, CHIEF SURG SERV, 80- *Concurrent Pos:* Gastrointestinal res fel, 64-65; attend staff, Milwaukee County Gen Hosp, 64- & Wood Vet Admin Hosp, 65-; Vet Admin clin investr, 65-68; staff attend, St Joseph's Hosp & Mt Sinai Hosp, Milwaukee, Wis. *Mem:* Am Fedn Clin Res; fel Am Col Surg; Am Gastroenterol Soc; Asn Acad Surg; Cent Surg Asn. *Res:* General surgery; parenteral nutrition; gastrointestinal motility; gastric and pancreatic physiology. *Mailing Add:* Surg Serv Vet Admin Hosp Milwaukee WI 53193

SCHULTER-ELLIS, FRANCES PIERCE, b Helena, Ala, Sept 22, 23; m 42; c 2. ANATOMY, PHYSICAL ANTHROPOLOGY. *Educ:* Birmingham Southern Col, BS, 52; Emory Univ, MS, 54; George Washington Univ, PhD(anat), 72. *Prof Exp:* Instr biol, Chamblee High Sch, Ga, 60-61; instr zool, anat & physiol, Marjorie Webster Jr Col, 61-65; ASST PROF ANAT, SCH MED, UNIV MD, BALTIMORE, 72- *Concurrent Pos:* Res collabr, Div Phys Anthropol, Smithsonian Inst, 80- *Mem:* Human Biol Coun; Am Asn Phys Anthropologists; Am Anthrop Asn; AAAS; Am Asn Anatomists. *Res:* Craniometry, with special emphasis on temporal bone and cranial base variations, middle and inner ear disease, otitis media, human variation and asymmetry; bone aging, morphology of human hand skeleton. *Mailing Add:* Dept of Anat Univ Md Sch Med 655 W Baltimore St Baltimore MD 21201

SCHULTES, RICHARD EVANS, b Boston, Mass, Jan 12, 15; m 59; c 3. BOTANY. *Educ:* Harvard Univ, AB, 37, MA, 38, PhD(econ bot), 41. *Hon Degrees:* MH, Nat Univ Colombia, 53. *Prof Exp:* Collabr, Inst Biol, Nat Univ Mex, 38, 39 & 41; Nat Res Coun fel, Inst Natural Sci, Nat Univ Colombia, 41; hon res fel, Bot Mus, 41-54, curator, Ames Orchid Herbarium, 54-58, lectr econ bot, Univ, 58-70, exec dir, Bot Mus, 68-70, Mangelsdorf prof natural sci, 75-80, prof, 70-80, JEFFREY PROF BIOL, HARVARD UNIV, 80-, CURATOR ECON BOT, BOT MUS, 58-, DIR, MUS, 70- *Concurrent Pos:* Rubber researcher, Rubber Develop Corp, Colombia, 42-43; jungle explor & botanist, USDA, 43-54; collabr, 54-55; collabr, Northern Inst Agr, Brazil, 46; Guggenheim fel, 50; ed, Bot Mus Leaflets Harvard Univ, 58- & Econ Bot, 63-; adj prof pharmacog, Sch Pharm, Univ Ill, 75- *Honors & Awards:* Orden de la Victoria Regia, Colombian Govt. *Mem:* Nat Acad Sci; Col Acad Sci, Ecuador; Acad Sci, Argentina; fel Am Acad Arts & Sci; Linnean Soc. *Res:* Latin American ethnobotany, especially narcotics and poisons used by primitive peoples; orchid taxonomy; taxonomy of rubber plants. *Mailing Add:* Bot Mus Harvard Univ Oxford St Cambridge MA 02138

SCHULTHEIS, JAMES J, b Rochester, NY, Aug 22, 32; m 55; c 5. PHYSICS. *Educ:* John Carroll Univ, BS, 54; Univ Rochester, MS, 56. *Prof Exp:* Engr, Atomic Power Div, Westinghouse Elec Corp, 55-56; asst physicist, Argonne Nat Lab, 56-58; nuclear engr, 58-67, nuclear consult, 67-71, mgr mat systs reliability, Energy Res & Develop Admin, 71-77, mgr steam generator-coolant technol, 77-80, MGR, CERAMIC DEVELOPMENT LAB, KNOLLS ATOMIC POWER LAB, DEPT ENERGY, 80- *Mem:* Am Nuclear Soc. *Res:* Radiological physics; reactor physics; advanced reactor engineering; heat transfer; reactor control; steam generators; materials engineering. *Mailing Add:* 1139 Fernwood Dr Schenectady NY 12309

SCHULTHEISS, PETER M(AX), b Munich, Ger, Oct 18, 24; nat US; m 59; c 3. ELECTRICAL ENGINEERING. *Educ:* Yale Univ, BE, 45, MEng, 48, PhD(elec eng), 52. *Prof Exp:* From instr to assoc prof, 48-64, PROF ENG & APPL SCI, YALE UNIV, 64- *Mem:* Inst Elec & Electronics Engrs; Acoust Soc Am. *Res:* Communication theory; automatic control; applied mathematics; underwater acoustics. *Mailing Add:* 481 Shepard Ave Hamden CT 06514

SCHULTZ, ALBERT BARRY, b Philadelphia, Pa, Oct 10, 33; m 55; c 3. ENGINEERING MECHANICS. *Educ:* Univ Rochester, BS, 55; Yale Univ, MEng, 59, PhD(mech eng), 62. *Prof Exp:* Lectr mech eng, Yale Univ, 61-62; asst prof, Univ Del, 62-65; from asst prof to assoc prof, 65-71, PROF MAT ENG, UNIV ILL, CHICAGO CIRCLE, 71- *Concurrent Pos:* NIH spec res fel, Stockholm, 71-72; res career award, NIH, 75-80; assoc ed, J Biomech Eng, 76-; vis prof, Sahlgren Hosp, Gothenburg, Sweden, 78-79. *Mem:* Am Soc Biomech; Am Soc Mech Engrs; Int Soc Study Lumbar Spine (pres, 81-82); Am Soc Biomech (pres, 82-83). *Res:* Biomechanics; mechanical behavior of human spine. *Mailing Add:* Dept Mat Eng Univ Ill Box 4348 Chicago IL 60680

SCHULTZ, ALVIN LEROY, b Minneapolis, Minn, July 27, 21; m; c 4. INTERNAL MEDICINE, ENDOCRINOLOGY. *Educ:* Univ Minn, BA, 43, MD, 46, MS, 52. *Prof Exp:* Intern med, Ohio State Univ Hosp, 46-47; from instr to assoc prof, 52-65, PROF MED, MED SCH, UNIV MINN, MINNEAPOLIS, 65-, LECTR, 52-; CHIEF MED, HENNEPIN COUNTY MED CTR, 65- *Concurrent Pos:* Assoc dir, Radioisotope Lab, Minneapolis Vet Admin Hosp, 52-53, asst chief med serv, 53-54, consult, Radioisotope Lab & Med Serv, 54-; attend physician, Endocrine Clin, Univ Minn Hosps, 52-60, chief clin, 60-65; dir radioisotope Lab, Methodist Hosp, 55-59; dir med educ & res, Mt Sinai Hosp, 59-65. *Mem:* Endocrine Soc; Cent Soc Clin Res; Am Fedn Clin Res; fel Am Col Physicians; Am Thyroid Asn. *Res:* Diseases of metabolism and endocrinology, especially of the thyroid gland. *Mailing Add:* 5127 Irving Ave S Minneapolis MN 55419

SCHULTZ, ANDREW, JR, b Harrisburg, Pa, Aug 14, 13; m 39; c 2. ENGINEERING. *Educ:* Cornell Univ, BS, 36, PhD(admin eng), 41. *Prof Exp:* From instr to asst prof admin eng, Cornell Univ, 38-41; assoc prof, 46-50, prof & head dept, 50-61; vpres & dir res, Logistics Mgt Inst, Washington, DC, 61-63; from actg dean to dean, Col Eng, 63-72, actg dean, 78, SPENCER T OLIN PROF ENG, COL ENG, CORNELL UNIV, 72- *Concurrent Pos:* Dir, Chicago Pneumatic Tool Co, S I Handling Systs, Inc, Logistics Mgt Inst, Zurn Indust & Lexington Growth & Res. *Mem:* Am Soc Eng Educ; Am Inst Indust Engrs. *Res:* Statistical applications in engineering; operations research; industrial engineering. *Mailing Add:* 631 Highland Rd Ithaca NY 14850

SCHULTZ, ARNOLD MAX, b Altura, Minn, Sept 9, 20; m 49; c 5. PLANT ECOLOGY. *Educ:* Univ Minn, BSc, 41, MSc, 42; Univ Nebr, PhD(bot), 51. *Prof Exp:* Jr range conservationist, Soil Conserv Serv, USDA, 42; from asst specialist to specialist forestry, 49-66, ecologist, 66-77, PROF FORESTRY & RESOURCE MGT, AGR EXP STA, UNIV CALIF, BERKELEY, 77- *Mem:* AAAS; Soc Gen Systs Res; Ecol Soc Am. *Res:* Sampling and biometric techniques in range ecology; nutrient cycles and productivity in arctic tundra ecosystems; ecology of high mountain meadows; ecosystem management; interdisciplinary undergraduate programs. *Mailing Add:* Sch of Forestry & Conserv Univ of Calif Berkeley CA 94720

SCHULTZ, ARTHUR GEORGE, b Chicago, Ill, Sept 14, 42; m 69. ORGANIC CHEMISTRY. *Educ:* Ill Inst Technol, BSc, 66; Univ Rochester, PhD(chem), 70. *Prof Exp:* Res fel chem, Columbia Univ, 70-72; asst prof chem, Cornell Univ, 72-78; assoc prof, 78-81, PROF CHEM, RENSSELAER POLYTECH INST, 81- *Mem:* Am Chem Soc. *Res:* Natural products synthesis; synthetic and mechanistic organic photochemistry; organo-sulfur chemistry; synthetic organic and natural products chemistry. *Mailing Add:* Dept of Chem Rensselaer Polytech Inst Troy NY 12181

SCHULTZ, ARTHUR JAY, b Brooklyn, NY, July 15, 47. NEUTRON DIFFRACTION, INORGANIC CHEMISTRY. *Educ:* State Univ NY Stony Brook, BS, 69; Brown Univ, PhD(inorg chem), 73. *Prof Exp:* res assoc chem, Univ Ill, Urbana, 73-76; res assoc, 76-78, ASST CHEMIST, ARGONNE NAT LAB, 78- *Mem:* Am Chem Soc; Am Crystallog Asn; AAAS. *Res:* Time-of-flight single-crystal neutron diffraction; transition metal coordination chemistry; organometallic chemistry; structural studies by x-ray and neutron diffraction; one-dimensional conductors. *Mailing Add:* Chem Div Argonne Nat Lab Argonne IL 60439

SCHULTZ, BLANCHE BEATRICE, b Palm, Pa, Aug 23, 20. MATHEMATICS. *Educ:* Ursinus Col, BS, 41; Univ Mich, MS, 49. *Prof Exp:* Teacher high sch, Pa, 41-42; from instr to assoc prof, 46-73, PROF MATH, URSINUS COL, 73-, ASST DEAN COL, 77- *Mem:* Am Math Soc; Math Asn Am. *Mailing Add:* Off of Dean Ursinus Col Collegeville PA 19426

SCHULTZ, CRAMER WILLIAM, b Laurel, Mont, May 2, 26; m 49; c 4. PHYSICS. *Educ:* Univ Calif, BA, 48; Univ Southern Calif, PhD(physics), 55. *Prof Exp:* Assoc prof, 53-64, PROF PHYSICS, CALIF STATE UNIV, LONG BEACH, 64- *Res:* Cryogenics; solid state physics. *Mailing Add:* Dept of Physics Calif State Univ Long Beach CA 90804

SCHULTZ, DAVID HAROLD, b Park Falls, Wis, Sept 10, 42; m 65; c 2. COMPUTER SCIENCE, NUMERICAL ANALYSIS. *Educ:* Univ Wis-Madison, BS, 65, MS, 67, PhD(comput sci), 70. *Prof Exp:* Co-supvr data processing, Surv Res Lab, 65-70, res asst numerical anal, Comput Sci Dept, 68-76, asst prof math, 70-76, ASSOC PROF MATH, UNIV WIS-MILWAUKEE, 76- *Concurrent Pos:* Reviewer, Math Rev; consult, Argonne Nat Lab, 77-78. *Mem:* Soc Indust & Appl Math; Asn Comput Mach. *Res:* Numerical analysis; discrete model theory; fluid flow problems; numerical solutions of differential equations. *Mailing Add:* Dept of Math Univ of Wis Milwaukee WI 53202

SCHULTZ, DAVID MICHAEL, b Akron, Ohio, Apr 25, 48. MARINE GEOCHEMISTRY. *Educ:* Hartwick Col, BA, 70; Univ RI, PhD(oceanog), 74. *Prof Exp:* Fel oceanog, Naval Res Lab, 74-75; PHYS SCIENTIST MARINE ORG GEOCHEM, US GEOL SURV, DEPT INTERIOR, 75- *Res:* Sediment organic geochemistry in the marine environment, including environmental assessment and resource evaluation research; hydrocarbon geochemistry; study of humic substances in sediments and sedimentary rocks. *Mailing Add:* Nat Ctr MS 973 US Geol Surv Reston VA 22092

SCHULTZ, DONALD GENE, b Milwaukee, Wis, Aug 28, 28; m 53; c 3. ELECTRICAL ENGINEERING. *Educ:* Univ Santa Clara, BSEE, 52; Univ Calif, Los Angeles, MS, 55; Purdue Univ, PhD(automatic control), 62. *Prof Exp:* Assoc prof, 62-66, PROF ELEC ENG, UNIV ARIZ, 66-, HEAD SYSTS & INDUST ENGR DEPT, 74- *Concurrent Pos:* Consult, Los Alamos Sci Lab. *Mem:* Inst Elec & Electronics Engrs. *Res:* Automatic control; stability. *Mailing Add:* Dept of Elec Eng Univ of Ariz Tucson AZ 85721

SCHULTZ, DONALD PAUL, b Detroit, Mich, Feb 7, 30; m 51; c 4. ENVIRONMENTAL CONTAMINATION EVALUATION. *Educ:* Concordia Teachers Col, BS, 54; Auburn Univ, PhD(plant physiol), 67. *Prof Exp:* Prin & teacher, St Stephen Lutheran Sch, 54-62; fel, Pesticide Metab, Univ Mo-Columbia, 67-70; fel herbicide metab, Fish Pesticide Res Lab, US Dept Interior, Mo, 70-71, fel, Southeastern Fish Control Lab, Ga, US Dept Interior, 71-80; MEM STAFF, ENVIRON CONTAMINATION EVAL, FISH & WILDLIFE SERV, ATLANTA, 80- *Mem:* AAAS; Aquatic Plant Mat Soc. *Res:* Uptake and metabolism of pesticides; influence of pesticides on metabolic processes. *Mailing Add:* US Fish & Wildlife Serv R B Russell Bldg AE/ECE Atlanta GA 30303

SCHULTZ, DONALD RAYMOND, b North Tonawanda, NY, Nov 2, 18; m 42; c 4. INORGANIC CHEMISTRY. *Educ:* Univ Mich, BS, 40, MS, 52, PhD(chem), 54. *Prof Exp:* Anal chemist, Pa Salt Mfg Co, 40; anal res chemist, McGean Chem Co, 40-42; res engr, Trojan Powder Co, 42-44; res engr, Inorg Res Brine Prods, Mich Chem Corp, 46-50; res engr, Boron Hydrides Eng Res Inst, Univ Mich, 51-54; SR PATENT LIAISON, CENT RES DEPT, 3M CO, 54- *Concurrent Pos:* Lectr, Bethel Col, 65-66. *Mem:* AAAS; Am Chem Soc; Am Inst Chemists. *Res:* Preparation properties and uses of magnesia; inorganic bromides; thermography; coordination chemistry of copper, nickel, cobalt; patent literature; boron hydrides in liquid ammonia; vinyl polymerization with boron alkyls; photoconductivity. *Mailing Add:* 2592 Sumac Ridge White Bear Lake MN 55110

SCHULTZ, DUANE ROBERT, b Bay City, Mich, June 24, 34; m 61; c 1. IMMUNOLOGY, PROTEIN CHEMISTRY. *Educ:* Univ Mich, BS, 57, MS, 60, PhD(microbiol), 64. *Prof Exp:* Staff immunologist, 66-71, ASSOC PROF MED, SCH MED, UNIV MIAMI, 71-; STAFF IMMUNOLOGIST, CORDIS LABS, 66- *Concurrent Pos:* NIH fel immunol, Walter Reed Army Inst Res, 64-66. *Res:* Isolation, purification and function of the nine components of complement. *Mailing Add:* Univ of Miami Sch of Med Dept of Med PO Box 016960 Miami FL 33101

SCHULTZ, EDWARD, b Suffern, NY, Dec 4, 40; m 66; c 2. ANATOMY. *Educ:* Ithaca Col, BA, 62, BS, 65; Temple Univ, PhD(anat), 73. *Prof Exp:* Asst prof, 75-81, ASSOC PROF ANAT, UNIV WIS-MADISON, 81- *Concurrent Pos:* Muscular Dystrophy Asn Can fel, McGill Univ, 73-75. *Mem:* Am Asn Anatomists; AAAS; Am Phys Ther Asn. *Res:* Skeletal muscle regeneration; trophic influence of nerve on muscle; satellite cells; aging. *Mailing Add:* Dept Anat Univ Wis Madison WI 53706

SCHULTZ, EVERETT HOYLE, JR, b Winston-Salem, NC, Sept 13, 27; m 55; c 4. MEDICINE, RADIOLOGY. *Educ:* Bowman Gray Sch Med, MD, 52. *Prof Exp:* Asst prof radiol, Univ Fla, 58-61; assoc prof, Univ NC, 61-67; chief radiol, St Anthony's Hosp, 67-75. *Concurrent Pos:* Ed consult, Yearbk Cancer, 64- *Mem:* AAAS; Radiol Soc NAm; fel Am Col Radiol. *Res:* Clinical research in human gastrointestinal diseases, particularly pancreatic diseases. *Mailing Add:* St Anthony's Hosp 601 12th St N St Petersburg FL 33705

SCHULTZ, FRANKLIN ALFRED, b Whittier, Calif, Mar 27, 41; m 65. ANALYTICAL CHEMISTRY, ELECTROCHEMISTRY. *Educ:* Calif Inst Technol, BS, 63; Univ Calif, Riverside, PhD(chem), 67. *Prof Exp:* Res chemist, Beckman Instruments, Inc, Calif, 67-68; asst prof chem, 68-73, assoc prof, 73-77, PROF CHEM, FLA ATLANTIC UNIV, 77- *Mem:* AAAS; Am Chem Soc; Electrochem Soc. *Res:* Electrochemistry of binuclear transition metal complexes; redox chemistry of inorganic compounds as models for biological electron transfer; analytical applications of ion-selective electrodes; theory of membrane electrode potentials. *Mailing Add:* Dept of Chem Fla Atlantic Univ Boca Raton FL 33432

SCHULTZ, FREDERICK HERMAN CARL, b Hanks, NDak, June 11, 21; m 49; c 3. PHYSICS. *Educ:* Univ NDak, PhB, 42; Univ Idaho, MS, 50; Wash State Univ, PhD(physics), 67. *Prof Exp:* Instr physics, Univ NDak, 42-44 & 46-48, NDak State Univ, 44 & Mont Sch Mines, 50-55; asst prof, Mont State Univ, 55-61; assoc prof, Minot State Col, 61-63; instr, Wash State Univ, 63-68; chmn dept, 68-77, PROF PHYSICS, UNIV WIS-EAU CLAIRE, 68- *Concurrent Pos:* Dir seismog sta, US Coast & Geod Surv, 55-61; energy consult, 77- *Mem:* Am Asn Physics Teachers; Seismol Soc Am; Optical Soc Am; Sigma Xi. *Res:* Seismology; small Montana earthquakes; interaction of polarized infrared radiation with materials and surfaces. *Mailing Add:* Dept of Physics Univ of Wis Eau Claire WI 54701

SCHULTZ, FREDERICK JOHN, b Davenport, Iowa, Oct 12, 29; m 55; c 4. ORGANIC CHEMISTRY, RESEARCH ADMINISTRATION. *Educ:* Augustana Col, Ill, BA, 52; DePauw Univ, MA, 56; Univ Iowa, PhD(chem), 60. *Prof Exp:* Res chemist, 59-62, sr res chemist, 62-65, prod develop mgr, 65-68, mgr res, Res Div, 68-75, dir, 75-78, VPRES RES & DEVELOP, LORILLARD DIV, LOEW'S THEATRES, INC, 78- *Mem:* AAAS; Am Chem Soc; NY Acad Sci; Am Inst Chemists. *Res:* Composition of tobacco and tobacco smoke; relation of composition to biological activity and organoleptic properties; selective filtration of tobacco smoke; analytical methods development; new products in areas of tobacco and food products. *Mailing Add:* Lorillard Res Ctr PO Box 21688 Loew's Theatre Inc Lorillard Div Greensboro NC 27420

SCHULTZ, GERALD EDWARD, b Red Wing, Minn, Sept 2, 36; m 64; c 1. VERTEBRATE PALEONTOLOGY. *Educ:* Univ Minn, BS, 58, MS, 61; Univ Mich, PhD(geol), 66. *Prof Exp:* From asst prof to assoc prof geol, 64-74, PROF GEOL, W TEX STATE UNIV, 74- *Concurrent Pos:* NSF res grant Pleistocene vert, Tex Panhandle, 70-72. *Mem:* Soc Vert Paleont; Am Soc Mammal; Paleont Soc; Am Quaternary Asn; Sigma Xi. *Res:* Vertebrate paleontology, especially late Cenozoic vertebrates and stratigraphy of the High Plains; late Tertiary and Pleistocene microvertebrate faunas and paleoecology. *Mailing Add:* Dept of Geosci WTex State Univ Canyon TX 79015

SCHULTZ, GILBERT ALLAN, b Camrose, Alta, Nov 25, 44; m 69; c 2. DEVELOPMENTAL BIOLOGY. *Educ:* Univ Alta, BSc, 65, MSc, 66; Univ Calgary, PhD(biol), 70. *Prof Exp:* Nat Res Coun Can fel, Weizmann Inst Sci, 70 & Med Ctr, Univ Colo, Denver, 71-72; asst prof, 72-77, ASSOC PROF MED BIOCHEM, FAC MED, UNIV CALGARY, 77- *Mem:* Can Soc Cell Biol; Am Soc Cell Biol; Soc Develop Biol; Soc Develop Biol. *Res:* Study of gene expression during early development of mammalian embryos. *Mailing Add:* Div of Med Biochem Fac of Med Univ of Calgary Calgary AB T2N 1N4 Can

SCHULTZ, HARRY PERSHING, b Racine, Wis, Mar 9, 18; m 43; c 3. ORGANIC CHEMISTRY. *Educ:* Univ Wis, BS, 42, PhD(org chem), 46. *Prof Exp:* Res chemist, Nat Defense Res Comt, Univ Wis, 42-45 & Merck & Co, Inc, NJ, 46-47; from asst prof to assoc prof chem, 47-52, PROF CHEM, UNIV MIAMI, 52-, CHMN DEPT, 72- *Mem:* Am Chem Soc. *Res:* Synthesis organic nitrogen heterocycles; organic reduction; chemical topology; polypeptides. *Mailing Add:* Dept of Chem Univ of Miami Coral Gables FL 33124

SCHULTZ, HARRY WAYNE, b Burlington, Iowa, June 13, 30; m 55; c 3. PHARMACEUTICAL CHEMISTRY. *Educ:* Univ Iowa, BS, 52, MS, 57, PhD(pharmaceut chem), 59. *Prof Exp:* Asst prof, 59-66, ASSOC PROF PHARMACEUT CHEM, ORE STATE UNIV, 66- *Mem:* Am Pharmaceut Asn; Am Chem Soc. *Res:* Organic pharmaceutical chemistry; relationship of chemical structure to pharmacological activity. *Mailing Add:* Dept of Pharmaceut Chem Ore State Univ Sch of Pharm Corvallis OR 97331

SCHULTZ, HARVEY ALBERT, b Tampico, Ill, Jan 4, 13; m 39; c 3. RADIOBIOLOGY. *Educ:* NCent Col, BA, 33; Univ Ill, AM, 35, PhD(physics), 37. *Prof Exp:* Asst physics, Univ Ill, 33-37; physicist, B F Goodrich Co, 37-49; assoc supvr, Armour Res Found, 49-50; physicist, Argonne Nat Lab, 50-70, info specialist, Ctr Human Radiobiol, 70-78; RETIRED. *Mem:* Am Phys Soc. *Res:* Spectroscopy; molecular structure; high polymer physics; rheology; ionization; biophysics; information technology; demography; history; genealogy. *Mailing Add:* 335 Fifth St Downers Grove IL 60515

SCHULTZ, HERMAN SOLOMON, b New York, NY, Sept 15, 24; m 53; c 3. POLYMER CHEMISTRY. *Educ:* City Col New York, BS, 44; Brooklyn Col, MA, 49; Polytech Inst Brooklyn, PhD(org chem), 56. *Prof Exp:* Res chemist, Nepera Chem Co, NY, 48-51; Tech Tape Corp, NJ, 53-54, Nopco Chem Co, 54-55 & Atlantic Refining Co, Pa, 55-56; sr scientist, Cent Res Lab, GAF Corp, Pa, 56-72; mgr polymer res & develop, Cent Res Lab, Itek Corp,

72-76; CHIEF SCIENTIST, CHEM PROD DIV, WATERS ASN, INC, 76- *Mem:* Am Chem Soc. *Res:* Polymerization techniques and catalysts; monomer and polymer structure versus properties and end uses, applied polymer technology, characterization and purification; organic synthesis, especially catalytic methods; carbon monoxide chemistry; hydrogenation, dehydrogenation and oxidation processes; chromatography science. *Mailing Add:* 13 Richard Rd Lexington MA 02173

SCHULTZ, HILBERT KENNETH, b Butternut, Wis, Oct 27, 35; m 57; c 4. SYSTEMS ANALYSIS, COMPUTER SYSTEMS. *Educ:* Univ Wis-Oshkosh, BS, 59; Univ Wis-Madison, MS, 62, PhD(comput sci), 71. *Prof Exp:* Comput analyst supvr, AC Electronics, Inc, 59-61; teacher math, Univ Wis-Oshkosh, 62-63 & 64-66; comput programmer & supvr numerical anal, Univ Wis-Madison, 66-68; assoc prof bus math, 70-80, PROF BUS, UNIV WIS-OSHKOSH, 80- *Concurrent Pos:* Consult govt & indust, 77-79 & med & retail, 80-81. *Mem:* Opers Res Soc Am; Am Prod & Inventory Control Soc; Am Inst Decision Sci. *Res:* Theoretical and practical analysis of transportation problems; development of new computer programs for nonlinear programming; mathematical programming models for use in optimization in industry; systems analysis and design of computer systems. *Mailing Add:* Col of Bus Admin Univ of Wis Oshkosh WI 54901

SCHULTZ, HYMAN, b Brooklyn, NY, July 11, 31; m 57; c 2. ANALYTICAL CHEMISTRY. *Educ:* Brooklyn Col, BS, 56; Pa State Univ, PhD(anal chem), 62. *Prof Exp:* Sr res engr, Rocketdyne Div, NAm Aviation, Inc, Calif, 62-67; scientist & head gas anal sect, Isotopes, Teledyne, Inc, NJ, 67-71; res supvr anal res & serv, Pittsburgh Energy Res Ctr, US Bur Mines, 71-75, res supvr anal res & serv, Pittsburgh Energy Res Ctr, 75-77, BR CHIEF ANAL CHEM, PITTSBURGH ENERGY TECHNOL CTR, DEPT ENERGY, 77- *Mem:* AAAS; Sigma Xi; Am Chem Soc. *Res:* Determination of trace materials in complex natural matrices; analysis of coal and the products of coal research; trace toxic materials in coal and their fate when coal is utilized; standardization of analytical methods for coal conversion materials. *Mailing Add:* Pittsburgh Energy Technol Ctr PO Box 10940 Pittsburgh PA 15236

SCHULTZ, IRWIN, b New York, NY, July 29, 29; m 55; c 5. MEDICINE. *Educ:* NY Univ, BA, 49, MD, 54; Harvard Univ, MSH, 60, ScD(trop med), 64. *Prof Exp:* Asst prof microbiol & med, Med Sch, Northwestern Univ, 61-64; asst prof med, Sch Med, Wash Univ, 65-69; ASSOC CLIN PROF MED, COL MED, ST LOUIS UNIV, 69- *Concurrent Pos:* Mem, Nat Inst Allergy & Infectious Dis, 59-61. *Mem:* AAAS; Am Fedn Clin Res; Am Col Physicians; Am Soc Microbiol. *Res:* Infectious diseases; epidemiology; pathogenesis of viral infections; host defense mechanisms in infectious disease; vaccine effectiveness. *Mailing Add:* 158 Mayfair Plaza Florrisant MO 63033

SCHULTZ, J(EROME) S(AMSON), b Brooklyn, NY, June 25, 33; m 55; c 3. CHEMICAL ENGINEERING, BIOENGINEERING. *Educ:* Columbia Univ, BS, 54, MS, 56; Univ Wis, PhD(biochem), 58. *Prof Exp:* Chem engr, Lederle Labs, Am Cyanamid Co, 58-59, in chg fermentation pilot plant, 59-61, group leader biochem res, 61-64; from asst prof to assoc prof, 64-70, PROF CHEM ENG, UNIV MICH, ANN ARBOR, 70-, CHMN DEPT, 77- *Concurrent Pos:* Res Career Develop Award, NIH, 70-75. *Mem:* Am Soc Artificial Internal Organs; AAAS; Am Chem Soc; Am Inst Chem Engrs. *Res:* Biochemical engineering; production of chemicals and pharmaceuticals by fermentation; kinetics; transport phenomena in membranes; compatibility of biomaterials; artificial organs; transport in blood and tissues; photochemical processes. *Mailing Add:* Dept of Chem Eng Univ of Mich Ann Arbor MI 48104

SCHULTZ, JACK C, b Chicago, Ill, Jan 4, 47. INSECT ECOLOGY, PLANT-INSECT ECOLOGY. *Educ:* Univ Chicago, AB, 69; Univ Wash, PhD(zool), 75. *Prof Exp:* Res instr, 75-80, RES ASST PROF, DEPT BIOL SCI, DARTMOUTH COL, 81- *Concurrent Pos:* Vis fel, Dept Entom, Cornell Univ, 78-79. *Mem:* Ecol Soc Am; Entom Soc Am; Lipidopterists Soc; Soc Study Evolution; Bot Soc Am. *Res:* Coevolutionary interactions among trees, insects and birds; chemical and physiological responses of trees to insects; foraging and predator-avoidance behavior of insects; tropical ecology. *Mailing Add:* Dept of Biol Sci Dartmouth Col Hanover NH 03755

SCHULTZ, JAMES EDWARD, b Sheboygan, Wis, Dec 25, 39; m 63; c 1. MATHEMATICS. *Educ:* Univ Wis-Madison, BS, 63; Ohio State Univ, MS, 67, PhD(math educ), 71. *Prof Exp:* Instr math, High Sch, Wis, 63-68; admin assoc, 68-71, asst prof, 71-78, ASSOC PROF MATH, OHIO STATE UNIV, 78- *Concurrent Pos:* Vis asst prof math, Mich State Univ, 73-74; vis asst prof educ, Univ Chicago, 74-75. *Mem:* Math Asn Am. *Res:* Mathematics preparation of elementary teachers. *Mailing Add:* Dept of Math Ohio State Univ Columbus OH 43210

SCHULTZ, JANE SCHWARTZ, b New York, NY, July 28, 32; m 55; c 3. IMMUNOGENETICS. *Educ:* Hunter Col, BA, 53; Columbia Univ, MS, 55; Univ Mich, MS, 67, PhD(human genetics), 70. *Prof Exp:* Res chemist, Gen Foods Corp, 54-55 & Forest Prod Lab, USDA, 55-58; sci teacher, Pearl River High Sch, NY, 58-59; res assoc, 70-71 & 72-75, ASST PROF HUMAN GENETICS, UNIV MICH, ANN ARBOR, 75-, ASST DEAN CURRICULUM, 79-; GENETICIST, VET ADMIN MED CTR, 72- *Concurrent Pos:* Sr res investr, Dept Immunohaemetology, State Univ Leiden, 71-72; Vet Admin rep, Genetics Study Sect, NIH, 73-77; chief, Div Prog Develop & Review, Vet Admin Res Serv, 76-79. *Mem:* Am Asn Immunologists; Genetics Soc Am; Am Soc Human Genetics; Am Asn Clin Histocompatability Testing. *Res:* Elucidation of the immunological functions controlled by genetically determined transplantation antigens in mouse, rat and man. *Mailing Add:* Vet Admin Med Ctr 2215 Fuller Rd Ann Arbor MI 48105

SCHULTZ, JAY WARD, b Detroit, Mich, Feb 9, 37; m 58; c 2. METALLURGY. *Educ:* Mich Technol Univ, BS, 58; Univ Mich, Ann Arbor, MSE, 60, PhD(metall eng), 65. *Prof Exp:* Asst res engr, Off Res Admin, Univ Mich, Ann Arbor, 60-64; res metallurgist alloy develop, Int Nickel Co, Inc, 64-65, res metallurgist corrosion, 66-70, supvr dry corrosion & nickel chem, 70-76, chem res mgr, 76-78; mgr res, 78-80, dir, 80-82, VPRES, INCO ALLOY PROD CO, 82- *Mem:* Nat Asn Corrosion Engrs; Am Soc Metals; Indust Res Inst. *Res:* Dry corrosion; alloy development; organometallic chemistry; electroplating, polymers; research management. *Mailing Add:* Inco Res & Develop Ctr Suffern NY 10901

SCHULTZ, JEROLD M, b San Francisco, Calif, June 21, 35; m 60; c 4. MATERIALS SCIENCE. *Educ:* Univ Calif, Berkeley, BS, 58, MS, 59; Carnegie Inst Technol, PhD(metall), 65. *Prof Exp:* Intermediate engr mat res, Westinghouse Res Labs, 59-61; from asst prof to assoc prof metall, 65-73, PROF METALL, UNIV DEL, 73- *Concurrent Pos:* Vis asst prof, Stanford Univ, 68; vis prof, Univ Mainz, 74-75; Humboldt sr scientist, Univ Saarbrücken, 77-78. *Mem:* Am Phys Soc; Am Crystallog Asn. *Res:* Polymeric materials; phase transformations; x-ray diffraction technology; crystal imperfections. *Mailing Add:* Dept of Chem Eng Univ of Del Newark DE 19711

SCHULTZ, JOHN E, b Nowata, Okla, Mar 5, 36; m 55; c 3. ORGANIC CHEMISTRY. *Educ:* Westminster Col, Mo, BA, 58; Univ Ill, PhD, 63. *Prof Exp:* From asst prof to assoc prof, 64-70, chmn dept, 74-77, PROF CHEM, WESTMINSTER COL, MO, 70-, ASST ACAD DEAN, 77- *Mem:* Am Chem Soc. *Res:* Small ring carbocyclic compounds and free radical reactions; information retrieval; computers in education. *Mailing Add:* Dept of Chem Westminster Col Fulton MO 65251

SCHULTZ, JOHN LAWRENCE, b Brooklyn, NY, June 22, 32. INFORMATION SCIENCE. *Educ:* St John's Univ, BS, 54; Univ Minn, PhD(chem), 59. *Prof Exp:* Asst inorg chem, Univ Minn, 54-56; res chemist, Pigments Dept, 57, info chemist, Patent Div, Textile Fibers Dept, 58-64, sr info specialist, Secy Dept, 64-73, SR INFO SPECIALIST, INFO SYSTS DEPT, E I DU PONT DE NEMOURS & CO, INC, 74- *Mem:* Am Chem Soc. *Res:* Solution calorimetry; heats of formation of metal ion complexes in aqueous solution; heats of ion exchange processes; storage and retrieval of chemical information. *Mailing Add:* Cent Report Index Info Syst Dept E I du Pont de Nemours & Co Wilmington DE 19898

SCHULTZ, JOHN RUSSELL, b Lanark, Ill, Apr 26, 08. GEOLOGY. *Educ:* Univ Ill, BA, 31; Northwestern Univ, MS, 33; Calif Inst Technol, PhD(geol), 37. *Prof Exp:* Asst geol, Northwestern Univ, 31-33; Nat Res Coun fel, Harvard Univ & Calif Inst Technol, 38; asst geologist, Standard Oil Co Calif, Saudi Arabia, 38-40; geologist, US Engrs Off, Miss, 41-43, geologist, Panama Canal, 46-47; assoc prof geol, Brown Univ, 47-49; chief geologist, US Waterways Exp Sta, 49-56; staff geologist, 56-75, CONSULT, HARZA ENG CO, 75- *Concurrent Pos:* Mem US comt on large dams, 73- *Res:* Engineering geology; geology of dam sites; flood control projects; airfields. *Mailing Add:* 35 Mayflower Rd Winchester MA 01890

SCHULTZ, JOHN WILFRED, b Portland, Ore, Sept 15, 31. PHYSICAL CHEMISTRY. *Educ:* Ore State Col, BS, 53; Brown Univ, PhD(phys chem), 57. *Prof Exp:* Instr chem, Univ Wash, 56-58; from asst prof to assoc prof chem, Naval Postgrad Sch, 66-75; ASSOC PROF CHEM, NAVAL ACAD, 75- *Concurrent Pos:* Soc Appl Spectros; Coblentz Soc; Am Phys Soc; Am Chem Soc. *Res:* Molecular spectroscopy; infrared and Raman intensities; spectra of solids. *Mailing Add:* Dept of Chem US Naval Acad Annapolis MD 21402

SCHULTZ, JONAS, b Brooklyn, NY, Mar 15, 35; m 58; c 3. PHYSICS. *Educ:* Columbia Univ, AB, 56, MA, 59, PhD(physics), 62. *Prof Exp:* Physicist, Nevis Cyclotron Labs, Columbia Univ, 61-63 & Lawrence Radiation Lab, Univ Calif, 63-66; assoc prof, 66-70, dean grad div, 73-76, PROF PHYSICS, UNIV CALIF, IRVINE, 70- *Concurrent Pos:* Assoc prog dir elem particle physics, NSF, 71-72. *Mem:* Am Phys Soc. *Res:* Elementary particle physics; studies of high energy phenomena. *Mailing Add:* Dept of Physics Univ of Calif Irvine CA 92717

SCHULTZ, JULIUS, b Rochester, NY, May 7, 14; m 42. BIOCHEMISTRY. *Educ:* Univ Mich, BS, 36, PhD(biol chem), 40. *Prof Exp:* Res assoc, Sch Med, Univ Pa, 39-41; asst, Off Sci Res & Develop & Comt Med Res, 42-43; res chemist, Wyeth Inst Appl Biochem, 44; asst, Sch Med, Univ Pa, 46-47; res biochemist, Jewish Hosp, 47-49; prin investr, Res Inst, Temple Univ, 49-50, asst res prof biochem, Fels Res Inst, Sch Med, 50-57; res assoc prof biochem, Hahnemann Med Col, 57-63, res prof biol chem, 63-68, dir, Inst Biochem Studies Cancer, 57-68; DIR PAPANICOLAOU CANCER RES INST, 68-, PRES, 72- *Concurrent Pos:* Adj prof pharmacol, Sch Med, Univ Miami, 68-70, biochem, 69-; mem adv bd, Cancer Biochem-Biophys, 74-, Fla Cancer Control & Res Adv Bd. *Mem:* AAAS; Am Chem Soc; Am Soc Biol Chem; Am Asn Cancer Res; English Biochem Soc. *Res:* Protein metabolism; metabolism of toxic agents; organic synthesis; proteolytic enzymes; nutrition; phosgene poisoning; serum protein synthesis in cancer; chromoprotein in experimental leukemic tumors; structure and function of myeloperoxidase, lysozomes of neutrophiles. *Mailing Add:* Papanicolaou Cancer Res Inst PO Box 016188 Miami FL 33101

SCHULTZ, LEONARD G, geology, see previous edition

SCHULTZ, LEONARD PETER, b Albion, Mich, Feb 2, 01; m 27; c 3. ICHTHYOLOGY. *Educ:* Albion Col, AB, 24; Univ Mich, MS, 26; Univ Wash, PhD(ichthyol), 32. *Hon Degrees:* DSc, Albion Col, 64. *Prof Exp:* Instr high sch, Mich, 24-25; asst zool, Univ Mich, 25-27; asst prof, Mich State Norm Col, 27-28; instr ichthyol, Univ Wash, 28-32, asst prof fisheries, 32-36; asst cur in-chg, Div Fishes, 36-38, cur in-chg, 38-65, cur & sr scientist, 65-68, EMER ZOOLOGIST, US NAT MUS, SMITHSONIAN INST, 68- *Concurrent Pos:* Univ Mich Mus exped, Western US, 26 & Wis, 28; leader, US Bur Fisheries Surv, Glacier Nat Park, 34; leader fisheries res, Yellowstone Nat Park, 36; naturalist, USS Bushnell Exped Hydrograph Surv, Phoenix & Samoa Islands, 39; Smithsonian Inst-US Dept State Ichthyol exped, Marcaibo Basin, Venezuela, 42; ichthyologist, Appl Fish Lab, Wash, 50; res assoc, Univ Md & Chesapeake Biol Lab, 68-72. *Mem:* AAAS; Am Soc Ichthyologists & Herpetologists (vpres, 37); Am Fisheries Soc; Am Soc Limnol & Oceanog; Soc Syst Zool; Arctic Inst NAm. *Res:* Life history of fishes; revisions of genera and families; spawning habits; classification, taxonomy, anatomy and races of fishes. *Mailing Add:* Scientists Cliffs Port Republic MD 20676

SCHULTZ, LINDA DALQUEST, b Yakima, Wash, Feb 23, 47; m 69. INORGANIC CHEMISTRY. *Educ:* Southern Methodist Univ, BA, 67, MS, 71; NTex State Univ, PhD(chem), 75; Registry Med Technologists, cert, 71. *Prof Exp:* Res technologist biochem, Univ Tex Southwestern Med Sch Dallas, 67-69; med technologist, Parkland Mem Hosp, 69-71; teaching asst chem, NTex State Univ, 71-74; res assoc sci, Howard Payne Univ, 75-76; fel, Tex Christian Univ, 76-78; ASSOC PROF, TARLETON STATE UNIV, 78- *Mem:* Am Chem Soc. *Res:* Kinetic and mechanism studies of substituted transition metal carbonyl complexes. *Mailing Add:* Rte 4 Box 187H Brownwood TX 76801

SCHULTZ, LORIS HENRY, b Mondovi, Wis, Feb 9, 19; m 49; c 3. DAIRY SCIENCE. *Educ:* Univ Wis, BS, 41, PhD, 49; Univ Minn, MS, 42. *Prof Exp:* From asst prof to prof animal husb, Cornell Univ, 49-57; PROF DAIRY SCI, UNIV WIS-MADISON, 57- *Mem:* Am Soc Animal Sci; Am Dairy Sci Asn (pres, 82); Nat Mastitis Coun (pres, 80). *Res:* Physiology of lactation; intermediary metabolism; metabolic disorders. *Mailing Add:* Dept Dairy Sci Univ Wis Madison WI 53706

SCHULTZ, MARTIN C, b Philadelphia, Pa, Aug 29, 26; m 51; c 4. SPEECH PATHOLOGY, AUDIOLOGY. *Educ:* Temple Univ, BA, 50; Univ Mich, MA, 52; Univ Iowa, PhD, 55. *Prof Exp:* Res assoc, Univ Iowa, 53-54; instr, Sch Speech, Northwestern Univ, 54-55; assoc otolaryngol, phys med & psychol, Univ Pa, 55-58, dir speech & hearing ctr, Univ Hosp, 55-58; supvr res lab, Cleveland Hearing & Speech Ctr, 58-60; asst prof, Univ Mich, 60-65; assoc prof speech, Ind Univ, Bloomington, 65-73; dir training in speech path & audiol, Develop Eval Clin, 72-77, DIR, HEARING & SPEECH DIV, CHILDREN'S HOSP MED CTR, 73-; PROF COMMUN DISORDERS, EMERSON COL, 72- *Concurrent Pos:* Off Voc Rehab grant, Univ Pa, 55-58; NIH grant, Cleveland Hearing & Speech Ctr, 59-60; NIH grant, Univ Mich, 60-64; consult, State Dept Health, Pa, 57 & Woods Schs Except Children, 57-58; adj prof, Sch Educ, Boston Univ, 72-; assoc otolaryngol, Harvard Med Sch, 74-; res affil, Res Lab Electronics, Mass Inst Technol, 74-; prin investr & res grant, US Dept Educ, 80-84. *Honors & Awards:* Editor's Award, J Speech & Hearing Disorders, Am Speech & Hearing Asn, 74. *Mem:* AAAS; Acoust Soc Am; Am Speech & Hearing Asn; Int Soc Phonetic Sci; Sigma Xi. *Res:* Speech and hearing sciences; design methodology; clinical processes and models; hearing and language development in children. *Mailing Add:* Children's Hosp Med Ctr 300 Longwood Ave Boston MA 02115

SCHULTZ, MARTIN H, b Boston, Mass, Dec 6, 40; m 65. COMPUTER SCIENCE. *Educ:* Calif Inst Technol, BS, 61; Harvard Univ, PhD(math), 65. *Prof Exp:* Asst prof math, Case Western Reserve Univ, 65-68; assoc prof, Calif Inst Technol, 68-70; PROF COMPUT SCI, YALE UNIV, 70-, CHMN DEPT, 74- *Mem:* Am Math Soc; Soc Indust & Appl Math; Asn Comput Mach. *Res:* Numerical analysis; computational complexity. *Mailing Add:* Dept of Comput Sci 306 Dunhan Lab Yale Univ New Haven CT 06520

SCHULTZ, MYRON GILBERT, b New York, NY, Jan 6, 35; m 59; c 3. EPIDEMIOLOGY. *Educ:* NY State Vet Col, Cornell Univ, DVM, 58; Albany Med Col, MD, 62; London Sch Hyg & Trop Med, DCMT, 67. *Prof Exp:* Pvt pract vet med, 58-62; epidemic intel serv officer, 63-65, CHIEF PARASITIC DIS BR, NAT CTR DIS CONTROL, USPHS, 67- *Concurrent Pos:* Clin assoc prof prev med, Emory Univ, 67-, clin asst prof med, 71- *Mem:* Fel Am Col Physicians; Am Soc Trop Med & Hyg; Royal Soc Trop Med & Hyg. *Res:* Epidemiology, clinical tropical medicine; clinical drug evaluation. *Mailing Add:* Parasitic Dis Br 1600 Clifton Rd NE Atlanta GA 30333

SCHULTZ, PETER BERTHOLD, b Bucharest, Rumania, Oct 24, 46; m 78. ENTOMOLOGY. *Educ:* Univ Calif, Davis, BS, 68; Midwestern Univ, MS, 72; Va Polytech Inst & State Univ, PhD(entom), 78. *Prof Exp:* Instr entom, US Air Force, 69-73; regulatory inspector, Va Dept Agr, 73-78; ENTOMOLOGIST, VA TRUCK & ORNAMENTALS RES STA, 78- *Mem:* Entom Soc Am. *Res:* Insect research on ornamental plants and small fruits. *Mailing Add:* 1444 Diamond Springs Rd Virginia Beach VA 23455

SCHULTZ, PETER CHARLES, b Brooklyn, NY, Dec 3, 42; m 66; c 2. CERAMICS, MATERIALS SCIENCE. *Educ:* Rutgers Univ, New Brunswick, BS, 64, PhD(ceramics), 67. *Prof Exp:* Sr ceramist, 67-71, sr res ceramist, 71-74, res mgr optical waveguides, 74-80, MGR EXPLOR RES, SULLIVAN PARK RES CTR, CORNING GLASS WORKS, 80- *Concurrent Pos:* Rev ed, Glass Notes, 75-78. *Honors & Awards:* Weyl Int Glass Sci, Int Glass Comn & Pa State Univ, 77; Indust Res 100 Award, 81. *Mem:* Fel Am Ceramic Soc. *Res:* High temperature inorganic materials research, including electronic glasses, magnetic glass-ceramics, high temperature oxide glasses; glass optical waveguide materials and fabrication processes. *Mailing Add:* Corning Glass Works Sullivan Park Corning NY 14830

SCHULTZ, PETER FRANK, b Oshkosh, Wis, Mar 23, 40; m 66; c 2. EXPERIMENTAL HIGH ENERGY PHYSICS. *Educ:* Univ Wis-Madison, BS, 62; Univ Ill, Urbana, MS, 64, PhD(physics), 69. *Prof Exp:* Res assoc physics, Univ Ill, Urbana, 69-72; res assoc, Argonne Nat Lab, 72-76, asst physicist, 76-81; MEM TECH STAFF, BELL TEL LAB, NAPERVILLE, ILL, 81- *Mem:* Am Phys Soc. *Res:* Elementary particle physics; acceleration technology; ion sources; telecommunications. *Mailing Add:* Argonne Nat Lab Argonne IL 60439

SCHULTZ, PETER HEWLETT, b New Haven, Conn, Jan 22, 44; m 67. ASTROGEOLOGY. *Educ:* Carleton Col, BA, 66; Univ Tex, PhD(astron), 72. *Prof Exp:* Resident res assoc, Nat Acad Sci-Nat Res Coun, Univ Santa Clara, 73-75, res assoc physics, NASA Ames Res Ctr, 75-76; STAFF SCIENTIST, LUNAR & PLANETARY INST, 76- *Mem:* Sigma Xi; Am Geophys Union; AAAS. *Res:* Morphology of impact craters on planets; impact cratering mechanics; degradational processes on planetary surfaces; volcanic modification of planetary surfaces; seismic effects of impact crater formation. *Mailing Add:* Lunar & Planetary Inst 3303 NASA Rd 1 Houston TX 77058

SCHULTZ, PHYLLIS W, b Connersville, Ind, Mar 9, 25; m 54. DEVELOPMENTAL BIOLOGY. *Educ:* Univ Cincinnati, BA, 47, MS, 50; Univ Wis, PhD(zool), 57. *Prof Exp:* Preparator zool, Univ Wis, 54-55; chemist med ctr, Univ Colo, 55-57; res assoc embryol, Univ Ore, 57-59; res assoc & vis instr, Med Ctr, 59-61, asst prof zool, 61-70, fac fel, 64-65, PROF BIOL & ASST DEAN NATURAL & PHYS SCI, MED CTR, UNIV COLO, DENVER, 71- *Concurrent Pos:* Res grants, USPHS, 58-64 & NSF, 64-66. *Mem:* Am Soc Cell Biol. *Res:* Effects of teratogenic agents or antimetabolites on protein formation, ultrastructure and cytochemistry of the chick and mammalian embryo and mammalian placenta. *Mailing Add:* Dept of Biol Univ of Colo Denver Ctr 1100 14th St Denver CO 80202

SCHULTZ, RAY KARL, b Hereford, Pa, Aug 23, 37; m 64; c 4. CHEMISTRY. *Educ:* Muhlenberg Col, BS, 59; Lehigh Univ, MS, 61, PhD(rheology), 65. *Prof Exp:* Instr quant anal, Muhlenberg Col, 63; asst prof phys chem, 65-70, ASSOC PROF PHYS CHEM, URSINUS COL, 70- *Mem:* Am Chem Soc; Sigma Xi. *Res:* Rheological and mechanical properties of gels having relaxation times in the order of one second; equilibrium constants for formation of boratediol complexes; properties of poly(acrylic acid)-co-4-vinyl pyridine. *Mailing Add:* Dept Chem Ursinus Col Collegeville PA 19426

SCHULTZ, REINHARD EDWARD, b Chicago, Ill, Sept 13, 43; m 70; c 1. TOPOLOGY, MATHEMATICS. *Educ:* Univ Chicago, SB, 64, SM, 65, PhD(math), 68. *Prof Exp:* From instr to asst prof, 68-74, assoc prof, 74-80, PROF MATH, PURDUE UNIV, WEST LAFAYETTE, 80- *Concurrent Pos:* Purdue Res Found grant, 69, NSF res grant, 70-72. *Mem:* Am Math Soc. *Res:* Algebraic topology, differential topology; transformation groups. *Mailing Add:* Dept of Math Purdue Univ West Lafayette IN 47907

SCHULTZ, RICHARD MICHAEL, b Philadelphia, Pa, Oct 28, 42; m 65; c 2. BIOCHEMISTRY, BIOPHYSICS. *Educ:* State Univ NY Binghamton, BA, 64; Brandeis Univ, MA, 67, PhD(org chem), 69. *Prof Exp:* Asst prof, 71-78, ASSOC PROF BIOCHEM, STRITCH SCH MED, LOYOLA UNIV CHICAGO, 78- *Concurrent Pos:* NIH res fel biol chem, Harvard Med Sch, 69-71. *Mem:* Am Chem Soc; Am Soc Biol Chemists. *Res:* Mechanism of enzyme action, particularly the hydrolytic enzymes; peptide synthesis; peptide synthesis; coagulation enzyme purification and properties; thermodynamics of substrate binding and catalysis; association of aldehyde transition-state analoys to protease enzymes. *Mailing Add:* Dept Biochem Loyola Univ Stritch Sch Med Maywood IL 60153

SCHULTZ, RICHARD OTTO, b Racine, Wis, Mar 19, 30; m 52; c 3. MEDICINE, OPHTHALMOLOGY. *Educ:* Univ Wis, BA, 50, MSc, 54; MD, Albany Med Col, 56; Univ Iowa, MSc, 60. *Prof Exp:* Instr opthal, Univ Iowa, 59-60; assoc, Proctor Found, Sch Med, Univ Calif, San Francisco, 63-64; assoc prof, 64-68, PROF OPHTHAL, MED COL WIS, 68-; CHMN DEPT, 64-; DIR OPHTHAL, MILWAUKEE COUNTY GEN HOSP, 64- *Concurrent Pos:* NIH spec fel ophthal microbiol, Proctor Found Sch Med, Univ Calif, San Francisco, 63-64; consult, US Vet Admin Hosp, Wood, Wis & Milwaukee Children's Hosp, 64- *Mem:* Fel Am Acad Ophthal & Otolaryngol; fel Am Col Surg; AMA; Am Asn Res Vision & Ophthal; Am Ophthal Soc. *Res:* Ocular microbiology and immunology. *Mailing Add:* 8700 W Wisconsin Ave Milwaukee WI 53226

SCHULTZ, ROBERT GEORGE, b Rahway, NJ, Jan 11, 33; m 58; c 3. ORGANIC CHEMISTRY. *Educ:* Mass Inst Technol, SB, 54; Univ Ill, PhD, 58; Northeast Mo State Univ, MA, 80. *Prof Exp:* Res specialist, 58-69, GROUP LEADER, MONSANTO CO, 69- *Mem:* Am Chem Soc. *Res:* Organometallic chemistry; homogeneous catalysis; heterogeneous catalysis. *Mailing Add:* Monsanto Co St Louis MO 63167

SCHULTZ, ROBERT JOHN, b Detroit, Mich, Apr 19, 44; m 67; c 2. MEDICINAL CHEMISTRY. *Educ:* Wayne State Univ, BSc, 66; Brown Univ, PhD(org chem), 71. *Prof Exp:* Res assoc, Univ Mich, 70-73; indust fel, Starks Assoc, Inc, 73, supvr, 73-75, prin investr, 75-79, co-prin investr, 79-80, PRIN INVESTR, STARKS C P, INC, 80- *Mem:* Am Chem Soc; Sigma Xi. *Res:* Potential chemotherapeutic agents for anticancer screening programs. *Mailing Add:* 818 Roeder Rd Suite 510 Silver Spring MD 20910

SCHULTZ, ROBERT LOWELL, b Moscow, Idaho, Mar 18, 30; m 51; c 3. ANATOMY. *Educ:* Walla Walla Col, BA, 51, MA, 53; Univ Calif, Los Angeles, PhD(anat), 57. *Prof Exp:* Asst instr, 53-57, from instr to assoc prof, 57-74, PROF ANAT, SCH MED, LOMA LINDA UNIV, 74- *Concurrent Pos:* USPHS spec fel, Univ Calif, Los Angeles, 63-64. *Mem:* Electron Micros Soc Am; Am Asn Anat; Am Soc Cell Biol. *Res:* Electron microscopy and microanatomy of the nervous system. *Mailing Add:* Dept of Anat Loma Linda Univ Sch of Med Loma Linda CA 92354

SCHULTZ, RODNEY BRIAN, b Enid, Okla, Nov 2, 46; m 68; c 2. APPLIED PHYSICS, LASER FUSION. *Educ:* Okla State Univ, BS, 68; Univ Colo, MS, 71, PhD(astrophys), 74. *Prof Exp:* Asst solar physics, High Altitude Observ, 68-74; staff mem thermonuclear wepons design, 74-80, STAFF MEM APPLIED THEORETICAL PHYSICS DIV, THERMONUCLEAR APPLICATIONS GROUP, LOS ALAMOS NAT LAB, 74- *Res:* Laser fusion theory; thermonuclear weapons research. *Mailing Add:* Group X-2 MS 220 Los Alamos Nat Lab Los Alamos NM 87545

SCHULTZ, ROLAND JACK, b Caro, Mich, Aug 17, 29; m 57; c 2. POPULATION BIOLOGY, ICHTHYOLOGY. *Educ:* Mich State Univ, BS, 52, MS, 53; Univ Mich, PhD, 60. *Prof Exp:* Res assoc, Mus Zool, Univ Mich, 60-63; from asst prof to prof zool, 63-74, PROF BIOL, BIOL SCI GROUP, UNIV CONN, 75- *Concurrent Pos:* Ed, Copeia, Am Soc Ichthyologists & Herpetologists, 70-73; prog dir syst biol, NSF, 74-75. *Mem:* Am Soc Ichthyologists & Herpetologists; Soc Study Evolution; Ecol Soc Am; Am Genetic Asn; Am Soc Naturalists. *Res:* Evolution and ecology of viviparous fishes. *Mailing Add:* Biol Sci Group Ecol Sect Univ of Conn Storrs CT 06268

SCHULTZ, RONALD DAVID, b Freeland, Pa, Apr 21, 44; m 66; c 3. IMMUNOLOGY, VETERINARY VIROLOGY. *Educ:* Pa State Univ, BS, 66, MS, 67, PhD(microbiol), 70. *Prof Exp:* Res asst microbiol, Pa State Univ, 66-70; res assoc immunol, NY State Vet Col, 71-73, from asst prof to assoc prof immunol, Vet Virus Res Inst, Cornell Univ, 73-78, assoc dir, Dept Health Serv, Microbiol & Clin Lab, 73-78; prof, Dept Microbiol, Col Vet Med, Auburn Univ, 78-80; MEM FAC, NY STATE VET COL, CORNELL UNIV, 80- *Concurrent Pos:* Consult, Nat Cancer Inst, 72-78, Miles Lab, 75-, Corning Glass, 78- & Hybridoma Sci, 78-; res grants, NIH, USDA & Food & Drug Admin. *Mem:* Am Soc Microbiol; Conf Res Workers Animal Dis; Am Asn Vet Immunologists (pres, 75-80); US Animal Health Asn. *Res:* Developmental aspects of the immune response; cell-mediated immunity; immunoglobulins; clinical immunology; immunopathology; viral infections and the immune response; leukemia. *Mailing Add:* NY State Vet Col Cornell Univ Ithaca NY 14850

SCHULTZ, RONALD G(LEN), b Hammond, Ind, Nov 15, 31; m 56; c 1. ELECTRICAL ENGINEERING. *Educ:* Valparaiso Univ, BSEE, 53; Northwestern Univ, MS, 54; Univ Pittsburgh, PhD(elec eng), 59. *Prof Exp:* From instr to assoc prof elec eng, Univ Pittsburgh, 54-68; PROF ELEC ENG & CHMN DEPT, CLEVELAND STATE UNIV, 68-, DEAN, COL GRAD STUDIES, 73-, ASSOC VPRES ACAD AFFAIRS, 75- *Res:* Computers and control systems; nonlinear control systems. *Mailing Add:* Col of Grad Studies Cleveland State Univ Cleveland OH 44115

SCHULTZ, SHELDON, b New York, NY, Jan 21, 33; m 53; c 3. SOLID STATE PHYSICS. *Educ:* Stevens Inst Technol, ME, 54; Columbia Univ, PhD(physics), 59. *Prof Exp:* Res asst physics, Radiation Lab, Columbia Univ, 59-60; from asst prof to assoc prof, 60-71, PROF PHYSICS, UNIV CALIF, SAN DIEGO, 71- *Concurrent Pos:* Sloan Found fel, 62-64. *Mem:* Fel Am Phys Soc; Am Vacuum Soc. *Res:* Solid state physics; high purity metals; many body effects; magnetic resonance in metals. *Mailing Add:* Dept of Physics B-019 Univ of Calif San Diego La Jolla CA 92093

SCHULTZ, STANLEY GEORGE, b Bayonne, NJ, Oct 26, 31; m 60; c 2. PHYSIOLOGY. *Educ:* Columbia Col, BA, 52; NY Univ, MD, 56. *Prof Exp:* Intern, Bellevue Hosp, NY, 56-57, resident internal med, 57-58; instr biophys, Harvard Med Sch, 64-65, assoc, 65-67; from assoc prof to prof physiol, Sch Med, Univ Pittsburgh, 70-79; PROF PHYSIOL & CHMN DEPT, MED SCH, UNIV TEX, HOUSTON, 79- *Concurrent Pos:* USPHS res fel cardiol, Lenox Hill Hosp, 58-59; Nat Acad Sci-Nat Res Coun res fel biophysics, Harvard Med Sch, 59-62; UPSHS res career award, 69-72; estab investr, Am Heart Asn, 64-69; res career develop award, NIH, 69-72; consult, NIH; overseas fel, Churchill Col, Cambridge Univ, 76; consult, Nat Bd Med Examrs; ed, Am J Physiol, Physiol Review & Ann Review Physiol. *Mem:* AAAS; Am Heart Asn; Biophys Soc; Am Physiol Soc; Soc Gen Physiol. *Res:* Membrane physiology; intestinal absorption. *Mailing Add:* Dept of Physiol Univ Tex Houston TX 77025

SCHULTZ, TERRY WAYNE, b Beloit, Wis, Feb 26, 46; m 68; c 1. TERATOGENESIS. *Educ:* Austin Peay State Univ, BS, 68; Univ Ark, MS, 72; Univ Tenn, PhD(zool), 75. *Prof Exp:* Fel, Biol Div, Oak Ridge Nat Lab, 75-77; asst prof histol & cell biol, Dept Biol, Pan Am Univ, 77-80; res assoc, Biol Div, Oak Ridge Nat Lab, 80-82; ASST PROF HISTOL, DEPT ANIMAL SCI, COL VET MED, UNIV TENN, 82- *Concurrent Pos:* Fac partic, Biomed & Environ Sci, Inst Lawrence Livermore Lab, 78; consult, Biol Div, Oak Ridge Nat Lab, 79. *Mem:* Am Micros Soc; Soc Environ Toxicol & Chem; Electron Micros Soc Am. *Res:* In vitro teratogenesis testing and screening using frog embryos; structure activity relationships of industrial chemicals and environmental toxicity; short-term cytotoxicity testing. *Mailing Add:* Dept Animal Sci Col Vet Med Univ Tenn PO Box 1071 Knoxville TN 37901

SCHULTZ, THEODORE DAVID, b Chicago, Ill, Jan 6, 29; m 57; c 2. THEORETICAL PHYSICS. *Educ:* Cornell Univ, BEngPhys, 51; Mass Inst Technol, PhD(physics), 56. *Prof Exp:* NSF fel math physics, Univ Birmingham, 56-58; res assoc physics, Univ Ill, 58-59, res asst prof, 59-60; PHYSICIST, WATSON RES CTR, IBM CORP, 60- *Concurrent Pos:* Adj prof, Syracuse Univ, 61-62; vis assoc prof, NY Univ, 64-65; vis prof, Univ Munich, 79-80. *Mem:* Fel Am Phys Soc. *Res:* Theory of solids. and quantum statistical mechanics; quantum field theory. *Mailing Add:* IBM Watson Res Ctr Rm 28-140 Yorktown Heights NY 10598

SCHULTZ, THEODORE JOHN, b Jefferson City, Mo, Aug 16, 22. ACOUSTICS. *Educ:* Harvard Univ, SM, 47, PhD(acoustics), 53. *Prof Exp:* Instr, US Naval Acad, 44-46; res physicist, Naval Res Lab, 47-48; instr, Harvard Univ, 48-53, res fel acoustics, 53-55; asst chief acoustics, Douglas Aircraft Co, 56-60; consult electronics & acoustics, 60-66, PRIN SCIENTIST, BOLT BERANEK & NEWMAN INC, 66- *Mem:* Fel Acoust Soc Am; Am Soc Testing & Mat; Int Orgn Standardization. *Res:* Acoustic wattmeter; concert hall acoustics; undersea reverberation; acoustical testing of buildings and building materials; community noise; noise control in ordinances and building codes. *Mailing Add:* Bolt Beranek & Newman Inc 50 Moulton St Cambridge MA 02138

SCHULTZ, VINCENT, b Lakewood, Ohio, Mar 7, 22; m 48; c 3. ANIMAL ECOLOGY. *Educ:* Ohio State Univ, BSc, 46, MSc, 48, PhD(zool), 49; Va Polytech Inst, MSc, 54. *Prof Exp:* Wildlife biologist, US Fish & Wildlife Serv, 49-50; sr biologist, State Game & Fish Comn, Tenn, 50-52; asst prof wildlife mgt, Va Polytech Inst, 52-54; res fel biostatist, USPHS, Johns Hopkins Univ, 54-56; assoc prof biostatist & agr statistician, Univ Md, 56-59; ecologist environ sci br, Div Biol & Med, US AEC, 59-66; PROF ZOOL, WASH STATE UNIV, 66- *Res:* Application of statistical techniques to ecological research; radiation ecology. *Mailing Add:* Dept Zool Wash State Univ Pullman WA 99164

SCHULTZ, WARREN WALTER, b Emporia, Kans, Sept 3, 41; m 69; c 3. PATHOBIOLOGY. *Educ:* Kans State Univ, Emporia, BA, 64, MS, 66; Johns Hopkins Univ, ScD(pathobiol), 72. *Prof Exp:* Teaching asst microbiol, Kans State Univ, Emporia, 64-66; res virologist, Naval Med Res Inst, 66-68; teaching asst pop biol, Johns Hopkins Univ, 69; res virologist, Naval Med Res Inst, 71-78; INSTR CHEM & BIOL, US NAVAL ACAD, 78- *Concurrent Pos:* Head pathobiol, Dept Microbiol, Naval Med Res Inst, 74-, consult, Environ Health Effects Lab, 74- *Mem:* Am Soc Microbiol; AAAS; Undersea Med Soc. *Res:* Hyperbaric microbiology; viral hepatitis. *Mailing Add:* Dept of Chem US Naval Acad Annapolis MD 21402

SCHULTZ, WILLIAM C(ARL), b Sheboygan, Wis, July 30, 27; m 51; c 3. ELECTRICAL ENGINEERING. *Educ:* Univ Wis, BS, 52, MS, 53, PhD(elec eng), 58. *Prof Exp:* Asst, Univ Wis, 52-53, instr elec eng, 55-58; asst engr, Comput Lab, Allis-Chalmers Mfg Co, Wis, 53-55; asst engr, Cornell Aeronaut Lab, Inc, 58-70; head comput ctr, 70-75; ASSOC PROF TECHNOL, STATE UNIV COL NY, BUFFALO, 75- *Mem:* Inst Elec & Electronics Engrs; assoc fel Am Inst Aeronaut & Astronaut. *Res:* Computer sciences; computer facility management; administrative data processing; flight control systems; cockpit displays; human factors engineering. *Mailing Add:* State Univ of NY 1300 Elmwood Ave Buffalo NY 14222

SCHULTZ, WILLIAM CLINTON, b Bainbridge, NY, Sept 19, 37; m 61; c 2. SYNTHETIC ORGANIC CHEMISTRY. *Educ:* Dartmouth Col, AB, 59; Rutgers Univ, PhD(org chem), 63. *Prof Exp:* SR DEVELOP CHEMIST, SYNTHETIC CHEM DIV, EASTMAN KODAK CO, 63- *Mem:* Am Chem Soc; Soc Photog Scientists & Engrs. *Res:* Development of economical manufacturing processes for speciality organic chemicals. *Mailing Add:* 11 Sweet Birch Lane Rochester NY 14615

SCHULTZE, HANS-PETER, b Swinemuende, Ger, Aug 13, 37; m 65; c 3. VERTEBRATE PALEONTOLOGY. *Educ:* Univ Freiburg, BSc, 58; Univ Tuebingen, MSc, 62, PhD(paleont), 65. *Prof Exp:* Fel, Ger Sci Found, Naturhistoriska Ricksmuseet, Stockholm, 65-67; asst prof, Dept Paleont, Univ Goettingen, 67-70; fel, Ger Acad Exchange, Am Mus Natural Hist, NY & Field Mus, Chicago, 70-71; asst prof to assoc prof, Univ Goettingen, Ger, 71-78; asst prof, 78-81, ASSOC PROF, DEPT SYST & ECOL, UNIV KANS, 81-, CUR, MUS NATURAL HIST, 78- *Mem:* Palaeontologische Gesellschaft; Soc Vertebrate Paleontologists. *Res:* Morphology and evolution of fossil fishes and early tetrapods; histology of hard tissue. *Mailing Add:* Mus Natural Hist Univ of Kans Lawrence KS 66045

SCHULTZE, LOTHAR WALTER, b Berlin, Ger, Dec 5, 20; US citizen; m 47; c 3. SCIENCE EDUCATION. *Educ:* State Univ NY Albany, BA, 42; Pa State Univ, MS, 52, DEd(higher educ), 55. *Prof Exp:* Proj engr, US Rubber Co, 42-45; assoc prof sci, State Univ NY Albany, 52-58, dir admis, 58-66; DIR INSTNL RES, STATE UNIV NY COL FREDONIA, 66- *Mem:* Am Chem Soc; Asn Inst Res. *Res:* Science education for non-science majors; non-academic predictors of college success; mobility of students in transfer. *Mailing Add:* 38 Birchwood Dr Fredonia NY 14063

SCHULTZE, WALTER DONALD, b Philadelphia, Pa, Aug 3, 25; m 50; c 3. DAIRY BACTERIOLOGY. *Educ:* Univ Pa, BA, 48; Univ Wis, MS, 51; Univ Minn, PhD(dairy bact), 58. *Prof Exp:* Asst, Univ Wis, 48-51 & Univ Minn, 52-56; from instr to asst prof bact, WVa Univ, 58-61; RES BACTERIOLOGIST, GENETICS & MGT LAB, ANIMAL PHYSIOL & GENETICS INST, SCI & EDUC ADMIN-AGR RES, USDA, 61- *Concurrent Pos:* Consult, Nat Conf Interstate Milk Shipments, 73-, Bur Vet Med, Food & Drug Admin, 76- & Mastitis Expers Group, Int Dairy Fed, 76- *Mem:* Am Soc Microbiol; Am Dairy Sci Asn; Nat Mastitis Coun. *Res:* Dairy manufacturing; microbial spoilage of dairy products; bacterial physiology, especially of psychrophilic bacteria; bovine mastitis; raw milk quality. *Mailing Add:* 12706 Brunswick Lane Bowie MD 20715

SCHULZ, ALVIN GEORGE, b Mayfield, Ky, Sept 11, 19; m 44; c 1. NUCLEAR MEDICINE, ENVIRONMENTAL ENGINEERING. *Educ:* Univ Calif, Berkeley, AB, 44, PhD(physics, math), 52. *Prof Exp:* Res assoc nuclear physics, Radiation Lab, Univ Calif, 43-45; res engr, Appl Physics Lab, Johns Hopkins Univ, 45-47; res assoc nuclear physics, Radiation Lab, Univ Calif, 47-52; ASST TO DIR, APPL PHYSICS LAB, JOHNS HOPKINS UNIV, 52-, ASSOC PROF RADIOL, SCH MED, 65-, ASSOC PROF RADIOL SCI, SCH HYG & PUB HEALTH, 66- *Mem:* AAAS; Am Phys Soc; Soc Nuclear Med. *Res:* Systems engineering; nuclear medicine instrumentation; environmental impact analysis. *Mailing Add:* Appl Physics Lab Johns Hopkins Rd Laurel MD 20810

SCHULZ, ARTHUR R, b Brighton, Colo, Oct 9, 25; m 56. BIOCHEMISTRY, NUTRITION. *Educ:* Colo State Univ, BS, 50; Univ Calif, PhD, 56. *Prof Exp:* Res assoc, Univ Minn, 57-58; asst prof, Okla State Univ, 58-62; asst prof, 62-68, assoc prof biochem, 68-77, clin prof path, 77-80, ASSOC PROF PATH, SCH MED, IND UNIV, INDIANAPOLIS, 80- *Concurrent Pos:* NSF fel biochem, Swiss Fed Inst Technol, 56-57. *Res:* Enzymology of thyroid; enzyme kinetics. *Mailing Add:* Dept of Biochem Ind Univ Sch of Med Indianapolis IN 46202

SCHULZ, DALE METHERD, b Fairfield, Ohio, Oct 20, 18; m 47; c 2. PATHOLOGY. *Educ:* Miami Univ, BA, 40; Wash Univ, MS, 42, MD, 49. *Prof Exp:* Res chemist, Tretolite Co, 42-45; from intern to resident path, Barnes Hosp, St Louis, Mo, 49-51; from instr to assoc prof, 52-62, PROF PATH, SCH MED, IND UNIV, INDIANAPOLIS, 62-; PATHOLOGIST, METHODIST HOSP, INDIANAPOLIS, 66- *Concurrent Pos:* Fel, Med Ctr, Ind Univ, Indianapolis, 51-52. *Mem:* Am Asn Path & Bact; Int Acad Path. *Res:* Trace metals; fungus diseases; kidney diseases. *Mailing Add:* 9540 Copley Dr Indianapolis IN 46260

SCHULZ, DAVID ARTHUR, b Cleveland, Ohio, June 30, 34; m 57; c 5. MATERIALS SCIENCE, CERAMIC ENGINEERING. *Educ:* Ga Inst Technol, BCerE, 55; Univ Calif, Berkeley, MS, 57, PhD(eng sci), 61. *Prof Exp:* Develop engr, Niagara Develop Lab, Nat Carbon Co, Union Carbide Corp, 55-56; res engr, Inst Eng Res, Univ Calif, Berkeley, 59-60, engr, Inorg Mat Div, Lawrence Radiation Lab, 60-61; develop engr, Adv Mat Lab, Nat Carbon Co, 61-63, develop engr, Nuclear Prod Dept, Carbon Prod Div, 63-66, proj engr, Lawrenceburg Tech Opers, 66-67, proj coordr, 67; proj engr, 68-73, staff engr, 73-76, sr engr, 76-79, sr res scientist, 79-81, SR GROUP LEADER, PARMA TECH CTR, UNION CARBIDE CORP, 81- *Mem:* AAAS; Am Chem Soc; Am Ceramic Soc; Nat Inst Ceramic Engrs; Sigma Xi. *Res:* Process and product development relating to high-strength, high-modulus carbon fibers and carbon fiber reinforced composites. *Mailing Add:* Parma Tech Ctr 12900 Snow Rd Parma OH 44130

SCHULZ, DONALD NORMAN, b Buffalo, NY, May 24, 43; m 67; c 1. ORGANIC CHEMISTRY, POLYMER CHEMISTRY. *Educ:* State Univ NY Buffalo, BA, 65; Univ Mass, PhD(org chem), 71. *Prof Exp:* Res scientist, Cent Res Lab, Firestone Tire & Rubber Co, 71-75; group leader, org-polymer chem, 75-81; GROUP HEAD & RES ASSOC WATER SOLUABLE POLYMERS, CORP RES, EXXON RES & ENG CO, 81- *Concurrent Pos:* Asst ed, Isotopics, 79, ed, 80- *Mem:* AAAS; Am Chem Soc; Am Inst Chemists; Fel Asn Inst Chem. *Res:* Synthetic and mechanistic organoantimony, organophosphorus and organometallic chemistry; anionic and cationic polymerizations; polymer synthesis and modification. *Mailing Add:* Exxon Res & Eng Co Exxon Res Sci Labs PO Box 45 Linden NJ 07036

SCHULZ, E(LMER) H(ARRY), b Lockhart, Tex, Oct 30, 13; m 38; c 2. ELECTRICAL ENGINEERING. *Educ:* Univ Tex, BS, 35, MS, 36; Ill Inst Technol, PhD(elec eng), 47. *Prof Exp:* From instr to asst prof elec eng, Univ Tex, 36-42; asst prof, Ill Inst Technol, 42-46; from asst chmn to chmn, Elec Eng Dept, Armour Res Found, 46-51, mgr, Physics & Elec Eng Div, 51-53, asst dir, Res Opers, 53-58, vpres, 58-63; exec vpres & dir, 63-77, EMER DIR, ILL INST TECHNOL, 77- *Mem:* AAAS; Inst Elec & Electronics Engrs. *Res:* Electronic instrumentation. *Mailing Add:* 10 W 35th St Chicago IL 60616

SCHULZ, JAN IVAN, b Bratislava, Czech, Feb 3, 46; Can citizen. IMMUNOLOGY, INTERNAL MEDICINE. *Educ:* Univ Western Ont, MD, 70; FRCPSCan, 74. *Prof Exp:* Res fel immunol, Montreal Gen Hosp Res Inst, 74-77 & Institut de Cancerologie et d'immunogenetique, France, 77-78; INSTR IMMUNOL & INTERNAL MED, McGILL UNIV, 78- *Concurrent Pos:* Affil staff, Dept Immunol, Montreal Gen Hosp, 78-; mem staff, Dept Med, St Mary's Hosp, Montreal, 78-; asst physician, Dept Med, Royal Victoria Hosp, Montreal, 79- *Mem:* Am Col Physicians; Am Acad Allergy; Can Soc Allergy & Clin Immunol; Royal Soc Med; fel Am Col Physicians. *Res:* Experimental and clinical immunotherapy of cancer; therapy of atopic diseases. *Mailing Add:* 687 Pine Ave Montreal PQ H3A 1A1 Can

SCHULZ, JEANETTE, b East Alton, Ill, Nov 30, 19. PEDIATRICS. *Educ:* Columbia Univ, AB, 49; Yale Univ, MD, 52; Am Bd Pediat, dipl. *Prof Exp:* From intern to resident pediat, Univ Minn Hosps, 52-55; res instr, Univ Calif, Los Angeles, 56-58, asst prof, 58-63; assoc prof pediat, Univ Ill Col Med, 63-76; Clin dir, Ill State Pediat Inst, 63-76; MED DIR, CHILD DEVELOP SERV, ALASKA, 76- *Concurrent Pos:* Fel pediat hemat, Sch Med, Univ Calif, Los Angeles, 55-56, Bank of Am-Giannini Found res fel, 56-58. *Mem:* Am Soc Hemat; Am Soc Human Genetics. *Res:* Hematology; congenital defects; cytogenetics. *Mailing Add:* 3401 E 42nd Ave Anchorage AK 99504

SCHULZ, JOHANN CHRISTOPH FRIEDRICH, b Gottingen, Ger, July 6, 20; nat US; m 58; c 2. ORGANIC CHEMISTRY. *Educ:* Mt Union Col, BS, 44; Syracuse Univ, PhD(chem), 49. *Prof Exp:* Asst, Syracuse Univ, 42-48; instr org & phys chem, Hobart Col, 48-50; asst prof, Wagner Col, 50-57 & Washington Col, 57-60; PROF ORG & PHYS CHEM, WAGNER COL, 60- *Mem:* AAAS; fel Am Inst Chemists; Am Chem Soc; NY Acad Sci. *Res:* Organic synthesis. *Mailing Add:* Dept of Chem Wagner Col Staten Island NY 10301

SCHULZ, JOHN HAMPSHIRE, b New York, NY, Apr 10, 34; m 63; c 3. PAPER CHEMISTRY. *Educ:* Brooklyn Polytech Inst, BChemE, 55; Lawrence Univ, MS, 57, PhD(physics), 61. *Prof Exp:* Asst prof paper technol, Western Mich Univ, 61-63; mgr process develop, Paper & Bd Div, Continental Can Co, Ga, 63-69, tech dir, Hodge, 69-72, gen supt, 72-75; mgr res & develop, 75-80, TECH DIR, KRAFT DIV, ST REGIS PAPER CO, 80- *Mem:* Am Chem Soc; Tech Asn Pulp & Paper Indust. *Res:* Reaction of paper to stress; paper mill quality control; clay coating of paper; paper machine performance analysis. *Mailing Add:* St Regis Paper Co West Nyack NY 10994

SCHULZ, JOHN THEODORE, b Ames, Iowa, June 15, 29; m 53; c 5. ENTOMOLOGY. *Educ:* Iowa State Univ, PhD(entom), 57. *Prof Exp:* From asst prof to assoc prof entom, 57-67, actg chmn dept, 73-74, PROF ENTOM, NDAK STATE UNIV, 67-, CHMN DEPT, 74- *Mem:* AAAS; Entom Soc Am; Phytopath Soc; Sunflower Asn Am. *Res:* Insect transmission of plant diseases; economic entomology. *Mailing Add:* Dept Entom NDak State Univ Fargo ND 58105

SCHULZ, KARLO FRANCIS, b Zagreb, Yugoslavia, Sept 20, 17; Can citizen. PHYSICAL CHEMISTRY. *Educ:* Univ Zagreb, Chem Eng, 41, PhD(chem), 52. *Prof Exp:* Instr chem, Univ Zagreb, 41-47; res officer, Inst Med Res, Yugoslavia Acad, 47-59; res assoc, Clarkson Col Technol, 59-61; res assoc, Dept Mining & Metall, Univ Alta, 61-62; RES OFFICER, RES COUN ALTA, 62- *Mem:* Am Chem Soc; Chem Inst Can; Croatian Chem Soc. *Res:* Electrolytic coagulation of sols; complex ions in solutions; physical and optical properties of aerosols; electron spin resonance. *Mailing Add:* Alta Res Coun 11315-87th Ave Edmonton AB T6G 2C2 Can

SCHULZ, MICHAEL, b Petoskey, Mich, July 14, 43. SPACE PHYSICS, PLASMA PHYSICS. *Educ:* Mich State Univ, BS, 64; Mass Inst Technol, PhD(physics), 67. *Prof Exp:* Mem tech staff, Bell Tel Labs, 67-69; staff scientist, 72-80, MEM TECH STAFF, AEROSPACE CORP, 69-, RES SCIENTIST, 80- *Mem:* Am Phys Soc; Am Geophys Union. *Res:* Dynamics of partially ionized gases; theoretical plasma physics; adiabatic theory of charged particle motion; magnetospheric and radiation belt physics; solar wind; solar-terrestrial relationships. *Mailing Add:* Aerospace Corp Space Sci Lab PO Box 92957 Los Angeles CA 90009

SCHULZ, MILFORD DAVID, b Sister Bay, Wis, Dec 12, 09; m 37; c 1. RADIATION ONCOLOGY. *Educ:* NCent Col, BA, 31; Northwestern Univ, BMed, 35, MD, 36. *Prof Exp:* From asst to prof, 42-76, EMER PROF RADIATION THER, HARVARD MED SCH, 76- *Concurrent Pos:* Sr consult radiation therapist, Mass Gen Hosp, 42-; consult, Mass Eye & Ear Infirmary, 42- & Pondville State Hosp. *Mem:* Am Roentgen Ray Soc; Radiol Soc NAm; Am Radium Soc (pres, 58-59); fel Am Col Radiol; Am Soc Therapeut Radiol (pres, 64-65). *Res:* Radiation therapy; cancer management. *Mailing Add:* Dept Radiation Med Mass Gen Hosp Boston MA 02114

SCHULZ, NORMAN F, b McGregor, Minn, June 3, 18; m 48; c 4. CHEMICAL & METALLURGICAL ENGINEERING. *Educ:* Univ Minn, BChE, 39, MS, 50, PhD(chem eng, phys chem), 51. *Prof Exp:* Chemist, Talon, Inc, Pa, 39-41; res engr, Testing Lab, Am Gas Asn, Ohio, 41-42; RES ASSOC MINERAL RESOURCES RES CTR, UNIV MINN, MINNEAPOLIS, 52- *Mem:* Am Inst Mining, Metall & Petrol Engrs; Am Soc Testing & Mat. *Res:* Direct reduction, magnetic roasting and magnetic separation of iron and manganiferous iron ores; agglomeration of iron ore concentrates. *Mailing Add:* Mineral Resources Res Ctr Univ Minn Minneapolis MN 55455

SCHULZ, ROBERT J, b Brooklyn, NY, Jan 12, 27; m 51; c 3. MEDICAL PHYSICS. *Educ:* Queens Col, NY, BS, 50; Cornell Univ, MS, 57; NY Univ, PhD, 67. *Prof Exp:* Asst physicist radiol physics, Mem Hosp, Sloan Kettering Inst, 52-56; asst prof, Albert Einstein Col Med, Yeshiva Univ, 56-70; PROF RADIOL PHYSICS, YALE UNIV, 70- *Concurrent Pos:* Attend physicist, Montefiore Hosp, 57-68; chief physicist, Yale-New Haven Hosp. *Mem:* Asn Physicists Med; Am Col Radiol. *Res:* Applications of x-rays and radioactive materials to medical diagnostic and therapeutic problems. *Mailing Add:* Dept Therapeut Radiol Yale Univ New Haven CT 06520

SCHULZ, WALLACE WENDELL, b Basil Mills, Nebr, Feb 24, 26; m 47; c 2. INORGANIC CHEMISTRY. *Educ:* Univ Nev, BS, 49, MS, 50. *Prof Exp:* From res chemist to sr scientist, Hanford Atomic Prod Oper, Gen Elec Co, 50-65; sr res scientist, Battelle Northwest Labs, 65-69; staff chemist, Atlantic Richfield Hanford Co, 69-77, prin chemist, 77-80, CHIEF SCIENTIST, ROCKWELL HANFORD CO, 80- *Mem:* Am Chem Soc; Am Inst Mining, Metall & Petrol Engrs. *Res:* Solvent extraction chemistry; uranium-plutonium separations processes; fission product separations processes; electrochemistry. *Mailing Add:* Rockwell Hanford Co PO Box 800 Richland WA 99352

SCHULZ, WILLIAM, b Lakefield, Minn, Oct 14, 35. ANALYTICAL CHEMISTRY. *Educ:* Mankato State Col, BS, 61, MS, 65; La State Univ, PhD(anal org chem), 75. *Prof Exp:* Instr chem, Wis State Univ-La Crosse, 65-68; asst prof, 68-76, ASSOC PROF CHEM, EASTERN KY UNIV, 76- *Mem:* Am Chem Soc. *Res:* Cellulose sulfonyl carbamates; ion exchange resins for biochemical separations. *Mailing Add:* Dept Chem & Geochem Colo Sch Mines Golden CO 80401

SCHULZ, WILLIAM DONALD, b Brooklyn, NY, Oct 4, 25; m 61; c 3. THEORETICAL PHYSICS. *Educ:* Rensselaer Polytech Inst, BS, 49; Columbia Univ, PhD(physics), 54. *Prof Exp:* physicist, Lawrence Livermore Nat Lab, Univ Calif, 55-82; RETIRED. *Mem:* Am Phys Soc. *Res:* Use of digital computers in fluid dynamics, field theory and photon transfer. *Mailing Add:* 280 Stonewall Rd Berkeley CA 94705

SCHULZE, IRENE THERESA, b Washington, Mo, Feb 8, 29. VIROLOGY, BIOCHEMISTRY. *Educ:* St Louis Univ, BS, 52, PhD(microbiol), 62. *Prof Exp:* Res asst enzym & biochem, Pub Health Res Inst City New York, Inc, 65-68, assoc virol, 68-70; asst prof, 70-73, assoc prof, 73-80, PROF MICROBIOL, SCH MED, ST LOUIS UNIV, 80- *Concurrent Pos:* Fel microbiol, Vanderbilt Univ, 62-65; USPHS res grant, Sch Med, St Louis Univ, 71- *Mem:* AAAS; Am Soc Microbiol; Am Soc Biol Chemists. *Res:* Structure and chemical composition of large RNA-containing viruses, for example, influenza and oncogenic viruses; relationships between viral structure and biological activities; viral synthesis and virus-host relationships. *Mailing Add:* Dept of Microbiol St Louis Univ Sch of Med St Louis MO 63104

SCHULZE, KARL LUDWIG, b Aachen, Ger, Feb 28, 11; nat US; c 4. MICROBIOLOGY. *Educ:* Univ Berlin, Dr rer nat(bot), 39. *Prof Exp:* Fel, Kaiser-Wilhelm Inst Biol, Ger, 34-38; fel, Univ Wurzburg, 39, Univ Gottingen, 39-40 & Univ Berlin, 40-41; res dir yeast prod, paper & pulp indust, 41-45; asst prof, Munich Tech Univ, 46-49, privat-dozent, 49-51; res dir waste treatment, Int Agr Prod, Inc, 51-55; res instr sanit eng, 55-57, from asst prof to assoc prof, 57-73, EMER ASSOC PROF SANIT ENG, MICH STATE UNIV, 73- *Concurrent Pos:* Consult, Fairfield Eng Co, Marion, Ohio. *Mem:* Am Inst Biol Sci; Water Pollution Control Fedn; Soc Indust Microbiol; Inst Advan Sanit Res Int. *Res:* Microbiology of waste treatment; biological recovery of waste water; biotechnology; water pollution control. *Mailing Add:* 403 Kumquat Fairhope AL 36532

SCHULZE, R(OBERT) A(LLISON), b Memphis, Tenn, Oct 3, 20; m 43; c 3. CHEMICAL ENGINEERING. *Educ:* Ga Inst Technol, BS, 41. *Prof Exp:* Res supvr, 52-56, div head eng res, 56-58, chief supvr, Plant Tech Sect, 58-59, supt develop, 59-61, supt prod, 61-64, supt develop, 65-70, supt environ control, 70-73, PROJ MGR, E I DU PONT DE NEMOURS & CO, INC, 73- *Res:* Synthetic elastomers and monomers; high temperature reactions; diffusional processes; fluorine chemistry. *Mailing Add:* E I du Pont de Nemours & Co Inc Elastomer Chem Dept Wilmington DE 19898

SCHULZE, STEPHEN ROBERT, b Santa Barbara, Calif, Sept 9, 41; m 65; c 2. CHEMICAL ENGINEERING. *Educ:* Harvey Mudd Col, BS, 63; Mass Inst Technol, PhD(chem eng), 66. *Prof Exp:* SR DEVELOP ENGR, CELANESE CORP, SUMMIT, 66- *Res:* Polymer synthesis and processing for application to the plastics and film industry. *Mailing Add:* Celanese Corp 86 Morris Ave Summit NJ 07901

SCHULZE, WALTER ARTHUR, b Philadelphia, Pa, Dec 8, 43; m 71; c 1. MATERIALS SCIENCE, FERROELECTRICS. *Educ:* Pa State Univ, BS, 65, MS, 68, PhD(solid state sci), 73. *Prof Exp:* Res assoc, 74-80, SR RES ASSOC, MAT RES LAB, PA STATE UNIV, 80- *Mem:* Am Ceramic Soc. *Res:* Preparation and characterization of ferroelectric materials and devices; electrical properties of piezoelectric and high dielectric constant ceramics. *Mailing Add:* 259 Mat Res Lab Pa State Univ University Park PA 16802

SCHULZE, WILLIAM EUGENE, b Kiowa, Kans, Nov 27, 34. SYNTHETIC ORGANIC CHEMISTRY. *Educ:* Knox Col, Ill, AB, 56; Kans State Univ, MS, 62. *Prof Exp:* Chemist northern lab, USDA, Ill, 56-57 & 59-60; Nat Defense Educ Act fel, Kans State Univ, 61-64; synthesis org chemist, Calif, 64-79, ORG SURFACTANT SYNTHESIS CHEMIST, EMERY INDUSTS, INC, SC, 79- *Mem:* AAAS; Am Chem Soc; Am Asn Cereal Chemists; Inst Food Technol. *Res:* Cereal chemistry; products prepared from cereal grains and the modification of these products by processing methods, addition of surfactants and/or formula modification; organic surfactant synthesis; organic surface active materials. *Mailing Add:* PO Box 723 Mauldin SC 29662

SCHUM, GREGORY MICHAEL, b Colorado Springs, Colo. ECOLOGY. *Educ:* Univ NMex, BS, 71, MS, 72, PhD(biol), 75. *Prof Exp:* Res scientist biomath, Lovelace Biomed & Environ Res Inst, 74-78; ASST PROF BIOL, SAN DIEGO STATE UNIV, 79- *Mem:* Sigma Xi. *Res:* Computer and mathematical modeling of biological systems; theoretical ecology; radioecology; biostatistics. *Mailing Add:* Dept Biol San Diego State Univ San Diego CA 92182

SCHUMACHER, BERTHOLD WALTER, b Karlsruhe, Ger, Apr 15, 21; US citizen; m 55; c 2. EXPERIMENTAL PHYSICS, PHYSICS ENGINEERING. *Educ:* Stuttgart Tech Univ, dipl, 50, Dr rer nat, 53. *Prof Exp:* Design engr, Prof Berthold Lab, Ger, 53-54; res fel, Ont Res Found, 54-58, dir dept physics, 58-66; mgr electron beam technol, Westinghouse Res Labs, 66-77; PRIN ENGR RES, FORD MOTOR CO, 77- *Mem:* Am Phys Soc; Can Asn Physicists; Brit Inst Physics; Ger Physics Soc; Asn Ger Eng. *Res:* Vacuum and electron beam physics and technology; electron beam attenuation, fluorescence and single-scatter probes for measuring gas parameters; atmospheric electron probe for x-ray analysis of matter; high power electron guns with beam in air for welding and cutting. *Mailing Add:* 24635 Winona Dearborn MI 48124

SCHUMACHER, CLIFFORD RODNEY, b Waukegan, Ill, Dec 19, 29; m 50, 69; c 3. THEORETICAL PHYSICS. *Educ:* Wayne State Univ, BS, 51; Cornell Univ, PhD(theoret physics), 62; Haskell Indian Jr Col, AA, 75. *Prof Exp:* Physicist, Air Develop Ctr, Wright-Patterson AFB, 51-54; mem tech staff, Bell Tel Labs, 54-57; mem, Inst Adv Study, 61-62; fels, NSF, Princeton Univ, 62-63 & Enrico Fermi, Chicago, 63-65; assoc prof physics, Pa State Univ, 65-70; vis assoc prof physics & vis fel, Lab Nuclear Studies, Cornell Univ, 70-73; adj prof physics & astron, Univ Kans, 73-76; Instr physics, Haskell Indian Jr Col, 76-80; MEM STAFF ELECTROMAGNETIC SIGNATURE, NAVAL SHIP RES & DEVELOP CTR, 80- *Concurrent Pos:* Vis asst physicist, Brookhaven Nat Lab, 63; prof math sci dept, Haskell Indian Jr Col, 72-; vpres gov bd, Lawrence Indian Ctr, Inc, 73-75, pres, 75- *Mem:* Am Phys Soc. *Res:* Theory of structure and interaction of elementary particles; analysis of high energy phenomena; microwave generators and electronics; electromagnetic interactions of the deuteron; meson resonances; American Indian traditions and science education. *Mailing Add:* Control Br Code 2734 Naval Ship Res & Develop Ctr Annapolis MD 21402

SCHUMACHER, DIETMAR, b Yugoslavia, May 28, 42; US citizen; m 70. PETROLEUM GEOLOGY, PALEONTOLOGY. *Educ:* Univ Wis-Madison, BS, 64, MS, 67; Univ Mo-Columbia, PhD(geol), 72. *Prof Exp:* From asst prof to assoc prof geosci, Univ Ariz, 70-77; res geologist, 77-79, res supvr, 79-81, SR GEOL SPECIALIST, PHILLIPS PETROL CO, 81- *Mem:* AAAS; Geol Soc Am; Paleont Soc; Am Asn Petrol Geologists. *Res:* Petroleum geology and geochemistry; micropaleontology and biostratigraphy; stratigraphy and sedimentation. *Mailing Add:* Phillips Petrol Co PO Box 1967 Houston TX 77001

SCHUMACHER, GEBHARD FRIEDERICH B, b Osnabruck, WGer, June 13, 24; m 58; c 2. OBSTETRICS & GYNECOLOGY, IMMUNOLOGY. *Educ:* Univ Gottingen, MD, 51. *Prof Exp:* Intern gen med, Med Sch, Univ Tubingen, 51-52; resident in biochem, Max Planck Inst Biochem, 52-53 & Max Planck Inst Virus Res, 53-54; resident obstet & gynec, Med Sch, Univ Tubingen, 54-59, sci asst, 59-62, docent, 62 & 64-65; res assoc immunol, Inst Tuberc Res, Col Med, Univ Ill, 62-63; res assoc & asst prof obstet & gynec, Univ Chicago, 63-64; assoc prof obstet & gynec & asst prof biochem, Albany Med Col, 65-67; res scientist, Div Labs & Res, NY State Dept Health, 65-67; assoc prof, 67-73, PROF OBSTET & GYNEC, PRITZKER SCH MED, UNIV CHICAGO, 73-, CHIEF SECT REPRODUCTIVE BIOL, 71- *Concurrent Pos:* Ger Sci Found grant, 55-62; NIH grants; Ford Found funds; app fac mem, Div Comt on Immunol, 72-; consult & task force mem, World

Health Orgn, Human Reprod Unit, 72-77; mem med adv bd, Int Fertil Res Prog, Triangle Park, NC, 77-; reviewer & ad hoc consult, Nat Inst Child Health & Human Develop, Bethesda, Md, 73- *Mem:* Ger Soc Biol Chemists; Am Asn Pathologists; Soc Study Reprod; Am Soc Andrology; Europe Soc Immunol. *Res:* Biology of human reproduction; birth control; infertility; endocrinology-protein metabolism; serum proteins; immunology; inflammation and nonspecific resistance; trauma. *Mailing Add:* Dept of Obstet & Gynec Univ of Chicago Sch of Med Chicago IL 60637

SCHUMACHER, GEORGE ADAM, b Trenton, NJ, Sept 22, 12; m 41; c 4. MEDICINE. *Educ:* Pa State Univ, BS, 32; Cornell Univ, MD, 36. *Prof Exp:* From asst to assoc prof clin med, Cornell Med Ctr, New York, 46-50; chmn div neurol, 50-68, prof neurol, 50-77, EMER PROF NEUROL, UNIV VT, 77- *Concurrent Pos:* From asst attend neurologist to dir neurol serv, Bellevue Hosp, New York, 46-50; mem med adv bd, Nat Multiple Sclerosis Soc, 49-, chmn, 64-66; attend neurologist, Med Ctr Hosp, Vt, 50-; consult, Hosps, NY & Vt, 50-; mem prog proj comt, Nat Inst Neurol Dis & Blindness, 62-64; vis scientist, Arctic Health Res Lab, USPHS, 67-68; vis prof human ecol, Inst Arctic Biol, Univ Alaska, 67-68. *Mem:* Am Neurol Asn; Asn Res Nerv & Ment Dis; fel Am Acad Neurol. *Res:* Headache; pain; multiple sclerosis; spinal cord physiology. *Mailing Add:* Dept of Neurol Univ of Vt Col of Med Burlington VT 05401

SCHUMACHER, GEORGE JOHN, b Lindenwold, NJ, Dec 19, 24; m 49; c 3. PHYCOLOGY. *Educ:* Bucknell Univ, BS, 48; Cornell Univ, MS, 49, PhD(bot, vert zool), 53. *Prof Exp:* Instr, Cornell Univ, 52-53; from instr to assoc prof biol, 53-61, chmn dept, 59-66, PROF BIOL, STATE UNIV NY BINGHAMTON, 61- *Mem:* Am Phycol Soc; Int Phycol Soc. *Res:* Ecology and taxonomy of freshwater algae, populations and eutrophication. *Mailing Add:* Dept of Biol Sci State Univ NY Binghamton NY 13901

SCHUMACHER, H RALPH, b Montreal, Que, Feb 14, 33; m 65; c 2. INTERNAL MEDICINE, RHEUMATOLOGY. *Educ:* Ursinus Col, Collegeville, Pa, BS, 55; Univ Pa, MD, 59. *Prof Exp:* Intern, Denver Gen Hosp, 59-60; resident, Wadsworth Vet Admin Hosp, Los Angeles, 60-62, fel rheumatol, 62-63; fel, Robert Brigham Hosp, Boston, 65-67; asst prof, 67-72, assoc prof, 72-79, PROF MED, SCH MED, UNIV PA, 79- *Concurrent Pos:* Staff physician & chief arthritis sect, Vet Admin Hosp, 67-, dir, Rheumatol Ctr, 77-; actg chief, Arthritis Sect, Sch Med, Univ Pa, 68-80. *Mem:* Am Rheumatism Asn; Am Fedn Clin Res; Electron Micros Soc Am. *Res:* Pathogenic studies in the rheumatic diseases using light and electron microscopy, electron probe analysis, tissue culture and immunoelectron microscopy; crystal induced arthritis and rheumatoid arthritis. *Mailing Add:* Arthritis Sect Univ of Pa Hosp Philadelphia PA 19104

SCHUMACHER, IGNATIUS, b Munjor, Kans, Apr 1, 28; m 54; c 7. ORGANIC CHEMISTRY, MEDICINAL CHEMISTRY. *Educ:* Univ Kans, BS, 58; Univ Mich, PhD(med chem), 62. *Prof Exp:* Org researcher, 62-64, sr org chemist, 64-73, RES SPECIALIST, MONSANTO CO, 73- *Mem:* Am Chem Soc. *Res:* Pharmaceutical chemicals; medicinal agents; microbiocidal agents; process development; phosphate esters; nitrobenzenes; flame retardant chemicals. *Mailing Add:* Monsanto Co 800 N Lindbergh Blvd St Louis MO 63166

SCHUMACHER, JOSEPH CHARLES, b Peru, Ill, Sept 15, 11; m 33; c 4. INDUSTRIAL CHEMISTRY. *Educ:* Univ Southern Calif, AB, 46. *Prof Exp:* Res chemist & prod supvr, Carus Chem Co, Ill, 31-40; mem res develop & orgn staff, Fine Chem, Inc, Calif, 40-41, vpres & dir res, Western Electrochem Co, 41-54; dir res, Am Potash & Chem Corp, 54-66, vpres rare earth div, 66-68; vpres electrochem, Vanadium & Rare Earth Div, Kerr-McGee Chem Corp, 68-72; pres, 72-77, CHMN OF THE BD, J C SCHUMACHER CO, 77- *Concurrent Pos:* Trustee, Whittier Col, 68-77. *Mem:* Am Chem Soc; Electrochem Soc. *Res:* Industrial electrochemistry; chlorates perchlorates and manganese compounds; organic chemistry; photochemicals; boron. *Mailing Add:* J C Schumacher Co 580 Airport Rd Oceanside CA 92054

SCHUMACHER, JOSEPH NICHOLAS, b Downers Grove, Ill, May 2, 28; m 50; c 9. ORGANIC CHEMISTRY. *Educ:* St Procopius Col, BS, 50; Ohio State Univ, MSc, 52, PhD(org chem), 54. *Prof Exp:* Asst res found, Ohio State Univ, 50-51, asst univ, 51-54; res chemist, 54-68, group leader, 68-78, SECT HEAD, R J REYNOLDS TOBACCO CO, 78- *Mem:* Am Chem Soc. *Res:* Natural products; carbohydrates; chromatography. *Mailing Add:* R J Reynolds Tobacco Co Winston-Salem NC 27101

SCHUMACHER, ROBERT E, b Heron Lake, Minn, Oct 14, 18; m 45; c 4. AQUATIC BIOLOGY, FISHERIES MANAGEMENT. *Educ:* Univ Minn, BS, 50. *Prof Exp:* Aquatic biologist, Fisheries Res Unit, State Dept Conserv, Minn, 50-57, res biologist, 57-65; dist fisheries mgr, 65-71, REGIONAL FISHERIES MGR, MONT DEPT FISH & GAME, 71- *Mem:* Am Fisheries Soc. *Res:* Fisheries management and research; aquatic ecology; trout population levels and dynamics. *Mailing Add:* 1227 Fifth St W Kalispell MT 59901

SCHUMACHER, ROBERT THORNTON, b Berkeley, Calif, Sept 29, 30; m 54; c 2. MUSICAL ACOUSTICS. *Educ:* Univ Nev, BS, 51; Univ Ill, MS, 53, PhD(physics), 55. *Prof Exp:* Instr physics, Univ Wash, 55-57; from asst prof to assoc prof, 57-66, PROF PHYSICS, CARNEGIE-MELLON UNIV, 66- *Concurrent Pos:* NSF sr fel, 65-66. *Mem:* Fel Am Phys Soc. *Res:* Nuclear magnetic and electron spin resonance. *Mailing Add:* Dept of Physics Carnegie-Mellon Univ Pittsburgh PA 15213

SCHUMACHER, ROY JOSEPH, b Covington, Ky, Mar 15, 42; m 65; c 2. ORGANIC CHEMISTRY. *Educ:* Xavier Univ, Ohio, BS, 64, MS, 67; Univ Cincinnati, PhD(chem), 71. *Prof Exp:* Chemist, 71-75, res group leader, MC/B Mfg Chemists, 74-78, mkt mgr, 78-81, SR ANAL CHEMIST, MONSANTO RES CORP, 81- *Mem:* Am Chem Soc. *Res:* Ylid chemistry; organic synthesis and product development. *Mailing Add:* 3518 Grandview Ave Sharonville OH 45241

SCHUMACHER, WILLIAM JOHN, b Jersey City, NJ, Mar 11, 36; m 69; c 1. CHEMICAL ENGINEERING. *Educ:* Cornell Univ, BChE, 58, PhD(chem eng), 64. *Prof Exp:* Prof chem eng, Nat Univ Trujillo, 65-70; CHEM ENGR, STANFORD RES INST, 71- *Mem:* Am Inst Chem Engrs; Am Chem Soc. *Res:* Chemical process economics. *Mailing Add:* 1003 Almanor Ave Menlo Park CA 94025

SCHUMAKER, JOHN ABRAHAM, b Marshall, Ill, July 24, 25. MATHEMATICS. *Educ:* Univ Ill, BS, 46, AM, 47; NY Univ, PhD(math educ), 59. *Prof Exp:* Instr math, Univ Ill, 46-47; from instr to asst prof, MacMurray Col, 47-53; instr, Grinnell Col, 53-55; from asst prof to assoc prof, Montclair State Col, 55-61; dir, NSF in-serv insts, 62-68, PROF MATH & CHMN DEPT, ROCKFORD COL, 61- *Concurrent Pos:* Vis prof, NSF Inst, Univ Vt, 62-73. *Mem:* AAAS; Am Math Soc; Math Asn Am. *Res:* Number theory; history of mathematics; statistics. *Mailing Add:* 911 Woodridge Dr Rockford IL 61108

SCHUMAKER, LARRY L, b Aberdeen, SDak, Nov 5, 39; m 63; c 1. MATHEMATICS. *Educ:* SDak Sch Mines & Technol, BS, 61; Stanford Univ, MS, 62, PhD(math), 66. *Prof Exp:* Lectr comput sci, Stanford Univ, 66; vis asst prof math, Math Res Ctr, Univ Wis-Madison, 66-68; from asst prof to assoc prof math, Univ Tex, 68-74, prof, 74-79; PROF MATH, TEXAS A&M UNIV, COLLEGE STA, 80- *Concurrent Pos:* Vis assoc prof, Math Res Ctr, Univ Wis, 73-74; vis prof math, Univ Munich, 74-75, Free Univ Berlin, Hahn Meitner Atomic Energy Inst, 78-79 & Univ Sao Paulo, Brazil, 81. *Mem:* Am Math Soc; Soc Indust & Appl Math; Math Asn Am. *Res:* Classical approximation theory; total positivity; spline functions. *Mailing Add:* Dept Math Texas A&M Univ College Station TX 77843

SCHUMAKER, ROBERT LOUIS, b Sapulpa, Okla, July 28, 20; m 50; c 3. PHYSICS, MATHEMATICS. *Educ:* Tex Western Col, BS, 43; Univ Ariz, MS, 54. *Prof Exp:* From instr to asst prof physics & math, 46-61, asst dir, Schellenger Res Labs, 59-70, dir comput ctr, 67-70, dir admis, 70-77, physicist & head data anal sect, Schellenger Res Labs, 56-77, ASSOC PROF PHYSICS & MATH, UNIV TEX, EL PASO, 61- *Mem:* Am Meteorol Soc; Am Asn Physics Teachers. *Res:* Spectrography of high energy spark discharges; propagation and characteristics of atmospheric pressure oscillations, particularly ray-tracing techniques. *Mailing Add:* Dept of Physics Univ of Tex El Paso TX 79968

SCHUMAKER, VERNE NORMAN, b McCloud, Calif, Sept 16, 29; m 51; c 2. PHYSICAL BIOCHEMISTRY. *Educ:* Univ Calif, AB, 52, PhD(biophys), 55. *Prof Exp:* Jr res biophysicist, Virus Lab, Univ Calif, 54-55, assoc res biophysicist, 55-56; Am Cancer Soc fel, Lab Animal Morphol, Brussels, Belg, 56-57; from asst prof to assoc prof biochem, Univ Pa, 57-65; assoc prof chem, 65-66, PROF CHEM, UNIV CALIF, LOS ANGELES, 66- *Concurrent Pos:* John Simon Guggenheim fel, 64-65. *Mem:* AAAS; Biophys Soc; Am Soc Biol Chemists. *Res:* Immunochemistry, structure and function of lipoproteins, chromatin structure; hydrodynamic theory and methodology. *Mailing Add:* Dept of Chem Univ of Calif Los Angeles CA 90024

SCHUMAN, LEONARD MICHAEL, b Cleveland, Ohio, Mar 4, 13; m 54; c 2. EPIDEMIOLOGY. *Educ:* Oberlin Col, AB, 34; Western Reserve Univ, MSc, 39, MD, 40; Am Bd Prev Med, dipl. *Prof Exp:* Chief div venereal dis control, State Dept Pub Health, Ill, 47-49, actg chief div commun dis, 49-50, dep dir in charge div prev med, 50-51, 53-54; epidemiologist, Cold Injury Res Team, US Dept Defense, Korea, 51-53; assoc prof pub health, 54-57, PROF EPIDEMIOL, SCH PUB HEALTH, UNIV MINN, MINNEAPOLIS, 57- *Concurrent Pos:* Rockefeller Found fel nutrit, Vanderbilt Univ, 46; vis lectr, Sch Med, Univ Ill, 47-54; lectr, Sch Nursing, Mem Hosp, Springfield, Ill, 47-54, guest lectr, 52-; comn officer, USPHS, 41-47; officer-in-chg, SE Nutrit Res Univ, USPHS, 45-47, consult, Commun Dis Ctr, 55-; chmn, Coun on Res, Am Col of Prev Med, 59-64, Epidemiol Sect, Am Pub Health Asn, 67; Chronic Dis Div, 64-72, Div Radiol Health, 61-69, Nat Cancer Inst, 58-, Minn State Health Dept, 55-, Hennepin County Gen Hosp, 55-, USDA, 61-, Air Pollution Med Prog, 58 & Calif State Health Dept, 62; mem, Nat Adv Comt Gamma Globulin Eval, 52-53; adv comt polio vaccine field trials, Nat Found Infantile Paralysis, 52-55; adv polio vaccine eval ctr, Univ Mich, 53-55; adv nat cancer control comt, NIH, 59-62, accident prev res study sect, 63-66; adv comt, Nat Coop Leukemia Study, 59-63; adv field studies bd, Nat Adv Cancer Coun, 61-62; adv nat adv comt bio-effects radiation, USPHS, 66-69, task force smoking & health, 67-68; mem, Nat Adv Urban & Indust Health Coun, 68-69, Nat Adv Environ Control Coun, 69-71; mem comt health protection & dis prev adv, Secy, Health, Educ & Welfare, 69-71 & cancer res ctr rev comt, Nat Cancer Inst, 71-75; fel coun epidemiol, Am Heart Asn, chmn, Conf Chronic Dis Training Prog Dirs, 60-72, panel biomet & epidemiol, Nat Cancer Inst, 61-62, Nat Conf Res Methodology in Community Health & Prev Med, 62 & Surgeon Gen Adv Comt Smoking & Health, 62-64. task group on smoking, Nat Heart, Lung & Blood Inst, 78-; task group on interstitial lung dis, Nat Heart, Lung & Blood Inst/NIH, 78-; steering comt, Nutrit Res, Agency for Int Develop, US Dept of State, 78-; policy bd, Mid-Career Med Fels, Bush Found, 78- *Mem:* Am Epidemiol Soc (pres, 78); Am Thoracic Soc; Am Venereal Dis Asn; Asn Teachers Prev Med; NY Acad Sci. *Res:* Epidemiology of communicable disease, non-communicable disease and cancer. *Mailing Add:* Sch of Pub Health Univ Minn Minneapolis MN 55455

SCHUMAN, ROBERT PAUL, b Milwaukee, Wis, May 17, 19; m 49; c 3. NUCLEAR CHEMISTRY, PHYSICAL CHEMISTRY. *Educ:* Univ Denver, BS, 41; Ohio State Univ, MS, 44, PhD(chem), 46. *Prof Exp:* Chemist metall lab, Univ Chicago, 44-45, Knolls Atomic Power Lab, Gen Elec Co, 47-57, Atomic Energy Div, Phillips Petrol Co, 57-66 & Idaho Nuclear Corp, 66-69; assoc prof chem, Robert Col, Istanbul, 69-71; assoc prof chem, Bogazici Univ, Turkey, 71-77; vis prof, Nuclear Eng, Iowa State Univ, 77-78; sr phys chemist, Idaho Nat Eng Lab, Allied Chem Corp, 78-79; sr phys chemist, Exxon Nuclear, 79-80; SR PHYS CHEMIST, EG&G IDAHO, INC, 80- *Concurrent Pos:* Fulbright grant, Sri Venkateswara Univ, India, 65-66. *Mem:* Am Nuclear Soc; Am Chem Soc; Am Phys Soc. *Mailing Add:* 1766 Rainier St Idaho Falls ID 83401

SCHUMAN, STANLEY HAROLD, b St Louis, Mo, Dec 29, 25; m; c 8. EPIDEMIOLOGY, PUBLIC HEALTH. *Educ:* Wash Univ, MD, 48; Univ Mich, MPH, 60, DrPH, 62; Am Bd Pediat, dipl, 60. *Prof Exp:* Clin instr pediat, Sch Med, Wash Univ, 54-59; from asst prof to prof epidemiol, Sch Pub Health, Univ Mich, Ann Arbor, 62-73; PROF EPIDEMIOL IN FAMILY PRACT COL MED, MED UNIV SC, 74-, PROF PEDIAT, 76- *Concurrent Pos:* Proj dir, SC Pesticide Study Ctr, Environ Protection Agency, 81- *Mem:* Am Pub Health Asn; Am Acad Family Pract; Am Epidemiol Soc; Soc Epidemiol Res. *Res:* Epidemiology of heat waves in United States' cities; human sweat studies in population survey; screening for cystic fibrosis; population surveys of injuries due to accidents; accident prevention; field trials with young drivers; epidemiology in family practice; computers in medicine; immunotoxicology; cancer of the esophagus. *Mailing Add:* Dept of Family Pract Col of Med Med Univ of SC Charleston SC 29401

SCHUMAN, WILLIAM JOHN, JR, b Baltimore, Md, Jan 23, 30; m 52; c 3. MECHANICS. *Educ:* Univ Md, BS, 52; Pa State Univ, MS, 54, PhD(eng mech), 65. *Prof Exp:* Asst prof mech, US Air Force Inst Tech, 54-57; sr engr, Martin Co, Martin Marietta Corp, 57; aero res engr, 57-62, RES PHYSICIST, US ARMY BALLISTIC RES LAB, 62- *Mem:* Am Soc Mech Engrs; Am Acad Mech. *Res:* Dynamic response of structures, including determination of high explosive blast parameters and details of loading; primary structures; cylindrical and conical shells; design of blast/thermal hardened electronic shelters. *Mailing Add:* US Army Ballistic Res Lab Attn DRDAR-BLT Aberdeen Proving Ground MD 21005

SCHUMANN, EDWARD LEWIS, b Indianapolis, Ind, Aug 1, 23; m 47; c 3. ORGANIC CHEMISTRY, MEDICINAL CHEMISTRY. *Educ:* Ind Univ, BS, 43; Univ Mich, MS, 49, PhD(pharmaceut chem), 50. *Prof Exp:* Chemist, Linde Air Prods Co, 43-44; res chemist, Wm S Merrell Co, 49-57; res assoc, 57-65, mgr clin drug regulatory affairs, 65-68, DIR DRUG REGULATORY AFFAIRS, PROD RES & DEVELOP, UPJOHN CO, 68- *Mem:* AAAS; Am Fedn Clin Res; Am Col Clin Pharmacol & Chemother; Am Chem Soc. *Res:* Antispasmodics local anesthetics; histamine antagonists; central nervous system agents; cardiac-cardiovascular drugs; enzyme inhibitors; hormone antagonists. *Mailing Add:* 809 Dukeshire Ave Kalamazoo MI 49008

SCHUMANN, THOMAS GERALD, b Los Angeles, Calif, Mar 15, 37. ELEMENTARY PARTICLE PHYSICS. *Educ:* Calif Inst Technol, BS, 58; Univ Calif, Berkeley, MA, 60, PhD(physics), 65. *Prof Exp:* Res assoc physics, Brookhaven Nat Lab, 65-67; asst prof, City Col New York, 67-71; lectr, 71-74, asst prof, 74-76, ASSOC PROF PHYSICS, CALIF POLYTECH STATE UNIV, SAN LUIS OBISPO, 76- *Mem:* Am Phys Soc. *Res:* Experimental high energy physics using bubble chambers. *Mailing Add:* Dept of Physics Calif Polytech State Univ San Luis Obispo CA 93407

SCHUMAR, JAMES F(RANK), b Elyria, Ohio, Feb 13, 17; m 49; c 5. METALLURGICAL ENGINEERING. *Educ:* Case Inst Technol, BS, 39. *Prof Exp:* Chief inspector, Wolverine Tube Div, Calumet & Hecla Consol Copper, Inc, Mich, 39-41, sr metallurgist, 41-46; actg dir metall div, Argonne Nat Lab, 46-48, assoc dir metall div, 48-60; chmn metall dept, Gen Atomic Div, Gen Dynamics Corp, 60-63; SR METALLURGIST, ARGONNE NAT LAB, 63- *Mem:* Am Soc Metals; Am Inst Mining, Metall & Petrol Engrs; Am Nuclear Soc. *Res:* Fabrication techniques for uranium, thorium, zirconium, plutonium, beryllium and their alloys; nuclear fuels and fuel element development, metallic and ceramic; coordination of fast reactor for space propulsion. *Mailing Add:* Argonne Nat Lab 9700 Cass Ave Argonne IL 60440

SCHUMER, WILLIAM, b Chicago, Ill, June 29, 26; div; c 2. SURGERY, BIOCHEMISTRY. *Educ:* Ill Inst Technol, 44-45; Chicago Med Sch, MB, 49, MD, 50; Univ Ill, MS, 66; Am Bd Surg, dipl. *Prof Exp:* Asst prof surg, Chicago Med Sch, 59-65, asst prof cardiovasc res, 64-65; from assoc prof to prof surg, Univ Ill, Vet Admin West Side Hosp, 67-75, chief surg, 67-75; prof surg & chmn & prof biochem, Univ Health Sci, Chicago Med Sch & chief surg, 75-80, CHIEF, GEN SURG SECT, VA MED CTR, NORTH CHICAGO, 80- *Concurrent Pos:* Mem attend staff, Mt Sinai Hosp, Chicago, Ill, 62-65, asst chief surg, 63-64; mem attend staff, Vet Admin Hines Hosp, 60-63 & Vet Admin West Side Hosp, 63-64; dir surg serv, Sacramento County Med Ctr & Univ Calif, Davis, 65-67; mem, Am Bd Surg; mem med staff, Highland Park Hosp, Naval Reg Med Ctr, Great Lakes, 76- & St Mary's Nazareth Hosp Ctr, Chicago, 78- *Honors & Awards:* Morris L Parker Res Award, 76. *Mem:* Am Col Surg; Am Physiol Soc; Shock Soc (pres, 78); Cent Surg Asn; Cent Soc Clin Res. *Res:* Effect of trauma or shock on cell metabolism; correlation of cell biochemistry, physiology and anatomy in humans and animals in shock. *Mailing Add:* Univ Health Sci Chicago Med Sch Va Med Ctr of North Chicago North Chicago IL 60064

SCHUMM, BROOKE, JR, b Shanghai, China, Oct 8, 31; US citizen; m 55; c 4. ELECTROCHEMICAL & CHEMICAL ENGINEERING. *Educ:* Rensselaer Polytech Inst, BS, 53; Univ Rochester, MS, 62, PhD(chem eng), 66. *Prof Exp:* Team leader chem warfare, US Army, 53-55; indust methods engr film processing, Eastman Kodak Co, 55-57, develop engr coatings, 57-58; fel chem engr, Univ Rochester, 58-62; SR TECHNOL ASSOC BATTERIES, UNION CARBIDE CORP, 62- *Concurrent Pos:* Union Carbide fel, Univ Rochester, 60-62. *Mem:* Electrochem Soc. *Res:* Industrial coatings, fuel cell batteries, primary electrochemical cells and energy conversion. *Mailing Add:* Battery Prod Div PO Box 6056 Cleveland OH 44101

SCHUMM, DOROTHY ELAINE, b Dayton, Ohio, Aug 4, 43. BIOCHEMISTRY. *Educ:* Earlham Col, BA, 65; Univ Chicago, MS, 66, PhD(biochem), 69. *Prof Exp:* Res assoc biochem, Ben May Lab Cancer Res, Univ Chicago, 69-70; res assoc, 71-73, clin instr, 73-74, instr biochem, 74-75, asst prof, 75-79, ASSOC PROF PHYSIOL CHEM, SCH MED, OHIO STATE UNIV, 79- *Mem:* AAAS; Am Asn Cancer Res; NY Acad Sci; Asn Women in Sci. *Res:* Chemical carcinogenesis; oncogenesis; RNA synthesis and transport; aging. *Mailing Add:* Dept of Physiol Chem Ohio State Univ Sch of Med Columbus OH 43210

SCHUMM, STANLEY ALFRED, b Kearny, NJ, Feb 22, 27; m 50; c 3. GEOMORPHOLOGY, WATERSHED MANAGEMENT. *Educ:* Upsala Col, AB, 50; Columbia Univ, PhD(geol), 55. *Prof Exp:* Geologist, US Geol Surv, 54-67; assoc prof geol, 67-70, assoc dean, 73-74, PROF GEOL, COLO STATE UNIV, 70- *Concurrent Pos:* Vis lectr, Univ Calif, 59-60; prof affil, Colo State Univ, 63; mem nat comt, Int Union Quaternary Res, 63-69; fel, Univ Sydney, 64-65; cor mem comn hillslope evolution & mem comn appl geomorphol, Int Geog Union, 65; vis geol scientist, Am Geol Inst, 66; vis scientist, Polish Acad Sci, 69; distinguished lectr, Univ Tex, 70; vis prof, Univ de los Andes, Venezuela, 72 & Econ Geol Res Unit, Univ Witwatersrand, SAfrica, 75; prin investr res projs, Nat Sci Found, US Army Res Off, Nat Park Serv, Off of Water Res & Technol, US Geol Surv & Colo Agr Exp Sta; co-investr, US Army Corps of Engrs, Bur of Sports Fisheries & Wildlife & the Fed Hwy Admin; consult, Reg Transp Dist, Denver, Cameron Eng Co, Atlantic Richfield Oil Co & DDI Explor, Paris, Integral Ltd, Medellin, Manawatu bd, New Zealand, corp of engrs, Ohio River Div & US Dept of Justice. *Honors & Awards:* Horton Award, Am Geophys Union, 59; Kirk Bryan Award, Geol Soc Am, 79. *Mem:* AAAS; Geol Soc Am; Am Geophys Union; Am Soc Civil Engrs; Am Quaternary Asn. *Res:* Stream morphology; paleohydrology. *Mailing Add:* Dept of Earth Resources Colo State Univ Ft Collins CO 80521

SCHUNDER, MARY COTHRAN, b Tulsa, Okla, Sept 28, 31; m 56; c 3. GROSS ANATOMY, CYTOHISTOCHEMISTRY. *Educ:* Tex Christian Univ, BA, 53, MA, 70; Baylor Univ, PhD(anat), 76. *Prof Exp:* Staff microbiol, Univ Dallas, 64-69; instr biol, Tex Christian Univ, 69-70; ASSOC PROF ANAT & CHMN DEPT, TEX COL OSTEOP MED, 70-; ASSOC GRAD FAC MEM BASIC HEALTH SCI, NORTH TEX STATE UNIV, 78- *Concurrent Pos:* HEW training grant, Bur Health Prof, 72-75; consult anat, Nat Bd Examrs for Osteop Physicians & Surgeons, 75-; rep, Anat Bd State Tex, 70-, vpres, 78- *Mem:* Sigma Xi. *Res:* Calcium metabolism; histochemical localization of calcium and lipid in calcified tissue and gut. *Mailing Add:* Tex Col of Osteop Med Camp Bowie at Montgomery Ft Worth TX 76107

SCHUNK, ROBERT WALTER, b New York, NY. PLASMA TRANSPORT, NUMERICAL SIMULATIONS. *Educ:* NY Univ, BS, 65; Yale Univ, PhD(phys fluids), 70. *Prof Exp:* Inst Sci & Technol fel space physics, Univ Mich, 70-71; res assoc geophys, Yale Univ, 71-73; res assoc space physics, Univ Calif, San Diego, 73-76; assoc prof, 76-79, PROF PHYSICS, UTAH STATE UNIV, 79- *Concurrent Pos:* Assoc ed, J Geophys Res, 77-80; mem, Comt Solar Terrestrial Res, Geophysics Res Bd, Nat Acad Sci, 79-; mem, Nat Ctr Atmospheric Res Comput Divisions Adv Panel, 80-; prin investr, Solar Terrestrial Theory Prog, 80- *Mem:* Am Geophys Union; AAAS. *Res:* Planetary atmospheres, ionospheres and magnetospheres; solar wind. *Mailing Add:* Dept Physics Utah State Univ Logan UT 84322

SCHUNN, ROBERT ALLEN, b Martins Ferry, Ohio, July 15, 36; m 59; c 3. INORGANIC CHEMISTRY. *Educ:* Univ Ohio, BS, 58; Mass Inst Technol, PhD(inorg chem), 63. *Prof Exp:* RES CHEMIST, CENT RES DEPT, E I DU PONT DE NEMOURS & CO, INC, 63- *Mem:* Am Chem Soc. *Res:* Preparative inorganic chemistry, especially of transition metal compounds; heterogeneous catalysis; organometallic chemistry. *Mailing Add:* Cent Res Dept Exp Sta E I du Pont de Nemours & Co Wilmington DE 19898

SCHUPF, NICOLE, b New York, NY, Jan 20, 43; m 68; c 1. PHYSIOLOGICAL PSYCHOLOGY. *Educ:* Bryn Mawr Col, BA, 64; NY Univ, PhD(psychol), 70. *Prof Exp:* Res assoc, Rockefeller Univ, 69-71; instr neurol, Med Sch, NY Univ, 74-77; ASST PROF PSYCHOL, MANHATTANVILLE COL, 77- *Concurrent Pos:* Adj asst prof neurol, Med Sch, NY Univ, 77- *Mem:* AAAS; Soc Neurosci. *Res:* Neuroimmunology; metabolic and nutritional determinants of body weight regulation and food intake. *Mailing Add:* Dept of Psychol Manhattanville Col Purchase NY 10577

SCHUPP, GUY, b Blackwater, Mo, Oct 20, 33; m 62; c 2. NUCLEAR PHYSICS. *Educ:* Mo Valley Col, BS, 54; Iowa State Univ, PhD(physics), 62. *Prof Exp:* Res scientist, Indust Reactor Labs, US Rubber Co, NJ, 62-64 & Res Ctr, 64; asst prof physics, 64-70, ASSOC PROF PHYSICS, UNIV MO-COLUMBIA, 70- *Concurrent Pos:* Sabbatical, Argonne Nat Lab, 71-72. *Mem:* AAAS; Am Phys Soc; Am Asn Physics Teachers. *Res:* Nuclear spectroscopy; atomic excitation and ionization phenomena; Mössbauer scattering; neutron activation analysis and tracer studies. *Mailing Add:* Dept of Physics Univ of Mo Columbia MO 65211

SCHUPP, ORION EDWIN, III, b Wilmington, Del, Jan 28, 32; m 55; c 3. ANALYTICAL CHEMISTRY. *Educ:* Univ Del, BS, 53; Ohio State Univ, PhD(chem), 58. *Prof Exp:* Res chemist, 58-63, sr res chemist, 63-69, res assoc anal chem, 69, LAB HEAD, EASTMAN KODAK CO, 69- *Mem:* Am Chem Soc. *Res:* Molecular weight and chemical composition of polymers, gel permeation chromatography; liquid chromatography; gas chromatography; polarography of complex ions for determination of stability constants. *Mailing Add:* 363 Meadowbriar Rd Rochester NY 14616

SCHUPP, PAUL EUGENE, b Cleveland, Ohio, Mar 12, 37:; m 66. MATHEMATICS. *Educ:* Case Western Reserve Univ, BA, 59; Univ Mich, Ann Arbor, MA, 61, PhD(math), 66. *Prof Exp:* Asst prof math, Univ Wis-Madison, 66-67; from asst prof to assoc prof, 67-75, assoc mem, Ctr Advan Study, 73-74, PROF MATH, UNIV ILL, URBANA, 75- *Concurrent Pos:* Vis mem, Courant Inst, 69-70; John Simon Guggenheim mem fel, 77-78. *Mem:* Am Math Soc; London Math Soc. *Res:* Theory of infinite groups and decision problems in algebraic systems; automate theory. *Mailing Add:* Dept of Math Univ of Ill Urbana IL 61801

SCHUR, PETER HENRY, b Vienna, Austria, May 9, 33; US citizen; m 63; c 2. INTERNAL MEDICINE, IMMUNOLOGY. *Educ:* Yale Univ, BS, 55; Harvard Univ, MD, 58. *Prof Exp:* Assoc, 67-69, asst prof, 69-72, assoc prof, 72-77, PROF MED, HARVARD MED SCH, 78- *Concurrent Pos:* Helen Hay Whitney fel, Rockefeller Univ, 64-67. *Mem:* Am Soc Clin Invest; Am Asn Immunol; Am Col Physicians; Am Rheumatism Asn; Am Fedn Clin Res. *Res:* Rheumatology; systemic lupus. *Mailing Add:* Robert B Brigham Hosp Boston MA 02120

SCHURLE, ARLO WILLARD, b Clay Center, Kans, Oct 30, 43; m 63. MATHEMATICS. *Educ:* Univ Kans, BA, 64, MA, 66, PhD(math, topology), 67. *Prof Exp:* Asst prof math, Ind Univ, Bloomington, 67-71; assoc prof math, Univ NC, Charlotte, 71-78; fulbright prof math, Univ Liberia, 78-80; ASSOC PROF MATH, UNIV NC, CHARLOTTE, 80- *Mem:* Math Asn Am; Am Math Soc. *Res:* Geometric topology, including decompositions of three-space; compactifications and dimension theory. *Mailing Add:* Dept of Math Univ of NC Charlotte NC 28223

SCHURMAN, GLENN AUGUST, b La Center, Wash, Sept 6, 22; m 44; c 3. MECHANICAL ENGINEERING. *Educ:* State Col Wash, BS, 44; Calif Inst Technol, MS, 47, PhD(mech eng), 50. *Prof Exp:* Res engr, Nat Adv Comt Aeronaut, 44-46; from res engr to sr res engr, Calif Res Corp, 50-60, mgr producing res, 60-63, sr staff engr, 63-65, dist supt, Calif Co Div, Chevron Oil Co, 65-69; div prod supt, Standard Oil Co Tex, 69-71; asst gen mgr prod, Calco Div, 71-74, vpres & gen mgr prod, Denver, 74-75, managing dir, Chevron Petrol UK Ltd, 75-82, VPRES, STANDARD OIL CO CALIF, 82- *Concurrent Pos:* Distinguished lectr, Soc Petrol Engrs, 78. *Mem:* Nat Acad Eng; Am Inst Mining, Metall & Petrol Engrs; Am Soc Mech Engrs. *Res:* Auto-ignition of gases near heated surface; aerodynamics and fluid dynamics of gas turbines; oil production and geophysics. *Mailing Add:* Standard Oil Co Calif 225 Bush St San Francisco CA 94104

SCHURMEIER, HARRIS MCINTOSH, b St Paul, Minn, July 4, 24; m 49; c 4. AERONAUTICAL ENGINEERING. *Educ:* Calif Inst Technol, BS, 45, MS, 48, AeroE, 49. *Prof Exp:* From res engr to chief aerodyn div, Jet Propulsion Lab, 48-58, dep sergeant prog dir, 58-59, chief systs div, 59-62, mgr Ranger proj, 62-65, mgr Mariner Mars 1969 Proj, 66-69, dep asst lab dir flight proj, 69-76, mgr Voyager Proj, 72-76, asst lab dir energy & technol applications, 76-81, ASSOC LAB DIR UTILITARIAN PROG, CALIF INST TECHNOL, 81- *Concurrent Pos:* Mem manned space flight steering comt, NASA, 59-60, res adv comt missile & space vehicle aerodyn, 60-62. *Honors & Awards:* Exceptional Sci Achievement, Exceptional Serv & Distinguished Serv Medals, NASA, Astronaut Eng Award, 65 & 81; Von Karman Lectr, 75. *Mem:* AAAS; Supersonic Tunnel Asn; fel Am Inst Aeronaut & Astronaut. *Res:* Space exploration. *Mailing Add:* Calif Inst of Technol 4800 Oak Grove Dr Pasadena CA 91103

SCHURR, GARMOND GAYLORD, b Almont, NDak, Sept 7, 18; m 45; c 4. CHEMISTRY. *Educ:* NDak State Univ, BS(chem), 40. *Prof Exp:* Group leader, Paint Res, Sherwin-Williams Co, 46-58, asst dir, 58-66, dir, 66-74, dir, Res Ctr, 74-79, tech advr, 79-82; CONSULT, 82- *Mem:* Am Chem Soc; Am Soc Testing & Mat; Nat Asn Corrosion Eng; Fedn Socs Coatings Technol. *Res:* Applications of polymeric resins in protective coatings; corrosion control by means of protective coatings. *Mailing Add:* 6220 W 127th Place Palos Heights IL 60464

SCHURR, JOHN MICHAEL, b Pittsfield, Mass, Nov 10, 37; m 58; c 2. PHYSICAL CHEMISTRY, MOLECULAR BIOPHYSICS. *Educ:* Yale Univ, BS, 59; Univ Calif, Berkeley, PhD(biophys), 64. *Prof Exp:* NIH fel chem, Univ Ore, 64-66; from asst prof to assoc prof, 66-78, PROF CHEM, UNIV WASH, 78- *Concurrent Pos:* Vis scientist, Swiss Fed Water Inst, 74. *Mem:* Biophys Soc; Am Phys Soc; Am Chem Soc. *Res:* Coherent cynamic light scattering, pulsed laser optical techniques and NMR relaxation; macromolecular diffusion, including deformational brownian motions; cooperative association phenomena of polypeptides and polynucleotides; interaction of electromagnetic radiation; cooperative association phenomena in polypeptides and polynucleotides. *Mailing Add:* Dept of Chem Univ of Wash Seattle WA 98195

SCHURR, KARL M, b Logan Co, Ohio, Feb 28, 34; m 56; c 3. ENTOMOLOGY, POLLUTION BIOLOGY. *Educ:* Bowling Green State Univ, BA, 56, MA, 58; Univ Minn, PhD(entom, bot), 61. *Prof Exp:* Res asst, Univ Minn, 58-61; asst prof, 61-71, ASSOC PROF BIOL, BOWLING GREEN STATE UNIV, 71- *Concurrent Pos:* Grants, Fed Res, 58-61, NSF, 63-, US Dept Health, Educ & Welfare, 66- adj prof, Med Col Ohio; consult Ohio State Univ, 63, Greeley & Hansen Co, Ill, 65, Columbus Labs, Battelle Mem Res Inst, 70- & Holmes County Pub Health Dept & Regional Planning Comn, 71-; res consult marine pollution, Col Law, Univ Toledo & J&S Steel Co; res consult mariculture, Auburn Univ. *Mem:* Int Asn Advan Earth & Environ Sci (vpres, 77-78); World Mariculture Soc; AAAS; Entom Soc Am; Marine Technol Soc. *Res:* Invertebrate physiology, growth and development. *Mailing Add:* Dept of Biol Bowling Green State Univ Bowling Green OH 43403

SCHURRER, AUGUSTA, b New York, NY, Oct 11, 25. MATHEMATICS. *Educ:* Hunter Col, AB, 45; Univ Wis, MA, 47, PhD(math), 52. *Prof Exp:* Computer, Off Sci Res & Develop, 45; PROF MATH, UNIV NORTHERN IOWA, 50- *Concurrent Pos:* NSF fac fel, Univ Mich, 57-58; mem panel suppl pub, Sch Math Study Group, 61-65. *Mem:* Am Math Soc; Math Asn Am. *Res:* Mathematical analysis; zeros of polynomials; mathematics education; teacher education. *Mailing Add:* Dept of Math Univ of Northern Iowa Cedar Falls IA 50613

SCHUSSLER, M(ORTIMER), b Indianapolis, Ind, Jan 2, 23; m 43; c 2. METALLURGICAL ENGINEERING. *Educ:* Purdue Univ, BS, 43. *Prof Exp:* Res metallurgist, Caterpillar Tractor Co, Ill, 46-49; asst head metall dept, Union Carbide Nuclear Co, Tenn, 49-55, sect leader reactive metals, Union Carbide Metals Co, 55-60; engr in chg, Phys Metall Br, Tech Dept, Stellite Div, Union Carbide Corp, Ind, 60-66; SR SCIENTIST, FANSTEEL INC, 66- *Mem:* Am Soc Metals; Am Inst Mining, Metall & Petrol Engrs. *Res:* Refractory and reactive metals; superalloys; aluminum casting alloys; cast iron and steel; materials of construction for aerospace, chemical, nuclear and earthmoving applications. *Mailing Add:* H/K Porter Co, INc Fansteel Inc North Chicago IL 60064

SCHUSTEK, GEORGE W(ILLIAM), JR, b Oak Park, Ill, May 10, 15; m 44; c 3. CHEMICAL ENGINEERING. *Educ:* Univ Chicago, BS, 37, MBA, 51. *Prof Exp:* Res chemist, US Gypsum Co, 37-42; chem engr, Standard Oil Co (Ind), 46-48, group leader, 48-53, sect leader, Res Dept, 54-62, res supvr res & develop, Am Oil Co, 62-69, sr res scientist, 69-74; RETIRED. *Mem:* Am Chem Soc; Am Inst Chem Engrs. *Res:* Petroleum processes. *Mailing Add:* 1119 Country Club Dr Boone IA 50036

SCHUSTER, BURTON GORDON, physics, see previous edition

SCHUSTER, CHARLES ROBERTS, JR, b Woodbury, NJ, Jan 24, 30; m 53; c 5. PSYCHOLOGY, PHARMACOLOGY. *Educ:* Gettysburg Col, AB, 51; Univ NMex, MS, 53; Univ Md, PhD(psychol), 62. *Prof Exp:* Asst instr endocrinol & res biologist, Temple Med Sch, 53-55; jr scientist, Smith, Kline & French Labs, 55-57; res assoc psychopharmacol, Univ Md, 61-63; asst prof pharmacol, Med Sch, Univ Mich, Ann Arbor, 63-69, lectr psychol, 66-69; assoc prof pharmacol & psychiat, 69-72, PROF PSYCHIAT, PHARMACOL & PHYSIOL SCI, UNIV CHICAGO, 72- *Mem:* AAAS; Am Psychol Asn; Am Soc Pharmacol. *Res:* Psychological and physiological dependence on drugs; role of interoceptive processes in the control of behavior. *Mailing Add:* Dept of Psychiat Univ of Chicago Chicago IL 60637

SCHUSTER, DANIEL BRADLEY, b Milwaukee, Wis, Dec 22, 18; m 54; c 2. PSYCHIATRY. *Educ:* Univ Wis, BA, 41, MD, 43; Am Bd Psychiat & Neurol, dipl, 49. *Prof Exp:* Intern, Milwaukee Sanitarium, 43, resident, 46; intern, Germantown Hosp & Dispensary, Philadelphia, 44; resident psychiat & neurol, Univ Wis Hosps & Vet Admin Hosp, Mendota, 47-48; from instr to assoc prof, 49-69, dep chmn, 71-78, CLIN PROF PSYCHIAT, SCH MED & DENT, UNIV ROCHESTER, 70- *Concurrent Pos:* Vet Admin fel psychiat, Sch Med & Dent, Univ Rochester, 48-49; asst resident, Strong Mem Hosp, 48-49, asst psychiatrist, 49-60, sr assoc psychiatrist, 60-69, psychiatrist, 70-; psychiatrist, Rochester Munic Hosp, 49-; preceptor, Rochester State Hosp, 51-; consult, Sampson Base Hosp, US Dept Air Force, 51-55 & Vet Admin Hosp, Canadaigua, 52-; mem div psychoanal med, Col Med, State Univ NY Downstate Med Ctr, 56-61 & grad div psychoanal med, 61. *Mem:* AAAS; Am Psychoanal Asn; Geront Soc; Am Psychiat Asn; NY Acad Sci. *Res:* Clinical psychiatry; psychoanalysis; electroencephalography; aging. *Mailing Add:* Strong Mem Hosp 300 Crittenden Blvd Rochester NY 14642

SCHUSTER, DAVID ISRAEL, b Brooklyn, NY, Aug 13, 35; m 62. ORGANIC CHEMISTRY. *Educ:* Columbia Univ, BA, 56; Calif Inst Technol, PhD(chem, physics), 61. *Prof Exp:* Fel org photochem, Univ Wis, 60-61; from asst prof to assoc prof chem, 61-69, dir grad studies, Dept Chem, 74-78, PROF CHEM, NY UNIV, 69- *Concurrent Pos:* Alfred P Sloan fel, 67-69; vis fel, Royal Inst Gt Brit, 68-69; NSF sci fac fel, 75-76; vis prof, Yale Univ, 75-76. *Mem:* Am Soc Photobiol; Sigma Xi; Am Chem Soc; Inter-Am Photochem Soc; AAAS. *Res:* Mechanistic organic photochemistry; organic reaction mechanisms; spectroscopy and magnetic resonance; free radical chemistry; flash photolysis; biochemistry of Schizophrenia; mechanism of action of anti-psychotic drugs; characterization of dopamine receptors in the brain; photobiological processes; synthesis of prostaglandins. *Mailing Add:* Dept of Chem NY Univ New York NY 10003

SCHUSTER, DAVID J, b Memphis, Tenn, Aug 29, 47; m 71. HOST PLANT RESISTANCE, PEST MANAGEMENT. *Educ:* Kans State Univ, BS, MS, 70; Okla State Univ, PhD(entom), 73. *Prof Exp:* Res assoc entom, Okla State Univ, 73-75; asst prof, 75-80, ASSOC PROF ENTOM, AGR RES & EDUC CTR, UNIV FLA, BRADENTON, 80- *Mem:* Entom Soc Am; Sigma Xi. *Res:* Pest management of insect and mite pests of vegetables; interactions of insecticides, biological control and host plant resistance are emphasized. *Mailing Add:* Agr Res & Educ Ctr 5007 60th St E Bradenton FL 33508

SCHUSTER, DAVID MARTIN, b New York, NY, May 18, 39; m 67. MATERIALS SCIENCE, METALLURGICAL ENGINEERING. *Educ:* Mass Inst Technol, SB, 61; Cornell Univ, MS, 64, PhD(mat sci), 67. *Prof Exp:* Actg res assoc, Cornell Univ, 66-67; mem tech staff, 67-69, supvr, Composite Mat Develop Div, 69-77, DEPT MGR, SANDIA NAT LABS, 77- *Mem:* Am Soc Testing & Mat; Am Soc Metals; Am Inst Mining, Metall & Petrol Engrs; Soc Exp Stress Anal. *Res:* Growth and properties of crystals and whiskers; high temperature metallurgy and dispersion strengthening; plasma- jet spray-quenching; photoelastic stress analysis; discontinuously reinforced fiber composites and continuous filament composite materials. *Mailing Add:* Dept 8310 Mats Sandia Nat Labs Livermore CA 94550

SCHUSTER, FREDERICK LEE, b Brooklyn, NY, Jan 23, 34; m 60; c 2. PROTOZOOLOGY, ELECTRON MICROSCOPY. *Educ:* Brooklyn Col, BS, 56; Univ Calif, Berkeley, MA, 58, PhD(protozoan ultrastruct), 62. *Prof Exp:* Res specialist electron micros, Langley Porter Neuropsychiat Inst, 62-63; res assoc biol, Argonne Nat Lab, 63-66; from asst prof to assoc prof, 66-74, PROF BIOL, BROOKLYN COL, 74- *Mem:* Soc Protozool; Am Soc Cell Biol; Electron Micros Soc Am; Am Microscopical Soc; Am Sco Microbiol. *Res:* Pathogenic free-living Protozoa; Protozoan ultrastructure; morphogenesis of Protozoa. *Mailing Add:* Dept of Biol Col Brooklyn NY 11210

SCHUSTER, GARY BENJAMIN, b New York, NY, Aug 6, 46; m 68; c 2. PHOTOCHEMISTRY. *Educ:* Clarkson Col Technol, BS, 68; Univ Rochester, PhD(chem), 71. *Prof Exp:* Res asst chem, Univ Rochester, 68-71; phys sci asst radiation chem, US Army, 71-73; res assoc chem, Columbia Univ, 73-75; asst prof, 75-80, ASSOC PROF CHEM, UNIV ILL, 80- *Concurrent Pos:* NIH fel, 74-75. *Mem:* Am Chem Soc; Am Soc Photobiol; Sigma Xi. *Res:* Energy partitioning in exothermic organic chemical reactions; chemical formation of electronically excited states. *Mailing Add:* Box 58 Roger Adams Lab Univ of Ill Urbana IL 61801

SCHUSTER, GEORGE SHEAH, b Geneva, Ill, Sept 22, 40; m 63; c 1. MICROBIOLOGY, CELL BIOLOGY. *Educ:* Wash Univ, AB, 62; Northwestern Univ, DDS & MS, 66; Univ Rochester, PhD(microbiol), 70. *Prof Exp:* PROF MICROBIOL, CELL BIOL & MOLECULAR BIOL, SCH DENT & MED, MED COL GA, 70- *Mem:* AAAS; Tissue Cult Asn. *Res:* Viral carcinogenesis; metabolic functions of cells and the effects of virus infection on these; dental caries. *Mailing Add:* Dept of Oral Biol Med Col of Ga Augusta GA 30912

SCHUSTER, INGEBORG I M, b Frankfurt, Ger, Oct 30, 37: US citizen. PHYSICAL ORGANIC CHEMISTRY. *Educ:* Univ Pa, BA, 60; Carnegie Inst Technol, MS, 63, PhD(chem), 65. *Prof Exp:* Huff fel org chem, Bryn Mawr Col, 65-67; asst prof chem, 67-73, ASSOC PROF CHEM, PA STATE UNIV, OGONTZ CAMPUS, 73- *Mem:* Am Chem Soc. *Res:* Nuclear magnetic resonance spectroscopy. *Mailing Add:* 3340 Jeffrey Dr Dresher PA 19025

SCHUSTER, JAMES J(OHN), b Pottsville, Pa, Dec 13, 35; m 58; c 3. CIVIL ENGINEERING, TRANSPORTATION. *Educ:* Villanova Univ, BCE, 57, MCE, 61; Purdue Univ, PhD(civil eng), 64. *Prof Exp:* From instr to assoc prof, 58-70, PROF CIVIL ENG, VILLANOVA UNIV, 70-, DIR INST TRANSP STUDIES, 65- *Concurrent Pos:* Consult, Northern Calif Transit Demonstration Proj, 65-66; mem origin & destination comt, Hwy Res Bd, Nat Acad Sci-Nat Res Coun, 65- *Mem:* Inst Traffic Engrs; Am Soc Civil Engrs; Am Soc Eng Educ. *Res:* Origin-destination; vehicular trip prediction; modal split analysis; generation; distribution; assignment. *Mailing Add:* Dept of Civil Eng Villanova Univ Villanova PA 19085

SCHUSTER, JOSEPH L, b Teague, Tex, May 21, 32; m 57; c 4. RANGE MANAGEMENT, ECOLOGY. *Educ:* Tex A&M Univ, BS, 54, PhD(range mgt), 62; Colo State Univ, MS, 59. *Prof Exp:* Range conservationist, US Soil Conserv Serv, 54-59 & US Forest Serv, 61-64; asst prof range mgt, Tex Tech Univ, 64-69, prof & chmn dept, 69-72; PROF RANGE SCI & HEAD DEPT, TEX A&M UNIV, 72- *Concurrent Pos:* Range mgt consult, Bur Land Mgt, 64. *Mem:* Soc Range Mgt; Soil Conserv Soc Am; Wildlife Soc. *Res:* Forest overstory-understory relations; research technique development; range improvement practices. *Mailing Add:* Dept of Range Sci Tex A&M Univ College Station TX 77843

SCHUSTER, MICHAEL FRANK, b Mexia, Tex, May 29, 29; m 51; c 7. ECONOMIC ENTOMOLOGY. *Educ:* Tex A&M Col, BS, 55, MS, 61; Miss State Univ, PhD(entom), 71. *Prof Exp:* Asst entomologist, Tex Agr Exp Sta, Weslaco, Tex, 55-71; from asst prof to assoc prof entom, Miss Agr & Forest Exp Sta, 71-78; PROF ENTOM, AGR EXP STA, TEX A&M UNIV, 78- *Concurrent Pos:* Consult entomologist, US AID, Brazil, 67. *Mem:* Entom Soc Am; Orgn Biol Control; Sigma Xi. *Res:* Development of insect controls based on natural regulating factors, such as host plant resistance and biological control; resistance in plants is identified, evaluated and utilized; natural enemies are evaluated for effectiveness. *Mailing Add:* Agr Res & Exten Ctr 17560 Coit Rd Dallas TX 75252

SCHUSTER, ROBERT LEE, b Chehalis, Wash, Aug 29, 27; m 55; c 4. GEOLOGY & CIVIL ENGINEERING. *Educ:* State Col Wash, BS, 50; Ohio State Univ, MS, 52; Purdue Univ, MS, 58, PhD(civil eng), 60; Imp Col, London, dipl, 65. *Prof Exp:* Geologist, Snow, Ice & Permafrost Res Estab, Corps Engrs, US Army, 52-55; instr civil engr & eng geol, Purdue Univ, 56-60; from assoc prof to prof civil eng, Univ Colo, 60-67; prof civil eng & chmn dept, Univ Idaho, 67-74; chief engr, Eng Br, 74-79, GEOLOGIST, US GEOL SURV, 79- *Concurrent Pos:* NSF sci fac fel, Imp Col, London, 64-65; NATO sr fel sci, Imp Col, Univ London, 74; chmn, Joint Am Soc Civil Engrs-Geol Soc Am-Asn Eng Geol Comt on Eng Geol, 74-78; chmn eng geol comt, Transp Res Bd, Nat Res Coun-Nat Acad Sci, 77-81; mem exec comt, US Nat Comt of Int Soc Soil Mech & Found Eng, 78-82, chmn, 81. *Mem:* Asn Eng Geol; Geol Soc Am; Am Soc Civil Engrs; Geol Soc London; Int Asn Eng Geol. *Res:* Slope stability; soil and rock properties; engineering geology. *Mailing Add:* Eng Geol Br US Geol Surv MS 903 Box 25046 Denver CO 80225

SCHUSTER, RUDOLF MATHIAS, b Altmuehldorf, Ger, Apr 8, 21; nat US; m 43; c 2. BOTANY. *Educ:* Cornell Univ, BSc, 45, MSc, 46; Univ Minn, PhD(entom, bot), 48. *Prof Exp:* Instr bot, Univ Minn, 48-50; asst prof, Univ Miss, 50-53 & Duke Univ, 53-56; asst prof bot & cur bryophyta, Univ Mich, 56-57; assoc prof, 57-60, dir herbarium, 64-70, PROF BOT, UNIV MASS, AMHERST, 60- *Concurrent Pos:* NSF grants, 53-72 & 76-84; Guggenheim fel, 55-56 & 67; Fulbright prof, Univ Otago, NZ, 61-62. *Honors & Awards:* Award, Arctic Inst NAm, 60 & 66. *Mem:* Am Bryol & Lichenological Soc; Brit Bryol Soc. *Res:* Systematics, ecology and distribution patterns of North American, Arctic and Antipodal Hepaticae; phylogeny of the Archegoniates; plant geography; taxonomy of Mutillid wasps. *Mailing Add:* Dept of Bot Univ of Mass Amherst MA 01003

SCHUSTER, SANFORD LEE, b Hastings, Nebr, Sept 28, 38; m 67; c 2. SOLID STATE PHYSICS. *Educ:* Univ Nebr, Lincoln, BS, 60, MS, 63, PhD(physics), 69. *Prof Exp:* From asst prof to assoc prof physics, 68-74, PROF PHYSICS, MANKATO STATE UNIV, 74- *Mem:* Am Phys Soc; Am Asn Physics Teachers; Am Crystallog Asn. *Res:* Thermal diffuse scattering of x-rays by metals. *Mailing Add:* Dept of Physics Mankato State Univ Mankato MN 56001

SCHUSTER, SEYMOUR, b Bronx, NY, July 31, 26; m 54; c 2. MATHEMATICS. *Educ:* Pa State Univ, BA, 47, PhD(math), 53; Columbia Univ, AM, 48. *Prof Exp:* Asst math, Pa State Univ, 49-51, instr, 51-52; from instr to assoc prof, Polytech Inst Brooklyn, 53-58; assoc prof, Carleton Col, 58-63; res fel, Univ Minn, Minneapolis, 62-63, assoc prof math, 63-68; chmn dept, 73-76, PROF MATH, CARLETON COL, 68- *Concurrent Pos:* Fel, Univ Toronto, 52-53; vis assoc prof, Univ NC, Chapel Hill, 61; dir col geom proj, Minn Math Ctr, 64-74, Acad Year Inst for Col Teachers, 66-67; NSF sci fac fel, 70-71; vis scholar, Univ Calif, Santa Barbara, 70-71; guest scholar,

Western Mich Univ, 76 & vis scholar, Western Mich Univ, 81. *Mem:* Am Math Soc; Math Soc Can; Sigma Xi; Math Asn Am. *Res:* Graph theory; projective and non-Euclidean geometry; mathematical film production. *Mailing Add:* Carleton Col Northfield MN 55057

SCHUSTER, TODD MERVYN, b June 27, 33; US citizen. BIOPHYSICAL CHEMISTRY. *Educ:* Wayne State Univ, AB, 58, MS, 60; Wash Univ, PhD(molecular biol), 63. *Prof Exp:* USPHS fel, Max Planck Inst, 63-66; asst prof biol, State Univ NY Buffalo, 66-70; assoc prof, 70-75, chmn dept, 77-81, PROF BIOL, UNIV CONN, 75- *Concurrent Pos:* Consult, NIH, 71-75. *Mem:* AAAS; Am Chem Soc; Am Soc Biol Chem; Biophys Soc. *Res:* Physical biochemistry of proteins and protein-nucleic acid interactions. *Mailing Add:* Dept Biol Sci Box U-125 Univ Conn Storrs CT 06268

SCHUSTER, WILLIAM JOHN, b Elkhart, Ind, Mar 21, 48. ASTRONOMY. *Educ:* Case Western Reserv Univ, BS, 70; Univ Ariz, PhD(astron), 76. *Prof Exp:* INVESTR, INST ASTRON, MEX NAT UNIV, 73- *Mem:* Am Astron Soc; Royal Astron Soc. *Res:* Photometric astronomy; calibration of photometric indices; chemical compositions, evolutionary status and effective temperatures of stars; subdwarf stars, high velocity stars, Be stars, solar type stars. *Mailing Add:* Observ Astronomico Nacional Apartado Postal 877 Ensenada Baja Calif Mexico

SCHUSTERMAN, RONALD JAY, b New York, NY, Sept 3, 32; m 57; c 3. ETHOLOGY. *Educ:* Brooklyn Col, BA, 54; Fla State Univ, MA, 58, PhD(psychol), 61. *Prof Exp:* NSF res fel, Yerkes Labs Primate Biol, 61-62; asst prof psychol, San Fernando Valley State Col, 62-63; psychobiologist, Stanford Res Inst, 63-71; mgr animal behav, 69-71; PROF PSYCHOL & BIOL, CALIF STATE UNIV, HAYWARD, 72- *Concurrent Pos:* Prin investr, NSF grant, Stanford Res Inst, 63-70; Off Naval Res Contract, 67-71 & Calif State Univ, Hayward, 71-; lectr psychol, Calif State Univ, Hayward, 64-71. *Mem:* Fel AAAS; Animal Behav Soc. *Res:* Animal behavior and communication; discrimination learning; biological sonar; animal psychophysics. *Mailing Add:* Dept of Psychol Calif State Univ Hayward CA 94542

SCHUT, ROBERT N, b Hudsonville, Mich, Mar 6, 32; m 60; c 4. MEDICINAL CHEMISTRY. *Educ:* Hope Col, AB, 54; Mass Inst Technol, PhD(org chem), 58. *Prof Exp:* Res chemist, 59-62, group leader org chem, 62-65, sr res chemist, 65-66, sect head, 66-71, dir med chem dept, Miles Res Div, 71-75, DIR CHEM DEPT, CORP RES, MILES LABS, INC, 75- *Mem:* AAAS; Am Chem Soc; Royal Soc Chem; Sigma Xi; fel Am Inst Chemists. *Res:* Synthesis of compounds of potential therapeutic interest. *Mailing Add:* Chem Dept Miles Labs Inc 1127 Myrtle St Elkhart IN 46514

SCHUTT, DALE W, b Oak Park, Ill, Oct 1, 38. INSTRUMENTATION. *Educ:* Univ Ill, BS, 61; Univ Notre Dame, MS, 63. *Prof Exp:* Test equip design engr, Missile Div, Bendix Corp, 61-64; res asst, Univ Notre Dame, 64-66, asst prof specialist, 66-70, assoc prof specialist, 70-77; RES ASSOC & SUPVR PHYSICS DEPT, VA POLYTECH INST & STATE UNIV, 77- *Concurrent Pos:* Consult, Custom Electron Apparatus, Electro-optics. *Mem:* Inst Elec & Electronics Engrs. *Res:* Instrumentation used in basic research studies in the area of intermediate energy physics including detectors, wire chambers, data acquisition. *Mailing Add:* Dept of Physics Va Polytech Inst & State Univ Blacksburg VA 24061

SCHUTTE, A(UGUST) H(ENRY), b Boston, Mass, Dec 1, 07; m 35; c 2. CHEMICAL ENGINEERING. *Educ:* Dartmouth Col, AB, 29; Mass Inst Technol, MS(chem eng) & MS(chem eng practice), 30. *Prof Exp:* Asst dir & dir tech serv div, Stand Oil Co, Sumatra, 31-34; res & develop engr, W M Kellogg Co, 34-35; process design & proj engr, Lummus Co, 35-42, proj engr, 42-47, vpres, 48, process develop & eval, 48-57, mgr New York Div, 57-60; sr staff, Eng Div, 60-72, SR CONSULT, PERTO-CHEM & CONSTRUCTION PROJ, ARTHUR D LITTLE, INC, 72- *Res:* Development of new devices; engineering and management consulting to developing countries. *Mailing Add:* 2 Whitman Circle Lexington MA 02173

SCHUTTE, JULIA ANN, b Louisville, Ky, Oct 1, 50; m 70. BOTANY, LICHENOLOGY. *Educ:* Jacksonville Univ, BS, 72; Ohio State Univ, PhD(bot), 76. *Prof Exp:* Teaching assoc bot, Ohio State Univ, 72-76; asst prof, 76-82, ASSOC PROF BIOL, COE COL, 82- *Concurrent Pos:* Consult, Ecol Consults Inc, 78- *Mem:* AAAS; Ecol Soc Am; Am Bryol & Lichenological Soc; Am Inst Biol Sci; Bot Soc Am. *Res:* Plant ecology; lichen community ecology. *Mailing Add:* Dept of Biol Coe Col Cedar Rapids IA 52402

SCHUTTE, WILLIAM CALVIN, b Ponca, Nebr, May 14, 41; m 62; c 3. PHYSICAL CHEMISTRY. *Educ:* Wayne State Col, BAE, 62; Univ SDak, MNS, 67, PhD(phys chem), 72. *Prof Exp:* Teacher, S Sioux City Pub Sch, 62-67; ASST PROF CHEM, UNIV SDAK, 70- *Concurrent Pos:* Grant gen res fund, Univ SDak, 72-73 & 74-75, Exxon Educ Found, 76-77 & NSF, Acad Yr Proj, 77-78 & 78-79. *Mem:* Am Chem Soc; Sigma Xi. *Res:* Study of metal concentrations in walleye, paddlefish and morels. *Mailing Add:* Dept of Chem Univ of SDak Vermillion SD 57069

SCHUTZ, BERNARD FREDERICK, b Paterson, NJ, Aug 11, 46. THEORETICAL ASTROPHYSICS, MATHEMATICAL PHYSICS. *Educ:* Clarkson Col Technol, BSc, 67; Calif Inst Technol, PhD(physics), 72. *Prof Exp:* NSF fel physics, Univ Cambridge, 71-72; res fel physics, Yale Univ, 72-73, instr, 73-74; lectr astrophysics, 74-76, READER IN GEN RELATIVITY, UNIV COL S WALES, 76- *Mem:* Am Phys Soc; Royal Astron Soc; Sigma Xi; Int Astron Union. *Res:* General relativity and relativistic astrophysics; structure and stability of rotating stars. *Mailing Add:* Dept Appl Math & Astron Univ Col S Wales PO Box 78 Cardiff Wales

SCHUTZ, BOB EWALD, b Brownfield, Tex, Sept 6, 40; m 68; c 2. ASTRODYNAMICS, REMOTE SENSING. *Educ:* Univ Tex, BS, 63, MS, 66, PhD(aerospace eng), 69. *Prof Exp:* Teaching asst, 65-69, asst prof, 69-77, assoc prof, 77-81, PROF AEROSPACE ENG, UNIV TEX, AUSTIN, 81-

Mem: AAAS; Am Inst Aeronaut & Astronaut; Am Astron Soc. *Res:* Rotation of the earth; estimation theory applied to orbit determination and geodynamics; applications of digital computers. *Mailing Add:* Dept Aerospace Eng Univ Tex Austin TX 78712

SCHUTZ, DONALD FRANK, b Orange, Tex, Sept 22, 34; m 58; c 2. GEOCHEMISTRY. *Educ:* Yale Univ, BS, 56, PhD(geol), 64; Rice Univ, MA, 58. *Prof Exp:* Instr geol, Kinkaid Sch, 58-60, res staff geologist, Yale Univ, 64; scientist, Isotopes, Inc, 64-65, dir, Proj Pinocchio, 65-66, mgr nuclear opers, 66-70, vpres & gen mgr, Westwood Labs, 70-75, PRES, TELEDYNE ISOTOPES, 75- *Mem:* Am Geophys Union; Air Pollution Control Asn; Am Inst Mining, Metall & Petrol Engr; Geol Soc Am; Am Asn Petrol Geologists. *Res:* Radiochemical tests for clandestine nuclear weapons tests; neutron activation analysis of trace elements in sea water; nuclear reactor environmental monitoring, isotope geochemistry, geochromometry, nuclear fuel analysis; radiotraced applications in enhanced oil recovery and refining; synfuel processes. *Mailing Add:* Teledyne Isotopes 50 Van Buren Ave Westwood NJ 07675

SCHUTZ, WILFRED M, b Eustis, Nebr, Jan 26, 30; m 57; c 3. GENETICS, STATISTICS. *Educ:* Univ Nebr, BS, 57, MS, 59; NC State Univ, PhD(genetics, statist), 62. *Prof Exp:* Res geneticist, NC State Univ & Agr Res Serv, USDA, 62-68; PROF STATIST & HEAD, BIOMET & INFO SYSTS CTR, INST AGR & NATURAL RESOURCES, UNIV NEBR, LINCOLN, 68- *Mem:* Am Soc Agron; Biomet Soc; Am Statist Asn. *Res:* Quantitative genetics, statistics and computing. *Mailing Add:* Biomet & Info Systs Ctr Univ of Nebr Lincoln NE 68583

SCHUTZBACH, JOHN STEPHEN, b Pittsburgh, Pa, Mar 3, 41; m 62; c 4. BIOCHEMISTRY, MICROBIOLOGY. *Educ:* Edinboro State Col, BS, 63; Univ Pittsburgh, PhD(microbiol), 69. *Prof Exp:* Technician microbiol, Univ Pittsburgh, 65; res assoc, Med Col Wis, 71-72, asst prof biochem, 72-73; ASST PROF MICROBIOL, UNIV ALA, BIRMINGHAM, 73- *Concurrent Pos:* Fel, Med Col Wis, 69-71. *Mem:* Am Chem Soc; Am Soc Microbiol; Am Soc Biol Chemists. *Res:* Enzyme mechanisms; biosynthesis of macromolecules, particularly cell membrane constituents of mammalian cells. *Mailing Add:* Dept Microbiol Univ Ala Birmingham AL 35294

SCHUTZENHOFER, LUKE A, b East St Louis, Ill, Feb 14, 39; m 60; c 5. GAS DYNAMICS, ROTORDYNAMICS. *Educ:* St Louis Univ, BS, 60; Univ Ala, MSE, 70, PhD, 78. *Prof Exp:* Aerospace engr struct design, 60-62 aerospace engr struct vibrations, 62-64, aerospace engr unsteady gas dynamics, 64-81, BR CHIEF, SERVOMECH & SYSTS STABILITY BR, MARSHALL SPACE FLIGHT CTR, NASA, 81- *Res:* Structural vibrations; unsteady fluid and gas dynamics; applications of stochastic process theory; aero-structural interaction phenomena; statistical communication theory; stability theory; rotordynamics. *Mailing Add:* FD 21 Bldg 4610 NASA Marshall Space Flight Ctr Huntsville AL 35812

SCHUTZMAN, ELIAS, b New York, NY, Jan 16, 25; m 60. ELECTRICAL ENGINEERING. *Educ:* NY Univ, BEE, 51, MEE, 53. *Prof Exp:* Res asst, NY Univ, 51-52, instr elec eng, 52-56, eng scientist, 56-59, asst dir, Grad Ctr, 59-66, adj assoc prof elec eng, 58-68; actg prog dir eng systs, 68, staff assoc, Elec Sci & Anal Prog, 68-72, PROG DIR, ELEC & OPTICAL COMMUN PROG, ENG DIV, NAT SCI FOUND, 72- *Concurrent Pos:* Asst dir lab electrosci res & sr res scientist, NY Univ, 66-68. *Mem:* Am Soc Eng Educ; Inst Elec & Electronics Engrs. *Res:* Large scale computer communications networks; electronic circuits; digital systems; optical communication systems. *Mailing Add:* Div Elec Comput & Systs Eng Nat Sci Found Washington DC 20550

SCHUUR, JERRY D, b Kalamazoo, Mich, Jan 14, 36; m 62; c 3. MATHEMATICS. *Educ:* Univ Mich, BS, 57, MA, 58, PhD(math), 63. *Prof Exp:* Engr, Boeing Airplane Co, 57; physicist, Cornell Aeronaut Lab, 59; teaching fel math, Univ Mich, 58-62, lectr, 62; from asst prof to assoc prof, 63-76, PROF MATH, MICH STATE UNIV, 76- *Concurrent Pos:* Off Naval Res fel & consult, 68-69; fel, Ital Nat Res Coun, 70; vis prof, Univ Florence, 77. *Mem:* Am Math Soc. *Res:* Ordinary differential equations. *Mailing Add:* Dept of Math Mich State Univ East Lansing MI 48824

SCHUURMANN, FREDERICK JAMES, b East Grand Rapids, Mich, Jan 16, 40; m 64; c 2. MATHEMATICS. *Educ:* Calvin Col, BS, 62; Mich State Univ, MS, 63, PhD(math), 67. *Prof Exp:* Asst prof, 67-76, ASSOC PROF MATH, MIAMI UNIV, 76- *Concurrent Pos:* Vis res assoc, Aerospace Res Labs, Wright-Patterson AFB, Ohio, 73-74. *Mem:* Asn Comput Mach; Math Asn Am; Soc Indust & Appl Math. *Res:* Numerical analysis, especially computational problems of approximation theory; computational problems of multivariate statistical analysis. *Mailing Add:* Dept of Math & Statist Miami Univ Oxford OH 45056

SCHUURMANS, DAVID MEINTE, b Ithaca, Mich, Apr 11, 28; m 51; c 2. INDUSTRIAL MICROBIOLOGY. *Educ:* Albion Col, BA, 49; Mich State Univ, MS, 51, PhD(bact), 54. *Prof Exp:* Jr bacteriologist, City Health Dept, Jackson, Mich, 49-50; bacteriologist, Div Antibiotics & Fermentation, 53-55, chief, Tissue Culture Unit, 57-61, chief, Antibiotic Screening Sect, 65-77 & Fermentation Sect, 68-77, chief, Div Antibiotics & Fermentation, 77-80, CHIEF, TISSUE CULTURE & ANTIBIOTIC ASSAY SECT, MICH DEPT PUB HEALTH, 61-, DEP CHIEF, BIOL PROD PROG, 80 *Mem:* Am Soc Microbiol. *Res:* Development of antitumor antibiotics; development and production of bacterial vaccines. *Mailing Add:* 2620 Wilson Ave Lansing MI 48906

SCHUURMANS, HENDRIK J L, b Malang, Indonesia, Dec 26, 28; US citizen; m 56, 74; c 5. POLYMER CHEMISTRY. *Educ:* State Univ Leiden, BS, 52, MS, 55, PhD(phys chem), 57. *Prof Exp:* Sr res chemist, Monsanto Co, Tex, 56-61; supvr, mgr & sr develop assoc, Mobil Chem Co, NJ & NY, 61-67; tech dir, Stein-Hall & Co, Inc, NY, 67-71; res dir, M&T Chem Inc, NJ, 71-74, dir new ventures, 74-75; DIR RES & DEVELOP, PLASTICS DIV, ICI AM

INC, 75- *Concurrent Pos:* Consult, Med Br, Univ Tex, 58-59. *Mem:* Am Phys Soc; Am Chem Soc; Am Asn Textile Chemists & Colorists; Tech Asn Pulp & Paper Indust. *Res:* Natural and synthetic polymer evaluation; polymer synthesis, production and processing; thermodynamics and kinetics of rate processes; catalysis studies. *Mailing Add:* ICI Am Inc Wilmington DE 19897

SCHUYLER, ALFRED E, b Salamanca, NY, July 10, 35; m 68. BOTANY, TAXONOMY. *Educ:* Colgate Univ, AB, 57; Univ Mich, AM, 58, PhD(bot), 63. *Prof Exp:* Asst cur, 62-69, chmn bot dept, 62-75, ASSOC CUR, ACAD NATURAL SCI, PHILADELPHIA, 69- *Concurrent Pos:* Am Philos Soc traveling grants, 63-64, 66 & 72 & res grant, Franklin Inst, 70; vis prof, Mich State Univ, 66, Univ Mont Biol Sta, 78 & 82, Rutgers Univ, Camden, 81; vis lectr, Swarthmore Col, 67-70, 78 & 82; res assoc, Morris Arboretum, Univ Pa, 71-; ed, Bartonia, 71-; mem adv comt, Syst Resources Bot, NSF, 72-74; care & maintenance bot col, Acad Natural Sci, NSF, 72-77, assoc ed, Sci Publ, 78- *Mem:* Am Soc Plant Taxon; Bot Soc Am; Am Inst Biol Scientists. *Res:* Taxonomic research in the Cyperaceae; biology of aquatic vascular plants; environmental consulting. *Mailing Add:* Dept of Bot Acad of Natural Sci 19th & Parkway Philadelphia PA 19103

SCHUYTEMA, EUNICE CHAMBERS, b Rochester, NY, Feb 4, 29; m 54; c 1. MEDICAL MICROBIOLOGY. *Educ:* Cornell Univ, BS, 51, MS, 54; Univ Iowa, PhD, 56. *Prof Exp:* Res biochemist, Abbott Labs, 56-68; asst prof biol chem, Univ Ill Med Ctr, 68-71; ASST PROF MICROBIOL, RUSH PRESBY ST LUKE'S MED CTR, 71-, ASST DEAN PRECLIN CURRICULUM, RUSH MED COL, 79- *Mem:* Am Chem Soc; Am Soc Microbiol. *Res:* Nucleic acid chemistry; anaerobes; bacteriophage. *Mailing Add:* Dept of Microbiol Rush-Presby-St Luke's Med Ctr Chicago IL 60612

SCHWAB, ARTHUR WILLIAM, b Minneapolis, Minn, July 17, 17; m 45; c 4. ORGANIC CHEMISTRY. *Educ:* Univ Minn, BChem, 41; Bradley Univ, PhD(chem), 52. *Prof Exp:* Chemist, WPoint Mfg Co, 41-42; RES CHEMIST, NORTHERN REGIONAL RES LAB, USDA, 42- *Mem:* Am Chem Soc; Am Oil Chem Soc. *Res:* Fundamental research on the chemistry of vegetable oils and modification of these oils for industrial utilization. *Mailing Add:* 2223 W Albany Ave Peoria IL 61604

SCHWAB, BERNARD, b Worcester, Mass, Dec 26, 26; m 57; c 3. CLINICAL MICROBIOLOGY. *Educ:* Clark Univ, AB, 49; Univ Mass, MS, 51; Nat Registry Microbiol, registered, 64, specialist med microbiol, 69, specialist food microbiol, 75. *Prof Exp:* Bacteriologist, Vt State Bur Labs, 52-62; bacteriologist in-chg lab, City of Kingston, NY, 62-64; chief bacteriologist, Erie Co Lab, Buffalo, 63-68; microbiologist in-chg diag & spec probs sect, 68-73, sr staff officer microbiol staff, Meat & Poultry Inspection Prog, Sci Serv Staff, Food & Safety Qual Serv, 73-77, st staff officer microbiol div, 77-80, CHIEF, MED MICROBIOL BR, MICROBIOL DIV, SCI FOOD SAFETY & QUAL SERV, USDA, 81- *Mem:* Am Soc Microbiol; fel Am Asn Vet Lab Diagnosticians; Soc Gen Microbiol; Soc Appl Microbiol. *Res:* Public health microbiology; meat and poultry microbiology related to consumer protection programs; swine mycobacteriology, staphylococcus enterotin, antibiotics, species determination. *Mailing Add:* Rm 103 Bldg 318 Sci Agr Res Ctr-East USDA Beltsville MD 20705

SCHWAB, FREDERIC LYON, b Brooklyn, NY, Jan 8, 40; m 65; c 4. SEDIMENTOLOGY. *Educ:* Dartmouth Col, AB, 61; Univ Wis, MS, 63; Harvard Univ, PhD(geol), 68. *Prof Exp:* From asst prof to assoc prof geol, 67-75, PROF GEOL, WASHINGTON & LEE UNIV, 75- *Concurrent Pos:* NSF sci fac fel, Univ Edinburgh, 71-72; consult ed, McGraw-Hill Dict Sci & Technol, Encycl Geol Sci & Encycl Energy; NATO sr scientist, Univ Grenoble, 77-78. *Mem:* Int Asn Sedimentologists; Geol Soc London; Geol Soc Am; Soc Econ Mineralogists & Paleontologists; Soc Precambrian Geologists. *Res:* Depositional environments, provenance and sedimentary tectonics of precambrian of the Blue Ridge; geochemistry of sedimentary rocks; sedimentation and tectonic history of the Cordilleran belt; sedimentation trends through time; Eocambrian Appalachian sediments. *Mailing Add:* Shenandoah Rd Lexington VA 24450

SCHWAB, FREDERICK CHARLES, b Meadville, Pa, Mar 1, 37; m 61; c 3. POLYMER CHEMISTRY. *Educ:* Cleveland State Univ, BChE, 61; Union Col, NY, MS, 66; Univ Akron, PhD(polymer sci), 69. *Prof Exp:* Chemist insulation develop, Gen Elec Co, 61-66; ASSOC CHEMIST POLYMERS, MOBIL CHEM CO, 69- *Mem:* Am Chem Soc. *Res:* Synthesis, characterization and mechanical properties of block polymers. *Mailing Add:* 34 Spear St Metuchen NJ 08840

SCHWAB, GLENN O(RVILLE), b Gridley, Kans, Dec 30, 19; m 51; c 3. AGRICULTURAL ENGINEERING. *Educ:* Kans State Univ, BS, 42; Iowa State Univ, MS, 47, PhD(agr eng, soils). 51. *Prof Exp:* From instr to prof agr eng, Iowa State Univ, 46-56; PROF AGR ENG, OHIO STATE UNIV, 56- *Concurrent Pos:* Consult, Off State Exp Sta, USDA, 59-62. *Honors & Awards:* Hancock Brick & Tile Drainage Eng Award, Am Soc Agr Engrs, 68. *Mem:* AAAS; life fel Am Soc Agr Engrs; Am Soc Eng Educ; AAAS; Soil Conserv Soc Am. *Res:* Agricultural drainage; irrigation; erosion and flood control; agricultural hydrology. *Mailing Add:* Dept of Agr Eng Ohio State Univ 2073 Neil Ave Columbus OH 43210

SCHWAB, HELMUT, b Nurnberg, Ger, Apr 3, 29; nat US; m 53; c 2. ANALYTICAL CHEMISTRY, PHYSICAL CHEMISTRY. *Educ:* Rutgers Univ, BS, 51, PhD(chem), 57. *Prof Exp:* Asst, Rutgers Univ, 53-54; res chemist, Nat Cash Register Co, 56-59, sect head, 59-72, MGR COLOR REACTION CHEM, APPLETON PAPERS INC, 73- *Mem:* Am Chem Soc; Soc Photograph Scientists & Engrs. *Res:* Heat and pressure recording media; color forming systems; photochromic systems; carbonless papers; color-blocked dyes; paper chemistry. *Mailing Add:* 136 Crestview Dr Appleton WI 54911

SCHWAB, JOHN HARRIS, b Minn, Nov 20, 27; m 51; c 4. BACTERIOLOGY, IMMUNOLOGY. *Educ:* Univ Minn, BA, 49, MS, 50, PhD(bact), 53. *Prof Exp:* Asst bact, Univ Minn, 49-53; from instr to assoc prof, 53-67, PROF BACT & IMMUNOL, MED SCH, UNIV NC, CHAPEL HILL, 67- *Concurrent Pos:* NIH fel, Lister Inst, London, Eng, 60-61; mem, Med Res Coun Rheumatism Res Unit, Taplow, Eng, 68-69; Josiah Macy, Jr Found fac scholar, 75-76. *Mem:* AAAS; Am Soc Microbiol; Soc Exp Biol & Med; Am Asn Immunol. *Res:* Bacterial immunosuppressants; microbial factors in chronic inflammatory diseases; toxicity of bacterial cell walls; experimental models of rheumatic carditis and rheumatoid arthritis; significance of autoimmunity against heart. *Mailing Add:* Dept Bact & Immunol Sch Med Univ NC Chapel Hill NC 27514

SCHWAB, JOHN J, b Cumberland, MD, Feb 10, 23; m 45; c 1. PSYCHIATRY, PSYCHOSOMATIC MEDICINE. *Educ:* Univ Ky, BS, 46; Univ Louisville, MD, 46; Univ Ill, MS, 49; Am Bd Internal Med, dipl, 55; Am Bd Psychiat & Neurol, dipl, 64. *Prof Exp:* From asst resident to resident med, Louis Gen Hosp, Ky, 49-50; internist & psychosomaticist, Holzer Clin, Gallipolis, Ohio, 54-59; resident psychiat, Col Med, Univ Fla, 59-61, from instr to asst prof, 62-65, from assoc prof to prof psychiat & med, 65-74, chief psychosom consult serv, 61-64, dir consult-liaison prog, 64-67; PROF PSYCHIAT & BEHAV SCI, SCH MED, UNIV LOUISVILLE, 74- *Concurrent Pos:* Med fel, Col Med, Univ Ill, 48-49; fel psychosom med, Duke Univ, 51-52; NIMH career teacher award, 62-64; internist, Yokohama Army Hosp, Japan, 52-54; state trustee, Ment Health Fedn Ohio, 58-61; proj dir res grant, 65-68; prin investr, NIMH Res Grant, 69-73; chmn epidemiol studies rev comt, Ctr Epidemiol Studies, NIMH, 73-75; chmn coun res & develop, Am Psychiat Asn, 74-75. *Mem:* Fel Acad Psychosom Med (pres, 70-71); fel Am Asn Social Psychiat (pres, 71-73); AMA; fel Am Psychiat Asn; fel Am Col Psychiat. *Res:* Applicability, both theoretical and practical, of psychiatric concepts to general medicine; establishing guidelines for the identification and management of medical patients whose illnesses are complicated by emotional distress; sociocultural aspects of mental illness; psychiatric epidemiology. *Mailing Add:* Dept of Psychiat & Behav Sci Univ of Louisville Sch of Med Louisville KY 40232

SCHWAB, LINDA SUE, b St Louis, Mo, Oct 25, 51. MEDICINAL CHEMISTRY, NEUROCHEMISTRY. *Educ:* Wells Col, BA, 73; Univ Rochester, MS, 75, PhD(chem), 78. *Prof Exp:* Fel, 77-78, ASSOC NEUROCHEM, CTR BRAIN RES, SCH MED, UNIV ROCHESTER, 78- *Mem:* Am Chem Soc. *Res:* Chemistry of heterocycles. *Mailing Add:* Ctr Brain Res Med Ctr Univ Rochester Box 605 Rochester NY 14642

SCHWAB, MICHAEL, b New York, NY, Aug 9, 39; m 68; c 2. MATERIALS SCIENCE. *Educ:* Calif Inst Technol, BS, 61; Univ Calif, Berkeley, PhD(physics), 68. *Prof Exp:* Physicist, Lawrence Berkeley Lab, 68-69; PHYSICIST MAT SCI, LAWRENCE LIVERMORE LAB, 69- *Mem:* Am Phys Soc; AAAS. *Res:* Spectroscopy; nuclear and electron magnetic resonance; materials science; radiation damage; metallurgy. *Mailing Add:* 6215 Harwood Ave Oakland CA 94618

SCHWAB, PETER AUSTIN, b Utica, NY, Mar 29, 37; m 58; c 4. POLYMER CHEMISTRY. *Educ:* Regis Col, BS, 59; Kans State Univ, PhD(org chem), 64. *Prof Exp:* Res scientist polymer chem, Petrochem Lab, Continental Oil Co, Okla, 64-68, sr polymer chemist, Conoco Plastics Div, Conn, 68-72, SUPV GROUP LEADER, RESIN DEVELOP LAB, CONTINENTAL OIL CO, OKLA, 72- *Res:* Free radical and cationic polymerizations; vinyl polymerizations in solution, suspension or emulsion; synthetic organic and oxirene chemistry. *Mailing Add:* Petrochem Sect Res & Dev Div Continental Oil Co Ponca City OK 74601

SCHWAB, ROBERT G, b Park Rapids, Minn, Mar 1, 32; m 51; c 3. PHYSIOLOGY. *Educ:* Univ Minn, BS, 58, MS, 65; Univ Ariz, PhD(zool), 66. *Prof Exp:* Asst prof, 64-74, ASSOC PROF WILDLIFE BIOL, COL AGR & ENVIRON SCI, UNIV CALIF, DAVIS, 74- *Mem:* Am Soc Mammalogists; Cooper Ornith Soc. *Res:* Environmental physiology; mammalogy; ornithology. *Mailing Add:* Dept of Wildlife & Fisheries Biol Univ of Calif Davis CA 95616

SCHWAB, WALTER EDWIN, b Mexico City, Mex, Jan 4, 41; US citizen; m 64. NEUROBIOLOGY. *Educ:* Georgetown Univ, BS, 64; Va State Col, MS, 71; Univ Md, MS, 73, PhD(zool), 74. *Prof Exp:* Fel res assoc, Dept Develop & Cell Biol, Univ Calif, Irvine, 74-77; ASST PROF NEUROBIOL, DEPT BIOL, VA POLYTECH INST & STATE UNIV, 77- *Mem:* Am Soc Zoologists; AAAS; Am Inst Biol Sci. *Res:* Physiology and morphology of intracellular communication in primitive animals, primarily coelenterates. *Mailing Add:* Dept Biol Va Polytech Inst & State Univ Blacksburg VA 24061

SCHWABE, ARTHUR DAVID, b Varel, Ger, Feb 1, 24; US citizen; m 46. MEDICINE, GASTROENTEROLOGY. *Educ:* Univ Calif, Berkeley, AB, 51; Univ Chicago, MD, 56. *Prof Exp:* From intern to assoc resident, 56-59, chief resident, 60-61, from instr to assoc prof, 61-71, actg chmn dept, 72, vchmn dept, 72-74, PROF MED, MED CTR, UNIV CALIF, LOS ANGELES, 71-, CHIEF GASTROENTEROL, DEPT MED, 67- *Concurrent Pos:* Ambrose & Gladys Bowyer fel med, Univ Calif, Los Angeles, 58 & 59; USPHS fel gastroenterol, 59-60; chief gastroenterol, Harbor Gen Hosp, Torrance, Calif, 62-67; consult, Vet Admin Ctr, Los Angeles, 64- *Mem:* Fel Am Col Physicians; Am Fedn Clin Res; Am Asn Study Liver Dis; Am Gastroenterol Asn; Soc Exp Biol & Med. *Res:* Intestinal fat absorption; familial Mediterranean Fever; carotene and vitamin A metabolism. *Mailing Add:* Dept of Med Ctr of Health Sci Univ of Calif Los Angeles CA 90024

SCHWABE, CALVIN WALTER, b Newark, NJ, Mar 15, 27; m 51; c 2. EPIDEMIOLOGY, PARASITOLOGY. *Educ:* Va Polytech Inst, BS, 48; Univ Hawaii, MS, 50; Auburn Univ, DVM, 54; Harvard Univ, MPH, 55, ScD(trop pub health), 56. *Prof Exp:* Assoc prof parasitol & chmn dept, Sch Med, American Univ Beirut, 56-57, assoc prof parasitol & trop health & chmn dept trop health, Schs Pub Health & Med, 57-62, prof parasitol & epidemiol & asst dir, Sch Pub Health, 62-66; chmn dept epidemiol & prev med, Sch Vet Med, Univ Calif, Davis, 66-70, assoc dean, 70-71, prof epidemiol, Sch Med, 67-81, PROF EPIDEMIOL, SCH VET MED, UNIV CALIF, DAVIS, 66-; PROF EPIDEMIOL, UNIV CALIF, SAN FRANCISCO, 67- *Concurrent Pos:* USPHS res fel, Harvard Univ, 54-56 & Cambridge Univ, 72-73; Fulbright fel, MaKerere Univ Col, Kenya, 61, Cambridge Univ, 72-73 & Univ Khartoum, 79-80; consult, Nat Acad Sci-Nat Res Coun, 61 & 72-; mem, WHO Secretariat, 64-66, consult, 60-; consult, Pan Am Health Orgn, 61- *Mem:* Am Soc Trop Med & Hyg; Am Soc Parasitol; Am Vet Med Asn. *Res:* Tropical public health and agriculture; veterinary medicine and human health; invertebrate physiology; parasitism; history of veterinary medicine. *Mailing Add:* Dept of Epidemiol & Prev Med Univ of Calif Davis CA 95616

SCHWABE, CHRISTIAN, b Flensburg, Ger, May 10, 30; US citizen. BIOLOGICAL CHEMISTRY. *Educ:* Univ Hamburg, DDS, 55; Univ Iowa, DDS, 60, MS, 63, PhD, 65. *Prof Exp:* Pvt pract, Ger, 55-56; res asst, Clinton Corn Processing Co, Iowa, 56-57; res asst stomatol, Col Dent, Univ Iowa, 57-60; instr biochem, Col Med, 63; instr biol chem, Sch Dent Med, Harvard Univ, 65, assoc, 66-67, asst prof, 67-71; assoc prof, 71-76, PROF BIOCHEM, MED UNIV SC, 76- *Concurrent Pos:* NIH career develop award, 66. *Mem:* Sigma Xi; Am Chem Soc; Am Soc Biol Chemists; Endocrine Soc; Int Asn Dent. Res. *Res:* Connective tissue; enzymology; protein chemistry; chemical endocrinology. *Mailing Add:* Dept of Biochem Med Univ of SC Charleston SC 29401

SCHWAIGHOFER, JOSEPH, b Annaberg, Austria, Apr 16, 24. ENGINEERING MECHANICS. *Educ:* Graz Tech Inst, Dipl Ing, 51; Pa State Univ, MS, 57, PhD(eng mech), 58; Graz Univ, Dr Tech(civil eng), 65. *Prof Exp:* Asst prof eng mech, Pa State Univ, 58-59; from asst prof to assoc prof civil eng, 59-69, PROF CIVIL ENG, UNIV TORONTO, 69- *Concurrent Pos:* ASTEF French Govt res fel, Univ Nancy, 61. *Mem:* Soc Exp Stress Anal; Am Soc Testing & Mat. *Res:* Photoelasticity and experimental stress analysis; structural engineering. *Mailing Add:* Dept of Civil Eng Univ of Toronto Toronto ON M5S 1A1 Can

SCHWALB, MARVIN N, b New York, NY, May 23, 41; m 62; c 3. MYCOLOGY, MICROBIOLOGY. *Educ:* State Univ NY Buffalo, BA, 63, PhD(biol), 67. *Prof Exp:* Asst prof biol, Bridgewater State Col, 68-69; from instr to assoc prof, 69-78, PROF MICROBIOL, NJ MED SCH, UNIV MED & DENT, NJ, 78- *Concurrent Pos:* Fel, Brandeis Univ, 67-68. *Mem:* Am Soc Microbiol; Mycol Soc Am. *Res:* Biochemical and genetic regulation of development in higher fungi; recombinant DNA genetic systems in higher fungi. *Mailing Add:* Dept of Microbiol NJ Med Sch Univ Med & Dent NJ Newark NJ 07103

SCHWALBE, LARRY ALLEN, b Austin, Tex, Feb 3, 45; m 68; c 2. SOLID STATE PHYSICS. *Educ:* Univ Ill, BS, 68, MS, 69, PhD(physics), 73. *Prof Exp:* Fel physics, Tech Univ Munich, 73-75; fel, 75-77, MEM STAFF PHYSICS, LOS ALAMOS NAT LAB, 77- *Res:* High pressure diamond cell and energy dispersive x-ray diffraction techniques applied to equation of state studies; nondestructive testing including x-ray fluorescence analysis and archeology. *Mailing Add:* Los Alamos Nat Lab M-1 MS-912 Los Alamos NM 87545

SCHWALL, DONALD V, b Nicolaus, Calif, July 2, 31; m 55; c 3. FOOD TECHNOLOGY, POULTRY SCIENCE. *Educ:* Calif State Polytech Col, BS, 53; Tex A&M Univ, MS, 60; Purdue Univ, PhD(food technol), 62. *Prof Exp:* Head poultry prod res & develop, Food Res Div, Armour & Co, 62-70; dir qual assurance & res & develop, 70-76, DIR RES & DEVELOP, VAN CAMP SEA FOOD DIV, RALSTON PURINA CO, 76- *Concurrent Pos:* Mem res coun, Poultry & Egg Inst Am, 65-, res award, 71. *Mem:* Inst Food Technologists; Poultry Sci Asn; World Poultry Sci Asn. *Res:* Direction and coordination of sea food research programs. *Mailing Add:* Van Camp Sea Food Div 4245 Sorrento Valley Blvd San Diego CA 92121

SCHWALL, RICHARD JOSEPH, b Evanston, Ill, Oct 11, 49. ATMOSPHERIC POLLUTION, ANALYTICAL CHEMISTRY. *Educ:* Calif Inst Technol, BS, 71; Northwestern Univ, PhD(anal chem), 77. *Prof Exp:* PROG MGR, ROCKWELL INT ENVIRON MONITORING & SERV CTR, 77- *Mem:* Am Chem Soc. *Res:* Wide-band fast fourier transform faradaic admittance measurements with application to analysis and kinetic studies; visibility degradation measurements and theory; statistical analysis of pollution data. *Mailing Add:* 2421 W Hillcrest St Newbury Park CA 91320

SCHWALM, FRITZ EKKEHARDT, b Arolsen, Ger, Feb 17, 36; m 62; c 3. ZOOLOGY, DEVELOPMENTAL PHYSIOLOGY. *Educ:* Univ Marburg, PhD(zool), 64. *Prof Exp:* Lectr Ger, Folk Univ, Sweden, 59-60; res assoc exp embryol, Univ Marburg, 64-65; Anglo Am Corp SAfrica advan res fel electron micros, Univ Witwatersrand, 66-67; trainee, Univ Va, 68; res assoc embryol, Univ Notre Dame, 68-70; asst prof, 70-74, actg chmn, 79-81, ASSOC PROF BIOL SCI, ILL STATE UNIV, 74- *Mem:* AAAS; Soc Develop Biol; Ger Zool Soc; Am Soc Zoologists. *Res:* Ultrastructure and biochemistry of oogenesis and embryogenesis in insects. *Mailing Add:* Dept Biol Sci Ill State Univ Normal IL 61761

SCHWALM, MIZUHO K, b Tokyo, Japan, Sept 23, 40; m 77. SOLID STATE PHYSICS. *Educ:* Tokyo Gakugei Univ, BA, 64; Univ Wyo, MS, 70; Mont State Univ, PhD(physics), 78. *Prof Exp:* Asst instr, Univ Utah, 79-80; asst prof physics, Moorehead State Univ, 81-82; MEM STAFF, PHYSICS DEPT, UNIV NDAK, 82- *Res:* Methods for studying electronic structure and transport in disordered two-dimensional systems; computation of optical selection rules; modest size electron energy band calculations. *Mailing Add:* Dept Physics Univ NDak Grand Forks ND 58105

SCHWALM, WILLIAM A, b Portsmouth, NH, March 3, 47; m 77. SURFACE PHYSICS, SOLID STATE PHYSICS. *Educ:* Univ NH, BS, 69; Mont State Univ, PhD(physics), 78. *Prof Exp:* Fel physics, Univ Utah, 78-79; instr, 79-80; ASST PROF PHYSICS, UNIV NDAK, 80- *Mem:* Am Asn

Physics Teachers; Am Phys Soc; Soc Physics Students. *Res:* Electronic structure of surfaces and thin films; transport properties in two dimensional systems; electrostatics of semi-infinite lattices; mathematical and computational methods. *Mailing Add:* Physics Dept Univ N Dak Grand Forks ND 58202

SCHWAN, HERMAN PAUL, b Aachen, Ger, Aug 7, 15; nat US; m 49; c 5. BIOPHYSICS, BIOMEDICAL ENGINEERING. *Educ:* Univ Frankfurt, PhD(biophys), 40, Dr habil, 46. *Prof Exp:* Asst, Kaiser Wilhelm Biophys, 37-40, res assoc, 40-45, admin dir, 45-47; res specialist, US Naval Base, Pa, 47-50; asst prof physics in med, 50-60, asst prof phys med, 50-52, chmn biomed electronic eng, 61-73, ASSOC PROF PHYS MED, SCH MED, UNIV PA, 52-, PROF ELEC ENG, MOORE SCH ELEC ENG & PROF ELEC ENG IN PHYS MED, SCH MED, 57-, PROF BIOENG, SCH ENG, 75- *Concurrent Pos:* Asst prof, Univ Frankfurt, 46-55, vis prof, 62; vis MacKay prof, Univ Calif, Berkeley, 56; lectr, Johns Hopkins Univ, 62-66; sci mem, Max Planck Inst Biophys, 62-; consult, Gen Elec Co, 57-76, US Army & US Navy, 57-71 & NIH, 61-76; mem nat comt C95, Am Nat Stands Inst, 61- & Nat Acad Sci-Nat Res Coun, 67-73; mem nat adv coun environ health, Dept Health, Educ & Welfare, 69-71; Vis W W Clide prof, Univ Utah, Salt Lake, 80; Alexander von Humboldt US sr scientist award, 80. *Honors & Awards:* Cert of Commendation, Dept Health, Educ & Welfare, 66 & 72; Awards, Inst Elec & Electronics Eng, 53, 63 & 67; Rajewsky Prize for Biophys, 74. *Mem:* Fel AAAS; Biophys Soc; Biomed Eng Soc; fel Inst Elec & Electronics Eng; Nat Acad Eng. *Res:* Impedance measurement techniques and electrodes for biological dielectric research; biophysics of nonionizing radiation; biomedical engineering; electrical and acoustical properties of tissues and cells; electrical properties of biological membranes and biopolymers; electrical engineering. *Mailing Add:* Dept of Bioeng D3 Univ of Pa Philadelphia PA 19104

SCHWAN, THEODORE CARL, b Florida, Ohio, June 17, 18; m 44; c 4. ORGANIC CHEMISTRY, POLYMER CHEMISTRY. *Educ:* Valparaiso Univ, AB, 41; Univ Notre Dame, MS, 49, PhD(chem), 53. *Prof Exp:* Phys tester & chem analyst, US Rubber Co, Ind, 38-39, asst to res chemist, 41-42; chem analyst, Ind Steel Prods Co, 40-41; from instr to assoc prof chem, 48-62, chmn dept, 57-59, PROF CHEM, VALPARAISO UNIV, 62- *Concurrent Pos:* Res & develop chemist, Continental-Diamond Fibre Corp, Ind, 53-58; grant, Petrol Res Fund, Am Chem Soc, 59 & 63; Univ Ky prof, Univ Indonesia, Int Coop Admin, 59-61, chief of party, 61-62; UN Educ Sci & Cult Orgn vis prof, Haile Selassie Univ, 68-70; prof chem, Col Med & Med Sci, King Faisal Univ, Dammam, Saudi Arabia, 77-79, chmn dept, 78-79. *Mem:* AAAS; Am Chem Soc. *Res:* Copolymerization of unsaturated organic compounds by free radical and heterogeneous catalyst systems; water as a fuel additive for internal combustion engines. *Mailing Add:* Dept of Chem Valparaiso Univ Valparaiso IN 46383

SCHWAN, THOMAS JAMES, b Medina, NY, June 19, 34; m 61; c 3. MEDICINAL CHEMISTRY. *Educ:* St Bonaventure Univ, BS, 56, MS, 58; State Univ NY Buffalo, PhD(org chem), 65. *Prof Exp:* Res fel med chem, State Univ NY Buffalo, 64-65; sr res chemist, 65-68, unit leader org chem sect, 68-78, mgr, 78-80, DIR DEVELOP PLANNING, NORWICH-EATON PHARMACEUT, 80- *Mem:* Am Chem Soc. *Res:* Synthesis and transformations of nitrogen heterocycles; enzyme inhibitors; preparation of compounds of potential pharmacological activity; reaction mechanisms. *Mailing Add:* 8 Hillview Dr Norwich NY 13815

SCHWANDT, PETER, b Gottingen, Ger, Apr 7, 39; US citizen; m 63; c 1. NUCLEAR PHYSICS. *Educ:* Ind Univ, Bloomington, BS, 61; Univ Wis-Madison, MS, 63, PhD(physics), 67. *Prof Exp:* Res assoc nuclear physics, Univ Wis-Madison, 67-68 & Univ Colo, Boulder, 68-69; from asst prof to assoc prof, 69-80, PROF PHYSICS, IND UNIV, BLOOMINGTON, 80- *Mem:* Am Phys Soc. *Res:* Medium-energy physics; reaction mechanisms; spin dependent interactions; potential models for composite particle scattering; heavy-ion interactions. *Mailing Add:* Dept of Physics Ind Univ Bloomington IN 47401

SCHWARCZ, ERVIN H, b Cleveland, Ohio, Aug 22, 24; m 48; c 4. PHYSICS. *Educ:* Ohio State Univ, BS, 45; Univ Mich, MS, 48, PhD(physics), 55. *Prof Exp:* Res physicist, Lawrence Radiation Lab, Univ Calif, 54-67; PROF PHYSICS, STANISLAUS STATE COL, 67- *Mem:* AAAS; Am Asn Physics Teachers; Am Phys Soc. *Res:* Nuclear structure and optical model analysis of elastic and quasi-elastic scattering. *Mailing Add:* Dept Physics Stanislaus State Col Turlock CA 95380

SCHWARCZ, HENRY PHILIP, b Chicago, Ill, July 22, 33; m 64. STABLE ISOTOPES. *Educ:* Univ Chicago, BA, 52; Calif Inst Technol, MSc, 55, PhD(geol), 60. *Prof Exp:* Res assoc isotopic geochem, Enrico Fermi Inst Nuclear Studies, Univ Chicago, 60-62; from asst prof to assoc prof, 62-72, PROF GEOL, McMASTER UNIV, 72- *Concurrent Pos:* Mem mineral, geochem & petrol subcomt, Nat Adv Coun Res-Geol Soc Can, 65-72; Fulbright fel, Nuclear Geol Lab, Univ Pisa, 68-69; mem subcomt isotopes & geochronology, Assoc Comt Geod & Geophys, Nat Res Coun Can, 72-74, mem subcomt meteorites, 77-; vis prof, Hebrew Univ Jerusalem, 75-76; vis scientist, Res Lab Archeol, Oxford Univ, 78. *Mem:* Fel Geol Soc Am; fel Geol Asn Can; Geochem Soc. *Res:* Stable isotope geochemistry; meteorites; archeology; geochronology of cave deposits; disposal of radioactive waste. *Mailing Add:* Dept of Geol McMaster Univ Hamilton ON L8S 4M1 Can

SCHWARK, WAYNE STANLEY, b Vita, Man, May 19, 42; m 63; c 2. PHARMACOLOGY, TOXICOLOGY. *Educ:* Univ Guelph, DVM, 65, MSc, 67; Univ Ottawa, PhD(pharmacol), 70. *Prof Exp:* Lectr physiol & pharmacol, Ont Vet Col, Univ Guelph, 65-67; biologist pharmacol div, Food & Drug Dir, Ont, 67-70, res scientist, 70-71; asst prof, 72-77, ASSOC PROF PHARMACOL, NY STATE COL VET MED, CORNELL UNIV, 77- *Concurrent Pos:* Vet consult med sch, Univ Ottawa, 69-70; vis lectr, NY State Vet Col, Cornell Univ, 71; consult, Food & Drug Admin, 77- *Mem:* Am Soc Vet Physiol & Pharmacol; Can Vet Med Asn; Soc Neurosci. *Res:*

Neurochemistry and neuropharmacology; toxicological aspects of environmental pollutants; neurochemical and neuropharmacological basis of epileptic disorders; clinical pharmacology and medicine. *Mailing Add:* Dept Phamacol Cornell Univ Col Vet Med Ithaca NY 14853

SCHWARTING, ARTHUR ERNEST, b Waubay, SDak, June 8, 17; m 41; c 3. PHARMACOGNOSY. *Educ:* SDak State Univ, BS, 40; Ohio State Univ, PhD(pharmacog), 43. *Prof Exp:* Assoc prof pharmacog, Univ Nebr, 43-49; dir, Am Found Pharmaceut Educ, 74-80; dean Sch Pharm, 70-80, PROF PHARMACOG, UNIV CONN, 49- *Concurrent Pos:* Ed, Lloydia, 60-76; vis prof, Univ Munich, 68-69; consult drug efficacy, Food & Drug Admin, 75-77. *Honors & Awards:* Res Achievement Award, Am Pharmaceut Asn, 64. *Mem:* AAAS; Am Pharmaceut Asn; Am Soc Pharmacog; Acad Pharmaceut Sci. *Res:* Ergot culture; biosynthesis; alkaloid chemistry. *Mailing Add:* 330 Capstan Dr Cape Haze Placida FL 33946

SCHWARTZ, ABRAHAM, b New York, NY, June 13, 16; m 40; c 3. MATHEMATICS. *Educ:* City Col New York, BS, 36; Mass Inst Technol, MS, 37, PhD(math), 39. *Prof Exp:* Res math, Inst Advan Study, 39-41; from instr to asst prof, Pa State Univ, 41-48; from instr to assoc prof, 48-65, dean, 66-70, provost, 70-71, PROF MATH, CITY COL NEW YORK, 66- *Mem:* Am Math Soc; Math Asn Am. *Res:* Metric differential geometry; matrix algebra; high dimensional Riemannian manifolds. *Mailing Add:* Dept Math City Col NY 138th St at Convent Ave New York NY 10031

SCHWARTZ, ABRAHAM, b Rockville Centre, NY, Apr 4, 43. PHYSICAL CHEMISTRY, BIOMATERIALS. *Educ:* Bradley Univ, BA, 65; Case Inst Technol, MS, 67; Case Western Reserve Univ, PhD(phys chem), 69. *Prof Exp:* Biophysicist, Aerospace Med Res Lab, 69-73; instr mat sci, Cornell Univ, 73-77; SR CHEMIST, RES TRIANGLE INST, 77- *Mem:* Am Phys Soc; Am Soc Artificial Internal Organs. *Res:* Electron microscopy; structural and morphology of natural and synthetic polymers; thrombus formation and hard tissues. *Mailing Add:* Res Triangle Inst Research Triangle Park NC 27709

SCHWARTZ, ALAN LEE, b Chicago, Ill, Dec 8, 41; m 65; c 2. MATHEMATICS. *Educ:* Mass Inst Technol, BS, 63; Univ Wis-Madison, MS, 64, PhD(math), 68. *Prof Exp:* Asst prof math, 68-74, ASSOC PROF MATH, UNIV MO-ST LOUIS, 74- *Mem:* AAAS; Am Math Soc; Math Asn Am. *Res:* Harmonic analysis; integral transformations; orthogonal expansion. *Mailing Add:* Dept of Math Univ of Mo St Louis MO 63121

SCHWARTZ, ALAN SHELDON, b Detroit, Mich, Mar 21, 36. CHEMICAL & NUCLEAR ENGINEERING. *Educ:* Wayne State Univ, BS, 58, MS, 61, PhD(chem eng), 65. *Prof Exp:* Mem staff, Gen Atomic Co, 63-76, dir, Govt Int Progs Div, 76-77, dir advan progs, 77-80; MEM STAFF, SRS INT INC, 80- *Mem:* Am Chem Soc; Am Nuclear Soc. *Mailing Add:* SRS Int Inc PO Box 3396 Engelwood CO 80155

SCHWARTZ, ALAN WILLIAM, b New York, NY, Sept 9, 35; m 60; c 2. EXOBIOLOGY, ORGANIC GEOCHEMISTRY, CHEMICAL EVOLUTION. *Educ:* NY Univ, BA, 57; Fla State Univ, MS, 62, PhD(biochem), 65. *Prof Exp:* AEC fel, Biomed Res Group, Los Alamos Sci Lab, 65-67; NASA resident res assoc, Exobiol Div, Ames Res Ctr, NASA, 67-68; assoc prof exobiol, 68-70, PROF EXOBIOL, UNIV NIJMEGEN, 70- *Mem:* AAAS; Royal Neth Chem Soc; Geochem Soc; Am Soc Biol Chemists; Am Chem Soc. *Res:* Chemical evolution. *Mailing Add:* Dept of Exobiol Univ of Nijmegen Toernooiveld Nijmegen 6525ED Netherlands

SCHWARTZ, ALBERT, b Cincinnati, Ohio, Sept 13, 23. SYSTEMATIC ZOOLOGY. *Educ:* Univ Cincinnati, BA, 44; Univ Miami, MS, 46; Univ Mich, PhD(mammal), 52. *Prof Exp:* Instr zool, Univ Miami, 46-48; cur vert zool, Charleston Mus, 52-56; from instr to asst prof biol, Albright Col, 56-60; independent res, 60-67; assoc prof biol, 67-72, PROF BIOL, MIAMI-DADE JR COL, 72- *Concurrent Pos:* NSF res grants, 57-61 & 69-72. *Mem:* Am Soc Ichthyologists & Herpetologists; Am Soc Mammal; Lepidopterists' Soc; Soc Syst Zool; Am Ornith Union. *Res:* Mammalogy and herpetology; herpetofauna of West Indies; systematics and natural history of North American mammals, amphibians and reptiles; herpetogeography and systematics of West Indies. *Mailing Add:* 10000 SW 84th St Miami FL 33173

SCHWARTZ, ALBERT B, b Philadelphia, Pa, Dec 26, 22; m 63; c 1. CHEMICAL ENGINEERING. *Educ:* Univ Pa, BS, 44. *Prof Exp:* Chem engr, Anthracite Industs Lab, 44-45; chem engr, 45-49, group leader, 49-56, supv technologist, 56-62, res assoc, 62-64, supvr, 64-70, group mgr, 70-72, sr scientist, 72-81, SECT MGR, MOBIL RES & DEVELOP CORP, 81- *Mem:* Am Chem Soc; Catalysis Soc; Am Inst Chem Engrs. *Res:* Research and development of catalysts and adsorbents with their applications. *Mailing Add:* Mobil Res & Develop Corp Paulsboro NJ 08066

SCHWARTZ, ALBERT TRUMAN, b Freeman, SDak, May 8, 34; m 58; c 2. BIOPHYSICAL CHEMISTRY, HISTORY OF CHEMISTRY. *Educ:* Univ SDak, AB, 56; Oxford Univ, BA, 58, MA, 60; Mass Inst Technol, PhD(phys chem), 63. *Prof Exp:* Res chemist, Miami Valley Labs, Procter & Gamble Co, Ohio, 63-66; from asst prof to assoc prof, 66-78, dean fac, 74-76, PROF CHEM, MACALESTER COL, 78-, CHMN DEPT, 80- *Concurrent Pos:* Asst, Mass Inst Technol, 58-63; mem, State & District Comt Selection Rhodes Scholar, 58-63; Arthur Lee Haines lectr & vis scientist, Univ SDak, 65; Macalester fac for fel, Thermochem Lab, Univ Lund, 68; vis researcher, Univ Mass, 72-73; vis prof & NSF fel, Univ Wis-Madison, 79-80. *Mem:* AAAS; Am Chem Soc. *Res:* Chemical education; history of chemistry; physicochemical properties of macromolecules, particularly conformation and aggregation of proteins; solution calorimetry; preparative electrophoresis; equilibrium properties of ion exchange resins. *Mailing Add:* Macalester Col St Paul MN 55105

SCHWARTZ, ALICE GRIFFIN, molecular genetics, see previous edition

SCHWARTZ, ALLAN JAMES, b New York, NY, Dec 8, 39. PSYCHIATRY. *Educ:* Columbia Univ, BA, 61, MA, 66; Rensselaer Polytech Inst, MS, 67; Univ Rochester, PhD(psychol), 73. *Prof Exp:* Staff writer, Crowell-Collier Publ Co, 61-62; chmn sci dept, Riverdale Country Sch, 62-68; asst prof, 71-80, ASSOC PROF PSYCHIAT, SCH MED, UNIV ROCHESTER, 80- *Concurrent Pos:* Mem & chmn, Ment Health Ann Prog Surv, Am Col Health Asn, 73-; staff develop consult, Delphi House Drug Treatment Ctr, 73-75; group therapist & supvr, Rochester Ment Health Ctr, 73-76. *Mem:* Am Col Health Asn; Am Psychol Asn; Am Asn Sex Educr, Counr & Therapists; Int Transactional Anal Asn. *Res:* Epidemiology of mental disorders; non-verbal behavior, communication process and outcome in therapeutic, supervisory and consultative relationships; education in human sexuality and treatment of sexual dysfunction. *Mailing Add:* Box 617 Strong Mem Hosp 260 Crittenden Blvd Rochester NY 14642

SCHWARTZ, ANTHONY, b New York, NY, July 30, 40; m 63; c 2. IMMUNOLOGY, VETERINARY MEDICINE. *Educ:* Cornell Univ, DVM, 63; Ohio State Univ, PhD(med microbiol), 72; Am Col Vet Surg, dipl, 71. *Prof Exp:* Small animal pract, Ft Hill Animal Hosp, NY, 63-66; res vet viral immunol, US Army, Ft Detrick, Md, 66-68; resident surg, New York Animal Med Ctr, 68-69; teaching assoc vet surg & res assoc med microbiol, Ohio State Univ, 69-72, asst prof & head small animal surg, 73; asst prof comp med, Sch Med, Yale Univ, 73-79; assoc prof comp med, 79, ASSOC PROF & HEAD, DEPT SMALL ANIMAL SURGERY, SCH VET MED, TUFTS UNIV, 79-, ACTG CHMN SURGERY, 81- *Concurrent Pos:* Fel, Ohio State Univ, 72-73. *Mem:* AAAS; Am Vet Med Asn; Am Asn Immunol; Am Col Vet Surg. *Res:* Basic aspects of cellular immunology, specifically vasoamines and delayed hypersensitivity; small animal general veterinary surgery. *Mailing Add:* Dept Surg Sch Vet Med Tufts Univ 350 S Huntington Ave Boston MA 02130

SCHWARTZ, ANTHONY MAX, b Philadelphia, Pa, July 31, 08; m 36; c 2. SURFACE CHEMISTRY. *Educ:* Cornell Univ, BChem, 28, PhD(org chem), 31. *Prof Exp:* Res chemist, Nat Aniline & Chem Co, RI, 43-44; res assoc, Harris Res Labs, Inc, Gillette Co, DC, 44-57, asst dir, 57-67, prin scientist, Gillette Res Inst, 67-73; CONSULT, 73- *Concurrent Pos:* Adj res assoc, Lehigh Univ, 78- *Honors & Awards:* Honor Scroll, Am Inst Chemists, 78. *Mem:* Am Chem Soc; Am Oil Chem Soc; hon mem Am Soc Test & Mat; Soc Cosmetic Chemists; Am Inst Chemists. *Res:* High polymers; cellulose derivatives; detergents and surface active agents; textile proccessing; colloid chemistry; detergency; capillary and interfacial phenomena. *Mailing Add:* 2260 Glenmore Terr Rockville MD 20850

SCHWARTZ, ARNOLD, b New York, NY, Mar 1, 29; m 56; c 2. PHARMACOLOGY, BIOCHEMISTRY. *Educ:* Brooklyn Col Pharm, BS, 51; Ohio State Univ, MS, 57; State Univ NY, PhD(pharmacol), 61. *Prof Exp:* From asst prof to assoc prof pharmacol, Baylor Col Med, 62-69, prof pharmacol & head div myocardial biol, 69-72, prof cell biophys & pharmacol & chmn dept cell biophys, 72-77; DIR DEPT PHARMACOL & CELL BIOPHYS, COL MED, UNIV CINCINNATI, 77- *Concurrent Pos:* Nat Heart Inst fel biochem, Inst Psychiat, Maudsley Hosp, Univ London, 60-61 & fel physiol, Univ Aarhus, 61-62; USPHS res career develop award, 64-74; NSF grant, 65-67; mem study sect CV-A, NIH, 72-76. *Mem:* Am Soc Cell Biol; Am Soc Pharmacol & Exp Therapeut; Brit Biochem Soc; Int Study Group for Res in Cardiac Metabolism; Am Soc Biol Chem. *Res:* Mechanism of cardiac glycoside action on a biochemical level; etiology of congestive heart failure and ischemia. *Mailing Add:* Dept of Cell Pharmacol & Cell Biophys Univ of Cincinnati Cincinnati OH 45267

SCHWARTZ, ARNOLD EDWARD, b Rochester, NY, Dec 15, 35; m 59; c 6. CIVIL ENGINEERING, SOIL MECHANICS. *Educ:* Univ Notre Dame, BSCE, 58, MSCE, 60; Ga Inst Technol, PhD(civil eng), 63. *Prof Exp:* From asst prof to assoc prof, 63-72, head dept civil eng, 67-69, dean grad sch & div univ res, 69-70, PROF CIVIL ENG, CLEMSON UNIV, 72-, DEAN GRAD STUDIES & UNIV RES, 70- *Concurrent Pos:* Mem spec comt nuclear principles & appln, Hwy Res Bd, Nat Acad Sci-Nat Res Coun, 64-69; mem exec comt, Southern Conf Grad Schs, 72-; mem, US Coun Grad Schs. *Mem:* Am Soc Civil Engrs. *Res:* Soil mechanics and foundation engineering; highway materials and quality control testing; pavement design. *Mailing Add:* Grad Sch Clemson Univ Martin Hall Clemson SC 29631

SCHWARTZ, ARTHUR GERALD, b Baltimore, Md, Mar 13, 41. CELL BIOLOGY, CANCER. *Educ:* Johns Hopkins Univ, BA, 61; Harvard Univ, PhD(bact, immunol), 68. *Prof Exp:* asst prof, 72-77, ASSOC PROF MICROBIOL, FELS RES INST MED SCH, TEMPLE UNIV, 77- *Concurrent Pos:* Jane Coffin Childs grant, Oxford Univ, 68-71 & Albert Einstein Col Med, 71-72. *Mem:* Am Asn Cancer Res; Geront Soc. *Res:* Chemical carcinogenesis in vitro; inhibition of tumor formation in vivo. *Mailing Add:* Fels Res Inst Dept Microbiol Temple Univ Med Sch Philadelphia PA 19140

SCHWARTZ, ARTHUR HAROLD, b New York, NY, Apr 6, 36; div; c 1. PSYCHIATRY, ACADEMIC ADMINISTRATION. *Educ:* Columbia Univ, AB, 57; Harvard Med Sch, MD, 61. *Prof Exp:* Intern, Univ Ill Res & Educ Hosps, 61-62; Vet Admin fel, Yale Univ Med Ctr, 62-64; USPHS fel, 64-65; dir psychiat, Dana Psychiat Clin, Yale-New Haven Hosp, 67-68; chief, In-Patient Serv, Conn Ment Health Ctr, 68-69, assoc dir, Gen Clin Div, 69-71, assoc psychiatrist-in-chief, 71-72, actg psychiatrist-in-chief, 72; assoc prof psychiat, Mt Sinai Sch Med, 72-81, dir, Ambulatory Serv, Dept Psychiat, 72-81; PROF PSYCHIAT, COL MED & DENT NJ, RUTGERS MED SCH, 81- *Concurrent Pos:* Actg clin dir, Newport County Ment Health Clin, 66-67; asst prof psychiat, Yale Univ Sch Med, 67-71, assoc prof clin psychiat, 71-72; consult, Hosp of St Raphael, New Haven, Conn, 70-71, Vet Admin Hosp, West Haven, Conn, 71-72 & Vet Admin Hosp, Bronx, NY, 72- *Mem:* AAAS; Am Psychoanal Asn; Am Psychopath Asn; fel NY Acad Med; Am Psychiat Asn. *Res:* Group process including group therapy and therapeutic communities; professional student values and attitudes; clinical psychiatry. *Mailing Add:* Dept Psychiat Box 101 Col Med & Dent NJ Rutgers Med Sch Piscataway NJ 08854

SCHWARTZ, B(ERNARD), b Yonkers, NY, July 20, 24; m; c 3. CERAMICS. *Educ:* Alfred Univ, BS, 48; Mass Inst Technol, ScD(ceramics), 51. *Prof Exp:* Mem staff ceramics, Mass Inst Technol, 48-52; head ceramics group, Electronic Div, Sylvania Elec Prod, Inc, 52-54; res engr, Res Ctr, Burroughs Corp, 54-58; mgr component develop, Semiconductor & Mat Div, Radio Corp Am, 58-63; SR ENGR, IBM CORP, 63- *Mem:* Fel Am Ceramic Soc; Nat Inst Ceramic Engrs; sr mem Inst Elec & Electronics Engrs. *Mailing Add:* IBM Corp Rt 52 Hopewell Junction NY 12533

SCHWARTZ, BENJAMIN L, b Pittsburgh, Pa, Jan 11, 26; m 56; c 3. OPERATIONS RESEARCH. *Educ:* Carnegie Mellon Univ, BS, 46, MS, 47; Stanford Univ, PhD(oper res), 65. *Prof Exp:* Asst prof math, Duquesne Univ, 50-53; asst div chief, Battelle Mem Inst, 53-58; suboff tech dir, Monterey Lab, 58-64; mem tech staff, Inst Defense Anal, 65-67; subdept head, Mitre Corp, 67-70; CONSULT, 70- *Concurrent Pos:* Vis assoc prof, US Naval Postgrad Sch, 63-65; vis prof, George Washington Univ, 66-; adj prof, Am Univ, 69-72, Georgetown Univ, 82- *Mem:* Fel AAAS; Am Math Soc; Opers Res Soc Am; Asn Comput Mach; Math Asn Am. *Res:* Mathematics. *Mailing Add:* 216 Apple Blossom Ct Vienna VA 22180

SCHWARTZ, BENJAMIN SAM, microbiology, deceased

SCHWARTZ, BERNARD, b Toronto, Ont, Nov 12, 27; nat US; m 54; c 3. OPHTHALMOLOGY, PHYSIOLOGY. *Educ:* Univ Toronto, MD, 51; Univ Iowa, MS, 53, PhD(physiol), 59; Am Bd Opthal, dipl, 56. *Prof Exp:* Assoc prof ophthal, Col Med, State Univ NY Downstate Med Ctr, 58-68; PROF OPHTHAL, SCH MED, TUFTS UNIV & - OPHTHALMOLOGIST-IN-CHIEF, TUFTSNEW ENG MED CTR, 68- *Mem:* Asn Res Vision & Ophthal; fel Am Col Surg; fel Am Acad Ophthal & Otolaryngol; fel NY Acad Med; Fr Soc Ophthal. *Res:* Metabolism and permeability of the lens and cornea; physiology of intraocular fluid formation; patho-physiology of cataract and glaucoma. *Mailing Add:* Tufts-New Eng Med Ctr 171 Harrison Ave Boston MA 02111

SCHWARTZ, BERTRAM, b New York, NY, Nov 1, 24; m 48; c 2. SURFACE CHEMISTRY. *Educ:* NY Univ, BS, 49. *Prof Exp:* Mem tech staff, Interchem Corp, 51-52, Sylvania Elec Prod Co, 52-54 & Hughes Aircraft Co, 54-60; MEM TECH STAFF, BELL LABS, INC, 60- *Mem:* Am Phys Soc; Electrochem Soc. *Res:* Chemistry of solid surfaces; chemical etching of solids; semiconductor material preparation; semiconductor device fabrication techniques. *Mailing Add:* 321 Orenda Circle Westfield NJ 07090

SCHWARTZ, BRIAN B, b Brooklyn, NY, Apr 15, 38; m 61; c 2. THEORETICAL PHYSICS, SCIENCE EDUCATION. *Educ:* City Col NY, BS, 59; Brown Univ, PhD(physics), 63. *Prof Exp:* Teaching asst physics, Brown Univ, 59-61; res assoc, Rutgers Univ, 63-65; leader theoret physics group, Nat Magnet Lab, Mass Inst Technol, 65-77; dean, Sch Sci, prof physics, 77-80, DEAN RES, BROOKLYN COL, 78- *Concurrent Pos:* Assoc prof physics, Mass Inst Technol, 69-74; co-dir, NATO Advan Study Inst Large Scale Appl Superconductivity, Entreve, Italy, 73 & Small Scale Devices, Gardone Riviera, Italy, 77; superconductor mat sci, Sintra, Portugal, 80. *Mem:* Fel Am Phys Soc. *Res:* Low temperature physics; superconductivity; type II superconductors; Josephson junctions; response of ferromagnetic metals; many-body problem; scientific manpower projection and utilization; physics education for the science and non-science major; small business; high technology. *Mailing Add:* Dean Res Brooklyn Col of CUNY Booklyn NY 11210

SCHWARTZ, CHARLES, b Seattle, Wash, Nov 22, 09; m 38; c 2. MEDICINAL CHEMISTRY. *Educ:* Univ Wash (Seattle), BS, 30, MS, 31, PhD, 35. *Prof Exp:* Retail pharmacist, Seattle, Wash, 29-35; chemist, Nat Bur Stands, 35-46; admin pharmacist, Pharm Div, US Vet Admin, Calif & Washington, DC, 46-50; prof pharm, 50-75, EMER PROF PHARM, SCH PHARM, SOUTHWESTERN OKLA STATE UNIV, 75- *Mem:* Am Pharmaceut Asn. *Mailing Add:* 2 Adams St Apt 906 Denver CO 80206

SCHWARTZ, CHARLES LEON, b New York, NY, June 9, 31; m 52; c 3. THEORETICAL PHYSICS. *Educ:* Mass Inst Technol, SB, 52, PhD(physics), 54. *Prof Exp:* Res assoc physics, Mass Inst Technol, 54-56; res assoc, Stanford Univ, 56-57, asst prof, 57-60; from asst prof to assoc prof, 60-67, PROF PHYSICS, UNIV CALIF, BERKELEY, 67- *Mem:* Am Phys Soc. *Res:* Theoretical studies of atoms, nuclei and elementary particles; interaction of science with human affairs. *Mailing Add:* Dept Physics Univ Calif Berkeley CA 94720

SCHWARTZ, COLIN JOHN, b Angaston, SAustralia, May 1, 31; m 58; c 4. ANATOMIC PATHOLOGY, EXPERIMENTAL PATHOLOGY. *Educ:* Univ Adelaide, MB, BS, 54, MD, 59; FRCP. *Prof Exp:* Resident med & surg, Royal Adelaide Hosp, Australia, 55; vice master, Lincoln Univ Col, Univ Adelaide, 57, actg master, 58; specialist pathologist, Inst Med Vet Sci, 62-67, head div med res, 67; prof path, Fac Med, McMaster Univ, 68-76; head dept cardiovasc dis res, Cleveland Clin Found, 76-78; PROF PATH, UNIV TEX HEALTH SCI CTR SAN ANTONIO, 78- *Concurrent Pos:* Nat Health & Med Res Coun Australia res fel exp path, Univ Adelaide, 56-58; C J Martin overseas res fel cardiovasc dis, Dept Med, Oxford Univ, 59-61; Nuffield Comt res grant, 59-61; Med Res Coun Gt Brit fel, 61; Nat Heart Found Australia res grant, 62-66; NIH int fel cardiovasc path, C T Miller Hosp, Univ Minn, 67; Med Res Coun Can res grant, 68-; fel coun on arteriosclerosis, Am Heart Asn, 67, mem exec comt coun; dir, Southam Labs, Chedoke Hosps, 70-76; mem, Heart, Lung & Blood Res Rev Comt. *Mem:* Am Asn Path & Bact; NY Acad Sci; Can Asn Path; Am Heart Asn; Int Acad Path. *Res:* Myocardial infarction and the etiology and pathogenesis of atherosclerosis and thrombosis; endothelial structures; lipid transport and metabolism. *Mailing Add:* Dept of Path 7703 Floyd Curl Dr San Antonio TX 78284

SCHWARTZ, DANIEL ALAN, b San Antonio, Tex, Oct 21, 42; m 69; c 2. X-RAY ASTRONOMY, COSMOLOGY. *Educ:* Washington Univ, BS, 63; Univ Calif, San Diego, MS, 66, PhD(physics), 69. *Prof Exp:* Lectr physics, Univ Calif, San Diego, 68-70, asst res physicist, 69-70; Nat Res Coun resident res assoc, Goddard Space Flight Ctr, NASA, 70-71; from staff scientist to sr scientist x-ray astron, Am Sci & Eng, Inc, 71-73; PHYSICIST, SMITHSONIAN ASTROPHYS OBSERV, 73- *Concurrent Pos:* Lectr astron dept, Harvard Univ, 81- *Mem:* Am Astron Soc; Am Phys Soc; Int Astron Union. *Res:* Experiment development and observation of extragalactic x-rays to study isotropy of the x-ray background and mechanism of source emission; development of x-ray imaging systems for spectral studies of cosmic x-rays. *Mailing Add:* Ctr Astrophys 60 Garden St Cambridge MA 02138

SCHWARTZ, DANIEL EVAN, b Hollywood, Calif, Oct 6, 52; m 74. FLUVIAL SEDIMENTOLOGY, PETROLEUM ENGINEERING. *Educ:* Univ Calif, Berkeley, AB, 74; Univ Tex, Dallas, PhD(geol), 78. *Prof Exp:* RES ENGR PROD, SHELL DEVELOP CO, 78- *Mem:* Geol Soc Am; Int Asn Sedimentologists; Soc Econ Paleontologists & Mineralogists. *Res:* Sedimentology of the braided-to-meandering transition zone of the Red River; applications of scanning electron microscopy to petroleum engineering; petrology and diagenesis of clastic petroleum reservoirs. *Mailing Add:* Shell Develop Co PO Box 481 Houston TX 77001

SCHWARTZ, DANIEL M(AX), b San Francisco, Calif, Mar 22, 13; m 37; c 2. MECHANICAL ENGINEERING, MANAGEMENT. *Educ:* Stanford Univ, AB, 33. *Prof Exp:* Mech engr, Pac Gear & Tool Works, Calif, 33-36; mech engr, Dept of Water & Power, City of Los Angeles, 36-37; mech design engr, Falk Corp, Wis, 37-40; develop engr, Dravo Corp, Pa, 40-46; vpres in charge eng & dir, Eimco Corp, 46-63, sr vpres, 63-66, gen mgr, Tractor Div, 65-66; sr staff engr, Ground Vehicle Systs, Res & Develop Div, Lockheed Missiles & Space Co, 66-67, mgr construct equip syst, 67-72, prog mgr army progs, 72-78; PRES, FOOTHILL ENG, INC, 78- *Mem:* Fel Am Soc Mech Engrs; Soc Automotive Engrs. *Res:* Government proposals, engineering management; machine design and development of heavy duty equipment; heavy transmissions, clutches; shipyard cranes; mining and milling machinery; construction equipment; loaders and tractors. *Mailing Add:* Foothill Eng Inc 517 Outlook Dr Los Altos CA 94022

SCHWARTZ, DONALD, b Scarsdale, NY, Dec 27, 27; m 50; c 4. CHEMISTRY. *Educ:* Univ Mo, BS, 49; Mont State Col, MS, 51; Pa State Univ, PhD(chem, fuel tech), 55. *Prof Exp:* Chemist, Gen Elect Co, 51-53; asst, Pa State Univ, 53-55; asst prof chem, Villanova Univ, 55-57; res chemist, Esso Res Lab, La, 57-58; asst prof chem, Moorhead State Col, 58-59; prof chem, NDak State Univ, 59-65; reg specialist, Cent Am, NSF-Am Chem Soc, 65-66; prog dir, NSF, 66-68; prof chem & assoc dean, Grad Sch, Memphis State Univ, 68-70; dean advan studies, Fla Atlantic Univ, 70-71; vpres acad affairs, 71-74, actg pres, State Univ NY Col Buffalo, 74; chancellor, Ind Univ-Purdue Univ, 74-78; CHANCELLOR, UNIV COLO, 78- *Concurrent Pos:* Consult, Baroid Div, Nat Lead Co, 60-64; consult vpres, Mid-South Res Assocs, 68-70; bd dir, Ind Comn Humanities, 74- *Mem:* AAAS; Am Chem Soc. *Res:* Humic acids; coordination compounds of titanium; zirconium; science education; elucidation of structure of coal. *Mailing Add:* Off Chancellor Univ Colo Colorado Springs CO 80907

SCHWARTZ, DONALD ALAN, b Brooklyn, NY, Mar 5, 26; m 52; c 3. PSYCHIATRY. *Educ:* Case Western Reserve Univ, MD, 52. *Prof Exp:* From instr to assoc clin prof psychiat, Sch Med, Univ Calif, Los Angeles, 58-69; assoc prof psychiat, Sch Med, Univ Calif, Irvine, 69-71; from assoc prof to prof psychiat & chief adult psychiat, Neuropsychiat Inst, 71-74; MED COODR, BENJAMIN RUSH CTR, ST JOSEPH HOSP, ORANGE, CALIF, 80- *Concurrent Pos:* Chief inpatient serv, Neuropsychiat Inst, Univ Calif, Los Angeles, 59-61; dep dir, Los Angeles County Dept Ment Health, 61-69; chief psychiat inpatient serv, Orange County Med Ctr, 69-71; adj prof psychiat, Sch Med, Univ Calif, Los Angeles, 74- *Mem:* AMA; fel Am Psychiat Asn. *Res:* Psychopathology; administrative medicine. *Mailing Add:* 17772 17th St Tustin CA 92680

SCHWARTZ, DREW, b Philadelphia, Pa, Nov 15, 19; m 42; c 1. GENETICS. *Educ:* Pa State Col, 42; Columbia Univ, MA, 48, PhD(bot), 50. *Prof Exp:* Res assoc cytogenetics, Univ Ill, 50-51; sr biologist, Biol Div, Oak Ridge Nat Lab, 51-62; prof biol, Western Reserve Univ, 62-64; PROF GENETICS, IND UNIV, BLOOMINGTON, 64- *Mem:* AAAS; Genetics Soc Am; Am Soc Nat. *Res:* Genetic control of enzyme synthesis and regulation of gene action. *Mailing Add:* Dept Biol Ind Univ Bloomington IN 41401

SCHWARTZ, EDITH RICHMOND, b Karlsruhe, US citizen; c 3. BIOCHEMISTRY, ORTHOPEDICS. *Educ:* Columbia Univ, AB, 52, MA, 55; Cornell Univ, PhD(biochem), 64. *Prof Exp:* Res assoc biochem, Univ Tex, 66-69; vis asst prof, Univ Ill, 69-70; res assoc pediat, Sch Med, Univ Va, 70-71, res assoc orthop, 71-72, from asst prof to assoc prof orthop, 75-78; PROF ORTHOP SURG, SCH MED, TUFTS UNIV, 78- *Concurrent Pos:* Damon Runyon fel, Albert Einstein Col Med, 64-66. *Mem:* Orthop Res Soc; Fedn Am Soc Exp Biol; Rheumatism Asn. *Res:* Connective tissue research; osteoarthritis; sulfated proteoglycon metabolism in articular cartilage; human chondrocyte cultures. *Mailing Add:* Dept Orthop Surg Sch Med 136 Harrison Ave Boston MA 02116

SCHWARTZ, EDWARD, b Dec 25, 32; US citizen; m 58; c 3. TOXICOLOGY, PHARMACOLOGY. *Educ:* Philadelphia Col Pharm & Sci, BS, 55; Univ Pa, VMD, 59; Jefferson Med Col, PhD(pharmacol), 63; LaSalle Exten Univ, dipl comput programming, 69. *Prof Exp:* Sr toxicologist, Hoffman-LaRoche, Inc, 62-65; sr res assoc, Warner-Lambert Res Inst, 65-70, head dept toxicol, 70, dir dept toxicol, 70-77, assoc dir toxicol, 77; dir, 77-81, SR DIR PATH & TOXICOL, SCHERING-PLOUGH CORP, 81- *Mem:* Am Vet Med Asn; Soc Toxicol; Am Soc Pharmacol & Exp Therapeut; Europ Soc Study Drug Toxicity; Can Soc Toxicol. *Res:* Drug safety evaluation studies in animals; specific research in utilization of isoenzymes in diagnostic problems in dogs. *Mailing Add:* Dept Toxicol Box 32 Lafayette NJ 07848

SCHWARTZ, ELMER G(EORGE), b Pittsburgh, Pa, July 16, 27; m 47; c 5. NUCLEAR ENGINEERING, MATERIALS SCIENCE. *Educ:* US Merchant Marine Acad, BS, 50; Carnegie Inst Technol, MS, 60, PhD(nuclear eng), 64. *Prof Exp:* Develop engr, Bettis Atomic Power Lab, Westinghouse Elec Corp, 52-59, develop engr, Atomic Power Div, 60-61; assoc prof eng, 64-72, PROF ENG, UNIV SC, 72- *Concurrent Pos:* Consult, Carolinas-Va Nuclear Power Assocs, 64-68; res partic, Savannah River Lab, 66; vis assoc prof, Carnegie-Mellon Univ, 71-72; tech assoc, E R Johnson Assocs, Inc, 77-78. *Mem:* Am Soc Mech Engrs; Am Soc Metals. *Res:* Nuclear waste management; powder metallurgy compaction; mechanical properties of materials. *Mailing Add:* Univ of SC Col of Eng Columbia SC 29208

SCHWARTZ, EMANUEL ELLIOT, b New York, NY, Oct 14, 23; m 46; c 2. MEDICINE, RADIOLOGY. *Educ:* NY Univ, BA, 46; State Univ NY, MD, 50. *Prof Exp:* Intern, Jewish Hosp Brooklyn, 50-51; resident radiol, Yale-New Haven Med Ctr, 51-54; instr, Sch Med, Univ Chicago, 54-55; asst radiother, Hosp Joint Dis, New York, 55-56; asst radiol, Albert Einstein Med Ctr, 57-61, assoc, 61-65; assoc prof & dir div radiation ther & nuclear med, Sch Med, Univ Va, 65-67; radiologist, Coatesville Hosp, 67-71; ASSOC PROF RADIOL, HAHNEMANN MED COL & HOSP, 71- *Concurrent Pos:* AEC fel, Argonne Cancer Res Hosp, Univ Chicago, 54-55; USPHS fel, Biol Div, Oak Ridge Nat Lab, 56-57; instr, Sch Med, Yale Univ, 53-54. *Mem:* Radiation Res Soc; Am Roentgen Ray Soc; Radiol Soc NAm; AMA; Am Asn Cancer Res. *Res:* Radiographic manifestations of chest disease, particularly in renal patients, and with complications of medical practice. *Mailing Add:* Hahnemann Med Col & Hosp 230 N Broad St Philadelphia PA 19102

SCHWARTZ, FRANK JOSEPH, b New Castle, Pa, Nov 20, 29. ICHTHYOLOGY. *Educ:* Univ Pittsburgh, BS, 50, MS, 52, PhD(ichthyol, ecol), 54. *Prof Exp:* Asst zool, Univ Pittsburgh, 50-55; asst prof, Univ WVa, 55-57; Md Dept Res & Educ biologist, Chesapeake Biol Lab, Univ Md, 57-61, res assoc prof, biol, 61-67, prof, 67; assoc prof, 68-71, PROF BIOL, INST MARINE SCI, UNIV NC, 71- *Concurrent Pos:* Assoc ed, Chesapeake Sci, 64-74; ed, Trans Am Fisheries Soc, 66-68 & Copeia, Am Soc Ichthyol & Herpet, 68-72; mem, Gulf & Caribbean Fisheries Inst & Int Oceanog Found. *Mem:* Am Inst Fishery Res Biologists; Int Acad Fishery Scientists; Int Oceanog Found; Am Fish Soc; Brit Fisheries Soc. *Res:* Taxonomy; distribution, ecology and life histories of marine and freshwater fishes; turtles; crayfishes. *Mailing Add:* Inst Marine Sci Univ of NC Morehead City NC 28557

SCHWARTZ, GARY PAUL, b Memphis, Tenn, May 25, 45. SURFACE CHEMISTRY. *Educ:* Univ Wash, BS, 67; Univ Calif, Berkeley, MS, 69, PhD(chem), 75. *Prof Exp:* MEM TECH STAFF CHEM, BELL LABS, MURRAY HILL, 75- *Mem:* Am Vacuum Soc; Sigma Xi; Am Phys Soc. *Res:* Surface and interfacial studies resulting from reactive gas-solid and solid-solid interactions. *Mailing Add:* Bell Labs 600 Mountain Ave Murray Hill NJ 07974

SCHWARTZ, GERALD PETER, b Cleveland, Ohio, Mar 20, 38; m 63; c 3. BIOCHEMISTRY. *Educ:* John Carroll Univ, BS, 60; Univ Pittsburgh, PhD(biochem), 64. *Prof Exp:* Res assoc biochem, Med Dept, Brookhaven Nat Lab, 64-66, asst scientist, 66-68; ASST RES PROF BIOCHEM, MT SINAI SCH MED, 66- *Mem:* AAAS; Am Chem Soc. *Res:* Isolation of enzymes; study of enzyme action; synthesis of peptides of biological interest. *Mailing Add:* Dept Biochem Mt Sinai Sch of Med New York NY 10029

SCHWARTZ, GERALDINE COGIN, b New York, NY, Apr 4, 23; m 43; c 2. PHYSICAL CHEMISTRY. *Educ:* Brooklyn Col, BA, 43; Columbia Univ, MA, 45, PhD(chem), 48. *Prof Exp:* Asst physics, SAM Labs, Manhattan Proj, Columbia Univ, 43; USPHS res fel, Tuberc Res Lab, 48 & Sloan Kettering Inst Cancer Res, 49, inst fel phys chem, 50-52; instr chem, Adelphi Col, 53 & Queens Col, NY, 53-54; asst prof, Bard Col, 58-62; chemist, 64-71, adv engr, Components Div, 71-78, SR ENGR, GEN TECHNOL DIV, IBM CORP, 78- *Mem:* Am Vacuum Soc; Sigma Xi; Electrochem Soc. *Res:* Physical chemistry of proteins; thin films; anodic oxidation and reactive ion etching. *Mailing Add:* IBM Corp East Fishkill Facil Dept 206 Bldg 300-48A Hopewell Junction NY 12533

SCHWARTZ, HAROLD LEON, b Brooklyn, NY, Mar 14, 33; m 56; c 3. ENDOCRINOLOGY, BIOCHEMISTRY. *Educ:* Brooklyn Col, BS, 57; NY Univ, MS, 61, PhD(physiol), 64. *Prof Exp:* Res assoc med, State Univ NY Downstate Med Ctr, 57-64, instr, 64-66; biochemist, Endocrine Res Lab, Montefiore Hosp & Med Ctr & asst prof biochem, Albert Einstein Col Med, 67-76; ASSOC PROF MED, UNIV MINN COL MED, 76-, ASSOC DIR, DIV ENDOCRINOL & METAB, DEPT MED, 81- *Concurrent Pos:* USPHS fel, Nat Inst Med Res, London, Eng, 66-67. *Mem:* AAAS; NY Acad Sci; Am Thyroid Asn; Endocrine Soc. *Res:* Thyroid hormone biosynthesis and metabolism; mechanisms of hormone action; chemistry of thyroid proteins. *Mailing Add:* Univ of Minn Col of Med Mayo Bldg Minneapolis MN 55455

SCHWARTZ, HEINZ (GEORG), b Landsberg, Ger, Jan 15, 24; US citizen; m 50; c 1. PATHOLOGY. *Educ:* Rutgers Univ, New Brunswick, BS, 53, PhD(biochem), 57; Temple Univ, MD, 61. *Prof Exp:* Res asst biochem, Merck Inst Therapeut Res, Rahway, 50-57; intern, Abington Hosp, Pa, 61-62; resident path, Temple Univ Hosp, 62-65, instr, 65-66; asst prof & assoc dir, 66-70, assoc prof path & assoc dir clin labs, 70-78, PROF PATH & DIR CLIN LABS, THOMAS JEFFERSON UNIV HOSP, 78- *Concurrent Pos:* Consult, Vet Admin Hosp, Coatesville, 67- & Children's Heart Hosp, 78- *Mem:* AMA; Am Asn Clin Path; Am Asn Clin Chem; Col Am Path. *Res:* Lipid analysis; immunoglobuline analysis. *Mailing Add:* Dept of Path Clin Labs Thomas Jefferson Univ Hosp Philadelphia PA 19107

SCHWARTZ, HENRY GERARD, JR, b St Louis, Mo, Aug 3, 38; m 60; c 2. ENVIRONMENTAL HEALTH ENGINEERING. *Educ:* Wash Univ, St Louis, BS, 61, MS, 62; Calif Inst Technol, PhD(environ health eng), 66. *Prof Exp:* Res fel environ health eng, Calif Inst Technol, 65-66; sr engr, 66-76, vpres & mgr, Environ Div, Sverdrup & Pracel & Assoc, Inc, 76-80, VPRES,

PRIN CORP, SVERDRUP CORP, 78- *Concurrent Pos:* Mgt adv group, US Environ Protection Agency, 81- *Honors & Awards:* Edward Bartow Award, Am Chem Soc, 66. *Mem:* Nat Soc Prof Engrs; Am Soc Civil Engrs; Am Acad Environ Engrs; Water Pollution Control Fedn; Air Pollution Control Asn. *Res:* Adsorption and microbial degradation of pesticides in aqueous solutions; water recovery and reuse in space vehicles; water and air pollution control. *Mailing Add:* 10 Deerfield Rd St Louis MO 63124

SCHWARTZ, HERBERT, b Limerick, Pa, Mar 8, 25; m 58; c 2. ORGANIC & BIOLOGICAL CHEMISTRY. *Educ:* Univ Freiburg, Ger, dipl, 55; Univ Utrecht, PhD(chem), 65. *Prof Exp:* Res chemist, Vineland Chem Co, 55-57; chemist anal chem, Food & Drug Admin, Washington, DC, 57-58; chemist biochem, Grad Hosp, Philadelphia, 58-59; res assoc, Inst Org Chem, Univ Utrecht, 59-65; R & D CONSULT CHEM, BIOVIVAN RES INST, 63- *Concurrent Pos:* Adj prof chem, Cumberland County Col, 69-75 & Camden County Col, 77-78. *Mem:* Am Chem Soc; AAAS. *Res:* Biologically active chemistry; investigation into biochemically induced human interactions based upon chronobiology and sociobiology; environmental chemistry; synthetic plant hormones. *Mailing Add:* Biovivan Res Inst PO Box 266 Vineland NJ 08360

SCHWARTZ, HERBERT C, b New Haven, Conn, May 8, 26; m 58; c 3. MEDICINE, PEDIATRICS. *Educ:* Yale Univ, AB, 48; State Univ NY, MD, 52. *Prof Exp:* Intern med, Vet Admin Hosp, Newington, Conn, 52-53, intern pediat, Grace-New Haven Community Hosp, 53; med resident, Univ Serv, Kings County Hosp, 53-54 & Stanford Univ Hosp, 54-55; instr, Univ Utah, 58-60; from asst prof to assoc prof, 60-68, chmn dept, 69-71, PROF PEDIAT, SCH MED, STANFORD UNIV, 68- *Concurrent Pos:* Clin & res fel med, Univ Utah, 55-56, res fel, 56-57, res fel biochem, 57-58; Markle scholar acad med, 62. *Mem:* Am Fedn Clin Res; Soc Pediat Res; Am Soc Clin Invest; Am Pediat Soc; Am Soc Hemat. *Res:* Hemoglobin structure and synthesis in mammalian erythrocytes; effects of pregnancy on hemoglobin AIc in diabetic women; structure and function relationship of hemoglobins in deep diving mammals. *Mailing Add:* Dept of Pediat Stanford Univ Sch of Med Stanford CA 94305

SCHWARTZ, HOWARD JULIUS, b New York, NY, Nov 24, 36; m 62; c 3. MEDICINE, ALLERGY. *Educ:* Brooklyn Col, BA, 56; Albert Einstein Col Med, MD, 60. *Prof Exp:* Res fel, Harvard Med Sch, 66-68; USPHS trainee, 68-71, asst prof, 71-74, asst clin prof, 74-77, ASSOC CLIN PROF MED, SCH MED, CASE WESTERN RESERVE UNIV, 77- *Concurrent Pos:* Clin res fel allergy & immunol, Mass Gen Hosp, 66-68; assoc physician, Univ Hosps, Cleveland, 71-, chief allergy clin, 72-; consult, Hillcrest Hosp, Cleveland & Mt Sinai Hosp, Cleveland; chmn, Comt Insects, Am Acad Allergy. *Mem:* Am Asn Immunologists; fel Am Acad Allergy; fel Am Col Chest Physicians; Am Thoracic Soc. *Res:* Allergic respiratory disease, including the interaction of rhinitis and asthma; insect allergy- bee, wasp, hornet and yellow jacket; immunology. *Mailing Add:* 3609 Park East Cleveland OH 44122

SCHWARTZ, ILSA ROSLOW, b Brooklyn, NY, Aug 20, 41; m 64; c 2. NEUROANATOMY, AUDITORY SYSTEM. *Educ:* Vassar Col, AB, 62; Yale Univ, MS, 64, PhD(molecular biophys), 68. *Prof Exp:* Res assoc, Ctr Neural Sci, Ind Univ, Bloomington, 70-73, asst prof anat & physiol, 73-77; asst prof, 77-81, ASSOC PROF SURG IN RESIDENCE, DIV HEAD & NECK SURG, SCH MED, UNIV CALIF, LOS ANGELES, 81- *Concurrent Pos:* NIH fel & res fel neuroanat, Albert Einstein Col Med, 68-69; USPHS biomed sci res support grant, Ind Univ, Bloomington, 70-72, NIH res grants, 72-81; vis res anatomist, Sch Med, Univ Calif, Los Angeles, 76-77. *Mem:* AAAS; Am Asn Anat; Asn Res Otolaryngol; Soc Neurosci. *Res:* Synaptic organization; synaptic development; structural and functional correlations of auditory and vestibular neural activity; autoradiographic studies of chemical properties of neurons in the auditory system. *Mailing Add:* 6617 Maryland Dr Los Angeles CA 90048

SCHWARTZ, IRA, b New York, NY, May 16, 47; m 68; c 3. BIOCHEMISTRY, MOLECULAR BIOLOGY. *Educ:* City Univ New York, BS, 68, PhD(biochem), 73. *Prof Exp:* Lectr, Dept Chem, City Col New York, 68-73; fel, Roche Inst Molecular Biol, 73-75; asst prof biochem, Univ Mass, 75-80; ASST PROF BIOCHEM, NY MED COL, 80- *Mem:* AAAS; Am Chem Soc. *Res:* Identification of the ribosomal components necessary for binding of tRNA, mRNA and nonribosomal protein factors; study of regulation of expression of genes for proteins involved in translation; molecular cloning. *Mailing Add:* Dept of Biochem NY Med Col Valhalla NY 10595

SCHWARTZ, IRA A(RTHUR), b Brooklyn, NY, Mar 8, 15; m 56; c 2. METALLURGY. *Educ:* City Col New York, BS, BME, 42; Stevens Inst Technol, MS, 50. *Prof Exp:* Sr eng draftsman, Hull Design Div, NY Naval Shipyard, US Dept Army, 42-46, metallurgist, Mat Lab, 46-52, supvry metallurgist, 52-58, head, Wrought Metals & Radiographic Sect, 58-63, sr task leader, Naval Appl Sci Lab, 63-65, gen metallurgist, Off Chief Engrs, 65-80, res coordr metall & civil eng probs, 69-80; CONSULT WELDING METALL & NON-DESTRUCTIVE TESTING, 80- *Concurrent Pos:* Metall consult, Corp Coun, NY, 59-60. *Mem:* Am Soc Metals; Am Foundrymen's Soc. *Res:* Foundry metallurgy involving casting of ferrous and nonferrous alloys by sand, shell and lost-wax methods; physical metallurgy of wrought metals, particularly heat treatment and notch-toughness; nondestructive testing radiography and ultrasonics; metallurgical failures; general metallurgical problems. *Mailing Add:* 8303 The Midway Annandale VA 22003

SCHWARTZ, IRVING LEON, b Cedarhurst, NY, Dec 25, 18; m 46; c 3. PHYSIOLOGY, MEDICINE. *Educ:* Columbia Col, AB, 39; NY Univ, MD, 43. *Prof Exp:* Intern, Third Med Div, Bellevue Hosp, New York, 43-44, asst resident, 46-47; from asst to assoc, Rockefeller Inst, 52-58; sr scientist & attend physician hosp, Med Res Ctr, Brookhaven Nat Lab, 58-61; prof physiol & chmn dept, Col Med, Univ Cincinnati, 61-65; prof physiol & biophys, chmn dept physiol & dean grad sch biol sci, 65-80, GOLDEN & HAROLD LAMPORT DISTINGUISHED SERV PROF-AT-LARGE & DIR CTR POLYPEPTIDE & MEMBRANE RES, MT SINAI SCH MED, 80- *Concurrent Pos:* NIH fel, Col Med, NY Univ, 47-50; Porter fel, Rockefeller Inst, 50-51, Am Heart Asn fel, 51-52; from asst physician to assoc physician, Rockefeller Hosp Inst, 52-58; res collabr, Med Res Ctr, Brookhaven Nat Lab, 61-; exec officer, Biomed Sci Doctoral Prog, City Univ New York, 68-70. *Mem:* Am Physiol Soc; Soc Exp Biol & Med; Harvey Soc; Biophys Soc; Am Fedn Clin Res. *Res:* Membrane and transport phenomena; mechanism of hormone action; conformation-structure-activity relationships of peptides and proteins. *Mailing Add:* Dept Physiol Mt Sinai Sch Med 100th St & Fifth Ave New York NY 10029

SCHWARTZ, IRVING ROBERT, b New York, NY, May 7, 23; m 51; c 3. MEDICINE, HEMATOLOGY. *Educ:* NY Univ, AB, 47; State Univ NY, MD, 51. *Prof Exp:* Intern, Montefiore Hosp, Bronx, NY, 51-52; resident internal med, Bronx Vet Admin Hosp, 52-53 & Ohio State Univ Hosp, Columbus, 53-54; resident hemat, Cardeza Found, Jefferson Med Col, 54-55; asst dir, Sacks Dept Hemat, Albert Einstein Med Ctr, 58-74; asst prof, 65-73, ASSOC PROF MED, TEMPLE UNIV, 73-; dir sacks dept hemat, 74-80, HEAD, DIV HEMAT, ALBERT EINSTEIN MED CTR, 80- *Concurrent Pos:* USPHS res fel, Jefferson Med Col, 55-57; Sacks res fel, Albert Einstein Med Ctr, 57-58. *Mem:* Am Soc Hemat; AMA; Am Col Physicians; Transplantation Soc; NY Acad Sci. *Res:* Cancer chemotherapy; bone marrow transplantation; radiation effects; hemoglobinopathies; leukoagglutinins; bone marrow preservation. *Mailing Add:* 408 Upland Rd Elkins Park PA 19117

SCHWARTZ, JACK, b New York, NY, May 4, 31; m 57; c 2. ENGINEERING PHYSICS. *Educ:* City Col NY, BS, 53; Harvard Univ, AM, 54, PhD(physics), 58. *Prof Exp:* Res assoc, Brookhaven Nat Lab, 57-60; mem tech staff, RCA Labs, David Sarnoff Res Ctr, NJ, 60-64; MEM TECH STAFF, SANDERS ASSOCS, INC, 64- *Mem:* Am Phys Soc; NY Acad Sci; Sigma Xi. *Res:* Scientific applications of lasers; nonlinear optics; magnetic resonance phenomena; magnetism in thin ferromagnetic films; atomic beams; system analysis; operations research; solar energy; conversion of radiation to mechanical energy; finite element computation applied to heat transfer problems; computer modeling of radar systems. *Mailing Add:* Defensive Systs Div Sanders Assocs Inc 95 Canal St Nashua NH 03060

SCHWARTZ, JACOB THEODORE, b New York, NY, Jan 9, 30; m 50; c 2. MATHEMATICS. *Educ:* City Col New York, BS, 48; Yale Univ, MA, 49, PhD, 51. *Prof Exp:* From instr to asst prof math, Yale Univ, 52-57; assoc prof, 57-59, PROF MATH & COMPUT SCI, COURANT INST MATH SCI, NY UNIV, 59- *Mem:* Nat Acad Sci. *Res:* Physics and functional analysis; physical mathematics; probability. *Mailing Add:* Dept Math NY Univ New York NY 10003

SCHWARTZ, JAMES F, b Milwaukee, Wis, Oct 28, 29; m 56; c 3. PEDIATRICS, NEUROLOGY. *Educ:* Swarthmore Col, BA, 51; Rochester Univ, MD, 55. *Prof Exp:* From asst prof to assoc prof, 63-70, PROF PEDIAT, SCH MED, EMORY UNIV, 70-, PROF NEUROL, 75- *Concurrent Pos:* Nat Inst Neurol Dis & Blindness spec fel pediat neurol, Columbia-Presby Med Ctr, 60-63. *Mem:* Fel Am Acad Pediat; fel Am Acad Neurol; Am Neurol Asn; Child Neurol Soc (pres, 75-76); Am Pediat Soc. *Res:* Neurological aspects of development; muscle and convulsive disorders in infancy and childhood. *Mailing Add:* Dept of Pediat Emory Univ Sch of Med Atlanta GA 30303

SCHWARTZ, JAY W(ILLIAM), b Scranton, Pa, Sept 28, 34; m 70; c 2. ELECTRICAL ENGINEERING. *Educ:* Univ Pa, BS, 56; Yale Univ, MEng, 60, PhD(elec eng), 64. *Prof Exp:* Mem tech staff, Res & Eng Support Div, Inst Defense Anal, 63-67; vis assoc prof elec eng, Polytech Inst Brooklyn, 67-68; mech tech staff, Sci & Tech Div, Inst Defense Anal, Va, 68-72; CONSULT TO ASSOC DIR RES SPACE & COMMUN SCI & TECHNOL, NAVAL RES LAB, 72- *Concurrent Pos:* Mem ad hoc sci group, Tactical Satellite Commun, 67-68; chmn optical commun working group, Navy Laser Technol Prog Off, 72-; mem, Mil Man in Space Panel, 78- *Mem:* Inst Elec & Electronics Engrs. *Res:* Communication satellite systems; military communications; data processing in space vehicles; communication theory; military space systems. *Mailing Add:* Naval Res Lab Code 7005 Washington DC 20375

SCHWARTZ, JEFFREY, b New York, NY, Jan 3, 45; m 70. ORGANOMETALLIC CHEMISTRY. *Educ:* Mass Inst Technol, SB, 66; Stanford Univ, PhD(chem), 70. *Prof Exp:* NIH fel, Columbia Univ, 70; ASST PROF CHEM, PRINCETON UNIV, 70- *Mem:* Am Chem Soc; Royal Soc Chem. *Res:* Applications of organometallic chemistry to organic synthesis; novel organometallic complexes; intramolecular organometallic redox reactions. *Mailing Add:* Dept of Chem Princeton Univ Princeton NJ 08540

SCHWARTZ, JEFFREY H, b Richmond, Va, Mar 6, 48. EVOLUTIONARY BIOLOGY, PHYSICAL ANTHROPOLOGY. *Educ:* Columbia Univ, BA, 69, MS, 73, PhD(phys anthrop), 74. *Prof Exp:* Adj lectr, Lehman Col, 73-74; ASST PROF PHYS ANTHROP, UNIV PITTSBURGH, 74- *Concurrent Pos:* Staff osteologist, Am Sch Oriental Res, 70-; res assoc, Carnegie Mus Natural Hist, 76- *Mem:* Am Asn Phys Anthrop; AAAS; Soc Syst Zool; Soc Vert Paleont. *Res:* Evolutionary theory and systematics; primate phylogeny and paleontology; human and faunal remains of the circum-Mediterranean and Near East; general physical anthropology and vertebrate paleontology. *Mailing Add:* Dept of Anthrop Univ of Pittsburgh Pittsburgh PA 15260

SCHWARTZ, JEFFREY LEE, b Far Rockaway, NY, Aug 19, 43. MICROBIAL BIOCHEMISTRY. *Educ:* Brooklyn Col Pharm, BS, 66; Univ Wis-Madison, MS, 68, PHD(pharm biochem), 71. *Prof Exp:* Res fel microbial biochem, Wesleyan Univ, 71-73; res fel, 73-74, RES INVESTR MICROBIAL BIOCHEM, SQUIBB INST MED RES, 74- *Mem:* Am Soc Microbiol; Am Chem Soc. *Res:* Investigating the production of new antibiotics from various microorganisms and the development of novel and sensitive methods for antibiotic detection. *Mailing Add:* Squibb Inst for Med Res PO Box 4000 Princeton NJ 08540

SCHWARTZ, JEROME LAWRENCE, b Birmingham, Ala, July 4, 38; m 64; c 2. CHEMISTRY. *Educ:* Univ SC, BS, 61, MS, 64; Univ Del, PhD(phys-org chem), 70. *Prof Exp:* Chemist polymer chem, 63-65, res chemist photog chem, 68-71, mkt rep clin instrumentation, 71-73, appl lab supvr clin chem, 73-75, mgr tech serv clin chem instrumentation, 76-78, SR methods res supvr, 78-79, RES & DEVELOP MGR, E I DU PONT DE NEMOURS & CO INC, 79- *Res:* Development of instrumentation and methodology for the automation of clinical chemistry tests. *Mailing Add:* Glasgow Site-Bldg 100 Clin Systs Div-Du Pont Co Wilmington DE 19898

SCHWARTZ, JOAN POYNER, b Ont, Can, Aug 19, 43; m 67. NEOROBIOLOGY, NEUROPHARMACOLOGY. *Educ:* Cornell Univ, AB, 65; Harvard Univ, PhD(biol chem), 71. *Prof Exp:* Instr pharmacol, Dept Pharm, Rutgers Med Sch, 70-71; staff fel, Lab Neuroanat & Neurosci, Nat Inst Neurol & Commun Disorders & Stroke, 72-76; RES CHEMIST, LAB PRECLIN PHARM, NAT INST MENTAL HEALTH, 76- *Mem:* Am Soc Pharmaceut & Exp Therapeut; Soc Neurosci; Am Soc Neurochem; AAAS. *Res:* Nerve growth factor: regulation of synthesis and mechanism of actions; catecholamine-mediated regulation of gene expression via cyclic adenosine monophosphate levels. *Mailing Add:* White Bldg Lab Preclin Pharm Nat Inst Mental Health St Elizabeths Hosp Washington DC 20032

SCHWARTZ, JOHN T, b Hazelton, Pa, Aug 28, 26; m 56; c 6. OPHTHALMOLOGY, EPIDEMIOLOGY. *Educ:* Dartmouth Col, AB, 47; Univ Notre Dame, MS, 50; Jefferson Med Col, MD, 55; Harvard Univ, MPH, 63. *Prof Exp:* Intern med, Madison Gen Hosp, 55-56; head dept ophthal, Naval Base Dispensary, Norfolk, Va, 59-61; asst prof, Sch Med, Univ Mo-Columbia, 61-62; head sect ophthal field & develop res, Nat Inst Neurol Dis & Blindness, 63-68; dep chief dept ophthal, USPHS Hosp, Baltimore, 68-69; head sect ophthal field & develop res, Nat Eye Inst, 69-75; spec asst to dir, Div Hosp & Clin & chief, Dept Ophthal, 76-79, ASSOC DIR MED AFFAIRS, BUR MED SERV, HEALTH SERV ADMIN, USPHS, 81- *Concurrent Pos:* Clin asst prof ophthal, Sch Med, Univ Mo, 63-64; asst clin prof, George Washington Univ, 65-73; consult ophthal, USPHS Hosp, Baltimore, 69-; Nat Health Exam Surv, Nat Ctr Health Statist, 69-; guest worker, Geront Res Ctr, Nat Inst Aging, 79-80; consult ophthalmoepidemiol, Bur Med Devices, Food & Drug Admin, 80-81. *Mem:* Am Acad Ophthal; AMA; Int Soc Twin Studies; Am Eye Study Club; Soc Epidemiol Res. *Res:* Epidemiologic and genetic investigations of etiology of ocular disorders. *Mailing Add:* 18000 Marden Lane Sandy Spring MD 20860

SCHWARTZ, JOSEPH A, b New York, NY, Jan 3, 38. HIGH ENERGY PHYSICS, BIOPHYSICS. *Educ:* Univ Calif, Berkeley, AB, 59, PhD(physics), 64. *Prof Exp:* Res assoc physics, Lawrence Radiation Lab, 64; field worker, Student Non-Violent Coord Comt, 64-65; fel biol & biophys, Col Physicians & Surgeons, Columbia Univ, 65-67; assoc prof physics, Richmond Col, NY, 67-76; ASSOC PROF PHYSICS, COL STATEN ISLAND, 76- *Concurrent Pos:* Consult, interdisciplinary prog res & training in biol sci, Col Physicians & Surgeons, Columbia Univ, 67-68. *Mem:* AAAS. *Res:* Genetics and IQ; science and social control; scientific practice and social structure. *Mailing Add:* Dept of Physics Col of Staten Island Staten Island NY 10301

SCHWARTZ, JOSEPH BARRY, b Richmond, Va, June 11, 41; m 64; c 3. PHARMACEUTICAL CHEMISTRY. *Educ:* Med Col Va, BS, 63; Univ Mich, MS, 65, PhD(pharmaceut chem), 67. *Prof Exp:* Sr res pharmacist, Merck, Sharp & Dohme Res Labs, West Point, Pa, 67-72, res fel, 72-81; PROF PHARMACEUT, PHILADELPHIA COL PHARM & SCI, 81- *Mem:* AAAS; Am Pharmaceut Asn; Acad Pharmaceut Sci; Am Chem Soc. *Res:* Drug release from wax matrices; physical and chemical properties affecting drug availability; dosage from design. *Mailing Add:* Philadelphia Col Pharm & Sci 43rd St & Kingsessing Mall Philadelphia PA 19104

SCHWARTZ, JOSEPH ROBERT, b Chicago, Ill, Feb 17, 19; m 42; c 5. PHYSICAL CHEMISTRY, ORGANIC CHEMISTRY. *Educ:* Univ Chicago, BS, 41, MS & PhD(chem), 48. *Prof Exp:* Res assoc, Univ Calif, Los Angeles, 48-50 & Radioisotope Unit, Long Beach Vet Hosp, 50-53; from asst prof to assoc prof, 53-70, PROF CHEM, LOYOLA UNIV LOS ANGELES, 70-, CHMN DEPT, 74- *Mem:* AAAS; Am Chem Soc; Am Crystallog Asn. *Res:* Physical organic research; relation of mechanism to structure; color of C-nitroso compounds; determination of molecular interactions through x-ray crystallographic studies. *Mailing Add:* Dept of Chem Loyola Univ of Los Angeles Los Angeles CA 90045

SCHWARTZ, JUDAH LEON, b Brooklyn, NY, July 13, 34; m 60; c 3. SCIENCE EDUCATION. *Educ:* Yeshiva Univ, BA, 54; Columbia Univ, AM, 57; NY Univ, PhD(physics), 63. *Prof Exp:* Asst physics, Columbia Univ, 54-57; reactor physicist, Am Mach & Foundry Co, 57; instr physics, Israel Inst Technol, 57-58; mem tech staff weapons physics, G C Dewey Corp, 58-61; sr physicist, Autometric Corp, 61-62 & G C Dewey Corp, 62-63; instr physics, NY Univ, 61-63; fel, Lawrence Radiation Lab, 63-64; physicist, 63-66; sr res scientist, Educ Res Ctr, 66-72, PROF ENGR SCI & EDUC, MASS INST TECHNOL, 73- *Concurrent Pos:* Consult Sci, Tech & World Affairs Prog, Carnegie Endowment for Int Peace, 63- & For Serv Inst, Dept State Educ Develop Ctr; assoc ed, Am J Physics, 72-; assoc ed, Int J Math Educ, 72-; hon res assoc, Dept Psychol, Harvard Univ, 74-75. *Mem:* AAAS; Am Phys Soc; Am Soc Engr Educ; Am Asn Physics Teachers. *Res:* Science and mathematics education; computer graphics; computer generated films; cognitive psychology and the development of mathematical competence in children. *Mailing Add:* Sch of Engr Mass Inst Technol Cambridge MA 02139

SCHWARTZ, LARRY LEE, b Fremont, Ohio, July 24, 35; m 69; c 2. PHYSICAL CHEMISTRY. *Educ:* Case Western Reserve Univ, AB, 57, MS, 59, PhD(phys chem), 63. *Prof Exp:* Res assoc nuclear chem, Argonne Nat Lab, 62-64; chemist, 64-76, DEP DIV LEADER EARTH SCI DIV NUCLEAR CHEMIST, LAWRENCE LIVERMORE LAB, 76- *Mem:* AAAS. *Res:* Chemical and radiochemical effects of nuclear explosions; radioactive waste disposal. *Mailing Add:* PO Box 808 Livermore CA 94550

SCHWARTZ, LEANDER JOSEPH, b Newton, Wis, Jan 10, 32; m 64; c 2. MICROBIOLOGY. *Educ:* Wis State Univ, Platteville, BS, 57; Univ Wis, MS, 59, PhD(plant physiol), 63. *Prof Exp:* Asst prof bot, Fox Valley Ctr, Univ Wis, 63-69, dean, 69-72; ASSOC PROF ENVIRON SCI, UNIV WIS-GREEN BAY, 69-, CHMN DEPT BIOL, 72-75. *Mem:* AAAS; Bot Soc Am; Am Inst Biol Sci; Am Soc Microbiol. *Res:* Aquatic microbiology; resource recovery; anaerobic digestion of high strength liquid waste streams using upflow reactors; application of sludges on agricultural lands. *Mailing Add:* Col of Environ Sci Univ Wis Green Bay WI 54302

SCHWARTZ, LELAND DWIGHT, b Enid, Okla, July 26, 25; m 54; c 3. POULTRY PATHOLOGY. *Educ:* Okla State Univ, DVM, 53; Univ Ga, MS, 63. *Prof Exp:* Vet, pvt pract, 53-55; vet, Hartsel Ranch, 55-56; inspection livestock, Animal & Plant Health Insepction Serv, USDA, 56-59 & poultry, 59-61; instr avian path, Univ Ga, 61-64; VET, EXTEN, PA STATE UNIV, 64- *Mem:* Sigma Xi; Am Vet Med Asn; Am Asn Avian Pathologists. *Res:* Unidentified viral infections of commercial chickens. *Mailing Add:* 115 Animal Indust Bldg Pa State Univ University Park PA 16802

SCHWARTZ, LEON JOSEPH, b New York, NY, Jan 28, 43; m 67; c 2. MATERIALS SCIENCE. *Educ:* City Col New York, BEng, 64; City Univ New York, MEng, 66, PhD(metall), 70. *Prof Exp:* Chemist, Photoconductors, 70-74, MATS SCIENTIST, PITNEY-BOWES, INC, STAMFORD, CONN, 74- *Mem:* Electrochem Soc; Soc Photog Scientists & Engrs. *Res:* Materials research on a phenomenalogical level; inorganics, especially metals, semiconductors, ceramics, intermetallic compounds; solid state diffusion and photoconductivity; materials, electronic, paper; graphic arts; design of experiments, human factors. *Mailing Add:* 30 Briarcliff Dr Monsey NY 10952

SCHWARTZ, LEONARD H, b New York, NY, Nov 25, 32; m 59; c 3. CHEMISTRY. *Educ:* City Col New York, BS, 54; NY Univ, PhD(chem), 61. *Prof Exp:* From asst prof to assoc prof, 63-71, PROF CHEM, CITY COL NY, 71- *Concurrent Pos:* Exec officer, PhD Prog chem, City Univ New York, 71-78. *Mem:* Am Chem Soc; Royal Soc Chem. *Res:* Organic chemistry. *Mailing Add:* Dept of Chem City Col of New York New York NY 10031

SCHWARTZ, LOWELL MELVIN, b Brooklyn, NY, Dec 1, 34. PHYSICAL CHEMISTRY. *Educ:* Mass Inst Technol, SB, 56, ScD(chem eng), 59; Calif Inst Technol, MS, 57. *Prof Exp:* Chem engr, Dept Appl Physics, Chr Michelsens Inst, Norway, 59-60 & Esso Res & Eng Co, Standard Oil Co NJ, 60-61; res assoc chem, Princeton Univ, 62-63; res instr, Dartmouth Col, 63-65; from asst prof to assoc prof chem, 65-76, PROF CHEM, UNIV MASS, BOSTON, 76- *Mem:* Royal Soc Chem. *Res:* Physical properties of oxocarbon complexation chemistry of cyclohexaamy loses statistical treatment of data. *Mailing Add:* Dept of Chem Univ of Mass Boston MA 02125

SCHWARTZ, LYLE H, b Chicago, Ill, Aug 2, 36; div; c 2. MATERIALS SCIENCE. *Educ:* Northwestern Univ, BSc, 59, PhD(mat sci), 64. *Prof Exp:* From asst prof to assoc prof, 64-72, asst chmn, Dept of Mat Sci & Eng, 73-78, PROF MAT SCI, NORTHWESTERN UNIV, EVANSTON, 72-, DIR, MAT RES CTR, 79- *Concurrent Pos:* Consult, Solid State Sci Div, Argonne Nat Lab, 66-; visitor, Bell Tel Labs, 72-73; mem, Nat Res Coun panel to select NSF doctoral fels in eng, 74-77, chmn, 76 & 77. *Mem:* Am Phys Soc; Mat Res Soc; Am Crystallog Asn; Am Inst Mining, Metall & Petrol Engrs; Am Soc Metall. *Res:* X-ray and neutron diffraction; Mossbauer effect; spinodal alloys; alloy catalysts. *Mailing Add:* Dept of Mat Sci Technol Inst Northwestern Univ Evanston IL 60201

SCHWARTZ, M(URRAY) A(RTHUR), b New York, NY, Nov 13, 20; m 44; c 2. CERAMIC ENGINEERING. *Educ:* Alfred Univ, BS, 43. *Prof Exp:* Ceramic engr, Bendix Aviation Corp, 43-44; Streator Drain Tile Co, 46-47, Fairchild Engine & Airplane Corp, 47-51 & Oak Ridge Nat Lab, 51; supvr ceramics, Aeronaut Res Lab, US Dept Air Force, 51-59; mgr, Aeronutronic Div, Ford Motor Co, 59-60; mat appln, United Tech Ctr, United Aircraft Corp, 60-65; asst dir ceramics div, Ill Inst Technol Res Inst, 65-71; coord engr, Dept Pub Works, Chicago, 71-72; supvr nonmetallic mat res, Tuscaloosa Res Lab, 72-74, staff ceramic eng, 74-80, PROG MGR, US BUR MINES, 80- *Concurrent Pos:* Exec secy, Interagency Comt Mat, 75-79; ed, News From Washington, Bulletin Am Ceramic Soc, 76- *Honors & Awards:* US Air Force sustained superior performance award, 58. *Mem:* Fedn Mats Soc; fel Am Ceramic Soc (vpres, 81-82); fel Am Inst Chem; Am Soc Metals; Am Inst Ceramic Engrs. *Res:* Nonmetallic materials; recycling of waste materials; utilization of mineral resources; industrial ceramics; new materials; basic behavior; refractories; whitewares; glass; aerospace, nuclear and electronic applications; environmental quality; energy conservation. *Mailing Add:* US Dept of Interior Bur of Mines 2401 E St NW Washington DC 20241

SCHWARTZ, MARTIN, b Worcester, Mass, Nov 23, 25; m 53; c 1. PLANT PHYSIOLOGY, BIOCHEMISTRY. *Educ:* Johns Hopkins Univ, AB, 49, MS, 51; Univ Wis, PhD, 52. *Prof Exp:* Vis investr, Kaiser Wilhelm Inst Cell Physiol, Berlin, 52-53; res assoc, NY Univ, 53-54; USPHS fel, Inst Phys-Chem Biol, Paris, France, 54-56; asst prof biol, Univ Chicago, 57-60 & Univ Pa, 60-64; mem res staff, Res Inst Advan Study, 64-69; PROF BIOL SCI & CHMN BIOL SCI, UNIV MD, BALTIMORE COUNTY, 69- *Mem:* AAAS; fel Am Soc Plant Physiologists; Am Soc Biol Chemists; Biophys Soc. *Res:* Photosynthesis; bioenergetics. *Mailing Add:* Dept of Biol Sci Univ of Md Baltimore County Catonsville MD 21228

SCHWARTZ, MARTIN ALAN, b New York, NY, July 5, 40; m 61; c 3. ORGANIC CHEMISTRY. *Educ:* Dartmouth Col, AB, 62; Stanford Univ, PhD(org chem), 66. *Prof Exp:* From asst prof to assoc prof chem, 66-76, PROF CHEM, FLA STATE UNIV, 76-, CHMN DEPT, 77- *Concurrent Pos:* Sr ed, J Org Chem, Am Chem Soc, 71- *Mem:* Am Chem Soc. *Res:* Synthesis of natural products. *Mailing Add:* Dept of Chem Fla State Univ Tallahassee FL 32306

SCHWARTZ, MAURICE EDWARD, b Laurinburg, NC, Sept 28, 39; m 65; c 2. THEORETICAL CHEMISTRY. *Educ:* Presby Col (SC), BS, 61; Vanderbilt Univ, PhD(chem), 66. *Prof Exp:* NSF & Ramsey fels, Oxford Univ, 66; res fel, Princeton Univ, 67-68; asst prof & sr scientist, Radiation Lab, 68-73, ASSOC PROF CHEM, UNIV NOTRE DAME, 73- *Concurrent Pos:* Vis prof, Univ Calif, Berkeley, 72; NATO sr fel sci, Univ Uppsala, Sweden & Oxford Univ, England, 73; assoc prog dir quantum chem, NSF, 76-77. *Mem:* Am Chem Soc; Am Phys Soc; Am Asn Univ Profs. *Res:* Quantum chemistry; photoelectron spectroscopy; radiation chemistry; surface chemistry and catalysis. *Mailing Add:* Dept of Chem Univ of Notre Dame Notre Dame IN 46556

SCHWARTZ, MAURICE LEO, b Ft Worth, Tex, Sept 27, 25; m 50; c 5. GEOLOGICAL OCEANOGRAPHY, SCIENCE EDUCATION. *Educ:* Columbia Univ, BA, 63, MS, 64, PhD(geol), 66. *Prof Exp:* Lab instr geol, Columbia Univ, 63-66; lectr, Brooklyn Col, 64-68; from asst prof to assoc prof geol & educ, 68-75, PROF GEOL & EDUC, WESTERN WASH UNIV, 75-; PRES, COASTAL CONSULT, INC, 81- *Concurrent Pos:* Fulbright-Hayes res scholar, Inst Oceanog & Fishing Res, Athens, Greece, 73-74; Nat Acad Sci specialist exchange prog visit to USSR, 78. *Mem:* Geol Soc Am; Nat Asn Geol Teachers; Am Asn Univ Profs; The Coastal Soc; Am Shore & Beach Preservation Asn. *Res:* Beach processes; sea level changes; tidal cycle sedimentation; geologic models; earth science education; raised and submerged terraces; archeology; barrier islands; beach cusps. *Mailing Add:* Dept Geol Western Wash Univ Bellingham WA 98225

SCHWARTZ, MELVIN, b New York, NY, Nov 2, 32; m 53; c 3. PHYSICS. *Educ:* Columbia Univ, AB, 53, PhD(physics), 58. *Prof Exp:* Res assoc, Brookhaven Nat Lab, 56-57, assoc physicist, 57-58; from asst prof to prof physics, Columbia Univ, 58-66; PROF PHYSICS, STANFORD UNIV, 66- *Concurrent Pos:* Sloan fel, 59-63; Guggenheim fel, Guggenheim Found, 68. *Honors & Awards:* Prize, Am Phys Soc, 64. *Mem:* Nat Acad Sci; fel, Am Phys Soc. *Res:* High energy experimental particle physics. *Mailing Add:* Dept of Physics Stanford Univ Stanford CA 94305

SCHWARTZ, MELVIN J, b Brooklyn, NY, Oct 8, 28; m 52; c 2. THEORETICAL PHYSICS. *Educ:* Brooklyn Col, BS, 51; State Univ Iowa, PhD(physics), 58. *Prof Exp:* Instr physics, Univ Minn, 57-59; res assoc, Rutgers Univ, 56-57; lectr, Univ Minn, 57-59; res assoc, Syracuse Univ, 59-61; assoc prof, Adelphi Univ, 61-64; res scientist, NY Univ, 64-66; ASSOC PROF PHYSICS, ST JOHN'S UNIV, NY, 66- *Concurrent Pos:* Nat Sci Found res grant, 61-64; NASA res grant, 64-66. *Mem:* AAAS; Am Phys Soc; NY Acad Sci. *Res:* Quantum field theory; correspondence principle quantization of electrodynamics; collisionless plasmas; general relativistic kinetic theory of plasmas; social effects of science. *Mailing Add:* Dept of Physics St John's Univ Jamaica NY 11432

SCHWARTZ, MICHAEL AVERILL, b New York, NY, Aug 4, 30; m 54; c 2. PHARMACEUTICAL CHEMISTRY. *Educ:* Brooklyn Col Pharm, BS, 52; Columbia Univ, MS, 56; Univ Wis, PhD(pharm), 59. *Prof Exp:* Sr res scientist prod develop, Bristol Labs, Inc, 59-63; from asst prof to prof, State Univ NY, Buffalo, 63-78, 63-70, asst dean, 66-70, dean, Sch Pharm, 70-76; PROF PHARM & DEAN COL, UNIV FLA, 78- *Concurrent Pos:* USPHS grant, 64-69. *Mem:* fel AAAS; Am Pharmaceut Asn; fel Acad Pharmaceut Sci; Am Chem Soc; Am Soc Hosp Pharmacol. *Res:* Pharmaceutics; chemistry of penicillins and drug allergy; models for enzymes; drug stability. *Mailing Add:* J Hillis Miller Health Ctr Univ of Fla Box J-4 Gainesville FL 32610

SCHWARTZ, MICHAEL MUNI, b Chicago, Ill, Aug 30, 43; m 70; c 1. INDUSTRIAL CHEMISTRY. *Educ:* Northwestern Univ, BA, 64; Fla State Univ, MS, 67, PhD(org chem), 70. *Prof Exp:* RES CHEMIST, AMOCO CHEM CO, 70- *Mem:* Am Chem Soc. *Mailing Add:* 1141 Monticello Dr Aurora IL 60506

SCHWARTZ, MISCHA, b New York, NY, Sept 21, 26; m 57, 70; c 1. COMPUTER COMMUNICATIONS, DIGITAL COMMUNICATIONS. *Educ:* Cooper Union, BEE, 47; Polytech Inst Brooklyn, MEE, 49; Harvard Univ, PhD(appl physics), 51. *Prof Exp:* Asst proj engr, Sperry Gyroscope Co, 47-49, proj engr, 49-52; from asst prof to prof elec eng, Polytech Inst Brooklyn, 52-74, head dept, 61-65; PROF ELEC ENG & COMPUT SCI, COLUMBIA UNIV, 74- *Concurrent Pos:* NSF sci fac fel, Ecole Normale Superieure, Paris, 65-66; consult, Montefiore Hosp, 55-56; indust consult; mem, US Nat Comt, Int Union Radio Sci, 78-81; vis scientist, IBM Res, 80; Nippon Tel & Tel, 81. *Mem:* Fel AAAS; Asn Comput Mach; fel Inst Elec & Electronics Engrs; Sigma Xi; Am Asn Univ Professors. *Res:* Communication theory; computer communications; signal processing. *Mailing Add:* Dept Elec Eng Columbia Univ 1322 SW Mudd New York NY 10027

SCHWARTZ, MORTON ALLEN, b Brooklyn, NY, Mar 12, 28; m 62. DRUG METABOLISM. *Educ:* City Col, NY, BS, 50; Univ Wis, MS, 52, PhD(biochem), 54. *Prof Exp:* Biochemist, Path Dept, Mercy Hosp, Pittsburgh, 54-56; res fel biophys, Sloan-Kettering Inst, 56-58; asst dir, Drug Metab Lab, 58-71, head sect drug disposition, 71-74, asst dir, 74-79, ASSOC DIR, DEPT BIOCHEM & DRUG METAB, HOFFMANN-LA ROCHE INC, 80. *Mem:* Am Chem Soc; Am Soc Pharmacol & Exp Therapeut; NY Acad Sci; Acad Am Pharmaceut Asn; AAAS. *Res:* Metabolism of drugs; relationship between drug metabolism and biological activity. *Mailing Add:* Dept Biochem & Drug Metab Hoffmann-La Roche Inc Nutley NJ 07110

SCHWARTZ, MORTON DONALD, b Chicago, Ill, Oct 11, 36; m 58; c 2. COMPUTERS, INSTRUMENTATION. *Educ:* Univ Calif, Los Angeles, BS, 58, MS, 60, PhD(eng), 64. *Prof Exp:* Sr engr, NAm Aviation, 64-66; sr scientist, TRW, 66-70; PROF ELEC ENG, CALIF STATE UNIV, LONG BEACH, 70- *Concurrent Pos:* Consult, St Mary Med Ctr, Long Beach, Calif, 70-, Hughes Aircraft Co, 78-; ed, J Clin Eng, 75-; mem, Bd Dir, Am Bd Clin Engrs, 75- *Mem:* Inst Elec & Electronics Engrs; Am Soc Elec Engrs. *Res:* Computer applications in medicine including instrumentation for cardiac catheterization, pacemaker and firemen paramedic systems. *Mailing Add:* Dept Elec Eng Calif State Univ Long Beach CA 90840

SCHWARTZ, MORTON K, b Wilkes-Barre, Pa, Oct 22, 25; m 66; c 2. BIOCHEMISTRY, CLINICAL CHEMISTRY. *Educ:* Lehigh Univ, BA, 48; Boston Univ, MA, 49, PhD(biochem), 52. *Prof Exp:* From instr to assoc prof, 54-71, PROF BIOCHEM, SLOAN-KETTERING DIV, MED COL, CORNELL UNIV, 71- *Concurrent Pos:* Res fel, Sloan-Kettering Div, Med Col, Cornell Univ, 52-54; res fel, Sloan-Kettering Inst Cancer Res, 52-55; asst, Surg Metab Sect, Sloan-Kettering Inst Cancer Res, 55-56, assoc mem, Div Biochem, 57-, mem & lab head, Inst, 69-, assoc field coordr, Human Cancer, 75-81; dir clin res training, Mem Hosp for Cancer & Allied Dis, 71-81, vpres lab affairs & dep gen dir, 77-81, attend biochemist & chmn, Dept Biochem, 67- *Honors & Awards:* Van Slyke Award, Am Asn Clin Chem. *Mem:* Am Soc Biol Chemists; Am Chem Soc; Harvey Soc; Acad Clin Lab Phys & Scientists; Am Gastroenterol Asn. *Res:* Enzyme kinetics; serum enzymes; tumor associated antigens; hormone receptor; automation. *Mailing Add:* Mem Hosp for Cancer & Allied Dis 1275 York Ave New York NY 10021

SCHWARTZ, NATHAN, b Peoria, Ill, Nov 18, 22; m 45. APPLIED MATHEMATICS. *Educ:* Univ Ill, BS, 44; Cornell Univ, PhD(theoret physics), 50. *Prof Exp:* Instr physics, Cornell Univ, 50-53; physicist, Electronics Lab, Gen Elec Co, 53-65; PROF ELEC ENG, SYRACUSE UNIV, 65- *Mem:* Am Phys Soc; Inst Elec & Electronics Engrs. *Res:* Magnetic and dielectric materials; continuing engineering education; communications and control. *Mailing Add:* Dept of Elec Eng Syracuse Univ Syracuse NY 13210

SCHWARTZ, NEENA BETTY, b Baltimore, Md, Dec 10, 26. PHYSIOLOGY. *Educ:* Goucher Col, BA, 48; Northwestern Univ, MS, 50, PhD, 53. *Prof Exp:* From instr to assoc prof physiol, Col Med, Univ Ill, 53-57; dir biol lab, Inst Psychosom & Psychiat Res & Training, Michael Reese Hosp, 57-61; from assoc prof to prof physiol, Univ Ill Col Med, 61-70, prof neuroendocrinol, 70-73, asst dean, Col Med, 68-70; prof physiol, Med Sch, 73-74, prof biol & chmn dept, 74-77, DEERING PROF NEUROBIOL & PHYSIOL, NORTHWESTERN UNIV, EVANSTON, 81- *Mem:* Endocrine Soc (pres elect, 81-82); Am Physiol Soc; Soc Study Reproduction (pres, 77-78); Brit Soc Study Fertil. *Res:* Endocrinology; reproduction; environmental control of pituitary. *Mailing Add:* 1215 Chancellor St Evanston IL 60201

SCHWARTZ, NEWTON, b New York, NY, Aug 1, 25; m 49; c 2. SOLID STATE CHEMISTRY. *Educ:* City Col NY, BS, 47; Stevens Inst Technol, MS, 50; Univ Southern Calif, PhD(chem), 55. *Prof Exp:* Instr chem, Stevens Inst Technol, 47-49; res chemist, Maimonides Hosp, Brooklyn, 49-50; fel & lectr chem, Univ Southern Calif, 54-56; mem tech staff, 56-66, dept head struct anal thin film mat, 66-70, SUPVR THIN FILM MAT RES DEPT, BELL TEL LABS, INC, 70- *Concurrent Pos:* Div ed, J Electrochem Soc. *Mem:* AAAS; Am Vacuum Soc; Am Chem Soc; Electrochem Soc. *Res:* Physical organic chemistry; free radical chemistry; formation and properties of thin metallic and inorganic films. *Mailing Add:* Bell Tel Labs Murray Hill NJ 07974

SCHWARTZ, NORMAN MARTIN, b New York, NY, Nov 9, 35; m 69; c 2. BIOLOGY. *Educ:* Hunter Col, BA, 56; Syracuse Univ, MS, 59; Univ Chicago, PhD(microbiol), 63. *Prof Exp:* NIH res fel microbiol, Yale Univ, 63-64; asst prof, 64-80, ASSOC PROF BIOL, CITY COL NEW YORK, 80- *Res:* Mutagenesis; microbial genetics. *Mailing Add:* Dept of Biol City Col of New York New York NY 10031

SCHWARTZ, NORMAN VINCENT, b Toronto, Ont, Oct 6, 33; m 64; c 2. RUBBER CHEMISTRY. *Educ:* Univ Toronto, BA, 57, MA, 58, PhD(org chem), 60. *Prof Exp:* Europ Res Assocs res fel org chem, Oxford Univ, 60-61; RES CHEMIST, DUNLOP RES CTR, 62- *Mem:* Am Chem Soc; Chem Inst Can; NAm Thermal Anal Soc. *Res:* Polymer chemistry; thermal methods. *Mailing Add:* Dunlop Res Ctr Sheridan Park ON L5K 1Z8 Can

SCHWARTZ, PAUL HENRY JR, b Baltimore, Md, Dec 19, 36; m 61; c 4. ENTOMOLOGY. *Educ:* Univ Md, BS, 59, MS, 61; Univ Fla, PhD(entom), 64. *Prof Exp:* Res entomologist, Agr Res Serv, USDA, 61-64; entomologist, USPHS, 64-65; res entomologist, 65-69, asst to chief, Fruit Insects Res Br, Entom Res Div, 69-72, staff specialist, 72-73, STAFF SCIENTIST, SCI & EDUC ADMIN-AGR RES, USDA, 73- *Mem:* Entom Soc Am. *Res:* Chemical and other methods for control of insect pests. *Mailing Add:* 17600 Princess Anne Dr Olney MD 20832

SCHWARTZ, PAULINE MARY, b Philadelphia, Pa, Aug 8, 47; m 75. PHARMACOLOGY, BIOCHEMISTRY. *Educ:* Drexel Univ, BS, 70; Univ Mich, MS, 71, PhD(med chem), 75. *Prof Exp:* Teaching fel chem, Univ Mich, 70-71; res scholar cancer chemother, Los Angeles County-Univ Southern Calif Cancer Ctr, 75-76; cancer res training fel, 76; res assoc path, Sch Med, Univ Southern Calif, 76-77; fel, dept pharmacol, 77-80, RES ASSOC DEPT PHARMACOL, YALE UNIV, 80- *Concurrent Pos:* Prin investr, Young Investrs Grant, Yale Univ. *Honors & Awards:* Wilsson R Earle Award, Nat Tissue Culture Asn, 74. *Mem:* Am Chem Soc; Am Soc Microbiol; Am Asn Cancer Res. *Res:* Mechanism of action of antineoplastic and antiviral agents; design and develop selective chemotherapy. *Mailing Add:* 101 Hammonasset Meadows Rd Madison CT 06443

SCHWARTZ, PETER LARRY, b Chicago, Ill, July 11, 40; m 64. CLINICAL BIOCHEMISTRY, MEDICAL EDUCATION. *Educ:* Univ Wis-Madison, BS, 61; Wash Univ, MD, 65. *Prof Exp:* lectr clin biochem, 71-77, SR LECTR CLIN BIOCHEM, MED SCH, UNIV OTAGO, NZ, 77- *Concurrent Pos:* Australian Res Grants Comt fel biochem, Monash Univ, Australia, 65-68. *Mem:* Fel Am Inst Chemists; Australasian & New Zealand Asn Med Educ. *Res:* Improved methods of medical and biochemical education; self-learning systems; computer-assisted instruction. *Mailing Add:* Dept of Clin Biochem Univ of Otago Med Sch Box 913 Dunedin New Zealand

SCHWARTZ, RALPH JEROME, b Chicago, Ill, Mar 14, 19; m 66. SPEECH PATHOLOGY, AUDIOLOGY. *Educ:* Northwestern Univ, BS, 41; Marquette Univ, MA, 48; Purdue Univ, PhD(speech path, audiol), 58. *Prof Exp:* Head speech clin, Am Red Cross, McPherson, Kans, 47-52; speech clinician, Inst Logopedics, 52-53; speech therapist & actg head speech & hearing dept, Children's Rehab Inst, Inc, Baltimore, Md, 53-55; asst prof logopedics, Univ Wichita & Inst Logopedics, 57-63; from asst prof to assoc prof speech, 63-71, ASSOC PROF SPEECH PATH & AUDIOL, UNIV NORTHERN IOWA, 71- *Mem:* Am Speech & Hearing Asn; Acoust Soc Am; Int Asn Logopedics & Phoniatrics; Am Asn Phonetic Sci; Int Soc Phonetic Sci. *Res:* Voice; diagnosis and appraisal; phonology; speech and hearing in the blind. *Mailing Add:* Dept Commun Dis Unin Northern Iowa Cedar Falls IA 50614

SCHWARTZ, RICHARD DEAN, b Hutchinson, Kans, Apr 17, 41; m 78. ASTRONOMY, ASTROPHYSICS. *Educ:* Kans State Univ, BS, 63; Union Theol Sem, MDiv, 66; Univ Wash, MS, 70, PhD(astron), 73. *Prof Exp:* Res asst atomic collision physics, Columbia Radiation Lab, Columbia Univ, 64-68; res teaching asst astron, Univ Wash, 68-73; astronomer pre-main sequence astron, Lick Observ, Univ Calif, Santa Cruz, 73-75; ASST PROF ASTRON, UNIV MO, 75- *Concurrent Pos:* Mem user's comt, Kitt Peak Nat Observ, 76-77; Copernicus prin investr, NASA grant, 76-78. *Mem:* Am Astron Soc; Int Astron Union. *Res:* Observational and theoretical pre-main sequence astronomy; T Tauri stars; Herbig-Haro objects; circumstellar dust shells; post-main sequence astronomy; white dwarfs; planetary nebulae. *Mailing Add:* Dept of Physics 8001 Natural Bridge Rd St Louis MO 63121

SCHWARTZ, RICHARD F(REDERICK), b Albany, NY, May 31, 22; div; c 5. ELECTROMAGNETICS, ACOUSTICS. *Educ:* Rensselaer Polytech Inst, BEE, 43, MEE, 48; Univ Pa, PhD(elec eng), 59. *Prof Exp:* Res asst physics, Rensselaer Polytech Inst, 46, asst elec eng, 46-48, instr, 48; develop engr, Adv Develop Sect, Radio Corp Am, NJ, 48-51; instr elec eng, Moore Sch Elec Eng, Univ Pa, 51-53, from assoc to res assoc, 53-59, from asst prof to assoc prof, 59-74, chmn grad group elec eng, 68-73; dept head, 73-79, PROF ELEC ENG, MICH TECHNOL UNIV, 73- *Concurrent Pos:* Consult, Marquette Univ, 78, Singer Corp, 80 & John Wiley & Sons, 81. *Mem:* AAAS; Am Soc Eng Educ; sr mem Inst Elec & Electronics Engrs; Nat Soc Prof Engrs; Acoust Soc Am. *Res:* Microwave theory and techniques; electromagnetic theory; antennas; communication engineering; electromagnetic compatability; musical acoustics; electroacoustics; electrical measurements. *Mailing Add:* Dept of Elec Eng Mich Technol Univ Houghton MI 44931

SCHWARTZ, RICHARD JOHN, b Waukesha, Wis, Aug 12, 35; m 57; c 8. SOLAR CELLS. *Educ:* Univ Wis, BSEE, 57; Mass Inst Technol, SMEE, 59, ScD(elec eng), 62. *Prof Exp:* Mem tech staff solid state develop, David Sarnoff Res Ctr, RCA Corp, 57-58; sr scientist, Energy Conversion, Inc, 61-64; assoc prof elec eng, 64-71, PROF ELEC ENG, PURDUE UNIV, LAFAYETTE, 71-, ASST HEAD SCH, 72- *Concurrent Pos:* Consult, RCA Corp, 65- *Mem:* Inst Elec & Electronics Engrs. *Res:* Solid state devices; direct energy conversion; semiconducting materials. *Mailing Add:* Sch of Elec Eng Purdue Univ West Lafayette IN 47907

SCHWARTZ, ROBERT, b New Haven, Conn, Dec 17, 22; m 47; c 3. PEDIATRICS. *Educ:* Yale Univ, BS, 43, MD, 47. *Prof Exp:* Intern, Children's Med Serv, Bellevue Hosp, 47-48; asst pediat, Col Med, NY Univ, 48-49, instr, 49; res fel, Harvard Med Sch, 49-51, res assoc med, 51-53, instr pediat, 53-54, assoc, 55-58; from assoc prof to prof pediat, Sch Med, Case Western Reserve Univ, 59-74; PROF MED SCI, BROWN UNIV, 74-; DIR PEDIAT METAB & NUTRIT, RI HOSP, 74- *Concurrent Pos:* Fel med, Children's Hosp, Boston, 49-51, NIH fel, 49-51; fel med, Thorndike Mem Lab, Boston City Hosp, 51-53; asst resident, Bellevue Hosp, 48-49, resident physician, 49; asst physician, Children's Hosp, 53-56, chief diabetic clin, 54-58, assoc physician & chief metab, 56-58; sr asst surgeon, Thorndike Mem Lab, Boston City Hosp, 51-53; res collabr, Brookhaven Nat Lab, 59-66; assoc pediatrician, Babies & Children's Hosp, Cleveland, 59-74; staff pediatrician, Metrop Gen Hosp, 59-74; dir dept pediat, Cleveland Metrop Gen Hosp, 67-74. *Mem:* AAAS; Am Soc Pediat Res; Am Fedn Clin Res; Am Acad Pediat; Pediat Soc. *Res:* Pediatrics metabolism; physiology. *Mailing Add:* Dept Pediat RI Hosp Providence RI 02902

SCHWARTZ, ROBERT BERNARD, b Brooklyn, NY, Sept 2, 29; m 56; c 2. NEUTRON DOSIMETRY, NUCLEAR PHYSICS. *Educ:* Union Univ, NY, BS, 51; Yale Univ, PhD(physics), 55. *Prof Exp:* Asst physicist, Brookhaven Nat Lab, 55-58; res assoc, Atomic Energy Res Estab, Harwell, Eng, 58-59; asst physicist, Brookhaven Nat Lab, 59-60; physicist, US Naval Res Lab, 60-62; PHYSICIST, US NAT BUR STAND, 62- *Mem:* Am Phys Soc. *Res:* Neutron spectroscopy by time-of-flight; neutron personnel dosimetry. *Mailing Add:* US Nat Bur of Stand Washington DC 20234

SCHWARTZ, ROBERT DAVID, b Brooklyn, NY, Apr 3, 41; m 64; c 2. INDUSTRIAL MICROBIOLOGY. *Educ:* Brooklyn Col, BS, 64; Long Island Univ, MS, 67; Rutgers Univ, PhD(microbial genetics), 69. *Prof Exp:* Technician metab res, Col Physicians & Surgeons, Columbia Univ, 64-65; med technologist, Middlesex Gen Hosp, New Brunswick, NJ, 68-69; res assoc oncogenic virol, Germfree Life Res Ctr, Life Sci Ctr, Nova Univ Advan Technol, 69-70; res biologist, Exxon Res & Eng Co, 70-76; proj scientist, Union Carbide Corp, 76-80; WITH BIOLOGICAL SCI SECT, STAUFFER CHEMICAL CO, 80- *Mem:* AAAS; Am Soc Microbiol; Soc Indust Microbiol; Sigma Xi. *Res:* fermentation process development; enzymatic hydroxylation; biotransformation; pollution control; single cell protein; microbial genetics; microbial energy production. *Mailing Add:* Stauffer Chemical Co 1200 South 47th St Richmond CA 94804

SCHWARTZ, ROBERT DONALD, b New York, NY, Mar 15, 24; m 47; c 4. ANALYTICAL CHEMISTRY. *Educ:* City Col NY, BS, 43; Univ Buffalo, PhD(inorg chem), 51. *Prof Exp:* Res chemist, Tonawanda Labs, Linde Air Prods Co, 43-48; asst, Univ Buffalo, 48-51; res chemist, Electro Refractories & Abrasives Corp, 51-52; explor & prod res lab, Shell Develop Co, 52-66; sect

leader anal res, United Gas Corp, 66-69, MGR ANAL RES & SERV DIV, PENNZOIL CO, 69- *Concurrent Pos:* Instr, Fillmore Col, Buffalo, 49-51. *Mem:* AAAS; Am Soc Test & Mat; Am Chem Soc; Am Inst Chem. *Res:* Hydrocarbon analysis; reducing action of aluminum powder in aqueous solution; separation techniques; origin and migration of petroleum; gas chromatography. *Mailing Add:* Pennzoil Co PO Box 6199 Shreveport LA 71106

SCHWARTZ, ROBERT NELSON, b New Haven, Conn, Feb 4, 40; m 71. PHYSICAL CHEMISTRY. *Educ:* Univ Conn, BA, 62, MS, 65; Univ Colo, Boulder, PhD(chem), 69. *Prof Exp:* Fel chem, Univ Ill, Chicago Circle, 69-70, asst prof, 70-76, assoc prof, 76-81; vis assoc prof chem, Univ Calif, Los Angeles, 79-81; MEM TECH STAFF, HUGHES RES LAB, 81- *Concurrent Pos:* Vis scholar, Univ Calif, Los Angeles, 79-80; adj prof phys & astron, Calif State Univ, Northridge, 81- *Mem:* Sigma Xi; Am Phys Soc; Am Chem Soc. *Res:* Magnetic resonance; molecular structure and relaxation phenomena; optical image processing. *Mailing Add:* Hughes Res Labs 3011 Malibu Canyon Rd Malibu CA 90265

SCHWARTZ, ROBERT SAUL, b Brooklyn, NY, Apr 20, 42; m 65; c 2. ANALYTICAL CHEMISTRY. *Educ:* Brooklyn Col, BS, 63; City Univ New York, PhD(anal chem), 74. *Prof Exp:* Chemist pharmaceut res, Dept Health & Welfare, Food & Drug Admin, 74-75; RES CHEMIST ANAL RES, US CUSTOMS SERV, TREAS DEPT, 75- *Mem:* Am Chem Soc. *Res:* Analysis and detection of trace quantities of organic vapors; electroanalytical chemistry; instrumentation. *Mailing Add:* US Treas Dept 1301 Constitution Ave NW Washington DC 20037

SCHWARTZ, ROBERT STEWART, b East Orange, NJ, Mar 14, 28; m 63; c 1. HEMATOLOGY. *Educ:* Seton Hall Col, BS, 50; NY Univ, MD, 54. *Prof Exp:* From intern to resident med, Montefiore Hosp, NY, 54-56; resident, New Haven Hosp, Conn, 56-57; clin fel hemat, 57-58, res fel, 58-60, from instr to assoc prof, 60-71, PROF MED, NEW ENG MED CTR, SCH MED, TUFTS UNIV, 71- *Concurrent Pos:* Dir blood bank, New Eng Med Ctr Hosp, 61-, chief clin immunol sect, 66-; consult, Collab Comt Transplantation & Immunol, NIH, 65- *Mem:* Am Soc Clin Invest; Am Asn Immunol; Am Fedn Clin Res; Am Soc Hemat; Transplantation Soc. *Res:* Autoimmunity; experimental leukemia. *Mailing Add:* Dept Med 171 Harrison Ave Boston MA 02111

SCHWARTZ, RUTH, b Berlin, Ger, Oct 9, 24. NUTRITION. *Educ:* Univ London, BSc, 47, PhD(nutrit biochem), 59. *Prof Exp:* Res asst biochem, Postgrad Med Sch, Univ London, 48-49; biochemist, Med Res Coun, Uganda, 50-56; res fel nutrit biochem, Med Sch, Wash Univ, 57-60; lectr nutrit, London Sch Hyg & Trop Med, 60-63; res assoc nutrit biochem, Mass Inst Technol, 63-65; asst nutrit, Univ Conn, 65-70; ASSOC PROF NUTRIT, NY STATE COL HUMAN ECOL, CORNELL UNIV, 70- *Mem:* AAAS; Am Inst Nutrit; Brit Nutrit Soc. *Res:* Magnesium requirements; protein-mineral interactions; availability of minerals. *Mailing Add:* Div of Nutrit Sci Cornell Univ Ithaca NY 14853

SCHWARTZ, SAMUEL, b Minneapolis, Minn, Apr 13, 16; m 37; c 9. MEDICAL RESEARCH. *Educ:* Univ Minn, BS, 38, MD, 43. *Prof Exp:* Intern, Univ Minn Hosps, 42-43; group leader res, Manhattan Proj, Univ Chicago, 43-46; from asst prof to assoc prof, 48-61, PROF EXP MED, UNIV MINN, MINNEAPOLIS, 61- *Concurrent Pos:* Commonwealth Fund fels, Univ Minn, Carlsberg Lab, Copenhagen & Karolinska Inst, Sweden, 46-48; USPHS res career award exp med, Nat Inst Gen Med Sci, 63-; vis prof, Hebrew Univ, Jerusalem, 61-62. *Mem:* Am Soc Biol Chem; Am Soc Clin Invest; Am Asn Cancer Res; Soc Exp Biol & Med. *Res:* Porphyrin and bile pigment metabolism; modification of radiosensitivity by metalloporphyrins. *Mailing Add:* Dept of Med Univ of Minn Minneapolis MN 55455

SCHWARTZ, SAMUEL MEYER, b Winnipeg, Man, Feb 15, 29; m 54; c 3. MEDICINAL CHEMISTRY. *Educ:* Univ Man, BSc, 52; Univ Minn, PhD(med chem), 56. *Prof Exp:* Assoc prof pharmaceut chem, Sch Pharm, George Washington Univ, 56-64; scientist admin, 64-78, ASSOC DIR SCI REV, DIV RES GRANTS, NIH, 78- *Mem:* AAAS; Am Chem Soc. *Res:* Pharmacology; biochemistry. *Mailing Add:* Div Res Grants Bethesda MD 20014

SCHWARTZ, SANFORD BERNARD, b Cheyenne, Wyo, Sept 9, 25; div; c 4. COMPUTER SCIENCES. *Educ:* Univ Colo, BS, 50, MA, 55, PhD, 59. *Prof Exp:* Physicist, Nat Bur Standards, 51-54; asst prof physics, Univ Nev, 58-59; assoc res scientist, Martin Co, 59-66; res scientist, Advan Res Labs, Douglas Aircraft Corp, 66-69, Douglas Advan Res Lab, 69-70, mgr systs programming, 70-80, SR SPECIALIST PLANNING, MCDONNELL DOUGLAS AUTOMATION CO, 80- *Mem:* Asn Comput Mach. *Res:* Physics of solar corona; astrophysical cross-sections; plasma physics; computer systems, especially measurement and evaluation of performance. *Mailing Add:* McDonnell-Douglas Automation Co K19-86 3855 Lakewood Blvd Long Beach CA 90846

SCHWARTZ, SEYMOUR I, b New York, NY, Jan 22, 28; m 49; c 3. THORACIC SURGERY. *Educ:* Univ Wis, BA, 47; NY Univ, MD, 50; Am Bd Surg & Am Bd Thoracic Surg, dipl. *Prof Exp:* Chief resident, Strong Mem Hosp, Rochester, NY, 56-57; from instr to assoc prof, 57-66, PROF SURG, UNIV ROCHESTER, 67-, DIR SURG RES, 62- *Concurrent Pos:* From asst surgeon to assoc surgeon, Strong Mem Hosp, Rochester, 57-63, sr assoc surgeon, 63-67, sr surgeon, 67-; Markle scholar acad med, 60-65; mem sci adv comt, Cent Clin Res Ctr, Roswell Park Mem Inst. *Mem:* Fel Am Col Surg; Soc Univ Surgeons; Am Surg Asn; AMA; Am Asn Thoracic Surg. *Res:* Portal hypertension; vascular surgery; platelets. *Mailing Add:* Univ of Rochester Med Ctr 601 Elmwood Ave Rochester NY 14642

SCHWARTZ, SHELDON, b New York, NY, July 21, 19; m 44; c 2. MEDICINE. *Educ:* Rensselaer Polytech Inst, BS, 40; NY Univ, MD, 43; Am Bd Internal Med, dipl, 52. *Prof Exp:* ASSOC PROF CLIN MED, MED CTR, NY UNIV, 47- *Concurrent Pos:* Chief arthritis clin, Bellevue Hosp; dir med, Hillcrest Hosp. *Mem:* Am Rheumatism Asn; fel Am Col Physicians. *Res:* Arthritis. *Mailing Add:* Dept of Med NY Univ Med Sch New York NY 10016

SCHWARTZ, SOLOMON SAMUEL, radiology, see previous edition

SCHWARTZ, SORELL LEE, b Buffalo, NY, Sept 13, 37; m 63; c 2. PHARMACOLOGY. *Educ:* Univ Md, BS, 59; Med Col Va, PhD(pharmacol), 63. *Prof Exp:* Head pharmacol div, US Naval Med Res Inst, 66-68; assoc dir, Int Ctr Interdisciplinary Studies Immunol, 75-79, PROF PHARMACOL, SCH MED, GEORGETOWN UNIV, 68- *Mem:* Am Asn Immunologists; Soc Toxicol; Am Soc Pharmacol & Exp Therapeut; Reticuloendothelial Soc. *Res:* Cellular toxicology; immuno toxicology; molecular pharmacology; pharmacokinetics. *Mailing Add:* Dept Pharmacol Georgetown Univ Sch Med Washington DC 20007

SCHWARTZ, STEPHEN EUGENE, b St Louis, Mo, June 18, 41; m 80; c 1. PHYSICAL CHEMISTRY. *Educ:* Harvard Univ, AB, 63; Univ Calif, Berkeley, PhD(chem), 68. *Prof Exp:* Fulbright fel & Ramsay Mem fel. Cambridge Univ, 68-69; asst prof chem, State Univ NY, Stony Brook, 69-75; assoc chemist, 75-77 CHEMIST, BROOKHAVEN NAT LAB, 77- *Mem:* AAAS; Am Chem Soc; Am Phys Soc. *Res:* Physical chemistry; atmospheric chemistry; chemical kinetics; design, conduct and interpretation of measurements of trace atmospheric constituents; laboratory studies of gas and aqueous-phase kinetics; modeling gas-phase and heterogeneous atmospheric reactions; interpretation of residence times and scales of transport. *Mailing Add:* Dept of Energy & Environ Brookhaven Nat Lab Upton NY 11973

SCHWARTZ, STEPHEN MARK, b Boston, Mass, Jan 1, 42; m 64; c 2. PATHOLOGY, CARDIOVASCULAR DISEASES. *Educ:* Harvard Univ, AB, 63; Boston Univ, MD, 67; Univ Wash, PhD(path), 74. *Prof Exp:* Asst dir labs, Long Beach Naval Regional Med Ctr, 73-74; asst prof, 74-80, ASSOC PROF PATH, UNIV WASH, 80- *Mem:* AAAS. *Res:* Structure, function and pathology of arterial endothelium; cell replication in endothelium. *Mailing Add:* Dept of Path Univ of Wash Seattle WA 98195

SCHWARTZ, STEVEN OTTO, b Hungary, July 6, 11; m 42; c 3. HEMATOLOGY. *Educ:* Northwestern Univ, BS, 32, MS, 35, MD, 36; Am Bd Internal Med, dipl, 42. *Prof Exp:* Prof internal med, Cook County Grad Sch Med, 39-68; asst prof med, Univ Ill, 42-47; prof hemat, Chicago Med Sch, 47-55; assoc prof, 55-59, prof, 59-79, EMER PROF MED, SCH MED, NORTHWESTERN UNIV, CHICAGO, 79- *Concurrent Pos:* Chief hemat clin, Mandel Clin & assoc hematologist, Michael Reese Hosp, 38-50; attend hematologist & dir hemat dept, Cook County Hosp, 39-68; hematologist, Hektoen Inst Med Res, 45-68; consult, Chicago State Hosp, 41-49, Highland Park Hosp, 50- Mother Cabrini Hosp, 51-, Columbus Hosp, 55- & Hines Vet Admin Hosp, 56-; assoc, Mt Sinai Hosp, 48-51; attend hematologist, WSide Vet Hosp, 55-56; sr attend physician, Northwestern Mem Hosp, 55- *Mem:* Am Col Physicians; Int Soc Hematol; Am Soc Hematol; Am Med Asn; Am Soc Internal Med. *Mailing Add:* 645 N Michigan Ave Chicago IL 60611

SCHWARTZ, STUART CARL, b New York, NY, July 12, 39; m 61; c 2. ELECTRICAL ENGINEERING. *Educ:* Mass Inst Technol, BS & MS, 61; Univ Mich, PhD(info & control), 66. *Prof Exp:* Res engr, Jet Propulsion Lab, Calif Inst Technol, 61-62; from asst prof to assoc prof elec eng, 66-74, assoc dean, Sch Eng & Appl Sci, 77-80, PROF ELEC ENG, PRINCETON UNIV, 74- *Concurrent Pos:* Ed, J Appl Math, 70; Guggenheim Mem Found fel, 72. *Mem:* Inst Math Statist; Inst Elec & Electronics Engrs; Soc Indust & Appl Math. *Res:* Application of probability and stochastic processes to problems in statistical communication and systems theory. *Mailing Add:* Dept of Elec Eng Princeton Univ Princeton NJ 08540

SCHWARTZ, THEODORE BENONI, b Philadelphia, Pa, Feb 14, 18; m 48; c 6. MEDICINE. *Educ:* Franklin & Marshall Col, BS, 39; Johns Hopkins Univ, MD, 43; Am Bd Internal Med, dipl. *Prof Exp:* Intern med, Johns Hopkins Univ, 43-44; resident, Salt Lake Gen Hosp, 46-48; assoc, Duke Univ, 50-52, asst prof, 53-55; from assoc prof to prof, Col Med, Univ Ill, 55-70; CHMN DEPT INTERNAL MED, RUSHPRESBYST LUKE'S MED CTR, 70-; PROF & CHMN DEPT, RUSH MED SCH, 71- *Concurrent Pos:* Damon Runyon sr clin fel, 40-52; fel, Nassau, asst chief med serv, Vet Admin Hosp, Durham, NC, 53-55; dir endocrinol & metab, Presby-St Luke's Hosp, Chicago, Ill, 55-; ed, Year Book Endocrinol, 64-; mem, Am Bd Internal Med, 70-79 & Am Bd Med Specialties, 71-79. *Mem:* Endocrine Soc; Am Soc Clin Invest; Am Diabetes Asn; fel Am Col Physicians; Am Fedn Clin Res. *Res:* Endocrinology; protein metabolism. *Mailing Add:* 1637 Judson Ave Evanston IL 60201

SCHWARTZ, TOBIAS LOUIS, b Ft Wayne, Ind, Sept 8, 28; m 49; c 3. BIOPHYSICS, PHYSIOLOGY. *Educ:* City Col New York, BEE, 49; State Univ NY Buffalo, PhD(biophys), 66. *Prof Exp:* Design engr, Niagara Transformer Corp, NY, 54-58; USPHS fel lab neurophysiol, Col Physicians & Surgeons, Columbia Univ, 65-68; asst prof biol sci, 68-71, ASSOC PROF BIOL SCI, UNIV CONN, 71- *Concurrent Pos:* Nat Inst Neurol Dis & Stroke res grant, 69; instr res, Lab Cellular Neurobiol, Nat Ctr Sci Res, France, 74-75; mem, Marine Biol Lab Corp, Woods Hole, Mass. *Mem:* AAAS; Biophys Soc; Soc Gen Physiol; Soc Neurosci. *Res:* Diffusion phenomena in membranes; active transport; mechanisms of membrane excitability; membrane diffusion theory. *Mailing Add:* Biol Sci Group Univ of Conn Storrs CT 06268

SCHWARTZ, WILLIAM BENJAMIN, b Montgomery, Ala, May 16, 22; c 3. INTERNAL MEDICINE. *Educ:* Duke Univ, MD, 45; Am Bd Internal Med, dipl, 56. *Prof Exp:* Intern & asst resident med, Univ Chicago Clins, 45-46; from instr to assoc prof, 50-58, chmn dept, 71-76, PROF MED, MED

SCH, TUFTS UNIV, 58-, VANNEVAR BUSH PROF, 76- *Concurrent Pos:* Res fel, Harvard Med Sch, 48-50; fel, Boston Children's Hosp, 49-50; Markle scholar, 50-55; asst, Peter Bent Brigham Hosp, 48-50; from asst physician to sr physician, New Eng Med Ctr, 50-; estab investr, Am Heart Asn, 56-; chmn gen med study sect, NIH, 65-; chmn sci adv bd, Nat Kidney Found, 68-70; chmn health policy adv bd, Rand Corp, 70-, prin adv, Health Sci Prog, 77-; Endicott prof & physician in chief, New Eng Med Ctr Hosps, 71-76. *Mem:* Nat Inst Med; Am Acad Clin Invest; Am Acad Arts & Sci; Am Soc Nephrol (pres, 74-75). *Res:* Renal disease; acid-base and electrolyte physiology; health economics; computer-aided decision making; public policy. *Mailing Add:* Dept of Med Tufts Univ Sch of Med Boston MA 02111

SCHWARTZ, WILLIAM JOSEPH, b Philadelphia, Pa, Mar 28, 50; m 79. NEUROSCIENCE. *Educ:* Univ Calif, Irvine, BS, 71; Univ Calif, San Francisco, MD, 74. *Prof Exp:* Res assoc, Lab Neurophysiol, NIMH, 75-77 & Lab Cerebral Metab, 77-78; intern, Univ Calif, San Francisco, 74-75, neurol resident, 78-81; INSTR NEUROL, MED SCH, HARVARD UNIV, 81-, ASST, MASS GEN HOSP, 81- *Mem:* Am Acad Neurol; Soc Neurosci; AAAS. *Res:* Clinical neurology; neural regulation of circadian rhythmicity. *Mailing Add:* Dept Neurol Mass Gen Hosp Harvard Med Sch Boston MA 94143

SCHWARTZ, WILLIAM LEWIS, b Columbus, Ohio, Dec 11, 31; m 53; c 2. VETERINARY PATHOLOGY. *Educ:* Ohio State Univ, BSc, 53, DVM, 57; Tex A&M Univ, MS, 70. *Prof Exp:* Pvt pract, 57-60; dist vet, Ohio Dept Agr, 60-63, vet diagnostician, 63-64; asst prof diag vet med, Ga Coastal Plain Exp Sta, Univ Ga, 64-67; res assoc vet path & toxicol, 67, asst prof, 67-70, PATHOLOGIST, TEX VET MED DIAG LAB, TEX A&M UNIV, 70- *Concurrent Pos:* Consult mem health adv comt, Tex Specific Pathogen Free Swine Accrediting Agency, Inc, 71-75. *Mem:* Am Vet Med Asn; Am Asn Swine Practitioners; Am Asn Vet Lab Diagnosticians; Sigma Xi. *Res:* Diagnostic veterinary pathology and related fields; diseases of swine. *Mailing Add:* Tex Vet Med Diag Lab Drawer 3040 College Station TX 77840

SCHWARTZBACH, STEVEN DONALD, b Bronx, NY, May 24, 47; m 68; c 2. PLANT PHYSIOLOGY, MOLECULAR BIOLOGY. *Educ:* State Univ NY, Buffalo, BA, 69; Brandeis Univ, PhD(biol), 75. *Prof Exp:* Fel molecular biol, Oak Ridge Nat Lab, 74-76; asst prof, 76-81, ASSOC PROF CELL BIOL, UNIV NEBR-LINCOLN, 81- *Concurrent Pos:* Am Cancer Soc fel, 75-76. *Mem:* Am Soc Plant Physiol. *Res:* Photoregulation of chloroplast development; organelle nucleic acids. *Mailing Add:* 303 Lyman Hall Univ of Nebr Lincoln NE 68588

SCHWARTZBECK, RICHARD ARTHUR, weed science, see previous edition

SCHWARTZBERG, HENRY G, b New York, NY, Oct 12, 25; m 55; c 3. CHEMICAL ENGINEERING, FOOD ENGINEERING. *Educ:* Cooper Union, BChE, 49; NY Univ, MChE, 54; PhD(chem eng), 66. *Prof Exp:* Chem engr, Chem & Radiol Labs, Army Chem Ctr, 50-53; res specialist process develop, Tech Ctr, Gen Foods Corp, 54-66; assoc prof chem eng, NY Univ, 66-73; PROF FOOD PROCESS ENG, UNIV MASS, 73- *Concurrent Pos:* Consult, Clairol Co, 66-67, Gen Foods Corp, 66-, Am Nat Res Cross, 67-74 & Devro, Inc, 68-77. *Mem:* Am Inst Chem Engrs; Inst Food Technol; Am Chem Soc. *Res:* Microwave heating; freeze concentration, food texturization by extrusion; membrane permeation; solid-liquid extraction; expression; freezing and thawing; evaporation; energy storage by brines; drying. *Mailing Add:* 493 S Pleasant St Amherst MA 01002

SCHWARTZMAN, ROBERT M, b New Haven, Conn, Nov 7, 26; m 60; c 3. DERMATOLOGY, IMMUNOLOGY. *Educ:* Univ Pa, MD, 52; Univ Minn, MPH, 58, PhD(dermatopath), 59. *Prof Exp:* Instr vet med, Univ Minn, 53-59; from asst prof to assoc prof dermat, 59-67, PROF DERMAT, SCH VET MED, UNIV PA, 67-, ASST PROF COMP DERMAT, GRAD SCH MED, 62- *Concurrent Pos:* Morris Animal Found award, 57-59; USPHS res career develop award, 63-72. *Mem:* Soc Invest Dermat; Am Soc Dermatopath; Am Soc Allergy; Am Vet Med Asn; Am Col Vet Dermat. *Res:* Veterinary and comparative dermatology. *Mailing Add:* Dept of Dermat Univ of Pa Sch of Vet Med Philadelphia PA 19174

SCHWARZ, ANTON, b Munich, Ger, May 26, 27; nat US; m 52; c 2. MEDICAL RESEARCH. *Educ:* Maximilian Univ, Ger, MD, 51. *Prof Exp:* Intern internal med, hosp, Munich, Ger, 51-52; intern, St John's Hosp, Long Island, 52-53; resident physician, Dobbs Ferry Hosp, 53-54; sr res assoc pediat, Children's Hosp Res Found, Col Med, Univ Cincinnati, 54-56; asst dir virus res, Res Div, Pitman-Moore Co, 56-63, dir virus res, Res Div, Pitman-Moore Div, 63-65, dir human health res & develop labs, 65-71, dir biol res & develop & biol labs, 71-75, med dir, Europ Area, Dow Chem Co, 75-77; dir corp med res, Int Region II, 77-80, DIR MED SCI, SCHERING-PLOUGH RES DIV, 81- *Honors & Awards:* Grand Officio Brazilian Order of Merit of Med, 67; Wolferine Frontiersman Award, 68. *Mem:* AAAS; Sigma Xi; Am Med Asn; NY Acad Sci; Soc Exp Biol & Med. *Res:* Medical sciences; research administration. *Mailing Add:* Schering-Plough Corp 60 Orange St Bloomfield NJ 07003

SCHWARZ, E(RIC) G(EORGE), b Boston, Mass, July 31, 31; m 58; c 3. CHEMICAL ENGINEERING. *Educ:* Mass Inst Technol, SB, 53, SM, 54. *Prof Exp:* Chem engr, 54-65, group leader, 65-77, SR DEVELOP SCIENTIST, CHEM & PLASTICS, RES & DEVELOP DEPT, UNION CARBIDE CORP, 77- *Mem:* Am Chem Soc. *Res:* Application development; silicone elastomers; surfactants; cellular plastics; reinforced plastics; silane coupling agents. *Mailing Add:* Union Carbide Corp Sillicones & Urethane Intermediates Div Tarrytown NY 10591

SCHWARZ, ECKHARD C A, b Luebeck, Ger, Nov 13, 30; US citizen; m 60; c 4. POLYMER SCIENCE. *Educ:* Univ Hamburg, Diplom, 56; McGill Univ, PhD(org chem), 62. *Prof Exp:* Chemist, E B Eddy Co, 57-59; sr res chemist, E I du Pont de Nemours & Co, 62-68, Kimberly-Clark Corp, 68-72 & E I du

Pont de Nemours & Co, Ger, 72-73; dir res, Presto Prod, Inc, 73-74; PRES, BIAX-FIBERFILM CORP, 74- *Mem:* Am Chem Soc. *Res:* Research and development immodification of commodity polymers; design and development of fiber and film processes. *Mailing Add:* 115 N Park Ave Neenah WI 54956

SCHWARZ, FRANK, b Timisoara, Roumania, June 2, 24; US citizen; m 49; c 2. ELECTRICAL ENGINEERING. *Educ:* City Col New York, BEE, 50; Univ Conn, MEE, 61. *Prof Exp:* Develop engr, Spellman TV Co, 50 & Sigma Elec Co, 50-51; proj engr, Sorensen & Co, Inc, 51-53; proj & dept mgr & consult electrooptics, 53-69, MGR ADVAN DEVELOP DEPT, BARNES ENG CO, 69- *Mem:* Sr mem Inst Elec & Electronics Engrs; Optical Soc Am. *Res:* Infrared instruments and electrooptical systems, including infrared horizon sensors, radiometers, trackers, thermal imaging systems. *Mailing Add:* 156 Thunderhill Dr Stamford CT 06902

SCHWARZ, HANS JAKOB, b Leysin, Switzerland, Feb 3, 25; nat US; m 52; c 2. ORGANIC CHEMISTRY, BIOCHEMISTRY. *Educ:* Univ Basel, PhD(chem), 51. *Prof Exp:* Fel, Nat Res Coun Can, 51-53; res chemist, Res Div, Cleveland Clin, 53-54, res assoc, 54-55, asst mem staff, 55-58, mem staff, 58-59; biochem res, 59-63, head metab unit, 63-68, assoc head, Biochem Sect, 68-73, DIR, DRUG METAB SECT, SANDOZ PHARMACEUT DIV, SANDOZ, INC, 73- *Mem:* Am Chem Soc. *Res:* Isolation and structure of natural products; synthesis of polypeptides and labelled drugs; metabolism of drugs. *Mailing Add:* Drug Metab Sect Bldg 404 Sandoz Pharmaceut Route 10 East Hanover NH 07936

SCHWARZ, HAROLD A, b Nebr, Apr 1, 28; m 53; c 4. PHYSICAL CHEMISTRY. *Educ:* Univ Omaha, BA, 48; Notre Dame Univ, PhD(chem), 52. *Prof Exp:* Assoc chemist, 51-59, chemist, 59-66, SR CHEMIST, BROOKHAVEN NAT LAB, 66- *Mem:* Am Chem Soc; Radiation Res Soc. *Res:* Radiation and photochemistry. *Mailing Add:* Chem Dept Brookhaven Nat Lab Upton NY 11973

SCHWARZ, HELMUT JULIUS, b Wuppertal, Ger, Nov 20, 15; m 50; c 2. APPLIED PHYSICS, ELECTRON PHYSICS. *Educ:* Univ Bonn, PhD(physics), 40. *Prof Exp:* Asst, High Vacuum Lab & asst prof gaseous electronics, Univ Bonn, 40; head labs electronic tubes & vacuum physics, Tech Insts, 42-44; mem staff high frequency res, Ger Govt, 44-45; dir pvt found phys sci, 45-49; head dept electron physics, Brazilian Ctr Physics Res, 50-54; prof appl physics, Univ Brazil, 51-57; dir, Inst Appl Physics, Brazilian Air Force, 55-57; dir projs electron physics, Radio Corp Am, 57-60; sci adv, Hamilton Stand Div, United Aircraft Corp, 60-62, sr staff res scientist, Res Labs, 62-63; PROF PHYSICS, RENSSELAER POLYTECH INST, 63- *Concurrent Pos:* Consult, CBS Lab, 63-65, VEECO Instruments Inc, 63- & Ion Physics Corp, 65-; curric chmn engr physics, Rensselaer Hartford Grad Ctr, 65-77; US coordr, US-Japan Coop Sci Prog Laser Interaction with Matter, 72-; vis prof, Univ Brazil, 74-75, prof, 75-; co-organizer & ed, Laser Interaction & Related Plasma Phenomena. *Honors & Awards:* I-R 100 Award, 69; NASA Award, 70; A Cressy Morrison Award, NY Acad Sci, 70; NASA Invention Award, NASA, 72. *Mem:* Am Phys Soc; fel Am Inst Physics; Electron Micros Soc Am; sr mem Inst Elec & Electronics Engrs; sr mem Brazilian Soc Phys. *Res:* Vacuum physics; thin films by vacuum evaporation; quantum electronics; reflection of an electron beam from standing light wave (Kapitza-Dirac effect); laser interaction with matter; quantum mechanical modulation of electron beam by laser (Schwarz-Hora effect). *Mailing Add:* 49 Carver Circle Simsbury CT 06070

SCHWARZ, HENRY P, biochemistry, deceased

SCHWARZ, JAMES ALAN, surface chemistry, see previous edition

SCHWARZ, JOHN HENRY, b North Adams, Mass, Nov 22, 41. THEORETICAL PHYSICS, HIGH ENERGY PHYSICS. *Educ:* Harvard Univ, AB, 62; Univ Calif, Berkeley, PhD(physics), 66. *Prof Exp:* Instr physics, Princeton Univ, 66-68, lectr, 68-69, asst prof, 69-72; RES ASSOC THEORET PHYSICS, LAURITSEN LAB, CALIF INST TECHNOL, 72- *Concurrent Pos:* Guggenheim fel, 78-79. *Mem:* Am Phys Soc. *Res:* Theoretical research in particle physics; properties of hadrons; dual resonance models; supensymmetry. *Mailing Add:* Dept Physics Lauritsen Lab Calif Inst Technol Pasadena CA 91125

SCHWARZ, JOHN ROBERT, b Passaic, NJ, Oct 8, 44; m 74. MARINE MICROBIOLOGY. *Educ:* Rensselaer Polytech Inst, BS, 67, PhD(biol), 72. *Prof Exp:* Res assoc, Univ Md, College Park, 72-75; ASST PROF MICROBIOL, MOODY COL, TEX A&M UNIV SYST, 76-, ASST DEAN ACAD AFFAIRS, 78- *Mem:* Am Soc Microbiol; Soc Indust Microbiol; AAAS; Sigma Xi. *Res:* Marine microbial ecology; biodegradation; microbial production on non-conservative gases in the marine environment. *Mailing Add:* Dept of Marine Biol PO Box 1675 Galveston TX 77553

SCHWARZ, JOHN SAMUEL PAUL, b Chicago, Ill, Mar 6, 32; m 56; c 1. INDUSTRIAL ORGANIC CHEMISTRY. *Educ:* Univ Ill, BS, 54; Univ Calif, PhD(org chem), 58. *Prof Exp:* Res chemist synthetic lubricants, Exxon Res & Eng Co, NJ, 57-58; sr res scientist pharmaceut res, Squibb Inst Med Res, 60-68; sr res chemist, Nease Chem Co, 68-72; PRES, PURE SYNTHETICS, INC, 73- *Mem:* Am Chem Soc; Inst Food Technologists. *Res:* Isolation, structure, stereochemistry of biologically-active natural products; synthesis and chemistry of tetracyclines and penicillins; acyclic isoimide-imide rearrangement; process research, development, production and marketing of fine organic chemicals. *Mailing Add:* 107 Highland Ave Ridgewood NJ 07450

SCHWARZ, KLAUS W, b Heidelberg, Ger, Mar 12, 38; US citizen; m 62; c 2. PHYSICS. *Educ:* Harvard Univ, BA, 60; Univ Chicago, MS, 62, PhD(physics), 67. *Prof Exp:* Asst prof physics, Univ Chicago, 69-76; RES STAFF MEM, IBM WATSON RES CTR, 76- *Mem:* Am Phys Soc. *Res:* Experimental research in quantum liquids and solid state. *Mailing Add:* IBM Watson Res Ctr PO Box 218 Yorktown Heights NY 10598

SCHWARZ, M ROY, anatomy, immunology, see previous edition

SCHWARZ, MAURICE JACOB, b Northampton, Eng, Sept 13, 39; US citizen; m 65; c 2. ORGANIC CHEMISTRY. *Educ:* Univ Ore, BA, 62, PhD(chem), 65. *Prof Exp:* Develop chemist, Geigy Chem Corp, RI, 67-69, group leader develop, 69-71, develop mgr, Ciba-Geigy Facil, NJ, 71-75, dir chem develop, 75-78, DIR PROD, PHARMACEUT DIV, CIBA-GEIGY CORP, 78- *Mem:* Am Chem Soc; Pharmaceut Mfrs Asn. *Res:* Process development and research; management. *Mailing Add:* Ciba-Geigy Corp 556 Morris Ave Summit NJ 07901

SCHWARZ, MEYER, b Amsterdam, Holland, Nov 6, 24; nat US; m 56; c 2. ORGANIC CHEMISTRY. *Educ:* Univ Geneva, BSc, 46, PhD(org chem), 50. *Prof Exp:* Res assoc chem, Fla State Univ, 50-52; res chemist, Sprague Elec Co, Mass, 52-56; chemist, Harry Diamond Labs, 56-64; CHEMIST, AGR ENVIRON QUAL INST, AGR RES SERV, USDA, 64- *Mem:* The Chem Soc; Am Chem Soc. *Res:* Organic synthesis and reaction mechanisms; dielectric materials; polymers; organic fluorine; phosphorus compounds; natural products as related to insect chemistry; insect hormones, pheromones, attractants and repellents. *Mailing Add:* Agr Envrn Qual Inst 319 B007 Beltsville Agr Res Ctr-W Beltsville MD 20705

SCHWARZ, OTTO JOHN, b Chicago, Ill, Oct 19, 42; m 65; c 2. PLANT PHYSIOLOGY, BIOCHEMISTRY. *Educ:* Univ Fla, BSA, 64; NC State Univ, MS, 67, PhD(plant physiol), 70. *Prof Exp:* NIH fel, Biol Div, Oak Ridge Nat Lab, 69-71; asst prof, 71-77, ASSOC PROF PLANT PHYSIOL, UNIV TENN, KNOXVILLE, 77- *Concurrent Pos:* NIH biomed sci grant, Univ Tenn, Knoxville, 71-72; vis investr, Comp Animal Res Lab, Oak Ridge Assoc Univ, 79- *Mem:* Am Soc Plant Physiol. *Res:* Regulation of pyrimidine nucleoside phosphorylating enzymes; chemical regulation of secondary product formation in plants-paraquat induced oleoresin synthesis in Pinus; food chain transport of synfuels. *Mailing Add:* Dept Bot Univ Tenn Knoxville TN 37916

SCHWARZ, RALPH J, b Hamburg, Ger, June 13, 22; nat US; m 51; c 2. ELECTRICAL ENGINEERING. *Educ:* Columbia Univ, BS, 43, MS, 44, PhD(elec eng), 49. *Prof Exp:* From asst to prof elec eng, 43-76, chmn dept elec eng & comput sci, 58-65, 71-72, assoc dean acad affairs, Sch Eng & Appl Sci, 72-76, THAYER-LINDSLEY PROF ELEC ENG, COLUMBIA UNIV, 76-, V DEAN, 76- *Concurrent Pos:* Adv, Inst Int Educ, 51-70; vis assoc prof, Univ Calif, Los Angeles, 56; vis scientist, IBM Res Ctr, 69-70; trustee, Assoc Univs, Inc, 80- *Mem:* Am Soc Eng Educ; Pattern Recognition Soc; fel Inst Elec & Electronics Engrs; Soc Indust & Appl Math; AAAS. *Res:* Communication theory and information processing; system analysis; pattern recognition. *Mailing Add:* Dept Elec Eng Columbia Univ New York NY 10027

SCHWARZ, RICARDO, b Valdivia, Chile, July 5, 42; m 66; c 2. SOLID STATE PHYSICS. *Educ:* Univ Chile, EE, 67; Univ Va, PhD(physics), 72. *Prof Exp:* Asst prof physics, Univ Chile, 66-68 & Univ Va, 72; vis asst prof physics, Univ Ill, 73-75; PHYSICIST, ARGONNE NAT LAB, 75- *Mem:* Am Phys Soc. *Res:* Mechanical properties of solids; ultrasonics. *Mailing Add:* Mat Sci Div Argonne Nat Lab 9700 S Cass Ave Argonne IL 60439

SCHWARZ, RICHARD HOWARD, b Easton, Pa, Jan 10, 31; m 55; c 4. OBSTETRICS & GYNECOLOGY. *Educ:* Jefferson Med Col, MD, 55; Am Bd Obstet & Gynec, dipl, 63, cert, 74. *Prof Exp:* Assoc obstet & gynec, Tulane Univ, 59-63; from instr to assoc prof, Sch Med, Univ Pa, 63-73, prof obstet & gynec, 73-78, dir, Jerrold R Giolding Div Fetal Med, 71-78; PROF OBSTET & GYNEC & CHMN DEPT, STATE UNIV NY DOWNSTATE MED CTR, 78- *Mem:* AAAS; fel Am Col Obstet & Gynec; Am Gynec & Obstet Soc; Infectious Disease Soc Obstet & Gynec (pres). *Res:* Perinatal and placental physiology; high risk obstetrics; diabetes; infectious disease. *Mailing Add:* State Univ NY Downstate Med Ctr 450 Clarkson Ave Brooklyn NY 11203

SCHWARZ, STEVEN E, b Los Angeles, Calif, Jan 29, 39; m 63. ELECTRICAL ENGINEERING. *Educ:* Calif Inst Technol, BS, 59, MS, 61, PhD(elec eng), 64; Harvard Univ, AM, 62. *Prof Exp:* Mem tech staff, Hughes Res Labs, 62-64; from asst prof to assoc prof elec eng, 64-74, PROF ELEC ENG, UNIV CALIF, BERKELEY, 74- *Concurrent Pos:* Guggenheim fel, IBM Corp Res Lab, Zurich, 71-72. *Mem:* Sr mem Inst Elec & Electronics Engrs; Am Phys Soc. *Res:* Lasers; quantum electronics. *Mailing Add:* Dept of Elec Eng Univ of Calif Berkeley CA 94720

SCHWARZ, THOMAS WERNER, b Berlin, Ger, July 21, 16; nat US; m 50; c 2. PHARMACEUTICAL CHEMISTRY, PHARMACY. *Educ:* Univ Calif, BS, 41, MS, 43, PhD(pharmaceut chem), 52. *Prof Exp:* From instr to asst prof 51-59, ASSOC PROF PHARM & PHARMACEUT CHEM, SCH PHARM, UNIV CALIF, SAN FRANCISCO, 59- *Concurrent Pos:* Guest prof, Pharmaceut Inst, Swiss Fed Inst Technol, 60-61. *Mem:* Am Chem Soc; Am Pharmaceut Asn. *Res:* Relation of chemical constitution to pharmacological action; drug formulation; hydrocolloids; history of health science. *Mailing Add:* Sch of Pharm Univ of Calif San Francisco CA 94143

SCHWARZ, WILLIAM MERLIN, JR, b Hartford, Conn, Nov 13, 34; m 55; c 4. ELECTROCHEMISTRY, PHYSICAL CHEMISTRY. *Educ:* Pa State Univ, 56; Univ Wis, PhD(phys chem), 61. *Prof Exp:* Proj assoc, Univ Wis, 61-63; sr engr, Int Bus Mach Corp, 63-64; chemist, Nat Bur Stand, DC, 64-68; scientist, 68-70, SR SCIENTIST, XEROX CORP, 70- *Mem:* Am Chem Soc; Electrochem Soc; Am Inst Chemists. *Res:* Electrode kinetics; xerographic development; polarography; photoelectrophoresis; xerographic processes and materials. *Mailing Add:* Xerox Corp 800 Phillips Rd Webster NY 14580

SCHWARZ, WINFRED MAX, b St Louis, Mo, Mar 28, 14; m 41. PHYSICS. *Educ:* Wash Univ, AB, 36, MS, 38: Ohio State Univ, PhD(physics), 47. *Prof Exp:* Asst metal res eng, Exp Sta, Ohio State Univ, 41-42; instr physics, Ind Univ, 42-46; from asst prof to prof, 46-79, EMER PROF PHYSICS, UNION COL, NY, 79- *Mem:* Am Phys Soc; Am Asn Physics Teachers; AAAS; Sigma Xi. *Res:* Beta-ray spectroscopy; gamma rays of tungsten and molybdenum; nuclear physics; electricity and magnetism; geophysics; mathematical modeling. *Mailing Add:* Dept of Physics Union Col Schenectady NY 12308

SCHWARZER, CARL G, b San Francisco, Calif, Apr 20, 17; m 37; c 1. ORGANIC CHEMISTRY. *Prof Exp:* Chemist, Shell Develop Co, 37-67; dir res & develop, Apogee Chem Co, 67-71; pres, Appl Resins & Technol, 71-73; mgr & chemist, Indust Tank, Inc, J & J Disposal, Inc, 74-76; waste mgt specialist, State Calif Health Serv, Hazardous Mat Mgt Sect, 76-80; TECH SPECIALIST AEROJET GEN ENVIRON STAFF & PROG MGR HAZARDOUS WASTE MAT, AEROJET ENERGY CONVERSION CO, 80- *Concurrent Pos:* Consult, US, Mex, Europe & China; mem bd dirs, World Asn Solid Waste Transfer & Exchange. *Mem:* Am Chem Soc; Am Civil Eng Asn. *Res:* Synthesis of organic and epoxy resins; hydrocarbon resin surface coatings; manufacture and applications of epoxy, peroxide, phenolic compounds and resins; industrial waste; disposal management in the environmental systems and technology; surveillance and management of hazardous waste materials; resource recovery and reuse of industrials; environmental chemistry disciplines. *Mailing Add:* Aerojet Gen Environ Staff PO Box 13222 Dept 0200 Sacramento CA 95813

SCHWARZER, THERESA FLYNN, b Troy, NY, Apr 14, 40; m 61; c 1. GEOLOGY, GEOCHEMISTRY. *Educ:* Rensselaer Polytech Inst, BS, 63, MS, 66, PhD(geol), 69. *Prof Exp:* Instr geol, State Univ NY Albany, 69; res fel remote sensing, Rice Univ, 69-72; sr res geologist, 72-74, res specialist, Exxon Prod Res Co, 74-76, sr res specialist, 76-78, sr explor geologist, 78-80, proj leader, Tex Offshore, 80-81, DIST PROD GEOLOGIST, ETEX DIV, EXXON CO, 81- *Concurrent Pos:* Chairwoman women geoscientists comt, Am Geol Inst, 73-77. *Mem:* Geol Soc Am; Am Asn Petrol Geologists; Soc Explor Geophysicists; Geochem Soc. *Res:* Inorganic and organic geochemistry; remote sensing; multivariate statistical techniques; interpretation and integration of geophysical, geological and geochemical data for hydrocarbon exploration. *Mailing Add:* 17915 Echobend Spring TX 77373

SCHWARZSCHILD, ARTHUR ZEIGER, b New York, NY, Mar 24, 30; m 52; c 3. NUCLEAR PHYSICS. *Educ:* Columbia Univ, BA, 51, MA, 56, PhD(physics), 57. *Prof Exp:* Res assoc physics, Columbia Univ, 57-58; res assoc physics, 58-60, assoc physicist, 61-63, physicist, 63-70, dept chmn & heal nuc physics, 78-81, SR PHYSICIST, BROOKHAVEN NAT LAB, 70-, CHMN, PROG ADV COMN, 75- *Concurrent Pos:* NATO fel, 66-67; mem, Nuclear Sci Adv Comn, Dept Energy, NSF, 81- *Mem:* Fel Am Phys Soc; Am Phys Soc; AAAS; Sigma Xi. *Res:* Heavy ion nuclear reactions; nuclear spectroscopy; measurements of electromagnetic transition probabilities for excited nuclear states; instrumentation for very short lifetime measurements. *Mailing Add:* Dept of Physics Brookhaven Nat Lab Upton NY 11973

SCHWARZSCHILD, MARTIN, b Potsdam, Ger, May 31, 12; nat US; m 45. ASTRONOMY, ASTROPHYSICS. *Educ:* Univ Gottingen, PhD(astron), 35. *Hon Degrees:* DSc, Swarthmore Col, 60, Columbia Univ, 73. *Prof Exp:* Nansen fel, Univ Oslo, 36-37; Littauer fel, Harvard Univ, 37-40; lectr astron, Columbia Univ, 40-44, asst prof, 44-47; prof, 47-51, Higgins prof, 51-79, EMER HIGGINS PROF ASTRON, PRINCETON UNIV, 79- *Concurrent Pos:* Vpres, Int Astron Union, 64-70. *Honors & Awards:* Newcomb Cleveland Prize, AAAS, 57; Draper Medal, Nat Acad Sci, 61; Eddington Medal, Royal Astron Soc, 63, Gold Medal, 69; Bruce Medal, Astron Soc Pac, 65; Rittenhouse Medal, Rittenhouse Astron Soc, 66; Albert A Michelson Award, Case Western Reserve Univ, 67; Dannie Heineman Prize, Acad Learning, Gottingen, 67; Prix Janssen Award, Soc Astron France, 70. *Mem:* Nat Acad Sci; Am Astron Soc (pres, 70-72). *Res:* Theory of stellar structure and evolution. *Mailing Add:* Princeton Univ Observ Peyton Hall Princeton NJ 08540

SCHWASSMAN, HORST OTTO, b Berlin, Ger, Aug 31, 22; m 60; c 1. BIOLOGY, PHYSIOLOGY. *Educ:* Univ Munich, Cand rer nat, 52; Univ Wis-Madison, PhD(zool), 62. *Prof Exp:* Lectr zool, Univ Wis-Madison, 62-63; USPHS fel, Univ Calif, Los Angeles, 63-65, asst res anatomist, 65-67; from asst res physiologist to assoc res physiologist, Scripps Inst Oceanog, 67-70; assoc prof psychol & biol, Dalhousie Univ, 70-72, prof, 72; assoc prof zool, 72-78, PROF ZOOL, UNIV FLA, 78- *Mem:* Asn Trop Biol; Am Soc Ichthyologists & Herpetologists. *Res:* Animal behavior; sensory physiology; visual system; circadian and biological rhythms; neurophysiology of vision in vertebrates. *Mailing Add:* Dept of Zool Univ Fla Gainesville FL 32611

SCHWEBEL, SOLOMON LAWRENCE, b New York, NY, Oct 21, 16; m 49; c 2. THEORETICAL PHYSICS. *Educ:* City Col New York, BS, 37; NY Univ, MS, 47, PhD, 54. *Prof Exp:* Instr physics, City Col New York, 46-50; res scientist, Inst Math Sci, NY Univ, 52-54; instr physics, Brooklyn Col, 54-55; staff scientist, Missiles & Space Div, Lockheed Aircraft Corp, 55-61; assoc prof physics, Univ Cincinnati, 61-64; ASSOC PROF PHYSICS, BOSTON COL, 64- *Mem:* Am Phys Soc; Am Asn Physics Teachers. *Mailing Add:* Dept Physics Boston Col Chestnut Hill MA 02167

SCHWEBER, SILVAN SAMUEL, b Strasbourg, France, Apr 10, 28; nat US; m 65. THEORETICAL PHYSICS. *Educ:* City Col New York, BS, 47; Univ Pa, MS, 49; Princeton Univ, PhD(physics), 52. *Prof Exp:* Asst instr, Univ Pa, 47-49; instr, Princeton Univ, 51-52; NSF fel, Cornell Univ, 52-54; res physicist, Carnegie Inst Technol, 54-55; assoc prof, 55-61, chmn dept, 58-61 & 74-76, chmn sch sci, 62-64 & 73-74, PROF PHYSICS, BRANDEIS UNIV, 61- *Concurrent Pos:* Vis prof, Mass Inst Technol, 61-62 & 69-70 & Hebrew Univ, Jerusalem, 71-72. *Mem:* Am Phys Soc; AAAS; Sigma Xi. *Res:* Field theory; statistical mechanics; history of science. *Mailing Add:* Dept of Physics Brandeis Univ Col Arts & Sci Waltham MA 02154

SCHWEDA, PAUL, b Vienna, Austria, May 28, 23; m 55. TOXICOLOGY. *Educ:* Univ Vienna, dipl chem, 51, PhD(anal toxicol), 55. *Prof Exp:* Demonstr anal toxicol, Inst Forensic Med, Univ Vienna, 51-55, asst, 55-58; res chemist, McGill Univ, 59-61; from asst toxicologist to toxicologist, Off Chief Med Examr, State of Md, 61-74; ASSOC DIR, NAT MED SERV, 72- *Concurrent Pos:* Lectr, Sch Hyg & Pub Health, Johns Hopkins Univ, 65-72; from instr to assoc prof, Sch Med, Univ Md, 67-74. *Mem:* Am Chem Soc; Int Asn Forensic Toxicol; Austrian Chem Soc. *Res:* Analytical toxicology of new drugs and their metabolites; thin-layer chromatography of toxicologically significant substances; instrumental methods for the detection of poisons in biological material and autopsy specimen. *Mailing Add:* Nat Med Serv 2300 Stratford Ave Willow Grove PA 19090

SCHWEE, LEONARD JOSEPH, b Omaha, Nebr, Mar 19, 36; m 61; c 3. PHYSICS, ELECTRICAL ENGINEERING. *Educ:* Creighton Univ, BS, 60. *Prof Exp:* RES PHYSICIST MAGNETISM, NAVAL SURFACE WEAPONS CTR, 60- *Mem:* Inst Elec & Electronics Engrs. *Res:* Magnetic thin films (permalloy), and their application to devices such as magnetometers, recorders, and computer memories (the crosstie memory). *Mailing Add:* Naval Surface Weapons Ctr Silver Spring MD 20910

SCHWEGMAN, CLETUS W, b Brookville, Ind, Apr 27, 14; m; c 2. SURGERY. *Educ:* Univ Cincinnati, BM, 39, MD, 40; Am Bd Surg, dipl, 48. *Prof Exp:* Instr chem, Xavier Univ, Ohio, 33-35; instr pharmacol, Col Med, Univ Cincinnati, 36-37; asst, Alfred Kuhn Diag Lab, Cincinnati Gen Hosp, 37-39; from asst resident to chief resident surg, Hosp Univ Pa, 46-48, instr, Sch Med, 48-50, lectr, Grad Sch Med, 48-60, assoc, Sch Med, 50-52, asst prof clin surg, 52-59, assoc prof surg, 60-73, PROF SURG, SCH MED & GRAD SCH MED, UNIV PA, 60- *Concurrent Pos:* Assoc surgeon, Hosp Univ Pa, 48-, dir tumor clin, 55-, ward chief, Div Surg, 60-; from asst secy to assoc secy, Am Bd Surg, 49-; attend surgeon, Vet Admin Hosp, Philadelphia, 55-; vis lectr, Seton Hall Col Med & Dent, 59- *Mem:* AMA; Am Surg Asn; Am Col Surg. *Res:* Absorption of ascitic fluid by the defunctionalized colon. *Mailing Add:* Univ of Pa Hosp 3400 Spruce St Philadelphia PA 19104

SCHWEGMANN, JACK CARL, b Denver, Colo, Nov 4, 25; m 47; c 2. PLANT PATHOLOGY. *Educ:* Tulane Univ, BS, 48; Univ Okla, MS, 50; La State Univ, PhD(plant path), 53. *Prof Exp:* Plant pathologist, Chalmette Works, Kaiser Aluminum & Chem Corp, 53-54, sr plant pathologist, 54-56, supvr air control, 56-58, supvr fume abatement, Metals Div, 58, coordr air control activ, 58-67, DIR ENVIRON SERV, KAISER ALUMINUM & CHEM CORP, 67- *Mem:* AAAS; Sigma Xi; Am Phytopath Soc; Air Pollution Control Asn; NY Acad Sci. *Res:* Air and stream pollution effects on plants and animals; diseases and insect pests of ornamental plants and vegetable crops. *Mailing Add:* Kaiser Aluminum & Chem Corp 300 Lakeside Dr Oakland CA 94604

SCHWEICKERT, RICHARD ALLAN, b Sonora, Calif, Feb 7, 46; m 67; c 2. GEOLOGY, TECTONICS. *Educ:* Stanford Univ, BS, 67, PhD(geol), 72. *Prof Exp:* Geologist, Texaco Inc, 71-72 & US Geol Surv, 73; asst prof geol, Calif State Col, Sonoma, 72, Calif State Univ, San Jose, 73 & Calif State Univ, San Francisco, 73; asst prof, 73-78, ASSOC PROF GEOL, COLUMBIA UNIV, 78- *Mem:* Geol Soc Am; Am Geophys Union; Soc Econ Paleontologists & Mineralogists. *Res:* Tectonics of orogenic belts and convergent plate boundaries; Paleozoic and Mesozoic tectonic evolution of the western cordillera of the United States; stratigraphy and structure of western Sierra Nevada; origin of melanges. *Mailing Add:* Lamont-Doherty Geol Observ Palisades NY 10964

SCHWEIGER, JAMES W, b Osage, Iowa, Oct 13, 29; c 2. DENTISTRY, PROSTHODONTICS. *Educ:* Univ Iowa, DDS, 54, MS, 57. *Prof Exp:* Instr prosthetic dent, Dent Sch, Univ Iowa, 57-58, asst prof dent technol, 58-59, asst prof otolaryngol & maxillofacial surg, Sch Med, 59-65, assoc prof, Sch Dent, 65-69; CHIEF DENT SERV & DIR MAXILLOFACIAL PROSTHETIC CTR, VET ADMIN CTR, WILMINGTON, 70-, COORDR RES, 81- *Concurrent Pos:* Consult, Coun Dent Educ, Thomas Jefferson Univ Hosp, Wilmington Med Ctr Surg & Dent & Children's Hosp Philadelphia, Temple Univ. *Mem:* Fel Am Col Prosthodont; assoc mem Am Acad Ophthal & Otolaryngol; fel Am Acad Maxillofacial Prosthodontics (pres, 81-82); Am Dent Asn. *Res:* Development of facial plastics for maxillofacial prosthodontics. *Mailing Add:* Dent Serv Vet Admin Ctr Wilmington DE 19805

SCHWEIGER, MARVIN I, b Middletown, NY, Feb 10, 23; m 80; c 2. AERONAUTICAL ENGINEERING. *Educ:* Rensselaer Polytech Inst, BAeroE, 48. *Prof Exp:* Asst, Res Labs, Gen Elec Co, 47; res engr, Res Dept, United Aircraft Corp, 48-55, head propulsion sect, Res Labs, 55-61, chief propulsion, 61-62; vpres, Bowles Eng Corp, Md, 62-67; mgr, Aerothermo, 67-71, mgr preliminary design, 71-73, mgr, Internal Aero, 73-78, proj mgr contracted res, Columbus Aircraft Div, 78-80, TECH DIR RES & TECHNOL, NAM AIRCRAFT OPERS, ROCKWELL INT CORP, 80- *Mem:* Assoc fel Am Inst Aeronaut & Astronaut. *Res:* Aerodynamics; propulsion; control and aircraft. *Mailing Add:* Rockwell Int Corp 4300 E Fifth Ave Columbus OH 43216

SCHWEIGERT, BERNARD SYLVESTER, b Alpha, NDak, Mar 29, 21; m 43; c 2. FOOD SCIENCE. *Educ:* Univ Wis, BS, 43, MS, 44, PhD(biochem), 46. *Prof Exp:* Asst, Univ Wis, 45-46; assoc prof biochem & nutrit, Agr & Mech Col, Tex, 46-48; from asst prof to assoc prof biochem, Univ Chicago, 48-60, head div biochem nutrit, 48-60, asst dir & dir res, Am Meat Inst Found; prof food sci & chmn dept, Mich State Univ, 60-70; PROF FOOD SCI & TECHNOL & CHMN DEPT, UNIV CALIF, DAVIS, 70- *Honors & Awards:* Babcock-Hart Award, Inst Food Technologists, 74; Nicholas Appert Award, Inst Food Technologists, 81. *Mem:* AAAS; Am Chem Soc; Soc Exp Biol & Med; Am Inst Nutrit; Inst Food Technologists. *Res:* Amino acid metabolism and microbiological methods; reproduction and lactation; stability of nutrients; nutrition and dental caries; vitamin B-12 and nucleic acid metabolism; meat flavor; irradiation of foods. *Mailing Add:* Dept of Food Sci & Technol Univ of Calif Davis CA 95616

SCHWEIGHARDT, FRANK KENNETH, b Passaic, NJ, May 12, 44; m 68; c 2. MOLECULAR SPECTROSCOPY, FUEL/COAL SCIENCE. *Educ:* Seton Hall Univ, BS, 66; Duquesne Univ, PhD(phys chem), 70. *Prof Exp:* Asst to dean pharmaceut chem, Sch Pharm, Duquesne Univ, 70-71; fel Nat Res Coun, US Bur Mines, 71-72 res chemist, Dept Energy, 72-79; RES ASSOC, AIR PROD & CHEM, INC, 79- *Concurrent Pos:* Chemist,

Allegaheny County Morgue, 79-71; lectr, Chem Dept, Duquesne, 70; consult anal & forensic chem, 70- *Mem:* Am Chem Soc; Spectros Soc; Anal Soc; AAAS; Sigma Xi. *Res:* Determination of physico-chemical properties of solvent-refined coal liquifaction feed and product streams; defining of analytical methods, particularly separation technology at the macro and molecular levels; utilization of the data base with process engineering to define the mechanism of coal liquifaction and construction of a demo plant. *Mailing Add:* Corp Res & Develop Div Air Prod & Chem, Inc Box 538 Allentown PA 18105

SCHWEIKER, GEORGE CHRISTIAN, b Philadelphia, Pa, Feb 17, 24; m 50; c 5. CHEMISTRY, RESEARCH & DEVELOPMENT ADMINISTRATION. *Educ:* Temple Univ, AB, 49, AM, 52, PhD(chem), 53. *Prof Exp:* Instr chem, Drexel Univ, 50-53; res chemist, Hooker Chem Corp, 53-56, supvr polymer res, 56-57; mgr res, Velsicol Chem Corp, 57-60; mgr plastics res, Celanese Corp, 60-65; dir chem & polymers, Develop Div, Borg-Warner Corp, 65-71; DIR RES & DEVELOP, PQ CORP, 71- *Mem:* Fel AAAS; fel Royal Soc Chem; Am Chem Soc; Indust Res Inst; Soc Chem Indust. *Res:* Polymers; organic syntheses; rearrangements; industrial and agricultural chemicals; fire retardants; plastics and plastics additives; inorganic chemicals; research and development management. *Mailing Add:* 233 Shawnee Rd Ardmore PA 19003

SCHWEIKER, JERRY W, b Oshkosh, Wis, July 1, 31. ENGINEERING. *Educ:* Univ Ill, BS, 55, MS, 57, PhD(theoret & appl mech), 61. *Prof Exp:* Res asst theoret & appl mech, Univ Ill, 55-57, instr, 57-61; sr engr, McDonnell Aircraft Corp, 61-65; prof eng mech, St Louis Univ, 65-71; VPRES, ENG DYNAMICS INT, 71- *Mem:* Am Soc Eng Educ; Soc Exp Stress Anal. *Res:* Structural dynamics; noise control. *Mailing Add:* Eng Dynamics Int 8420 Delmar Blvd Suite 302 St Louis MO 63124

SCHWEIKERT, DANIEL GEORGE, b Bemidji, Minn, June 15, 37; m 61; c 3. COMPUTER AIDED DESIGN. *Educ:* Yale Univ, BE, 59; Brown Univ, ScM, 62, PhD(numerical anal), 66. *Prof Exp:* Res engr, Gen Dynamics/Elec Boat, 61-64; mem tech staff comput applns, Bell Tel Labs, 66-72, supvr, Bell Labs, 72-80; DIR COMPUT-AIDED DESIGN, UNITED TECHNOL MICROELECTRON CTR, 80- *Concurrent Pos:* Assoc ed, Trans Comput Aided Design Int Circles & Systems, Inst Elec & Electronics Engrs, 81-; mem, Prog Comt, Design Automation Conf, 80- *Mem:* Sr mem Inst Elec & Electronics Engrs; Asn Comput Mach. *Res:* Development of systems for the computer-aided design of integrated circuits. *Mailing Add:* 1365 Garden of the Gods Rd United Technol Microelectron Ctr Colorado Springs CO 80907

SCHWEIKERT, EMILE ALFRED, b Flawil, Switz, Sept 10, 39; m 65; c 3. ANALYTICAL CHEMISTRY. *Educ:* Univ Toulouse, Licensee in sci, 62; Univ Paris, Dr(anal chem), 64. *Prof Exp:* Res asst res ctr metall chem, Nat Ctr Sci Res, Vitry, France, 63-65; sci consult, Europ Nuclear Energy Agency, Orgn Econ Coop & Develop, Paris, 65; scientist, Swiss Govt Deleg, Atomic Energy Matters, Switz, 65-66; asst prof anal chem & asst res chemist, 66-70, assoc prof anal chem & assoc res chemist, 70-74, PROF CHEM, TEX A&M UNIV, 74-, DIR, CTR TRACE CHARACTERIZATION, 68- *Concurrent Pos:* Adj asst prof grad sch, Col Med, Baylor Univ, 68- *Mem:* Am Chem Soc; NY Acad Sci; Swiss Asn Atomic Energy. *Res:* Analytical chemistry, especially nuclear activation analysis; administration of scientific affairs. *Mailing Add:* Ctr for Trace Characterization Tex A&M Univ College Station TX 77843

SCHWEINFURTH, STANLEY P, b Brooklyn, NY, Apr 23, 26; m 55; c 1. GEOLOGY. *Educ:* Univ Cincinnati, BS, 52, MS, 53. *Prof Exp:* Geologist, Stand Oil Co, Tex, 53-54 & Calif Explor Co, 54-59; GEOLOGIST, US GEOL SURV, 62- *Mem:* Am Asn Petrol Geol; Geol Soc Am. *Res:* Organic fuels; exploration and resources; field geologic mapping. *Mailing Add:* 956 Nat Ctr US Geol Surv Reston VA 22092

SCHWEINLER, HAROLD CONSTANTINE, b Tacoma, Wash, June 1, 22; m 45. PHYSICS. *Educ:* Carnegie Inst Technol, BS, 43, MS, 44; Mass Inst Technol, PhD, 51. *Prof Exp:* Instr physics, Carnegie Inst Technol, 43-44; jr physicist, Metall Lab, Univ Chicago, 44-45; physicist, Oak Ridge Nat Lab, 45-48; asst prof physics, Mass Inst Technol, 51-52, mem solid state & molecular theory group, 52-54; physicist, Oak Ridge Nat Lab, 54-79; FORD FOUND PROF PHYSICS, UNIV TENN, KNOXVILLE, 63- *Concurrent Pos:* Lectr, Univ Tenn, Knoxville, 47-48 & 58-63. *Mem:* Am Phys Soc; Am Asn Physics Teachers. *Res:* Nuclear reactor theory; magnetic susceptibility; defects in solids; molecular potential energy curves; theory of solids; mathematical physics. *Mailing Add:* Rte 2 Box 398 Rockwood TN 37854

SCHWEINSBERG, ALLEN ROSS, b Ellwood City, Pa, May 5, 42; m 69. MATHEMATICAL ANALYSIS. *Educ:* Univ Pittsburgh, BS, 62, MS, 65, PhD(math), 69. *Prof Exp:* Instr math, Univ Pittsburgh, 67-69; asst prof, 69-76, ASSOC PROF MATH, BUCKNELL UNIV, 76- *Mem:* Am Math Soc; Math Asn Am. *Res:* Operator theory. *Mailing Add:* Dept of Math Bucknell Univ Lewisburg PA 17837

SCHWEISS, JOHN FRANCIS, b St Louis, Mo, June 25, 25; m 50; c 5. MEDICINE. *Educ:* St Louis Univ, MD, 48. *Prof Exp:* Asst surg, 52-57, from instr to assoc prof, 57-71, ASSOC PROF PEDIAT & PROF SURG, SCH MED, ST LOUIS UNIV, 71-, DIR SECT ANESTHESIOL, 62- *Concurrent Pos:* Resident, Presby Hosp, New York, 54-56; chief anesthesiol, Cardinal Glennon Mem Hosp, 56-; pvt pract. *Mem:* Am Soc Anesthesiol; AMA; Int Anesthesia Res Soc. *Res:* Anesthesiology. *Mailing Add:* St Louis Univ Sch of Med 1402 S Grande Blvd St Louis MO 63104

SCHWEISTHAL, MICHAEL R, anatomy, see previous edition

SCHWEITZER, CARL EARLE, b Flint, Mich, Jan 19, 14:; m 41; c 2. ORGANIC CHEMISTRY. *Educ:* Kalamazoo Col, AB, 36, MS, 37; Northwestern Univ, PhD(chem), 41. *Prof Exp:* Asst chem, Northwestern Univ, 37-40; patents consult, Polymer Prod Dept, E I du Pont de Nemours & Co, Inc, 41-81; RETIRED. *Mem:* AAAS; Sigma Xi. *Res:* Polymers and plastics, particularly delrin acetal resin. *Mailing Add:* 205 Alapocas Dr Wilmington DE 19803

SCHWEITZER, DONALD GERALD, b New York, NY, Mar 2S, 30; m 52; c 2. REACTOR PHYSICS. *Educ:* City Col New York, BS, 51; Syracuse Univ, PhD(chem), 55. *Prof Exp:* Chemist, Appl Sci Dept, 55-74, HEAD, HIGH TEMPERATURE GAS-COOLER REACTOR SAFETY DIV, BROOKHAVEN NAT LAB, 74- *Mem:* Am Inst Mining, Metall & Petrol Eng. *Res:* Reactor safety; graphite research, chemistry of liquid metals; superconductivity; radiation damage; photochemistry. *Mailing Add:* Fission Prod Chem Brookhaven Nat Lab Upton NY 11973

SCHWEITZER, EDMUND OSCAR, III, b Evanston, Ill, Oct 31, 47; m 77. ELECTRICAL ENGINEERING. *Educ:* Purdue Univ, BS, 68, MS, 71; Wash State Univ, PhD(elec eng), 77. *Prof Exp:* Elec engr radar syst, Nat Security Agency, 68-73; elec engr, Probe Syst Inc, 73-74; res asst elec power, Wash State Univ, 74-77; asst prof, Ohio Univ, 77-79; ASST PROF ELEC POWER, WASH STATE UNIV, 79- *Mem:* Inst Elec & Electronics Engrs. *Res:* Application of microprocessors to electric power systems protection; revenue metering of electric energy; digital signal processing using microprocessors. *Mailing Add:* Dept of Elec Eng Wash State Univ Pullman WA 99164

SCHWEITZER, GEORGE KEENE, b Poplar Bluff, Mo, Dec 5, 24; m 48; c 3. INORGANIC CHEMISTRY, PHILOSOPHY OF SCIENCE. *Educ:* Cent Col, Mo, BA, 45; Univ Ill, MS, 46, PhD(inorg chem), 48; Columbia Univ, MA, 59; NY Univ, PhD(philos of relig), 64; Cent Col, Mo, ScD(hist of sci), 64. *Prof Exp:* Asst chem, Cent Col, Mo, 43-45; from asst prof to assoc prof, 48-58, prof, 60-70, DISTINGUISHED PROF CHEM, UNIV TENN, KNOXVILLE, 70- *Mem:* Am Philos Asn; Am Chem Soc; Hist Sci Soc. *Res:* Photoelectron spectroscopy; electron-induced fluorescence; microwave-acoustic spectroscopy; history and philosophy of science. *Mailing Add:* Dept of Chem Univ of Tenn Knoxville TN 37916

SCHWEITZER, HOWARD CHRISTOPHER, b Chicago, Ill, Feb 12, 46. AUDITORY SCIENCE, BIOMEDICAL ENGINEERING. *Educ:* Northern Ill Univ, BA, 68; Univ Md, MA, 71, PhD(audiol), 74. *Prof Exp:* Dir educ audiol, NAm Philips Corp, 74-75; RES ASSOC AUDITION, UNIV MD, 75-; RES AUDIOLOGIST, VET ADMIN HOSP, WASHINGTON, DC, 77- *Mem:* Acoust Soc Am; Am Speech & Hearing Asn; Acad Rehabilitative Audiol; Am Auditory Soc; Int Soc Audiol. *Res:* Rehabilitative audiology; biomedical engineering for the auditorily impaired. *Mailing Add:* Vet Admin Hosp Auditory Lab 50 Irving St NW Washington DC 20422

SCHWEITZER, JEFFREY STEWART, b New York, NY, May 6, 46; m 70. NUCLEAR PHYSICS, NUCLEAR LOGGING. *Educ:* Carnegie Inst Technol, BS, 67; Purdue Univ, MS, 69, PhD(physics), 72. *Prof Exp:* Res fel nuclear physics, Calif Inst Technol, 72-74; SR RES PHYSICIST, SCHLUMBERGER LTD, 74- *Concurrent Pos:* Reviewer, Sci Fac Prof Develop, NSF, 81. *Mem:* Am Phys Soc. *Res:* Experimental work in gamma-ray spectroscopy, neutron and gamma-ray interactions, low energy compound nuclear reactions and development of nuclear well logging tools for spectroscopic analysis. *Mailing Add:* Schlumberger-Doll Res Ctr PO Box 307 Ridgefield CT 06877

SCHWEITZER, JOHN WILLIAM, b Covington, Ky, Apr 23, 41. SOLID STATE PHYSICS. *Educ:* Thomas More Col, AB, 60; Univ Cincinnati, MS, 62, PhD(physics), 66. *Prof Exp:* Asst prof, 66-72, assoc prof, 72-78, PROF PHYSICS, UNIV IOWA, 78- *Mem:* Am Phys Soc. *Res:* Localized magnetic states; itinerant electron magnetism; mixed configuration rare earth compounds. *Mailing Add:* Dept Physics & Astron Univ of Iowa Iowa City IA 52242

SCHWEITZER, LELAND RAY, b Merna, Nebr, July 23, 41; m 71; c 2. AGRONOMY, VEGETABLE CROPS. *Educ:* Ore State Univ, BS, 66, MS, 69; Mich State Univ, PhD(crop sci), 72. *Prof Exp:* Int Agr Ctr study fel, Off Seed Testing Sta, Wageningen, Neth, 72; SEED PHYSIOLOGIST, ASGROW SEED CO, 72- *Mem:* Am Soc Agron; Asn Off Seed Anal. *Res:* Seed physiology, technology and testing. *Mailing Add:* Asgrow Res Ctr PO Box 1235 Twin Falls ID 83301

SCHWEITZER, PAUL JEROME, b New York, NY, Jan 16, 41; m 70. OPERATIONS RESEARCH, APPLIED MATHEMATICS. *Educ:* Mass Inst Technol, BS(physics) & BS(math), 61, ScD(physics), 65. *Prof Exp:* Consult, Lincoln Lab, Mass Inst Technol, 64-65; staff mem, Weapons Systs Eval Div, Inst Defense Anal, 65-66, Jason Div, 66 & Weapons Systs Eval Div, 66-72; staff mem, IBM Thomas J Waston Res Ctr, 72-77; PROF OPERS RES & COMPUT & INFO SYSTS, GRAD SCH MGT, UNIV ROCHESTER, 77- *Concurrent Pos:* Consult, Airborne Instruments Lab, NY, 62-63; mem staff, Am Univ, 69-70; vis mem fac, Israel Inst Technol, 70-72; mem staff, Haifa Univ, 72; consult, Israel Aircraft Industs, 72. *Mem:* Opers Res Soc Am; Inst Mgt Sci. *Res:* Military operations research; mathematical programming; stochastic processes; telecommunications and computer networks. *Mailing Add:* Grad Sch of Mgt Univ of Rochester Rochester NY 14627

SCHWEITZER, WALTER GARELD, JR, b Toledo, Ohio, Nov 2, 24; m 50; c 3. LASER PHYSICS. *Educ:* Am Univ, BS, 47; Univ Mich, MS, 48; Univ Md, PhD, 62. *Prof Exp:* physicist, Nat Bur Standards, 48-81; lectr physics, Montgomery Col, 81- *Concurrent Pos:* Fel, Dept Com, Sci & Technol, 74-75; mem senate com comt staff, 74-75. *Mem:* Am Phys Soc; fel Optical Soc Am. *Res:* Optical hyperfine structure and atomic beam absorption spectroscopy; isotope shifts; zeeman filter and atomic beam standards; interferometry; laser stabilization, spectroscopy and wave length standards. *Mailing Add:* 14223 Briarwood Terrace Rockville MD 20853

SCHWEIZER, ALBERT EDWARD, b Philadelphia, Pa, Mar 31, 43; m 61; c 3. INORGANIC CHEMISTRY. *Educ:* West Chester State Col, BS, 64; Rutgers Univ, MS, 68; Calif Inst Technol, PhD(chem), 74. *Prof Exp:* Sr res chemist, Cent Res Labs, Mobil Res & Develop Corp, 64-76; SR RES CHEMIST, INDUST CHEM RES & DEVELOP, AIR PROD & CHEM, INC, 76- *Mem:* Am Chem Soc. *Res:* Synthesis, mechanistic studies and thermal properties; process development; catalysis; zeolites and transition metal chemistry. *Mailing Add:* Air Prods & Chemicals Inc PO Box 538 Allentown PA 18105

SCHWEIZER, BERTHOLD, b Cologne, Ger, July 20, 29; nat US; m 61; c 1. MATHEMATICS. *Educ:* Mass Inst Technol, SB, 51; Ill Inst Technol, MS, 54, PhD(math), 56. *Prof Exp:* Instr math, Ill Inst Technol, 56-57; asst prof, San Diego State Col, 57-58; vis asst prof, Univ Calif, Los Angeles, 58-60; assoc prof, Univ Ariz, 60-65 & Univ Mass, Amherst, 65-68; prof, Univ Ariz, 68-70; PROF MATH, UNIV MASS, AMHERST, 70- *Mem:* AAAS; Am Math Soc; Math Asn Am. *Res:* Probabilistic geometry; algebra of functions; functional equations. *Mailing Add:* Dept of Math & Statist Univ of Mass Amherst MA 01003

SCHWEIZER, EDWARD E, b Joliet, Ill, Apr 6, 33; m 53; c 2. PLANT PHYSIOLOGY, AGRONOMY. *Educ:* Univ Ill, BS, 56, MS, 57; Purdue Univ, PhD(plant physiol), 62. *Prof Exp:* PLANT PHYSIOLOGIST, CROPS RES LAB, COLO STATE UNIV, USDA, 61- *Mem:* Weed Sci Soc Am; Am Soc Plant Physiol; Am Soc Sugar Beet Technol. *Res:* Weed research in sugar beets; integrated pest management. *Mailing Add:* Crops Res Lab Colo State Univ USDA Ft Collins CO 80523

SCHWEIZER, EDWARD ERNEST, b Shanghai, China, Dec 7, 28; US citizen; m 68; c 7. ORGANIC CHEMISTRY. *Educ:* NDak State Univ, BS, 51, MS, 53; Mass Inst Technol, PhD(org chem), 56. *Prof Exp:* Sr chemist, Argos Establecimiento de Productos Colorantes, Arg, 51-52; sr res chemist, Minn Mining & Mfg Co, 56-59; res assoc org chem, Univ Minn, 59-60, instr, 60; asst prof chem, Hofstra Col, 60-61; from asst prof to assoc prof, 61-72, PROF CHEM, UNIV DEL, 72- *Concurrent Pos:* Fulbright teaching award, Univ Madrid, 68-69. *Mem:* Am Chem Soc; Royal Soc Chem. *Res:* Carbene chemistry; reactions of phosphonium compounds; heterocyclics. *Mailing Add:* Dept of Chem Univ of Del Newark DE 19711

SCHWEIZER, FELIX, b Cologne, Ger, Sept 1, 27; US citizen; m 59; c 3. RADIATION PHYSICS, THEORETICAL PHYSICS. *Educ:* Rensselaer Polytech Inst, BS, 51, MS, 54; Univ Calif, Los Angeles, PhD(physics), 60. *Prof Exp:* Mem tech staff space physics, Space Technol Labs Inc, 60-62; scientist specialist, Jet Propulsion Lab, Calif Inst Technol, 62-64; asst prof physics, San Fernando Valley State Col, 64-67; PHYSICIST, NAVAL PLANT REP OFFICE, POMONA, 67- *Concurrent Pos:* Mem, Working Group Infrared & Lasers, Joint Dept Defense-Metrol & Calibration Coord Group, 68- *Mem:* Am Phys Soc. *Res:* Nuclear physics; electromag theory; radiometry; photometry; lasers; classical mechanics; anomalies in relativity and quantum mechanics. *Mailing Add:* PO Box 141 Pomona CA 91769

SCHWELB, OTTO, b Budapest, Hungary, Mar 27, 31; Can citizen; m 66; c 3. INTEGRATED OPTICS, MICROWAVE DEVICES. *Educ:* Univ Tech Sci, Budapest, dipl, 54; McGill Univ, PhD(elec eng), 78. *Prof Exp:* Mem sci staff, Res & Develop Div, Northern Elec Co, 57-67; ASST PROF ELEC ENG, CONCORDIA UNIV, 67- *Concurrent Pos:* Lectr, Univ Ottawa, 62-66; consult, Ainslie Antenna Corp, 69-71, Mitec Electronics Ltd, 75-76 & Can Elec Asn, 78-80. *Mem:* Inst Elec & Electronics Engrs; Optical Soc Am. *Res:* Integrated optics; surface acoustic wave devices; microwave components; electromagnetic wave propagation in stratified and periodic media. *Mailing Add:* Dept Elec Eng Concordia Univ 1455 De Maisonneuve Blvd W Montreal PQ H3G 1M8 Can

SCHWELITZ, FAYE DOROTHY, b Milwaukee, Wis, June 17, 31. CELL BIOLOGY. *Educ:* Alverno Col, BA, 53; Purdue Univ, MS, 67, PhD(cell biol), 71. *Prof Exp:* NIH trainee, Purdue Univ, 69-71; asst prof biol, 71-78, ASSOC PROF BIOL, UNIV DAYTON, 78- *Mem:* Electron Micros Soc Am; Am Soc Plant Physiol; Biophys Soc; Am Soc Cell Biol. *Res:* Role of cyclic Adenine Monophosphatase in Euglena; photosynthetic mutants of Euglena; correlation of structural changes with functional and biochemical changes; chloroplast development. *Mailing Add:* Dept of Biol Univ of Dayton Dayton OH 45469

SCHWENDEMAN, JOSEPH RAYMOND, JR, b Fargo, NDak, Dec 13, 30; m 52; c 3. PHYSICAL GEOGRAPHY, RESOURCE GEOGRAPHY. *Educ:* Univ Ky, BA, 56, MS, 57; Ind Univ, PhD(geog), 67. *Prof Exp:* Asst prof phys geog, Univ NDak, 62-63; staff instr, Ind Univ, 63-64; asst prof phys geog & chmn dept geog, Univ NDak, 64-66; chmn dept, 66-76, DEAN UNDERGRAD STUDIES & PROF GEOG & CHMN DEPT, EASTERN KY UNIV, 76- *Concurrent Pos:* Co-dir, Geog Studies & Res Ctr, 68- *Mem:* Asn Am Geog. *Res:* Climatology; regional potential studies; planners. *Mailing Add:* Dean of Undergrad Studies Eastern Ky Univ Richmond KY 40475

SCHWENDEMAN, RICHARD HENRY, b Chicago, Ill, Aug 26, 29; m 53; c 3. PHYSICAL CHEMISTRY. *Educ:* Purdue Univ, BS, 51; Univ Mich, MS, 52, PhD, 56. *Prof Exp:* Res fel chem, Harvard Univ, 55-57; from asst prof to assoc prof, 57-69, PROF CHEM, MICH STATE UNIV, 69- *Mem:* Am Chem Soc; Am Phys Soc. *Res:* Determination of molecular structure and collisional relaxation rates by microwave spectroscopy and infrared laser spectroscopy; theoretical studies in molecular spectra and molecular dynamics. *Mailing Add:* Dept of Chem Mich State Univ East Lansing MI 48824

SCHWENDER, CHARLES FREDERICK, b Buffalo, NY, July 22, 41; m 63. MEDICINAL CHEMISTRY. *Educ:* State Univ NY Buffalo, BS, 63, PhD(med chem), 68. *Prof Exp:* Scientist org chem, Warner-Lambert Res Inst, 67-71, sr scientist, Org Chem, 71-77; res assoc, 77, dir, Allergy Pulmonary Sect, 79-80, DIR, IMMUNOCHEM SECT, DEPT CHEM, PARKE-DAVIS PHARMACEUT RES DIV, WARNER-LAMBERT CO, 80- *Mem:* Am Chem Soc; Am Pharmaceut Asn; AAAS. *Res:* Organic medicinal chemistry; synthesis of cardiopulmonary agents; antianginal, bronchodilator, antiallergic, anti-inflammatory and immunomodulating agents; agent effective in the alleviation of emphysema; use of emzymes and receptor binding as models for drug design. *Mailing Add:* Parke-Davis Pharmaceut Res Div Warner-Lambert Co 2800 Plymouth Rd Ann Arbor MI 48105

SCHWENDIMAN, L(YSLE) C(HRISTIAN), b Sugar City, Idaho, June 2, 17; m 42; c 4. CHEMICAL ENGINEERING. *Educ:* Univ Idaho, BS, 39; Am Bd Health Physics, Dipl. *Prof Exp:* Tool engr, Boeing Aircraft Co, 42-45, supvr, 46-47; methods engr, Gen Elec Co, 48-51, supvr radiochem stand, 52-54, sr radiol engr, 54-56, supvr equip & instrumentation, 57-61, mgr particulate & gaseous waste res, Hanford Labs, 62-65; mgr particulate & gaseous waste res, 65-68, mgr air pollution chem, 68-70, res assoc atmospheric anal, 70-72, mgr particulate & gaseous waste res, Atmospheric Sci Dept, 72-80, TECH PROG MGR RES, NAT RES COUN, URANIUM RECOVERY STUDIES, PAC NORTHWEST LABS, BATTELLE MEM INST, 80- *Concurrent Pos:* Lectr, Joint Ctr Grad Studies, Univ Wash, 60- *Mem:* Am Nuclear Soc; Am Chem Soc; Am Inst Chem Engrs; Health Physics Soc; Air Pollution Control Asn; AAAS. *Res:* Radiological engineering; radiochemical methods; air pollution sampling and control methods; radioactive waste management; environmental effects of nuclear power reactors; uranium mill effluents control. *Mailing Add:* 6335 W Willamette Kennewick WA 99336

SCHWENK, FRED WALTER, b Dickinson, NDak, July 29, 38; m 63; c 2. PLANT PATHOLOGY, VIROLOGY. *Educ:* NDak State Univ, BS, 60, MS, 64; Univ Calif, Berkeley, PhD(plant path), 69. *Prof Exp:* Lab technician plant path, Univ Calif, Berkeley, 64-66; asst prof, 69-74, ASSOC PROF PLANT PATH, KANS STATE UNIV, 74- *Mem:* AAAS; Am Phytopath Soc. *Res:* Soybean pathology; teaching of undergraduate plant pathology. *Mailing Add:* Dept Plant Path Dickens Hall Kans State Univ Manhattan KS 66506

SCHWENKER, J(OHN) E(DWIN), b Bartlesville, Okla, June 27, 28; m 50; c 2. ELECTRICAL ENGINEERING. *Educ:* Univ Okla, BS, 52; Rutgers Univ, MS, 56. *Prof Exp:* Mem tech staff, 52-59, head logic technol res dept, 59-68, head data systs dept, 68-72, HEAD DATA APPLN ENG DEPT, BELL TEL LABS, INC, 72- *Mem:* AAAS; Inst Elec & Electronics Engrs. *Res:* Data communications; computers. *Mailing Add:* Data Appln Eng Dept Bell Tel Labs Inc Holmdel NJ 07733

SCHWENKER, ROBERT FREDERICK, JR, b Ann Arbor, Mich, July 3, 20; m 43; c 4. CELLULOSE CHEMISTRY, POLYMER CHEMISTRY. *Educ:* Univ Pa, AB, 48. *Prof Exp:* Asst biol, Wistar Inst, Univ Pa, 46-48; lab asst chem, Rutgers Univ, 48-49, asst instr, 49-51; chemist, Textile Res Inst, 51-55, group leader org chem, 55-60, assoc res dir, 60-66, dir chem & chem processing, 66; assoc dir res & develop, 66-74, dir res & develop, 74-75, vpres res & develop, 75-82, MEM BD DIRS, PERSONAL PROD CO, JOHNSON & JOHNSON, 74-, VPRES SCI TECHNOL, 82- *Honors & Awards:* Am Dyestuff Reporter Award, 65. *Mem:* Am Chem Soc; Fiber Soc; Tech Asn Pulp & Paper Indust; fel Am Inst Chemists; Sigma Xi. *Res:* Structure of cellulose derivatives; thermal degradation of high polymers; structure and properties of fibers; chemical specialties. *Mailing Add:* Res & Develop Personal Prod Co Johnson & Johnson Milltown NJ 08850

SCHWENSFEIR, ROBERT JAMES, JR, b Hartford, Conn, June 27, 34; m 67; c 3. NUCLEAR SCIENCE. *Educ:* Wesleyan Univ, BA, 56; Trinity Col, Conn, MS, 60; Brown Univ, PhD(physics), 66. *Prof Exp:* Exp physicist, Pratt & Whitney Aircraft Div, United Aircraft Corp, 56-60; res asst solid state physics, Brown Univ, 60-66; res assoc metal physics, Adv Mat Res & Develop Lab, Pratt & Whitney Aircraft Div, United Aircraft Corp, 66-68; asst prof physics, Bucknell Univ, 68-74; nuclear criticality safety engr, Naval Prod Div, United Nuclear Corp, 74-76, nuclear criticality safety specialist, 76-79; MGR NUCLEAR SAFETY & MAT, TEX INSTRUMENTS INC, 79- *Res:* Nuclear criticality safety research. *Mailing Add:* Tex Instruments 34 Forest St M/S 10-17 Attleboro MO 02703

SCHWENTERLY, STANLEY WILLIAM, III, b Philadelphia, Pa, Aug 18, 45. CRYOGENICS, SUPERCONDUCTING MAGNETS. *Educ:* Yale Univ, BS, 67; Cornell Univ, PhD(physics), 73. *Prof Exp:* RES STAFF MEM PHYSICS, OAK RIDGE NAT LAB, 72- *Mem:* Am Phys Soc; Cryogenic Soc Am; Sigma Xi. *Res:* Research and development on cryogenic materials and equipment for application in nuclear fusion and other types of energy systems. *Mailing Add:* Oak Ridge Nat Lab Bldg 9204-1 PO Box Y Oak Ridge TN 37830

SCHWENZER, KATHRYN SARAH, b Buffalo, NY. BIOCHEMISTRY. *Educ:* State Univ NY Buffalo, BA, 70; Univ Miami, PhD(chem), 74. *Prof Exp:* Teaching asst chem, Univ Miami, 70-71 & 74, res asst kinetics & bioinorg chem, 71-74; trainee affinity chromatography, St Jude Children's Hosp, 74-75, trainee, Reyes Syndrome Metab, 75-77; MEM STAFF DIAG, ABBOTT LABS, 77- *Mem:* Am Chem Soc; Am Soc Microbiol; Am Diabetes Asn. *Res:* Diagnostives for the clinical laboratory; fluoresence polarization immunnoassays for therapeutive drug monitoring. *Mailing Add:* Rte 43 & Rte 137 North Chicago IL 60064

SCHWEPPE, EARL JUSTIN, b Trenton, Mo, Sept 28, 27; m 48; c 3. COMPUTER SCIENCE, MATHEMATICS. *Educ:* Mo Valley Col, BS, 48; Univ Ill, MS, 50, PhD(math), 55. *Prof Exp:* Asst math, Univ Ill, 51-55; instr, Univ Nebr, 55-57; asst prof, Iowa State Univ, 57-61; mathematician, Dept Defense, 61-63; res asst prof comput sci & math, Univ Md, College Park, 63-65, assoc prof, 65-67; PROF COMPUT SCI, SCH BUS, UNIV KANS, 67- *Concurrent Pos:* Consult, Fed Systs Div, IBM Corp, 65- *Mem:* Am Math Soc; Math Asn Am; Asn Comput Mach. *Res:* Abstract algebra; projective geometry; graph and network theory; automata theory; information structures; computer language design and translation; machine description and design; simulation; consequent prodecures; computer science curriculum development. *Mailing Add:* Comput Ctr Univ of Kans Sch of Bus Lawrence KS 66044

SCHWEPPE, JOHN S, b Chicago, Ill, May 8, 17; m 43; c 3. MEDICINE. *Educ:* Harvard Univ, AB, 39; Northwestern Univ, MD, 44, MS, 46. *Prof Exp:* Fel internal med, Mayo Clin, 47-50; res assoc biochem, 55-60, assoc med, 60-62, from asst prof to assoc prof, 63-78, PROF MED & BIOCHEM, MED SCH, NORTHWESTERN UNIV, CHICAGO, 78- *Concurrent Pos:* Mem res dept, Northwestern Mem Hosp, 60-; fel coun arteriosclerosis, Am Heart Asn.

Mem: Endocrine Soc; Am Fedn Clin Res; Am Asn Cancer Res; fel Am Col Physicians. *Res:* Cyclic adenosine monophosphate; protein kinases in endocrine and malignant tissues; control of gene expression; oncology. *Mailing Add:* Rm 949W 845N Michigan Ave Chicago IL 60611

SCHWEPPE, JOSEPH L(OUIS), b Trenton, Mo, Jan 11, 21; m 42; c 3. ENGINEERING. *Educ:* Univ Mo, BS, 42, MS, 46; Univ Mich, PhD(chem eng), 50. *Prof Exp:* Jr chem engr, Tenn Valley Authority, Ala, 42-43; asst chem eng, Univ Mo, 46; chem engr, E I du Pont de Nemours & Co, Tex, 49-52; res engr, C F Braun & Co, Calif, 52-54, sr chem engr, 54-56, proj engr, 56-58; from assoc prof to prof mech eng, Univ Houston, 58-63, chmn dept, 59-63; PRES, HOUSTON ENG RES CORP, 60- *Concurrent Pos:* Lectr, Univ Southern Calif, 54-56 & Univ Calif, Los Angeles, 55. *Mem:* Instrument Soc Am; Inst Elec & Electronics Engrs; Am Soc Mech Engrs; Nat Soc Prof Engrs; Am Inst Chem Engrs. *Res:* Project engineering; process instrumentation; computer control. *Mailing Add:* Houston Eng Res Corp PO Box 3246 Houston TX 77001

SCHWER, JOSEPH FRANCIS, b Georgetown, Ohio, July 25, 36; m 57; c 2. AGRONOMY, PLANT PHYSIOLOGY. *Educ:* Ohio State Univ, BSc, 57; Univ Ky, MSc, 59; Pa State Univ, PhD(genetics, breeding), 62. *Prof Exp:* Sr plant physiologist, Greenfield Labs, Eli Lilly & Co, Ind, 62-64, head Western Field Res, 65-66, head plant sci res, Lilly Res Labs Ltd, Eng, 66-69, PLANT SCI FIELD RES-INT, ELI LILLY & CO, 69- *Mem:* Am Soc Agron; Weed Sci Soc Am. *Res:* New pesticides and plant growth regulators. *Mailing Add:* Greenfield Labs Eli Lilly & Co Box 708 Greenfield IN 46140

SCHWERDT, CARLTON EVERETT, b New York, NY, Jan 2, 17; m 45; c 3. VIROLOGY. *Educ:* Stanford Univ, AB, 39, MA, 40, PhD(biochem), 46. *Prof Exp:* Res assoc chem, Stanford Univ, 43-47; asst prof biochem, Sch Hyg & Pub Health, Johns Hopkins Univ, 47-50; from asst res biochemist to assoc res biochemist, Virus Lab, Univ Calif, 50-57; assoc prof med microbiol, 57-61, PROF MED MICROBIOL, STANFORD UNIV, 61- *Mem:* Fel AAAS; Am Chem Soc; Soc Exp Biol & Med; Am Soc Biol Chemists; fel NY Acad Sci. *Res:* Physical and chemical characterization and biology of replication of animal viruses; crystallization of polio virus particles. *Mailing Add:* Dept of Med Microbiol Stanford Univ Stanford CA 94305

SCHWERDTFEGER, CHARLES FREDERICK, b Philadelphia, Pa, July 20, 34; m 63; c 4. PHYSICS. *Educ:* Villanova Univ, BSc, 56; Univ Notre Dame, PhD(physics), 61. *Prof Exp:* Res assoc physics, Univ Basel, 61-62 & Ind Univ, 62-63; from asst prof to assoc prof, 63-73, PROF PHYSICS, UNIV BC, 73- *Mem:* Am Phys Soc; Can Asn Physicists. *Res:* Electronic properties of solids; electron spin resonance studies in semiconductors. *Mailing Add:* Dept Physics Univ BC Vancouver BC V6T 1W5 Can

SCHWERDTFEGER, WERNER, b Koeln, Ger, July 12, 09; m 33; c 3. METEOROLOGY, GEOPHYSICS. *Educ:* Univ Leipzig, DrPhil, 31; Univ Konigsberg, DrPhil habil(meteorol), 37. *Prof Exp:* With Ger Meteorol Serv, 31-48; sci adv, Nat Meteorol Serv, Arg, 48-56 & Naval Hydrographical Serv, 57-61; PROF METEOROL, UNIV WIS-MADISON, 62- *Concurrent Pos:* Docent, Univ Konigsberg, 36-38 & Univ Vienna, 42-43; privatdocent, Univ Munich, 47-48; prof, Arg Sch Adv Meteorol, 49-51 & Univ Buenos Aires, 57; vis scientist, Univ Melbourne, 58, Carnegie Inst Technol, Inst Geophys, Univ Calif, Los Angeles, High Altitude Observ, Boulder, Colo, Univ Wis & polar res group, US Weather Bur, DC, 59-60. *Mem:* Am Meteorol Soc; Am Geophys Union; Ger Meteorol Soc; Arg Sci Soc. *Res:* Synoptic and polar meteorology; general circulation. *Mailing Add:* Dept of Meteorol Univ of Wis Madison WI 53706

SCHWERER, FREDERICK CARL, b Pittsburgh, Pa, Feb 1, 41; m 64; c 2. APPLIED PHYSICS, MATERIALS SCIENCE. *Educ:* Pa State Univ, BS, 62; Cornell Univ, PhD(appl physics), 67. *Prof Exp:* Scientist, Physics Div, US Steel Res Ctr, 67-76, ASSOC RES CONSULT, BASIC RES, US STEEL RES LAB, 76- *Concurrent Pos:* Prin investr, Apollo Lunar Sci Prog, 71-76. *Mem:* AAAS; Am Inst Mining, Metall & Petrol Engrs; Am Soc Nondestructive Testing; Am Soc Testing & Mat; Am Phys Soc. *Res:* Experimental and theoretical studies of transport and magnetic properties of metals and alloys; mixed metal oxides and industrial minerals; mathematical modeling of two-phase flow in porous media; theoretical and experimental studies of electromagnetically induced fluid flows in liquid metals. *Mailing Add:* US Steel Res Ctr MS 98 Monroeville PA 15146

SCHWERING, FELIX, b Cologne, Ger, June 4, 30. ELECTRICAL ENGINEERING, THEORETICAL PHYSICS. *Educ:* Aachen Tech Univ, BS, 51, MS, 54, PhD(elec eng), 57. *Prof Exp:* Asst prof theoret physics, Aachen Tech Univ, 56-58; physicist, US Army Elec Lab, NJ, 58-61; proj leader radar res, Telefunken Co, Ulm, Ger, 61-64; RES PHYS SCIENTIST, US ARMY ELEC LAB, 64- *Concurrent Pos:* Vis prof, Rutgers Univ, 74- *Honors & Awards:* J T Bolljahn Award, Inst Radio Eng, 61. *Mem:* Inst Elec & Electronics Engrs. *Res:* Electromagnetic theory, particularly guided and free space propagation of electromagnetic waves; beam wave guides; antenna theory; periodic structures; diffraction and scatter theory; theoretical and electron optics; millimeter ware antennas and propagation. *Mailing Add:* US Army Commun Res & Develop Command Ctr Commun Sci Ft Monmouth NJ 07703

SCHWERT, DONALD PETERS, b Wellsville, NY, Dec 12, 49. QUATERNARY GEOLOGY, SOIL ECOLOGY. *Educ:* Allegheny Col, BS, 72; State Univ NY, MS, 75; Univ Waterloo, PhD(earth sci), 78. *Prof Exp:* ASST PROF GEOL, NDAK STATE UNIV, 78- *Concurrent Pos:* Fel, Univ Waterloo, 78- *Mem:* Geol Soc Am; Coleopterists Soc; Am Quaternary Asn. *Res:* Use of fossils to determine Quaternary distributions of insects; systematics and ecology of terrestrial Oligochaeta. *Mailing Add:* Dept Geol NDak State Univ Fargo ND 58105

SCHWERT, GEORGE WILLIAM, b Denver, Colo, Jan 27, 19; m 43; c 2. BIOCHEMISTRY. *Educ:* Carleton Col, BA, 40; Univ Minn, PhD(biochem), 43. *Prof Exp:* Asst agr biochem, Univ Minn, 41-42, instr, 42-43; biochemist, Sharp & Dohme, Inc, Pa, 43-44; instr & res assoc biochem, Duke Univ, 46-48, from asst prof to prof, 48-59; chmn dept, 59-74, PROF BIOCHEM, COL MED, UNIV KY, 59- *Concurrent Pos:* Markle scholar, 49-54; consult, NIH, 59-62. *Mem:* AAAS; Am Chem Soc; Am Soc Biol Chemists. *Res:* Mechanisms of enzyme action; hydrolases; dehydrogenases; transaminases; relation of protein structure to biological activity. *Mailing Add:* Dept of Biochem Univ of Ky Col of Med Lexington KY 40506

SCHWERZEL, ROBERT EDWARD, b Rockville Center, NY, Dec 14, 43; div. PHOTOCHEMISTRY, PHYSICAL ORGANIC CHEMISTRY. *Educ:* Va Polytech Inst & State Univ, BS, 65; Fla State Univ, PhD(phys org chem), 70. *Prof Exp:* Fel photochem, Cornell Univ, 70-71; fel magnetic resonance, Brown Univ, 71-72; res chemist org chem, Syva Res Inst, 72-73; res chemist photochem, 73-78, prin res scientist, 78-80, SR RES SCIENTIST PHOTOCHEM, BATTELLE MEM INST, 80- *Concurrent Pos:* Adj prof, Ohio State Univ, 82- *Mem:* Am Chem Soc; AAAS; Inter-Am Photochem Soc; Int Solar Energy Soc; Sigma Xi. *Res:* Novel applications of photochemistry and spectroscopy, including photochemical utilization of solar energy, optical data storage and processing, photoelectrochemical formation of fuels, development of improved laser dyes and exploratory studies on artificial photosynthetic systems; use of laser-produces x-ray for x-ray absorption fine structure spectroscopy. *Mailing Add:* Battelle Mem Inst Columbus Lab 505 King Ave Columbus OH 43201

SCHWERZLER, DENNIS DAVID, b St Louis, Mo, Dec 23, 44; m 67; c 2. MECHANICAL ENGINEERING. *Educ:* Univ Mo-Rolla, BS, 66; Purdue Univ, Lafayette, MS, 68, PhD(mech eng), 71. *Prof Exp:* Assoc sr res engr, 71-74, DEVELOP ENGR, ENG STAFF, GEN MOTORS RES LABS, 74- *Mem:* Am Soc Mech Engrs. *Res:* Vehicle structural dynamics; application of finite element techniques to vehicle structures; experimental dynamic testing of vehicle structures. *Mailing Add:* Vibration Struct & Mass Projs Gen Motors Eng Staff Tech Ctr Warren MI 48090

SCHWETMAN, HERBERT DEWITT, b Waco, Tex, Aug 1, 11; m 39; c 3. ELECTRONICS, PHYSICS. *Educ:* Baylor Univ, BA, 32; Univ Tex, MA, 37, PhD(physics), 52; Harvard Univ, MS, 47. *Prof Exp:* Jr operator, Western Union Tel Co, 28-33; teacher pub schs, Tex, 34-41; instr electronics, Harvard Univ, 41-47; PROF PHYSICS & CHMN DEPT, BAYLOR UNIV, 47- *Mem:* Am Phys Soc; Am Asn Physics Teachers; sr mem Inst Elec & Electronics Engrs. *Res:* Mathematics; application of Laplace transforms to analysis of electric circuits and physical problems; electronic analog computers; mechanical harmonic analyzers and synthesizers; ultrasonic and microwave attenuation. *Mailing Add:* Dept of Physics Box 6367 Waco TX 76703

SCHWETTMAN, HARRY ALAN, b Cincinnati, Ohio, Aug 16, 36; m 58; c 3. PHYSICS. *Educ:* Yale Univ, BS, 58; Rice Univ, MA, 60, PhD(physics), 62. *Prof Exp:* Res assoc, 62-64, asst prof, 64-66, assoc prof, 66-77, PROF PHYSICS, STANFORD UNIV, 77- *Concurrent Pos:* Sloan res fel, 66-72. *Res:* Low temperature physics; development of superconducting accelerator; application of low temperature physics and nuclear physics to medicine. *Mailing Add:* Dept of Physics Stanford Univ Stanford CA 94305

SCHWETZ, BERNARD ANTHONY, b Cadott, Wis, Nov 27, 40; m 62; c 2. TOXICOLOGY, TERATOLOGY. *Educ:* Univ Wis-Stevens Point, BS, 62; Univ Minn, St Paul, DVM, 67; Univ Iowa, MS, 68, PhD(pharmacol), 70. *Prof Exp:* TOXICOLOGIST, DOW CHEM CO, 70-, DIR TOXICOL RES LAB, 77- *Mem:* Indust Veterinarian's Asn; Environ Mutagen Soc; Soc Toxicol; Behav Teratology Soc; NY Acad Sci. *Res:* Reproduction; hepatotoxicity; mutagenesis. *Mailing Add:* 1803 Bldg Health & Environ Res Dow Chem Co Midland MI 48640

SCHWIDERSKI, ERNST WALTER, b Satticken, Ger, Feb 24, 24; nat US; m 59; c 1. APPLIED MATHEMATICS. *Educ:* Karlsruhe Tech Univ, Dipl math, 52, Dr rer nat, 55. *Prof Exp:* Sci asst & instr math, Math Inst, Karlsruhe Tech Univ, 48-55; head traffic theory br, Stand Elektrik Co, Ger, 55-57; SR RES MATHEMATICIAN, DAHLGREN LAB, US NAVAL SURFACE WEAPONS CTR, 58- *Concurrent Pos:* Prof lectr, Am Univ, 58-67; adj prof, Va Polytech Inst & State Univ, 68- *Mem:* Am Phys Soc; Am Geophys Union. *Res:* Ordinary and partial differential equations; integral equations; real and complex analysis; numerical analysis; mathematical theory of inviscid and viscous fluid flow; ocean tides and currents. *Mailing Add:* 102 Bell St Fredericksburg VA 22401

SCHWIESOW, RONALD LEE, b Pittsburgh, Pa, May 22, 40; m 62; c 3. ATMOSPHERIC PHYSICS, PHYSICAL OPTICS. *Educ:* Purdue Univ, BS, 62; Johns Hopkins Univ, PhD(physics), 68; Pa State Univ, MS, 74. *Prof Exp:* Jr instr physics, Johns Hopkins Univ, 62-66, res asst crystal spectros, 67-68; Nat Res Coun res fel atmospheric spectros, Res Labs, Environ Sci Serv Admin, 68-70; PHYSICIST, ENVIRON RES LABS, NAT OCEANIC & ATMOSPHERIC ADMIN, 70- *Concurrent Pos:* Vis scientist, Riso Nat Lab, Denmark, 78-79. *Mem:* Am Meteorol Soc; Royal Meterol Soc; Optical Soc Am. *Res:* Remote measurement of meteorological parameters using lasers; micrometeorology of the boundary layer; inelastic scattering spectroscopy applied to environmental problems; infrared transmission of atmospheric gases; Doppler laser wind instrumentation; atmospheric vortices; cloud dynamics. *Mailing Add:* Nat Oceanic & Atmospheric Admin R45X1 325 Broadway RL3-007 Boulder CO 80303

SCHWIMMER, SIGMUND, b Cleveland, Ohio, Sept 20, 17; m 41; c 2. ENZYMOLOGY, FOOD BIOCHEMISTRY. *Educ:* George Washington Univ, BS, 41; Georgetown Univ, PhD(biochem), 43. *Prof Exp:* Jr chemist, USDA, Washington, DC, 41-43, from asst chemist to chemist, 43-58, prin chemist, Western Regional Res Lab, 58-65, chief chemist, 65-74, EMER CHIEF RES BIOCHEMIST, WESTERN REGIONAL RES LAB, USDA, 75- *Concurrent Pos:* NSF sr fel, Carlsberg Found Biol Inst & Royal

Vet & Agr Col, Denmark, 58-59; res assoc, Calif Inst Technol, 63-65, head enzyme technol invests, 67-71; sr biochemist, UN Indust Develop Orgn Centre Indust Res, Haifa, Israel, 73-74; guest lectr, Dept Nutrit Sci, Univ Calif, Berkeley, 75- Mem: Am Soc Biol Chem; Inst Food Technol. Res: Enzymology; plant and food biochemistry. Mailing Add: Western Regional Res Ctr USDA 800 Buchanan St Berkeley CA 94710

SCHWINCK, ILSE, b Hamburg, Ger, May 24, 23. DEVELOPMENTAL GENETICS. Educ: Univ Tübingen, Dr rer nat(biol, biochem), 50. Prof Exp: Ger Res Asn fel insect physiol, Univ Munich, 51-54; Karl-Hescheler Found fel develop genetics, Univ Zurich, 54-56; res fel, Albert Einstein Col Med, 56, Col Med, NY Univ, 56-57 & Columbia Univ, 57-58; guest investr develop genetics, Biol Lab, Cold Spring Harbor, 59-60; Ger Res Asn grant & investr, Max Planck Inst, Mariensee, Ger, 60-62; asst prof biol, 62-74, ASSOC PROF BIOL, UNIV CONN, 74- Concurrent Pos: Fulbright advan res fel, 56-58. Mem: Am Soc Cell Biol; Genetics Soc Am; Soc Develop Biol; NY Acad Sci; Swiss Genetics Soc. Res: Developmental and biochemical genetics; enzyme action; control of insect development. Mailing Add: Biol Sci Group Univ Conn Box U-42 Storrs CT 06268

SCHWIND, RICHARD G(ROBE), b Elyria, Ohio, Jan 13, 34; m 61. MECHANICAL ENGINEERING. Educ: Mass Inst Technol, SB, 55, SM, 56, ScD(mech eng), 62. Prof Exp: Res specialist fluid mech, Thompson-Ramo-Wooldridge Co, Ohio, 56-58; res scientist, Lockheed Missiles & Space Co, 62-69; res scientist, 69-80, SR RES SCIENTIST, NIELSEN ENG & RES, INC, 80- Mem: Am Inst Aeronaut & Astronaut; Am Soc Mech Engrs. Res: External and internal experimental aerodynamics and heat transfer, particularly in windmills, airplanes, helicopters, missiles, turbomachinery, sprays, orifices and mixed convection boundary layers. Mailing Add: Nielsen Eng & Res Inc 510 Clyde Ave Mountain View CA 94043

SCHWIND, ROGER ALLEN, b Rochester, NY, Oct 4, 42; m 66; c 2. CHEMICAL ENGINEERING, PHYSICAL CHEMISTRY. Educ: Univ Rochester, BS, 64; Wash Univ, MS, 67, DSc(chem eng), 68. Prof Exp: Sr res chemist & group leader separations res group, Mound Lab, Monsanto Res Corp, Monsanto Co, 67-79; PRES, ISOTEC, INC, 79- Mem: Am Inst Chem Engrs. Res: Counter current separation methods, including distillation, chemical exchange and thermal and mass diffusion with emphasis towards isotope separation. Mailing Add: 8241 Dry Creek Circle Dayton OH 45459

SCHWINDEMAN, JAMES ANTHONY, b Cincinnati, Ohio, Oct 30, 55. HERBICIDE SYNTHESIS. Educ: Miami Univ, BS, 77; Ohio State Univ, PhD(org chem), 81. Prof Exp: Grad teaching asst org chem, Ohio State Univ, 77-78, assoc, 78-81; SR RES CHEMIST AGR CHEM, PPG INDUST, 81- Mem: Am Chem Soc; Royal Soc Chem. Res: Synthesis and evaluation of novel herbicidal compounds. Mailing Add: P P G Indust PO Box 31 Baberton OH 44203

SCHWING, GREGORY WAYNE, b Cincinnati, Ohio, Sept 30, 46; m 67; c 3. ORGANIC CHEMISTRY, AGRCHEMICALS. Educ: Purdue Univ, BS, 69; Univ Minn, PhD(organic chem), 72. Prof Exp: Res chemist agrchem, 72-77, sr res chemist, 77-78, RES SUPVR HERBICIDES, BIOCHEM DEPT, E I DU PONT DE NEMOURS & CO, INC, 78- Mem: Am Chem Soc. Res: Selective crop herbicides, industrial herbicides, plant growth modifiers, fungicides, insecticides and nematocides; synthesis and evaluation of new classes of compounds for agrichemical utility. Mailing Add: Dept Biochem Exp Sta Bldg 324 E I du Pont de Nemours & Co Inc Wilmington DE 19898

SCHWING, KARL JOSEF, b Balzfeld, Ger, Feb 27, 97; nat US. CHEMISTRY. Educ: Univ Freiburg, PhD(chem), 22. Prof Exp: Instr chem, Univ Freiburg, 22-23; res chemist, I G Farben Indust, 23-24, E I du Pont de Nemours & Co, NJ, 24-25, Amalgamated Dye & Chem Co, 25-29 & Barrett Co, 29-31; assoc prof chem & physics, 31-40, prof chem & chmn dept, 40-72, EMER PROF CHEM, UPSALA COL, 72- Mem: AAAS; Am Chem Soc. Res: Anthraquinone dyes; protein chemistry; isolation of amino acids from natural sources; coal tar products; stereoisomerism in the cyclohexane series; use of polyethylene films as a matrix for spectral measurements. Mailing Add: 154 Bergen Ave Ridgefield Park NJ 07660

SCHWING, RICHARD C, b Buffalo, NY, Dec 8, 34; m 56; c 4. ENVIRONMENTAL POLICY, CHEMICAL ENGINEERING. Educ: Univ Mich, BS, 57, MS, 58, PhD(chem eng), 63. Prof Exp: Sr res engr, 63-77, staff res engr, 77-81, SR STAFF RES ENGR, GEN MOTORS RES LABS, 81- Mem: AAAS; Am Chem Soc; Pub Choice Soc; Sigma Xi. Res: Pollution control of internal combustion engines; measurement of corporate externalities; air pollution epidemiology regression analysis; risk-benefit, cost-benefit analyses; risk assessments; technology assessments; forecasting. Mailing Add: Societal Anal Dept 12 Mile & Mound Rd Warren MI 48090

SCHWINGER, JULIAN SEYMOUR, b New York, NY, Feb 12, 18; m 47. PHYSICS. Educ: Columbia Univ, AB, 36, PhD(physics), 39. Hon Degrees: DSc, Purdue Univ, 61, Harvard Univ, 62, Columbia Univ, 66. Prof Exp: Nat Res Coun fel, Columbia Univ, 39-40; res assoc, Univ Calif, 40-41; from instr to asst prof, Purdue Univ, 41-43; mem staff, Radiation Lab, Mass Inst Technol, 43-45; from assoc prof to prof physics, Harvard Univ, 45-66, Higgins prof, 66-75; PROF PHYSICS, UNIV CALIF, LOS ANGELES, 75- Concurrent Pos: Mem staff, Metall Lab, Univ Chicago, 43; vis prof, Univ Calif, Los Angeles, 61. Honors & Awards: Nobel Prize in Physics, 65; C L Mayer Nature of Light Award, 49; Prize, Nat Acad Sci, 49; Einstein Award, 51; Nat Medal Sci in Physics, 64. Mem: Nat Acad Sci; AAAS; Am Phys Soc; Am Acad Arts & Sci; NY Acad Sci. Res: Nuclear and high energy physics; wave guide and electromagnetic theory; variational methods; quantum electrodynamics and field theory; foundations of quantum mechanics; many-particle systems; quantum gravitational theory. Mailing Add: Dept of Physics Univ of Calif Los Angeles CA 90024

SCHWINGHAMER, ERWIN A, microbial genetics, biology, see previous edition

SCHWINTZER, CHRISTA ROSE, US citizen. NITROGEN FIXATION, WETLAND ECOLOGY. Educ: Berea Col, BA, 62; Univ Mich, MA, 63, PhD(bot), 69. Prof Exp: Fel, Mo Bot Garden, 69-71; from asst prof to assoc prof ecol, Univ Wis-Green Bay, 71-78; RES ASSOC, HARVARD UNIV FOREST, 78- Concurrent Pos: Res assoc, Biol Sta, Univ Mich, 72-77. Mem: Ecol Soc Am; Brit Ecol Soc; Bot Soc Am; Am Soc Plant Physiologists. Res: Ecology of actinomycete-nodulated nitrogen fixing plants; ecology of northern bogs, swamps and fens emphasizing vegetation and nutrient status; physiological ecology of wetland plants. Mailing Add: Harvard Forest Harvard Univ Petersham MA 01366

SCHWIRZKE, FRED, b Schwiebus, Ger, Aug 21, 27; m 58; c 3. PHYSICS. Educ: Karlsruhe Tech Univ, MS, 53, Dr rer nat(physics), 59. Prof Exp: Scientist, Max-Planck Inst Physics & Astrophys, 59-61; group supvr plasma physics res, Inst Plasma Physics, Munich, Ger, 61-62; staff mem plasma physics, Gen Atomic Div, Gen Dynamics Corp, Calif, 62-67; ASSOC PROF PHYSICS, NAVAL POSTGRAD SCH, 67- Mem: Am Phys Soc; Inst Elec & Electronics Engrs; Sigma Xi. Res: Plasma physics; controlled thermonuclear fusion; turbulence and anomalous diffusion of plasmas confined in magnetic fields; laser produced plasmas; self-generated magnetic fields; plasma diagnostics; impurities and plasma wall effects; plasma sheaths; ionization and charge exchange cross sections. Mailing Add: Dept of Physics Naval Postgrad Sch Monterey CA 93940

SCHWITTERS, ROY FREDERICK, b Seattle, Wash, June 20, 44; m 65; c 2. PHYSICS. Educ: Mass Inst Technol, SB, 66, PhD(physics), 71. Prof Exp: Res assoc high energy physics, Stanford Univ, 71-74; from asst prof to assoc prof exp high energy physics, Stanford Linear Accelerator Ctr, 74-79; PROF PHYSICS, HARVARD UNIV, 79- Concurrent Pos: Assoc ed, Annual Reviews of Nuclear & Particle Sci, 78- Mem: Am Phys Soc. Res: Experimental high energy physics; development of large solid angle detection apparatus for use with high energy colliding beams; study of hadron production in electron-position collisions. Mailing Add: Physics Dept Harvard Univ Cambridge MA 02138

SCHWOEBEL, RICHARD LYNN, b New Rockford, NDak, Dec 26, 31; m 54; c 2. PHYSICS. Educ: Hamline Univ, BS, 53; Cornell Univ, PhD(eng physics), 62. Prof Exp: Sr engr, Gen Mills, Inc, 55-57; staff mem, 62-65, supvr, 65-69, MGR RADIATION & SURFACE PHYSICS RES DEPT, SANDIA LABS, 69- Concurrent Pos: Vis prof, Cornell Univ, 71. Mem: Fel Am Phys Soc; fel Am Inst Chemists. Res: Oxidation of metals; defect nature and transport properties of oxides; microgravimetry; electron microscopy and diffraction; crystal growth processes; surface morphology; nuclear waste management. Mailing Add: Dept 5110 Sandia Labs Albuquerque NM 87115

SCHWOERER, F(RANK), b New York, NY, Sept 5, 22; m 49; c 1. MECHANICAL ENGINEERING. Educ: Webb Inst Naval Archit, BS, 44; Mass Inst Technol, MS, 46. Prof Exp: Develop engr, Aviation Gas Turbine Div, Westinghouse Elec Corp, 47-51, supvr compressor develop, 51-55, mgr adv develop, 55-57, adv engr, Bettis Atomic Power Lab, 57-59, mgr adv reactor develop, 59-64; mgr eng, NUS Corp, 64-65, tech dir, 65-66, vpres, 66-68; assoc, Pickard Lowe & Assocs, 68-75; TECH DIR, NUCLEAR PROJS INC, 75- Mem: Am Soc Mech Engrs; Am Nuclear Soc. Res: Nuclear reactor engineering, economics and project management. Mailing Add: Nuclear Projs Inc 5 Choke Cherry Rd Rockville MD 20850

SCHY, ALBERT ABE, b Przemysl, Poland, July 30, 20; m 57; c 4. AEROSPACE ENGINEERING, SYSTEMS CONTROL THEORY. Educ: Univ Chicago, BS, 42. Prof Exp: Aerospace engr control eng, 49-55, sect head, 55-60, asst br head, 60-66, br head, 66-78, ASST BR HEAD CONTROL ENG, NASA LANGLEY RES CTR, 78- Honors & Awards: Spec Achievement Award, NASA Langley Res Ctr, 70. Mem: Am Inst Aeronaut & Astronaut; Am Automatic Control Coun. Res: Dynamics and control of aerospace vehicles; computer aided control system design. Mailing Add: NASA Langley Res Ctr MS-161 Hampton VA 23665

SCHYVE, PAUL MILTON, b Rochester, NY, May 16, 44. PSYCHIATRY, PSYCHOPHARMACOLOGY. Educ: Univ Rochester, BA, 66, MD, 70, dipl psychiat, 74. Prof Exp: Instr psychiat, Univ Rochester, 73-74; chief psychiat, US Air Force Regional Hosp, 74-75; staff psychiatrist, US Air Force Med Ctr, Wright-Patterson AFB, 75-76; unit chief, 76-77, assoc dir, 77-79, CLIN DIR, LAB BIOL PSYCHIAT, ILL STATE PSYCHIAT INST, 79- Concurrent Pos: Regional med consult, US Air Force Med Corps, 74-75; res assoc, Dept Psychiat, Univ Chicago, 76-80; asst prof, Dept Psychiat, Univ Chicago, 80-; attend mem, Dept Psychiat, Michael Reese Hosp, 80- Mem: Am Psychiat Asn. Res: Psychobiology of schizophrenia and affective illness; psychiatric diagnosis. Mailing Add: Ill State Psychiat Inst 1601 W Taylor St Chicago IL 60612

SCIALDONE, JOHN JOSEPH, b Vitulazio, Italy, July 25, 26; US citizen; m 52; c 2. MECHANICAL ENGINEERING, AEROSPACE ENGINEERING. Educ: Univ Naples, dipl eng, 49, DE(mech & aerospace eng), 69; Carnegie Inst Technol, BS, 53; Univ Pittsburgh, MS, 60. Prof Exp: Pneumatic engr, Air Brake Div, Westinghouse Air Brake Co, 53-57, analyst, 57-62, sr analyst, Astronuclear Lab, Westinghouse Elec Corp, 62-64; asst mgr advan res, Test & Eval Div, 64-68, actg off head, 68-70, STAFF ENGR, GODDARD SPACE FLIGHT CTR, NASA, 70- Concurrent Pos: Adj prof physics & math, Capitol Inst Technol, Kensington, Md, 76; consult, invest comts on vacuum, internal flow & contamination probs of NASA spacecraft; prin investr, Int Sci Comts on Mat in Space Environ. Mem: Inst Environ Sci; Am Vacuum Soc; Am Soc Testing & Mat. Res: Vacuum research and technology; space technologies; surface physics; kinetic theory; surface contamination; rarified gas dynamics; environmental testing; lubrication in space; instrumentation. Mailing Add: Instrument Div Systs Br Code 725 Goddard Space Flight Ctr NASA Greenbelt MD 20771

SCIAMMARELLA, CAESAR AUGUST, b Buenos Aires, Arg, Aug 22, 26; m 49, 68; c 2. ENGINEERING MECHANICS. *Educ:* Univ Buenos Aires, Dipl Eng, 50; Ill Inst Technol, PhD(eng), 60. *Prof Exp:* Supvr design & stress anal, Hormigon Elastico Inversor, 51-53; spec assignment engr, Ducilo, Inc, 53-54; tech dir, Zofra, Inc, 55-56; sr researcher reactor eng, Arg Atomic Energy Comn, 56-57; assoc res engr, Ill Inst Technol, 58-59, instr, 59-60; prof eng sci & mech, Univ Fla, 61-67; prof appl mech & aerospace eng, Polytech Inst Brooklyn, 67-72; PROF APPL MECH, MECH ENG & AEROSPACE & DIR EXP STRESS LAB, ILL INST TECHNOL, 72- *Concurrent Pos:* Prof, Arg Army Eng Sch, 52-57 & Univ Buenos Aires, 56-57; lectr, Brit Sci Res Coun, 66; NSF vis lectr, Europe, 66. *Mem:* Am Soc Mech Engrs; Soc Exp Stress Anal; Am Astronaut Soc; Am Soc Testing & Mat. *Res:* Experimental mechanics with particular emphasis in optical techniques; applications of experimental mechanics to the mechanics of materials; studies on the mechanism of failure of materials simple and composite. *Mailing Add:* Dept of Mech & Aerospace Eng Ill Inst of Technol Chicago IL 60616

SCIARINI, LOUIS J(OHN), b Branford, Conn, June 30, 15; m 53; c 1. ORGANIC CHEMISTRY. *Educ:* Pavia Univ, Italy, PhD(org chem), 39. *Prof Exp:* Asst chem microbiol, Fordham Univ, 40-45; res asst org chem, 46-62, RES ASSOC PHARMACOL, YALE UNIV, 63- *Mem:* AAAS; Am Chem Soc. *Res:* Mechanism of enzyme action; fermentation; wood-destroying fungi; chemical control of digitalis therapy; detoxication mechanisms; anti-viral and cancer chemotherapeutic agents. *Mailing Add:* Dept of Pharmacol Yale Univ New Haven CT 06520

SCIARRA, DANIEL, b Sansevero, Italy, Aug 19, 18; nat US; m 46, 59, 72; c 6. MEDICINE. *Educ:* Harvard Univ, BA, 40, MD, 43; Am Bd Psychiat & Neurol, dipl, 49. *Prof Exp:* Instr neurol, Harvard Med Sch, 44-45; from instr to assoc prof, 47-67, PROF CLIN NEUROL, COL PHYSICIANS & SURGEONS, COLUMBIA UNIV, 67- *Concurrent Pos:* Attend neurologist, Neurol Inst. *Mem:* Asn Res Nerv & Ment Dis; Am Neurol Asn; Am Acad Neurol. *Res:* Epilepsy; multiple sclerosis; brain tumors. *Mailing Add:* Neurol Inst 710 W 168th St New York NY 10032

SCIARRA, JOHN J, b Brooklyn, NY, Dec 28, 27; m 64; c 4. INDUSTRIAL PHARMACY. *Educ:* St John's Univ, NY, BS, 51; Duquesne Univ, MS, 53; Univ Md, PhD(pharm), 57. *Prof Exp:* Asst pharm, Duquesne Univ, 51-53; instr, Univ Md, 54-57; from asst prof to prof pharmaceut chem, St John's Univ, NY, 57-74, dir grad div, 66-73, asst dean col pharm & allied health professions, 72-73; prof indust pharm & dean, Brooklyn Col Pharm, 75-76, EXEC DEAN, ARNOLD & MARIE SCHWARTZ COL PHARM & HEALTH SCI, LONG ISLAND UNIV, 77- *Concurrent Pos:* Consult, 60; mem, Nat Formulary Adv Comt & adv panel pharmaceut, US Pharmacopeia Comt. *Mem:* Am Pharmaceut Asn; fel, Acad Pharmaceut Sci; fel, Soc Cosmetic Chem; Soc Cosmetic Chem (pres, 80). *Res:* Pharmacy; physical pharmacy; aerosol science and technology; particle size distribution. *Mailing Add:* Arnold & Marie Schwartz 75 DeKalb Ave at Univ Plaza Brooklyn NY 11201

SCIARRA, JOHN J, b West Haven, Conn, Mar 4, 32; m 60; c 3. OBSTETRICS & GYNECOLOGY. *Educ:* Yale Univ, BS, 53; Columbia Univ, MD, 57, PhD(anat), 64. *Prof Exp:* Am Cancer Soc fel, 64-65; asst prof obstet & gynec, Col Physicians & Surgeons, Columbia Univ, 65-68; prof obstet & gynec & head dept, Med Sch, Univ Minn, Minneapolis, 68-73; PROF OBSTET & GYNEC & CHMN DEPT, SCH MED, NORTHWESTERN UNIV, 73- *Concurrent Pos:* NIH spec fel, 65-68; mem nat med comt, Planned Parenthood-World Pop, 71- *Honors & Awards:* Carl G Hartman Award, Am Fertil Soc, 64. *Mem:* Am Col Obstet & Gynec; Am Fertil Soc; Am Col Surgeons; Am Asn Anatomists; Soc Gynec Invest. *Res:* Reproductive physiology and endocrinology. *Mailing Add:* Dept of Obstet & Gynec Northwestern Univ Sch of Med Chicago IL 60611

SCIARRONE, BARTLEY JOHN, b Jersey City, NJ, Nov 24, 26; m 65; c 1. PHARMACEUTICS. *Educ:* Rutgers Univ, BS, 52, MS, 55; Univ Wis, PhD(phys pharm), 60. *Prof Exp:* Instr pharmaceut chem, Col Pharm, Rutgers Univ, 54-55; asst, Univ Wis, 56-59; from asst prof to assoc prof, 58-69, asst dean, 81, PROF PHARM, COL PHARM, RUTGERS UNIV, NEW BRUNSWICK, 69- *Mem:* AAAS; Am Chem Soc; Am Pharmaceut Asn. *Res:* Kinetics and mechanisms of interactions in pharmaceutical systems. *Mailing Add:* Sch Pharm Rutgers Univ New Brunswick NJ 08903

SCIDMORE, ALLAN K, b Grafton, NDak, Mar 11, 27; m 53; c 4. ELECTRICAL ENGINEERING. *Educ:* Univ NDak, BS, 51; Univ Wis, MS, 53, PhD(elec eng), 58. *Prof Exp:* Res asst chem eng, 51-52, res fel elec eng, 53-54, res asst, 54-55, proj asst, 56-57, asst prof, 58-63, proj head, Digital Comput Lab, 57-59, assoc prof elec eng, 63-69, assoc dir, Univ Indust Res Prog, 76-80, PROF ELEC & COMPUT ENG, UNIV WIS-MADISON, 69- *Concurrent Pos:* Dir, Nat Eng Consortium, 77-80. *Mem:* Inst Elec & Electronics Engrs; Int Soc Biotelemetry. *Res:* Linear and digital circuit design and application. *Mailing Add:* Dept of Elec & Comput Eng Univ of Wis 1425 Johnson Dr Madison WI 53706

SCIDMORE, WRIGHT HARWOOD, b Saratoga Springs, NY, July 20, 25; m 51; c 3. OPTICS. *Educ:* Columbia Univ, BS, 50. *Prof Exp:* Staff mem, 50-58, chief, Optical Design Lab, Frankford Arsenal, US Army, 58-77; CONSULT OPTICAL DESIGN, SCIDMORE & SCIDMORE, 77- *Concurrent Pos:* Consult mil optical instruments, Int Sci Prog, 68-77. *Honors & Awards:* Meritorious Civilian Serv Award, US Army, 71; Karl Fairbanks Mem Award, Soc Photo-Optical Instrumentation Engrs, 73. *Mem:* Optical Soc Am; Sigma Xi. *Res:* Geometrical optics; lens design; military optical instruments. *Mailing Add:* 1173 Old Lincoln Hwy Langhorne PA 19047

SCIFRES, CHARLES JOEL, b Foster, Okla, June 1, 41; m 61; c 2. RANGE SCIENCE, WEED SCIENCE. *Educ:* Okla State Univ, BS, 63, MS, 65; Univ Nebr, PhD(agron, bot), 68. *Prof Exp:* Asst res agronomist, Range Ecol, Agr Res Serv, USDA, 65-68; asst prof range mgt, 68-69, assoc prof range ecol & improvements, 69-76, PROF RANGE SCI, PROF RANGE ECOL & DEPT RANGE SCI, TEX A&M UNIV, 76- *Mem:* Weed Sci Soc Am; Soc Range Mgt; Sigma Xi. *Res:* Development of vegetation manipulation systems for rangeland resources management for maximum productivity of usable products from the resource while maintaining its ecological integrity; persistence and modes of dissipation of herbicides from the range ecosystem; life history of key range species and community dynamics following vegetation manipulation. *Mailing Add:* Dept of Range Sci Tex A&M Univ College Station TX 77843

SCIFRES, DONALD RAY, b Lafayette, Ind, Sept 10, 46; m 69; c 4. PHYSICS, ELECTROOPTICS. *Educ:* Purdue Univ, Lafayette, BS, 68; Univ Ill, MS, 70, PhD(elec eng), 72. *Prof Exp:* RES SCIENTIST, & MGR, XEROX PALO ALTO RES CTR, 72- *Mem:* Am Phys Soc; fel Inst Elec & Electronics Engrs; fel Optical Soc Am. *Res:* Integrated optics and electro-optical devices; lasers. *Mailing Add:* Xerox Palo Alto Res Ctr 3333 Coyote Hill Rd Palo Alto CA 94304

SCIGLIANO, J MICHAEL, b Omaha, Nebr, Nov 22, 41; m 64; c 2. CHEMICAL & INDUSTRIAL ENGINEERING. *Educ:* Iowa State Univ, BS(chem eng) & BS(indust admin), 64, MS, 65; Washington Univ, DSc(chem eng), 71. *Prof Exp:* Process engr textile fibers, Monsanto Corp Eng, 65-68, sr engr polymers & petrochem, 68-72, process design supvr ABS resins, 72-75; process engr mgr nitration prod, 75-77, MGR PROCESS DESIGN CHEM GROUP, AIR PROD & CHEM, 77- *Mem:* Am Inst Chem Engrs; Nat Soc Prof Engrs. *Res:* Polymer solution thermodynamics; polymer characterization; polymer devolatilization; homogeneous catalysis; industrial equipment mortality. *Mailing Add:* Air Prod & Chem PO Box 538 Allentown PA 18105

SCINTA, JAMES, b Buffalo, NY. OIL SHALE PROCESSING, COAL CONVERSION. *Educ:* Cornell Univ, BS, 73; State Univ NY at Buffalo, MS, 75, PhD(chem eng), 77. *Prof Exp:* Res engr, 77-79, SECT SUPVR, PHILLIPS PETROL CO, 79- *Mem:* Am Inst Chem Eng; Am Chem Soc. *Res:* Processes for recovering hydrocarbons from oil shale. *Mailing Add:* 92-E Phillips Petrol Co Bartlesville OK 74004

SCIORE, EDWARD, b July 13, 55. DATABASE SYSTEMS. *Educ:* Yale Univ, BA, 76; Princeton Univ, PhD(comput sci), 80. *Prof Exp:* ASST PROF COMPUT SCI, STATE UNIV NY, STONY BROOK, 80- *Mem:* Asn Comput Mach. *Res:* Database systems, especially the semantics of data; database design methodologies; improved data description languages. *Mailing Add:* Dept Comput Sci State Univ NY Stony Brook NY 11794

SCIPIO, L(OUIS) ALBERT, II, b Juarez, Mex, Aug 22, 22; US citizen; m 42; c 3. SPACE SCIENCES. *Educ:* Tuskegee Inst, BS, 43; Univ Minn, BCE, 48, MS, 50, PhD, 54. *Prof Exp:* Instr archit & mech drawing, Tuskegee Inst, 46; struct engr, Long & Thorshov, 48-50; lectr aeronaut eng, Univ Minn, Minneapolis, 52-61; assoc prof mech, Howard Univ, 61-62; prof phys sci, Univ PR, 62-63; aerospace eng, Univ Pittsburgh, 63-67; prof aerospace eng & dir grad studies eng & archit, 67-70, UNIV PROF SPACE SCI, HOWARD UNIV, 70- *Concurrent Pos:* Fulbright prof, Cairo Univ, 55-56; consult, NASA Knowledge Availability Systs Ctr, Univ Pittsburgh, John Wiley & Sons, Inc & Winzen Res Inc. *Honors & Awards:* Steinman Award, 58. *Mem:* AAAS; Soc Natural Philos; Am Phys Soc; Am Inst Aeronaut & Astronaut; Int Asn Bridge & Struct Engrs. *Res:* Continuum mechanics; aerothermoelasticity; shell structures; viscoelasticity. *Mailing Add:* Grad Sch Howard Univ Washington DC 20059

SCISSON, SIDNEY EUGENE, b Danville, Ark, Feb 4, 17; m 42; c 2. ENGINEERING. *Educ:* Okla State Univ, BS, 39. *Prof Exp:* Civil engr, US Corps Engrs, Tulsa, 39-42 & Pate Eng Co, Tulsa, 45-48; PRES, FENIS & SCISSON, INC, 48- *Mem:* Nat Acad Eng; Am Inst Mining, Metall & Petrol Engrs; Am Gas Asn; Nat Gas Processors Asn. *Mailing Add:* Fenis & Scisson Inc PO Box 15609 Tulsa OK 74112

SCIUCHETTI, LEO A, b Harrison, Idaho, Apr 7, 13; m 43; c 2. PHARMACOGNOSY. *Educ:* Idaho State Col, BS, 40; Wash State Univ, MS, 42; Univ Wash, PhD(pharmacog), 57. *Prof Exp:* Lab asst pharmaceut chem, Idaho State Col, 39-40; instr, Creighton Univ, 42-43; prof pharm, Louisville Col Pharm, 43-46; asst prof, Ore State Univ, 46-48, assoc prof pharmacog, 48-59, prof & chmn dept, 59-66; assoc dir undergrad sci ed, 66-67, assoc prog dir, undergrad study prog, 66-73, mgr student-oriented prog, NSF, 73-77; CONSULT, 77- *Concurrent Pos:* USPHS grant, 64-67. *Mem:* Fel AAAS; Am Soc Pharmacog; Am Pharmaceut Asn; Acad Pharmaceut Sci; NY Acad Sci. *Res:* Alkaloid biogenesis in Solanaceae; growth regulator studies with medicinal plants; phytochemical screening of plants. *Mailing Add:* 5075 SW Angel St Beaverton OR 97005

SCIULLI, FRANK J, b Philadelphia, Pa, Aug 22, 38; m 65; c 2. EXPERIMENTAL PHYSICS, ELEMENTARY PARTICLE PHYSICS. *Educ:* Univ Pa, AB, 60, MS, 61, PhD(K-meson decay), 65. *Prof Exp:* Res assoc particle physics, Univ Pa, 65-66; res fel particle physics, Calif Inst Technol, 66-68, from asst prof to prof, 69-81; PROF PHYSICS, COLUMBIA UNIV, 81- *Mem:* AAAS; Am Phys Soc. *Res:* Weak interactions of elementary particles, particularly K-meson decays and neutrino interactions. *Mailing Add:* Physics Dept Columbia Univ New York NY 10027

SCIULLI, PAUL WILLIAM, b Pittsburgh, Pa, Aug 14, 47; m 73. BIOLOGICAL ANTHROPOLOGY, DENTAL ANTHROPOLOGY. *Educ:* Univ Pittsburgh, BA, 69, PhD(anthrop), 74. *Prof Exp:* Instr phys anthrop, Univ Pittsburgh, 73-74; vis asst prof, 74-76, ASST PROF PHYS ANTHROP, OHIO STATE UNIV, 76- *Concurrent Pos:* Consult breeding prog, SMI Chinchilla Farm, 75-78; res award, Col Soc & Behav Sci, Ohio State Univ, 75 & 79. *Mem:* Sigma Xi; Am Asn Phys Anthropologists; Am Asn Human Genetics. *Res:* Biocultural adaptations of prehistoric eastern woodland ameridians and genetic interactions in the production of coat color in the chinchilla. *Mailing Add:* Dept Anthrop Ohio State Univ Columbus OH 43210

SCIUMBATO, GABRIEL LON, b La Junta, Colo, Sept 12, 45; m 67; c 1. PLANT PATHOLOGY. *Educ:* Univ Eastern NMex, BA, 68; La State Univ, MS, 69, PhD(plant path). 73. *Prof Exp:* Technician plant path, La State Univ, 72-73; fel, Tex A&M Univ, 73-75; agronomist res & develop, US Borax Corp, 75-76; ASST PLANT PATHOLOGIST, MISS STATE UNIV, 76- *Mem:* Weed Sci Soc; Am Phytopath Soc. *Res:* Control of foliar cotton, soybean and rice diseases. *Mailing Add:* MAFES Delta Br Stoneville MS 38776

SCKERL, MAX MICHAEL, plant physiology, weed science, see previous edition

SCLAIR, MORTON H, b Bangor, Maine, Nov 18, 42; m 66; c 2. MOLECULAR BIOLOGY, MICROBIOLOGY. *Educ:* Univ Maine, BS, 64; Pa State Univ, MS, 65, PhD(biophys), 70. *Prof Exp:* Trainee genetics, Dept Bact & Immunol, Sch Med, Univ NC, 69-72; asst prof, 72-75, assoc prof & asst curric coordr biol, 75-80, PROF BIOL & CURRIC COORDR BIOL, ERIE COMMUNITY COL, CITY CAMPUS, 80- *Concurrent Pos:* Cancer res scientist, Dept Viral Oncol, Roswell Park Mem Cancer Inst, 73- *Mem:* Am Soc Microbiol; AAAS. *Res:* restriction enzyme mapping in SV40 virus mutants; gene splicing; gene transfer. *Mailing Add:* Dept Biol 121 Ellicott St Buffalo NY 14230

SCLAR, CHARLES BERTRAM, b Newark, NJ, Mar 16, 25; m 46; c 2. PETROLOGY, ORE DEPOSITS. *Educ:* City Col New York, BS, 46; Yale Univ, MS, 48, PhD(geol), 51. *Prof Exp:* Instr geol, Ohio State Univ, 49-51; res geologist, Battelle Mem Inst, 51-53, prin geologist, 53-57, asst consult, 57-62, res assoc, 62-65, assoc chief chem physics div & dir high-pressure res lab, 65-68; PROF GEOL, LEHIGH UNIV, 68-, CHMN DEPT GEOL SCI, 76- *Mem:* Fel Geol Soc Am; Soc Econ Geol; Geochem Soc; fel Mineral Soc Am; Am Geophys Union. *Res:* Petrology, geochemistry, mineralogy, high-pressure synthesis, phase equilibria and phase transformation; igneous and metamorphic petrology; shock metamorphism; shock effects in lunar minerals; mineral deposits and industrial applications of mineralogy. *Mailing Add:* Dept Geol Sci Williams Hall 31 Lehigh Univ Bethlehem PA 18015

SCLATER, JOHN GEORGE, b Edinburgh, Scotland, June 17, 40; m 68. OCEANOGRAPHY, GEOPHYSICS. *Educ:* Univ Edinburgh, BSc, 62; Cambridge Univ, PhD(geophys), 66. *Prof Exp:* NSF res grant, Scripps Inst Oceanog, Univ Calif, San Diego, 65-67, asst geophys res, 67-72, lectr geol, Univ, 71-72; assoc prof oceanog & marine geophys, 72-76, PROF MARINE GEOPHYSICS, MASS INST TECHNOL, 76- *Concurrent Pos:* Dir, Joint Prog Oceanog Woods Hole Oceanog Inst & Mass Inst Technol, 81. *Honors & Awards:* Rosenstiel award in Oceanography, 79. *Mem:* fel Am Geophys Union; fel Geol Soc Am. *Res:* Application of the theory of plate tectonics to the ocean environment. *Mailing Add:* Dept of Earth & Planetary Sci Mass Inst of Technol Cambridge MA 02139

SCLOVE, STANLEY LOUIS, b Charleston, WVa, Nov 25, 40; m 62; c 2. STATISTICS. *Educ:* Dartmouth Col, AB, 62; Columbia Univ, PhD(math statist), 67. *Prof Exp:* Res assoc statist, Stanford Univ, 66-68; asst prof, Carnegie-Mellon Univ, 68-72; assoc prof, 7-81, PROF MATH, UNIV ILL, CHICAGO CIRCLE, 81- *Concurrent Pos:* Consult, Alcoa Res Labs, Pa, 69; vis asst prof statist & educ, Stanford Univ, 71-72; vis assoc prof independent energy & mgt sci, Northwestern Univ, 80-81. *Mem:* Am Statist Asn; Inst Math Statist; Opers Res Soc Am. *Res:* Multivariate statistical analysis; regression analysis; linear statistical models. *Mailing Add:* Dept of Math Univ Ill Chicago Cirlce 819 Marion Ave Highland Park IL 60035

SCOBEY, ELLIS HURLBUT, b Kelso, Wash, Sept 15, 11; m 35; c 4. GEOLOGY. *Educ:* Cornell Col, AB, 33; Univ Iowa, MS, 35, PhD(geol), 38. *Prof Exp:* Asst geol, Univ Iowa, 35-38; asst geologist, Gulf Oil Corp, Ind, 38-44; geologist, Bay Petrol Corp, 44-47; dist geologist, Southern Minerals Corp, Tex, 47-51; chief geologist, Guy Mabee Drilling Co, 51-65 & Mabee Petrol Corp, 65-75; VPRES & TREAS, McFARLAND & SCOBEY, INC, 75- *Mem:* Soc Econ Paleontologists & Mineralogists; Am Asn Petrol Geologists. *Res:* Sedimentation; stratigraphy and petroleum geology in Illinois Basin; petroleum geology in West Texas. *Mailing Add:* 2 Chatham Ct Midland TX 79701

SCOBEY, ROBERT P, b Providence, RI, Sept 10, 38; m 60; c 3. PHYSIOLOGY, NEUROPHYSIOLOGY. *Educ:* Worcester Polytech Inst, BSEE, 60; Clark Univ, MA, 62; Johns Hopkins Univ, PhD(physiol), 68. *Prof Exp:* Asst prof neurophysiol, 68-77, ASSOC PROF NEUROL & PHYSIOL, SCH MED, UNIV CALIF, DAVIS, 77- *Res:* Neurophysiology of central nervous system; vision. *Mailing Add:* Dept Neurol Univ of Calif Sch of Med Davis CA 95616

SCOBY, DONALD RAY, b Sabetha, Kans, Mar 18, 31; c 1. ENVIRONMENTAL BIOLOGY. *Educ:* Kans State Univ, BS, 57; Nebr State Teachers Col, MS, 60; NDak State Univ, PhD(bot, ecol), 68. *Prof Exp:* Instr & prin high sch, Kans, 57-60; instr high sch, Colo, 61-65, chmn sci dept, 65-66; instr gen biol & sci methods, 67-68, asst prof biol & ecol, 68-71, assoc prof biol & ecol, 71-78, PROF BIOL, NORTH DAK STATE UNIV, 78- *Concurrent Pos:* Environ consult, Lutheran Social Serv, Minn, 70-73. *Mem:* Am Inst Biol Sci; Ecol Soc Am; Sigma Xi; Nat Asn Biol Teachers. *Res:* Energy efficiency; land use ecology; environmental education procedures; practices for environmental self sufficiency; application of ecological and biological principles to organic farming methods. *Mailing Add:* Dept Bot & Biol NDak State Univ Fargo ND 58105

SCOCCA, JOHN JOSEPH, b Philadelphia, Pa, Mar 23, 40; m 66; c 2. BIOCHEMISTRY, MOLECULAR BIOLOGY. *Educ:* Johns Hopkins Univ, BA, 61, PhD(biochem), 66. *Prof Exp:* NIH fel, McCollum-Pratt Inst, 66-68, asst prof, Univ, 68-72, ASSOC PROF BIOCHEM, SCH HYG & PUB HEALTH, JOHNS HOPKINS UNIV, 72- *Mem:* Am Soc Biol Chemists; Am Chem Soc. *Res:* Membrane biology; macromolecular transport; nucleic acid metabolism. *Mailing Add:* Sch of Hyg & Pub Health Johns Hopkins Univ Baltimore MD 21205

SCOFIELD, DILLON FOSTER, b Norfolk, Va, Aug 10, 43; m 71. PHYSICS, MATERIALS SCIENCE. *Educ:* George Washington Univ, BS, 65, MS, 66, PhD(solid state physics), 69. *Prof Exp:* Independent systs analyst, 60-67; res analyst solid state & high energy physics, Foreign Technol Div, Air Force Systs Command, 67-70, res physicist solid state physics, Aerospace Res Labs, 70-71; Nat Res Coun assoc, Wright-Patterson AFB, 72-74; MEM STAFF PHOTO PROD DEPT, EXP STA, E I DU PONT DE NEMOURS & CO, INC, 74- *Concurrent Pos:* Pres, Appl Sci, Inc, 77- *Mem:* AAAS; Am Phys Soc; Inst Elec & Electronics Engrs. *Res:* Ab initio quantum mechanical treatments of atomic, molecular and solid state physics; physical theory of photographic process, thin film fluid flow, mechanical and magnetic composites; high level languages for minicomputers; computer science. *Mailing Add:* Photo Prod Dept E-352 Exp Sta E I du Pont de Nemours & Co Inc Wilmington DE 19895

SCOFIELD, GORDON L(LOYD), b Huron, SDak, Sept 29, 25; m 47; c 2. MECHANICAL ENGINEERING. *Educ:* Purdue Univ, BS, 46; Univ Mo, MS, 49; Univ Okla, PhD, 68. *Prof Exp:* Instr mech eng, SDak State Col, 46-47; asst, Univ Mo-Rolla, 47-48, from instr to prof, 48-69; PROF MECH ENG & ENG MECH & HEAD DEPT, MICH TECHNOL UNIV, 69- *Concurrent Pos:* Consult, Naval Ord Test Sta, Calif. *Mem:* Am Soc Mech Engrs; Soc Automotive Engrs (pres, 77); Am Soc Eng Educ; Am Inst Aeronaut & Astronaut. *Res:* Heat transfer and energy conversion. *Mailing Add:* Dept of Mech Eng & Eng Mech Mich Technol Univ Houghton MI 49931

SCOFIELD, HERBERT TEMPLE, b West Lafayette, Ind, May 16, 09; m 60. PLANT PHYSIOLOGY. *Educ:* Cornell Univ. AB, 30, PhD(plant physiol), 37. *Prof Exp:* Asst plant physiol, Cornell Univ, 31-36, instr, 36-37; instr bot, Ohio State Univ, 37-40, asst prof, 40-43; from asst prof to prof, 46-72, head dept, 50-63, EMER PROF BOT, N C STATE UNIV, 72- *Concurrent Pos:* Agent, Bur Entom & Plant Quarantine, USDA, 39; consult acad affairs to rector, Agrarian Univ, Peru, 59, 61-62, 63-65, 67-79, 70-72. *Res:* Tobacco physiology. *Mailing Add:* 1306 Banbury Rd Raleigh NC 27607

SCOFIELD, JAMES HOWARD, b Gary, Ind, Oct 10, 33; m 59; c 3. THEORETICAL PHYSICS. *Educ:* Ind Univ, BS, 55, MS, 57, PhD(theoret physics), 60. *Prof Exp:* Res assoc theoret physics, Stanford Univ, 60-62; PHYSICIST, UNIV CALIF, LAWRENCE LIVERMORE LAB, 62- *Mem:* Am Phys Soc. *Res:* Atomic structure calculations; interaction of electrons and x-rays with atoms. *Mailing Add:* Lawrence Livermore Lab Livermore CA 94550

SCOGGIN, JAMES F, JR, b Laurel, Miss, Aug 3, 21; m 48; c 3. PHYSICS, ELECTRICAL ENGINEERING. *Educ:* Miss State Univ, BS, 41; US Mil Acad, BS, 44; Johns Hopkins Univ, MA, 51; Univ Va, PhD(physics), 57; Indust Col Armed Forces, grad(nat security), 62. *Prof Exp:* Physicist, Signal Corps, US Army, 51-53 & 54-55 & Defense Atomic Support Agency, 58-61, engr, Adv Res Proj Agency, 62-65, proj mgr ground surveillance systs, Electronics Command, 66-68; assoc prof elec eng, 68-75, PROF ELEC ENG, THE CITADEL, 75- *Mem:* Am Phys Soc; sr mem Inst Elec & Electronics Engrs; Am Nuclear Soc; Precision Measurements Asn; Am Soc Mech Engrs. *Res:* Micrometeorology; cellular convection; tropical communications; surveillance systems; artillery sound ranging; nuclear energy; precision electrical measurements. *Mailing Add:* The Citadel Charleston SC 29409

SCOGGIN, JOHN KYLE, insect toxicology, see previous edition

SCOGGIN, WILLIAM ALLEN, b Norfolk, Va, Feb 12, 26; m 51; c 5. OBSTETRICS & GYNECOLOGY. *Educ:* Univ Va, BA, 49, MD, 53. *Prof Exp:* From instr to asst prof obstet & gynec, Sch Med, Univ Va, 60-64; assoc prof, Sch Med, Western Reserve Univ, 64-66; PROF OBSTET & GYNEC & CHMN, MED COL GA, 66- *Concurrent Pos:* NIH fel obstet & gynec, Univ Va Hosp, 62-63; USPHS grant, 65-; Cleveland Diabetes Asn grant, 66; consult, Vet Admin Hosp Augusta, Macon City & Milledgeville State Hosps, 66- *Mem:* AAAS; AMA; Am Col Obstetricians & Gynecologists; Soc Gynec Invest. *Res:* Fetomaternal exchange mechanisms; amniochorionic membrane dynamics; diabetes in pregnancy. *Mailing Add:* Dept of Obstet & Gynec Med Col of Ga Augusta GA 30902

SCOGGINS, JAMES R, b Aragon, Ga, Sept 22, 31; m 52; c 2. METEOROLOGY. *Educ:* Berry Col, AB, 52; Pa State Univ, BS, 54, MS, 60, PhD(meteorol), 66. *Prof Exp:* Mathematician, Lockheed Aircraft Corp, Ga, 57-58; meteorologist, Nuclear Lab, 59-60; meteorologist, Aerospace Environ Div, NASA Marshall Space Flight Ctr, 60-67; assoc prof, 67-69, asst dean opers, 71-73, dir, Ctr Appl Geosci, 73-75, assoc dean res, 75-77, PROF METEOROL, COL GEOSCI, TEX A&M UNIV, 69-, HEAD DEPT METEOROL, 80- *Concurrent Pos:* Consult, Tex Dept Water Resources, 73- *Mem:* Am Meteorol Soc; Am Geog Soc; Am Geophys Union; AAAS. *Res:* Mesometeorology and weather modification. *Mailing Add:* Dept of Meteorol Tex A&M Univ College Station TX 77843

SCOGIN, RON LYNN, b Corpus Christi, Tex, Oct 6, 41; m 67; c 1. PLANT CHEMISTRY. *Educ:* Univ Tex, Austin, BA, 64, PhD(bot), 68. *Prof Exp:* Asst prof bot, Ohio Univ, 68-71; asst prof, 72-76, ASSOC PROF BOT, CLAREMONT GRAD SCH, 76-, CHMN DEPT, 79- *Concurrent Pos:* NSF fel, Univ Durham, Eng, 70-71. *Res:* Biochemical systematics and evolution; biochemical systematics of angiosperms. *Mailing Add:* Rancho Santa Ana Botanic Garden 1500 N College Claremont CA 91711

SCOLA, DANIEL ANTHONY, b Worcester, Mass, July 11, 29; m 53; c 4. CHEMISTRY, MATERIALS SCIENCE. *Educ:* Clark Univ, BA, 52; Williams Col, MA, 54; Univ Conn, PhD(org & phys chem), 59. *Prof Exp:* Lab asst chem, Williams Col, 52-54; res chemist, Durez Plastics Co, NY, 55; lab asst, Univ Conn, 55-57, asst instr, 57-58; sr res chemist, Monsanto Res Corp, Mass, 58-64, res group leader, 64-65; sr res scientist, United Aircraft Res Labs, Conn, 65-66; sr res engr, Res Labs, Norton Co, Mass, 66-67; sr res scientist & supvr org mat res, 66-74, SR MAT SCIENTIST, UNITED

TECHNOL RES CTR, EAST HARTFORD, 74- *Concurrent Pos:* Adj fac mem, Univ Hartford, 69-; dir & chmn relig educ comt, St Augustine Church, Glastonbury, 69- *Mem:* AAAS; Am Chem Soc. *Res:* Materials research, especially fiber reinforced polymeric materials; interface effects in composite materials; influence of environment on mechanical properties of composites; surface effects in adhesive bonding; synthesis of moisture resistant laminating resins, coatings and adhesives; synthesis and evaluation of high temperature polymeric materials. *Mailing Add:* 83 Stone Post Rd Glastonbury CT 06033

SCOLARO, REGINALD JOSEPH, b Tampa, Fla, Oct 19, 39; m 66; c 2. INVERTEBRATE PALEONTOLOGY, PALEOECOLOGY. *Educ:* Univ Fla, BA, 60, BS, 62, MS, 64; Tulane Univ, PhD(paleont), 68. *Prof Exp:* Intern, Smithsonian Inst, 67-68; res fel, Univ Ga, 68-69; assoc prof, 69-79, chmn dept, 71-79, PROF GEOL, RADFORD COL, 79- PROJ GEOLOGIST, GULF OIL EXPLOR & PROD CO, 79- *Mem:* Geol Soc Am; Paleont Soc; Paleont Res Inst. *Res:* Taxonomy and paleoecology of tertiary and recent Cheilostome Bryozoa. *Mailing Add:* Gulf Oil Explor & Prod Co PO Box 61590 New Orleans LA 70161

SCOLES, GRAHAM JOHN, b England, UK; Can citizen. PLANT BREEDING, CYTOGENETICS. *Educ:* Univ Reading, UK, BSc, 73; Univ Manitoba, MSc, 75, PhD(plant sci), 79. *Prof Exp:* ASST PROF CYTOGENETICS, UNIV SASK, CAN, 79- *Mem:* Can Genetics Soc. *Res:* Interspecific hybridization and cross-compatibility in crop species. *Mailing Add:* Crop Sci Dept Univ Sask Saskatoon SK S7N 0W0 Can

SCOLMAN, THEODORE THOMAS, b Duluth, Minn, Oct 27, 26; m 5 55; c 2. NUCLEAR PHYSICS. *Educ:* Beloit Col, BS, 50; Univ Minn, PhD(physics), 56. *Prof Exp:* Staff mem physics, Weapon Div, 56-62, test div, 62-66, assoc group leader, 66-69, asst div leader physics, Test Div, 72-78, PROG MGR, FULL TESTING, LOS ALAMOS NAT LAB, UNIV CALIF, 78- *Mem:* Am Phys Soc. *Res:* Nuclear weapons test and development; mass spectroscopy. *Mailing Add:* Los Alamos Nat Lab PO Box 1663 Los Alamos NM 87545

SCOMMEGNA, ANTONIO, b Barletta, Italy, Aug 26, 31; US citizen; m 58; c 3. REPRODUCTIVE PHYSIOLOGY. *Educ:* Univ Bari, MD, 53; Am Bd Obstet & Gynec, dipl & cert reprod endocrinol, 74. *Prof Exp:* Intern, New Eng Hosp, Boston, Mass, 54-55; resident obstet & gynec, 56-58, fel, Dept Human Reproduction, 60-61, res assoc, 61, dir sect Gynec & endocrinol, 65-81, ATTEND PHYSICIAN, DEPT OBSTET & GYNEC, MICHAEL REESE HOSP & MED CTR, 61-, CHMN DEPT, 69-; PROF OBSTET & GYNEC, PRITZKER SCH MED, UNIV CHICAGO, 69- *Concurrent Pos:* Pvt practice, 61-64; fel, Steroid Training Prog, Worcester Found, Exp Biol & Clark Univ, 64-65; assoc prof, Chicago Med Sch, 65-69. *Mem:* Fel Am Col Obstet & Gynec; AMA; Am Fertil Soc; Soc Study Reproduction; fel Int Fertil Soc. *Res:* Infertility and fertility; steroid chemistry; human reproduction; intrauterine contraceptive medication; hormones. *Mailing Add:* Dept Obstet & Gynec Med Ctr Michael Reese Hosp 2900 S Ellis Ave Chicago IL 60616

SCOPP, IRWIN WALTER, b New York, NY, Dec 8, 09; m 42; c 1. ORAL MEDICINE, PERIODONTICS. *Educ:* City Col New York, BS, 30; Columbia Univ, DDS, 34; State Univ NY, cert pedag, 35. *Prof Exp:* Asst chief dent serv, Vet Admin Hosp, North Little Rock Ark, 44-49, chief dent serv, Vet Admin Regional Off, 49-54, CHIEF DENT SERV, VET ADMIN HOSP, NEW YORK, 54-; PROF PERIODONT, DIR DEPT MED & DIR CONTINUING EDUC, COL DENT, NY UNIV, 54- *Concurrent Pos:* Consult, Goldwater Hosp, New York, 66- *Honors & Awards:* Hershfeld Medal, Northeastern Soc Periodont; Samuel Charles Miller Mem Award, Am Acad Oral Med, 71. *Mem:* Am Acad Periodont; Am Acad Oral Med; fel Am Col Dent; fel Am Pub Health Asn; Sigma Xi (pres, 64-66). *Res:* Dentistry; dental medicine. *Mailing Add:* New York Univ 342 E 26th St New York NY 10010

SCORA, RAINER WALTER, b Mokre, Silesia, Poland, Dec 5, 28; US citizen; m 71; c 3. BOTANY. *Educ:* DePaul Univ, BS, 55; Univ Mich, MS, 58, PhD(bot), 64. *Prof Exp:* Master prep sch, Mich, 58-60; from asst botanist to assoc botanist, 64-75, PROF BOT, UNIV CALIF, RIVERSIDE, 75- *Concurrent Pos:* NSF res grant, 65-71. *Honors & Awards:* Cooley Award, Am Inst Biol Sci, 68. *Mcm:* Phytochem Soc NAm; Bot Soc Am; Int Asn Bot Gardens; Int Orgn Biosyst; Int Soc Plant Taxon. *Res:* Biosystematics of the genus Monarda; taxonomy of subfamily Aurantioideae; phenolic and essential oil constituents of partheuium subfamily Aurantioideae; history, origin and evolution of citrus. *Mailing Add:* Dept Bot & Plant Sci Univ Calif Riverside CA 92521

SCORDELIS, ALEXANDER COSTICAS, b San Francisco, Calif, Sept 27, 23; m 48; c 2. STRUCTURAL & CIVIL ENGINEERING. *Educ:* Univ Calif, Berkeley, BS, 48; Mass Inst Technol, ScM, 49. *Prof Exp:* Struct designer, Pac Gas & Elec Co, 48; from instr to assoc prof, 49-62, PROF CIVIL & STRUCT ENG, UNIV CALIF, BERKELEY, 62- *Concurrent Pos:* Asst dean, Col Eng, Univ Calif, 62-65. *Honors & Awards:* Moissieff Award, Am Soc Civil Engrs, 76; Western Elec Award, Am Soc Eng Educ, 78; Axion Award, Hellenic Am Prof Soc, 79. *Mem:* Nat Acad Eng; fel Am Soc Civil Engrs; Am Concrete Inst. *Res:* Analysis and design of complex structural systems, especially reinforced and prestressed concrete shell and bridge structures. *Mailing Add:* Univ of Calif 729 Davis Hall Berkeley CA 94720

SCORDILIS, STYLIANOS PANAGIOTIS, b Bridgeport, Conn, Nov 13, 48. PROTEIN BIOCHEMISTRY, CELL PHYSIOLOGY. *Educ:* Princeton Univ, AB, 69; State Univ NY, PhD(biophys), 75. *Prof Exp:* Fel, Muscular Dystrophy Asn Am, 75-78; ASST PROF BIOL, SMITH COL, 78- *Mem:* Am Soc Cell Biol; Biophys Soc; Electron Micros Soc Am; Am Soc Zool. *Res:* Regulation of and energy transduction in muscle and non-muscle motility; contractile proteins and their interactions; role of fixed charge potentials in biological systems. *Mailing Add:* Dept of Biol Sci Smith Col Northampton MA 01063

SCORPIO, RALPH M, biochemistry, physiology, see previous edition

SCORSONE, FRANCESCO G, b Palermo, Italy, June 12, 20; US citizen; m 45; c 2. MATHEMATICS. *Educ:* Univ Palermo, PhD(math), 45. *Prof Exp:* From asst prof to assoc prof math, Hartwick Col, 61-65; assoc prof, 65-66, PROF MATH, EASTERN KY UNIV, 66- *Res:* Differential equations; mathematical analysis. *Mailing Add:* Dept of Math Eastern Ky Univ Richmond KY 40475

SCOTFORD, DAVID MATTESON, b Cleveland, Ohio, Jan 7, 21; m 47; c 4. PETROLOGY, STRUCTURAL GEOLOGY. *Educ:* Dartmouth Col, AB, 46; Johns Hopkins Univ, PhD(geol), 50. *Prof Exp:* Asst prof, 50-60, chmn dept, 60-79, PROF GEOL, MIAMI UNIV, 60- *Concurrent Pos:* Fulbright lectr grant, Turkey, 64-65; NSF travel grant, Brazil, 66; consult, Turkish Geol Surv, 65 & Shell Develop Co; fel, Univ Liverpool, 80-81. *Mem:* Fel Geol Soc Am; Mineral Soc Am. *Res:* Metamorphic petrology; structural geology; stratigraphy; shale mineralogy and petrography; feldspar structural and geochemistry studies related to geothermometry. *Mailing Add:* Dept Geol Miami Univ Oxford OH 45051

SCOTT, ALAN JOHNSON, b Chicago, Ill, Dec 26, 33; m 54; c 1. PALEONTOLOGY. *Educ:* Univ Ill, BS, 55, PhD(geol), 58. *Prof Exp:* Tech asst, Ill State Geol Surv, 54-58; from asst prof to assoc prof, 58-70, PROF GEOL, UNIV TEX, AUSTIN, 70- *Concurrent Pos:* Researcher, Ill State Geol Surv, 59. *Mem:* Soc Econ Paleont & Mineral; Geol Soc Am. *Res:* Micropaleontology, conodonts and chitinozoans; paleocology and biostratigraphy of upper paleozoic sediments. *Mailing Add:* Dept Geol Sci Col Natural Sci Univ of Tex Austin TX 78712

SCOTT, ALASTAIR IAN, b Glasgow, Scotland, Apr 10, 28; m 50; c 2. ORGANIC CHEMISTRY. *Educ:* Glasgow Univ, BSc, 49, PhD(chem), 52, DSc(chem), 63. *Hon Degrees:* MA, Yale Univ, 68. *Prof Exp:* Fel chem, Ohio State Univ, 52-53 & Birbeck Col, Univ London, 54-56; fel, Glasgow Univ, 56-57, lectr, 57-62; prof, Univ BC, 62-65 & Univ Sussex, 65-68; prof chem, Yale Univ, 68-77; prof chem, Tex A&M Univ, 77-80; prof org chem, Univ Edinburgh, 80-82; DAVIDSON PROF SCI, TEX A&M UNIV, 82- *Concurrent Pos:* Roche Found fel, 63-65. *Honors & Awards:* Corday Morgan Medal, 64; E Guenther Award, Am Chem Soc, 75. *Mem:* Fel Royal Soc; Am Chem Soc; The Chem Soc; Brit Biochem Soc; Swiss Chem Soc. *Res:* Chemistry and biochemistry of biologically significant molecules. *Mailing Add:* Dept of Chem Tex A&M Univ College Station TX 77843

SCOTT, ALBERT DUNCAN, b Cupar, Sask, Nov 1, 21; m 47; c 3. SOIL CHEMISTRY. *Educ:* Univ Sask, BSA, 43; Cornell Univ, PhD(soils), 49. *Prof Exp:* From asst prof to assoc prof, 50-58, PROF SOILS, IOWA STATE UNIV, 59- *Mem:* Clay Minerals Soc; fel Am Soc Agron; fel Soil Sci Soc Am; Int Soc Soil Sci. *Res:* Forms, reactions and plant availability of potassium in soils and minerals; clay mineralogy. *Mailing Add:* Dept of Agron Iowa State Univ Ames IA 50010

SCOTT, ALLEN, b Louisa, Ky, Jan 22, 48; m 77. ORGANIC CHEMISTRY. *Educ:* Ohio Univ, BS, 69; Purdue Univ, PhD(org chem), 75. *Prof Exp:* Fel, Mass Inst Technol, 75-77; SCIENTIST ORG CHEM, UPJOHN CO, 77- *Concurrent Pos:* NIH Res Serv fel, 75-77. *Mem:* Am Chem Soc. *Res:* Synthesis of pharmaceutical compounds; development of synthetic methods and tools. *Mailing Add:* UpJohn Co 7265-91-1 Kalamazoo MI 49001

SCOTT, ALWYN C, b Worcester, Mass, Dec 25, 31; m 58; c 2. SOLID STATE ELECTRONICS. *Educ:* Mass Inst Technol, BS, 52, MS, 58, ScD(elec eng), 61. *Prof Exp:* Engr, Sylvania Physics Lab, 52-54; from instr to assoc prof elec eng, Mass Inst Technol, 61-65; PROF COMPUT & ELEC ENG, UNIV WIS-MADISON, 65- *Concurrent Pos:* Guest prof, Univ Bern, 65-66; Belgian-Am Educ Found guest lectr, Univ Louvain, 66; researcher, Cybernet Lab, Univ Naples, Italy, 69-70. *Res:* Experimental and theoretical aspects of solid state device theory and nonlinear wave propagation including semiconductors; superconductors, laser media, high density logic systems and neurophysics. *Mailing Add:* Dept of Elec & Comput Eng Univ of Wis Madison WI 53706

SCOTT, ANDREW EDINGTON, b Newport, Scotland, Apr 27, 19; Can citizen; m 46; c 1. ORGANIC CHEMISTRY. *Educ:* Res fel chem, Ont Res Found, 50-52; res chemist, Elec Reduction Co Can, Ltd, 53-55; res fel chem, Ont Res Found, 59-60; lectr, Bristol Univ, 60-62; from asst prof to assoc prof, 63-66, head dept, 65-66, PROF CHEM, UNIV WESTERN ONT, 66-, DEAN FAC SCI, 66- *Prof Exp:* Res fel chem, Ont Res Found, 50-52; res chemist, Elec Reduction Co Can, Ltd, 53-55; res fel chem, Ont Res Found, 59-60; lectr, Bristol Univ, 60-62; from asst prof to assoc prof, 63-66, head dept, 65-66, prof chem, 66-79, dean fac sci, 66-79, EMER PROF, UNIV WESTERN ONT, 79- *Mem:* Fel Can Inst Chem. *Res:* Lignin chemistry; chemistry of condensed phosphates. *Mailing Add:* 451 Westmount Dr London ON N6K 1X4 Can

SCOTT, ARTHUR FLOYD, b Dickson, Tenn, Jan 10, 44; m 66; c 2. VERTEBRATE ZOOLOGY, HERPETOLOGY. *Educ:* Austin Peay State Col, BS, 65, MAEd, 67; Auburn Univ, PhD(zool), 76. *Prof Exp:* Instr biol, Univ S Ala, 67-70; asst prof, Union Col, Ky, 74-77; field rep zool, Ky Nature Preserves Comn, 77-78; asst prof, 78-80, ASSOC PROF BIOL, AUSTIN PEAY STATE UNIV, 80- *Mem:* Soc Study Amphibians & Reptiles. *Res:* Ecology, natural history and distribution of amphibians and reptiles in Kentucky and Tennessee. *Mailing Add:* Dept of Biol Austin Peay State Univ Clarksville TN 37040

SCOTT, BRUCE ALBERT, b Trenton, NJ, Feb 23, 40; m 62; c 2. PHYSICAL CHEMISTRY, INORGANIC CHEMISTRY. *Educ:* Rutgers Univ, BS, 62; Pa State Univ, PhD(chem), 65. *Prof Exp:* Res chemist, Eastern Lab, E I du Pont de Nemours & Co, 66-67; RES STAFF MEM, SOLID STATE CHEM, THOMAS J WATSON RES CTR, IBM CORP, 67-, MGR ORG SOLID STATE, 72- *Mem:* Am Chem Soc; Am Phys Soc. *Res:* Electric and magnetic properties of solids; crystal chemistry; crystal growth; phase equilibria; kinetics and mechanisms of film growth; solid state transformations. *Mailing Add:* Thomas J Watson Res Ctr IBM Corp Box 218 Yorktown Heights NY 10598

SCOTT, BRUCE L, b Waco, Tex, Oct 8, 32; m 54; c 3. THEORETICAL NUCLEAR PHYSICS. *Educ:* Calif Inst Technol, BS, 53; Univ Ill, MS, 55; Univ Calif, Los Angeles, PhD(physics), 60. *Prof Exp:* Consult physics, Atomics Int Div, NAm Aviation Inc, 57-60; asst prof, Univ Southern Calif, 60-65; assoc prof, 65-68, PROF PHYSICS, CALIF STATE UNIV, LONG BEACH, 68- *Concurrent Pos:* Consult, TRW Systs, Inc, 61-72. *Mem:* Am Asn Physics Teachers; Am Phys Soc. *Res:* Nuclear many-body problem; nucleon-nucleon interaction; electron-hydrogen scattering; 3-body problem. *Mailing Add:* Dept of Physics Calif State Univ Long Beach CA 90840

SCOTT, CHARLES COVERT, b Sparta, Ill, Jan 18, 09; m 33; c 2. PHARMACOLOGY. *Educ:* Mo Valley Col, BS, 29; Univ Mo, MS, 33; Univ Chicago, PhD(physiol) & MD, 37. *Prof Exp:* Prof physiol, Chicago Col Osteop, 34-36; intern med, Billings Hosp, Chicago, 38; asst prof physiol, Sch Med, Univ Tex, 39-40; asst in med, Univ Chicago, 40-41; pharmacologist, Res Labs, Eli Lilly & Co, Ind, 41-47; head dept gen pharmacol, 47-48; internist, Inlow Clin, Ind, 48-50; dir clin pharmacol, Warner-Chilcott Labs, 50-54, pharmacol, 54-57, res, 57-58, vpres basic sci, 58-63, vpres sci affairs, 63-67, dir med regulatory document, Warner-Lambert Res Inst, 67-74; RETIRED. *Mem:* AAAS; Am Soc Pharmacol & Exp Therapeut; AMA; NY Acad Sci; Pharmacol Soc Can. *Res:* Gastrointestinal physiology; secondary shock; pharmacology of analgesic, cardiac, diuretic, antispasmodic and central nervous system drugs. *Mailing Add:* 19419 Spook Hill Rd Freeland MD 21053

SCOTT, CHARLES D(AVID), b Chaffee, Mo, Oct 24, 29; m 56; c 3. CHEMICAL ENGINEERING & BIOCHEMICAL ENGINEERING. *Educ:* Univ Mo, BS, 51; Univ Tenn, MS, 62, PhD(chem eng), 66. *Prof Exp:* Develop engr, Y-12 Plant, Nuclear Div, 53-57, develop engr, Oak Ridge Nat Lab, 57-67, group leader bio eng, Sect Chief Chem Technol Div, 70-76, ASSOC DIV DIR, CHEM TECHNOL DIV, OAK RIDGE NAT LAB, UNION CARBIDE CORP, 76- *Concurrent Pos:* Vis lectr, Univ Tenn, 66-70, adj prof, 70- *Honors & Awards:* IR-100 Award, 71, 77, 78 & 79; Am Asn Clin Chem Award, 80; E O Lawrence Mem Award, Dept Energy, 80. *Mem:* AAAS; Am Inst Chem Engrs; Am Chem Soc; Am Asn Clin Chem. *Res:* Separations technology, heterogeneous kinetics; biotechnology; energy production. *Mailing Add:* Bldg 4505 Oak Ridge Nat Lab PO Box X Oak Ridge TN 37830

SCOTT, CHARLES EDWARD, b Philadelphia, Pa, Aug 26, 29; m 55; c 3. CHEMISTRY. *Educ:* St Joseph's Col, Pa, BS, 52; Univ Notre Dame, PhD(chem), 57. *Prof Exp:* Res chemist, US Rubber Co, NJ, 55-58; sect chief, Sun Oil Co, 58-63; asst dir carbon & elastomer res, Columbian Carbon Co, 63-72; ASST DIR PETROCHEM RES, CITIES SERV CO, 72- *Mem:* Am Chem Soc. *Res:* Petrochemical processing; carbon black development; new elastomers; flame retardants; intumescent coatings. *Mailing Add:* Cities Service Co PO Box 300 Tulsa OK 74102

SCOTT, CHARLES ELLIOTT, b Philadelphia, Pa, Nov 27, 35; m 56; c 4. CHEMICAL ENGINEERING. *Educ:* Drexel Univ, BS, 60; Univ Pa, MSE, 68. *Prof Exp:* Develop engr process res & develop, Atlantic Refining Co, 57-62; res engr explor catalytic res, Houdry Labs, Air Prod & Chem Co, 62-68, supvr comput oper, 68-69; dir math & comput applns, 69-70, mgr alumina clay proj, 70-72, DIR PROCESS RES & ENG, ALUMINA RES DIV, REYNOLDS METALS CO, 72- *Mem:* Am Inst Chem Engrs; Am Inst Mining, Metall & Petrol Engrs. *Res:* Kinetics; thermodynamics; hydrometallurgy; crystallization; liquid solids separations; fluid bed technology; mathematical modelling; process research and development; alumina production; alumina chemicals. *Mailing Add:* Alumina Res Div Reynolds Metals Co Bauxite AR 72011

SCOTT, CHARLES JAMES, b St Paul, Minn, Apr 16, 29; m 51; c 6. AERONAUTICAL ENGINEERING. *Educ:* Univ Minn, BS, 51, MS, 54, PhD, 64. *Prof Exp:* Scientist, Rosemount Aeronaut Labs, 52-65, ASSOC PROF MECH ENG, UNIV MINN, MINNEAPOLIS, 65- *Concurrent Pos:* NATO fel, Univ Naples, 65-66. *Mem:* Am Inst Aeronaut & Astronaut. *Res:* Aerothermodynamics. *Mailing Add:* Dept of Mech Eng Univ of Minn Minneapolis MN 55455

SCOTT, CHARLEY, b Meridian, Miss, June 10, 23; m 47; c 2. MECHANICAL ENGINEERING. *Educ:* Miss State Univ, BS, 44; Ga Inst Technol, MSME, 50; Purdue Univ, PhD(heat transfer, thermodyn), 53. *Prof Exp:* Instr drawing, Miss State Univ, 46-47; instr drawing & physics, Meridian Munic Jr Col, 47; instr mech eng, Univ WVa, 47-48; asst prof, Miss State Univ, 49-51, from assoc prof to prof, 53-63, res thermodynamicist, 61-63; from asst dean to dean grad sch, 63-76, actg dean, Capstone Col Nursing, 78-79, asst acad vpres, 73-76, PROF MECH ENG, UNIV ALA, TUSCALOOSA, 63-66 & 69-, ASSOC ACAD VPRES, 76- *Concurrent Pos:* Asst engr, Manhattan proj, Oak Ridge Nat Lab, 44-46; fel univ admin, Ctr Study Higher Educ, Univ Mich, 62-63; dir instrn, Univ Ala, Huntsville, 63-66, prof, 66-69, dir acad affairs, 66-68, dir div eng, 66-68, dir div grad studies, 68-69; dir, Univ Libr, Univ Ala, Tuscaloosa, 72. *Mem:* Am Soc Eng Educ; fel Am Soc Mech Engrs. *Res:* Heat transfer; thermodynamics. *Mailing Add:* PO Box 1336 University AL 35486

SCOTT, DAN DRYDEN, b Petersburg, Tenn, Apr 1, 28; m 55; c 2. ANALYTICAL CHEMISTRY, SCIENCE EDUCATION. *Educ:* Middle Tenn State Univ, BS, 50; George Peabody Col, MA, 54, PhD(sci ed, chem), 63. *Prof Exp:* Teacher high sch, Tenn, 52-55; from instr to assoc prof, 55-65, PROF CHEM & PHYSICS, MID TENN STATE UNIV, 65-, CHMN, 81- *Concurrent Pos:* Consult chemist, Samsonite, Inc, 64- *Mem:* AAAS; Am Chem Soc; fel Am Inst Chem. *Res:* Curricula for beginning college chemistry; analysis of trace amounts of alkalai metals. *Mailing Add:* Dept of Chem Box 68 Mid Tenn State Univ Murfreesboro TN 37131

SCOTT, DAVID ALEXANDER, anatomy, physiology, see previous edition

SCOTT, DAVID BYTOVETZSKI, b Providence, RI, May 8, 19; m 43, 65; c 5. MEDICAL & HEALTH SCIENCES. *Educ:* Brown Univ, AB, 39; Univ Md, DDS, 43; Univ Rochester, MS, 44. *Hon Degrees:* Dr, Col Med & Dent, NJ, Univ Louis Pasteur, France. *Prof Exp:* Carnegie fel, Univ Rochester, 43-44; mem staff, Nat Inst Dent Res, 44-56, chief lab histol & path, 56-65; Thomas J Hill distinguished prof phys biol, Sch Dent, Case Western Reserve Univ & prof anat, Sch Med, 65-75, dean, 69-75; dir, Nat Inst Dent Res, NIH, 76-81; CONSULT, 82- *Concurrent Pos:* USPHS, 44-65; mem gen res support prog adv comt, NIH, 72- *Honors & Awards:* Arthur S Flemming Award, 55; Award, Res in Mineralization, Int Asn Dent Res, 68. *Mem:* Am Dent Asn; Am Acad Forensic Sci; Electron Micros Soc Am; Am Col Dent; Int Asn Dent Res. *Res:* Physical biology; biological mineralization; histology and embryology of tooth structure by physical methods; dental caries; methods for age estimation in forensic odontology. *Mailing Add:* 10448 Wheatridge Dr Sun City AZ 85373

SCOTT, DAVID EVANS, b Los Angeles, Calif, June 27, 38; m 61; c 2. ANATOMY, NEUROENDOCRINOLOGY. *Educ:* Willamette Univ, BA, 60; Univ Southern Calif, MS, 65, PhD(anat), 67. *Prof Exp:* Instr neuroanat & histol, Med Sch, Univ Southern Calif, 65-67; from asst prof to assoc prof, 67-76, PROF ANAT, MED SCH, UNIV ROCHESTER, 76- *Concurrent Pos:* NIH grant, 68-; USPHS career develop award, 71-76; NSF grant, 78-80. *Mem:* Soc Neurosci; Am Asn Anat; Am Asn Neuropath; Electron Micros Soc Am. *Res:* Electron microscopy; brain-endocrine interaction. *Mailing Add:* Dept of Anat Univ of Rochester Med Sch Rochester NY 14642

SCOTT, DAVID FREDERICK, b Watertown, Mass, Mar 18, 40; m 63; c 3. BIOCHEMISTRY. *Educ:* Northeastern Univ, BA, 63; Ind Univ, Indianapolis, PhD(biochem), 68. *Prof Exp:* USPHS fel oncol, Univ Wis, 68-71; Brown-Hazen grant, 71-72, ASST PROF CELL & MOLECULAR BIOL, MED COL GA, 71- *Mem:* Am Asn Dent Res; Am Asn Lab Animal Sci; Sigma Xi; Am Asn Cancer Res; Am Chem Soc. *Res:* Intermediary metabolism; metabolic regulation; granulocytic function; biochemical oncology; enzymology; lipid metabolism and obesity. *Mailing Add:* Dept of Cell & Molecular Biol Med Col of Ga Augusta GA 30902

SCOTT, DAVID KNIGHT, b North Ronaldsay, Scotland, Mar 2, 40; m 66; c 3. NUCLEAR PHYSICS. *Educ:* Edinburgh Univ, BSc, 62; Oxford Univ, DPhil(nuclear physics), 67. *Prof Exp:* Res officer, Nuclear Physics Lab, Oxford Univ, 70-73, res fel nuclear physics, Balliol Col, 67-70, sr res fel, 70-73; physicist, Lawrence Berkeley Lab, Univ Calif, 73-75, sr scientist nuclear sci, 75-80; PROF PHYSICS, NAT SUPERCONDUCTING CYCLOTRON LAB, MICH STATE UNIV, 80- *Mem:* Am Phys Soc; AAAS; Europ Phys Soc. *Res:* Study of nuclear structure and reaction mechanisms using heavy ion collisions; particularly interested in relation of high energy and low energy phenomena. *Mailing Add:* Nat Superconducting Cyclotron Lab Mich State Univ E Lansing MI 48824

SCOTT, DAVID MAXWELL, b Glasgow, Scotland, Apr 30, 20; Can citizen; m 48; c 4. ZOOLOGY. *Educ:* McGill Univ, BSc, 42, MSc, 47, PhD, 49. *Prof Exp:* Lectr zool, McGill Univ, 48-51; from asst prof to assoc prof, 51-64, PROF ZOOL, UNIV WESTERN ONT, 64- *Mem:* Am Ornith Union; Brit Ornith Union. *Res:* Ornithology, particularly reproductive biology of passerines. *Mailing Add:* Dept of Zool Univ of Western Ont London ON N6A 5B8 Can

SCOTT, DAVID MORRIS, b Evanston, Ill, Feb 20, 33; m 55; c 4. COMPOSITE LEPTON MODELS. *Educ:* Mass Inst Technol, BS, 65; Ohio State Univ, PhD(physics), 69. *Prof Exp:* Jr engr, Delco Prods, Gen Motors, 55-58; res physicist group leader, Mound Lab, Monsanto Res Corp, 58-64; res asst, Ohio State Univ, Columbus, 65-69, res assoc, 69-70; asst prof, 70-75, assoc prof, 75-80, PROF PHYSICS, OHIO STATE UNIV, MANSFIELD, 80- *Mem:* Am Phys Soc; Am Asn Physics Teachers. *Res:* High energy or elementary particle physics including heavy quark production and composite lepton models. *Mailing Add:* Ohio State Univ 1680 Univ Dr Mansfield OH 44906

SCOTT, DAVID PAUL, b Montreal, Que, Apr 4, 26; m 49; c 4. BIOPHYSICS, BIOMETRICS. *Educ:* McGill Univ, BSc, 47, MSc, 49; Univ BC, PhD(zool), 56. *Prof Exp:* Biologist, Dept Maritime Fisheries, Prov Que, 49-50; biologist, BC Game Comn, 51-55; res scientist, Dept Environ, Freshwater Inst, Fisheries Res Bd Can, 56-70, res scientist, Dept Environ, Freshwater Inst, 70-79, RES SCIENTIST, WESTERN REGION, CAN DEPT FISHERIES & OCEANS, 79- *Concurrent Pos:* Hon lectr, Univ Western Ont, 56-66 & Univ Toronto, 61-64. *Mem:* NY Acad Sci; Am Fisheries Soc. *Res:* Fisheries biometrics; physiology and histopathology of fishes associated with pollution. *Mailing Add:* Dept of Environ Freshwater Inst Fisheries & Marine Serv Winnipeg MB R3T 2N6 Can

SCOTT, DAVID ROBERT MAIN, b Toronto, Ont, Aug 30, 21; m 44; c 4. SILVICULTURE. *Educ:* Univ Va, BA, 42; Yale Univ, MF, 47, PhD(forestry), 50. *Prof Exp:* Res forester, Forestry Br, Dom Dept Resources & Develop, 50-51; forester, Div Res, Ont Dept Lands & Forests, 51-55; from asst prof to assoc prof silvicult, 55-64, assoc dean col forestry, 64-69, PROF SILVICULT, UNIV WASH, 64- *Concurrent Pos:* Lectr, Inst Forest Biol, NC State Col, 60. *Mem:* Soc Am Foresters; Ecol Soc Am; Can Inst Forestry. *Mailing Add:* Col of Forest Resources Univ of Wash Seattle WA 98195

SCOTT, DAVID WILLIAM, b Trenton, NJ, Feb 4, 43; m 67; c 2. IMMUNOLOGY. *Educ:* Univ Chicago, MS, 64; Yale Univ, PhD(immunol), 69. *Prof Exp:* Jane Coffin Childs Mem Fund fel, Sch Path, Oxford Univ, 69-70; asst prof immunol, 71-74, assoc prof, 74-78, PROF IMMUNOL, DUKE UNIV, 79- *Mem:* AAAS; Am Asn Immunol; Am Soc Exp Pathologists; Brit Soc Immunol. *Res:* Immunologic tolerance; differentiation of immunologic competence; cellular interactions among lymphocytes. *Mailing Add:* Div of Immunol Box 3010 Duke Univ Med Ctr Durham NC 27710

SCOTT, DON, b Brooklyn, NY, July 8, 25; m 46; c 3. BIOCHEMISTRY, FOOD SCIENCE. *Educ:* Cornell Univ, BS, 44, MS, 45; Univ Chicago, MBA, 70; Ill Inst Technol, PhD, 50. *Prof Exp:* Bacteriologist & biochemist, Vita-Zyme Labs, Ill, 45-46, tech dir, 51-54; instr bact, Ill Inst Technol, 46-50; res bacteriologist, Jackson Lab, E I du Pont de Nemours & Co, 50-51; vpres, Fermco Labs, Inc, 54-66, vpres & gen mgr, Fermco Div, G D Searle & Co, 66-72, pres, Searle Biochemics Div, 72-75, tech dir, New Ventures Div, 73-75; PRES, FERMCO BIOCHEMICS INC, 75- *Mem:* Am Chem Soc; Am Asn Clin Chemists; Inst Food Technol; Am Inst Chem Engrs. *Res:* Microbial enzymes; food stabilization; clinical analytical procedures; research management; organizational structure. *Mailing Add:* Fermco Biochemics Inc 2638 Delta Lane Elk Grove Village IL 60007

SCOTT, DONALD, JR, b Oyster Bay, NY, Oct 16, 09; m 53; c 2. NEUROPHYSIOLOGY. *Educ:* Univ London, PhD(biophys), 39. *Prof Exp:* Assoc neurophysiol, Johnson Found, 39-48, assoc neurol, Sch Med, 39-S4, asst prof anat, 49-53, from asst prof to assoc prof, 53-77, PROF PHYSIOL, SCH MED, UNIV PA, 77- *Concurrent Pos:* Foreign investr award res, Turku Univ, 72. *Mem:* Am Physiol Soc; Brit Physiol Soc. *Res:* Influence on neural regeneration of proteosynthesis; identification and excitation of dentinal receptor in tooth; influence of heat, cold, pressure, anesthetics and microcirculation on receptor; role of metabolism and inorganic ions on receptor function; membrane physiology of receptor. *Mailing Add:* Dept of Physiol Univ of Pa Sch of Med Philadelphia PA 19104

SCOTT, DONALD ALBERT, b Campville, NY. Nov 20, 17; m 46; c 2. ORGANIC CHEMISTRY. *Educ:* Cornell Col, AB, 39; Univ Ariz, MS, 41; Univ Iowa, PhD(org chem), 52. *Prof Exp:* Instr chem, Univ Ariz, 41-42 & Cornell Col, 42-43, 46-49; asst prof, Wash & Jefferson Col, 51-54; assoc prof, 54-57, chmn dept, 54-71, PROF CHEM, DREW UNIV, 57- *Concurrent Pos:* NSF fac fel, Univ Calif, Los Angeles, 60-61. *Mem:* Am Chem Soc. *Res:* Structure of natural organic products; glycosides from bark; electrophilic substitution on carbon attached to sulfur. *Mailing Add:* Dept of Chem Drew Univ Madison NJ 07940

SCOTT, DONALD CHARLES, b Washington, DC, Jan 6, 20; m 42; c 5. LIMNOLOGY, FISH BIOLOGY. *Educ:* Univ Mich, BS, 42; Ind Univ, PhD(zool), 47. *Prof Exp:* Asst, Ind Univ, 42-47; from instr to assoc prof zool, 47-65, chmn div biol sci, 67-72, prof, 65-80, EMER PROF ZOOL, UNIV GA, 80- *Concurrent Pos:* Biologist, USPHS, 51-52; staff assoc, Div Inst Prog, NSF, 64-65. *Mem:* AAAS; Am Soc Ichthyologists & Herpetologists; Am Fisheries Soc; Soc Syst Zool; fel Am Inst Fishery Res Biol. *Res:* ichthyology. *Mailing Add:* Dept Zool Univ Ga Athens GA 30602

SCOTT, DONALD HOWARD, b Indianapolis, Ind, July 11, 34; m 56; c 4. PHYTOPATHOLOGY. *Educ:* Purdue Univ, BS, 56; Univ Ill, MS, 64, PhD(plant path), 68. *Prof Exp:* Field rep grain dealers, 56-62; res asst plant path, Univ Ill, 62-64, asst exten plant pathologist, 64-68; assoc prof, 68-80, PROF & EXTEN PLANT PATHOLOGIST, PURDUE UNIV, LAFAYETTE, 80- *Concurrent Pos:* Consult, 78- *Mem:* Am Phytopath Soc; Sigma Xi. *Res:* Diseases and disease control of agronomic crops; effects of crop rotation and tillage practices on disease development; interaction of insects, nematodes, and disease on crop yield losses. *Mailing Add:* Dept of Bot & Plant Path Purdue Univ Life Sci Bldg Lafayette IN 47907

SCOTT, DONALD RAY, b Wichita Falls, Tex, Apr 27, 34; m 58; c 3. PHYSICAL & ANALYTICAL CHEMISTRY. *Educ:* Univ Tex, Austing, xBA Austin, BA, 56; Univ Houston, MS, 60, PhD(phys chem), 65. *Prof Exp:* Res chemist clay & anal chem, Texaco Res Lab, 56-61; instr & res fel spectros & quantum chem, Dept Chem, Univ Tex, Austin, 64-65; asst prof, Tex Tech Univ, 65-67; scientist polymer photo decomposition, Lockheed-Ga Mat Sci Lab, 67-71; sect chief environ anal chem, US Environ Protection Agency, 71-73; assoc prof spectros, Dept Chem, SDak Tech Univ, 73-75; br chief environ anal chem, US Environ Protection Agency, 75-78; dir & res scientist environ phys & anal chem, Inst Appl Sci, NTex State Univ, 78-80; res chemist & br chief, Environ Methods Div, 80-81, RES ADVISOR, US ENVIRON PROTECTION AGENCY, 81- *Concurrent Pos:* Fel, Theoret Chem Group, Univ Tex, Austin, 64-65; consult, Intersoc Comt Heavy Metals, 74-75 & Environ Protection Agency, 78-; adj prof chem dept, NTex State Univ, 78-80. *Mem:* Am Chem Soc. *Res:* Electronic spectroscopy; quantum chemistry; environmental analytical chemistry; computer application to chemistry; theoretical predictions of toxicity. *Mailing Add:* MD-78A US Environ Protection Agency Research Triangle Park NC 27711

SCOTT, DONALD S(TRONG), b Edmonton, Alta, Dec 17, 22; m 45; c 2. CHEMICAL ENGINEERING, PHYSICAL CHEMISTRY. *Educ:* Univ Alta, MSc, 46; Univ Ill, PhD(chem eng), 49. *Prof Exp:* Jr petrol engr, Imp Oil, Ltd, 44-45; chem engr, Nat Res Coun Can, 46-47; asst prof chem eng, Univ BC, 49-56, assoc prof, 56-64; chmn dept, 64-69, actg dean eng, 69-70, PROF CHEM ENG, UNIV WATERLOO, 64- *Concurrent Pos:* Vis prof, Univ Cambridge, 63-64, assoc dean eng, 80- *Mem:* Fel Am Inst Chem Engrs; Am Chem Soc; fel Chem Inst Can; Can Soc Chem Engrs (vpres & pres, 70-72); Am Inst Mining, Metall & Petrol Engrs. *Res:* Kinetics; reactor design; catalysis; extractive metallurgy; conversion of biomass and cool to liquids. *Mailing Add:* Dept of Chem Eng Univ of Waterloo Waterloo ON N2L 3G1 Can

SCOTT, DONALD WILLIAM, physical chemistry, deceased

SCOTT, DWIGHT BAKER MCNAIR, b Coldwater, Mich, May 5, 07; m 36; c 2. BIOCHEMISTRY. *Educ:* Vassar Col, AB, 29; Radcliffe Col, PhD(biochem), 36. *Prof Exp:* Biochemist, Thorndike Mem Hosp, Boston, 29-31; Huntington Mem Hosp, 33-34; asst biol chem, Harvard Med Sch, 34-36, Univ Col Hosp Med Sch, London, 36-38 & Pa Hosp Nervous & Ment Dis, 41-42; instr pediat, Johns Hopkins Univ, 42-43; instr chem, Wellesley Col, 43-45; assoc pediat & physiol chem, Children's Hosp, Philadelphia, 47-53; asst prof med & physiol chem, Sch Med, 54-57, physiol, 57-65, from asst prof to assoc prof biochem, 65-72, prof biochem, 72-76, PROF EMER, SCH VET MED, UNIV PA, 76- *Mem:* AAAS; Am Soc Microbiol; Am Soc Biol Chem; Am Chem Soc; Brit Biochem Soc. *Res:* Carbohydrate metabolism and cancer; the role of zinc in female reproductive system. *Mailing Add:* 426 S 26th St Philadelphia PA 19146

SCOTT, EARLE STANLEY, b Bellingham, Wash, Oct 16, 22; m 44; c 7. INORGANIC CHEMISTRY. *Educ:* Reed Col, BA, 49; Univ Ill, PhD(inorg chem), 52. *Prof Exp:* Instr chem, Univ Calif, 52-55; asst prof, Amherst Col, 55-60; vis prof, Earlham Col, 60-62; assoc prof, 62-68, PROF CHEM, RIPON COL, 68- & CHMN DEPT, 78- *Mem:* AAAS; Am Chem Soc. *Res:* Chemical education. *Mailing Add:* Dept of Chem Ripon Col Ripon WI 54971

SCOTT, EDWARD JOSEPH, b Chicago, Ill, May 29, 13; m 40; c 1. MATHEMATICS. *Educ:* Maryville Col, Tenn, BA, 36; Vanderbilt Univ, MA, 37; Cornell Univ, PhD(math), 43. *Prof Exp:* Asst math, Univ Md, 37-39; instr, Lawrence Inst Technol, 39-43; instr, Cornell Univ, 43-46; from instr to assoc prof, 46-64, PROF MATH, UNIV ILL, URBANA, 64- *Res:* Partial differential equations; wave propagation. *Mailing Add:* Dept of Math Univ of Ill 273 Altgeld Hall Urbana IL 61801

SCOTT, EDWARD ROBERT DALTON, b Heswall, Eng, Mar 22, 47; m 80. COSMOCHEMISTRY, PLANETOLOGY. *Educ:* Univ Cambridge, BA, 68, PhD(mineral), 72. *Prof Exp:* Researcher geophys, Univ Calif, Los Angeles, 72-75; researcher mineral, Univ Cambridge, Eng, 75-78; res fel, Dept Terrestrial Magnetism, Carnegie Inst Wash, 78-80; RES SCIENTIST, INST METEORITICS, UNIV NMEX, 80- *Mem:* Meteorit Soc; Am Geophys Union; Mineral Soc. *Res:* Origin and formation of meteorites; composition, mineralogy and trace element distributions; analysis by electron probe and neutron activation analysis. *Mailing Add:* Inst Meteoritics Dept Geol Univ NMex Albuquerque NM 87131

SCOTT, EDWARD W, b Tulia, Tex, Nov 21, 09; m 33; c 3. GEOLOGY. *Educ:* Univ Calif, Los Angeles, BA, 32. *Prof Exp:* Geologist, Union Oil Co, Calif, 33-44, dist geologist, 44-53, chief geologist, Williston Basin, 53-54, geol coordr, 54-59, mgr opers, Can Div, 59-61, vpres explor, Union Oil Co Can, 61-67, mgr explor res, Union Oil Co Calif, 67-74; GEOLOGIST, RESOURCE ASSESSMENT GROUP, US GEOL SURV, 75- *Mem:* Am Asn Petrol Geol. *Res:* Exploration research in petroleum; basin assessment and evaluation with relation to hydrocarbon potential. *Mailing Add:* US Geol Surv 24000 Avila Rd Laguna Niguel CA 92677

SCOTT, EION GEORGE, b Glasgow, Scotland, May 3, 31; US citizen; m 57; c 3. PLANT PHYSIOLOGY, PLANT BIOCHEMISTRY. *Educ:* Glasgow Univ, BSc, 54; Univ Calif, Davis, PhD(plant physiol), 58. *Prof Exp:* Nuffield fel plant physiol, Univ Col Swansea, Wales, 58-60; asst prof, Univ Southern Calif, 60-62; chmn dept hort, WVa Univ, 62-69, prof hort & horticulturist, 62-73, prof agr biochem, 69-73; consult scientist hort, Gen Elec Co, 73-75, tech dir, Controlled Environ Agr Oper, 75-79, mgr, 78-80; GEN MGR, CONTROLLED ENVIRON AGRON OPER, CONTROL DATA CORP, 80- *Mem:* AAAS; Am Soc Hort Sci. *Res:* Trace element metabolism; plant organ culture; plant environment interactions photobiology. *Mailing Add:* Control Data Corp 75 Bidwell St St Paul MN 55107

SCOTT, ELIZABETH LEONARD, b Ft Sill, Okla, Nov 23, 17. MATHEMATICAL STATISTICS, BIOSTATISTICS ASTRONOMY. *Educ:* Univ Calif, AB, 39, PhD(astron, math statist), 49. *Prof Exp:* Asst statist, 39-41, asst astron, 41-42 & 44-46, assoc astron & instr, Exten Div, 46-47, assoc math & asst statist lab, 42-48, lectr, res assoc & instr, 50-51, from asst prof to assoc prof statist, 51-62, PROF STATIST, UNIV CALIF, BERKELEY, 62-, CO-HEAD GROUP BIOSTATIST, 73- *Concurrent Pos:* Chmn dept statist, Univ Calif, 68-73, asst dean, Col Lett & Sci, 65-67. *Honors & Awards:* Liege Medal, 55; Cleveland Prize, AAAS, 58. *Mem:* fel AAAS (vpres, 70-71); Am Astron Soc; fel Inst Math Statist (pres, 77-78); fel Royal Statist Soc; Int Statist Inst. *Res:* Applications of statistics to astronomy, medicine, biology and meteorology; methodology of evaluation cloud-seeding experiments; biological systems; distribution of galaxies in space; expansion of clusters; carcinogenesis. *Mailing Add:* Statist Lab Univ of Calif Berkeley CA 94720

SCOTT, ERIC JAMES YOUNG, b Gourock, Scotland, May 8, 24; nat US; m 59. CHEMISTRY. *Educ:* Glasgow Univ, BSc, 45, PhD, 48. *Prof Exp:* Nat Res Coun Can fel photochem, 48-50; AEC fel & res assoc radiation chem, Univ Notre Dame, 50-52; sr res chemist, 52-75, ASSOC CHEMIST, MOBIL RES & DEVELOP CORP, 75- *Mem:* Am Chem Soc. *Res:* Oxidation; kinetics of gas reactions; petroleum chemistry; chemical kinetics; homogeneous and heterogeneous catalysis; combustion. *Mailing Add:* Mobil Res & Develop Corp PO Box 1025 Princeton NJ 08540

SCOTT, FRANCIS LESLIE, b Cork, Ireland, July 3, 28; m 75; c 4. MEDICINAL CHEMISTRY, ORGANIC CHEMISTRY. *Educ:* Univ Col, Cork, BSc, 48, MSc, 49, PhD, 52; Nat Univ Ireland, DSc, 57; Royal Inst Chem, CChem, 75. *Prof Exp:* Demonstr chem, Univ Col, Cork, 48-49, asst, 49-51, lectr org chem, 51-53; Lilly fel, Univ Calif, Los Angeles, 53-55, lectr org chem, 55-57; proj leader, Explor Group, Pennsalt Chem Corp, Pa, 57-59, group leader, 59-60; prof chem & head dept, Univ Col, Cork, 60-73; vis prof, Univ Calif, Los Angeles, 73; DIR CHEM RES, PHARM DIV, PENNWALT CORP, 73- *Concurrent Pos:* Orgn Econ Coop & Develop sr fels, Switz, 64 & Poland, 65. *Mem:* Am Chem Soc; Royal Soc Chem; fel Inst Chem Ireland; Royal Irish Acad. *Res:* Mechanisms of inorganic and organic reactions; perchloryl chemistry; sulfur nitrogen, phosphorous and halogen compounds; high nitrogen heterocycles; neighboring group studies; halogenation reactions and electrochemistry; drug design; QSAR studies; neurochemistry; chemical toxicology. *Mailing Add:* Pennwalt Corp Pharm Div PO Box 1710 Rochester NY 14603

SCOTT, FRANKLIN JAMES, organic chemistry, polymer chemistry, see previous edition

SCOTT, FRASER WALLACE, b Montreal, Que, Nov 21, 46. METABOLISM, DIABETES. *Educ:* McGill Univ, BSc, 69, MSc, 72; Queen's Univ, PhD(biochem), 76. *Prof Exp:* Fel cancer res, Cancer Res Unit, Univ Alta, 76-77; RES SCIENTIST NUTRIT, DEPT NAT HEALTH & WELFARE, CAN, 77- *Mem:* Can Biochem Soc; Can Soc Nutrit Sci. *Res:* Hazardous effects of dietary carbohydrates, particularly in high risk segments of the population such as diabetics. *Mailing Add:* Nutrit Res Div Health Protection Br Tunney's Pasture Ottawa ON K1A 0L2 Can

SCOTT, FREDERICK ARTHUR, b Albany, NY, Mar 6, 25; m 51; c 2. ANALYTICAL CHEMISTRY. *Educ:* Rensselaer Polytech Inst, BS, 48, MS, 49, PhD, 52. *Prof Exp:* Sr scientist, Hanford Lab, Gen Elec Co, 52-65; chem div, Pac Northwest Labs, Battelle Mem Inst, 65-70; Wadco, 70-71; sr scientist, 71-80, MGR, WESTINGHOUSE HANFORD CO, 80- *Mem:* Am Chem Soc; Am Nuclear Soc. *Res:* Analytical instrument and methods development; sodium technology. *Mailing Add:* Westinghouse Hanford Co Richland WA 99352

SCOTT, FREDRIC WINTHROP, b Greenfield, Mass, Nov 22, 35; m 57; c 3. VETERINARY VIROLOGY, FELINE MEDICINE. *Educ:* Univ Mass, BS, 58; Cornell Univ, DVM, 62, PhD(vet virol), 68; Am Col Vet Microbiol, dipl. *Prof Exp:* Vet, Rutland Vet Clinic, Vt, 62-64; res vet, Plum Island Animal Dis Lab, Agr Res Serv, 64-65; Nat Inst Allergy & Infectious Dis res fel virol Cornell Univ, 65-68, asst prof, 68-73, assoc prof, 73-78, PROF VET VIROL, NY STATE COL VET MED, CORNELL UNIV, 78-, DIR, CORNELL FELINE HEALTH CTR, 74- *Concurrent Pos:* Prin investr res grant, State Agr Exp Sta, 69-79; USPHS prin investr res grant, Nat Inst Allergy & Infectious Dis, 70-73, co-investr res grant, Nat Inst ChildHealth & Human Develop, 71-74, prin investr res grant, Div Res Resources, 74-77; prin investr res contract, Nat Inst Allergy & Infectious Dis, 75-; mem, Int Working Teams on Small Enveloped RNA Viruses, Caliciviruses and Parvoviruses, WHO-Food & Agr Orgn Prog Comp Virol; fel, Mark L Morris Animal Found. *Mem:* Am Vet Med Asn; Conf Res Workers Animal Dis; Am Asn Feline Practitioners (pres, 76-78). *Res:* Feline and bovine viral diseases; feline infectious pertionitis; feline panleukopenia; feline respiratory diseases; bovine winter dysentery; antiviral compounds; intrauterine viral infections and teratology; maternal immunity; immunology. *Mailing Add:* Dept Microbiol Col Vet Med Cornell Univ Ithaca NY 14853

SCOTT, GARLAND ELMO, JR, b Greensboro, NC, Nov 30, 38; m 61; c 2. CERAMICS. *Educ:* NC State Univ, BS, 61, MS, 64, PhD, 71. *Prof Exp:* Res asst solid state res, NC State Univ, 61-67; ceramist, Monsanto Co, 67-69; res ceramist, Gen Elec Co, 69-76, mgr, Lamp Div, 76-78; asst prof ceramics, 77-80, PROF MAT ENG, CALIF STATE POLYTECH INST, 80- *Mem:* Am Ceramic Soc. *Res:* Solid state sintering; behavior of glass with low silica content. *Mailing Add:* 424 Adrian Ct Claremont CA 91711

SCOTT, GARY WALTER, b Topeka, Kans, Jan 19, 43; m 66; c 2. CHEMICAL PHYSICS. *Educ:* Calif Inst Technol, BS, 65; Univ Chicago, PhD(chem physics), 71. *Prof Exp:* NSF fel, Univ Pa, 71-72, NIH fel, 72-74; asst prof, 74-80, ASSOC PROF CHEM, UNIV CALIF, RIVERSIDE, 80- *Concurrent Pos:* Vis scholar, Wesleyan Univ, 80-81. *Mem:* Am Phys Soc. *Res:* Experimental chemical physics; spectroscopic studies of excited molecular states; development of short pulse lasers; applications of lasers to studies of the photophysics of n electron aromatics, fluorescent dyes, polymer photostabilizers, stabilized polymers, and hydrogen-bonded molecules. *Mailing Add:* Dept of Chem Univ of Calif Riverside CA 92521

SCOTT, GENE E, b Oberlin, Kans, June 11, 29; m 54; c 2. PLANT BREEDING. *Educ:* Kans State Univ, BS, 51, MS, 55, PhD(agron), 63. *Prof Exp:* Agent corn invests, 54-55, RES AGRONOMIST, AGR RES SERV, USDA, 55- *Mem:* Am Soc Agron; Crop Sci Soc Am. *Res:* Insect and disease resistance in corn; aspects of corn improvement. *Mailing Add:* Dept of Agron Box 5248 Miss State Univ Mississippi State MS 39762

SCOTT, GEORGE CLIFFORD, b Shumway, Ill, Dec 6, 26; c 7. VETERINARY MEDICINE. *Educ:* Univ Ill, BS, 50, DVM, 52. *Prof Exp:* Vet, Vet Pract, 52-58; asst vet med dir, Smith Kline & French Labs, 58-64; dir res & develop, Vetco, Johnson & Johnson, 64-66 & Animal Div, Schering Corp, 66-67; dir, 67-74, VPRES RES & DEVELOP, ANIMAL HEALTH PROD DIV, SMITH-KLINE BECKMAN CORP, 74- *Mem:* Am Vet Med Asn; Soc Study Reprod; Am Dairy Sci Asn; Am Soc Animal Sci; Am Poultry Sci Asn. *Res:* Parasites of domestic animals, nutrition of ruminants and control of diseases in domestic animals. *Mailing Add:* 800 Hessian Circle West Chester PA 19380

SCOTT, GEORGE DAVID, b Toronto, Ont, Jan 2, 18; m 48; c 3. PHYSICS. *Educ:* Univ Toronto, BA, 39, MA, 40, PhD(physics), 46. *Prof Exp:* Instr radio mech, Royal Can Air Force, 41-43; from asst prof to assoc prof, 56-62, assoc chmn dept, 62-68, PROF PHYSICS, UNIV TORONTO, 62- *Mem:* Am Phys Soc; Electron Micros Soc Am; Can Asn Physicists (secy, 59-62); Optical Soc Am. *Res:* Thin metal films; structure of liquids; relativity. *Mailing Add:* Dept of Physics Univ of Toronto Toronto ON M5S 1A7 Can

SCOTT, GEORGE PRESCOTT, b Pittsfield, Mass, Sept 17, 21; m 47; c 5. ORGANIC CHEMISTRY, PHILOSOPHY OF SCIENCE. *Educ:* Worcester Polytech Inst, BS, 43; Univ Rochester, PhD(chem), 49. *Prof Exp:* Assoc prof, 49-56, actg head dept, 59-60, 61-62, PROF CHEM, UNIV S DAK, VERMILLION, 56- *Concurrent Pos:* Res assoc, Univ Ill, 53-55; Fulbright lectr, UAR, 64-65; vis scholar, Univ Tex, Austin, 74. *Mem:* Am Chem Soc. *Res:* Polymers; telomers; free radical kinetics; history and philosophy of science; chemical ascillations. *Mailing Add:* Dept of Chem Univ of SDak Vermillion SD 57069

SCOTT, GEORGE TAYLOR, b Troy, NY, Sept 10, 14; m 43; c 2. PHYSIOLOGY. *Educ:* Union Univ, NY, AB, 38; Harvard Univ, MA, 40, PhD(physiol), 43. *Prof Exp:* From instr to prof zool, 43-60, head, Dept Zool, 57-60, head, Dept Biol, 60-67, prof biol, Oberlin Col, 60-80. *Concurrent Pos:* Trustee, Marine Biol Lab, Woods Hole, 56-73; trustee, Bermuda Biol Sta, 55-, pres, 67-77. *Mem:* AAAS; Am Soc Zool; Soc Gen Physiol; NY Acad Sci. *Res:* Marine antifouling; cellular electrolyte physiology; ion transport and exchange; physiology of psychotherapeutic drugs; pigment cell biology. *Mailing Add:* Dept Biol 10 Orchard St Woods Hole MA 02543

SCOTT, GEORGE VANE, b Jersey City, NJ, May 10, 17; m 59; c 3. COLLOID CHEMISTRY. *Educ:* St Peter's Col, BS, 39; Polytech Inst Brooklyn, PhD(chem), 49. *Prof Exp:* RES CHEMIST, COLGATE-PALMOLIVE CO, 41- *Mem:* AAAS; Am Chem Soc; Soc Cosmetic Chem. *Res:* Detergents; foam; detergency; toilet articles. *Mailing Add:* 1927 W Broad St Scotch Plains NJ 07076

SCOTT, GEORGE WILLIAM, b Cape Charles, Va, Apr 2, 17; m 43; c 3. ORGANIC CHEMISTRY. *Educ:* Col of William & Mary, BS, 38; Univ Va, MS, 41, PhD(org chem), 42. *Prof Exp:* Res chemist, Jackson Lab, 42-55, RES CHEMIST, NEOPRENE WORKS, E I DU PONT DE NEMOURS & CO, INC, 55- *Mem:* Am Chem Soc. *Res:* Polymerization of dienes; emulsion and colloidal chemistry. *Mailing Add:* 4706 Kittyhawk Way Louisville KY 40207

SCOTT, GEORGE WILLIAM, JR, b Auburn, NY, Feb 20, 12; m 39; c 3. PHYSICS. *Educ:* Wesleyan Col, BA, 34; Cornell Univ, AM, 35, PhD(physics), 38. *Prof Exp:* Asst physics, Cornell Univ, 34-38; Haskins Lab fel appl electronics, Mass Inst Technol, 38-40, res assoc, 40-41; res physicist, Armstrong Cork Co, 41-42, asst chief physicist, 42-46, asst mgr phys res, 46-52, mgr, 52-59, gen mgr phys res, 59-77; RETIRED. *Honors & Awards:* Award, Welding Soc, 44; Resistance Welder Mfrs Asn Award, 45; Inst Elec & Electronics Engrs Award, 45. *Mem:* Am Phys Soc. *Res:* Quartz crystal resonators; positive ion sources; high energy ion accelerators for nuclear physics; aluminum alloy spotwelding; induction and dielectric heating; calendering and mixing of plastic materials. *Mailing Add:* 1307 Hillcrest Rd Lancaster PA 17603

SCOTT, HAROLD GEORGE, b Williams, Ariz, Aug 20, 25; m 48; c 9. ENTOMOLOGY. *Educ:* Univ NMex, BS, 50, MS, 53, PhD, 57. *Prof Exp:* Entomologist, Med Field Serv Sch, Ft Sam Houston, US Army, Tex, 50-51, air res & develop Command, Kirtland AFB, US Air Force, NMex, 51-55, Commun Dis Ctr, USPHS, 55-67, Hosp, New Orleans, 67-69, Environ Health Serv, 69-71 & Environ Protection Agency, 71; prof trop med, 71-76, CONSULT COMMUNITY MED, TULANE UNIV, 76- *Mem:* Entom Soc Am; Soc Syst Zool; Sci Res Soc Am. *Res:* Public health and systematic entomology. *Mailing Add:* Dept of Community Med Tulane Univ Med Ctr New Orleans LA 70112

SCOTT, HARRY ELDON, entomology, deceased

SCOTT, HENRY WILLIAM, JR, b Graham, NC, Aug 22, 16; m 42; c 4. SURGERY. *Educ:* Univ NC, AB, 37; Harvard Univ, MD, 41; Am Bd Surg, dipl, 48. *Prof Exp:* Asst surg, Harvard Med Sch, 43-44, Cushing fel neurosurg, 44-45; asst surg, Sch Med, Johns Hopkins Univ, 46, from instr to assoc prof, 47-51; PROF SURG & HEAD DEPT, SCH MED & SURGEON-IN-CHIEF, UNIV HOSP, VANDERBILT UNIV, 52-, DIR, SECT SURG SCI, 75- *Concurrent Pos:* Chief surg consult, Vet Admin Hosp, 52-; mem, Am Bd Surg, 56-62, rep to adv bd, Med Specialties; mem, Nat Bd Med Examr, 65-; mem study sect B, USPHS & chmn, 66-70. *Mem:* Soc Clin Surg (pres, 71); Soc Univ Surgeons (pres, 60); Am Surg Asn (treas, 58-65, pres, 73-74); Am Col Surgeons (treas, 67-, pres, 75-76); Soc Surg Alimentary Tract (pres, 70-71). *Res:* Physiology and physiopathology of cardiovascular diseases; gastrointestinal disorders; surgical aspects of cancer. *Mailing Add:* Dept Surg Vanderbilt Univ Med Ctr Nashville TN 37232

SCOTT, HERBERT ANDREW, b Marion, Va, Mar 29, 24; m 47; c 2. POLYMERIZATION, HEAT TRANSFER. *Educ:* Va Polytech Inst, BS, 44, MS, 47. *Prof Exp:* Chem engr, Tenn Eastman Co, 47-59, supt glycol dept, 59-64, supt polymers div, 65-68; plant mgr, Holston Defense Corp, Tenn, 68-71; dir systs develop, 71-73, SUPT ENG, TENN EASTMAN CO, 73- *Mem:* Am Inst Chem Engrs; Sigma Xi; Am Mgt Asn; Nat Soc Prof Engrs. *Res:* Hydrogenation; polyester polymers; polyurethane elastomers. *Mailing Add:* Tenn Eastman Co Kingsport TN 37662

SCOTT, HOWARD ALLEN, b Ft Smith, Ark, Aug 12, 26; m 50; c 4. PLANT PATHOLOGY. *Educ:* Memphis State Col, BS, 49; Univ Mont, MA, 54; Univ Calif, PhD(plant path), 59. *Prof Exp:* Asst specialist plant path, Univ Calif, 54-59; plant pathologist virol, Crops Res Div, USDA, Md, 59-67; assoc prof, 67-68, PROF PLANT PATH, UNIV ARK, FAYETTEVILLE, 68- *Mem:* Am Phytopath Soc; Soc Invert Path. *Res:* Purification; electron microscopy; serological studies of plant and insect viruses. *Mailing Add:* Virol & Biocontrol Lab Rte 11 Univ Farms Fayetteville AR 72701

SCOTT, HUBERT DONOVAN, b Tarboro, NC, Apr 26, 44; m 68. SOIL SCIENCE. *Educ:* NC State Univ, BS, 66, MS, 68; Univ Ky, PhD(soil sci), 71. *Prof Exp:* assoc prof, 71-80, PROF SOIL PHYSICS, UNIV ARK, FAYETTEVILLE, 80- *Mem:* Am Soc Agron; Soil Sci Soc Am. *Res:* Movement of water and water soluble substances in the soil and their subsequent uptake by plants. *Mailing Add:* Dept of Agron Univ of Ark Fayetteville AR 72701

SCOTT, HUGH LAWRENCE, JR, b Baltimore, Md, Jan 10, 44; m 66; c 1. BIOPHYSICS. *Educ:* Purdue Univ, BS, 65, PhD(physics), 70. *Prof Exp:* Res assoc physics, Univ Utah, 70-72; asst prof, 72-76, ASSOC PROF PHYSICS, OKLA STATE UNIV, 76- *Concurrent Pos:* NSF grant, 74. *Mem:* Am Phys Soc; Biophys Soc; AAAS. *Res:* Development and analysis of theoretical models, using statistical mechanics for lipid monolayer, lipid bilayer and biological membrane thermodynamic behavior. *Mailing Add:* Dept of Physics Okla State Univ Stillwater OK 74014

SCOTT, HUGH LOGAN, III, b Lexington, Ky, Oct 19, 40; m 63; c 2. EXPERIMENTAL NUCLEAR PHYSICS. *Educ:* Univ Ky, BS, 62, MS, 66, PhD(physics), 67. *Prof Exp:* Res fel physics, Bartol Res Found, 67-69; asst prof, Univ Ga, 69-76; MEM TECH STAFF, SANDIA LABS, 76- *Mem:* Am Phys Soc. *Res:* Nuclear spectroscopy; decay schemes; spin-parities of nuclear states; analog states and elemental analysis via proton-induced x-rays. *Mailing Add:* Div 5423 Sandia Labs Albuquerque NM 87115

SCOTT, J(OHN) D(ONALD), Canadian; m 56; c 2. GEOTECHNICAL ENGINEERING. *Educ:* Queen's Univ, Ont, BSc, 54; Univ Ill, Urbana, MSc, 58, PhD(soil mech), 64. *Prof Exp:* Engr, Hardy & Ripley, Consult, 54-57; res asst civil eng, Univ Ill, Urbana, 57-60; asst prof, Univ Waterloo, 60-64, assoc prof, 64-66; prof & chmn dept civil eng, Univ Ottawa, 66-78; sr geotech engr, R M Hardy & Assocs Ltd, 78-80; AOSTRA PROF & CHAIR, UNIV ALBERTA, 80- *Concurrent Pos:* Private consult, 57-78; Nat Res Coun res grant, Univ Waterloo, 61-65 & Univ Ottawa, 65-78; Ont Res Coun res grant, Univ Waterloo, 64-65; vis scientist, Nat Res Coun Can, 65-66; dir & consult engr, Fondex Ltd, 71-74; Ont Ministry Transp & Commun res grant, 75-78; Nat Res Coun Can res grant, 78-; adj res prof civil eng, Univ Alta, 78-; Aostra res grant, 80-; geotech engr consult, 80- *Mem:* Eng Inst Can; Am Soc Civil Engrs; Can Geotech Soc (treas, 75-78); Can Inst Mining. *Res:* Slope stability; foundation performance; oil sand geotechnique; oil sand mining; tailings dams. *Mailing Add:* Dept Civil Eng Univ Alberta Edmonton AB T6G 2G7 Can

SCOTT, J(AMES) L(OUIS), b Memphis, Tenn, May 22, 29; m 53; c 2. MATERIALS SCIENCE, CERAMICS. *Educ:* Univ Tenn, BS, 52, MS, 54, PhD(metall), 57. *Prof Exp:* Instr chem eng, Univ Tenn, 53-56; metallurgist, 56-65, head ceramics lab, 65-74, MGR, FUSION REACTOR MAT PROG, METALS & CERAMICS DIV, OAK RIDGE NAT LAB, 74- *Concurrent Pos:* Mem, high temperature fuels comt, Atomic Energy Comn, 61-71; chmn, Special Purpose Mat Task Group, Dept Energy, 76- *Mem:* Fel Am Nuclear Soc; fel Am Soc Metals; Am Ceramic Soc. *Res:* Fabrication and irradiation behavior of reactor materials. *Mailing Add:* Oak Ridge Nat Lab C-103 5500 PO Box X Oak Ridge TN 37830

SCOTT, JAMES ALAN, b Adrian, Mich, Aug 17, 43; m 65; c 1. ANALYTICAL CHEMISTRY, NYLON POLYMERS. *Educ:* Bowling Green State Univ, BS, 64, MS, 65. *Prof Exp:* From chemist to supvr, 65-73, asst chief chemist, Plastics Dept, 73-77, SR PROD SPECIALIST, E I DU PONT DE NEMOURS & CO, INC, 78- *Mem:* Am Chem Soc; Soc Plastics Indust; Soc Electroplated Plastics. *Res:* Analytical chemistry of fluorocarbons and fluorocarbon polymers; atomic absorption spectrophotometry; flame emission spectrophotometry; thermal analysis; analysis automation; flame retardant thermoplastics. *Mailing Add:* 9 Jacqueline Dr Wellington Hills Hockessin DE 19707

SCOTT, JAMES ALLAN, b Boulder, Colo, Sept 15, 48. ECOLOGY, ENTOMOLOGY. *Educ:* Univ Colo, Boulder, BA, 68; Univ Calif, Berkeley, PhD(entom), 72. *Prof Exp:* Fel entom, Univ Calif, Davis, 73-75; FEL ECOL & SYSTS ANAL, NATURAL RESOURCE ECOL LAB, COLO STATE UNIV, 75- *Res:* Systems analysis and modeling of grassland invertebrates; field work and analysis of grassland invertebrates. *Mailing Add:* Natural Resource Ecol Lab Colo State Univ Ft Collins CO 80523

SCOTT, JAMES FLOYD, b Beverly, NJ, May 4, 42; m 63; c 2. SOLID STATE PHYSICS. *Educ:* Harvard Univ, AB, 63; Ohio State Univ, PhD(physics), 66. *Prof Exp:* Res fel physics, Ohio State Univ, 66; mem tech staff, Bell Tel Labs, NJ, 66-72; PROF PHYSICS & ASTROPHYS, UNIV COLO, BOULDER, 72- *Concurrent Pos:* Sci Res Coun sr vis fel physics, Univ Edinburgh, 70-71 & Osford Univ, 76-77; consult, Los Alamos Nat Labs, 74- & IBM, Zurich, 82; lectr, USSR Acad Sci, 77-81 & Japan Soc Promotion Sci, 80. *Mem:* Am Phys Soc. *Res:* Inelastic scattering of laser light from solid state excitations. *Mailing Add:* Dept of Physics Univ of Colo Boulder CO 80309

SCOTT, JAMES HENRY, b Marlboro, NY, Apr 19, 30; m 53; c 3. GEOPHYSICS, GEOLOGY. *Educ:* Union Col, NY, BS, 51. *Prof Exp:* With Beers & Heroy, 51, Phillips Petrol Co, 51-54, USAEC, 54-62, US Geol Surv, Colo, 62-67 & US Bur Mines, 67-74; GEOPHYSICIST, US GEOL SURV, 74- *Mem:* Soc Explor Geophys; Soc Prof Well Log Analysts. *Res:* Well logging for exploration and evaluation of mineral deposits. *Mailing Add:* US Geol Surv Mail Stop 964 Box 25046 Fed Ctr Denver CO 80225

SCOTT, JAMES J, b Wiota, Wis, Apr 22, 28; m 47; c 5. MINING ENGINEERING. *Educ:* Mo Sch Mines, BS, 50; Univ Wis, MS, 59, PhD(mining eng), 62. *Prof Exp:* Mine engr, Bethlehem Steel Co, Pa, 50-53, mine foreman, 53-57; from instr to asst prof mining, Univ Wis, 57-63; assoc prof, Univ Mo-Rolla, 63-65, chmn depts mining & petrol, 70-76, prof mining, 65-80. *Concurrent Pos:* Gen mgr, Black River Mine, Marble Cliff Quarries Co, 67; asst dir mining res, US Bur Mines, 70-; adj prof mining eng, Univ Mo-Rolla, 80- *Mem:* Am Inst Mining, Metall & Petrol Engrs; Soc Exp Stress Anal; Can Inst Mining & Metall. *Res:* Field rock mechanics; mine operational problems; experimental stress analysis; photoelasticity; model studies; stress distribution problems; mine and research management. *Mailing Add:* Dept of Mining Eng Univ of Mo Rolla MO 65401

SCOTT, JAMES MICHAEL, b San Diego, Calif, Sept 20, 41; m 66; c 2. ENDANGERED SPECIES. *Educ:* San Diego State Univ, BS, 66, MA, 70; Ore State Univ, PhD(zool), 73. *Prof Exp:* Biol aide, US Bur Commercial Fisheries, 66-68; asst curator vertebrates, Nat Hist Mus, Ore State Univ, 69-73, researcher, Dept Fisheries & Wildlife, 73-74; BIOLOGIST IN CHARGE, MAUNA LOA FIELD STA, US FISH & WILDLIFE SERV, 74- *Concurrent Pos:* Instr ornithol, Malheur Environ Field Sta, Pac Univ, 72 & 73; leader, Maui Forest Bird Recovery Team, 75-79, Hawaii Forest Bird Recovery Team, 75-; mem, Am Ornithologists Union Conserv, 74-75 & 75-76, Sci Adv Bd, Nature Conserv Hawaii Forest Bird Proj, 81- *Mem:* Am Ornithologists Union; Ecol Soc Am; The Wildlife Soc; AAAS. *Res:* Determining limiting factors for endangered species and devising methods for estimating their numbers which are statisticly sound and cost efficient; author or coauthor of over 40 publications. *Mailing Add:* Patuxent Wildlife Res Ctr US Fish & Wildlife Serv PO Box 44 Hawaii Nat Park HI 96718

SCOTT, JERRY BENJAMIN, b Ennis, Tex, Nov 29, 30; m 53; c 2. PHYSIOLOGY. *Educ:* Sam Houston State Univ, BS, 52; ETex State Univ, MS, 54; Univ Okla, PhD(physiol), 65. *Prof Exp:* Res assoc physiol, Sch Med, Univ Okla, 61-65, asst prof, 65-66; assoc prof, 66-73, PROF PHYSIOL, MICH STATE UNIV, 73- *Concurrent Pos:* NIH career develop award, Mich State Univ, 70-; estab investr, Am Heart Asn, Univ Okla, 65-66 & Mich State Univ, 66-70. *Mem:* Am Physiol Soc; Soc Exp Biol & Med. *Res:* Investigation into the factors that act locally to control blood flow through peripheral vascular beds including heart, skeletal muscle and kidney. *Mailing Add:* Dept of Physiol Mich State Univ East Lansing MI 48824

SCOTT, JOHN CAMPBELL, b Edinburgh, Scotland, Oct 5, 49; m 75. PHYSICS. *Educ:* Univ St Andrews, BSc, 71; Univ Pa, PhD(physics), 75. *Prof Exp:* Asst prof physics, Cornell Univ, 75-80; MEM RES STAFF, SAN JOSE RES LAB, IBM CORP, 80- *Mem:* AAAS; Am Phys Soc. *Res:* Experimental solid state physics; magnetic properties of solids; low dimensional conductors; quasi-one-dimensional magnetic materials; electronic properties of polymers. *Mailing Add:* IBM Res Lab K32-281 5600 Cottle Rd San Jose CA 95193

SCOTT, JOHN DELMOTH, b San Antonio, Tex, Aug 8, 44; m 67; c 3. CHEMICAL PHYSICS, MOLECULAR SPECTROSCOPY. *Educ:* Baylor Univ, BS, 67; NTex State Univ, PhD(chem), 74. *Prof Exp:* Teacher, John Marshall High Sch, 67-69; res fel, NTex State Univ, 75; res fel, La State Univ, 75-78; ASST PROF CHEM, UNIV MONT, 78- *Concurrent Pos:* Res fels, Robert A Welch Found, 75 & Energy Res & Develop Admin, 75-78. *Mem:* Am Chem Soc; Optical Soc Am. *Res:* Experimental and theoretical investigation of excited electronic states of molecules, principally molecular Rydberg states; experimental studies include vacuum-ultraviolet field effect, particularly magnetic and electric spectroscopy. *Mailing Add:* Dept Chem Univ Mont Missoula MT 59812

SCOTT, JOHN E(DWARD), JR, b Portsmouth, Va, Nov 29, 27; m 52; c 4. AEROSPACE ENGINEERING. *Educ:* Va Polytech Inst, BS, 48; Purdue Univ, MS, 50; Princeton Univ, MA, 53, PhD(aeronaut eng), 59. *Prof Exp:* Instr mech eng, Va Polytech Inst, 48; asst, Purdue Univ, 48-50; sr scientist, Exp, Inc, Va, 51; asst, Princeton Univ, 52-54, actng tech dir, Proj Squid, 54-56; assoc prof aeronaut eng, 56-62, res dir, Astronaut Div, 56-60, head aerospace div, Res Labs Eng Sci, 60-67, chmn dept aerospace eng & eng physics, 72-77, chmn dept mech & aerospace eng, 80-82, PROF AEROSPACE ENG, UNIV VA, 62- *Concurrent Pos:* Dir proj Squid, 62-67; liaison scientist, Br Off, Off Naval Res, London, 67-68; prog mgr res atomic interactions basic to macroscopic properties of cases, Univ Va, 68- *Mem:* AAAS; Am Phys Soc; Am Inst Aeronaut & Astronaut. *Res:* Gas dynamics; propulsion; astronautics; molecular physics. *Mailing Add:* Sch of Eng & Appl Sci Univ of Va Charlottesville VA 22903

SCOTT, JOHN MARSHALL WILLIAM, b Ipswich, Suffolk, UK, Nov 2, 30; m 55; c 3. CHEMISTRY. *Educ:* Univ London, BSc, 53, PhD(chem), 56. *Prof Exp:* Temporary sci officer, Serv Electronics Res Lab, Harlow, UK, 55-57; Nat Res Coun Can fel chem, 57-59; temporary lectr, Queen Mary Col, Univ London, 59-60; res chemist, Am Cyanamid Co, 60-62; assoc prof, 62-67, head dept, 68-69, 70-72, PROF CHEM, MEMORIAL UNIV, 67- *Concurrent Pos:* Hon vis prof, Univ Calgary, 69-70. *Res:* Organic mechanisms; physical and organic chemistry. *Mailing Add:* Dept of Chem Mem Univ St John's NF A1C 5S7 Can

SCOTT, JOHN PAUL, b Kansas City, Mo, Dec 17, 09; m 33, 79; c 4. ZOOLOGY, PSYCHOLOGY. *Educ:* Univ Wyo, BA, 30; Oxford Univ, BA, 32; Univ Chicago, PhD(zool), 35. *Prof Exp:* Asst, Univ Chicago, 32-35; assoc prof zool, Wabash Col, 35-42, prof, 42-45, chmn dept, 35-45; res assoc & chmn div behav studies, Jackson Mem Lab, 45-57, sr staff scientist, 57-65, trustee, 46-49; res prof, 65-68, Ohio Regents Prof Psychol, 68-80, EMER REGENTS PROF PSYCHOL, BOWLING GREEN STATE UNIV, 80- *Concurrent Pos:* Vis prof, Univ Chicago, 58; fel, Ctr Adv Study Behav Sci, 63-64. *Honors & Awards:* Jordan Prize, 47. *Mem:* AAAS; Am Soc Zool; Int Soc Develop Psychobiol (pres, 73-); Int Soc Res Aggression (pres, 73-74); Behav Genetics Asn (pres, 75-76). *Res:* Embryology and physiological genetics of the guinea pig; genetics and behavior of Drosophila; sociobiology; genetics and social behavior of dogs, mice and other mammals; development of behavior. *Mailing Add:* Ctr for Res on Social Behav Bowling Green State Univ Bowling Green OH 43403

SCOTT, JOHN STANLEY, b Hamilton, Ont, July 14, 29; m 56; c 2. GEOLOGY. *Educ:* McMaster Univ, BSc, 53; Univ Ill, Urbana, PhD(geol), 60. *Prof Exp:* Geologist, Photog Surv Corp Ltd, Can, 53-57; geologist, Geol Surv Can, 60-67; consult geologist, H G Acres & Co Ltd, Can, 67-69; res scientist, 69-74, DIR, TERRAIN SCI DIV, GEOL SURV CAN, 74- *Concurrent Pos:* Mem assoc comt geotech res, Nat Res Coun Can, 61-66. *Mem:* Geol Soc Am; fel Geol Asn Can. *Res:* Engineering geology; hydrogeology as related to construction; stability of slopes in overconsolidated shales. *Mailing Add:* Geol Surv of Can 601 Booth St Ottawa ON K1A 0E8 Can

SCOTT, JOHN W(ALTER), b Berkeley, Calif, May 27, 19; m 42; c 5. CHEMICAL ENGINEERING. *Educ:* Univ Calif, BS, 41, MS, 51. *Prof Exp:* Res chemist, 46-56, sr res chemist, 56-57, supvr res engr, 57-59, supvr petrol process develop, 60-64, mgr petrol process res & develop div, 64-67, V PRES PROCESS RES, CHEVRON RES CO, STANDARD OIL CO, CALIF, 67- *Concurrent Pos:* Chmn & mem adv bd, Chem Eng Dept, Univ Calif, Berkeley, 74-81. *Honors & Awards:* Award in Chem Eng Pract, Am Inst Chem Eng. *Mem:* AAAS; Am Chem Soc; Am Inst Chem Eng. *Res:* Physical chemistry; adsorption; synthetic fuels; processing; catalytic hydrogenation; hydrocracking; catalysis. *Mailing Add:* 576 Standard Ave Richmond CA 94802

SCOTT, JOHN WARNER, b Rochester, NY, Sept 27, 48; m 75; c 2. HORTICULTURE. *Educ:* Mich State Univ, BS, 70, MS, 74; Ohio State Univ, PhD(hort), 78. *Prof Exp:* Res technician, Mich State Univ, 70-75; res assoc hort, Ohio State Univ, 75-78, asst prof, 78-81; ASST PROF VEG CROPS, UNIV FLA, 81- *Concurrent Pos:* Mem staff, Bradenton Agr Res & Educ Ctr, 81- *Mem:* Am Soc Hort Sci. *Res:* Breeding, genetics, and culture of vegetable crops, especially tomatoes; selection methodology. *Mailing Add:* Bradenton Agr Res & Educ Ctr 5007 60th St E Bradenton FL 33508

SCOTT, JOHN WATTS, JR, b Oct 5, 38; US citizen; m 66. NEUROANATOMY, NEUROPHYSIOLOGY. *Educ:* Ala Col, AB, 61; Univ Mich, Ann Arbor, PhD(psychol), 65. *Prof Exp:* NIMH fel, Rockefeller Univ, 65-67, asst prof physiol psychol, 67-69; asst prof, 69-76, ASSOC PROF ANAT, SCH MED, EMORY UNIV, 76- *Concurrent Pos:* Nutrit Found grant, Emory Univ, 70-72, NSF grant, 71-73, 78-, NIMH res develop award, 71-76; Nat Inst Neurol & Commun Disorders & Stroke grant, 78- *Mem:* Am Asn Anatomists; Soc Neurosci. *Res:* Olfactory projections to the lateral hypothalamus, physiological properties of feedback circuits of the olfactory bulb, organization of the olfactory projection system. *Mailing Add:* Dept Anat Sch of Med Emory Univ Atlanta GA 30322

SCOTT, JOHN WILSON, b Toronto, Ont, July 7, 15; m 41; c 2. NEUROPHYSIOLOGY. *Educ:* Univ Toronto, BA, 37, MA, 38, MD, 41. *Prof Exp:* Dir EEG dept, Toronto Gen Hosp, 50; lectr physiol, 50-56, assoc prof, 56-60, PROF PHYSIOL, UNIV TORONTO, 60- *Concurrent Pos:* Fel med, Univ Toronto, 47-48; fel EEG, Montreal Neurol Inst, McGill Univ, 49; Nuffield fel, Nat Hosp, Queen Sq, London, Eng, 49-50; consult, Sunnybrook Hosp, 51-65 & Inst Aviation Med, Royal Can Air Force, 59; mem panel auditory prob, Defence Res Bd Can, 54-; chmn personnel res comt, Royal Can Navy, 56-65, chmn oper effectiveness of personnel, 66-70. *Mem:* EEG Soc; Soc Neurosci; Can Neurol Soc; Am Asn Hist Med; Can Med Asn. *Res:* Electroencephalography. *Mailing Add:* 15 Braemar Ave Toronto ON M5P 2L1 Can

SCOTT, JOSEPH LEE, b Delano, Calif, Mar 18, 43; m 64; c 3. BOTANY, CYTOLOGY. *Educ:* Univ Calif, Santa Barbara, AB, 65, MA, 67; Univ Calif, Irvine, PhD(biol), 71. *Prof Exp:* Asst prof, 70-76, ASSOC PROF BIOL, COL WILLIAM & MARY, 76- *Mem:* Phycol Soc Am; Int Phycol Soc; Brit Phycol Soc. *Res:* Development and ultrastructure of algae, particularly cell division and reproductive differentiation in red algae. *Mailing Add:* Dept of Biol Col of William & Mary Williamsburg VA 23185

SCOTT, JUNE ROTHMAN, b New York, NY, Nov 28, 40; m 66. MICROBIAL GENETICS. *Educ:* Swarthmore Col, BA, 61; Mass Inst Technol, PhD(microbiol), 64. *Prof Exp:* Guest investr, Rockefeller Univ, 64-66, res assoc, 66-69; asst prof, 69-75, assoc prof, 75-81, PROF MICROBIOL, SCH MED, EMORY UNIV, 81- *Concurrent Pos:* Nat Cancer Inst fel, 65-66. *Mem:* Am Soc Microbiol; Genetics Soc Am; Am Soc Virol. *Res:* Plasmids; bacterial genetics; lysogeny. *Mailing Add:* Dept of Microbiol Sch of Med Emory Univ Atlanta GA 30322

SCOTT, KENNETH ELSNER, b Webster, Mass, May 18, 26; m 52; c 4. MECHANICAL ENGINEERING. *Educ:* Worcester Polytech Inst, BS, 48, MS, 54. *Prof Exp:* From instr to assoc prof mech eng, 48-65, Alden prof eng & inst dir audiovisual develop, 72-75, PROF MECH ENG, WORCESTER POLYTECH INST, 65-, DIR INSTRNL TV, 72-, DIR COMPUTER AIDED DESIGN LAB, 81- *Honors & Awards:* Western Elec Fund Award, Am Soc Eng Educ, 73. *Mem:* Am Soc Mech Engrs; Am Soc Eng Educ; Sigma Xi. *Res:* Education; innovator of teaching methods; pioneer in use of individually prescribed instruction methods and use of audio-visuals in supporting these methods at Worcester Polytechnic Institute. *Mailing Add:* Dept Mech Eng Worcester Polytech Inst Worcester MA 01609

SCOTT, KENNETH JOHN, JR, marine ecology, see previous edition

SCOTT, KENNETH RICHARD, b New York, NY, Apr 17, 34; m 52; c 2. MEDICINAL CHEMISTRY, ANALYTICAL CHEMISTRY. *Educ:* Howard Univ, BS, 56; Univ Buffalo, MSc, 59; Univ Md, PhD(pharm chem), 66. *Prof Exp:* Asst pharm, biochem & anal chem, Univ Buffalo, 56-59; from instr to assoc prof, 60-75, PROF ANAL CHEM & INORG PHARMACEUT CHEM, COL PHARM, HOWARD UNIV, 75-, ASST DEAN STUDENT AFFAIRS & RECRUITMENT, 71- *Concurrent Pos:* Consult, S F Durst Co, 66-67 & NIH, 67-68; proj dir sem recruitment & retention minority disadvantaged students health professions, Howard Univ, 71; consult, Student Nat Pharmaceut Asn, 72 & Student Health Manpower Conf, 72; actg chmn, Dept Biomed Chem, 76. *Mem:* Am Chem Soc; Am Asn Cols Pharm; Am Pharmaceut Asn; Nat Pharmaceut Asn; fel Am Inst Chemists. *Res:* Synthetic chemistry, spiranes, carbazoles, steroids and biological testing; analytical chemistry, newer techniques in the development of assay procedures of pharmaceutical preparations. *Mailing Add:* Col of Pharm Howard Univ Fourth & College St NW Washington DC 20059

SCOTT, KENNETH WALTER, b Cleveland, Ohio, May 18, 25; m 67; c 4. POLYMER CHEMISTRY. *Educ:* Univ Mich, BS, 46; Princeton Univ, AM, 48, PhD(chem), 49. *Prof Exp:* Sr res chemist, Eastman Kodak Co, 49-55; res scientist, 55-57, sect head basic rubber res, 57-67, mgr basic polymer res, 67-73, mgr New Prod Res, 74-77, MGR TRANSP PROD RES, RES DIV, GOODYEAR TIRE & RUBBER CO, 77- *Mem:* Am Phys Soc; Am Chem Soc. *Res:* Viscoelastic behavior; chemistry and physics of high polymers. *Mailing Add:* Res Div Goodyear Tire & Rubber Co Akron OH 44316

SCOTT, KEVIN M, b Iowa City, Iowa, Aug 3, 35; m 61; c 2. GEOLOGY. *Educ:* Univ Calif, Los Angeles, BA, 57, MA, 60; Univ Wis, PhD(geol), 64. *Prof Exp:* Geologist, US Geol Surv, 59-60; proj assoc geol, Univ Wis, 61-64; NATO fel, Univ Edinburgh, 64-65; GEOLOGIST, WATER RESOURCES DIV, US GEOL SURV, 65- *Mem:* Am Asn Petrol Geol. *Res:* Sedimentology of marine and fluvial systems; sedimentary structures and their hydrodynamic interpretation; fluvial morphology; changes in sedimentologic parameters and mineralogy of sediments; environmental geomorphology; sedimentology and hazards assessment of lahars. *Mailing Add:* US Geol Surv 5391 Kenosha Ln Irvine CA 92715

SCOTT, L(YLE) JAMES, b Milroy, Minn, Apr 9, 13; m 36; c 2. ELECTRICAL ENGINEERING. *Educ:* Univ Minn, BEE, 35. *Prof Exp:* Mem tech staff equip design, Bell Tel Labs, 36-55, supvr switching eng, 55-58, head, Switching Studies Dept, 58-62 & Toll Switching Systs Requirements Dept, 62-71, head, Local Switching Systs Eng Dept, 71-76; RETIRED. *Res:* Fundamental long range planning for local switching systems. *Mailing Add:* 11 Woodland Dr Colts Neck NJ 07722

SCOTT, LAWRENCE TRESSLER, b Ann Arbor, Mich, June 11, 44; m 66; c 4. ORGANIC CHEMISTRY. *Educ:* Princeton Univ, AB, 66; Harvard Univ, PhD(org chem), 70. *Prof Exp:* Asst prof org chem, Univ Calif, Los Angeles, 70-75; asst prof, 75-77, assoc prof, 77-80, PROF CHEM, UNIV NEV, RENO, 80- *Concurrent Pos:* Petrol Res Fund grant, 70-73, 75-77, 78-80; NSF grant, 73-76, 79-82; NIH grant, 79-82; NATO sr scientist award, 81. *Mem:* AAAS; Am Chem Soc; Royal Soc Chem. *Res:* Organic syntheses and the chemical consequences of cyclic conjugation; aromaticity and pericyclic reactions; annulenes, azulenes, nonbenzenoid quinones, homoaromatic ions, cyclic polyacetylenes, and hydrocarbons; thermal rearrangements of aromatic compounds. *Mailing Add:* Dept Chem Univ Nev Reno NV 89557

SCOTT, LAWRENCE VERNON, b Anthony, Kans, Jan 28, 17; m 45; c 3. VIROLOGY. *Educ:* Phillips Univ, BA, 40; Univ Okla, MS, 47; Johns Hopkins Univ, ScD, 50. *Prof Exp:* From asst prof to assoc prof bact, 50-58, PROF MICROBIOL, SCH MED, UNIV OKLA HEALTH SCI CTR, 58-, CHMN DEPT, 61- *Concurrent Pos:* Consult, St Anthony & Vet Admin Hosps. *Mem:* Sigma Xi; Am Soc Microbiol; fel Am Acad Microbiol; NY Acad Sci; Am Soc Trop Med & Hyg. *Res:* Viral diseases of man; influenza; herpes simplex; Rous sarcoma; arboviruses. *Mailing Add:* Dept of Microbiol & Immunol Univ Okla Hlth Sci Ctr Box 26901 Oklahoma City OK 73190

SCOTT, LAWRENCE WILLIAM, b Manhattan, Kans, June 10, 24; m 49; c 3. FOOD SCIENCE, ANALYTICAL CHEMISTRY. *Educ:* Kans State Univ, BS, 51, MS, 54; Univ Mo-Columbia, PhD(food sci & nutrit), 70. *Prof Exp:* res & qual control chemist, Gen Lab, Utah-Idaho Sugar Co, 54-61; ASSOC PROF CHEM, UNIV WIS-RIVER FALLS, 61- *Mem:* AAAS; Inst Food Technologists; Am Chem Soc. *Res:* Metabolic products of filamentous fungi; consumer service food nutrient surveys; vitamin C; fat in ground meats; design of new experiments and modification of old to present interesting science to non-science students. *Mailing Add:* Dept of Chem Univ of Wis River Falls WI 54022

SCOTT, LEE R, JR, mechanical engineering, see previous edition

SCOTT, LELAND LATHAM, b Elba, Ill, Mar 31, 19; m 46; c 3. MATHEMATICS. *Educ:* Southern Ill Univ, BS, 47; Univ Ill, MS, 48, PhD(math), 51. *Prof Exp:* Asst math, Univ Ill, 47-51; from asst prof to assoc prof, Univ Miss, 51-57; from assoc prof to prof, Southwestern at Memphis, 57-62; assoc prof, 62-64, PROF MATH, UNIV LOUISVILLE, 64-, PROF GRAD SCH, 69- *Concurrent Pos:* Ford Found fac fel, 55-56. *Mem:* Am Math Soc; Math Asn Am; Asn Symbolic Logic. *Mailing Add:* Dept of Math Univ of Louisville Grad Sch Louisville KY 40208

SCOTT, LEONARD LEWY, JR, b Little Rock, Ark, Oct 17, 42; m 60; c 2. ALGEBRA. *Educ:* Vanderbilt Univ, BA, 64; Yale Univ, MA, 66, PhD(math), 68. *Prof Exp:* Instr math, Univ Chicago, 68-70; asst prof, Yale Univ, 70-71; assoc prof, 71-77, PROF MATH, UNIV VA, 78- *Concurrent Pos:* Mem ctr advan studies, Univ Va, 71-73; vis assoc prof, Univ Mich, 74-75; vis prof, Yale Univ, 78. *Mem:* Am Math Soc. *Res:* Finite permutation groups; representation theory; cohomology; algebraic groups. *Mailing Add:* Dept of Math Univ of Va Charlottesville VA 22903

SCOTT, LINUS ALBERT, b Jacksonville, Fla, June 8, 23; m 43; c 2. MECHANICAL ENGINEERING. *Educ:* Univ Fla, BME, 48, MSE, 51; Case Inst Technol, PhD(mech eng), 60. *Prof Exp:* From instr to asst prof mech eng, Univ Fla, 48-57; instr, Case Inst Technol, 57-58 & 59-60; assoc prof, Univ Fla, 60-62; prof, Univ Toledo, 63; PROF ENERGY CONVERSION & CHMN DEPT, UNIV S FLA, 64- *Mem:* Instrument Soc Am; Am Soc Mech Engrs. *Res:* Instrumentation and automatic control of industrial operations. *Mailing Add:* Col of Eng Univ of S Fla Tampa FL 33620

SCOTT, MACK TOMMIE, b Grand Junction, Tenn, Dec 4, 31; m 58; c 2. ANIMAL SCIENCE, VETERINARY MEDICINE. *Educ:* Tenn State Univ, BS, 58; Tuskegee Inst, DVM, 62. *Prof Exp:* Instr clin vet med, Tuskegee Inst, 62-63; ASST PROF RES VET PHYSIOL & DIR EXP ANIMAL HOSP, MEHARRY MED COL, 63- *Mem:* Am Vet Med Asn; Am Asn Lab Animal Sci. *Res:* Laboratory animal nutrition and diseases; cellular physiology; experimental production of kernicterus and study of the pathogenesis of hemolytic anemia and jaundice in new born rabbits. *Mailing Add:* 6128 Beal's Ln Nashville TN 37218

SCOTT, MARION B(OARDMAN), b Ashland, Nebr, Dec 9, 12; m 42; c 2. CIVIL ENGINEERING. *Educ:* Univ Nebr, BSCE, 34; Purdue Univ, MSCE, 44. *Prof Exp:* Engr, State of Nebr Bur Rd & Irrig, 34-37; instr engr drawing, Purdue Univ, 37-41, instr civil eng, 42-44; engr, Third Locks Proj, CZ, 41-42; process engr & asst to head physics dept, Curtiss-Wright Res Lab, 44-46; from asst prof to assoc prof, 46-57, head struct eng, 62-64, asst dean, 64-68, PROF CIVIL ENG, PURDUE UNIV, 57-, ASSOC DEAN ENG, 68- *Mem:* AAAS; Am Soc Civil Engrs; Rwy Eng Asn; Soc Exp Stress Anal; Am Soc Eng Educ. *Res:* Analysis, stress measurement and performance of structural steel bridges, buildings and structural components. *Mailing Add:* Dept of Struct Eng Purdue Univ West Lafayette IN 47907

SCOTT, MARTHA RICHTER, b Dallas, Tex, July 8, 41; m 62. MARINE GEOCHEMISTRY. *Educ:* Rice Univ, BA, 63, PhD(geol), 66. *Prof Exp:* NSF fel geol, Yale Univ, 66-67; res assoc geol & oceanog, Fla State Univ, 67-69, 70-71; res assoc, 71-74, vis asst prof oceanog, 74-75, ASST PROF OCEANOG, TEX A&M UNIV, 75- *Mem:* Am Geophys Union; Am Geol Inst; Am Soc Oceanog; Geochem Soc; AAAS. *Res:* Interaction of land-derived materials with sea water; uranium series isotopes in sea water and sediments; adsorption chemistry in marine environment; incorporation of trace metals into ferromanganese deposits; chemistry of plutonium isotopes in the environment. *Mailing Add:* Dept of Oceanog Tex A&M Univ College Station TX 77843

SCOTT, MARVIN WADE, b Clifton Forge, Sept 6, 36; m 62; c 2. BOTANY, MICROBIOLOGY. *Educ:* Hampden-Sydney Col, BS, 59; Va Polytech Inst & State Univ, PhD(bot), 68. *Prof Exp:* Chmn dept sci, Lynchburg Pub Sch Syst, Va, 59-60; res asst bot, Longwood Col, 60-62; instr biol, Hampden-Sydney Col, 62-63; assoc prof, 66-71, PROF BIOL, LONGWOOD COL, 71-, CHMN DEPT NATURAL SCI, 70- *Mem:* AAAS; Bot Soc Am. *Res:* Isolation and fermentation studies of Streptococcus lactis variety tardus; genetics and cytology studies of species of Iliamn. *Mailing Add:* Stevens Hall Longwood Col Farmville VA 23901

SCOTT, MARY JEAN (MRS E C H SILK), b Brooklyn, NY, Nov 8, 31; m 59; c 3. MEDICAL PHYSICS, NUCLEAR PHYSICS. *Educ:* St Lawrence Univ, BS, 52; Johns Hopkins Univ, PhD(physics), 58. *Prof Exp:* Vis asst physics, Brookhaven Nat Lab, 55, jr res assoc, 55-58; asst prof, Bryn Mawr Col, 58; vis res assoc nuclear physics, Atomic Energy Res Estab, Eng, 58-60; res assoc, Univ Witwatersrand, 60-61, lectr physics, 61-67; med physicist, Johannesburg Gen Hosp, 67-80; SR MED PHYSICIST, HILLBROW HOSP, JOHANNESBURG, 80- *Mem:* AAAS; Am Phys Soc; SAfrican Asn Physicists Med; SAfrican Inst Physics; SAfrican Soc Nuclear Med (secy-treas, 74-78). *Res:* Proton polarization; radiobiology; effects of fractionated radiation therapy on cell populations and determination of cell parameters. *Mailing Add:* Dept Med Physics Hillbrow Hosp Johannesburg South Africa

SCOTT, MECKINLEY, b Shillong, India, Mar 1, 35; m 65; c 1. APPLIED MATHEMATICS, STATISTICS. *Educ:* Presidency Col Calcutta, India, BS, 55; Gauhati Univ, India, MS, 57; Univ NC, Chapel Hill, PhD(statist), 64. *Prof Exp:* Asst prof math, Colo Sch Mines, 64-65; from asst prof to assoc prof, 65-74, PROF MATH, UNIV ALA, TUSCALOOSA, 74- *Mem:* Inst Math Statist. *Res:* Applied probability; theory of queues. *Mailing Add:* Dept of Math Col of Arts & Sci Univ of Ala in Tuscaloosa University AL 35486

SCOTT, MILTON LEONARD, b Tempe, Ariz, Feb 21, 15; m 38; c 2. NUTRITION. *Educ:* Univ Calif, AB, 37; Cornell Univ, PhD(nutrit), 45. *Prof Exp:* Vitamin chemist, Coop G L F Mills, Inc, Buffalo, NY, 37-42; fel, 42-44, res assoc, 44-45, from asst prof to assoc prof, 45-53, Jacob Gould Schurman prof, 76, PROF NUTRIT, CORNELL UNIV, 53-, CHMN DEPT POULTRY SCI, 76- *Concurrent Pos:* Fel, Tech Univ Denmark, 61; consult, Feed & Pharmaceut Industs. *Honors & Awards:* Awards, Am Feed Mfrs, 52, Nat Turkey Fedn, 58, Distillers Feed Res Coun, 64; Borden Award, 65; Calcium Carbonate Co Nat Feed Ingredients Asn travel award, 65; NY Farmers Award, 71; Borden Award, Am Inst Nutrit, 77. *Mem:* AAAS; Am Inst Nutrit; Am Poultry Sci Asn; Am Soc Animal Sci; Soc Exp Biol & Med. *Res:* Biochemistry. *Mailing Add:* Dept of Poultry Sci Cornell Univ Ithaca NY 14853

SCOTT, NORMAN JACKSON, JR, b Santa Monica, Calif, Sept 30, 34; m 56; c 2. HERPETOLOGY, VERTEBRATE ECOLOGY. *Educ:* Humboldt State Col, BS, 56, MS, 62; Univ Southern Calif, PhD, 69. *Prof Exp:* Prof zool, Univ Costa Rica, 64-66; course coordr, Orgn Trop Studies, Miami, 66-70; asst prof biol sci, Univ Conn, 58-74; BIOLOGIST, US FISH & WILDLIFE SERV, UNIV N MEX, 74-, ADJ ASSOC PROF BIOL, 75- *Mem:* Am Soc Ichthyologists & Herpetologists; Ecol Soc Am; Soc Syst Zool; Am Soc Zoologists; Asn Trop Biol. *Res:* Arid land ecology; primate ecology; tropical biology. *Mailing Add:* Nat Fish & Wildlife Lab Dept of Biol Sci Univ of N Mex Albuquerque NM 87131

SCOTT, NORMAN R(OSS), b Brooklyn, NY, May 15, 18; m 50; c 4. COMPUTER ENGINEERING. *Educ:* Mass Inst Technol, BS & MS, 41; Univ Ill, PhD(elec eng), 50. *Prof Exp:* Asst prof elec eng, Univ Ill, 46-50; from asst prof to prof & assoc dean, Col Eng, 51-68, dean, Dearborn Campus, 68-71, PROF ELEC & COMPUT ENG, UNIV MICH, ANN ARBOR, 71- *Concurrent Pos:* Ed, Trans Electronic Comput, Inst Elec & Electronics Engrs, 61-65; mem math & comput sci res adv comt, AEC, 62-65. *Mem:* Asn Comput Mach; fel Inst Elec & Electronics Engrs. *Res:* Engineering and logical design of electronic computers. *Mailing Add:* Dept of Elec & Comput Eng Univ of Mich Ann Arbor MI 48109

SCOTT, NORMAN ROY, b Spokane, Wash, Sept 6, 36; m 61; c 3. AGRICULTURAL ENGINEERING. *Educ:* Wash State Univ, BSAE, 58; Cornell Univ, PhD(heat transfer), 62. *Prof Exp:* From asst prof to assoc prof, 62-76, PROF AGR ENG, CORNELL UNIV, 76-, CHMN DEPT, 78- *Mem:* Am Soc Agr Engrs; Am Soc Eng Educ; Am Soc Heat, Refrig & Air-Conditioning Engrs; Instrument Soc Am; NY Acad Sci. *Res:* Biological engineering study of poultry involving heat transfer and physiological responses; biomathematical modeling of animal systems; animal calorimetry; electronic instrumentation in biological measurements. *Mailing Add:* Dept of Agr Eng Cornell Univ Riley-Robb Hall Ithaca NY 14850

SCOTT, PAUL BRUNSON, b Flint, Mich, Sept 8, 37; m 60. FLUID DYNAMICS, PHYSICS. *Educ:* Mass Inst Technol, SB & SM, 59, ScD(aeronaut eng), 65. *Prof Exp:* Mem staff vehicle anal, Space Tech Labs, 59-60; res staff molecular beam res, Mass Inst Technol, 65, asst prof aeronaut eng, 65-67; asst prof aerospace eng, Univ Southern Calif, 67-72; prin scientist, Xonics, Inc, 72-78; PRES, UNIV CONSULTS, INC, 78- *Concurrent Pos:* Ford Found fel. *Mem:* AAAS; Am Phys Soc. *Res:* Rarefied gas dynamics; molecular beams; intermolecular collisions; x-ray imaging; chemical kinetics; isotope separation, chemical and ultraviolet lasers. *Mailing Add:* 17500 Lemarsh St Northridge CA 91325

SCOTT, PETER CARLTON, b Seattle, Wash, Mar 20, 40. PLANT PHYSIOLOGY. *Educ:* Ore State Univ, BS, 63; Purdue Univ, Lafayette, PhD(plant physiol), 66. *Prof Exp:* Instr chem, Univ Calif, Santa Cruz, 66-67; instr chem, 69-72, chmn dept math & sci, 72-73, DIR DIV SCI & TECHNOL, LINN-BENTON COMMUNITY COL, 73- *Concurrent Pos:* Herman Frasch Found grant, Ore State Univ, 67-69; res assoc, Ore State Univ, 69- *Res:* Physiology of plant growth regulators. *Mailing Add:* Linn-Benton Community Col 6500 SW Pacific Blvd Albany OR 97321

SCOTT, PETER DOUGLAS, b Kingston, Pa, Dec 13, 42; m 65; c 2. BIOMEDICAL ENGINEERING. *Educ:* Cornell Univ, BS, 65, MS, 68, PhD(elec eng), 71. *Prof Exp:* Asst prof, 70-77, ASSOC PROF ELEC ENG, STATE UNIV NY BUFFALO, 77- *Concurrent Pos:* Asst prof, Dept Biophys Sci, State Univ NY Buffalo, 75-; plus, Surg Res Comput Lab, Buffalo Gen Hosp, 75- *Mem:* Sigma Xi; Inst Elec & Electronics Engrs; Am Soc Eng Educ; Comt Social Responsibility in Eng. *Res:* Cardiac electrophysiology; automated intensive care unit monitoring; systems theory; cybernetics. *Mailing Add:* 403 Voorhees Ave Buffalo NY 14216

SCOTT, PETER HAMILTON, b Providence, RI, Apr 6, 36; m 60; c 3. CHEMISTRY. *Educ:* Brown Univ, ScB, 60; Lehigh Univ, PhD(chem), 65. *Prof Exp:* Sr res chemist, Olin Res Ctr, Olin Mathieson Chem Corp, 65-67, sr res chemist II, 68-70; closure res mgr, 70-75, ASST DIR RES, DEWEY & ALMY CHEM DIV, W R GRACE & CO, 75- *Mem:* Am Chem Soc; Sci Res Soc Am; Soc Plastics Engrs; Am Asn Textile Chem & Colorists. *Res:* Reactions of nitrenes and nitrenelike intermediates; mechanisms of oxirane polymerization; organo-sulfur and heterocyclic chemistry; polyurethane chemistry, especially flame retardant polyurethanes; sealant compounds. *Mailing Add:* Dewey & Almy Chem Div W R Grace & Co 55 Hayden Ave Lexington MA 02173

SCOTT, PETER JOHN, b Toronto, Can, July 2, 48. TAXONOMY. *Educ:* Univ Alta, BSc Hons, 70; Mem Univ Nfld, PhD(taxonomy), 73. *Prof Exp:* ASSOC PROF BOT & CUR HERBARIUM, MEM UNIV NFLD, 73- *Mem:* Sigma Xi. *Res:* Flora of Newfoundland: origin, history and relationships with other floras. *Mailing Add:* Biol Dept Mem Univ Nfld St John's NF A1B 3X9 Can

SCOTT, PETER LESLIE, b San Francisco, Calif, May 14, 33; m 77; c 3. PHYSICS. *Educ:* Univ Calif, Berkeley, AB, 55, PhD(physics), 62; Univ Mich, MA, 57. *Prof Exp:* NSF fel, 62-63; asst prof physics, Stanford Univ, 63-66; ASSOC PROF PHYSICS, UNIV CALIF, SANTA CRUZ, 66- *Concurrent Pos:* Alfred P Sloan fel, 64-68; Fulbright-Hays fel, Galway, Ireland, 70-71. *Mem:* Am Phys Soc. *Res:* Magnetic resonance; solid state spectroscopy. *Mailing Add:* Nat Sci Div Univ of Calif Santa Cruz CA 95064

SCOTT, PETER MICHAEL, b Blackpool, Eng, Aug 20, 38; UK & Can citizen; m 63; c 2. ORGANIC CHEMISTRY. *Educ:* Cambridge Univ, BA, 59. PhD(org chem), 62, MA, 63. *Prof Exp:* NATO fel, Univ Calif, Berkeley, 62-64; fel, Univ BC, 64-65; RES SCIENTIST ANAL & ORG CHEM, CAN DEPT NAT HEALTH & WELFARE, 65- *Concurrent Pos:* Chmn, Joint Mycotoxins Comt, 76- *Mem:* Chem Inst Can; Can Inst Food Sci & Technol; Asn Off Anal Chemists. *Res:* Mycotoxins and other fungal metabolites, isolation, structure determination and analysis in foodstuffs. *Mailing Add:* Health Protection Br Health & Welfare Can Ottawa ON K1A 0L2 Can

SCOTT, RALPH ASA, JR, b Sterling, Ill, July 23, 30; m 59; c 2. ANALYTICAL CHEMISTRY, RADIOCHEMISTRY. *Educ:* Univ Ill, BS, 52; Univ Okla, MS, 54; Tex A&M Univ, PhD(plant physiol, biochem, org chem), 57. *Prof Exp:* Radiochemist, Okla Res Inst, 52-53; res plant breeder, W Atlee Burpee Seed Co, Calif, 54-55; prin res chemist & dir waste eval proj, Int Minerals & Chem Corp, Fla, 57-58; res plant physiologist, Olin Mathieson Chem Corp, NY, 58; plant physiologist, Cotton Res Ctr, Crops Res Div, Agr Res Serv, USDA, Phoenix, Ariz, 58-61, sr res plant physiologist, Boll Weevil Res Lab, Starkville, Miss, 61-62; chief chemist, US Dept Defense, US Air Force, 6571st Aeromed Res Lab, Holloman Air Force Base, NMex, 62-64, sr chemist, Nat Test Tech, Joint Chiefs Staff, Deseret Test Ctr, Ft Douglas, Utah, 65-66; chief div chem, Dept Pub Health, DC, 66-67; chief nationwide aquatic plant control prog, Off Chief Engrs, 67-69, CHIEF PHYS SCIENTIST, EXPLOSIVES SAFETY BD, DEPT DEFENSE, 69- *Concurrent Pos:* Int sci adv, Secy State, 69-; personal rep Secy Defense, Chem Munition Safety, Okinawa. *Honors & Awards:* Patent Award & Outstanding Performance Eval Award, US Govt, 65. *Mem:* Am Chem Soc (chmn, Chem Health & Safety Div, 78-80 & 83-84, vchmn, 81-82); Am Soc Plant Physiol; Am Soc Agron. *Res:* Residue analysis, quality control and toxicology; air and water pollution analytical analysis control; allergies; carcinogenic chemicals mode of action; virological and microbiological chemistry as related to biological warfare analysis. *Mailing Add:* 2819 Elsmore St Fairfax VA 22031

SCOTT, RALPH CARMEN, b Bethel, Ohio, June 7, 21; m 45; c 3. INTERNAL MEDICINE, CARDIOLOGY. *Educ:* Univ Cincinnati, BS, 42, MD, 45; Am Bd Internal Med, dipl; Am Bd Cardiovasc Dis, dipl. *Prof Exp:* Resident & asst path, Col Med, Univ Cincinnati, 48-49, from instr to assoc prof med, 50-68; dir cardiac clin, Cincinnati Gen Hosp, 65 75; PROF MED, COL MED, UNIV CINCINNATI, 68- *Concurrent Pos:* Fel internal med & cardiol, Univ Cincinnati, 49-57; asst clinician internal med & cardiol, Cincinnati Gen Hosp, 50-51; clinician internal med, 52-, clinician cardiol, 52-55, asst chief clinician, 56-64, from asst attend physician to attend physician, 58-; attend physician, Vet Admin Hosp, 54-61, Holmes Hosp, 57- & Providence Hosp, Cincinnati, 71-; consult, US Air Force Hosp, Wright-Patterson Air Force Base, 60-, Vet Admin Hosp, 62-, Good Samaritan Hosp, 67-, Jewish Hosp, 68- & Children's Hosp, 68-; fel coun clin cardiol, Am Heart Asn. *Mem:* AMA; Int Cardiovasc Soc; fel Am Col Physicians; fel Am Col Chest Physicians; Am Heart Asn. *Res:* Electrocardiography. *Mailing Add:* 2955 Alpine Terr Cincinnati OH 45028

SCOTT, RALPH MASON, b Leemont, Va, Nov 23, 21; m 46; c 3. RADIOLOGY. *Educ:* Univ Va, BA, 47; Med Col Va, MD, 50. *Prof Exp:* Radiotherapist, Robert Packer Hosp, Sayre, Pa, 57-59; asst prof radiol, Sch Med, Univ Chicago, 59-60; assoc prof, Sch Med, Univ Louisville, 60-64, prof radiol, 64-77, dir radiation ther, 60-77; prof radiol & chmn, Dept Radiation Ther, Sch Med, Univ Md, 78-80. *Mem:* Am Radium Soc; Am Col Radiol; Am Roentgen Ray Soc; Radiol Soc NAm; Asn Univ Radiol. *Res:* Clinical radiation therapy. *Mailing Add:* 8586 Beacon Point Dr Pasadena MD 21122

SCOTT, RAYMOND PETER WILLIAM, b Erith, Eng, June 20, 24; m 46; c 2. PHYSICAL CHEMISTRY. *Educ:* Univ London, BSc, 46, DSc(chem), 58; FRIC, 58. *Prof Exp:* Lab mgr phys chem, Benzole Prod Res Labs, 50-60; div mgr phys chem, Unilever Res Labs, 60-69; DIR DEPT PHYS CHEM, HOFFMANN-LA ROCHE INC, 69- *Honors & Awards:* Chromatography Award, Am Chem Soc, 77; Tswett Medal Chromatography, Int Chromatography Symp, 78. *Mem:* Brit Chem Soc; Am Chem Soc. *Res:* Separations technology; gas chromatography; liquid chromatography; exclusion chromatography; gas chromatography/mass spectroscopy; liquid chromatography/mass spectroscopy; general physical chemical instrumentation; computer technology and data processing. *Mailing Add:* Hoffmann-LaRoche Inc Nutley NJ 07110

SCOTT, RICHARD ALBERT, b La Grange, Ind, Oct 20, 21; m 51. PALEOBOTANY, PLANT MORPHOLOGY. *Educ:* DePauw Univ, BA, 43, MA, 49; Univ Mich, PhD, 52. *Prof Exp:* Instr biol, Harvard Univ, 52-55; PALEOBOTANIST, US GEOL SURV, 55- *Mem:* Bot Soc Am. *Res:* Tertiary wood and fruits; Mesozoic palynology. *Mailing Add:* Paleont & Stratig Br US Geol Surv Denver Fed Ctr Denver CO 80225

SCOTT, RICHARD ANTHONY, b Cork, Ireland, May 5, 36; m 67. APPLIED MATHEMATICS. *Educ:* Univ Col, Cork, BSc, 57, MSc, 59; Calif Inst Technol, PhD(eng sci), 64. *Prof Exp:* Lectr appl mech, Calif Inst Technol, 64-65, res fel, 65-67; asst prof, 67-71, assoc prof, 71-77, PROF ENG MECH, UNIV MICH, ANN ARBOR, 77- *Concurrent Pos:* Consult, Am Math Soc Math Rev, 68- *Mem:* Am Soc Mech Engrs; Am Acad Mech; Sigma Xi. *Res:* Wave propogation in solids; elastic wave propagation; linear, nonlinear and random vibrations of solids; dynamics. *Mailing Add:* 204 W Eng Univ of Mich Ann Arbor MI 48109

SCOTT, RICHARD LYNN, analytical chemistry, see previous edition

SCOTT, RICHARD ROYCE, b Fairfield, Ala, Mar 19, 33; m 69; c 1. FLUID MECHANICS. *Educ:* Univ Miss, BSME, 60; Univ Ala, PhD(eng mech), 68. *Prof Exp:* Proj engr, Procter & Gamble, Inc, 60-62; asst prof systs eng, Wright State Univ, 68-77; ASSOC PROF MECH ENG, UNIV SOUTHWESTERN LA, 77- *Res:* Supersonic fluidics; pollution control of automotive engines. *Mailing Add:* Dept of Mech Eng Box 4-4170 Univ of Southwestern La Lafayette LA 40501

SCOTT, RICHARD WALTER, b Modesto, Calif, June 30, 41; m 61; c 2. PLANT ECOLOGY. *Educ:* Univ Wyo, BS, 64, MS, 66; Univ Mich, MA, 69, PhD(plant ecol), 72. *Prof Exp:* NDEA fel plant ecol, Univ Mich, 66-69; asst prof biol, Albion Col, 69-75; INSTR BIOL, CENT WYO COL, 75- *Concurrent Pos:* Dir natural areas, Albion Col, 69-74, dir wilderness prog, 73-75. *Mem:* Sigma Xi; Am Polar Asn. *Res:* Mountain ecosystems and plant community structure; research includes Alpine plant communities of Western North America and human impact on wilderness environments. *Mailing Add:* Div of Life & Phys Sci Cent Wyo Col Riverton WY 82501

SCOTT, ROBERT ALLEN, b Dixon, Ill, Apr 25, 53. BIOPHYSICAL CHEMISTRY, BIOINORGANIC CHEMISTRY. *Educ:* Univ Ill, Urbana, BS, 75; Calif Inst Technol, PhD(chem), 80. *Prof Exp:* NIH fel, Stanford Univ, 79-81; ASST PROF INORG CHEM, UNIV ILL, URBANA, 81- *Mem:* Am Chem Soc; AAAS. *Res:* Inorganic and physical aspects of biologically important systems; kinetics of electron transfer in metalloenzymes and extended x-ray absorption fine structure studies of metalloproteins and models. *Mailing Add:* Sch Chem Sci 466 Noyes Box 9 Univ Ill 505 S Mathew St Urbana IL 61801

SCOTT, ROBERT BLACKBURN, b Wilmington, Del, July 22, 37; m 62. GEOLOGY. *Educ:* Univ Ala, BS, 60; Rice Univ, PhD(geol), 65. *Prof Exp:* Res geologist, Yale Univ, 65-67; asst prof geol, Fla State Univ, 67-71; ASSOC PROF GEOL, TEX A&M UNIV, 71- *Concurrent Pos:* Petrologist, Trans-Atlantic Geotraverse Proj, Nat Oceanic & Atmospheric Admin, 71- *Mem:* AAAS; Geochem Soc; Geol Soc Am; Mineral Soc Am; Am Geophys Union. *Res:* Marine volcanism; oceanic basalt geochemistry and petrology; seawater-basalt reactions and equilibria. *Mailing Add:* Dept of Geol Tex A&M Univ College Station TX 77843

SCOTT, ROBERT BLACKBURN, JR, b Greensboro, NC, Nov 11; m 36; c 4. ORGANIC CHEMISTRY. *Educ:* Pa State Univ, BS, 34, MS, 35; Univ Va, PhD(org chem), 49. *Prof Exp:* Chemist org chem, E I du Pont de Nemours & Co, 35-45; from assoc prof to prof, Univ Ala, 48-63; prof & chmn dept, 63-77, EMER PROF ORG CHEM, UNIV MISS, 77- *Mem:* Am Chem Soc. *Res:* Mechanisms; steric effects; reactions of aliphatic sulfonyl and sulfinyl compounds and 1, 3-glycols and diketones. *Mailing Add:* 406 Country Club Rd Oxford MS 38655

SCOTT, ROBERT BRADLEY, b Petersburg, Va, Nov 7, 33; m 58; c 3. INTERNAL MEDICINE, HEMATOLOGY. *Educ:* Univ Richmond, BS, 54; Med Col Va, MD, 58. *Prof Exp:* From intern to resident internal med, Bellevue & Mem Hosps, New York, 58-61; fel biol, Mass Inst Technol, 63-64, res assoc, 64-65; from asst prof to assoc prof med, 65-74, PROF MED, PATH & BIOCHEM, MED COL VA, VA COMMONWEALTH UNIV, 74- *Concurrent Pos:* Am Cancer Soc res scholar, 63-65; clin fel med, Mass Gen Hosp, 64-65; dir, Lab Hemat Res, 66- *Mem:* Fel Am Col Physicians; Am Fedn Clin Res; Am Asn Cancer Res; Am Soc Clin Oncol; Am Soc Hemat. *Res:* Genetic counseling in sickle cell anemia; control of differentiation in normal and leukemic blood cell; cell biology. *Mailing Add:* Dept of Med Med Col of Va Richmond VA 23298

SCOTT, ROBERT EDWARD, b Crystal Springs, Miss, Oct 19, 22; m 45; c 3. ANALYTICAL CHEMISTRY. *Educ:* Univ Tex, BA, 43, MA, 44. *Prof Exp:* Anal chemist, New Prod Develop Lab, Gen Elec Co, Mass, 48-53; res anal chemist & group leader, Chem Div, Pittsburgh Plate Glass Co, 53-65; sr res supvr, Inorg Phys Res Dept, 65-67, SR RES SUPVR CHEM DIV, ANAL LABS, PPG INDUSTS, INC, 68- *Mem:* Am Chem Soc. *Res:* Wet chemical, ultraviolet-visible-infrared spectrophotometric, polarographic, x-ray, emission spectrographic and gas chromatographic analytical techniques applied to chlorosilanes, silicones, phenolics, autoxidation process hydrogen peroxide, chrome chemicals and chlorinated hydrocarbons. *Mailing Add:* PPG Industs Inc PO Box 4026 Corpus Christi TX 78408

SCOTT, ROBERT FOSTER, b Alberta, Can, June 23, 25; m 54; c 3. PATHOLOGY. *Educ:* Univ Alberta, BSc, 49, MD, 51; FRCP, 58. *Prof Exp:* Asst prof path, Univ BC, 57-58, clin instr, 58-59; asst prof, 59-63, assoc prof, 63-66, PROF PATH, ALBANY MED COL, 66- *Concurrent Pos:* Fel, Nat Res Coun Can, 54-55; Life Insurance Med Res Found, 56-57; mem, Cardiovasc Study Sect, NIH, 64-68; Path Study Sect, NIH, 73-77; exec mem, Arterrosclerosis Coun, Am Heart Asn, 71-73; asst to dean acad affairs, Albany Med Col, 79-80, assoc to dean, 80- *Res:* Kinetics of arterial wall cells with regard to atherosclerosis utilizing experimental models. *Mailing Add:* Dept Path Albany Med Col 47 New Scotland Ave Albany NY 12208

SCOTT, ROBERT LANE, b Santa Rosa, Calif, Mar 20, 22; m 44; c 4. PHYSICAL CHEMISTRY. *Educ:* Harvard Univ, SB, 42; Princeton Univ, MA, 44, PhD(chem), 45. *Prof Exp:* Asst chem, Princeton Univ, 42-43, Manhattan Proj, 44-45; scientist, Manhattan Proj, Los Alamos Sci Lab, 45-46; Jewett fel, Univ Calif, 46-48; from asst prof to assoc prof, 48-60, chmn dept, 70-75, PROF CHEM, UNIV CALIF, LOS ANGELES, 60- *Concurrent Pos:* Guggenheim fel, 55; NSF sr fel, 61-62; Fulbright award, 68-69. *Mem:* AAAS; Am Chem Soc; Am Phys Soc. *Res:* Statistical thermodynamics of liquids and solutions; high polymer solutions; fluorocarbon solutions; hydrocarbon solutions; critical phenomena; tricritical points; solubility and phase equilibria. *Mailing Add:* Dept of Chem Univ of Calif Los Angeles CA 90024

SCOTT, ROBERT NEAL, b Pawtucket, RI, Mar 8, 41; m 63; c 2. INDUSTRIAL CHEMISTRY. *Educ:* Brown Univ, ScB, 63; Northwestern Univ, PhD(chem), 68. *Prof Exp:* Sr res chemist polymer chem, 67-71, group leader org res & develop, 71-75, sect leader org & inorg res & develop, 75-78, SECT MGR ORG & INORG RES & DEVELOP, OLIN CORP, 78- *Mem:* Am Chem Soc; Am Soc Lubrication Engrs. *Res:* High temperature polymers; synthetic lubricants; surfactants textile chemicals; hydrazine applications and derivative chemistry. *Mailing Add:* Olin Corp 275 Winchester Ave New Haven CT 06511

SCOTT, ROBERT NELSON, b St John, NB, Apr 30, 33; m 72; c 5. ELECTRICAL ENGINEERING. *Educ:* Univ NB, BSc, 55. *Hon Degrees:* DSc, Acadia Univ, 81. *Prof Exp:* Engr, Northern Elec Co, Ltd, 55-56; from asst prof to assoc prof, 56-67, exec dir, Bio-Eng Inst, 65-79, PROF ELEC ENG, UNIV NB, 67-, DIR, BIO-ENG INST, 80- *Mem:* Inst Elec & Electronics Engrs; fel Can Med & Biol Eng Soc; Int Soc Electrophysiol Kinesiology. *Res:* Electronic instrumentation and circuit design; medical applications of electronics, particularly electronics aids for the physically handicapped; clinical engineering. *Mailing Add:* Univ of NB Bio-Eng Inst PO Box 4400 Fredericton NB E3B 5A3 Can

SCOTT, ROBERT W, b Davenport, Iowa, June 7, 36; m 62; c 3. GEOLOGY, PALEONTOLOGY. *Educ:* Maryknoll Col, BA, 58; Univ Wyo, BA, 60, MA, 61; Univ Kans, PhD(geol), 67. *Prof Exp:* Asst geol, Univ Kans, 61-66; asst prof, Waynesburg Col, 66-70; asst prof, Univ Tex, Arlington, 70-74; sr res scientist, 74-77, RES SUPVR, AMOCO PROD CO, 77- *Mem:* Am Asn Petrol Geol; Paleont Soc. *Res:* Growth and evolution of Early Cretaceous bivalves and stratigraphy and sedimentary environments of Lower Cretaceous rocks in western interior and Gulf Coast of the United States. *Mailing Add:* Amoco Prod Co Res Ctr PO Box 591 Tulsa OK 74102

SCOTT, RONALD E, b Leslie, Sask, Mar 25, 21; US citizen; c 1. ELECTRICAL ENGINEERING. *Educ:* Univ Toronto, BASc, 43, MASc, 46; Mass Inst Technol, ScD(elec eng), 50. *Prof Exp:* Res assoc elec eng, Mass Inst Technol, 46-50, asst prof, 50-55; prof, Northeastern Univ, 55-60, dean eng, 60-67; dean eng, Col Petrol & Minerals, Dhahran, 67-78; PROJ HEAD, NAT INST ELEC & ELECTRONICS, ALGERIA, 78- *Mem:* Inst Elec & Electronics Engrs; Am Soc Eng Educ; Soc Am Mil Engrs. *Res:* Circuit theory solid state microelectronics reliability and medical electronics. *Mailing Add:* INELEC/IAP Boumerdes Algeria

SCOTT, RONALD F(RASER), b London, Eng, Apr 9, 29; m 59; c 3. CIVIL ENGINEERING. *Educ:* Glasgow Univ, BSc, 51; Mass Inst Technol, SM, 53, ScD(soil mech), 55. *Prof Exp:* Asst soil mech, Mass Inst Technol, 51-55; soil engr, Corps Engrs, US Dept Army, 55-57; div soil engr, Racey, MacCallum & Assocs, Ltd, Can, 57-58; from asst prof to assoc prof civil eng, 58-67, PROF CIVIL ENG, CALIF INST TECHNOL, 67- *Concurrent Pos:* Churchill fel, Churchill Col, Eng, 72; Guggenheim fel, 72. *Honors & Awards:* Norman Medal, Am Soc Civil Engrs, 73. *Mem:* Nat Acad Eng; Am Soc Civil Engrs; Am Geophys Union. *Res:* Soil engineering and mechanics; soil dynamics; earthquake engineering. *Mailing Add:* 2752 N Santa Anita Ave Altadena CA 91001

SCOTT, RONALD MCLEAN, b Detroit, Mich, Apr 16, 33; m 57; c 2. BIOCHEMISTRY. *Educ:* Wayne State Univ, BS, 55; Univ Ill, PhD(biochem), 59. *Prof Exp:* From asst prof to assoc prof, 59-68, PROF CHEM, EASTERN MICH UNIV, 68- *Concurrent Pos:* Exchange prof, Coventry Univ, Eng, 71-72; vis lectr, Warwick Univ, Eng, 72. *Mem:* Am Chem Soc; Sigma Xi. *Res:* Enzymology; biopolymer; organic polymers. *Mailing Add:* Dept of Chem Eastern Mich Univ Ypsilanti MI 48197

SCOTT, ROY ALBERT, III, b Pottsville, Pa, Mar 22, 34; m 58; c 2. PHYSICAL CHEMISTRY, MOLECULAR BIOLOGY. *Educ:* Cornell Univ, AB, 58, PhD(chem), 64. *Prof Exp:* Asst prof chem, Cornell Univ, 63-66; asst prof biophys, Univ Hawaii, 66-68; ASSOC PROF BIOCHEM & MOLECULAR BIOL, OHIO STATE UNIV, 68- *Mem:* Am Chem Soc; Am Phys Soc. *Res:* Physical chemistry of biological macromolecules. *Mailing Add:* Dept of Biochem Col of Biol Sci Ohio State Univ Columbus OH 43210

SCOTT, RUSSELL, JR, b Houston, Tex, Oct 25, 25; m 54; c 4. UROLOGY. *Educ:* Univ Pa, MD, 50; Am Bd Urol, dipl, 60. *Prof Exp:* Intern, Hosp Univ Pa, 50-51; mem fac, Army Med Serv Grad Sch, DC, 52-53; instr urol res, Univ Mich, 54-57; from instr to assoc prof urol, 57-60, head div urol, 61-77, PROF UROL, BAYLOR COL MED, 72-; CLIN PROF UROL, UNIV COLO, 77- *Concurrent Pos:* Trustee, Am Bd Urol. *Mem:* Am Urol Asn (dir educ); Clin Soc Genito-Urinary Surg; Am Asn Genito-Urinary Surg; Am Col Surg; Soc Pediat Urol. *Mailing Add:* PO Box 4257 Aspen CO 81612

SCOTT, SHERYL ANN, b Wilmington, Del, Feb 16, 49. DEVELOPMENTAL NEUROBIOLOGY. *Educ:* Duke Univ, BS, 71; Yale Univ, PhD(biol), 76. *Prof Exp:* Fel neurobiol, Med Ctr, McMaster Univ, 76-77 & Carnegie Inst Washington, 78-79; ASST PROF NEUROBIOL, STATE UNIV NY STONY BROOK, 79- *Concurrent Pos:* Fels, Multiple Sclerosis Soc Can, 76-77, HEW Pub Health Serv, 77 & 78- & Grass Found, 78. *Mem:* Soc Neurosci. *Mailing Add:* Dept of Neurobiol & Behav State Univ of NY Stony Brook NY 11794

SCOTT, STEVEN DONALD, b Ft Frances, Ont, June 4, 41; m 63; c 2. ECNOMIC GEOLOGY, GEOCHEMISTRY. *Educ:* Univ Western Ont, BSc, 63, MSc, 64; Pa State Univ, PhD(geochem), 68. *Prof Exp:* Res assoc geochem, Pa State Univ, 68-69; asst prof, 69-72, assoc prof, 72-79, PROF GEOCHEM, UNIV TORONTO, 79-, ASSOC CHMN, 80- *Concurrent Pos:* Lectr, Ore Deposits Workshop, Univ Toronto, 74-; Can rep, Int Asn Genesis of Ore Deposits, 74- & Int Mineral Asn, 75- *Honors & Awards:* Waldemar Lindgren Citation, Soc Econ Geologists. *Mem:* Mineral Soc Am; Mineral Asn Can; Geol Asn Can; Soc Econ Geol; Can Inst Mining & Metal. *Res:* Physical geochemistry; ore forming processes by field and experimental methods; sulfide mineralogy; synthesis and crystal chemistry of metallic sulfides and arsenides; sulfides in meteorites; massive copper-zinc ores; fluid inclusions. *Mailing Add:* Dept Geol Univ Toronto Toronto ON M5S 1A1 Can

SCOTT, STEWART MELVIN, b Sherman, Tex, Oct 14, 26; m 60; c 1. CARDIOVASCULAR SURGERY, THORACIC SURGERY. *Educ:* Baylor Univ, MD, 51. *Prof Exp:* Asst chief cardiovasc surg, 59-62, ASSOC CHIEF STAFF FOR RES & CHIEF CARDIOVASC SURG SECT, VET ADMIN HOSP, 62- *Concurrent Pos:* Clin instr, Woman's Med Col Pa, 52-56; assoc clin prof, Duke Univ Med Ctr, 68- *Mem:* Fel Am Col Surgeons; Int Cardiovasc Soc; Am Asn Thoracic Surgeons; Soc Thoracic Surgeons; AMA. *Res:* Cardiac, pulmonary and vascular diseases. *Mailing Add:* Vet Admin Hosp Asheville NC 28805

SCOTT, THOMAS A, b Tremont, La, Jan 10, 30; m 52; c 2. PHYSICS. *Educ:* Univ Pa, BA, 52; Harvard Univ, MS, 53, PhD(physics), 59. *Prof Exp:* From asst prof to assoc prof physics, Univ Fla, 58-65, prof, 66-80, chmn dept, 71-73. *Mem:* Fel Am Phys Soc; Int Soc Nuclear Quadrupole Resonance Spectros. *Res:* Nuclear resonance; solid state and low temperature physics. *Mailing Add:* 3001 SW 4 Ct Gainesville FL 32601

SCOTT, THOMAS WALTER, b Sewickley, Pa, Nov 10, 29; m 53; c 4. SOIL FERTILITY. *Educ:* Pa State Univ, BS, 52; Kans State Univ, MS, 56; Mich State Univ, PhD(soil sci), 59. *Prof Exp:* From asst prof to assoc prof, 59-74, PROF SOIL SCI, CORNELL UNIV, 74-, MEM DEPT AGRON, 77- *Concurrent Pos:* Travel grants from Cornell Univ & NY lime & fertilizer industs to Cambridge Univ, 66-67; USAID assignment to PR, 73- *Mem:* Am Soc Agron; Soil Sci Soc Am. *Res:* Undergraduate teaching; animal waste management; soil fertility research and extension; soil fertility research on tropical soils. *Mailing Add:* Dept of Agron Bradfield Hall Cornell Univ Ithaca NY 14853

SCOTT, TOM E, b Cleveland, Ohio, Sept 10, 33; m 59; c 4. METALLURGY. *Educ:* Case Inst Technol, BS, 56, MS, 58, PhD(phys metall), 62. *Prof Exp:* Res metallurgist, Int Nickel Co, Ind, 61-63; asst prof mech metall, 63-69, assoc prof metall, 69-72, PROF METALL, IOWA STATE UNIV, 72-, SECT CHIEF, AMES LAB, 75- *Mem:* Am Soc Metals; Am Inst Mining, Metall & Petrol Engrs; Nat Asn Corrosion Engrs. *Res:* Hydrogen embrittlement; embrittlements; ferrous alloys; deformation; fracture mechanisms. *Mailing Add:* 205 Metals Develop Bldg Iowa State Univ Ames IA 50011

SCOTT, TOM KECK, b St Louis, Mo, Aug 4, 31; m 53; c 4. PLANT PHYSIOLOGY. *Educ:* Pomona Col, BA, 54; Stanford Univ, MA, 59, PhD(biol), 61. *Prof Exp:* Teaching fel biol, Stanford Univ, 56-60, res asst, 57-61; res assoc, Princeton Univ, 61-63; from asst prof to assoc prof, Oberlin Col, 63-69; asst prof, 69-72, chmn biol curriculum, 70-75, PROF BOT & CHMN DEPT, UNIV N C, CHAPEL HILL, 72- *Concurrent Pos:* Vis res fel, Univ Nottingham, 67-68; Fulbright lectr, 72-73; assoc, Danforth Found, 73- *Mem:* Fel AAAS; Bot Soc Am; Am Soc Plant Physiol; Soc Develop Biol; Soc Gen Physiol. *Res:* Plant growth and development; auxin relationships and transport; growth regulator interactions; hormone physiology. *Mailing Add:* Dept of Bot Univ of NC Chapel Hill NC 27514

SCOTT, VERNE H(ARRY), b Salem, Ore, June 19, 24; m 48; c 3. CIVIL ENGINEERING, HYDROLOGY. *Educ:* Univ Mich, BS, 45, MS, 48; Colo State Univ, PhD(irrig eng), 59. *Prof Exp:* Res & irrig engr, hydrol, 46-47, assoc prof irrig, 48-63, chmn dept water sci & eng, 64-71, PROF WATER SCI & CIVIL ENG & HYDROLOGIST, UNIV CALIF, DAVIS, 63-, DIR CAMPUS WORK-LEARN PROG, 71- *Mem:* Am Soc Eng Educ; Am Soc Civil Engrs; Am Soc Agr Engrs; Am Geophys Union. *Res:* Ground water and water resources. *Mailing Add:* Dept of Land Air & Water Resources Univ of Calif Davis CA 95616

SCOTT, W(ILLARD) FRANK, b Salt Lake City, Utah, Nov 23, 19; m 46. GEOLOGY. *Educ:* Univ Utah, BS, 41, MS, 47; Univ Wash, PhD(geol), 54. *Prof Exp:* Actg instr geol, Univ Utah, 46-48; instr, Univ Wash, 48-51; from asst prof to assoc prof, 51-66, assoc dean grad sch, 66-68, chmn environ sci prog, 75-77, PROF GEOL, WASH STATE UNIV, 66-, CHMN GEOL, 76- *Concurrent Pos:* Petrol geol consult, 46- *Mem:* Geol Soc Am; Am Asn Petrol Geologists; Paleont Soc; Soc Econ Paleont & Mineral. *Res:* Stratigraphy; paleontology; marine and petroleum geology. *Mailing Add:* Dept of Geol Wash State Univ Pullman WA 99164

SCOTT, WALTER ALVIN, b Los Angeles, Calif, Feb 1, 43; m 70. BIOCHEMISTRY, CELL BIOLOGY. *Educ:* Calif Inst Technol, BS, 65; Univ Wis, PhD(physiol chem), 70. *Prof Exp:* Fel cell biol dept biophys & biochem, Univ Calif, San Francisco, 70-73; fel tumor virol, Dept Microbiol, Med Sch, Johns Hopkins Univ, 73-75; ASST PROF BIOCHEM, SCH MED, UNIV MIAMI, 75- *Concurrent Pos:* NSF fel, 70-71; Jane Coffin Childs Mem Fund fel, 71-72; NIH fel, 72-73 & 74-75; NIH grant, 75-78 & 78-81; NSF grant, 78-79. *Mem:* Am Soc Microbiol; AAAS. *Res:* Structure and function of Simian Virus 40 chromatin; recombination involved in integration and excision of SV40 from cell chromosomes; transformation of pancreatic islet cells by SV40 mutants. *Mailing Add:* Dept of Biochem PO Box 016129 Miami FL 33101

SCOTT, WALTER NEIL, b Evansville, Ind, Mar 2, 35; m 59. MEDICINE, PHYSIOLOGY. *Educ:* Western Ky State Col, BS, 56; Univ Louisville, MD, 60. *Prof Exp:* Intern, New Eng Center Hosp, 60-61; resident, 61-62; fel med, Mass Mem Hosps, 62-63; USPHS res fel, Biophys Lab, Harvard Med Sch, 63-65; spec fel biochem, Mass Inst Technol, 65-66; asst prof biophys, 68-71, asst prof ophthal, 70-74, ASSOC PROF PHYSIOL & OPHTHAL, MT SINAI SCH MED, 74-, ASST DEAN RES, 75- *Concurrent Pos:* Estab investr, Am Heart Asn, 71-76; mem cornea task force, Nat Eye Inst, 72, mem vision res prog comt, 75- *Mem:* Fel NY Acad Sci; Am Soc Cell Biol; Am Chem Soc; Am Physiol Soc; Endocrine Soc. *Res:* Biochemistry and physiology of membrane transport of ions, amino acids and water. *Mailing Add:* Dept of Physiol Mt Sinai Sch of Med New York NY 10029

SCOTT, WALTER TANDY, b Haskell, Tex, Dec 12,12; m 43; c 3. MATHEMATICS. *Educ:* Rice Univ, BA, 33, MA, 35, PhD(math), 38. *Prof Exp:* Asst math, Northwestern Univ, 38; instr, Ill Inst Technol, 39; instr, Univ Mich, 39-40; from instr to assoc prof, Northwestern Univ, 40-61; prof, 61-80, EMER PROF, ARIZ STATE UNIV, 61- *Mem:* AAAS; Am Math Soc; Math Asn Am; Soc Indust & Appl Math. *Res:* Continued fraction theory; theory of summation of series; geometric function theory. *Mailing Add:* Dept of Math Ariz State Univ Tempe AZ 85281

SCOTT, WILLIAM, b Edmonton, Alta, Can, Mar 12, 37. FOREST SOILS, SOIL SCIENCE. *Educ:* Univ BC, BSF, 63; Ore State Univ, MS, 70, PhD(forest soils), 73. *Prof Exp:* Forester, BC Forest Serv, Victoria, 63-65; soil survr, Can Dept Agr, Vancouver, 65-67; res asst, Ore State Univ, 67-72; res scientist, Dept Environ, Can Forest Serv, 72-74; RES SCIENTIST LAND MGT, WEYERHAEUSER CO, 74- *Mem:* Am Soc Agron; Soc Am Foresters; Sigma Xi. *Res:* Evaluating the impact of various equipment and operations on soil disturbance and resultant losses in productivity; species-site relationships; effect of N fixing brush species on Douglas-fir regeneration; edaphic factors influencing Douglas fir regeneration and plantation performance. *Mailing Add:* Weyerhaeuser Co PO Box 420 Centralia WA 98531

SCOTT, WILLIAM ADDISON, III, b Indianapolis, Ind, Apr 27, 40; m 66; c 1. BIOCHEMISTRY, GENETICS. *Educ:* Univ Ill, Urbana, BS, 62; Calif Inst Technol, PhD(biochem), 67. *Prof Exp:* Guest investr biochem genetics & US Pub Health Serv grant, 67-69, res assoc, 69-71, asst prof, 71-77, ASSOC PROF BIOCHEM GENETICS, DEPT CELL PHYSIOL & IMMUNOL, ROCKEFELLER UNIV, 77- *Mem:* AAAS; Sigma Xi; Harvey Soc. *Res:* Biochemical basis of morphology; membrane structure and function. *Mailing Add:* Dept Cell Physiol & Immunol Rockefeller Univ New York NY 10021

SCOTT, WILLIAM BEVERLEY, b Toronto, Ont, July 7, 17; m 42; c 2. ICHTHYOLOGY. *Educ:* Univ Toronto, BA, 42, PhD(zool). 50. *Prof Exp:* Actg curator, Royal Ont Mus, 48-50; cur dept ichthyol & herpet, 50-76, assoc dir mus, 73-76; EXEC DIR, HUNTSMAN MARINE LAB, ST ANDREWS, NB, 76- *Concurrent Pos:* Assoc prof, Univ Toronto, 63, prof, 68- *Honors & Awards:* Centennial Medal, Govt Can, 67, Silver Jubilee Medal, 77. *Mem:* Am Soc Ichthyol & Herpet (pres, 73); Can Soc Zool; Am Fisheries Soc; Soc Systs Zool; Fel Am Soc Fish Res Biologists. *Res:* Systematics and distribution of Canadian freshwater fishes and Northwest Atlantic fishes, particularly salmonids, myctophids and scombroides; food and feeding; commercial fisheries. *Mailing Add:* Huntsman Marine Lab St Andrews NB E0G 2X0 Can

SCOTT, WILLIAM D(OANE), b Lakewood, Ohio, Feb 17, 31; m 59; c 2. CERAMICS ENGINEERING. *Educ:* Univ Ill, BS, 54; Univ Calif, Berkeley, MS, 59, PhD(eng sci), 61. *Prof Exp:* Res fel, Univ Leeds, 61-63; asst prof eng, Univ Calif, Berkeley & Lawrence Radiation Lab, 64-65; PROF ENG, UNIV WASH, 65- *Mem:* Fel Am Ceramic Soc. *Res:* Nucleation and growth of crystals in glass; mechanical properties of ionic solids and oxides; structure of grain boundaries. *Mailing Add:* Div of Ceramic Eng FB-10 Univ of Wash Seattle WA 98105

SCOTT, WILLIAM EDWARD, b Middletown, Conn, Sept 6, 47; m 70; c 1. GEOLOGY. *Educ:* St Lawrence Univ, BS, 69; Univ Wash, MS, 71, PhD(geol), 74. *Prof Exp:* GEOLOGIST, US GEOL SURV, 74- *Mem:* AAAS; Geol Soc Am; Am Quaternary Asn. *Res:* Quaternary stratigraphy and tectonics of the Wasatch Front, Utah; quaternary history and climate change in Bonneville Basin and southeastern Idaho. *Mailing Add:* US Geol Surv Fed Ctr Denver CO 80225

SCOTT, WILLIAM EDWIN, b Rome, NY, Apr 8, 18; m 41; c 3. CHEMISTRY. *Educ:* Hamilton Col, NY, BS; Swiss Fed Inst Technol, DTechSc, 41. *Prof Exp:* Res chemist, 41-56, asst to dir res, 56-59, res coordr, 59-63, dir res admin, 63-69, DIR RES TECH SERVS, HOFFMAN-LA ROCHE, INC, 69- *Mem:* Am Chem Soc; NY Acad Sci; The Chem Soc. *Res:* Structure and synthesis of organic medicinal compounds; purification and structure determination of natural products; synthesis of steroid analogs. *Mailing Add:* Res Div Kingsland Rd Hoffman-La Roche Inc Nutley NJ 07110

SCOTT, WILLIAM JAMES, JR, b New York, NY, Dec 8, 37; m 62. TERATOLOGY, DEVELOPMENTAL BIOLOGY. *Educ:* Univ Ga, DVM, 61; George Washington Univ, PhD(anat), 69. *Prof Exp:* Dir teratology, Woodard Res Corp, 64-68; Pharmaceut Mfrs Asn Found fel, 69-71, asst prof res pediat, 71-73, assoc prof res pediat, 73-78, PROF RES PEDIAT, CHILDREN'S HOSP RES FOUND, 78- *Concurrent Pos:* Vet consult, Sch Med, George Washington Univ, 64-69. *Mem:* Teratology Soc; Am Asn Lab Animal Sci. *Res:* Determination of the mechanisms by which environmental factors interfere with embryonic development to produce congenital malformations. *Mailing Add:* Div of Path Embryol Children's Hosp Res Found Cincinnati OH 45229

SCOTT, WILLIAM RAYMOND, b Bloomingburg, Ohio, June 25, 19; m 45; c 3. ALGEBRA. *Educ:* Ohio State Univ, BA, 40, MA, 41, PhD, 47. *Prof Exp:* Res assoc math, Ohio State Univ, 47-48; instr, Univ Mich, 48-49; from asst prof to prof, Univ Kans, 49-65, actg chmn dept, 59-61; PROF MATH, UNIV UTAH, 65- *Concurrent Pos:* NSF fel, 55-56; managing ed, Rocky Mountain J of Math, 70- *Mem:* Am Math Soc; Math Asn Am. *Res:* Theory of groups. *Mailing Add:* Dept of Math Univ of Utah Salt Lake City UT 84112

SCOTT, WILLIAM TAUSSIG, b Yonkers, NY, Mar 16, 16; m 42; c 5. ATMOSPHERIC PHYSICS, PHILOSOPHY OF SCIENCE. *Educ:* Swarthmore Col, BA, 37; Univ Mich, PhD(physics), 41. *Prof Exp:* Instr physics, Amherst Col, 41-44; asst prof math & physics, Deep Springs Jr Col, 44-45; from instr to prof physics, Smith Col, 45-61; PROF PHYSICS, UNIV NEV, RENO, 61- *Concurrent Pos:* Res fel, Yale Univ, 59-60; vis prof, Univ Nev, 61-62, dir prog philos inquiry, 70-; consult, Brookhaven Nat Lab, 47-53, Nat Bur Stand, 54-58; res prof, Atmospheric Sci Ctr, Desert Res Inst, 64-; sr mem, Linacre Col, Oxford Univ, 69-70; mem anal comt, Higher Educ progs on Sci, Technol & Human Values Res Proj, Univ Mich, 75. *Mem:* Fel Am Phys Soc; Am Asn Physics Teachers; Am Meteorol Soc. *Res:* Philosophy of science in atmospheric physics; theory of multiple scattering of fast charged particles; interaction of science and religion; theory of cloud droplet growth by condensation and coalescence. *Mailing Add:* Dept of Physics Univ of Nev Reno NV 89557

SCOTT, WILLIAM WALLACE, b Utica, NY, Oct 1, 20; m 42; c 4. MYCOLOGY. *Educ:* Univ Vt, AB, 48, MS, 50; Univ Mich, PhD(bot), 55. *Prof Exp:* Res asst plant path, Univ Vt, 48-50; from assoc prof to prof bot, Va Polytech Inst, 55-64; assoc prog dir, NSF, 64-66; dean, Madison Col, Va, 66-68, chmn dept bot, 68-75, assoc dean grad sch, 75-78, PROF BOT, EASTERN ILL UNIV, 68- *Concurrent Pos:* Vis prof, Univ Wis, 60. *Mem:* Fel AAAS; Bot Soc Am; Mycol Soc Am; Brit Mycol Soc. *Res:* Cryptogamic botany; aquatic fungi; fungus diseases of fish; marine microbiology. *Mailing Add:* Dept of Bot Eastern Ill Univ Charleston IL 61920

SCOTT, WILLIAM WALLACE, b Kansas City, Kans, Jan 27, 13; m 36; c 1. PHYSIOLOGY. *Educ:* Univ Mo, AB, 34; Univ Chicago, PhD(physiol), 38, MD, 39. *Hon Degrees:* DSc, Univ Mo, 74. *Prof Exp:* Res assoc surg, Univ Chicago, 41-43, from instr to assoc prof urol, 43-46; prof, 46-74, DAVID HALL McCONNELL PROF UROL, SCH MED, JOHNS HOPKINS UNIV, 75-, UROLOGISTINCHG, HOPKINS HOSP, 46- *Concurrent Pos:* Consult, US Naval Hosp, Bethesda, Clin Ctr, NIH & Walter Reed Gen Hosp, Washington, DC. *Mem:* Am Physiol Soc; Endocrine Soc; Am Asn Cancer Res; Am Asn Genito-Urinary Surg; Am Urol Asn. *Res:* Endocrine relations in prostatic disease; renal circulation. *Mailing Add:* Room 500 Brady Urol Inst Johns Hopkins Hosp Baltimore MD 21205

SCOTTER, GEORGE WILBY, b Cardston, Alta, Jan 16, 33; m 59; c 2. ECOLOGY. *Educ:* Utah State Univ, BSc, 59, MSc, 62, PhD(range sci), 68. *Prof Exp:* Res scientist ecol, Can Wildlife Serv, 59-66; asst prof range ecol, Utah State Univ, 66-68; res scientist ecol, 68-77, prog leader parks res, 77-78, CHIEF CAN WILDLIFE SERV, 78- *Mem:* Ecol Soc Am; Soc Wildlife Mgt; Soc Range Mgt; Can Bot Asn. *Res:* Wildlife-range relationships and alpine research; wildland management and wilderness recreation research. *Mailing Add:* 4115 Aspen Dr W Edmonton AB T6J 2B5 Can

SCOTT-WALTON, BARRY LOUIS, b Buffalo, NY, Sept 4, 46; m 74. SOLID STATE PHYSICS, OPERATIONS ANALYSIS. *Educ:* Univ Calif, Santa Cruz, BA, 68, MS, 71, PhD(physics), 74. *Prof Exp:* Fel solid state physics, Ames Lab, Iowa State Univ & Dept Energy, 73-74; resource analyst, SRI Int, 74-80; sr energy analyst, INTASA Inc, 80-81; STAFF ENGR, FAIRCHILD INC, 81- *Mem:* Am Phys Soc; AAAS. *Res:* Energy and environmental impacts of new technologies and their policy implications, including the impacts of synthetic fuels technolgies; vortex nucleation in superconductors. *Mailing Add:* Fairchild Inc 3420 Central Expressway Santa Clara CA 95051

SCOUTEN, CHARLES GEORGE, b Atlanta, Ga, Nov 21, 40; m 64; c 2. ORGANIC CHEMISTRY, POLYMER SCIENCE. *Educ:* Univ Ga, BS, 68; Purdue Univ, PhD(org chem), 75. *Prof Exp:* Proj mgr mat, Xerox Prod Technol, 73-77; STAFF CHEMIST COAL SCI, EXXON CORP RES LABS, 78- *Mem:* Am Chem Soc. *Res:* Application of physical organic chemistry and polymer physics to development of new improved processes for utilizing coal and other alternate fuels. *Mailing Add:* Exxon Corp Res Lab PO Box 45 Linden NJ 07036

SCOUTEN, WILLIAM HENRY, b Corning, NY, Feb 12, 42; m 65; c 2. ENZYMOLOGY, PROTEIN CHEMISTRY. *Educ:* Houghton Col, BA, 64; Univ Pittsburgh, PhD(biochem), 69. *Prof Exp:* NIH fel, State Univ NY Stony Brook, 69-71; ASST PROF CHEM, BUCKNELL UNIV, 71- *Concurrent Pos:* Fulbright fel, 76; NSF fac develop fel, State Agr Univ, Wageningen. *Mem:* Am Chem Soc; Am Soc Cell Biol. *Res:* DNA replication; multienzyme complexes; DNA-binding proteins; protein chemistry; solid state biochemistry; affinity chromatography. *Mailing Add:* Dept of Chem Bucknell Univ Lewisburg PA 17837

SCOVELL, WILLIAM MARTIN, b Wilkes-Barre, Pa, Jan 16, 44; m 65; c 2. BIOINORGANIC CHEMISTRY. *Educ:* Lebanon Valley Col, BS, 65; Univ Minn, Minneapolis, PhD(inorg chem), 69. *Prof Exp:* Teaching assoc gen chem, Univ Minn, 65-69, res assoc inorg chem, 69; researcher phys biochem, Princeton Univ, 69-70, instr phys chem, 70-71, gen chem, 71-72; vis asst prof chem, State Univ NY Buffalo, 72-74; ASSOC PROF CHEM, BOWLING GREEN STATE UNIV, 74- *Concurrent Pos:* Consult, NL Industs, Inc, 70- & Smith, Kline & French Labs, 75. *Mem:* Am Chem Soc. *Res:* Interaction of metal ions and complexes of therapeutic value with proteins and nucleic acids; binding studies; use of vibrational spectroscopy, spectroscopy (Raman) in elucidating structure and conformation of biological macromolecules; studies of nucleosome structure. *Mailing Add:* Dept of Chem Hayes Hall Bowling Green State Univ Bowling Green OH 43403

SCOVIL, HENRY EVELYN DERRICK, b Victoria, BC, Can, July 25, 23; m 49; c 1. SOLID STATE PHYSICS. *Educ:* Univ BC, BA, 48, MA, 49; Oxford Univ, PhD(physics), 51. *Prof Exp:* Nuffield res fel, Oxford Univ, 51-52; asst prof, Univ BC, 52-55; mem tech staff ferrite devices, 55-59, supvr microwave maser amplifiers, 59-61, dept head masers, 61-64, DIR SOLID STATE DEVICE LAB, BELL TEL LABS, 64- *Honors & Awards:* Stuart Ballantine Medal, Franklin Inst, 61; Morris N Liebmann Award, Inst Elec & Electronics Engr, 75. *Mem:* Nat Acad Eng. *Res:* Device development. *Mailing Add:* Bell Tel Labs Murray Hill NJ 07974

SCOVILL, JOHN PAUL, b Fort Benning, Ga, Jan 16, 48; m 71; c 1. DRUG DESIGN. *Educ:* Cent Mich Univ, BSc, 70; Univ Mich, MSc, 73, PhD(med chem), 75. *Prof Exp:* RES CHEMIST, DIV EXP THERAPEUT, WALTER REED ARMY INST RES, 75. *Mem:* Am Chem Soc. *Res:* Design and preparation of potential chemotherapeutic agents; synthesis and mechanistic studies of organosulfur and organoselenium compounds, nitrogen heterocycles, and transition metal complexes. *Mailing Add:* Div Exp Therapeut Walter Reed Army Inst Res Washington DC 20012

SCOVILL, WILLIAM ALBERT, b Battle Creek, Mich, Nov 26, 40; m 68; c 2. SURGERY. *Educ:* Univ Mich, BS, 63, MD, 66; Univ Ill, MS, 73. *Prof Exp:* Instr surg, Sch Med, Univ Ill, 72-74; asst prof surg & physiol, 74-77, ASSOC PROF SURG & PHYSIOL, ALBANY MED COL, 77- *Concurrent Pos:* Dir, Trauma Serv, Albany Med Ctr, 74-, dir, Burn Treat Ctr, 75- *Mem:* Am Col Surgeons; Asn Acad Surg; Am Burn Asn; Reticuloendothelial Soc. *Res:* Influence of trauma, burn injury or surgery on humoral and cellular aspects of reticuloendothelial host defense function. *Mailing Add:* Dept of Surg Albany Med Col Albany NY 12208

SCOVILLE, HERBERT, JR, b New York, NY, Mar 16, 15; c 4. PHYSICAL CHEMISTRY. *Educ:* Yale Univ, BS, 37; Univ Rochester, PhD(phys chem), 42. *Prof Exp:* From asst to assoc chem, Nat Defense Res Comt contract, Univ Rochester, 41-44; res assoc, Northwestern Univ, 44-45; res assoc, Univ Ill, 45; tech aide & actg secy, Insect & Rodent Control Comt, Nat Res Coun, 45-46; sr scientist, AEC contract, Los Alamos Sci Lab, Calif, 46-48; tech dir, Armed Forces Spec Weapons Proj, 48-55; from asst dir to dep dir, Cent Intel Agency, 55-63; asst dir sci & tech, Arms Control & Disarmament Agency, 63-69; dir arms control prog, Carnegie Endowment Int Peace, 69-71; AUTHOR & CONSULT, 69- *Concurrent Pos:* Vpres, Arms Control Asn; consult, Carnegie Endowment Int Peace. *Mem:* Fedn Am Sci. *Res:* Photochemistry; gas absorption; aerosols; nuclear and radiation effects; scientific intelligence; arms control and strategic studies; political science; national security; foreign policy. *Mailing Add:* 6400 Georgetown Pike McLean VA 22101

SCOVILLE, RICHARD ARTHUR, b Torrington, Conn, Feb 14, 35. MATHEMATICS. *Educ:* Yale Univ, BA, 56, MA, 57, PhD(math), 62. *Prof Exp:* Asst prof, 61-74, ASSOC PROF MATH, DUKE UNIV, 74- *Concurrent Pos:* Lectr, Ehime Univ, Japan, 66-67. *Mem:* Am Math Soc. *Res:* Ergodic theory; measure-preserving transformations; sums of dependent random variables. *Mailing Add:* Dept of Math Duke Univ Durham NC 27706

SCOW, ROBERT OLIVER, b Dos Cabezas, Ariz, Nov 17, 20; m 48; c 4. PHYSIOLOGY, ENDOCRINOLOGY. *Educ:* Univ Calif, AB, 43, MA, 44, MD, 46. *Prof Exp:* Intern, San Francisco Hosp, 46 & Presby Hosp, NY, 47-48; from sr asst surgeon to surgeon, 48-59, MED DIR, NIH, 59-, CHIEF SECT ENDOCRINOL, LAB NUTRIT & ENDOCRINOL, NAT INST ARTHRITIS, METAB & DIGESTIVE DIS, 61- *Concurrent Pos:* Guggenheim fel, 55; vis prof exp med & cancer res, Hebrew Univ-Hadassah Med Sch, Israel, 65-66; vis prof pediat, Univ Oulu, 75; vis scientist, Ctr Biochem & Molecular Biol, Nat Ctr Sci Res, France, 77; fel, Coun Arteriosclerosis, Am Heart Asn. *Mem:* Am Physiol Soc; Endocrine Soc; Am Asn Anatomists. *Res:* Hormonal influences on growth of striated musculature and bone; hormonal control of fat and carbohydrate metabolism; diabetes; perfusion of isolated organs; role of capillaries and lipoprotein lipase in metabolism of chylomicrons; hormonal regulation of lipoprotein lipase; lipid transport by lateral movement in cell membranes. *Mailing Add:* Rm 8-D-14 Bldg 10 Nat Inst of Health Bethesda MD 20014

SCOZZIE, JAMES ANTHONY, b Erie, Pa, Nov 3, 43; m 70. ORGANIC CHEMISTRY. *Educ:* Gannon Col, AB, 65; Case Western Reserve Univ, MS, 68, PhD(chem), 70. *Prof Exp:* Jr res chemist, Cent Res Dept, Lord Corp, 65; res chemist, 70-72, sr res chemist, 72-76, res supvr pharmaceut, 76-78, GROUP LEADER AGR CHEM, DIAMOND SHAMROCK CORP, 78- *Mem:* Am Chem Soc; NY Acad Sci. *Res:* Structure and chemistry of peptide antibiotics; synthesis of biologically active compounds; pesticides; process studies of organic compounds; commercial evaluation; nutrition and animal health; herbicides; plant growth regulants; cardiovascular agents and antiinflammatory agents. *Mailing Add:* T R Evans Res Ctr PO Box 348 Diamond Shamrock Corp Painesville OH 44077

SCRABA, DOUGLAS G, b Blairmore, Alta, Apr 17, 40. BIOCHEMISTRY, VIROLOGY. *Educ:* Univ Alta, BSc, 61, BEd, 63, PhD(biochem), 68. *Prof Exp:* Lectr chem, North Alta Inst Technol, 63-64; asst prof, 70-73, ASSOC PROF BIOCHEM, UNIV ALTA, 73- *Concurrent Pos:* Med Res Coun Can, centennial fel, Univ Geneva, 68-70. *Mem:* Can Biochem Soc; Am Soc Microbiol; Soc Gen Microbiol; Micros Soc Can. *Res:* Structure and assembly of mammalian and bacterial viruses. *Mailing Add:* Dept of Biochem Univ of Alta Edmonton AB T6G 2E1 Can

SCRAFANI, JOSEPH THOMAS, b Passaic, NJ, Aug 24, 39. PHARMACOLOGY, MEDICAL EDUCATION. *Educ:* Rutgers Univ, BS, 61, MS, 64; Univ Mich, PhD(pharmacol), 69. *Prof Exp:* Res fel, NY State Res Inst Neurochem & Drug Addiction, 69-71; med educ mgr, 71-73, assoc dir educ, 73-74, assoc dir prof serv, 74-81, DIR MED EDUC, SCHERING LABS, DIV SCHERING-PLOUGH CORP, 81- *Concurrent Pos:* Lectr pharmacol, Sch Dent, Fairleigh Dickinson Univ, 69-72; assoc res scientist pharmacol, NY State Narcotic Addiction Control Comn, 71-72. *Mem:* NY Acad Sci; Am Soc Hosp Pharmacists; Am Pharmaceut Asn; AAAS. *Mailing Add:* Schering-Plough Corp Galloping Hill Rd Kenilworth NJ 07033

SCRANTON, BRUCE EDWARD, b Pittsfield, Ill, May 5, 46; m 68; c 4. MATHEMATICAL ANALYSIS, OPERATIONS RESEARCH. *Educ:* Northern Ill Univ, BS, 68; Purdue Univ, MS, 71, PhD(math), 74. *Prof Exp:* Sr assoc opers res, Daniel H Wagner, Assocs, 74-82; SR SYST ENGR, GEN ELEC, 82- *Mem:* Am Math Soc; Math Asn Am; Inst Elec & Electronics Engrs. *Res:* Design evaluation and application of operations research and real time; computer models with military applications. *Mailing Add:* Gen Elec Valley Forge Space Ctr Philadelphia PA 19301

SCRANTON, MARY ISABELLE, b Atlanta, Ga, Feb 28, 50; m 81. MARINE BIOGEOCHEMISTRY. *Educ:* Mount Holyoke Col, BA, 72; Mass Inst Technol, PhD(oceanog), 77. *Prof Exp:* Nat Acad Sci-Nat Res Coun resident res assoc, US Naval Res Lab, 77-79; ASST PROF CHEM OCEANOG, MARINE SCI RES CTR, STATE UNIV NY STONY BROOK, 79- *Mem:* Am Geophys Union; Am Soc Limnol & Oceanog; Sigma Xi. *Res:* Investigations of sources, sinks and distributions of reduced gases in the marine environment; interactions of biological processes and chemical cycles. *Mailing Add:* Marine Sci Res Ctr State Univ NY Stony Brook NY 11794

SCRIABINE, ALEXANDER, b Yelgava, Latvia, Oct 26, 26; nat US; m 64; c 2. PHARMACOLOGY. *Educ:* Cornell Univ, MS, 54; Univ Mainz, MD, 58. *Prof Exp:* Res asst pharmacol, Med Sch, Cornell Univ, 51-54; pharmacologist, Res Labs, Chas Pfizer & Co, Maywood, NJ, 54-56, sr pharmacologist, 59-61, supvr, 61-63, mgr, Chas Pfizer & Co, Groton, Conn, 63-66; chief pharmacologist, Div Cardiol, Philadelphia Gen Hosp, 66-67; sr res fel, Merck Inst Therapeut Res, 67-69, dir cardiovasc res, 69-72, sr dir pharmacol, 72-73, exec dir pharmacol, 73-78; ASSOC PROF PHARMACOL, SCH MED, UNIV PA, 75-; assoc dir biol res, Wyeth Labs, Inc, 78-79; DIR, MILES INST PRECLIN PHARMACOL, 79- *Concurrent Pos:* Asst prof pharmacol, Sch Med, Univ Pa, 67-75; mem coun thrombosis, Am Heart Asn. *Mem:* Am Soc Pharmacol & Exp Therapeut; Ger Pharmacol Soc; Am Soc Clin Pharmacol & Therapeut; Int Study Group Cardiac Metab Res; Int Soc Heart Res. *Res:* Cardiovascular, autonomic and renal pharmacology; antihypertensives, diuretics, antianginal agents; cardiotonics; antithrombotics; pharmacology of tetrahydrozoline, hydroxyzine, benzthiazide, polythiazide, benzquinamide, prazosin, clonidine, germine monoacetate, timolol. *Mailing Add:* Miles Inst Preclin Pharmacol PO Box 1956 New Haven CT 06509

SCRIBNER, BELDING HIBBARD, b Chicago, Ill, Jan 18, 21; m 42; c 4. MEDICINE. *Educ:* Univ Calif, AB, 41; Stanford Univ, MD, 45. *Prof Exp:* From intern to resident med, San Francisco Hosp, 44-47; from asst prof to assoc prof, 51-62, PROF MED, SCH MED, UNIV WASH, 62-, HEAD DIV NEPHROL, 80- *Concurrent Pos:* Fel, Mayo Found, Univ Minn, 47-51; mem staff, Vet Admin Hosp, Seattle, 51-57. *Mem:* Am Soc Clin Invest; AMA; fel Am Col Physicians. *Res:* Fluid and electrolyte balance and kidney disease as pertaining to medicine; nephrology; dialysis. *Mailing Add:* Dept of Med Univ of Wash Sch of Med Seattle WA 98195

SCRIBNER, JOHN DAVID, b Portage, Wis, June 28, 41; m 78; c 1. ORGANIC CHEMISTRY, ONCOLOGY. *Educ:* Univ Wis-Madison, BS, 63, PhD(oncol), 67, BA, 70. *Prof Exp:* NSF fel, Ger Cancer Res Ctr, Heidelberg, 67-68; NIH training grant, Univ Wis-Madison, 68-71; CHMN DEPT CHEM CARCINOGENESIS, PAC NORTHWEST RES FOUND & FRED HUTCHINSON CANCER RES CTR, 71- *Mem:* AAAS; Am Chem Soc; Am Asn Cancer Res. *Res:* Mechanisms of chemical carcinogenesis; theoretical and organic chemistry of carcinogens. *Mailing Add:* PO Box 1267 North Bend WA 98045

SCRIMGEOUR, KENNETH GRAY, b Vancouver, BC, Sept 10, 34; m 58; c 2. BIOCHEMISTRY. *Educ:* Univ BC, BA, 56, MSc, 57; Univ Wash, PhD(biochem), 61. *Prof Exp:* Res assoc biochem, Univ Wash, 61-62; from asst to assoc, Scripps Clin & Res Found, 62-67; assoc prof, 67-81, PROF BIOCHEM, UNIV TORONTO, 81- *Mem:* Can Biochem Soc. *Res:* Enzymology; pteridine chemistry. *Mailing Add:* Dept of Biochem Univ of Toronto Toronto ON M5S 1A8 Can

SCRIMGER, EDWARD BRANTLY, JR, mathematics, see previous edition

SCRIMSHAW, NEVIN STEWART, b Milwaukee, Wis, Jan 20, 18; m 41; c 5. NUTRITION. *Educ:* Ohio Wesleyan Univ, BA, 38; Harvard Univ, MA, 39, PhD(physiol), 41, MPH, 59; Univ Rochester, MD, 45; Am Bd Nutrit, cert, 64. *Hon Degrees:* DPS, Ohio Wesleyan Univ, 61; ScD, Univ Rochester, 74. *Prof Exp:* Instr embryol & comp anat, Ohio Wesleyan Univ, 41-42; intern, Gorgas Hosp, CZ, 43-46; asst resident physician obstet & gynec, Strong Mem Hosp & Genesee Hosp, Rochester, NY, 48-49; dir, Inst Nutrit Cent Am & Panama, Guatemala, 49-61; dir, Clin Res Ctr, 62-66, PROF HUMAN NUTRIT & HEAD DEPT NUTRIT & FOOD SCI, MASS INST TECHNOL, 61-, PRIN INVESTR, CLIN RES CTR, 62- *Concurrent Pos:* Fel nutrit & endocrinol, Dept Vital Econ, Univ Rochester, 42-43, Rockefeller Found fel, Dept Obstet & Gynec, 46-47, Merck Nat Res Coun fel natural sci, 47-49; vis lectr trop pub health, Harvard Univ, 68-; mem, Food & Nutrit Bd, Nat Acad Sci-Nat Res Coun, 67-, mem exec comt, 68-, mem, Comt Int Nutrit Progs, 64-, chmn, 68-, mem, Task Force Genetic Alteration Food Crops, 73-, mem, Task Force Food-Health-Pop Prob, 73-; mem, Adv Comt Med Res, WHO, 71-, chmn, 73-78; trustee, Rockefeller Found, 71-; vpres, Int Union Nutrit Sci, 72-, pres, 78-81; mem, US Del Joint Comt, US-Japan Coop Med Sci Prog, 74-; chmn food & nutrit sect, Am Pub Health Asn, 63, mem res comt, 65, chmn ad hoc task force nutrit, 70; mem lectr prog, Inst Food Technol, 69-70, mem, Int Award Jury, 69-72, chmn, 74; mem expert work group on world hunger, UN Univ, 75; sr adv, World Hunger Prog, 75- *Honors & Awards:* Osborne-Mendel Award, Am Inst Nutrit, 60; Order of Rodolfo Robles, Govt Guatemala, 61; Int Award, Inst Food Technol, 69; Joseph Goldberger Award Clin Nutrit, AMA, 69. *Mem:* Nat Acad Sci; Nat Inst Med; AAAS; Am Inst Nutrit; Am Soc Clin Nutrit. *Res:* Clinical and public nutrition; amino acid protein metabolism; nutrition and infection. *Mailing Add:* Dept of Nutrit & Food Sci Mass Inst of Technol Cambridge MA 02139

SCRIVEN, L E(DWARD), (II), b Battle Creek, Mich, Nov 4, 31; m 52; c 3. ENGINEERING SCIENCE. *Educ:* Univ Calif, Berkeley, BS, 52; Univ Del, MChE, 54, PhD(chem eng), 56. *Prof Exp:* Res engr, Shell Develop Co, 56-59; from asst prof to assoc prof, 59-66, PROF CHEM ENG, UNIV MINN, 66-, ASSOC HEAD, 74- *Concurrent Pos:* Adv ed, Prentice-Hall, Inc; guest investr, Rockefeller Inst, 63; vis prof, Univ Pa, 67, Univ Fed Rio de Janeiro, 69 & Univ Witwatersrand, 74; Guggenheim fel, 69-70; assoc ed, J Fluid Mech, 69-75. *Honors & Awards:* Colburn Award, Am Inst Chem Engrs, 60, Walker Award, 77. *Mem:* Nat Acad Eng; Am Inst Chem Engrs; Am Phys Soc; Soc Petrol Engrs; The Chem Soc. *Res:* Interface, contact line and micellar physics; capillarity and small-scale free-surface flows; dynamic instability and pattern; finite element methods. *Mailing Add:* 2044 Cedar Lake Pkwy Cardinal Point Minneapolis MN 55416

SCRIVER, CHARLES ROBERT, b Montreal, Que, Nov 7, 30; m; c 4. PEDIATRICS, GENETICS. *Educ:* McGill Univ, BA, 51, MD, CM, 55; FRCPS(C), 61; FRSC, 73. *Prof Exp:* From intern to jr asst resident med, Royal Victoria Hosp, Montreal, 55-56; jr asst resident, Montreal Children's Hosp, 57 & Med Ctr, Boston, Mass, 57-58; McLaughlin traveling fel, Univ Col, London Hosp, 58-60; chief resident pediat, Montreal Children's Hosp, 60-61, dir deBelle Lab Biochem Genet, 61-; lectr pediat, 62-63, from asst prof to assoc prof, 63-69, PROF PEDIAT, MCGILL UNIV, 69-, PROF BIOL, 77- *Concurrent Pos:* Markle fel, 61-66; assoc physician, Dept Pediat Med, Montreal Children's Hosp, 63-65, physician, 65-; Med Res Coun assoc, 69- *Honors & Awards:* Wood Gold Medal, McGill Univ, 55; Royal Col Physicians & Surgeons, Can Medal, 61; F Mead Johnson Award, Am Acad Pediat, 68, Borden Award, 73; Borden Award, Nutrit Soc Can, 69; Allan Award, Am Soc Human Genetics, 78; Gardner Int Award, 79; McLaughlin Medal, Royal Soc Can, 81. *Mem:* Am Acad Pediat; Am Soc Clin Invest; Am Soc Clin Nutrit; Am Soc Human Genetics; Am Pediat Soc. *Res:* Biochemical genetics; membrane transport; genetic screening; amino acid metabolism; phosphate metabolism. *Mailing Add:* Montreal Children's Hosp Res Inst 2300 Tupper St Montreal PQ H3H 1P3 Can

SCROGGIE, LUCY E, b Knoxville, Tenn, May 29, 35. ANALYTICAL CHEMISTRY. *Educ:* Univ Tenn, BS, 57, MS, 59; Univ Tex, PhD(anal chem), 61. *Prof Exp:* Anal chemist, anal chem div, Oak Ridge Nat Lab, 61-66; anal chemist res & develop dept chem & plastics div, Union Carbide Corp, 66-69; anal chemist indust & radiol hyg br, Div Environ Res & Develop, 70-75, res chemist, Lab Br, Div Environ Planning, 75-80, mgt trainee, Off Natural Resources, 80-81, PROJ MGR, DIV NATURAL RESOURCE OPERS, TENN VALLEY AUTH, 81- *Mem:* Am Chem Soc; Am Conf Govt Indust Hygienists. *Res:* Analytical methods development; spectrophotometry; industrial hygiene chemistry; analytical chemistry applied to air and water quality and industrial hygiene. *Mailing Add:* Tenn Valley Auth 306 Evans Bldg Knoxville TN 37902

SCROGGS, JAMES EDWARD, b Little Rock, Ark, Apr 20, 26; m 48; c 3. MATHEMATICS. *Educ:* Univ Ark, BA, 49; Univ Houston, MA, 54; Rice Inst, PhD(math), 57. *Prof Exp:* From asst prof to assoc prof math, Univ Ark, 57-62; asst prof, Univ Tex, 62-64; PROF MATH, UNIV ARK, FAYETTEVILLE, 64-, CHMN DEPT, 66- *Mem:* Am Math Soc; Math Asn Am; Soc Indust & Appl Math. *Res:* Functional and complex analysis; Banach and Hilbert spaces. *Mailing Add:* Dept of Math Univ of Ark Fayetteville AR 72701

SCRUGGS, JAMES ANDERS, pharmacy, see previous edition

SCUDAMORE, HAROLD HUNTER, b Wayne City, Ill, Dec 8, 15; m 42; c 4. MEDICINE. *Educ:* Mont State Col, BS, 37; Northwestern Univ, MS, 40, PhD(zool), 42, MD, 45; Am Bd Internal Med, dipl, 55; Am Bd Gastroenterol, dipl, 60. *Prof Exp:* Asst zool, Northwestern Univ, 37-39, asst sci, 39-42, instr, 42-43, asst pharmacol, 43; intern, Evanston Hosp, 45-46; fel med, Mayo Grad Sch Med, Univ Minn, 49-51, from instr to assoc prof, 52-71; CLIN ASSOC PROF MED, SCH MED, UNIV WIS, 71-; CHIEF GASTROENTEROL, MONROE CLIN, 71- *Concurrent Pos:* Mem staff, Mayo Clin, 51-71. *Mem:* AAAS; Am Gastroenterol Asn; fel Am Col Physicians; fel Am Col Gastroenterol; Am Soc Int Med. *Res:* Gastroenterology, especially malabsorption syndromes and diseases of the intestines; radioisotope studies; diseases of pancreas, stomach and postgastrectomy states. *Mailing Add:* Monroe Clin 1515 Tenth St Monroe WI 53566

SCUDDAY, JAMES FRANKLIN, b Alpine, Tex, Sept 16, 29; m 50; c 3. VERTEBRATE BIOLOGY, WILDLIFE BIOLOGY. *Educ:* Sul Ross State Univ, BS, 52; Univ Idaho, MNS, 62; Tex A&M Univ, PhD(wildlife sci), 71. *Prof Exp:* Teacher independent sch dist, Tex, 52-54 & 56-61; instr biol, Sul Ross State Univ, 61-66; res asst wildlife sci, Tex A&M Univ, 67-69; from asst prof to assoc prof, 69-76, PROF BIOL, SUL ROSS STATE UNIV, 76- *Concurrent Pos:* NSF res partic syst bot, Okla State Univ, 64. *Mem:* Herpet League; Am Soc Mammal; Soc Study Amphibians & Reptiles; Sigma Xi; Soc Syst Zool. *Res:* Ecology and systematics of vertebrate animals. *Mailing Add:* Dept of Biol Sul Ross State Univ Alpine TX 79830

SCUDDER, CHARLES LEE, psychopharmacology, see previous edition

SCUDDER, GEOFFREY GEORGE EDGAR, b Kent, Eng, Mar 18, 34; m 58. ENTOMOLOGY. *Educ:* Univ Wales, BSc, 55; Oxford Univ, DPhil(entom), 58. *Prof Exp:* Instr zool, 58-60, from asst prof to assoc prof, 60-68, PROF ZOOL, UNIV BC, 68-, CUR SPENCER ENTOM MUS, 58- *Concurrent Pos:* Royal Soc & Nuffield Found Commonwealth bursary, Imp Col, Univ London, 64-65. *Honors & Awards:* Gold Medal, Entom Soc Can, 75. *Mem:* Soc Study Evolution; Entom Soc Can; Can Soc Zool; fel Royal Entom Soc London; fel Royal Soc Can. *Res:* Systematics; evolution; entomology of Hemiptera; comparative morphology of insects; freshwater insect ecology and evolution. *Mailing Add:* Dept of Zool Univ of BC Vancouver BC V6T 2A9 Can

SCUDDER, HARVEY ISRAEL, b Elmira, NY, Jan 2, 19; m 45; c 2. PUBLIC HEALTH, BIOLOGY. *Educ:* Cornell Univ, BS, 39, PhD(pub health), 53. *Prof Exp:* Asst entomologist, Boyce Thompson Inst Plant Res, 41; jr entomologist, USPHS, Fla, 42-43, state malaria control entomologist, Ala, 43-44, Carter Mem Lab, Ga, 44-46; chief div malaria control & sanit, Standard-Vacuum Oil Co, Sumatra, 47; tech coordr & officer in chg vector control field sta, State Dept Pub Health, Calif, 51-54; res biologist, Tech Develop Labs, Commun Dis Ctr, USPHS, Ga, 54-56, sect chief, Health Res Facil, Div Res Grants, NIH, 56-57, exec secy microbiol, virol & rickettsial study sect, 57-59; staff asst, Nat Cancer Inst, 59-61, chief virol res resources br, 61-62; asst to chief div res grants, NIH, 62; chief res training grants, Nat Inst Gen Med Sci, 62-65; manpower consult, Div Community Health Serv, USPHS, 65-66; head div biol & health sci, 67-70, actg head div sci & math, 68-69, actg chmn dept biol sci, 70-71, coordr health sci, 71-72, PROF MICROBIOL, CALIF STATE UNIV, HAYWARD, 67- *Concurrent Pos:* Mem microbiol fel rev panel, NIH, 58-60; mem, Moss Landing Marine Labs, 67-70, chmn policy bd, 69-70; mem bd trustees, St Rose Hosp, Hayward, 69-74 & 77- chmn, 73-74; trustee, Marine Ecol Inst, Redwood City, 71-, actg chmn, 74-; mem bd dir, East Bay Found Health Careers Educ, 72-, chmn, 74-76; mem community adv comt, Fairmont Hosp, San Leandro, 74- *Mem:* AAAS; Am Soc Allied Health Professions; Am Soc Trop Med & Hyg; Entom Soc Am; Am Soc Microbiol. *Res:* Environmental sanitation and public health; health manpower; medical entomology. *Mailing Add:* Dept of Biol Sci Calif State Univ Hayward CA 94542

SCUDDER, HENRY J, III, b Brooklyn, NY, Sept 26, 35; c 4. INFORMATION SCIENCE. *Educ:* Cornell Univ, BEngPhys, 58, MEE, 60; Univ Calif, Berkeley, PhD(elec eng), 64. *Prof Exp:* Engr, Advan Electronics Ctr, 58-60, INFO SCIENTIST, RES & DEVELOP CTR, GEN ELEC CO, 64- *Concurrent Pos:* NSF fel, 62. *Mem:* Inst Elec & Electronics Engrs. *Res:* Information theory; pattern recognition; communication theory; data transmission and processing; learning machines; acoustic noise measurements; computer aided tomography; nondestructive evaluation. *Mailing Add:* Gen Elec Res & Develop Ctr Schenectady NY 12345

SCUDDER, JACK DAVID, b Sao Paulo, Brazil, Sept 28, 47; US citizen; m 69; c 1. PLASMA PHYSICS. *Educ:* Williams Col, BA, 69; Univ Md, College Park, MS, 72, PhD(plasma physics), 75. *Prof Exp:* RES PHYSICIST SPACE PLASMA PHYSICS, NASA, GODDARD SPACE FLIGHT CTR, 69- *Concurrent Pos:* Max Planck fel, Max Planck Soc, 77. *Honors & Awards:* Mariner 10 Sci Award, NASA, 74; Int Sun Earth Explorer Team Award, NASA, 78. *Mem:* Am Geophys Union. *Res:* Kinetic physics of space magneto plasmas with emphasis on transport phenomena. *Mailing Add:* NASA Mail Code 692 Goddard Space Flight Ctr Greenbelt MD 20771

SCUDDER, WALTER TREDWELL, b Elmira, NY, Aug 28, 20; m 51; c 3. WEED SCIENCE. *Educ:* Cornell Univ, BS, 41, PhD(veg crops), 51; La State Univ, MS, 43. *Prof Exp:* Asst hort, La State Univ, 41-43; teacher, NY, 43-44; asst veg crops, Cornell Univ, 46-49; instr, 49-50; assoc horticulturist, SC Truck Exp Sta, 50-53; horticulturist, US Marine Corps, 53-55; assoc horticulturist, 55-68, PROF HORT & HORTICULTURIST, AGR RES & EDUC CTR, UNIV FLA, 68- *Mem:* Weed Sci Soc Am; Am Soc Hort Sci; Potato Asn Am. *Res:* Chemical and biological weed control in vegetable and field crops; herbicide evaluation; persistence and degradation of herbicide residues in soil; weed species identification, terminology and distribution. *Mailing Add:* Dept of Hort Agr Res & Educ Ctr Univ of Fla Sanford FL 32771

SCULLEY, JOHN DAMIAN, organic chemistry, see previous edition

SCULLY, ERIK PAUL, b Ossining, NY, Oct 22, 49. ZOOLOGY, POPULATION BIOLOGY. *Educ:* Fordham Univ, BS, 71; Univ RI, PhD(biol), 76. *Prof Exp:* Lectr ecol, Univ Calif, Irvine, 76-78; INSTR BIOL, TOWSON STATE UNIV, 78- *Mem:* AAAS; Soc Study Evolution; Ecol Soc Am; Animal Behav Soc; Sigma Xi. *Res:* Behavioral ecology and population biology of invertebrates, specifically marine invertebrates; mechanisms of resource utilization and intraspecific competition; use of the computer for instructional purposes. *Mailing Add:* Dept of Biol Sci Towson State Univ Towson MD 21204

SCULLY, FRANK E, JR, b Brooklyn, NY, Mar 23, 47; m 71. CHEMISTRY. *Educ:* Spring Hill Col, BS, 68; Purdue Univ, PhD(chem), 73. *Prof Exp:* Instr org chem, Yale Univ, 73-75; asst prof chem sci, 75-80, ASSOC PROF CHEM, OLD DOMINION UNIV, 80- *Res:* Photosensitized oxygenations of cyclopropanes, vinylcyclopropanes, vinylcyclopropanols and norbornyl systems as a probe for an ionic mechanism of dioxetane formation; unsaturated alkoxide systems as an internal trap for intermediates in the reaction of singlet oxygen with olefins; use and effect of crown ethers in singlet oxygenations. *Mailing Add:* Dept of Chem Old Dominion Univ Norfolk VA 23508

SCULLY, MARLAN ORVIL, b Caspar, Wyo, Aug 3, 39; m 58; c 3. PHYSICS. *Educ:* Univ Wyo, BS, 61; Yale Univ, MS, 63, PhD(physics), 65. *Prof Exp:* Physicist, Gen Elec Co, 61-62; instr physics, Yale Univ, 65-67; from asst prof to assoc prof, Mass Inst Technol, 67-71; prof physics & optical sci, Univ Ariz, 70-80; MEM FAC, DEPT PHYSICS & ASTRON, UNIV NMEX, 80- *Concurrent Pos:* Consult, United Aircraft Res Lab, 65-, Los Alamos Sci Lab, 70-, US Army, Redstone, 71-; Sci Appln Inc, 76- & Litton Indust, 76- mem, Joint Coun Quantum Electronics; John Simon Guggenheim & Alfred P Sloan fels; adv to pres, Rice Univ. *Honors & Awards:* Adolph Lomb Medal, Optical Soc Am, 70. *Mem:* Fel AAAS; fel Am Phys Soc; fel Am Optical Soc. *Res:* Neutron and low temperature physics; laser physics; quantum statistical mechanics; solid state physics and quantum optics. *Mailing Add:* Dept Physics & Astron Univ NMex 800 Yale Blvd NE Albuquerque NM 87131

SCULLY, ROBERT EDWARD, b Pittsfield, Mass, Aug 31, 21. PATHOLOGY. *Educ:* Col of the Holy Cross, AB, 41; Harvard Med Sch, MD, 44. *Prof Exp:* Asst clin prof, 59-63, assoc prof, 63-69, PROF PATH, HARVARD MED SCH, 70- *Concurrent Pos:* From assoc pathologist to pathologist, Mass Gen Hosp, 58- *Mem:* AMA; Int Soc Gynec Pathologists; Soc Gynec Oncol; Int Acad Path. *Res:* Gynecologic and testicular pathology and endocrinology. *Mailing Add:* Mass Gen Hosp Boston MA 02114

SCURRY, MURPHY TOWNSEND, b Houston, Tex, May 25, 33; m 55; c 2. MEDICINE, ENDOCRINOLOGY. *Educ:* Univ Tex, Austin, BA, 54; Univ Tex Med Br Galveston, MD, 58. *Prof Exp:* Rotating intern, Univ Pa, 59; resident med, Univ Mich, Ann Arbor, 61, NIH fel, 61-63; asst prof med, 66-72, ASSOC PROF MED, UNIV TEX MED BR GALVESTON, 72- *Concurrent Pos:* Consult, USPHS Hosp, Galveston, Tex, 70- *Mem:* Endocrine Soc; Am Diabetes Asn; Am Fedn Clin Res; Am Col Physicians. *Res:* Secretion of parathyroid hormone. *Mailing Add:* Dept of Med Univ of Tex Med Br Galveston TX 77550

SEABAUGH, PYRTLE W, b Millersville, Mo, Sept 14, 35; m 59; c 1. ANALYTICAL CHEMISTRY, APPLIED STATISTICS. *Educ:* Southeast Mo State Col, BS, 56; Iowa State Univ, PhD(inorg chem), 61; Univ Dayton, MBA, 71. *Prof Exp:* Fel struct chem, Univ Wis, 61-63; sr res chemist, 63-67, res specialist, 67-74, SR ANAL SPECIALIST, MONSANTO RES CORP, MOUND LAB, 74- *Mem:* AAAS; Am Chem Soc; Am Crystallog Asn; Sigma Xi; Am Inst Physics. *Res:* Development of x-ray fluorescence and diffraction techniques; experimental design; interpretation of research and development data via applied statistics and numerical analysis; financial modeling; structural and pollution chemistry. *Mailing Add:* Monsanto Res Corp Mound Lab Miamisburg OH 45342

SEABLOOM, ROBERT W, b St Paul, Minn, Aug 15, 32. MAMMALOGY. *Educ:* Univ Minn, BA, 53, MS, 58, PhD(wildlife mgt), 63. *Prof Exp:* From asst prof to assoc prof biol, 61-75, PROF BIOL, UNIV NDAK, 75- *Concurrent Pos:* Vis scientist, Whiteshell Nuclear Res Estab, Atomic Energy Can Ltd, 71-72. *Mem:* Am Soc Mammal; Wildlife Soc; Ecol Soc Am. *Res:* Vertebrate population ecology; mammalian systematics, life histories, and distributions; adrenal function in small mammal populations. *Mailing Add:* Dept of Biol Univ of NDak Grand Forks ND 58202

SEABORG, GLENN THEODORE, b Ishpeming, Mich, Apr 19, 12; m 42; c 6. NUCLEAR CHEMISTRY. *Educ:* Univ Calif, Los Angeles, AB, 34; Univ Calif, Berkeley, PhD(chem), 37. *Hon Degrees:* Forty-six from US & foreign univs & cols, 51-78. *Prof Exp:* Res assoc chem, 37-39, prof, 39-71, dir nuclear chem res, Lawrence Berkeley Lab, 46-58 & 72-75, chancellor, 58-61, fac res lectr, 59, UNIV PROF CHEM, UNIV CALIF, BERKELEY, 71-, DIR NUCLEAR CHEM RES, LAWRENCE BERKELEY LAB, 46-58, 72-, ASSOC DIR LAB, 54-61, 72- *Concurrent Pos:* Sect chief metall lab, Univ Chicago, 42-46; mem gen adv comt, AEC, 46-50, mem hist adv comt, 58-61, chmn, AEC, 61-71; mem joint comn radioactivity, Int Coun Sci Unions, 46-56; mem, President's Sci Adv Comt, 59-61; mem, Pac Coast Comt, Am Coun Educ, 59-61; mem exec comt & chmn steering comt chem study, Chem Educ Mat Study, NSF, 59-74, mem bd, 60-61 & adv coun col chem, 62-67; mem, Fed Coun Sci & Technol, 61-71; mem, Fed Radiation Coun, 61-71; mem, Nat Aeronaut & Space Coun, 61-71; mem comn humanities, Am Coun Learned Socs & Coun Grad Schs, 62-65; mem sci adv comt, Pac Sci Ctr Found, 63-77; mem, Nat Coun Marine Res & Eng Develop, 66-71; mem sc adv bd, Robert Welch Found, 57-; trustee, Educ Serv, Inc, 61-67 & Pac Sci Ctr Found, 62-77; trustee, Sci Serv, 65-, pres, 66-; bd trustees, Swed Coun Am, 76- *Honors & Awards:* Nobel Prize in Chem, 51; Award Pure Chem, Am Chem Soc, 47, Nichols Medal, 48, Parsons Award, 64, Gibbs Medal, 66, Marshall Madison Award, 72 & Priestley Medal, 79; Ericsson Gold Medal, Am Soc Swed Engrs, 48; Perkin Medal, Am Sect, Brit Soc Chem Indust, 57; Edison Found Award, 58; Enrico Fermi Award, AEC, 59; Priestley Mem Award, Dickinson Col, 60; Sci & Eng Award, Fedn Eng Socs, Drexel Inst, 62; Swed Am Yr, Vasa Order Am, 62; Franklin Medal, Franklin Inst, 63; Leif Erikson Award, Leif Erikson Found, 64; Arches of Sci Award, Pac Sci Ctr, 68; Chem Pioneer, Am Inst Chemists, 68, Gold Medal Award, 73; Prometheus Award, Nat Elec Mfrs Asn, 69; Oliver Townsend Award, Atomic Indust Forum, 71. *Mem:* Nat Acad Sci; fel AAAS (pres, 72); Am Chem Soc; fel Am Nuclear Soc; fel Am Phys Soc. *Res:* Heavy ion reactions; transuranium elements. *Mailing Add:* Lawrence Berkeley Lab Univ of Calif Berkeley CA 94720

SEABORN, JAMES BYRD, b Panama City, Fla, Dec 15, 32; m 53; c 5. THEORETICAL NUCLEAR PHYSICS. *Educ:* Fla State Univ, BS, 60, MS, 62; Univ Va, PhD(nuclear theory), 65. *Prof Exp:* Asst prof physics, Univ Richmond, 65-66; res assoc, Univ Frankfurt, 66; asst prof, North Tex State Univ, 67-69; vis lectr, Iowa State Univ, 69-70; ASSOC PROF PHYSICS, UNIV RICHMOND, 70- *Res:* Nuclear structure studies; electromagnetic interactions in atomic nuclei. *Mailing Add:* Dept Physics Univ Richmond Richmond VA 23173

SEABROOK, WILLIAM DAVIDSON, b Ottawa, Ont, Apr 2, 35; m 60; c 2. INSECT NEUROPHYSIOLOGY. *Educ:* Carleton Univ, Can, BSc, 60, MSc, 64; Univ London, PhD(zool), 67. *Prof Exp:* Biologist, Govt Can, 60-62; PROF BIOL, UNIV NB, FREDERICTON, 67-, RES CONSULT, BIO-ENG INST, 67- *Mem:* Can Soc Zool; Can Entom Soc; Am Entom Soc. *Res:* Sensory physiology and behaviour of insects, particularly chemical senses. *Mailing Add:* Dept of Biol Univ of NB Fredericton NB E3B 5A3 Can

SEABURG, PAUL ALLEN, structural engineering, see previous edition

SEADER, J(UNIOR) D(EVERE), b San Francisco, Calif, Aug 16, 27; m 50, 61; c 8. CHEMICAL ENGINEERING. *Educ:* Univ Calif, BS, 49, MS, 50; Univ Wis, PhD(chem eng), 52. *Prof Exp:* Instr chem eng, Univ Wis, 51-52; res engr, Calif Res Corp, Standard Oil Co, Calif, 52-57, group supvr chem process design, 57, supvr eng res, 58-59; sr res engr, Rocketdyne Div, N Am Aviation, Inc, 59-60, res specialist, 60-61, prin scientist, 60-65; prof chem eng, Univ Idaho, 65-66; chmn dept, 75-78, PROF CHEM ENG, UNIV UTAH, 66-, ADJ PROF MAT SCI & ENG IN MECH ENG, 69- *Concurrent Pos:* Eve instr, eng exten, Univ Calif, 54-59. *Mem:* Am Inst Aeronaut & Astronaut; Am Inst Chem Engrs. *Res:* Ablation; rocket engine cooling; heat, mass and momentum transport; chemical kinetics; thermodynamics; physical properties; flammability; process design; fuel processes. *Mailing Add:* Dept of Chem Eng Univ of Utah Salt Lake City UT 84112

SEAGER, CARLETON HOOVER, b North Plainfield, NJ, July 18, 43; m 65. PHYSICS. *Educ:* Dartmouth Col, AB, 65; Princeton Univ, PhD(solid state physics), 69. *Prof Exp:* RES PHYSICIST, SANDIA LABS, 69- *Mem:* Am Phys Soc. *Res:* Electronic transport in insulators and semiconductors; ionic transport; defects in solids. *Mailing Add:* Sandia Labs Western Elec Co Albuquerque NM 87115

SEAGER, SPENCER LAWRENCE, b Ogden, Utah, Mar 10, 35; m 60; c 3. PHYSICAL CHEMISTRY. *Educ:* Univ Utah, BS, 57, PhD(phys chem), 62. *Prof Exp:* From asst prof to assoc prof chem, 61-69, PROF CHEM, WEBER STATE COL, 69-, CHMN DEPT, 68- *Mem:* Am Chem Soc. *Res:* Gas chromatography; gas phase diffusion. *Mailing Add:* Dept of Chem Weber State Col 2503 Ogden UT 84408

SEAGLE, EDGAR FRANKLIN, b Lincolnton, NC, June 27, 24; m 58; c 4. OCCUPATIONAL SAFETY & HEALTH. *Educ:* Univ NC, Chapel Hill, AB, 49; Univ Fla, BCE, 61; Univ NC, MSPH, 54; Univ Tex, DrPH(environ & occup health), 74; Am Acad Environ Engrs, dipl, 75. *Prof Exp:* Sanit consult, Div Epidemiol, NC State Bd Health, 54-56; chief, Indust Hyg Sect, Charlotte City Health Dept, NC, 56-59; engr, Div Radiol Health, USPHS, 61-66, chief, Prog Planning Off, 66-68, dir, Off Planning Strategy, 68-69, sr indust hyg engr, 69-75, dir occup safety, 75-78; ASST DIR, FELS OFF NAT ACAD SCI, 78- *Concurrent Pos:* Consult engr, 78- *Mem:* Am Soc Civil Engrs; Am Pub Health Asn. *Res:* Radiological health; industrial hygiene; occupational safety; sanitation. *Mailing Add:* 14108 Heathfield Ct Rockville MD 20853

SEAGONDOLLAR, LEWIS WORTH, b Hoisington, Kans, Sept 30, 20; m 42; c 3. PHYSICS. *Educ:* Kans State Teachers Col, AB, 41; Univ Wis, PhM, 43, PhD(physics), 48. *Prof Exp:* Instr physics, Univ Kans, 47-48, from asst prof to assoc prof, 48-60, prof, 60-65; head dept, 65-75, PROF PHYSICS, NC STATE UNIV, 65- *Concurrent Pos:* Civilian with Manhattan proj, Los Alamos Sci Lab, 59-60 & Hanford Lab, 62- *Mem:* Fel AAAS; fel Am Phys Soc; Am Asn Physics Teachers. *Res:* Low energy nuclear physics; nuclear spectroscopy; Van de Graaff generators. *Mailing Add:* Dept of Physics NC State Univ Raleigh NC 27650

SEAGRAVE, JOHN DORRINGTON, b Bronxville, NY, Jan 23, 26; m 51; c 2. NUCLEAR PHYSICS, OPTICAL PHYSICS. *Educ:* Calif Inst Technol, BS, 46, MS, 48, PhD(physics), 51. *Prof Exp:* MEM STAFF PHYSICS, LOS ALAMOS SCI LAB, 51- *Mem:* Fel AAAS; Am Optical Soc; fel Am Phys Soc. *Res:* Optical physics and detectors; interactive image processing and pattern recognition; structure of very light nuclei and fast neutron scattering. *Mailing Add:* Los Alamos Sci Lab P-1 MS455 Los Alamos NM 87545

SEAGRAVE, RICHARD C(HARLES), b Westerly, RI, Dec 31, 35; m 59; c 1. CHEMICAL ENGINEERING. *Educ:* Univ RI, BS, 57; Iowa State Univ, MS, 59, PhD(chem eng), 61. *Prof Exp:* Asst prof chem eng, Univ Conn, 61-62; res fel, Calif Inst Technol, 62-63, asst prof, 63-66; assoc prof, 66-71, PROF CHEM ENG, IOWA STATE UNIV, 71- *Mem:* Am Inst Chem Engrs. *Res:* Transport phenomena; reactor dynamics; biomedical engineering. *Mailing Add:* Dept of Chem Eng Iowa State Univ Ames IA 50010

SEALANDER, JOHN ARTHUR, JR, b Detroit Lakes, Minn, Dec 9, 17; m 47; c 3. ZOOLOGY. *Educ:* Luther Col, AB, 40; Mich State Univ, MS, 42; Univ Ill, PhD(zool), 49. *Prof Exp:* Asst zool, Mich State Univ, 40-42; asst zool & physiol, Univ Ill, 46-48; from asst prof to assoc prof zool, 49-59, PROF ZOOL, UNIV ARK, FAYETTEVILLE, 59- *Concurrent Pos:* USPHS spec fel, Inst Arctic Biol, Univ Alaska, 63-64; mem staff, Rocky Mt Biol Lab, 57; investr biol sta, Queen's Univ, Ont, 58; res assoc, Univ Ga, 68. *Mem:* AAAS; Am Soc Zool; Ecol Soc Am; Am Soc Mammal; Am Physiol Soc. *Res:* Comparative physiology; acclimatization of mammals to environmental temperature changes; natural history and ecology of mammals. *Mailing Add:* 1527 Markham Rd Fayetteville AR 72701

SEALE, DIANNE B, b Birmingham, Ala, April 15, 45; m 73. ECOSYSTEMS, POPULATIONS. *Prof Exp:* Fel, Nat Environ Health Asn, Pa State Univ, 73-74, instr environ sci, 73; res scientist, Ill Inst Technol, 74-75; res assoc, Dept Biol, Pa State Univ, 75-80; RES ASSOC, CTR GREAT LAKES STUDIES, UNIV WIS, MILWAUKEE, 80- *Concurrent Pos:* Vis instr, Northwestern Univ, 74-75; prin investr, NSF grants, 75-78 & 78-80. *Mem:* Sigma Xi; Am Soc Limnol & Oceanog; Ecol Soc Am; Am Soc Ichthyologists & Herpetologists; Int Asn Great Lakes Res. *Res:* Impact of suspension feeders on ecosystem processes; factors regulating suspension feeding dynamics; plant animal interactions; amphibian breeding behavior and larval community structure; nutrient release by amphibians and by Mysis relicta; phytoplankton ecology. *Mailing Add:* Ctr Great Lakes Studies Univ Wis Box 413 Milwaukee WI 53201

SEALE, MARVIN ERNEST, b Edmonton, Alta, June 7, 22; m 53; c 4. ANIMAL BREEDING. *Educ:* Univ Alta, BSc, 48; Univ Minn, MS, 51, PhD(animal breeding), 65. *Prof Exp:* From asst prof to assoc prof, Univ Man, 51-66, head dept, 73-80, PROF ANIMAL SCI, 66-, ASSOC DEAN & DIR, GLENLEA RES STA, 80- *Mem:* Am Soc Animal Sci; Can Soc Animal Prod; Genetics Soc Can. *Res:* Development of new breeds of livestock; inheritance of quantitative traits; evaluation of heterosis. *Mailing Add:* W 309 Agr Univ of Man Winnipeg MB R3T 2N2 Can

SEALE, RAYMOND ULRIC, b Snyder, Tex, Aug 19, 34; m 55; c 1. ANATOMY, EXPERIMENTAL EMBRYOLOGY. *Educ:* Eastern NMex Univ, BS, 56; Wash Univ, AM, 58; Univ Minn, PhD, 63. *Prof Exp:* Asst prof anat, Col Dent, Baylor Univ, 63-65; instr, Univ Tex Southwestern Med Sch, 65-66; asst prof, Sch Med, Univ Colo, Denver, 66-71; assoc prof, 71-80, PROF ANAT, RUSH MED COL, 80- *Concurrent Pos:* Vis instr, Southern Methodist Univ, 65-66; spec instr, Med Ctr, Baylor Univ, 63-66; AMA consult gross anat, Fac Med, Univ Saigon, 70. *Mem:* AAAS; NY Acad Sci; Am Asn Anat. *Res:* Developmental aspects of acquired immunological tolerance; morphogenetic movement in chick embryos in vitro; role of catecholamines in differentiation; mosaic and regulative capacity of organ primordia. *Mailing Add:* 2713 W 39th Pl Chicago IL 60632

SEALE, ROBERT L(EWIS), b Rosenberg, Tex, Mar 18, 28; m 47; c 4. NUCLEAR ENGINEERING. *Educ:* Univ Houston, BS, 47; Univ Tex, MS, 51, PhD(physics), 53. *Prof Exp:* Nuclear engr, Gen Dynamics Corp, Tex, 53-57, proj engr, 57-59, chief nuclear opers, 59-61; PROF NUCLEAR ENG, UNIV ARIZ, 61-, HEAD DEPT, 69- *Concurrent Pos:* Lectr, Southern Methodist Univ, 55-60; consult, Los Alamos Sci Lab, 61 & Sandia Corp, NMex, 66-; mem bd dir, Eng Coun Prof Develop, 72- *Mem:* Am Asn Physics Teachers; Am Phys Soc; Am Nuclear Soc; Nat Soc Prof Engrs. *Res:* Radiation shielding; nuclear reactor operations and safety; use of nuclear reactors. *Mailing Add:* Dept of Nuclear Eng Univ of Ariz Tucson AZ 85721

SEALS, RUPERT GRANT, b Shelbyville, Ky, Aug 32; m 54; c 4. DAIRY INDUSTRY. *Educ:* Fla Agr & Mech Univ, BS, 53; Univ Ky, MS, 56; Wash State Univ, PhD(dairy chem), 60. *Prof Exp:* Instr dairying, Fla Agr & Mech Univ, 54-55; res asst dairy sci, Wash State Univ, 55-59; assoc prof dairy mfg, Tenn Agr & Ind State, 59-64; res assoc, Iowa State Univ, 64-66, asst prof, 66-69; prof food chem & dean sch agr & home econ, Fla A&M Univ, 69-77; ASSOC DEAN & PROF ANIMAL SCI, COL AGR, UNIV NEV, 77- *Concurrent Pos:* Coordr spec prog, Coop State Res Serv, USBA, 74- *Mem:* Inst Food Technologists. *Res:* Amino acids in peanuts; milk proteins; lipid and flavor chemistry. *Mailing Add:* Univ of Nev Col of Agr Reno NV 89507

SEALY, ROGER CLIVE, b Wells, Eng, Sept 26, 48. BIOPHYSICS. *Educ:* Univ Leeds, BSc, 69, PhD(phys chem), 73. *Prof Exp:* Res fel chem, Univ York, 72-74; res asst phys chem, Univ Oxford, 74-76; res assoc radiol, 76-79, ASST PROF RADIOL, BIOCHEM & MED, COL WIS, 79- *Mem:* Biophys Soc; Am Soc Photobiol; Int Pigment Cell Soc; Royal Soc Chem. *Res:* Free radicals in biology; photochemistry and photobiology; applications of electron spin resonance; radical reactions of melanins, catecholamines. *Mailing Add:* Nat Biomed ESR Ctr Med Col Wis 8701 Watertown Plank Rd Milwaukee WI 53226

SEAMAN, DONALD EDWARD, b Hornell, NY, Aug 3, 25; m 55; c 3. AGRONOMY, WEED SCIENCE. *Educ:* Alfred Univ, BA, 50; Ohio State Univ, MSc, 52; Purdue Univ, PhD(plant physiol), 57. *Prof Exp:* Plant physiologist, USDA, Fla, 57-62; asst res botanist, Univ Calif, Davis, 62-66; agr officer, Food & Agr Orgn, Bangkok, Thailand, 66-67; sr scientist, Syracuse Univ Res Corp, 67-68; vis weed scientist, Int Rice Res Inst, Philippines, 68-69; AGRON SPECIALIST & LECTR AGRON, UNIV CALIF, DAVIS, 69- *Mem:* Am Soc Agron; Weed Sci Soc Am. *Res:* Cultural practices and production systems for rice; weed control in rice. *Mailing Add:* Rice Exp Sta PO Box 306 Biggs CA 95917

SEAMAN, EDNA, b Warsaw, Poland, July 2, 32; nat US; m 56; c 3. BIOLOGY. *Educ:* Brooklyn Col, BS, 56; Univ Ill, PhD(microbiol), 60. *Prof Exp:* Fel biochem, Brandeis, 60-68; asst prof biol, 68-73; ASSOC PROF BIOL, UNIV MASS, BOSTON, 74-, CHMN DEPT, 78- *Res:* Molecular biology; interrelations of DNA, RNA and proteins; bacterial transformations; synthesis of nucleic acids in subcellular systems. *Mailing Add:* Dept of Biol Univ of Mass Boston MA 02125

SEAMAN, GEOFFREY VINCENT F, b Uxbridge, Eng, Nov 24, 32; m 58; c 4. PHYSICAL BIOCHEMISTRY, BIOMATERIALS. *Educ:* Royal Col Sci, London, BSc, 55; Cambridge Univ, PhD(biophys), 58. *Prof Exp:* Fel med, Univ Cambridge, 57-60; Beit Mem res fel, Univ Cambridge, 60-61 & Univ Cologne, 61-62; sr asst radiotherapeut, Univ Cambridge, 62-66; asst prof neurol, 66-68, assoc prof neurol & biochem, 68-73, PROF NEUROL & BIOCHEM, UNIV ORE HEALTH SCI CTR, 73- *Concurrent Pos:* Res fel neurol, Med Sch, Univ Ore, 63-64; ed newslett, Int Soc Biorheology, 69; ed, Biorheaology, 72; mem adv comt to NASA, Univ Space Res Asn, 72. *Mem:* Am Soc Biol Chemists; Am Chem Soc; Biophys Soc; Int Soc Biorheology (secy gen, 69); NY Acad Sci. *Res:* Surface properties of biological cells, especially blood cells; flow properties of blood and cell suspensions; composition and molecular structure of the glycoprotein components of cellular membranes; biocompatibility of surfaces. *Mailing Add:* Dept of Neurol Univ of Ore Health Sci Ctr Portland OR 97201

SEAMAN, GERALD ROBERT, b Pottsville, Pa, May 20, 27. MICROBIOLOGY. *Educ:* Williams Col, BA, 45; Fordham Univ, MS, 47, PhD(zool), 49. *Prof Exp:* Instr biol chem sch med, Creighton Univ, 49-50; instr physiol med br, Univ Tex, 50-51, from asst prof to assoc prof, 51-58, assoc prof microbiol, 59-63; prof biol sci, Hunter Col, 63-66; prof biol, Roosevelt Univ, 66-80. *Mem:* AAAS; Soc Protozool; Soc Exp Biol & Med; Soc Gen Microbiol; Am Soc Microbiol. *Res:* Metabolism of freeliving and parasitic Protozoa; cell permeability; metabolism of pyruvate and acetate by microbes and animal tissues; protein synthesis. *Mailing Add:* 6007 N Sheridan Rd Chicago IL 60626

SEAMAN, GREGORY G, b Alma, Mich, Jan 6, 38; m 62; c 2. ENVIRONMENTAL PHYSICS. *Educ:* Col Wooster, AB, 59; Yale Univ, MS, 60, PhD(physics), 65. *Prof Exp:* Appointee nuclear physics, Los Alamos Sci Lab, 64-66; fel, Rutgers Univ, 66-68; from asst prof to assoc prof nuclear physics, Kans State Univ, 68-76; prod specialist, 76-78, APPLN MGR, INSTRUMENT DIV, CANBERRA INDUSTS, 79- *Mem:* Am Phys Soc; Am Asn Physics Teachers. *Res:* Coulomb excitation; Ericson fluctuations; Doppler shift attenuation measurements of nuclear lifetimes; trace element analysis of foods by x-ray fluorescence. *Mailing Add:* Canberra Industs 45 Gracey Ave Meriden CT 06450

SEAMAN, LYNN, b De Queene, Ark, Aug 28, 33; m 57; c 4. CIVIL ENGINEERING, STRUCTURES. *Educ:* Univ Calif, Berkeley, BS, 59; Mass Inst Technol, PhD(civil eng), 61. *Prof Exp:* Civil engr, 61-67, PHYSICIST, SRI INT, 67- *Mem:* Am Soc Civil Engrs. *Res:* Structural mechanics, shell buckling, structural dynamics; materials science, equations of state for soil and other porous media, crack growth and fracturing. *Mailing Add:* SRI Int 333 Ravenswood Ave Menlo Park CA 94025

SEAMAN, RICHARD ERIC, polymer physics, textile physics, see previous edition

SEAMAN, RONALD L, b Seaman, Ohio, Feb 10, 47; m 77; c 4. BIOMEDICAL ENGINEERING, NEUROPHYSIOLOGY. *Educ:* Univ Cincinnati, BS, 70; Duke Univ, PhD(biomed eng), 75. *Prof Exp:* Res assoc, Duke Univ, 74; res fel, Univ Tex Health Sci Ctr, Dallas, 75-76, instr physiol, 76-79; RES ENGR, ENG EXP STA, GA INST TECHNOL, 79- *Mem:* Inst Elec & Electronics Engrs; AAAS; Int Microwave Power Inst; Soc Neurosci; Bioelectromagnetics Soc. *Res:* Microwave biological effects, primarily neural systems; electromagnetic wave interactions with biological tissues; dielectric properties; microwave exposure devices. *Mailing Add:* Biomed Res Div Eng Exp Sta Ga Inst Technol Atlanta GA 30332

SEAMAN, WILLIAM B, b Chicago, Ill, Jan 5, 17; m 44; c 2. RADIOLOGY. *Educ:* Harvard Med Sch, MD, 41. *Prof Exp:* Instr radiol, Sch Med, Yale Univ, 48-49; from instr to prof, Sch Med, Washington Univ, 49-56; PROF RADIOL & CHMN DEPT, COL PHYSICIANS & SURGEONS, COLUMBIA UNIV, 56- *Concurrent Pos:* Dir radiol serv, Presby Hosp, New York, 56-, bd trustees, Picker Found; chmn comt radiol, Nat Acad Sci, Nat Coun, 69-73; mem bd chancellors, Am Col Radiol, 75-78. *Mem:* Am Roentgen Ray Soc (pres, 73-74); Soc Gastrointestinal Radiol (pres, 73-74); Radiol Soc NAm Asn Univ Radiol (pres, 56). *Res:* Diagnostic roentgenology. *Mailing Add:* Dept of Radiol Columbia Univ Col Phys & Surg New York NY 10032

SEAMAN, WILLIAM LLOYD, b Charlottetown, PEI, July 16, 34; m 59. PLANT PATHOLOGY. *Educ:* McGill Univ, BSc, 56; Univ Wis, PhD, 60. *Prof Exp:* Asst plant path, Univ Wis, 56-60; res officer, 60-73, RES SCIENTIST, CAN DEPT AGR, 73- *Mem:* Am Phytopath Soc; Can Phytopath Soc. *Res:* cereal grain diseases; disease survey. *Mailing Add:* Agr Can Res Sta K W Neatby Bldg CEF Ottawa ON K1A 0C6 Can

SEAMANS, DAVID A(LVIN), b Lawrence, Kans, June 13, 27; m 57; c 2. ELECTRICAL ENGINEERING. *Educ:* Univ Kans, BS, 50, MS, 56; Ore State Univ, PhD, 68. *Prof Exp:* Jr engr, Black & Veatch, Consult Engrs, 50-52; instr elec eng, Univ Kans, 53-54; from instr to asst prof, 54-63, ASSOC PROF ELEC ENG, WASH STATE UNIV, 63- *Mem:* Inst Elec & Electronics Engrs; Simulation Coun. *Res:* Analog and digital computer technology; solid state devices. *Mailing Add:* Dept of Elec Eng Wash State Univ Pullman WA 99163

SEAMANS, R(OBERT) C(HANNING), JR, b Salem, Mass, Oct 30, 18; m 42; c 5. AERONAUTICAL ENGINEERING. *Educ:* Harvard Univ, BS, 39; Mass Inst Technol, MS, 42, ScD(instrumentation), 51. *Hon Degrees:* DSc, Rollins Col, 62, NY Univ, 67; DEng, Norwich Acad, 71, Notre Dame Univ, 74, Rensselaer Polytech Inst, 74, Univ Wyoming, 75, George Washington Univ, 75, Lehigh Univ, 76. *Prof Exp:* From Instr to assoc prof aeronaut eng, Mass Inst Technol, 41-55, staff engr instrumentation lab, 41-45, proj leader, 45-50, chief engr Proj Meteor, 50-55, dir flight control lab, 53-55; mgr airborne systs lab & chief systs engr, Airborne Systs Dept, Radio Corp Am, 55-58, chief engr, Missile Electronics & Controls Div, RCA Corp, 58-60; assoc adminr, NASA, 60-65, dep adminr, 65-68; Jerome Clarke Hunsaker prof aeronaut & astronaut, Mass Inst Technol, 68-69; Secy of the Air Force, 69-73; pres, Nat Acad Eng, 73-74; adminr, US ERDA, 74-77; dean eng, 78-81, HENRY R LUCE PROF ENVIRON & PUB POLICY, MASS INST TECHNOL, 77- *Concurrent Pos:* Mem subcomt automatic stabilization & control, Nat Adv Comt Aeronaut, 48-58 & group instrumentation & spec comt space technol, 58-59; consult, Sci Adv Bd, US Air Force, 57-59, mem, 59-62, assoc adv, 62-67; nat deleg, Adv Group Aerospace Res & Develop, NATO, 66-69; consult to adminr, NASA, 68-69; mem bd overseers, Harvard Univ. *Honors & Awards:* Naval Ord Develop Award, 45; Lawrence Sperry Award, Am Inst Aeronaut & Astronaut, 51; NASA Distinguis-ed Serv Medal, 65 & 69; Goddard Trophy, 68; Dept Air Force Exceptional Civilian Serv Award; Dept Defense Distinguished Pub Serv Medal; Gen Thomas D White US Air Force Space Trophy; Ralph Coats Roe Medal, Am Soc Mech Engrs. *Mem:* Nat Acad Eng (pres, 73-74); fel Am Astronaut Soc; fel Inst Elec & Electronics Engrs; hon fel Am Inst Aeronaut & Astronaut; AAAS. *Res:* Administration; instrumentation. *Mailing Add:* Mass Inst Technology Rm G40-443 77 Massachusetts Ave Cambridge MA 02139

SEAMON, ROBERT EDWARD, b Worcester, Mass, May 18, 39. NUCLEAR PHYSICS. *Educ:* Worcester Polytech Inst, BS, 61; Yale Univ, MS, 63, PhD(physics), 68. *Prof Exp:* Res staff mem nuclear reactor physics, 69-71, STAFF MEM NUCLEAR PHYSICS, LOS ALAMOS SCI LAB, 71- *Concurrent Pos:* Staff mem, Nuclear Data Sect, Int Atomic Energy Agency, Vienna, Austria, 77-78. *Mem:* Am Phys Soc; Am Nuclear Soc. *Res:* Evaluated nuclear data files (ENDF/B) and associated processing codes used in weapons calculations; phase-shift analysis of nucleon-nucleon scattering data; nucleon-nucleon potentials. *Mailing Add:* Group TD-6 Los Alamos Sci Lab PO Box 1663 Los Alamos NM 87545

SEANOR, DONALD A, b Gatley, Eng, June 10, 36; m 60; c 2. CHEMISTRY. *Educ:* Bristol Univ, BSc, 57, PhD(phys chem), 61. *Prof Exp:* Nat Res Coun Can fel catalysis, 61-63; from res chemist to sr res chemist, Chemstrand Res Ctr, Inc, Monsanto Co, NC, 63-67; scientist res labs div, 67-70, scientist info technol group, 70-71, SR SCIENTIST SPEC MAT TECHNOL CTR, XEROX CORP, 71- *Concurrent Pos:* Guest lectr, NY State Col Environ Sci & Forestry, Syracuse, 75. *Mem:* The Chem Soc; Am Chem Soc. *Res:* Surface chemistry; solid state physics and chemistry; triboelectricity; polymers; photoconductivity and conduction in polymers; tribology; materials development. *Mailing Add:* 264 Garnsey Rd Pittsford NY 14534

SEAQUIST, ERNEST RAYMOND, b Vancouver, BC, Nov 19, 38; m 66; c 2. ASTRONOMY. *Educ:* Univ BC, BASc, 61; Univ Toronto, MA, 62, PhD(astron), 66. *Prof Exp:* Lectr, 65-66, from asst prof to assoc prof, 66-78, PROF & ASSOC CHMN, UNIV TORONTO, 78- *Mem:* Am Astron Soc. *Res:* Galactic and extragalactic radio sources. *Mailing Add:* Dept of Astron Univ of Toronto Toronto ON M5S 2R8 Can

SEARCY, A(LAN) W(INN), b Covina, Calif, Oct 12, 25; m 45; c 3. MATERIALS SCIENCE, CHEMISTRY. *Educ:* Pomona Col, AB, 46; Univ Calif, PhD(chem), 50. *Prof Exp:* Asst chem, Univ Calif, 47-48, chemist, Radiation Lab, 48-49 & 50; from instr to asst prof, Purdue Univ, 49-54; from assoc prof to prof ceramic eng, 54-59, prof eng sci, 59-60, fac asst to chancellor, 63-64, vchancellor, 64-67, Miller res prof, 70-71, PROF MAT SCI, UNIV CALIF, BERKELEY, 60- *Concurrent Pos:* Fulbright lectr, Physics Inst, Arg, 60-61; consult, Los Alamos Sci Lab, Calif, 55-59 & Lawrence Radiation Lab, 56-61, assoc div head, Inorg Mat Div, 61-64; consult, adv res proj agency, US Dept Defense, 58-60; prin investr, Lawrence Berkeley Lab, 60-; mem, Nat Res Coun Comt on high temperature chem, 61-70; Guggenhiem fel, 67-68. *Mem:* AAAS; fel Am Ceramic Soc; Am Chem Soc. *Res:* Compositions of vapors at high temperatures and low pressures; thermodynamics of high temperature reactions; kinetics of gas-solid reactions and vaporization; thermodynamics of surfaces. *Mailing Add:* Dept of Mat Sci & Mineral Eng Univ of Calif Berkeley CA 94720

SEARCY, CHARLES JACKSON, b Beaver, Okla, Feb 14, 35; m 61; c 2. MATHEMATICS. *Educ:* Panhandle A&M Col, BS, 57; Okla State Univ, MS, 63, EdD(math), 67. *Prof Exp:* Instr math, Cent State Col, Okla, 65-67; asst prof, 67-80, ASSOC PROF MATH, NMEX HIGHLANDS UNIV, 80- *Mem:* Math Asn Am. *Res:* Topology; algebra. *Mailing Add:* Dept of Math NMex Highlands Univ Las Vegas NM 87701

SEARCY, DENNIS GRANT, b Portland, Ore, Sept 25, 42; m 66; c 1. CELL PHYSIOLOGY. *Educ:* Ore State Univ, BS, 64; Univ Calif, Los Angeles, PhD(zool), 68. *Prof Exp:* NIH trainee, Univ Calif, Los Angeles, 68-69; fel, Calif Inst Technol, 69-71; asst prof, 71-78, ASSOC PROF ZOOL, UNIV MASS, AMHERST, 78- *Concurrent Pos:* Vis scholar, Oxford, 78-79. *Mem:* AAAS; Int Orgn Mycoplasmology; Soc Cell Biol. *Res:* Evolution; origin of eukaryotic cells; histones; chromatin structure; physiology of mycoplasmas and primitive organisms. *Mailing Add:* Dept of Zool Univ of Mass Amherst MA 01003

SEARIGHT, THOMAS KAY, b Vermillion, SDak, June 3, 29; m 54; c 2. GEOLOGY. *Educ:* Univ Mo, AB, 51, MA, 52; Univ Ill, PhD, 59. *Prof Exp:* Geologist, State Geol Surv, Mo, 52-54; from asst prof to assoc prof, 59-74, PROF GEOL, ILL STATE UNIV, 74- *Concurrent Pos:* Res affil, Ill State Geol Surv, 62- *Mem:* Geol Soc Am; Soc Econ Paleont & Mineral; Am Asn Petrol Geologists. *Res:* Pennsylvania stratigraphy and sedimentation of the mid-continent region. *Mailing Add:* Dept of Geol Ill State Univ Normal IL 61761

SEARLE, CAMPBELL L(EACH), b Winnipeg, Man, July 24, 26; Can citizen; m 53; c 4. ELECTRONICS. *Educ:* Queen's Univ, Ont, BSc, 47; Mass Inst Technol, SM, 51. *Prof Exp:* Mem staff, Div Sponsored Res, Mass Inst Technol, 51-56, from instr to prof elec eng, 56-74; prof psychol & elec eng, Queen's Univ, Ont, 74-79; PROF ELEC ENG, MASS INST TECHNOL, 79- *Mem:* Inst Elec & Electronics Engrs; Acoust Soc Am. *Res:* auditory and speech perception. *Mailing Add:* Dept Elec Eng & Comput Sci Mass Inst Technol Cambridge MA 02159

SEARLE, CLARK WELLINGTON, solid state physics, see previous edition

SEARLE, GILBERT LESLIE, b Napa, Calif, Aug 8, 24; m 54; c 3. PHYSIOLOGY, BIOCHEMISTRY. *Educ:* Univ Calif, Berkeley, AB, 49, PhD(physiol), 54. *Prof Exp:* From jr res physiologist to asst res physiologist, Univ Calif, Berkeley, 54-56; asst chief, 56-77, PRIN SCIENTIST, NUCLEAR MED RES, VET ADMIN HOSP, 77-, CHIEF CARBOHYDRATE METABOLISM, 80- *Concurrent Pos:* Lectr physiol, Univ Calif, San Francisco. *Mem:* Am Physiol Soc; Endocrine Soc. *Res:* Kinetics of energy metabolites in man; diabetes and drug action. *Mailing Add:* Vet Admin Hosp 42nd Ave & Clement St San Francisco CA 94121

SEARLE, GORDON WENTWORTH, b Providence, RI, Mar 9, 20; m 45; c 3. PHYSIOLOGY. *Educ:* Univ Ill, BS, 41, MD, 45; Northwestern Univ, MS, 49, PhD(physiol), 51. *Prof Exp:* Asst physiol, Northwestern Univ, 48-51; asst prof, Albany Med Col, Union, NY, 51-52; asst prof, 52-55, ASSOC PROF PHYSIOL, COL MED, UNIV IOWA, 55- *Concurrent Pos:* Vis res prof, Med Sch, Univ Newcastle, 64-65. *Mem:* AAAS; Am Physiol Soc; Soc Exp Biol & Med. *Res:* Intestinal absorption; bile secretion. *Mailing Add:* Dept of Physiol & Biophys Univ of Iowa Iowa City IA 52242

SEARLE, JOHN RANDOLPH, b Wilmington, Del, Jan 20, 47; m 73; c 2. BIOMEDICAL ENGINEERING. *Educ:* Wake Forest Univ, BS, 70; NC State Univ, BS, 70; Duke Univ, PhD(biomed eng), 75. *Prof Exp:* Biomed engr, Vet Admin, 75-77; biomed engr, 77-80, ASST PROF BIOMED ENG, MED COL GA, 80- *Mem:* AAAS; Asn Advan Med Instrumentation; Inst Elec & Electronics Engrs; Eng Med & Biol. *Res:* Ectopic beat detection and recording with portable hybrid computer, mathematical model and computer simulation of neural sensory coding. *Mailing Add:* Dept of Biomed Engr CI-100 Med Col of Ga Augusta GA 30912

SEARLE, NORMA ZIZMER, b New York, NY, Jan 26, 25; m 49. PHYSICAL CHEMISTRY. *Educ:* Hunter Col, BA, 46; NY Univ, PhD(phys chem), 59. *Prof Exp:* Control chemist, Purepac Pharmaceut Co, 46; res chemist, Montefiore Hosp, New York, 47-53; chemist, New York Dept Health, 53-54; chemist, 57-69, sr res chemist, 69-74, GROUP HEAD, AM CYANAMID CO, 74- *Mem:* Am Chem Soc; Am Soc Photobiol. *Res:* Ultraviolet, near-infrared and infrared spectrophotometry; molecular structure; radiometry; photochemistry of plastics and additives; mass spectroscopy; fluorescence and phosphorescence; chemiluminescence. *Mailing Add:* Grandview Gardens 106D Finderne Ave Bridgewater NJ 08807

SEARLE, ROGER, b Wilmington, Del, July 24, 36; m 61; c 2. ORGANIC CHEMISTRY. *Educ:* Oberlin Col, BA, 58; Univ Ill, PhD(org chem), 63. *Prof Exp:* RES CHEMIST, EASTMAN KODAK CO, 63- *Mem:* AAAS; Am Chem Soc. *Res:* Physical organic chemistry; organic photochemistry. *Mailing Add:* 68 Sagamore Dr Rochester NY 14617

SEARLE, SHAYLE ROBERT, b Wanganui NZ, Apr 26, 28; m 58; c 2. STATISTICS. *Educ:* Victoria Univ Wellington, BA, 49, MA, 50; Cambridge Univ, dipl math stat, 53; Cornell Univ, PhD(animal breeding), 59. *Prof Exp:* Actuarial asst, Colonial Mutual Life Ins Co, NZ, 50-51; res statistician, NZ Dairy Bd, 53-62; res asst animal breeding, 56-58, res assoc, 58-59, from asst prof to assoc prof biol statist, 62-69, PROF BIOL STATIST, NY STATE COL AGR, CORNELL UNIV, 69- *Concurrent Pos:* Fulbright travel award, 56-59. *Mem:* Fel Am Statist Asn; Biomet Soc; fel Royal Statist Soc. *Res:* Computing; linear models; variance components. *Mailing Add:* NY State Col of Agr Cornell Univ 337 Warren Hall Ithaca NY 14850

SEARLES, ARTHUR LANGLEY, b Nashua, NH, Aug 8, 20; m. ORGANIC CHEMISTRY. *Educ:* NY Univ, BA, 42, PhD(chem), 46. *Prof Exp:* Asst, Squibb Inst Med Res, 44; instr org chem, NY Univ, 46-48, asst prof, 48-56, assoc prof chem, 56-73, chmn dept, 70-72, PROF CHEM, COL MT ST VINCENT, 73- *Mem:* Am Chem Soc; Royal Soc Chem. *Res:* Nitrogen heterocycles; organo-metallics; beta-ketoanilides. *Mailing Add:* Dept of Chem Col of Mt St Vincent Bronx NY 10471

SEARLES, RICHARD BROWNLEE, b Riverside, Calif, June 19, 36; m 57; c 3. PHYCOLOGY. *Educ:* Pomona Col, BA, 58; Univ Calif, Berkeley, PhD(bot), 65. *Prof Exp:* Asst prof bot, 65-69, ASSOC PROF BOT, DUKE UNIV, 69- *Mem:* Phycol Soc Am; Int Phycol Soc. *Res:* Marine phycology; morphology; taxonomy and ecology of benthic marine algae. *Mailing Add:* Dept of Bot Duke Univ Durham NC 27706

SEARLES, SCOTT, JR, b Minneapolis, Minn, Oct 15, 20; m 47, 59; c 5. ORGANIC CHEMISTRY. *Educ:* Univ Calif, Los Angeles, BA, 41, MA, 42; Univ Minn, PhD(org chem), 47. *Prof Exp:* Asst chem, Univ Minn, 42-43; res chemist, Am Cyanamid Co, Conn, 44-45; instr chem, Univ Minn, 46; instr, Univ Ill, 47-49; asst prof, Northwestern Univ, 49-52; assoc prof, Kans State Univ, 52-62, prof, 62-66; PROF CHEM, UNIV MO-COLUMBIA, 66- *Concurrent Pos:* NSF sr fel, Calif Inst Technol & Cambridge Univ, 62-63. *Mem:* AAAS; Am Chem Soc; Royal Soc Chem. *Res:* Small ring heterocyclic compounds; rearrangements; reaction mechanisms; ionic catalysis. *Mailing Add:* Dept of Chem Univ of Mo Columbia MO 65201

SEARLES, STUART KENNETH, lasers, see previous edition

SEARLS, CRAIG ALLEN, b Bremerton, Wash, Feb 27, 54. EXPLORATION GEOPHYSICS, ELECTROMAGNETICS. *Educ:* Univ Puget Sound, BS, 76; Univ Calif, Los Angeles, MS, 78, PhD(geophysics & space physics), 81. *Prof Exp:* Sci intern, Northwest Asn Col & Univ Advan Sci, Pac Northwest Div, Batelle Mem Inst, 76; GEOPHYSICIST, WESTERN ELEC, SANDIA NAT LAB, 81- *Mem:* Am Geophys Union; AAAS. *Res:* Design, monitoring, and analysis of geophysical experiments to determine parameters critical to both underground storage of oil and gas and the extraction of gas from unconventional resources. *Mailing Add:* Sandia Nat Lab Albuquerque NM 87185

SEARLS, JAMES COLLIER, b Mitchell, SDak, Aug 22, 26; m 47; c 4. ANATOMY. *Educ:* Cornell Col, BA, 50; Univ Iowa, DDS, 55, PhD(anat), 66. *Prof Exp:* Fel, Nat Inst Dent Res, 62-66; ASST PROF ORTHOD & ANAT, UNIV IOWA, 66- *Mem:* Am Asn Anatomists; Int Asn Dent Res. *Res:* Radioisotopic studies of the cartilagenous nasal septum and its role in maxillofacial growth. *Mailing Add:* Dept of Oral Biol & Anat Univ of Iowa Iowa City IA 52240

SEARLS, ROBERT L, b Madison, Wis, Oct 26, 31; m 61; c 4. BIOCHEMISTRY, EMBRYOLOGY. *Educ:* Univ Wis, BS, 53; Univ Calif, Berkeley, PhD(biochem), 60. *Prof Exp:* Fel embryol, Brandeis Univ, 60-63; asst prof biol, Univ Va, 63-68; assoc prof, 68-74, PROF BIOL, TEMPLE UNIV, 74- *Mem:* AAAS; Am Chem Soc; Soc Develop Biol; Int Soc Develop Biol. *Res:* Oxidative metabolism; chemical basis of morphogenesis and differentiation. *Mailing Add:* Dept of Biol Temple Univ Philadelphia PA 19122

SEARS, ALAN ROY, b Brooklyn, NY, Jan 28, 42; m 69; c 2. PHYSICAL CHEMISTRY. *Educ:* Brooklyn Col, BS, 63; Yale Univ, PhD(chem), 71. *Prof Exp:* With USPHS, 67-69; res fel chem, Calif Inst Technol, 71-73; sr scientist, Rohm and Haas Co, 73-74; STAFF SCIENTIST CHEM, GEN ELEC RES & DEVELOP CTR, 74- *Mem:* Am Chem Soc; Electrochem Soc. *Res:* Surface chemistry; electrochemistry; electrokinetic phenomena. *Mailing Add:* Gen Elec Res & Develop Ctr PO Box 8 Schenectady NY 12301

SEARS, BARRY, b Long Beach, Calif, June 6, 47; m 69; c 1. BIOCHEMISTRY, BIOPHYSICAL CHEMISTRY. *Educ:* Occidental Col, AB, 68; Ind Univ, PhD(chem), 71. *Prof Exp:* Instr med, Sch Med, Boston Univ, 75-78; consult biochem, Arthur D Little Inc, 78; STAFF MEM MOLECULAR BIOPHYS, NAT MAGNET LAB, MASS INST TECHNOL, 78- *Mem:* Biophys Soc. *Res:* Application of nuclear magnetic resonance to biochemistry. *Mailing Add:* Nat Magnet Lab Mass Inst of Technol Cambridge MA 02139

SEARS, CHARLES EDWARD, b Utica, Mich, Feb 3, 11; m 37; c 4. ECONOMIC GEOLOGY, ENGINEERING GEOLOGY. *Educ:* Va Polytech Inst, BS, 32, MS, 35; Colo Sch Mines, DSc, 53. *Prof Exp:* Instr mining eng, from asst prof to assoc prof geol, 46-77, EMER PROF GEOL, VA POLYTECH INST & STATE UNIV, 77- DIR SEISMOL OBSERV, 62- *Concurrent Pos:* Consult geologist. *Mem:* Geol Soc Am. *Res:* Hydrothermal alteration and mineralization at the Climax Molybdenum deposit, Climax, Colorado; geology and petrology; kimberlites; geothermal studies of Virginia areas. *Mailing Add:* Box 522 Blacksburg VA 24060

SEARS, CURTIS THORNTON, JR, b Wareham, Mass, Aug 3, 38; m 60; c 2. INORGANIC CHEMISTRY, ORGANOMETALLIC CHEMISTRY. *Educ:* WVa Wesleyan Col, AB, 61; Univ NC, PhD(chem), 66. *Prof Exp:* NATO fel, 66-67; asst prof chem, Univ SC, 67-71; asst prof, 71-77, ASSOC PROF CHEM, GA STATE UNIV, 77- *Honors & Awards:* O'Haus Award, Nat Sci Teachers Asn, 73. *Mem:* Am Chem Soc; Royal Soc Chem. *Res:* Chemistry of second and third row transition metals in low oxidation states. *Mailing Add:* Dept of Chem Ga State Univ Atlanta GA 30303

SEARS, DAVID ALAN, b Portland, Ore, Oct 20, 31; m 58; c 3. INTERNAL MEDICINE, HEMATOLOGY. *Educ:* Yale Univ, BS, 53; Univ Ore, MS, 58, MD, 59; Am Bd Internal Med, dipl, 66, cert hemat, 74. *Prof Exp:* Intern, Sch Med & Dent, Univ Rochester, 59-60, resident med, 60-62, trainee hemat, 62-63, asst prof med, 66-69; assoc prof med & head div hemat, 69-77, PROF MED & HEAD DIV HEMAT, UNIV TEX MED SCH SAN ANTONIO, 77- *Concurrent Pos:* Assoc physician, Strong Mem Hosp, Rochester, NY, 66-69; consult, Highland Hosp, 66-69 & Audie Murphy Vet Admin Hosp, San Antonio, 73- *Mem:* Am Soc Hemat; Am Fedn Clin Res; Int Soc Hemat; fel Am Col Physicians. *Res:* Hemolytic disease; heme pigment metabolism; erythrocyte membrane. *Mailing Add:* Dept of Med Univ of Tex Med Sch San Antonio TX 78284

SEARS, DONALD RICHARD, b Wilmington, Del, July 23, 28; c 1. ENVIRONMENTAL SCIENCE & ENGINEERING. *Educ:* Lawrence Col, BS, 50; Cornell Univ, PhD(phys chem), 58. *Prof Exp:* Asst chem, Cornell Univ, 50-52; chemist, Inst Paper Chem, Lawrence Col, 54; asst chem, Cornell Univ, 54-57; res fel chem phys, Mellon Inst, 58-63; res staff mem, Oak Ridge Nat Lab, 63-68; develop specialist, Oak Ridge Y-12 Plant, 68-72; vis scientist, Nat Ctr Atmospheric Res, 72-73; dir, Air Pollution Eng Lab, Civil Eng Dept, WVa Univ, 73-75; res scientist, Lockheed Res & Eng Ctr, 75-79; PROJ MGR ENVIRON ENG, GRAND FORKS ENERGY TECHNOL CTR, 79- *Mem:* AAAS; Air Pollution Control Asn; Am Chem Soc; AAAS; Sigma Xi. *Res:* Characterization and control of particulate emissions; analysis of trace element and organic emissions from combustion of low rank western coals. *Mailing Add:* PO Box 8213 Univ Sta Dept Energy Technol Ctr Grand Forks ND 58202

SEARS, DUANE WILLIAM, b Denver, Colo, Mar 23, 46; m 69; c 2. IMMUNOLOGY, BIOCHEMISTRY. *Educ:* Colo Col, BS, 68; Columbia Univ, PhD(biophys chem), 74. *Prof Exp:* Fel, Albert Einstein Col Med, 74-77; ASST PROF IMMUNOL & BIOCHEM, UNIV CALIF, SANTA BARBARA, 77- *Mem:* Am Asn Immunologists; NY Acad Sci; AAAS; Am Chem Soc. *Res:* Structural analysis of major histocompatibility complex antigens; immunogenetic analysis of cytotoxic T lymphocyte reactivities; biochemical analysis of cytotoxic T lymphocyte target antigens. *Mailing Add:* Dept Biol Sci Univ Calif Santa Barbara CA 93106

SEARS, ERNEST ROBERT, b Rickreall, Ore, Oct 15, 10; m 36, 50; c 4. PLANT CYTOGENETICS. *Educ:* Ore State Col, BS, 32; Harvard Univ, AM, 34, PhD(biol), 36; Univ Göttingen, DSc, 70. *Prof Exp:* GENETICIST, AGR RES SERV, USDA, 36- *Concurrent Pos:* Fulbright res fel, Ger, 58. *Honors & Awards:* Stevenson Award, 51; Hoblitzelle Award, 58; USDA Award, 58; Distinguished Serv Award, Gamma Sigma Delta, 58; Ore State Univ Distinguished Serv Award, 73; Award Excellence, Genetics Soc Can, 77. *Mem:* Nat Acad Sci; Genetics Soc Am (pres, 78-79); Am Soc Agron; Bot Soc Am; Genetics Soc Can. *Res:* Origin, evolution, cytogenetics of wheat. *Mailing Add:* USDA 108 Curtis Hall Univ of Mo Columbia MO 65201

SEARS, HAROLD FREDERICK, b Wilmington, Del, Feb 20, 47; m 68; c 2. BEHAVIORAL BIOLOGY. *Educ:* Northwestern Univ, BA, 69; Univ NC, PhD(zool), 76. *Prof Exp:* Instr, 74-77, ASST PROF BIOL, UNIV SC, UNION, 77- *Mem:* AAAS; Sigma Xi; Animal Behav Soc; Am Ornithologists Union; Brit Ornithologists Union. *Res:* Vertebrate communication and display behavior; evolution of display; invertebrate homing and orientation. *Mailing Add:* Dept of Biol Univ of SC Union SC 29379

SEARS, J KERN, b Harper, Kans, May 13, 20; m 50; c 4. PLASTICS CHEMISTRY. *Educ:* Harding Col, BS, 42; Univ Mo, MA, 45, PhD(org chem), 47. *Prof Exp:* Asst instr, Univ Mo, 47; assoc prof, Harding Col, 47-51; res chemist, 51-71, RES SPECIALIST, MONSANTO CO, 71- *Mem:* AAAS; Tech Asn Pulp & Paper Indust; Soc Plastics Eng. *Res:* Organic chemistry; compatibility and solventability; resin modification by external additives; polymer testing and evaluation; plasticizer chemistry. *Mailing Add:* Monsanto Co PO Box 150 St Louis MO 63166

SEARS, JACK WOOD, b Cordell, Okla, Aug 12, 18; m 43; c 3. GENETICS. *Educ:* Harding Col, BS, 40; Univ Tex, MA, 42, PhD(genetics), 44. *Prof Exp:* Instr zool, Univ Tex, 44-45; PROF BIOL & HEAD DEPT, HARDING UNIV, 45- *Concurrent Pos:* Mem, Ark State Healing Arts Bd, 72- *Mem:* Fel AAAS; Genetics Soc Am; Am Inst Biol Sci; Am Fisheries Soc. *Res:* Cytogenetics and genetics of Drosophila; aquatic ecology; ecological relationships in Little Red River, Arkansas. *Mailing Add:* Dept of Biol Box 941 Harding Univ Searcy AR 72143

SEARS, JOHN T, b LaCrosse, Wis, Nov 15, 38; m 71; c 4. CHEMICAL ENGINEERING. *Educ:* Univ Wis, BS, 60; Princeton Univ, PhD(chem eng), 65. *Prof Exp:* Asst chem engr, Nuclear Eng Dept, Brookhaven Nat Lab, 64-68; res engr, Esso Res & Eng Co, NJ, 68-69; asst prof, 69-77, assoc prof,

77-81, PROF CHEM ENG, WVA UNIV, 81- *Mem:* Am Inst Chem Engrs; Am Nuclear Soc. *Res:* Radiation chemistry and processing; fluidized beds; air pollution control. *Mailing Add:* Dept of Chem Eng WVa Univ Morgantown WV 26506

SEARS, KARL DAVID, b Cedar Falls, Iowa, Mar 31, 41; m 65; c 2. CHEMISTRY. *Educ:* Iowa State Univ, BA, 63; Univ Wash, PhD(org chem), 68. *Prof Exp:* RES CHEMIST, ITT RAYONIER INC, 68- *Mem:* Am Chem Soc. *Res:* Cellulose, pulping and bleaching chemistry as well as the chemistry of noncellulogic constituents present in wood and bark and their conversion to commercial products. *Mailing Add:* ITT Rayonier Inc Shelton WA 98594

SEARS, LEO A, b Teaneck, NJ, Feb 10, 27; m 52; c 4. CHEMICAL ENGINEERING. *Educ:* Cornell Univ, BChE, 50. *Prof Exp:* Chem engr, 50-62, sr res engr, 62-66, supvr chem eng, 66-69, RES ASSOC, E I DU PONT DE NEMOURS & CO, INC, 69- *Mem:* Am Chem Soc. *Res:* Polymer synthesis and fabrication. *Mailing Add:* 5 Stable Lane Wilmington DE 19803

SEARS, MARKHAM KARLI, b San Luis Obispo, Calif, May 3, 46; m 69; c 1. INSECT ECOLOGY. *Educ:* Univ Calif, Davis, BSc, 69, PhD(entom), 74. *Prof Exp:* From res assoc to teaching asst, 72-74, ASST PROF ENTOM, UNIV GUELPH, 75- *Concurrent Pos:* Mem subcomt woody ornamentals, flowers & turf, Ont Crop Protection Comt, 75- *Mem:* Sigma Xi; Entom Soc Am; Can Entom Soc. *Res:* Ecology of insects affecting turfgrasses and woody ornamentals; biology and systematics of immature Coleoptera. *Mailing Add:* Dept of Environ Biol Univ of Guelph Guelph ON N1G 2W1 Can

SEARS, MARVIN LLOYD, b New York, NY, Sept 16, 28; m 50; c 4. OPHTHALMOLOGY. *Educ:* Princeton Univ, AB, 49; Columbia Univ, MD, 53. *Prof Exp:* Intern, Columbia Bellevue Hosp, 53-54; from asst resident to chief resident, Wilmer Inst Ophthal, 54-61; PROF OPHTHAL & VISUAL SCI & CHMN DEPT, SCH MED, YALE UNIV, 61-, CHIEF, YALENEW HAVEN MED CTR, 61- *Concurrent Pos:* Robert Weeks Kelly fel ophthal, 57-58; NIH trainee, 59-60; consult to Surgeon Gen, USPHS & mem visual sci study sect, Nat Inst Neurol Dis & Blindness, 62-66; mem bd sci coun, Nat Eye Inst, 70-; mem adv panel, US Pharmacopeia, 75-80. *Honors & Awards:* New Eng Ophthal Soc Award, 69; Friedenwald Award, Asn Res Vision & Ophthal, 77. *Mem:* AMA; Am Acad Ophthal & Otolaryngol; Am Ophthal Soc; Am Col Surgeons; Asn Res Vision & Ophthal. *Res:* Diseases of the eye. *Mailing Add:* Dept of Ophthal Yale Univ Sch of Med New Haven CT 06510

SEARS, MILDRED BRADLEY, b New Castle, Pa, Feb 19, 33. INORGANIC CHEMISTRY, CHEMICAL ENGINEERING. *Educ:* Col Wooster, BA, 54; Univ Fla, PhD(inorg chem), 58. *Prof Exp:* RES STAFF MEM, OAK RIDGE NAT LAB, 58-70 & 72- *Mem:* Am Chem Soc; Sigma Xi. *Res:* Engineering and environmental assessments of the nuclear fuel cycle, including possible future waste treatment methods; chemistry of uranium and thorium carbides. *Mailing Add:* 130 Monticello Rd Oak Ridge TN 37830

SEARS, PAUL GREGORY, b Somerset, Ky, Sept 5, 24; m 51; c 1. PHYSICAL CHEMISTRY. *Educ:* Univ Ky, BS, 50, PhD(chem), 53. *Prof Exp:* Asst, Univ Ky, 50-53, from instr to asst prof, 53-57; chemist, Monsanto Chem Co, 57-59; assoc prof, 59-62, PROF CHEM, UNIV KY, 62- *Mem:* Am Chem Soc; Electrochem Soc; Sigma Xi; AAAS. *Res:* Electrochemistry; nonaqueous solution chemistry; reactions in molten systems. *Mailing Add:* Dept of Chem Univ of Ky Lexington KY 40506

SEARS, RAYMOND ERIC JOHN, b Wellington, NZ, July 2, 34; m 62; c 4. NUCLEAR MAGNETIC RESONANCE. *Educ:* Univ Victoria, NZ, BSc, 57, MSc, 59; Univ Calif, Berkeley, PhD(physics), 66. *Prof Exp:* Res assoc chem, Mass Inst Technol, 66-67; asst prof, 67-80, ASSOC PROF PHYSICS, NTEX STATE UNIV, 80- *Mem:* AAAS; Am Phys Soc. *Mailing Add:* Dept of Physics NTex State Univ Denton TX 76203

SEARS, RICHARD LANGLEY, b Boston, Mass, Mar 27, 31; m 73; c 1. ASTROPHYSICS. *Educ:* Harvard Univ, AB, 53; Ind Univ, MA, 55, PhD(astrophys), 58. *Prof Exp:* Vis fel astron, Princeton Univ, 58; instr, Ind Univ, 58-59; asst, Lick Observ, Univ Calif, 59-61; res fel physics, Calif Inst Technol, 60-61; sr res fel, 61-64; vis asst prof physics & astron, Vanderbilt Univ, 64-65; asst prof astron, 65-70, ASSOC PROF ASTRON, UNIV MICH, ANN ARBOR, 70- *Concurrent Pos:* Mem, Int Astron Union. *Mem:* AAAS; Am Astron Soc; Royal Astron Soc. *Res:* Stellar interiors and evolution; stellar photometry; theoretical astrophysics. *Mailing Add:* Dept of Astron Univ of Mich Ann Arbor MI 48109

SEARS, ROBERT F, JR, b Warren Co, Ky, June 13, 41; m 65; c 1. PHYSICS. *Prof Exp:* EDCentre Col, BA, 63; Univ Colo, PhD(physics), 68. *Prof Exp:* From asst prof to assoc prof, 68-78, PROF PHYSICS, AUSTIN PEAY STATE UNIV, 78- *Mem:* Am Asn Physics Teachers; Am Phys Soc. *Res:* Study of antiproton-proton interactions resulting in the production of a single pion; high energy physics. *Mailing Add:* Dept of Physics Austin Peay State Univ Clarksville TN 37040

SEARS, TIMOTHY STEPHEN, b Boston, Mass, Sept 29, 45; m 75. PHOTOCHEMISTRY, PHYSICAL CHEMISTRY. *Educ:* Boston Univ, AB, 67; Univ Calif, Davis, CPhil, 70, PhD(chem), 73. *Prof Exp:* Fel chem, Univ Calgary, 73-74; sessional instr chem, 74-76; PROCESS ENGR, KAISER ALUMINUM & CHEM CORP, 76- *Mem:* Am Chem Soc; Royal Soc Chem. *Res:* Kinetics; flash and laser photolysis; electron spin resonance; mass spectrometry; radiation chemistry. *Mailing Add:* Kaiser Aluminum & Chem Corp 3400 Taylor Way Tacoma WA 98421

SEARS, WILLIAM R(EES), b Minneapolis, Minn, Mar 1, 13; m 36; c 2. AERODYNAMICS. *Educ:* Univ Minn, BAeroE, 34; Calif Inst Technol, PhD(aeronaut), 38. *Prof Exp:* Asst aeronaut, Calif Inst Technol, 34-37; from instr to asst prof, 37-41; chief aerodynamicist, Northrop Aircraft Inc, Calif, 41-46; prof aeronaut eng & dir grad sch aeronaut, Cornell Univ, 46-64; dir ctr appl math, 63-67, J L Given prof eng, 63-74; PROF AEROSPACE &

MECH ENG, UNIV ARIZ, TUCSON, 74- *Concurrent Pos:* Consult, Calspan Corp; ed, J Aerospace Sci, Inst Aerospace Sci. *Mem:* Am Inst Aeronaut & Astronaut, 57-63. *Honors & Awards:* Vincent Bendix Award, 65; Ludwig Prandtl Ring, Deutsche Gesellschaft fur Luft- und Raumfahrt, 74; G Edward Pendray Award, Am Inst Aeronaut & Astronaut, 75. *Mem:* Nat Acad Sci; Nat Acad Eng; fel Am Acad Arts & Sci; hon fel Am Inst Aeronaut & Astronaut; fel Int Acad Astronaut. *Res:* Fluid mechanics; wing and boundary layer theory; wind tunnels. *Mailing Add:* Dept of Aerospace & Mech Eng Univ of Ariz Tucson AZ 85721

SEASE, JOHN WILLIAM, b New Brunswick, NJ, Nov 10, 20; m 43; c 4. ELECTROCHEMISTRY. *Educ:* Princeton Univ, AB, 41; Calif Inst Technol, PhD(org chem), 46. *Prof Exp:* Asst inorg chem, Calif Inst Technol, 41-42, asst, Nat Defense Res Comt, 42-45; instr org chem, 46-48, from asst prof to assoc prof, 48-58, PROF CHEM, WESLEYAN UNIV, 58- *Mem:* AAAS; Am Chem Soc. *Res:* Electrochemistry of organic compounds. *Mailing Add:* Dept of Chem Wesleyan Univ Middletown CT 06457

SEASTROM, CHARLES C, metallurgical engineering, see previous edition

SEATON, JACOB ALIF, b Wellington, Kans, Jan 2, 31; m 55; c 3. INORGANIC CHEMISTRY. *Educ:* Wichita State Univ, BS, 53, MS, 55; Univ Ill, PhD(inorg chem), 58. *Prof Exp:* Asst chemist chem eng div, Argonne Nat Lab, 57-58; proj engr polymer br mat lab, Wright Air Develop Ctr, 58-60; sr staff mem inorg res, Spencer Chem Co, 60-62; asst prof chem, Sam Houston State Col, 62-66; head dept chem, 66-78, PROF CHEM, STEPHEN F AUSTIN STATE UNIV, 66-, CHMN DEPT, 78- *Mem:* Fel Am Inst Chem; Am Chem Soc. *Res:* Non-aqueous solvents; inorganic polymers; transition and inner-transition metal compounds. *Mailing Add:* Dept of Chem Stephen F Austin State Univ Nacogdoches TX 75961

SEATON, VAUGHN ALLEN, b Abilene, Kans, Oct 11, 28; m 54; c 2. VETERINARY PATHOLOGY. *Educ:* Kans State Univ, BS & DVM, 54; Iowa State Univ, MS, 57. *Prof Exp:* From instr to assoc prof, 55-64, PROF VET PATH & HEAD DEPT, COL VET MED, IOWA STATE UNIV, 64-, HEAD VET MED DIAG LAB, 74- *Concurrent Pos:* Mem, Conf Vet Lab Diagnosticians. *Mem:* Am Pub Health Asn; Am Vet Med Asn; Am Col Vet Toxicol. *Res:* Pulmonary adenomatosis in Iowa cattle; infectious diseases; veterinary toxicology. *Mailing Add:* Vet Diag Lab Col of Vet Med Iowa State Univ Ames IA 50010

SEATON, WILLIAM HAFFORD, b Black Oak, Ark, Oct 22, 24; m 44; c 2. CHEMICAL ENGINEERING. *Educ:* Univ Ark, BSChE, 50; Ohio State Univ, MS, 55, PhD(chem eng), 58. *Prof Exp:* Chem engr, Monsanto Chem Co, 50-53; res assoc, Ohio State Res Found, 53-55; sr res engr, 58-67, RES ASSOC, TENN EASTMAN CO, 67- *Honors & Awards:* Dudley Medal, Am Soc Testing & Mat, 77. *Mem:* Am Inst Chem Engrs; Nat Soc Prof Engrs; Am Soc Testing & Mat. *Res:* Chemical process data; unit operations research and development. *Mailing Add:* Tenn Eastman Co Kingsport TN 37662

SEATZ, LLOYD FRANK, b Winchester, Idaho, June 2, 19; m 49; c 1. SOIL FERTILITY. *Educ:* Univ Idaho, BS, 40; Univ Tenn, MS, 41; NC State Univ, PhD(agron), 49. *Prof Exp:* Asst agron, Univ Tenn, 40-41; asst, NC State Univ, 41-42 & 46-47; from asst prof to assoc prof, 47-55, prof, 55-68, CLYDE B AUSTIN DISTINGUISHED PROF AGR, UNIV TENN, KNOXVILLE, 68-, HEAD DEPT, 61- *Concurrent Pos:* Agronomist & asst chief soils & fertilizer res br, Tenn Valley Authority, 53-55. *Mem:* Am Soc Agron; Soil Sci Soc Am. *Res:* Phosphorus and trace element reactions and availability in soils; factors affecting crop response to fertilization. *Mailing Add:* Dept of Plant & Soil Sci Univ of Tenn Knoxville TN 37916

SEAVEY, MARDEN HOMER, JR, b Preston, Cuba, Jan 12, 29; US citizen; m 55, 63; c 5. SOLID STATE PHYSICS. *Educ:* Harvard Univ, AB, 52; Northeastern Univ, MS, 56; Harvard Univ, PhD, 70. *Prof Exp:* Physicist, Air Force Cambridge Res Ctr, 52-55, Lincoln Lab, Mass Inst Technol, 55-62, Air Force Cambridge Res Labs, 62-70 & Philips Res Lab, Netherlands, 70-72; PRIN ENGR, EQUIP DIV, RAYTHEON CO, 72- *Mem:* Am Phys Soc. *Res:* Resonance phenomena and acoustic effects in ordered magnetic systems; laser gyroscopes; radiation effects in large scale integrated circuits. *Mailing Add:* 21 Depot St Westford MA 01886

SEAWRIGHT, JACK ARLYN, b Ware Shoals, SC, Sept 9, 41; m 62; c 2. ENTOMOLOGY, GENETICS. *Educ:* Clemson Univ, BS, 64, MS, 65; Univ Fla, PhD(entom), 69. *Prof Exp:* RES ENTOMOLOGIST, INSECTS AFFECTING MAN & ANIMALS LAB, USDA, 68- *Concurrent Pos:* Asst prof, 70-80, prof dept entom, Univ Fla, 80- *Mem:* Entom Soc Am; Am Mosquito Control Asn. *Res:* Genetics of insects with emphasis on genetics control mechanisms; toxicology of chemosterilants in insects. *Mailing Add:* Entom Dept PO Box 14565 1700 SW 23rd Dr Univ Fla Gainesville FL 32604

SEAY, GLENN EMMETT, b Tahlequah, Okla, Mar 9, 26; m 59; c 3. PHYSICS. *Educ:* Univ Okla, BS, 50, MS, 53, PhD(physics), 57. *Prof Exp:* Mem staff, Los Alamos Sci Lab, Univ Calif, 47-62; div supvr, Sandia Corp, 62-64; dept mgr, 64-68; mgr dept exp physics, Systs Sci & Software, La Jolla, Calif, 68-70; mgr systs & software div, 70-76; GROUP LEADER, LOS ALAMOS SCI LAB, UNIV CALIF, 76- *Mem:* Am Phys Soc. *Res:* Flash radiography; atomic spectroscopy; shock waves in gases and solids; detonation physics; initiation of detonation. *Mailing Add:* 101 San Ildefonso Rd Los Alamos NM 87544

SEAY, THOMAS NASH, b Cincinnati, Ohio, Sept 29, 32; m 58; c 2. ENTOMOLOGY. *Educ:* Univ Fla, BSA, 55; Univ Ky, MSA, 63, PhD(biol sci), 67. *Prof Exp:* Asst prof biol, 66-70, ASSOC PROF BIOL, GEORGETOWN COL, 70-, DIR ENVIRON SCI, 74- *Mem:* Entom Soc Am; Am Mosquito Control Asn. *Res:* Mosquito biology; other medically important Diptera; history of medical entomology. *Mailing Add:* Dept of Biol Georgetown Col Georgetown KY 40324

SEBALD, ANTHONY VINCENT, b US. ELECTRICAL ENGINEERING, SYSTEMS SCIENCE. *Educ:* Gannon Col, BEE, 63; Univ Ill, MSEE, 75, PhD(elec eng), 76. *Prof Exp:* Assoc engr, IBM Corp, 64-68; prof eng, Univ Catolica de Valparaiso, 69-72; ASST PROF SYST SCI, UNIV CALIF, SAN DIEGO, 76- *Mem:* AAAS; Inst Elec & Electronics Engrs. *Res:* Energy and air pollution policy analysis; solar heating and cooling of buildings; estimation and control in systems which are incompletely specified. *Mailing Add:* Dept of Appl Mech B-010 Univ of Calif San Diego La Jolla CA 92037

SEBAN, RALPH A, b May 11, 17. MECHANICAL ENGINEERING. *Educ:* Univ Calif, Berkeley, PhD(mech eng), 48. *Prof Exp:* PROF MECH ENG, UNIV CALIF, BERKELEY, 52- *Mem:* Nat Acad Eng; Am Soc Mech Engrs. *Mailing Add:* Dept of Mech Eng 6169 Etcheverry Hall Berkeley CA 94720

SEBASTIAN, ANTHONY, b Youngstown, Ohio, July 11, 38; m 64. MEDICINE, NEPHROLOGY. *Educ:* Univ Calif, Los Angeles, BS, 60; Univ Calif, San Francisco, MD, 65. *Prof Exp:* From intern internal med to resident, Moffitt Hosp, 65-68, asst resident physician, 70-71, asst prof, 71-78, ASSOC PROF MED, UNIV CALIF, SAN FRANCISCO, 78- *Concurrent Pos:* Bank Am-Giannini Found fel renal dis, Univ Calif, San Francisco, 68-70. *Mem:* Am Soc Nephrol; Am Fedn Clin. *Res:* Am Soc Clin Invest; Int Soc Nephrol. *Res:* Renal and acid-base physiology and pathophysiology; renal acidosis; interrelationship of hydrogen ion and electrolyte transport in the kidney; renal tubular disorders. *Mailing Add:* Dept of Med 1202 Moffitt Hosp Univ of Calif San Francisco CA 94143

SEBASTIAN, JOHN FRANCIS, b San Diego, Calif, Nov 20, 39; m 67; c 2. PHYSICAL ORGANIC CHEMISTRY, BIOCHEMISTRY. *Educ:* San Diego State Col, BS, 61; Univ Calif, Riverside, PhD(org chem), 65. *Prof Exp:* NIH fel enzyme catalysis, Northwestern Univ, 65-67; asst prof chem, 67-72, assoc prof, 72-81, PROF CHEM, MIAMI UNIV, 81- *Concurrent Pos:* Res Corp grant, 68- *Mem:* AAAS; Am Chem Soc; Royal Soc Chem. *Res:* Mechanisms of enzyme catalysis; enzyme model systems; nuclear magnetic resonance spectroscopy; organometallic and heterocyclic chemistry; applications of molecular orbital theory. *Mailing Add:* Dept of Chem Miami Univ Oxford OH 45056

SEBASTIAN, LESLIE PAUL, b Tata, Hungary, July 11, 23; Can citizen; m 49; c 3. WOOD SCIENCE. *Educ:* Univ Forestry & Timber Indust, Hungary, ForEngr, 49; State Univ NY Col Forestry, Syracuse Univ, MSc, 65, PhD(wood sci), 71. *Prof Exp:* Demonstr forest utilization, Univ Forestry & Timber Indust, Hungary, 49-50, asst, 50-52, adj, 52-56; asst prof wood technol, Fac Forestry, Univ BC, 57-59; from asst prof to assoc prof, 59-75, PROF WOOD SCI, FAC FORESTRY, UNIV NB, 75- *Mem:* Int Asn Wood Anatomists; Forest Prod Res Soc; Soc Wood Sci & Technol; Tech Asn Pulp & Paper Indust; Can Inst Forestry. *Res:* Anatomical and physical properties of wood. *Mailing Add:* Fac Forestry Univ NB Fredericton NB E3B 5A3 Can

SEBASTIAN, RICHARD LEE, b Hutchinson, Kans, June 22, 42; m 64; c 2. SIGNAL PROCESSING, PATTERN RECOGNITION. *Educ:* Princeton Univ, AB, 64; Univ Md, College Park, PhD(physics), 70. *Prof Exp:* Staff scientist, 69-72, chief scientist, 72, div mgr, 72-74, VPRES RES, ENSCO, INC, SPRINGFIELD, VA, 74- *Mem:* Am Phys Soc; Inst Elec & Electronics Eng; Soc Explor Geophysics. *Res:* Signal processing applications; geophysics including acoustic seismic and electromagnetic waves; source localization and classification and wave propagation. *Mailing Add:* 5400 Port Royal Rd Springfield VA 22192

SEBEK, OLDRICH KAREL, b Prague, Czech, July 3, 19; nat US; m 59; c 1. MICROBIAL PHYSIOLOGY, INDUSTRIAL MICROBIOLOGY. *Educ:* Charles Univ, Prague, ScD(microbiol & bot), 46. *Prof Exp:* Asst microbiol, Charles Univ, 45-47; int fel fermentation, J E Seagram & Sons, Inc, 47-48; res assoc microbiol, Rutgers Univ, 48-49; fel chem & enzymol, Fordham Univ, 49-50; Muelhaupt scholar biol, Ohio State Univ, 50-52; SR SCIENTIST, UPJOHN CO, 52- *Concurrent Pos:* Abstractor, Chem Abstr, 50-70; vis scientist & res assoc, Univ Calif, Berkeley, 66-67; ed, Appl Microbiol, 68-71; vis prof, Nat Polytech Inst, Mexico City, 73; US rep, Int Comn Appl Microbial Genetics, Int Asn Microbiol Socs, 74- *Mem:* Am Soc Microbiol; Am Chem Soc. *Res:* Microbiol metabolism and biochemistry; biosynthesis and biotransformation of microbial products, antibiotics, carotenoids, pigments, amino acids, steroids. *Mailing Add:* Infectious Dis Res Upjohn Co Kalamazoo MI 49001

SEBESTA, CHARLES FREDERICK, b North Braddock, Pa, Mar 6, 14; m 45; c 7. MATHEMATICS. *Educ:* Univ Pittsburgh, AB, 34, MA, 38, PhD, 56. *Prof Exp:* Teacher high sch, Pa, 34-43; instr math, Univ Pittsburgh, 46-54, asst prof, 54-56; assoc prof, 56-65, head dept, 56-74 & 78-79, PROF MATH, DUQUESNE UNIV, 65- *Mem:* Math Asn Am; Sigma Xi. *Res:* Abstract algebra; partial differential equations; analytic function theory. *Mailing Add:* Dept of Math Duquesne Univ Pittsburgh PA 15219

SEBESTA, HENRY ROBERT, mechanical & control engineering, see previous edition

SEBETICH, MICHAEL J, b Nanty-Glo, Pa, Feb 25, 43. LIMNOLOGY, ECOLOGY. *Educ:* Duquesne Univ, BS, 65; Col William & Mary, MA, 69; Rutgers Univ, PhD(ecol, limnol), 72. *Prof Exp:* Asst prof, William Paterson Col, 72-73; aquatic biologist, US Geol Surv Water Resources Div, 73-77; ASSOC PROF BIOL, WILLIAM PATERSON COL, 77- *Mem:* Ecol Soc Am; Am Soc Limnol & Oceanog; AAAS; Am Inst Biol Sci; Int Asn Theoret & Appl Limnol. *Res:* Nutrient cycling in freshwater ecosystems. *Mailing Add:* Dept of Biol William Paterson Col Wayne NJ 07470

SEBO, STEPHEN ANDREW, b Budapest, Hungary, June 10, 34; m 68. ELECTRICAL ENGINEERING. *Educ:* Budapest Polytech Univ, MS, 57; Hungarian Acad Sci, PhD(elec eng), 66. *Prof Exp:* Elec engr, Budapest Elec Co, Hungary, 57-61; from asst prof to assoc prof elec power eng, Budapest Polytech Univ, 61-68; assoc prof elec eng, 68-74, PROF ELEC ENG, OHIO STATE UNIV, 74- *Concurrent Pos:* Consult engr, State Power Bd, Hungary, 61-64 & Columbus & Southern Ohio Elec Co, 69-; Ford Found fel, 67-68; consult & res, Am Elec Power Serv Corp, 72-; res engr, Elec Power Res Inst, 75- *Mem:* Inst Elec & Electronics Engrs; Int Conf Large Elec Systs. *Res:* Electric power systems; high-voltage power transmission; power system analysis; electric power generation; high-voltage technique; power system economics. *Mailing Add:* Dept of Elec Eng Ohio State Univ 2015 Neil Ave Columbus OH 43210

SEBORG, DALE EDWARD, b Madison, Wis, Mar 29, 41; m 67. CHEMICAL ENGINEERING. *Educ:* Univ Wis-Madison, BSc, 64; Princeton Univ, PhD(chem eng), 69. *Prof Exp:* Res asst chem eng, Princeton Univ, 64-68; from asst prof to prof chem & petrol eng, Univ Alta, 68-77; PROF CHEM & NUCLEAR ENG, UNIV CALIF, SANTA BARBARA, 77-, CHMN DEPT, 78- *Mem:* Am Inst Chem Engrs; Instrument Soc Am. *Res:* Process control; computer control techniques; applied mathematics. *Mailing Add:* Dept of Chem & Nuclear Eng Univ of Calif Santa Barbara CA 93106

SEBRANEK, JOSEPH GEORGE, b Richland Ctr, Wis, Feb 22, 48; m 70; c 1. MEAT SCIENCES. *Educ:* Univ Wis, Platteville, BS, 70; Univ Wis, Madison, MS, 71, PhD(meat sci & food sci), 74. *Prof Exp:* Fel, Nat Cancer Inst, 74-75; asst prof meat sci, 75-81, ASSOC PROF ANIMAL SCI & FOOD TECH, IOWA STATE UNIV, 81- *Mem:* Inst Food Technologists; Am Soc Animal Sci; Am Meat Sci Asn; Am Chem Soc. *Res:* Meat processing, food additives, dehydration of processed meats, curing reactions, use of nitrite, color development and processed meat quality. *Mailing Add:* 215 Meat Lab Iowa State Univ Ames IA 50011

SECCO, ETALO ANTHONY, b Dominion, NS, Nov 8, 28; m 53; c 6. PHYSICAL CHEMISTRY. *Educ:* St Francis Xavier Univ, BSc, 49; Laval Univ, DSc(chem), 53. *Prof Exp:* Instr gen chem, St Francis Xavier Univ, 49-50; instr phys chem, Laval Univ, 52-53; res assoc, Ind Univ, 53-55; from asst prof to assoc prof chem, 55-64, PROF CHEM, ST FRANCIS XAVIER UNIV, 64- *Concurrent Pos:* NATO overseas fel, Cavendish Lab, Cambridge Univ, 61-62. *Mem:* Am Chem Soc; NY Acad Sci; fel Chem Inst Can; Royal Soc Chem; fel Am Inst Chemists. *Res:* Kinetics of heterogeneous reactions; diffusion in solids; reaction of metals with oxides, sulfides and selenides at high temperatures; phase equilibria at high temperatures; radiotracers; structural problems; solid state decomposition kinetics; electrical conductivity studies. *Mailing Add:* Dept of Chem St Francis Xavier Univ Antigonish NS B2G 1C0 Can

SECHI-ZORN, BICE, b Cagliari, Italy, May 20, 28; m 55. ELEMENTARY PARTICLE PHYSICS. *Educ:* Univ Cagliari, PhD(physics), 52. *Prof Exp:* Asst physics, Univ Padua, 52-56; assoc, Brookhaven Nat Lab, 56-62; asst prof, Univ Md, 62-68; vis physicist, Nat Lab Frascati, Italy, 68-69; assoc prof, 69-76, PROF PHYSICS, UNIV MD, COLLEGE PARK, 76- *Mem:* Am Phys Soc. *Res:* Search for new particles in electron-positron intearctions; study of total cross sections and strange particle production of negative pions in hydrogen at the highest available energy 360 GeV. *Mailing Add:* Dept of Physics Univ of Md College Park MD 20742

SECHLER, DALE TRUMAN, b Pleasant Hope, Mo, Nov 30, 26; m 54; c 3. PLANT BREEDING. *Educ:* Univ Mo, BS, 50, MEd, 54, PhD(plant breeding), 60. *Prof Exp:* Teacher high schs, Mo, 50-S5; instr field crops, Univ Mo, 55-60; asst prof agron, Univ Fla, 60-67; assoc prof, 67-75, PROF AGRON, UNIV MO-COLUMBIA, 75- *Mem:* Am Soc Agron. *Res:* Genetics and improvement of wheat and oats; grain crops production; plant breeding; international agronomy. *Mailing Add:* Dept of Agron 106 Curtis Hall Univ of Mo Columbia MO 65201

SECHRIEST, RALPH EARL, b Warren, Pa, Oct 31, 35; m 60; c 3. ECONOMIC ENTOMOLOGY. *Educ:* Thiel Col, BA, 58; Bowling Green State Univ, MA, 59; Ohio State Univ, PhD(entom), 62. *Prof Exp:* Asst prof zool, animal ecol & entom, Carthage Col, 62-64; asst entomologist, 64-71, ASSOC ENTOMOLOGIST CORN TEAM, PESTICIDE PERFORMANCE & EVAL 83, ILL NATURAL HIST SURV, UNIV ILL, URBANA, 71-, ASST PROF AGR ENTOM, UNIV, 71- *Concurrent Pos:* Ohio Acad Sci fel, 66. *Mem:* Entom Soc Am. *Res:* Insecticide performance evaluation of corn and stored products. *Mailing Add:* 172 Natural Resources Bldg Ill Natural Hist Surv Urbana IL 61801

SECHRIST, CHALMERS FRANKLIN, JR, b Glen Rock, Pa, Aug 23, 30; m 57; c 2. AERONOMY, IONOSPHERIC PHYSICS. *Educ:* Johns Hopkins Univ, BE, 52; Pa State Univ, MS, 54, PhD(elec eng), 59. *Prof Exp:* From asst elec eng to instr, Pa State Univ, 52-55, asst ionosphere res lab, 55-59; sr engr, HRB-Singer, Inc, 59-63; staff engr, 63-65; from asst prof to assoc prof elec eng, 61-71, PROF ELEC ENG, UNIV ILL, URBANA-CHAMPAIGN, 71- *Concurrent Pos:* Mem comn III, Int Union Radio Sci; mem joint comt, Int Asn Geomagnetism & Aeronomy & Int Asn Meteorol & Atmospheric Physics, 75- *Mem:* Inst Elec & Electronics Engrs; Am Geophys Union; Am Meteorol Soc. *Res:* Physics and chemistry of the lower ionosphere; interactions between the stratosphere, mesosphere and lower ionosphere. *Mailing Add:* Aeronomy Lab Dept Elec Eng Univ of Ill Urbana-Champaign Urbana IL 61801

SECHRIST, JOHN WILLIAM, b Manila, Philippines, Feb 22, 42; US citizen; m 64. NEUROANATOMY, DEVELOPMENTAL BIOLOGY. *Educ:* Wheaton Col, Ill, BS, 64; Univ Ill, PhD(anat), 67. *Prof Exp:* From instr to asst prof neuroanat, Sch Med, Univ Pittsburgh, 67-72; asst prof anat, Col Med, Univ Ariz, 72-76; lectr anat, Univ Ibadan, Nigeria, 76-79; ASSOC PROF BIOL, WHEATON COL, 79- *Mem:* AAAS; Am Asn Anatomists; Am Soc Cell Biol. *Res:* Investigation of cytologic and metabolic changes during neuroblast differentiation and the retrograde reaction; comparative studies of earliest neurons in both vertebrates and invertebrates. *Mailing Add:* Dept Biol Wheaton Col Wheaton IL 60187

SECHZER, JERI ALTNEU, b New York, NY, Nov 1, 30; m 48; c 3. PHYSIOLOGICAL PSYCHOLOGY, NEUROBIOLOGY. *Educ:* NY Univ, BS, 56; Univ Pa, MA, 61, PhD(psychol), 62. *Prof Exp:* Res fel physiol psychol, Sch Med, Univ Pa, 61-63, USPHS fel, 63-64; asst prof physiol psychol & anat, Col Med, Baylor Univ, 64-66; res scientist, Dept Rehab Med & Anat, NY Univ Med Ctr, 66-70; asst prof psychiat, 70-71, ASSOC PROF PSYCHIAT, MED COL, CORNELL UNIV, 71- *Mem:* Am Psychol Asn; Am Asn Anatomists; Am Physiol Soc; Soc Neurosci; Asn Women in Sci. *Res:* Learning and memory; interhemispheric mechanisms; early development. *Mailing Add:* 180 East End Ave New York NY 10028

SECHZER, PHILIP HAIM, b New York, NY, Sept 13, 14; m 48; c 3. ANESTHESIOLOGY. *Educ:* City Col New York, BS, 34; NY Univ, MD, 38; Am Bd Anesthesiol, dipl, 47. *Prof Exp:* Intern, Harlem Hosp, New York, 38-40; resident, Fordham Hosp, 41-42, dir anesthesiol & asst prof, Postgrad Med Sch, NY Univ, 55-56; asst prof anesthesiol, Sch Med & physician-anesthetist, Hosp Univ Pa, 56-64; from assoc prof to prof anesthesiol, Col Med, Baylor Univ, 64-66; PROF ANESTHESIOL, STATE UNIV NY DOWNSTATE MED CTR, 66-; DIR ANESTHESIOL, MAIMONIDES MED CTR, 66-, MED DIR, 73-, DIR PAIN THER CTR, 72- *Concurrent Pos:* Consult, USPHS Marine Hosp, Staten Island, NY, 48-; dir anesthesiol, Seton Hosp, New York, 50-55; attend anesthesiologist, Vet Admin Hosps, New York, 55-56 & Philadelphia, 58-59; consult, Harlem Hosp, New York, 56- & Vet Admin Hosps, Philadelphia, 60-63 & Houston, 64-66; chief Baylor anesthesiol sect, Methodist Hosp, Houston; area consult, Vet Admin, DC, 64-; ed, Commun in Anesthesiol, 70-77; hon police surgeon, New York, 74-; mem, Nat Bd Acupuncture Med. *Mem:* Fel Am Col Clin Pharmacol; fel Am Col Anesthesiol; Sigma Xi; fel Am Col Physicians; AMA. *Res:* Circulatory and respiratory physiology; statistical methods and experimental design; evaluation of new drugs and anesthetic methods. *Mailing Add:* Dept of Anesthesiol Maimonides Med Ctr Brooklyn NY 11219

SECKEL, GUNTER RUDOLF, b Osnabruck, Ger, Nov 4, 23; nat US; m 65. OCEANOGRAPHY. *Educ:* Univ Wash, BS, 50, MS, 54. *Prof Exp:* Asst oceanog, Univ Wash, 50-53; oceanogr biol lab, Bur Com Fisheries, US Fish & Wildlife Serv, Hawaii, 53-63, supvry res oceanogr, 63, chief trade wind zone oceanog prog, 63-67, chief oceanog prog, 67-70; res oceanogr, 70-77, CHIEF PAC ENVIRON GROUP, NAT MARINE FISHERIES SERV, NAT OCEANIC & ATMOSPHERIC ADMIN, 77- *Mem:* Am Geophys Union; Am Soc Limnol & Oceanog. *Res:* Physical oceanography; climatic oceanography of Hawaiian waters; mechanisms producing seasonal and longer term changes in distribution of properties in north Pacific; structure of Pacific north equatorial current. *Mailing Add:* Nat Marine Fisheries Serv c/o Fleet Numerical Weather Cent Monterey CA 93940

SECKLER, BERNARD DAVID, b New York, NY, Feb 14, 25; m 53; c 2. MATHEMATICS. *Educ:* Brooklyn Col, BA, 45; Columbia Univ, MA, 48; NY Univ, PhD(appl math), 58. *Prof Exp:* Instr math, Long Island Univ, 48-53; lectr, Brooklyn Col, 47-54, instr, 57-58; asst appl math, NY Univ, 54-58; assoc prof math, Pratt Inst, 58-64; chmn dept, 68-72, PROF MATH, C W POST COL, LONG ISLAND UNIV, 64- *Mem:* Math Asn Am; Soc Indust & Appl Math. *Res:* Asymptotic expansions; geometrical and asymptotical solution of diffraction problems; Russian abstracting and translating of applied mathematics; translating of probability journal. *Mailing Add:* Dept of Math C W Post Col Long Island Univ Greenvale NY 11548

SECOR, DONALD TERRY, JR, b Oil City, Pa, Nov 22, 34; m 59; c 3. GEOPHYSICS, GEOLOGY. *Educ:* Cornell Univ, BS, 57, MS, 59; Stanford Univ, PhD(geol), 62. *Prof Exp:* Asst prof geol, 62-65, assoc prof, 65-81, PROF GEOL, UNIV SC, 81-, CHMN DEPT, 77- *Mem:* Fel Geol Soc Am; Am Geophys Union. *Res:* Rock mechanics. *Mailing Add:* Dept of Geol Univ of SC Columbia SC 29208

SECOR, JACK BEHRENT, b Indianapolis, Ind, Aug 18, 23. PHYSIOLOGICAL ECOLOGY. *Educ:* Butler Univ, BS, 48; Wash State Univ, PhD(bot), 57. *Prof Exp:* Botanist, US Geol Surv, 56-57; range conservationist, US Forest Serv, 57-58; Labatt fel bot, Univ Western Ont, 59-60; instr, Dept Natural Sci, Mich State Univ, 60-63; res asst biochem, Va Polytech Inst, 63-65; res scientist assoc, Univ Tex, Austin, 66-67; from asst prof to assoc prof biol, 67-77, PROF BIOL, EASTERN NMEX UNIV, 77- *Mem:* Ecol Soc Am. *Res:* Gypsumland ecosystems. *Mailing Add:* Dept of Life Sci Eastern NMex Univ Portales NM 88130

SECOR, ROBERT M(ILLER), b New York, NY, Mar 21, 32; m 56; c 2. CHEMICAL ENGINEERING. *Educ:* NY Univ, BChE, 52; Yale Univ, DEng, 58. *Prof Exp:* Asst, Yale Univ, 52-55; res engr, Eastern Lab, 56-64, sr res engr, Eng Technol Lab, 64-74, res assoc, 74-78, RES ASSOC, CENT RES & DEVELOP DEPT, E I DU PONT DE NEMOURS & CO, INC, 78- *Mem:* Am Chem Soc; Am Inst Chem Engrs. *Res:* Diffusion; mass transfer; chemical kinetics; applied mathematics; phase rule; optical isomerism; polymer processing. *Mailing Add:* Cent Res & Develop Dept Exp Sta E I du Pont de Nemours & Co Inc Wilmington DE 19898

SECORD, DAVID CARTWRIGHT, b Guelph, Ont, June 6, 33; m 57; c 3. LABORATORY ANIMAL MEDICINE. *Educ:* Ont Vet Col, DVM, 58; Univ Toronto, MVSc, 61. *Prof Exp:* From asst prof to assoc prof exp surg, 61-74, PROF EXP SURG, FAC MED, UNIV ALTA, 74-, DIR ANIMAL CARE, 61- *Concurrent Pos:* Med Res Coun Can grants, 69-64; chmn, Bd Examr Vet Med, Alta, 61-74. *Mem:* Can Asn Lab Animal Sci; Can Vet Med Asn; Am Asn Lab Animal Sci; Am Vet Med Asn; Am Asn Lab Animal Practitioners. *Res:* Canine gastroenterology; physiology of renal function; exercise physiology. *Mailing Add:* Dept Exp Surg Fac Med Univ Alta Edmonton AB T6G 2G7 Can

SECORD, ROBERT N, b Newton, Mass, Dec 20, 20; m 44; c 4. CHEMICAL ENGINEERING. *Educ:* Mass Inst Technol, BS, 42, MS, 47. *Prof Exp:* Chem engr, 47-51, head appl res sect, New Prods Res Dept, 51-61, eng mgr, Oxides Div, 61-66, dir process develop, 66-70, res dir, 70-77, DIR CAB-O-SIL RES & DEVELOPMENT, CABOT CORP, 77- *Mem:* Am Chem Soc; Am Inst Chem Engrs. *Res:* Processes for high temperature chemical reactions. *Mailing Add:* Cabot Corp Concord Rd Billerica MA 01821

SECOY, DIANE MARIE, b Kenton, Ohio, Oct 31, 38; m 70. VERTEBRATE BIOLOGY. *Educ:* Ohio State Univ, BS, 60, MS, 62; Univ Colo, PhD(herpet), 68. *Prof Exp:* Asst cur zool & paleont, Mus, Univ Colo, 67-68; asst prof, 68-72, ASSOC PROF BIOL, UNIV REGINA, 72- *Mem:* Sigma Xi; Am Soc Ichthyologists & Herpetologists; Herpetologists League; Soc Study Amphibians & Reptiles; Can Soc Zoologists. *Res:* Reptilian morphology; thermal ecology of reptiles and amphibians; history of pest control; avian ecology. *Mailing Add:* Dept of Biol Univ of Regina Regina SK S4S 0A2 Can

SECREST, BRUCE GILL, b Iowa City, Iowa, July 20, 36; m 64. MATHEMATICS, AERONAUTICAL ENGINEERING. *Educ:* Iowa State Univ, BS, 58, MS, 62, PhD(math), 64. *Prof Exp:* Assoc engr, Douglas Aircraft Co, Inc, 59; asst math, Iowa State Univ, 59-63, instr, 63-64; asst prof, Univ Nebr, 64-66; MEM TECH STAFF, TEX INSTRUMENTS, INC, 66- *Mem:* Am Math Soc. *Res:* Propagation of waves in fluid mechanics; methods of solution in applied mathematics. *Mailing Add:* 1228 Seminole Dr Richardson TX 75080

SECREST, DONALD H, b Akron, Ohio, Jan 3, 32; m 58; c 2. PHYSICAL CHEMISTRY. *Educ:* Univ Akron, BS, 55; Univ Wis, PhD(theoret chem), 61. *Prof Exp:* Instr phys chem, Univ Wis, 60-61; asst prof, 62-67, ASSOC PROF PHYS CHEM, UNIV ILL, URBANA, 67- *Concurrent Pos:* Vis scientist, Max Planck Inst, Gottingen, Ger, 71-72; assoc ed, J Chem Physics, 77-79. *Mem:* Fel Am Phys Soc; Soc Indust & Appl Math. *Res:* Atomic and molecular scattering problems; molecular structure of small systems, especially development of mathematical techniques for handling quantum mechanical problems; on-line application of computing machinery. *Mailing Add:* 115 Noyes Lab Univ of Ill Urbana IL 61801

SECREST, EVERETT LEIGH, b Tioga, Tex, Jan 5, 28; m 48; c 2. RESEARCH ADMINISTRATION, SYSTEMS SCIENCE. *Educ:* NTex State Col, BS, 47, MS, 48; Mass Inst Technol, PhD(physics), 51. *Prof Exp:* From asst prof to assoc prof physics, NTex State Col, 51-54; chief nuclear physics, Convair Div, Gen Dynamics Corp, 54-57; sect chief proj physics atomic energy div, Babcock & Silcox Co, 57-58, asst mgr physics & math, 58-59; chief appl res, Gen Dynamics/Ft Worth, 59-63, chief scientist, 63-64; assoc dean eng grad studies & res, Univ Okla, 64-65; pres res found, 65-72, grad dean, 65-68, vchancellor advan studies & res, 68-72, CONTINENTAL NAT BANK PROF MGT SCI, TEX CHRISTIAN UNIV, 72-, VCHANCELLOR FINANCE & PLANNING, 81- *Concurrent Pos:* Consult, Gen Dynamics/Ft Worth, 52-54; guest of the inst syst dynamics group & opers res ctr, Mass Inst Technol, 72. *Mem:* Am Phys Soc; Am Nuclear Soc; Am Soc Eng Educ; Soc Comput Simulation. *Res:* Management science with emphasis on applications of systems dynamics to complex social and economic structures; university administration. *Mailing Add:* 2415 Wabash Ave Ft Worth TX 76109

SECRIST, JOHN ADAIR, III, b Vincennes, Ind, Sept, 26, 47; m 68; c 2. NUCLEOSIDE SYNTHESIS, DRUG SYNTHESIS. *Educ:* Univ Mich, BS, 68; Univ Ill, PhD(org chem), 72. *Prof Exp:* Fel, Harvard Univ, 72-73; asst prof chem, Ohio State Univ, 73-79; sr chemist, 79-80, HEAD, BIOORG SECT, SOUTHERN RES INST, 80- *Concurrent Pos:* Mem, Exam Comt, Org Chem Subcomt, Am Chem Soc, 75-80. *Mem:* Am Chem Soc; Chem Soc; AAAS. *Res:* Synthetic organic chemistry; biochemistry; chemotherapy. *Mailing Add:* Southern Res Inst PO Box 3307-A Birmingham AL 35255

SEDAR, ALBERT WILLIAM, b Cambridge, Mass, Dec 20, 22; m 53; c 4. MICROSCOPIC ANATOMY. *Educ:* Brown Univ, AB, 43, MS, 48; Univ Iowa, PhD(zool), 53. *Prof Exp:* Asst gen biol, Brown Univ, 46-48; asst histol, Univ Iowa, 50, asst cytol, 51-52; instr zool & histol, Syracuse Univ, 52-53; NIH res fel cytol, Rockefeller Inst, 53-55; from asst prof to assoc prof anat, 55-66, PROF ANAT, JEFFERSON MED COL, 67- *Concurrent Pos:* USPHS career develop award, 66-71. *Mem:* Am Soc Cell Biol; Electron Micros Soc Am; Am Asn Anatomists. *Res:* Histology; cytophysiology; electron microscopy; fine structure of cells; electron histochemistry of cells; ultrastructure of cells and tissues. *Mailing Add:* Dept of Anat Jefferson Hall Jefferson Med Col Philadelphia PA 19107

SEDAT, JOHN WILLIAM, b Culver City, Calif, Aug 17, 42; m 75. MOLECULAR BIOLOGY, CHEMISTRY. *Educ:* Pasadena Col, BA, 63; Calif Inst Technol, PhD(biol), 70. *Prof Exp:* Fel, Helen Hay Whitney Found, 70-73; staff scientist, Lab Molecular Biol, Med Res Coun, 73-74; vis scientist, Dept Cell Biochem, Hadassah Med Sch, Jerusalem, Israel, 74-75; res assoc, Dept Radiobiol, Yale Univ Sch Med, 75-78; ASST PROF MOLECULAR BIOL, UNIV CALIF SCH MED, SAN FRANCISCO, 78- *Res:* Chromosome and interphase nuclear architecture. *Mailing Add:* Dept of Biochem & Biophys Univ of Calif San Francisco CA 94143

SEDBERRY, JOSEPH E, JR, b Shreveport, La, Sept 18, 25; m 53; c 3. AGRONOMY, SOIL CHEMISTRY. *Educ:* Centenary Col, BS, 49; La State Univ, Baton Rouge, MS, 52, PhD(agron), 54. *Prof Exp:* Agronomist, NLa Exp Sta, La State Univ, Baton Rouge, 54-55; agronomist, Lion Oil Co, Monsanto Chem Co, 55-58; agronomist, Am Potash Inst, 58-63; PROF AGRON, LA STATE UNIV, BATON ROUGE, 63- *Concurrent Pos:* Ford Found consult, Latin Am, 65-66; res grants, Geigy Chem Co, Eagle Picher Co, Sherwin Williams Co & Am Cyanamid Chem Co, 67- *Mem:* Am Soc Agron; Soil Sci Soc Am. *Res:* Soil testing and fertility with major emphasis on effect of major, secondary and micronutrients on yield; chemical composition of food and fiber crops. *Mailing Add:* Dept of Agron La State Univ Baton Rouge LA 70803

SEDELOW, SALLY YEATES, b Greenfield, Iowa, Aug 10, 31; m 58. COMPUTER SCIENCE, LINGUISTICS. *Educ:* Univ Iowa, BA, 53; Mt Holyoke Col, MA, 56; Bryn Mawr Col, PhD(Eng lit), 60. *Prof Exp:* Instr Eng, Smith Col, 59-60; asst prof, Parsons Col, 60-61 & Rockford Col, 61-62; human factors scientist, Systs Develop Corp, 62-64; asst prof Eng, St Louis Univ, 64-66; assoc prof Eng & comput & info sci, Univ NC, Chapel Hill, 66-70; PROF COMPUT SCI & LING, UNIV KANS, 70-, ASSOC DEAN COL

LIBERAL ARTS & SCIS, 81- *Concurrent Pos:* Off Naval Res res grant automated lang, Univ NC, Chapel Hill & Univ Kans, 64-74; consult, Syst Develop Corp, 64-67; mem, Adv Panel, Instnl Comput Serv Sect, NSF, 68-70, Comput Applns Res Sect, 70-71, Adv Comt Comput Activities, 72-; vis scientist, NSF-Asn Comput Mach Vis Scientist Prog, 69-70; NSF grant, Univ Kans, 71-72; prog dir, Techniques & Systs Prog, NSF, 74-76; chmn group comput in lang & lit, Modern Lang Asn Am, 77-78; mem US deleg comput-based natural-lang processing, USSR, 78. *Mem:* Asn Comput Mach; Asn Comput Ling; Am Soc Info Sci; Ling Soc Am; Modern Lang Asn Am. *Res:* Computer-based language and literature analysis; stylistics; semantics; computing in the humanities. *Mailing Add:* Dept of Comput Sci Univ of Kans Lawrence KS 66045

SEDELOW, WALTER ALFRED, JR, b Ludlow, Mass, Apr 17, 28; m 58. COMPUTER SCIENCE, SOCIOLOGY. *Educ:* Amherst Col, BA, 47; Harvard Univ, MA, 51, PhD, 57. *Prof Exp:* Instr, Williams Col, 48-50; from instr to asst prof, Amherst Col, 54-60; assoc prof sociol & chmn dept, Parsons Col, 60-61; Jane Addams assoc prof & chmn dept, Rockford Col, 61-62; human factors scientist, Syst Develop Corp, 62-64; assoc prof sociol, chmn dept sociol & anthrop & dir health orgn res prog, St Louis Univ, 64-66; from assoc prof to prof comput & info sci & sociol, Univ NC, Chapel Hill, 66-70, dean, Sch Libr Sci, 67-70; PROF COMPUT SCI & SOCIOL, UNIV KANS, 70- *Concurrent Pos:* Consult, Life Sci Div, McDonnell Aircraft Corp, 64-66; res prof, Inst Res Soc Sci, Univ NC, Chapel Hill, prin investr, NASA res proj grant & Higher Educ Act fel prog, 68-70; mem, Comt Info Technol, Am Coun Learned Socs, 68-70; vis scientist, NSF-Asn Comput Mach Vis Scientist Prog, 69-70; prin investr, NSF study grant, Univ Kans & mem, Adv Comt Proj Alternative Approaches Mgt & Financing Univ Comput Ctrs, Univ Denver, 71-72; consult, Col Human Ecol, Mich State Univ, 73-74; dir, Networking Sci, Div Math & Comput Sci, NSF, 75 & 76; mem, Oversight Comt, Info Networks Technol Assessment Proj, Columbus Labs, Battelle Mem Inst, 75-76; mem, Adv Panel Comput Applns, Nat Endowment Humanities, 75-76; Menninger Found fel interdisciplinary studies, 77-; consult biotechnol resources, NIH, 78- *Mem:* AAAS; Asn Comput Mach; Am Soc Info Sci; fel Am Sociol Asn; Soc Gen Systs Res. *Res:* Computer-assisted language analysis; information systems; public uses of computers, including education applications; human factors in computer based systems; computer to computer communication networks; sociology of science and technology; sociology of culture. *Mailing Add:* Dept of Comput Sci Univ of Kans Lawrence KS 66045

SEDENSKY, JAMES ANDREW, b Bridgeport, Conn, Aug 6, 36. CARDIOVASCULAR PHYSIOLOGY, PULMONARY PHYSIOLOGY. *Educ:* Fairfield Univ, BS, 58; Univ Tenn, Memphis, PhD(physiol, biophys), 66. *Prof Exp:* NSF trainee biomath, NC State Univ, 66-67, NIH trainee, 67-69; from instr to asst prof physiol, 69-76, ASSOC PROF PHYSIOL, SCH MED, WAYNE STATE UNIV, 76- *Concurrent Pos:* NIH fac educ develop award, 73. *Mem:* AAAS; Math Asn Am; Am Statist Asn; Am Physiol Soc; Am Thoracic Soc. *Res:* Computer simulation and statistical analysis of biomedical systems; electrical impedance plethysmography. *Mailing Add:* Dept of Physiol Wayne State Univ Sch of Med Detroit MI 48201

SEDGWICK, ROBERT T, b Rome City, Ind, Aug 2, 33; m 66; c 1. MECHANICS, MATERIALS SCIENCE. *Educ:* Tri-State Col, BSME, 59; Mich State Univ, MS, 60, PhD(mat sci), 65. *Prof Exp:* Asst instr mech, Mich State Univ, 60-65; scientist, Space Sci Lab, Gen Elec Co, Pa, 65-69; CONVENTIONAL MUNITIONS PROG MGR, SYSTS, SCI & SOFTWARE, 69- *Mem:* Soc Eng Sci. *Res:* Dislocation mechanics; continuum mechanics; elastic-plastic-hydrodynamic material flow; hypervelocity and ballistic impact studies; Eulerian and Lagrangian numerical code development; shaped charge and fragmentation munitions calculations; fuel-air explosives; conventional warhead design. *Mailing Add:* 1515 San Dieguito Dr Del Mar CA 92014

SEDLACEK, WILLIAM ADAM, b Glendive, Mont, Feb 22, 36; m 63; c 2. ATMOSPHERIC CHEMISTRY. *Educ:* Univ Wyo, BS, 58, PhD(phys chem), 65. *Prof Exp:* Res chemist shale oil & petrol res sta, US Bur Mines, 59-60; NSF fel, Univ Fla, 65-66; STAFF MEM, LOS ALAMOS SCI LAB, UNIV CALIF, 66- *Mem:* Am Geophys Union; Am Chem Soc. *Res:* Ternary fission, activation analysis; nuclear reactions, nuclear experimental techniques and environmental pollution; atmospheric dynamics; Aitken nuclei; trace elements and ozone. *Mailing Add:* Los Alamos Sci Lab PO Box 1663 Los Alamos NM 87545

SEDLAK, BONNIE JOY, b Oak Park, Ill, Jan 30, 43. CELL BIOLOGY, DEVELOPMENTAL BIOLOGY. *Educ:* Northwestern Univ, BA, 65, PhD(biol), 74; Case Western Reserve Univ, MA, 68. *Prof Exp:* Instr biol, Northwestern Univ, 71-72; res assoc biochem, Rush Med Col, 74-75; asst prof biol, Smith Col, 75-77; ASST PROF BIOL, STATE UNIV NY COL PURCHASE, 77- *Mem:* Am Soc Cell Biol; AAAS; Soc Develop Biol; Electron Micros Soc Am. *Res:* Cellular aspects of development and endocrine control in insects. *Mailing Add:* Div of Natural Sci State Univ of NY Col Purchase NY 10577

SEDLAK, JOHN ANDREW, b Bridgeport, Conn, May 17, 34. ORGANIC CHEMISTRY. *Educ:* Wesleyan Univ, BA, 55; Tufts Univ, MS, 56; Ohio State Univ, PhD(org fluorine chem), 60. *Prof Exp:* Res chemist, 60-66, sr res chemist, 66-77, PROJ LEADER, AM CYANAMID CO, 77- *Mem:* AAAS; Am Chem Soc; Tech Asn Pulp & Paper Indust. *Res:* Fluorinated monomers; polynuclear aromatic hydrocarbons; polyelectrolytes; paper chemicals. *Mailing Add:* Am Cyanamid Co 1937 W Main St Stamford CT 06904

SEDLAK, MICHAEL, b Whitaker, Pa, May 12, 29. ORGANIC CHEMISTRY, ANALYTICAL CHEMISTRY. *Educ:* Rutgers Univ, BSc, 51, PhD(org chem), 57. *Prof Exp:* Chemist, Arvey Corp, 51; asst, Rutgers Univ, 54-56; res technologist, Mobil Oil Corp, 57-62, sr res chemist, 62-67, RES ASSOC MOBIL RES & DEVELOP CORP, 67- *Mem:* Soc Appl Spectros; Am Chem Soc. *Res:* Organic synthesis; organic-analytical methods. *Mailing Add:* Mobil Res & Develop Corp Paulsboro NJ 08066

SEDLET, JACOB, b Milwaukee, Wis, Apr 4, 22; m 44, 68; c 2. PHYSICAL CHEMISTRY. *Educ:* Univ Wis, BS, 45; Purdue Univ, PhD(chem), 51. *Prof Exp:* Asst chemist metall lab, Univ Chicago, 44-46; asst, Purdue Univ, 46-48, asst instr, 48-50; assoc chemist, 50-75, CHEMIST, AGRONNE NAT LAB, 75- *Mem:* AAAS; Health Physics Soc; Am Chem Soc. *Res:* Analytical chemistry; radiochemistry; environmental chemistry. *Mailing Add:* Argonne Nat Lab 9700 S Cass Ave Argonne IL 60439

SEDMAN, YALE S, b Detroit, Mich, May 22, 29; m 55; c 3. ENTOMOLOGY. *Educ:* Ariz State Univ, BS, 50; Univ Utah, MS, 52; Univ Wis, PhD(entom), 55. *Prof Exp:* Asst entom, Univ Utah, 50-52; asst, Univ Wis, 52-54; from asst prof to assoc prof, 55-65, PROF BIOL SCI, WESTERN ILL UNIV, 65- *Mem:* Soc Syst Zool. *Res:* Systematics of Diptera, especially family Syrphidae. *Mailing Add:* Dept of Biol Sci Western Ill Univ Macomb IL 61455

SEDNEY, R(AYMOND), b McKeesport, Pa, Dec 16, 27; m 50; c 9. FLUID DYNAMICS, APPLIED MATHEMATICS. *Educ:* Carnegie Inst Technol, BS, 48, MS, 50, DSc(math), 51. *Prof Exp:* Asst math, Carnegie Inst Technol, 48-51; aerodynamicist, Douglas Aircraft Co, 51-53; mathematician, Res Lab Br, Aberdeen Proving Ground, US Dept Army, 53-55, from res engr to chief wind tunnel br, Ballistic Res Lab, 55-66; prin res scientist, Res Inst Advan Study, Martin Marietta Corp, Md, 66-71; res physicist, 71-76, CHIEF FLUID DYNAMICS RES GROUP, BALLISTIC RES LAB, ABERDEEN PROVING GROUND, 76- *Mem:* Am Inst Aeronaut & Astronaut; Am Phys Soc. *Res:* Fluid mechanics; flow visualization; heat transfer. *Mailing Add:* Launch & Flight Div Ballistics Res Labs Aberdeen Proving Ground MD 21005

SEDOR, EDWARD ANDREW, b East Chicago, Ind, June 24, 39. ORGANIC CHEMISTRY. *Educ:* Lake Forest Col, Ill, BA, 61; Mich State Univ, PhD(org chem), 66. *Prof Exp:* Res chemist, Archer-Daniels-Midland Co, 65-67, sr res chemist, 67-73; MKT COORDR, ASHLAND CHEM CO, 73-, GROUP LEADER ADDITIVE CHEM, 74-; SECT MGR, SHEREX CHEM CO, 79- *Mem:* Am Chem Soc; Am Oil Chemists's Soc. *Res:* Fundamental chemistry, processing technology and applications research of fatty derivatives including amines, alcohols, quaternaries andesters; applications areas-emulsifiers, surfactants; plasticizers, mining technology, fabric softeners. *Mailing Add:* Sherex Chem Co Box 646 Dublin OH 43017

SEDRA, ADEL S, b Egypt, Nov 2, 43. ELECTRONICS, CIRCUIT THEORY. *Educ:* Cairo Univ, BSc, 64; Univ Toronto, MASc, 68, PhD(elec eng), 69. *Prof Exp:* Instr & res engr, Cairo Univ, 64-66; from asst prof to assoc prof, 69-78, PROF ELEC ENG, UNIV TORONTO, 78- *Concurrent Pos:* Consult, Elec Eng Consociates Ltd, 69-; Nat Res Coun Can grant, Univ Toronto, 69-; assoc ed, Inst Elec & Electronics Engrs Trans Circuits & Systs, 81- *Mem:* Inst Elec & Electronics Engrs. *Res:* Electronic circuit design; active network theory and design; active filters; analog and digital instrumentation; digital filters; switched-capacitor networks; computer-aided design; speech recognition. *Mailing Add:* Dept of Elec Eng Univ of Toronto Toronto ON M5S 1A4 Can

SEDRANSK, JOSEPH HENRY, b New York, NY, Mar 3, 38; m 67. STATISTICS. *Educ:* Univ Pa, BS, 58; Harvard Univ, PhD(statist), 64. *Prof Exp:* From asst prof to assoc prof statist, Iowa State Univ, 63-69; from assoc prof to prof, Univ Wis-Madison, 69-74; prof statist sci, State Univ NY Buffalo, 74-78; PROF MATH & STATIST, STATE UNIV NY ALBANY, 78- *Mem:* Inst Math Statist; Am Statist Asn. *Res:* Theory of sampling from finite populations; Bayesian methods; fisheries and forestry statistics. *Mailing Add:* Dept of Math State Univ of NY Albany NY 12222

SEDRIKS, ARISTIDE JOHN, b Riga, Latvia, May 15, 38; m 62; c 3. CORROSION, METALLURGY. *Educ:* Univ Wales, BSc, 59, PhD(phys metall), 62. *Prof Exp:* Res scientist, Defense Standards Labs, Sydney, 62-66; head, Metall Dept, Martin-Marietta Labs, Baltimore, 66-71; CORROSION SECT MGR, INT NICKEL, INC, SUFFERN, 71- *Concurrent Pos:* Corrosion adv comt mem, Elec Power Res Inst, 78- *Mem:* Nat Asn Corrosion Engrs. *Res:* Electrochemistry; fracture; failure analysis; nickel alloys; stainless steels; light alloys. *Mailing Add:* Int Nickel Co Inc Sterling Forest Suffern NY 10901

SEE, JOHN BRUCE, b Newcastle, Australia, July 15, 43; m 69; c 3. PYROMETALLURGY, PROCESS METALLURGY. *Educ:* Univ New South Wales, BSc, 65, PhD(metall), 71. *Prof Exp:* Asst prof metall & mat sci, Mass Inst Technol, 70-74; res group leader pyrometall, Nat Inst Metall, Johannesburg, 74-78; ASSOC PROF METALL ENG, MACKAY SCH MINES, UNIV NEV, 78- *Concurrent Pos:* Vis scientist, Francis Bitter Nat Magnet Lab, 72-74; mem, Phys Chem Comt, Extractive Metall Div, Am Inst Metall Engrs, 73-74; lectr, Dept Metall, Univ Witwatersrand, South Africa, 76-78. *Mem:* Am Inst Metall Engrs; Brit Inst Mining & Metall; Brit Inst Metall. *Res:* Pyrometallurgy, atomization of liquid metals; production of ferro-alloys; copper losses to slags. *Mailing Add:* Dept of Chem & Metall Eng Univ of Nev Reno NV 89557

SEEBACH, J ARTHUR, JR, b Philadelphia, Pa, May 17, 38; m 59. MATHEMATICS. *Educ:* Gettysburg Col, BA, 59; Northwestern Univ, MA, 62, PhD(math), 68. *Prof Exp:* Asst prof math, 65-71, ASSOC PROF MATH, ST OLAF COL, 71- *Concurrent Pos:* Vis assoc prof, Swiss Fed Inst Technol, 70; assoc ed, Am Math Monthly, 70-; ed, Math Mag, 76- *Mem:* Am Math Soc; Math Asn Am. *Res:* Algebraic topology, especially categorical homotopy and category theory; point set topology. *Mailing Add:* Dept of Math St Olaf Col Northfield MN 55057

SEEBASS, A RICHARD, III, b Denver, Colo, Mar 27, 36; m 58; c 2. AERODYNAMICS, APPLIED MATHEMATICS. *Educ:* Princeton Univ, BSE, 58, MSE, 61; Cornell Univ, PhD(aerospace eng), 62. *Prof Exp:* From asst prof to assoc prof aerospace eng, Cornell Univ, 62-75, assoc dean res & grad progs, 72-75; PROF AEROSPACE & MECH ENG & MATH, UNIV

ARIZ, 75- *Concurrent Pos:* Consult, Inst Defense Anal, 64-65, Dept Transp, 67-71, Gen Appl Sci Labs, 68-, Flow Res, 76 & Boeing Co; consult, Nat Acad Sci, 67-70, mem comt on SST-Sonic Boom, 70-71; mem staff, NASA Hq, 66-67; adv, Interagency Aircraft Noise Abatement Prog, 68-70; fac assoc, Boeing Sci Res Labs, 70; assoc ed, Physics of Fluids; mem, NASA RTAC panel on basic res, 74-77; mem Nat Res Coun Aeronaut & Space Eng Bd & Air Force Studies Bd, 77- *Mem:* AAAS; assoc fel Am Inst Aeronaut & Astronaut; Soc Indust & Appl Math; Am Soc Mech Engrs. *Res:* Aerodynamics and fluid mechanics. *Mailing Add:* Dept of Aerospace & Mech Eng Univ of Ariz Tucson AZ 85721

SEEBOHM, PAUL MINOR, b Cincinnati, Ohio, Jan 13, 16; m 42; c 1. MEDICINE. *Educ:* Univ Cincinnati, AB, 38, MD, 41; Am Bd Internal Med, cert allergy. *Prof Exp:* Asst resident physician, Cincinnati Gen Hosp, 46-48; resident allergy, Roosevelt Hosp, New York, 48-49; assoc internal med, 49-51, dir allergy clin, 49-70, from asst prof to assoc prof internal med, 51-59, PROF INTERNAL MED, COL MED, UNIV IOWA, 59-, EXEC ASSOC DEAN COL, 70- *Concurrent Pos:* Mem spec med adv group, Vet Admin, 72-76; chmn allergenic extract rev panel, Food & Drug Admin, 74; pres, Iowa State Bd Health, 76-78; mem bd dirs, Iowa Health Systs Agency, 76-80. *Mem:* Fel Am Col Physicians; Cent Soc Clin Res; fel Am Acad Allergy (secy, pres, 66). *Res:* Pulmonary function in chronic respiratory disease. *Mailing Add:* Univ of Iowa Col of Med Iowa City IA 52240

SEEBURGER, GEORGE HAROLD, b Phillips, Wis, July 20, 35; m 59; c 2. SCIENCE EDUCATION, BIOLOGY. *Educ:* Wis State Univ, Stevens Point, BS, 57; Univ Ga, MEd, 62, EdD(sci educ), 64. *Prof Exp:* Teacher high sch, Wis, 57-60; from asst prof to assoc prof, 64-76, PROF BIOL, UNIV WIS-WHITEWATER, 76- *Mem:* Am Inst Biol Sci; Am Soc Mammal; Am Soc Ichthyologists & Herpetologists. *Res:* Preparation of high school biology teachers; ichthyology, fishes of Wisconsin; mammalogy. *Mailing Add:* Dept of Biol Univ of Wis Whitewater WI 53190

SEED, HARRY BOLTON, b Bolton, Eng, Aug 19, 22; US citizen; m 53; c 2. SOIL MECHANICS, EARTHQUAKE ENGINEERING. *Educ:* King's Col, London, BSc, 43, PhD(civil eng), 47; Harvard Univ, SM, 48. *Prof Exp:* Asst lectr civil eng, King's Col, London, 43-47; instr soil mech, Grad Sch Eng, Harvard Univ, 48-49; found engr, Thomas Worcester, Inc, Mass, 49-50; from asst prof to assoc prof, 50-60, PROF CIVIL ENG, UNIV CALIF, BERKELEY, 60- *Concurrent Pos:* Mem, US Del Soil & Found Engr, USSR, 59; mem, Hwy Res Bd, Nat Acad Sci-Nat Res Coun, 60-, exec comt dept soils geol & found, 63-66; mem comt Alaskan earthquake, Nat Acad Sci, 64-; mem comt earthquake eng res, Nat Acad Eng, 66-68; mem US Comt Large Dams & Earthquake Eng Res Inst; consult, State Calif Dept Water Resources, 62-, US Bur Reclamation, 64-66, NASA, 65-68, Oak Ridge Nat Lab, 65-, US Secy Interior, 66-68, US Army Corps Engr, 67- & Venezuela, 67- *Honors & Awards:* Middlebrook Award, Am Soc Civil Engrs, 58, 64, 66, 71, Thomas Fitch Rowland Award, 61, Res Prize, 62, Croes Medal, 62, 64, Norman Medal, 68, Wellington Prize, 68. *Mem:* Nat Acad Eng; Am Soc Civil Engrs; Am Soc Testing & Mat; Seismol Soc Am. *Res:* Strength and deformation characteristics of soils under static, dynamic and earthquake loading conditions; field behavior of soils, foundations and earth structures under static and earthquake loadings. *Mailing Add:* 441 Davis Hall Univ of Calif Berkeley CA 94720

SEED, JOHN RICHARD, b Paterson, NJ, Apr 27, 37; m 59; c 2. MICROBIOLOGY, PARASITOLOGY. *Educ:* Lafayette Col, AB, 59; Yale Univ, PhD(microbiol), 63. *Prof Exp:* Res assoc biol, Haverford Col, 62-63; from asst prof to assoc prof, Tulane Univ, 65-73, prof, 73-74; PROF BIOL & HEAD DEPT BIOL, MICROBIOL & PARASITOL LAB, TEX A&M UNIV, 74- *Concurrent Pos:* Am Cancer Soc fel, 62-63. *Mem:* Fel AAAS; Am Inst Biol Sci; Am Soc Microbiol; Soc Protozool; Am Soc Parasitol. *Res:* Immunological and physiological studies on parasitic protozoan infections, especially African trypanosomiasis. *Mailing Add:* Dept of Biol Tex A&M Univ College Station TX 77843

SEED, RANDOLPH WILLIAM, b Chicago, Ill, May 1, 33; m 68; c 5. SURGERY, BIOCHEMISTRY. *Educ:* Harvard Univ, BA, 54; Univ Chicago, MD, 60, PhD(biochem), 65. *Prof Exp:* chmn dept surg, Grant Hosp, Chicago, 70-76; ASST PROF SURG, MED SCH, NORTHWESTERN UNIV, 71- *Concurrent Pos:* Attend surg, Vet Admin Res Hosp, Chicago, 68- *Mem:* Am Thyroid Asn. *Res:* Human thyroid cancer; human thyroid tissue culture and biosynthesis of thyroglobulin. *Mailing Add:* Prudential Plaza Chicago IL 60601

SEED, THOMAS MICHAEL, microbiology, see previous edition

SEEDS, MICHAEL AUGUST, b Danville, Ill, Dec 14, 42. ASTRONOMY. *Educ:* Univ Ill, Urbana, BS, 65; Ind Univ, Bloomington, MS & PhD(astron), 70. *Prof Exp:* ASST PROF ASTRON, FRANKLIN & MARSHALL COL, 70- *Mem:* AAAS; Am Astron Soc; Royal Astron Soc. *Res:* Photometry of short period variable stars and eclipsing binaries; narrow band photometry; undergraduate astronomy instruction, methods and materials. *Mailing Add:* J R Grundy Observ Franklin & Marshall Col Lancaster PA 17604

SEEDS, NICHOLAS WARREN, b Circleville, Ohio, Dec 25, 42; m 64; c 2. BIOCHEMISTRY. *Educ:* Univ NMex, BS, 64; Univ Iowa, PhD(biochem), 68. *Prof Exp:* NSF fel, NIH, 68-70; ASSOC PROF BIOPHYS & GENETICS, MED CTR, UNIV COLO, DENVER, 70- *Mem:* Am Soc Biol Chemists; AAAS; Am Soc Cell Biol. *Res:* Developmental neurobiology; microtubules. *Mailing Add:* Dept of Biochem/Biophys & Genetics Univ of Colo Denver CO 80220

SEEFELDT, VERN DENNIS, b Lena, Wis. ANATOMY. *Educ:* Wis State Univ, La Crosse, BS, 55; Univ Wis, PhD(phys educ). *Prof Exp:* Asst prof phys educ, Mich State Univ, 66-69; asst prof, Univ Wis-Madison, 69-71; assoc prof, 71-76, PROF PHYS EDUC, MICH STATE UNIV, 76- *Concurrent Pos:* Dir, Youth Sports Inst. *Mem:* Am Asn Health, Phys Educ & Recreation; Soc Study Human Biol. *Res:* Motor development; interrelationship of physical growth, motor development and academic achievement in pre-school and elementary aged clildren. *Mailing Add:* Room 213 Women's Intramural Bldg Mich State Univ East Lansing MI 48824

SEEFRIED, ADOLF VON, cell physiology, virology, see previous edition

SEEGAL, RICHARD FIELD, b Newport, RI, Feb 13, 45; m 69; c 2. PHYSIOLOGICAL PSYCHOLOGY. *Educ:* Brown Univ, AB, 66; Emory Univ, MA, 70; Univ Ga, PhD(physiol psychol), 72. *Prof Exp:* Fel endocrinol biobehav sci, Univ Conn, 72-74; res assoc neurochem, Dept Pharmacol, Mich State Univ, 77-78; RES SCIENTIST VIROL, NY STATE DEPT HEALTH, 74- *Mem:* AAAS; Soc Neurosciences. *Res:* Interaction of central nervous system infection, viruses, with behavior and neurochemistry and neuroendocrinology; behavior endocrine interactions. *Mailing Add:* Div of Lab & Res NY State Dept of Health Albany NY 12201

SEEGER, CHARLES RONALD, b Columbus, Ohio, Jan 31, 31; m 61; c 2. STRUCTURAL GEOLOGY, GEOPHYSICS. *Educ:* Ohio State Univ, BSc, 53; George Washington Univ, MS, 58; Univ Pittsburgh, PhD(earth & planetary sci), 66. *Prof Exp:* Analyst, Weapons Systs Eval Div, Inst Defense Anal, 58-60; earth sci analyst, Sci & Tech Intel Ctr, US Navy, 60-63; Nat Acad Sci-Nat Res Coun fel, NASA-Goddard Space Flight Ctr, 66-68; from asst prof to assoc prof, 68-77, PROF GEOL & GEOPHYS, WESTERN KY UNIV, 77- *Mem:* AAAS; Am Geophys Union; Geol Soc Am; Meteoritical Soc. *Res:* Geological and geophysical invesiigations of astroblemes, cryptoexplosion structures, volcanic and impact craters and other geological structures; tectonics of plate boundaries; lunar geology and geochemistry; planetology. *Mailing Add:* Dept of Geog & Geol Western Ky Univ Bowling Green KY 42101

SEEGER, PHILIP ANTHONY, b Evanston, Ill, Feb 19, 37; m 59; c 3. PHYSICS OF MATERIALS. *Educ:* Rice Inst, BA, 58; Calif Inst Technol, PhD(physics), 63. *Prof Exp:* Res fel low energy nuclear physics, Calif Inst Technol, 62-64; STAFF MEM WEAPONS NEUTRON RES FACIL, LOS ALAMOS SCI LAB, 64- *Mem:* Am Phys Soc; Int Astron Union. *Res:* Calculation of stellar nucleosynthesis and the semiempirical atomic mass law; neutron time-of-flight experiments in nuclear physics, materials science and biophysics. *Mailing Add:* Los Alamos Sci Lab PO Box 1663 MS 805 Los Alamos NM 87545

SEEGER, ROBERT CHARLES, b Salem, Ore, May 9, 40; m 64; c 1. IMMUNOLOGY, PEDIATRICS. *Educ:* Willamette Univ, BA, 62; Univ Ore, MS & MD, 66. *Prof Exp:* Pediat intern, Med Sch, Univ Minn, 66-67, resident, 67-68; clin assoc immunol, NIH, 68-72; spec fel tumor immunol, Nat Cancer Inst, Univ Col, Univ London, 72-74; asst prof, 74-77, ASSOC PROF PEDIAT IMMUNOL, UNIV CALIF, LOS ANGELES, 77- *Concurrent Pos:* Res career develop award, Nat Cancer Inst, 75. *Mem:* Am Asn Cancer Res; Soc Pediat Res; Am Asn Immunologists. *Res:* Pediatric tumor immunology; childhood neuroblastoma with studies of tumor associated antigens; immune responses which kill tumor cells; chemo-immunotherapy in nude mice; human monocyte subsets. *Mailing Add:* Dept of Pediat Univ of Calif Sch of Med Los Angeles CA 90024

SEEGERS, WALTER HENRY, b Fayette Co, Iowa, Jan 4, 10; m 35; c 1. PHYSIOLOGY, BIOCHEMISTRY. *Educ:* Univ Iowa, BA, 31, MS, 32, PhD(biochem), 34. *Hon Degrees:* ScD, Wartburg Col, 53 & Med Col Ohio, 78; MD, Justus Liebig Univ, Ger, 74. *Prof Exp:* Res assoc nutrit, Univ Iowa, 34-35, res assoc path, 37-42; res assoc nutrit & nitrogen metab, Antioch Col, 36-37; res, Parke, Davis & Co, Mich, 42-45; from assoc prof physiol to prof, 45-48, chmn dept physiol & pharmacol, 46-73, SEEGERS PROF PHYSIOL & PHARMACOL, SCH MED, WAYNE STATE UNIV, 48-, TRAITEL PROF HEMAT, 64-, CHMN DEPT PHYSIOL, 73- *Concurrent Pos:* Prof, Univ Detroit, 46-50; vis prof, Baylor Univ, 50; Brown mem lectr, Am Heart Asn, 49, Harvey lectr, 52; Reilly lectr, Notre Dame Univ, 59; John G Gibson, II lectr, Col Physicians & Surgeons, Columbia Univ, 60; Behringwerke lectr, Marburg/Lahn, Ger, 62; Lakey hon lectr, Rho Chi, 64; Beaumont lectr, Wayne County Med Soc, 66; Nat Sci Coun vis prof, Nat Taiwan Univ, 75. Chmn panel blood coagulation, Nat Res Coun, 53-57; USPHS res grants, Univ Detroit; Sigma Xi res award, 57; Commonwealth Fund res award, 57-58; Henry Ford Hosp chmn, Nat Comt Platelet Conf, 60; mem, Ctr Health Educ, 61; mem, Mayor's Comt Rehab Narcotic Addicts, Detroit, 61-75; hon mem fac med, Univ Chile; mem bd regents, Wartburg Col, 66-; Shirley Johnson Greenwalt mem lectr. *Honors & Awards:* Co-recipient, Ward Burdick Award, Am Soc Clin Pathologists, 50 & James F Mitchell Found Award, 69; Am Nat Red Cross Sci Adv Bd Centennial Recognition, 69; Mich Minuteman Governor's Award, 73; H P Smith Award, Am Soc Clin Pathologists. *Mem:* Am Physiol Soc; Int Soc Hemat; fel Am Inst Chemists; fel Am Soc Clin Pharmacol & Therapeut; fel NY Acad Sci. *Res:* Nutrition; vitamins; protein metabolism; isolation and chemical characterization of plasma proteins; mechanisms of blood clotting; integrative physiology; hemostatic agents. *Mailing Add:* Dept of Physiol Wayne State Univ Detroit MI 48201

SEEGMILLER, DAVID W, b Nephi, Utah, Jan 6, 34; m 54; c 4. ELECTROCHEMISTRY. *Educ:* Brigham Young Univ, BS, 56, MS, 58; Univ Calif, Berkeley, PhD(nuclear chem), 63. *Prof Exp:* US Air Force, 58-, nuclear res officer, 58-60, from assoc prof to prof chem, US Air Force Acad, 62-76, dep dept head, 75-76, chief scientist, US Air Force European Off Aerospace Res & Develop, London, 76-78, dep dept head, 78-80, PROF & ACTG HEAD DEPT CHEM & BIOL SCI, US AIR FORCE ACAD, 80- *Concurrent Pos:* Res & Develop Award, US Air Force, 71. *Mem:* Am Chem Soc. *Res:* Electrochemistry and physical chem of fused salt systems; nuclear chemistry and reactions; thermochemical measurements; high energy-density batteries. *Mailing Add:* Dept of Chem & Biol Sci US Air Force Acad CO 80840

SEEGMILLER, JARVIS EDWIN, b St George, Utah, June 22, 20; m 50; c 4. BIOCHEMISTRY. *Educ:* Univ Utah, AB, 42; Univ Chicago, MD, 48. *Prof Exp:* Asst, US Bur Mines, Utah, 41; asst, Nat Defense Res Comt, Northwestern Tech Inst, 42-44; asst med, Univ Chicago, 47-48; intern, Marburg Div, Hopkins Hosp, 48-49; biochemist, Nat Inst Arthritis & Metab Dis, 49-51; res assoc, Thorndike Mem Lab, Harvard Med Sch, 52-53; vis investr, Pub Health Res Inst, NY, 53-54; chief sect human biochem genetics & asst sci dir, Nat Inst Arthritis & Metab Dis, 54-69; PROF DEPT MED & DIR DIV RHEUMATOLOGY, SCH MED, UNIV CALIF, SAN DIEGO, 69- *Concurrent Pos:* Vis scientist, Univ Col Hosp Sch Med, London, 64-65; vis scientist, Basel Inst Immunol, Switz & Sir William Dunn Sch Path, Oxford, Eng, 75-76. *Mem:* Nat Acad Sci; Harvey Soc; Am Soc Biol Chemists; Am Rheumatism Asn; Am Fedn Clin Res. *Res:* Enzymology; intermediary carbohydrate and purine metabolism; biochemistry of liver disease; hereditary metabolic diseases; arthritis; human genetics. *Mailing Add:* Dept Med M-013 Sch Med Univ Calif La Jolla CA 92093

SEEGMILLER, ROBERT EARL, b Salt Lake City, Utah, July 8, 43; m 63; c 7. EMBRYOLOGY. *Educ:* Univ Utah, BS, 65, MS, 67; McGill Univ, PhD(genetics), 70. *Prof Exp:* Res assoc develop biol, Univ Colo, 70-72; assoc prof, 72-80, PROF ZOOL, BRIGHAM YOUNG UNIV, 80- *Concurrent Pos:* Dipl, Pharmaceut Mfrs Asn Found, 70-72; res starter grant, 73; Basil O'Connor res starter grant, Nat Found March of Dimes, 74-76. *Mem:* Teratology Soc; Soc Develop Biol. *Res:* Drug and gene induced defects of the endochondral skeleton in relation to limb and palate development in laboratory animals; epidemiological assessment of birth defects in human populations. *Mailing Add:* Dept of Zool Brigham Young Univ Provo UT 84601

SEEHRA, MOHINDAR SINGH, b W Pakistan, Feb 14, 40; m 63; c 2. SOLID STATE PHYSICS. *Educ:* Punjab Univ, India, BSc, 59; Aligarh Muslin Univ, MSc, 62; Univ Rochester, PhD(physics), 69. *Prof Exp:* Lab instr chem, Arya Col, India, 59-60; lectr physics, Jain Col, India, 62-63; from asst prof to assoc prof, 69-77, PROF PHYSICS, WVA UNIV, 77- *Concurrent Pos:* Alfred P Sloan Found res fel, 73-76; NSF & Dept of Energy res grants. *Mem:* Am Phys Soc. *Res:* Phase transitions and critical phenomena; magnetic resonance and spin-spin relaxation; magnetic optical and transport properties; properties of pyrite and other minerals in coal. *Mailing Add:* Dept of Physics WVa Univ Morgantown WV 26506

SEELAND, DAVID ARTHUR, b St Paul, Minn, Nov 14, 36; m 61; c 2. GEOLOGY. *Educ:* Univ Minn, BA, 59, MS, 61; Univ Utah, PhD(geol), 68. *Prof Exp:* GEOLOGIST, US GEOL SURV, 61-63 & 67- *Mem:* Geol Soc Am; Soc Econ Paleont & Mineral. *Res:* Sedimentology, particularly early Paleozoic marine shelf paleocurrents and depositional environments of Tertiary fluvial rocks; structure and stratigraphy of the northern Rocky Mountains. *Mailing Add:* US Geol Surv Box 25046 Fed Ctr Denver CO 80225

SEELBACH, CHARLES WILLIAM, b Buffalo, NY, Dec 13, 23; m 46; c 3. POLYMER CHEMISTRY, INDUSTRIAL CHEMISTRY. *Educ:* Cornell Univ, AB, 48; Case Western Reserve Univ, MS, 51; Purdue Univ, PhD, 55. *Prof Exp:* Res chemist, Standard Oil Co, Ohio, 48-52; anal chemist, Purdue Univ, 52-55; res chemist, Esso Res & Eng Co, 55-57, asst sect head res lab, Esso Standard Oil Co, 57-58, sect head explor res, Esso Res & Eng Co, 58-61, chem coordr, Esso Int, Inc, 61-63, mgr polymers div, Esso Chem Co, Inc, NY, 63-66, mgr elastomers new investments & planning div, 66-67; dir indust chem develop, 67-69, dir hydrocarbon raw mat develop, 69-71, mgr com develop plastics dept, 71-77, MGR COM DEVELOP PETROCHEM DEVELOP DEPT, USS CHEM DIV, US STEEL CORP, 77- *Mem:* AAAS; Am Oil Chem Soc; NY Acad Sci; Soc Plastics Indust; Com Develop Asn. *Res:* Hydrocarbon stability; synthesis antioxidants; liquid thermal diffusion; separation of hydrocarbons and lipids; polymerization catalysis; plastic and elastomer synthesis; chemical intermediate syntheses; metal alkyl derivatives; olefin-diolefin derivatives; oxygenated derivatives. *Mailing Add:* USS Chem Div Rm 2858 US Steel Corp 600 Grant St Pittsburgh PA 15230

SEELEY, DONALD BERNARD, b Stratford, Conn, Nov 29, 20; m 43. MICROBIOLOGY. *Educ:* UnivConn, BS, 42; Univ Mass, MS, 47, PhD(bact), 49. *Prof Exp:* Chg bact labs antibiotic screening, Chas Pfizer & Co, Conn, 49, dir biol labs, 50-61, HEAD, FERMENTATION DEVELOP LABS, CHEM PROD RES & DEVELOP, PFIZER, INC, 61- *Honors & Awards:* Eli Lilly Award, 50. *Mem:* Soc Indust Microbiol. *Res:* Quaternary ammonium germicides; antibiotic research and production; organic acids. *Mailing Add:* Fermentation Res & Develop Pfizer Inc Eastern Point Rd Groton CT 06340

SEELEY, HARRY WILBUR, b Bridgeport, Conn, Mar 5, 17; m 40; c 3. BACTERIOLOGY. *Educ:* Univ Conn, BS, 41, MS, 42; Cornell Univ, PhD(bact), 47. *Prof Exp:* Instr dairy sci, Univ Conn, 43-45; from asst prof to assoc prof bact, 47-55, chmn sect microbiol, div biol sci, 64-68, actg chmn dept microbiol, 77-78, PROF BACT, CORNELL UNIV, 55- *Concurrent Pos:* Guggenheim fel, 58. *Mem:* Am Soc Microbiol; Am Acad Microbiol; Brit Soc Gen Microbiol; Brit Soc Appl Bact. *Res:* Classification and physiology of lactic acid bacteria and related organisms; microbial nutrition; aquatic microbiology. *Mailing Add:* Dept Microbiol Cornell Univ Ithaca NY 14850

SEELEY, JOHN GEORGE, b North Bergen, NJ, Dec 21, 15; m; c 5. FLORICULTURE. *Educ:* Rutgers Univ, BSc, 37, MSc, 40; Cornell Univ, PhD(floricult), 48. *Prof Exp:* Asst, NJ Exp Sta, 37-40, garden supt, 40-41; res instr floricult, Cornell Univ, 41-43; asst agronomist bur plant indust, Soils & Agr Eng, USDA, Ga, 43-44; chemist in charge rubber mat lab, Wright Aeronaut Corp, NJ, 44-45; res instr floricult, Cornell Univ, 45-48, asst prof, 48-49; prof, Pa State Univ, 49-56; head dept, 56-70, PROF FLORICULT, CORNELL UNIV, 56- *Honors & Awards:* Soc Am Florists Outstanding Res Award, 65; Leonard Vaughan Res Award, 50. *Mem:* Am Acad Florists; AAAS; fel Am Soc Hort Sci; Int Soc Hort Sci. *Res:* Nutrition and plant physiology; soils; soil aeration; light and temperature. *Mailing Add:* Dept of Floricult Cornell Univ Ithaca NY 14853

SEELEY, MILLARD GARFIELD, b Tucson, Ariz, Aug 2, 15. ORGANIC CHEMISTRY. *Educ:* Univ Ariz, BS, 38, MS, 39; Stanford Univ, PhD(org chem), 48. *Prof Exp:* Instr chem, Univ Ariz, 39-42; res chemist, B F Goodrich Co, 42-45; from instr to assoc prof, 45-58, prof, 58-80, EMER PROF CHEM, UNIV ARIZ, 80- *Concurrent Pos:* Cottrell grant, Res Corp, NY. *Mem:* Assoc Am Chem Soc. *Res:* Ultraviolet spectroscopy of organic isomers; composition and constitution of gums and mucilages. *Mailing Add:* Dept of Chem Univ of Ariz Tucson AZ 85721

SEELEY, ROBERT D, b Kansas City, Kans, May 15, 23; m 46; c 3. PHYSICAL CHEMISTRY. *Educ:* Tex A&I Univ, BS, 50, MS, 51; Wayne State Univ, PhD(phys chem), 59. *Prof Exp:* Asst instr chem, Tex A&I Univ, 50-51; instr gen sci & chem, McCook Jr Col, 51-52; asst instr chem, Wayne State Univ, 53-54; mat engr tire div, US Rubber Co, 54-59; sr chemist, Chemstrand Res Ctr, Inc, 59-62; staff mem high polymer res, Sandia Corp, 62-65; assoc prof chem, 65-68, PROF CHEM, CENT MO STATE UNIV, 68- *Mem:* AAAS; Sigma Xi. *Res:* Structural, surface and performance characteristics of high polymers; chemical sorption; reaction kinetics phenomena studies. *Mailing Add:* RR 3 Box 176 Warrensburg MO 64093

SEELEY, ROBERT DUDLEY, b North Bergen, NJ, Mar 9, 19; m 45; c 4. BIOCHEMISTRY. *Educ:* Rutgers Univ, BS, 40, PhD(biochem), 45. *Prof Exp:* Asst res specialist, Rutgers Univ, 45-47; instr biochem col pharm 45-46; head nutrit lab, Anheuser-Busch, Inc, 47-50, dir yeast sect, 50-54, assoc dir res, 54-75, dir yeast prod res, 75-81; tech dir, S&R Food Co, Inc, 73-81; RETIRED. *Mem:* AAAS; Soc Exp Biol & Med; Am Asn Cereal Chem; Inst Food Technol; Am Chem Soc. *Res:* Protein metabolism; protein and vitamin nutrition; yeast, other microbiological fermentations and SCP, yeast isolates, protein, glycan and extracts; bakery, egg and other food products. *Mailing Add:* Box 813 Payson AZ 85541

SEELEY, ROD R, b Rupert, Idaho, Dec 29, 45; m 65; c 2. REPRODUCTIVE PHYSIOLOGY. *Educ:* Idaho State Univ, BS, 68; Utah State Univ, MS, 71, PhD(physiol), 73. *Prof Exp:* Asst prof, 73-77, ASSOC PROF PHYSIOL, IDAHO STATE UNIV, 77-, ASSOC PROF BIOL, 80- *Mem:* AAAS; Sigma Xi; Soc Study Reprod. *Res:* The study of neural and endocrine mechanisms that regulate smooth-muscle motility in the testicular capsule and neural and endocrine mechanisms that control ovulation. *Mailing Add:* Dept of Biol Idaho State Univ Pocatello ID 83209

SEELEY, SCHUYLER DRANNAN, b Huntington, Utah, Aug 5, 39; m 62; c 5. PLANT CHEMISTRY. *Educ:* Brigham Young Univ, BS, 64; Utah State Univ, MS, 67; Cornell Univ, PhD(pomol), 71. *Prof Exp:* Res assoc pomol, Cornell Univ, 71; asst prof, 71-77, ASSOC PROF PLANT SCI, UTAH STATE UNIV, 77- *Honors & Awards:* J H Gourley Medal, Am Soc Hort Sci, 75. *Mem:* Am Soc Hort Sci. *Res:* Hormonal physiology of fruit tree dormancy; mathematical modeling of chill units and growing degree hours for fruit tree physiodates; instrumental ultramicroanalysis of plant hormones. *Mailing Add:* Dept of Plant Sci UMC 48 Utah State Univ Logan UT 84322

SEELEY, THOMAS DYER, b Bellefonte, Pa, June 17, 52; m 79. BEHAVIORAL ECOLOGY, SOCIOBIOLOGY. *Educ:* Dartmouth Col, AB, 74; Harvard Univ, PhD(biol), 78. *Prof Exp:* Jr fel, Soc Fels, Harvard Univ, 78-80; ASST PROF BIOL, YALE UNIV, 80- *Concurrent Pos:* Sci leader, Expedition Thailand, Nat Geog Soc, 79-80. *Mem:* Animal Behav Soc; Int Union Study Social Insects; Int Bee Res Asn. *Res:* Physiological, behavioral, and ecological studies of the biology of social insects, especially the honeybee. *Mailing Add:* Biol Dept Yale Univ PO Box 6666 New Haven CT 06511

SEELIG, MILDRED SYLVIA, b New York, NY, Aug 20, 20; m 41; c 2. MEDICINE, NUTRITION. *Educ:* Hunter Col, AB, 42; NY Med Col, MD, 45; Columbia Univ, MPH, 50. *Prof Exp:* Intern med, Orange County Hosp, Calif, 45-46; health officer, New York Dept Health, 48-50; asst dir med lit, Lederle Labs, Am Cyanamid Co, 51-53, dir, 57-60; assoc med dir med writing, William D McAdams, NY, 54-56; assoc dir clin pharm, E R Squibb & Sons, Inc, 60-65, dir med affairs, Squibb Int, NY, 65-67; dir med affairs, Bristol Int, 67-69; dir biomed anal, Schering Corp, Bloomfield, 69-73; ASST PROF CLIN MED, MED CTR, NY UNIV, 73- *Concurrent Pos:* Pharmacol assoc, New York Med Col, 65-67, adj assoc prof, 67-; res assoc, Maimonides Med Ctr, Brooklyn, 67-; attend physician, Goldwater Mem Hosp, 73- *Mem:* AMA; fel Am Col Nutrit. *Res:* Magnesium; vitamin D; nutritional and steroid factors involved in cardiovascular and renal disease; D-penicillamine therapy of autoimmune diseases; influence of nutritional factors in treatment of chronic diseases; Candida infection and diagnosis. *Mailing Add:* Dept of Clin Med NY Univ New York NY 10016

SEELY, DONALD RANDOLPH, b Santa Rosa, Calif, Jan 15, 28; m 54; c 3. GEOLOGY. *Educ:* Pomona Col, BA, 49; Univ Okla, MS, 55, PhD(geol), 62. *Prof Exp:* Geologist-geophysicist, Standard Oil, Tex, 55-56; instr geol & chmn dept, Okla City Univ, 59-62; RES GEOLOGIST, JERSEY PROD RES CO, CREOLE PETROL CORP, EXXON PROD RES CO, 62- *Mem:* Am Asn Petrol Geologists; Geol Soc Am; Am Geophys Union. *Res:* Structural geology; geology of oceanic trenches; wrench faults; orogenic belts; interpretation of geophysical data. *Mailing Add:* Exxon Prod Res Co PO Box 2189 Houston TX 77001

SEELY, GILBERT RANDALL, b Bellingham, Wash, Jan 18, 29; m 56; c 4. PHYSICAL CHEMISTRY. *Educ:* Harvard Univ, AB, 50; Univ Calif, PhD(chem), 54. *Prof Exp:* Chemist, Gen Elec Co, NY, 53-54; fel boron chem, Univ Wash, Seattle, 56-57; chemist phys chem dept, Shell Develop Co, 57-62; investr, 62, sr res scientist, 62-72, SR INVESTR, C F KETTERING RES LAB, 72- *Mem:* AAAS; Am Chem Soc; Inter-Am Photochem Soc; Am Soc Photobiol; Int Solar Energy Soc. *Res:* Photochemistry of chlorophyll and porphyrins; photochemistry and energy transfer in polymeric systems; environmental applications. *Mailing Add:* C F Kettering Res Lab Yellow Springs OH 45387

SEELY, J RODMAN, b Willard, Utah, July 28, 27; m 55; c 3. PEDIATRICS. *Educ:* Univ Utah, BS, 50, MD, 52, PhD(biol chem), 64. *Prof Exp:* Intern pediat, Salt Lake Gen Hosp, 52-53, asst resident, 53-56; res instr, Col Med, Univ Utah, 57-58; asst prof, Sch Med, Univ Wash, 58-63; assoc prof, 64-76, prof, 76-79, CLIN PROF PEDIAT, SCH MED, UNIV OKLA, 79-; DIR, GENETICS DIAGNOSTIC CTR, PRESBYTARIAN HOSP, OKLAHOMA CITY, 80- *Concurrent Pos:* Asst pediatrician, Salt Lake Gen Hosp, 55-58; dir premature ctr, Univ Hosp, Univ Wash, 60-63. *Mem:* AAAS; Am Acad Pediat; Endocrine Soc; NY Acad Sci. *Res:* Biochemistry; production and metabolism of adrenocortical steroids in normal and abnormal infants and children; human biochemical genetics; cytogenetics; intrauterine diagnosis. *Mailing Add:* Univ Okla Health Sci Ctr PO Box 26901 Oklahoma City OK 73190

SEELY, JUSTUS FRANDSEN, b Mt Pleasant, Utah, Feb 11, 41; m 65; c 3. STATISTICS, MATHEMATICS. *Educ:* Utah State Univ, BS, 63, MS, 65; Iowa State Univ, PhD(statist), 69. *Prof Exp:* Instr appl statist & comput sci, Utah State Univ, 64-65; ASSOC PROF STATIST, ORE STATE UNIV, 69- *Honors & Awards:* George W Snedecor Award, Iowa State Univ, 68. *Mem:* Inst Math Statist; Am Statist Asn. *Res:* Development of statistical computer programs; linear model theory; experimental design; mathematical statistcs. *Mailing Add:* Dept of Statist Ore State Univ Corvallis OR 97331

SEELY, ROBERT T, b Bryn Mawr, Pa, Feb 26, 32; m 58; c 4. MATHEMATICAL ANALYSIS. *Educ:* Haverford Col, BS, 53; Mass Inst Technol, PhD(math), 58. *Prof Exp:* Instr math, Harvey Mudd Col, 58-59, asst prof, 59-61; NATO fel, 61-62; from asst prof to assoc prof, Brandeis Univ, 63-67, prof, 67-72; PROF MATH, UNIV MASS, BOSTON, 72- *Concurrent Pos:* Sloan Found fel, 65-67. *Mem:* Am Math Soc; Math Asn Am. *Res:* Partial differential equations. *Mailing Add:* Dept of Math Univ of Mass Boston MA 02125

SEELY, SAMUEL, b New York, NY, May 7, 09; m 51; c 2. PHYSICS, ELECTRICAL ENGINEERING. *Educ:* Polytech Inst Brooklyn, EE, 31; Stevens Inst Technol, MS, 32; Columbia Univ, PhD(physics), 36. *Prof Exp:* Lectr physics, Polytech Inst Brooklyn, 35; from instr to asst prof elec eng, City Col New York, 36-46; assoc prof electronics, Grad Sch, US Naval Acad, 46-47; prof elec eng, Univ Syracuse, 47-56, chmn dept, 51-56; prof, Case Inst Technol, 56-64, head dept, 56-59; ed consult, 64-67; guest prof, Chalmers Univ Technol & Lund Inst Technol, Sweden, 67-68; vis prof elec eng, Univ Mass, Amherst, 68-69, coordr res & assoc grad dean, Grad Sch, 69-70; prof elec eng, Univ Conn, 71-72; PROF ELEC ENG, UNIV RI, 72- *Concurrent Pos:* Mem staff, Radiation Lab, Mass Inst Technol, 41-46; Fulbright lectr, Athens Polytech, 59-60; head eng sect, NSF, 61-63; vis prof, Johns Hopkins Univ, 65, City Col New York, 66 & Okla State Univ, 67. *Mem:* Fel Am Phys Soc; Am Soc Eng Educ; fel Inst Elec & Electronics Engrs. *Res:* Diamagnetism; nuclear physics; electronic circuits; microwave and longwave antennas; digital systems. *Mailing Add:* RD 1 Clearview Dr Bradford RI 02808

SEEMAN, MARY VIOLETTE, b Lodz, Poland, Mar 24, 35; Can citizen; m 59; c 3. PSYCHIATRY. *Educ:* McGill Univ, BA, 55, MD, 60; FRCPCan, 68. *Prof Exp:* Res psychiatrist, Fullbourne Hosp, Cambridge, 65-67; psychiatrist, Toronto Western Hosp, 67-75; HEAD ACTIVE TREATMENT CLIN, CLARKE INST PSYCHIAT, 75-; assoc prof, 75-80, PROF, UNIV TORONTO, 80- *Mem:* Can Psychiat Asn; Can Med Asn. *Res:* Clinical research in schizophrenia. *Mailing Add:* Clarke Inst of Psychiat 250 College St Toronto ON M5T 1R8 Can

SEEMAN, NADRIAN CHARLES, b Chicago, Ill, Dec 16, 45. MOLECULAR BIOPHYSICS, X-RAY CRYSTALLOGRAPHY. *Educ:* Univ Chicago, BS, 66; Univ Pittsburgh, PhD(biochem, crystallog), 70. *Prof Exp:* Res assoc biol, Columbia Univ, 70-72; Damon Runyon Found fel, Mass Inst Technol, 72-73, NIH fel biophys, 73-76, res assoc biol, 76-77; ASST PROF BIOL, STATE UNIV NY ALBANY, 77- *Honors & Awards:* Sidhu Award, Pittsburgh Diffraction Soc, 74. *Mem:* Am Crystallog Asn. *Res:* Structural aspects of the storage, expression and transmission of biological information; molecular recognition. *Mailing Add:* Dept of Biol State Univ NY Albany NY 12222

SEEMAN, PHILIP, b Winnipeg, Man, Feb 8, 34; m 59; c 3. NEUROPHARMACOLOGY, CELL BIOLOGY. *Educ:* McGill Univ, BSc, 55, MSc, 56, MD, 60; Rockefeller Univ, PhD(life sci), 66. *Prof Exp:* Intern med, Harper Hosp, Detroit, 60-61; from asst prof to assoc prof pharmacol, 67-71, PROF PHARMACOL, UNIV TORONTO, 71-, CHMN DEPT, 77- *Concurrent Pos:* Med Res Coun Can fel, Univ Cambridge, 66-67. *Mem:* AAAS; Am Soc Pharmacol & Exp Therapeut; Biophys Soc; Am Soc Cell Biol; Pharmacol Soc Can. *Res:* Membrane biology; cell actions of anesthetics, tranquilizers and narcotics; nerve-muscle pharmacology; membrane ultrastructure; freeze-etch electron microscopy; biology of schizophrenia; erythrocyte membrane biophysics and physiology. *Mailing Add:* Dept of Pharmacol Univ of Toronto Toronto ON M5S 2R8 Can

SEERLEY, ROBERT WAYNE, b Indianapolis, Ind, Oct 6, 30; m 51; c 2. ANIMAL SCIENCE, ANIMAL NUTRITION. *Educ:* Purdue Univ, BS, 52; Mich State Univ, MS, 57, PhD(animal nutrit), 60. *Prof Exp:* Exten swine specialist, Purdue Univ, 62-54; asst, Mich State Univ, 56-60; from asst prof to assoc prof animal sci, SDak State Univ, 60-67; assoc prof, 67-80, PROF ANIMAL SCI, UNIV GA, 80- *Concurrent Pos:* AID consult, Korea, 65. *Mem:* Am Soc Animal Sci. *Res:* Amino acids, minerals and vitamins in animal nutrition; building design and space requirements for animal environment. *Mailing Add:* Dept of Animal Sci Univ of Ga Athens GA 30601

SEERY, DANIEL J, b Philadelphia, Pa, Dec 17, 33; m 60; c 3. CHEMICAL KINETICS, FUEL SCIENCE. *Educ:* St John's Univ, BS, 55; Pa State Univ, MS, 58, PhD(fuel technol), 62. *Prof Exp:* Fel chem, Univ Minn, 62-64; res scientist, 64-66, sr res scientist kinetics & heat transfer group, 66-77, prin scientist combustion sci sect, 78-81, MGR COMBUSTION SCI, UNITED TECHNOL RES CTR, 81- *Mem:* Am Chem Soc; Am Phys Soc; Combustion Inst. *Res:* Chemical kinetics of combustion behind shock waves and in flames; dissociation of simple molecules; heterogeneous combustion in dust flames; catalytic combustion and combustion generated air pollution. *Mailing Add:* Silver Lane United Technol Res Ctr East Hartford CT 06108

SEERY, VIRGINIA LEE, b New York, NY, July 23, 34. BIOCHEMISTRY. *Educ:* Seton Hill Col, AB, 56; Duke Univ, MA, 58; Univ Wash, PhD(biochem), 68. *Prof Exp:* Res associateship, Ore State Univ, 68-70; NIH trainee, Scripps Clin & Res Found, 70-72; asst prof biochem, Emory Univ, 72-79; ASSOC PROF BIOCHEM, WESTERN ILL UNIV, 79- *Mem:* Am Chem Soc; AAAS. *Res:* Structure, function and interactions of proteins and enzymes; binding of small molecules to macromolecules; allosteric effectors; photoaffinity labeling; application of physical methods such as ultracentrifugation, fluorescence and ultraviolet spectroscopy. *Mailing Add:* Dept Chem Wester Ill Univ Macomb IL 61455

SEEVER, GALEN LATHROP, b Wichita, Kans, Aug 3, 34; m 65; c 1. MATHEMATICS. *Educ:* Univ Kans, AB, 56, MA, 57; Univ Calif, Berkeley, PhD(math), 63. *Prof Exp:* Lectr math, Univ Calif, Los Angeles, 63-65; asst prof, Calif Inst Technol, 65-68; vis assoc prof, 68-70, ASSOC PROF MATH, UNIV TEX, AUSTIN, 70- *Res:* Functional analysis. *Mailing Add:* Dept of Math Univ of Tex Austin TX 78712

SEEVERS, DELMAR OSWELL, b St John, Kans, June 26, 19; m 43; c 1. PHYSICS. *Educ:* Duke Univ, BS, 41, PhD, 51. *Prof Exp:* Physicist, Bur Ord, US Dept Navy, 41-45; teaching assoc physics, Duke Univ, 46-51; res physicist, 51-55, sr res physicist, 55-56, res assoc, 56-60, SR RES ASSOC PHYSICS, CHEVRON RES CO, 60- *Mem:* Am Phys Soc. *Res:* Cosmic rays; nuclear and neutron physics; nuclear magnetic and electron paramagnetic resonance; physics of solid-liquid interfaces. *Mailing Add:* Chevron Res Co PO Box 446 La Habra CA 90631

SEEVERS, ROBERT EDWARD, b Okanogan, Wash, Mar 18, 35; m 56; c 4. PHYSICAL CHEMISTRY. *Educ:* Portland State Col, BS, 63; Ore State Univ, PhD(chem), 68. *Prof Exp:* Sr analyst, Reynolds Metals Co, 60-61; chemist, Ore Steel Mills, 61-63; res asst chem, Ore State Univ, 66-67; asst prof, 67-74, assoc prof, 74-80, PROF CHEM, SOUTHERN ORE COL, 80- *Mem:* Am Chem Soc. *Res:* Solid state chemistry, especially electrical properties of alkali-halide crystals and semiconductors; quantum chemistry. *Mailing Add:* Dept of Chem Southern Ore Col Ashland OR 97520

SEEWALD, DAVID ALLAN, b New York, NY, Jan 16, 42; c 2. BIOPHYSICAL CHEMISTRY. *Educ:* Brooklyn Col, BS, 62; Yale Univ, PhD(chem), 67; Univ Conn, MD, 76. *Prof Exp:* Res assoc inorg chem, Brookhaven Nat Lab, 66-68; NIH fel biophys chem, Univ Minn, Minneapolis, 68-70; asst prof biochem, Univ Bridgeport, 70-72; RESEARCHER MED, SCH MED, UNIV CONN, 72-; RESIDENT INTERNAL MED, ST MARYS HOSP, WATERBURY, CONN, 76- *Concurrent Pos:* Sigma Xi fel biophys chem, Univ Bridgeport, 71-72; fel endocrinol, Vet Admin Hosp, East Orange, NJ, 79-80, Vet Admin Hosp, Mt Sinai Hosp, Bronx NY, 80-81. *Mem:* AAAS; Am Chem Soc. *Res:* Hot atom chemistry; inorganic reaction kinetics; artificial membranes; enzyme kinetics. *Mailing Add:* 1924 E 17 St Brooklyn NY 11229

SEFF, KARL, b Chicago, Ill, Jan 23, 38; div. PHYSICAL CHEMISTRY, CRYSTALLOGRAPHY. *Educ:* Univ Calif, Berkeley, BS, 59; Mass Inst Technol, PhD(phys chem), 64. *Prof Exp:* Scholar chem, Mass Inst Technol, 64; scholar, Univ Calif, Los Angeles, 64-67, asst res chemist, 67-68; from asst prof to assoc prof, 68-75, PROF CHEM, UNIV HAWAII, 75- *Mem:* Am Crystallog Asn; Am Chem Soc. *Res:* Intrazeolitic chemistry and complex structure; transition metal organic disulfide complexes; structures of molecules of organic or biochemical interest; computer techniques. *Mailing Add:* Dept of Chem Univ of Hawaii Honolulu HI 96822

SEFFL, RAYMOND JAMES, b Chicago, Ill, Sept 21, 27; m 51; c 2. ORGANIC CHEMISTRY. *Educ:* Univ Ill, BS, 50; Univ Colo, PhD(org chem), 54. *Prof Exp:* Jr res chemist, Velsicol Corp, 50-51; sr res chemist, M W Kellog Co div, Pullman, Inc, 54-57; chief chemist, Titan Chem Co, 57-58; LAB MGR, CHEM DIV, 3M CO, 58- *Mem:* Am Chem Soc. *Res:* Organic fluorine chemistry; synthesis and commerical product development. *Mailing Add:* Chem Div 3M Co 3M Ctr St Paul MN 55101

SEGA, GARY ANDREW, b Cleveland, Ohio, Mar 23, 41; m 71; c 2. MOLECULAR GENETICS. *Educ:* Case Inst Technol, BS, 63; Univ Tex, Austin, MA, 66; La State Univ, Baton Rouge, PhD(genetics), 71. *Prof Exp:* Investr, 71-73, RES STAFF MEM MOLECULAR GENETICS, BIOL DIV, OAK RIDGE NAT LAB, 73- *Mem:* AAAS; Environ Mutagen Soc; Sigma Xi. *Res:* Molecular mechanisms of mutation induction in the mouse, including dosimetry of chemical mutagens in the germ cells and DNA repair. *Mailing Add:* Biol Div Oak Ridge Nat Lab PO Box Y Oak Ridge TN 37830

SEGAL, ALAN H, b Pittsburgh, Pa, Dec 5, 21; m 48; c 2. DENTISTRY. *Educ:* Univ Pittsburgh, BS, 45, DDS, 46, MDS, 70. *Prof Exp:* Assoc prof dent anat, 59-70, PROF GRAD PERIODONT, SCH DENT, UNIV PITTSBURGH, 71- *Concurrent Pos:* Res grant, 63-66; mem, Coun Med TV. *Mem:* Am Dent Asn; Am Col Dentists; Am Acad Periodontists. *Res:* Dental anatomy; preclinical operative dentistry. *Mailing Add:* Univ Pittsburgh Sch Dent C-117 Salk Hall Pittsburgh PA 15237

SEGAL, ALEXANDER, b Novograd-Volynsky, USSR, Oct 10, 34; m 60; c 1. ACOUSTICS, ELECTROACOUSTICS. *Educ:* Polytech Inst Kiev, MS, 58; Inst Textile & Light Indust Leningrad, PhD(noise abatement), 73. *Prof Exp:* Sr elec engr, State Proj Inst Commun Kiev, 66-68; sr sci assoc, Sci Res Inst Labor Hygiene, Kiev, 68-76; MEM TECH STAFF ACOUST, WYLE LAB, 78- *Concurrent Pos:* Expert, Proj Inst Kievproject, 73-76; consult, Country Kiev Noise Control Dept Kiev, 71-76. *Res:* Community and industrial noise control; effect of noise on worker productivity; aircraft acoustics. *Mailing Add:* 5222 Trojan Ave 316 San Diego CA 92115

SEGAL, ALVIN, b New York, NY, Mar 21, 29; div; c 2. BIOCHEMISTRY, CANCER. *Educ:* Univ Long Island, BS, 51 & 58; NY Univ, MS, 61, PhD(org chem), 65. *Prof Exp:* Pharmacist, Univ Hosp, New York, 58-59; org chemist, Ortho Pharmaceut Corp, 59-61; teaching fel chem, NY Univ, 61-63, univ fel, 63-64, USPHS fel environ med, Col Med, 64-66; asst prof pharmacog, Col Pharm, Univ Tenn, Memphis, 66-68; assoc res scientist environ med, 68-70, res scientist, 70-73, sr res scientist, 73-76, RES ASSOC PROF ENVIRON MED, MED CTR, NY UNIV, 76- *Mem:* AAAS; Am Chem Soc; Am Asn Cancer Res; Environ Mutagen Soc. *Res:* Steroids; natural products chemistry; mechanisms of chemical carcinogenesis. *Mailing Add:* Dept of Environ Med NY Univ Med Ctr 550 1st Ave New York NY 10016

SEGAL, ARTHUR CHERNY, b Newark, NJ, July 22, 38; c 2. MATHEMATICS. *Educ:* Univ Fla, BS, 58; Univ Ariz, MS, 62; Tex Christian Univ, PhD(math), 66. *Prof Exp:* Physicist, ARO, Inc, Tenn, 58-59; asst prof math, Judson Col, 62-64, Univ Tex, Arlington, 65-66 & Tex A&M Univ, 66-67; chmn dept, 75-78, ASSOC PROF MATH, UNIV ALA, BIRMINGHAM, 67- *Mem:* Math Asn Am. *Res:* Biomathematics. *Mailing Add:* Dept of Math Univ of Ala Birmingham AL 35294

SEGAL, BERNARD L, b Montreal, Que, Feb 13, 29; m 63. INTERNAL MEDICINE, CARDIOLOGY. *Educ:* McGill Univ, BSc, 50, MD, CM, 55; Am Bd Internal Med, dipl, 63; Am Bd Cardiovasc Dis, dipl, 64. *Prof Exp:* Asst med, Sch Med, Johns Hopkins Univ, 56-57; clin asst, St George's Hosp, London, 59-60; assoc med, 61-62, assoc prof, 62-72, PROF MED, HAHNEMANN MED COL & HOSP, 72-, DIR, LIKOFF CARDIOVASC INST, 80- *Concurrent Pos:* Teaching fel, Harvard Med Sch, 57-58 & Sch Med, Georgetown Univ, 58-59; USPHS fel, St George's Hosp, London, Eng, 59-60; Southeast Heart Asn Pa grants, 61-63 & 64-65; NIH grant, 62-64, res grant, 65-68; jr attend, Vet Admin Hosp & Hahnemann Med Col & Hosp, 61-; consult, Hoffmann-La Roche, Inc, 62-63; ed, Eng & Pract Med & Theory & Prac Auscultation; head, Auscultation Unit, Hahnemann Med Col & Hosp, 66-80. *Mem:* Fel Am Col Physicians; fel AMA; fel Am Col Cardiol; fel Am Col Chest Physicians; fel NY Acad Sci. *Res:* Atherosclerosis and coronary heart disease; author of over 270 publications. *Mailing Add:* 1156 Red Rose Lane Villanova PA 19085

SEGAL, BERNICE G, b Brooklyn, NY, Sept 5, 29; m 52; c 2. PHYSICAL CHEMISTRY. *Educ:* Radcliffe Col, BA, 50; Columbia Univ, PhD(chem), 55. *Prof Exp:* Asst phys chem, Columbia Univ, 55-58, lectr chem, Barnard Col, 58-64, from asst prof to assoc prof, 64-75, PROF CHEM & CHMN DEPT, BARNARD COL, 75- *Concurrent Pos:* Lectr, Columbia Univ, 57. *Mem:* Am Phys Soc; Am Chem Soc. *Res:* Paramagnetic resonance; x-ray crystallography. *Mailing Add:* Dept of Chem Barnard Col New York NY 10027

SEGAL, DAVID S, b Montreal, Que, Aug 7, 42; US citizen; m 63; c 3. NEUROPHARMACOLOGY, NEUROPSYCHOLOGY. *Educ:* Univ Calif, Santa Barbara, BA, 65; Univ Calif, Irvine, PhD(psychobiol), 70. *Prof Exp:* NIMH fel, 70-72, from asst prof to assoc prof, 72-78, PROF PSYCHIAT, UNIV CALIF, SAN DIEGO, 78- *Concurrent Pos:* Regional ed, Pharmacol, Biochem & Behav, 73-; NIMH res scientist develop award, 73-78. *Mem:* AAAS; Soc Neurosci. *Res:* Neurochemical substrates of arousal; drug-induced changes in brain biosynthetic enzymes in response to environmental changes; long-term effects of drugs on behavior and neurochemical mechanisms of adaptation. *Mailing Add:* Dept of Psychiat Univ of Calif at San Diego La Jolla CA 92093

SEGAL, EARL, b New York, NY, Dec 29, 23; m 54; c 2. ENVIRONMENTAL PHYSIOLOGY. *Educ:* Univ Southern Calif, BA, 49; Univ Calif, Los Angeles, MA, 53, PhD(zool), 55. *Prof Exp:* From asst prof to assoc prof biol, Kans State Teachers Col, 55-60; asst prof, Rice Univ, 60-63; assoc prof, 63-72, PROF BIOL, CALIF STATE UNIV, NORTHRIDGE, 72- *Concurrent Pos:* NSF lectr, NMex Highlands Univ, 58; lectr, Woods Hole Marine Biol Lab, 61; lectr, Marine Lab, Duke Univ, 62 & 63; coordr & lectr oceanog, US Naval Missile Range, Point Mugu, 65; Fulbright lectr, Penang, Malaysia, 71-72; US Info Serv lectr, SE Asia, 72; chmn bd govs, Southern Calif Ocean Studies Consortium, 76- *Mem:* Sigma Xi; Am Soc Zoologists; Marine Biol Asn UK. *Res:* Physiological ecology of poikilotherms; acclimation and physiological responses to stress. *Mailing Add:* Dept of Biol Calif State Univ 18111 Nordhoff St Northridge CA 91324

SEGAL, GERALD A, b Pittsburgh, Pa, Dec 1, 34; m 59; c 4. THEORETICAL CHEMISTRY. *Educ:* Amherst Col, AB, 56; Carnegie Inst Technol, PhD(chem), 66. *Prof Exp:* NSF fel, Bristol Univ, 66-67; from asst prof to assoc prof, 67-75, PROF CHEM & CHMN DEPT, UNIV SOUTHERN CALIF, 75- *Concurrent Pos:* Sloan Found fel, 71-; sr Fulbright fel, France, 73-74. *Mem:* Am Phys Soc; Am Chem Soc. *Res:* Molecular orbital theory; theoretical spectroscopy. *Mailing Add:* Dept of Chem Univ of Southern Calif Los Angeles CA 90007

SEGAL, HAROLD JACOB, b Winnipeg, Man, Mar 6, 41; m 70; c 1. PHARMACY ADMINISTRATION. *Educ:* Univ Man, BScPharm, 62; Purdue Univ, MS, 66, PhD(pharm admin), 68. *Prof Exp:* Pharmacist, Crescentwood Pharm Ltd, 62-65; res assoc & Can Dept Nat Health & Welfare fel, Comn Pharmaceut Serv, Toronto, 68-70; ASSOC PROF PHARM, FAC PHARM, UNIV TORONTO, 70-, FAC MED, DIV COMMUNITY HEALTH, DEPT HEALTH ADMIN, 75- *Res:* Pharmaceutical and health product marketing; health care delivery systems planning; economics of health care. *Mailing Add:* Fac Pharm Univ Toronto Toronto ON M5S 1A1 Can

SEGAL, HAROLD LEWIS, b New York, NY, Nov 18, 24; m 45; c 2. BIOCHEMISTRY. *Educ:* Carnegie Inst Technol, BS, 47; Univ Minn, MS, 50, PhD(biochem), 52. *Prof Exp:* Instr, Univ Minn, 51-52; res assoc zool, Univ Calif, Los Angeles, 52-54; asst prof biochem, Univ Pittsburgh, 54-59; assoc prof pharmacol, St Louis Univ, 59-64; chmn dept, 64-67, PROF CELL & MOLECULAR BIOL, STATE UNIV NY BUFFALO, 64-, GRAD DIR, 80- *Mem:* AAAS; Am Chem Soc; Am Soc Biol Chemists; NY Acad Sci. *Res:* Metabolic regulation. *Mailing Add:* Div of Cell & Molec Biol State Univ of NY Buffalo NY 14260

SEGAL, IRVING EZRA, b New York, NY, Sept 13, 18; m 55; c 3. MATHEMATICS, THEORETICAL PHYSICS. *Educ:* Princeton Univ, AB, 37; Yale Univ, PhD(math), 40. *Prof Exp:* Instr math, Harvard Univ, 41; res assoc, Princeton Univ, 42-43; asst, Inst Advan Study, 46, Guggenheim fel, 46-47; from asst prof to prof, Univ Chicago, 48-60; PROF MATH, MASS INST TECHNOL, 60- *Concurrent Pos:* Guggenheim fel, 51-52 & 67-68; vis assoc prof, Columbia Univ, 53-54; vis prof, Univ Paris, 65 & State Univ Col Pisa, 72. *Mem:* Nat Acad Sci; Am Math Soc; Am Phys Soc; AAAS; Am Astron Asn. *Res:* Harmonic analysis; operator rings in Hilbert space; analysis in infinite-dimensional spaces; quantum field and particle theory; astrophysics; nonlinear relativistic partial differential equations. *Mailing Add:* Rm 2-244 Mass Inst of Technol Cambridge MA 02139

SEGAL, JACK, b Philadelphia, Pa, May 9, 34; m 55; c 2. TOPOLOGY. *Educ:* Univ Miami, BS, 55, MS, 57; Univ Ga, PhD(math), 60. *Prof Exp:* From instr to assoc prof, 60-70, chmn dept, 75-78, PROF MATH, UNIV WASH, 70- *Concurrent Pos:* NSF fel, 63-64; Fulbright fel, 69-70. *Mem:* Am Math Soc; Math Asn Am. *Res:* Point-set topology; manifolds; dimension and fixed point theory; mapping; abstract spaces; inverse limit spaces; shape theory. *Mailing Add:* Dept of Math Univ of Wash Seattle WA 98195

SEGAL, MARK, b Montreal, Que, Sept 21, 35; m 59; c 3. PHARMACOLOGY. *Educ:* McGill Univ, BSc, 56, MSc, 57, PhD(pharmacol), 60. *Prof Exp:* NIMH fel pharmacol, Univ Mich, 60-62; sr pharmacologist, Ayerst, McKenna & Harrison Ltd, 62-64; from asst prof to assoc prof pharmacol, Dalhousie Univ, 64-73; SR RES PHARMACOLOGIST, PSYCHIAT RES LAB, DEPT PSYCHIAT, HADASSAH MED ORGN, 74- *Concurrent Pos:* Med Res Coun Can grant, 64-; vis prof pharmacol, Hadassah Med Sch, Hebrew Univ, Jerusalem, 71-72; vis prof pharmacol & exp therapeut, Sch Med, Boston Univ, 74; ed-in-chief, Rev Pure & Appl Pharmacol Sci, 80- *Mem:* Am Soc Pharmacol & Exp Therapeut; Pharmacol Soc Can; Can Physiol Soc; Int Soc Biochem Pharmacol; Israel Soc Physiol Pharmacol. *Res:* Evaluation of antihypertensives under chronic stress-induced conditions; mechanisms of tolerance and physical dependence; psychochemicals; biochemistry and pharmacology of affective disorders and of stress; interaction between tetrahydrocannabinols (THC) and other psychochemicals at blood-brain barrier; pharmacology and biochemistry of drugs influencing sexual behavior; mechanisms of drug-induced sterotypy; magnesium and cardiac infarction. *Mailing Add:* Hadassah Med Orgn Dept Psychiat PO Box 12000 il-91 120 Jerusalem Israel

SEGAL, MOSHE, b Haifa, Israel, June 3, 34; m 61; c 3. OPERATIONS RESEARCH. *Educ:* Israel Inst Technol, BS, 56, Ing, 56; Johns Hopkins Univ, DEng, 61. *Prof Exp:* Mem tech staff, 61-64, supvr opers res meth- odology, 64-77, SUPVR OPERS RES TECH, BELL TEL LABS, INC, 77- *Concurrent Pos:* Vis scientist, Lady Davies fel, tech, Israel Inst Technol, 76-77. *Mem:* Opers Res Soc Am. *Res:* Queueing theory; communications networks; linear and non-linear mathematical programming; optimization techniques for the design of networks. *Mailing Add:* Bell Tel Labs Inc Rm WB 1A-346 Holmdel NJ 07733

SEGAL, SANFORD LEONARD, b Troy, NY, Oct 11, 37; m 59; c 3. MATHEMATICS. *Educ:* Wesleyan Univ, BA, 58; Univ Colo, PhD(math), 63. *Prof Exp:* From instr to assoc prof, 63-77, PROF MATH, UNIV ROCHESTER, 77- *Concurrent Pos:* Fulbright res fel, Univ Vienna, 65-66; vis lectr, Univ Nottingham, Eng, 72-73. *Mem:* AAAS; Am Math Soc; Math Asn Am; London Math Soc; Soc Sociol Study Sci. *Res:* Elementary and analytic number theory; functional equations; history of science. *Mailing Add:* Dept of Math Univ of Rochester Rochester NY 14627

SEGAL, STANTON, b Camden, NJ, Sept 6, 27; m 56; c 2. MEDICINE, BIOCHEMISTRY. *Educ:* Princeton Univ, AB, 48; Harvard Med Sch, MD, 52. *Hon Degrees:* MA, Univ Pa, 71. *Prof Exp:* Res assoc, Sch Med, Univ Pa, 49-50; intern, Med Ctr, Cornell Univ, 52-53; resident med, Hosp Univ Pa, 53-54; clin assoc, NIH, 54-57; resident med, Hosp Univ Pa, 57-58; NIH sr investr, 58-65, chief sect diabetes & intermediary metab, Nat Inst Arthritis & Metab Dis, 65-66; PROF PEDIAT & CHIEF LAB MOLECULAR DIS & METAB, SCH MED, UNIV PA, 66-, PROF MED, 70-, ATTEND PHYSICIAN, HOSP, 70- *Concurrent Pos:* Vis scientist, Nat Inst Med Res, London, Eng, 63-64; mem metab study sect, NIH, 67-71, mem metab & diabetes training comt, Nat Inst Arthritis, Metab & Digestive Dis, 71-73; mem ment retardation comt, Nat Inst Child Health & Human Develop, 75-79; sr physician, Children's Hosp, Philadelphia. *Mem:* Asn Am Physicians; Am Soc Clin Invest; Endocrine Soc; Am Soc Biol Chemists; Brit Biochem Soc. *Res:* Intermediary metabolism; endocrinology; human genetics; inherited metabolic diseases. *Mailing Add:* Children's Hosp Philadelphia PA 19104

SEGAL, WILLIAM, b Montreal, Que, Dec 22, 22; nat US; m 51; c 2. MICROBIOLOGY. *Educ:* McGill Univ, BS, 43; Univ Wis, MS, 48; Rutgers Univ, PhD(microbiol), 52. *Prof Exp:* Bacteriologist, Clin Bact Lab, Royal Victoria Hosp, 44-45; asst bacteriologist, Univ Wis, 47-48; vis investr, Pub Health Res Inst, NY, 52-57; asst prof microbiol, Sch Med, 58-66, assoc prof biol, 66-68, PROF BIOL, UNIV COLO, BOULDER, 68- *Concurrent Pos:* Vis scientist, Sch Med, Hebrew Univ, Israel, 68; NIH spec res fel, Nat Ctr Sci Res, France, 68-69. *Mem:* AAAS; Am Soc Microbiol; Brit Soc Gen Microbiol. *Res:* Intermediates in bacterial nitrogen-fixation; bacterial transformation of organic sulfur compounds; biochemistry and genetics of mycobacteria; biochemistry of tuberculous host-parasite interrelationship; pathogenicity and immunogenicity of tubercle bacillus; microbial ecology. *Mailing Add:* Dept of Biol Univ of Colo Boulder CO 80302

SEGALL, BENJAMIN, b New York, NY, July 23, 25; m 53; c 3. THEORETICAL PHYSICS. *Educ:* Brooklyn Col, BS, 48; Univ Ill, MS, 49, PhD(physics), 51. *Prof Exp:* Fel, Univ Ill, 51-52; fel, Copenhagen Inst Theoret Physics, Denmark, 52-53; res physicist, Radiation Lab, Univ Calif, 53-54; res physicist, Res & Develop Ctr, Gen Elec Co, NY, 55-68; PROF PHYSICS, CASE WESTERN RESERVE UNIV, 68- *Res:* Theoretical solid state and nuclear physics. *Mailing Add:* Dept of Physics Case Western Reserve Univ Cleveland OH 44106

SEGALL, HAROLD NATHAN, b Jassy, Romania, Oct 17, 97; Can citizen; m 34; c 2. CLINICAL MEDICINE. *Educ:* McGill Univ, MD, CM, 20. *Prof Exp:* Asst cur, Med Mus, McGill Univ, 20-21; demonstr med, 26-47, lectr, 47-49, ASST PROF MED, MCGILL UNIV, 49- *Concurrent Pos:* Fel, Res Dept Path, Royal Victoria Hosp, 21-22; Walcott fel, Harvard Univ, 22-23; Dalton scholar cardiol, Mass Gen Hosp, 23-24; sr physician & chief dept cardiol, Jewish Gen Hosp, 34-60; consult physician, 60-; Louis Gross mem lectr, 62; vpres, Nat Heart Found Can; pres, Que Heart Found, 65-67. *Mem:* Am Heart Asn; fel Am Col Physicians; Can Cardiovasc Soc; fel Royal Soc Arts; Can Med Asn. *Res:* History of medicine. *Mailing Add:* 4100 Cote des Neiges Rd #19 Montreal PQ H3H 1W8 Can

SEGALL, STANLEY, b Baltimore, Md. May 12, 30; m 54; c 2. ORGANIC CHEMISTRY, FOOD TECHNOLOGY. *Educ:* Northeastern Univ, SB, 53; Mass Inst Technol, 54-57, PhD(food tech), 57. *Prof Exp:* Chief chemist, Blue Seal Extract Co, Mass, 51-54; dir res, Rudd-Melikian, Inc, 57-68; ASSOC PROF BIOL & ENVIRON SCI, DREXEL UNIV, 68-, ASSOC PROF NUTRIT & FOOD & HEAD DEPT, 74- *Mem:* Am Chem Soc; Inst Food Technol. *Res:* Environmental and toxicological studies; taste and odor; flavor chemistry; food processing; public health aspects of automated industrial feeding. *Mailing Add:* Dept of Nutrit & Food Drexel Univ Philadelphia PA 19104

SEGALL, STEPHEN BARRETT, b Newark, NJ, Oct, 2, 42; m 65; c 4. PHYSICS. *Educ:* Columbia Col, BA, 64; Univ Md, MSc, 72, PhD(physics), 72. *Prof Exp:* PRIN SCIENTIST, FREE ELECTRON LASERS & DIR RES, KMS FUSION, INC, 72- *Res:* Laser-plasma interaction physics and free electron laser development. *Mailing Add:* 1349 King George Blvd Ann Arbor MI 48104

SEGALOFF, ALBERT, b West Haven, Conn, July 25, 16; m 40; c 3. ENDOCRINOLOGY, CLINICAL MEDICINE. *Educ:* Yale Univ, BS, 37; Wayne State Univ, MS, 39, MD, 43; Am Bd Internal Med, dipl, 52. *Prof Exp:* Intern, William J Seymour Hosp, Eloise, Mich, 43-44; asst med, Sch Med & asst vis physician, Hosp, Vanderbilt Univ, 44-45; from instr to assoc prof med, 45-63, PROF MED, SCH MED, TULANE UNIV, 63-, ADJ PROF 75-; CLIN PROF PATH, SCH MED, LA STATE UNIV, 77- *Concurrent Pos:* Dir endocrine res, Alton Ochsner Med Found, 45-67, dir res, 61-62; mem staff, Dept Internal Med & consult oncol, Ochsner Clin, New Orleans, 45-; vis staff, Tulane Unit, Charity Hosp, 45-50, from vis physician to sr vis physician, 50-65, consult, 65-; attend physician, Ochsner Found Hosp, 47-; chmn clin studies comt, Cancer Chemother Nat Serv Ctr, 56-57, mem endocrinol panel, 56-59, 60-, clin panel, 56-59, 62-65, planning comt, 57 & hormone eval comt, 57-62, chmn, 60-, mem clin trials task force, 66-; consult, Nat Cancer Inst, 56-, chmn coop breast cancer group, 56-78, mem cent oncol group, 62-71, mem solid tumor task force & breast cancer task force, 66-70; mem revision comt, US Pharmacopoeia, 60, 62, 66; from assoc managing ed to ed, Steroids, 63-; consult endocrinol, USPHS Hosp, New Orleans, 64-70; mem drug efficacy study & chmn panel drugs for reproductive syst disturbances, Nat Acad Sci-Nat Res Coun, 66-69; vis prof oncol, Cancer Res Inst, Med Ctr, Univ Calif, 67; assoc ed, Cancer Res, 69-73; consult, Food & Drug Admin, 71; US rep, Int Bd Ed Cancer, Excerpta Medica. *Honors & Awards:* Ciba Award, Endocrine Soc, 51; Wayne State Univ Col Med Distinguished Serv Citation, 66. *Mem:* Am Soc Clin Invest; Sigma Xi; Am Soc Clin Oncol; Am Soc Clin Pharmacol & Therapeut; Endocrine Soc. *Res:* Steroid metabolism; clinical investigations; cancer chemotherapy; internal medicine; oncology. *Mailing Add:* Alton Ochsner Med Found 1520 Jefferson Hwy New Orleans LA 70121

SEGAR, WILLIAM ELIAS, b Indianapolis, Ind, Dec 16, 23; m 54; c 2. PEDIATRICS. *Educ:* Ind Univ, BS, 44, MD, 47; Am Bd Pediat, dipl, 55. *Prof Exp:* Instr pediat, Yale Univ, 51-53; from asst prof to prof, Sch Med, Ind Univ, 55-67; prof, Mayo Grad Sch Med, 67-70; PROF PEDIAT, UNIV WIS-MADISON, 70-, CHMN DEPT, 75- *Mem:* AAAS; Soc Pediat Res; AMA; Am Fedn Clin Res. *Res:* Water and electrolyte metabolism; renal physiology. *Mailing Add:* Dept of Pediat Univ of Wis Madison WI 53706

SEGARRA, JOSEPH M, b Vinaroz, Spain, Dec 25, 22; nat US; m; c 4. NEUROLOGY. *Educ:* Univ Barcelona, Lic, 46; Univ Madrid, DMed, 52. *Prof Exp:* Vis asst, Univ Paris Hosp, 50; physician, Neurol Inst Barcelona, Spain, 50-52; asst resident neurol, Boston City Hosp, 54-55; chief resident, New Eng Med Ctr, 55-56; MEM STAFF, VET ADMIN HOSP, 56-; ASSOC PROF NEUROL, SCH MED, TUFTS UNIV, 76-; ASSOC PROF, SCH MED, BOSTON UNIV, 67- *Concurrent Pos:* Res fel, Nat Ctr Sci Res, France, 58-60; Rockefeller Found res fel, Boston City Hosp, 53-54; asst prof neurol, Sch Med, Tufts Univ, 66-76. *Mem:* Acad Neurol. *Res:* Neuropathology and clinical neurology. *Mailing Add:* 94 Pleasant St Arlington MA 02174

SEGATTO, PETER RICHARD, b New York, NY, June 4, 28; m 54; c 3. ANALYTICAL CHEMISTRY, PHYSICAL CHEMISTRY. *Educ:* Univ Adelphi, AB, 53; Rutgers Univ, PhD(chem), 58. *Prof Exp:* Res chemist, 57-62, res chem assoc, 62-69, res assoc electronic mat & prod develop, 69-72, mgr tech prod dept, 72-77, portfolio mgr electronic/elec projs, 77-78, DIR TECH STAFF SERV, CORNING GLASS WORKS, 78- *Mem:* Am Chem Soc; Electrochem Soc. *Res:* Electrochemical analysis; thermodynamics; instrumental methods of analysis; instrumentation; electronic materials research; dielectrics; resister and magnetic materials; product development; vacuum technology; environmental chemistry; catalysis. *Mailing Add:* Res & Develop Labs Corning Glass Works Corning NY 14830

SEGEL, IRWIN HARVEY, b Staten Island, NY, Dec 29, 35; c 2. BIOCHEMISTRY. *Educ:* Rensselaer Polytech Inst, BS, 57; Univ Wis, MS, 60, PhD(biochem), 62. *Prof Exp:* NSF fel, 62-63; USPHS res fel, 63-64; from asst prof to assoc prof, 64-73, PROF BIOCHEM, UNIV CALIF, DAVIS, 73- *Mem:* AAAS; Am Soc Biol Chemists; Am Soc Plant Physiol; Am Chem Soc; Am Soc Microbiol. *Res:* Microbial biochemistry; enzymology and regulation of sulfur and nitrogen metabolism in microorganisms; membrane transport systems; glycogen metabolism. *Mailing Add:* Dept of Biochem & Biophys Univ of Calif Davis CA 95616

SEGEL, L(EONARD), b Cincinnati, Ohio, Apr 16, 22; m 44; c 3. AERONAUTICAL & MECHANICAL ENGINEERING. *Educ:* Univ Cincinnati, BSAE, 47; State Univ NY, Buffalo, MS, 53. *Prof Exp:* Res engr, Flight Res Dept, Cornell Aeronaut Lab, Inc, 47-56, prin engr, Vehicale Dynamics Dept, 56-57, head res sect, 57-60, asst dept head, 60-63, staff scientist, Appl Mech Dept, 63-66; lectr mech eng, 67-68, assoc prof, 68-75, PROF MECH ENG, UNIV MICH, ANN ARBOR, 75-, HEAD, PHYS FACTORS GROUP, HWY SAFETY RES INST, 67- *Concurrent Pos:* Technion, Israel Inst Technol, 78. *Honors & Awards:* Crompton-Lancester Medal, Brit Inst Mech Engrs, 58. *Mem:* Am Soc Mech Engrs; Am Inst Aeronaut & Astronaut; Human Factors Soc; Am Soc Testing & Mat; fel Inst Mech Engrs. *Res:* Flight mechanics; vehicle stability and control; man-vehicle relationships; mobility of off-road vehicles; linear systems; tire mechanics; rotary-wing phenomena; tire-vehicle system dynamics. *Mailing Add:* Dept of Mech Eng Univ of Mich Huron Pkwy & Baxter Rd Ann Arbor MI 48109

SEGEL, LEE AARON, b Boston, Mass, Feb 5, 32; m 58; c 4. APPLIED MATHEMATICS, THEORETICAL BIOLOGY. *Educ:* Harvard Univ, AB, 53; Mass Inst Technol, PhD(math), 59. *Prof Exp:* Res fel, Aerodyn Div, Nat Phys Lab, Eng, 58-60; from asst prof to prof math, Rensselaer Polytech Inst, 60-73; head dept, 73-78, PROF APPL MATH, WEIZMANN INST SCI, ISRAEL, 73-, DEAN, FAC MATH SCI, 77-; RES PROF, RENSSELAER POLYTECH INST, 73- *Concurrent Pos:* Vis assoc prof, Mass Inst Technol, 63-64; vis assoc prof, Sch Med, Cornell Univ & vis scientist, Sloan-Kettering Inst, 68-69; Guggenheim fel & vis prof, Weizmann Inst Sci, 71-72; Vinton Hayes sr fel & vis prof appl math, Harvard Univ, 78-79. *Mem:* Am Math Soc; Soc Indust & Appl Math; Israel Math Soc; AAAS. *Res:* Theoretical biology, especially chemotaxis and neurotransmitter release; theoretical physical chemistry; theoretical ecology; general applied mathematics. *Mailing Add:* Dept Appl Math Weizmann Inst Sci Rehovot Israel

SEGEL, RALPH E, b New York, NY, Aug 29, 29; m 60; c 3. PHYSICS. *Educ:* Mass Inst Technol, SB, 48; Johns Hopkins Univ, PhD(physics). *Prof Exp:* Res assoc physics, Johns Hopkins Univ, 55; res assoc, Brookhaven Nat Lab, 55-56; physicist, US Air Force, 56-61; assoc physicist, Argonne Nat Lab, 61-70, sr physicist, 70-76; PROF PHYSICS, NORTHWESTERN UNIV, 66- *Concurrent Pos:* Sr res officer, Oxford Univ, 58-59; Humboldt Found award, Tech Univ Munich, 78. *Mem:* Fel Am Phys Soc. *Res:* Studies of the structure of the nucleus using nuclear reactions and other means. *Mailing Add:* Dept of Physics Northwestern Univ Evanston IL 60201

SEGEL, STANLEY LEWIS, b Philadelphia, Pa, Aug 23, 32; m 58; c 3. SOLID STATE PHYSICS. *Educ:* Allegheny Col, BS, 53; Univ Del, MS, 56; Iowa State Univ, PhD(physics, metall), 63. *Prof Exp:* Instr physics, Robert Col, 57-58; asst prof, Kalamazoo Col, 62-67; assoc prof, 67-76, PROF PHYSICS, QUEEN'S UNIV, ONT, 76-, ASSOC PROF ART, 76- *Mem:* Am Asn Physics Teachers; Phys Soc Japan. *Res:* Nuclear magnetic and quadrupole resonance. *Mailing Add:* Dept of Physics Queen's Univ Kingston ON K7L 3N6 Can

SEGELKEN, WARREN GEORGE, b Jamaica, NY, Mar 13, 26; m 57; c 3. MAGNETIC RESONANCE. *Educ:* Rutgers Univ, BS, 50, PhD(physics), 55. *Prof Exp:* Asst, Rutgers Univ, 50-52; res physicist, Gen Elec Co, 55-67; assoc prof, 67-72, PROF PHYSICS, ASHLAND COL, 72-, CHMN DEPT, 70- *Mem:* Am Asn Physics Teachers; Sigma Xi; Am Phys Soc. *Res:* Solid state physics; nuclear and electronic paramagnetic resonance. *Mailing Add:* Dept of Physics Ashland Col Ashland OH 44805

SEGELMAN, ALVIN BURTON, b Boston, Mass, Sept 27, 31; m 72; c 2. PHARMACOGNOSY, PHYTOCHEMISTRY. *Educ:* Mass Col Pharm, BS, 54, MS, 67; Univ Pittsburgh, PhD(pharmacog), 71. *Prof Exp:* Chief pharmacist, Kenmore Prof Pharmacy, 54-61; dir pharmaceut serv, Bell Pharm Co, 61-65; fel, Mass Col Pharm, 65-67; instr pharmacog & microbiol, Univ Pittsburgh, 67-71; asst prof, 71-74, ASSOC PROF PHARMACOG, RUTGERS UNIV, 74- *Concurrent Pos:* Consult, Cliniderm Labs, Boston, 57-65. *Mem:* AAAS; Am Soc Pharmacog; Acad Pharmaceut Sci; fel Linnean Soc London; Am Soc Econ Botany. *Res:* Isolation, purification and structure elucidation of biologically active natural products; design of phytochemical screening and isolation methods; alkaloids, antibiotics, anti-tumor and psychotomimetric substances in higher plants; microbiology; microbial transformations and fermentations; medicinal plant tissue culture. *Mailing Add:* Dept of Pharmacog Rutgers Univ PO Box 789 New Brunswick NJ 08903

SEGELMAN, FLORENCE PETTLER, pharmacognosy, phytochemistry, see previous edition

SEGERS, RICHARD GEORGE, b Cincinnati, Ohio, July 4, 28; m 56; c 4. MATHEMATICS, OPERATIONS RESEARCH. *Educ:* Univ Dayton, BS, 50; Purdue Univ, MS, 52, PhD(math), 56. *Prof Exp:* Mem tech staff, Networks Dept, Bell Tel Labs, Inc, 55-59; sr mathematician, Vitro Labs, 59-63; res consult, Gen Precision Labs, 63-64; RES CONSULT, EXXON CORP, 64- *Concurrent Pos:* Vis assoc prof, Grad Sch Bus, Univ Chicago, 69-70; adj fac mem, Dept Math & Physics, Fairleigh Dickinson Univ, 71- *Mem:* Am Math Soc; Soc Indust & Appl Math. *Res:* Optimal control, statistics and game theory. *Mailing Add:* Exxon Corp Math Systs Box 153 Florham Park NJ 07932

SEGHERS, BENONI HENDRIK, b Willebroek, Belgium, Dec 24, 44; Can citizen. ETHOLOGY, ICHTHYOLOGY. *Educ:* Univ BC, BSc, 67, PhD(zool), 73. *Prof Exp:* Lectr, Univ Man, 72-73; lectr, 74-75, ASST PROF ZOOL, UNIV WESTERN ONT, 76- *Concurrent Pos:* Fel, Univ Man, 72-74. *Mem:* Can Soc Zool; Animal Behav Soc; Soc Study Evolution; Am Soc Ichthyologists & Herpetologists. *Res:* Behavior, ecology and evolution of fishes; biology of the fishes of Trinidad, West Indies; anti-predator adaptations in vertebrates; zoogeography; limnology. *Mailing Add:* Dept of Zool Univ of Western Ont London ON N6A 5B8 Can

SEGLIE, ERNEST AUGUSTUS, b New York, NY, Aug 8, 45. NUCLEAR PHYSICS. *Educ:* Cooper Union, BS, 67; Univ Mass, PhD(nuclear physics), 73. *Prof Exp:* Assoc physics, Rensselaer Polytech Inst, 73-75; res assoc & lectr physics, Yale Univ, 75-79; RES ANALYST, INST DEFENSE ANALYSES, 79- *Mem:* Am Phys Soc. *Res:* Heavy ion physics, nuclear scattering and reaction theories and fusion reactions. *Mailing Add:* Inst for Defense Analyses 400 Army-Navy Dr Arlington VA 22202

SEGMULLER, ARMIN PAUL, b Nuremberg, Ger, Aug 15, 24; m 53; c 5. CRYSTALLOGRAPHY. *Educ:* Univ Erlangen, MS, 50, PhD(crystallog), 54. *Prof Exp:* Sci asst metall, Clausthal Tech Univ, 55-59; res staff mem, Res Lab, IBM Corp, Zurich, Switz, 59-66, RES STAFF MEM, THOMAS J WATSON RES CTR, IBM CORP, 66- *Mem:* Am Crystallog Asn. *Res:* X-ray diffractometry; x-ray small angle interferences; modulated structures; laboratory automation. *Mailing Add:* IBM T J Watson Res Ctr PO Box 218 Yorktown Heights NY 10598

SEGNER, EDMUND PETER, JR, b Austin, Tex, Mar 28, 28; m 52; c 5. STRUCTURAL ENGINEERING. *Educ:* Univ Tex, BS, 49, MS, 52; Tex A&M Univ, PhD(struct eng), 62. *Prof Exp:* Engr, United Gas Pipe Line Co, La, 49-50; sr struct engr, Gen Dynamics Corp, Tex, 51-52 & 53-54; engr, Forrest & Cotton, Inc, 53; from instr to assoc prof civil eng, Tex A&M Univ, 54-63; prof civil eng & struct group coordr, Univ Okla, 63-65; prof civil eng, Univ Ala, Tuscaloosa, 65-76, asst dean res & grad studies, 68-71, assoc dean eng, 71-76; PROF CIVIL ENG & ASSOC V PRES RES & GRAD STUDIES, MEMPHIS STATE UNIV, 76- *Concurrent Pos:* Consult, 54-; ed, Civil Eng Bull, 56-57. *Mem:* Am Soc Civil Engrs; Am Soc Eng Educ; Nat Soc Prof Engrs; Am Concrete Inst; Int Asn Bridge & Struct Engrs. *Res:* Design and analysis of structural steel and reinforced concrete structures; openings in flexural members; splices in tensile reinforcing bars; bond in reinforced concrete design and various flexural studies involving reinforced concrete and structural steel. *Mailing Add:* Memphis State Univ Memphis TN 38152

SEGNER, WAYNE PHILIP, food microbiology, see previous edition

SEGOVIA, ANTONIO, b Asuncion, Paraguay, Nov 3, 32; m 60; c 1. GEOLOGY. *Educ:* Nat Univ Paraguay, BS, 54; Pa State Univ, PhD(geol), 63. *Prof Exp:* Geologist, Ministry Pub Works, Paraguay, 56; field geologist, Bolivian Gulf Oil Corp, 57; geologist, Photogeol Unit, Gulf Oil Corp, NJ, 57-58, consult, Western Explor Div, 58-60; adv photogeol, Nat Geol Surv, Colombia, 60-61; asst prof geol & head dept, Sch Petrol Eng, Eastern Univ Venezuela, 61-64 & Cent Univ Venezuela, 64-66; sr res scientist, Tulsa Res Ctr, Sinclair Oil Corp, 66-69; ASSOC PROF GEOL, UNIV MD, COLLEGE PARK, 69- *Concurrent Pos:* Consult, Skelly Oil Corp, 65-66; mem, Bd Dirs, Geosysts Inc, 72-76; consult archaeol, Cath Univ Am, 73-75 & Am Univ, 74-75; vis res prof, Cent Univ Venezuela, 75. *Mem:* AAAS; fel Geol Soc Am; Soc Petrol Engrs; Am Asn Petrol Geologists; Am Inst Mining, Metall & Petrol Engrs. *Res:* Photogeology; geomorphology; engineering geology; petroleum geology; structural geology; seismicity of regmites, especially deformation of Pleistocene surfaces; geological study of nuclear sites; South American geology. *Mailing Add:* Dept of Geol Univ of Md College Park MD 20740

SEGOVIA, JORGE, b Martinez, Arg, Mar 2, 34; m 63; c 2. COMMUNITY HEALTH, SOCIOMEDICAL SCIENCES. *Educ:* Univ Buenos Aires, MD, 59, MPH, 61. *Prof Exp:* Head health educ sect sociomed sci, Sch Pub Health, Univ Buenos Aires, 63-66; head med sociol sect, Ctr Educ Med Invest Clin Buenos Aires, 64-68; mem prof staff med sociol, Ctr Latino Am Admin Med Buenos Aires, 68-71; res assoc sociomed sci, Columbia Univ Sch Pub Health, 71-73; asst prof & consult med care prog, Health & Community, Univ Campinas, Brazil, 73-75; ASSOC PROF SOCIAL MED, MEM UNIV NFLD, 76- *Concurrent Pos:* Milbank fac fel, Milbank Mem Fund NY, 65-71. *Mem:* Can Pub Health Asn; Am Col Prev Med; Am Pub Health Asn; Am Sociol Asn. *Res:* Comparative health systems; health policy formulation in developing countries; multivariate analysis of social and health indicators in developing countries; health effects of environmental hazzards. *Mailing Add:* Div Of Community Med Mem Univ of Nfld St John's NF A1C 5S7 Can

SEGRE, DIEGO, b Milano, Italy, Feb 3, 22; nat US; m 52; c 2. IMMUNOLOGY. *Educ:* Univ Milano, DVM, 47; Univ Nebr, MS, 54; Univ Wis, PhD(vet sci), 57. *Prof Exp:* Asst prof infectious dis, Univ Milano, 47-51; asst animal pathologist, Univ Nebr, 52-55; res asst vet sci, Univ Wis, 55-57, asst prof, 57-60; PROF VET MICROBIOL & PUB HEALTH, COL VET MED, UNIV ILL, URBANA, 60- *Mem:* AAAS; Soc Exp Biol & Med; Am Asn Immunologists; Conf Res Workers Animal Dis; Am Col Vet Microbiol. *Res:* Mechanisms of immunity and immunological tolerance; maturation and cytokinetics of the immune response; immunology of aging. *Mailing Add:* Col of Vet Med Univ of Ill Urbana IL 61801

SEGRE, EMILIO GINO, b Tivoli, Italy, Feb 1, 05; nat US; m 72; c 3. NUCLEAR PHYSICS, PARTICLE PHYSICS. *Educ:* Univ Rome, PhD(physics), 28. *Hon Degrees:* Dr, Univ Palermo, 59; PhD, Gustavus Adolphus Col, 67. *Prof Exp:* Asst prof physics, Univ Rome, 30-32; assoc prof, 32-35; prof & dir lab, Univ Palermo, 35-38; res assoc, Radiation Lab, 38-43, physicist & group leader, Los Alamos Sci Lab, 43-46, prof physics, 46-72, EMER PROF PHYSICS, UNIV CALIF, BERKELEY, 72-; PROF NUCLEAR PHYSICS, UNIV ROME, 74- *Concurrent Pos:* Rockefeller fel, Hamburg & Amsterdam, 31-32; vis prof, Univ Ill, 51-52; hon prof, San Marcos Univ, Peru; Guggenheim fel, Univ Rome, 58, Fulbright fel. *Honors & Awards:* Nobel Prize in Physics, 59; Hofmann Medal, Heidelberg Acad. *Mem:* Nat Acad Sci; fel Am Phys Soc; Heidelberg Acad; Nat Acad Lincei, Italy; Uruguayan Soc Sci. *Res:* History of physics; slow neutrons; chemical elements technetrim, astatine, plutonium and of the antiproton. *Mailing Add:* Dept of Physics Univ of Calif Berkeley CA 94720

SEGRE, GINO C, b Florence, Italy, Oct 4, 38; US citizen; m 62; c 2. THEORETICAL PHYSICS. *Educ:* Harvard Univ, AB, 59; Mass Inst Technol, PhD(physics), 63. *Prof Exp:* NSF fel physics, Europ Orgn Nuclear Res, Geneva, Switz, 63-65; res assoc, Lawrence Radiation Lab, Univ Calif, 65-69; assoc prof, 69-74, PROF, UNIV PA, 74- *Concurrent Pos:* A P Sloan Found fel, 63-71; Guggenheim fel, 75-76. *Mem:* Am Phys Soc. *Res:* Elementary particle physics. *Mailing Add:* Dept of Physics Univ of Pa Philadelphia PA 19104

SEGRE, MARIANGELA BERTANI, b Milan, Italy, Oct 4, 27; US citizen; m 52; c 2. IMMUNOBIOLOGY. *Educ:* Univ Milan, Dr Sc, 49. *Prof Exp:* Res asst infectious dis, Univ Milan, 49-51; vis investr, Animal Dis Res Inst, Weybridge, Eng, 51; bacteriologist, Montecatini Corp, Milan, 51-52 & Nebr State Dept Health, 53-54; res assoc, 63-73, ASST PROF IMMUNOL, UNIV ILL, URBANA, 73- *Res:* Mechanism of antibody formation; immunologic tolerance; immunologic aspects of aging; cytokinetics of the immune response; mechanisms of immunologic memory; immunological methods. *Mailing Add:* Ctr Zoonoses & Comp Med Univ of Ill Col of Vet Med Urbana IL 61801

SEGREST, JERE PALMER, b Dothan, Ala, Aug 16, 40; m 66. CELL BIOLOGY, MOLECULAR BIOPHYSICS. *Educ:* Vanderbilt Univ, BA, 62, MD, 67, PhD(biochem), 69. *Prof Exp:* Resident path, Univ Hosp, Vanderbilt Univ, 68-70; staff assoc, Lab Exp Path, Nat Inst Arthritis, Metab & Digestive Dis, 70-74; ASSOC PROF PATH & ASST PROF BIOCHEM, MED CTR, UNIV ALA, 74-, ASST PROF MICROBIOL, SCIENTIST COMPREHENSIVE CANCER CTR & ASST SCIENTIST INST DENT RES, 75- *Concurrent Pos:* Europ Molecular Biol Orgn fel, Nat Ctr Sci Res, Gif-sur-Yvette, France, 73; mem, NIH Study Sect Molecular Cytol, 78. *Mem:* AAAS; Am Chem Soc; Am Soc Cell Biol; Am Soc Exp Path; Biophys Soc. *Res:* Protein-lipid interactions in membrane and plasma lipoproteins; structure and function of human erythrocyte glycophorin; fusion of lipid vesicles to membranes of mammalian cells in culture; relevant diseases such as atherosclerosis and cancer. *Mailing Add:* Dept of Path Biochem & Microbiol Univ of Ala Med Ctr Birmingham AL 35294

SEGUIN, FREDRICK HAMPTON, theoretical astrophysics, hydrodynamics, see previous edition

SEGUIN, JEROME JOSEPH, b North Bay, Ont, Sept 27, 24; m 52; c 6. PHYSIOLOGY. *Educ:* Univ West Ont, BSc, 50, MSc, 52, PhD(physiol), 56. *Prof Exp:* Demonstr & asst, 50-57, lectr, 58-60, asst prof, 60-63, ASSOC PROF PHYSIOL, UNIV WESTERN ONT, 63- *Concurrent Pos:* McEachern sr med fel, Muscular Dystrophy Asn Can, 58-63; guest investr, Inst Muscle Dis, Inc, NY, 62-63. *Mem:* Can Physiol Soc; Soc Neurosci; Int Asn Study Pain. *Res:* Muscle receptor physiology; neurophysiology of pain. *Mailing Add:* Dept of Physiol Health Sci Ctr Univ of Western Ont London ON N6A 5B8 Can

SEGUIN, LOUIS-ROCH, b Rigaud, Que, Apr 26, 20; m 50; c 4. FISHERIES. *Educ:* Col Bourget, BA, 43; Univ Laval, BSc, 47; Univ Montreal, MSc, 54. *Prof Exp:* Biologist, Laurentian Fish Hatchery, Que, 47-49; biologist & dir, Eastern Twp Fishery Sta, Que Dept Fish & Game, 50-61, chief biol, 62-63; prof fish culture, Univ Laval, 63; chief wildlife biologist, Can Int Paper Co, 63-71; exec dir, Que Fedn Camping & Caravaning, 71-72; head fishery sect, Appl Res Ctr Feeding Sci, Univ Que, Montreal, 72-76; CONSULT FISHERY BIOLOGIST & MGR, JAMES BAY RESERVOIRS, QUE, 76-; PROF AQUACULT, COL ST FELICIEN, QUEBEC, 80- *Concurrent Pos:* Gen mgr, Que Outfitters Asn, 73- *Mem:* Am Inst Fishery Res Biologists. *Res:* Trout culture; building and management of lakes; outdoor recreation management. *Mailing Add:* RR 5 Coaticook PQ J1A 2S4 Can

SEGUIN, MAURICE KRISHOLM, b Cedars, Que, May 30, 38. GEOPHYSICS, GEOLOGY. *Educ:* McGill Univ, MSc, 63, PhD(geophys), 65. *Hon Degrees:* Degree, Royal Inst Technol, Stockholm, 68. *Prof Exp:* Geophysicist, Iron Ore Co, Can, 64-65; lectr, Royal Inst Technol, Stockholm, 65-68; assoc res, Soquem, Que, 68; asst prof, 69-72, ASSOC PROF GEOPHYS, LAVAL UNIV, 72- *Concurrent Pos:* Mem, Comt Geol & Geophys, Nat Res Coun Can, 69. *Mem:* French-Can Asn Advan Sci; Europ Asn Explor Geophys; Europ Asn Geophys. *Res:* Applied geophysics; paleomagnetism; permafrost. *Mailing Add:* Dept of Geol Laval Univ Quebec PQ G1K 7P4 Can

SEGUIN, WARD RAYMOND, b Monpelier, Vt, Aug 28, 42; m 67; c 3. METEOROLOGY. *Educ:* Fla State Univ, BS, 65, MS, 67, PhD(meteorol), 72. *Prof Exp:* Fel meteorol, Univ Va, 72-73; RES SCIENTIST METEOROL, NAT OCEANIC & ATMOSPHERIC ADMIN, DEPT COM, 73- *Mem:* Am Meteorol Soc. *Res:* Study of energy and momentum transfers in the tropical marine atmospheric boundary layer. *Mailing Add:* 11007 Dayton Silver Spring MD 20902

SEGUNDO, JOSE PEDRO, b Montevideo, Uruguay, Oct 6, 22; c 5. NEUROPHYSIOLOGY. *Educ:* Univ Repub Uruguay, BS, 42, MD, 49. *Prof Exp:* Instr physiol, Univ Repub Uruguay, 50-57; head dept electrobiol, Inst Biol Sci, Montevideo, 57-60; instr anat, 53-55, PROF ANAT, HEALTH SCI CTR, UNIV CALIF, LOS ANGELES, 60- *Mem:* Am Physiol Soc; Biophys Soc; Soc Neurosci; LatinAm Ciencias Fisiologicas. *Res:* Functional organization of multisensory areas of the nervous system; interneuronal communication. *Mailing Add:* Dept of Anat Univ of Calif Los Angeles CA 90024

SEGURA, GONZALO, JR, b Cuba, Nov 25, 19; nat US. RADIOCHEMISTRY. *Educ:* Emory Univ, AB, 42, MS, 43. *Prof Exp:* Instr math, Emory Univ, 43-44; asst physics, Columbia Univ, 44; chemist, Tenn Eastman Corp, 45-46; instr chem, Finch Col, 46-51; radiochemist, Foster D Snell, Inc, 51-52, chief radiochemist, 52-59; RES SCIENTIST, PHILIP MORRIS, INC, 59- *Mem:* Am Chem Soc; Am Nuclear Soc. *Res:* Radiotracers; detergency; syntheses. *Mailing Add:* 3522 Grove Ave Richmond VA 23221

SEHE, CHARLES THEODORE, b Geneva, Ill, Feb 26, 23; m 53; c 5. DEVELOPMENTAL BIOLOGY, ENDOCRINOLOGY. *Educ:* NCent Col, Ill, AB, 50; Univ Iowa, MS, 53, PhD(zool), 57. *Prof Exp:* Asst embryol, Univ Iowa, 52-57; asst prof endocrinol, Univ Ill, Urbana, 57-58; asst prof embryol & endocrinol, Univ Cincinnati, 58-61; assoc prof embryol & comp anat, NCent Col, Ill, 61-64; res assoc prof develop biol & endocrinol, Stanford Med Ctr, 64-71; prof develop biol & endocrinol, 71-77, MEM BIOL FAC, MANKATO STATE COL, 77- *Concurrent Pos:* Resident res assoc, Argonne Nat Lab, 62-63; consult biol, Teacher Training Prog, Inst Nuclear Sci & Eng, Argonne Nat Lab, 64. *Mem:* AAAS; Am Soc Zool. *Res:* Developmental and secretory characteristics of the ultimobranchial body of vertebrates; hormonal factors in sexual behavioral development. *Mailing Add:* Dept of Biol Mankato State Col Mankato MN 56001

SEHGAL, OM PARKASH, b Rawal Pindi, India, July 22, 32; m 62; c 2. PLANT PATHOLOGY, VIROLOGY. *Educ:* Univ Lucknow, MSc, 53; Univ Wis, PhD(plant path), 61. *Prof Exp:* Res asst virol, Indian Agr Res Inst, 55-57; res asst plant path, Univ Wis, 58-61; fel virol, Univ Ariz, 61-63; asst prof field crops & plant path, 63-68, assoc prof plant path & biol sci, 69-78, PROF PLANT PATH & BIOL SCI, UNIV MO-COLUMBIA, 78- *Honors & Awards:* Birbal Sahni Mem Gold Medal, Lucknow Univ, 53. *Mem:* AAAS; Am Phytopath Soc; Soc Gen Microbiol; Am Soc Microbiol. *Res:* Viral structure and genetics. *Mailing Add:* Dept of Plant Path Univ of Mo-Columbia Columbia MO 65201

SEHGAL, PRAVINKUMAR B, b Bombay, India, Sept 11, 49; m 72; c 1. VIROLOGY, INTERFERON. *Educ:* Seth G S Med Col, MB & BS, 73; Rockefeller Univ, PhD(virol & cell biol), 77. *Prof Exp:* Intern, King Edward Mem Hosp, 71-72; fel, 77-79, ASST PROF VIROL, ROCKEFELLER UNIV, 79- *Concurrent Pos:* Assoc ed, J Interferon Res, 79; Irma T Hirschl Award, Irma T Hirschl Trust, 81. *Mem:* AAAS; NY Acad Sci; Am Soc Microbiol; Am Soc Virol. *Res:* Regulation of human interferon production and the molecular biology of the human interferon system; mechanism of inhibition of mammalian RNA synthesis by halobenzimidazole ribosides. *Mailing Add:* Rockefeller Univ 1230 York Ave New York NY 10021

SEHGAL, PREM P, b Patiala, India, Nov 16, 34; m 61; c 1. PLANT PHYSIOLOGY. *Educ:* Univ Delhi, BSc, 54, MSc, 56; Harvard Univ, AM, 61; Duke Univ, PhD(bot), 64. *Prof Exp:* Asst prof bot, B R Col, Agra, 56-57; lectr, Ramjas Col, Delhi, 57-58; res asst, Duke Univ, 61-64, NSF res assoc, 64-65; NIH proj assoc biochem, Univ Wis, Madison, 65-66; asst prof, 66-69, assoc prof, 69-77, PROF BIOL, E CAROLINA UNIV, 77- *Concurrent Pos:* NC Bd Sci & Tech res grant, 67-70; NSF Cosip grant, 69-70. *Mem:* Am Soc Plant Physiol; Bot Soc Am; Brit Soc Exp Biol; Int Soc Plant Morphol; NY Acad Sci. *Res:* Interaction of hormones with nitrogen compounds, especially in chlorophyll production; biochemistry of plant tissue cultures with special reference to enzymatic changes; urease. *Mailing Add:* Dept of Biol E Carolina Univ Greenville NC 27834

SEHGAL, S(ATYA) B(HUSHAN), b India, Sept 22, 34; m 60; c 3. SOIL MECHANICS. *Educ:* Punjab Univ, India, BA, 54, BSc, 57, MSc, 58; Ohio State Univ, PhD(civil eng), 65. *Prof Exp:* Asst prof civil eng, Punjab Eng Col, Chandigarh, India, 58-66, assoc prof, 66-69; dean eng, 75-78, PROF CIVIL ENG, DETROIT INST TECHNOL, 69-, CHMN DEPT, 70-, DEAN, SCH TECHNOL & APPL SCI, 78- *Concurrent Pos:* Dir soils eng, Mich Testing Engrs, Inc, 69- & Construct Testing & Inspection, 76-; consult, Detroit Inst Technol, 69-70. *Mem:* Am Soc Civil Engrs; Am Soc Eng Educ. *Res:* Soil stabilization. *Mailing Add:* 2727 Second Ave Detroit MI 48232

SEHGAL, SURENDRA N, b Khushab, India, Feb 10, 32; Can citizen; m 61; c 2. MICROBIOLOGY. *Educ:* Banaras Hindu Univ, BPharm, 52, MPHarm, 53; Bristol Univ, PhD(microbiol), 57. *Prof Exp:* Asst prof pharm, Birla Col Pharm, 53-55; fel microbiol, Coun Sci & Indust Res, India, 55; Nat Res Coun Can fel, 58-60; sr scientist microbiol, 60-69, head microbial technol, 69-74, ASST DIR, DEPT MICROBIOL, AYERST RES LABS, 74- *Concurrent Pos:* Adj assoc prof microbiol, Concordia Univ, Montreal. *Mem:* Am Soc Microbiol; Can Soc Microbiol; Chem Inst Can; Soc Indust Microbiol. *Res:* Industrial microbiology; bioconversion of organic compounds; antibiotic fermentations; microbial chemistry. *Mailing Add:* Ayerst Res Labs PO Box 6115 Montreal PQ H3C 3J1 Can

SEHGAL, SURINDER K, b Hoshiarpur, India, Apr 22, 38; m 66; c 2. ALGEBRA. *Educ:* Panjab Univ, India, BA, 57, MA, 59; Univ Notre Dame, PhD(math), 65. *Prof Exp:* Lectr math, DAV Col, Hoshiarpur, 59-61; teaching asst, Univ Notre Dame, 61-63; from teaching asst to asst prof, 63-71, ASSOC PROF MATH, OHIO STATE UNIV, 71- *Mem:* Am Math Soc. *Res:* Algebra; group theory. *Mailing Add:* Dept of Math Ohio State Univ Columbus OH 43210

SEHMEL, GEORGE ALBERT, b Puyallup, Wash, Apr 8, 32; m 58; c 3. CHEMICAL ENGINEERING, AEROSOL PHYSICS. *Educ:* Univ Wash, Seattle, BS, 55, PhD(chem eng), 61; Univ Ill, MS, 56. *Prof Exp:* Engr, Gen Elec Co, NY, 57-58 & Wash, 61-63, sr engr, 63-65; STAFF ENGR, PAC NORTHWEST LABS, BATTELLE MEM INST, 65- *Concurrent Pos:* Lectr, Ctr Grad Study at Hanford, 64-69. *Mem:* Am Inst Chem Engrs. *Res:* Program management of aerosol physics research; aerosol particulate mass transfer behavior; meteorology; particulate deposition and resuspension; sampling of aerosols; evaluation of nuclear reactor fuel elements; heat transfer technology. *Mailing Add:* Atmos Sci Dept Pac Northwest PO Box 999 Richland WA 99352

SEHON, ALEC, b Romania, Dec 18, 24; Can citizen; m 50; c 2. IMMUNOLOGY. *Educ:* Univ Manchester, BSc, 48, MSc, 50, PhD(phys chem), 51, DSc, 65. *Prof Exp:* Demonstr chem, Univ Manchester, 48-49 & Nat Res Labs, 51-52; res assoc chem, Calif Inst Technol & Inst Biochem, Univ Uppsala, 52-53; asst prof exp med, McGill Univ, 53-59, from asst prof to prof chem, 56-69, hon lectr biochem, 59-69; PROF IMMUNOL & HEAD DEPT, FAC MED, UNIV MAN, 69- *Concurrent Pos:* Co-dir, Div Immunochem & Allergy, Royal Victorian Hosp, Montreal, 53-59; biophys chemist, McGill Univ Clin, Montreal Gen Hosp, 60-69; Nat Res Coun Can sr res fel, John Simon Guggenheim Mem Found fel & res assoc, Harvard Univ, 63-64; mem, Res Grants Comt, Med Res Coun Can, 64-69; chmn, Gordon Res Conf Immunochem & Immunobiol, 66; dir, NATO Advan Studies Insts, Val Morin, Que, 68, Minaki, Ont, 70; RR Inst res award, Univ Man & Shering travel fel, Can Soc Clin Invest, 73; vis scientist, Walter & Eliza Hall Inst, Melbourne Univ Col, London & Med Res Coun Can, 73-74. *Mem:* Fel AAAS; Am Asn Immunologists; fel Am Acad Allergy; sci fel Am Col Allergists; Can Soc Immunologists (vpres, 67-69, pres, 69-71). *Res:* Antigen-antibody systems involved in common allergies; development of immunosuppressive therapeutic regimens; tumor immunology; immunodiagnostics. *Mailing Add:* Dept of Immunol Fac of Med Univ of Manitoba Winnipeg MB R3T 2N2 Can

SEIB, DAVID HENRY, b Exeter, Calif, Jan 23, 43; m 65; c 3. ELECTRICAL ENGINEERING. *Educ:* Calif Inst Technol, BS, 64; Stanford Univ, MS, 65, PhD(elec eng), 70. *Prof Exp:* Staff scientist solid state physics, tech staff, Aerospace Corp, 69-76; MEM TECH STAFF VI ELEC ENG, SCI CTR, ROCKWELL INT, 76- *Mem:* Am Phys Soc; Inst Elec & Electronics Engrs. *Res:* Semiconductor device research, specifically charge coupled devices and infrared detective arrays; integrated optics devices. *Mailing Add:* 2948 Pemba Dr Costa Mesa CA 92626

SEIB, PAUL A, b Poseyville, Ind, Jan 8, 36; m 58; c 2. ORGANIC CHEMISTRY, BIOCHEMISTRY. *Educ:* Purdue Univ, BS, 58, MS, 63, PhD(biochem), 65. *Prof Exp:* Asst prof org chem, Inst Paper Chem, 65-70; ASSOC PROF GRAIN SCI, KANS STATE UNIV, 70- *Mem:* Am Chem Soc; Am Asn Cereal Chemists; Inst Food Technologists. *Res:* Cereal chemistry; chemistry of vitamin C. *Mailing Add:* Dept of Grain Sci Kans State Univ Manhattan KS 66510

SEIBEL, ERWIN, b Schwientochlowitz, Ger, Apr 29, 42; US citizen; m 68; c 1. OCEANOGRAPHY. *Educ:* City Univ New York, BS, 65; Univ Mich, MS, 66, PhD(oceanog), 72. *Prof Exp:* Logistics officer, US Army Corps Engrs, 67-69; master instr, US Army Engr Sch, 69-70, sect head, 70-71; assoc res oceanog & asst proj dir, Great Lakes Res Div, Univ Mich, Ann Arbor, 72-78, asst dir, Mich Sea Grant Prog, 75-78; PROF OCEANOG & GEOL & DIR, TIBURON CTR ENVIRON STUDIES, SAN FRANCISCO STATE UNIV, 78- *Mem:* AAAS; Am Geophys Union; Geol Soc Am; Marine Technol Soc; Soc Econ Paleontologists & Mineralogists. *Res:* Multidisciplinary approach to the solution of San Francisco Bay Area and adjacent Pacific Ocean environmental problems by monitoring and modeling the physical, effect relationship between nearshore ice, topography, sediments, economic, social and cultural variables involved; investigation of the effect of nuclear power plant operation on the biological, chemical, geological and physical facets of the aquatic environment. *Mailing Add:* Tiburon Ctr for Environ Studies Sch of Sci San Francisco CA 94132

SEIBEL, FREDERICK TRUMAN, b Corning, NY, May 30, 41; m 65; c 1. COMPUTER SCIENCE, PHYSICS. *Educ:* Yale Univ, BS, 63; Duke Univ, PhD(physics), 68. *Prof Exp:* Staff mem, Los Alamos Sci Lab, 68-77; sr prof tech staff, Princeton Plasma Physics Lab, Princeton Univ, 77-81; DIR, AUTOMATION & CONTROL, SYST & ADVAN TECHNOL, MERCK & CO, INC, 81- *Mem:* Sigma Xi. *Res:* Developing computerized data acquisition facilities for plasma physics. *Mailing Add:* 95 Herron Town Land Princeton NJ 08540

SEIBEL, HUGO RUDOLF, b Radautz, Rumania, Nov 9, 37; m 64. ANATOMY, ELECTRON MICROSCOPY. *Educ:* Brooklyn Col, BS, 60; Univ Rochester, PhD(anat), 67. *Prof Exp:* Col sci asst & instr biol, Brooklyn Col, 60-62; instr anat, Univ Rochester, 66-67; from asst prof to assoc prof, 67-75, PROF ANAT, MED COL VA, 75-, DIR ELECTRON MICROS DIV, 67- *Concurrent Pos:* A D Williams grant, Med Col Va, 67-69, NIH grant, 68-71. *Mem:* AAAS; Soc Study Reproduction; Am Asn Anatomists; Pan-Am Asn Anatomists; Transplantation Soc. *Res:* Kidney and heart transplantation; electron microscopy and functional correlates of thyroid and pineal. *Mailing Add:* Dept of Anat Med Col of Va Richmond VA 23219

SEIBEL, WERNER, b Krenau, WGer, Sept 27, 43; US citizen; m 67; c 2. GROSS ANATOMY, DENTAL RESEARCH. *Educ:* Brooklyn Col, BA, 65; Hofstra Univ, MA, 68; Med Col Va, Va Commonwealth Univ, PhD(anat), 73. *Prof Exp:* Asst anat, histol & neuroanat, Med Col Va, Va Commonwealth Univ, 68-72; instr, 72-73, asst prof, 73-77, ASSOC PROF DENT ANAT, SCH DENT, UNIV MD, 77- *Concurrent Pos:* NDEA fel, 68. *Mem:* Am Asn Anatomists; Sigma Xi. *Res:* Structure of odontogenesis; histochemistry and cytochemistry of normal rodent tooth development; development of palate; protein transport through rat placenta. *Mailing Add:* Dept Anat Sch Dent Univ Md Baltimore MD 21201

SEIBER, JAMES N, b Hannibal, Mo, Sept 21, 40; m 67; c 2. ORGANIC CHEMISTRY. *Educ:* Bellarmine Col, Ky, AB, 61; Ariz State Univ, MS, 64; Utah State Univ, PhD(org chem), 66. *Prof Exp:* Res chemist, Dow Chem Co, 66-69; asst prof, 69-74, ASSOC PROF ENVIRON TOXICOL, UNIV CALIF, DAVIS, 74- *Concurrent Pos:* Vis scientist, Pesticides & Toxic Substances Effects Lab, US Environ Protection Agency, Fla, 73-74. *Mem:* AAAS; Am Chem Soc. *Res:* Isolation, structure determination, synthesis and reactions of biologically active chemicals, particularly pesticides, insect pheromones and plant-derived poisons; origin and fate of toxic chemicals in the environment; analytical chemistry of pesticides and pollutants. *Mailing Add:* Dept of Environ Toxicol Univ of Calif Davis CA 95616

SEIBERT, MICHAEL, b Lima, Peru, Nov 15, 44; US citizen; m 75; c 2. PHOTOBIOLOGY, PLANT PHYSIOLOGY. *Educ:* Pa State Univ, University Park, BS, 66; Univ Pa, MS, 67, PhD(molecular biol & biophys), 71. *Prof Exp:* Mem tech staff, GTE Labs, 71-77; SR SCIENTIST & TASK LEADER, PHOTOBIOL CONVERSION OF SOLAR ENERGY, SOLAR ENERGY RES INST, 77- *Concurrent Pos:* Scientist, Exp Sta, E I du Pont de Nemours & Co, 65-68; mem local comt, 3rd Int Conf on the Conversion

& Storage of Solar Energy. *Mem:* Biophys Soc; AAAS; Int Solar Energy Soc; Am Soc Photobiol; Am Soc Plant Physiologists. *Res:* Photobiological conversion of solar energy; primary photochemical processes in photosynthesis; photomorphogenesis and cryopreservation of plant tissue culture; agricultural applications of lighting. *Mailing Add:* SERI 1617 Cole Blvd Golden CO 80401

SEIBERT, RICHARD ALBERT, b Minneapolis, Minn, Mar 16, 13; wid. CHEMISTRY. *Educ:* Aurora Col, BS, 39; Stanford Univ, MS, 40, PhD(chem), 43. *Prof Exp:* Res assoc, Off Sci Res & Develop, Stanford Univ, 42-45; fel, Iowa State Col, 46-47; instr chem, Hartnell Col, 47-48; chmn sci & eng div, Orange Coast Col, 48-50; asst prof, 50-55, ASSOC PROF PHARMACOL, BAYLOR COL MED, 55- *Mem:* AAAS; Am Chem Soc; Soc Exp Biol & Med; Am Soc Pharmacol & Exp Therapeut. *Res:* Drug enzymology and metabolism; synthetic organic chemistry; statistics. *Mailing Add:* Dept of Pharmacol Baylor Col of Med Houston TX 77025

SEIBOLD, CAROL DUKE, b San Francisco, Calif, July 1, 43; m 64; c 1. PHOTOGRAPHIC CHEMISTRY. *Educ:* Creighton Univ, BS, 65; Univ Nebr, MS, 67, PhD(chem), 72. *Prof Exp:* Assoc prof chem, Bemidji State Col, 68-69; res chemist, Environ Res Corp, 72-73; MGR & SR CHEMIST, 3M CO, 73- *Mem:* Am Chem Soc; Soc Photog Scientists & Engrs. *Res:* Mechanisms and kinetics of photographic development. *Mailing Add:* 624 S Lexington Pky St Paul MN 55116

SEIDAH, NABIL GEORGE, clinical biochemistry, biophysical chemistry, see previous edition

SEIDE, PAUL, b Brooklyn, NY, July 22, 26; m 51; c 2. ENGINEERING MECHANICS. *Educ:* City Col New York, BCivEng, 46; Univ Va, MAeroE, 52; Stanford Univ, PhD(eng mech), 54. *Prof Exp:* Aeronaut res scientist, Nat Adv Comn Aeronaut, 46-52; res asst eng mech, Stanford Univ, 52-53; res engr, Northrup Aircraft, Inc, 53-55; head methods & theory sect, Space Technol Lab, 55-61; staff engr, Aerospace Corp, 61-65; PROF CIVIL ENG, UNIV SOUTHERN CALIF, 65- *Concurrent Pos:* NSF sr fel, 64-65; consult, Aerospace Corp, 65-68 & Northrop Corp, 69, Novair Div, 72-77; Albert Alberman vis prof, Technion, Israel Inst Technol, 75. *Mem:* Am Soc Mech Engrs; Am Soc Civil Engrs; Am Acad Mech. *Res:* Stability of structures; nonlinear elasticity; shell analysis. *Mailing Add:* Dept of Civil Eng Univ of Southern Calif Los Angeles CA 90007

SEIDEHAMEL, RICHARD JOSEPH, b Cleveland, Ohio, Dec 26, 40; m 63; c 3. PHARMACOLOGY. *Educ:* Univ Toledo, BS, 63; Ohio State Univ, MSc, 65, PhD, 68. *Prof Exp:* Sr scientist, 69-71, sr investr, 71-74, SR RES ASSOC, MEAD JOHNSON RES CTR, 74- *Mem:* Am Soc Pharmacol & Exp Therapeut; AAAS; NY Acad Sci. *Res:* Respiratory, cardiovascular, ocular and autonomic pharmacology. *Mailing Add:* Mead Johnson Res Ctr Evansville IN 47721

SEIDEL, BARRY S(TANLEY), b Philadelphia, Pa, Aug 27, 32; m 53; c 2. FLUID MECHANICS. *Educ:* Univ Del, BSME, 53; Mass Inst Technol, SM, 56, ScD(mech eng), 59. *Prof Exp:* Design engr, Aviation Gas Turbine Div, Westinghouse Elec Co, 53-55; asst prof mech eng, Univ Del, 59-64; NSF res fel, Calif Inst Technol, 64-65; assoc prof mech & aerospace eng, 65-69, PROF MECH & AEROSPACE ENG, UNIV DEL, 69- *Concurrent Pos:* Vis, Cambirdge Univ, 76. *Mem:* Am Soc Mech Engrs; Am Inst Aeronaut & Astronaut. *Res:* Fluid mechanics of turbomachinery. *Mailing Add:* Dept of Mech & Aerospace Eng Col of Eng Univ of Del Newark DE 19711

SEIDEL, GEORGE ELIAS, JR, b Reading, Pa, July 13, 43; m 70. REPRODUCTIVE PHYSIOLOGY. *Educ:* Pa State Univ, University Park, BS, 65; Cornell Univ, MS, 68, PhD(physiol), 70. *Prof Exp:* NIH fel, Harvard Med Sch, 70-71; asst prof, 71-75, ASSOC PROF PHYSIOL, COLO STATE UNIV, 75- *Mem:* Am Dairy Sci Asn; Am Soc Animal Sci. *Res:* Spermatogenesis and spermiogenesis; in vitro fertilization; oogenesis; application of electron microscopy, statistics and computers to reproductive biology; mechanisms of hormone action. *Mailing Add:* Dept of Physiol & Biophys Colo State Univ Ft Collins CO 80523

SEIDEL, GEORGE MERLE, b Springfield, Mass, Aug 14, 30; m 54; c 3. SOLID STATE PHYSICS. *Educ:* Worcester Polytech Inst, BS, 52; Purdue Univ, MS, 55, PhD(physics), 58. *Prof Exp:* NSF fel, Univ Leiden, 58-59; res assoc & lectr physics, Harvard Univ, 59-62; from asst prof to assoc prof, 62-67, PROF PHYSICS, BROWN UNIV, 67- *Concurrent Pos:* Fulbright lectr, Atomic Ctr, Arg, 73-74. *Mem:* Am Phys Soc; AAAS; Fedn Am Scientist. *Res:* Low temperature physics, electronic properties of metals; magnetism. *Mailing Add:* Dept of Physics Brown Univ Providence RI 02912

SEIDEL, HENRY MURRAY, b Passaic, NJ, July 19, 22; m 45; c 3. PEDIATRICS. *Educ:* Johns Hopkins Univ, AB, 43, MD, 46. *Prof Exp:* From instr to asst prof pediat, 50-68, asst dean student affairs, 68-71, ASSOC PROF PEDIAT, SCH MED, JOHNS HOPKINS UNIV, 68-, ASSOC PROF MED CARE & HOSPS, 69-, ASSOC DEAN, SCH MED, 77- *Mem:* Fel Am Acad Pediat. *Res:* Malignancy; maternal attitudes, medical care staffing; delivery systems. *Mailing Add:* Sch Med Johns Hopkins Univ Baltimore MD 21205

SEIDEL, JOHN CHARLES, b Milwaukee, Wis, Sept 25, 33; m 63; c 1. BIOCHEMISTRY. *Educ:* Carroll Col, Wis, BS, 56; Univ Wis-Madison, MS, 59, PhD(biochem), 61. *Prof Exp:* From res asst to res assoc, Retina Found, 61-70; staff scientist, 70-73, SR STAFF SCIENTIST, BOSTON BIOMED RES INST, 73- *Concurrent Pos:* Res assoc, Harvard Univ, 68-69, assoc, 69- *Mem:* AAAS; Am Soc Biol Chemists; Am Chem Soc; Biophys Soc; NY Acad Sci. *Res:* Chemistry of muscle contraction; electron spin resonance. *Mailing Add:* Boston Biomed Res Inst 20 Staniford St Boston MA 02114

SEIDEL, MICHAEL EDWARD, b New York, NY, Jan 20, 45; m 70; c 2. VERTEBRATE ZOOLOGY, HERPETOLOGY. *Educ:* Univ Miami, BS, 67; NMex Highlands Univ, MS, 69; Univ NMex, PhD(biol), 73. *Prof Exp:* Instr, Univ NMex, 73-74; ASST PROF BIOL, MARSHALL UNIV, 74- *Mem:* Herpetologists League; Soc Study Amphibians & Reptiles; Am Soc Ichthyologists & Herpetologists. *Res:* Comparative physiology and ecology of reptiles; systematics of amphibians and reptiles. *Mailing Add:* Dept of Biol Sci Marshall Univ Huntington WV 25701

SEIDEL, THOMAS EDWARD, b Altoona, Pa, Oct 8, 35; m 60; c 3. PHYSICS, SOLID STATE ELECTRONICS. *Educ:* St Joseph's Col, Pa, BS, 57; Univ Notre Dame, MS, 59; Stevens Inst Technol, PhD(physics), 65. *Prof Exp:* Engr, Semiconductor Div, RCA Corp, 59-60; mem staff, Sarnoff Labs, 61-63 & 65-66; MEM STAFF, BELL LABS, 66- *Mem:* Electrochem Soc; Am Phys Soc; Inst Elec & Electronics Eng. *Res:* Ion implantation phenomena and applications to semiconductor devices. *Mailing Add:* Bell Labs 600 Mountain Ave Rm 2D414 Murray Hill NJ 07974

SEIDELMANN, PAUL KENNETH, b Cincinnati, Ohio, June 15, 37; m 60; c 2. ASTRONOMY, CELESTIAL MECHANICS. *Educ:* Univ Cincinnati, EE, 60, MS, 62, PhD(dynamical astron), 68. *Prof Exp:* Astronomer, 65-73, asst dir, 73-76, DIR, NAUTICAL ALMANAC OFF, US NAVAL OBSERV, 76- *Concurrent Pos:* Lectr, Cath Univ, 66; proj officer, Air Standards Coord Comt, 73-; vis asst prof, Univ Md, 73 & 75; vis assoc prof, U Md, 77. *Mem:* AAAS(secy, div dynamical astron); Am Astron Soc; Am Inst Navig (vpres, 78-79); Am Inst Aeronaut & Astronaut; Int Astron Union. *Res:* Dynamical astronomy; planetary research; general planetary theories; celestial navigation. *Mailing Add:* US Naval Observ Washington DC 20390

SEIDEN, DAVID, b New York, NY, Apr 14, 46; m 67; c 3. MORPHOLOGY, CELL BIOLOGY. *Educ:* City Univ New York, BS, 67; Temple Univ, PhD(anat), 71. *Prof Exp:* Teaching asst anat, Sch Med, Temple Univ, 68-70; instr, 71-73, ASST PROF ANAT, RUTGERS UNIV MED SCH, 73- *Mem:* AAAS; Am Asn Anatomists; NY Acad Sci. *Res:* Electron microscopy and cytochemistry of skeletal muscle and cardiac muscle. *Mailing Add:* Dept of Anat Rutgers Univ Med Sch Med Piscataway NJ 08854

SEIDEN, ESTHER, b Ropczyce, Poland, Mar 3, 08; nat US. STATISTICS. *Educ:* Stefan Batory Univ, Poland, MPhil, 31; Univ Calif, PhD(math statist), 49. *Prof Exp:* Teacher govt primary sch, Poland, 32-34 & Sokolov Girls Col, Jerusalem, 35-41; asst math statist, Univ Calif, 47-49, lectr, 49-50; asst prof statist, Univ Buffalo, 50-52; res assoc, Univ Chicago, 52-53, res assoc & asst prof, 53-54; asst prof math, Howard Univ, 54-55 & Northwestern Univ, 55-58; lectr, Int Statist Educ Ctr & consult, Indian Statist Inst, 58-59; asst prof math, Northwestern Univ, 59-61; assoc prof, 61-65, PROF STATIST, MICH STATE UNIV, 66- *Concurrent Pos:* Fulbright vis prof, Univ Istanbul, 65-66. *Mem:* Am Math Soc; Math Asn Am; fel Inst Math Statist. *Res:* Mathematical statistics, particularly design of experiments; application of electronic computers to mathematical statistics. *Mailing Add:* Dept of Statist & Probability Mich State Univ East Lansing MI 48824

SEIDEN, LEWIS S, b Chicago, Ill, Aug 1, 34; m 62; c 2. PSYCHOPHARMACOLOGY. *Educ:* Univ Chicago, BA, 56, BS, 58, PhD(biopsychol), 62. *Prof Exp:* Res assoc pharmacol, 63-64, from instr to asst prof pharmacol & psychiat, 65-72, assoc prof, 72-77, PROF PHARMACOL & PSYCHIAT, UNIV CHICAGO, 77- *Concurrent Pos:* USPHS fels pharmacol, Gothenburg Univ, 62-63 & Stanford Univ, 64-65; USPHS res grant, 65-, res career develop award, 67-77; career res scientist, 77-82. *Mem:* Am Soc Pharmacol & Exp Therapeut; Am Psychol Asn; Soc Neurosci; Int Col Neuropsychopharmacol. *Res:* Relationships between behavior, drugs and biogenic amines in the brain. *Mailing Add:* Dept Pharmacol & Physiol Sci Univ of Chicago Chicago IL 60637

SEIDEN, PHILIP EDWARD, b Troy, NY, Dec 25, 34; m 54; c 2. PHYSICS. *Educ:* Univ Chicago, AB, 54, BS, 55, MS, 56; Stanford Univ, PhD(physics), 60. *Prof Exp:* Asst betatron, Univ Chicago, 55-56; scientist solid state physics, Missiles & Space Div, Lockheed Aircraft Corp, 56-59; NSF fel magnetism, Univ Grenoble, 60; mem staff, 60-66, mgr coop phenomena group, 66-70, mgr physics group, Res Ctr, 70-72, dir phys dept, Res Ctr, 72-76, dir gen sci dept, 76-77, STAFF MEM, RES CTR, IBM CORP, NY, 78- *Concurrent Pos:* Vis prof, Ind Univ, Bloomington, 67-68; mem, Solid State Sci Panel, Nat Acad Sci, 70-; Lady Davis vis scientist, Technion Inst, Israel, 74-75. *Mem:* Am Astron Soc; AAAS; Sigma Xi; fel Am Phys Soc. *Res:* Superconductivity; metals; magnetism; ferromagnetism; electrical properties of organic materials; galactic structure. *Mailing Add:* Res Ctr IBM Corp PO Box 218 Yorktown Heights NY 10598

SEIDENBERG, ABRAHAM, b Washington, DC, June 2, 16; m 39. MATHEMATICS. *Educ:* Johns Hopkins Univ, PhD(math), 43. *Prof Exp:* Mem staff, Radiation Lab, Mass Inst Technol, 44-45; from instr to assoc prof, 45-58, PROF MATH, UNIV CALIF, BERKELEY, 58- *Concurrent Pos:* Off Naval Res fel, Harvard Univ, 48-49; Guggenheim fel, 53-54. *Mem:* Am Math Soc; Math Asn Am. *Res:* Algebraic geometry; algebra. *Mailing Add:* Dept of Math Univ of Calif Berkeley CA 94720

SEIDENSTICKER, RAYMOND GEORGE, b Elmhurst, Ill, May 27, 29; m 60; c 2. APPLIED PHYSICS. *Educ:* Carnegie Inst Technol, BS, 51; Carnegie-Mellon Univ, PhD(elec eng), 67. *Prof Exp:* Engr, 51-54, RES PHYSICIST, RES LABS, WESTINGHOUSE ELEC CORP, 56- *Mem:* Electrochem Soc; Am Asn Crystal Growth. *Res:* Preparation of semiconductor materials; materials research; theory and practice of crystal growth. *Mailing Add:* 319 Castlegate Rd Pittsburgh PA 15221

SEIDER, WARREN DAVID, b Brooklyn, NY, Oct 20, 41; m 65. CHEMICAL ENGINEERING, COMPUTER SCIENCE. *Educ:* Polytech Inst Brooklyn, BS, 62; Univ Mich, MS, 63, PhD(chem eng), 66. *Prof Exp:* Res assoc chem eng, Univ Mich, 66-67; asst prof, 67-71, ASSOC PROF CHEM & ELEC ENG, UNIV PA, 71- *Concurrent Pos:* Mem, Comput Aids for Chem

Engrs Educ Comt, 69-71, chmn, 71-; vis assoc prof, Mass Inst Technol, 74-75. *Mem:* Am Chem Soc; Am Inst Chem Engrs; Asn Comput Mach; Am Soc Eng Educ. *Res:* Process analysis, simulation and design; computer methods; thermodynamic and physical properties; applied mathematics; energy conservation and conversion processes. *Mailing Add:* Dept of Chem Eng Univ of Pa Philadelphia PA 19174

SEIDERS, VICTOR MANN, b Chicago, Ill, Jan 7, 31; m 65; c 2. GEOLOGY. *Educ:* Franklin & Marshall Col, BS, 58; Princeton Univ, MA, 60, PhD(geol), 62. *Prof Exp:* GEOLOGIST, US GEOL SURV, 62- *Mem:* AAAS; Geol Soc Am. *Res:* Mapping of metamorphic and volcanic rocks in Venezuela, Puerto Rico, Virginia, New England and North Carolina; mapping of Franciscan rocks in Santa Lucia range, California. *Mailing Add:* US Geol Surv 345 Middlefield Rd Menlo Park CA 94025

SEIDL, FREDERICK GABRIEL PAUL, b New York, NY, June 12, 18; div; c 3. MATHEMATICAL PHYSICS, NUCLEAR PHYSICS. *Educ:* Univ Pa, PhD(physics), 43. *Prof Exp:* Assoc physicist, Metall Lab, Univ Chicago, 42-44, Los Alamos Sci Lab, 44-46, Argonne Nat Lab, 46-48 & Brookhaven Nat Lab, 48-55; physicist, Boeing Co, 55-59, Lawrence Radiation Lab, Univ Calif, 59-65 & Inst Space Studies, NASA, 65-71; PHYSICIST, PLASMA PHYSICS LAB, PRINCETON UNIV, 72- *Mem:* Am Phys Soc. *Res:* Numerical calculations of tokamak plasmas, stellar collisions, and underground nuclear explosions; construction of neutron velocity selectors; neutron resonances; light-nuclear reactions; standard neutron source; cosmic-ray asymmetries. *Mailing Add:* Plasma Physics Lab Princeton Univ PO Box 451 Princeton NJ 08540

SEIDL, MILOS, b Budapest, Hungary, May 24, 23; m 61; c 1. PLASMA PHYSICS. *Educ:* Prague Tech Univ, BSc, 47, PhD(phys electronics), 49, DSc(physics), 63. *Prof Exp:* Mem staff, Res Inst Vacuum Electronics, Prague, 49-53, group leader vacuum devices, 53-58; group leader plasma physics, Inst Plasma Physics, Prague, 59-68; vis scientist, Stanford Univ, 68-69; PROF PLASMA PHYSICS, STEVENS INST TECHNOL, 69- *Concurrent Pos:* Lectr, Prague Tech Univ, 60-68; Int Atomic Energy Agency fel, Culham Lab, UK Atomic Energy Authority, 62-63. *Mem:* Am Vacuum Soc; AAAS; Sigma Xi; fel Am Phys Soc. *Res:* Plasma production, heating and instabilities. *Mailing Add:* Dept of Physics Stevens Inst of Technol Hoboken NJ 07030

SEIDLER, RAMON JOHN, b Floral Park, NY, Aug 10, 41; m; c 3. MICROBIOLOGY. *Educ:* San Fernando Valley State Col, BA, 64; Univ Calif, Davis, PhD(microbiol), 68. *Prof Exp:* Asst prof biol, San Fernando Valley State Col, 67; fel, Univ Tex M D Anderson Hosp & Tumor Inst, 70; asst prof, 70-77, ASSOC PROF MICROBIOL, ORE STATE UNIV, 77- *Concurrent Pos:* USPHS fel, Univ Tex M D Anderson Hosp & Tumor Inst, 70-71. *Mem:* Am Soc Microbiol; Brit Soc Gen Microbiol. *Res:* Molecular systematics; aquatic microbiology; bacteriolytic bacteria, structure and function. *Mailing Add:* Dept of Microbiol Ore State Univ Corvallis OR 97331

SEIDLER, ROSEMARY JOAN, b New Orleans, La, Oct 4, 39. ANALYTICAL CHEMISTRY, INORGANIC CHEMISTRY. *Educ:* Loyola Univ, BS, 61; Tulane Univ, PhD(anal chem), 66. *Prof Exp:* Asst prof, 66-73, ASSOC PROF CHEM, CENTENARY COL LA, 73- *Concurrent Pos:* Qual control chemist, O J Beauty Lotion, 78- *Mem:* Sigma Xi; Am Chem Soc. *Res:* Magnetic properties of alpha-amido acid metal complexes; metal complexes of azo dyes. *Mailing Add:* Dept of Chem Centenary Col Shreveport LA 71104

SEIDMAN, ARTHUR HERBERT, b New York, NY, Jan 7, 23; m 49; c 2. ELECTRICAL ENGINEERING. *Educ:* City Col New York, BEE, 51; Hofstra Univ, MA, 58. *Prof Exp:* Sr engr, Sperry Gyroscope Co, Rand Corp, 54-59; lectr elec eng, City Col New York, 59-63; actg dean, Sch Eng, 75-78, PROF, PRATT INST, BROOKLYN, 63- *Concurrent Pos:* Adv ed, Solid State Technol, 60- *Mem:* Am Soc Eng Educ; Inst Elec & Electronics Engrs; AAAS. *Res:* Electronic circuits; microelectronic devices and processes; teaching methods. *Mailing Add:* Pratt Inst 215 Ryerson St Brooklyn NY 11205

SEIDMAN, DAVID NATHANIEL, b Brooklyn, NY, July 5, 38; m 73; c 3. MATERIALS SCIENCE. *Educ:* NY Univ, BS, 60, MS, 62; Univ Ill, PhD(phys metall), 65. *Prof Exp:* Res assoc mat sci, 64-66; from asst prof to assoc prof mat sci & eng, 66-76, PROF MAT SCI & ENG, CORNELL UNIV, 76- *Concurrent Pos:* Vis scientist, Israel Inst Technol, 69-70; Guggenheim fel, 72-73. *Honors & Awards:* Robert Lansing Hardy Gold Medal, Am Inst Metall Engrs, 67. *Mem:* Am Phys Soc; Am Inst Mining, Metall & Petrol Engrs. *Res:* Point and line imperfections in metals; field ion microscopy; radiation damage in metals. *Mailing Add:* Dept of Mat Sci & Eng 130 Bard Hall Cornell Univ Ithaca NY 14850

SEIDMAN, IRVING, b Brooklyn, NY, Oct 3, 30; m 56; c 3. PATHOLOGY. *Educ:* Univ Va, BA & MD, 51. *Prof Exp:* Asst prof, 61-66, ASSOC PROF PATH, MED CTR, NY UNIV, 66- *Concurrent Pos:* NIH fel path, Med Ctr, NY Univ, 58-60. *Mem:* Am Soc Exp Path; Am Asn Path & Bact. *Res:* Experimental oncology. *Mailing Add:* Dept of Path NY Univ Med Ctr New York NY 10016

SEIDMAN, MARTIN, b Brooklyn, NY, June 20, 21; m 44; c 8. CARBOHYDRATE CHEMISTRY. *Educ:* Brooklyn Col, AB, 41; Okla State Univ, MS, 48; Univ Wis, PhD(biochem), 50. *Prof Exp:* Chemist, P J Schweitzer Co, 41-42; asst sci aide, US Dept Navy, 42-43; instr gen & org chem, Okla State Univ, 46; res asst biochem, Univ Wis, 48-50; res chemist, Visking Co Div, Union Carbide Corp, 50-55 & Salvo Chem Co, 55-57; group leader process res, 57-71, sr scientist, Fermentation Lab, 71-73, GROUP LEADER, STARCH SYRUPS & FERMENTATION LAB, A E STALEY MFG CO, 73- *Mem:* AAAS; Am Chem Soc; Am Inst Chemists; Royal Soc Chem. *Res:* Syrup, starch and cellulose chemistry; fermentation; enzymes; process research. *Mailing Add:* Res Ctr A E Staley Mfg Co Decatur IL 62525

SEIDMAN, STEPHEN BENJAMIN, b New York, NY, Apr 13, 44; m 69; c 1. MATHEMATICAL SOCIOLOGY. *Educ:* City Col New York, BS, 64; Univ Mich, Ann Arbor, MA, 65, PhD(math), 69. *Prof Exp:* Asst prof math, NY Univ, 69-72; asst prof, 72-76, ASSOC PROF MATH, GEORGE MASON UNIV, 76- *Mem:* Am Math Soc; Am Anthrop Asn; Int Network Social Network Anal; Math Asn Am. *Res:* Mathematical sociology; graph theory; mathematical anthropology. *Mailing Add:* Dept of Math George Mason Univ Fairfax VA 22030

SEIDMAN, THOMAS ISRAEL, b New York, NY, Jan 7, 35; m 69. APPLIED MATHEMATICS. *Educ:* Univ Chicago, AB, 52; Columbia Univ, MA, 53; NY Univ, MS, 54, PhD(math), 59. *Prof Exp:* Res asst, Courant Inst Math Sci, NY Univ, 55-58; mathematician, Lawrence Radiation Lab, Univ Calif, Berkeley, 58-60; lectr math, Univ Calif, Los Angeles, 60-61; mem, Math Res Ctr, Univ Wis, 61-62; mathematician, Boeing Sci Res Lab, Wash, 62-64; assoc prof math, Wayne State Univ, 64-67 & Carnegie-Mellon Univ, 67-72; ASSOC PROF MATH, UNIV MD, BALTIMORE COUNTY, 72- *Mem:* Am Math Soc; Soc Indust & Appl Math. *Res:* Control theory, especially boundary control for diffusion processes; computational methods for ill-posed problems; partial differential equations; numerical analysis. *Mailing Add:* Dept Math Univ Md Baltimore MD 21228

SEIELSTAD, GEORGE A, b Detroit, Mich, Dec 8, 37; m 65; c 3. RADIO ASTRONOMY. *Educ:* Dartmouth Col, AB, 59; Calif Inst Technol, PhD(physics), 63. *Prof Exp:* Asst prof physics, Univ Alaska, 63-64; from res fel to sr res fel, 64-72, RES ASSOC RADIO ASTRON, CALIF INST TECHNOL, 72-; STAFF MEM, OWENS VALLEY RADIO OBSERV, 66- *Concurrent Pos:* Docent, Chalmers Univ Technol, 69-70; fel, John Simon Guggenheim Mem Found, 69-70; vis assoc prof astron & elec eng, Univ Ill, Urbana-Champaign, 78. *Mem:* AAAS; Am Astron Soc; Astron Soc Pac; Int Astron Union; Int Sci Radio Union. *Res:* Interferometry; polarimetry; extragalactic radio sources; galactic magnetic field; supernovae; galactic nuclei. *Mailing Add:* Owens Valley Radio Observ PO Box 387 Big Pine CA 93513

SEIF, ROBERT DALE, b Cincinnati, Ohio, May 25, 27; m 50; c 4. BIOMETRY. *Educ:* Ohio State Univ, BS, 50, MS, 52; Cornell Univ, PhD, 57. *Prof Exp:* From asst prof biomet to assoc prof agron, 56-69, PROF AGRON, UNIV ILL, URBANA, 69- *Concurrent Pos:* Health, Educ & Welfard grant, Univ Minn, 65. *Mem:* Am Soc Agron; Crop Sci Soc Am; Biomet Soc. *Res:* Biological statistics; data processing applied to agriculture, especially agronomy and horticulture. *Mailing Add:* Dept of Agron Univ of Ill Urbana IL 61801

SEIFER, ARNOLD DAVID, b Newark, NJ, Apr 22, 40. APPLIED MATHEMATICS, SYSTEM ANALYSIS & DESIGN. *Educ:* Rensselaer Polytech Inst, BS, 62, MS, 64, PhD(math), 68. *Prof Exp:* Res specialist appl math, Elec Boat Div, Gen Dynamics Corp, 67-73; mathematician sr staff, Appl Phys Lab, Johns Hopkins Univ, 73-75; sr staff engr, Electronics & Space Div, Emerson Elec Co, 76-; MEM STAFF, EQUIP DEVELOP LABS, RAYTHEON CO, 80- *Mem:* Soc Indust & Appl Math; Acoust Soc Am; Inst Elec & Electronics Engrs; Am Math Soc. *Res:* Interdisciplinary analytical problems of radar system design; radar detection and tracking; analysis and systems design of fire control systems. *Mailing Add:* Equip Develop Labs Raytheon Co 430 Boston Post Rd Wayland MA 01778

SEIFERT, GEORGE, b Jena, Ger, Mar 4, 21; nat US; m 48; c 2. APPLIED MATHEMATICS. *Educ:* State Univ NY, AB, 42; Cornell Univ, MA, 48, PhD(math), 50. *Prof Exp:* Asst prof math, Univ Nebr, 50-55; assoc prof, 55-62, PROF MATH, IOWA STATE UNIV, 62- *Concurrent Pos:* Mem staff, Res Inst Advan Study, 59-60. *Mem:* Am Math Soc; Math Asn Am; Soc Indust & Appl Math. *Res:* Nonlinear ordinary differential equations; volterra integral equations; functional differential equations. *Mailing Add:* Dept of Math Iowa State Univ Ames IA 50011

SEIFERT, HOWARD STANLEY, b Reynoldsville, Pa, Feb 17, 11; m 33; c 3. PHYSICS. *Educ:* Carnegie Inst Technol, BS, 32, MS, 34; Calif Inst Technol, PhD(physics), 38. *Prof Exp:* Teacher high sch, Pa, 32-34; asst prof physics, Kalamazoo Col, 37-40; res physicist, Westinghouse Elec & Mfg Co, 40-42; from asst proj engr to chief liquid rocket sect, Jet Propulsion Lab, Calif Inst Technol, 42-46; chief appl physics div, 46-51, staff engr, 51-54, lectr, 45-48; mem res staff, Ramo-Woolridge Co, 54-56; staff engr, Space Tech Labs, Inc, 56-59; dir adv planning, United Tech Ctr, 60-64, mgr phys sci lab, 64-66, CONSULT, CHEM SYSTS DIV, UNITED TECHNOLOG CORP, 66-; PROF AEROSPACE ENG, STANFORD UNIV, 60- *Concurrent Pos:* Lectr, Carnegie Inst Technol, 42 & US Army Premeteorol Sch, Pomona Col, 43; vis prof, Univ Calif, Los Angeles, 55-59; mem, Off Plans & Progs, Jet Propulsion Lab, Calif Inst Technol, 71-72; Aramco, Saudi Arabia. *Honors & Awards:* Pendray Award Lit, Am Inst Aeronaut & Astronaut, 62. *Mem:* Fel Am Inst Aeronaut & Astronaut (pres, Am Rocket Soc, 60); Int Astronaut Fedn (vpres, 61); Am Asn Physics Teachers; Am Soc Eng Educ; Int Acad Astronaut. *Res:* Chemical and electrical propulsion; space systems; solar and wind energy. *Mailing Add:* 11 Pearce Mitchell Pl Stanford CA 94305

SEIFERT, KARL EARL, b Orangeville, Ohio, Mar 16, 34; m 54; c 3. GEOLOGY. *Educ:* Bowling Green State Univ, BS, 56; Univ Wis, MS, 59, PhD(geol), 63. *Prof Exp:* Phys scientist, Geotech Br, Air Force Cambridge Res Labs, 64-65; from asst prof to assoc prof, 65-72, PROF GEOL, IOWA STATE UNIV, 72- *Mem:* Am Geophys Union; Geochem Soc; Geol Soc Am. *Res:* Behavior and geochemistry of igneous and metamorphic rocks as a function of their environment and rare earth element distribution in anorthosite complexes and oceanic basalts. *Mailing Add:* Dept of Earth Sci Iowa State Univ Ames IA 50010

SEIFERT, RALPH LOUIS, JR, b Alma, Mich, Jan 4, 43. MATHEMATICS. *Educ:* Ind Univ, AB, 63; Univ Calif, Berkeley, MA, 66, PhD(math), 68. *Prof Exp:* Asst prof math, Ind Univ, Bloomington, 68-70; asst prof, 70-76, ASSOC PROF MATH, HANOVER COL, 76- *Concurrent Pos:* Writer, CEMREL-Comprehensive Sch Math Proj, 70-74. *Mem:* Am Math Soc; Math Asn Am; Asn Symbolic Logic; Sigma Xi. *Res:* Foundations of mathematics; general algebra. *Mailing Add:* Dept of Math Hanover Col Hanover IN 47243

SEIFERT, WILLIAM EDGAR, JR, b Bozeman, Mont, Dec 21, 48; m 69; c 1. ANALYTICAL BIOCHEMISTRY. *Educ:* Marietta Col, BS, 70; Purdue Univ, West Lafayette, MS, 73, PhD(biochem), 75. *Prof Exp:* Supvr, 75-76, sr res assoc, 76-77, RES SCIENTIST, ANAL CHEM CTR, 77- & ASST PROF, DEPT BIOCHEM & MOLECULAR BIOL, MED SCH, UNIV TEX HEALTH SCI CTR, HOUSTON, 78- *Mem:* Am Soc Mass Spectrometry. *Res:* Biochemical applications of mass spectrometry; stable isotopes to study biochemical reactions; biochemical applications of x-ray energy spectrometry; investigation of neurological disfunction by mass spectrometry. *Mailing Add:* Univ of Tex Health Sci Ctr Med Sch PO Box 20708 Houston TX 77030

SEIFERT, WILLIAM W(ALTHER), b Troy, NY, Feb 22, 20; m 43; c 4. ELECTRICAL ENGINEERING, SYSTEMS ANALYSIS. *Educ:* Rensselaer Polytech Inst, BEE, 41; Mass Inst Technol, SM, 47, ScD(elec eng), 51. *Prof Exp:* Instr elec eng, Rensselaer Polytech Inst, 41-44; mem res staff, Field Sta, 44-45, from asst to res assoc, Dynamic Anal & Control Lab, 45-51, mem res staff, 51-57, from assoc prof to prof elec eng, 57-70, asst dir, Dynamic Anal Control Lab, 52-55, actg dir, 56, asst to dean eng, 59-62, asst dean, 62-67, dir proj transport, 64-70, PROF CIVIL ENG, MASS INST TECHNOL, 70- *Mem:* Sr mem Inst Elec & Electronics Eng. *Res:* Transportation, computation and control; engineering education; computer modelling of socioeconomic systems; transportation problems in developing countries; environmental problems. *Mailing Add:* 7 Longfellow Rd Wellesley Hills MA 02181

SEIFERT, WOLFGANG K, b Obernigk, Ger, Jan 18, 31; m 59; c 2. ORGANIC CHEMISTRY. *Educ:* Inst Technol, Munich, BS, 52, MS, 56, PhD(org chem), 58; Univ Colo, MS, 60. *Prof Exp:* NSF fel phys org chem with Prof S J Cristol, Univ Colo, 58-60; res chemist, Chevron Res Co, 60-64, proj leader, 65-69, SR RES ASSOC, CHEVRON OIL FIELD RES CO, RICHMOND, 69- *Concurrent Pos:* Teacher, petrol chem, Extension Div, Univ Calif, Berkeley, 78; mem, US-USSR Joint Working Group Oil Experts, 78- *Honors & Awards:* Organic Geochem Award, Geochem Soc, 73. *Mem:* Am Chem Soc; Ger Chem Soc; Geochem Soc. *Res:* Organic geochemistry; petroleum chemistry; natural product petroleum chemistry; petroleum exploration; analytical chemistry; synthetic organic chemistry; natural products. *Mailing Add:* 436 Nova Albion Way San Rafael CA 94903

SEIFF, ALVIN, b Kansas City, Mo, Feb 26, 22; div; c 4. SPACE SCIENCE, ATMOSPHERIC SCIENCE. *Educ:* Univ Mo, BS, 42. *Prof Exp:* Res engr, Tenn Valley Authority, 42-44; tech supvr mass spectros, Uranium Isotope Separation Plant, Oak Ridge, Tenn, 44-46; instr physics, Univ Tenn, 46-48; aeronaut res scientist & chief supersonic free-flight res br, Ames Res Ctr & Aeronaut Lab, 48-63, chief vehicle environ div, 63-72, staff scientist, Dir Off, 72-76, SR STAFF SCIENTIST, SPACE SCI DIV, AMES RES CTR, NASA, 76- *Concurrent Pos:* Mem sci steering group, Pioneer Venus Proj, NASA, 72-82; mem res coun, Off Advan Res & Technol, NASA, 71-74; mem entry sci team, Viking Mission to Mars, 69-76; mem adv comt basic res, NASA, 71-73; mem grad fac aerospace eng, Univ Kans, 79; mem proj sci group, Galileo Orbiter-Probe Mission to Jupiter, 79- *Honors & Awards:* Group Achievement Award, Planetary Atmosphere Exp Test Proj, NASA, 71, Outstanding Sci Achievement Medal, 78. *Mem:* Assoc fel Am Inst Aeronaut & Astronaut; Am Astron Soc; Am Geophys Union. *Res:* Measurement of atmospheres of Mars and Venus; preparing an in-situ experiment for atmosphere of Jupiter; problems of hypervelocity entry into atmospheres of earth and other planets; boundary layers and viscous flows. *Mailing Add:* Mail Stop 245-1 Ames Res Ctr NASA Moffett Field CA 94035

SEIFFERT, STEPHEN LOCKHART, b Iowa, Nov 16, 42. NUCLEAR MATERIALS, METALLURGICAL PHYSICS. *Educ:* NMex State Univ, BS, 67; Univ Utah, MS, 72, PhD(mat sci), 74. *Prof Exp:* Physicist nuclear effects, White Sands Missile Range, 67; res asst, Univ Utah, 70-73; collaborator metal physics, Dept Res Fund, Centre d'Etude Nucleaires, Grenoble, France, 73-75; sr metallurgist nuclear mat, EG&G Idaho Inc, 76-79, scientist light water safety res, 79-81; SR STAFF MEM, BDM CORP, 81- *Concurrent Pos:* Affil prof metal, Idaho Nat Eng Lab Educ Prog, 77- *Mem:* Am Phys Soc; Am Inst Physics; Am Nuclear Soc; Am Soc Testing & Mat; Optical Soc Am. *Res:* Nuclear materials applications and reactor safety research; mechanical properties changes; radiation damage in metals. *Mailing Add:* 1801 Randolph Rd SE BDM Corp Albuquerque NM 87106

SEIFRIED, HAROLD EDWIN, b Suffern, NY, Apr 23, 46; m 70; c 2. BIOCHEMICAL PHARMACOLOGY, TOXICOLOGY. *Educ:* Univ Rochester, BS, 68; Cornell Univ, MS, 71, PhD(biochem), 73; Am Bd Toxicol, dipl. *Prof Exp:* Sr chemist protein & lipid chem & cosmetic ingredient toxicity, Explor Prod Res, Avon Prod Inc, 73-74; Roche fel & guest worker carcinogen metab & enzymology activation deactivation, Nat Inst Arthritis, Diabetes, Digestive & Kidney Dis, NIH, 74-76; biochem toxicologist indust hyg, occup & environ health, Stanford Res Inst, 76-77; GUEST WORKER, TRANSMETHYLATION OF FLUORINATED CATECHOLAMINES & INTERACTION WITH NEUROTRANSMITTERS, NAT INST ARTHRITIS, METAB & DIGESTIVE DIS, NIH, 77-; SR TOXICOLOGIST & PRIN INVESTR, NAT CANCER INST, 77-; SR TOXICOLOGIST, ENVIRON PROTECTION AGENCY, TRACOR JITCO INC, 77- *Mem:* Am Col Toxicol; Am Indust Hygiene Asn; Am Chem Soc; Soc Toxicol. *Res:* Chemical carcinogenesis; metabolism; toxicology; carbinogen and poly-cyclic aromatic hydrocarbon metabolism and binding to nucleic acid; enzymology of activation/deactivation; lipid biosynthesis; toxic substances relating to occupational exposure and carcinogenesis. *Mailing Add:* Tracor Jitco Inc 1776 E Jefferson St Rockville MD 20852

SEIFTER, ELI, b Cleveland, Ohio, Apr 17, 19; m 46; c 1. NUTRITION. *Educ:* Ohio State Univ, AB, 48; Univ Pa, PhD(bot), 53. *Prof Exp:* Asst instr bot, Univ Pa, 50-52; res biochemist, Monsanto Chem Co, 52-57; biochemist, Lond Island Jewish Hosp, NY, 57-62; asst prof, 62-72, ASSOC PROF BIOCHEM, ALBERT EINSTEIN COL MED, 72-, ASSOC PROF SURG, 76- *Mem:* AAAS; Am Chem Soc; Am Inst Nutrit. *Res:* Metabolic pathways; amino acids; metabolic effects. *Mailing Add:* Dept of Surg 1300 Morris Park Ave Bronx NY 10461

SEIFTER, SAM, b Cleveland, Ohio, Dec 1, 16; m 43; c 2. BIOCHEMISTRY. *Educ:* Ohio State Univ, BA, 39; Western Reserve Univ, MS & PhD(biochem), 44. *Prof Exp:* Asst immunol, Western Reserve Univ, 40-44, instr, Med Sch, 44-45, sr instr immunochem, 45; asst prof biochem, Long Island Col Med, 45-49; assoc prof, Col Med, State Univ NY Downstate Med Ctr, 49-53; biochemist, Long Island Jewish Hosp, 54-56; assoc prof, 56-61, actg chmn biochem, 75-76, PROF BIOCHEM, ALBERT EINSTEIN COL MED, 61-, CHMN BIOCHEM, 76- *Mem:* Am Chem Soc; Am Soc Biol Chemists. *Res:* Protein chemistry; enzymology; immunochemistry; connective tissues. *Mailing Add:* Dept of Biochem Albert Einstein Col of Med New York NY 10461

SEIGEL, ARNOLD E(LLIOTT), b Washington, DC, July 16, 23; m 51; c 3. PHYSICS, MECHANICAL ENGINEERING. *Educ:* Univ Md, BS, 44; Mass Inst Technol, MS, 47; Univ Amsterdam, ScD, 52. *Prof Exp:* Mech engr, Signal Corps, US Dept Army, 45 & US Naval Res Lab, 45-46; air conditioning engr, Wm Brown Consult Engrs, 47; mech engr & physicist, 48-61, CHIEF BALLISTICS DEPT, US NAVAL ORD LAB, 61- *Concurrent Pos:* Lectr, Univ Md, 54-; consult, 58- *Mem:* Am Inst Physics; Am Inst Aeronaut & Astronaut. *Res:* Gas dynamics; interior ballistics; thermodynamics; hydrodynamics; high speed flow; stress waves in solids; aeronautical engineering. *Mailing Add:* Ballistics Dept US Naval Ord Lab Silver Spring MD 20910

SEIGER, MARVIN BARR, b New York, NY, Nov 18, 26; m 60; c 3. GENETICS. *Educ:* Duquesne Univ, BS, 50; Univ Tex, MA, 53; Univ Calif, Los Angeles, MA, 59; Univ Toronto, PhD(genetics), 62. *Prof Exp:* Vis asst prof genetics, Purdue Univ, 62-63; res assoc, Univ Notre Dame, 63-64; NIH trainee biol, Univ Rochester, 64-65; asst prof, 65-68, ASSOC PROF GENETICS, WRIGHT STATE UNIV, 68- *Mem:* Soc Study Evolution; Genetics Soc Am; Am Soc Zool; Animal Behavior Soc. *Res:* Population dynamics; quantitative inheritance; behavior and ecological genetics. *Mailing Add:* Dept of Biol Sci Wright State Univ Col Glenn Hwy Dayton OH 45431

SEIGLE, L(ESLIE) L(OUIS), b Dumbarton, Scotland, June 13, 17; m 50; c 3. PHYSICAL METALLURGY. *Educ:* Cooper Union, BChE, 41; Univ Pa, MS, 48; Mass Inst Technol, ScD, 52. *Prof Exp:* Res metallurgist, Int Nickel Co, 38-46; proj leader, Univ Pa, 46-48; instr metall, Drexel Inst Technol, 48; res asst labs, Gen Elec Corp, 48 & Mass Inst Technol, 48-51; head fundamental metall sect, Sylvania Elec Prod, Inc, Gen Tel & Electronics Corp, 51-56, mgr metall lab, Res Labs, 56-65; PROF MAT SCI, STATE UNIV NY, STONY BROOK, 65- *Concurrent Pos:* Adj prof, NY Univ, 52-60; mem refractory metals panel, Mat Adv Bd, Nat Acad Sci, 55-65 & comt on coatings, 66-69; NY Univ exchange metall deleg, Moscow Steel Inst, USSR, 57; vis prof, Univ Pittsburgh, 64-65. *Mem:* Am Soc Metals; Am Inst Mining, Metall & Petrol Engrs; Am Powder Metall Inst. *Res:* Thermodynamics of alloys, diffusion and sintering of metals; protective coatings. *Mailing Add:* 1 Saywood Lane Stony Brook NY 11790

SEIGLER, DAVID STANLEY, b Wichita Falls, Tex, Sept 11, 40; m 61; c 2. ORGANIC CHEMISTRY, BOTANY. *Educ:* Southwestern State Col, Okla, BS, 61; Univ Okla, PhD(org chem), 67. *Prof Exp:* Assoc chem, Northern Regional Lab, USDA, 67-68; fel bot, Univ Tex, Austin, 68-70; asst prof, 70-76, ASSOC PROF BOT, UNIV ILL, URBANA, 76- *Concurrent Pos:* Fulbright Hays lectr, 76. *Mem:* Bot Soc Am; Am Chem Soc. *Res:* Phytochemistry; study of secondary plant compounds; biochemical systematics. *Mailing Add:* Dept of Botany Univ of Ill Urbana IL 61801

SEIGLER, HILLIARD FOSTER, b Asheville, NC, Apr 19, 34; m 61; c 4. SURGERY, IMMUNOLOGY. *Educ:* Univ NC, BA, 56, MD, 60. *Prof Exp:* NIH res fel immunogenetics, 65-67, asst prof surg, 67-70, asst prof immunol, 69-70, CO-PROG DIR, CLIN CANCER RES UNIT, MED CTR, DUKE UNIV, 70-, assoc prof surg & immunol, 71-78, PROF SURG 78- *Concurrent Pos:* Clin investr, Vet Admin Hosp, Durham, NC, 67-70, chief surg, 71-72. *Honors & Awards:* Henry C Fordham Award, 62. *Mem:* Transplantation Soc; Am Col Surgeons; Int Primatol Soc; Asn Acad Surgeons; Soc Univ Surgeons. *Res:* Immunogenetics of transplantation; tumor immunology. *Mailing Add:* Box 3917 Dept Surg Duke Univ Med Ctr Durham NC 27710

SEIGLIE, GEORGE A, micropaleontology, see previous edition

SEIKEN, ARNOLD, b New York, NY, Feb 23, 28; m 55; c 3. MATHEMATICS. *Educ:* Syracuse Univ, BA, 51; Univ Mich, MA, 54, PhD(math), 63. *Prof Exp:* Instr math, Southern Ill Univ, 58-60; asst prof, Oakland Univ, 61-64; assoc prof, Univ RI, 64-67; ASSOC PROF MATH, UNION COL, 67-, CHMN DEPT, 68- *Mem:* Am Math Soc; Math Asn Am. *Res:* Differential geometry, particularly theory of connections. *Mailing Add:* Dept of Math Union Col Schenectady NY 12308

SEIL, FREDRICK JOHN, b Nova Sova, Yugoslavia, Nov 9, 33; US citizen; m 55; c 2. NEUROLOGY, NEUROSCIENCE. *Educ:* Oberlin Col, AB, 56; Stanford Univ, MD, 60. *Prof Exp:* Resident neurol, Stanford Univ, 61-64, fel, 64-65; fel neurol, Mt Sinai Hosp, NY & Albert Einstein Col Med, 65-66; asst prof neurol, Stanford Univ, 69-75; assoc prof neurol, Univ Ore Health Sci Ctr, 76-78; PROF NEUROL, ORE HEALTH SCI UNIV, 78- *Concurrent Pos:* Staff neurologist, Vet Admin Hosp, Palo Alto, 69-76; clin investr, Vet Admin Hosp, Portland, Ore, 76-79, staff neurologist, 79-81; dir, Vet Admin Off Regeneration Res Prog, 81- *Mem:* Int Brain Res Orgn; Soc Neurosci; AAAS; Am Neurol Asn; Am Asn Neuropathologists. *Res:* Tissue culture studies of structure and function of the nervous system, of myelination and demyelination, of the pathophysiology of neurotoxic agents, and of neural development and plasticity. *Mailing Add:* Off Regeneration Res Prog Vet Admin Med Ctr Portland OR 97201

SEILER, DAVID GEORGE, b Green Bay, Wis, Dec 17, 40; m 63; c 2. SOLID STATE PHYSICS. *Educ:* Case Western Reserve Univ, BS, 63; Purdue Univ, Lafayette, MS, 65, PhD(physics), 69. *Prof Exp:* Physicist, Nat Bur Standards, 72-73; temp asst prof, 69-70, asst prof, 70-72, ASSOC PROF PHYSICS, NTEX STATE UNIV, 73- *Mem:* Am Phys Soc; Optical Soc Am. *Res:* Semiconductors; energy band structures; scattering mechanisms. *Mailing Add:* Dept of Physics North Tex State Univ Denton TX 76203

SEILER, GERALD JOSEPH, b New Rockford, NDak, June 4, 49; m 74; c 1. PLANT BREEDING, GERM PLASM. *Educ:* NDak State Univ, BA, 71, MS, 73, PhD(bot), 80. *Prof Exp:* Fel bot & biol, NDak State Univ, 71-73; asst, State Biol Surv Kans, 73-74; res technician agron & crop physiol, 74-80, RES BOTANIST, AGR RES SERV, USDA, BUSHLAND, TEX, 80- *Concurrent Pos:* Curator wild sunflower germ plasm, Agr Res Serv, US Dept Agr, 80-; US coordr, Food & Agr Orgn, UN, Rome Italy, 81- *Mem:* Am Soc Plant Taxonomist; Agron Soc Am; Crop Sci Soc Am; Bot Soc Am. *Res:* Breeding of native species of sunflowers for specific characters of insect pest and disease resistance for commercial production; incompatibility of the species and development of techniques for interspecific crossing and physiology of stress and drought in wild species. *Mailing Add:* PO Drawer 10 Bushland TX 79012

SEILER, STEVEN WING, b Glen Ridge, NJ, May 31, 50; m 72. PLASMA PHYSICS. *Educ:* Cornell Univ, BA, 72; Princeton Univ, MA, 74, PhD(physics), 77. *Prof Exp:* Res assoc neutron diagnostics, Plasma Physics Lab, Princeton Univ, 77-79; SR RES PHYSICIST, R&D ASSOCS, 79- *Mem:* Am Phys Soc; Sigma Xi. *Res:* Neutron and alpha particle diagnostics on fusion research tokamaks and micro instability research on Q-machines. *Mailing Add:* R&D Assocs 1401 Wilson Blvd Arlington VA 22209

SEILHEIMER, JACK ARTHUR, b Kalamazoo, Mich, Nov 12, 35; m 54; c 4. ZOOLOGY, LIMNOLOGY. *Educ:* Western Mich Univ, BS, 60; Univ Louisville, PhD(zool), 63. *Prof Exp:* Instr limnol, Univ Louisville, 62; from instr to assoc prof, 63-73, PROF BIOL, SOUTHERN COLO STATE COL, 73- *Concurrent Pos:* Vis lectr, Colo-Wyo Acad Sci, 65 & 66; consult water pollution, Pueblo City County Health Dept, 66- *Mem:* AAAS; Am Soc Limnol & Oceanog; Ecol Soc Am. *Res:* Stream ecology; algology; plankton; ichthyology; pollution biology; radioecology. *Mailing Add:* Dept of Biol Southern Colo State Col Pueblo CO 81005

SEIM, HENRY JEROME, b Granite Falls, Minn, Mar 20, 19; m 46; c 2. ANALYTICAL CHEMISTRY. *Educ:* St Olaf Col, BA, 41; Mont Sch Mines, MS, 43; Univ Wis, PhD(chem), 49. *Prof Exp:* Asst chem, Mont Sch Mines, 41-43, instr, 45-46; res & anal chemist, Boeing Airplane Co, 43-45; asst chem, Univ Wis, 46-49; from instr to assoc prof, Univ Nev, 49-62; mgr chem res, Res Div, Allis-Chambers, Wis, 62-67, dir, 67-69; MGR ANAL RES & SERV, CTR TECHNOL, KAISER ALUMINUM & CHEM CORP, 69- *Mem:* Am Chem Soc; Electrochem Soc; Am Soc Testing & Mat. *Res:* Instrumental analysis; ion exchange; electrochemistry. *Mailing Add:* Ctr for Technol Kaiser Aluminum & Chem Corp PO Box 877 Pleasanton CA 94566

SEINER, JOHN MILTON, b Upper Darby, Pa, Feb 23, 44; m 68; c 4. AEROSPACE ENGINEERING, ACOUSTICS. *Educ:* Drexel Univ, BSME, 67; Pa State Univ, MSAE, 69, PhD(aeorspace eng), 74. *Prof Exp:* AEROSPACE ENGINEER JET NOISE, NASA LANGLEY RES CTR, 74- *Res:* Supersonic jet noise; nonlinear acoustics; physics of high speed turbulence; laser velocimetry and raman spectroscopy. *Mailing Add:* 103 Wharf Row Yorktown VA 23690

SEINFELD, JOHN H, b Elmira, NY, Aug 3, 42. CHEMICAL ENGINEERING. *Educ:* Univ Rochester, BS, 64; Princeton Univ, PhD(chem eng), 67. *Prof Exp:* PROF CHEM ENG & EXEC OFFICER, CALIF INST TECHNOL, 67- *Concurrent Pos:* Camille & Henry Dreyfus Found teacher-scholar grant, 72. *Honors & Awards:* Donald P Eckman Award, Am Automatic Control Coun, 70; Curtis W McGraw Res Award, Am Soc Eng Educ, 76; Allan P Colburn Award, Am Inst Chem Engrs, 76. *Mem:* Am Inst Chem Engrs; Am Chem Soc; Air Pollution Control Asn; Am Soc Eng Educ; Sigma Xi. *Res:* Optimization and control of chemical systems; air pollution. *Mailing Add:* Dept of Chem Eng Calif Inst of Technol Pasadena CA 91125

SEIPEL, JOHN HOWARD, b Pittsburgh, Pa, Nov 9, 25; m 59; c 4. NEUROLOGY, BIOPHYSICS. *Educ:* Carnegie Inst Technol, BS, 46, MS, 47; Harvard Univ, MD, 54; Northwestern Univ, PhD(chem), 58. *Prof Exp:* Intern, Pa Hosp, Philadelphia, 54-55, resident surg, 55-56; res scientist, Nat Cancer Inst, 56-58; asst resident neurol, Mt Alto Vet Admin Hosp, Washington, DC, 58; chief resident, Georgetown Univ Hosp, 59 & DC Gen Hosp, 60; clin instr neurol, 61-78, ASST PROF NEUROL, GEORGETOWN UNIV HOSP, 78- DIR NEUROL RES, FRIENDS MED SCI RES CTR, INC, 66-; 66- *Concurrent Pos:* Res fel neurol, Georgetown Univ Hosp, 60-61; Greenwalt fel neuroanat, NY Univ, 61; chief neurol lab, Georgetown Clin Res Inst, Fed Aviation Admin, 61-66, sr aviation med examr, Aviation Med Serv, 61-, consult neurol, 72-; consult neurol, Res Div, Md State Dept Ment Hyg & Spring Grove State Hosp, 66-78; staff neurologist, Neurol Serv, US Vet Admin Hosp, Washington, DC, 67-69, chief electrodiag sect, 68-69; dir neurol res, Md Psychiatric Res Ctr, 69-78. *Honors & Awards:* S Weir Mitchell Award, 66; Spec Serv Award, Fed Aviation Agency, 66. *Res:* Biophysics of the cerebral circulation; rheoencephalography and the application of physical science and technology to the solution of medical problems, particularly in neurology, geriatrics and aerospace medicine. *Mailing Add:* 5335 Summit Dr Fairfax VA 22030

SEIREG, ALI A, b Mahalla, Egypt, Oct 26, 27; US citizen; m 54; c 2. SYSTEMS DESIGN, ROBOTICS. *Educ:* Univ Cairo, BSc, 48; Univ Wis, PhD(mech eng), 54. *Prof Exp:* Lectr mech eng, Univ Cairo, 54-56; adv engr res & develop, Falk Corp, 56-59; prof theory appl mech, Marquette Univ, 59-65; PROF MECH ENG, UNIV WIS-MADISON, 65- *Concurrent Pos:* Consult, Falk Corp, 59-, Vet Admin Res, 64-, NSF, 80-82, & Jet Propulsion Lab, 81-82. *Honors & Awards:* George Washington Award, Am Soc Eng Educ, 70; Richard Mem Award, Am Soc Mech Engrs, 73; E P Connell Award, Am Gear Mfg Asn, 74. *Mem:* Am Soc Mech Engrs; Am Soc Eng Educ; Soc Exp Stress Anal; Am Gear Mfg Asn. *Res:* Mechanical systems analysis; computer aided design; robotics; biomechanics; rehabilitation devices; underwater systems; gears and power transmission; friction lubrication and wear. *Mailing Add:* Dept Mech Eng Univ Wis 1513 University Ave Madison WI 53706

SEITCHIK, JEROLD ALAN, b Philadelphia, Pa, Jan 26, 35. SOLID STATE PHYSICS. *Educ:* Univ Del, BS, 56; Univ Pa, PhD(physics), 63. *Prof Exp:* Mem tech staff, Physics Res, Bell Tel Labs, 63-65; sr physicist, Univac Div, Sperry Rand Corp, 65-75; MEM TECH STAFF, TEX INSTRUMENTS, INC, 75- *Mem:* Am Phys Soc. *Res:* Nuclear magnetic resonance; transport properties of thin films; acoustic delay lines; magnetic bubble domains. *Mailing Add:* Tex Instruments Inc PO Box 225621 Dallas TX 75265

SEITZ, EUGENE W, b Regina, Sask, Sept 27, 35; m 63; c 2. MICROBIAL BIOCHEMISTRY. *Educ:* Univ Sask, BSA, 57; Ore State Univ, MSc, 59, PhD(microbiol), 62. *Prof Exp:* Res asst bact, Ore State Univ, 57-59; res fel biochem, 59-62; Microbiol Res Inst, Res Br, Can Dept Agr, 62-63, res officer, 63-64, res scientist, Food Res Inst, 64-67, proj leader flavor res, 67-73, GROUP LEADER FLAVOR RES & DEVELOP, INT FLAVORS & FRAGRANCES, INC, 67- *Mem:* Am Chem Soc; Am Dairy Sci Asn; Can Soc Microbiol; Am Soc Microbiol. *Res:* Creation of and evaluation of natural flavors and fragrances; biogenesis of flavor compounds by microorganisms, especially fermentation and enzyme production by microorganisms and design of microbial and enzymatic processes. *Mailing Add:* Res Ctr Int Flavors & Fragrances Inc Union Beach NJ 07735

SEITZ, FREDERICK, b San Francisco, Calif, July 4, 11; m 35. PHYSICS. *Educ:* Stanford Univ, AB, 32; Princeton Univ, PhD(physics), 34. *Hon Degrees:* Twenty-four from US & foreign univs & cols, 57-78. *Prof Exp:* Proctor fel, Princeton Univ, 34-35; from instr to asst prof physics, Univ Rochester, 35-37; res physicist, Gen Elec Co, 37-39; from asst prof to assoc prof physics, Randall Morgan Lab Physics, Univ Pa, 39-42; prof & head dept, Carnegie Inst Technol, 42-49; res prof, Univ Ill, 49-65, dir, Control Systs Lab, 51-52, tech dir, 52-57, head, Dept Physics, 57-64, dean, Grad Sch & vpres res, 64-65; pres, Nat Acad Sci, Washington, DC, 62-69; pres, Rockefeller Univ, 68-78; RETIRED. *Concurrent Pos:* Dir training prog atomic energy, Oak Ridge Nat Lab, 46-47; sci adv, NATO, 59-60; vpres, Int Union Pure & Appl Physics, 60-; consult educ comn inquiry, Ministry Educ, India, 64-; chmn, Sci Adv Coun, Ill, 64-; Midwest Sci Adv Comt, 65-; mem gov bd, Am Inst Physics, 54-, chmn gov bd, 54-59; mem, Naval Res Adv Comt, 55-, chmn, 60-62; mem, Defense Sci Bd, 58-72, vchmn, 61-62, chmn, 63-72; mem policy adv bd, Argonne Nat Lab, 58-; mem, President's Sci Adv Comt, 62-; mem, President's Comt Nat Medal Sci, 62-, chmn, 62-63; mem statutory vis comt, Nat Bur Stand, 62-66; Grad Res Ctr Southwest, 63-66; liaison comt sci & technol, Libr of Cong, 63-; educ & adv bd, Guggenheim Mem Found, 65; bd dirs, Res Corp, Tex Instruments Inc, 71-, Akzona Inc, 73- & Ogden Corp, 77- bd trustees, Nutrit Found, Rockefeller Found, 64-77, Rockefeller Univ, 66-78, Res Corp, 66-, Princeton Univ, 68-72, Inst Int Educ, 71- & Woodrow Wilson Nat Fel Found, 72-; mem, Inst Defense Anal, 70-; mem, Nat Cancer Adv Bd, 72-74, 77-; mem, Belg Am Educ Found. *Honors & Awards:* Franklin Medal, Franklin Inst, 65; Hoover Medal, 67; Nat Sci Medal, 73. *Mem:* Nat Acad Sci; Am Acad Arts & Sci; Am Crystallog Asn; Am Soc Metals; fel Am Phys Soc (pres, 61). *Res:* Theory of solids; nuclear physics. *Mailing Add:* Rockefeller Univ 1230 York Ave New York NY 10021

SEITZ, LARRY MAX, b Hutchinson, Kans, June 30, 40; m 62; c 1. ANALYTICAL BIOCHEMISTRY, CEREAL CHEMISTRY. *Prof Exp:* Asst prof chem, Kans State Univ, 66-71; RES CHEMIST, US GRAIN MKT RES LAB, AGR RES SERV, USDA, 71- *Mem:* Am Asn Cereal Chemists; Am Chem Soc; AAAS. *Res:* Mycotoxins; fungal metabolites; growth of fungi on cereal grains; composition of cereal grains. *Mailing Add:* 3008 Conrow Dr Manhattan KS 66502

SEITZ, MARTIN GEORGE, b St Louis, Mo, May 12, 44; m 68; c 2. GEOCHEMISTRY, CHEMISTRY. *Educ:* Univ Mo-Rolla, BS, 66; Washington Univ, St Louis, PhD(physics), 71. *Prof Exp:* Fel geochem, Geophys Lab, Carnegie Inst Washington, 71-74; sr engr, Singer Simulation Prods, Singer Co, 74-75; GEOCHEMIST, ARGONNE NAT LAB, 75- *Mem:* Am Geophys Union; Geochem Soc; AAAS. *Res:* Chemistry of trace elements in groundwater and rock; immobilization of radionuclides in rock; chemistry of uranium, thorium and plutonium in crystal-magma systems. *Mailing Add:* Argonne Nat Lab 9700 S Cass Ave Argonne IL 60439

SEITZ, WESLEY DONALD, b Wapakoneta, Ohio, Sept 29, 40; m 64; c 2. AGRICULTURAL ECONOMICS, ENVIRONMENTAL MANAGEMENT. *Educ:* Ohio State Univ, BS, 62, MS, 64; Univ Calif, Berkeley, PhD(agr econ), 68. *Prof Exp:* Asst prof bus admin, 68-70, from asst prof to assoc prof agr econ, 68-74, assoc dir, Inst Environ Studies, 74-82, PROF AGR ECON, UNIV ILL, URBANA, 74-, HEAD AGR ECON & PROF, INST ENVIRON STUDIES, 82- *Concurrent Pos:* Mem Ill Environ Agency Task Force on Agr Nonpoint Sources of Pollution, 77-78. Mem strip mined land reclamation task force, Argonne Nat Lab, 72-73; mem adv comt, Ill Environ Protection Agency on Appln of Sludge on Agr Land, 73-74; Off Water Res & Technol res grants, 73 & 74; chmn, Coun Agr Sci & Technol Task Force Rev Environ Protection Agency Proposed Guidelines for Registering Pesticides, 75; chmn, NCent Regional Strategy Comt Natural Resources, 75-76; US Environ Protection Agency grants, 76 & 78. *Mem:* Am Agr Econ Asn; Am Econ Asn; Soil Conserv Soc Am. *Res:* Alternative policies for the control of non-point sources of water pollution from agriculture; impact of major developments on the social, economic and natural environments. *Mailing Add:* 2203 Fletcher Urbana IL 61801

SEITZ, WILLIAM RUDOLF, b Orange, NJ, May 5, 43; m 69; c 2. ANALYTICAL CHEMISTRY. *Educ:* Princeton Univ, AB, 65; Mass Inst Technol, PhD(chem), 70. *Prof Exp:* Res chemist, Environ Protection Agency, 70-73; instr, 73-75, asst prof chem, Univ Ga, 75-76; ASST PROF CHEM, UNIV NH, 76- *Mem:* Am Chem Soc. *Res:* Analytical applications of chemiluminescence; fundamental aspects of chemiluminescence; flame photometry of nonmetals. *Mailing Add:* Dept of Chem Univ of NH Durham NH 03824

SEKA, WOLF, b Klagenfurt, Austria, May 15, 39; m 63; c 2. LASER PHYSICS, SPECTROSCOPY. *Educ:* Univ Tex, PhD(physics), 65. *Prof Exp:* Nat Res Coun fel, Univ BC, Can, 65-68; foreign scientist, French Atomic Energy Comn, France, 68-70; vis scientist, Europ Space Res Inst, 70-72; res scientist, Univ Bern, Switz, 72-76; SR SCIENTIST, LAB LASER ENERGETICS, UNIV ROCHESTER, 76- *Mem:* Am Phys Soc. *Res:* High power solid state laser physics; yttrium-aluminum-garnet and glass oscillator development; laser plasma interaction experiments. *Mailing Add:* Lab Laser Energetics 250 E River Rd Rochester NY 14627

SEKANINA, ZDENEK, b Mlada Boleslav, Czech, June 12, 36; m 66; c 1. PLANETARY SCIENCES, ASTROPHYSICS. *Educ:* Charles Univ, dipl physicist, 59, PhD(astron), 63. *Prof Exp:* Astronr, Stefanik Observ, Czech, 59-66 & Ctr Numerical Math, Charles Univ, 67-68; physicist, Smithsonian Astrophys Observ, 69-80; PHYSICIST, JET PROPULSION LAB, CALIF INST TECHNOL, 80- *Concurrent Pos:* Assoc, Harvard Col Observ, 69- *Mem:* Int Astron Union; Am Astron Soc. *Res:* Physics and dynamics of comets; interplanetary particles; meteors. *Mailing Add:* Jet Propulsion Lab Calif Inst Technol 4800 Oak Grove Dr Pasadena CA 91109

SEKAR, VAITHILINGAM, b Tamil, India, Nov 29, 52; m 82. RECOMBINANT DNA. *Educ:* Univ Madras, India, BSc, 72, MSc, 74; NMex State Univ, PhD(biochem), 79. *Prof Exp:* Fel, NMex State Univ, 80, mem Sloan-Kettering Cancer Ctr, 81; RES ASSOC, UNIV GA, 82- *Mem:* Sigma Xi; NY Acad Sci; AAAS. *Res:* Mechanism of action of interferon. *Mailing Add:* Univ Ga Athens GA 30601

SEKELJ, PAUL, b Novi Sad, Yugoslavia, Jan 21, 04; nat Can; m 38; c 2. PHYSIOLOGY, BIOPHYSICS. *Educ:* Baden Inst Technol, dipl, 27, Dr Ing, 33. *Prof Exp:* Asst prof physiol, 48-64, asst prof exp med, 65-67, ASSOC PROF PHYSIOL, McGILL UNIV, 64-, ASSOC PROF EXP MED, 67- *Concurrent Pos:* Consult, Montreal Children's Hosp, 48-56, dir dept biophys, 56-; res assoc, Royal Victoria Hosp, 50, assoc scientist, 67. *Mem:* Am Phys Soc; Biophys Soc; Inst Elec & Electronics Engrs; Can Physiol Soc; Am Physiol Soc. *Res:* Techniques and instrumentation for studies on circulation in man; photoelectricity; biological transducers; computers. *Mailing Add:* Dept of Physiol McGill Univ Montreal PQ H3G 1Y6 Can

SEKELLICK, MARGARET JEAN, b New Haven, Conn, Aug 15, 43. ANIMAL VIROLOGY. *Educ:* Univ Conn, BA, 65, MS, 67. *Prof Exp:* Res asst develop genetics, 67-69, res asst virol, 69-81, RES ASSOC BIOL, UNIV CONN, 81- *Mem:* AAAS; Am Soc Microbiol; Soc Gen Microbiol. *Res:* Animal virus-host cell interactions; mechanisms of cell killing and persistent infection by viruses; mechanisms of induction and action of interferon. *Mailing Add:* Microbiol Sect Univ of Conn Storrs CT 06268

SEKERKA, IVAN, b Prague, Czech, Dec 8, 27; Can citizen; m 58; c 1. ANALYTICAL CHEMISTRY, CORROSION. *Educ:* Charles Univ, Prague, BS, 50, MS, 52, PhD(phys chem), 55; Tech Univ, Ostrava, PhD(phys chem), 59. *Prof Exp:* Chemist anal chem, Nat Inst Mat Protection, 51-53, res scientist phys chem, 53-61; res mgr, Nat Inst Motor Vehicles, 62-68; RES SCIENTIST PHYS CHEM, NAT WATER RES INST, 69- *Res:* Electroanalytical chemistry; ion selective electrodes; water quality parameters; water chemistry. *Mailing Add:* Nat Water Res Inst PO Box 5050 Burlington ON L7Y 4A6 Can

SEKERKA, ROBERT FLOYD, b Wilkinsburg, Pa, Nov 27, 37; m 60; c 2. PHYSICS, METALLURGY. *Educ:* Univ Pittsburgh, BS, 60; Harvard Univ, AM, 61, PhD(physics), 66. *Prof Exp:* Technician metall, Westinghouse Res Labs, 55-58, sr engr, 65-68, mgr physics of mat sect, 68, mgr mat growth & properties dept, 68-69; lectr, 65-66 & 67-69, assoc prof metall & mat sci, 69-71, PROF METALL & MAT SCI, CARNEGIE-MELLON UNIV, 71- *Concurrent Pos:* Consult, Nat Bur Standards & Bel Tel Labs Inc; assoc ed, J Crystal Growth. *Mem:* Am Phys Soc; Am Inst Mining, Metall & Petrol Engrs. *Res:* Magnetism; solidification; crystals; applied mathematics; morphological stability; transport processes. *Mailing Add:* Dept of Metall & Mat Sci Carnegie-Mellon Univ Pittsburgh PA 15213

SEKHON, SANT SINGH, b Ludhiana, India, June 20, 31; m 62; c 2. ZOOLOGY, CYTOLOGY. *Educ:* Govt Col, Ludhiana, India, BSc, 52; Panjab Univ, India, BSc(hons), 54, MSc, 56; Univ Iowa, PhD(zool), 62. *Prof Exp:* Res assoc cytol, Univ Iowa, 61-67; RES BIOLOGIST, VET ADMIN HOSP, 67-; res anatomist, 67-80, ASSOC RES ANATOMIST, SCH MED, UNIV CALIF, LOS ANGELES, 80- *Mem:* AAAS; Electron Micros Soc Am; Am Soc Cell Biol; Am Asn Anat. *Res:* Fine structure of germ cells; sense organs of insects; secretion; general cell structure; process of aging in the central nervous system. *Mailing Add:* Med Res Vet Admin Hosp 5901 E Seventh St Long Beach CA 90804

SEKI, HAJIME, b Nishinomiya, Japan, Feb 11, 29; m 66; c 3. SURFACE PHYSICS, ELECTROCHEMISTRY. *Educ:* Res asst physics, Metals Res Lab, Brown Univ, 53-54 & Univ Pa, 54-61; res staff mem, 61-67, proj mgr, 67-77, RES STAFF MEM, RES DIV, IBM CORP, 77- *Mem:* AAAS; Am Phys Soc; Phys Soc Japan. *Res:* Solid state physics of semiconductors, junction, surface phenomenon, photoconductivity; cryogenics of liquid helium, superfluidity, superconductivity; ultrasonic attenuation in crystals; molecular solids; organic surface and interface physics; electrochemistry. *Mailing Add:* IBM Corp Res Lab 5600 Cottle Rd San Jose CA 95193

SEKI, RYOICHI, b Toyama, Japan, Jan 13, 40; m 67. THEORETICAL NUCLEAR PHYSICS, ATOMIC PHYSICS. *Educ:* Waseda Univ, Japan, BS, 62; Northeastern Univ, MS, 64, PhD(physics), 68. *Prof Exp:* Res assoc physics & fel, Univ Denver, 67-68; fel, Univ Ga, 68-69; asst prof, 69-72, assoc prof 72-76, PROF PHYSICS, CALIF STATE UNIV, NORTHRIDGE, 76- *Concurrent Pos:* Consult, Lawrence Radiation Lab, Univ Calif, Berkeley, 74-; vis assoc, Calif Inst Technol, 78- *Mem:* Am Phys Soc; Phys Soc Japan. *Res:* Theoretical intermediate energy physics, including interaction of mesons with nuclei and atoms. *Mailing Add:* Dept of Physics & Astron Calif State Univ Northridge CA 91324

SEKULA, BERNARD CHARLES, b Philadelphia, Pa, Dec 29, 51; m 77; c 1. LIPID BIOCHEMISTRY, ANAEROBIC YEAST GROWTH. *Educ:* Drexel Univ, BA, 74, MS, 76, PhD(biochem), 79. *Prof Exp:* Res asst, Drexel Univ, 74-76, teaching asst biochem, bot, life sci, 76-77, res asst, 77-79; trainee, Fels Res Inst, 79-81; SR MICROBIOL CHEMIST, BEST FOODS RES & ENG CTR, 81- *Mem:* Am Oil Chemists' Soc; AAAS. *Res:* Biochemistry of steroids and other lipids; structure/function relationship of sterols and sterol metabolism in anaerobic yeast; glucocorticoid receptor regulation. *Mailing Add:* Best Foods Res & Eng Ctr 1120 Commerce Ave Union NJ 07083

SEKULA, STANLEY TED, b Niagara Falls, NY, Jan 30, 27; m 57. PHYSICS. *Educ:* Univ Buffalo, BA, 51; Cornell Univ, PhD(physics), 59. *Prof Exp:* PHYSICIST, OAK RIDGE NAT LAB, 58- *Concurrent Pos:* Vis prof, Mid East Tech Univ, Ankara, 63-64. *Mem:* Sigma Xi; Am Phys Soc. *Res:* Superconductivity; radiation damage in solids. *Mailing Add:* Solid State Div Oak Ridge Nat Lab PO Box X Oak Ridge TN 37830

SEKULER, ROBERT W, b Elizabeth, NJ, May 5, 39; m 61; c 3. VISION. *Educ:* Brandeis Univ, BA, 60; Brown Univ, ScM, 63, PhD(psychol), 64. *Prof Exp:* Fel, Mass Inst Technol, 64-65; asst prof, 65-68, assoc prof, 68-73, PROF PSYCHOL, NORTHWESTERN UNIV, 77-, PROF OPTHAL, MED SCH, 77-, PROF NEURBIOL & PHYSIOL, 81- *Concurrent Pos:* Mem, Adv Panel Sensory Physiol, NSF, 74-77, Steering Comt Physiol Optics, Am Acad Optometry, 81-; sr vpres, Optronix Corp, 79-; consult, Nat Inst Aging, 81- *Mem:* Am Acad Optometry; Soc Neurosci; Asn Res Vision & Opthal; Optical Soc Am; Geront Soc. *Mailing Add:* Neurosci Lab Northwestern Univ 2021 Sheridan Rd Evanston IL 60201

SEKUTOWSKI, DENNIS G, b Hamtramck, Mich, Aug 14, 48; m 75. CATALYSIS, INORGANIC CHEMISTRY. *Educ:* Wayne State Univ, BS, 70; Univ Ill, PhD(inorg chem), 75. *Prof Exp:* Res chemist catalysis, Max Planck Inst Coal Res, Muelheim, WGer, 75-77; res assoc, Tex A&M Univ, 77-78; res chemist catalysis, Oxirane Int, 79-81; res chemist catalysis, Arco Chem Co, 81; RES CHEMIST CATALYSIS, MINERALS & CHEM DIV, ENGELHARD MINERALS & CHEM CORP, 81- *Mem:* Am Chem Soc; Sigma Xi. *Res:* Homogeneous and heterogeneous catalysis, especially in relationship to the petrochemical industry. *Mailing Add:* Engelhard Minerals & Chem Corp Menlo Park CN 28 Edison NJ 08801

SELANDER, RICHARD BRENT, b Garfield, Utah, July 21, 27; m 50. ENTOMOLOGY. *Educ:* Univ Utah, BS, 50, MS, 51; Univ Ill, PhD, 54. *Prof Exp:* Instr biol, Univ Utah, 54; asst taxonomist, Ill Natural Hist Surv, 54-58; from asst prof to prof entom, 58-77, PROF GENETICS & DEVELOP, UNIV ILL, URBANA, 77- *Mem:* AAAS; Soc Syst Zool; Entom Soc Am. *Res:* Classification, phylogeny and biology of Meloidae; classification and phylogeny of Coleoptera. *Mailing Add:* Dept of Entom Univ of Ill Urbana IL 61801

SELANDER, ROBERT KEITH, b Garfield, Utah, July 21, 27; m 51; c 2. ZOOLOGY. *Educ:* Univ Utah, BS, 50, MS, 51; Univ Calif, PhD(zool), 56. *Prof Exp:* From instr to prof zool, Univ Tex, Austin, 56-74; PROF BIOL, UNIV ROCHESTER, 74- *Concurrent Pos:* Res fel, Am Mus Natural Hist, 60-61; Guggenheim fel, 65; Rand fel, 71. *Honors & Awards:* Walker Prize, 69; Painton Award, 70. *Mem:* Soc Syst Zool; Soc Study Evolution; Am Soc Naturalists; fel Am Ornith Union; fel AAAS. *Res:* Vertebrate systematics and ethology; population genetics; ecological genetics. *Mailing Add:* Dept of Biol Univ of Rochester Rochester NY 14627

SELANDER, WILLIAM NILS, Can citizen. APPLIED MATHEMATICS, ENGINEERING. *Educ:* Univ Toronto, BASc, 58, MA, 59, PhD(math), 69. *Prof Exp:* Engr, 59-63, RES OFFICER PHYSICS, CHALK RIVER NUCLEAR LABS, ATOMIC ENERGY CAN LTD, 66- *Mem:* Math Asn Am. *Res:* Fluid dynamics; differential equations. *Mailing Add:* Math & Computation Br Chalk River Nuclear Labs Atomic Energy Can Ltd Chalk River ON K0J 1J0 Can

SELBERG, ATLE, b Langesund, Norway, June 14, 17; m 47; c 2. MATHEMATICS. *Educ:* Univ Oslo, PhD(math), 43. *Hon Degrees:* Dr, Univ Trondheim, Norway. *Prof Exp:* Res fel Math, Univ Oslo, 42-47; assoc prof, Syracuse Univ, 48-49; mem, 47-48, permanent mem, 49-51, PROF, INST ADVAN STUDY, 51- *Honors & Awards:* Fields Medal & Prize, Int Cong Mathematicians, 50. *Mem:* Am Math Soc; Am Acad Arts & Sci; Norweg Acad Sci & Letters; Royal Norwegian Soc Sci; Royal Swedish Acad Sci. *Res:* Number theory; analysis. *Mailing Add:* 7 Maxwell Lane Princeton NJ 08540

SELBIN, JOEL, b Washington, DC, Aug 20, 31; m 55; c 4. INORGANIC CHEMISTRY. *Educ:* George Washington Univ, BS, 53; Univ Ill, PhD(chem), 57. *Prof Exp:* From asst prof to assoc prof, 57-67, dir grad studies, Chem Dept, 77-81, PROF CHEM, LA STATE UNIV, BATON ROUGE, 67- *Concurrent Pos:* Petrol Res Fund int fac award, Rome, Italy, 63-64; vis prof, Univ Calif, Berkeley, 72 & Harvard Univ, 82; Danforth Assoc. *Mem:* Am Chem Soc; AAAS; Sigma Xi. *Res:* Bioinorganic chemistry; physical chemical studies on complex inorganic compounds, mainly spectral properties of transition metal complexes. *Mailing Add:* Dept Chem La State Univ Baton Rouge LA 70803

SELBY, HENRY M, b US, Sept 20, 18; m 51; c 3. MEDICINE. *Educ:* La State Univ, MD, 43; Am Bd Radiol, dipl, 50. *Prof Exp:* ASST PROF CLIN RADIOL, MED COL, CORNELL UNIV, 51- *Concurrent Pos:* Asst attend radiologist, NY Hosp, 51 & James Ewing Hosp, 51-; assoc attend roentgenologist, Mem Hosp, 51-; dir radiol, Prev Med Inst, Strang Clin, 65- *Mem:* Am Radium Soc; Am Col Radiol. *Res:* Radiology. *Mailing Add:* 57 W 57th St New York NY 10019

SELBY, LLOYD A, b Denver, Colo, Feb 7, 36; m 63; c 4. VETERINARY MEDICINE, EPIDEMIOLOGY. *Educ:* Colo State Univ, BS, 59, DVM, 61; Tulane Univ, MPH, 64, DrPH(epidemiol), 67; Am Bd Vet Pub Health, dipl. *Prof Exp:* Intern vet med, Vet Hosp, Col Vet Med, Colo State Univ, 60-61;

Epidemic Intel Serv officer, USPHS, 61-63; epidemiologist, Div Hyg & Trop Med, Sch Med, Tulane Univ, 65-67, res assoc epidemiol, 65-67; asst prof community health & med pract, Med Sch & Vet Microbiol, Sect Vet Pub Health, Vet Sch, 67-70, ASSOC PROF VET MICROBIOL, COL VET MED & ASSOC PROF COMMUNITY HEALTH & MED PRACT, DIV COMMUNITY HEALTH SCI, UNIV MO-COLUMBIA, 70- Concurrent Pos: Consult, Mo Crippled Children's Serv, 67-73. Mem: Am Vet Med Asn; Am Pub Health Asn; NY Acad Sci; Asn Teachers Vet Pub Health & Prev Med (pres, 77-79). Res: Study of trace substances as related to human and animal health; congenital malformations; infectious disease of public health importance, particularly zoonoses; study of relationship between companion animals and the social-mental well being of their owners and respective families. Mailing Add: Dept of Vet Microbiol Univ of Mo Col of Vet Med Columbia MO 65201

SELBY, PAUL BRUCE, b Owatonna, Minn, Dec 5, 45; m 70; c 1. MAMMALIAN GENETICS. Educ: Westmar Col, BA, 67; Univ Tenn, PhD(biomed sci), 72. Prof Exp: Res assoc radiation genetics, Gesellschaft fur Strahlen-und Umweltforschung, Neuherberg, Ger, 72-75; RES ASSOC MUTAGENESIS, OAK RIDGE NAT LAB, 75- Concurrent Pos: Mem, Nat Res Coun Comt Biol Effects Ionizing Radiations, 77- & Genetic Effects Subcommittee, 77- Mem: Genetic Soc Am; Environ Mutagen Soc. Res: Radiation and chemical mutagenesis in mice; study of induction and nature of dominant mutations that cause malformations of skeleton; induction of specific-locus mutations; cytogenetics; genetic risk estimation. Mailing Add: Biol Div PO Box Y Oak Ridge TN 37830

SELDEN, DUDLEY BYRD, b Oakhill, WVa, Nov 24, 11; m 39. MATHEMATICS. Educ: Univ Richmond, BS, 32; Purdue Univ, MS, 61. Prof Exp: Asst dir, Ballistic Res Labs, Md, US Army, 46-47, chief proj officer, White Sands Proving Ground, NMex, 48-49, chief tech unit, Off Chief Ord, Washington, DC, 51-53, chief eng officer, Japan Ord Command, Oppama, Japan, 54-55, exec officer, Ballistic Missile Agency, Ala, 57-58, US Army Guided Missile Rep, Brit Ministry of Supply, Eng, 58-60; from instr to assoc prof, 61-74, EMER ASSOC PROF MATH, HAMPDEN-SYDNEY COL, 74- Mem: Math Asn Am. Res: Teaching under graduate mathematics; development of military weapons, especially guided missiles. Mailing Add: Dept of Math Hampden-Sydney Col Hampden-Sydney VA 23943

SELDEN, GEORGE, b Cleveland, Ohio, Oct 13, 15; m; c 2. ORGANIC CHEMISTRY, CHEMICAL ENGINEERING. Educ: Case Western Reserve Univ, BS, 36, MS, 39, PhD(org chem), 42. Prof Exp: Chemist, Upco Co, 36-39; resin chemist & head resin & varnish lab, Finishes Div, Interchem Corp, 41-47; factory mgr, Upco Co, USM Corp, 47-79, pres, 49-79, bus dir, Bostile Div, 79-81; PRES, SELDEN CHEM CONSULTS, INC, 81- Mem: Fel AAAS; Am Chem Soc; Am Soc Testing & Mat; Am Concrete Inst. Res: Factors affecting the adhesion of paint films to metals. Mailing Add: 2 Bratenahl Pl Apt 10D Cleveland OH 44108

SELDIN, DONALD WAYNE, b New York, NY, Oct 24, 20; m 42; c 3. INTERNAL MEDICINE. Educ: NY Univ, AB, 40; Yale Univ, MD, 43. Prof Exp: From instr to asst prof internal med, Yale Univ, 48-51; from asst prof to assoc prof, 51-52, PROF INTERNAL MED & CHMN DEPT, UNIV TEX HEALTH SCI CTR DALLAS, 52- Mem: Am Soc Clin Invest; Asn Am Physicians; Am Col Physicians; Am Fedn Clin Res; Royal Soc Med. Res: Electrolyte and water metabolism; renal function; diabetes; adrenal gland. Mailing Add: Dept of Internal Med Univ Tex Health Sci Ctr 5323 Harry Hines Blvd Dallas TX 75235

SELDIN, EMANUEL JUDAH, b Brooklyn, NY, Mar 20, 27; m 52; c 2. ENGINEERING PHYSICS. Educ: Brooklyn Col, BA, 49; Univ Wis, MS, 51; Univ Buffalo, PhD(physics), 58. Prof Exp: Asst physics, Univ Wis, 49-53 & Univ Buffalo, 53-57; PHYSICIST, PARMA TECH CTR, CARBON PROD DIV, UNION CARBIDE CORP, 57- Concurrent Pos: Lectr, Baldwin-Wallace Col, 64. Mem: Am Phys Soc; Am Carbon Soc. Res: Processing, mechanical and thermal properties of carbon and graphite. Mailing Add: Union Carbide Corp Carbon Prod Div PO Box 6116 Cleveland OH 44101

SELDIN, JONATHAN PAUL, b New York, NY, Jan 30, 42. MATHEMATICAL LOGIC. Educ: Oberlin Col, BA, 64; Pa State Univ, MA, 66; Univ Amsterdam, Dr Math, 68. Prof Exp: Temp lectr pure math, Univ Col Swansea, Wales, 68-69; ASST PROF MATH, SOUTHERN ILL UNIV, CARBONDALE, 69- Mem: AAAS; Asn Symbolic Logic; Am Math Soc; Math Asn Am. Res: Combinatory logic; Gentzen and Prawitz proof theoretic techniques. Mailing Add: Dept of Math Southern Ill Univ Carbondale IL 62901

SELDNER, MICHAEL, b Los Angeles, Calif, July 24, 48; m 67; c 2. PHYSICS, ASTRONOMY. Educ: Rutgers Univ, AB, 72; Princeton Univ, PhD(physics), 77. Prof Exp: LECTR PHYSICS, PRINCETON UNIV, 77- Mem: Am Astron Soc. Res: Cosmology distribution of matter in the universe; infrared radiation in the galaxy. Mailing Add: Dept of Physics Jadwin Hall Princeton Univ Princeton NJ 08540

SELEGUE, JOHN PAUL, b Lorain, Ohio, Dec 31, 52. METAL CLUSTER COMPLEXES. Educ: Miami Univ, Oxford, Ohio, BS, 74; Mass Inst Technol, PhD(chem), 79. Prof Exp: Assoc, Yale Univ, 78-80; ASST PROF CHEM, UNIV KY, LEXINGTON, 80- Mem: Am Chem Soc; Sigma Xi. Res: Synthetic organotransition metal chemistry using spectroscopic and x-ray diffraction techniques; metallacumulene and carbide complexes; metal clusters; reactions of coordinated ligands. Mailing Add: Dept Chem Univ KY Lexington KY 40506

SELF, GLENDON DANNA, b Waveland, Ark, Jan 1, 38; m 60. OPERATIONS RESEARCH, STATISTICS. Educ: Univ Ark, BS, 58, MS, 59; Okla State Univ, PhD(indust eng), 63; Univ Tex, JD, 79. Prof Exp: Qual control engr, Sandia Corp, 59-60, consult, 61-63; sr opers analyst, Gen Dynamics/Ft Worth, 63-64, proj opers analyst, 64-65; from asst prof to assoc

prof opers res, Tex A&M Univ, 65-69; systs engr, 69-70, VPRES, ELECTRONIC DATA SYSTS CORP, 71- Concurrent Pos: Adj prof math, Tex Christian Col, 64-65; consult, Gulf Sch Suppl Educ Ctr, 67, Ctr Naval Anal, 68-69 & Nat Bur Standards, 68-; vis prof mech eng, Univ Tex, 78. Mem: Am Statist Asn; Opers Res Soc Am; Inst Mgt Sci; Am Soc Eng Educ. Res: Non-separable and multi-decision variable dynamic programming solutions; cost modeling of research and development; maintainability-reliability interface; large-scale computer systems software development for the utilities; application of operations research contract law. Mailing Add: Electronic Data Systs Corp 7171 Forest Lane Dallas TX 75230

SELF, HAZZLE LAYFETTE, b Clairette, Tex, Aug 1, 20; m 43; c 4. ANIMAL SCIENCE. Educ: Agr & Mech Col, Tex, BS, 48; Tex Tech Col, MS, 50; Univ Wis, PhD(animal husb, genetics), 54. Prof Exp: Asst prof animal husb, Tarleton State Col, 48-52; assoc, Univ Wis, 53-54, asst prof, 54-59; assoc prof, 59-61, PROF ANIMAL HUSB, IOWA STATE UNIV, 61-, IN CHG EXP FARMS, 60- Honors & Awards: Animal Mgt award, Am Soc Animal Soc, 78. Mem: AAAS; Am Soc Animal Sci; Am Forage & Grassland Coun. Res: Physiology of reproduction; breeding and artificial insemination; environmental effects on farm animals. Mailing Add: Room 20 Curtiss Hall Iowa State Univ Ames IA 50011

SELF, JOHN TEAGUE, b Spur, Tex, Sept 28, 06; m 37; c 2. ZOOLOGY, PARASITOLOGY. Educ: Baylor Univ, BA, 31, MA, 32; Univ Okla, PhD(zool), 36. Prof Exp: From instr to prof, 35-67, chmn dept zool, 46-57, prof lab pract & parasitol, 69-77, res assoc, Stovall Mus, 47-69, REGENTS PROF ZOOL, UNIV OKLA, 67-, EMER PROF LAB PRACT & PARASITOL, SCH MED, HEALTH SCI CTR, 77- CUR PARSITES, STOVALL MUS, 69- Concurrent Pos: Chief, Pre-prof Adv Health Professions, Col Arts & Sci, Univ Okla, 73-77. Mem: AAAS; Am Soc Parsitol; Am Micros Soc (pres, 70); Am Soc Zoologists; Am Soc Trop Med & Hyg. Res: Pentastomida of reptiles; host reactions by mammalian hosts to pentastomes; human pentastomiasis; cestodes and trematodes of wildlife. Mailing Add: Dept Zool Univ Okla Norman OK 73609

SELF, STEPHEN, b London, Eng, Oct 26, 46. VOLCANOLOGY. Educ: Leeds Univ, BSc, 70; Imp Col Sci & Technol, PhD(geol), & DIC, 74. Prof Exp: Fel geol, Victoria Univ, NZ, 74-76; higher sci officer, Inst Geol Sci, UK, 76-77; res assoc, Goddard Inst Space Studies, NASA, & Dartmouth Col, 77-79; ASST PROF GEOL, ARIZ STATE UNIV, 80- Concurrent Pos: Vis scientist, Los Alamos Nat Lab, 78; vis prof, Mich Technol Univ, 79. Mem: Am Geophys Union; Geol Soc Am; Int Unquaternary Res; Int Asn Sedimentologists; NZ Geol Soc. Res: Quantitative volcanology; generation of volcanic rocks; quaternary geology; sedimentology. Mailing Add: Dept Geol Ariz State Univ Tempe AZ 85287

SELFRIDGE, RALPH GORDON, b London, Eng, July 30, 27; m 65. MATHEMATICS. Educ: Mass Inst Technol, BS, 47; Cornell Univ, MA, 53; Univ Ore, PhD(math), 53. Prof Exp: Mathematician, US Naval Ord Test Sta, Calif, 51-59; assoc prof math, Miami Univ, 59-61; assoc prof math, 61-72, dir comput ctr, 65-72, PROF COMPUT SCI, UNIV FLA, 72- Mem: Am Math Soc; Asn Comput Mach; Math Asn Am. Res: Numerical and harmonic analysis; computing technology. Mailing Add: 512 Weil Hall Univ of Fla Gainesville FL 32611

SELGRADE, JAMES FRANCIS, b Washington, DC, Apr 25, 46; m 70; c 2. MATHEMATICS. Educ: Boston Col, BA, 68; Univ Wis-Madison, MS, 69, PhD(math), 73. Prof Exp: Asst prof, 73-79, ASSOC PROF MATH, NC STATE UNIV, 79- Mem: Am Math Soc; Sigma Xi. Res: Qualitative theory of ordinary differential equations, global analysis and biomathematics. Mailing Add: Dept Math NC State Univ Raleigh NC 27650

SELIG, ERNEST THEODORE, b Harrisburg, Pa, Nov 25, 33; m 57; c 3. GEOTECHNICAL ENGINEERING, SOIL MECHANICS. Educ: Cornell Univ, BME, 57; Ill Inst Technol, MS, 60, PhD(civil eng), 64. Prof Exp: Res engr, Mech Div, IIT Res Inst, 57-66, mgr, Soil Mech Sect, 66-68; from assoc prof to prof civil eng, State Univ NY Buffalo, 68-78; PROF CIVIL ENG, UNIV MASS, 78- Concurrent Pos: Geotech eng consult, govt & private orgn, 68-; tech ed, Geotech Testing J, Am Soc Testing & Mat, 78- Mem: Am Soc Civil Engrs; Am Soc Testing & Mat; Transp Res Bd; Am Railway Eng Asn. Res: Dynamic behavior of soils; stress, strain and moisture instrumentation for soils; soil compaction and compaction equipment performance; soil-structure interaction; analysis of buried flexible and rigid culverts; behavior of railroad ballast and mechanics of track structure performance. Mailing Add: Marston Hall Dept Civil Eng Univ Mass Amherst MA 01003

SELIG, WALTER S, b Frankfurt am Main, Ger, Apr 13, 24; US citizen; m; c 3. ANALYTICAL CHEMISTRY. Educ: Roosevelt Univ, BS, 51; Miami Univ, MS, 52. Prof Exp: Chemist, R Lavin & Sons, Inc, Ill, 53-54; Simoniz Co, 54-59 & Sandia Corp, Calif, 59-60; chemist, 60-69, group leader org anal, 69-77, RESEARCHER, LAWRENCE LIVERMORE LAB, UNIV CALIF, 77- Concurrent Pos: US AEC res & teaching fel & vis prof, Dept Org Chem, Hebrew Univ, Israel, 72-73. Res: Research and development of analytical methods for organic materials; applications of ion-selective electrodes to organic and inorganic analysis; methods development in organic materials analysis, especially plastics and high explosives. Mailing Add: Lawrence Livermore Lab Code L-310 PO Box 808 Livermore CA 94550

SELIGA, THOMAS A, b Hazleton, Pa, Dec 3, 37; m 63; c 2. ATMOSPHERIC SCIENCES, ELECTRICAL ENGINEERING. Educ: Case Inst Technol, BS, 59; Pa State Univ, MS, 61, PhD(elec eng), 65. Prof Exp: Instr elec eng, Pa State Univ, 61-65, asst prof, 65-69; prog dir aeronomy, NSF, 67-68; PROF ELEC ENG, OHIO STATE UNIV, 69-, DIR ATMOSPHERIC SCI, 71- Concurrent Pos: Mem rep, Univ Corp Atmospheric Res, 73-; consult, Environ Anal Asn Inc, 73- Mem: Inst Elec & Electronics Engrs; Am Geophys Union; AAAS. Res: Radar meteorology; ionospheric wave propagation; air pollution effects on forests; climatic variability; acid precipitation. Mailing Add: Atmospheric Sci Prog 2015 Neil Ave Columbus OH 43210

SELIGER, HOWARD HAROLD, b New York, NY, Dec 4, 24; m 44; c 2. PHYSICS, PHOTOBIOLOGY. *Educ:* City Col New York, BA, 43; Purdue Univ, MS, 48; Univ Md, PhD(physics), 54. *Prof Exp:* Asst instr physics, Purdue Univ, 48; prof leader radioactivity, Nat Bur Standards, 48-58; res assoc biophys, 58-63, assoc prof, 63-68, PROF BIOL, JOHNS HOPKINS UNIV, 68- *Concurrent Pos:* Guggenheim fel, 58-59; consult, Off Naval Res, 63-65; mem comt biol effects increased solar ultraviolet, Nat Acad Sci, 81. *Honors & Awards:* Meritorious Serv Award, US Dept Com, 58. *Mem:* AAAS; fel Am Phys Soc; Radiation Res Soc; Am Soc Biol Chemists; Am Soc Photobiol (pres, 80-81). *Res:* Radioactivity standardization; bioluminescence; excited states of biological molecules; marine biology of bioluminescent dinoflagellates; photometry. *Mailing Add:* Dept of Biol Johns Hopkins Univ Baltimore MD 21218

SELIGER, WILLIAM GEORGE, b Chicago, Ill, Oct 8, 22; m 45; c 7. ANATOMY, DENTISTRY. *Educ:* Northwestern Univ, BS, 45, DDS, 46; Univ Wis, PhD(anat), 64. *Prof Exp:* Assoc prof anat, Colo State Univ, 64-68; prof anat & coordr, Sch Dent, Med Col Ga, 68-71; prof & chief oral med & chmn, Dept Anat, 71-81, PROF ANAT, SCH MED, TEX TECH UNIV, 71- *Concurrent Pos:* Nat Inst Dent Res fel, 62-64; NIH career res award, 66-68. *Mem:* Am Asn Anat; Int Asn Dent Res; World Asn Vet Anat; Am Asn Vet Anat. *Res:* Gross anatomy; histology; embryology; cytology; bone disease; tissue fluid movement through bone; periodontal disease; steroid secreting cells. *Mailing Add:* Dept of Oral Med Tex Tech Univ Sch of Med Lubbock TX 79430

SELIGMAN, GEORGE BENHAM, b Attica, NY, Apr 30, 27; m 59; c 2. MATHEMATICS. *Educ:* Univ Rochester, BA, 50; Yale Univ, MA, 51, PhD(math), 54. *Prof Exp:* Fine instr math, Princeton Univ, 54-56; from instr to assoc prof, 56-65, chmn dept, 74-77, PROF MATH, YALE UNIV, 65- *Concurrent Pos:* Fulbright lectr, Univ Munster, 58-59. *Mem:* Am Math Soc; Math Asn Am. *Res:* Lie algebras, especially semi-simple Lie algebras. *Mailing Add:* Dept Math Yale Univ New Haven CT 06520

SELIGMAN, ROBERT BERNARD, b Brooklyn, NY, Dec 30, 24; m 51; c 2. ORGANIC CHEMISTRY. *Educ:* Univ NC, BS, 48, PhD(org chem), 53. *Prof Exp:* Res chemist, 53-54, leader, Org Sect, 54-55, supvr, 55-57, asst mgr tobacco res, 57-58, develop, 58-59, mgr, 59-64, asst dir tobacco res & develop, 64-66, dir develop, 66-71, com develop, 71-76, VPRES RES & DEVELOP, PHILIP MORRIS USA, 76- *Mem:* Am Chem Soc; NY Acad Sci. *Res:* Synthetic tuberculostats; tobacco chemistry; consumer product development. *Mailing Add:* Philip Morris Res Ctr PO Box 26583 Richmond VA 23261

SELIGMAN, STEPHEN JACOB, b Brooklyn, NY, Feb 4, 31; div; c 2. INFECTIOUS DISEASES. *Educ:* Harvard Univ, AB, 42; NY Univ, MD, 56. *Prof Exp:* fel infectious dis, Univ Calif, Los Angeles, 61-63, asst prof med, 63-68; assoc prof, 68-81, PROF MED, STATE UNIV NY DOWNSTATE MED CTR, 81- *Concurrent Pos:* NIH grant staphylococcal L forms, Infectious Dis Sect, State Univ NY Downstate Med Ctr, 68-; consult, Vet Admin Hosp, Brooklyn, 70- & St Mary's Hosp Cath Med Ctr, Brooklyn, 71- *Mem:* AAAS; Infectious Dis Soc Am; Am Soc Microbiol; Soc Exp Biol & Med; Am Fedn Clin Res. *Res:* Resistance of bacteria to antibiotics, particularly the penicillins; methicillin resistant staphylococci; L forms; computer applications on bacteriologic data. *Mailing Add:* Infectious Dis Sect State Univ NY Downstate Med Ctr Brooklyn NY 11203

SELIGMANN, EDWARD BAKER, JR, b Buffalo, NY, Oct 28, 24; m 46; c 2. MICROBIOLOGY. *Educ:* Mich State Col, BS, 48, MS, 49, PhD, 51. *Prof Exp:* Asst, Mich State Col, 48-51; bacteriologist, Microbiol Div, Army Chem Corps Labs, Ft Detrick, Md, 51-53, Process Develop Div, 53-54, sect chief, Assessment Div, 54-57, asst chief methods res & agent eval br, 57-59; sect chief lab control activities, Div Biol Standards, NIH, 59-68, chief, 68-72, DIR DIV CONTROL ACTIVITIES, BUR BIOLOGICS, FOOD & DRUG ADMIN, 72- *Concurrent Pos:* Mem, WHO Expert Adv Panel Biol Standardization; mem, US Pharmacopoeia Comt Rev, 75- *Mem:* AAAS; Am Soc Microbiol. *Res:* Prophylactic and therapeutic biological preparations; freeze drying; aerobiology; disinfectants and sterilization; water and sewage microbiology; mycology. *Mailing Add:* Div of Control Activities Bur of Biol Food & Drug Admin Bethesda MD 20014

SELIGSON, DAVID, b Philadelphia, Pa, Aug 12, 16; m 49; c 3. PATHOLOGY, BIOCHEMISTRY. *Educ:* Univ Md, BS, 40; Johns Hopkins Univ, ScD(biochem), 42; Univ Utah, MD, 46. *Hon Degrees:* MA, Yale Univ, 65. *Prof Exp:* Res biochemist, USDA, 42-43; chief hepatic & metab dis lab, Walter Reed Army Med Ctr, 43-45; USPHS fel, Univ Pa, 49-51, assoc prof clin chem in med, Grad Sch Med & dir div biochem, Grad Hosp, 53-58; assoc prof, 59-69, PROF MED & PATH, SCH MED, YALE UNIV, 69-, CHMN DEPT LAB MED, 71-, DIR CLIN LABS, YALENEW HAVEN MED CTR, 58- *Concurrent Pos:* Medici Publici & Med Alumni Asn fel, Col Med, Univ Utah, 66. *Honors & Awards:* Donald D VanSlyke Award, Am Asn Clin Chemists, 70, Ames Award, 71. *Mem:* Fel Am Soc Clin Pathologists; fel Col Am Pathologists; fel Am Col Physicians; Am Soc Clin Invest; Am Asn Clin Chemists (pres, 61-62). *Mailing Add:* Yale-New Haven Med Ctr 6022 CB 789 Howard Ave New Haven CT 06504

SELIKOFF, IRVING JOHN, b New York, NY, Jan 15, 15; m 46. ENVIRONMENTAL MEDICINE, PUBLIC HEALTH. *Educ:* Columbia Univ, BS, 35; Royal Cols, Scotland, MD, 41; Am Bd Prev Med, dipl, 68. *Prof Exp:* Fel path, Mt Sinai Hosp, New York, 41; intern med, Newark Beth Israel Hosp, NJ, 43-44; resident, Sea View Hosp, New York, 44-47; physician, Paterson Clin, NJ, 47-68; PROF COMMUNITY MED, MT SINAI SCH MED, 68-, PROF MED, 70-, DIR ENVIRON SCI LAB, 64- *Concurrent Pos:* Consult, numerous govt agencies, 55-; ed-in-chief, Environ Res, 68- & Amer J Indust Med, 80-; consult, Am Cancer Soc, 71- *Honors & Awards:* Lasker Award, Am Pub Health Asn, 55; Poiley Award & Medal, NY Acad Sci, 74; Haven Emerson Award, Pub Health Asn NY, 75; Nat res award, Am Cancer Soc, 77. *Mem:* NY Acad Sci (pres, 69-70, gov, 70-); fel Am Pub Health Asn; fel Am Col Chest Physicians; Soc Occup & Environ Health (pres, 73-74). *Res:* Health effects of environmental factors, including environmental and occupational cancer. *Mailing Add:* Environ Sci Lab Mt Sinai Sch of Med New York NY 10029

SELIM, MOSTAFA AHMED, b Cairo, Egypt, June 11, 35; US citizen; m 64. OBSTETRICS & GYNECOLOGY, GYNECOLOGIC ONCOLOGY. *Educ:* Alexandria Univ, PNS, 54; Cairo Univ, MBBCH, 59. *Prof Exp:* Intern, Ahmed Maher Hosp, Egypt, 60; house officer, Royal Infirmary, UK, 61-62, Lister Hosp, 62-63 & Fairfield Gen Hosp, 63; residency, Womans Hosp, St Lukes Hosp Ctr, 64-66, chief resident, 66-67; fel pelvic cancer surg & res, Roswell Park Mem Inst, 67-68; pvt pract, Dar El Shiefa Hosp, Egypt, 69-70; instr, 70-71, sr instr, 71-72, asst prof, 72-74, ASSOC PROF REPROD BIOL, CASE WESTERN RESERVE UNIV, 75- *Concurrent Pos:* Intern, St Vincents Hosp, NY, 63-64; dir, Div Gynec Oncol, Cleveland Metrop Gen Hosp, 70- & Div Gynec Serv, 72- *Mem:* Am Col Obstet & Gynec; Am Col Surgeons; Am Fertility Soc. *Res:* Improved methods of early diagnosis of gynecologic cancer and protocols for treatment with irradiation, chemotherapy and radical surgery; improve irradiation response by increasing the blood flow by chemical and physical factors. *Mailing Add:* Dept Obstet & Gynec Cleveland Metrop Gen Hosp Cleveland OH 44109

SELING, THEODORE VICTOR, b Lansing, Mich, Mar 27, 28; m 52; c 2. ELECTRICAL ENGINEERING, RADIO ASTRONOMY. *Educ:* Mich State Univ, BS, 49; Univ Mich, MSE, 60, PhD(elec eng), 69. *Prof Exp:* Engr, Pub Utilities Comn, State Mich, 49-50; ionosphere data anal elec engr, US Army Signal Corp, 50-52; proj engr, AC Spark Plug Div, Gen Motors Corp, 52-54, sr proj engr, 54-60 & Defense Systs Div, 60-62; assoc res engr, 62-69, RES SCIENTIST RADIO ASTRON, UNIV MICH RADIO ASTRON OBSERV, 69- *Concurrent Pos:* Consult microwave receiving systs, Environ Res Inst-Mich, 73-74 & 81-82. *Mem:* Inst Elec & Electronics Engrs; Am Astron Soc. *Res:* Radio astronomy instrumentation; centimeter wave radiometers and associated electronic systems. *Mailing Add:* Univ of Mich 949 Dennison Bldg Ann Arbor MI 48109

SELISKAR, CARL EDWARD, plant pathology, see previous edition

SELKE, WILLIAM A, b Newburgh, NY, June 16, 22; m 52; c 3. CHEMICAL ENGINEERING. *Educ:* Mass Inst Technol, SB, 43, SM, 47; Yale Univ, DEng, 49. *Prof Exp:* Engr, State Water Comn Proj, Yale Univ, 47; assoc chem eng, Columbia Univ, 49-50, asst prof, 50-55, eng mgr, Atomic Energy Comn Proj, 54-55; dir fundamental res, Peter J Schweitzer, Inc, 55-57, DIR RES, SCHWEITZER DIV, KIMBERLY-CLARK CORP, 58- *Concurrent Pos:* Engr, E I du Pont de Nemours & Co, 51. *Mem:* AAAS; Am Chem Soc; Tech Asn Pulp & Paper Indust; Am Inst Chem Engrs; fel NY Acad Sci. *Res:* Thermodynamics; ion exchange; nuclear engineering; dielectric materials; tobacco; paper making. *Mailing Add:* Schweitzer Div Kimberly-Clark Corp Lee MA 01238

SELKER, MILTON LEONARD, b Detroit, Mich, Nov 2, 15; m 41; c 2. PHYSICAL ORGANIC CHEMISTRY. *Educ:* Western Reserve Univ, BS, 36, MA, 37, PhD(phys org chem), 40. *Prof Exp:* Lab asst qual anal, Western Reserve Univ, 35-36, org chem, 37; rubber res chemist, Bell Tel Labs, Inc, 40-46; engr, Kahn Co, 46-52 & Clevite Corp, 52-64, dir, Mech Res Div, 64-69; dir, Gould Mat Technol Lab, Gould Inc, 69-71, vpres, 71-75, vpres res & develop, 76-77, consult, 78-81. *Mem:* Am Chem Soc. *Res:* Physical organic chemistry; rubber-metal bearings; plating of metals; rubber recycling; metal-organic bonding; thin film technology. *Mailing Add:* 3175 Morley Rd Shaker Heights OH 44122

SELKIRK, JAMES KIRKWOOD, b New York, NY, Dec 3, 38; m 61; c 2. CHEMICAL CARCINOGENESIS, BIOCHEMISTRY. *Educ:* NY State Col Environ Sci Forestry, BS, 64; Upstate Med Ctr Syracuse, PhD(biochem), 69. *Prof Exp:* Fel, McArdle Lab Cancer Res, Univ Wis, 69-72; staff fel, Chem Nat Cancer Inst, 72-75, sr staff fel, 74-75; group leader chem carcinogenesis, 75-78, SR SCIENTIST, BIOL DIV, OAK RIDGE NAT LAB, 78- *Concurrent Pos:* Lectr, Biomed Grad Sch, Univ Tenn, 76-80, sr lectr, 80-; assoc ed, Carciongenesis, 79-, Cancer Res, 82-85; mem, Breast Cancer Task Force, NIH, 80-81; mem, Comt Pyrene & Andogs, Nat Acad Sci, 81. *Mem:* Am Asn Cancer Res; Sigma Xi; NY Acad Sci; AAAS; Am Soc Biol Chemists. *Res:* Mechanism of action of chemical carcinogens in in vivo and in vitro systems; the enzymatic pathways involved and species variability. *Mailing Add:* Oak Ridge Nat Lab PO Box Y Oak Ridge TN 37830

SELKURT, EWALD ERDMAN, b Edmonton, Alta, Mar 13, 14; US citizen; m 41; c 2. PHYSIOLOGY. *Educ:* Univ Wis, BA, 37, MA, 39, PhD(zool), 41. *Prof Exp:* Asst zool & physiol, Univ Wis, 37-41; instr med physiol, Col Med, NY Univ, 41-44; from instr to assoc prof, Sch Med, Western Reserve Univ, 44-58; prof & chmn dept, 58-76, DISTINGUISHED PROF PHYSIOL, SCH MED, IND UNIV, INDIANAPOLIS, 76- *Concurrent Pos:* Mem subcomt shock, Comt Med & Surg, Nat Res Coun, 53-58; mem cardiovasc study sect, Nat Heart Inst, 63-67; Nat Sci fel, Univ Gottingen, 64-65. *Mem:* Fel Am Physiol Soc (pres-elect, 75); fel Soc Exp Biol & Med; fel Harvey Soc; fel Am Heart Asn; fel Am Soc Nephrology. *Res:* Physiology of circulation and kidney. *Mailing Add:* Dept of Physiol Univ of Ind Sch of Med Indianapolis IN 46202

SELL, DARRELL, telephone engineering management, see previous edition

SELL, GEORGE ROGER, b Milwaukee, Wis, Feb 7, 37; m 58; c 6. MATHEMATICS. *Educ:* Marquette Univ, BS, 57, MS, 58; Univ Mich, PhD(math), 62. *Prof Exp:* Benjamin Pierce instr math, Harvard Univ, 62-64; asst prof, Univ Minn, Minneapolis, 64-67; assoc prof, Univ Southern Calif, 67-68; assoc head, Sch Math, 70-71, assoc prof, 68-73, PROF MATH, SCH MATH, UNIV MINN, MINNEAPOLIS, 73-, ASSOC DIR, INST MATH & APPLICATIONS, 81- *Concurrent Pos:* Mathematician, Inst Defense Anal, NJ, 66; vis prof, Univ Florence, 71-72, Univ Palermo, 75, Tech Univ Warsaw, 75, Japan Soc Prom Sci, 77 & Australian Nat Univ, 79; prog dir, NSF, 77-78. *Mem:* Am Math Soc; Math Asn Am; Soc Indust & Appl Math. *Res:* Topological dynamics and the qualitative theory of ordinary differential equations with applications in celestial mechanics, control theory and biological systems; integral equations; applied mathematics. *Mailing Add:* Sch of Math Univ of Minn Minneapolis MN 55455

SELL, HAROLD MELVIN, b Waseca, Minn, June 7, 05; m 39; c 2. BIOCHEMISTRY. *Educ:* NCent Col, AB, 29; Mich State Univ, MS, 31; Univ Wis, PhD(biochem), 38. *Prof Exp:* Asst chem, NCent Col, 27-29; asst organ chem, Mich State Univ, 29-31; res chem, Gen Foods Corp, 31-35; asst biochem, Univ Wis, 35-39; assoc chemist, Bur Plant Indust, USDA, 39-45; res prof agr chem, 45-61, prof, 61-75, EMER PROF BIOCHEM, MICH STATE UNIV, 75- *Mem:* AAAS; Am Chem Soc; Am Soc Plant Physiol; Am Inst Biol Sci; Am Soc Biol Chem. *Res:* Biochemical genetic studies of sex expression in high plants; isolation, characterization and metabolism of plant growth regulators; effect of plant hormone derivatives on biological activity. *Mailing Add:* Dept of Biochem Mich State Univ East Lansing MI 48824

SELL, JEFFREY ALAN, b Anderson, Ind, Sept 18, 52; div. CHEMICAL PHYSICS. *Educ:* Purdue Univ, BS, 74; Calif Inst Technol, PhD(chem), 79. *Prof Exp:* Assoc sr res scientist, 78-80, SR RES SCIENTIST PHYSICS, GEN MOTORS RES LABS, 80- *Concurrent Pos:* Lectr physics & math, Lawrence Inst Technol, 81- *Mem:* Optical Soc Am; Am Chem Soc. *Res:* Tunable diode laser spectroscopy; ultraviolet photoelectron spectroscopy; visible laser spectroscopy of rare earth crystals; thermodynamics; Raman spectroscopy. *Mailing Add:* Dept Physics Gen Motors Res Lab Warren MI 48090

SELL, JERRY LEE, b Adel, Iowa, Feb 6, 31; m 53; c 2. ANIMAL NUTRITION. *Educ:* Iowa State Univ, BS, 57, MS, 58, PhD(poultry nutrit), 60. *Prof Exp:* Assoc prof animal sci, Univ Man, 60-66; assoc prof animal sci, 66-68, prof animal nutrit, NDak State Univ, 68-76; PROF ANIMAL NUTRIT, IOWA STATE UNIV, 76- *Concurrent Pos:* Chmn poultry subcomt, Comt Animal Nutrit, Nat Res Coun Can, 62-64. *Honors & Awards:* Poultry Nutrition Research Award, Am Feed Mfrs, 78. *Mem:* AAAS; Am Inst Nutrit; Am Inst Biol Sci; Am Poultry Sci Asn; World Poultry Sci Asn. *Res:* Energy efficiency of chickens and turkeys; metabolism of minerals. *Mailing Add:* Dept of Animal Sci Iowa State Univ Ames IA 50011

SELL, JOHN EDWARD, b Gainesville, Fla, June 14, 41. BIOCHEMISTRY, IMMUNOLOGY. *Educ:* Mich State Univ, BS, 63; Univ Wis-Madison, MS, 67; Univ Cincinnati, PhD(biochem), 71. *Prof Exp:* Res assoc microbiol, Univ Mich, Ann Arbor, 71-73, res assoc internal med, 73-76; RES ASSOC BIOCHEM, MICH STATE UNIV, 80- *Mem:* AAAS; Am Chem Soc. *Res:* Biochemistry of neonatal respiration; carcinofetal antigens; cellular fluorescence specroscopy. *Mailing Add:* Dept Biochem Mich State Univ East Lansing MI 48824

SELL, KENNETH W, b Valley City, NDak, Apr 29, 31; m 50; c 4. BLOOD BANKING. *Educ:* Univ NDak, BA, 53; Harvard Med Sch, MD, 56; Cambridge Univ, PhD(immunopath), 68. *Prof Exp:* Intern & resident, Bethesda Naval Hosp, 56-59, mem pediat staff, 59-60; dir, Navy Tissue Bank, Md, 60-70; chmn, Dept Clin & Exp Immunol, Navy Med Res Inst, 70-77; SCI DIR, NAT INST ALLERGY & INFECTIOUS DIS, NIH, 77-; CLIN PROF, DEPT PEDIAT, GEORGETOWN SCH MED, 73- *Concurrent Pos:* Command officer, Navy Med Res Inst, 74-77; lectr, Found Advan Educ Sci, NIH, 60-; dir, Transplantation Serv, Nat Naval Med Ctr, 71-77; lectr, Uniformed Serv Univ Health Sci, 77- *Mem:* Am Asn Tissue Banks; Soc Cryobiol; Transplantation Soc; Am Acad Pediat; Am Col Path. *Res:* Clinical immunology and transplantation with contributions to immunoparasitology and immune regulation of responses to viral diseases; experimental and clinical study of immunosuppression for organ transplantation. *Mailing Add:* Nat Inst Allergy & Infectious Dis Bldg 10 Rm 11C103 NIH Bethesda MD 20205

SELL, NANCY JEAN, b Milwaukee, Wis, Jan 18, 45. CHEMICAL PHYSICS. *Educ:* Lawrence Univ, BA, 67; Northwestern Univ, MS, 68, PhD(chem physics), 72. *Prof Exp:* Asst prof, 71-77, ASSOC PROF CHEM & PHYSICS, UNIV WIS-GREEN BAY, 77-, CHMN DEPT, 81-, COORDR, GRAD PROG ENVIRON SCI, 81- *Concurrent Pos:* Consult, Allis Chalmers, 74-76 & Gen Portland, Inc, 75-78, Chem Specialty Prod Co, 81 & numerous law firms. *Mem:* Am Phys Soc; Am Chem Soc; AAAS; Am Soc Testing & Mat; Sigma Xi. *Res:* Industrial resource recovery and subsequent industrial energy conservation; industrial pollution control. *Mailing Add:* Col of Environ Sci Univ of Wis Green Bay WI 54302

SELL, SARAH H WOOD, b Birmingham, Ala, Mar 20, 13; m 52; c 2. PEDIATRICS. *Educ:* Berea Col, AB, 34; Vanderbilt Univ, MS, 38, MD, 48; Am Bd Pediat, dipl, 54. *Prof Exp:* Intern pediat, Vanderbilt Univ Hosp, 48-49; resident, Cincinnati Children's Hosp, 49-51; instr microbiol & pediat, Sch Med, La State Univ, 51-53; instr pediat, Sch Med, Tulane Univ, 53-54; from instr to prof, 54-78, EMER PROF PEDIAT, SCH MED, VANDERBILT UNIV, 78- *Concurrent Pos:* Res fel microbiol & pediat, Sch Med, La State Univ, 51-53; med consult, Tenn State Dept Pub Health. *Mem:* Am Pediat Soc; Am Acad Pediat; Am Col Chest Physicians; Infectious Dis Soc Am; Am Soc Microbiol. *Res:* Infectious disease of children, especially Hemophilus influenzae, respiratory infections and immunizations; bacterial polysaccharide vaccines in infants and young children; natural history of etitis media in infants and young children. *Mailing Add:* Dept of Pediat Vanderbilt Univ Sch of Med Nashville TN 37232

SELL, STEWART, b Pittsburgh, Pa, Jan 20, 35; c 4. PATHOLOGY, IMMUNOLOGY. *Educ:* Col William & Mary, BS, 56; Univ Pittsburgh, MD, 60; Am Bd Path, dipl, 66; Am Bd Lab Immunol, 81. *Prof Exp:* Intern & asst resident path, Mass Gen Hosp, 60-62; res assoc, NIH, 62-64; from instr to assoc prof, Sch Med, Univ Pittsburgh, 65-70; from assoc prof to prof path, Sch Med, Univ Calif, San Diego, 70-82; PROF PATH & CHMN DEPT, PATH LAB MED, UNIV TEX HEALTH SCI CTR, HOUSTON, 82- *Concurrent Pos:* Nat Inst Allergy & Infectious Dis spec fel, Univ Birmingham, Eng, 64-65 & res career develop award, 65-70; mem adv path study sect B, NIH, 72-76. *Mem:* AAAS; Brit Soc Immunol; Am Asn Immunologists; NY Acad Sci; Am Soc Exp Path. *Res:* Immunology and pathology, lymphocyte receptors; alpha fetoprotein; chemical carcinogenesis; syphilis; shope fibroma. *Mailing Add:* Dept Path Sch Med Univ Calif at San Diego La Jolla CA 92093

SELLARS, JOHN R(ANDOLPH), b Ft Stanton, NMex, Mar 1, 25; m 50; c 3. AERONAUTICAL ENGINEERING. *Educ:* NMex State Univ, BS, 45; Univ Mich, MS, 50, PhD(aeronaut eng), 52. *Prof Exp:* Res assoc, Appl Physics Lab, Johns Hopkins Univ, 45-46; res assoc, Univ Mich, 46-52, asst prof, 52-55; mem tech staff, TRW Systs, 55-58, mgr aerodyn dept, 58-61, dir aerosci lab, 61-66, mgr systs labs eng oper, 66-69, mgr, Res & Technol Opers, Appl Technol Div, TRW Syts, 69-81, VPRES & GEN MGR, ENERGY TECHNOL DIV, TRW ENERGY DEVELOP GROUP, 81- *Mem:* Am Inst Aeronaut & Astronaut; Sigma Xi. *Res:* Reentry systems; stability of flow; heat transfer. *Mailing Add:* TRW Energy Group One Space Park Redondo Beach CA 90278

SELLAS, JAMES THOMAS, b Chicago, Ill, Dec 29, 24; m 51. ORGANIC CHEMISTRY. *Educ:* Univ Iowa, PhD(chem), 54. *Prof Exp:* Chemist, Stand Oil Co, 53-59, Aerojet-Gen Corp, Gen Tire & Rubber Co, 59-71 & Aerojet Solid Propulsion Co, 71-75, sr chem specialist, Aerojet Solid Propulsion Co, 75-78, SR CHEM SPECIALIST, AEROJET TACTICAL SYST CO, 78- *Mem:* Am Chem Soc. *Res:* Polymer chemistry; development of new and novel class of controllable high burning rate propellants for thrust vector control and controllable solid rocket application; expanding the technology of extinguishable solid propellants and the use of new oxidizers; expanding technology of ultra high burning rate propellants. *Mailing Add:* 3708 Lynwood Way Sacramento CA 95825

SELLE, JAMES EDWARD, b Waukesha, Wis, Sept 1, 31; m 58; c 2. METALLURGICAL ENGINEERING, MATERIALS ENGINEERING. *Educ:* Univ Wis, BS, 55, MS, 56; Univ Cincinnati, PhD(metall eng), 67. *Prof Exp:* Res engr, Gen Motors Res Staff, Mich, 56-58 & Dayton Malleable Iron Co, Ohio, 58; sr res chemist, Mound Lab, Monsanto Res Corp, 58-67, group leader, 67-70, sr res specialist, 70-73; res staff mem, Oak Ridge Nat Lab, 74-80; SR RES SPECIALIST, ENERGY SYST GROUP, ROCKWELL INT, GOLDEN, COLO, 80- *Honors & Awards:* Wilson Award, Am Soc Metals, 72. *Mem:* Am Soc Metals; Sigma Xi. *Res:* Equilibrium diagrams; allotropic transformations; compatibility; nuclear reactor fuels studies; high temperature reactions; liquid metal corrosion. *Mailing Add:* 4755 W 101 St Place Westminster CO 80030

SELLECK, GEORGE WILBUR, b Sask, Can, Jan 28, 24; m 48; c 2. PLANT ECOLOGY, WEED SCIENCE. *Educ:* Univ Sask, BSA, 50, MSc, 53; Univ Wis, PhD(bot), 59. *Prof Exp:* Weed ecologist, Univ Sask, 53-55, instr ecol, 56, asst prof, 56-60; sr proj mgr, Monsanto Co, 60-63, mgr agr sales, Monsanto Europe, 63-66, mgr agr develop, 66-68, regional mgr mkt develop, 68-73, sr develop assoc, Monsanto Co, 73-75; PROF HORT & SUPT RES FARM, CORNELL UNIV, 75- *Mem:* AAAS; Ecol Soc Am; Weed Sci Soc Am; Can Soc Agron; Agr Inst Can. *Res:* Ecology of native vegetation; life history of perennial weeds; agricultural pesticides; weed control in horticultural crops; fertilization practise in potatoes and turf in relation to nitrate pollution in underground water. *Mailing Add:* Long Island Hort Res Lab 39 Sound Ave Riverhead NY 11901

SELLERS, ALFRED MAYER, b Philadelphia, Pa, Feb 23, 24; m 52; c 2. MEDICINE. *Educ:* Duke Univ, BS & MD, 51; Am Bd Internal Med, dipl, 58, recert, 75. *Hon Degrees:* MA, Univ Pa, 71. *Prof Exp:* Asst instr, 52-54, instr, 54-56, assoc, 56-59, asst prof, 59-66, chief hypertension clin, Univ Hosp, 61-71, ASSOC PROF MED, UNIV HOSP & MED SCH, UNIV PA, 66- *Concurrent Pos:* Attend physician, Vet Admin Hosp, Philadelphia, 67-; mem coun high blood pressure res & mem med adv bd & fel coun clin cardiol, Am Heart Asn. *Mem:* AAAS; fel Am Col Physicians; Am Fedn Clin Res; fel Am Col Cardiol; fel Am Col Chest Physicians. *Res:* Internal medicine; cardiology; hypertension. *Mailing Add:* Dept of Med Univ of Pa Hosp 3600 Spruce St Philadelphia PA 19104

SELLERS, ALVIN FERNER, b Somerset, Pa, Aug 9, 17; m 42; c 3. VETERINARY PHYSIOLOGY. *Educ:* Univ Pa, VMD, 39; Ohio State Univ, MS, 40; Univ Minn, PhD, 49. *Prof Exp:* Asst, Ohio State l)niv, 39-40; instr animal physiol, Univ Minn, 40-42 & 46-49, assoc prof vet physiol, 49-54, prof vet physiol & pharmacol & head div, 54-60; PROF PHYSIOL, NY STATE VET COL, CORNELL UNIV, 60- *Concurrent Pos:* Guggenheim fel, Physiol Lab, Cambridge & Rowett Res Inst, Scotland, 57-58. *Mem:* Am Physiol Soc; Soc Exp Biol & Med; Am Gastroenterol Asn. *Res:* Ruminant digestive tract; absorption; blood flow. *Mailing Add:* Dept of Physiol Biochem & Pharma NY State Vet Col Cornell Univ Ithaca NY 14850

SELLERS, ALVIN LOUIS, b Philadelphia, Pa, Oct 16, 16; m 42; c 3. PHYSIOLOGY. *Educ:* Univ Calif, Los Angeles, BA, 40; Univ Calif, MD, 43. *Prof Exp:* Intern med, Univ Calif Hosp, 43-44; resident, Permanente Hosp, 44-46; res assoc, 50-70, SR RES ASSOC, CEDARS OF LEBANON HOSP, 70-; CLIN PROF MED, UNIV CALIF, LOS ANGELES, 79- *Concurrent Pos:* Nat Res Coun res fel, St Mary's Hosp Med Sch, Eng, 47-48; res fel, Cedars of Lebanon Hosp, Los Angeles, 48-49; assoc clin prof med, Univ Southern Calif, 56-73. *Mem:* Soc Exp Biol & Med; Am Physiol Soc; Am Heart Asn. *Res:* Physiology of the kidneys; hypertension. *Mailing Add:* Inst for Med Res Cedars-Sinai Med Ctr Los Angeles CA 90029

SELLERS, CLETUS MILLER, JR, b Harrisonburg, Va, Sept 6, 44; m 70. ENVIRONMENTAL PHYSIOLOGY. *Educ:* Hampden-Sydney Col, BA, 66; James Madison Univ, MS, 70; Va Polytech Inst & State Univ, PhD(zool), 73. *Prof Exp:* Asst prof biol, 73-81, ASSOC PROF BIOL, JAMES MADISON UNIV, 81- *Mem:* Am Soc Zoologists; Sigma Xi. *Res:* Development and implementation of biological monitoring systems for rapid detection and quantification of environmental toxicant effects. *Mailing Add:* Dept of Biol James Madison Univ Harrisonburg VA 22807

SELLERS, DONALD ROSCOE, b Kansas City, Mo, June, 24, 46; m 68; c 2. TOXIC MATERIALS DETECTION, CLINICAL CHEMISTRY. *Educ:* Univ Mo, AB, 68, MS, 70, PhD(biochem), 72. *Prof Exp:* Head, Stress Biochem Lab, Wright Patterson AFB, Ohio, 72-77; SR BIOCHEMIST, MIDWEST RES INST, 77- *Mem:* AAAS; Am Chem Soc; Sigma Xi. *Res:* Development of methodologies and instrumentation that employ biological mechanisms to detect chemicals of interest in the environment and workplace. *Mailing Add:* 5913 N Cleveland Kansas City MO 64119

SELLERS, DOUGLAS EDWIN, b Santa Maria, Calif, Nov 25, 31; m 51; c 2. ANALYTICAL CHEMISTRY. *Educ:* Ft Hays Kans State Col, BS, 53; Kans State Univ, MS, 55, PhD(chem), 58. *Prof Exp:* Asst prof chem, Kans State Univ, 57-58 & Univ Southern Ill, 58-64; res specialist, Monsanto Res Corp, 64-66, group leader electrochem, explosives & gas anal, 66-69, anal mgr, 69-78; RETIRED. *Mem:* Am Chem Soc. *Res:* Instrumental methods of chemical analysis, particularly polarography and ultraviolet visible techniques. *Mailing Add:* RR 2 Box 35 Wakeeney KS 67672

SELLERS, EDWARD ALEXANDER, b Winnipeg, Man, Sept 14, 16; m 39; c 3. PHARMACOLOGY. *Educ:* Univ Man, MD, 39; Univ Toronto, PhD(physiol), 47. *Prof Exp:* Res assoc physiol, 45-46, asst prof pharmacol, 46-48, from assoc prof to prof physiol, Banting & Best Dept Med Res, 48-58, chief dept defence med res labs, 55-58, head dept pharmacol, 58-66, assoc dean fac med, 65-68, dir, Banting & Best Diabetes Ctr, 78-81, PROF PHARMACOL, FAC MED, UNIV TORONTO, 58-, CO-DIR, BANTING & BEST DIABETES CTR, 81- *Concurrent Pos:* Chmn, Personnel Res Comt, Royal Can Navy, 53-56; mem gov coun, Univ Toronto, 72-74. *Mem:* Am Physiol Soc; Am Soc Pharmacol & Exp Therapeut; Pharmacol Soc Can (pres, 65-66); Can Physiol Soc; Nutrit Soc Can. *Res:* Thyroid nutritional physiology; physiological adaptive phenomena; drug action. *Mailing Add:* Dept Pharmacol Univ Toronto Fac Med Toronto ON M5S 1A8 Can

SELLERS, EDWARD MONCRIEFF, b Victoria, BC, June 12, 41. CLINICAL PHARMACOLOGY. *Educ:* Univ Toronto, MD, 65; Harvard Univ, PhD(pharmacol), 71; FRCP(C) & Am Bd Internal Med, dipl internal med, 72; FACP, 77. *Prof Exp:* Clin & res fel med, Mass Gen Hosp, 68-72; instr pharmacol, Harvard Univ, 70-71; head, Clin Res Unit, Clin Inst Addiction Res Found, 73; dir, Div Clin Pharmacol, Clin Inst Addiction Res Found & Toronto Western Hosp, 75; assoc prof pharmacol, 74-80, assoc prof fac med, 76-80, PROF PHARMACOL & MED, UNIV TORONTO, 80- *Concurrent Pos:* Assoc ed, Drug Metab Rev, 74- *Mem:* Am Soc Pharmacol & Exp Therapeut; Am Soc Clin Pharmacol & Therapeut; Pharmacol Soc Can; Can Soc Clin Invest; Am Fedn Clin Res. *Res:* Drug interactions; protein binding; drug metabolism and toxicology; drug treatment of alcohol withdrawal. *Mailing Add:* Pharmacol & Med Dept Univ Toronto Toronto ON M5S 2S1 Can

SELLERS, ERNEST E(DWIN), b Manhattan, Kans, Aug 17, 25; m 49; c 4. ELECTRICAL ENGINEERING. *Educ:* Kans State Univ, BS, 48, MS, 49. *Prof Exp:* Res engr, Res Labs, Radio Corp Am, NJ, 49-51; instr elec eng, Kans State Univ, 51-52; RES ENGR, MANAGING DIR OFF, INST SCI & TECHNOL, UNIV MICH, ANN ARBOR, 52- *Concurrent Pos:* Sr engr, Tex Instruments Co, 59; head, Univ Mich Tech Inst Radar Lab, 63-66. *Mem:* AAAS; Inst Elec & Electronics Engrs; Instrument Soc Am. *Res:* Electronics systems analysis; air defense; combat surveillance; detection and control theory; radar; television; countermeasures; navigation; radio astronomy; microwave propagation and reflection; signal handling; data processing; data display; bio-medical engineering. *Mailing Add:* 2105 Copley Ann Arbor MI 48104

SELLERS, F(REDERICK) BURTON, b Kankakee, Ill, June 23, 18; m 41; c 2. CHEMICAL ENGINEERING. *Educ:* Univ Ill, BS, 40. *Prof Exp:* Process engr, Tex Co, Okla & NY, 40-47, tech asst, Texaco Develop Corp, 47-53, asst to mgr tech div, 53-55, asst mgr, 55-62, tech sect legal dept, Texaco, Inc, 62-64, mgr, 64-68, asst mgr, 68-72, mgr, Texaco Develop Corp, 72-80, DIR, TEXACO BRASIL SOUTH AM, 81- *Concurrent Pos:* Asst to exec vpres, Carthage Hydrocol, 51-52. *Mem:* Am Inst Chem Engrs. *Res:* Petroleum; production of synthesis gas from gas, oil and coal; patent licensing. *Mailing Add:* Texaco Brasil South Am Caixa Postal 520 20000 Rio de Janeiro Brazil

SELLERS, FRANCIS BACHMAN, b Washington, NC, Mar 22, 30; m 58; c 2. ATOMIC PHYSICS, NUCLEAR PHYSICS. *Educ:* Wake Forest Col, BS, 54; Univ Kans, PhD(physics), 60. *Prof Exp:* Sr physicist, Phys Res Dept, Allied Res Assocs, Inc, Mass, 60-62, head physics res dept, 62-64; head dept, 64-80, VPRES RADIATION PHYSICS, PANAMETRICS INC, 81- *Mem:* Am Phys Soc; Sigma Xi; Am Geophys Union; Am Meteor Soc. *Res:* Interaction of nuclear particles with matter; production and measurement of x-radiation; measurement of atmospheric and extraterrestrial parameters; radiation detection techniques for rocket and satellite applications; atmospheric physics. *Mailing Add:* Radiation Physics Dept Panametrics Inc 221 Crescent St Waltham MA 02154

SELLERS, FRANK JAMIESON, b Winnipeg, Man, Mar 10, 28; m 61; c 3. PEDIATRIC CARDIOLOGY. *Educ:* Univ Man, BSc, 54; Queen's Univ, Ont, MD & CM, 55. *Prof Exp:* From asst prof to assoc prof pediat, Univ Sask, 63-70; ASSOC PROF PEDIAT, UNIV OTTAWA, 70- *Mem:* Can Med Asn; Can Pediat Soc; Can Cardiovasc Soc; Can Soc Clin Invest. *Res:* Congenital heart disease; rheumatic fever. *Mailing Add:* Children's Hosp of Eastern Ont 401 Smyth Rd Ottawa ON K1H 8L1 Can

SELLERS, JOHN WILLIAM, b Wausau, Wis, Apr 13, 16; m 44; c 2. ORGANIC CHEMISTRY, CHEMICAL ENGINEERING. *Educ:* Univ Ill, BS, 42; Ohio State Univ, PhD(chem), 49. *Prof Exp:* Tech dir foods, Food Mat Corp, 37-40; jr chem engr rubber, Firestone Tire & Rubber Co, 42-45, sr res chemist, 49-51; sr res chemist, Chem Div, Pittsburgh Plate Glass Co, 51-57, supvry org res, 57-58; head, Org Res Sect, Petrol Chems, Inc, 58-59; sr supvr org res, Chem Div, Pittsburgh Plate Glass Co, 59-63 & Rubber Chem Res, 63-65; tech adv to mgt & dir corp res, Tenneco Chem, Inc, 65-67; dir res & develop, Paterson Paper Co, 67-68, vpres tech, 68-70; mgr indust waste mgt, Procon, Inc, 70-71 & environ control, H J Heinz Co, 71-73; VPRES OPERS, INTERSCIENCE, INC, 73- *Mem:* AAAS; Am Chem Soc; Soc Plastics Eng; Water Pollution Control Fedn; Am Inst Chem Eng. *Res:* Organic synthesis; high polymers; plastics; vulcanization and reinforcement of elastomers; oxidation of hydrocarbons; kinetics and mechanisms; market development; management. *Mailing Add:* Interscience Inc 5025 W Grace St Tampa FL 33607

SELLERS, PETER HOADLEY, b Philadelphia, Pa, Sept 12, 30; m 58; c 4. MATHEMATICS. *Educ:* Univ Pa, PhD(math), 65. *Prof Exp:* Programmer math, Johnson Found, Univ Pa, 58-61; master, Kangaru Sch, Embu, Kenya, 61-63; fel math, Johnson Found, Univ Pa, 65-66; res assoc, 66-72, ASSOC PROF MATH, ROCKEFELLER UNIV, 72-, SR RES ASSOC, 74- *Mem:* Am Math Soc; Math Asn Am; Soc Indust & Appl Math; Kenya Math Soc. *Res:* Combinatorial analysis; homological theories applied to chemistry. *Mailing Add:* Dept of Math Rockefeller Univ New York NY 10021

SELLERS, THOMAS F, JR, b Atlanta, Ga, Apr 9, 27; m 49; c 3. PREVENTIVE MEDICINE, INFECTIOUS DISEASES. *Educ:* Emory Univ, BS, 46, MD, 50. *Prof Exp:* Res fel infectious dis, Sch Med, Emory Univ, 55-57 & Med Col, Cornell Univ, 57-58; asst prof med, 58-60, PROF PREV MED, SCH MED, EMORY UNIV, 60- *Concurrent Pos:* Mem adv comt health, Appalachian Regional Comn, 65-67; staff mem community med, Cent Middlesex Hosp, London, Eng, 74-75. *Mem:* Am Col Physicians; Am Pub Health Asn; Am Col Prev Med; Asn Teachers Prev Med. *Mailing Add:* Dept of Prev Med Emory Univ Sch of Med Atlanta GA 30303

SELLERS, W(ILLIAM) WALLACE, JR, b Wilmington, NC, Jan 24, 17; m 46. CHEMICAL ENGINEERING. *Educ:* Col William & Mary, BS, 37; Vanderbilt Univ, MS, 41. *Prof Exp:* Control chemist, Ethyl-Dow Chem Co, 37-40, res chemist, 41-42, chief chemist, 42-44; res chemist, Int Nickel Co, 44-54, head electrochem sect, Res Lab, 54-57, electroplating specialist, Res & Develop Div, Sales, Nickel Sales Dept, 66-77; GEN SALES MGR, PLATING & CHEM INDUST SALES & EXPORT SALES, INCO INC, 77- *Honors & Awards:* Gold Medal, Electroplaters Soc, 49, Silver Medal & George Hogaboom Award, 66. *Mem:* Electrochem Soc; Electroplaters Soc; Soc Automotive Engrs; Nat Asn Corrosion Engrs; fel Am Inst Chemists. *Res:* Extraction and absorption of bromine; synthesis of ethylendibromide; electrochemistry; electrodeposition of metals, including mickel, chromium and copper. *Mailing Add:* INCO Plating & Chem Indust Sales One New York Plaza New York NY 10004

SELLIN, HELEN GILL, b New York, NY, June 22, 39; m 62; c 2. PHOTOCHEMISTRY, IMMUNOBIOLOGY. *Educ:* Univ Chicago, BS, 60, PhD(biochem), 64. *Prof Exp:* Res assoc biochem, animal housing quarters & hosp, Sch Med, Univ Ill, 64-65 & Dept Biochem, Columbia Univ, 65-67; RES ASSOC BIOCHEM, UNION CARBIDE, BIOL DIV, OAK RIDGE NAT LAB, 68- *Res:* Photochemistry of iodinated nucleic acids; transfer factor; in vitro protein synthesis of biologically active enzymes; DNA methylation; asparaginase, thyroglobulin biosynthesis; virology and tissue culture. *Mailing Add:* Biol Div Oak Ridge Nat Lab Box Y Oak Ridge TN 37830

SELLIN, IVAN ARMAND, b Everett, Wash, Aug 16, 39; m 62; c 2. ATOMIC PHYSICS. *Educ:* Harvard Univ, BS, 59; Univ Chicago, SM, 60, PhD(physics), 64. *Prof Exp:* Instr physics, Univ Chicago, 64-65; asst prof, NY Univ, 65-67; res physicist, Oak Ridge Nat Lab, 67-70; assoc prof, 70-74, PROF PHYSICS, UNIV TENN, KNOXVILLE, 74-, PROJ DIR, UNIV TENN & OAKRIDGE NAT LAB, 70-; CONSULT, NSF, 80- *Concurrent Pos:* Lectr, Univ Chicago, 61-64; consult, Oak Ridge Nat Lab, 70-; vis prof, Orgn Am States, 72; NSF grants; NASA grants, Off Naval Res Contracts, Dept Energy contracts, Univ Tenn, 72-82; mem adv comt atomic & molecular physics, Nat Acad Sci, 73-76; chmn, Fourth Int Conf Beam-Foil Spectros, 75; guest prof, Swedish Natural Sci Res Coun, 78; sr Fulbright Hays grant, Germany, 77; guest prof, Cent Atomico Bariloche, Argentina, 81. *Honors & Awards:* Sr US Scientist Award, Alexander von Humboldt Found, 77. *Mem:* Fel Am Phys Soc. *Res:* Physics of ion beams; structure and collisions of heavy ions; physics of highly ionited matter. *Mailing Add:* PO Box X Oak Ridge TN 37830

SELLINGER, OTTO ZIVKO, b Zagreb, Yugoslavia, Sept 14, 29; nat US; m 55; c 4. NEUROCHEMISTRY. *Educ:* Mass Inst Technol, SB, 54; Tulane Univ, PhD(biochem), 58. *Prof Exp:* NIH fel, Lab Physiol Chem, Univ Louvain, Belgium, 58-59; NIH fel biochem, Ist Superiore Sanita, Rome, Italy, 59-60; asst prof biochem & med, Med Sch, Tulane Univ, 60-64; Fulbright vis prof biochem, Univ of the Repub, Uruguay, 64-65; assoc res pharmacologist, 65-68, RES SCIENTIST, MENT HEALTH RES INST, UNIV MICH, ANN ARBOR, 68- *Concurrent Pos:* Fogarty Int Scientist Award, Univ Claude Bernaud, Villerbanne, France. *Mem:* Am Soc Neurochem; Am Soc Biol Chemists; Am Soc Cell Biol; Am Soc Pharmacol & Exp Therapeut; Int Soc Neurochem. *Res:* Neurochemistry; methylations in brain; convulsant drug mechanisms. *Mailing Add:* Ment Health Res Inst Univ of Mich Ann Arbor MI 48109

SELLMER, GEORGE PARK, b Milwaukee, Wis, Mar 12, 18; m 43; c 2. ZOOLOGY. *Educ:* Upsala Col, AB, 48; Rutgers Univ, MS, 52, PhD(zool), 59. *Prof Exp:* From instr to assoc prof, 48-61, chmn dept, 58-79, PROF BIOL, UPSALA COL, 61- *Mem:* Soc Sci Study Sex; Am Asn Sex Educr, Councr & Therapists. *Res:* Anatomy and ecology of bivalve mollusks; human sexuality; biological control of insect pests. *Mailing Add:* Dept of Biol Upsala Col East Orange NJ 07019

SELLMYER, DAVID JULIAN, b Joliet, Ill, Sept 28, 38; m 62; c 2. SOLID STATE PHYSICS. *Educ:* Univ Ill, BS, 60; Mich State Univ, PhD(physics), 65. *Prof Exp:* From asst prof to assoc prof metall & mat sci, Ctr Mat Sci, Mass Inst Technol, 65-72; assoc prof, 72-75, PROF PHYSICS, UNIV NEBR, LINCOLN, 75-, CHMN DEPT, 78- *Concurrent Pos:* Consult, US Air Force Cambridge Res Lab, Bedford, Mass, 71-72 & Date Electron, Norfolk, Nebr, 79- *Honors & Awards:* Tech Brief Award, NASA, 73. *Mem:* AAAS; fel Am Phys Soc; Sigma Xi. *Res:* Low temperature solid state physics; electronic structure and magnetism in metallic compounds and alloys; physics of metallic glasses; amorphous magnetism; electronic and magnetic properties of low dimensional conductors; physics of thin films. *Mailing Add:* Behlen Lab Dept Physics Astron Univ Nebr Lincoln NE 68588

SELLNER, KEVIN GREGORY, b Albany, NY, Oct 11, 49. BIOLOGICAL OCEANOGRAPHY, ALGAL PHYSIOLOGY. *Educ:* Clark Univ, AB, 71; Univ SC, MS, 73; Dalhousie Univ, PhD(oceanog), 78. *Prof Exp:* Res asst algal physiol, Univ SC, 71-73; ASST CURATOR ALGAL PHYSIOL, ACAD NAT SCI PHILADELPHIA, 78- *Mem:* Am Soc Limnol & Oceanog; Phycol Soc Am. *Res:* Primary production and the flux of labile dissolved organic matter, including dissolved saccharides and dissolved amino acids; carbon flow in the plankton. *Mailing Add:* Acad Nat Sci Philadelphia Benedict Estuanne Res Lab Benedict MD 20612

SELLNER, RONALD GEORGE, b Audubon, NJ, Sept 11, 45. PHYSIOLOGY, ENDOCRINOLOGY. *Educ:* Pa State Univ, BS, 67, PhD(physiol), 71. *Prof Exp:* Asst prof biol med, Univ Mo-Kansas City, 73-78; prof physiol & actg chmn dept, Sch Med, St Georges Univ, Grenada, Wis, 78-79; ASST DEAN UNDERGRAD MED EDUC, PEORIA SCH MED, UNIV ILL, 79- *Concurrent Pos:* NIH staff fel physiol, Nat Inst Arthritis Metab & Digestive Dis, 71-73; lectr, Found Advan Educ in Sci, Inc, 72-73. *Mem:* AAAS; Soc Study Reprod; Am Asn Sex Educ, Coun & Ther. *Res:* Female reproductive physiology and endocrinology; human sexuality. *Mailing Add:* Peoria Sch of Med 123 SW Glendale Ave Peoria IL 61605

SELLO, STEPHEN , b Budapest, Hungary, Oct 28, 21; US citizen; m 48; c 2. TEXTILE CHEMISTRY. *Educ:* Pazmany Peter Univ, Budapest, dipl chem, 45, PhD(org chem), 47. *Prof Exp:* Chemist, Goldberger Textile Corp, Hungary, 48-51; chief chemist, Aniline Tech Serv, 51-53; assoc prof textile chem, Budapest Tech Univ, 53-56; head develop lab, Texstyle Corp, NJ, 57-58; res chemist, Chicopee Mfg Corp, 58-59; group leader, 59-68, res mgr, 68-74, res assoc textile chem res, Tech Ctr, Garfield, 75-81, MGR EXPLOR CHEM, J P STEVENS & CO, INC, NY, 81- *Concurrent Pos:* Lectr, Budapest Tech Univ, 51-56, postgrad course for chem engrs, 53-56: mem res adv comt, Hungarian Textile Res Inst, 53-56; mem, Info Coun Fabric Flammability, chmn res comt, 72; tech expert, UN Indust Develop Orgn, 72- *Honors & Awards:* Serv Award, Chem Abstr Serv, 75; Educ Serv Award, Plastic Inst Am, 75. *Mem:* NY Acad Sci; Fiber Soc; Fiber 72, 78, 79; mem, Res Adv Comt Radiation, NC State Univ, 75-77; co-ed, Flammability Bull, 75-; mem, Adv Comt Cooper Union Res Found, 77- Am Chem Soc; Am Asn Textile Chem & Colorists. *Res:* Chemical modification of cotton with activated vinyl compounds; polyfunctional polycarbamates; reversible crosslinks in cotton; flame retardant modification of textiles; shrinkproofing of wool with polyaziridines; durable antistatic finishes; hydrophilic topical finishes; permanent setting of wool; elastomeric textiles. *Mailing Add:* 43 Reservoir Pl Cedar Grove NJ 07009

SELLS, BRUCE HOWARD, b Ottawa, Ont, Aug 15, 30; m 53; c 4. BIOCHEMISTRY. *Educ:* Carleton Univ, BSc, 52; Queen's Univ, Ont, MA, 54; McGill Univ, PhD(biochem), 57. *Prof Exp:* Damon Runyon res fels, Lab Animal Morphol, Free Univ Brussels, 57-59 & State Serum Inst, Copenhagen, Denmark, 59-60; cancer res scientist, Roswell Park Mem Inst, 60-61; res assoc, Columbia Univ, 61-62; from asst prof to assoc prof, Lab Biochem, St Jude Children's Res Hosp & Dept Biochem, Univ Tenn, Memphis, 62-73, mem, Hosp, 68-72; PROF & DIR MOLECULAR BIOL, MED SCH, MEM UNIV NFLD, 72-, ASSOC DEAN, BASIC MED SCI, 79- *Concurrent Pos:* Vis res scientist, Inst Animal Genetics, Univ Edinburgh, 69-70; mem biochem grants comt, Med Res Coun Can, 73; assoc ed, Can J Biochem, 74; Killam sr res fel, Inst Molecular Biol, Univ Paris, 78-79; exchange scientist coop res prog, French Nat Ctr Sci Res/US Nat Res Coun; sci officer, Nat Cancer Inst, 79-81. *Mem:* Can Biochem Soc (pres); Am Soc Biol Chemists; Am Soc Microbiol. *Res:* Nucleic acids; biosynthesis of ribosomes; studies on growth and growth hormone effects; ribosome topography; capillary fragility. *Mailing Add:* Labs Molecular Biol Fac Med Mem Univ of Nfld St John's NF A1B 3V6 Can

SELLS, GARY DONNELL, b New Hartford, Iowa, Aug 5, 32; m 53; c 4. PLANT PHYSIOLOGY. *Educ:* Univ Northern Iowa, BA, 54, MA, 59; Iowa State Univ, PhD(plant physiol), 65. *Prof Exp:* Teacher high schs, Iowa, 54-62; assoc prof, 65-71, PROF PHYSIOL, NORTHEAST MO STATE UNIV, 71- *Mem:* AAAS; Am Inst Biol Sci. *Res:* Physiology; botany; developmental anatomy. *Mailing Add:* Dept of Biol Northeast Mo State Univ Kirksville MO 63501

SELLS, JACKSON S(TUART), b Buffalo, NY, Dec 27, 20; m 41; c 2. ELECTRICAL ENGINEERING. *Educ:* Univ Miami, BS, 46, MS, 50; Purdue Univ, BSEE, 52. *Prof Exp:* Asst prof elec eng & physics, 46-55, assoc prof elec eng, 55-65, PROF ELEC ENG, UNIV MIAMI, 65- *Concurrent Pos:* Consult, Mercy Hosp, Fla, 53-60 & City of Miami, 60-80. *Mem:* Am Soc Eng Educ; Illum Eng Soc; Inst Elec & Electronics Engrs; Am Sci Affil; Simulations Coun. *Res:* Servomechanisms; radiotelemetry; control and network theories. *Mailing Add:* Dept of Elec Eng Univ of Miami Coral Gables FL 33124

SELLS, JEAN THURBER, b Butte, Nebr, May 24, 40; m 62; c 2. MATHEMATICS. *Educ:* Nebr Wesleyan Univ, AB, 61; Univ Minn, Minneapolis, MA, 63, PhD(math), 66. *Prof Exp:* Asst prof math, Tex A&I Univ, 66-67; asst prof, Univ Louisville, 67-70; from asst prof to assoc prof, Frostburg State Col, 70-72; assoc prof, Coker Col, 73-75; asst prof, Fordham Univ, 75-76; ASSOC PROF MATH, SACRED HEART UNIV, 76-, CHMN, DEPT MATH, 81- *Mem:* Am Math Soc; Math Asn Am; Nat Coun Teachers Math. *Mailing Add:* 36 September Lane Weston CT 06880

SELLS, ROBERT LEE, b Lancaster, Ohio, Oct 14, 25; m 47; c 2. PHYSICS. *Educ:* Univ Mich, BS, 48; Univ Notre Dame, PhD(physics), 53. *Prof Exp:* From asst prof to assoc prof physics, Rutgers Univ, 53-63; prof, 63-73, DISTINGUISHED TEACHING PROF PHYSICS & ASTRON & CHMN DEPT, STATE UNIV NY COL GENESEO, 73- *Honors & Awards:* Centennial of Sci Award, Univ Notre Dame, 65; Citation for Distinguished Serv, Am Asn Physics Teachers, 69. *Mem:* Am Asn Physics Teachers; Am Phys Soc. *Res:* Theoretical physics; atomic and nuclear physics; solid state physics; teaching physics. *Mailing Add:* Dept of Physics State Univ of NY Col Geneseo NY 14454

SELLSTEDT, JOHN H, b Minneapolis, Minn, June 11, 40; m 61; c 2. MEDICINAL CHEMISTRY. *Educ:* Univ Minn, BS, 62, PhD(org chem), 65. *Prof Exp:* Sr res chemist, Wyeth Labs, Inc, 65-69, group leader, 69-77, MGR RES ANAL CHEM, RES & DEVELOP LABS, WYETH LABS DIV, AM HOME PROD CORP, 77- *Res:* Antiallergy and cardiovascular research; mass spectroscopy; cephalosporins and penicillins. *Mailing Add:* Res & Develop Labs Wyeth Labs Lancaster Pike & Morehall Rd Radnor PA 19088

SELMAN, ALAN L, b New York, NY, Apr 2, 41; m 63; c 2. THEORETICAL COMPUTER SCIENCE, MATHEMATICAL LOGIC. *Educ:* City Col Univ NY, BS, 62; Univ Calif, Berkeley, MA, 64; Pa State Univ, PhD(math), 70. *Prof Exp:* Instr math, Pa State Univ, 68-70; lectr, Carnegie-Mellon Univ, 70-72; asst prof, Fla State Univ, 72-77; ASSOC PROF COMPUT SCI, IOWA STATE UNIV, 77- *Concurrent Pos:* Res Mathematician, Carnegie-Mellon Univ, 70-72; NSF grant, 75-77 & 77-79. *Mem:* Asn Symbolic Logic; Asn Comput Mach. *Res:* Low level automata based complexity; studies on whether certain computational problems can be feasibly computed versus whether they are intractable for practical computing. *Mailing Add:* Dept of Comput Sci Iowa State Univ Ames IA 50011

SELMAN, CHARLES MELVIN, b Brenham, Tex, Jan 18, 37; m 60; c 2. ORGANIC POLYMER CHEMISTRY, ORGANOMETALLIC CHEMISTRY. *Educ:* Southwestern Univ, BS, 59; NTex State Univ, MS, 66, PhD(chem), 68. *Prof Exp:* Res chemist, Dow Chem Co, 60-63; SR POLYMERIZATION CHEMIST, PHILLIPS PETROL CO, 67- *Mem:* Am Chem Soc. *Res:* Polymerization reactions of organic molecules catalyzed with organometallic compounds. *Mailing Add:* 5120 Parsons Dr Bartlesville OK 74003

SELMAN, KELLY, b Cleveland, Ohio, July 22, 42. CELL BIOLOGY, REPRODUCTIVE BIOLOGY. *Educ:* Univ Mich, BA, 64; Harvard Univ, MA, 65, PhD(biol), 72. *Prof Exp:* Instr biol, Simmons Col, 67-68 & Univ Va, 71-72; fel anat, Harvard Univ Med Sch, 72-74; asst prof, 74-79, ASSOC PROF ANAT, COL MED, UNIV FLA, 79- *Mem:* Am Soc Cell Biol; AAAS; Am Asn Anat; Am Soc Zoologists. *Res:* Oogenesis and fertilization. *Mailing Add:* Dept Anat Col Med Univ Fla Gainesville FL 32610

SELMANOFF, MICHAEL KIDD, b Minneapolis, Minn, July 18, 49; m 75; c 2. NEUROBIOLOGY, REPRODUCTIVE NEUROENDOCRINOLOGY. *Educ:* Earlham Col, BA, 70; Univ Conn, PhD(neurobiol), 74. *Prof Exp:* Fel, Dept Obstet, Gynec & Reprod Sci, Reprod Endocrinol Ctr, Sch Med, Univ Calif, San Francisco, 74-77; asst prof, 77-82, ASSOC PROF, DEPT PHYSIOL, SCH MED, UNIV MD, 82- *Mem:* Endocrine Soc; Soc Neurosci; Am Physiol Soc. *Res:* Role of tuberoinfundibular dopaminergic neurons in the release of prolactine and luteinizing hormone from the anterior pituitary gland. *Mailing Add:* Dept Physiol Sch Med Univ Md 655 W Baltimore Rd Baltimore MD 20201

SELMECZI, JOSEPH GABOR, b Banhida, Hungary, Apr 12, 30; US citizen; m 54; c 2. CHEMICAL ENGINEERING, ENVIRONMENTAL ENGINEERING. *Educ:* Tech Univ Sopron, Hungary, Geol Engr Dipl Eng, 53. *Prof Exp:* Lab supvr, 68-70, mgr labs, 70-71, mgr process develop, 71-72, mgr res, 72-74, mgr res & develop, Dravo Lime Co, 74-75, vpres res & develop, 75, MGR SUPT TECH DEVELOP, DRAVO CORP, 76- *Mem:* AAAS; Am Inst Chem Engrs; Am Chem Soc; Soc Mining Engrs; NY Acad Sci. *Res:* Processing and utilization of coal; ferrous and nonferrous mineral processing and extraction; air pollution control; solid and liquid waste disposal; energy alternatives; lime utilization. *Mailing Add:* Dravo Corp 3600 Neville Rd Pittsburgh PA 15225

SELOVE, WALTER, b Chicago, Ill, Sept 11, 21; m 55. PARTICLE PHYSICS. *Educ:* Univ Chicago, BS, 42, MS, 48, PhD(physics), 49. *Prof Exp:* Asst instr electronics, Univ Chicago, 42-43; mem staff, Radiation Lab, Mass Inst Technol, 43-45; from jr physicist to assoc physicist, Argonne Nat Lab, 47-50; from instr to asst prof physics, Harvard Univ, 50-56; assoc prof, 56-61, PROF PHYSICS, UNIV PA, 61- *Concurrent Pos:* Mem staff, Radiation Lab, Univ Calif, 53-54; Nat Sci Found fel, 56; Guggenheim fel, 71-72. *Mem:* Fel Am Phys Soc. *Res:* Radar receivers; nuclear and particle physics. *Mailing Add:* Dept of Physics Univ of Pa Philadelphia PA 19104

SELOVER, JAMES CARROLL, b Los Angeles, Calif, Mar 25, 29; m 51; c 5. ORGANIC CHEMISTRY. *Educ:* Rutgers Univ, BS, 50; Stanford Univ, MS, 52, PhD(org chem), 53. *Prof Exp:* Res chemist, M W Kellogg Co, Pullman, Inc, 53-55; sr res chemist, Richfield Oil Corp, 55-59; tech dir new prods & quality control, Pilot Chem Co, 59; sr chem economist, Stanford Res Inst, 59-68, dir long range planning serv, 68-69; planning systs mgr, 69-71, MGR CORP PLANNING, BECHTEL CORP, 71-, EXEC ENGR, 73- *Mem:* Am Chem Soc; Sigma Xi; Am Inst Chem Engrs. *Res:* Management consulting and corporate research planning. *Mailing Add:* 12401 Hilltop Dr Los Altos Hills CA 94022

SELOVER, THEODORE BRITTON, JR, b Cleveland, Ohio, Jan 13, 31; m 55; c 3. PHYSICAL CHEMISTRY. *Educ:* Brown Univ, ScB, 52; Western Reserve Univ, MS, 57. *Prof Exp:* Jr chemist, 52, chemist, 54-57, sr chemist & proj leader basic res, 57-60, tech specialist, 60-62, sr res chemist, 62-69, res assoc, 69-71, INFO SPECIALIST, STANDARD OIL CO, OHIO, 71- *Mem:* Am Chem Soc; Am Soc Testing & Mat; Am Phys Soc; Am Ceramic Soc; Sigma Xi. *Res:* Plasma chemistry; high temperature materials; fused salt batteries; heterogeneous catalysis; aqueous capacitors; information awareness/retrieval; thermodynamic and transport property data. *Mailing Add:* 3575 Traver Rd Shaker Heights OH 44122

SELPH, WADE EDWARD, b Oklahoma City, Okla, June 26, 30; m 55; c 2. NUCLEAR PHYSICS, NUCLEAR ENGINEERING. *Educ:* Okla Univ, BS, 53, MS, 54. *Prof Exp:* Weapons officer nuclear, US Navy 54-58; nuclear specialist shielding & weapons effects, LTV Vought Aeronautics, 58-65; staff mem radiation transport, Radiation Res Assocs, 65-68; mgr prog develop nuclear res, 68-80, TECH ADVR, IRT CORP, 80- *Mem:* Am Nuclear Soc.

Res: Development of new radiation detection systems; measurement of radiation fields; development and use of radiation transport analysis computer codes; weapons effects and weapon system analysis. *Mailing Add:* IRT Corp PO Box 80817 San Diego CA 92138

SELSER, WILL LINDSEY, b Hattiesburg, Miss, May 28, 16; m 39; c 3. SCIENCE EDUCATION, BIOLOGY. *Educ:* Univ Fla, BS, 46 & 48, EdD, 62. *Prof Exp:* Instr biol & sci ed, Univ Fla, 61-62, asst prof, 62-64; chmn sci div, Polk Jr Col, 64-65; assoc prof biol, ECarolina Col, 65-66; PROF SCI, NORTHEAST MO STATE UNIV, 66- *Mem:* AAAS; Nat Sci Teachers Asn; Nat Asn Res Sci Teaching. *Res:* Endocrinology; adrenals; elementary science education. *Mailing Add:* Sci Div Northeast Mo State Univ Kirksville MO 63501

SELSKY, MELVYN IRA, b Brooklyn, NY, June 25, 33; m 63; c 2. BOTANY. *Educ:* Brooklyn Col, BA, 54, MA, 56; Univ Ill, PhD(plant virol), 60. *Prof Exp:* Substitute teacher biol, Brooklyn Col, 54-56; asst bot, Univ Ill, 56-57 & plant virol, 57-59, res assoc, 60; from asst prof to assoc prof, 60-72, PROF BIOL, BROOKLYN COL, 72- *Concurrent Pos:* Nat Cancer Inst grant, 64-66; fel, Yale Univ, 69-70. *Mem:* AAAS; Am Soc Microbiol; NY Acad Sci. *Res:* Organelle transfer RNAs; chloroplast development in Euglena gracilis; blue-green algae. *Mailing Add:* Dept of Biol Brooklyn Col Brooklyn NY 11210

SELTER, GERALD A, b Windsor, Ont, May 3, 40; m 63; c 3. ORGANIC CHEMISTRY. *Educ:* Wayne State Univ, BS, 62; Wash State Univ, PhD(chem), 66. *Prof Exp:* Fel, Univ Calif, Berkeley, 66-67 & 68; asst prof, 68-74, assoc prof, 74-80, PROF ORG CHEM, SAN JOSE STATE UNIV, 80- *Concurrent Pos:* Lectr, Univ Calif, Berkeley, 67-68. *Mem:* Am Chem Soc. *Res:* Reactivity of alpha-pentadienyl esters; solvolytic reactivity of allylic halides and esters, especially the mechanisms of the neighboring group participation in such reactivity. *Mailing Add:* Dept Chem San Jose State Univ San Jose CA 95192

SELTIN, RICHARD JAMES, b Chicago, Ill, Nov 4, 27; m 53; c 3. VERTEBRATE PALEONTOLOGY. *Educ:* Univ Wyo, BS, 49; Univ Chicago, MS, 54, PhD(paleont), 56. *Prof Exp:* From instr to assoc prof, 56-69, PROF NATURAL SCI, MICH STATE UNIV, 69-, CONSULT, UNIV MUS, 57-, CHMN NATURAL SCI, 74- *Concurrent Pos:* Am Philos Soc grants, 58, 60, 62, 64, 66. *Mem:* Soc Vert Paleont; Soc Econ Paleont & Mineral; Soc Study Evolution. *Res:* Primitive reptiles and amphibians. *Mailing Add:* Dept of Natural Sci Mich State Univ East Lansing MI 48823

SELTMANN, HEINZ, b Frankfurt am Main, Ger, Sept 8, 24; nat US. PLANT PHYSIOLOGY. *Educ:* Drew Univ, BA, 49; Univ Chicago, MS, 50, PhD(bot), 53. *Prof Exp:* Asst, Univ Chicago, 50-53; asst prof bot, Barnard Col, Columbia Univ, 53-56; from asst prof to assoc prof, 56-74, PROF BOT, NC STATE UNIV, 74- PLANT PHYSIOLOGIST, USDA, 56- *Mem:* Am Soc Plant Physiologists; Am Soc Agron. *Res:* Physiology of tobacco plant; plant growth regulators. *Mailing Add:* Dept of Botany NC State Univ Raleigh NC 27650

SELTSER, RAYMOND, b Boston, Mass, Dec 17, 23; m 46; c 2. PREVENTIVE MEDICINE, PUBLIC HEALTH. *Educ:* Boston Univ, MD, 47; Johns Hopkins Univ, MPH, 57; Am Bd Prev Med, dipl, 69. *Prof Exp:* Asst med, Sch Med, Boston Univ, 48-51; asst chief med info & intel br, Off Surgeon Gen, US Dept Army, 53-56; epidemiologist, Div Int Health, USPHS, 56-57; from asst prof to assoc prof epidemiol, 57-66, from assoc prof to prof chronic dis, 63-69, PROF EPIDEMIOL, JOHNS HOPKINS UNIV, 66-, ASSOC DEAN, SCH HYG & PUB HEALTH, 67- *Concurrent Pos:* Resident med & infectious dis, Mass Mem Hosp, 48-51; asst med, Sch Med, Harvard Univ, 50-51; consult, NIMH, 58-70, Nat Cancer Inst, 64-71, Fed Radiation Coun, 66-68, Nat Inst Environ Health Sci, 67-71, Bur Radiol Health, Dept Health, Educ & Welfare, 68-71 & Off Biomet, Nat Inst Neurol Dis & Stroke, 73-; fel coun epidemiol, Am Heart Asn, 65-, mem exec comt coun stroke, 69-72; vis prof, Med Col Pa, 66-69; mem coun pub health consult, Nat Sanitation Found, 67-69; secy, Asn Sch Pub Health, 69-71; mem bd overseers, Am J Epidemiol, 71-; chmn adv comt radiation registry physicians, Div Med Sci, Nat Acad Sci-Nat Res Coun, 72-; mem, Nat Coun Radiation Protection & Measurements, 73-; chmn biomet & epidemiol contract rev comt, Nat Cancer Inst, 73-; secy-treas, Am Bd Prev Med, 74-; chmn, Comt Human Volunteers, Johns Hopkins Univ, 77- *Mem:* Fel AAAS; fel Am Pub Health Asn; fel Am Col Prev Med; fel Am Heart Asn; Int Epidemiol Asn. *Res:* Streptococcal disease; poliomyelitis; hemorrhagic fever; influenza; ionizing radiation effects; cerebral vascular disease. *Mailing Add:* Dept of Epidemiol Johns Hopkins Univ Baltimore MD 21205

SELTZER, ALBERT PINCUS, b Myrepolia, Romania, Aug 12, 03; nat; m 44; c 2. SURGERY. *Educ:* Temple Univ, MD, 28; Univ Pa, MSc, 41, DSc, 42; Univ NC, LLD, 54. *Prof Exp:* Intern, St Joseph's Hosp, 28-29 & Northwestern Gen Hosp, 30-31; resident, Univ Pa Hosps, 31-33, clin prof otolaryngol, Univ, 55-58, ASSOC PROF OTORHINOLARYNGOL & HUMAN COMMUN, SCH MED, UNIV PA, 58-; CHIEF PLASTIC SURG, ST LUKE'S & CHILDREN'S MED CTR, 50- *Concurrent Pos:* Asst chief ear, nose & throat, St Luke's & Children's Med Ctr, 45-; chief otolaryngol, Philadelphia Gen Hosp, 50- & Mercy-Douglass Hosp, 55-; sr attend, Albert Einstein Med Ctr, 57-, emer chief dept otolaryngol, North Div; chief dept plastic & reconstruct surg, Community Hosp; attend plastic surgeon, St Joseph's Hosp; clin assoc prof, Hahnemann Med Col & Hosp; Smith, Kline & French Co res grants. *Mem:* AMA; Nat Med Asn; fel Am Col Surgeons; Am Acad Ophthal & Otolaryngol; fel Royal Soc Med. *Res:* Plastic surgery. *Mailing Add:* 2104 Spruce St Philadelphia PA 19103

SELTZER, CARL COLEMAN, b Boston, Mass, June 1, 08; m 30; c 3. PHYSICAL ANTHROPOLOGY. *Educ:* Harvard Univ, AB, 29, PhD(phys anthrop), 33. *Prof Exp:* Anthropologist, Constitution Clinic, Presby Hosp, New York, 30-31; Nat Res Coun fel, Harvard Univ, 33-35, res asst, Fatigue Lab, 37-38, res assoc anthrop, 38-39, res assoc phys anthrop, 39-42, res fel, Peabody Mus, 42-63, res grant, Sch Pub Health, 42-47, anthropologist, Dept Hyg, 47-56, res assoc, 63-68, SR RES ASSOC BIOL ANTHROP, SCH PUB HEALTH, HARVARD UNIV, 68-, HON RES ASSOC PHYS ANTHROP, PEABODY MUS, 74- *Concurrent Pos:* Consult, Off Indian Affairs, US Dept Interior, 37-42; res assoc, Robert B Brigham Hosp, Boston, 40-; res assoc, Adolescent Unit, Children's Hosp, 57-; fel, Coun Epidemiol, Am Heart Asn, 64-; consult, Vet Admin Outpatient Clinic, Boston, 65- & Framingham Heart Study, Boston Univ, 71-73; vis prof nutrit, Tufts Univ, 79- *Mem:* AAAS; Am Asn Phys Anthrop; Am Anthrop Asn; NY Acad Sci; Soc Epidemiol Res. *Res:* Human constitution; constitutional medicine; growth and development; obesity. *Mailing Add:* 39 Williston Rd Brookline MA 02146

SELTZER, EDWARD, b Chelsea, Mass, Oct 28, 11; m 41; c 3. CHEMICAL ENGINEERING, FOOD SCIENCE. *Educ:* Harvard Univ, BS, 33. *Prof Exp:* Res chemist & chem engr, Walter Baker Co Div, Gen Foods Corp, Mass, 34-39, res chemist & proj leader, Cent Res Lab, NJ, 39-42, from chem engr to head processing eng div, 41-46; chief res engr, Thomas J Lipton, Inc, NJ, 46-59, asst dir tech res, 59-69; PROF FOOD PROCESS ENG, COOK COL, RUTGERS UNIV, NEW BRUNSWICK, 69- *Mem:* Am Chem Soc; Am Inst Chem Engr; Inst Food Technol; Res & Develop Assocs Mil Food & Packaging Systs. *Res:* Food research; process engineering; spray drying; dehydration; research administration. *Mailing Add:* Dept of Food Sci Cook Col Rutgers Univ Box 231 New Brunswick NJ 08903

SELTZER, JAMES EDWARD, b Lebanon, Pa, Apr 15, 36. ELECTROMAGNETICS, MATHEMATICAL STATISTICS. *Educ:* US Mil Acad, BS, 58; Purdue Univ, MSE, 63, PhD(eng), 71. *Prof Exp:* RES ENGR, HARRY DIAMOND LABS, 67- *Mem:* Inst Elec & Electronics Engrs; Union Radio Scientists. *Res:* Analysis and simulation of radar systems including backscatter from terrain and complex targets; evaluation of clutter effects. *Mailing Add:* Advan Res Lab US Army Adelphi MD 20783

SELTZER, JO LOUISE, b St Louis, Mo, July 10, 42; m 63; c 3. BIOCHEMISTRY. *Educ:* Wash Univ, AB, 63, PhD(pharmacol), 69. *Prof Exp:* Res assoc, Dept Pharmacol, 70-72, res instr biochem, 72-78, RES ASST PROF MED, DIV DERMAT, SCH MED, WASH UNIV, 78- *Mem:* Sigma Xi. *Res:* Neutral proteases of human skin including collagenase. *Mailing Add:* Div of Dermat Dept of Med Wash Univ Sch of Med St Louis MO 63110

SELTZER, LEON Z(EE), b Chicago, Ill, Apr 17, 14; m 40; c 1. AERONAUTICAL ENGINEERING. *Educ:* Univ Mich, BSE, 40; Univ Ill, PhC, 34. *Prof Exp:* Aeronaut engr, Douglas Aircraft Co, Calif, 40-41; prof aeronaut eng & chmn dept, Va Polytech Inst, 41-47 & WVa Univ, 49-63; PROF AEROSPACE ENG & DEAN, PARKS COL, ST LOUIS UNIV, 63- *Mem:* Am Soc Eng Educ; Soc Automotive Engrs; Am Inst Aeronaut & Astronaut; Am Helicopter Soc. *Res:* Theoretical and applied aerodynamics, including flying and flight testing. *Mailing Add:* 8021 Orlando Dr Clayton MO 63105

SELTZER, MARTIN S, b New York, NY, Apr 8, 37; m 60; c 3. SOLID STATE PHYSICS, PHYSICAL METALLURGY. *Educ:* NY Univ, BMetalEng, 58, Yale Univ, MEng, 60, DEng(metall), 62. *Prof Exp:* Res scientist, N V Philips Gloeilampenfabrieken, 62-63; fel, Dept Metall, Battelle Mem Inst, 63-77; MEM STAFF, PORTER, WRIGHT, MORRIS & ARTHUR, 77- *Mem:* AAAS; Am Ceramic Soc. *Res:* Self diffusion and mechanical properties of inorganic binary compounds. *Mailing Add:* Porter Wright Morris & Arthur 37 W Broad St Columbus OH 43215

SELTZER, RAYMOND, b New York, NY, May 27, 35; m 66; c 2. POLYMER CHEMISTRY, ORGANIC CHEMISTRY. *Educ:* City Col New York, BS, 56; Purdue Univ, PhD(org chem), 61. *Prof Exp:* Res chemist, Eastman Kodak Co, 61-63 & M&T Chem, Inc, Am Can Co, NY, 63-68; RES ASSOC, PLASTICS & ADDITIVES DIV, RES DEPT, CIBA-GEIGY CHEM CO, 68-, ASSOC DIR, 76- *Mem:* Am Chem Soc; Sigma Xi; NY Acad Sci; Soc Plastic Engrs. *Res:* Synthesis, characterization, evaluation and application of novel polymeric systems; developmental novel epoxy and other thermosetting resins; ultraviolet curable resins; high temperature stable polymers; film, coatings, adhesive, casting and composite applications. *Mailing Add:* Plastic & Additives Div Res Dept Saw Miller River Rd Ardsley NY 10502

SELTZER, SAMUEL, b Philadelphia, Pa, Feb 3, 14; m 46; c 1. DENTISTRY. *Educ:* Univ Pa, DDS, 37. *Prof Exp:* Assoc prof oral histol & path, Sch Dent, Univ Pa, 59-67; PROF ENDODONT, SCH DENT, TEMPLE UNIV, 67- *Mem:* AAAS; fel Am Col Dent; NY Acad Sci. *Res:* Biological aspects of dental pulp disease; injury of dental pulp and mechanisms of repair. *Mailing Add:* Dept Endodont Temple Univ Sch Dent Philadelphia PA 19140

SELTZER, STANLEY, b New York, NY, Feb 25, 30; m 52; c 1. PHYSICAL CHEMISTRY, ORGANIC CHEMISTRY. *Educ:* City Col, BS, 50; Harvard Univ, AM, 56, PhD(chem), 58. *Prof Exp:* Phys chem analyst, M W Kellogg Co Div, Pullman, Inc, 50-52; from res assoc to chemist, 58-73, SR CHEMIST, BROOKHAVEN NAT LAB, 73- *Concurrent Pos:* Vis prof, Cornell Univ, 64-65; NIH spec fel, 69-70; vis prof, Brandeis Univ, 69-70; lectr, Columbia Univ, 69-73; vis prof, State Univ NY, Stony Brook, 74 & 77, adj prof, 78- *Mem:* Am Chem Soc. *Res:* Mechanisms of reaction in organic and biochemical systems; kinetic isotope effects. *Mailing Add:* Dept of Chem Brookhaven Nat Lab Upton NY 11973

SELTZER, STANLEY, b Brooklyn, NY, Aug 8, 25; m 51; c 4. CHEMICAL ENGINEERING. *Educ:* Cooper Union, BChE, 47; Univ Mich, MS, 48, PhD(chem eng). 51. *Prof Exp:* Chem engr, Chem Mat Dept, Mass, 51-60, process engr, Silicone Prods Dept, Waterford, 60-61, eng leader, 61-65, mgr process eng, 66-69, mgr intermediates mfg, 69-79, MGR ADVAN TECHNOL, GEN ELEC CO, 79- *Mem:* Am Chem Soc; Am Inst Chem Engrs. *Res:* Advanced incineration systems; fluidized bed reactions; process control computers. *Mailing Add:* 2481 McGovern Dr Schenectady NY 12309

SELUND, ROBERT B(ERNARD), b La Crosse, Wis, Jan 25, 07; m 34; c 1. CHEMICAL ENGINEERING. *Educ:* Univ Minn, BS, 30. *Prof Exp:* Chem engr, Standard Oil Co (Ind), 30-40, res group leader, 41-51, res sect leader, 52-61, tech serv sect leader, Am Oil Co, 61-77; RETIRED. *Mem:* Am Chem Soc; Am Inst Chem Engrs. *Res:* Asphalt; motor oils; wax; crude oil distillation and coking; petroleum refining. *Mailing Add:* 250 Seventh Ave S Naples FL 33940

SELVA, RONALD JOSEPH, b Canonsburg, Pa, Sept 11, 41; m 63; c 2. MATHEMATICS, NUCLEAR PHYSICS. *Educ:* Washington & Jefferson Col, BA, 63; Univ Pittsburgh, MS, 65. *Prof Exp:* Programmer nuclear design, Bettis Atomic Power Lab, Westinghouse Elec Corp, 65-68; sr analyst nuclear consult, KPA Nuclear Inc, 68-70; PRIN MATHEMATICIAN NUCLEAR DESIGN, BETTIS ATOMIC POWER LAB, WESTINGHOUSE ELEC CORP, 70- *Mem:* Asn Comput Mach. *Res:* Solution for the neutron transport equation in varying geometries and dimensions using discrete ordinates technique; solution of the neutron diffusion equation with depletion capability. *Mailing Add:* Bettis Atomic Power Lab PO Box 79 West Mifflin PA 15122

SELVAGGI, JERRY ANTHONY, b Manhattan, NY, May 8, 22; m 50; c 4. ELECTRICAL ENGINEERING, APPLIED MATHEMATICS. *Educ:* Pratt Inst, BEE, 48; Pa State Univ, MS, 62. *Prof Exp:* Elec designer, Am Elec Power Co, 48-49, Long Island Lighting Co, 49-51 & Gibbs & Hill Consult, 51-52; distrib engr, Pa Elec Co, 52-57; dir eng, 57-68, ASSOC PROF & DIR ENG RES, GANNON COL, 68- *Concurrent Pos:* Consult, Elec Mat Co, 54-, Erie Malleable Iron Co, 55-, Talon Inc, 62-, Lord Mfg Co, 66-, Army Electronic Command, Ft Monmouth, NJ, 67-, Elgin Electronics, 68-, Eriez Magnetics, 69-, Meadville Forging, 71-, Ga Kaolin Co, 75-, Dayton Malleable Inc, 75- & Casting Serv, 76. *Mem:* Inst Elec & Electronics Engrs. *Res:* Application of mathematics in linear and nonlinear dynamic systems; ferroresonance; subharmonic generation; magnetostatics; development of operational techniques in nonlinear differential equations. *Mailing Add:* Dept of Eng Gannon Col Perry Sq Erie PA 16501

SELVERSTON, ALLEN ISRAEL, b Chicago, Ill, Jan 17, 36; m 63; c 4. NEUROPHYSIOLOGY, COMPARATIVE PHYSIOLOGY. *Educ:* Univ Ore, MA, 64, PhD(neurophysiol), 67. *Prof Exp:* Res assoc neurophysiol, Stanford Univ, 67-69; assoc prof neurophysiol, 74-76, assoc prof, 76-81, PROF BIOL, UNIV CALIF, SAN DIEGO, 81- *Concurrent Pos:* USPHS fel, 67-69; Alexander von Humboldt sr fel, 82-83. *Mem:* AAAS. *Res:* Animal behavior; neural mechanisms underlying behavior; integrative activity of invertebrate ganglia. *Mailing Add:* Dept of Biol Univ of Calif at San Diego La Jolla CA 92037

SELVESTER, RONALD H, b McArthur, Calif, Aug 19, 20; m; c 3. CARDIOLOGY. *Educ:* Loma Linda Univ, MD, 51. *Prof Exp:* Intern, Los Angeles County Gen Hosp, 50-51, resident internal med, 51-52; chief chest med serv, Los Angeles County Harbor Gen Hosp, 54-55, resident internal med, 55-56; NIH res fel, 56-58; assoc dir cardiopulmonary lab, White Mem Med Ctr, 59-62; from asst clin prof to assoc clin prof, 64-68, assoc prof, 68-71, PROF MED, SCH MED, UNIV SOUTHERN CALIF, 71-; CARDIAC PHYSIOLOGIST, RANCHO LOS AMIGOS HOSP, 62-, DIR BIOMATH & EKG RES GROUP, 65-, CHIEF CARDIOL, 67- *Concurrent Pos:* Instr, Loma Linda Univ, Loma Linda & Los Angeles, 58-62, asst prof, 62-; mem, Cardiovasc B Study Sect, NIH, 68-72, chmn, 72- *Mem:* AMA; Am Heart Asn. *Res:* Cardiovascular, hemodynamics, electrophysiology, computer modeling of the electric field of the heart and computer application to cardiology. *Mailing Add:* Cardiol Dept Univ of Southern Calif Downey CA 90242

SELVIDGE, HARNER, b Columbia, Mo, Oct 16, 10; m 33; c 4. ELECTRONICS. *Educ:* Mass Inst Technol, 32, MS, 33; Harvard Univ, SM, 34, SD(commun eng), 37. *Prof Exp:* Instr physics & commun eng, Harvard Univ, 35-38; assoc prof elec eng, Kans State Col, 38-41; sr engr, Carnegie Inst Technol, 41-42; appl physics lab, Johns Hopkins Univ, 42-45; dir spec prods develop, Bendix Aviation Corp, 45-56, staff engr, 56-60, vpres & gen mgr, Meteorol Res, Inc, Calif, 60-69; CONSULT, ALTA ASSOCS, 69- *Concurrent Pos:* Mem, Harvard-Mass Inst Technol Eclipse Exped, Russia, 36; consult engr, Am Phenolic Corp, 38-42; assoc engr, Taylor Tube Co, Ill, 39-40; dir res, Fournier Inst, 42-45. *Mem:* Am Meteorol Soc; fel Inst Elec & Electronics Engrs; assoc fel Am Inst Aeronaut & Astronaut. *Res:* Antennas; propagation and transmission lines; vacuum tubes; proximity fuses; fire control radar; guided missile control systems; nucleonics; industrial instrumentation and controls; meteorological systems. *Mailing Add:* Alta Assocs Box 1128 Sedona AZ 86336

SELVIN, BEATRICE L, b Hartford, Conn, Oct 13, 22. ANESTHESIOLOGY. *Educ:* Univ Mich, Ann Arbor, BA, 42; New York Med Col, MD, 45; Am Bd Anesthesiol, dipl. *Prof Exp:* Asst attend anesthesiologist, Columbia-Presby Med Ctr, 48-54; part-time anesthesiologist, Stamford Hosp, 54-56; asst attend anesthesiologist, Mem Ctr for Cancer, New York, 56 & James Ewing Hosp, 56; Instr anesthesiol, Med Col, Cornell Univ, 60; asst prof, 64-68, ASSOC PROF ANESTHESIOL, HOSP, UNIV MD, BALTIMORE CITY, 68- *Concurrent Pos:* Instr & assoc anesthesiol, Columbia-Presby Med Ctr, 48-54. *Mem:* AMA; Am Soc Anesthesiol. *Mailing Add:* Dept of Anesthesiol Univ of Md Hosp Baltimore MD 21201

SELWITZ, CHARLES MYRON, b Springfield, Mass, July 20, 27; m 55; c 2. ORGANIC CHEMISTRY. *Educ:* Worcester Polytech Inst, BS, 49; Univ Cincinnati, PhD(chem), 53. *Prof Exp:* Asst inorg chem, Univ Cincinnati, 49-50; res chemist, 53-55, group leader, 55-61, res chemist, 61-72, res assoc, 72-74, sect supvr, 74-76, GULF RES & DEVELOP CO, PITTSBURGH, 72-, DIR SYNTHETIC CHEM, 76- *Mem:* Am Chem Soc; Catalyst Soc. *Res:* Oxidation of organic compounds; chemical abstracts; free radical chemistry; organo-metallics; oxychlorination; phenols; coal chemistry; dcetylene chemistry; high temperature polymers. *Mailing Add:* 1169 Princeton Rd Monroeville PA 15146

SELWYN, PHILIP ALAN, b New York, NY, Feb 12, 45; m 66. CHEMICAL PHYSICS, FLUID MECHANICS. *Educ:* Univ Rochester, BS, 65; Mass Inst Technol, PhD(chem physics), 70. *Prof Exp:* Res assoc, Mass Inst Technol, res staff mem geophys fluid mech, Inst Defense Anal, 70-76; PROG MGR ANTISUBMARINE WARFARE & HYDRODYNAMICS, OCEAN MONITORING & CONTROL DIV, TACTICAL TECHNOL OFF, DEFENSE ADVAN RES PROJS AGENCY, 76- *Mem:* Am Phys Soc; Am Geophys Union. *Res:* Nonequilibrium statistical mechanics; atmospheric and oceanic fluid mechanics; sensor technology; operations analysis; turbulence. *Mailing Add:* Defense Advan Res Projs Agency 1400 Wilson Blvd Arlington VA 22209

SELYE, HANS, b Vienna, Austria, Jan 26, 07; Can citizen; m 78; c 4. PHYSIOLOGY. *Educ:* Ger Univ Prague, MD, 29, PhD(biochem), 31; McGill Univ, DSc, 42. *Hon Degrees:* DSc, Univ Windsor, 55, Cath Univ Chile, 56, Hahnemann Med Col, 62, Univ Guelph, Can, 73; MD, Univ Münster, 66, Univ Cagliari, Sardinia, 67, Karl-Franzens Univ, Graz, 67, J E Purkyne Univ, Czech, 69, Laval Univ, 75; LLD, Philadelphia Col, 75, Univ Alberta, 78. *Prof Exp:* Asst exp path, Ger Univ Prague, 29-31; Rockefeller res fel biochem, Johns Hopkins Univ, 31 & res fel biochem, McGill Univ, 32-33; lectr biochem, McGill Univ, 33-34, asst prof, 34-37, from asst prof to assoc prof histol, 37-45; prof & dir, 45-76, EMER PROF EXP MED & SURG, INST EXP MED & SURG, UNIV MONTREAL, 76- *Concurrent Pos:* Consult to Surgeon Gen, US Army, 47-57; pres, Int Inst Stress, Montreal, 76-; mem coun arteriosclerosis, Am Heart Asn. *Honors & Awards:* Many honors & awards from US & Europe, 46- *Mem:* Fel Am Geriat Soc; Endocrine Soc; Soc Exp Biol & Med; Am Soc Clin Invest. *Res:* Endocrinology; stress; cardiac necroses; calcium metabolism; anaphylactoid inflammation; thrombohemorrhagic phenomena; steroid anesthesia. *Mailing Add:* Int Inst Stress 2900 Edouard Montpetit Blvd Montreal PQ H3C 3J7 Can

SELZER, ARTHUR, b Lwow, Poland, July 3, 11; nat US; m 36; c 2. MEDICINE, CARDIOLOGY. *Educ:* Univ Lwow, MB, 35; Cracow Univ, MD, 36; Am Bd Internal Med, dipl, 43. *Prof Exp:* Asst, 41-42, clin instr, 42-47, from asst clin prof to clin prof, 47-76, EMER CLIN PROF MED, MED SCH, STANFORD UNIV, 76- CLIN PROF MED, SCH MED, UNIV CALIF, SAN FRANCISCO, 60- *Concurrent Pos:* Chief cardiol & dir cardiopulmonary lab, Pac Med Ctr, 59-; consult, US Naval Hosp, Oakland, Letterman Gen Hosp. *Mem:* Am Fedn Clin Res; Int Cardiovasc Soc; fel Am Col Physicians; fel Am Col Cardiol. *Res:* Clinical cardiovascular physiology; operable heart disease; coronary artery disease; heart failure; pharmacology of digitalis. *Mailing Add:* Pac Med Ctr Clay & Webster Sts San Francisco CA 94115

SELZER, MELVIN LAWRENCE, b New York, NY, Feb 3, 25; m 57; c 3. PSYCHIATRY. *Educ:* Tulane Univ, BS, 49, MD, 52; Am Bd Psychiat & Neurol, dipl, 59. *Prof Exp:* Intern, Univ Mich Hosp, 52-53; resident psychiat, Ypsilanti State Hosp, 54-57; assoc psychiatrist, Health Serv, Med Sch, Univ Mich, Ann Arbor, 57-59, from instr to prof psychiat, 59-78; CLIN PROF, DEPT PSYCHIAT, UNIV CALIF, SAN DIEGO, 81- *Concurrent Pos:* Examr, Am Bd Psychiat & Neurol, 62-68; mem comt alcohol & drugs, Nat Safety Coun, 63-72; resource consult, President's Comt Traffic Safety, 64-65; mem fac, Inst Continuing Legal Educ, Univ Mich-Wayne State Univ Law Schs, 65-70; mem criminal code revision comt, State Bar Mich, 66-69; ed referee, J Studies Alcohol, 67- & Am J Psychiat, 69-; mem fac, Pract Law Inst, NY, 68-71; consult, Fed Aviation Admin, 69, US Dept Transp, 69- & Archdiocese of Detroit, 72; consult ed, Life Threatening Behav, 70-; res psychiatrist, Hwy Safety Res Inst, 70-75; mem res rev comt, Nat Inst Alcohol Abuse & Alcoholism, 76-78. *Mem:* Fel Am Psychiat Asn; Asn Am Med Cols; fel Am Col Psychiat. *Res:* Psychoanalytic therapy; student mental health; alcoholism; psychological aspects of traffic accidents. *Mailing Add:* 6967 Paseo Laredo La Jolla CA 92037

SEMAN, GABRIEL, b Budapest, Hungary, Sept 3, 25; m 52; c 5. VIROLOGY, CYTOLOGY. *Educ:* Univ Paris, BS, 46, MD, 54. *Prof Exp:* Gen practitioner, France, 54-61; res assoc, Res Ctr Cancerology & Radiobiol, Paris, 61-64; Eli Lilly res fel, Univ Tex M D Anderson Hosp & Tumor Inst Houston, 64-65; sr res assoc & head dept cytol & electron micros, Inst Cancerology & Immunogenetics, Villejuif, France, 65-68; ASSOC PROF VIROL & ASSOC VIROLOGIST, UNIV TEX M D ANDERSON HOSP & TUMOR INST HOUSTON, 68- *Mem:* AAAS; Am Asn Cancer Res; Tissue Cult Asn. *Res:* Ultrastructure cytology; normal and leukemic cytohematology; viral oncology; electron microscopy. *Mailing Add:* Dept of Molecular Carcinogenesis & Virol M D Anderson Hosp & Tumor Inst Houston TX 77025

SEMAN, GEORGE WILLIAM, b Pittsburgh, Pa, May 29, 40. ELECTRICAL ENGINEERING. *Educ:* Carnegie Inst Technol, BS, 62, MS, 64, PhD(elec eng), 66. *Prof Exp:* Res engr space syst, Avco Corp, 66-67; res engr, nuclear weapons effects, EG&G Inc, 67-68; sr res engr nuclear weapons effects, Ion Physics Corp, 68-69; RES MGR ELEC CABLES, GEN CABLE, PIRELLI CABLE CORP, 69- *Mem:* Sr mem Inst Elec & Electronics Engrs. *Res:* New cable designs; evaluation of electrical and mechanical performance of extruded and laminar dielectric transmission and distribution cables. *Mailing Add:* Pirelli Cable Corp 800 Rahway Ave Union NJ 07083

SEMANCIK, JOSEPH STEPHEN, b Barton, Ohio, June 9, 38; m 63. PATHOLOGY, VIROLOGY. *Educ:* Western Reserve Univ, AB, 60; Purdue Univ, MS, 62, PhD(path), 64. *Prof Exp:* Asst plant pathologist & lectr plant path, Univ Calif, Riverside, 64-69; assoc prof plant path, Univ Nebr, Lincoln, 69-72; assoc prof, 72-74, PROF PLANT PATH, UNIV CALIF, RIVERSIDE, 74-, CHMN DEPT, 80- *Concurrent Pos:* USPHS grants, 65-68 & 69-73; assoc ed, Virol, 71-73 & Phytopathology, 74-76; NSF awards, 73-75, 75-78 & 78-81; Guggenheim fel, 78. *Honors & Awards:* Alexander von Humboldt Found Prize, 75. *Mem:* AAAS; fel Am Phytopath Soc. *Res:* Purification and characterization of pathogenic nucleic acids; cell biology; viroids; viroid-cell interactions. *Mailing Add:* Dept of Plant Path Univ of Calif Riverside CA 92502

SEMAR, CARY LLOYD, space physics, see previous edition

SEMBA, KAZUE, b Tsuchiura, Japan, Jan 13, 49; m 72. PSYCHOBIOLOGY, NEUROSCIENCE. *Educ:* Tokyo Univ Educ, BEd, 71, MA, 73; Rutgers Univ, PhD(psychobiol), 79. *Prof Exp:* Res asst, Inst Aminal Behav, Rutgers Univ, 75-76, teaching asst physiol & exp psychol, Dept Psychol, 76-77; fel, Dept Vet Physiol & Pharmacol, Iowa State Univ, 79-80; res specialist, Col Med & Dent NJ, 80-81, assoc behav & brain sci, 81-82, INSTR, RUTGERS MED SCH, UNIV MED & DENT NJ, 81- *Concurrent Pos:* Grant-in-aid, Japan Soc NY, 78 & NJ State fel, 77-78. *Honors & Awards:* Young Psychologist Award, 76. *Mem:* Soc Neurosci; Am Psychol Asn; Sigma Xi; NY Acad Sci; Am Asn Univ Professors. *Res:* Sensorimotor control of the vibrissae; sensory mechanisms in the spinal cord. *Mailing Add:* Dept Anat Univ Med & Dent NJ Rutgers Med Sch Piscataway NJ 08854

SEMEGEN, STEPHEN THOMAS, b Akron, Ohio, Dec 28, 18; m 43; c 4. CHEMISTRY. *Educ:* Univ Akron, BS, 40. *Prof Exp:* Res chemist, Quaker Rubber Corp, Pa, 40-41; res chemist, B F Goodrich Rubber Co, 41-47, group head rubber res, 47-53, actg dir, 53-54, group head compounding res, 54-56, mgr rubber & plastics tech, 56-60, mgr prod res, 60-64; dir US tech adv serv, Natural Rubber Bur, 64-68, vpres, 68-69, pres, Malaysian Rubber Bur, 69-76, PRES, NATURAL RUBBER CO, 76- *Mem:* AAAS; Am Inst Chem; Am Chem Soc; Am Forestry Asn. *Res:* Rubber chemistry: latex technology; compounding polymerization; vulcanization; radiation chemistry; plastics; synthetic leather; natural rubber agriculture. *Mailing Add:* Natural Rubber Co 15 Atterbury Blvd Hudson OH 44236

SEMEL, MAURIE, b NY, Jan 18, 23; m 50; c 3. ENTOMOLOGY. *Educ:* Cornell Univ, PhD(entom), 54. *Prof Exp:* Grad asst, 49-54, asst prof, 54-59, ASSOC PROF ENTOM, LONG ISLAND HORT RES LAB, CORNELL UNIV, 59- *Concurrent Pos:* Vis sr scientist, Int Potato Ctr, Lima, Peru, 72-73; mem adv coun agr, NY State Dept Agr & Mkt. *Mem:* Entom Soc Am; NY Acad Sci; Entom Soc Can; Potato Asn Am; Sigma Xi. *Res:* Control of insects affecting vegetable and ornamental crops. *Mailing Add:* Dept of Entom Long Island Hort Res Lab Riverhead NY 11901

SEMELUK, GEORGE PETER, b Coleman, Alta, Apr 14, 24; m 49; c 3. PHYSICAL CHEMISTRY. *Educ:* Univ Alta, BSc, 47, MSc, 49; Ill Inst Technol, PhD(kinetics), 55; Cambridge Univ, PhD(kinetics), 60. *Prof Exp:* Res chemist, Lamp Div, Gen Elec Co, Ohio, 53-55; proj engr, Electrochem Labs, Inc, Okla, 55-58; assoc prof, 60-67, PROF CHEM, UNIV NB, 67- *Concurrent Pos:* Consult, Dow Chem Can, Ltd, 64- *Mem:* Fel AAAS; fel Chem Inst Can; Am Chem Soc; The Chem Soc. *Res:* Unimolecular decompositions; structure and chemistry of excited states; photosensitized decompositions. *Mailing Add:* Dept of Chem Univ of NB Fredericton NB E3B 5A3 Can

SEMENIUK, FRED THEODOR, b Edmonton, Alta, Jan 3, 15; nat US; m 56; c 2. PHARMACEUTICAL CHEMISTRY. *Educ:* Univ Alta, BSc, 39; Purdue Univ, PhD(pharmaceut chem), 47. *Prof Exp:* Asst instr pharmaceut chem, Purdue Univ, 41-46; instr, Univ Wis, 46-47; from asst prof to assoc prof, 47-51, PROF PHARMACEUT CHEM, UNIV NC, CHAPEL HILL, 51- *Mem:* AAAS; Am Chem Soc; Am Pharmaceut Asn. *Res:* Organic medicinals; organic chemical nomenclature. *Mailing Add:* Sch of Pharm Univ of NC Chapel Hill NC 27514

SEMENIUK, GEORGE, b Edmonton, Alta, May 2, 10; nat US; m 39; c 3. PLANT PATHOLOGY. *Educ:* Univ Alta, BSc, 32, MSc, 34; Iowa State Col, PhD(mycol), 38. *Prof Exp:* Asst plant path, Univ Alta, 30-34; asst, Exp Sta, Iowa State Col, 38-39, res assoc, 39-44, from res asst prof to res assoc prof, Col, 44-52; prof, 52-75, EMER PROF PLANT SCI & MICROBIOL, SDAK STATE UNIV, 75- *Concurrent Pos:* Res asst biologist, Nat Res Coun Can, 44-45. *Mem:* AAAS; Mycol Soc Am; Am Inst Biol Sci; Am Phytopath Soc. *Res:* Mycotoxicology; alfalfa and wheat root diseases; mycology of feed spoilage. *Mailing Add:* Dept Plant Sci SDak State Univ Brookings SD 57007

SEMENUK, NICK SARDEN, b Nestow, Alta, June 16, 37; m 63; c 3. ORGANIC CHEMISTRY, INFORMATION SCIENCE. *Educ:* Univ Alta, BSc, 58; Purdue Univ, PhD(chem), 64. *Prof Exp:* Sr res chemist org div, Olin Mathieson Chem Co, 63-65, chem div, 65-69; info res scientist, Squibb Inst Med Res, New Brunswick, 69-71, dir sci info dept, 71-76, SECT HEAD, SQUIBB INST MED RES, PRINCETON, 76- *Mem:* AAAS; Am Chem Soc; Chem Inst Can; Drug Info Asn. *Res:* Pharmaceutical chemistry; cyclic adenosine monophosphate. *Mailing Add:* Squibb Inst for Med Res PO Box 4000 Princeton NJ 08540

SEMERJIAN, HRATCH G, b Istanbul, Turkey, Oct 22, 43; US citizen; m 69; c 2. FLUID MECHANICS, COMBUSTION. *Educ:* Robert Col, Turkey, BS, 66; Brown Univ, MSc, 68, PhD(eng), 72. *Prof Exp:* Lectr chem, Univ Toronto, 72-73; res engr, Pratt & Whitney Aircraft, United Technol Corp, 73-77; GROUP LEADER COMBUSTION, THERMAL PROCESS DIV, NAT BUR STANDARDS, 77- *Concurrent Pos:* Res fel, Univ Toronto, 71-73. *Mem:* Am Inst Aeronaut & Astronaut; Am Soc Mech Engrs; Combustion Inst; Sigma Xi. *Res:* Pollutant formation in flames; combustion modelling and diagnostics; gas turbine combustion; particle sizing techniques; radiative heat transfer; fluid mechanics. *Mailing Add:* Nat Bur of Standards Bldg 221 Rm B252 Washington DC 20234

SEMKEN, HOLMES ALFORD, JR, b Knoxville, Tenn, Jan 28, 35; m 57; c 2. VERTEBRATE PALEONTOLOGY. *Educ:* Univ Tex, BS, 58, MA, 60; Univ Mich, PhD(geol), 65. *Prof Exp:* Mus intern geol, Smithsonian Inst, 60-61 & summer 62; from asst prof to assoc prof, 65-73, PROF GEOL, UNIV IOWA, 73- *Mem:* Geol Soc Am; Paleont Soc; Soc Vert Paleont; Am Soc Mammal; Am Quaternary Asn. *Res:* Paleoecology and biogeography of Pleistocene and Holocene mammals, especially rodents; archaeological geology, especially zoology archaeology; vertebrate paleontology. *Mailing Add:* Dept Geol Univ Iowa Iowa City IA 52242

SEMLER, CHARLES EDWARD, b Dayton, Ohio, Dec 27, 40; m 62; c 2. HIGH TEMPERATURE MINERALOGY, MATERIALS TESTING. *Educ:* Miami Univ, BA, 62, MS, 65; Ohio State Univ, PhD(mineral), 68. *Prof Exp:* Res engr ceramics, Ferro Corp, 64-65; sr res engr mat res, Monsanto Res Corp, 68-70; asst prof geol, Wash Univ, 70-71; sr res mineral refractories, Dresser Indust, 71-74; asst prof, 74-80, ASSOC PROF, OHIO STATE UNIV, 80-, DIR CERAMIC ENG, 74- *Concurrent Pos:* Abstractor, Am Chem Soc, 71-74; chmn Spalling Comt, Am Soc Testing & Mat, 75-; chmn refractories comt, Am Foundrymen's Soc, 76-; adv comt, Interceram, WGer, 78-; NSF Exchange Scientist, India, 76; vis prof, Sydney, Australia, 81. *Mem:* Fel Am Ceramic Soc; Am Soc Testing & Mat; Nat Inst Ceramic Eng. *Res:* Refractories testing by destructive and non-destructive methods; high temperature phase equilibrium relations of oxide materials; microstructure of materials; thermal shock of materials; test development. *Mailing Add:* Dept of Ceramics Ohio State Univ Columbus OH 43210

SEMLYEN, ADAM, b Gherla, Romania, Jan 10, 23. ELECTRICAL ENGINEERING. *Educ:* Timisoara Polytech Inst, Dipl Ing, 50; Iasi Polytech Inst, Dr Ing, 65. *Prof Exp:* Lectr power apparatus, Timisoara Polytech Inst, 50-58, from assoc prof to prof power systs, 58-69; vis assoc prof elec eng, 69-71, assoc prof, 71-74, PROF ELEC ENG, UNIV TORONTO, 74- *Concurrent Pos:* Engr, Power Sta Timisoara, Romania, 49-51; consult, Regional Power Authority, Timisoara, 60-69 & Elec Eng Consociates, 70-; Nat Res Coun Can grant, Univ Toronto, 71- *Mem:* Inst Elec & Electronics Engrs; Int Conf Large Elec Systs. *Res:* Power system dynamics; power system optimization; switching transients in high voltage systems. *Mailing Add:* Dept Elec Eng Univ Toronto Toronto ON M5S 1A4 Can

SEMMELHACK, MARTIN F, b Appleton, Wis, Nov 19, 41; m 73; c 1. ORGANIC CHEMISTRY. *Educ:* Univ Wis, Madison, BS, 63; Harvard Univ, AM, 65, PhD(org chem), 67. *Prof Exp:* NIH fel, Stanford Univ, 67-68; from asst prof to prof org chem, Cornell Univ, 68-78; PROF ORG CHEM, PRINCETON UNIV, 78- *Concurrent Pos:* Fel, Alfred P Sloan Found, 72-74; teacher-scholar award, Camille and Henry Dreyfuss Found, 73-78; Guggenheim fel, 78-79. *Mem:* Am Chem Soc; The Chem Soc. *Res:* Synthesis of biologically active compounds; organometallic reagents and electrochemical techniques in organic synthesis. *Mailing Add:* Dept of Chem Princeton Univ Princeton NY 08540

SEMMES, JOSEPHINE, b Hazlehurst, Miss, Nov 2, 16; div; c 3. PHYSIOLOGICAL PSYCHOLOGY. *Educ:* Univ Chicago, BA, 43; Yale Univ, PhD(psychol), 49. *Prof Exp:* Asst, Yerkes Labs Primate Biol, 45-50; asst prof psychobiol, Yale Univ, 49-50; res assoc neurol, Col Med, NY Univ, 51-53; res fel, Nat Inst Ment Health, 52-54; res assoc neurol, Sch Med, NY Univ, 54-61; res psychologist, Lab Psychol, 61-75, CHIEF SECT NEUROPSYCHOL, BEHAV SCI RES BR, DIV EXTRAMURAL PROGS, NAT INST MENT HEALTH, 75- *Concurrent Pos:* Mem exp psychol study sect, Div Res Grants, NIH; pres, Assembly of scientists, Nat Inst Ment Health, Nat Inst Neurol Dis & Stroke & Nat Eye Inst, 73. *Mem:* Fel AAAS; Int Brain Res Orgn; Psychonomic Soc; Am Psychol Asn. *Res:* Behavioral effects of cerebral lesions; differences between the hemispheres; somesthetic function. *Mailing Add:* Rm 10-C-06 Parklawn Bldg 5600 Fishers Lane Rockville MD 20857

SEMMLOW, JOHN LEONARD, b Chicago, Ill, Mar 12, 42. BIOENGINEERING, BIOMEDICAL ENGINEERING. *Educ:* Univ Ill, Champaign, BS, 64; Univ Ill Med Ctr, PhD(physiol), 70. *Prof Exp:* Sr engr, Motorola, Inc, 64-66; instr physiol optics, Univ Calif, Berkeley, 69-70; asst prof bioeng, Univ Ill, Chicago, 71-77; asst prof physiol, Med Sch, Rush Univ, Chicago, 71-77; asst prof elec eng, 77-80, ASSOC PROF SURG, MED SCH & ASSOC PROF ELEC ENG, RUTGERS UNIV, 81- *Mem:* Inst Elec & Electronics Engrs; Sigma Xi; NY Acad Sci. *Res:* Eye movement and other physiological motor control systems; design and development of bioinstrumentation for noninvasive diagnosis, particularly in cardiology and neurology. *Mailing Add:* Dept Elec Eng Rutgers Univ Piscataway NJ 08901

SEMON, MARK DAVID, b Milwaukee, Wis, Mar 27, 50. PHYSICS, MATHEMATICS. *Educ:* Colgate Univ, AB, 71; Colo Univ, MS, 73; Univ Colo, PhD(physics), 76. *Prof Exp:* ASST PROF PHYSICS, BATES COL, 76- *Concurrent Pos:* Fac fel, Bates Col, 77-79. *Mem:* Am Phys Soc. *Res:* Quantum scattering theory; phase transitions and critical phenomena; quantum field theory; aharonov-bohm effect. *Mailing Add:* Dept of Physics Bates Col Lewiston ME 04240

SEMON, WALDO LONSBURY, b Demopolis, Ala, Sept 10, 98; m 20; c 3. CHEMISTRY. *Educ:* Univ Wash, Seattle, BS, 20, PhD(chem), 23. *Hon Degrees:* ASLD, Univ Wash, Seattle, 46; DSc, Kent State Univ, 81. *Prof Exp:* Anal chemist, Falkenburg Co, Wash, 18; instr chem, Univ Wash, Seattle, 20-26; res chemist & chem engr, B F Goodrich Co, 26-40, dir synthetic rubber res, 40-43, dir pioneering res, 43-54, dir polymer res, 54-58, dir rubber res, 58-63; RES PROF, KENT STATE UNIV, 63- *Concurrent Pos:* Chem engr, Everett Gas Works, Wash, 21; vpres & dir res, Hycar Chem Co, 40-42; vpres & dir, Farm Chemurgic Coun, 43-60; dir, Concepts Develop Inst, Ohio, 76- *Honors & Awards:* Modern Pioneer Award, Nat Asn Mfrs, 40; Goodyear Medal, Am Chem Soc, 45; Distinguished Award, Akron Coun Sci Socs, 60; 3rd Int Synthetic Rubber Gold Medal, London, Elliot Cresson Gold Medal, Franklin Inst & Am Inst Chem Eng Award, 64. *Mem:* Am Chem Soc; Am Inst Chem Eng. *Res:* Hydroxylamine and oximes; complexes of sulfur; rubber chemistry; antioxidants; synthetic copolymers, nitrile and deuterio rubber; rubber to metal adhesion; brass plating; polyvinyl chloride; Koroseal; butadiene; directive polymers; reactions of oxygen dissolved in water. *Mailing Add:* 79 Atterbury Blvd 110 Hudson OH 44236

SEMON, WARREN LLOYD, b Boise, Idaho, Jan 17, 21; m 45; c 4. MATHEMATICS. *Educ:* Univ Chicago, SB, 44; Harvard Univ, MS, 49, PhD(appl math), 54. *Prof Exp:* Instr math, Hobart Col, 46-47; res assoc comput lab, Harvard Univ, 49-55, lectr appl math & asst dir comput lab, 55-61; head appl math dept, Sperry Rand Res Ctr, Mass, 61-64; mgr comput

& anal, Burroughs Res Ctr, Pa, 64-67; PROF COMPUT SCI, SYRACUSE UNIV, 67-, DIR SYSTS & INFO SCI, 68-, DEAN, SCH COMPUT & INFO SCI, 77- *Concurrent Pos:* Consult, US Air Force, 57-61 & Nat Security Agency, 58-59; ed-in-chief, Comput Soc of Inst of Elec & Elec Engrs, 75- *Mem:* Asn Comput Mach; fel Inst Elec & Electronics Engrs; Math Asn Am; Sigma Xi. *Res:* Digital computer systems and applications; switching theory; automata theory. *Mailing Add:* Sch Comput & Info Sci Syracuse Univ Syracuse NY 13210

SEMONIN, RICHARD GERARD, b Akron, Ohio, June 25, 30; m 51; c 4. ATMOSPHERIC PHYSICS, PRECIPITATION CHEMISTRY. *Educ:* Univ Wash, Seattle, BSc, 55. *Prof Exp:* Res asst radar meteorol, 55-56, from res assoc to assoc prof sci, 56-65, prof, 65-71, asst head atmospheric sci sect, 70-80, PRIN SCIENTIST, ILL STATE WATER SURV, 71-, ASST CHIEF, 80- *Concurrent Pos:* NSF grants, 58-60 & 61-; US Army Res & Develop Labs grant, 62-64; Dept Energy contract, 69-; Dept Interior contract, 71-; prof atmospheric sci, Univ Ill, 75- *Mem:* Fel AAAS; fel Am Meteorol Soc; Weather Modification Asn; Nat Weather Asn. *Res:* Microphysical processes necessary or attendant to the formation of clouds and precipitation; weather modification, controlled and inadvertent; causes and distribution of acid deposition. *Mailing Add:* Ill State Water Surv 605 E Springfield Champaign IL 61820

SEMPLE, ROBERT B(AYLOR), b St Louis Co, Mo, Aug 18, 10; m 33; c 5. CHEMICAL ENGINEERING. *Educ:* Mass Inst Technol, BS, 32, MS, 33. *Hon Degrees:* DEng, Wayne State Univ. *Prof Exp:* Res chemist, Monsanto Chem Co, Mo, 33-34, pilot plant supt, 35-39, asst dir, Develop Dept, 39-44, mgr petrol chem sales, 44-46, dir develop dept, 47-49; pres, Wyandotte Chem Corp, 49-71, chmn bd, BASF Wyandotte Corp, 71-81; RETIRED. *Mem:* Am Chem Soc; Am Inst Chem Engrs. *Res:* Peroxide catalyst for polymerization of styrene. *Mailing Add:* 333 Fort St 11th Floor Detroit MI 48226

SEMRAD, JOSEPH EDWARD, b Renfrow, Okla, Aug 15, 05; m 31; c 3. ZOOLOGY. *Educ:* Creighton Univ, PhB, 27; St Louis Univ, MS, 31; Northwestern Univ, PhD(zool), 35. *Prof Exp:* Asst, St Louis Univ, 27-29; instr, Loyola Univ, Ill, 29-32, from asst prof to assoc prof biol, 37-39, actg head dept, 39-42; dir, In-Serv Inst, 65-77, from assoc prof to prof, 45-72, EMER PROF ZOOL, DEPAUL UNIV, 72- *Concurrent Pos:* Fel, La State Univ, 59. *Mem:* AAAS; Am Soc Parasitol; Am Soc Trop Med & Hyg. *Res:* Parasitology; trichinosis; chick embryology; effects of ultraviolet on protoplasm. *Mailing Add:* 1122 Lunt Ave Apt 70 Chicago IL 60626

SEMRAU, KONRAD (TROXEL), b Chico, Calif, June 5, 19. CHEMICAL ENGINEERING. *Educ:* Univ Calif, BS, 48, MS, 49. *Prof Exp:* Asst tech engr, Carbide & Carbon Chem Co Div, Union Carbide & Carbon Corp, 46; chem engr, 50-63, SR CHEM ENGR, SRI INT, 63- *Mem:* Am Inst Chem Engrs; Am Chem Soc; Sigma Xi; Air Pollution Control Asn. *Res:* Dust and mist collection; fine particle technology; air pollution control engineering; mass transfer. *Mailing Add:* SRI Int 333 Ravenswood Ave Menlo Park CA 94025

SEMTNER, ALBERT JULIUS, JR, b Oklahoma City, Okla, May 25, 41; m 69; c 2. OCEANOGRAPHY. *Educ:* Calif Inst Technol, BS, 63; Univ Calif, Los Angeles, MA, 65; Princeton Univ, PhD(geophys fluid dynamics), 73. *Prof Exp:* Lt comdr oceanog, Nat Oceanic & Atmospheric Admin, 68-73; adj asst prof meteorol, Univ Calif, Los Angeles, 73-76; STAFF SCIENTIST OCEANOG, NAT CTR ATMOSPHERIC RES, 76- *Concurrent Pos:* Consult, Rand Corp, 74-75. *Res:* Numerical simulation of ocean circulation; prediction of climatic changes with coupled models of the atmosphere, the ocean and sea ice. *Mailing Add:* Nat Ctr for Atmospheric Res PO Box 3000 Boulder CO 80307

SEMTNER, PAUL JOSEPH, b Seminole, Okla, May 9, 45; m 70; c 3. ECONOMIC ENTOMOLOGY, INSECT ECOLOGY. *Educ:* Okla State Univ, BS, 67, MS, 70, PhD(entom), 72. *Prof Exp:* Res assoc entom, Okla State Univ, 72-73; instr, Connors State Col, 73-74; ASST PROF ENTOM, VA POLYTECH INST & STATE UNIV, 74- *Mem:* Entom Soc Am; Sigma Xi. *Res:* Pest management of tobacco insect pests and effects of the environment on their abundance. *Mailing Add:* Va Polytech Inst & State Univ Southern Piedmont Ctr Blackstone VA 23824

SEN, AMAR KUMAR, b Calcutta, India, Mar 14, 27; m 56; c 2. PHYSIOLOGY. *Educ:* Univ Calcutta, MSc, 49, MB & BS, 55; Univ London, PhD(physiol), 60. *Prof Exp:* Instr physiol, Sch Med, Vanderbilt Univ, 60-61; sci pool officer, S K M Hosp, Calcutta, India, 62; dir clin res, Sandoz Ltd, Bombay, 62-63; asst prof physiol, Sch Med, Vanderbilt Univ, 63-66; assoc prof, 66-70, PROF PHARMACOL, FAC MED, UNIV TORONTO, 70- *Concurrent Pos:* Consult pharmacologist, Addiction Res Found, Ont. *Mem:* Am Physiol Soc; Can Biochem Soc; Can Pharmacol Soc; Can Physiol Soc. *Res:* Transport of electrolytes and non-electrolytes across the cell membrane. *Mailing Add:* Dept of Pharmacol Univ of Toronto Fac of Med Toronto Can

SEN, AMIYA K, b Calcutta, India, Dec 14, 30; m 63. ELECTRICAL ENGINEERING, PLASMA PHYSICS. *Educ:* Indian Inst Sci, Bangalore, dipl, 52; Mass Inst Technol, SM, 58; PhD(elec eng), 63. *Prof Exp:* Test engr elec eng, Gen Elec Co, 53-54, design anal engr, 54-55; teaching asst, Mass Inst Technol, 56-57, instr, 57-58; from instr to assoc prof, 58-74, PROF ELEC ENG, COLUMBIA UNIV, 74- *Concurrent Pos:* Various NSF grants, 65-; mem, Adv Subcomt, NSF, 80-82. *Mem:* Am Phys Soc; Am Geophys Union; Inst Elec & Electronic Engrs. *Res:* Energy conversion; plasma and space physics; magnetohydrodynamics; author or coauther of over 50 scientific journal publications. *Mailing Add:* Dept of Elec Eng Mudd Bldg Columbia Univ New York NY 10027

SEN, BUDDHADEV, b India, Aug 7, 23; nat US; m 56; c 2. PHYSICAL INORGANIC CHEMISTRY. *Educ:* Univ Calcutta, India, BSc, 45, MSc, 47, DPhil(sci), 54. *Prof Exp:* Lectr chem, City Col Calcutta, India, 48 & Jadavpur Univ, India, 48-56; fel, La State Univ, 54-56, from vis asst prof to asst prof, 56-60; vis asst prof, Univ Alta, 60-61; from asst prof to assoc prof, 61-72, PROF CHEM, LA STATE UNIV, BATON ROUGE, 72- *Concurrent Pos:* Petrol Res Fund int grant, Univ Col London, 66-67; chmn freshman chem prog, Dept Chem, La State Univ, 76. *Res:* Coordination chemistry of transition and post-transition elements; thermodynamics of chelates; properties of mixed solvents. *Mailing Add:* Dept of Chem La State Univ Baton Rouge LA 70803

SEN, DIPAK KUMAR, b Patna, India, Feb 28, 36. MATHEMATICAL PHYSICS. *Educ:* Patna Univ, India, MSc, 54; Univ Paris, DresSci(physics), 58. *Prof Exp:* From lectr to assoc prof, 58-77, PROF MATH, UNIV TORONTO, 77- *Mem:* Am Math Soc; Can Math Soc. *Res:* Relativity; cosmology. *Mailing Add:* Dept of Math Univ of Toronto Toronto ON M5S 2R8 Can

SEN, GANES C, b Varanasi, India, Jan 17, 45; m 73; c 2. MOLECULAR BIOLOGY. *Educ:* Calcutta Univ, BSc, 65, MSc, 67; McMaster Univ, PhD(biochem), 74. *Prof Exp:* Fel molecular biol, Yale Univ, 74-76, res assoc, 76-78; ASST MEM MOLECULAR BIOL, SLOAN-KETTERING CANCER CTR, 78-, HEAD, LAB ONCOGENIC VIRUSES & INTERFERONS, 81-; ASST PROF, GRAD SCH MED SCI, CORNELL UNIV, 79- *Mem:* Am Soc Microbiol; Am Soc Virol; NY Acad Sci. *Res:* Molecular mechanisms of various actions of interferons including the actions on replication of and neoplastic transformation by RNA tumor viruses. *Mailing Add:* 1275 York Ave New York NY 10021

SEN, PRANAB KUMAR, b Calcutta, India, Nov 7, 37; m 63; c 2. BIOSTATISTICS. *Educ:* Univ Calcutta, India, BSc, 55, MSc, 57, PhD(statist), 62. *Prof Exp:* Asst prof statist, Univ Calcutta, India, 61-64 & Univ Calif, Berkeley, 64-65; from asst prof biostatist to assoc prof, 65-70, prof statist, 70-80, PROF BIOSTATIST, UNIV NC, CHAPEL HILL, 70-, ADJ PROF STATIST, 80- *Concurrent Pos:* US Air Force Systs Command contract statist anal, Univ NC, 71-78; Richard Merton Guest Prof, Univ Freiburg, Ger, 74-75. *Mem:* Fel Inst Math Statist; fel Am Statist Asn; Int Statist Inst. *Res:* Nonparametric methods; multivariate analysis; order statistics; weak convergence; nonparametric statistics and sequential procedures. *Mailing Add:* Dept of Biostatist Univ of NC Chapel Hill NC 27514

SENA, ELISSA PURNELL, b Brooklyn, NY, Nov 17, 44. MOLECULAR BIOLOGY. *Educ:* Cornell Univ, BS, 65, MS, 66; Univ Wis-Madison, PhD(molecular biol), 72. *Prof Exp:* Researcher genetics & molecular biol, Univ Calif, Berkeley, 70-75; asst prof molecular biol, 75-76, ASST PROF BIOL, DEPT BIOL, CASE WESTERN RESERVE UNIV, 76- *Mem:* Genetics Soc Am. *Res:* Control of DNA replication and recombination; organelle biogenesis. *Mailing Add:* Dept of Biol Case Western Reserve Univ Cleveland OH 44106

SENAY, LEO CHARLES, JR, b Fall River, Mass, Jan 18, 27; m 51; c 7. PHYSIOLOGY. *Educ:* Harvard Univ, AB, 49; State Univ Iowa, PhD(physiol), 57. *Prof Exp:* From instr to assoc prof, 57-68, PROF PHYSIOL, SCH MED, ST LOUIS UNIV, 68- *Concurrent Pos:* NIH career develop award, 65-70; Anglo-Am fel, SAfrica, 70-71; vis prof appl physiol, Univ Witwatersrand, 71; consult, NIH. *Mem:* AAAS; Am Physiol Soc; Soc Exp Biol & Med. *Res:* Environmental physiology, particularly human responses to heat stress and exercise; body fluid dynamics. *Mailing Add:* Dept of Physiol St Louis Univ Sch of Med St Louis MO 63104

SENBUPTA, GAUTAM, b Gaibandha, Bangladesh, Sept 1, 45; m 72; c 2. MECHANICAL & AEROSPACE ENGINEERING. *Educ:* Univ Calcutta, BSc Hons, 63; Indian Inst Technol, Kharagpur, BTech Hons, 66; Univ Southampton, PhD(struct acoust), 70. *Prof Exp:* Spec engr acoust fatigue, Eng Sci Data Univ, London, 70-71; resident res assoc struct dynamics, Langley Res Ctr, NASA, 72-73; sr specialist, 73-80, PRIN ENGR NOISE CONTROL, BOEING CO, 73- *Concurrent Pos:* Reviewer, J Sound & Vibration, Shock & Vibration Digest, Am Inst Aeronaut & Astronaut J, 70-; resident res assoc, Langley Res Ctr, NASA-Nat Acad Sci, 72-73; dir educ, Pac Northwest Sect, Am Inst Aeronaut & Astronaut, 78-80. *Honors & Awards:* Cert Recognition Creative Achievement, Boeing Co, 76, 1st Ann Inventors Award, 77 & 80; Outstanding Tech Contrib, Am Inst Aeronaut & Astronaut, 78. *Mem:* fel Am Inst Aeronaut & Astronaut; Acoust Soc India; Acoust Soc Am. *Res:* Vibration and noise control, especially cabin noise, airframe noise, aeroacoustics, sonic fatigue, wave propagation, periodic structures, matrix methods, correlation techniques and intrinsic structural tuning; solid state physics, especially semiconductors, photovoltaic cells and energy conversion; physics. *Mailing Add:* MS 73-16 Boeing Co Seattle WA 98124

SENCER, DAVID JUDSON, b Grand Rapids, Mich, Nov 10, 24; m 51; c 3. MEDICINE. *Educ:* Univ Mich, MD, 51; Harvard Sch Pub Health, MPH, 58. *Prof Exp:* Med consult tuberculosis, USPHS, 55; med officer in charge, Muscogee County TB Field Res Facil, 55-59; prog officer, Bur State Serv, USPHS, Washington, DC, 59-60; asst chief, Ctr Dis Control, 60-64, dep chief, 64-66, dir, 66-77; sr vpres med & sci affairs, Becton Dickinson & Co, 77-81; COMNR, NEW YORK HEALTH DEPT, 82- *Concurrent Pos:* Mem, WHO Comt Int Surveillance Communicable Dis, 67-76; mem, US Deleg World Health Assembly, 68-76; mem, Int Comn Assessment Smallpox Eradication, 77; consult, Epidemiol Training Progs, WHO, India, 79. *Honors & Awards:* Rosenau Prize, Am Pub Health Asn, 76. *Mem:* Am Soc Trop Med & Hyg; Int Epidemiol Asn. *Mailing Add:* Dept Health New York NY 10007

SENCIALL, IAN ROBERT, b Nottingham, Eng, June 2, 38; m 62; c 3. BIOCHEMISTRY. *Educ:* Univ London, BS, 61; Univ Birmingham, PhD(biochem), 67. *Prof Exp:* Org res chemist, Fisons Pest Control Ltd, Eng, 61-64; res biochemist, 67-70, lectr, 70-73, asst prof, 73-77, ASSOC PROF BIOCHEM, SCH MED, MEM UNIV NFLD, 77- *Mem:* Can Biochem Soc. *Res:* Studies on the biosynthesis and metabolism of steroid carboxylic acids by the human and by animals; steroid metabolism in essential hypertension. *Mailing Add:* Sch of Med Mem Univ of Nfld St John's NF R1B 3V6 Can

SENCINDIVER, JOHN COE, b Martinsburg, WVa, Aug 21, 48; m 73; c 2. SOIL SCIENCE. *Educ:* WVa Univ, BS, 70, PhD(agron soil sci), 77. *Prof Exp:* NDEA fel, 71-74; soil scientist reclamation, Forest Serv, 75-78; ASST PROF SOIL SCI, W Va UNIV, 78- *Concurrent Pos:* Soil scientist soil surv, USDA Soil Conserv Serv, 71-75. *Mem:* Soil Sci Soc Am; Am Soc Agron; Soil Conserv Soc Am; Int Soc Soil Sci; Am Coun Reclamation Res. *Res:* Soil genesis and classification; overburden and minesoil properties; surface mine reclamation. *Mailing Add:* Div Plant & Soil Sci WVa Univ Morgantown WV 26506

SENDELBACH, ANTON G, b Waumandee, Wis, Mar 23, 24; m 56; c 4. DAIRY SCIENCE, GENETICS. *Educ:* Wis State Univ, River Falls, BS, 54; Univ Wis, MS, 56, PhD(dairy sci), 60. *Prof Exp:* From instr to assoc prof, 56-75, PROF DAIRY SCI, UNIV WIS-MADISON, 75- *Mem:* Am Dairy Sci Asn. *Res:* Dairy sire and cow evaluation for dairy herd improvement. *Mailing Add:* Dept Dairy Sci Animal Sci Bldg Univ of Wis Madison WI 53706

SENDERS, JOHN W, US citizen. INDUSTRIAL ENGINEERING. *Educ:* Harvard Univ, AB, 48. *Prof Exp:* Consult eng, 48-50; res psychologist, Aero Med Lab, Wright Patterson AFB, 50-56; head, Dept Psychol, Arctic Aero Med Lab, US Air Force, Fairbanks, 56-57; prin res scientist, Minneapolis-Honeywell Regulator Co, 57-62; prin scientist & consult, Bolt, Beranek & Newman, Inc, 62-70; vis prof, 73, PROF, DEPT INDUST ENG, UNIV TORONTO, 74- *Concurrent Pos:* Mem, Comt Bio-Astronaut, Nat Acad Sci-Nat Res Coun, 59-60, Man-in-Space Comt, Space Sci Bd, 60-62, Comt Hearing, Bio-acoust & Bio-mech, 62-, Highway Safety Comt, Highway Res Bd, 65 & 72-, Comt Vision, 70-, Road Characteristics Comt, 72- & Indust Eng Grant Selection Comt, 74-77; lectr & sr res assoc psychol, Brandeis Univ, 65-72; sr lectr mech eng, Mass Inst Technol, 66-67; pres, Senders Assoc, Inc, 68-73; sr res assoc, Univ Calif, Santa Barbara, 79-80; adj prof eng & psychol, Univ Maine, Orono, 81-; consult, various indust, govt agencies, res co, & legal firms. *Mem:* Sr mem Inst Elec & Electronics Engrs; fel Soc Eng Psychologists; fel Am Psychol Asn; fel AAAS; assoc fel Am Inst Aeronaut & Astronaut. *Res:* Models of visual monitoring behavior; quantification of mental workload; nature and source of human error; design of electronic publications systems; human perceptual motor skill; human information processing; author or coauthor of over 50 publications. *Mailing Add:* Keneggy West Columbia Falls ME 04623

SENDLEIN, LYLE V A, b St Louis, Mo, May 11, 33; m 55; c 3. GEOLOGICAL ENGINEERING, GEOPHYSICS. *Educ:* Wash Univ, St Louis, BS, 58, AM, 60; Iowa State Univ, PhD(geol soil eng), 64. *Prof Exp:* From instr to prof geol & geophys, Iowa State Univ, 60-77; DIR, COAL EXTRACTION & UTILIZATION RES CTR, SOUTHERN ILL UNIV, CARBONDALE, 77- *Concurrent Pos:* Consult, Atlantic Ref Co, Tex, 57 & Alpha Portland Cement Co, Mo, 58; consult engr, H M Reitz, 59-60 & US Gypsum Co, Ill, 60-; asst div chief, Energy & Minerals Resources Res Inst, Iowa State Univ, 75- *Mem:* Geol Soc Am; Am Geophys Union; Soc Explor Geophys; Nat Water Well Asn. *Res:* Engineering geology related to urban and rural problems; ground water investigations of pollution from sanitary landfills, coal mines and other sources; mining and reclamation research in coal mines. *Mailing Add:* Coal Res Ctr Southern Ill Univ Carbondale IL 62901

SENDRA, JOSEPH CHARLES, b Beacon, NY, Nov 16, 41; m 64; c 2. ORGANOMETALLIC & INORGANIC CHEMISTRY. *Educ:* Marist Col, BA, 64; Purdue Univ, PhD(chem), 70. *Prof Exp:* SR RES CHEMIST MOTOR OILS, TEXACO INC, 69- *Mem:* Am Chem Soc. *Res:* Motor oil crankcase additives; finished motor oils. *Mailing Add:* Texaco Inc Box 509 Beacon NY 12508

SENDROY, JULIUS, JR, b Zombor, Hungary, Sept 26, 00; nat US; m 32; c 2. PHYSIOLOGICAL CHEMISTRY. *Educ:* City Col New York, BS, 23; Columbia Univ, MA, 25, PhD(biochem), 26; Am Bd Clin Chem, dipl. *Hon Degrees:* ScD, St Bonaventure Univ, 54. *Prof Exp:* From asst chem to assoc, Rockefeller Inst Hosp, 26-37; prof chem & head dept exp med, Sch Med, Univ Loyola, Ill, 37-48; chief chemist, US Naval Med Res Inst, Bethesda, 48-70, sci adv, 65-60, spec sci asst, Bur Med & Surg, Navy Med Dept, 67-70; expert chemist, Navy Med Neuropsychiat Res Unit, 71-77. *Concurrent Pos:* Guest scientist, Cambridge Univ & Kaiser Wilhelm Inst Biol, Ger, 28; consult, La Rabida-Jackson Park Sanitarium, Chicago, Ill, 44-48, US Army Chem Warfare Labs, 60- & Naval Med Sch, 62; assoc exam, Nat Bd Med Exam, 42; mem bd, US Civil Serv Exam Sci & Tech Personnel, 49, from vchmn to chmn, 54-67; mem biochem study sect, USPHS, 50-53; chmn symp comt instrumentation, NIH, 61; mem, Nat Res Coun, 62-68; mem bd dirs, Nat Registry Clin Chem, 67-72. *Honors & Awards:* Van Slyke Award, 62; Ames Award, 68. *Mem:* Am Soc Biol Chem; Am Chem Soc; Aerospace Med Asn; Undersea Med Soc; fel Am Asn Clin Chem (pres, 64). *Res:* Physical chemistry of blood gases and electrolytes; acid-base balance; gasometric and photoelectric methods of analysis; carbon monoxide chemistry; air contamination; respiratory physiology; body surface area; mineral metabolism; clinical chemistry. *Mailing Add:* 16560 Casero Rd San Diego CA 92128

SENEAR, ALLEN EUGENE, b Chicago, Ill, Nov 2, 19; m 48; c 4. ANALYTICAL CHEMISTRY. *Educ:* Williams Col, Mass, BA, 41, Calif Inst Technol, PhD(org chem), 46. *Prof Exp:* Asst radiochem, Williams Col, Mass, 40; asst chem, Calif Inst Technol, 41-43, Comt Med Res contract, 43-45; fel, Univ Ill, 46-47; from instr to asst prof chem, Univ Calif, 47-55; RES ENGR, BOEING CO, 55- *Mem:* Am Chem Soc; Soc Appl Spectros. *Res:* Synthetic organic chemistry, especially monomer synthesis; polymer preparation. *Mailing Add:* 1446 92nd Ave NE Bellevue WA 98004

SENECA, HARRY, b Beirut, Lebanon, July 24, 09; m 48. INTERNAL MEDICINE, BACTERIOLOGY. *Educ:* Am Univ Beirut, MD, 33; Tulane Univ, MS, 43; Am Bd Internal Med, dipl. *Prof Exp:* Instr bact & parasitol, Med Sch, Am Univ Beirut, 33-37; from asst prof to assoc prof bact & parasitol & lectr trop dis, Royal Col Med, Iraq, 37-40; Rockefeller fel, Tulane Univ, 41; from instr to asst prof trop med, Tulane Univ, 42-43; ASSOC PROF UROL (MICROBIOL), COL PHYSICIANS & SURGEONS, COLUMBIA UNIV, 47-, RES ASSOC, 52- *Concurrent Pos:* Instr path, Med Sch, Am Univ Beirut, 35-36; dir, Govt Bact, Parasitol & Vaccine Insts, Baghdad, Iraq, 37-40; attend physician, Royal Hosp, Baghdad, 37-40, Charity Hosp, New Orleans, La, 41-44 & Columbia Presby Hosp, 47-; consult, Schering Corp, NJ, 46-51 & Chas Pfizer & Co, Inc, NY, 51-54; mem, Chagos Dis Found, Rio de Janeiro, Brazil, 73- *Honors & Awards:* Iraq Govt Award, 39; Brazil Govt Award, 59; Henderson Award, 64; Physicians Recognition Award, AMA, 70-81; Hugh Young Award, 76. *Mem:* Am Soc Trop Med & Hyg; Am Soc Parasitol; Am Geriat Soc; Am Soc Microbiol; fel Am Col Physicians. *Res:* Experimental medicine in relation to treatment and diagnosis; gastrointestinal diseases; bacterial and parasitic diseases; hemoflagellates; sepsis and septic shock; E histolytica; antibacterials and antibiotics; oxysteroids; antihistaminics; bacterial resistance; neoplastic diseases; pyelonephritis. *Mailing Add:* 401 Park Pl Ft Lee NJ 07024

SENECAL, GERARD, b Atwood, Kans, July 27, 29. PHYSICS. *Educ:* St Benedict's Col, Kans, BS, 51; Univ Mich, MA, 57; Kans State Univ, PhD(physics), 63. *Prof Exp:* Air Force Cambridge Res Labs res asst, Kans State Univ, 61-62; from instr to assoc prof physics, 62-72, actg chmn dept, 66-68 & chmn dept, 68-72, PRES, BENEDICTINE COL, 72- *Concurrent Pos:* Lectr-consult, Mobile Lab Prog, Oak Ridge Inst Nuclear Studies, 66-; proj dir, Undergrad Res Participation Grants St Benedict's Col, 66-67 & 68-69; NSF sci faculty fel, Univ Calif, Berkeley, 71-72. *Mem:* Am Phys Soc; Am Asn Physics Teachers. *Res:* Electrical and magnetic properties of thin evaporated semiconducting films; electrical properties of polymer materials, particularly polyethylene crystals. *Mailing Add:* Off of the Pres Benedictine Col Atchison KS 66002

SENECAL, VANCE E(VAN), b Phillipston, Pa, Aug 16, 21; m 45; c 4. CHEMICAL ENGINEERING. *Educ:* Slippery Rock State Teachers Col, BS, 43; Carnegie Inst Technol, BS, 47, MS, 48, DSc(chem eng), 51. *Prof Exp:* Develop engr, Pittsburgh Coke & Chem Co, 48; res engr, Exp Sta, 51-56, res proj engr, 56-59, res proj supvr, 59-60, res supvr, 60-62, res mgr, 62-66, develop mgr, 66-67, res mgr chem eng, Eng Technol Lab, 67-69, lab dir, 69-77, MGR ENG RES, E I DU PONT DE NEMOURS & CO, INC, 77- *Mem:* Am Inst Chem Engrs; Am Chem Soc; Sigma Xi. *Res:* Solid deformation mechanics; liquid dynamics; heat transfer; fluid distribution. *Mailing Add:* Eng Dept Louviers E I du Pont de Nemours & Co Inc Wilmington DE 19898

SENECHAL, LESTER JOHN, b Chicago, Ill, June 10, 34; m 63; c 2. MATHEMATICS. *Educ:* Ill Inst Technol, BS, 56, MS, 58, PhD(math), 63. *Prof Exp:* Instr math, Ill Inst Technol, 59-60 & Univ Tenn, 60-62; asst prof, Univ Ariz, 63-65 & Univ Mass, Amherst, 66-68; assoc prof, 68-75, PROF MATH, MT HOLYOKE COL, 75- *Concurrent Pos:* Fulbright lectr, Brazil, 65; vis prof, Rijksuniversitijt te Groningen, Neth, 74-75 & Acad Sci USSR, 78-79. *Mem:* Am Math Soc; Neth-Am Acad Circle. *Res:* Abstract analysis; matrix theory; combinatorial algebra. *Mailing Add:* Dept Math Clapp Lab Mt Holyoke Col South Hadley MA 01075

SENECHAL, MARJORIE LEE, b St Louis, Mo, July 18, 39; m 63; c 2. MATHEMATICAL CRYSTALLOGRAPHY, DISCRETE GEOMETRY. *Educ:* Univ Chicago, BS, 60; Ill Inst Technol, MS, 62, PhD(math), 65. *Prof Exp:* Lectr, 66-67, asst prof, 67-74, assoc prof, 74-78, PROF MATH, SMITH COL, 78- *Concurrent Pos:* Sabbatical, Univ Gronirgen, Netherlands, 74-75; exchange scientist, Inst Crystall Moscow, Nat Acad Sci, 78-79; mem, Adv Comt USSR Eastern Eruop, Comn Int Relations, Nat Acad Sci, 82. *Mem:* Am Math Soc; Sigma Xi. *Res:* Application of discrete geometry, including symmetry theory and the theory of tessellations to physical chemical and biological problems; history of the science of structure of matter. *Mailing Add:* Clark Sci Ctr Smith Col Northampton MA 01063

SENECHALLE, DAVID ALBERT, b Chicago, Ill, July 8, 40; m 63; c 1. MATHEMATICS. *Educ:* Univ Tex, BA, 65, PhD(functional anal), 67. *Prof Exp:* Res sci asst math, Univ Tex, Austin, 62-65; eng scientist, Tracor, Inc, 65-67; asst prof math, Univ Ga, 67-70; asst prof math, State Univ NY Col New Platz, 70-74, assoc prof, 74-78; SR SCIENTIST, TRACOR, INC, 78- *Mem:* Am Math Soc. *Res:* Functional analysis; electronic counter-measures. *Mailing Add:* Tracor Inc 6500 Tracor Lane Austin TX 78721

SENFF, ROBERT E, b Sheridan, Wyo, Mar 9, 38; m 61. ANIMAL PHYSIOLOGY. *Educ:* St Mary's Col, Calif, BS, 60; Univ of the Pac, MA, 62; Purdue Univ, PhD(animal physiol), 66. *Prof Exp:* ASSOC PROF BIOL, UNIV WIS-LA CROSSE, 65- *Mem:* AAAS. *Res:* Insect physiology; electrophysiology of the insect heart; physiology invertebrate nervous systems. *Mailing Add:* Dept of Biol Univ of Wis La Crosse WI 54601

SENFT, ALFRED WALTER, b Windsor, Colo, Oct 20, 24; m 48; c 3. TROPICAL MEDICINE, PARASITOLOGY. *Educ:* Univ Calif, BA, 48; Harvard Univ, MD, 52, MPH, 56; Univ London, DTM&H, 53. *Prof Exp:* Mem staff, Jagaum Hosp, New Guinea, 54-55; assoc, Falmouth Med Assocs, Mass, 56-58; investr, Marine Biol Lab, Woods Hole, Mass, 56-58; assoc prof, 68-74, PROF MED SCI, BROWN UNIV, 74- *Concurrent Pos:* Pvt pract, 56-; res grants, NIH, 57-, NSF, 64- & Rockefeller Found, 72-; consult, Merck Inst Therapeut Res, 65- & Rockefeller Found, 71; mem sci deleg, US-Japan Prog Med Sci, 72; consult schistosomiasis, WHO, 74-75. *Honors & Awards:* A Cressy Morrison Award, NY Acad Sci, 65. *Mem:* Am Soc Parasitologists; Am Soc Trop Med & Hyg; NY Acad Sci; Royal Soc Trop Med & Hyg. *Res:* Physiology, nutrition and electron microscopy of schistosomes; biochemistry; amino acid and nucleotide biochemistry of schistosomes; extraction and characterization of proteolytic enzymes and their use as diagnostic skin test. *Mailing Add:* Dept of Med Sci Brown Univ Providence RI 02912

SENFT, JOHN FRANKLIN, b York, Pa, Apr 13, 33; m 58; c 2. FOREST PRODUCTS. *Educ:* Pa State Univ, BS, 55, MF, 59; Purdue Univ, PhD(wood tech), 67. *Prof Exp:* Instr forestry, Pa State Univ, 57-59; from instr forestry to asst prof wood sci, 59-71, ASSOC PROF WOOD SCI, PURDUE UNIV,

WEST LAFAYETTE, 71- *Mem:* Forest Prod Res Soc; Soc Wood Sci & Technol; Am Soc Test & Mat. *Res:* Mechanical properties of wood; stress rating of lumber, wood anatomy, and mechanical properties. *Mailing Add:* Dept Forestry & Nat Resources Purdue Univ West Lafayette IN 47907

SENFT, JOSEPH PHILIP, b York Co, Pa, Oct 2, 36; m 59; c 3. PHYSIOLOGY, PLANT NUTRITION. *Educ:* Juniata Col, BS, 59; State Univ NY Buffalo, MA, 61, PhD(biol), 65. *Prof Exp:* Fel physiol, Sch Med, Univ Md, 64-65, res assoc, 65-66, instr, 66-67; from asst prof to assoc prof, Rutgers Univ, New Brunswick, 67-72; vis prof, Juniata Col, 72-73, assoc prof, 73-77; RES SCIENTIST, RODALE RES CTR, 77- *Concurrent Pos:* USPHS res grant, 68-75; mem corp, Marine Biol Lab, Woods Hole. *Mem:* AAAS; Am Asn Cereal Chemists; Am Physiol Soc; Biophys Soc; Soc Gen Physiol. *Res:* Nutritional quality of amaranth grain as possible food source; relationships between soil and plant nutrients for optimum nutritional quality of plant food products. *Mailing Add:* Rodale Res Ctr Box 323 RD 1 Kutztown PA 19530

SENFTLE, FRANK EDWARD, b Buffalo, NY, May 4, 21; m 49; c 6. PHYSICS. *Educ:* Univ Toronto, BS, 42, MA, 44, PhD(physics), 47. *Prof Exp:* Lectr chem, physics & math, St Michael's Col, Toronto, 40-46; physicist in charge radiation lab, Dept Mines & Resources, Ont, Can, 47-49; res assoc, Mass Inst Technol, 49-51; physicist in charge nucleonics group, 51-60, head solid state physics group, 60-65, HEAD PHYSICS LAB, US GEOL SURV, 65- *Concurrent Pos:* Lectr, Ottawa Univ, 47-49; vis res prof, Howard Univ, 65-66 & 70-81. *Mem:* Am Phys Soc; Am Inst Mining, Metall & Petrol Eng. *Res:* Development of instruments and methods in nuclear and solid state physics applied to geochemical processes; magnetic properties of crystalline materials. *Mailing Add:* US Geol Surv Stop 990 Reston VA 22092

SENFTLEBER, FRED CARL, b Roslyn, NY, Nov 19, 48; m 71; c 2. ANALYTICAL CHEMISTRY. *Educ:* Univ Tampa, BS, 70; Southern Ill Univ, PhD(anal chem), 77. *Prof Exp:* Res assoc separation chem, Bucknell Univ, 75-76; instr anal & inorg chem, Providence Col, 76-77, asst prof, 77-78; ASST PROF ANAL CHEM, MURRAY STATE UNIV, 78- *Mem:* Am Chem Soc. *Res:* Studies into changes in metabolic pathways brought about by various pathological conditions; studies involving the use of transition metal complexes in the catalysis of electrochemical reactions. *Mailing Add:* Dept of Chem & Geol Murray State Univ Murray KY 42071

SENGBUSCH, HOWARD GEORGE, b Buffalo, NY, Dec 14, 17; m 42; c 2. PARASITOLOGY. *Educ:* State Univ NY, BS, 39; Univ Buffalo, EdM, 47; NY Univ, MS & PhD(parasitol), 51. *Prof Exp:* Teacher pub sch, NY, 39-41; asst zool, Univ Buffalo, 46-47; instr gen biol, 51-52, from asst prof to assoc prof biol, 52-57, univ res found grant, 56 & 61, dir, Great Lakes Lab, 65-67, dean fac arts & sci, 65-70, res grant, 70, prof biol, 57-81, EMER PROF, STATE UNIV NY BUFFALO, 81- *Concurrent Pos:* NSF grant, Mt Lake Biol Sta, Univ Va, 55-56; mem USAEC radiation safety prog, USPHS, Nev, 57, scientist dir, 80-; with Max Planck Inst, 57-58; NIH fel, La State Univ, Cent Am, 60: Fulbright fel, Cent Philippines Univ, 62-63; vis prof, Univ Mysore, 69-70; consult, Roswell Park Mem Inst, NY, 63-; fac exchange scholar, State Univ NY, 74-; res assoc, Bishop Mus, 77-78 & Buffalo Mus Sci, 81- *Mem:* Am Soc Parasitol; Entom Soc Am; fel Am Inst Biol Sci; Am Soc Acarology; Soc Syst Zool. *Res:* Physiology, ecology and taxonomy of soil mites; survey of dog heartworm, Dirofilaria immitis, in west New York; survey of toxoplasma antibodies in west New York. *Mailing Add:* Dept of Biol 1300 Elmwood Ave Buffalo NY 14222

SENGE, GEORGE H, b Braunschweig, Ger, Oct 10, 37; US citizen. MATHEMATICS. *Educ:* Univ Calif, Berkeley, BA, 60; Univ Calif, Los Angeles, MA, 61, PhD(math), 65; Univ Wis-Madison, MS, 77. *Prof Exp:* Asst prof math, Univ Calif, San Diego, 65-68 & Univ Wis-Milwaukee, 68-74; asst prof math, Lawrence Univ, 75-76; STAFF ENGR, HUGHES AIRCRAFT CO, 77- *Mem:* Am Math Soc; Math Asn Am. *Res:* Digital signal processing and synthetic aperture radar systems; information theory and digital communication systems; sequential machines. *Mailing Add:* 3437 Mountain View Ave Los Angeles CA 90066

SENGEL, RANDAL ALAN, b Liberal, Kans, Jan 8, 48; m 71; c 1. PSYCHOPATHOLOGY, SCHIZOPHRENIA. *Educ:* Univ Okla, BA, 70, MA, 73, PhD(human ecol), 76. *Prof Exp:* Res assoc behav sci, Vet Admin Hosp, 77-80, RES HEALTH SCIENTIST, VET ADMIN, 81- *Concurrent Pos:* Consult, Task Force Ecopsychiat Data Base, Am Psychiat Asn, 76-78; Nat Res Serv fel, 80. *Mem:* AAAS. *Res:* Cognitive and neuropsychological deficits in schizophrenia. *Mailing Add:* Behav Sci Labs 151A Vet Admin Hosp 921 NE 13 Oklahoma City OK 73104

SENGER, CLYDE MERLE, b Portland, Ore, June 25, 29; m 51; c 6. ZOOLOGY, PARASITOLOGY. *Educ:* Reed Col, BA, 52; Purdue Univ, MS, 53; Utah State Univ, PhD, 58. *Prof Exp:* Co-op agent parasitol, Mont State Univ, 53-55 & Utah State Univ, 55-56; asst prof zool, Univ Mont, 57-63; assoc prof, 63-66, chairperson biol, 73-77, PROF BIOL, WESTERN WASH UNIV, 66- *Mem:* AAAS; Am Soc Mammal; Am Soc Parasitol; Am Inst Biol Sci. *Res:* Chemotaxonomy of lilies; taxonomy and life history of ectoparasites; ecology of bats. *Mailing Add:* Dept of Biol Western Wash Univ Bellingham WA 98225

SENGERS, JAN V, b Heiloo, Netherlands, May 27, 31; m 63; c 4. FLUID PHYSICS. *Educ:* Univ Amsterdam, Drs, 55, PhD(physics), 62. *Prof Exp:* Res asst physics, Van der Waals Lab, Univ Amsterdam, 53-55, res assoc, 55-63; physicist, Nat Bur Stand, 63-67; assoc prof, 68-74, PROF INST PHYS SCI & TECHNOL UNIV MD, COLLEGE PARK, 74- *Concurrent Pos:* Physicist, Nat Bur Stand, 68-; Jr Cornelis Gelderman Vis Prof, Delft Technol Univ, Netherlands, 74-75. *Honors & Awards:* Nat Bur Stand Awards, 66, 68, 69, 70 & 77. *Mem:* AAAS; fel Am Phys Soc; Am Soc Mech Engrs; Am Inst Chem Engrs; Am Chem Soc. *Res:* Kinetic theory; transport phenomena; critical phenomena and fluctuation phenomena in gases and liquids. *Mailing Add:* Inst Phys Sci & Technol Univ Md College Park MD 20742

SENGERS, JOHANNA M H LEVELT, b Amsterdam, Netherlands, Mar 4, 29; m 63; c 4. THERMAL PHYSICS. *Educ:* Univ Amsterdam, Drs, 54, PhD(physics), 58. *Prof Exp:* Wetenschappelijk ambtenaar, Van Der Waals Lab, Univ Amsterdam, 54-58; res assoc inst theoret chem, Univ Wis, 58-59; wetenschappelijk ambtenaar, Van Der Waals Lab, Univ Amsterdam, 59-63; physicist, Heat Div, Inst Basic Standards, 63-78, PHYSICIST & SUPVR, THERMO PHYSICS DIV, NAT ENG LAB, NAT BUR STANDARDS, 78- *Concurrent Pos:* Lectr, Cath Univ Louvain, 71; res assoc inst theor physics, Univ Amsterdam, 74-75; Regent's prof, Dept Chem, Univ Calif, Los Angeles, 82. *Honors & Awards:* Nat Bur Stand Performance Awards, 68 & 69, Spec Achievement Award, 71; Silver Medal Award, Dept of Com, 72, Gold Medal Award, 78. *Mem:* Netherlands Phys Soc; Am Soc Mech Engrs; Am Phys Soc; Europ Phys Soc. *Res:* Thermodynamic properties of dilute and dense gases; critical phenomena; equation of state, theoretical and experimental. *Mailing Add:* Div 544 Nat Bur Standards Washington DC 20234

SEN GUPTA, BARUN KUMAR, b Jamshedpur, India, July 31, 31; m 56; c 2. MICROPALEONTOLOGY, MARINE GEOLOGY. *Educ:* Calcutta Univ, BSc, 51, MSc, 54; Cornell Univ, MS, 61; Indian Inst Technol, Kharagpur, PhD(geol), 63. *Prof Exp:* From asst lectr to lectr geol, Indian Inst Technol, Kharagpur, 55-66; Nat Res Coun Can fel, Atlantic Oceanog Lab, Bedford Inst, 66-68, temporary res scientist, 68; asst prof geol, Univ Ga, 69-72, assoc prof, 72-79, prof, 79; PROF GEOL, LA STATE UNIV, 80- *Concurrent Pos:* NSF res grants, 69-72 & 75-78; vis prof, Univ Fed Rio Grande Do Sul, Porto Alegre, Brazil. *Mem:* AAAS; fel Geol Soc Am; fel Cushman Found Foraminiferal Res; Paleont Soc; Soc Econ Paleont Mineralogists. *Res:* Stratigraphy, ecology, and paleoecology of cenozoic benthic foraminifera. *Mailing Add:* Dept of Geol La State Univ Baton Rouge LA 70803

SENGUPTA, BHASKAR, b New Delhi, India, Feb 7, 44; m 70. OPERATIONS RESEARCH. *Educ:* Indian Inst Technol, BTech, 65; Columbia Univ, MS, 73, EngScD, 76. *Prof Exp:* Proj engr elec eng, Crompton Greaves Ltd, 65-69; syst engr comp sci, IBM World Trade Corp, 69-71, Serv Bur Co, 71-72; ASST PROF OPER RES, STATE UNIV NY STONY BROOK, 76- *Concurrent Pos:* Consult, Turner Construct Co, 76- *Mem:* Inst Mgt Sci; Oper Res Soc Am. *Res:* Stochastic models in inventory, production and health care. *Mailing Add:* Dept of Appl Math & Statist State Univ of NY Stony Brook NY 11794

SENGUPTA, DIPAK L(AL), b Batisha, Bangladesh, Mar 1, 31; m 62; c 2. ELECTRONICS. *Educ:* Univ Calcutta, BSc, 50, MSc, 52; Univ Toronto, PhD(elec eng), 58. *Prof Exp:* Res fel electronics, Gordon McKay Lab Appl Physics, Harvard Univ, 59; res assoc, Radiation Lab, Univ Univ, 59-61, assoc res physicist, 61-63; asst prof elec eng, Univ Toronto, 63-64; asst dir electronics, Cent Electronics Eng Res Inst Pilani, India, 64-65; lectr elec eng, 65-66, assoc res engr, 65-68, RES SCIENTIST LAB, UNIV MICH, ANN ARBOR, 68- *Mem:* Inst Elec & Electronics Engrs; AAAS; Sigma Xi; Int Union Radio Sci. *Res:* Electromagnetic theory; antennas; plasma physics; interaction of electromagnetic waves and plasmas; acoustic and electromagnetic waves; electromagnetic interference. *Mailing Add:* Radiation Lab Dept of ECE Univ of Mich Ann Arbor MI 48109

SENGUPTA, SAILES KUMAR, b Bankura, India, Jan 1, 35; US citizen; m 69; c 2. OPERATIONS RESEARCH, SIMULATION. *Educ:* Univ Calcutta, BSc, 53, MSc, 56; Univ Calif, Berkeley, PhD(statist), 69. *Prof Exp:* Lectr math, WBengal Educ Serv, 57-62; teaching res asst statist, Univ Calif, Berkeley, 63-64 & 65-67; asst prof math, Univ Mo-Kansas City, 69-76; assoc prof, 76-81, PROF MATH, SDAK SCH MINES & TECHNOL, 81- *Mem:* Inst Math Statist; Am Statist Asn; Am Math Asn; Am Inst Decision Sci; Sigma Xi. *Res:* Probability theory; theory of games; dynamic programming; design of experiments in concrete research; multivariate statistical analysis of geochemical data; stochastic models for resource allocation; statistical forecasting. *Mailing Add:* Dept of Math Sci S Dak Sch Mines & Technol Rapid City SD 57701

SENGUPTA, SISIR K, b Cuttack, India, Jan 1, 26; m 64; c 1. ORGANIC CHEMISTRY, CANCER. *Educ:* Univ Calcutta, BSc, 47, MSc, 52; Jadavpur Univ, PhD(org synthesis), 59. *Prof Exp:* Res assoc chem, Mass Inst Technol, 59-61; res assoc, Children's Cancer Res Found, Boston, 61-64; Royal Cancer Inst vis fel, Chester Beatty Res Inst, Eng, 64-65, res assoc cancer chemother, 65-66; RES ASSOC CHEM & CANCER CHEMOTHER, SIDNEY FARBER CANCER CTR, 66-; ASSOC CHEM, HARVARD COL, 66- *Concurrent Pos:* Res assoc, Harvard Col, 62-64. *Honors & Awards:* Cunningham Mem Award, Presidency Col, Calcutta, India, 52. *Mem:* Am Chem Soc. *Res:* Synthetic organic chemistry; cancer chemotherapy and biochemistry. *Mailing Add:* Sidney Farber Cancer Ctr 35 Binney St Boston MA 02115

SENGUPTA, SUMEDHA, b India, Feb 17, 43; US citizen; m 69; c 2. COMPUTER SCIENCE, STATISTICS. *Educ:* Patna Univ, BS, 62, MS, 64; Indian Inst Technol, PhD(statist), 68. *Prof Exp:* Lectr, Nat Col Bus, 76-78; res scientist statist res, Inst Atmospheric Sci, 78-80; sr res statistician, Res Inst Geochem, 80-81; STATISTICIAN RELIABILITY & QUAL CONTROL, MPI-CONTROL DATA, 81- *Concurrent Pos:* Consult, Ace Elec Co, Kans, 71, Marion Lab, 76, Jackson County, Kans, 76, & to assoc adminr, Regional Hosp, SDak, 82- *Mem:* Sigma Xi; Am Statist Asn; Inst Math Statist; Grad Women Sci. *Res:* Bayesian inference in life testing and reliability; statistical methodology in metereology and atmospheric science; quality and process control. *Mailing Add:* 3011 Country Club Dr Rapid City SD 57701

SENHAUSER, DONALD ALBERT, b Dover, Ohio, Jan 30, 27; m 61; c 2. PATHOLOGY, IMMUNOPATHOLOGY. *Educ:* Columbia Univ, AB, 48, MD, 51. *Prof Exp:* Intern, Roosevelt Hosp, New York, 51-52; asst resident & instr path, Columbia Presby Hosp, 55-56; asst resident, Cleveland Clin Found, Ohio, 56-58, sr resident, 58-59, clin assoc, 59-61, staff physician, 61-63; from assoc prof to prof path, Univ Mo-Columbia, 63-75, vchmn dept, 66-75, asst dean acad affairs, 69-71; PROF PATH & CHMN DEPT, COL MED, OHIO STATE UNIV, 75- *Concurrent Pos:* Fel path, Cleveland Clin

Found, Ohio, 56-59; travelling fel immunol res, 60-61; consult, Study Group, WHO, 71- *Mem:* AAAS; Am Soc Clin Path; Col Am Path; Int Acad Path; Am Soc Exp Path. *Res:* Ultrastructural studies of the immunopathology of lymphocyte-target cell interaction; role of lipid molecules in cell membrane structural and antigenic integrity apheresis and immunosuppression. *Mailing Add:* Dept of Path Ohio State Univ Col of Med Columbus OH 43210

SENICH, DONALD, b Cleveland, Ohio, Sept 5, 29; m 52; c 4. SOIL MECHANICS. *Educ:* Univ Notre Dame, BSME, 53; Iowa State Univ, MS, 61, PhD(soil mech), 66. *Prof Exp:* Resident engr, US Army, Frankfurt Am Main, WGer, 61-63, chief nuclear eng, Nuclear Power Field Off, Ft Belvoir, Va, 66-67, officer in chg, US Army Reactor, Ft Greely, Alaska, 67, chief construct engr, Mil Assistance Command, Vietnam, 68-69, staff scientist, Apollo Lunar Explor Off, NASA, 69-73; dir div, Energy Resources Res, 73-78, div dir, Integrated Basic Res, 78-79, dir div, Problem Focused Res, 79-81, DIV DIR, INDUST SCI & TECHNOL INNOVATION, NSF, 81- *Mem:* Sigma Xi. *Res:* Soil mechanics; physical and surface chemistry; development of fundamental knowledge to aid in the solution of major problems in the areas of discipline sciences. *Mailing Add:* Nat Sci Found Washington DC 20550

SENIOR, BORIS, b Priluki, Russia, Apr 24, 23; US citizen; m 54; c 3. PEDIATRICS, ENDOCRINOLOGY. *Educ:* Univ Witwatersrand, Mb, BCh, 46; MRCP, 53, FRCP, 70. *Prof Exp:* Res asst, Univ Col Hosp, London, 51-54; Coun Sci & Indust Res sr bursar, Univ Cape Town, 54-55; asst prof pediat, Sch Med, Boston Univ, 62-63; from asst prof to assoc prof, 63-69, PROF PEDIAT, SCH MED, TUFTS UNIV, 70-, CHIEF PEDIAT ENDOCRINOL, NEW ENG MED CTR, 63- *Mem:* Endocrine Soc; Am Pediat Soc. *Res:* Disorders of carbohydrate metabolism; carbohydrate-lipid interrelationships. *Mailing Add:* Tufts New Eng Med Ctr 171 Harrison Ave Boston MA 02111

SENIOR, JOHN BRIAN, b Cleveleys, Eng, Oct 11, 36. INORGANIC CHEMISTRY. *Educ:* Univ London, BSc, 58; McMaster Univ, PhD(chem), 62. *Prof Exp:* Dept Sci Indust Res-NATO fel chem, Birkbeck Col, London, 62-63; fel, Univ Western Ont, 63-64; asst prof chem, St Paul's Col, Man, 64-66; asst prof, 66-70, ASSOC PROF CHEM, UNIV SASK, 70- *Mem:* The Chem Soc; Chem Inst Can. *Res:* Chemistry of acidic nonaqueous solvent systems; halogen cations and oxycations. *Mailing Add:* Dept of Chem & Chem Eng Univ of Sask Saskatoon SK S7H 0W0 Can

SENIOR, JOHN ROBERT, b Philadelphia, Pa, July 17, 27; m 52; c 3. INTERNAL MEDICINE, GASTROENTEROLOGY. *Educ:* Pa State Univ, BS, 50; Univ Pa, MD, 54. *Prof Exp:* Instr med, Univ Pa, 57-59; res fel, Harvard Med Sch, 59-62; asst prof med & assoc bochem, Univ Pa, 62-68, assoc prof med, 68-78, assoc prof community med, 74-76, clin prof med, 78-80; CLIN PROF MED, ALBANY MED CTR, 81-; VPRES CLIN AFFAIRS, STERLING-WINTHROP RES INST, RENSSELAER, NY, 81- *Concurrent Pos:* Nat Inst Arthritis & Metab Dis res & training grants gastroenterol, Philadelphia Gen Hosp, 62-71; consult, US Naval Reg Med Ctr, Philadelphia, 66-, Nat Bd Med Examr & Am Bd Internal Med, 70-; dir clin invest, Presby-Univ Pa Med Ctr, 71-73; Carnegie Corp & Commonwealth Fund grant comput based exam, Philadelphia, 71-73; dir clin res Clin Res Ctr, Grad Hosp, Univ Pa, 73-74, dir, Emergency Serv & Spec Treatment Unit Alchol-Related Disorders & dir Off Eval, 74-79; dir regulatory proj, E R Squibb & Sons, NJ, 79-81; rear admiral, Med Corps, US Naval Reserve & dep fleet surgeon & comdr-in -chief, Pac Fleet, US Naval Health Sci Educ & Training Command, Bethesda, 80-; adj prof med, Univ Pa, 80- *Mem:* Am Soc Clin Invest; Am Soc Clin Pharmacol & Therapeut; Am Asn Study Liver Dis (pres); Am Gastroenterol Asn; fel Am Col Physicians. *Res:* Lipid metabolism; biochemistry; cell physiology; computer science; medical information processing; hepatic and central nervous effects of ethanol; viral and drug-induced hepatitis; evaluation of clinical competence. *Mailing Add:* Sterling-Winthrop Res Inst Rensselaer NY 12144

SENIOR, THOMAS BRYAN ALEXANDER, b Menston, Eng, June 26, 28; m 57; c 4. ELECTROMAGNETICS. *Educ:* Univ Manchester, BSc, 49, MSc, 50; Cambridge Univ, PhD(appl math), 54. *Prof Exp:* From sci officer to sr sci officer, Radar Res & Develop Estab, Ministry of Supply, Eng, 52-57; res assoc, 57-58, from assoc res mathematician to res mathematician, 58-61, prof elec eng, univ & assoc dir, lab, 61-75, DIR, RADIATION LAB, UNIV MICH, ANN ARBOR, 75- *Concurrent Pos:* Ed, Radio Sci, 73-79; chmn, Nat Comt, Int Union Radio Sci, 82- *Mem:* Fel Inst Elec & Electronics Engrs. *Res:* Theoretical problems in scattering and diffraction of electromagnetic and acoustical waves; radio wave propagation; optics. *Mailing Add:* Radiation Lab Univ Mich 4072 E Eng Bldg Ann Arbor MI 48109

SENITZER, DAVID, b New York, NY, Oct 9, 44; m 66; c 2. IMMUNOLOGY, MICROBIOLOGY. *Educ:* City Col New York, BS, 66; La State Univ, PhD(microbiol), 69; Am Bd Med Lab Immunol, dipl. *Prof Exp:* Res assoc immunol, Col Physicians & Surgeons, Columbia Univ, 69-72; asst prof microbiol, 72-77, ASSOC PROF MICROBIOL & PATH, MED COL OHIO, 78- *Honors & Awards:* Fac Educ Develop Award, Wayne State Univ, 73. *Mem:* AAAS; Am Soc Microbiol; Am Asn Immunologists; Am Soc Clin Pathologists; Am Asn Clin Histocompatibility Testing. *Res:* Immunochemistry of nucleic acids, autoimmune disease mechanisms, monoclonal antibody. *Mailing Add:* Dept Microbiol CS 10008 Med Col Ohio Toledo OH 43614

SENITZKY, BENJAMIN, b Vilno, Poland, Nov 15, 26; nat US; m 50; c 3. PHYSICS. *Educ:* Columbia Univ, BS, 48, PhD, 56. *Prof Exp:* Mem tech staff, Bell Tel Labs, Inc, 56-59; physicist, Tech Res Group, Inc, 59-66; ASSOC PROF ELECTROPHYS, POLYTECH INST NEW YORK, 66-, ASST HEAD DEPT, 74- *Mem:* Am Phys Soc. *Res:* Atomic beam resonance techniques for study of hyperfine structure in atomic spectra; high field breakdown in semiconductors; millimeter wave amplification using resonance saturation effects. *Mailing Add:* Dept of Elec Eng Polytech Inst of New York Farmingdale NY 11735

SENKLER, GEORGE HENRY, JR, b Postville, Iowa, Oct 25, 45; m 72. PHYSICAL ORGANIC CHEMISTRY. *Educ:* Hamline Univ, BS, 67; Princeton Univ, MA, 72, PhD(chem), 75. *Prof Exp:* SR RES CHEMIST, CHEM DYES & PIGMENTS DEPT, E I DU PONT DE NEMOURS & CO, 74- *Mem:* Am Chem Soc. *Res:* Studies on the stereochemistry of organophosphorus, arsenic and sulfur compounds; development of industrially important heterogeneous dehydrogenation reactions; organic pigment research. *Mailing Add:* Dept of Chem Dyes & Pigments Exp Sta E I du Pont de Nemours & Co Wilmington DE 19898

SENKO, MICHAEL EDWARD, b Gary, Ind, June 24, 31. INFORMATION SYSTEMS, COMPUTER SCIENCE. *Educ:* Purdue Univ, BS, 53; Univ Calif, PhD(chem), 56. *Prof Exp:* Res staff mem, Res Ctr, 56-68, mgr info sci, IBM Res, 68-74, MEM RES STAFF, MATH SCI DEPT, IBM RES CTR, YORKTOWN HEIGHTS, NY, 74- *Concurrent Pos:* Pub affairs fel, Brookings Inst, 65; mem, US Nat Comt, CODATA, 68-75, mem, Comput Use Task Group, 75-; nat lectr, Asn Comput Mach, 74; mem, Int Fedn Info Processing Soc Working Groups, 75- *Mem:* Am Crystallog Asn; Asn Comput Mach; NY Acad Sci; Sigma Xi. *Res:* Data base systems structure; data base systems languages; information systems science; theoretical physics. *Mailing Add:* IBM Res Yorktown Heights NY 10598

SENKOWSKI, BERNARD ZIGMUND, b Dearborn, Mich, Feb 2, 27; m 52; c 2. PHARMACEUTICAL CHEMISTRY. *Educ:* Rutgers Univ, AB, 51, MS, 60, PhD(chem), 65. *Prof Exp:* Chemist, Hoffmann-La Roche Inc, 57-62, head anal res, 62-65, asst dir qual control, 65-70, dir qual control, 70, asst vpres, 71-77, dir pharmaceut opers, 72-77; V PRES MFG & ENG, ALCON LABS, 77- *Concurrent Pos:* Lectr, Rutgers Univ, 65-70; mem rev comt, US Pharmacopoeia, 70-75; mem comt vitamins, Nat Formulary. *Mem:* Fel AAAS; Sigma Xi; Am Chem Soc; fel Acad Pharmaceut Sci; fel Am Inst Chemists. *Res:* Corporate manufacturing, domestic and international; facilities planning; GMP, OSHA regulatory compliance; analytical research; quality control; pharmaceutical operations. *Mailing Add:* Alcon Labs Inc PO Box 1959 Ft Worth TX 76101

SENKUS, MURRAY, b Redberry, Sask, Aug 31, 14; nat US; m 38; c 4. CHEMISTRY. *Educ:* Univ Sask, BSc, 34, MSc, 36; Univ Chicago, PhD(phys org chem), 38. *Prof Exp:* Instr chem, N Park Col, 37-38; chemist, Com Solvents Corp, 38-50; dir res & develop, Daubert Chem Corp, 50-51; dir chem res, 51-60, asst dir res, 60-64, dir res, 64-76, dir sci affairs, 76-79, CONSULT TOBACCO INST, R J REYNOLDS TOBACCO CO, 79- *Mem:* AAAS; NY Acad Sci; Am Chem Soc. *Res:* Tobacco and synthetic organic chemistry; insecticides; recovery of fermentation products; chemotherapeutic agents; chemistry of flavors. *Mailing Add:* Res Dept RJ Reynolds Tobacco Co Winston-Salem NC 27102

SENKUS, RAYMOND, physical chemistry, see previous edition

SENN, HARRY V, b Miami, Fla, May 27, 25; m 46; c 4. METEOROLOGY. *Educ:* Univ Wis, BBA, 50, MS, 56. *Prof Exp:* Asst meteorol, Univ Wis, 55-56; assoc prof, 56-77, PROF RADAR METEOROL, UNIV MIAMI, 77- *Concurrent Pos:* Consult, US Weather Bur, 60-; stormfury, US Navy, 65-75. *Mem:* Am Meteorol Soc. *Res:* Radar and cloud physics; tropical and severe storms; airborne radar; satellite meteorology; tropical cumulus, convection, winds; air pollution meteorology; solar energy. *Mailing Add:* Remote Sensing Lab Univ of Miami PO Box 248003 Coral Gables FL 33124

SENN, MILTON J E, b Milwaukee, Wis, Mar 23, 02; m 32; c 1. PEDIATRICS, PSYCHIATRY. *Educ:* Univ Wis, BS, 25, MD, 27. *Prof Exp:* Instr pediat, Univ Wash, St Louis, 29-33; assoc, Med Col, Cornell Univ, 33-37; Commonwealth Fund fel psychiat, New York Hosp & Philadelphia Child Guid Clin, 37-39; from asst prof to prof pediat & psychiat, Med Col, Cornell Univ, 39-48; Sterling prof pediat, 48-70, chmn dept, 51-63, dir, Child Study Ctr, 48-66, EMER STERLING PROF PEDIAT & PSYCHIAT, YALE UNIV, 70- *Concurrent Pos:* Assoc New York Hosp, 33-37, attend pediatrician, 37-48. *Mem:* Am Pediat Soc; Am Orthopsychiat Asn; fel Am Acad Pediat; fel NY Acad Med. *Res:* Integration of psychiatry and pediatrics; psychological development of infants and children. *Mailing Add:* 275A Heritage Village Southbury CT 06488

SENN, TAZE LEONARD, b Newberry, SC, Oct 16, 17; m 39; c 3. HORTICULTURE. *Educ:* Clemson Col, BS, 39; Univ Md, MS, 50, PhD, 58. *Prof Exp:* Asst horticulturist, Clemson Col, 39-40, asst botanist, 40-41, assoc prof hort, 46-56; asst plant pathologist, Univ Tenn, 41-43 & 46; agriculturist, Eastern Lab, USDA, 56-58; prof, 58-81, EMER PROF HORT & HEAD DEPT, CLEMSON UNIV, 81- *Mem:* Fel AAAS; fel am Soc Hort Sci. *Res:* Active compounds of marine plants; physiological aspects of plant propagation; tobacco chemistry; horticultural physiology; post-harvest physiology of horticultural crops; horticultural therapy. *Mailing Add:* 201 Strawberry Lane Clemson SC 29631

SENNE, JOSEPH HAROLD, JR, b St Louis, Mo, Nov 9, 19; m 46; c 1. CIVIL ENGINEERING. *Educ:* Wash Univ, BS, 48; Univ Mo, MS, 51; Iowa State Univ, PhD, 61. *Prof Exp:* Asst construct engr, Laclede Christy Clay Prod Co, Mo, 41-42; from instr to asst prof civil eng, Mo Sch Mines, 48-54; asst prof, Iowa State Univ, 54-63; PROF CIVIL ENG, UNIV MO-ROLLA, 63-, CHMN DEPT, 65- *Mem:* Am Soc Eng Educ; Am Soc Civil Engrs; Nat Soc Prof Engrs. *Res:* Welded wire fabric in reinforced concrete beams and pipe; structural design; orbital mechanics; satellite tracking. *Mailing Add:* Dept of Civil Eng Univ of Mo Rolla MO 65401

SENNELLO, LAWRENCE THOMAS, b New York City, NY, Feb 4, 37; m 62; c 4. PHARMACOKINETICS, DRUG ANALYSIS. *Educ:* Lake Forest Sch Mgt, Ill, MBA, 80; Univ Ill, Urbana, BS, 59, PhD(chem), 68. *Prof Exp:* Teaching asst chem, Univ Ill, Urbana, 66-67; group leader, Anal Chem Res, 69-70, SECT MGR, CHEM PHARMACOL, ABBOTT LABS, NORTH CHICAGO, 71- *Mem:* Am Chem Soc; Sigma Xi; NY Acad Sci. *Res:* Analytical chemistry methodology. *Mailing Add:* 408 W Hawthorne Ct Lake Bluff IL 60044

SENNER, JOHN WILLIAM, b Newton, Kans, Nov, 3, 44; m 66. EVOLUTIONARY GENETICS, PRIMATOLOGY. *Educ:* Bethel Col, BA, 67; State Univ NY, Stony Brook, PhD(ecol & evolution), 76. *Prof Exp:* Assoc, Univ Calif, San Diego, 76-78, instr biomet & fundamentals pop biol, 78; ASST SCIENTIST GENETICS, ORE REGIONAL PRIMATE RES CTR, 78- *Concurrent Pos:* Mem, Comt Nonhuman Primates, Inst Lab Animal Resources, Nat Res Coun, 79-82. *Mem:* Soc Syst Zool; Soc Study Evolution; AAAS. *Res:* Evolutionary and medical genetics of primates; genetics of protein polymorphisms; estimation of effective population size; inbreeding depression; heritability of medically important traits; genetics of primate birth defects. *Mailing Add:* Ore Regional Primate Res Ctr 505 NW 185 Ave Beaverton OR 97006

SENOFF, CAESAR V, b Toronto, Ont, Apr 30, 39; m 68. INORGANIC CHEMISTRY. *Educ:* Univ Toronto, BSc, 61, MA, 63, PhD(chem), 65. *Prof Exp:* Fel chem, Clarkson Col Technol, 65-67 & Univ Tex, Austin, 67-68; asst prof, 68-73, ASSOC PROF CHEM, UNIV GUELPH, 73- *Mem:* Am Chem Soc; Chem Inst Can; Royal Soc Chem. *Res:* Coordination chemistry of transition elements. *Mailing Add:* Dept of Chem Univ of Guelph Guelph ON N1G 2W1 Can

SENOZAN, NAIL MEHMET, b Istanbul, Turkey, Sept 13, 36; m 61. PHYSICAL CHEMISTRY. *Educ:* Brown Univ, ScB, 60; Univ Calif, Berkeley, PhD(chem), 65. *Prof Exp:* PROF CHEM, CALIF STATE UNIV, LONG BEACH, 64- *Mem:* Am Chem Soc; Am Phys Soc. *Res:* Solid state chemistry; biophysical chemistry. *Mailing Add:* Dept Chem Calif State Univ Long Beach CA 90840

SENSEMAN, DAVID MICHAEL, b Dayton, Ohio, Dec 6, 48; m 81. NEUROPHYSIOLOGY, ANIMAL BEHAVIOR. *Educ:* Kent State Univ, BS, 71; Princeton Univ, PhD(biol), 77. *Prof Exp:* asst mem, Monell Chem Senses Ctr, 77-81, RES ASST PROF PHYSIOL, SCH DENT MED, UNIV PA, 78- *Concurrent Pos:* NIH fel, 76-78; res grant, Nat Inst Dent Res, 78-81. *Honors & Awards:* Merck Award, 71. *Mem:* AAAS; Biophys Soc. *Res:* Biophysics and neuropharmacology of exocrine and endocrine gland function. *Mailing Add:* Sch Dent Med Univ Pa Philadelphia PA 19104

SENSENIG, CHESTER, b New Holland, Pa, June 13, 29; m 50; c 3. MATHEMATICS. *Educ:* Franklin & Marshall Col, BS, 52; NY Univ, PhD(math), 58. *Prof Exp:* asst math, Lehigh Univ, 52-54; instr, Bucknell Univ, 55-56; asst prof, Lafayette Col, 56-58; mem staff, NY Univ, 58-59; mem tech staff, Space Tech Labs, Calif, 59-61; MEM RES STAFF MATH, NY UNIV, 61-, ASSOC PROF, 65- *Res:* Partial differential equations; elasticity; hydrodynamics. *Mailing Add:* Dept of Math NY Univ Bronx NY 10453

SENSIPER, S(AMUEL), b Elmira, NY, Apr 26, 19; m 50; c 3. MICROWAVE ENGINEERING, ANTENNA ENGINEERING. *Educ:* Mass Inst Technol, SB, 39, ScD, 51; Stanford Univ, EE, 41. *Prof Exp:* Asst, Stanford Univ, 39-41; from asst proj engr to sr proj engr & res sect head, Microwave Equip, Sperry Gyroscope Co, NY, 41-48, consult, 48-50; mem staff, Res Lab Electronics, Mass Inst Technol, 49-51; res physicist & head, antenna sect, Microwave Lab, Hughes Aircraft Co, 51-53, head circuits & anal sect, Electron Tube Lab, 53-58, sr staff physicist, Physics Lab, 58-60; dir, Command & Control Labs, Space Electronics Corp, 60-63, assoc sr div mgr electronics opers, 63-64, dir eng, Electronic Systs, 64, mgr, Res & Ed Div, Space-Gen Corp, 64-67; mgr antenna syst lab, TRW Systs Group, 67-70; CONSULT ANTENNAS, ELECTROMAGNETICS & MICROWAVES, 70- *Concurrent Pos:* Instr, Univ Southern Calif, 55-57 & 79-81. *Mem:* Fel AAAS; fel Inst Elec & Electronics Engrs; Sigma Xi. *Res:* Systems theory and analysis, communications systems and components; electromagnetic theory; microwave electron tubes and devices; antennas and transmission components; microwave test equipment. *Mailing Add:* PO Box 3102 Culver City CA 90230

SENTER, HARVEY, b Brooklyn, NY, Dec 22, 36; m 59; c 5. MATHEMATICS. *Educ:* Yeshiva Univ, BA, 58, MS, 59, PhD(math), 63. *Prof Exp:* Asst prof, 63-68, ASSOC PROF MATH, FAIRLEIGH DICKINSON UNIV, 68- *Mem:* NY Acad Sci; Am Math Soc; Math Asn Am. *Res:* Three dimensional Dirichlet problem associated with plane lamina. *Mailing Add:* Fairleigh Dickinson Univ 1000 River Rd Teaneck NJ 07666

SENTERFIT, LAURENCE BENFRED, b Sarasota, Fla, July 30, 29; m 57; c 3. MICROBIOLOGY, IMMUNOLOGY. *Educ:* Univ Fla, BS, 49, MS, 50; Johns Hopkins Univ, ScD(pathobiol), 55; Am Bd Med Microbiol, dipl, 66. *Prof Exp:* Instr ophthal microbiol, Sch Med, Johns Hopkins Univ, 54-58; chief microbiologist & dir lab exp path, Charlotte Mem Hosp, NC, 58-64; res scientist, Chas Pfizer & Co, Inc, 64-66; assoc prof path & asst prof microbiol, Sch Med, St Louis Univ, 66-70; ASSOC PROF MICROBIOL, MED COL, CORNELL UNIV, 70-; DIR LAB MICROBIOL, NEW YORK HOSP, 70- *Concurrent Pos:* Attend microbiologist, Hosp for Spec Surg; attend microbiologist, Burke Rehab Ctr. *Mem:* Fel Am Pub Health Asn; Am Soc Microbiol; Am Asn Immunologists; Soc Exp Biol & Med; fel Royal Soc Health. *Res:* Immunology of parasitic diseases; vaccines for respiratory agents, particularly parainfluenza, respiratory syncytial virus and mycoplasma pneumonia; immunopathology and hypersensitivity. *Mailing Add:* Dept of Microbiol Cornell Univ Med Col New York NY 10021

SENTI, FREDERIC R(AYMOND), b Cawker City, Kans, Apr 29, 13; m 39; c 3. RESEARCH ADMINISTRATION. *Educ:* Kans State Univ, BS, 36; Johns Hopkins Univ, PhD(chem), 39. *Prof Exp:* Asst chemist, Eastern Regional Res Lab, Bur Agr & Indust Chem, USDA, 41-42, assoc chemist, 42-45, chemist, 45-47, prin chemist, 47-48, chief, Anal Phys Chem & Physics Sect, Northern Utilization Res & Develop Div, 49-54, Cereal Crops Sect, 54-59, dir, North Region Res Lab, 59-65, dept adminr nutrit, Consumer & Indust, USDA, 64-72, asst adminr, Nat Prog Staff, 72-74; res assoc, 74-77, ASSOCS DIR, LIFE SCI RES OFF, FEDS AM SOC EXP BIOL, 77- *Concurrent Pos:* Lectr physics & chem, Grad Sch, Temple Univ, 46-48; consult, Agency Int Develop, Govt India, 66-68; mem, Panel World Food Supply, Pres Sci Adv Comt, 66-67; mem, Bd Trustees, Am Type Cult Collection, 62-67, chmn, 68-69; mem, Liaison Panel, Food Protection Comt, Nat Res Coun, 71-74; chmn, Task Group on Gen Recognized As Safe New Plant Varieties, Food & Drug Admin, USDA, 72-74, chief staff officer, Comt Processed Foods for Develop Countries & Domestic Food Distrib Prog, 64-74 vchmn, Comt Food & Nutrit Res, 72-74; USDA rep, Patent Policy Comt, Fed Coun Sci & Technol, 64-74 & Indust Asn Tech Comt Aflatoxin, Food & Drug Admin, USDA, 72-74. *Mem:* Am Chem Soc; Inst Food Technologists; fel AAAS; Am Crystallog Asn; Am Asn Cereal Chemists. *Res:* Structure and solution properties of starches and microbial polysaccharides; mycotoxins; cereal and oilseed chemistry and technology; development of processed foods for food assistance programs; safety evaluation of food additives. *Mailing Add:* 2601 N Pollard St Arlington VA 22207

SENTILLES, F DENNIS, JR, b Donaldsonville, La, Aug 7, 41; m 63; c 2. MATHEMATICS. *Educ:* Francis T Nicholls State Col, BS, 63; La State Univ, MS, 65, PhD(math), 67. *Prof Exp:* Instr math, La State Univ, 66-67; asst prof, 67-70, ASSOC PROF MATH, UNIV MO-COLUMBIA, 70- *Mem:* Am Math Soc. *Res:* Abstract functional analysis; application of functional analytic techniques to specific problems in function and measure spaces. *Mailing Add:* Dept of Math Univ of Mo Columbia MO 65211

SENTMAN, DAVIS DANIEL, b Iowa City, Iowa, Jan 19, 45. MAGNETOSPHERIC & SOLAR TERRESTRIAL PHYSICS. *Educ:* Univ Iowa, BA, 71, MS, 73, PhD(physics), 76. *Prof Exp:* Res assoc, Univ Iowa, 76-77; RES GEOPHYSICIST PHYSICS, INST GEOPHYS & PLANETARY PHYSICS, UNIV CALIF, LOS ANGELES, 78- *Mem:* Am Geophys Union. *Res:* Physics of planetary magnetospheres; solar terrestrial interactions. *Mailing Add:* Inst Geophys & Planetary Physics 405 Hilgard Ave Los Angeles CA 90024

SENTMAN, LEE H(ANLEY), III, b Chicago, Ill, Jan 27, 37; m 59; c 2. AERONAUTICAL & ASTRONAUTICAL ENGINEERING. *Educ:* Univ Ill, BS, 58; Stanford Univ, PhD(aeronaut, astronaut), 65. *Prof Exp:* Sr dynamics engr, Lockheed Missiles & Space Co, Calif, 59-65; asst prof, 65-60, assoc prof, 69-79, PROF AERONAUT & ASTRONAUT ENG, UNIV ILL, URBANA, 79- *Concurrent Pos:* Vis prof aerospace eng, Univ Ariz, 71-72; consult, various aerospace companies. *Mem:* Am Inst Aeronaut & Astronaut; Am Phys Soc; Optical Soc Am. *Res:* Chemical lasers, unstable resonators; rotational nonequilibrium effects, vibrational relaxation of excited molecules, fluid dynamics; kinetic theory and statistical mechanics. *Mailing Add:* Dept Aeronaut & Astronaut Univ Ill 101 Trans Bldg Urbana IL 61801

SENTURIA, BEN HARLAN, b St Louis, Mo, Nov 3, 10; m 42; c 2. OTOLARYNGOLOGY. *Educ:* Washington Univ, MD, 35; Am Bd Otolaryngol, dipl, 39. *Prof Exp:* Assoc prof clin otol, 45-75, CLIN PROF OTOLARYNGOL, SCH MED, WASHINGTON UNIV, 75- *Concurrent Pos:* Dir, Otol Dept, Jewish Hosp, 53-72, emer dir, 72-; ed, Annals, Otol, Rhinol & Laryngol, 66-82, assoc ed, 82-; mem staff, Barnes, Children's, Jewish, McMillan & St John's Mercy Hosps, St Louis. *Mem:* Am Laryngol, Rhinol & Otol Soc; Am Otol Soc (vpres, 71-72, pres, 72-73); AMA; Am Acad Ophthal & Otolaryngol; Southern Med Asn. *Res:* Diseases of external auditory canal; middle ear effusions and deafness. *Mailing Add:* Annals Publ Co 4949 Forest Park Blvd St Louis MO 63108

SENTURIA, JEROME BASIL, b San Antonio, Tex, Dec 2, 38; m 62; c 2. COMPARATIVE PHYSIOLOGY, ENVIRONMENTAL PHYSIOLOGY. *Educ:* Univ Calif, Los Angeles, BA, 60; Rice Univ, MA, 63; Univ Tex, PhD(zool), 67. *Prof Exp:* Asst prof biol, 66-71, asst dean, Col Arts & Sci, 77-81, ASSOC PROF BIOL, CLEVELAND STATE UNIV, 71- *Concurrent Pos:* Nat Heart Inst fel, Heart Lab, Malmo, Sweden, 67-68; mem Hibernation Info Exchange. *Mem:* AAAS; Am Inst Biol Sci; Am Soc Zool; Am Physiol Soc; Am Heart Asn. *Res:* Cardiovascular physiology in hibernating mammals; seasonal variation in the physiology of hibernating mammals. *Mailing Add:* Dept of Biol Cleveland State Univ 1983 E 24th Cleveland OH 44115

SENTURIA, STEPHEN DAVID, b Washington, DC, May 25, 40; m 61; c 2. SOLID STATE PHYSICS, ELECTRONICS. *Educ:* Harvard Univ, BA, 61; Mass Inst Technol, PhD(physics), 66. *Prof Exp:* Mem res staff, 66-67, asst prof, 67-70, ASSOC PROF ELEC ENG, CTR MAT SCI & ENG, MASS INST TECHNOL, 70- *Mem:* AAAS; Am Phys Soc; Inst Elec & Electronics Engrs; sr mem Instrument Soc Am. *Res:* Studies of crystalline, amorphous and polymeric semiconductors; the charge-flow transistor sensing device; electronic instrumentation. *Mailing Add:* Rm 13-3010 Dept of Elec Eng 77 Massachusetts Ave Cambridge MA 02139

SENTZ, JAMES CURTIS, b Littlestown, Pa, Sept 24, 27; m 59; c 3. PLANT SCIENCE, EXPERIMENTAL STATISTICS. *Educ:* Pa State Univ, BS, 49; NC State Univ, MS, 51, PhD(agron), 53. *Prof Exp:* Asst statistician, NC State Univ, 52-54; res agronomist, Agr Res Serv, USDA, 54-57; from asst prof to assoc prof agron & plant genetics, 57-75, training officer, Int Agr Progs, Univ Minn, St Paul, 71-75; res adv, Tech Asst Bur, USAID, Washington, DC, 75-77; assoc prof & training officer, Col Agr, Univ Minn, St Paul, 77-80. *Concurrent Pos:* Cornell Univ Grad Educ Prog vis prof, Col Agr, Univ Philippines, 66-68. *Mem:* Am Soc Agron; Crop Sci Soc Am; Genetics Soc Am; Biomet Soc. *Res:* Population and quantitative genetics; Zea Mays and plant breeding; experimental statistics; grain legumes. *Mailing Add:* 1040 W City Rd G2 St Paul MN 55112

SENUM, GUNNAR IVAR, b Kristiansand, Norway, Nov 10, 48; US citizen. PHYSICAL CHEMISTRY. *Educ:* Brooklyn Col, BS, 70; State Univ NY, PhD(chem), 75. *Prof Exp:* Asst chemist, 76-78, assoc chemist, 78-81, CHEMIST, BROOKHAVEN NAT LAB, 81- *Mem:* Am Chem Soc; Am Phys Soc; AAAS. *Res:* Atmospheric chemistry, analytical instrumentation for tracing and tagging using fluorocarbons. *Mailing Add:* Environ Chem Div Bldg 426 Brookhaven Nat Lab Upton NY 11973

SENUS, WALTER JOSEPH, b Rome, NY, Feb 5, 46; m 68; c 4. SATELLITE GEODESY, ELECTRONIC SURVERYING. *Educ:* Syracuse Univ, BS, 67, MS, 71; Univ Hawaii, PhD(geodesy/geophysics). *Prof Exp:* Staff physicist, Rome Air Develop Ctr, 68-72; electron engr, Res & Develop, US Coast Guard, 72-78; CHIEF SCIENTIST, DEFENSE MAPPING AGENCY, 78- *Concurrent Pos:* Prof math, Northern Va Community Col, 74-; lectr math, George Mason Univ, 76-81; assoc prof, George Washington Univ, 76- *Mem:* Am Geophys Union. *Res:* The application of satellite technology to furthering the fields of geodesy and geophysics; defining the physical fields of the earth and other bodies in our solar system. *Mailing Add:* 12238 Westwood Hills Dr Herndon VA 22070

SENYK, GEORGE, b Kharkov, Ukraine, May 6, 26; US citizen; m 55; c 2. IMMUNOLOGY, MICROBIOLOGY. *Educ:* Univ Frankfurt, 46-49; Univ San Francisco, BS, 66; Univ Calif, San Francisco, PhD(microbiol), 71. *Prof Exp:* Lectr, San Francisco State Col, 70; fel biochem, 71, trainee, Dept Clin Path & Lab Med & lectr med technol-clin microbiol, 72-73, asst prof clin path & lab med & training coordr curriculum med technol-clin microbiol, 73-77, asst dir, Grad Prog Clin Lab Sci-Clin Microbiol, 74-77, RES MICROBIOLOGIST, DEPT MICROBIOL, UNIV CALIF, SAN FRANCISCO, 77- *Mem:* AAAS; Am Soc Microbiol; Am Asn Immunologists. *Res:* Role of cellular immunity in resistance to infections; in vitro correlates of cellular immunity. *Mailing Add:* 2319 32nd Ave San Francisco CA 94116

SENZEL, ALAN JOSEPH, b Los Angeles, Calif, May 26, 45; m 69; c 2. TOXICOLOGY, ANALYTICAL CHEMISTRY. *Educ:* Calif State Univ, Long Beach, BS, 67; Univ Calif, Los Angeles, MS, 69, PhD(anal chem), 70. *Prof Exp:* Assoc ed, Anal Chem & Mem Exec Comt, Div Anal Chem, Am Chem Soc, 70-74; anal methods ed, asn off anal chemists, 74-78; head info off, Chem Indust Inst Toxicol, 78-79; SR CHEMIST, DEL GREEN ASSOC, INC, FOSTER CITY, CALIF, 81- *Concurrent Pos:* Consult environ chem & eng, 78- *Mem:* AAAS; Am Chem Soc; Instrument Soc Am; Asn Off Anal Chemists; Soc Environ Chem & Toxicol. *Res:* Toxicology of bulk, commodity chemicals; analytical methodology for agricultural products, foods, feeds, beverages, drugs, pesticides, cosmetics, color additives, and other commodities important in public health; chemical literature and journal publication; air pollution measurement. *Mailing Add:* 7704 Audubon Dr Raleigh NC 27609

SEO, EDDIE TATSU, b Los Angeles, Calif, July 12, 35; m 64; c 2. BATTERY ENGINEERING. *Educ:* Univ Calif, Los Angeles, BS, 59; Univ Calif, Riverside, PhD(chem), 64. *Prof Exp:* Res assoc chem, Univ Kans, 64-65; mem tech staff, TRW Systs Group, 65-77; mem staff, Res & Develop Div, Gates Rubber Co, 77-80, MEM STAFF, RES & DEVELOP DIV, GATES CORP, 80- *Mem:* Am Chem Soc; Electrochem Soc; Royal Soc Chem. *Res:* Electrochemical energy conversion and storage. *Mailing Add:* Gates Corp 900 S Broadway PO Box 5887 Denver CO 80217

SEO, JOHN S, b Aiea, Hawaii, June 9, 26; m 60; c 4. BACTERIOLOGY, MYCOLOGY. *Educ:* Syracuse Univ, BA, 51, MS, 54, PhD(microbiol), 59. *Prof Exp:* Res asst bact, Syracuse Univ, 54-56; res assoc microbiol & biochem, Cornell Univ, 59-62, anal chemist, 62-64; sr res microbiologist, Ciba Pharmaceut Co, NJ, 64-69; sect head microbiol, Hess & Clark Div, Richardson-Merrell Inc, Ohio, 69-70; bacteriologist, Technicon Corp, NY, 70-73; sr res & develop scientist, Pfizer, Inc, Conn, 73-81; RES ASSOC GEN DIAG, WARNER-LAMBERT CO, 81- *Mem:* Am Soc Microbiol. *Res:* Production of cellulases by fungi; biochemistry and microbiology of the rumen in relation to utilization on non-protein nitrogen and production of volatile fatty acids; chemotherapy of animal diseases; research and development of diagnostic products for microbiology. *Mailing Add:* Gen Diag Warner-Lambert 170 Tabor Rd Morris Plains NJ 07950

SEO, STANLEY TOSHIO, b Honolulu, Hawaii, Mar 5, 28. CHEMISTRY. *Educ:* Univ Hawaii, BS, 50, MS, 52. *Prof Exp:* Chemist, 55-64, SUPVRY RES CHEMIST, COMMODITY TREAT, HANDLING & TRANSP LAB, AGR RES SERV, USDA, 64- Mem. *Mem:* AAAS; Am Chem Soc; Entom Soc Am. *Res:* Commodity treatment by fumigation, heat, low temperatures and use of gamma radiation; chemical factors affecting the infestation of fruit by fruitflies. *Mailing Add:* Fruit Fly Invests PO Box 2280 Honolulu HI 96804

SEON, BEN KUK, b Fukuoka-Ken, Japan, May 5, 36; m 66; c 3. IMMUNOLOGY, CANCER. *Educ:* Osaka Univ, MS, 63, PhD(biochem), 66. *Prof Exp:* Fel biochem, Osaka Univ, 66-67; from cancer res scientist to sr cancer res scientist, 67-75, assoc cancer res scientist, 75-78, CANCER RES SCIENTIST V, ROSWELL PARK MEM INST, 78- *Mem:* AAAS; Sigma Xi; Am Asn Immunologists; Am Asn Cancer Res. *Res:* Utilization of hybridoma technology for cancer; immunochemical characterization of tumor-associated cell membrane antigens. *Mailing Add:* Immunol Res Dept Roswell Park Mem Inst 666 Elm St Buffalo NY 14263

SEPERICH, GEORGE JOSEPH, b Chicago, Ill, Mar 18, 44; m 68; c 1. FOOD SCIENCE, MEAT CHEMISTRY. *Educ:* Loyola Univ, BS, 67; Mich State Univ, MS, 72, PhD(food sci), 76. *Prof Exp:* Dir educ prog, Mich Dept Labor, 75-76; ASST PROF AGR, DIV AGR, ARIZ STATE UNIV, 76- *Mem:* Inst Food Technologists; AAAS; Am Meat Sci Asn; Am Soc Animal Sci. *Res:* Muscle food constituents; muscle turnover and metabolism; isolation and characterization of food and muscle food proteins and muscle cellular physiology and biochemistry related to exercise and pathology. *Mailing Add:* Div Agr Ariz State Univ Tempe AZ 85281

SEPINWALL, JERRY, b Montreal, Que, Dec 14, 40; m 63; c 3. PSYCHOPHARMACOLOGY, PHYSIOLOGICAL PSYCHOLOGY. *Educ:* McGill Univ, BA, 61; Cornell Univ, MA, 63; Univ Pa, PhD(psychol), 66. *Prof Exp:* Sr scientist, 66-71, res group chief, 71-75, RES SECT HEAD, HOFFMANN-LA ROCHE, INC, 75- *Concurrent Pos:* Instr, Brooklyn Col, 67 & Montclair State Col, 70. *Mem:* Soc Neurosci; Am Soc Pharmacol & Exp Therapeut; Am Psychol Asn; Behav Pharmacol Soc; NY Acad Sci. *Res:* Pharmacology of antianxiety agents; physiology and neurochemistry of motivation and learning. *Mailing Add:* Dept Pharmacol Hoffmann-La Roche Inc Nutley NJ 07110

SEPKOSKI, J(OSEPH) J(OHN), JR, b Presque Isle, Maine, July 26, 48; m 71; c 1. PALEONTOLOGY, GEOLOGY. *Educ:* Univ Notre Dame, BS, 70; Harvard Univ, PhD(geol), 77. *Prof Exp:* Instr geol, Univ Rochester, 74-77, asst prof, 77-78; asst prof, 78-82, ASSOC PROF GEOL, UNIV CHICAGO, 82-; RES ASSOC, FIELD MUS NATURAL HIST, 80- *Mem:* AAAS; Paleont Soc; Sigma Xi. *Res:* Evolutionary paleobiology and paleoecology, with particular emphasis on diversification and distribution of marine invertebrates, especially in the early Paleozoic; Cambrian and Vendian paleontology and stratigraphy; geostatistics. *Mailing Add:* Dept of Geophys Sci Univ of Chicago Chicago IL 60637

SEPKOSKI, JOSEPH JOHN, b Cleveland, Ohio, July 30, 21; m 47; c 5. ORGANIC CHEMISTRY. *Educ:* John Carroll Univ, BS, 43; Univ Notre Dame, MS, 50; Rutgers Univ, MBA, 56. *Prof Exp:* Anal chemist, Cleveland Graphite Bronze Co, 42-43; prod chemist, Schering Corp, 50-53; develop chemist, Celanese Corp Am, 53-55; sr chemist, Chicopee Mfg Corp, 55-57, res supvr, 57-62; group leader, Thatcher Mfg Co, 62-63; sr res chemist, Indust Chem Div, Allied Chem Corp, 63-67 & Plastics Div, 67-68, group leader, 68-74, tech serv supvr spec chem, Plastics Div, 74-81, TECH COORDR, ALLIED FIBERS & PLASTICS CO, ALLIED CORP, 81- *Mem:* Fel Am Inst Chem; Am Chem Soc. *Res:* Thermosetting resins, reinforced and non-reinforced; urethanes; low molecular weight polyethylene. *Mailing Add:* 323 West Shore Trail Sparta NJ 07871

SEPMEYER, L(UDWIG) W(ILLIAM), b East St Louis, Ill, Nov 6, 10; m 36; c 1. ELECTRICAL ENGINEERING. *Educ:* Univ Calif, BS, 33. *Prof Exp:* Consult engr, Calif, 34-41; asst, Univ Calif, Los Angeles, 34-37 & 40-41; engr, Lansing Mfg Co, Calif, 39-40; systs engr, Elec Res Prods Div, Western Elec Co, 41-42; engr, Div War Res, Univ Calif, 42-45 & Calif Inst Technol, 45; elec engr, US Naval Ord Test Sta, 45-51; engr, Rand Corp, 51-56 & Eng Systs Develop Corp, 56-63; CONSULT ENGR, 63- *Concurrent Pos:* Consult, 47- & US Naval Ord Test Sta, 51-57. *Mem:* Fel Acoust Soc Am; fel Audio Eng Soc; Am Soc Test & Mat; Inst Noise Control Eng USA; Inst Elec & Electronics Engrs. *Res:* Architectural acoustics; noise control; acoustical instrumentation; electrical sound recording and reproduction. *Mailing Add:* 1862 Comstock Ave Los Angeles CA 90025

SEPPALA, LYNN G, b Watertown, SDak, May 21, 46; m 80. OPTICAL DESIGN. *Educ:* SDak State Univ, BS, 68; Univ Rochester, PhD(optics), 74. *Prof Exp:* Optical designer, ITEK Corp, 74-76; OPTICAL ENGR, LAWRENCE LIVERMORE LAB, 76- *Mem:* Optical Soc Am; Int Soc Optical Eng. *Mailing Add:* Lawrence Livermore Lab Univ of Calif Livermore CA 94550

SEPPI, EDWARD JOSEPH, b Price, Utah, Dec 16, 30; m 53; c 3. PHYSICS, MATHEMATICS. *Educ:* Brigham Young Univ, BS, 52; Univ Idaho, MS, 56; Calif Inst Technol, PhD(physics), 62. *Prof Exp:* Jr engr, Geneva Steel Co, 51; lab instr, Brigham Young Univ, 51-52; physicist, Hanford Labs, Gen Elec Co, 52-58; res asst physics, Calif Inst Technol, 58-60, Gen Elec fel, 60-62, univ fel, 62; staff physicist, Inst Defense Anal, 62-64; head res area physics group, 64-66, res area dept head, 66-68, head exp facil dept, Stanford Linear Accelerator Ctr, 68-74; mgr med diag inst, 74-76, eng mgr, 76-77, div mgr, 77-78, tech dir, 78-80, SR SCIENTIST, VARIAN ASSOCS, 80- *Concurrent Pos:* Consult, Inst Defense Anal, 64- *Mem:* Am Phys Soc. *Res:* High energy, nuclear and solid state physics; lasers; medical diagnostic instrumentation; research administration. *Mailing Add:* 320 Dedalera Dr Portola Valley CA 94025

SEPSY, CHARLES FRANK, b Rochester, NY, May 19, 24; m 45; c 2. MECHANICAL ENGINEERING. *Educ:* Univ Tenn, Knoxville, BME, 49; Univ Rochester, MSc, 51. *Prof Exp:* Asst mech eng, Univ Rochester, 50-51; res assoc, Res Found, 51-56, from instr to assoc prof, 56-67, PROF MECH ENG, OHIO STATE UNIV, 67- *Concurrent Pos:* Consult, Owens-Corning Fiberglas, 58-, Bender & Assocs, Consult Engrs, 60-65 & Off Civil Defense, 63-; educ consult, NAm Heating, Air Conditioning Wholesalers Asn, 64-; consult, CVI Corp, 65- *Honors & Awards:* Carrier Award, Am Soc Heating, Refrig & Air-Conditioning Engrs, 67. *Mem:* Am Soc Heating, Refrig & Air-Conditioning Engrs; Am Soc Eng Educ; Inst Environ Sci. *Res:* Internal control of the environment for man and machines with respect to regulating temperature, humidity, contaminants, noise and distribution; system simulation and energy requirements of building environmental control systems. *Mailing Add:* Dept of Mech Eng Ohio State Univ Columbus OH 43210

SEPUCHA, ROBERT CHARLES, b Salem, Mass, June 2, 43; m 66; c 3. CHEMICAL PHYSICS, PHYSICAL OPTICS. *Educ:* Mass Inst Technol, SB, 65, SM, 67; Univ Calif, San Diego, PhD(eng physics), 71. *Prof Exp:* Sr res scientist, Aerodyne Res Inc, 71-76; physicist, High Energy Laser Syst Proj Off, US Army, 76-78; prof mgr, 79-80, ASST DIR, SPACE DEFENSE TECHNOL DIV, DIRECTED ENERGY OFF, DEFENSE ADVAN RES PROJ AGENCY, 80- *Mem:* Am Phys Soc; Optical Soc Am. *Res:* Advanced high energy laser technology programs which may head to eventual space-based weapon systems; high-power chemical lasers; acquisition tracking and precision pointing; large-apecture beam control. *Mailing Add:* Directed Energy Off Defense Advan Res Proj Agency 1400 Wilson Blvd Arlington VA 22209

SEQUEIRA, JOEL AUGUST LOUIS, b Bombay, India, July 13, 47; US citizen; m 73; c 1. PHARMACOKINETICS, PHYSICAL PHARMACY. *Educ:* Univ Bombay, BPharm, 69; Columbia Univ, MS, 72; State Univ NY, Buffalo, PhD(pharmaceut), 76. *Prof Exp:* Sr res scientist, Pharmaceut Res & Develop, Johnson & Johnson Res, 76-78; SECT LEADER, PHARMACEUT RES & DEVELOP, SCHERING CORP, 78- *Mem:* Acad Pharmaceut Sci; Am Pharmaceut Asn; Soc Invest Dermat. *Res:* Topical dosage form design; topical pharmacokinetics; percutaneous absorption; aerosol dosage form design. *Mailing Add:* Schering Corp 80 Orange St Bloomfield NJ 07003

SEQUEIRA, LUIS, b San Jose, Costa Rica, Sept 1, 27; m 54; c 4. PLANT PATHOLOGY. *Educ:* Harvard Univ, BA, 49, MA, 50, PhD(biol), 52. *Prof Exp:* Parker traveling fel from Harvard Univ, Biol Inst, Brazil, 52-53; from asst plant pathologist to dir, Coto Res Sta, United Fruit Co, Costa Rica, 53-60; res assoc plant path, NC State Univ, 60-61; assoc prof, 61-64, prof plant path, 64-78, PROF PLANT PATH & BACT, UNIV WIS-MADISON, 78- *Concurrent Pos:* NSF sr fel, Univ Reading, 70-71; ed-in-chief, Phytopath, 79-81. *Mem:* Nat Acad Sci; fel Am Phytopath Soc; Bot Soc Am; Mycol Soc Am; Am Soc Plant Physiol. *Res:* Soil microbiology; root diseases; plant growth regulators; physiology of parasitism. *Mailing Add:* Dept of Plant Path Univ of Wis Madison WI 53706

SEQUIN, CARLO HEINRICH, b Winterthur, Switz, Oct 30, 41; m 68; c 2. ELECTRONICS, COMPUTER SCIENCE. *Educ:* Univ Basel, Switz, dipl, 65, PhD(physics), 69. *Prof Exp:* Mem tech staff MOS integrated circuits, Bell Tel Labs, 70-76; vis lectr logic design microprocessors, 76-77, ASSOC PROF COMPUT SCI, UNIV CALIF, BERKELEY, 77- *Mem:* Inst Elec & Electronics Engrs; Asn Comput Mach. *Res:* Mutual influence of advanced computer architecture and VLSI technology; modular multiprocessor computer networks; efficient hardware implementation of computer functions through special purpose integrated circuits. *Mailing Add:* Dept of Elec Eng & Comput Sci Univ of Calif Berkeley CA 94720

SERAD, GEORGE, b Philadelphia, Pa, Feb 26, 39; m 67; c 1. CHEMICAL ENGINEERING. *Educ:* Drexel Inst Technol, BS, 61; Univ Pa, MS, 62, PhD(chem eng), 64. *Prof Exp:* Lab asst chem res, Scott Paper Co, Pa, 58 & 59; engr aide, Texaco Inc, NJ, 60 & 61; res engr, Celanese Res Co, 64-70, res engr, Celanese Fibers Co, 70-73, tech group leader, 73-75, TECH MGR, CELANESE FIBERS CO, 75- *Mem:* Am Inst Chem Engrs; Am Chem Soc. *Res:* Transport phenomena; electrochemistry; catalysis; fibers and plastics processing. *Mailing Add:* Celanese Fibers Co PO Box 32414 Charlotte NC 28232

SERAFETINIDES, EUSTACE A, b Athens, Greece, June 4, 30; m 65. PSYCHIATRY. *Educ:* Nat Univ Athens, MD, 53; Royal Col Physicians & Surgeons, dipl psychol med, 59; Univ London, PhD(psychol med), 64. *Prof Exp:* Clin asst-res assoc, Maudsley Hosp, Inst Psychiat, Univ London, 57-65; assoc prof psychiat, neurol & behav sci, Sch Med, Univ Okla, 65-71; vis assoc prof psychiat, 71-72, PROF, DEPT PSYCHIAT & MEM, BRAIN RES INST, UNIV CALIF, LOS ANGELES, 72-; ASSOC CHIEF OF STAFF RES, VET ADMIN HOSP BRENTWOOD, LOS ANGELES, 72- *Concurrent Pos:* NIMH res scientist development award, 67-72. *Mem:* Am Col Neuropsychopharmacol; Royal Col Psychiat; EEG Soc. *Res:* Electro-clinical and psychopharmacological investigations of brain-behavior relationships; epilepsy; cerebral dominance consciousness and schizophrenia. *Mailing Add:* Dept of Psychiat Univ of Calif Los Angeles CA 90024

SERAFIN, FRANK G, b Passaic, NJ, Oct 8, 35. SURFACE CHEMISTRY, GAS-SOLID INTERACTIONS. *Educ:* Wesleyan Univ, Middletown, Conn, BA, 57; Northeastern Univ, Boston, MS, 68 & 76. *Prof Exp:* Chemist, 60-68, group leader, 68-72, res assoc, 72-82, SR RES ASSOC, W R GRACE & CO, CAMBRIDGE, 82- *Mem:* Am Chem Soc; Soc Appl Spectros; Royal Soc Chem; Sigma Xi. *Res:* Cement surfaces and reactivities. *Mailing Add:* 31 Livingston Dr Peabody MA 01960

SERAFIN, JOHN AUGUSTUS, b Stafford Springs, Conn, July 26, 38. NUTRITION. *Educ:* Univ Conn, BS, 60, MS, 62; Cornell Univ, PhD(animal nutrit), 68. *Prof Exp:* Res asst poultry nutrit, Univ Conn, 60-62; res asst animal nutrit, Cornell Univ, 63-68; RES NUTRITITIONIST, PATUXENT WILDLIFE RES CTR, US FISH & WILDLIFE SERV, 68- *Res:* Bile acid metabolism; bile acids in avian species; biological properties of plant proteins; nutritional requirements of wild, rare and/or endangered species. *Mailing Add:* Patuxent Wildlife Res Ctr Laurel MD 20708

SERAFIN, ROBERT JOSEPH, b Chicago, Ill, Apr 22, 36; m 61; c 4. RADAR ENGINEERING, RADAR METEOROLOGY. *Educ:* Univ Notre Dame, BS, 58; Northwestern Univ, MS, 61; Ill Inst Technol, PhD(elec eng), 72. *Prof Exp:* Engr elec eng radar, Hazeltine Res Corp, 60-62; res engr radar signal process, IIT Res Inst, 60-69, sr engr, 69-73, res assoc radar meteorol, 70-73; mgr field oberv facil radar meteoral instrumentation, 73-81, DIR, ATMOSPHERIC TECH DIV, NAT CTR ATMOSPERIC RES, 81- *Mem:* Am Meteorol Soc; Inst Elec & Electronics Engrs; Sigma Xi. *Res:* Doppler radar signal processing theory and implementation; random signal theory; atmospheric turbulence, severe storms, tornadoes and damaging winds. *Mailing Add:* Nat Ctr for Atmospheric Res PO Box 3000 Boulder CO 80307

SERAFINI, ANGELA, b Sassoferrato, Italy, July 27, 13; nat. BACTERIOLOGY, CYTOLOGY. *Educ:* Wayne State Univ, BA, 50; Univ Mich, MS, 56; Registry Med Technol, cert, 33; Nat Registry Microbiol, registered, 61. *Prof Exp:* Med technologist, Wayne County Gen Hosp, Eloise, Mich, 33-35, sr bacteriologist, mycologist, parasitologist & instr, 44-55; sr bacteriologist, supvr med technologists & instr med technol, Grace Hosp, Detroit, 35-44; from asst res microbiologist to assoc res microbiologist, Parke, Davis & Co, 56-70; instr med technol, Sch Med, Wayne State Univ, 70-72, res asst, 72-78; RETIRED. *Mem:* Am Soc Microbiol. *Res:* Respiratory human viruses; tumor viruses of animals and man; immunology; cytology. *Mailing Add:* 1550 Cherboneau Pl Apt 111 Detroit MI 48207

SERAPHIN, BERNHARD OTTO, b Berlin, Ger, Nov 4, 23; nat US; m 58; c 2. SOLID STATE PHYSICS. *Educ:* Friedrich Schiller Univ, dipl, 50; Humboldt Univ, PhD(physics), 51. *Prof Exp:* Sci asst, Inst Solid State Res, Ger, 50-52; physicist, Res Lab, Siemens-Schuckertwerke Co, Co, 52-56; chief semiconductor team, Physics Lab, Brown Bovery Co, Switz, 56-59; head, Semiconductor Br, Michelson Lab, US Dept Navy, 59-70; PROF OPTICAL SCI, OPTICAL SCI CTR, UNIV ARIZ, 70- *Concurrent Pos:* Liaison scientist, Off Naval Res, London, 65-67; guest prof, Tech Univ Denmark, 69-70, Univ VI Paris, Univ Strasbourg, Univ Nice. *Mem:* Fel Am Phys Soc. *Res:* Modulation spectroscopy; electroreflectance; energy band structure and optical properties of solids; material science aspects of solar energy conversion. *Mailing Add:* Optical Sci Ctr Univ of Ariz Tucson AZ 85721

SERAT, WILLIAM FELKNER, b Chicago, Ill, Nov 14, 29; m 53; c 3. AGRICULTURAL ENVIRONMENTALCHEMISTRY, ENVIRONMENTAL CHEMICAL DYNAMICS. *Educ:* Univ Colo, AB, 51; Iowa State Univ, MS, 53; Univ Calif, Los Angeles, PhD(biochem), 58. *Prof Exp:* Res asst biochem, US Atomic Energy proj, 56-58; tech rep, Rohm and Haas Co, 58-62; res chemist, Calif State Dept Health, 62-69, coord & prin investr, Community Studies in Pesticides, 69-79; PRES, HARTSHORN CO, 79- *Concurrent Pos:* Lectr biol & biochem, St Mary's Col, Calif, 64-72. *Mem:* Am Chem Soc; Soc Environ Toxicol & Chem. *Res:* environmental and health aspects of pesticides; physico-chemical aspects of environment. *Mailing Add:* 12 Camelford Ct Moraga CA 94556

SERBER, ROBERT, b Philadelphia, Pa, Mar 14, 09; m 33, 79; c 2. PHYSICS. *Educ:* Lehigh Univ, BS, 30; Univ Wis, PhD(physics), 34. *Hon Degrees:* DSc, Lehigh Univ, 72. *Prof Exp:* Nat Res Coun fel physics, Univ Calif, 34-36, res assoc, 36-38; from asst prof to assoc prof, Univ Ill, 38-45; prof, Univ Calif, 45-51; prof, 51-77, chmn dept, 75-77, EMER PROF PHYSICS, COLUMBIA UNIV, 77- *Concurrent Pos:* Res assoc, Metall Lab, Univ Chicago, 42-43; sr scientist, Los Alamos Sci Lab, Univ Calif, 43-45; mem, Atomic Bomb Group, Mariana, 45, dir physics measurements, Atomic Bomb Mission to Japan, 45; consult, Douglas Aircraft Co, 46-51 & Brookhaven Nat Lab, 51-; mem, Solvay Conf, Brussels, 48; sci policy comt, Stanford Linear Accelerator Ctr; high energy physics comt, Argonne Nat Lab; vis comt physics, Lehigh Univ; Guggenheim fel, 57; mem adv comts, Fermi Nat Lab, 67-72 & Los Alamos Meson Physics Facil, 78-82; trustee, Assoc Univs, 74-81. *Mem:* Nat Acad Sci; fel Am Phys Soc (pres, 71); Am Acad Arts & Sci; Explorers Club. *Res:* Atomic and molecular structure; cosmic rays; quantum field theory; nuclear physics; particle accelerators; meson theory. *Mailing Add:* 450 Riverside Dr New York NY 10027

SERCARZ, ELI, b Bronx, NY, Feb 14, 34; m 55; c 4. IMMUNOLOGY, CELL BIOLOGY. *Educ:* San Diego State Col, BA, 55; Harvard Univ, MA, 56, PhD(bact, immunol), 60. *Prof Exp:* From asst prof to assoc prof microbiol, 63-70, PROF BACTERIOL, UNIV CALIF, LOS ANGELES, 70- *Concurrent Pos:* Fel bact, Harvard Med Sch, 60-62; fel virol, Mass Inst Technol, 62-63; grants, NSF, 63-69, NIH, 67-81 & Am Heart Asn, 69-72; consult, Eye Res Lab, Cedars-Sinai Med Ctr, 66-69; Guggenheim fel, Nat Inst Med Res, London, 70-71. *Mem:* Am Soc Microbiol; Am Asn Immunol; Nat Inst Med Res London. *Res:* Cell cooperation; iridium gene control; tritium cell specificity; immune unresponsiveness; idrotyke regulation. *Mailing Add:* Dept of Bacteriol Univ of Calif Los Angeles CA 90024

SERDAREVICH, BOGDAN, b Vel Bukovica, Yugoslavia, Dec 3, 21; m 64; c 1. CHEMISTRY. *Educ:* Univ Zagreb, MSc, 55; Swiss Fed Inst Technol, PhD(org chem & biochem), 61. *Prof Exp:* Res assoc peptide chem, Univ Pittsburgh, 61-63; sr res assoc org chem, Swiss Fed Inst Technol, 63-64; asst prof lipid chem, Univ Western Ont, 64-75; PRES SERDARY RES LABS, INC, 72- *Concurrent Pos:* USPHS fel, 61-63; res grants, Swiss Nat Res Coun, 63-64 & Med Res Coun Can, 64- *Mem:* Sr mem Chem Inst Can; NY Acad Sci; Am Oil Chemists Soc. *Res:* Research and synthesis of lipids; lipid metabolism in relation to atherosclerosis and aging process; cell membranes structure and function. *Mailing Add:* Serdary Res Labs Inc PO Box 5036 London ON N6G 2R7 Can

SERDENGECTI, SEDAT, b Izmit, Turkey, July 28, 27; m 58; c 2. CONTROL & SYSTEMS ENGINEERING. *Educ:* Syracuse Univ, BS, 51; Calif Inst Technol, MS, 52, PhD(mech eng), 55. *Prof Exp:* Fel, Calif Inst Technol, 55-57; res engr, Turkish Gen Staff, 57-58 & Chevron Res Corp, Calif, 58-61; asst prof physics, 61-63, asst prof control systs eng, 63-65, assoc prof control systs, 65-71, PROF ENG, HARVEY MUDD COL, 71- *Concurrent Pos:* Consult, Metaflo Res Corp, Calif, 59-61, Chevron Res Corp, 61-64 & Gen Motors Corp, Mich, 65- *Res:* Applied mathematics and mechanics; rock physics; stress analysis; optimalizing control systems; computer science. *Mailing Add:* Dept of Eng Harvey Mudd Col Claremont CA 91711

SERDUKE, FRANKLIN JAMES DAVID, b Berkeley, Calif, May 23, 42; m 63; c 2. NUCLEAR PHYSICS. *Educ:* San Francisco State Univ, AB, 64; Univ Calif, Davis, MA, 66, PhD(physics), 70. *Prof Exp:* Asst physicist, Physics Div, Argonne Nat Lab, 73-76; PHYSICIST, LAWRENCE LIVERMORE NAT LAB, 76- *Mem:* Am Phys Soc; Am Geophys Union. *Res:* Theoretical nuclear physics; nuclear shell theory; few body problems; nuclear matter; pion-nucleus interactions; numerical modeling; Speakeasy computer language. *Mailing Add:* Lawrence Livermore Nat Lab PO Box 808 L-10 Livermore CA 94550

SERDULA, KENNETH JAMES, reactor physics, see previous edition

SERENE, JOSEPH WILLIAM, b Indiana, Pa, Apr 4, 47; m 69. LOW TEMPERATURE PHYSICS, SUPERFLUID FERMI LIQUIDS. *Educ:* Dartmouth Col, AB, 69; Cornell Univ, PhD(physics), 74. *Prof Exp:* Fel, Stanford Univ, 74-75; guest prof physics, Nordic Inst Theoret Atomic Physics, 75-76; asst prof, State Univ NY, Stony Brook, 76-79; ASST PROF APPL PHYSICS, YALE UNIV, 79- *Res:* Theoretical condensed matter physics; superfluid helium 3, superconductivity and superfluids in neutron stars. *Mailing Add:* Becton Ctr 2157 Yale Sta New Haven CT 06520

SERFLING, ROBERT JOSEPH, b Kalamazoo, Mich, Jan 23, 39; m 61; c 2. MATHEMATICAL STATISTICS, PROBABILITY. *Educ:* Ga Inst Technol, BS, 63; Univ NC, Chapel Hill, PhD(math statist), 67. *Prof Exp:* Res statistician, Res Triangle Inst, 67; from asst prof to assoc prof statist, Fla State Univ, 67-75, prof, 75-79; PROF MATH SCI, JOHNS HOPKINS UNIV, 79- *Concurrent Pos:* Statistician & chmn, Assessment Admin Rev Comn, State of Fla, 73-77; vis statist adv, NSF, 77-78. *Mem:* Fel Am Statist Asn; fel Inst Math Statist; Biometrics Soc; Am Math Soc; Math Asn Am. *Res:* Probability theory; statistical inference; stochastic processes; sampling of finite populations. *Mailing Add:* Dept Math Sci Johns Hopkins Univ Baltimore MD 21218

SERFOZO, RICHARD FRANK, b Detroit, Mich, Mar 29, 39; m 62; c 1. OPERATIONS RESEARCH. *Educ:* Wayne State Univ, BS, 61; Univ Wash, MA, 65; Northwestern Univ, PhD(appl math), 69. *Prof Exp:* Prof engr, Ford Motor Co, 62; oper res analyst, Boeing Co, 62-68; vis asst prof oper res, Cornell Univ, 72; ASST PROF OPER RES, SYRACUSE UNIV, 69-72, 73- *Mem:* Am Math Soc; Oper Res Soc Am; Inst Mgt Sci. *Res:* Applied probability; semi-stationary processes; thinning of point processes, control of queues. *Mailing Add:* Oper Res Ctr Bell Tel Labs Holmdel NJ 07733

SERGEANT, DAVID ERNEST, b Hangchow, China, Jan 17, 27; Can citizen; m 54; c 3. BIOLOGY, ECOLOGY. *Educ:* Cambridge Univ, BSc, 48, MSc, 49, PhD(zool), 53. *Prof Exp:* Biologist fisheries biol, Fisheries Res Bd, Can Biol Sta, St John's, Nfld, 51-55 & Arctic Unit, Montreal, 55-65; BIOLOGIST, CAN FISHERIES & OCEANS DEPT, ARCTIC BIOL STA, 65- *Mem:* Am Soc Mammal; Int Union Conserv Nature & Natural Resources. *Res:* Study of life history, population dynamics of sea mammals and advice towards the management of exploited species. *Mailing Add:* Arctic Biol Sta PO Box 400 Ste-Anne de Bellevue PQ H9X 3L6 Can

SERGOVICH, FREDERICK RAYMOND, b Toronto, Ont, Nov 1, 33; m 60; c 2. CYTOLOGY, CYTOGENETICS. *Educ:* McMaster Univ, BA, 60; Univ Western Ont, PhD(anat), 64. *Prof Exp:* DIR CYTOGENETICS LAB, CHILDREN'S PSYCHIAT RES INST, 64- *Concurrent Pos:* Lectr, Med Sch, Univ Western Ont, 64-66, asst prof, 66-72; grants, Med Res Coun Can, 64-71, Ont Ment Health Fedn, 66-69 & 71-72 & Ont Cancer Treatment & Res Fedn, 69-72; consult, Victoria Hosp, London, Ont, 65- *Mem:* Am Soc Human Genetics; Can Asn Anat; Can Soc Cell Biol. *Res:* Human cytogenetics; correlation of clinical expression with chromosomes in lesion in mental retardation syndromes; fluorescence analysis of chromosomes in primary malignancies. *Mailing Add:* 1385 Commissioners W London ON N6K 1E2 Can

SERIF, GEORGE SAMUEL, b Saskatoon, Sask, Apr 5, 28; m 48; c 3. BIOCHEMISTRY. *Educ:* McMaster Univ, BSc, 51, MSc, 53, PhD(biochem), 56. *Prof Exp:* Mem tech staff, DuPont of Can, 52-54; Hoffmann-La Roche fel, agr biochem, Univ Minn, 56-57; mem staff, Scripps Clin & Res Found, Calif, 57-58; from asst prof to assoc prof biochem, Sch Med, Univ SDak, 58-62; from asst prof to assoc prof, 62-67, prof biochem & molecular biol & chmn faculty, 67-71, PROF BIOCHEM & CHMN DEPT, OHIO STATE UNIV, 71- *Mem:* Am Soc Biol Chem; Am Chem Soc; Soc Exp Biol & Med; NY Acad Sci. *Res:* Mechanism of hormone action; carbohydrate metabolism; metabolism of fluoro derivatives; antimetabolites. *Mailing Add:* Dept of Biochem Col Biol Sci Ohio State Univ 484 W 12th Ave Columbus OH 43210

SERIFF, AARON JAY, b Eagle Pass, Tex, Apr 26, 24; m 51; c 2. GEOPHYSICS. *Educ:* Univ Tex, BS, 44; Calif Inst Technol, PhD(physics), 51. *Prof Exp:* Instr math & physics, Univ Tex, 44-46; asst physics, Calif Inst Technol, 50; SR RES ASSOC, SHELL DEVELOP CO, 51- *Concurrent Pos:* Ed, Geophysics, 73-75. *Mem:* Am Geophys Union; Seismol Soc Am; Europ Asn Explor Geophys; Soc Explor Geophys. *Res:* Seismology; cosmic rays; exploration geophysics. *Mailing Add:* Shell Develop Co Houston TX 77001

SERIO, CHARLES S, b Grenada, Miss, Aug 26, 46; m 69; c 3. IMMUNOLOGY, MICROBIOLOGY. *Educ:* Univ Miss, BS, 69, MS, 73, PhD(immunol), 75. *Prof Exp:* Res fel, St Jude Children's Res Hosp, 75-77; asst biologist immunol, Argonne Nat Lab, 77-81; IMMUNOLOGIST, WILLIAM BEAUMONT ARMY MED CTR, 81- *Mem:* Int Soc Res Reticuloendothelial Systs; Brit Soc Immunol; Sigma Xi; Can Soc Immunol. *Res:* Immunobiology of macrophage functions in relation to tumor cell growth and inhibition. *Mailing Add:* Dept Clin Invest William Beaumont Army Med Ctr El Paso TX 79920

SERKES, KENNETH DEAN, b St Louis, Mo, Aug 18, 26; m 48; c 3. SURGERY. *Educ:* Yale Univ, BS, 50; Washington Univ, MD, 51; Am Bd Surg, dipl, 57. *Prof Exp:* Assoc surg, Jewish Hosp St Louis, 56-62, asst dir, 62-67; asst to dir, Albert Einstein Med Ctr, Pa, 67-68; assoc clin res, 68-70, assoc dir clin res, 70-72, MED DIR ARTIFICIAL ORGANS DIV, BAXTER/TRAVENOL LABS, INC, 72- *Concurrent Pos:* From instr to asst prof, Sch Med, Washington Univ, 56-57; assoc prof, Sch Med, Temple Univ, 67-68; asst prof, Northwestern Univ, 68- *Mem:* AAAS; fel Am Col Surg; Am Soc Artificial Internal Organs; NY Acad Sci. *Res:* Shock; blood volume; membrane and bubble oxygenation; artificial kidneys; organ preservation; general surgery; development of artificial kidneys; organ preservation; development of artificial organs; peritoneal dialysis research and development. *Mailing Add:* Baxter/Travenol Labs Inc One Baxter Pkwy Deerfield IL 60015

SERKOWSKI, KRZYSZTOF, b Warsaw, Poland, Dec 8, 30; US citizen; m 57; c 2. ASTROPHYSICS. *Educ:* Wroclaw Univ, MS, 54; Warsaw Univ, Dr Math & Phys Sci(astrophys), 58. *Hon Degrees:* DSc, Australian Nat Univ, 70. *Prof Exp:* Asst astron observ, Univ Warsaw, 50-52 & 54-59; astronr, Lowell Observ, 59-61 & 65-66; docent astron, Univ Warsaw, 62-65, assoc dean Col math & physics, 64-65; sr res fel, Mt Stromlo Observ, Canberra, Australia, 66-70; assoc prof astrophys, 70-79, RES PROF LUNAR & PLANETARY LAB, UNIV ARIZ, 79- *Concurrent Pos:* NSF grants, 70-; mem, Instrument Definition Team, NASA Large Space Telescope, 73-75. *Mem:* Int Astron Union; Am Astron Soc; Polish Astron Soc (secy, 58). *Res:* Polarization of starlight; techniques of astronomical polarimetry and spectrophotometry; measurements of stellar radial velocities and search for planets around stars. *Mailing Add:* Lunar & Planetary Lab Univ of Ariz Tucson AZ 85721

SERLIN, IRVING, b New York, NY, Apr 3, 23; m 50; c 2. POLYMER CHEMISTRY. *Educ:* City Col, BS, 43; Columbia Univ, MA, 47, PhD(org chem), 50. *Prof Exp:* Res chemist, Am Diet Aids, Inc, 43-44; lab instr org chem, Columbia Univ, 47-49; res assoc biochem, 51-53; res chemist, Cent Res Labs, Donut Corp Am, 50-51; assoc scientist, Brookhaven Nat Lab, 53-56; res chemist, Shawinigan Resins Corp, 56-65; res specialist, 65-70, SR RES SPECIALIST, MONSANTO CO, 70- *Concurrent Pos:* Mem, Int Physiol

Cong, Belg, 56. *Mem:* Am Chem Soc. *Res:* Organic chemistry; synthesis of new resins for reprographic systems; synthesis of high temperature resins; pressure sensitive adhesive basic research. *Mailing Add:* Monsanto Co 190 Grochmal Ave Indian Orchard MA 01151

SERLIN, OSCAR, b New York, NY, Aug 10, 17; m 51; c 2. SURGERY. *Educ:* Dalhousie Univ, MD & CM, 41; Am Bd Surg, dipl, 52. *Prof Exp:* Chief surg serv, Vet Admin Hosp, Lebanon, 56-57 & Philadelphia, 57-67; chief surg serv, 67-75, CHIEF OF STAFF, VET ADMIN HOSP, EAST ORANGE, 75-PROF SURG, COL MED NJ, COL MED & DENT NJ, 71- *Concurrent Pos:* Clin prof, Sch Med, Temple Univ, 58-67. *Mem:* Fel Am Col Surg. *Res:* Chemotherapy in treatment of cancer. *Mailing Add:* Vet Admin Hosp East Orange NJ 07019

SERNAS, VALENTINAS A, b Klaipeda, Lithuania, Nov 3, 38; US citizen; m 62; c 2. MECHANICAL & AEROSPACE ENGINEERING. *Educ:* Univ Toronto, BASc, 61, MASc, 64, PhD(mech eng), 67. *Prof Exp:* Asst prof, 66-71, assoc prof, 71-79, PROF MECH ENG, RUTGERS UNIV, NEW BRUNSWICK, 79- *Mem:* Am Soc Mech Engrs; Sigma Xi; Optical Soc Am. *Res:* Heat transfer; boiling and condensation; natural connection; interferometry applied to heat transfer. *Mailing Add:* Dept Mech & Aero Eng Rutgers Univ New Brunswick NJ 08903

SERNE, ROGER JEFFREY, b Lakewood, Ohio, Mar 20, 46; m 68; c 2. GEOCHEMISTRY, ANALYTICAL CHEMISTRY. *Educ:* Univ Wash, BS(chem) & BS(oceanog), 69. *Prof Exp:* Res scientist, 69-76, sr res scientist, 76-78, sect mgr, 78, STAFF SCIENTIST WATER & LAND RESOURCES, BATTELLE NORTHWEST LABS, 78- *Mem:* Am Soc Agron; Soil Sci Soc Am. *Res:* Migration of hazardous wastes in geologic environment; adsorption mechanisms of trace constituents onto geomedia. *Mailing Add:* Battelle Northwest Labs PO Box 999 Sigma 5 3000 Richland WA 99352

SERNKA, THOMAS JOHN, b Cleveland, Ohio, July 26, 41; m 69. MEDICAL PHYSIOLOGY, MEDICAL BIOPHYSICS. *Educ:* Oberlin Col, BA, 63; Harvard Univ, MA, 66; Univ Iowa, PhD(physiol, biophys), 69. *Prof Exp:* NIH fel, Univ Calif, San Francisco, 69-71; from instr to asst prof physiol, Univ Tex Med Sch Houston, 71-74; asst prof, 74-75, assoc prof physiol & biophys, med sch, La State Univ, Shreveport, 75-76; ASSOC PROF PHYSIOL, WRIGHT STATE UNIV, DAYTON, 76- *Concurrent Pos:* Nat Inst Alcohol Abuse & Alcoholism grant, 76-80. *Mem:* Am Physiol Soc; Biophys Soc; Soc Exp Biol & Med. *Res:* Gastric mucosal transport and metabolism. *Mailing Add:* Dept of Physiol Wright State Univ Dayton OH 45435

SEROVY, GEORGE K(ASPAR), b Cedar Rapids, Iowa, Aug 29, 26; m 71; c 5. MECHANICAL ENGINEERING. *Educ:* Iowa State Univ, BS, 48, MS, 50, PhD(mech eng), 58. *Prof Exp:* Asst mech eng, Iowa State Univ, 48-49; aeronaut res scientist, Nat Adv Comt Aeronaut, 49-53; from asst prof to assoc prof mech eng, 53-60, asst dir eng res inst, 68-72, PROF MECH ENG, IOWA STATE UNIV, 60-, ASST TO DEAN, COL OF ENG, 72- *Concurrent Pos:* Mem Nat Acad Sci propulsion adv panel, US Air Force Systs Command, 69-75. *Mem:* Fel Am Soc Mech Engrs; Int Asn Hydraul Res. *Res:* Fluid mechanics of turbomachinery; aircraft propulsion; internal flow; heat transfer. *Mailing Add:* Dept of Mech Eng Iowa State Univ Ames IA 50011

SERRANO, LOUIS JOSEPH, b New York, NY, Apr 10, 31; m 53; c 3. LABORATORY ANIMAL MEDICINE. *Educ:* Univ Miami, Fla, BS, 57; Auburn Univ, DVM, 61. *Prof Exp:* USPHS fels lab animal med & physiol, Sch Med, Univ Calif, Los Angeles, 61-62 & Sch Med, Univ Mich, 62-63; biologist, group leader & dir lab animal resources, Biol Div, Oak Ridge Nat Lab, 63-77; dir vet med, Microbiol Assocs, 77-79; DIR ANIMAL RESOURCES, NCI-FREDERICK CANCER RES FACIL, 79- *Concurrent Pos:* Assoc ed, Lab Animal Sci; consult, Nat Ctr Toxicol Res, Food & Drug Admin & Nat Res Coun-Inst Lab Animal Resources, Nat Cancer Inst, 75- *Mem:* Am Vet Med Asn; Am Asn Lab Animal Sci; Am Soc Lab Animal Practitioners; Am Asn Indust Veterinarians. *Res:* Environmental influences on experimental animals; development and operation of isolation-type animal facilities; application of computer technology to storage and analysis of animal reproduction data; control of diseases of lab rodents. *Mailing Add:* Frederick Cancer Res Facil Nat Cancer Inst PO Box B Frederick MD 21701

SERRIN, JAMES B, b Evanston, Ill, Nov 1, 26; m 52; c 3. MATHEMATICS. *Educ:* Univ Ind, PhD(math), 51. *Hon Degrees:* DSc, Univ Sussex, 72. *Prof Exp:* Instr math, Mass Inst Technol, 52-54; from asst prof to assoc prof, 54-60, head, Sch Math, 64-65, PROF MATH & AERO ENG, UNIV MINN, MINNEAPOLIS, 60- *Concurrent Pos:* Vis prof, Univ Chicago, 64 & 75 & Johns Hopkins Univ, 66; vis fel, Univ Sussex, 67, 72 & 76. *Mem:* Nat Acad Sci; Math Asn Am; Soc Natural Philos; fel AAAS; Am Math Soc. *Res:* Partial differential equations; theoretical fluid mechanics; thermodynamics. *Mailing Add:* Dept Math Univ Minn Minneapolis MN 55455

SERSON, PAUL HORNE, b Ottawa, Ont, Dec 24, 23. MAGNETISM. *Educ:* Univ Toronto, BA, 46, MA, 49, PhD(physics), 51. *Prof Exp:* Geophysicist, Dom Observ, 46-62, chief div geomagnetism, 62-70, CHIEF DIV GEOMAGNETISM, EARTH PHYSICS BR, CAN DEPT ENERGY, MINES & RESOURCES, 70- *Res:* Instruments for measuring earth's magnetic field. *Mailing Add:* Prescott Hwy Ottawa ON K1R 7L2 Can

SERTH, ROBERT WILLIAM, b Rochester, NY, Aug 30, 41; m 64; c 1. CHEMICAL ENGINEERING. *Educ:* Univ Rochester, BS, 63; State Univ NY, Buffalo, PhD(chem eng), 69; Univ Ariz, MA, 70. *Prof Exp:* Asst prof chem eng, Univ Puerto Rico, 71-74; sr res engr energy & environ, Monsanto Res Corp, 74-77, res specialist, 77-78; ASSOC PROF CHEM ENG, TEX A&I UNIV, 78- *Mem:* Am Inst Chem Engrs; Air Pollution Control Asn; AAAS. *Res:* Fluid mechanics; rheology; applied mathematics; pollution control. *Mailing Add:* Dept of Chem Eng Tex A&I Univ Kingsville TX 78363

SERVADIO, GILDO JOSEPH, b Ridgefield, Conn, Jan 27, 29; m 55; c 3. FOOD SCIENCE. *Educ:* Tufts Univ, BS, 52; Univ Mass, MS, 55, PhD(food technol), 61. *Prof Exp:* Proj leader, Pillsbury Co, 55-58; instr packaging, Univ Mass, 58-61; sr scientist, Mead Johnson & Co, 61-63; res mgr, Beech-Nut Life Savers, Inc, NY, 63-65, assoc dir res, 65-67; dir res & develop labs, 67-75, VPRES RES & DEVELOP LABS, HEUBLEIN INC, HARTFORD, 75- *Concurrent Pos:* Mem, Wash Lab Comt, Nat Canners Asn, 65-, Res & Develop Assocs, US Army Natick Labs, 65 & Distilled Spirits Inst, 69-; chmn tech comt, Vinegar Inst, 70-; chmn comt food protection, Grocery Mfrs Asn, 70- *Mem:* Inst Food Technol; Am Asn Cereal Chemists. *Res:* Food and beverage chemistry; food colorimetry; baking, infant nutrition and nutritional products technology; chemistry and processing of fruits, vegetables and formulated foods; technology of wines, beers and distilled spirits; research administration. *Mailing Add:* Res & Develop Lab 430 New Park Ave Hartford CT 06101

SERVAES, TAHIRA MINHAJ, quantum physics, statistical mechanics, see previous edition

SERVAIS, RONALD ALBERT, b La Crosse, Wis, Apr 6, 42; m 64; c 2. AEROTHERMOCHEMISTRY, AERODYNAMICS. *Educ:* St Louis Univ, BS, 63, MS, 66; Wash Univ, DSc(chem eng), 69. *Prof Exp:* Assoc engr, McDonnell Aircraft Corp, 63-64, engr, 64-66; asst prof mech eng, Univ Mo-Rolla, 68-72; res scientist, US Air Force Mat Lab, 73-74; CHMN CHEM ENG, UNIV DAYTON, 74- *Concurrent Pos:* Consult, Davis-Standard Co, 67-70, Thermo-Systs, Inc, 69-70, Eng Dynamics Int, 70-, A J Celis & Assocs, 71- & Monsanto Enviro-Chem Systs, Inc, 72-; partner, Creative Eng Consult & Assocs, 73- *Mem:* Air Pollution Control Asn; Am Inst Aeronaut & Astronaut; Am Inst Chem Engrs; Nat Soc Prof Engrs; Am Soc Eng Educ. *Res:* Numerical solution of equations describing reacting; viscous, conducting, and diffusing flow fields, including reentry physics and air pollution modeling; aerodynamics of automobiles and trucks; performance of materials exposed to intense radiant heating. *Mailing Add:* Dept Chem Eng Univ Dayton Dayton OH 45469

SERVAITES, JEROME CASIMER, b Dayton, Ohio, Sept 15, 44. PLANT PHYSIOLOGY, BIOCHEMISTRY. *Educ:* Univ Dayton, BS, 68, MS, 72; Univ Ill, Urbana-Champaign, PhD(biol), 76. *Prof Exp:* Teaching asst, Dept Biol, Univ Dayton, 70-72; res asst, Dept Agron, Univ Ill, 72-75, res assoc, 76; res assoc, Dept Hort, Univ Wis, 76-77, fel agron, 77-78; plant physiologist res, Sci & Educ Admin-Agr Res, USDA, 78-80; MEM FAC, BIOL DEPT, VA POLYTECH INST & STATE UNIV, 80- *Mem:* AAAS; Am Soc Agron; Am Soc Plant Physiol. *Res:* Photosynthetic carbon metabolism and photorespiration in crop plants; biochemical mechanisms and processes limiting yield of crop plants. *Mailing Add:* Biol Dept Va Polytech Inst & State Univ Blacksburg VA 24061

SERVE, MUNSON PAUL, b Medina, NY, Nov 26, 39; m 69. ORGANIC CHEMISTRY, BIOCHEMISTRY. *Educ:* Univ Notre Dame, BS, 61, PhD(org chem), 64. *Prof Exp:* Am Cancer Soc fel, Univ Chicago, 64-65; asst prof, 65-75, PROF CHEM WRIGHT STATE UNIV, 75- *Concurrent Pos:* Vis scientist, NIH, 75-76 & Toxic Hazzards Br, US Air Force, 80- *Mem:* Am Chem Soc; Sigma Xi. *Res:* Photochemistry; photolysis of benzotriazoles; shift reagents in organic structure determinations; chemical toxicology of enviromental pollutants. *Mailing Add:* Dept of Org Biochem Wright State Univ Glenn Hwy Dayton OH 45431

SERVI, I(TALO) S(OLOMON), b Gallarate, Italy, Oct 3, 22; m 50; c 3. PHYSICAL METALLURGY. *Educ:* Milan Univ, Dr, 46; Mass Inst Technol, MS, 49, ScD, 51. *Prof Exp:* Asst metall, Mass Inst Technol, 48-51; res metallurgist, Metals Res Labs, Union Carbide Metals Co, 51-56, staff metallurgist, 56-58, group mgr, 58-59; dir res, Metals Div, Kelsey-Hayes Co, 59-60, tech dir, 60-61; vpres & tech dir, Spec Metals, Inc, 61-62; staff scientist, Ledgemont Lab, Kennecott Copper Co, 62-65, asst dir res, 66-76, dir prod develop, 76-78, dir new venture technol, Lexington Develop Ctr, 78-81; CONSULT ENG, 81- *Concurrent Pos:* Instr, Adult Educ Ctr, Niagara Falls, NY, 53-54. *Mem:* Fel Am Soc Metals; Am Inst Mining, Metall & Petrol Engrs; fel Inst Metall. *Res:* Physical and mechanical behavior of metals and alloys; organizational communication. *Mailing Add:* 3 Angier Rd Lexington MA 02173

SERVIS, KENNETH L, b Indianapolis, Ind, July 27, 39; m 68; c 3. PHYSICAL CHEMISTRY, ORGANIC CHEMISTRY. *Educ:* Purdue Univ, BS, 61; Calif Inst Technol, PhD(chem), 65. *Prof Exp:* Am-Yugoslavia Cultural Exchange fel, Rudjer Boskovic Inst, Univ Zagreb, Yugoslavia, 64-65; asst prof, 65-68, ASSOC PROF CHEM, UNIV SOUTHERN CALIF, 68- *Concurrent Pos:* Alfred P Sloan fel, 69-71; Guggenheim fel, 73-74; Fulbright Hays Award, Univ Zagreb, 74. *Mem:* Am Chem Soc; Royal Soc Chem; Croatian Chem Soc. *Res:* Structure and reactivity of organic compounds; molecular rearrangements; nuclear magnetic resonance spectroscopy. *Mailing Add:* 14 Gaucho Dr Rolling Hills Estates CA 90274

SERVIS, ROBERT EUGENE, b Lansing, Mich, June 28, 41; m 69. BIO-ORGANIC CHEMISTRY. *Educ:* Univ Mich, BS, 63; NY Univ, MS, 66, PhD(chem), 69, MD, 74. *Prof Exp:* Res scientist, NY Univ, 69-74; RES SCIENTIST, DEPT MED RES, BLODGETT MED CTR, 74- *Mem:* AAAS; Am Chem Soc; NY Acad Sci; Am Inst Chemists. *Res:* Natural products; alkaloids; bioorganic chemistry; gas chromatography; mass spectrometry of biological materials. *Mailing Add:* 3226 Dorais Dr NE Grand Rapids MI 49505

SERVOS, KURT, b Anrath, Ger, Dec 20, 28; nat US. MINERALOGY. *Educ:* Rutgers Univ, BS, 52; Yale Univ, MS, 54. *Prof Exp:* Sr cur geol, NY State Mus, 56-57; asst prof mineral, Stanford Univ, 57-60; independent geologist, 60-67; PROF GEOL, MENLO COL, 67- *Concurrent Pos:* Geologist, Stanford Res Inst, 67-69. *Mem:* Mineral Soc Am; Am Crystallog Asn; Mineral Asn Can; Geol Soc Am. *Res:* Crystallography. *Mailing Add:* 1281 Mills St Menlo Park CA 94025

SERVOSS, REVA R, physical chemistry, see previous edition

SERWAY, RAYMOND A, b Frankfort, NY, June 26, 36; m 59; c 4. SOLID STATE PHYSICS. *Educ:* Syracuse Univ, BA, 59; Univ Colo, MS, 61; Ill Inst Technol, PhD(physics), 67. *Prof Exp:* Teaching asst physics, Univ Colo, 59-61; res physicist, Rome Air Develop Ctr, 61-63; assoc physicist, IIT Res Inst, 63-67; from asst prof to prof physics, Clarkson Col Technol, 67-80; PROF PHYSICS & HEAD DEPT, JAMES MADISON UNIV, 80- *Concurrent Pos:* Vis guest prof, IBM Zurich Res Lab, Switz, 74. *Mem:* AAAS; Am Phys Soc; Am Asn Physics Teachers; Sigma Xi. *Res:* Thin-film solar cells and semiconducting solar cell materials exhibiting the photovoltaic effect; magnetic resonance spectroscopy; electron spin resonance absorption spectroscopy in inorganic systems; paramagnetic defect centers in irradiated solids; crystalline field splitting; structure of inorganic molecules. *Mailing Add:* Dept of Physics James Madison Univ Harrisonburg VA 22807

SERWER, PHILIP, b Brooklyn, NY, Feb 5, 42; m 66; c 3. VIROLOGY, MACROMOLECULE FRACTIONATION. *Educ:* Univ Rochester, AB, 63; NY Med Col, MS, 68; Harvard Univ, PhD(biophysics), 73. *Prof Exp:* Fel res, Calif Inst Technol, 72-75, sr res fel, 75-76; asst prof, 76-81, ASSOC PROF BIOCHEM, UNIV TEX HEALTH SCI CTR, SAN ANTONIO, 81- *Mem:* Am Soc Virologists; Electrophoresis Soc; Biophys Soc; Am Soc Biol Chemists; Electron Microscopy Soc Am. *Res:* Mechanisms of assembly of viruses, isolating characterizing and quantitating precursors of viruses, using bacteriophages as a model virus. *Mailing Add:* Dept Biochem San Antonio TX 78284

SESCO, JERRY ANTHONY, b Pensacola, Fla, July 26, 39; m 61; c 2. FORESTRY, ECONOMICS. *Educ:* Univ Ga, BS, 61; Auburn Univ, MS, 62; Southern Ill Univ, PhD(econ), 74. *Prof Exp:* From forester to res forester, 63-74, PROJ LEADER, N CENT FOREST EXP STA, US FOREST SERV, 74- *Mem:* Soc Am Foresters; Forest Prod Res Soc; Sigma Xi; Am Econ Asn. *Res:* Forest products marketing and economics. *Mailing Add:* Ranger Sta US Forestry Serv 2221 Walnut Murphysboro IL 62966

SESHADRI, KALKUNTE S, b Jagalur, India, May 11, 24; m 51; c 2. PHYSICAL CHEMISTRY. *Educ:* Mysore Univ, BSc, 45, MSc, 47; Ore State Univ, PhD(phys chem), 60. *Prof Exp:* Lectr chem, Cent Col, Bangalore, 45-56; lectr phys chem, Maharani's Col, Mysore, 60; fel Nat Res Coun Can, 60-62; res assoc, Ohio State Univ, 62-66; res chemist, 66-68, SR RES CHEMIST, GULF RES & DEVELOP CO, 68- *Mem:* NY Acad Sci; Am Chem Soc; Am Phys Soc. *Res:* Infrared molecular structure determination, intensity measurement and band shape analysis; surface and catalytic studies by magnetic resonance and optical spectroscopic techniques; study of coal, coal liquids, and polymers by proton, carbon-13, silicon-29, fluorine-19 and nitrogen-15 nuclear magnetic resonance spectroscopy and fourier transform infrared spectroscopy. *Mailing Add:* Gulf Res & Develop Co PO Drawer 2038 Pittsburgh PA 15230

SESHADRI, SENGADU RANGASWAMY, b Madras City, India, Oct 25, 28; m 59. APPLIED PHYSICS, ELECTRICAL ENGINEERING. *Educ:* Madras Univ, MA, 51; Indian Inst Sci, Bangalore, dipl, 53; Harvard Univ, PhD(appl physics), 59. *Prof Exp:* Lectr electronics, Madras Inst Tech, 53-55; res fel appl physics, Harvard Univ, 59-60 & 61-63; prin sci officer, Electronics Res & Develop Estab, Bangalore, 60-61; consult, Appl Res Lab, Sylvania Elec Prod Inc, Mass, 62-63, sr eng specialist, 63-68; PROF ELEC ENG, UNIV WIS-MADISON, 68- *Concurrent Pos:* Vis prof, Univ Toronto, 65; NSF sr fel, Calif Inst Technol, 70-71. *Mem:* Sr mem Inst Elec & Electronics Eng. *Res:* Electromagnetic scattering and diffraction; surface waves; antennas in anisotropic media; plasma instabilities; nonlinear waves. *Mailing Add:* Dept of Elec & Comput Eng Univ of Wis Madison WI 53706

SESHADRI, VANAMAMALAI, b Madras, India, Apr 25, 28; m 49; c 2. MATHEMATICAL STATISTICS. *Educ:* Univ Madras, BA, 50, MA, 57; Okla State Univ, PhD, 61. *Prof Exp:* Teacher, Pub Schs, Ceylon, 50-54; asst lectr math, Mandalay Univ, 54-57; asst, Okla State Univ, 57-60; asst prof, Southern Methodist Univ, 60-62, asst prof math statist, 62-64; assoc prof math, 65-70, PROF MATH, McGILL UNIV, 70- *Mem:* Am Statist Asn; Inst Math Statist. *Res:* Statistical inference; distribution theory, characterization of distributions; applications of characterization to goodness of fit. *Mailing Add:* Burnside Hall 805 Sherbrooke St W Montreal PQ H3A 2K6 Can

SESHU, LILLY HANNAH, b Coimbatore, India, July 9, 25; m. MATHEMATICS. *Educ:* Univ Travancore, India, BSc, 44, MSc, 46; Univ Ill, PhD(math), 56. *Prof Exp:* Asst, Univ Ill, 53-56; instr, Syracuse Univ, 56-58; instr math, Univ Toronto, 58-65; asst prof, Univ Ill, Urbana, 65-72; ASSOC PROF MATH, PORTLAND STATE UNIV, 72- *Mem:* Am Math Soc. *Res:* Analytic number theory; complex variable theory. *Mailing Add:* Dept of Mathematics Portland State Univ Portland OR 97207

SESONSKE, ALEXANDER, b Gloversville, NY, June 20, 21; m 52; c 2. NUCLEAR ENGINEERING, CHEMICAL ENGINEERING. *Educ:* Rensselaer Polytech Inst, BChE, 42; Univ Rochester, MS, 47; Univ Del, PhD(chem eng), 50. *Prof Exp:* Chem engr, Chem Construct Corp, 42-43; res assoc, S A M Labs, Columbia Univ, 43; chem engr, Houdaille-Hershey Corp, 43-45; res engr, Columbia Chem Div, Pittsburgh Plate Glass Co, 45-46; mem staff, Los Alamos Sci Lab, Univ Calif, 50-54; assoc prof, 54-58, PROF NUCLEAR & CHEM ENG, PURDUE UNIV, 58- *Concurrent Pos:* Mem staff, Los Alamos Sci Lab, 58-59, consult, 60-62; mem rev comt, Argonne Nat Lab, 65-68 & 75-81; consult, Oak Ridge Nuclear Lab, 62-65 & United Nuclear Corp, 63. *Mem:* Fel Am Nuclear Soc; Am Soc Eng Educ; Am Inst Chem Engrs. *Res:* Nuclear reactor engineering; heat transfer; nuclear fuel cycle analysis. *Mailing Add:* Sch of Nuclear Eng Purdue Univ West Lafayette IN 47907

SESSA, DAVID JOSEPH, b Hackensack, NJ, Mar 3, 38; div; c 4. ORGANIC BIOCHEMISTRY. *Educ:* Tufts Univ, BS, 59. *Prof Exp:* Assoc chemist, Agr Res Serv, USDA, 63-68, res chemist org biochem, Northern Regional Res Ctr, 68-81. *Mem:* Am Oil Chemists Soc; NY Acad Sci; Inst Food Technologists. *Res:* Composition and properties of Soybean meal and proteins; lipid chemistry and its relationship to flavor; characterization of complex lipids of soybeans, oxidation of phospholipids and oxidative stability during processing. *Mailing Add:* Northern Regional Res Ctr 1815 N University St Peoria IL 61604

SESSA, GRAZIA L, b Italy; US citizen; m; c 2. BIOCHEMISTRY. *Educ:* Univ Rome, PhD(biol), 58. *Prof Exp:* Fel, Brit Cancer Campaign, Oxford, 60-63; Fulbright scholar, Res Inst Pub Health, New York, 63-64; res fel, Sch Med, NY Univ, 64-65, asst res scientist, 65-67, asst prof microbiol, 68-70; asst prof pharmacol, 70-75, SPEC TRAINING DIR LAB, MT SINAI HOSP, 75-; asst prof pharmacol, Mt Sinai Med Sch, 70-75, dir, Clin Lab Training, Mt Sinai Hosp, 70-79; mem staff clinical chem, Monmouth Med Ctr, Long Branch, NY, 79-81; MEM STAFF, MERCK INT DIV, 81- *Res:* Interaction of drugs with brain membranes; functions of the blood-brain barrier. *Mailing Add:* Merck Int Div PO Box 2000 Rahway NJ 07065

SESSION, JOHN JOE, b Grandfield, Okla, Mar 25, 28; m 59. IMMUNOGENETICS, CYTOGENETICS. *Educ:* Tillotson Col, BS, 49; Tex Southern Univ, MS, 55; Queen's Univ, Ont, PhD(biol), 66. *Prof Exp:* Instr high sch, 55-56; res asst immunogenetics, Baylor Col Med, 57-59, res assoc, 61-62; instr, 59-61 & 62-63, from asst prof to assoc prof, 66-75, PROF BIOL & HEAD DEPT, TEX SOUTHERN UNIV, 75- *Concurrent Pos:* Res assoc exp biol, Baylor Col Med, 62-63; lectr, In-Serv Inst Biol, Tex Southern Univ, 66-68, Fac Res Found grant, 67-68, lectr, Summer Sch Inst, 68; prog dir & prin investr biomed res improv prog; prog dir ungrad hons res training prog, Tex Southern Univ, 72-80. *Mem:* AAAS. *Res:* Karyology and immunology of murine leukemias; significance of the thymus gland during immunogenesis and leukemogenesis. *Mailing Add:* Dept of Biol Tex Southern Univ Houston TX 77004

SESSIONS, JOHN TURNER, JR, b Atlanta, Ga, July 8, 22; m 50. MEDICINE. *Educ:* Emory Univ, BS, 43, MD, 45; Am Bd Gastroenterol, dipl, 68. *Prof Exp:* Intern, Kings County Hosp, Brooklyn, 45-46; intern & resident, Grady Mem Hosp, Atlanta, 48-50; asst med, Sch Med, Boston Univ, 50-52; from asst prof to assoc prof, 52-64, PROF MED, SCH MED, UNIV NC, CHAPEL HILL, 64- *Concurrent Pos:* Res assoc, Evans Mem Hosp, Boston, 50-52; mem training comt gastroenterol & nutrit, Nat Inst Arthritis, Metab & Digestive Dis, 68-; ed, Viewpoints Digestive Dis, 68- *Mem:* AAAS; Am Col Physicians; Am Gastroenterol Asn; Am Fedn Clin Res; Am Asn Study Liver Dis; Am Clin & Climat Asn. *Res:* Biochemical and physiologic aspects of gastroenterology and hepatology. *Mailing Add:* Dept of Med Univ of NC Sch of Med Chapel Hill NC 27514

SESSLE, BARRY JOHN, b Sydney, Australia, May 28, 41; m 67; c 2. NEUROPHYSIOLOGY, ORAL BIOLOGY. *Educ:* Univ Sydney, BDS, 63, BSc & MDS, 65; Univ New South Wales, PhD(physiol), 69. *Prof Exp:* Fel physiol, Med Sch, Univ New South Wales, 65-68; vis assoc orofacial neurophysiol, Nat Inst Dent Res, 68-70; assoc prof dent, 71-76, PROF & CHMN, DIV BIOL SCI, FAC DENT & PROF PHYSIOL, FAC MED, UNIV TORONTO, 77- *Concurrent Pos:* mem, Can Med Res Coun, dent sci grants comt, 79-; vis prof, Can Med Res Coun, Univ BC, 80- *Honors & Awards:* Oral Sci Award, Int Asn Dent Res, 76. *Mem:* Int Asn Study Pain; Soc Neurosci; Int Asn Dent Res; Can Physiol Soc. *Res:* Neural basis of facial and oropharyngeal function; general sensory and motor neurophysiology; perceptual and behavioral correlates. *Mailing Add:* Fac of Dent Univ of Toronto Toronto ON M5G 1G6 Can

SESSLER, ANDREW M, b Brooklyn, NY, Dec 11, 28; m 51; c 3. THEORETICAL PHYSICS. *Educ:* Harvard Univ, BA, 49; Columbia Univ, MS, 51, PhD(physics), 53. *Prof Exp:* Asst physics, Columbia Univ, 49-52; NSF fel, Cornell Univ, 53-54; from asst prof to assoc prof physics, Ohio State Univ, 54-61; theoret physicist, 61-73, dir, 73-80, THEORET PHYSICIST, LAWRENCE BERKELEY LAB, UNIV CALIF, 80- *Concurrent Pos:* Mem high energy physics adv panel, US AEC, 69-72; mem comt on high energy physics, Argonne Univ, 71-73; chmn sci policy bd, Stanford Synchrotron Radiation Lab, 76-78; chmn advan fuels adv comt, Elec Power Res Inst, 78-81; chmn comt on Isabelle, Brookhaven Nat Lab, 80-; mem review comt, Plasma Physics Lab, Princeton Univ, 81- *Honors & Awards:* E O Lawrence Award, US AEC, 70. *Mem:* AAAS; fel Am Phys Soc; Sigma Xi. *Res:* Theory of particle accelerators; plasma physics. *Mailing Add:* Lawrence Berkeley Lab Univ Calif Berkeley CA 94720

SESSLER, JOHN CHARLES, b Newark, NJ, Feb 14, 32; m 54; c 7. PHYSICS, OPERATIONS RESEARCH. *Educ:* Rutgers Univ, BA, 56; Univ Southern Calif, MA, 61; Georgetown Univ, PhD, 70. *Prof Exp:* Res engr, Rocketdyne Div, NAm Aviation, Inc, 56-60; assoc scientist, Opers Model Eval Group Off, Tech Opers, Inc, 60-62; opers analyst, Ctr Naval Anal, Univ Rochester, 62-72; sr prog analyst, Drug Abuse Coun, 72-78; EVAL COODR USPHS, 78- *Concurrent Pos:* Marine Corps opers anal group rep, Staff, Commanding Gen, Fleet Marine Force, Atlantic, 64-65, Pac, 67-68; opers eval group rep, Comdr Attack Carrier Striking Force, Seventh Fleet, 70-71. *Mem:* Am Phys Soc; Opers Res Soc Am. *Res:* Analysis of control systems for large liquid propellant rocket engines; simulation of air battles; operations analysis; low energy nuclear physics; social program evaluation. *Mailing Add:* 4401 Lee Hwy #43 Arlington VA 22207

SESSLER, JOHN GEORGE, b Syracuse, NY, Apr 8, 20; m 53; c 4. MECHANICAL ENGINEERING, METALLURGICAL ENGINEERING. *Educ:* Syracuse Univ, BS, 50, MS, 62. *Prof Exp:* Res engr, Syracuse Univ, 50-60, sr res engr, 60-72; consult, 72-76, TECH CONSULT, ENGR PROD LIABILITY & ACCIDENT RECONSTRUCT, 76- *Concurrent Pos:* Contrib ed, Aerospace Struct Metals Handbk, Belfour-Stulen, Inc, Traverse City, Mich, 69- *Honors & Awards:* NASA Minor Award, NASA, 68. *Mem:* Am Soc Testing & Mat; Am Inst Mining, Metall & Petrol Engrs. *Res:* Mechanical behavior of metals and alloys, including creep, fatigue, notch behavior and fracture. *Mailing Add:* 121 Jean Ave Syracuse NY 13210

SESSOMS, STUART MCGUIRE, b Autryville, NC, July 16, 21; m 44; c 2. INTERNAL MEDICINE. *Educ:* Univ NC, BS, 43; Med Col Va, MD, 46; Am Bd Internal Med, dipl. *Prof Exp:* Intern, US Marine Hosp, Baltimore, 46-47, resident internal med, 47-50, asst chief med serv & chg med outpatient dept, 50-52; asst resident med, Mem Ctr Cancer & Allied Dis, New York, 52-53; mem Clin Med & Surg Br, Nat Cancer Inst, NIH, 53-54, actg chief, Gen Med Br, 54, asst dir, Clin Ctr, 55-57, asst dir, Nat Cancer Inst, 58, chief cancer chemother, Nat Serv Ctr, 58-62, assoc dir chemother, 60-62, dep dir, NIH, 62-68; prof med & health admin & dir hosp, Duke Univ, 68-75; SR VPRES, NC BLUE CROSS & BLUE SHIELD, 76- *Concurrent Pos:* Clin instr, Sch Med, George Washington Univ, 53-54. *Honors & Awards:* Meritorious Serv Medal, USPHS, 64 & 66. *Mem:* AMA; Am Hosp Asn; Am Pub Health Asn; NY Acad Sci. *Res:* Cancer chemotherapy. *Mailing Add:* Box 2291 Durham NC 27702

SESTANJ, KAZIMIR, b Zagreb, Yugoslavia, Nov 11, 27; Can citizen; wid. ORGANIC CHEMISTRY, MEDICINAL CHEMISTRY. *Educ:* Univ Zagreb, dipl, 55, PhD(org chem), 61. *Prof Exp:* Res chemist, Pliva Pharmaceut & Chem Works, Yugoslavia, 54-63; fel org photochem, Harvard Univ, 63-64; fel synthetic carcinostatics, Children's Cancer Res Found, Boston, Mass, 64-65; RES CHEMIST, AYERST LABS DIV, AYERST, MCKENNA & HARRISON LTD, 65-, SECT HEAD, CHEM DEPT, 80- *Mem:* Am Chem Soc; NY Acad Sci; Chem Inst Can. *Res:* Synthetic organic chemistry; peptide synthesis; drug metabolism; chemistry of odors; synthetic pharmaceuticals; inhibitors aldose reductase. *Mailing Add:* 745 Place Fortier #606 St Laurent PQ H4L 5A6 Can

SETH, KAMAL KISHORE, b Lucknow, India, Mar 10, 33; m 62; c 3. NUCLEAR PHYSICS. *Educ:* Univ Lucknow, BSc, 51 & 53, MSc, 54; Univ Pittsburgh, PhD(physics), 57. *Prof Exp:* Lectr, Univ Pittsburgh, 54-56; res assoc, Brookhaven Nat Lab, 56-57; res assoc, Duke Univ, 57-61; from asst prof to assoc prof, 61-74, PROF PHYSICS, NORTHWESTERN UNIV, EVANSTON, 74- *Concurrent Pos:* Vis scientist, Saclay Nuclear Res Ctr, France, 67; vis prof, Univ Tokyo, 71; consult, Oak Ridge Assocs Univs, Lewis Res Lab, NASA & Oak Ridge Nat Lab. *Mem:* Fel Am Phys Soc. *Res:* Nuclear structure, low and medium energy nuclear spectroscopy; neutron cross sections and charged particle induced reactions; pion spectroscopy. *Mailing Add:* Dept of Physics Northwestern Univ Evanston IL 60201

SETH, RAJINDER SINGH, b Lahore, India, June 11, 37; Can citizen; m 63; c 2. PULP & PAPER TECHNOLOGY. *Educ:* Panjab Univ, India, BSc, 57, MSc, 58; Univ Alberta, Can, PhD(physics), 69. *Prof Exp:* Lectr, DAV Col, India, 58-60, Govt Col, India, 60-64; sr res physicist, Consolidated Bathurst Inc, Can, 69-71; res scientist, 71-77, SR SCIENTIST & HEAD, FIBRE & PAPER PHYSICS SECT, PULP & PAPER RES INST, CAN, 77- *Mem:* Can Asn Physicists; Tech Asn Pulp & Paper Indust; Can Pulp & Paper Asn. *Res:* Structure and physical properties of wood pulp fibres and paper. *Mailing Add:* 570 St John's Blvd Pointe Claire PQ H9R 3J9 Can

SETH, SHARAD CHANDRA, b Madhya Pradesh, India, Nov 1, 42. COMPUTER SCIENCE, ELECTRICAL ENGINEERING. *Educ:* Univ Jabalpur, BE, 64; Indian Inst Technol, Kanpur, MTech, 66; Univ Ill, Urbana, PhD(elec eng), 70. *Prof Exp:* Asst prof, 72-75, ASSOC PROF COMPUT SCI, UNIV NEBR-LINCOLN, 75- *Honors & Awards:* NSF LOCI grant, 77. *Mem:* Asn Comput Mach; Inst Elec & Electronics Engrs. *Res:* Digital systems; design and maintenance of reliable digital systems; theory of automata and formal languages. *Mailing Add:* Dept of Comput Sci Univ of Nebr Lincoln NE 68508

SETHARES, GEORGE C, b Hyannis, Mass, Oct 16, 30; m 52; c 4. MATHEMATICS. *Educ:* Boston Univ, BMus, 53; Univ Mass, MA, 59; Harvard Univ, PhD(math), 67. *Prof Exp:* Instr math, Boston Univ, 59-64; res mathematician, Air Force Cambridge Res Labs, 64-73; assoc prof, 73-80, PROF MATH, BRIDGEWATER STATE COL, 80- *Concurrent Pos:* Lectr, Northeastern Univ, 67-68. *Res:* Analytic function theory; Teichmüller mappings; network theory; automata theory; computer science. *Mailing Add:* Bridgewater State Col Bridgewater MA 02324

SETHARES, JAMES C(OSTAS), b Hyannis, Mass, Dec 13, 28; m 73; c 3. SOLID STATE PHYSICS, ELECTRICAL ENGINEERING. *Educ:* Univ Mass, BSEE, 59; Mass Inst Technol, SMEE, 62. *Prof Exp:* Teaching asst elec eng, Mass Inst Technol, 59-62; RES PHYSICIST, MICROWAVE PHYSICS LAB, AIR FORCE CAMBRIDGE RES LABS, 62- *Concurrent Pos:* Lectr, Boston Univ, 60-63 & Lowell Technol Inst, 63-69. *Honors & Awards:* Marcus D O'Day Mem Award, Air Force Cambridge Res Labs, 69. *Mem:* Inst Elec & Electronics Engrs. *Res:* Microwave magnetics research for analog signal processing directly at microwave frequencies and for tunable nanosecond time delays for phased array antennas; liquid crystal displays for microwaves and millimeter waves. *Mailing Add:* Cambridge Res Labs RADC-EEAC Hanscom AFB Bedford MA 01731

SETHER, LOWELL ALBERT, b Iola, Wis, Aug 5, 31; m 63; c 3. ANATOMY. *Educ:* Concordia Col, Minn, BA, 60; Univ NDak, MS, 62, PhD(anat), 64. *Prof Exp:* Asst prof, 64-74, ASSOC PROF ANAT, MED COL WIS, 74- *Concurrent Pos:* Consult, 25th Ed, Dorlands Med Dictionary. *Mem:* Am Asn Anat. *Res:* Morphology and experimental pathology of bone and cartilage; histology of structure and circulation of tympanic membrane. *Mailing Add:* 4538 Menomonee River Pkwy Milwaukee WI 53225

SETHI, DHANWANT S, b Rawalpindi, WPakistan, Dec 13, 37; m 66; c 2. PHYSICAL CHEMISTRY. *Educ:* Delhi Col, BSc, 56; Hindu Col, MSc, 58; NY Univ, PhD(chem), 67. *Prof Exp:* Jr sci officer, AEC, India, 58-59; tech asst chem, Dir Gen Health Servs, India, 59-62; lectr, NY Univ, 66-67; NSF vis scientist, Nat Ctr Atmospheric Res, Colo, 68-69; asst res geophysicist, Inst Geophys, Univ Calif, Los Angeles, 69; PROF CHEM, UNIV BRIDGEPORT, 69-, CHMN DEPT, 80- *Concurrent Pos:* Res collab, Brookhaven Nat Lab, 72- *Mem:* AAAS; Am Chem Soc; Air Pollution Control Asn. *Res:* Gas phase kinetics, photochemistry, flash photolysis and kinetic absorption spectroscopy. *Mailing Add:* Dept of Chem Univ of Bridgeport Bridgeport CT 06602

SETHI, JITENDER K, b Lahore, India, Oct 16, 39; US citizen; m 64; c 2. PHARMACY, IMMUNOLOGY. *Educ:* Punjab Univ, BS, 60, MS, 62; Univ Iowa, PhD(pharm), 72. *Prof Exp:* Prof serv rep pharmaceut, Pfizer India Ltd, 62-67; res & teaching asst pharm, Univ Iowa, 67-72; fel tumor immunol, Sloan Kettering Inst, NY, 72-74, res assoc immunodiagnosis, 74-81; SR SCIENTIST, WARNER-LAMBERT CO, NJ, 81- *Concurrent Pos:* Instr, Cornell Univ Grad Sch Med Sci, 75-81. *Mem:* Am Asn Cancer Res; Tissue Cult Asn; Brit Soc Immunol. *Res:* Research related to tumor antigens, particularly human sarcomas to determine and to clinically evaluate if these could be of immunodiagnostic value; role and specificity of complement in complement mediated antigen antibody reactions. *Mailing Add:* Warner Lambert Co 170 Tabor Rd Morris Plains NJ 07950

SETHIAN, JOHN DASHO, b Washington, DC, Mar 20, 50; m 77. PLASMA PHYSICS. *Educ:* Princeton Univ, AB, 72; Cornell Univ, MS, 74, PhD(appl physics), 76. *Prof Exp:* Res assoc plasma physics, Univ Md, 76-77; RES PHYSICIST PLASMA PHYSICS, US NAVAL RES LAB, 77- *Mem:* Am Phys Soc. *Res:* Intense relativistic electron beams; electron beam induced CTR magnetic confinement systems; plasma heating and collective ion acceleration; generation and propagation of intense beams. *Mailing Add:* US Naval Res Lab Code 6762 Washington DC 20375

SETHNA, PATARASP R(USTOMJI), b Bombay, India, May 26, 23; nat US; m 54; c 4. MECHANICS, MATHEMATICS. *Educ:* Univ Bombay, BE, 45 & 46; Univ Mich, MSE, 48, PhD(eng mech), 53. *Prof Exp:* Instr, Univ Mich, 52-53; sr engr, Res Lab Div, Bendix Aviation Corp, 53-56; from asst prof to assoc prof, 56-63, PROF AERONAUT & ENG MECH, UNIV MINN, MINNEAPOLIS, 63-, HEAD DEPT, 66- *Concurrent Pos:* Vis prof, Brown Univ, 65-66; vis sr scientist, Univ Calif, Berkeley, 70; vis prof, Univ Warwick, 72; vis scholar, Stanford Univ, 77; comt mem, Nat Res Coun Comt Adv to Air Army Res Off, 78- *Mem:* Am Soc Mech Engrs; Am Inst Aeronaut & Astronaut. *Res:* Dynamical systems; nonlinear oscillation theory; applied mechanics. *Mailing Add:* 107 Aerospace Eng Bldg Univ of Minn Minneapolis MN 55455

SETHNESS, EDWARD DOUGLAS, JR, b San Antonio, Tex, Jan 13, 45. ENVIRONMENTAL ENGINEERING, HYDROLOGY. *Educ:* Univ Tex, Austin, BS, 71, MS, 73. *Prof Exp:* Proj engr hydraul, Gilbert Assocs, Inc, 72-74; sr civil engr hydrol, Radian Corp, 74-76; REGIONAL MGR ENVIRON, CAMP DRESSER & McKEE INC, 76- *Concurrent Pos:* Vpres, Moore & Sethness, Inc, 75- *Mem:* Am Soc Civil Engrs; Soc Mining Engrs; Air Pollution Control Asn; Health Phys Soc. *Res:* Advancement of the offset reflecting surfaces concept for floating breakwaters and working vessels. *Mailing Add:* Camp Dresser & McKee Inc 3445 Executive Center Dr Austin TX 78731

SETHURAMAN, JAYARAM, b Hubli, India, Oct 3, 37; m 65; c 2. MATHEMATICAL STATISTICS, PROBABILITY. *Educ:* Madras Univ, MA, 58; Indian Statist Inst, Calcutta, PhD(statist), 62. *Prof Exp:* Lectr statist, Indian Statist Inst, 61-62; assoc prof, 65-68, PROF STATIST, FLA STATE UNIV, 68- *Concurrent Pos:* Fels, Univ NC, Chapel Hill, 62-63, Mich State Univ, 63-64 & Stanford Univ, 64-65; mem, Indian Statist Inst, 67-; US Army Res Off res grant, 72-82; vis prof statist, Univ Mich, 74-75; vis prof & actg head, Indian Statist Inst, Bangalore, 79-80. *Mem:* Fel Inst Math Statist; fel Am Statist Asn; Int Statist Inst. *Res:* Probability; stochastic processes. *Mailing Add:* Dept Statist Fla State Univ Tallahassee FL 32306

SETHURAMAN, S, b Madras, India, Dec 16, 39; m 66; c 2. METEOROLOGY. *Educ:* Univ Roorkee, ME, 69; Colo State Univ, PhD(fluid mech), 72. *Prof Exp:* Lectr civil eng, Bakthavatsalam Polytech, Madras, 66-69; METEOROLOGIST, BROOKHAVEN NAT LAB, 72- *Mem:* Am Meteorol Soc; Am Geophys Union. *Res:* Geophysics, air-sea interaction, atmospheric turbulence, atmospheric diffusion, planetary boundary layer. *Mailing Add:* Meteorol Brookhaven Nat Lab Upton NY 11973

SETIAN, LEO, b Providence, RI, July 22, 30; m 57; c 5. ELECTRICAL ENGINEERING. *Educ:* Brown Univ, AB, 55; Univ RI, MS, 66; Mont State Univ, PhD(elec eng), 71. *Prof Exp:* Electronic eng, Underwater Sound Lab, 57-63 & Electronics Res Lab, 66-68; from asst prof to assoc prof, 70-79, PROF ELEC ENG, JOHN BROWN UNIV, 79- *Mem:* Am Sci Affiliation. *Res:* Moisture measurement in living foliage using an open-wire transmission line. *Mailing Add:* Dept of Elec Eng John Brown Univ Siloam Springs AR 72761

SETLER, PAULETTE ELIZABETH, b Pittsburgh, Pa, Jan 1, 38. PHARMACOLOGY, PHYSIOLOGY. *Educ:* Seton Hill Col, BA, 59; Univ Pa, PhD(physiol), 70. *Prof Exp:* Res assoc pharmacol, McNeil Labs, 59-62; from jr pharmacologist to pharmacologist, Smith Kline & French Labs, 62-66; instr physiol, Sch Dent Med, Univ Pa, 68; supvr, Churchill Col, Cambridge Univ, 71-72; sr investr pharmacol, Smith Kline & French Labs, 72-77, asst dir biol res, 77-80; WITH MCNEIL PHARMACEUTICAL, 80- *Concurrent Pos:* Res assoc, Physiol Lab, Cambridge Univ, 70-72. *Mem:* Am Physiol Soc; Soc Neurosci; AAAS. *Res:* Pharmacology of biogenic amines as studied behaviorally and biochemically and the interaction of amine neurotransmitters in regulation of behavior; the pharmacology of psychotropic drugs; control of ingestive behavior and body fluid balance. *Mailing Add:* McNeil Pharmaceutical McKean Rd Spring House PA 19477

SETLIFF, EDSON CARMACK, b Indianola, Miss, Nov 3, 41; m 69; c 2. FOREST PATHOLOGY, FOREST MYCOLOGY. *Educ:* NC State Univ, BS, 63; Yale Univ, MF, 64; State Col Environ Sci & Forestry, Syracuse Univ, PhD(forest mycol), 70. *Prof Exp:* Res assoc, Dept Plant Path, Univ Wis, 70-73; res scientist forest path, Cary Arboretum, NY Bot Garden, 73-77; res assoc, Dept Environ & Forest Biol, Col Environ Sci & Forestry, State Univ NY, Syracuse, 77-80; MEM STAFF, FORINTEK CAN CORP, 80- *Concurrent Pos:* Adj assoc prof, Vassar Col, 75- & Univ BC. *Mem:* Am Phytopath Soc; Mycol Soc Am; Sigma Xi. *Res:* Taxonomy of tropical Polyporales; physiology and cultural morphology of wood decay fungi; mushroom culture; etiology of tree root diseases; tree disease diagnosis; cytology and fine structure of Polyporales; wood products pathology. *Mailing Add:* Dept Environ & Forest Biol State Univ NY Syracuse NY 13210

SETLIFF, FRANK LAMAR, b Lake Charles, La, Sept 21, 38; m 62; c 2. ORGANIC CHEMISTRY. *Educ:* McNeese State Univ, BS, 60; Tulane Univ, MS, 62, PhD(org chem), 66. *Prof Exp:* Teaching asst org chem, Tulane Univ, 60-62, res asst, 64-66; asst prof, Little Rock Univ, 66-69; assoc prof, 69-74, chmn dept, 73-75, PROF CHEM, UNIV ARK, LITTLE ROCK, 74- *Mem:* Am Chem Soc; NY Acad Sci; Sigma Xi. *Res:* Small ring compounds; non-benzenoid aromatics; heterocyclic compounds; fluorination reactions. *Mailing Add:* Dept of Chem Univ of Ark Little Rock AR 72204

SETLOW, JANE KELLOCK, b New York, NY, Dec 17, 19; m 42; c 4. BIOPHYSICS. *Educ:* Swarthmore Col, BA, 40; Yale Univ, PhD, 60. *Prof Exp:* Asst biophys, Dept Radiol, Sch Med, Yale Univ, 59-60; biologist, Biol Div, Oak Ridge Nat Lab, 60-74; BIOLOGIST, BIOL DEPT, BROOKHAVEN NAT LAB, 74- *Res:* Molecular biology; ultraviolet action spectra; photoreactivation; cellular repair mechanisms; bacterial recombination. *Mailing Add:* Biol Dept Brookhaven Nat Lab Upton NY 11973

SETLOW, PETER, b New Haven, Conn, June 1, 44; m 65; c 2. BIOCHEMISTRY. *Educ:* Swarthmore Col, BA, 64; Brandeis Univ, PhD(biochem), 69. *Prof Exp:* NSF fel, Stanford Univ, 68-71; from asst prof to assoc prof 71-80, PROF BIOCHEM, UNIV CONN, 80- *Mem:* Am Soc Biol Chemists; Am Soc Microbiol. *Res:* Biochemical regulation of differentiation; bacterial sporulation and germination. *Mailing Add:* Univ Conn Health Ctr Farmington CT 06032

SETLOW, RICHARD BURTON, b New York, NY, Jan 19, 21; m 42; c 4. BIOPHYSICS. *Educ:* Swarthmore Col, AB, 41; Yale Univ, PhD(physics), 47. *Prof Exp:* Asst physics, Med Sch, Yale Univ, 41-42, from asst instr to assoc prof, Univ, 42-61; biophysicist, Oak Ridge Nat Lab, 61-69, sci dir biophys & cell physiol, 69-74; SR BIOPHYSICIST, BROOKHAVEN NAT LAB, 74-, CHMN, BIOL DEPT, 79- *Concurrent Pos:* Prof, Univ Tenn, 67-74, dir, Oak Ridge Grad Sch, 72-74; adj prof biochem, State Univ NY Stony Brook, 75- *Mem:* Nat Acad Sci; Am Acad Arts & Sci; Biophys Soc; Radiation Res Soc; Environ Mutagen Soc. *Res:* Far ultraviolet spectroscopy; ionizing and nonionizing radiation; molecular biophysics; action of light on proteins viruses and cells; nucleic acids; repair mechanisms; environmental carcinogenesis. *Mailing Add:* Biol Dept Brookhaven Nat Lab Upton NY 11973

SETO, BELINDA P L, b Canton, China, July 25, 48; US citizen; m 75; c 1. VIROLOGY. *Educ:* Univ Calif, Davis, BS, 70; Purdue Univ, PhD(microbiol), 74. *Prof Exp:* Staff fel, Nat Heart, Lung & Blood Inst, NIH, 74-80; RES CHEMIST, BUR BIOLOGICS, FOOD & DRUG ADMIN, 80- *Concurrent Pos:* Lectr, Howard Univ, 77. *Mem:* Am Soc Biol Chemists. *Res:* Human non-A and non-B hepatitis to isolate the soluble antigen associated with the hepatitis virus, to develop radioimmunoassay for testing, and structural studies of the viral DNA. *Mailing Add:* 9006 Burdette Rd Bethesda MD 20817

SETO, FRANK, b Los Angeles, Calif, Mar 12, 25; m 55; c 2. ZOOLOGY. *Educ:* Berea Col, BA, 49; Univ Wis, MS, 50, PhD(zool), 53. *Prof Exp:* Asst prof, Exten Div, Univ Wis, 53-56; asst prof zool, Berea Col, 56-62; asst prof, 64-69, assoc prof, 69-80, PROF ZOOL, UNIV OKLA, 81- *Concurrent Pos:* NSF res grant, Berea Col, 60-61; USPHS spec fel, Oak Ridge Nat Lab, 62-64, USPHS res grant, 75; Am Cancer Soc grant, 65-68. *Mem:* Soc Study Evolution; Am Genetics Asn; Am Soc Zoologists; Soc Develop Biologists; Soc Exp Hemat. *Res:* Developmental biology and immunology. *Mailing Add:* Dept Zool Univ Okla Norman OK 73069

SETO, JANE MEI-CHUN, b China, May 15, 27; US citizen; m 58; c 2. INTERNAL MEDICINE. *Educ:* Kwang-Ha Med Col, China, MD, 51; Queen's Univ Belfast, cert med, 57; Tulane Univ, cert trop med, 67. *Prof Exp:* Intern med, Regina Grey Nun's Hosp, Sask, 57-58; resident internal med, Providence Hosp, Seattle, 58-59; physician, Health Ctr, Univ Wash, 59-60; physician, Austin State Sch, Tex, 61-62; res asst cancer chemother, Univ Tex M D Anderson Hosp & Tumor Inst, 64-66; serologist, La State Bd Health, 67-69; instr internal med, Sch Med, 69-70, RES ASSOC ELECTROSCI & BIOPHYS RES GROUP & NIH FEL, SCH ENG, TULANE UNIV, 69- *Mem:* Fel Royal Soc Health; AMA; Am Pub Health Asn. *Res:* Electromagnetic induced biological effects; dynamics of biological cells. *Mailing Add:* 4824 Purdue Dr Metairie LA 70003

SETO, JOSEPH TOBEY, b Tacoma, Wash, Aug 3, 24; m 59; c 2. VIROLOGY, ELECTRON MICROSCOPY. *Educ:* Univ Minn, BS, 49; Univ Wis, MS, 55, PhD(bact), 57. *Prof Exp:* Asst bact, Sch Med, Univ Ill, 50-53; res assoc, Fermentation Div, Upjohn Co, Mich, 57; res virologist, Med Ctr, Univ Calif, Los Angeles, 58-59; asst prof biol, San Francisco State Col, 59-60; from asst prof to assoc prof microbiol, 60-67, chmn dept microbiol & pub health, 64-75, PROF MICROBIOL, CALIF STATE UNIV, LOS ANGELES, 67- *Concurrent Pos:* Consult & res virologist, US Naval Biol Lab, Univ Calif, 60-63; guest prof, Inst Virol, Univ Giessen, 65-66, 72-73 & 79-80; Humboldt Found sr scientist award, 72; WHO res exchange worker, 72. *Mem:* AAAS; Am Soc Microbiol; fel Am Acad Microbiol; Electron Micros Soc Am; NY Acad Sci. *Res:* Characterization of myxovirus and paramyxovirus glycoproteins; electron microscopy of RNA from large RNA viruses; persistent infections of paramyxoviruses in tissue cultures. *Mailing Add:* Dept of Microbiol & Pub Health Calif State Univ Los Angeles CA 90032

SETO, YEB JO, b China, July 31, 30; US citizen; m 58; c 2. ELECTRONICS, PLASMA PHYSICS. *Educ:* Univ Idaho, BS, 57; Univ Wash, MS, 60; Univ Tex, PhD(elec eng), 64. *Prof Exp:* Engr-in-training, Taiwan Power Co, China, 50-51; jr engr, Boeing Airplane Co, Wash, 57-58, res assoc engr, 58-60; from instr to asst prof elec eng, Univ Houston, 60-66; instr, Univ Tex, 61-64; assoc prof, 66-70, PROF ELEC ENG, TULANE UNIV, 70-, DIR ELECTROSCI & BIOPHYS RES GROUP, 69-; PRES & DIR, SEALONG, INC, 72- *Concurrent Pos:* Fac res engr, Univ Tex, 63-64; NSF res grant, 66-67 & 69-72; NIH res grant, 69-72; consult assoc, Advan Technol Consults Corp, 70- *Mem:* AAAS; Inst Elec & Electronics Engrs; Am Phys Soc; Am Soc Eng Educ; Am Soc Oceanog. *Res:* Waves and oscillations in moving and deforming plasma; biological effects of microwave; quantum effects in DNA. *Mailing Add:* Dept of Elec Eng Tulane Univ New Orleans LA 70118

SETSER, CAROLE SUE, b Warrenton, Mo, Aug 26, 40; m 69; c 3. FOOD SCIENCE. *Educ:* Univ Mo-Columbia, BS, 62; Cornell Univ, MS, 64; Kans State Univ, PhD(foods, nutrit), 71. *Prof Exp:* Instr food sci, 64-66, asst to dean col home econ, 66-68, asst prof, 74-81, ASSOC PROF FOOD SCI, KANS STATE UNIV, 81- *Mem:* Inst Food Technologists; Am Home Econ Asn; Sigma Xi; Am Asn Cereal Chemists; Am Meat Sci Asn. *Res:* Sensory physical and chemical evaluation of nutritive and oxidative changes in foods; functions of hydrocolloids in baked products. *Mailing Add:* Dept of Foods & Nutrit Kans State Univ Manhattan KS 66506

SETSER, DONALD W, b Great Bend, Kans, Jan 2, 35; m 69; c 3. PHYSICAL CHEMISTRY. *Educ:* Kans State Univ, BS, 54, MS, 56; Univ Wash, PhD(phys chem), 61. *Prof Exp:* Fel phys chem, Univ Wash, 61-62; NSF fel, Cambridge Univ, 62-63; from asst prof to assoc prof, 63-69, PROF PHYS CHEM, KANS STATE UNIV, 70- *Concurrent Pos:* Alfred P Sloan fel, 68-70. *Honors & Awards:* Midwest Award, Am Chem Soc, 81. *Mem:* Am Chem Soc; Am Phys Soc; Royal Soc Chem. *Res:* Chemical kinetics; spectroscopy of small molecules; energy transfer. *Mailing Add:* Dept of Chem Kans State Univ Manhattan KS 66502

SETTERFIELD, GEORGE AMBROSE, b Halifax, NS, Aug 29, 29; m 51; c 5. CYTOLOGY. *Educ:* Univ BC, BA, 51; Univ Wis, PhD(bot), 54. *Prof Exp:* Instr genetics & cytol, Univ BC, 54-56; asst res officer biophys, Nat Res Coun Can, 56-57, assoc res officer, 58-62; assoc prof, 62-64, chmn dept, 63-68, PROF BIOL, CARLETON UNIV, 64- *Concurrent Pos:* Vis prof, Laval Univ, 68-69; assoc ed, Can J Botany, 70-78 & Can J Biochem, 77-; mem adv comt biol, Nat Res Coun Can, 72-75, mem grant selection comt plant biol, 72-76, chmn, 74-75; mem adv comt acad planning, Coun Ont Univs, 73-; vis scientist, Nat Res Coun Lab, Saskatoon, Sask, 77-78. *Mem:* AAAS; fel Royal Soc Can; Can Soc Plant Physiologists; Can Soc Cell Biol (pres, 74-75); Soc Develop Biologists. *Res:* Experimental cytology; relation of structure to function in plant cells; plant hormones and growth processes; somatic cell genetics of plants; physiology of cell division; fine structure of nuclei. *Mailing Add:* Dept Biol Carleton Univ Ottawa ON K1S 5B6 Can

SETTERGREN, CARL DAVID, b Chicago, Ill, Dec 12, 35; m 65; c 1. FORESTRY, WATERSHED MANAGEMENT. *Educ:* Univ Mo, BSF, 58, MS, 60; Colo State Univ, PhD(watershed mgt), 67. *Prof Exp:* From instr ecol to assoc prof forest hydrol, 64-77, PROF FOREST HYDROL, UNIV MO-COLUMBIA, 77- *Mem:* Soc Am Foresters; Am Water Resources Asn. *Res:* Forest hydrology; forest influences. *Mailing Add:* Sch of Forestry Univ of Mo Columbia MO 65201

SETTERQUIST, ROBERT ALTON, polymer chemistry, organometallic chemistry, see previous edition

SETTERSTROM, CARL A(LBERT), b Brooklyn, NY, May 2, 15; m 40; c 2. CHEMICAL ENGINEERING. *Educ:* Polytech Inst, Brooklyn, BChE, 36. *Prof Exp:* Sci asst plant physiol, Boyce Thompson Inst Plant Res, 36-40; from tech rep to gen mgr, Textile Fibers Dept, Union Carbide Corp, 40-54; spec projs mgr, Chas Pfizer & Co, Inc, 54-58; asst dir, Res & Develop Div, Sun Oil Co, 58-59; asst to pres, Avisun Corp, 59; gen mgr mkt, 60; vpres, Rexall Chem Co, NJ, 60-68; MANAGING PARTNER, HARRINGTON RES CO, 68- *Concurrent Pos:* Pres, PNC Co, 70-79. *Mem:* Am Chem Soc; Commercial Develop Asn; Am Inst Chemists. *Res:* New product development; corporate acquisitions and evaluations; marketing of polymers; corporate profit strategies; plastics and fibers technology. *Mailing Add:* 11 Timberline Rd Hohokus NJ 07423

SETTINE, ROBERT LOUIS, b Newburgh, NY, Nov 23, 32; c 2. ORGANIC CHEMISTRY. *Educ:* Fla State Univ, BS, 55, MS, 58; Univ Colo, PhD, 62. *Prof Exp:* Chemist, Naval Stores Lab, USDA, 55-56 & 60-61, Fruit & Veg Lab, 62-63 & Naval Stores Lab, 63-64; asst prof pharmaceut chem, Univ Miss, 64-69; ASSOC PROF CHEM, UNIV ALA, BIRMINGHAM, 69-, DIR, GC/MS CTR, 77- *Mem:* Am Chem Soc (treas, 72); Sigma Xi. *Res:* Terpene chemistry; natural products related to tetrahydracannibinols. *Mailing Add:* Dept of Chem Univ of Ala Birmingham AL 35294

SETTLE, DOROTHY MILLER, b Hutchinson, Kans, Apr 3, 25; m 53. ANALYTICAL CHEMISTRY, RADIOCHEMISTRY. *Educ:* Southeast Mo State Col, BS & BA, 45; Univ Iowa, MS, 47. *Prof Exp:* Instr chem, San Diego State Col, 48-52; anal chemist geol, Calif Inst Technol, 57-59; Univ Calif, San Diego, 60-62; radio chemist, Gulf Gen Atomic, San Diego, 63-68; anal chemist geochem, 68-77, SR SCIENTIST BIOGEOCHEM, CALIF INST TECHNOL, 77- *Mem:* Am Chem Soc. *Res:* Natural occurrences of lead and alkalinc earths in plants, animals and waters of marine and terrestrial ecosystems and in the atmosphere by stable isotope dilution analyses using ultra-clean techniques. *Mailing Add:* Div of Geol & Planetary Sci Calif Inst of Technol Pasadena CA 91125

SETTLE, FRANK ALEXANDER, JR, b Nashville, Tenn, Sept 19, 37; wid; c 3. ANALYTICAL CHEMISTRY. *Educ:* Emory & Henry Col, BS, 60; Univ Tenn, PhD(chem), 64. *Prof Exp:* From asst prof to assoc prof, 64-74, PROF CHEM, VA MIL INST, 74- *Concurrent Pos:* NSF res fel, Va Polytech Inst & State Univ, 72-73; instr, Am Chem Soc Comput & Electronics Short Courses, 72-73 & 75-76; consult, NSF Comput Enriched Module Proj, Ill Inst Technol, 74-76 & Tenn Eastman Co, 77; instr, Microprocessor Short Courses, Va Mil Inst, 76 & 78; consult, Bendix Environ & Process Instruments Div,

79; proj dir, Sci Instrument Info & Curricula Proj, 80- *Mem:* Am Chem Soc. *Res:* Computer interfacing of chemical instrumentation; computer-based information systems. *Mailing Add:* Dept of Chem Va Mil Inst Lexington VA 24450

SETTLE, RICHARD GREGG, b Ft Worth, Tex, Sept 4, 49; m 72. NEUROPSYCHOLOGY, PSYCHOPHYSICS. *Educ:* Colgate Univ, BA, 72; Univ Mo-Columbia, MA, 73, PhD(psychol), 75. *Prof Exp:* Fel psychol, Monell Chem Senses Ctr, 75-80, ASSOC RES DEPT SURG, UNIV PA, 80- *Mem:* AAAS. *Res:* Structure and function of the hippocampus; neuroanatomical and physiological basis of learning and memory; genetic and environmental influences on alcoholism in humans and alcohol consumption in animals; taste sensation and perception. *Mailing Add:* Monell Chem Senses Ctr Univ of Pa Philadelphia PA 19104

SETTLE, WILBUR JEWELL, b Barren Co, Ky. BOTANY. *Educ:* Centre Col, Ky, AB, 62; Ohio State Univ, MSc, 65, PhD(bot), 69. *Prof Exp:* Asst prof biol, Bowling Green State Univ, 69-70; asst prof, 70-80, ASSOC PROF BIOL, STATE UNIV NY COL ONEONTA, 80- *Concurrent Pos:* Res Found State Univ NY fac res fel, 71. *Mem:* AAAS; Bot Soc Am; Am Soc Plant Taxonomists; Int Asn Plant Taxonomists; Soc Econ Bot. *Res:* Plant biosystematics, especially the genus Blephilia. *Mailing Add:* Dept of Biol State Univ of NY Oneonta NY 13820

SETTLEMIRE, CARL THOMAS, b Dayton, Ohio, July 14, 37; m 60; c 3. BIOCHEMISTRY. *Educ:* Ohio State Univ, BS, 59, MS, 61; NC State Univ, PhD(biochem), 67. *Prof Exp:* Instr nutrit, Ohio Agr Res & Develop Ctr, 61-62; NIH trainee biochem, NC State Univ, 62-66; NIH fel, Ohio State Univ, 66-69; asst prof biochem, 69-74, ASSOC PROF BIOL & CHEM, BOWDOIN COL, 74- *Concurrent Pos:* Mem, Nat Student Support Rev Comt, Dept Health, Educ & Welfare, 68-70. *Mem:* AAAS; Am Chem Soc. *Res:* Membrane biochemistry and ion transport in whole cells and in mitochondria; membrane changes in cystic fibrosis. *Mailing Add:* Dept Chem Bowdoin Col Brunswick ME 04011

SETTLEMYER, KENNETH THEODORE, b Arnold, Pa, Dec 19, 35; m 64; c 3. TAXONOMIC BOTANY. *Educ:* Pa State Univ, BS, 57, MEd, 61, DEd(biol sci), 71. *Prof Exp:* Instr biol, Freeport Area Joint Schs, Pa, 57-66; from asst prof to assoc prof, 66-72, chmn dept, 78-81, PROF BIOL SCI, LOCK HAVEN STATE COL, 72- *Concurrent Pos:* Partic, NSF Inserv Inst, Univ Pittsburgh, 60-61. *Mem:* AAAS; Am Inst Biol Sci; Nat Asn Biol Teachers; Bot Soc Am; Am Soc Plant Taxonomists. *Res:* Taxonomy of woody plants. *Mailing Add:* Dept of Biol Sci Lock Haven State Col Lock Haven PA 17745

SETTLES, GARY STUART, b Maryville, Tenn, Oct, 9, 49. TURBULENT & SEPARATED FLOWS. *Educ:* Univ Tenn, BS, 71, PhD(mech & aerospace eng), 76. *Prof Exp:* Res scientist, Princeton Combustion Labs, Div Flow Res Corp, 75-77; RES SCIENTIST & LECTR FLUID MECH, MECH & AEROSPACE ENG DEPT, PRINCETON UNIV, 77- *Concurrent Pos:* Consult, Ketron, Inc, 79-, Am Meter Div, Singer Corp, 80-81, Aerodyn Lab, Boeing Com Airplane Co, 80-81. *Mem:* Am Inst Aeronaut & Astronaut; Am Soc Mech Engrs; Optical Soc Am; Soc Photo-Optical Instrumentation Engrs; AAAS. *Res:* Fluid mechanics, specializing in experimental methods, high-speed flows, turbulent boundary layers, and shock waves; optical flow visualization techniques, especially schlieren methods; energy conservation; scientific writing and photography; combustion. *Mailing Add:* 4 Halsey Rd Kendall Park NJ 08824

SETTLES, HARRY EMERSON, b Denver, Colo, Dec 19, 40; m 67; c 3. ANATOMY. *Educ:* Wabash Col, AB, 63; Tulane Univ, PhD(anat), 67. *Prof Exp:* From instr to asst prof anat, NY Med Col, 69-78; ASST PROF ANAT, UNIV S DAK, 78- *Mem:* Sigma Xi; AAAS. *Res:* Experimental embryology; regeneration; electron microscopy. *Mailing Add:* Dept of Anat Univ of SDak Sch of Med Vermillion SD 57069

SETTLES, RONALD DEAN, b Lawrence, Kans, Feb 12, 38; m 63; c 3. PHYSICS, MATHEMATICS. *Educ:* Va Polytech Inst, BS, 59, MS, 61; La State Univ, PhD(physics), 64. *Prof Exp:* SR STAFF PARTICLE PHYSICS, MAX PLANCK INST PHYSICS & ASTROPHYS, 64- *Res:* Elementary particle physics; ultra-high energy cosmic ray interactions. *Mailing Add:* Max Planck Inst for Physics & Astrophys D-8000 Munich 40 Fohringer Ring 6 Germany

SETTOON, PATRICK DELANO, b Amite, La, Feb 15, 34; m 56; c 3. BIOCHEMISTRY, FOOD CHEMISTRY. *Educ:* Southeastern La Univ, BS, 57; La State Univ, Baton Rouge, MS, 61, PhD, 67. *Prof Exp:* Chemist, Union Carbide Corp, 57-58; from instr to assoc prof, 58-69, prof chem & chmn dept chem & physics, 69-80, DEAN, COL SCI & TECHNOL, SOUTHEASTERN LA UNIV, 80- *Mem:* Am Inst Chemists; Am Chem Soc. *Res:* Mechanisms involved in food decomposition; accessory growth factors for microorganisms. *Mailing Add:* Southeastern La Univ Box 401 Hammond LA 70401

SETZLER-HAMILTON, EILEEN MARIE, b Fremont, Ohio, Apr 28, 43; m 79. MARINE ECOLOGY, FISH BIOLOGY. *Educ:* Col of St Mary of Springs, BA, 65; Univ Del, MS, 69; Univ Ga, PhD(zool), 77. *Prof Exp:* Fisheries biologist, Southwest Fisheries Ctr, Nat Marine Fisheries Serv, Nat Oceanic & Atmospheric Admin, 74; RES ASSOC FISH ECOL, CTR ENVIRON & ESTUARINE STUDIES, CHESAPEAKE BIOL LAB, UNIV MD, 75- *Mem:* Am Fisheries Soc; Sigma Xi; Estuarine Res Fedn; Atlantic Estuarine Res Soc (secy-treas, 78-79). *Res:* Fish ecology; population dynamics of estuarine species; estuarine food webs; larval and juvenile fish biology; roles of fish in energetics of estuarine nursery areas; striped bass biology. *Mailing Add:* Ctr Environ & Estuarine Studies Chesapeake Biol Lab Univ Md PO Box 38 Solomons MD 20688

SEUBOLD, FRANK HENRY, JR, b Chicago, Ill, Nov 16, 22; m 42; c 2. ORGANIC CHEMISTRY, PUBLIC HEALTH ADMINISTRATION. *Educ:* Northwestern Univ, BS, 43; Univ Calif, Los Angeles, PhD(chem), 48. *Prof Exp:* Jr chemist, Shell Develop Co, 43-45, chemist, 47-52; asst prof chem, Northwestern Univ, 52-54; res chemist, Union Oil Co Calif, 54-59; sr chemist, Aerojet-Gen Corp Div, Gen Tire & Rubber Co, 59-63, tech dept mgr, Space-Gen Corp, Calif, 63-71; dir proj mgt & planning div, Health Maintenance Orgn Serv, Health Serv & Ment Health Admin, 71-74, assoc bur dir, Health Serv Admin, 74-76, dir div health maintenance orgns, Bur Med Serv, Health Serv Admin, 76-77, dir div health maintenance develop, Off Asst Secy Health, 77-78, dep dir, Div Intramural Res, Nat Ctr Health Serv Res,79-81, DIR, HEALTH MAINTENANCE ORGNS, OFF ASST SECY HEALTH, DEPT HEALTH & HUMAN SERV, 80- *Mem:* Am Chem Soc. *Res:* Mechanisms of organic reactions free radical processes; oxidations of hydrocarbons; reaction of organic peroxides; polymerization; heterogeneous catalysis; solid rocket propellants; encapsulation; immunochemistry; biological and chemical detection systems and instrumentation; health care delivery systems; health maintenance organization; health services research. *Mailing Add:* Off Health Maintenance Orgns 12420 Parklawn Dr Rockville MD 20857

SEUFERT, LUDWIG E, organic chemistry, inorganic chemistry, see previous edition

SEUFERT, WOLF D, b Düsseldorf, Ger, Apr 17, 35; m 61; c 2. BIOPHYSICS, MOLECULAR BIOLOGY. *Educ:* Univ Dusseldorf, Dr Med, 60. *Hon Degrees:* DSc, Univ Provence Marseille, 79. *Prof Exp:* Intern med, Hosp Nördlingen, Ger, 61-62; res assoc physiol, Univ Heidelberg, 63-64; med res scientist, Dept Basic Res, Eastern Pa Psychiat Inst, 64-65; guest investr biophys, Rockefeller Univ, 66-67; asst prof, 67-70, ASSOC PROF BIOPHYS, FAC MED, UNIV SHERBROOKE, 70- *Mem:* Biophys Soc. *Res:* Physico-chemical characteristics of biological membranes and membrane models; medical instrumentation; biomedical engineering. *Mailing Add:* Dept of Biophys Univ of Sherbrooke Fac of Med Sherbrooke PQ J1H 5N4 Can

SEUFZER, PAUL RICHARD, b Cleveland, Ohio, Dec 23, 21; m 44. INORGANIC CHEMISTRY, RESEARCH ADMINISTRATION. *Educ:* Western Reserve Univ, BS, 43, MS, 49, PhD(inorg chem), 51. *Prof Exp:* Anal chemist, Harshaw Chem Co, 43-44; shift foreman, Tenn Eastman Corp & Corps Engrs, US Army, Tenn, 44-46; res chemist, Argonne Nat Lab, 51-53; supvr chem dept, 53-63, SUPT DEVELOP LAB, TECH DIV, GOODYEAR ATOMIC CORP, 63- *Mem:* AAAS; Am Chem Soc. *Res:* Physical inorganic chemistry of fluorine and uranium. *Mailing Add:* Develop Lab Tech Div Goodyear Atomic Corp Piketon OH 45661

SEUGLING, EARL WILLIAM, JR, b Little Falls, NJ, Jan 6, 33; m 66; c 3. PHARMACY, CHEMICAL ENGINEERING. *Educ:* Rutgers Univ, BS, 55; Ohio State Univ, MSc, 57, PhD(pharm), 61. *Prof Exp:* Sr pharmaceut scientist, Vick Div Res, Richardson Merrell Inc, 60-63; res mgr, Res Dept, Strong Cobb Arner Inc, 63-65, dir res, 65-69; dir res, Block Drug Co, 69-78; CONSULT PHARMACEUT/DENT, COSMETIC, TOILETRIES DEVELOP, QUAL CONTROL /QUAL ASSURANCE PROD, 78- *Mem:* Am Pharmaceut Asn; Acad Pharmaceut Sci; Am Inst Chem Eng; Am Chem Soc. *Res:* Ionic and adsorptive exchange reactions in pharmaceutical sciences; product and process development, specifically, improved granulation, compression and advanced tablet coating techniques; development of dental, pharmaceutical, cosmetic and toiletry products; research administration; technical management. *Mailing Add:* PO Box 1295 44 Courtney Pl Palm Coast FL 32037

SEUS, EDWARD J, b New York, NY, Jan 30, 35; m 57; c 4. ORGANIC CHEMISTRY, PHOTOGRAPHIC CHEMISTRY. *Educ:* Queens Col, NY, BS, 56; Univ Minn, PhD(org chem), 60. *Prof Exp:* Res chemist, Chem Div, 60-65, sr res chemist, Photo Mat Div, 65-72, tech assoc Film Emulsion Div, 72-75, SUPVR DEVELOP COLOR PRODS, EASTMAN KODAK CO, 75- *Honors & Awards:* R Max Goepp, Jr Mem Prize Chem, 56. *Mem:* Am Chem Soc; Soc Photograph Scientists & Engrs. *Res:* Synthesis of olefins via organophorous intermediates; chemistry of stilbenes; Vilsmeier formylation; preparation of photomaterials; development of color films. *Mailing Add:* Eastman Kodak Co Kodak Park Bldg 30 Rochester NY 14650

SEVACHERIAN, VAHRAM, b Nov 25, 42; US citizen. ENTOMOLOGY, APPLIED STATISTICS. *Educ:* Univ Calif, Los Angeles, BA, 64; Calif State Univ, Los Angeles, MA, 66; Univ Calif, Riverside, PhD(entom), 70. *Prof Exp:* Asst zool, Calif State Univ, Los Angeles, 64-66; res asst entom, 66-70, lectr entom, asst res entomologist, lectr statist & asst res statistician, 71-72, asst prof, 72-81, ASSOC PROF STATIST & ENTOM, UNIV CALIF, RIVERSIDE, 81- *Mem:* Entom Soc Am; Ecol Soc Am; Entom Soc Can; Am Statist Soc. *Res:* Systems analysis; sampling techniques; statistical ecology; integrated pest management; economic thresholds in agriculture. *Mailing Add:* Dept Entom Univ Calif Riverside CA 92521

SEVALL, JACK SANDERS, b Jan 12, 46; US citizen. BIOCHEMISTRY. *Educ:* Willamette Univ, BA, 67; Purdue Univ, PhD(biochem), 71. *Prof Exp:* Lab instr biochem, Purdue Univ, 69-70; res assoc biol, Calif Inst Technol, 71-74; asst prof biochem, Tex Tech Univ, 74-80; SR SCIENTIST, WADLEY INSTS MOLECULAR MED, 80- *Concurrent Pos:* Damon Runyon Mem Fund Cancer Res fel, Calif Inst Technol, 72-74; NSF res grant, 75, NIH res grants, 76-79 & 81-84, Roger A Welch res grant, 77-80. *Mem:* Soc Cell Biol; Biophys Soc; AAAS; Am Soc Biol Chemists. *Res:* Eukaryotic gene structure; nonhistone chromosomal protein role in gene structure and function. *Mailing Add:* Dept of Chem Tex Tech Univ Lubbock TX 79409

SEVENAIR, JOHN P, b Somerville, NJ, Oct 12, 43. BIO-ORGANIC CHEMISTRY. *Educ:* Mass Inst Technol, BS, 65; Univ Notre Dame, PhD(chem), 70. *Prof Exp:* Res assoc chem, Ga Inst Technol, 69-71 & Univ Ala, 71-72; teaching res fel, Tulane Univ, 72-74; ASST PROF CHEM, XAVIER UNIV, 74- *Mem:* Am Chem Soc; Nat Speleol Soc. *Res:* Model systems for the elucidation of biological reaction pathways; chemistry of humic substances. *Mailing Add:* Dept of Chem Xavier Univ New Orleans LA 70125

SEVENANTS, MICHAEL R, b Two Rivers, Wis, Mar 16, 38; m 62; c 3. FOOD CHEMISTRY. *Educ:* Univ Calif, Davis, BS, 61, PhD(agr chem), 65. *Prof Exp:* CHEMIST, PROCTOR & GAMBLE CO, 65-, GROUP LEADER, 70- *Mem:* Am Chem Soc; Am Oil Chemists Soc. *Res:* Chemical identification and sensory correlation of natural flavorous components in foods. *Mailing Add:* Procter & Gamble Co 6071 Center Hill Ave Cincinnati OH 45224

SEVENICH, RICHARD ANTHONY, b St Paul, Minn, Dec 20, 40; m 61; c 4. REACTOR PHYSICS. *Educ:* Col St Thomas, BS, 62; Iowa State Univ, PhD(physics), 67. *Prof Exp:* Assoc prof physics, Univ Wis-Platteville, 67-74; sr scientist core physics, Hanford Eng Develop Lab, 74-80; assoc prof nuclear eng, Joint Ctr Grad Study, 78-80; MEM FAC, PHYSICS DEPT, UNIV WIS, PLATTEVILLE, 80- *Mem:* Am Nuclear Soc; Am Asn Physics Teachers; Sigma Xi. *Res:* Neutron kinetics of nuclear reactors. *Mailing Add:* Physics Dept Univ Wis Platteville WI 53818

SEVER, DAVID MICHAEL, b Canton, Ohio, Feb 21, 48; m 69; c 2. HERPETOLOGY. *Educ:* Ohio Univ, BS, 70, MS, 71; Tulane Univ, PhD(biol), 74. *Prof Exp:* Asst prof, 74-77, ASSOC PROF BIOL, ST MARY'S COL, IND, 77-, CHMN DEPT, 80- *Concurrent Pos:* Res grants, Highlands Biol Sta Inc, 73 & 75, Ind Acad Sci 75, Am Philos Soc, 77 & Nat Res Soc, 79. *Mem:* AAAS; Am Inst Biol Sci; Am Soc Icthyologists & Herpetologists; Herpetologists League; Soc Study Amphibians & Reptiles. *Res:* Systematics, ecology and morphology of salamanders. *Mailing Add:* Dept of Biol St Mary's Col Notre Dame IN 46556

SEVER, JOHN LOUIS, b Chicago, Ill, Apr 11, 32; m 56; c 3. PEDIATRICS, MICROBIOLOGY. *Educ:* Univ Chicago, BA, 51; Northwestern Univ, BS, 52, MS, 56, MD, PhD(microbiol), 57. *Prof Exp:* Instr microbiol, Med Sch, Northwestern Univ, 54-60; head sect infectious dis, Nat Inst Neurol Dis & Stroke, 60-71; assoc prof, 63-73, PROF PEDIAT, SCH MED, GEORGETOWN UNIV, 73-, PROF OBSTET & GYNEC, 80-; CHIEF INFECTIOUS DIS BR, NAT INST NEUROL & COMMUN DISORDERS, DIS & STROKE, 71- *Concurrent Pos:* Resident pediat, Chicago Children's Mem Hosp, Ill, 57-60; mem res & clin staff, DC Children's Hosp. *Mem:* Am Soc Microbiol; AMA; Soc Pediat Res; Am Asn Immunologists; Am Epidemol Soc. *Res:* Infectious diseases; virology; perinatal infections; vaccines; chronic infections of central nervous system. *Mailing Add:* Nat Inst of Neurol & Commun Disorders Bethesda MD 20205

SEVERANCE, DEAN CHARLES, b Chester, Vt, Sept 8, 23; m 55; c 2. PHYSICS. *Educ:* Univ Vt, BS, 44, MS, 51. *Prof Exp:* From instr to asst prof physics, Tex Tech Col, 56-61; asst prof, 61-63, ASSOC PROF PHYSICS, NORWICH UNIV, 63- *Mem:* AAAS; Am Asn Physics Teachers. *Res:* Elementary particle theory; basic concepts of physics. *Mailing Add:* Dept of Physics Norwich Univ Northfield VT 05663

SEVERIN, CHARLES HILARION, b Bendena, Kans, Sept 3, 96. BOTANY. *Educ:* Univ Chicago, BS, 25, MS, 27, PhD(bot), 30. *Hon Degrees:* LLD, St Mary's Col, Minn, 75. *Prof Exp:* High sch teacher, De La Salle Inst, 20-33; prof, 33-75, EMER PROF BIOL, ST MARY'S COL, MINN, 75- *Concurrent Pos:* Asst, Univ Chicago, 30; instr, De Paul Univ, 32-33. *Mem:* AAAS; Bot Soc Am; Ecol Soc Am; Am Genetic Asn; hon mem Nat Asn Biol Teachers (pres, 55). *Res:* Plant anatomy and ecology; morphology of botany; anatomy of roots of the lower monocotyls; anatomy of roots and seedlings of emergent spermatophytes. *Mailing Add:* Dept of Biol St Mary's Col Winona MN 55987

SEVERIN, CHARLES MATTHEW, b Youngstown, Ohio, Dec 4, 48. NEUROANATOMY. *Educ:* St Louis Univ, BA, 70, MS, 72, PhD(anat), 75. *Prof Exp:* Asst anat, Sch Med, St Louis Univ, 73-74; ASST PROF ANAT, UNIV TEX MED BR GALVESTON, 78- *Mem:* Sigma Xi; Soc Neurosci. *Res:* Efferent projections of the globus pallidus, using selective silver impregnation, autoradiography and horseradish peroxidase. *Mailing Add:* Dept of Anat Univ of Tex Med Br Galveston TX 77550

SEVERIN, MATTHEW JOSEPH, b Omaha, Nebr, Aug 7, 33; m 58; c 4. MEDICAL MICROBIOLOGY. *Educ:* Creighton Univ, BS, 55, MS, 60; Univ Nebr, PhD(med microbiol), 68. *Prof Exp:* Bacteriologist, Clin Labs, Immanuel Hosp, Omaha, 58-60; asst prof biol, Univ Omaha, 61-63; dir labs, Omaha-Douglas County Health Dept, 63-73; PROF MED MICROBIOL, CREIGHTON UNIV, 72-, DEAN STUDENTS, SCH MED, 75- *Concurrent Pos:* USPHS grants, 63-; lectr, Col St Mary, Nebr, 67-75; asst prof, Sch Med, Creighton Univ, 68-; asst prof, Col Med, Univ Nebr, 72-77; lectr, St Joseph's Sch Nursing, 72- *Mem:* Fel Am Soc Clin Scientists; Am Soc Microbiol; fel Am Pub Health Asn; Infectious Dis Soc Am. *Res:* Venereal disease agents and streptococcal disease agents and their chemotherapeutic sensitivities. *Mailing Add:* Med Dean's Off Creighton Univ Sch of Med Omaha NE 68178

SEVERINGHAUS, CHARLES WILLIAM, b Ithaca, NY, Sept 3, 16; m 41, 71; c 3. WILDLIFE MANAGEMENT. *Educ:* Cornell Univ, BS, 39. *Prof Exp:* Conserv worker, State Conserv Dept, 39-41, asst game res investr, 41, game res investr, 41-59, dist game mgr, 41-44, leader deer mgt res, 44-56, leader big game mgt invests, 56-61, supv wildlife biologist, 61-74, prin wildlife biologist, 74-77; RETIRED. *Concurrent Pos:* Consult wildlife biologist, Cornell Univ, 77- *Honors & Awards:* Achievement Award, Wildlife Soc, 51; Conserv Award, Am Motors Corp, 62; Wildlife Conservationist Award, Nat Wildlife Fedn & Sears-Roebuck Found, 65; Conserv Award, Sullivan County, NY, 66. *Mem:* Wildlife Soc; Am Soc Mammalogists. *Res:* Game management; life history, population dynamics, ecology, reproduction and management of white-tailed deer and black bear. *Mailing Add:* 4665 Picard Rd Voorheesville NY 12186

SEVERINGHAUS, JOHN WENDELL, b Madison, Wis, May 6, 22; m 48; c 4. MEDICINE. *Educ:* Haverford Col, BS, 43; Columbia Univ, MD, 49; Am Bd Anesthesiol, dipl, 58. *Hon Degrees:* Dr med, Univ Copenhagen, Denmark, 79. *Prof Exp:* Staff physicist, Radiation Lab, Mass Inst Technol, 43-45; staff physician, Sage Hosp, Ganado, Ariz, 51 & Embudo Hosp, NMex, 51; res assoc physiol, Univ Pa, 51-53; sr asst surgeon, Clin Ctr, USPHS, 53-56, surgeon, 56-58; from asst prof to assoc prof, 58-65, PROF ANESTHESIA, MED CTR, UNIV CALIF, SAN FRANCISCO, 65-, DIR ANESTHESIA RES, CARDIOVASC RES INST, 58- *Concurrent Pos:* Fel, Fac Anesthetists, Royal Col Surgeons, London, 75. *Mem:* Am Soc Anesthesiol; Am Physiol Soc; Am Soc Clin Invest; NY Acad Sci. *Res:* Pulmonary physiology; control of respiration; physiologic effects in anesthesia; electrodes for blood and tissue oxygen and carbon dioxide tension. *Mailing Add:* Dept Anesthesia Univ Calif Med Ctr San Francisco CA 94122

SEVERN, CHARLES B, pediatrics, neonatology, see previous edition

SEVERNS, WILLIAM H(ARRISON), JR, chemical engineering, see previous edition

SEVERS, WALTER BRUCE, b Pittsburgh, Pa, June 10, 38; m 70; c 5. PHARMACOLOGY. *Educ:* Univ Pittsburgh, BS, 60, MS, 63, PhD(pharmacol), 65. *Prof Exp:* Instr pharmacol, Univ Pittsburgh, 64-65; USPHS fel, 65-66; USPHS fel, Lab Chem Pharmacol, Nat Heart Inst, 66-68; from asst prof to assoc prof, 68-77, PROF PHARMACOL, HERSHEY MED CTR, PA STATE UNIV, 77- *Concurrent Pos:* Asst prof, Ohio Northern Univ, 65-66. *Mem:* AAAS; Am Soc Pharmacol & Exp Therapeut; Am Fedn Clin Res; Am Physiol Soc; Sigma Xi. *Res:* Hypertension; renin-angiotensin system; interaction between angiotensin and the central nervous system; salt/water balance. *Mailing Add:* Dept of Pharmacol Pa State Univ Hershey Med Ctr Hershey PA 17033

SEVERSIKE, LEVERNE K, b Des Moines, Iowa, Nov 5, 36. AEROSPACE ENGINEERING. *Educ:* Iowa State Univ, BS, 58, MS, 61, PhD(aerospace eng), 64. *Prof Exp:* Res asst gas dynamics, Eng Exp Sta, 60-63, from instr to asst prof, 63-76, ASSOC PROF AEROSPACE ENG, IOWA STATE UNIV, 76- *Mem:* Am Inst Aeronaut & Astronaut; Am Astronaut Soc; Am Soc Aerospace Educ; Planetary Soc. *Res:* Vehicle flight mechanics; flight and reentry trajectories; optimization techniques; gas dynamics; optimal controls. *Mailing Add:* 2961 Northwestern Ames IA 50010

SEVERSON, ARLEN RAYNOLD, b Clarkfield, Minn, Dec 5, 39; m 62; c 4. BIOLOGICAL STRUCTURE, CELL PHYSIOLOGY. *Educ:* Concordia Col, Moorhead, Minn, BA, 61; Univ NDak, MS, 63, PhD(anat), 65. *Prof Exp:* Res collabr histochem, Brookhaven Nat Lab, 65-67; asst prof anat, Sch Med, Ind Univ, Indianapolis, 67-72, res assoc orthop, 68-69; assoc prof, 72-79, PROF BIOMED ANAT, SCH MED, UNIV MINN, DULUTH, 79- *Concurrent Pos:* USPHS fel, 65-67, spec fel, 71; guest worker, Nat Inst Dent Res, Md, 71; res collabr hemat, Brookhaven Nat Lab, 76; assoc ed, Anat Rec, 78-; consult ed, Gerodont, 82- *Mem:* Am Asn Anatomists; Am Soc Cell Biol. *Res:* Histochemistry, biochemistry and cellular physiology of connective tissue, bone and teeth; proteoglycan and collagen metabolism; bone cell origin and metabolism; effects of hormones on connective tissue, bone and cartilage metabolism; hematology. *Mailing Add:* Dept Biomed Anat Sch Med Univ Minn Duluth MN 55812

SEVERSON, DONALD E(VERETT), b Minneapolis, Minn, Dec 16, 19; m 47; c 5. CHEMICAL ENGINEERING. *Educ:* Univ Minn, BChE, 41, PhD(chem eng), 58. *Prof Exp:* Res chem engr, Md Res Labs, Ford, Bacon, & Davis Inc, DC, 43-45; assoc prof, 49-58, PROF CHEM ENG, UNIV N DAK, 58-, CHMN DEPT, 71-, CHESTER FRITZ DISTINGUISHED PROF, 77- *Concurrent Pos:* Asst dir res contract, Univ NDak-US Army Qm Corps, 49-53; dir res contract, NSF grant, 57-59; dir res contracts, Univ NDak-Great Northern Rwy, 59-64 & 65-71; prin investr, Off Coal Res Proj Lignite, 72-; consult, Coal Res Lab, US Bur Mines, 64- *Mem:* Am Chem Soc; Am Inst Chem Engrs; Am Soc Eng Educ. *Res:* Food dehydration; mass transfer in evaporation; drying; coal research; gasification; high pressure technology. *Mailing Add:* Dept of Chem Eng Univ of NDak Grand Forks ND 58202

SEVERSON, KIETH EDWARD, b Albert Lea, Minn, Dec 22, 36; m 61; c 2. RANGE SCIENCE, WILDLIFE ECOLOGY. *Educ:* Univ Minn, BA, 62; Univ Wyo, MS, 64, PhD(range mgt), 66. *Prof Exp:* Instr range ecol, SDak State Univ, 66-67, asst prof wildlife ecol, 67-70; range scientist, Rapid City, SDak, 70-77, WILDLIFE BIOLOGIST, ROCKY MOUNTAIN FOREST & RANGE EXP STA, US FOREST SERV, 77- *Mem:* Soc Range Mgt; Wildlife Soc. *Res:* Effects of grazing by domestic livestock on wildlife habitat, especially big game; habitat requirements of blue grouse; domestic livestock distribution patterns and influences on riparian habitat. *Mailing Add:* Rocky Mt Forest & Range Exp Sta Ariz State Univ Tempe AZ 85281

SEVERSON, ROLAND GEORGE, b Malta, Mont, Apr 1, 24; m 45; c 4. ORGANIC CHEMISTRY. *Educ:* Mont State Col, BS, 46; Purdue Univ, MS, 48, PhD(chem), 51. *Prof Exp:* Asst chem, Purdue Univ, 46-48, asst instr, 48-50; from instr to assoc prof, 50-58, PROF CHEM, UNIV N DAK, 58-, CHMN DEPT, 60- *Mem:* Am Chem Soc. *Res:* Organometallics; synthesis of substituted organosilanes; organosilicon chemistry. *Mailing Add:* Dept of Chem Univ of NDak Grand Forks ND 58202

SEVERSON, RONALD CHARLES, b Tracy, Minn, Nov 14, 45; m 69. GEOCHEMISTRY. *Educ:* Univ Minn, BS, 67, MS, 72, PhD(pedology), 74. *Prof Exp:* Soil scientist, USDA Soil Conserv Serv, Minn, 65-67; soil analyst, US Cold Regions Res & Eng Lab, NH, 68-69; res asst, Soil Sci Dept, Univ Minn, St Paul, 70-74; SOIL SCIENTIST GEOCHEM, BR REGIONAL GEOCHEM, US GEOL SURV, 74- *Concurrent Pos:* Instr soil genesis & geog, Dept Plant & Earth Sci, Univ Wis-River Falls, 73. *Mem:* Am Soc Agron; Soil Sci Soc Am. *Res:* Spatial distribution of elements in soil materials and their changes with cultural activities. *Mailing Add:* US Geol Surv Stop 925 Box 25046 Denver Fed Ctr Denver CO 80225

SEVERUD, FRED N, b June 8, 99; US citizen. STRUCTURAL ENGINEERING. *Educ:* Norwegian Inst Technol, dipl eng, 23. *Prof Exp:* CONSULT & FOUNDER, SEVERUD-PERRONE-STRUM-BANDEL, 27- *Honors & Awards:* Am Gold Medal, Am Inst Architects, 58; Franklin Award, Franklin Inst, 62; Ernest E Howard Award, Am Soc Civil Engrs, 64. *Mem:* Nat Acad Eng; Am Soc Civil Engrs. *Mailing Add:* Severud-Perrone-Strum-Bandel 485 Fifth Ave New York NY 10017

SEVIAN, WALTER ANDREW, b Copiague, NY, Sept 16, 40; m 64; c 3. APPLIED MATHEMATICS, DATA PROCESSING. *Educ:* State Univ NY Stony Brook, BS, 62, MS, 64, PhD(appl math), 70. *Prof Exp:* Asst prof math, Southhampton Col, 70-71; SYSTS ENGR ENERGY SYSTS ANAL, BROOKHAVEN NAT LAB, 72- *Concurrent Pos:* Adj asst prof math, State Univ NY Stony Brook, 74-75. *Mem:* Am Geophys Union; Asn Comput Users. *Res:* Computerized model/data couplings in environmental assessment of energy systems; free surface motion in groundwater hydrology; algorithm development for microcomputers. *Mailing Add:* Bldg 475 Brookhaven Nat Lab Upton NY 11973

SEVIK, MAURICE, b Istanbul, Turkey, Mar 19, 23; US citizen; m 53; c 2. AEROSPACE ENGINEERING. *Educ:* Univ London, DIC, 46; Pa State Univ, PhD(eng mech), 63. *Prof Exp:* Mem staff, Bristol Aircraft Ltd & Hawker-Siddeley Ltd, 46-59; prof aerospace eng, Pa State Univ, 59-68, prof, 68-72, dir, Garfield Thomas Water Tunnel, 69-72; ASSOC TECH DIR ACOUST, NAVAL SHIP RES & DEVELOP CTR, 72- *Concurrent Pos:* Consult, Int Bus Mach Corp, 64-65 & Off Res Anal, US Air Force, 65-66; vis prof, Cambridge Univ, 70, fel, Churchill Col, 70. *Mem:* Am Soc Mech Engrs; fel Acoust Soc Am. *Res:* Acoustics. *Mailing Add:* Naval Ship Res & Develop Ctr Bethesda MD 20034

SEVILLA, MICHAEL DOUGLAS, b San Jose, Calif, Feb 16, 42; m 63; c 3. PHYSICAL CHEMISTRY, BIOPHYSICAL CHEMISTRY. *Educ:* San Jose State Col, BS, 63; Univ Wash, PhD(phys chem), 67. *Prof Exp:* Instr, Univ Wash, 67-68; res chemist, Atomics Int Div, NAm Rockwell Corp, 68-70; asst prof, 70-76, ASSOC PROF CHEM, OAKLAND UNIV, 76- *Mem:* AAAS; Am Chem Soc; Sigma Xi; Radiation Res Soc; Am Soc Photobiol. *Res:* Electron spin resonance spectroscopy, particularly as an aid to understanding free radical mechanisms induced by radiation effects on biological molecules. *Mailing Add:* Dept Chem Oakland Univ Rochester MI 48063

SEVIN, E(UGENE), b Chicago, Ill, Jan 5, 28; m 51; c 3. SOLID MECHANICS. *Educ:* Ill Inst Technol, BS, 49, PhD(eng mech), 58; Calif Inst Technol, MS, 51. *Prof Exp:* Assoc res engr struct mech, Armour Res Found, 51-53, res engr, 53-58, sr res engr, 58-61, asst dir res, Mech Res Div, 61-63, dir res, IIT Res Inst, 63-70; prof mech eng & head dept, Ben Gurion Univ, Israel, 70-74; CHIEF STRATEGIC STRUCT DIV, DEFENSE NUCLEAR AGENCY, US DEPT OF DEFENSE, 74- *Concurrent Pos:* Eve instr, Ill Inst Technol, 55-63, adj prof, 63-; mem adv comts, Dept Defense Agencies, 55- *Mem:* Am Soc Mech Engrs. *Res:* Analytical design; structural dynamics; vibrations; numerical methods; computer applications of structural design; nuclear weapons effects. *Mailing Add:* US Dept Defense 6801 Telegraph Rd Alexandria VA 22310

SEVOIAN, MARTIN, b Methuen, Mass, Mar 28, 19; m 54; c 2. VETERINARY MEDICINE. *Educ:* Univ Mass, BS, 49; Univ Pa, VMD, 53; Cornell Univ, MS, 54; Am Col Vet Microbiol, dipl. *Prof Exp:* Asst prof path, Cornell Univ, 54-55; PROF VET SCI, UNIV MASS, AMHERST, 55- *Mem:* Am Vet Med Asn. *Res:* Infectious diseases, especially neoplasms. *Mailing Add:* Paige Labs Univ of Mass Amherst MA 01002

SEVON, WILLIAM DAVID, III, b Andover, Ohio, July 22, 33; m 57; c 2. GEOLOGY. *Educ:* Ohio Wesleyan Univ, BA, 55; Univ SDak, MA, 58; Univ Ill, PhD(geol), 61. *Prof Exp:* Lectr geol, Univ Canterbury, 61-65; GEOLOGIST, PA GEOL SURV, 65- *Mem:* AAAS; Geol Soc Am; Soc Econ Paleontologists & Mineralogists; Am Quaternary Asn. *Res:* Sedimentology of Appalachian Devonian; Quaternary sedimentology of northeastern Pennsylvania. *Mailing Add:* Pa Geol Surv Harrisburg PA 17120

SEVY, ROGER WARREN, b Richfield, Utah, Nov 6, 23; m 48; c 2. PHARMACOLOGY. *Educ:* Univ Vt, MS, 48; Univ Ill, PhD(physiol), 51, MD, 54. *Prof Exp:* Asst physiol, Col Med, Univ Ill, 48-51, instr, 51-54; asst prof, 54-57, head dept, 57-73, dean, Sch Med, 73-78, PROF PHARMACOL, SCH MED, TEMPLE UNIV, 56- *Mem:* AAAS; Am Physiol Soc; Am Soc Pharmacol & Exp Therapeut; Endocrine Soc. *Res:* Cardiovascular pharmacology; vascular smooth muscle; hypertension; adrenal hormones and cardiovascular-renal function; pharmacology of platelets. *Mailing Add:* Dept of Pharmacol Temple Univ Sch of Med Philadelphia PA 19140

SEWARD, THOMAS PHILIP, III, b Brooklyn, NY, May 2, 39; m 65; c 2. APPLIED PHYSICS. *Educ:* Wesleyan Univ, BA, 61; Harvard Univ, MS, 63, PhD(appl physics), 67. *Prof Exp:* Res mat scientist, 67-69, sr res mat scientist, 69-74, RES SUPVR, RES & DEVELOP LABS, CORNING GLASS WORKS, 74- *Mem:* Am Ceramic Soc; Optic Soc Am. *Res:* Structure propertids and composition of glass and glass ceramics; photochromic glass; interaction of light with glasses and ceramics. *Mailing Add:* Res & Develop Labs Corning Glass Works Corning NY 14830

SEWARD, WILLIAM DAVIS, b Richmond, Va, Mar 14, 38; m 60. SOLID STATE PHYSICS. *Educ:* Univ Richmond, BS, 60; Cornell Univ, PhD(physics), 65. *Prof Exp:* Res assoc physics, Univ Ill, 65-67; asst prof, Univ Utah, 67-73; asst prof physics, Pomona Col, 73-76, assoc prof, 76-81; ENG STAFF, ENG RES ASSOCS, MCLEAN, VA, 81- *Mem:* Am Phys Soc. *Res:* Solid helium; computer aided instruction, maintenance and testing. *Mailing Add:* Eng Res Assocs 1517 Westbranch Dr McLean VA 22102

SEWELL, CURTIS, JR, b Iowa Park, Tex, Apr 14, 24; m 45; c 3. ELECTRONICS ENGINEERING, COMPUTER HARDWARE. *Educ:* Hardin Col, 41-42; Tex Tech Col, 42-43; Univ NH, 43; Va Polytech Inst, 44. *Prof Exp:* Electronics engr, Los Alamos Sci Lab, 46-57; mgr eng div, Isotopes, Inc, NJ, 57-62; ELECTRONICS ENGR, LAWRENCE LIVERMORE LAB, 62- *Res:* Electronic circuit design; nuclear and laboratory instrumentation; digital computers; feedback amplifiers; microcomputers and systems for control and data processing. *Mailing Add:* 1625 Alviso Pl Livermore CA 94550

SEWELL, DUANE CAMPBELL, b Oakland, Calif, Aug 15, 18; m 43; c 1. PHYSICS. *Educ:* Col of the Pac, AB, 40. *Prof Exp:* Asst, Radiation Lab, 40-41, physicist, 41-52, physicist, Lawrence Radiation Lab, 52-59, assoc dir, Lawrence Livermore Lab, Univ Calif, 59-73, dep dir, 73-78; asst secy defense prog, 78-81, CONSULT, DEPT ENERGY, 81- *Concurrent Pos:* Mem, Gov Radio Defense Adv Comt, State of Calif, 60-; sci officer to gen adv comt, AEC, 63-68. *Mem:* Am Phys Soc. *Res:* Uranium-235 mass spectrograph development; high energy neutron cross sections; magnetic field measurements. *Mailing Add:* Asst Secy Defense Prog US Dept Energy Washington DC 20545

SEWELL, FRANK ANDERSON, JR, b Atlanta, Ga, June 25, 34; m 58; c 1. ELECTRONIC PHYSICS. *Educ:* Vanderbilt Univ, BA, 56; Emory Univ, MA, 58; Brown Univ, PhD(physics), 66. *Prof Exp:* Instr physics, Emory Univ, 57-58; sr engr, Sperry Gyroscope Co, 58-60, res staff mem, 65-73, mgr optoelectronics dept, 73-78, DIR, SEMICONDUCTOR LAB, SPERRY RES CTR, SPERRY RAND CORP, 78- *Mem:* Sr mem Inst Elec & Electronics Engrs; Am Phys Soc; Soc Photog Scientists & Engrs. *Res:* Semiconductor device physics; electrophotography; high resolution x-ray and electron beam lithography. *Mailing Add:* 47 Tarleton Rd Newton Centre MA 02159

SEWELL, HOMER B, b Red Bird, Mo, Aug 4, 20. ANIMAL NUTRITION. *Educ:* Univ Mo, BS, 53, MS, 63; Univ Ky, PhD(ruminate nutrit), 65. *Prof Exp:* County agt, 53-58, from asst prof to assoc prof, 58-72, PROF ANIMAL HUSB, EXTEN, UNIV MO-COLUMBIA, 72- *Mem:* Am Soc Animal Sci. *Res:* Beef cattle feeding; stability of vitamin A liver stores of ruminants. *Mailing Add:* Dept of Animal Husb Univ of Mo Exten Columbia MO 65201

SEWELL, JOHN I, b Cedartown, Ga, Aug 28, 33; m 60; c 2. AGRICULTURAL ENGINEERING. *Educ:* Univ Ga, BSAE, 54; NC State Univ, MSAE, 58, PhD(agr eng), 62. *Prof Exp:* Instr agr eng, NC State Univ, 60-62; from asst prof to prof agr eng, 62-77, assoc head dept, 73-77, ASST DEAN, AGR EXP STA, UNIV TENN, KNOXVILLE, 77- *Mem:* Sr mem Am Soc Agr Engrs. *Res:* Land grading in alluvial lands for improved surface drainage; animal waste management; infrared aerial remote sensing; irrigation; pond sealing. *Mailing Add:* Asst Dean Agr Exp Sta 104 Morgan Hall Univ of Tenn Knoxville TN 37916

SEWELL, KENNETH GLENN, b Sherman, Tex, July 26, 33; m 54; c 2. PHYSICS. *Educ:* Okla State Univ, BS, 57; Southern Methodist Univ, MS, 60; Tex Christian Univ, PhD(physics), 64. *Prof Exp:* Aerodyn engr, Chance Vought Aircraft Corp, 57-60; res scientist, LTV Res Ctr, Ling-Tempco Vought Inc, 60-61, sr scientist, 64-67; assoc prof physics, Abilene Christian Col, 67-68; sr scientist, LTV Res Ctr Ling-Tempco Vought, Inc, Dallas, 68-69, tech dir Isoray, 69-70; dir res & develop, 70-74, engr mgr, 74-78, GEN MGR, TEX DIV, VARO INC, 78- *Mem:* Am Phys Soc; Optical Soc Am; Inst Elec & Electronics Engrs. *Res:* Photoelectric devices; infrared, x-ray imaging, research and development management; nonlinear optics; atomic physics; electrooptics; infrared techniques. *Mailing Add:* 7661 La Bolsa Dallas TX 75240

SEWELL, RAYMOND F, b Seffner, Fla, Feb 20, 23; m 50; c 6. ANIMAL NUTRITION. *Educ:* Univ Fla, BSA, 49, MS, 50; Cornell Univ, PhD, 52. *Prof Exp:* Asst, Univ Fla, 50; from asst prof to assoc prof animal husb, Univ, Ga, 52-60, prof animal sci, 60-67; dir livestock res, Ralston Purina Co, 67-78; DIR NUTRIT & TECH SERV, COSBY-HODGES MILLING CO, 78- *Mem:* Am Soc Animal Sci; Am Dairy Sci Asn; Am Asn Lab Animal Sci; Am Fisheries Soc; Am Inst Nutrit. *Res:* Nutritional requirements of swine, dairy cattle, beef cattle, horses, laboratory species, catfish, rabbits, canine and feline. *Mailing Add:* Cosby-Hodges Milling Co PO Box 10767 Birmingham AL 35202

SEWELL, WINIFRED, b Newport, Wash, Aug 12, 17. INFORMATION SCIENCE, PHARMACY. *Educ:* Wash State Univ, AB, 38; Columbia Univ, BS, 40. *Hon Degrees:* DSc, Philadelphia Col Pharm & Sci, 79. *Prof Exp:* Jr asst librn, Columbia Univ, 40-42; librn, Wellcome Res Labs, NY, 42-46; sr librn, Squibb Inst Med Res, NJ, 46-61; med subj heading specialist, Nat Libr Med, 61-62, dep chief bibliog serv div, 62-64, head drug lit prog, 64-70; coordr drug info servs, Heath Sci Ctr, Univ Md, Baltimore City, 70-74. *Concurrent Pos:* Ed, Unlisted Drugs, 49-59 & 61-64; mem comn pharmaceut abstr, Int Fedn Pharmaceut, 58-60; ad hoc comt on patent off steroid code, 59-60; comt current med terminology, AMA, 62-64; consult, Winthrop Labs, 63; comt mod methods handling chem info, Nat Acad Sci-Nat Res Coun, 64-67; adj lectr med lit, Univ Md, 69-; ed health affairs ser & Gale Info Guides, 72-81; consult, Nat Health Planning Info Ctr, 75-81. *Honors & Awards:* Pub Award Sci Tech Div, Spec Libr Asn, 66; Eliot Prize, Med Libr Asn, 77. *Mem:* Drug Info Asn (vpres, 65-66, pres, 70-71); Spec Libr Asn (pres, 60-61); Am Libr Asn; Am Soc Info Sci; fel Med Libr Asn. *Res:* Coordination of chemical and biomedical terminology, especially in on-line information retrieval systems; library science; drug information centers; medical information transfer. *Mailing Add:* 6513 76th Pl Cabin John MD 20818

SEXSMITH, DAVID RANDAL, b Niagara Falls, Ont, June 8, 33; nat US; m 53; c 3. ORGANIC CHEMISTRY. *Educ:* Kenyon Col, AB, 55; Univ Rochester, PhD(chem), 59. *Prof Exp:* Res chemist, Am Cyanamid Co, 58-65, group leader, 65-66; mgr res, Power Chem Div, 66-72, dir res, 72-74, vpres res, 74-80, VPRES TECHNOL, DREW CHEM CORP LAB, 80- *Mem:* Am Chem Soc; Am Soc Testing & Mat; Tech Asn Pulp & Paper Indust; Nat Asn Corrosion Engr. *Res:* Polymer application; water and waste treatment. *Mailing Add:* Res & Develop Lab One Drew Chem Plaza Boonton NJ 07005

SEXSMITH, FREDERICK HAMILTON, b Ft Erie, Ont, Mar 30, 29; US citizen; m 64; c 2. CHEMISTRY. *Educ:* Queen's Univ, Ont, BA, 51, MA, 53; Princeton Univ, MA, 54, PhD(phys chem), 57. *Prof Exp:* Supvr, Chicopee Mfg Co, 56-62, dir res specialty chem, Refined Prod Co, 62-64 & Refined Prod Co Div, Millmaster-Onyx, 64-65; sect head, Ethicon Inc, 65-66; mgr Res & Develop Div, Hughson Chem Co Div, 66-80, DIR RES, CHEM PROD GROUP, LORD CORP, 80- *Concurrent Pos:* Textile Res Inst fel, Princeton Univ, 57. *Mem:* Am Chem Soc; Chem Inst Can; Fiber Soc; Am Asn Textile Chemists & Colorists; Am Inst Chemists. *Res:* Applied polymer chemistry; colloid science; surface chemistry; emulsion polymerization; textile finishes; adhesives for elastomers; polyurethane coatings; rubber chemicals. *Mailing Add:* Lord Chem Prod Div 2000 W Grandview Blvd Erie PA 16512

SEXSMITH, ROBERT G, b Regina, Can, Apr 13, 38; m 64; c 3. STRUCTURAL ENGINEERING. *Educ:* Univ BC, BASc, 61; Stanford Univ, MS, 63, Engr, 66, PhD(civil eng), 67. *Prof Exp:* Design engr, Phillips, Barratt & Partners, 63-64; from asst prof to assoc prof struct eng, Cornell Univ, 67-76; res scientist, Western Forest Prod Lab, 76-79; sr engr, 79-81, PRIN, BUCKLAND AND TAYLOR LTD, 81- *Mem:* Am Concrete Inst; Am Soc Civil Engrs; Can Soc Civil Eng (struct div exec comt, 77-). *Res:* Application of probabilistic concepts to structural engineering; structural mechanics. *Mailing Add:* Buckland and Taylor Ltd 1591 Bowser North Vancouver BC V7P 2Y4 Can

SEXTON, ALAN WILLIAM, b Newark, NJ, Mar 25, 25; m 46; c 3. PHYSIOLOGY. *Educ:* Mont State Univ, BS, 50; Univ Mo, MA, 52, PhD(physiol), 55. *Prof Exp:* Instr physiol, Med Sch, Univ Mo, 54-55; instr human growth, 55-59, physiologist, Child Res Coun, 55-62, asst prof physiol, 59-63, asst prof phys med, 63-70, ASSOC PROF PHYS MED, MED SCH, UNIV COLO, DENVER CTR, 70- *Concurrent Pos:* Mgt consult, Nat Heart, Lung & Blood Inst. *Mem:* Am Physiol Soc; Soc Exp Biol & Med. *Res:* Physiology of muscle contraction; effects of hormones on muscle contractility. *Mailing Add:* Dept Phys Med & Rehab C-243 Univ Colo Health Sci Ctr Denver CO 80262

SEXTON, EDWIN LEON, biochemistry, nutrition, see previous edition

SEXTON, MICHAEL RAY, b High Point, NC, May 1, 41; m 68; c 3. ENERGY SYSTEMS, TURBOMACHINERY. *Educ:* Va Polytech Inst & State Univ, BS, 66, MS, 73, PhD(mech eng), 80. *Prof Exp:* Eng officer, US Navy, 66-71; instr mech eng, Va Polytech Inst & State Univ, 73-74; nuclear staff engr, Bechtel Power Corp, 74-75; proj engr, Rural Electrification Admin, 75-78, chief power plants, 78; instr, Va Polytech Inst & State Univ, 78-79; ASST PROF MECH ENG, UNIV VA, 79- *Mem:* Am Soc Mech Engrs; Am Soc Heating, Refrigeration & Air Conditioning Engrs; Am Soc Naval Engrs; Am Soc Eng Educ. *Res:* Experimental measurement of flow field parameters in the rotating components of turbomachines; semi-empirical modeling of the transient behavior of flows in axial-flow compressors. *Mailing Add:* 285 Turkey Ridge Rd Charlottesville VA 22901

SEXTON, OWEN J, b Philadelphia, Pa, July 11, 26; m 52; c 4. ECOLOGY, VERTEBRATE ZOOLOGY. *Educ:* Oberlin Col, BA, 51; Univ Mich, MA, 53, PhD(vert natural hist), 57. *Prof Exp:* From instr to assoc prof, 55-68, exec officer dept, 64-66, PROF BIOL, WASHINGTON UNIV, 68- *Concurrent Pos:* NSF fel, Univ Chicago, 66-67; trop consult, UNESCO, 74-75; prof zool, Univ Mich Biol Sta, 75- *Mem:* Ecol Soc Am; Am Soc Ichthyologists & Herpetologists; Asn Trop Biol. *Res:* Reproductive cycles in tropical vertebrates; predation in reference to color polymorphism and mimicry; habitat structure; tropical versus temperate biology; amphibian development; reptilian hibernation. *Mailing Add:* Dept of Biol Washington Univ St Louis MO 63130

SEXTON, ROBERT ROSS, b Canton, Ill, May 13, 22; m 43; c 4. MEDICINE, OPHTHALMOLOGY. *Educ:* Bradley Univ, BS, 44; Univ Ill, Chicago, MD, 46; Univ Iowa, MS, 61. *Prof Exp:* Res fel ocular infection, Univ Calif, San Francisco, 61, instr ophthal, 61; asst prof, Univ Miami, 62-66; from assoc prof to prof ophthal, Univ Tex Health Sci Ctr Dallas, 66-78; RETIRED. *Mem:* AMA; Asn Res Vision & Ophthal; Am Acad Ophthal & Otolaryngol. *Mailing Add:* 110 W 11th St Silver City NM 88061

SEXTRO, RICHARD GEORGE, b Odell, Nebr, Dec 31, 44; m 67; c 2. ENVIRONMENTAL SCIENCES. *Educ:* Carnegie Inst Technol, BS, 67; Univ Calif, Berkeley, MS, 69, PhD(nuclear chem), 73. *Prof Exp:* Fel nuclear chem, Lawrence Berkeley Lab, 74-75 & energy policy, Nat Sci Found, 75-76; Energy assessment, 76-82, STAFF SCIENTIST, INDOOR AIR QUALITY, LAWRENCE BERKELEY LAB, 82- *Mem:* AAAS; Sigma Xi. *Res:* Measurement of indoor air pollutants, with emphasis on concentrations of radon and progeny in indoor air. *Mailing Add:* Lawrence Berkeley Lab Bldg 90-3118 Berkeley CA 94720

SEYB, EDGAR JOHN, JR, b Pretty Prairie, Kans, Sept 14, 23; m 53; c 1. ELECTROCHEMISTRY. *Educ:* Sterling Col, BA, 46; Univ Kans, PhD(chem), 50. *Prof Exp:* Lab asst, Univ Kans, 46-48; res chemist, United Chromium Inc, 50-55; res supvr, Metal & Thermit Corp, 55-62, M & & T Chem, Inc, 62-67, res mgr, 67-68, RES DIR, M & T CHEM, INC, 69- *Mem:* Am Chem Soc; Electrochem Soc; Inst Metal Finishing; Am Soc Testing & Mat; Am Electroplaters Soc. *Res:* Superoxide chemistry; chromium, tin, zinc and nickel deposition; electrodeposition. *Mailing Add:* 48 Brookside Rd Freehold NJ 07728

SEYB, LESLIE PHILIP, b Franklin, Iowa, May 11, 15; m 39; c 2. ENVIRONMENTAL CHEMISTRY. *Educ:* Coe Col, AB, 35; Univ Iowa, MS, 37, PhD(org chem), 39. *Prof Exp:* Chem asst, Patent Dept, Phillips Petrol Co, 39-42; res chemist & group leader, Diamond Alkali Co, 42-50, mgr res, 50-53, assoc dir res, 53-63; chief phys sci, Pac Northwest Water Lab, Environ Protection Agency, 64-67, asst prog dir eutrophication, 67-71, asst dir, 71-78; RETIRED. *Mem:* Am Chem Soc. *Res:* Fatty acids; wetting agents; textile bleaching; heterocyclic N-compounds; ethylene derivatives; N-chloro organic; chloro hydrocarbons; textile flameproofing; pesticides; xylene derivatives; metallo organics; acetylene derivatives; water pollution and industrial waste control; water and analytical chemistry. *Mailing Add:* 2960 NW Jackson St Corvallis OR 97330

SEYBERT, DAVID WAYNE, b Hazleton, Pa, May 2, 50; m 72. ENZYMOLOGY. *Educ:* Bloomsburg State Col, BA, 72; Cornell Univ, PhD(biochem), 76. *Prof Exp:* Res assoc, Med Ctr, Duke Univ, 76-79; ASST PROF CHEM, DUQUESNE UNIV, 79- *Concurrent Pos:* NIH prin investr, Duquesne Univ, 80- *Mem:* Am Chem Soc; AAAS. *Res:* Enzymology of biological oxidation, with particular emphasis on hemoproteins and cytochrome P-450 catalyzed steroid hydroxylations. *Mailing Add:* Dept Chem Duquesne Univ Pittsburgh PA 15282

SEYBOLD, VIRGINIA SUSAN (DICK), b Milwaukee, Wis, March 23, 51; m 72. NEUROSCIENCE, PAIN PATHWAYS. *Educ:* Col William & Mary, BS, 73; Univ Minn, PhD(pharmacol), 77. *Prof Exp:* Instr, 78-80, ASST PROF NEUROANAT, DEPT ANAT, UNIV MINN, 80- *Mem:* Soc Neurosci. *Res:* Determination of transmitter-coded neuronal cirucitry in the spinal cord using immunohistochemical, labeling via retrograde transport and autoradiographic methods with focus on pathways for pain and analgesia. *Mailing Add:* Dept Anat Univ Minn 4-135 Jackson Hall 321 Church St SE Minneapolis MN 55455

SEYDEL, FRANK DAVID, b Davenport, Iowa, May 15, 44; m 70; c 2. BIOETHICS, BIOCHEMISTRY. *Educ:* Iowa Wesleyan Col, BS, 66; Iowa State Univ, PhD(biochem, cell biol), 73; Princeton Theol Sem, MDiv, 76. *Prof Exp:* Asst prof chem, Univ Tenn, 76-79; ASSOC PROF CHEM, FRIENDS UNIV, WICHITA, 80- *Concurrent Pos:* Minister, Iowa Conf United Methodist Church, 74- *Mem:* Am Inst Biol Sci; Soc Protozool. *Res:* Ethics of genetic manipulation. *Mailing Add:* Dept Chem Friends Univ Wichita KS 67212

SEYDEL, HORST GUNTER, b Berlin, Ger, Aug 5, 29; US citizen; m 58; c 3. RADIOTHERAPY, RADIOBIOLOGY. *Educ:* Univ Frankfurt, MD, 55; Wayne State Univ, MS, 61. *Prof Exp:* From instr to asst prof radiol, Wayne State Univ, 61-64; asst prof, Univ Md, Baltimore, 64-68; assoc prof, Univ Pa, 68-73; assoc prof, 73-77, PROF RADIOTHER & NUCLEAR MED, JEFFERSON MED COL, THOMAS JEFFERSON UNIV, 77-, SR RADIOTHERAPIST, UNIV HOSP, 75- *Concurrent Pos:* Consult, Vet Admin Hosp, Perry Point, Md, 66-68; chief dept radiother, Am Oncol Hosp, Philadelphia, 68-75. *Mem:* Am Radium Soc; Am Soc Therapeut Radiol; Radiation Res Soc; Radiol Soc NAm; Am Col Radiol. *Res:* Cellular radiobiology; radiation carcinogenesis; clinical research in radiotherapy. *Mailing Add:* Thomas Jefferson Univ Hosp Philadelphia PA 19107

SEYER, FRED A, b Stettler, Alta, May 7, 40; m 63; c 1. CHEMICAL ENGINEERING. *Educ:* Univ Alta, BScChE, 63; Univ Del, MS, 65, PhD(fluid mech), 68. *Prof Exp:* Asst prof chem eng, Univ Alta, 67-77, prof, 77-80; WITH SYNCRUDE, 80- *Mem:* Am Inst Chem Engrs; Am Chem Soc; Chem Inst Can. *Res:* Fluid mechanics in the special area of non-Newtonian fluids. *Mailing Add:* Syncrude Postal Bag 4009 Ft McMurray AB T9H 3L1 Can

SEYER, JEROME MICHAEL, b Oran, Mo, Jan 2, 37; m 69; c 2. BIOCHEMISTRY. *Educ:* Univ Mo-Columbia, BS, 59, PhD(biochem), 66. *Prof Exp:* Orthop res fel, Mass Gen Hosp, Boston, 66-69. Prof Exp: Res asst biochem, Univ Mo-Columbia, 65-66; res assoc orthop res, Mass Gen Hosp, Boston, 66-71; res assoc orthop res, Children's Hosp, Boston, 71-74; asst prof, 74-80, ASSOC PROF BIOCHEM, UNIV TENN, MEMPHIS, 80-; RES CHEMIST, VET ADMIN HOSP, MEMPHIS, 74- *Concurrent Pos:* Res assoc, Harvard Med Sch, 66- *Mem:* AAAS; Am Chem Soc; Orthop Res Soc. *Res:* Biological mechanism of calcification of bone and dental enamel and development of cartilage collagen; special emphasis of the two above areas along protein sequence analysis; diseases in connective tissues with special reference to fibrosis of lung, liver and scar tissue and amino acid sequence of collagen. *Mailing Add:* Dept of Biochem Univ of Tenn 1030 Jefferson Ave Memphis TN 38104

SEYFERT, CARL K, JR, b Pecos, Tex, Feb 12, 38; m 60; c 2. STRUCTURAL GEOLOGY, PETROLOGY. *Educ:* Vanderbilt Univ, BA, 60; Stanford Univ, PhD(geol), 65. *Prof Exp:* From instr to asst prof geol, Queens Col, NY, 64-67; chmn dept, 67-72, assoc prof, 67-72, PROF GEOL, STATE UNIV NY COL BUFFALO, 72- *Concurrent Pos:* Geol Soc Am Penrose grant, Stanford Univ, 62-64, Shell grant fundamental res, 62-64; Sigma Xi grant, Queens Col, NY, 65-68; Res Found State Univ NY grant, State Univ NY Col Buffalo, 69-72. *Mem:* AAAS; Geol Soc Am; Am Geophys Union; Nat Asn Geol Teachers; Sigma Xi. *Res:* Igneous and metamorphic petrology and structural geology; compositional variation within granitic plutons; paleomagnetism and geotectonics; reconstruction of large scale movements of continents throughout geologic time. *Mailing Add:* Dept of Geosci State Univ of NY Buffalo NY 14222

SEYFERTH, DIETMAR, b Chemnitz, Ger, Jan 11, 29; nat US; m 56; c 3. ORGANOMETALLIC CHEMISTRY. *Educ:* Univ Buffalo, BA, 51; Harvard Univ, MA, 53, PhD(inorg chem), 55. *Hon Degrees:* Dr, Univ Aix-Marseille III. *Prof Exp:* Res chemist, Dow Corning Corp, 55-56; res assoc, Harvard Univ, 56-57; from instr to assoc prof, 57-65, PROF CHEM, MASS INST TECHNOL, 65- *Concurrent Pos:* Regional ed, J Organometallic Chem, 63-81, coord ed, Organometallic Chem Rev, 64-81; Guggenheim fel, 68; ed, Organometallics, Am Chem Soc, 81- *Honors & Awards:* Frederic Stanley Kipping Award, 72. *Mem:* Am Chem Soc; Royal Soc Chem; fel Ger Acad Scientists Leopoldina; fel AAAS. *Res:* Main group, especially silicon and mercury and transition metal organometallic chemistry; organophosphorus chemistry; organic synthesis. *Mailing Add:* Dept of Chem Mass Inst of Technol Cambridge MA 02139

SEYFRIED, THOMAS NEIL, b Flushing, NY, July 25, 46; m 73; c 3. NEUROBIOLOGY. *Educ:* St Francis Col, Maine, BA, 68; Ill State Univ, MS, 73; Univ Ill, PhD(genetics), 76. *Prof Exp:* Fel neurogenetics, 76-79, ASST PROF, DEPT NEUROL, SCH MED, YALE UNIV, 79- *Mem:* Genetics Soc Am; AAAS; Am Soc Neurochem; Int Soc Neurochem. *Res:* Cellular localization and function of brain gangliosides; developmental genetics of inherited epilepsy in mice; genetic control of brain myelinogenesis. *Mailing Add:* Dept Neurol Sch Med Yale Univ New Haven CT 06510

SEYLER, CHARLES EUGENE, b Eustis Fla, June, 2, 48. PLASMA PHYSICS. *Educ:* Univ SFla, BA, 70, MA, 72; Univ Iowa, PhD(physics), 75. *Prof Exp:* Res scientist plasma physics, Courant Inst Math Sci, NY Univ, 75-78; staff mem, Los Alamos Nat Lab, 78-81; ASST PROF PLASMA PHYSICS ELEC ENG, CORNELL UNIV, 81- *Concurrent Pos:* Vis staff mem, Los Alamos Nat Lab, 81- *Res:* Equilibrium, stability and transport of plasmas with applications to the development of controlled thermonuclear fusion reactors. *Mailing Add:* Phillips Hall Sch Elec Eng Cornell Univ Ithaca NY 14853

SEYLER, RICHARD G, b Du Bois, Pa, June 14, 33; m 64. NUCLEAR PHYSICS. *Educ:* Pa State Univ, BS, 55, MS, 59, PhD(physics), 61. *Prof Exp:* Vis asst prof, 61-63, from asst prof to assoc prof, 63-73, PROF PHYSICS, OHIO STATE UNIV, 73- *Mem:* Am Phys Soc. *Res:* Theoretical low-energy nuclear physics. *Mailing Add:* Dept of Physics Ohio State Univ Columbus OH 43210

SEYMOUR, ALLYN H, b Seattle, Wash, Aug 1, 13; m 40; c 3. RADIATION ECOLOGY, FISH BIOLOGY. *Educ:* Univ Wash, BS, 37, PhD, 56. *Prof Exp:* Jr scientist, State Dept Fisheries, Wash, 40-41; asst scientist, Int Fisheries Comn, 42-47; res assoc & asst dir appl fisheries lab, Univ Wash, 48-56; marine biologist, Div Biol & Med, US AEC, DC, 56-58; asst dir lab radiation biol, 58-63, prof fisheries, Col Fisheries, 63-79 dir lab radiation ecol, 66-78, EMER PROF, COL FISHERIES, UNIV WASH, 79- *Concurrent Pos:* Chmn panel radioactivity in the marine environ & mem panel nuclear merchant ships, Nat Res Coun. *Mem:* Am Fisheries Soc; Am Soc Limnol & Oceanog; Am Inst Fishery Res Biol; Health Physics Soc; Nat Shellfisheries Asn. *Res:* Biological distribution of radioisotopes; aquatic radioecology. *Mailing Add:* Col Fisheries Univ Wash Seattle WA 98195

SEYMOUR, KEITH GOLDIN, b Fairfax, Mo, Jan 25, 22; m 43; c 2. PESTICIDE CHEMISTRY, FORMULATIONS. *Educ:* Iowa State Univ, BS, 43, MS, 50; Tex A&M Univ, PhD(soil chem), 54. *Prof Exp:* Chemist, Tex Div, Dow Chem Co, 54-59, res specialist, 59-65, group leader, Bioprod Dept, 65-71, RES MGR, AGR PROD DEPT, DOW CHEM CO, 71- *Mem:* Asn Official Anal Chemists; Am Soc Testing & Mat; Fel AAAS; Am Chem Soc; NY Acad Sci. *Res:* Colloid, surface, agricultural and physical chemistry; pesticide formulations and application systems. *Mailing Add:* 6003 Sturgeon Creek Pkwy Midland MI 48640

SEYMOUR, MICHAEL DENNIS, b St Cloud, Minn, May 17, 50. ANALYTICAL CHEMISTRY. *Educ:* St John's Univ, BA, 72; Univ Ariz, PhD(anal chem), 78. *Prof Exp:* ASST PROF CHEM, HOPE COL, 78- *Mem:* Am Chem Soc. *Res:* Determination of acidic pollutants in rainfall; application of linear functions to the analysis of titration data; use of product induced x-ray emission for analysis of trace metals in the environment. *Mailing Add:* Dept of Chem Hope Col Holland MI 49423

SEYMOUR, RICHARD JONES, b Harrisburg, Pa, Aug 28, 29; c 1. OCEANOGRAPHY. *Educ:* US Naval Acad, BS, 51; Univ Calif, San Diego, PhD(oceanog), 74. *Prof Exp:* Vpres, Wire Equip Mfg Co, Inc, 51-59; head rocket develop, Elkton Div, Thiokol Chem Corp, 59-62; chief engr, United Technol Div, United Aircraft Corp, 62-69; res asst oceanog, Scripps Inst Oceanog, Univ Calif, San Diego, 70-73; STAFF OCEANOGR, CALIF DEPT BOATING & WATERWAYS, 74- *Res:* Sediment transport; wave measurement and analysis; coastal processes. *Mailing Add:* Calif Dept Boating & Waterways Scripps Inst of Oceanog AO22 La Jolla CA 92093

SEYMOUR, ROLAND LEE, b Palestine, Ill, Oct 12, 39. MYCOLOGY. *Educ:* Eastern Ill Univ, BS, 61; Va Polytech Inst & State Univ, PhD(bot), 65. *Prof Exp:* Asst bot, Eastern Ill Univ, 61-65; res asst, Va Polytech Inst & State Univ, 61-65, asst prof biol, 65-66; vis instr bot, Duke Univ, 66-67; asst prof biol, Univ Pittsburgh, 67-70; asst prof, 70-74, ASSOC PROF BOT, OHIO STATE UNIV, 74- *Concurrent Pos:* NSF grant, Univ Pittsburgh, 68-70; NSF grant, Ohio State Univ, 70-, Arctic Inst NAm grant, 72-74; consult mycologist, Bausch & Lomb, 72- *Mem:* Mycol Soc Am; Asn Trop Biol. *Res:* Aquatic mycology; role of aquatic fungi in tropical rainforest ecosystem; systematics and distribution of tropical aquatic phycomycetes; fungal parasites of mosquito and black fly of Mexico and West Africa. *Mailing Add:* Dept of Bot Ohio State Univ Columbus OH 43210

SEYMOUR, VIRGINIA ANNE, b Mass, July 30, 48. PLANT PHYSIOLOGY. *Educ:* Tufts Univ, BS, 72; Univ Wash, MS, 75, PhD(plant physiol), 80. *Prof Exp:* FEL, DEPT LAND, AIR & WATER RESOURCES, UNIV CALIF, DAVIS, 81- *Concurrent Pos:* Vis prof, Plant Ecol Group, Univ Andes, Venezuela, 82. *Mem:* AAAS; Am Soc Plant Physiologists; Sigma Xi. *Res:* Plant water relations; energy budgets; environmental effects on stomatal conductance. *Mailing Add:* Dept Land Air & Water Resources Univ Calif Davis CA 95616

SFAT, MICHAEL R(UDOLPH), b Timisoara, Rumania, Oct 28, 21; nat US; m 48; c 2. CHEMICAL ENGINEERING. *Educ:* Cornell Univ, BChE, 43, MChE, 47. *Prof Exp:* Res assoc chem eng, Cornell Univ, 43-44; asst microbiologist, Merck & Co, Inc, 47-51; sr microbiologist, 51-52; chem engr, Labs, Pabst Brewing Co, 52-54; res dir, Rahr Malting Co, 54-58, coordr res & develop, 58-60, vpres res & develop, 60-69, PRES, BIO-TECH RESOURCES, INC, 62- *Mem:* Am Chem Soc; Am Soc Brewing Chem; Am Soc Microbiol; Am Inst Chem Engrs; Inst Food Technol. *Res:* Industrial fermentations; malting; enzymes; bioengineering. *Mailing Add:* Bio-Tech Resources Inc Seventh & Marshall Manitowoc WI 54220

SFERRA, PASQUALE RICHARD, b St Louis, Mo, Sept 2, 27; m 50; c 4. ENTOMOLOGY. *Educ:* Washington Univ, AB, 52; Rutgers Univ, MSc, 55, PhD(entom), 57. *Prof Exp:* Asst prof entom, Exp Sta, State Univ NY Col Agr, Cornell Univ, 56-62, asst prof biol, 62-63; assoc prof, 63-73, PROF BIOL, COL OF MT ST JOSEPH, 73- *Concurrent Pos:* Leave of absence, biol sci adv, US Environ Protection Agency, 79-82. *Mem:* AAAS; Entom Soc Am; Am Inst Biol Sci; Sigma Xi. *Res:* Respiratory pacing in insects; insect toxicology; carbohydrate metabolism in insects; taxonomy of desert insects. *Mailing Add:* 5645 Candlelite Terrace Cincinnati OH 45238

SFORZA, PASQUALE M, b New York, NY, Mar 5, 41; m 63; c 3. FLUID MECHANICS. *Educ:* Polytech Inst Brooklyn, BAeE, 61, MS, 62, PhD(astronaut), 65. *Prof Exp:* Res fel aerospace eng, Polytech Inst Brooklyn, 61-62, res asst, 62-63; res assoc aerospace eng, Polytech Inst Brooklyn, 63-65, from asst prof to assoc prof, 65-77, PROF MECH & AEROSPACE ENG, POLYTECH INST NEW YORK, 77- *Concurrent Pos:* Pres, Flowpower, Inc, 78-; assoc ed, Am Inst Aeronaut & Astronaut J. *Honors & Awards:* Technol Achievement Award, Am Inst Aeronaut & Astronaut, 77. *Mem:* Assoc fel Am Inst Aeronaut & Astronaut; Am Soc Mech Engrs; Sigma Xi; NY Acad Sci; Int Solar Energy Soc. *Res:* Theoretical and experimental fluid mechanics; high temperature energy transfer; urban environmental studies; wind engineering; energy conversion. *Mailing Add:* Polytech Inst New York Rte 110 Farmingdale NY 11735

SFORZINI, RICHARD HENRY, b Rochester, NY, July 25, 24; m 47; c 7. AEROSPACE ENGINEERING. *Educ:* US Mil Acad, BSc, 47; Mass Inst Technol, MechE, 54. *Prof Exp:* Instr ord, US Mil Acad, 54-56, asst prof, 56-57; proj dir missile systs, Res & Develop Div, Army Rocket & Guided Missile Agency, Redstone Arsenal, Ala, 58-59; engr, Huntsville Div, Thiokol Chem Corp, Ala, 59-62, mgr eng dept, 62-64, dir eng, Space Booster Div, Brunswick, Ga, 64-66; vis prof, 66-67, PROF AEROSPACE ENG, AUBURN UNIV, 67- *Mem:* Assoc fel Am Inst Aeronaut & Astronaut; Sigma Xi. *Res:* Aircraft and missile propulsion systems, especially internal ballistics, combustion, air-augmented rockets, ignition, swirling flow through nozzles and problems of very large solid-propellant rockets; aerodynamics. *Mailing Add:* Dept Aerospace Eng Auburn Univ Auburn AL 36849

SGOUTAS, DEMETRIOS SPIROS, b Thessaloniki, Greece, Sept 2, 29; US citizen; m 61; c 2. BIOCHEMISTRY, CLINICAL CHEMISTRY. *Educ:* Univ Thessaloniki, BS, 54; Univ Ill, Urbana, PhD, 63. *Prof Exp:* Res assoc food chem, Univ Ill, Urbana, 63-64, asst prof, 64-65; asst prof chem, Univ Thessaloniki, 65-66; asst prof food chem, Univ Ill, Urbana, 66-70; from asst prof to assoc prof path, 70-74, PROF PATH & LAB MED, MED SCH, EMORY UNIV, 75-, DIR, RADIOIMMUNOASSAY LAB, 73- *Concurrent Pos:* Prin investr, Chicago & Ill Heart Asn grants, 64-69; NIH grants, 67-; prof allied health professions, Emory Univ, 70- *Mem:* Am Chem Soc; Am Oil Chemists Soc; Am Soc Biol Chemists; Am Asn Clin Chemists. *Res:* Lipid metabolism as related to cardiovascular diseases. *Mailing Add:* Dept of Path Emory Univ Med Sch Atlanta GA 30322

SGUROS, PETER LOUIS, microbial physiology, deceased

SHA, WILLIAM T, b Shanghai, China, Sept 13, 28; US citizen; m 57; c 3. NUCLEAR ENGINEERING, NUCLEAR SCIENCE. *Educ:* Polytech Inst Brooklyn, BS, 58; Columbia Univ, DESc, 64. *Prof Exp:* Engr, Combustion Eng Inc, 57-60; fel scientist, Atomic Power Div, Westinghouse Elec Corp, 60-67; sr nuclear engr & mgr anal modelling sect, Components Technol Div, 67-80, SR CONSULT, THERMAL HYDAULICS, 80- *Mem:* Am Nuclear Soc. *Res:* Reactor dynamics; system stability; nuclear-thermal-hydraulic interaction calculation; multiphase fluid mechanics and heat transfer. *Mailing Add:* Div of Reactor Physics Bldg 308 Argonne Nat Lab Argonne IL 60439

SHAAD, DOROTHY JEAN, b Newton, Mass, Aug 16, 09. OPHTHALMOLOGY, PSYCHOLOGY. *Educ:* Univ Kans, AB, 29; Bryn Mawr Col, MA, 30, PhD(exp psychol), 34; Univ Kans, MD, 44. *Prof Exp:* Asst, Howe Lab Ophthal, Harvard Med Sch, 31-32; instr, St Mary Col, Kans, 34; clin technician, Manhattan Eye, Ear & Throat Hosp, New York, 35-38; intern, Duke Univ Hosp, 44-45; assoc ophthal, Med Ctr, Univ Kans, 45-46, asst prof, 66-77, assoc res vision & ophthal, 71-77; RETIRED. *Concurrent Pos:* Practicing ophthalmologist, 45-69. *Res:* Light perception and dark adaptation; binocular vision. *Mailing Add:* 2322 West 51st St Shawnee Mission KS 66205

SHA'AFI, RAMADAN ISSA, b Nabi-Rubien, Palestine, June 9, 38; Jordanian citizen; c 2. BIOPHYSICS, PHYSIOLOGY. *Educ:* Univ Ill, BS, 62, MS, 63, PhD(biophys), 65. *Prof Exp:* Fel, Harvard Med Sch, 65-67, instr biophys, 67-69; asst prof physiol, Am Univ Beirut, 69-72; from asst prof to assoc prof, 72-78, PROF PHYSIOL, UNIV CONN HEALTH CTR, 78- *Mem:* Biophys Soc; Am Physiol Soc; Soc Gen Physiol. *Res:* Mechanism of water and solute transport across mammalian red and white cells. *Mailing Add:* Dept of Physiol Univ of Conn Health Ctr Farmington CT 06032

SHAAK, GRAIG DENNIS, b Harrisburg, Pa, Oct 18, 42; m 75; c 1. PALEOECOLOGY. *Educ:* Shippensburg State Col, BS, 67; Ind Univ, MAT, 69; Univ Pittsburgh, PhD(geol), 72. *Prof Exp:* Asst cur paleontol, Dept Natural Sci, 72-78, asst prof zool, 75-80, chmn dept paleontol, 78-79, asst dir, 79-80, ADJ PROF GEOL, FLA STATE MUS, UNIV FLA, 73-, CHMN DEPT NATURAL SCI, 79-, ASSOC DIR, 80- *Concurrent Pos:* Diving officer, Dept Natural Sci, Univ Fla, 74-, asst prof, Ctr Latin Am Studies, 75- *Mem:* Soc Econ Paleontologists & Mineralogists; Paleont Soc; Geol Soc Am; Paleont Res Inst; Int Paleont Asn. *Res:* Diversity, structure, and evolution of shallow benthic marine communities; succession in late Pleistocene freshwater communities; echinoid evolution, biogeography and biometrics. *Mailing Add:* Fla State Mus Univ Fla Gainesville FL 32611

SHAATH, NADIM ALI, b Jaffa, Palestine, Dec 10, 45; m 67; c 1. ORGANIC CHEMISTRY, MEDICINAL CHEMISTRY. *Educ:* Univ Alexandria, BSc, 67; Univ Minn, PhD(org chem), 73. *Prof Exp:* Teaching assoc chem, Univ mMinn, 67-72, res specialist med chem, 72-75; from asst prof to assoc prof chem, State Univ NY, Purchase, 75-81; RES DIR, FELTON INT, 81- *Concurrent Pos:* Teaching assoc, Exten Div, Univ Minn, 70-73; prin investr multiple grants, 76- *Mem:* Am Chem Soc; AAAS. *Res:* Neuromuscular junction blocking or paralysing drugs; nuclear magnetic resonance shift reagents; mechanism of organic reactions; metabolism of narcotic stimulants; flavors and fragrances. *Mailing Add:* Felton Int 599 Johnson Ave Brooklyn NY 11237

SHABANOWITZ, HARRY, b Brooklyn, NY, Nov 11, 18; m 43; c 2. MATHEMATICS. *Educ:* City Col New York, BS, 49; Columbia Univ, MA, 50; Syracuse Univ, PhD(math educ), 74. *Prof Exp:* Sr engr, Westinghouse Elec Corp, 51-65 & Gen Elec Co, 65-66; assoc prof, 66-80, PROF MATH, ELMIRA COL, 80- *Concurrent Pos:* Spec lectr, 57-65. *Mem:* Am Math Soc; NY Acad Sci. *Res:* Research and development of high sensitivity television camera tubes; theoretical and experimental investigation of the factors limiting television camera tube performance; study of high quantum efficiency photoemissive surfaces; secondary electron emission; electron optical geometry. *Mailing Add:* Dept Math Elmira Col Elmira NY 14901

SHABEL, BARRIE STEVEN, b New York, NY, Aug 31, 38; m 62; c 1. METALLURGY. *Educ:* Mass Inst Technol, SB, 59; Rensselaer Polytech Inst, MMetE, 61; Syracuse Univ, PhD(solid state sci), 67. *Prof Exp:* Mat engr, zirconium/columbium alloys, Knolls Atomic Power Lab, 59-60, mat engr radiation damage, 60-63; res engr aluminum alloys, Phys Metall Div, Alcoa Res Labs, 66-74; 66-74, sr res engr, 74-75; sr res engr mech & metalworking, Eng Properties & Design Div, Alcoa Labs, 75-78, sr res engr, STAFF ENGR MECH & ALUMINUM ALLOYS, ALLOY TECHNOL DIV, ALCOA TECH CTR, 80- *Mem:* Am Soc Metals; Am Metall Soc; Inst Mining, Metall & Petrol Engrs. *Res:* Physical and mechanical metallurgy of aluminum alloys; mechanics of sheet metal forming, plasticity; application of statistics to industrial research. *Mailing Add:* Alcoa Tech Ctr Alcoa Center PA 15069

SHABICA, ANTHONY CHARLES, JR, b Meadville, Pa, Nov 20, 15; m 40; c 3. ORGANIC CHEMISTRY. *Educ:* Brown Univ, ScB, 38; Pa State Univ, MS, 39, PhD(org chem), 42. *Prof Exp:* Jr chemist, Calco Chem Co, 37 & 39; asst, Pa State Univ, 39-42; sr chemist, Merck & Co, Inc, 42-46; head develop dept, CIBA Pharmaceut Co, 46-48, dir develop res, 48-67, vpres develop & control, 67-81; ADJ PROF, COL VIRGIN ISLANDS, 81- *Concurrent Pos:* Mem bd, NJ Coun Res & Develop, 68-, chmn, 76-77; res assoc, Woods Hole Oceanog Inst. *Mem:* Am Pharmaceut Asn; Am Chem Soc; fel Am Inst Chemists; fel NY Acad Sci; Int Pharmaceut Fedn. *Res:* Heterocyclic chemistry; natural products; mechanism of the polymerization of olefins; steroidal sapogenins and related compounds alkaloids; process research, development and design. *Mailing Add:* Box 1631 Destin FL 32541

SHABICA, CHARLES WRIGHT, b Elizabeth, NJ, Jan 2, 43; m 67; c 2. MARINE SCIENCES, LIMNOLOGY. *Educ:* Brown Univ, AB, 65; Univ Chicago, PhD(evolutionary biol), 71. *Prof Exp:* Res asst marine biol, Woods Hole Oceanog Inst, 66-67; assoc prof, 71-80, PROF EARTH SCI, NORTHEASTERN ILL UNIV, 80-, ASSOC CHMN DEPT, 75- *Concurrent Pos:* Partic, Ctr Grad Studies, Field Mus Natural Hist, 68-; vpres, Village Printers, NC, 71-74; coordr, Kaskaskia Plan, Northeastern Univ, 74-77; vis prof, Col VI, 80-81; prin investr marine sci curric, NSF grant, 81-84, earth watch exped, 80- *Honors & Awards:* Furcifer Macminahan Award, Field Mus Natural Hist, 69. *Mem:* Am Asn Petrol Geologists; Soc Econ Paleontologists & Mineralogists; Am Meteorol Soc; AAAS. *Res:* Coastal processes; Pennsylvanian stratigraphy. *Mailing Add:* 326 Ridge Ave Winnetka IL 60093

SHABICA, STEPHEN VALE, b Newark, NJ, Apr 16, 45; c 2. OCEANOGRAPHY. *Educ:* Brown Univ, BA, 69; Ore State Univ, MS, 74, PhD, 76. *Prof Exp:* Res asst oceanog, Sch Oceanog, Ore State Univ, 69-70; sta sci leader antarctic marine biol, Palmer Sta, Antarctica, NSF, 70-71; res asst oceanog, Sch Oceanog, Ore State Univ, 71-74, proj dir, Netarts Bay Studies, 75-76; consult, Lockheed Marine Biol, Calif, 76; RES OCEANOGRAPHER, COASTAL FIELD RES LAB, NAT PARK SERV, NAT SPACE TECH LABS, BAY ST LOUIS, 77- *Concurrent Pos:* Field marine biologist, Natural Sci Ctr, Wildcliff, NY, 71-; res asst estuarine biol, Sch Oceanog, Ore State Univ, 72; consult, Wilsey & Ham Inc, Portland, 74-76. *Mem:* Ecol Soc Am; Am Littoral Soc; Int Oceanog Found; Am Polar Soc; Sigma Xi. *Res:* Barrier Island dynamics; near shore processes; Barrier Island ecology; estuarine and near shore oceanography; reproductive biology and general ecology of Antarctic molluscs; intertidal and estuarine ecology of temperate and polar regions. *Mailing Add:* Coastal Field Res Lab Nat Space Tech Labs Sta Bay St Louis MS 39529

SHACK, ROLAND VINCENT, b Chicago, Ill, Jan 15, 27; m 57; c 4. OPTICS. *Educ:* Univ Md, BS, 49; Am Univ, BA, 51; Univ London, PhD(physics), 65. *Prof Exp:* Physicist, Nat Bur Standards, 49-57 & Perkin-Elmer Corp, 57-64; res assoc, 64-65, assoc prof, 65-70, PROF OPTICS, UNIV ARIZ, 70- *Mem:* Optical Soc Am. *Res:* Optical image evaluation and testing; interferometry; systems analysis. *Mailing Add:* Optical Sci Ctr Univ of Ariz Tucson AZ 85721

SHACK, WILLIAM JOHN, b Pittsburgh, Pa, Jan 12, 43; m 75; c 1. APPLIED MECHANICS. *Educ:* Mass Inst Technol, BS, 64; Univ Calif, Berkeley, MS, 65, PhD(appl mech), 68. *Prof Exp:* From asst prof to assoc prof, Mass Inst Technol, 68-75; SCIENTIST, ARGONNE NAT LAB, 76- *Mem:* Am Soc Mech Engrs. *Res:* Solid mechanics; fracture mechanics; biomechanics; polymer processing. *Mailing Add:* Argonne Nat Lab Argonne IL 60439

SHACKELFORD, CHARLES L(EWIS), b Wagoner, Okla, Oct 19, 18; m 45; c 1. ELECTRONICS. *Educ:* Okla State Univ, BS, 41; Univ Mo, MS, 42. *Prof Exp:* Repairman, Porum Tel Co, 35-40; asst, Univ Mo, 41-42; engr, Westinghouse Elec Corp, Pa, 42, NJ, 42-52; engr, Chatham Electronics Div,

Tung-Sol Elec, Inc, 52-66, chief engr, Power Tube Div, NJ, 66-69; SR ENGR, ELECTRON TUBE DIV, INT TEL & TEL CORP, 69- Mem: Sr mem Inst Elec & Electronics Engrs. Res: Electron emission; conduction of electricity through gases and vapors. Mailing Add: 3916 Oakland Rd Bethlehem PA 18017

SHACKELFORD, ROBERT G, b Atlanta, Ga, Oct 25, 36; m 62; c 2. ELECTROOPTICS. Educ: Ga Inst Technol, BEE, 59, MSEE, 62, MSPhys, 67. Prof Exp: Assoc aircraft engr, Lockheed-Ga Div, Lockheed Aircraft Corp, 59; res asst microwave eng, 59-62, from asst res engr to res engr, 62-68, sr res physicist, 68-69, assoc chief spec tech div, 69-75, chief, Electrooptics Div, 75-77, PRIN RES SCIENTIST & ASSOC DIR, ELECTROMAGNETICS LAB, ENG EXP STA, GA INST TECHNOL, 77- Mem: Inst Elec & Electronics Engrs. Res: Electromagnetic theory; dielectric properties of materials; laser design and development; atmospheric propagation in the infrared-visible spectrum. Mailing Add: 5833 W Fayetteville Rd College Park GA 30349

SHACKELFORD, SCOTT ADDISON, b Long Beach, Calif, Aug 11, 44; m 69; c 2. ORGANIC CHEMISTRY, NOBLE GAS COMPOUND CHEMISTRY. Educ: Simpson Col, BA, 66; Northern Ariz Univ, MA, 68; Ariz State Univ, PhD(org chem), 73. Prof Exp: Teaching asst chem, Northern Ariz Univ, 66-68 & Ariz State Univ, 68-72; res chemist, Frank J Seiler Res Lab, 72-74, prin investr & div chief energetic chem, 74-77; Air Force WGer exchange scientist, Inst For Chem Antrieb & Verfahrenstech, 78-80; CHIEF, CHEM RES & DEVELOP SECT, AIR FORCE ROCKET PROPULSION LAB, 80-, PROPELLANT CHEM TASK MGR, 82- Concurrent Pos: Lectr, Dept Chem, US Air Force Acad, 74-78, asst prof, 78-; secy, Joint Tech Coord Group, 75-77; prin investr org synthesis & mech, 81- Honors & Awards: Award Cert Sci Achievement, Dept Air Force, 74, Award Cert Chem Invention, 75 & 77; AFSC Tech Achievement Award, 77. Mem: Am Chem Soc. Res: Mechanistic elucidation of thermochemical and synthetic reactions via kinetic isotope effects and deuterium labeling; selective organic compound xenon difluoride fluorination; new synthetic transformations for energetic aliphatic chemistry; chemical propulsion concepts. Mailing Add: Air Force Rocket Propulsion Lab Edwards AFB CA 93523

SHACKELFORD, WALTER MCDONALD, b Birmingham, Ala, Jan 8, 45; m 69; c 1. ANALYTICAL CHEMISTRY. Educ: Univ Miss, BS, 67; Ga Inst Technol, PhD(anal chem), 71. Prof Exp: Chemist, E I du Pont de Nemours & Co, Inc, Chattanooga Nylon Plant, 67; res assoc, Univ New Orleans, 73-74; RES CHEMIST, ATHENS ENVIRON RES LAB, US ENVIRON PROTECTION AGENCY, 74- Concurrent Pos: Chemist, Edgewood Arsenal, Md, 71-73. Mem: Sigma Xi; Am Chem Soc; Am Soc Mass Spectrometry. Res: Trace analysis of water for organic compounds using gas chromatography-mass spectrometry; computer systems; applications of mini-computers in analytical chemistry. Mailing Add: 470 Ponderosa Dr Athens GA 30605

SHACKLE, DALE RICHARD, b Caldwell, Ohio, Oct 4, 41; m 65; c 2. CHEMISTRY. Educ: Marietta Col, BS, 63; Ohio Univ, PhD(chem), 69. Prof Exp: Chemist process improv, Goodyear Atomic Corp, 63-65; teaching asst chem, Ohio Univ, 65-69; proj leader paper coatings, 69-74, sect head, 74-77, mgr process eng, 77-79, ASSOC DIR RES, MEAD CORP, 79- Res: Specialty coatings for paper and the materials used in these coatings. Mailing Add: Cent Res Lab Mead Corp Chillicothe OH 45601

SHACKLEFORD, JOHN MURPHY, b Mobile, Ala, Dec 22, 29; m 54; c 2. ANATOMY. Educ: Spring Hill Col, BS, 57; Univ Ala, PhD(anat), 61. Prof Exp: From instr to assoc prof anat, Med Ctr, Univ Ala, 61-72, asst prof dent, 64-72; chmn dept, 72-80, PROF ANAT, COL MED, UNIV SOUTH ALA, 72- Concurrent Pos: NIH res grants, 62-72. Mem: Am Asn Anatomists. Res: Cytochemistry and histophysiology of exocrine glands; electron microscopy of bones and teeth. Mailing Add: Dept Anat Col Med Univ SAla Mobile AL 36688

SHACKLETT, COMER DRAKE, physical organic chemistry, see previous edition

SHACKLETT, ROBERT LEE, b Calif, Apr 5, 26; Div; c 2. PHYSICS. Educ: Calif State Univ, Fresno, AB, 49; Calif Inst Technol, PhD(physics), 56. Prof Exp: From asst prof to assoc prof physics, 55-65, asst acad vpres, 67-68; asst dean sch grad studies, 68-75, actg dean sch grad studies, 75-76, prof, 65-79, EMER PROF PHYSICS, CALIF STATE UNIV, FRESNO, 79- Concurrent Pos: NSF fel, Univ Uppsala, 61-62. Honors & Awards: Co-inventor, Digital Commun Syst, US Patent Off, 75. Mem: Am Phys Soc; Am Asn Physics Teachers; fel Am Sci Affil; Sigma Xi. Res: physics of consciousness. Mailing Add: 5015 Winsford Court Newark CA 94560

SHACKLETTE, HANSFORD THRELKELD, b Henderson, Ky, Sept 1, 14. BOTANY. Educ: Univ Ky, BS, 35, MS, 37; Univ Mich, PhD(bot), 63. Prof Exp: Instr bot, Univ Ky, 37-41 & Colgate Univ, 55-56; asst prof, Hanover Col, 57 & Georgetown Col, 57-61; RES BOTANIST, US GEOL SURV, 61- Honors & Awards: US Geol Surv Award, 66; US Dept Interior Meritorious Serv Award, 73. Mem: Arctic Inst NAm; Brit Bryol Soc. Res: Arctic and north boreal soil-plant relationships; distribution and ecology of bryophytes; element content of plants related to soil chemistry; use of plants in mineral prospecting. Mailing Add: Regional Geochem Br US Geol Surv Fed Ctr Bldg 25 Denver CO 80225

SHACTER, JOHN, b Vienna, Austria, Sept 26, 21; nat US; m 47; c 2. CHEMICAL ENGINEERING. Educ: Univ Pa, BS, 43. Prof Exp: Supvr develop, Union Carbide Corp, SAM Labs, Columbia Univ, 43-44; uranium isotope separation design & opers anal, Oak Ridge, Tenn, 44-56, new proj planning & eval, Union Carbide Develop Co, NY, 56-58, asst dir tech planning, Union Carbide Corp, 58-60, mgr planning & mgr nept res, 60-66, dir, AEC Combined Opers Planning in Oak Ridge & Washington, DC, 66-72, ASST TO PRES & MGT-TECH CONSULT, NUCLEAR DIV, UNION CARBIDE CORP, 72- Concurrent Pos: Lectr mgt & eng, 53-; consult, US Dept Defense, 55-56 & East-West Int Inst, Laxenburg, Austria, 78-; mem mgt & technol comt, Nat Acad Sci, 78-; Nat coordr of energy educ, Multieng-Soc Coord Comt on Energy, 78-; founded John Shacter Assocs, mgt & tech consult & workshops, 77- Mem: Am Inst Chem Engrs; Inst Mgt Sci; Am Mgt Asn. Res: Process design and evaluation, separation processes and cascades; operations analysis and planning, energy planning, technical, financial and business planning; management and leadership of seminars. Mailing Add: 107 Westoverlook Dr Oak Ridge TN 37830

SHADBOLT, C ALLAN, b Benito, Man, July 25, 27; m 56; c 3. HORTICULTURE, PLANT PHYSIOLOGY. Educ: Univ Man, BSA, 49, MS, 52; Univ Wis, PhD(hort, plant physiol), 55. Prof Exp: Asst oleiculturist, Univ Calif, Riverside, 55-62; dir field res & develop, N Cent Region, 62-65, NAT DIR FIELD RES & DEVELOP, THOMPSON-HAYWARD CHEM CO, 65- Mem: Weed Sci Soc Am. Res: Agricultural chemical research and development. Mailing Add: Thompson-Hayward Chem Co PO Box 2383 Kansas City KS 66110

SHADDUCK, JOHN ALLEN, b Toledo, Ohio, Apr 22, 39; m 60; c 2. COMPARATIVE PATHOLOGY, VIROLOGY. Educ: Ohio State Univ, DVM, 63, MSc, 65, PhD(vet path), 67; Am Col Vet Pathologists, dipl. Prof Exp: Fel vet path, Ohio State Univ, 63-67, from asst prof to assoc prof vet path, 67-73; from assoc prof to prof comp path, Univ Tex Health Sci Ctr, Dallas, 73-80; PROF VET PATH & HEAD DEPT, COL VET MED, UNIV ILL, 80- Concurrent Pos: Fel comp virol & neuropath, Univ Munich, 67-68; consult indust, fed govt, Food & Drug Admin & WHO; prin investr grants & contracts; ed, Vet Path. Mem: AAAS; Am Vet Med Asn; Am Soc Exp Path; Am Col Vet Path. Res: Viral oncology; ophthalmic pathology; infectious diseases; host-parasite relationships; immunoregulatory events; comparative and functional aspects of inflammation. Mailing Add: Dept Vet Path Col Vet Med Univ Ill Urbana IL 61801

SHADDY, JAMES HENRY, b Everett, Wash, Aug 30, 38; m 66. ECOLOGY, ENTOMOLOGY. Educ: Okla State Univ, BS, 62, MS, 64; Mich State Univ, PhD(entom), 70. Prof Exp: Res technician, Mich State Univ, 67-68; ASSOC PROF ECOL, NORTHEAST MO STATE UNIV, 69- Mem: Audubon Soc; Ecol Soc Am; Entom Soc Am; Nat Asn Col Teachers Agr. Res: Environmental assessment; Collembola taxonomy and biology; aquatic biology; strip mine revegetation. Mailing Add: Sci Div Northeast Mo State Univ Kirksville MO 63501

SHADE, ELWOOD B, b Hollidaysburg, Pa, Aug 9, 13; div. FORESTRY, BIOLOGICAL SCIENCES. Educ: Juniata Col, BA, 35; Pa State Univ, BSF, 46, MF, 47. Prof Exp: Pub sch instr, Pa, 41-44 & Md, 44-45; forester, US Forest Serv, 47-55; park forester, City of Portland, Ore, 55-56; naturalist, Nat Park Serv, 56-57; asst prof, 57-60, ASSOC PROF FORESTRY, UNIV ARK, MONTICELLO, 60- Mem: Soc Am Foresters. Res: Forest and outdoor recreation. Mailing Add: Dept of Forestry Univ of Ark Box 2528 Monticello AR 71655

SHADE, JOHN WILLIAM, geochemistry, mineralogy, see previous edition

SHADE, JOYCE ELIZABETH, b Louisville, Ky, Oct 30, 53. SYNTHETIC INORGANIC CHEMISTRY. Educ: Univ Louisville, BA, 75, PhD(chem), 80. Prof Exp: Asst chem, Univ Louisville, 75-80; res fel, Ohio State Univ, 80-82; ASST PROF CHEM, US NAVAL ACAD, 82- Concurrent Pos: Instr chem, Univ Louisville, 79; physics teacher, Presentation Acad, 77-79. Mem: Am Chem Soc; Sigma Xi. Res: Syntheses and characterization of cyclopentadienyl-type iron complexes; identification of diastereomeric isomers. Mailing Add: 1220 Chambers Rd 425B Columbus OH 43212

SHADE, RAY W(ALTON), b Souderton, Pa, Jan 11, 27; m 52; c 1. CHEMICAL ENGINEERING. Educ: Mass Inst Technol, SB, 49, SM, 51; Rensselaer Polytech Inst, PhD(chem eng), 64. Prof Exp: Chem engr, Knolls Atomic Power Lab, Gen Elec Co, 51-53 & Res & Develop Ctr, 53-66, mgr polymer processing, 66-68, mgr proc eng br, 68-70; assoc prof bio-environ eng, Rensselaer Polytech Inst, 70-77, chmn environ eng curriculum, 71-77; CHEM ENGR, GEN ELEC CO, 77- Mem: Am Chem Soc; Am Inst Chem Engrs. Res: Chemical and polymer processing; vacuum technology and thin vacuum deposited films; electroless plating. Mailing Add: 19 El Dorado Dr Clifton Knolls NY 12207

SHADE, ROBERT EUGENE, b Dayton, Ohio, Nov 10, 42; m 70; c 2. PHYSIOLOGY, ENDOCRINOLOGY. Educ: Ind Univ, PhD(physiol), 70. Prof Exp: USPHS training grant, Med Sch, Univ Mo, 70-72; from asst prof to assoc prof physiol & biophys, Ctr Health Sci, Univ Tenn, Memphis, 72-78; ASSOC PROF PHYSIOL, SCH MED, UNIV SC, COLUMBIA, 78- Mem: Am Physiol Soc. Res: Renal-endocrine regulation of salt and water metabolism. Mailing Add: Dept of Physiol & Biophys Univ SC Sch of Med Columbia SC 29209

SHADER, LESLIE ELWIN, b Ft Collins, Colo, July 18, 35; m 58; c 3. MATHEMATICS. Educ: Colo State Univ, BS, 57, MS, 61; Univ Colo, Boulder, PhD(math), 69. Prof Exp: Teacher math, High Sch, Colo, 57-58 & Wyo, 58-59; asst, Colo State Univ, 59-61; instr, Univ Wyo, 61-63; instr, Univ Colo, Boulder, 65-66 & 67-68; from instr to asst prof, 68-73, assoc prof, 73-81, PROF MATH, UNIV WYO, 81- Mem: Am Math Soc; Math Asn Am. Res: Polynomials over a finite field; matrix theory; combinatorics; number theory. Mailing Add: Dept of Math Univ of Wyo Laramie WY 82070

SHADOFF, LEWIS ALLAN, analytical chemistry, mass spectrometry, see previous edition

SHADOMY, HELEN JEAN, mycology, microbiology, see previous edition

SHADOMY, SMITH, b Denver, Colo, Aug 29, 31; m 56; c 2. MEDICAL MICROBIOLOGY. *Educ:* Univ Calif, Los Angeles, BA, 56, PhD(microbiol), 63. *Prof Exp:* Instr biol, San Fernando Valley State Col, 61-62; asst prof infectious dis, 65-71, assoc prof, 71-77, PROF MED & MICROBIOL, DEPT MED, MED COL VA, 77- *Concurrent Pos:* Mem fac, Mil Nursing Pract & Res, Dept Nursing, Walter Reed Army Inst Res, 65-66 & Otolaryngol Basic Sci Course, Armed Forces Inst Path, 66. *Mem:* Int Soc Human & Animal Mycol; Brit Mycol Soc; Am Soc Microbiol; Asn Mil Surgeons US; Infectious Dis Soc Am. *Res:* Chemotherapeutic evaluations; environmental microbiology; medical mycology; patient isolation; chemotherapeutic studies in bacterial and fungal diseases; epidemiology of mycotic infections. *Mailing Add:* Div of Infectious Dis Med Col Va Commonwealth Univ Richmond VA 23298

SHADOWEN, HERBERT EDWIN, b Fredonia, Ky, Sept 11, 26; m 50; c 3. VERTEBRATE ZOOLOGY. *Educ:* Berea Col, BA, 50; Univ Ky, MS, 51; La State Univ, PhD(zool), 56. *Prof Exp:* Assoc prof zool, La Polytech Inst, 55-61; PROF BIOL, WESTERN KY UNIV, 61- *Mem:* Am Soc Mammal; Am Ornith Union. *Res:* Small-mammal population studies; taxonomy of amphibians and reptiles. *Mailing Add:* Dept of Biol Western Ky Univ Bowling Green KY 42102

SHAEFFER, JOSEPH ROBERT, b New York, NY, June 3, 35; m 57; c 3. MOLECULAR BIOLOGY, BIOCHEMISTRY. *Educ:* Mass Inst Technol, SB, 56; Univ Rochester, PhD(biophys), 62. *Prof Exp:* Res fel biochem, Univ Ky, 62-65; asst physicist, Univ Tex M D Anderson Hosp & Tumor Inst, 65-68, asst biologist, 68-71, assoc biologist, 71-76; vis assoc prof med, Peter Bent Brigham Hosp, Boston, 76-77; INVESTR, CTR BLOOD RES, 77-; ASSOC PROF MED BIOCHEM, HARVARD MED SCH, 78- *Concurrent Pos:* USPHS fel, 62-64. *Mem:* Biophys Soc; Am Soc Biol Chemists; NY Acad Sci; Am Soc Hematol. *Res:* Hemoglobin biosynthesis. *Mailing Add:* Ctr for Blood Res 800 Huntington Ave Boston MA 02115

SHAEIWITZ, JOSEPH ALAN, b Brooklyn, NY, Oct 12, 52. CHEMICAL ENGINEERING. *Educ:* Univ Del, BS, 74; Carnegie-Mellon Univ, MS, 76, PhD(chem eng), 78. *Prof Exp:* ASST PROF CHEM ENG, UNIV ILL, 78- *Mem:* Am Inst Chem Engrs; Am Chem Soc; AAAS; Am Soc Eng Educ. *Res:* Mass transfer of surfactants near solid-liquid and liquid-liquid interfaces as related to surfactant adsorption and fat digestion; diffusion and migration of colloidal particles, especially diffusiophoresis and thermophoresis. *Mailing Add:* Dept of Chem Eng 1209 W Calif St Urbana IL 61801

SHAER, ELIAS HANNA, b Beit-Jala, Israel, Aug 2, 41; US citizen; m 70; c 2. PHYSICAL & ANALYTICAL CHEMISTRY. *Educ:* Austin Peay State Univ, BS, 66; Univ Miss, MS, 70, PhD(phys chem), 77. *Prof Exp:* Lab instr chem, Univ Miss, 66-70; dir chem, Div Contractors, Vulcan Waterproofing Co, 70-73; lab instr chem, Univ Miss, 73-77; sr res chemist, 77-80, SCIENTIST RES & DEVELOP, DRACKETT CO, 80- *Mem:* Am Chem Soc. *Res:* Kinetics solvent effect on the rate of methyl radicals combination; thermodynamics of liquids and liquid mixtures; cleaning compositions and emulsions. *Mailing Add:* Drackett Co 5020 Spring Grove Ave Cincinnati OH 45232

SHAER, NORMAN ROBERT, b Boston, Mass, Mar 31, 37; m 58; c 2. COMPUTER SCIENCE, ELECTRICAL ENGINEERING. *Educ:* Tufts Univ, BSEE, 58; New York Univ, MEE, 60. *Prof Exp:* Mem tech staff, Bell Tel Labs, 58-63, supvr systs eng, 63-66, dept head electronic switching, 66-69; vpres bus info systs, Comput Systs Labs, 69-71; mgr comput sci, 72-74, HEAD, DEPT COMPUT SCI, BELL TEL LABS, 74- *Mem:* AAAS; Inst Elec & Electronics Engrs. *Res:* Use of computers for large scale, real time systems; design and implementation. *Mailing Add:* Bell Tel Labs Crawfords Corner Rd Holmdel NJ 07733

SHAFAI, LOTFOLLAH, b Maraghen, Iran, Mar 17, 41; Can citizen; m 66; c 2. MICROWAVES, ELECTRONICS. *Educ:* Univ Tehran, BSc, 63; Univ Toronto, MSc, 66, PhD(elec eng), 69. *Prof Exp:* Lectr elec eng, Univ Man, 69-70, from asst prof to assoc prof, 70-76; vis scientist appl electromagnetic, Commun Res Ctr, Ottawa, 76-77; vis prof, Electromagnetic Inst, Tech Univ Denmark, 77-79; PROF ELEC ENG, UNIV MAN, 79- *Mem:* Sr mem Inst Elec & Electronics Engrs; Am Geophys Union. *Res:* Antennas; electromagnetic scattering and diffraction; wave guides; computer solution of field problems; optics. *Mailing Add:* Dept Elec Eng Univ Man Winnipeg MB R3T 2N2 Can

SHAFER, A WILLIAM, b Great Bend, Kans, Nov 1, 27; m 50; c 2. MEDICINE. *Educ:* Univ Kans, BA, 50, MD, 54. *Prof Exp:* Assoc hemat, Scripps Clin & Res Found, 59-60, assoc mem, 60-66, head hemat, 64-66; assoc prof lab med, Health Sci Ctr, Univ Okla, 66-70, from asst prof to prof med, 66-73, prof path & med, Col Med & dir clin labs, Med Ctr, Univ Ky, 73-75; DIR, SOUTH EASTERN MICH RED CROSS BLOOD CTR, 75- *Concurrent Pos:* Clin prof med & adj prof allied health, Wayne State Univ, 76- *Mem:* Col Am Physicians; Am Bd Internal Med; Am Bd Path; Am Fedn Clin Res; fel Am Soc Clin Path. *Res:* Metabolism of normal, abnormal and stored erythrocytes. *Mailing Add:* South Eastern Mich Red Cross Blood Ctr Box 351 Detroit MI 48232

SHAFER, JULES ALAN, b New York, NY, Nov 21, 37; m 59; c 3. PHYSICAL ORGANIC CHEMISTRY, BIOCHEMISTRY. *Educ:* City Col New York, BChE, 59; Polytech Inst Brooklyn, PhD(chem), 63. *Prof Exp:* Fel chem, Polytech Inst Brooklyn, 62-63 & Harvard Univ, 63-64; from asst prof to assoc prof, 64-77, PROF BIOL CHEM, UNIV MICH, ANN ARBOR, 77- *Concurrent Pos:* NIH grants, 65-80; Rackham res grant, 66-67; NATO vis prof, Univ Rome. *Mem:* AAAS; Am Chem Soc; Am Soc Biol Chemists; NY Acad Sci. *Res:* Mechanisms and models of enzyme action, especially enzymic catalysis of hydrolytic reactions and reactions involving pyridoxal phosphate; functions of proteins on cell surfaces. *Mailing Add:* Dept of Biol Chem Univ of Mich Ann Arbor MI 48109

SHAFER, M(ERRILL) W(ILBERT), b Grier City, Pa, July 25, 28; m 54; c 4. SOLID STATE CHEMISTRY, MATERIALS SCIENCE. *Educ:* Susquehanna Univ, BA, 52; Pa State Univ, MS, 54, PhD(ceramic tech), 56. *Prof Exp:* Asst, Pa State Univ, 54-56; res chemist, Res Lab, 56-72, MGR, SOLID STATE CHEM, IBM RES LAB, 72- *Mem:* Am Ceramic Soc; Am Phys Soc; Electrochem Soc; NY Acad Sci. *Res:* High temperature and solid state chemistry involving oxides, fluorides and sulfides; synthesis and evaluation of magnetic materials, particularly the rare earths; synthesis and evaluation of physical properties of electronic materials; especially magnetic, luminesent and semiconducting properties; flouride gasses and wide band gap insulators for electronic packaging. *Mailing Add:* T J Watson Res Ctr IBM Corp Box 218 Yorktown Heights NY 10598

SHAFER, PAUL RICHARD, b Springfield, Ohio, June 17, 23; m 46; c 3. ORGANIC CHEMISTRY. *Educ:* Oberlin Col, BA, 47; Univ Wis, PhD(chem), 51. *Prof Exp:* Fel, Univ Ill, 51-52; from instr to assoc prof, 52-63, PROF CHEM, DARTMOUTH COL, 63- *Concurrent Pos:* NSF fel, Calif Inst Technol, 59-60. *Mem:* Am Chem Soc; Royal Soc Chem. *Res:* Natural products; reaction mechanisms; nuclear magnetic resonance of fast exchange reactions. *Mailing Add:* Dept of Chem Dartmouth Col Hanover NH 03755

SHAFER, RICHARD HOWARD, b New Rochelle, NY, July 20, 44; m 74. BIOPHYSICAL CHEMISTRY. *Educ:* Yale Univ, BA, 66; Harvard Univ, MA, 69, PhD(chem physics), 72. *Prof Exp:* Fel, Univ Calif, San Diego, 73-75; ASST PROF CHEM & PHARMACEUT CHEM, UNIV CALIF, SAN FRANCISCO, 75- *Mem:* Am Chem Soc; Biophys Soc. *Res:* Physical chemistry of nucleic acids; drug-nucleic acid interactions and hydrodynamic properties of high polymers. *Mailing Add:* Dept of Pharmaceut Chem Univ of Calif San Francisco CA 94143

SHAFER, ROBERT E, b San Francisco, Calif, June 2, 36; m 68. HIGH SPEED ELECTRONICS, ACCELERATOR DESIGN. *Educ:* Stanford Univ, BS, 58; Univ Calif, Berkeley, PhD(physics), 66. *Prof Exp:* Res assoc, Mass Inst Technol, 66-69; PHYSICIST RES & DEVELOP, FERMI NAT ACCELERATOR LAB, 69- *Mem:* Am Inst Physics. *Res:* High energy physics experiments; designing and building 1000 giga electron volt superconducting accelerator. *Mailing Add:* Mail Sta 345 Fermilab Box 500 Batavia IL 60510

SHAFER, SHELDON JAY, b Passaic, NJ, June 17, 48. ORGANIC CHEMISTRY. *Educ:* Fairleigh Dickinson Univ, BS, 70; State Univ NY, Albany, PhD(org chem), 76. *Prof Exp:* Res fel org chem, Univ Calif, Santa Cruz, 76-77; DEVELOP CHEMIST, PLASTICS DIV, GEN ELEC CO, 77- *Mem:* Am Chem Soc. *Res:* Physical organic chemistry; reaction mechanisms; organic electron transfer reactions; organosulfur chemistry. *Mailing Add:* Gen Elec Co One Plastics Div Pittsfield MA 01201

SHAFER, STEPHEN JOEL, b Philadelphia, Pa, Dec 28, 39; m 70. BIOCHEMICAL & DEVELOPMENTAL GENETICS. *Educ:* Haverford Col, BA, 63; Univ Pa, MS, 65; Temple Univ, PhD(biochem genetics), 72. *Prof Exp:* Res asst genetics, Haverford Col, 65-66; res assoc biochem genetics, Temple Univ, 72-73; asst prof, 73-78, ASSOC PROF BIOL, DOWLING COL, 78- *Mem:* Genetics Soc Am; NY Acad Sci; AAAS; Am Soc Zool. *Res:* Aspects of gene regulation involving transcriptional and translational control systems during eukaryotic development. *Mailing Add:* Dept of Biol Dowling Col Oakdale NY 11769

SHAFER, STEPHEN QUENTIN, b Barrytown, NY, Dec 18, 44; m 66; c 2. EPIDEMIOLOGY, NEUROEPIDEMIOLOGY. *Educ:* Harvard Univ, BA, 66; Columbia Univ, MD, 70, MPH, 77, MA, 79; Am Bd Internal Med, dipl, 75. *Prof Exp:* Intern & resident, Harlem Hosp Ctr, 70-72, clin fel neurol, 72-74, resident med, 74-75; clin scholar med, Johnson Clin Scholars Prog, 76-78, ASST PROF PUB HEALTH & NEUROL, SERGIEVSKY CTR, COLUMBIA UNIV, 78- *Concurrent Pos:* Asst attend physician, Harlem Hosp Ctr, 75-78; res assoc med, Columbia Col Physicians & Surgeons, 76-78. *Mem:* Am Pub Health Asn; Int Soc Cardiol; Am Fedn Clin Res; Soc Epidemiol Res. *Res:* Cerebrovascular disease; environmental health; chronic disease epidemiology; neuroepidemiology; epilepsy. *Mailing Add:* G H Sergievsky Ctr 630 W 168th St New York NY 10032

SHAFER, THOMAS HOWARD, b Columbus, Ohio, Jan 23, 48; m 70; c 2. PLANT PHYSIOLOGY, DEVELOPMENTAL BIOLOGY. *Educ:* Duke Univ, BS, 70; Ohio State Univ, MS, 73, PhD(bot), 75. *Prof Exp:* Res assoc develop plant physiol, Ohio State Univ, 75-76; vis asst prof, Denison Univ, 76-77 & Univ Ill, 77-78; ASST PROF, UNIV NC-WILMINGTON, 78- *Mem:* Am Soc Plant Physiologists; Bot Soc Am; AAAS. *Res:* Relation of plant hormones to the synthesis of gene products; gene activation in early embryogenesis. *Mailing Add:* Dept of Biol Univ of NC Wilmington NC 28406

SHAFER, WILLIAM GENE, b Toledo, Ohio, Nov 15, 23; m 43. ORAL PATHOLOGY. *Educ:* Univ Toledo, BS, 47; Ohio State Univ, DDS, 47; Univ Rochester, MS, 50; Am Bd Oral Path, dipl, 52. *Prof Exp:* From instr to assoc prof, 50-59, chmn dept, 56-59, PROF ORAL PATH, SCH DENT, IND UNIV, INDIANAPOLIS, 59-, DENT CANCER COORDR, 52- *Concurrent Pos:* Consult, US Vet Admin, 53- & Surgeon Gen, US Dept Air Force, 60-; secy-treas, Am Bd Oral Path, 61- *Mem:* AAAS; Soc Exp Biol & Med; Am Dent Asn; fel Am Acad Oral Path (vpres, 54, pres, 57); NY Acad Sci. *Res:* Experimental dental caries; salivary glands and endocrines; x-ray irradiation; experimental salivary gland tumors; tissue culture. *Mailing Add:* Dept of Oral Path Ind Univ Sch of Dent Indianapolis IN 46202

SHAFFER, BERNARD W(ILLIAM), b New York, NY, Aug 7, 24; m 47; c 2. ENGINEERING. *Educ:* City Col New York, BME, 44; Case Inst Technol, MS, 47; Brown Univ, PhD(appl math), 51. *Prof Exp:* Aeronaut res scientist, Nat Adv Comt Aeronaut, Ohio, 44-47; res assoc, Grad Div, Appl Math, Brown Univ, 47-50; from asst prof to prof mech eng, NY Univ, 50-73, proj dir, Res Div, 51-73; PROF MECH & AEROSPACE ENG, POLYTECH INST NEW YORK, 73- *Concurrent Pos:* Spec lectr, Case Inst Technol,

46-47. *Honors & Awards:* Richards Mem Award Outstanding Achievement, Am Soc Mech Engrs, 68. *Mem:* Fel Am Soc Mech Engrs; Am Soc Eng Educ; assoc fel Am Inst Aeronaut & Astronaut. *Res:* Stress analysis; elasticity; plasticity; kinematics; mechanics of metal cutting; analysis of filament inforced plastics. *Mailing Add:* 18 Bayside Dr Great Neck NY 11023

SHAFFER, CHARLES FRANKLIN, b Pittsburgh, Pa, Oct 9, 40; m 64; c 3. IMMUNOLOGY, TRANSPLANTATION BIOLOGY. *Educ:* Univ Pittsburgh, BS, 63, MS, 65; Univ Pa, PhD(biol), 68. *Prof Exp:* Pa scholar exp med, Dept Med Genetics, Sch Med, Univ Pa, 68-71; asst prof, 71-77, ASSOC PROF BIOL, WITTENBERG UNIV, 77- *Concurrent Pos:* Adj assoc prof microbiol & immunol, Med Sch, Wright State Univ, 77- *Mem:* Transplantation Soc; Am Asn Immunologists. *Res:* Immunologic and genetic aspects of tissue and organ transplantation. *Mailing Add:* Dept of Biol Wittenberg Univ Springfield OH 45501

SHAFFER, CHARLES HENRY, JR, b Washington, DC, Nov 20, 13; m 40; c 2. MICROBIOLOGY. *Educ:* Univ Md, BS, 38. *Prof Exp:* Bacteriologist, HEW, 42-45 & Div Antibiotics, Food & Drug Admin, 45-63; asst supvr, USDA, 63-70; supvr microbiologist, US Environ Protection Agency, 70-78; RETIRED. *Concurrent Pos:* Consult, TRACOR-JITCO Sci Mgt Serv Inc, 78-79. *Mem:* Am Soc Microbiol; Am Soc Testing & Mat; Soc Indust Microbiol. *Res:* Development and testing of new disinfectants for tuberuocidal activity. *Mailing Add:* 622 Rollins Ave Rockville MD 20852

SHAFFER, CHARLES V(ERNON), b Melbourne, Fla, Feb 22, 22; m 44; c 3. ELECTRICAL ENGINEERING. *Educ:* Univ Fla, BEE, 44, MSE, 60; Stanford Univ, PhD(elec eng), 65. *Prof Exp:* Asst res prof electronic ord, 46-51, assoc prof, 51-66, grad council, 65-68, asst dean grad sch, 69-71, PROF ELEC ENG, UNIV FLA, 66- *Concurrent Pos:* Consult, US Army Missile Command, 71-74; dir, Northeast Regional Data Ctr, State Univ Systs Fla, 72-74; mem tech staff, Bell Labs, Denver, Colo, 70-, Holmdel, NJ, 76- & IBM, Gen Systs Div, Boca Raton, Fla, 78- *Honors & Awards:* Award, NASA, 70. *Mem:* Am Soc Eng Educ; Inst Elec & Electronics Engrs. *Res:* Network theory and design; computer communications; system science; microcomputers. *Mailing Add:* Dept Elec Eng Univ Fla Gainesville FL 32611

SHAFFER, DAVID, b Johannesburg, SAfrica, Apr 20, 36; Brit citizen; c 2. CHILD PSYCHIATRY. *Educ:* Univ London, MB, BS, 61; MRCP, 64; FRCPsych, 81. *Prof Exp:* Lectr pediat, Univ Col Hosp, London, 64-65; registr psychiat, Maudsley Hosp, London, 65-69; sr registr & lectr child psychiat, Inst Psychiat, London, 69-74; sr lectr, 74-77, DIR DEPT CHILD PSYCHIAT, NY STATE PSYCHIAT INST, 77-; PROF CLIN PSYCHIAT & PEDIAT, COL PHYSICIANS & SURGEONS, COLUMBIA UNIV, 77- *Concurrent Pos:* von Ameringen fel, Found Fund Psychiat, Yale Univ, 67-68. *Honors & Awards:* Fellowes Medal Med, Univ London, 59. *Mem:* Asn Child Psychiat & Psychol, London (treas, 75-77); Am Acad Child Psychiat; Am Psychiat Asn; Brit Pediat Asn; Royal Col Psychiat, London (secy, 75-77). *Res:* Relationships between brain damage and psychiatric disorder in children; suicide and depression in childhood; psychological aspects of enuresis; classification of child psychiatric disorders. *Mailing Add:* Dept of Child Psychiat 722 W 168th St New York NY 10032

SHAFFER, DAVID BRUCE, b Berea, Ohio, Feb 17, 46; m 79. RADIO ASTRONOMY. *Educ:* Carnegie-Mellon Univ, BS, 68; Calif Inst Technol, PhD(astron), 74. *Prof Exp:* Teaching asst physics, Calif Inst Technol, 71-73; instr astron, Yale Univ, 73-75; asst scientist radio astron, Nat Radio Astron Observ, 75-77; assoc scientist, 77-79; STAFF SCIENTIST, VERY LONG BASELINE INTERFEROMETRY GROUP, PHOENIX CORP, 79- *Mem:* Am Astron Soc; Int Astron Union; Int Sci Radio Union. *Res:* Long baseline radio interferometry of compact extragalactic radio sources, galaxies and quasars. *Mailing Add:* Phoenix Corp c/o Code 974 NASA/GSFC Greenbelt MD 20771

SHAFFER, DOROTHY BROWNE, b Vienna, Austria, Feb 12, 23; nat US; m 43, 78; c 3. MATHEMATICS. *Educ:* Bryn Mawr Col, AB, 43; Radcliffe Col, MA, 45, PhD, 62. *Prof Exp:* Mem staff, Dynamic Anal & Control Lab, Mass Inst Technol, 45-47; asst, Harvard Univ, 48; consult, Corning Glass Works, 49-50; assoc mathematician, Cornell Aeronaut Lab, 52-56; staff mathematician, Dunlap & Assocs, Inc, 58-60; lectr, Univ Conn, Stamford Br, 63; from asst prof to assoc prof, 63-75, PROF MATH, FAIRFIELD UNIV, 75- *Concurrent Pos:* NSF fac fel, Courant Inst Math Sci, NY Univ, 69-70; Prof develop fel, Res Div, IBM Corp, 80; vis prof, Imperial Col Sci & Technol, London 78, Univ Md, College Park & Univ Calif, San Francisco, 80. *Mem:* Am Math Soc; Math Asn Am; Sigma Xi; Asn Women in Math; NY Acad Sci. *Res:* Conformal mapping and level curves of Green's Function; operations research; theoretical aerodynamics; polynomials; univalent functions; potential theory; special functions. *Mailing Add:* Dept Math Fairfield Univ Fairfield CT 06430

SHAFFER, DOUGLAS HOWERTH, b Danville, Pa, Oct 31, 28; m 52; c 2. MATHEMATICS. *Educ:* Carnegie Inst Technol, BS, 50, MS, 51, PhD, 53. *Prof Exp:* Instr math, Carnegie Inst Technol, 53-54; res mathematician, 54-63, fel mathematician, 63-65, adv mathematician, 65-75, consult mathematician, 75-79, MGR MATH, WESTINGHOUSE ELEC CORP, 79- *Mem:* Am Statist Asn; Soc Indust & Appl Math. *Res:* Applied and statistical mathematics; design of experiments; mathematics education. *Mailing Add:* Westinghouse Res Labs Pittsburgh PA 15235

SHAFFER, EDWARD C(HARLES), engineering physics, see previous edition

SHAFFER, GARY W, organic chemistry, photochemistry, see previous edition

SHAFFER, GEORGE EMERY, JR, physical chemistry, chemical engineering, see previous edition

SHAFFER, HARRY LEONARD, b Boston, Mass, Dec 15, 33; m 60; c 6. ELECTRICAL ENGINEERING. *Educ:* Northeastern Univ, BSEE, 62, MSEE, 64. *Prof Exp:* Res engr speech res, GTE Sylvania Appl Res Lab, 64-70, ENG SPECIALIST DIGITAL SIGNAL PROCESSING RES, EASTERN DIV, GTE SYLVANIA ELECTRONICS SYSTS GROUP, 70- *Concurrent Pos:* NSF grant, 63-64. *Mem:* Inst Elec & Electronics Engrs. *Res:* Development of algorithms to digitally process speech and modem signals, in real-time on mini-computers and micro-processors; extensive study into algorithms for secure-speech transmission on communications channels; digital signal processing. *Mailing Add:* 55 Howard Ave Lynnfield MA 01940

SHAFFER, JAMES GRANT, medical education, medical microbiology, deceased

SHAFFER, JAY CHARLES, b Sunbury, Pa, July 21, 38; m 69. SYSTEMATIC ENTOMOLOGY. *Educ:* Bucknell Univ, BS, 61; Cornell Univ, PhD(syst entom), 67. *Prof Exp:* Vis res assoc entom, Smithsonian Inst, 66-67; from asst prof to assoc prof, 68-81, PROF BIOL, GEORGE MASON UNIV, 81- *Concurrent Pos:* Assoc ed, Biotropica, 72- *Mem:* AAAS; Asn Trop Biol; Lepidop Soc. *Res:* Systematics and biology of the Pyralidae, Lepidoptera; origin, development and present status of the insect fauna of Aldabra atoll. *Mailing Add:* Dept of Biol George Mason Univ Fairfax VA 22030

SHAFFER, JOHN CLIFFORD, b Towanda, Pa, May 3, 38; m 66; c 2. PHYSICS. *Educ:* Franklin & Marshall Col, BS, 60; Univ Del, MS, 62, PhD(physics), 66. *Prof Exp:* Asst prof, 65-68, assoc prof, 68-75, PROF PHYSICS, NORTHERN ILL UNIV, 75-, CHMN DEPT, 73- *Mem:* AAAS; Am Phys Soc. *Res:* Optical properties of solids; luminescence; band structure of solids; disordered solids; surface physics. *Mailing Add:* Dept of Physics Northern Ill Univ De Kalb IL 60115

SHAFFER, JOHN WHITCOMB, b Harrisburg, Pa, Jan 6, 32; m 53; c 2. BEHAVIORAL SCIENCES, STATISTICS. *Educ:* Pa State Univ, BS, 53, MS, 54, PhD(psychol), 57. *Prof Exp:* Chief behav sci, Friends Med Sci Res Ctr, Inc, 63-67; from instr to asst prof, 57-78, ASSOC PROF MED PSYCHOL, SCH MED, JOHNS HOPKINS UNIV, 78- *Concurrent Pos:* Consult, Social Security Admin, 65-, Friends Med Sci Res Ctr, Inc, 67-, Md Dept Health & Ment Hyg, 67-, Md Med Legal Found, 68- & Md Med Chirurgical Fac, 75- *Mem:* Am Psychol Asn; Am Statist Asn; AAAS. *Res:* Research design; statistical analysis; psychological measurement and evaluation; psychopharmacology; traffic safety; suicide prevention; alcohol and drug addiction; precursors of heart disease and cancer. *Mailing Add:* Dept of Med Psychol Johns Hopkins Hosp Baltimore MD 21205

SHAFFER, LAWRENCE BRUCE, b Delta, Ohio, Oct 14, 37; m 59; c 4. PHYSICS. *Educ:* Ohio State Univ, BSc, 59; Univ Wis, MSc, 60, PhD(physics), 64. *Prof Exp:* Asst prof physics, Hiram Col, 63-70, chmn dept, 64-70; PROF PHYSICS & CHMN DEPT, ANDERSON COL, IND, 70- *Concurrent Pos:* Res Corp grants, 64-; teaching equip grants, NSF, 65-67 & Kettering Found, 65-; NASA res grants, 66-69; guest scientist, Inst Solid State Res, Nuclear Res Ctr, Julich GmbH, WGer, 77-78. *Mem:* AAAS; Am Phys Soc; Am Asn Physics Teachers; Am Crystallog Asn. *Res:* Thermodynamics of liquids and solutions using x-ray methods; measurement of dislocations and interstitial atom content in crystal surfaces by x-ray methods. *Mailing Add:* Dept of Physics Anderson Col Anderson IN 46011

SHAFFER, LOUIS RICHARD, b Sharon, Pa, Feb 7, 28; m 55; c 3. CONSTRUCTION ENGINEERING. *Educ:* Carnegie-Mellon Univ, BS, 50; Univ Ill, Urbana, MS, 57, PhD(systs civil eng), 61. *Prof Exp:* Asst to master mech, Nat Castings Co, Pa, 50-52, asst to dir eng, Sharon Steel Corp, 53-54; instr eng, 55-56, from asst prof to assoc prof, 61-65, PROF CIVIL ENG, UNIV ILL, URBANA, 65-; TECH DIR CONSTRUCT ENG RES LAB, US ARMY, 76- *Concurrent Pos:* Asst dir, Tech Dir Construct Eng Res Lab, US Army, 69-70 & dep dir, 70-76; chmn res comt, Proj Mgt Inst, 73-; coordr, Int Working Comn on Orgn & Mgt Construct, 74-; chmn US Nat comt, Int Coun Bldg Res, 77- *Honors & Awards:* Walter L Huber Res Prize, Am Soc Civil Engrs, 67. *Mem:* Am Soc Civil Engrs (chmn, Tech Coun Res, 76-77). *Res:* Modern construction management with emphasis on technical innovation to increase productivity of management on all levels. *Mailing Add:* 2203 Pond St Urbana IL 61801

SHAFFER, MORRIS FRANK, b Revere, Mass, Feb 2, 10; m 43, 59; c 2. MEDICAL MICROBIOLOGY. *Educ:* Mass Inst Technol, SB, 30; Oxford Univ, PhD(bact), 34, DSc(microbiol), 73. *Prof Exp:* Asst biol & bact, Mass Inst Technol, 30-31; fel bact, Harvard Univ, 34-35, Nat Res Coun fel med, 35-36, asst bact, 36-38; res assoc div microbiol, Squibb Inst Med Res, NJ, 38-42; assoc bact & immunol, Harvard Med Sch, 42-43; from assoc prof to prof bact, Sch Med, Tulane Univ La, 43-73, chmn dept, 48-73; dean grad sch biomed sci, Col Med & Dent NJ, 73-77; COORDR OFF RES, MED SCH, LA STATE UNIV, 78-; EMER PROF, TULANE UNIV, 78- *Concurrent Pos:* Sr bacteriologist, Mass Antitoxin & Vaccine Lab, 42-43; consult virus & rickettsia sect, Commun Dis Ctr, USPHS; consult, Tulane-Colombia Proj, Int Coop Admin; mem comn measles & mumps, Bd Prev Epidemic Dis in US Army; mem comn enteric infections, Armed Forces Epidemiol Bd; chmn microbiol & immunol study sect, NIH, chmn microbiol res training comt, Div Gen Med Sci, mem comt int res fels; mem comt, Lederle Med Fac Awards. *Mem:* Am Soc Microbiol (vpres, 70-71, pres, 71-72); Soc Exp Biol & Med; Am Soc Trop Med & Hyg; Am Asn Immunol. *Mailing Add:* Sch of Med La State Univ 1542 Tulane Ave New Orleans LA 70112

SHAFFER, PATRICIA MARIE, b Los Angeles, Calif, June 11, 28. BIOCHEMISTRY. *Educ:* San Francisco Col Women, BA, 52; Stanford Univ, MS, 59; Univ Calif, San Diego, PhD(chem), 75. *Prof Exp:* Asst prof chem, San Diego Col Women, 59-68; student counr, 59-78, assoc prof, 71-81, PROF CHEM, UNIV SAN DIEGO, 81- *Concurrent Pos:* NATO fel, Univ Newcastle upon Tyne, England, 80-81. *Res:* Metabolism of primidine deoxyribonucleosides in Neurospora crassa aspergillus nidulans and in mammalian systems and in mammalian systems. *Mailing Add:* Dept of Chem Univ of San Diego San Diego CA 92110

SHAFFER, ROBERT LYNN, b Long Beach, Calif, Dec 29, 29; m 58; c 1. MYCOLOGY, TAXONOMY. *Educ:* Kans State Col, BS, 51, MS, 52; Cornell Univ, PhD, 55. *Prof Exp:* From instr to asst prof bot, Univ Chicago, 55-60; from asst prof to assoc prof, 60-70, PROF BOT, UNIV MICH, ANN ARBOR, 70-, CUR FUNGI, HERBARIUM, 60-, DIR, 75- *Mem:* Mycol Soc Am (secy-treas, 68-71, vpres, 71-72, pres, 72-73); NAm Mycol Asn; Int Asn Plant Taxonomists. *Res:* Taxonomy of fungi, especially Agaricales. *Mailing Add:* Herbarium Univ of Mich Ann Arbor MI 48109

SHAFFER, RONALD JAY, fracture mechanics, earth science, see previous edition

SHAFFER, RUSSELL ALLEN, b Philadelphia, Pa, Nov 3, 33; m 58; c 4. THEORETICAL PHYSICS. *Educ:* Drexel Univ, BS, 56; Johns Hopkins Univ, PhD(physics), 62. *Prof Exp:* Res assoc physics, Vanderbilt Univ, 62-64; asst prof, 64-67, ASSOC PROF PHYSICS, LEHIGH UNIV, 67- *Mem:* Am Asn Physics Teachers. *Res:* Quantum field theory; theory of elementary particle interactions; weak and electromagnetic interactions; lepton physics. *Mailing Add:* Dept of Physics Bldg 16 Lehigh Univ Bethlehem PA 18015

SHAFFNER, CLYNE SAMUEL, b Freeland, Mich, Apr 18, 14; m 51; c 2. POULTRY SCIENCE. *Educ:* Mich State Col, BS, 38, MS, 40; Purdue Univ, PhD(physiol), 47. *Prof Exp:* Asst poultry, Mich State Col, 38-40; asst, Purdue Univ, 40-41, instr poultry husb, 41-42, fed-state grading supvr, 42-44; prof poultry physiol, 47-55, head, Dept Poultry Sci, 55-72, prof, 55-80, EMER PROF POULTRY SCI, UNIV MD, COLLEGE PARK, 80- *Concurrent Pos:* Vis prof, Univ Alexandria, 61. *Mem:* Soc Exp Biol & Med; fel Poultry Sci Asn (pres, 62); Am Soc Animal Sci; World Poultry Sci Asn. *Res:* Avian endocrinology; sperm physiology. *Mailing Add:* Dept of Poultry Sci Univ of Md College Park MD 20740

SHAFFNER, RICHARD OWEN, b Chicago, Ill, June 12, 38; div; c 2. GAS DISCHARGE PHYSICS. *Educ:* Ill Inst Technol, BSEE, 60, Mass Inst Technol, SMEE, 62; Case Western Reserve Univ, PhD(elec eng), 74. *Prof Exp:* Engr discharge lamps, Lighting Bus Group, Gen Elec Co, Ohio, 68-71, sr engr, 71-75, sr design engr, 75-78; sr staff scientist discharge plasmas, 78-79, mgr, Daymax Div, 80, SR PROJ ENGR, ILC TECHNOL INC, 81- *Mem:* Am Phys Soc; Inst Elec & Electronics Engrs; Sigma Xi. *Res:* Radiation from discharge plasmas and physical chemistry associated with discharge. *Mailing Add:* ILC Technol Inc 399 Java Dr Sunnyvale CA 94086

SHAFI, MOHAMMAD, b Peshawar, Pakistan, May 18, 37; m 63; c 3. SYSTEMS SERVICES, INFORMATION SYSTEMS. *Educ:* Islamia Col, Pakistan, BSc, 56; Peshawar Univ, MSc, 58; Georgetown Univ, MS, 61, PhD(physics), 63; Univ NMex, MA, 71. *Prof Exp:* Asst physics, Georgetown Univ, 58-63; instr, Swarthmore Col, 63-64; sr lectr, Univ Karachi, 64-65; lectr, Univ West Indies, Trinidad, 65-67; lectr & res assoc, Univ NMex, 67-68, asst prof, 68-69; consult, 69-71, sr res physicist, 71-72, sr systs analyst, 72-74, leading analyst, 74-76, mgr PSRO systs, 76-81, DIR SYSTS SERV, HANCOCK DIKEWOOD SERV, 81- *Concurrent Pos:* Res assoc, Univ NMex, 69-71, lectr, 71- *Mem:* AAAS; Am Phys Soc; Am Asn Physics Teachers; Am Soc Pub Admin; Am Mgt Asn. *Res:* Structure of diatomic molecules; theoretical and computer modeling of geomagnetic field; systems analysis; design, development and installation of management information systems for large programs; management of personnel and resources for operating large systems. *Mailing Add:* 1500 Calle del Ranchero NE Albuquerque NM 87106

SHAFIQ, SAIYID AHMAD, b Sitapur, India, Dec 29, 29; m 55; c 3. CELL BIOLOGY. *Educ:* Oxford Univ, DPhil(cytol), 54. *Prof Exp:* Lectr zool, Univ Dacca, 54-59; Fulbright fel anat, Univ Wash, 59-60; res assoc cell biol, Inst Muscle Dis, 60-63, asst mem, 63-69, assoc mem, 69-74; ASSOC PROF NEUROL, STATE UNIV NY DOWNSTATE MED CTR, 74- *Mem:* Am Asn Anatomists. *Res:* Cytology; muscle pathology; electron microscopy. *Mailing Add:* Dept of Neurol State Univ NY Downstate Med Ctr Brooklyn NY 11203

SHAFIT-ZAGARDO, BRIDGET, b Bronx, NY, May 6, 52; m 76. HUMAN GENETICS. *Educ:* C W Post Col, BS, 73; NY Univ, MS, 78; City Univ New York, MPhil, 80; Mt Sinai Sch Med, PhD(genetics), 81. *Prof Exp:* RES ASSOC, DEPT CELL BIOL, ALBERT EINSTEIN COL MED, 81- *Mem:* Am Soc Human Genetics; Am Soc Cell Biol. *Res:* Molecular organization of primate genomes; inherited disorders in man; somatic cell genetics; human gene polymorphisms. *Mailing Add:* 1691 N Jerusalem Rd East Meadow NY 11554

SHAFIZADEH, FRED, b Teheran, Iran, Jan 26, 24; US citizen; m 54; c 1. ORGANIC CHEMISTRY. *Educ:* Tech Inst Teheran, BS, 46; Univ Birmingham, PhD(org chem), 50. *Hon Degrees:* DSc, Univ Birmingham, 72. *Prof Exp:* Res fel chem, Univ Birmingham, 50-52; res assoc physics, Pa State Univ, 52-53; assoc supvr, Res Found, Ohio State Univ, 53-58; mgr pioneering res, Weyerhaeuser Co, Wash, 58-66; DIR WOOD CHEM RES LABS & PROF CHEM, UNIV MONT, 66- *Mem:* Am Chem Soc; The Chem Soc. *Res:* Carbohydrate, wood and cellulose chemistry; chemistry of cellulosic fuels and fires; plant extractives; scientific publications and industrial patents. *Mailing Add:* Wood Chem Lab Univ of Mont Missoula MT 59801

SHAFLAND, JAMES L, human anatomy, see previous edition

SHAFRITZ, DAVID ANDREW, b Philadelphia, Pa, Oct 5, 40; m 64; c 3. MOLECULAR BIOLOGY, MEDICINE. *Educ:* Univ Pa, AB, 62, MD, 66. *Prof Exp:* Res assoc, Molecular Dis Br, Sect Human Biochem, Nat Heart & Lung Inst, 68-71; from instr to asst prof med, Harvard Med Sch, 71-73; asst prof, 73-77, assoc prof, 76-81, PROF MED & CELL BIOL, ALBERT EINSTEIN COL MED, 81- *Concurrent Pos:* Nat Inst Arthritis, Metab & Digestive Dis spec res fel, Gastrointestinal Unit, Mass Gen Hosp, 71-73; Nat Inst Arthritis, Metab & Digestive Dis res career develop award, 75-; assoc ed, Hepatology. *Honors & Awards:* Merril lectr, Am Asn Study Liver Dis, 78. *Mem:* AAAS; Am Asn Study Liver Dis; Am Soc Biol Chemists; Am Soc Clin Invest; Harvey Soc. *Res:* Mammalian protein synthesis and RNA metabolism; properties of mammalian cellular membranes in normal and transformed cells; liver regeneration and regulation of cellular differentiation, hepatitis B virus infection, chronic liver disease and primary liver cancer; diseases of liver and intestine. *Mailing Add:* Albert Einstein Col Med 1300 Morris Park Ave Bronx NY 10461

SHAFROTH, STEPHEN MORRISON, b Denver, Colo, June 12, 26; m 54; c 3. ATOMIC PHYSICS. *Educ:* Harvard Univ, BA, 47; Johns Hopkins Univ, PhD(physics), 53. *Prof Exp:* From instr to asst prof physics, Northwestern Univ, 53-59; res physicist, France, 59 & Bartol Res Found, 60-67; assoc prof, 67-70, PROF PHYSICS, UNIV NC, CHAPEL HILL & TRIANGLE UNIVS NUCLEAR LAB, DURHAM, 70- *Concurrent Pos:* Vis lectr, Temple Univ, 65; lectr & consult, US Naval Res Lab, 66-; adv bd, Nuclear Data Sheets, 66-78; assoc ed, Atomic Data & Nuclear Data Tables, 75-; ed, Scintillation Spectros of Gamma Radiation. *Mem:* Fel Am Phys Soc. *Res:* Experimental nuclear physics; high resolution x-ray spectroscopy following atomic excitation by heavy ions accelerated by a tandem Van de Graaff; resonant inelastic x-ray scattering. *Mailing Add:* Dept of Physics Univ of NC Chapel Hill NC 25714

SHAFTAN, GERALD WITTES, b New York, NY, Apr 15, 26; m 49; c 2. SURGERY. *Educ:* Brown Univ, AB, 45; NY Univ, MD, 49. *Prof Exp:* Asst instr, 56-57, from instr to assoc prof, 57-68, PROF SURG, STATE UNIV NY DOWNSTATE MED CTR, 68- *Concurrent Pos:* Consult, Vet Admin Hosp, Brooklyn, 64-; chief surg serv, Kings County Hosp Ctr, Brooklyn, 72- *Mem:* Am Col Surgeons; Asn Acad Surg; Am Soc Surg of Hand; Am Asn Surg of Trauma. *Res:* Management of multiple trauma and shock; control of bleeding and healing of fractures. *Mailing Add:* Dept of Surg State Univ of NY Downstate Med Ctr Brooklyn NY 11203

SHAFTMAN, DAVID HARRY, b Philadelphia, Pa, Aug 27, 24; m 44, 75; c 4. MATHEMATICS. *Educ:* Univ Chicago, BS, 48, MS, 49. *Prof Exp:* Asst mathematician, Naval Reactors Div & Reactor Eng Div, 50-55, assoc mathematician, Reactor Eng Div & Reactor Physics Div, 55-69, assoc mathematician, Appl Physics Div, 69-74, mathematician, Appl Physics Div, 74-77, MATHEMATICIAN, REACTOR ANAL & SAFETY DIV, ARGONNE NAT LAB, 77- *Mem:* AAAS; Am Math Soc; Am Nuclear Soc. *Res:* Reactor design and development; theoretical reactor physics; theory and application of functional analysis. *Mailing Add:* Reactor Anal & Safety Div Argonne Nat Lab Argonne IL 60439

SHAGASS, CHARLES, b Montreal, Que, May 19, 20; nat US; m 42; c 3. PSYCHIATRY. *Educ:* McGill Univ, BA, 40, MD, CM, 49, dipl, 53; Univ Rochester, MS, 41. *Prof Exp:* Asst psychol, Allan Mem Inst Psychiat, McGill Univ, 45-48, asst & assoc dir res, Dept Psychol, 47-50, resident psychiat, 50-52, from lectr to asst prof psychiat, Univ & dir dept electrophysiol, Inst, 52-58; from assoc prof to prof psychiat, Univ Iowa, 58-66; PROF PSYCHIAT, TEMPLE UNIV, 66-; DIR, TEMPLE CLIN SERV, EASTERN PA PSYCHIAT INST, 66- *Concurrent Pos:* Clin asst, Royal Victoria Hosp, 53-55, asst psychiatrist, 56-58; mem, B Study Sect, NIMH, 63-67, Extramural Res Adv Comt, 69-70 & Clin Prog Projs Study Sect, 70-74 & 79-82. *Mem:* Soc Biol Psychiat; Am Electroencephalog Soc; fel Am Psychiat Asn; Am Psychopath Asn; fel Am Col Neuropsychopharmacol. *Res:* Neurophysiological aspects of psychiatric illness, emotion and learning; psychosomatic relationships; objective tests for psychiatric diagnosis; experimental psychopathology; psychopharmacology. *Mailing Add:* Dept of Psychiat Temple Univ Sch of Med Philadelphia PA 19140

SHAH, ASHOK CHANDULAL, b Palanpur, India, Apr 25, 39; m 66; c 1. PHARMACEUTICS. *Educ:* Univ Bombay, BSc (hons), 59, BSc, 61; Univ Wis, MS, 63, PhD(pharm), 65. *Prof Exp:* SR SCIENTIST, UPJOHN CO, 65- *Mem:* Am Pharmaceut Asn; fel Acad Pharmaceut Sci. *Res:* Chemical kinetics in solutions; physical properties of solids, including phase behavior, and surface, crytal, thermal, mechanical and dissolution properties; formulation of new solid drug dosage forms. *Mailing Add:* Upjohn Co Kalamazoo MI 49001

SHAH, BABUBHAI VADILAL, b Bombay, India, Feb 6, 35; m 66; c 2. STATISTICS. *Educ:* Univ Bombay, BS, 55, MS, 57, PhD(statist), 60. RPXRes assoc statist, Iowa State Univ, 59-62; res analyst, Karamchand Premchand Ltd, India, 62-66; statistician, 66-68, mgr, 68-71, assoc dir, 72-75, CHIEF SCIENTIST, RES TRIANGLE INST, 76- *Mem:* Am Statist Asn; Soc Indust & Appl Math; Inst Math Statist; Asn Comput Mach; Royal Statist Soc. *Res:* Data analysis in complex sample surveys, microsimulation models, optimization techniques. *Mailing Add:* Res Triangle Inst PO Box 12194 Research Triangle Park NC 27709

SHAH, BHUPENDRA K, b Visnagar, India, Dec 8, 35; US citizen; m 58; c 2. STATISTICS, BIOMETRICS. *Educ:* Univ Baroda, BS, 55, MS, 57; Yale Univ, PhD(statist), 68. *Prof Exp:* Lectr statist, Univ Baroda, 57-64; statistician, E I du Pont de Nemours & Co, 68-69; res math statistician, Info Sci Div, 69-70, ASSOC RES SCIENTIST BIOMET, ROCKLAND RES INST, 70- *Concurrent Pos:* Consult med statist, Nat Inst Neurol Dis & Strokes, Washington, DC, 69-71, Impact Nuclear Power Plants; NIMH res grant, 73; Fulbright scholar; Daxina fel. *Mem:* Biomet Soc; Inst Math Statist; Sigma Xi; Am Statist Asn; Economet Soc. *Res:* Application of statistics and computers to medical research; developing statistical theory to help establish bioequivalence of two pharmaceuticals. *Mailing Add:* Rockland Res Inst Orangeburg NY 10962

SHAH, BHUPENDRA UMEDCHAND, b Bombay, India, June 15, 38; m 63; c 2. METALLURGY. *Educ:* Birla Eng Col, India, BEng, 59; Mich State Univ, MSc, 61, PhD(metall), 67; Univ Akron, MBA, 76. *Prof Exp:* Proj engr, Bausch & Lomb, NY, 62-63; RES SPECIALIST METALL, RES DIV, TIMKEN CO, 67- *Mem:* Am Inst Mining, Metall & Petrol Engrs; Am Soc Metals; Am Foundrymen's Soc. *Res:* Development of new steelmaking processes and strand casting. *Mailing Add:* Res Div Timken Co Canton OH 44706

SHAH, DINESH CHHABILDAS, b Rangoon, Burma, Mar 28, 41; m 68; c 1. PROCESS ENGINEERING, ENVIRONMENTAL SCIENCES. *Educ:* Banaras Hindu Univ, BSc, 64; Univ Wis, MS, 65. *Prof Exp:* Chem engr process, Sylvania Chem Div, Gen Tel & Elec Co, 64-65; conceptual design engr math modeling, Deco Gen Elec Co, 65-68; staff process engr environ control processes, Marathon Battery Co, 68-74; head, Environ Process Lab, Esb-Ray-O-Vac Technol Co, 74-78; PROJ MGR, EXIDE CORP, 78- *Mem:* Am Inst Chem Engrs; Air Pollution Asn; Filtration Soc. *Res:* Development of processes to treat waste water containing heavy metals; evaluation and design of energy saving processes; economic analysis of legislation related to battery industry; develop mathematical models for fuel cells systems; definition and notification rira regulators. *Mailing Add:* 514 Anne Lane Fairless Hills PA 19030

SHAH, DINESH OCHHAVLAL, b Bombay, India, Mar 31, 38; m 68; c 2. BIOPHYSICS. *Educ:* Univ Bombay, BS, 59, MS, 61; Columbia Uni, PhD(biophys), 65. *Prof Exp:* Nat Res Coun-NASA resident res assoc, Ames Res Ctr, NASA, 67-68; res assoc surface chem, Lamont Geol Observ, Columbia Univ, 68-70; from asst prof to assoc prof, 70-75, PROF ANESTHESIOL, BIOPHYS & CHEM ENG, UNIV FLA, 75- *Concurrent Pos:* Consult, Barnes-Hind Pharmaceut, Inc, 72- & Sun Oil Co, 73- *Honors & Awards:* Excellence Teaching Award, Univ Fla, 72, President's Scholar Award & Outstanding Serv Award, 75; Best Paper Award, Int Cong Chem & Technol, India, 78. *Mem:* AAAS; Am Soc Eng Educ; Am Chem Soc; Am Inst Chem Engrs; Am Soc Anesthesiol. *Res:* Surface chemistry of biological systems and processes; lung surfactant; corneal surface; biomembranes; biomaterials; emulsification of fat; lipoproteins and mechanisms of anesthesia. *Mailing Add:* Dept of Anesthesiol Univ of Fla Gainesville FL 32611

SHAH, GHULAM M, b Srinagar, India, May 22, 37; m 62; c 3. ANALYTICAL MATHEMATICS, APPLIED MATHEMATICS. *Educ:* Univ Jammu & Kashmir, India, BA, 56; Aligarh Muslim Univ, India, MA, LLB & dipl statist, 58; Univ Wis-Milwaukee, PhD(math), 66. *Prof Exp:* Lectr math, Amar Singh Col, India, 58-60; jr lectr, Regional Eng Col, Srinagar, 60-61, lectr, 61-63; asst, Univ Wis-Milwaukee, 63-66, asst prof, 66-70; assoc prof, 70-75, chmn dept, 73-80, PROF MATH, UNIV WIS-WAUKESHA, 75- *Res:* Zeros of polynomials in complex variables; differential equations and analytic function theory. *Mailing Add:* Dept of Math Univ of Wis Waukesha WI 53186

SHAH, GOVINDLAL M, atomospheric physics, radiation, see previous edition

SHAH, HARESH C, b Godhra, India, Aug 7, 37; m 65. CIVIL ENGINEERING. *Educ:* Univ Poona, BS, 59; Stanford Univ, MS, 60, PhD(civil eng), 63. *Prof Exp:* Teaching asst civil eng, Stanford Univ, 61-62; actg asst prof, San Jose State Col, 62; from instr to assoc prof civil & mech eng, Univ Pa, 62-68; assoc prof, 68-73, PROF CIVIL ENG, STANFORD UNIV, 73-, DIR, JOHN A BLUME EARTHQUAKE ENG CTR, 76- *Concurrent Pos:* Mem, Earthquake Eng Res Inst; scientist, Struct Mech Assocs: Analysts & Consults, 65- *Mem:* Am Soc Civil Engrs; Am Inst Aeronaut & Astronaut; Am Soc Eng Educ; Am Concrete Inst; Seismological Soc Am. *Res:* Structural mechanics; application of theory of probability and statistics to civil engineering problems; earthquake engineering. *Mailing Add:* Dept of Civil Eng Stanford Univ Stanford CA 94305

SHAH, ISHWARLAL D, b Rangoon, Burma, May 8, 35; m 63. METALLURGICAL ENGINEERING. *Educ:* Univ Bombay, BSc, 56; Univ Mo-Rolla, BS, 58; Purdue Univ, MS, 61; Stanford Univ, PhD(metall eng), 67. *Prof Exp:* Res asst metall eng, Purdue Univ, 58-61; res chemist, Delta Res, Ill, 61-63; res asst mineral eng, Stanford Univ, 63-67, res assoc, 67-68; RES METALLURGIST, US BUR MINES, 68- *Mem:* Am Inst Mining, Metall & Petrol Engr; Am Soc Metals. *Res:* Fundamentals of roasting of copper sulphide ores; solubilities and diffusion of gases in metals at high temperatures; extractive metallurgy of copper-nickel sulfides, production of alumina, iron and steel making. *Mailing Add:* US Bur of Mines Labs PO Box 1660 Twin Cities MN 55111

SHAH, JAGDEEP C, b Surat, India, Sept 3, 42; m 67. SOLID STATE PHYSICS. *Educ:* Univ Bombay, BSc, 62; Mass Inst Technol, PhD(solid state physics), 67. *Prof Exp:* Teaching asst physics, Rensselaer Polytech Inst, 62-63; res asst, Mass Inst Technol, 63-67; MEM TECH STAFF, BELL LABS, 67- *Mem:* Am Inst Physics. *Res:* Optical and electrical properties of semiconductors; high intensity effects and non-equilibrium phenomena in semiconductors; electron-hole liquids in semiconductors, amorphous solids; picosecond spectroscopy in semiconductors. *Mailing Add:* Bell Labs Holmdel NJ 07733

SHAH, KANTI L, b Aligarh, India, Jan 6, 35; m 56; c 3. ENVIRONMENTAL SCIENCES, WATER RESOURCES. *Educ:* Aligarh Muslim Univ, India, BS, 55; Univ Kans, MS, 63; Univ Okla, PhD(environ sci), 69. *Prof Exp:* Asst engr, Irrig Dept, State of Uttar Pradesh, India, 55-59; city engr, Munic Corp, India, 59-60; lectr civil eng, M G Polytech, Hathras, India, 60-61; sanit engr, Kans State Dept Health, 63-67; res assoc, Univ Okla, 69; sanit engr, Pa Dept Health, 70; from asst prof to assoc prof, 70-76, PROF CIVIL ENG, OHIO NORTHERN UNIV, 76- *Concurrent Pos:* Consult water qual mgt, Pa Dept Health, 70. *Mem:* Water Pollution Control Fedn; Am Soc Civil Engrs. *Res:* Interdisciplinary approach to environmental and water resources, especially wastewater and stream water quality. *Mailing Add:* Dept of Civil Eng Ohio Northern Univ Ada OH 45810

SHAH, KEERTI, b Ranpur, India, Nov 2, 28; m 67. VIROLOGY. *Educ:* B J Med Col, Poona, India, MBBS, 51; Johns Hopkins Univ, MPH, 57, DrPH, 63. *Prof Exp:* From intern to resident gen med, Sassoon Hosp, Poona, India, 51-53; asst res officer virol, Virus Res Ctr, Poona, 53-58, res officer, 58-61; res assoc pathobiol, 62-63, from asst prof to assoc prof, 63-74, PROF PATHOBIOL, SCH HYG, JOHNS HOPKINS UNIV, 74- *Mem:* AAAS; Am Soc Microbiol; Am Asn Immunologists. *Res:* Biology of DNA tumor viruses. *Mailing Add:* Dept of Pathobiol Johns Hopkins Univ Sch Hyg Baltimore MD 21205

SHAH, MANESH J(AGMOHAN), b Bombay, India, July 9, 32; US citizen; m 60; c 2. CHEMICAL ENGINEERING, MATHEMATICS. *Educ:* Tech Inst Bombay, BS, 53, MS, 55; Univ Mich, MSChE, 57; Univ Calif, Berkeley, PhD(chem eng), 61. *Prof Exp:* Assoc engr phys chem, Int Bus Mach Corp, 60-62, staff engr process control, 62-65, adv engr, 65-69, sr control systs engr, Data Processing Div, 69-72, sr engr, Gen Systs Div, 72-80, CONSULT ENGR, DATA PROCESSING DIV, IBM CORP, 81- *Concurrent Pos:* Adj prof, Univ Puerto Rico, 78-79; sr lectr, Stanford Univ, 80- *Mem:* Am Inst Chem Engrs. *Res:* Process simulation and control; electric birefringence of colloids; heat transfer and fluid mechanics in non-Newtonian fluids; applied mathematics in chemical engineering. *Mailing Add:* 1788 Frobisher Way San Jose CA 95124

SHAH, PRADEEP L, b Poona, India, Oct 17, 44; m 74; c 1. ELECTRICAL ENGINEERING, QUANTUM ELECTRONICS. *Educ:* Indian Inst Technol, BTech, 66; Rice Univ, PhD(elec eng), 70. *Prof Exp:* Supvr optics, Hycel Inc, 71-72; adj asst prof, Rice Univ, 72-73; MGR METAL OXIDE SEMICONDUCTORS TECHNOL, COMPLEMENTARY METAL OXIDE SEMICONDUCTORS CTR, TEX INSTRUMENTS, 73- *Concurrent Pos:* Res assoc, Rice Univ, 70-72. *Mem:* Inst Elec & Electronics Engrs. *Res:* Development of very large scale integrated circuits spanning areas of solid state physical electronics such as materials science, device physics and electronic circuit and system design and analysis. *Mailing Add:* Tex Instruments PO Box 225012 M/S 82 Dallas TX 75265

SHAH, RAMESH TRIKAMLAL, b Padra, India, Sept 13, 34; m 57; c 2. MECHANICAL ENGINEERING. *Educ:* Univ Baroda, BE, 56; Tech Univ Mech Eng, Magdeburg, Ger, DrIng(mech eng), 59. *Prof Exp:* Prof mech eng, Univ Baroda, 56-67 & Ill Inst Technol, 67-68; PROF AERONAUT & MECH ENG, CALIF STATE POLYTECH UNIV, SAN LUIS OBISPO, 68- *Concurrent Pos:* Consult, Jyoti Ltd, Sayaji Iron Works, Metrop Springs & Buganda Steel, Gaskets & Oil Seals, 60-67; consult, Maurey Mfg, Versionall Steel Press & Southern Calif Edison & O'Connar Eng, 67- *Mem:* Am Soc Mech Engrs; Am Soc Heating, Refrig & Air-Conditioning Engrs; Asn Ger Engrs; Indian Inst Engrs. *Res:* Mechanical design; stress analysis. *Mailing Add:* Dept of Mech Eng Calif State Polytech Univ San Luis Obispo CA 93401

SHAH, SHANTILAL NATHUBHAI, b Dhulia, India, Aug 5, 30; m 56; c 3. BIOCHEMISTRY, NEUROCHEMISTRY. *Educ:* Univ Bombay, BS, 51; Univ Nagpur, BSc, 54, MSc, 56; Univ Ill, Urbana, PhD, 60. *Prof Exp:* Res asst, Univ Ill, Urbana, 56-60; Inst Metab Res res fel, Highland Hosp, Oakland, Calif, 60-62; asst res physiologist & Alameda County Heart Asn fel, Univ Calif, Berkeley, 62-65; lectr, Sardar Patel Univ, India, 65-67; res specialist, Sonoma State Hosp, 69-73; assoc res biochemist, Univ Calif, San Francisco, 73-78; assoc res biochemist, 78-80, RES BIOCHEMIST II, LANGLEY-PORTER NEUROPSYCHIAT INST, CALIF, 80- *Concurrent Pos:* NIH grants, Sonoma State Hosp, Calif, 68- *Mem:* AAAS; Am Inst Nutrit; Biochem Soc; Int Soc Neurochem; Am Soc Neurochem. *Res:* Lipid metabolism of the central nervous system and other tissues. *Mailing Add:* Langley-Porter Neuropsychiat Inst Brain Behav Res Ctr Sonoma Develop Ctr Eldridge CA 95431

SHAH, SHEILA, b Zanzibar, Tanzania, Mar 14, 45; US citizen; m 73; c 1. PATHOLOGY. *Educ:* Bombay Univ, MD, 68. *Prof Exp:* Intern med, KEM Hosp, Bombay, 68-69; resident, 70-74, asst prof & pathologist, 74-78, DIR HEMAT LAB PATH, W VA UNIV HOSP, 78- *Concurrent Pos:* Pathologist, Cancer & Leukemia Group B, 76- *Mem:* Int Acad Path. *Res:* Platelet function abnormalities in myeloproliferative disorders related to morphological abnormalities. *Mailing Add:* Dept of Path WVa Univ Med Ctr Morgantown WV 26506

SHAH, SURENDRA P, b Bombay, India, Aug 30, 36; US citizen; m 62; c 2. CIVIL ENGINEERING, STRUCTURAL ENGINEERING. *Educ:* Col Eng, Bombay, India, BS, BVM, 59; Lehigh Univ, MS, 60; Cornell Univ, PhD(struct eng), 65. *Prof Exp:* Design engr, Modjeski & Masters, Pa, 60-62; res asst struct eng, Cornell Univ, 64-65; res assoc, 65-66; asst prof mat eng, Univ Ill, Chicago Circle, 66-73, prof civil eng & mat eng, 73-81; PROF CIVIL ENG, NORTHWESTERN UNIV, 81- *Concurrent Pos:* Develop engr, Res Labs, Portland Cement Asn, 66; consult, Corning Glass Works, 67, US Gypsum Co, 74-75 & Sci Mus Va, 76-77; vis assoc prof, Mass Inst Technol, 69-70; vis prof, Delft Univ Technol, 76-77; NSF res grants, 78-; consult, Holderbark Mgt, Ltd, Switz; mem tech comt, Hwy Res Bd; mem ad-hoc comt, Nat Acad Sci; consult, Amoco Res. *Honors & Awards:* Rilem Gold Medal, 80. *Mem:* Fel Am Concrete Inst; Am Soc Civil Engrs; Prestress Concrete Inst. *Res:* Relating macroscopic mechanical behavior of concrete to its microscopic properties; developing fiber-reinforced concrete; micromechanics of composite materials; fracture of brittle solids; application of ferrocement to low cost housing; properties of concrete, fiber reinforced concrete and ferrocement. *Mailing Add:* Civil Eng Northwestern Univ Evanston IL 60201

SHAH, SWARUPCHAND MOHANLAL, b Deesa, India, Dec 30, 05; m 26; c 1. MATHEMATICAL ANALYSIS. *Educ:* Univ Bombay, BA, 27; Univ London, MA, 30, PhD(math), 42, DLitt(math), 51. *Hon Degrees:* DSc, Univ Kentucky, 79. *Prof Exp:* Sr lectr math, Muslim Univ, India, 30-47, reader, 47-53, prof & chmn dept, 53-58; vis prof, Univ Wis, 58-59, vis prof, Math Res Ctr, 59; vis prof, Northwestern Univ, 59-60 & Univ Kans, 60-66; prof, 66-76, EMER PROF MATH, UNIV KY, 76- *Concurrent Pos:* Ed, Math Student, 57-59; vis prof, Univ Tex, Arlington, 77; vis prof, Univ Brasilia, Brazil, 79. *Mem:* Am Math Soc; fel Nat Inst Sci India; fel Indian Acad Sci; fel Royal Soc Edinburgh; London Math Soc. *Res:* Theory of functions of a complex variable, particularly entire and meromorphic functions; Fourier analysis; difference equations; approximation theory; theory of numbers. *Mailing Add:* Dept Math Univ Ky Lexington KY 40506

SHAH, VIPINCHANDRA LAXMICHAND, b Bombay, India, Dec 2, 33; m 56; c 2. HEAT TRANSFER, FLUID MECHANICS. *Educ:* V J Tech Inst, BE, 55; Univ London, DIC, 58, MSc, 61; Brown Univ, PhD(eng), 68. *Prof Exp:* Engr, Mercantile & Indust Develop Co, Bombay, 55-56; design draughtsman, Wayne Pump Co, London, 57; res asst, Col Aeronaut Eng, 59-62; sr tech officer, Dir Tech Develop & Prod, Ministry of Defense, India, 63-64; teaching asst, Brown Univ, 64-68; from asst prof to assoc prof, 68-77, PROF ENERGETICS, UNIV WIS-MILWAUKEE, 77- *Res:* Numerical solution of heat and mass transfer in laminar and tubulent boundary layers for Newtonian and non-Newtonian fluids. *Mailing Add:* Dept of Eng Univ of Wis Milwaukee WI 53201

SHAHANI, KHEM MOTUMAL, b Hyderabad Sind, India, Sept 3, 23; nat US; m 54; c 4. FOOD TECHNOLOGY, BIOCHEMISTRY. *Educ:* Univ Bombay, BSc, 43; Univ Wis, PhD(dairy technol, biochem), 50. *Prof Exp:* Instr agr, King George V Agr Col, India, 43-45; fel dairy technol, Univ Ill, 50-51; bus consult chem, Int Bus Consults, India, 52-53; res assoc dairy technol, Ohio State Univ, 53-57; assoc prof, 57-61, PROF DAIRY & FOOD TECHNOL, UNIV NEBR, LINCOLN, 61- *Concurrent Pos:* Inst Food Technologists sci lectr; mem adv comt food hyg, WHO. *Honors & Awards:* Borden Award, 64; Gamma Sigma Delta Int Award Distinguished Serv to Agr, 66; Sigma Xi Outstanding Scientist Award, 77; Pfizer Award, 77; Nordica Interaction Award, 77. *Res:* Bioprocessing; food enzymes and their immobilzation and application; products; antibiotics in milk; mode of action of antibiotics and milk and microbial lipase; lysozymes; other enzymes; cultured dairy foods; lactase and proteases immobilization and their uses. *Mailing Add:* Dept of Food Sci Univ of Nebr Lincoln NE 68583

SHAHBENDER, R(ABAH) A(BD-EL-RAHMAN), b Damascus, Syria, July 23, 24; m 54; c 3. ELECTRICAL ENGINEERING. *Educ:* Cairo Univ, BEE, 46; Wash Univ, St Louis, MSEE, 49; Univ Ill, PhD(elec eng), 51. *Prof Exp:* Engr, Anglo-Egyptian Oilfields, Ltd, Egypt, 46-48; sr res engr, Honeywell Controls Div, Pa, 51-55; develop engr, Radio Corp Am, 55-58, sr staff mem, Res Labs, 58-61, head digital device res, 61-72, head appl electronics res, 72-75, TECH STAFF, RCA LABS, 75- *Concurrent Pos:* Chmn dept electronics physics, Evening Div, La Salle Col, 60-67. *Honors & Awards:* Indust Res-100 Award, 64 & 69. *Mem:* AAAS; fel Inst Elec & Electronics Engrs; Sigma Xi. Sci. *Res:* Behavior of nonlinear automatic control systems and adaptive systems; nondestructive testing by means of ultrasonics; digital computer memory systems; digital video systems; kinescope displays. *Mailing Add:* RCA Labs Princeton NJ 08540

SHAHEEN, DONALD G, b Trenton, NJ, Sept 5, 30; m 55; c 3. ANALYTICAL CHEMISTRY. *Educ:* Pa State Univ, BS, 53; NY Univ, MS, 58. *Prof Exp:* Chemist, Callery Chem Co, 55-59; sr chemist, Reaction Motors Div, Thiokol Chem Corp, 59-63; mgr, Chem Dept, Life Systs Div, Hazleton Labs, Inc, Va, 63-69; res mgr, Biospherics, Inc, 69-76; V PRES & TECH DIR, DEGESCH AM INC, 76- *Mem:* Am Chem Soc; Am Microchem Soc; Am Soc Testing & Mat. *Res:* Organic microanalyses; analytical method development; instrumental trace and functional group analyses; thermal stability; decomposition studies; phase diagram studies. *Mailing Add:* Degesch Am Inc 275 Triangle Dr Weyers Cave VA 24486

SHAHEEN, ESBER IBRAHIM, rheology, chemical engineering, see previous edition

SHAHIDI, FREYDOON, b Tehran, Iran, June 19, 47; m 77; c 1. AUTOMORPHIC FORMS. *Educ:* Tehran Univ, BS, 69; Johns Hopkins Univ, PhD(math), 75. *Prof Exp:* Vis mem math, Inst Advan Studies, 75-76; vis asst prof math, Ind Univ, Bloomington, 76-77; asst prof, 77-82, ASSOC PROF MATH, PURDUE UNIV, WEST LAFAYETTE, 82- *Concurrent Pos:* Prin investr, NSF, 79-; vis prof, Univ Toronto, Can, 81-82. *Mem:* Am Math Soc. *Res:* Theory of automorphic forms, logarithm functions and group representations. *Mailing Add:* Dept Math Purdue Univ West Lafayette IN 47907

SHAHIDI, NASROLLAH THOMAS, b Meshed, Iran, Dec 11, 26; US citizen; c 3. HEMATOLOGY. *Educ:* Univ Montpellier, dipl, 47; Sorbonne, MD, 54. *Prof Exp:* Resident pediat, Hosp for Sick Children, Paris, France, 54-56; asst resident, Baltimore City Hosp, Md, 56-57; instr, Harvard Med Sch, 60-63; asst prof, Children's Hosp, Zurich, Switz, 64-66; dir pediat hemat, Children's Hosp, 70-77; assoc prof, 66-70, PROF PEDIAT, CTR HEALTH SCI, UNIV WIS-MADISON, 70- *Concurrent Pos:* Res fel, Harvard Med Sch, 57-60; asst physician, Children's Hosp Med Ctr, Boston, 60-63; vis investr, Swiss Nat Found, 64-66; hematologist, Children's Hosp, Wis, 66. *Mem:* Am Pediat Soc; Am Soc Hemat; Am Soc Pediat Res; affil Royal Soc Med. *Res:* Red cell 2, 3-diphosphoglycerate and oxygen transport; androgens and erythropoiesis; acquired and congenital thrombocytopenic purpura; red cell metabolism, glucose-6-phosphate dehydrogenase deficiency and drug-induced hemolytic anemias. *Mailing Add:* Dept Pediat Ctr for Health Sci Univ of Wis-Madison Madison WI 53706

SHAHIED, ISHAK IBRAHIM, b Egypt, Apr 22, 36; US citizen. BIOCHEMISTRY, NUTRITION. *Educ:* Eastern Nazarene Col, BA, 59; Univ Tenn, MS, 64; Colo State Univ, PhD, 73. *Prof Exp:* Chemist, Johnson & Johnson Co, NJ, 61-62 & Schering Corp, NJ, 62-63; sr chemist, US Air Force, Ohio, 73-74; teacher & researcher biochem, Univ Mo-Kansas City, 75-77; PROF BIOCHEM, SCH MED, ST GEORGE'S UNIV, 77-, CHMN DEPT, 80- *Res:* Effect of hormones on lipid metabolism; effect of various lipids on enzymic activities; relationships between glycolytic enzymes. *Mailing Add:* St George's Univ Sch of Med PO Box 7 St George's Grenada British West Indies

SHAHIN, JAMAL KHALIL, b Bethlehem, Jordan, Mar 5, 31; US citizen; m 58; c 3. MATHEMATICS. *Educ:* Univ Calif, Berkeley, BA, 60; Lehigh Univ, MS, 62, PhD(math), 65. *Prof Exp:* Asst math, Lehigh Univ, 60-62, from instr to asst prof, 62-66; assoc prof, 66-68, PROF MATH & CHMN DEPT, SALEM STATE COL, 68- *Mem:* Am Math Soc; Math Asn Am. *Res:* Differential geometry in affine space; Euclidean and Riemannian geometry. *Mailing Add:* Dept of Math Salem State Col Salem MA 01970

SHAHIN, MICHAEL M, b Isfahan, Iran, Sept 7, 32; m 58; c 1. PHYSICAL CHEMISTRY. *Educ:* Univ Birmingham, BSc, 55, PhD(phys chem), 58. *Prof Exp:* Nat Res Coun Can res fel phys chem, 58-60; res chemist, E I du Pont de Nemours & Co, 60-61; res assoc, Sch Med, Yale Univ, 61-63; sr scientist, Res Div, 63-68, lab mgr xerographic sci, 68-72 & imaging res, 72-73, mgr, 73-78, MGR TECH PLANNING, CORP RES, XEROX CORP, 78- *Mem:* Am Chem Soc; Am Phys Soc; The Chem Soc. *Res:* Photochemistry; gas-phase kinetics; chemical reactions in electrical discharges; radiation chemistry; gas chromatography; mass spectrometry; ion-molecule reactions; ionization phenomena. *Mailing Add:* Webster Res Ctr Xerox Corp 800 Phillips Rd Webster NY 14580

SHAHINIAN, PAUL, b Richmond, Va, June 17, 21; m 51; c 1. METALLURGY. *Educ:* Va Polytech Inst, BS, 43; Mass Inst Technol, SM, 47; Univ Md, PhD(metall), 59. *Prof Exp:* Metallurgist, Curtiss-Wright Corp, 43-45; asst prof physics, Richmond Prof Inst, 47-48; metallurgist, 48-59, sect head mech properties, 59-66, supvry res physicist, 66-72, assoc supt, Metall Div, 72-74, consult thermostruct mat, 74-77, SECT HEAD, PERFECTION THERMOSTRUCT MAT, US NAVAL RES LAB, 77- *Honors & Awards:* Nat Res Lab Appl Sci Award, 80. *Mem:* Am Inst Mining, Metall & Petrol Engrs; Am Soc Metals; Sigma Xi. *Res:* Effects of metallurgical variables and gaseous environment on the high-temperature mechanical properties of metals; creep and fatigue; high temperature fracture mechanics. *Mailing Add:* US Naval Res Lab Washington DC 20375

SHAHN, EZRA, b New York, NY, Nov 12, 33. MOLECULAR BIOLOGY, BIOPHYSICS. *Educ:* Bard Col, AB, 55; Univ Pa, PhD(molecular biol), 65. *Prof Exp:* Biophysicist, Off Math Res, Nat Inst Arthritis & Metab Dis, 58-60; fel bacteriophage, Wistar Inst, 65-66; asst prof biol, 66-70, ASSOC PROF BIOL, HUNTER COL, 71- *Concurrent Pos:* NSF res grant, 67-69, cause grant, 77-80. *Res:* Mathematical models of biological systems; mechanisms of genetic recombination of bacteriophage; effects of ultraviolet light on bacteriophage; thermodynamics of membrane function; science education. *Mailing Add:* Dept Biol Sci Hunter Col New York NY 10021

SHAHRIK, H ARTO, b Istanbul, Turkey, June 22, 23; US citizen; m 62; c 2. CYTOLOGY, ORAL BIOLOGY. *Educ:* Univ Istanbul, Lic es sc, 47, BDS, 50; Tufts Univ, DMD, 59. *Prof Exp:* Intern pediat dent & res, Forsyth Dent Ctr, Boston, Mass, 55-56, clin fel oral biol, 56-57; sr res fel histochem & cytochem & asst mem, Inst Stomatol Res, 59-63; assoc res specialist, Sci Resources Found, 63-64, assoc res clinician & assoc mem oral biol, 64-67, res specialist, head histochem & cytochem & mem oral biol, 67-76. *Concurrent Pos:* Asst clin prof, Dept Oral Health Serv, Sch Dent Med, Tufts Univ, 78- *Mem:* AAAS; NY Acad Sci; Inst Asn Dent Res; Am Dent Asn. *Res:* Tissues of the oral cavity in health and disease, oxidative enzymes; keratinization; salivary fluids and cells; tobacco smoke toxicity on human oral and bronchial cells. *Mailing Add:* Sci Resources Found 489 Common St Belmont MA 02178

SHAHROKHI, FIROUZ, b Tehran, Iran, July 29, 38; US citizen; c 2. AEROSPACE ENGINEERING. *Educ:* Univ Okla, BSME, 61, PhD(mech eng), 66. *Prof Exp:* Design engr, Boeing Co, Wash, 61-62; res engr, Res Inst, Okla Univ, 62-65; asst prof, La State Univ, New Orleans, 65-66; from asst prof to assoc prof, 66-76, PROF AEROSPACE ENG & DIR SPACE INST, UNIV TENN, 76- *Honors & Awards:* Nat Outstanding Event Award, Inst Aeronaut & Astronaut, 69. *Mem:* Am Inst Aeronaut & Astronaut; Am Soc Mech Engrs. *Res:* Sensor technology radiating heat transfer; remote sensing for earth resources; radiative heat transfer in boundary layer flow. *Mailing Add:* Space Inst Univ of Tenn Tullahoma TN 37388

SHAIKH, A(BDUL) FATTAH, b Sukkur, WPakistan, Aug 13, 37; m 67; c 3. STRUCTURAL ENGINEERING. *Educ:* Univ Karachi, BE, 60; Univ Hawaii, MS, 64; Univ Iowa, PhD(struct eng), 67. *Prof Exp:* Asst engr, Water & Power Develop Auth, WPakistan, 60-62; instr struct eng, Univ Iowa, 66-67; from asst prof to assoc prof, 67-81, PROF STRUCT ENG, UNIV WIS-MILWAUKEE, 81- *Honors & Awards:* Martin P Korn Award, Prestressed Concrete Inst, 71. *Mem:* Am Concrete Inst; Prestressed Concrete Inst; Am Soc Civil Engrs. *Res:* Deflections of concrete structures; connections in precast-prestressed concrete; behavior of concrete structures. *Mailing Add:* Dept of Civil Eng Univ of Wis Milwaukee WI 53201

SHAIKH, BADARUDDIN, biochemistry, analytical chemistry, see previous edition

SHAIN, ALBERT LEOPOLD, b Brussels, Belg, Dec 7, 42; US citizen; m 66; c 2. PHYSICAL CHEMISTRY, POLYMER CHEMISTRY. *Educ:* Univ Calif, Los Angeles, BS, 65; Wash Univ, PhD(phys chem), 69. *Prof Exp:* Fel, Inst Phys Chem, Univ Amsterdan, 69-70 & Univ Calif, Los Angeles, 70-71; res assoc chem physics, Univ Del, 71-73; mem staff elaschem, 73-80, MEM STAFF, POLYMER PROD DEPT, EXP STA, E I DU PONT DE NEMOURS & CO, INC, 80- *Mem:* AAAS; Am Chem Soc; Am Phys Soc. *Res:* Magnetic resonance and optical spectroscopy of molecular excited states; polymer chemistry and physics, polymer flammability. *Mailing Add:* Exp Sta Polymer Prod-353 E I du Pont de Nemours & Co Wilmington DE 19898

SHAIN, IRVING, b Seattle, Wash, Jan 2, 26; m 47; c 4. ELECTROANALYTICAL CHEMISTRY. *Educ:* Univ Wash, BS, 49, PhD(chem), 52. *Prof Exp:* From instr to prof chem, Univ Wis-Madison, 52-75, chmn dept, 67-70, vchancellor, 70-75; prof chem, provost & vpres acad affairs, Univ Wash, 75-77; PROF CHEM & CHANCELLOR, UNIV WIS-MADISON, 77- *Mem:* Am Chem Soc; Int Soc Electrochem; Electrochem Soc. *Res:* Instrumental analysis; polarography; kinetics of electrode reactions. *Mailing Add:* 158 Bascom Hall Univ of Wis 500 Lincoln Dr Madison WI 53706

SHAIN, STEPHEN A, chemical engineering, see previous edition

SHAIN, SYDNEY A, b Chicago, Ill, Aug 31, 40; m 67; c 2. BIOCHEMISTRY, ENDOCRINOLOGY. *Educ:* Univ Ill, BS, 62; Univ Calif, Berkeley, PhD(biochem), 68. *Prof Exp:* Res assoc, Sch Med, Univ Pa, 70-71; from asst to assoc found scientist, 71-76, FOUND SCIENTIST & DIR DEPT CELLULAR & MOLECULAR BIOL, SOUTHWEST FOUND RES & EDUC, 77- *Concurrent Pos:* Pop Coun fel, Weizmann Inst Sci, Rehovoth, Israel, 68-70; res assoc, Audie L Murphy Mem Vet Hosp, 76-; adj assoc prof, Dept Physiol, Health Sci Ctr, Univ Tex, 78-81, adj prof, 81- *Mem:* Endocrine Soc; Am Soc Andrology; Am Asn Cancer Res; Am Soc Biol Chemists; NY Acad Sci. *Res:* Pathophysiology of diseases of aging, normal and abnormal function in male accessories and genitalia; carcinogenesis in male accessories. *Mailing Add:* Southwest Found for Res & Educ PO Box 28147 San Antonio TX 78284

SHAIN, WILLIAM ARTHUR, b Louisville, Ky, Feb 16, 31; m 53; c 4. FORESTRY. *Educ:* Univ Ga, BSF, 53, MF, 56; Mich State Univ, PhD(forestry), 63. *Prof Exp:* Forester, Int Paper Col, 53; instr forestry, Miss State Univ, 56-59; asst prof forest mensuration, 61-70, assoc prof, 70-81, PROF DEPT FORESTRY, CLEMSON UNIV, 81- *Mem:* Soc Am Foresters; Am Soc Photogram. *Res:* Forest sampling techniques; aerial photogrammetry. *Mailing Add:* Dept of Forestry Clemson Univ Clemson SC 29631

SHAININ, DORIAN, b San Francisco, Calif, Sept 26, 14; m 40; c 7. AERONAUTICAL ENGINEERING, QUALITY CONTROL. *Educ:* Mass Inst Technol, SB, 36. *Prof Exp:* Engr, Hamilton Standard Div, United Aircraft Corp, 36-43, chief inspector, 43-52; chief engr, Rath & Strong, Inc, 52-57, vpres & dir statist eng, 57-76; PRES, DORIAN SHAININ, CONSULT, INC, 76- *Concurrent Pos:* Lectr, Univ Conn, 50-, fac assoc, Sch Bus Admin, 64-; lectr, Am Mgt Asn, 51-78; consult med staff, Newington Children's Hosp, 57-; lectr, Assoc Bus Progs, London, Eng, 67-70 & Kwaliteitsdienst voor de Industrie, Rotterdam, Neth, 71-76. *Honors & Awards:* Brumbaugh Award, Am Soc Qual Control, 51, Edwards Medal, 69. *Mem:* Fel AAAS; fel Am Soc Qual Control (exec secy, 53-54, vpres, 54-57); Am Statist Asn; Acadamician Int Acad Qual & Productivity Improv. *Res:* Plant operating cost reduction; statistical quality control; reliability engineering; accelerated life testing; statistically designed experiments in research and development; creative and analytical methods of problem solving; product liability prevention; management. *Mailing Add:* 35 Lakewood Circle S Manchester CT 06040

SHAINOFF, JOHN RIEDEN, b Pittsburgh, Pa, Oct 9, 30; m 59. BIOPHYSICS. *Educ:* Univ Pittsburgh, BS, 51, MS, 54, PhD(biophys), 56. *Prof Exp:* Asst biophys, Univ Pittsburgh, 51-56; fel chem, Yale Univ, 56-57; res assoc, 57-59, mem asst staff, 60-63, mem staff, 63-75, actg dir atherosclerosis thrombosis res, 75-76, assoc dir, 76-78, DIR, THROMBOSIS RES SECT, RES DIV, CLEVELAND CLIN FOUND, 80- *Mem:* Am Soc Biol Chem; Biophys Soc; Am Heart Asn; Int Soc Thrombosis & Haemostasis; Am Asn Path. *Res:* Protein chemistry; blood coagulation; arteriosclerosis. *Mailing Add:* Res Div Cleveland Clin Found Cleveland OH 44106

SHAIR, FREDRICK H, b Denver, Colo, May 25, 36; m 64; c 3. CHEMICAL ENGINEERING. *Educ:* Univ Ill, Urbana, BS, 57; Univ Calif, Berkeley, PhD(chem eng), 63. *Prof Exp:* Res engr, Space Sci Lab, Gen Elec Co, 61-65; from asst prof to assoc prof, 65-77, PROF CHEM ENG, CALIF INST TECHNOL, 77- *Mem:* Am Inst Chem Engrs; Am Phys Soc; Am Chem Soc. *Res:* Plasma chemistry; nonequilibrium electrical discharges relating to chemical synthesis and separations; kinetics and transport associated with ecological systems; dispersion of pollutants; indoor air quality. *Mailing Add:* Dept of Chem Eng Calif Inst of Technol Pasadena CA 91109

SHAIR, ROBERT C, b New York, NY, Aug 2, 25; m 49; c 2. CHEMICAL ENGINEERING, PHYSICAL CHEMISTRY. *Educ:* City Col New York, BChE, 47; Polytech Inst Brooklyn, MChE, 49, PhD(chem eng), 54. *Prof Exp:* Dir res, Alkaline Battery Div, Gulton Industs, Inc, 59-63, vpres res, 63-71; mgr energy prod res & develop, Motorola, Inc, Ft Lauderdale, Fla, 71-79; MGR ENG, CENTEC CORP, 79- *Mem:* Electrochem Soc; Inst Elec & Electronics Engrs. *Res:* Batteries; energy conversion; electrochemistry; power sources; energy engineering; environmental engineering. *Mailing Add:* 4921 Sarazen Dr Hollywood FL 33021

SHAKE, ROY EUGENE, b Claremont, Ill, July 3, 32; m 57; c 6. PLANT ECOLOGY. *Educ:* Eastern Ill Univ, BS, 54; Univ Wis-Madison, MS, 56. *Prof Exp:* From instr to asst prof biol, Abilene Christian Col, 58-62; asst, Univ Fla, 62-64; prof, Polk Co Jr Col, 64-65; asst prof, 65-67, ASSOC PROF BIOL, ABILENE CHRISTIAN UNIV, 67- *Res:* Collecting and identifying reptiles and fish in West Central Texas; actinomycete activity in lake water; succession in lentic environments. *Mailing Add:* Dept of Biol Abilene Christian Col Abilene TX 79601

SHAKESHAFT, ROBIN, b Leamington Spa, Eng, June 3, 47. PHYSICS. *Educ:* Univ London, BSc, 68; Univ Nebr, PhD(physics), 72. *Prof Exp:* Res assoc, NY Univ, 72-75; asst prof, 75-80, ASSOC PROF PHYSICS, TEX A&M UNIV, 80- *Concurrent Pos:* Prin investr, NSF, 77-; vis asst prof physics, NY Univ, 78-79. *Mem:* Inst Physics. *Res:* Theoretical atomic physics, in particular, scattering theory, variational principles, quantum electrodynamics. *Mailing Add:* Dept of Physics Tex A&M Univ College Station TX 77843

SHAKHASHIRI, BASSAM ZEKIN, b Enfeh, Lebanon, Oct 9, 39, US citizen. CHEMISTRY. *Educ:* Boston Univ, AB, 60; Univ Md, College Park, MSc, 65, PhD(chem), 68. *Prof Exp:* Res assoc, Univ Ill, Urbana, 67-68, vis asst prof chem, 68-70; asst prof, 70-76, assoc prof, 76-80, PROF CHEM, UNIV WIS-MADISON, 80- *Concurrent Pos:* Danforth Assoc, 80-; Consult, Exxon Educ Found, Chicago Mus Sci & Indust, 81. *Mem:* AAAS; Am Chem Soc (chmn, Chem Educ Div, 81); Royal Soc Chem; Nat Sci Teachers Asn. *Res:* Inorganic reaction mechanisms; innovations in undergraduate and graduate education in chemistry; lecture demonstrations. *Mailing Add:* Dept of Chem Univ of Wis Madison WI 53706

SHAKIN, CARL M, b New York, NY, Feb 17, 34; m 55; c 2. NUCLEAR PHYSICS. *Educ:* NY Univ, BS, 55; Harvard Univ, PhD(theoret physics), 61. *Prof Exp:* Instr physics, Mass Inst Technol, 60-63, NSF fel, 63-65, from asst prof to assoc prof, 65-70; assoc prof, Case Western Reserve Univ, 70-73; PROF PHYSICS, BROOKLYN COL, 73- *Concurrent Pos:* Consult, Lawrence Radiation Lab & Brookhaven Nat Lab. *Mem:* Fel Am Phys Soc. *Res:* Nuclear theory; nuclear structure; nuclear reactions; intermediate energy physics. *Mailing Add:* Dept of Physics Brooklyn Col Brooklyn NY 11210

SHAKLEE, FRANCIS S(OWERSBY), physics, electrical engineering, see previous edition

SHAKLEE, JAMES BROOKER, b Salina, Kans, Mar 29, 45; m 65; c 2. FISH BIOLOGY, BIOCHEMICAL GENETICS. *Educ:* Colo State Univ, BS, 68, MS, 74; Yale Univ, MPhil, 70, PhD(biol), 72. *Prof Exp:* Res assoc develop genetics, Univ Ill, 72-73 & 74-75; ASST PROF ZOOL, UNIV HAWAII & ASST MARINE BIOLOGIST, HAWAII INST MARINE BIOL, 75- *Concurrent Pos:* NIH fel, Univ Ill, 74-75. *Mem:* Soc Study Evolution; Am Soc Ichthyologists & Herpetologists; Am Soc Zoologists; Sigma Xi; Soc Develop Biol. *Res:* Study of the developmental, physiological and evolutionary genetics of fishes primarily by analyzing their isozymes and other proteins. *Mailing Add:* Dept of Zool Univ of Hawaii Honolulu HI 96822

SHAKUN, WALLACE, b New York, NY, July, 21, 34; m 58; c 3. FINANCIAL MANAGEMENT, THERMOECONOMICS. *Educ:* City Univ New York, BME, 58; Univ Vt, MS, 65; Univ Glasgow, PhD(math), 69; Univ Louisville, MBA, 76. *Prof Exp:* Advan design engr prod develop, Gen Elec Co, 60-66; res & develop dir fans, Torin Corp, 69-72; advan design engr com prod, Gen Elec Co, 72-78; vpres engr com prod, Modernfold, 78-80; SR RES ENGR, ENERGY MAT SCI LAB, ENG EXP STA, GA INST TECHNOL, 80- *Concurrent Pos:* Vis asst prof, Univ Vt, 60-65; vis asst prof, Univ Louisville, 72-78; pres, W W Shakun Consults, 80- *Mem:* Assoc fel Royal Aeronaut Soc. *Res:* Program development based on strategic planning requiring a multidisciplinary approach in order to ascertain the impact of new technologies on hardware development. *Mailing Add:* Eng Exp Sta Ga Inst Technol Atlanta GA 30332

SHALABY, RAGAA ABDEL FATTAH, biophysics, see previous edition

SHALABY, SHALABY W, b Dayrut, Egypt, Jan 3, 38; m 65; c 4. BIOMATERIALS, POLYMER SCIENCE. *Educ:* Ain Shams Univ, Egypt, BSc, 58; Univ Lowell, MS, 63, PhD(chem), 66, PhD(polymer sci), 67. *Prof Exp:* Asst forensic chem, Medico-Legal Dept, Egypt, 59-60; instr polymer sci, Univ Lowell, 65-67; instr math, Belvidere Sch, Mass, 66-67; lectr polymer sci, Col Appl Sci, Egypt, 67-68; sr res chemist, Allied Chem Corp, NJ, 69-74; prin scientist, 74-78, MGR POLYMER RES SECT, ETHICON, INC, 78- *Concurrent Pos:* Researcher, Nat Res Ctr, Cairo, 67-68; NASA res assoc, Old Dominion Univ, Va, 68-69. *Mem:* Sigma Xi; Am Chem Soc; NY Acad Sci; Am Phys Soc; Soc Plastics Engrs. *Res:* Synthesis and modification of macromolecules; study of structure-properties relationships and assessment of pertinent physical and structural parameters; structural design and development of new polymeric materials for biomedical applications; organometallic chemistry. *Mailing Add:* Ethicon Inc Rte 22 Somerville NJ 08876

SHALATI, MOHAMAD DEEB, b Damascus, Syria, Jan 17, 47; US citizen; m 75; c 2. POLYMER SCIENCE. *Educ:* Damascus Univ, Syria, BSc, 71; Eastern Mich Univ, MSc, 74; Univ Mich, PhD(chem, macromolecular sci & eng), 79. *Prof Exp:* Res scientist, Miami Valley Labs, Procter & Gamble Co, 79-80; RES SCIENTIST INDUST RES & DEVELOP, INT MINERALS & CHEM CORP, 80- *Mem:* Am Chem Soc; Sigma Xi. *Res:* Polymer synthesis and characterization; coating; controlled release drug delivery systems. *Mailing Add:* Int Mineral & Chem Corp PO Box 207 Terre Haute IN 47808

SHALAWAY, SCOTT D, b Pottstown, Pa, Aug 13, 52; m 75. NONGAME WILDLIFE, HABITAT MANAGEMENT. *Educ:* Univ Del, BS, 74; Northern Ariz Univ, MS, 77; Mich State Univ, PhD(wildlife ecol), 79. *Prof Exp:* Resource specialist impact statements, Mich Dept Nat Resources, 80; vis asst prof biol, Dept Zool, 80-81, asst prof ornith, Univ Okla Biol Sta, 81, ASST PROF WILDLIFE, DEPT ZOOL, OKLA STATE UNIV, 81- *Concurrent Pos:* Mem, Animal Res Coun, Okla City Zoo, 80- *Mem:* Wildlife Soc; Am Ornithologists Union; Wilson Ornith Soc; Am Soc Mammalogists; Ecol Soc Am. *Res:* Breeding biology, behavior and habitat requirements of nongame and endangered species of wildlife; eastern bluebird biology; black-tailed prairie dog habitat impacts. *Mailing Add:* Dept Zool Okla State Univ Stillwater OK 74078

SHALE, DAVID, b Christchurch, NZ, Mar 22, 32; US citizen; m 66; c 2. MATHEMATICS. *Educ:* Univ NZ, MSc, 53; Univ Chicago, PhD(math), 60. *Prof Exp:* Lectr math, Univ Toronto, 59-61; instr, Univ Calif, Berkeley, 61-62, asst prof, 61-64; from asst prof to assoc prof, 64-70, PROF MATH, UNIV PA, 70- *Concurrent Pos:* Temporary mem, Inst Advan Study, 63-64. *Mem:* Am Math Soc. *Res:* Abstract analysis and applications, especially to quantum theory. *Mailing Add:* Dept of Math Univ of Pa Philadelphia PA 19174

SHALEK, ROBERT JAMES, b Chicago, Ill, Apr 15, 22, m 51, c 6. BIOPHYSICS. *Educ:* Univ Ill, BA, 43; Southern Methodist Univ, MA, 48; Rice Inst, MA, 50, PhD(biophys), 53. *Prof Exp:* Instr radiol physics, Univ Tex M D Anderson Hosp & Tumor Inst, 50-53; USPHS fel, Univ London, 53-54; from asst physicist to assoc physicist, 54-60, PHYSICIST, UNIV TEX M D ANDERSON HOSP & TUMOR INST, 60-, PROF BIOPHYS, 65- *Concurrent Pos:* Consult, Oak Ridge Inst Nuclear Studies, 53-61. *Mem:* Am Phys Soc; Radiation Res Soc; Biophys Soc; Am Asn Physicists in Med (pres, 66); Brit Inst Radiol. *Res:* Radiation chemistry; radiological physics. *Mailing Add:* Physics Dept Univ of Tex M D Anderson Hosp & Tumor Inst Houston TX 77030

SHALEN, PETER BROCK, mathematics, see previous edition

SHALER, AMOS J(OHNSON), b Harrow, Eng, July 8, 17; US citizen; m 43; c 3. METALLURGY, POLLUTION CONTROL. *Educ:* Mass Inst Technol, SB, 40, ScD(phys metall), 47. *Prof Exp:* Asst, New Consol Gold Fields, SAfrica, 40-42; heat treatment supt, Cent Ord Factory, 42; res & develop engr, C H Hirtzel & Co, Ltd, 42-43; tech dir, Indust Rys Equip Co, 43-45; mem staff, Div Indust Coop, Mass Inst Technol, 44-47, from asst prof to assoc prof phys metall, 47-53; prof metall & head dept, Pa State Univ, 53-60; PRES, AMOS J SHALER, INC, CONSULTS, 65-; VPRES, MGD, INC, 79- *Concurrent Pos:* Sci liaison officer, Off Naval Res, 50-51; dir, Belg-Am Educ Found, 58-; consult, 60-; spec consult to asst secy gen, NATO, 69-70. *Honors & Awards:* Award, Am Inst Mining, Metall & Petrol Engrs, 51; Cert of Appreciation, US Off Naval Res, 51; Award, Am Soc Metals, 57; Award, Am Powder Metall Inst, 59; Cert of Appreciation, US Mission to NATO, 70. *Mem:* Am Soc Metals; Brit Inst Metals; Int Oceanog Found. *Res:* Waste recycling; chemical oceanography; water purification; control of estuary waters; powder metallurgy; refractory materials; materials systems; new products and processes; economics of innovation. *Mailing Add:* 705 W Park Ave State College PA 16801

SHALIT, HAROLD, b Philadelphia, Pa, May 9, 19; m 42; c 2. ORGANIC CHEMISTRY. *Educ:* Univ Pa, AB, 41; Pa State Univ, MS, 43; Polytech Inst Brooklyn, PhD(org chem), 48. *Prof Exp:* Sr res assoc, Polytech Inst Brooklyn, 46-48; res chemist, Standard Oil Co Ind, 48-51; res chemist, Houdry Process Corp, 51-58; sect head explor & fuel cell res, 58-63; dir phys chem res, 63-72, mgr catalytic res, 72-76, SR RES ASSOC, ARCO CHEM DIV, ATLANTIC RICHFIELD CO, 76- *Concurrent Pos:* Adj prof chem, Drexel Univ, 74- *Mem:* Am Chem Soc; Catalysis Soc. *Res:* Physical, organic, petroleum and electro-organic chemistry; high pressure reactions; kinetics; catalysis. *Mailing Add:* Arco Chem Co 3801 W Chester Pike Newtown Square PA 19073

SHALITA, ALAN REMI, b New York, NY, Mar 22, 36; m 60; c 2. DERMATOLOGY, BIOCHEMISTRY. *Educ:* Brown Univ, AB, 57; Free Univ Brussels, BS, 60; Bowman Gray Sch Med, MD, 64. *Prof Exp:* Training grant fel dermat, Med Ctr, NY Univ, 68-70, from instr to asst prof dermat, 70-73; asst prof dermat, Col Physicians & Surgeons, Columbia Univ, 73-75; assoc prof, 75-79, head, Div Dermat, 75-80, PROF MED, STATE UNIV NY DOWNSTATE MED CTR, 79-, CHMN, DEPT DERMAT, 80- *Concurrent Pos:* USPHS spec fel biochem, Med Ctr, NY Univ, 70-72; dep dir div finance, Nat Prog Dermat, 70-; Dermat Found grant, 76. *Mem:* AAAS; NY Acad Sci; Soc Invest Dermat; Am Fedn Clin Res; fel Am Acad Dermat. *Res:* Factors involved in the pathogenesis of acne vulgaris, including cutaneous lipogenesis and microbial lipids and lipolytic enzymes. *Mailing Add:* Div Dermat State Univ NY Downstate Med Ctr Brooklyn NY 11203

SHALLA, THOMAS ALLEN, b Grand Island, Nebr, May 7, 33; m 55; c 2. PLANT PATHOLOGY. *Educ:* Colo State Univ, BS, 55; Univ Calif, PhD(plant path), 58. *Prof Exp:* Instr & jr plant pathologist, 59-60, from asst prof to assoc prof, 60-70, PROF PLANT PATH, UNIV CALIF, DAVIS, 70- *Concurrent Pos:* Ed, Virology, 74- *Mem:* AAAS; fel Am Phytopath Soc. *Res:* Electron microscopy of virus infected plant cells; pome fruit viruses. *Mailing Add:* Dept of Plant Path Univ of Calif Davis CA 95616

SHALLCROSS, FRANK V(AN LOON), b Philadelphia, Pa, Nov 9, 32; m 56; c 2. PHYSICAL CHEMISTRY, SOLID STATE DEVICE TECHNOLOGY. *Educ:* Univ Pa, AB, 53; Brown Univ, PhD(chem), 58. *Prof Exp:* Chemist, M & C Nuclear, Inc, Mass, 57-58; MEM TECH STAFF, DAVID SARNOFF RES CTR, RCA CORP, 58- *Mem:* AAAS; Am Chem Soc; Am Inst Chemists. *Res:* Solid state physical chemistry; thin films; photoconductive materials; solid state image sensors; semiconductors; charge-coupled devices; integrated circuit technology. *Mailing Add:* 12 Jeffrey Lane Princeton Junction NJ 08550

SHALLENBERGER, ROBERT SANDS, b Pittsburgh, Pa, Apr 11, 26; m 51; c 4. FOOD CHEMISTRY, FOOD TECHNOLOGY. *Educ:* Univ Pittsburgh, BS, 51; Cornell Univ, MS, 53, PhD(biochem, hort, plant physiol), 55. *Prof Exp:* Assoc technologist chem, Gen Foods Corp, 55-56; asst prof biochem, 56-60, assoc prof food sci & technol, 60-66, PROF BIOCHEM, CORNELL UNIV, 66- *Mem:* Am Chem Soc. *Res:* Chemical reactions affecting color, flavor, texture and nutritive value in processed foods; carbohydrate structure and reactions. *Mailing Add:* Dept of Food Sci & Technol NY State Agr Exp Sta Cornell Univ Geneva NY 14456

SHALUCHA, BARBARA, b Springfield, Vt, Dec 9, 15. HORTICULTURE. *Educ:* Univ Vt, PhB, 37, MS, 38; Ohio State Univ, PhD(hort), 47. *Prof Exp:* Dow asst, Conn Col, 38-42; instr bot, 42-43; asst, Exp Sta, Ohio Univ, 43-45; asst cur pub educ, Brooklyn Bot Garden, 45-47; from instr to asst prof, 47-71, ASSOC PROF BOT, IND UNIV, BLOOMINGTON, 71- *Concurrent Pos:* Am Asn Univ Women & Nat Coun State Garden Clubs fel, Wye Col, Univ London, 54; vis prof, Cornell Univ, 70-71 & Royal Bot Garden, Kew, Eng; pres, Nat Civic Garden Ctrs, Inc, 75-77. *Mem:* Bot Soc Am; Am Soc Hort Sci; Am Hort Soc; Nat Sci Teachers Asn; Int Soc Hort Sci. *Res:* Extraction of auxins from plant tissues; environmental horticulture and horticulture education; civic garden centers. *Mailing Add:* Dept of Bot Ind Univ Bloomington IN 47401

SHALVOY, RICHARD BARRY, b Norwalk, Conn, Apr 26, 49; m 72; c 1. SURFACE PHYSICS, ANALYTICAL CHEMISTRY. *Educ:* Rensselaer Polytech Inst, BS, 71; Brown Univ, ScM, 74, PhD(physics), 77. *Prof Exp:* Res fel, Univ Ky, 76-78; sr physicist electron spectros, 78-80; RES CHEMIST ANALYTICAL RES, STAUFFER CHEM CO, 80- *Mem:* Am Phys Soc; Am Vacuum Soc; Am Chem Soc. *Res:* Characterization of catalysts and metals using electron spectroscopy; chemical bonding in semiconductors; analytical surface chemistry. *Mailing Add:* Stauffer Chem Co Eastern Res Ctr Dobbs Ferry NY 10522

SHAM, LU JEU, b Hong Kong, China, Apr 28, 38; m 65; c 2. THEORETICAL PHYSICS, SOLID STATE PHYSICS. *Educ:* Univ London, BSc, 60, Imp Col, ARCS, 60; Cambridge Univ, PhD(solid state physics), 63. *Prof Exp:* Physicist, Univ Calif, San Diego, 63-65, asst res physicist & lectr physics, 65-66; asst prof, Univ Calif, Irvine, 66-67; reader appl math, Queen Mary Col, Univ London, 67-68; assoc prof physics, 68-74, PROF PHYSICS, UNIV CALIF, SAN DIEGO, 74- *Concurrent Pos:* Vis prof, Max Planck Inst Solid State Res, Stuttgart, WGer, 78; Humbolt Found award, 81. *Mem:* fel Am Phys Soc. *Res:* Lattice dynamics; electron-phonon interaction; electronic properties in solids; semiconductors. *Mailing Add:* Dept Physics Univ Calif San Diego La Jolla CA 92037

SHAMAN, PAUL, b Portland, Ore, Mar 30, 39; m 64; c 2. STATISTICS. *Educ:* Dartmouth Col, AB, 61; Columbia Univ, MA, 64, PhD(statist), 66. *Prof Exp:* From asst res scientist to assoc res scientist, NY Univ, 64-67; res assoc, Stanford Univ, 67-68; from asst prof to assoc prof statist, Carnegie-Mellon Univ, 68-77; ASSOC PROF STATIST, UNIV PA, 77- *Mem:* Am Statist Asn; Inst Math Statist. *Res:* Time series analysis. *Mailing Add:* Dept of Statist Univ of Pa Philadelphia PA 15213

SHAMBAUGH, GEORGE FRANKLIN, b Columbus, Ohio, Nov 3, 28; m 53; c 3. ENTOMOLOGY. *Educ:* Wilmington Col, AB, 50; Ohio State Univ, MSc, 51, PhD(entom), 53. *Prof Exp:* Entomologist & asst chief pesticides br, Natick Qm Res & Eng Command, 55-62; assoc prof, 62-72, PROF ENTOM, OHIO AGR RES & DEVELOP CTR & OHIO STATE UNIV, 72- *Mem:* AAAS; Am Soc Zoologists; Am Entom Soc. *Res:* Electrophysiology of insect nerves and muscles; insect sense physiology; insect attractants and repellent; insect digestive enzymes. *Mailing Add:* 1574 Sunset Lane Wooster OH 44691

SHAMBELAN, CHARLES, b Philadelphia, Pa, Mar 16, 30; m 56; c 2. SYNTHETIC FIBERS. *Educ:* Temple Univ, BA, 51, MA, 55; Univ Pa, PhD(phys chem), 59. *Prof Exp:* Chemist, Frankford Arsenal, 51-55; res chemist, 58-64, res supvr, 64, res assoc, 73, RES FEL, E I DUPONT DE NEMOURS & CO, INC, 77- *Mem:* Am Chem Soc. *Res:* Polymers; nonwoven fabrics; synthetic fibers. *Mailing Add:* Exp Sta E I DuPont De Nemours & Co Wilmington DE 19898

SHAMBERGER, RAYMOND J, b Munising, Mich, Aug 23, 34; m 59; c 6. BIOCHEMISTRY. *Educ:* Alma Col, BS, 56; Ore State Univ, MS, 60; Univ Miami, PhD(biochem), 63. *Prof Exp:* Asst, Ore State Univ, 57-59 & Univ Southern Calif, 63; dir res, Sutton Res Corp, Calif, 63-64; sr cancer res scientist, Roswell Park Mem Inst, 64-69; MEM STAFF, CLEVELAND CLIN FOUND, 69- *Concurrent Pos:* Prof, Cleveland State Univ, 70-; mem comts nutrit & path, Fedn Am Socs Exp Biol & Med. *Mem:* Am Asn Cancer Res; Am Soc Clin Pathologists; Am Asn Clin Chemists. *Res:* Chemistry of trace metals; mechanisms of cancer formation; enzyme chemistry. *Mailing Add:* Cleveland Clin Found 9500 Euclid Ave Cleveland OH 44106

SHAMBLIN, JAMES E, b Holdenville, Okla, Mar 24, 32; m 59; c 1. MECHANICAL ENGINEERING, INDUSTRIAL ENGINEERING. *Educ:* Univ Tex, BSME, 54, MSME, 62, PhD(mech eng), 64. *Prof Exp:* Test engr, Pratt & Whitney Aircraft Div, United Aircraft Corp, 54-55; res engr, Southwest Res Inst, 55-60; teaching asst mech eng, Univ Tex, 60-62, instr, 62-64; from asst prof to assoc prof, 64-69, PROF INDUST ENG, OKLA STATE UNIV, 69-, DIR, CTR LOCAL GOVT TECHNOL, 75- *Mem:* Am Inst Indust Engrs; Am Soc Eng Educ; Am Pub Works Asn. *Res:* Application of engineering and management technology to problems of local government. *Mailing Add:* 505 Engineering N Okla State Univ Stillwater OK 74074

SHAMBURGER, JOHN HERBERT, b Meridian, Miss, Nov 22, 25; m 48; c 4. ENGINEERING GEOLOGY. *Educ:* Univ Miss, BS, 49. *Prof Exp:* Civil engr, 49-51, geologist, 53-62, CHIEF, ENG GEOL APPLICATIONS GROUP, GEOTECH LAB, WATERWAYS EXP STA, US ARMY CORP ENGRS, 62- *Mem:* Asn Eng Geol; Am Soc Photogram; Am Mil Engrs; Int Geog Union. *Res:* Waterborne acoustic sensors for engineering problems; alluvial environment of deposition suitability for engineering requirements; groundwater containment at disposal sites; remote imagery interpretation methodology. *Mailing Add:* Geotech Lab PO Box 631 Vicksburg MS 39180

SHAMES, DAVID MARSHALL, b Norfolk, Va, Dec 27, 39. NUCLEAR MEDICINE. *Educ:* Univ Va, BA, 61; Yale Univ, MD, 65. *Prof Exp:* Intern internal med, Yale-New Haven Hosp, 65-66; staff assoc kinetic anal metab systs, Math Res Br, NIH, 66-69; asst resident internal med, Johns Hopkins Hosp, 69-70; NIH fel, 70-71; asst prof, 71-75, assoc prof radiol, 75-80, ASSOC CLIN PROF, UNIV CALIF, SAN FRANCISCO, 80- *Concurrent Pos:* Nat Insts Gen Med Sci res career develop award, 72-77. *Mem:* Soc Nuclear Med; Am Fedn Clin Res. *Res:* Kinetic analysis of nuclear medicine tracer data using the computer, especially the cardiovascular, cerebrovascular and renal systems. *Mailing Add:* Dept of Radiol Univ of Calif San Francisco CA 94143

SHAMES, IRVING H, b Boston, Mass, Oct 31, 23; m 54; c 2. ENGINEERING. *Educ:* Northeastern Univ, BS, 48; Harvard Univ, MS, 49; Univ Md, PhD, 53. *Prof Exp:* From instr to asst prof, Univ Md, 49-55; asst prof, Stevens Inst Technol, 55-57; prof eng sci & chmn dept, Pratt Inst, 57-62, actg chmn physics, 60-61; prof & head, Div Interdisciplinary Studies & Res Eng, 62-69, fac prof eng & appl sci, 69-72, PROF ENG SCI & CHMN DEPT, STATE UNIV NY BUFFALO, 72- *Concurrent Pos:* Vis lectr, Ord Lab, US Dept Navy, 52-55 & Res Lab, 53-55; vis prof, Haifa Univ, 69. *Mem:* Am Soc Eng Educ. *Res:* Dynamics and mechanics. *Mailing Add:* Parker Eng Bldg State Univ of NY Buffalo NY 14214

SHAMIR, ADI, b Tel Aviv, Israel, July 6, 52. COMPUTER SCIENCE. *Educ:* Tel Aviv Univ, BSc, 72; Weizmann Inst, MSc, 75, PhD(comput sci), 77. *Prof Exp:* Res asst, Univ Warwick, 76; instr, 77-78, ASST PROF COMPUT SCI, MASS INST TECHNOL, 78- *Res:* Combinatorics; algorithms; cryptography; semantics. *Mailing Add:* Lab Comput Sci Mass Inst of Technol Cambridge MA 02139

SHAMIS, SIDNEY S, b Norwalk, Conn, July 19, 20; m 42; c 2. ELECTRICAL ENGINEERING. *Educ:* Cooper Union, BSEE, 47; Stevens Inst Technol, MS, 50. *Prof Exp:* Instr advan commun eng, Army Air Force Off Electronics Sch, 42-44, course supvr, 44-46; electronics engr advan develop sect, Allen B Dumont Labs, Inc, 46-50, sect head, 50-52; from asst prof to prof elec eng, NY Univ, 52-73, assoc dean sch eng & sci, 72-73; prof elec eng & assoc dean eng, 73-81, ACTG DEAN ENG, POLYTECH INST NY, 81- *Concurrent Pos:* Arthur M Loew Found grant transistor techniques, 54-55; dir grad ctr at Bell Labs, 57-59, assoc dir lab electrosci res, 62-68; consult, Sprague Elec Co, 64-65, Eon Corp, 65-67 & Digital Device Corp, 65-67. *Mem:* Inst Elec & Electronics Engrs; Am Soc Eng Educ. *Res:* Electronic circuits; active networks; device technology. *Mailing Add:* Dept Eng Polytech Inst NY 333 Jay St Brooklyn NY 11201

SHAMMA, MAURICE, b Cairo, Egypt, Dec 14, 26; nat US; m 55; 55; c 1. NATURAL PRODUCTS CHEMISTRY. *Educ:* Berea Col, AB, 51; Univ Wis, PhD(chem), 55. *Prof Exp:* Fel, Wayne State Univ, 55-56; from asst prof to assoc prof, 56-66, PROF CHEM, PA STATE UNIV, UNIVERSITY PARK, 66- *Mem:* Am Chem Soc. *Res:* Isolation, characterization and synthesis of natural products, particularly alkaloids; synthesis of new nitrogen heterocycles. *Mailing Add:* Dept of Chem Pa State Univ University Park PA 16802

SHAMOIAN, CHARLES ANTHONY, b Worcester, Mass, Oct 5, 31; m 61; c 2. PSYCHIATRY, BIOCHEMICAL PHARMACOLOGY. *Educ:* Clark Univ, AB, 54, MA, 56; Tufts Univ, PhD(physiol), 60, MD, 66. *Prof Exp:* Instr physiol, Med Sch, Tufts Univ, 61-62, res assoc pharmacol, 63-66; intern med, Bellevue Hosp, New York, 66-67; fel psychiat, 67-70, instr, 70-71, asst prof, 71-78, ASSOC PROF CLIN PSYCHIAT, CORNELL UNIV-NEW YORK HOSP, 78-, DIR GERIATRIC SERV, WESTCHESTER DIV NY HOSP, 79- *Concurrent Pos:* Asst attend psychiatrist, Payne Whitney Psychiat Clin, 71-78, assoc attend psychiatrist, 78- *Mem:* AAAS; Am Physiol Soc; Am Psychopath Asn; Am Psychiat Asn; NY Acad Med. *Res:* Catecholamine metabolism in affective illnesses; geriatric psychopharm. *Mailing Add:* New York Hosp Cornell 21 Bloomingdale Rd White Plains NY 10605

SHAMOO, ADIL E, b Baghdad, Iraq, Aug 1, 41; m 67; c 1. PHYSIOLOGY, BIOPHYSICS. *Educ:* Univ Baghdad, 62; Univ Louisville, MS, 66; City Univ New York, PhD(physiol, biophys), 70. *Prof Exp:* Instr physics, Univ Louisville, 65-68; from asst to assoc biophys, Mt Sinai Sch Med, 68-71, asst prof physiol & biophys, 71-73; asst prof, 73-75, ASSOC PROF RADIATION BIOL & BIOPHYS, SCH MED & DENT, UNIV ROCHESTER, 75- *Concurrent Pos:* Guest worker, Nat Inst Neurol Dis & Stroke, 72-73; guest prof, Max-Planck Inst Biophysics, Frankfurt, 77-78; co-ed-in-chief, J Membrane Biochem. *Mem:* Am Asn Biol Chemists; NY Acad Sci; Biophys Soc; Am Physiol Soc. *Res:* Physiology and biochemistry of membrane transport; membrane biochemistry-lipid membranes. *Mailing Add:* Dept of Radiation Biol & Biophys Univ of Rochester Sch Med & Dent Rochester NY 14642

SHAMOS, MICHAEL IAN, b New York, NY, Apr 21, 47; m 73. COMPUTER SCIENCES. *Educ:* Princeton Univ, AB, 68; Vassar Col, MA, 70; Am Univ, MS, 72; Yale Univ, MS, 73, MPhil, 74, PhD(comput sci), 78; Duquesne Univ, JD, 81. *Prof Exp:* Assoc engr comput sci, IBM Corp, 68-70; supvry programmer, Nat Cancer Inst, NIH, 70-72; teaching fel, Yale Univ, 72-75; ASST PROF MATH & COMPUT SCI, CARNEGIE-MELLON UNIV, 75-; PRES, UNILOGIC, LTD, 79- *Concurrent Pos:* Consult, various law firms. *Mem:* Asn Comput Mach; Math Asn Am; Nat Sci Teachers Asn; Soc Indust & Appl Math; Sigma Xi. *Res:* Theoretical computer science; graph theory; discrete mathematics; computational geometry; combinatorics; analysis of algorithms; computers and law. *Mailing Add:* Dept of Math & Comput Sci Carnegie-Mellon Univ Pittsburgh PA 15213

SHAMOS, MORRIS HERBERT, b Cleveland, Ohio, Sept 1, 17; m 42; c 1. BIOPHYSICS, LABORATORY MEDICINE. *Educ:* NY Univ, AB, 41, MS, 43, PhD(physics), 48. *Prof Exp:* From instr to assoc prof, 42-59, PROF PHYSICS, NY UNIV, 59-; SR VPRES & CHIEF SCI OFFICER, TECHNICON CORP, 75- *Concurrent Pos:* Consult, US AEC, 56-69, Nat Broadcasting Co, 57-65 & UN Info Serv, 58; chmn dept physics, Washington Sq Col, NY Univ, 57-70; sr vpres res & educ, Technicon Corp, 70-75; mem adv coun, NY Polytech Inst, 80- *Mem:* Fel AAAS; Am Phys Soc; sr mem Inst Elec & Electronics Engrs; Nat Sci Teachers Asn (pres-elect, 66-67, pres, 67-68); NY Acad Sci (rec secy, 77-79, vpres, 80-81, pres, 82). *Res:* Atomic and nuclear physics; cosmic rays; electron scattering; physical electronics; high energy physics; nuclear detectors and instrumentation; biophysics, electrical properties of hard tissues; biophysical theory of aging. *Mailing Add:* Dept of Physics NY Univ New York NY 10003

SHAMSIE, JALAL, b Delhi, India, Jan 29, 30; Can citizen; m 59; c 2. CHILD PSYCHIATRY. *Educ:* Punjab Univ, India, BSc, 47; Punjab Univ, Pakistan, MBBS, 53; FRCP(C), 62. *Prof Exp:* Dir child & child adolescent serv psychiat, Douglas Hosp, Montreal, Que, 61-71; asst prof, McGill Univ, 67-71; asst prof, 72-80, PROF PSYCHIAT, UNIV TORONTO, 80- *Concurrent Pos:* Dir Res & Educ, Thistletown Regional Ctr Children & Adolescents, Toronto, 72-80; consult child psychiat, Clarke Inst, 76- *Mem:* Royal Col Psychiatrists, Gt Brit; Can Psychiat Asn. *Res:* Adolescent psychiatry; administrative psychiatry. *Mailing Add:* 32 Grovetree Rd Rexdale ON M9V 2Y2 Can

SHAN, ROBERT KUOCHENG, b Gaoan, China, Nov 9, 27; m 63; c 1. AQUATIC ECOLOGY. *Educ:* Taiwan Norm Univ, BS, 56; Univ BC, MS, 62; Ind Univ, Bloomington, PhD(zool), 67. *Prof Exp:* Asst fishery biol, Nat Taiwan Univ, 55-56, asst zool, 56-59; res assoc, Ind Univ, Bloomington, 67-69; from asst prof to assoc prof, 69-75, PROF BIOL, FAIRMONT STATE COL, 75- *Mem:* Am Inst Biol Sci; Am Soc Limnol & Oceanog; Ecol Soc Am. *Res:* Systematics and ecology of marine copepods; ecology and genetics of chydorid cladocerans. *Mailing Add:* Dept of Biol Fairmont State Col Fairmont WV 26554

SHANA'A, JOYCE A, mathematics education, applied mathematics, see previous edition

SHANAHAN, PATRICK, b Clyde, Ohio, Aug 4, 31; m 53; c 9. MATHEMATICS. *Educ:* Univ Notre Dame, BA, 53; Ind Univ, PhD(math), 57. *Prof Exp:* From instr to assoc prof, 57-67, PROF MATH, COL OF THE HOLY CROSS, 67- *Concurrent Pos:* NSF sci fac fel, Harvard Univ, 66-67. *Mem:* Am Math Soc; Math Asn Am; London Math Soc. *Res:* Differential topology; equivariant version of the Atiyah-singer index theorem, and its applications to gemetric and topological problems. *Mailing Add:* Dept Math Col Holy Cross Worcester MA 01610

SHANBERGE, JACOB N, b Milwaukee, Wis, Jan 14, 22; m 53; c 4. PATHOLOGY, HEMATOLOGY. *Educ:* Marquette Univ, BS, 42, MD, 44. *Prof Exp:* Assoc dir, Milwaukee Blood Ctr, 48; asst chief lab serv, Vet Admin Ctr Hosp, Wood, Wis, 52-55 & West Roxbury, Mass, 55-60; Nat Heart Inst spec res fel, Zurich, Switz, 60-61; assoc dir path, Michael Reese Hosp & Med Ctr, Chicago, 62-64; dir hemat labs & blood bank & assoc in path, Evanston Hosp, Ill, 64-69; dir dept path & lab med, Mt Sinai Med Ctr, 69-79; CHIEF COAGULATION & HEMOSTASIS, WILLIAM BEAUMONT HOSP, 79- *Concurrent Pos:* Res fel biochem, Sch Med, Marquette Univ, 48; assoc path, Peter Bent Brigham Hosp, Boston, 55-60. *Mem:* AAAS; Col Am Path; Am Asn Path; Int Soc Thrombosis & Haemostasis; Am Soc Clin Path. *Res:* Blood coagulation. *Mailing Add:* 3601 W 13 Mile Rd Clin Labs William Beaumont Hosp Royal Oak MI 48072

SHANBOUR, LINDA LIVINGSTON, b Oklahoma City, Okla, Mar 15, 42; div; c 3. PHYSIOLOGY, BIOPHYSICS. *Educ:* Cent State Univ, BS, 63; Univ Okla, MS, 65; Univ Ala, PhD(biophys), 68. *Prof Exp:* Instr physiol, Med Ctr, Univ Okla, 68-70, asst prof physiol & biophys, 70-71; ASSOC PROF PHYSIOL, UNIV TEX MED SCH HOUSTON, 71- *Concurrent Pos:* Physiologist, Vet Admin Hosp, Oklahoma City, 68-70; res assoc, Dept Med, Med Ctr, Univ Okla, 68-71, Manahan grant, Med Sch, 70-71; USPHS grant, Univ Tex Med Sch Houston, 72-, NIMH res scientist develop award, 73-78; consult, Gen Med Study Sect A, NIH, 72; consult, Study Sect, Nat Inst Alcohol Abuse & Alcoholism, 74-78. *Mem:* AAAS; Am Fedn Clin Res; Biophys Soc; Soc Exp Biol & Med; Am Physiol Soc. *Res:* Gastrointestinal physiology, biophysics, biochemistry and pathology with emphasis on alcoholism. *Mailing Add:* Dept of Physiol Univ of Tex Med Sch Houston TX 77025

SHANBROM, EDWARD, b West Haven, Conn, Nov 29, 24; m 46; c 4. INTERNAL MEDICINE, HEMATOLOGY. *Educ:* Allegheny Col, BS, 47; Univ Buffalo, MD, 51; Am Bd Internal Med, dipl, 61. *Prof Exp:* Intern, E J Meyer Mem Hosp, Buffalo, 51-52; resident med, Gorgas Hosp, Ancon, CZ, 52-53; resident, Vet Admin Hosp, West Haven, Conn, 53-55; res fel, Sch Med, Yale Univ, 55-56; chief leukemia-lymphoma sect, Dept Hemat, City of Hope Med Ctr, Duarte, Calif, 56-58; dir med oncol & hemat & assoc chief clin serv, Orange County Gen Hosp, Orange, 58-64; med dir & dir res, Hyland Labs, Los Angeles, 64-; ASSOC CLIN PROF MED, UNIV CALIF MED SCH, IRVINE, 76- *Concurrent Pos:* Staff physician, St Joseph Hosp, Orange, Calif, 58-; clin instr, Med Ctr, Univ Calif, Los Angeles, 61-65, asst clin prof, 65-69, assoc clin prof med & path, 69-; vis prof, Makerere Univ, Uganda, 71. *Honors & Awards:* Sci & Res Achievement Award, Nat Hemophilia Found, 66. *Mem:* Fel Am Col Physicians; Am Soc Hemat; Am Asn Cancer Res; Am Fedn Clin Res; Transplantation Soc. *Res:* Leukemias and lymphomas; cancer chemotherapy; purification of antihemophilic factor for practical therapy; isolation of histocompatibility typing sera. *Mailing Add:* 2252 Liane Lane Santa Ana CA 92705

SHAND, JULIAN BONHAM, JR, b Columbia, SC, Nov 6, 37; m 63; c 3. SOLID STATE PHYSICS. *Educ:* Univ SC, BS, 59; Univ NC, Chapel Hill, PhD(physics), 65. *Prof Exp:* Asst prof physics, Univ Ga, 64-67; Dana prof & chmn dept, 67-73, PROF COMPUT SCI, BERRY COL, 73-, DANA PROF PHYSICS, 81- *Mem:* Am Phys Soc; Am Asn Physics Teachers; Sigma Xi. *Res:* Electrons in metals; pseudopotentials; positron annihilation in solids. *Mailing Add:* 112 Parkway Dr Rome GA 30161

SHAND, MICHAEL LEE, b Stockton, Calif, July 2, 46; m 69. SOLID STATE PHYSICS, OPTICS. *Educ:* Princeton Univ, AB, 68; Univ Pa, MSc, 69, PhD(physics), 73. *Prof Exp:* Res assoc physics, Univ Paris, 73-74; vis asst prof, Ariz State Univ, 75-76; staff physicist, Allied Chem Corp, 76-80, SR RES PHYSICIST, ALLIED CORP, 80- *Concurrent Pos:* Res assoc fel, French Foreign Ministry, 73-74. *Mem:* Sigma Xi; Am Phys Soc; Inst Elec & Electronics Engrs. *Res:* Raman scattering; quantum optics; nonlinear optics; laser physics. *Mailing Add:* Corp Res Ctr PO Box 1021R Morristown NJ 07960

SHANDLEY, PAUL DAVID, b Niagara Falls, NY, Nov 15, 24; m 47; c 2. PHYSICS. *Educ:* Mich Col Mining & Technol. BS, 49; Univ Rochester, MS, 53. *Prof Exp:* From instr to asst prof, 52-64, admin asst, 65-77, actg head dept, 74-75, ASSOC PROF PHYSICS, MICH TECHNOL UNIV, 64- *Res:* Physical properties of natural and artificial magnetite; instrumentation for the quantitative determination of magnetite in ores. *Mailing Add:* Dept of Physics Mich Technol Univ Houghton MI 49931

SHANDS, HARLEY CECIL, psychiatry, deceased

SHANDS, HENRY LEE, plant genetics, plant breeding, see previous edition

SHANDS, JOSEPH WALTER, JR, b Jacksonville, Fla. Nov 1. 30; m 55; c 4. MEDICAL MICROBIOLOGY. *Educ:* Princeton Univ, AB. 52; Duke Univ, MD, 56. *Prof Exp:* Fel microbiol, 61-64, from asst prof to prof immunol & med microbiol, Col Med, 67-76, PROF MED & CHIEF DIV INFECTIOUS DIS, UNIV FLA, 76- *Concurrent Pos:* Ed, J Infection & Immunity, 70-78; mem bacteriol & mycol study sect, NIH. 71-74. *Mem:* Am Soc Microbioloeists; Reticuloendothelial Soc; NY Acad Sci; Infectious Dis Soc Am; Am Asn Immunologists. *Res:* Endotoxin; pathogenesis of infection; host-parasite relationships. *Mailing Add:* Dept of Med Box J 277 M S B Univ of Fla Gainesville FL 32610

SHANE, CHARLES DONALD, b Auburn, Calif, Sept 6, 95; m 20; c 2. ASTRONOMY. *Educ:* Univ Calif, AB, 15, PhD(astron), 20. *Hon Degrees:* LLD, Univ Calif, 65. *Prof Exp:* Instr math, 20-22, instr math & astron, 22-24, from asst prof to prof astron, 24-45, astronr, 45-63, dir, 45-58, EMER ASTRONR, LICK OBSERV, UNIV CALIF, 63- *Mem:* Nat Acad Sci; Am Astron Soc; Am Philos Soc. *Res:* Stellar spectra; solar spectrum; celestial photography; distribution of nebulae. *Mailing Add:* Dept Astron Lick Observ Univ Calif Santa Cruz CA 95064

SHANE, HAROLD D, b New York, NY, Jan 22, 36; m 62; c 2. MATHEMATICAL STATISTICS. *Educ:* Mass Inst Technol, SB, 57; NY Univ, MS, 62, PhD(math), 68. *Prof Exp:* Engr electronics, Elec Div, Daystrom Inc. 58-61; instr math, Sch Eng, Cooper Union, 62-68; from asst prof to assoc prof, 68-75, PROF MATH, BARUCH COL, 76-, CHMN DEPT, 71- *Mem:* Am Math Soc; Math Asn Am; Inst Math Statist. *Res:* Nonparametric statistical theory and methodology; inequalities for order statistics; mathematical applications to political science and management. *Mailing Add:* Dept of Math Baruch Col New York NY 10010

SHANE, JOHN DENIS, b Gooding, Idaho, Aug 9, 52; m 76; c 2. PALEOPALYNOLOGY, ORGANIC MATTER ANALYSIS. *Educ:* Brigham Young Univ, BS, 77; Ariz State Univ, PhD(bot), 82. *Prof Exp:* Geol field asst, US Geol Surv, 79, grad student appointee, 79-81; SR GEOLOGIST, HQ PALEONT, EXPLOR DEPT, EXXON CO, 81- *Mem:* Sigma Xi; Am Asn Stratig Palynologists; Int Orgn Paleobot; Int Asn Angiosperm Paleobot. *Res:* Organic matter analysis; Mesozoic palynology; fossil fungal spores. *Mailing Add:* Exxon Co PO Box 2189 Mercer 2-2 Houston TX 77001

SHANE, JOHN RICHARD, b San Diego, Calif, Sept 13, 36; m 59; c 2. MAGNETISM. *Educ:* Univ Maine. BS, 58; Mass Inst Technol, PhD(solid state physics). 63. *Prof Exp:* Mem res staff solid state physics. Sperry Rand Res Ctr, 63-68; asst prof, 68-70, ASSOC PROF PHYSICS, UNIV MASS, BOSTON, 70- *Mem:* Am Phys Soc. *Res:* Magnetic properties of matter; antiferromagnetism; antiferromagnetic and paramagnetic resonance; spin-lattice relaxation. *Mailing Add:* Dept of Physics Univ of Mass Boston MA 02125

SHANE, PRESSON S, b Junction City, Kans, Feb 2, 20; m 50; c 4. CHEMICAL ENGINEERING. *Educ:* Univ Kans, BS, 41; Mass Inst Technol, MS, 46. *Prof Exp:* Tech supt, Heavy Water Dept, E I du Pont de Nemours & Co, Inc, 46-57; asst to gen mgr, McGean Chem Co, 57-58; dir, Solid Propellant Div, Atlantic Res Corp, 58-60, vpres, 60-63; partner, Columbia Assocs, 63-64; pres, Wash Technol Assocs, Inc, 64-67; PROF ENG ADMIN, GEORGE WASHINGTON UNIV, 68- *Mem:* Am Inst Aeronaut & Astronaut; Am Inst Chem Engrs. *Res:* Aerospace developments; management of advanced technology. *Mailing Add:* Dept of Eng Admin & Opers Res George Washington Univ Washington DC 20006

SHANE, ROBERT S, b Chicago, Ill, Dec 8, 10; m 36; c 3. MATERIALS SCIENCE, APPLIED CHEMISTRY. *Educ:* Univ Chicago, BS, 30, PhD(chem), 33. *Prof Exp:* Res chemist, Nat Aniline Div, Allied Chem & Dye Corp, 34-35; chemist, Stein-Hall Mfg Co, 35-36; chemist, Fuel Antioxidants, Universal Oil Prod Co, 36; tech dir, Western Adhesives Co, 37-40; res chemist, Gelatin Prod Co, 41-42; plant supt, Amecco Chem, Inc, 42-43; group leader, Bausch & Lomb Optical Co, 43-35; owner, dry cleaning bus, 46-52; proj supvr govt contract res, Wyandotte Chem Corp, 52-54; asst dir new prod develop, Am Cyanamid Co, 54-55; mgr chem ceramics, Com Atomic Power Dept, Westinghouse Elec Corp, 55-57; nucleonics specialist, Bell Aircraft Corp, 57-58; consult engr, Light Mil Electronics Dept, Gen Elec Co, 58-64, res engr, Laminated Prod Dept, 64-66, systs specialist radiation effects, Spacecraft Dept, 66-67, major design rev, Reentry Systs, 67-69, mgr parts, Mat & Processes Eng, Space Systs Orgn, 69-70; staff scientist, Nat Mat Adv Bd, Nat Acad Sci, 70-76; PRIN, SHANE ASSOCS, INC, 76- *Concurrent Pos:* Guest instr, Pa State Univ, 56; consult, US Dept Defense, 76- *Honors & Awards:* Gold Key Award, Gen Elec Co, 63; Award of Merit, Am Soc Testing & Mat, 74. *Mem:* Am Chem Soc; fel Am Soc Testing & Mat; fel Am Inst Chem Engrs; Am Soc Metals. *Res:* Materials engineering; radiation effects; energy transmission; surface phenomena; plastics fabrication; physical chemistry. *Mailing Add:* 7821 Carrleigh Pkwy Springfield VA 22152

SHANE, SAMUEL JACOB, b Yarmouth, NS, May 17, 16; m 72; c 4. INTERNAL MEDICINE. *Educ:* Dalhousie Univ, BSc, 36, MD, CM, 40; FRCP(C). *Prof Exp:* From asst med dir to med dir, Point Edward Hosp, Sydney, NS, 49-57; from asst prof to assoc prof med, Dalhousie Univ, 57-68; assoc prof med, Fac Med, Univ Toronto, 68-81; dir cardiovasc unit, Sunnybrook Hosp, 68-81; CONSULT CARDIOLOGIST, SURREY MEM HOSP, SURREY, BC, 81- *Concurrent Pos:* Med dir tuberc div, Halifax Tuberc Hosp & Health Ctr, 57-64; cardiologist, Halifax Children's Hosp, 57-68; dir cardiac unit, Victoria Gen Hosp, 58-68; Can Tuberc Asn traveling fel, 60; consult, NS Rehab Ctr, 60-68 & Cardiol Halifax Infirmary, 64-68. *Mem:* Am Col Cardiol; Am Thoracic Soc; Am Col Physicians; Am Col Chest Physicians. *Res:* Diseases of chest and heart; cardiovascular hemodynamics and catheterization; clinical pharmacology. *Mailing Add:* Suite 116 Surrey Health Sci Ctr 13798 94 Ave Surrey BC V3V 1N1 Can

SHANEBROOK, J(OHN) RICHARD, b Syracuse, NY, July 10, 38; m 67; c 2. MECHANICAL ENGINEERING. *Educ:* Syracuse Univ, BME, 60, MME, 63, PhD(mech eng), 65. *Prof Exp:* From asst prof to assoc prof, 65-75, PROF MECH ENG, UNION COL, NY, 75- *Concurrent Pos:* NSF res grants, 67-72; Eng Found Res grant, 73-75. *Mem:* Am Soc Mech Engrs; Am Soc Eng Educ; Sigma Xi; Int Soc Biomech; Am Inst Physics. *Res:* Study of three-dimensional boundary layers, both laminar and turbulent; fluid dynamics of artificial heart valves and cardiac assist devices; energy conservation. *Mailing Add:* Dept of Mech Eng Steinmetz Hall Union Col Schenectady NY 12308

SHANEFIELD, DANIEL J, b Orange, NJ, Apr 29, 30; m 64; c 2. PHYSICAL CHEMISTRY. *Educ:* Rutgers Univ, BS, 56, PhD(phys chem). 62. *Prof Exp:* Sr tech specialist phys chem, ITT Fed Labs, 62-67; SR RES CHEMIST, WESTERN ELEC CO, 67- *Mem:* Am Chem Soc; Electrochem Soc; fel Am Inst Chemists; Am Ceramic Soc. *Res:* Electrochemical crystal growth from aqueous and nonaqueous solutions; new electronic memory devices. *Mailing Add:* Western Elec Co PO Box 900 Princeton NJ 08540

SHANER, DALE LESTER, plant physiology, weed science, see previous edition

SHANER, GREGORY ELLIS, b Portland, Ore, Dec 19, 42; m 64; c 2. PLANT PATHOLOGY. *Educ:* Ore State Univ, BS, 64, PhD(plant path), 68. *Prof Exp:* asst prof, 68-75, ASSOC PROF PLANT PATH, PURDUE UNIV, WEST LAFAYETTE, 75- *Mem:* Am Phytopath Soc; Crop Sci Soc Am; Am Soc Agron. *Res:* Plant disease epidemiology; development of improved varieties of wheat and oats; nature and genetics of disease resistance in small grains. *Mailing Add:* Dept of Bot & Plant Path Purdue Univ Life Sci Bldg West Lafayette IN 47906

SHANEYFELT, DUANE L, b Hastings, Nebr, Nov 16, 34; m 63; c 1. POLYMEP CHEMISTRY, APPLIED CHEMISTRY. *Educ:* Hastings Col, BA, 56; Univ Nebr, MS. 59, PhD(org chem), 62. *Prof Exp:* Res chemist, Niagara Chem Div, FMC Corp, 61-64; fel, Coal Chem Res Proj, Mellon Inst Sci, 64-67; group leader, Res & Develop Div, Kraftco Corp, 67-72; sr chemist res & develop, 72-75, res supvr, 75-76, DIR RES & DEVELOP, MASURY-COLUMBIA CO, 77- *Mem:* Am Oil Chem Soc; Fel Am Inst Chemists; Am Chem Soc. *Res:* Oxygen and nitrogen heterocyclic organic chemistry; organic sulfur compounds; agricultural chemistry; chemistry of coal tar derivatives; organic chemistry of ammonia; detergents, cleaners and degreasers, particularly maintenance specialties, emulsions, polymer coatings and systems; floor finishes, coatings and maintenance systems. *Mailing Add:* Res & Develop 1502 N 25th St Melrose Park IL 60160

SHANFIELD, HENRY, b Toronto, Ont, May 17, 23; US citizen; m 50; c 2. PHYSICAL CHEMISTRY, CHEMICAL ENGINEERING. *Educ:* Univ Toronto, BASc, 46, MASc, 57, PhD(phys chem, chem eng), 51. *Prof Exp:* Sr res scientist, Nat Res Coun Can, 47-48; res engr, Esso Eng & Res Ctr, Standard Oil Co, 51-53; asst dir res, Paper-Mate Mfg Div, Gillette Co, 53-58; mgr chem lab, Aeronutronic Div, Philco-Ford Corp, Newport Beach, 58-68; dir res & eng, Polymetrics, Inc, 68-71; dir eng, Foremost Water Systs, 71; mgr water systs, KMS Technol Ctr, 71-74; ASSOC PROF CHEM, UNIV HOUSTON, 74- *Mem:* AAAS; Am Chem Soc; Am Inst Aeronaut & Astronaut; Combustion Inst; Sigma Xi. *Res:* Chemical kinetics; thermodynamics; electrochemistry; membrane transport phenomena; thin layer chromatography; semipermeable membranes. *Mailing Add:* Dept of Chem Cullen Blvd Houston TX 77004

SHANGRAW, RALPH F, b Rutland, Vt, June 11, 30; m 55; c 3. INDUSTRIAL PHARMACY. *Educ:* Mass Col Pharm, BS, 52, MS, 54; Univ Mich, PhD(pharmaceut chem). 58. *Prof Exp:* From asst prof to assoc prof. 58-71, PROF PHARM & CHMN DEPT, SCH PHARM, UNIV MD, BALTIMORE CITY, 71- *Concurrent Pos:* Mem, XIX Revision Comt, US Pharmacopeia & XX Revision Comt, 75-80. *Mem:* Am Pharmaceut Asn; fel Acad Pharmaceut Sci; Soc Cosmetic Chemists; Am Asn Cols Pharm. *Res:* Rheology; aerosols; direct tablet compression; emulsion and suspension formulation and evaluation; pharmaceutical technology. *Mailing Add:* Univ of Md Sch of Pharm 636 W Lombard St Baltimore MD 21201

SHANHOLTZ, VERNON ODELL, b Slanesville, WVa, Apr 22, 35; m 65; c 2. AGRICULTURAL ENGINEERING. *Educ:* WVa Univ, BS, 58, MS, 63; Va Polytech Inst & State Univ, PhD(civil eng), 70. *Prof Exp:* Hydraul engr, Agr Res Serv, 58-63; res chemist, 66-70, asst prof, 70-78, ASSOC PROF SOIL & WATER CONSERV, VA POLYTECH INST & STATE UNIV, 78- *Mem:* Am Geophys Union; Am Soc Agr Engrs; Soil & Water Conserv Soc Am. *Res:* Modeling agricultural watershed systems. *Mailing Add:* Dept of Agr Eng Va Polytech & State Univ Blacksburg VA 24060

SHANHOLTZER, WESLEY LEE, b Cumberland, Md, Jan 25, 38; m 66; c 2. SOLID STATE PHYSICS. *Educ:* WVa Univ, BS, 62, MS, 64, PhD(physics), 68. *Prof Exp:* Asst prof, 66-73, ASSOC PROF PHYSICS, MARSHALL UNIV, 73- *Mem:* Sigma Xi; Am Asn Physics Teachers. *Res:* Electron spin resonance studies of conduction electrons paramagnetic susceptibility in lithium metal; electron spin resonance of doped semiconductor crystals. *Mailing Add:* Dept of Physics Marshall Univ Huntington WV 25701

SHANK, BRENDA MAE BUCKHOLD, b Cleveland, Ohio, Sept 25, 39; m. CELL PHYSIOLOGY. *Educ:* Western Reserve Univ, BA, 61, PhD(biophys), 66; Rutgers Med Sch, MD, 76. *Prof Exp:* Res biophysicist, Lawrence Radiation Lab, Univ Calif, 66-68, NIH fel biophys, Donner Lab Med Physics, 68-69; asst prof radiol, Case Western Reserve Univ, 69; asst prof physiol, Rutgers Med Sch, 69-74; FEL, MEM SLOAN-KETTERING CANCER CTR, 76- *Mem:* AAAS; NY Acad Sci; Radiol Soc NAm; Radiation Res Soc. *Res:* Osmotic adaptation in tissue-culture cells; flour beetle, tribolium confusum, regarding effects of radiation and weightlessness in biosatellite; electronic counting of erythrocytes; membrane properties and growth control of cultured cells; radiation kinetics. *Mailing Add:* Dept of Radiation Ther Mem Sloan-Kettering Cancer Ctr New York NY 10021

SHANK, CHARLES PHILIP, b Pittsburgh, Pa, Feb 6, 41; m 63; c 4. POLYMER CHEMISTRY. *Educ:* Univ Dayton, BS, 63, MS, 65; Univ Akron, PhD(polymer sci). 68. *Prof Exp:* Res chemist, NCR Corp, 68-73; DEVELOP CHEMIST, PLASTICS DIV, GEN ELEC CO, 73- *Mem:* Am Chem Soc. *Res:* Characterizations and use of polymers and copolymers, particularly impact modification of polymers and copolymer sequence distribution and its effect on properties. *Mailing Add:* Plastics Div Gen Elec Co Selkirk NY 12158

SHANK, CHARLES VERNON, b Mt Holly, NJ, July 12, 43. ELECTRICAL ENGINEERING. *Educ:* Univ Calif, Berkeley, BS, 65, MS, 66, PhD(elec eng), 69. *Prof Exp:* MEM TECH STAFF, BELL TEL LABS, 69- *Res:* Quantum electronics. *Mailing Add:* Bell Tel Labs 600 Mountain Ave Murray Hill NJ 07974

SHANK, DANIEL BOYD, b Jewell Co, Kans, Nov 5, 14; m 41. AGRONOMY. *Educ:* Univ Nebr, BS, 35; Iowa State Univ, PhD(genetics), 41. *Prof Exp:* Asst prof agron, Univ Ark, 41-46; assoc agronomist, SDak State Univ, 46-52, assoc prof, 46-52, prof agron, 52-80, agronomist, Exp Sta, 52-80. *Mem:* Assoc Am Soc Agron. *Res:* Corn breeding and genetics; top-root ratios of inbred and hybrid maize; irradiation; colchicine treatment of corn; homeostasis; stalk quality in corn; cold tolerance in maize; drouth resistance; multi-eared corn work. *Mailing Add:* RFD 3 Sunnyview Brookings SD 57007

SHANK, GEORGE DEANE, b Muncie, Ind, July 17, 40; m 62; c 2. NUMERICAL ANALYSIS. *Educ:* Purdue Univ, BSEE, 62; Univ Md, PhD(appl math), 68. *Prof Exp:* Math analyst, Comput Usage Co, 63-68; from res mathematician to advan res mathematician, 68-74, SR RES MATHEMATICIAN, DENVER RES CTR, MARATHON OIL CO, 74- *Mem:* Soc Indust & Appl Math; Am Math Soc; Asn Comput Mach; Sigma Xi. *Res:* Computational methods for solving problems of flow in porous media and other oil industry problems. *Mailing Add:* Marathon Oil Denver Res Ctr PO Box 269 Littleton CO 80160

SHANK, HERBERT S, b Orange, NJ, Sept 25, 27. MATHEMATICS. *Educ:* Univ Chicago, BA, 49, MS, 52; Cornell Univ, PhD, 69. *Prof Exp:* Mathematician, Inst Syst Res, Univ Chicago, 54-59, mathematician, Labs Appl Scis, 59-65; mem prof staff, Ctr Naval Anal, 65-68; res assoc, Cornell Univ, 68-70; Nat Res Coun fel, 70-71, ASSOC PROF MATH, UNIV WATERLOO, 71- *Concurrent Pos:* Instr, Ill Inst Technol, 57-58; vis prof, Queen's Univ, 81; vis scientist, Cornell Univ, 81-82. *Mem:* Am Math Soc; Math Asn Am. *Res:* Graph theory; combinatorial mathematics; operations research; electrical network theory. *Mailing Add:* Dept Combinatorics & Optimiz Univ Waterloo Waterloo ON N2L 3G1 Can

SHANK, KENNETH EUGENE, b Lancaster, Pa, Oct 26, 49; m 70; c 3. RADIOLOGICAL & ENVIRONMENTAL HEALTH. *Educ:* Elizabethtown Col, BS, 71; Purdue Univ, MS, 73, PhD(bionucleonics), 75. *Prof Exp:* Oper res anal, Defense Activ, 71-72; res assoc environ assessment, Oak Ridge Nat Lab, 75-80; MEM STAFF, US DEPT ENERGY, OAK RIDGE, TENN, 80- *Honors & Awards:* Glenn L Jenkins Award, Purdue Univ, 76. *Mem:* Health Physics Soc; Am Indust Hyg Asn; Am Pub Health Asn. *Res:* Determining the environmental and health impacts of nuclear and nonnuclear energy systems. *Mailing Add:* US Dept Energy PO Box E Oak Ridge TN 37830

SHANK, LOWELL WILLIAM, b Hagerstown, Md, June 28, 39; m 63; c 2. CHEMISTRY. *Educ:* Goshen Col, BS, 61; Ohio State Univ, MSc, 64, PhD(anal chem), 66. *Prof Exp:* Asst prof, 66-74, ASSOC PROF ANAL CHEM, WESTERN KY UNIV, 74- *Mem:* Am Chem Soc. *Res:* Analysis of ancient metals. *Mailing Add:* Dept of Chem Western Ky Univ Bowling Green KY 42101

SHANK, MAURICE E(DWIN), b Brooklyn, NY, Apr 22, 21; m 48; c 3. AERONAUTICAL PROPULSION, MECHANICAL ENGINEERING. *Educ:* Carnegie Inst Technol, BS, 42; Mass Inst Technol, ScD, 49. *Prof Exp:* Instr metall, Mass Inst Technol, 46-49, from asst prof to assoc prof mech eng, 49-60; dir advan mat, 60-70, mgr mat eng & res, 70-71, DIR ENG TECHNOL, COM PRODS DIV, PRATT & WHITNEY AIRCRAFT GROUP, UNITED TECHNOLOGIES CORP, 72- *Concurrent Pos:* Consult ed, McGraw-Hill Bk Co; mem res & technol adv coun, NASA, 73-77, mem advr comt aeronaut, 78-; mem comt res, NSF, 74-77. *Mem:* Soc Automotive Engrs; fel Am Soc Mech Engrs; fel Am Inst Mining, Metall & Petrol Engrs; fel Am Soc Metals; assoc fel Am Inst Aeronaut & Astronaut. *Res:* Advancing state-of-the-art technology in engine aerodynamic components, noise and emission reduction, fuel systems and controls, materials and structures to assure competitive engine performance, weight and cost. *Mailing Add:* Com Prods Div (EB2A) United Technologies Corp East Hartford CT 06108

SHANK, PETER R, b Ithaca, NY, Feb 17, 46; m 70; c 1. VIROLOGY. *Educ:* Cornell Univ, BS, 68; Univ NC, Chapel Hill, PhD(virol), 73. *Prof Exp:* Fel, Univ Calif, San Francisco, 73-78; ASST PROF BIOL & MED, BROWN UNIV, 78- *Mem:* Am Soc Microbiol; AAAS; Soc Gen Microbiol. *Res:* Molecular mechanisms by which RNA tumor viruses transform cells with focus on the structure of the proviral DNA and factors which govern its expression. *Mailing Add:* Div Biol & Med Brown Univ Providence RI 02912

SHANK, ROBERT ELY, b Louisville, Ky, Sept 2, 14; m 42; c 3. MEDICINE. *Educ:* Westminster Col, Mo, AB, 35; Washington Univ, MD, 39. *Prof Exp:* From intern to house physician, Barnes Hosp, Mo, 39-41; resident physician, St Louis Isolation Hosp, 41; asst resident physician & asst, Rockefeller Inst Hosp, 41-46; assoc mem, Pub Health Res Inst, New York, 46-48; DANFORTH PROF PREV MED & HEAD DEPT, SCH MED, WASHINGTON UNIV, 48- *Concurrent Pos:* With nutrit surv, Nfld, 48-; spec consult, USPHS, 49-53; mem food & nutrit bd, Nat Res Coun, 50-71; mem adv comt metab, Surgeon Gen, US Dept Army, 56-60 & adv comt nutrit, 60-72; mem sci adv comt, Nat Vitamin Found, 58-61; mem human ecol study sect, NIH, 59-63 & nutrit study sect, 64-68; mem prof adv comt, Nat Found, 61-62 & Nat Adv Coun Child Health & Human Develop, 69-73; mem, Clin Appln & Prev Adv Comt, Nat Heart, Lung & Blood Inst, 76-80. *Mem:* Am Soc Biol Chemists; Am Soc Clin Invest; Soc Exp Biol & Med; Asn Am Physicians; Am Inst Nutrit. *Res:* Metabolism of progressive muscular dystrophy; cirrhosis of the liver; infectious hepatitis and homologous serum jaundice; appraisal of nutritional status; iron deficiency; relationship between nutrients and hormonal function. *Mailing Add:* Dept of Prev Med Washington Univ Sch of Med St Louis MO 63110

SHANKEL, DELBERT MERRILL, b Plainview, Nebr, Aug 4, 27; m 58; c 3. MICROBIOLOGY. *Educ:* Walla Walla Col, BA, 50; Univ Tex, PhD(bact), 60. *Prof Exp:* Instr sci & math, Walla Walla Col & res scientist bact, San Antonio Col, 54-55; res scientist bact, Univ Tex, 56-59; from asst prof to assoc prof, 59-68, from assoc dean to actg dean arts & sci, 69-74, PROF BACT, UNIV KANS, 68-, EXEC VCHANCELLOR, 74- *Concurrent Pos:* Consult, Cramer Chem Co, 59- & NCent Asn Cols & Sec Schs, 73-; NIH sr fel, Univ Edinburgh, 67-68. *Mem:* AAAS; Am Soc Microbiologists; Genetics Soc Am; Radiation Res Soc; Brit Soc Gen Microbiol. *Res:* Genetic effects of radiations and chemicals and interactions of repair processes; mutagenesis and antimutagenesis. *Mailing Add:* 1520 Learnard Ave Lawrence KS 66045

SHANKLAND, DANIEL LESLIE, b San Diego, Calif, June 18, 24; m 55; c 3. NEUROPHYSIOLOGY. *Educ:* Colo State Col, BS, 48; Univ Ill, MS, 52, PhD(entom), 56. *Prof Exp:* Salesman, Stauffer Chem Co, 52 & Farm Air Serv, 52-54; res rep, Stauffer Chem Co, 55-57; prof entom, Purdue Univ, West Lafayette, 57-76; prof entom & head dept, Miss State Univ, 76-80; PROF ENTOM & HEAD DEPT, UNIV FLA, 80- *Mem:* AAAS; Entom Soc Am; Sigma Xi. *Res:* Physiology; neurophysiology, especially neurotoxic action of insecticides. *Mailing Add:* Dept Entom & Nematol Univ Fla Gainesville FL 32611

SHANKLAND, ROBERT SHERWOOD, b Willoughby, Ohio, Jan 11, 08; m 31, 71; c 5. PHYSICS. *Educ:* Case Western Reserve Univ, BS, 29, MS, 33; Univ Chicago, PhD(physics), 35. *Prof Exp:* Physicist, Radio Sect, Nat Bur Stand, 29-30; from instr to assoc prof, 30-41, head dept, 40-58, AMBROSE SWASEY PROF PHYSICS, CASE WESTERN RESERVE UNIV, 41- *Concurrent Pos:* Asst, Univ Chicago, 34-36, instr, 36; chmn hydrophone adv comt, US Navy, 42-44; chmn underwater sound measurements adv comt, 44-46; physicist & consult, Nat Defense Res Comt, 42-46; dir underwater sound ref labs, Off Sci Res & Develop, 42-46, rep, UK, 43; trustee, Cleveland Hearing & Speech Ctr, 46-61 & Andrews Sch for Girls, 60-; mem acoust panel, Underwater Sound Comt, Nat Res Coun, 47-48, mem div phys sci, 51-54; consult, Phillips Patroleum Co, Atomic Energy Div, 55-66 & Idaho Nuclear Corp, 66-70; dir, Assoc Midwest Univs, 58-61, vpres, 59-60, pres, 60-61. *Mem:* Fel AAAS; fel Am Phys Soc; fel Acoust Soc Am; Optical Soc Am; Am Asn Physics Teachers. *Res:* Acoustics and architectural acoustics; underwater sound; atomic physics and nuclear energy. *Mailing Add:* Dept of Physics Case Western Reserve Univ Cleveland OH 44106

SHANKLE, ARTHUR THOMPSON, electrical engineering, see previous edition

SHANKLE, ROBERT JACK, b Ga, Sept 17, 23; m 52; c 2. DENTISTRY. *Educ:* Emory Univ, DDS, 48; Am Bd Endodontics, dipl. *Prof Exp:* Instr crown & bridge prothodont, Sch Dent, Emory Univ, 49-51; from assoc prof to prof oper dent, 51-66, PROF ENDODONT & CHMN DEPT, SCH DENT, UNIV NC, CHAPEL HILL, 66- *Concurrent Pos:* Consult, Womack Army Hosp, Ft Knox, Ky, Ft Benning, Ga & Ft Dix, NJ; dir admis, Sch Dent, Univ NC, Chapel Hill, 64-75, ed, NC Dent J, 72-77; dir pub rels & develop, 75- *Mem:* Am Dent Asn; fel Am Asn Endodont; fel Am Col Dent; fel Int Col Dent. *Res:* Endodontics. *Mailing Add:* Univ of NC Sch of Dent Chapel Hill NC 27514

SHANKLIN, JAMES ROBERT, JR, b Bluefield, WVa, Dec 28, 41; m 66; c 2. SYNTHETIC ORGANIC CHEMISTRY, MEDICINAL CHEMISTRY. *Educ:* Yale Univ, BA, 64; Univ Va, PhD(chem), 72. *Prof Exp:* Teacher, Va Episcopal Sch, 64-66; fel, Wayne State Univ, 71-73; sr res chemist, 73-80, GROUP MGR CARDIOVASCULAR SYNTHESIS, A H ROBINS CO, 80- *Concurrent Pos:* Adj fac mem, Va Commonwealth Univ, 73- *Mem:* Am Chem Soc; Sigma Xi. *Res:* Organosulfur chemistry; heterocyclic chemistry; medicinal chemistry specializing in the cardiovascular and central nervous system areas. *Mailing Add:* 1211 Sherwood Ave Richmond VA 23220

SHANKLIN, MILTON D(AVID), b Kansas City, Mo, Aug 17, 24; m 45; c 3. AGRICULTURAL ENGINEERING. *Educ:* Univ Mo, BS, 51, MS, 53, PhD(agr eng), 58. *Prof Exp:* Field engr, Portland Cement Asn, 53-55; instr agr eng, Univ Mo, 55-58; proj leader, Climatic Lab, USDA, Mo, 58-60; assoc prof, 60-64, PROF AGR ENG, UNIV MO-COLUMBIA, 64- *Mem:* Am Soc Agr Engrs; Int Soc Biometeorol. *Res:* Animal calorimetry; heat transfer in animal shelters. *Mailing Add:* 104 Agr Eng Bldg Univ of Mo Columbia MO 65201

SHANKS, CARL HARMON, JR, b Martinsville, Ohio, May 20, 32; m 55; c 3. ENTOMOLOGY. *Educ:* Wilmington Col, BS, 54; Ohio State Univ, MSc, 55; Univ Wis, PhD(entom), 60. *Prof Exp:* ENTOMOLOGIST, WASH STATE UNIV, 59-, SUPT, SOUTHWESTERN WASTE RES UNIT, 80- *Mem:* Entom Soc Am. *Res:* Biology and control of arthropod pests of small fruits and vegetables; plant resistance to insects and mites; biological control of weeds. *Mailing Add:* Wash State Univ Southwestern Wash Res Unit Vancouver WA 98665

SHANKS, DANIEL, b Chicago, Ill, Jan 17, 17; m 47; c 3. MATHEMATICS. *Educ:* Univ Chicago, BS, 37; Univ Md, PhD(math), 54. *Prof Exp:* Physicist, Aberdeen Proving Ground, 40; physicist & mathematician, Naval Ord Lab, Naval Ship Res & Develop Ctr, 41-57, mathematician, Comput & Math Dept, 57-76, mathematician, Nat Bur Standards, 77; MATHEMATICIAN, DEPT MATH, UNIV MD, COLLEGE PARK, 77- *Mem:* Am Math Soc. *Res:* Number theory; numerical analysis and analysis; summability; computing machinery; servo-mechanisms; theoretical physics. *Mailing Add:* Dept of Math Univ of Md College Park MD 20742

SHANKS, JAMES BATES, b Steubenville, Ohio, June 17, 17; m 43, 74; c 3. HORTICULTURE. *Educ:* Ohio State Univ, PhD, 49. *Prof Exp:* Assoc prof, 49-56, PROF HORT, UNIV MD, COLLEGE PARK, 56- *Concurrent Pos:* Mem, Plant Growth Regulator Working Group. *Mem:* Am Soc Hort Sci; Am Inst Biol Sci. *Res:* Greenhouse flowering crops. *Mailing Add:* Dept of Hort Univ of Md College Park MD 20742

SHANKS, JAMES CLEMENTS, JR, b Detroit, Mich, Oct 15, 21; m 50; c 3. SPEECH PATHOLOGY. *Educ:* Mich State Univ, BA, 43; Univ Denver, MA, 49; Northwestern Univ, PhD(speech path), 57. *Prof Exp:* Instr speech, Iowa State Teachers Col, 49-50; asst prof speech path, Syracuse Univ, 52-55; from asst prof to assoc prof, 55-67, PROF SPEECH PATH & CLIN DIR SPEECH PATH SERV, SCH MED, IND UNIV, INDIANAPOLIS, 67- *Concurrent Pos:* Consult, New Castle State Hosp, 59. *Mem:* Am Speech & Hearing Asn; Am Cleft Palate Asn. *Res:* Speech disorders involving function of the larynx and valum manifested as deviations of voice quality and vocal resonance. *Mailing Add:* Sch of Med Dept of Speech Path Ind Univ Indianapolis IN 46202

SHANKS, ROGER D, b Libertyville, Ill, May 30, 51; m 71. DAIRY CATTLE BREEDING. *Educ:* Univ Ill, BS, 74; Iowa State Univ, MS, 77, PhD(animal sci), 79. *Prof Exp:* ASST PROF GENETICS, UNIV ILL, 79- *Mem:* Am Agr Econ Asn; Am Dairy Sci Asn; Am Genetic Asn; Biomet Soc; Genetics Soc Am. *Res:* Genetic and economic aspects of dairy cattle improvement programs including evaluation, selection, and mating designs. *Mailing Add:* Dept Dairy Sci 315 Animal Sci Lab Univ Ill 1207 W Gregory Dr Urbana IL 61801

SHANKS, SUSAN JANE, b Toledo, Ohio. SPEECH PATHOLOGY. *Educ:* Univ Toledo, BEd, 57; Bowling Green State Univ, MA, 60; La State Univ, PhD(speech path), 66. *Prof Exp:* Teacher, St Pius X Sch, 57-58; grad asst speech pathologist, Bowling State Univ, 58-59; speech pathologist, Samuel Gompers Rehab Ctr, 60-63; asst prof, Univ South Fla, 67-68; asst prof, Stephen F Austin State Univ, 68-70; PROF SPEECH PATH, CALIF STATE UNIV, FRESNO, 70- *Mem:* Am Speech & Hearing Asn. *Res:* Voice disorders; language disorders in children and adults. *Mailing Add:* Dept of Speech Path Calif State Univ Fresno CA 93740

SHANKS, WAYNE C, III, b Detroit, Mich, Aug 26, 47; m 70. GEOCHEMISTRY. *Educ:* Mich State Univ, BS, 69; La State Univ, MS, 71; Univ Southern Calif, PhD(geol), 76. *Prof Exp:* Teaching asst geol, La State Univ, 70-71; res asst, Univ Southern Calif, 71-75; asst prof geol, Univ Calif, Davis, 75-77; ASST PROF GEOL & GEOPHYSICS, UNIV WIS, MADISON, 77- *Concurrent Pos:* Instr geol, Pierce Col, Calif, 73-75; NSF traineeship, 74. *Mem:* Sigma Xi; Soc Econ Paleontologists & Mineralogists; Geochem Soc. *Res:* Geochemistry of hydrothermal and geothermal ore fluids; origin of ore deposits and stable isotope geochemistry. *Mailing Add:* Dept of Geol & Geophysics Univ of Wis Madison WI 53706

SHANMUGAN, K SAM, b India, Jan 6, 43; US citizen; m 68; c 2. COMMUNICATION SYSTEMS, SIGNAL PROCESSING. *Educ:* Madras Univ, India, BE, 64; Indian Inst Sci, ME, 66; Okla State Univ, PhD(elec eng), 70. *Prof Exp:* Res assoc elec eng, Okla State Univ, 70-71 & Univ Kans, 71-73; assoc prof, Wichita State Univ, 73-78; mem tech staff, Bell Labs, NJ, 78-80; PROF ELEC ENG, UNIV KANS, 80- *Concurrent Pos:* Consult, Boeing Aircraft, Wichita, 74-75 & United Telephone, 80; assoc dir, Image Processing Lab, Univ Kans, 80- *Mem:* Inst Elec & Electronics Engrs; Am Soc Eng Educ. *Res:* Image processing; general systems theory; modeling and analysis of communication systems. *Mailing Add:* Elec Eng Dept Univ Kans Lawrence KS 66044

SHANNETTE, GARY WAYNE, b Highland Park, Mich, Jan 24, 37; m 61; c 2. METALLURGICAL ENGINEERING. *Educ:* Mich Technol Univ, BS, 59; Iowa State Univ, MS, 66, PhD(metall), 68. *Prof Exp:* Metallurgist, Aluminum Co Am, 60-63; asst metall, Ames Lab, USAEC, 63-68; asst prof, 68-74, ASSOC PROF METALL ENG, MICH TECHNOL UNIV, 74- *Concurrent Pos:* NSF res grants, 70-72 & 76-81. *Mem:* Am Soc Metals. *Res:* Physics of metals, solid state thermodynamics. *Mailing Add:* Dept of Metall Eng Mich Technol Univ Houghton MI 49931

SHANNON, CHARLES FRANCIS, biochemistry, immunology, see previous edition

SHANNON, CLAUDE ELWOOD, b Gaylord, Mich, Apr 30, 16; m 49; c 3. APPLIED MATHEMATICS. *Educ:* Univ Mich, BS, 36; Mass Inst Technol, MS & PhD(math), 40. *Hon Degrees:* MSc, Yale Univ, 54; DSc, Univ Mich, 61. *Prof Exp:* Asst elec eng & math, Mass Inst Technol, 36-39; Nat Res Coun fel, Princeton Univ, 40, res mathematician, Nat Defense Res Comt, 40-41; res mathematician, Bell Tel Labs, Inc, 41-57; Donner prof sci, 58-80, PROF ELEC ENG, MASS INST TECHNOL, 57-, EMER DONNER PROF SCI, 80- *Concurrent Pos:* Fel, Ctr Advan Study in Behav Sci, 57-58. *Honors & Awards:* Noble Prize, Inst Elec Eng, 39, Liebmann Prize, Inst Radio Eng, 49; Ballantine Medal, Franklin Inst, 55. *Mem:* Nat Acad Sci; Am Math Soc; Inst Elec & Electronics Engrs; Am Acad Arts & Sci. *Res:* Boolean algebra and switching circuits; communication theory; mathematical cryptography; computing machines. *Mailing Add:* Dept of Elec Eng Mass Inst of Technol Cambridge MA 02139

SHANNON, EDWARD LEO, food science, see previous edition

SHANNON, EMROY LAUD, plant pathology, see previous edition

SHANNON, FREDERICK DALE, b Akron, Ohio, June 10, 31; m 57; c 1. ORGANIC CHEMISTRY, POLYMER CHEMISTRY. *Educ:* Univ Akron, BS, 53, MS, 59, PhD(chem), 64. *Prof Exp:* Res chemist, Inst Rubber Res, Univ Akron, 53-54 & 56-58; instr, 58-60, assoc prof, 60-62 & 64-65, PROF CHEM, HOUGHTON COL, 65-, DIR SUMMER SCH, 71-, ACAD DEAN, 73- *Mem:* Am Chem Soc; Am Sci Affil; Am Asn Higher Educ; Am Conf Acad Deans. *Res:* Cyclic dienes; cationic polymerization; molecular structure determination. *Mailing Add:* Off of Acad Dean Houghton Col Houghton NY 14744

SHANNON, IRA LENWOOD, b McGehee, Ark, Oct 12, 18; m 51; c 4. BIOLOGY, CHEMISTRY. *Educ:* Pac Univ, BS, 47; Univ Ore, DMD, 51; Univ Calif, MSD, 55. *Prof Exp:* Instr dent med, Sch Dent, Univ Calif, US Air Force, 54-55, chief exp dent, Sch Aerospace Med, 55-67; DIR ORAL DIS RES LAB, VET ADMIN HOSP, 67-; PROF BIOCHEM, UNIV TEX DENT BR HOUSTON, 67- *Mem:* Fel Am Col Dentists; Soc Exp Biol & Med; Endocrine Soc. *Res:* Oral biology; clinical chemistry; parotid fluid steroids in stress; parotid gland physiology; etiology of peridontal disease. *Mailing Add:* Vet Admin Hosp 2002 Holcombe Blvd Houston TX 77031

SHANNON, JACK CORUM, b Halls, Tenn, Feb 27, 35; m 55; c 2. PLANT PHYSIOLOGY. *Educ:* Univ Tenn, BS, 58; Univ Ill, MS, 59, PhD(plant physiol), 62. *Prof Exp:* Res asst hort, Univ Ill, 58-60, res asst plant physiol, 60-62; asst prof, Purdue Univ, 62-63; plant physiologist, Crop Res Div, Agr Res Serv, USDA, 63-71; assoc prof, 71-74, PROF HORT PHYSIOL, PA STATE UNIV, 74- *Mem:* Am Soc Plant Physiologists; Am Soc Agron; Crop Sci Soc Am; Am Asn Cereal Chemists; Am Soc Hort Sci. *Res:* Study of sugar movement into Zea mays L kernels and the utilization of these sugars in starch biosynthesis. *Mailing Add:* 1455 Park Hills Ave State College PA 16801

SHANNON, JACK DEE, b McAlester, Okla, Oct 18, 43. METEOROLOGY. *Educ:* Univ Okla, BS, 65, MS, 72, PhD(meteorol), 75. *Prof Exp:* ASST METEOROLOGIST, ARGONNE NAT LAB, 76- *Mem:* Am Meteorol Soc; Royal Meteorol Soc; AAAS. *Res:* Numerical modeling of regional air pollution; objective placement of sensors. *Mailing Add:* Bldg 181 Argonne Nat Lab Argonne IL 60439

SHANNON, JAMES AUGUSTINE, b Hollis, NY, Aug 9, 04; m 33; c 2. PHYSIOLOGY. *Educ:* Col Holy Cross, AB, 25; NY Univ, MD, 29, PhD(physiol), 35. *Hon Degrees:* DSc, Col Holy Cross, 52, Duke Univ, 58, Providence Col, 58, Loyola Univ, Ill, 59, Cath Univ Am, 60, WVa Univ, 60, Univ Md, 65, NY Univ, 65 & Jefferson Med Col, 65; LLD, Univ Notre Dame, 57; LHD, Yeshiva Univ, 62; MD, Cath Univ Louvain, 64 & Karolinska Inst, Sweden, 64; plus many others. *Prof Exp:* Intern, Bellevue Hosp, New York, 29-31; from asst physiol to assoc prof med, Col Med, NY Univ, 31-46; dir, Squibb Inst Med Res, 46-49; assoc dir chg res, Nat Heart Inst, 49-52, assoc dir, NIH, 52-55, dir, 55-68; scholar in residence, Nat Acad Sci, 68-70; prof & spec asst to pres, 70-75, adj prof biomed sci, 75-80, EMER PROF, ROCKEFELLER UNIV, 80-; VIS SCHOLAR, NAT LIBR MED, NIH, 75- *Concurrent Pos:* Clin asst vis physician, NY Univ Med Div, Bellevue Hosp, New York, 31-32, asst vis physician, 38-42, assoc vis neuropsychiatrist, Third Psychiat Serv, 44; guest investr, Physiol Labs, Cambridge Univ, 36; ed, J Soc Exp Biol & Med, 40; dir res serv, Goldwater Mem Hosp, 41-46, actg dir, NY Univ Med Div, 44-45; mem bd dirs, Gorgas Mem Inst Trop & Prev Med, 54; mem bd trustees, Whitehead Inst Med Res, 74- Consult to Secy of War, 41-45, Off Surgeon Gen, 46-49, President's Sci Adv Comt, 59-65 & adv comt res, AID, 63-68. Mem malaria conf, Nat Res Coun, 41-46, chmn, Atabrine Conf, mem subcomt coord malarial studies, Bd Coord Malarial Studies & chmn panel clin testing antimalarials; chmn malaria study sect, NIH, 45-47, mem, 47-49; mem nat comt, Int Union Physiol Sci, 55-62; expert adv panel malaria, WHO, 56-66, adv comt med res, 59-63; adv comt med res, Pan-Am Health Orgn, 62-66; standing comt, Fed Coun Sci & Technol, 59-65, Dept Health, Educ & Welfare alternate rep, 65; US deleg, US-Japan Coop Med Sci Comt, 65-68; mem coun, Nat Acad Sci, 58-71, exec comt, 72-73; scholar human biol, Univ Colo, 77- *Honors & Awards:* Medal for Merit, 48; Sci Award, NY Univ, 58; Mendel Medal, Villanova Univ, 61; Pub Welfare Medal, Nat Acad Sci, 62; Rockefeller Pub Serv Award, 64; Distinguished Serv Medal, USPHS, 66; Modern Med Distinguished Achievement Award, 66; Fed Civilian Serv Award, 66; John M Russell Award, Markle Found, 66; Abraham Flexner Award, Asn Am Med Cols, 66; Alan Gregg Lect, 66; Presidential Award for Civilian Serv, 67; Nat Medal for Sci, 75; Int Award, Nat Soc Res Admin, 75; plus other awards from nat groups. *Mem:* Nat Acad Sci; Am Acad Arts & Sci; AAAS; Am Physiol Soc; Soc Exp Biol & Med. *Res:* Pharmacology; clinical investigation in chemotherapy; secretory mechanisms of the renal tubule; renal control of water and electrolyte balance; functional aspects of renal disease; measurement of glomerular filtration. *Mailing Add:* 8302 SW Homewood St Portland OR 97225

SHANNON, JAMES GROVER, plant breeding, see previous edition

SHANNON, JERRY A, JR, b Meshoppen, Pa, Mar 31, 24; m 54; c 4. SCIENCE EDUCATION, BIOLOGY. *Educ:* Pa State Teachers Col, Mansfield, BS, 48; Peabody Col, MA, 49; Cornell Univ, EdD, 57. *Prof Exp:* Supvr biol, Demonstration Sch, Peabody Col, 49-50; high sch teacher, Ind, 50-51 & NY, 51-52; instr biol & conserv, Wis State Col, Oshkosh, 53; from instr to asst prof elem sch sci, Iowa State Teachers Col, 53-56; assoc prof biol & conserv, 56-64, PROF SCI EDUC & BIOL, STATE UNIV NY, COL ONEONTA 64- *Concurrent Pos:* Grants, State Univ NY, plant taxon, Univ Northern Iowa, 61, NSF, Univ NC, 65; biol educ, Univ Rochester, 68; sci educ, Univ Colo, 72. *Mem:* Nat Asn Biol Teachers; Conserv Educ Asn; Nat Sci Teachers Asn. *Res:* Science and environmental education; local flora. *Mailing Add:* Dept Sci Educ State Univ NY Col Oneonta NY 13820

SHANNON, LARRY J(OSEPH), b Williston, NDak, Apr 10, 37; m 57; c 2. CHEMICAL ENGINEERING. *Educ:* Univ Seattle, BS, 59; Univ Calif, Berkeley, PhD(chem eng), 63. *Prof Exp:* Design engr, Aerospace Div, Boeing Co, 59; sr res engr, United Tech Ctr, United Aircraft Corp, 63-69; sr chem engr, 69-72, prin chem engr, 72-76; dir, Environ Mat Sci Div, 76-79, EXEC DIR, ENG & APPL SCI GROUP, MIDWEST RES INST, 79- *Concurrent Pos:* Lectr, Rockhurst Col, 70- *Mem:* Air Pollution Control Asn; Am Inst Aeronaut & Astronaut; Sigma Xi. *Res:* Environmental sciences; air pollution control technology; solid waste management; chemical kinetics; catalysis; combustion dynamics. *Mailing Add:* Midwest Res Inst 425 Volker Blvd Kansas City MO 64110

SHANNON, LELAND MARION, b Fullerton, Calif, Oct 24, 27; m 49; c 5. PLANT BIOCHEMISTRY. *Educ:* Univ Calif, Los Angeles, BS, 49, MS, 51; Rutgers Univ, PhD(plant physiol), 54. *Prof Exp:* Res assoc, Rutgers Univ, 51-54; from instr to assoc prof biochem, Univ Calif, Los Angeles, 54-68; PROF BIOCHEM, UNIV CALIF, RIVERSIDE, 68- *Mem:* Am Soc Plant Physiologists; Am Soc Biol Chemists; Brit Biochem Soc. *Res:* Glycoproteins; protein chemistry; lectins; plant cell-cell interaction. *Mailing Add:* Dept of Biochem Univ of Calif Riverside CA 92502

SHANNON, MICHAEL CARLYLE, plant genetics, see previous edition

SHANNON, ROBERT DAY, b Highland Park, Mich, Aug 28, 35; m 66; c 2. SOLID STATE CHEMISTRY, INORGANIC CHEMISTRY. *Educ:* Univ Ill, Champaign, BS, 57, MS, 59; Univ Calif, Berkeley, PhD(ceramic eng), 64. *Prof Exp:* Res assoc, Univ Ill, 59-60; RES CERAMIST, E I DU PONT DE NEMOURS & CO, INC, 64- *Concurrent Pos:* Res assoc, McMaster Univ, 71-72; assoc prof, Univ Grenoble, 72-73. *Mem:* Mineral Soc Am; Am Chem Soc; Am Inst Physics. *Res:* Crystal growth; synthesis of inorganic oxides; high pressure synthesis; crystallography; solid electrolytes. *Mailing Add:* E I du Pont de Nemours & Co Inc Exp Sta Wilmington DE 19898

SHANNON, ROBERT RENNIE, b Mt Vernon, NY, Oct 3, 32; m 54; c 6. OPTICS. *Educ:* Univ Rochester, BS, 54, MA, 57. *Prof Exp:* Staff physicist, Itek Corp, 59-62; dept mgr optical design, 62-67, dir advan tech labs, 67-69; PROF OPTICAL SCI, UNIV ARIZ, 69- *Concurrent Pos:* Topical ed, Optical Soc Am, 75-78. *Mem:* Fel Optical Soc Am; fel Soc Photo-Optical Instrument Engrs (pres, 79-80). *Res:* Applied optics, especially lens design, image analysis, optical testing, laser application, and application of computers to engineering problems; atmospheric optics; massive optics design and fabrication. *Mailing Add:* Optical Sci Ctr Univ of Ariz Tucson AZ 85721

SHANNON, SPENCER SWEET, JR, b Philadelphia, Pa, Apr 15, 27; div; c 4. EXPLORATION GEOCHEMISTRY, ORE GENESIS. *Educ:* Amherst Col, AB, 49; Yale Univ, MSc, 50; Univ Idaho, PhD(geol), 64. *Prof Exp:* Mineral economist, US Bur Mines, Washington, DC, 53-55; geologist, AEC, Rawlins, Wyo, 55-57; mining engr, US Bur Mines, Denver, Colo, 57-61; asst prof geol, Univ Idaho, 63-65; sr geologist, Minerals Div, Phillips Petrol Co, Utah, 65-66; res mgr, Navarro Explor Co Ltd, Windhoek, Nambia, 66-67; asst prof geol, Weber State Col, 67-68; assoc prof, Univ Tex, El Paso, 68-75; staff geologist, US Energy Res & Develop Admin, 75-78; STAFF MEM, LOS ALAMOS NAT LAB, N MEX, 78- *Concurrent Pos:* Consult to var corp clients. *Mem:* Fel Geol Soc Am; Am Inst Prof Geologists; Soc Econ Geologists; Geol Soc SAfrica; Asn Explor Geochemists. *Res:* Instruction, research, and participation in systematic exploration for mineral deposits using geology, geochemistry, and geophysics; examination and evaluation of mines and prospects; relation of volcanism to genesis of ore deposits. *Mailing Add:* Los Alamos Nat Lab Univ Calif PO Box 1663 Los Alamos NM 87545

SHANNON, STANTON, b Phoenix, Ariz, Dec 28, 28; m 57; c 2. SOIL CHEMISTRY. *Educ:* Univ Ariz, BS, 52, MS, 53; Univ Calif, Davis, PhD(plant physiol), 61. *Prof Exp:* Sr lab technician, Citrus Exp Sta, Dept Soils & Plant Nutrit, Univ Calif, Riverside, 56-57; res asst plant anal, Univ Calif, Davis, 57-61; asst prof, 61-68, ASSOC PROF VEG CROPS, NY STATE COL AGR, CORNELL UNIV, 68- *Mem:* Am Soc Plant Physiologists; Am Soc Hort Sci. *Res:* Post harvest physiology of vegetable crops; plant biochemistry; mineral element nutrition; cultural practices for mechanically harvested vegetables, water relations and photosynthetic efficiency. *Mailing Add:* NY State Agr Exp Sta Geneva NY 14456

SHANNON, STEPHEN RANDALL, high energy physics, see previous edition

SHANNON, WILBURN ALLEN, JR, b Springfield, Tenn, June 21, 41; m 64. MEDICAL RESEARCH, CYTOCHEMISTRY. *Educ:* Mid Tenn State Univ, BS, 64; Vanderbilt Univ, MA, 67, PhD(biol), 70. *Prof Exp:* Res assoc path, Harvard Med Sch & Mass Gen Hosp, 70-71; res assoc, Sch Med, Johns Hopkins Univ & Sinai Hosp Baltimore, 71-75; DIR, RES MORPHOLOGY & CYTOCHEM UNIT, GEN MED RES SERV, VET ADMIN HOSP, 75-; ASST PROF CELL BIOL, SOUTHWESTERN MED SCH, 74- *Concurrent Pos:* USPHS fel, Harvard Med Sch & Mass Gen Hosp, Boston, 70-71; Nat Cancer Inst fel, Sch Med, Johns Hopkins Univ & Sinai Hosp Baltimore, 71- *Mem:* Am Soc Cell Biol; Electron Micros Soc Am; Histochem Soc. *Res:* Ultracytochemistry, especially development of methods and application to normal and pathological tissue studies; endocrinology; mitochondriology. *Mailing Add:* Dept of Cell Biol Gen Med Res Serv Vet Admin Hosp Dallas TX 75216

SHANNON, WILLIAM MICHAEL, b Mt Holly, NJ, Oct 11, 40; m 64; c 3. MICROBIOLOGY. *Educ:* Univ Ala, Tuscaloosa, BS, 62; Loyola Univ, La, MS, 65; Tulane Univ, PhD(microbiol), 69. *Prof Exp:* Radioisotope res technician, Vet Admin Hosp, Birmingham, Ala, 62-63; res asst endocrinol, Med Units, Univ Tenn, Memphis, 63-64; res asst virol, Loyola Univ, La, 64-65; res asst, Sch Med, Tulane Univ, 64-66, NASA fel, 66-69; res virologist, 69-71, sr virologist, 72-74, HEAD MICROBIOL, VIROL DIV, SOUTHERN RES INST, 75- *Mem:* AAAS; Am Soc Microbiol; NY Acad Sci; Am Asn Cancer Res; Brit Soc Gen Microbiol. *Res:* Biochemistry of adenovirus-infected cells; antiviral chemotherapy; oncogenic viruses, especially murine leukemia viruses; herpesviruses; virus-host cell interactions. *Mailing Add:* Southern Res Inst 2000 Ninth Ave S Birmingham AL 35205

SHANOR, LELAND, b Butler, Pa, July 21, 14; m 40; c 2. MYCOLOGY. *Educ:* Maryville Col, AB, 35; Univ NC, MA, 37, PhD(bot), 39. *Hon Degrees:* DSc, Ill Wesleyan Univ, 61. *Prof Exp:* Asst biol, Maryville Col, 33-35; asst bot, Univ NC, 35-39; instr, Clemson Col & Univ Ill, 39-43; pathologist, USDA, 43-44; res mycologist, George Washington Univ, 44-45; res assoc, Canal Zone Lab, Univ Pa, 46; from asst prof to prof bot, Univ Ill, 46-56, cur mycol collections, 48-56; prof bot & head dept biol sci, Fla State Univ, 56-62; dean div advan studies, Fla Inst Continuing Univ Studies, 62-64; sect head

div sci personnel & educ, NSF, 64, div dir undergrad educ in sci, 65; chmn dept, 65-73, PROF BOT, UNIV FLA, 65- *Concurrent Pos:* Dir, Highlands Mus Natural Hist, Univ NC, 39; Guggenheim fel, 51-52; mem adv comt, Canal Zone Biol Area, 54-; trustee, Highlands Biol Sta, Univ NC, 57-, pres, 58-63; trustee, Fairchild Trop Garden, 66- *Mem:* AAAS; Bot Soc Am; Mycol Soc Am (secy-treas, 50-53, pres, 54). *Res:* Culture of entomogenous fungi; cytology of Saprolegniaceae; distribution, morphology and taxonomy of aquatic fungi. *Mailing Add:* Dept of Bot Univ of Fla Gainesville FL 32611

SHANSKY, MICHAEL STEVEN, b Milwaukee, Wis, May 3, 43; m 68; c 1. VISUAL PHYSIOLOGY, PSYCHOLOGY. *Educ:* Marquette Univ, BA, 66; Syracuse Univ, PhD(psychol), 74. *Prof Exp:* Asst prof physiol optics, 71-77, ASSOC PROF VISUAL SCI, ILL COL OPTOM, 77-, CHMN DEPT VISUAL SCI & DIR RES, 72- *Concurrent Pos:* Guest lectr, DePaul Univ & Northeastern Ill Univ, 73- *Mem:* AAAS; Asn Res Vision & Ophthal. *Res:* Neurophysiology of vision; information processing in the vertebrate visual system; visual perception; polysensory integration. *Mailing Add:* Ill Col Optom Chicago IL 60616

SHANTARAM, RAJAGOPAL, b Poona, India, Mar 29, 39; m 69. MATHEMATICAL STATISTICS. *Educ:* Ferguson Col, India, BS, 59; Univ Poona, MS, 61; Pa State Univ, PhD(math), 66. *Prof Exp:* Asst prof math & statist, State Univ NY Stony Brook, 66-71; asst prof, 71-74, ASSOC PROF MATH & STATIST, UNIV MICH-FLINT, 74- *Mem:* Am Math Soc; Math Asn Am; Am Statist Asn. *Res:* Characteristic functions; limit distributions; mathematical statistics; mathematical modeling; operations research. *Mailing Add:* Dept of Math Univ of Mich Flint MI 48503

SHANTEAU, ROBERT MARSHALL, b Los Angeles, Calif, June 24, 47; m 80. TRANSPORTATION SCIENCE. *Educ:* San Jose State Univ, BS, 70; Univ Calif, Berkeley, MS, 76, PhD(civil eng), 80. *Prof Exp:* ASST PROF CIVIL ENG, PURDUE UNIV, 80- *Mem:* Opers Res Soc Am; Inst Transp Engrs. *Res:* Application of mathematical and physical principles to problems in transporation, including traffic signal timing, speed monitoring and control, mass transit operations and airport design and operation. *Mailing Add:* Civil Eng Bldg Purdue Univ West Lafayette IN 47907

SHANTHAVEERAPPA, TOTADA RAMAIAH, neuroanatomy, histochemistry, see previous edition

SHANTHIKUMAR, JEYAVEERASINGAM GEORGE, b Sri Lanka, July 1, 50; m 77; c 2. PRODUCTION SYSTEMS, STOCHASTIC MODELS. *Educ:* Univ Sri Lanka, BSc, 72; Univ Toronto, MASc, 77, PhD(indust eng), 79. *Prof Exp:* Asst lectr prod & mech eng, Univ Sri Lanka, 73-75; teaching asst indust eng, Univ Toronto, 75-79; ASST PROF INDUST ENG, SYRACUSE UNIV, 79- *Concurrent Pos:* Consult, Syracuse Res Inc, 82- *Mem:* Opers Res Soc Am; Am Inst Indust Engrs; Inst Mgt Sci; Inst Elec & Electronics Engrs; Asn Comput Mach. *Res:* Develop models to understand the behavior to obtain performance measures and to design production systems; develop efficient techniques to derive solutions to stochastic and deterministic models of production systems. *Mailing Add:* 200 Eden Roc Circle Dewitt NY 13214

SHANTZ, RICHARD CHARLES, food science, see previous edition

SHANTZ, ROBERT FRANCIS, metallurgy, chemical engineering, see previous edition

SHAPERE, DUDLEY, b Harlingen, Tex, May 27, 28; div; c 2. PHILOSOPHY OF SCIENCE, HISTORY OF SCIENCE. *Educ:* Harvard Univ, BA, 49, MA, 55, PhD(philos), 57. *Prof Exp:* Instr philos, Ohio State Univ, 57-60; from asst prof to prof, Univ Chicago, 60-72; prof, Univ Ill, Urbana-Champaign, 72-75; PROF PHILOS, UNIV MD, COLLEGE PARK, 75- *Concurrent Pos:* Vis assoc prof, Rockefeller Univ, 65-66; consult, Comn Undergrad Educ Biol Sci, 65-71; spec consult & prog dir, Hist & Philos Sci Prog, NSF, 66-75; vis prof, Harvard Univ, 68; NSF res grants, 70-72, 73-75, 76-78; mem, Inst Advan Study, Princeton, NJ, 78-79. *Mem:* Am Philos Asn; Philos Sci Asn; Hist Sci Soc; AAAS; Am Psychol Asn. *Res:* Characteristics of explanation; the relations of theory, observation, and experiment and the nature of change and innovation in the development of science. *Mailing Add:* Comt Hist & Philos Sci 1131 Skinner Hall Univ of Md College Park MD 20742

SHAPIRA, RAYMOND, b New Bedford, Mass, June 29, 28; m 56; c 3. BIOCHEMISTRY, NEUROCHEMISTRY. *Educ:* Univ NMex, BS, 50; Fla State Univ, PhD(chem), 54. *Prof Exp:* Res biochemist, Biol Div, Oak Ridge Nat Lab, 54-57; from asst prof to assoc prof, 58-71, PROF BIOCHEM, EMORY UNIV, 72- *Concurrent Pos:* Fulbright lectr, Weizmann Inst Sci, 67. *Mem:* AAAS; Am Chem Soc; Fedn Am Socs Exp Biol; Am Soc Biol Chemists; Am Soc Neurochem. *Res:* Studies on the structure, metabolism and function of myelin proteins; induction of tolerance in experimental allergic encephalomyelitis; studies on myelin from patients with multiple sclerosis. *Mailing Add:* Dept of Biochem Emory Univ Woodruff Med Ctr Atlanta GA 30322

SHAPIRA, YAACOV, b Haifa, Israel, Jan 9, 38. PHYSICS. *Educ:* Brandeis Univ, BA, 60; Mass Inst Technol, PhD(physics), 64. *Prof Exp:* MEM RES STAFF SOLID STATE PHYSICS, NAT MAGNET LAB, MASS INST TECHNOL, 64- *Mem:* Am Phys Soc. *Res:* Ultrasonic behavior of solids; Fermi surface; high field superconductors; magnetic phase transitions; magnetic semiconductors. *Mailing Add:* Nat Magnet Lab 170 Albany St Cambridge MA 02139

SHAPIRO, ALAN ELIHU, b New York, NY, Jan 6, 42; m 72. HISTORY OF SCIENCE. *Educ:* Polytech Inst Brooklyn, BS, 62, MS, 65; Yale Univ, MPhil, 69; PhD(hist sci), 70. *Prof Exp:* Instr physics, St John's Univ, NY, 65-66; NATO fel, Cambridge Univ, 70-71; asst prof hist sci, Oberlin Col, 71-72; asst prof, 72-75, ASSOC PROF HIST SCI, UNIV MINN, MINNEAPOLIS, 75- *Mem:* AAAS; Am Hist Asn; Hist Sci Soc; Soc Hist Technol. *Res:* History of physical sciences from the sixteenth to nineteenth centuries; Newton; optics; mechanics. *Mailing Add:* Univ of Minn Sch of Physics Minneapolis MN 55455

SHAPIRO, ALVIN, b Jersey City, NJ, Apr 20, 30; m 71; c 4. NUCLEAR SCIENCE & ENGINEERING. *Educ:* Polytech Inst Brooklyn, BME, 51; Univ Cincinnati, MS, 62, PhD(physics), 68. *Prof Exp:* Engr, Allis-Chalmers Mfg Co, 55-58 & Gen Elec Co, 58-62; from instr to assoc prof, 62-78, PROF NUCLEAR ENG, UNIV CINCINNATI, 78- *Concurrent Pos:* Consult, Mound Lab, Monsanto Res Corp, 70- *Mem:* Am Nuclear Soc; Am Phys Soc. *Res:* Methods of neutron and photon transport; nuclear reactor physics and radiation shielding; neutron dosimetry. *Mailing Add:* Mail Location 163 Univ of Cincinnati Cincinnati OH 45221

SHAPIRO, ALVIN PHILIP, b Nashville, Tenn, Dec 28, 20; m 51; c 2. INTERNAL MEDICINE. *Educ:* Cornell Univ, AB, 41, Long Island Col Med, MD, 44. *Prof Exp:* Res fel, Cincinnati Gen Hosp, 48-49; instr internal med, Col Med, Univ Cincinnati, 49-51; asst prof, Univ Tex Southwestern Med Sch Dallas, 51-56; from asst prof to assoc prof, 56-60, assoc dean acad affairs, 71-75, vchmn med, 75-77, PROF MED, SCH MED, UNIV PITTSBURGH, 67-, ACTG CHMN DEPT, 77- *Concurrent Pos:* Asst clinician, Cincinnati Gen Hosp, 48-49, clinician & asst attend physician, 49-51; attend physician, Parkland Mem & Vet Admin Hosps, Dallas, Tex, 51-56 & Presby Hosp, Pittsburgh, 56- *Mem:* AAAS; Am Psychosom Soc; AMA; Am Heart Asn; Asn Am Med Cols. *Res:* Hypertension; experimental hypertension; psychosomatic disorders. *Mailing Add:* Dept of Internal Med Univ of Pittsburgh Sch of Med Pittsburgh PA 15261

SHAPIRO, ANATOLE MORRIS, b Syracuse, NY, June 28, 23; m 45; c 2. PHYSICS. *Educ:* Univ Buffalo, BA, 44; Cornell Univ, PhD(physics), 52. *Prof Exp:* Assoc physicist, Brookhaven Nat Lab, 52-54; res fel & lectr, Harvard Univ, 54-56, asst prof physics, 56-58; assoc prof, 58-65, PROF PHYSICS, BROWN UNIV, 65- *Mem:* Am Asn Physics Teachers; fel Am Phys Soc; Italian Phys Soc. *Res:* Nuclear physics; high energy particle interactions; proton-proton and pion-proton elastic and inelastic cross sections; production and decay of K-mesons and hyperons; hybrid systems for interactions above 100 GeV/c. *Mailing Add:* Dept of Physics Brown Univ Providence RI 02912

SHAPIRO, ARTHUR MAURICE, b Baltimore, Md, Jan 6, 46; m 69. POPULATION BIOLOGY. *Educ:* Univ Pa, BA, 66; Cornell Univ, PhD(entom), 70. *Prof Exp:* Asst prof biol, Richmond Col, NY, 70-72; asst prof, 72-75, ASSOC PROF ZOOL, UNIV CALIF, DAVIS, 75- *Concurrent Pos:* Consult, Staten Island Inst Arts & Sci, 70-71; City Univ New York Res Found fel, Richmond Col, NY, 71-72. *Mem:* AAAS; Ecol Soc Am; Soc Study Evolution; Entom Soc Can; Am Entom Soc. *Res:* Genetics and ecology of colonizing species; adaptive strategies of weedy insects and plants; coevolution of insect-plant relationships; historical biogeography of the Andean region; phenology; biogeography and systematics of Pieridae and Hesperiidae. *Mailing Add:* Dept of Zool Univ of Calif Davis CA 95616

SHAPIRO, ASCHER H(ERMAN), b Brooklyn, NY, May 20, 16; m 39; c 5. FLUID DYNAMICS, BIOMEDICAL ENGINEERING. *Educ:* Mass Inst Technol, SB, 38, ScD(mech eng), 46. *Hon Degrees:* DrSci, Univ Salford, Eng, 78. *Prof Exp:* Asst mech eng, 39-40, from instr to prof, 40-62, Ford prof eng, 62-75, chmn fac, 64-65, head dept mech eng, 65-74, INST PROF MECH ENG, MASS INST TECHNOL, 75- *Concurrent Pos:* Consult mech engr, 38-; vis prof, Cambridge Univ, 55-56; Akroyd Stuart Mem lectr, Nottingham Univ, 56; mem subcomt, Nat Adv Comt Aeronaut, US Air Force; tech adv panel aeronaut, Off Secy Defense; chmn, Nat Comt Fluid Mech Films, 62-65 & 71-, mem, 65-; mem sci adv bd, US Air Force, 64-66; mem sci & pub policy comt, Nat Acad Sci, 73-77. *Honors & Awards:* Navy Ord Develop Award, 45; Army-Navy Cert Merit, 47; Richards Mem Award, 60 & Worcester Reed Warner Medal, 65, Am Soc Mech Engrs; Lamme Award, Am Soc Eng Educ, 77. *Mem:* Nat Acad Sci; Nat Acad Eng; fel Am Acad Arts & Sci; fel Am Soc Mech Engrs; fel Am Inst Aeronaut & Astronaut. *Res:* Fluid mechanics; supersonic flow of gases; gas turbine power plant; jet and rocket propulsion; dynamics and thermodynamics of compressible fluid flow; biomedical engineering; cardiovascular function. *Mailing Add:* Dept of Mech Eng Mass Inst of Technol Cambridge MA 02139

SHAPIRO, BENNETT MICHAELS, b Philadelphia, Pa, July 14, 39; m 62. BIOCHEMISTRY. *Educ:* Dickinson Col, BS, 60; Jefferson Med Col, MD, 64. *Prof Exp:* Intern med, Hosp, Univ Pa, 64-65; res assoc, Lab Biochem, Nat Heart Inst, 65-68; vis scientist, Pasteur Inst, Paris, 68-69; chief sect cellular differentiation, Nat Heart & Lung Inst, 69-70; assoc prof, 70-78, PROF BIOCHEM, MED SCH, UNIV WASH, 78- *Mem:* AAAS; Am Chem Soc; Am Soc Microbiol; Am Soc Cell Biol; Am Soc Biol Chemists. *Res:* Regulation of enzyme activity; regulation of nitrogen metabolism; role of the membrane in fertilization and development. *Mailing Add:* Dept of Biochem Univ of Wash Med Sch Seattle WA 98105

SHAPIRO, BERNARD, b Philadelphia, Pa, May 22, 25; m 49; c 3. NUCLEAR MEDICINE. *Educ:* Univ Pa, MD, 51; Am Bd Nuclear Med, dipl, 72. *Prof Exp:* From house officer to resident internal med, Hosp, Univ Pa, 51-53; Am Cancer Soc fel, Norweg Hydro Inst, Oslo, 53-54; Southeast Pa Heart Asn fel, Univ Pa, 54-55, Am Heart Asn fel, 55-56; head radioisotope lab, South Div, 56-66, HEAD RADIATION RES LAB, ALBERT EINSTEIN MED CTR, PHILADELPHIA, 56-, HEAD DEPT NUCLEAR MED, 66-; CLIN PROF RADIOL, SCH MED, TEMPLE UNIV, 78- *Concurrent Pos:* Clin assoc prof radiol, Sch Med, Temple Univ, 67-78. *Mem:* AMA; Am Chem Soc; Radiation Res Soc; Soc Nuclear Med; NY Acad Sci. *Res:* Clinical radioisotopes; radiation research. *Mailing Add:* Dept of Nuclear Med Albert Einstein Med Ctr Philadelphia PA 19141

SHAPIRO, BERNARD LYON, b Montreal, Que, June 16, 32; US citizen; m 60; c 2. ORGANIC CHEMISTRY, NUCLEAR MAGNETIC RESONANCE. *Educ:* McGill Univ, BSc, 52; Harvard Univ, AM, 54, PhD(org chem), 57. *Prof Exp:* Res fel chem, Harvard Univ, 56-58; res fel, Mellon Inst, 58-64; assoc prof, Ill Inst Technol, 64-68; admin officer, 68-71, PROF CHEM, TEX A&M UNIV, 68- *Concurrent Pos:* Ed, Ill Inst Technol Nuclear Magnetic Resonance Newsletter, 58- & Nuclear Magnetic Resonance Abstracts Serv, Preston Tech Abstracts Co, 64-; consult, Res Div,

W R Grace & Co, 64- & Shell Develop Co, 66. *Mem:* AAAS; Am Chem Soc; Am Phys Soc. *Res:* Organic chemistry; especially stereochemistry of haloketones; aliphatic fluorine compounds; organophosphorus compounds; nature of coupling constants, especially involving fluorine and phosphorous. *Mailing Add:* Dept of Chem Tex A&M Univ College Station TX 77843

SHAPIRO, BERT IRWIN, b New York, NY, Jan 14, 41; m 62; c 2. NEUROPHYSIOLOGY, TOXINOLOGY. *Educ:* Swarthmore Col, BA, 62; Harvard Univ, MA, 65, PhD(biol), 67. *Prof Exp:* Instr biol & gen educ, 67-68, from asst prof to assoc prof biol, Harvard Univ, 68-77; MEM STAFF, NAT INST GEN MED SCI, 77- *Concurrent Pos:* Mem, Bermuda Biol Sta. *Mem:* Am Soc Zoologists; Soc Gen Physiologists; Biophys Soc; Int Soc Toxinol; Soc Neurosci. *Res:* Neurophysiology, particularly of conduction mechanisms; action of pharmacological compounds, especially toxins; purification and structure of protein toxins, especially from invertebrates. *Mailing Add:* Cellular & Molecular Nat Inst Gen Med Sci Westwood Bldg Bethesda MD 20014

SHAPIRO, BURTON LEONARD, b New York, NY, Mar 29, 34; m 58; c 3. ORAL BIOLOGY, GENETICS. *Educ:* NY Univ, DDS, 58; Univ Minn, MSD, 62, PhD(genetics), 66. *Prof Exp:* Teaching asst, 61-62, instr, 62-66, assoc prof, 66-70, dir grad studies, 71-75, PROF ORAL PATH, SCH DENT, UNIV MINN, MINNEAPOLIS, 70-, CHMN DEPT ORAL BIOL, 68- *Concurrent Pos:* Consult, lectr & cytologist, Minn Oral Cancer Detection, 63-66 & Wyo State Bd Health, 66-70; geneticist & oral pathologist, Cleft Palate-Maxillofacial Clin, Univ Minn, 65-69; mem, Grad Fac Dent & Genetics, oral biol Grad Sch, Univ Minn, Minneapolis, 66-, mem med staff, Univ Minn Hosp, 67-; chmn health sci policy and rev coun, 74-; exec comt grad sch, 74-; mem bd dirs, Minn Chapter Cystic Fibrosis Found, 75- *Mem:* AAAS; Am Dent Asn; fel Am Acad Oral Path; Int Asn Dent Res; Am Soc Human Genetics. *Res:* Enzyme histochemistry; mongolism; cystic fibrosis; palatal anthropometry and congenital malformation; oral cytodiagnosis, genetics and oral disease; cleft palate microforms in American Indians; temporomandibular joint disorders; oral ectoderm development biology. *Mailing Add:* Dept of Oral Biol Univ Minn Minneapolis MN 55455

SHAPIRO, CAREN KNIGHT, b Berkeley, Calif, Apr 19, 45; m 72. MEDICAL MICROBIOLOGY, IMMUNOBIOLOGY. *Educ:* Univ Calif, Davis, AB, 67; Univ Wis, MS, 71, PhD(med microbiol), 72. *Prof Exp:* Res assoc, Ind Univ, 73-76; res affil, Roswell Park Mem Inst, 77; ASST PROF BIOL, D'YOUVILLE COL, NY, 77- *Mem:* Sigma Xi; NY Acad Sci; Am Soc Microbiol; AAAS. *Mailing Add:* 112 Parkledge Dr Snyder NY 14226

SHAPIRO, CHARLES SAUL, b Brooklyn, NY, June 16, 36; m 56; c 3. PHYSICS. *Educ:* Brooklyn Col, BS, 57; Syracuse Univ, MS, 60, PhD(physics), 65. *Prof Exp:* Jr physicist, Int Bus Mach Corp, 57-59, assoc physicist, 59; teaching asst physics, Syracuse Univ, 59-60; guest jr res assoc reactor physics, Brookhaven Nat Lab, 61-64, res collabr, 64; staff mem physics, Int Bus Mach Corp, 64-67; from asst prof to assoc prof, 67-75, PROF PHYSICS, SAN FRANCISCO STATE UNIV, 75- *Concurrent Pos:* Consult, Canfield Press & Worth Publ Co; guest researcher, Stockholm Int Peace Res Inst, 73-74. *Mem:* Am Phys Soc; Am Nuclear Soc. *Res:* Radiation transport; neutron thermalization; shielding and dosimetry; reactor physics; numerical analysis; disarmament; relations of science and humanities; science and society; social responsibility of science; science education; arms control and disarmament. *Mailing Add:* Dept of Physics San Francisco State Univ San Francisco CA 94132

SHAPIRO, DAVID JORDON, b Brooklyn, NY, Apr 13, 46. BIOCHEMISTRY. *Educ:* Brooklyn Col, BS, 67; Purdue Univ, PhD(biochem), 72. *Prof Exp:* Helen Hay Whitney Found fel biochem, Med Sch, Stanford Univ, 72-73; biol, 73-74; asst prof, 74-78, ASSOC PROF BIOCHEM, UNIV ILL, URBANA, 78- *Mem:* Am Chem Soc; Sigma Xi; Am Soc Biol Chemists; AAAS. *Res:* Control of gene expression and messenger RNA synthesis in animal cells; nucleic acid hybridization and use of immunologic techniques to isolate specific messenger RNAs in hormone dependent development. *Mailing Add:* Dept of Biochem Univ of Ill Urbana IL 61801

SHAPIRO, DAVID M, b New York, NY, June 9, 29; m 50; c 3. BIOCHEMISTRY. *Educ:* Queens Col, NY, BS, 51; Johns Hopkins Univ, PhD(biochem), 61. *Prof Exp:* Chemist, Sun Chem Co, 51-54; instr chem, Brooklyn Col, 54-55; chemist, Nopco Chem Co, 55-56; res assoc biol chem, Univ Mich, 61-64; asst prof biochem, Woman's Med Col Pa, 64-69; ASST PROF BIOCHEM, UNIV TEX HEALTH SCI CTR SAN ANTONIO, 69-, DIR STUDENT SERV, 73- *Concurrent Pos:* Fel, Inst Sci & Technol, Univ Mich, 61-62; NIH fel, 62-63. *Mem:* AAAS. *Res:* Photosynthesis and electron transport; protein synthesis in bacteriophage-infected systems. *Mailing Add:* Dept of Biochem Univ of Tex Health Sci Ctr San Antonio TX 78229

SHAPIRO, DONALD M, b Pittsburgh, Pa, Nov 15, 35; m 56; c 3. APPLIED MATHEMATICS, COMPUTER SCIENCE. *Educ:* Univ Pittsburgh, BS, 56; Wash Univ, ScD(appl math), 66. *Prof Exp:* Reactor physicist, United Aircraft Corp, 56 & Internuclear Corp, 57; res assoc appl math, Washington Univ, 63-64; asst prof psychiat, Univ Mo, 64-66; asst prof appl math, Washington Univ, 66-67; PROF BIOSTATIST, NY MED COL, 67- *Mem:* AAAS; Asn Comput Mach; Soc Indust & Appl Math; Opers Res Soc Am; Data Processing Mgt Asn. *Res:* Use of computers and statistics in both research and hospital administration. *Mailing Add:* Info Processing Ctr NY Med Col PO Box 31 Valhalla NY 10595

SHAPIRO, DOUGLAS YORK, b Houston, Tex, July 25, 41; m 75. BEHAVIORAL ECOLOGY. *Educ:* Harvard Univ, BA, 64; Case Western Reserve Univ, MD, 68; Cambridge Univ, PhD(animal behav), 77. *Prof Exp:* Med intern, New York Hosp & Cornell Med Ctr, 68-69; res assoc neurol, Nat Inst Neurol Dis & Stroke, NIH, 69-71; clin asst psychiat, W Suffolk Hosp, Eng, 73-75; asst prof, 77-81, ASSOC PROF ANIMAL BEHAV, DEPT MARINE SCI, UNIV PR, 81- *Concurrent Pos:* Vis prof pharmacol, Ponce

Med Sch, PR, 78-80. *Mem:* Animal Behav Soc; Am Soc Ichthyologists & Herpetologists; Ecol Soc Am. *Res:* Behavioral aspects of socially controlled female-to-male sex reversal in coral reef fish; formation and development of fish social groups; ecological determinants of group size and spatial dispersion. *Mailing Add:* Dept Marine Sci Univ PR Mayaguez PR 00708

SHAPIRO, EDWIN SEYMOUR, b Los Angeles, Calif, June 20, 28; m 62; c 1. MATHEMATICS. *Educ:* Univ Calif, MA, 51; Univ Pittsburgh, PhD, 62. *Prof Exp:* Mathematician, US Naval Radiol Defense Lab, Calif, 51-69; assoc prof, 69-78, PROF QUANT METHODS, UNIV SAN FRANCISCO, 78- *Mem:* Am Math Soc; Opers Res Soc Am; Math Asn Am. *Res:* Military operations; applied mathematics. *Mailing Add:* Col of Bus Admin Univ of San Francisco San Francisco CA 94117

SHAPIRO, EUGENE, b New York, NY, Dec 26, 44; m 69. METALLURGICAL & MATERIALS ENGINEERING. *Educ:* Polytech Inst Brooklyn, BS, 65; Drexel Inst, MS, 67, PhD(mat eng), 69. *Prof Exp:* Res engr, Metals Res Lab, 69-76, GROUP SUPVR, OLIN CORP, 76- *Mem:* Am Soc Metals; Am Inst Mining, Metall & Petrol Engrs; Am Soc Testing & Mat. *Res:* Fracture and ductility; hot working; formability; alloy development. *Mailing Add:* Olin Corp 91 Shelton Ave New Haven CT 06504

SHAPIRO, GILBERT, b Philadelphia, Pa, Mar 17, 34; m 58; c 3. PARTICLE PHYSICS. *Educ:* Univ Pa, BA, 55; Columbia Univ, MA, 57, PhD(physics), 59. *Prof Exp:* Res assoc physics, Nevis Cyclotron Lab, Columbia Univ, 59-61; physicist, Lawrence Radiation Lab, Univ Calif, 61-63, asst prof, Univ, 63-67, ASSOC PROF PHYSICS, UNIV CALIF, BERKELEY, 67- *Concurrent Pos:* NSF sr fel, Saclay Nuclear Res Ctr, France, 65-66. *Mem:* Am Phys Soc. *Res:* Particle and muon physics; polarized proton targets. *Mailing Add:* Dept of Physics 366 LeConte Hall Univ of Calif Berkeley CA 94720

SHAPIRO, HARRY LIONEL, b Boston, Mass, Mar 19, 02; m 38; c 3. BIOLOGICAL ANTHROPOLOGY. *Educ:* Harvard Univ, AB, 23, AM, 25, PhD(anthrop), 26. *Prof Exp:* Tutor anthrop, Harvard Univ, 25-26; from asst cur to cur, 26-70, chmn dept anthrop, 42-70, EMER CHMN, AM MUS NAT HIST. *Concurrent Pos:* Res prof anthrop, Univ Hawaii, 30-33; prof, Columbia Univ, 39-73; consult, Qm Gen, US Army, 46-52; mem comt race & cult, UNESCO, 50; chmn comt behav sci, Nat Acad Sci, 58-60; mem bd, Field Found, Inc, 66-72 & L Wise Serv, 58-; prof anthrop, Univ Pittsburgh, 70-71. *Honors & Awards:* Theodore Roosevelt Distinguished Serv Medal, 64; NY Acad Sci Award, 77. *Mem:* Nat Acad Sci; Am Anthrop Asn (pres, 48); Am Asn Phys Anthropologists (secy, 35-39); Am Acad Arts & Sci; Am Ethnol Soc (pres). *Res:* Biological anthropology, with emphasis on genetical evolution and environmental effects on biological development. *Mailing Add:* Dept of Anthrop Am Mus of Nat Hist New York NY 10027

SHAPIRO, HARVEY LEE, mathematics, psychology, see previous edition

SHAPIRO, HERMAN SIMON, b New York, NY, Aug 29, 29. BIOCHEMISTRY, GENETICS. *Educ:* City Col New York, BS, 51; Columbia Univ, PhD(biochem), 57. *Prof Exp:* Asst biochem, Col Physicians & Surgeons, Columbia Univ, 51-52, res biochemist, 56-57, from res assoc to asst prof biochem, 58-69, ASSOC PROF BIOCHEM, COL MED NJ, 69- *Mem:* Brit Biochem Soc. *Res:* Elucidation of nucleotide sequences of the DNA of diverse cellular sources, especially the correlation of structure and function of these macromolecules. *Mailing Add:* Dept of Biochem Col of Med of NJ 100 Bergen St Newark NJ 07103

SHAPIRO, HOWARD MAURICE, b Brooklyn, NY, Nov 8, 41; m 64; c 2. MEDICINE, BIOENGINEERING. *Educ:* Harvard Univ, BA, 61; NY Univ, MD, 65. *Prof Exp:* Asst res scientist, NY Univ, 62-65; from intern to asst resident surg, Bellevue Hosp, 65-67; res assoc math statist & appl math, Biomet Br, Nat Cancer Inst, 67-70; sr staff fel, Baltimore Cancer Res Ctr, 70-71; resident surg, Col Med, Univ Ariz, 71-72; from asst dir med systs & instrumentation to dir clin res diag prod, G D Searle & Co, 72-76; asst to chmn, Cancer & Leukemia Group B, 76-77, chief cytokinetics, 77-81, PRES, SIDNEY FARBER CANCER INST, 81- *Concurrent Pos:* Consult clin metrol & lectr path, Harvard Med Sch, 76- *Mem:* AAAS; Am Asn Cancer Res; Am Soc Clin Oncol; Am Soc Hemat; Inst Elec & Electronics Engrs. *Res:* Biomedical instrumentation and computing; oncology and hematology; analytical and theoretical biology; medical education and communication. *Mailing Add:* 283 Highland Ave West Newton MA 02165

SHAPIRO, IRVING, b Newark, NJ, Mar 3, 32; m 60; c 3. AUDIOLOGY. *Educ:* Western Mich Univ, BS, 58; Syracuse Univ, AM, 60; Western Reserve Univ, PhD(clin audiol), 64. *Prof Exp:* Instr otolaryngol, Med Sch, Univ Chicago, 64-66; audiologist, Vet Admin West Side Hosp, Chicago, 66-67; DIR COMMUN DISORDERS, HARBOR GEN HOSP, 67-; ASST PROF OTOLARYNGOL, MED SCH, UNIV CALIF, LOS ANGELES, 69-, LECTR HEAD & NECK SURG, 76- *Mem:* Am Speech & Hearing Asn; Am Audiol Soc; Int Soc Audiol. *Res:* Pediatric audiology; ototoxic drugs; systems for hearing aid evaluation. *Mailing Add:* Harbor Gen Hosp 1000 W Carson St Torrance CA 90509

SHAPIRO, IRVING MEYER, b London, Eng, Oct 28, 37; m 65; c 1. BIOCHEMISTRY. *Educ:* London Hosp Med Col, LDSRCS BDS, 61; Univ Liverpool, MSc, 64; Univ London, PhD(biochem), 68. *Prof Exp:* Vis scientist biochem, Forsyth Dent Ctr, Boston, 64-66; from asst prof to assoc prof, 69-76, actg chmn dept, 75-80, PROF BIOCHEM, SCH DENT MED, UNIV PA, 76-, CHMN DEPT, 80- *Concurrent Pos:* Consult biochem, Koch Light Chem, Ltd, Eng, 67-70; res consult, Vet Admin Hosp, Philadelphia, 76- *Honors & Awards:* Basic Sci Award, Int Asn Dent Res, 74. *Mem:* AAAS; Biochem Soc; Royal Soc Med; Bone & Tooth Soc; Int Asn Dent Res. *Res:* Role of mitochondria in the initiation of the mineralization process; use of mineralized tissues in the diagnosis and treatment of lead poisoning. *Mailing Add:* Dept Biochem & Ctr Oral Hlth Res Univ of Pa Sch of Dent Med Philadelphia PA 19174

SHAPIRO, IRWIN IRA, b New York, NY, Oct 10, 29; m 59; c 2. PHYSICS, ASTRONOMY. *Educ:* Cornell Univ, BA, 50; Harvard Univ, MS, 51, PhD(physics), 55. *Prof Exp:* Staff mem physics & astron, Lincoln Lab, 54-70, PROF GEOPHYS & PHYSICS, MASS INST TECHNOL, 67- *Honors & Awards:* Michelson Medal, Franklin Inst, 75. *Mem:* Nat Acad Sci; fel Am Phys Soc; fel Am Geophys Union; Am Astron Soc; Int Astron Union. *Res:* Dynamical, radar and radio astronomy; experimental general relativity. *Mailing Add:* 17 Lantern Lane Lexington MA 02173

SHAPIRO, IRWIN LOUIS, b New York, NY, Jan 2, 32; m 63; c 2. BIOCHEMISTRY. *Educ:* Univ Iowa, BA, 53; Univ Del, MS, 59, PhD(chem), 62. *Prof Exp:* Fel biochem, Wistar Inst, Univ Pa, 61-63, assoc, 63-69; sr biochemist, J T Baker Chem Co, 69-73; ASST PROF CHEM, MONMOUTH COL, 74- *Concurrent Pos:* Instr, Sch Dent, Univ Pa, 63-65, asst prof, Sch Vet Med, 66-69; lectr, Philadelphia Col Pharm, 64-65. *Mem:* AAAS; Am Inst Nutrit; Am Asn Clin Chemists; Am Chem Soc; Am Oil Chemists Soc. *Res:* Triglyceride metabolism; cholesterol metabolism; nutritional biochemistry; inborn errors of metabolism; isotope applications in medicine; isotope instrumentation; clinical biochemistry. *Mailing Add:* Dept of Chem Monmouth Col West Long Branch NJ 07764

SHAPIRO, JACK SOL, b Brooklyn, NY, Nov 3, 41; m 70; c 2. MATHEMATICS. *Educ:* Brooklyn Col, BS, 63; Yeshiva Univ, MA, 66, PhD(math), 70. *Prof Exp:* Asst prof, 70-78, ASSOC PROF MATH, BARUCH COL, CITY UNIV NEW YORK, 78- *Mem:* Am Math Soc; Math Asn Am. *Res:* Functional analysis and operator theory. *Mailing Add:* Dept of Math Baruch Col New York NY 10010

SHAPIRO, JACOB, b New York, NY, Sept 4, 25; m 48; c 2. BIOPHYSICS, RADIOLOGICAL HEALTH. *Educ:* City Col New York, BS, 44; Brown Univ, MS, 48; Univ Rochester, PhD(biophys), 54. *Prof Exp:* Instr physics, Univ RI, 46-47; tech adv nuclear energy, Opers Off, AEC, NY, 48-50; res assoc radiation biol, Univ Rochester, 53-55; supvr radiation anal, Elec Boat Div, Gen Dynamics Corp, 55-61; LECTR BIOPHYS IN ENVIRON HEALTH, SCH PUB HEALTH & UNIV HEALTH PHYSICIST, HARVARD UNIV, 61- *Mem:* Am Phys Soc; Health Physics Soc. *Res:* Radiation shielding, detection and dosimetry; health physics; nuclear reactor hazards and control. *Mailing Add:* Harvard Univ Health Serv 75 Mt Auburn St Cambridge MA 02138

SHAPIRO, JAMES ALAN, b Chicago, Ill, May 18, 43; m 64; c 1. MICROBIOLOGY, MOLECULAR GENETICS. *Educ:* Harvard Col, BA, 64; Cambridge Univ, PhD(genetics), 68. *Prof Exp:* Fel, Pasteur Inst, Paris, 67-68 & Harvard Med Sch, 68-70; invited prof genetics, Univ Havana, 70-72; fel, Brandeis Univ, 72-73; asst prof, 73-78, ASSOC PROF MICROBIOL, UNIV CHICAGO, 78- *Concurrent Pos:* Mem, Working Group Prod Useful Substances Microbiol Means, US/USSR Sci Exchange Prog, NSF, 75-78. *Mem:* Genetics Soc Am; Soc Gen Microbiol; AAAS; Brit Genetical Soc. *Res:* Microbial hydrocarbon metabolism; antibiotic resistance; bacterial plasmids; DNA insertion elements; genetics of industrial microorganisms; Pseudomonas genetics and physiology. by fermentation. *Mailing Add:* Dept of Microbiol Univ of Chicago Chicago IL 60637

SHAPIRO, JAMES NORMAN, b Niagara Falls, NY, Nov 14, 40; m 70; c 2. GEOPHYSICS. *Educ:* Mass Inst Technol, BS, 62; Univ Calif, Los Angeles, MS, 65, PhD(physics), 70. *Prof Exp:* Res asst, Raytheon Co, 62-64; ASST PROF GEOPHYS, TEX A&M UNIV, 71- *Mem:* Soc Explor Geophysicists; Am Geophys Union; Sigma Xi. *Res:* High pressure physics; equations of state of earth material; mathematical techniques in geophysics; digital signal processing. *Mailing Add:* Amoco Prods Co Security Life Bldg Denver CO 80202

SHAPIRO, JEFFREY HOWARD, b New York, NY, Dec 27, 46; m 69; c 2. ELECTRICAL ENGINEERING. *Educ:* Mass Inst Technol, SB, 67, SM, 68, EE, 69, PhD(elec eng), 70. *Prof Exp:* Asst prof elec eng, Case Western Reserve Univ, 70-73; ASSOC PROF ELEC ENG, MASS INST TECHNOL, 73- *Concurrent Pos:* NSF res grants, 71-77; consult, Lincoln Lab, Mass Inst Technol, 77- *Mem:* Inst Elec & Electronics Engrs; Optical Soc Am. *Res:* Communication theory for optical channels; wave propagation in turbulent and turbid media; quantum communication theory. *Mailing Add:* Dept of Elec Eng & Comput Sci Mass Inst of Technol Cambridge MA 02139

SHAPIRO, JEROME LEE, environmental & nuclear engineering, see previous edition

SHAPIRO, JESSE MARSHALL, b Minneapolis, Minn, Nov 20, 29; m 51; c 3. MATHEMATICS. *Educ:* Univ Minn, BA, 50, MA, 51, PhD(math), 54. *Prof Exp:* Asst math, Univ Minn, 51-53, instr, 53-54; from instr to prof, Ohio State Univ, 54-69; prof, Augsburg Col, 69-71; assoc prof, 71-80, PROF MATH, BEN GURION UNIV OF THE NEGEV, ISRAEL, 80-, DEAN FAC NATURAL SCI, 80- *Mem:* AAAS; Am Math Soc; Math Asn Am; Inst Math Statist. *Res:* Statistics; probability limit theorems. *Mailing Add:* Dept Math Ben Gurion Univ Negev Beersheba Israel

SHAPIRO, JOEL ALAN, b New York, NY, Feb 23, 42; m 65; c 2. THEORETICAL HIGH ENERGY PHYSICS. *Educ:* Brown Univ, ScB, 62; Cornell Univ, PhD(theoret physics), 67. *Prof Exp:* Vis res physicist, Univ Calif, Berkeley, 67-69; res assoc high energy physics, Univ Md, College Park, 69-71; asst prof, 71-76, ASSOC PROF HIGH ENERGY PHYSICS, RUTGERS UNIV, 76- *Res:* Theoretical models for the strong interactions. *Mailing Add:* Dept of Physics Rutgers Univ New Brunswick NJ 08903

SHAPIRO, JOHN LAWTON, b Maury Co, Tenn, May 8, 15; m 42; c 4. PATHOLOGY. *Educ:* Vanderbilt Univ, BA, 38, MD, 41. *Prof Exp:* From instr to assoc prof, 47-56, head dept, 56-71, prof, 56-80, EMER PROF PATH, MED SCH, VANDERBILT UNIV, 80- *Concurrent Pos:* Consult, Nashville Vet Hosp. *Mem:* Am Soc Exp Path; Am Asn Path & Bact; AMA; Am Soc Clin Path; Int Acad Path. *Res:* Rickettisal diseases. *Mailing Add:* Vanderbilt Univ Hosp Nashville TN 37232

SHAPIRO, JOSEPH, b Montreal, Que, May 24, 29; m 52; c 2. LIMNOLOGY. *Educ:* McGill Univ, BSc, 50; Univ Sask, MSc, 52; Yale Univ, PhD(limnol), 57. *Prof Exp:* Res assoc limnol, Univ Wash, 56-58, res instr, 58-59; asst prof sanit eng, Johns Hopkins Univ, 59-64; assoc prof geol & geophys, 64-70, PROF GEOL & GEOPHYS, LIMNOL RES CTR, UNIV MINN, MINNEAPOLIS, 70-, ASSOC DIR, 64- *Mem:* AAAS; Am Soc Limnol & Oceanog; Int Asn Theoret & Appl Limnol. *Res:* Chemical, physical and biological phenomena occurring in natural waters. *Mailing Add:* Limnol Res Ctr Univ of Minn Minneapolis MN 55455

SHAPIRO, LARRY JAY, b Chicago, Ill, July 6, 46; m 68; c 1. HUMAN GENETICS. *Educ:* Washington Univ, AB, 68, MD, 71. *Prof Exp:* Intern & resident pediat, St Louis Children's Hosp, 71-73; res assoc genetics, NIH, 73-75; asst prof pediat & genetics, 75-81, ASSOC PROF IN RESIDENCE PEDIAT & GENETICS, SCH MED, UNIV CALIF, LOS ANGELES, HARBOR GEN HOSP CAMPUS, 81- *Mem:* AAAS; Am Soc Human Genetics; Am Fedn Clin Res; fel Am Acad Pediat. *Res:* Pediatrics, with emphasis on inborn errors of metabolism, lysosomal storage diseases, mucopolysaccharidoses and disorders of sulfated steroid metabolism. *Mailing Add:* Div Med Genetics Harbor Gen Hosp 1000 W Carson St Torrance CA 90509

SHAPIRO, LEE TOBEY, b Chicago, Ill, Dec 12, 43; m 70. ASTRONOMY. *Educ:* Carnegie Inst Technol, BS, 66; Northwestern Univ, MS, 68, PhD(astron), 74. *Prof Exp:* ASST PROF ASTRON & ASTROPHYS & DIR ABRAMS PLANETARIUM, MICH STATE UNIV, 74- *Mem:* Am Astron Soc; Royal Astron Soc; Int Planetarium Soc. *Res:* Late type giants and subgiants in close binaries; membership, size and configuration of the Local Group of Galaxies; development and statistics of planetariums throughout the world. *Mailing Add:* Abrams Planetarium Mich State Univ East Lansing MI 48824

SHAPIRO, LEONARD DAVID, b San Francisco, Calif, Dec 4, 43. MATHEMATICS. *Educ:* Reed Col, BA, 65; Yale Univ, PhD(math), 69. *Prof Exp:* From instr to asst prof math, Univ Minn, Minneapolis, 70-76, vis prof econ, 76-77; CHMN DEPT MATH SCI, N DAK STATE UNIV, FARGO, 77- *Concurrent Pos:* Vis scholar econ, Univ Calif, Berkeley, 77. *Mem:* Am Math Soc; Math Asn Am; Econometric Soc. *Res:* Topological dynamics; minimal sets; diophantine approximation; mathematical economics. *Mailing Add:* Dept of Math Sci NDak State Univ Fargo ND 58105

SHAPIRO, LORIN JAMES, ethology, animal behavior, see previous edition

SHAPIRO, LORNE, b Montreal, Que, Nov 8, 12; m 42; c 7. INTERNAL MEDICINE, HEMATOLOGY. *Educ:* McGill Univ, BA, 34, MD, 39, dipl internal med, 49; FRCP(C), 48. *Prof Exp:* Res fel hemat, Royal Victoria Hosp, 46; res asst, Postgrad Sch Med, Univ London, 47-48; from demonstr to asst prof, 49-68, assoc prof, 68-76, PROF MED, McGILL UNIV, 76- *Concurrent Pos:* Consult, Queen Mary Vet Hosp, 48-66, hon consult, 67; consult, St Anne's Mil Hosp, 48-66 & Montreal Children's Hosp, 77; from asst physician to assoc physician, Royal Victoria Hosp, 57-70, physician, 70-, assoc dir div hemat, 69-; mem acute leukemia coop group B, NIH, 62; chmn panel blood & related probs, Defence Res Bd Can, 62-66; consult, Kenyatta Nat Hosp, Nairobi, Kenya, 68-69; sr lectr, Univ Col, Hairobi, 68-69. *Mem:* Fel Am Col Physicians; fel Int Soc Hemat. *Res:* Clinical investigations in leukemias and lymphomas. *Mailing Add:* Div of Hemat Royal Victoria Hosp Montreal PQ H3A 1A1 Can

SHAPIRO, LUCILLE, b New York, NY, July 16, 40; m 60; c 1. MOLECULAR BIOLOGY, BIOCHEMISTRY. *Educ:* Brooklyn Col, AB, 62; Albert Einstein Col Med, PhD(molecular biol), 66. *Prof Exp:* Jane Coffin Childs fel, 66-67; from asst prof to assoc prof, 67-77, SEIGFRIED VILMANN PROF MOLECULAR BIOL, ALBERT EINSTEIN COL MED, 77-, CHMN DEPT, 78- *Concurrent Pos:* Hirschl career scientist award, 76-; *Honors & Awards:* Spirit of Achievement Award, 78. *Mem:* AAAS; Harvey Soc; Am Soc Biol Chemists; Am Soc Microbiol. *Res:* Microbial developmental biology and molecular biochemistry. *Mailing Add:* Dept of Molecular Biol Albert Einstein Col of Med Bronx NY 10461

SHAPIRO, MARK HOWARD, b Boston, Mass, Apr 18, 40; m 61; c 3. NUCLEAR PHYSICS, ATMOSPHERIC PHYSICS. *Educ:* Univ Calif, Berkeley, AB, 62; Univ Pa, MS, 63, PhD(physics), 66. *Prof Exp:* Res fel physics, Kellogg Radiation Lab, Calif Inst Technol, 66-68; res assoc, Nuclear Struct Res Lab, Univ Rochester, 68-70; from asst prof to assoc prof, 70-78, PROF PHYSICS, CALIF STATE UNIV, FULLERTON, 78- *Concurrent Pos:* Res Corp grant & fac res grant, 71-72; vis assoc, Kellogg Radiation Lab, Calif Inst Technol, 76-; Calif Inst Technol President's venture fund grant, 77-78; US Geol Surv grant, 78-79. *Mem:* AAAS; Am Phys Soc; Am Asn Physics Teachers; Am Geophys Union. *Res:* Nuclear structure physics; nuclear reaction physics; laboratory nuclear astrophysics; applications of nuclear physics in geophysics; nuclear safety. *Mailing Add:* Dept of Physics Calif State Univ Fullerton CA 92634

SHAPIRO, MARTIN, b New York, NY, Mar 18, 37; m 67; c 2. ENTOMOLOGY, MICROBIOLOGY. *Educ:* Brooklyn Col, AB, 58; Cornell Univ, MS, 61; Univ Calif, Berkeley, PhD(entom), 66. *Prof Exp:* Entomologist, USDA, Tex, 65-66; res entomologist, Int Minerals & Chem Corp, 66-70; USPHS fel insect path, Boyce Thompson Inst Plant Res, 70-72; entomologist, Maag & Easterbrooks, Inc, 72-73; mem staff, Res Unit Vector Path, Mem Univ Nfld, 73-75; MEM STAFF, GYPSEY MOTH METHODS DEVELOP LAB, USDA, 75- *Concurrent Pos:* Consult, Int Minerals & Chem Corp, 70-73. *Mem:* Soc Invert Path; Entom Soc Am; Tissue Cult Asn; Int Orgn Biol Control. *Res:* Insect pathology and tissue culture. *Mailing Add:* Gypsy Moth Methods Develop Lab USDA Otis AFB MA 02542

SHAPIRO, MAURICE A, b Denver, Colo, June 4, 17; m 45; c 6. ENVIRONMENTAL HEALTH ENGINEERING, PUBLIC HEALTH. *Educ:* Johns Hopkins Univ, AB, 41; Univ Calif, Berkeley, MEng, 49. *Prof Exp:* Asst sanit engr, USPHS, 41-47, field officer, United Yugoslav Relief Fund Am, 47-48; eng res assoc, Am Pub Health Asn, 49-51; asst sanit eng, 51-69, PROF ENVIRON HEALTH ENG, GRAD SCH PUB HEALTH, UNIV PITTSBURGH, 69- *Concurrent Pos:* Vis prof, Israel Inst Technol, 65-66; found dir, Westernport Bay Environ Study, Victoria, Australia, 73-74, vis mem sci fac, Univ Melbourne, 73-74; vis lectr, Monash Univ, 73-74. *Mem:* Am Soc Civil Engrs; Am Water Works Asn; Am Pub Health Asn; Am Pub Works Asn; Soc Environ & Occupational Health. *Res:* Water and air pollution control; health aspects of energy conversion and water quality; radioactive wastes disposal; environmental health aspects of energy conversion, environmental health planning. *Mailing Add:* Grad Sch of Pub Health Univ of Pittsburgh Pittsburgh PA 15261

SHAPIRO, MAURICE MANDEL, cosmic ray physics, astrophysics, see previous edition

SHAPIRO, NATHAN, b Boston, Mass, July 16, 24; m 51; c 2. GENETICS. *Educ:* Univ Wis, BS, 49, MS, 50; Purdue Univ, PhD(genetics), 63. *Prof Exp:* Mycologist, Mat Testing Lab, NY Naval Shipyard, 51-53; res asst, Biol Dept, Brookhaven Nat Lab, 56-59; asst prof zool, Smith Col, 59-70; PROF BIOL, EASTERN CONN STATE COL, 70- *Res:* Radiation genetics; plant growth hormones. *Mailing Add:* Dept of Biol Eastern Conn State Col Willimantic CT 06226

SHAPIRO, NORMAN ZALMAN, mathematics, computer science, see previous edition

SHAPIRO, PAUL JONATHON, b Baltimore, Md, Sept 10, 52; m 79; c 2. MECHANICAL ENGINEERING. *Educ:* Mass Inst Technol, BS, 73, MS, 75, PhD(fluid mech), 77. *Prof Exp:* Fel, Lady Davis Scholorship Found, 77; staff fel, Nat Inst Health, 78-79; MEM TECH STAFF, PHILIPS LAB, NORTH AM PHILIPS CORP, 79- *Mem:* NY Acad Sci; AAAS; Sigma Xi. *Res:* Development of long life spaceborne mechanical refrigerator; x-ray diffraction studies of functioning muscle specimens; boundary-layer transition studies. *Mailing Add:* 71 N Moger Ave Mt Kisco NY 10549

SHAPIRO, PHILIP, b Brooklyn, NY, Sept 10, 23; m 51; c 2. NUCLEAR PHYSICS, MEDICAL PHYSICS. *Educ:* Brooklyn Col, BS, 48; Univ Iowa, PhD(physics), 53. *Prof Exp:* Asst physics, Univ Iowa, 48-53; physicist, Radiation Div, 53-66, Nuclear Physics Div, 66-71, Cyclotron Br, 71-74, PHYSICIST, CYCLOTRON APPLN BR, US NAVAL RES LAB, 74- *Mem:* AAAS; Sigma Xi; Am Phys Soc; Am Asn Physicists in Med. *Res:* Neutron radiotherapy; dosimetry; nuclear reactions. *Mailing Add:* Cyclotron Appln Br US Naval Res Lab Washington DC 20375

SHAPIRO, RALPH, b Malden, Mass, Nov 9, 22; m 45; c 3. DYNAMIC METEOROLOGY. *Educ:* Bridgewater Col, BS, 43; Mass Inst Technol, MS, 48, DSc(meteorol), 50. *Prof Exp:* Asst, Pressure Change Proj, Mass Inst Technol, 47-50; meteorologist, Planetary Atmospheres Proj, Lowell Observ, 50-51; proj scientist, Geophys Res Directorate, Hanscom AFB, 51-57, assoc chief, Meteorol Develop Lab & chief, Atmospheric Dynamics Br, Air Force Cambridge Res Ctr, 57-75, chief, Climatol & Dynamics Br, Air Force Geophys Labs, 75-80; SR SCIENTIST, SYSTS & APPL SCI CORP, 80- *Mem:* AAAS; Am Geophys Union; fel Am Meteorol Soc; foreign mem Royal Meteorol Soc; Sigma Xi. *Res:* Mathematical modeling of large-scale atmospheric circulations; numerical weather prediction; numerical analysis of partial differential equations; digital filter design; statistical weather prediction; flux of solar radiation through the atmosphere. *Mailing Add:* Systs & Appl Sci Corp 109 Massachusetts Ave Lexington MA 02173

SHAPIRO, RAYMOND E, b New York, NY, Oct 20, 27; m 64; c 2. CHEMISTRY. *Educ:* City Col New York, BS, 48; Ohio State Univ, PhD(phys chem soils), 52. *Prof Exp:* Soil chemist, Soil & Water Conserv Res Div, Agr Res Serv, USDA, 53-65; res chemist, Div Pharmacol, Intermediary Metab Br, US Food & Drug Admin, 65-70, sci coordr, Bur Foods, 70-73, sci coordr, Epidemiol Unit, 73-76; ASST DIR TOXICOL COORD, NAT INST ENVIRON HEALTH SCI, 76- *Concurrent Pos:* Guggenheim fel, Rothamsted Exp Sta, Herpenden, Eng, 62. *Mem:* Fel AAAS; Am Col Toxicol; Soc Environ Geochem & Health; Am Chem Soc; Soc Epidemiol Res. *Res:* Soil aeration; chemistry of submerged soils; kinetics of ion migration in soil systems; mycotoxins; metabolism; toxicology. *Mailing Add:* 1724 Quail Ridge Rd Raleigh NC 27609

SHAPIRO, ROBERT, b New York, NY, Nov 28, 35; m 64; c 1. BIOCHEMISTRY, ORGANIC CHEMISTRY. *Educ:* City Col New York, BS, 56; Harvard Univ, AM, 57, PhD(chem), 59. *Prof Exp:* NATO fel chem, Cambridge Univ, 59-60; fel biochem, Sch Med, 60-61, from asst prof to assoc prof, 61-70, PROF CHEM, NY UNIV, 70- *Honors & Awards:* USPHS Career Develop Award, 71. *Mem:* AAAS; Am Chem Soc; Royal Soc Chem. *Res:* Chemistry of nucleic acids; chemical mutagenesis and carcinogenesis; heterocyclic compounds. *Mailing Add:* Dept of Chem NY Univ New York NY 10003

SHAPIRO, ROBERT ALLEN, b Long Branch, NJ, Aug 14, 30; m 53; c 3. INDUSTRIAL ENGINEERING. *Educ:* Okla State Univ, BS, 53, MS, 64, PhD(indust eng), 65. *Prof Exp:* Div prod engr, Shell Oil Co, 53-61; assoc prof, 64-72, asst to pres, 67-68, PROF INDUST ENG, & ASSOC VPRES ADMIN & FINANCE, UNIV OKLA, 72-, DIR SCH ENG, 65- *Concurrent Pos:* Consult, Okla Mgt Study Comt, 67, US Army & USPHS, 67- *Mem:* Am Inst Indust Engrs; Am Soc Petrol Engrs; Am Soc Eng Educ; Am Soc Qual Control. *Res:* Operations research, including recurrent processes, modern organization theory, econometric models of decisions under uncertainty and statistical quality control. *Mailing Add:* Dept of Indust Eng Univ of Okla Norman OK 73069

SHAPIRO, ROBERT HOWARD, b New Haven, Conn, July 18, 35; m 56; c 3. ORGANIC CHEMISTRY. *Educ:* Univ Conn, BS, 61; Stanford Univ, PhD(chem), 64. *Prof Exp:* NSF fel chem, Royal Vet & Agr Col, Denmark, 64-65; from asst prof to assoc prof chem, Univ Colo, Boulder, 65-74, prof, 74-80; PROF & DEPT HEAD CHEM, JAMES MADISON UNIV, HARRISONBURG, VA, 80- *Concurrent Pos:* Consult, Criminal Lawyers, 66- *Mem:* Am Chem Soc; Royal Soc Chem. *Res:* Reaction mechanisms; mass spectrometry; environmental chemistry; natural products chemistry. *Mailing Add:* Dept Chem James Madison Univ Harrisonburg VA 22801

SHAPIRO, RUBIN, b Chicago, Ill, Nov 7, 24; div; c 2. CHEMISTRY. *Educ:* Univ Ill, BS, 48; Univ Wis, PhD(anal chem), 53. *Prof Exp:* Res chemist, 53-57, supvr, 57-68, res assoc, 68-77, SR RES ASSOC, TECH SERV DEPT, AM CAN CO, 77- *Mem:* Am Chem Soc; Am Soc Mass Spectrometry; Soc Appl Spectros. *Res:* Emission, mass and atomic absorption spectroscopy; gas chromatography; analytical chemistry. *Mailing Add:* Tech Serv Dept Am Can Co Barrington IL 60010

SHAPIRO, SAM, b New York, NY, Feb 12, 14; m 38; c 2. EPIDEMIOLOGY, STATISTICS. *Educ:* Brooklyn Col, BS, 33. *Prof Exp:* Chief, Natality Anal Br, Nat Off Vital Statist, USPHS, 47-54; sr study dir, Nat Opinion Res Ctr, 54-55; assoc dir, Div Res & Statist, Health Ins Plan of Greater New York, 55-59; vpres & dir, 59-73; PROF HEALTH CARE ORGN, SCH HYG & PUB HEALTH, JOHNS HOPKINS UNIV & DIR, HEALTH SERV RES & DEVELOP CTR, JOHNS HOPKINS MED INSTS, 73- *Concurrent Pos:* Lectr pub health, Sch Pub Health & Admin Med, Columbia Univ, 61-; adj prof community med, Mt Sinai Sch Med, 72-; consult to var insts & orgns. *Honors & Awards:* Merit Award, New York City Pub Health Asn, 72. *Mem:* Inst of Med of Nat Acad Sci; fel Am Pub Health Asn; fel Am Statist Asn; fel Am Heart Asn; fel Am Epidemiol Asn. *Res:* Evaluative research in organization; delivery; economics; quality of health care. *Mailing Add:* Health Serv Res & Develop Ctr Johns Hopkins Med Insts Baltimore MD 21205

SHAPIRO, SAMUEL S, b Brooklyn, NY, July 13, 30; m 56; c 2. APPLIED STATISTICS. *Educ:* City Col New York, BBA, 52; Columbia Univ, MS, 54; Rutgers Univ, MS, 61, PhD(statist), 64. *Prof Exp:* Statist qual control engr, Pittsburgh Plate Glass Co, 56-58; statistician, Res & Develop Ctr, Gen Elec Co, NY, 58-67; statistician, Prog Methodology, Inc, 67-72; PROF STATIST, FLA INT UNIV, 72- *Concurrent Pos:* Lectr, Union Col, 65-66; UN tech adv, Indian Statist Inst, 66. *Mem:* Inst Math Statist; Am Statist Asn. *Res:* Testing for distributional assumptions. *Mailing Add:* Math Sci Dept Fla Int Univ Miami FL 33136

SHAPIRO, SANDOR SOLOMON, b Brooklyn, NY, July 26, 33; m 54; c 2. HEMATOLOGY. *Educ:* Harvard Univ, BA, 54, MD, 57. *Prof Exp:* Intern, Harvard Med Serv, Boston City Hosp, 57-58; asst surgeon, Div Biol Stand, NIH, USPHS, 58-60; asst resident, Boston City Hosp, 60-61; NIH spec fel, Mass Inst Technol, 61-64; from instr to assoc prof, 64-72, PROF MED, CARDEZA FOUND, JEFFERSON MED COL, 72-, ASSOC DIR, FOUND, 78- *Concurrent Pos:* Mem hemat study sect, NIH, 72-76 & 78-79; mem med adv coun, Nat Hemophilia Found, 73-; chmn, Pa State Hemophilia Adv Comt, 74-76. *Mem:* Am Soc Clin Invest; Am Soc Hemat; Am Asn Immunologists; Int Soc Thrombosis & Hemostasis; Am Fedn Clin Res. *Res:* Hemostasis and thrombosis, prothrombin metabolism, hemophilia. *Mailing Add:* Cardeza Found 1015 Walnut St Philadelphia PA 19107

SHAPIRO, SEYMOUR, b New York, NY, Feb 16, 24; m 47; c 1. BOTANY. *Educ:* Univ Mich, BS, 47, PhD(bot), 52. *Prof Exp:* Instr bot, Univ Mich, 50-51, res assoc, 51-52; res collabr biol, Brookhaven Nat Lab, 53, assoc botanist, NY, 53-61; assoc prof biol, Univ Ore, 61-64; head dept, 64-68, actg dean arts & sci, 68-70, actg head dept, 71-72, actg dean fac natural sci & math, 75-78, PROF BOT, UNIV MASS, AMHERST, 64-, DEAN FAC NATURAL SCI & MATH, 78- *Concurrent Pos:* Consult, NSF, 62-69, vis scientist, Inst Atomic Sci in Agr, Wageningen, Neth, 70-71. *Mem:* AAAS; Am Soc Plant Physiologists; Am Soc Develop Biol; Bot Soc Am. *Res:* Regeneration, adventitious bud production and somatic mutations in woody plants; morphogenesis of higher plants. *Mailing Add:* Dept of Bot Univ of Mass Amherst MA 01002

SHAPIRO, SIDNEY, b Boston, Mass, Dec 4, 31; m 60; c 2. SOLID STATE PHYSICS. *Educ:* Harvard Univ, AB, 53, AM, 55, PhD(appl physics), 59. *Prof Exp:* Res asst appl physics, Harvard Univ, 55-59; physicist, Arthur D Little, Inc, 59-64; mem tech staff, Bell Labs, Inc, NJ, 64-67; assoc prof, 67-73, PROF ELEC ENG, UNIV ROCHESTER, 73-, ASSOC DEAN, COL ENG & APPL SCI, 74- *Concurrent Pos:* Vis prof, Physics Lab I, Tech Univ Denmark, 72-73. *Mem:* Fel Am Phys Soc; sr mem Inst Elec & Electronics Engrs. *Res:* Superconductivity; electron tunneling; Josephson effect; microwave phenomena and devices involving superconducting junctions and weak links. *Mailing Add:* Dept of Elec Eng Univ of Rochester Rochester NY 14627

SHAPIRO, STANLEY, b Brooklyn, NY, Jan 3, 37; m 58; c 3. RESEARCH MANAGEMENT. *Educ:* City Col New York, BChe, 60; Rensselaer Polytech Inst, MS, 64; Lehigh Univ, PhD(metall), 66. *Prof Exp:* Res engr, Pratt & Whitney, 60-61; res engr, Res Lab, United Aircraft Corp, 61-64; instr & res asst, Lehigh Univ, 64-66; res sci supvr, Metals Res Labs, Olin Corp, 66-79; PRES, REVERE RES, INC, 79- *Mem:* Am Inst Metal Engrs; Am Soc Metals; AAAS; Am Soc Testing & Mats; Am Mgt Asn. *Res:* Non-ferrous metals research and development, alloy and process research. *Mailing Add:* PO Box 1352 Edison NJ 08837

SHAPIRO, STANLEY KALLICK, b Montreal, Que, Mar 20, 23; nat US; m 45. MICROBIOLOGY, BIOCHEMISTRY. *Educ:* McGill Univ, BSc, 44, MSc, 45; Univ Wis, PhD(microbiol), 49. *Prof Exp:* Asst prof bact, Iowa State Univ, 49-54; assoc biochemist, Argonne Nat Lab, 54-69; PROF BIOL SCI, UNIV ILL, CHICAGO CIRCLE, 69-, HEAD DEPT, 74- *Mem:* AAAS; Am Soc Microbiol; Am Soc Biol Chemists; Sigma Xi. *Res:* Microbial physiology and biochemistry; sulfonium biochemistry, transmethylation, polyamine biosynthesis, sulfur amino acid metabolism. *Mailing Add:* Dept of Biol Sci Univ of Ill at Chicago Circle Chicago IL 60680

SHAPIRO, STANLEY LELAND, b Oakland, Calif, Jan 27, 41; m 71. PHYSICS. *Educ:* Univ Calif, Berkeley, AB, 62; Univ Calif, Santa Barbara, MA, 64, PhD(physics), 67. *Prof Exp:* Guest worker, Nat Bur Stand, 65; mem tech staff, Bell Labs, 67-69 & Gen Tel & Electronics Labs, NY, 69-72; MEM STAFF, LOS ALAMOS SCI LAB, UNIV CALIF, 72- *Concurrent Pos:* Assoc ed, Optics Letters, 79- *Mem:* Am Phys Soc; Optom Soc Am. *Res:* Lasers; nonlinear optical effects; short optical pulses; molecular physics; fast relaxation phenomena. *Mailing Add:* Rm B268 Bldg 221 Nat Bur Standards Washington DC 20234

SHAPIRO, STANLEY SEYMOUR, b Brooklyn, NY, Sept 22, 40; m 65; c 3. BIOCHEMISTRY. *Educ:* Brooklyn Col, BS, 63; Univ Del, PhD(biochem), 66. *Prof Exp:* NIH fel molecular biol, Albert Einstein Col Med, 66-68; sr biochemist, 68-76, RES FEL, HOFFMANN-LA ROCHE INC, 76- *Concurrent Pos:* Mem coadj staff, Rutgers Univ, Newark, 69-70. *Mem:* AAAS; NY Acad Sci; Am Soc Biol Chemists; Am Chem Soc; Soc Complex Carbohydrates. *Res:* Mechanism of enzymes action; role of vitamins in glycosaminoglycan and glycoprotein biosynthesis; biochemistry of retinoids; role of vitamins in glycosaminglycan synthesis. *Mailing Add:* Dept of Biochem Nutrit 340 Kingsland St Nutley NJ 07110

SHAPIRO, STEPHEN D, b New York, NY, Feb 18, 41; m 69; c 1. COMPUTER & INFORMATION SCIENCE. *Educ:* Columbia Univ, BS, 63, MS, 64, PhD(digital syst), 67. *Prof Exp:* Mem tech staff comput software algorithms, Bell Tel Lab, 67-71; prof comput sci, Dept Elec Eng, Stevens Inst Technol, 74-80; PROF ELEC ENG, STATE UNIV NY STONY BROOK, 80- *Concurrent Pos:* Consult info processing, var comn & indust orgn, 71-; consult dir comput sci educ prog, Bell Labs, 76-; NSF grant, 76-; chmn elec eng dept, Comput Sci Comn, 78- *Mem:* Sigma Xi; sr mem Inst Elec & Electronics Engrs; Asn Comput Mach. *Res:* Information processing; software engineering; picture processing; telecommunications. *Mailing Add:* Dept of Elec Eng State Univ NY Stony Brook NY 11794

SHAPIRO, STEPHEN MICHAEL, b Pittsfield, Mass, June 21, 41; m 71; c 2. SOLID STATE PHYSICS. *Educ:* Union Col, BS, 63; Johns Hopkins Univ, PhD(physics), 69. *Prof Exp:* Res assoc, Physics Lab, Univ Paris, 69-70; res assoc, Brookhaven Nat Lab, 71-73; vis physicist, Riso Nat Lab, Denmark, 73-74; PHYSICIST, BROOKHAVEN NAT LAB, 74- *Mem:* Am Phys Soc. *Res:* Neutron scattering studies of phase transitions, magnetic phenomenon and solid electrolytes. *Mailing Add:* Dept of Physics 510B Brookhaven Nat Lab Upton NY 11973

SHAPIRO, STEWART, b Springfield, Mass, Mar 21, 37; m; c 2. DENTISTRY, PUBLIC HEALTH. *Educ:* Boston Col, BA, 58; Tufts Univ, DMD, 62; Harvard Univ, MScH, 69. *Prof Exp:* Res assoc oral physiol, Dent Sch, Tufts Univ, 62-63, instr oral physiol & oral diag, 64-65, staff mem, Forsyth Dent Ctr, 65-66; asst prof community dent, Sch Dent, Univ Md, 69-72; PROF FAMILY PRACT & COMMUNITY HEALTH, COLS MED & HEALTH, PROF COMMUNITY DENT, COL DENT & CHMN DIV COMMUNITY DENT, UNIV OKLA, 72- *Concurrent Pos:* Pvt pract dent, 62-68; lectr epidemiol, Sch Hyg & Pub Health, Johns Hopkins Univ, 69-70, assoc, 70-72; consult, Job Corps Prog, Dept Labor, 70-72, Vet Admin Hosp, Muskogee, Okla, 72- & Head Start, Div Dent Health, Dept Health, Educ & Welfare, 73- *Mem:* Am Dent Asn; Int Asn Dent Res; Am Pub Health Asn. *Mailing Add:* Div of Community Dent Univ of Okla Sch of Dent Oklahoma City OK 73190

SHAPIRO, STUART, b Brooklyn, NY, 1952. SECONDARY METABOLISM, BIOTECHNOLOGY. *Educ:* Washington Square Col, NY Univ, BA, 71; Univ Ill, Urbana-Champaign, MS, 76; Worcester Polytech Inst, PhD(biomed sci), 81. *Prof Exp:* Res asst bio-org chem, Worcester Found Exp Biol, Inc, 78-79; fel biol, Dalhousie Univ, 81-82; RES CHEMIST, MOLECULAR GENETICS & BIOCHEM GROUP, BIO LOGICALS, INC, 82- *Mem:* Am Soc Microbiol; Soc Indust Microbiol; Chem Inst Can; AAAS. *Res:* Microbial biochemistry; natural products chemistry; fermentation technology; stereochemistry of enzymic reactions. *Mailing Add:* Bio Logicals Inc 20 Victoria St Suite 405 Toronto ON M5C 2N8 Can

SHAPIRO, STUART CHARLES, b New York, NY, Dec 30, 44; m 72. COMPUTER SCIENCE. *Educ:* Mass Inst Technol, SB, 66; Univ Wis, MS, 68, PhD(comput sci), 71. *Prof Exp:* From asst prof to assoc prof, Ind Univ, 72-78; asst prof, 77-78, ASSOC PROF COMPUT SCI, STATE UNIV NY, BUFFALO, 78- *Concurrent Pos:* Teaching asst, Comput Sci Dept, Univ Wis, 66-67; NSF grant & actg chmn, Comput Sci Dept, State Univ NY, Buffalo, 78- *Mem:* Asn Comput Mach; Asn Comput Ling; Inst Elec & Electronics Engrs; Soc Study Artificial Intel; Soc Interdisciplinary Study of Mind. *Res:* Artificial intelligence; representation of knowledge; inference; natural language understanding. *Mailing Add:* Dept of Comput Sci 4226 Ridge Lea Rd Amherst NY 14226

SHAPIRO, STUART LOUIS, b New Haven, Conn, Dec 6, 47; m 71. ASTROPHYSICS. *Educ:* Harvard Univ, AB, 69; Princeton Univ, MA, 71, PhD(astrophys sci), 73. *Prof Exp:* Lab instr physics, Harvard Col, 67-69; teaching asst astron, Princeton Univ, 73; res assoc, 73-75, instr, 74-75, asst prof, 75-77, ASSOC PROF ASTRON, CTR RADIOPHYS & SPACE SCI, CORNELL UNIV, 77- *Mem:* Am Astron Soc; Int Astron Union. *Res:* Theoretical problems in relativistic astrophysics and high-energy astrophysics; black hole physics; the physics of compact objects, such as white dwarfs, neutron stars and black holes; x ray astronomy; cosmology; dynamical astronomy. *Mailing Add:* Ctr for Radiophys & Space Res 426 Space Sci Bldg Cornell Univ Ithaca NY 14853

SHAPIRO, VICTOR LENARD, b Chicago, Ill, Oct 16, 24; m 48; c 4. MATHEMATICAL ANALYSIS. *Educ:* Univ Chicago, BS, 47, MS, 49, PhD(math), 52. *Prof Exp:* Instr math, Ill Inst Technol, 48-52; from instr to prof, Rutgers Univ, 52-60; prof, Univ Ore, 60-64; PROF MATH, UNIV CALIF, RIVERSIDE, 64- *Concurrent Pos:* Asst, Univ Chicago, 51-52; mem, Inst Advan Study, 53-55 & 58-59, NSF fel, 54-55. *Mem:* Am Math Soc; Math Asn Am. *Res:* Harmonic analysis; partial differential equations. *Mailing Add:* Dept of Math Univ of Calif Riverside CA 92502

SHAPIRO, WILLIAM, b Newark, NJ, Dec 8, 27; m 51; c 3. INTERNAL MEDICINE, CARDIOLOGY. *Educ:* Duke Univ, AB, 47, MA, 48, MD, 54. *Prof Exp:* Intern, Mt Sinai Hosp, New York, 54-55; jr asst resident internal med, Duke Hosp, Durham, NC, 55-56, res fel cardiol, 56-57, sr asst resident, 57-58; from instr to asst prof, Med Col Va, 60-65; asst prof, 65-68, assoc prof, 68-81, PROF INTERNAL MED, UNIV TEX HEALTH SCI CTR DALLAS, 81-; CHIEF CARDIOVASC SECT, VET ADMIN HOSP, 68- *Concurrent Pos:* Consult, Vet Admin Hosp, Dallas, 65-68 & Coronary Care Comt, Am Heart Asn, 68- *Mem:* Am Fedn Clin. *Res:* Am Physiol Soc; fel Am Col Physicians; Am Heart Asn; Am Col Cardiol. Res: Clinical cardiology; cardiovascular physiology; digitalis pharmacodynamics. *Mailing Add:* Dept of Internal Med Univ of Tex Health Sci Ctr Dallas TX 75235

SHAPIRO, WILLIAM RICHARD, b Pittsburgh, Pa, May 1, 36; m 59; c 2. NEUROLOGY. *Educ:* Univ Calif, Los Angeles, BA, 58; Univ Calif, San Francisco, MD, 61; Am Bd Psychiat & Neurol, dipl, 69. *Prof Exp:* Intern med, King County Hosp, Seattle, 61-62; asst resident neurol, New York Hosp, 63-66; staff assoc neuro-oncol, Nat Cancer Inst, 66-69; assoc neuro-oncol, Sloan-Kettering Inst Cancer Res, 69-78; from asst prof to assoc prof, 69-77, PROF NEUROL, MED COL, CORNELL UNIV, 77- *Concurrent Pos:* Asst attend neurologist, New York Hosp, 69-73, assoc attend neurologist, 73-77; asst attend physician, Mem Hosp Cancer & Allied Dis, 69-73, assoc attend physician, 73-77, attend physician, 77- consult, Nat Cancer Inst, 69-; Sloan-Kettering Inst Cancer Res res grant, 70-76; Nat Inst Neurol Dis & Stroke res career develop award, 71; Nat Cancer Inst res grant, 74- *Mem:* Am Neurol Asn; NY Acad Sci; Am Acad Neurol; Am Asn Cancer Res; Am Soc Clin Oncol. *Res:* Neuro-oncology; chemotherapy of experimental and clinical brain tumors. *Mailing Add:* Mem Hosp for Cancer & Allied Dis 1275 York Ave New York NY 10021

SHAPIRO, ZALMAN MORDECAI, b Canton, Ohio, May 12, 20; m 45; c 3. CHEMISTRY. *Educ:* Johns Hopkins Univ, AB, 42, MA, 45, PhD(phys chem), 48. *Prof Exp:* Res assoc, Johns Hopkins Univ, 42-46, jr instr chem, 46-48; sr scientist res labs, Westinghouse Elec Corp, 48-49, sr scientist, Bettis Atomic Power Div, 49-50, supv scientist, 50-53, mgr phys chem sect, 53-54, mgr chem metall sect, 54-55, asst mgr, Reactor Design Sub-Div, 55-57; pres, Nuclear Mat & Equip Corp, 57-70; exec asst to mgr, Breeder Reactor Div, 71-73, DIR FUSION POWER SYSTS DEPT, WESTINGHOUSE ELEC CORP, 73- *Concurrent Pos:* Chmn, Isotope & Radiation Enterprises, Ltd, 64-68; pres, Nuclear Decontamination Corp & vpres, Arco Chem Co, 68-70; vpres, Kawecki Berylco Industs. *Mem:* AAAS; Am Nuclear Soc; Am Chem Soc; Electrochem Soc; Am Soc Metals. *Res:* Chemical erosion of steel; carbonyl chemistry; flame reactions of metallic halides; zirconium, hafnium, uranium and plutonium chemistry; metallurgy; fusion power systems technology. *Mailing Add:* Westinghouse Fusion Power Systs PO Box 10864 Pittsburgh PA 15236

SHAPLEY, ALAN HORACE, geophysics, see previous edition

SHAPLEY, JAMES LOUIS, b Asotin, Wash, Mar 9, 20; m 47; c 3. AUDIOLOGY, SPEECH PATHOLOGY. *Educ:* Univ Wash, BA, 47, MA, 52; Univ Iowa, PhD(audiol), 54. *Prof Exp:* Assoc instr speech, Univ Wash, 47-51; chief audiologist, Houston Speech & Hearing Ctr, Tex, 54-56; from instr to asst prof audiol, Univ Iowa, 56-60; CHIEF AUDIOL & SPEECH PATH, VET ADMIN HOSP, SEATTLE, 60- *Concurrent Pos:* Clin assoc prof, Univ Wash, 61- *Mem:* Acoust Soc Am; Am Speech & Hearing Asn. *Res:* Psychoacoustics; clinical audiology. *Mailing Add:* Audiol & Speech Path Vet Admin Hosp Seattle WA 98108

SHAPLEY, JOHN ROGER, b Manhattan, Kans, Apr 15, 46; m 70; c 1. INORGANIC CHEMISTRY. *Educ:* Univ Kans, BS, 67; Harvard Univ, PhD(chem), 72. *Prof Exp:* Assoc, Stanford Univ, 71-72; asst prof, 72-78, ASSOC PROF CHEM, UNIV ILL, URBANA, 78- *Concurrent Pos:* NSF fel, 71-72; A P Sloan Found fel, 78-80; teacher-scholar, Camille & Henry Dreyfus Found, 78-83. *Mem:* Am Chem Soc. *Res:* Organotransition metal chemistry; synthesis and characterization of novel compounds; metal clusters; catalysis; dynamic nuclear magnetic resonance. *Mailing Add:* Dept of Chem Univ of Ill Urbana IL 61801

SHAPLEY, LLOYD STOWELL, b Cambridge, Mass, June 2, 23; m 55; c 2. MATHEMATICS, MATHEMATICAL ECONOMICS. *Educ:* Harvard Univ, AB, 48; Princeton Univ, PhD(math), 53. *Prof Exp:* Mathematician, Rand Corp, 48-49; Henry B Fine instr math, Princeton Univ, 52-54; mathematician, Rand Corp, 54-55; sr res fel math, Calif Inst Technol, 55-56; MATHEMATICIAN, RAND CORP, 56- *Concurrent Pos:* Mem ed bd, Int J Game Theory, 70-, Math Prog, 71-, J Math Econ, 74- & Math Opers Res, 75- *Mem:* Am Math Soc; Math Prog Soc; fel Economet Soc; fel Am Acad Arts & Sci. *Res:* Game theory, both pure and applied to economics and political science. *Mailing Add:* Rand Corp 1700 Main St Santa Monica CA 90406

SHAPLEY, ROBERT M, b New York, NY, Oct 7, 44; m 66; c 2. NEUROPHYSIOLOGY, BIOPHYSICS. *Educ:* Harvard Univ, AB, 65; Rockefeller Univ, PhD(biophys), 70. *Prof Exp:* Fel physiol, Northwestern Univ, 70-71 & Cambridge Univ, 71-72; asst prof, 72-76, ASSOC PROF NEUROPHYSIOL, ROCKEFELLER UNIV, 76- *Mem:* Int Brain Res Orgn. *Res:* Visual neurophysiology in vertebrates; mathematical analysis of neural networks. *Mailing Add:* Rockefeller Univ 1230 York Ave New York NY 10021

SHAPPIRIO, DAVID GORDON, b Washington, DC, June 18, 30; m 53; c 2. PHYSIOLOGY, BIOCHEMISTRY. *Educ:* Univ Mich, BS, 51; Harvard Univ, AM, 53, PhD(biol), 55. *Prof Exp:* NSF fel, Cambridge Univ, 55-56; Nat Res Coun-Am Cancer Soc fel, Univ Louvain, 56-57; from instr to assoc prof zool, 57-67, prof zool, 67-75, actg chmn dept cell & molecular biol, 75-76, assoc chmn 76-78, PROF BIOL SCI, 75- & ACTG CHMN DIV BIOL SCI, UNIV MICH, ANN ARBOR, 78- *Concurrent Pos:* Danforth assoc, Danforth Found, 68-; consult develop biol textbooks, res grant appl, NIH, NSF. *Mem:* AAAS; Am Soc Cell Biol; Brit Soc Exp Biol; Am Soc Zoologists; Entom Soc Am. *Res:* Physiology and biochemistry of insect development and diapause; respiratory enzymology; cell biology; biology of wasps. *Mailing Add:* Div of Biol Sci Univ of Mich Ann Arbor MI 48109

SHAPRAS, PETER, b Rokiskis, Lithuania, Feb 23, 25; m 62; c 3. ANALYTICAL CHEMISTRY. *Educ:* Johns Hopkins Univ, BS, 55. *Prof Exp:* Res chemist, 55-67, res specialist, 67-73, SR RES SPECIALIST ANAL CHEM, MONSANTO CO, 73- *Mem:* Am Chem Soc. *Res:* Gas chromatography; infrared spectroscopy; trace analysis; polymer characterization; electrochemistry. *Mailing Add:* Monsanto Co 730 Worcester St Indian Orchard MA 01151

SHAPTON, WILLIAM ROBERT, b Lansing, Mich, June 25, 41; m 63; c 2. MECHANICAL ENGINEERING. *Educ:* Mich State Univ, BS, 62, MS, 63; Univ Cincinnati, PhD(vibrations), 68. *Prof Exp:* Systs engr, Missile Div, Bendix Corp, 63-64, engr, Automation & Measurement Div, 64-65; assoc prof vibration, Univ Cincinnati, 65-79; PROF MECH ENG, MICH TECHNOL UNIV, 79- *Concurrent Pos:* Consult, Automation & Measurement Div, Bendix Corp, 65-, Gen Elec Co, 69-70, Mound Lab, Monsanto Res Corp, 72-78, NASA, 76-82 & Cincinnati Milacron, 77- *Mem:* Soc Automotive Engrs; Am Soc Mech Engrs; Am Soc Eng Educ. *Res:* Vibration, shock and measurement of mechanical systems; seismic response of structures; machine tool dynamics; experimental engineering. *Mailing Add:* 1200 Eighth Ave Houghton MI 49931

SHARAWY, MOHAMED, b Cairo, Egypt, Mar 13, 41; m 65; c 3. ANATOMY. *Educ:* Cairo Univ, PNS, 58, DDS, 62; Univ Rochester, PhD(anat), 70. *Prof Exp:* Intern oral surg, Sch Dent, Cairo Univ, 62, instr, 62-65; Fulbright fel, Inst Int Educ, 65-68; UAR scholar, Univ Rochester, 68-70; asst prof, Sch Dent, 70-73, assoc prof, 73-78, PROF ORAL BIOL & ANAT & COORD ANAT DENT, MED COL GA, 78- *Res:* Fine structural and biochemical studies of the adrenal cortex and salivary gland. *Mailing Add:* Dept of Oral Biol Med Col of Ga Augusta GA 30902

SHARBAUGH, AMANDUS HARRY, b Richmond, Va, Mar 28, 19; m 40; c 2. CHEMISTRY, PHYSICS. *Educ:* Western Reserve Univ, AB, 40; Brown Univ, PhD(chem), 43. *Prof Exp:* Res assoc, Res Lab, 42-61, liaison scientist, 61-64, mgr dielec studies, 64-71, MGR PLASMA PHYSICS BR, GEN ELEC CO, 71- *Concurrent Pos:* Fel physics, Union Univ, NY, 44-48; secy, Conf Elec Insulation, 54, vchmn, 55, chmn 56; mem adv comt, US Dept Defense, 56-57; mem conf elec insulation & dielec behav, Nat Acad Sci; US Adv to CIGRE; Holder world's record microwave communication. *Mem:* Electrochem Soc; Inst Elec & Electronics Engrs. *Res:* Dielectric behavior; magnetron design; electronic breakdown and conduction; microwave spectroscopy. *Mailing Add:* Gen Elec Res & Develop Ctr The Knolls Schenectady NY 12309

SHARBER, JAMES RANDALL, b Clarksville, Tenn, Aug 13, 41; m 74; c 1. SPACE PHYSICS, AURORAL PHYSICS. *Educ:* Murray State Col, BA, 63; Tex A&M Univ, PhD(physics), 72. *Prof Exp:* Res asst scientist, Div Atmospheric & Space Sci, Univ Tex, Dallas, 66-72; vis asst prof physics, US Naval Acad, 72-74; ASSOC PROF PHYSICS & SPACE SCI, FLA INST TECHNOL, 74- *Concurrent Pos:* consult, Southwest Res Inst, 82- *Mem:* Am Geophys Union; Am Asn Physics Teachers; Am Inst Physics. *Res:* Analysis of particle data taken by polar satellite; descriptions of the electron and ion fluxes incident on the earth's auroral regions to determine the processes responsible for the entry of solar wind particles into the magnetosphere and their subsequent acceleration and precipitation to produce auroras. *Mailing Add:* Dept Physics & Space Sci Fla Inst Technol Melbourne FL 32901

SHARDA, SATISH CHANDER, b Delhi, India, May 11, 46. POLYMER SCIENCE, POLYMER ENGINEERING. *Educ:* Panjab Univ, India, BS, 67; Mont State Univ, MS, 69; Calif Inst Technol, PhD(chem eng), 74. *Prof Exp:* Sr res chemist, Monsanto Co, 74-76; STAFF ENGR, IBM CORP, 76- *Mem:* Soc Rheology; Brit Soc Rheology; Am Inst Chem Engrs; Am Chem Soc; Soc Plastics Engrs. *Res:* Polymer material; characterization, rheology and engineering of new polymeric materials. *Mailing Add:* 23 Benthaven Pl Boulder CO 80303

SHARE, GERALD HARVEY, b New York, NY, Oct 9, 40. X-RAY ASTRONOMY. *Educ:* Queens Col, NY, BS, 61; Univ Rochester, PhD(physics), 66. *Prof Exp:* Nat Acad Sci-Nat Res Coun resident res assoc cosmic radiation, 66-68, RES PHYSICIST, NAVAL RES LAB, 68- *Mem:* AAAS; Am Phys Soc; Am Astron Soc; Sigma Xi. *Res:* Cosmic x-and-gamma radiation. *Mailing Add:* Code 7128.4 Naval Res Lab Washington DC 20375

SHARE, LEONARD, b Detroit, Mich, Oct 14, 27; m 49; c 3. PHYSIOLOGY. *Educ:* Brooklyn Col, AB, 47; Oberlin Col, AM, 48; Yale Univ, PhD(physiol), 51. *Prof Exp:* USPHS fel physiol, Sch Med, Western Reserve Univ, 51-52; from instr to prof physiol, 52-69; PROF PHYSIOL & BIOPHYS & CHMN DEPT, UNIV TENN CTR HEALTH SCI, MEMPHIS, 69- *Mem:* AAAS; Int Soc Neuroendocrinol; Endocrine Soc; Am Physiol Soc. *Res:* Water and electrolyte metabolism; vasopressin secretion; metabolism. *Mailing Add:* Dept of Physiol & Biophys Univ of Tenn Ctr Health Sci Memphis TN 38163

SHARE, NORMAN N, b Montreal, Que, Dec 25, 30; m 56; c 1. NEUROPHARMACOLOGY. *Educ:* Univ Montreal, BPh, 58; McGill Univ, PhD(pharmacol), 62. *Prof Exp:* Fel, Columbia Univ, 62-64; chief pharmacologist, Charles E Frosst & Co, 64-65, mgr, Dept Pharmacol, 65-71, asst dir res biol, Dept Pharmacol, 71-79, dir pharmacol, 79-81, SR DIR NEUROPSYCHOPHARMACOL, MERCK INST THERAPEUT RES, 82- *Mem:* Pharmacol Soc Can; Am Soc Pharmacol & Exp Therapeut; NY Acad Sci. *Res:* Chronic obstructive lung disease. *Mailing Add:* Merck Inst Therapeut Res W26-208 West Point PA 19486

SHARER, ARCHIBALD WILSON, b Dayton, Ohio, Sept 19, 19; m 41; c 3. ZOOLOGY. *Educ:* Ohio State Univ, BS, 43; Univ Mich, MS, 48, PhD(zool), 59. *Prof Exp:* Asst zool, Univ Mich, 46-50; instr biol, Fla State Univ, 50-53; instr, Lake Forest Col, 53-56; instr zool, Duke Univ, 58-60; assoc prof biol, 60-63, chmn div sci, 63-77, PROF BIOL, NC WESLEYAN COL, 63- *Mem:* Am Soc Ichthyologists & Herpetologists; Am Inst Biol Sci. *Res:* Behavior, ecology and natural history of vertebrates; herpetology. *Mailing Add:* Dept of Biol NC Wesleyan Col Rocky Mount NC 27801

SHARF, DONALD JACK, b Detroit, Mich, Aug 4, 27; m 52; c 2. SPEECH & HEARING SCIENCES. *Educ:* Wayne State Univ, BA, 51, MA, 52; Univ Mich, PhD(speech sci), 58. *Prof Exp:* Asst ed, G & C Merriam Co, 57-61; asst prof speech, State Univ NY Buffalo, 61-64; from asst prof to assoc prof, 64-73, PROF SPEECH SCI, UNIV MICH, ANN ARBOR, 73- *Mem:* Am Speech & Hearing Asn; Acoust Soc Am; Int Soc Phonetic Sci; Am Asn Phonetic Sci. *Res:* Acoustic and perceptual aspects of speech communication. *Mailing Add:* Univ of Mich Speech & Hearing Sci Ann Arbor MI 48109

SHARGEL, LEON DAVID, b Baltimore, Md, Nov 18, 41; m 67; c 2. PHARMACOLOGY, DRUG METABOLISM. *Educ:* Univ Md, BS, 63; George Washington Univ, PhD(pharmacol), 69. *Prof Exp:* Assoc res biologist, Sterling-Winthrop Res Inst, NY, 69-71; group leader, 72-75; asst prof, 75-77, ASSOC PROF, PHARM & PHARMACOL, COL PHARM & ALLIED HEALTH PROF, NORTHEASTERN UNIV, 77- *Mem:* AAAS; Am Soc Pharmacol & Exp Therapeut; Sigma Xi. *Res:* Physiological disposition of drugs, drug metabolism, biopharmaceutics; pharmacokinetics. *Mailing Add:* Col of Pharm & Allied Health Prof Northeastern Univ Boston MA 02115

SHARGOOL, PETER DOUGLAS, b Feb 25, 35; Can citizen; m 61; c 2. PLANT BIOCHEMISTRY. *Educ:* Univ London, BSc, 62; Univ Alta, MSc, 65, PhD(plant biochem), 68. *Prof Exp:* Res worker biochem, Wellcome Res Labs, Eng, 54-62; Nat Res Coun Can grant, 68-73, assoc prof, 73-79, PROF BIOCHEM, UNIV SASK, 79- *Concurrent Pos:* Med Res Coun grant, 75-77, Nat Sci & Engr Res Coun grant, 77-; Nat Res Coun res contract, 80- *Mem:* Can Soc Plant Physiologists; Can Biochem Soc; Int Asn Plant Tissue Culture. *Res:* Mechanisms regulating the biosynthesis of amino acids in plants and animals. *Mailing Add:* Dept Biochem Health Sci Bldg Univ Sask Saskatoon SK S7N 0W0 Can

SHARITZ, REBECCA REYBURN, b Wytheville, Va, Aug 10, 44. ECOLOGY, BOTANY. *Educ:* Roanoke Col, BS, 66; Univ NC, Chapel Hill, PhD(bot), 70. *Prof Exp:* Asst prof biol, Saginaw Valley Col, 70-71; adj asst prof bot, 72-77, ASSOC RES ECOLOGIST, SAVANNAH RIVER ECOL LAB, UNIV GA, 77- *Concurrent Pos:* Res assoc, Univ NC, 71; plant ecologist, US Energy Res & Develop Admin, 75-76. *Mem:* Sigma Xi; Ecol Soc Am; Am Inst Biol Sci. *Res:* Plant population ecology; structure and diversity of plant communities; uptake and turnover of radionuclides in plant communities. *Mailing Add:* Savannah River Ecol Lab Drawer E Univ of Ga Aiken SC 29801

SHARKAWI, MAHMOUD, b Cairo, Egypt, May 26, 35; m 70; c 4. PHARMACOLOGY. *Educ:* Cairo Univ, BPharm, 57; Univ Minn, Minneapolis, MSc, 61; Univ Calif, San Francisco, PhD(pharmacol), 64. *Prof Exp:* Lectr pharmacol, Cairo Univ, 64-65; res assoc, Univ Ill, 65-66; res assoc, Stanford Univ, 66-67; from instr to asst prof, 68-73, assoc prof, 73-80, PROF PHARMACOL, FAC MED, UNIV MONTREAL, 80- *Mem:* AAAS; Int Soc Biochem Pharmacol; Am Soc Pharmacol & Exp Therapeut; Pharmacol Soc Can. *Res:* Interactions between disulfiram-life compounds and centrally acting drugs. *Mailing Add:* Dept of Pharmacol Univ of Montreal Fac of Med Montreal PQ H3C 3J7 Can

SHARKEY, JOHN BERNARD, b Elizabeth, NJ, Sept 5, 40; m 63; c 1. INORGANIC CHEMISTRY, INSTRUMENTATION. *Educ:* NY Univ, BA, 64, MSc, 68, PhD(phys chem), 70. *Prof Exp:* Anal chemist, Engelhard Industs, NJ, 62-66; asst prof, 70-77, assoc prof, 77-79, PROF CHEM & PHYS SCI & CHAIRPERSON DEPT, PACE UNIV, 77- *Mem:* Am Chem Soc; AAAS; NY Acad Sci. *Res:* Polymorphism in inorganic compounds; trace analysis of metals by absorption spectroscopy; instrumental analysis. *Mailing Add:* Dept of Chem Pace Univ New York NY 10038

SHARKEY, MARGARET MARY, b New York, NY, Apr 28, 26. CELL BIOLOGY. *Educ:* Fordham Univ, BS, 54, MS, 60; St John's Univ, NY, PhD(cell biol), 72. *Prof Exp:* Teaching asst cytol, histol & embryol, St John's Univ, NY, 69-70; asst prof cell biol, histol & embryol, St Thomas Aquinas Col, 70-72; RES ADMINR VIROL & CELL BIOL PROJ GRANTS, AM CANCER SOC, 72- *Mem:* Am Soc Cell Biol; AAAS; NY Acad Sci. *Res:* In vitro lymphocyte stimulation with phytomitogens as a probe for the study of biochemical differences in the surface behavior of normal and malignant cells. *Mailing Add:* Am Cancer Soc 777 Third Ave New York NY 10017

SHARKOFF, EUGENE GIBB, physics, see previous edition

SHARMA, GHANSHYAM D, b Delhi, India, Feb 28, 31; m 61; c 1. MARINE GEOLOGY, GEOCHEMISTRY. *Educ:* Benares Hindu Univ, BSc, 52; Swiss Fed Inst Technol, MS, 58; Univ Mich, PhD(geol), 61. *Prof Exp:* Res engr, Sinclair Res, Inc, 61-63; asst prof, 63-69, assoc prof, 69-74, prof marine geol & geochem, Inst Marine Sci, 74-78, PROF MARINE SCI, ALASKA SEA GRANT, UNIV ALASKA, FAIRBANKS, 78- *Honors & Awards:* Pres Award, Am Asn Petrol Geologists. *Mem:* Am Asn Petrol Geologists; Soc Econ Paleontologists & Mineralogists; Am Geophys Union. *Res:* Concentration and distribution of elements in marine water and sediments of arctic and subarctic in Alaska; study of diagenesis to reconstruct the paleoecology and environments of deposition; sediment transport and distribution on continental shelf. *Mailing Add:* Alaska Sea Grant Prog Univ of Alaska Fairbanks AK 99701

SHARMA, GOPAL CHANDRA, b Churi-Ajitgarh, India, Apr 18, 32; US citizen; m 60; c 2. PHARMACOLOGY, CANCER. *Educ:* Agra Univ, BS, 53, DVM, 58; Univ Mo-Columbia, MS, 66, PhD(med pharmacol), 69. *Prof Exp:* Officer prev immunization, Dept Animal Husb, Govt India, 58-59, vet surgeon asst, 59-61; res asst genetics, Indian Coun Agr Res, 61-65; res asst med pharmacol, Univ Mo-Columbia, 66-67, Nat Cancer Inst spec proj fel, Med Sch, 67-69; asst prof pharmacol, Sch Med, Univ NDak, 69-70; sr res scientist cancer res, 70-73, dir plant res, Am Med Ctr, Denver, 73-77, PHARMACOLOGIST, PHARMACOL & TOXICOL BR, DIV VET MED RES, BUR VET MED, FOOD & DRUG ADMIN, HEW, 77- *Res:* Evaluation of anticancer drugs; effect of cancer on disposition of drugs in the body; drug toxicities and prevention; drug distribution and interaction; cyclic adenosine monophosphate; comparative pharmacology; drug interaction and analytical microdetection of drug and chemical residue in the tissue of food animals, effect of drugs on the metabolism of other drugs. *Mailing Add:* Food & Drug Admin Bldg 339D ARC Beltsville MD 20705

SHARMA, GOPAL KRISHAN, b Hoshiarpur, India, Mar 24, 37; m 66. ECOLOGY. *Educ:* Univ Mo-Columbia, BS, 61, MS, 62, PhD(bot), 67. *Prof Exp:* Teaching asst bot, Univ Mo-Columbia, 62-66; instr, Prestonsburg Community Col, Ky, 66-67; chmn div biol sci, 67-68; assoc prof, 68-76, PROF BIOL SCI, UNIV TENN, MARTIN, 76- *Concurrent Pos:* Instr, Cult Enrichment Prog, Prestonsburg, Ky, 66; NSF fel, Univ Mich, 68-69; res fel econ bot, Harvard Univ, 76-77. *Mem:* AAAS; Am Inst Biol Sci; Bot Soc Am; Ecol Soc Am. *Res:* Ecology and ethnobotany of Cannabis; cuticular features as indicators of environmental pollution. *Mailing Add:* Dept of Biol Univ of Tenn Martin TN 38238

SHARMA, GOVIND C, b Udaipur, India, Mar 3, 44; m 68. PLANT SCIENCE. *Educ:* Univ Udaipur, India, BS, 64; Univ Fla, MAgr, 65; Kans State Univ, PhD(veg crops), 70. *Prof Exp:* Res asst, Pesticide Lab, Univ Fla, 65-66; agr coordr, Peace Corps, 66; assoc prof, 70-73, PROF PLANT SCI & CHMN DEPT NATURAL RESOURCES & ENVIRON STUDIES, ALA A&M UNIV, 73- *Mem:* Am Soc Hort Sci; Am Soc Agron; Sigma Xi. *Res:* Triticale breeding; plant breeding; new fertilizer evaluation in cash crops; remote sensing in agricultural resource management; host plant resistance and pesticide analysis. *Mailing Add:* PO Box 183 Ala A&M Univ Normal AL 35762

SHARMA, JAGADISH, b Calcutta, India, Dec 15, 23; US citizen; m 51; c 2. SOLID STATE PHYSICS, ELECTRON SPECTROSCOPY. *Educ:* Calcutta Univ, BS, 44, MS, 47, PhD(physics). 53. *Prof Exp:* Nat Inst Res fel thermoluminescence, Khaira Physics Lab, Calcutta Univ, 53-54; res fel color ctr, Nat Res Coun, Div Elec Eng, Ottawa, Can, 55-57; lectr dept physics, Indian Inst Technol, Kharagpur, 58-61; asst prof radiation damage, 65-67; res assoc, Dept Aerospace & Mech Sci, Princeton Univ, 61-64; res physicist, Div Explosives & Electron Spectros, Energetic Mat Res & Develop Comn, US Army, 67-80; PHYSICIST, NAVAL SURFACE WEAPONS CTR, 80- *Mem:* Am Phys Soc. *Res:* Fluorescence; thermoluminescence; color centers; radiation damage; solid state physics of explosives and propellants; Auger, uv, x-ray photoelectron spectroscopy of explosives and propellants. *Mailing Add:* Naval Surface Weapons Ctr White Oak Silver Springs MD 20910

SHARMA, JAGDEV MITTRA, b Punjab, India, June 28, 41; m 69. MICROBIOLOGY, VIROLOGY. *Educ:* Punjab Univ, India, BVSc, 61; Univ Calif, Davis, MS, 64, PhD(comp path), 67. *Prof Exp:* Jr specialist avian med, Univ Calif, Davis, 62-66; poultry pathologist, Wash State Univ, 67-71; VET MED OFFICER, REGIONAL POULTRY RES LAB, SCI & EDUC ADMIN-AGR RES, USDA, 71-, ASST PROF DEPT OF PATH, MICH STATE UNIV, 74-, PRIN INVESTR, 80- *Mem:* Am Vet Med Asn; Am Asn Avian Pathologists; Int Asn Comp Res Leukemia & Related Dis; Am Soc Microbiol; World Vet Poultry Asn. *Res:* Avian tumor immunology; mechanisms of virus-induced neoplasms. *Mailing Add:* Regional Poultry Res Lab 3606 E Mt Hope Rd East Lansing MI 48823

SHARMA, MADAN LAL, b Faridkot, India, Aug 28, 34; Can citizen; m 68. ENTOMOLOGY, ECOLOGY. *Educ:* Univ Punjab, India, BSc, 54 & 56, MSc, 57; Univ Paris, DSc(entom), 65. *Prof Exp:* Scientist, Agr Dept, French Govt, 65-66; lectr, 66-68, asst prof, 68-70, assoc prof, 70-78, PROF ENTOM, UNIV SHERBROOKE, 78- *Concurrent Pos:* French Govt fel, Nat Inst Agron Res, 71; res fel, Quebec-France & France-Can Mission, Nat Inst Agron Res, France, 81. *Res:* Biology and ecology of Aphids and Coccids; bibliography of Aphidoidea. *Mailing Add:* Dept of Biol Univ of Sherbrooke Sherbrooke PQ J1K 2R1 Can

SHARMA, MANGALORE GOKULANAND, bMulki, India,Nov 3, 27; US citizen; m 62; c 2. BIOMECHANICS, RHEOLOGY. *Educ:* Univ Mysore, India, BE, 52; Indian Inst Sci, DIISc, 54; Pa State Univ, PhD(eng mech), 60. *Prof Exp:* Design engr, Hindustan Aeronaut, 54-57; res asst eng mech, 57-60, asst prof, 60-64, assoc prof, 64-75, PROF ENG MECH, PA STATE UNIV, 75- *Concurrent Pos:* Vis prof, Indian Inst Sci, 67-68; consult, Gen Tire & Rubber Co, 64-68 & Fed Hgy Admin, 81- *Mem:* Am Soc Rheology; Am Soc Testing & Mat; Am Acad Mech; Am Soc Testing & Mat Comt Composite Mat. *Res:* Analysis of hemodynamic flow through blood vessels; fluid dynamical contribution to atherosclerosis; rheology of blood vessels; effect of hypertension on rheological properties; physical properties of biopolymers used in cardiac assist devices; mechanics of composite materials and their failure analysis; viscoplasticity of metals at elevated temperatures. *Mailing Add:* Pa State Univ 227 Hammond Bldg University Park PA 16802

SHARMA, MINOTI, bioenergetics, biochemical endocrinology, see previous edition

SHARMA, MOHESWAR, b Jhanji, India; US citizen; m 62; c 2. ORGANIC CHEMISTRY. *Educ:* Calcutta Univ, BS, 53, MS, 56, PhD(chem), 62. *Prof Exp:* Fel chem, Tufts Univ, 63-65, Univ Alta, 65-67; vis lectr, Univ Southampton, 67-72; CANCER RES SCIENTIST CARBOHYDRATES, ROSWELL PARK MEM INST, 72- *Mem:* Am Chem Soc. *Res:* Carbohydrates; cell membranes. *Mailing Add:* 281 Coronation Dr Amherst NY 14226

SHARMA, RABINDER KUMAR, b Kampala, Uganda, May 19, 46; US citizen. DEMOGRAPHY, PUBLIC HEALTH. *Educ:* Makerere Univ, BA, 69; Univ Pa, MA, 70, PhD(demog), 75. *Prof Exp:* Instr, 73-75, dir, Health Policy Admin, 75-80, ASST PROF PUBLIC HEALTH, UNIV PITTSBURGH, 75-, ASST PROF GRAD SCH PUBLIC & INT AFFAIRS, 80- *Concurrent Pos:* Pop Coun acad fel, NY, 69-74. *Mem:* AAAS; Am Pub Health Asn; Pop Asn Am; Int Union Study Pop; Am Sociol Asn. *Res:* Health planning and health policy formulation. *Mailing Add:* Grad Sch of Pub Health Univ of Pittsburgh Pittsburgh PA 15261

SHARMA, RAGHUBIR PRASAD, b Bharatpur, India, Sept 9, 40; m 58; c 2. PHARMACOLOGY, TOXICOLOGY. *Educ:* Univ Rajasthan, BVSc, 59; Univ Minn, St Paul, PhD(pharmacol), 68; Am Bd Vet Toxicol, dipl, 74. *Prof Exp:* Clin vet, Govt Rajasthan, India, 59-60; instr pharmacol, Univ Rajasthan, 60-61; asst prof, Uttar Pradesh Agr Univ, India, 61-64; asst prof, 69-75, assoc prof, 69-80, PROF & TOXICOLOGIST ANIMAL, DAIRY & VET SCI, UTAH STATE UNIV, 80- *Concurrent Pos:* NIH grant, Utah State Univ, 69-72, NIMH res grant, 70-71; Food & Drug Admin res grant, 74-77. *Mem:* Am Soc Pharmacol & Exp Therapeut; Soc Toxicol; Am Col Vet Toxicol; Am Vet Med Asn. *Res:* Pharmacology and toxicology of selected chemicals; mechanisms, metabolism and biochemical alterations; neurochemical alterations and molecular interactions. *Mailing Add:* 465 West 550 N Logan UT 84321

SHARMA, RAM ASHREY, b Azamgarh, India, Sept 5, 43; m 61; c 2. MEDICINAL CHEMISTRY. *Educ:* Univ Gorakhpur, India, BS, 63, MS, 66; Univ Roorkee, PhD(chem), 70. *Prof Exp:* Asst prof chem, K N Govt Col Gyanpur, Varanasi, India, 66-68; res assoc, Coun Sci & Indust Res, New Delhi, 68-70; asst prof, Univ Roorkee, 70-71; CANCER RES SCIENTIST MED CHEM, ROSWELL PARK MEM INST, BUFFALO, 71- *Mem:* Am Chem Soc. *Res:* Synthesis and biological evaluation of metabolite analogs of purines and pyrimidines of potential medicinal interest. *Mailing Add:* 4105 A Harlem Rd Snyder NY 14226

SHARMA, RAM RATAN, b Jaipur, India, Oct 6, 36; c 1. PHYSICS. *Educ:* Maharaja's Col, Jaipur, BS, 58; Univ Bombay, MS, 62; Univ Calif, Riverside, MA, 64, PhD(physics), 65. *Prof Exp:* Lectr physics & chem, Indian Inst, Jaipur, 57-58; sci officer physics, Atomic Energy Estab, Bombay, 58-62; asst, Univ Calif, Riverside, 62-65; res assoc, Purdue Univ, West Lafayette, 65-68; assoc prof, 68-73, PROF PHYSICS, UNIV ILL, CHICAGO CIRCLE, 73- *Concurrent Pos:* Advan Res Proj Agency fel, Purdue Univ, West Lafayette, 65-68; res assoc, Argonne Nat Lab, 71-; vis scientist, Atomic Energy Res Estab, Eng, 74; vis prof, Univ Liverpool, 75. *Mem:* Am Phys Soc. *Res:* Solid state physics; properties of magnetic ions in solids and biological systems; bound-excitons in nonmetals; electron-nuclear interactions in solids; shielding effects; polarizabilities of ions; surface color-centers; nuclear fusion. *Mailing Add:* Dept of Physics Univ of Ill at Chicago Circle Chicago IL 60680

SHARMA, RAMESH C, b Delhi, India, June 5, 31. NUCLEAR PHYSICS, SOLID STATE PHYSICS. *Educ:* Univ Delhi, BSc, 50, MSc, 52, MA, 53; Univ Toronto, PhD(nuclear physics), 59. *Prof Exp:* Lectr physics, Ramjas Col, Delhi, 55-56; res asst, Univ Toronto, 56-59; res fel, Ont Cancer Inst, Can, 59-60; lectr, Ramjas Col, Delhi, 60-61; lectr, Col Eng & Technol, Delhi, 61-62; asst prof, 62-69, ASSOC PROF PHYSICS, SIR GEORGE WILLIAMS CAMPUS, CONCORDIA UNIV, 69- *Concurrent Pos:* Nat Res Coun Can grant, 64-65. *Mem:* Am Soc Eng Educ; Can Asn Physicists. *Res:* Angular distribution of alpha particles from oriented nuclei and the distribution on the nuclear surface. *Mailing Add:* Dept of Physics 1455 Boul De Maisonneuve W Montreal PQ H3G 1M8 Can

SHARMA, RAMESH DUTT, chemical physics, see previous edition

SHARMA, RAMESHWAR KUMAR, b Jammu, India, Dec 15, 35; m 65. MEDICINAL CHEMISTRY. *Educ:* Univ Jammu & Kashmir, BS, 53; Birla Inst Technol, India, BS, 58; Univ Conn, PhD(med chem), 63. *Prof Exp:* Assoc res chemist, Sterling Winthrop Res Inst, 63; lectr med chem, State Univ NY Buffalo, 63-64; sr res scientist, Regional Res Labs, India, 64-65; res assoc steroids, Univ Miss, 65-67; fel biochem steroids, Worcester Found Exp Biol, 67-68; group leader chem & biochem, Thomas J Lipton, Inc, 68-69; asst prof biochem, med units, 69-78, PROF BIOCHEM CTR HEALTH SCI, UNIV TENN, MEMPHIS, 78- CHIEF STEROID BIOCHEMIST, VET ADMIN HOSP, MEMPHIS, 69- *Concurrent Pos:* Vis prof, McArdle Lab Cancer Res, Madison, Wi, 74-75. *Mem:* AAAS; Am Soc Biol Chemists; fel Acad Pharmaceut Sci; fel Am Inst Chemists; Am Chem Soc. *Res:* Regulatory mechanisms of hormones at cellular level in normal and tumor tissues; steroid biochemistry. *Mailing Add:* 2827 Flowerwood Rd Memphis TN 38128

SHARMA, RAN S, b Ruppura, Gujarat, India, June 9, 37; nat US. BIOSTATISTICS, MATHEMATICAL STATISTICS. *Educ:* Gujarat Univ, India, BA, 59, MA, 61; Univ Calif, Los Angeles, PhD(biostatist), 66. *Prof Exp:* Asst, Univ Calif, Los Angeles, 62-66; biostatistician, Riker Labs, 66; sr statistician, E R Squibb & Sons, Inc, 66-70; asst prof, Sch Med, Temple Univ, 68-74, assoc prof biomet & actg chmn dept, 74-80; WITH ORTHO PHARMACEUTICAL CORP, 80- *Concurrent Pos:* Res asst, Bur Econ & Statist, Gujarat State, 61-62; part-time biostatist consult, 63-65. *Mem:* Biomet Soc; Am Statist Asn. *Res:* Use of multivariate techniques in repeated measures and in related topics; non-parametrics; bioassay; repeated measures; pair comparisons. *Mailing Add:* Ortho Pharmaceutical Corp Route 202--Res Bldg Rariton NJ 08869

SHARMA, SANSAR C, b Pirthipur, India, Mar 10, 38; m 70. NEUROBIOLOGY. *Educ:* Panjab Univ, India, BSc, 61, MSc, 62; Univ Edinburgh, PhD(physiol), 67. *Prof Exp:* Lectr, DAV Col, Ambala, India, 62-63; fel, Univ Edinburgh, 64-68; NIH grant neurobiol, Washington Univ, 68-72; ASSOC PROF OPHTHAL, NEW YORK MED COL, 72- *Concurrent Pos:* NSF grant, 74-75; Nat Eye Inst grant, 75- *Mem:* AAAS; Am Physiol Soc; Soc Neurosci; NY Acad Sci; Brit Soc Develop Biol. *Res:* Formation of specific nerve connections in the visual system; developmental neurophysiology of the spinal cord. *Mailing Add:* Dept of Ophthal New York Med Col New York NY 10029

SHARMA, SANTOSH DEVRAJ, b Kenya, Feb 24, 34. OBSTETRICS & GYNECOLOGY. *Educ:* B J Med Sch, Poona, India, MB & BS, 60; Am Bd Obstet & Gynec, dipl, 77. *Prof Exp:* From lectr to sr lectr obstet & gynec, Med Sch Makerere Univ, Kampala, Uganda, 67-72; asst prof obstet & gynec, Sch Med, Howard Univ, Washington DC, 72-74; assoc prof, 74-78, PROF OBSTET & GYNEC, JOHN A BURN SCH MED, HONOLULU, 78- *Mem:* Fel Royal Col Obstetricians & Gynecologists; fel Am Col Obstetricians & Gynecologists; Am Soc Colposcopy & Cervical Path. *Res:* Clinical uses of prostagrandins in obstetrics and gynecology. *Mailing Add:* 1319 Punahou St #801 Honolulu HI 96826

SHARMA, UDHISHTRA DEVA, b Amritsar, India, Aug 16, 28; m 59; c 1. ANIMAL SCIENCE, BIOLOGY. *Educ:* Punjab Univ, BVSc, 48; Univ Ill, Urbana, MS, 54, PhD(reproductive physiol), 57. *Prof Exp:* Res asst animal genetics, Indian Vet Res Inst, 49-53; res assoc germ cell physiol, Am Found Biol Res, Wis, 57-58; prof animal genetics, Postgrad Col Animal Sci, Indian Vet Res Inst, 58-64; prof animal husb & head dept, Punjab Agr Univ, 64-65; vis prof anat, Med Ctr, Univ Ark, Little Rock, 65-66; PROF BIOL, ALA STATE UNIV, 66- *Mem:* Soc Study Reproduction. *Res:* Physiology of reproduction, artificial insemination and preservation of bovine semen at room temperatures; animal sciences and veterinary medicine; biological sciences. *Mailing Add:* 4438 Eley Ct Montgomery AL 36106

SHARMA, VINAY KUMAR, b Montgomery, WPakistan; US citizen; m 64; c 2. INDUSTRIAL PHARMACY, PHARMACY. *Educ:* Panjab Univ, BPharm, 58, MPharm, 63; Univ Iowa, MS, 67; Purdue Univ, PhD(indust pharm), 75. *Prof Exp:* Res pharmacist, Sherwood Drug Co, 67-68; scientist, Warner-Lambert Co, 68-72; fel, NIH, 75-76; SR RES PHARMACIST, A H ROBINS CO, 76- *Mem:* Am Pharmaceut Asn. *Res:* Design of controlled-release dosage forms; development and use of instrumentation in process control as applied to compressed tablet and coated tablet technology. *Mailing Add:* A H Robins Co Inc 1211 Sherwood Ave Richmond VA 23220

SHARNOFF, MARK, b Cleveland, Ohio, July 26, 35; m 59; c 3. MOLECULAR PHYSICS, SOLID STATE PHYSICS. *Educ:* Univ Rochester, BS, 57; Harvard Univ, PhD(physics), 63. *Prof Exp:* Nat Acad Sci-Nat Res Coun resident res assoc, Nat Bur Stand, 63-65; from asst prof to assoc prof, 65-74, PROF PHYSICS, UNIV DEL, 74- *Concurrent Pos:* Regional ed, J Luminescence, 69-; NIH spec fel & vis assoc prof biophys, Pa State Univ, 72-73. *Mem:* AAAS; Am Phys Soc; Biophys Soc; Am Chem Soc. *Res:* Dynamic nuclear polarization; electron spin resonance of free radicals and transition metal ions; optical properties of coordination complexes; microwave-optical studies of isomerization and energy transport in organic systems; holographic interferometry of biological tissues. *Mailing Add:* Dept of Physics Univ of Del Newark DE 19711

SHARP, A C, JR, b Lorenzo, Tex, July 16, 32; m 55; c 3. MAGNETISM. *Educ:* Tex A&I Univ, BS, 57, MS, 58; Tex A&M Univ, PhD(physics), 65. *Prof Exp:* Instr physics, Univ Tex, Arlington, 58-61; asst prof, Tex Woman's Univ, 64-65; PROF PHYSICS, McMURRY COL, 65- *Mem:* Am Phys Soc; Am Asn Physics Teachers; Optical Soc Am. *Res:* Polymer solution theory using polyisobutylene-n-alkane systems; magnetic properties of thin permalloy films. *Mailing Add:* Dept of Physics McMurry Col Abilene TX 79605

SHARP, A(RNOLD) G(IDEON), b Worcester, Mass, May 16, 23. MECHANICAL ENGINEERING. *Educ:* Tufts Univ, BS, 45; Worcester Polytech Inst, MS, 53. *Prof Exp:* Instr mech eng, Worcester Polytech Inst, 46-53; asst prof civil eng, Univ Mass, 53-58; res engr, 58-63, res assoc, 63-78, RES SPECIALIST, WOODS HOLE OCEANOG INST, 78- *Concurrent Pos:* Lectr, Lincoln Col, Northeastern Univ, 60-61. *Mem:* Soc Exp Stress Anal; Soc Naval Architects & Marine Engrs. *Res:* Applied mechanics; stress analysis; structural design; properties of materials; oceanographic instrumentation; deep-submergence vehicle design. *Mailing Add:* PO Box 434 Woods Hole MA 02543

SHARP, ALLAN ROY, b Hamilton, Ont, Nov 3, 46; m 71; c 3. BIOPHYSICS, APPLIED PHYSICS. *Educ:* McMaster Univ, BSc, 67; Univ Waterloo, MSc, 69, PhD(physics), 73. *Prof Exp:* Fel, Univ Toronto, 72-74; lectr, Univ Natal, 74-75; asst prof, 75-79, ASSOC PROF PHYSICS, UNIV NB, 79- *Concurrent Pos:* Nat Sci Eng Res Coun Can res grant, 76- *Mem:* Can Asn Physicists. *Res:* Nuclear magnetic resonance studies of interactions of molecules with biopolymers, primarily water with cellulose; effects of these molecules on wood properties; materials science of wood. *Mailing Add:* Dept of Physics Univ of NB Fredericton NB E3B 5A3 Can

SHARP, BYRON JAMES, geology, see previous edition

SHARP, DAVID HOWLAND, b Buffalo, NY, Oct 14, 38; m 65; c 2. THEORETICAL PHYSICS. *Educ:* Princeton Univ, AB, 60; Calif Inst Technol, PhD(physics), 64. *Prof Exp:* NSF fel physics, Princeton Univ, 63-64, res assoc, 64-65; res fel, Munich Tech Univ, 65-66; res fel, Calif Inst Technol, 66; instr, Palmer Phys Lab, Princeton Univ, 66-67; asst prof physics, Univ Pa, 67-74; MEM STAFF, LOS ALAMOS SCI LAB, 74- *Concurrent Pos:* Consult, Jason Div, Inst Defense Anal, 60-66 & Lawrence Livermore Lab, Univ Calif, Livermore, 64-66; guest partic, Battelle Rencontres Math & Physics, 69; mem, Bd Hons Examrs, Swarthmore Col, 72; mem, J Robert Oppenheimer Mem Comt, 76-, chmn, 78. *Mem:* AAAS; Asn Math Physicists; Int Soc Gen Relativity & Gravitation; fel Am Phys Soc. *Res:* Elementary particle physics; theory of gravitation. *Mailing Add:* Los Alamos Sci Lab PO Box 1663 Los Alamos NM 87545

SHARP, DEXTER BRIAN, b Chicago, Ill, June 14, 19; m 45; c 3. CHEMISTRY. *Educ:* Carleton Col, BA, 41; Univ Nebr, MA, 43, PhD(chem), 45. *Prof Exp:* Asst chem, Univ Nebr, 41-45; res chemist chem dept, Exp Sta, E I du Pont de Nemours & Co, Inc, 45-46; Am Chem Soc fel & instr, Univ Minn, 46-47; from asst prof to assoc prof chem, Kans State Col, 47-51; res chemist, 51-54, group leader, 54-68, mgr res & develop, 68-75, environ sci dir, 75-78, DIR, ENVIRON SCI, MONSANTO AGR PROD CO, 78- *Mem:* Am Chem Soc; Weed Sci Soc Am. *Res:* Mechanisms of organic reactions; oxidation; pesticides; gas-liquid chromatography. *Mailing Add:* 13042 Weathersfield Dr 800 N Lindbergh Blvd Creve Coeur MO 63141

SHARP, EDWARD A, b Milwaukee, Wis, Oct 3, 20. MATHEMATICS, COMPUTER SCIENCE. *Educ:* St Louis Univ, AB, 43, AM, 56. *Prof Exp:* ASSOC PROF MATH, CREIGHTON UNIV, 57-, DIR COMPUT CTR, 66- *Mem:* Am Math Soc; London Math Soc; Soc Indust & Appl Math. *Mailing Add:* Dept of Math Creighton Univ Omaha NE 68178

SHARP, EUGENE LESTER, b Spokane, Wash, Nov 19, 26; m 54; c 4. PLANT PATHOLOGY. *Educ:* Univ Idaho, BS, 49; Iowa State Col, MS, 51, PhD(plant path), 53. *Prof Exp:* Asst plant path, Iowa State Col, 49-53; res plant path, Biol Lab, Chem Corps, US Dept Army, 55-57; asst plant pathologist, 57-62, assoc plant pathologist, 62-67, PROF PLANT PATH, MONT STATE UNIV, 67-, HEAD DEPT, 73- *Concurrent Pos:* Sigma Xi Fac Res Award, Mont State Univ, 70. *Honors & Awards:* Sr Scientist Award, Alexander von Humboldt Found, 75. *Mem:* Fel AAAS; Am Phytopath Soc. *Res:* Cereal pathology; genetics of pathogenicity and disease resistance with emphasis on cereal rusts; host-pathogen interactions from a genetic and environmental basis. *Mailing Add:* Dept of Plant Path Mont State Univ Bozeman MT 59715

SHARP, GEORGE ROBERT, solid mechanics, see previous edition

SHARP, GERALD DUANE, b Twin Falls, Idaho, July 28, 33; m 54; c 2. RUMINANT NUTRITION, LIVESTOCK EVALUATION. *Educ:* Univ Idaho, BS, 55, MS, 62; Wash State Univ, PhD(animal nutrit), 69. *Prof Exp:* Animal scientist, Caldwell Br Exp Sta, Univ Idaho, 62-64, Swine Herdsman, 64-66; asst dairy scientist, Wash State Univ, 69-70; asst prof, Fort Hays Kans State Col, 70-72, prof & farm supt, 72-76; assoc prof, 76-79, PROF & CHAIR, ANIMAL SCI DEPT, CALIF STATE POLYTECH UNIV, POLOMA, 79- *Mem:* Sigma Xi; Am Soc Animal Sci; Coun Agr Sci & Technol. *Mailing Add:* Animal Sci Dept Calif State Polytech Univ 3801 W Temple Ave Pomona CA 91768

SHARP, GERALD WHITE, physics, see previous edition

SHARP, HENRY, JR, b Nashville, Tenn, Oct 14, 23; m 57; c 2. MATHEMATICS. *Educ:* Vanderbilt Univ, BE, 47; Duke Univ, AM, 50, PhD(math), 52. *Prof Exp:* Res assoc, Johns Hopkins Univ, 52-53; asst prof math, Ga Inst Technol, 53-56; from asst prof to assoc prof, 58-67, PROF MATH, EMORY UNIV, 67- *Concurrent Pos:* NSF fac fel, 64-65, res grant, 68-69. *Mem:* Am Math Soc; Math Asn Am. *Res:* Point-set topology, dimension theory and graph theory. *Mailing Add:* Dept of Math Emory Univ Atlanta GA 30322

SHARP, HOMER FRANKLIN, JR, b Lithonia, Ga, Sept 5, 36; m 61; c 2. ZOOLOGY, ECOLOGY. *Educ:* Emory Univ, BA, 59; Univ Ga, MS, 62, PhD(zool), 70. *Prof Exp:* Asst prof biol, LaGrange Col, 62-63; from instr to asst prof, 63-71, ASSOC PROF BIOL, OXFORD COL, EMORY UNIV, 71- *Mem:* Am Soc Mammalogists. *Res:* Bioenergetics of populations; diversity of benthic communities. *Mailing Add:* Dept of Biol Oxford Col Emory Univ Oxford GA 30267

SHARP, JAMES H, b Moosejaw, Sask, Apr 20, 34; m; c 4. PHYSICAL CHEMISTRY, CHEMICAL PHYSICS. *Educ:* Univ BC, BA, 57, MSc, 60; Univ Calif, Riverside, PhD(phys chem), 64. *Prof Exp:* Fel org solid state, Nat Res Coun Can, 63-64; scientist, Physics Res Lab, 64-68, mgr, Chem Physics Res Br, Res & Eng Sci Div, 68-71, mgr, Org Solid State Physics, Rochester Corp Res Ctr, 71-72, technol ctr mgr, Info Technol Group, 72-74, RES MGR, XEROX RES CENTRE CAN, XEROX CORP, 74- *Mem:* Am Phys Soc; Am Chem Soc. *Res:* Photochemistry; photolyses and photophysics of organic materials; electron spin resonance; photoconductivity and transport phenomenon; optical sensitization and energy transfer; spectroscopy of the organic solid state. *Mailing Add:* Xerox Res Centre Can 2480 Dunwin Dr Mississauga ON L5L 1J9 Can

SHARP, JAMES JACK, b Glasgow, Scotland, July 22, 39; m 63; c 3. CIVIL ENGINEERING. *Educ:* Glasgow Univ, BSc, 61, MSc, 63; Univ Strathclyde, ARCST, 61, PhD(hydraul), 69. *Prof Exp:* Exec engr, Govt Malawi, 63-66; lectr civil eng, Univ Strathclyde, 66-70; PROF ENG, MEM UNIV NFLD, 70- *Mem:* Am Soc Civil Engrs; Brit Inst Civil Engrs. *Res:* Hydraulics; densimetric phenomena; energy dissipation. *Mailing Add:* Fac of Eng Mem Univ of Nfld St John's NF A1B 3X5 Can

SHARP, JOHN ARTHUR, b Liverpool, Eng, Apr 24, 29; Can citizen; m 55; c 3. PHYSICAL CHEMISTRY. *Educ:* Univ Liverpool, BSc, 50, PhD(chem), 53. *Prof Exp:* Fel photochem, Nat Res Coun Can, 53-55; res chemist, 55-65, res leader, 65-69, res sect leader, 69-71, res group mgr, 71-79, RES SCIENTIST, CHEM RES LAB, CAN INDUSTS LTD, 79- *Mem:* Chem Inst Can; Can Inst Mining & Metall. *Res:* Reaction kinetics; electrochemistry; polymer and inorganic chemistry; mineral processing. *Mailing Add:* CIL Inc 2101 Hadwen Rd Mississauga ON L5K 2L3 Can

SHARP, JOHN BUCKNER, b Maynardville, Tenn, Nov 5, 20; m 49; c 2. FORESTRY. *Educ:* Univ Tenn, BS, 43, MS, 45; Duke Univ, MF, 47; Harvard Univ, MPA, 50, DPA, 52. *Prof Exp:* Carnegie Corp fel, Harvard Univ, 50-52; dist forester, 47-49, assoc exten forester, 52-57, STATE EXTEN FORESTER, AGR EXTEN SERV, UNIV TENN, KNOXVILLE, 57- *Mem:* Soc Am Foresters. *Res:* Farm forestry; forestry administration. *Mailing Add:* 5052 Mountain Crest Dr Knoxville TN 37918

SHARP, JOHN MALCOLM, JR, b St Paul, Minn, Mar 11, 44; m 67; c 2. HYDROGEOLOGY. *Educ:* Univ Minn, BGeolE, 67; Univ Ill, MS & PhD(hydrogeol), 74. *Prof Exp:* Civil engr, US Air Force, 67-71; ASST PROF GEOL, UNIV MO-COLUMBIA, 74- *Mem:* Am Inst Mining Engrs; Geol Soc Am. *Res:* Energy transport in porous media; flood-plain hydrogeology; economics of water resource development. *Mailing Add:* 101 Geol Bldg Univ of Mo Columbia MO 65211

SHARP, JOHN ROLAND, b Joplin, Mo, Dec 5, 49; m 79; c 1. AQUATIC TOXICOLOGY, PHYSIOLOGICAL ECOLOGY. *Educ:* Southwest Mo State Col, BS, 71; Tex A&M Univ, PhD(biol), 79. *Prof Exp:* Res assoc, Tex A&M Univ, 78-79; ASST PROF BIOL, ZOOL & BIOL FISHES, INTRO AQUATIC TOXICOL, SOUTHEAST MO STATE UNIV, 80- *Concurrent Pos:* Instr marine ichthyol, Gulf Coast Res Lab, 76 & 81-82. *Res:* Individual and interactive effects of environmental stressors on the physiology and developmental biology of marine and freshwater fishes, particularly the embryo-larval life history stages; ecology of fishes. *Mailing Add:* Dept Biol Southeast Mo State Univ Cape Girardeau MO 63701

SHARP, JOHN TURNER, b Jamestown, NY, Jan 18, 27; m 49; c 5. INTERNAL MEDICINE. *Educ:* Univ Buffalo, MD, 49. *Prof Exp:* Intern med, Bellevue Hosp, New York, 49-50; resident internal med, Vet Admin Hosp, Buffalo, 52-54; Am Heart Asn res fel cardiopulmonary physiol & clin cardiol, Buffalo Gen Hosp & Sch Med, State Univ NY Buffalo, 54-57; Am Heart Asn estab investr, 57-59; PROF DIR PULMONARY DIS SERV, VET ADMIN HOSP, HINES, 59-; PROF MED, UNIV ILL COL MED, 67- *Concurrent Pos:* Nat Heart Inst res grants, 59-62 & 64-79; assoc prof, Univ Ill Col Med, 64-67. *Mem:* Am Soc Clin Invest; Am Col Physicians; fel Am Col Chest Physicians; fel Am Col Cardiol; Am Physiol Soc. *Res:* Cardiopulmonary physiology; respiratory physiology, particularly the mechanics of respiration and respiratory muscle function in normal and diseased man; human hemodynamics in health and disease; epidemiology of chronic respiratory diseases. *Mailing Add:* PO Box 7 Hines IL 60141

SHARP, JONATHAN HAWLEY, b Bridgeton, NJ, Apr 29, 43; m 73; c 2. CHEMICAL OCEANOGRAPHY, BIOLOGICAL OCEANOGRAPHY. *Educ:* Lehigh Univ, BA, 65, MS, 67; Dalhousie Univ, PhD(oceanog), 72. *Prof Exp:* Fel oceanog, Scripps Inst Oceanog, Univ Calif, San Diego, 72-73; ASST PROF CHEM OCEANOG, COL MARINE STUDIES, UNIV DEL, 73- *Concurrent Pos:* Consult, Org Am States, 72-74; mem Md Environ Res Guidance Comt, 77-80. *Mem:* AAAS; Am Soc Limnology & Oceanog; Phycol Soc Am; Am Chem Soc. *Res:* Organic chemistry of seawater and physiology of marine phytoplankton algae. *Mailing Add:* Col of Marine Studies Univ of Del Lewes DE 19958

SHARP, JOSEPH CECIL, b Salt Lake City, Utah, May 30, 34; m 56; c 2. NEUROBIOLOGY, EXPERIMENTAL PSYCHOLOGY. *Educ:* Univ Utah, BS, 57, MS, 58, PhD(psychol), 61. *Prof Exp:* Chief behav radiation, Walter Reed Army Inst Res, 60-67, chief exp psychol, 67-68; dep comn environ health, Dept Health, State NY, 69-70; dep dir neuropsychiat, Walter Reed Army Inst Res, 71-74; DEP DIR LIFE SCI, NASA AMES RES CTR, 74- *Mem:* Am Psychol Asn; Radiation Res Soc; Int Soc Chronobiol; Sigma Xi. *Res:* Central nervous system and radiation effects; space biology and medicine; experimental psychology, drug abuse and neuroendocrinology. *Mailing Add:* Off of Life Sci Dir Code 200-7 NASA Ames Res Ctr Moffett Field CA 94035

SHARP, KENNETH GEORGE, b Dec 24, 43; US citizen; m 67; c 1. INORGANIC CHEMISTRY. *Educ:* Univ Calif, Riverside, BA, 65; Rice Univ, PhD(chem), 69. *Prof Exp:* Nat Res Coun-Nat Bur Stand fel, Nat Bur Stand, Washington, DC, 69-71; asst prof inorg chem, Univ Southern Calif, 71-80; WITH DOW CORNING CORP, 80- *Mem:* Am Chem Soc. *Res:* Inorganic synthesis via energetic intermediates; high-temperature chemistry; silicon and fluorine chemistry. *Mailing Add:* Corporate Res Dow Corning Corp Midland MI 48640

SHARP, LEE AJAX, b Salt Lake City, Utah, Mar 27, 22; m 47; c 1. RANGE MANAGEMENT. *Educ:* Utah State Agr Col, BS, 48, MS, 49, PhD, 66. *Prof Exp:* From instr to assoc prof forestry & range mgt, 49-71, PROF RANGE MGT, UNIV IDAHO, 71-, CHAIRPERSON RES MGT, 77- *Mem:* Soc Range Mgt. *Res:* Salt desert shrub revegetation and evaluation; grazing management programs for seeded ranges. *Mailing Add:* Dept of Range Mgt Univ of Idaho Moscow ID 83843

SHARP, LOUIS JAMES, IV, b Washington, DC, Oct 13, 44; m 68; c 3. POLYMER CHEMISTRY. *Educ:* Univ Notre Dame, BS, 66; Calif Inst Technol, PhD(chem), 70. *Prof Exp:* Res fel, Radiation Lab, Univ Notre Dame, 69-72; asst prof chem, Marian Col, 72-74; dir resin res & develop, Lily Indust Coatings Inc, 74-80; group leader synthesis, Betz Labs, 80-81; MGR POLYMER CHEM, MIDLAND DEXTER CORP, 81- *Mem:* Am Chem Soc; Sigma Xi. *Res:* Synthesis and rheology of resins for coatings, including polyesters, acrylics, urea-formaldehyde resins, silicones, melamines, alkyds, water-based resins, high solids resins and ultraviolet cured resins. *Mailing Add:* Midland Dexter Corp E Water St Waukegan IL 60085

SHARP, PHILIP ALLEN, b Falmouth, Ky, June 6, 44; m; c 2. MOLECULAR BIOLOGY, VIROLOGY. *Educ:* Union Col, BA, 66; Univ Ill, Urbana, PhD(chem), 69. *Prof Exp:* Fel biophys chem & molecular biol, Calif Inst Technol, 69-71; res staff virol & molecular biol, Cold Spring Harbor Lab, 71-74; ASSOC PROF, CTR CANCER RES & DEPT BIOL, MASS INST TECHNOL, 74- *Concurrent Pos:* Consult, Biogen Ltd, 75- *Honors & Awards:* Fac Res Award, Am Cancer Soc, 74. *Mem:* Am Chem Soc; Am Soc Microbiol. *Res:* The molecular biology of Adenovirus; the control of viral transcription and the identification of functions of genes involved in transformation of normal mammalian cells to malignant cells. *Mailing Add:* Ctr Cancer Res Rm E17-529B Mass Inst of Technol Cambridge MA 02139

SHARP, RICHARD DANA, b Brooklyn, NY, June 17, 30; m 59; c 2. MAGNETOSPHERIC PHYSICS, IONOSPHERIC PHYSICS. *Educ:* Mass Inst Technol, BS, 52, PhD(physics), 56. *Prof Exp:* SR STAFF SCIENTIST, LOCKHEED PALO ALTO RES LAB, 56- *Mem:* Am Phys Soc; Am Geophys Union. *Res:* Hot plasma measurements in the magnetosphere; satellite experiments on auroral phenomena. *Mailing Add:* Lockheed Res Lab Dept 52-12 3251 Hanover St Bldg 205 Palo Alto CA 94304

SHARP, RICHARD LEE, b Kansas City, Mo, Sept 14, 35; m 64; c 1. CHEMICAL TOXICOLOGY. *Educ:* William Jewell Col, AB, 61; Purdue Univ, PhD(org chem), 66. *Prof Exp:* Prod chemist, 66-67, develop chemist, 67-69, supvr synthetic org chem, Synthetic Chem Div, 69-73, TECH ASSOC HEALTH & SAFETY LAB, EASTMAN KODAK CO, 73- *Mem:* Am Chem Soc; Am Indust Hyg Asn. *Res:* Directive effects in the hydroboration of functionally substituted olefins and related compounds; synthesis of fine organic chemicals; toxicity testing of organic chemicals. *Mailing Add:* Kodak Park Works Bldg 320 Eastman Kodak Co Rochester NY 14650

SHARP, ROBERT PHILLIP, b Oxnard, Calif, June 24, 11; m 38; c 2. GEOMORPHOLOGY. *Educ:* Calif Inst Technol, BS, 34, MS, 35; Harvard Univ, AM, 36, PhD(geol), 38. *Prof Exp:* Instr geol, Univ Ill, 38-43; prof, Univ Minn, 45-47; chmn div geol sci, 52-68, PROF GEOMORPHOL, CALIF INST TECHNOL, 47- *Concurrent Pos:* Condon lectr, Univ Ore, 60. *Honors & Awards:* Kirk Bryan Award, Geol Soc Am, 64; NASA Except Sci Achievement Medal, 71; Penrose Medal, Geol Soc Am, 78. *Mem:* Nat Acad Sci; fel Geol Soc Am; Am Geophys Union; Glaciol Soc; fel Am Acad Arts & Sci. *Res:* Glaciology; glacial geology; arid region geomorphology; planetary surfaces. *Mailing Add:* Dept of Geol & Planetary Sci Calif Inst of Technol Pasadena CA 91125

SHARP, ROBERT RICHARD, b Newport News, Va, May 15, 41; m 68; c 1. PHYSICAL CHEMISTRY. *Educ:* Case Western Reserve Univ, AB & MS, 65, PhD(chem), 68. *Prof Exp:* NSF fel, Oxford Univ, 67-69; asst prof, 69-74, ASSOC PROF CHEM, UNIV MICH, ANN ARBOR, 74- *Mem:* Am Chem Soc; AAAS; Sigma Xi. *Res:* Nuclear magnetic resonance of chemical and biological systems. *Mailing Add:* Dept of Chem Univ of Mich Ann Arbor MI 48104

SHARP, ROBERT THOMAS, b Detroit, Mich, Aug 13, 22; nat Can; m 48; c 4. THEORETICAL PHYSICS. *Educ:* McGill Univ, BSc, 48, MSc, 50, PhD(theoret physics), 53. *Prof Exp:* Asst prof physics, Univ Alta, 51-53; assoc prof appl math, 53-66, PROF PHYSICS, MCGILL UNIV, 66- *Concurrent Pos:* Nuffield fel, Imp Col, Univ London, 57-58; vis prof, Univ Ill, Urbana, 66-67; assoc mem, Appl Math Res Ctr, Univ Montreal, 74-; vis scientist, Inst Hautes Etudes Sci, Bures-s-Yvette, France, 81-82. *Mem:* Am Phys Soc; Can Asn Physicists. *Res:* Elementary particles; nuclear forces; group representations. *Mailing Add:* Dept of Physics McGill Univ Montreal PQ H3A 2T6 Can

SHARP, TERRY EARL, b Chicago, Ill, Nov 5, 35; m 58; c 3. CHEMICAL PHYSICS. *Educ:* Carnegie Inst Technol, BS, 57; Univ Calif, Berkeley, PhD(chem), 62. *Prof Exp:* Nat Res Coun res assoc mass spectrometry, Nat Bur Standards, 62-64; assoc res scientist, Lockheed Palo Alto Res Labs, 64-67, res scientist, 67-69; prin res scientist assoc, Ford Motor Co Sci Res Labs, 69-72; STAFF SCIENTIST, LOCKHEED PALO ALTO RES LABS, 72- *Mem:* Am Phys Soc; Am Chem Soc; Am Soc Mass Spectrometry; fel Am Inst Chem. *Res:* Mass spectrometry and ionization in gases; theory of energy transfer in gases; atomic cross sections; negative ion formation; laser-materials interactions; aging of polymers; decomposition of explosives. *Mailing Add:* Lockheed Palo Alto Res Lab Palo Alto CA 94304

SHARP, THOMAS JOSEPH, b Hattiesburg, Miss, Oct 15, 44; m 70; c 2. ALGEBRA. *Educ:* Univ Southern Miss, BS, 65; Auburn Univ, MS, 66, PhD(math), 71. *Prof Exp:* Teaching asst math, Auburn Univ, 66-69; ASST PROF MATH, W GA COL, 69- *Mem:* Am Math Soc; Math Asn Am. *Res:* Characterization of projection-invariant subgroups of abelian groups and their relationship to fully-invariant subgroups; study of big subgroups and little homomorphisms. *Mailing Add:* Dept of Math W Ga Col Carrollton GA 30117

SHARP, WILLIAM BROOM ALEXANDER, b Glengarnock, Scotland, May 12, 42; m 67; c 3. CORROSION, MATERIALS SCIENCE. *Educ:* Univ Cambridge, BA, 64, MA, 67; Univ London, MSc, 68; Univ Ottawa, PhD(chem), 76. *Prof Exp:* Res officer high temperature oxidation res, Cent Elec Res Lab, Eng, 64-69; assoc scientist corrosion res, Pulp & Paper Res Inst, Can, 75-78; RES ENGR CORROSION & MAT, WESTVACO RES LAB, 78- *Mem:* Brit Inst Corrosion Sci & Technol; Brit Inst Metall; Electrochem Soc; Nat Asn Corrosion; Tech Asn Pulp & Paper Indust. *Res:* Mechanisms and rates of propagation of localized corrosion of stainless steels; mechanisms of corrosion in pulp and paper mill equipment. *Mailing Add:* Westvaco Corp 11101 Johns Hopkins Rd Laurel MD 20810

SHARP, WILLIAM EDWARD, III, b Del Norte, Colo. SPACE PHYSICS, ATOMIC PHYSICS. *Educ:* William Jewell Col, BA, 62; Univ NH, MS, 65; Univ Colo, PhD(astro-geophys), 70. *Prof Exp:* Instr physics, Stetson Univ, 64-66; RES SCIENTIST, UNIV MICH, 70- *Concurrent Pos:* Lectr, Univ Mich, 72- *Mem:* Am Geophys Union. *Res:* Chemical and physical processes occurring in the aurora. *Mailing Add:* Space Physics Res Lab 2455 Hayward Ann Arbor MI 48107

SHARP, WILLIAM R, b Akron, Ohio, Sept 13, 36. CELL BIOLOGY, MICROBIOLOGY. *Educ:* Univ Akron, BS, 63, MS, 64; Rutgers Univ, PhD(bot), 67. *Prof Exp:* NSF fel & NIH grant, Case Western Reserve Univ, 67-69; asst prof, 69-78, ASSOC PROF MICROBIOL, OHIO STATE UNIV, 78- *Concurrent Pos:* Fulbright Hays fel, Ctr Nuclear Energy in Agr, Univ Sao Paulo, 71, 73, & 74; vis prof, Orgn Am States, 72. *Mem:* AAAS; Bot Soc Am; Am Soc Plant Physiologists. *Res:* Cellular aspects of plant growth and development; propagation and genetic engineering. *Mailing Add:* Dept of Microbiol Ohio State Univ Columbus OH 43210

SHARPE, CHARLES BRUCE, b Windsor, Ont, Apr 8, 26; nat US; m 54; c 5. ELECTRICAL ENGINEERING. *Educ:* Univ Mich, BS, 47, PhD(elec eng), 53; Mass Inst Technol, SM, 49. *Prof Exp:* Asst, High Voltage Lab, Mass Inst Technol, 47-49; res assoc, Willow Run Res Ctr, 49-50, res assoc electronics defense group, 51-53 & 55-60, from asst prof to assoc prof, 55-60, PROF ELEC ENG, UNIV MICH, ANN ARBOR, 61- *Mem:* Sr mem Inst Elec & Electronics Engrs. *Res:* Network synthesis; microwave circuit theory; theory and application of ferrites; microwave properties of ferroelectrics; synthesis of nonuniform transmission lines; electromagnetic sounding problems in geophysics. *Mailing Add:* Dept of Elec Eng Univ of Mich Ann Arbor MI 48109

SHARPE, DAVID MCCURRY, b Orange, NJ, Jan 2, 38; m 61; c 2. PHYSICAL GEOGRAPHY. *Educ:* Syracuse Univ, BS, 60, MS, 63; Southern Ill Univ, Carbondale, PhD(geog), 68. *Prof Exp:* Jr forester, Forest Serv, USDA, Mt Hood Nat Forest, 60-61; FAC GEOG, SOUTHERN ILL UNIV, CARBONDALE, 66- *Concurrent Pos:* NSF grant, Div Environ Biol, Oak Ridge Nat Lab, 72-74. *Mem:* Asn Am Geogr; AAAS. *Res:* Ecology and biogeography of regional forest ecosystems including impact of forest resource use and land use change; interaction between relict forest stands separated by nonforest land use. *Mailing Add:* Dept of Geog Southern Ill Univ Carbondale IL 62901

SHARPE, GRANT WILLIAM, b Kentfield, Calif, May 15, 25; m 48; c 9. FORESTRY. *Educ:* Univ Wash, BS & MF, 51, PhD, 56. *Prof Exp:* From asst prof to assoc prof forestry, Univ Mich, Ann Arbor, 56-67; PROF OUTDOOR RECREATION, COL FOREST RESOURCES, UNIV WASH, 67- *Concurrent Pos:* Soc Am Foresters vis scientist lectr, NSF. *Mem:* Asn Interpretive Naturalists. *Res:* Recreational use of wild lands. *Mailing Add:* Col of Forest Resources Univ of Wash Seattle WA 98195

SHARPE, LAWRENCE, b London, Eng, Dec 25, 30. PSYCHIATRY. *Educ:* Univ London, MB & BS, 54, dipl psychol med, 61. *Prof Exp:* House surgeon & physician, Highlands Hosp, London, Eng, 54-55; registr, Cell Barnes Hosp, St Alban's, 57; sr house officer & registr, Maudsley Hosp, London, 58-61; fel pediat & psychiat, Johns Hopkins Hosp, 62-63, instr pediat & psychiat, Johns Hopkins Univ, 63-65; asst prof psychiat, State Univ NY Downstate Med Ctr, 66-67; asst prof psychiat, Col Physicians & Surgeons, Columbia Univ, 67-76; MEM STAFF, DEPT NEUROPHARMACOL NIDA ADDICTION RES CTR, 77- *Concurrent Pos:* Consult, Md Children's Ctr, Boys Village of Md, Barrett Sch for Girls & McKim's Boys Haven, 63-65; psychiatrist, Res Found Ment Hyg, Inc, 67-; res psychiatrist biomet res, NY State Dept Ment Hyg, Inc, 67- *Mem:* Royal Col Psychiat; Royal Soc Med. *Mailing Add:* Dept of Neuropharmacol NIDA Addiction Res Ctr Lexington KY 40583

SHARPE, LOUIS HAUGHTON, b Port Maria, Jamaica, WI, Jan 31, 27; m 68. PHYSICAL CHEMISTRY. *Educ:* Va Polytech Inst, BS, 50; Mich State Univ, PhD(phys chem), 57. *Prof Exp:* Engr, State Hwy Dept, Mich, 54-55; mem tech staff, 55-59, supvr adhesives & surface chem, 59-65, supvr surface chem appl res, 65-68, SUPVR ADHESIVES ENG & DEVELOP, BELL LABS, 68- *Concurrent Pos:* Ed, J Adhesion. *Honors & Awards:* Adhesives Award, Am Soc Test & Mat, 68. *Mem:* Am Chem Soc; fel Am Inst Chem; Am Soc Test & Mat; fel NY Acad Sci. *Res:* Surface chemistry; adhesion; adhesives; mechanical properties of polymers. *Mailing Add:* Bell Labs Murray Hill NJ 07974

SHARPE, MICHAEL JOHN, b Sydney, Australia, Mar 15, 41; m 66. MATHEMATICS. *Educ:* Univ Tasmania, BSc, 63; Yale Univ, MA, 65, PhD(math), 67. *Prof Exp:* Asst prof, 67-73, assoc prof, 73-77, PROF MATH, UNIV CALIF, SAN DIEGO, 77- *Concurrent Pos:* Vis prof, Univ Paris, 73-74. *Mem:* Inst Math Statist; Am Math Soc. *Res:* Probability theory; Markov processes; continuous parameter martingales; potential theory. *Mailing Add:* Dept of Math Univ of Calif PO Box 109 La Jolla CA 92093

SHARPE, ROGER STANLEY, b Omaha, Nebr, Mar 31, 41; m 62; c 3. ZOOLOGY. *Educ:* Munic Univ Omaha, BA, 63; Univ Nebr, MS, 65, PhD(zool), 68. *Prof Exp:* Asst prof, 68-72, ASSOC PROF BIOL, UNIV NEBR, OMAHA, 72- *Mem:* Am Ornith Union; Cooper Ornith Soc; Wilson Ornith Soc; Animal Behavior Soc. *Res:* Avian reproductive behavior; zoogeography of Great Plains avifauna; avian ecology and behavior. *Mailing Add:* Dept of Biol Univ of Nebr Omaha NE 68101

SHARPE, THOMAS R, b Milwaukee, Wis, Nov 25, 44; m 68. HEALTH CARE ADMINISTRATION, STATISTICS. *Educ:* Univ Ill, BS, 70; Univ Miss, MS, 73, PhD(health care admin), 75. *Prof Exp:* Staff pharmacist, Northwestern Univ Hosp, 70-71; grad res asst health care, Admin Dept, 71-74, RES ASST PROF, RES INST PHARMACEUT SCI & ASST DIR ADMIN SCI RES, UNIV MISS, 74- *Concurrent Pos:* Charles R Walgreen Mem fel, Am Found Pharmaceut Educ, 72-74; consult, Nat Ctr Health Serv Res, 75-, Miss State Bd Health, 76- & Drug Info Designs Inc, 78- *Mem:* Am Pharmaceut Asn; Am Pub Health Asn; Am Inst Decision Sci; Am Sociol Asn; Am Heart Asn. *Res:* Clinical role of pharmacist; patient compliance; sociology of occupations and professions; epidemiology of hypertension; computer applications to pharmacy; social indicators; rural health, optimum delivery of comprehensive health care. *Mailing Add:* Res Inst of Pharmaceut Sci Univ of Miss University MS 38677

SHARPE, WILLIAM D, b Canton, Ohio, July 18, 27. PATHOLOGY, HISTORY OF MEDICINE. *Educ:* Univ Toronto, BA, 50; Univ Buffalo, MA, 53; Johns Hopkins Univ, MD, 58. *Prof Exp:* Intern med, Jersey City Med Ctr, 58-59; resident path, Pa Hosp, 59-63; asst prof, 63-68, CLIN ASSOC PROF PATH, COL MED & DENT NJ, 68- *Concurrent Pos:* Fel path, Pa Hosp, Philadelphia, 59-63; asst instr, Sch Med, Univ Pa, 60-63; dir labs, Cabrini Med Ctr, New York. *Mem:* Int Acad Path; Mediaeval Acad Am; Am Philol Asn; Am Asn Pathologists & Bacteriologists; Col Am Pathologists. *Res:* Chronic radiation intoxication in human beings; ancient, medieval and colonial American medical history. *Mailing Add:* Cabrini Med Ctr 227 E 19th St New York NY 10003

SHARPE, WILLIAM NORMAN, JR, b Pittsboro, NC, Apr 15, 38; m 59; c 2. MECHANICAL ENGINEERING. *Educ:* NC State Univ, BS, 60, MS, 61; Johns Hopkins Univ, PhD(mech), 66. *Prof Exp:* Instr mech, Johns Hopkins Univ, 65-66; asst prof mech, Mich State Univ, 66-70, assoc prof, 70-75, prof, 75-78; PROF MECH ENG & CHMN DEPT, LA STATE UNIV, 78- *Mem:* Am Soc Mech Engrs; Am Soc Eng Educ; Soc Exp Stress Anal; Am Soc Testing & Mat. *Res:* Experimental mechanics, especially strain measurement by laser interferometry; vibration measurement. *Mailing Add:* 289 South Donmoor Baton Rouge LA 70806

SHARPLES, FRANCES ELLEN, b Brooklyn, NY, Feb 5, 50. ECOLOGY, MAMMALOGY. *Educ:* Barnard Col, AB, 72; Univ Calif, Davis, MA, 74, PhD(zool), 78. *Prof Exp:* Teaching asst zool & ecol, Univ Calif, Davis, 72-78; RES ASSOC ENVIRON IMPACT ASSESSMENT, OAK RIDGE NAT LAB, 78- *Mem:* AAAS; Ecol Soc Am; Am Soc Mammal. *Res:* Vertebrate terrestrial ecology; ecology and evolution of mammals; environmental impact assessment; endangered species status and preservation. *Mailing Add:* Environ Sci Div Oak Ridge Nat Lab Oak Ridge TN 37830

SHARPLES, GEORGE CARROLL, b Toledo, Ohio, Dec 17, 18; m 44; c 2. HORTICULTURE. *Educ:* Univ Ariz, BS, 41, MS, 48. *Prof Exp:* Asst horticulturist, 48-58, res assoc hort, 58-62, from asst horticulturist to assoc horticulturist, 62-72, HORTICULTURIST, AGR EXP STA, UNIV ARIZ, 72- *Mem:* Am Soc Hort Sci; Am Asn Advan Sci. *Res:* Grape nutrition and culture; citrus nutrition; lettuce seed physiology and precision planting. *Mailing Add:* Agr Exp Sta Univ of Ariz PO Box 1308 Mesa AZ 85201

SHARPLESS, NANSIE SUE, b West Chester, Pa, Oct 11, 32. BIOCHEMISTRY. *Educ:* Oberlin Col, BA, 54; Wayne State Univ, MS, 56, PhD(chem), 70. *Prof Exp:* Med technologist pharmacol, Henry Ford Hosp, Detroit, 56-62, med technologist virol, 62-67; res assoc biochem, Mayo Clinic & Mayo Found, 70-74, Nat Inst Neurol Dis & Stroke spec trainee, 71-74, sr res fel neurol, 74; ASST PROF PSYCHIATRY, ALBERT EINSTEIN COL MED, 75- *Mem:* AAAS; Am Chem Soc; NY Acad Sci; Soc for Neurosci; Soc Exp Biol & Med; Am Asn Clin Chemists. *Res:* Biogenic amines in neurologic and mental disorders; immunoglobulins; serum and cerebrospinal fluid proteins; metabolism of L-Dopa, L-3-0-methyldopa & L-5HTP in patients; brain neurotransmitter amines. *Mailing Add:* Dept of Psychiatry Albert Einstein Col of Med Bronx NY 10461

SHARPLESS, SETH KINMAN, b Anchorage, Alaska, May 21, 25; m 47; c 2. PHARMACOLOGY, PHYSIOLOGICAL PSYCHOLOGY. *Educ:* Univ Chicago, MA, 51; McGill Univ, PhD(psychol), 54. *Prof Exp:* Res assoc psychol, McGill Univ, 54-55; asst prof, Yale Univ, 55-57; asst prof pharmacol & sr res fel, Albert Einstein Col Med, 57-64, assoc prof pharmacol, 64-69; PROF PSYCHOL, UNIV COLO, BOULDER, 69- *Concurrent Pos:* NIH career develop fel, 61-69; mem rev comt psychol serv fel, NIMH, 71-, mem exp psychol study sect, NIH, 71- *Mem:* Am Psychol Asn; Philos Sci Asn; Asn Symbolic Logic; Am Physiol Soc; Am Soc Pharmacol & Exp Therapeut. *Res:* Neuropharmacology; physiological basis of behavior; drugs on central nervous system. *Mailing Add:* Dept of Psychol Univ of Colo Boulder CO 80309

SHARPLESS, STEWART LANE, b Milwaukee, Wis, Mar 29, 26. ASTRONOMY. *Educ:* Univ Chicago, PhB, 48, PhD(astron), 52. *Prof Exp:* Carnegie fel, Mt Wilson & Palomar Observs, 52-53; astronomer, US Naval Observ, 53-64, dir, Astron & Astrophys Div, 63-64; PROF ASTRON & DIR C E KENNETH MEES OBSERV, UNIV ROCHESTER, 64- *Concurrent Pos:* Dir-at-large, AURA, Inc, 66-69. *Mem:* AAAS; Am Astron Soc; Int Astron Union. *Res:* Galactic structure; spectroscopy. *Mailing Add:* Dept of Physics & Astron Univ of Rochester Rochester NY 14627

SHARPLESS, THOMAS KITE, cytology, biomedical engineering, see previous edition

SHARPLEY, ROBERT CALDWELL, b Chicago, Ill, Jan 31, 46; m 66; c 2. MATHEMATICAL ANALYSIS. *Educ:* Univ Tex, BA, 68, MA, 69, PhD(math), 72. *Prof Exp:* Vis asst prof math, La State Univ, 72; asst prof, Oakland Univ, 72-76; asst prof, 76-78, ASSOC PROF MATH, UNIV SC, 78- *Concurrent Pos:* Proj dir & fac fel, Oakland Univ, 73-74 & NSF res grant, 77-; vis assoc prof math, McMaster Univ, 78-79. *Mem:* Am Math Soc; Sigma Xi. *Res:* Interpolation of operators; Fourier analysis; functional analysis; spaces of measurable functions, Sobolev and Besov spaces; singular integral operator; mathematical analysis. *Mailing Add:* Dept Math Comput Sci & Statist Univ of SC Columbia SC 29208

SHARRAH, PAUL CHESTER, b Jamesport, Mo, Oct 31, 14; m 36; c 2. PHYSICS. *Educ:* William Jewell Col, AB, 36; Univ Mo, PhD(physics), 42. *Prof Exp:* Instr physics & math, William Jewell Col, 38-40; from asst prof to assoc prof, 42-55, chmn dept, 57-59, PROF PHYSICS, UNIV ARK, FAYETTEVILLE, 55-, DIR PLANETARIUM, 70- *Concurrent Pos:* Physicist, US Naval Ord Lab, Washington, DC, 44-46. *Mem:* AAAS; Am Phys Soc; Am Asn Physics Teachers; Am Crystallog Asn; Int Soc Planetarium Educr. *Res:* X-ray and neutron diffraction by liquids. *Mailing Add:* Dept of Physics Univ of Ark Fayetteville AR 72701

SHARTS, CLAY MARCUS, b Long Beach, Calif, Feb 9, 31; m 52; c 4. FLUORINE CHEMISTRY, ORGANIC CHEMISTRY. *Educ:* Univ Calif, BS, 52; Calif Inst Technol, PhD(chem), 59. *Prof Exp:* Asst, Calif Inst Technol, 55-58; res chemist, Explosives Dept, E I du Pont de Nemours & Co, 58-62; assoc prof, 62-71, PROF CHEM, SAN DIEGO STATE UNIV, 71- *Concurrent Pos:* NSF sci fac fel, Univ Cologne, 71-72; consult, Technicon Instruments corp, 73-; vpres, S & S Polymer Consults Co, 75- *Mem:* AAAS; Am Chem Soc; NY Acad Sci. *Res:* Small-ring and organic fluorine compounds; spiropolymers; perfluorocarbons as oxygen carriers in artificial blood. *Mailing Add:* PO Box 15487 San Diego CA 92115

SHASHA, BARUCH, b Bagdad, Iraq, Mar 15, 31; US citizen; m 57; c 4. AGRICULTURAL CHEMISTRY. *Educ:* Hebrew Univ, Jerusalem, PhD(chem), 61. *Prof Exp:* Chemist, Ministry Health, Govt Israel, 60-61; asst prof chem, Hebrew Univ Jerusalem, 61-62 & Purdue Univ, West Lafayette, 62-63; CHEMIST, NORTHERN REGIONAL LAB, 63- *Res:* Sulfur chemistry, especially xanthate chemistry; thionocarbonate; carbohydrate chemistry, particularly starch and monosaccharides; pesticides, especially in areas of controlled release. *Mailing Add:* 4921 N Dawn Dr Peoria IL 61614

SHASHIDHARA, NAGALAPUR SASTRY, b Mysore, India, Aug 13, 40; m 71; c 1 APPLIED FLUID MECHANICS, HYDROTHERMAL ENGINEERING. *Educ:* Mysore Univ, BS, 61; Indian Inst Sci, MS, 64; Rutgers Univ, MS & Phd(fluid mech), 71. *Prof Exp:* Asst engr fluid mech, Simpson & Group Co, Bangalore, India, 61-62; sr sci officer hydrodynamics, Indian Inst Sci, 62-66; res asst fluid mech, Rutgers Univ & Princeton Univ, 66-71; SUPVR HYDROTHERMAL ENG, EBASCO SERV, INC, 71- *Concurrent Pos:* Res scientist rheology, E I du Pont de Nemours & Co, Inc, 67; consult fluid mech & other hydrothermal probs to many US & foreign elec utilities. *Mem:* Int Asn Hydraulic Res; Am Geophys Union; Sigma Xi; Asn Sci Workers India (secy, 62-66). *Res:* Dispersion in air and water of thermal, radioactive and chemical effluents from industrial facilities and their effects on the environment. *Mailing Add:* 81 Primrose Dr New Providence NJ 07974

SHASHOUA, VICTOR E, b Kermanshah, Iran, Nov 15, 29; nat US; m 55; c 3. BIOCHEMISTRY. *Educ:* Univ London, BSc, 51; Loughborough Col Tech, Eng, dipl, 51; Univ Del, PhD(org chem), 56. *Prof Exp:* Res chemist, E I du Pont de Nemours & Co, Inc, 51-64, res assoc, 64-68; mem neurosci res prog, Mass Inst Technol, 64-68, res assoc biol, 68-70; asst prof, 70-75, ASSOC PROF BIOL CHEM, HARVARD MED SCH, 75-, ASSOC BIOCHEMIST, MCLEAN HOSP, 70- *Mem:* Am Chem Soc; Am Neurochem Soc; Int Soc Neurochem; Soc Neurosci; Am Soc Cell Biol. *Res:* Neurochemistry; behavior and biochemistry. *Mailing Add:* Harvard Med Sch Dept of Biol Chem Boston MA 02115

SHASKAN, EDWARD GREGORY, neurochemistry, neuropharmacology, see previous edition

SHATKIN, AARON JEFFREY, b Providence, RI, July 18, 34; m 57; c 1. BIOCHEMISTRY, VIROLOGY. *Educ:* Bowdoin Col, AB, 56; Rockefeller Univ, PhD(microbiol), 61. *Prof Exp:* Sr asst scientist virol, Cell Biol Sect, Nat Inst Health, 61-63, res biochemist, 63-68; assoc mem, 68-71, mem, 71-77, HEAD ROCHE INST MOLECULAR BIOL, 77- *Concurrent Pos:* Vis prof, Georgetown Univ, 68; guest investr, Salk Inst, Calif, 68-69; mem molecular biol study sect, NSF, 71-74; instr, Cold Spring Harbor Lab, 72-74; ed, J Virology, 73-77; adj prof, Rockefeller Univ, 78. *Mem:* AAAS; Am Soc Biol Chem; Am Soc Microbiol; NY Acad Sci; Harvey Soc. *Res:* Structure and function of animal cells and viruses; biochemistry of virus replication. *Mailing Add:* Dept of Cell Biol Roche Inst of Molecular Biol Nutley NJ 07110

SHATOFF, LARRY DAVID, mathematics, see previous edition

SHATTES, WALTER JOHN, b Oceanside, NY, May 27, 24; m 60; c 2. EXPERIMENTAL PHYSICS. *Educ:* Union Col, BS, 50; Rutgers Univ, PhD(physics), 56. *Prof Exp:* Res physicist, Tung-Sol Elec Co, 55-62; SR PHYSICIST, AIRCO 62- *Mem:* Am Vacuum Soc; Am Phys Soc. *Res:* Vacuum technology; physical vapor deposition; superconductors; semiconductors; semiconductor devices and materials; thin films, cryogenics. *Mailing Add:* 70 Beverly Rd Bloomfield NJ 07003

SHATTUCK, THOMAS WAYNE, b Denver, Colo, Aug 10, 50; m 78. PHYSICAL CHEMISTRY. *Educ:* Lake Forest Col, BA, 72; Univ Calif, Berkeley, PhD(chem), 76. *Prof Exp:* ASST PROF CHEM, COLBY COL, 76- *Concurrent Pos:* Vis asst prof, Univ Maine, Orono, 78. *Mem:* Am Chem Soc; Am Phys Soc; Sigma Xi. *Res:* Solid state nuclear magnetic resonance; nuclear quadrupole resonance of transition metal complexes; liquid crystal phase transitions. *Mailing Add:* Dept of Chem Colby Col Waterville ME 04901

SHATYNSKI, STEPHEN ROBERT, b Woodbury, NJ, Aug 16, 49; m 71; c 1. METALLURGY, MATERIALS SCIENCE. *Educ:* Bowling Green State Univ, BS, 71; Syracuse Univ, MS, 74; Ohio State Univ, PhD(metall), 76. *Prof Exp:* Fel phys chem, Max Planck Inst Iron Res, 76-77; ASST PROF MAT ENG, RENSSELAER POLYTECH INST, 77- *Concurrent Pos:* Dep ed, J Reviews High Temp Mat, 77- *Mem:* Am Soc Metals; Am Inst Metall Engrs; Electrochem Soc. *Res:* Oxidation; hot corrosion; reaction kinetics; catalysis; thermodynamics of alloys; diffusion; interfacial phenomena; tribology; physical metallurgy; chemical metallurgy. *Mailing Add:* Dept of Mat Eng Rensselaer Polytech Inst Troy NY 12181

SHATZ, STEPHEN S, b New York, NY, Apr 27, 37; m 58; c 2. MATHEMATICS. *Educ:* Harvard Univ, AB, 57, AM, 58, PhD(math), 62. *Prof Exp:* Instr math, Stanford Univ, 62-63; actg asst prof, 63-64; from asst prof to assoc prof, 64-69, PROF MATH, UNIV PA, 69- *Concurrent Pos:* Vis lectr, Haverford Col, 66; mem, Res Ctr, Physics & Math, Univ Pisa, 66-67. *Mem:* Am Math Soc. *Res:* Algebraic geometry. *Mailing Add:* Dept of Math Univ of Pa Philadelphia PA 19104

SHAUCK, MAXWELL EUSTACE, JR, mathematics, see previous edition

SHAUDYS, EDGAR T, b Washingtons Crossing, Pa, Nov 23, 28; m 52; c 4. AGRICULTURAL ECONOMICS. *Educ:* Wilmington Col, BS, 50; Ohio State Univ, MS, 52, PhD(agr econ), 54. *Prof Exp:* Teaching asst biol, Wilmington Col, 47-50; res asst, 50-54, PROF AGR ECON, OHIO STATE UNIV, 54- *Mem:* Am Soc Farm Mgrs & Rural Appraisers; Am Agr Econ Asn. *Res:* Farm management production and organization; land tenure and farm real estate taxation; cost of production studies for crops and livestock. *Mailing Add:* Dept of Agr Econ & Rural Sociol Ohio State Univ Columbus OH 43210

SHAUGHNESSY, THOMAS PATRICK, b Dedham, Mass, July 12, 42; m 67; c 2. SEMICONDUCTOR PROCESSING, MICROLITHOGRAPHY. *Educ:* Boston Col, BS, 64, PhD(physics), 70. *Prof Exp:* Asst silicon photovoltaics, Boston Col, 72-75; group leader, Spire Corp, 75-79; MGR PROCESS ENG, GCA CORP, BURLINGTON, 79- *Mem:* Am Vacuum Soc; Electrochem Soc; Inst Elec & Electronics Engrs. *Res:* Selicon integrated process development; photolithography; electron beam lithography; photoresist chemistry; reactive ion etch; ion implantation; anneal techniques; diffusion; depostions; device modeling and testing. *Mailing Add:* GCA Corp 209 Burlington Rd Bedford MA 01730

SHAULIS, NELSON JACOB, b Somerset, Pa, Sept 10, 13; m 41; c 2. VITICULTURE. *Educ:* Pa State Col, BS, 35, MS, 37; Cornell Univ, PhD(soils), 41. *Prof Exp:* Asst soil technol, Pa State Col, 35-37, asst county agent, 37-38, asst pomol, 38-41, instr, 42-44; coop agent, Soil Conserv Serv, US Dept Agr, 38-41, asst soil conservationist, 42-44; from asst prof to prof pomol, 44-67, PROF VITICULT, EXP STA, NY STATE COL AGR & LIFE SCI, CORNELL UNIV, 67- *Concurrent Pos:* Fulbright res scholar, Australia, 67-68. *Mem:* Am Soc Hort Sci; Am Soc Agron; Soil Sci Soc Am; Am Soc Enol. *Res:* Vineyard sites; grapevine physiology; vineyard mechanization and management including mineral nutrition, rootstocks and canopy microclimate. *Mailing Add:* Dept of Pomol & Viticult NY State Agr Exp Sta Geneva NY 14456

SHAVER, ALAN GARNET, b Brockville, Ont, Dec 17, 46; m 69; c 1. ORGANOMETALLIC CHEMISTRY, INORGANIC CHEMISTRY. *Educ:* Carleton Univ, BSc, 69; Mass Inst Technol, PhD(chem), 72. *Prof Exp:* Fel, Univ Western Ont, 72-75; asst prof, 75-79, ASSOC PROF CHEM, MCGILL UNIV, 79- *Mem:* Chem Inst Can. *Res:* Synthesis and characterization of new types of complexes; special interest in optically active organometallic complexes and in complexes with catenated sulfur ligands. *Mailing Add:* Dept Chem McGill Univ Montreal PQ H3Z 2K6 Can

SHAVER, EVELYN LOUISE, b London, Ont, Aug 21, 31. CYTOGENETICS, REPRODUCTIVE BIOLOGY. *Educ:* Univ Wester Ont, BSc, 54, MSc, 58, PhD(anat), 68. *Prof Exp:* Res asst micro-anat, Univ Western Ont, 54-60; res technician biol, Atomic Energy of Can Ltd, 60-64; demonstr, 64-66, from lectr to assoc prof, 66-79, PROF ANAT, UNIV WESTERN ONT, 79- *Mem:* Am Asn Anat; Can Asn Anat; Teratology Soc; Can Soc Cell Biol; Soc Study Reproduction. *Res:* Factors influencing the chromosome complement of pre- and postimplantation embryos; invitro fertilization. *Mailing Add:* Dept of Anat Univ of Western Ont London ON N6A 5C1 Can

SHAVER, GAIUS ROBERT, b Pasadena, Calif, Aug 19, 49. PLANT ECOPHYSIOLOGY. *Educ:* Stanford Univ, BS, 72, AM, 72; Duke Univ, PhD(bot), 76. *Prof Exp:* Res assoc ecol, San Diego State Univ & Univ Alaska, 76-78; ASST SCIENTIST ECOL, ECOSYSTS CTR, MARINE BIOL LAB, 79- *Concurrent Pos:* Instr biol, San Diego State Univ, 77-78. *Mem:* Am Ecol Soc; Brit Ecol Soc; Soc Am Naturalists; AAAS. *Res:* Ecology of plants; ecology of arctic tundras; mineral nutrition, growth and ecophysiology of plants. *Mailing Add:* Ecosysts Ctr Marine Biol Lab Woods Hole MA 02543

SHAVER, JOHN RODNEY, b Philadelphia, Pa, Nov 7, 16. EMBRYOLOGY. *Educ:* Univ Pa, AB, 38, PhD, 50. *Prof Exp:* Asst prof zool, Univ Mo, 49-54; fel, Calif Inst Technol, 54-56; PROF ZOOL, MICH STATE UNIV, 56- *Mem:* Am Soc Zoolgists (secy, 67-69); Soc Develop Biol; Soc Study Reproduction. *Res:* Reproductive physiology. *Mailing Add:* Dept of Zool Mich State Univ East Lansing MI 48824

SHAVER, KENNETH JOHN, b Auburn, NY, Dec 18, 25; m 48; c 1. FOOD CHEMISTRY. *Educ:* Syracuse Univ, BS, 48, PhD(chem), 52. *Prof Exp:* RES CHEMIST, MONSANTO CO, 52-, GROUP LEADER, 64-, RES MGR, 78- *Mem:* Am Chem Soc; Int Asn Dent Res; Inst Food Technologists; Sigma Xi. *Res:* Food phosphates; food preservatives. *Mailing Add:* 32 Millbrook Lane St Louis MO 63122

SHAVER, PAUL MERL, b Marion, NY, Apr 19, 22; m 49; c 2. SCIENCE EDUCATION. *Educ:* Syracuse Univ, AB, 42, MS, 47. *Prof Exp:* Teacher high sch, 42-44, 47-60; asst prof phys sci, 60-63, asst prof chem, 63-64, assoc prof physics, 64-65, assoc prof geophys, 65-67, ASSOC PROF EARTH SCI, STATE UNIV NY COL OSWEGO, 67- *Concurrent Pos:* Consult, Cent NY Study Coun, 62; lectr, St Lawrence Valley Educ TV Coun, 63; mem comt earth sci, Univ NY, Regents External Degree, 74-69. *Mem:* Nat Sci Teachers Asn; Am Phys Soc; Nat Educ Asn. *Res:* The use of independent study as a method of instruction. *Mailing Add:* Dept of Earth Sci State Univ of NY Col at Oswego Oswego NY 13126

SHAVER, ROBERT HAROLD, b North Henderson, Ill, Sept 8, 22; m 45; c 4. GEOLOGY. *Educ:* Univ Ill, BS, 47, MS, 49, PhD(geol), 51. *Prof Exp:* Asst geol, Univ Ill, 47-50; from asst prof to prof, Univ Miss, 51-56, chmn dept, 52-56; assoc prof, 56-64, asst chmn dept, 67-72, actg chmn, 70, PROF GEOL, IND UNIV, BLOOMINGTON, 64-; HEAD GEOL SECT, IND GEOL SURV, 56- *Concurrent Pos:* Co-ed J Paleont, 64-69. *Mem:* Fel Geol Soc Am; Paleont Soc; Soc Econ Paleont & Mineral (pres-elect, 75-76, pres, 76-77); Am Asn Petrol Geol. *Res:* Invertebrate paleontology; Ostracoda and Silurian reef faunas; stratigraphy, Silurian and Devonian. *Mailing Add:* Dept of Geol Ind Univ Bloomington IN 47401

SHAVER, ROBERT JOHN, b Ridgway, Pa, May 20, 27; m 51. ZOOLOGY, PARASITOLOGY. *Educ:* St Bonaventure Univ, BS, 50; Univ Notre Dame, MS, 52, PhD, 54. *Prof Exp:* Res asst, Univ Notre Dame, 51-54; parasitologist, 54-66, group leader, 60-64, planning coordr, 64-70, asst dir, 71-72, res dir, 72-75, MGR ANIMAL SCI FIELD RES & DEVELOP, DOW CHEM CO, 75-, OPER MGR HEALTH & ENVIRON RES, 75- *Concurrent Pos:* Lab instr, St Mary's Col, 51-53. *Mem:* AAAS; Am Soc Parasitol; assoc mem Am Asn Vet Parasitol. *Res:* Screening, evaluation and development of nutrition products and chemotherapeutics for domestic animals and poultry. *Mailing Add:* Health & Environ Res Dow Chem Co Midland MI 48640

SHAVER, ROY ALLEN, b Rushville, Ill, Aug 4, 31; m 59; c 3. ORGANIC CHEMISTRY. *Educ:* Western Ill Univ, BS, 53, MS, 56. *Prof Exp:* From instr to assoc prof, 56-77, PROF CHEM & CHMN DEPT, UNIV WIS-PLATTEVILLE, 77- *Mem:* Am Chem Soc; Royal Soc Chem. *Res:* Nonbenzenoid aromaticity-electrophilic reactions of the tropylium ion; time predictions on cheese rancidification. *Mailing Add:* Dept of Chem Univ of Wis Platteville WI 53818

SHAVITT, ISAIAH, b Kutno, Poland, July 29, 25; m 57; c 1. THEORETICAL CHEMISTRY. *Educ:* Israel Inst Technol, BSc, 50, dipl eng, 51; Cambridge Univ, PhD(theoret chem), 57. *Prof Exp:* Instr chem, Israel Inst Technol, 53-54 & 56-57, lectr, 57-58; res assoc theoret chem, Naval Res Lab, Univ Wis, 58-59; asst prof chem, Brandeis Univ, 59-60; staff chemist, IBM Watson Sci Comput Lab, Columbia Univ, 60-62; sr lectr chem, Israel Inst Technol, 62-63, assoc prof, 63-67; STAFF MEM THEORET CHEM, BATTELLE MEM INST, 67- *Concurrent Pos:* Mem nat coun, Info Processing Asn Israel, 66-67; adj prof chem, Ohio State Univ, 68- *Mem:* Am Chem Soc; Asn Comput Mach; Am Phys Soc. *Res:* Molecular quantum mechanics; computational methods. *Mailing Add:* Battelle Mem Inst 505 King Ave Columbus OH 43201

SHAW, A(LEXANDER) J(OHN), b Vancouver, BC, May 7, 20; m 47; c 2. CHEMICAL ENGINEERING, ENVIRONMENTAL TECHNOLOGY. *Educ:* Univ BC, BASc, 44, dipl bus mgt, 62. *Prof Exp:* Shift supvr, BC Distillery, 44-46; from res engr to chief chemist & develop engr, Western Chem Industs, Ltd, 46-68; CHEM ENGR, B H LEVELTON & ASSOCS LTD, 68- *Mem:* Sr mem Chem Inst Can. *Res:* Process and product development, environmental quality studies, waste management; vitamins; proteins, fats, oils; alpha-glyceryl ethers; nucleotides; production biochemicals and medicinal chemicals; air and water quality studies; hazardous chemical disposal; air and water pollution control; energy from biomass. *Mailing Add:* 4427 W Fifth Ave Vancouver BC V6R 1S4 Can

SHAW, ALAN BOSWORTH, b Englewood, NJ, Mar 28, 22; wid; c 2. GEOLOGY. *Educ:* Harvard Univ, AB, 46, AM, 49, PhD(geol), 49. *Prof Exp:* Asst prof geol, Univ Wyo, 49-55; area paleontologist, Shell Oil Co, Colo, 55-60; consult paleontologist, 60-61; res assoc, 61, res sect supvr paleont & palynol, 61-65, spec res assoc, Okla, 65-68, consult geologist, Denver Div Explor, 68-70, district geologist, 70-71, consult geologist, 71-76, chief paleontologist, 76-77, mgr geol, Chicago Br, 77-82, RES CONSULT, AMOCO PROD RES,STANDARD OIL CO, OKLA, 82- *Mem:* Paleont Soc (pres, 68); Soc Econ Paleont & Mineral; Am Asn Petrol Geol; Paleont Asn. *Res:* Invertebrate paleontology and carbonate stratigraphy. *Mailing Add:* Amoco Prod Co Res Ctr PO Box 591 Tulsa OK 74102

SHAW, BARBARA RAMSAY, b Newton, NJ. BIOPHYSICAL CHEMISTRY. *Educ:* Bryn Mawr Col, AB, 65; Univ Wash, MS, 67, PhD(phys chem), 73. *Prof Exp:* Res fel biophys chem, Ore State Univ, 73-75; ASST PROF CHEM, DUKE UNIV, 75- *Mem:* AAAS. *Res:* Protein-nucleic acid interaction in chromatin and subunit structure of chromatin; association of collagen model polypeptides and thermodynamic analysis of their thermal transitions. *Mailing Add:* Dept of Chem Duke Univ Durham NC 27706

SHAW, C FRANK, III, b Mt Vernon, NY, Mar 17, 44; m 66; c 2. INORGANIC CHEMISTRY. *Educ:* Univ Del, BS, 66; Northwestern Univ, PhD(inorg chem), 70. *Prof Exp:* NSF grant, dept chem, Purdue Univ, Lafayette, 70-72; fel chem, McGill Univ, 72-74; lectr, 74-75, ASST PROF CHEM, UNIV WIS-MILWAUKEE, 75- *Concurrent Pos:* Book rev ed, Can J Spectroscopy, 73- *Mem:* Am Chem Soc; Royal Soc Chem; Sigma Xi; Spectros Soc Can. *Res:* Applications of spectroscopy to structural problems in organometallic and bioinorganic chemistry. *Mailing Add:* Dept of Chem Univ of Wis Milwaukee WI 53201

SHAW, CHARLES BERGMAN, JR, b Dallas, Tex, June 7, 27; m 50, 66; c 2. PHYSICS, APPLIED MATHEMATICS. *Educ:* Calif Inst Technol, BS, 47; Univ Southern Calif, MS, 50, PhD(physics), 58. *Prof Exp:* Lab assoc physics, Univ Southern Calif, 47-49, lectr math, 52-54; res asst, Los Alamos Sci Lab, 49; physicist, Nat Bur Standards, 51; sr scientist, Missile Systs Div, Lockheed Aircraft Corp, 54-56; mem tech staff, Res Labs, Hughes Aircraft Co, 56-64; sr scientist, Electro-Optical Systs Inc, 64-66; sr tech specialist phys sci, Autonetics Div, NAm Aviation, Inc, 66-68; group scientist phys sci, 68-70, mem tech staff, 70-71, GROUP LEADER FLUID PHYSICS, SCI CTR, ROCKWELL INT, 71- *Concurrent Pos:* Vis prof, Loyola Univ, Calif, 60. *Mem:* Am Phys Soc; Am Math Soc; Soc Indust & Appl Math; Inst Elec & Electronics Engrs; Am Welding Soc. *Res:* Plasma diagnostics; arc physics; physics of welding processes; computational physics; integral equations; improperly posed problems; reconstruction from projections; holographic interferometry; laser-generated plasmas; interaction of laser radiation with structural material. *Mailing Add:* Sci Ctr Rockwell Int 1049 Camino Dos Rios Thousand Oaks CA 91360

SHAW, CHARLES GARDNER, b Springfield, Mass, Aug 12, 17; m 40; c 3. PHYTOPATHOLOGY, MYCOLOGY. *Educ:* Ohio Wesleyan Univ, BA, 38; Pa State Col, MS, 40; Univ Wis, PhD(bot, plant path), 47. *Prof Exp:* Instr, Bot Lab, Ohio Wesleyan Univ, 37-38; lab asst, Pa State Col, 38-40; lab asst, Univ Wis, 41-43, asst, 46-47; instr plant path & jr plant pathologist, 47-48, asst prof & asst plant pathologist, 48-51, assoc prof & assoc plant pathologist, 51-57, actg chmn dept, 60-61, chmn dept, 61-72, PROF & PLANT PATHOLOGIST, WASH STATE UNIV, 57- *Concurrent Pos:* Consult, US Agency Int Develop Pakistan Agr Univ, 69-70 & 72; vis prof plant path, Dept Bot, Univ Auckland, NZ, 75. *Mem:* Mycol Soc Am; Am Phytopath Soc; Brit Mycol Soc; Int Soc Plant Path; Am Soc Plant Taxon. *Res:* Saprots of conifers; vectoring or wood decay fungi, delignification of wood; taxonomy of Peronosporaceae. *Mailing Add:* Dept of Plant Path Wash State Univ Pullman WA 99163

SHAW, CHARLES GARDNER, III, b Colfax, Wash, June 30, 48; m 70; c 1. FOREST PATHOLOGY. *Educ:* Wash State Univ, BSc, 70; Ore State Univ, PhD(plant path), 75. *Prof Exp:* Scientist forest path, Forest Res Inst, NZ Forest Serv, 74-77; RES PLANT PATHOLOGIST, FOREST SCI LAB, JUNEAU, ALASKA, 77- *Mem:* Soc Am Foresters; Am Phytopath Soc; Australian Plant Path Soc; NZ Inst Foresters. *Res:* Root rot diseases of forest trees, particularly Armillaria; tree growth responses to various diseases and levels thereof. *Mailing Add:* Forest Sci Lab PO Box 909 Juneau AK 99802

SHAW, CHARLES RAYMOND, b Indianapolis, Ind, Feb 28, 21; m 42; c 1. ONCOLOGY. *Educ:* NY Univ, MD, 46; Am Bd Psychiat & Neurol, dipl, 59. *Prof Exp:* Resident internal med, Cornell Infirmary, 47-49, asst prof med nutrit, Cornell Univ, 49-51; resident psychiat, Neuropsychiat Inst, Univ Mich, 53-56, child psychiatrist & res dir, Hawthorn Ctr, 56-67; PROF BIOL & CHIEF SECT MED GENETICS, UNIV TEX M D ANDERSON TUMOR INST, 67-, ASSOC PEDIATRICIAN & ASSOC PROF PEDIAT, INST, 75-, CLIN ASSOC PROF, DEPT PSYCHIAT, MED SCH, UNIV TEX, HOUSTON, 75- *Mem:* Genetics Soc Am; Am Asn Cancer Res. *Res:* Biochemical genetics; chemical carcinogenesis. *Mailing Add:* Dept of Biol Univ of Tex M D Anderson Hosp & Tumor Inst Houston TX 77025

SHAW, CHENG-MEI, b Chang-Hua, Taiwan, Oct 24, 26; m 51; c 4. NEUROPATHOLOGY. *Educ:* Taihoku Gym, dipl, 46; Nat Taiwan Univ, MD, 50. *Prof Exp:* Resident surg, Nat Taiwan Univ Hosp, 50-53 & neuropsychiat, 53-54; fel neurosurg, Lahey Clin, 54-55; resident neurosurg, Col Med, Baylor Univ, 55-58; res fel path, Col Med, Baylor Univ, 58-60; from res instr to assoc prof, 60-74, PROF PATH, SCH MED, UNIV WASH, 74- *Concurrent Pos:* Nat Multiple Sclerosis Soc res fel, 60-63. *Mem:* Am Asn Neuropath; Int Acad Path; Reticuloendothelial Soc; Am Soc Exp Path. *Res:* Immunopathology; etiology and pathogenesis of experimental allergic encephalitis; mechanisms of immunological adjuvants; morphological studies of malformation of human central nervous system. *Mailing Add:* Dept of Path Univ of Wash Sch of Med RJ05 Seattle WA 98195

SHAW, DAVID GEORGE, b Los Angeles, Calif, Apr 20, 45; m 69. CHEMICAL OCEANOGRAPHY, ORGANIC CHEMISTRY. *Educ:* Univ Calif, Los Angeles, BS, 67; Harvard Univ, AM, 69, PhD(chem), 71. *Prof Exp:* NSF fel, Harvard Univ, 71-72; res assoc chem oceanog, Marine Sci Inst, Univ Conn, 72-73; asst prof, 73-76, ASSOC PROF, INST MARINE SCI, UNIV ALASKA, 76- *Mem:* AAAS; Geochem Soc; Am Chem Soc; Am Soc Limnol & Oceanog. *Res:* Transport and reactivity of organic chemicals in marine systems; organic trace analysis; environmental quality. *Mailing Add:* Inst Marine Sci Univ of Alaska Fairbanks AK 99701

SHAW, DAVID HAROLD, b Grants Pass, Ore, Jan 18, 41; m 63; c 3. PHYSIOLOGY, PHARMACOLOGY. *Educ:* Univ Nebr, BS, 63, MS, 65; Univ of the Pac, PhD(physiol, pharmacol), 69. *Prof Exp:* Asst physiol, Univ Nebr, 63-64, asst & res assoc cell physiol, 64-65, instr physiol, 65-66; instr & res assoc physiol & pharmacol, Univ of the Pac, 67-69; asst prof, 69-73, ASSOC PROF ORAL BIOL, COL DENT, UNIV NEBR, LINCOLN, 73- *Mem:* AAAS; Int Asn Dent Res; Tissue Cult Asn; Am Soc Cell Biol. *Res:* Oxygen toxicity in cultured cells; drug effects on cells in vitro; experimental carcinogenesis. *Mailing Add:* Dept of Oral Biol Univ of Nebr Col of Dent Lincoln NE 68588

SHAW, DAVID T, b China, Mar 13, 38; m 61; c 2. ELECTROMECHANICAL ENGINEERING. *Educ:* Nat Taiwan Univ, BS, 59; Purdue Univ, MS, 61, PhD(nuclear eng), 64. *Prof Exp:* From asst prof to assoc prof, 64-74, PROF ELEC ENG, STATE UNIV NY BUFFALO, 74-, DIR LAB FOR POWER & ENVIRON STUDIES, 78- *Concurrent Pos:* NSF res initiation grant, 65-67; consult, Bell Aerosystem Co, NY, 66-69 & Jet Propulsion Lab, Calif, 68-; vis assoc, Dept Environ Eng Sci, Calif Inst Technol, 70-71; vis prof, Univ Paris, 76; consult, Atomic Energy Comn, Paris, 77- *Mem:* Am Nuclear Soc; Inst Elec & Electronics Engrs; Am Soc Mech Engrs; Am Soc Eng Educ; Am Inst Aeronaut & Astronaut. *Res:* Control of particulate emissions into the atmosphere; acoustic agglomeration; atmospheric nucleation processes; aerosol measurement techniques; aerosol physics; energy conversion. *Mailing Add:* Lab for Power & Environ Studies 4232 Ridge Lea Rd Buffalo NY 14214

SHAW, DENIS MARTIN, b St Annes, Eng, Aug 20, 23; m 46; c 3. GEOCHEMISTRY. *Educ:* Cambridge Univ, BA, 43, MA, 48; Univ Chicago, PhD(geochem), 51. *Prof Exp:* From lectr to assoc prof, 48-60, chmn dept, 53-59, 62-66, PROF GEOL, McMASTER UNIV, 60-, DEAN GRAD STUDIES, 78- *Concurrent Pos:* Vis prof, Ecole Nat Superieure de Geol, France, 59-60 & Inst Mineral, Univ Geneva, 66-67; exec ed, Geochimica et Cosmochimica Acta, 70- *Honors & Awards:* Miller Medal, Royal Soc Can, 81. *Mem:* Geochem Soc; fel Royal Soc Can; Geol Asn Can; Mineral Asn Can (pres, 64-65); Geol Soc Am. *Res:* Spectrochemistry; chemical mineralogy. *Mailing Add:* Dept of Geol McMaster Univ Hamilton ON L8S 4L8 Can

SHAW, DEREK HUMPHREY, b Maidstone, Eng, Apr 27, 37; Can citizen; m 60; c 2. CARBOHYDRATE CHEMISTRY, MICROBIAL BIOCHEMISTRY. *Educ:* Univ Cape Town, BSc, 59, PhD(carbohydrate chem), 65. *Prof Exp:* Prod chemist, Seravac Labs Ltd, Cape Town, SAfrica, 60-63; Nat Res Coun Can fel biosci, Ottawa, Ont, 65-67; res scientist marine carbohydrates, Fisheries Res Bd Can, 67-72, div head fisheries technol, St John's, Nfld, 72-74; head, Marine Prod Div, Nfld Biol Sta, 75-76, HEAD, MICROBIAL CHEM SECT, NORTHWEST ATLANTIC FISHERIES CTR, 76- *Concurrent Pos:* Adj prof chem, Mem Univ Nfld. *Mem:* Royal Soc Chem; fel Chem Inst Can. *Res:* Marine carbohydrates; gas chromatography of carbohydrate derivatives; microbial polysaccharides from bacteria pathogenic to fish; biochemistry of fish diseases. *Mailing Add:* Northwest Atlantic Fisheries Ctr PO Box 5662 St John's NF A1C 5X1 Can

SHAW, DON W, b Pecan Gap, Tex, Dec 26, 37; m 59; c 2. PHYSICAL CHEMISTRY. *Educ:* East Tex State Univ, BS, 58; Baylor Univ, PhD(phys chem), 65. *Prof Exp:* Instr chem, Dallas Inst, 58-61; mem tech staff, 65-72, sr scientist, 72-77, head, Explor Mat Br, 78-79, DIR, MAT SCI LAB, TEX INSTRUMENTS, INC, 79- *Concurrent Pos:* Assoc ed, J Crystal Growth; div ed, J Electrochem Soc. *Mem:* Electrochem Soc; Am Asn Crystal Growth; Am Chem Soc; Sigma Xi. *Res:* Crystal growth mechanisms; kinetics of vapor phase epitaxial growth of semiconductors; materials for solid state microwave devices; preparation and properties of gallium arsenide. *Mailing Add:* Tex Instruments Inc PO Box 225936 MS 147 Dallas TX 75265

SHAW, EDGAR ALBERT GEORGE, b Middlesex, Eng, July 10, 21; Can citizen; m 45; c 2. PHYSICS. *Educ:* Univ London, BSc, 48, PhD(physics), 50. *Prof Exp:* Tech officer, UK Ministry Aircraft Prod & Brit Air Comn, US, 40-46; from asst res officer to sr res officer, 50-74, PRIN RES OFFICER, DIV PHYSICS, NAT RES COUN CAN, 74-, HEAD ACOUST SECT, 75- *Concurrent Pos:* Lectr, Univ Ottawa, 58-; mem, Comt Hearing, Bio-Acoust & Biomech, Nat Res Coun-Nat Acad Sci, 65-; chmn, Int Comn Acoust, 75-78. *Honors & Awards:* Rayleigh Medal, Inst Acoust, Brit, 79. *Mem:* Fel Acoust Soc Am (pres, 73); fel Royal Soc Can; Brit Inst Physics; Can Asn Physicists. *Res:* Electroacoustics; psychoacoustics; physiological acoustics; acoustic measurements; wave acoustics; urban noise. *Mailing Add:* Div Physics Nat Res Coun Can Ottawa ON K1A 0R6 Can

SHAW, EDWARD IRWIN, b New York, NY, Jan 17, 27; m 56; c 3. RADIATION BIOLOGY. *Educ:* Univ Mo, AB, 48, MA, 50; Univ Tenn, PhD(zool, radiation biol), 55. *Prof Exp:* Asst zool, Univ Mo, 48-51 & Univ Tenn, 52-55; res assoc biol div, Oak Ridge Nat Lab, 55-56; from asst prof to assoc prof, 56-66, chmn dept, 68-78, PROF RADIATION BIOPHYS, UNIV KANS, 66- *Concurrent Pos:* Instr, Univ Tenn, 55; consult, Menninger Found, Kans, 57-62 & AAAS, 71-75; dir, Radiation Protection, Energy Res Develop Admin Training Grant, 74-77. *Mem:* Fel AAAS; Radiation Res Soc; Health Physics Soc. *Res:* Radiation biophysics; radiation effects at the cell level; metabolism of radioactively labelled organic compounds as internal emitters; health physics; mutation-induction and recovery from pre-mutational lesions. *Mailing Add:* Dept of Radiation Biophys Univ of Kans Nuclear Reactor Ctr Lawrence KS 66045

SHAW, ELDEN K, b Brigham, Utah, Aug 20, 34; m 57; c 4. ELECTRICAL ENGINEERING. *Educ:* Utah State Univ, BS, 56; Stanford Univ, MS, 57, PhD(elec eng), 67. *Prof Exp:* Sr res engr, Litton Industs Tube Corp, 60-66; from asst prof to assoc prof, 66-77, PROF ELEC ENG, SAN JOSE STATE UNIV, 77- *Concurrent Pos:* Res asst, Stanford Univ, 64-66; consult, S F D Labs, Inc, 66-70. *Mem:* Inst Elec & Electronics Engrs. *Res:* Steady state plasma discharges; crossed field microwave tubes, electron optics. *Mailing Add:* Dept of Elec Eng San Jose State Univ San Jose CA 95114

SHAW, ELLIOTT NATHAN, b Youngstown, Ohio, Apr 6, 20; m 55. BIOCHEMISTRY. *Educ:* Mass Inst Technol, SB, 41, PhD(chem), 43. *Prof Exp:* Res assoc, Squibb Inst Med Res, 43-48; vis investr biochem, Rockefeller Inst, 48-50, asst, 50-51, assoc, 51-57; from assoc prof to prof, Tulane Univ, 57-65; SR BIOCHEMIST, BROOKHAVEN NAT LAB, 65- *Concurrent Pos:* Fel, Nat Cancer Inst, 49-50. *Mem:* Am Chem Soc; Am Soc Biol Chem; Harvey Soc; NY Acad Sci. *Res:* Chemical structure and biological action; antimetabolites; enzyme active centers; proteolytic enzymes. *Mailing Add:* Dept of Biol Brookhaven Nat Lab Upton NY 11973

SHAW, ELLSWORTH, b Chicago, Ill, Mar 7, 20; m 43; c 6. SOIL SCIENCE, AGRICULTURAL CHEMISTRY. *Educ:* Univ Chicago, BS, 41; Univ Ariz, PhD(soil chem), 49. *Prof Exp:* Res chemist, Testing Mat, Kellogg Switchboard & Supply Co, 41-42; plant indust sta, US Dept Agr, 49-52; consult agr, 53-70; PLANT & SOIL SCIENTIST & LAB & FIELD DIR, GAC PRODUCE, MEXICO, 70- *Concurrent Pos:* Res assoc agr chem & soils, Univ Ariz, 60; independent agr consult, Ariz & Calif. *Mem:* Am Chem Soc; Am Soc Agron; fel Am Inst Chem; Sigma Xi. *Res:* Application of radioisotopes to soil and plant nutritional problems; effect of fumigants on soil; availability of soil zinc to plants; soil and fertilizer need to plants through measurement of nitrogen uptake. *Mailing Add:* 3602 E Flower Tucson AZ 85716

SHAW, ELWOOD R, b Clark Co, Ohio, Sept 29, 18; m 56; c 1. ANALYTICAL CHEMISTRY. *Educ:* Cedarville Col, AB, 40, BS, 41; Ohio State Univ, MSc, 56. *Prof Exp:* Instr math & chem, Cedarville Col, 40-41, prof chem, 46-54; teacher high schs, Ohio, 41-42, 45-46; asst prof chem & res chemist, Antioch Col, 54-59; res assoc, 59-67, SR RES ASSOC CHEM, C F KETTERING RES LAB, 67- *Mem:* Am Chem Soc. *Res:* Hydrothermal research; germanates and silicates; organic synthesis; substituted hydrazines; metalloporphins; photosynthesis. *Mailing Add:* 1102 Clifton Rd Xenia OH 45385

SHAW, EMIL GILBERT, b San Antonio, Tex, June 22, 22; m 50; c 3. BIOCHEMISTRY, NUTRITION. *Educ:* Southwest Tex State Col, BS, 47, MA, 48; Tex A&M Univ, PhD(bionutrit), 67. *Prof Exp:* Instr & prof biol, East Tex State Col, 48-50; chief lab serv, US Army Hosp, Ft Chaffee, 50-51; biochemist, Fourth Army Area Med Lab, Ft Sam Houston, 51-52, Surg Res Univ, Brooke Army Med Ctr, 52-53 & Tripler Gen Hosp, Honolulu, Hawaii, 53-55; chief of serv, Wilford Hall, US Air Force Hosp, Lackland Air Force Base, 55-56; liaison officer, Off Surgeon Gen, US Army Chem Ctr, Edgewood, Md, 56-58; dep chief environ systs div, 58-72, CHIEF ENVIRON SCI DIV, US AIR FORCE SCH AEROSPACE MED, 72- *Res:* Physiological effects of exposure to exotic atmospheres for prolonged periods upon the mineral metabolism of man and experimental animals. *Mailing Add:* Environ Sci Div Air Force Sch of Aerospace Med Brooks Air Force Base TX 78235

SHAW, EUGENE, b Burlington, Iowa, Aug 3, 25; m 56; c 4. MICROBIOLOGY, VIROLOGY. *Educ:* Northwestern Univ, BS, 49; Univ Iowa, MS, 55, PhD(microbiol), 63. *Prof Exp:* With Med Serv Corps, US Army, 51-70; SR SCIENTIST, VIROL DIV, ORTHO RES FOUND, 70- *Mem:* Am Soc Microbiol; Tissue Cult Asn; NY Acad Sci. *Res:* Enteroviruses; infectious hepatitis. *Mailing Add:* 908 Sherwood Rd Bridgewater Township NJ 08807

SHAW, FREDERICK CARLETON, b Boston, Mass, July 8, 37; m 58; c 2. INVERTEBRATE PALEONTOLOGY. *Educ:* Harvard Univ, AB, 58, PhD(geol), 65; Univ Cincinnati, MS, 60. *Prof Exp:* From instr to asst prof geol, Mt Holyoke Col, 63-68; asst prof, 68-71, chmn, Dept Geol & Geog, 72-81, ASSOC PROF GEOL, LEHMAN COL, 71-, DEAN NATURAL & SOCIAL SCI, 81- *Concurrent Pos:* Geol Soc Am res grant, 65; instr & dir social sci training prog, Mt Hermon Sch, 65-66. *Mem:* AAAS; Paleont Soc. *Res:* Systematics and paleoecology of Paleozoic invertebrates; Ordovician biostratigraphy. *Mailing Add:* Dept of Geol & Geog Herbert H Lehman Col Bronx NY 10468

SHAW, GAYLORD EDWARD, b London, Ont, Mar 10, 39; m 65; c 2. ANIMAL PHYSIOLOGY. *Educ:* Graceland Col, Iowa, BA, 62; Univ Ill, Urbana, MS, 66, PhD(vet med sci), 70. *Prof Exp:* Res asst pathol & hyg, Col Med, Univ Ill, 62-63; instr biol, Graceland Col, 63-64; res asst physiol & pharmacol, Col Vet Med, Univ Ill, 64-69, res asst vet biol structure, 69-70; ASSOC PROF ANAT & PHYSIOL MICROBIOL, KENT STATE UNIV, 70- *Concurrent Pos:* Lab dir, Caries Susceptibility Testing & Res Ctr, 78-82. *Mem:* AAAS; Sigma Xi. *Res:* Oral leukocyte infiltration and phagocytic activity; oral lactobacillus counts as a clinical parameter of caries activity. *Mailing Add:* Kent State Univ Good Frank Ave NW Canton OH 44720

SHAW, GLENN EDMOND, b Butte, Mont, Dec 5, 38; m 57; c 4. ATMOSPHERIC PHYSICS. *Educ:* Mont State Univ, BS, 63; Univ Southern Calif, MS, 65; Univ Ariz, PhD, 71. *Prof Exp:* Mem tech staff, Hughes Aircraft, 63-65; asst prof, 71-74, ASSOC PROF GEOPHYS, GEOPHYS INST, UNIV ALASKA, 74- *Mem:* Am Meteorol Soc; Am Geophys Union; Royal Meteorol Soc. *Res:* Laser profiling of lower and upper atmosphere; atmospheric optics; atmospheric radiation; agrometeorology. *Mailing Add:* Geophys Inst Univ of Alaska College AK 99701

SHAW, GORDON LIONEL, b Atlantic City, NJ, Sept 20, 32; m 58; c 3. THEORETICAL PHYSICS. *Educ:* Case Inst Technol, BS, 54; Cornell Univ, PhD(theoret physics), 59. *Prof Exp:* Res assoc theoret physics, Ind Univ, 58-60 & Univ Calif, San Diego, 60-62; asst prof physics, Stanford Univ, 62-65; assoc prof, 65-68, PROF PHYSICS, UNIV CALIF, IRVINE, 68- *Mem:* Am Phys Soc. *Res:* Theory of strong interactions of elementary particles. *Mailing Add:* Dept of Physics Univ of Calif Irvine CA 92664

SHAW, HARRY, JR, b Miami, Fla, Feb 6, 27; m 49; c 2. APPLIED MATHEMATICS. *Educ:* Emory Univ, BA, 49; Univ Miami, MS, 51. *Prof Exp:* Instr math, Marion Mil Inst, 51-52; asst, Univ NC, 52-54 & Univ Md, 54-56; assoc mathematician, 56-61, SR MATHEMATICIAN, APPL PHYSICS LAB, JOHNS HOPKINS UNIV, 61- *Mem:* Asn Comput Mach. *Res:* Numerical analysis. *Mailing Add:* Appl Physics Lab Johns Hopkins Univ Laurel MD 20810

SHAW, HERBERT RICHARD, b San Mateo, Calif, Dec 7, 30; m 51. GEOLOGY. *Educ:* Univ Calif, Berkeley, PhD(geol), 59. *Prof Exp:* GEOLOGIST, EXP MINERAL & GEOCHEM BR, US GEOL SURV, 59- *Mem:* Geol Soc Am; Am Geophys Union. *Res:* Experimental and field geologic investigations relating to interpretation of igneous rocks. *Mailing Add:* Exp Mineral & Geochem Br 345 Middlefield Rd Menlo Park CA 94025

SHAW, JAMES EDWARD, organic chemistry, see previous edition

SHAW, JAMES HARLAN, b Tyler, Tex, May 8, 46. WILDLIFE ECOLOGY, WILDLIFE RESEARCH. *Educ:* Stephen F Austin Univ, BS, 68; Yale Univ, MFS, 70, PhD(wildlife ecol), 75. *Prof Exp:* Teaching asst biol, Yale Univ, 73-74, teaching fel ecol, 74; asst prof wildlife ecol, 74-81, ASSOC PROF ZOOL, OKLA STATE UNIV, 81- *Mem:* Wildlife Soc; Ecol Soc Am; Am Soc Mammalogists; Animal Behav Soc. *Res:* Biology of the Carnivora; prey-predator relations; ecology and behavior of free-living vertebrates. *Mailing Add:* Sch of Biol Sci Okla State Univ Stillwater OK 74074

SHAW, JAMES HEADON, b Sharon, Ont, Jan 1, 18; nat US; m 43; c 2. BIOCHEMISTRY. *Educ:* McMaster Univ, BA, 39; Univ Wis, MS, 41, PhD(biochem), 43. *Hon Degrees:* MA, Harvard Univ, 55. *Prof Exp:* Res assoc nutrit, Univ Wis, 43-45; instr, 45-47, assoc, 47-48, asst prof dent med, 48-55, assoc prof biol chem, 55-65, PROF NUTRIT, SCH DENT MED, HARVARD UNIV, 65-, DIR TRAINING CTR, CLIN SCHOLARS ORAL BIOL, 72- *Concurrent Pos:* Asst ed, Nutrit Rev, 46-; consult, Forsyth Dent Infirmary Children, 47-63; mem comt dent, Med Sci Div, Nat Res Coun, 53-62, comt diet phosphate & dent caries, food & nutrit bd, Div Biol & Agr, 58-63; career investr, USPHS, 60- *Mem:* AAAS; Soc Exp Biol & Med; Am Inst Nutrit; Int Asn Dent Res. *Res:* Oral disease in rodents and subhuman primates; nutritional relationships to the development, calcification, metabolism and disease susceptibility of the oral structures. *Mailing Add:* Sch Dent Harvard Univ 188 Longwood Ave Boston MA 02115

SHAW, JAMES SCOTT, b Grand Junction, Colo, Oct 13, 42; m 67; c 1. ASTRONOMY. *Educ:* Yale Univ, AB, 64; Univ Pa, PhD(astron), 70. *Prof Exp:* Asst prof, 70-77, ASSOC PROF ASTRON, UNIV GA, 77- *Mem:* Sigma Xi; Int Astron Union; Am Astron Soc. *Res:* Eclipsing binary stars; intrinsic variable stars; photoelectric photometry. *Mailing Add:* Dept of Physics & Astron Univ of Ga Athens GA 30602

SHAW, JANE E, b Worcester, Eng, Feb 3, 39. PHYSIOLOGY, CLINICAL PHARMACOLOGY. *Educ:* Univ Birmingham, BS, 61, PhD(physiol), 64. *Prof Exp:* Staff scientist, Worcester Found Exp Biol, 64-70; sr scientist, 70-72, PRIN SCIENTIST, ALZA RES, 72- *Mem:* AAAS; NY Acad Sci; Am Phys Soc. *Res:* Elucidation of the physiological role of the prostaglandins; mechanism of action of analeptics; mechanism of gastric secretion; physiology and pharmacology of skin. *Mailing Add:* Alza Res 950 Page Mill Rd Palo Alto CA 94304

SHAW, JOHN GORDON, plant pathology, see previous edition

SHAW, JOHN H, b Sheffield, Eng, Jan 25, 25; m 49; c 4. PHYSICS. *Educ:* Cambridge Univ, BA, 46, MA, 50, PhD(physics), 51. *Prof Exp:* From lectr to assoc prof, 53-64, PROF PHYSICS, OHIO STATE UNIV, 64- *Mem:* Am Meteorol Soc; fel Optical Soc Am; Royal Meteorol Soc. *Res:* Infrared spectroscopy; infrared studies of atmospheric gaseous constituents. *Mailing Add:* Dept of Physics Ohio State Univ Columbus OH 43210

SHAW, JOHN THOMAS, b Philadelphia, Pa, Sept 12, 25; m 46; c 3. ORGANIC CHEMISTRY. *Educ:* Temple Univ, AB, 50, MA, 52, PhD, 54. *Prof Exp:* Res chemist, Org Chem Div, Am Cyanamid Co, 54-63; asst prof chem, Am Int Col, 63-65; assoc prof chem, 65-68, PROF CHEM, GROVE CITY COL, 68- *Concurrent Pos:* Res grant, Petrol Res Fund, 73-75, 76-77 & 78-80. *Mem:* Am Chem Soc; Sigma Xi. *Res:* Synthesis and reactions of nitrogen heterocycles. *Mailing Add:* 520 Woodland Ave Grove City PA 16127

SHAW, KENNETH C, b Cincinnati, Ohio, Sept 18, 32; m 55; c 4. ZOOLOGY. *Educ:* Univ Cincinnati, BS, 54; Univ Mich, MS, 58, PhD(zool), 66. *Prof Exp:* Asst zool, Univ Mich, 56-60, instr, 60-61; asst prof, 63-76, ASSOC PROF ZOOL, IOWA STATE UNIV, 76- *Mem:* AAAS; Am Soc Zoologists; Am Inst Biol Sci; Animal Behav Soc. *Res:* Acoustical behavior of Homoptera and Orthoptera. *Mailing Add:* Dept of Zool & Entom Iowa State Univ Ames IA 50010

SHAW, KENNETH NOEL FRANCIS, b Vancouver, BC, Dec 4, 19; m 46; c 3. BIOCHEMISTRY. *Educ:* Univ BC, BA, 40, MA, 42; Iowa State Col, PhD(bio-org chem), 51. *Prof Exp:* Instr chem, Univ BC, 40-42; chemist, Inspection Bd UK & Can, 42-43; supvr pharmaceut prod, Ayerst, McKenna & Harrison, Ltd, 43-47; from instr to res asst, Iowa State Univ, 47-51; res assoc, Wash State Univ, 51-52; from instr to asst res prof biochem, Col Med, Univ Utah, 52-57; sr res fel, Calif Inst Technol, 57-64; assoc prof, 64-77, PROF PEDIAT, SCH MED, UNIV SOUTHERN CALIF, 77-; DIR, METAB SECT, MED GENETICS DIV, CHILDRENS HOSP LOS ANGELES, 64- *Mem:* Soc Pediat Res; Am Soc Biol Chem; Am Chem Soc; Royal Soc Chem. *Res:* Chemistry and metabolism of amino acids; urinary phenol and indole acids; neural tumors; inherited metabolic disorders; mental diseases of biochemical origin. *Mailing Add:* Childrens Hosp of Los Angeles PO Box 54700 Los Angeles CA 90054

SHAW, LEONARD G, b Toledo, Ohio, Aug 15, 34; m 61; c 3. SYSTEMS ANALYSIS, ELECTRICAL ENGINEERING. *Educ:* Univ Pa, BS, 56; Stanford Univ, MS, 57, PhD(elec eng), 61. *Prof Exp:* Res asst, Dept Elec Eng, Stanford Univ, 59-60; asst prof, 60-64, assoc prof, 64-75, PROF ELEC ENG, POLYTECH INST NY, 75- *Concurrent Pos:* Vis prof, Tech Univ Eindhoven, Neth, 70; consult signal processing, Mgt Div, Sperry Syst, 73-; Nat Ctr Sci Res assoc, Automatic Control Lab, Univ Nantes, France, 76-77. *Mem:* Inst Elec & Electronics Engrs; Oper Res Soc; Am Soc Eng Educ; AAAS. *Res:* Optimal filtering; stochastic control; spectral analysis; control of traffic and message queues; reliability. *Mailing Add:* Dept of Elec Eng Polytech Inst NY Brooklyn NY 11201

SHAW, M(ELVIN) P, b Brooklyn, NY, Aug 16, 36; m 59; c 2. SOLID STATE PHYSICS & ELECTRONICS. *Educ:* Brooklyn Col, BS, 59; Case Inst Technol, MS, 63, PhD(physics), 65. *Prof Exp:* Exp physicist & scientist-in-chg microwave physics, Res Labs, United Aircraft Corp, 64-70; PROF ELEC ENG & MAT SCI, WAYNE STATE UNIV, 70- *Concurrent Pos:* Lectr, Trinity Col, Conn, 65-66; adj asst prof, Rensselaer Polytech Inst, 68-70; vis lectr, Yale Univ, 69-70; consult, Energy Conversion Devices, 70-; adv, Nat Res Coun Comt, 75-78; dir, Res Inst Eng Sci, Wayne State Univ, 76-77. *Mem:* Fel Am Phys Soc; sr mem Inst Elec & Electronics Engrs. *Res:* Amorphous solar cells; cyclotron resonance; electron spin resonance; superconductivity; solid state microwave sources; crystal growth and purification of metals and semiconductors; switching in crystalline and amorphous semiconductors. *Mailing Add:* Dept of Elec Eng Wayne State Univ Detroit MI 48202

SHAW, MARGARET ANN, b Louisville, Ky, Apr 29, 33. PHARMACY. *Educ:* Univ Ky, BS, 55; Univ Fla, PhD(pharm), 61. *Prof Exp:* Pharm practice, 55-58; asst prof pharm, Univ NC, 61-65; asst prof, 65-69, assoc prof, 69-80, PROF PHARM, COL PHARM, BUTLER UNIV, 80- *Mem:* Am Soc Hosp Pharmacists. *Res:* Isotonic solutions; aerosols. *Mailing Add:* Butler Univ Col of Pharm Indianapolis IN 46207

SHAW, MARGERY WAYNE, b Evansville, Ind, Feb 15, 23; div; c 1. HUMAN GENETICS, LEGAL GENETICS. *Educ:* Univ Ala, AB, 45; Columbia Univ, MA, 46; Univ Mich, MD, 57; Univ Houston, JD, 73. *Hon Degrees:* ScD, Univ Evansville, 77. *Prof Exp:* Instr zool, Univ Alaska, 51-53; from instr to assoc prof human genetics, Univ Mich, 58-67; assoc prof, 67-69, prof biol, Univ Tex M D Anderson Hosp & Tumor Inst, 69-75, PROF GENETICS & DIR MED GENETICS CTR, UNIV TEX HEALTH SCI CTR HOUSTON, 71- *Concurrent Pos:* Mem genetics study sect, NIH, 66-70, training comt, 70-74; mem med adv bd, Nat Genetics Found, 72- *Mem:* Am Soc Human Genetics; Am Soc Cell Biol; Tissue Cult Asn; Genetics Soc Am (pres, 77-78); Environ Mutagen Soc. *Res:* Inherited diseases; human chromosomes. *Mailing Add:* Univ of Tex Med Genetics Ctr 6420 Lamar Fleming Blvd Houston TX 77025

SHAW, MICHAEL, b Barbados, BWI, Feb 11, 24; m 48; c 4. PLANT PATHOLOGY, PLANT PHYSIOLOGY. *Educ:* McGill Univ, BSc, 46, MSc, 47, PhD(bot, plant path), 49. *Hon Degrees:* PhD, Univ Sask, 71; DSc, McGill Univ, 75. *Prof Exp:* Nat Res Coun Can fel, Bot Sch, Cambridge Univ, 49-50; from assoc prof to prof plant physiol, Univ Sask, 50-67, head dept biol, 61-67; dean agr sci, 67-75, vpres acad develop, 75-80, PROF AGR BOT, UNIV BC, 67-, VPRES & PROVOST, 81- *Concurrent Pos:* Vis researcher, Hort Res Labs, Univ Reading, 58-59; ed, Can J Bot, 64-79; vpres, Biol Coun Can, 71, pres, 72; mem adv comt biol, Nat Res Coun Can, 71-73; mem, Sci Coun Can, 76-; mem, Natural Sci & Eng Res Coun Can, 78-80. *Honors & Awards:* Gold Medal, Can Soc Plant Physiol, 71; Flavelle Medal, Royal Soc Can, 76. *Mem:* AAAS; Am Soc Plant Physiol; fel Royal Soc Can; Can Soc Plant Physiol; Can Bot Asn. *Res:* Host-parasite relations of obligate plant parasites. *Mailing Add:* Vpres Acad Develop Univ BC Vancouver BC V6T 1W5 Can

SHAW, MILTON C(LAYTON), b Philadelphia, Pa, May 27, 15; m 39; c 2. MECHANICAL ENGINEERING, TRIBOLOGY. *Educ:* Drexel Inst, BS, 38; Univ Cincinnati, MEngSc, 40, ScD(chem physics), 42. *Hon Degrees:* Dr, Cath Univ Leuven, 70. *Prof Exp:* Res engr, Cincinnati Milling Mach Co, 38-42; chief mat br, Nat Adv Comt Aeronaut, 42-46; from assoc prof to prof mech eng, Mass Inst Technol, 46-61, head mach tool div, 53-61; head dept mech eng, Carnegie-Mellon Univ, 61-75, dir processing res inst, 70-71, univ prof, 74-77; PROF ENG, ARIZ STATE UNIV, 77- *Concurrent Pos:* Guggenheim fel, 56; Fulbright vis prof, Aachen Tech Univ, 57; vis prof, Univ Birmingham, 60, 61 & 64; Springer prof, Univ Calif, Berkeley, 72; distinguished guest prof, Ariz State Univ, 76; consult, various co, 46- *Honors & Awards:* Westinghouse Award, Am Soc Eng Educ, 56; Hersey Award, Am Soc Mech Engrs; Gold Medal, Am Soc Tool & Mfg Eng, 58; Wilson Award, Am Soc Metals, 71. *Mem:* Nat Acad Eng; fel Am Soc Mech Engrs; fel Am Soc Lubrication Engrs; hon mem Soc Mfg Eng; fel Am Acad Arts & Sci. *Res:* Metal cutting; lubrication, friction and wear; behavior of materials. *Mailing Add:* Ariz State Univ ECG 247 Tempe AZ 85287

SHAW, MONTGOMERY THROOP, b Ithaca, NY, Sept 11, 43; m 66; c 1. POLYMER SCIENCE. *Educ:* Cornell Univ, BChE & MS, 66; Princeton Univ, MA, 68, PhD(chem), 70. *Prof Exp:* Chemist polymer thermodyn, Union Carbide Corp, 70-74, proj scientist polymer rheology, 74-76; ASSOC PROF, DEPT CHEM ENG, UNIV CONN, 76- *Mem:* Am Chem Soc; Soc Rheology; Sigma Xi. *Res:* Research directed at relating rheological functions of high-polymer melts to the chemical structure of the polymer, and developing the theory and experiments to substantiate these relationships. *Mailing Add:* Inst of Mat Sci Univ of Conn Storrs CT 06268

SHAW, NOLAN GAIL, b Forsan, Tex, Oct 2, 29; m 67; c 5. GEOLOGY. *Educ:* Baylor Univ, AB, 51; Southern Methodist Univ, MS, 56; La State Univ, PhD(paleont), 66. *Prof Exp:* From asst prof to prof, 55-78, WILLIAM C WOOLF PROF CHAIR GEOL, CENTENARY COL LA, 78-, CHMN DEPT, 74- *Mem:* Am Asn Petrol Geologists; fel Geol Soc Am; Sigma Xi. *Res:* Paleontology. *Mailing Add:* Dept of Geol Centenary Col of La Shreveport LA 71105

SHAW, PAUL DALE, b Morton, Ill, Aug 12, 31; m 55. BIOCHEMISTRY. *Educ:* Bradley Univ, BS, 53; Univ Ill, PhD(biochem), 57. *Prof Exp:* Res fel chem, Harvard Univ, 58-60; from asst prof to assoc prof, 60-74, PROF BIOCHEM, UNIV ILL, URBANA, 74- *Mem:* Am Chem Soc; Am Soc Biol Chemists. *Res:* Chemistry and biochemistry of natural products; metabolism of fungi. *Mailing Add:* Dept of Plant Path Univ of Ill Urbana IL 61801

SHAW, PHILIP EUGENE, b St Petersburg, Fla, July 21, 34; m 59; c 3. ORGANIC CHEMISTRY. *Educ:* Duke Univ, BS, 56; Rice Univ, PhD(chem), 60. *Prof Exp:* Res assoc chem, Sterling-Winthrop Res Inst Div, Sterling Drug, Inc, 60-65; chemist, 65-72, RES LEADER, CITRUS AND SUBTROP PROD LAB, US DEPT AGR, 72- *Mem:* Am Chem Soc; Inst Food Technologists. *Res:* Isolation and identification of natural food flavors and insect attractants; chemistry of nutrients. *Mailing Add:* Citrus & Subtrop Prods Lab US Dept of Agr Box 1909 Winter Haven FL 33880

SHAW, RALPH ARTHUR, b Peoria, Ill, Dec 27, 30; m 55; c 2. METABOLISM, ENDOCRINOLOGY. *Educ:* Northwestern Univ, BS, 54, MD, 62; Purdue Univ, MS, 56, PhD(biochem), 58. *Prof Exp:* Consult, Children's Mem Hosp, 59-61, fel biochem, 61-62; intern, Evanston Hosp, Ill, 62-63; resident med, Hahnemann Hosp, 63-65, from sr instr med to assoc prof med & biochem, 66-72, dir clin chem lab, 70-71, PROF MED & RES PROF BIOCHEM, HAHNEMANN MED COL, 72-, ASSOC VPRES HEALTH AFFAIRS, 71- *Concurrent Pos:* Mem bd, Action for Brain Injured Children, Inc; fel biochem & med, Sch Med, Northwestern Univ, 58-61; USPHS fel, Hahnemann Hosp, 65-66. *Mem:* Am Fedn Clin Res; Am Diabetes Asn; Am Geriat Soc; NY Acad Sci; Am Schizophrenia Found. *Res:* Diabetes mellitus. *Mailing Add:* Dept of Med Hahnemann Med Col Philadelphia PA 19102

SHAW, RICHARD FRANCIS, b Lawrence, Mass, Feb 22, 52. OCEANOGRAPHY. *Educ:* Univ Maine, PhD(oceanog), 81. *Prof Exp:* Res asst, Dept Oceanog, Univ Maine, 73-79; consult coordr, Human Sci Res Inc, 79-80; regional coordr & consult, Kathryn Chandler Assocs, Inc & Market Facts, Inc, 81; RES ASSOC IV, COASTAL ECOL LAB, CTR WETLAND RESOURCES, LA STATE UNIV, 81- *Concurrent Pos:* Prin investr, Ira C Darling Ctr, Univ Maine, 79-80. *Mem:* Am Fisheries Soc; Am Soc Ichthyologists & Herpetologists; Am Soc Limnol & Oceanog; Estuarine Res Soc. *Res:* Ecology, population dynamics, growth rates, condition factors, age determination, recruitment, migration and transport of larval fishes. *Mailing Add:* Ctr Wetland Resources La State Univ Baton Rouge LA 70803

SHAW, RICHARD GREGG, b Wilmington, Del, Nov 21, 29; m 57; c 3. POLYMER CHEMISTRY. *Educ:* Cornell Univ, AB, 51; Univ Pa, MS, 52; Ind Univ, PhD, 60. *Prof Exp:* Group leader opers div, Union Carbide Corp, 60-75, technol mgr wire & cable, Polyethylene Div, 75-77, mkt mgr wire & cable, Domestic Int Liaison, 77-78; CONSULT, 78- *Mem:* Am Chem Soc; Inst Elec & Electronics Engrs; Soc Photog Scientists & Engrs. *Res:* Polymer free radical chemistry; photosensitive systems; polymer property predictions; polymer synthesis and modification; engineered plastic materials design; physics of dielectrics. *Mailing Add:* RD 1 Remsen NY 13438

SHAW, RICHARD JOHN, b Fall River, Mass, Jan 15, 39; m 65; c 2. FLORICULTURE, ORNAMENTAL HORTICULTURE. *Educ:* Univ RI, BS, 61; Univ Mo, MS, 63, PhD(hort), 66. *Prof Exp:* Asst prof hort, La State Univ, Baton Rouge, 66-70; asst prof, 70-76, ASSOC PROF PLANT & SOIL SCI, UNIV RI, 76- *Mem:* Am Soc Hort Sci; Am Hort Soc. *Res:* Effects of environment, growth regulators, growing media and fertilizers on the production of greenhouse crops. *Mailing Add:* Dept of Plant & Soil Sci Univ of RI Kingston RI 02881

SHAW, RICHARD JOSHUA, b Ogden, Utah, June 25, 23; m 47; c 3. BOTANY. *Educ:* Utah State Univ, BS, 48, MS, 50; Claremont Grad Sch, PhD(bot), 61. *Prof Exp:* From asst prof to assoc prof bot, 50-69, PROF BIOL, UTAH STATE UNIV, 69- *Mem:* Am Soc Plant Taxon; Bot Soc Am; Int Asn Plant Taxon. *Res:* Taxonomic botany; biosystematics. *Mailing Add:* Dept of Biol Utah State Univ Logan UT 84321

SHAW, RICHARD P(AUL), b Brooklyn, NY, June 23, 33; m 61; c 2. ENGINEERING, OCEANOGRAPHY. *Educ:* Polytech Inst Brooklyn, BS, 54; Columbia Univ, MS, 55, PhD(appl mech), 60. *Prof Exp:* Sr instr appl mech, Polytech Inst Brooklyn, 56-57; asst prof eng sci, Pratt Inst, 57-62; from assoc prof to prof eng sci, 62-80, PROF CIVIL ENG, STATE UNIV NY BUFFALO, 80- *Concurrent Pos:* Nat Res Coun-Environ Sci Serv Admin fel, Joint Tsunami Res Effort, Univ Hawaii, 69-70, Nat Oceanog & Atmospheric Admin sr res assoc, 73-74; Am Coun Educ Govt exchange fel, Int Decade Ocean Explor, NSF, 77-78; pres, Technol Systs Res Inc. *Mem:* Am Soc Civil Engrs; Am Geophys Union; Am Soc Mech Engrs; Acoust Soc Am; Marine Technol Soc. *Res:* Numerical methods (boundary integral/element methods); wave motion (acoustic, eleastic, water); ocean engineering and oceanography; structures and solid mechanics; oceanography. *Mailing Add:* Dept Civil Eng State Univ of NY Buffalo NY 14214

SHAW, ROBERT BLAINE, b Commerce, Tex, May 24, 49; m 76. AGROSTOLOGY, GRASS TAXONOMY. *Educ:* Southwest Tex State Univ, BS, 74; Tex A&M Univ, MS, 76, PhD(range sci), 79. *Prof Exp:* Res assoc, Range Sci Dept, Tex A&M Univ, 78-79; instr biol, Southwest Tex State Univ, 79-80; ASST PROF PLANT TAXON, SCH FORESTRY, UNIV FLA, 80- *Mem:* Soc Range Mgt; Am Soc Plant Taxonomists; Bot Soc Am. *Res:* Evolution, ecology, anatomy, morphology and systematics of the grasses; distribution, composition and evolution of the North American grasslands. *Mailing Add:* Sch Forest Resources & Conserv Univ Fla 312 Newins-Ziegler Hall Gainesville FL 32611

SHAW, ROBERT FLETCHER, b Montreal, Que, Feb 16, 10; m 35. ENGINEERING, EDUCATION ADMINISTRATION. *Educ:* McGill Univ, BE, 33. *Hon Degrees:* DSc, McMaster Univ, 67; DEng, NS Tech Col, 67. *Prof Exp:* From engr & estimator to asst to vpres, Found Co Can Ltd, 37-43, from shipyard mgr, Pictou, NS, to mgr eng & asst to pres, 43-58, exec vpres, Foundation Co Can Ltd, 58-62, pres & dir, 62-63; vprin admin, McGill Univ, 68-71; dep minister, Environ Can, 71-75; pres, Monenco Pipeline Consult Ltd, 75-78; CONSULT, MONTREAL ENG CO LTD, 78- *Concurrent Pos:* Vpres, dir & chief engr, Defense Construct Ltd, 51-52; with NATO, 52; past mem, Sci Coun Can & Nat Design Coun; mem Can Environ Adv Coun; past chmn Fed/Provincial Atlantic Fisheries Comt; past co-chmn BC Fed/Provincial Fisheries Comt; spec adv, Minister Indust Develop, Nfld, 78-79. *Honors & Awards:* Companion of the Order of Can, 67; Govt Can Centennial Medal, 67; Julian C Smith Medal, Eng Inst Can, 67, Sir John Kennedy Medal, 79; Syst & Cybernet Award, Inst Ele & Electronics Engrs, 67. *Mem:* Eng Inst Can (pres, 75-76). *Mailing Add:* 3980 Cote des Neiges Rd Apt c29 Montreal PQ H3H 1W2 Can

SHAW, ROBERT HAROLD, b Madrid, Iowa, June 26, 19; m 45; c 3. AGRICULTURAL METEOROLOGY. *Educ:* Iowa State Univ, BS, 41, MS, 42, PhD(agr climat), 49. *Prof Exp:* From asst prof to assoc prof, 48-57, PROF AGR CLIMAT, IOWA STATE UNIV, 57- *Concurrent Pos:* Mem comt meteorol and climat, Am Soc Agron, 60, 63-66, chmn, 65-66; mem working group biometeorol, Am Meteorol Soc, 63-66; assoc ed climat, Agron J, 64-66; mem comt agr meteorol, Am Meteorol Soc, 65-66; mem panel teaching climat, Am Asn Geographers, 66-67; mem panel natural resource sci, Comn Educ Agr and Nat Resources, Nat Res Coun, 66-68; mem working group, Instructions in Climat, World Meteorol Orgn, 67-68; mem comt meteorol and climat, Agr Bd, Nat Res Coun, 4 yrs. *Mem:* Fel AAAS; fel Am Soc Agron; Sigma Xi; fel Soil Sci Soc Am; Am Meteorol Soc. *Res:* Water use; weather statistics; evaluation of microclimate; crop-weather relationships; solar-wind energy climatology. *Mailing Add:* Climat-Meteorol Iowa State Univ Ames IA 50010

SHAW, ROBERT REEVES, b Bokoshe, Okla, June 9, 36; m 62; c 4. MATERIALS SCIENCE, CERAMICS. *Educ:* Univ Wash, BS, 59, MS, 60; Mass Inst Technol, SM, 65, ScD(ceramics), 67. *Prof Exp:* Res engr, Boeing Corp, 59-60; res trainee, Gen Elec Res Lab, 60-62; res asst ceramics, Mass Inst Technol, 62-67; sr res physicist, Am Optical Corp, 67-77; prof supvr, Phys Sci Lab, P R Mallory & Co, Inc, 77-81; ADV ENGR, IBM CORP, 81- *Mem:* Am Ceramic Soc. *Res:* Glass structure and properties; composite materials; optical phenomena in crystal and glass systems; phase separation; electron microscopy; microstructure-controlled phenomena; battery reactions and systems. *Mailing Add:* 5 Pine Ridge Rd Poughkeepsie NY 02603

SHAW, ROBERT WAYNE, b Davenport, Iowa, Sept 9, 47; m 69. SPECTROSCOPY. *Educ:* Iowa State Univ, BS, 69; Princeton Univ, PhD(chem), 74. *Prof Exp:* Res chemist, Indust Tape Lab, 3M Co, 68; fel Dept Chem, Univ Calif, Los Angeles, 73-75; RES CHEMIST, ANAL CHEM DIV, OAK RIDGE NAT LAB, 75- *Mem:* Am Chem Soc; AAAS; Sigma Xi; Optical Soc Am. *Res:* New spectroscopic methods and instrumentation for analytical and physical chemical research. *Mailing Add:* Anal Chem Div Oak Ridge Nat Lab Oak Ridge TN 37830

SHAW, ROBERT WAYNE, b Bartlesville, Okla, July 10, 49. BIOPHYSICAL CHEMISTRY. *Educ:* WVa Univ, BA, 71; Pa State Univ, PhD(biochem), 76. *Prof Exp:* Fel biochem, Inst Enzyme Res, Univ Wis, 76-81; ASST PROF CHEM, TEX TECH UNIV, 81- *Mem:* AAAS; Am Chem Soc. *Res:* Mechanism of a variety of physiologically important metalloenzymes; electron paramagnetic resonance; optical spectroscopies coupled to rapid kinetic methods. *Mailing Add:* Dept Chem PO Box 4260 Tex Tech Univ Lubbock TX 79409

SHAW, RODERICK WALLACE, b Drummondville, Que, July 30, 38; m 62; c 2. METEOROLOGY. *Educ:* Queen's Univ, Ont, BSc, 61; Univ Toronto, MA, 66; McGill Univ, PhD(meteorol), 70. *Prof Exp:* Meteorol analyst, Cent Anal Off, Can Meteorol Serv, Que, 66-67; res scientist, Atmospheric Environ Serv, 70-75; RES SCIENTIST, ENVIRON PROTECTION SERV, ENVIRON CAN, 75- *Mem:* Can Meteorol Soc. *Res:* Air pollution meteorology; long range transport of air pollutants and sink mechanisms. *Mailing Add:* Environ Protection Serv 5151 George St Halifax NS Can

SHAW, RODNEY, b Rotherham, UK, May 9, 37; m 63; c 2. OPTICS. *Educ:* Leeds Univ, BS, 58; Cambridge Univ, PhD(physics), 61. *Prof Exp:* Res scientist, Ilford Ltd, UK, 61-64; lectr appl physics, Hull Univ, UK, 64-67; prin lectr photog sci, Polytech Cent London, 67-70; res scientist, Ciba-Geigy Photochemie, Switz, 70-73; PRIN SCIENTIST PHYSICS, XEROX CORP, 73- *Concurrent Pos:* Ed, Photog Sci & Eng, 77- *Mem:* Optical Soc Am; Soc Photog Scientists & Engrs. *Res:* Application of image evaluation methodologies to unconventional imaging processes. *Mailing Add:* Xerox Corp 800 Phillips Rd W 147 Webster NY 14580

SHAW, ROGER WALZ, b Chicago, Ill, May 29, 34; m 56; c 3. SOLID STATE PHYSICS. *Educ:* Univ Rochester, BS, 55; Univ Ill, MS, 56, PhD(physics), 59. *Prof Exp:* Asst physics, Univ Ill, 55-58, res assoc, 59-60; from asst prof to assoc prof, Rensselaer Polytech Inst, 60-67; SR RES SPECIALIST,

ELECTRONICS DIV, MONSANTO CO, 67- *Concurrent Pos:* Vis staff mem, Los Alamos Sci Lab, 66-67. *Mem:* Am Phys Soc. *Res:* Experimental physics of solids at low temperature; superconductivity; physics of magnetic thin films, particularly magnetic bubble materials; physics of semiconductors. *Mailing Add:* Electronics Div Monsanto Co 800 N Lindbergh Blvd St Louis MO 63166

SHAW, ROSS FRANKLIN, zoology, see previous edition

SHAW, STANLEY MINER, b Parkston, SDak, July 4, 35; m 62; c 3. BIONUCLEONICS, MEDICAL RESEARCH. *Educ:* SDak State Univ, BS, 57, MS, 59; Purdue Univ, PhD(bionucleonics), 62. *Prof Exp:* Instr pharmaceut chem, SDak State Univ, 60-62; from asst prof to assoc prof, 62-71, PROF BIONUCLEONICS, PURDUE UNIV, LAFAYETTE, 71- *Concurrent Pos:* Lederle pharm fac awards, 62 & 65; res award, Parenteral Drug Asn, 70. *Mem:* AAAS; Am Pharmaceut Asn; Acad Pharm Practice; Sigma Xi. *Res:* Exploration of the utilization of radioactive isotopes for the study of pharmacological agents and the diagnosis of disease states. *Mailing Add:* Dept of Bionucleonics Purdue Univ Lafayette IN 47907

SHAW, VERNON REED, b Bellefontaine, Ohio, Apr 10, 37; m 66. ANALYTICAL CHEMISTRY. *Educ:* Wittenberg Univ, BS, 64; Univ Ill, MS, 66, PhD(chem), 68. *Prof Exp:* Asst, Univ Ill, 64-68; asst prof chem, Adrian Col, 68-73; asst prof, 73-77, ASSOC PROF CHEM, UNIV EVANSVILLE, 77- *Mem:* Am Chem Soc. *Res:* Gas chromatography of metal halide using fused salt liquid phases. *Mailing Add:* Dept of Chem Univ of Evansville Evansville IN 47702

SHAW, WALTER NORMAN, b Penns Grove, NJ, Dec 12, 23; m 52; c 3. BIOLOGICAL CHEMISTRY. *Educ:* Duke Univ, BA, 44; Univ Pa, PhD, 56. *Prof Exp:* Asst instr biochem, Univ Pa, 51-54, instr in res med, Univ Hosp, 56-58, assoc, 58-61; sr pharmacologist, 61-66, sr biochemist, 66-69, res scientist, 69-75, RES ASSOC, LILLY RES LABS, 75- *Mem:* AAAS; Am Diabetes Asn. *Res:* Hormonal control of lipid and carbohydrate metabolism; study of disease states in genetically determined disease states in laboratory animals. *Mailing Add:* Lilly Res Labs Dept M860 Indianapolis IN 46206

SHAW, WARREN A(RTHUR), b Wichita, Kans, Mar 10, 25; m 50; c 2. STRUCTURAL & CIVIL ENGINEERING. *Educ:* Univ Kans, BS, 49, MS, 52; Univ Ill, Urbana, PhD(civil eng), 62. *Prof Exp:* Instr eng mech, Univ Kans, 49-52; res engr, 52-62, dir struct div, 62-72, HEAD CIVIL ENG DEPT, US NAVAL CIVIL ENG LAB, 72- *Mem:* Am Soc Civil Engrs; Am Concrete Inst; Sigma Xi. *Res:* Engineering mechanics; structural dynamics; blast resistance of structures and structural elements; nuclear weapons effects research. *Mailing Add:* US Naval Civil Eng Lab Port Hueneme CA 93043

SHAW, WARREN CLEATON, b Roanoke Rapids, NC, May 8, 22; m 53; c 3. AGRONOMY, PLANT PHYSIOLOGY. *Educ:* NC State Univ, BS, 43, MS, 47; Ohio State Univ, PhD(agron, plant physiol), 49. *Prof Exp:* Asst instr agron, NC State Univ, 45-47; instr, Ohio State Univ, 47-49; asst prof, NC State Univ, 49-50; leader weed res, 50-64, pesticide coordr, 64-66, asst dir plant sci res div, 66-72, mem nat prof staff, 72-81, NAT RES PROG LEADER, SCI & EDUC, AGR RES SERV, USDA, 81- *Concurrent Pos:* Consult, Rockefeller Found; mil consult, Dept Defense, 57-78. *Honors & Awards:* Superior Serv Award, US Dept Agr, 62. *Mem:* AAAS; fel Weed Sci Soc Am (pres, 62-64); fel Am Soc Agron; Am Soc Plant Physiol. *Res:* Plant science; plant ecology; weed science; pests and their control; agricultural chemistry; pesticides; air pollution and environmental quality. *Mailing Add:* Agr Res Serv Sci & Educ USDA Beltsville MD 20705

SHAW, WILFRID GARSIDE, b Cleveland, Ohio, May 30, 29; m 53; c 2. INORGANIC CHEMISTRY. *Educ:* Oberlin Col, AB, 51; Univ Cincinnati, MS, 53, PhD(phys org chem), 57. *Prof Exp:* Sr chemist, 56-59, tech specialist, 59-62, sr res chemist, 62-71, res assoc, 71-74, SR RES ASSOC, STANDARD OIL CO, OHIO, 75- *Mem:* Am Chem Soc; Catalysis Soc. *Res:* Heterogeneous and homogeneous catalysis; petrochemical processes and catalysts; characterization of solids, liquid crystals; phototropy; molecular structure; petroleum processes. *Mailing Add:* Standard Oil Res Ctr 4440 Warrensville Center Rd Cleveland OH 44128

SHAW, WILLIAM S, b Glace Bay, NS, Oct 20, 24; m 50; c 6. GEOLOGY. *Educ:* St Francis Xavier Univ, BSc, 45; Mass Inst Technol, PhD(geol), 51. *Prof Exp:* Geologist, Geol Surv Can, 49-52; sr geologist, Dominion Oil Co Div, Standard Oil Co Calif, 52-56, div stratigrapher, Calif Co Div, 56-57; consult geologist, Rodgers, Seglund & Shaw, 57-68; PROF GEOL & CHMN DEPT, ST FRANCIS XAVIER UNIV, 68-; PRES, CREIGNISH MINERALS LTD, 78- *Concurrent Pos:* Mem bd dirs, Deuterium of Can, Ltd, 69-81; Dep, Ministry Mines & Energy, NS, 79-80; mem, Vol Econ Planning Bd, NS, 69- *Mem:* Am Asn Petrol Geol; Can Inst Mining & Metall; Geol Soc Am; fel Geol Asn Can; Can Soc Petrol Geologists. *Res:* Oil and gas exploration; geology of evaporites; mineral exploration. *Mailing Add:* Dept of Geol St Francis Xavier Univ Antigonish NS B0H 1C0 Can

SHAW, WILLIAM WESLEY, b Pittsburgh, Pa, May 12, 46; m 69; c 2. WILDLIFE CONSERVATION, RESOURCE MANAGEMENT. *Educ:* Univ Calif, Berkeley, BA, 68; Utah State Univ, MS, 71; Univ Mich, Ann Arbor, PhD(natural resources), 74. *Prof Exp:* ASST PROF NATURAL RESOURCES, UNIV ARIZ, 74- *Mem:* Wildlife Soc; Asn Interpretive Naturalists. *Res:* Values of wildlife resources and management of wildlife for non-consumptive uses. *Mailing Add:* Sch Renewable Natural Resources Univ of Ariz Tucson AZ 85721

SHAWCROFT, ROY WAYNE, b LaJara, Colo, Aug 17, 38; m 67; c 2. SOIL PHYSICS, MICROMETEOROLOGY. *Educ:* Colo State Univ, BS, 61, MS, 65; Cornell Univ, PhD(soil sci), 70. *Prof Exp:* SOIL SCIENTIST, SCI & EDUC ADMIN-AGR RES, US DEPT AGR, 61-65, 70- *Mem:* Am Soc Agron; Soil Sci Soc Am. *Res:* Plant, soil, water and atmospheric relations in semi-arid region of central plains United States; dryland and irrigated agriculture. *Mailing Add:* Cent Great Plains Res Sta USDA Sci & Educ Admin Agr Res Akron CO 80720

SHAWE, DANIEL REEVES, b Gardnerville, Nev, May 24, 25; m 51; c 3. GEOLOGY. *Educ:* Stanford Univ, BS, 49, MS, 50, PhD(geol), 53. *Prof Exp:* Geologist, 51-69, chief br Rocky Mt mineral resources, 69-72, GEOLOGIST, US GEOL SURV, 72- *Honors & Awards:* Meritorious Serv Award, US Dept Interior, 72. *Mem:* AAAS; fel Geol Soc Am; Soc Econ Geol; Am Inst Mining, Metall & Petrol Eng. *Res:* Ore deposits; geology uranium in sedimentary rocks; geology beryllium in volcanic rocks; resources fluoride in United States; structure in Great Basin. *Mailing Add:* 8920 W Second Ave Lakewood CO 80226

SHAWL, STEPHEN JACOBS, b San Francisco, Calif, June 18, 43; m 66; c 2. ASTRONOMY. *Educ:* Univ Calif, Berkeley, AB, 65; Univ Tex, Austin, PhD(astron), 72. *Prof Exp:* Asst prof, 72-76, ASSOC PROF PHYSICS & ASTRON, UNIV KANS, 76- *Mem:* Int Astron Union; Am Astron Soc. *Res:* Polarimetry of cool stars; motions of globular clusters. *Mailing Add:* Dept of Physics & Astron Univ of Kans Lawrence KS 66045

SHAWYER, BRUCE L R, b Kirkcaldy, Scotland, May 12, 37; m 66; c 4. PURE MATHEMATICS. *Educ:* St Andrews Univ, BSc, 60, PhD(math), 63. *Prof Exp:* Asst lectr math, Univ Nottingham, 62-64, lectr, 64-66; from asst prof to assoc prof, 66-76, PROF MATH, UNIV WESTERN ONT, 76- *Mem:* Math Asn Am; Edinburgh Math Soc; London Math Soc; Can Math Soc. *Res:* Summability of series and integrals; approximation of series. *Mailing Add:* Dept Math Fac Sci Univ Western Ont London ON N6A 5B9 Can

SHAY, JERRY WILLIAM, b Dallas, Tex, Nov 7, 45. CELL BIOLOGY, CELL GENETICS. *Educ:* Univ Tex, Austin, BA, 66, MA, 69; Univ Kans, PhD(physiol & cell biol), 72. *Prof Exp:* Fel marine biol, Marine Biol Lab, 72; fel molecular cellular & develop biol, Univ Colo, 72-75; ASST PROF CELL BIOL, UNIV TEX HEALTH SCI CTR, 75- *Concurrent Pos:* NIH fel, 72-73; Muscular Dystrophy Asn fel, 73-75; res grants, NIH, Muscular Dystrophy Asn & Am Heart Asn, 75-; course coordr genetics & develop, Southwestern Med Sch, 76-; mem exec comt, Cancer Ctr, 77-78; chmn grad admis comt, Dept Cell Biol, Grad Sch Biomed Sci, 76-78; adj asst prof, Univ Tex, 77-; adj staff mem, W Alton Jones Cell Sci Ctr, 77-, course dir, 76-; NIH res career develop award, 78-83. *Mem:* Am Soc Cell Biol; Tissue Culture Asn; Electron Micros Soc Am; Sigma Xi; NY Acad Sci. *Res:* Somatic cell genetics; cell enucleation and hybridization; analysis of heart cell contraction; the role of the nucleus and cytoplasm in cell transformation and differentiation; scanning and transmission electron microscopy. *Mailing Add:* Dept Cell Biol 5323 Harry Hines Blvd Dallas TX 75235

SHAY, JOSEPH LEO, b Albany, NY, Mar 12, 42; m 63; c 2. SOLID STATE PHYSICS. *Educ:* Manhattan Col, BEE, 63; Stanford Univ, MS, 64, PhD(elec eng), 67. *Prof Exp:* Mem tech staff, 67-74, HEAD INFRARED PHYSICS & ELECTRONICS RES DEPT, BELL LABS, 74- *Mem:* Am Phys Soc. *Res:* Optical properties and electronic structure of semiconductors; properties of ordered ternary semiconductors; photovoltaic solar cells; electrochromic display devices. *Mailing Add:* Rm 4C310 Bell Labs Holmdel NJ 07733

SHAY, JUNIOR RALPH, b Bird City, Kans, Jan 8, 18; m 43; c 6. PLANT PATHOLOGY. *Educ:* Univ Ark, BS, 39; Univ Wis, MS, 41, PhD(plant path), 43. *Prof Exp:* Asst plant path, Univ Wis, 39-43; asst prof, Univ Ark, 43-45; from asst to prof, 45-66, head dept bot & plant path, 54-66; prof plant path, 66-73, PROF BOT & ASST DEAN RES, ORE STATE UNIV, 73- *Concurrent Pos:* Chmn comt remote sensing for agr purposes, Nat Acad Sci; mem Ore task force, Pac Northwest Regional Comn, Proj on Land Resource Inventory, 74-78. *Mem:* Am Phytopath Soc (secy, 63-66). *Res:* Disease resistance in tree fruits; physiologic races venturia inaequalis; fruit diseases. *Mailing Add:* Off of Dean of Res Ore State Univ Corvallis OR 97331

SHAY, LUCAS KING, bacterial physiology, bacterial genetics, see previous edition

SHAYA, STEVEN ALAN, b Brooklyn, NY, June 22, 48; c 1. SURFACTANTS, COSMETICS. *Educ:* Brooklyn Col, BS, 69; Univ Wis, PhD(phys chem), 74. *Prof Exp:* Group leader, 74-80, SECT HEAD RES & DEVELOP, PROCTER & GAMBLE CO, 80- *Res:* Physical chemistry of surfactants; Rayleigh light spectroscopy from mesomorphic systems. *Mailing Add:* Procter & Gamble Co 6110 Center Hill Rd Cincinnati OH 45224

SHAYEGANI, MEHDI, b Rasht, Iran, Apr 2, 26; m 61; c 3. MEDICAL MICROBIOLOGY. *Educ:* Univ Tehran, PharmD, 53; Univ Pa, MS, 58, PhD(med microbiol), 61. *Prof Exp:* Dir, Mobile Unit Lab & Public Health Lab, Iran, 52-56; instr med microbiol, Med Sch, Univ Pa, 58-61; res assoc, Inst Microbiol, Rutgers Univ, 61-62; res assoc, microbiol & vet med, Dept Commun Med, Sch Med, Univ Pa, 62-68, asst prof, Sch Med & Dept path, 68-72; DIR, BACTERIOL LABS, NY STATE DEPT HEALTH, ALBANY, 73-; ASSOC PROF MICROBIOL, DEPT OBSTET & GYNECOL, ALBANY MED SCH, 81- *Concurrent Pos:* Prin investr grants, 61-; lectr, Sch Med Technol, Albany Med Ctr Hosp, 75- *Mem:* Fel Am Acad Microbiol; Am Soc Microbiol; Reticuloendothelial Soc; Sigma Xi. *Res:* Nonspecific cell-mediated immunity to bacteria and virus in mice infected and alicited with staphylococci and its antigens; pathogenicity of Yersinia enterocolitica and its prevelance and adaptation to environment. *Mailing Add:* 23 Fairway Ave Delmar NY 12054

SHAYKEWICH, CARL FRANCIS, b Winnipeg, Man, July 18, 41; m 67. SOIL PHYSICS. *Educ:* Univ Man, BSA, 63, MSc, 65; McGill Univ, PhD(soil physics), 68. *Prof Exp:* Asst prof, 67-74, ASSOC PROF SOIL PHYSICS, UNIV MAN, 74- *Mem:* Am Soc Agron; Can Soc Soil Sci. *Res:* Soil physics, especially water relations in soil-plant-atmosphere system. *Mailing Add:* Dept of Soil Sci Univ of Man Winnipeg MB R3T 2N2 Can

SHE, CHIAO-YAO, b Fukien, China, Aug 4, 36; m 64; c 2. QUANTUM ELECTRONICS, SOLID STATE PHYSICS. *Educ:* Nat Taiwan Univ, BS, 57; NDak State Univ, MS, 61; Stanford Univ, PhD(elec eng), 64. *Prof Exp:* Asst prof elec eng, Univ Minn, 64-68; from asst prof to assoc prof physics,

68-74, PROF PHYSICS, COLO STATE UNIV, 74- *Mem:* Am Phys Soc; fel Optical Soc Am; Inst Elec & Electronics Engr. *Res:* Optical properties of solids; light scattering; spectroscopy; non-linear optical processes. *Mailing Add:* Dept of Physics Eng Bldg Colo State Univ Ft Collins CO 80523

SHEA, DANIEL FRANCIS, b Springfield, Mass, Aug 2, 37; m 66; c 1. MATHEMATICS. *Educ:* Am Int Col, BA, 59; Syracuse Univ, MS, 61, PhD(math), 66. *Prof Exp:* From asst prof to assoc prof, 65-72, PROF MATH, UNIV WIS-MADISON, 72- *Concurrent Pos:* Vis assoc prof, Purdue Univ, 70-71; vis prof, Calif Inst Technol. *Mem:* Math Asn Am; Am Math Soc. *Res:* Functions of a complex variable; tauberian theory; asymptotics; functional equations. *Mailing Add:* Dept of Math Univ of Wis Madison WI 53706

SHEA, JAMES H, b Eau Claire, Wis, Dec 20, 32; m 60; c 2. GEOLOGY. *Educ:* Univ Wis, BS, 58, MS, 60; Univ Ill, PhD(geol), 64. *Prof Exp:* Geologist, Texaco, Inc, 60-61; admin asst sec sch curric, Earth Sci Curric Proj, Am Geol Inst, 64-65, asst to dir, 65-66; asst prof geol, Univ Tenn, 66-67; assoc prof geol, 67-74, PROF EARTH SCI, UNIV WIS-PARKSIDE, 74- *Mem:* AAAS; fel Geol Soc Am; Am Asn Petrol Geologists; Nat Asn Geol Teachers; Soc Econ Paleont & Mineral. *Res:* Paleozoic stratigraphy; recent sediments; geological education; Pleistocene history; secondary school curriculum. *Mailing Add:* Dept of Geol Univ of Wis-Parkside Kenosha WI 53141

SHEA, JOHN RAYMOND MICHAEL, JR, b Burlington, Vt, Oct 9, 38; m 68. ANATOMY, HISTOLOGY. *Educ:* Rensselaer Polytech Inst, BS, 60; McGill Univ, MSc, 62, PhD(anat), 65; Univ Surrey, MSc, 75. *Prof Exp:* From sessional lectr to lectr anat, McGill Univ, 65-68; asst prof, 68-74, ASSOC PROF ANAT, JEFFERSON MED COL, 74- *Honors & Awards:* Christian R & Mary F Lindback Award, 70. *Mem:* Anat Soc Gr Brit & Ireland; Am Asn Anat. *Res:* Cytology; nuclear morphology; cytophotometric analysis. *Mailing Add:* Dept of Anat Jefferson Med Col Philadelphia PA 19107

SHEA, JOSEPH F(RANCIS), b New York, NY, Sept 5, 26; m 47; c 5. ENGINEERING MECHANICS. *Educ:* Univ Mich, BS, 46, MS, 50, PhD(eng mech), 55. *Prof Exp:* Instr eng mech, Univ Mich, 48-50 & 53-55; res mathematician, Bell Tel Labs, 50-53, engr, 55-59; dir advan systs, AC Spark Plug Div, Gen Motors Corp, 59-61; space prog dir, Space Tech Labs, Thompson Ramo Wooldridge, Inc, 61-62; dep dir systs eng, Off Manned Space Flight, NASA, 62-63, mgr Apollo Spacecraft Prog, Manned Spacecraft Ctr, 63-67, dep asst adminr manned space flight, Washington, DC, 67-68; vpres & gen mgr equip div, Raytheon Co, 68-69, sr vpres & gen mgr, 69-75, sr vpres & group exec, 75-78, SR V PRES & SPEC ASST TO PRES, SUBSIG DIV, ELECTROMAGNETIC SYSTS DIV, RAYTHEON SERV CO, 78- *Honors & Awards:* Arthur S Flemming Award, 65. *Mem:* Nat Acad Sci; Nat Acad Eng; fel Am Astronaut Soc; fel Am Inst Aeronaut & Astronaut. *Res:* Guidance and navigation, both radio and inertial; systems engineering; space technology. *Mailing Add:* Raytheon Serv Co 141 Spring St Lexington MA 02193

SHEA, MICHAEL FRANCIS, b Henderson, Ill, Sept 22, 33; m 61; c 5. ENGINEERING PHYSICS. *Educ:* Ill Benedictine Col, BS, 55; Univ Notre Dame, PhD(nuclear physics), 60. *Prof Exp:* Fel, Univ Notre Dame, 60-61; physicist, Midwestern Univs Res Asn, 61-64; res scientist space physics, Lockheed Palo Alto Res Labs, 64-67; assoc physicist, Argonne Nat Lab, 67-69; PHYSICIST, FERMI NAT ACCELERATOR LAB, 69- *Mem:* Am Phys Soc. *Res:* Bremstrahlung production; nuclear resonance fluorescence; space radiation measurements; satellite instrumentation; particle accelerator beam diagnostic instrumentation and measurements; computer control systems and microprocessor instrumentation. *Mailing Add:* Accelerator Div PO Box 500 Batavia IL 60510

SHEA, MICHAEL JOSEPH, b Eau Claire, Wis, Sept 4, 39; m 66; c 2. EXPERIMENTAL SOLID STATE PHYSICS. *Educ:* Marquette Univ, BS, 61; Univ Minn, Minneapolis, MS, 66; Bryn Mawr Col, PhD(physics), 69. *Prof Exp:* ASSOC PROF PHYSICS, CALIF STATE UNIV, SACRAMENTO, 69-, CHMN DEPT, 74- *Mem:* Am Asn Physics Teachers; Int Solar Energy Soc. *Res:* Photoproperties of lead monoxide; contact effects in solids; solar energy; holography. *Mailing Add:* Dept of Physics Calif State Univ Sacramento CA 95819

SHEA, PHILIP ALAN, b Malden, Mass, Aug 17, 40; m 65. BIOCHEMISTRY, NEUROBIOLOGY. *Educ:* Am Int Col, BA, 67; Ind Univ, PhD(biochem), 75. *Prof Exp:* Fel behavior, 75-77, ASST PROF NEUROCHEM & NEUROBIOL, DEPT PSYCHIAT, INST PSYCHIAT RES, MED CTR, IND UNIV, 77- *Mem:* Am Soc Neurochem; Soc Neurosci. *Res:* Neurochemistry of mental disorders in humans. *Mailing Add:* Inst of Psychiat Res Ind Univ Med Ctr Indianapolis IN 46202

SHEA, PHILIP JOSEPH, b Groton, NY, Dec 11, 21; m 49; c 3. PHARMACOLOGY, PHYSIOLOGY. *Educ:* Syracuse Univ, BS, 52, MS, 56. *Prof Exp:* Pharmacologist, Biochem Lab, 56-62, Human Health Labs, 62-72, Chem Biol Res Labs, 72, res specialist, 72-80, RES ASSOC, DOW CHEM CO, 80- *Mem:* AAAS; NY Acad Sci; Sigma Xi. *Res:* Cardiovascular-renal physiology and pharmacology; autonomic pharmacology; drug screening and evaluation. *Mailing Add:* Dow Chem Co PO Box 68511 Indianapolis IN 46268

SHEA, RICHARD FRANKLIN, b Boston, Mass, Sept 13, 03; m 30; c 3. ELECTRONICS, NUCLEAR INSTRUMENTATION. *Educ:* Mass Inst Technol, BS, 24. *Prof Exp:* Radio engr, Am Bosch Corp, 25-28, Amrad, Mass, 28-29, Kolster Radio Co, NJ, 29 & Atwater-Kent, Pa, 29-30; chief engr, Pilot Radio Corp, Mass, 30-31, Freed-Eisemann, NY, 32-34 & Fada Radio Co, 34-37; sect engr, Gen Elec Co, 37-50, mgr adv planning, Labs Dept, 50-54, res liaison, 54-55, consult engr, Knolls Atomic Power Lab, 55-63; CONSULT, 63- *Concurrent Pos:* Consult, War Assets Bd; ed consult, John Wiley & Sons, Inc; ed-in-chief, Nuclear & Plasma Sci Soc, Inst Elec & Electronics Engrs. *Honors & Awards:* Nuclear & Plasma Sci Soc Spec Award, 73. *Mem:* Fel Inst Elec & Electronics Engrs. *Res:* Design of radio receivers; circuits and novel application of new materials; application of electronics in nuclear field; solid state circuits and applications. *Mailing Add:* 255 Inner Dr E Venice FL 33595

SHEA, STEPHEN MICHAEL, b Galway, Ireland, Apr 25, 26. PATHOLOGY. *Educ:* Nat Univ Ireland, BSc, 48, MB & BCh, 50, MSc, 51, MD, 59; Am Bd Path, dipl, 60. *Prof Exp:* Asst lectr pharmacol, Univ Col, Dublin, 53-56; resident path, Mallory Inst Path, Boston City Hosp, 56-59; asst prof, Univ Toronto, 59-61; from instr path to instr math biol, Harvard Med Sch, 61-64, from assoc to assoc prof path, 65-73; PROF PATH, RUTGERS MED SCH, COL MENT & DENT NJ, 73- *Concurrent Pos:* NIH grants, 62 & 73; assoc pathologist, Mass Gen Hosp, 72-73. *Mem:* Am Asn Path & Bact; Electron Micros Soc Am; Am Soc Exp Path; Soc Math Biol; Biophys Soc. *Res:* Kinetic, morphometric and quantitative aspects of tissue and cellular structure; ultrastructure and microvascular permeability. *Mailing Add:* Dept of Path Rutgers Med Sch Piscataway NJ 08854

SHEA, TIMOTHY EDWARD, b Newton, Mass, Aug 6, 98; m 22; c 6. ELECTRICAL ENGINEERING. *Educ:* Mass Inst Technol, SB & SM, 19; Harvard Univ, SB, 19. *Hon Degrees:* ScD, Columbia Univ, 46; EngD, Case Inst Technol, 49. *Prof Exp:* Instr physics, Mass Inst Technol, 18-20; mem staff, Bell Tel Labs, New York, 21-39; dir war res, Columbia Univ, 41-45; pres, Teletype Corp, Chicago, 48-49; asst vpres, AT&T, New York, 50-52; vpres & gen mgr, Sandia Atomic Labs, Albuquerque, 52-54; vpres mfg, Western Elec Co, New York, 54-56, vpres personnel, 56-58, vpres eng & dir, 58-63; CONSULT, NAT ACAD SCI, 63- *Concurrent Pos:* Founder, Underwater Sound Lab, US Navy, 41; vpres, Bell Tel Labs, New York, 52-53, dir, 58-63; consult, US Navy, 55-; founder, Western Elec Eng Res Ctr, Princeton, NJ, 59; chmn undersea warfare comt, Nat Acad Sci, 64-72. *Honors & Awards:* Presidential Merit Medal, 46; Distinguished Civilian Serv Medal, 68. *Mem:* Emer mem Nat Acad Eng; fel Inst Radio Engrs; fel Acoust Soc Am. *Res:* Submarine detection devices; transmission networks and wave filters. *Mailing Add:* 92 Pine Grove Ave Summit NJ 07901

SHEA, TIMOTHY GUY, b Elmhurst, Ill, Aug 22, 39; m 66; c 1. ENVIRONMENTAL ENGINEERING. *Educ:* Loyola Univ Los Angeles, BS, 62; Univ Calif, Berkeley, MS, 63, PhD(environ eng), 68. *Prof Exp:* Res engr, Water Pollution Control Plant, Los Angeles County Sanit Dists, Calif, 63; asst mgr res & develop lab, Eng-Sci, Inc, 67-70, dir advan eng, Tech Ctr, 71-72; dir water qual control systs, Enviro-Eng Inc, 72-77; CHIEF ENVIRON ENG, TOUPS CORP, 77- *Mem:* Water Pollution Control Fedn; Int Asn Water Pollution Res (actg secy-treas, 67-69). *Res:* All aspects of environmental engineering related to water quality management, waste treatment, aquatic ecosystem modelling, resource allocation institutions, and storm water treatment. *Mailing Add:* Toups Corp 1370 Piccard Dr Rockville MD 20850

SHEALY, CLYDE NORMAN, b Columbia, SC, Dec 4, 32; m 59; c 3. HOLISTIC MEDICINE, NEUROSURGERY. *Educ:* Duke Univ, BSc & MD, 56; Humanistic Psychol Inst, PhD(psychol), 77. *Prof Exp:* Asst med, Sch Med, Duke Univ, 56-57; asst surg, Wash Univ, 57-58; teaching fel, Sch Med, Harvard Univ, 62-63; sr instr neurosurg, Sch Med, Western Reserve Univ, 63-66, asst prof, 66; chief, Dept Neurosurg, Gundersen Clin & Lutheran Hosp, LaCrosse, Wis, 66-71; CLIN ASSOC, DEPT PSYCHOL, UNIV WIS-LACROSSE, 71- *Concurrent Pos:* Asst clin prof neurosurg, Sch Med, Univ Wis, 67-74; assoc clin prof, Sch Med, Univ Minn, 70-75; sr dolorologist, Pain & Health Rehab Ctr; pres, Holos Inst Health. *Mem:* Am Holistic Med Asn (pres, 78-80); Am Asn Neurol Surgeons; AMA; Am Asn Study Pain; Am Asn Study Headache. *Res:* Holistic medicine, integration of body, mind, emotion, and spirit; psychophysiologic basis of stress. *Mailing Add:* Rte 2 Welsh Coulee LaCrosse WI 54601

SHEALY, DAVID LEE, b Newberry, SC, Sept 16, 44; m 69. OPTICS. *Educ:* Univ Ga, BS, 66, PhD(physics): 73. *Prof Exp:* Syst analyst, Dept Physics, Univ Ga, 73; ASST PROF PHYSICS, UNIV ALA, BIRMINGHAM, 73- *Concurrent Pos:* Consult, Dept Physics, Univ Ga, 75- *Mem:* Optical Soc Am; Acoust Soc Am; Am Asn Physics Teachers; Am Phys Soc; Am Inst Aeronaut & Astronaut. *Res:* Formulation and implementation of new optical design techniques based on analytical expressions for the illuminance and the caustic surface of an optical system. *Mailing Add:* Dept Physics Univ Ala Birmingham AL 35294

SHEALY, HARRY EVERETT, JR, b Columbia, SC, Oct 24, 42; m 65; c 2. BIOLOGY, BOTANY. *Educ:* Univ SC, BS, 65, MS, 71, PhD(biol), 72. *Prof Exp:* Fel plant sci, Univ Man, 72-73; ASSOC PROF BIOL, UNIV SC, 73- *Mem:* Bot Soc Am. *Res:* Biology of reproduction in seed plants; vascular plant systematics. *Mailing Add:* Div of Sci & Math 171 University Pkwy Aiken SC 29801

SHEALY, OTIS LESTER, b Little Mountain, SC, Oct 3, 23; m 50; c 4. ORGANIC CHEMISTRY, TEXTILES. *Educ:* Newberry Col, AB, 44; Univ NC, PhD(chem), 50. *Hon Degrees:* ScD, Newberry Col, 68. *Prof Exp:* Instr org chem, Univ NC, 48-49; res chemist, 50-52, res supvr, 52-55, res mgr, 55-59, prod develop mgr, 59-64, res dir, 64-66, TECH DIR, E I DU PONT DE NEMOURS & CO, INC, 66- *Mem:* Fel Brit Textile Inst; Am Chem Soc; Fiber Soc; NY Acad Sci. *Res:* Polyester and polyamide fibers engineering of sheet structures. *Mailing Add:* 109 Walnut Ridge Rd Wilmington DE 19807

SHEALY, Y(ODER) FULMER, b Chapin, SC, Feb 26, 23; m 50; c 3. ORGANIC CHEMISTRY, MEDICINAL CHEMISTRY. *Educ:* Univ SC, BS, 43; Univ Ill, PhD(chem), 49. *Prof Exp:* Chemist, Nat Defense Res Comt, 43-45; asst chem, Univ Ill, 45-47; Abbot Labs fel, Univ Minn, 49-50; res chemist, Upjohn Co, 50-56; asst prof chem, Univ SC, 56-57; sr chemist, 57-59, sect head, 59-66, DIV HEAD, SOUTHERN RES INST, 66- *Mem:* AAAS; NY Acad Sci; Int Soc Heterocyclic Chem; Am Chem Soc; Acad Pharmaceut Sci. *Res:* Heterocyclic compounds; triazenes; steroids; anticancer agents; nucleoside analogs; folic acid analogs; hydrazines and azo compounds; antiviral agents; retinoids. *Mailing Add:* Southern Res Inst 2000 Ninth Ave S Birmingham AL 35255

SHEAN, GERALD MICHAEL, JR, b Washington, DC, Feb 19, 27; m 55; c 6. ELECTROCHEMISTRY. *Educ:* Carleton Col, BA, 50; Univ Mo, PhD(plant physiol), 58. *Prof Exp:* Prin high sch, Mont, 50-51; RES CHEMIST, NAT INST ARTHRITIS METAB & DIGESTIVE DIS, 58- *Mem:* Am Chem Soc; Am Soc Plant Physiol. *Res:* Electrochemistry of permselective oil and porous membranes; transport properties of oil membranes; artificial membrane models of biological membranes; carrier mechanisms for ionic movement across porous and liquid ion exchanger membranes. *Mailing Add:* Lab of Chem Phys Nat Inst of Arthritis Metab & Digestive Dis Bethesda MD 20014

SHEAR, CHARLES ROBERT, b Chicago, Ill, Jan 20, 42; m 66. ANATOMY, NEUROBIOLOGY. *Educ:* Univ Ill, BS, 65; Columbia Univ, MA, 67, PhD(biol sci), 69. *Prof Exp:* Leverhulme Trust vis fel, Univ Hull, 69-70; instr, Emory Univ, 70-71, asst prof anat, 71-80; MEM FAC DEPT ANAT, SCH MED, UNIV MD, BALTIMORE, 80- *Mem:* AAAS; Am Asn Anat; Am Soc Cell Biol; Am Soc Zoologists. *Res:* Ultrastructural aspects of skeletal muscle growth, development and regeneration; cellular organization and function of the neural retina; electron microscopy. *Mailing Add:* Dept Anat Univ Md Sch Med Baltimore MD 21201

SHEAR, CORNELIUS BARRETT, b Vienna, Va, Sept 24, 12; m 35; c 3. PLANT PHYSIOLOGY. *Educ:* Univ Md, BS, 34, MS, 38. *Prof Exp:* Agent, Crops Res Div, Sci & Educ Admin, Agr Res, USDA, 33-35, asst sci aide, 35-39, from jr physiologist to sr plant physiologist, 39-63, prin res plant physiologist, 63-77; RETIRED. *Honors & Awards:* J H Gourley Award, 59. *Mem:* Int Soc Hort Sci; fel Am Soc Hort Sci. *Res:* Mineral nutrition of fruit trees and tissue analysis as means of determining their nutrient status; physiology of corking and relation of nutrition, especially calcium to quality in apples. *Mailing Add:* 4218 Kenny St Beltsville MD 20705

SHEAR, DAVID BEN, b Boston, Mass, Jan 26, 38; div; c 2. BIOPHYSICS. *Educ:* Swarthmore Col, BA, 59; Brandeis Univ, PhD(biophys), 66. *Prof Exp:* NIH fel, Univ Buffalo, 66-67; asst prof physics, Univ Ga, 67-69; asst prof, 67-73, ASSOC PROF BIOCHEM, UNIV MO-COLUMBIA, 73- *Mem:* Biophys Soc. *Res:* Applications of thermodynamics, kinetics and statistical mechanics to biology; bioenergetics; muscle contraction; photosynthesis; mathematical models in biology. *Mailing Add:* 1523 St Michael Dr Columbia MO 65201

SHEAR, LEROY, b Baltimore, Md, Feb 20, 33; m 55; c 2. INTERNAL MEDICINE, NEPHROLOGY. *Educ:* Johns Hopkins Univ, BA, 53; Univ Md, MD, 57; Am Bd Internal Med, dipl, 59. *Prof Exp:* Res fel nutrit & metab, Western Reserve Univ, 61-62; USPHS trainee, Cleveland Metrop Gen Hosp, 62-63, assoc physician, 66-69; sr instr med, Case Western Reserve Univ, 66-67, asst prof, 67-69; assoc prof, Sch Med & dir nephrol sect, Sch Med, Temple Univ, 69-73; dir renal sect, Med Ctr Western Mass, Springfield, 73-77; clin assoc prof, 73-76, CLIN PROF MED, SCH MED, TUFTS UNIV, 76-; MED DIR, WESTERN MASS KIDNEY CTR, SPRINGFIELD, 77- *Mem:* AAAS; Am Fedn Clin Res; Am Soc Artificial Internal Organs; Am Soc Nephrol; Soc Exp Biol & Med. *Res:* Metabolic aspects of renal and hepatic disease. *Mailing Add:* Baystate Med Ctr 759 Chestnut St Springfield MA 01107

SHEAR, WILLIAM ALBERT, b Coudersport, Pa, July 5, 42; m 80. BIOLOGY. *Educ:* Col Wooster, BA, 63; Univ NMex, MS, 65; Harvard Univ, PhD(evolutionary biol), 71. *Prof Exp:* Asst prof biol, Concord Col, 70-74; assoc prof, 74-80, PROF BIOL, HAMPDEN-SYDNEY COL, 81- *Concurrent Pos:* Res assoc, Am Mus Natural Hist, 78- *Honors & Awards:* John Peter Mettauer Award, 80. *Mem:* Sigma Xi; Am Arachnol Soc. *Res:* Behavior, taxonomy and biogeography of arachnids and myriapods; early evolution of land animals; revisions of families and genera of Opiliones and Diplopoda, especially North American forms; web-building behavior of spiders; Devonian fossils of arachnids and myriapods. *Mailing Add:* Dept of Biol Hampden-Sydney Col Hampden-Sydney VA 23943

SHEARD, JOHN LEO, b Southbridge, Mass, Feb 24, 24; m 47; c 4. INORGANIC CHEMISTRY. *Educ:* Harvard Univ, AB, 45, AM, 47; Univ Minn, PhD(chem), 53. *Prof Exp:* Instr chem, Northeastern Univ, 46-47; res chemist, Electrochem Div, 52-70, staff scientist, 70-78, RES ASSOC, ELECTRONICS DIV, E I DU PONT DE NEMOURS & CO, INC, 78- *Mem:* Am Ceramic Soc. *Res:* Fabrication of multilayer capacitors; ferrocyanides and ferricyanides; oxygen fluorides; acrylonitrile and pulp bleaching; precious metal compositions for solid state circuitry. *Mailing Add:* 88 Sundow Trail Williamsville NY 14221

SHEARD, MICHAEL HENRY, b Manchester, Eng, Aug 23, 27; US citizen; m 52; c 3. PSYCHIATRY, NEUROPHARMACOLOGY. *Educ:* Univ Manchester, MB & ChB, 51, MD, 64; Am Bd Psychiat & Neurol, dipl, 61; Royal Col Physicians, DPM, 62. *Prof Exp:* NIMH fel psychiat, Yale Univ, 62-64; from res assoc psychiat & pharmacol to assoc prof psychiat res, 64-78, PROF PSYCHIAT RES, YALE UNIV, 78- *Concurrent Pos:* Consult, Conn Dept Corrections, 58- *Mem:* Fel Am Psychiat Asn; fel Royal Col Physicians. *Res:* Relationship between brain and behavior. *Mailing Add:* Dept of Psychiat Yale Univ Sch of Med New Haven CT 06520

SHEARER, CHARLES M, b Ashland, Ohio, July 30, 31; m 58. ANALYTICAL ORGANIC CHEMISTRY. *Educ:* ETenn State Col, BA, 53; Univ Detroit, MS, 64, PhD(chem), 68. *Prof Exp:* Chemist, Columbus Coated Fabrics, 54-55; res chemist, Parke, Davis & Co, 57-66; UNIT SUPVR, WYETH LABS, 68- *Mem:* AAAS; NY Acad Sci; Am Inst Chemists; Am Chem Soc. *Res:* Analysis and determination of rates of degradation of pharmaceuticals. *Mailing Add:* 380 Arden Rd Conshohocken PA 19428

SHEARER, DUNCAN ALLAN, b Kamsack, Sask, Feb 15, 20; m 46; c 2. ANALYTICAL CHEMISTRY. *Educ:* Univ Sask, BA, 48, MA, 50; Univ Toronto, PhD(org chem), 54. *Prof Exp:* Res scientist, Can Dept Agr, 54-73, sr res scientist, 73-80; RETIRED. *Mem:* Fel Chem Inst Can; Spectros Soc Can. *Res:* Lignin; organo-mercury chemistry; analytical methods in agriculture; pheromones of the honeybee. *Mailing Add:* 1182 Gateway Rd Ottawa ON K2C 2W9 Can

SHEARER, EDMUND COOK, b Birmingham, Ala, May 20, 42; m 66; c 3. PHYSICAL CHEMISTRY. *Educ:* Ark Polytech Col, BS, 64; Univ Ark, PhD(chem), 69. *Prof Exp:* Asst prof, 68-74, ASSOC PROF CHEM, FT HAYS STATE UNIV, 74- *Mem:* Am Chem Soc. *Res:* Reaction kinetics, atmospheric precipitation studies; chemical species in reservoirs. *Mailing Add:* Dept of Chem Ft Hays State Univ Hays KS 67601

SHEARER, GREG OTIS, b Washington, DC, May 2, 47; m 68; c 4. PHYSICAL ORGANIC CHEMISTRY. *Educ:* Iowa State Univ, BS, 69; Creighton Univ, MS, 71; Univ Kans, PhD(med chem), 76. *Prof Exp:* ASST PROF CHEM, CREIGHTON UNIV, 75- *Mem:* Am Chem Soc. *Res:* Mechanistic studies of organic and biochemical reactions. *Mailing Add:* Dept of Chem Creighton Univ 2500 California St Omaha NE 68178

SHEARER, J(ESSE) LOWEN, b Marengo, Ill, Apr 25, 21; m 44; c 3. MECHANICAL ENGINEERING. *Educ:* Ill Inst Technol, BS, 44; Mass Inst Technol, SM, 50, ME, 52, ScD, 54. *Prof Exp:* Eng trainee, Sundstrand Mach Tool Co, 39-44; asst mech eng, Mass Inst Technol, 49-51, from instr to assoc prof, 51-63, supvr automatic control systs div, 58-63; Rockwell prof eng, 63-74, dir systs & controls lab, 64-76, PROF MECH ENG, PA STATE UNIV, 74- *Concurrent Pos:* Guest scientist, Swedish Inst Textile Res, 56-57; consult; chmn component comt, Am Automatic Control Coun, 61-63, chmn tech comt components, Int Fedn Automatic Control, 66-69; vis prof, Tokyo Inst Technol, 69; guest scientist, Royal Inst Technol, Sweden, 70; tech ed, Am Soc Mech Engrs J Dynamic Systs, Measurement & Control, 76- *Honors & Awards:* Donald P Eckman Award, Instrument Soc Am, 65; Richards Mem Award, Am Soc Mech Engrs, 66. *Mem:* Fel Am Soc Mech Engrs; Am Soc Eng Educ; Instrument Soc Am; Am Inst Aeronaut & Astronaut. *Res:* Automatic control systems; mechanical, electrical and fluid control systems; design of engineering systems; materials recycling and resource recovery systems. *Mailing Add:* 136 Redwood Lane College Township PA 16801

SHEARER, JAMES WELLES, b New York, NY, July 3, 24; m 51; c 2. PLASMA PHYSICS. *Educ:* Mass Inst Technol, BS, 45, PhD, 50. *Prof Exp:* Physicist, Tracerlab, Inc, 51-57; PHYSICIST, LAWRENCE LIVERMORE LAB, UNIV CALIF, 57- *Mem:* Am Phys Soc; Am Meteorol Soc. *Res:* Fusion plasmas; electron and ion beams; x-ray and neutron radiations. *Mailing Add:* Lawrence Livermore Lab L-637 PO Box 5511 Livermore CA 94550

SHEARER, NEWTON HENRY, JR, b Lynchburg, Va, Nov 29, 20; m 55; c 2. ORGANIC CHEMISTRY. *Educ:* Lynchburg Col, AB, 41; Univ Va, MS, 44, PhD(org chem), 46. *Prof Exp:* Res chemist, 46-52, sr res chemist, 52-61, mgr, Eastman Res AG, Switz, 61-63, res assoc, 63-65, mgr tech info serv, 66-81, MGR TECH INFO SERV, EASTMAN CHEM DIV, TENN EASTMAN CO, 81- *Mem:* Am Chem Soc. *Res:* Condensation polymers; polyolefins; adhesives; organometallics; technical information storage, retrieval and analysis. *Mailing Add:* Res Labs Tenn Eastman Co Kingsport TN 37662

SHEARER, RAYMOND CHARLES, b Anaheim, Calif, June 3, 35; m 56; c 10. FORESTRY. *Educ:* Utah State Univ, BS, 57, MS, 59. *Prof Exp:* SULVICULTURIST, INTERMOUNTAIN FOREST & RANGE EXP STA, FOREST SERV, USDA, 57- *Mem:* Soc Am Foresters; Forest Hist Soc. *Res:* Regeneration of Larix occidentalis and Picea engelmannii including seed production, seed dissemination, germination, causes of seedling mortality and development; cutting methods and growth and mortality in western larch forests. *Mailing Add:* Forestry Sci Lab Drawer G Missoula MT 59806

SHEARER, THOMAS ROBERT, b South Bend, Ind, Aug 11, 42; m 64; c 2. BIOCHEMISTRY. *Educ:* Beloit Col, BA, 64; Univ Wis, MS, 67, PhD(biochem), 69. *Prof Exp:* Fel biochem, Univ Wis, 69; asst prof, 69-74, assoc prof, 74-80, PROF NUTRIT & DIR DIV, DENT & MED SCHS, ORE HEALTH SCI UNIV, 80- *Concurrent Pos:* Sabbatical biochem, Univ Wis, 76. *Res:* Effects of toxic amounts of fluoride on intermediary metabolism in animals; selenium distribution in animals and biological materials; mechanism of selenium, induced calaracl. *Mailing Add:* Dept of Biochem Univ of Ore Dent Sch Portland OR 97201

SHEARER, WILLIAM MCCAGUE, b Zanesville, Ohio, June 24, 26; m 54; c 2. SPEECH & HEARING SCIENCE. *Educ:* Ind Univ, BA, 51; Western Mich Univ, MA, 54; Univ Denver, PhD(speech), 58. *Prof Exp:* Asst prof speech path, Minot State Col, 54-56; PROF COMMUN DISORDERS, NORTHERN ILL UNIV, 58- *Concurrent Pos:* Fel, Sch Med, Stanford Univ, 63-64; vis prof, Commun Sci Lab, Univ Fla, 68-69. *Mem:* Am Speech & Hearing Asn; Am Asn Phonetic Sci. *Res:* Anatomy of speech and hearing. *Mailing Add:* Speech & Hearing Clin Northern Ill Univ De Kalb IL 60115

SHEARER, WILLIAM THOMAS, b Detroit, Mich, Aug 23, 37. ALLERGY, IMMUNOLOGY. *Educ:* Univ Detroit, BS, 60; Wayne State Univ, PhD(biochem), 66; Wash Univ, MD, 70. *Prof Exp:* Asst pediat, Wash Univ, 70-72, from instr to prof, 72-78; PROF PEDIAT, MICROBIOL & IMMUNOL, BAYLOR COL MED, 78- *Concurrent Pos:* Res award, Detroit News Found, 65; fel chem, Ind Univ, 66-67; res fel, USPHS, 72-74; res scholar award, Cystic Fibrosis Found, 74; dir div immunol, St Louis Children's Hosp, 74-76, dir div allergy & immunol, 76-78; from assoc pediatrician to pediatrician, Barnes Hosp, 76-78; fac res award, Am Cancer Soc, 77; head sect allergy & immunol, Baylor Col Med, 78-; chief allergy & immunol serv, Tex Children's Hosp, Houston, 78-; dir, Allergy & Immunol Training Prog, Baylor Col Med, 79- *Mem:* Sigma Xi; Am Asn Immunologists; fel Am Acad Pediat; Soc Pediat Res; fel Am Acad Allergy. *Res:* Tumor immunology; interaction of antibody and complement with cell membrane antigens; immunodeficiency diseases of children; allergic disorders of children; cystic fibrosis. *Mailing Add:* Dept of Pediat 1200 Moursund Ave Houston TX 77030

SHEARN, ALLEN DAVID, b Chicago, Ill, May 27, 42; m 64; c 1. DEVELOPMENTAL GENETICS. *Educ:* Univ Chicago, BA, 64; Calif Inst Technol, PhD(genetics), 69. *Prof Exp:* Helen Hay Whitney Found res fel molecular biophys & biochem, Yale Univ, 68-71; from asst prof to assoc prof,

71-81, PROF BIOL, JOHNS HOPKINS UNIV, 81- *Concurrent Pos:* Consult, Genetic Biol Adv Panel, NSF, 72-75. *Mem:* AAAS; Soc Develop Biol; Genetics Soc Am. *Res:* Applying the techniques of molecular biology to the study of the regulation of development in higher organisms. *Mailing Add:* Dept of Biol Johns Hopkins Baltimore MD 21218

SHEARN, MARTIN ALVIN, b New York, NY, Dec 19, 23; m 51; c 3. INTERNAL MEDICINE, RHEUMATOLOGY. *Educ:* Ohio Univ, AB, 43; New York Med Col, MD, 49; Am Bd Internal Med, dipl, 56. *Prof Exp:* From intern to resident med, Bellevue Hosp, New York, 49-52, from clin asst vis physician to asst attend physician, 53-55; DIR MED EDUC, KAISER FOUND HOSP, OAKLAND, 56-; CLIN PROF MED, UNIV CALIF, SAN FRANCISCO, 75- *Concurrent Pos:* Res fel cardiol, Sch Med, Stanford Univ, 52-53; instr, Med Sch, NY Univ, 53-55; from instr to asst clin prof med, Med Ctr, Univ Calif, San Francisco, 59-68, assoc prof med, Sch Med, 68-75, clin prof, 75-; consult, Vet Admin Hosp; attend physician, Highland Hosp, Oakland; chmn, Northern Calif Sect, Arthritis Found, 66; ed, Rheumatic Dis, Med Clin NAm; prof med, Univ Fed de Alagoas, Brazil. *Mem:* AMA; Am Heart Asn; fel Am Col Physicians; Am Fedn Clin Res. *Res:* Connective tissue disorders; rheumatic diseases; medical history; author of over 50 publications. *Mailing Add:* 1815 Arlington Ave El Cerrito CA 94530

SHEASLEY, WILLIAM DAVID, b Youngstown, Ohio, Oct 31, 46; m 69; c 2. PHYSICAL CHEMISTRY, POLYMER SCIENCE. *Educ:* Grove City Col, BS, 68; Ohio State Univ, MS, 70, PhD(phys chem), 72. *Prof Exp:* Fel chem lasers, Cornell Univ, 72-73; sr chemist, 73-79, RES SECT MGR, ROHM AND HAAS CO, 79- *Mem:* Am Chem Soc; Soc Rheology. *Res:* Analytical research, materials and polymer characterization; particular emphasis on surface analysis, microscopy and rheology. *Mailing Add:* Rohm and Haas Co Box 219 Bristol PA 19007

SHEATS, GEORGE FREDERIC, b Reno, Nev, Dec 19, 27; m 53; c 3. PHYSICAL CHEMISTRY. *Educ:* Univ Calif, BS, 51; Univ Rochester, PhD(phys chem), 55. *Prof Exp:* Res chemist, Am Cyanamid Co, 55-62; assoc prof chem, 62-69, chmn dept comput sci, 70-75, PROF CHEM, STATE UNIV NY COL PLATTSBURGH, 69- *Mem:* Am Chem Soc. *Res:* Absorption spectroscopy; microcalorimetry; ion chromatography; kinetics of aromatic nitration; lumninescence of inorganic complexes. *Mailing Add:* Dept Chem State Univ of NY Col Plattsburg NY 12901

SHEATS, JOHN EUGENE, b Atlanta, Ga, Dec 20, 39; m 72; c 1. ORGANOMETALLIC CHEMISTRY, PHYSICAL ORGANIC CHEMISTRY. *Educ:* Duke Univ, BS, 61; Mass Inst Technol, PhD(chem), 66. *Prof Exp:* Asst prof chem, Bowdoin Col, 65-70; assoc prof, 70-78, PROF, RIDER COL, 78- *Mem:* Am Chem Soc; Sigma Xi. *Res:* Mechanism of decomposition of benzenediazonium ion; synthesis and properties of substituted Cobalticinium salts and other organo-transition metal compounds; preparation of organo-metallic polymers; biomedical applications of organometallic compounds. *Mailing Add:* Dept of Chem Rider Col Lawrenceville NJ 08648

SHECHMEISTER, ISAAC LEO, b Windaw, Latvia, June 11, 13; nat US; m 38; c 2. MEDICAL MICROBIOLOGY. *Educ:* Univ Calif, AB, 34, MA, 35, PhD(bact), 49; Am Bd Microbiol, dipl. *Prof Exp:* Asst bact, Univ Calif, 36-39, lectr epidemiol, Sch Pub Health, 46, prin bacteriologist, Infectious Dis Proj, 46-50; asst prof bact & immunol, Sch Med, Washington Univ, 50-52, asst prof microbiol, 52-53, assoc prof bact, Sch Dent, 53-57; assoc prof microbiol, 57-64, PROF MICROBIOL, SOUTHERN ILL UNIV, 64- *Concurrent Pos:* Consult, Radiol Defense Lab, US Dept Navy, Calif, 46-51; spec fel biophys, Statens Seruminstitut, Denmark, 66-67. *Mem:* Am Soc Microbiol; Am Asn Immunol. *Res:* Electron microscopy of antigen-antibody reactions; animal virology and immunology; dental caries. *Mailing Add:* Dept Microbiol Southern Ill Univ Carbondale IL 62901

SHECHTER, HAROLD, b New York, NY, July 12, 21. ORGANIC CHEMISTRY. *Educ:* Univ SC, BS, 41; Purdue Univ, PhD(chem), 46. *Prof Exp:* Asst chem, Purdue Univ, 41-42; from asst prof to assoc prof, 46-70, PROF CHEM, OHIO STATE UNIV, 70- *Mem:* Am Chem Soc. *Res:* Nitration of saturated hydrocarbons; mechanics of addition reactions of oxides of nitrogen; synthesis of polynitro compounds; kinetics of neutralization of pseudo acids; mechanisms of reactions of hydrazoic acid; homomorphic ring strain; chemistry of small ring compounds; alkylation of ambident ions; decomposition of carbenes. *Mailing Add:* Dept of Chem Ohio State Univ Columbus OH 43210

SHECHTER, LEON, b New York, NY, Dec 19, 12; m 37. ORGANIC CHEMISTRY, POLYMER CHEMISTRY. *Educ:* Univ SC, BS, 33, MS, 34; Univ Cincinnati, PhD(org chem), 37. *Prof Exp:* Asst, Univ Cincinnati, 34-37; res chemist, Union Carbide Plastics Co, 37-44, head coating resins res, 44-52, sect head plastics res, 52-56, asst dir res, 56-58, resident dir, 58-59, dir, 60-61, dir polymer res & develop, 61-63, dir appln res & develop, 63-64, vpres res & develop, 64-67, vpres res & develop chem & plastics, Union Carbide Corp, 67-74, vpres exploratory technol, Patents & Licensing Chem & Plastics, 74-77; CONSULT, 77- *Mem:* Am Chem Soc. *Res:* Alkyds; vinyl polymers; silicones; epoxy resins; phenolics; research and development management-long range research chemicals and plastics; patent management and licensing. *Mailing Add:* 22 Harvey Dr Summit NJ 07901

SHECHTER, YAAKOV, b Tel Aviv, Israel, Feb 11, 34; US citizen; m 59. HUMAN GENETICS, GENETIC COUNSELING. *Educ:* Univ Calif, Los Angeles, BSc, 59, PhD(plant sci), 65, cert med mycol, 67. *Prof Exp:* Res asst agr sci, Univ Calif, Los Angeles, 60-64, fel med mycol, Sch Med, 65-66; lectr bot, Univ Southern Calif, 66-67; res biochemist, Sch Med, Univ Calif, Los Angeles, 67-69; from asst prof to assoc prof, 69-76, PROF BIOL SCI, LEHMAN COL, 76- *Concurrent Pos:* Adj curator, NY Bot Garden, 69-; consult, Human Affairs Res Ctr, NY; vis assoc prof, Stein-Moore Lab, Rockefeller Univ, 75-76; lectr, Dept Pediat, Div Genetics, Col Physicians & Surgeons, Columbia Univ, 80- *Mem:* Sigma Xi; NY Acad Sci; Inst Soc, Ethics & Life Sci; Am Soc Human Genetics. *Res:* Human genetics; genetics of keratins; genetic counseling. *Mailing Add:* Dept of Biol Sci Herbert H Lehman Col Bronx NY 10468

SHEDD, DONALD POMROY, b New Haven, Conn, Aug 4, 22; m 46; c 4. SURGERY. *Educ:* Yale Univ, BS, 44, MD, 46. *Prof Exp:* Intern surg, Yale Univ, 46-47, from asst resident to resident, 50-53, from instr to assoc prof, 53-67; CHIEF DEPT HEAD & NECK SURG, ROSWELL PARK MEM INST, 67-; ASSOC RES PROF, STATE UNIV NY BUFFALO, 70- *Concurrent Pos:* Harvey Cushing fel surg res, Yale Univ, 49-50; Markle scholar med sci, 53-58; mem head & neck cancer group, Nat Head & Neck Cancer Cadre, 73- *Mem:* Soc Univ Surg; Soc Head & Neck Surg (treas, 71-, pres, 76-77); Am Col Surg; Sigma Xi. *Res:* Oncology, particularly in head and neck cancer; physiology of deglution; speech rehabilitation. *Mailing Add:* Dept Head & Neck Surg Roswell Park Mem Inst Buffalo NY 14263

SHEDLARSKI, JOSEPH GEORGE, JR, b Forty Fort, Pa, Mar 15, 39. MICROBIAL BIOCHEMISTRY. *Educ:* King's Col, Pa, BS, 61; St John's Univ, NY, MS, 63; Princeton Univ, MA, 66, PhD(biochem sci), 69; La State Univ, DDS, 81. *Prof Exp:* Instr biol, Col Misericordia, 63-64; asst prof biol, Univ New Orleans, 71-75, assoc prof, 76-77. *Concurrent Pos:* Can Nat Cancer Inst fel, McMaster Univ, 69-71; res award, Am Asn Dent, 81. *Mem:* AAAS; Am Soc Microbiol; Am Chem Soc; Int Union Biochem; Am Dent Asn. *Res:* Microbial cell wall/sheath structure; biogenesis; regulation; sugar transport in bacteria. *Mailing Add:* 1418 Airline Dr Bossier City LA 71112

SHEDLER, GERALD STUART, b New York, NY, May 8, 39; m 68. OPERATIONS RESEARCH, COMPUTER SCIENCE. *Educ:* Amherst Col, BA, 61; Tufts Univ, MA, 64. *Prof Exp:* Asst scientist appl math, Res & Advan Develop Div, Avco Corp, 62-64; res staff mem comput sci, T J Watson Res Ctr, IBM Corp, 65-70; actg assoc prof oper res, Stanford Univ, 73-74; RES STAFF MEM COMPUT SCI, SAN JOSE RES LAB, IBM CORP, 70-73, 74- *Concurrent Pos:* Actg assoc prof, Dept Oper Res, Stanford Univ, 75-76; vis lectr, Math Asn Am, 77-81; consult assoc propf dept oper res, Stanford Univ, 78-80; lectr dept info sci, Victoria Univ, NZ, 79. *Mem:* Asn Comput Mach. *Res:* Stochastic processes and their applicationse; discrete event simulation of stochastic systems; computer system performance analysis. *Mailing Add:* IBM San Jose Res Lab K51/61F 5600 Cottle Rd San Jose CA 95193

SHEDLOVSKY, LEO, colloid chemistry, electrochemistry, deceased

SHEDRICK, CARL F(RANKLIN), b South Bend, Ind, Aug 2, 20; m 46; c 3. CHEMICAL ENGINEERING. *Educ:* Purdue Univ, BS, 42; Columbia Univ, MSE, 48. *Prof Exp:* Res engr, E I du Pont de Nemours & Co, Inc, NJ, 42-50, tech economist, Polychem Dept, Del, 50-67, CHEM ENG, PLASTICS DEPT, E I DU PONT DE NEMOURS & CO, INC, 67- *Mem:* Am Chem Soc; Am Inst Chem Engrs. *Res:* Process development of plastic materials; process and equipment design; applications research; economic evaluation. *Mailing Add:* 2535 Deepwood Dr Wilmington DE 19810

SHEEHAN, BERNARD STEPHEN, b Halifax, NS, July 25, 35; m 59; c 4. INFORMATION SYSTEMS. *Educ:* NS Tech Col, BE, 57; Mass Inst Technol, SM, 61; Univ Conn, PhD(elec eng), 65. *Prof Exp:* Engr, Can Gen Elec Co, 57-58; lectr eng, St Mary's Univ, NS, 58-59; teaching asst, Mass Inst Technol, 59-61; instr, Univ Conn, 61-65; dean arts & sci, St Mary's Univ, NS, 65-67; asst to acad vpres, 67-69, dir, Off Instnl Res, 69-81, PROF FAC MGT, UNIV CALGARY, 81- *Concurrent Pos:* Can Coun res grant, 73-74; consult, Alta Advan Educ & Manpower, 75-77. *Mem:* Asn Instnl Res (vpres, 74-75, pres, 75-76). *Res:* Analysis in management, including institutional and system-wide problems in planning, resource allocation and decision processes; information technology. *Mailing Add:* Fac Mgt MA 526 Univ Calgary Calgary AB T2N 1N4 Can

SHEEHAN, DESMOND, b Aldershot, Eng, Apr 8, 31; m 57; c 4. ORGANIC CHEMISTRY. *Educ:* Univ Reading, BSc, 55; Yale Univ, MS, 61, PhD(chem), 64. *Prof Exp:* Sci asst chem, Ministry Supply, Eng, 47-50, exp officer, 52 & 55-56; res chemist, Microcell Ltd, 56-58 & Am Cyanamid Co, Conn, 58-65; dir res, Techni-Chem Co, Conn, 65-70; sr res assoc, 70-72, MGR ORG RES, CORP RES LAB, ALLIED CHEM CORP, MORRISTOWN, 72- *Mem:* Fel Am Chem Soc; The Chem Soc. *Res:* Synthetic organic chemistry; reaction mechanism. *Mailing Add:* 31 Maple Ave Mendham NJ 07945

SHEEHAN, JAMES ELMER, b Waukegan, Ill, Feb 26, 44; m 68; c 2. MATERIALS SCIENCE. *Educ:* Univ Wis, BS, 66, MS, 67; Rensselaer Polytech Inst, PhD(mat sci), 73. *Prof Exp:* Develop engr metall & ceramics, Ford Sci Lab, 67-69; res engr, Savannah River Lab, 72-74; STAFF SCIENTIST & BR MGR CERAMICS, GEN ATOMIC CO, 74- *Mem:* Am Soc Metals; Am Ceramic Soc. *Res:* Fabrication of powder metals and ceramics; physical properties of ceramics creep and mechanical behavior. *Mailing Add:* Gen Atomic Co PO Box 81608 San Diego CA 92138

SHEEHAN, JOHN CLARK, b Battle Creek, Mich, Sept 23, 15; m 41; c 3. ORGANIC CHEMISTRY. *Educ:* Battle Creek Col, BS, 37; Univ Mich, MS, 38, PhD(org chem), 41. *Hon Degrees:* DSc, Univ Notre Dame, 63. *Prof Exp:* Res assoc, Nat Defense Res Comt Proj, Univ Mich, 41; res chemist, Merck & Co, Inc, NJ, 41-46; from asst prof to prof chem, 46-76, EMER PROF ORG CHEM, MASS INST TECHNOL, 76- *Concurrent Pos:* Sci liaison officer, Off Naval Res, 53-54; Reilly lectr, Univ Notre Dame, 53; Swiss-Am Found lectr, 58; ed-in-chief, Org Syntheses, 58; McGregory lectr, Colgate Univ, 58; Bachmann lectr, Univ Mich, 60; Dakin Mem lectr, Adelphi, 61. *Honors & Awards:* Am Chem Soc Awards, 51 & 59; Medal, Synthetic Org Chem Mfrs Asn, 68; Outstanding Achievement Award, Univ Mich, 71. *Mem:* Nat Acad Sci; Am Chem Soc; Am Acad Arts & Sci; NY Acad Sci; Royal Soc Chem. *Res:* Synthetic penicillin; lactams; amino acids; peptides; alkaloids; steroids and the synthesis of high explosives. *Mailing Add:* Dept of Chem Mass Inst of Technol Cambridge MA 02139

SHEEHAN, JOHN FRANCIS, b Portsmouth, NH, July 28, 06; m 35. CLINICAL CYTOLOGY. *Educ:* Univ NH, BS, 28, MS, 30; Univ Iowa, PhD(zool), 45. *Prof Exp:* Asst zool, Univ NH, 28-30; from instr to assoc prof biol, 30-49, res assoc prof exfoliative cytol, 48-67, PROF BIOL,

CREIGHTON UNIV, 49-, PROF PATH, SCH MED, 67-, PROF GYNEC, 75- *Concurrent Pos:* Mem adj med staff, St Joseph Hosp, 72, chief, Cytol Lab, 78- *Mem:* Sigma Xi; Am Asn Anat; Am Soc Clin Pathologists; Am Soc Cytol; fel Am soc Colposcopy & Cervical Pathol. *Res:* Cytology cancer cell; exfoliative gynecologic cytology; colpomicroscopy; ultracentrifuge; cytoplasm. *Mailing Add:* Dept Path Sch Med Creighton Univ Omaha NE 68178

SHEEHAN, THOMAS JOHN, b Brooklyn, NY, Apr 13, 24; m 50; c 3. ORNAMENTAL HORTICULTURE. *Educ:* Dartmouth Col, AB, 48; Cornell Univ, MS, 51, PhD(floricult, plant breeding & physiol), 52. *Prof Exp:* Asst floricult, Cornell Univ, 48-52; asst horticulturist, Exp Sta, Univ Ga, 52-54; asst ornamental horticulturist, Agr Exten Serv, 54-56 & Exp Sta, 56-63, assoc ornamental horticulturist, 63-67, ornamental horticulturist, Exp Sta, 67-81, PROF ORNAMENTAL HORTICULTURE, UNIV FLA, 81- *Concurrent Pos:* Vis prof, Univ Hawaii, 62-63; consult floriculture, Food & Agr Orgn, UN, 71 & 74-75. *Mem:* Am Hort Soc. *Res:* Nutrition and other cultural factors of orchids; photoperoid and photoperiod-temperature studies and growth tailoring compounds and their use with floricultural crops; Orchidaceae, Amryllidaceae and Zingiberaceae. *Mailing Add:* Dept of Ornamental Hort Univ of Fla Gainesville FL 32611

SHEEHAN, WILLIAM C, b Macon, Ga, Oct 31, 25; m 46; c 3. ORGANIC CHEMISTRY. *Educ:* Mercer Univ, AB, 49; Inst Textile Technol, MS, 51; Univ Tenn, PhD(org chem), 56. *Prof Exp:* Res chemist, Bibb Mfg Co, Ga, 49 & 51-53; instr chem, Univ Tenn, 55; res chemist, E I du Pont de Nemours & Co, Va, 56-59; head textile sect, Southern Res Inst, 59-62, asst head phys sci div, 62-64, head polymer div, 64-65; dir fiber res, Phillips Petrol Co, Okla, 65-70, dir res, 70-73, tech vpres, 73-79, VPRES MKT, PHILLIPS FIBERS CORP, 79-, MEM BD DIRS, 75- *Concurrent Pos:* Mem comt textile functional finishing, Nat Res Coun, 65-74. *Mem:* Am Chem Soc; Am Mgt Asn; Indust Res Inst; AAAS; Textile Res Inst. *Res:* Fiber and polymer chemistry; textile finishing and auxiliaries. *Mailing Add:* PO Box 66 Greenville SC 29602

SHEEHAN, WILLIAM FRANCIS, b Chicago, Ill, Oct 19, 26; m 53; c 7. PHYSICAL CHEMISTRY, QUANTUM CHEMISTRY. *Educ:* Loyola Univ, Ill, BS, 48; Calif Inst Technol, PhD(chem), 52. *Prof Exp:* Chemist, Shell Develop Co, 52-55, chmn dept, 72-79; PROF CHEM, UNIV SANTA CLARA, 55- *Mem:* Am Chem Soc; Sigma Xi. *Res:* Valence; structural chemistry; thermodynamics; quantum chemistry. *Mailing Add:* Dept of Chem Univ of Santa Clara Santa Clara CA 95053

SHEEHE, PAUL ROBERT, b Buffalo, NY, Dec 8, 25; m 48; c 5. EPIDEMIOLOGY. *Educ:* Univ Buffalo, BSBA, 48, MBA, 54; Univ Pittsburgh, ScD(biostatist), 59. *Prof Exp:* Statistician, Erie County Health Dept, NY, 50-52; teaching fel statist, Univ Buffalo, 52-54; statistician, Pratt & Letchworth, 54-57; assoc biostatistician, Roswell Park Mem Inst, 59-65; assoc prof biostatist, 65-69, PROF PREV MED, STATE UNIV NY UPSTATE MED CTR, 69- *Mem:* Fel Am Col Epidemiol; Am Epidemiol Soc. *Res:* Statistics; epidemiol. *Mailing Add:* Dept of Prev Med State Univ NY Upstate Med Ctr Syracuse NY 13210

SHEEHY, THOMAS W, b Columbia, Pa, May 20, 21; m 44; c 4. MEDICINE, HEMATOLOGY. *Educ:* St Vincent Col, BS, 47; Syracuse Univ, MD, 51; Baylor Col Med, MS, 55; Am Bd Internal Med, dipl, 58. *Prof Exp:* From intern to resident med, Brooke Gen Hosp, US Army, 51-55, asst chief, Walter Reed Gen Hosp, 56-59, chief med div & hemat, Army Trop Res Lab, PR, 59-62, chief dept gastroenterol res, Walter Reed Army Inst Res, 62-65, med consult, Vietnam, 65-66, chief gen med & dir educ & med res, Walter Reed Gen Hosp, 66-67; prof med & assoc dir div nutrit & clin res ctr, NUTRIT & CLIN RES CTR, MED CTR, UNIV 67-72, CHIEF MED SERV & CO-CHMN DEPT MED, MED CTR, UNIV ALA, BIRMINGHAM, 69- *Concurrent Pos:* Studentship, Walter Reed Army Inst Res, 55-56, fel hemat, 56-57; from asst prof to assoc prof, Sch Med, Univ PR, 59-62; assoc prof, George Washington Univ, 63-65; mem hemat study sect, NIH, 62-65 & 71-75. *Mem:* Am Fedn Clin Res; Am Soc Hemat; Asn Mil Surg US; fel Am Col Physicians; Am Gastroenterol Asn. *Res:* Study of folic acid metabolism, minimal daily requirements; gastroenterology, small bowel metabolism, absorption, function, enzymes; tropical disease, malaria, scrub typhus, tropical sprue. *Mailing Add:* Dept of Med Univ of Ala Med Ctr Birmingham AL 35294

SHEELER, JOHN B(RIGGS), b Anita, Iowa, Oct 25, 21; m 45; c 5. CHEMICAL ENGINEERING, CIVIL ENGINEERING. *Educ:* Iowa State Univ, BS, 50, PhD(chem & soil eng), 56. *Prof Exp:* Res assoc, 50-56, asst prof civil eng, 56-59, ASSOC PROF CIVIL & CHEM ENG, IOWA STATE UNIV, 59- *Concurrent Pos:* Mem, Hwy Res Bd, Nat Acad Sci-Nat Res Coun, 51. *Mem:* AAAS; Am Inst Chem Engrs; Am Chem Soc. *Res:* Soil mechanics, engineering and stabilization; physico-chemical phenomena in soils. *Mailing Add:* 474 Town Eng Bldg Iowa State Univ Ames IA 50010

SHEELEY, EUGENE C, b Tiffin, Ohio, Jan 4, 33. AUDIOLOGY. *Educ:* Heidelberg Col, BA, 54; Western Reserve Univ, MA, 55; Univ Pittsburgh, PhD(audiol), 64. *Prof Exp:* Audiologist, Cincinnati Speech & Hearing Ctr, 55-60; asst res audiol, Univ Pittsburgh, 61 & 63-64; dir hearing test & child study ctr, NMex Sch Deaf, 64-67; PROF DEPT COMMUNICATIVE DISORDERS & DIR AUDIOL PROG, SPEECH & HEARING CTR, UNIV ALA, TUSCALOOSA, 67- *Concurrent Pos:* Asst clin audiol, Univ Pittsburgh, 62; spec instr, Univ Eastern NMex, 65-67; consult, Partlow State Sch & Hosp, Tuscaloosa, 68-74; chmn commun skills comt, 74-; consult hearing conserv progs, Ala Industs, 72- *Mem:* Am Asn Ment Deficiency; Acoust Soc Am; Am Speech-Language-Hearing Asn; A G Bell Asn Deaf; Am Auditory Soc. *Res:* Signal detection; noise exposure. *Mailing Add:* Univ Ala Speech & Hearing Ctr PO Box 1903 University AL 35486

SHEELEY, RICHARD MOATS, b Hershey, Pa, Nov 9, 34; m 60; c 4. MEDICINAL CHEMISTRY, FOOD CHEMISTRY. *Educ:* Univ Utah, BS, 57; Pa State Univ, MS, 59; Brigham Young Univ, PhD(org chem), 64. *Prof Exp:* Res chemist, Lederle Labs, Am Cyanamid Co, 63-67; asst prof chem, Shippensburg State Col, 67-69; asst prof, 69-74, ASSOC PROF CHEM, DICKINSON COL, 74- *Mem:* Am Chem Soc. *Res:* Structure elucidation; stereochemistry; design and synthesis of drugs. *Mailing Add:* Dept of Chem Dickinson Col Carlisle PA 17013

SHEELINE, RANDALL D(AVID), b New York, NY, Apr 10, 17; m 42; c 2. ORDNANCE ENGINEERING, INERT CARRIER PROCESS ENGINEERING. *Educ:* Polytech Inst Brooklyn, BChE, 38; Univ Mich, MSChE, 40. *Prof Exp:* Indust engr, Essex Rubber Co, 40-41; chem engr, Picatinny Arsenal, 41-44 & BuOrd, US Dept Navy, 44-55; prog mgr advan processing, Rocketdyne Div, NAm Rockwell Corp, 55-71; processing consult, 71; prof mgr, Chem Systs Div, United Technologies, 72-81; CONSULT, UNITED TECHNOLOGIES, QUADREX & GWR ASSOCIATES, 81- *Mem:* Am Inst Chem Engrs; Am Chem Soc; Am Ord Asn. *Res:* Solid propellant research, development and applications; advanced continuous processing of solid propellants; pyrotechnics; high explosives; radioactive wastes. *Mailing Add:* 6213 Camino Verde San Jose CA 95119

SHEELY, W(ALLACE) F(RANKLYN), b Albany, NY, Nov 28, 31; m 55; c 2. METALLURGICAL ENGINEERING. *Educ:* Rensselaer Polytech Inst, BMetE, 53, MMetE, 56, PhD, 57. *Prof Exp:* Res assoc, Rensselaer Polytech Inst, 53-57; res metallurgist, Union Carbide Metals Co, 57-60; sr metallurgist, Div Res, USAEC, 60-68; sr staff engr, Chem & Metall Div, Pac Northwest Labs, Battelle Mem Inst, 68-69, assoc div mgr, 69-70; mgr appl res, Mat & Technol Dept, 70-76, mgr, Chem Eng Dept, 76-80, MGR MAT TECHNOL, WESTINGHOUSE-HANFORD CO, 80- *Concurrent Pos:* Dept Com sci & technol fel, 65-66. *Mem:* Am Soc Metals; Am Nuclear Soc. *Res:* Plasticity and mechanical properties; nuclear metallurgy and chemistry. *Mailing Add:* Westinghouse-Hanford Co PO Box 1970 Richland WA 99352

SHEEN, SHUH-JI, b Wookiang, China, Mar 21, 31; m 59; c 5. PLANT GENETICS. *Educ:* Chung Hsing Univ, Taiwan, BS, 53; NDak State Univ, MS, 58; Univ Minn, PhD(plant genetics), 62. *Prof Exp:* Asst agron, Chung Hsing Univ, Taiwan, 54-56; asst prof biol, Hanover Col, 62-66; from asst prof to assoc prof agron, 66- 74, assoc prof, 74-79, PROF PLANT PATH, UNIV KY, 74- *Concurrent Pos:* NSF acad res exten grant, 65-66; USDA contract grants tobacco & health probs, 67-82. *Mem:* AAAS; Am Chem Soc; Genetic Soc Am; Am Phytopath Soc; Am Soc Plant Physiol. *Res:* Genetics and physiology of polyphenols and proteins in tobacco and forage crops as relates to leaf quality or disease resistance. *Mailing Add:* Dept Plant Pathol Agr Sci Ctr N Univ Ky Lexington KY 40506

SHEER, M(AXINE) LANA, b Brooklyn, NY, June 14, 45; m 78. PHYSICAL CHEMISTRY, POLYMER CHEMISTRY. *Educ:* Emory Univ, BS, 65, MS, 67, PhD(phys chem), 69. *Prof Exp:* Res chemist, Stauffer Chem Co, 69-73; res chemist, 73-77, tech specialist, 77-79, prod specialist, 79-80, FINANCIAL ANALYST, E I DU PONT DE NEMOURS & CO, INC, 81- *Mem:* AAAS; Am Chem Soc; Sigma Xi. *Res:* Nuclear magnetic resonance; infrared and ultraviolet spectroscopy; computer applications to molecular spectral theory; Raman spectroscopy; applications of spectroscopy to polymeric materials; development of thermoplastic engineering materials; process development for injection molded engineering plastics; market and product management of engineering plastics; financial forecasting. *Mailing Add:* Polymer Prod Dept D-11164-3 Wilmington DE 19898

SHEERAN, PATRICK JEROME, b Meade Co, Ky, Aug 29, 42; m 63; c 4. PESTICIDE CHEMISTRY. *Educ:* Bellarmine Col, BS, 64; Univ Vt, PhD(chem), 68. *Prof Exp:* RES SUPERVR PROCESS DEVELOP, BIOCHEM DEPT, EXP STA, E I DU PONT DE NEMOURS & CO, INC, 68- *Res:* Organic synthesis involving 4-8 membered heterocycles; biologically active organic compounds. *Mailing Add:* RD 2 Box 260A Landenberg PA 19350

SHEERAN, STANLEY ROBERT, b Elizabeth, NJ, Nov 19, 16; m 43; c 3. CHEMICAL MANAGEMENT, MANUFACTURING MANAGEMENT. *Educ:* St Vincent Col, BS, 38; Univ Notre Dame, MS, 39, PhD(org chem), 41. *Prof Exp:* Chemist, E I du Pont de Nemours & Co, 41-42, prod supvr, 42-44, supvr prod develop, 44-45, supvr tech sales develop, 45-46, mgr tech sales & develop, Del, 46-51, mgr opers, NY, 51-52, mgr Midwest sales develop, 53-58, mgr chem develop, Del, 59-63; vpres mkt chem div, Archer Daniels Midland Co, Minn, 63-66; vpres, Tenneco Chem Inc, 66-68, sr vpres, 68-70, exec vpres, 70-71, vpres, 71-81; PRES, SHEERAN ASSOC INC, 81- *Mem:* AAAS; fel Am Inst Chem; Am Mgt Asn; Mfg Chem Asn; Am Chem Soc. *Res:* Acetylene separation; polyvinyl alcohol and acetate resins; solubility and process of acetylene; cyanide chemistry; oxidation with peroxides; protective coating resins; plastics; industrial chemicals and specialities; paper and textile chemicals; management. *Mailing Add:* Sheeran Assoc Inc 18 Highland Dr Summit NJ 07901

SHEETS, DONALD GUY, b Mt Vernon, NY, Nov 20, 22; m 50. CHEMISTRY. *Educ:* Cent Col, Mo, AB, 44; Univ Mich, MS, 47, PhD(pharmaceut chem), 50. *Prof Exp:* Lab asst chem, Cent Col, Mo, 43-44, instr physics, 44; res chemist, Monsanto Chem Co, 44-45; asst prof anal chem, Miss State Col, 49-50; prof gen chem, St Louis Col Pharm, 50-62; PROF GEN & PHYS CHEM, US NAVAL ACAD, 62- *Mem:* Am Chem Soc. *Res:* Reactions of phthalic anhydride; derivatives of thiophene; derivatives of thianaphthene. *Mailing Add:* Dept of Chem US Naval Acad Annapolis MD 21402

SHEETS, GEORGE HENKLE, b Washington Court House, Ohio, Apr 22, 15; m 41; c 2. PAPER CHEMISTRY, CHEMICAL ENGINEERING. *Educ:* Ohio State Univ, BChE, 37; Inst Paper Chem, MS, 39, PhD(chem), 41. *Prof Exp:* Develop engr res & develop, Mead Corp, 41-50, div mgr oper mgt, 50-60, managing dir, 60-61, exec vpres corp mgt, 62-80; RETIRED. *Mem:* Tech Asn Pulp & Paper Indust (pres, 69-70); Can Pulp & Paper Asn. *Res:* Pulping; papermaking. *Mailing Add:* 60 Harmon Terr Dayton OH 45419

SHEETS, HERMAN E(RNEST), b Dresden, Ger, Dec 24, 08; nat US; m 42; c 6. MECHANICAL & OCEAN ENGINEERING. *Educ:* Dresden Tech Univ, dipl, 34; Prague Tech Univ, DrTechSci(appl mech), 36. *Prof Exp:* Dir res, St Paul Eng & Mfg Co, Minn, 42-44; proj engr, Elliott Co, Pa, 44-46; eng mgr, Goodyear Aircraft Corp, Ohio, 46-53; dir res & develop, Elec Boat Div, Gen Dynamics Corp, 53-66, vpres eng & res, 66-69; PROF OCEAN ENG & CHMN DEPT, UNIV RI, 69- *Concurrent Pos:* Mem marine bd, Nat Acad Eng; mem, Nat Acad Sci-Nat Acad Eng sci & eng adv comt to Nat Oceanic & Atmospheric Admin. *Mem:* Nat Acad Eng; Am Soc Mech Engrs; Soc Naval Archit & Marine Engrs; Am Soc Naval Engrs; Am Inst Aeronaut & Astronaut. *Res:* Ocean engineering systems; hydrodynamics. *Mailing Add:* Dept of Ocean Eng Univ of RI Kingston RI 02881

SHEETS, RALPH WALDO, b Point Cedar, Ark, Apr 18, 35; m 62; c 2. ENVIRONMENTAL CHEMISTRY. *Educ:* Henderson State Col, BS, 66; Univ Ark, MS, 69, PhD(phys chem), 71. *Prof Exp:* Fel surface chem, Ames Lab, AEC, 70-71; asst prof, 71-76, ASSOC PROF CHEM, SOUTHWEST MO STATE UNIV, 76- *Concurrent Pos:* Sci translr Russ, Consults Bur, Plenum Publ Corp, 71-, Faraday Press Inc, 71-72 & Allerton Press Inc, 72-76. *Mem:* Am Chem Soc; Sigma Xi. *Res:* Chemical characterization of natural water systems; chemisorption and heterogeneous catalysis; infrared and ultraviolet spectroscopy of adsorbed species. *Mailing Add:* Dept of Chem Southwest Mo State Univ Springfield MO 65802

SHEETS, RAYMOND FRANKLIN, b Bentley, Ill, June 15, 14; m 46; c 3. INTERNAL MEDICINE. *Educ:* Carthage Col, AB, 36; Univ Ill, MS & MD, 40. *Prof Exp:* Intern, 40-41, from resident to assoc prof, 46-59, chmn div hemat, Dept Internal Med, 68-70, dir hemat outpatient clins, Univ Hosp, 71-74, PROF INTERNAL MED, UNIV IOWA, 59- *Concurrent Pos:* Attend physician & consult, Vet Hosp. *Mem:* Soc Nuclear Med; Soc Exp Biol & Med; Am Soc Internal Med; Am Soc Hemat; Asn Am Med Cols. *Res:* Blood diseases; clinical hematology and oncology. *Mailing Add:* Univ Iowa Hosps Iowa City IA 52240

SHEETS, ROBERT CHESTER, meteorology, see previous edition

SHEETS, THOMAS JACKSON, b Asheville, NC, Dec 11, 26; m 52; c 2. PLANT PHYSIOLOGY. *Educ:* NC State Col, BS, 51, MS, 54; Univ Calif, PhD, 59. *Prof Exp:* Res instr, NC State Col, 51-54; res agronomist, Agr Res Serv, USDA, Calif, 54-59, plant physiologist, Delta Br Exp Sta, Miss, 59-60 & Md, 60-65; assoc prof entom & crop sci, 65-69, PROF ENTOM, CROP SCI & HORT SCI, NC STATE UNIV, 69- *Concurrent Pos:* Ed, Weed Sci, 71-73; Ed-in-chief, Weed Sci Soc Am 74-78. *Mem:* Coun Agr Sci & Technol; fel Weed Sci Am (vpres, 80, pres-elect, 81, pres, 82). *Res:* Movement, persistence and modes of detoxification of herbicides; physiologic and agronomic research in weed and vegetation control; pesticide residues. *Mailing Add:* Pesticide Residue Res Lab NC State Univ PO Box 5215 Raleigh NC 27650

SHEETZ, DAVID P, b Colebrook, Pa, Dec 4, 26; m 46; c 3. PHYSICAL CHEMISTRY. *Educ:* Lebanon Valley Col, BS, 48; Univ Nebr, MS, 51, PhD(chem), 52. *Prof Exp:* Res chemist, 52-56, proj leader, 56-59, group leader, 59-65, asst lab dir, 65-66, lab dir, 66-67, asst dir res & develop, Midland Div, 67-71, dir res & develop, Mich Div, 71-78, vpres & dir, 78-80, CORP DIR RES & DEVELOP, DOW CHEM CO, 80- *Mem:* Am Chem Soc; Sigma Xi; Am Inst Chemists. *Res:* Polymer, colloid and organic chemistry. *Mailing Add:* Res & Develop 2020 Dow Center Midland MI 48640

SHEFER, JOSHUA, b Leipzig, Ger, Nov 1, 24; US citizen; m 50; c 3. ELECTRICAL ENGINEERING. *Educ:* Israel Inst Technol, BSc, 48; Univ London, PhD(elec eng), 55. *Prof Exp:* Res engr electronics res lab, Israeli Ministry Defence, 48-52 & 56-58; sci attache, Israeli Embassy, London, 58-60; res fel, Harvard Univ, 60-62; mem tech staff, Bell Tel Labs, 62-67; MEM TECH STAFF, RCA LABS, 67- *Concurrent Pos:* Lectr microwave theory & technol, Israel Inst Technol, 57-58; consult, Technol Co Mass, 61-62. *Mem:* Inst Elec & Electronics Engrs; Sigma Xi. *Res:* Electromagnetic theory; antenna and propagation studies; microwaves; mobile radio; display devices; television systems. *Mailing Add:* 223 Gallup Rd Princeton NJ 08540

SHEFFER, ALBERT L, II, b Lewistown, Pa, Aug 7, 29; m 54; c 4. CLINICAL IMMUNOLOGY, ALLERGY. *Educ:* Franklin & Marshall Col, BS, 52; George Washington Univ, MD, 56. *Prof Exp:* Fel pulmonary dis, Grad Hosp & Henry Phipps Inst, 57-58; res med, Grad Hosp, Philadelphia, 56-60; fel appl immunol & allergy, Med Ctr, Temple Univ, 61; attend physician, Rockefeller Univ Hosp, 61-62; guest investr, Rockefeller Univ, 62; assoc clin prof, Harvard Med Sch, 66; DIR ALLERGY CLIN, BETH ISRAEL HOSP, BOSTON, 69- & PETER BENT BRIGHAM HOSP, BOSTON, 71- *Concurrent Pos:* Allergy consult, Harvard Community Health Plan, Boston, 69-80; allergy sect chief, New Eng Deaconess Hosp, Boston, 72-; asst allergy, Children's Hosp Med Ctr, Boston, 74-; consult, US Pharmacopei, 75- & Parenteral Drug Asn, 81-; dir allergy training prog, Robert B Brigham Hosp, Boston, 76-80 & Brigham & Women's Hosp, 80- *Honors & Awards:* Honors Achievement Award, Angiology Res Found, 65. *Mem:* Am Acad Allergy. *Res:* Pathogenesis and treatment of asthma, auophylaxis, urticaria, and angioedema. *Mailing Add:* 110 Francis St Boston MA 02215

SHEFFER, HOWARD EUGENE, b Schenectady, NY, Oct 3, 18; m 44; c 6. ORGANIC CHEMISTRY. *Educ:* Union Col, NY, BS, 39; Rensselaer Polytech Inst, MS, 40; Cornell Univ, PhD(org chem), 43. *Prof Exp:* Res chemist, Carbide & Carbon Chem Co, WVa, 43-45; from asst prof to assoc prof, 45-60, PROF CHEM, UNION COL, NY, 60- *Concurrent Pos:* Consult, Schenectady Varnish Co, 47-; NSF fac fel, Univ Del, 61-62; Fulbright prof, 68-69, Neste Oil Found grant, Tech Univ Helsinki, 75-76. *Mem:* Am Chem Soc. *Res:* Organics; colloids; wire enamels; insulation varnishes; condensation polymerization; cationic polymerization; osmometry. *Mailing Add:* Dept Chem Union Col Schenectady NY 12308

SHEFFER, RICHARD DOUGLAS, b Portland, Ind, Apr 19, 42; m 69. CYTOGENETICS, BIOSYSTEMATICS. *Educ:* Purdue Univ, BS, 70; Univ Hawaii, PhD(hort), 74. *Prof Exp:* Res assoc, Univ Hawaii, 74-75; asst prof, Univ NB, 75-76; instr, Montclair State Col, 76-77; asst prof, 77-81, ASSOC PROF GENETICS, IND UNIV NORTHWEST, 81- *Mem:* AAAS; Am Genetics Asn; Am Soc Plant Taxon; Int Asn Plant Taxon; Soc Study Evolution. *Res:* Cytogenetics and cytotaxonomy of the genus anthurium. *Mailing Add:* Dept Biol Ind Univ Northwest Gary IN 46408

SHEFFI, YOSEF, b Jerusalem, Israel. TRANSPORTATION SYSTEMS, OPERATIONS RESEARCH. *Educ:* Israel Inst Technol, BSc, 75; Mass Inst Technol, SM, 77, PhD(transp), 78. *Prof Exp:* Asst prof, 78-80, ASSOC PROF TRANSP SYST, MASS INST TECHNOL, 80- *Concurrent Pos:* Sr oper res analyst, Transp Syst Ctr, US Dept Transp, 78-79; consult, 78-81. *Mem:* Transp Res Bd; Oper Res Soc Am; Inst Transp Engrs. *Res:* Transportation systems analysis; travel demand models; network analysis; performance of transportation facilities. *Mailing Add:* Dept of Civil Eng 77 Massachusetts Ave Cambridge MA 02139

SHEFFIELD, HARLEY GEORGE, b Detroit, Mich, Jan 10, 32; m 59; c 2. MEDICAL PARASITOLOGY, ELECTRON MICROSCOPY. *Educ:* Wayne State Univ, BS, 53, MS, 58; La State Univ, PhD(med parasitol), 62. *Prof Exp:* Res biologist, Parke, Davis & Co, 58-59; from scientist to sr scientist, 62-73, SCIENTIST DIR, NIH, 73- *Mem:* Am Soc Parasitol; Am Soc Trop Med & Hyg; Soc Protozool. *Res:* Electron microscopy of parasitic protozoa, especially toxoplasma and related organisms; electron microscopy of parasitic nematode intestine and other tissues. *Mailing Add:* MIDP Nat Inst Allergy & Infectious Dis NIH Bethesda MD 20205

SHEFFIELD, JOEL BENSON, b Brooklyn, NY, Dec 30, 42; m 65; c 1. CELL BIOLOGY, VIROLOGY. *Educ:* Brandeis Univ, AB, 63; Univ Chicago, PhD(biol), 70. *Prof Exp:* Guest investr virol, Rockefeller Univ, 63-64; fel cell membranes, Dutch Cancer Inst, 70-71; asst mem virol, Inst Med Res, 71-77; ASST PROF BIOL, TEMPLE UNIV, 77- *Concurrent Pos:* Res fel, Int Agency Res Cancer, WHO, 70; Nat Cancer Inst fel, 71; fac assoc, Rutgers Univ, 74- *Mem:* AAAS; Am Soc Cell Biol; Am Soc Microbiol. *Res:* Structure and biogenesis of cellular and viral membranes. *Mailing Add:* Dept of Biol Temple Univ Philadelphia PA 19122

SHEFFIELD, JOHN, b Purley, Eng, Dec 15, 36; m 64; c 2. PLASMA PHYSICS. *Educ:* London Univ, BSc, 58, MSc, 62, PhD(plasma physics), 66. *Prof Exp:* Exp officer plasma physics, Harwell Lab, UK Atomic Energy Authority, 58-61; Culham Lab, 61-66; asst prof plasma physics, Univ Tex, Austin, 66-71; prin sci officer fusion res, Culham Lab, UK Atomic Energy Authority, 71-77; ASSOC DIR, FUSION ENERGY DIV, OAK RIDGE NAT LAB, 77- *Mem:* Fel Am Phys Soc; Am Nuclear Soc. *Res:* Magnetic fusion; magnetic confinement schemes; diagnostics and technology for fusion. *Mailing Add:* Oak Ridge Nat Lab PO Box Y Oak Ridge TN 37830

SHEFFIELD, L THOMAS, b Montgomery, Ala, Oct 25, 28; m 54; c 2. MEDICINE. *Educ:* Emory Univ, BA, 49; Univ Ala, MD, 54. *Prof Exp:* Intern, Michael Reese Hosp, Chicago, Ill, 54-55; asst med res, Univ Hosp & Vet Admin Hosp, Birmingham, Ala, 57-59; NIH cardiovasc res fel, Mass Mem Hosp & Sch Med, Boston Univ, 59-60 & Med Ctr, Univ Ala, Birmingham, 60-62; from instr to assoc prof, 62-73, PROF MED, UNIV ALA, BIRMINGHAM, 73-, DIR ECG LAB & EXERCISE LAB, 62- *Concurrent Pos:* Attend physician, Univ Hosp, Birmingham, 63-; mem, Am Heart Asn. *Mem:* AAAS; Am Fedn Clin Res; AMA; fel Am Col Cardiol. *Res:* Clinical cardiology; exercise electrocardiography; work physiology; computer-aided diagnosis. *Mailing Add:* Univ Ala Med Ctr Univ Sta Birmingham AL 35294

SHEFFIELD, ROY DEXTER, b Dorsey, Miss, Sept 5, 22; m 46. MATHEMATICS. *Educ:* Univ Miss, BA, 48, MA, 49; Univ Tenn, PhD(math), 56. *Prof Exp:* Asst prof math, Univ Miss, 51-56; sr nuclear engr, Gen Dynamics/Convair, 56-57; prof math, Univ Miss, 57-63; prof, Miss State Univ, 63-71; PROF MATH, UNIV MISS, 71-, CHMN DEPT, 73- *Concurrent Pos:* Consult, Gen Dynamics/Convair, 57-61. *Mem:* Am Math Soc; Math Asn Am; Soc Indust & Appl Math. *Res:* Functional analysis; linear algebra; nonlinear programming. *Mailing Add:* Dept of Math Univ of Miss University MS 38677

SHEFFIELD, WILLIAM JOHNSON, b Nashua, NH, May 9, 19; m 55; c 3. PHARMACY. *Educ:* Univ NC, BS, 42, MS, 49, PhD(pharm), 54. *Prof Exp:* From asst prof to assoc prof, 52-68, PROF PHARM, COL PHARM, UNIV TEX, AUSTIN, 68-, ASST DEAN COL, 56-58 & 68- *Mem:* AAAS; Acad Pharmaceut Sci; Am Pharmaceut Asn. *Mailing Add:* Col of Pharm Univ of Tex Austin TX 78712

SHEFFY, BEN EDWARD, b Luxemburg, Wis, Mar 12, 20; m 48; c 2. NUTRITION, MICROBIOLOGY. *Educ:* Univ Wis, BS, 48, MS, 50, PhD, 51. *Prof Exp:* CASPARY PROF NUTRIT & ASST DIR J A BAKER INST ANIMAL HEALTH, CORNELL UNIV, 51- *Concurrent Pos:* Guggenheim fel, Cambridge Univ, 59-60; NIH spec fel, Univ Munich, 66-67; nutrit consult, NY Zool Soc; consult, Joint Comn Rural Reconstruction, Republic China, 74-75. *Mem:* Brit Nutrit Soc; Am Asn Lab Animal Sci. *Res:* Nutrition and disease interrelationships. *Mailing Add:* J A Baker Inst Animal Health Cornell Univ Ithaca NY 14850

SHEFTER, ELI, b Philadelphia, Pa, Sept 10, 36; m 61; c 2. MEDICINAL CHEMISTRY, PHARMACEUTICS. *Educ:* Temple Univ, BSc, 58; Univ Wis, PhD(phys pharm & chem), 63. *Prof Exp:* Nat Gen Med Sci fel, 64-65; asst prof, 66-69, ASSOC PROF PHARMACEUT, SCH PHARM, STATE UNIV NY BUFFALO, 69- *Concurrent Pos:* Pfeiffer fel, Am Fedn Pharmaceut Educ, 72. *Mem:* Fel Am Acad Pharmaceut Sci; AAAS; Am Crystallog Asn; Am Chem Soc; Am Pharmaceut Asn. *Res:* Correlations of structure and pharmacological activity; crystallographic studies on nucleic acid components and complexes of these fragments; phase transformations of solid pharmaceuticals. *Mailing Add:* Dept of Pharmaceut State Univ NY Sch Pharm Amherst NY 14260

SHEHADI, WILLIAM HENRY, b Providence, RI, June 30, 06; m 55; c 2. RADIOLOGY. *Educ:* Am Univ Beirut, DDS, 27, MD, 31; Am Bd Radiol, dipl, 41. *Prof Exp:* Instr anat, Schs Med & Dent, Am Univ Beirut, 31-33, asst radiologist, 32-39; asst prof radiol, Sch Med, Univ Vt, 41-42; dir, Mt Vernon Hosp, NY, 42-48; prof radiol & dir dept, New York Polyclin Med Sch, 48-60; dir dept, United Hosp, Port Chester, NY, 61-67; DIR DEPT RADIOL, GRASSLANDS HOSP, VALHALLA, NY, 68-; PROF RADIOL, NEW YORK MED COL, 69- *Concurrent Pos:* Trainee radiol, Am Univ Beirut, 32-39; asst radiologist, Mary Fletcher Hosp, Burlington, Vt, 41-42; instr radiol, New York Med Col, 43-47; consult, St Joseph's Hosp, Yonkers, 43-71; trustee, Am Univ Beirut, 56-; consult, Food & Drug Admin, 75, Westchester County Med Ctr, Valhalla, NY, 76; chmn comt safety contrast media, Int Soc Radiol, 69. *Mem:* Am Roentgen Ray Soc; Radiol Soc NAm; AMA; fel Am Geog Soc; fel Am Col Radiol. *Mailing Add:* 27 Byram Shore Rd Greenwich CT 06830

SHEIBLEY, FRED EASLY, b Cleveland, Ohio, Dec 18, 06. ORGANIC CHEMISTRY. *Educ:* Case Inst, BS, 31, PhD(org chem), 39; Univ Pa, MS, 37. *Prof Exp:* Asst org lab, Case Inst, 31-33; res chemist, Grasselli Chem Dept, E I du Pont de Nemours & Co, 33-35; asst instr, Univ Pa, 35-37; instr, Case Inst, 37-41; res chemist, Carborundum Co, NY, 41-43 & Battelle Mem Inst, 44-46; asst prof chem, Univ Ky, 46-47; res chemist, Gen Tire & Rubber Co, 47-49; chief chemist, Hefco Labs, Mich, 49-52; res chemist, B F Goodrich Chem Co, Ohio, 52-54 & Palmer Chem Co, 54-55; from asst prof to assoc prof chem, 55-72, EMER ASSOC PROF CHEM, CLEVELAND STATE UNIV, 72- *Mem:* Am Chem Soc. *Res:* Synthesis of monomers; pure heterocyclic chemistry. *Mailing Add:* 1921 E 97th St Cleveland OH 44106

SHEID, BERTRUM, b Brooklyn, NY, Apr 19, 37. BIOCHEMISTRY. *Educ:* City Col New York, BS, 56; Brooklyn Col, MA, 60; Univ Conn, PhD(biochem), 65. *Prof Exp:* Fel biochem, Col Physicians & Surgeons, Columbia Univ, 65-67; asst prof path, Albert Einstein Col Med, 67-69; asst prof, 69-75, ASSOC PROF PHARMACOL, STATE UNIV NY, DOWNSTATE MED CTR, 75- *Mem:* AAAS; Am Chem Soc; Am Biol Scientists; NY Acad Sci. *Res:* Nucleic acid metabolism in normal and malignant tissues; experimental cancer chemotherapy. *Mailing Add:* Dept of Pharmacol State Univ NY Downstate Med Ctr Brooklyn NY 11203

SHEIH, CHING-MING, b Taiwan, Aug 11, 36; m 66; c 2. FLUID MECHANICS, ATMOSPHERIC PHYSICS. *Educ:* Nat Taiwan Univ, BS, 62; Colo State Univ, MS, 65; Pa State Univ, PhD(aerospace eng), 69. *Prof Exp:* Res assoc teaching, Dept Aerospace Eng, Pa State Univ, 69-70, res assoc, Ctr Air Environ Studies, 70-74; METEOROLOGIST, ATMOSPHERIC PHYSICS SECT, ARGONNE NAT LAB, 74- *Mem:* Am Meteorol Soc. *Res:* Numerical and physical simulations of pollutant dispersion in the atmosphere. *Mailing Add:* Argonne Nat Lab Bldg 181 Argonne IL 60439

SHEIKH, KAZIM, b Hyderabad, Pakistan, Sept 21, 36; Brit citizen; m 69; c 2. OCCUPATIONAL EPIDEMIOLOGY, ENVIRONMENTAL EPIDEMIOLOGY. *Educ:* Univ Karachi, Pakistan, MB & BS, 60; Royal Col Surgeons & Physicians, Eng, DIH, 73. *Prof Exp:* Intern & resident, Nat Health Serv Gen Hosp, London & Southeast Eng, 60-70; med officer, Slough Indust Health Serv, Eng, 70-74; epidemiologist, Med Res Coun, UK, 74-78; med adv, BOC Ltd, London, 78-80; ASST PROF EPIDEMIOL, SCH PUB HEALTH, UNIV MICH, 81- *Concurrent Pos:* Mem, Am Heart Asn. *Mem:* Am Pub Health Asn; hon fel Royal Col Physicians; Soc Epidemiologic Res; Royal Soc Med; Brit Soc Social Med. *Res:* Medical care and community health research in stroke, and in chronic physical and mental disability; occupational epidemiology; occupational and general environmental epidemiology, and epidemiological methods. *Mailing Add:* Dept Epidemiol Sch Pub Health Univ Mich 109 Observatory St Ann Arbor MI 48109

SHEINAUS, HAROLD, b New York, NY, Sept 5, 18; m 49; c 2. PHARMACY. *Educ:* City Col New York, BS, 39, Columbia Univ, BS, 49, MS, 51; Purdue Univ, PhD(pharm, pharmaceut chem), 55. *Prof Exp:* Instr pharm, Columbia Univ, 51-52; dir develop & process lab, Carroll Dunham Smith Pharmacol Co, 54-60; sr scientist, Warner-Lambert Res Inst, 61-63; dept head pharmaceut res & develop, 64-70, dir pharmaceut prod develop, 70-79, DIR CONCEPT DEVELOP, PROD DIV, BRISTOL-MYERS CO, 79- *Mem:* Fel AAAS; Am Chem Soc; Am Pharmaceut Asn; Acad Pharmaceut Sci. *Res:* Application of new developmental materials and techniques to pharmacy; aerosol pharmaceuticals; emulsions; sustained action formulations; preservatives; effervescent products; solubilization techniques. *Mailing Add:* 132 Wildwood Terr Watchung NJ 07060

SHEINESS, DIANA KAY, b Corpus Christi, Tex, Oct 1, 47. RETROVIRUSES, RETROVIRAL ONCOGENES. *Educ:* Univ Tex, Austin, BA, 67; Columbia Univ, MA, 73, PhD(cell biol), 74. *Prof Exp:* Fel genetics, Univ Edinburgh, Scotland, 74-75 & microbiol, Med Sch, Univ Calif, 76-81; ASST PROF BIOCHEM, LA STATE MED CTR, 81- *Mem:* Am Soc Microbiol. *Res:* Elucidating the function in normal cells of genes that have served as progenitors for retroviral oncogenes. *Mailing Add:* Dept Biochem La State Med Ctr 1901 Perdido St New Orleans LA 70112

SHEINGOLD, ABRAHAM, b New York, NY, Feb 17, 17; m 41; c 2. ELECTRONICS. *Educ:* City Col New York, BS, 36, MS, 37. *Prof Exp:* Instr high schs, NY, 36-43; instr elec commun, Mass Inst Technol, 43-46; from asst prof to assoc prof, 46-54, PROF ELECTRONICS, US NAVAL POSTGRAD SCH, 54- *Mem:* Inst Elec & Electronics Engrs. *Mailing Add:* 3281 Trevis Way Carmel CA 93921

SHEINGORN, MARK ELLIOT, b New York, NY, Dec 3, 44; m 72. MATHEMATICS. *Educ:* Dartmouth Col, AB, 65; Univ Wis-Madison, MS, 67, PhD(math), 70. *Prof Exp:* Nat Res Coun fel, Nat Bur Standards, 70-72; asst prof math, Hofstra Univ, 72-73; from asst prof to assoc prof, 73-82, PROF MATH, BARUCH COL, 82- *Concurrent Pos:* Nasa fel, Univ Wis, 66-68; NSF grant, 73-81; vis mem, Inst Advan Study, Princeton, 74-75 & 81; mem, Inst Mittag-Leffler, Sweden, 77-; vis lectr, Univ Ill, Urbana, 78-79. *Mem:* Am Math Soc. *Res:* Complex variables; analytic number theory; automorphic forms. *Mailing Add:* 1200 Broadway New York NY 10001

SHEININ, ERIC BENJAMIN, b Chicago, Ill, Dec 23, 43; m 65, 76; c 3. PHARMACEUTICAL CHEMISTRY. *Educ:* Univ Ill, Urbana, BS, 65; Univ Ill Med Ctr, PhD(pharmaceut chem), 71. *Prof Exp:* Res chemist anal & pharmaceut chem, 71-79, SUPVRY CHEMIST, FOOD & DRUG ADMIN, 79- *Mem:* Sigma Xi; Am Chem Soc; Am Soc Mass Spectrom; Acad Pharmaceut Sci. *Res:* Use of nuclear magnetic resonance spectroscopy and mass spectrometry; development of methodology for the analysis of pharmaceutical preparations; laboratory evaluation of analytical methodology included in new drug applications. *Mailing Add:* Food & Drug Admin HFD-420 200 C St SW Washington DC 20204

SHEININ, ROSE, b Toronto, Ont, May 18, 30; m 51; c 3. BIOCHEMISTRY, VIROLOGY. *Educ:* Univ Toronto, BSc, 51, MSc, 53, PhD(biochem), 56. *Prof Exp:* Res assoc tumor virol, Ont Cancer Inst, 58-76; asst prof med biophys, 67-72, assoc prof, 72-75, chmn dept, 75-81, PROF MICROBIOL & PARASITOL, UNIV TORONTO, 75- *Concurrent Pos:* Fel, Brit Empire Cancer Campaign, 56-58; vis prof, Med Res Coun, 72, sci officer, 74-; Josiah Macy Jr Fac Scholar award, 81-82. *Mem:* Can Biochem Soc (pres, 75); Can Soc Cell Biol (pres, 73); Am Soc Microbiol; fel Am Acad Microbiol; fel Royal Soc Chem. *Res:* Tumor virology; chromatin structure and replication; biochemical genetics. *Mailing Add:* Dept of Microbiol & Parasitol Univ of Toronto Toronto ON M5S 1A1 Can

SHEINSON, RONALD SWIREN, b Philadelphia, Pa, Dec 16, 42; m 68. PHYSICAL CHEMISTRY. *Educ:* Temple Univ, BA, 64; Mass Inst Technol, PhD(chem physics), 70. *Prof Exp:* RES CHEMIST, US NAVAL RES LAB, 70- *Mem:* Am Phys Soc; Sigma Xi; Am Chem Soc. *Res:* Spectroscopy; chemiluminescence; gas phase oxidation mechanisms; combustion suppression; electron paramagnetic resonance. *Mailing Add:* US Naval Res Lab Washington DC 20375

SHEKELLE, RICHARD BARTEN, b Ventura, Calif, Mar 24, 33; m 52; c 5. EPIDEMIOLOGY. *Educ:* Univ Chicago, AB, 52, AM, 58, PhD(human develop), 62. *Prof Exp:* Res assoc psychiat, Univ Ill, Chicago, 59-61, res assoc prev med, 61-65, from instr to assoc prof, 65-74; assoc prof, 74-75, PROF PREV MED, RUSH-PRESBY-ST LUKE'S MED CTR, 75- *Concurrent Pos:* Fel Am Heart Asn Coun Epidemiol. *Mem:* Am Pub Health Asn; Biomet Soc; Soc Epidemiol Res. *Res:* Epidemiology of cardiovascular diseases and cancer. *Mailing Add:* Dept of Prev Med Rush-Presby-St Luke's Med Ctr Chicago IL 60612

SHELANSKI, MICHAEL L, b Philadelphia, Pa, Oct 5, 41; m 63; c 3. NEUROPATHOLOGY, PHARMACOLOGY. *Educ:* Univ Chicago, MD, 66, PhD(physiol), 67. *Prof Exp:* Intern path, Albert Einstein Col Med, 67-68, fel neuropath, 68-69, asst prof, 69-71; staff investr neurobiol, Lab Biochem Genetics, Nat Heart & Lung Inst, 71-73; Guggenheim fel, Inst Pasteur, Paris, 73-74; assoc prof neuropath, Harvard Med Sch, 74-78; PROF PHARMACOL & CHMN DEPT, MED SCH, NY UNIV, 78- *Concurrent Pos:* NIH res grant, Albert Einstein Col Med, 68-73, Nat Inst Neurol Dis & Stroke teacher-investr award, 70-71 & 73-74, asst prof in residence, Col, 71-73. *Mem:* Am Soc Cell Biol; Am Asn Neuropath; Am Soc Neurochem. *Res:* Microtubule and neurofilaments; physical biochemistry of self-assembly; chemistry of senile and pre-senile dementias; neuronal differentiation. *Mailing Add:* Dept of Pharmacol 350 First Ave New York NY 10016

SHELBURNE, JOHN DANIEL, b Washington, DC, Aug 27, 43; m 66; c 2. PATHOLOGY. *Educ:* Univ NC, Chapel Hill, AB, 66; Duke Univ, PhD(path), 71, MD, 72. *Prof Exp:* Intern, 72-73, asst prof, 73-78, ASSOC PROF PATH, MED CTR, DUKE UNIV, 78-; assoc dir, 73-77, DIR DIAGNOSTIC ELECTRON MICROS LAB, DUKE MED CTR & VET ADMIN HOSP, DURHAM, 77- *Mem:* Int Acad Path; Am Asn Pathologists; Electron Micros Soc Am. *Res:* Lysosomes; autophagy; surgical pathology; x-ray microanalysis; ion microscopy. *Mailing Add:* Dept Path Duke Univ Med Ctr Durham NC 27710

SHELBY, CHARLES EDWIN, b Salem, Ky, July 19, 25; m 55; c 4. ANIMAL GENETICS. *Educ:* Univ Ky, BS, 48, MS, 49; Iowa State Univ, PhD(animal breeding, genetics), 52. *Prof Exp:* Asst, Univ Ky, 48-49; geneticist range livestock exp sta, Agr Res Serv, USDA, Mont, 52-55, beef cattle breeding res, Colo, 55-59, dir regional swine breeding lab, Iowa State Univ, 59-70, liaison officer, Ky State Univ, 70-74; GENETICIST, STORED-PROD INSECTS RES & DEVELOP LAB, AGR RES SERV, USDA, 74- *Mem:* Am Soc Animal Sci; Genetics Soc Am; Am Genetic Asn; Biomet Soc; Entom Soc Am. *Res:* Population genetics; genetics of resistance and susceptibility of insects to insecticide treatment. *Mailing Add:* Box 22578 Savannah GA 31403

SHELDEN, HAROLD RAYMOND, II, b Indianapolis, Ind, July 7, 42; m 65. ORGANIC CHEMISTRY. *Educ:* Loma Linda Univ, BA, 64; Univ Calif, Irvine, PhD(org chem), 69. *Prof Exp:* Asst prof, 69-74, assoc prof, 74-79, PROF CHEM, LOMA LINDA UNIV, LA SIERRA CAMPUS, 79-, CHMN DEPT, 80- *Mem:* Am Chem Soc. *Res:* Mechanisms of organic reactions. *Mailing Add:* Dept Chem Loma Linda Univ La Sierra Campus Riverside CA 92505

SHELDEN, ROBERT MERTEN, b Troy, Mont, Mar 23, 38; m 64; c 3. REPRODUCTIVE PHYSIOLOGY, EMBRYOLOGY. *Educ:* Univ Mont, BA, 64, PhD(zool), 68. *Prof Exp:* Asst prof biol, Moorhead State Col, 68-71; res assoc, Dept Obstet & Gynec, Ohio State Univ, 73-75; ASST PROF, DEPT OBSTET & GYNEC, RUTGERS MED SCH, 76- *Concurrent Pos:* Minn State Col Bd res grant, 68-69; NIH fel reprod endocrinol, Dept Obstet & Gynec, Ohio State Univ, 71-73. *Mem:* AAAS; Soc Study Reprod. *Res:* Endocrine regulation of the uterine environment; immunogenic potentials of primate reproductive organs. *Mailing Add:* Dept of Obstet & Gynec Univ Heights Piscataway NJ 08854

SHELDON, ANDREW LEE, b Greenfield, Mass, Apr 22, 38; m 63; c 2. ZOOLOGY, ECOLOGY. *Educ:* Colby Col, BA, 60; Cornell Univ, PhD(zool), 66. *Prof Exp:* Asst res zoologist, Sagehen Creek Field Sta, Univ Calif, 64-67; res assoc, Resources for the Future, Inc, 67-69; asst prof zool, 69-73, assoc prof, 73-77, PROF ZOOL, UNIV MONT, 78- *Concurrent Pos:* Off Water Resources Res grant, Univ Mont, 71-73; vis scientist, Oak Ridge Nat Lab, 77-78. *Mem:* AAAS; Ecol Soc Am; Am Soc Limnol & Oceanog; Soc Study Evolution; Am Fisheries Soc. *Res:* Community structure and dynamics; comparative ecology; running water biology; biometrics. *Mailing Add:* Dept of Zool Univ of Mont Missoula MT 59801

SHELDON, DONALD RUSSELL, b Binghamton, NY, Jan 17, 31; m 53; c 2. SCIENCE ADMINISTRATION. *Educ:* Susquehanna Univ, AB, 53; Hofstra Univ, MA, 54; Purdue Univ, PhD(biochem), 60. *Prof Exp:* Assoc sci, Res Found, Ill Inst Technol, 60-61; sr scientist, Microbiol, Assoc, Inc, Md, 61-63; prog analyst int sci & tech develop, Dept Defense, 63-66; sr staff mem, Inst Defense Anal, Va, 66-72; mem narcotics res mgt group, Off Sci & Technol, Exec Off Pres, 72-73; CHIEF RES & ENG DIV, DRUG ENFORCEMENT ADMIN, DEPT JUSTICE, 73- *Concurrent Pos:* Mem res & develop subcomt, Cabinet Comt Int Narcotics Control, 73-75; chmn S&T functional working group, Drug Rev Task Force, Exec Off Pres, 75. *Mem:* AAAS; Am Chem Soc; Am Pub Health Asn. *Res:* Research and development planning and administration; technology applications management; narcotic and dangerous drugs; forensic science; epidemiology. *Mailing Add:* 1428 Trapline Ct Vienna VA 22186

SHELDON, ERIC, b Oct 24, 30; Brit citizen; m 59; c 1. THEORETICAL NUCLEAR PHYSICS, ASTROPHYSICS. *Educ:* Univ London, BSc, 51, Hons, 52, PhD(sci), 55, DSc(physics), 71. *Prof Exp:* Lectr & demonstr physics, Acton Tech Col, Eng, 52-55; assoc physicist, IBM Res Lab, Switz, 57-59; res assoc physics, Swiss Fed Inst Technol, 59-63, privat dozent, 63-64, prof, 64-69; vis prof, Univ Tex, Austin, 69-70; PROF PHYSICS, UNIV LOWELL, 70- *Concurrent Pos:* NSF sr foreign scientist fel & vis prof, Univ Va, 68-69. *Mem:* Fel AAAS; fel Brit Inst Physics; The Chem Soc; Royal Inst Gt Brit; fel Am Phys Soc. *Res:* Theoretical nuclear physics involving nuclear reaction mechanism and nuclear structure studies in the low and intermediate energy range; astrophysics. *Mailing Add:* Dept of Physics Univ of Lowell Lowell MA 01854

SHELDON, HUNTINGTON, b New York, NY, Jan 14, 30; m 55; c 2. PATHOLOGY, MEDICINE. *Educ:* McGill Univ, BA, 51; Johns Hopkins Univ, MD, 56. *Prof Exp:* From asst to instr path, Johns Hopkins Univ, 56-59; from asst prof to assoc prof, 59-66, PROF PATH, MCGILL UNIV, 66-, STRATHCOME PROF, 80- *Concurrent Pos:* From intern to asst resident, Johns Hopkins Hosp, 56-59; from asst to instr path, Johns Hopkins Univ, 56-59; vis prof, Harvard Univ, 72; co-ed, Intro to Study Dis, 77. *Mem:* Am Soc Cell Biol; Am Soc Exp Path; Biophys Soc; Int Acad Path. *Res:* Application of electron microscopy to problems in pathology. *Mailing Add:* Dept Path McGill Univ 3775 Univ St Montreal PQ H3A 2B4 Can

SHELDON, JOHN WILLIAM, b Miami, Fla, Nov 21, 33; m 79; c 3. CHEMICAL PHYSICS, FLUID DYNAMICS. *Educ:* Purdue Univ, BS, 55, MS, 59; Tex A&M Univ, PhD(nuclear eng), 64. *Prof Exp:* Res engr, NASA, 55, head gaseous electronics sect, 64-66; from asst prof to assoc prof eng sci, Fla State Univ, 66-72; assoc prof phys sci, 72-76, chmn dept, 74-77, PROF PHYS SCI, FLA INT UNIV, 76- *Mem:* Am Phys Soc; Am Chem Soc; Am Vacuum Soc. *Res:* Atomic collision phenomena, measurement of collision cross sections by beam techniques; ionospheric flow and probe theory; electrical phenomena accompanying shock waves in two-phase flows. *Mailing Add:* Dept of Phys Sci Fla Int Univ Tamiami Trail Miami FL 33199

SHELDON, JOSEPH KENNETH, b Ogden, Utah, Nov 11, 43; m 65; c 2. INSECT ECOLOGY. *Educ:* Col Idaho, BS, 66; Univ Ill, PhD(entom), 72. *Prof Exp:* Assoc prof, 71-81, PROF BIOL, EASTERN COL, 81- *Mem:* AAAS; Ecol Soc Am; Am Entom Soc (vpres, 82); Am Sci Affil. *Res:* Biology and taxonomy of Chrysopidae; insect mimicry. *Mailing Add:* Dept Biol Eastern Col St Davids PA 19087

SHELDON, RICHARD P, b Tulsa, Okla, Oct 25, 23; m 66. GEOLOGY. *Educ:* Yale Univ, BS, 50; Stanford Univ, PhD, 56. *Prof Exp:* Geologist, US Geol Surv, 47-57; geologist, Lion Oil Co, 57-58; from geologist to asst chief geologist, 58-72, chief geologist, 72-77, RES GEOLOGIST, US GEOL SURV, 77- *Mem:* AAAS; Geol Soc Am; Soc Econ Geol; Am Asn Petrol Geologists; Soc Econ Paleontologists & Mineralogists. *Res:* Sedimentary petrology; physical stratigraphy; sedimentary mineral deposits. *Mailing Add:* US Geological Survey Mail Stop 953--Nat Ctr Reston VA 22092

SHELDON, VICTOR LAWRENCE, b Maysville, Mo, Sept 24, 21; m 46; c 4. SOILS, FERTILIZERS. *Educ:* Univ Mo, BS, 43, MA, 48, PhD(soils, plant physiol), 50. *Prof Exp:* Asst prof soils, Univ Mo, 52-55; agronomist & consult, Olin Mathieson Chem Corp, 55-61; mgr agr serv, John Deere Chem Co, 61-66; mgr tech serv, Esso Chem Co, Standard Oil, NJ, 66-67; vpres mkt, Esso Pakistan Fertilizer Co, Karachi, 67-69; PROF AGR & CHMN DEPT, WESTERN ILL UNIV, 69-; PRES, VLS ASSOC, 76- *Concurrent Pos:* Leader deleg to CENTO Agr Conf, US State Dept; consult, VLS Assoc, 72-76, Tenn Valley Authority, Int Inst Trop Agr & Int Fertilizer Develop Ctr. *Mem:* Soil Sci Soc Am, Am Soc Plant Physiol; Am Soc Agron; Sigma Xi. *Res:* Efficiency of phosphorus uptake from various compounds; influence of phosphorus on metabolism of plants; biodegradation of pesticides; fatty acids in soybean oil according to planting site and genotype; fertilizer marketing plan for nigeria; management systems for fertilizer operaters. *Mailing Add:* 221 Woodchuck Ln Macomb IL 61455

SHELDON, WALTER HERMAN, b Berlin, Ger, Feb 21, 11; nat US; m 40; c 3. PATHOLOGY. *Educ:* Univ Catania, MD, 35. *Prof Exp:* Asst instr path, Univ Pavia, 36-38; house officer, Children's Hosp, Boston, 38-39; resident, Boston Lying-in-Hosp, 39 & Free Hosp for Women, 40; instr, Harvard Med Sch, 40-43; asst prof, Sch Med, Emory Univ, 43-46, from assoc prof to prof & chmn dept, 47-60; prof, 60-76, EMER PROF PATH & EMER PROF COMP MED SCH MED, JOHNS HOPKINS UNIV, 76- *Concurrent Pos:* Resident, Peter Bent Brigham Hosp, 40-42; res assoc, Boston Lying-in-Hosp, 42-43; chief pathologist, Grady Mem Hosp, 43-54 & Hosp, Emory Univ, 49-60. *Mem:* Am Asn Path & Bact; Am Fedn Clin Res; Int Acad Path; Soc Exp Biol & Med; Med Mycol Soc of Americas. *Res:* Pathology and pathogenesis of infectious diseases. *Mailing Add:* Dept of Path Johns Hopkins Univ Hosp Baltimore MD 21205

SHELDON, WILLIAM GULLIVER, b New York, NY, Jan 13, 12; m 43; c 2. ECOLOGY. *Educ:* Yale Univ, BA, 33; Cornell Univ, MS, 47, PhD(vert zool), 48. *Prof Exp:* Leader coop wildlife res unit, US Fish & Wildlife Serv, 48-72; RESEARCHER & WRITER, 72- *Concurrent Pos:* Mem, US Nat Mus Exped, Can, 30-32 & Am Mus Natural Hist Exped, China & Tibet, 34-35. *Honors & Awards:* John Pierce Mem Conserv Award. *Mem:* Wildlife Soc; Ecol Soc Am; Am Soc Mammal; Am Ornith Union. *Res:* Biology and ecology of wild birds and mammals. *Mailing Add:* Brewster MA 02631

SHELDON, WILLIAM ROBERT, b Ft Lauderdale, Fla, May 17, 27; c 2. PHYSICS. *Educ:* Univ Mo, BS, 50, MS, 56, PhD(physics), 60. *Prof Exp:* Sr physicist, Rocketdyne Div, NAm Aviation, Inc, 60; res specialist space physics, Aerospace Div, Boeing Co, 60-66; res scientist cosmic ray physics, Southwest Ctr Advan Studies, 66-68; assoc prof, 68-73, PROF PHYSICS, UNIV HOUSTON, 73- *Concurrent Pos:* Proj leader, Joint French-US Cosmic Ray Exped, Mont Blanc Tunnel; proj leader rocket and balloon measurements of x-rays and electric fields at Roberval and Ft Churchill, Can, Ft Yukon, Alaska, Kiruna, Sweden, Siple Sta, Antarctica and the Kerguelen Islands; leader US team, French-USSR ARAKS experiment, 74-75. *Mem:* Am Phys Soc; Am Geophys Union; Sigma Xi. *Res:* Cosmic rays; high energy muons; auroral particle precipitations; x-rays in the atmosphere. *Mailing Add:* Dept of Physics Univ of Houston Houston TX 77004

SHELDRAKE, RAYMOND, JR, b Paterson, NJ, Sept 7, 23; m 54; c 4. HORTICULTURE. *Educ:* Rutgers Univ, BS, 49; Cornell Univ, MS, 50, PhD(veg crops, plant path, soils), 52. *Prof Exp:* Asst, NY Exp Sta, Geneva, 49-52; exten veg specialist, Univ Ga, 52-54; from asst prof to assoc prof, 54-69, PROF VEG CROPS, CORNELL UNIV, 69- *Mem:* Am Soc Hort Sci; Potato Asn Am. *Res:* Critical temperatures for growth of higher plants; plastics and plant growing. *Mailing Add:* Dept of Veg Crops Cornell Univ Ithaca NY 14853

SHELDRICK, PETER, b Newark, NJ, Jan 22, 36. MOLECULAR BIOLOGY, VIROLOGY. *Educ:* Brown Univ, Providence, RI, BA, 58; Univ Calif, Berkeley, PhD(chem), 62. *Prof Exp:* Sr researcher, 68-77, MASTER RESEARCHER, NAT CTR SCI RES, FRANCE, 77- *Concurrent Pos:* Mem, Herpes Virus Study Group, Int Comt Taxon Viruses, 76- *Mem:* Europ Molecular Biol Orgn. *Res:* Structure and function of herpes virus genomes: DNA base sequence orgnaization; transcription of RNA; in vivo polypeptide synthesis; enzymatic activities. *Mailing Add:* Inst Rech Sci Sur Le Cancer B P No 8 94802 Villejuif Cedex France

SHELEF, MORDECAI, b Suvalki, Poland, June 28, 31; m 55; c 2. CATALYSIS, FUEL SCIENCE. *Educ:* Israel Inst Technol, BSc, 56, MSc, 59; Pa State Univ, PhD(fuel sci), 66. *Prof Exp:* Res scientist, Israel Mining Industs, Haifa, 56-63; res asst, Pa State Univ, 63-66; prin res scientist, 69-73, staff scientist, 73-77, mgr fuels & lubricants dept, 77-81, MGR CHEM DEPT, RES STAFF, FORD MOTOR CO, 81- *Mem:* Am Chem Soc; Catalysis Soc. *Res:* Development of new fuel sources; kinetics and mechanism of surface reactions; chemisorption; carbon gasification; mineral dressing. *Mailing Add:* Res Staff PO Box 2053 Dearborn MI 48121

SHELESNYAK, MOSES CHIAM, b Chicago, Ill, June 6, 09; m 42; c 2. BIODYNAMICS, PHYSIOLOGY. *Educ:* Univ Wis, BA, 30; Columbia Univ, PhD(anat), 33. *Prof Exp:* Asst endocrinol, Columbia Univ, 33-35; instr physiol & pharmacol, Chicago Med Sch, 35-36; Gen Educ Bd fel child develop, NY Asn Care Jewish Children, 36-38, dean boys, 38-40; Freidsam res fel endocrine pediat, Beth Israel Hosp, New York, 40-42; head ecol br, med sci div & actg head biophys br, US Off Naval Res, 46-49; dir, Arctic Inst NAm, DC, 49-50; sr scientist, Dept Exp Biol, Weizmann Inst Sci, 50-56, assoc, 56-57, prof endocrine & reproductive physiol, 58-61, prof biodynamics & head dept, 61-68; assoc dir, 67-68, dir interdisciplinary commun prog, Off Asst Secy Sci, 68-77, RES ASSOC, SMITHSONIAN INST, 77- *Concurrent Pos:* Res assoc, Mt Sinai Hosp, 36-40; guest lectr, Columbia Univ, 37-38; vis prof geog, McGill Univ, 48; lectr, Johns Hopkins Univ, 49-50; hon consult, Panel Human Ecol Arid Zones, UNESCO, mem bd, 54-72; Marks fel & univ fel, Birmingham Univ, 57-58; consult & mem comn, Palais des Sci, World's Fair, Brussels, 58; mem Israel comt, Zool Sta, Naples; mem res comt, Int Planned Parenthood Fedn, 59-72; mem selection & adv comt, Int Training Prog Physiol Reproduction, Worcester, Mass, 59-; vis prof, Col France, Paris, 60; mem neuroendocrinol panel, Int Brain Res Orgn, 61-; mem expert adv comt human reproduction, WHO, 65-70; chmn bd, Interdisciplinary Commun Assocs, 69-; dir, Int Prog Pop Analysis, 72-77; mem Israel comt, Int Biol Prog. *Honors & Awards:* Oliver Bird Prize, 58. *Mem:* Fel AAAS; fel Soc Res Child Develop; fel Arctic Inst NAm; Soc Exp Biol & Med; Am Physiol Soc. *Res:* Reproduction and endocrine physiology; environmental physiology and human ecology; interdisciplinary communications; population dynamics; social biology. *Mailing Add:* River House Cherryfield Rd Drayden MD 20630

SHELINE, GLENN ELMER, b Flint, Mich, Mar 31, 18; m 48; c 1. MEDICINE. *Educ:* Univ Calif, BS, 39, PhD(physiol), 43, MD, 48. *Prof Exp:* Nat Res Coun fels, Univ Chicago, 49-50 & Univ Calif, San Francisco, 50-51; consult, US Naval Radiol Defense Lab, 53; from asst prof to assoc prof, 55-64, PROF RADIOL, SCH MED, UNIV CALIF, SAN FRANCISCO, 64- *Concurrent Pos:* Commonwealth Fund fel, Royal Marsden Hosp, London, 57; consult, San Francisco Gen Hosp, 57-, San Francisco Vet Admin Hosp, 70 & AEC; dir radiation ther, Nat Cancer Inst. *Mem:* Soc Nuclear Med (vpres); Am Radium Soc; Radiation Oncol Roentgen Ray Soc (vpres); Am Thyroid Asn (vpres); Radiol Soc NAm. *Res:* Radiation therapy and effects; radiobiology. *Mailing Add:* Dept of Radiol Univ of Calif Sch of Med San Francisco CA 94143

SHELINE, RAYMOND KAY, b Port Clinton, Ohio, Mar 31, 22; m 51; c 7. NUCLEAR CHEMISTRY. *Educ:* Bethany Col, BS, 43; Univ Calif, PhD(chem), 49. *Prof Exp:* Asst, Bethany Col, 40-42; asst, Manhattan Proj, Columbia Univ, 43-45; jr scientist, Los Alamos Sci Lab, Univ Calif, 45-46, asst, Univ, 46-49; instr, Inst Nuclear Studies, Univ Chicago, 49-51; res participant, Oak Ridge Inst Nuclear Studies, 51-52; assoc prof chem, 52-55, distinguished prof physics, 66-67, PROF CHEM, FLA STATE UNIV, 55-, PROF PHYSICS, 59- *Concurrent Pos:* Res chemist, Merck Chem Co, 46; Fulbright res prof & Guggenheim fel, Niels Bohr Inst, Coepnhagen, Denmark, 55-56 & 57-58, Ford res prof, 57-58; Guggenheim fel, 64; Nordita prof, Univ Lund & Copenhagen Univ, 71-72; consult, NSF, Los Alamos Sci Lab, Univ Calif & Oak Ridge Nat Lab, 61-; Gillon lectureship, Nat Univ Zaire, Kinshasa, 76. *Honors & Awards:* Niels Bohr Inst Silver Cup; Am Inst Physics Citation, 63, Alexander von Humboldt sr scientist award, 76. *Mem:* Royal Danish Acad Sci & Letters; Am Chem Soc; fel Am Phys Soc. *Res:* Nuclear spectroscopy by decay scheme studies and Van de Graaff excitation; coulomb excitation; correlation of experimental data with nuclear models; muonic x-ray studies; metal carbonyls, especially the production and structure of uranium carbonyls. *Mailing Add:* Dept of Chem Fla State Univ Tallahassee FL 32306

SHELKIN, BARRY DAVID, b Brooklyn, NY, Oct 11, 28; m 52; c 3. GEOLOGY. *Educ:* Brooklyn Col, BS, 55. *Prof Exp:* Cartog aide, US Coast & Geod Surv, 55-56; geologist, Gulf Oil Corp, 56-60, Span Gulf Oil Co, 60-63 & Nigerian Gulf Oil Co, 63-64; sr photointerpreter, Data Anal Ctr, Itek Corp, 64-65; sr scientist, Autometric Oper, Raytheon Co, 65-69, head terrain sci sect, 69-70; chief, Terrain Sci Div, 70-73, chief, Support Div, Defense Mapping Agency, 73-81, CHIEF, ANAL DIV, DEFENSE MAPPING AGENCY, HYDROGRAPHIC TOPOGRAPHIC CTR, US ARMY TOPOG COMMAND, 81- *Mem:* Geol Soc Am; Am Asn Petrol Geologists; Am Soc Photogram. *Res:* Geological research, terrain, and environmental analysis through the medium of aerial photography; administration of cartographic contracts. *Mailing Add:* 8206 Chancery Ct Alexandria VA 22308

SHELL, DONALD LEWIS, b Worth Twp, Sanilac Co, Mich, Mar 1, 24; m 46, 73; c 2. MATHEMATICS. *Educ:* Mich Technol Univ, BS, 44; Univ Cincinnati, MS, 51, PhD(math), 59. *Prof Exp:* Instr math, Mich Technol Univ, 46-49; mathematician, Gen Elec Co, 51-52, numerical analyst, 52-53, supvr systs anal & synthesis, 53-54, mgr comput tech develop, 54-56, mgr, Evendale Comput, 56-57, comput consult specialist, 57-59, mgr digital anal & comput, Knolls Atomic Power Lab, 60-61, eng math, adv tech lab, 61-63, mgr comput appln & processing telecommun & info processing opers, 63-66, mgr eng, Info Serv Dept, 66-68, mgr automation studies, Res & Develop Ctr, 68-69, mgr info servs tech planning, 69-71, mgr info servs qual assurance, 71-72; chmn bd & gen mgr, Robotics, Inc, 72-75; mgr file systs, 75-76, mgr technol systs, 76-78, mgr appln systs, 78-80, MGR MARK III SYSTS, GEN ELEC INFO SERV CO, 80- *Mem:* Math Asn Am; Asn Comput Mach. *Res:* Numerical computation; applications of digital computers; sorting. *Mailing Add:* Gen Elec Info Serv Co 401 N Washington Rockville MD 20850

SHELL, EDDIE WAYNE, b Chapman, Ala, June 16, 30; m 53. FISH BIOLOGY. *Educ:* Auburn Univ, BS, 52, MS, 54; Cornell Univ, PhD(fishery biol), 59. *Prof Exp:* Asst fisheries, Auburn Univ, 52-54 & Cornell Univ, 56-58; asst fish culturist, 59-61, assoc prof fisheries, 61-70, PROF FISHERIES, AUBURN UNIV, 70-, HEAD DEPT, 73- *Concurrent Pos:* Dir Int Ctr Aquaculture, 73. *Mem:* AAAS; Am Fisheries Soc. *Mailing Add:* Dept of Fish & Allied Agr Auburn Univ Auburn AL 36830

SHELL, FRANCIS JOSEPH, b Medicine Lodge, Kans, Mar 27, 22; m 44; c 3. PHYSICAL CHEMISTRY. *Educ:* Ft Hays Kans State Col, AB & MS, 49; Univ Ky, PhD(phys chem), 53. *Prof Exp:* Res chemist, 52-57, asst dir tech serv div, 57-66, mgr tech serv, 66-81, SR CHEM ASSOC, PHILLIPS PETROL CO, 81- *Mem:* Am Chem Soc; Am Petrol Inst; Soc Petrol Engrs. *Res:* Non-aqueous solutions; oil well cements; drilling fluids; fracturing; colloids. *Mailing Add:* Phillips Petrol Co 309 Short St Bartlesville OK 74004

SHELL, JOHN WELDON, b Waxahachie, Tex, Apr 20, 25; m 52; c 2. PHARMACEUTICAL CHEMISTRY. *Educ:* Univ Colo, BA, 49, BS, 53, PhD(pharmaceut chem), 54. *Prof Exp:* Asst chem, Univ Colo, 49-53; res assoc physics, Upjohn Co, 54-57, res scientist in prod res, 57-60, sr res scientist, 60-62; dir qual control, Allergan Pharmaceut, 62-64, dir res, 64-68; assoc dir, Inst Pharmaceut Chem Div, 68-71, dir ophthal res, 71-73, VPRES & DIR CLIN OPHTHAL, ALZA CORP, 73- *Concurrent Pos:* Vis grad lectr, Univ Southern Calif, 65-66; adj prof, 72-77, prof, Med Ctr, Univ Calif, San Francisco, 77- mem, Res Prevent Blindness, Inc. *Mem:* Am Pharmaceut Asn; fel Acad Pharmaceut Sci; Asn Res Vision & Ophthal. *Res:* Cyrstallography; x-ray analysis; biopharmaceutics; biochemistry; ocular pharmacology. *Mailing Add:* Alza Corp 950 Page Mill Rd Palo Alto CA 94304

SHELL, LESTER CRANE, b Decatur City, Iowa, Oct 1, 12; m 41. EMBRYOLOGY, PHYSIOLOGY. *Educ:* Cent Methodist Col, AB, 34; Univ Iowa, MS, 39, PhD, 59. *Prof Exp:* Asst sci, Cent Methodist Col, 34-36, from instr to assoc prof, 37-59; prof biol & head dept, Univ Dubuque, 59-63; vis prof, Macalester Col, 63; prof biol & head dept, Millikin Univ, 63-78; mem staff, Cent Methodist Col, 78-80; EMER PROF BIOL, MILLIKIN UNIV, 80- *Concurrent Pos:* NSF grant chromatography, Kans State Univ; NSF grant plant biochem, Inst Paper Chem & NSF grant radioactive isotopes, Cornell Col, 59; NSF comp physiol, Carleton Col, 61. *Mem:* AAAS; Am Chem Soc; Am Soc Zool; Nat Sci Teachers Asn; Nat Asn Biol Teachers. *Res:* Distribution mitotic figures in rana pipiens; distribution radioisotopes in various organs of treated and control white mice; reserpine-thyroxine interrelationship; distribution of sulfhydryl groups in developing cell; premedical education; effect of drugs on oxygen uptake for various body tissues. *Mailing Add:* 205 N Church PO Box 46 Fayette MD 65248

SHELLABARGER, CLAIRE J, b College Corner, Ohio, Oct 23, 24; m 48; c 3. RADIOBIOLOGY, ENDOCRINOLOGY. *Educ:* Miami Univ, AB, 48; Ind Univ, MA, 49, PhD(zool), 52. *Prof Exp:* Asst, Ind Univ, 50-52; jr scientist, Brookhaven Nat Lab, 52-53, asst scientist, 53-54, assoc scientist, 54-57, scientist, 58-60, asst to chmn dept med, 59-60; prof zool & coordr, Kresge Radioisotope Labs, Med Sch, Univ Mich, Ann Arbor, 60-68; asst chmn med dept, 68-70, sr scientist & head radiobiol div, Brookhaven Nat Lab, Upton, 70-80; PROF PATH, STATE UNIV NY STONY BROOK, 80- *Concurrent Pos:* Lectr, Adelphi Col, 56; USPHS fel, Nat Inst Med Res, Eng, 57-58 & Inst Cancer Res, London, 66-67. *Mem:* Am Soc Zool; Soc Exp Biol & Med; Am Soc Exp Path; Radiation Res Soc; Am Physiol Soc. *Res:* Radiation carcinogenesis. *Mailing Add:* Dept Path Health Sci Ctr State Univ NY Stony Brook NY 11794

SHELLENBARGER, ROBERT MARTIN, b Sacramento, Calif, June 25, 36; m 59; c 5. PHYSICAL CHEMISTRY. *Educ:* Col Pac, BS, 57; Univ NC, PhD(phys chem), 63. *Prof Exp:* Res chemist, 62-71, SUPVR RES & DEVELOP, E I DU PONT DE NEMOURS & CO, INC, 71- *Mem:* AAAS. *Res:* Structure and properties of synthetic fibers and nonwoven fabrics. *Mailing Add:* 3804 Valleybrook Dr Wilmington DE 19808

SHELLENBERGER, CARL H, b York, Pa, Sept 11, 35; m 59; c 3. PHYSIOLOGY, PHARMACOLOGY. *Educ:* Muhlenberg Col, BS, 58; State Univ NY, PhD(physiol), 68. *Prof Exp:* Res asst anesthesiol, Med Sch, Univ Pa, 59-61; mem staff pharmacol dept, Endo Labs, Inc, 67-70; clin scientist, Consumer Prod Div, Warner-Lambert Co, 70-73; asst dir, Sandoz, Inc, 73-75, assoc dir, 75-78, sr assoc dir clin res, 78-81; DIR CLIN AFFAIRS, WARNER-LAMBERT CO, 81- *Mem:* AAAS; Am Pharmaceut Asn; NY Acad Sci. *Res:* Fibrinolysis; neuropharmacology; glucose and fat metabolism; adrenal gland metabolism; respiratory and analgesic pharmacology; clinical investigation of proprietary and ethical drugs; medical instrumentation. *Mailing Add:* Warner-Lambert Co Tabor Rd Morris Plains NJ 07950

SHELLENBERGER, DONALD J(AMES), b Altoona, Pa, Mar 30, 28; m 49; c 2. CHEMICAL ENGINEERING. *Educ:* Pa State Univ, BS, 50. *Prof Exp:* Asst indust hygienist, State Bur Indust Hyg, Pa, 50-51; process engr, Day & Zimmermann, Inc, 51-55; process engr, Jones & Laughlin Steel Corp, 55-56, sr process engr, 56-58, supvr chem eng servs, 58-64, supvr blast furnace res, 64-67, planning engr, 67-69, develop engr blast furnaces, 69-77; sr staff engr, 77-81, ASST DIR TECH OPERS, KOPPERS CO, INC, 81- *Mem:* Am Inst Mining, Metall & Petrol Engrs; Asn Iron & Steel Engrs. *Res:* Development of blast furnaces, ancillary equipment and iron ore agglomeration facilities; coordination of research and development in coal carbonization, byproducts, ore agglomerization and metallurgical processes. *Mailing Add:* Koppers Co Inc Pittsburgh PA 15219

SHELLENBERGER, JOHN ALFRED, b Moline, Ill, Jan 8, 00; m 38; c 3. CEREAL CHEMISTRY. *Educ:* Univ Wash, BS, 28; Kans State Univ, MS, 29; Univ Minn, PhD(agr chem), 34. *Prof Exp:* Chemist, Fisher Flouring Mills, 25-29; asst prof chem & asst agr chemist, Univ Idaho, 30-31; asst grain respiration res, Univ Minn, 32-34, instr agr biochem, 34-35; head prod control, Mennel Milling Co, Ohio, 36-39; head biochem lab, Rohm and Haas Co, Pa, 39-42; tech adv, Corp Promotion Interchange, Chancellor Exchequer, Arg, 42-44; distinguished prof flour & feed milling industs, Flour & Feed Grains Inst & cereal chemist, Agr Exp Sta, 45-71, EMER DISTINGUISHED PROF FLOUR & FEED MILLING INDUSTS, FLOUR & FEED GRAINS INST, KANS STATE UNIV, 71- *Concurrent Pos:* Consult, Armour Res Found, Arg, 42-43 & US Grain Mkt Res Ctr, 72-; food specialist, Inst Inter-Am Affairs Mission, Peru, 46 & Costa Rica, 48; chmn US deleg, Food & Agr Orgn, Colombia, 49; deleg, US AID, Guatemala, 70-71; consult, Grain Mkt Res Ctr, USDA, Manhattan, Kans, 71-74. *Honors & Awards:* C H Bailey Gold Medal, Int Asn Cereal Chem, 75. *Mem:* AAAS; Am Chem Soc; Am Asn Cereal Chem (pres, 50); Inst Food Technol; Int Asn Cereal Chem (pres, 66-68). *Res:* Wheat quality; enzymes in baking; respiration of cereal grains; flour milling; technology and biochemistry of barley; microchemical analysis; malting. *Mailing Add:* Shellenberger Hall Kans State Univ Manhattan KS 66506

SHELLENBERGER, MELVIN KENT, b Pittsburg, Kans, Oct 29, 36; m 59; c 4. NEUROPHARMACOLOGY. *Educ:* Kans State Col Pittsburg, BS, 58; Univ Wash, MS, 62, PhD(pharmacol), 65. *Prof Exp:* Lab technician, Pharmacol Dept, Upjohn Co, 59-60; lab instr dent, med, pharm & pharmacol courses, Univ Wash, 60-65, lectr pharm & pharmacol courses, 62-65; from instr to asst prof, 67-74, ASSOC PROF PHARMACOL, UNIV KANS MED CTR, 74- *Concurrent Pos:* Nat Inst Neurol Dis & Stroke fel pharmacol, Univ Mich, 65-66, NIMH trainee neuropsychopharmacol, 66-67; res assoc, Kans Ctr Ment Retardation & Human Develop, 71-; NIMH career develop res award, Univ Kans Med Ctr, 72-77. *Mem:* Int Soc Neurochem; Am Soc Pharmacol & Exp Therapeut; Soc Neurosci. *Res:* Correlating possible chemical mediators in the brain with electrical, physiological and behavioral events. *Mailing Add:* Dept Pharmacol Univ Kans Med Ctr Kansas City KS 66103

SHELLENBERGER, PAUL ROBERT, b Dover, Pa, May 28, 35; m 57; c 2. DAIRY SCIENCE. *Educ:* Pa State Univ, BS, 57, MS, 59; Iowa State Univ, PhD(animal nutrit), 64. *Prof Exp:* Area dairy specialist, Agr Ext Serv, Tex A&M Univ, 64-66; acting assoc prof agr, Tarleton State Col, 66-67; asst prof dairy sci, 67-72, assoc prof, 72-77, PROF DAIRY SCI, PA STATE UNIV, UNIVERSITY PARK, 77- *Mem:* Nat Asn Col & Teachers Agr; Am Dairy Sci Asn; Am Soc Animal Sci. *Mailing Add:* 203 Borland Lab University Park PA 16802

SHELLENBERGER, THOMAS E, b Havre, Mont, May 3, 32; m 53; c 3. BIOCHEMISTRY, TOXICOLOGY. *Educ:* Mont State Univ, BS, 54, MS, 55; Kans State Univ, PhD(biochem), 61. *Prof Exp:* Res asst chem, Mont State Univ, 54-55; asst instr, Kans State Univ, 55-60; biochemist, Stanford Res Inst, 60-66, mgr biochem toxicol labs, 66; chmn dept toxicol, Gulf South Res Inst, 66-72; actg dep dir, Nat Ctr Toxicol Res, 77-78, CHIEF DIV COMP

PHARMACOL, NAT CTR TOXICOL RES, FOOD & DRUG ADMIN, 72- *Concurrent Pos:* Assoc prof biochem, Univ Ark, Little Rock, 74- *Mem:* AAAS; NY Acad Sci; Am Chem Soc; Soc Toxicol; Am Col Vet Toxicologists. *Res:* Metabolism of carcinogens; comparative endocrinology; reactions and mechanisms of organophosphates; hazards of pesticides to fish and wildlife; poultry nutrition, vitamins and protein. *Mailing Add:* Nat Ctr Toxicol Res Food & Drug Admin Jefferson AR 72079

SHELLEY, AUSTIN L(INN), b New Ross, Ind, Apr 9, 22; m 48; c 2. ELECTRICAL ENGINEERING. *Educ:* Univ Ky, BS, 47; Purdue Univ, MS, 52, PhD(elec eng), 58. *Prof Exp:* Instr elec eng, Miss State Col, 47-49; from instr to asst prof, 50-61, ASSOC PROF ELEC ENG, PURDUE UNIV, WEST LAFAYETTE, 61-, EXEC ASST TO HEAD SCH, 64- *Mem:* Illum Eng Soc; Inst Elec & Electronics Engrs; Am Soc Eng Educ. *Res:* Circuits; machinery; servomechanisms. *Mailing Add:* Sch of Elec Eng Purdue Univ West Lafayette IN 47907

SHELLEY, CRAIG ALAN, organic chemistry, computer science, see previous edition

SHELLEY, DONALD L(OUIS), b Cleveland, Ohio, Jan 28, 37; m 64; c 4. MATERIALS & POLYMER SCIENCE. *Educ:* Cath Univ, AB, 59, MS, 61, PhD(physics), 65. *Prof Exp:* Res asst physics, Cath Univ, 59-64; asst prof, Calif State Col Long Beach, 64-67; res physicist, Res & Develop Ctr, Armstrong Cork Co, Lancaster, 67-73, SR RES SCIENTIST, RES & DEVELOP CTR, ARMSTRONG WORLD INDUSTS, 73- *Concurrent Pos:* Part time consult, Teledyne, Calif, 65. *Mem:* Am Phys Soc; Am Chem Soc. *Res:* Ultrasonics applied to solids and gases; polymer physics, especially thermodynamic and electrical properties. *Mailing Add:* Armstrong Res & Develop 2500 Columbia Ave Lancaster PA 17604

SHELLEY, EDWARD GEORGE, b Watford City, NDak, Jan 8, 33; m 52; c 2. SPACE PHYSICS. *Educ:* Ore State Univ, BS(physics) & BS(math), 59; Stanford Univ, MS, 61, PhD(nuclear physics), 67. *Prof Exp:* Res scientist, 59-73, staff scientist, 73-80, SR STAFF SCIENTIST, LOCKHEED RES LABS, 80- *Concurrent Pos:* Res assoc physics, Stanford Univ, 65-68. *Mem:* Am Geophys Union. *Res:* Magnetospheric physics, primarily in area of satellite observations of space plasmas. *Mailing Add:* Lockheed Res Labs B/205 3251 Hanover D52/12 Palo Alto CA 94304

SHELLEY, EDWIN F(REEMAN), b New York, NY, Feb 19, 21; m 41; c 2. COMMUNICATIONS, SYSTEMS ENGINEERING. *Educ:* Columbia Univ, AB, 40, BSEE, 41; Harvard Univ, cert, 57. *Prof Exp:* Proj engr, Propeller Div, Curtiss-Wright Corp, NJ, 41-47; pres & chief engr, Am Chronoscope Corp, 48-50; co-founder, vpres & gen mgr, Bulova Res & Develop Labs, Inc, 50-57; dir advan progs, US Industs, Inc, 57-60, vpres, 60-64, pres, Robodyne Div, 58-60; pres, E F Shelley & Co, Inc, 65-71, chmn bd, 71-75; DIR, CTR ENERGY POLICY & RES, NY INST TECHNOL, 75- *Concurrent Pos:* Consult, Wilson Mech Instrument Co, 45-47 & US Off Educ, 77-; spec consult, Mercury Totalizer Co, Inc, 49-50; pres, Nat Coun Aging, 68-71; mem bd dirs, Ctr Community Change; mem bd trustees, NY Inst Technol; mem bd trustees, Nova Univ. *Mem:* AAAS; sr mem Inst Elec & Electronics Engrs; Am Inst Aeronaut & Astronaut; Am Phys Soc; Newcomen Soc NAm. *Res:* Automatic machines and computing equipment; electronic instrumentation; application of information systems to social organization; energy policy; public education techniques. *Mailing Add:* NY Inst Technol Old Westbury NY 11568

SHELLEY, ROBERT DUNCAN, material science, deceased

SHELLEY, WALTER BROWN, b St Paul, Minn, Feb 6, 17; m 42, 80; c 3. DERMATOLOGY. *Educ:* Univ Minn, BS, 40, PhD(physiol), 41, MB & MD, 43. *Hon Degrees:* MD, Univ Uppsala, Sweden, 77. *Prof Exp:* Asst physiol, Univ Minn, 38-41; instr, Col St Thomas, 42-43; instr, Univ Pa, 46-47, asst instr dermat, 47-49; instr, Dartmouth Col, 49-50; from asst prof to prof dermat, Sch Med, Univ Pa, 50-80, chmn dept, 65-80; PROF DERMAT, PEORIA SCH MED, UNIV ILL, 80- *Concurrent Pos:* Pvt pract; chief clin, Univ Hosp, 51-56 & 65-66; regional consult, US Vet Admin, 55-59; mem comt cutaneous dis, Nat Res Coun, 55-59, mem coun, 61-64; Pollitzer lectr, NY Univ, 56; Rauschkolb Mem lectr, Univ Chicago, 57; Prosser White Oration, Univ London, 57; consult, Surgeon Gen, US Army, 58-61 & US Air Force, 58-61; mem comn cutaneous dis, Armed Forces Epidemiol Bd, 58-61, dep dir, 59-61; consult, Philadelphia Gen Hosp, 60-65, chief dermat serv, 65-67; mem & dir, Am Bd Dermat, 60-69, past pres; consult dermatologist, Children's Hosp Philadelphia, 65-80. *Honors & Awards:* Soc Cosmetic Chem Award, 55; Hellerstrom Medal, Karolinska Inst, Sweden, 71; Am Med Writers Asn Award, 73; Dohi Medalist, Nagoya, Japan, 81. *Mem:* Soc Invest Dermat (past pres); Am Physiol Soc; Am Dermat Asn (past pres); Am Acad Dermat (past pres); Asn Prof Dermat (past pres). *Res:* Physiology of the skin, especially the eccrine and apocrine sweat gland, sebaceous gland and pruritus; allergic states. *Mailing Add:* Univ Ill Col Med Peoria Sch Med PO Box 1649 Peoria IL 61656

SHELLEY, WILLIAM J, b Wichita, Kans, Mar 15, 22; m 54. CHEMICAL ENGINEERING. *Educ:* Univ Mich, BS, 48, MSE, 49. *Prof Exp:* Prod engr uranium div, Mallinckrodt Chem Works, 49-50, admin asst, 50-55, prod control mgr, 55-61, vpres & mgr, 61-67; asst to vpres, 67-71, DIR & VPRES NUCLEAR LICENSING & REGULATIONS, KERR-MCGEE OIL INDUSTS, KERR-MCGEE CORP, 71- *Mem:* Am Inst Chem Engrs; Am Chem Soc; Am Mgt Asn. *Mailing Add:* Kerr-McGee Corp Kerr-McGee Bldg Oklahoma City OK 73102

SHELLHAAS, JAMES LEE, immunology, microbiology, see previous edition

SHELLHAMER, DALE FRANCIS, b Tamaqua, Pa, Dec 4, 42; m 71; c 2. ORGANIC CHEMISTRY. *Educ:* Univ Calif, Irvine, BA, 69; Univ Calif, Santa Barbara, PhD(org chem), 74. *Prof Exp:* Assoc prof chem, 74-81, PROF CHEM, POINT LOMA COL, 81- *Concurrent Pos:* Am Heart Asn grant, 78. *Mem:* Am Chem Soc. *Res:* Electrophilic additions to alkenes, alkynes and dienes; physical organic properties of fluorinated hydrocarbons. *Mailing Add:* Dept of Chem 3900 Lomaland Dr San Diego CA 92106

SHELLHAMER, ROBERT HOWARD, b Plymouth, Pa, June 3, 25; m 55; c 4. ANATOMY, HISTOCHEMISTRY. *Educ:* Temple Univ, MA, 48, PhD(anat), 52. *Prof Exp:* From instr to assoc prof, 51-65, PROF ANAT, SCH MED & SCH DENT, IND UNIV, INDIANAPOLIS, 65-, ASST TO DEAN STUDENT AFFAIRS, SCH MED, 76- *Res:* Gross anatomy; vascular system; histochemistry of the life cycle of the lamprey. *Mailing Add:* Dept of Anat Ind Univ Indianapolis IN 46202

SHELLHAMMER, HOWARD STEPHEN, b Woodland, Calif, Aug 30, 35; m 56; c 1. VERTEBRATE ZOOLOGY. *Educ:* Univ Calif, Davis, BA, 57, PhD(zool), 61. *Prof Exp:* From asst prof to assoc prof, 61-70, PROF BIOL SCI, SAN JOSE STATE UNIV, 70- *Concurrent Pos:* Consult. *Mem:* Am Soc Mammal; Animal Behav Soc; AAAS; Wildlife Soc. *Res:* evolution and ecology of harvest mice and other Caliornia mammals; fire ecology; behavior and ecology of Douglas tree squirrels. *Mailing Add:* Dept Biol Sci San Jose State Univ San Jose CA 95192

SHELLY, EUGENE PAUL, b Philadelphia, Pa, June 26, 29. MATHEMATICS. *Educ:* Pa State Univ, BS, 52; Carnegie Inst Technol, PhD(math), 57. *Prof Exp:* Instr math, Carnegie Inst Technol, 56-57; fel, Univ Md, 57-58; mathematician, E I du Pont de Nemours & Co, 58-59; numerical analyst, Knolls Atomic Power Lab, Gen Elec Co, 59-62; assoc prof math, Univ Conn, 62-80. *Concurrent Pos:* Vis prof math, Col Virgin Islands. *Mem:* Am Math Soc. *Res:* Applied mathematics; numerical analysis. *Mailing Add:* Dept Math Univ Conn Storrs CT 06268

SHELLY, JAMES H, b Zanesville, Ohio, Nov 28, 32; m 56; c 3. MATHEMATICS, COMPUTER SCIENCE. *Educ:* Oberlin Col, BA, 54; Univ Ill, Urbana, AM, 56, PhD(math), 59. *Prof Exp:* Assoc engr, 59-62, sr assoc engr, 62-64, staff engr, 64-66, proj engr, 66-67, adv engr, 67-73, SR ENGR, IBM CORP, 73- *Mem:* Asn Comput Mach; Soc Indust & Appl Math. *Res:* Processor and systems design and development; logical design; switching theory; combinatorial mathematics. *Mailing Add:* IBM Corp PO Box 390 Poughkeepsie NY 12602

SHELLY, JOHN RICHARD, b Sellersville, Pa, Jan 19, 49; m 74; c 1. FOREST PRODUCTS ENGINEERING. *Educ:* Pa State Univ, BS, 70; Univ Calif, Berkeley, MS, 77. *Prof Exp:* Res asst, Forest Prod Lab, Univ Calif, Berkeley, 74-81; ASST PROF FOREST PROD, DEPT FORESTRY, UNIV KY, 81- *Concurrent Pos:* Extension specialist, Coop Extension, Univ Calif, 77-78. *Mem:* Forest Prod Res Soc; Soc Wood Sci & Technol; Sigma Xi. *Res:* Principles and practice of wood drying methods, in particular energy efficiency in commercial lumber drying operations; the theory of the flow of fluids through porous materials. *Mailing Add:* 204 TP Cooper Bldg 0073 Dept Forestry Univ Ky Lexington KY 40546

SHELOKOV, ALEXIS JOANN, b China, Oct 18, 19; nat US; m 47; c 1. VIROLOGY. *Educ:* Stanford Univ, AB, 43, MD, 48; Am Bd Microbiol, dipl pub health & med virol; Am Bd Prev Med, dipl. *Prof Exp:* Physiologist, Climatic Res Lab, US War Dept, 43-44; res asst physiol, Stanford Univ, 46-47; res asst med, Sch Med, Boston Univ, 48-49, instr, 48-50; med officer, Lab Infectious Dis, Nat Inst Allergy & Infectious Dis, NIH, 50-57, dir, Mid Am Res Unit, CZ, 57-61, chief lab trop virol, Nat Inst Allergy & Infectious Dis, 59-63, chief lab virol & rickettsiol, Div Biologics Standards, NIH, 63-68; prof microbiol & chmn dept, Univ Tex Health Sci Ctr San Antonio, 68-81; PROF EPIDEMIOL, SCH HYG & PUB HEALTH, JOHNS HOPKINS UNIV, 81-, DIR, VACCINE RES INST, 81- *Concurrent Pos:* House officer, Mass Mem Hosps, Boston, 47-50; asst pediat, Harvard Med Sch, 49-50 & Georgetown Univ, 53-57; consult, DC Gen Hosp, 55-57, Gorgas & Coco Solo Hosps, CZ, 58-61, Pan Am Health Orgn, 58-63 & 71, Fogarty Int Ctr, NIH, 71 & 75 & Geog Med Br, Nat Inst Allergy & Infectious Dis, 72-; mem sci adv bd, Gorgas Mem Inst, Panama, 59-72; exec coun, Am Comt Arthropod-Borne Viruses, 60-67; US Deleg Virus Dis, USSR, 61; panel for arboviruses, Nat Inst Allergy & Infectious Dis, 62-66; ad hoc mem, Int Ctr Comt; mem sci adv bd, WHO Reference Serum Bank, Yale Univ, 64-68; chmn, US Deleg Hemorrhagic Fevers, USSR, 65 & 69; mem virol study sect, NIH, 68-70; mem bd trustees, Am Type Cult Collection, 69-72; vis prof, Fac Med & Inst Hyg, Univ of the Republic, Uruguay, 71; bd sci counr, Nat Inst Dent Res, 71-75; mem viral dis panel, US-Japan Coop Med Sci Prog, 71-76; mem, Adv Bd Virol, CRC Press, 75-80; mem sci adv bd, Gorgas Mem Inst Trop & Preventive Med, 76- *Honors & Awards:* Order of Rodolfo Robles, Guatemala, 59. *Mem:* Am Epidemiol Soc; Soc Exp Biol & Med; Am Soc Trop Med & Hyg; Am Asn Immunol; Infectious Dis Soc Am. *Res:* Epidemiology; preventive medicine; infectious diseases. *Mailing Add:* Dept Epidemiol Sch Hyg & Pub Health Johns Hopkins Univ Baltimore MD 21205

SHELSON, W(ILLIAM), b Toronto, Ont, June 18, 22; m 58; c 2. ENERGY ANALYSIS, SYSTEM PLANNING. *Educ:* Univ Toronto, BASc, 44, PhD, 52; Pa State Univ, MS, 47. *Prof Exp:* Stress analyst, Curtiss-Wright Corp, 47-48; res assoc appl math, Brown Univ, 48-49; mech engr, Can Stand Asn, 50-51; res engr, Hydro-Elec Power Comn, Ont, 52-56, chmn, Opers Res Group, 56-67; mgr oper res, 67-74, mgr fuel resources planning, 75-80, MGR ENERGY RESOURCES PLANNING, ONT HYDRO, 80- *Concurrent Pos:* Special lectr, Univ Toronto, 56-57. *Mem:* Can Oper Res Soc. *Res:* Operations research; systems analysis; stress analysis; energy analysis and planning of electric power systems; evaluation and optimization of primary energy supply alternatives. *Mailing Add:* 53 Evanston Dr Downsview ON M3H 5P4 Can

SHELSTAD, KENNETH ALVIN, b Glenavon, Sask, Sept 25, 25; m 49; c 4. CHEMICAL ENGINEERING, PHYSICAL CHEMISTRY. *Educ:* Univ Sask, BE, 47; Dalhousie Univ, MSc, 52; Univ Toronto, PhD(chem eng), 58. *Prof Exp:* Asst prof chem eng, NS Tech Col, 48-54; spec lectr, Univ Toronto, 54-58; asst prof, McGill Univ, 58-62, res eng, Imp Oil Enterprises Ltd, 62-64; assoc prof chem eng, 64-77, MEM FAC ENG SCI, UNIV WESTERN ONT, 77- *Concurrent Pos:* Res grants, Nat Res Coun Can, 59-62, 64- & Dept Univ Affairs, 65-; res engr, Atomic Energy Can, 61; consult, NS Res Found, 50-52. *Mem:* Can Soc Chem Eng. *Res:* Contact catalysis; air pollution control; chemical process design and development. *Mailing Add:* Fac Eng Sci Univ Western Ont London ON N6A 5B8 Can

SHELTON, DAMON CHARLES, b Richland, Ind, Apr 4, 22; m 43; c 2. BIOCHEMISTRY. *Educ:* Purdue Univ, BSA, 47, MS, 49, PhD(agr biochem), 50. *Prof Exp:* Instr agr chem, Purdue Univ, 49-50, fel, 51-52; pvt bus, 52-53; from assoc prof to prof agr biochem, WVa Univ, 53-60, from assoc prof to prof med biochem, Sch Med, 60-67; res mgr, 67-75, RES DIR, RALSTON PURINA CO, 75- *Concurrent Pos:* Assoc animal nutritionist, Ala Polytech Inst, 50-51. *Mem:* Am Chem Soc; Am Inst Nutrit; Am Soc Cell Biol; Am Soc Microbiol; Am Soc Biol Chem. *Res:* Blood proteins; amino acids; antibiotics and vitamins in nutrition and pathology; microbiology; mineral and antibiotic interrelationships; lipid-protein interactions; biological transport-peptides and amino acids. *Mailing Add:* 9338 Lincoln Dr St Louis MO 63127

SHELTON, EMMA, b Urbana, Ill, June 10, 20. CELL BIOLOGY, ELECTRON MICROSCOPY. *Educ:* Brown Univ, PhD(biol), 49. *Prof Exp:* Jr biologist, Nat Cancer Inst, 44-46, res biologist, 49-78; secy, Am Soc Cell Biol, 78-81; RETIRED. *Concurrent Pos:* Vis biologist, Lab Electron Micros, Villejuif, France, 63-64. *Mem:* Fel AAAS; Am Soc Cell Biol; Am Asn Path; Histochem Soc; Am Asn Cancer Res. *Res:* Fine structure of ribosomes, enzymes, immunoglobulins; electron microscopy of cell interactions in the immune response. *Mailing Add:* 8410 Westmount Terrace Bethesda MD 20817

SHELTON, FRANK HARVEY, b Flagstaff, Ariz, Oct 4, 24; m 48; c 3. NUCLEAR PHYSICS. *Educ:* Calif Inst Technol, BS, 49, MS, 50, PhD(physics), 52. *Prof Exp:* Res analyst, NAm Aviation, Inc, 50; mem staff, Sandia Corp, 51-55; tech dir, Armed Forces Spec Weapons Proj, US Dept Defense, 55-59; sr scientist, Nuclear Div, Kaman Aircraft Corp, 59-68, VPRES & CHIEF SCIENTIST, KAMAN SCI CORP, 68- *Concurrent Pos:* Mem subcomt civil defense, Nat Acad Sci, 57; mem sci adv group effects, Defense Nuclear Agency, Dept Defense, 74- *Mem:* Fel Am Phys Soc. *Res:* Military effects of nuclear weapons and missile applications; peaceful uses of nuclear detonations. *Mailing Add:* 1500 Garden of Gods Rd Colorado Springs CO 80907

SHELTON, GEORGE CALVIN, b Tex, Apr 26, 23; m 49; c 2. VETERINARY PARASITOLOGY. *Educ:* Tex A&M Univ, DVM, 48; Auburn Univ, MS, 52; Univ Minn, PhD(vet microbiol), 65. *Prof Exp:* Asst prof vet bact & parasitol, Univ Mo, 49-51; res assoc, Auburn Univ, 52; from asst prof to prof vet bact & parasitol, Univ Mo-Columbia, 52-59, prof vet microbiol, Sch Vet Med, 59-73, assoc, Col Vet Med, 69-73, assoc dean acad affairs, 71-73; DEAN, COL VET MED, TEX A&M UNIV, 73- *Concurrent Pos:* NSF fac fel, 61-62. *Mem:* Am Vet Med Asn; Am Soc Parasitol; Conf Res Workers Animal Dis. *Res:* Internal parasites of ruminants. *Mailing Add:* Col of Vet Med Tex A&M Univ College Station TX 77843

SHELTON, JACK L, b Brown Co, Tex, Sept 12, 35; m 61. CHEMICAL ENGINEERING. *Educ:* Mass Inst Technol, BS, 58; Rice Univ, PhD(chem eng), 65. *Prof Exp:* Sr res engr, 64-76, ENG SUPVR, AMOCO PROD CO, STANDARD OIL CO (IND), 76- *Mem:* Am Inst Chem Engrs; Soc Petrol Engrs. *Res:* Radiant heat transfer with chemical reactions; numerical solution of partial differential equations; flow of fluids in porous media. *Mailing Add:* Amoco Prod Co Security Life Bldg Denver CO 80202

SHELTON, JAMES CHURCHILL, b Kansas City, Mo; m 63; c 4. MATERIALS SCIENCE, APPLIED PHYSICS. *Educ:* Cornell Univ, BEP, 63, PhD(mat sci), 73. *Prof Exp:* Instr nuclear reactor eng, US Naval Nuclear Power Sch, 63-69; mem tech staff mat res & integrated optics, Bell Labs, 72-80; WITH CORPORATE PRODUCT PLANNING, WESTERN ELEC CO, 80- *Mem:* AAAS; Inst Elec & Electronics Engrs; Am Phys Soc; Optical Soc Am; Am Vacuum Soc. *Res:* Integrated optics, especially semiconductor laser sources, optical waveguides, switches, modulators, polarizers and detectors; surface physics, especially surface segregation, electron beam-solid interactions and diagnostics. *Mailing Add:* Western Elec Co 475 South St Morristown NJ 07960

SHELTON, JAMES EDWARD, b Allais, Ky, Sept 26, 29; m 53; c 2. SOIL CHEMISTRY, SOIL FERTILITY. *Educ:* Univ KY, BS, 53, MS, 57; NC State Univ, PhD(soils), 60. *Prof Exp:* From instr to asst prof, 59-78, ASSOC PROF SOILS, NC STATE UNIV, 78- *Mem:* Am Soc Agron; Soil Sci Soc Am; Int Soc Soil Sci; Am Soc Hort Sci. *Res:* Role of fertilizers in soil-plant relationships. *Mailing Add:* Mountain Hort Crops Res Sta RFD 2 Box 249 Fletcher NC 28732

SHELTON, JAMES MAURICE, b Collinwood, Tenn, July 27, 24; m 50; c 4. ANIMAL BREEDING, GENETICS. *Educ:* Univ Tenn, BS, 48; Agr & Mech Col Tex, MS, 53, PhD(genetics), 57. *Prof Exp:* Instr animal husb, Univ Tenn, 48-50; instr, Agr & Mech Col Tex, 50-53; assoc prof animal sci, Am Univ Beirut, 54-55; from asst prof to assoc prof, 56-67, PROF ANIMAL SCI, TEX AGR EXP STA, TEX A&M UNIV, 67- *Mem:* Am Soc Animal Sci; Soc Study Reproduction; Am Genetic Asn; Sigma Xi; Soc Range Mgt. *Res:* Physiology and production of sheep, angora goats and beef cattle; animal production; improvement of animal performance through genetic changes; environmental modification of endocrine stimulation. *Mailing Add:* Dept Animal Sci Tex A&M Univ College Station TX 77843

SHELTON, JAMES REID, b Allerton, Iowa, Jan 16, 11; m 34; c 3. ORGANIC CHEMISTRY, POLYMER SCIENCE. *Educ:* Univ Iowa, BS, 33, MS, 34, PhD(org chem), 36. *Prof Exp:* Asst org chem, Univ Iowa, 35-36; instr chem, 36-41, from asst prof to assoc prof org chem, 41-48, dean grad studies, 66-67, prof org chem, 49-77, prof polymer sci, 68-77, EMER PROF CHEM & MACROMOL SCI, CASE WESTERN RESERVE UNIV, 77- *Mem:* AAAS; Am Chem Soc. *Res:* Mechanism of oxidation and antioxidant action in rubber and related systems; mechanism of organic reactions; high polymers; organic sulfur compounds; reaction of free radicals with olefins; reactions of peroxides. *Mailing Add:* Dept of Chem Case Western Reserve Univ Cleveland OH 44106

SHELTON, JOHN C, b Renovo, Pa, June 8, 37; m 62. ORGANIC CHEMISTRY. *Educ:* Lock Haven State Col, BS, 59; Cornell Univ, PhD(org chem), 64. *Prof Exp:* Instr chem, City Col San Francisco, 64-65; from asst prof to assoc prof org chem, 65-73, PROF ORG CHEM, CALIF STATE COL HAYWARD, 73- *Mem:* Am Chem Soc. *Res:* Highly strained bicyclic ring compounds. *Mailing Add:* Dept of Chem Calif State Univ Hayward CA 94542

SHELTON, JOHN WAYNE, b China Spring, Tex, Dec 28, 28; m 49; c 2. GEOLOGY. *Educ:* Baylor Univ, BA, 49; Univ Ill, MS, 51, PhD(geol), 53. *Prof Exp:* Asst, Univ Ill, 50-52; geologist, Shell Oil Co, 53-63; from asst prof to assoc prof, 63-70, PROF GEOL, OKLA STATE UNIV, 70- *Concurrent Pos:* Consult, Continental Oil Co, 64- *Mem:* Geol Soc Am; Soc Econ Paleont & Mineral; Am Asn Petrol Geologists. *Res:* Sedimentation; structural geology. *Mailing Add:* Dept of Geol Okla State Univ Stillwater OK 74074

SHELTON, JOHN WINTHROP, physics, see previous edition

SHELTON, KEITH RAY, b Chatham, Va, Jan 11, 41; m 65; c 3. BIOCHEMISTRY. *Educ:* Univ Va, BA, 63; Univ Ill, Urbana, PhD(biochem), 68. *Prof Exp:* Res assoc biochem, Rockefeller Univ, 67-69; Nat Res Coun Can fel, 69-70; asst prof, 70-76, ASSOC PROF BIOCHEM, MED COL VA, VA COMMONWEALTH UNIV, 76- *Mem:* Am Soc Cell Biol; Am Soc Biol Chemists; Am Chem Soc. *Res:* Metabolism and function of nuclear proteins. *Mailing Add:* Dept of Biochem Med Col of Va Richmond VA 23298

SHELTON, ROBERT DUANE, electrical engineering, computer science, see previous edition

SHELTON, ROBERT SCHEMBER, chemotheraphy, deceased

SHELTON, ROBERT WAYNE, b Springfield, Ill, Dec 3, 23; m 46; c 3. ORGANIC CHEMISTRY. *Educ:* Ill Col, AB, 49; Univ Iowa, PhD(chem), 54. *Prof Exp:* Res chemist, E I du Pont de Nemours & Co, 53-56; assoc prof, 56-60, head dept, 58-66, PROF CHEM, WESTERN ILL UNIV, 60- *Mem:* Am Chem Soc. *Res:* Synthesis; organophosphorus compounds. *Mailing Add:* Dept of Chem Western Ill Univ Macomb IL 61455

SHELTON, RONALD M, b Shipman, Ill, July 11, 31; m 53; c 2. MATHEMATICS. *Educ:* Univ Ill, BS, 53, MS, 57, PhD(math educ), 65. *Prof Exp:* From asst prof to assoc prof, 60-61, PROF MATH, MILLIKIN UNIV, 71-, CHMN DEPT, 63- *Concurrent Pos:* Consult, Decatur Pub Schs, 67. *Mem:* Math Asn Am. *Res:* Teaching of mathematics at the college level. *Mailing Add:* Dept of Math Millikin Univ Decatur IL 62522

SHELTON, RUSSELL D, theoretical physics, see previous edition

SHELTON, WILFORD NEIL, b Dalton, Ga, Dec 29, 35; m 65; c 3. ELECTRON PHYSICS. *Educ:* Univ Calif, Los Angeles, AB, 58; Fla State Univ, PhD(physics), 62. *Prof Exp:* From res asst to res assoc, 60-63, from actg asst prof to assoc prof, 63-76, PROF PHYSICS, FLA STATE UNIV, 76- *Mem:* Am Phys Soc. *Res:* Electron scattering on atoms and molecules; resonant charge exchange between atoms; electron-impact ionization of atoms; electron-photon angular correlations; states of nuclei; fourier transform infrared spectroscopy. *Mailing Add:* Dept of Physics Fla State Univ Tallahassee FL 32306

SHELTON, WILLIAM LEE, b Tulsa, Okla, May 28, 39; m 65; c 1. FISHERIES. *Educ:* Okla State Univ, BS, 61, MS, 64; Univ Okla, PhD(zool), 72. *Prof Exp:* Fishery biologist, US Corps Engrs, Tulsa Dist, 67; ASST LEADER, ALA COOP FISHERY UNIT, US FISH & WILDLIFE SERV, AUBURN UNIV, 71- *Mem:* Am Soc Ichthyologists; Am Fisheries Soc; Sigma Xi. *Res:* Fishery biology in reservoirs and rivers; reproductive biology of fishes. *Mailing Add:* Ala Coop Fishery Res Unit Auburn Univ Auburn AL 36830

SHELUPSKY, DAVID I, b New York, NY, Dec 9, 37; m 63. PHYSICS. *Educ:* City Col New York, BS, 59; Princeton Univ, MA, 61, PhD(physics), 65. *Prof Exp:* from instr to asst prof, 64-71, ASSOC PROF PHYSICS, CITY COL NEW YORK, 72- *Mem:* Am Math Soc; Am Phys Soc; Math Asn Am. *Res:* Axiomatic quantum field theory; algebraic methods in statistical mechanics. *Mailing Add:* Dept of Physics City Col of New York New York NY 10031

SHELVER, WILLIAM H, b Ortonville, Minn, May 31, 34; m 58. MEDICINAL CHEMISTRY, ORGANIC CHEMISTRY. *Educ:* NDak State Univ, BS, 56, MS, 57; Univ Va, PhD(org chem), 62. *Prof Exp:* From asst prof to assoc prof pharmaceut chem, 60-68, PROF PHARMACEUT SCI, NDAK STATE UNIV, 68-, . *Mem:* Am Chem Soc; Am Pharmaceut Asn. *Res:* Development of relationships between structure and biological activity by synthesis of new compounds; measurement of physical properties of new and existing compounds, especially in analgesic and hypotensive drugs. *Mailing Add:* Dept of Pharmaceut Chem NDak State Univ Fargo ND 58102

SHEMA, BERNARD FRANCIS, b Montgomery, Minn, Oct 11, 15; m 42; c 4. MICROBIOLOGY. *Educ:* Univ Minn, BS, 39, MS, 41. *Prof Exp:* Agent, Bur Plant Indust, US Dept Agr, Minn, 40-41; asst plant path, Inst Paper Chem, 41-54; chief microbiologist, 54-71, dir biol res, 71-74, MGR ENVIRON & REGULATORY AFFAIRS, BETZ LABS, INC, 74- *Mem:* AAAS; Soc Indust Microbiol; Am Soc Microbiol; Tech Asn Pulp & Paper Indust; Am Soc Testing & Mat. *Res:* Microbiology of pulp and paper; physiology of fungi; chemistry of wood decay; industrial fungicides and bactericides. *Mailing Add:* Betz Labs Inc Somerton Rd Trevose PA 19047

SHEMANCHUK, JOSEPH ALEXANDER, b Wostok, Alta, Apr 28, 27; m 51; c 2. VETERINARY ENTOMOLOGY. *Educ:* Univ Alta, BScAgr, 50, MSc, 58. *Prof Exp:* Entomologist med entom, Household Med Entom Unit, Can Dept Agr, Ottawa, 50-51 & Dominion Entom Lab, Saskatoon, 51-55; ENTOMOLOGIST VET-MED ENTOM, AGR CAN RES STA, LETHBRIDGE, 55- *Concurrent Pos:* Scientist exchange fel, Nat Res Coun Can & USSR Acad Sci, 71, Nat Res Coun Can & Czechoslovak Acad Sci, 80. *Mem:* Entom Soc Can; Am Mosquito Control Asn; Can Soc Zool. *Res:* Behavior, culture and biological control of blood-sucking flies; development of repellents for protection of man and livestock; epidemiology of insect-borne diseases in livestock. *Mailing Add:* Agr Can Res Sta Lethbridge AB T1J 4B1 Can

SHEMANO, IRVING, b San Francisco, Calif, June 23, 28; m 56; c 2. PHARMACOLOGY. *Educ:* Univ Calif, AB, 50, MS, 51; Univ Man, PhD(pharmacol), 56. *Prof Exp:* Asst pharmacologist, Abbott Labs, 51-53; sr pharmacologist, Smith Kline & French Labs, 56-60; dir macrobiol res labs, Merrell-Nat Labs, 60-70, head dept immunol & endocrinol, 70-74, group dir, Clin Pharmacol Dept, 74-78; DIR, CLIN INVEST, ADRIA LABS, 78- *Mem:* Am Soc Pharmacol & Exp Therapeut; Pharmacol Soc Can; Soc Exp Biol & Med; Am Soc Clin Pharmacol & Therapeut. *Res:* Immunopharmacology; gastrointestinal pharmacology; autonomic pharmacology; metabolic diseases pharmacology. *Mailing Add:* Adria Lab Inc PO Box 16529 Columbus OH 43216

SHEMANSKY, DONALD EUGENE, b Moose Jaw, Sask, Apr 28, 36. ATMOSPHERIC PHYSICS. *Educ:* Univ Sask, BE, 58, MSc, 60, PhD(auroral physics), 66. *Prof Exp:* Physicist, Bristol Aero Industs, Ltd, 60-61; res asst, Univ Sask, 61-66; jr physicist, Kitt Peak Nat Observ, Ariz, 66-69; res asst prof physics, Univ Pittsburgh, 69-74; res assoc prof physics, Univ Mich, 74-78; res assoc, Univ Ariz, 78-79; SR RES SCIENTIST, TUCSON LABS, SPACE SCI INST, UNIV SOUTHERN CALIF, 79- *Concurrent Pos:* Assoc ed, J Geophys Res, 81-84; prin investr, NASA grants. *Mem:* Am Geophys Union; Am Astron Soc. *Res:* Physics of ionium plasma torus and Jupiter, Saturn and Titan atmosphere-magnetosphere interactions; interstellar medium and cygnus loop study in extreme ultraviolet; theoretical physicsof gas-surface interactions. *Mailing Add:* Space Sci Inst Univ Southern Calif Tucson Labs 3625 E Ajo Way Tucson AZ 85713

SHEMDIN, OMAR H, b Zakho, Iraq, Sept 12, 39; US citizen; m 65; c 3. OCEANOGRAPHIC ENGINEERING, OCEANOGRAPHY. *Educ:* Mass Inst Technol, BSc, 61, MSc, 62; Stanford Univ, PhD(eng), 66. *Prof Exp:* Asst prof civil eng, Stanford Univ, 66-67; from asst prof to assoc prof, 67-77, PROF COASTAL ENG, UNIV FLA, 77- *Concurrent Pos:* Consult, Esso Res & Eng Co, 68-; consult res scientist, Naval Res Lab, 70-72, dir lab, 72-; consult res oceanographer, Nat Oceanic & Atmospheric Admin, 71-72. *Mem:* Am Geophys Union; Am Soc Civil Engrs; Am Meteorol Soc. *Res:* Air-sea interaction; coastal and near shore precesses. *Mailing Add:* Dept of Coastal & Oceanog Eng Univ of Fla Gainesville FL 32601

SHEMENSKI, ROBERT MARTIN, b Martins Ferry, Ohio, June 17, 38; m 60; c 3. METALLURGICAL ENGINEERING. *Educ:* Univ Cincinnati, MetE, 61; Ohio State Univ, PhD(metall eng), 64. *Prof Exp:* Mem tech staff, Bell Tel Labs, 66-67; sr scientist, Battelle Mem Inst, 67-70; sr scientist, Fabric Develop Dept, 70-77, PRIN METALL, GOODYEAR TIRE & RUBBER CO, 77- *Mem:* Am Soc Metals; Am Inst Mining, Metall & Petrol Engrs; Nat Asn Corrosion Engrs. *Res:* Anger spectroscopy; secondary ion mass spectrometry; iron filamentary single crystals metallic dissolution kinetics; internal friction; properties of beryllium; scanning electron microscopy; failure analyses; fatigue; fiber reenforcement systems; x-ray photoelectron spectroscopy. *Mailing Add:* Goodyear Tire & Rubber Co 1144 E Market St Akron OH 44316

SHEMER, JACK EVVARD, b Phoenix, Ariz, Aug 22, 40; m 63; c 1. COMPUTER SCIENCE, ELECTRICAL ENGINEERING. *Educ:* Occidental Col, BA, 62; Ariz State Univ, MS, 65; Southern Methodist Univ, PhD(elec eng), 68. *Prof Exp:* Syst engr, Comput Dept, Gen Elec Co, 62-67; subsect mgr, Xerox Data Systs, 68-72, prin scientist & area mgr, Xerox Palo Alto Res Ctr, El Segundo, 73-76; vpres systs eng, Transaction Technol Inc, Citicorp, 77-79; PRES & CHIEF EXEC OFFICER, TERADATA CORP, 80- *Concurrent Pos:* Tech ed, Computer, 73-76. *Mem:* Inst Elec & Electronics Engrs; Asn Comput Mach. *Res:* Computer architecture; file and database management, performance analysis; queueing theory and applications; automatic control systems; digital image coding and display. *Mailing Add:* 270 Oceano Dr Los Angeles CA 90049

SHEMILT, L(ESLIE) W(EBSTER), b Souris, Man, Dec 25, 19; m 46; c 2. CHEMICAL ENGINEERING. *Educ:* Univ Toronto, BASc, 41, PhD(phys chem), 47; Univ Man, MSc, 46. *Prof Exp:* Lab supvr, Defence Industs, Ltd, 41-42, supvr tech dept & acid plant supvr, 42-44; lectr chem, Univ Man, 44-45; spec lectr, Univ Toronto, 45-47; from asst prof to prof, Univ BC, 47-61; prof chem eng & head dept, Univ NB, 61-69; dean fac eng, 69-79, PROF CHEM ENG, MCMASTER UNIV, 69- *Concurrent Pos:* Vis prof, Univ Col, London, 59-60 & Ecole Polytech Lausanne, 75; chmn, NB Res & Productivity Coun, 62-69; sci adv, Prov NB, 64-69; chmn, Atlantic Prov Inter-Univ Comt on Sci, 66-69; mem, Nat Res Coun Can, 66-69; ed, Can J Chem Eng, 67-; chmn tech adv comt, Nuclear Fuel Waste Mgt, 79- *Honors & Awards:* T P Hoar Prize, Inst Corrosion Sci & Technol, 80. *Mem:* Am Chem Soc; fel Am Inst Chem Engrs; fel Chem Inst Can (pres, 70-71); fel Eng Inst Can; Can Res Mgt Asn. *Res:* Fundamentals of corrosion; chemical engineering thermodynamics; industrial wastes; mass transfer; process dynamics. *Mailing Add:* Fac Eng McMaster Univ Hamilton ON L8S 4L7 Can

SHEMIN, DAVID, b New York, NY, Mar 18, 11; m 37, 63; c 2. BIOCHEMISTRY. *Educ:* City Col, BS, 32; Columbia Univ, AM, 33, PhD(biochem), 38. *Prof Exp:* Asst biochem, Col Physicians & Surg, Columbia Univ, 35-37, immunochem & virus res, 37-40, from instr to prof biochem, 40-68; PROF BIOCHEM, NORTHWESTERN UNIV, 68- *Concurrent Pos:* Lectr & scientist, Karolinska Inst, Stockholm & Swedish Med Res Coun, 47; Harvey lectr, 54; Guggenheim fel, 56 & 70; Commonwealth fel, 65; vis prof, Weizman Inst Sci; mem study sect, NIH, NSF; Fogarty scholar, NIH, 80-83; dep dir, Cancer Ctr, Northwestern Univ. *Mem:* Nat Acad Sci; AAAS; Am Soc Biol Chem; Am Chem Soc; Am Acad Arts & Sci. *Res:* Biosynthesis of porphyrins B12; porphyria enzymology; protein structure; control systems; microbiology; chlorophyll synthesis. *Mailing Add:* Dept Biochem & Molecular Biol Northwestern Univ Evanston IL 60201

SHEN, BENJAMIN SHIH-PING, b Hangzhou, China, Sept 14, 31; nat US; m 71; c 1. ASTROPHYSICS, NUCLEAR PHYSICS. *Educ:* Assumption Col, AB, 54; Clark Univ, AM, 56; Univ Paris, DSc d'Etat (physics), 64. *Hon Degrees:* MA, Univ Pa, 71; ScD, Assumption Col, 72. *Prof Exp:* Asst prof physics, State Univ NY Albany, 56-59; assoc prof space sci, Sch Eng, NY Univ, 64-66; from assoc prof to prof astron & astrophys, 66-72, chmn dept astron & dir Flower & Cook Observ, 73-79, assoc univ provost, 79-80, chmn Coun Grad Deans, 79-81, actg univ provost, 80-81, REESE W FLOWER PROF ASTRON & ASTROPHYS, UNIV PA, 72- *Concurrent Pos:* Consult, Space Sci Lab, Gen Elec Co, 61-68, Am Inst Physics, 65, 72-75 & Cosmic Physics Div, Am Phys Soc, 72-75; guest staff mem, Brookhaven Nat Lab, 63-64, 65-70; gen chmn, Int Conf Spallation Nuclear Reactions & Their Appln in Astrophys & Radiother, 75. *Mem:* Fel AAAS; Am Astron Soc; fel Am Phys Soc; Int Astron Union; fel Royal Astron Soc. *Res:* Astrophysical spallation nuclear reactions; variable galaxies and quasars; cosmic rays; nuclear cascade; high-energy shielding and radiologic dosimetry. *Mailing Add:* Dept of Astron & Astrophys Univ of Pa Philadelphia PA 19174

SHEN, CHE-KUN JAMES, b Taipei, Taiwan, 1949. BIOCHEMISTRY, MOLECULAR BIOLOGY. *Educ:* Nat Taiwan Univ, BS, 71; Univ Calif, Berkeley, PhD(biochem), 77. *Prof Exp:* Elec officer electronics & mech radar div, Navy Repub China, 71-73; NIH res fel biol, Calif Inst Technol, 78-80; ASST PROF GENETICS, UNIV CALIF, 80- *Mem:* Sigma Xi. *Res:* Molecular genetics of eukeryotic gene expression. *Mailing Add:* Div of Biol Calif Inst of Technol Pasadena CA 91125

SHEN, CHIH-KANG, b Chekiang, China, Sept 21, 32; m 64; c 1. SOIL MECHANICS. *Educ:* Nat Taiwan Univ, BS, 56; Univ NH, MS, 60; Univ Calif, Berkeley, PhD(soil mech), 65. *Prof Exp:* Asst prof, Loyola Univ, Calif, 65-70; asst prof, 70-76, assoc prof, 76-80, PROF CIVIL ENG, UNIV CALIF, DAVIS, 80- *Concurrent Pos:* Res assoc, Univ Calif, Los Angeles, 66-; mem Hwy Res Bd, Nat Acad Sci-Nat Res Coun, 66- *Mem:* Am Soc Civil Engrs; Int Soc Soil Mech & Found Engrs. *Res:* Soil stabilization and compaction; flexible pavement design; shear strength of unsaturated soils. *Mailing Add:* Dept of Civil Eng Univ of Calif Davis CA 95616

SHEN, CHI-NENG, b Peiping, China, July 18, 17; m 47; c 2. CONTROL SYSTEMS, ENGINEERING SYSTEMS. *Educ:* Nat Tsing Hua Univ, China, BEng, 39; Univ Minn, MS, 50, PhD(eng), 54. *Prof Exp:* Instr mech eng, Univ Minn, 51-54; asst prof, Dartmouth Col, 54-58; from assoc prof to prof mech eng, 58-67, PROF ELEC & SYSTS ENG, RENSSELAER POLYTECH INST, 73- *Concurrent Pos:* Vis prof mech eng, Mass Inst Technol, 67-68; consult. *Mem:* Am Soc Mech Engrs; Am Nuclear Soc; Am Inst Aeronaut & Astronaut; Am Soc Eng Educ; Sigma Xi. *Res:* Martian vehicle navigation, including obstacle detection, terrain modeling and park selection; nuclear reactor stability for kinetics and two-phase flow phenomena; automatic controls, including nonlinear control systems and estimation theory; guidance and navigation. *Mailing Add:* Dept of Elec & Systs Eng Rensselaer Polytech Inst Troy NY 12181

SHEN, CHIN-WEN, b Shanghai, Oct 14, 24; m; c 3. OIL WELL DRILLING, ENHANCED OIL RECOVERY. *Educ:* Nat Chiao Tung Univ, BS, 46; Univ Tulsa, MS, 65; Tex A&M Univ, PhD(petrol eng), 69. *Prof Exp:* Mining engr coal mining, Fusin Colliery Co, China, 46-48; petrol engr drilling & production, Chinese Petrol Corp, 48-64; RES SCIENTIST THERMAL RECOVERY, GETTY OIL CO, HOUSTON, 69- *Mem:* Am Soc Petrol Engrs. *Res:* Steam displacement. *Mailing Add:* 11618 Cherry Knoll Houston TX 77077

SHEN, CHUNG YI, b Canton, China, May 23, 37; US citizen; m 61; c 3. APPLIED MATHEMATICS. *Educ:* Ore State Univ, BS, 60, MS, 63, PhD(math), 68. *Prof Exp:* ASST PROF MATH, SIMON FRASER UNIV, 67- *Concurrent Pos:* Fel, Carnegie-Mellon Univ, 68-69; Nat Res Coun Can res grants, 69 & 72. *Mem:* Am Math Soc; Soc Indust & Appl Math. *Res:* Mathematical foundation of classical thermodynamics; infinite systems in statistical mechanics. *Mailing Add:* Dept Math Simon Fraser Univ Burnaby BC V5A 1S6 Can

SHEN, CHUNG YU, b Peiping, China, Dec 15, 21; nat US; m 54; c 3. CHEMICAL ENGINEERING. *Educ:* Nat Southwest Assoc Univ, China, BS, 42; Univ Louisville, MChE, 50; Univ Ill, PhD, 54. *Prof Exp:* From group leader to sect leader, Cent Chem Works, China, 42-49; sr chem engr, Inst Indust Res, Univ Louisville, 50-52; scientist, 54-60, SR ENG FEL, MONSANTO CO, 60- *Honors & Awards:* Du Bois Award, Monsanto Co, 58. *Mem:* AAAS; Sigma Xi; Am Oil Chem Soc; Am Inst Chem Engrs. *Res:* Chemical kinetics; fluidization; organic processing; industrial phosphates; sequestrants; detergents; spray-drying. *Mailing Add:* Monsanto Co 800 N Lindbergh Blvd St Louis MO 63166

SHEN, D(AVID) W(EI) C(HI), b Shanghai, China, Jan 4, 20; nat US. ELECTRICAL ENGINEERING. *Educ:* Nat Tsing Hua Univ, China, BSc, 39; Univ London, PhD(elec eng), 48. *Prof Exp:* Lectr elec eng, Nat Univ Amoy, China, 40-44; with Marconi Wireless & Tel Co, Eng, 44-45; elec engr, Messrs Yangtse, Ltd, 46-48; sr lectr elec eng, Adelaide Univ, 50-53; vis asst prof, Univ Ill, 53-54, Mass Inst Technol, 54 & City Col New York, 55; from asst prof to assoc prof, 55-66, PROF ELEC ENG, MOORE SCH ELEC ENG, UNIV PA, 66- *Concurrent Pos:* Mem res staff, Stromberg-Carlson Div, Gen Dynamics Corp, NY; consult, CDC Control Serv, Inc, 55-; mem, Franklin Inst. *Mem:* Am Soc Eng Educ; fel Inst Elec & Electronics Engrs; fel Brit Inst Elec Eng; Tensor Soc; fel AAAS. *Res:* Electrical machinery; analogue computers; optimal and adaptive control theory; control in biological systems. *Mailing Add:* Moore Sch of Elec Eng Univ of Pa Philadelphia PA 19104

SHEN, HSIEH WEN, b Peking, China, July 13, 31; m 56. HYDRAULICS. *Educ:* Univ Mich, BS, 53, MS, 54; Univ Calif, Berkeley, PhD(hydraul), 61. *Prof Exp:* Hydraul engr, US Army Corps Engrs, 55-56; struct engr, Giffels & Vallet, Inc, 56; res engr hydraul, Inst Eng Res, Univ Calif, 56-61; hydraul engr, Harza Eng Co, 61-63; assoc prof hydraul eng, 64-68, PROF HYDRAUL ENG, COLO STATE UNIV, FT COLLINS, 68- *Concurrent Pos:* Freeman fel, Am Soc Civil Engrs, 65-66; Guggenheim fel, 72. *Honors & Awards:* Horton Award, Am Geophys Union. *Res:* Various aspects of fluvial hydraulics, including meandering, local scour, sediment transport under wind, stable channel shape and change of bed forms. *Mailing Add:* Dept of Civil Eng Colo State Univ Ft Collins CO 80521

SHEN, KELVIN KEI-WEI, b Liao-pei, China, Sept 29, 41; m 68. ORGANIC CHEMISTRY. *Educ:* Nat Taiwan Univ, BS, 64; Univ Mass, Amherst, MS, 66, PhD(chem), 68. *Prof Exp:* Guest scientist, Brookhaven Nat Lab, 66-68; res fel, Yale Univ, 68-69; instr chem, Drexel Univ, 69-70; asst prof, Calif State Univ, Los Angeles, 70-72; res chemist, 72-80, SR RES CHEMIST, US BORAX RES CORP, 80- *Concurrent Pos:* Petrol Res Fund grant, Calif State Univ, Los Angeles, 72. *Mem:* AAAS; Am Chem Soc; Soc Plastics Engrs. *Res:* Chemistry of small ring compounds; organometallic chemistry; fire retardants in plastics; x-ray crystallography; photochemistry; syntheses of herbicides; environmental studies of pesticides. *Mailing Add:* US Borax Res Corp 412 Crescent Way Anaheim CA 92801

SHEN, LIANG CHI, b Chekiang, China, Mar 17, 39; US citizen; m 65; c 2. ELECTRICAL ENGINEERING. *Educ:* Nat Taiwan Univ, BS, 61; Harvard Univ, SM, 63, PhD(appl physics), 67. *Prof Exp:* Asst assoc prof, 67-77, PROF ELEC ENG & CHMN DEPT, UNIV HOUSTON, 77- *Concurrent Pos:* Consult, Harvard Univ, 73- *Mem:* Inst Elec & Electronics Engrs; Am Asn Univ Profs; AAAS; Am Soc Eng Educ; Sigma Xi. *Res:* Antennas; microwaves; electromagnetic wave propagation in earth; well-logging. *Mailing Add:* Dept of Elec Eng Univ of Houston Houston TX 77004

SHEN, MEI-CHANG, b Shanghai, China, Oct 3, 31; m 64; c 2. APPLIED MATHEMATICS. *Educ:* Taiwan Univ, BSc, 54; Brown Univ, PhD(appl math), 63. *Prof Exp:* Res assoc appl math, Brown Univ, 62-63; vis mem, Courant Inst Math Sci, NY Univ, 63-65; from asst prof to assoc prof, 65-70, PROF APPL MATH, UNIV WIS-MADISON, 70- *Concurrent Pos:* Vis prof, Courant Inst Math Sci, NY Univ, 71-72; vis fel, Calif Inst Tech, 76. *Mem:* Am Math Soc; Soc Indust & Appl Math. *Res:* Asymptotic methods; biofluid-dynamics; nonlinear wave propagation; plasma dynamics; geophysical fluid dynamics. *Mailing Add:* Dept of Math Univ of Wis Madison WI 53706

SHEN, MITCHEL C, physical chemistry, deceased

SHEN, PETER KO-CHUN, b China, Oct 28, 38; US citizen; m 65; c 1. REACTOR PHYSICS. *Educ:* Nat Taiwan Univ, BS, 61; Univ Minn, MS, 65; Kans State Univ, PhD(nuclear eng), 70. *Prof Exp:* Res assoc nuclear shielding, Kans State Univ, 69-70; supv nuclear engr reactor physics & fuel mgt, Southern Calif Edison Co, 70-75; assoc prof reactor physics & fuel cycle, Joint Ctr Grad Study, Univ Wash, 75-79, dean, Joint Ctr Grad Study, 77-79, AFFIL PROF NUCLEAR ENG, UNIV WASH, 79-; TECHNICIAN & DIR, WASHINGTON PUB POWER SUPPLY SYST, 80- *Mem:* Am Nuclear Soc. *Res:* Nuclear fuel cycle core physics, thermal hydraulic and nuclear power plant design and operation. *Mailing Add:* Washington Pub Power Supply Syst PO Box 968 Richland WA 99352

SHEN, S(HAN) F(U), b Shanghai, China, Aug 31, 21; m 50; c 2. AERONAUTICAL ENGINEERING. *Educ:* Nat Cent Univ, China, BS, 41; Mass Inst Technol, ScD(aeronaut eng), 49. *Prof Exp:* Res assoc math, Mass Inst Technol, 48-50; from asst prof to prof, Univ Md, 50-61; PROF AERONAUT ENG, GRAD SCH AERONAUT ENG, CORNELL UNIV, 61-, JOHN EDSON SWEET PROF ENG, 78- *Concurrent Pos:* Guggenheim fel, 57-58; vis prof, Univ Paris, 64-65 & 69-70 & Tech Univ Vienna, 77. *Honors & Awards:* Achievement Award, Wash Acad Sci, 59. *Mem:* Cor mem Int Acad Astronaut; Acad Sinica Repub China. *Res:* Aerodynamics; rarefied gasdynamics; fluid mechanics. *Mailing Add:* Sibley Sch Mech & Aerospace Eng Cornell Univ Ithaca NY 14853

SHEN, SAMUEL YI-WEN, b Tientsin, China, Jan 4, 19; m 51; c 1. CHEMISTRY, PHYSICS. *Educ:* Yenching Univ, China, BSc, 41; Columbia Univ, MA, 51, EdD, 58. *Prof Exp:* Lectr chem, Rutgers Univ, 56-57; from asst prof to assoc prof, 57-64, PROF CHEM, LONG ISLAND UNIV, ZECKENDORF CAMPUS, 64- *Concurrent Pos:* Lectr, Polytech Inst New York, 61- *Mem:* Am Chem Soc. *Res:* Chromatography; nonaqueous titrations; spectrophotometric analysis; chelate chemistry; electrochemistry. *Mailing Add:* Dept Chem Zeckendorf Campus Long Island Univ Brooklyn NY 11201

SHEN, SHELDON SHIH-TA, b Shanghai, China, Nov 22, 47; US citizen; c 2. CELL PHYSIOLOGY. *Educ:* Univ Mo, BS, 69; Univ Calif, Berkeley, PhD(physiol), 74. *Prof Exp:* Fel cancer biol, Univ Calif, Berkeley, 74-77, asst res zoologist cell biol, 77-79; ASST PROF ZOOL, IOWA STATE UNIV, 79-

Concurrent Pos: NIH fel, 74-76; USPHS, NIH grant, 77-79, NSF grant, 80-83. *Mem:* Sigma Xi; Soc Develop Biol; Am Soc Cell Biol; AAAS. *Res:* Use of ion-selective microelectrodes for investigating ion activities regulation of sea urchin egg activation; study of alteration of ion and nutrient transport with tumorigenesis of the mouse mammary gland. *Mailing Add:* Dept Zool Iowa State Univ Ames IA 50011

SHEN, SIN-YAN, b Singapore, Nov 12, 49; m 73. LOW TEMPERATURE PHYSICS. *Educ:* Univ Singapore, BS, 69; Ohio State Univ, MS, 70, PhD(low temp physics), 73. *Prof Exp:* ASST PROF PHYSICS, NORTHWESTERN UNIV, 74- *Concurrent Pos:* Scientist, Agronne Nat Lab, 74- *Mem:* Am Phys Soc. *Res:* Surface second sound; superfluidity; surface phenomena in liquid helium; thermodynamics; hydrodynamics; acoustics; statistical mechanics; transport properties; Fermi liquids; quantum fluids; experimental ultra low temperature physics; cryogenics; fluid mechanics. *Mailing Add:* Dept of Physics Northwestern Univ Evanston IL 60201

SHEN, TSUNG YING, b Peking, China, Sept 28, 24; nat US; m 53; c 6. ORGANIC CHEMISTRY. *Educ:* Nat Cent Univ, China, BSc, 46; Univ London, dipl, 48; Univ Manchester, PhD(org chem), 50, DSc, 78. *Prof Exp:* Fel, Ohio State Univ, 50-52; res assoc, Mass Inst Technol, 52-56; res fel synthetic org chem, 56-67, assoc dir, 67-69, dir synthetic chem res, 69-71, sr dir med chem, 71-74, exec dir med chem, 74-76, VPRES MEMBRANE & ARTHRITIS RES, MERCK SHARP & DOHME RES LABS, 76- *Concurrent Pos:* Vis chem prof, Univ Calif, Riverside, 73. *Honors & Awards:* Galileo Medal Sci Achievement, Univ Pisa, 76; Rene Descarte Silver Medal, Univ Paris, 77; Medal of Merit, Giornate Mediche Int del Collegium Biol Europa, 77; Burger Award, Am Chem Soc, 80. *Mem:* Am Chem Soc; NY Acad Sci; AAAS. *Res:* Medicinal chemistry; anti-inflammatory and immunopharmacological agents, viral and cancer chemotherapy; nucleosides, carbohydrate derivatives and membrane receptor regulators. *Mailing Add:* Merck Sharp & Dohme Res Labs Rahway NJ 07065

SHEN, VINCENT Y, b US. COMPUTER SCIENCES, SOFTWARE ENGINEERING. *Educ:* Nat Taiwan Univ, BS, 64; Princeton Univ, PhD(elec eng), 69. *Prof Exp:* Asst prof, 69-74, ASSOC PROF COMPUT SCI, PURDUE UNIV, WEST LAFAYETTE, 74- *Mem:* Asn Comput Mach. *Res:* Software engineering and software science; computer operating systems; programming languages; switching theory. *Mailing Add:* Dept of Comput Sci Purdue Univ West Lafayette IN 47907

SHEN, Y(UNG) C(HUNG), b China, Dec 16, 21; nat US; m 57; c 2. AERONAUTICS, MATHEMATICS. *Educ:* Nat Cent Univ China, BS, 42; Calif Inst Technol, MS, 52, PhD(aeronaut, math), 56. *Prof Exp:* Aerodyn engr, Propulsion Corp, 56-57; res aerodynamicist, Aerojet-Gen Corp, Gen Tire & Rubber Co, 57-60; sr scientist, Norair Div, Northrop Corp, 60-63; mem sr staff, Hughes Aircraft Co, 63-64; mgr aerophys, Nat Eng Sci Co, 64-66; head aerodyn, Gen Dynamics/Pomona, 66-70; MEM TECH STAFF, AEROSPACE CORP, 70- *Res:* Fluid mechanics; flight dynamics; reentry physics; engineering cybernetics; missile and space performance analysis. *Mailing Add:* 776 Valle Vista Sierra Madre CA 91024

SHEN, YUAN-SHOU, b Peking, China, Dec 12, 21; m 48; c 2. PHYSICAL METALLURGY. *Educ:* Nat Southwest Assoc Univ, BS, 43; Ore State Univ, MS, 64, PhD(mat sci), 68. *Prof Exp:* Assoc prof metall, Cheng Kung Univ, Taiwan, 61-62; res metallurgist, Wah Chang Albany Corp, Ore, 65-67; sr res staff, P R Mallory & Co Inc, Mass, 67-78; res scientist, 78-80, SR RESEARCH SCIENTIST, ENGELHARD INDUSTS, PLAINVILLE, 80- *Mem:* Am Soc Metals; Metall Soc; Am Soc Testing & Mat. *Res:* Phase diagram; intermetallic compound; composite material; alloy development; electric contact material; silver alloy; powder metallurgy. *Mailing Add:* 6 Shackford Rd Reading MA 01867

SHEN, YUEN-RON, b Shanghai, China, Mar 25, 35; m 64. SOLID STATE PHYSICS. *Educ:* Nat Taiwan Univ, BS, 56; Stanford Univ, MS, 59; Harvard Univ, PhD(solid state physics), 63. *Prof Exp:* From asst prof to assoc prof, 64-70, PROF PHYSICS, UNIV CALIF, BERKELEY, 70- *Mem:* Fel Am Phys Soc. *Res:* Quantum electronics. *Mailing Add:* Dept of Physics Univ of Calif Berkeley CA 94720

SHEN, YVONNE FENG, b Hu-Nan, China, Sept 11, 42; US citizen; m 68; c 2. ORGANIC CHEMISTRY. *Educ:* Tunghai Univ, Taiwan, BS, 64; Univ Mass, PhD(org chem), 68. *Prof Exp:* Fel, Princeton Univ, 68-69, Drexel Univ, 69-70 & Univ Southern Calif, 70-71; jr res scientist, City Hope Med Ctr, 71-73; CHIEF CHEMIST, ORANGE COUNTY WATER DIST, 74- *Mem:* Am Chem Soc; Am Water Works Asn; Water Pollution Control Fedn. *Res:* Chemistry aspects of water and wastewater treatment. *Mailing Add:* Orange County Water Dist PO Box 8300 Fountain Valley CA 92708

SHENDRIKAR, ARUN D, b Gulberga, India, July 10, 38; m 66; c 2. ENVIRONMENTAL CHEMISTRY. *Educ:* Osmania Univ, India, BS, 57, MS, 61; Durham Univ, PhD(anal chem), 66. *Prof Exp:* Lectr chem, V V Sci Col, India, 61-62; lectr in-chg, 62-63; lectr, Osmania Univ, 62-63; asst prof, Environ Sci Inst, La State Univ, 66-73; sr fel aerosol, Nat Ctr Atmospheric Res, 73-74; sr res chemist, Oil Shale Corp, 74-76; tech dir, O A Labs, Indianapolis, 76-78; tech staff specialist, Meteorol Res Inc, Altadena, 78-80; SR CHEMIST, RES TRIANGLE INST, 80- *Concurrent Pos:* Mem adv comt, Colo Air Pollution Control Comt, 74- *Mem:* Assoc mem Royal Inst Chem; Sigma Xi; Am Soc Testing & Mat. *Res:* Interpretation of chemical data to investigate mechanisms of aerosol formation and modification; application of analytical chemistry for process performance evaluation; development of new source performance standards, artifacts and inhalable particulate matter sampling. *Mailing Add:* 1910 Paloma St Pasadena CA 91104

SHENEFELT, RAY ELDON, b Spokane, Wash, Oct 2, 33; m 57; c 4. TERATOLOGY. *Educ:* Univ Wis-Madison, BS, 59, MD, 63. *Prof Exp:* Intern path, Univ Wis Hosps, 63-64; resident path, Univ Iowa Hosps, 64-66; fel path, Dartmouth Med Sch, 66-69; asst prof pediat & path, Cincinnati

Childrens Hosp, 69-73; med officer teratol, Nat Ctr Toxicol Res, 74-79; INSTR PEDIAT & PATHOL, LE BONHEUR CHILDREN'S HOSP, 80- *Concurrent Pos:* Asst prof path, Med Sch, Univ Ark, 73-79. *Mem:* Teratol Soc; Pediat Path Club. *Res:* Pathologic sequence in development of malformations. *Mailing Add:* Dept Pathol Le Bonheur Children's Hosp 848 Adams St Jefferson AR 38103

SHENEFELT, ROY DAVID, b Evanston, Ill, Jan 27, 09; m 32; c 2. ENTOMOLOGY. *Educ:* Spokane Col, AB, 32; State Col Wash, MS, 35, PhD(entom), 40. *Prof Exp:* From instr to asst prof zool, State Col Wash, 35-46; from asst prof to prof, 46-77, EMER PROF ENTOM, UNIV WIS-MADISON, 77- *Mem:* Entom Soc Am; Entom Soc Can. *Res:* Taxonomy of Braconidae. *Mailing Add:* 630 N Oak St Oregon WI 53575

SHENEMAN, JACK MARSHALL, b Grand Rapids, Mich, Mar 26, 27; m 57; c 2. MICROBIOLOGY. *Educ:* Mich State Univ, BS, 52, MS, 54, PhD(microbiol), 57. *Prof Exp:* Asst microbiol, Mich State Univ, 54-57; res assoc, Wis Malting Co, 57-61, asst dir res, 61-63; sr food scientist, Eli Lilly & Co, 63-69; res microbiologist, Basic Veg Prod Inc, 69-75; FOOD TECHNOL SPECIALIST, FOOD & DRUG SECT, CALIF DEPT HEALTH SERV, 75- *Mem:* AAAS; Am Soc Microbiol; Inst Food Technologists; Asn Food & Drug Officials. *Res:* Industrial fermentations; food flavors and preservatives; microbiology of dehydrated vegetable products; new product and process development in vegetable dehydration; food hazard microorganisms; bacterial spores; microbiological quality control methods; food and drug regulation. *Mailing Add:* Food & Drug Sect Calif Dept Health Serv 714 P St Sacramento CA 95814

SHENFIL, LEON, b Berlin, Ger, May 17, 23; US citizen; m 47; c 3. PHYSICS. *Educ:* Calif Inst Technol, BS, 47, MS, 48, PhD(physics, math), 52. *Prof Exp:* Physicist, Aerojet-Gen Corp Div, Gen Tire & Rubber Co, 52-53, sr engr, 53-56, mgr preliminary design dept, 56-59, appl mech sr dept, 59-65, mgr study ctr, 65-67, sr scientist, solid rocket opers, 67-69, staff eng opers, Aerojet Nuclear Systs Co, 69-72, mgr arctic surface effect vehicle prog, Aerojet-Gen Corp, 72-75, SR SCIENTIST, AEROJET ENERGY CONVERSION CO, 75- *Mem:* Am Inst Aeronaut & Astronaut. *Res:* Low angle x-ray diffraction; infrared optics; liquid rocket combustion instability analysis; nuclear and solid rocket preliminary design; fossil fuel energy. *Mailing Add:* Aerojet Energy Conversion Co Box 13222 Sacramento CA 95813

SHENG, HWAI-PING, b Johore, Malaysia, July 18, 43; Singapore citizen. MEDICAL PHYSIOLOGY. *Educ:* Univ Singapore, BSc, 66, Hons, 67; Baylor Col Md, PhD(physiol), 71. *Prof Exp:* Lectr pharmacol, Univ Hong Kong, 71-74; ASST PROF PHYSIOL, BAYLOR COL MED, 75- *Mem:* Am Physiol Soc; AAAS; Soc Exp Biol & Med. *Res:* Growth, nutrition and body composition. *Mailing Add:* Dept Physiol Baylor Col of Med Houston TX 77030

SHENG, MING NAN, organic chemistry, see previous edition

SHENG, PING, b Shanghai, China, Aug 5, 46; m 70; c 2. SOLID STATE PHYSICS. *Educ:* Calif Inst Technol, BS, 67; Princeton Univ, PhD(physics), 71. *Prof Exp:* Vis mem, Sch Natural Sci, Inst Advan Study, Princeton, NJ, 71-73; mem tech staff physics, RCA David Sarnoff Res Ctr, 73-80; MEM STAFF, CORP RES CTR, EXXON RES & ENG, 80- *Mem:* Am Phys Soc. *Res:* Electrical transport in inhomogeneous systems; liquid crystals; ferromagnetic transmission resonance; polaron; diffraction optics. *Mailing Add:* Corp Res Ctr Exxon Res & Eng PO Box 45 Linden NJ 07036

SHENG, YEA-YI PETER, b Shanghai, China, Aug 3, 46; m 70. FLUID MECHANICS, ENVIRONMENTAL SCIENCES. *Educ:* Nat Taiwan Univ, BS, 68; Case Western Reserve Univ, MS, 72, PhD(mech & aerospace eng), 75. *Prof Exp:* Res assoc environ, Case Western Reserve Univ, 75-77, sr res assoc, 77-78; assoc consult, 78-79, CONSULT METEOROL & OCEANOG, AERONAUT RES ASSOC, PRINCETON, 79- *Mem:* Am Geophys Union; Am Soc Mech Engrs; Int Asn Gr Lakes Res; AAAS. *Res:* Flow and dispersion of contaminants in the aquatic and atmospheric environments; resuspension and transport of sediments in shallow waters; turbulent transport processes in stratified environments; turbulence modeling; computational fluid dynamics. *Mailing Add:* Aeronaut Res Assocs PO Box 2229 Princeton NJ 08540

SHENITZER, ABE, b Warsaw, Poland, Apr 2, 21; nat US; m 52; c 2. MATHEMATICS. *Educ:* Brooklyn Col, BA, 50; NY Univ, MSc, 51, PhD, 54. *Prof Exp:* Asst, Inst Math Sci, NY Univ, 52-55; mem staff, Bell Tel Labs, Inc, 55-56; from instr to asst prof math, Rutgers Univ, 56-58; assoc prof, Adelphi Univ, 58-63, prof, 63-69; PROF MATH, ARTS & EDUC, YORK UNIV, 69- *Mem:* Am Math Soc. *Res:* Group theory; differential equations; approximation theory. *Mailing Add:* Dept of Math York Univ Downsview ON M3J 2R3 Can

SHENK, JOHN STONER, b Lancaster Co, Pa, July 25, 33; m 52; c 4. AGRONOMY, PLANT BREEDING. *Educ:* Pa State Univ, BS, 65; Mich State Univ, MS, 67, PhD, 69. *Prof Exp:* Asst prof, 70-74, assoc prof, 74-81, PROF AGRON, PA STATE UNIV, 78- *Mem:* Am Soc Agron; Am Forage & Grassland Coun. *Res:* Plant breeding and genetics; development and utilization of chemical and bioassay technique for the production of new plant varieties with improved nutritional quality; chemical infrared and bioassay; computer analysis of infrared data. *Mailing Add:* Dept of Agron 222 Tyson Bldg Pa State Univ University Park PA 16802

SHENK, WILLIAM E(DWIN), b Erie, Pa, June 5, 06; m 35; c 4. ELECTRICAL ENGINEERING. *Educ:* Mass Inst Technol, SB, 28, SM, 29. *Prof Exp:* Lab res engr, US Steel Corp, NJ, 29-35, res engr in-chg physics, 35-43; mgr qual control, Am Transformer Co, 43-44, engr mfg, 44-47, gen eng mgr, 47-48, tech dir, 48-50; chief elec engr, McKay Mach Co, Ohio, 50-56, dir elec eng, 56-61; vpres, Abbey-Etna Mach Co, 61-81; CONSULT, 82- *Honors & Awards:* Inst Elec & Electronics Engrs Prize, 56. *Mem:* Am Soc

Metals; Asn Iron & Steel Engrs; sr mem Inst Elec & Electronics Engrs. *Res:* Automation; computer and servo control; rotary welding transformers; magnetic material improvement and absolute measurement; high temperature pyrometry; furnace control; high pressure measurement; transformer core development; induction heating; transient stability limit of power systems. *Mailing Add:* 7154 Stockport Dr Lambertville MI 48144

SHENKEL, CLAUDE W, JR, b Lyons, Kans, Apr 29, 19; m 41; c 2. GEOLOGY. *Educ:* Kans State Col, BS, 41; Univ Colo, MS, 47, PhD(geol), 52. *Prof Exp:* From asst prof to assoc prof geol, 49-58, PROF GEOL, KANS STATE UNIV, 58- *Concurrent Pos:* Consult, Spec Res Proj, East Venezuelan Basin, 56-57, res geol, Andes Mountains, SAm, 65, spec res geol, SAm, 65-66. *Mem:* Fel Geol Soc Am; Am Inst Prof Geol; Am Asn Petrol Geologists. *Res:* Regional stratigraphic analysis of San Juan and Paradox Basins; petroleum and sub-surface geology. *Mailing Add:* Dept of Geol Kans State Univ Manhattan KS 66502

SHENKER, MARTIN, b New York, NY, Aug 12, 28; m 49; c 3. OPTICS. *Educ:* NY Univ, AB, 48, MS, 51. *Prof Exp:* Jr actuary, New York City Teachers' Retirement Bd, 48-49; inspector, 49-50, jr physicist, 50-51, optical designer, 51-57, asst chief optical designer, 57-60, chief optical designer, 60-73, V PRES OPTICAL DESIGN, FARRAND OPTICAL CO, 73- *Mem:* Fel Optical Soc Am; Soc Photo-Optical Instrument Engrs. *Res:* Optical design; geometrical optics. *Mailing Add:* Farrand Optical Co 117 Wall St Valhalla NY 10595

SHENKIN, HENRY A, b Philadelphia, Pa, June 25, 15; m 41; c 4. NEUROSURGERY. *Educ:* Univ Pa, AB, 35; Jefferson Med Col, MD, 39. *Prof Exp:* Charles Harrison Frazier traveling fel from Univ Pa to dept physiol & brain tumor registry, Sch Med, Yale Univ, 41-42; DIR NEUROSURG, EPISCOPAL HOSP, 58-; PROF NEUROSURG, MED COL PA, 74- *Concurrent Pos:* Assoc prof neurol surg, Div Grad Med, Univ Pa, 60-67; clin prof neurosurg, Sch Med, Temple Univ, 67- *Mem:* Am Asn Neurol Surg; Soc Neurol Surg; Am Col Surg. *Res:* Cerebral circulation and the metabolism of the neurosurgical patient. *Mailing Add:* Episcopal Hosp Front & Lehigh Ave Philadelphia PA 19125

SHENOI, BELLE ANANTHA, b Mysore, India, Dec 23, 29; m 61; c 2. ELECTRICAL ENGINEERING. *Educ:* Univ Madras, BS, 51; Indian Inst Sci, Bangalore, DIISc, 55; Univ Ill, MS, 58, PhD(elec eng), 62. *Prof Exp:* From teaching asst to instr elec eng, Univ Ill, 56-62; from asst prof to assoc prof, 62-67, fac res fel, 63, grad col grant, 63-67, PROF ELEC ENG, UNIV MINN, MINNEAPOLIS, 71- *Concurrent Pos:* NSF grant, 64-68. *Mem:* Fel Inst Elec & Electronics Engrs (pres, Circuits & Systs Soc, 75). *Res:* Digital filters and signal processing; theory and design of networks; analysis of systems. *Mailing Add:* Dept Elec Eng Univ Minn Minneapolis MN 55455

SHEPARD, BUFORD MERLE, b Dexter, Ga, Apr 10, 42; m 60. ENTOMOLOGY, ECOLOGY. *Educ:* Mid Tenn State Univ, BS, 66; Univ Ga, MS, 68; Tex A&M Univ, PhD(entom), 71. *Prof Exp:* Entomologist, Hillsborough County Health Dept, 68-69; asst prof entom, Univ Fla, 71-72; asst prof, 72-78, assoc prof, 78-80, PROF ENTOM, CLEMSON UNIV, 80- *Mem:* Entom Soc Am; Entom Soc Can. *Res:* Insect ecology and biological control with primary emphasis on insect pest management. *Mailing Add:* Dept Entom Clemson Univ Clemson SC 29631

SHEPARD, CHARLES CARTER, b Ord, Nebr, Dec 18, 14; m 39. INFECTIOUS DISEASES. *Educ:* Northwestern Univ, BS, 36, MS, 38, MB, 40, MD, 41. *Prof Exp:* Commissioned officer med, USPHS, 41-79, commissioned officer med, NIH, 42-48, Biochem Inst Uppsala, Sweden, 48-49, NIH, 49-50 & Rocky Mountain Lab, 50-53, CHIEF LEPROSY & RICKETTSIA BR, CTR DIS CONTROL, USPHS, 54- *Concurrent Pos:* Vis prof, Univ Ala, 56-60; mem comn rickettsial dis, Armed Forces Epidemiol Bd, 59-72; adj assoc prof, Univ NC, 64- & Emory Univ, 76-; chmn leprosy panel, Japan-US coop med sci prog, 65-77; mem steering comts, Therapy of Leprosy, WHO, 76- & Immunol of Leprosy, WHO, 78- *Honors & Awards:* Gorgas Medal & Kimble Methodol Award, 62; Philip R Edwards Award, 64; World Leprosy Day Award, 70; Ambaj Nath Bose Bequest, 74; Raoul Folleraux Award, 78; Richard & Hilda Rosenthal Award, 79. *Mem:* AAAS; Int Leprosy Asn; Am Soc Microbiol; Soc Exp Biol & Med; Am Asn Immunol. *Res:* Infectious diseases, especially leprosy and rickettsiae. *Mailing Add:* Ctr for Dis Control US Pub Health Serv Atlanta GA 30333

SHEPARD, DAVID C, b Montpelier, Vt, Mar 13, 29; m 52; c 2. BIOLOGY. *Educ:* Stanford Univ, AB, 51, PhD, 57. *Prof Exp:* From instr to assoc prof, 56-65, PROF BIOL, SAN DIEGO STATE UNIV, 65- *Mem:* Gerontol Soc; AAAS; Am Soc Cell Biol. *Res:* Cell growth and division; cell aging. *Mailing Add:* Dept of Biol San Diego State Univ San Diego CA 92182

SHEPARD, EDWIN REED, b Springfield, Ohio, June 24, 17; m 40; c 5. ORGANIC CHEMISTRY. *Educ:* Wittenberg Col, AB, 38; Ohio State Univ, PhD(org chem), 42. *Prof Exp:* Org chemist, 42-51, head dept org chem res, 51-57, head dept appln res, 58-66, res assoc, Prod Develop Div, 66-72, RES ADV, ELI LILLY & CO, 73- *Mem:* NY Acad Sci; AAAS; Am Chem Soc. *Res:* Chemotherapy, especially antibiotics; cardiovascular drugs; agricultural and food chemicals. *Mailing Add:* Prod Develop Div Eli Lilly & Co 307 E McCarty St Indianapolis IN 46206

SHEPARD, HARVEY KENNETH, b Chicago, Ill, Sept 19, 38; m 62; c 1. THEORETICAL HIGH ENERGY PHYSICS. *Educ:* Univ Ill, Urbana, BS, 60; Calif Inst Technol, MS, 62, PhD(physics), 66. *Prof Exp:* Consult, Rand Corp, Calif, 61-65; lectr & res fel high energy physics, Univ Calif, Santa Barbara, 65-67 & Univ Calif, Riverside, 67-69; asst prof, 69-73, assoc prof, 73-79, PROF PHYSICS, UNIV NH, 79- *Concurrent Pos:* Mem, Inst Advan Study, 77-78. *Mem:* Am Phys Soc; Sigma Xi. *Res:* High energy theoretical physics; theoretical elementary particle physics; mathematical physics. *Mailing Add:* Dept of Physics Univ of NH Durham NH 03824

SHEPARD, JAMES F, b Rhinebeck, NY, Nov 16, 41; m 61; c 2. PLANT PATHOLOGY, PLANT VIROLOGY. *Educ:* Cornell Univ, BS, 59; Univ Calif, Davis, MS, 65, PhD(plant path), 67. *Prof Exp:* Res plant pathologist, Univ Calif, Davis, 67; from asst prof to prof plant path, Mont State Univ, 67-76; PROF PLANT PATH & HEAD DEPT, KANS STATE UNIV, 76- *Mem:* Am Phytopath Soc; Potato Asn Am. *Res:* Mesophyll protoplast culture and selection. *Mailing Add:* Dept of Plant Path Kans State Univ Manhattan KS 66506

SHEPARD, JOSEPH WILLIAM, b St Paul, Minn, Aug 16, 22; m 43. PHYSICAL CHEMISTRY. *Educ:* Wayne State Univ, BS, 43; Univ Mich, MS, 47, PhD(chem), 52. *Prof Exp:* Res chemist, Eng Div, Chrysler Corp, 47-49; dir, Imaging Res Lab, 52-68, tech dir Microfilm Prod Div, 68-80, tech dir Duplicating Prod Div, 75-78, MGR COM & ENG PROD DEPT, MINN MINING & MFG CO, 80- *Mem:* AAAS; Am Chem Soc; Electrochem Soc; Soc Photog Scientists & Engrs. *Res:* Surface and crystal chemistry; colloids; solid state; photochemistry. *Mailing Add:* Com & Eng Prod Dept 3M Co 3M Ctr St Paul MN 55101

SHEPARD, JUNE SMITH, cytogenetics, see previous edition

SHEPARD, KENNETH LEROY, b Hahira, Ga, Aug 5, 37; m 55; c 2. MEDICINAL CHEMISTRY. *Educ:* Stetson Univ, BS, 59; Univ NC, Chapel Hill, PhD(org chem), 63. *Prof Exp:* Mem staff, Chem Res & Develop Labs, Edgewood Arsenal, US Army, Md, 63-65; sr res chemist, 65-74, res fel, 74-75, SR RES FEL, MED CHEM DEPT, MERCK, SHARP & DOHME RES LABS, WEST POINT, 75- *Mem:* AAAS; Am Chem Soc. *Res:* Synthesis of potential therapeutic agents. *Mailing Add:* Merck Sharp & Dohme Res Lab Sunneytown Pike West Point PA 19486

SHEPARD, KENNETH WAYNE, b Columbus, Ohio, Jan 2, 41; m 62; c 2. ACCELERATOR PHYSICS. *Educ:* Univ Chicago, BS, 62; Dartmouth Col, MA, 64; Stanford Univ, PhD(physics), 70. *Prof Exp:* Res asst, Calif Inst Technol, 70-73, res assoc, 73-75; PHYSICIST, ARGONNE NAT LAB, 75- *Mem:* Am Phys Soc. *Res:* Development of high-field, radio-frequency superconducting devices for use in particle accelerators; investigation of the properties of thin superconducting films; development of superconducting thin-film devices. *Mailing Add:* 6000 Oakwood 4-L Lisle IL 60532

SHEPARD, MARION L(AVERNE), b Owosso, Mich, Dec 20, 37; m 62; c 1. MATERIALS SCIENCE, METALLURGICAL ENGINEERING. *Educ:* Mich Tech, BS, 59; Iowa State Univ, MS, 60, PhD(metall), 65. *Prof Exp:* Anal engr, Pratt & Whitney Aircraft Div, United Aircraft Corp, 60-62, proj metallurgist, 65-67, sr proj metallurgist, 67; from asst prof to assoc prof, 67-78, PROF MECH ENG, DUKE UNIV, 78-, ASSOC DEAN, SCH ENG, 77- *Mem:* Am Soc Mech Engrs; Am Soc Eng Educ. *Res:* Phase equilibria in cryobiological systems; response of materials to chemical and thermal fields; precipitation hardening. *Mailing Add:* Dept Mech Eng & Mat Sci Duke Univ Durham NC 27706

SHEPARD, MAURICE CHARLES, b River Falls, Wis, Feb 29, 16; wid; c 3. MEDICAL BACTERIOLOGY. *Educ:* Univ Wis, BS, 39, MS, 40; Duke Univ, PhD(microbiol), 53. *Prof Exp:* Asst bact, Univ Wis, 39-40; instr, Univ Mass, 40-44; coordr field labs, Veneral Dis Div, USPHS, Washington, DC, 45-48, dir spec veneral dis res unit, NC, 49-52 & Ark, 52-53; chief div bact, US Naval Med Field Res Lab, 53-75, CONSULT PREV MED, NAVAL REGIONAL MED CTR, 75- *Mem:* Am Soc Microbiol; NY Acad Sci. *Res:* Biology of mycoplasma; ureaplasmas T-strains; etiology of nongonococcal urethritis. *Mailing Add:* Occup & Prev Med US Naval Reg Med Ctr Camp Lejeune NC 28542

SHEPARD, PAUL FENTON, b Ann Arbor, Mich, Jan 27, 42; m 63; c 2. PARTICLE PHYSICS. *Educ:* Col William & Mary, BS, 63; Princeton Univ, MA, 66, PhD(physics), 69. *Prof Exp:* Adj asst prof physics, Univ Calif, Los Angeles, 69-73; asst prof, 74-79, ASSOC PROF PHYSICS & ASTRON, UNIV PITTSBURGH, 79- *Mem:* AAAS; Am Phys Soc. *Res:* High energy experimental particle physics; electromagnetic form factors of elementary particles; applications of solid state devices to high energy physics. *Mailing Add:* Dept Physics & Astron Univ Pittsburgh Pittsburgh PA 15260

SHEPARD, RICHARD HANCE, b Tulsa, Okla, Jan 18, 22; m 45; c 3. MEDICINE. *Educ:* Washington & Lee Univ, AB, 43; Johns Hopkins Univ, MD, 46. *Prof Exp:* Intern, Johns Hopkins Hosp, 46-47; fel path, Univ Pa, 49-50; fel, Johns Hopkins Univ, 50-52; resident, Chest Serv, Columbia Div, Bellevue Hosp, 52-53; from instr to asst prof environ med, 53-57, from instr to asst prof med, 55-61, assoc prof physiol, 70-72, ASSOC PROF ENVIRON, SCH HYG & PUB HEALTH, JOHNS HOPKINS UNIV, 58-, ASSOC PROF MED, 61-, PROF PHYSIOL & BIOMED ENG, 72- *Concurrent Pos:* Res fel, Johns Hopkins Univ, 51-52, Nat Res Coun fel, 53-55. *Mem:* Am Thoracic Soc; Am Physiol Soc; Am Soc Clin Invest; fel NY Acad Sci. *Res:* Pulmonary diffusion and distribution in normal subjects and in patients with pulmonary diseases. *Mailing Add:* Dept Biomed Eng Johns Hopkins Univ Med Sch Baltimore MD 21205

SHEPARD, ROBERT ANDREWS, b Gaziantep, Turkey, Oct 22, 23; m 49; c 4. ORGANIC CHEMISTRY. *Educ:* Yale Univ, BS, 44, PhD(chem), 50. *Prof Exp:* Instr chem, Yale Univ, 46-50; from instr to assoc prof chem, 50-58, chmn dept chem, 58-68, dean Col Lib Arts, 68-76, PROF CHEM, NORTHEASTERN UNIV, 58- *Mem:* Am Chem Soc. *Res:* Organic fluorine chemistry; marine chemistry; diazo compounds. *Mailing Add:* Dept of Chem Northeastern Univ Boston MA 02115

SHEPARD, ROBERT STANLEY, b Washington, DC, June 19, 27; m 50; c 4. PHYSIOLOGY, PHARMACOLOGY. *Educ:* George Washington Univ, BS, 50, MS, 51; Univ Iowa, PhD(physiol), 55. *Prof Exp:* From spec instr to assoc prof, 55-70, PROF PHYSIOL, SCH MED, WAYNE STATE UNIV, 70- *Concurrent Pos:* Lectr, Mercy Col, Mich, 58-61 & Grace Hosp, 62-81. *Mem:* Am Physiol Soc. *Res:* Lathyrism; blood coagulation; muscle and cardiovascular physiology; teaching techniques. *Mailing Add:* Dept of Physiol Wayne State Univ Sch of Med Detroit MI 48201

SHEPARD, THOMAS H, b Milwaukee, Wis, May 22, 23; m 47; c 3. PEDIATRICS. *Educ:* Amherst Col, AB, 45; Univ Rochester, MD, 48. *Prof Exp:* Asst resident pediat, Albany Med Col, 49-50; chief resident, Univ Rochester, 50-52; fel endocrinol, Med Sch, Johns Hopkins Univ, 54-55; from instr to assoc prof, 55-68, PROF PEDIAT, SCH MED, UNIV WASH, 68-, HEAD CENT LAB HUMAN EMBRYOL, 62- *Concurrent Pos:* Res assoc embryol, Dept Anat & vis asst prof, Col Med, Univ Fla, 61-62; vis investr, Dept Embryol, Carnegie Inst Wash, 62 & fetal lab, Dept Pediat, Copenhagen Univ, 63. *Mem:* AAAS; Am Pediat Soc; Teratology Soc (pres, 68). *Res:* Human embryology and teratology; clinical pediatrics; development of the thyroid; embryo explantation and organ culture; metabolism of Achondroplastic Dwarfism. *Mailing Add:* Dept of Pediat Univ of Wash Sch of Med Seattle WA 98195

SHEPARDSON, JOHN U, b Winchendon, Mass, May 4, 20; m 42; c 3. ANALYTICAL CHEMISTRY. *Educ:* Univ Mass, BS, 42; Rensselaer Polytech Inst, MS, 48, PhD(anal chem), 50. *Prof Exp:* Analyst, Lever Bros Co, 46-47; mgr control dept, Uranium Div, Mallinckrodt Chem Works, 50-59, mgr tech admin, 59-64, dir control, Winthrop Labs, Sterling Drug, 64-76; tech dir, Cis Radiopharmaceut Inc, 76-79; CHIEF CHEMIST, ASTRO CIRCUIT CORP, 80- *Mem:* AAAS; Am Soc Qual Control; Am Chem Soc. *Res:* Organic analytical reagents; inorganic separations; organic analysis; pharmaceuticals. *Mailing Add:* 11 Hitchinpost Rd Chelmsford MA 01824

SHEPHARD, RONALD W(ILLIAM), b Portland, Ore, Nov 22, 12; m 40; c 2. INDUSTRIAL ENGINEERING. *Educ:* Univ Calif, AB, 35, PhD(math), 40, Univ Karlsruche, W Germany, Phd(econ sci), 80. *Prof Exp:* Asst, Univ Calif, 36-40, res assoc, Bur Pub Admin, 40-42, instr math, 41-42, lectr math econ, 46; statist consult, Bell Aircraft Corp, NY, 43-46; asst prof math & econ, NY Univ, 47-50; sr staff mem, Rand Corp, Calif, 50-52; mgr systs anal dept, Sandia Corp, 52-56; chmn, Indust Eng Dept, 60-64, chmn, Opers Res Ctr, 66-72, chmn, Dept Indust Eng & Opers Res, 70-76, PROF ENG SCI, UNIV CALIF, BERKELEY, 56- *Concurrent Pos:* Consult, Off Naval Res, 43-46, Sandia Corp, 58, Europ Prod Agency, 59-60, Mkt Res Corp Am, 61-67 & Laurence Livermore Lab, 69-; Miller prof res, 77-78. *Honors & Awards:* Humboldt Prize, 77. *Mem:* Am Math Soc; fel Economet Soc; Inst Math Statist; Inst Mgt Sci; Opers Res Soc Am. *Res:* Mathematical economics; operations research. *Mailing Add:* Dept of Indust Eng & Opers Res Univ of Calif Berkeley CA 94720

SHEPHARD, ROY JESSE, b London, Eng, May 8, 29; m 58; c 2. PHYSIOLOGY, MEDICINE. *Educ:* Univ London, BSc, 49, MB & BS, 52, PhD(sci), 54, MD, 59. *Prof Exp:* Asst prof prev med, Univ Cincinnati, 56-58; sr sci officer, Chem Defence Res Estab, UK Ministry Defence, 58-59, prin sci officer, 59-64; PROF APPL PHYSIOL & PREV MED, UNIV TORONTO, 64-, PROF PHYSIOL, 66-, PROF MED, INST MED SCI, 68-, ASSOC PROF PHYS EDUC, SCH PHYS & HEALTH EDUC, 71-, DIR, SCH PHYS & HEALTH EDUC, 79- *Concurrent Pos:* Fulbright scholar, Univ Cincinnati, 56-58; consult, Toronto Rehab Ctr, 57-, Gage Inst Chest Dis, 71- & Univ Que, Trois Rivieres, 71-; vpres, Int Comt Phys Fitness Res. *Honors & Awards:* Philip Noel Baker Res Prize, UNESCO. *Mem:* Brit Physiol Soc; Can Physiol Soc; Am Physiol Soc; Brit Med Res Soc; Am Asn Health, Phys Educ & Recreation. *Res:* Cardiorespiratory physiology with particular reference to endurance fitness, sport medicine and the environment. *Mailing Add:* Sch Phys & Health Educ Univ Toronto Toronto ON M5S 1A1 Can

SHEPHARD, WILLIAM DANKS, b Gary, Ind, July 8, 33; m 59. EXPERIMENTAL HIGH ENERGY PHYSICS. *Educ:* Wesleyan Univ, BA, 54; Univ Wis, MS, 55, PhD, 62. *Prof Exp:* Asst physics, Univ Wis, 54-60; asst prof, Univ Ky, 60-63; from asst prof to assoc prof, 63-73, PROF PHYSICS, UNIV NOTRE DAME, 73- *Concurrent Pos:* Guest jr res asst, Brookhaven Nat Lab, 57-58, guest assoc physicist, 60-; Fulbright fel, Max Planck Inst Physics, 62-63; guest physicist & consult, Argonne Nat Lab, 63-; guest physicist, Nat Accelerator Lab, 71-; consult, Oak Ridge Nat Lab, 61-63; guest prof physics, Fac Math & Natural Sci, Univ Nijmegen, Netherlands, 75-76. *Mem:* Am Phys Soc; Sigma Xi. *Res:* Elementary particle physics; high energy interactions; experiments in hadronic multiparticle production and hadron spectroscopy involving various experimental techniques. *Mailing Add:* Dept of Physics Univ of Notre Dame Notre Dame IN 46556

SHEPHERD, ALBERT PITT, JR, b Lexington, Miss, Dec 29, 43; m 65; c 1. PHYSIOLOGY. *Educ:* Millsaps Col, BS, 66; Univ Miss, PhD(physiol), 71. *Prof Exp:* Asst instr physiol, Univ Tex Med Sch Houston, 72-73; asst prof, Col Med, Univ Calif, Irvine, 73-74; asst prof, 74-77, ASSOC PROF PHYSIOL, UNIV TEX HEALTH SCI CTR SAN ANTONIO, 74- *Mem:* Am Physiol Soc; Microcirc Soc; Int Soc Oxygen Transport to Tissue; Am Heart Asn. *Res:* Intestinal circulation; control of microcirculation. *Mailing Add:* Dept of Physiol Univ of Tex Health Sci Ctr San Antonio TX 78284

SHEPHERD, B(URCHARD) P(OST), b Portland, Ore, May 30, 12; m 48; c 4. MECHANICAL ENGINEERING. *Educ:* Ore State Col, BS, 36. *Prof Exp:* Engr, Dow Chem Co, Mich & NC, 36-41; construct engr, Am Baptist Mission, Burma, 46-49; chief mech eng sect, US AEC, Idaho, 49-51; chief engr, Rocky Flats Plant, Dow Chem Co, 51-63, eng consult, 63-64, activation mgr, Dow Aerospace Serv, 64-66, opers mgr, 66-69, res specialist, Tex Div, Freeport, 69-76; RETIRED. *Mem:* Am Soc Mech Engrs. *Res:* Marine fouling; brine waste disposal; coastal engineering problems. *Mailing Add:* 10015 Fairview Rd Tillamook OR 97141

SHEPHERD, BENJAMIN ARTHUR, b Woodville, Miss, Jan 28, 41; c 2. ZOOLOGY. *Educ:* Tougaloo Col, BA, 61; Atlanta Univ, MA, 63; Kans State Univ, PhD(zool), 70. *Prof Exp:* Instr biol, Tougaloo Col, 63-65; asst zool, Kans State Univ, 66-69; from instr to asst prof, 69-73, asst chmn dept zool, 76-78, actg chmn, 78, assoc prof, 73-79, PROF ZOOL, SOUTHERN ILL UNIV, CARBONDALE, 79-, ASSOC VPRES ACAD AFFAIRS, 79- *Mem:* Am Soc Zoologists; Soc Study Reproduction; AAAS; Am Asn Anatomists; Sigma Xi. *Res:* Epididymal histophysiology of the mammal including effects of androgens and age on the viability and fertilizing capacity of spermatazoa; influence of olfactory stimulation on estrous induction. *Mailing Add:* Dept of Zool Southern Ill Univ Carbondale IL 62901

SHEPHERD, D(ENNIS) G(RANVILLE), b Ilford, Eng, Oct 6, 12; nat US; m 39; c 3. MECHANICAL ENGINEERING, AERONAUTICAL & ASTRONAUTICAL ENGINEERING. *Educ:* Univ Mich, BSE, 34. *Prof Exp:* Engr, Power Jets, Ltd, Eng, 40-46; chief exp engr, Gas Turbine Div, A V Roe Can, 46-48; from asst prof to prof, 48-78, dir, 65-72, EMER PROF MECH ENG, CORNELL UNIV, 78- *Concurrent Pos:* Guggenheim fel, 54-55; Orgn Europ Econ Coop fel, 60-61; consult, Curtiss-Wright Corp, Bendix-Westinghouse Automotive Air Brake Co, Continental Engine Co & Carrier Corp. *Honors & Awards:* Worcester Reed Warner Medal, Am Soc Mech Engrs, 76. *Mem:* AAAS; Am Soc Mech Engrs; Brit Inst Mech Eng. *Res:* Thermal engineering, especially turbomachinery, gas turbines, wind power and jet propulsion. *Mailing Add:* Dept of Mech & Aerospace Eng Cornell Univ Ithaca NY 14853

SHEPHERD, DAVID PRESTON, b Center, Tex, Aug 2, 40; m 68. RADIATION BIOLOGY, ZOOLOGY. *Educ:* Lamar Univ, BS, 63; Tex A&M Univ, MS, 67, PhD(biol), 70. *Prof Exp:* Instr zool, Tex A&M Univ, 69-70; asst prof, 70-77, ASSOC PROF BIOL, SOUTHEASTERN LA UNIV, 77- *Mem:* AAAS. *Res:* Radiation; physiology; ecology; herpetology; archeology. *Mailing Add:* Dept of Biol Sci Southeastern La Univ Hammond LA 70402

SHEPHERD, FLOYD, b La Grange, Ga, Nov 24, 41. POLYMER CHEMISTRY, SPECIALTY CHEMICALS. *Educ:* Univ Akron, BS, 64, PhD(polymer sci), 72; Ohio State Univ, MBA, 81. *Prof Exp:* Chemist synthetic rubber, Goodyear Tire & Rubber Co, 64-69, sr res chemist polyester fibers, 71-75; proj scientist coatings, Union Carbide Corp, 75-77; LAB SUPVR, OWENS/CORNING FIBERGLAS, 77- *Mem:* Am Chem Soc. *Res:* Organic polymer chemistry; chemical reactions on polymers; marine antifouling coatings; polymer structure-property relationships; specialty chemicals development; fiberglass binders and sizes. *Mailing Add:* Owens/Corning Fiberglas PO Box 415 Granville OH 43023

SHEPHERD, FREEMAN DANIEL, JR, b Boston, Mass, June 7, 36; m 59; c 3. PHYSICS, ELECTRONICS. *Educ:* Mass Inst Technol, BS & MS, 59; Northeastern Univ, PhD(elec eng), 65. *Prof Exp:* Staff scientist, Air Force Cambridge Res Labs, 57-59, group leader infrared devices, 66-76, CHIEF ELECTRONIC DEVICE TECHNOL BR, ROME AIR DEVELOP CTR, HANSCOM AFB, 77- *Concurrent Pos:* Assoc mem adv group electron devices, Spec Devices Working Group, 70-76; mem, Working Group Basic Mech Radiation Effects, 71-76; Air Force rep, Comt Electromagnetic Detection Devices, Nat Mat Adv Bd-Nat Res Coun-Nat Acad Sci, 71-72. *Honors & Awards:* Tech Achievement Award, US Air Force Systs Command, 70. *Mem:* Inst Elec & Electronics Engrs; Sigma Xi; Instrument Soc Am. *Res:* Design, fabrication and test of infrared and electrooptical devices; measurement of noise; electron transport processes and radiation effects. *Mailing Add:* Electronic Device Technol Br Rome Air Develop Ctr Hanscom AFB MA 01731

SHEPHERD, GORDON GREELEY, b Sask, Can, June 19, 31; m 53; c 3. AERONOMY, SPACE PHYSICS. *Educ:* Univ Sask, BSc, 52, MSc, 53; Univ Toronto, PhD(molecular spectros), 56. *Prof Exp:* From asst prof to assoc prof physics, Univ Sask, 57-69; PROF PHYSICS, YORK UNIV, 69- *Concurrent Pos:* Mem ed adv bd, Planetary & Space Sci. *Mem:* Optical Soc Am; Can Asn Physicists; Am Geophys Union; fel Can Aeronaut & Space Inst; fel Royal Soc Can. *Res:* Interferometric spectroscopy of airglow and aurora from the ground; rockets and satellites; morphology of low energy auroral electron precipitation and excitation processes of auroral emissions by these electrons. *Mailing Add:* Centre for Res in Exp Space Sci York Univ Downsview ON M3J 1P3 Can

SHEPHERD, GORDON MURRAY, b Ames, Iowa, July 21, 33; m 59; c 3. NEUROPHYSIOLOGY. *Educ:* Iowa State Univ, BS, 55; Harvard Med Sch, MD, 59; Oxford Univ, PhD(neurophysiol), 62. *Prof Exp:* Res assoc biophys, NIH, 62-64; vis scientist neurophysiol, Karolinska Inst, Sweden, 64-66; asst prof, 67-68, assoc prof physiol, 69-81, PROF NEUROSCIENCE, SCH MED, YALE UNIV, 81- *Concurrent Pos:* USPHS fel, 59-62, spec fel, 64-66 & res grant, 66-; assoc fel, Retina Found, Boston, 66-67 & dept biol, Mass Inst Technol, 67; vis assoc prof, Neurol Inst, Univ Pa, 71-72; mem study sect, NIH, 75- *Mem:* Soc Neurosci; Am Physiol Soc; Int Brain Res Orgn; assoc Physiol Soc London. *Res:* Synaptic organization of the olfactory bulb; receptor properties of the isolated muscle spindle; properties of neuronal dendrites; mechanisms of cortical integration; energy metabolism of synapses. *Mailing Add:* Dept of Physiol Yale Univ Sch of Med New Haven CT 06510

SHEPHERD, HERNDON GUINN, JR, b Schuyler, Va, Mar 14, 27. CLINICAL CHEMISTRY, TOXICOLOGY. *Educ:* Univ Va, BS, 50; Loyola Univ, Ill, MS, 58, PhD(biochem), 59; Nat Registry Clin Chem, cert; Am Bd Bioanal, cert, 76. *Prof Exp:* Anal chemist, E I du Pont de Nemours & Co, 50-55; Chicago Heart Asn asst, Loyola Univ, Ill, 58; lab dir, Mason-Barron Labs, 59-78; VPRES & TECH DIR, CENTRAL PATHOL REGIONAL LAB, CHICAGO, 78- *Concurrent Pos:* Lectr, Stritch Sch Med, Loyola Univ, Ill; consult, Narcotic Control Div, State Dept Pub Safety, Ill; instr & clin chemist, Grant Hosp, Chicago, 64-; instr, Augustana Hosp Chicago, 64-, clin chemist, 75-; vpres, C&C Med Equip & Leasing Co, 68-76; secy qual control bd, Biomed Div, Damon Corp, Mass, 71-; adj assoc prof, Stritch Sch Med, Loyola Univ, 72. *Honors & Awards:* Samuel Natelson award, Am Asn Clin Chemists, 78. *Mem:* Am Chem Soc; Am Asn Clin Chem, Am Inst Chemists. *Res:* Clinical chemical methodology; clinical endocrinology. *Mailing Add:* Central Pathol Regional Labs 2060 N Clark St Chicago IL 60614

SHEPHERD, HURLEY SIDNEY, b Oxford, NC, Dec 17, 50. PLANT MOLECULAR BIOLOGY, ORGANELLE GENETICS. *Educ:* Univ NC, BS, 73; Duke Univ, PhD(bot), 78. *Prof Exp:* Res assoc, Univ Calif, San Diego, 79-81; ASST PROF BOT & BIOCHEM, UNIV KANS, 81- *Mem:* Genetics Soc Am; Am Soc Plant Physiologists; Plant Molecular Biol Asn; AAAS. *Res:* Control of gene expression in plants due to environmental and developmental effects and interactions between the nuclear and organelle genomes. *Mailing Add:* Dept Bot Univ Kans Lawrence KS 66045

SHEPHERD, JAMES WILLIS, b Indianapolis, Ind, Oct 29, 19; m 50; c 3. ORGANIC CHEMISTRY. *Educ:* Ohio State Univ, BSc, 49, MSc, 51; Purdue Univ, PhD, 54. *Prof Exp:* Dir com res, Callery Chem Co, 54-68; SR RES SPECIALIST, MOBAY CHEM CO, DIV BAYCHEM CORP, 68- *Res:* Aliphatic nitro compounds; boron hydrides; organo-boron compounds; organometallics; high energy fuels and propellants; epoxy foams; urethane systems; electroless plating. *Mailing Add:* New Prods Dept New Plastics & Penn-Lincoln Pkwy W Pittsburgh PA 15205

SHEPHERD, JIMMIE GEORGE, b Lone Oak, Tex, Sept 2, 23; m 46; c 2. PHYSICS. *Educ:* North Tex State Univ, BS, 47, MA, 51. *Prof Exp:* Teacher high sch, Tex, 47-53; petrol engr, Sun Oil Co, 53-57; asst prof physics, Lamar State Col, 57-66, ASSOC PROF PHYSICS, LAMAR UNIV, 66- *Concurrent Pos:* Sci teaching consult, Lamar Area Sch Study Coun, 66, 67 & 68. *Mem:* AAAS; Am Asn Physics Teachers. *Res:* Search for magnetic monopoles. *Mailing Add:* Dept of Physics PO Box 10046 Beaumont TX 77710

SHEPHERD, JOHN PATRICK GEORGE, b West Wickham, Eng, May 11, 37; m 63; c 2. SOLAR ENERGY. *Educ:* Univ London, BSc & ARCS, 58, PhD(electron physics) & dipl, Imp Col, 62. *Prof Exp:* Res asst electron physics, Imp Col, Univ London, 61-63; res assoc, Case Inst Technol, 63-65, asst prof, 65-66; sr sci officer, Royal Radar Estab, Eng, 66-69; assoc prof physics, 69-75, PROF PHYSICS, UNIV WIS-RIVER FALLS, 75- *Concurrent Pos:* Consult, 3M Co, 71- *Mem:* Am Phys Soc. *Res:* Band structure of solids; deHass van Alphen effect in metals and alloys, pseudo potential models of band structure of same; laser and nonlinear optics; band structure of semiconductors; solar energy; optical design; electro-chemical studies. *Mailing Add:* Dept of Physics Univ of Wis River Falls WI 54022

SHEPHERD, JOHN THOMPSON, b Northern Ireland, May 21, 19; m 45; c 2. PHYSIOLOGY. *Educ:* Queen's Univ Belfast, MB & BCh, 45, MCh, 48, MD, 51, DSc, 56. *Prof Exp:* House physician, Royal Victoria Hosp, Belfast, Northern Ireland, 45-46, extern surgeon, 46; lectr physiol, Queen's Univ Belfast, 47-53; Anglo-French Med Exchange bursary, 57; assoc prof, 57-62, dir res, Mayo Found, 69-77, PROF PHYSIOL, MAYO GRAD SCH MED, UNIV MINN, 62-, DEAN MAYO MED SCH, 77- *Concurrent Pos:* Leathem traveling fel & Fulbright scholar, 53-54; consult, Mayo Clin, 57- & Northern Ireland Hosps; chmn physiol sect, Mayo Found, 66-74. *Honors & Awards:* Carl J Wiggers Award, Am Physiol Soc, 78; Gold Heart Award, Asn Am Physicians, 78. *Mem:* Am Heart Asn (pres, 75-76). *Res:* Heart and peripheral circulation of man and animals in health and disease, especially hemodynamics. *Mailing Add:* Mayo Clin & Found Rochester MN 55901

SHEPHERD, JOSEPH EMMETT, b Joliet, Ill, Mar 7, 53; m 79; c 1. COMBUSTION, GAS DYNAMICS. *Educ:* Univ SFla, BS, 76; Calif Inst Technol, PhD(appl physics), 81. *Prof Exp:* MEM TECH STAFF, SANDIA NAT LABS, 80- *Mem:* Am Phys Soc; AAAS; Sigma Xi. *Res:* Modeling of rapid evaporation of superheated liquids; compressible flow in porous materials; gasdynamics of explosions; turbulent combustion of high-temperature gases. *Mailing Add:* Div 2513 Sandia Nat Lab PO Box 5800 Albuquerque NM 87185

SHEPHERD, JULIAN GRANVILLE, b Lutterworth, Eng, Dec 16, 42; US citizen; m 66; c 1. INVERTEBRATE PHYSIOLOGY. *Educ:* Cornell Univ, BA, 64; Harvard Univ, PhD(biol), 72. *Prof Exp:* Res scientist insect reproduction, Int Ctr Insect Physiol & Ecol, 72-74; fel, Harvard Univ, 74-75; ASST PROF BIOL, STATE UNIV NY BINGHAMTON, 75- *Mem:* AAAS. *Res:* Development and physiology of invertebrate, mainly insect, spermatazoa. *Mailing Add:* Dept of Biol Sci State Univ of NY Binghamton NY 13901

SHEPHERD, MARK, JR, b Dallas, Tex, Jan 18, 23; m 45; c 3. ELECTRICAL ENGINEERING. *Educ:* Southern Methodist Univ, BS, 42; Univ Ill, Urbana, MS, 47; PhD, Rensselaer Polytech Inst, 79. *Hon Degrees:* PhD, Southern Methodist Univ, 66. *Prof Exp:* Test engr, Gen Elec Co, 42-43; engr, Farnsworth TV & Radio Corp, 47-48; proj engr, Geophys Serv Inc, 48-51, from asst chief engr to chief engr, Semiconductor Design, 52-54, asst vpres, Semiconductor-Components Div, 54-55, gen mgr, 54-61, vpres, 55-61, exec vpres, 61-66, chief opers officer, 61-69, pres, 67-76, CHIEF EXEC OFFICER, TEX INSTRUMENTS INC, 69-, CHMN, 76-; from asst chief engr to chief engr, Semiconductor Design, 52-54, asst vpres & gen mgr, Semiconductor-Components Div, 54-55, vpres & gen mgr, Semiconductory-Components Div, 55-61, exec vpres & chief oper officer, 61-66, pres & chief oper officer, 67-69, pres & chief exec officer, 69-76, CHMN & CHIEF EXEC OFFICER, TEX INSTRUMENTS INC, 76-, MEM, BD DIRS, 63- *Mem:* Nat Acad Eng; Inst Elec & Electronics Engrs; Soc Explor Geophys. *Res:* Solid state control systems. *Mailing Add:* Tex Instruments Inc PO Box 225474 MS 236 Dallas TX 75265

SHEPHERD, RAYMOND EDWARD, b Joliet, Ill, Aug 21, 41; m 62; c 1. PHYSIOLOGICAL CHEMISTRY. *Educ:* Bethel Col, BS, 62; Univ Mont, MS, 68; Wash State Univ, PhD(exercise physiol), 74. *Prof Exp:* Instr biol, Graceville High Sch, 64-66; instr physiol, Dakota State Col, 68-70; NIH fel, Brown Univ, 74-76, from instr to asst prof physiol chem, 76-78; assoc prof exercise physiol, Univ Toledo, 78-80; ASST PROF PHYSIOL, LOUISIANA STATE UNIV MED CTR, 80- *Concurrent Pos:* Fel, Nat Inst Arthritis Metab & Digestive Dis, 74. *Mem:* NY Acad Sci; AAAS; Am Col Sports Med; Am Physiol Soc; Sigma Xi. *Res:* Regulation of adenylate cyclase, protein kinase, and triglyceride lipase in fat cells by hormones and fatty acids. *Mailing Add:* Dept Physiol Louisiana State Univ 1901 Perdido St New Orleans LA 70112

SHEPHERD, RAYMOND LEE, b Arkadelphia, Ark, Oct 13, 26; m 50; c 3. GENETICS, PLANT PATHOLOGY. *Educ:* Ouachita Baptist Col, 50; Univ Ark, MS, 60; Auburn Univ, PhD(plant breeding), 65. *Prof Exp:* Proprietor retail grocery bus, 54-57; res asst plant breeding, Univ Ark, 57-60; asst agron, 60-65, SUPVRY RES AGRONOMIST, AUBURN UNIV, 65- *Mem:* Am Soc Agron. *Res:* Genetics and breeding investigations on cotton, especially the development of basic breeding stocks which are resistant to nematodes and diseases. *Mailing Add:* Dept of Agron & Soils Auburn Univ Auburn AL 36830

SHEPHERD, REX E, b Greenville, Ohio, Nov 27, 45. REDOX REACTIONS, MODELING CATALYTIC REACTIVITIES. *Educ:* Purdue Univ, BS, 67; Stanford Univ, MS, 69, PhD(inorg chem), 71. *Prof Exp:* Fel, Dept Chem, Yale Univ, 71-72 & State Univ NY, Buffalo, 72-73; vis asst prof, Purdue Univ, 73-75; asst prof, 75-81, ASSOC PROF INORG ANAL, DEPT CHEM, UNIV PITTSBURGH, 81- *Concurrent Pos:* Consult, Maynard Metals, Inc, 74-75. *Mem:* Am Chem Soc. *Res:* Mechanistic inorganic chemistry as related to transition metal complexes, bioinorganic systems, catalytic activation of small molecules and photochemistry studied by physical chemical methods. *Mailing Add:* Dept Chem Univ Pittsburgh Pittsburgh PA 15260

SHEPHERD, ROBERT JAMES, b Clinton, Okla, June 5, 30; m 78; c 3. PLANT PATHOLOGY, VIROLOGY. *Educ:* Okla State Univ, BS, 54, MS, 56; Univ Wis, PhD(plant path), 59. *Prof Exp:* Asst plant path, Okla State Univ, 54-55; asst, Univ Wis, 56-58, res assoc, 58-59, asst prof, 59-61; asst prof, Univ Calif, Davis, 61-65; assoc prof, Univ Ark, 65-66; assoc prof & assoc plant pathologist, 66-72, PROF PLANT PATH, UNIV CALIF, DAVIS, 72- *Concurrent Pos:* Assoc ed, Phytopath, 65-66; ed, Virol, 71-74; chmn plant virus subcomt, Int Comt Taxonomy Viruses; assoc ed, J Gen Virol, 78-81. *Honors & Awards:* Ruth Allen Award, Am Phytopath Soc, 81. *Mem:* Fel Am Phytopath Soc; Soc Gen Microbiol. *Res:* Characterization and description of plant viruses; epidemiology and control of plant virus diseases; recombinant DNA vectors for plants. *Mailing Add:* Dept Plant Path Univ Calif Davis CA 95616

SHEPHERD, W(ILLIAM) G(ERALD), b Ft William, Ont, Aug 28, 11; nat US; m 36; c 3. ELECTRICAL ENGINEERING. *Educ:* Univ Minn, BS, 33, PhD(physics), 37. *Prof Exp:* Mem tech staff, Bell Tel Labs, NJ, 37-47; assoc dean inst technol, 54-56, head dept elec eng, 56-63, vpres acad admin, 63-73, prof elec eng, 47-79, dir, Space Sci Ctr, 74-79, EMER PROF ELEC ENG, UNIV MINN, MINNEAPOLIS, 79- *Concurrent Pos:* Consult, Bendix Aviation Corp, 49-63, Gen Elec Co, 55-63 & Control Data, 58-63; US Comn VII chmn, Int Sci Radio Union, 53-57 & Int Comn VII, 57-63; mem eng sci panel, NSF, 58-61, eng div adv comt, 64-69; mem adv group electron devices, Dept Defense, 58-68, chmn, 62-68; mem space technol adv comt, NASA, 64-69. *Honors & Awards:* Citation, Bur Ships, 47; Medal of Honor, Nat Electronics Conf, 65. *Mem:* Nat Acad Eng; fel Inst Elec & Electronics Engs (vpres, 65-66, pres, 66-67); Am Phys Soc. *Res:* Microwave electronics; physical electronics, especially electron emission. *Mailing Add:* 103 Space Sci Ctr 100 Union St SE Minneapolis MN 55455

SHEPHERD, WILLIAM LLOYD, b Okla, Oct 2, 15; m 39; c 1. MATHEMATICS. *Educ:* Okla State Univ, BS, 38, MS, 41. *Prof Exp:* Instr math, Southwestern Col (Kans), 43-45; asst prof, Okla State Univ, 46-47; instr, Univ Tex, 47; instr, Univ Ore, 48-52; asst prof math & physics, Tex Western Col, 52-60; mathematician, White Sands Missile Range, US Dept Army, NMex, 60-73, res mathematician, Res Proj Off, Instrumentation Directorate, 73-80; CONSULT, 80- *Mem:* Am Math Soc; Math Asn Am; Soc Indust & Appl Math. *Res:* Mathematics for missile range instrumentation problems; digital signal processing; number theoretic considerations in interferometric angle measurements. *Mailing Add:* 2104 Atlanta Ave El Paso TX 79930

SHEPLEY, LAWRENCE CHARLES, b Washington, DC, Aug 11, 39. COSMOLOGY. *Educ:* Swarthmore Col, BA, 61; Princeton Univ, MA, 63, PhD(physics), 65. *Prof Exp:* Res physicist, Univ Calif, Berkeley, 65-67; asst prof, 67-70, ASSOC PROF PHYSICS, UNIV TEX, AUSTIN, 70-, ASSOC DIR, CTR RELATIVITY THEORY, 71- *Concurrent Pos:* NSF grant, 68-; vchmn grad affairs, Physics Dept, Univ Tex, Austin, 71-73. *Mem:* Am Phys Soc; Am Asn Physics Teachers. *Res:* Cosmological models; equivalent lagrangians. *Mailing Add:* Dept Physics Univ Tex Austin TX 78712

SHEPP, ALLAN, b New York, NY, Apr 2, 28; m 48; c 2. PHOTOGRAPHIC CHEMISTRY, COLOR SCIENCE. *Educ:* Oberlin Col, BA, 48; Cornell Univ, PhD(phys chem), 53. *Prof Exp:* Fel div pure chem, Nat Res Coun Can, 53-55; chemist, Tech Opers, Inc, 55-69, dir chem, 65-69; SR SCIENTIST, RES LABS, TECH CONTROL CTR, POLAROID CORP, CAMBRIDGE, 69- *Concurrent Pos:* Vpres confs, Soc Photog Scientists & Engrs, 71-75, vpres publs, 75- *Mem:* Am Phys Soc; Soc Photog Sci & Eng; Am Chem Soc. *Res:* Photographic theory; color; developers, image evaluation, evaporated and polymer systems; photochemistry, free radical kinetics, luminescence; color duplication theory. *Mailing Add:* 68 Shade St Lexington MA 02173

SHEPP, LAWRENCE ALAN, b Brooklyn, NY, Sept 9, 36; m 62; c 3. MATHEMATICS. *Educ:* Polytech Inst Brooklyn, BS, 58; Princeton Univ, MA, 60, PhD(math), 61. *Prof Exp:* Instr probability & statist, Univ Calif, Berkeley, 61-62; MEM TECH STAFF MATH, BELL LABS, 62- *Concurrent Pos:* Mem comt appl math, Nat Acad Sci, 74-77; vis scientist math dept, Mass Inst Technol, 75; adj prof, Columbia Univ & The Neurological Inst, 74- *Honors & Awards:* Paul - Levy Prize, Inst Henri Poincare, Paris, 66. *Mem:* Fel Inst Math Statist; Am Math Soc; Math Asn Am; AAAS. *Res:* Probability and statistics; stochastic processes; Gaussian measure theory; analysis; asymptotics; random walk; limit theorems; computered tomography; medical imaging; reconstruction of pictures from projections. *Mailing Add:* Bell Tel Labs Murray Hill NJ 07974

SHEPPARD, ALAN JONATHAN, b Parkersburg, WVa, Oct 11, 27; m 60. NUTRITIONAL BIOCHEMISTRY, ANIMAL NUTRITION. *Educ:* Ohio State Univ, BS, 51; Va Polytech, MS, 54; Univ Ill, MS, 56, PhD(animal nutrit), 59. *Prof Exp:* Agronomist, Northern Va Pasture Res Sta, 53; res asst animal sci, Agr Exp Sta, Univ Ill, Urbana, 59-60; chief lipid res sect, 60-70, RES CHEMIST, DIV NUTRIT, FOOD & DRUG ADMIN, 60-, CHIEF, FATS & ENERGY SECT, 70- *Concurrent Pos:* Instr grad sch, USDA, 60-63; actg chief macronutrient res br, Food & Drug Admin, 67; mem sub comn 9,12 di-cis-linoleic acid, Oils & Fats Sect, Int Union of Pure & Appl Chem, 74-78; adj prof chem, Am Univ, 77-; assoc prof, Human Nutrit Prog, Howard Univ, 77- *Mem:* Am Inst Nutrit; Am Oil Chem Soc; Am Soc Animal Sci; Am Dairy Sci Asn; Asn Off Anal Chem. *Res:* Gas chromatography of vitamins; nutritional-metabolic studies in the lipid and fatty acid fields; interface between research and application to regulatory problems. *Mailing Add:* Div of Nutrit HFF-268 200 C St SW Washington DC 20204

SHEPPARD, ALBERT PARKER, b Griffin, Ga, June 6, 36; m 78; c 2. ELECTRONICS, RESEARCH ADMINISTRATION. *Educ:* Oglethorpe Univ, BS, 58; Emory Univ, MS, 59; Duke Univ, PhD(elec eng), 65. *Prof Exp:* Instr physics, Univ Ala, 59-60; sr engr, Martin Co, Fla, 60-63; radio physicist, US Army Res Off, NC, 63-65; head, Spec Tech Br, Eng Exp Sta, 65-71, chief, Chem Sci & Mat Div, 71-72, assoc dean, Col Eng, 72-74, actg vpres res, 80, PROF ELEC ENG, GA INST TECHNOL, 72-, ASSOC VPRES RES, 74- *Concurrent Pos:* Lectr, DeKalb Col, 67-71; secy-treas, Microwave & Electronic Consults, Atlanta. *Mem:* Sr mem Inst Elec & Electronics Engrs; Am Soc Eng Educ; Nat Soc Prof Engrs; Int Solar Energy Soc; Int Microwave Power Inst. *Res:* Millimeter and submillimeter wave technology; microwave engineering and electromagnetic radiation hazards; alternate energy microcomputer applications. *Mailing Add:* 3591 Norwich Dr Tucker GA 30084

SHEPPARD, ASHER R, b Brooklyn, NY, Apr 4, 43; m 65; c 3. MEMBRANE BIOPHYSICS. *Educ:* Union Col, BS, 63; State Univ NY Buffalo, MS, 71, PhD(physics), 75. *Prof Exp:* Nat Inst Environ Health Sci fel environ biophys, Inst Environ Med, NY Univ Med Ctr, 74-76; Nat Inst Environ Health Sci fel environ biophys, Brain Res Inst, Univ Calif, Los Angeles, 76-78; RES PHYSICIST, PETTIS VET ADMIN HOSP, LOMA LINDA, CALIF, 78- *Concurrent Pos:* Asst res prof physiol, Loma Linda, Calif, 79-; sci adv to WHO, 80-, Dept Energy, 80- *Mem:* AAAS; Am Phys Soc; Bioelectronmagnetics Soc; Soc Neurosci. *Res:* Biological effects of electric and magnetic fields; physiological effects of fields at cell membrane surfaces and biophysical modeling of cell environment in fields; determination of health criteria for field exposures. *Mailing Add:* Res Serv-151 J L Pettis Mem Vet Hosp Loma Linda CA 92357

SHEPPARD, CHESTER STEPHEN, b Buffalo, NY, Sept 27, 27; m 52; c 2. ORGANIC CHEMISTRY. *Educ:* Canisius Col, BS, 52; Univ Pittsburgh, MLS, 55, PhD(org chem), 61. *Prof Exp:* Jr fel coal chem, Mellon Inst Indust Res, 52-61; res chemist, Lucidol Div, Wallace & Tiernan, Inc, 62-63; group leader res, 63-65, supvr res, 66-70, MGR RES, LUCIDOL DIV, PENNWALT CORP, 71- *Mem:* Am Chem Soc; Am Inst Chem; The Chem Soc. *Res:* Nitrogen chemistry; free radicals; peroxides; aliphatic azo chemistry; foamed polymers; polymerization; plasticizers; stabilizers; organic blowing agents; hydrazine chemistry. *Mailing Add:* Lucidol Div Pennwalt Corp 1740 Military Rd Buffalo NY 14240

SHEPPARD, DAVID E, b Chester, Pa, Jan 16, 38; m 60; c 3. BIOCHEMICAL GENETICS. *Educ:* Amherst Col, BA, 59; NIJohns Hopkins Univ, PhD(biochem genetics), 63. *Prof Exp:* Asst prof biol, Reed Col, 63-65; NIH fel, Univ Calif, Santa Barbara, 65-66; asst prof, 67-69, ASSOC PROF BIOL, UNIV DEL, 69- *Concurrent Pos:* NIH fel, Univ BC, 73. *Mem:* Genetics Soc Am; Am Soc Microbiol. *Res:* Transduction; feed-back inhibition; genetic control of protein synthesis; arabinose operon. *Mailing Add:* Dept of Biol Sci Univ of Del Newark DE 19711

SHEPPARD, DAVID W, b Quincy, Mass, Dec 28, 27; m 52; c 2. PHYSICS. *Educ:* Gordon Col, BA, 52; Andover Newton Theol Sch, BD, 56; Brown Univ, MA, 61; Ohio State Univ, PhD(physics), 68; Univ Pittsburgh, MLS, 77. *Prof Exp:* Pastor, Congregational Church, Dunstable, Mass, 54-57 & Riverpoint Congregational Church, West Warwick, RI, 57-61; instr physics, Defiance Col, 61-64, asst prof, 64-65; chem dept physics, Thiel Col, 75-77, asst prof, 68-80; ASSOC PROF, WVA WESLEYAN COL, 80- *Mem:* Am Phys Soc; Am Asn Physics Teachers. *Res:* Nuclear magnetic resonance. *Mailing Add:* PO Box 68 WVa Wesleyan Col Buckhannon WV 26201

SHEPPARD, DONALD M(AX), b Port Arthur, Tex, Mar 21, 37; m 58; c 2. MECHANICAL ENGINEERING. *Educ:* Lamar State Univ, BS, 60; Tex A&M Univ, MS, 62; Ariz State Univ, PhD(mech eng), 69. *Prof Exp:* Design engr, Collins Radio Co, 60-61; asst mech eng, Tex A&M Univ, 61-62, Univ Ariz, 62-63 & Southwest Res Inst, 63-64; instr, Ariz State Univ, 64-68, NSF fel, 67-68; from asst prof to assoc prof eng sci, 69-77, asst chmn coastal & oceanog eng, 77-78, ASSOC PROF COASTAL & OCEANOG ENG, UNIV FLA, 77-, ACTG CHMN COASTAL & OCEANOG ENG, 78- *Concurrent Pos:* Instr, San Antonio Col, 63-64. *Res:* Stratified shear flows internal waves coastal hydraulics; nearshore sediment transport; geophysical fluid mechanics. *Mailing Add:* Dept of Coastal & Oceanog Eng Univ of Fla Gainesville FL 32611

SHEPPARD, DOUGLAS MURRAY, b Hamilton, Ont, Sept 19, 39; m 67; c 2. PHYSICS. *Educ:* McMaster Univ, BSc, 60; Mass Inst Technol, PhD(physics), 64. *Prof Exp:* Sci collabr physics, State Univ Utrecht, 64-67; res assoc, 67-69, asst prof, 69-72, ASSOC PROF PHYSICS, UNIV ALTA, 72- *Mem:* Am Asn Physics Teachers; Can Asn Physicists. *Res:* Investigation of nuclear properties from the gamma ray decay of nuclei excited by low energy nuclear bombardment and gamma ray polarization; investigation of nuclear structure through bombardment at medium energy. *Mailing Add:* Dept of Physics Nuclear Res Ctr Univ of Alta Edmonton AB T6G 2E1 Can

SHEPPARD, ERWIN, b New York, NY, May 27, 21; m 43; c 2. PHYSICAL CHEMISTRY. *Educ:* City Col, BS, 42; Polytech Inst Brooklyn, PhD(chem), 51. *Prof Exp:* Res assoc phys biochem, Med Col, Cornell Univ, 49-57; staff chemist, 57-58, PHYS RES SUPVR, S C JOHNSON & SON, INC, 58- *Mem:* Am Chem Soc; Electron Micros Soc Am; Soc Appl Spectros; Sigma Xi; AAAS. *Res:* Physical chemistry of polymeric and colloidal systems; organic coatings; surface chemistry; aerosol technology; electrokinetic and light scattering investigations; electron microscopy and corrosion studies. *Mailing Add:* 120 Westminster Sq Racine WI 53402

SHEPPARD, HERBERT, b New York, NY, June 14, 22; m 47; c 2. BIOCHEMISTRY. *Educ:* Cornell Univ, BS, 48; Univ Calif, PhD(biochem), 53. *Prof Exp:* Asst, Nutrit Lab, Cornell Univ, 48; assoc chemist, Biochem Res, Gen Foods Corp, Inc, 49; asst, Univ Calif, 49-50; assoc dir biochem pharmacol, Ciba Pharmaceut Co, NJ, 53-62, head, 62-67; sect head biochem pharmacol, 67-72, DIR DEPT CELL BIOL, HOFFMANN-LA ROCHE, INC, 72- *Mem:* AAAS; Am Soc Pharmacol & Exp Therapeut; Am Chem Soc; Sigma Xi. *Res:* Cyclic adenosine monophosphate metabolism; metabolism of nervous tissue; steroid hormone action; lipid metabolism. *Mailing Add:* 33 Highwood Rd West Orange NJ 07052

SHEPPARD, JOHN CLARENCE, b San Pedro, Calif, June 4, 23; m 50; c 3. RADIOCHEMISTRY, INORGANIC CHEMISTRY. *Educ:* San Diego State Col, AB, 49; Washington Univ, MA, 54, PhD(chem), 55. *Prof Exp:* Chemist, US Naval Radiol Defense Lab, 49-51; asst, Washington Univ, 52-55; chemist, Hanford Labs, Gen Elec Co, 55-57; asst prof chem, San Diego State Col, 57-60; chemist, Hanford Labs, Gen Elec Co, 60-63; sr res scientist chem dept, Battelle Mem Inst, 65-71; assoc nuclear engr, Eng Res Div, 72-77, PROF CHEM ENG & ANTHROP, WASH STATE UNIV, 77- *Mem:* Am Chem Soc; AAAS; Sigma Xi. *Res:* Electron transfer reactions between ions in aqueous solution; solvent extraction of actinide elements; activation analysis; atmospheric chemistry. radiocarbon dating. *Mailing Add:* Dept Chem Eng Wash State Univ Pullman WA 99164

SHEPPARD, JOHN RICHARD, b Minneapolis, Minn, Dec 29, 44; m 68; c 2. CELL BIOLOGY, BIOCHEMISTRY. *Educ:* Univ Minn, Minneapolis, BA, 65; Univ Colo, Boulder, PhD(chem), 69. *Prof Exp:* NIH fel biochem, Princeton Univ, 69-70; asst prof neurol, Univ Colo, Denver, 70-72; asst prof, 72-75, ASSOC PROF GENETICS, UNIV MINN, MINNEAPOLIS, 75-, ASST DIR GENETICS, DIGHT INST HUMAN GENETICS, 72- *Concurrent Pos:* Sci adv, Nat Ataxia Found, 74- & Leukemia Task Force, 75-; mem, Am Cancer Soc Adv Comt Biochem & Carcinogenesis, 78-82; Jackson Mem lectr, Med Sch, Northwestern Univ, 75. *Mem:* Am Asn Cancer Res; Am Soc Biol Chemists; Am Soc Cell Biol; Soc Neurosci; Tissue Cult Asn. *Res:* The role of the plasma membrane in biological regulation, specifically cyclic nucleotide, plasma membrane enzyme and hormonal studies using cultured fibroblasts and nerve cells. *Mailing Add:* Dight Inst for Human Genetics Univ of Minn Minneapolis MN 55455

SHEPPARD, MOSES MAURICE, b Hendersonville, NC, Sept 5, 28; m 51; c 2. SCIENCE EDUCATION. *Educ:* ECarolina Col, BS, 52, MA, 58; Ohio State Univ, PhD(sci ed, physics), 66. *Prof Exp:* Teacher pub schs, Norfolk County, 52-53; qual engr, Ford Motor Co, 53-54; teacher pub schs, Norfolk County, 54-58, sci coordr, 58-61; instr sci educ & math, Ohio State Univ, 62-63; from asst prof to assoc prof, 63-74, PROF SCI EDUC, E CAROLINA UNIV, 74- *Concurrent Pos:* Partic, NSF Acad Year Inst, Ohio State Univ, 61-62; fel earth sci, Southwest Ctr Advan Study, Tex, 68. *Mem:* Nat Sci Teachers Asn; Asn Educ Teachers Sci; Nat Asn Res Sci Teaching. *Res:* Science teaching on both the secondary school and college level. *Mailing Add:* Dept of Sci Educ E Carolina Univ Greenville NC 27834

SHEPPARD, RICHARD A, b Lancaster, Pa, May 14, 30; m 57. GEOLOGY. *Educ:* Franklin & Marshall Col, BS, 56; Johns Hopkins Univ, PhD(geol), 60. *Prof Exp:* GEOLOGIST, US GEOL SURV, 60- *Honors & Awards:* Spec Act Award, US Geol Surv, 66. *Mem:* AAAS; Geol Soc Am; Mineral Soc Am; Clay Minerals Soc; Soc Econ Geol. *Res:* Geology of Cascade Mountains, especially petrology of Cenozoic volcanic rocks; distribution and genesis of zeolites in sedimentary rocks. *Mailing Add:* US Geol Surv Box 25046 Fed Ctr Denver CO 80225

SHEPPARD, ROGER FLOYD, b Barberton, Ohio, July 25, 45; m 70. ENTOMOLOGY, INSECT PATHOLOGY. *Educ:* Ohio Univ, BS, 67; Ohio State Univ, MS, 73, PhD(entom), 76. *Prof Exp:* ASST PROF BIOL, CONCORD COL, 76- *Mem:* Am Entom Soc; Soc Invert Path. *Res:* Baculovirus diseases of insects. *Mailing Add:* Dept of Biol Concord Col Athens WV 24712

SHEPPARD, WILLIAM ARTHUR, organic chemistry, see previous edition

SHEPPARD, WILLIAM JAMES, b Boston, Mass, Apr 10, 31; m 55; c 2. FUEL SCIENCE. *Educ:* Oberlin Col, AB, 52; Harvard Univ, MA, 54, PhD(chem), 59. *Prof Exp:* Instr chem, Swarthmore Col, 58-64; sr chem economist, 64-73, assoc sect mgr, 73-75, SR FUELS & ENERGY RES, BATTELLE MEM INST, 75- *Mem:* AAAS; Am Chem Soc; Sigma Xi; Int Asn Energy Economists. *Res:* Planning and supervision of research in fuels and energy sciences; economic and technical analysis of markets for products and processes for energy generation; fuel production and environmental control. *Mailing Add:* 505 King Ave Columbus OH 43201

SHEPPE, WILLIAM MARCO, JR, b Wheeling, WVa, Feb 2, 24; m 55; c 2. PSYCHIATRY. *Educ:* Univ Va, BA, 45, MD, 48. *Prof Exp:* From instr to assoc prof, 54-72, clin assoc prof, 72-76, CLIN PROF PSYCHIAT, SCH MED, UNIV VA, 76-; MED DIR, DC WILSON PSYCHIAT-NEUROL HOSP, 72- *Concurrent Pos:* Consult, US Vet Admin, 60. *Mem:* AMA; Am Psychiat Asn. *Res:* Psychotherapy. *Mailing Add:* 2101 Arlington Blvd Charlottesville VA 22901

SHEPPERD, WAYNE DELBERT, b Sterling, Colo, June 28, 47; m 70; c 2. FORESTRY, SILVICULTURE. *Educ:* Colo State Univ, BS, 70, MS, 74. *Prof Exp:* Forestry res technician, Rocky Mountain Forest & Range Exp Sta, 70-76, forest silviculturist, Rio Grande Nat Forest, 76-78, RES FORESTER, ROCKY MOUNTAIN FOREST & RANGE EXP STA, US FOREST SERV, 78- *Mem:* Sigma Xi; Soc Am Foresters. *Res:* Silviculture of sub alpine forests; growth and yield prediction; silviculture of aspen. *Mailing Add:* Rocky Mt Forest & Range Exp Sta 240 W Prospect Ft Collins CO 80521

SHEPPERSON, JACQUELINE RUTH, b Hopewell, Va, Feb 10, 35. PARASITOLOGY. *Educ:* Va State Col, BS, 54; NC Col, Durham, MS, 56; Howard Univ, PhD(zool), 64. *Prof Exp:* Inst biol, Ft Valley State Col, 55-59; asst prof zool, Howard Univ, 64-65; assoc prof, 65-68, PROF BIOL, WINSTON-SALEM STATE UNIV, 68-, CHMN SCI DEPT, 67- *Mem:* Wildlife Dis Asn. *Res:* Survey studies of helminths in wild mammals; chemical relationships of host and parasite; physiological studies on plant parasitic nemotodes. *Mailing Add:* Dept of Natural Sci Winston-Salem State Univ Winston-Salem NC 27102

SHEPRO, DAVID, b Holyoke, Mass, Feb 14, 24; m 48; c 2. CARDIOVASCULAR PHYSIOLOGY. *Educ:* Clark Univ, BA, 48, MA, 50; Boston Univ, PhD, 58. *Prof Exp:* Instr biol, Simmons Col, 50-52, from asst prof to prof, 53-68; PROF BIOL, BOSTON UNIV, 68-, ASSOC PROF SURG, 71- *Concurrent Pos:* Mem corp, Marine Biol Lab, Woods Hole, 66-72, clerk of corp, 72-; ed-in-chief, J Microvascular Res. *Mem:* Microcirc Soc; Sigma Xi; Soc Gen Physiol; Am Physiol Soc; Am Soc Cell Biol. *Res:* Communication and interaction between endothelium and blood; calcium flux and release reaction in thrombocytes; homeostasis and the pulmonary microvasculature. *Mailing Add:* Dept of Biol Boston Univ Boston MA 02215

SHEPS, CECIL GEORGE, b Winnipeg, Man, July 24, 13; nat US; m 37; c 1. PREVENTIVE MEDICINE. *Educ:* Univ Man, MD, 36; Yale Univ, MPH, 47; Am Bd Prev Med, dipl, 50. *Hon Degrees:* DSc, Chicago Med Sch, 70. *Prof Exp:* Asst dep minister, Dept Pub Health, Sask, Can, 45-46; Rockefeller Found fel, Yale Univ, 46-47; assoc prof pub health admin, Univ NC, 47-51, res prof health planning, 52-53; lectr prev med, Harvard Med Sch, 54-58, clin prof, 58-60; prof, Grad Sch Pub Health, Univ Pittsburgh, 60-65; prof community med, Mt Sinai Sch Med, 66-68; dir health serv res ctr, 69-71, vchancellor health sci, 71-76, PROF SOCIAL MED, UNIV NC, CHAPEL HILL, 69- *Concurrent Pos:* Spec consult, Training Div Commun Dis Ctr, USPHS, 48-51; WHO traveling fel, 51; gen dir, Beth Israel Hosp, Boston, 53-60 & Beth Israel Med Ctr, New York, 65-68; mem & chmn health serv study sect, NIH, 55-62; mem, Nat Adv Comt Chronic Dis & Health of Aged, 57-61; nat planning comt, White House Conf Aging, 59-61; consult med affairs, Welfare Admin, Dept Health, Educ & Welfare, Washington, DC. *Honors & Awards:* Miles Award Sci Achievement, Can Pub Health Asn, 70; chmn higher educ pub health, Millbank Mem Found Comn, 72-76. *Mem:* Inst of Med of Nat Acad Sci; Am Pub Health Asn; Asn Teachers Prev Med. *Res:* Social medicine; medical and hospital administration. *Mailing Add:* Chase Hall 132A Univ NC Chapel Hill NC 27514

SHEPS, LILLIAN, b Montreal, Que, Can, Aug 23, 27; m 67. PLANT PHYSIOLOGY, DESERT ECOLOGY. *Educ:* Sir George Williams Univ, BSc, 48; Washington Univ, PhD(bot), 64. *Prof Exp:* Control chemist, Lymans Ltd Pharamaceut, Can, 48-50 & 51-52; res technician steroid chem, Med Ctr, Columbia Univ, 53-56; res asst bot, Earhart Plant Res Lab, Calif Inst Technol, 56-58, Nat Ctr Sci Res, France, 58-59 & Mo Bot Garden, 59-63; res assoc, Washington Univ, 64-65 & Desert Res Inst, Univ Nev, Reno, 65-75; CONSULT BOT, SCI ENG SYSTS INC, 75- *Concurrent Pos:* Consult lab chem natural prod, NIH, 63- *Mem:* AAAS; Bot Soc Am; Ecol Soc Am; Human Ecol Soc. *Res:* Ecology and physiology of plant interactions; role of allelopathic substances in natural plant communities; effect of environment on plant growth and natural distribution; biological rhythms in plants; relationship of mycorrhiza to growth of desert and montane plants. *Mailing Add:* PO Box 134 Naramata BC V0H 1N0 Can

SHER, ALVIN HARVEY, b St Louis, Mo, Aug 15, 41; m 63; c 3. NUCLEAR CHEMISTRY, SEMICONDUCTOR PHYSICS. *Educ:* Wash Univ, AB, 63, AM, 65; Simon Fraser Univ, PhD(nuclear chem), 67. *Prof Exp:* Res chemist, 68-72, sect chief semi-conductor processing, 72-75, asst chief, Electronic Technol Div, 75-77, DEPT DIR, CTR ELECTRONICS & ELEC ENG, NAT BUR STANDARDS, 78- *Concurrent Pos:* Analyst, Nat Bur Standards Off Progs, 76. *Mem:* Am Soc Testing & Mat; Inst Elec & Electronics Engrs. *Res:* Development of measurement methods relating to reliability of semiconductor microelectronic devices. *Mailing Add:* Rm B-358 Metrol Bldg Nat Bur Standards Washington DC 20234

SHER, ARDEN, b St Louis, Mo, July 5, 33; m 55; c 3. PHYSICS. *Educ:* Wash Univ, St Louis, BS, 55, PhD(physics), 59. *Prof Exp:* Res assoc physics, Wash Univ, St Louis, 59; NSF fel, Saclay Nuclear Res Ctr, France, 60; sr engr, Cent Res Labs, Varian Assocs, Calif, 61-67; assoc prof physics, Col William & Mary, 67-72, dir appl sci, 70-76, prof physics, 72-79; MEM STAFF, SRI INT, 79- *Concurrent Pos:* Consult, Langley Res Ctr, NASA, 68-69 & 72; consult prof mat sci, Stanford Univ, 82- *Mem:* Fel Am Phys Soc. *Res:* Solid state physics. *Mailing Add:* Phys Electron Dept SRI Int Menlo Park CA 94025

SHER, IRVING HAROLD, b Philadelphia, Pa, July 10, 24; m 49; c 2. INFORMATION SYSTEMS, COMPUTER SCIENCE. *Educ:* Univ Pa, BA, 44; Johns Hopkins Univ, ScD(biochem), 53. *Prof Exp:* Res scientist, Mt Sinai Hosp, 53-54 & Nat Drug Co, Philadelphia, 54-57; sr info scientist, Smith, Kline, French Labs, 57-62; vpres res & develop, Inst Sci Info, 62-68 & Info Co Am, 68-70; vpres opers & prod, 3i Co, Philadelphia, 70-71; group mgr, Franklin Inst Res Labs, 72-74; mgr info systs, Univ City Sci Ctr, 74-78, DIR QUALITY CONTROL, INST SCI INFO, PHILADELPHIA, 78- *Honors & Awards:* McCollum Res Prize, Johns Hopkins Univ, 51. *Mem:* AAAS; Am Chem Soc; Am Soc Info Sci; Sigma Xi. *Res:* Information gathering, analysis, storage, indexing, retrieval and presentation. *Mailing Add:* 2192 Lantern Lane Lafayette Hill PA 19444

SHER, LAWRENCE D, b Philadelphia, Pa, Dec 26, 33. BIOMEDICAL ENGINEERING. *Educ:* Drexel Univ, BS, 56; Univ Pa, PhD(biomed eng), 63. *Prof Exp:* From instr elec eng to asst prof biomed eng, Moore Sch, Univ Pa, 59-71; SR SCIENTIST, BOLT BERANEK AND NEWMAN, INC, 71- *Mem:* AAAS; Soc Info Display. *Res:* Accident prevention in skiing; 3-D computer displays; computer technology in biology and medicine. *Mailing Add:* Bolt Beranek and Newman Inc 10 Moulton St Cambridge MA 02238

SHER, RICHARD B, b Flint, Mich, Jan 21, 39; m 62; c 2. TOPOLOGY. *Educ:* Mich Technol Univ, BS, 60; Univ Utah, MS, 64, PhD(math), 66. *Prof Exp:* From asst prof to assoc prof math, Univ Ga, 66-74; PROF MATH, UNIV NC, GREENSBORO, 74-, HEAD DEPT, 80- *Mem:* Math Asn Am; Am Math Soc; Inst Advan Study. *Res:* Point set topology; piecewise linear topology; shape theory; infinite-dimensional manifolds; theory of retracts. *Mailing Add:* Dept of Math Univ of NC Greensboro NC 27412

SHER, RUDOLPH, b New York, NY, May 28, 23; m 52; c 2. NUCLEAR ENGINEERING. *Educ:* Cornell Univ, AB, 43; Univ Pa, PhD(physics), 51. *Prof Exp:* Staff mem radiation lab, Mass Inst Technol, 43-46; assoc physicist nuclear eng, Brookhaven Nat Lab, 51-61; assoc prof, 61-70, PROF MECH ENG, STANFORD UNIV, 70- *Concurrent Pos:* Vis scientist, Comm a l'Energie Atomique, France, 58-59 & A B Atomenergi, Sweden, 68-69; consult, Brookhaven Nat Lab, 70-; ed, Progress in Nulcear Energy, 75-; vis staff mem, Int Atomic Energy Agency, 78-79. *Mem:* Am Nuclear Soc; Am Phys Soc; Inst Nuclear Mat Mgt. *Res:* Nuclear reactor physics; nuclear data; nuclear safeguards. *Mailing Add:* Dept Mech Eng Stanford Univ Stanford CA 94305

SHER, STEPHANIE ELLSWORTH, b Phoenix, Ariz, Nov 13, 38; m 67; c 2. IMMUNOLOGY. *Educ:* Brigham Young Univ, BA, 60; Univ Pa, PhD(immunol), 67. *Prof Exp:* Vis asst prof microbiol, Sch Med, Pahlavi Univ, Iran, 67-68; res assoc immunol, Childrens Hosp Philadelphia, 68-71; sr res chemist, Collabr Res Inc, 72; res assoc cognitive info processing group, 73-78, res assoc, Res Lab Electronics & Dept Biol, 78-80, RES SCIENTIST, DEPT BIOL, MASS INST TECHNOL, 80- *Concurrent Pos:* Fel, NIH & NSF, 68-71. *Mem:* AAAS; Asn Women in Sci; Am Asn Immunologists. *Res:* Preparation of artificial skin for research in cell motility and cell aging; artificial skin for grafting to burn patients. *Mailing Add:* 36-657 Res Lab of Electronics Mass Inst Technol Cambridge MA 02139

SHERA, E BROOKS, b Oxford, Ohio, Aug 28, 35; m 56; c 2. NUCLEAR PHYSICS. *Educ:* Case Western Reserve Univ, BA, 56, PhD(physics), 62; Univ Chicago, MS, 58. *Prof Exp:* Instr physics, Case Western Reserve Univ, 61-62; resident res assoc, Argonne Nat Lab, 62-64; STAFF MEM, LOS ALAMOS SCI LAB, 64- *Mem:* Fel Am Phys Soc; AAAS. *Res:* Muonic x-ray studies; electron and proton scattering; neutron-capture gamma ray studies; low energy nuclear physics; nuclear structure. *Mailing Add:* Los Alamos Nat Lab PO Box 1663 Los Alamos NM 87545

SHERALD, ALLEN FRANKLIN, b Frederick, Md, Nov 15, 42. DEVELOPMENTAL GENETICS. *Educ:* Frostburg State Col, BS, 64; Univ Va, PhD(biol), 73. *Prof Exp:* Teacher sci, Montgomery County Pub Schs, 64-66; res assoc genetics, Univ Va, 73-74; trainee genetics & biochem, Cornell Univ, 74-76; asst prof, 76-80, ASSOC PROF, GEORGE MASON UNIV, 80- *Mem:* AAAS; Genetics Soc Am. *Res:* Drosophila; biochemistry; sclerotization. *Mailing Add:* Dept Biol George Mason Univ Fairfax VA 22030

SHERBECK, L ADAIR, b New Norway, Alta, July 24, 22; m 43; c 3. POLYMER CHEMISTRY. *Educ:* Univ Alta, BSC, 47; McGill Univ, PhD(chem), 51. *Prof Exp:* From res chemist to sr res chemist, 51-59, supvr technol, 59-64, sr supvr nomex technol, 64-80, RES ASSOC, TEXTILE FIBERS DEPT, TECH DIV, E I DU PONT DE NEMOURS & CO, INC, 80- *Mem:* Am Chem Soc. *Res:* Wood and cellulose chemistry; addition and condensation polymerization; fiber production and properties. *Mailing Add:* Nomex Tech Textile Fibers Div E I du Pont de Nemours & Co Wilmington DE 19898

SHERBERT, DONALD R, b Wausau, Wis, Feb 24, 35; m 58; c 2. MATHEMATICAL ANALYSIS. *Educ:* Univ Wis, BS, 57; Stanford Univ, PhD(math), 62. *Prof Exp:* From instr to asst prof, 62-68, ASSOC PROF MATH, UNIV ILL, URBANA, 68-, DIR UNDERGRAD PROG, 80- *Mem:* Am Math Soc; Math Asn Am. *Res:* Functional analysis. *Mailing Add:* Dept Math Univ Ill Urbana IL 61801

SHERBINE, K BRUCE, b Johnstown, Pa, Mar 6, 38; m 60; c 1. ZOOLOGY, MARINE BIOLOGY. *Educ:* Gettysburg Col, AB, 60; Temple Univ, MS, 64; Pa State Univ, PhD(zool), 69. *Prof Exp:* Teacher high sch, Pa, 60-65; teaching asst zool, Pa State Univ, 65-68; instr genetics & ecol, Gettysburg Col, 68-69; asst prof, 69-78, ASSOC PROF & CHMN BIOL, LYCOMING COL, 78- *Concurrent Pos:* NSF jr scientist, Stanford Univ, TeVega Oceanog Exped XVI, Gulf of Calif, 67; vis assoc prof biol, NC State Univ. *Mem:* Am Inst Biol Sci; Am Soc Zool; Am Soc Ichthyologists & Herpetologists; Animal Behav Soc. *Res:* Factors influencing the dispersion patterns of brookside plethodontid salamanders; biological oceanography, particularly distribution of demersal fish of continental shelf; behavior and ecology of land crab including the Gecarcinus Lateralis; animal behavior as population regulating mechanism. *Mailing Add:* Dept of Biol Lycoming Col Williamsport PA 17701

SHERBLOM, ANN P, b New Haven, Conn, July 31, 49; m 74. GLYCOPROTEINS, MUCIN BIOSYNTHESIS. *Educ:* Bates Col, BS, 71; Dartmouth Col, PhD(chem), 75. *Prof Exp:* Vis asst prof, Dept Chem, Dartmouth Col, 76; res assoc, Dept Biol, Bowdoin Col, 76-77 & Okla State Univ, 77-80; ASST PROF, DEPT BIOCHEM, UNIV MAINE, ORONO, 80- *Mem:* Am Chem Soc. *Res:* Analysis of aggregates in proteoglycans from cartilage; isolation and characterization of tumor cell glycoproteins; factors influencing sialic acid content of mucin-type glycoproteins. *Mailing Add:* Dept Biochem Univ Maine Orono ME 04469

SHERBON, JOHN WALTER, b Lewiston, Idaho, Oct 31, 33; m 57; c 2. DAIRY CHEMISTRY. *Educ:* Washington State Univ, BS, 55; Univ Minn, MS, 58, PhD(dairy sci), 63. *Prof Exp:* From asst prof to assoc prof, 63-77, PROF FOOD SCI, CORNELL UNIV, 77- *Mem:* Assoc referee, Asn Off Anal Chem Am Dairy Sci Asn; Inst Food Technol; Am Chem Soc. *Res:* Physical state of fat in dairy and other food products; analysis for protein content of milk; protein gelation; chemical instrumentation in agricultural chemistry. *Mailing Add:* Dept of Food Sci Cornell Univ Ithaca NY 14853

SHERBOURNE, ARCHIBALD NORBERT, b Bombay, India, July 8, 29; Can citizen; m 59; c 6. STRUCTURAL ENGINEERING & MECHANICS. *Educ:* Univ London, BSc, 53; Lehigh Univ, BSCE, 55, MSCE, 57; Cambridge Univ, MA, 59, PhD(eng), 60; Univ London, DSc(appl math), 70. *Prof Exp:* Engr, Brit Rwys, 48-52; engr, Greater London Coun, 52-54; instr civil & mech eng, Lehigh Univ, 54-57; engr, US Steel Corp, Calif, 56; sr asst res eng, Cambridge Univ, 57-61; assoc prof, 61-63, chmn dept civil eng, 64-66, dean fac eng, 66-74, PROF CIVIL ENG, UNIV WATERLOO, 63- *Concurrent Pos:* Vis sr lectr, Univ Col, Univ London, 63-64; Orgn Econ Coop & Develop res fel, Swiss Fed Inst Technol, 64; vis prof, Univ West Indies, 69-70; Nat Res Coun sr res fel, Nat Lab Civil Eng, Portugal, 70; W Ger Acad Exchange fel, 75; NATO sr scientist fel & vis lectureship, Western Europe, 75-76; vis prof, Ecole Polytech Fed, Lausanne, Switz, 75-77, Mich Technol Univ, 80-81 & 81-83; consult/adv tech educ, Orgn Am States, Inter Am Develop Bank & Can Int Develop Agency; Gleddon sr vis fel, Univ Western Australia, 78. *Mem:* Fel Brit Inst Struct Engrs; fel Royal Soc Arts; Int Asn Bridge & Struct Engrs; Am Acad Mech. *Res:* Design of steel structures. *Mailing Add:* Fac of Eng Univ of Waterloo Waterloo ON N2L 3G1 Can

SHERBURNE, JAMES AURIL, b Milo, Maine, Aug 8, 41; m 63; c 2. ECOLOGY. *Educ:* Univ Maine, BA, 67, MS, 69; Cornell Univ, PhD(ecol), 72. *Prof Exp:* Ecol consult wildlife proj, African Wildlife Leadership Found, Botswana, 74-75; dep dir, Peace Corps Environ Prog, Smithsonian Inst, 72-74, dir, 75-78; UNIT LEADER, COOP WILDLIFE RES UNIT, UNIV MAINE, 78- *Concurrent Pos:* Ecol consult, Ctr Natural Areas, 72-73 & Off Ecol, Smithsonian Inst, 72-74; ecol consult, Environ Protection Agency, 78-; mem, Survival Serv Comn & Am Comt Int Conserv; directorate, Man & Biosphere Prog. *Mem:* AAAS; Sigma Xi; Ecol Soc Am; Int Union Conserv Nature & Natural Resources; Entom Soc Am. *Res:* Pesticide residues in vertebrates; chemical interactions between plants and vertebrates, particularly frugiverous birds and secondary chemicals, affecting behavior; developing wildlife and natural resource management projects internationally, particularly Africa, South America, and Asia; methods of plant dispersal by vertebrates. *Mailing Add:* Maine Wildlife Coop Res Unit Univ Maine Orono ME 04473

SHERBY, OLEG D(IMITRI), b Shanghai, China, Feb 9, 25; nat US; m 49; c 4. MATERIALS SCIENCE. *Educ:* Univ Calif, BS, 47, MS, 49, PhD(metall), 56; Univ Sheffield, DMet, 68. *Prof Exp:* Asst metall, Univ Calif, 47-49, res metallurgist, Inst Eng Res, 49-56; NSF fel, Univ Sheffield, 56-57; sci liaison officer metall, US Off Naval Res, Eng, 57-58; assoc prof, 58-62, PROF MAT SCI, STANFORD UNIV, 62- *Concurrent Pos:* Consult, Los Alamos Nat Lab, 59-, Lockheed Palo Alto Res Lab, 61-64 & Lawrence Livermore Nat Lab, 65-; fel, Univ Paris, France, 67-68. *Honors & Awards:* Dudley Medal, Am Soc Testing & Mat, 58; Centennial Medal, Am Soc Mech Engrs, 80. *Mem:* Nat Acad Eng; Am Inst Mining, Metall & Petrol Engrs; fel Am Soc Metals. *Res:* Theoretical and experimental aspects of mechanical behavior of solids and diffusion in solids. *Mailing Add:* Dept of Mat Sci & Eng Stanford Univ Stanford CA 94305

SHERCK, CHARLES KEITH, b Willard, Ohio, July 27, 22; m 46; c 2. FOOD SCIENCE. *Educ:* Miami Univ, BA, 47. *Prof Exp:* Chemist, Am Home Prod Corp, 47-50, mgr mfg, 50-54; mgr qual control, 54-59, mgr res opers, 59-64, mgr grocery prod res & develop, 64-69, dir corp res & develop, 70-77, dir, Res & Develop Facil & Tech Serv, 78-81, DIR RES & DEVELOP ADMIN, PILLSBURY CO, 81- *Concurrent Pos:* Bd dir, AACC, 73-74. *Mem:* Am Asn Cereal Chem; Inst Food Technol. *Res:* Management food research and development. *Mailing Add:* Pillsbury Co 311 Second St SE Minneapolis MN 55414

SHERDEN, DAVID J, b Washington, DC, Oct 26, 40; m 63; c 2. PHYSICS. *Educ:* Univ San Francisco, BS, 62; Univ Chicago, MS, 64, PhD(physics), 70. *Prof Exp:* PHYSICIST, STANFORD LINEAR ACCELERATOR CTR, 69- *Res:* Experimental elementary particle physics; high energy electron and photon interactions. *Mailing Add:* Stanford Linear Accelerator Ctr PO Box 4349 Stanford CA 94305

SHEREBRIN, MARVIN HAROLD, b Winnipeg, Man, Mar 23, 37; m 66; c 3. BIOPHYSICS, BIOMEDICAL ENGINEERING. *Educ:* Univ Man, BSc, 60; Univ Western Ont, MSc, 63, PhD(biophys), 65. *Prof Exp:* Res asst biophys, 60-65, asst prof, 67-73, ASSOC PROF BIOPHYS, FAC MED, UNIV WESTERN ONT, 73- *Concurrent Pos:* Can Med Res Coun fel, Weizmann Inst Sci, 65-67, Can Med Res Coun res scholar, 67-72. *Mem:* Inst Elec & Electronics Eng; Can Med & Biol Eng Soc; Biophys Soc. *Res:* Olfaction in insects; mechanochemistry of contractile systems; conformational changes in biological membranes; biological control systems; electronics systems in hospitals. *Mailing Add:* Dept Biophys Univ Western Ont Fac Med London ON N6A 5C1 Can

SHERER, GLENN KEITH, b Allentown, Pa, May 11, 43; m 70. DEVELOPMENTAL BIOLOGY. *Educ:* Muhlenberg Col, BS, 64; Temple Univ, PhD(biol), 72. *Prof Exp:* Res fel, NIH, 72-73, guest worker cell biol, 73; res assoc med, Col Physicians & Surgeons, Columbia Univ, 73-75; assoc med, Med Univ SC, 75-77, asst prof res med, 77-80; ASST PROF BIOL, BOWDOIN COL, 80- *Concurrent Pos:* NIH res fel, Col Physicians & Surgeons, Columbia Univ, 74-75 & Med Univ SC, 75-76. *Mem:* AAAS; Am Soc Cell Biol; Am Soc Zool; Soc Develop Biol; Tissue Cult Asn. *Res:* Epithelial-mesenchymal interactions in liver development; development of embryonic microvasculature; cell culture; tissue interaction in vertebrate organogenesis; embryonic development of the liver. *Mailing Add:* Dept Biol Bowdoin Col Brunswick ME 04011

SHERER, JAMES PRESSLY, b Rock Hill, SC, Aug 25, 39; m 61; c 2. ORGANIC CHEMISTRY. *Educ:* Erskine Col, BA, 61; Duke Univ, MA, 63, PhD(org chem), 66. *Prof Exp:* Res assoc, E I du Pont de Nemours & Co, Inc, 65-82. *Mem:* Am Chem Soc. *Res:* Synthesis and reactions of dicationoid aromatic systems containing one or more quaternary nitrogen atoms at bridgehead positions; research and development of synthetic fibers; synthesis of nitrogen heterocyclic compounds. *Mailing Add:* 1796 Balfoure Dr Charleston SC 29409

SHERER, SANKEY, inorganic physical chemistry, see previous edition

SHERF, ARDEN FREDERICK, b Brooklyn Center, Minn, Aug 7, 16; m 42; c 4. PLANT PATHOLOGY. *Educ:* Univ Minn, BS, 39; Univ Nebr, PhD(plant path), 48. *Prof Exp:* Res asst plant path, Univ Minn, 38-39; asst, Univ Nebr, 39-42, asst path & asst exten plant pathologist, 46-49; from asst prof to assoc prof bot & plant path, Iowa State Univ, 49-54; from assoc prof to prof plant path, 54-81, exten plant pathologist, 54-81, EMER PROF PLANT PATH, CORNELL UNIV, 81- *Concurrent Pos:* Exten plant pathologist, Iowa State Univ, 49-54; consult, Brit Ministry Agr, 68 & New SWales Dept Agr, Australia, 75. *Mem:* AAAS; fel Am Phytopath Soc. *Res:* Soil chemical and seed treatments; vegetable disease diagnosis. *Mailing Add:* Dept of Plant Path Cornell Univ Ithaca NY 14853

SHERGALIS, WILLIAM ANTHONY, b Hazleton, Pa, May 25, 41; m 64; c 2. ANALYTICAL & PHYSICAL CHEMISTRY. *Educ:* Univ Pa, BS, 62; Drexel Univ, MS, 64; Temple Univ, PhD(phys chem), 69. *Prof Exp:* Assoc prof chem, Widener Col, 68-78, chmn sci, 78-81; PROF CHEM & ACAD DEAN, CARDINAL NEWMAN COL, 81- *Mem:* Am Chem Soc; Sigma Xi; AAAS. *Res:* Electro-analytical techniques and their applications to chemical and biochemical systems. *Mailing Add:* Cardinal Newman Col 7701 Florissant Rd St Louis MO 63121

SHERIDAN, JANE CONNOR, b Griffith, Australia; US citizen; m 60. ANALYTICAL CHEMISTRY. *Educ:* Univ Sydney, BSc, 48; Rutgers Univ, PhD(soils), 56. *Prof Exp:* Res off soil chem, Commonwealth Sci & Indust Res Orgn, Australia, 48-57; chemist, Mich State Univ, 57-59; proj leader anal chem, Evans Res & Develop Corp, 59-64; sr anal chemist, 66-71, mgr anal res, 71-72, DIR QUAL CONTROL, HOFFMANN-LA ROCHE, INC, 72-, ASST VPRES, 76- *Concurrent Pos:* Asst prof fine arts, NY Univ, 60-66; mem, US Gen Comt Revision, 75-80. *Mem:* AAAS; NY Acad Sci; Am Chem Soc; Acad Pharmaceut Sci; Am Soc Qual Control. *Res:* Administration of development and implementation of analytical techniques characterizing pharmaceuticals and fine chemicals. *Mailing Add:* Dept of Qual Control Hoffmann-La Roche Inc Nutley NJ 07110

SHERIDAN, JOHN FRANCIS, b Brooklyn, Ny, June 2, 49; m 72; c 4. IMMUNOLOGY, MICROBIOLOGY. *Educ:* Fordham Univ, BS, 72; Rutgers Univ, MS, 74, PhD(microbiol), 76. *Prof Exp:* Pub Health Serv fel div immunol, Med Ctr, Duke Univ, 76-78; res assoc immunol, 78-79, instr, 79-82, ASST PROF, DIV COMP MED, JOHNS HOPKINS UNIV, 82- *Mem:* Am Soc Microbiol; AAAS. *Res:* Infection and immunity; cellular immunology; virology-herpesviruses, rotaviruses. *Mailing Add:* Div of Comp Med Johns Hopkins Univ Baltimore MD 21218

SHERIDAN, JOHN JOSEPH, III, b Providence, RI, Feb 2, 45. CATALYSIS, MINERAL BENEFICIATION. *Educ:* Stevens Inst Technol, Hoboken, NJ, BE, 67; Univ Ill, Champaign, MS, 69, PhD(chem eng), 71. *Prof Exp:* Sr res engr, Process Res, Engelhard Minerals & Chem, Inc, 71-76; SR PRIN DEVELOP ENGR, PROCESS DESIGN, DEVELOP & JOINT VENTURE MGT, AIR PROD & CHEM, INC, 76- *Mem:* Am Inst Chem Engrs; Am Chem Soc. *Res:* Properties of reversible metal hydrides; hydrogenation chemistry, particularly unsaturated hydrocarbons over metallic surfaces; gas and metal interactions; gas separations via chemical complexation or absorption. *Mailing Add:* Air Prod & Chem Inc Box 538 Allentown PA 18105

SHERIDAN, JOHN ROGER, b Helena, Mont, Sept 24, 33; m 59; c 2. ATOMIC PHYSICS, CHEMICAL PHYSICS. *Educ:* Reed Col, BA, 55; Univ Wash, PhD(physics), 64. *Prof Exp:* Res engr, Boeing Co, 55-60; res asst physics, Univ Wash, 60-63, assoc, 63-64; from asst prof to assoc prof, 64-71, head dept, 67-76 & 78-80, PROF PHYSICS, UNIV ALASKA, FAIRBANKS, 71- *Concurrent Pos:* Danforth assoc, 66-; vis scientist, Stanford Res Inst, 68-69; vis prof, Queen's Univ Belfast, 75-76. *Mem:* Sigma Xi; fel Am Phys Soc; Am Asn Physics Teachers; AAAS. *Res:* Use of photon coincidence techniques in laboratory studies of reactions of atoms, molecules; metastable and long-lived atomic, molecular reactions using molecular beams; optical calibration using photon coincidence; quenching and radiative lifetimes of excited atoms and molecules. *Mailing Add:* Dept of Physics Univ of Alaska Fairbanks AK 99701

SHERIDAN, JUDSON DEAN, b Greeley, Colo, Nov 10, 40; m 63; c 2. CELL PHYSIOLOGY, CELL BIOLOGY. *Educ:* Hamline Univ, BS, 61; Oxford Univ, DPhil(neurophysiol), 65. *Prof Exp:* Res assoc neurophysiol & neuropharmacol, Neurophysiol Lab, Harvard Med Sch, 65-66, instr neurobiol, 66-68; from asst prof to assoc prof zool, 68-76, prof genetics & cell biol, 76-79, PROF ANAT, MED SCH, UNIV MINN, MINNEAPOLIS, 79- *Concurrent Pos:* USPHS fel, 65-68; assoc ed develop physiol, Develop Biol, 71-73; Nat Cancer Inst career develop award, 72; consult cell biol study sect, NSF, NIH, 72-; sr res fel, Dept Biochem, Univ Glasgow, Scotland, 74-75. *Mem:* AAAS; Am Soc Cell Biol; NY Acad Sci; Soc Develop Biol; Brit Physiol Soc. *Res:* Cellular communication via specialized points of cell-to-cell contacts, especially during development and abnormal cell growth. *Mailing Add:* Dept Anat 4-135 Jackson Hall Univ of Minn Minneapolis MN 55455

SHERIDAN, LAURENCE WARD, b Buffalo, NY, June 30, 07; m 37; c 1. MATHEMATICS, METEOROLOGY. *Educ:* Canisius Col, BA, 28; Cath Univ, MA, 29, PhD(mech), 32; NY Univ, MS, 41. *Prof Exp:* Asst math, Cath Univ, 30-32; instr high schs, NY, 32-33; prof math & chmn dept, Univ Scranton, 33-36; instr high schs, NY, 36-37; prof math & physics & chmn dept math, Col Mt St Vincent, 37-42; asst meteorologist, US Weather Bur, 42-46; assoc prof math, St Thomas Univ, 46-52; res engr, Aeronaut Div, Minneapolis-Honeywell Regulator Co, 52-53; sr physicist, Eng Res & Develop Div, Gen Mills, Inc, 53-55; res engr, Aircraft Div, Fairchild Eng & Airplane Corp, 55-60; assoc prof math, Pa State Univ, 60-73; RETIRED. *Concurrent Pos:* Lectr, Wilson Col, 59-60; staff engr, Washington, DC Lab, Link Aviation, Inc, 60- *Mem:* Am Meteorol Soc; Math Asn Am; assoc fel Am Inst Aeronaut & Astronaut. *Res:* Physics; aerodynamics; theoretical and wind-tunnel testing; long and short range forecasting by statistical methods. *Mailing Add:* RD 4 Box 843 Altoona PA 16601

SHERIDAN, MICHAEL FRANCIS, b Springfield, Mass, Feb 20, 40; m 64; c 3. PETROLOGY, VOLCANOLOGY. *Educ:* Amherst Col, AB, 62; Stanford Univ, MS, 64, PhD(geol), 65. *Prof Exp:* Geologist, US Geol Surv, 64-74; instr geol, Amherst Col, 65-66; from asst prof to assoc prof, 66-76, PROF GEOL, ARIZ STATE UNIV, 76- *Concurrent Pos:* Consult geologist, 69-; NASA Surtsey Exped, 70; vis prof, Univ Tokyo, 72-73; sr Fulbright-Hays scientist, Iceland, 78 & Antarctic Exped, 78. *Mem:* Geol Soc Am; Int Asn Volcanol & Chem Earth's Interior; Mineral Soc Am; Am Geophys Union. *Res:* Physical processes in volcanology; ash-flow tuff field relationships and mineralogy. *Mailing Add:* Dept of Geol Ariz State Univ Tempe AZ 85281

SHERIDAN, MICHAEL N, b Augusta, Tex, Sept 5, 37; m 58; c 3. ANATOMY, ELECTRON MICROSCOPY. *Educ:* Stephen F Austin State Col, BS, 58; Med Col Va, PhD(anat), 63. *Prof Exp:* Instr anat, Med Col Va, 62-63, asst prof, 64-66; from asst prof to assoc prof anat, Sch Med & Dent, Univ Rochester, 66-77, prof, 77-80; MEM FAC, UNIFORMED SERV UNIV HEALTH SCI, 80- *Concurrent Pos:* NIH fel biochem, Inst Animal Physiol, Cambridge, Eng, 63-64. *Mem:* AAAS; Am Soc Cell Biol; Am Asn Anat. *Res:* Electron microscopy of steroid secretors; central nervous system. *Mailing Add:* Uniformed Serv Univ Health Sci 4301 Jones Bridge Rd Bethesda MD 20014

SHERIDAN, PETER STERLING, b Portland, Maine, Mar 1, 44; m 67. INORGANIC CHEMISTRY. *Educ:* Kenyon Col, Ohio, BA, 66; Northwestern Univ, Evanston, PhD(chem), 71. *Prof Exp:* Lectr chem, Univ Kent, Canterbury, UK, 70-71; fel chem, 71-72; fel chem, Univ Southern Calif, 72-74; asst prof chem, State Univ NY Binghamton, 74-80; ASST PROF CHEM, COLGATE UNIV, 80- *Mem:* Am Chem Soc. *Res:* Photochemical reactions of transition metal complexes. *Mailing Add:* Dept Chem Colgate Univ Hamilton NY 13346

SHERIDAN, RICHARD COLLINS, b Trotwood, Ohio, Aug 19, 29; m 57; c 4. CHEMISTRY. *Educ:* Murray State Col, BS, 56; Univ Ky, MS, 61. *Prof Exp:* Chemist, B F Goodrich Chem Co, 56-58; RES CHEMIST, DIV CHEM DEVELOP, TENN VALLEY AUTHORITY, 60- *Mem:* Am Chem Soc. *Res:* Synthesis of oxamide; pyrolysis of urea phosphate; preparation of ammonium polyphosphates; history of chemistry; preparation of new nitrogen-phosphorus fertilizer compounds; melamine phosphate; recovery of uranium from phosphate rock. *Mailing Add:* 105 Terrace St Sheffield AL 35660

SHERIDAN, RICHARD P, b Detroit, Mich, Mar 10, 39; m 62; c 2. PLANT PHYSIOLOGY, BIOLOGY. *Educ:* Univ Ore, BA, 62, MA, 63, PhD(biol), 67. *Prof Exp:* NIH fel, Scripps Inst Oceanog, Univ Calif, San Diego, 67-68; asst prof, 68-74, ASSOC PROF BOT, UNIV MONT, 74- *Concurrent Pos:* NSF res grant, 69-71. *Mem:* Phycol Soc Am; Am Soc Plant Physiologists. *Res:* Algal physiology with emphasis on the photosynthetic mechanisms. *Mailing Add:* Dept of Bot Univ of Mont Missoula MT 59812

SHERIDAN, ROBERT E, b Hoboken, NJ, Oct 11, 40; m 66; c 3. GEOLOGY, GEOPHYSICS. *Educ:* Rutgers Univ, BA, 62; Columbia Univ, MA, 65, PhD(geol), 68. *Prof Exp:* Res asst, Lamont Geol Observ, NY, 62-68, res scientist, 68; asst prof, 68-73, assoc prof, 73-81, PROF GEOL, UNIV DEL, 81- *Concurrent Pos:* WAE appointment, US Geol Surv, 75-; coordr, Marine Geol & Geophys Prog, Col Marine Studies, Univ Del, 78-80; vis prof, Rutgers Univ, 79. *Mem:* Geol Soc Am; Am Geophys Union; Am Asn Petrol Geol; Nat Maritime Hist Soc. *Res:* Geology of the continental margin off eastern North America; stratigraphy of the Western North Atlantic; discovery of USS Monitor; recovery of oldest oceanic sediments; development of pulsation tectonic theory. *Mailing Add:* Dept of Geol Univ of Del Newark DE 19711

SHERIDAN, WILLIAM, b Cohoes, NY, Dec 1, 30; m 59; c 3. GENETICS. *Educ:* City Col New York, BA, 54; Univ Stockholm, Fil Lic, 62, Fil Dok(genetics), 68. *Prof Exp:* Instr genetics, Inst Genetics, Univ Stockholm, 60-61; res assoc, Lab Radiation Genetics, Sweden, 62-68; docent, Inst Genetics, Univ Stockholm, 68-73, actg dir inst, 70-71; HEAD MAMMALIAN GENETICS SECT, NAT INST ENVIRON HEALTH SCI, NIH, 73- *Concurrent Pos:* Asst ed, Mutation Res, 74- *Mem:* Genetics Soc Am; Environ Mutagen Soc. *Res:* Mammalian genetics; environmental mutagenesis; radiation genetics. *Mailing Add:* Mammalian Genetics Sect Nat Inst of Environ Health Sci Research Triangle Park NC 27709

SHERIDAN, WILLIAM FRANCIS, b Lakeland, Fla, Dec 4, 36; m 64; c 2. GENETICS, CELL BIOLOGY. *Educ:* Univ Fla, BSA, 58, MS, 60; Univ Ill, PhD(cell biol), 65. *Prof Exp:* Teaching asst bot, Univ Fla, 58-61; teaching asst, Univ Ill, 61-63; USPHS trainee biol, 63-65; instr, Yale Univ, 65-66, res fel sch med, 66-68; asst prof, Univ Mo-Columbia, 68-75; assoc prof, 75-80, PROF BIOL, UNIV NDAK, 80- *Concurrent Pos:* Fulbright res award, 77-78; vis prof, Dept Physiol, Carlsberg Res Lab, Copenhagen, 77-78; hon fel, Univ Minn, 81-82. *Res:* Maize genetics and embryo development; chromosome structure; tissue culture of cereals and its genetic applications. *Mailing Add:* Dept of Biol Univ of NDak Grand Forks ND 58201

SHERIDON, NICHOLAS KEITH, b Detroit, Mich, Dec 8, 35; m 61; c 3. ELECTROOPTICS. *Educ:* Wayne State Univ, BS, 57, MS, 59. *Prof Exp:* Asst physicist systs div, Bendix Corp, 60-62, physicist res labs, 62, sr physicist, 64-67; sr physicist res labs, 67-71, scientist, 71-72, sr scientist, 72-75, PRIN SCIENTIST, PALO ALTO RES CTR, XEROX CORP, 75- *Mem:* Optical Soc Am; Inst Elec & Electronics Eng; Soc Photog Instrumentation Eng; Soc Photog Scientists & Engrs. *Res:* Electrography, nom-impact printing; electronic imaging devices; electrophotography; optical and acoustical holography; optical data processing; electron physics; surface chemistry; display devices, gaseous electronics. *Mailing Add:* Xerox Corp Palo Alto Res Ctr 3333 Coyote Hill Rd Palo Alto CA 94304

SHERIF, MEHMET A, b Istanbul, Turkey, Aug 26, 33; m 59; c 2. SOIL MECHANICS. *Educ:* Robert Col, Istanbul, BS, 57; Ariz State Univ, MS, 62; Princeton Univ, MA, 63, PhD(eng), 64. *Prof Exp:* From asst prof to assoc prof, 63-77, PROF CIVIL ENG, UNIV WASH, 77- *Concurrent Pos:* Mem comt C-3, Hwy Res Bd, Nat Acad Sci-Nat Res Coun, 63- *Mem:* Am Soc Civil Engrs; Am Soc Testing & Mat. *Res:* Concrete and asphalt; shear and viscoelastic behavior of cohesive soils; stress distribution in earth masses. *Mailing Add:* 124 More Hall Dept of Civil Eng Univ of Wash Seattle WA 98105

SHERIFF, ROBERT EDWARD, b Mansfield, Ohio, Apr 19, 22; m 45; c 6. EXPLORATION GEOPHYSICS. *Educ:* Wittenberg Univ, AB, 43; Ohio State Univ, MS, 47, PhD(physics), 50. *Prof Exp:* Physicist, Manhattan Proj, 44-46; from geophysicist to chief geophysicist, Standard Oil Co, Calif, 50-75; sr vpres, Seiscom-Delta Inc, 75-80; PROF, UNIV HOUSTON, 80- *Concurrent Pos:* Adj prof geophysics, Univ Houston, 73- *Honors & Awards:* Kauffman Gold Medal, Soc Explor Geophysicists, 69. *Mem:* Hon mem Soc Explor Geophysicists (1st vpres, 72-73); Europ Asn Explor Geophysicists; Sigma Xi; Am Asn Petrol Geologists; AAAS. *Res:* Techniques of geophysical interpretation, including data acquisition and data processing techniques. *Mailing Add:* 12911 Butterfly Lane Houston TX 77024

SHERINS, RICHARD J, b Brooklyn, NY, July 6, 37; m 60; c 3. ENDOCRINOLOGY, ANDROLOGY. *Educ:* Univ Calif, Los Angeles, BA, 59, San Francisco, MD, 63. *Prof Exp:* Fel endocrinol, Univ Wash, 67-69; fel, Nat Cancer Inst, 69-70, sr investr endocrinol, Endocrinol & reproduction res br, 70-77, DEVELOP ENDOCRINOL BR, NAT INST CHILD HEALTH & HUMAN DEVELOP, NIH, 77- *Concurrent Pos:* Assoc clin prof obstet & gynec, Sch Med, George Washington Univ, 75- *Mem:* Am Fedn Clin Res; Endocrine Soc; Am Col Physicians; Am Fertility Soc; Am Soc Andrology (treas, 79-81, pres, 82-83). *Res:* Disorders of male reproduction; control of pituitary gonadotropin secretion. *Mailing Add:* Develop Endocrinol Br NIH Bldg 10 Rm 10 B09 Bethesda MD 20205

SHERK, FRANK ARTHUR, b Stayner, Ont, May 20, 32; m 54; c 4. MATHEMATICS. *Educ:* McMaster Univ, BA, 54, MSc, 55; Univ Toronto, PhD(math), 57. *Prof Exp:* Lectr math, 57-61, asst prof, 61-65, assoc prof, 65-81, PROF MATH, UNIV TORONTO, 81- *Mem:* Am Math Soc; Can Math Cong. *Res:* Projective geometry; regular maps; discrete groups. *Mailing Add:* Dept of Math Univ of Toronto Toronto ON M5S 1A3 Can

SHERK, FRED T, b Lake Park, Iowa, Mar 21, 29; m 53; c 2. CHEMICAL ENGINEERING. *Educ:* Iowa State Univ, BS, 51. *Prof Exp:* Chem engr, Phillips Chem Co, 51-55 & Phillips Petrol Co, 55-64, SECT MGR PROCESS EVAL RES & DEVELOP, PHILLIPS PETROL CO, 64- *Mem:* Am Inst Chem Engrs. *Res:* Petroleum and petrochemical process development, process design and evaluation. *Mailing Add:* Phillips Petrol Co 636 Adams Bldg Bartlesville OK 74003

SHERLOCK, PAUL, b New York, NY, Oct 7, 28; m 52; c 3. INTERNAL MEDICINE, GASTROENTEROLOGY. *Educ:* Queens Col, NY, BS, 50; Cornell Univ, MD, 54. *Prof Exp:* Nat Cancer Inst trainee, Sloan-Kettering Inst Cancer Res, 59-60, Am Cancer Soc res fel, 60-62, assoc, Inst Cancer Res, 62-78, chief gastroenterol serv, Cancer Ctr, 70-78, MEM, SLOAN-KETTERING INST CANCER RES, 78-, CHMN DEPT MED, MEM SLOAN-KETTERING CANCER CTR, 78- *Concurrent Pos:* Assoc prof med, Med Col, Cornell Univ, 70-75, prof, 75-; attend physician, Mem Sloan-Kettering Cancer Ctr, 70-; attend physician, New York Hosp, 75-; vis physician, Rockefeller Univ Hosp, 78-; consult, N Shore Univ Hosp, 78-; mem large bowel cancer proj working cadre & diag radiol comt, Nat Cancer Inst; mem task force on colon & rectal cancer, Am Cancer Soc; mem subspecialty bd gastroenterol, Am Bd Internal Med; assoc ed, Am J Digestive Dis; ed, Medilex Digest-Oncol, 80-; mem nat comt, Digestive Dis, 77-79; chmn adv bd, Nat Digestive Dis, 81- *Honors & Awards:* Int Cong Gastroenterol Cert & Gold Medal, Prague, 68. *Mem:* Fel Am Col Physicians; fel Am Col Gastroenterol; Am Asn Study Liver Dis; Am Gastroenterol Asn; Am Soc Gastrointestinal Endoscopy (secy). *Res:* Pathogenesis, diagnosis and treatment of premalignant and malignant disorders of the gastrointestinal tract. *Mailing Add:* 425 E 67th St New York NY 10021

SHERMA, JOSEPH A, b Newark, NJ, Mar 2, 34; m 61; c 1. ANALYTICAL CHEMISTRY. *Educ:* Upsala Col, BS, 55; Rutgers Univ, PhD(anal chem), 58. *Prof Exp:* Assoc prof anal chem, 58-75, PROF ANAL CHEM, LAFAYETTE COL, 75- *Concurrent Pos:* Sabbatical leave researcher, Perrine Primate Lab, Environ Protection Agency, 72; vis researcher, Argonne Nat Lab, Iowa State Univ, Syracuse Univ Res Corp, Hosp Univ Pa, Waters Assocs & Whatman Inc. *Mem:* Am Inst Chem; Am Chem Soc; Soc Appl Spectros; Sigma Xi. *Res:* Ion exchange and solution chromatography; analytical separations; pesticide analysis; quantitative thin-layer chromatography. *Mailing Add:* Dept of Chem Lafayette Col Easton PA 18042

SHERMAN, ALBERT HERMAN, b Philadelphia, Pa, Mar 5, 21; m 44; c 3. ORGANIC CHEMISTRY. *Educ:* Rutgers Univ, BS, 42, MS, 50, PhD(org chem), 53. *Prof Exp:* Chemist, Rare Chems Div, Nopco Chem Co, 47-49; asst anal chem, Rutgers Univ, 49-52; sr chemist, Nitrogen Div, Allied Chem Corp, 52-57; res chemist, Atlas Powder Co, 57-71 & ICI Am, Inc, 71-80. *Mem:* Am Chem Soc. *Res:* Surfactants; detergents; textile additives; organic synthesis; cosmetic chemistry. *Mailing Add:* 1426 Fresno Rd Wilmington DE 19803

SHERMAN, ALFRED ISAAC, b Toronto, Ont, Sept 4, 20; US citizen; m 44; c 3. OBSTETRICS & GYNECOLOGY. *Educ:* Univ Toronto, MD, 43; Am Bd Obstet & Gynec, dipl; Bd Gynec Oncol, dipl, 74. *Prof Exp:* From sr intern to asst resident obstet & gynec, Hamilton Gen Hosp, Ont, 44-45; fel path, Univ Rochester, 46-47; intern, St Louis Maternity & Barnes Hosps, 47-48; asst resident, 49-50; fel obstet & gynec, Sch Med, Washington Univ, 50-51, from instr to prof obstet & gynec, 51-65; PROF OBSTET & GYNEC, SCH MED, WAYNE STATE UNIV, 67-; DIR, DEPT OBSTET & GYNEC RES & EDUC, SINAI HOSP, DETROIT, 75-; DIR, DEPT OBSTET & GYNEC ONCOL, BEAUMONT HOSP, ROYAL OAK, 75- *Concurrent Pos:* Res asst cancer, Sch Med, Washington Univ, 48-49, instr radiother, 53-67; resident, Barnard Hosp, 50-51; consult & vis physician, St Louis City Hosp; consult, Mallinckrodt Inst Radiol, Homer G Phillips, St Luke's & Jewish Hosps; civilian consult, US Air Force; co-dir cytogenetics lab, John Hartford Found, Mo, 62-67. *Mem:* Radium Soc; Am Col Obstet & Gynec; Endocrine Soc; Soc Gynec Invest; Soc Gynec Oncol. *Mailing Add:* Dept Obstet & Gynec Res & Educ Sinai Hosp Detroit MI 48235

SHERMAN, ANTHONY MICHAEL, polymer chemistry, see previous edition

SHERMAN, BURTON STUART, b Brooklyn, NY, Nov 12, 30; m 52; c 4. ANATOMY. *Educ:* NY Univ, BA, 51, MS, 56; State Univ NY Downstate Med Ctr, PhD(anat), 60. *Prof Exp:* Res asst leukemia, Sloan-Kettering Inst Cancer Res, 51-52; res chemist, Jewish Hosp Brooklyn, NY, 52-56, res assoc biochem, 59-60; asst, 56-59, from instr to asst prof, 60-71, ASSOC PROF ANAT, STATE UNIV NY DOWNSTATE MED CTR, 71- *Concurrent Pos:* Vis scientist, Strangeways Res Lab, Eng, 64-65. *Mem:* Am Asn Anat; AAAS. *Res:* Leukemia research; osteogenesis; calcification of collagen and macromolecules; tissue and organ culture; vitamin A metabolism, biochemistry and effects on growth and proliferation of tissues; developmental anatomy. *Mailing Add:* Dept Anat State Univ NY Downstate Med Ctr Brooklyn NY 11203

SHERMAN, BYRON WESLEY, b St Louis, Mo, Sept 20, 35; m 55; c 4. ELECTRICAL ENGINEERING. *Educ:* Univ Mo, BS, 57, MS, 59, PhD(elec eng), 66. *Prof Exp:* Asst instr elec eng, Univ Mo, 57-59; eng consult, Columbia Pictures Corp, Calif, 60-61 & Wells Eng, 61-62; electronics engr, McDonnell Aircraft Corp, 62-63; instr, 63-66, asst prof elec eng, 66-81, PROF, UNIV MO-COLUMBIA, 81- *Concurrent Pos:* Eng consult, Audience Studies, Inc, Calif, 66-67; summer fac fel, NASA Manned Spacecraft Ctr, 67-68, consult, 68-; consult, Lockheed Electronics Corp, Tex, 67-68 & Inst Bioeng Res, Univ Mo, 68- *Mem:* Inst Elec & Electronics Engrs. *Res:* Electric field instrumentation. *Mailing Add:* RD 1 Columbia MO 65201

SHERMAN, CHARLES HENRY, b Fall River, Mass, Dec 16, 28; m 51; c 2. PHYSICS. *Educ:* Mass Inst Technol, BS, 50; Univ Conn, MS, 57, PhD(physics), 62. *Prof Exp:* Physicist, Tracerlab, Inc, 50-53; physicist, US Navy Underwater Sound Lab, 53-63; assoc dir res, Parke Math Labs, Inc, Mass, 63-71; head appl res br, Transducer Div, 71-74, HEAD TRANSDUCER & ARRAYS DIV, NEW LONDON LAB, NAVAL UNDERWATER SYSTS CTR, 74- *Concurrent Pos:* Adj prof dept ocean eng, Univ RI, 75- *Mem:* Fel Acoust Soc Am; Am Phys Soc. *Res:* Acoustics; theoretical physics; solid state physics. *Mailing Add:* New London Lab Naval Underwater Systs Ctr New London CT 06320

SHERMAN, CHRISTINE ANN, computational physics, atmospheric science, see previous edition

SHERMAN, CHRISTOPHER, b New Brunswick, NJ, Aug 18, 22; m 50; c 2. PHYSICS. *Educ:* Univ Wis, BA, 47; Princeton Univ, PhD(physics), 55. *Prof Exp:* Proj engr, Sprague Elec Co, 55-56; scientist, Avco Corp, 56-61; prin scientist, GCA Corp, 61-70; SCIENTIST, AIR FORCE GEOPHYS LAB, 70- *Mem:* Am Phys Soc. *Res:* Nuclear magnetic resonance; plasma and atmospheric physics. *Mailing Add:* Air Force Geophys Lab Hanscom Air Force Base Bedford MA 01731

SHERMAN, D(ONALD) R, b Cleveland, Ohio, Aug 2, 35; m 60; c 3. STRUCTURAL ENGINEERING. *Educ:* Case Inst Technol, BS, 57, MS, 60; Univ Ill, PhD(struct eng), 64. *Prof Exp:* Engr, Pittsburgh Testing Lab, 57-58; design engr, Aerojet-Gen Corp, 63; engr, Esso Res & Eng Co, 64-66; assoc prof, 66-72, PROF STRUCT, UNIV WIS-MILWAUKEE, 72- *Mem:* Am Soc Civil Engrs; Soc Exp Stress Anal; Struct Stability Res Coun. *Res:* Stability of structural steel columns; tubular structures; equipment design for seismic loads. *Mailing Add:* Col of Eng Univ of Wis Box 784 Milwaukee WI 53201

SHERMAN, DOROTHY HELEN, b Stanley, Iowa, Nov 18, 05. SPEECH PATHOLOGY, STATISTICS. *Educ:* Univ Iowa, BA, 31, MA, 38, PhD(speech path), 51. *Prof Exp:* Teacher, Pub Schs, 25-48; asst & part-time instr speech path, 48-51, prof, 51-72, EMER PROF SPEECH PATH, UNIV IOWA, 72- *Concurrent Pos:* Vis asst prof & res assoc res found, Ohio State Univ, 54-55; consult & dir res acoust lab, US Naval Sch Aviation Med, 54-55; ed, J Speech & Hearing Res, 58-62. *Honors & Awards:* Honors of the Asn, Am Speech & Hearing Asn, 72. *Mem:* Fel Am Speech & Hearing Asn; Sigma Xi. *Res:* Psychological scaling of speech deviations and evaluation of relationships among perceptual, acoustical and physiological data to make inferences useful for diagnosis and therapy and development of theory. *Mailing Add:* 4 Oak Park Ct Iowa City IA 52240

SHERMAN, EDWARD, b New York, NY, Feb 8, 19; m 45; c 2. TECHNICAL MANAGEMENT, ORGANIC CHEMISTRY. *Educ:* Univ Ill, BS, 40; Lehigh Univ, MS, 47, PhD(chem), 49; Northwestern Univ, MBA, 70. *Prof Exp:* Asst org chem, Univ Ala, 40-41; jr inspector, US Food & Drug Admin, 41-42; asst oil chem, Lehigh Univ, 46-47; res assoc high nitrogen compounds, Ill Inst Technol, 49-50; group leader chem res, 50-64, sect leader, 64-71, coordr tech & admin serv, 71-72, asst dir chem res & develop, 72-78, mgr spec projs, 78-80, CHEM PROD MGR, QUAKER OATS CO, 80- *Mem:* AAAS; Am Chem Soc; Polyurethane Mfrs Asn. *Res:* Chemical product development and marketing; environmental sciences; industrial hygiene; furans; tetrahydrofurans; lactones; lactams; aromatics; ring cleavage; polymers; photochemistry; levulinic acid; cycloaliphatics; nitrogen heterocycles; nitroaminoguanidine; nitroguanyl azide; nitroaminotetrazole; pharmaceuticals; oil oxidation; hemin and hemochromogens; resins. *Mailing Add:* Chem Res & Mkt Quaker Oats Co PO Box 3514 Merchandise Mart Sta Chicago IL 60654

SHERMAN, FRANK EDWARD, b Pittsburgh, Pa, Oct 31, 14; m 38; c 3. PATHOLOGY. *Educ:* Univ Pittsburgh, MD, 38. *Prof Exp:* Instr path, Rush Med Col, Univ Ill, 40-43; instr, Sch Med, Univ Pittsburgh, 43-45; pathologist, Butler County Mem Hosp, Pa, 45-48; pathologist, Passavant Hosp, Pittsburgh & Suburban Gen Hosp, Bellevue, 48-50; from asst prof to assoc prof, 50-66, prof, 66-80, EMER PROF PATH, SCH MED, UNIV PITTSBURGH, 80- *Concurrent Pos:* Pathologist, Sewickley Valley Hosp, Pa, 43-45 & Vet Admin Hosp, Aspinwall, 50-54; assoc pathologist, Children's Hosp Pittsburgh, 54- *Mem:* Am Soc Clin Path; AMA; fel Col Am Path; Int Acad Path. *Res:* Fluorescent antibody techniques adapted to homologous proteins; anatomy of congenital heart disease. *Mailing Add:* Children's Hosp 125 DeSoto Pittsburgh PA 15213

SHERMAN, FRED, b Minneapolis, Minn, May 21, 32; m 58; c 3. GENETICS, BIOPHYSICS. *Educ:* Univ Minn, BA, 53; Univ Calif, Berkeley, PhD(biophys), 58. *Prof Exp:* Fel genetics, Univ Wash, 59-60 & Lab Physiol Genetics, France, 60-61; from sr instr to assoc prof, 61-71, prof, 71-81, WILSON PROF RADIATION BIOL & BIOPHYS, SCH MED & DENT, UNIV ROCHESTER, 81- *Concurrent Pos:* Instr, Cold Spring Harbor Lab, 70- *Mem:* AAAS; Genetics Soc Am; Am Soc Microbiol; Biophys Soc. *Res:* Mutational alteration of yeast cytochrome C; yeast genetics; cytoplasmic inheritance; cytochrome deficient mutants of yeast; amino acid changes in cytochrome C; DNA changes in yeast genes. *Mailing Add:* Sch Med & Dent Univ Rochester Rochester NY 14642

SHERMAN, FREDERICK GEORGE, b McGregor, Mich, Apr 16, 15; m 42; c 3. BIOLOGY. *Educ:* Univ Tulsa, BS, 38; Northwestern Univ, PhD(physiol), 42. *Prof Exp:* Fel, Sch Med, Wash Univ, St Louis, 46; from instr to prof biol, Brown Univ, 46-60; prof zool & chmn dept, Syracuse Univ, 60-68, prof biol, 68-82. *Concurrent Pos:* Fel, Picker Found, 51-52; res collabr, Brookhaven Nat Lab, 53-56 & 58-68; vis scientist, NIH, Bethesda, 57, spec fel, 67-68. *Mem:* Am Physiol Soc; fel Geront Soc; Soc Develop Biol; Soc Gen Physiol(secy, 57-59); Sigma Xi. *Res:* Biochemical changes associated with aging; regulation of protein synthesis. *Mailing Add:* Dept Biol Syracuse Univ Syracuse NY 13210

SHERMAN, FREDERICK S, b San Diego, Calif, Apr 14, 28; m 53; c 2. MECHANICS. *Educ:* Harvard Univ, BS, 49; Univ Calif, MS, 50, PhD(mech eng), 54. *Prof Exp:* Instr mech eng, Univ Calif, 54-56; aeronaut res engr mech br, Off Naval Res, US Dept Navy, Washington, DC, 56-58; asst prof mech eng, 58-59, assoc prof, 59-65, prof aeronaut sci, 65-70, asst dean, Col Eng, 73-80, PROF MECH ENG, UNIV CALIF, BERKELEY, 70- *Concurrent Pos:* Mem fluid mech subcomt, Nat Adv Comt Aeronaut, 57-58. *Res:* Fluid mechanics; rarefied gas dynamics; cloud physics and stratified fluid flows; non-linear instability; free convertion. *Mailing Add:* Dept of Mech Eng Univ of Calif Berkeley CA 94720

SHERMAN, GARY JOSEPH, b Bellaire, Ohio, Dec 18, 41; m 64; c 3. MATHEMATICS. *Educ:* Bowling Green State Univ, BS, 63, MA, 68; Ind Univ, Bloomington, PhD(math), 71. *Prof Exp:* Asst prof, 71-78, PROF MATH, ROSE-HULMAN INST TECHNOL, 78- *Mem:* Am Math Soc; Math Asn Am. *Res:* Group theory; partially ordered groups. *Mailing Add:* Dept of Math Rose-Hulman Inst Technol Terre Haute IN 47803

SHERMAN, GEORGE CHARLES, b Pasadena, Calif, Mar 4, 38; m 59; c 5. PHYSICAL OPTICS. *Educ:* Stanford Univ, BS, 60; Univ Calif, Los Angeles, MS, 65, PhD(meteorol), 69. *Prof Exp:* Mem tech staff, Aerospace Corp, 65-68; res assoc optics, Dept Physics & Astron & Inst Optics, Univ Rochester, 69-70, asst prof optics, Inst Optics, 70-76; staff electro-optic scientist, Itek Corp, 76-79; MEM PROF STAFF, SCHLUMBERGER-DOLL RES CTR, 79- *Mem:* Optical Soc Am. *Res:* Radiation, propagation, diffraction and scattering of waves; atmospheric optics; oil exploration. *Mailing Add:* Schlumberger-Doll Res Ctr PO Box 307 Ridgefield CT 06877

SHERMAN, GERALD PHILIP, b Philadelphia, Pa, Mar 20, 40; m 66; c 2. PHARMACOLOGY, PHARMACY. *Educ:* Philadelphia Col Pharm & Sci, BSc, 63, MSc, 65, PhD(pharmacol), 67. *Prof Exp:* NIH fel, Univ Pittsburgh, 67-68; asst prof physiol & pharmacol, Univ Pittsburgh, 68-69; asst prof mat med, 69-70, Univ Ky, from asst prof to assoc prof clin pharm, 70-78; dir undergrad studies, 78-80, PROF PHARMACOL, UNIV TOLEDO, 80-, CHMN, DEPT PHARMACOL, 81- *Mem:* Am Asn Col Pharm; Am Soc Clin Pharmacol & Therapeut. *Res:* Clinical drug efficacy studies; autonomic and cardiovascular pharmacology. *Mailing Add:* Col of Pharm Univ of Toledo Toledo OH 43606

SHERMAN, GORDON R, b Menomonee, Mich, Feb 24, 28; m 51; c 2. COMPUTER SCIENCES, OPERATIONS RESEARCH. *Educ:* Iowa State Univ, BS, 53; Stanford Univ, MS, 54; Purdue Univ, PhD(math), 60. *Prof Exp:* Assoc prof math, 60-69, prof, 69-73, head dept comput sci, 70-73, PROF MATH & COMPUT SCI, UNIV TENN, KNOXVILLE, 73-, DIR, COMPUT CTR, 60- *Concurrent Pos:* NASA res grant, 62-70, grant data entry systs, 74-75; NSF grant, 71-72; chmn, Knoxville/Knox County Comput Adv Comt, 75. *Mem:* Asn Comput Mach; Soc Indust & Appl Math; Opers Res Soc Am; Am Statist Asn; Sigma Xi. *Res:* Optimization of discrete functions; application of digital computers. *Mailing Add:* Comput Ctr Univ Tenn Knoxville TN 37916

SHERMAN, HAROLD, b Newark, NJ, Oct 19, 21; m 43; c 2. PHYSICS. *Educ:* Brooklyn Col, AB, 42; NY Univ, PhD, 56. *Prof Exp:* PhysProf Exp: Physicist, Signal Corps, US Dept Army, Ohio, 42-44; electronics engr, Fada Radio, NY, 44; physicist, Premier Crystal Labs, 44-47; asst physics, NY Univ, 48-49, res assoc, 52-56; instr, St Peter's Col, 49-51; sr engr, A B Dumont Labs, NJ, 51-52; sr scientist, Avco Corp, Conn, 56; SR RES PROJ PHYSICIST, SCHLUMBERGER-DOLL RES CTR, 56- *Mem:* Am Phys Soc; Inst Elec & Electronics Engrs; Sigma Xi. *Res:* Gas discharges; nuclear instrumentation; nuclear well logging. *Mailing Add:* 24 Webster Rd Ridgefield CT 06877

SHERMAN, HARRY LOGAN, b Anniston, Ala, Dec 5, 27; m 55; c 4. BOTANY, ECOLOGY. *Educ:* Jacksonville State Univ, BS, 55; Univ Tenn, Knoxville, MS, 58; Vanderbilt Univ, PhD(biol), 69. *Prof Exp:* Instr & res asst bot, Univ Tenn, Knoxville, 57-59; from asst prof to assoc prof biol, 61-69, PROF BIOL SCI & HEAD DEPT, MISS UNIV WOMEN, 69- *Mem:* Am Inst Biol Sci; Am Soc Plant Taxon; Int Soc Plant Taxon. *Res:* Biosystematics, including cyto- and chemo-taxonomy and reproductive biology; taxonomy. *Mailing Add:* Dept of Biol Sci Miss Univ for Women Columbus MS 39701

SHERMAN, HERBERT, b Brooklyn, NY, Feb 24, 20; m 42; c 2. ELECTRICAL ENGINEERING. *Educ:* City Col New York, BEE, 40; Polytech Inst Brooklyn, MEE, 49, DEE, 55. *Prof Exp:* Tech adv to chief contracting off, NY Signal Corps Procurement Dist, US Signal Corps, 40-44; mem res & develop prog & chief plans, Rome Air Develop Ctr, 46-52; group leader med technol & staff mem res & develop, Lincoln Lab, Mass Inst Technol, 52-76; LECTR HEALTH POLICY & MGT DEPT & ASSOC DIR FOR TECHNOL, CTR ANAL HEALTH PRACTICES, HARVARD SCH PUB HEALTH, 72- *Concurrent Pos:* Consult, Proj Charles, 50, Proj Barnstable, 58, Proj Atlantis, 59, Polaris Commun Comt, US Navy, 59 & Nat Ctr for Health Serv Res, 72-81; consult to Asst Secy Defense, 56-58; mem assoc staff, Peter Bent Brigham Hosp, 58-72; consult to spec asst to President for Aviation Facil Planning, 59; mem staff, Beth Israel Hosp, 69-; prin res assoc & mem fac med, Harvard Med Sch, 70-; mem telecommun & comput appln bd, Nat Res Coun, 77-80. *Mem:* Fel AAAS; fel Inst Elec & Electronics Engrs; fel Soc Advan Med Systs; Biomed Eng Soc. *Res:* Communications theory; quantum and continuous signal design; pattern recognition; systems and biomedical engineering; space technology; mathematical modelling of physiological systems; health services research. *Mailing Add:* Harvard Sch of Pub Health 677 Huntington Ave Boston MA 02115

SHERMAN, IRWIN WILLIAM, b New York, NY, Feb 12, 33; m 66; c 2. ZOOLOGY, PARASITOLOGY. *Educ:* City Col New York, BS, 54; Northwestern Univ, MS, 59, PhD(biol), 60. *Prof Exp:* Asst protozool, Univ Fla, 54; lab technician, US Army, 54-56; teacher, Yonkers Bd Educ, 56-57; asst parasitol, Northwestern Univ, 57-60; NIH fel, Rockefeller Inst, 60-62; from asst prof to assoc prof, 62-73, chmn, Dept Biol, 74-79, PROF ZOOL, UNIV CALIF, RIVERSIDE, 73-, DEAN, COL NATURAL & AGR SCI, 81- *Concurrent Pos:* Guggenheim Mem Found fel, Carlsberg Found, Copenhagen, 67; eve lectr biol, City Col New York, 57, 60-62; spec NIH fel, Nat Inst Med Res, Mill Hill, Eng, 73-74; mem trop med & parasitol study sect, NIH, 70-74 & 79-80; chmn ad hoc, Study Group Parasitic Dis, Dept Army, 77-78; mem steering comt Malaria Chemother, World Health Orgn, 78- *Mem:* AAAS; Soc Protozool; Am Soc Parasitol; Am Soc Tropical Med & Hygiene. *Res:* Biochemistry and physiology of intracellular parasites; heterogeneity of enzymes; parasitic immunity. *Mailing Add:* Dept of Biol Univ of Calif Riverside CA 92521

SHERMAN, JACQUES LAWRENCE, JR, b Washington, DC, June 24, 16; m 41; c 2. INTERNAL MEDICINE. *Educ:* Univ Ky, BS, 37; Georgetown Univ, MD, 48. *Prof Exp:* Chief resident med serv, Walter Reed Army Hosp, US Army, 51-52, asst chief med serv & cardiologist, Army Hosp, Ft Belvoir, Va, 53-56, chief med serv, Army Hosp, Munich, Ger, 56-59, chief dept metab, Walter Reed Army Inst Res, 59-61, chief res div, Med Res & Develop Command, 61-64; chief med serv, Coney Island Div, Maimonides Hosp, 64-67; med dir, Maimonides Med Ctr, 67-71; ASSOC CHIEF OF STAFF, VET ADMIN HOSP, NORTHPORT, 71-; DEAN CLIN CAMPUS & PROF MED, HEALTH SCI CTR, STATE UNIV NY STONYBROOK, 71- *Mem:* AAAS; Am Fedn Clin Res; AMA; Am Col Physicians; NY Acad Sci. *Res:* Metabolis aspects of disease; structure and function of arterio-venous anastamoses; physiology. *Mailing Add:* Off of Chief of Staff Vet Admin Hosp Northport NY 11768

SHERMAN, JAMES H, b Detroit, Mich, Mar 14, 36; m 65; c 2. PHYSIOLOGY. *Educ:* Univ Mich, BS, 57; Cornell Univ, PhD(cell physiol), 63. *Prof Exp:* From res assoc to asst prof, 63-71, asst dir, Off Allied Health Educ, Dept Postgrad Med, 72-77, ASSOC PROF PHYSIOL, MED SCH, UNIV MICH, ANN ARBOR, 71- *Mem:* Biophys Soc; NY Acad Sci; Am Physiol Soc. *Res:* Cell membrane permeability; intracellular pH; active transport of amino acids in tumor cells; surface properties of cell membranes. *Mailing Add:* Dept Physiol Med Sch Univ Mich Ann Arbor MI 48104

SHERMAN, JEROME KALMAN, b Brooklyn, NY, Aug 14, 25; m 52; c 3. ANATOMY, CRYOBIOLOGY. *Educ:* Brown Univ, AB, 47; Western Reserve Univ, MS, 49; Univ Iowa, PhD(zool), 54. *Prof Exp:* Asst biol, Western Reserve Univ, 47-49; from asst to res assoc urol, Univ Iowa, 49-54; res assoc, Am Found Biol Res, 54-58; from asst prof to assoc prof, 59-66, PROF ANAT, MED COL, UNIV ARK MED SCI, LITTLE ROCK, 67- *Concurrent Pos:* Consult, Am Breeders Serv, 55-56, Winrock Farm, 59-60, Idant Corp, 72-73, Dow Chem Co, 77- & semen banking; mem adv bd, Am Type Cult Collections, 73-77; Lederle med fac award, 61-63; Fulbright sr res award, Univ Munich, Ger, 65-66; spec chair prof, Nat Chung-Hsin Univ, Taiwan, 73-74. *Mem:* Am Asn Anat; Soc Cryobiol; Sigma Xi; Am Asn Tissue Banks; Soc Exp Biol & Med. *Res:* Effects of cooling, freezing and rewarming on protoplasm of various cells and tissues; low temperature preservation of living cells, especially mammalian gametes; fertility and sterility; cytology; ultrastructural and biochemical cryoinjury of cellular organelles; cyrobanking of human semen. *Mailing Add:* Dept of Anat Med Col Univ of Ark for Med Sci Little Rock AR 72205

SHERMAN, JOHN EDWIN, b Brooklyn, NY, Jan 18, 22; m 45; c 3. INFORMATION SCIENCE. *Educ:* Hofstra Col, BA, 50. *Prof Exp:* Physicst, US Naval Air Missile Test Ctr, 51-53; design engr, McDonnell Aircraft Corp, 53-54; math analyst analog comput, 54-56, group engr, 56-57, sect leader, 57-59, dept mgr hybrid comput, 59-66, div mgr, 66-69, div mgr data processing, 69-75, DIV MGR SCI COMPUT, LOCKHEED MISSILE & SPACE CO, 75- *Concurrent Pos:* Pres, Simulation Coun, Inc, 59-60, dir, 60-66, dir pub, 64-74; dir, Am Fedn Info Processing Socs, 62-72. *Mem:* Inst Elec & Electronics Engrs; Simulation Coun. *Res:* Analog and hybrid computing; digital computing; data processing. *Mailing Add:* 1647 Grant Rd Mountain View CA 94040

SHERMAN, JOHN FOORD, b Oneonta, NY, Sept 4, 19; m 44; c 2. PHARMACOLOGY. *Educ:* Union Univ, NY, BS, 49; Yale Univ, PhD(pharmacol), 53. *Hon Degrees:* ScD, Albany Col Pharm, 70. *Prof Exp:* Pharmacologist, Lab Trop Dis, Nat Microbiol Inst, 53-56, dep chief extramural progs, Nat Inst Arthritis & Metab Dis, 56-61, assoc dir extramural progs, Nat Inst Neurol Dis & Blindness, 61-62, Nat Inst Arthritis & Metab Dis, 62-63 & NIH, 64-68, dep dir, NIH, 68-74; VPRES, ASN AM MED COL, 74- *Mem:* Inst Med-Nat Acad Sci; Sigma Xi; AAAS; Nat Soc Med Res (pres, 79-); Nat Multiple Sclerosis Soc. *Res:* Pharmacology of the central nervous system; chemotherapy; medical research and education administration. *Mailing Add:* Asn Am Med Cols One Dupont Circle NW Washington DC 20036

SHERMAN, JOHN WALTER, b Auburn, NY, Aug 19, 45; m 70, 80. PALEOLIMNOLOGY. *Educ:* Hamilton Col, BA, 67; Univ Vt, MS, 72; Univ Del, PhD(geol), 76. *Prof Exp:* Sr biologist diatom ecol, 75-77, PROG MGR RIVER ECOL, ACAD NATURAL SCI PHILADELPHIA, 77- *Mem:* Am Soc Limnol & Oceanog; Sigma Xi; Int Asn Great Lakes Res; AAAS. *Res:* Paleolimnology, especially diatom taxonomy, ecology and relations with other microfossils and sediment properties of cores; use of artificial periphyton substrates for river pollution monitoring. *Mailing Add:* Div of Limnol & Ecol 19th & The Parkway Philadelphia PA 19103

SHERMAN, JOSEPH E, b Chicago, Ill, July 27, 19; m 45; c 3. MICROBIOLOGY, FOOD TECHNOLOGY. *Educ:* Univ Ill, BS, 39. *Prof Exp:* Bacteriologist, Vet Admin Hosp, Wis, 39-41; res labs, Swift & Co, Ill, 46-60; group leader microbiol res ctr, Kraftco Corp, 60-69; tech dir, Runyon Lab, 69-73; qual assurance mgr, Schulze & Burch Biscuit Co, 73-81; CONSULT, SHERMAN FOOD LAB, 82- *Mem:* Am Soc Microbiol; Inst Food Technologists; Am Soc Qual Control; Soc Indust Microbiol. *Res:* Medical and forensic microbiology. *Mailing Add:* 3925 N Triumvera Dr Apt 12B Glenview IL 60025

SHERMAN, KENNETH, b Boston, Mass, Oct 6, 32; m 58; c 3. BIOLOGICAL OCEANOGRAPHY. *Educ:* Suffolk Univ, BS, 54; Univ RI, MS, 60. *Hon Degrees:* DSc, Suffolk Univ, 79. *Prof Exp:* Instr conserv educ, Mass Audubon Soc, 54-55; fishery aide, US Bur Com Fisheries, Mass, 55-56; teacher high sch, Mass, 59-60; fishery res biologist zooplankton ecol, US Bur Com Fisheries, Hawaii, 60-63, Maine, 63-71; coord, Marine Resources Monitoring Assessing & Prediction Prog, 71-73, chief resource assessment div, US Dept Com, Nat Oceanic & Atmospheric Admin, Washington, DC, 73-75, LAB DIR & CHIEF, MARINE ECOSYST DIV, US DEPT COM, NAT OCEANIC & ATMOSPHERIC ADMIN, NAT MARINE FISHERIES SERV, NARRAGANSETT, RI, 75- *Concurrent Pos:* Mem biol oceanog comt, Int Coun Explor Sea, 72-; US proj officer, Plankton Sorting Ctr, Szczecin, Poland, 73-; adj prof, Grad Sch Oceanog, Univ RI, 80. *Mem:* AAAS; Am Soc Limnol & Oceanog; Ecol Soc Am; Am Soc Zool; Am Soc Ichthyol & Herpet. *Res:* Tuna oceanography; zooplankton ecology; Atlantic herring biology; distribution and abundance of epipelagic marine copepods; estuarine ecology; taxonomy of marine copepods; predator prey relationships of pelagic fishes; plankton in ecosystems; productivity of living marine resources. *Mailing Add:* Nat Marine Fisheries Serv Lab RR-7A Box 522A Narragansett RI 02882

SHERMAN, KENNETH ELIOT, b Long Branch, NJ, Dec 21, 55; m 80. VIROLOGY. *Educ:* Cook Col, BS, 76; Rutgers Univ, PhD(microbiol), 80. *Prof Exp:* Adj fac microbiol, Middlesex County Col, 78-80; FEL, RES LABS, AM RED CROSS, 80- *Mem:* Am Soc Microbiol; AMA; Sigma Xi. *Res:* Viral hepatitis with emphasis on the epidemiology of non-A, non-B hepatitis and biochemical marker of liver disease; relationship of baculoviruses with arboviruses invertebrate hosts. *Mailing Add:* Res Labs Am Red Cross 9312 Old Georgetown Rd Bethesda MD 20814

SHERMAN, LOUIS ALLEN, b Chicago, Ill, Dec 16, 43; m 69; c 2. PHOTOSYNTHESIS, MEMBRANE STRUCTURE. *Educ:* Univ Chicago, BS, 65, PhD(biophysics), 70. *Prof Exp:* Fel photosynthesis, Cornell Univ, 70-72; asst prof, 72-77, ASSOC PROF BIOL SCI, UNIV MO, 77- *Concurrent Pos:* Fulbright res fel, Univ Leiden, Netherlands, 79-80. *Mem:* Biophys Soc; Am Soc Microbiol; Am Soc Photobiol; AAAS; Plant Physiol. *Res:* Photosynthesis and the structure of photosynthetic membranes; isolation of photosynthetic mutants in cyanobacteria; isolation of photosynthetic membrane components; cloning of photosynthesis genes on specially designed hybrid plasmids. *Mailing Add:* Div Biol Sci Univ Mo Tucker Hall Columbia MO 65211

SHERMAN, MALCOLM J, b Chicago, Ill, July 28, 39; m 63; c 2. MATHEMATICS. *Educ:* Univ Chicago, BS & MS, 60; Univ Calif, Berkeley, PhD(math), 64. *Prof Exp:* Asst prof math, Univ Calif, Los Angeles, 64-68; asst prof, 68-70, ASSOC PROF MATH, STATE UNIV NY, ALBANY, 70- *Mem:* Am Math Soc; Math Asn Am. *Res:* Functional analysis and operator theory, particularly invariant subspaces of Hardy classes of Hilbert space valued functions. *Mailing Add:* Dept of Math State Univ NY Albany NY 12222

SHERMAN, MARTIN, b Newark, NJ, Nov 21, 20; div; c 2. ENTOMOLOGY, INSECT TOXICOLOGY. *Educ:* Rutgers Univ, BSc, 41, MSc, 43; Cornell Univ, PhD(insect toxicol), 48. *Prof Exp:* Res asst entom, Cornell Univ, 45-48; entomologist, Beech-Nut Packing Co, 48-49; asst prof entom, Univ & asst entomologist, Agr Exp Sta, 49-52, assoc prof & assoc entomologist, 52-58, PROF ENTOM & ENTOMOLOGIST, AGR EXP STA, UNIV HAWAII, 58- *Concurrent Pos:* Fulbright scholar, Univ Tokyo, 56-57 & State Entom Lab & Royal Vet & Agr Col, Denmark, 66; vis prof, Rutgers Univ, 73. *Mem:* Am Chem Soc; Entom Soc Am; Soc Toxicol; Soc Environ Toxicol & Chem; Int Soc Study Xenobiotics. *Res:* Comparative vertebrate and insect toxicology; insecticide residue analysis; insecticide formulation; metabolism of insecticides. *Mailing Add:* Dept of Entom 3050 Maile Way Honolulu HI 96822

SHERMAN, MERRY RUBIN, b New York, NY, May 14, 40. ENDOCRINE BIOCHEMISTRY. *Educ:* Wellesley Col, BA, 61; Univ Calif, Berkeley, MA, 63, PhD(biophysics), 66. *Prof Exp:* NIH fel, Weizmann Inst, 66-67 & Nat Inst Dent Res, 68-69; res assoc, 70-71, assoc, 71-76, ASSOC MEM, SLOAN-KETTERING INST, 76- *Concurrent Pos:* Vis investr, Cardiovascular Res Inst, Univ Calif, San Francisco, 75-76; assoc prof biochem, Grad Sch Med Sci, Cornell Univ, 77-; ed, J Biol Chem. *Mem:* Am Soc Biol Chemists; Endocrine Soc; Am Asn Cancer Res. *Res:* Steroid hormone receptors and responses. *Mailing Add:* Sloan-Kettering Inst 1275 York Ave New York NY 10021

SHERMAN, MICHAEL, b New York, NY, Sept 7, 38. APPLIED MATHEMATICS. *Educ:* NY Univ, AB & BS, 60; Stanford Univ, MS, 61; Case Inst Technol, PhD(eng), 65. *Prof Exp:* Engr, Rand Corp, 65-69; PRES, DELPHI INFO SCI CORP, 69- *Res:* Numerical analysis; computer sciences; systems analysis. *Mailing Add:* 844 2nd St Santa Monica CA 90403

SHERMAN, MICHAEL IAN, b Montreal, Que, Sept 27, 44; m 68. DEVELOPMENTAL BIOLOGY. *Educ:* McGill Univ, BS, 65; State Univ NY Stony Brook, PhD(molecular biol), 69. *Prof Exp:* Fel, Dept Path, Univ Oxford, 69-70 & Dept Zool, 70-71; asst mem cell biol, 71-75, assoc mem, 76-81, MEM, ROCHE INST MOLECULAR BIOL, 81- *Concurrent Pos:* Mem rev panel, NASA, 78; mem human embryol develop study sect, NIH, 79-81; adj assoc prof human genetics, Columbia Col Physicians & Surgeons, 80- *Mem:* Tissue Cult Asn; Develop Biol Soc. *Res:* Biochemistry and biology of differentiation of mouse embryos and teratocarcinoma cells in vivo and in vitro. *Mailing Add:* Dept of Cell Biol Roche Inst of Molecular Biol Nutley NJ 07110

SHERMAN, NORMAN K, b Kingston, Ont, Jan 28, 35; m 60; c 5. NUCLEAR PHYSICS, RADIATION PHYSICS. *Educ:* Royal Mil Col, Ont, rmc, 56; Queen's Univ, Ont, BSc, 57, MSc, 59, PhD(physics), 62. *Prof Exp:* Lectr physics, Royal Mil Col, Ont, 59-60; lectr, Queen's Univ, Ont, 61-62; NATO fel nuclear physics, Univ Paris, 62-64 & Yale Univ, 64-65; asst prof physics, McGill Univ, 65-68; assoc res officer x-rays and nuclear radiations, 68-75, SR RES OFFICER X-RAYS & NUCLEAR RADIATIONS, DIV PHYSICS, NAT RES COUN CAN, 75- *Concurrent Pos:* Res assoc accelerator lab, Univ Sask, 65; user zero gradient synchrotron, Argonne Nat Lab, 66-68; ed, Youth Sci News, 73-76; mem ad hoc comt synchrotron radiation, Nat Res Coun, 77; actg head, Electron Linac Lab, Nat Res Coun, 77-; secy, Comt Intermediate & High Energy Physics, NSERC, 78-; proj mgr, Can Synchrotron Radiation Fac, 78- *Honors & Awards:* Farrington Daniels Award Achievement Radiation Dosimetry, Am Asn Physicists Med, 75. *Mem:* AAAS; Am Phys Soc; NY Acad Sci; Can Asn Physicists; Youth Sci Found (pres, 76-78). *Res:* Superconducting nuclear particle detector; magnesium photofission; lithium phototritons; proton scattering; shielding; radiation-damage reversal; de-excitation neutrons; bremsstrahlung spectra, radiators, filters, depth dose; photoneutron fine structure by time-of-flight; photon total absorption; liquid-deuterium. *Mailing Add:* Physics Div Nat Res Coun Ottawa ON K1H 6C2 Can

SHERMAN, PATSY O'CONNELL, b Minneapolis, Minn, Sept 15, 30; m 53; c 2. POLYMER CHEMISTRY, APPLIED CHEMISTRY. *Educ:* Gustavus Adolphus Col, BA, 52. *Prof Exp:* Chemist cent res dept, 52-57, chemist chem div, 57-67, res specialist, 67-70, sr res specialist, 70-73, res mgr chem resources div, 73-81, MGR TECH EDUC, MINN MINING & MFG CO, 82- *Mem:* Am Chem Soc. *Res:* Fluorine-containing polymers. *Mailing Add:* Minn Mining & Mfg Co 3M Ctr Bldg 224-2N-09 St Paul MN 55144

SHERMAN, PAUL DWIGHT, JR, b San Diego, Calif, May 18, 42; m 63; c 2. INDUSTRIAL ORGANIC CHEMISTRY. *Educ:* Univ NH, BS, 64; Brown Univ, PhD(org chem), 70. *Prof Exp:* PROJ SCIENTIST, UNION CARBIDE CORP, 68-, GROUP LEADER & TECHNOL MGR, 76- *Mem:* Am Chem Soc. *Res:* Application of analytical techniques for the solution of industrial process problems; organic-analytical chemistry; hydroformylation process development. *Mailing Add:* 1014 Knob Way South Charleston WV 25309

SHERMAN, PAUL WILLARD, b July 6, 49; US citizen. EVOLUTIONARY BIOLOGY, ANIMAL BEHAVIOR. *Educ:* Stanford Univ, BA, 71; Univ Mich, MS, 74, PhD(biol), 76. *Prof Exp:* Miller fel zool, Univ Calif, Berkeley, 76-78, asst prof psychol, 78-80; ASST PROF NEUROBIOL & BEHAV, CORNELL UNIV, 80- *Honors & Awards:* A B Howell Award, Cooper Ornith Soc, 74; A M Jackson Award, Am Soc Mammalogists, 77. *Mem:* AAAS; Animal Behav Soc; Cooper Ornith Soc. *Res:* Evolution and elaboration of social behavior. *Mailing Add:* Neruobiol & Behav Dept Cornell Univ Ithaca NY 14850

SHERMAN, PAULINE M, b New York, NY, Aug 27, 21; m 49. GAS DYNAMICS, CONDENSED PARTICULATES. *Educ:* Univ Calif, Berkeley, MSE, 55. *Prof Exp:* Res assoc, Univ Mich, 52-53; res engr, Univ Calif, 53-56; assoc res engr, 56-58, from lectr to assoc prof, 58-71, PROF AEROSPACE ENG, UNIV MICH, ANN ARBOR, 71- *Concurrent Pos:* Consult, Adv Group Aeronaut Res & Develop, 61; Environ Protection Agency, 71-72 & Lawrence Berkeley Lab, 77- *Mem:* Am Inst Aeronaut & Astronaut. *Res:* Gas dynamics. *Mailing Add:* Dept Aerospace Eng Univ Mich Ann Arbor MI 48109

SHERMAN, PHILIP M(ARTIN), b Norwalk, Conn, July 10, 30; m 55; c 3. STRATEGIC PLANNING, COMPUTER SCIENCE. *Educ:* Cornell Univ, BEPhys, 52; Yale Univ, MEng, 56, PhD(elec eng), 59. *Prof Exp:* Engr, Sperry Gyroscope Co, NY, 52-55; instr elec eng, Yale Univ, 57-59; engr, Bell Tel Labs, 59-63, supvr, 63-67, dept head, 67-69; mgr info systs, 69-76, MGR TECHNOL PLANNING, WEBSTER RES CTR, XEROX CORP, 76- *Mem:* Inst Elec & Electronics Engrs; Asn Comput Mach. *Res:* Computer programming and analysis; systems analysis; computer language studies; computer data management. *Mailing Add:* Webster Res Ctr Xerox Corp 800 Phillips Rd Webster NY 14580

SHERMAN, ROBERT GEORGE, b Charlevoix, Mich, Mar 22, 42; m 65; c 2. NEUROPHYSIOLOGY, ZOOLOGY. *Educ:* Alma Col, BS, 64; Mich State Univ, MS, 67, PhD(zool), 69. *Prof Exp:* USPHS fel, Univ Toronto, 69-70, spec fel, 70-71; from asst prof to assoc prof physiol, Clark Univ, 71-78; PROF & CHMN ZOOL, MIAMI UNIV, 78- *Mem:* Am Soc Zool; NY Acad Sci; Soc Gen Physiologists; Soc Neurosci; Electron Microscopy Soc Am. *Res:* Structure and function of synapses in arthropods; ultrastructure of arthropod muscle; cardiac physiology of arthropods; development of nerve and muscle. *Mailing Add:* Dept of Zool Miami Univ Oxford OH 45056

SHERMAN, ROBERT HOWARD, b Chicago, Ill, Nov 18, 29. PHYSICAL CHEMISTRY, CRYOGENICS. *Educ:* Ill Inst Technol, BS, 51; Univ Calif, PhD(chem), 55. *Prof Exp:* STAFF MEM, LOS ALAMOS SCI LAB, 55- *Concurrent Pos:* Consult, Argonne Nat Lab, 59-60. *Mem:* Am Chem Soc; Am Phys Soc. *Res:* Thermodynamics, especially at low temperatures; liquid helium; critical point phenomena; hydrogen isotope technology (tritium). *Mailing Add:* Group Q-10 Los Alamos Sci Lab PO BOx 1663 Los Alamos NM 87545

SHERMAN, ROBERT JAMES, b Bristow, Iowa, July 28, 40; m 62; c 1. BOTANY, ECOLOGY. *Educ:* Coe Col, BA, 62; Ore State Univ, MS, 66, PhD(bot), 68. *Prof Exp:* Teacher high sch, Iowa, 62-64; asst prof biol, Univ Colo, Colorado Springs, 68-70; chmn dept, 75-78, asst prof, 70-80, PROF BIOL, SONOMA STATE UNIV, 80- *Concurrent Pos:* Consult grasslands biome, Int Biol Prog, 69-70; NSF grants; Dept Health, Educ & Welfare grant. *Mem:* Ecol Soc Am. *Res:* Structure and pattern of Pinus ponderosa forests; fire ecology; autotutorial instruction. *Mailing Add:* Dept Biol Sonoma State Univ Rohnert Park CA 94928

SHERMAN, ROBERT S, b Pawtucket, RI, May 17, 09; m 42; c 3. MEDICINE. *Educ:* Brown Univ, PhB, 31; Harvard Med Sch, MD, 35. *Prof Exp:* Intern, Mem Hosp, Pawtucket, RI, 35-36; intern med, Long Island Col Hosp, Brooklyn, 36-37, resident radiol, 37-39; Fel, Mem Hosp, NY, 39-40, clin asst, 40, asst attend roentgenologist, 41; from asst prof to assoc prof clin radiol, Med Col, Cornell Univ, 47-58, clin prof, 58-80; RETIRED. *Concurrent Pos:* Jr asst resident, Tuberc Div, Boston City Hosp, 35; res radiologist, Pondville Hosp, Wrentham, Mass, 40; assoc attend roentgenologist, Mem Hosp, NY, 41-48, attend roentgenologist, 49-, chmn dept diag radiol, 49-68; consult roentgenologist, Cornwall Hosp, NY, 48-50; attend roentgenologist & chmn dept diag radiol, James Ewing Hosp, 49-; consult, Dept Diag Roentgenol, Strang Clin, 54-61 & Morristown Mem Hosp, NJ; consult radiol, NY Infirmary; corp consult radiol, IBM Corp, 67-77; consult, Health Examinetics, Inc, NY, 69-75. *Mem:* AAAS; Am Geriat Soc; Radiol Soc NAm; Am Col Radiol; James Ewing Soc. *Res:* Radiology; health screening through diagnostic radiology. *Mailing Add:* Squire Rd Roxbury CT 06783

SHERMAN, ROGER TALBOT, b Chicago, Ill, Sept 30, 23; m 52; c 5. SURGERY. *Educ:* Kenyon Col, AB, 46; Univ Cincinnati, MD, 48; Am Bd Surg, dipl, 57. *Prof Exp:* Fel path, St Luke's Hosp, Chicago, 49-50; asst resident surgeon, Cincinnati Gen Hosp, 50-55, instr surg, Col Med, Univ Cincinnati, 55-56; from asst prof to prof, Col Med, Univ Tenn, Memphis, 59-72; PROF SURG & CHMN DEPT, COL MED, UNIV S FLA, 72- *Mem:* Am Surg Asn; Am Asn Surg of Trauma. *Res:* Surgical infections, shock and trauma. *Mailing Add:* Med Ctr 12901 N 30th St Tampa FL 33612

SHERMAN, RONALD, b Philadelphia, Pa, Sept 5, 41; wid; c 2. ELECTRICAL ENGINEERING, APPLIED MATHEMATICS. *Educ:* Univ Pa, BSEE, 62, PhD(elec eng), 65; Columbia, MBA, 82. *Prof Exp:* Mem tech staff radar systs, 65-67, mem tech staff ocean systs, 67-70, supvr electromagnetic pulse eng & design principles group, 70-76, supvr systs anal & planning group, 76-80, SUPVR FINANCIAL MODELING STUDIES GROUP, BELL LABS, 80- *Concurrent Pos:* Vis sr lectr, Stevens Inst Technol, 69-71, assoc prof elec eng, 71-77, prof, 77-80. *Mem:* Inst Elec & Electronics Engrs. *Res:* Electromagnetics; effect of pulsed fields on communications systems; estimation and control theory; adaptive tracking; statistics; clustering algorithm development; financial model development. *Mailing Add:* Bell Labs 600 Mountain Ave Murray Hill NJ 07974

SHERMAN, SAMUEL MURRAY, b Pittsburgh, Pa, Jan 4, 44; m 69. NEUROSCIENCES, OPHTHALMOLOGY. *Educ:* Calif Inst Technol, BS, 65; Univ Pa, PhD(neuroanat), 69. *Prof Exp:* USPHS fel, Australian Nat Univ, 70-72; from asst prof to prof physiol, Sch Med, Univ Va, 72-78; prof anat, Dept Anat Sci, 79-80, PROF NEUROBIOL & BEHAV, STATE UNIV NY, STONY BROOK, 80- *Concurrent Pos:* NSF res grant, 73-; USPHS res grant, 75-; USPHS res career develop award, 75-80; mem, Visual Sci B Study Sect, NIH, 75-79. *Mem:* Soc Neurosci; Am Physiol Soc; Am Asn Anat; Asn Res Vision & Ophthal. *Res:* Neurophysiology, neuroanatomy and behavior of mammalian visual system with emphasis on postnatal visual development. *Mailing Add:* Dept Neurobiol & Behav State Univ of NY Stony Brook NY 11794

SHERMAN, SEYMOUR, b New York, NY, Dec 4, 24; m 55; c 2. SYSTEMS DESIGN, SYSTEMS SCIENCE. *Educ:* City Col New York, BEE, 47; Harvard Univ, MS, 48; NY Univ, PhD(math), 62. *Prof Exp:* Pres, Compudat Sci Systs, Inc, 68-71; pres, Seymour Sherman & Co, 71-72; vpres new prod develop, Utility Comput Systs, Inc, Evers Systs Corp, 72-75; SR SYSTS MGR & ASST VPRES, MERRILL LYNCH, PIERCE, FENNER & SMITH, INC, 75- *Concurrent Pos:* Instr, City Col New York, 48-49. *Mem:* Soc Mgt & Info Syst; Asn Comput Mach; Inst Elec & Electronics Engrs; Inst Mgt Sci. *Res:* Management sciences; computer sciences and management information systems. *Mailing Add:* 17 Timber Dr North Caldwell NJ 07006

SHERMAN, THOMAS FAIRCHILD, b Ithaca, NY, May 25, 34; m 70; c 5. BIOLOGY. *Educ:* Oberlin Col, AB, 56; Oxford Univ, DPhil(biochem), 60. *Prof Exp:* Vis asst prof zool, Oberlin Col, 60-61; res fel hist sci, Yale Univ, 61-62; vis asst prof zool, Pomona Col, 62-65; res fel math biol, Harvard Univ, 65-66; asst prof biol, 66-68, assoc prof, 68-79, PROF BIOL, OBERLIN COL, 68- *Res:* Vascular branching; connective tissue transport; history of science. *Mailing Add:* Dept Biol Oberlin Col Oberlin OH 44074

SHERMAN, THOMAS LAWRENCE, b Los Angeles, Calif, Nov 17, 37. MATHEMATICS. *Educ:* Univ Calif, Los Angeles, AB, 59; Univ Utah, MS, 61, PhD(math), 63. *Prof Exp:* Mem, US Army Math Res Ctr, Univ Wis, 63-64; from asst prof to assoc prof, 64-74, PROF MATH, ARIZ STATE UNIV, 74- *Mem:* Am Math Soc; Math Asn Am; Soc Indust & Appl Math. *Res:* Ordinary differential equations. *Mailing Add:* Dept of Math 120 E McKellips Tempe AZ 85281

SHERMAN, THOMAS OAKLEY, b Brooklyn, NY, May 6, 39; m 61; c 3. MATHEMATICS. *Educ:* Mass Inst Technol, BS, 60, PhD(math), 64. *Prof Exp:* Mem staff math, Inst Advan Study, 64-65; asst prof, Brandeis Univ, 65-69; asst prof, 69-70, ASSOC PROF MATH, NORTHEASTERN UNIV, 70- *Res:* Lie groups; harmonic analysis; numerical analysis. *Mailing Add:* Dept Math Northeastern Univ Boston MA 02115

SHERMAN, WARREN V, b London, Eng, Jan 7, 37; m 63; c 2. RADIATION CHEMISTRY, PHOTOBIOLOGY. *Educ:* Univ London, BSc, 58, PhD(org chem), 61. *Prof Exp:* Fulbright res fel chem, Brandeis Univ, 61-63; res fel, US Army Natick Lab, 63-64 & Israel Atomic Energy Comn, 64-66; res fel radiation lab, Univ Notre Dame, 66-68; assoc prof, 68-74, PROF CHEM, CHICAGO STATE UNIV, 74- *Concurrent Pos:* NSF fac develop grant, 79-80; vis prof physics, Ill Inst Technol, 79-80. *Mem:* Am Chem Soc; Royal Soc Chem; fel Europ Molecular Biol Orgn; Royal Inst Chem; Am Soc Photobiol. *Res:* Photochemistry and high-energy radiation chemistry of organic and biological compounds; visual pigments. *Mailing Add:* Dept of Phys Sci Chicago State Univ Chicago IL 60628

SHERMAN, WAYNE BUSH, b Lena, Miss, Feb 25, 40; m 63; c 1. PLANT BREEDING, HORTICULTURE. *Educ:* Miss State Univ, BS, 61, MS, 63; Purdue Univ, PhD(hort), 66. *Prof Exp:* Asst prof hort, 66-72, assoc prof, 72-78, PROF HORT, UNIV FLA, 78- *Mem:* Am Soc Hort Sci; Am Pomol Soc. *Res:* Fruit crops. *Mailing Add:* Dept of Fruit Crops 1181 McCarty Hall Univ of Fla Gainesville FL 32611

SHERMAN, WILLIAM REESE, b Seattle, Wash, Jan 18, 28; m 51; c 2. ORGANIC CHEMISTRY, BIOCHEMISTRY. *Educ:* Columbia Univ, AB, 51; Univ Ill, PhD(org chem), 55. *Prof Exp:* Sr res chemist, Abbott Labs, 55-59, group leader, 59-61; res asst, 61-63, res asst prof, 63-69, assoc prof, 69-75, PROF BIOCHEM, DEPT PSYCHIAT, SCH MED, WASHINGTON UNIV, 75-, PROF BIOL CHEM, DEPT BIOL CHEM, 78- *Mem:* Am Chem Soc; Int Soc Neurochem; Am Soc Neurochem; Am Soc Mass Spectrometry; Fedn Am Socs Exp Biol. *Res:* Biochemistry of inositols and inositides; biochemical applications of gas chromatography-mass spectrometry. *Mailing Add:* Dept of Psychiat Washington Univ Sch of Med St Louis MO 63110

SHERMAN, ZACHARY, b New York, NY, Oct 26, 22; m 47; c 2. STRUCTURAL ENGINEERING, MECHANICAL ENGINEERING. *Educ:* City Col New York, BCE, 43; Polytech Inst Brooklyn, MCE, 53, PhD(mech, struct), 69; Stevens Inst Technol, MME, 68. *Prof Exp:* Stress analyst, Gen Dynamics, Calif & Tex, 43-45; sr stress analyst, Repub Aviation Corp, 45-47; struct designer, Cent RR of NJ, 48-49; struct engr, Parsons, Brinckerhoff, Hall & MacDonald, New York, 49-51; designer-in-chg, F L Ehasz, 51-52; engr-in-chg, Loewy-Hydropress Co, 52-54; from assoc prof to prof civil eng, Univ Miss, 54-59; prin engr, Repub Aviation Corp, 59-62; in-chg stress anal lab, Stevens Inst Technol, 62-67; lectr civil eng, City Col New York, 67-69; assoc prof aerospace eng, Pa State Univ, 69-73; CONSULT ENGR, 73- *Concurrent Pos:* Consult engr, S S Kenworthy Eng & Concrete Eng Co, Tenn, 54-58; independent consult engr, indust & ins, 58-; NSF int travel grant to Int Aeronaut Fedn Cong, 71; adj prof civil eng, Sch Eng, Cooper Union, 73- *Mem:* Fel Am Soc Civil Engrs; Am Inst Aeronaut & Astronaut; Am Soc Eng Educ. *Res:* Dynamics and vibrations; optimization; tornado resistant construction; design; elasticity. *Mailing Add:* 109 N Broadway White Plains NY 10603

SHEROCKMAN, ANDREW ANTOLCIK, b Raccon, Pa, July 19, 13; m 43. INORGANIC CHEMISTRY. *Educ:* Dubuque Univ, BA, 35; Univ Pittsburgh, MA, 45, PhD, 55. *Prof Exp:* Teacher high sch, Pa, 35-42; prof chem, Evansville Col, 46-55; dir naval reactor training & tech educ, Bettis Atomic Power Lab, Westinghouse Elec Corp, 55-59; SUPVR TECH INFO SERV, NAT STEEL CORP, 59- *Concurrent Pos:* Consult. *Mem:* Fel AAAS; Am Chem Soc; Nat Sci Teachers Asn. *Res:* Technical information and editing; science education. *Mailing Add:* Res & Develop Dept Box 596-B McMichael Rd Pittsburgh PA 15205

SHERR, ALLAN ELLIS, b Detroit, Mich, July 26, 26; m 55; c 3. ORGANIC CHEMISTRY, TOXICOLOGY. *Educ:* Wayne State Univ, BS, 48, MS, 51, PhD(chem), 56. *Prof Exp:* Chief chemist, Radioactive Prods, Inc, Mich, 51; res chemist, Conn, 55-57, tech rep new prod develop dept, NY, 57-58, res chemist, 58-60, group leader res div, Conn, 60-66, group leader, 67-77, Am Cyanamid Co; tech dir, Glendale Optical Co, 71-77; coordr toxic chem regist, Cent Res Div, 77-79, APPROVALS MGR, TOXICOL DEPT, CHEMICALS GROUP, AM CYANAMID CO, 79- *Concurrent Pos:* Mem comt safe use of lasers & masers, Am Nat Standards Inst; chief US del, Inst Standards Orgn Comt Eye Safety, 74-80; sci adv, Glendale Optical Co, 77- *Mem:* AAAS; Soc Plastics Eng; Sigma Xi; Indust Safety Equipment Asn; Am Chem Soc. *Res:* Synthetic organic chemistry; preparation and properties of polymers; additives to modify properties of polymers; personal safety equipment as respirators, safety spectacles, laser goggles, hearing protectors and head protection; optical plastics, flame retardance; toxicology; national and international health and safety regulations. *Mailing Add:* Am Cyanamid Co Bound Brook NJ 08805

SHERR, EVELYN BROWN, b Dublin, Ga, Dec 19, 46; m 79. MARINE ECOLOGY. *Educ:* Emory Univ , BS, 69; Duke Univ, PhD(zool), 74. *Prof Exp:* Res assoc microbiol, Univ Ga, 74-75, RES ASSOC MARINE ECOL, MARINE INST, UNIV GA, 75- *Mem:* AAAS; Am Soc Limnol & Oceanog; Ecol Soc Am; Am Soc Microbiol. *Res:* Nitrogen cycle in coastal ecosystems; dynamics of coastal phytoplankton production; carbon flows in a salt marsh estuary by analysis of the stable carbon isotope composition of organic matter; ecological roles of heterotrophic microprotozoa. *Mailing Add:* Marine Inst Univ Ga Sapelo Island GA 31327

SHERR, RUBBY, b Long Branch, NJ, Sept 14, 13; m 36; c 2. NUCLEAR PHYSICS. *Educ:* NY Univ, BA, 34; Princeton Univ, PhD(physics), 38. *Prof Exp:* Asst radioactivity, Harvard Univ, 38-39, instr nuclear physics, 39-42; staff mem radiation lab, Mass Inst Technol, 42-44; staff mem, Manhattan Proj, Los Alamos Sci Lab, Univ Calif, 44-46; from asst prof to assoc prof, 46-58, PROF PHYSICS, PRINCETON UNIV, 58- *Mem:* Fel Am Phys Soc. *Res:* Radar systems; radioactivity; nuclear structure. *Mailing Add:* Dept of Physics Princeton Univ Princeton NJ 08540

SHERR, STANLEY I, b Washington, DC, Oct 17, 34; m 63; c 3. BIOCHEMISTRY. *Educ:* George Washington Univ, BS, 57, MS, 58, PhD(biochem), 64. *Prof Exp:* Res assoc biochem, Harvard Univ, 63-65; asst prof, 65-71, ASSOC PROF BIOCHEM, UNIV MED & DENT NJ, 72- *Mem:* AAAS; Am Soc Microbiol. *Res:* Pulmonary fat embolism and its relation to trauma; lipid metabolism in bacteria and fungi; intestinal absorption and metabolism of lipids. *Mailing Add:* Dept Biochem NJ Med Sch Univ Med & Dent NJ Newark NJ 07103

SHERRARD, JOSEPH HOLMES, b Waynesboro, Va, June 12, 42; m 64. ENVIRONMENTAL ENGINEERING. *Educ:* Va Mil Inst, BS, 64; Sacramento State Col, MS, 69; Univ Calif, Davis, PhD(civil eng), 71. *Prof Exp:* Jr civil engr, Calif Div Hwy, 64-65; Zurn Industs fel, Cornell Univ, 71-72; asst prof bioeng, Okla State Univ, 72-74; ASSOC PROF CIVIL ENG, VA POLYTECH INST & STATE UNIV, 74- *Mem:* Am Soc Civil Engrs; Am Water Works Asn; Water Pollution Control Fedn. *Res:* Biological and chemical wastewater treatment. *Mailing Add:* Dept of Civil Eng Va Polytech Inst & State Univ Blacksburg VA 24060

SHERREN, ANNE TERRY, b Atlanta, Ga, July 1, 36; m 66. ANALYTICAL CHEMISTRY. *Educ:* Agnes Scott Col, BA, 57; Univ Fla, PhD(chem), 61. *Prof Exp:* Instr chem, Tex Woman's Univ, 61-63, asst prof, 63-66; chmn dept, 75-78, assoc prof, 66-76, PROF CHEM, NORTH CENT COL, ILL, 76-, CHMN DEPT, 81- *Mem:* AAAS; Am Chem Soc; Am Inst Chem; Coblentz Soc. *Res:* Turbidity measurements; technetium chemistry; neutron activation analysis; electrochemistry; absorption spectrophotometry. *Mailing Add:* Dept of Chem NCent Col Naperville IL 60540

SHERRER, ROBERT E(UGENE), b Abilene, Kans, Aug 20, 23; m 56; c 2. ENGINEERING MECHANICS. *Educ:* Univ Kans, BS, 48; Univ Wis, MS, 53, PhD(eng mech), 58. *Prof Exp:* Engr, Allis-Chalmers Mfg Co, 48-52; instr eng mech, Univ Wis, 52-57, asst prof, 57-60; ASSOC PROF MECH ENG, UNIV WASH, 60- *Concurrent Pos:* Consult, Forest Prod Lab, Madison, Wis, 56-58 & Boeing Co, 60- *Mem:* Am Soc Eng Educ. *Res:* Fluid and solid mechanics; mechanical vibration; structural analysis; materials; dynamics. *Mailing Add:* Dept of Mech Eng Univ of Wash Seattle WA 98105

SHERRICK, JOSEPH C, b Monmouth, Ill, June 4, 17; m 44; c 3. PATHOLOGY. *Educ:* Monmouth Col, Ill, BA, 37; Harvard Med Sch, MD, 41. *Prof Exp:* Demonstr path, Sch Med, Western Reserve Univ, 43-44; fel, Med Sch, Northwestern Univ, 51-52; instr, Northwestern Univ, 53-54, assoc, 54-55; asst prof, Univ Ill Col Med, 56-59; from asst prof to assoc prof, 56-67, PROF PATH, MED SCH, NORTHWESTERN UNIV, CHICAGO, 67- *Concurrent Pos:* Ill Div Am Cancer Soc grant, 63-67. *Mem:* AAAS; Asn Clin Sci (pres, 64); Col Am Path; Am Soc Clin Path; Am Asn Path & Bact. *Res:* Cancer research; clinical pathology. *Mailing Add:* Dept of Path Northwestern Univ Med Sch Chicago IL 60611

SHERRILL, BETTE CECILE BENHAM, b Vernon, Tex, Aug 7, 44; m 63; c 2. PHYSICAL CHEMISTRY, BIOCHEMISTRY. *Educ:* NMex State Univ, BS, 66; Tex Christian Univ, PhD(phys chem), 73. *Prof Exp:* Asst scientist rocket telemetry, Phys Sci Lab, White Sands Missile Range, 62-66; res fel membrane transp, Dept Internal Med, Univ Tex Health Sci Ctr, 73-75, instr, 75-77, asst prof cholesterol metab & membrane transp, 77-81; ASST PROF LIPOPROTEIN METAB & MEMBRANE TRANSP, DEPTS MED & BIOCHEM, BAYLOR COL MED, 81- *Concurrent Pos:* Res asst chem, NMex State Univ, 66-67; res fel, Robert A Welch Res Found, 73 & NIH grant, 73-75; consult, Sherrill Eng Consults, Inc, Irving, Tex, 78-; consult & pres, Sherrill Environ Consult Inc, Houston, 81-; estab investr, Am Heart Asn. *Mem:* Am Heart Asn; Am Chem Soc; Biophys Soc; Sigma Xi; fel Am Inst Chemists. *Res:* Membrane transport; hepatic transport kinetics of intestinal and serum lipoproteins; thermodynamic properties of lipids; liquid diffusion studies. *Mailing Add:* Baylor Col Med 6565 Fannin Houston TX 77030

SHERRILL, EUGENE A(LLAN), b Valparaiso, Nebr, June 16, 20; m 40; c 6. HYDROMECHANICS, ELECTROHYDRAULICS. *Educ:* LaSalle Exten Univ, cert, 52. *Prof Exp:* Draftsman, Prod Div, 41-42, technician, 42-45, engr, 47-55, sr engr, Bendix Missile Systs Div, 55-59, chief engr, 59-64, div staff engr, 64-70, supvry engr, 70-76, STAFF ENGR, BENDIX AEROSPACE SYSTS DIV, MISHAWAKA, 76- *Mem:* Am Inst Aeronaut & Astronaut; Soc Automotive Engrs; Am Soc Photogram. *Res:* Spacecraft auxiliary power systems; missile auxiliary power and inertial guidance systems; mass transportation guidance systems; photogrammetric devices. *Mailing Add:* Bendix Aerospace Systs Div 400 S Beiger St Mishawaka IN 46544

SHERRILL, J(OSEPH) C(YRIL), b Philadelphia, Pa, Nov 18, 17; m 42; c 3. CHEMICAL ENGINEERING. *Educ:* Pa State Univ, BS, 41, MS, 47, PhD(chem), 52. *Prof Exp:* Asst petrol res, Pa State Univ, 41-47, instr textile chem, 47-52; prof detergency res & asst dean, Tex Woman's Univ, 52-57; sect head detergency eval, Armour & Co, 57-58, mgr soap res, 58-59, sales mgr pvt brand detergents, Armour Grocery Prod Co, 59-69; mkt mgr, Darrill Industs, Inc, 69-71; PRES, SHERRILL ASSOCS, INC, 71- *Mem:* Am Inst Chemists; Am Inst Chem Engrs. *Res:* Detergency evaluation; forces bonding soils to surfaces, especially fabric surfaces; ultrasonic methods for evaluation of detergency. *Mailing Add:* 2360 Maple Rd Homewood IL 60430

SHERRILL, MAX DOUGLAS, b Hickory, NC, Jan 2, 30; m 55; c 5. SOLID STATE PHYSICS. *Educ:* Univ NC, BS, 52, PhD(physics), 61. *Prof Exp:* Physicist, Gen Elec Res & Develop Ctr, 60-67; assoc prof physics, 67-75, PROF PHYSICS, CLEMSON UNIV, 75- *Mem:* Am Phys Soc. *Res:* Electrical and magnetic properties of metals, particularly superconductivity. *Mailing Add:* Dept of Physics & Astron Clemson Univ Clemson SC 29631

SHERRILL, WILLIAM MANNING, b San Antonio, Tex, Feb 23, 36; m 58; c 3. RADIOPHYSICS. *Educ:* Univ Tex, BA & BS, 57; Rice Univ, MS, 59. *Prof Exp:* Anal engr, Pratt & Whitney Aircraft Div, United Aircraft Corp, Conn, 58-59; res engr, 59-63, sr res engr, 63-66, mgr intercept & direction finding res, 66-71, asst dir dept appl electromagnetics, 71-74, DIR DEPT RADIO LOCATION SCI, SOUTHWEST RES INST, 74- *Mem:* Inst Elec & Electronics Eng; Am Astron Soc; Sigma Xi. *Res:* Ionospheric propagation and mode angular spectra; radio location research; high frequency radio direction finding; solar system radio astronomy. *Mailing Add:* Southwest Res Inst 6220 Culebra Rd San Antonio TX 78285

SHERRIS, JOHN C, b Colchester, Eng, Mar 8, 21; m 44; c 2. MICROBIOLOGY. *Educ:* Univ London, MRCS & LRCP, 44, MB & BS, 48, MD, 50; Am Bd Med Microbiol, dipl, 61; FRCPath. *Hon Degrees:* Dr med, Karolinska Inst, Sweden, 75. *Prof Exp:* House surgeon & physician med, King Edward VII Hosp, Windsor, Eng, 44-45; trainee path & microbiol, Stoke Mandeville Hosp, 45-48, sr registr, 48-50; sr registr, Radcliffe Infirmary, Oxford, 50-52; lectr bact, Univ Manchester, 53-56, sr lectr, 56-59; assoc prof microbiol, 59-63, chmn dept, 70-80, PROF MICROBIOL, SCH MED, UNIV WASH, 63- *Concurrent Pos:* Chmn, Am Bd Med Microbiol, 71-73; vchmn Am Acad Microbiol, 76-78. *Honors & Awards:* Becton- Dickinson Award, Am Soc Microbiol, 78. *Mem:* Fel Am Acad Microbiol; Am Soc Microbiol (pres-elect, 81); Brit Asn Clin Path; Brit Soc Gen Microbiol. *Res:* Clinical microbiology; chemotherapy; pathogenesis of infection. *Mailing Add:* Dept of Microbiol & Immunol SC-42 Univ of Wash Seattle WA 98195

SHERRITT, GRANT WILSON, b Hunter, NDak, Mar 27, 23; m 52; c 3. ANIMAL SCIENCE. *Educ:* Iowa State Univ, BS, 48; Univ Ill, MS, 49; Pa State Univ, PhD(animal husb), 61. *Prof Exp:* Asst animal sci, Univ Ill, 48-49; instr animal husb, 49-61, asst prof animal sci, 62-81, ASSOC PROF ANIMAL SCI, PA STATE UNIV, 81- *Concurrent Pos:* Mem comt, Nat Swine Indust, 63. *Mem:* AAAS; Am Soc Animal Sci. *Res:* Crossbreeding and selection experiments in swine breeding; swine management studies, especially as related to the sow. *Mailing Add:* Dept of Animal Sci Pa State Univ University Park PA 16802

SHERROD, LLOYD B, b Goodland, Kans, Mar 5, 31; m 63; c 2. ANIMAL NUTRITION. *Educ:* SDak State Univ, BS, 58; Univ Ark, MS, 60; Okla State Univ, PhD(animal nutrit), 64. *Prof Exp:* Asst animal scientist, Univ Hawaii, 64-67; assoc prof animal sci, Res Ctr, Tex Tech Univ, 67-73, prof, 73-79; PROF CHEM, FRANK PHILLIPS COL, BORGER, TEX, 79- *Mem:* AAAS; Am Inst Biol Sci; Am Soc Agron; Am Dairy Sci Asn; Am Soc Animal Sci. *Res:* Ruminant animal nutrition research with emphasis on factors influencing ration component digestibility, nutrient utilization and retention and nutrient requirements. *Mailing Add:* PO Box 1017 Pantex TX 79068

SHERROD, THEODORE ROOSEVELT, b Ala, July 29, 15; m 41; c 1. PHARMACOLOGY. *Educ:* Talladega Col, AB, 38; Univ Chicago, MS, 41; Univ Ill, PhD(pharmacol), 45, MD, 49. *Prof Exp:* From instr to assoc prof, 45-58, PROF PHARMACOL, UNIV ILL COL MED, 58- *Mem:* Am Soc Pharmacol & Exp Therapeut; Soc Exp Biol & Med. *Res:* Cardiovascular and renal pharmacology. *Mailing Add:* Dept of Pharmacol Univ of Ill Col of Med Chicago IL 60612

SHERRY, ALLAN DEAN, b Viroqua, Wis, Oct 13, 45; m 65; c 2. BIOINORGANIC CHEMISTRY. *Educ:* Wis State Univ, LaCrosse, BS, 67; Kans State Univ, PhD(inorg chem), 71. *Prof Exp:* Fel bioinorg chem, NIH, 71-72; asst prof, 72-80, ASSOC PROF CHEM, UNIV TEX, DALLAS, 80- *Mem:* Am Chem Soc. *Res:* Aqueous lanthanide chemistry; lanthanides as probes of calcium sites in proteins; fluorescence and NMR spectroscopy of metalloproteins. *Mailing Add:* Dept of Chem PO Box 688 Richardson TX 75080

SHERRY, CLIFFORD JOSEPH, b Chicago, Ill, Jan 16, 43; m 69; c 3. NEUROPHYSIOLOGY. *Prof Exp:* Res assoc pharmacol, Med Sch, Univ Ill, 74-75; instr, 75-77, ASST PROF BIOL, TEX A&M UNIV, 77- *Mem:* Neurosci Soc. *Res:* Neurophysiology, especially the relationship beteen single neuron activity and behavior; neuroembryology; behavioral teratology; teratology; psychobiology and psychopharmacology, especially hallucinogens; psychobiology of reproductive and sexual behavior. *Mailing Add:* Dept Biol Tex A&M Univ College Station TX 77843

SHERRY, EDWIN J, b Jamaica, NY, Nov 10, 33; m 65; c 2. MATHEMATICS. *Educ:* Fordham Univ, AB, 57, MA, 59 & 61; Yeshiva Univ, PhD(math), 64. *Prof Exp:* Instr math & physics, Brooklyn Prep Sch, 58-59; res asst, Univ NMex, 63-64; mem tech staff, Sandia Labs, 65-67; MEM TECH STAFF, JET PROPULSION LAB, CALIF INST TECHNOL, 67- *Concurrent Pos:* Vis lectr, Univ NMex, 65-67. *Mem:* Am Math Soc; NY Acad Sci. *Res:* Partial differential equations; operations research and analysis of the planetary quarantine problem; development of a computer model to simulate the microbial accumulation on a spacecraft during assembly; the problem of assaying low levels of microbial contamination. *Mailing Add:* PO Box 822 La Canada CA 91011

SHERRY, HOWARD S, b New York, NY, Nov 18, 30; m 55; c 4. PHYSICAL INORGANIC CHEMISTRY, CHEMICAL ENGINEERING. *Educ:* NY Univ, BSChE, 57; State Univ NY Buffalo, MA, 62, PhD(phys chem), 63. *Prof Exp:* Res chem engr, Union Carbide Metals Co, 57-59; Union Carbide fel, 62-63; sr res chem appl res & develop div, Mobil Res & Develop Corp, 63-65; vis lectr chem, Univ Colo, 65-66; sr res chem cent res div, Mobil Res & Develop Corp, 66-69, res assoc, 69-71, res assoc appl res div, 71-77; tech mgr,

Res & Develop Div, 77-80, VENTURE MGR ZEOLITES, PQ CORP, 80- *Concurrent Pos:* Mem panel rare earths, Nat Acad Sci, 69. *Mem:* Am Chem Soc; Am Inst Chem Engrs; Mineral Soc Am; Catalysis Soc; Int Zeolite Asn. *Res:* Catalysis; ion exchange in zeolites; zeolite science and technology and catalysis; rare earth chemistry. *Mailing Add:* 416 S Crawford Rd Cherry Hill NJ 08003

SHERRY, PETER BURUM, b Augusta, Ga, Mar 22, 25. PHYSICAL CHEMISTRY. *Educ:* Ga Inst Technol, BS, 49, MS, 51; Univ Va, PhD, 56. *Prof Exp:* Fulbright fel, Oxford Univ, 55-56, Ramsay Mem fel, 56-57; asst prof, 57-67, ASSOC PROF CHEM, GA INST TECHNOL, 67- *Mem:* AAAS; Am Chem Soc; Am Phys Soc. *Res:* Solid state chemistry; application of quantum mechanics to the theory of solids; surface chemistry of well characterized surfaces; transport properties of solids. *Mailing Add:* Sch of Chem Ga Inst of Technol Atlanta GA 30332

SHERRY, SOL, b New York, NY, Dec 8, 16; m 46; c 2. MEDICINE. *Educ:* NY Univ, BA, 35, MD, 39. *Hon Degrees:* DSc, Temple Univ, 80. *Prof Exp:* Fel med, Col Med, NY Univ, 39-41; intern & resident, Bellevue Hosp, 41-42 & 46; asst, NY Univ, 46-47; from instr to asst prof, 47-51; asst prof, Univ Cincinnati, 51-54; from assoc prof to prof med, Sch Med, Washington Univ, 54-68; PROF INTERNAL MED & CHMN DIV MED, SCH MED, TEMPLE UNIV, 68-, DIR THROMBOSIS RES CTR, 71- *Concurrent Pos:* Dir, May Inst Med Res, Cincinnati, Ohio, 51-54 & med serv, Jewish Hosp, 54-58; chmn coun thrombosis, Am Heart Asn; chmn subcomt clin invest, Int Comt Haemostasis & Thrombosis; chmn coun thrombosis, Int Soc Cardiol; former chmn thrombosis, thrombolytic agents & gen clin res, NIH & task force on thrombosis, Nat Acad Sci-Nat Res Coun; selections comt for career res, Vet Admin; emer consult, US Army & Develop Command; NIH career res award. *Honors & Awards:* Typhus Comn Medal, US Army; Robert Grant Medal, Inst Soc Thrombosis & Haemostasis; John Phillips Medal, Am Col Physicians; Founder's Medal, Am Col Cardiol. *Mem:* Am Soc Clin Invest; Asn Am Physicians; Int Soc Cardiol; Int Soc Thrombosis & Haemostasis (pres); Asn Prof Med (pres). *Res:* Thrombosis research; fibrinolysis, coagulation and hemostasis. *Mailing Add:* Dept of Internal Med Temple Univ Sch of Med Philadelphia PA 19140

SHERSHIN, ANTHONY CONNORS, b Clifton, NJ, Oct 16, 39; m 68; c 3. OPERATIONS RESEARCH, MATHEMATICS. *Educ:* Georgetown Univ, AB, 61; Univ Fla, MS, 63, PhD(math), 67. *Prof Exp:* Opers res anal autonetics div, NAm Rockwell Corp, 63-64; asst prof math, Univ SFla, 67-72; assoc prof, 72-74, ASSOC PROF MATH, FLA INT UNIV, 74- *Mem:* Am Math Asn; Opers Res Soc Am. *Res:* Graph theory; networks; computer algorithms. *Mailing Add:* Dept of Math Sci Fla Int Univ Miami FL 33199

SHERWIN, ALLAN LEONARD, b Montreal, Jan 29, 32; m 64; c 1. NEUROLOGY, IMMUNOCHEMISTRY. *Educ:* McGill Univ, BSc, 53, MD & CM, 57, PhD(immunochem), 65; FRCPS(C), 64. *Prof Exp:* Life Ins Med Res Fund fel, 60-61, instr neurol, 62-65, asst prof neurol & asst neurologist, 65-71, ASSOC PROF NEUROL & NEUROLOGIST, McGILL UNIV, 72- *Concurrent Pos:* Markle scholar acad med, 62-67. *Mem:* Am Acad Neurol; Can Neurol Soc; Can Med Asn. *Res:* Clinical neuropharmacology; antiepileptic drugs. *Mailing Add:* Dept of Neurol McGill Univ Montreal PQ H3A 2A7 Can

SHERWIN, DUANE O, psychiatry, neurology, see previous edition

SHERWIN, MARTIN BARRY, b New York, NY, July 27, 38; m 64; c 2. CHEMICAL ENGINEERING. *Educ:* City Col New York, BChE, 60; Polytech Inst Brooklyn, MS, 63; City Univ New York, PhD(chem eng), 67. *Prof Exp:* Jr process engr, Sci Design Co, 60-62; process develop engr, Halcon Int, Inc, 62-64; lectr chem eng, City Col New York, 64-66; staff engr, Chem Systs, Inc, 66-68, mgr process develop, 68-69, dir res & develop, 69-71, vpres res & develop, 71-78, managing dir, Chem Systs Int, Ltd, 79-80; WITH W R GRACE & CO, 80- *Mem:* Am Inst Chem Engrs; Am Chem Soc. *Res:* Development of new and improved processes for the production of petrochemical intermediates. *Mailing Add:* W R Grace & Co 7379 Rt 32 Columbia MD 21044

SHERWIN, RUSSELL P, b New London, Conn, Mar 11, 24; m 48; c 3. PATHOLOGY. *Educ:* Boston Univ, MD, 48. *Prof Exp:* Instr path, Georgetown Univ, 49-50; instr, Boston Univ, 53-55, assoc, 55-61, asst prof, 61-62; asst prof, 62-63, Hastings assoc prof, 63-69, HASTINGS PROF PATH, SCH MED, UNIV SOUTHERN CALIF, 69- *Concurrent Pos:* Asst, Harvard Univ, 56-62; mem path ref panel asbestosis & neoplasia, Int Union Against Cancer, 65-; sci consult oncol, Vet Admin, Washington, DC, 71-74; mem subcomt exp biol, Nat Cancer Inst, 72-75; sci consult, Am Cancer Soc; mem res grants, Am Lung Asn, Air Qual Health Adv Comt State Calif. *Mem:* Am Soc Exp Path; Am Asn Cancer Res; Int Acad Path; AAAS. *Res:* Air quality standards and pollutant effects; cancer, specifically breast, lung and adrenal gland cancer; diseases of the lung, especially emphysema and fibrosis; histoculture; pathobiology; tissue culture; electromicroscopy; cinemicrography; histochemistry. *Mailing Add:* Dept of Path Univ of Southern Calif Sch Med Los Angeles CA 90033

SHERWOOD, A GILBERT, b Lloydminster, Sask, June 17, 30; m 53; c 2. PHYSICAL CHEMISTRY. *Educ:* Univ Man, BSc, 53, MSc, 58; Univ Alta, PhD(photochem), 64. *Prof Exp:* Fel, Univ Alta, 64-65; Nat Res Coun fel, 65-66; asst prof, 66-77, ASSOC PROF CHEM, SIMON FRASER UNIV, 77- *Mem:* Chem Inst Can. *Res:* Gas phase photochemistry; free radical kinetics; photoelectrochemistry; electrochemical storage of solar energy. *Mailing Add:* Dept of Chem Simon Fraser Univ Burnaby BC V5A 1S6 Can

SHERWOOD, ALBERT E(DWARD), b New Haven, Conn, Sept 19, 30; m 53; c 2. CHEMICAL ENGINEERING. *Educ:* Mass Inst Technol, SB & SM, 57; Univ Calif, Berkeley, PhD(chem eng), 64. *Prof Exp:* Chem engr, Esso Res & Eng Co, 57-58; res assoc molecular physics, Univ Md, 64-65; CHEMIST, LAWRENCE LIVERMORE NAT LAB, UNIV CALIF, 65- *Mem:* Am

Chem Soc; Am Nuclear Soc; Am Inst Chem Engrs. *Res:* Energy and mass transport; industrial applications of nuclear explosions; equations of state; mathematical modeling of in-situ coal gasification; tritium technology; containment and capture systems. *Mailing Add:* Lawrence Livermore Nat Lab Univ of Calif Livermore CA 94550

SHERWOOD, ALDEN G, b Lloydminster, Sask, June 17, 30; m 53; c 2. PHYSICAL CHEMISTRY. *Educ:* Univ Man, BSc, 53, MSc, 58; Univ Alta, PhD(chem), 64. *Prof Exp:* ASSOC PROF CHEM, SIMON FRASER UNIV, 66- *Mem:* Chem Inst Can. *Res:* Gas phase photochemistry; photoelectrochemistry; solar to electrical power conversion and storage. *Mailing Add:* Dept of Chem Simon Fraser Univ Burnaby BC V5A 1S6 Can

SHERWOOD, ARTHUR ROBERT, b Berkeley, Calif, Sept 6, 36; div; c 2. PLASMA PHYSICS. *Educ:* Pomona Col, BA, 58; Univ Calif, Berkeley, PhD(physics), 67. *Prof Exp:* Physicist, Lawrence Radiation Lab, 67, STAFF MEM PHYSICS, LOS ALAMOS SCI LAB, UNIV CALIF, 67- *Mem:* Am Phys Soc. *Res:* Experimental plasma physics, especially as related to the controlled thermonuclear reactor program. *Mailing Add:* 4332 Sycamore St Los Alamos NM 87544

SHERWOOD, BOB EDWIN, b Presho, SDak, May 10, 46; m 66; c 1. MEDICINAL CHEMISTRY, DRUG DELIVERY. *Educ:* SDak State Univ, BS, 68, MS, 69; Univ Wash, PhD(med chem), 73. *Prof Exp:* RES CHEMIST MED CHEM, COLUMBUS LABS, BATTELLE MEM INST, 73- *Mem:* Am Chem Soc; Sigma Xi. *Res:* Prodrug synthesis; development of chemical organ replacement devices and generation of immunoproteins for varied applications. *Mailing Add:* Battelle Mem Inst 505 King Ave Columbus OH 43201

SHERWOOD, BRUCE ARNE, b Laporte, Ind, Dec 12, 38; m 59; c 3. SPEECH SYNTHESIS. *Educ:* Purdue Univ, BS, 60; Univ Chicago, MS, 63, PhD(physics), 67. *Prof Exp:* Asst prof physics, Calif Inst Technol, 66-69; asst prof, 69-75, ASSOC PROF, COMPUT BASED EDUC RES LAB & DEPT PHYSICS, UNIV ILL, URBANA-CHAMPAIGN, 75- & ASSOC PROF, DEPT LING, 82- *Concurrent Pos:* Secy, Comn Int Confer Univ, Universal Esperanto Asn, Rotterdam, Neth, 80- *Mem:* Am Phys Soc; Am Asn Physics Teachers; AAAS; Ling Soc Am; Esperanto Studies Asn Am. *Res:* Design and development of Plato computer-based education system; computer-based physics teaching; multi-lingual speech synthesis; esperanto studies. *Mailing Add:* 252 Eng Res Lab 103 S Mathews Urbana IL 61801

SHERWOOD, JESSE EUGENE, b Pittsburgh, Pa, Dec 27, 22. ATOMIC PHYSICS. *Educ:* Univ Pittsburgh, BS, 43; Univ Md, MS, 52; Univ Ky, PhD(physics), 73. *Prof Exp:* Physicist, Nat Bur Standards, 49-53; physicist, Oak Ridge Nat Lab, 53-61; physicist, Lawrence Radiation Lab, 61-64; asst prof physics, Univ Miss, 64-66; staff physicist, Oak Ridge Tech Enterprises, 66-69; lectr physics, Univ Ky, 69-73; sr res officer nuclear physics res unit, Univ of Witwatersrand, Johannesburg, South Africa, 73; vis asst prof, NC State Univ, Raleigh, 75-76; from asst prof to assoc prof physics, Valdosta State Col, 76-80; ASSOC PROF CHEM, MIDWESTERN STATE UNIV, 80-81. *Mem:* Am Phys Soc. *Res:* Measurement of nuclear moments; magnetic behavior of the neutron; polarized ion sources; polarization of photoneutrons; measurement of fast neutron polarization from reactions; production and properties of negative ions. *Mailing Add:* Dept Chem Midwestern State Univ Wichita Falls TX 76308

SHERWOOD, LOUIS MAIER, b New York, NY, Mar 1, 37; m 66; c 2. ENDOCRINOLOGY, METABOLISM. *Educ:* Johns Hopkins Univ, AB, 57; Columbia Univ, MD, 61. *Prof Exp:* NIH trainee endocrinol & metab, Col Physicians & Surgeons, Columbia Univ, 64-68; assoc med, Harvard Med Sch, 68-69; from asst prof to assoc prof, 69-72; PROF MED, DIV BIOL SCI PRITZKER SCH MED, UNIV CHICAGO, 72-; PHYSICIAN-IN-CHIEF & CHMN DEPT MED, MICHAEL REESE HOSP, 72- *Concurrent Pos:* Chief endocrine unit, Beth Israel Hosp, Boston, Mass, 68-72; assoc physician, 71-72; attend physician, West Roxbury Vet Admin Hosp, 71-72; trustee, Michael Reese Hosp & Med Ctr, 74-77; mem gen med B study sect, NIH, 75-79; Macy Found fel, vis scientist, Weizmann Inst, Israel, 78-79. *Mem:* Endocrine Soc; Am Soc Biol Chem; Am Fedn Clin Res; Cent Soc Clin Res; Am Soc Clin Invest. *Res:* Protein chemistry, correlations between structure and function; polypeptide hormones-parathyroid hormones; human placental lactogen; correlations of structure-function and factors regulating synthesis and secretion. *Mailing Add:* Dept of Med Michael Reese Hosp & Med Ctr Chicago IL 60616

SHERWOOD, MARTHA ALLEN, b Eugene, Ore, Nov 8, 48. MYCOLOGY. *Educ:* Univ Ore, BA, 70; Cornell Univ, PhD(mycol), 77. *Prof Exp:* Fel mycol, Cornell Univ, 77; CRYPTOGAMIC BOTANIST, FARLOW HERBARIUM, HARVARD UNIV, 77- *Mem:* Mycol Soc Am; Am Bryol & Lichenol Soc. *Res:* Morphology and taxonomy of ascomycetes such as fungi, including lichens and monographic studies in the Ostropales and Phacidiales. *Mailing Add:* Farlow Herbarium Harvard Univ Cambridge MA 02138

SHERWOOD, ROBERT TINSLEY, b West Orange, NJ, Feb 21, 29; m 55; c 3. PLANT PATHOLOGY. *Educ:* Cornell Univ, BS, 52, MS, 54; Univ Wis, PhD, 58. *Prof Exp:* Res asst prof plant path, NC State Univ, 58-69, prof, 69-71; PLANT PATHOLOGIST, USDA, 58- *Concurrent Pos:* Adj prof, Pa State Univ, 71- *Mem:* Am Phytopath Soc; Soc Nematol. *Res:* Physiology of parasitism; forage crop disease; fungal diseases of plants. *Mailing Add:* US Regional Pasture Res Labs US Dept of Agr University Park PA 16802

SHERWOOD, WILLIAM CULLEN, b Washington, DC, Feb 8, 32; m 58; c 3. GEOCHEMISTRY. *Educ:* Univ Va, BA, 54, MA, 58; Lehigh Univ, PhD(geol), 61. *Prof Exp:* Mat res analyst, Va Hwy Res Coun, 61-67; asst prof geol, Univ Va, 67-70; asst prof environ sci, 70-72; assoc prof geol, 72-73, PROF GEOL, JAMES MADISON UNIV, VA, 73- *Concurrent Pos:* Mem subcomt on fundamentals of binder-aggregate adhesion, Hwy Res Bd, Nat Acad Sci-Nat Res Coun, 65-67; lectr, Univ Va, 66-67; fac consult, Va Hwy

Res Coun. *Mem:* Geochem Soc; Geol Soc Am; Nat Asn Geol Teachers; Am Inst Prof Geologists. *Res:* Erosion and sedimentation control; land use planning; geochemistry of weathering and soils; chemistry of natural waters; environmental geology. *Mailing Add:* Dept of Geol James Madison Univ Harrisonburg VA 22801

SHESHTAWY, ADEL A, b Zefta, Egypt, Feb 1, 40; US citizen; m 69; c 2. PETROLEUM ENGINEERING, EARTH SCIENCE. *Educ:* Cairo Univ, BS, 63; NMex Inst Mining & Technol, MSc, 74. *Prof Exp:* Resident drilling engr, Co Oriental Des Petrol Egypt, 63-66; petrol eng supvr contractor, Phillips Petrol Co, Egypt, 66-68; dist mgr, Sontrach, Algeria, 68-72; drilling supvr petrol eng, Mobil Explor & Producing Serv, 74; sr engr, Amoco Int Oil Co, 74-75; asst prof, NMex Inst Mining & Technol, 75-76; ASSOC PROF PETROL ENG, OKLA UNIV, 76-; PRES, INT PETROL ENG CORP, 78- *Mem:* Soc Petrol Eng; Am Petrol Inst; Int Asn Oil Well Drilling Contractors. *Res:* Deep oil and gas well drilling optimization; offshore operations; computer application in oil well drilling. *Mailing Add:* Int Petrol Eng Corp Suite 10A 710 Asp Norman OK 73070

SHESTAKOV, ALEKSEI ILYICH, b Yugoslavia, Feb 8, 49; US citizen. NUMERICAL ANALYSIS, COMPUTATIONAL PHYSICS. *Educ:* Univ Calif, Berkeley, BS, 70, MA, 73, PhD(appl math), 75. *Prof Exp:* PHYSICIST MAGNETIC FUSION ENERGY, LAWRENCE LIVERMORE NAT LAB, UNIV CALIF, 76- *Mem:* Am Math Soc; Am Phys Soc. *Res:* Developing numerical models for use in problems arising in magnetic fusion energy; calculations; solution of linear systems. *Mailing Add:* L-561 Lawrence Livermore Nat Lab PO Box 5509 Livermore CA 94556

SHETH, ATUL C, b Bombay, India, Dec 2, 41; US citizen; m 65; c 2. SYNTHETIC FUELS TECHNOLOGY. *Educ:* Univ Bombay, India, BChemEng, 64; Northwestern Univ, MS, 69, PhD(chem eng), 73. *Prof Exp:* Shift supvr, Esso Standard Eastern Inc, 64-67; chem operator, Riker Labs, 67; process engr, Armour Indust Chem Co, 69; clerk, Charlotte Charles Inc, 71-72; fel chem eng, Argonne Nat Lab, 72-74, chem engr, 74-80; CHEM ENGR, EXXON RES & ENG CO, 80- *Concurrent Pos:* Tech leader seed reprocessing team, Dept Energy & NASA, 78-80. *Mem:* Am Inst Chem Engrs. *Res:* Alternate energy fields such as nuclear reactors, high-temp electric batteries, magnetohydrodynamics and coal liquefaction; catalytic coal gasification process with Exxon. *Mailing Add:* 15723 Crest Brook Dr Houston TX 77059

SHETH, BHOGILAL, b Bombay, India, Sept 18, 31; US citizen. PHYSICAL PHARMACY, PHARMACEUTICAL CHEMISTRY. *Educ:* Gujerat Univ, India, BPharm, 52; Univ Mich, MS, 55, PhD(pharmaceut chem), 61. *Prof Exp:* Sect head prod develop, Alcon Labs, 60-64; group leader pharm res, Warner-Lambert Co, 64-68; assoc prof, 68-74, PROF PHARMACEUT, COL PHARM, UNIV TENN, 74- *Concurrent Pos:* Consult, var pharmaceut cos, 68- *Mem:* Am Pharmaceut Asn; Acad Pharmaceut Sci; Am Chem Soc; AAAS; Am Soc Hosp Pharmacists. *Res:* Pharmaceutical research and development; surface chemistry applications to dosage forms; rheology; drug dissolutions; product formulations. *Mailing Add:* Div Drug Technol Col Pharm Univ of Tenn Memphis TN 38163

SHETLAR, DAVID JOHN, b Columbus, Ohio, June 30, 46; m 68; c 1. ENTOMOLOGY, URBAN PEST MANAGEMENT. *Educ:* Univ Okla, BS, 69, MS, 75; Pa State Univ, PhD(entomol), 77. *Prof Exp:* Instr & curator, 75-76, ASST PROF TEACHING & RES, DEPT ENTOMOL, PA STATE UNIV, 77- *Mem:* Sigma Xi; Entomol Soc Am. *Res:* Pest management of greenhouse, ornamental plants, turf and christmas trees. *Mailing Add:* Dept Entomol 106 Patterson Pa State Univ University Park PA 16802

SHETLAR, MARTIN DAVID, b Wichita, Kans, Aug 28, 38; m 66; c 1. PHOTOCHEMISTRY, PHOTOBIOLOGY. *Educ:* Kans State Univ, BS, 60; Univ Calif, Berkeley, PhD(chem), 65. *Prof Exp:* Biophysicist, Donner Lab, Univ Calif, Berkeley, 65-68; asst prof, 68-76, ASSOC PROF CHEM & PHARMACEUT CHEM, SCH PHARM, UNIV CALIF, SAN FRANCISCO, 76- *Concurrent Pos:* AEC fel, 66-68. *Mem:* AAAS; Am Chem Soc; Am Soc Photobiol; Int-Am Photochem Soc; Sigma Xi. *Res:* Photochemistry and free radical chemistry in nucleic acid-protein systems; organic photochemistry; photochemical kinetics. *Mailing Add:* Sch of Pharm Univ of Calif San Francisco CA 94143

SHETLAR, MARVIN ROY, b Bayard, Kans, Apr 3, 18; m 40; c 3. BIOCHEMISTRY. *Educ:* Kans State Univ, BS, 40; Ohio State Univ, MS, 43, PhD(biol chem), 46. *Prof Exp:* Asst milling indust, Kans State Univ, 38-40; asst, Ohio State Univ, 41-42, instr agr chem, 44-46; Am Cancer Soc fel, Sch Med, Univ Okla, 46-47, res assoc, 47-50, from asst prof to prof biochem, 53-64, res prof, 64-66; prof, Univ Tex Med Br, Galveston, 66-73; assoc chmn dept, 72-75, PROF BIOCHEM & DERMAT, HEALTH SCI CTR, TEX TECH UNIV, 77- *Concurrent Pos:* Chief res lab, Vet Admin Hosp, 50-57; NIH sr res fel, 57-62; vis prof, Univ Calif-Univ Airlangga Proj Med Educ Indonesia, 64-66 & Col Med, Univ King Faisal, Dammam, Saudi Arabia, 79-81; mem, Am Bd Clin Chem. *Mem:* Am Chem Soc; Am Inst Chem; Soc Exp Biol & Med; Am Asn Biol Chem; Am Asn Clin Chem. *Res:* Animal glycoproteins and mucopolysaccharides. *Mailing Add:* Dept of Dermat Tex Tech Univ Sch Med Lubbock TX 79430

SHETLER, STANWYN GERALD, b Johnstown, Pa, Oct 11, 33; m 63; c 2. PLANT TAXONOMY. *Educ:* Cornell Univ, BS, 55, MS, 58; Univ Mich, PhD, 79. *Prof Exp:* Asst cur, 62-63, assoc cur, 63-81, dir, Flora NAm Prog, 71-80, CUR, DEPT BOT, SMITHSONIAN INST, 81- *Concurrent Pos:* Pres, Audubon Naturalist Soc Cent Atlantic States, Inc, 74-77. *Mem:* AAAS; Am Soc Plant Taxon; Bot Soc Am; Am Inst Biol Sci; Arctic Inst NAm. *Res:* Taxonomy and ecology of Campanula; flora and vegetation of the Arctic, especially Alaska; history of Russian botany; biological data storage and retrieval. *Mailing Add:* Dept of Bot NMNH 166 Smithsonian Inst Washington DC 20560

SHETTERLY, DONIVAN MAX, b Des Moines, Iowa, Oct 29, 46; m 66; c 2. PHYSICS, MATHEMATICS. *Educ:* Cent Col, BA, 68; Univ Wis-Madison, MA, 70. *Prof Exp:* Assoc physicist, 70-74, physicist, 74-80, SR PHYSICIST, GLASS TECHNOL SECT, OWENS-ILLINOIS INC, TOLEDO, 80- *Mem:* Am Ceramic Soc; Sigma Xi. *Res:* Heat transfer; glass forming; process control; phase separation in glass; glass homogeneity. *Mailing Add:* 3033 Gallatin Rd Toledo OH 43606

SHETTLE, ERIC PAYSON, b New York, NY, Nov 23, 43; m 65; c 2. ATMOSPHERIC PHYSICS. *Educ:* Johns Hopkins Univ, BA, 65; Univ Wis-Madison, MA, 67. *Prof Exp:* Asst, Dept Physics, Univ Wis, 66-68, res asst, Dept Meteorol, 68-72; instr & res assoc, Dept Physics, Univ Fla, 72-73; PHYSICIST, AIR FORCE GEOPHYS LAB, 73- *Mem:* Optical Soc Am; Am Meteorol Soc; Am Geophys Union; AAAS. *Res:* The optical properties of the atmosphere, especially the atmospheric aerosols and their effects on radiative transfer of light in scattering atmospheres. *Mailing Add:* Atmospheric Optics Br Air Force Geophys Lab Hanscom AFB Bedford MA 01731

SHEVCHIK, NIGEL JOHN, solid state physics, see previous edition

SHEVENELL, THOMAS CORTLAND, b Dover, NH, Apr 2, 48; m 75. OCEANOGRAPHY, SEDIMENTOLOGY. *Educ:* Univ NH, BA, 70; Columbia Univ, MPhil, 74. *Prof Exp:* Res assoc & instr sedimentology, Univ NH, 73-74; OCEANOGR PHYS OCEANOG, & PHYS SCI PROJ MGR, NORMANDEAU ASSOCS INC, 74- *Mem:* Limnol & Oceanog; Soc Econ Paleontologists & Mineralogists; Int Asn Sedimentologists. *Mailing Add:* Normandeau Assocs Inc Nashua Rd Bedford NH 03102

SHEVIAK, CHARLES JOHN, b Chicago, Ill, May 31, 47; m 68. PLANT SYSTEMATICS. *Educ:* Univ Ill, Urbana, BS, 70, MS, 72; Harvard Univ, PhD(plant syst), 76. *Prof Exp:* Dir, Ill Endangered Plants Proj, Natural Land Inst, 77-78; CUR BOT, NY STATE MUS, 78- *Mem:* AAAS; Am Soc Plant Taxonomists; Sigma Xi. *Res:* Systematics, ecology and biogeography of North American orchids; biogeography, especially forest-grassland relationships; evolution of colonizing species; northeastern floristics. *Mailing Add:* Cur of Bot NY State Mus Albany NY 12234

SHEVLIN, PHILIP BERNARD, b Mineola, NY, June 28, 39. ORGANIC CHEMISTRY. *Educ:* Lafayette Col, BS, 61; Yale Univ, MS, 63, PhD(chem), 66. *Prof Exp:* Res assoc chem, Brookhaven Nat Lab, 65-66 & 68-70; asst prof, 70-74, ASSOC PROF CHEM, AUBURN UNIV, 74- *Mem:* Am Chem Soc. *Res:* Nuclear magnetic resonance studies of chemical kinetics; liquid and gas photochemistry; chemistry of atomic carbon. *Mailing Add:* Dept of Chem Auburn Univ Auburn AL 36830

SHEVLIN, THOMAS S, b Marietta, Ohio, July 14, 20; m 44; c 4. CERAMIC ENGINEERING. *Educ:* Ohio State Univ, BCerE, 42, MSc, 47, PhD, 54. *Prof Exp:* Res engr, Ohio State Univ, 46-55, asst prof ceramic eng, 55-61; assoc prof, Univ Wash, 61-64; SUPVR CERAMIC, PHYS SCI LAB, CENT RES LABS, 3M CO, 64- *Concurrent Pos:* Consult, Oak Ridge Nat Lab, 51-64, mem adv comt, 54-58; mem refractory mat study comt, Mat Adv Bd, Nat Acad Sci, 54-55, mem rocket nozzles & vanes comt, 58-60; C Paul Stocker vis prof mech eng, Ohio Univ, Athens, 81-82. *Mem:* AAAS; fel Am Ceramic Soc; Inst Food Technologists; Nat Inst Ceramic Engrs (pres, 78-79). *Res:* High temperature inorganic, cermets and mineralogical ceramics; phase equilibrium; food heating and reconstitution; high temperature filtration. *Mailing Add:* Advan Progs Res Lab Cent Res 3M Co St Paul MN 55101

SHEW, DELBERT CRAIG, b Canton, Ohio, Dec 29, 40; m 67. MASS SPECTROMETRY. *Educ:* Hanover Col, AB, 62; Ind Univ, MS, 66; Univ Ark, PhD(chem), 69. *Prof Exp:* Res chemist, E I du Pont de Nemours & Co, 68-71; assoc prof math, Washington Tech Inst, 71-72; RES CHEMIST, R S KERR ENVIRON RES LAB, ENVIRON PROTECTION AGENCY, 72- *Concurrent Pos:* Consult legal aspects environ pollution, various law firms, 74- *Mem:* Am Soc Mass Spectrometry. *Res:* Isolation of organic pollutants from ground water and identification using electron impact and chemical ionization mass spectrometry. *Mailing Add:* R S Kerr Environ Res Lab-EPA PO Box 1198 Ada OK 74820

SHEWAN, WILLIAM, b Chicago, Ill, May 24, 14; m 49; c 6. ELECTRICAL ENGINEERING, MATHEMATICS. *Educ:* Valparaiso Univ, BS, 50; Univ Notre Dame, MS, 52; Purdue Univ, PhD(elec eng), 60. *Prof Exp:* Jr eng, Northern Ind Pub Serv Co, 45-46; instr electronics, Valparaiso Tech Univ, 46-50; fron instr to assoc prof, 52-57, chmn dept, 57-76, actg dean, Col Eng, 78-80, PROF ELEC ENG, VALPARAISO UNIV, 80- *Mem:* Sr mem Instrument Soc Am; sr mem Inst Elec & Electronics Engrs; Am Soc Eng Educ. *Res:* Nonlinear circuit analysis; variable speed drives for rotating machines-solid state devices; numerical methods in systems engineering. *Mailing Add:* Gellersen Ctr Valparaiso Univ Valparaiso IN 46383

SHEWCHUN, JOHN, b Toronto, Ont, Aug 14, 38; m 63; c 1. SOLID STATE PHYSICS & ELECTRONICS. *Educ:* Univ Toronto, BASc, 60; Univ Waterloo, MASc, 61, PhD(elec eng), 63. *Prof Exp:* Fel mat sci, Brown Univ, 64-65; mem tech staff solid state physics, RCA Labs, 65-66; asst prof mat sci, 66-68, actg chmn dept, 67-69, ASSOC PROF ENG PHYSICS, McMASTER UNIV, 68-, CHMN DEPT, 69- *Concurrent Pos:* Spec lectr, City Col New York, 66-67; E W R Steacie Mem fel, Nat Res Coun Can, 72-74; exchange scientist, Soviet Acad Sci, 72. *Mem:* AAAS; Am Phys Soc; Inst Elec & Electronics Engrs; Am Vacuum Soc; Can Asn Physicists. *Res:* Metal-oxide-semiconductor and semiconductor-oxide semiconductor structures; tunneling devices and spectroscopy; ion implantation; epitaxial growth of semiconductor thin films; ellipsometry; semiconductor lasers; device physics and transport in thin films; microelectronics; large scale integrated circuits; solar cells. *Mailing Add:* Solar Cells LTD 3327 D Mainway PO Box 1025 Burlington ON L7P 3S9 Can

SHEWMAKER, JAMES EDWARD, b Paragould, Ark, Jan 22, 22; m 46; c 5. PHYSICAL CHEMISTRY. *Educ:* Harding Col, BS, 44; Univ Nebr, MS, 49, PhD(phys chem), 51. *Prof Exp:* Res chemist, Esso Res & Eng Co, 51-58, sr chemist, 58-61, res assoc, 61-73, RES ASSOC, EXXON RES & ENG CO, 73- *Mem:* AAAS; Am Chem Soc; Water Pollution Control Fedn; NY Acad Sci. *Res:* Surfactants and detergents; biodegradability; demulsification; oilfield chemicals; radiation chemistry; trace metal contaminants in petroleum; pollution control. *Mailing Add:* 1370 S Martine Ave Scotch Plains NJ 07076

SHEWMON, PAUL G(RIFFITH), b Rochelle, Ill, Apr 18, 30; m 52; c 3. METALLURGY. *Educ:* Univ Ill, BSc, 52; Carnegie Inst Technol, MS & PhD(metall eng), 55. *Prof Exp:* Res engr, Res Lab, Westinghouse Elec Corp, 55-58; from asst prof to prof metall eng, Carnegie Inst Technol, 58-67; assoc dir metall div, Argonne Nat Lab, 67-68, dir mat sci div, 69-73; dir, Div Mat Res, NSF, 73-75; PROF METALL ENG & CHMN DEPT, OHIO STATE UNIV, 75- *Concurrent Pos:* NSF fel, 64-65; mem, Adv Com Reactor Safeguards, US Nuclear Regulatory Comn, 77-, chmn, 82. *Honors & Awards:* Alfred Noble Prize, 60; Howe Medal, Am Soc Metals, 77. *Mem:* Nat Acad Eng; Am Inst Mining, Metall & Petrol Engrs; Am Nuclear Soc; fel Am Soc Metals. *Res:* Physical metallurgy; nuclear materials; kinetics of reactions in solids. *Mailing Add:* Dept of Metall Eng Ohio State Univ Columbus OH 43210

SHI, YUN YUAN, b Nanking, China, Sept 26, 32; m 60; c 3. AERONAUTICS, APPLIED MATHEMATICS. *Educ:* Nat Taiwan Univ, BSc, 55; Brown Univ, MSc, 58; Calif Inst Technol, PhD(aeronaut, math), 63. *Prof Exp:* Res asst eng physics, Brown Univ, 57-58; scholar & teaching asst, Calif Inst Technol, 58-62; res specialist, Missile & Space Syst Div, Douglas Aircraft Co, 62-63; asst prof eng & sci, Carnegie Inst Technol, 63-65; SR SCIENTIST RES & DEVELOP, McDONNELL DOUGLAS ASTRONAUTICS CO, 65- *Mem:* AAAS; fel Am Inst Aeronaut & Astronaut; sr mem Inst Elec & Electronics Engrs. *Res:* Wave propagation in anelastic solids; fluid mechanics; magneto-hydrodynamics; nonlinear oscillations; singular perturbation methods; astronomical science; electromagnetic wave scattering from turbulent plasma; optimal control and estimation; digital signal processing. *Mailing Add:* Res & Develop McDonnell Douglas Astronautics Co 5301 Bolsa Ave Huntington Beach CA 92647

SHIAO, DANIEL DA-FONG, b Kiangsi, China, Apr 6, 37; c 2. PHYSICAL CHEMISTRY, PHYSICAL BIOCHEMISTRY. *Educ:* Nat Taiwan Univ, BS, 58; NMex Highlands Univ, MS, 63; Univ Minn, PhD(phys chem), 68. *Prof Exp:* Fel, Yale Univ, 68-70; SR RES CHEMIST, EASTMAN KADAK, CO, 70- *Mem:* Am Chem Soc. *Res:* Physical chemistry at colloidal interfaces; mathemedical modeling of diffusion processes and heterogeneous catalysis. *Mailing Add:* Res Labs Eastman Kodak Co Kodak Park Rochester NY 14650

SHIBATA, EDWARD ISAMU, b Gallup, NMex, Mar 1, 42; m 73. EXPERIMENTAL HIGH ENERGY PHYSICS. *Educ:* Mass Inst Technol, SB, 64, PhD(physics), 70. *Prof Exp:* Res assoc physics, Northeastern Univ, 70-72; asst prof, 72-78, ASSOC PROF PHYSICS, PURDUE UNIV, WEST LAFAYETTE, 78- *Mem:* Am Phys Soc. *Res:* Experimental study of baryon exchange reactions; meson and baryon spectroscopy; electron-positron colliding beam physics. *Mailing Add:* Dept of Physics Purdue Univ West Lafayette IN 47907

SHIBATA, SHOJI, b Kyoto, Japan, Nov 12, 27; m 58; c 2. PHARMACOLOGY. *Educ:* Nara Med Col, Japan, MD, 52; Kyoto Univ, PhD(pharmacol), 57. *Prof Exp:* Japanese Govt fel, 54-57; instr pharmacol, Sch Med, Kyoto Univ, 57-59; asst prof, Sch Med, Univ Miss, 63-66; assoc prof, 67-69, PROF PHARMACOL, SCH MED, UNIV HAWAII, MANOA, 70- *Concurrent Pos:* Instr & lectr, Sch Med, Univ Southern Calif, 60-61; assoc prof pharmacol & chmn dept, Col Pharm, Kyoto Univ, 62-63. *Mem:* Am Soc Pharmacol & Exp Therapeut; Am Soc Physiol. *Res:* Cardiovascular pharmacology and natural products. *Mailing Add:* Dept of Pharmacol Univ of Hawaii Sch of Med Honolulu HI 96822

SHIBKO, SAMUEL ISSAC, b Bargoed, Wales, Oct 2, 27. BIOCHEMISTRY. *Educ:* Univ Birmingham, BSc, 54; Imp Col, dipl, 58, Univ London, PhD(biochem), 58. *Prof Exp:* Res assoc, McCollum Pratt Inst, Johns Hopkins Univ, 58-60; asst biochemist dept food sci & technol, Univ Calif, Davis, 60-64; instr nutrit & food sci, Mass Inst Technol, 64-65, asst prof, 65-67; rev scientist, 67-72, spec asst to dir toxicol div, 72-76, actg chief SPAL, 76-77, CHIEF CONTAMINANTS & NATURAL TOXICANTS EVAL BR, FOOD & DRUG ADMIN, 77- *Concurrent Pos:* Gen referee toxicol tests, Asn Off Anal Chemists, 74- *Mem:* AAAS; Soc Exp Biol & Med; NY Acad Sci; Soc Toxicol; Soc Environ Geochem & Health. *Res:* Food toxicology; evaluation of safety of food additives, and hazards associated with contamination of the food supply with heavy metals, industrial chemicals and natural toxicants; techniques for establishing safety of food chemicals. *Mailing Add:* HFF-195 Div of Toxicol Food & Drug Admin 200 C St SW Washington DC 20204

SHIBLES, RICHARD MARWOOD, b Brooks, Maine, Feb 12, 33; m 64; c 1. AGRONOMY. *Educ:* Univ Maine, BS, 56; Cornell Univ, MS, 58, PhD(field crops), 61. *Prof Exp:* From asst prof agron to assoc prof agron, 60-69, PROF AGRON, IOWA STATE UNIV, 69- *Mem:* Fel AAAS; Am Soc Agron; Crop Sci Soc Am; Am Soc Plant Physiol. *Res:* Soybean physiology: photosynthesis, growth, development, yield. *Mailing Add:* Dept of Agron Iowa State Univ Ames IA 50011

SHIBLEY, GEORGE P, virology, immunology, see previous edition

SHIBLEY, JOHN LUKE, b Gentry, Ark, Apr 12, 19; m 48; c 4. ZOOLOGY. *Educ:* Univ Okla, BS, 41; Univ Ga, MS, 49, PhD(zool), 56. *Prof Exp:* Instr zool, Univ Ga, 49-50; assoc prof, 50-56, PROF BIOL, LA GRANGE COL, 56- *Res:* Population survival of Euglena with ultraviolet irradiation treatment. *Mailing Add:* Dept of Biol La Grange Col La Grange GA 30240

SHICHI, HITOSHI, b Nagoya, Japan, Dec 20, 32; m 62; c 2. BIOCHEMISTRY, BIOPHYSICS. *Educ:* Nagoya Univ, BS, 55, MS, 57; Univ Calif, Berkeley, PhD, 62. *Prof Exp:* Res biochemist, Univ Calif, Berkeley, 62; instr biochem, Nagoya Univ, 62-63; instr, Univ Tokyo, 63-67; res chemist, Nat Inst Neurol Dis & Stroke, 67-69, res chemist, Lab Vision Res, Nat Eye Inst, 69-81; PROF & ASST DIR, INST BIOL SCI, OAKLAND UNIV, ROCHESTER, 81- *Mem:* Biophys Soc; Japanese Biochem Soc; Am Soc Photobiol; Am Soc Biol Chem; Asn Res Vision & Ophthal. *Res:* Drug metabolism; biochemistry of the visual process. *Mailing Add:* Inst Biol Sci Oakland Univ Rochester MI 48063

SHICHMAN, D(ANIEL), b Brooklyn, NY, Aug 20, 28; m 49; c 3. MECHANICAL ENGINEERING. *Educ:* Univ Mich, BS, 50; Stevens Inst Technol, MS, 61. *Prof Exp:* Develop engr, Nylon Div, E I du Pont de Nemours & Co, Del, 50-51; develop engr, Atomic Energy Div, Ind, 51-53; res engr, Mech Eng Dept, Res Ctr, Uniroyal, Inc, 53-60, mgr fiber eng res, 60-66, mgr eng res, 66-78; dir res & develop, NRM Corp Div, Condec Corp, 78-80. *Mem:* Sigma Xi; Am Chem Soc; Nat Soc Prof Engrs (vpres, 74-76). *Res:* Process equipment development for chemical, rubber and plastic industry; sprayed metals; synthetic fiber and automation; process equipment for rubber and plastics industry. *Mailing Add:* 20 Copper Kettle Rd Trumbull CT 06611

SHICK, PHILIP E(DWIN), b Kendallville, Ind, Jan 7, 18; m 63; c 2. CHEMICAL ENGINEERING. *Educ:* Harvard Univ, SB, 39; Lawrence Col, MS, 41, PhD(phys chem), 43. *Prof Exp:* Res chemist, Masonite Corp, Miss, 43-45; res proj leader, WVa Pulp & Paper Co, 45-48; res supvr, Mead Corp, 48-56, tech asst to vpres res, 56; tech dir mill div, Owens-Ill Glass Co, 56-60, tech dir forest prod div, 60-63, actg dir res & eng, 63-65, dir res, 65-66, SR RES SCIENTIST, FOREST PROD DIV, OWENS-ILL, INC, 66- *Mem:* Can Pulp & Paper Asn; Am Chem Soc; Am Tech Asn Pulp & Paper Indust. *Res:* High temperature thermodynamics; chemistry of lignin; pulping and papermaking; neutral sulfite semichemical recovery. *Mailing Add:* Forest Prod Div Owens-Ill Inc One Sea Gate Toledo OH 43666

SHICKLUNA, JOHN C, b Port Colborne, Ont, May 25, 23; US citizen; m 53; c 1. SOIL FERTILITY. *Educ:* Univ Toronto, BSA, 50; Mich State Univ, MS, 51, PhD(soil sci), 61. *Prof Exp:* Chemist, Can Packers, Ltd, 51-52; soil technologist, 52-60, soil chemist, 60-64, from asst prof to assoc prof soil sci, 64-70, PROF SOIL SCI, MICH STATE UNIV, 70- *Concurrent Pos:* Consult agr chem dept, Univ Ryukyus, 67-68. *Mem:* Soil Conserv Soc Am; Soil Sci Soc Am; Am Soc Agron; Sigma Xi; Nat Asn Cols & Teachers Agr. *Res:* Evaluation of the availability of the major, secondary and micronutrient elements to various plants and their effect on growth and plant response. *Mailing Add:* Dept of Crop & Soil Sci Mich State Univ East Lansing MI 48823

SHIDA, MITSUZO, b Hamamatsu, Japan, Oct 2, 35; m 59; c 2. CHEMISTRY. *Educ:* Kyoto Univ, BS, 58; Polytech Inst Brooklyn, PhD(chem), 64. *Prof Exp:* Sr res chemist, W R Grace & Co, 63-66; sr res scientist, Plastic Div, Allied Chem Corp, 66; mgr polymer physics, 66-70, MGR POLYMER RES DEPT, CHEMPLEX CO, ROLLING MEADOWS, 70- *Mem:* Am Chem Soc; Soc Rheol; Chem Soc Japan. *Res:* Polymer physical chemistry, especially solution properties; morphological and rheological aspects of polymer science. *Mailing Add:* 68 Timberlake Dr Barrington IL 60010

SHIDELER, GERALD LEE, b Detroit, Mich, May 19, 38; m 63; c 2. SEDIMENTOLOGY, MARINE GEOLOGY. *Educ:* Mich State Univ, BS, 63; Univ Ill, MS, 65; Univ Wis, PhD(geol), 68. *Prof Exp:* Explor geologist, Mobil Oil Co, summer 63; teaching asst geol, Univ Ill, Urbana, 63-65; teaching asst, Univ Wis, Madison, 65-66, res asst, 66-68; asst prof, Old Dom Univ, 68-72, assoc prof geol & oceanog, 72-74; MARINE GEOLOGIST, OFF MARINE GEOL, US GEOL SURV, CORPUS CHRISTI, TEX. 74- *Concurrent Pos:* Nat Acad Sci exchange scientist, Poland. *Mem:* AAAS; Geol Soc Am; Soc Econ Paleont & Mineral. *Res:* Modern sedimentation of coastal regions and continental shelves; Paleozoic and Cenozoic sedimentation and stratigraphy. *Mailing Add:* US Geol Surv PO Box 6732 Off of Marine Geol Corpus Christi TX 78411

SHIDELER, ROBERT WEAVER, b Joliet, Ill, Apr 25, 13; m 48; c 2. BIOCHEMISTRY. *Educ:* Goshen Col, AB, 34; Univ Chicago, MS, 41; Univ Tex, PhD, 56. *Prof Exp:* Teacher high sch, NDak, 35-36, Ind, 36-40; instr sci, Independence Jr Col, Iowa, 41-42; instr, US Army Air Force Training Sch, Wis, 42-44; assoc prof chem, 46-50, prof chem & chmn dept chem, 54-77, chmn natural sci area, 66-77, EMER HAROLD & LUCY CABE DISTINGUISHED PROF CHEM, HENDRIX COL, 78- *Mem:* AAAS; Am Chem Soc; NY Acad Sci. *Res:* Methods in investigating intermediary metabolism; individual differences in mineral metabolism. *Mailing Add:* 1903 Jefferson St Conway AR 72032

SHIDEMAN, FREDERICK EARL, b Albion, Mich, Oct 16, 15; m 39; c 4. PHARMACOLOGY. *Educ:* Albion Col, BA, 36; Univ Wis, PhD(pharmacol), 41; Univ Mich, MD, 46. *Prof Exp:* Univ fel, Univ Mich, 42-43, from instr to assoc prof pharmacol, 43-52; prof pharmacol & toxicol, Univ Wis, 52-62, chmn dept, 54-62; PROF PHARMACOL & HEAD DEPT, UNIV MINN, MINNEAPOLIS, 62- *Concurrent Pos:* Mem pharmacol & exp therapeut study sect, USPHS, 60-65; spec adv bd postgrad med, NIH, 63-75; pharmacol & toxicol training comt, 65-69, ed comt, Annual Rev Pharmacol, 66-70; chmn adv comt abuse of depressant & stimulant drugs, Food Drug Admin, 66-68; mem, Joint Food & Drug Admin-NIMH Psychotomimetics Adv Comt, 67-71; chmn pharmacol test comt, Nat Bd Med Exam, 68-73; sci adv comt, Bur of Narcotics & Dangerous Drugs, US Dept Justice, 68-75; mem narcotic addiction & drug abuse comt, NIMH, 71-75; chmn, Drug Res Bd, Nat Acad Sci, 72-76; vpres & pres & mem bd trustees, US Pharmacopeia Conv; mem & vchmn exec comt, Nat Coun Drugs, 76-78, chmn, 78-80. *Mem:* Am Soc Pharmacol & Exp Therapeut (treas, 60-62, pres, 63-64); Soc Exp Biol & Med; fel Royal Soc Med; hon mem Korean Med Asn; Pharmacol Soc Japan.

Res: Hyperventilation; addiction to narcotic analgesics; effect of drugs on intermediary metabolism; metabolism of thiobarbiturates; renal tubular transport mechanisms; cardiac catecholamines and inotropic responses to drugs; anticonvulsant pyrimidines; psychopharmacology. *Mailing Add:* Dept of Pharmacol Univ of Minn Minneapolis MN 55455

SHIDLOVSKY, IGAL, b Haifa, Israel, Oct 13, 36; m 63; c 2. CHEMISTRY. *Educ:* Israel Inst Technol, BSc, 61; Hebrew Univ Jeruslaem, MSc, 63, PhD(inorg chem), 68. *Prof Exp:* Res assoc chem, Pittsburgh Univ, 68-69; MEM TECH STAFF, RCA LABS, 69- *Mem:* Electrochem Soc. *Res:* Electro-optics; photochromics; magnetic and intermetallic materials; solid state chemistry. *Mailing Add:* Org Chem RCA Labs Princeton NJ 08540

SHIEH, HANG SHAN, b Hunan, China, Aug 5, 30; Can citizen; m 65. MICROBIOLOGY. *Educ:* Nat Taiwan Univ, BSc, 54; McGill Univ, MSc, 60, PhD(agr bact), 63. *Prof Exp:* SCIENTIST, FISHERIES RES BD CAN, DEPT FISHERIES & OCEANS, 62- *Mem:* Can Soc Microbiol. *Res:* Microbial biochemistry; fish diseases. *Mailing Add:* Dept Fisheries & Oceans PO Box 550 Halifax NS B3J 2R3 Can

SHIEH, KENNETH KUANG-ZEN, b Keelung, Taiwan, Feb 15, 36; US citizen; m 66; c 2. INDUSTRIAL MICROBIOLOGY. *Educ:* Taiwan Prov Col Agr, BS, 61; Ill Inst Technol, MS, 65, PhD(microbiol), 69. *Prof Exp:* Sr res microbiologist, 68-75, RES ASSOC, CENT RES DEPT, CORN PRODS SECT, ANHEUSER-BUSCH, INC, 75- *Mem:* Am Soc Microbiol. *Res:* Production of enzymes from a microbial origin for transformation of one kind of carbohydrate to another. *Mailing Add:* Anheuser-Busch Inc 1101 Wyoming St St Louis MO 63118

SHIEH, LEANG-SAN, b Tainan, China, Jan 10, 34; US citizen; m 62; c 2. DIGITAL CONTROL SYSTEMS, NETWORK THEORY. *Educ:* Nat Taiwan Univ, BS, 58; Univ Houston, MS, 68, PhD(elec eng), 70. *Prof Exp:* Design engr, Taiwan Florescent Lamp Co, 60-61; power systs engr, Taiwan Elec Power Co, 61-65; asst prof, 71-74, assoc prof, 74-78, PROF CONTROL SYSTS, UNIV HOUSTON, 78- *Concurrent Pos:* Vis prof, Inst Univ Polit, Venezuela, 76-77; vis scientist, Battelle Columbus Lab, 77 & Math Res Ctr, Univ Wis-Madison, 79. *Mem:* Inst Elec & Electronics Engrs; Am Soc Elec Engrs. *Res:* Model reduction, identification, realization and adaptive control of multivariable control systems. *Mailing Add:* Dept Elec Eng Univ Houston Cent Campus Houston TX 77004

SHIEH, LIAU JANG, air pollution, meteorology, see previous edition

SHIEH, PAULINUS SHEE-SHAN, b Nanchang, China, Apr 5, 31; m 60; c 3. NUCLEAR ENGINEERING, PHYSICS. *Educ:* Nat Taiwan Univ, BS, 55; Univ SC, MS, 58; NC State Univ, PhD(nuclear eng), 69. *Prof Exp:* Asst prof physics & chmn dept, King's Col, Pa, 60-63; instr, NC State Univ, 63-69; from asst prof to assoc prof nuclear eng, Miss State Univ, 69-79; sr nuclear engr, C P & L, 79-81; SUPVR NUCLEAR ANAL, H L & P, TEX, 79- *Concurrent Pos:* Vis prof, Pinstech, Pakistan, 76-77. *Mem:* AAAS; Am Nuclear Soc; Am Soc Eng Educ. *Res:* Neutron transport theory; radiation measurements; nuclear power. *Mailing Add:* 771 Seacliff Dr Houston TX 77062

SHIEH, YUCH-NING, b Chan-hua, Taiwan, Feb 15, 40; m 66; c 2. GEOCHEMISTRY, PETROLOGY. *Educ:* Nat Taiwan Univ, BS, 62; Calif Inst Technol, PhD(geochem), 69. *Prof Exp:* Fel geochem, McMaster Univ, Can, 68-72; asst prof, 72-79, ASSOC PROF GEOCHEM, PURDUE UNIV, 79- *Concurrent Pos:* Vis scientist, Inst Earth Sci, Acad Sinica, Taipei, China, 80-81; assoc ed, Isotope Geosci, 82- *Mem:* Geochem Soc; Am Geophys Union; Geol Soc China. *Res:* Oxygen, carbon and hydrogen isotopes in igneous and metamorphic rocks; sulfur isotopes in ore deposits and coals; stable isotope studies of active geothermal systems. *Mailing Add:* Dept Geosci Purdue Univ West Lafayette IN 47907

SHIELD, RICHARD THORPE, b Swalwell, Eng, July 9, 29; m 58; c 2. MECHANICS. *Educ:* Univ Durham, BSc, 49, PhD(appl math), 52. *Prof Exp:* Res assoc appl math, Brown Univ, 51-53; sr res fel, A R E Ft Halstead, Eng, 53-55; from asst prof to prof, Brown Univ, 55-65; prof appl mech, Calif Inst Technol, 65-70; PROF THEORET & APPL MECH & HEAD DEPT, UNIV ILL, URBANA, 70- *Concurrent Pos:* Guggenheim mem fel, Univ Durham, 61-62; co-ed, J Appl Math & Physics, 65-, assoc ed, J Appl Mech, 79-; Alcoa vis prof, Univ Pittsburgh, 70-71; distinquished scholar, Calif Inst Technol, 82. *Mem:* Fel AAAS; fel Am Acad Mech (pres, 77-78); Am Soc Mech Engrs; Sigma Xi; Soc Rheology. *Res:* Elasticity, plasticity; stability theory. *Mailing Add:* Univ Ill 104 S Wright St Urbana IL 61801

SHIELDS, ALLEN LOWELL, b New York, NY, May 7, 27; m 56; c 3. MATHEMATICS. *Educ:* City Col New York, BS, 49; Mass Inst Technol, PhD(math), 52. *Prof Exp:* Instr math, Tulane Univ, 52-54, asst prof, 54-55; from asst prof to assoc prof, 56-64, chmn dept, 75-77, PROF MATH, UNIV MICH, ANN ARBOR, 64- *Concurrent Pos:* Mem, US Nat Comt Math, 74-77. *Mem:* Am Math Soc; Math Asn Am. *Res:* Mathematical analysis. *Mailing Add:* Dept of Math Univ of Mich Ann Arbor MI 48109

SHIELDS, BRUCE MACLEAN, b Wilkinsburg, Pa, Sept 27, 22; m 51; c 2. METALLURGICAL ENGINEERING, METALLURGY. *Educ:* Carnegie Inst Technol, BS, 44; Mass Inst Technol, MS, 52. *Prof Exp:* Metall observer, Homestead Works, Carnegie Ill Steel, 42-43 & 46-47; res technologist metall, South Works, US Steel Corp, 47-50; res asst, Mass Inst Technol, 50-51; chief develop metallurgist, Duquesne Works, 51-54, chief process metallurgist, 54-56, asst chief metallurgist, 56-57, chief metallurgist, 57-60, chief metallurgist, South Works, 60-65, mgr process metall, 65-68, mgr tubular prod metall, 68-72, gen mgr process metall, 72-75, gen mgr customer tech serv, 75-78, DIR METALL ENG, US STEEL CORP, 78- *Mem:* Fel Am Soc Metals; Am Inst Mining, Metall & Petrol Engrs; Am Soc Testing & Mat; Brit Metals Soc; Am Iron & Steel Inst. *Res:* Physical chemical reactions of iron and steelmaking, including both the equilibrium relationships and the reaction kinetics; transformation characteristics of alloy steel systems. *Mailing Add:* US Steel Corp 600 Grant St Pittsburgh PA 15230

SHIELDS, DENNIS, b London, Eng, Sept 9, 48; m 75. CELL BIOLOGY, BIOCHEMISTRY. *Educ:* Univ York, Eng, BA, 71; Nat Inst Med Res, London, PhD(biochem), 74. *Prof Exp:* Fel cell biol, Rockefeller Univ, 74-77; ASST PROF ANAT, ALBERT EINSTEIN COL MED, 78- *Honors & Awards:* Solomon A Berson Award, Am Diabetes Asn, 78. *Mem:* Am Soc Cell Biol; Biochem Soc; Endocrine Soc. *Res:* Biosynthesis and subcellular compartmentation of secretory and membrane proteins; pancreatic islet hormone biosynthesis; post-translational modifications of proteins. *Mailing Add:* Dept Anat 1300 Morris Park Ave Bronx NY 10461

SHIELDS, FLETCHER DOUGLAS, b Nashville, Tenn, Oct 27, 26; m 48; c 4. PHYSICS. *Educ:* Tenn Polytech Inst, BS, 47; Vanderbilt Univ, MS, 48, PhD(physics), 56. *Prof Exp:* Res physicst, Carbide & Carbon Chem Corp, 48-49; from asst prof to assoc prof physics, Middle Tenn State Col, 49-59; assoc dean lib arts, 76-79, PROF PHYSICS, UNIV MISS, 59- *Mem:* Fel Acoust Soc Am. *Res:* Thermal relaxation processes in gas by means of sound absorption measurements; energy and mometum accommodation of gas molecules on solid surfaces. *Mailing Add:* Dept Physics Univ Miss Oxford MS 38677

SHIELDS, GEORGE SEAMON, b Bombay, NY, Oct 18, 25; m 48; c 5. INTERNAL MEDICINE, COMPUTER MEDICINE. *Educ:* Mass Inst Technol, SB, 48; Cornell Univ, MD, 52. *Prof Exp:* Intern, Bellvue Hosp, New York, 52-53, resident, 53-54; USPHS res fel hemat, State Univ NY Downstate Med Ctr, 54-56; resident, Salt Lake County Gen Hosp, 56-57; Am Cancer Soc fel biochem & hemat, Col Med, Univ Utah, 57-60, instr internal med, 59-61; from asst prof to assoc prof, Col Med, Univ Cincinnati, 61-70; dir med systs, Good Samaritan Hosp, 69-75; VPRES, MICRO-MED, INC, 80- *Concurrent Pos:* Med dir, Winton Hills Med Ctr, 73-75, Wesley Hall Home, 75-, Riverview Home, 78- & Three Rivers Home, 78-; pres, Sycamore Prof Asn Inc, 71- *Mem:* Biomed Eng Soc; Soc Comput Med; Soc Advan Med Systs; Am Fedn Clin Res; Am Chem Soc. *Res:* Biochemistry, protein, enzymology, nucleic acids, trace metals, copper; hematology, anemias, leukemias, pathogenesis; computer applications. *Mailing Add:* 4903 Vine St Cincinnati OH 45217

SHIELDS, GERALD FRANCIS, b Anaconda, Mont, Nov 9, 43; m 67; c 2. CYTOGENETICS, MOLECULAR EVOLUTION. *Educ:* Carroll Col, BA, 66; Cent Wash State, MS, 70; Univ Toronto, PhD(zool), 74. *Prof Exp:* Teacher biol, Billings Cent High Sch, 66-68; NSF res asst, Cent Wash State Col, 68-70; teaching asst, Dept Zool, Univ Toronto, 70-74; ASST PROF ZOOL, INST ARCTIC BIOL, UNIV ALASKA, 75- *Concurrent Pos:* Nat Res Coun fel, 72-74. *Mem:* Am Ornith Union; Soc Study Syst Zool; Soc Study Evolution; Can Soc Genetics & Cytol; Sigma Xi. *Res:* Cytogenetics and chromosomal evolution in insects and vertebrates; DNA evolution in vertebrates; rates of chromosome and DNA change. *Mailing Add:* Inst Arctic Biol Univ of Alaska Fairbanks AK 99701

SHIELDS, HOWARD WILLIAM, b Tomotla, NC, May 19, 31; m 60; c 3. SOLID STATE PHYSICS. *Educ:* Univ NC, BS, 52; Pa State Univ, MS, 53; Duke Univ, PhD(physics), 56. *Prof Exp:* Res assoc physics, Duke Univ, 56-57; from asst prof to assoc prof, 58-66, PROF PHYSICS, WAKE FOREST UNIV, 66- *Concurrent Pos:* Sloan Found res fel, 63-65; vis prof, Yale Univ, 68-69. *Mem:* Fel Am Phys Soc; Radiation Res Soc. *Res:* Electron spin resonance; studies made on irradiation damage in organic solids. *Mailing Add:* Dept of Physics Wake Forest Univ Winston-Salem NC 27109

SHIELDS, JAMES EDWIN, b Marion, Ind, July 29, 34; m 62; c 1. BIOCHEMISTRY, ENTOMOLOGY. *Educ:* DePauw Univ, AB, 56; Univ Calif, Berkeley, PhD(biochem), 61. *Prof Exp:* USPHS fel, Univ Zurich, 60-62; asst prof chem, Case Western Reserve Univ, 62-68; sr biochemist, 68-76, RES SCIENTIST, LILLY RES LABS, ELI LILLY & CO, 77-; FOUNDER & PRES, AMARYLLIS RES INST, 78- *Concurrent Pos:* Adj prof chem, Indiana Univ & Purdue Univ, 79- *Mem:* Am Chem Soc; Lepidopterists Soc; AAAS. *Res:* Peptide and protein chemistry; horticulture. *Mailing Add:* Lilly Res Labs Eli Lilly & Co 307 E McCarty St Indianapolis IN 46285

SHIELDS, JIMMIE LEE, b St Louis, Mo, Aug 9, 34; m 65; c 2. ENVIRONMENTAL PHYSIOLOGY. *Educ:* Cent Methodist Col, AB, 56; Univ Mo, AM, 58, PhD(physiol), 62. *Prof Exp:* Instr physiol, Univ Mo, 62-64, asst prof, 64-65; res physiologist, Fitzsimons Gen Hosp, Denver, 65-68; mem staff, 68-74, asst dir health info progs, 74-77, ASST DIR PREV EDUC & CONTROL & ACTG DEP DIR, DIV HEART & VASCULAR DIS, NAT HEART, LUNG & BLOOD INST, 78- *Concurrent Pos:* Res assoc, Space Sci Res Ctr, Univ Mo, 64-65, res consult, 65-68. *Mem:* Am Physiol Soc. *Res:* Altitude and arctic, metabolic and performance aspects of environmental physiology. *Mailing Add:* Health Info Progs Nat Heart, Lung & Blood Inst Bethesda MD 20014

SHIELDS, JOAN ESTHER, b Cambridge, Mass, Oct 11, 34. ORGANIC CHEMISTRY. *Educ:* Regis Col, Mass, AB, 56; Tufts Univ, MS, 58; Boston Col, PhD(org chem), 66. *Prof Exp:* Instr chem, Regis Col, Mass, 58-63; fel, Max Planck Inst Coal Res, 66-68; asst prof, 68-71, ASSOC PROF CHEM, C W POST COL, LONG ISLAND UNIV, 71- *Mem:* Am Chem Soc. *Res:* Organometallic chemisitry; organosulfur and nitrogen heterocyclics and photochemical cycloadditions. *Mailing Add:* Dept of Chem C W Post Col Long Island Univ Greenvale NY 11548

SHIELDS, JOHN ALLEN, JR, b Youngstown, Ohio, May 12, 46; m 68; c 3. METALLURGY ENGINEERING. *Educ:* Case Western Reserve Univ, BS, 68, MS, 71, PhD(metall & mat sci), 75. *Prof Exp:* Jr metallurgist, Aluminum Co, 68-69; asst metall engr, EBR II, Argonne Nat Lab, 74-76, metall engr, 76-78, mgr, Reactor & Mfg Mat Support Sect, 78-79; asst prof metall eng, Wayne State Univ, 79-81; SR RES METALLURGIST, RES LAB, CLIMAX MOLYBDENUM CO, 81- *Concurrent Pos:* Adj prof nuclear eng, La State Univ, 78-79; metall consult, var orgn including Argonne Nat Lab, 79-81; adj prof metall eng, Wayne State Univ, 82- *Mem:* Am Inst Mining Metall & Petrol Engrs Metall Soc; Sigma Xi; Am Soc Metals. *Res:* Metallurgy of molybdenum metal, molybdenum base alloys and magnetic alloys; hot deformation of nickel and nickel-base alloys. *Mailing Add:* Climax Molybdenum Co PO Box 1568 Ann Arbor MI 48106

SHIELDS, LORA MANEUM, b Choctaw, Okla, Mar 13, 12; m 31; c 1. BIOLOGY. *Educ:* Univ NMex, BS, 40, MS, 42; Unv Iowa, PhD(bot), 47. *Prof Exp:* Assoc prof biol, NMex Highlands Univ, 47-54, prof biol & head dept, 51-78, dir, Environ Health Div, 72-78; RESEARCHER & INSTR, NAVAJO COMMUNITY COL, SHIPROCK, NMEX, 78- *Concurrent Pos:* Res grants, AEC, NIH, NSF, Sigma Xi & Squibb & Searle. *Mem:* AAAS; Ecol Soc Am (vpres, 62-63). *Res:* Plant nitrogen sources and leaf nitrogen content; soil algae; nuclear effects on vegetation; serum lipids; hypoglycemic principles in plants; serum lipids in Spanish and Anglo-Americans; birth anomalies in the Navajo uranium district. *Mailing Add:* Navajo Commun Col Shiprock Campus PO Box 580 Shiprock NM 87420

SHIELDS, LORAN DONALD, b San Diego, Calif, Sept 18, 36; m 57; c 4. ANALYTICAL CHEMISTRY, ACADEMIC ADMINISTRATION. *Educ:* Univ Calif, Riverside, BA, 59; Univ Calif, Los Angeles, PhD(chem), 64. *Prof Exp:* From asst prof to assoc prof chem, 63-67, chmn fac coun, 67, vpres admin, 67-70, actg pres, 70-71, PROF CHEM, CALIF STATE UNIV, FULLERTON, 67-, PRES, 71- *Concurrent Pos:* Consult, Calif State Senate for Legis in Support of Res in Calif State Cols, 68-69 & NSF, 70; mem exec comt, Coun of Pres, Calif State Univ & Cols Syst, 73-, chmn, 75-76; resource leader, Res Corp Conf for Pub Univ Sci Dept Chairs, Ala, 74; mem, Nat Sci Bd, 74-80, mem budget comt, Progs Comt, Sci Educ Adv Comt, 74- & Nat Comt on Coop Educ. *Mem:* Am Inst Chemists; Sigma Xi; AAAS; Am Chem Soc; Am Col Pub Rels Asn. *Res:* Transition metal coordination chemistry; instrumental methods of analytical chemistry. *Mailing Add:* Off of the Pres Calif State Univ Fullerton CA 92634

SHIELDS, PAUL CALVIN, b South Haven, Mich, Nov 10, 33; m 62; c 3. PURE MATHEMATICS. *Educ:* Colo Col, AB, 56; Yale Univ, MA, 58, PhD(math), 59. *Prof Exp:* CLE Moore instr math, Mass Inst Technol, 59-61; asst prof, Boston Univ, 61-63; asst prof, Wayne State Univ, 63-69; vis scholar & res assoc, Stanford Univ, 70-73; vis lectr, Univ Warwick, Coventry Eng, 73-74; assoc prof, 74-76, PROF MATH, UNIV TOLEDO, 76- *Concurrent Pos:* Res assoc, Willow Run Lab, Univ Mich, 60; vis prof elec eng, Cornell Univ, 78, Stanford Univ, 80-82. *Mem:* Am Math Soc; Inst Elec & Electronics Eng. *Res:* Ergodic theory; information theory; statistical mechanics; operator theory; linear algebra. *Mailing Add:* Dept of Math Univ of Toledo Toledo OH 43606

SHIELDS, ROBERT JAMES, b Philadelphia, Pa, Apr 23, 34; m 58. PARASITOLOGY. *Educ:* East Stroudsburg State Col, BS, 55; Ohio State Univ, MS, 59, PhD(zool), 62. *Prof Exp:* Instr zool, Ohio State Univ, 62-63; instr biol, 63-65, asst prof, 65-70. assoc prof, 70-76, PROF BIOL, CITY COL NEW YORK, 77-, CHMN DEPT, 78. *Mem:* Am Soc Parasitol; Am Soc Zoologists; Am Micros Soc. *Res:* Life-histories, ecology and physiology of marine and fresh-water copepods parasitic on fishes. *Mailing Add:* Dept of Biol City Col of New York New York NY 10031

SHIELDS, ROBERT PIERCE, b Nashville, Tenn, June 11, 32; m 60; c 2. VETERINARY PATHOLOGY, BIOCHEMISTRY. *Educ:* Auburn Univ, DVM, 56, MVS, 59; Univ Ark, Little Rock, MS, 66; Mich State Univ, PhD(path), 72. *Prof Exp:* Instr path, Auburn Univ, 56-59; pathologist, Ralston Purina Co, 59-62; resident pathologist, Med Ctr, Univ Ark, Little Rock, 65-66; assoc prof path, Auburn Univ, 66-72; ASSOC PROF PATH, DIV COMP MED, COL VET MED & DIR, ANIMAL RESOURCE DIAG LAB, UNIV FLA, 72- *Concurrent Pos:* NIH fel chem path, Univ Ark, 62-65, spec fel path, Mich State Univ, 70-72. *Mem:* Am Col Vet Pathologists; Am Vet Med Asn. *Res:* Biochemistry and pathology associated with neuromuscular diseases; nutritional pathology; creatine metabolism. *Mailing Add:* PO Box J6 JHM Health Ctr Univ of Fla Col Vet Med Gainesville FL 32611

SHIELDS, THOMAS WILLIAM, b Ambridge, Pa, Aug 17, 22; m 48; c 3. THORACIC SURGERY. *Educ:* Kenyon Col, BA, 43; Temple Univ, MD, 47; Am Bd Surg, dipl, 55; Bd Thoracic Surg, dipl, 56. *Hon Degrees:* DSc, Kenyon, 78. *Prof Exp:* Intern, Allegheny Gen Hosp, Pittsburgh, 47-48; resident, New Eng Deaconess Hosp, Boston, 48-49, Passavant Mem Hosp, Chicago, 49-50 & Vet Admin Res Hosp, Chicago, 54-55; sr resident, Chicago Munic Tuberc Sanitarium, 55-56; instr, 56-57, assoc, 57-62, assoc prof, 64-68, PROF SURG, NORTHWESTERN UNIV, CHICAGO, 68-, CHIEF SURG SERV, VET ADMIN LAKESIDE HOSP, 68- *Concurrent Pos:* Allan B Kanavel fel surg, Passavant Mem Hosp, Chicago, 49-50; thoracic surgeon, Vet Admin Res Hosp, 56-57, mem staff thoracic surgeons, 57-; assoc surg staff, Passavant Mem Hosp, 56-57, attend surgeon, 58-72; attend thoracic surgeon, Chicago Munic Tuberc Sanitarium, 56-68 & attend surgeon, Northwestern Mem Hosp, 72- *Mem:* Western Surg Asn; Am Col Surg; Am Asn Thoracic Surg; Soc Thoracic Surg; Cent Surg Asn. *Res:* Clinical cancer research; editor and contributor to surgical, thoracic surgical, and cancer literature. *Mailing Add:* Vet Admin Lakeside Hosp 333 E Huron St Chicago IL 60611

SHIELDS, WALTER JOSEPH, JR, b Santa Ana, Calif, March 15, 48; m 71. ECOLOGICAL CLASSIFICATION. *Educ:* Univ Wash, Seattle, BS, 74; Univ Idaho, MS, 76; Univ Wis, Madison, PhD(soil sci), 79. *Prof Exp:* RES FORESTER ECOL & SOILS FORESTRY, RES DIV, CROWN ZELLERBACH CORP, ORE, 79- *Mem:* Soc Am Foresters; Soil Sci Soc Am; Am Soc Photogrammetry. *Res:* Relationship between soil properties and forest pathology; hardwood soil-site productivity; ecological classification; forest meteorology; computerized geographic information systems; soil moisture and soil temperature regime. *Mailing Add:* Forestry Res Div Crown Zellerbach Corp Box 368 Wilsonville OR 97070

SHIER, DOUGLAS ROBERT, b Cleveland, Ohio, Oct 16, 46. OPERATIONS RESEARCH, APPLIED MATHEMATICS. *Educ:* Harvard Univ, AB, 68; London Sch Econ, PhD(oper res), 73. *Prof Exp:* Res statistician, Ctr Dis Control, USPHS, 68-70; res assoc, Nat Bur Standards, 73-74; asst prof quant methods, Univ Ill, 74-75; mathematician, Nat Bur Standards, 75-80; ASSOC PROF MATH SCI, CLEMSON UNIV, 80- *Mem:* Am Statist Asn; Math Asn Am; Opers Res Soc Am. *Res:* Mathematical and statistical modeling; network and location problems; environmental sciences. *Mailing Add:* Dept Math Sci Clemson Univ Clemson SC 29631

SHIER, WAYNE THOMAS, b Harriston, Ont, Dec 1, 43; m 69; c 3. BIOCHEMISTRY. *Educ:* Univ Waterloo, BSc, 66; Univ Ill, Urbana, MS, 68, PhD(chem), 70. *Prof Exp:* Res assoc biochem, Salk Inst, 70-72, asst res prof, 72-80; ASSOC PROF, DEPT PHARMACEUT CELL BIOL, UNIV MINN, 80- *Concurrent Pos:* Am Cancer Soc Dernham jr fel, 70-71; consult, Tokyo Tanabe Co, Ltd, 71 & Marcel Dekker, Inc, 79-; USPHS res grant, 72-80; Cystic Fibrosis Found res grant, 78-80 & Nat Sci Found Res Grant, 80- *Mem:* AAAS; Am Soc Biol Chemists; NY Acad Sci; Am Chem Soc; Acad Pharmaceut Sci. *Res:* Structure and synthesis of glycoproteins; biochemistry of cell membranes; phospholipases; cystic fibrosis; cyclic nucleotides; lipids; cytotoxic mechanisms; regulation of prostaglandin synthesis. *Mailing Add:* Dept Pharmaceut Cell Biol Col Pharm Health Sci Unit F Univ Minn Minneapolis MN 55455

SHIFFLER, DONALD ALBERT, JR, chemical engineering, see previous edition

SHIFFMAN, BERNARD, b New York, NY, June 23, 42; m 65; c 2. MATHEMATICS, COMPLEX MATHEMATICS. *Educ:* Mass Inst Technol, BS, 64; Univ Calif, Berkeley, PhD(math), 68. *Prof Exp:* Moore instr math, Mass Inst Technol, 68-70; asst prof, Yale Univ, 70-73; assoc prof, 73-77, PROF MATH, JOHNS HOPKINS UNIV, 77- *Concurrent Pos:* Mem, Inst Advan Study, 75; res fel, Alfred P Sloan Found, 73-75; Woodrow Wilson fac develop award, 79; vis prof, Univ Paris, 81. *Mem:* Am Math Soc; Inst Hautes Etudes Sci. *Res:* Several complex variables. *Mailing Add:* Dept of Math Johns Hopkins Univ Baltimore MD 21218

SHIFFMAN, CARL ABRAHAM, b Boston, Mass, Nov 14, 30; m 56; c 2. PHYSICS. *Educ:* Mass Inst Technol, BS, 52; Oxford Univ, DrPhil, 56. *Prof Exp:* Physicist, Nat Bur Standards, 56-60 & Mass Inst Technol, 60-67; PROF PHYSICS, NORTHEASTERN UNIV, 67- *Res:* Low temperature physics; superconductivity. *Mailing Add:* Dept of Physics Northeastern Univ Huntington Ave Boston MA 02115

SHIFFMAN, MAX, b New York, NY, Oct 30, 14; div; c 2. MATHEMATICS, AERODYNAMICS. *Educ:* City Col New York, BS, 35; NY Univ, MS, 36, PhD(math), 38. *Prof Exp:* Instr math, St John's Univ, NY, 38-39 & City Col New York 38-42; res mathematician, US Army, US Off Naval Res & Appl Math Panel, US Off Sci Res & Develop, NY Univ, 41-48, assoc prof math, 46-49; prof, Stanford Univ, 49-66; prof math, Calif State Univ, Hayward, 67-79; MATHMATICIAN & OWNER, MATHEMATICO, 70- *Concurrent Pos:* Res mathematician, Rand Co, Santa Monica, Calif, 51; consult, US Govt. *Mem:* Math Asn Am; AAAS; Am Math Soc; Soc Indust & Appl Math; Am Soc Prof Consult. *Res:* Minimal surfaces; stationary extremals; groups; conformal mapping; potential theory; complex variable; calculus of variations; hydrodynamics; aerodynamics; partial differential equations; games; probability; topological and linear space methods in analysis; non-measurable sets. *Mailing Add:* 16913 Meekland Ave No 7 Hayward CA 94541

SHIFFMAN, MORRIS A, b New York, NY, Oct 12, 22; m 50; c 2. ENVIRONMENTAL HEALTH. *Educ:* Middlesex Univ, DVM, 44; Univ Mich, MPH, 45; Nat Vet Sch, Alfort, France, DVet, 49; Univ Pa, MGA, 57, PhD, 67. *Prof Exp:* Qual control supvr, Gen Ice Cream Corp, 45; sr veterinarian, UN Relief & Rehab Admin, 46-47; food & drug sanit supvr, Milwaukee Health Dept, 49-53; chief milk & food sanit, Phila Dept Pub Health, 53-64; assoc prof environ sanit, 64-69, PROF ENVIRON HEALTH, UNIV NC, CHAPEL HILL, 69- *Concurrent Pos:* Mem subcomt food sanit, Nat Res Coun, 59-62, chmn, 62-65; mem food estab sanit adv comt, USPHS, 60-63; adv panel zoonoses, WHO, 61-72; mem comt sanit eng & environ, Nat Acad Sci-Nat Res Coun, 62-65; mem adv panel food hyg, WHO, 72- & Sci Adv Comt, Pan-Am Zoonoses Ctr, 72- *Mem:* AAAS; Am Soc Pub Admin. *Res:* Administration of environmental health programs; environmental health policy; project-impact studies in developing countries. *Mailing Add:* Dept of Environ Sci & Eng Univ of NC Sch of Pub Health Chapel Hill NC 27514

SHIFLET, THOMAS NEAL, b Marysville, Tex, July 25, 30; m 53; c 2. RANGE MANAGEMENT, ECOLOGY. *Educ:* Tex A&M Univ, BS, 51; Univ Calif, Berkeley, MS, 67; Univ Nebr, PhD(range mgt), 72. *Prof Exp:* Consult area range mgt, 57-60, state range consult, 60-67, staff range consult, 67-70, regional range consult, 70-74, chief range consult, 74-75, DIV DIR ECOL SCI, SOIL CONSERV SERV, USDA, 75- *Concurrent Pos:* Range conservationist, Soil Conserv Serv, USDA, 53-54, work unit conservationist, 54-57. *Mem:* AAAS; Soc Range Mgt; Soil Conserv Soc Am; Sigma Xi; Coun Agr Sci & TEchnol. *Mailing Add:* USDA Soil Conserv Serv PO Box 2890 Washington DC 20013

SHIFLETT, LILBURN THOMAS, b Adamsville, Ala, Feb 4, 21; m 42; c 2. MATHEMATICS. *Educ:* Univ N Ala, BS, 46; George Peabody Col, MA, 48, PhD(math), 63. *Prof Exp:* Teacher high sch, Ark, 46-48; from instr to assoc prof, 48-58, dir div honors, 65-67, PROF MATH, SOUTHWEST MO STATE UNIV, 58- HEAD DEPT MATH, 68- *Res:* Geometry; statistics. *Mailing Add:* Southwest Mo State Univ 901 S National Springfield MO 65802

SHIFLETT, RAY CALVIN, b Levensworth, Wash, Dec 3, 39; m 59; c 2. MATHEMATICS. *Educ:* Eastern Wash State Col, BA, 63; Ore State Univ, MS, 65, PhD(math), 67. *Prof Exp:* NSF res asst, Ore State Univ, 66-67; asst prof math, Wells Col, 67-75, chmn dept, 69-75; assoc prof, 75-80, PROF MATH, CALIF STATE UNIV, FULLERTON, 80- *Mem:* Math Asn Am; Am Math Soc. *Res:* Analysis, especially measure theory, doubly stochastic measures and Markov operators. *Mailing Add:* Dept of Math Calif State Univ Fullerton CA 92634

SHIFRINE, MOSHE, b Harbin, China, Apr 29, 28; nat US; m 56, 72; c 7. MICROBIOLOGY. *Educ:* Univ Calif, BS, 52, MS, 53, PhD(microbiol), 58. *Prof Exp:* Jr specialist poultry husb, Univ Calif, Davis, 58, asst specialist avian med, 58-64; microbiologist, Agr Res Serv, USDA, Kenya, 64-68; res immunologist, Radiobiol Lab, 68-71, ASSOC PROF IN RESIDENCE

MICROBIOL, RADIOBIOL LAB, UNIV CALIF, DAVIS, 68-, PROF IN RESIDENCE IMMUNOL, SCH VET MED, 69-, ADJ PROF IMMUNOL, DEPT VET MICROBIOL, UNIV, 71-, RES IMMUNOLOGIST, LAB ENERGY RELATED HEALTH RES, 71- *Mem:* AAAS; Am Asn Immunol; Int Soc Biometeorol; Sigma Xi; Int Asn Comp Leukemia Res. *Res:* Radiation and environmental immunology. *Mailing Add:* Lab Energy-Related Health Res Univ of Calif Davis CA 95616

SHIGEISHI, RONALD A, b Vancouver, BC, Apr 5, 39; m 68. PHYSICAL CHEMISTRY. *Educ:* Univ Toronto, BSc, 61; Queen's Univ, PhD(chem), 65. *Prof Exp:* Nat Res Coun fel, 65-67; ASST PROF CHEM, CARLETON UNIV, 67- *Concurrent Pos:* Nat Res Coun res grants, 67-69. *Res:* Surface chemistry of gas-metal systems. *Mailing Add:* Dept of Chem Carleton Univ Ottawa ON K1S 5B6 Can

SHIGLEY, JOSEPH E(DWARD), b Delphi, Ind, Apr 10, 09; m 34; c 2. MECHANICAL ENGINEERING. *Educ:* Purdue Univ, BS, 31 & 32; Univ Mich, MS, 46. *Prof Exp:* From assoc prof to prof, 57-78, EMER PROF MECH ENG, UNIV MICH, ANN ARBOR, 78- *Concurrent Pos:* Res writer & consult. *Honors & Awards:* Mechanisms Award, Am Soc Mech Engrs, 74; Worcester Reed Warner Medal, 77. *Mem:* Fel Am Soc Mech Engrs. *Res:* Kinematic and dynamic analysis and computer simulation of mechanical systems. *Mailing Add:* Rte 1 Box 64E Pinecone Beach Roscommon MI 48653

SHIGO, ALEX LLOYD, b Duquesne, Pa, May 8, 30; m 54; c 2. PLANT PATHOLOGY. *Educ:* Waynesburg Col, BS, 56; Univ WVa, MS, 58, PhD(plant path), 59. *Prof Exp:* Plant pathologist, 59-74, CHIEF PLANT PATHOLOGIST & LEADER, PIONEER PROJ, US FOREST SERV, 74- *Concurrent Pos:* Lectr, Univ Maine; adj prof, Univ NH. *Honors & Awards:* New Eng Logger Award Outstanding Res, 73; Award of Achievement, NY Arborist Asn, 74; Super Serv Award, USDA, 74; Award Merit, Am Phytopath Soc, New Eng Div, 74; Super Serv Award, Md Arborist Asn, 75; Ciba-Giegy Award, Am Phytopath Soc, 75. *Mem:* Mycol Soc Am; Am Phytopath Soc. *Res:* Decay and discoloration in living trees; physiology of wood-inhabiting fungi; diseases of northern hardwoods; fungi parasitic on other fungi; myco-parasites. *Mailing Add:* Northeastern Forest Exp Sta Box 640 Durham NH 03824

SHIH, ARNOLD SHANG-TEH, b Shanghai, China, May 17, 43; US citizen; m 69; c 2. PHYSICS. *Educ:* Univ Calif, Berkeley, AB, 65; Columbia Univ, PhD(physics), 72. *Prof Exp:* Physicist surface chem, Nat Bur Standards, 72-75; RES PHYSICIST SURFACE PHYSICS, NAVAL RES LAB, 75- *Mem:* Am Phys Soc; Am Vacuum Soc. *Res:* Electronic properties at the surface of solids; Van der Waals forces between atoms and solid surfaces. *Mailing Add:* Naval Res Lab Code 6832 4555 Overlook Ave Washington DC 20375

SHIH, CHANG-TAI, b Amoy, China, Aug 15, 34; Can citizen; m 63; c 2. SYSTEMATICS, BIOLOGICAL OCEANOGRAPHY. *Educ:* Nat Taiwan Univ, BSc, 58; McGill Univ, PhD(marine sci), 66. *Prof Exp:* Asst prof biol, Lakehead Univ, 66-67; scientist res group & cur zool, 67-79, CUR CRUSTACEANS, NAT MUS NATURAL SCI, 79- *Mem:* Am Soc Limnol & Oceanog; Ecol Soc Am; Soc Study Evolution; Sigma Xi; Plankton Soc Japan. *Res:* Systematics and zoogeography of Hyperiidea and Calanoida; taxonomy and ecology of marine zooplankton of northern waters of northern hemisphere. *Mailing Add:* Nat Mus of Natural Sci Ottawa ON K1A 0M8 Can

SHIH, CHING-YUAN G, b Taiwan, China, May 25, 34; m 67; c 2. PLANT PHYSIOLOGY, CROP BREEDING. *Educ:* Chung Hsing Univ, Taiwan, BS, 58; Nat Taiwan Univ, MS, 62; Univ Calif, Davis, PhD(plant physiol), 68. *Prof Exp:* Fel veg crops, Univ Calif, Davis, 68-69; res assoc, 69-71, adj asst prof, 78-81, ADJ ASSOC PROF BOT, UNIV IOWA, 81-, DIR, UNIV SCANNING ELECTRON MICROS LAB, 71- *Mem:* AAAS; Electron Micros Soc Am; Am Soc Cell Biol. *Res:* Structure of phloem cells in relation to translocation; plant hormones in relation to nucleic acid synthesis; virus-host-relationship in cultured cells; scanning electron microscopy in biology; biological microsculptures. *Mailing Add:* Scanning Electron Micros Lab Univ Iowa 40ZB Iowa City IA 52242

SHIH, CORNELIUS CHUNG-SHENG, b Rukuan, Formosa, Nov 15, 31; m 60; c 4. FLUID MECHANICS. *Educ:* Nat Taiwan Univ, BS, 54; Mich State Univ, MS, 57, PhD(fluid mech), 59. *Prof Exp:* Res asst fluid mech, Mich State Univ, 56-59; assoc prof civil eng, Auburn Univ, 59-65; PROF ENG MECH, UNIV ALA, HUNTSVILLE, 65-, HEAD FLUID DYNAMICS LAB, RES INST, 69- *Mem:* Am Soc Civil Engrs; Eng Soc Japan. *Res:* Hydraulic open-channel flows, secondary flows; fluid amplifiers; vortex motions. *Mailing Add:* Dept of Fluid & Thermal Eng Univ of Ala Box 1247 Huntsville AL 35807

SHIH, FREDERICK F, b China, Dec 11, 36; US citizen; m 77; c 1. FOOD SCIENCE & TECHNOLOGY. *Educ:* Fort Hays State Univ, MS, 66; La State Univ, PhD(chem), 76. *Prof Exp:* Assoc prof chem, Maryville Col, 66; RES CHEMIST, USDA, 76- *Mem:* Am Chem Soc; Sigma Xi. *Res:* Textile research on the improvement of cotton fabrics with chemical treatments; chemical and enzymatide modification of oil seed proteins for the improvement of functional properties. *Mailing Add:* SRRC-USDA PO Box 19687 New Orleans LA 70179

SHIH, HANSEN S T, b Shanghai, China, April 15, 42. LASER PHYSICS, NONLINEAR OPTICS. *Educ:* Mass Inst Technol, BS, 65, MS, 68; Harvard Univ, PhD(appl physics), 70. *Prof Exp:* Res assoc, Dept Physics & Optical Sci Ctr, Univ Ariz, Tuscon, 71-75; res physicist, Naval Res Lab, 75-76; sr res physicist, Tech Ctr, Libby-Omens-Ford, 77-79; TECH SPECIALIST & PROJ MGR, XEROX CORP, 79- *Mem:* Am Phys Soc. *Res:* Laser physics; nonlinear optics; acoustics; process modelling of physical processes of industrial interests, including vacuum film deposition, color, fluid dynamics and acoustics. *Mailing Add:* 81 Redwood Dr Penfield NY 14526

SHIH, HSIANG, b Chungking, China, Nov 11, 43; m 70. POLYMER CHEMISTRY. *Educ:* Nat Taiwan Univ, BS, 65; Yale Univ, MPh, 68, PhD(chem), 69. *Prof Exp:* Fel chem, Stanford Univ, 69-70; res chemist, 70-75, SR RES CHEMIST, PIONEERING RES LAB, TEXTILE FIBERS DEPT, E I DU PONT DE NEMOURS & CO, 75- *Mem:* Am Chem Soc. *Res:* Polymer chemistry and its industrial applications; thermodynamics and other physical chemistry fields. *Mailing Add:* Pioneering Res Lab E I du Pont de Nemours & Co Inc Wilmington DE 19898

SHIH, HSIO CHANG, b Wuchang, Hupei, China, Apr 1, 37; m 71. PHYSICS. *Educ:* Ohio Univ, BSME, 58; Ill Inst Technol, MS, 62, PhD(physics), 68. *Prof Exp:* Mech designer, Precision Transformer Corp, 58-60; asst prof physics, Ill Inst Technol, 68; lectr, 67-68, actg chmn dept, 71, ASSOC PROF PHYSICS, ROOSEVELT UNIV, 68- *Concurrent Pos:* Chmn dept physics & eng sci, 73-77. *Mem:* Am Phys Soc; Am Asn Physics Teachers. *Res:* Electrodynamics. *Mailing Add:* Dept of Physics Roosevelt Univ Chicago IL 60605

SHIH, JAMES WAIKUO, b China, July 24, 41; US citizen; m 68; c 2. VIROLOGY, IMMUNOCHEMISTRY. *Educ:* Chung Hsing Univ, Taiwan, BS, 64. *Prof Exp:* Mem staff, Molecular Anat Prog, Oak Ridge Nat Lab, 71-78; assoc prof microbiol, Div Molecular Virol & Immunol, Georgetown Univ, 78-80; RES MICROBIOLOGIST, HEPATITIS BR, DIV BLOOD & BLOOD PROD, BUR BIOLOGICS, FOOD & DRUG ADMIN, 80- *Concurrent Pos:* Res assoc pharm, Sch Pharm, Univ Wis, 70; vis fel biochem, Nat Heart & Lung Inst, NIH, 70-71. *Mem:* Am Soc Microbiol. *Res:* Identification of antigenic systems of viruses and characterization of structure-function relationship by immunochemical procedures; specific application in research of viral hepatitis and respiratory disease pathogens. *Mailing Add:* Bur Biologics Bldg 29 Rm 324 8800 Rockville Pike Bethesda MD 20205

SHIH, JEAN CHEN, b Yunan, China, Jan 29, 42; US citizen; m 69; c 2. AGING RESEARCH, PHARMACY. *Educ:* Nat Taiwan Univ, Taipei, BS, 64; Univ Calif, Riverside, PhD(biochem), 68. *Prof Exp:* Scholar biochem, Dept Biol Chem & Psychiat, Sch Med, Univ Calif, Los Angeles, 68-70; asst res biochemist, 70-74; asst prof, 74-79, ASSOC PROF BIOCHEM, SCH PHARM, UNIV SOUTHERN CALIF, 79- *Concurrent Pos:* Vis assoc prof pharmacol, Dept Pharmacol, Sch Med, Univ Calif, Los Angeles, 81. *Mem:* Am Soc Biol Chemists; Am Soc Neurochem; Soc Neurosci; Am Asn Col Pharm; AAAS. *Res:* Molecular mechanism of neurotransmission with emphasis on the structure and function relationship of membrane proteins in central nervous systems; regulation of enzymes and receptors, and their implicaiton in aging and in disease states. *Mailing Add:* Sch Pharm Univ Southern Calif 1985 Zonal Ave Los Angeles CA 90033

SHIH, KWANG KUO, b China, Oct 13, 32; m 64; c 2. SOLID STATE DEVICES & PHYSICS. *Educ:* Nat Taiwan Univ, BS, 53; Purdue Univ, MS, 56; Va Polytech Inst, MS, 59; Stanford Univ, MS, 61, PhD(elec eng), 66. *Prof Exp:* Engr, Sunbeam Corp, 56-57; engr, Hewlett Packard Co, 61-62; res asst, Stanford Univ, 64-66; RES STAFF MEM RES CTR, IBM CORP, 66- *Mem:* Fel Am Inst Chemists; Electrochem Soc; Am Phys Soc; Inst Elec & Electronics Engrs; Sigma Xi. *Res:* Electroluminescence; growth of III-V ternary compounds, defects in silicon and the physics of semiconductors; thin film devices; reactive evaporation. *Mailing Add:* IBM Res Ctr PO Box 218 Yorktown Heights NY 10598

SHIH, THOMAS YUTZONG, b Taipei, Taiwan, July 10, 39; m 68; c 1. BIOCHEMISTRY, MOLECULAR BIOLOGY. *Educ:* Nat Taiwan Univ, MB, 65; Calif Inst Technol, PhD(biochem, chem), 69. *Prof Exp:* Asst biol, Calif Inst Technol, 66-69; res assoc biochem, Brandeis Univ, 69-71; vis fel molecular biol, 71-72; vis assoc molecular biol, Lab Biol of Viruses, 73-77, MEM STAFF, LAB OF TUMOR VIRUS GENETICS NAT INST ALLERGY & INFECTIOUS DIS, 78- *Mem:* AAAS; Am Chem Soc; Biophys Soc. *Res:* Molecular biology of heredity; mechanisms of gene regulation in eukaryotic cells; chemical structure and biochemical activities of chromatin; interactions of viruses and cells; biophysical chemistry of macromolecules. *Mailing Add:* 6820 Marbury Rd Bethesda MD 20014

SHIH, TSUNG-MING ANTHONY, b Taipei, Taiwan, Oct 8, 44; US citizen; m 70; c 2. PHARMACOLOGY. *Educ:* Kaohsiung Med Col, Taiwan, BS, 67; Univ Pittsburgh, PhD(pharmacol), 74. *Prof Exp:* Teaching asst, Columbia Univ, 68-69; teaching asst, 69-71, NIH trainee, 72-74, res asst III, Dept Psychiat, Univ Pittsburgh, 74-76, res assoc, 76-78; pharmacologist, Biomed Lab, Chem Systs Lab, 78-80, PHARMACOLOGIST, US ARMY MED RES INST CHEM DEF, ABERDEEN PROVING GROUND, MD, 80- *Concurrent Pos:* Fel, Western Psychiat Inst & Clin, Univ Pittsburgh, 74-76. *Mem:* Sigma Xi; Am Chem Soc; AAAS; Am Mgt Asn; Soc Neurosci. *Res:* Central neuropharmacological mechanisms of action of anticholinesterases; transport of choline from plasma, via choline in the brain, to acetylcholine in the brain; possible acetylcholine storage function of platelets. *Mailing Add:* US Army Med Res Inst Chem Defense Bldg E-3100 Aberdeen Proving Ground MD 21010

SHIH, VIVIAN EAN, b China, Dec 27, 34; US citizen; m 65; c 2. PEDIATRICS. *Educ:* Col Med, Nat Taiwan Univ, MD, 58. *Prof Exp:* Dir animo acid lab, Joseph P Kennedy Jr Mem Labs, 67-75, asst neurol, 68-75, ASSOC PROF NEUROL, MASS GEN HOSP & HARVARD UNIV MED SCH, 75- *Concurrent Pos:* Consult & co-prin investr, Mass Metab Disorders Prog, Mass Dept Pub Health, 67-80; consult amino acid metab dis, Walter E Fernald State Sch, Waltham, Mass, 68- & Wrentham State Sch, Wrentham, Mass, 68-70; consult pediat, Cambridge Hosp, Cambridge, Mass, 69-; asst prof neurol, Harvard Med Sch, 70-75; assoc, Ctr Human Genetics, 71- *Mem:* Soc Pediat Res; Am Acad Pediat; Am Asn Human Genetics; Am Asn Foreign Med Grads. *Res:* Biochemical genetics and hereditary metabolic disorders. *Mailing Add:* Amino Acid Lab Mass Gen Hosp Boston MA 02114

SHILEPSKY, ARNOLD CHARLES, b Norwalk, Conn, Dec 10, 44; m 68; c 2. MATHEMATICS, COMPUTER SCIENCES, GENERAL. *Educ:* Wesleyan Univ, AB, 66; Univ Wis-Madison, PhD(math), 71. *Prof Exp:* Asst prof, Ark State Univ, 71-74; asst prof, 74-79, chmn, Div Phys & Math Sci, 78-81, ASSOC PROF MATH, WELLS COL, 79- *Concurrent Pos:* Proj dir, Exxon Comput Litevvoy grant, 81-82. *Mem:* Math Asn Am; Am Math Soc; Asn Women Math. *Res:* Geometric topology; properties of embeddings in Euclidean spaces. *Mailing Add:* Dept of Math Wells Col Aurora NY 13026

SHILES, EUGENE JOSEPH, solid state physics, magnetism, see previous edition

SHILLADY, DONALD DOUGLAS, b Norristown, Pa, Aug 27, 37; m 68; c 2. THEORETICAL CHEMISTRY. *Educ:* Drexel Univ, BS, 62; Princeton Univ, MA, 65; Univ Va, PhD(chem), 70. *Prof Exp:* Fel chem, Univ Va, 69-70; ASSOC PROF CHEM, ACAD DIV, VA COMMONWEALTH UNIV, 70- *Mem:* Am Chem Soc; Sigma Xi. *Res:* Quantum chemistry, ab initio and semiempirical computational methods applied to chemical bonding and interpretation of circular dichroism and magnetic circular dichroism. *Mailing Add:* Dept Chem Va Commonwealth Univ 914 W Franklin St Richmond VA 23284

SHILLING, PAUL R, b Canton, Ohio, Jan 24, 27; m 47; c 2. BIOLOGY, GENETICS. *Educ:* Ohio State Univ, BA, 48, PhD(hort, plant breeding), 52. *Prof Exp:* Asst prof biol, Malone Col, 57-60; assoc prof, Hartwick Col, 60-65; prof, 65-67; assoc prof, Rensselaer Polytech Inst, 67-72; dir div natural sci, Mattatuck Community Col, 72-77; chmn, Div Natural Sci & Math, Cent Va Community Col, 77-80; DIR NATURAL & HEALTH RELATED SCI, JOHNSON COUNTY COMMUNITY COL, 80- *Mem:* AAAS; Bot Soc Am; Nat Asn Biol Teachers. *Res:* Investigation of the genetic character in the tomato; effects of variations in chromosome number on total protein and amino acid syntheses in tomato, pepper and tobacco. *Mailing Add:* Div Natural & Health Related Sci Johnson County Community Col Overland Park KS 66210

SHILLING, WILBUR LEO, b St Joseph, Mo, Aug 30, 21; m 42; c 4. ORGANIC CHEMISTRY, POLYMER CHEMISTRY. *Educ:* Univ Mo, AB, 42; Univ Notre Dame, MS, 47; Ohio State Univ, PhD(chem), 49. *Prof Exp:* Res chemist, Mallinckrodt Chem Works, 42-46; sr res chemist, Crown Zellerbach Corp, 49-69, supvr polymer-fiber res, 69-72, res assoc, 72-77, proj mgr, Pioneering Res, 78-81; CONSULT, 82- *Mem:* Am Chem Soc; Tech Asn Pulp & Paper Indust. *Res:* Cellulose and carbohydrates; lignin and lignans; consumer paper products; applied polymer research; advanced technology assessment. *Mailing Add:* 1702 N E Ione Loop Camas WA 98607

SHILLINGTON, JAMES KEITH, b Clarion, Iowa, Nov 4, 21. ORGANIC CHEMISTRY. *Educ:* Iowa State Col, BS, 43; Cornell Univ, PhD(chem), 52. *Prof Exp:* Instr chem, Evansville Col, 46-48 & Amherst Col, 52-53; from asst prof to assoc prof, 53-66, PROF CHEM, WASHINGTON & LEE UNIV, 66- *Concurrent Pos:* NSF res grant, 56-57. *Mem:* Am Chem Soc. *Res:* Macro carbon rings; optical resolution; resolving agents. *Mailing Add:* Dept of Chem Washington & Lee Univ Lexington VA 24450

SHILLITOE, EDWARD JOHN, b Hull, Eng, Sept 13, 47. ORAL CANCER. *Educ:* Univ London, BDS, 71, PhD(immunol), 76. *Prof Exp:* Fel virol, Dept Microbiol, Hershey Med Ctr, Pa State Univ, 76-78; ASST PROF ORAL PATH, DENT SCH, UNIV CALIF, SAN FRANCISCO, 78- *Res:* Etiology of oral cancer, utilizing immunological and virological methods. *Mailing Add:* Dept Oral Med Sch Dent Univ Calif San Francisco CA 94143

SHILMAN, AVNER, b Tel Aviv, Israel, Aug 28, 23; US citizen; m 72. ANALYTICAL CHEMISTRY, PHYSICAL CHEMISTRY. *Educ:* Columbia Univ, MS, 53, MA, 57; Polytech Inst Brooklyn, PhD(chem), 61. *Prof Exp:* Mgr pharm, Shilman Pharmacy, 45-48 & 50-51; fel, Polytech Inst Brooklyn, 61-63; from asst prof to assoc prof chem, 63-68, PROF CHEM, NEWARK COL ENG, 68- *Mem:* Am Chem Soc. *Res:* Analytical methods and physical chemical principles of chromatographic and electrophoresis processes. *Mailing Add:* 150 East 18th St Apt 11D New York NY 10003

SHILS, MAURICE EDWARD, b Atlantic City, NJ, Dec 31, 14; m 39; c 2. MEDICINE, NUTRITION. *Educ:* Johns Hopkins Univ, BA, 37, ScD(nutrit, biochem), 40; NY Univ MD, 58. *Prof Exp:* Asst biochem, Sch Hyg & Pub Health, Johns Hopkins Univ, 40-41, instr, 41-42; asst biochemist, Edgewood Arsenal, US Dept Army, 42-43; food technologist, Off Qm Gen, 43-45; exec secy subcomt nutrit & indust fatigue, Nat Res Coun, 45-46; instr nutrit & indust hyg, Sch Pub Health, Columbia Univ, 46-49, asst prof nutrit, 49-54; res assoc, Sloan-Kettering Inst, 57-59, head, Surg Metab Lab, 59 & metab lab, 61, assoc mem, 60, asst prof biochem, Sloan-Kettering Div, 59-62, asst prof med, 62-67, assoc prof, 67-79, PROF MED, MED COL, CORNELL UNIV, 79- *Concurrent Pos:* Attend physician, Mem Hosp, New York, 67-72; attend physician, 72-; dir clin nutrit; exec secy, Comn Pub Health, NY Acad Med, 76- *Mem:* AAAS; Am Inst Nutrit; Am Soc Clin Nutrit; Soc Exp Biol & Med; Harvey Soc. *Res:* Clinical nutrition research; nutrition and metabolism; trace elements in man; intravenous nutrition. *Mailing Add:* Mem Sloan-Kettering Cancer Ctr 1275 York Ave New York NY 10021

SHILTS, JAMES LEONARD, b South Bend, Ind, Oct 9, 25. PHYSICS, ASTRONOMY. *Educ:* Univ Notre Dame, BS, 49, PhD(physics), 61. *Prof Exp:* Instr, 61-64, ASST PROF PHYSICS, UNIV NOTRE DAME, 64- *Mem:* Am Phys Soc; Am Asn Physics Teachers. *Res:* Photoelectric emission from clean and coated metal surfaces in the near and vacuum ultraviolet; density of electron energy states in metals. *Mailing Add:* Dept of Physics Univ of Notre Dame Notre Dame IN 46556

SHIM, BENJAMIN KIN CHONG, b Honolulu, Hawaii, May 21, 29; m 53; c 5. PHYSICAL CHEMISTRY. *Educ:* Univ Rochester, BS, 52; Northwestern Univ, PhD(phys chem), 56. *Prof Exp:* Chemist, Esso Res & Eng Co, 56-62; sr chemist, Lord Corp, 62-68; SR RES CHEMIST, CALSICAT DIV,

MALLINCKRODT, INC, 68- *Mem:* Am Chem Soc. *Res:* Heterogeneous catalysts-preparation; characterization and process research and development. *Mailing Add:* Calsicat Div 1707 Gaskell Ave Mallinckrodt Inc Erie PA 16503

SHIMABUKURO, FRED ICHIRO, b Honolulu, Hawaii, Sept 3, 32; m 67; c 1. RADIO ASTRONOMY. *Educ:* Mass Inst Technol, BS, 55, MS, 56; Calif Inst Technol, PhD(elec eng), 62. *Prof Exp:* Mem tech staff, Hughes Aircraft Co, 56-58; mem tech staff, Electronics Res Lab, 62-74, STAFF SCIENTIST, AEROSPACE CORP, 74- *Mem:* Am Astron Soc; Inst Elec & Electronics Engrs. *Res:* Solar radio astronomy; millimeter-wave propagation. *Mailing Add:* Aerospace Corp 2350 E El Segundo Blvd El Segundo CA 90245

SHIMABUKURO, MARY ABRAHAMSEN, b Morgantown, WVa, Jan 24, 38; m 65; c 2. PLANT PHYSIOLOGY. *Educ:* Univ Wis, BS, 59; Univ Minn, MS, 62, PhD(plant physiol), 64. *Prof Exp:* Instr biol, Eastern Mich Univ, 63; Am Asn Univ Women res fel, Hebrew Univ, Israel, 64-65; asst prof, 66-73, assoc prof, 73-77 PROF BIOL, MOORHEAD STATE COL, 77- *Concurrent Pos:* Sigma Xi grant-in-aid, 66; Sigma Delta Epsilon grant-in-aid, 67. *Mem:* AAAS; Am Soc Plant Physiol. *Res:* Plant tissue culture; physiology of seed germination. *Mailing Add:* Dept of Biol Moorhead State Col Moorhead MN 56560

SHIMABUKURO, RICHARD HIDEO, b Hakalau, Hawaii, Sept 20, 33; m 65. PLANT PHYSIOLOGY. *Educ:* Univ Hawaii, BS, 56; Univ Minn, MS, 62, PhD(plant physiol), 64. *Prof Exp:* RES PLANT PHYSIOLOGIST, METAB & RADIATION RES LAB, USDA, 64- *Honors & Awards:* Foreign Res Scientist Award, Japanese Govt, 73. *Mem:* AAAS; Am Soc Plant Physiol; Weed Sci Soc Am; Scand Soc Plant Physiologists. *Res:* Metabolism of chemical pesticides in plants; mechanism of action of herbicidal chemicals in plants and their metabolism in different plant organs. *Mailing Add:* Metab & Radiation Res Lab State Univ Sta Fargo ND 58102

SHIMADA, KATSUNORI, b Tokyo, Japan, Mar 12, 22; nat US; m 54; c 2. ELECTRICAL ENGINEERING. *Educ:* Univ Tokyo, BS, 45; Univ Minn, MS, 54, PhD(elec eng), 58. *Prof Exp:* Engr, Tokyo Shibaura Elec Co, Japan, 45-49; instr elec eng, Univ Minn, 54-58; assoc prof, Univ Wash, 58-64; resident res appointee, 64-65, RES GROUP SUPVR, JET PROPULSION LAB, CALIF INST TECHNOL, 65- *Concurrent Pos:* Consult, Boeing Co, Wash, 61-63. *Mem:* Inst Elec & Electronics Engrs; Am Inst Physics. *Res:* Thermionic energy conversion, plasma, noise. *Mailing Add:* Jet Propulsion Lab Calif Inst Technol Pasadena CA 91103

SHIMADA, STEVEN GLEN, b Seattle, Wash, Oct 3, 48; m 70. PHYSIOLOGY. *Educ:* Univ Wash, BS, 70; Univ Southern Calif, MS, 74, PhD(biomed eng), 77. *Prof Exp:* Fel, Dept Epidemiol & Pub Health, Sch Med, Yale Univ, 77-80; vis asst fel, 77-81, ASST FEL PHYSIOL, JOHN B PIERCE FOUND LAB, 81-; RES AFFIL EPIDEMIOL & PUB HEALTH, SCH MED, YALE UNIV, 80- *Concurrent Pos:* NIH fel, 78-80. *Res:* Control of the cardiovascular and thermoregulatory systems in mammals. *Mailing Add:* John B Pierce Found Lab 290 Congress Ave New Haven CT 06519

SHIMAMOTO, YOSHIO, b Honolulu, Hawaii, Oct 4, 24; m 55; c 2. THEORETICAL PHYSICS, MATHEMATICS. *Educ:* Univ Hawaii, AB, 48; Harvard Univ, AM, 51; Univ Rochester, PhD(physics), 54. *Prof Exp:* Assoc physicist, 54-58, physicist, 58-64, chmn dept appl math, 64-75, SR SCIENTIST, BROOKHAVEN NAT LAB, 64- *Concurrent Pos:* Vis res prof digital comput lab, Univ Ill, Urbana, 64, consult dept comput sci, 67-; mem math & comput sci res adv comt, US AEC, 65-, chmn, 69-71; adj prof dept math statist, Columbia Univ, 71-72; vis prof math inst, Hanover Tech Univ, 72-73; assoc ed, J Comput Physics, 75-77. *Honors & Awards:* Sr Scientist Award, Alexander von Humboldt-Stiftung, 72. *Mem:* Am Phys Soc. *Res:* Reactor and particle physics; computer design; graph theory. *Mailing Add:* Dept of Appl Math Brookhaven Nat Lab Upton NY 11973

SHIMAMURA, TETSUO, b Yokohama, Japan, Feb 18, 34; m 60; c 2. PATHOLOGY. *Educ:* Yokohama Munic Univ, MD, 59. *Prof Exp:* Intern med, US Army Med Command, Japan, 59-60; intern, Bexar County Hosp, 60-61; residency in path, Sch Med, Washington Univ, 61-64; resident, Methodist Hosp, Houston, Tex, 64-65; res asst, Baylor Sch Med, & resident res assoc, Vet Admin Hosp, Houston, 65-66; asst prof, Baylor Sch Med, 66; asst prof, Univ SDak, 67-68; from asst prof to assoc prof, 68-75, PROF PATH, RUTGERS MED SCH, 75- *Mem:* Int Acad Path; Am Soc Nephrol; Int Soc Nephrol. *Res:* Renal pathology; experimental amyloidosis and hydronephrosis; experimental chronic renal disease; nutrition and glomerular diseases. *Mailing Add:* Dept of Path Rutgers Med Sch Piscataway NJ 08854

SHIMAN, ROSS, b Washington, DC, May 22, 38. BIOCHEMISTRY. *Educ:* Columbia Col, BA, 60; Univ Calif, Berkeley, PhD(biochem), 65. *Prof Exp:* Res chemist, NIH, 65-68; ASSOC PROF BIOL CHEM, M S HERSHEY MED CTR, PA STATE UNIV, 69- *Concurrent Pos:* NIH fel, 66-67. *Mem:* Am Chem Soc; Am Soc Biol Chemists. *Res:* Mechanism of phenylalanine hydroxylase action; regulation of enzyme expression and activity in mammalian cells. *Mailing Add:* Dept of Biol Chem Hershey Med Ctr Pa State Univ Hershey PA 17033

SHIMANUKI, HACHIRO, b Kahului, Hawaii, July 25, 34; m 58. INSECT PATHOLOGY, APICULTURE. *Educ:* Univ Hawaii, BA, 56; Iowa State Univ, PhD(bact), 63. *Prof Exp:* Res microbiologist, 63-66, invest leader bioenviron bee lab, 66-72, microbiologist, 72-75, LAB CHIEF, BIOENVIRON BEE LAB, AGR RES SERV, USDA, 75- *Honors & Awards:* J I Hambleton Mem Award, 78. *Mem:* Am Soc Microbiol; Entom Soc Am; Soc Invert Path; Am Beekeeping Fedn; Sigma Xi. *Res:* Diseases of honey bees; computer simulation of honey bee populations. *Mailing Add:* Bioenviron Bee Lab Agr Res Ctr-E Beltsville MD 20705

SHIMAOKA, KATSUTARO, b Nara, Japan, Sept 4, 31; m 56; c 2. MEDICINE, ONCOLOGY. *Educ:* Keio Univ, Japan, MD, 55. *Prof Exp:* Intern, St Luke's Hosp, Denver, Colo, 56-57; resident med, Louisville Gen Hosp, Ky, 57-58; resident, Roswell Park Mem Inst, 58-59, fel, 59-61; res asst, Univ Col Hosp Med Sch, London, 61-63; sr res assoc, 63-65, sr cancer res scientist, 65-67, cancer res internist I, 67-69, cancer res internist II, 69-79, RES INTERNIST, ROSWELL PARK MEM INST, 79- *Concurrent Pos:* Res asst prof med, State Univ NY, Buffalo, 71-75, assoc chief cancer physiol, 72-; chief Endocrinol Clin, E J Meyer Mem Hosp, Buffalo, 74-, mem consult staff med, 75-; attend physician, Vet Admin Ctr, Buffalo, 79- *Mem:* Endocrinol Soc; Am Asn Cancer Res; Soc Nuclear Med; Am Soc Clin Oncol; Am Thyroid Asn. *Res:* Thyroid and iodine metabolism; radiation induced cancer; cancer chemotherapy; lymphoma and leukemia; parathyroid and calcium metabolism. *Mailing Add:* Dept Clin Pharmacol & Therapeut Roswell Park Mem Inst 666 Elm St Buffalo NY 14263

SHIMAZAKI, TATSUO, b Tokyo, Japan, June 28, 25; m 55; c 3. ATMOSPHERIC PHYSICS, SPACE PHYSICS. *Educ:* Univ Tokyo, BSc &MSc, 49, PhD(geophys) & DSc, 59. *Prof Exp:* Res asst inst atmospherics, Nagoya Univ, 49-50; res officer, Radio Res Labs, Tokyo, Japan, 50-60; fel, Nat Res Coun Can, 60-62; res officer, Radio Res Labs, Tokyo, Japan, 62-63; physicist, Cent Radio Propagation Lab, Colo, 63-65; physicist inst telecommun sci & aeronomy, Environ Sci Serv Admin, 65-70; vis prof, Univ Ill, 70-71; physicist, Environ Res Labs, Nat Oceanic & Atmospheric Admin, 71-74; SPACE SCIENTIST, AMES RES CTR, NASA, 74- *Concurrent Pos:* Mem, US Nat Comt, Int Union Radio Sci; mem, US Comt Exten to Standard Atmosphere; consult, Ionosphere Res Lab, Pa State Univ, 72-74. *Honors & Awards:* Tanakadate Prize, Soc Geomagnetism & Geoelec Japan, 59. *Mem:* Am Meteorol Soc; Am Geophys Union; Phys Soc Japan; Soc Geomagnetism & Geoelec Japan. *Res:* Chemical reactions and dynamical processes in the stratosphere, mesosphere and thermosphere; theoretical modeling of distributions of neutral and ionized constituents in the planetary upper atmosphere. *Mailing Add:* Space Sci Div Ames Res Ctr NASA Mountain View CA 94035

SHIMI, ISMAIL N, b Cairo, Egypt, Sept 9, 38; m 58. STATISTICS, OPERATIONS RESEARCH. *Educ:* Ain Shams Univ, Cairo, BSc, 57; Univ NC, Chapel Hill, PhD(statist), 64. *Prof Exp:* From instr to asst prof math, Ain Shams Univ, Cairo, 57-67; lectr, Univ Calif, Riverside, 63-64, asst prof, 64-65; from asst prof to assoc prof statist, Fla State Univ, 67-75; PROG MGR, MATH & INFO SCI DIRECTORATE, AIR FORCE OFF SCI RES, 75- *Concurrent Pos:* Consult, Autonetics Div, NAm Aviation, Calif, 64; opers res & statist area dir, Coca-Cola Export Co, Mid East, 67. *Mem:* Inst Math Statist. *Res:* Branching processes; random elements in abstract spaces; reliabiligy problems; stochastic inventory problems. *Mailing Add:* Air Force Off of Sci Res Washington DC 20332

SHIMIZU, C SUSAN, b Gilroy, Calif, Jan 30, 24; m 60. BIOCHEMISTRY, PHYSIOLOGY. *Educ:* NY Univ, BA, 46; Syracuse Univ, MA, 48, PhD(physiol), 51. *Prof Exp:* AEC & NIH fel, Brookhaven Nat Lab & Univ Chicago, 50-52; res assoc endocrinol, Sch Med, Stanford Univ, 52-59 & Children's Hosp, Los Angeles, 59-63; asst prof, Sch Med, Univ Southern Calif, 63-68; asst prof, Sch Med, Univ Calif, Los Angeles, 68-71; ASST PROF SURG & PATH, SCH MED, UNIV SOUTHERN CALIF, 71- *Concurrent Pos:* NIH career develop award, Sch Med, Univ Southern Calif, 63-68. *Mem:* AAAS; Radiation Res Soc; Am Asn Cancer Res; Endocrine Soc; Am Physiol Soc. *Res:* Viral oncology. *Mailing Add:* 1841 Hollyvista Ave Los Angeles CA 90027

SHIMIZU, HIROSHI, b Kyoto, Japan, Aug 21, 24; m 51; c 2. OTOLARYNGOLOGY, AUDIOLOGY. *Educ:* Kyoto Prefectural Univ Med, MD, 49, MScD, 55. *Prof Exp:* Asst otolaryngol, Kyoto Prefectural Univ Med, 50-56, instr, 56-57; clin fel, White Mem Hosp, Los Angeles, 57-58; resident otolaryngol, Johns Hopkins Hosp, 58; res fel audiol, Johns Hopkins Univ, 58-60; instr, Kyoto Prefectural Univ Med, 60-63; asst prof, 63-67, ASSOC PROF OTOLARYNGOL, SCH MED, JOHNS HOPKINS UNIV, 67-, DIR HEARING & SPEECH CTR, 76- *Concurrent Pos:* NIH res grants, 65-68 & 67-70. *Mem:* Am Auditory Soc; Am Speech & Hearing Asn; Japan Soc Otolaryngol; Japan Soc Audiol; Acoust Soc Am. *Res:* Auditory evoked potentials in both normal listeners and patients. *Mailing Add:* Dept Laryngol & Otol Sch Med Johns Hopkins Univ Baltimore MD 21205

SHIMIZU, NOBUYOSHI, b Osaka-city, Japan, Aug 10, 41; m 67; c 1. CELL BIOLOGY, HUMAN GENETICS. *Educ:* Nagoya Univ, BA, 65; Inst Molecular Biol, MSc, 67, PhD(molecular biol), 70. *Prof Exp:* Res assoc, Inst Molecular Biol, 70-71; res biologist, Univ Calif, 71-74 & Yale Univ, 74-76; asst prof, 77-79, ASSOC PROF RES & TEACHING, UNIV ARIZ, 79- *Concurrent Pos:* Res biologist, Yale Univ, 74-75, vis asst prof, 77; jr fac res award, Am Cancer Soc, 78-80. *Mem:* NY Acad Sci; AAAS; Tissue Cult Asn; Am Soc Cell Biol; Am Soc Biol Chemists. *Res:* Genetic control of mammalian cell surface functions with emphasis on receptor-mediated hormonal signal transfer mechanisms and malignant transformation; parasexual approaches to human genetics and chromosome mapping. *Mailing Add:* Dept of Cellular & Develop Biol Univ of Ariz Tucson AZ 85721

SHIMIZU, YUZURU, b Gifu, Japan, Jan 17, 35; m 63; c 2. NATURAL PRODUCTS CHEMISTRY, PHARMACOGNOSY. *Educ:* Hokkaido Univ, BS, 58, MS, 60, PhD(pharm sci), 63. *Prof Exp:* Scientist, Worcester Found Exp Biol, 63-64; res assoc dept chem, Univ Ga, 64-65; instr pharm sci, Hokkaido Univ, 65-69; asst prof pharmacog, 69-73, assoc prof, 73-77, PROF PHARMACOG, UNIV RI, 77- *Concurrent Pos:* Water resources grant, 71-75; Dept Health, Educ & Welfare grant, 74-; chmn marine natural prod sect, Gordon Res Conf, 75- *Honors & Awards:* Award, Matsunaga Sci Found, Japan, 69. *Mem:* Am Chem Soc; Am Soc Pharmacog; Pharmaceut Soc Japan. *Res:* Isolation, structural elucidation and synthesis of natural products, especially of marine origins; marine pharmacognosy. *Mailing Add:* Col Pharm Univ RI Kingston RI 02881

SHIMKIN, MICHAEL BORIS, b Tomsk, Siberia, Oct 7, 12; US citizen; m 38; c 3. CANCER. *Educ:* Univ Calif, AB, 33, MD, 37; Am Bd Internal Med, dipl, 50; Am Bd Prev Med, dipl, 59. *Prof Exp:* Resident internal med, John Sealy Hosp, Tex, 37-38; Nat Cancer Inst sr fel, Harvard Univ, 38-39; from asst surgeon to med dir, Nat Cancer Inst, 39-63; prof med, Sch Med & chief cancer biol, Fels Res Inst, Temple Univ, 63-69, asst vpres res, Health Serv Ctr, 66-69; prof, 69-80, EMER PROF COMMUNITY MED & ONCOL, SCH MED, UNIV CALIF, SAN DIEGO, 80- *Concurrent Pos:* Consult med res mission, Off Sci Res & Develop, Russia, 43-44, UNRRA, 44-45 & US Army, 44-45; adv US del, Int Health Cong, WHO, 46; clin prof & dir lab exp oncol, Med Sch, Univ Calif, 47-54; sci ed, J Nat Cancer Inst, 55-60; assoc dir field studies, Nat Cancer Inst, 60-63; ed, Cancer Res, Am Asn Cancer Res, 64-69; coordr, San Diego-Imp County Regional Med Prog, 69-74. *Mem:* Soc Exp Biol & Med; fel Am Pub Health Asn; Am Asn Cancer Res; fel Am Col Physicians; fel Am Col Prev Med. *Res:* Mammary and pulmonary tumors in mice; biologic effects of carcinogens; bio-assay and pharmacology; experimental clinical chemotherapy of cancer; cancer statistics; international aspects of medicine, especially in Soviet Union; administration of research. *Mailing Add:* Dept of Community Med Sch Med Univ of Calif at San Diego La Jolla CA 92093

SHIMM, ROBERT A, b New York, NY, Jan 30, 26; m 58; c 3. INTERNAL MEDICINE. *Educ:* Columbia Univ, AB, 45, MD, 48; Am Bd Internal Med, dipl, 56, recert, 77. *Prof Exp:* Intern med, Presby Hosp, New York, 49-50, jr asst resident, 50-51; sr asst resident, Duke Hosp, Durham, NC, 51-52; NIH trainee cardiol, Mt Sinai Hosp, New York, 52-53; resident med, Bellevue Hosp, 55-56; instr, 56-59, assoc, 59-62, from asst prof to assoc prof med, 62-76, CLIN PROF MED, ALBERT EINSTEIN COL MED, 76- *Mem:* Am Soc Internal Med; Am Col Physicians. *Res:* Medical administration; comprehensive ambulatory private health care. *Mailing Add:* 1180 Morris Park Ave Bronx NY 10461

SHIMONY, ABNER, b Columbus, Ohio, Mar 10, 28; m 51; c 2. THEORETICAL PHYSICS, PHILOSOPHY OF SCIENCE. *Educ:* Yale Univ, BA, 48, PhD(philos), 53; Univ Chicago, MA, 50; Princeton Univ, PhD(physics), 62. *Prof Exp:* Instr philos, Yale Univ, 52-53; asst prof, Mass Inst Technol, 59-62, assoc prof, 62-68; assoc prof, 68-73, PROF PHYSICS & PHILOS, BOSTON UNIV, 73- *Concurrent Pos:* Sr NSF fel, 66-67; fel, Am Coun Learned Soc, 67 & Guggenheim Found fel, 72-73; Luce prof cosmol, Mt Holyoke Col, 81. *Mem:* Am Philos Soc; Am Phys Soc. *Res:* Foundations of quantum mechanics; foundations of statistical mechanics; philosophy of physics; naturalistic epistemology. *Mailing Add:* Dept of Physics Boston Univ 111 Cummington St Boston MA 02215

SHIMOTAKE, HIROSHI, b Dec 6, 28; US citizen; m 60; c 3. CHEMICAL ENGINEERING. *Educ:* Nihon Univ, Tokyo, BS, 51; Northwestern Univ, MS, 57, PhD(chem eng), 60. *Prof Exp:* Res engr, Whirlpool Res Labs, 60-63; CHEM ENGR & GROUP LEADER, ARGONNE NAT LAB, 63- *Honors & Awards:* IR-100 Award, 68. *Mem:* Am Chem Soc; Electrochem Soc Japan; Japanese Soc Chem Engrs; Electrochem Soc. *Res:* Energy conversion and storage; high energy electrochemical cells and batteries. *Mailing Add:* 726 Franklin St Hinsdale IL 60521

SHIMP, NEIL FREDERICK, b Akron, Ohio, Aug 19, 27; m 49; c 2. ANALYTICAL CHEMISTRY. *Educ:* Mich State Univ, BS, 50, MS, 51; Rutgers Univ, PhD, 56. *Prof Exp:* Res chemist citrus exp sta, Univ Fla, 51-52; asst prof, Rutgers Univ, 56-57; assoc chemist, 57-63, chemist head anal chem sect, 63-73, PRIN CHEMIST, ILL STATE GEOL SURV, 73- *Mem:* Am Chem Soc; Soc Appl Spectros; Am Soc Test & Mat. *Res:* Geochemistry; trace elements; instrumental analysis; coal chemistry; environmental geology; spectrochemistry. *Mailing Add:* 361 Natural Resources Bldg Ill State Geol Surv 615 E Peabody Dr Champaign IL 61820

SHIMURA, GORO, b Hamamatsu, Japan, Feb 23, 30; m 59; c 2. MATHEMATICS. *Educ:* Univ Tokyo, BS, 52, DSc(math), 59. *Prof Exp:* Asst prof math, Univ Tokyo, 57-61; prof, Univ Osaka, 61-64; vis prof, 62-64, PROF MATH, PRINCETON UNIV, 64- *Concurrent Pos:* Res mem, Nat Ctr Sci Res, Paris, France, 57-58; mem, Inst Advan Study, 58-59, 67, 70-71 & 74-75; John Simon Guggenheim fel, 70-71. *Mem:* Am Math Soc; Math Soc Japan. *Res:* Number theory; automorphic functions; algebraic geometry. *Mailing Add:* Fine Hall Princeton Univ Princeton NJ 08540

SHIN, BAK C, b Cheju, Korea, June 11, 36; m 65; c 4. IMMUNOLOGY, BIOCHEMISTRY. *Educ:* Chonnam Univ, Korea, MD, 61; Okla State Univ, PhD(biochem), 73. *Prof Exp:* Fel pharmacol, State Univ NY Downstate Med Ctr, 68-69; fel biochem, Okla State Univ, 73-74; intern, Brooklyn-Cumberland Med Ctr, 74-75; resident pediat, St Jude Children's Res Hosp, Memphis, 75-77; FEL ALLERGY & IMMUNOL, DEPT PEDIAT, MED COL VA, 77- *Mem:* Sigma Xi; AMA; Am Acad Allergy. *Res:* Biochemical studies of immunological hypersensitivity reaction; IgE-mediated and cell-mediated reaction; biochemical and immunological studies of sarcoidosis and other granulomatous diseases. *Mailing Add:* Dept of Pediat Allergy & Immunol Box 225 MCV Sta Richmond VA 23298

SHIN, HYUNG KYU, b Kochang, Korea, Sept 3, 33; m 63; c 3. PHYSICAL CHEMISTRY, THEORETICAL CHEMISTRY. *Educ:* Univ Utah, BS, 59, PhD(phys chem), 61. *Prof Exp:* Res chemist, Nat Bur Standards, Washington, DC, 61-63; fel theoret chem, Cornell Univ, 63-65; from asst prof to assoc prof 65-67, assoc prof 67-70, chmn dept, 76-80, PROF PHYS CHEM, UNIV NEV, RENO, 70- *Concurrent Pos:* Petrol Res Fund grant, 65-67; Air Force Off Sci Res grant, 67-; vis res prof, Univ Calif, Berkeley, 80; Petrol Res Fund grant, 81- *Honors & Awards:* Award, Sigma Xi Soc, 61. *Mem:* Am Phys Soc; Sigma Xi; Am Chem Soc. *Res:* Theory of inelastic collisions; theory of non-equilibrium rate processes; hydrogen bonding. *Mailing Add:* Dept Chem Univ Nev Reno NV 89557

SHIN, JOSEPH BOKKYUN, physics, space science, see previous edition

SHIN, KIU HI, b Pusan, Korea, Nov 11, 29; US citizen; m; c 3. CHEMISTRY. *Educ:* Seoul Nat Univ, BS, 52; Univ Frankfurt, MS, 58, PhD(chem), 60. *Prof Exp:* Fel & res assoc, Cornell Univ, 60-62; Nat Res Coun Can fel, 62-63; staff chemist res labs, UniRoyal Co, Can, 63-66; staff chemist, 66-75, SR RES CHEMIST, ETHYL CORP, 75- *Mem:* Am Chem Soc; Korean Chem Soc; Korean Scientists & Engrs Am. *Res:* Organic synthesis and catalysis; antioxidants; oxidation; synthesis of fine chemicals. *Mailing Add:* Ethyl Corp Gulf States Rd PO Box 341 Baton Rouge LA 70805

SHIN, MYUNG SOO, b Seoul, Korea, May 5, 30; m 60; c 3. RADIOLOGY. *Educ:* Seoul Nat Univ, MD, 56, PhD(radiol), 67. *Prof Exp:* Instr radiol, Sch Med, Seoul Nat Univ, 63-67, asst prof, 67-68; from asst prof to assoc prof, 69-75, PROF RADIOL, SCH MED, UNIV ALA, BIRMINGHAM, 75- *Concurrent Pos:* Consult, Radiol Serv, Vet Admin Hosp, Birmingham, 68- *Mem:* AMA; fel Am Col Radiol; Radiol Soc NAm; Am Roentgen Ray Soc; Asn Univ Radiol. *Mailing Add:* Dept of Diag Radiol Univ of Ala Hosp Birmingham AL 35233

SHIN, SEUNG-IL, b Wonju City, Korea, Nov 10, 38. GENETICS, CELL BIOLOGY. *Educ:* Brandeis Univ, BA, 64, PhD(biochem), 69. *Prof Exp:* Dutch Orgn Sci Res fel, State Univ Leiden, 69-70; mem, Basel Int Immunol, 70-72; asst prof, 72-77, assoc prof, 77-81, PROF GENETICS, ALBERT EINSTEIN COL MED, 82- *Concurrent Pos:* Fac res award, Am Cancer Soc, 76-81; mem, Scientific Adv Comt, Damon Runyon-Walter Winchell Cancer Fund, 77-82; vis prof microbiol, Seoul Nat Univ, Korea, 79. *Mem:* AAAS; Genetics Soc Am; Am Soc Cell Biol; Am Asn Cancer Res; Am Diabetes Asn. *Res:* Molecular genetics of somatic cells; tumor biology; eticologic mechanisms of insulin-dependent diabetes mellitus. *Mailing Add:* Dept Genetics Albert Einstein Col Med Bronx NY 10461

SHIN, YONG AE IM, b Seoul, Korea, Aug 2, 33; m 61; c 3. INORGANIC CHEMISTRY, MOLECULAR BIOLOGY. *Educ:* Tift Col, BA, 56; Ohio State Univ, MSc, 58, PhD(chem), 60. *Prof Exp:* Res fel chem, Univ Ill, 61-62; res assoc chem, Ohio State Univ, 62-64; fel inorg chem, 65-67, RES CHEMIST, GERONT RES CTR, NIH, 67- *Res:* Stereospecificity in coordination compounds; the role of metals in nucleic acids and proteins; structure and function of nucleic acids and nucleoproteins. *Mailing Add:* NIH Geront Res Ctr Baltimore City Hosps Baltimore MD 21224

SHIN, YONG-MOO, b Seoul, Korea, June 14, 31; m 56; c 2. NUCLEAR PHYSICS. *Educ:* Yonsei Univ, Korea, BS, 57; Univ Pa, MS, 60, PhD(physics), 63. *Prof Exp:* Res assoc, Univ Tex, 63-64, asst prof, 64-65; from asst prof to assoc prof, 65-75, PROF PHYSICS & DIR ACCELERATOR LAB, UNIV SASK, 75- *Mem:* Can Asn Physics; Can Nuclear Soc; Am Phys Soc. *Res:* Nuclear structure and reaction mechanism. *Mailing Add:* Dept of Physics Univ of Sask Saskatoon SK S7H 0W0 Can

SHINBROT, MARVIN, b Brooklyn, NY, May 30, 28; m 48; c 3. MATHEMATICS. *Educ:* Syracuse Univ, BS, 48, MA, 49; Stanford Univ, PhD(math), 60. *Prof Exp:* Aeronaut res scientist, Nat Adv Comt Aeronaut, 49-57; res scientist, Lockheed Missile Systs Div, 57-61; instr math, Univ Chicago, 61-62; asst prof, Univ Calif, Berkeley, 62-65; assoc prof, Northwestern Univ, Evanston, 65-67, prof, 67-73; PROF MATH, UNIV VICTORIA, 73- *Concurrent Pos:* Vis prof, Univ Victoria, BC, 72-73; mem grant selection comt pure & appl math, Nat Res Coun Can, 75-78; mem, Can Math Soc Coun, 75-78; chmn res comt, Can Math Soc, 78-80; ed J Integral Equations; spec lectr, Soc Indust & Appl Math, 75-76. *Mem:* Am Math Soc; Math Asn Am; fel Royal Soc Can. *Res:* Integral and differential equations; statistical mathematics; applied mathematics; hydrodynamics. *Mailing Add:* Dept Math Univ Victoria Victoria BC V8W 2Y2 Can

SHINDALA, ADNAN, b Mosul, Iraq, July 1, 37; m 64; c 1. SANITARY ENGINEERING. *Educ:* Univ Baghdad, BSc, 58; Va Polytech Inst, MSc, 61, PhD(civil eng), 64. *Prof Exp:* Asst resident engr, Govt Iraq, 59-60; asst prof civil eng, Lehigh Univ, 64-65; lectr, Univ Baghdad, 65-67; from asst prof to assoc prof sanit eng, 67-77, PROF ENVIRON ENG, MISS STATE UNIV, 77- *Mem:* Am Soc Civil Engrs; Water Pollution Control Fedn; Am Water Works Asn; Am Water Resources Asn. *Res:* Water resources engineering. *Mailing Add:* Dept of Sanit Eng Box 3544 State College MS 39762

SHINDLER, DAVID BRUCE, biology, microbiology, see previous edition

SHINE, ANDREW J(OSEPH), b Cass, WVa, Jan 3, 22; m 46; c 5. MECHANICAL ENGINEERING. *Educ:* Rensselaer Polytech Inst, BME, 46, MME, 47; Ohio State Univ, PhD(mech eng), 57. *Prof Exp:* Asst, Univ Minn, 47-48; instr & asst, Rensselaer Polytech Inst, 48-49; from asst prof to assoc prof, 49-58, PROF MECH ENG & HEAD DEPT, US AIR FORCE INST TECHNOL, 58- *Mem:* Am Soc Mech Engrs; Am Soc Eng Educ. *Res:* Heat transfer; fluid flow. *Mailing Add:* US Air Force Inst of Technol Wright-Patterson AFB Dayton OH 45433

SHINE, DANIEL PHILLIP, b Chicago, Ill, Aug 10, 34. COSMETIC CHEMISTRY. *Educ:* Xavier Univ, BS, 55, MS, 57; Univ Akron, PhD(chem), 61. *Prof Exp:* Instr chem, Villa Madonna Col, 61-64; RES CHEMIST, ANDREW JERGENS CO, 64- *Res:* Analysis of cosmetics, fats, oils and waxes. *Mailing Add:* Andrew Jergens Co 2535 Spring Grove Ave Cincinnati OH 45214

SHINE, HENRY JOSEPH, b London, Eng, Jan 4, 23; m 53; c 2. ORGANIC CHEMISTRY. *Educ:* London Univ, BSc, 44, PhD(chem), 47. *Prof Exp:* Chemist, Shell Develop Co, Eng, 44-45; res fel org chem, Iowa State Univ, 48-49; res fel, Calif Inst Technol, 49-51; res chemist, US Rubber Co, 51-54; from asst prof to assoc prof chem, 54-60, prof, 60-68, chmn dept, 69-75, PAUL WHITFIELD HORN PROF CHEM, TEX TECH UNIV, 68- *Mem:* AAAS; Am Chem Soc; Royal Soc Chem; Sigma Xi. *Res:* Reaction mechanisms; aromatic rearrangements; organosulfur chemistry; ion radical reactions; electron spin spectroscopy. *Mailing Add:* Dept of Chem Tex Tech Univ Lubbock TX 79409

SHINE, ROBERT JOHN, b Orange, NJ, May 21, 41; m 67; c 3. ORGANIC CHEMISTRY. *Educ:* Seton Hall Univ, BS, 62; Pa State Univ, PhD(org chem), 66. *Prof Exp:* Teaching asst, Pa State Univ, 62; res chemist, Walter Reed Army Inst Res, 67-69; asst prof chem, Trinity Col, DC, 69-71; from asst prof to assoc prof, 71-74, PROF CHEM, RAMAPO COL, NJ, 74- *Mem:* Am Chem Soc. *Res:* Structural determination of alkaloids; chemistry of organic sulfur and organic selenium compounds. *Mailing Add:* Sch of Theoret & Appl Sci Ramapo Col Mahwah NJ 07430

SHINE, TIMOTHY D, b New York, NY, June 6, 39. ORGANIC CHEMISTRY. *Educ:* Merrimack Col, BS, 60; Univ Conn, PhD(org chem), 67. *Prof Exp:* Asst inst chem, Univ Conn, 62-66; res assoc, Univ Mich, 66-67; asst prof, 67-71, assoc prof, 71-77, PROF CHEM, CENT CONN STATE COL, 77- *Mem:* Sigma Xi; Am Chem Soc. *Res:* Acyl and alkoxy group migrations between oxygen and nitrogen in oo-aminophenols; sulfur and nitrogen in o-aminothiophenols. *Mailing Add:* Cent Conn State Col 1516 Stanley St New Britain CT 06050

SHINE, WILLIAM MORTON, b St Louis, Mo, Nov 24, 12; m 46; c 4. ORGANIC CHEMISTRY. *Educ:* Wash Univ, St Louis, BS, 34; Univ Ill, MS, 37. *Prof Exp:* Res chemist med sch, Wash Univ, St Louis, 34-36; res chemist, Univ Ill, 36-37; chemist, Pfanstiehl Chem Co, 37-41; sect leader res & chem develop plastics dept, Gen Elec Co, 41-45; mkt develop chemist, Gen Aniline & Film Corp, 45-50; dir mkt develop, Arnold Hoffman & Co, Inc, 50-53; dir develop dept, Celanese Corp Am, 53-55, techno-com dir cent tech dept, 55-59, vpres, Celanese Develop Co, 59-63; PRES, WILLIAM M SHINE CONSULT SERV, 63- *Mem:* Am Chem Soc; Soc Plastics Eng; Chem Develop Asn; Chem Mkt Res Asn; fel Am Inst Chem. *Res:* Organic synthesis; polymer chemistry; international technology; marketing research; corporate planning; technical-economics evaluations; acquisition studies. *Mailing Add:* William M Shine Consult Serv PO Box 61 Brooklyn NY 11202

SHINEFIELD, HENRY R, b Paterson, NJ, Oct 11, 23; div; c 2. MEDICINE, PEDIATRICS. *Educ:* Columbia Univ, AB, 44, MD, 48; Am Bd Pediat, dipl. *Prof Exp:* From asst prof to assoc prof pediat, Med Col, Cornell Univ, 59-65; CHIEF PEDIAT, KAISER FOUND HOSP, 65-; CLIN PROF, SCH MED, UNIV CALIF, SAN FRANCISCO, 68- *Concurrent Pos:* Nat Found res fel, 59-61; Lederle med fac award, 61-63; assoc clin prof, Univ Calif, San Francisco, 66-68; chief pediat, Permanente Med Group, San Francisco; mem bact & mycol study sect, Res Rev Br, NIH, 70-74. *Mem:* Inst Med-Nat Acad Sci; fel Am Acad Pediat; Soc Pediat Res; Infectious Dis Soc Am; Am Pediat Soc. *Res:* Infectious diseases; epidemiology; medical care. *Mailing Add:* 2200 O'Farrell St San Francisco CA 94115

SHINEMAN, RICHARD SHUBERT, b Albany, NY, May 21, 24. INORGANIC CHEMISTRY. *Educ:* Cornell Univ, AB, 45; Syracuse Univ, MS, 50; Ohio State Univ, PhD(inorg chem), 57. *Prof Exp:* From inst to asst prof chem, Purdue Univ, 59-62; PROF CHEM, STATE UNIV NY COL, OSWEGO, 62- *Concurrent Pos:* Chmn dept chem, State Univ NY Col, Oswego, 62-67. *Mem:* AAAS; Am Chem Soc. *Res:* Inorganic nitrogen chemistry; x-ray crystallography. *Mailing Add:* Dept of Chem State Univ of NY Col Oswego NY 13126

SHINER, EDWARD ARNOLD, b Chicago, Ill, Feb 18, 24; m 51; c 3. ORGANIC CHEMISTRY. *Educ:* Northwestern Univ, BS, 47; Univ Wis, PhD(chem), 51. *Prof Exp:* Instr chem, Univ Wis-Milwaukee, 47-48; res chemist, Food Prod Div, 51-60, mgr food casing develop, 60-65, tech mgr, 65-69, asst dir res & develop, 69-73, DIR RES & DEVELOP, UNION CARBIDE CORP, 73- *Mem:* Am Chem Soc. *Res:* Cellulose; lignin; polymer science. *Mailing Add:* Res & Develop Dept Union Carbide Corp 6733 W 65th St Chicago IL 60638

SHINER, VERNON JACK, JR, b Laredo, Tex, Aug 11, 25; m 46; c 3. PHYSICAL ORGANIC CHEMISTRY. *Educ:* Tex Western Col, BS, 47; Cornell Univ, PhD(chem), 50. *Prof Exp:* Res assoc org chem, State Agr Exp Sta, NY, 47; Fulbright scholar, London Univ, 50-51; Du Pont fel, Harvard Univ, 51-52; from instr to assoc prof chem, 52-60, chmn dept, 62-67, dean, Col Arts & Sci, 73-78, PROF CHEM, IND UNIV, BLOOMINGTON, 60- *Mem:* Am Chem Soc; Royal Soc Chem; Sigma Xi. *Res:* Kinetics and mechanisms of organic reactions; deuterium isotope rate effects. *Mailing Add:* Dept of Chem Ind Univ Bloomington IN 47401

SHING, YUH-HAN, b Anhwei, China, June 18, 41; Can citizen; m 67; c 3. THIN FILM MATERIALS, DEVICE PHYSICS. *Educ:* Taiwan Normal Univ, BSc, 63; Univ Calgary, MSc, 69, PhD(physics), 72. *Prof Exp:* Nat Res Coun fel physics, McGill Univ, 72-74, reader & res assoc, 74-76, reader, 76-79; mem res staff solar energy, Xerox Res Ctr, Can, 79-80; SR SCIENTIST MAT, ARCO SOLAR INDUST, 80- *Mem:* Am Phys Soc; Inst Elec & Electronics Engrs; Electrochem Soc. *Res:* Synthesis and characterization of energy conversion materials; electronic and optical properties of thin film; material synthesis techniques for amorphous and crystalline semiconductors using sputtering, glow-discharge and melt-spinning. *Mailing Add:* Arco Solar Indust 911 Wilshire Blvd Los Angeles CA 90017

SHINGLETON, HUGH MAURICE, b Stantonsburg, NC, Oct 11, 31; c 3. OBSTETRICS & GYNECOLOGY, ONCOLOGY. *Educ:* Duke Univ, AB, 51, MD, 57; Am Bd Obstet & Gynec, dipl. *Prof Exp:* Intern, Jefferson Med Col Hosp, 57-58; asst resident obstet & gynec, NC Mem Hosp, Chapel Hill, 60-61 & Margaret Hague Maternity Hosp, Jersey City, NJ, 62; resident, NC Mem Hosp, Chapel Hill, 62-63, chief resident, 63-64; from instr to asst prof obstet & gynec, Sch Med, Univ NC, Chapel Hill, 64-69, asst prof path, 68-69; assoc prof, 69-74, asst prof, 69-81, PROF OBSTET & GYNEC, SCH MED, UNIV ALA, BIRMINGHAM, 74-, ASSOC PROF PATH, 81-, CHMN DEPT, MED CTR, 78- *Concurrent Pos:* Am Cancer Soc fel, Mem Hosp, Chapel Hill, NC, 62-63; Nat Cancer Inst spec fel, Col Physicians & Surgeons, Columbia Univ, 66-67. *Mem:* Am Col Obstet & Gynec; Am Col Surgeons; AMA; Soc Gynec Oncol (secy-treas, 81); Am Gynec Soc. *Res:* Gynecologic oncology; use of electron microscope and clinical research. *Mailing Add:* Dept of Obstet & Gynec Univ of Ala Sch of Med Birmingham AL 35294

SHININGER, TERRY LYNN, b Tillamook, Ore, Oct 28, 41; m 63; c 2. DEVELOPMENTAL BIOLOGY, PLANT PHYSIOLOGY. *Educ:* Univ Ore, BA, 63, MA, 64; Univ Mass, Amherst, PhD(bot), 69. *Prof Exp:* Instr biol, Mankato State Col, 64-65; NSF grant res assoc, Stanford Univ, 68-69; asst prof bot, Univ Minn, Minneapolis, 69-71; Maria Moors Cabot Found fel, Harvard Univ, 71-72; asst prof, 73-79, ASSOC PROF BIOL, UNIV UTAH, 79- *Mem:* Soc Develop Biol; Am Soc Plant Physiol. *Res:* Hormones; differentiation; host-parasite physiology and biochemistry. *Mailing Add:* Dept Biol Univ Utah Salt Lake City UT 84112

SHINKAI, ICHIRO, b Japan, Dec 4, 41; m 66; c 2. ORGANIC & ANALYTICAL CHEMISTRY. *Educ:* Doshisha Univ, BSc, 64, MSc, 66; Kyushu Univ, PhD(org chem), 71. *Prof Exp:* Res asst & lectr org chem, Kyushu Univ, 66-72; res assoc dept chem, Univ Ala, 72-76; RES FEL PROCESS CHEM, MERCK, SHARP & DOHME RES LABS, MERCK & CO, INC, 76- *Mem:* Am Chem Soc; Japan Chem Soc. *Res:* Synthetic organic chemistry; reaction mechanisms of heterocycles; reactive intermediate. *Mailing Add:* 121 N Cathage Place Westfield NJ 07090

SHINKAI, JOHN H, b Tokyo, Japan, Aug 23, 21; nat US. PHARMACEUTICAL CHEMISTRY. *Educ:* Philadelphia Col Pharm, BS, 44; Univ Wis, MS, 45, PhD(pharmaceut chem), 49. *Prof Exp:* Assoc prof pharmaceut chem col pharm, Loyola Univ, La, 49-57; asst prof pharmaceut chem, Rutgers Univ, New Brunswick, 57-60; assoc prof, 60-80. *Mem:* AAAS; Am Chem Soc; Am Pharmaceut Asn. *Res:* Organic medicinals; synthesis. *Mailing Add:* 213 Horizon Dr Edison NJ 08817

SHINKMAN, PAUL G, b New York, NY, June 18, 36; m 69. PHYSIOLOGICAL PSYCHOLOGY. *Educ:* Harvard Univ, AB, 58; Univ Mich, AM, 62, PhD(psychol), 62. *Prof Exp:* Instr psychol, Univ Mich, 61-62, NIMH fel, Brain Res Lab, 64-66; vis asst prof psychobiol, Univ Calif, Irvine, 66-67; from asst prof to assoc prof psychol & neurobiol, 67-77, PROF PSYCHOL & NEUROBIOL, UNIV NC, CHAPEL HILL, 77-, DIR EXP PSYCHOL PROG, 75- *Mem:* Am Psychol Asn; Psychonomic Soc; Soc Neurosci. *Res:* Central nervous system and behavior. *Mailing Add:* Dept of Psychol Univ of NC Chapel Hill NC 27514

SHINN, DENNIS BURTON, b Keene, NH, Sept 2, 39; m 60; c 3. INORGANIC CHEMISTRY. *Educ:* Univ NH, BS, 61, MS, 64; Mich State Univ, PhD(chem), 68. *Prof Exp:* Adv develop engr, 68-70, engr in charge chem appln, 70-72, prog mgr high intensity discharge mat, 72-78, PROG MGR MAT ENG LAB, SYLVANIA LIGHTING CTR, 78- *Mem:* Am Chem Soc; Am Crystallog Asn; Am Ceramic Soc; Sigma Xi. *Res:* Synthesis and properties of solid state inorganic materials. *Mailing Add:* High Intensity Discharge Mat Lab Sylvania Lighting Ctr Danvers MA 01923

SHINN, JEFFREY N(ORLAND), b Washington, Pa, Feb 5, 29; m 55; c 3. MECHANICAL ENGINEERING. *Educ:* Univ Conn, BS, 51, MS, 53; Yale Univ, MEng, 53, DEng, 57. *Prof Exp:* Mgr controls eng, 56-76, MGR GAS TURBINE DEPT, GEN ELEC CO, 76- *Mem:* Am Soc Mech Engrs. *Res:* Fluid power control systems. *Mailing Add:* Gas Turbine Dept One River Rd Schenectady NY 12306

SHINN, JOSEPH HANCOCK, b Atlantic City, NJ, Jan 4, 38; m 75; c 2. METEOROLOGY, POLLUTION ECOLOGY. *Educ:* Del Valley Col, BS, 59; Cornell Univ, MS, 62; Univ Wis-Madison, PhD(meteorol), 71. *Prof Exp:* Phys sci aide microclimate, Agr Res Serv, USDA, 59-62; proj asst meteorol, Univ Wis-Madison, 62-67; res meteorologist, US Army Electronics Command, Ft Huachuca, 67-70 & White Sands Missile Range, 70-73; METEOROLOGIST POLLUTANT EFFECTS, ENVIRON SCI DIV, LAWRENCE LIVERMORE LAB, 73- *Concurrent Pos:* Chmn, US Army Electronics Command Res Bd, 71-72; adv tactical environ support study, US Army Intel Sch, 72-73; br chief automatic meteorol systs, US Army Atmospheric Sci Lab, 72-73; dep sect chief environ sci div, Lawrence Livermore Lab, 77- *Mem:* Sigma Xi; Am Meteorol Soc; Air Pollution Control Asn. *Res:* Dynamics of the atmospheric boundary layer; inhalation exposure and suspension of toxic particles; processes of deposition of gases and particles on vegetation; forest meteorology; air pollution meteorology. *Mailing Add:* Lawrence Livermore Lab L-524 PO Box 5507 Livermore CA 94550

SHINNAR, REUEL, b Vienna, Austria, Sept 15, 23; US citizen; m 48. CHEMICAL ENGINEERING. *Educ:* Israel Inst Technol, BSc, 45; Columbia Univ, ScD(chem eng), 57. *Prof Exp:* Chem engr indust, 45-54; asst prof chem eng, Israel Inst Technol, 58-62; res assoc aeronaut eng, Princeton Univ, 62-64; prof, 64-79, DISTINGUISHED PROF CHEM ENG, CITY COL NEW YORK, 79- *Mem:* AAAS; NY Acad Sci; Am Inst Chem Engrs; Am Chem Soc; Am Inst Aeronaut & Astronaut. *Res:* Process dynamics and control; process design and economics; policy research in problems of energy; chemical reactor design. *Mailing Add:* Dept of Chem Eng City Col of New York New York NY 10031

SHINNERS, CARL W, b Milwaukee, Wis, Aug 13, 28; m 54; c 3. PHYSICS. *Educ:* Marquette Univ, PhB, 52; La State Univ, MS, 60, PhD(nuclear spectros), 65. *Prof Exp:* Instr physics, La State Univ, 59-63; assoc prof, 65-67, chmn dept, 67-71, PROF PHYSICS, UNIV WIS-WHITEWATER, 67- *Concurrent Pos:* Wis State res grants, 68 & 70; NSF grants, 70 & 71. *Mem:* AAAS; Am Phys Soc; Am Asn Physics Teachers. *Res:* Beta and gamma ray spectroscopy; nuclear structures; solar energy and energy education. *Mailing Add:* Dept of Physics Univ of Wis Whitewater WI 53190

SHINNERS, STANLEY MARVIN, b New York, NY, May 9, 33; m 56; c 3. ELECTRICAL ENGINEERING, EDUCATION. *Educ:* City Col New York, BEE, 54; Columbia Univ, MS, 59. *Prof Exp:* Engr, Western Elec Co, 53-55; staff engr, Electronics Div, Otis Elevator Co, 55-56; proj engr, Polarad Electronics Corp, 56-57 & Consol Avionic Corp, 57-58; SR RES SECT HEAD, SPERRY SYSTS MGT DIV, SPERRY RAND CORP, 58- *Concurrent Pos:* Adj prof, Polytech Inst Brooklyn, 59-71, Cooper Union, 66-73 & 79- & NY Inst Technol, 74- *Mem:* Fel Inst Elec & Electronics Engrs; Am Soc Eng Educ. *Res:* Control systems and systems engineering. *Mailing Add:* 28 Sagamore Way North Jericho NY 11753

SHINNICK-GALLAGHER, PATRICIA L, b Chicago, Ill, July 28, 47; m 74; c 2. NEUROPHARMACOLOGY, NEUROPHYSIOLOGY. *Educ:* Univ Ill, BS, 70; Loyola Univ Chicago, PhD(pharmacol), 74. *Prof Exp:* Pharmacist, Nosek Apothecary, 71-73; res assoc neurophysiol, Sch Med, Loyola Univ Chicago, 74-75; instr, 75-76, asst prof, 76-81, ASSOC PROF PHARMACOL, UNIV TEX MED BR, GALVESTON, 81- *Mem:* AAAS; Am Pharmaceut Asn; Am Soc Pharmacol Exp Therapy. *Res:* Pharmacological and physiological dissection of reflex pathways in the isolated spinal cord; analysis of drug action on ganglionic and neuromuscular transmission. *Mailing Add:* Dept of Pharmacol & Toxicol Univ of Tex Med Br Galveston TX 77550

SHINOHARA, MAKOTO, b Naha, Japan, Jan 30, 37; m 64; c 2. POLYMER CHEMISTRY, POLYMER SCIENCE. *Educ:* Tokyo Inst Technol, BSc, 60, MSc, 62; State Univ NY Col Forestry, Syracuse Univ, PhD(phys chem), 69. *Prof Exp:* Res Found fel, State Univ NY Col Forestry, Syracuse Univ, 64-69; proj chemist, Dow Corning Corp, 69-74; sr proj chemist, 74-75; res assoc, Int Playtex, Inc, 75-78; MGR MOLDING COMPOUND RES & DEVELOP, MORTON CHEM CO, 78- *Mem:* Am Chem Soc; Am Geog Soc; Sigma Xi; AAAS; NY Acad Sci. *Res:* Structure-mechanical, electrical and physico-chemical property relation in thermo-plastic and thermosetting polymers; polymer composites and toughening; polymer characterization; mechanisms and kinetics of polymerization, polyaddition, polycondensation and ring-opening polymerization; water soluble polymers and gels; organo-silicone polymers. *Mailing Add:* Woodstock Res Ctr Morton Chem Co 1275 Lake Ave Woodstock IL 60098

SHINOZUKA, MASANOBU, b Tokyo, Japan, Dec 23, 30; m 54; c 3. CIVIL ENGINEERING, ENGINEERING MECHANICS. *Educ:* Kyoto Univ, BS, 53, MS, 55; Columbia Univ, PhD(civil eng), 60. *Prof Exp:* Res asst, 59-61, from asst prof to assoc prof, 61-69, prof, 69-77, RENWICK PROF CIVIL ENG, COLUMBIA UNIV, 77- *Concurrent Pos:* US coordr, US-Japan Joint Seminars; res analyst, US Air Force, 67-68; consult, Jet Propulsion Lab, 68- & Kawasaki Heavy Indust, Kobe, Japan, 71; res struct engr, Naval Civil Eng Lab, 70. *Honors & Awards:* Walter L Huber Civil Eng Res Prize, Am Soc Civil Engrs, 72; Am Freudenthal Medal, Am Soc Civil Engrs. *Mem:* Am Soc Civil Engrs; Am Soc Mech Engrs; Am Inst Aeronaut & Astronaut; Am Soc Mat. *Res:* Structural reliability analysis; random vibration; inelasticity; structural analysis. *Mailing Add:* 610 Mudd Columbia Univ New York NY 10027

SHIONO, RYONOSUKE, b Kobe, Japan, Nov 12, 23; m 58; c 3. CRYSTALLOGRAPHY. *Educ:* Osaka Univ, MSc, 45, DSc(physics), 60. *Prof Exp:* Instr physics, Osaka Univ, 49-56; res assoc lectr, 56-61, asst res prof, 61-65, assoc res prof crystallog, 66-69, ASSOC PROF CRYSTALLOG, UNIV PITTSBURGH, 69- *Concurrent Pos:* Vis prof, Univ Sao Paulo, 69. *Mem:* Am Crystallog Asn; Royal Soc Chem; Chem Soc Japan; Phys Soc Japan. *Res:* Crystal structure analysis and application of computer in crystallography. *Mailing Add:* Dept of Crystallog Univ of Pittsburgh Pittsburgh PA 15260

SHIOTA, TETSUO, b Los Angeles, Calif, Jan 1, 23; m 48; c 3. BIOCHEMISTRY. *Educ:* Roosevelt Col, BS, 48; Univ Ill, MS, 50, PhD(bact), 53. *Prof Exp:* Res assoc, NIH, Bethesda, Md, 53-60, sr scientist microbiol, 60-67; assoc prof, 67-71, PROF MICROBIOL, UNIV ALA, BIRMINGHAM, 71-, ASSOC PROF BIOCHEM, 69- *Concurrent Pos:* Sr scientist, Cancer Res & Training Prog, Univ Ala, Birmingham, 72- *Mem:* Am Soc Microbiol; Am Soc Biol Chemists. *Res:* Biochemistry of pteridines and folic acid compounds in bacteria and mammalian cells. *Mailing Add:* Dept of Microbiol Univ of Ala Birmingham AL 35294

SHIOYAMA, TOD KAY, b Seattle, Wash, Aug 16, 51. ANALYTICAL CHEMISTRY, INORGANIC CHEMISTRY. *Educ:* Western Wash State Col, BS, 73; Wash State Univ, PhD(anal), 78. *Prof Exp:* CHEMIST RES, PHILLIPS PETROL CO, 78- *Mem:* Am Chem Soc. *Res:* Catalysis; kinetics. *Mailing Add:* Phillips Petrol Co 87G PRC Bartlesville OK 74004

SHIP, IRWIN I, b New York, NY, July 11, 32; m 56; c 3. ORAL MEDICINE. *Educ:* Harvard Univ, DMD, 56; Univ Pa, MSc, 65. *Prof Exp:* Intern oral surg & med, Mass Gen Hosp, Boston, 56-57; prin investr oral med, Nat Inst Dent Res, 57-60; from asst prof to assoc prof, 60-66, dir hosp educ, 63-73, chmn dept oral med, 73-78, PROF ORAL MED & CHMN SCH DENT MED, UNIV PA, 66-, DIR CLIN RES CTR, 78- *Concurrent Pos:* Asst chief dent res, DIR RURAL DENT HEALTH PROG, ROBERT JOHNSON FOUND, Philadelphia Gen Hosp, 60-63, chief, 63-73; consult, US Army, Ft Dix, 61-73 & Walter Reed Army Hosp, 74-75; vis prof & chief dept oral med, Hebrew Univ Jerusalem-Hadassah Sch Dent Med, 69-70, vis prof & consult, 72; asst oral surg, Presby Univ Pa Med Ctr; staff mem, Univ Pa Hosp; attend dentist, Children's Hosp Philadelphia. *Honors & Awards:* Samuel Charles Miller Award, Am Acad Oral Med, 77; Tasman Award for Outstanding Serv to Dent Med, 78. *Mem:* Am Asn Dent Schs; Am Acad Oral Med; Soc Dent Handicapped; Int Asn Dent Res. *Res:* Clinical oral medicine; epidemiology and biometry of oral diseases. *Mailing Add:* Dept of Oral Med Univ of Pa Sch of Dent Med Philadelphia PA 19174

SHIPCHANDLER, MOHAMMED TYEBJI, b Surat, India, May 19, 41; m 71. MEDICINAL CHEMISTRY, ORGANIC CHEMISTRY. *Educ:* Univ Bombay, BSc, 62, BSc, 64; Univ Minn, Minneapolis, PhD(med chem), 69. *Prof Exp:* NIH fel & res assoc med chem, Univ Kans, 68-70; NIH fel & res assoc natural prod chem, Col Pharm, Ohio State Univ, 70-72; instr, Columbus Tech Inst, Ohio, 72-73; RES CHEMIST, COM SOLVENTS CORP, TERRE HAUTE, IND, 73- *Mem:* Am Chem Soc. *Res:* Synthesis of medicinal agents and natural products. *Mailing Add:* Res Dept Com Solvents Corp Terre Haute IN 47808

SHIPE, EMERSON RUSSELL, b Knoxville, Tenn, July 28, 47; m 76; c 2. AGRONOMY. *Educ:* Univ Tenn, BS, 69; Western Ky Univ, MS, 70; Va Polytech Inst & State Univ, PhD(agron), 78. *Prof Exp:* Teaching asst, Western Ky Univ, 69-70; agriculturalist, US Peace Corps, Cent Am, 73-75; teaching asst, Va Polytech Inst & State Univ, 75-78; asst prof soil & crop sci, Tex Agr Exp Sta, 78-80; ASST PROF AGRON & SOILS, CLEMSON UNIV, 80- *Mem:* Am Soc Agron; Crop Sci Soc Am; Am Genetic Asn. *Res:* Improvement of forage legumes for pasture through a plant breeding program; adaptation of new species; seedling growth; persistence; production; quality. *Mailing Add:* Dept Agron & Soils Clemson Univ Clemson SC 29631

SHIPE, WILLIAM FRANKLIN, b Middletown, Va, Mar 8, 20; m 48; c 2. FOOD SCIENCE. *Educ:* Va Polytech Inst, BS, 41; Cornell Univ, PhD(dairy chem), 49. *Prof Exp:* Instr dairy mfg, Va Polytech Inst, 45-46; from asst to assoc prof dairy indust, 46-60, PROF FOOD SCI, CORNELL UNIV, 61- *Concurrent Pos:* Res assoc, NC State Col, 56; travel fel, Cornell Univ, 62; res consult, Dept Agr & Mkt, 63; Nat Inst Res Dairying fel, Reading, Eng, 70 & 79. *Mem:* Am Chem Soc; Am Dairy Sci Asn; Int Food Technologists. *Res:* Enzymatic changes in food products; flavor and texture of foods. *Mailing Add:* Dept of Food Sci Cornell Univ Ithaca NY 14850

SHIPINSKI, JOHN, b Wisconsin Rapids, Wis, Aug 25, 32; m 66. MECHANICAL ENGINEERING. *Educ:* Univ Wis, BSME, 60, MSME, 63, PhD(mech eng), 67. *Prof Exp:* Engr, Deere & Co, 67-75 & Chicago Pneumatic, 75-76; ENGR, WARNER ELEC CO, 76- *Honors & Awards:* Dugald Clerk Prize, Inst Mech Engrs, London, 72. *Mem:* Soc Automotive Engrs; Am Soc Mech Engrs; Am Soc Agr Engrs. *Res:* Electromagnetic clutches and brakes; clutches and brakes; diesel engines; energy technology; supercharging of engines. *Mailing Add:* Warner Elec Co Beloit WI 53511

SHIPKOWITZ, NATHAN L, b Chicago, Ill, Mar 29, 25; m 56; c 4. MICROBIOLOGY. *Educ:* Univ Ill, BS, 49, MS, 50; Mich State Univ, PhD(bact, pub health), 52. *Prof Exp:* Asst prof vet sci, Univ Mass, 52-54; asst res bacteriologist, Hooper Found, Med Ctr, Univ Calif, San Francisco, 54-58; bacteriologist & virologist, Path Dept, Good Samaritan Hosp, Portland, Ore, 59-62; sr res microbiologist, 63-75, ASSOC RES FEL, ABBOTT LABS, 76- *Mem:* AAAS; Am Soc Microbiol. *Res:* Virology. *Mailing Add:* Abbott Labs North Chicago IL 60064

SHIPLEY, EDWARD NICHOLAS, b Baltimore, Md, Jan 26, 34; m 63; c 3. DATABASE TECHNOLOGY, COMMUNICATION NETWORKS. *Educ:* Johns Hopkins Univ, AB, 54, PhD(physics), 58. *Prof Exp:* From instr to asst prof physics, Northwestern Univ, 58-63; mem tech staff, Bellcomm, Inc, Washington, DC, 63-72; MEM TECH STAFF, BELL LABS, 72- *Concurrent Pos:* Consult, Argonne Nat Lab, 59-63; co-investr, Mariner-Mars Mission, 71. *Mem:* Am Phys Soc. *Res:* Low energy nuclear reactions; lifetimes of excited nuclear states; hyperfragment decay modes; K meson reactions; lunar surface mechanical properties; Martian atmospheric phenomena; maintenance and operations of telephone switching systems; database administration. *Mailing Add:* Bell Labs Bldg Rm 2F401 Crawford Corners Rd Holmdel NJ 07733

SHIPLEY, GEORGE GRAHAM, b London, Eng, Nov 18, 37. BIOPHYSICS. *Educ:* Univ Nottingham, Eng, BSc, 59, PhD(phys chem), 63. *Prof Exp:* Scientist biophys, Unilever Res Lab, Eng, 63-69, sect leader, 69-71; asst res prof med, 71-74, asst prof biochem, 73-74, ASSOC PROF BIOCHEM & ASSOC RES PROF MED, SCH MED, BOSTON UNIV, 74- *Mem:* AAAS; Am Chem Soc; Am Crystallog Asn; Am Heart Asn; Am Soc Biol Chemists. *Res:* Structure and function of biological lipids, cell membranes and serum lipoproteins and their relationship to pathological processes, notably atherosclerosis and hyperlipidemia. *Mailing Add:* Dept Med Sch Med Boston Univ 80 E Concord St Boston MA 02118

SHIPLEY, GEORGE LEWIS, b Marion, Ohio, Aug 14, 47; m 73. CELL & DEVELOPMENTAL BIOLOGY. *Educ:* Univ Calif, Santa Barbara, BA, 73, PhD(cell biol), 78. *Prof Exp:* Fel biol, Univ Fla, 78-80; NIH fel, 80-82, FLOW GEN FEL, MASS INST TECHNOL, 82- *Mem:* Am Soc Cell Biol. *Res:* Molecular mechanisms of self and non-self recognition at the cellular level using heterothallic plasmodial slime molds as a model system. *Mailing Add:* Dept Biol Rm 56-720 Mass Inst Technol Cambridge MA 02139

SHIPLEY, JAMES PARISH, JR, b Clovis, NMex, Jan 3, 45; m 62; c 3. APPLIED MATHEMATICS, SYSTEMS SCIENCE. *Educ:* NMex State Univ, BS, 66; Univ NMex, MS, 69, PhD(elec eng), 73. *Prof Exp:* Staff mem electronics, 66-73, solar energy, 73-76, systs sci, 76-78, GROUP LEADER SAFEGUARDS SYSTS, LOS ALAMOS NAT LAB, 78- *Mem:* Inst Elec & Electronics Engrs; AAAS; Inst Nuclear Mat Mgt. *Res:* Nuclear safeguards systems; systems science; statistical decision theory. *Mailing Add:* Safeguards Systs Los Alamos Nat Lab Los Alamos NM 87545

SHIPLEY, MICHAEL THOMAS, b Kansas City, Mo, Apr 22, 41; m 76; c 1. NEUROANATOMY, NEUROPHYSIOLOGY. *Educ:* Univ Mo, Kansas City, BA, 67; Mass Inst Technol, PhD(neurosci), 72. *Prof Exp:* Fel anat, Univ Aarhus, 72-74; asst prof, Univ Lausanne, 74-78; ASST PROF CELL BIOL & ANAT, MED SCH, NORTHWESTERN UNIV, 78- *Concurrent Pos:* Prin investr, NIH grant, 82-; Woodrow Wilson fel. *Mem:* Soc Neurosci; Am Asn Anatomists. *Res:* Neuroanatomy and physiology of sensory-lumbic interactions in cerebral cortex and neuroanatomy; neurochemistry of ontogenetic development of central (olfactory) nervous system circuitry. *Mailing Add:* Dept Cell Biol & Anat Med Sch Northwestern Univ 303 E Chicago Ave Chicago IL 60611

SHIPLEY, THORNE, b New York, NY, Apr 11, 27; m 71; c 2. OPHTHALMOLOGY, PSYCHOLOGY. *Educ:* Johns Hopkins Univ, BA, 49; New Sch Social Res, MA, 53; NY Univ, PhD(psychol), 55. *Prof Exp:* Instr psychol, Long Island Univ, 53-55; res psychol, Am Optical Co, 55-58; NIH spec fel, Imp Col, Univ London, 58-59 & Fac Med, Univ Paris, 59-60; assoc prof visual sci, Med Sch & assoc prof neuropsychol, Sch Arts & Sci, 60-77, PROF VISUAL SCI, MED SCH & PROF NEUROPSYCHOL, SCH ARTS & SCI, UNIV MIAMI, 77- *Mem:* AAAS; Am Psychol Asn; Soc Neurosci; Soc Social Responsibility in Sci; Optical Soc Am. *Res:* Theoretical psychology; sensory communication; sense function in children; cognition; communication and learning disabilities; psychology. *Mailing Add:* Dept of Ophthal Univ of Miami Med Sch Miami FL 33152

SHIPMAN, C(HARLES) WILLIAM, b Phillipsburg, NJ, Aug 29, 24; m 46; c 3. CHEMICAL ENGINEERING. *Educ:* Mass Inst Technol, SB, 48, SM, 49, ScD(chem eng), 52. *Prof Exp:* Instr chem eng, Mass Inst Technol, 49-50, asst combustion res, 50-52, res assoc, 55-58; asst prof chem eng, Univ Del, 52-55; from asst prof to prof, Worcester Polytech Inst, 58-74, dean grad studies, 71-74; assst dir, Corp Res Dept, 78-80, ENGR, CABOT CORP, 74-, MGR CARBON BLACK RES & DEVELOP, 82- *Concurrent Pos:* Consult, Avco Corp, 58-65, United Aircraft Corp, 65-74 & Kennecott Corp, 68-74. *Mem:* Am Chem Soc; Am Inst Chem Engrs; Combustion Inst. *Res:* Thermodynamics; combustion; mass transfer; fine particles technology. *Mailing Add:* Cabot Corp Billerica Tech Ctr Concord Rd Billerica MA 01821

SHIPMAN, CHARLES, JR, b Ventura, Calif, Nov 1, 34; m 73; c 2. VIROLOGY. *Educ:* Univ Calif, Los Angeles, AB, 56; Calif State Univ, Fresno, MA, 63; Ind Univ, PhD(microbiol), 66. *Prof Exp:* Assoc res microbiologist, Parke-Davis & Co, 66-68; asst prof biol, 68-74, asst prof microbiol, Med Sch, 68-75, ASSOC PROF ORAL BIOL, SCH DENT, UNIV MICH, ANN ARBOR, 74-, ASSOC PROF MICROBIOL, MED SCH, 75-, MEM, DENT RES INST, 68- *Concurrent Pos:* Consult, Coun Dent Educ, 72-73. *Mem:* Am Soc Microbiol; Tissue Cult Asn. *Res:* Antiviral action of nucleoside antibiotics on herpes simplex virus. *Mailing Add:* Dept Microbiol Univ Mich Ann Arbor MI 48109

SHIPMAN, HAROLD R, b Rock Rapids, Iowa, Feb 20, 11; m 38; c 2. SANITARY ENGINEERING. *Educ:* Univ Minn, BS, 37, MS, 48; Am Acad Environ Engrs, dipl. *Prof Exp:* Dir div rural sanit, dir div hotels, resorts & restaurants, regional engr & dist engr coord, Minn State Dept Health, 37-50; sanit engr, Am Red Cross, Korea, 51; sanit engr, WHO, Turkey, 52-54 & Egypt, 54-58; sanit engr & chief br environ sanit, Pan-Am Health Orgn, 58-62; water & wastes adv, 62-76, chief, Water Supply Sect, 63-76, CONSULT, ASIAN DEVELOP BANK, WORLD BANK, 76- *Concurrent Pos:* Consult, Govt Turkey, 52-54, Govt Egypt, 54-58 & numerous eng firms, 76-; chmn subcomt water resources, UN, 71-72. *Honors & Awards:* Centennial Fel Award, Johns Hopkins Univ, 76. *Mem:* Am Soc Civil Engrs; Nat Soc Prof Engrs; Am Water Works Asn; Am Pub Health Asn; Inter-Am Asn Sanit Engrs. *Res:* Management, financing, appraisal and design of water supply and sewerage systems internationally. *Mailing Add:* 7108 Edgevale St Chevy Chase MD 20815

SHIPMAN, HARRY LONGFELLOW, b Hartford, Conn, Feb 20, 48; m 70; c 2. ASTROPHYSICS, PHYSICS. *Educ:* Harvard Univ, BA, 69; Calif Inst Technol, MS, 70, PhD(astron), 71. *Prof Exp:* J W Gibbs instr astron, Yale Univ, 71-73; asst prof physics, Univ Mo, St Louis, 73-74; asst prof, 74-77, assoc prof, 77-81, PROF PHYSICS, UNIV DEL, 81- *Concurrent Pos:* Guest investr, Kitt Peak Nat Observ, 72-74 & Copernicus Satellite Prog, NASA, 74-; astronomer, McDonnell Planetarium, 73-74; prin investr grants, NSF, 74-, Res Corp, 74-76, Univ Del Res Found, 75-76 & NASA, 76-79 & 81; John Simon Guggenheim Mem fel, 80-81. *Mem:* Sigma Xi; Am Astron Soc; AAAS; Am Asn Physics Teachers; Astron Soc Pac. *Res:* Analysis of stellar spectra via stellar-atmosphere calculations; white-dwarf stars and other final stages of stellar evolution; theoretical astrophysics. *Mailing Add:* Dept of Physics Univ of Del Newark DE 19711

SHIPMAN, LESTER LYNN, b Topeka, Kans, Mar 28, 47; m 69. THEORETICAL CHEMISTRY. *Educ:* Washburn Univ, BA & BS, 69; Univ Kans, PhD(chem), 72. *Prof Exp:* Fel chem, Cornell Univ, 72-74; appointee, Argonne Nat Lab, 74-75, res assoc chem, 75-76, asst chemist, 76-80, chemist, 80-81; RES SCIENTIST, E I DU PONT DE NEMOURS & CO, INC, 81- *Concurrent Pos:* Consult, Norwich Pharmacal Co, 73-75. *Mem:* Biophys Soc; Am Soc Photobiol; Am Chem Soc; Plant Growth Regulator Soc Am; Am Soc Plant Physiologists. *Res:* Ab initio molecular quantum mechanics; conformational and intermolecular potential energy functions; primary events of photosynthesis; structure-activity relationships; theoretical biophysical chemistry; molecular aspects of chemical carcinogenesis; mechanisms of energy transfer; theory of excitons in molecular aggregates. *Mailing Add:* Cent Res & Develop Dept Exp Sta E I du Pont de Nemours & Co Inc Wilmington DE 19898

SHIPMAN, ROBERT DEAN, b Moundsville, WVa, May 12, 21; m 46; c 2. FOREST ECOLOGY, SILVICULTURE. *Educ:* Univ Mich, BSF & MF, 42; Mich State Univ, PhD(forestry), 52. *Prof Exp:* Asst forest soils, Childs-Walcott Forest, Conn, 42; munic park forester, Oglebay Park, Wheeling, WVa, 47; agr aide, US Forest Serv, 49, mem staff, 52-58; asst forest res, Mich State Univ, 50-51; assoc prof forestry, Clemson Univ, 58-63; assoc prof forest ecol, 63-75, PROF FOREST ECOL, SCH FOREST RESOURCES, PA STATE UNIV, 75- *Concurrent Pos:* Moderator Northeast Weed Control Conf, NY, 64; mem, Soc Am Foresters Nat Task Force on Herbicides, 75-76. *Mem:* Soil Sci Soc Am; Soc Am Foresters; Ecol Soc Am; Weed Sci Soc Am; Sigma Xi. *Res:* Tree physiology and soils; silvics and herbicides. *Mailing Add:* Sch of Forest Resources Pa State Univ University Park PA 16802

SHIPMAN, ROSS LOVELACE, b Jackson, Miss, Nov 20, 26; m 48; c 1. GEOLOGY. *Educ:* Univ Miss, BA, 50. *Prof Exp:* Geologist, Miss State Geol Surv, 49-50; jr geologist, Humble Oil & Refining Co, 50-51, dist geologist, 51-55; petrol consult, 55-67; asst exec dir, Am Geol Inst, 67-71; res prog mgr, Bur Econ Geol & Div Natural Resources & Environ, 71-75, assoc dir admin, Marine Sci Inst, 75-79, ASSOC VPRES, RES ADMIN, UNIV TEX, AUSTIN, 79- *Mem:* Fel Geol Soc Am; Am Asn Petrol Geol; Am Inst Prof Geol. *Res:* Petroleum exploration and production; mining exploration; environmental geology; marine geophysics. *Mailing Add:* Univ Tex Main Bldg 201 Austin TX 78712

SHIPMAN, WILLIAM H, b Los Molinas, Calif, Aug 19, 22; m 47; c 1. RADIOCHEMISTRY. *Educ:* San Jose State Col, BS, 49. *Prof Exp:* Radio chemist, US Naval Radiol Defense Lab, 50-69, oceanog chemist, Naval Ocean Systs Ctr, 69-79; RETIRED. *Concurrent Pos:* Consult, Radiation Detection Corp, 59-64; consult, Found for Nutrit & Stress Res, 66-68 & Sea World, 76- *Mem:* AAAS; Am Chem Soc. *Res:* Analytical chemistry; radioecology; oceanography. *Mailing Add:* 4051 Calavo Dr La Mesa CA 92041

SHIPP, JOSEPH CALVIN, b Northport, Ala, Feb 10, 27; m 62; c 1. MEDICINE. *Educ:* Univ Ala, BS, 48; Columbia Univ, MD, 52. *Prof Exp:* Intern & asst resident med, Presby Hosp, New York, 52-54; Nat Res Coun res fel, Harvard Med Sch, 54-56; res fel biochem, Oxford Univ, 58-59; instr med, Harvard Med Sch, 59-60; from asst prof to assoc prof med, Med Col, Univ Fla, 60-68, prof & dir clin res ctr, 68-70, dir diabetes res & training prog, 64-70; PROF MED & CHMN DEPT, COL MED, UNIV NEBR MED CTR, 70- *Concurrent Pos:* Sr asst resident, Peter Bent Brigham Hosp, 56-57, chief resident physician, 57-58, jr assoc, 59-60; sr investr, Boston Med Found, 59-60; Markle scholar, 61; res fel biochem, Univ Munich, 65-66. *Mem:* Am Diabetes Asn; Am Fedn Clin Res. *Res:* Endocrinology; diabetes; acting of hormones at the cellular level. *Mailing Add:* Dept of Med Univ Nebr Col of Med Omaha NE 68105

SHIPP, OLIVER ELMO, b Big Creek, Miss, June 13, 28; m 52; c 3. ENTOMOLOGY, PLANT PHYSIOLOGY. *Educ:* Miss State Univ, BS, 52, MS, 58; Tex A&M Univ, PhD(entom), 63. *Prof Exp:* Asst county agent, Miss Exten Serv, 54-56; asst prof cotton insect res, Tex A&M Univ, 60-63; res biologist, 63-68, MEM STAFF FIELD RES, CHEMAGRO CORP, 68- *Mem:* Entom Soc Am; Southern Weed Sci Soc. *Res:* Tenacity of insecticide residues on field crops; penetration characteristics of plant tissue by insecticides; insect control; rearing techniques for laboratory insect cultures; herbicide evaluation and development. *Mailing Add:* 218 Valleywood Dr East Collierville TN 38017

SHIPP, RAYMOND FRANCIS, b Hay Springs, Nebr, June 1, 31; m 66; c 3. AGRONOMY. *Educ:* Univ Nebr, BS, 53, MS, 58; Pa State Univ, PhD(agron), 62. *Prof Exp:* Soil scientist, Pa State Dept Health, 62-66 & US Dept Interior Bur Reclamation, 66-72; exten agronomist, 72-77, ASSOC PROF AGRON EXTEN, PA STATE UNIV, 78- *Mem:* Fel AAAS; Soil Sci Soc Am; Sigma Xi. *Res:* The use of sewage sludge by-products from municipal waste water treatment plants for the enhancement of crop production. *Mailing Add:* Dept of Agron Pa State Univ University Park PA 16802

SHIPP, ROBERT LEWIS, b Tallahassee, Fla, Aug 22, 42; m 64; c 2. ICHTHYOLOGY. *Educ:* Spring Hill Col, BS, 64; Fla State Univ, MS, 66, PhD(biol), 70. *Prof Exp:* Instr biol, Fla A&M Univ, 68-70; asst prof biol, 71-75, ASSOC PROF BIOL, UNIV S ALA, 75- *Mem:* Am Soc Ichthyologists & Herpetologists; Am Fisheries Soc; Soc Syst Zool. *Res:* Marine zoogeography; fish systematics and phylogeny; artificial reef development; development of Guatemalan fisheries; river ecology. *Mailing Add:* Dept of Biol Univ of SAla Mobile AL 36688

SHIPP, WILLIAM STANLEY, b Little Rock, Ark, July 11, 39; m 62; c 1. BIOPHYSICS. *Educ:* Univ Chicago, PhD(biophys), 65. *Prof Exp:* Nat Acad Sci-Nat Res Coun res fel bact genetics, Genetics Inst, Univ Cologne, 65-66; Am Cancer Soc res fel, Max Planck Inst Biol, Ger, 66-67; asst prof, 67-72, ASSOC PROF MED SCI, BROWN UNIV, 72-, ASST PROVOST, 80- *Res:* Bacterial genetics; bacterial electron transport and oxidative phosphorylation systems; digital signal processing; local area networks; operating systems. *Mailing Add:* Provost Off Brown Univ Box 1857 Providence RI 02912

SHIPPY, DAVID JAMES, b Oelwein, Iowa, July 26, 31; m 54; c 2. ENGINEERING MECHANICS. *Educ:* Iowa State Univ, BS, 53, MS, 54, PhD(theoret & appl mech), 63. *Prof Exp:* Aerophysics engr, Gen Dynamics Corp, 54-56; instr physics & eng, Graceland Col, 56-64; from asst prof to assoc prof eng mech, 64-78, NSF grant, 66-67, PROF ENG MECH, UNIV KY, 78- *Concurrent Pos:* Instr, Iowa State Univ, 60-61; Air Force Off Sci Res grant, 75-78; NSF grants, 81- *Mem:* Am Soc Eng Educ. *Res:* Rigid body dynamics; nonlinear oscillations; numerical methods in solid mechanics, especially the Boundary Integral Equation Method. *Mailing Add:* Dept Eng Mech Anderson Hall Univ Ky Lexington KY 40506

SHIPSEY, EDWARD JOSEPH, b New York, NY, Aug 22, 38; m; c 2. PHYSICAL CHEMISTRY. *Educ:* Stanford Univ, BS, 60; Ohio State Univ, PhD(phys chem), 67. *Prof Exp:* RES ASSOC PHYSICS, UNIV TEX, AUSTIN, 72- *Res:* Theory and computation of atomic and molecular collisions. *Mailing Add:* Dept of Physics Univ of Tex Austin TX 78712

SHIPTON, HAROLD W(ILLIAM), b Birmingham, Eng, Sept 29, 20; m 47; c 1. ELECTRONICS. *Educ:* Shrewsbury Tech Col, Eng, EE, 38. *Prof Exp:* Electronic develop engr, Burden Neurol Inst, Bristol, Eng, 46-47; res assoc med electronics, 57-61, assoc prof, 61-67, PROF MED ELECTRONICS, COL MED, UNIV IOWA, 67-, DIR BIOENG RESOURCE FACIL, 68- *Concurrent Pos:* Consult ed, Electroencephalog & Clin Neurophysiol; mem ed comt, Ann Rev Biophysics & Bioeng, 74-79. *Mem:* Brit Inst Electronics & Radio Engrs; Inst Elec & Electronics Engrs; Am Electroencephalog Soc. *Res:* Methods for the transduction, transformation and display of electrophysiological variables; biomedical engineering. *Mailing Add:* Univ of Iowa Col of Med Iowa City IA 52242

SHIRANE, GEN, b Nishinomiya, Japan, May 15, 24; m 50; c 2. SOLID STATE PHYSICS. *Educ:* Univ Tokyo, BE, 47, DSc(physics), 54. *Prof Exp:* Res assoc physics, Tokyo Inst Technol, Japan, 48-52; res assoc, Pa State Univ, 52-55, asst prof, 55-56; assoc physicist, Brookhaven Nat Lab, 56-57; res physicist, Res Labs, Westinghouse Elec Corp, 57-58, adv physicist, 59-63; physicist, 63-68, SR PHYSICIST, BROOKHAVEN NAT LAB, 68- *Honors & Awards:* Buckley Prize, Am Physics Soc, 73; Warren Award, Am Crystallog Asn, 73. *Mem:* Am Phys Soc; Phys Soc Japan. *Res:* Neutron scattering; magnetism; lattice dynamics. *Mailing Add:* Dept of Physics Brookhaven Nat Lab Upton NY 11973

SHIRAZI, MOSTAFA AYAT, b Najaf, Iraq, Sept 27, 32; US citizen; m 61; c 3. FLUID DYNAMICS. *Educ:* Calif State Polytech Col, BS, 59; Univ Wash, MS, 61; Univ Ill, Urbana, PhD(mech eng), 67. *Prof Exp:* Assoc res engr, Boeing Co, Wash, 61; sr res engr, Hercules Inc, Md, 67-69; res mech engr, 69-80, SR RES SCIENTIST, CORVALLIS ENVIRON RES LAB, ENVIRON PROTECTION AGENCY, 80- *Mem:* Am Soc Mech Engrs. *Res:* Analysis of jet diffusion for the prediction of heated plume behavior in large bodies of water; jet diffusion; ecosystems modeling and analysis. *Mailing Add:* Corvallis Environ Res Lab Environ Protection Agency Corvallis OR 97330

SHIRER, DONALD LEROY, b Cleveland, Ohio, May 10, 31. COMPUTER SCIENCES, ENGINEERING PHYSICS. *Educ:* Case Western Reserve Univ, BS, 52; Ohio State Univ, MSc, 53, PhD(physics), 57. *Prof Exp:* Res assoc, Res Found, Ohio State Univ, 57; from asst prof to prof physics, Valparaiso Univ, 57-78; adj prof elec eng, 80-81, DIR, COMPUTER-BASED INSTRUCTION LAB, UNIV ARIZ, TUSCON, 81- *Concurrent Pos:* Consult, Argonne Nat Lab, 58-65; NSF fel, Univ Ill, 71-72; assoc ed, Am J Physics, 71-76; vis prof elec eng, Univ Ariz, 78-79. *Mem:* Am Phys Soc; Am Asn Physics Teachers; Acoust Soc Am; Asn Develop Comput-Based Instruction Systs. *Res:* Educational uses of computers; speech and music synthesis; acoustics. *Mailing Add:* Dept Elec Eng Univ Ariz Tuscon AZ 85721

SHIRER, HAMPTON WHITING, b Newton, Mass, Aug 8, 24; m 47; c 5. PHYSIOLOGY. *Educ:* Washburn Univ, BS, 45; Univ Kans, MD, 48. *Prof Exp:* Intern, Med Ctr, Univ Kans, 48-49, USPHS res fel, 49-51, instr surg, 53-54, from instr to asst prof physiol, 54-61; head biophys group biol sci & systs dept, Gen Motors Defense Res Labs, 61-63; asst prof physiol, Univ Mich, 63-64; assoc prof physiol, Dept Comp Biochem & Physiol & Dept Elec Eng, 64-67, prof elec eng, physiol & cell biol, 67-73, PROF PHYSIOL & CELL BIOL, UNIV KANS, 73- *Concurrent Pos:* Lederle med fac award, 56-59. *Mem:* AAAS; Biophys Soc; Am Meteorol Soc; Inst Elec & Electronics Eng. *Res:* Bioelectricity; cardiovascular regulation; physiological instrumentation; biotelemetry. *Mailing Add:* Dept of Physiol & Cell Biol Univ of Kans Lawrence KS 66044

SHIRES, GEORGE THOMAS, b Waco, Tex, Nov 22, 25; m 48; c 3. SURGERY. *Educ:* Univ Tex, BS, 44, MD, 48. *Prof Exp:* From asst prof to prof surg & chmn dept, Southwest Med Sch, Univ Tex, Dallas, 57-74; chmn & prof surg, Sch Med, Univ Wash, 74-75; PROF SURG & CHMN DEPT, MED COL, CORNELL UNIV, 75- *Concurrent Pos:* Consult, Surgeon Gen, Army & NIH; ed, Surg, Gynec & Obstet, 82- *Mem:* Am Asn Surg Trauma; Am Surg Asn (secy, 69-74, pres, 79-80); Am Col Surg (pres, 82); Soc Univ Surg; Soc Int Surg. *Res:* Surgical trauma. *Mailing Add:* Dept Surg Cornell Univ Med Col 1300 York Ave New York NY 10021

SHIRES, THOMAS KAY, b Buffalo, NY, July 12, 35; m 61; c 3. CELL BIOLOGY. *Educ:* Colgate Univ, BA, 57; Univ Okla, MS, 61, PhD(med sci), 65. *Prof Exp:* Res lectr depts anat & urol, Sch Med, Univ Okla, 65-68; res fel, McArdle Cancer Res Inst, Univ Wis-Madison, 68-72; asst prof, 72-75, assoc prof, 75-81, PROF PHARMACOL, COL MED, UNIV IOWA, 81- *Concurrent Pos:* Vis prof, Univ Wis-Madison, 81-82. *Mem:* Am Asn Cancer Res; NY Acad Sci; Am Soc Pharmacol & Exp Therapeut; Am Soc Cell Biol. *Res:* Rough endoplasmic reticulum protein synthesis; chemical carcinogenesis; toxic reactions of the liver. *Mailing Add:* Dept of Pharmacol Univ of Iowa Iowa City IA 52240

SHIRK, AMY EMIKO, b Honolulu, Hawaii, July 14, 46. INORGANIC CHEMISTRY. *Educ:* Univ Hawaii, BS, 68; Northwestern Univ, PhD(chem), 73. *Prof Exp:* Res assoc mat sci, Northwestern Univ, 73-74; RES ASSOC CHEM, ILL INST TECHNOL, 74- *Concurrent Pos:* Mem tech staff chem, Bell Labs, 77-78. *Mem:* Am Chem Soc; Sigma Xi. *Res:* Infrared and Raman spectroscopy; molecular structure; inorganic syntheses. *Mailing Add:* Ill Inst of Technol 3300 S Dearborn Chicago IL 60616

SHIRK, B(RIAN) THOMAS, b Schoeneck, Pa, Sept 20, 41; m 66. SOLID STATE SCIENCE, ELECTRICAL ENGINEERING. *Educ:* Pa State Univ, BS, 63, PhD(solid state sci), 68. *Prof Exp:* Res scientist, Stackpole Carbon Co, 68-72; tech dir, Lydall Magnetics Co, 72-75; PRES, HOOSIER MAGNETICS, INC, 75- *Mem:* Inst Elec & Electronics Engrs; Am Ceramic Soc. *Res:* Magnetic oxides and glasses; single crystal growth and characterization; research and development of ferrites. *Mailing Add:* Hoosier Magnetics Inc 2001 Cosby Rd Washington IN 47501

SHIRK, JAMES SILER, b Chambersburg, Pa, Mar 7, 40. SPECTROSCOPY, LASER CHEMISTRY. *Educ:* Col Wooster, BA, 62; Univ Calif, Berkeley, PhD(chem), 66. *Prof Exp:* Res assoc chem, Imp Col, Univ London, 66-67; Nat Acad Sci-Nat Res Coun res assoc fel spectros, Nat Bur Standards, 67-69; asst prof chem, 69-75, ASSOC PROF CHEM, ILL INST TECHNOL, 75- *Concurrent Pos:* Mem tech staff, Bell Labs, Murray Hill, NJ, 77-78. *Mem:* Am Chem Soc; Am Phys Soc; Sigma Xi. *Res:* Infrared and ultraviolet spectroscopy; low temperature chemistry; matrix isolation studies; lasers; analytical instrumentation; raman spectroscopy. *Mailing Add:* Dept of Chem Ill Inst of Technol Chicago IL 60616

SHIRK, PAUL DAVID, b Waterloo, Iowa, June 7, 48. MOLECULAR GENETICS, MOLECULAR ENDOCRINOLOGY. *Educ:* Univ Northern Iowa, BA, 70; Tex A&M Univ, MS, 75, PhD(zool), 78. *Prof Exp:* Res assoc, Univ Ore, 78-79, NIH fel, 79-81; ASST PROF, ORE STATE UNIV, 81- *Mem:* Am Soc Zoologists; AAAS. *Res:* Hormonal control of yolk polypeptide expression in Drosophila; morphogenesis of the corpora allata and juvenile hormone biosynthesis in the cecropia silkmoth. *Mailing Add:* 3310 Oxbow Way Eugene OR 97401

SHIRK, RICHARD JAY, b Tyrone, Pa, Feb 10, 30; m 51; c 4. BACTERIOLOGY, DATA PROCESSING. *Educ:* Pa State Univ, BS, 51. *Prof Exp:* Bacteriologist fermentation process develop, Heyden Chem Corp, 51-53; bacteriologist, 53-55, res bacteriologist food res group, 55-64 & bact chemother group, 64-74, SR TECH SYSTS ANALYST, AM CYANAMID CO, 74- *Mem:* Data Processing Mgt Asn. *Res:* Antibiotic fermentations; food technology; antioxidants; food preservatives; food coatings; bioassays; experimental infections; chemotherapy of animal diseases; statistical analysis; computer programming; computerized biological screening systems; research and development computer applications. *Mailing Add:* Agr Res Ctr Am Cyanamid Co PO Box 400 Princeton NJ 08540

SHIRKEY, HARRY CAMERON, b Cincinnati, Ohio, July 2, 16; m 58; c 3. PEDIATRICS. *Educ:* Univ Cincinnati, BS, 39, MD, 45, DSc(pharm), 76; Am Bd Pediat, dipl, 52; Am Bd Clin Toxicol, dipl, 76. *Prof Exp:* Assoc prof pharm, Col Pharm, Univ Cincinnati, 40-41; pharmacist, Children's Hosp, 41-42; asst pharmacol, Col Med, Univ Cincinnati, 43-46 & 48-53, instr pediat, 53-57, asst clin prof, 57-60; prof pediat, Med Col Ala, 60-68; prof pediat & chmn dept & prof pharmacol, Sch Med, Univ Hawaii, 68-71; prof pediat & chmn dept, Med Ctr, Tulane Univ, 71-77. *Concurrent Pos:* Resident, Children's Hosp, Cincinnati, 48-51; assoc prof pharmacol, Col Pharm, Univ Cincinnati, 48-60; mem rev comt & chmn panel pediat, US Pharmacopeia, 52-; dir pediat, Cincinnati Gen Hosp, 53-60; chmn admis comt, Nat Formulary, 60-; med & admin dir, Children's Hosp, 60-68; dir, Jefferson County Poison Control Ctr, 60-68; mem staff, Univ Hosp, 60-68; consult, Baptist Hosp, Crippled Children's Hosp & Clin & St Vincent Hosp, 60-68; prof pharmacol, Samford Univ, 60-68; med & exec dir, Kauikeolani Children's Hosp, 68-71; dir pediat serv, Charity Hosp New Orleans, 71-77; mem adv comt drug efficacy study, Nat Res Coun-Nat Acad Sci, mem drug res bd, 71-74. *Mem:* Fel Am Acad Pediat; Am Pediat Soc; Am Soc Pharmacol & Exp Therapeut. *Mailing Add:* 2019 Alexandria Pike Highland Heights KY 41076

SHIRLEY, BARBARA ANNE, b Muskogee, Okla, Oct 15, 36. PHYSIOLOGY, ENDOCRINOLOGY. *Educ:* Okla Baptist Univ, BA, 56; Univ Okla, MS, 61, PhD(physiol), 64. *Prof Exp:* Asst, Univ Okla, 58-62; asst prof zool, 64-70, assoc prof, 70-79, PROF ZOOL, UNIV TULSA, 79- *Mem:* AAAS; Am Soc Zool; assoc Am Physiol Soc. *Res:* Reproduction; pituitary gonadotropins and ovarian steroids. *Mailing Add:* Natural Sci Div Univ Tulsa Tulsa OK 74104

SHIRLEY, DAVID ALLEN, b Knoxville, Tenn, Sept 15, 18; m 41; c 4. ORGANIC CHEMISTRY. *Educ:* Univ Tenn, BS, 39, MS, 40; Iowa State Univ, PhD(chem), 43. *Prof Exp:* Res assoc, Iowa State Col, 43-44; res chemist, E I du Pont de Nemours & Co, Del, 44-47; from asst prof to assoc prof chem, Tulane Univ, 47-52; assoc prof, 52-62, head dept, 62-79, prof, 62-79, EMER PROF CHEM, UNIV TENN, KNOXVILLE, 79- *Mem:* AAAS; Am Chem Soc; The Chem Soc; Sigma Xi. *Res:* Organic chemistry and synthesis; organometallic and heterocyclic compounds; chemotherapy; natural products. *Mailing Add:* Dept of Chem Univ of Tenn Knoxville TN 37916

SHIRLEY, DAVID ARTHUR, b North Conway, NH, Mar 30, 34; m 56; c 5. CHEMICAL PHYSICS. *Educ:* Univ Maine, BS, 55; Univ Calif, Berkeley, PhD(chem), 59. *Hon Degrees:* ScD, Univ Maine, 78. *Prof Exp:* Fel chem, Lawrence Radiation Lab, Univ Calif, 58-59; lectr chem, 59-60, from asst prof to assoc prof, 60-67, from vchmn to chmn dept, 68-75, PROF CHEM, UNIV CALIF, BERKELEY, 67- *Concurrent Pos:* NSF fels, Oxford Univ, 66-67 & Free Univ Berlin, 70; assoc ed, J Chem Physics, 74-76; assoc dir, Lab & head, Mat & Molecular Res Div, Lawrence Berkeley Lab, 75-80, dir, 80- *Honors & Awards:* Ernest O Lawrence Award, USAEC, 72. *Mem:* Nat Acad Sci; AAAS; Am Chem Soc; Am Phys Soc; Fedn Am Scientists. *Res:* Electron spectroscopy of atoms, molecules and solids with emphasis on surfaces and many-electron effects. *Mailing Add:* Dept of Chem Univ of Calif Berkeley CA 94720

SHIRLEY, FRANK CONNARD, b Minneapolis, Minn, Dec 18, 33; m 64; c 4. FOREST MANAGEMENT, FOREST ECONOMICS. *Educ:* Cornell Univ, AB, 55; State Univ NY Col Forestry, Syracuse, MF, 60; Univ Mich, Ann Arbor, PhD(forestry), 69. *Prof Exp:* Forester, US Forest Serv, 60-64; asst prof forest econ, Colo State Univ, 69-72; consult forest mgt policy & econ, 72-74; forest economist, 74-81, OPERS RES ANALYST, ST REGIS PAPER CO, 81- *Mem:* Am Econ Asn; Soc Am Foresters. *Res:* Forest land management in an affluent society. *Mailing Add:* Rt 1 Box 161 Vaughn WA 98394

SHIRLEY, HERSCHEL VINCENT, JR, b Alpharetta, Ga, Aug 29, 23; m 51; c 3. ANIMAL GENETICS, ANIMAL PHYSIOLOGY. *Educ:* Univ Ga, BSA, 49, MSA, 51, PhD(animal genetics & physiol), 55. *Prof Exp:* Assoc prof & assoc poultry geneticist, 55-75, PROF ANIMAL PHYSIOL & POULTRY GENETICIST, AGR EXP STA, UNIV TENN, KNOXVILLE, 75- *Mem:* Poultry Sci Asn; Am Genetic Asn. *Res:* Endocrinology of reproduction and stress physiology. *Mailing Add:* Dept of Animal Sci Agr Exp Sta Univ of Tenn Knoxville TN 37916

SHIRLEY, RAY LOUIS, b Berkeley Co, WVa, Dec 11, 12; m 43, 78; c 5. ANIMAL NUTRITION. *Educ:* WVa Univ, BS, 37, MS, 39; Mich State Univ, PhD(biochem), 49. *Prof Exp:* Asst agr chem, WVa Univ, 37-39; asst biochem, Mich State Univ, 39-41, asst prof, 41-42; res chemist, Hercules Powder Co, 42-47; asst prof biochem, Mich State Univ, 47-49; prof animal nutrit & biochemist, Univ Fla, 49-51; prof chem, Shepherd Col, 51-53; PROF ANIMAL SCI & ANIMAL NUTRITIONIST, UNIV FLA, 53- *Honors & Awards:* Gustav Bohstedt Award, Am Soc Animal Sci, 75. *Mem:* AAAS; Am Chem Soc; Soc Exp Biol & Med; Am Animal Sci; Am Inst Nutrit. *Res:* Nitrogen compounds and minerals, isotopes, enzymes, energy in diets. *Mailing Add:* 1523 NW 11th Rd Gainesville FL 32605

SHIRLEY, ROBERT LOUIS, b Fairview Village, Ohio, Jan 11, 33; m 55; c 3. ORGANIC CHEMISTRY. *Educ:* Col Wooster, BA, 55; Ohio State Univ, PhD(org chem), 60. *Prof Exp:* Res chemist, Jefferson Chem Co, Inc, 60-63, mem staff mkt develop, 63-70; mgr mkt develop, Ott Chem Co, 70-73; sales mgr, Story Chem Corp, 73-77; TECH SALES REP, UPJOHN POLYMER CHEM DIV, 77- *Concurrent Pos:* Tech sales rep, Upjohn Polymer Chemicals Div, 77- *Mem:* Soc Plastics Engrs; Soc Automotive Engrs. *Res:* Phosgene chemistry; isocyanates, specialty organic chemicals. *Mailing Add:* North Muskegon MI 49445

SHIRN, GEORGE AARON, b Williamsport, Pa, June 30, 21; m 46; c 2. PHYSICS. *Educ:* Columbia Univ, BS, 46; Rensselaer Polytech Inst, MS, 50, PhD(physics), 54. *Prof Exp:* SR SCIENTIST, RES & DEVELOP CTR, SPRAGUE ELEC CO, 54- *Mem:* Am Phys Soc; Electrochem Soc; Am Vacuum Soc. *Res:* Solid state physics; semiconductors; oxides; metals; thin films. *Mailing Add:* Res & Develop Ctr Sprague Elec Co Marshall St North Adams MA 01247

SHISHKEVISH, LEO J, b Leningrad, Russia, Dec 11, 26; US citizen; m 65; c 2. GEOLOGY. *Educ:* City Col New York, BS, 52; NY Univ, MS, 54, PhD, 64. *Prof Exp:* Geologist, Am Mus Natural Hist, 53-54, Mobil Oil Co, 54-61 & Lamont Geol Observ, 63-64; SR GEOLOGIST, GULF RES & DEVELOP CO, 64- *Mem:* Am Asn Petrol Geol. *Res:* Regional geology of West Africa. *Mailing Add:* 12422 Perthshire Houston TX 77024

SHIUE, CHYNG-YANN, b Tainan, Taiwan, Dec 15, 41; m 67; c 2. ORGANIC CHEMISTRY, MEDICINAL CHEMISTRY. *Educ:* Taiwan Normal Univ, BSc, 65; Brown Univ, PhD(chem), 70. *Prof Exp:* Asst org chem, Inst Chem, Acad Sinica, 64-65; res asst, Brown Univ, 66-70; res assoc, Univ Ky, 70-72; res assoc biochem pharmacol, 72-74; instr biochem, Brown Univ, 74-76; sr res assoc, 76-80, ASSOC CHEMIST, BROOKHAVEN NAT LAB, 80- *Mem:* Am Chem Soc. *Res:* Synthesis of radiopharmaceuticals and other biologically active compounds, especially antitumor agents; nuclear medicine. *Mailing Add:* Dept of Chem Brookhaven Nat Lab Upton NY 11973

SHIVANANDAN, KANDIAH, b Parit Buntar, Malaya, Aug 22, 29; US citizen; m 62; c 2. ASTROPHYSICS, COSMOLOGY. *Educ:* Univ Melbourne, BSc, 58; Univ Toronto, MA, 59; Cath Univ Am, PhD(physics), 69. *Prof Exp:* Tech asst, Weapons Res Estab, Melbourne, Australia, 50-57; radiation physicist, Australian Atomic Energy Comn, 57-58; res physicist, Mass Inst Technol, 59-64; PHYSICIST, NAVAL RES LAB, 65- *Concurrent Pos:* Consult mem, Fed Radiation Coun, 60-63 & Int Atomic Energy Asn, Vienna, 60-65; mem, US Nuclear Weapons Study Comt, 63-; adv mem, US Arms Control & Disarmament Agency, 66 & Europ Space Res Orgn, Paris, 68. *Mem:* Am Astron Soc; fel Royal Astron Soc; Europ Phys Soc; NY Acad Sci; Indian Inst Physics. *Res:* Biological effects of radiation from nuclear weapon tests; relativistic astrophysics and experimental infrared astronomy in relation to cosmology; infrared and submillimeter astronomy. *Mailing Add:* 4711 Overbrook Rd Washington DC 20016

SHIVE, DONALD WAYNE, b Hanover, Pa, June 24, 42; m 71. ANALYTICAL CHEMISTRY. *Educ:* Pa State Univ, BS, 64; Mass Inst Technol, PhD(chem), 69. *Prof Exp:* Asst prof, 69-74, assoc prof, 74-78, PROF CHEM, MUHLENBERG COL, 78- *Concurrent Pos:* Consult, J T Baker Chem Co, 79- *Honors & Awards:* Lindback Award, 78. *Mem:* Am Chem Soc. *Res:* Electrochemistry. *Mailing Add:* Dept Chem Muhlenberg Col Allentown PA 18104

SHIVE, JOHN BENJAMINE, JR, b Bennetsville, SC, July 14, 45. PLANT PHYSIOLOGY, BOTANY. *Educ:* Calif State Univ, BA, 68; Univ Md, MS, 72, PhD(plant physiol), 74. *Prof Exp:* Res assoc plant sci, Tex A&M Univ, 75-76; fel biol, Purdue Univ, 76-77; ASST PROF BIOL, WINTHROP COL, 77- *Mem:* Am Soc Plant Physiologists. *Res:* Biophysical mechanisms of gas exchange in plants; mode of action of growth regulators; separation of proteins by two dimensional polyacrylamide gel electrophoresis. *Mailing Add:* Dept of Biol Winthrop Col Rock Hill SC 29733

SHIVE, JOHN NORTHRUP, b Baltimore, Md, Feb 22, 13; m 39; c 3. ELECTRONICS. *Educ:* Rutgers Univ, BS, 34; Johns Hopkins Univ, PhD(physics), 39. *Prof Exp:* Jr instr physics, Johns Hopkins Univ, 37-39; mem tech staff, Bell Tel Labs, Inc, 39-60, dir educ & training, 60-68, mgr sci lects & demonstrations, 68-73; SPEC LECTR PHYSICS, GEORGIAN COURT COL, LAKEWOOD, NJ, 73- *Concurrent Pos:* Spec instr, Univ Rutgers, 45. *Mem:* Sr mem Inst Elec & Electronics Eng; Am Asn Physics Teachers. *Res:* Semiconductors; contact rectification; Geiger-Muller counters; thermoelectric and photoelectric effects; transistors; infrared military systems; engineering education. *Mailing Add:* 1370 W Front St Lincroft NJ 07738

SHIVE, PETER NORTHROP, b Plainfield, NJ, July 2, 41; m 64. GEOPHYSICS. *Educ:* Wesleyan Univ, BA, 64; Stanford Univ, PhD(geophys), 68. *Prof Exp:* Res assoc geophys, Stanford Univ, 68-69; asst prof geol, 69-72, assoc prof geol & physics, 72-76, PROF GEOL & PHYSICS, UNIV WYO, 76- *Mem:* AAAS; Am Geophys Union; Soc Terrestrial Magnetism & Elec; Soc Explor Geophys. *Res:* Rock magnetism; paleomagnetism; time series analysis; exploration seismology. *Mailing Add:* Dept of Geol Univ of Wyo Laramie WY 82070

SHIVE, ROBERT ALLEN, JR, b Dallas, Tex, Oct 27, 42; m 64; c 3. MATHEMATICS. *Educ:* Southern Methodist Univ, BA, 64, MS, 66; Iowa State Univ, PhD(math), 69. *Prof Exp:* Instr math, Iowa State Univ, 67-69; asst prof, 69-74, assoc prof, 74-79, PROF MATH & ASSOC DEAN, MILLSAPS COL, 79-, DIR INFO SYSTS, 81- *Concurrent Pos:* Consult comput; adm intern, Am Coun Educ, 78-79. *Mem:* Am Math Soc; Math Asn Am. *Res:* Integration theory; computers in education. *Mailing Add:* Dept of Math Millsaps Col Jackson MS 39210

SHIVELY, CARL E, b Laurelton, Pa, June 8, 36; m 58; c 3. BACTERIOLOGY. *Educ:* Bloomsburg State Col, BS, 58; Bucknell Univ, MS, 61; St Bonaventure Univ, PhD(biol), 68. *Prof Exp:* Instr bact, Bucknell Univ, 61; asst prof bact & genetics, State Univ NY Col Cortland, 63-65; asst prof bact & genetics, 68-71, assoc prof, 71-77, PROF BACT & BIOCHEM, ALFRED UNIV, 78-, HEAD, DIV BIOL SCI, 77- *Mem:* Am Soc Microbiol; Sigma Xi. *Res:* Biochemistry. *Mailing Add:* Dept of Biol Alfred Univ Alfred NY 14802

SHIVELY, CHARLES DEAN, b Dyersburg, Tenn, Feb 4, 44; m 66; c 2. PHARMACEUTICAL CHEMISTRY. *Educ:* Purdue Univ, BS, 67, PhD(indust & phys pharm), 72. *Prof Exp:* Sr scientist pharm develop, Alcon Labs, Inc, 71-75, prod mkt mgr, 75-76, res sect head, 76-77; MGR PHARM DEVELOP, COOPER LABS, INC, 77- *Concurrent Pos:* Lectr, Calif Bd Pharm Continuing Educ, 77-; adv bd mem, Nat Eye Res Found, 77- *Mem:* Am Pharmaceut Asn; Nat Eye Res Found; Sigma Xi. *Res:* Pharmaceutical dosage form development; pharmaceutical formulation; physical pharmacy; surface chemistry. *Mailing Add:* Cooper Labs Inc 455 E Middlefield Rd Mountain View CA 94043

SHIVELY, FRANK THOMAS, b Cuyahoga Falls, Ohio, Oct 31, 34; m 69. ELEMENTARY PARTICLE PHYSICS, COMPUTATIONAL PHYSICS. *Educ:* Oberlin Col, BA, 54; Yale Univ, MS, 57, PhD(physics), 61. *Prof Exp:* Asst physicist, Physics Dept, Yale Univ, 60-61; res physicist, Ctr Nuclear Studies, France, 61-63; res assoc, Lawrence Radiation Lab, Univ Calif, 63-66; sr researcher, Inst Nuclear Physics, Univ Paris, 66-68; mem staff, Los Alamos Meson Physics Facil, Univ Calif, 69-74; staff scientist & consult, Lawrence Berkeley Lab, Univ Calif, & Univ Calif, Los Angeles, 74-77; CONSULT & SR SCIENTIST, SCI SIMULATION, INC, 78- *Concurrent Pos:* Adj instr, Physics Dept, Univ Calif, Berkeley, 64; vis lectr, Colo Col, 75; dir consult, C/D Sci Consults, 75-78; lectr, Honors Prog, Univ NMex, 76; vis prof physics, Univ Calif, Los Angeles, 77. *Mem:* Am Phys Soc; Sigma Xi. *Res:* Strong, electromagnetic and weak interactions of particles and nuclei; particle beam propagation, radiation transport; atmospheric physics & remote sensing theory; simulation methodology; author or coauthor of over 50 publications. *Mailing Add:* 1094 Governor-Dempsey Dr Santa Fe NM 87501

SHIVELY, JAMES NELSON, b Moran, Kans, Feb 9, 25; m 53; c 3. VETERINARY PATHOLOGY. *Educ:* Kans State Univ, DVM, 46; Johns Hopkins Univ, MPH, 53; Univ Rochester, MS, 56; Colo State Univ, PhD, 71. *Prof Exp:* Officer in charge vet med, Army Med Lab, 46-52; res vet, Agr Res Prog, Univ Tenn, AEC, 54-55; chief vet virol, Div Vet Med, Walter Reed Army Inst Res, 56-60; vet, Res Br, Div Radiol Health, USPHS, 60-62, Radiol Health Lab, Colo, 62-68 & Path Sect, Div Biol Effects, Bur Radiol Health, Md, 68-70; assoc prof vet path, NY State Vet Col, Cornell Univ, 71-75; PROF VET SCI, UNIV ARIZ, 75- *Mem:* Am Vet Med Asn; Electron Micros Soc Am; Int Acad Path; Sigma Xi. *Res:* Pathology; electron microscopy. *Mailing Add:* Dept of Vet Sci Univ of Ariz Tucson AZ 85721

SHIVELY, JESSUP MACLEAN, b Monrovia, Ind, Nov 9, 35; m 59; c 2. BIOCHEMISTRY, MICROBIOLOGY. *Educ:* Purdue Univ, BS, 57, MS, 59, PhD(microbiol), 62. *Prof Exp:* Instr microbiol, Purdue Univ, 61-62; from asst prof to assoc prof, Univ Nebr, Lincoln, 62-70; chmn biochem sect, Biol Div, 70-71, assoc prof, 70-73, PROF BIOCHEM, CLEMSON UNIV, 73-, HEAD DEPT, 71- *Concurrent Pos:* NSF fel, Scripps Inst Oceanog, 65, grants, 65-67; USPHS grants, 66-69; fel, Inst Enzyme Res, Univ Wis-Madison, 68-69, Dept Physiol Chem, Med Sch, Johns Hopkins Univ, 69-70 & Med Div, Oak Ridge Assoc Univs, 71. *Mem:* AAAS; Am Soc Microbiol; Brit Soc Gen Microbiol; Am Soc Biol Chemists. *Res:* Lipids and membranes of bacteria; ribulose diphosphate carboxylase, autotrophic microbes. *Mailing Add:* Dept of Biochem Clemson Univ Clemson SC 29631

SHIVELY, JOHN ADRIAN, b Rossville, Ind, Oct 29, 22; m 45; c 4. PATHOLOGY, HEMATOLOGY. *Educ:* Ind Univ, BA, 44, MD, 46. *Prof Exp:* Lab asst physiol, Ind Univ, 43-44; clin pathologist, Clin Hosp, Bluffton, Ind, 52-54; asst prof path, Sch Med, Ind Univ, 54-57; pathologist, Manatee Mem Hosp, Bradenton, Fla, 57-62; assoc prof path, Col Med, Univ Ky, 62-63; pathologist, Univ Tex M D Anderson Hosp & Tumor Inst, 63-68; prof path, Sch Med, Univ Mo-Columbia, 68-71; chmn dept, 71-76, PROF PATH, UNIV TENN, MEMPHIS, 71-, V CHANCELLOR ACAD AFFAIRS, CTR HEALTH SCI, 76- *Mem:* AAAS; Col Am Pathologists; Am Soc Clin Path; Am Col Physicians. *Res:* Bone marrow failure; platelet physiology; oncology; medical education. *Mailing Add:* Ctr Health Sci Univ of Tenn 62 S Dunlap Memphis TN 38163

SHIVELY, JOHN ERNEST, b Chicago, Ill, Aug 25, 46; m 67; c 2. BIOCHEMISTRY. *Educ:* Univ Ill, Urbana, BS, 68, MS, 69, PhD(biochem), 75. *Prof Exp:* SCIENTIST IMMUNOCHEM, CITY RES INST, 75- *Res:* Microsequence studies on carcinoembryonic antigen and human plasma fibronectin. *Mailing Add:* City Res Inst 1450 E Duarte Rd Duarte CA 91010

SHIVELY, RALPH LELAND, b Mt Morris, Ill, Nov 22, 21; m 50. MATHEMATICS. *Educ:* Univ Mich, BSE, 47, MA, 48, PhD(math), 54. *Prof Exp:* From instr to asst prof math, Western Reserve Univ, 51-55, from asst prof to assoc prof, 56-61; assoc prof, Manchester Col, 55-56; assoc prof, Swarthmore Col, 61-64; sr mathematician, Oak Ridge Nat Lab, 64-65; PROF MATH & CHMN DEPT, LAKE FOREST COL, 65- *Concurrent Pos:* NSF fac fel, Univ Calif, Berkeley, 60-61; vis res fel, Comput Lab, Oxford Univ, 71-72. *Mem:* Am Math Soc; Math Asn Am. *Res:* Special functions of classical analysis. *Mailing Add:* Dept of Math Lake Forest Col Lake Forest IL 60045

SHIVERICK, KATHLEEN THOMAS, b Burlington, Vt, Dec 1, 43; c 1. BIOCHEMICAL PHARMACOLOGY, PHYSIOLOGY. *Educ:* Univ Vt, BS, 65, PhD(physiol), 74. *Prof Exp:* Res asst, Univ Vt, 65-68; fel endocrinol, McGill Univ, 74-76, res assoc pharmacol, 76-78; ASST PROF PHARMACOL, UNIV FLA, 78- *Concurrent Pos:* Fel, Am Lung Asn, 74-76; res assoc, Roche Develop Pharm Unit, McGill Univ, 76-78. *Res:* Endocrine pharmacology. *Mailing Add:* Dept of Pharmacol JHM Health Ctr Box J-267 Gainesville FL 32610

SHIVERS, CHARLES ALEX, b Goodlettsville, Tenn, Sept 16, 32; m 55; c 3. REPRODUCTIVE BIOLOGY, DEVELOPMENTAL BIOLOGY. *Educ:* George Peabody Col, BS, 55, MA, 56; Mich State Univ, PhD(zool), 61. *Prof Exp:* Instr chem, Cumberland Univ, 56-58, res asst develop, Mich State Univ, 59-60; USPHS fel, Fla State Univ, 61-63; from asst prof to assoc prof zool, 63-71, PROF ZOOL, UNIV TENN, KNOXVILLE, 71- *Mem:* AAAS; Am Soc Zoologists. *Res:* Immunochemical studies on fertilization mechanisms. *Mailing Add:* Dept of Zool Univ of Tenn Knoxville TN 37916

SHIVERS, RICHARD RAY, b Salina, Kans, Dec 18, 40; c 2. ZOOLOGY, CELL BIOLOGY. *Educ:* Univ Kans, AB, 63, MA, 65, PhD(zool), 67. *Prof Exp:* Asst prof, 67-77, ASSOC PROF ZOOL, UNIV WESTERN ONT, 77- *Mem:* Am Soc Cell Biol; Am Asn Anat; Can Asn Anat; Soc Neurosci; Pan-Am Asn Anat. *Res:* Electron microscopic anatomy of invertebrate nervous systems, especially that of the crayfish; freeze-fracture of nerve regeneration; neurosecretory portions of the crayfish optic ganglia; reptile blood-brain interface, ultrastructure and freeze-fracture of dystrophic muscle and blood cell membranes; freeze-fracture and ultrastructure of human brain tumor vascular systems. *Mailing Add:* Dept Zool Univ Western Ont London ON N6A 5B8 Can

SHKAROFSKY, ISSIE PETER, b Montreal, Que, July 4, 31; m 57; c 4. PLASMA PHYSICS, MICROWAVE ELECTRONICS. *Educ:* McGill Univ, BSc, 52, MSc, 53, PhD(physics), 57. *Prof Exp:* Res & develop fel, Res & Develop Labs, RCA Ltd, Ste Anne de Bellevue, 57-76; RES & DEVELOP FEL, MPB TECHNOL INC, STE ANNE DE BELLEVUE, 77- *Mem:* Can Asn Physicists; Am Phys Soc; Am Geophys Union. *Res:* Plasma kinetics and waves; fusion; lasers and microwaves; propagation; turbulence; space and ionosphere. *Mailing Add:* 1959 Clinton Ave Montreal PQ H3S 1L2 Can

SHKLAIR, IRVING L, b Montreal, Can, Jan 26, 24; US citizen; m 55; c 3. MICROBIOLOGY. *Educ:* Univ Ill, BS, 48, MS, 49; Mich State Univ, PhD(bact), 52. *Prof Exp:* HEAD MICROBIOL, DENT RES INST, US NAVY TRAINING STA, 52- *Honors & Awards:* US Navy Meritorious Civilian Award, 59. *Mem:* Am Soc Microbiol; Int Asn Dent Res. *Res:* Microorganisms of the oral cavity and their relationship to dental decay and periodontal disease. *Mailing Add:* Dental Res Inst Bldg 1H Naval Base Great Lakes IL 60088

SHKLAR, GERALD, b Montreal, Que, Dec 2, 24; nat US; m 48; c 3. ORAL PATHOLOGY. *Educ:* McGill Univ, BSc, 47, DDS, 49; Tufts Univ, MS, 52; Am Bd Oral Path, dipl; Am Bd Periodont, dipl. *Hon Degrees:* MA, Harvard Univ, 71. *Prof Exp:* Res assoc oral path & periodont, Sch Dent Med, Tufts Univ, 51-52, from instr to assoc prof, 52-60, assoc prof oral path & assoc res prof periodont, 60-61, prof oral path & chmn dept, 61-71; CHARLES A BRACKETT PROF ORAL PATH & CHMN DEPT ORAL MED & ORAL PATH, SCH DENT MED, HARVARD UNIV, 71- *Concurrent Pos:* Nat Res Coun Can dent res fel, 51-52; dir cancer training prog, Sch Dent Med, Tufts Univ, 52-71, prof dent hist, 60-63, lectr social dent, 63-71, lectr oral path, Forsyth Sch Dent Hygienists, 53-71, res prof periodont, 60-71; oral pathologist, Boston City Hosp, 61-; consult, Mass Gen Hosp, Peter Bent Brigham & Women's Hosp & Children's Hosp Med Ctr. *Mem:* Am Dent Asn; Am Acad Oral Path; Am Acad Periodont; fel Int Col Dentists; fel Am Col Dentists. *Res:* Tumors of mouth and jaws; experimental pathology of salivary glands and periodontal tissues; pathology and physiology of bone; experimental carcinogensis; histochemistry of oral diseases; ultrastructure oral tissues; radiation biology. *Mailing Add:* 33 Clinton Rd Brookline MA 02146

SHKLOV, NATHAN, b Winnipeg, Man, Aug 3, 18; m 51; c 1. MATHEMATICS. *Educ:* Univ Man, BA, 40; Univ Toronto, MA, 49. *Prof Exp:* Spec lectr math, Univ Sask, 51-52, from instr to assoc prof, 52-67, chmn comput ctr, 62-67; PROF MATH, UNIV WINDSOR, 67- *Concurrent Pos:* Consult, Defence Res Bd Can, 56-60; ed-in-chief, Can Comput Sci Asn, 66-71. *Mem:* Math Asn Am; Inst Math Statist; Can Math Soc; Statist Soc Can (pres, 72-74). *Res:* Non-associative algebras; statistical design of experiments. *Mailing Add:* Dept of Math Univ of Windsor Windsor ON N9B 3P4 Can

SHLANTA, ALEXIS, b Scranton, Pa, June 17, 37; m 65; c 2. ATMOSPHERIC PHYSICS. *Educ:* Univ Tex, El Paso, BS, 62, MS, 65; NMex Inst Mining & Technol, PhD(atmospheric physics), 72. *Prof Exp:* Res engr space physics & radar, NAm Aviation, Inc, 62-63; instr physics, Buena Vista Col, 66-67; PHYSICIST ATMOSPHERIC PHYSICS, NAVAL WEAPONS CTR, CHINA LAKE, 73- *Concurrent Pos:* Fel, Nat Oceanic & Atmospheric Admin, 72-73. *Mem:* Am Meteorol Soc; Am Geophys Union. *Res:* The determination and quantification of the effects of atmospheric conditions on the performance of tactical weapon systems. *Mailing Add:* Code 3173 Naval Weapons Ctr China Lake CA 93555

SHLEIEN, BERNARD, b New York, NY, Feb 5, 34; m 60; c 2. HEALTH PHYSICS. *Educ:* Univ Southern Calif, PharmD, 57; Harvard Univ, MS, 63; Am Bd Health Physics, dipl, 66. *Prof Exp:* Staff pharmacist, USPHS Hosp, Seattle, 57-59, anal chemist, Med Supply Depot, 59-60; asst to chief radiol intel fallout studies, Robert A Taft Sanit Eng Ctr, Bur Radiol Health, 60-62, chief dosimetry, Northeastern Radiol Health Lab, 63-70, chief environ radiation, 68-70; co-proj officer, Fed Radiation Coun-Nat Acad Sci Risk Eval, Dept Health, Educ & Welfare, 70-72, tech adv, Off Bur Dir, 72-78, ASST DIR SCI AFFAIRS, BUR RADIOL HEALTH, FOOD & DRUG ADMIN, 78- *Concurrent Pos:* Mem Intersoc Comn Ambient Air Sampling, chmn radioactive substances, 66-72; mem temporary staff, Fed Radiation Coun-Environ Protection Agency spec studies group, 70- *Mem:* AAAS; Health Physics Soc; Am Indust Hyg Asn; fel Am Pub Health Asn. *Res:* Radiation hazards; radioactive aerosols; population doses; radiation carcinogenesis, and standards setting; energy planning for radiation accidents. *Mailing Add:* 2421 Homestead Dr Silver Spring MD 20902

SHLOMING, ROBERT, applied statistics, see previous edition

SHMOYS, JERRY, b Warsaw, Poland, Oct 6, 23; US citizen; m 53; c 2. ELECTROPHYSICS. *Educ:* Cooper Union, BEE, 45; NY Univ, PhD(physics), 52. *Prof Exp:* Jr electronic engr, Marine Div, Bendix Aviation Corp, 45; asst proj engr, Res Labs, Sperry Gyroscope Co, 45-46; res asst, Physics Dept, NY Univ, 46-49, math res group, 49-52, res assoc, Inst Math Sci, 52-55; from instr to asst prof elec eng, 55-60, assoc prof electrophys, 60-68, prof electrophysics, 68-80, PROF ELEC ENG, POLYTECH INST NY, 80- *Concurrent Pos:* Mem US Comn B, Int Sci Radio Union, 66-; Nat Acad Sci-Nat Res Coun sr res fel, Ames Res Ctr, NASA, 67-68. *Mem:* Sr mem Inst Elec & Electronics Engrs; Am Phys Soc. *Res:* Diffraction and propagation of electromagnetic waves; antenna theory; plasma research. *Mailing Add:* Polytech Inst of NY Rt 110 Farmingdale NY 11735

SHNEOUR, ELIE ALEXIS, b Paris, France, Dec 11, 25; nat US; m 55; c 2. BIOCHEMISTRY, NEUROSCIENCES. *Educ:* Columbia Univ, BA, 47; Univ Calif, Berkeley, MA, 55, Univ Calif, Los Angeles, PhD(biol chem), 58. *Hon Degrees:* DSc, Bard Col, 68. *Prof Exp:* Asst dir res & develop, J A E Color Works, NY, 48-50; sr res technician, Univ Calif, Berkeley, 50-53, asst biochem, 53-55, asst, Univ Calif, Los Angeles, 55-58; Am Heart Asn res fel, Univ Calif, Berkeley, 58-62; res assoc genetics, Stanford Univ, 62-65; assoc prof molecular & genetic biol, Univ Utah, 65-69; vis res neurochemist, Div Neurosci, City of Hope Nat Med Ctr, Duarte, Calif, 69-71; dir res, Calbiochem, 71-74; PRES, BIOSYST ASSOCS, LTD & DIR RES, BIOSYSTS RES INST, 74- *Concurrent Pos:* Consult, Melpar Inc, 64-65, Gen Elec Co, 65- & NAm Aviation, Inc, 66-70 & other maj US & Foreign Corps, 74-; exec secy biol & explor Mars study group, Nat Acad Sci, 64-65; chmn regional biosci res coun manned earth orbiting missions, Am Inst Biol Sci, 66-; chmn sci adv prog, Am Soc Biol Chemists, 73-, mem sci & pub policy comt, 74-; mem sci adv coun, Cousteau Soc, Inc, 77-; mem bd dir, San Diego Biomed Inst, 81-; chmn, Sci Adv Bd, Quadroma, Inc, 81- *Mem:* Am Chem Soc; Int Soc Neurochem; NY Acad Sci; Am Soc Biol Chemists; Soc Neurosci. *Res:* Chemistry and intermediary metabolism of lipids and carotenoids; biopeosis; developmental neurochemistry; information processing by biological systems. *Mailing Add:* Biosysts Res Inst Biosysts Res Inst PO Box 1414 La Jolla CA 92038

SHNIDER, BRUCE I, b Ludzk, Poland, Jan 20, 20; nat US; m 42; c 3. INTERNAL MEDICINE, ONCOLOGY. *Educ:* Wilson Teachers Col, BS, 41; Georgetown Univ, MD, 48; Am Bd Internal Med, dipl, 55. *Prof Exp:* Intern, DC Gen Hosp, 48-49, from jr asst resident to chief resident, Georgetown Univ Hosp, 49-52, from instr to assoc prof med, 52-66, from asst prof to assoc prof pharmacol, 61-66, cancer coordr, 60-66, from asst dean to assoc dean, 61-79, prog dir clin cancer training, 70-75, dir, Breast Cancer Detection Demonstration Prog, 76-79, PROF MED & PHARMACOL, SCH MED, GEORGETOWN UNIV, 66- *Concurrent Pos:* Dir Tumor serv & cancer chemother res prog, Georgetown Univ Med Div, DC Gen Hosp, 57-, chief vis physician, 57-59, exec officer, 59-60, coord teaching activ, 61-; prin investr, East Coop Group Solid Tumor Chemother, 57-, chmn, 61-71; dir div oncol, Dept Med, Georgetown Univ, 61-80; consult, oncol clin & vis physician, Georgetown Univ Med Ctr, Holy Cross Hosp, Wash Hosp Ctr & Mt Alto Vet Hosp; consult, Clin Ctr, NIH; vis prof oncol, Sch Med, Tel Aviv Univ, 72-73 & Sch Med, Hebrew Univ, 79-80. *Mem:* Soc Internal Med; Am Soc Clin Oncol; fel Col Clin Pharmacol & Chemother; Am Asn Cancer Res; fel Am Col Physicians. *Res:* Medical oncology; clinical pharmacology; chemotherapy of cancer. *Mailing Add:* 610 Sisson St Silver Spring MD 20902

SHNIDER, RUTH WOLKOW, b Louisville, Ky, June 15, 15; m 47. APPLIED MATHEMATICS, PHYSICS. *Educ:* Wellesley Col, AB, 34; Univ Chicago, SM, 37. *Prof Exp:* Instr electronics, Univ Chicago, 42-43; instr physics, Ind Univ, 43-44; electronics engr, US Naval Res Lab, 44-52, from nuclear physicist to res physicist, US Naval Radiol Defense Lab, 52-69; prin res physicist & sr systs analyst, URS Res Co, San Mateo, Calif, 69-76; sr analyst, Ctr Planning & Res Inc, Palo Alto, Calif, 76-80; CONSULT, 80- *Mem:* AAAS; Oper Res Soc Am. *Res:* Correlation of experimental and theoretical analysis of nuclear weapons to provide predictive estimates of effects of nuclear bursts; development of procedures and criteria for evaluation of the efficiency of environmental monitoring networks. *Mailing Add:* 2745 Summit Dr Burlingame CA 94010

SHNIDER, SOL M, b Yorkton, Sask, June 13, 29; US citizen. MEDICINE. *Educ:* Univ Man, BSc & MD, 53; Am Bd Anesthesiol, dipl. *Prof Exp:* Intern, Winnipeg Gen Hosp, Man, 52-53; gen pract, Sask, 53-57; resident, Presby Hosp, New York, 57-59; instr anesthesiol, Col Physicians & Surgeons, Columbia Univ, 59, assoc, 60-62; from asst prof to assoc prof, 62-72, PROF ANESTHESIA, OBSTET & GYNEC, SCH MED, UNIV CALIF, SAN FRANCISCO, 72-, VCHMN DEPT ANESTHESIA, 73- *Concurrent Pos:* Mem, World Fedn Socs Anesthesiol; asst anesthesiologist, Presby Hosp, New York, 59-62. *Mem:* AMA; Am Soc Anesthesiol; fel Am Col Anesthesiol; Pan-Am Med Asn. *Res:* Obstetrical anesthesia; impact of maternal anesthesia on fetus and newborn. *Mailing Add:* Dept of Anesthesia Univ of Calif Med Ctr San Francisco CA 94143

SHNITKA, THEODOR KHYAM, b Calgary, Alta, Nov 21, 27. PATHOLOGY, CELL BIOLOGY. *Educ:* Univ Alta, BSc, 48, MSc, 52, MD, 53; Royal Col Physicians & Surgeons Can, cert path, 58; FRCP(C), 72. *Prof Exp:* From instr to assoc prof, 54-67, PROF PATH, UNIV ALTA, 67-, DIR ELECTRON MICROS UNIT, DEPT PATH, 68-, CHMN FAC MED, 80- *Concurrent Pos:* Jr intern, Univ Alta Hosp, 53-54, from asst resident to resident path, 54-59; fel, Sch Med, Johns Hopkins Univ, 59-60; Can Cancer Soc McEachern Mem fel, 59-60. *Mem:* Electron Micros Soc Am; Histochem Soc; Am Soc Cell Biol; Am Soc Exp Path; Int Acad Path. *Res:* Experimental and molecular pathology, utilizing techniques of enzyme cytochemistry and electron microscopy; cell structure and function; diagnostic electron microscopy. *Mailing Add:* Dept of Path Prov Lab Univ of Alta Edmonton AB T6G 2J2 Can

SHOAF, CHARLES JEFFERSON, b Roanoke, Va, July 22, 30; m 58; c 2. TEXTILE CHEMISTRY. *Educ:* Va Mil Inst, BS, 52; Purdue Univ, MS, 54, PhD(chem), 57; Del Law Sch, JD, 80. *Prof Exp:* Res chemist, E I du Pont de Nemours & Co, 57; instr chem, US Air Force Inst Technol, 57-59, asst prof, 59; res chemist, 59-63, patent chemist, 63-69, sr patent chemist, 69-74, patent agent, 74-80, PATENT ATTY, LEGAL DEPT, E I DU PONT DE NEMOURS & CO, INC, 80- *Mem:* Am Chem Soc. *Res:* Synthetic textile fibers. *Mailing Add:* E I du Pont de Nemours & Co Inc Legal Dept Wilmington DE 19898

SHOAF, MARY LA SALLE, b Milwaukee, Wis, Feb 29, 32; m 58; c 2. PHYSICAL CHEMISTRY. *Educ:* Cardinal Stritch Col, BA, 53; Univ Calif, MS, 55; Purdue Univ, PhD(phys chem), 60. *Prof Exp:* Phys chemist, US Dept Air Force, 58-59; assoc prof, ECarolina Univ, 61-63; mem sci fac, Tatnall Sch, Del, 64-66; from assoc prof to prof physics, West Chester State Col, 66-75, dean grad studies, 75-77; ASST DIR, PRINCETON PLASMA PHYSICS LAB, 78- *Concurrent Pos:* Consult, Am Phys Soc, 73- *Mem:* Fel Am Inst Chemists; Am Chem Soc; Am Phys Soc (dep exec secy, 73-78); AAAS. *Res:* Ion-induced fission reactions; determination of thermodynamic data for transition ions; technical management. *Mailing Add:* 1113 Independence Dr West Chester PA 19380

SHOBE, L(OUIS) RAYMON, b Waverly, Kans, Apr 22, 13; m 36; c 3. MATHEMATICS, ENGINEERING MECHANICS. *Educ:* Emporia State Univ, BS, 36; Kans State Univ, MS, 40. *Prof Exp:* Lab asst physics, Emporia State Univ, 35-36; teacher high schs, Kans, 36-38; instr math, Kans State Univ, 38-40 & Univ Kans, 40-41; instr math & mech, Gen Motors Inst, 41-46; assoc prof math, Bemidji State Teachers Col, 46-47; assoc prof math, 47-56, prof, 57-78, EMER PROF ENG MECH, UNIV TENN, KNOXVILLE, 78- *Concurrent Pos:* Consult, Oak Ridge Nat Lab, 59- *Mem:* Fel Am Soc Civil Engrs; Nat Soc Prof Engrs; Am Soc Eng Educ; Am Acad Mech. *Res:* Solid mechanics; stress analysis. *Mailing Add:* 1432 Tugaloo Dr Knoxville TN 37919

SHOBER, ROBERT ANTHONY, b St Louis, Mo, Oct 18, 48; m 76. COMPUTER SIMULATION, NUMERICAL ANALYSIS. *Educ:* Univ Fla, BSNES, 70, MS, 72; Mass Inst Technol, PhD(nuclear eng), 76. *Prof Exp:* Engr safety physics, Combustion Eng, Inc, 72-74; nuclear engr methods develop, Agronne Nat Lab, 76-79; MEM TECH STAFF, BELL LABS, 79- *Concurrent Pos:* Consult, Nat Eval Systs, Inc, 76; mem comput benchmarks probs comt, Am Nuclear Soc, 77- *Mem:* Am Nuclear Soc. *Res:* computer simulation methods; numerical methods for multidimensional diffusion problems; efficient numerical calculation. *Mailing Add:* Crawfords Corner Rd Bell Labs Holmdel NJ 07733

SHOCH, DAVID EUGENE, b Warsaw, Poland, June 10, 18; nat US; m 45; c 2. OPHTHALMOLOGY. *Educ:* City Col New York, BS, 38; Northwestern Univ, MS, 39, PhD(biochem), 43, BM, 45, MD, 46. *Prof Exp:* Intern, Cook County Hosp, 45-46; res fel, Med Sch, Northwestern Univ, 48-50; resident ophthal, Cook County Hosp, 50-52; clin asst, 52-56, assoc, 56-60, asst prof, 60-66, PROF OPHTHAL & CHMN DEPT, MED SCH, NORTHWESTERN UNIV, CHICAGO, 66- *Concurrent Pos:* Mem, Am Bd Ophthal, 69-80. *Mem:* AMA; Asn Res Vision & Ophthal; Am Col Surgeons; Am Acad Ophthal (pres,81); Am Ophthal Soc. *Res:* Biochemistry and diseases of the crystalline lens. *Mailing Add:* 1070 Hohfelder Rd Glencoe IL 60022

SHOCH, JOHN F, b Evanston, Ill. COMPUTER COMMUNICATIONS, DISTRIBUTED SYSTEMS. *Educ:* Stanford Univ, BA, 71, MS, 77, PhD(comput sci), 79. *Prof Exp:* Mem res staff, Xerox Palo Res Ctr, 71-80, EXEC ASST TO PRES & DIR, CORP POLICY COMT, XEROX CORP, 80- *Concurrent Pos:* Vis fac mem, Comput Sci Dept, Stanford Univ, 78; mem, Tech Adv Comt, US House Representatives, 81. *Mem:* Asn Comput Mach; Inst Elec & Electronics Engrs; Int Fedn Info Processing. *Res:* Computer communication and distributed systems; local computer networks; internetwork communication; packet radio; protocol design; programs which span machine boundaries. *Mailing Add:* Xerox Palo Alto Res Ctr 3333 Coyote Hill Rd Palo Alto CA 94304

SHOCHET, MELVYN JAY, b Philadelphia, Pa, Oct 31, 44; m 67; c 2. ELEMENTARY PARTICLE PHYSICS. *Educ:* Univ Pa, BA, 66; Princeton Univ, MA & PhD(physics), 72. *Prof Exp:* Res assoc, Enrico Fermi Inst, 72-73, instr, 73-75, asst prof, 75-78, PROF PHYSICS, UNIV CHICAGO, 79- *Mem:* Am Phys Soc; AAAS. *Res:* Experimental elementary particle physics. *Mailing Add:* Univ of Chicago 5630 S Ellis Ave Chicago IL 60637

SHOCK, D'ARCY ADRIANCE, b Fowler, Colo, June 13, 11; m 55; c 4. PHYSICAL CHEMISTRY. *Educ:* Colo Col, BS, 33; Univ Tex, MA, 46. *Prof Exp:* Chemist, Dow Chem Co, Mich, 33-36 & McGean Chem Co, 36-42; chief chemist, Int Minerals & Chem Corp, 42-44; instr chem, Univ Tex, 44-45; field correlator, Nat Gas Asn, 46-47, res scientist, 47-49; sr res chemist, Prod Res Lab, Continental Oil Co, 49-51, res group leader chem & metal sect, Prod Res Div, 51-56, mgr, Cent Res Div, 56-75, mgr, Mining Res Div, 75-78; CONSULT SOLUTION MINING & SLURRY TRANSPORT, 78- *Mem:* Am Chem Soc; Nat Asn Corrosion Eng; Am Inst Mining, Metall & Petrol Eng. *Res:* Corrosion of iron and steel in oil production and processing; anodic passivation; manufacture, transportation and storage of cryogenic gases; hydraulic fracturing technology; solution mining; waste disposal; solids pipelining; mining and milling of uranium and copper ores; coal mining research. *Mailing Add:* 233 Virginia Ponca City OK 74601

SHOCK, NATHAN WETHERILL, b Lafayette, Ind, Dec 25, 06; m 28; c 2. PHYSIOLOGY, PSYCHOLOGY. *Educ:* Purdue Univ, BS, 26, MS, 27, Univ Chicago, PhD(psychol), 30. *Hon Degrees:* DSc(geront), Purdue Univ, 54; LHD, Johns Hopkins Univ, 81. *Prof Exp:* Res assoc med, Univ Chicago, 30-31, res assoc pediat, 31-32; asst prof physiol, Sch Med & res assoc, Inst Child Welfare, Univ Calif, 32-41; chief, 41-76, EMER SCIENTIST, GERONT RES CTR, NAT INST AGING, 77- PHYSIOLOGIST, BALTIMORE CITY HOSPS, 41- *Concurrent Pos:* Ed, Macy Conf Aging, 50-54; asst ed, J Geront, 57-61, ed-in-chief, 63-69; mem, Md Comn Aging, 67-75. *Honors & Awards:* Geront Res Found Award, 56; Super Serv Award, Dept Health, Educ & Welfare, 65; Willard O Thompson Award, Am Geriat Soc, 65; Distinguished Serv to Res Award, Am Heart Asn, 65; First Annual Res Award, Geront Soc, 65. *Mem:* AAAS (chmn sect med sci, 59); fel Am Physiol Soc; fel Geront Soc (secy, 51-58, pres, 60); Am Geriat Soc; fel Am Psychol Asn. *Res:* Physiology of aging; cardiovascular physiology; physiology of exercise; renal physiology. *Mailing Add:* 6505 Maplewood Rd Baltimore MD 21212

SHOCK, ROBERT CHARLES, b Dayton, Ohio, July 18, 40; m 64; c 2. ALGEBRA, OPERATIONS RESEARCH. *Educ:* Bowling Green State Univ, BS, 62; Univ Ariz, MA, 64; Univ NC, Chapel Hill, PhD(math), 68. *Prof Exp:* From asst prof to assoc prof math, Southern Ill Univ, 68-78; PROF MATH & CHAIRPERSON DEPT, EAST CAROLINA UNIV, 78- *Mem:* Am Math Soc. *Res:* Non-commutative ring theory; linear programming. *Mailing Add:* Dept of Math East Carolina Univ Greenville NC 27834

SHOCKEY, DONALD ALBERT, b New Kensington, Pa, July 26, 41; m 68; c 1. MATERIALS SCIENCE. *Educ:* Grove City Col, BS, 63; Carnegie Inst Technol, MS, 65; Carnegie-Mellon Univ, PhD(metall, mat sci), 68. *Prof Exp:* Scientist, Ernst-Mach Inst Freiburg, Ger, 68-71; PHYSICIST, STANFORD RES INST, 71- *Res:* Fracture behavior of materials; fracture mechanics; response of materials to high rate loading; effects of environment, radiation, and microstructure on plasticity and fracture. *Mailing Add:* 467 Claremont Way Menlo Park CA 94025

SHOCKLEY, DOLORES COOPER, b Clarksdale, Miss, Apr 21, 30; m 57; c 4. PHARMACOLOGY. *Educ:* La State Univ, BS, 51; Purdue Univ, MS, 53, PhD(pharmacol), 55. *Prof Exp:* Asst pharmacol, Purdue Univ, 51-53; asst prof, 55-67, ASSOC PROF PHARMACOL, MEHARRY MED COL, 67- *Concurrent Pos:* Fulbright fel, Copenhagen Univ, 55-56; vis asst prof, Albert Einstein Col Med, 59-62; Lederle fac award, 63-66. *Mem:* AAAS; Am Pharmaceut Asn. *Res:* Measurement of non-narcotic analgesics; effect of drugs on stress conditions; effect of hormones on connective tissues; nutrition effects and drug action. *Mailing Add:* Dept of Pharmacol Meharry Med Col Nashville TN 37208

SHOCKLEY, G(ILBERT) R, b Mo, Sept 20, 19; m 43; c 2. CHEMICAL ENGINEERING. *Educ:* Univ Mo, BS, 42. *Hon Degrees:* CE, Univ Mo, 60, DE, 70. *Prof Exp:* Design chem engr, Monsanto Chem Co, 42-46; design & supvry engr, Wood Res Inst, 46-47; design chem engr, Goslin Birmingham Mfg Co, 47-49; asst mgr, Filter Div, Eimco Corp, 49-53; vpres, Metals Div, Olin Mathieson Chem Corp, 53-61; gen dir, Prod Develop Div, 61-74, GEN MGR OPERS SERV, MILL PROD DIV, REYNOLDS METALS CO, 74-, EXEC VPRES, REYNOLDS RES CORP, 66- *Mem:* NY Acad Sci; Am Chem Soc; Am Inst Chem Engrs; Am Soc Metals; Soc Automotive Engrs. *Mailing Add:* 207 Nottingham Rd Richmond VA 23221

SHOCKLEY, JAMES EDGAR, b Richmond, Va, Dec 26, 31; div; c 3. MATHEMATICS. *Educ:* Univ NC, AB, 57, AM, 59, PhD(math), 62. *Prof Exp:* Asst prof math, Col William & Mary, 61-64; assoc prof, Univ Wyo, 64-66; ASSOC PROF MATH, VA POLYTECH INST & STATE UNIV, 66- *Mem:* Am Math Soc; Math Asn Am. *Res:* Elementary number theory. *Mailing Add:* Dept of Math Va Polytech Inst & State Univ Blacksburg VA 24061

SHOCKLEY, THOMAS D(EWEY), JR, b Haynesville, La, Nov 2, 23; m 47; c 2. ELECTRICAL ENGINEERING. *Educ:* La State Univ, BS, 50, MS, 52; Ga Inst Technol, PhD(elec eng), 63. *Prof Exp:* Instr eng, La State Univ, 50-53; aerophys eng, Gen Dynamics/Ft Worth, 53-56; res engr, Ga Inst Technol, 56-58, asst prof elec eng, 58-63; assoc prof, Univ Ala, 63-64; prof, Univ Okla, 64-67; chmn dept, Memphis State Univ, 67-78; PRES, SSC, INC, 78- *Mem:* Inst Elec & Electronics Engrs; Am Soc Eng Educ; Nat Fire Protection Asn; Nat Soc Prof Engrs. *Res:* Microwave and antenna systems; computer systems. *Mailing Add:* 1526 Poplar Estates Pkwy Germantown TN 38138

SHOCKLEY, THOMAS E, b Rock Island, Tenn, Mar 15, 29; m 57; c 4. BACTERIOLOGY. *Educ:* Fisk Univ, BA, 49; Ohio State Univ, MSc, 52, PhD, 54. *Prof Exp:* Asst, Ohio State Univ, 50-52; asst prof, Meharry Med Col, 54-59; Rockefeller Found fel, 59-60; Am Cancer scholar, 60-61; assoc prof, 62-67, vchmn dept, 67-71, PROF MICROBIOL, MEHARRY MED COL, 67-, CHMN DEPT, 71- *Concurrent Pos:* Vis investr, Rockefeller Univ, 59-61. *Mem:* Am Soc Microbiol. *Res:* Microbial physiology and genetics; molecular biology; medical microbiology. *Mailing Add:* 4141 W Hamilton Rd Nashville TN 37218

SHOCKLEY, W(OODLAND) G(RAY), b Crisfield, Md, June 3, 14; m 39; c 2. CIVIL ENGINEERING, SOIL MECHANICS. *Educ:* Antioch Col, BS, 36. *Prof Exp:* Engr, Soils & Pavements Sect, Little Rock Dist, US Corps Engrs, 38-46, chief, Bituminous Sect, US Army Engrs, Waterways Exp Sta, 46-47, asst chief, Embankment & Found Br, 47-52, asst chief, Flexible Pavement Br, 52-53, chief, Embankment & Found Br, 53-58, asst chief, Soils Div, 58-63, chief, Mobility & Environ Systs Lab, 63-78, prog mgr mil eng, 78-80; CONSULT ENGR, 80- *Concurrent Pos:* Mem task group tech panel adv comt, Dept Housing & Urban Develop. *Honors & Awards:* Meritorious Civilian Serv Award, Dept Army. *Mem:* Am Soc Civil Engrs; Nat Soc Prof Engrs; Am Soc Testing & Mat. *Res:* Mobility research. *Mailing Add:* 326 Lake Hill Dr Vicksburg MS 39180

SHOCKLEY, WILLIAM, b London, Eng, Feb 13, 10; US citizen; m 33, 55; c 3. PHYSICS. *Educ:* Calif Inst Technol, BSc, 32; Mass Inst Technol, PhD(physics), 36. *Hon Degrees:* ScD, Univ Pa, 54, Rutgers Univ, 56. *Prof Exp:* Mem tech staff, Bell Tel Labs, 36-42; dir res antisubmarine warfare opers res group, Div War Res, Columbia Univ, 42-44; expert consult, Off Secy War, 44-45; res physicist, Bell Tel Labs, 45-54 & Beckman Instruments, Inc, 55-58; pres, Shockley Transistor Corp, 58-60, dir Shockley Transistor, Clevite Transistor Div, Clevite Corp, Calif, 60-63; Alexander M Poniatoff Prof eng sci, 63-74, EMER PROF ELEC ENG, STANFORD UNIV, 74- *Concurrent Pos:* Lectr, Princeton Univ, 46; mem sci adv panel, US Army, 51-; vis prof, Calif Inst Technol, 54; dep dir & dir res, Weapons Syst Eval Group, US Dept Defense, 54-55; exec consult, Bell Tel Labs, NJ, 63-75. *Honors & Awards:* Nobel Prize in Physics, 56; Liebmann Prize, Inst Elec & Electronics Eng, 52; Buckley Prize, Am Phys Soc, 53; Comstock Prize, Nat Acad Sci, 54; Holley Medal, Am Soc Mech Eng, 63. *Mem:* Nat Acad Sci; fel Am Phys Soc; fel Am Acad Arts & Sci; fel Inst Elec & Electronics Eng. *Res:* Ferromagnetic domains; semiconductors; plastic properties of metals; theory of solids; semiconductor amplifiers or transistors; mental tools for scientific thinking; operations research on human quality statistics. *Mailing Add:* 202 McCullough Stanford Univ Stanford CA 94305

SHOCKMAN, GERALD DAVID, b Mt Clemens, Mich, Dec 22, 25; m 49; c 3. MICROBIOLOGY, BIOCHEMISTRY. *Educ:* Cornell Univ, BS, 46; Rutgers Univ, PhD(microbiol), 50. *Prof Exp:* Res assoc, Pepper Labs, Hosp Univ Pa, 50-51; res assoc, Inst Cancer Res, Pa, 52-60; assoc prof, 60-66, PROF MICROBIOL, SCH MED, TEMPLE UNIV, 66-, CHAIRPERSON DEPT MICROBIOL & IMMUNOL, 74- *Concurrent Pos:* Res fel gen biochem, Inst Cancer Res, Pa, 51-52; Am Cancer Soc-Brit Empire Cancer Campaign exchange fel, 54-55; NIH res career develop award, 65-70; vis scientist, Lab Enzymol, Nat Ctr Sci Res, Gif-sur-Yvette, France, 68-69; prof, Univ Liege, 71-72. *Mem:* Am Soc Microbiol; Am Acad Microbiol; Am Soc Biol Chemists; Brit Soc Gen Microbiol. *Res:* Microbial growth; amino acid metabolism; bacterial cell walls and cell membranes; antibiotics and mode of action of antibiotics; cellular physiology. *Mailing Add:* Dept of Microbiol & Immunol Temple Univ Sch of Med Philadelphia PA 19140

SHODELL, MICHAEL J, b New York, NY, Mar 9, 41; m 68; c 2. CELL BIOLOGY. *Educ:* NY State Univ Stony Brook, BS, 62; Univ Calif, Berkeley, PhD(molecular biol), 68. *Prof Exp:* Vis prof tissue cult, Ctr Invest Polytechnic, Mex, 68; Damon Runyon fel cancer res, Imp Cancer Res Fund, London, 69, Am Cancer Soc fel, 69-71, head, Dept Cell Proliferation Studies, 71-75; asst prof, 75-80, PROF BIOL, C W POST COL, 80- *Res:* Regulation of growth in normal and neoplastic cells. *Mailing Add:* 13 Covert Port Washington NY 11050

SHOEMAKER, CARLYLE EDWARD, b Columbus, Ohio, Feb 19, 23; m 48; c 3. INORGAINC CHEMISTRY. *Educ:* Ohio State Univ BChE, 43; Univ Ill, MS, 46, PhD(inorg chem), 49. *Prof Exp:* Asst smoke munitions res, Univ Ill, 44-45, asst anal rubber res, 45-46 & asst inorg chem, 46-49; res chemist atomic energy, Monsanto Chem Co, 49-54; from sr res & develop chemist to group leader inorg & chem eng develop, J T Baker Chem Co, 54-60; mem tech staff, Bell Tel Labs, Inc, 60-64; res engr, Bethlehem Steel Corp, 64-72, sr res engr, 72-77; PROJ MGR, ELEC POWER RES INST, 78- *Mem:* Nat Asn Corrosion Engrs; Am Chem Soc; Am Soc Metals. *Res:* Analytical and preparative inorganic chemistry; surface chemistry of metals; corrosion. *Mailing Add:* Elec Power Res Inst PO Box 10412 Palo Alto CA 94303

SHOEMAKER, CHRISTINE ANNETTE, b Berkeley, Calif, July 2, 44. PEST MANAGEMENT MODELING, WATER QUALITY MODELING. *Educ:* Univ Calif, BS, 66; Univ Southern Calif, MS, 69, PhD(math), 71. *Prof Exp:* Vis asst syst ecologist entom, Univ Calif, Berkeley, 76-77; asst prof, 72-79, ASSOC PROF ENVIRON ENG, CORNELL UNIV, 79- *Concurrent Pos:* Panel mem, Study Pest Control, Nat Acad Sci, 72-73; co-organizer, Conf Resource Mgt, NATO, Parma, Italy, 78. *Mem:* Operations Res Soc Am; Entom Soc Am; Am Geophys Union; Biometric Soc; Entom Soc Can. *Res:* Application of operations research techniques to environmental problems, especially pesticide use and water quality management; mathematical modeling of pest management, ecosystems, nitrogen pollution of groundwater and sewage networks; optimization techniques and statistical analysis of environmental data. *Mailing Add:* Dept Environ Eng Cornell Univ Ithaca NY 14853

SHOEMAKER, CLARA BRINK, b Rolde, Netherlands, June 20, 21; US citizen; m 55; c 1. CRYSTALLOGRAPHY. *Educ:* State Univ Leiden, Doctoraal, 46, PhD(chem), 50. *Prof Exp:* Instr inorg chem, State Univ Leiden, 46-53; res assoc, Mass Inst Technol, 53-55; res assoc biochem lab, Harvard Med Sch, 55-56 & Mass Inst Technol, 58-70; res assoc chem, 70-75, RES ASSOC PROF CHEM, ORE STATE UNIV, 75- *Concurrent Pos:* Int Fedn Univ Women fel, Oxford Univ, 50-51; proj supvr chem, Boston Univ, 63-64; mem comn struct reports, Int Union Crystallog, 70-; mem crystallographic data comt, Am Crystallog Asn, 75-77. *Mem:* Am Crystallog Asn. *Res:* X-ray crystallography; crystal structures of metals and alloys. *Mailing Add:* Dept of Chem Ore State Univ Corvallis OR 97331

SHOEMAKER, DAVID POWELL, b Kooskia, Idaho, May 12, 20; m 55; c 1. SOLID STATE CHEMISTRY, STRUCTURAL CHEMISTRY. *Educ:* Reed Col, BA, 42; Calif Inst Technol, PhD(chem), 47. *Prof Exp:* Nat Defense Res Comt projs, Calif Inst Technol, 43-46, sr res fel, 48-51; Guggenheim fel, Inst Theoret Physics, Copenhagen, Denmark, 47-48; from asst prof to prof chem, Mass Inst Technol, 51-70; chmn dept chem, 70-80, PROF DEPT CHEM, ORE STATE UNIV, 70- *Concurrent Pos:* Consult res labs, Exxon Co USA, 57-; co-ed, Acta Crystallographica, Int Union Crystallog, 64-69 & mem exec comt, 62-68; chmn, US Nat Comt Crystallog, 67-69; vis scientist, Nat Ctr Sci Res, Grenoble, France, 67 & 78-79; mem vis comt, Chem Dept, Brookhaven Nat Lab, 74-79, chmn, 79; mem eval panel, Div Mat Sci, Nat Bur Standards, 78-80. *Mem:* AAAS; Am Acad Arts & Sci; Am Chem Soc; Am Phys Soc; Am Crystallog Asn (pres, 70). *Res:* Chemical crystallography; x-ray diffraction; metals and alloys; zeolites and catalytic materials. *Mailing Add:* Dept Chem Ore State Univ Corvallis OR 97331

SHOEMAKER, EDWARD MILTON, b Wilkinsburg, Pa, Jan 5, 29; m 70. APPLIED MATHEMATICS. *Educ:* Carnegie Inst Technol, MS, 51, PhD(math), 55. *Prof Exp:* Res engr, Chance Vought Aircraft, Inc, 55-56; res mathematician, Boeing Airplane Co, 56-60; assoc prof theoret & appl mech, Univ Ill, Urbana, 60-65; PROF MATH, SIMON FRASER UNIV, 65- *Concurrent Pos:* Consult, Sandia Labs, 62-70. *Mem:* Am Geophys Union; Int Soc Glaciol. *Res:* Glaciology; tectonophysics; solid mechanics. *Mailing Add:* Dept of Math Simon Fraser Univ Burnaby BC V5A 1S6 Can

SHOEMAKER, EUGENE MERLE, b Los Angeles, Calif, Apr 28, 28; m 51; c 3. GEOLOGY. *Educ:* Calif Inst Technol, BS, 47, MS, 48; Princeton Univ, MS, 54, PhD, 60. *Hon Degrees:* DSc, Ariz State Col, 65 & Temple Univ, 67. *Prof Exp:* Chief br astrogeol, US Geol Surv, 61-65, chief scientist, Ctr Astrogeol, 66-68; chmn div geol & planetary sci, 69-72, PROF GEOL, CALIF INST TECHNOL, 69-; GEOLOGIST, US GEOL SURV, 48- *Concurrent Pos:* Co-investr, TV Exp, Proj Ranger, 61-65, prin investr, Proj Surveyor, 63-68; vis prof, Calif Inst Technol, 62, res assoc, 64-68; actg dir manned space sci div, NASA, 63; prin investr field geol exp, Proj Apollo, 66-70. *Honors & Awards:* Wetherill Medal, Franklin Inst, 65; Arthur S Fleming Award, 66. *Mem:* Nat Acad Sci; Mineral Soc Am; Soc Econ Geol; Geochem Soc; Am Asn Petrol Geol. *Res:* Geology of the Colorado Plateau; meteorite impact and nuclear explosion craters; geology of the moon; paleomagnetism; planet-crossing asteroids; origin of the earth. *Mailing Add:* US Geol Survey 2255 N Gemini Dr Flagstaff AZ 86001

SHOEMAKER, FRANK CRAWFORD, b Ogden, Utah, Mar 26, 22; m 44; c 2. EXPERIMENTAL HIGH ENERGY PHYSICS. *Educ:* Whitman Col, AB, 43; Univ Wis, PhD(physics), 49. *Hon Degrees:* DSc, Whitman Col, 78. *Prof Exp:* Mem staff radiation lab, Mass Inst Technol, 43-45; asst, Univ Wis, 46-49, instr physics, 49-50; MEM FAC, PRINCETON UNIV, 50-, PROF PHYSICS, 62- *Concurrent Pos:* Vis scientist, Rutherford High Energy Lab, Eng, 65-66; head main ring sect, Nat Accelerator Lab, 68-69. *Mem:* Fel Am Phys Soc. *Res:* High energy accelerator design and construction; elementary particle physics. *Mailing Add:* 361 Walnut Lane Princeton NJ 08540

SHOEMAKER, GRADUS LAWRENCE, b Zeeland, Mich, Jan 18, 21; m 52; c 2. ORGANIC CHEMISTRY. *Educ:* Hope Col, AB, 44; Univ Ill, MS, 47, PhD(org chem), 49. *Prof Exp:* Asst org chem, Univ Ill, 46-47; res fel, Rutgers Univ, 49; from asst prof to assoc prof chem, 49-65, actg chmn dept, 63-64, chmn, 65-67 & 67-80, PROF CHEM, UNIV LOUISVILLE, 65- *Mem:* AAAS; Am Chem Soc. *Res:* Reactions of nitroparaffins; preparation and reactions of nitro Mannich bases; synthesis of alkylboranes and alkylboronic acids. *Mailing Add:* Dept Chem Univ of Louisville Louisville KY 40292

SHOEMAKER, JOHN DANIEL, JR, b Lawton, Okla, May 9, 39; m 72. CHEMISTRY. *Educ:* Univ Okla, BS, 60, MS, 62; Univ Kans, PhD(org chem), 67; La State Univ, Baton Rouge, MBA, 72. *Prof Exp:* Chemist, Esso Res Labs, Humble Oil & Ref Co, La, 66-70; chemist, Union Camp Corp, 72-78; res assoc, 78-80, SR RES ASSOC, ERLING RIIS LAB, INT PAPER CO, 80- *Mem:* AAAS; Tech Asn Pulp & Paper Indust; Am Chem Soc. *Res:* Chemistry of pulp bleaching; preparation of petroleum refining catalysts; Kraft pulping process; wood chemistry. *Mailing Add:* Int Paper Co Box 2787 Mobile AL 36601

SHOEMAKER, JON PHILIP, zoology, parasitology, see previous edition

SHOEMAKER, RICHARD LEE, b Grand Rapids, Mich, Dec 31, 44; m 68; c 3. CHEMICAL PHYSICS, QUANTUM OPTICS. *Educ:* Calvin Col, BS, 66; Univ Ill, PhD(phys chem), 71. *Prof Exp:* Vis scientist molecular physics, IBM Res Div, San Jose Calif, 71-72; from asst prof to assoc prof, 72-81, PROF OPTICAL SCI, OPTICAL SCI CTR, UNIV ARIZ, 81- *Concurrent Pos:* Alfred P Sloan fel, 76-80. *Mem:* Optical Soc Am; Am Phys Soc. *Res:* Coherent optical transient effects; nonlinear spectroscopic techniques; saturated absorption spectroscopy; molecular relaxation processes and molecular spectra. *Mailing Add:* Optical Sci Ctr Univ of Ariz Tucson AZ 85721

SHOEMAKER, RICHARD LEONARD, b Cullman, Ala, Sept 28, 31; c 4. PHYSIOLOGY. *Educ:* Auburn Univ, BS, 54, MS, 59; Univ Ala, Birmingham, PhD, 67. *Prof Exp:* Asst animal nutrit, Auburn Univ, 51-54; supvr animal care, 60-66, dir animal care dept, 64-67, assoc prof, 67-73, PROF PHYSIOL & BIOPHYS, MED CTR, UNIV ALA, BIRMINGHAM, 73- *Concurrent Pos:* Consult meteorologist, Eastern Airlines, 59-60. *Mem:* AAAS; Am Physiol Soc; Biophys Soc; NY Acad Sci. *Res:* Membrane transport, particularly the mechanisms involved in the secretion of HCl in the stomach. *Mailing Add:* Dept of Physiol Univ of Ala Med Ctr Birmingham AL 35294

SHOEMAKER, RICHARD NELSON, b Allentown, Pa, Nov 21, 21; m 47; c 2. MEDICAL EDUCATION. *Educ:* Lehigh Univ, PhD(microbiol), 50. *Prof Exp:* Instr biol sci, Lehigh Univ, 47-49; dir explor res, Pfizer, Inc, 52-55, tech mgr, 55-70; coordr med educ, Greater Del Valley Regional Med Prog, 70-73; DIR EDUC, MERCY HOSP, SCRANTON, PA, 73- *Concurrent Pos:* Med educ consult, Lackawanna County Med Soc, Pa, 71- *Mem:* Soc Indust Microbiol. *Res:* Microbiological conversions; antibiotics; vitamins; steroidal chemicals. *Mailing Add:* Mercy Hosp Scranton PA 18501

SHOEMAKER, RICHARD W, b Toledo, Ohio, Nov 8, 18; m 45; c 4. MATHEMATICS. *Educ:* Univ Toledo, BS, 40, MS, 42; Univ Chicago, cert, 43; Univ Mich, MA, 49, PhD(educ math). 54. *Prof Exp:* From asst prof to assoc prof, 46-58, chmn dept, 58-63, PROF MATH, UNIV TOLEDO, 58- *Mem:* Math Asn Am. *Mailing Add:* 2426 Meadow Wood Dr Toledo OH 43606

SHOEMAKER, ROBERT ALAN, b Toronto, Ont, July 9, 28; m 50; c 4. MYCOLOGY. *Educ:* Univ Guelph, BSA, 50, MSA, 52; Cornell Univ, PhD(mycol), 55. *Prof Exp:* Asst bot, Univ Guelph, 50-52; asst plant path, Cornell Univ, 52-55; asst mycologist, Plant Res Inst, 55-56, assoc mycologist, 56-57, mycologist, 57-65, sr mycologist, 65-67, HEAD MYCOL SECT, BIOSYSTEMATICS RES INST, CAN DEPT AGR, 67- *Concurrent Pos:* With inst specialized bot, Swiss Fed Inst Technol, 61-62. *Res:* Mycol Soc Am; Can Bot Asn; Can Phytopath Soc. *Res:* Taxonomy of Pyrenomycetes. *Mailing Add:* Biosystematics Res Inst Can Dept of Agr Ottawa ON K1A 0C6 Can

SHOEMAKER, ROY H(OPKINS), b Ogden, Utah, Oct 9, 23; m 54; c 3. CIVIL & HYDRAULIC ENGINEERING. *Educ:* Whitman Col, AB, 47; Ore State Univ, MS, 51, PhD, 56. *Prof Exp:* Instr civil eng, Ore State Univ, 49-50, 51-53, 54-56, from asst prof to assoc prof, 56-62; sr engr, Gen Elec Co, Richland, 59-60, 62-63, actg mgr reactor eng, 63-64, mgr thermal hydraul oper, Hanford Atomic Prod Dept, 64-67; mgr thermal hydraul subsect, Douglas United Nuclear, Inc, 67-68, mgr reactor technol subsect, 68-70, mgr reactor & fuels technol subsect, 70-71, consult engr, 71-73; consult engr, United Nuclear Industs, Inc, 73-75; res assoc, Pac Northwest Div, Battelle Mem Inst, 75-76; SR ENGR, UNITED NUCLEAR CORP INDUSTS, INC, 76- *Mem:* Am Soc Civil Engrs; Am Nuclear Soc. *Res:* Thermal and hydraulic analysis of reactor fuel performance and reactor cooling systems; reactor fuel design; design and analysis of pumping systems; hydraulics of closed conduits; nuclear safety analysis. *Mailing Add:* 7024 W Umatilla Ave Kennewick WA 99336

SHOEMAKER, VAUGHAN HURST, b Chicago, Ill, Apr 4, 38; Div. COMPARATIVE PHYSIOLOGY, ANIMAL PHYSIOLOGY. *Educ:* Earlham Col, AB, 59; Univ Mich, MA, 61, PhD(zool), 64. *Prof Exp:* Instr zool, Univ Mich, 64-65; from asst prof to assoc prof, 65-75, PROF ZOOL,

UNIV CALIF, RIVERSIDE, 75- *Concurrent Pos:* NIH fel, 65; NSF res grants, 66-81; mem adv panel, Pop Biol & Physiol Ecol, 79-82. *Mem:* AAAS; Am Soc Zool; Am Inst Biol Sci. *Res:* Water and electrolyte metabolism in terrestrial vertebrates. *Mailing Add:* Dept of Biol Univ of Calif Riverside CA 92521

SHOEMAKER, WILLIAM C, b Chicago, Ill, Feb 27, 23; m 53; c 4. SURGERY. *Educ:* Univ Calif, AB, 44, MD, 46. *Prof Exp:* Res fel surg, Harvard Med Sch, 56-59; from asst prof to prof surg, Chicago Med Sch, 59-69; prof surg, Mt Sinai Sch Med, 69-74, chief div surg metab, 71-74; PROF SURG, SCH MED, UNIV CALIF, LOS ANGELES, 74-, CHIEF ACUTE CARE CTR, HARBOR GEN HOSP, 74- *Concurrent Pos:* Dir dept surg res, Hektoen Inst Med Res, Cook County, Ill, 59-68; mem prog-proj rev comt B, Nat Heart Inst, 68-70; mem comt shock, Nat Res Coun-Nat Acad Sci, 69-71; chief third surg serv, Cook County Hosp, Ill; Nat Heart Inst res career award. *Mem:* AAAS; Am Physiol Soc; Soc Exp Biol & Med. *Res:* Regional hemodynamics and metabolism; hemorrhagic shock; hepatic physiology; electrolyte metabolism. *Mailing Add:* Harbor/Univ Calif Los Angeles Med Ctr 1000 W Carson Torrance CA 90509

SHOEMAN, DON WALTER, b Tracy, Minn, Feb 24, 41; m 67; c 1. PHARMACOLOGY. *Educ:* Macalester Col, BA, 65; Univ Minn, Minneapolis, PhD(pharmacol), 71. *Prof Exp:* Instr pharmacol, Univ Kans Med Ctr, Kansas City, 70-74, asst prof, 74-80; ASST PROF & CHMN DEPT PHYSIOL & PHARMACOL, NEW ENG COL OSTEOPATHIC MED, 80- *Mem:* Am Soc Pharmacol & Exp Therapeut. *Res:* Drug metabolism and clinical pharmacology. *Mailing Add:* Dept Physiol & Pharmacol New Eng Col Osteopathic Med Biddeford ME 04005

SHOENFIELD, JOSEPH ROBERT, b Detroit, Mich, May 1, 27. MATHEMATICS. *Educ:* Univ Mich, BS, 49, MS, 51, PhD(math), 52. *Prof Exp:* From instr to assoc prof, 52-65, PROF MATH, DUKE UNIV, 66- *Concurrent Pos:* NSF fel, 56-57. *Mem:* Am Math Soc; Asn Symbolic Logic. *Res:* Mathematical logic. *Mailing Add:* Dept of Math Duke Univ Durham NC 27706

SHOFFNER, JAMES PRIEST, b New Madrid, Mo, Jan 14, 28; m 56; c 3. ORGANIC CHEMISTRY. *Educ:* Lincoln Univ, Mo, BS, 51; DePaul Univ, MS, 56; Univ Ill, Chicago, PhD(org Chem), 65. *Prof Exp:* Res chemist, Corn Prod Co, 55-61; SR RES CHEMIST, UNIVERSAL OIL PRODS INC, 63- *Mem:* Am Chem Soc. *Res:* Synthesis of aromatic amines; rubber vulcanization; nuclear magnetic resonance spectroscopy; imine exchange reactions. *Mailing Add:* Corp Res Ctr Univeral Oil Prods Inc Des Plaines IL 60016

SHOFFNER, ROBERT NURMAN, b Junction City, Kans, Mar 2, 16; m 38; c 3. POULTRY GENETICS. *Educ:* Kans State Col, BS, 40, Univ Minn, MS, 42, PhD(animal genetics), 46. *Prof Exp:* From asst to assoc prof, 40-54, actg head dept, 65-66, PROF POULTRY HUSB, UNIV MINN, ST PAUL, 54- *Concurrent Pos:* Vis prof, Iowa State Univ, 57 & Univ Tex, Houston, 69; Fulbright scholar, Univ Queensland, 62. *Mem:* Fel AAAS; fel Poultry Sci Asn (2nd vpres, 64, 1st vpres, 65, pres, 66); Am Genetic Asn; Genetics Soc Am; World Poultry Sci Asn. *Res:* Avian genetics and cytogenetics; chromosome methodology, cytotaxonomy, quantitative genetics and genetic modification. *Mailing Add:* Dept of Animal Sci Univ of Minn St Paul MN 55101

SHOFFSTALL, GEORGE CARSON, JR, b Ashland, Pa, Nov 15, 29; m 51; c 5. MORPHOLOGY, RADIATION BIOLOGY. *Educ:* Pa State Univ, BS, 59, MS, 61, DEd(biol sci), 71. *Prof Exp:* Asst prof biol, Lock Haven State Col, 64-66; asst to dean, Col Sci, Pa State Univ, 66-80; DIR, WESTERN PA HOSP, PITTSBURGH, 80- *Concurrent Pos:* Dir, Para-Prof Med Aide Prog, Pa State Univ, 75-, Radiol Technologist Prog, 75-77 & Pilot Med Lab Technician Prog, 77- *Mem:* Fel AAAS; Asn Advan Med Instrumentation; Nat Asn Academies Sci (pres, 81-82). *Res:* Chief field of research interest has been the effects of ionizing radiation on the androecium of Coleus blumei benth, including microgametogenesis. *Mailing Add:* Western Pa Hosp 4800 Friendship Ave Pittsburgh PA 15224

SHOGER, ROSS L, b Aurora, Ill, Jan 14, 30; m 57; c 3. ZOOLOGY, DEVELOPMENTAL BIOLOGY. *Educ:* NCent Col, BA, 51; Purdue Univ, MS, 53; Univ Minn, PhD(zool), 59. *Prof Exp:* From instr to assoc prof, 59-69, chmn dept, 69-73, PROF BIOL, CARLETON COL, 69- *Concurrent Pos:* NSF sci fac fel, Waseda Univ, Japan, 68-69. *Mem:* AAAS; Am Inst Biol Sci; Soc Develop Biol; Am Soc Zool. *Res:* Experimental embryology development; node regression studies; differentiation in fresh water sponge. *Mailing Add:* Dept Biol Carleton Col Northfield MN 55057

SHOGREN, MERLE DENNIS, b Lindsborg, Kans, Nov 20, 26; m 74; c 4. CEREAL CHEMISTRY, BIOCHEMISTRY. *Educ:* Bethany Col, BS, 51; Kans State Univ, MS, 54. *Prof Exp:* RES FOOD TECHNOLOGIST CEREAL CHEM, USDA, 54- *Mem:* Sigma Xi; Am Asn Cereal Chemists; Am Chem Soc. *Res:* Improving breadmaking qualities of United States wheat (new varieties); improving nutritional qualities of bread-wheat flour. *Mailing Add:* US Grain Mkt Res 1515 College Ave Manhattan KS 66502

SHOHET, JUDA LEON, b Chicago, Ill, June 26, 37; m 69; c 3. PLASMA PHYSICS, ELECTRICAL ENGINEERING. *Educ:* Purdue Univ, BS, 58; Carnegie Inst Technol, MS, 60, PhD(elec eng), 61. *Prof Exp:* Asst prof elec eng, Johns Hopkins Univ, 61-66; assoc prof, 66-71, PROF ELEC ENG, UNIV WIS-MADISON, 71- *Concurrent Pos:* Consult, US Army Res & Develop Labs, Va, 61-63, Westinghouse Elec Corp, 63-66, 81, Trane Co, 68 & Argonne Nat Lab, 68-78; mem staff, Ctr Nuclear Study, Saclay, France, 69-70 & Los Alamos Sci Lab, 77- *Honors & Awards:* Frederick Emmons Terman Award, Am Soc Eng Educ, 77. *Mem:* AAAS; fel Inst Elec & Electronics Engrs; Sigma Xi; fel Am Phys Soc. *Res:* Controlled thermonuclear fusion; quantum electronics; waves and instabilities in plasmas; mathematical models of biological systems; electromagnetic theory and microwaves. *Mailing Add:* Dept of Elec & Comput Eng Univ of Wis Madison WI 53706

SHOKEIR, MOHAMED HASSAN KAMEL, b Mansoura, Egypt, July 2, 38; m 68; c 2. MEDICAL GENETICS. *Educ:* Cairo Univ, MB & ChB, 60, DCh, 63 & 64; Univ Mich, Ann Arbor, MS, 65, PhD(human genetics), 69. *Prof Exp:* Intern med, Cairo Univ Hosps, 60-61, resident orthop surg, 61-64; fel, Univ Mich, Ann Arbor, 64-66; res scholar, 66-69; from asst prof to assoc prof human genetics, 69-77, PROF PEDIAT & MED, UNIV SASK, 77-, DIR, DIV MED GENETICS, 75-, HEAD, DEPT PEDIAT, 79- *Concurrent Pos:* Queen Elizabeth II scientist grant, Univ Sask, 69-75; Med Res Coun Can grant, 70-; assoc prof pediat & head sect clin genetics, Univ Man, 72-75; counr genetics, Can Soc Clin Invest Coun, 73-75. *Mem:* Am Soc Human Genetics; Am Fedn Clin Res; Can Soc Clin Invest; Soc Pediat Res; fel Can Col Med Geneticists. *Res:* Genetics, biochemistry and immunology of copper containing enzymes and other metallo-proteins; neurobiology, especially of Huntington's chorea, Wilson's disease and parkinsonism; congenital malformations in man; genetic polymorphisms of proteins in man. *Mailing Add:* Div of Med Genetics Univ of Sask Saskatoon SK S7N 0X0 Can

SHOLANDER, MARLOW, b Topeka, Kans, Mar 13, 15; m 40; c 3. MATHEMATICS. *Educ:* Univ Kans, AB & AM, 40; Brown Univ, PhD(math), 49. *Prof Exp:* Instr math, Univ Kans, 38-40 & Brown Univ, 40-45; from instr to assoc prof, Wash Univ, 46-54; assoc prof, Carnegie Inst Technol, 54-60; prof, 60-80, EMER PROF MATH, CASE WESTERN RESERVE UNIV, 80- *Mem:* Am Math Soc; Math Asn Am. *Res:* Foundations of mathematics; lattice theory; theory of convex bodies. *Mailing Add:* Dept Math Case Western Reserve Univ Cleveland OH 44106

SHOLDT, LESTER LANCE, b Greeley, Colo, Aug 18, 38; m 62; c 2. MILITARY ENTOMOLOGY, MEDICAL ENTOMOLOGY. *Educ:* Colo State Univ, BS, 62, PhD(entom), 78; Univ Hawaii, MS, 64. *Prof Exp:* Res asst, Cotton Insect Lab, USDA, Ariz, 65-66; asst opers officer, Dis Vector Control Ctr, Calif, 66-67; div entomologist, 1st Marine Div, Vietnam, 68; head, Dept Entom, Prev Med Unit #2, Va, 69-72, Naval Med Res Unit #5, Ethiopia, 73-76; officer in charge, Dis Vector Ecol & Control Ctr, Fla, 78-81; HEAD, DIS VECTOR CONTROL SECT, PRE MED DIV, BUR MED & SURG, 81- *Mem:* Entom Soc Am; Am Mosquito Control Asn; Asn Military Surgeons of US; Sigma Xi. *Res:* Epidemiology and control of human lice and louse-borne diseases; insect space repellents for the protection of human subjects; malaria prevention and control; vector control in post-disaster situations. *Mailing Add:* Dis Vector Control Sect Prev Med Div Code MED31412 Bur Med & Surg Washington DC 20372

SHOLL, HOWARD ALFRED, b Northampton, Mass, Oct 14, 38; m 60; c 2. COMPUTER SCIENCES. *Educ:* Worcester Polytech Inst, BS, 60, MS, 63; Univ Conn, PhD(comput sci), 70. *Prof Exp:* Engr, US Army Signal Res & Develop Lab, 60-61; asst elec eng, Worcester Polytech Inst, 61-63; sr engr, Sylvania Elec Co, 63-66; from instr to asst prof, 66-75, ASSOC PROF ELEC ENG & COMPUT SCI, UNIV CONN, 75- *Concurrent Pos:* Leverhulme vis fel, Univ Edinburgh, 73-74; mem, Task Force Software Eng, Digital Syst Eval Comt, 75. *Mem:* Inst Elec & Electronics Engrs; Asn Comput Mach. *Res:* Digital systems design; engineering and analysis of software systems. *Mailing Add:* Dept of Elec Eng & Comput Sci Univ of Conn Box U-157 Storrs CT 06268

SHOLLENBERGER, CARL ALVIN, b Altoona, Pa, Nov 4, 46. FLUID MECHANICS. *Educ:* Pa State Univ, BS, 67; Calif Inst Technol, MS, 68, PhD(aeronaut), 71. *Prof Exp:* Res scientist, McDonnell Douglas Res Labs, 71-74, SR ENGR & SCIENTIST, DOUGLAS AIRCRAFT CO, MCDONNELL DOUGLAS CORP, 74- *Mem:* Am Inst Aeronaut & Astronaut. *Res:* Subsonic aerodynamics; multi-energy flows; fluid dynamics of high lift systems; flight in nature. *Mailing Add:* Douglas Aircraft Co 3855 Lakewood Blvd Long Beach CA 90846

SHOMAY, DAVID, b Brooklyn, NY, Aug 31, 24. ZOOLOGY. *Educ:* Long Island Univ, BS, 48; Univ Ill, MS, 49, PhD(zool), 55. *Prof Exp:* From asst to instr, 49-56, from instr to asst prof, 56-63, ASSOC PROF ZOOL, UNIV ILL, CHICAGO CIRCLE, 63- *Mem:* AAAS; Soc Vert Paleont; Am Soc Zoologists. *Res:* Comparative anatomy; invertebrate zoology; structure and evolution of nervous system. *Mailing Add:* Dept of Biol Sci Univ of Ill Box 4348 Chicago IL 60680

SHOMBERT, DONALD JAMES, b Pittsburgh, Pa, Oct 31, 28; m 55; c 4. PHYSICAL CHEMISTRY. *Educ:* Univ Pittsburgh, BS, 53, PhD(chem), 58. *Prof Exp:* Res assoc phys chem, Res Labs, Merck & Co, Inc, NJ, 58-61; mgr surface physics & chem, CBS Labs, Conn, 61-62; asst prof, 62-67, ASSOC PROF CHEM, DOUGLASS COL, RUTGERS UNIV, NEW BRUNSWICK, 67- *Mem:* Am Chem Soc; Inst Elec & Electronic Eng. *Res:* Semiconductor materials; thin-film depostion and device technology; physical measurements and electronic instrumentation. *Mailing Add:* Dept of Chem Douglass Col New Brunswick NJ 08903

SHOMURA, RICHARD SUNAO, b Honolulu, Hawaii, Aug 3, 28; m 52; c 3. FISH BIOLOGY. *Educ:* Univ Hawaii, BS, 50, MS, 61. *Prof Exp:* Fishery biologist, Bur Com Fisheries, US Fish & Wildlife Serv, 54-62, chief Indian Ocean Prog, 62-66, actg dep area dir, 66-68, dep area dir, 68-70, actg area dir, 69-70, assoc regional dir resource progs, 70-71, dir Tiburon Fisheries Lab, 71-73, DIR HONOLULU LAB, SOUTHWEST FISHERIES CTR, NAT MARINE FISHERIES SERV, NAT OCEANIC & ATMOSPHERIC ADMIN, 73- *Concurrent Pos:* Mem, Sea Grant Adv Coun, Univ Hawaii & Adv Subcomt Invert & Aquatic Biota, 73- *Honors & Awards:* Superior Performance Award, Nat Marine Fisheries Serv, Nat Oceanic & Atmospheric Admin, Dept Com, 67, Spec Achievement Award, 74, Outstanding Performance Rating Awards, 75 & 77. *Mem:* Am Fisheries Soc; Am Inst Fish Res Biol; Am Inst Biol Sci; Am Soc Ichthyol & Herpet; Ecol Soc Am. *Res:* Ecology of marine fishes. *Mailing Add:* Nat Marine Fisheries Serv Honolulu Lab PO Box 3830 Honolulu HI 96812

SHON, FREDERICK JOHN, b Pleasantville, NY, July 24, 26; m 46; c 1. NUCLEAR PHYSICS. *Educ:* Columbia Univ, BS, 46. *Prof Exp:* Jr engr, Publicker Alcohol Co, 46-47; proj engr, Thermoid Co, 47-48; opers physicist, Mound Lab, 48-52; reactor opers supvr, Lawrence Radiation Lab, Univ Calif, 52-61, lectr nuclear eng, 56-61; chief reactor oper & supvr licensing br, Div Licensing & Regulations, US AEC, 61-62, chief reactor & criticality safety br, Div Oper Safety, 63-67, asst dir nuclear facilities, 67-72; VCHMN ATOMIC SAFETY & LICENSING BD PANEL, US NUCLEAR REGULATORY COMN, 72- *Concurrent Pos:* Radiation chemist, Atomics Int Div, NAm Aviation, Inc, 51-52; consult, Aerojet-Gen Nucleonics Div, Gen Tire & Rubber Co, 58- & US AEC, 59-; physicist, Lawrence Radiation Lab, Univ Calif, 62-63; mem, Int Atomic Energy Agency Safety Adv Mission to the Spanish Junta De Energia Nuclear, 71-72. *Mem:* Am Nuclear Soc. *Res:* Nuclear reactor design and operation; neutron physics; radiation detection, measurement and safety. *Mailing Add:* US Nuclear Regulatory Comn Washington DC 20555

SHONE, ROBERT L, b Gary, Ind, July 28, 37; m 61; c 2. ORGANIC CHEMISTRY, MEDICINAL CHEMISTRY. *Educ:* Ind Univ, BS, 59; Mich State Univ, MS, 61, PhD(org chem), 65. *Prof Exp:* Res chemist, Swift & Co, 65-66; res fel, Ill Inst Technol, 66-67; sr investr, 67-71, RES SCIENTIST, G D SEARLE & CO, 71- *Mem:* Am Chem Soc; The Chem Soc. *Res:* Anti-viral and antihypertensive drugs; nucleic acids; enzyme inhibitors of nucleic acid metabolites; synthesis of nucleosides, amino acids and carbohydrates; antiallergy drugs; synthesis of pyrones. *Mailing Add:* G D Searle & Co PO Box 5110 Chicago IL 60680

SHONE, ROBERT TILDEN, b Rochester, NY, July 22, 28; m 54; c 2. PHOTOGRAMMETRY, FORESTRY. *Educ:* Syracuse Univ, BS, 49, MS, 54. *Prof Exp:* Photogram aide mapping, Army Map Serv, 52-53; sect mgr photogram prod sales, Bausch & Lomb Optical Co, 54-59; mem tech staff, Ramo-Wooldridge Div, Thompson Ramo Wooldridge, Inc, 59-61; sr staff engr, Librascope Div, Gen Precision Inc, 61-63; dept head photogram instrument res & develop, 63-67, tech dir, Spec Prod Div, 67-73, vpres spec prod develop, 73-81, DIR RES & DEVELOP, SCI OPTICAL PROD DIV, BAUSCH & LOMB, INC, 81- *Mem:* Can Inst Survrs; Am Soc Photogram. *Res:* Instrument accuracy studies; mapping instrument automation; system analysis; analytical photogrammetry; photographic interpretation; instrument development management. *Mailing Add:* Sci Optical Prod Div 1400 N Goodman St Rochester NY 14609

SHONEBARGER, F(RANCIS) J(OSEPH), b Sugar Grove, Ohio, Nov 2, 24; m 51; c 4. CERAMIC ENGINEERING. *Educ:* Ohio State Univ, BCerE & MS, 51, PhD, 61. *Prof Exp:* Glass technologist, Gen Elec Co, 54-61; glass technologist, Anchor Hocking Corp, 61-69, mgr explor res, 69-76; INSTR CERAMIC ENG, HOCKING TECH COL, 76- *Mem:* Am Ceramic Soc; Brit Soc Glass Technol. *Res:* Glasses to imbed electroluminescent phosphors; infrared glasses; glass surfaces, composition, physical properties and refractory reactions. *Mailing Add:* Hocking Tech Col Nelsonville OH 45764

SHONICK, WILLIAM, b Poland, Oct 3, 19; US citizen; m 41; c 1. BIOSTATISTICS, PUBLIC HEALTH. *Educ:* City Col New York, BS, 42; George Washington Univ, MA, 48; Univ Calif, Los Angeles, PhD(biostatist), 67. *Prof Exp:* Jr acct, Wm Janis CPA, New York, 42; statistician-economist, Off Price Admin, 43; bus agent, Local 203, United Fed Workers of Am-CIO, 44-45; teacher social studies, Montgomery County Sch Syst, Md, 45-51; pvt bus, 52-55; budget & statist anal, Fedn Jewish Philanthropies, New York, 55-61; coordr biostatist, Rehab Res & Training Ctr, Sch Med, Univ Southern Calif, 68-69; asst prof, 69-74, ASSOC PROF PUB HEALTH, SCH PUB HEALTH, UNIV CALIF, LOS ANGELES, 74- *Concurrent Pos:* NIH fel biostatist, Univ Calif, Los Angeles, 68; asst prof community med, Med Sch, Univ Southern Calif, 68-69. *Mem:* Am Statist Asn; Am Pub Health Asn; Opers Res Soc Am. *Res:* Quantitative methods applied to health services planning and administration; governmental policies and health services delivery. *Mailing Add:* Sch of Pub Health Univ of Calif Los Angeles CA 90024

SHONK, CARL ELLSWORTH, b Plymouth, Pa, Nov 11, 22; m 51; c 2. BIOCHEMISTRY. *Educ:* Bucknell Univ, BS, 48; MS, 49; Rutgers Univ, PhD(biochem, physiol), 62. *Prof Exp:* Chemist, E I du Pont de Nemours & Co, Pa, 48; biochemist, Merck & Co, Inc, 49-66; ASSOC PROF CHEM, CENT MICH UNIV, 66- *Mem:* AAAS; Am Chem Soc; NY Acad Sci; Biochem Soc; Am Inst Chemists. *Res:* Enzyme chemistry; cancer biochemistry; analytical biochemical methods. *Mailing Add:* Dept of Chem Cent Mich Univ Mt Pleasant MI 48859

SHONKWILER, RONALD WESLEY, b Chicago, Ill, Feb 20, 42. MATHEMATICS. *Educ:* Calif State Polytech Col, Kellogg-Voorhis, BS, 64; Univ Colo, Boulder, MS, 67, PhD(math), 70. *Prof Exp:* Aerospace engr, US Naval Ord Lab, 64-65; ASST PROF MATH, GA INST TECHNOL, 70- *Mem:* Soc Math Biol; Am Math Soc; Soc Indust & Appl Math. *Res:* Operator theory; mathematic biology. *Mailing Add:* Sch Math Ga Inst Technol Atlanta GA 30332

SHONLE, JOHN IRWIN, b Indianapolis, Ind, Oct 1, 33; m 71; c 6. MUSICAL ACOUSTICS. *Educ:* Wesleyan Univ, BA, 55; Univ Calif, Berkeley, MA, 57, PhD(physics), 61. *Prof Exp:* From asst prof to assoc prof physics, Reed Col, 60-67; assoc prof physics & astrophys, 67-73, PROF PHYSICS, UNIV COLO, DENVER, 73- *Concurrent Pos:* NSF sci fac fel, 66-67. *Mem:* AAAS; Am Asn Physics Teachers; Acoust Soc Am. *Res:* Physics teaching methods; psychoacoustics of music; environmental physics. *Mailing Add:* Dept of Physics Univ Colo Denver CO 80202

SHONTZ, CHARLES JACK, b Sewickley, Pa, Jan 2, 26; m 52. ANIMAL ECOLOGY, HUMAN ECOLOGY. *Educ:* Ind State Col, Pa, BS, 49; Univ Pittsburgh, MS, 53, PhD(zool), 62. *Prof Exp:* Teacher high sch, Pa, 49-55; Fulbright lectr sci, Kambawza Col, Burma, 55-56; teacher high sch, Pa, 56-57; asst prof biol, 57-59, assoc prof biol & physiol & head dept, 59-62, PROF

BIOL & PHYSIOL, CLARION STATE COL, 62-, DEAN ACAD SERV, 64-, ASSOC VPRES, ACAD AFFAIRS, 78- *Concurrent Pos:* NSF fac fel, 61-62; assoc vpres acad affairs & dean summer sessions, Clarion State Col. *Mem:* Am Soc Ichthyol & Herpet; Wilderness Soc; Am Nature Study Soc. *Res:* Effects of environment on the evolution of populations of fishes, especially the family Cyprinidae. *Mailing Add:* Clarion State Col Clarion PA 16214

SHONTZ, JOHN PAUL, b Meadville, Pa, Oct 11, 40; m 67; c 2. PLANT ECOLOGY. *Educ:* Edinboro State Col, BS, 62; Miami Univ, MA, 64; Duke Univ, PhD(bot), 67. *Prof Exp:* Teacher pub sch, Pa, 62; instr biol sci, Mt Holyoke Col, 67-68, asst prof, 68-74; asst prof, 74-76, ASSOC PROF BIOL, GRAND VALLEY STATE COLS, 76-, CHMN DEPT, 79- *Mem:* AAAS; Bot Soc Am; Ecol Soc Am. *Res:* Plant ecology with special interest in ecotypic variation, in plant species interaction and seed germination. *Mailing Add:* Dept of Biol Grand Valley State Cols Allendale MI 49401

SHONTZ, NANCY NICKERSON, b Pittsburgh, Pa, July 9, 42; m 67; c 2. PLANT ECOLOGY. *Educ:* Smith Col, AB, 64, PhD(biol), 69; Duke Univ, MA, 66. *Prof Exp:* Instr biol, ECarolina Univ, 66-67; instr bot, Univ Mass, 67-68; asst prof bot, Holyoke Community Col, 69-74; ADJ FAC BIOL, GRAND VALLEY STATE COLS, 74- *Mem:* AAAS; Am Soc Ichthyol & Herpet; Ecol Soc Am. *Res:* Electrophoresis of salamander proteins; seed germination studies; ecotypic variation. *Mailing Add:* 8747 Cottonwood Dr Jenison MI 29428

SHOOK, CLIFTON ARNOLD, b Lamont, Alta, Oct 10, 34; m 59; c 4. CHEMICAL ENGINEERING. *Educ:* Univ Alta, BSc, 56; Univ London, PhD(chem eng), 60. *Prof Exp:* From asst prof to assoc prof, 60-71, PROF CHEM ENG, UNIV SASK, 71- *Mem:* Chem Inst Can. *Res:* Fluid mechanics; heat transfer; mass transfer; fluid-particle systems; rheology; pipeline flow of suspensions. *Mailing Add:* Dept of Chem & Chem Eng Univ of Sask Saskatoon SK S5N 0W0 Can

SHOOK, THOMAS EUGENE, b Pasadena, Calif, Mar 10, 28; m 58; c 3. CHEMISTRY. *Educ:* Tex Tech Univ, BS, 51. *Prof Exp:* Res asst biochem, Ft Detrick, Md, 52-53, chief biochem br, 53-71, CHIEF DEVELOP & TECHNOL DIV, PINE BLUFF ARSENAL, US ARMY, 71-, ENVIRON COORDR, 72- *Mem:* Am Chem Soc; Am Inst Chemists; Sigma Xi; Am Statist Asn. *Res:* Physical-engineering sciences; statistics; production development; process evaluation; research management. *Mailing Add:* Develop & Technol Div Pine Bluff Arsenal Pine Bluff AR 71601

SHOOK, WILLIAM BEATTIE, b Columbus, Ohio, Oct 3, 28; m 50; c 4. CERAMICS ENGINEERING. *Educ:* Ohio State Univ, BCerE, 53, PhD(ceramics eng), 61. *Prof Exp:* Res asst ceramics res, Eng Exp Sta, Ohio State Univ, 50-53, res assoc, 53-55, supvr building res, 55-57, dir ceramics res, 57-63; vis prof, Indian Inst Technol, Kanpur, 63-65; from asst prof to assoc prof, 65-72, PROF CERAMICS ENG & CHMN DEPT, OHIO STATE UNIV, 72- *Honors & Awards:* Cramer Award, Am Ceramic Soc, 81. *Mem:* Fel Am Ceramic Soc; Am Soc Eng Educ; Am Ord Asn; Nat Inst Ceramic Engrs; Am Soc Nondestruct Testing. *Res:* Brittle failure mechanisms in impact testing, especially influence of elastic properties, density and geometry of test specimens on the response system; viscosity; measurement and interpretation in melting and crystallizing at non-equilibrium; nondestructive testing of ceramics. *Mailing Add:* Dept of Ceramics Eng 2041 N College Rd Columbus OH 43210

SHOOLERY, JAMES NELSON, b Worland, Wyo, June 25, 25; m 51; c 3. PHYSICAL CHEMISTRY. *Educ:* Univ Calif, BS, 48; Calif Inst Technol, PhD(chem), 52. *Prof Exp:* Dir appln lab, Varian Assocs, 52-62, mkt mgr anal inst div, Calif, 62-69; independent consult, 69-72; SR APPLN CHEMIST, VARIAN ASSOCS, 72- *Honors & Awards:* Sargent Award, 64. *Mem:* Am Chem Soc. *Res:* Microwave spectroscopy; chemical effects in nuclear magnetic resonance. *Mailing Add:* 2301 Bowdoin St Palo Alto CA 94306

SHOOMAN, MARTIN L, b Trenton, NJ, Feb 24, 34; m 62; c 2. COMPUTER ENGINEERING, ELECTRICAL ENGINEERING. *Educ:* Mass Inst Technol, SB & SM, 56; Polytech Inst Brooklyn, DEE, 61. *Prof Exp:* Teaching asst elec eng, Mass Inst Technol, 55-56; mem staff, Res & Develop Group, Sperry Gyroscope Co, NY, 56-58; from instr to assoc prof elec eng, 58-74, PROF ELEC ENG & COMPUT SCI & DIR, DIV COMPUT SCI, POLYTECH INST NY, FARMINGDALE, 81- *Concurrent Pos:* Consult govt & indust, 59-; vis assoc prof, Mass Inst Technol, 72-73. *Mem:* fel Inst Elec & Electronics Engrs; Asn Comput Mach. *Res:* Reliability theory and application to computer systems; reliability of electronic and mechanical systems; software engineering. *Mailing Add:* Dept of Elec Eng Long Island Ctr Rte 110 Farmingdale NY 11735

SHOOP, C ROBERT, b Chicago, Ill, Aug 12, 35; m 57; c 2. ECOLOGY. *Educ:* Southern Ill Univ, BA, 57; Tulane Univ, MS, 59, PhD(zool, bot), 63. *Prof Exp:* Instr zool & physiol, Wellesley Col, 62-64, asst prof biol sci, 64-69, res awards, 62-66; assoc prof zool, 69-74, PROF ZOOL, UNIV RI, 74- *Concurrent Pos:* US AEC res contract, 65-75; dir, Inst Environ Biol, 70-72; dir NIH training grant environ physiol, 70-72; collabr, Nat Park Serv, 78-; contracts, Dept Interior, 78-82 & Nat Marine Fisheries Serv, 80-81. *Honors & Awards:* Stoye Prize, Am Soc Ichthyol & Herpet, 60. *Mem:* AAAS; Am Inst Biol Sci; Am Soc Ichthyol & Herpet; Am Soc Mammal; Animal Behavior Soc. *Res:* Behavior and ecology of vertebrates; radiobiology. *Mailing Add:* Dept of Zool Univ of RI Kingston RI 02881

SHOOP, CLYDE EDWARD, b Pottsville, Pa, Sept 22, 24; m 51. PHARMACY. *Educ:* Philadelphia Col Pharm & Sci, BS, 51, MSci, 52. *Prof Exp:* Res assoc, 52-67, unit head, 57-59, res pharmacist, 67-74, SR RES PHARMACIST, MERCK & CO, INC, 74- *Mem:* Am Pharmaceut Asn; Acad Pharmaceut Sci. *Res:* Flavoring of pharmaceuticals; development of fluid and topical pharmaceuticals; rheology, suspension and semi-solid technology. *Mailing Add:* 538 Crescent Ave Lansdale PA 19446

SHOOP, GEORGE JEROME, agronomy, see previous edition

SHOOSMITH, JOHN NORMAN, b London, Eng, Oct 9, 34; US citizen; m 66; c 3. APPLIED MATHEMATICS, COMPUTER SCIENCE. *Educ:* Queen's Univ, Ont, BSc, 56; Col William & Mary, MS, 67; Univ Va, PhD(appl math), 73. *Prof Exp:* Comput specialist, Avro Aircraft Corp, Can, 56-59; aerospace technologist comput, Manned Spacecraft Ctr, 59-64, aerospace technologist, Gemini Prog, 64-65, HEAD COMPUT APPL, LANGLEY RES CTR, NASA, 65- *Concurrent Pos:* Asst prof lectr, George Washington Univ, 74- *Mem:* Asn Comput Mach; Am Inst Aeronaut & Astronaut; Soc Indust & Appl Math. *Res:* Numerical analysis, specifically high-order accurate numerical solutions to bondary-value problems of ordinary and partial differential equations. *Mailing Add:* Mail Stop 125 NASA Langley Res Ctr Hampton VA 23665

SHOOTER, ERIC MANVERS, b Mansfield, Eng, Apr 18, 24; m 49; c 1. BIOCHEMISTRY. *Educ:* Cambridge Univ, BA, 45, MA, 49, PhD(chem), 50; Univ London, DSc(biochem), 64. *Prof Exp:* Fel chem, Univ Wis, 49-50; sr scientist biochem, Brewing Indust Res Found, Eng, 50-53; lectr, Univ Col, Univ London, 53-64; assoc prof genetics, 64-68, prof genetics & biochem, 68-75, PROF NEUROBIOL & CHMN DEPT, SCH MED, STANFORD UNIV, 75- *Concurrent Pos:* USPHS int fel, Stanford Univ, 61-62. *Mem:* Brit Biochem Soc; Brit Biophys Soc; Am Soc Biol Chemists; Am Soc Neurochem; Int Soc Neurochem. *Res:* Physical chemistry of proteins; structure of normal and abnormal hemoglobins; genetic control of protein synthesis, replication of DNA; molecular neurobiology. *Mailing Add:* Dept of Neurobiol Stanford Univ Sch of Med Stanford CA 94305

SHOOTER, JACK ALLEN, b Austin, Tex, June 16, 40; m 77; c 3. ACOUSTICS, COMPUTER SCIENCE. *Educ:* Univ Tex, Austin, BS, 63. *Prof Exp:* res scientist assoc V acoust, 63-80, SPECIAL RES ASSOC, APPL RES LABS, UNIV TEX, AUSTIN, 80- *Mem:* Assoc mem Acoust Soc Am; Sigma Xi. *Res:* Underwater acoustics; physical acoustics; signal processing. *Mailing Add:* Appl Res Labs PO Box 8029 Austin TX 78712

SHOPE, RICHARD EDWIN, JR, b Philadelphia, Pa, Sept 4, 26; m 61; c 6. VIROLOGY, IMMUNOLOGY. *Educ:* Williams Col, BA, 47; Univ Wis, BS, 49; Cornell Univ, DVM, 59; Univ Minn, PhD(microbiol), 64. *Prof Exp:* Asst prof, 59-70, ASSOC PROF VET MED & MICROBIOL, UNIV MINN, ST PAUL, 70- *Concurrent Pos:* NIH career develop award, 64-68. *Mem:* Am Vet Med Asn; US Animal Health Asn; Am Asn Vet Clinicians. *Res:* Enteric and respiratory viral disease of domestic animals; mammalian leukemias and other tumors; immune tolerance and autoimmune diseases of domestic animals. *Mailing Add:* Dept of Vet Biol Col of Vet Med Univ of Minn St Paul MN 55101

SHOPE, ROBERT ELLIS, b Princeton, NJ, Feb 21, 29; m 58; c 4. VIROLOGY. *Educ:* Cornell Univ, BA, 51, MD, 54. *Prof Exp:* Intern, Grace-New Haven Community Hosp, Conn, 54-55, asst resident internal med, 57-58; mem staff virus labs, Rockefeller Found, NY, 58-59 & Belem Virus Lab, 59-65; assoc prof, 65-75, PROF EPIDEMIOL, SCH MED, YALE UNIV, 75- *Res:* Arboviruses. *Mailing Add:* Yale Arbovirus Res Unit 60 College St Box 3333 New Haven CT 06510

SHOR, AARON LOUIS, b New York, NY, Jan 13, 24; m 60. VETERINARY MEDICINE, ANIMAL NUTRITION. *Educ:* Cornell Univ, BS, 47, DVM, 53; Univ Del, MS, 49. *Prof Exp:* Field investr animal dis, Farm & Home Div, Am Cyanamid Co, 55-57, ruminant specialist, 57, field invest, Agr Div, 57-60, mgr, Clin Develop Lab & Poultry Prog, 63-77, regist coordr, Agr Div, 77-80; MGR CLIN DEVELOP, SMITH KLINE ANIMAL HEALTH PROD, 80- *Concurrent Pos:* Adj prof, Trenton State Col, 73-75. *Mem:* Am Vet Med Asn; Am Soc Animal Sci; Am Dairy Sci Asn; Poultry Sci Asn; Indust Vet Asn (secy, 65-70, pres, 71-72). *Res:* Development of drugs to prevent or treat disease or improve production efficiency of animals. *Mailing Add:* Smith Kline Animal Health Prod Am Cyanamid Co PO Box 400 West Chester NJ 19380

SHOR, ARTHUR JOSEPH, b New York, NY, June 10, 23; m 52; c 2. INORGANIC CHEMISTRY, CHEMICAL ENGINEERING. *Educ:* City Col New York, BChE, 43; Univ Tenn, MS, 64, PhD(chem), 67. *Prof Exp:* Assoc chem engr, Argonne Nat Lab, 46-56; res chem engr, IIT Res Inst, 56-57; MEM RES STAFF CHEM, OAK RIDGE NAT LAB, 58- *Mem:* Am Chem Soc; Sigma Xi. *Res:* Fused salt phase studies; effects of reactor irradiation on nuclear fuels and fertile materials; development of reverse osmosis membranes and apparatus for cleanup of waste and brackish waters. *Mailing Add:* Oak Ridge Nat Lab PO Box X Oak Ridge TN 37830

SHOR, GEORGE G, JR, b New York, NY, June 8, 23; m 50; c 3. MARINE GEOPHYSICS. *Educ:* Calif Inst Technol, BS, 44, MS, 48, PhD(seismol), 54. *Prof Exp:* Seismic party chief, Seismic Explor, Inc, 48-51; res asst, Calif Inst Technol, 51-53; from asst res geophysicist to res geophysicist, 53-69, prof marine geophys & sea grant prog mgr, 69-73, ASSOC DIR, SCRIPPS INST OCEANOG, UNIV CALIF, SAN DIEGO, 68- *Mem:* AAAS; Soc Explor Geophys; fel Geol Soc Am; fel Am Geophys Union. *Res:* Marine geophysics; structure, origin and properties of ocean floor; marine technology. *Mailing Add:* Scripps Inst of Oceanog A-005 La Jolla CA 92093

SHOR, STEVEN MICHAEL, b Manhattan, NY, Apr 5, 44; m 70. CHEMICAL ENGINEERING. *Educ:* Univ Mass, Amherst, BS, 65; Northwestern Univ, MS, 67; Iowa State Univ, PhD(chem eng), 70. *Prof Exp:* SR CHEM ENGR, 3M CO, 70- *Mem:* Am Inst Chem Engrs. *Res:* Small particle technology, especially as applies to grain size distribution involved in crystallization and precipitation processes; effects of various parameters on nucleation and growth kinetics. *Mailing Add:* 2660 Highwood Ave St Paul MN 55119

SHORB, ALAN MCKEAN, b Baltimore, Md, July 18, 38; m 60; c 3. MATHEMATICAL PROGRAMMING. *Educ:* Swarthmore Col, BA, 60; Cornell Univ, MA, 65; Univ Minn, Minneapolis, PhD(math), 69. *Prof Exp:* Instr, State Univ NY Binghamton, 64-66; from asst prof to assoc prof math,

Naval Postgrad Sch, 68-75; SYSTS ANALYST, DEVELOP ANAL ASSOCS, 76- *Concurrent Pos:* Res mathematician, Nat Bur Standards, 59-66; mathematician, Naval Electronics Lab Ctr, San Diego, 72-73. *Mem:* Soc Indust & Appl Math; Sigma Xi. *Res:* Computer simulation of social systems. *Mailing Add:* Develop Anal Assocs Cambridge MA 02139

SHORB, MARY SHAW, b Wahpeton, NDak, Jan 11, 07; m 29; c 3. MICROBIOLOGY. *Educ:* Col of Idaho, BS, 28; Johns Hopkins Univ, ScD(immunol), 33. *Prof Exp:* Tech asst res common cold, Abel Fund, Johns Hopkins Univ, 29-32, tech asst immunol, Sch Hyg & Pub Health, 31-32; bacteriologist, Bur Human Nutrit, USDA, Md, 42-44, Bur Dairy Indust, 44-46; Merck fel poultry husb, 47-49, res prof, 49-72, EMER RES PROF POULTRY HUSB, UNIV MD, COLLEGE PARK, 72- *Honors & Awards:* Hemat Res Found Award, 49; Mead-Johnson Award, 49. *Mem:* Am Soc Microbiol; Soc Exp Med & Biol; Soc Protozool; Soc Gen Microbiol; fel NY Acad Sci. *Res:* Immunology in pneumococcus infections; heterophile antigen in bacteria; food bacteriology; microbiological assays vitamins; chick and protozoan growth factors; lipids of protozoa and helminths; pleuropneumonia-like organisms. *Mailing Add:* Dept of Poultry Sci Animal Sci Bldg Univ of Md College Park MD 20742

SHORE, BRUCE WALTER, b Visalia, Calif, Feb 27, 35; c 2. ATOMIC PHYSICS. *Educ:* Col of Pacific, BS, 56; Mass Inst Technol, PhD(nuclear chem), 60. *Prof Exp:* Res chemist, Shell Oil Co, Calif, 56; res scientist, US Naval Radiol Defense Lab, 57; instr physics, Suffolk Univ, 57-60; analyst develop planning, Anal Serv, Inc, Va, 60-62; lectr astron & res fel astrophys, Harvard Col Observ, 62-68; assoc prof physics, Kans State Univ, 68-72; PHYSICIST, LAWRENCE LIVERMORE LAB, 72- *Concurrent Pos:* Sci Res Coun fel, Imp Col, Univ London, 70-71. *Mem:* Am Phys Soc; Int Astron Union. *Res:* Atomic structure and theoretical spectroscopy; photon physics. *Mailing Add:* Lawrence Livermore Lab Livermore CA 94550

SHORE, DAVID, b Detroit, Mich, Aug 12, 19; m 44; c 2. PHYSICS, AERONAUTICAL ENGINEERING. *Educ:* Univ Mich, BS, 41; Ohio State Univ, MS, 50. *Prof Exp:* Liaison, Nat Adv Comt Aeronaut-US Dept Air Force, 41-46; chief high speed aerodyn, Aircraft Lab, Wright Air Develop Ctr, 46, asst chief systs planning, Aircraft & Guided Missile Sect, 46-54; mgr systs synthesis, Missile & Surface Radar Dept, 54-58, chmn, Ballistic Missile Early Warning Syst, 58-59, assoc dir, Adv Mil Systs, 58-61, prog mgr, SAINT Satellite Inspector Syst, 61-62, chief systs eng, systs eng, eval & res, 62-65, chief engr, Commun Systs Div, 65-66, chief defense engr, Defense Electronic Prod, 66-69, div vpres plans & systs develop, 70-75, div vpres, Advan Progs Develop, 75-81, DIV VPRES BUS DEVELOP, RCA CORP, 81- *Concurrent Pos:* Mem, Army Sci Bd, 78- *Mem:* Am Inst Aeronaut & Astronaut; Am Ord Asn; Inst Elec & Electronics Engrs; Nat Security Indust Asn; Electronic Industs Asn. *Res:* Long range planning, allocation of investment resources, definition of customers requirements; selection, initiation and direction of major new systems programs; management of PRICE parametric model activity. *Mailing Add:* 1419 McLean Mews Ct McLean VA 22101

SHORE, FERDINAND JOHN, b Brooklyn, NY, Sept 23, 19; m 46; c 5. NUCLEAR PHYSICS. *Educ:* Queens Col, NY, BS, 41; Wesleyan Univ, MS, 43; Univ Ill, PhD(physics), 52. *Prof Exp:* Res physicist photom of pyrotech, Wesleyan Univ, 41-45, res physicist piezoelec, 45-46; asst physics, Univ Ill, 46-49, asst nuclear physics, 49-52; assoc physicist, Brookhaven Nat Lab, 52-60; assoc prof, 60-65, PROF PHYSICS, QUEENS COL, NY, 65- *Concurrent Pos:* Consult, Brookhaven Nat Lab, 61-; consult, Nat Coun Radiation Protection & Measurements, 62-70, consociate mem, 76- *Mem:* Sigma Xi; AAAS; Am Asn Physics Teachers; Am Phys Soc. *Res:* Pyrotechnics; piezoelectricity; decay schemes; reactor shielding; neutron cross sections; cryogenics; energy system analysis. *Mailing Add:* 77 Southern Blvd East Patchogue NY 11772

SHORE, FRED L, b Bakersfield, Calif, Sept 3, 42; m 64. ORGANIC CHEMISTRY. *Educ:* Fresno State Col, BS, 64; Ariz State Univ, PhD(chem), 71. *Prof Exp:* Asst prof, 70-76, ASSOC PROF CHEM, JACKSON STATE UNIV, 76- *Mem:* Am Chem Soc. *Res:* Isolation, identification and estimation of organic compounds of importance to living organisms; stereochemical and isotopic studies. *Mailing Add:* Dept of Chem Jackson State Univ Jackson MS 39217

SHORE, HERBERT BARRY, b Brooklyn, NY, Nov 18, 39. THEORETICAL SOLID STATE PHYSICS. *Educ:* Mass Inst Technol, BS, 61; Univ Calif, Berkeley, PhD(physics), 66. *Prof Exp:* Asst res physicist, Univ Calif, San Diego, 66-67, asst prof physics, 67-75; assoc prof, 75-79, PROF PHYSICS, SAN DIEGO STATE UNIV, 79- *Mem:* Am Phys Soc; AAAS. *Res:* theory of paraelectric resonance; resonance in biological systems; electron-hole liquid; theory of electron gas; impurities in semiconductors; metal-insulator transition. *Mailing Add:* Dept of Physics San Diego State Univ San Diego CA 92182

SHORE, JAMES HENRY, b Winston-Salem, NC, Apr 6, 40; m 63; c 2. PSYCHIATRY. *Educ:* Duke Univ, MD, 65. *Prof Exp:* Chief, Portland Area Indian Health Serv, 69-73; assoc prof, 73-75, PROF PSYCHIAT, MED SCH, UNIV ORE, 75-, CHMN DEPT, 75-, DIR, COMMUNITY PSYCHIAT TRAINING PROG, HEALTH SCI CTR, 75- *Concurrent Pos:* Chmn ment health res comt, Health Prog Systs Ctr, Indian Health Serv, Tucson, Ariz, 70-73; consult, Psychiat Educ Br, Div Manpower & Training Progs, NIMH, 74-80 & Nat Tribal Chmns Asn, Am Indian & Alaskan Native Ment Health Res & Develop Ctr, Portland, Ore, 74-81; mem dirs adv bd, Ore Ment Health Div, Salem, 75. *Honors & Awards:* Commendation Medal, Dept Health, Educ & Welfare, 72. *Mem:* Fel Am Psychiat Asn; AMA. *Res:* Psychiatric epidemiology among American Indians; psychiatric education; suicidology; effects of civil commitment. *Mailing Add:* Univ of Ore Health Sci Ctr 3181 SW Sam Jackson Park Rd Portland OR 97201

SHORE, JOHN EDWARD, b Slough, Gt Brit, Sept 2, 46; US citizen; m 69; c 1. INFORMATION THEORY, SPEECH PROCESSING. *Educ:* Yale Univ, BS, 68; Univ Md, PhD(theoret physics), 74. *Prof Exp:* RES SCIENTIST PHYSICS & COMPUT SCI, NAVAL RES LAB, 68- *Concurrent Pos:* Res publ award, Naval Res Lab, 71, 76 & 78; prof lectr comput sci, George Washington Univ, 78-; adj lectr elec engr, Univ Md, 80-. *Mem:* Asn Comput Mach; Inst Elec & Electronic Engrs; Am Phys Soc. *Res:* Information theory, especially the foundations and applications of maximum entropy and related techniques; software engineering; programming language design; speech processing. *Mailing Add:* 906 East Capitol St NE Washington DC 20002

SHORE, JOSEPH D, b New York, NY, Apr 2, 34; m 68; c 2. ENZYMOLOGY, PHYSICAL BIOCHEMISTRY. *Educ:* Cornell Univ, BS, 55; Univ Mass, MS, 57; Rutgers Univ, PhD(biochem), 63. *Prof Exp:* Muscular Dystrophy Asn fel, Nobel Med Inst, Stockholm, Sweden, 64-66; sr staff investr dept biochem, 66-79, HEAD DIV BIOCHEM RES, HENRY FORD HOSP, 79- *Concurrent Pos:* Adj assoc prof, Med Sch, Wayne State Univ. *Mem:* Am Chem Soc; Am Soc Biol Chem; Sigma Xi; Biophys Soc. *Res:* Blood coagulation; dehydrogenase mechanisms; transient kinetics and fluorescence techniques. *Mailing Add:* Dept Biochem Henry Ford Hosp 2799 W Grand Blvd Detroit MI 48202

SHORE, MILES FREDERICK, b Chicago, Ill, May 26, 29; m 53; c 3. PSYCHIATRY. *Educ:* Univ Chicago, AB, 48; Harvard Univ, BA, 50, MD, 54; Am Bd Psychiat & Neurol, dipl, 60. *Prof Exp:* Intern, Univ Ill Res & Educ Hosp, 55; resident psychiat, Mass Ment Health Ctr, 55-56 & Beth Israel Hosp, Boston, 59-61; instr, Harvard Med Sch, 64-65; from asst prof to prof psychiat, Sch Med, Tufts Univ, 71-75, assoc dean community affairs, 72-75, dir ment health ctr, 68-75; BULLARD PROF PSYCHIAT, HARVARD MED SCH, 75- *Concurrent Pos:* Chmn bd trustees, Boston Psychoanal Soc & Inst, 70-73; dir community & ambulatory ment, New Eng Med Ctr Hosp, 72-75; supt & area dir, Mass Ment Health Ctr, 75- *Mem:* Fel Am Psychiat Asn; Am Psychoanal Asn; Group Advan Psychiat; Am Col Psychiatrists. *Res:* Community psychiatry; psychoanalysis; psychohistory. *Mailing Add:* 62 Meadowbrook Rd Needham MA 02192

SHORE, MORIS LAWRENCE, b Russia, Dec 7, 27; US citizen; m 58; c 3. METABOLIC KINETICS, RADIOBIOLOGY. *Educ:* Southwestern Univ, Memphis, BA, 50; Univ Tenn, PhD(physiol), 54. *Prof Exp:* Staff mem Biophysics Br, US Navy Radiol Defense Lab, 54-61; asst prof physiol, Marquette Univ, 61-62; chief Biophysics & asst officer in command, Res Br Lab, 62-67, chief, Physiol & Biophysics Lab, 67-69, chief, Exp Studies Br, 69-70, DIR, DIV BIOL EFFECTS, BUR RADIOL HEALTH, DEPT HEALTH & HUMAN SERV, FOOD & DRUG ADMIN, 70- *Concurrent Pos:* Chief, Physiol Sect, Res Serv, Wood Vet Admin Ctr, 61-62. *Mem:* Radiation Res Soc; Health Physics Soc; Res Soc; NY Acad Sci. *Res:* Tracer kinetics; phospholipid metabolism; experimental atherosclerosis; reticulo-endothelial system function; effects of ionizing and nonionizing radiation; development of regulatory and voluntary health protection standards and guidelines. *Mailing Add:* Food & Drug Admin HFX-100 5600 Fishers Lane Rockville MD 20857

SHORE, NOMIE ABRAHAM, b Chicago, Ill, Oct 2, 23; div; c 2. PEDIATRICS, HEMATOLOGY. *Educ:* Univ Calif, Los Angeles, BA, 47; Univ Southern Calif, MD, 53. *Prof Exp:* Intern med, Los Angeles County Gen Hosp, 52-53; resident pediat, Children's Hosp Los Angeles, 53-55, fel hemat, 55-56; asst clin prof pediat, Univ Calif, Los Angeles, 57-60; asst prof, 61-68, ASSOC PROF PEDIAT, SCH MED, UNIV SOUTHERN CALIF, 68-; ASSOC HEMATOLOGIST, CHILDREN'S HOSP, LOS ANGELES, 61- *Concurrent Pos:* Consult pediat hemat, St John's Hosp, Santa Monica, 61-; mem hon staff, Santa Monica Hosp, 61- *Mem:* AMA; Am Soc Hemat; Am Acad Pediat; Am Asn Cancer Res. *Res:* Evaluating the effects of chemotherapeutic agents in treatment of leukemia and other neoplastic diseases; erythropoietin physiology; bone marrow stem cell kinetics. *Mailing Add:* Children's Hosp of Los Angeles 4650 Sunset Blvd Los Angeles CA 90027

SHORE, PARKHURST ALAN, b Washington, DC, Sept 21; m. PHARMACOLOGY. *Educ:* George Washington Univ, BS, 49, MS, 52; Georgetown Univ, PhD(biochem), 55. *Prof Exp:* Chemist, Nat Inst Arthritis & Metab Dis, 49-50, chemist, Chem Pharmacol Lab, Nat Heart Inst, 50-57, head sect biochem of drug action, 57-60, dep chief, Lab, 60-61; assoc prof, 61-63, assoc dean grad studies, 68-73, PROF PHARMACOL, SOUTHWESTERN MED SCH, UNIV TEX HEALTH SCI CTR DALLAS, 63- *Concurrent Pos:* Co-ed, Advan Pharmacol, 62-68; mem coun, Am Soc Pharmacol & Exp Therapeut, 68-71; mem psychopharmacol study sect, NIH, 63-67 & pharmacol & toxicol rev comn, 67-69; mem comn probs drug safety, Drug Res Bd, Nat Acad Sci, 67-70. *Honors & Awards:* Abel Award, Am Soc Pharmacol & Exp Therapeut, 59. *Mem:* AAAS; Soc Neurosci; Am Col Neuropsychopharmacol; Sigma Xi; Am Soc Pharmacol & Exp Therapeut. *Res:* Biochemistry and physiology of catecholamines; 5-hydroxytryptamine; histamine; membrane permeability; drug absorption; disposition and metabolism; neuropsychopharmacology. *Mailing Add:* Dept Pharmacol Southwest Med Sch Univ Tex Health Sci Ctr Dallas TX 75235

SHORE, RICHARD A, b Boston, Mass, Aug 18, 46; m 69; c 2. RECURSION THEORY. *Educ:* Hebrew Col, BJEI, 66; Harvard Univ, AB, 68; Mass Inst Technol, PhD(math), 72. *Prof Exp:* Instr, Univ Chicago, 72-74; asst prof, 74-78, ASSOC PROF MATH, CORNELL UNIV, 78- *Concurrent Pos:* Asst prof, Univ Ill, 77; vis assoc prof, Univ Conn, Storrs, 79 & Mass Inst Technol, 80. *Mem:* Am Math Soc; Asn Symbolic Logic. *Res:* Computability theory: degrees of difficulty of computability, recursively enumerable sets and degrees; generalizations of recursion theory and applications and effective mathematics. *Mailing Add:* Dept Math White Hall Cornell Univ Ithaca NY 14853

SHORE, RICHARD EUGENE, b Visalia, Calif, July 5, 37; m 57; c 2. DEVELOPMENTAL BIOLOGY. *Educ:* Col of Pac, BA, 59; Duke Univ, MA, 61, PhD(zool), 63. *Prof Exp:* Am Cancer Soc grant, Cancer Res Intramural Coun, St Louis Univ, 63-64, asst prof biol, 63-66; res assoc biol div, Oak Ridge Nat Lab, 66-70; asst prof, 70-73, ASSOC PROF BIOL, UNIV TOLEDO, 73- *Concurrent Pos:* Owens-Ill fundamental res grant, 69-71. *Mem:* AAAS. *Res:* Differentiation; changes in proteins during development in frog embryos and in beef eye lenses; regulation of differentiation and cell division in Porifera and vertebrate embryos. *Mailing Add:* Dept of Biol Univ of Toledo Toledo OH 43606

SHORE, S(IDNEY), civil engineering, deceased

SHORE, SAMUEL DAVID, b Lewistown, Pa, Nov 9, 37; m 64; c 2. MATHEMATICS. *Educ:* Juniata Col, BS, 59; Pa State Univ, MA, 61, PhD(gen topology), 64. *Prof Exp:* Instr math, Pa State Univ, 64-65; asst prof, 65-70, ASSOC PROF MATH, UNIV NH, 70- *Mem:* Am Math Soc; Math Asn Am. *Res:* Spaces of continuous functions; compactifications and extensions; ordered spaces. *Mailing Add:* Dept of Math Univ of NH Durham NH 03824

SHORE, SHELDON GERALD, b Chicago, Ill, May 8, 30. INORGANIC CHEMISTRY. *Educ:* Univ Ill, BS, 51; Univ Mich, MS, 54, PhD(chem), 57. *Prof Exp:* Instr chem, Univ Mich, 56-57; from asst prof to assoc prof, 57-62, PROF CHEM, OHIO STATE UNIV, 65- *Mem:* Am Chem Soc. *Res:* Synthesis and study of transition metal and non-metal cluster systems: polynuclear metal carbonyl hydrides, metalloboranes, and boron hydrides. *Mailing Add:* Dept of Chem Ohio State Univ Columbus OH 43210

SHORE, STEVEN NEIL, b New York, NY, July, 16, 53; m 74. THEORETICAL ASTROPHYSICS. *Educ:* State Univ NY, Stony Brook, MSc, 74; Univ Toronto, PhD(astron), 78. *Prof Exp:* Res assoc astron, Columbia Univ, 78-79, lectr, 79e; ASST PROF ASTRON, CASE WESTERN RESERVE UNIV, 79- *Concurrent Pos:* Shapley lectr astron, Am Astron Soc, 80-; vis asst prof astron, Ohio State Univ, 81. *Mem:* Am Astron Soc; Sigma Xi; Hist Sci Soc. *Res:* Magnetic fields in stellar structure and atmospheres; chemical evolution of the galaxy; ultraviolet spectroscopy; history of science. *Mailing Add:* Case Western Reserve Univ 1975 Taylor Rd East Cleveland OH 44112

SHORE, VIRGIE GUINN, b Lavaca, Ark, Oct 20, 28; m 52. BIOCHEMISTRY, PHYSIOLOGY. *Educ:* Univ Calif, AB, 50, PhD(biochem), 55. *Prof Exp:* Res asst physiol, Sch Med, Wash Univ, 57-58, from res instr to res asst prof, 58-61, asst prof, 61-63; BIOCHEMIST, BIO-MED DIV, LAWRENCE LIVERMORE LAB, UNIV CALIF, 63- *Concurrent Pos:* Mem, Metab Study Sect, NIH & exec comt coun on arteriosclerosis, Am Heart Asn. *Mem:* Am Physiol Soc. *Res:* Resonance energy transfer; structure of lipoproteins and membranes. *Mailing Add:* Bio-Med Div Lawrence Livermore Lab Livermore CA 94550

SHORER, PHILIP, DELETE THIS FIELD, b Brooklyn, NY, Dec, 9, 51. THEORETICAL ATOMIC PHYSICS. *Educ:* Stevens Inst Technol, BS, 74; Harvard Univ, AM & PhD(physics), 79. *Prof Exp:* Teaching fel physics, Dept Physics, Harvard Univ, 75-76, res asst, Dept Astron, 76-79; jr res assoc, Sci & Eng Res Coun, Daresbury Lab, 79-80; FEL, HARVARD-SMITHSONIAN CTR ASTROPHYS, 80- *Concurrent Pos:* Guest res assoc, Argonne Nat Lab, 80; res assoc, Radiation Lab, Univ Notre Dame. *Mem:* Am Phys Soc. *Res:* Relativistic approaches to atomic processes; determinations of atomic oscillator strengths, excitation energies, transition probabilities, and dynamic dipole polarizabilities using the relativistic random-phase approximation. *Mailing Add:* Radiation Lab Univ Notre Dame Notre Dame IN 46556

SHORES, DAVID AURTHER, b Towanda, Pa, Jan 10, 41; m 63; c 1. METALLURGICAL CHEMISTRY. *Educ:* Pa State Univ, BS, 62, MS, 64, PhD(mat sci), 67. *Prof Exp:* Fel metall, Ohio State Univ, 68-70; metallurgist, Large Steam Turbine Generator Div, 70-74, METALLURGIST HOT CORROSION, CORP RES & DEVELOP CTR, GEN ELEC CO, 74- *Mem:* Electrochem Soc; Am Inst Mining, Metall & Petrol Engrs. *Res:* High temperature surface stability of gas turbine alloys; thermochemistry and electrochemistry of corroding electrodes in molten salts; high temperature defect reactions in solid oxides. *Mailing Add:* Gen Elec Co PO Box 8 KI-3A46 Schenectady NY 12345

SHORES, THOMAS STEPHEN, b Kansas City, Kans, May 28, 42; m 68. MATHEMATICS. *Educ:* Univ Kans, BA, 64, MA, 65, PhD(math), 68. *Prof Exp:* Assoc prof, 68-77, dept vchmn, 76-79, PROF MATH, UNIV NEBR, LINCOLN, 77-, ACTG CHMN, 81- *Mem:* Am Math Soc; Math Asn Am. *Res:* Generalized solvable and nilpotent groups; structure theory for modules and commutative ring theory. *Mailing Add:* Dept of Math Univ of Nebr Lincoln NE 68508

SHOREY, HARRY HASLAM, entomology, see previous edition

SHORR, BERNARD, b New York, NY, July 5, 28; m 58. OPERATIONS RESEARCH. *Educ:* City Col NY, BA, 50; NY Univ, MS, 51, PhD, 70. *Prof Exp:* Meteorologist, Gen Elec Co, Wash, 51-55; staff mem div sponsored res, Mass Inst Technol, 56-58; res assoc opers res, 58-63, asst dir res, 63-66, assoc dir, 66-70, SECOND VPRES, CORP RES DIV, TRAVELERS INS CO, 70- *Concurrent Pos:* Lectr, Univ Conn, 70-77. *Mem:* Fel AAAS; Opers Res Soc Am; Inst Mgt Sci. *Res:* Management; financial and economic analysis. *Mailing Add:* Corp Res Div Travelers Ins Co 1 Tower Square Hartford CT 06115

SHORT, BYRON ELLIOTT, b Putnam, Tex, Dec 29, 01; m 37; c 2. MECHANICAL ENGINEERING. *Educ:* Univ Tex, BS, 26, MS, 30; Cornell Univ, MME, 36, PhD(mech eng), 39. *Prof Exp:* From instr to asst prof mech eng, 26-35, from assoc prof to prof, 36-73, chmn dept, 45-47, 51-53, actg dean, 48-49, in charge heat eng lab, 30-64, EMER PROF MECH ENG, UNIV TEX, AUSTIN, 73- *Concurrent Pos:* Consult, Defense Res Lab, Tex, 45-63, Tex Gulf Sulphur Co, 49-54, Oak Ridge Nat Lab, 56-59, Atomics Int, 61-63 & US Army Eng Corp, 64-68. *Mem:* AAAS; Am Soc Mech Engrs; Am Soc Eng Educ; Am Soc Heating, Refrig & Air-Conditioning Engrs. *Res:* Fluid flow; refrigeration; heat transfer. *Mailing Add:* Dept of Mech Eng Univ of Tex PO Box 7456 Austin TX 78712

SHORT, CHARLES ROBERT, b Rochester, NY, Nov 7, 38; m 64; c 2. PHARMACOLOGY. *Educ:* Ohio State Univ, DVM, 63, MS, 65; Univ Mo-Columbia, PhD, 69. *Prof Exp:* From instr to assoc prof pharmacol, Sch Med, Univ Mo-Columbia, 65-75; PROF VET PHARMACOL & TOXICOL, SCH VET MED, LA STATE UNIV, BATON ROUGE, 75-, VET DIAG TOXICOLOGIST, 76- *Concurrent Pos:* Spec fel med educ, Univ Southern Calif, 74. *Mem:* AAAS; NY Acad Sci; Am Soc Pharmacol & Exp Therapeutics; Am Col Vet Toxicologists. *Res:* Drug-disposition pharmacology in the fetus and neonate; chemical carcinogenesis. *Mailing Add:* Dept of Vet Physiol Louisiana State Univ Baton Rouge LA 70803

SHORT, DONALD RAY, JR, b Camp McCoy, Wis, Sept 13, 44; m 78; c 2. MATHEMATICS. *Educ:* Univ Calif, Los Angeles, BA, 65; Ore State Univ, PhD(math), 69. *Prof Exp:* From asst prof to assoc prof, 69-75, PROF MATH & DEAN, COL SCI, SAN DIEGO STATE UNIV, 75- *Mem:* Sigma Xi; Am Math Soc; Soc Indust & Appl Math. *Res:* Algebraic topology; cohomology theory; sheaf theory; spectral sequences; branched immersions. *Mailing Add:* Dept of Math San Diego State Univ San Diego CA 92182

SHORT, EVERETT C, JR, b Monett, Mo, Dec 27, 31; c 3. BIOCHEMISTRY. *Educ:* Kent State Univ, BS, 58; Colo State Univ, DVM, 62; Univ Minn, PhD(biochem), 68. *Prof Exp:* From instr to assoc prof, Col Vet Med, Univ Minn, St Paul, 64-73, prof biochem & assoc dean, 73-78; PROF & HEAD PHYSIOL SCI, COL VET MED, OKLA STATE UNIV, STILLWATER, 80- *Mem:* Am Soc Microbiol; Am Vet Med Asn; Soc Exp Biol Med; Soc Environ Toxicol & Chem. *Res:* Effects of toxic substances on aquatic organisms; enteric diseases of baby pigs. *Mailing Add:* Col Vet Med Okla State Univ Stillwater OK 74074

SHORT, FRANKLIN WILLARD, b Charleston, WVa, Feb 24, 28; m 57; c 2. MEDICINAL CHEMISTRY, CLINICAL DRUG DEVELOPMENT. *Educ:* Univ Buffalo, BA, 48; Columbia Univ, PhD(org chem), 52. *Prof Exp:* Jr chemist, Nat Aniline Div, Allied Chem Corp, 47-48; from assoc res chemist to sr res chemist, Parke, Davis & Co, 52-67, assoc lab dir org chem, 67-70, sect dir chem dept, 70-78, SR CLIN SCIENTIST, CLIN RES DEPT, WARNER-LAMBERT/PARKE-DAVIS PHARMACEUT RES DIV, 78- *Mem:* Am Chem Soc. *Mailing Add:* Clin Res Dept Pharmaceut Res Div 2800 Plymouth Rd Ann Arbor MI 48105

SHORT, HENRY LAUGHTON, b Penn Yan, NY, Apr 6, 34; m 62; c 2. ECOLOGY, WILDLIFE BIOLOGY. *Educ:* Swarthmore Col, BA, 56; Johns Hopkins Univ, MS, 59; Mich State Univ, PhD(fisheries, wildlife), 62. *Prof Exp:* Res asst vert ecol, Johns Hopkins Univ, 57-58; res asst fisheries & wildlife, Mich State Univ, 59-61; asst prof & mem grad fac forest recreation & wildlife, Colo State Univ, 61-63, wildlife nutritionist, Colo Coop Wildlife Res Unit, 61-63; wildlife biologist, Southern Forest Exp Sta, Forest Serv, USDA, 64-73, wildlife biologist, Rocky Mountain Forest & Range Exp Sta, 73-77; TERRESTRIAL ECOLOGIST, WESTERN ENERGY & LAND USE TEAM, FISH & WILDLIFE SERV, US DEPT INTERIOR, 77- *Concurrent Pos:* Cooperator, Int Biol Prog, 65; mem, Grad Fac Forestry, Stephen F Austin State Univ, 64-73 & Wildlife Sci, Tex A&M Univ, 69-73. *Mem:* Ecol Soc Am; Wildlife Soc; Am Soc Mammal; Am Soc Animal Sci. *Res:* Ecology and life history of migratory bats; anatomy, digestive physiology and nutrition of deer; determination of physiology and nutrition of deer; determination of physiological requirements of wild animals; forage quality for wild animals; predicted and determined quality of wildlife habitat. *Mailing Add:* Western Energy & Land Use Team 2625 Redwing Rd Ft Collins CO 80521

SHORT, JAMES HAROLD, b Leavenworth, Kans, July 9, 28; m 73; c 1. PHARMACOLOGY. *Educ:* Stanford Univ, BS, 50; Univ Kans, PhD(pharmaceut chem), 54. *Prof Exp:* Res chemist med chem, Abbott Labs, 56-71; res assoc, 72, asst prof pharmacol, Univ Louisville, 73-76; SUPVR CHEM, ADRIA LABS, 76- *Mem:* AAAS; Chem Soc Gt Brit; Am Chem Soc. *Res:* Synthesis and structure-activity relationships of anthrocycline antibiotics, cardiovascular agents and central nervous systems agents. *Mailing Add:* Adria Labs Inc PO Box 16529 Columbus OH 43216

SHORT, JAMES N, b Dayton, Ohio, Nov 14, 22; m 45; c 4. POLYMER CHEMISTRY, RESEARCH ADMINISTRATION. *Educ:* Univ Cincinnati, BChE, 45, MS, 47, ScD, 49. *Prof Exp:* Res chemist, Warren-Teed Labs, Ohio, 49-51; res chemist, 51-55, mgr solution polymerization sect, 55-59, rubber synthesis br, 59-66, rubber & carbon black processes br, 66-69 & chem processes br, 69-72, MGR PLASTICS DEVELOP BR, PHILLIPS PETROL CO, 72- *Mem:* Am Chem Soc; Soc Plastics Eng. *Res:* Stereospecific polymerization; polyolefins; synthetic rubber engineering plastics; fibers; technical direction; polymers. *Mailing Add:* 2360 Windsor Way Bartlesville OK 74003

SHORT, JOHN ALBERT, b Pittsburgh, Pa, Feb 2, 36; m 62; c 1. CELL BIOLOGY, HISTOLOGY. *Educ:* Univ Pittsburgh, BS, 57, PhD(anat & cell biol), 72. *Prof Exp:* Res asst, 63-67, res assoc, 71-75, res asst prof, 75-76, ASST PROF ANAT AND EMBRYOL, UNIV PITTSBURGH, 76- *Concurrent Pos:* Res biochemist, Vet Admin Med Ctr, 71-80, co-investr, 75-80. *Mem:* Fedn Am Scientists; Am Asn Anatomists; Am Soc Cell Biol. *Res:* Control of mammalian cell proliferation in vivo, including the effects of the thyroid hormones and glucocorticoids on this process. *Mailing Add:* 5753 Phillips Rd Gibsoma PA 15044

SHORT, LESTER LE ROY, JR, b Port Chester, NY, May 29, 33; m 55, 78; c 2. ORNITHOLOGY. *Educ:* Cornell Univ, BS, 55, PhD(vert zool), 59. *Prof Exp:* Asst vert zool, Cornell Univ, 54-59; instr biol, Adelphi Univ, 60-62, asst prof, 62; Chapman fel, Am Mus Natural Hist, 62-63; chief bird sect, Bird & Mammal Labs, US Fish & Wildlife Serv, 63-66; assoc cur, 66-68, CUR, AM MUS NATURAL HIST, 68- *Concurrent Pos:* Hon cur NAm birds, Smithsonian Inst, 63-66; adj prof, City Univ NY, 70- *Mem:* Soc Study Evolution; Am Ornith Union; Cooper Ornith Soc; Soc Syst Zool; Royal Australasian Ornith Union. *Res:* Systematic and evolutionary zoology; speciation; hybridization; taxonomy and classification of birds; avian ethology and ecology; zoogeography; ornithology. *Mailing Add:* Dept Ornith Am Mus Natural Hist New York NY 10024

SHORT, MICHAEL ARTHUR, b London, Eng, Aug 15, 30; US citizen; m 57; c 4. ANALYTICAL CHEMISTRY. *Educ:* Univ Bristol, Eng, BSc, 52, MSc, 57; Pa State Univ, PhD(fuel technol), 61. *Prof Exp:* Scientist, Gen Elec Co, Eng, 54-57; mem tech staff, Bell Telephone Lab, NJ, 61-64; engr, Assoc Elec Indust, 64-67; staff scientist, Ford Motor Co, Dearborn, Mich, 67-80; PRIN SCIENTIST, OCCIDENTAL RES CORP, CA, 80- *Concurrent Pos:* Lectr, Calif State Univ, Fullerton, 82. *Mem:* Am Crystallog Asn; Am Phys Soc; Am Chem Soc; Am Soc Metals; Microbeam Anal Soc. *Res:* Development of improved instrumentation and analytical techniques for X-ray diffraction, X-ray fluorescence and electron microprobe analysis. *Mailing Add:* Occidental Res Corp PO Box 19601 Irvine CA 92713

SHORT, NICHOLAS MARTIN, b St Louis, Mo, July 18, 27; m 61; c 1. GEOLOGY. *Educ:* St Louis Univ, BS, 51; Wash Univ, MA, 54; Mass Inst Technol, PhD(geol), 58. *Prof Exp:* Instr geol, Univ Mo, 54-55; geologist, Gulf Res & Develop Co, Pa, 57-59; geologist-physicist, Lawrence Radiation Lab, Univ Calif, 59-64; from asst prof to assoc prof geol, Univ Houston, 64-67; Nat Acad Sci res assoc, Planetology Br, 67-69, res geologist, Earth Resources Prog, 69-77, dir training, Regional Appln Prog, 77-81, RES SCIENTIST, GEOPHYS BR, GODDARD SPACE FLIGHT CTR, NASA, 81- *Mem:* Fel Geol Soc Am. *Res:* Geochemistry; astrogeology; shock effects in meteorite craters and underground nuclear explosion sites; remote sensing. *Mailing Add:* Eastern Regional Remote Sensing Goddard Space Flight Ctr NASA Greenbelt MD 20771

SHORT, OLIVER ALTON, b Trenton, NJ, Feb 24, 12; m; c 2. ELECTRONICS. *Educ:* Johns Hopkins Univ, BS, 34; Yale Univ, PhD(phys chem), 37. *Prof Exp:* Chemist, NJ Zinc Co, Pa, 37-41; chemist & res fel, E I du Pont de Nemours & Co, Inc, 46-77; RETIRED. *Mem:* Am Chem Soc. *Res:* Zinc pigments and alloys; chemical warfare protective equipment; ceramics; dielectric constants of dioxane-water mixtures; printed electronic circuits and components; noble metal chemistry. *Mailing Add:* 321 NE 18th Ave Ocala FL 32670

SHORT, PAUL HENRY, forest products, wood chemistry, see previous edition

SHORT, ROBERT ALLEN, b Dayton, Wash, Nov 7, 27; m 49; c 7. ELECTRICAL ENGINEERING, COMPUTER SCIENCE. *Educ:* Ore State Univ, BS, 49, BA, 52; Stevens Inst Technol, MS, 56; Stanford Univ, PhD(elec eng), 61. *Prof Exp:* Mem tech staff, Bell Tel Labs, 52-56; sr res engr, Stanford Res Inst, 56-66; PROF ELEC ENG & COMPUT SCI, ORE STATE UNIV, 66-, CHMN DEPT COMPUT SCI, 72- *Concurrent Pos:* Lectr, Santa Clara Univ, 65-66; mem gov bd, Inst Elec & Electronics Comput Soc, 70-72, 74-76, ed-in-chief, 71-75, spec tech ed, 77-; ed, Trans on Comput, Inst Elec & Electronics Engrs, 71-75. *Mem:* AAAS; Inst Elec & Electronics Engrs; Asn Comput Mach; Am Soc Cybernetics. *Res:* Information systems, computer science, logic design, switching theory, automata, fault-tolerant computing, coding theory, teaching effectiveness. *Mailing Add:* Dept of Comput Sci Ore State Univ Corvallis OR 97331

SHORT, ROBERT BROWN, b Changsha, China, Feb 28, 20; US citizen; m 47; c 3. PARASITOLOGY. *Educ:* Maryville Col, BA, 41; Univ Va, MS, 45; Univ Mich, PhD(zool), 50. *Prof Exp:* Instr math, Sewanee Mil Acad, 41-43; instr math & biol, Va Episcopal Sch, 43-44; from asst prof to assoc prof biol sci, 50-57, PROF BIOL SCI, FLA STATE UNIV, 57- *Concurrent Pos:* Mem study sect trop med & parasitol, NIH, 65-69; NIH spec res fel, Tulane Univ, La, 70-71. *Mem:* Am Soc Parasitol (vpres, 77, pres, 82); Am Soc Trop Med & Hyg; AAAS; Am Micros Soc. *Res:* Biology and cytogenetics of schistosomes and other trematodes. *Mailing Add:* Dept of Biol Sci Fla State Univ Tallahassee FL 32306

SHORT, ROLLAND WILLIAM PHILLIP, b Decatur, Ill, Dec 16, 22; m 69; c 1. CARBOHYDRATE CHEMISTRY. *Educ:* James Millikin Univ, AB, 49; Univ Ill, MS, 50, PhD(org chem), 53. *Prof Exp:* Sr res chemist, E I du Pont de Nemours & Co, 53-56; SR RES CHEMIST, RES & DEVELOP, AE STALEY MFG CO, 56- *Mem:* Am Chem Soc. *Res:* Diels-Alder reactions; synthesis of biphenyls; emulsion polymerization; organic films; chemical reaction of starch; pharmaceutical and food starches. *Mailing Add:* AE Staley Mfg Co Decatur IL 62521

SHORT, SARAH HARVEY, b Little Falls, NY, Sept 22, 24; m 46; c 3. NUTRITION, BIOCHEMISTRY. *Educ:* Syracuse Univ, BS, 46, PhD(nutrit), 70, EdD(instrnl technol), 75; State Univ NY, Upstate Med Ctr, MS, 66. *Prof Exp:* Researcher chem, Bristol Labs, 46-50; asst prof chem, State Univ NY, Upstate Med Ctr, 63-80; PROF NUTRIT, SYRACUSE UNIV, 66- *Concurrent Pos:* Bd adv, Am Coun Sci & Health, 78-; Int Cong Individualized Instr, 75-76; resource scholar, Heritage Found, 80- *Mem:* Am Dietetic Asn; Soc Nutrit Educ; Asn Educ Commun & Technol; Inst Food Technologists; Am Col Sports Med. *Res:* Nutrition education at university and medical school including developing and evaluating self instruction units using computer assisted instruction, audiovisual media and rate controlled speech; evaluation of trained athletes' diet using computer analysis. *Mailing Add:* Dept Human Nutrit Syracuse Univ Syracuse NY 13210

SHORT, TED H, b Wauseon, Ohio, Mar 13, 42; m 68; c 2. AGRICULTURAL ENGINEERING, HORTICULTURAL ENGINEERING. *Educ:* Ohio State Univ, BS, 65, MS, PhD(agr eng), 69. *Prof Exp:* Res assoc, Ohio State Univ, 65-69; asst prof, 69-74, ASSOC PROF AGR ENGR, OHIO AGR RES & DEVELOP CTR, 74- *Concurrent Pos:* Consult, TVA Waste Heat Prog, 75-76 & Bechtel Corp Waste Heat Study, 78; Greenhouse res exchange, Holland, 81. *Honors & Awards:* Concept of the Year, Am Soc Agr Engrs, 77. *Mem:* Sigma Xi; Solar Energy Soc; Int Soc Hort Sci; Am Soc Agr Engrs. *Res:* Energy conservation for greenhouses; mechanization of greenhouse growing systems; solar ponds for heating greenhouses and rural residences; passive solar greenhouse heating systems. *Mailing Add:* Dept of Agr Eng Ohio Agr Res & Develop Ctr Wooster OH 44691

SHORT, W(ILLIAM) LEIGH, b Calgary, Alta, Jan 30, 35; c 2. CHEMICAL & ENVIRONMENTAL ENGINEERING. *Educ:* Univ Alta, BSc, 56, MSc, 57; Univ Mich, PhD(chem eng), 62. *Prof Exp:* Proj engr, Edmonton Works, Can Industs Ltd, 57-59; res engr, Chevron Res Co, Calif, 62-67; from asst prof to prof chem eng, Univ Mass, Amherst, 67-79, assoc head dept, 69-76, head dept, 76-79; mgr, Houston Eng Div, 79-80, VPRES & DIR, ENVIRON ENG DIV, ENVIRON RES & TECHNOL INC, 80- *Concurrent Pos:* Pub Health Serv res grant & Co Dir Air Pollution training grant, 69-; consult, Kenics Corp, M W Kellogg & Arthur D Little, 69-, Environ Protection Agency, 70- & Gen Acct Off, 78; mem sci adv bd, Environ Protection Agency, 76- *Mem:* Am Inst Chem Engrs; Am Chem Soc; Air Pollution Control Asn; NY Acad Sci. *Res:* Chemical engineering applications in air and water pollution control; thermodynamics. *Mailing Add:* Environ Eng Group 6666 Harwin Dr Houston TX 77036

SHORT, WALLACE W(ALTER), b Ogdensburg, NY, May 21, 30; m 58; c 4. FLUID DYNAMICS, HIGH ENERGY LASERS. *Educ:* Mo Sch Mines, BS, 51; Calif Inst Technol, MS, 53, PhD(chem & elec eng), 58. *Prof Exp:* Prod supvr, Merck & Co, Inc, 51-52; res engr, Rocketdyne Div, N Am Aviation, Inc, 53; from res scientist to staff scientist, Convair Div, Gen Dynamics Corp, 58-62; mem tech staff, Gen Res Corp, 62-74; PRES, APPL TECHNOL ASSOCS, 75- *Concurrent Pos:* Consult, Inst Defense Anal, Washington, DC, 64-70. *Res:* Theoretical and experimental heat and mass transfer, especially evaporation, ablation and boundary layer flow; rocket propulsion, especially chemical and electrical devices; reentry phenomena; hypersonic wakes; radar scattering by plasmas; ballistic missile defense; high energy laser controls. *Mailing Add:* Appl Technol Assocs Box 9154 Albuquerque NM 87119

SHORT, WILLIAM ARTHUR, b West Chester, Pa, Feb 18, 25; m 50; c 2. ORGANIC CHEMISTRY, BIOCHEMISTRY. *Educ:* Furman Univ, BS, 50; Univ SC, MS, 52; Univ Ala, MS, 57, PhD(biochem), 61. *Prof Exp:* Res asst org chem & biochem, Southern Res Inst, 52-61; prof chem & chmn div natural sci & math, 61-77, PROF CHEM & CHMN DEPT, ATHENS STATE COL, ALA, 77- *Mem:* Am Chem Soc; fel Am Inst Chemists. *Res:* Carbohydrate chemistry. *Mailing Add:* Dept Chem Athens State Col Athens AL 35611

SHORTER, DANIEL ALBERT, b Goltry, Okla, May 20, 27; m 46; c 4. ENTOMOLOGY, ZOOLOGY. *Educ:* Northwestern Okla State Univ, BS, 49; Okla State Univ, MS, 60, PhD(entom), 66. *Prof Exp:* Instr pub schs, Kans, 49-58; dir admin, 72-75, PROF BIOL, NORTHWESTERN OKLA ST UNIV, 60-72, 75- *Mem:* Am Soc Mammal; Entom Soc Am. *Res:* Syrphidae of Oklahoma; ecology of the beaver. *Mailing Add:* Dept of Biol Northwestern Okla State Univ Alva OK 73717

SHORTER, ROY GERRARD, b London, Eng, Jan 11, 25; US citizen; m 48; c 2. EXPERIMENTAL MEDICINE. *Educ:* Univ London, MB, BS, 48, MD, 52; FRCPath, 71. *Prof Exp:* Fulbright travel award, 58-59; consult physician, Sect Path, 61-66, Sect Surg Res, 66-68 & Sect tissue & Org Transplantation, 68-71, consult physician exp med, Sect Anat Path, 71-75, prof path, 74-75, CONSULT PHYSICIAN EXP MED, SECT ANAT PATH & DEPT MED, MAYO CLIN & FOUND, 75-, PROF PATH & MED, MAYO MED SCH, 75- *Mem:* Am Asn Path & Bact; Am Gastroenterol Asn; Soc Exp Biol & Med; Brit Asn Clin Path; Brit Soc Gastroenterol. *Res:* Cytotoxicity of lymphocytes for colonic cells in patients with non-specific inflammatory bowel disease. *Mailing Add:* Sect Exp & Anatomic Path Mayo Clin 200 First St SW Rochester MN 55901

SHORTESS, DAVID KEEN, b Baltimore, Md, July 29, 30; m 49; c 4. GENETICS, PLANT PHYSIOLOGY. *Educ:* Lycoming Col, BA, 52; Pa State Univ, MEd, 59, PhD(genetics), 66. *Prof Exp:* Teacher high sch, Pa, 55-60; asst prof biol, Bloomsburg State Col, 61-63; actg head dept, 67-68, head dept, 68-72, ASSOC PROF BIOL, N MEX INST MINING & TECHNOL, 66- *Concurrent Pos:* Fulbright-Hays lectr, Univ Jordan, 77-78. *Mem:* AAAS; Am Genetic Asn. *Res:* Elaboration of genetic and physiological aspects of seed reserve proteins. *Mailing Add:* Dept Biol NMex Inst Mining & Technol Socorro NM 87801

SHORTLE, WALTER CHARLES, b Laconia, NH, Apr 26, 45; m 66; c 4. PLANT PATHOLOGY. *Educ:* Univ NH, BS, 68, MS, 70; NC State Univ, PhD(plant path), 74. *Prof Exp:* Res asst plant path, Univ NH, 68-70 & NC State Univ, 70-74; RES PLANT PATHOLOGIST, NORTHEASTERN FOREST EXP STA, US FOREST SERV, 74- *Mem:* Am Phytopath Soc. *Res:* Basic research in biochemistry and physiology of diseases which result in decay of wood in living trees. *Mailing Add:* Northeastern Forest Exp Sta Box 640 Durham NH 03824

SHORTRIDGE, ROBERT GLENN, JR, b Los Angeles, Calif, Aug 19, 45. CHEMICAL KINETICS. *Educ:* Loyola Univ, Los Angeles, BS, 67; Univ Calif, Irvine, PhD(chem), 71. *Prof Exp:* Res chem, Pa State Univ, 71-73; res assoc, Naval Res Lab, 73-75; asst res chemist, Dept Chem & Statewide Air Pollution Res Ctr, Univ Calif, Riverside, 75-77; MEM STAFF, BELL AEROS TEXTRON, BUFFALO, 77- *Mem:* Am Chem Soc; Sigma Xi. *Res:* Product and mechanistic studies of air pollution related chemical reactions; chemical identification of atmospheric contaminants. *Mailing Add:* Bell Aeros Textron PO Box 1 Mail Zone B49 Buffalo NY 14240

SHORTRIDGE, ROBERT WILLIAM, b Newport News, Va, Sept 1, 18; m 47; c 4. SCIENCE COMMUNICATIONS, TECHNOLOGY COMMUNICATIONS. *Educ:* Wabash Col, AB, 38; Ohio State Univ, PhD(org chem), 43. *Prof Exp:* Res chemist, Monsanto Chem Co, Ohio, 43-45; assoc chemist, Midwest Res Inst, 45-48; res chemist, Commercial Solvents Corp, 48-51; sr chemist, Midwest Res Inst, 53-57, head phys chem sect, 57-63, head org chem sect & asst dir chem div, 63-68; DIR TECH INFO CTR, UNIV MO, 68- *Mem:* AAAS; Sigma Xi. *Res:* Scientific and technological information transfer; non-metallic materials technology; separation and purification. *Mailing Add:* Tech Info Ctr Univ of Mo Oxford Hall Kansas City MO 64110

SHOSTAK, STANLEY, b Brooklyn, NY, Nov 3, 38; div; c 2. DEVELOPMENTAL BIOLOGY, PRIMATOLOGY. *Educ:* Cornell Univ, BA, 59; Brown Univ, ScM, 61, PhD(biol), 64. *Prof Exp:* NIH fel, Western Reserve Univ, 64-65; asst prof, 65-70, ASSOC PROF BIOL, UNIV PITTSBURGH, 70- *Mem:* Soc Develop Biol. *Res:* Investigates role of mitosis and migration in morphogenesis of Hydra; observes social patterns in caged squirrel monkey colony. *Mailing Add:* Dept of Biol Sci Univ of Pittsburgh Pittsburgh PA 15260

SHOTLAND, EDWIN, b Rulzheim, Ger, Dec 18, 08; nat US; m 46; c 2. PHYSICS. *Educ:* Univ Munich, BS, 31, MS, 32; Univ Heidelberg, Dr phil nat, 34. *Prof Exp:* Phys engr, Kurman Electronic Co, NY, 41-42, Kompolite Co, 42 & Kurman Electronic Co, NY, 45-46; sr proj anal engr, Chance Vought Aircraft, Inc, Conn, 46-48, Tex, 48-50; sr staff mem & physicist, 50-55, res proj supvr, 55-57, PRIN STAFF MEM, APPL PHYSICS LAB, JOHNS HOPKINS UNIV, 58- *Mem:* Am Phys Soc. *Res:* Dynamics of aircraft, missiles and artificial satellites; aeroelasticity of airframes; information theory and communication engineering; missile guidance and radar intelligence; investigation of communication by radio millimeter waves. *Mailing Add:* 418 E Indian Spring Dr Silver Spring MD 20901

SHOTT, LEONARD D, b Twin Falls, Idaho, June 10, 34; m 58; c 3. VETERINARY PATHOLOGY. *Educ:* Colo A&M Col, BS, 57; Colo State Univ, DVM, 59, PhD(vet path), 67; Am Col Vet Pathologists, dipl. *Prof Exp:* Vet, Hawthorne Vet Clin, 59-63; NIH trainee path, Colo State Univ, 63-67; vet pathologist, Hazleton Labs, Inc, 67-71; head dept, 71-81, SR HEAD, DEPT PATH, SYNTEX RES, 81- *Mem:* Am Col Vet Pathologists; Am Vet Med Asn; Int Acad Path. *Res:* Drug safety evaluation for human and veterinary pharmaceuticals; studies utilizing common laboratory animals and sophisticated laboratory techniques. *Mailing Add:* Syntex Res 3401 Hillview Ave Palo Alto CA 94304

SHOTTAFER, JAMES EDWARD, b Utica, NY, Dec 13, 30; m 53; c 2. MATERIALS SCIENCE, WOOD TECHNOLOGY. *Educ:* State Univ NY Col Forestry, Syracuse Univ, BS, 54, MS, 56; Mich State Univ, PhD(wood technol), 64. *Prof Exp:* Design group leader, Mat Design, United Aircraft Corp, 59-61; res group leader wood, Brunswick Corp, 61-62, res group leader physics, 62-64; assoc prof, 64-70, PROF WOOD TECHNOL, SCH FOREST RESOURCES, UNIV MAINE, ORONO, 70- *Concurrent Pos:* Consult, 64- *Mem:* Soc Wood Sci & Technol; Forest Prod Res Soc; Am Soc Testing & Mat. *Res:* Materials science and technology, especially on wood, adhesives, nonmetallic materials; study of adhesion and other surface phenomena; materials processing technology; operations analysis; research management. *Mailing Add:* Sch of Forest Resources Univ of Maine Orono ME 04473

SHOTTS, ADOLPH CALVERAN, b Rush Springs, Okla, Dec 28, 25; m 54; c 2. ORGANIC CHEMISTRY. *Educ:* Cent State Col, Okla, BS, 50. *Prof Exp:* Teacher & head sci & math, High Sch, NMex, 50-52; from asst res chemist to assoc res chemist, Continental Oil Co, 52-58; res chemist, Petrol Chem, Inc, S8-60; sect supvr anal chem, Cities Serv Res & Develop Co, 60-62; tech staff asst, Columbian Carbon Co, 62-64, asst to dir, Lake Charles Chem Res Ctr, 64-67, admin mgr, Technol & Planning Div, NJ, 67-68, mgr bus serv, Cities Serv Res & Develop Co, 68-74, prod mgr, Petrochem Sales Dept, Cities Serv Oil Co, 74-76, PROJ COORDR, ADMIN DIV, CHEM GROUP, CITIES SERV CO, 76- DEPT, CITIES SERV OIL CO, 74- *Concurrent Pos:* Mgr environ & safety affairs, Columbian Chem Co, 80. *Mem:* Am Chem Soc. *Res:* Organic chemical research as applied to petrochemicals; hydrocarbon oxidations. *Mailing Add:* Columbian Chem Co Box 37/841 Tulsa OK 74102

SHOTTS, EMMETT BOOKER, JR, b Jasper, Ala, Sept 23, 31; m 56; c 2. MEDICAL MICROBIOLOGY, VETERINARY MICROBIOLOGY. *Educ:* Univ Ala, BS, 52; Med Col Ala, cert, 53; Univ Ga, MS, 58, PhD, 66. *Prof Exp:* Asst microbiol & prev med, Sch Vet Med, Univ Ga, 56-57, res assoc path & parasitol, Southeastern Coop Deer Dis Study, 57-58; med bacteriologist, Vet Pub Health Lab, Commun Dis Ctr, USPHS, 59-62, res microbiologist, Rabies Invest Lab, 62-64; asst prof path & parasitol, 66-68, chief, Clin Microbiol Lab, 66-78, from asst prof to assoc prof, 69-76, PROF MED MICROBIOL, COL VET MED, UNIV GA, 76-, MEM GRAD FAC, 67-, CONSULT, MICROBIOL LAB, COL VET MED, 78- *Concurrent Pos:* Consult microbiol, Southeastern Comp Wildlife Dis Study, 66-; specialist, Pub Health & Med Lab Microbiol, Am Acad Microbiol. *Mem:* Fel Am Soc Microbiol; Wildlife Dis Asn; Am Fisheries Soc; Int Asn Aquatic Animal Med; Conf Res Workers Animal Dis. *Res:* Leptospira, serology, culture, isolation and identification; food borne diseases; diagnostic bacteriology; fluorescent antibody applications; virus-helminth interrelationships; zoonoses; diseases of fresh and salt water fish; Aeromonas, Edwardsiella and Flexibacter. *Mailing Add:* Dept of Med Microbiol Col Vet Med Univ of Ga Athens GA 30601

SHOTWELL, ODETTE LOUISE, b Denver, Colo, May 4, 22. ORGANIC CHEMISTRY. *Educ:* Mont State Col, BS, 44; Univ Ill, MS, 46, PhD(org chem), 48. *Prof Exp:* Asst inorg chem, Univ Ill, 44-48; chemist, Northern Regional Res Lab, Bur Agr & Indust Chem, 48-52, chemist, Northern Regional Res Lab, Agr Res Serv, 53-77, RES LEADER MYCOTOXIN ANAL & CHEM RES, NORTHERN REGIONAL RES CTR, SCI & EDUC ADMIN, USDA, 75- *Mem:* AAAS; Am Chem Soc; Am Oil Chem Soc; Am Asn Cereal Chemists; fel Asn Off Anal Chemists. *Res:* Synthetic organic chemistry; chemistry of natural products including isolation purification and characterization; antibiotics; microbial insecticides; mycotoxins. *Mailing Add:* Northern Regional Res Serv Lab Agr Res Serv USDA Peoria IL 61604

SHOTZBERGER, GREGORY STEVEN, b Lewistown, Pa, Jan 17, 48. PHARMACEUTICALS, CARDIOVASCULAR PHARMACOLOGY. *Educ:* Pa State Univ, BS, 69; State Univ NY, Buffalo, PhD(pharmacol), 74. *Prof Exp:* Res pharmacologist, 73-77, sr res pharmacologist, 77-81, PROJ MGR, E I DU PONT DE NEMOURS & CO, INC, 81- *Mem:* Am Col Clin Pharmacol; NY Acad Sci; Inflammation Res Asn. *Res:* Cardiovascular and gastrointestinal pharmacology; toxicology; local anesthetics; antiarrhythmic drugs; evaluation of the gastrointestinal effects of analgesic and antiinflammatory agents; new drug development. *Mailing Add:* Biochem Dept Pharmaceut Res & Develop Div E I Du Pont de Nemours & Co Inc Wilmington DE 19898

SHOUGH, HERBERT RICHARD, b Springfield, Ohio, Jan 7, 42; m 63; c 3. PHARMACOGNOSY, MEDICINAL CHEMISTRY. *Educ:* Univ Tenn, Memphis, BS, 64, PhD(pharm sci), 68. *Prof Exp:* From asst prof to assoc prof pharmacog, Col Pharm, Univ Utah, 68-78; assoc prof, 78-80, PROF HEALTH SCI CTR, COL PHARM, UNIV OKLA, 80-, ASST DEAN, 78- *Concurrent Pos:* Consult, Palmer Chem & Equip Co, Ga, 65-68; res comt grant, Univ Utah, 68-72; Am Cancer Soc inst grant, 73-74; Univ Utah res comt grant, 75-; Smith-Kline Corp Grant, 81-83. *Mem:* Phytochem Soc NAm; Am Asn Cols Pharm; Acad Pharmaceut Sci; Am Pharmaceut Asn; Am Soc Pharmacog. *Res:* Ergot alkaloid chemistry and biochemistry; pharmacy education. *Mailing Add:* Health Sci Ctr Univ of Okla Col of Pharm Oklahoma City OK 73190

SHOULBERG, R(OBERT) H(OWARD), b Upper Darby, Pa, Dec 16, 23; m 47; c 2. MECHANICAL ENGINEERING. *Educ:* Mass Inst Technol, SB, 48, SM, 49, ScD, 53. *Prof Exp:* Instr mech eng, Mass Inst Technol, 51-53; sect engr, Furnace Div, M W Kellogg Co, Pullman, Inc, 53-55; sr develop engr, Joseph Kaye & Co, 56-57; sr scientist, 57-64, lab head, 65-70, proj leader, 70-74, develop engr, Corp Venture Develop, 74-79, PROJ MGR, CORP NEW VENTURES, ROHM AND HAAS CO, 79- *Mem:* Am Soc Mech Engrs; Soc Rheol; Soc Plastics Eng; Am Inst Chem Engrs. *Res:* Mechanical and thermal properties of bulk polymers. *Mailing Add:* Rohm and Haas Co Independence Mall W Philadelphia PA 19105

SHOUMAN, A(HMAD) R(AAFAT), b Egypt, Aug 8, 29; m 60; c 5. MECHANICAL ENGINEERING. *Educ:* Cairo Univ, BS, 50; Univ Iowa, MS, 54, PhD(mech eng), 56. *Prof Exp:* Instr, Cairo Univ, 50-53; asst prof mech eng, Univ Wash, 56-60; assoc prof, 60-65, PROF MECH ENG, N MEX STATE UNIV, 65- *Concurrent Pos:* Consult, Boeing Co, 59-63, ARO Inc, 64, AiResearch Mfg Co, 66, NASA, 68, Serv Technol Corp, & E I du Pont de Nemours & Co, Inc, 69-70; vis prof, Laval Univ, 66; consult Nat Acad Sci-Nat Res Coun sr fel, Marshall Space Flight Ctr, NASA, 67. *Mem:* Fel AAAS; Am Soc Mech Engrs; Am Soc Eng Educ. *Res:* Thermodynamics; compressible fluids; gas turbines and heat transfer. *Mailing Add:* 1006 Bloomdale St Las Cruces NM 88001

SHOUP, CHARLES SAMUEL, JR, b Nashville, Tenn, Dec 10, 35; m 58; c 3. PHYSICAL CHEMISTRY. *Educ:* Princeton Univ, AB, 57; Univ Tenn, MS, 61, PhD(phys chem), 62. *Prof Exp:* Chemist, Oak Ridge Nat Lab, 57; prod specialist, Indust Prod Div, Goodyear Tire & Rubber Co, 57-58; chemist, Oak Ridge Nat Lab, 62-67; mgr spec projs, Electronics Div, Union Carbide Corp, NY, 67-68; vpres, Bell & Howell Schs, Inc, 68-69; mgr technol planning, Cabot Corp, 69-70, dir corp res, 70-73, vpres & gen mgr, Nat Res Corp, 70-73, VPRES & GEN MGR, E-A-R CORP, 73- *Concurrent Pos:* Mem steering comt tech physics, Am Inst Physics, 70- *Mem:* AAAS; Am Inst Physics; fel Am Inst Chemists; Am Chem Soc. *Res:* Infrared spectroscopy; surface chemistry; molecular force fields and structure; infrared spectra of adsorbed species; irreversible thermodynamics; technology transfer; technological innovation; new venture management; hearing protection. *Mailing Add:* E-A-R Div Cabot Corp 7911 Zionsville Rd Indianapolis IN 46268

SHOUP, JANE REARICK, b Kansas City, Mo, June 19, 41; m 62; c 2. ZOOLOGY. *Educ:* Univ Rochester, AB, 62; Univ Chicago, PhD(zool), 65. *Prof Exp:* Res assoc zool, Univ Chicago, 65-66; asst prof, 66-72, ASSOC PROF BIOL, PURDUE UNIV, CALUMET CAMPUS, 72-, HEAD DEPT, 74- *Concurrent Pos:* Bd mem nat abortion rights action league, 75-78. *Mem:* Bot Soc Am; Am Soc Cell Biol; AAAS; Inst Soc Ethics & Life Sci; Midwest Co Biol Teachers. *Res:* Fine structural aspects of the genetic control of development. *Mailing Add:* Dept of Biol Sci Purdue Univ Calumet Campus Hammond IN 46323

SHOUP, RICHARD GEORGE, b Pittsburgh, Pa, July 30, 43. COMPUTER SCIENCE. *Educ:* Carnegie-Mellon Univ, BS, 65, PhD(comput sci), 70. *Prof Exp:* Design engr, Berkeley Comput Corp, 70; RES SCIENTIST, XEROX PALO ALTO RES CTR, 70- *Mem:* Asn Comput Mach; Inst Elec & Electronics Engrs; Soc Info Display. *Res:* Computer graphics; digital video; imaging; system modelling; parapsychology. *Mailing Add:* Xerox Palo Alto Res Ctr 3333 Coyote Hill Rd Palo Alto CA 94304

SHOUP, ROBERT D, b Sinking Spring, Pa, Mar 14, 33; div; c 1. PHYSICAL INORGANIC CHEMISTRY. *Educ:* Albright Col, BS, 60; Univ Pittsburgh, PhD(inorg chem), 64. *Prof Exp:* Res chemist, W R Grace & Co, 64-68; sr res chemist, 68-75, RES SUPVR, CORNING GLASS WORKS, 75- *Mem:* Am Chem Soc; Am Ceramic Soc. *Res:* Boron hydride chemistry; chemistry of nuclear fuels, such as uranium dioxide, uranium carbide and uranium nitride; silicate materials research; catalysts and support systems for environmental pollution control; glass by non-melting techniques; synthetic flourohectorites by hydrathermal reactions. *Mailing Add:* Corning Glass Works Sullivan Park Corning NY 14870

SHOUP, TERRY EMERSON, b Troy, Ohio, July 20, 44; m 66. MECHANICAL ENGINEERING. *Educ:* Ohio State Univ, BS, 66, MS, 67, PhD(mech eng), 69. *Prof Exp:* Res asst mech eng, Ohio State Univ, 65-66, teaching asst, 67; teaching assoc, Ohio State Univ, 69; from asst prof to assoc prof, Rutgers Univ, 69-75; ASSOC PROF MECH ENG, UNIV HOUSTON,

75- *Concurrent Pos:* Ed-in-chief, Mechanism & Mach Theory, 77- *Mem:* Am Soc Mech Engrs; Am Soc Eng Educ. *Res:* Mechanisms; kinematic synthesis and analysis of linkages, machine design; dynamic analysis of machines and machine control systems; computer-aided design techniques. *Mailing Add:* Dept of Mech Eng Univ of Houston Houston TX 77004

SHOUPP, WILLIAM EARL, physics, engineering, deceased

SHOURD, MELVIN LEE, physiology, paleoecology, see previous edition

SHOVE, GENE C(LERE), b Havensville, Kans, Feb 18, 27; m 49; c 3. AGRICULTURAL ENGINEERING. *Educ:* Kans State Univ, BS, 52, MS, 53; Iowa State Univ, PhD(agr eng, theoret & appl mech), 59. *Prof Exp:* Asst agr eng, Kans State Univ, 52-53; asst, Iowa State Univ, 53-55, 56-58, ext agr engr, 55-56; assoc prof, 58-72, PROF AGR ENG, UNIV ILL, URBANA, 72- *Concurrent Pos:* Eng aid, USDA, 52-53. *Honors & Awards:* Paul A Funk Recognition Award, Col Agr, Univ Ill, 80. *Mem:* Am Soc Agr Engrs. *Res:* Crop drying and storage; feed and materials handling; farm building design and use; application of solar energy to grain drying. *Mailing Add:* 1208 W Peabody Dr Dept Agr Eng Univ Ill Urbana IL 61801

SHOVLIN, FRANCIS EDWARD, b Jamaica, NY, Oct 13, 29; m 57; c 5. ENDODONTICS, MICROBIOLOGY. *Educ:* City Col New York, BS, 57; Seton Hall Col, DDS, 61, MS, 65. *Prof Exp:* Nat Inst Dent Res fel, Seton Hall Col, 62-65; pvt pract endodont, 65-72; PROF ENDODONT & CHMN DEPT, COL MED & DENT NJ, 72- *Concurrent Pos:* Nat Inst Dent Res fels, 66-72 & 74-77; Omicron Kappa Upsilon, NJ Col Med & Dent, 71. *Mem:* Int Asn Dent Res; Am Soc Microbiol. *Res:* Microbiology of dental caries; cell wall components of cariogenic bacteria; intracellular polyphosphate storage in bacteria; tissue response to dental implants. *Mailing Add:* Dept of Endodont Col Med & Dent of NJ Newark NJ 07103

SHOW, IVAN TRISTAN, JR, b Belleville, Ill, May 12, 43. SYSTEMS ECOLOGY, MATHEMATICAL & NUMERICAL MODELING. *Educ:* Univ Southern Miss, BMEd, 66, MS, 73; Tex A&M Univ, PhD(oceanog & statist), 77. *Prof Exp:* Sr oceanographer, Sci Appl Inc, 77-80, div mgr, 79-80; PRES, INTERDISCIPLINARY SCI ASSOC, INC, 80- *Concurrent Pos:* Res assoc, Gulf Coast Res Lab, 72-82 & Hubbs-Sea World Res Inst, 79-82; consult, US Navy, 79-82, Nat Oceanic & Atmospheric Admin, 80-82. *Mem:* AAAS; Am Soc Limnol & Oceanog; Am Soc Naturalists. *Res:* Theoretical and applied systems ecology and biostatistics; effects of natural and man-made perturbations on marine ecosystem structure and function. *Mailing Add:* 1604 Calle Plumerias Encinitas CA 92024

SHOWALTER, DONALD LEE, b Louisville, Ky, Jan 22, 43; m 64; c 3. RADIOCHEMISTRY. *Educ:* Eastern Ky Univ, BS, 64; Univ Ky, PhD(chem), 70. *Prof Exp:* NASA grant radiochem anal extraterrestrial samples, under Dr Roman A Schmitt, Ore State Univ, 70-71; asst prof chem, Univ Wis-Stevens Point, 71-73; asst prof sci, Iowa Western Community Col, 73-76; ASSOC PROF CHEM, UNIV WIS-STEVENS PT, 76- *Concurrent Pos:* Consult radiation protection, Wis State health Lab, 80-81. *Mem:* Am Chem Soc. *Res:* Neutron activation applied to geochemical analysis; radiochemical solutions to problems of chemical analysis; environ monitoring of radioactivity. *Mailing Add:* Dept of Chem Univ of Wis Stevens Pt WI 54881

SHOWALTER, HOWARD DANIEL HOLLIS, b Broadway, Va, Feb 22, 48; m 73; c 1. BIO-ORGANIC CHEMISTRY. *Educ:* Univ Va, BA, 70; Ohio State Univ, PhD(nat prod chem), 74. *Prof Exp:* Fel org chem, Rice Univ, 74-76; res scientist, 76-80, SR RES SCIENTIST MED CHEM, WARNER LAMBERT/PARKE DAVIS PHARMACEUT RES, 80- *Mem:* Am Chem Soc; Int Soc Heterocyclic Chemistry. *Res:* Total synthesis of organic compounds of therapeutic significance, especially anthracylines, and nucleosides; new synthetic methodology; heterocyclic synthesis. *Mailing Add:* Warner Lambert 2800 Plymouth Rd Ann Arbor MI 48106

SHOWALTER, KENNETH, b Boulder, Colo, Apr 9, 49; m 70; c 2. CHEMICAL REACTION KINETICS. *Educ:* Ft Lewis Col, BS, 71; Univ Colo, PhD(chem), 75. *Prof Exp:* Res assoc chem, Univ Ore, 75-77, vis asst prof, 77-78; ASST PROF CHEM, W VA UNIV, 78- *Mem:* Am Chem Soc. *Res:* Chemical waves; multiple stationary states in dumped chemical systems. *Mailing Add:* Dept Chem WVa Univ Morgantown WV 26506

SHOWALTER, ROBERT KENNETH, b Middlebury, Ind, Feb 17, 16; m 43; c 1. HORTICULTURE, FOOD SCIENCE. *Educ:* DePauw Univ, AB, 38; Purdue Univ, MS, 40. *Prof Exp:* Asst hort, Purdue Univ, 38-43; asst chem, Allison Div, Gen Motors Corp, 43; chemist, US Rubber Co, 43-45; assoc prof hort, Exp Sta, 45-56, prof, 56-81, EMER PROF, HORT & FOOD SCI, UNIV FLA, 81- *Mem:* Fel AAAS; fel Am Soc Hort Sci; Inst Food Technologists. *Res:* Quality maintenance and evaluation of vegetables during handling, transportation and marketing; effects of mechanization of harvesting and handling on market quality of vegetables. *Mailing Add:* Dept of Veg Crops Univ of Fla Gainesville FL 32611

SHOWELL, JOHN SHELDON, b Camden, NJ, Oct 29, 25; m 51, 71; c 2. ORGANIC CHEMISTRY. *Educ:* Calif Inst Technol, BS, 46, MS, 47; Univ Minn, PhD(org chem), 51. *Prof Exp:* Fel org chem, Univ Ill, Urbana, 51-53; asst prof, Rutgers Univ, 53-55; res fel, Columbia Univ, 55-57; from res chemist to sr res chemist, Agr Res Serv, USDA, 57-66; assoc prog dir org chem, 66-68, assoc prog dir synthetic chem, 68-72, PROG DIR SYNTHETIC ORG & NATURAL PROD CHEM, NAT SCI FOUND, 72- *Mem:* Am Chem Soc; Royal Soc Chem. *Res:* Cyclopropane chemistry; monomer and polymer synthesis; lipid chemistry; organic synthesis; chemical applications of computers; x-ray crystallography. *Mailing Add:* Chem Div NSF 1800 G St NW Washington DC 20550

SHOWERS, MARY JANE C, b Iowa City, Iowa, June 30, 20. ANATOMY. *Educ:* Univ Chicago, BSc, 43; Univ Mich, MSc, 49, PhD(neuroanat), 57. *Prof Exp:* USPHS fel, Kresge Found, Mich, 47-58; staff nurse, Geneva Community Hosp, Ill, 41-42 & Chicago Mem Hosp, 42-43; instr sci, Sch Nursing, Christ Hosp, Ohio, 44-55, dir educ prog, 48-55; assoc prof biol, Our Lady Cincinnati Col, 58-62; asst prof anat, Col Med, Univ Ky, 62-64; from assoc prof to prof anat, Hahnemann Med Col, 64-73, head sect neuroanat, 68-73; prof anat, Philadelphia Col Osteop Med, 73-78; ADJ PROF ANAT, UNIV CINCINNATI MED SCH, 78- *Concurrent Pos:* Gelston fel med res, Anat Inst, Norway, 58; spec lectr, Rutgers Univ, 64-69; consult, Sch Nursing, Christ Hosp, 55-61 & Sch Nursing, Deaconess Hosp, 61-65; mem comp vert neuroanat comt, Study Sect, NIH, 63-67. *Honors & Awards:* Golden Apple Award, 69; Lindback Award, 70. *Mem:* AAAS; NY Acad Sci; Animal Behav Soc; Am Asn Neuropath; Am Asn Anat. *Res:* Additional motor areas of brain; comparative anatomy of the vertebrate nervous system. *Mailing Add:* Dept of Anat Univ of Cincinnati Col of Med Cincinnati OH 45267

SHOWERS, RALPH M(ORRIS), b Plainfield, NJ, Aug 7, 18; m 44; c 3. ELECTRONICS, COMMUNICATIONS. *Educ:* Univ Pa, BS, 39, MS, 41, PhD(eng), 50. *Prof Exp:* Lab asst, Farnsworth Radio & Tel Co, 39; testing engr, Gen Elec Co, Pa & NY, 40-41; lab asst, 41-43, instr elec eng, 42-43, res engr & lab supvr, 43-45, asst prof & proj supvr, 45-53, assoc prof, 53-58, PROF ELEC ENG, UNIV PA, 59- *Concurrent Pos:* Chmn, SCA A measurements, Int Spec Comt Radio Interference, 62-79, vpres, 73-79; chmn, Am Nat Standards Comt, 63, radio-elec coordr, 68-; vpres, US Nat Comt Int Electro-tech Comn, 75- *Mem:* Fel Inst Elec & Electronics Engrs; Opers Res Soc Am; Am Soc Eng Educ. *Res:* Electrical engineering; radio interference; solid-state electronics. *Mailing Add:* Moore Sch of Elec Eng Univ of Pa Philadelphia PA 19104

SHOWS, THOMAS BYRON, b Brookhaven, Miss, May 4, 38; m 59; c 2. HUMAN GENETICS, CELL GENETICS. *Educ:* San Diego State Univ, BA, 61; Univ Mich, MS, 63, PhD(biochem genetics) hon, 67. *Prof Exp:* head, Biochem Genetics Sect, 75-79, assoc chief, Dept Exp Biol, 79-80, RES PROF BIOL, ROSWELL PARK MEM INST, STATE UNIV NY, BUFFALO, 78-, DIR DEPT HUMAN GENETICS, 80- *Concurrent Pos:* USPHS fel, Yale Univ, 67-69. *Mem:* Sigma Xi; Genetics Soc Am; Am Soc Human Genetics; Am Soc Cell Biol; AAAS. *Res:* Human genetics: gene mapping and control of gene expression; biochemical and somatic cell genetics. *Mailing Add:* Dir Dept Human Genetics Roswell Park Mem Inst 666 Elm St Buffalo NY 14263

SHOZDA, RAYMOND JOHN, b Pittsburgh, Pa, Sept 5, 31; m 59; c 4. ORGANIC CHEMISTRY, INORGANIC CHEMISTRY. *Educ:* Carnegie Inst Technol, BS, 53, MS, 56, PhD(chem), 57. *Prof Exp:* Org chemist, Pittsburgh Consol Chem Co, 53-54; sr res chemist, 57-79, CHEMIST, PETROCHEM DEPT, E I DU PONT DE NEMOURS & CO, INC, 80- *Mem:* Am Chem Soc; Sigma Xi; NAm Thermal Anal Soc. *Res:* Industrial chemistry. *Mailing Add:* Petrochem Dept E I du Pont de Nemours & Co Wilmington DE 19898

SHPIZ, JOSEPH M, b Brooklyn, NY, Mar 12, 37; div; c 3. ELEMENTARY PARTICLE PHYSICS. *Educ:* Brooklyn Col, BSc, 58; Columbia Univ, AM, 61, PhD(physics), 63. *Prof Exp:* Mem tech staff, Bell Tel Labs, 62-64; asst prof, 64-70, ASSOC PROF PHYSICS, CITY COL NEW YORK, 70- *Concurrent Pos:* Guest asst physicist, Brookhaven Nat Lab, 65-73, guest physicist, 73-, vis physicist, 67, 73 & 80. *Mem:* Am Phys Soc; Italian Physics Soc; Sigma Xi. *Res:* Group theory; elementary particles. *Mailing Add:* Dept of Physics Convent Ave at 138th St New York NY 10031

SHRADER, JOHN STANLEY, b Yakima, Wash, Apr 17, 22; m 56; c 2. SCIENCE EDUCATION. *Educ:* Univ Wash, BS, 47, MA, 51, EdD, 57. *Prof Exp:* Asst zool, Univ Wash, 47-48; teacher pub schs, Wash, 48-55; asst zool, Univ Wash, 55-56; teacher pub schs, Wash, 56-57; from assoc prof to prof sci educ, Cent Wash State Col, 57-63; interim prof, Univ Fla, 63-64; PROF SCI EDUC, CENT WASH UNIV, 64- *Concurrent Pos:* NSF grant dir, Earth Sci Inst, 70-71. *Mem:* Nat Asn Res Sci Teaching; Asn Educ Teachers Sci; Nat Sci Teachers Asn; Northwest Sci Asn. *Res:* Instructional problems of beginning secondary science teachers in the Pacific Northwest; understanding of college chemistry by intermediate grade pupils; analysis of middle and junior high school teaching; false explorations in science. *Mailing Add:* Dept of Biol Cent Wash Univ Ellensburg WA 98926

SHRADER, KENNETH RAY, b Narrows, Ky, Oct 5, 20; m 45; c 3. PHARMACY ADMINISTRATION. *Educ:* Univ Ky, BS, 57; Purdue Univ, MS, 68, PhD(pharm admin), 70. *Prof Exp:* Asst prof, Sch Pharm, Auburn Univ, 68-71, assoc prof, 71; assoc prof & asst dean, Col Pharm, Univ Cincinnati, 71-73; PROF & DEAN, COL PHARM & HEALTH SCI, NORTHEAST LA UNIV, 73- *Concurrent Pos:* Pharm consult, Med Serv Admin, Ala Dept Pub Health, 68-71. *Mem:* Acad Pharmaceut Sci; Am Asn Cols Pharm; Am Pharmaceut Asn. *Res:* Health care delivery systems and the socio-economic aspects of pharmaceutical services. *Mailing Add:* Col Pharm & Health Sci Northeast La Univ Monroe LA 71209

SHRADER, WILLIAM D, b Bellflower, Mo, Oct 26, 12; m 35; c 3. SOILS. *Educ:* Univ Mo, BS, 35, MA, 41; Iowa State Univ, PhD(soils), 53. *Prof Exp:* Soil scientist soil conserv serv, USDA, 35-37; instr soils, Univ Mo, 37-42; soil scientist, US Forest Serv, 42-45; soil correlator, US Bur Plant Indust, Soils & Agr Eng, 45-52; from asst prof to prof, 52-81, EMER PROF SOILS, IOWA STATE UNIV, 81- *Concurrent Pos:* Consult, Govt Iran, 58-59 & Thailand, 62-; prof soils, fac agron & party chief, Iowa State Mission to Uruguay, 66. *Mem:* Am Soc Agron; Soil Sci Soc Am; Soil Conserv Soc Am. *Res:* Interpretation of soil properties in terms of plant growth. *Mailing Add:* Rt 2 Box 191 Hermann MO 65041

SHRAGER, PETER GEORGE, b Brooklyn, NY, Apr 18, 41; m 66. PHYSIOLOGY, BIOPHYSICS. *Educ:* Columbia Col, AB, 62; Columbia Univ, BS, 63; Univ Calif, Berkeley, PhD(biophys), 69. *Prof Exp:* NIH fel, Med Ctr, Duke Univ, 69-71; asst prof, 71-76, ASSOC PROF PHYSIOL, SCH

MED & DENT, UNIV ROCHESTER, 76- *Mem:* Am Physiol Soc; NY Acad Sci; Soc Gen Physiol; Biophys Soc. *Res:* Biophysics and biochemistry of cell membranes; molecular basis of excitation; cell electrophysiology; protein-lipid interactions in model systems. *Mailing Add:* Dept Physiol Box 642 Univ Rochester Med Ctr Rochester NY 14642

SHRAGO, EARL, b Omaha, Nebr, Apr 9, 28; m 55; c 3. BIOCHEMISTRY, MEDICINE. *Educ:* Univ Omaha, BA, 49; Univ Nebr, MD, 52. *Prof Exp:* From instr to asst prof med, 59-67, assoc prof, 67-71, PROF NUTRIT SCI, SCH MED, UNIV WIS-MADISON, 71-, PROF HEALTH SCI MED, 77-, PROF ASSOC, ENZYME INST, 61- *Concurrent Pos:* USPHS fel, 59-61. *Res:* Mechanisms of hormonal and metabolic control. *Mailing Add:* Dept of Med Univ of Wis Med Sch Madison WI 53706

SHRAUNER, BARBARA ABRAHAM, b Morristown, NJ, June 21, 34; m 65; c 2. PLASMA PHYSICS, BIOPHYSICS. *Educ:* Univ Colo, BA, 56; Harvard Univ, AM, 57, PhD(physics), 62. *Prof Exp:* Researcher statist mech & plasma physics, Free Univ Brussels, 62-64; resident res assoc plasma & space physics, Ames Res Ctr, NASA, 64-65; from asst prof to assoc prof elec eng, 66-77, PROF ELEC ENG, WASH UNIV, 77- *Concurrent Pos:* Am Asn Univ Women fel, 62-63; Air Force grant, 63-64; vis scientist, Los Alamos Sci Lab, 75-76. *Mem:* Am Phys Soc; Am Geophys Union; Am Asn Univ Profs. *Res:* Theoretical problems in plasma physics, including kinetic theory of plasmas and space plasmas; theoretical study of the effects of charge on blood clot formation; electron transport in gallium arsenic for Bab millimeter device. *Mailing Add:* Dept Elec Eng Wash Univ St Louis MO 63130

SHRAUNER, JAMES ELY, b Dodge City, Kans, Mar 10, 33; m 65; c 2. PHYSICS. *Educ:* Univ Kans, BS, 56; Columbia Univ, MA, 60; Univ Chicago, PhD(physics), 63. *Prof Exp:* Res asst biophys, Radio Res Lab, Columbia Univ, 56-58 & theoret physics, Enrico Fermi Inst Nuclear Res, Univ Chicago, 60-63; res assoc physics, Inst Theoret Physics, Stanford Univ, 63-65; from asst prof to assoc prof, 65-77, PROF PHYSICS, WASH UNIV, 77- *Concurrent Pos:* Vis scientist, Los Alamos Sci Lab, 75-76; assoc scientist, Ames Lab, Dept of Energy, 77- *Mem:* Fel Am Phys Soc; Fedn Am Sci. *Res:* Theoretical physics; quantum field and elementary particle theories. *Mailing Add:* Dept of Physics Wash Univ St Louis MO 63130

SHRAWDER, ELSIE JUNE, b Norristown, Pa, Nov 15, 38. CLINICAL BIOCHEMISTRY. *Educ:* Thiel Col, BA, 60; Univ Notre Dame, MS, 66, PhD(chem), 70. *Prof Exp:* Asst control chemist, Miles Labs, Inc, 60-63, assoc res biochemist, Ames Co, 63-68, res biochemist basic & appl res, 70-72; MEM STAFF, ABBOTT LABS CHICAGO, 76- *Mem:* Am Chem Soc; Am Asn Clin Chemists. *Res:* Enzymes, especially their structure and function; enzymes and their isoenzyme and their relation to diagnostic enzymology. *Mailing Add:* Abbott Labs AP-2 North Chicago IL 60064

SHREEVE, C(HARLES) A(LFRED), JR, b Baltimore, Md, Mar 29, 15; m 40; c 3. MECHANICAL ENGINEERING. *Educ:* Johns Hopkins Univ, BE, 35; Univ Md, MS, 43. *Prof Exp:* Engr, US Indust Alcohol Co, 35-37 & Babcock & Wilcox Co, 37-38, 39, 41; instr mech eng, Pratt Inst, 38-41; from asst prof to assoc prof, 41-50, head dept, 59-71, PROF MECH ENG, UNIV MD, COLLEGE PARK, 50- *Concurrent Pos:* Engr, US Naval Ord Lab, 45; consult, M W Kellogg Co, 46, Rogers & McGrath, Inc, 46- & Experiment, Inc, 53- *Mem:* Am Soc Mech Engrs. *Res:* Heat transfer; thermodynamics; turbomachinery; combustion; fluid flow; creativity. *Mailing Add:* 4612 Drexel Rd College Park MD 20740

SHREEVE, JEAN'NE MARIE, b Deer Lodge, Mont, July 2, 33. INORGANIC CHEMISTRY. *Educ:* Univ Mont, BA, 53; Univ Minn, MS, 56; Univ Wash, PhD(inorg chem), 61. *Prof Exp:* Teaching asst chem, Univ Minn, 53-55; asst, Univ Wash, 57-61; from asst prof to assoc prof, 61-67, PROF CHEM, UNIV IDAHO, 67-, HEAD DEPT, 73- *Concurrent Pos:* Fel, Cambridge Univ, 67-68; NSF fel, 67-68; hon US Ramsey fel, 67-68; Alfred P Sloan Found fel, 70-72; mem chem res eval panel, Air Force Off Sci Res, 72-76 & petrol res fund adv bd, Am Chem Soc, 75-78; vis prof, Univ Bristol, 77; Alexander von Humboldt sr scientist award, 78; mem adv comt chem, NSF, 78-82; mem chem div, Argonne Univ Asn Rev Comt, Argonne Nat Lab, 80-83. *Honors & Awards:* Garvan Medal, Am Chem Soc, 72; Flourine Award, Am Chem Soc, 78. *Mem:* Fel AAAS; Am Chem Soc. *Res:* Synthesis of inorganic fluorine-containing compounds. *Mailing Add:* Dept of Chem Univ of Idaho Moscow ID 83843

SHREEVE, WALTON WALLACE, b Muncie, Ind, Aug 2, 21; m 45; c 4. NUCLEAR MEDICINE, MEDICINE. *Educ:* DePauw Univ, BA, 43; Ind Univ, MD, 44; Western Reserve Univ, PhD(biochem), 51. *Prof Exp:* Lab instr biochem, Sch Med, Western Reserve Univ, 46-47, sr instr, 51-52; head radioisotope lab, US Naval Hosp, Oakland, Calif, 52-54; scientist & assoc physician, Biochem Div, Med Res Ctr, Brookhaven Nat Lab, 54-64, sr scientist & attend physician, 64-73; PROF MED, STATE UNIV NY STONY BROOK, 73-; CHIEF NUCLEAR MED, VET ADMIN MED CTR, NORTHPORT, 73-, DIR, SCH NUCLEAR MED TECHNOL, VET ADMIN HOSP, 75- *Concurrent Pos:* Res physician, radiosotope unit, Vet Admin Hosp, Cleveland, Ohio, 50-52; guest prof & NIH spec fel, Karolinska Inst, Sweden, 67; consult, Nassau County Med Ctr, 69- & WHO, India, 71; vis staff mem, Los Alamos Sci Lab, NMex, 72. *Mem:* Am Soc Biol Chemists; Endocrine Soc; Am Diabetes Asn; Soc Nuclear Med; NY Acad Sci. *Res:* Intermediary metabolism of carbohydrates, fats and amino acids; clinical applications of radioactive and stable nuclides in diabetes, liver disease and other endocrine, metabolic or nutritional disorders; isotope tracer methodology and uses in nuclear medicine. *Mailing Add:* Nuclear Med Serv Vet Admin Hosp Northport NY 11768

SHREFFLER, DONALD CECIL, b Kankakee, Ill, Apr 29, 33; m 57; c 2. GENETICS. *Educ:* Univ Ill, Urbana, BS, 54, MS, 58; Calif Inst Technol, PhD(genetics), 62. *Prof Exp:* Res assoc, 61-64, from asst prof to prof genetics, Med Sch, Univ Mich, Ann Arbor, 64-75; PROF GENETICS, WASH UNIV SCH MED, 75-, CHMN, 77- *Concurrent Pos:* Mem immunobiol study sect, NIH, 70-74. *Mem:* Inst Med-Nat Acad Sci; Genetics Soc Am; Am Soc Human Genetics; Transplantation Soc; Am Asn Immunol. *Res:* Mammalian biochemical genetics and immunogenetics; genetic control of variants in serum proteins and cellular antigens. *Mailing Add:* Dept of Genetics Wash Univ Sch of Med St Louis MO 63110

SHREFFLER, JACK HENRY, b Melrose Park, Ill, May 26, 44; m 70; c 1. METEOROLOGY, AIR POLLUTION. *Educ:* Univ Wis, BS, 65, MS, 67; Ore State Univ, PhD(oceanog), 75. *Prof Exp:* Aerospace engr, Manned Spacecraft Ctr, NASA, 67-70; phys scientist, 75-80, SUPVRY PHYS SCIENTIST, AIR RESOURCES LAB, NAT OCEANIC & ATMOSPHERIC ADMIN, 80- *Mem:* Am Meteorol Soc; Sigma Xi. *Res:* Numerical modeling related to air pollution meteorology; meteorological data analysis. *Mailing Add:* Environ Protection Agency MD80 Meteorol Div Research Triangle Park NC 27711

SHRENSEL, J(ULIUS), b Newark, NJ, Feb 6, 22; m 47; c 2. CHEMICAL ENGINEERING. *Educ:* Newark Col Eng, BS, 44; Stevens Inst Technol, MS, 49. *Prof Exp:* Engr, Baker & Co, Inc, 44-46; instr physics, Newark Col Eng, 46-51; res engr, Allied Chem & Dye Corp, 51-60, res engr, Nat Aniline Div, Allied Chem Corp, 60-63, supvr fiber process eng, Fibers Div, 63-65, proj mgr Mid E, Int Div, 65-69, mgr tech econ sect, eng dept, Specialty Chem Div, 69-71, MGR BUS ANAL SECT, PLANNING DEPT ALLIED CHEM CO, ALLIED CHEM CORP, 71- *Mem:* Am Chem Soc. *Res:* Plastics extrusion; equipment design; production of synthetic fibers; decision analysis; strategic planning. *Mailing Add:* 97 Laurel Dr Springfield NJ 07081

SHREVE, DAVID CARR, b Lafayette, Ind, May 25, 42. MATHEMATICS. *Educ:* NC State Univ, BS, 64; Rice Univ, PhD(math), 69. *Prof Exp:* Instr, Univ Minn, Minneapolis, 68-69, asst prof, 69-72; asst prof, Univ Wis-Milwaukee, 72-76, assoc prof, 76-81; RES MATHEMATICIAN, CITIES SERV CO, 81- *Mem:* Am Math Soc; Math Asn Am; Soc Indust & Appl Math. *Res:* Numerical analysis and Fourier analysis. *Mailing Add:* Prod Res Cities Serv Tech Ctr Box 3908 Tulsa OK 74102

SHREVE, GEORGE WILCOX, b Cincinnati, Ohio, Jan 11, 13; m 33; c 2. PHYSICAL CHEMISTRY. *Educ:* Stanford Univ, AB, 35, PhD(chem), 46. *Prof Exp:* Chemist, B Cribari & Sons, Calif, 35-36, Paraffine Co, 37 & Standard Oil Co, Calif, 37-38; res dir, Pac Can Co, Calif, 39-40; res group leader, Permenente Corp, 45; res chemist, Gen Elec Co, NY, 45-46; asst prof chem, Kenyon Col, 46-49; sr phys chemist, Stanford Res Inst, 49-53; res chemist, Monsanto Chem Co, 53-54; chief chemist, Hewlett-Packard Co, 54-57; RES & DEVELOP CONTRACTOR & CONSULT, 57- *Concurrent Pos:* Res Corp grant. *Mem:* AAAS; Am Chem Soc; NY Acad Sci. *Res:* Colloidal properties of non-alkali soaps; chromatography; phase systems of sodium soaps; surface potentials; adsorption; electrochemical cells; alcoholic fermentation, preservation and spoilage of food; protective linings for food containers; catalysis; lignin derivatives; air pollution; solid state chemistry; materials of electronics. *Mailing Add:* 20 Berenda Way Menlo Park CA 94025

SHREVE, LOY WILLIAM, b Smoke Hole, WVa, Oct 8, 26; m 51; c 3. FORESTRY, HORTICULTURE. *Educ:* WVa Univ, BSF, 51; Kans State Univ, MS, 67,PhD(hort), 72. *Prof Exp:* Serv forester, Ky Div Forestry, 54-57, asst dist forester, 57-59, dist forester, 59-63; exten forester fire control, Dept Hort & Forestry, Kans State Univ, 64-68, exten forester tree improv, Dept State & Exten Forestry, 68-76; AREA EXTEN HORTICULTURIST, DEPT HORT, TEX A&M UNIV, 76- *Concurrent Pos:* Mem tree improv comt, Walnut Coun, 72- *Mem:* Soc Am Foresters; Int Plant Propagators Soc Inc. *Res:* Development of practical and economical methods for production of genetic duplicates of forest tree species and horticultural varieties of trees and shrubs; breeding of walnuts, pecans and poplars. *Mailing Add:* PO Drawer 1849 Uvalde TX 78801

SHREVE, RONALD LEE, b Los Angeles, Calif, Oct 18, 30; m 62; c 1. GEOMORPHOLOGY, GLACIOLOGY. *Educ:* Calif Inst Technol, BS, 52, PhD(geol), 59. *Prof Exp:* Instr geol, Calif Inst Technol, 57-58; from instr to assoc prof geol & geophysics, 58-69, PROF GEOL & GEOPHYS, UNIV CALIF, LOS ANGELES, 69- *Concurrent Pos:* NSF fel, Swiss Fed Inst Technol, 58-59; hon res fel geol, Harvard Univ, 65-66, hon res assoc, 71-72; vis assoc prof, Univ Minn, 68; vis prof & Crosby lectr, Mass Inst Technol, 71-72; Sherman Fairchild Distinguished Scholar, Calif Inst Technol, 78-79. *Honors & Awards:* Kirk Bryan Award, Geol Soc Am, 69. *Mem:* AAAS; Geol Soc Am; Am Geophys Union; Int Glaciol Soc. *Res:* Geomorphology; glaciology; physical geology; tectonophysics. *Mailing Add:* Dept of Earth & Space Sci Univ of Calif Los Angeles CA 90024

SHRIER, STEFAN, b Mexico City, Mex, Nov 7, 42; US citizen. MACHINE INTELLIGENCE, NUMERICAL ANALYSIS. *Educ:* Columbia Univ, BS, 64, MS, 66; Brown Univ, PhD(appl math), 77. *Prof Exp:* Teaching fel appl math, Brown Univ, 71-72; chmn comput sci, Wellesley Col, 72-75; res asst appl math, Brown Univ, 75-76, specialist, Comput Lab, 76-77; sr engr, Booz, Allen & Hamilton, Inc, 77-79; dir, Softech, Inc, 79-80; MEM RES STAFF, SYST PLANNING CORP, 80- *Concurrent Pos:* Dir, Acad Comput Serv, Wellesley Col, 73-75; secy, New Eng Regional Comput Prog, 73-75; assoc prof & lectr statist, George Washington Univ, 81- *Mem:* Asn Comput Mach; Inst Elec & Electronics Engrs; Pattern Recognition Soc; Sigma Xi; Soc Indust & Appl Math. *Res:* Numerical analysis; operations research; pattern theory; machine intelligence; software engineering. *Mailing Add:* Syst Planning Corp 1500 Wilson Blvd Arlington VA 22209

SHRIFT, ALEX, b New York, NY, Apr 19, 23; m 55; c 3. PLANT PHYSIOLOGY. *Educ:* Brooklyn Col, AB, 44; Columbia Univ, AM, 48, PhD(plant physiol), 53. *Prof Exp:* Asst plant physiol, Columbia Univ, 46-51 & 52-53; instr pharmacog & plant physiol, Sch Pharm, Univ Calif, San Francisco, 53-55; asst prof bot, Univ Pa, 55-60; assoc res scientist, Lab Comp Biol, Kaiser Found Res Inst, 60-66; assoc prof, 66-69, PROF BIOL, STATE UNIV NY BINGHAMTON, 69- *Concurrent Pos:* NIH spec res fel bot &

microbiol, Univ Col, Univ London, 72-73. *Mem:* Bot Soc Am; Am Soc Plant Physiol; Am Soc Cell Biol; Am Soc Microbiol. *Res:* Sulfur and selenium metabolism; in plants and microorganisms. *Mailing Add:* Dept of Biol State Univ of NY Binghamton NY 13901

SHRIGLEY, EDWARD WHITE, b Lansdowne, Pa, Feb 20, 08; m 32; c 4. MICROBIOLOGY, INFECTIOUS DISEASES. *Educ:* Iowa State Univ, BS, 32, MS, 33; Harvard Univ, AM, 34; Univ Wis, PhD(genetics), 37, MD, 41; Am Bd Microbiol, dipl & cert pub health & bact. *Prof Exp:* Int Cancer Res fel, Sch Med, Yale Univ, 42-44, asst prof bact, 44-49; from assoc prof to prof microbiol, 49-75, chmn dept, 53-73, EMER PROF MICROBIOL, SCH MED, IND UNIV, INDIANAPOLIS, 76- *Concurrent Pos:* Mem, Nat Bd Med Examr, 53-57; mem, Comt Growth, Nat Res Coun, 55; consult, Sr Res Fel Comt, USPHS, 56-61 & Med Student Res Comt, 60-61; mem, Am Bd Microbiol, 60-62; USPHS microbiol training grants, 61-69 & spec fel, 64-65; vis prof bact, Univ Melbourne, 64-65; dir grad prog, Ind Univ-Purdue Univ, Indianapolis, 68-73; vis prof microbiol, Nat Univ San Agustin, Peru, 73-74; WHO consult med educ & microbiol, Govt Burma, 75. *Mem:* Fel AAAS; Soc Develop Biol (secy, 47-49); Am Acad Microbiol; Am Soc Microbiol; Am Asn Immunol. *Res:* Pseudomonas genetics; virology; virus-induced tumors. *Mailing Add:* 3240 E Via Celeste Tucson AZ 85718

SHRIGLEY, ROBERT LEROY, b Zanesville, Ohio, Apr 10, 29; m 52; c 3. SCIENCE EDUCATION. *Educ:* Ohio Univ, BS, 53, ME, 54; Pa State Univ, DEd, 68. *Prof Exp:* Asst prof educ, Ohio Univ, 55-63; sci adv, Kano Teachers Col, Nigeria, 63-65; assoc prof, 66-80, PROF SCI EDUC, PA STATE UNIV, 80- *Mem:* Nat Asn Res Sci Teaching; Sch Sci & Math Asn; Nat Sci Teachers Asn. *Res:* Attitude modification theory, preservice and in-service elementary teachers toward science. *Mailing Add:* 157 Chambers Bldg Pa State Univ University Park PA 16802

SHRIME, GEORGE P, b Fakeha, Lebanon, Nov 27, 40. ELECTRICAL ENGINEERING. *Educ:* Am Univ Beirut, BS, 62; Northwestern Univ, MS, 63, PhD(elec eng), 65. *Prof Exp:* Asst prof elec eng, Univ Hawaii, 65-66; sr engr, 65-69, BR MGR, SEMI-CONDUCTOR CIRCUITS DIV, TEX INSTRUMENTS, INC, 69- *Res:* Computer control of industrial processes; semi-conductor manufacturing; automatic control; deltamodulation. *Mailing Add:* 9611 Mill Trail Dr Dallas TX 75238

SHRIMPTON, DOUGLAS MALCOLM, b Nuneaton Warks, Eng, Mar 29, 35; Can citizen; m 56; c 4. PLANT BIOCHEMISTRY. *Educ:* Univ BC, BA, 57, MA, 58; Univ Chicago, PhD(plant biochem), 61. *Prof Exp:* Nat Res Coun Can fel, 61-63; enzyme chemist, Can Packers Ltd, Ont, 63-65; res officer biochem, 65-74, RES SCIENTIST, CAN FORESTRY SERV, 74- *Mem:* Can Soc Plant Physiol. *Res:* Formation of heartwood and wound response tissues in conifers; enzyme preparations and methods of preservation. *Mailing Add:* Can Forestry Service 1450 Government Victoria BC V8W 3E7 Can

SHRINER, DAVID SYLVA, b Spokane, Wash, July 20, 45; m 68. PHYTOPATHOLOGY, FOREST ECOLOGY. *Educ:* Univ Idaho, BS, 67; Pa State Univ, MS, 69; NC State Univ, PhD(plant path), 74. *Prof Exp:* RES ECOL, ENVIRON SCI DIV, OAK RIDGE NAT LAB, 74- *Mem:* Am Phytopath Soc; Am Ecol Soc; Air Pollution Control Asn; AAAS; Sigma Xi. *Res:* Effects of air pollutants on terrestrial ecosystems; biogeochemical cycling of pollutants; stress physiology of plants; plant host-parasite interactions. *Mailing Add:* Environ Sci Div Oak Ridge Nat Lab PO Box X Oak Ridge TN 37830

SHRINER, RALPH LLOYD, b St Louis, Mo, Oct 9, 99; m; c 1. ORGANIC CHEMISTRY. *Educ:* Wash Univ, BS, 21; Univ Ill, MS, 23, PhD(org chem), 25. *Prof Exp:* Instr chem, Wash Univ, 21-22; res assoc & asst prof, NY Agr Exp Sta, Geneva, 25-27; from asst prof to prof chem, Univ Ill, 27-41; prof & chmn dept, Ind Univ, 41-46; prof org chem, Univ Iowa, 47-63, head dept chem, 52-62; VIS PROF CHEM, SOUTHERN METHODIST UNIV, 63- *Concurrent Pos:* Mem chem panel cancer chemother, Nat Serv Ctr, Nat Cancer Inst, 59-62, chmn, 61-62; ed-in-chief, Chem Rev, Am Chem Soc, 50-66 & Org Syntheses Cumulative Indices, 71-76. *Mem:* AAAS; Am Chem Soc. *Res:* Syntheses and structure of organic compounds; anthocyanins and flavylium salts; lignin model compounds; synthetic drugs and stereoisomerism; organic chemical identification methods. *Mailing Add:* Dept Chem Southern Methodist Univ Dallas TX 75275

SHRIVASTAVA, PRAKASH NARAYAN, b Narsingpur, India, Sept 5, 40; m 68; c 3. RADIOLOGICAL PHYSICS. *Educ:* Univ Nagpur, BSc, 58, MSc, 61; Univ Tex, Austin, PhD(nuclear physics), 66. *Prof Exp:* Res assoc nuclear physics, Ctr Nuclear Studies, Univ Tex, Austin, 66-68; Ont Cancer Inst fel, Princess Margaret Hosp, Toronto, Ont, 68-69; DIR RADIOLOGIC PHYSICS, ALLEGHENY GEN HOSP, & MIDEAST CTR FOR RADIOLOGIC PHYSICS, ADJ ASSOC PROF, GRAD SCH OF PUB HEALTH, UNIV PITTSBURGH, 69- *Mem:* Am Asn Physicists in Med; Am Col Radiol; Am Pub Health Asn; Soc Photo-Optical Instrumentation Engrs; Soc Nuclear Med. *Res:* Computers in therapeutic and diagnostic radiology; precision techniques in radiation therapy and radiation biology. *Mailing Add:* Med Phys & Eng Allegheny Gen Hosp Pittsburgh PA 15212

SHRIVER, BRUCE DOUGLAS, b Buffalo, NY, Oct 18, 40; m 63; c 4. COMPUTER SCIENCE. *Educ:* Calif State Polytech Univ, BS, 63; W Coast Univ, MS, 68; State Univ NY Buffalo, PhD(comput sci), 71. *Prof Exp:* Res engr, Millard D Shriver Co Inc, 63-68; res asst comput sci, State Univ NY Buffalo, 68; NSF fel, 69-71; vis lectr, Aarhus Univ, 71-73; assoc prof, 73-75, prof, 75-81, ALFRED LAMSON PROF COMPUT SCI, UNIV SOUTHWESTERN LA, 81- *Concurrent Pos:* Consult educ, IBM Corp, 74-; proj investr, NATO grant, 74-75. *Mem:* Asn Comput Mach; Inst Elec & Electronics Engrs; Am Math Asn; Soc Indust & Appl Math. *Res:* Computer systems organization; virtual computer systems; multi-level-interpretation; mini and micro computer systems; performance measurement and evaluation; fault tolerant computing systems; simulation. *Mailing Add:* Dept of Comput Sci Box 4330 Univ of Southwestern La Lafayette LA 70501

SHRIVER, DAVID ALLEN, b Syracuse, NY, May 29, 42; m 64; c 2. GASTROINTESTINAL PHARMACOLOGY. *Educ:* Purdue Univ, BS, 66; Univ Iowa, MS, 68, PhD(pharmacol), 70. *Prof Exp:* Res scientist, Wyeth Labs, Div Am Home Prods, 70-77; GROUP LEADER GASTROINTESTINAL/AUTONOMICS/CNS PHARMACOL, ORTHO PHARMACEUT CORP, DIV JOHNSON & JOHNSON, 77- *Mem:* AAAS; NY Acad Sci. *Res:* Pharmacology of the gastrointestinal tract and in the central nervous system. *Mailing Add:* Div Pharmacol Ortho Pharmaceut Corp Raritan NJ 08869

SHRIVER, DUWARD F, b Glendale, Calif, Nov 20, 34; m 57; c 2. INORGANIC CHEMISTRY. *Educ:* Univ Calif, Berkeley, BS, 58; Univ Mich, PhD(chem), 61. *Prof Exp:* Chemist, Univ Calif Radiation Lab, Livermore, 58; from instr to assoc prof, 61-71, PROF CHEM, NORTHWESTERN UNIV, 71- *Concurrent Pos:* Mem, Mat Res Ctr, Northwestern Univ & Ctr Teaching Professions; Alfred P Sloan Found res fel, 67-69; vis prof, Univ Tokyo, 67 & Univ Western Ontario, 79; pres, Inorg Syntheses, Inc, 81- *Mem:* AAAS; Am Chem Soc; The Chem Soc; Electrochem Soc. *Res:* Synthesis and physical investigation of organometallics, solid-state superionic conductors, complexes and hydrides; infrared and Raman spectroscopy of inorganic and bioinorganic systems, homogenous and heterogenous catalysis. *Mailing Add:* Dept of Chem Northwestern Univ Evanston IL 60201

SHRIVER, ELLSWORTH HAROLD, b Betsy Layne, Ky, June 25, 21; m 44; c 3. RESEARCH ADMINISTRATION. *Educ:* Ohio State Univ, BChE, 42; Lawrence Col, MS, 48, PhD(chem), 50; Univ Cincinnati, MBA, 71. *Prof Exp:* Res engr labs, Mead Corp, 50-57, mgr new prod res, 57-60, asst dir prod planning, 60-63, dir new prod, Cincinnati Div, 63-65, corp planner, Dayton, 65-66, mgr inventory planning & control, Westlab Div, 67-68; tech dir org chem group, Glidden-Durkee Div, SCM Corp, 68-71; sr process engr, J E Atchison Consult, 71-74; mgr forming res, Huyck Corp, 74-79; DIR RES & DEVELOP, LINDSAY PAPER INDUST MGT ASN, LINDSAY WIRE, OHIO, 79- *Honors & Awards:* Steele Gold Medal, 50. *Mem:* Am Chem Soc; Tech Asn Pulp & Paper Indust. *Res:* Relationship of forming fabric geometry to paper and paperboard maxing. *Mailing Add:* Linday Wire 6151 Wilson Mills Rd 200 Cleveland OH 44143

SHRIVER, JOHN WILLIAM, b Fairmont, WVa, Aug 9, 49; m 80. MUSCLE CONTRACTION, NUCLEAR MAGNETIC RESONANCE. *Educ:* WVa Univ, BA, 71; Case Western Reserve Univ, PhD(chem), 77. *Prof Exp:* Fel biochem, Univ Alta, 77-81; ASST PROF MED BIOCHEM, SCH MED & ASST PROF CHEM, SOUTHERN ILL UNIV, 81- *Mem:* Biophys Soc; Sigma Xi. *Res:* Energetics of conformational state changes in myosin associated with energy transduction in muscle contraction; use of nuclear magnetic resonance in biophysical problems. *Mailing Add:* Dept Chem & Biochem Southern Ill Univ Carbondale IL 62966

SHRIVER, JOYCE ELIZABETH, b Quincy, Ill, Sept 14, 37. ANATOMY. *Educ:* William Jewell Col, AB, 59; Univ Kans, PhD(anat), 65. *Prof Exp:* Nat Inst Neurol Dis & Stroke fel, Col Physicians & Surgeons, Columbia Univ, 64-68; asst prof, 68-71, ASSOC PROF ANAT, MT SINAI SCH MED, 71-, MEM FAC, MT SINAI GRAD SCH BIOL SCI, 71- *Mem:* AAAS; Am Asn Anat; Am Soc Zoologists; Int Primatol Soc; Soc Neurosci. *Res:* Comparative and experimental neurology; study of limbic and rhinencephalic pathways, especially those arising from and projecting to the amygdala. *Mailing Add:* Dept of Anat Mt Sinai Sch of Med New York NY 10029

SHROCK, ROBERT RAKES, b Wawpecong, Ind, Aug 27, 04; m 33; c 2. PALEONTOLOGY, SEDIMENTOLOGY. *Educ:* Ind Univ, AB, 25, AM, 26, PhD(geol), 28. *Hon Degrees:* ScD, Ind Univ, 71. *Prof Exp:* Asst geol, Ind Univ, 23-26; asst geol, Univ Wis, 28-29, from instr to asst prof, 29-37; from asst prof to prof, 37-70, chmn dept geol, 49-65, EMER PROF GEOL, MASS INST TECHNOL, 70- *Concurrent Pos:* Sr lectr, Mass Inst Technol, 70-75. *Honors & Awards:* W H Twenhofel Medal, Soc Econ Paleontologists & Mineralogists, 76. *Mem:* Geol Soc Am; Paleont Soc (treas, 38-41); Soc Econ Paleontologists & Mineralogists (pres, 57); Am Asn Petrol Geologists; Nat Asn Geol Teachers (pres, 59). *Res:* Sedimentology; history of geology; index fossils; fossil invertebrates. *Mailing Add:* 18 Loring Rd Lexington MA 02173

SHRODE, ROBERT RAY, b Louisville, Colo, Oct 23, 19; m. ANIMAL BREEDING. *Educ:* Colo State Univ, BS, 43; Iowa State Univ, MS, 45, PhD(animal breeding), 49. *Prof Exp:* From assoc prof to prof genetics, Agr & Mech Col, Tex, 48-58; geneticist, Wm H Miner Agr Res Inst, NY, 58-60; pop geneticist, De Kalb Agr Asn, Inc, 60-66; PROF ANIMAL SCI, UNIV TENN, KNOXVILLE, 66- *Mem:* AAAS; Am Soc Animal Sci; Biometric Soc; Am Genetic Asn; Nat Asn Cols & Teachers Agr. *Res:* Quantitative genetics of beef cattle, swine, sheep and flour beetles; general biometrical genetics; computer applications; beef cattle breeding. *Mailing Add:* Dept of Animal Sci Univ of Tenn Knoxville TN 37916

SHRODER, JOHN FORD, JR, b Troy, NY, July 5, 39; m 66. GEOLOGY, GEOMORPHOLOGY. *Educ:* Union Col, BS, 61; Univ Mass, Amherst, MS, 63; Univ Utah, PhD(geol), 67. *Prof Exp:* Instr geol, Westminster Col, 66; lectr geol & geog, Univ Malawi, 67-69; asst prof geol, 69-74, ASSOC PROF GEOG & GEOL, UNIV NEBR, OMAHA, 74- *Concurrent Pos:* Grants, Univ Malawi, 68-69, improv undergrad prog NSF, 70- & Univ Nebr, Omaha, 70-71. *Mem:* AAAS; Geol Soc Am; Int Asn Quaternary Res. *Res:* Mass wasting; periglacial geomorphology; tropical geomorphology. *Mailing Add:* Dept of Geog & Geol Univ of Nebr Omaha NE 68101

SHROFF, ARVIN PRANLAL, b Surat, India, July 2, 33; US citizen; m 62; c 2. PHARMACEUTICAL CHEMISTRY. *Educ:* Univ Baroda, BS, 54; Duquesne Univ, MS, 58; Univ Md, PhD(pharmaceut chem), 62. *Prof Exp:* Lectr, Univ Col, Md, 61-63, fel, Univ, 62-63; sr scientist & group leader anal res, Ortho Res Found, 63-74; chemist, 74-75, chief Prod Surveillance Br, 75-81, DIR, DIV FIELD SCI, FOOD & DRUG ADMIN, 81- *Honors & Awards:* Philip B Hoffman Award, Johnson & Johnson, 72; Food & Drug

Admin Commendable Serv Award, 78. *Mem:* Am Chem Soc; Am Pharmaceut Asn; Am Microchem Soc; Soc Appl Spectros. *Res:* Steroids, alkaloids and heterocyclics; biotransformation, bioavailability and bioequivalence; pharmaceutical analyses and stability; chromatography; spectroscopy. *Mailing Add:* Food & Drug Admin 5600 Fishers Lane Rockville MD 20857

SHROFF, RAMESH N, b Jambusar, India, Apr 27, 37; m 65; c 2. POLYMER PHYSICS, POLYMER RHEOLOGY. *Educ:* St Xavier's Col, India, BS, 59; Lehigh Univ, MS, 61, PhD(chem), 66. *Prof Exp:* Sr res physicist, Goodyear Tire & Rubber Co, Ohio, 65-68; sr res scientist, 68-77, asst mgr polymer res, 77-81, RES ASSOC, CHEMPLEX CO, 81- *Res:* Rheology; extrusion; screw and die design; molecular weight and distribution; long-chain branching; morphology. *Mailing Add:* Chemplex Co Rolling Meadows IL 60008

SHROPSHIRE, WALTER, JR, b Washington, DC, Sept 4, 32; m 58; c 3. BIOPHYSICS, PLANT PHYSIOLOGY. *Educ:* George Washington Univ, BS, 54, MS, 56, PhD(plant physiol, photobiol), 58. *Prof Exp:* Plant physiologist, Astrophys Observ, Smithsonian Inst, 54-57; res fel biophys, Calif Inst Technol, 57-59; physicist, Div Radiation & Organisms, 59-64, ASST DIR, RADIATION BIOL LAB, SMITHSONIAN INST, 64- *Concurrent Pos:* Prof lectr, George Washington Univ, 63-; Smithsonian res award, 65-67; consult, Nat Acad Sci pre & postdoctoral fel award panels, 65-71; guest prof, Univ Freiburg, 68-69; mem coun, Am Asn Advan Sci, 67-77, mem comt coun affairs, 75-78; mem US Nat comt photobiol, Nat Res Coun, 73-75; chmn Am sect, Int Solar Energy Soc, 75-76. *Mem:* AAAS; Am Soc Plant Physiol; Biophys Soc; Mycol Soc Am; Int Solar Energy Soc. *Res:* Photobiology; action and transmission spectra; photomorphogenesis; seed germination; spectral distribution of solar radiation; cell physiology; phototropism and light growth responses of fungi. *Mailing Add:* Smithsonian Radiation Biol Lab 12441 Parklawn Dr Rockville MD 20852

SHROYER, DONALD ALLEN, b Anderson, Ind, Dec 26, 49; m 77. MEDICAL ENTOMOLOGY. *Educ:* Ball State Univ, BA, 72; Purdue Univ, MS, 74; Univ Notre Dame, PhD(biol), 79. *Prof Exp:* Med entomologist mosquito biol & virus transmission, Pac Res Unit, Res Corp, 78-80, MED ENTOMOLOGIST, ARBOVIRUS PROG, PAC BIOMED RES CTR, UNIV HAWAII, 80- *Mem:* AAAS; Am Mosquito Control Asn; Am Soc Trop Med & Hyg; Entomol Soc Am. *Res:* Mosquito biology, (especially bionomics, systematics, reproductive biology such as oviposition, egg hatching, diapause) and arbovirus transmission. *Mailing Add:* Arbovirus Prog PO box 1680 Honolulu HI 96806

SHRUM, EDGAR VAUGHAN, b Newport News, Va, Mar 26, 43; c 4. MICROPROCESSORS. *Educ:* Univ Richmond, BS, 65; Univ Va, PhD(physics), 71. *Prof Exp:* Fel physics, Brookhaven Nat Labs, 71-73; MEM TECH STAFF COMPUT SCI, BELL LABS, 73- *Mem:* Am Phys Soc; Asn Comput Mach. *Res:* Architecture and verification of very large scale integrated circuits. *Mailing Add:* Bell Labs Holmdel NJ 07733

SHRUM, JOHN W, b Jeannette, Pa, Apr 30, 25; m 47; c 3. GEOLOGY, SCIENCE EDUCATION. *Educ:* Pa State Univ, BS, 48; Bowling Green State Univ, MEd, 59; Ohio State Univ, PhD(earth sci, sci educ), 63. *Prof Exp:* Teacher pub schs, Ohio, 56-59; from instr to assoc prof geol & sci educ, Ohio State Univ, 60-68, actg dir acad year inst, 64; PROF SCI EDUC, UNIV GA, 67-, ASSOC DIR, BIOSCI TEACHING CTR, 77- *Concurrent Pos:* Dir teacher prep, Earth Sci Curric Proj, Colo, 64-66, Ga Sci Teacher Proj, 68-75; mem panel teacher prep, Coun Educ Geol Sci, 64-; mem inst eval panel, NSF, 64-75; field reader, US Off Educ Res Proposals, 65-72; chmn dept sci educ, Univ Ga, 67-74. *Mem:* Nat Sci Teachers Asn; Nat Asn Res Sci Teaching; Nat Asn Geol Teachers. *Res:* Evaluation of science instruction; photomacrography; biology science education; course development in geology. *Mailing Add:* 212 Alderhold Dept of Sci Educ Univ of Ga Athens GA 30601

SHRYOCK, A JERRY, b Canton, Ill, Apr 16, 30; m 50; c 2. MATHEMATICS. *Educ:* Bradley Univ, BS, 50; Ill State Univ, MS, 55; Univ Iowa, PhD(math educ), 62. *Prof Exp:* Mem fac math, 55-72, chmn dept, 70-76, PROF MATH, WESTERN ILL UNIV, 72- *Mem:* Math Asn Am. *Res:* Logic and its applications. *Mailing Add:* Dept of Math Western Ill Univ Macomb IL 61455

SHRYOCK, GERALD DUANE, b Sharon, Okla, Jan 24, 33; m 59; c 4. ORGANIC CHEMISTRY. *Educ:* Northwestern State Col, BS, 56; Okla State Univ, MS, 59; Univ of the Pac, PhD(chem), 66. *Prof Exp:* Instr chem, Murray State Col, 58-59 & Imp Ethiopian Col, 59-61; instr chem, Murray State Col, 61-62; from asst prof to assoc prof, 63-67, PROF CHEM, BLACK HILLS STATE COL, 67-, CHMN DIV SCI & MATH, 68- *Mem:* Am Chem Soc. *Res:* Carbohydrate chemistry. *Mailing Add:* 908 Spartan Dr Spearfish SD 57783

SHU, HOU SHING FRANK, b Chiangsee, China, July 20, 47. SYSTEMS ENGINEERING, COMPUTER SCIENCE. *Educ:* Nat Taiwan Univ, BS, 69; Univ Pa, MSE, 73, PhD(systs eng), 76. *Prof Exp:* SYSTS ENGR ELECTRONIC SCI & ENG, GEN ELEC RES & DEVELOP CTR, 76- *Mem:* Inst Elec & Electronics Engrs; Asn Comput Mach; Sigma Xi. *Res:* Software engineering; simulation and optimization techniques; computer systems architecture; manufacturing automation. *Mailing Add:* 1A Chapel Hill Rd Leonardo NJ 07737

SHU, LARRY STEVEN, b Kuala Lumpur, Malaysia, Mar 8, 36; US citizen; m 65; c 2. SOLID MECHANICS. *Educ:* Taiwan Cheng Kung Univ, BS, 58; Brown Univ, MS, 61, PhD(solid mech), 66. *Prof Exp:* Res scientist fiber-reinforced composites, Space Sci Lab, Gen Elec Co, 65-69; sr res chemist, Celanese Res Co, Celanese Corp, 69-70; mat scientist, 71-72, SR RES GROUP LEADER, CONSTRUCT MATS RES & DEVELOP, W R GRACE & CO, 72- *Mem:* Am Soc Mech Engrs; Am Soc Testing & Mat; NY Acad Sci. *Res:* Fiber-reinforced composites; materials science and engineering; building construction material research and development. *Mailing Add:* Res Lab Construct Prod Div W R Grace & Co 62 Whittemore Ave Cambridge MA 02140

SHUB, MICHAEL I, b Brooklyn, NY, Aug 17, 43; m 64. MATHEMATICS. *Educ:* Columbia Col, AB, 64; Univ Calif, Berkeley, MA, 66, PhD(math), 67. *Prof Exp:* Lectr math, Brandeis Univ, 67-68, from asst prof to assoc prof math, Univ Calif, Santa Cruz, 68-73; assoc prof, 73-75, PROF MATH, QUEENS COL, NY, 75- *Concurrent Pos:* NATO fel, 69; Sloan res fel, 72. *Mem:* Am Math Soc. *Res:* Orbit structure of discrete and continuous differentiable dynamical systems. *Mailing Add:* Dept of Math Queens Col Flushing NY 11367

SHUBA, RAYMOND J, b Jersey City, NJ, Feb 5, 23; m 48; c 4. ANALYTICAL CHEMISTRY. *Educ:* Columbia Univ, BS, 54; Rutgers Univ, PhD(anal chem), 58. *Prof Exp:* Res chemist, 58-62, STAFF CHEMIST, MARSHALL RES LAB, E I DU PONT DE NEMOURS & CO, INC, PHILADELPHIA, 62- *Mem:* Soc Appl Spectros. *Res:* Polymer characterization via nuclear magnetic resonance, infrared and ultraviolet spectroscopy, mass spectrometry and thermal analysis. *Mailing Add:* E I du Pont de Nemours & Co 3500 Grays Ferry Ave Philadelphia PA 19146

SHUBECK, PAUL PETER, b Elizabeth, NJ, Oct 21, 26; m 53; c 2. ECOLOGY, ENTOMOLOGY. *Educ:* Seton Hall Univ, BS, 50; Montclair State Col, AM, 55; Rutgers Univ, PhD(zool), 67. *Prof Exp:* Instr biol, Thomas Jefferson High Sch, 51-60; guid counsr, Battin High Sch, 61-67; from asst prof to assoc prof, 67-77, chmn dept, 76-79, PROF BIOL, MONTCLAIR STATE COL, 77- *Concurrent Pos:* Vis prof entom, Rutgers Univ, 80. *Mem:* Sigma Xi; Entom Soc Am; Ecol Soc Am; Nat Asn Biol Teachers; Coleopterists Soc. *Res:* Insect ecology and behavior; orientation of carrion beetles to carrion; phenology and flight activity of carrion beetles. *Mailing Add:* Dept of Biol Montclair State Col Upper Montclair NJ 07043

SHUBERT, BRUNO OTTO, b Ostrava, Czech, Apr 15, 34; m 60; c 1. MATHEMATICS, OPERATIONS RESEARCH. *Educ:* Czech Tech Univ, MS, 60; Charles Univ, Prague, PhD(probability, statist), 65; Stanford Univ, PhD(elec eng), 68. *Prof Exp:* Res assoc appl probability, Inst Info Theory & Automation, Czech Acad Sci, 64-68; vis asst prof math, Morehouse Col, 68; vis asst prof elec eng, Univ Colo, Boulder, 68-69; asst prof, 69-73, ASSOC PROF OPERS RES, NAVAL POSTGRAD SCH, 73- *Mem:* Inst Math Statist; Am Math Soc; Math Asn Am. *Res:* Stochastic models, theory of games, statistical decisions and learning. *Mailing Add:* Dept Opers Res/Systs Anal Naval Postgrad Sch Monterey CA 93940

SHUBERT, L ELLIOT, b St Louis, Mo, May 16, 43; c 1. PHYCOLOGY. *Educ:* Univ Mo-Kansas City, BS, 66; Univ Conn, PhD(phycol), 73. *Prof Exp:* asst prof, 73-78, ASSOC PROF BIOL, UNIV NDAK, 78- *Concurrent Pos:* Prin-investr, Dept of Interior Bur Reclamation grant, Univ NDak, 74-78; co-investr, Proj Reclamation, 75-80; co-dir, Inst for Energy & Coal Develop for Educators, 77-81; hon vis prof, Univ Durham, Eng, 80-81. *Mem:* Am Soc Limnol Oceanog; Phycol Soc Am; Sigma Xi; Brit Phycol Soc; Int Phycol Soc. *Res:* Freshwater algae-aquatic and soil; ecology, physiology and nutrition of algae; algal bioassays; algal succession on disturbed and natural soils; soil microcosms and acid rain; periphyton ecology of prairie lakes. *Mailing Add:* Dept of Biol Univ of NDak Grand Forks ND 58202

SHUBIK, PHILIPPE, b London, Eng, Apr 28, 21; US citizen; m 64; c 3. PATHOLOGY, ONCOLOGY. *Educ:* Oxford Univ, BMBCh, 43, DPhil, 49, DM, 71. *Prof Exp:* Demonstr path, Sir William Dunn Sch Path, Oxford Univ, 47-49; instr & biologist, Med Sch, Northwestern Univ, 49-50; cancer coordr, Chicago Med Sch, 50-53, prof oncol & dir dept, 53-68; Eppley Prof Oncol & Path & dir, Eppley Inst, Col Med, Univ Nebr Med Ctr, 68-80; RES FEL, QUEEN COL, OXFORD, ENG, 80- *Concurrent Pos:* Mem morphol study sect, NIH, 58-59, cell biol study sect, 58-60 & path study sect, 60-62; expert adv panel, WHO, 59-; Nat Adv Cancer Coun, 62-66 & sr mem, Nat Cancer Adv Bd, 70-; co-managing ed, Cancer Letters, 75-; pres, Toxicology Forum, 76-; toxicologist, Eppley Inst, Univ Nebr, dir, Eppley Inst for Res in Cancer. *Honors & Awards:* Co-recipient of Ernest W Bertner Mem Award, 78. *Mem:* Am Soc Path & Bact; Am Soc Exp Path; Am Asn Cancer Res; Am Soc Prev Oncol; Soc Toxicol. *Res:* Experimental pathology; chemical carcinogenesis; environmental and industrial cancer; toxicology; tumor biology. *Mailing Add:* Queen Col Univ of Nebr Col Med Oxford 0X2 6HG 68105 England

SHUBKIN, RONALD LEE, b New York, NY, Aug 27, 40; m 67; c 2. ORGANOMETALLIC CHEMISTRY. *Educ:* Univ NC, BS, 62; Univ Wis, PhD(inorg chem), 67; Mich State Univ, MBA, 81. *Prof Exp:* Res fel, Queen Mary Col, London, 66-67; res chemist, 67-77, sr res chemist, 77-79, res assoc, 79-81, RES SUPVR, ETHYL CORP, 81- *Concurrent Pos:* Instr, Wayne County Community Col; assoc prof, Oakland Community Col. *Mem:* Am Chem Soc. *Res:* Homogeneous catalysis; synthetic lubricants; industrial chemistry; organic chemistry. *Mailing Add:* Ethyl Corp 1600 W Eight Mile Rd Ferndale MI 48220

SHUCHAT, ALAN HOWARD, b Brooklyn, NY, Oct 6, 42; m 66; c 1. MATHEMATICAL ANALYSIS, OPERATIONS RESEARCH. *Educ:* Mass Inst Technol, SB, 63; Univ Mich, Ann Arbor, MS, 65, PhD(math), 69. *Prof Exp:* Asst prof math, Univ Toledo, 69-71 & Mt Holyoke Col, 71-74; asst prof, 74-77, ASSOC PROF MATH, WELLESLEY COL, 77- *Concurrent Pos:* Translr, Am Math Soc, 68-72; reviewer, Math Revs, 72- *Mem:* Am Math Soc; Math Asn Am; Opers Res Soc Am. *Res:* Functional analysis. *Mailing Add:* Dept of Math Wellesley Col Wellesley MA 02181

SHUCK, ARTHUR B, b Sioux City, Iowa, June 3, 18. METALLURGICAL ENGINEERING. *Educ:* SDak Sch Mines & Technol, BS, 42. *Prof Exp:* Asst to chief metallurgist, Metal Prod Div, Koppers Co, 42-49; assoc metall engr, Argonne Nat Lab, 49-59, plutonium fabrication group leader, 56-59, sr metall engr, 59-69, Procurement Serv Dept, 70-72, dir, Spec Mat & Serv Div, 72-75, prog mgr, Safeguards & Security Improv Progs, 75-80. *Mem:* Am Soc Metals; Am Nuclear Soc; Sigma Xi; AAAS; Inst Nuclear Mat Mgt. *Res:* Cast iron and malleable iron; reactor fuels; fabrication of reactor fuel elements and cores; plutonium fabrication; remote controlled fabrication of irradiated reactor fuels; nuclear materials management and safeguards. *Mailing Add:* OS 734 Forest Ave Winfield IL 60190

SHUCK, FRANK O, b Glasgow, Mont, Feb 19, 36; m 56; c 2. CHEMICAL ENGINEERING. *Educ:* Carnegie Inst Technol, BS, 58, MS, 60, PhD(chem eng), 62. *Prof Exp:* asst prof, 62-77, ASSOC PROF CHEM ENG, IOWA STATE UNIV, 77- *Mem:* Am Inst Chem Engrs. *Res:* Diffusion in binary and multicomponent liquids and liquid metals; mass transfer in liquid systems. *Mailing Add:* Dept of Chem Eng Iowa State Univ Ames IA 50010

SHUCK, JOHN WINFIELD, b Cumberland, Md, Apr 9, 40; m 64; c 1. MATHEMATICS, EDUCATION. *Educ:* Mass Inst Technol, BS, 63; Tufts Univ, MS, 68; Northeastern Univ, PhD(math), 69. *Prof Exp:* Asst prof math, Univ Mich, 69-70; asst prof math, Univ Rochester, 70-77; ASST PROF MATH, URSINUS COL, 77- *Mem:* Am Math Soc; Math Asn Am. *Res:* Algebraic number theory; non-Archimedean analysis and its applications to number theory; algebraic geometry; commutative algebra; Diophantine equations. *Mailing Add:* Dept of Math Ursinus Col Collegeville PA 19426

SHUCK, LOWELL ZANE, b Bluefield, WVa, Oct 23, 36. MECHANICAL ENGINEERING, PETROLEUM ENGINEERING. *Educ:* WVa Inst Technol, BSME, 58; WVa Univ, MSME, 65, PhD theoret & appl mech-biomech), 70. *Prof Exp:* Sales engr, WVa Armature Co, 58-59; from instr to assoc prof mech eng, WVa Inst Technol, 59-69, chmn dept, 65-69; res mech engr & proj leader, Morgantown Energy Res Ctr, 70-76; prof mech eng & mech & assoc dir eng, Exp Sta, WVa Univ, 76-80; PRES, TECHNOL DEVELOP INC, 81- *Concurrent Pos:* Consult, Railcar Div, Food Mach Corp, WVa, 65-66; NSF faculty fel, 68-69; res mech engr, Morgantown Energy Technol Ctr, 76-; Governor's appointee to WVa Coal & Energy Res Adv Comt, 77-81; sci adv to WVa Gov Jay Rockefeller IV, 78- *Honors & Awards:* Award, Am Soc Testing & Mat, 70; Ralph James Award, Am Soc Mech Engrs, 81. *Mem:* Am Soc Eng Educ; Am Soc Mech Engrs; Soc Petrol Engrs; Instrument Soc Am; Nat Soc Prof Engrs. *Res:* Vibrations; acoustics; data acquisition; metrology; biomechanics; rheology; theoretical and experimental stress analysis; design and development of transducers; instrumentation; biomechanics; petroleum, natural gas and coal in situ recovery technology research and development including theoretical, laboratory and field projects. *Mailing Add:* 401 Highview Place Morgantown WV 26505

SHUDDE, REX HAWKINS, b Santa Monica, Calif, Dec 25, 29; m 58; c 2. NUCLEAR CHEMISTRY. *Educ:* Univ Calif, Los Angeles, BS & AB, 52, Berkeley, PhD(chem), 56. *Prof Exp:* Sr res chemist, Atomics Int Div, NAm Aviation, Inc, 56-61; supvr reactor code develop, 61, supvr numerical applns, 61-62; assoc prof opers anal, 62-76, ASSOC PROF OPERS RES, NAVAL POSTGRAD SCH, 76- *Mem:* Opers Res Soc Am; Asn Comput Mach; Am Phys Soc. *Res:* Mathematics; electronics; operations research; mathematical programming; computer systems; numerical analysis. *Mailing Add:* Dept of Opers Res Code 55Su Monterey CA 93940

SHUE, ROBERT SIDNEY, b Burlington, NC, May 24, 43; m 67; c 2. POLYMER CHEMISTRY, ORGANOMETALLIC CHEMISTRY. *Educ:* Univ NC, Chapel Hill, AB, 64, PhD(org chem), 68. *Prof Exp:* Teaching asst org chem, Univ NC, Chapel Hill, 67-68; res chemist, Res Ctr, Phillips Petrol Co, 68-72, sr res chemist, 72-77, group leader, 77-78; mgr mkt develop, Phillips Eng Plastics, Phillips Chem Co, 78-80, GROUP LEADER, RES CTR, PHILLIPS PETROL CO, 80- *Mem:* Am Chem Soc; Soc Plastic Engrs. *Res:* Homogeneous transition metal catalyzed organic reactions; reaction mechanisms; synthesis, characterization and structure-property relationships of macromolecules. *Mailing Add:* Bldg 78-F PRC Phillips Petrol Co Bartlesville OK 74004

SHUEL, REGINALD WILLIAM, b Windsor, Ont, Mar 24, 20; m 53; c 3. PLANT PHYSIOLOGY, INSECT PHYSIOLOGY. *Educ:* Univ Toronto, BSA, 41, MSA, 48; Ohio State Univ, PhD(bot), 50. *Prof Exp:* From asst prof to assoc prof, 50-63, PROF APICULT, ONT AGR COL, UNIV GUELPH, 63- *Mem:* Am Soc Plant Physiol; Can Soc Plant Physiol; Am Inst Biol Sci; Int Bee Res Asn. *Res:* Nectar secretion; growth; insect polymorphism. *Mailing Add:* Dept of Environ Biol Ont Agr Col Univ Guelph Guelph ON N1G 2W1 Can

SHUEY, R(ICHARD) L(YMAN), b Chicago, Ill, May 7, 20; m 44; c 2. ELECTRONICS, INFORMATION SCIENCE. *Educ:* Univ Mich, BS(eng physics) & BS(eng math), 42; Univ Calif, MS, 47, PhD(elec eng), 50. *Prof Exp:* Engr, Radiation Lab, Univ Calif, 46-50; res assoc res lab, 50-55, mgr info studies sect, 55-65, mgr info studies br, Res & Develop Ctr, 65-75, STAFF CONSULT, RES & DEVELOP CTR, GEN ELEC CO, 75- *Concurrent Pos:* Adj prof, Rensselaer Polytech Inst, 53-59. *Mem:* Inst Elec & Electronics Engrs; Asn Comput Mach; Soc Mfg Engrs; AAAS. *Res:* Information theory; communications systems; computers; information handling systems. *Mailing Add:* Gen Elec Res & Develop Ctr PO Box 8 Schenectady NY 12309

SHUEY, WILLIAM CARPENTER, b Emporia, Kans, July 1, 24; m 43; c 4. CEREAL CHEMISTRY. *Educ:* Univ Wichita, BS, 48; NDak State Univ, MS, 67, PhD(cereal technol), 70. *Prof Exp:* Exp miller & baker, Gen Mills, Inc, 48-51, in chg exp milling & phys dough test sect, 51-62; res cereal food technologist in chg hard red spring & durum wheat qual lab, Agr Res Serv, USDA, 62-77, ADJ PROF CEREAL CHEM & TECHNOL, AGR EXP STA, NDAK STATE UNIV, 77- *Honors & Awards:* Carl Wilhelm Brabender Award, Am Asn Cereal Chem, 70. *Mem:* AAAS; Am Asn Cereal Chem. *Res:* Chemical composition of wheat and flour, their physical properties, finished products, influence of nutrition, temperature, disease, and other environmental factors on quality of wheat. *Mailing Add:* Dept of Cereal Chem NDak State Univ Fargo ND 58102

SHUFORD, RICHARD JOSEPH, b Hobart, Okla, Dec 20, 44. ORGANIC POLYMER CHEMISTRY. *Educ:* Stetson Univ, BS, 66; Southern Ill Univ, Carbondale, PhD(org chem), 71. *Prof Exp:* RES CHEMIST POLYMERS, ORG MAT LAB, ARMY MAT & MECH RES CTR, 71- *Mem:* Am Chem Soc; Sigma Xi; Catalysis Soc; Am Soc Nondestructive Testing; Soc Adv Mat & Process Eng. *Res:* Piezoelectric and pyroelectric polymers; polymer morphology; nondestructive evaluation of composites; fabrication and characterization of fiber reinforced composites; develop and evaluate quality control and cure monitoring techniques for composites. *Mailing Add:* Army Mat & Mech Res Ctr Watertown MA 02172

SHUGARMAN, PETER MELVIN, b Duluth, Minn, July 28, 27. PLANT PHYSIOLOGY, BIOCHEMISTRY. *Educ:* Univ Calif, Los Angeles, PhD(chlorophyll biosynthesis), 66. *Prof Exp:* Lab technician leukocyte metab, Dept of Med, Univ Calif, Los Angeles, 51-58 & chlorella physiol, Dept Bot & Plant Biochem, 58-66; asst prof cell physiol, 66-70, asst dean student affairs, 73-78, ASSOC PROF CELL PHYSIOL, UNIV SOUTHERN CALIF, 70-, ASST DEAN NATURAL SCI & MATH, 78- *Mem:* AAAS; Am Soc Plant Physiol; Am Inst Biol Sci. *Res:* Control of chlorophyll biosynthesis in Chlorella. *Mailing Add:* Dept Biol Sci Univ Southern Calif Los Angeles CA 90007

SHUGARS, JONAS P, b Liberty, Ky, Feb 8, 34; m 60; c 2. PLANT SCIENCE, SOIL SCIENCE. *Educ:* Univ Ky, BSA, 55, MS, 57; Univ Tenn, Knoxville, PhD(agr plant & soil sci), 70. *Prof Exp:* Teacher high sch, Ky, 59-60; ASSOC PROF HORT, BEREA COL, 60- *Mem:* Am Soc Hort Sci. *Res:* Plant nutrition; flower physiology of plants; pollen study related to allergic reactions. *Mailing Add:* Dept of Hort Berea Col Berea KY 40403

SHUGART, CECIL G, b Ennis, Tex, Oct 13, 30; m 55; c 2. NUCLEAR PHYSICS, POLYMER PHYSICS. *Educ:* North Tex State Univ, BA, 57; Univ Tex, Austin, MA, 61, PhD(nuclear physics), 68. *Prof Exp:* Staff asst physics, Southwestern Bell Tel Co, 57-58; res scientist, Defense Res Lab, Univ Tex, Austin, 58-61; assoc engr, Develop Lab, Int Bus Mach Corp, 61-62; asst prof physics & chmn dept, Hardin-Simmons Univ, 62-65; asst prof physics, Southwestern Univ, 65-66; res assoc nuclear physics, Univ Tex, Austin, 67-68; dir soc physics studies, Am Inst Physics, 68-70; assoc prof, 70-73, prof physics & head dept, Northeast La Univ, 73-77; PROF PHYSICS & CHMN DEPT, MEMPHIS STATE UNIV, 77- *Concurrent Pos:* Sci fac fel, NSF, 66-67; vis scientist, Am Asn Physics Teachers, 68-70. *Mem:* Fel AAAS; Am Phys Soc; Am Asn Physics Teachers. *Res:* Nuclear and polymer physics; atmospheric electricity; magnetics; physics education. *Mailing Add:* Dept of Physics Memphis State Univ Memphis TN 38152

SHUGART, HERMAN HENRY, JR, b El Dorado, Ark, Jan 19, 44; m 66; c 2. ECOLOGY, ZOOLOGY. *Educ:* Univ Ark, BS, 66, MS, 68, PhD(zool), 71. *Prof Exp:* ECOLOGIST, OAK RIDGE NAT LAB, 71- *Concurrent Pos:* Lectureship, asst to assoc prof, Dept Bot, Univ Tenn, 71- *Mem:* Am Ornith Union; Ecol Soc Am; AAAS. *Res:* Systems analysis in ecology; theoretical ecology; synecology; niche theory; mathematical ecology, use of multivariate statistics in ecology. *Mailing Add:* Environ Sci Div Bldg 1505 Oak Ridge Nat Lab Oak Ridge TN 37830

SHUGART, HOWARD ALAN, b Orange, Calif, Sept 21, 31; m 71. PHYSICS. *Educ:* Calif Inst Technol, BS, 53; Univ Calif, MA, 55, PhD, 57. *Prof Exp:* Teaching asst, 53-56, assoc, 57, lectr, 57-58, from actg asst prof to assoc prof, 58-67, PROF PHYSICS, UNIV CALIF, BERKELEY, 67- *Concurrent Pos:* Consult, Gen Dynamics/Convair, 60-61; mem comt nuclear constants, Nat Res Coun, 60-63; group leader, Lawrence Berkeley Lab, 64-79. *Mem:* Fel Am Phys Soc; fel Nat Speleol Soc; Sigma Xi. *Res:* Atomic and molecular beams; low energy nuclear physics; atomic and nuclear properties, including lifetimes, hyperfine structure, spins and static multipole moments. *Mailing Add:* Dept of Physics Univ of Calif Berkeley CA 94720

SHUGART, LEE RALEIGH, b Corbin, Ky, Dec 23, 31; m 52; c 3. BIOCHEMISTRY, MICROBIAL PHYSIOLOGY. *Educ:* East Tenn State Univ, BS, 51; Univ Tenn, MS, 62, PhD(microbiol), 65. *Prof Exp:* NIH fel biol, 65-67; BIOCHEMIST, BIOL DIV, OAK RIDGE NAT LAB, 67- *Mem:* Am Soc Microbiol; Am Chem Soc; fel Am Inst Chemists; Am Soc Biol Chemists; Sigma Xi. *Res:* Biochemical measurement of damage to DNA; mechanisms of protein synthesis in microorganisms; interaction of proteins with nucleic acids; isolation and characterization of nucleic acids. *Mailing Add:* Biol Div Oak Ridge Nat Lab Oak Ridge TN 37830

SHUKLA, KAMAL KANT, b India, Jan 1, 42. MUSCLE BIOCHEMISTRY. *Educ:* Agra Univ, India, BS, 61; Banaras Hindu Univ, MS, 63; State Univ NY Stony Brook, PhD(physiol & biophysics), 77. *Prof Exp:* Asst prof physics, K N Govt Col, India, 63; jr sci officer radiation physics, Inst Nuclear Med, India, 64-70; med assoc, Brookhaven Nat Lab, 71-73; lectr, 78-79, ASST PROF MUSCLE BIOCHEM, STATE UNIV NY STONY BROOK, 79- *Concurrent Pos:* Sr sci officer, Inst Nuclear Med, India, 70-81. *Res:* Muscle biochemistry, in particular the mechanism of adenosine triphosphate hydrolysis by acto-myosin and its relation to contractions. *Mailing Add:* Dept Physiol Health Sci Ctr State Univ NY Stony Brook NY 11794

SHUKLA, VISHWA NATH, b Kanpur, India, July 17, 47. CERAMICS ENGINEERING, MATERIAL SCIENCE. *Educ:* Indian Inst Technol, Kanpur, India, BTech, 69; Univ Ill, MS, 72, PhD(ceramics eng), 74. *Prof Exp:* Vis prof nuclear mat, Inst Energy Atomic, Brazil, 74-76; MEM TECH STAFF RES CERAMIC MAT, TEX INSTRUMENTS INC, 77- *Concurrent Pos:* Vis res assoc, Univ Ill, 76-77. *Mem:* Am Ceramic Soc; Nat Inst Ceramic Engrs. *Res:* Thermal and electrical properties of conducting oxides; oxide-metal interactions; contacts on semiconductors. *Mailing Add:* Tex Instruments Inc 34 Forest St Attleboro MA 02703

SHULDINER, PAUL W(ILLIAM), b New York, NY, June 19, 30; m 51; c 6. CIVIL ENGINEERING. *Educ:* Univ Ill, Urbana, BSCE, 51, MSCE, 53; Univ Calif, Berkeley, DrEng(transp), 61. *Prof Exp:* Instr civil eng, Ohio Northern Univ, 53-54, asst prof, 54-55; asst prof, Northwestern Univ, 60-63, assoc prof, 63-65; consult transp planning, Off Under Secy Transp, 65-66, sr transp engr, Off High Speed Ground Transp, US Dept Transp, 66-67, chief transp systs planning div, 68-69; fed exec fel, Brookings Inst, 70; dep dir nat transp planning study, Nat Acad Sci, 70-71; PROF CIVIL ENG & REGIONAL PLANNING, UNIV MASS, AMHERST, 71- *Concurrent Pos:*

Adv, Northeastern Ill Planning Comn, 64-65; mem Hwy Res Bd, Nat Acad Sci-Nat Res Coun. *Honors & Awards:* Walter L Huber Res Prize, Am Soc Civil Engrs, 66. *Mem:* AAAS; Am Soc Civil Engrs; Am Soc Eng Educ. *Res:* Transportation systems engineering; urban and regional planning. *Mailing Add:* Dept of Civil Eng Univ of Mass Amherst MA 01003

SHULER, CRAIG EDWARD, b Wichita, Kans, Aug 27, 38; m 60; c 4. FOREST PRODUCTS, WOOD SCIENCE & TECHNOLOGY. *Educ:* Colo State Univ, BS, 60, MS, 66, PhD(wood sci), 69. *Prof Exp:* Instr wood technol, Colo State Univ, 67-68; asst prof wood technol, Sch Forest Resources, Univ Maine, 69-75, assoc prof, 75-79; ASSOC PROF WOOD SCI & TECHNOL, COLO STATE UNIV, 79- *Mem:* Soc Wood Sci & Technol; Forest Prod Res Soc; Am Soc Testing & Mat; Sigma Xi. *Res:* Timber mechanics; particle board production and use; timber physics; residue utilization. *Mailing Add:* Wood Sci Lab Colo State Univ Ft Collins CO 80523

SHULER, KURT EGON, b Nürnberg, Ger, July 10, 22; nat US; m 44. THEORETICAL CHEMISTRY, CHEMICAL PHYSICS. *Educ:* Ga Inst Technol, BS, 42; Cath Univ, PhD(theoret chem), 49. *Prof Exp:* AEC fel, Appl Physics Lab, Johns Hopkins Univ, 49-51, sr staff mem, 51-55; mem sr staff, Nat Bur Stand, 55-58, consult to chief, Heat Div, 58-60, consult to dir, 60-61, sr res fel, 63-68; chmn dept, 68-70, PROF CHEM, UNIV CALIF, SAN DIEGO, 68- *Concurrent Pos:* Consult, Advan Res Proj Agency, Dept Defense, 61-74; spec asst to vpres res, Inst Defense Anal, 61-63; vis prof chem, Univ Calif, San Diego, 66-67; mem adv panel, Chem Sect, NSF, 73-75; Solvay Found fel, Solvay Inst, Univ Brussels, Belg, 75. *Honors & Awards:* Gold Medal, US Dept Com, 68. *Mem:* AAAS; fel Am Inst Chemists; Am Chem Soc; fel Am Phys Soc. *Res:* Statistical mechanics; nonlinear phenomena and processes; stochastic processes. *Mailing Add:* Dept Chem Univ Calif San Diego La Jolla CA 92093

SHULER, MICHAEL LOUIS, b Joliet, Ill, Jan 2, 47; m 72; c 3. CHEMICAL ENGINEERING, FOOD SCIENCE. *Educ:* Univ Notre Dame, BS, 69; Univ Minn, PhD(chem eng), 73. *Prof Exp:* asst prof, 74-79, ASSOC PROF CHEM ENG, CORNELL UNIV, 79- *Concurrent Pos:* Vis scholar, Univ Wash, 80-81; consult, Genex, 81- *Mem:* Am Inst Chem Engrs. *Res:* Biochemical engineering; novel food sources; mathematical models of individual cells; plant cell cultures; utilization of agricultural wastes; closed ecological life-support systems. *Mailing Add:* Sch of Chem Eng Cornell Univ Ithaca NY 14853

SHULER, PATRICK JAMES, b Joliet, Ill, Dec 11, 48; m 80. PETROLEUM & CHEM ENGINEERING. *Educ:* Univ Notre Dame, BS, 71; Univ Colo, MS, 74, PhD(chem eng), 78. *Prof Exp:* RES ENGR PETROL ENG, CHEVRON OIL FIELD RES CO, DIV STANDARD OIL CALIF, 78- *Mem:* Sigma Xi; Am Inst Chem Engrs; Soc Petrol Engrs. *Res:* Enhanced oil recovery by chemical flooding. *Mailing Add:* Chevron Oil Field Res Co PO Box 446 La Habra CA 90631

SHULER, ROBERT LEE, b West Columbia, SC, Mar 18, 26. SURFACE CHEMISTRY. *Educ:* Guilford Col, BS, 50; Georgetown Univ, MS, 60, PhD(chem), 69. *Prof Exp:* Chemist aeronaut fuels res, 54-61, res chemist biochem, 61-69, RES CHEMIST SURFACE CHEM, LAB CHEM PHYSICS, NAVAL RES LAB, 69- *Mem:* Am Chem Soc; Sigma Xi. *Res:* Study of the behavior of various types of polymers spread as monomolecular films on aqueous and nonaqueous liquids. *Mailing Add:* Apt 1512 5840 Cameron Run Alexandria VA 22303

SHULER, WOODFIN EPPS, physical chemistry, see previous edition

SHULKO, CAROL ANN, b Canton, Ohio, Feb 22, 49. POPULATION GENETICS. *Educ:* Bowling Green State Univ, BSEd, 70; Ohio State Univ, MS, 77, PhD(genetics), 79. *Prof Exp:* ASST PROF BIOL GENETICS, SOUTHEAST MO STATE UNIV, 79- *Mem:* AAAS. *Res:* Application of various molecular techniques to problems in evolutionary biology including subspecies and race differences; molecular and population genetic techniques to further study the origin and diversification of the Canidae. *Mailing Add:* Dept Biol Southeast Mo State Univ Cape Girardeau MO 63701

SHULL, CHARLES MORELL, JR, b Connellsville, Pa, Apr 8, 22; m 52; c 5. PHYSICAL CHEMISTRY, ANALYTICAL CHEMISTRY. *Educ:* Univ Tulsa, BS, 48; Univ Utah, MA, 50, PhD(chem), 53. *Prof Exp:* Instr chem, Univ Tulsa, 48-49; chemist, Newmont Explor, Ltd, 53-56; res metallurgist eng labs, Litton Data Systs, Inc, 56-58; asst prof chem, Colo Sch Mines, 59-64, assoc prof, 64-66; tech writer curric develop, Educ Develop Ctr, 66-69; assoc prof, 69-72, chmn dept, 74-80, PROF NATURAL SCI, SAN DIEGO STATE UNIV, 72-, ACTG ASSOC DEAN, IMPERIAL VALLEY CAMPUS, 80- *Concurrent Pos:* Consult curric res & writing, Ed Servs Inc, 66-67. *Mem:* Am Soc Eng Educ; Am Chem Soc; Royal Soc Chem; Am Inst Mining, Metall & Petrol Eng. *Res:* Reaction rates; formation constants and molecular structure of complex ions; curriculum development in science education. *Mailing Add:* Dept of Nat Sci San Diego State Univ San Diego CA 92182

SHULL, CLIFFORD GLENWOOD, b Pittsburgh, Pa, Sept 23, 15; m 41; c 3. SOLID STATE PHYSICS. *Educ:* Carnegie Inst Technol, BS, 37; NY Univ, PhD(nuclear physics), 41. *Prof Exp:* Asst, NY Univ, 37-41; res physicist, Tex Co, 41-46; from prin physicist to chief physicist, Oak Ridge Nat Lab, 46-55; PROF PHYSICS, MASS INST TECHNOL, 55- *Honors & Awards:* Buckley Prize, Am Phys Soc, 56. *Mem:* Nat Acad Sci; AAAS; fel Am Acad Arts & Sci; Am Phys Soc; Sigma Xi. *Res:* Solid state and neutron physics. *Mailing Add:* Dept of Physics Mass Inst of Technol Cambridge MA 02139

SHULL, DON LOUIS, b Bridgewater, Va, Aug 2, 35; m 59; c 2. PHYSICAL CHEMISTRY. *Educ:* Bridgewater Col, BA, 56; Univ Va, PhD(phys chem), 61. *Prof Exp:* Res chemist, Hercules Inc, 61-64; sr chemist, Texaco Exp Inc, 64-69, group leader, Texaco, Inc, 69-75; dir labs, Commonwealth Labs, Inc, 76-77; dir res & sci advisor, Va Gen Assembly, 77-80; EXEC DIR, VA FUEL

CONVERSION AUTHORITY, 81- *Mem:* Am Chem Soc; Sigma Xi. *Res:* Molecular spectroscopy; surface and colloid chemistry; chemical kinetics; analytical and testing; political science; information science. *Mailing Add:* Div Legis Serv PO Box 3-AG Richmond VA 23208

SHULL, FRANKLIN BUCKLEY, b Ann Arbor, Mich, Apr 23, 18; m 47; c 4. PHYSICS. *Educ:* Univ Mich, AB, 39, MA, 40, PhD(physics), 48. *Prof Exp:* Assoc physicist, US Naval Ord Lab, 41-46; from asst prof to assoc prof, 48-63, PROF PHYSICS, WASH UNIV, 63- *Mem:* Am Phys Soc. *Res:* Nuclear physics, especially beta-decay, nuclear reactions and polarization of nucleons. *Mailing Add:* Dept of Physics Wash Univ St Louis MO 63130

SHULL, HARRISON, b Princeton, NJ, Aug 17, 23; div; m 62; c 5. QUANTUM CHEMISTRY, ACADEMIC ADMINISTRATION. *Educ:* Princeton Univ, AB, 43; Univ Calif, PhD(phys chem), 48. *Prof Exp:* Assoc chemist, US Naval Res Lab, Washington, DC, 43-45; Nat Res Coun fel, Univ Chicago, 48-49; assoc scientist, Ames Lab, AEC, 49-54; asst prof phys chem, Iowa State Univ, 49-55; from assoc prof to prof chem, Ind Univ, Bloomington, 55-61, res prof, 61-79, vchancellor res & develop, 72-76; vpres acad affairs & provost, 79-82, PROF CHEM, RENSSELAER POLYTECH INST, 79-; CHANCELLOR & PROF CHEM, UNIV COLO, BOULDER, 82- *Concurrent Pos:* Guggenheim Found fel, 54-55; Sloan Res fel, 56-58; dir res comput ctr, Ind Univ, 59-63, actg chmn dept chem & actg dean grad sch, 65-66, dean, 66-72; mem comt awards under Fulbright Hays Act, Div Chem & Chem Technol, Nat Res Coun, 59-, chmn, 63-, mem comt phys chem, 63-66; mem panel surv chem, Westheimer Comt, 64-65; asst dir res, Quantum Chem Group, Sweden, 58-59; mem adv panel chem, NSF, 64-67, chmn, 66-67, sr fel, 68-69; consult, Off Sci Info Serv, 65-70; mem chem vis comt, Brookhaven Nat Lab, 67-69, chmn, 69-70; mem comt sci & pub policy, Nat Acad Sci, 69-72, mem coun & exec comt, 71-74; mem bd trustees, Argonne Univs Asn, 70-75; mem adv comt, Chem Abstr Serv, 72-75; consult ed, Allyn & Bacon; mem Naval Studies Bd, Nat Acad Sci, 73- & adv comn res, NSF, 74-76; actg dean fac, Ind Univ, 74. *Mem:* Nat Acad Sci; AAAS; fel Am Phys Soc; fel Am Acad Arts & Sci (pres, 80-); Am Chem Soc. *Res:* Quantum chemistry; theoretical and experimental molecular spectroscopy and structure. *Mailing Add:* Chancellor Univ Colo Boulder CO 80309

SHULL, JAMES JAY, b Chester, Pa, Sept 1, 29; m 52; c 2. MICROBIOLOGY, BIOCHEMISTRY. *Educ:* Pa State Col, BS, 51, MS, 55; Pa State Univ, PhD(microbiol), 63. *Prof Exp:* Res supvr microbiol, Wilmot Castle Co, 59-61; instr, Syracuse Univ, 61-63; sr res assoc, Am Sterilizer Co, 63-65; mgr biol & med sci lab, Gen Elec Co, 65-69, exp consult aerospace biol, 69-71; tech dir microbial protein prod, 72-74; vpres res & strategic planning, Ariz Feeds, 74-80; OPER MGR, VEGA BIOTECHNOL, INC, 80- *Mem:* Am Soc Microbiol; AAAS; Sigma Xi. *Res:* Gastrointestinal disease and antidiarrheal agents; animal nutrition and health; production of microbial protein; energy production through biological systems. *Mailing Add:* 4351 E Saranac Dr Tucson AZ 85718

SHULL, KENNETH HENRY, biochemistry, see previous edition

SHULLS, WELLS ALEXANDER, b Hudson, Wis, Oct 2, 16; m 42; c 1. MICROBIOLOGY. *Educ:* Mich State Univ, BS & MS, 39; Wayne State Univ, PhD, 57. *Prof Exp:* Assoc microbiologist, Parke, Davis & Co, 44-49; asst prof bact, Col Pharm, Detroit Inst Technol, 49-57; PROF MICROBIOL, UNIV COLO, 57- *Concurrent Pos:* Res assoc, Col Med, Wayne State Univ, 53-57. *Mem:* AAAS; Am Soc Microbiol. *Res:* Methane bacteria in soils and succession of bacteria in alpine soils in plant decay. *Mailing Add:* Dept of Biol Univ of Colo Boulder CO 80302

SHULMAN, CARL, b Chelsea, Mass, Jan 12, 17. ELECTRICAL ENGINEERING, OPTICS. *Educ:* Mass Inst Technol, BS, 38, MS, 39; Princeton Univ, MA, 48, PhD(physics), 57. *Prof Exp:* Res engr, Submarine Signal Co, Mass, 39-40 & Res Labs, Radio Corp Am, 40-55; assoc prof, 55-70, PROF ELEC ENG, CITY COL NEW YORK, 70- *Mem:* AAAS; Am Phys Soc; Inst Elec & Electronics Engrs; NY Acad Sci. *Res:* High frequency electronics; solid state physics; electromagnetic theory. *Mailing Add:* Dept of Elec Eng 140th St New York NY 10031

SHULMAN, GEORGE, b West New York, NJ, Sept 3, 14; m 43; c 4. INDUSTRIAL ORGANIC CHEMISTRY. *Educ:* City Col New York, BS, 36. *Prof Exp:* Res chemist, Insl-x Co, 37-39; res chemist, 39-40, plant chemist, 40-51, tech dir, 51-64, VPRES, PFISTER CHEM INC, 64- *Mem:* Am Chem Soc; Math Asn Am; Ny Acad Sci. *Res:* Organic synthesis; dye intermediates; thickeners for liquid hydrocarbons; plastics and plasticizers; textile chemicals. *Mailing Add:* 715 Winthrop Rd Teaneck NJ 07666

SHULMAN, HAROLD, b Newark, NJ, Feb 12, 25; m 58; c 3. MATHEMATICS. *Educ:* George Washington Univ, BS, 48; Johns Hopkins Univ, MA, 51; NY Univ, PhD(math), 58. *Prof Exp:* Tutor, Queens Col, NY, 52-54; assoc res scientist, Inst Math Sci, NY Univ, 54-60; sr analyst, Comput Usage Co, 60-62; prin comput engr, Repub Aviation Corp, 62-64; asst prof math, Hunter Col, 64-68; ASST PROF MATH, LEHMAN COL, 68- *Concurrent Pos:* Consult, Corps Engrs, Dept Defense, 57-59. *Mem:* Am Math Soc; Math Asn Am. *Res:* Numerical analysis; applied mathematics; statistics. *Mailing Add:* Dept of Math Herbert H Lehman Col Bronx NY 10468

SHULMAN, HERBERT BYRON, b Weehawken, NJ, June 29, 47; m 73. COMPUTER PERFORMANCE ANALYSIS, SYSTEMS ENGINEERING. *Educ:* Cornell Univ, AB, 68; Univ Calif, Berkeley, PhD(math), 72. *Prof Exp:* Instr math, Yale Univ, 72-74 & Univ Pa, 74-75; asst prof math, Belfer Grad Sch Sci, Yeshiva Univ, 75-78; MEM TECH STAFF, BELL TELEPHONE LABS, 78- *Concurrent Pos:* NSF grant, 72-78. *Res:* Queuing theory; traffic engineering. *Mailing Add:* 121 Clover Hill Rd Colts Neck NJ 07720

SHULMAN, HERMAN L, b New York, NY, Feb 24, 22; m 42; c 2. CHEMICAL ENGINEERING. *Educ:* City Col New York, BChE, 42; Univ Pa, MS, 48, PhD(chem eng), 50. *Prof Exp:* Chem engr, Gen Motors Corp, 42-43 & Barrett Div, Allied Chem & Dye Corp, 43-46; res chem engr, Publicker Industs, Inc, 46-47; from asst prof to prof, 48-77, assoc dir div res, 54-59, dir, 59-77, chmn dept, 59-64, dean grad sch, 64-77, vpres, 68-77, PROVOST, CLARKSON COL TECHNOL, 77-, DEAN SCH ENG, 68- *Mem:* Am Soc Eng Educ; Am Chem Soc; fel Am Inst Chem Engrs. *Res:* Mass transfer absorption; packed columns; ion exchange; gas-bubble columns; organic processes; flowmeters. *Mailing Add:* Clarkson Col of Technol Potsdam NY 13676

SHULMAN, JONES ALVIN, b Baltimore, Md, Sept 5, 36; m 58; c 2. INTERNAL MEDICINE. *Educ:* Univ Md, MD, 60; Am Bd Internal Med, dipl, 68. *Prof Exp:* Intern internal med, Univ Md Hosp, Baltimore, 60-61; asst resident med, Univ Wash, 61-62, R G Petersdorf fel infectious dis & med, 62-64, instr & chief resident med, Univ Wash Hosp, 66-67; from asst prof to assoc prof infectious dis, 70-74, coordr clin curric, 70-76, dir dept med & prev med, 72-76, PROF MED, EMORY UNIV, 74-, PROF PREV MED & COMMUNITY HEALTH, 76-, ASSOC DEAN CLIN EDUC, 76- *Mem:* Infectious Dis Soc Am. *Res:* Epidemiology of hospital infections; antibiotics, clinical pharmacology and efficacy studies. *Mailing Add:* Div Infectious Dis Sch Med Emory Univ Atlanta GA 30303

SHULMAN, LAWRENCE EDWARD, b Boston, Mass, July 25, 19; m 59; c 1. INTERNAL MEDICINE. *Educ:* Harvard Univ, AB, 41; Yale Univ, PhD(pub health), 45, MD, 49. *Prof Exp:* Res assoc, John B Pierce Found, Conn, 42-45; intern med, Johns Hopkins Hosp, 49-50, asst resident, 52-53, physician, 53; dir, Connective Tissue Div, Dept Med, 54-75, from instr to asst prof, 53-63, ASSOC PROF MED, SCH MED, JOHNS HOPKINS UNIV, 63- *Concurrent Pos:* Fel, Sch Med, Johns Hopkins Univ, 50-52; sr investr, Arthritis & Rheumatism Found, 57; assoc dir arthritis, musculoskeletal & skin dis, Nat Inst Arthritis, Diabetes & Digestive & Kidney Dis, 76- *Mem:* AAAS; Am Rheumatism Asn (pres, 74-75); Asn Am Med Cols; Am Fedn Clin Res; NY Acad Sci. *Res:* Connective tissue disorders, including rheumatic diseases, especially collagen disorders; immunologic and epidemiologic studies. *Mailing Add:* Bldg 31 Rm 9A35 NIH Bethesda MD 20205

SHULMAN, MORTON, b Chicago, Ill, July 7, 33; m 55; c 3. ANESTHESIOLOGY. *Educ:* Univ Ill, BS, 55, MD, 58. *Prof Exp:* Asst, 59-61, res fel, 61-62, from instr to asst prof, 63-70, ASSOC PROF ANESTHESIOL, UNIV ILL COL MED, 70- *Concurrent Pos:* Attend anesthesiologist, Vet Admin, 64- & Shriners Hosp Crippled Children, Chicago, 78; consult, Col Vet Med, Univ Ill, 68-70; vis prof, Univ Louisville, 69, Med Col Wis, 70, Mayo Clin, 78 & Brigham Women's Hosp, Harvard Univ, 81. *Mem:* Am Soc Anesthesiol; Int Anesthesia Res Soc. *Res:* Cardiovascular pharmacology of vasoactive drugs; pharmacology of respiratory drugs, new general anesthetics, local anesthetics and analgesics. *Mailing Add:* 1115 Thorn Tree Lane Highland Park IL 60035

SHULMAN, ROBERT GERSON, b New York, NY, Mar 3, 24; m 52; c 3. CHEMICAL PHYSICS. *Educ:* Columbia Univ, AB, 43, AM, 47, PhD(chem), 49. *Prof Exp:* AEC fel, Calif Inst Technol, 49-50; head semiconductor res, Hughes Aircraft Co, 50-53; MEM TECH STAFF, BELL LABS, INC, 53- *Concurrent Pos:* Rask Oersted lectr, Copenhagen Univ, 59; Guggenheim fel, Lab Molecular Biol, Med Res Coun Eng, 61; vis prof, Ecole Normale Superieur Univ, Paris, 62; Appleton lectr, Brown Univ, 65; Reilly lectr, Univ Notre Dame, 69; vis lectr, Princeton Univ, 71-72. *Mem:* Nat Acad Sci; Biophys Soc; fel Am Phys Soc. *Res:* Microwave spectroscopy; semiconductors; nuclear magnetic resonance; molecular orbital theory of transition metal complexes; radiation damage to DNA; metalloenzymes; phage genetics; paramagnetic metal ion complexes of nucleic acids; high resolution nuclear magnetic resonance of hemoglobin and tRNA. *Mailing Add:* Biophys Dept Bell Labs Mountain Ave Murray Hill NJ 07974

SHULMAN, SETH DAVID, b Lynn, Mass, Mar 11, 43; m 69; c 3. X-RAY ASTRONOMY. *Educ:* Harvard Univ, BA, 63; Columbia Univ, PhD(physics), 70. *Prof Exp:* Res physicist, E O Hulburt Ctr Space Res, 70-81, CONSULT X-RAY ASTRON, NAVAL RES LAB, 81-; PRES, BIOSCAN, INC, 80- *Mem:* Am Astron Soc; Am Phys Soc. *Res:* X-ray astronomy and studies of the interstellar medium; nuclear radiation detectors. *Mailing Add:* Bioscan Inc 4418 MacArthur Blvd NW Washington DC 20007

SHULMAN, SIDNEY, b Baltimore, Md, Aug 22, 23; m 45, 68; c 6. IMMUNOLOGY. *Educ:* George Washington Univ, BS, 44; Univ Wis, PhD(chem), 49. *Prof Exp:* Assoc, Allegany Ballistics Lab, US Army Ballistics Missile Agency, Md, 44-46; asst chem, Univ Wis, 46-48, proj assoc, 49-52, assoc immunochem, Sch Med, State Univ NY Buffalo, 52-54, asst prof, 54-58, assoc prof immunochem & biophys, 58-65, prof immunochem, 65-68, chmn dept microbiol, 68-69, PROF MICROBIOL, NEW YORK MED COL, 68-, DIR SPERM ANTIBODY LAB, 70-, RES PROF UROL, 73-, RES PROF OBSTET & GYNEC, 74- *Concurrent Pos:* Lederle med fac fel, 54-57; USPHS sr res fel, 58-62; NIH res career award, 63-68; consult immunol, Buffalo Vet Admin Hosp, 64-; Fulbright travel award, 65; Commonwealth Fund travel award, 65; vpres, Int Coord Comt Immunol Reproduction, 67-; assoc ed, Cryobiol, 69-; chmn workshop on immunoreproduction, 1st Int Cong Immunol, 71; assoc ed, Contraception, 73-; assoc ed, Int J Fertil; mem WHO task force immunol methods fertil regulation, 75- *Mem:* Int Soc Immunol Reproduction (vpres, 75); Am Chem Soc; assoc fel Am Col Obstet & Gynec; Am Soc Microbiol; Am Acad Allergy. *Res:* Tissue proteins; autoantibodies; cryobiology; urogenital tract antigens and enzymes; immunology of reproduction and infertility. *Mailing Add:* Sperm Antibody Lab New York Med Col New York NY 10029

SHULMAN, SOL, b Smorgon, White Russia, Nov 6, 29; US citizen; m 53; c 4. ORGANIC CHEMISTRY, POLYMER CHEMISTRY. *Educ:* Univ Wash, BS, 52; Univ Wis, MS, 54; NDak State Univ, PhD(chem), 63. *Prof Exp:* Teaching asst chem, Univ Wis, 53-54; res chemist, Archer-Daniels-Midland Co, Minn, 54-59; from instr to asst prof, NDak State Univ, 59-65; from assoc prof to prof chem, Moorhead State Col, 65-69, chmn dept, 66-69; head dept, 69-75, PROF CHEM, ILL STATE UNIV, 69- *Concurrent Pos:* Sr res assoc, Rice Univ, 75. *Mem:* Fel AAAS; Am Chem Soc; fel Am Inst Chemists. *Res:* Chemistry of lipids; derivatives of fats and oils, polyurethanes and synthesis. *Mailing Add:* Dept of Chem Ill State Univ Normal IL 61761

SHULMAN, STANFORD TAYLOR, b Kalamazoo, Mich, May 13, 42; m 64; c 3. PEDIATRICS, IMMUNOLOGY. *Educ:* Univ Cincinnati, BS, 63; Univ Chicago, MD, 67. *Prof Exp:* Intern-resident pediat, Univ Chicago, 67-69, chief resident, 69-70; fel, Univ Fla, 70-73, asst prof, 73-75, assoc prof pediat info dis & immunol, 75-79; PROF PEDIAT, MED SCH, NORTHWESTERN UNIV, 79-, ACTG CHMN, DEPT PEDIAT, 81- *Concurrent Pos:* Fel immunol, Inst Child Health, London, Eng, 70; mem, Fla Task Force Rheumatic Fever, 74-, Fla Heart Asn Task Force on Children, 74- & coun rheumatic fever, Am Heart Asn, 75-; Chief infectious dis, Children's Mem Hosp, Chicago, 79- *Mem:* Soc Pediat Res; Am Acad Pediat; Am Rheumatism Asn; Am Asn Immunol; AAAS. *Res:* Pathogenesis of rheumatic fever; immunotherapy of chronic aggressive hepatitis; clinical immunology. *Mailing Add:* Dept Pediat Med Sch Northwestern Univ 633 Clark St Evanston IL 60201

SHULMAN, YECHIEL, b Tel Aviv, Israel, Jan 28, 30; nat US; m 50; c 3. ENGINEERING, MANAGEMENT. *Educ:* Mass Inst Technol, SB(aeronaut eng), SB(bus & eng admin) & SM, 54, ScD(aeronaut & astronaut eng), 59; Univ Chicago, MBA, 73. *Prof Exp:* Res engr, Aeroelastic & Struct Res Lab, Mass Inst Technol, 54-56, asst, 57-59; asst prof mech eng, Tech Inst, Northwestern Univ, 59-62, assoc prof mech eng & astronaut, 62-67; res consult, Anocut Eng Co, 67-68, vpres advan eng, 69-72, dir electronic systs group, 70-72; V PRES CORP PLANNING, ALDEN PRESS, INC, JOHN BLAIR & CO, 72- *Concurrent Pos:* Consult, Am Mach & Foundry Co, 60-62 & Res Div, Gen Am Transp Corp, 62-67; mem res & develop comt, Nat Mach Tool Builders Asn, 68-72. *Mem:* Am Inst Aeronaut & Astronaut; Soc Mfg Engrs; Am Soc Eng Educ; Am Soc Mech Engrs; Graphic Commun Asn. *Res:* Electrochemical machining; digital control systems for process machinery; laser metrology, aerothermoelasticity; shell structures; astrodynamics and optimization; structural dynamics; flight mechanics. *Mailing Add:* 1248 Ash St Winnetka IL 60093

SHULT, ERNEST E, b Tonica, Ill, Sept 29, 33; m 57; c 2. ALGEBRA, COMBINATORICS. *Educ:* Southern Ill Univ, BA, 58, MA, 60; Univ Ill, PhD(math), 64. *Prof Exp:* Res assoc genetics yeast, Biol Res Lab, Southern Ill Univ, 54-57, chief theoretician, 58-61, instr math, 63-64, asst prof, 64-65; NSF fel, Univ Chicago, 65-66; from assoc prof to prof math, Southern Ill Univ, 66-70; prof, Univ Fla, 70-74; DISTINGUISHED REGENTS PROF MATH, KANS STATE UNIV, 74- *Concurrent Pos:* Mem, Inst Advan Study, 68-69. *Honors & Awards:* Leo Kaplan Res Prize, Sigma Xi, 70. *Mem:* Sigma Xi; Am Math Soc. *Res:* Abstract algebra; finite geometry; microbial genetics, especially yeast genetics; theory of finite groups. *Mailing Add:* Dept of Math Kans State Univ Manhattan KS 66506

SHULTS, WILBUR DOTRY, II, b Atlanta, Ga, Nov 24, 29; m 50; c 3. ANALYTICAL CHEMISTRY. *Educ:* Emory Univ, AB, 50, MS, 51; Ind Univ, PhD(chem), 66. *Prof Exp:* From jr chemist to assoc chemist, 51-55, from chemist to group leader, 57-67, asst div dir, 67-71, assoc div dir, 71-76, DIV DIR ANAL CHEM, OAK RIDGE NAT LAB, 76- *Mem:* Am Chem Soc. *Res:* Instrumental analysis. *Mailing Add:* Oak Ridge Nat Lab Oak Ridge TN 37830

SHULTZ, ALLAN R, b Huntington, Ind, Jan 8, 26; m 49; c 4. PHYSICAL CHEMISTRY. *Educ:* Manchester Col, AB, 48; Cornell Univ, PhD(chem), 53. *Prof Exp:* Res assoc chem, Mass Inst Technol, 52-54; res chemist, Minn Mining & Mfg Co, 54-63; RES CHEMIST, GEN ELEC RES & DEVELOP CTR, SCHENECTADY, 63- *Mem:* AAAS; Am Chem Soc. *Res:* Polymer chemistry and physics; radiation chemistry of polymers. *Mailing Add:* 111 Acorn Dr Scotia NY 12302

SHULTZ, CHARLES H, b Lancaster, Pa, May 29, 36. VOLCANIC GEOLOGY, IGNEOUS & METAMORPHIC PETROLOGY. *Educ:* Franklin & Marshall Col, BS, 58; Ohio State Univ, PhD(petrol), 62. *Prof Exp:* Geologist, Humble Oil & Refinery Co, 62-64; asst prof geol, Ohio State Univ, 64-70; assoc prof, 70-72, PROF GEOL, SLIPPERY ROCK STATE COL, 72- *Mem:* Geol Soc Am; Am Geophys Union; AAAS; Int Asn Volcanic & Chem Earth Interiors; Sigma Xi. *Res:* Tertiary volcanic petrology; tectonics and metamorphism of the Appalachian Mountains; volcanology of Antarctica; radar as a remote sensing device for geologic data. *Mailing Add:* Dept Geol Slippery Rock State Col Slippery Rock PA 16057

SHULTZ, FRED TOWNSEND, b Grinnell, Iowa, Mar 5, 23; m 61; c 4. GENETICS. *Educ:* Stanford Univ, AB, 47; Univ Calif, Berkeley, PhD(genetics), 52. *Prof Exp:* Asst poultry husb, 49-52, jr res geneticist, 52-53, RES ASSOC POULTRY HUSB, UNIV CALIF, 53-; DIR, BIOL FRONTIERS INST, 60- *Concurrent Pos:* Pres, Animal Breeding Consult, 52- *Honors & Awards:* Res Prize, Am Poultry Sci Asn, 53. *Mem:* Am Poultry Sci Asn; Genetics Soc Am; Soc Study Evolution; World Poultry Sci Asn; Nat Shellfisheries Asn. *Res:* Aquaculture; animal breeding; marine biology. *Mailing Add:* PO Box 313 Sonoma CA 95476

SHULTZ, GERALD L(EROY), b Richland Twp, Ind, Sept 30, 26; m 48; c 3. ELECTRICAL ENGINEERING. *Educ:* Univ Cincinnati, EE, 51; Univ Syracuse, MSEE, 60. *Prof Exp:* Tech engr, 51-54, assoc engr, 54-56, staff engr, 56-57, proj engr, 57-58, develop engr, 58-60, SR ENGR, IBM CORP, 60- *Mem:* AAAS; Sigma Xi; Asn Comput Mach. *Res:* Computer analysis of electrocardiograms; computer manipulation of radioisotope scan data; automated patient history; physiological monitoring; medical information systems. *Mailing Add:* 4305 SW Meadow Ridge Rd Rochester MN 55901

SHULTZ, LEONARD DONALD, b Boston, Mass, Apr 16, 45; m 69; c 2. CANCER. *Educ:* Northeastern Univ, BA, 67; Univ Mass, PhD(microbiol), 72. *Prof Exp:* Res asst cancer, Sch Med, Tufts Univ, 67-68; teaching asst microbiol, Univ Mass, 68-70, lectr immunol, 70-71; trainee, 72-74, res assoc cancer, 74-76, assoc staff scientist, 76-79, STAFF SCIENTIST, JACKSON LAB, 80- *Mem:* Am Soc Microbiol; Am Asn Immunologists. *Res:* The study of lymphoid cell differentiation and immunoregulatory mechanisms in tumorigenesis; immuno-deficiency diseases. *Mailing Add:* Jackson Lab Bar Harbor ME 04609

SHULTZ, WALTER, b Philadelphia, Pa, Nov 11, 31; m 58; c 3. BIOPHARMACEUTICS. *Educ:* Temple Univ, BS, 53; Philadelphia Col Pharm, MS, 54, PhD(pharmaceut chem), 61. *Prof Exp:* Develop chemist, 60-68, GROUP LEADER PHARMACEUT PROD DEVELOP, LEDERLE LABS DIV, AM CYANAMID CO, 68- *Mem:* AAAS; Am Chem Soc; Am Pharmaceut Asn; Acad Pharmaceut Sci. *Res:* Physical pharmacy; synthesis of steroid derivatives. *Mailing Add:* Pharmaceut Prod Develop Sect Lederle Labs Pearl River NY 10965

SHUM, ANNIE WAICHING, b US. COMPUTER SCIENCE, MATHEMATICAL MODELING. *Educ:* Univ Calif, Berkeley, BA, 72; Harvard Univ, MSc, 73, PhD(comput sci), 76. *Prof Exp:* Res staff comput sci, IBM Corp, 77-78; ASST PROF COMPUT SCI, DIV APPL SCI, HARVARD UNIV, 78- *Concurrent Pos:* Consult, BGS Systs Inc, 78-; res grant div appl sci, Harvard Univ, 78-79. *Mem:* Asn Comput Mach; Sigma Xi; Inst Elec & Electronics Engrs; Math Soc. *Res:* Queueing theory; mathematical models; operating system design and performance evaluation of computer systems; efficient computational algorithms of combinatoric problems. *Mailing Add:* Dept of Appl Sci Harvard Univ Cambridge MA 02138

SHUM, ARCHIE CHUE, b Hong Kong, Aug 13, 42; US citizen; m 73. CLINICAL MICROBIOLOGY, BIOCHEMISTRY. *Educ:* Idaho State Univ, BS, 68, MS, 70; Univ Iowa, PhD(microbiol), 73. *Prof Exp:* Asst prof microbiol, Calif State Univ, Los Angeles, 73-76; intern, clin labs, Univ Calif, Los Angeles, 76-77; CLIN MICROBIOLOGIST, ST JOHN'S HOSP, 77- *Concurrent Pos:* Consult, Santa Paula Hosp, Santa Paula, Calif & Pleasant Valley Hosp, Camarillo, Calif, 77; affil prof, Med Technol Prog, Calif State Univ, Dominguez Hills, 78. *Mem:* Am Soc Microbiol; AAAS; Sigma Xi. *Res:* Antimicrobial susceptibility testing on anaerobic bacteria of clinical significance. *Mailing Add:* St John's Hosp Oxnard CA 93030

SHUM, WAN-KYNG LIU, b Canton, China, Mar 11, 35; US citizen; m 64; c 2. BIOCHEMISTRY, ENDOCRINOLOGY. *Educ:* Nat Taiwan Univ, BS, 57; Univ Calif, Berkeley, MA, 60, PhD(biochem), 63. *Prof Exp:* Res assoc biochem, Children's Cancer Res Found, 66-68; asst biochemist, 68-71, asst prof, 71-80, ASSOC PROF BIOCHEM, UNIV TEX M D ANDERSON HOSP & TUMOR INST HOUSTON, 80- *Mem:* Endocrin Soc. *Res:* Primary and secondary protein structures especially in protein hormones and their structure-activity relationship. *Mailing Add:* Dept of Biochem Univ of Tex M D Anderson Hosp & Tumor Inst Houston TX 77025

SHUMACKER, HARRIS B, JR, b Laurel, Miss, May 20, 08; m 33; c 2. SURGERY. *Educ:* Univ Chattanooga, BS, 27; Vanderbilt Univ, MA, 28; Johns Hopkins Univ, MD, 32; Am Bd Surg, dipl, 46. *Prof Exp:* Instr surg, Sch Med, Yale Univ, 37-38; instr, Johns Hopkins Univ, 38-41, asst prof, 41-46; assoc prof, Sch Med, Yale Univ, 46-48; prof & chmn dept, 48-70, EMER DISTINGUISHED PROF SURG, IND UNIV-PURDUE UNIV MED CTR, 78-; PROF & SR ADV, DEPT SURG, UNIFORMED SERVS UNIV HEALTH SCI, 81- *Concurrent Pos:* Consult, Surgeon Gen, US Army, 50-55, mem adv comt, Environ Med, 57-61; vchmn, Am Bd Surg, 59-60; chmn surg sect, AMA, 60-61; vpres Int surg group, Int Soc Surg, 74-75, pres, 75- *Honors & Awards:* Distinguished Serv Award, Am Col Surgeons, 68. *Mem:* Fel Am Col Surgeons; Am Surg Asn (1st vpres, 60-61, secy, 64-68); Soc Clin Surg (pres, 60-62); Soc Univ Surg (pres, 50-51); Soc Vascular Surg (treas, 47-53, pres, 58-59). *Mailing Add:* Suite 411 St Vincent Prof Bldg 8402 Harcourt Rd Indianapolis IN 46260

SHUMAKER, JOHN BENJAMIN, JR, b Ames, Iowa, Jan 17, 26; m 54; c 1. OPTICAL PHYSICS. *Educ:* Iowa State Col, BS, 49; Yale Univ, PhD(chem), 52. *Prof Exp:* Analyst opers res, Opers Eval Group, Mass Inst Technol, 52-55; RES PHYSICIST, NAT BUR STANDARDS, 55- *Mem:* Optical Soc Am. *Res:* Plasma physics; plasma spectroscopy; spectral radiometry; physical optics. *Mailing Add:* Nat Bur Standards Washington DC 20234

SHUMAN, BERTRAM MARVIN, b Boston, Mass, May 2, 31; m 59; c 2. GEOPHYSICS, SPACE PHYSICS. *Educ:* Harvard Col, AB, 52; Boston Univ, AM, 68. *Prof Exp:* RES PHYSICIST GEOPHYS, AIR FORCE GEOPHYS LAB, 53- *Mem:* Am Geophys Union. *Res:* Magnetic field measurements in space using rocket and satellite-borne sensors. *Mailing Add:* 78 Hill St Lexington MA 02173

SHUMAN, CHARLES ROSS, b Harrisburg, Pa, Sept 18, 18; m 44; c 2. INTERNAL MEDICINE. *Educ:* Gettysburg Col, AB, 40; Temple Univ, MD, 43, MS, 49. *Hon Degrees:* DSc, Gettysburg Col, 73. *Prof Exp:* From instr to assoc prof, 49-63, clin prof, 63-66, PROF MED, SCH MED, TEMPLE UNIV, 66- *Concurrent Pos:* Consult, Vet Admin Hosp & Philadelphia Gen Hosp, 57-68; mem bd trustees, Am Diabetes Asn, 76-; pres, Philadelphia County Med Soc, 77- *Mem:* Am Col Physicians; Am Diabetes Asn; Am Fedn Clin Res; AMA. *Res:* Metabolism of carbohydrate, fat and protein; oral antiabetic agents; nutrition; disease. *Mailing Add:* Dept of Med Temple Univ Sch of Med Philadelphia PA 19140

SHUMAN, FRED LEON, JR, b Gulfport, Miss, May 30, 23; m 45; c 2. AGRICULTURAL & BIOLOGICAL ENGINEERING. *Educ:* Miss State Univ, BS, 52, MS, 61; Iowa State Univ, PhD(agr eng), 66. *Prof Exp:* Res asst, Dept Aerophys, Miss State Univ, 51-52; proj engr, Berry Div, Oliver Iron & Steel Corp, Miss, 52-55; proj engr, Dept Aerophys, 55-56, PROF AGR ENG, MISS STATE UNIV & ENGR, AGR EXP STA, 56- *Concurrent Pos:*

Processing Engr, A B McKay Food & Enology Lab & opers coordr, 56- *Mem:* Am Soc Agr Engrs; Am Soc Enologists. *Res:* Mechanical engineering; disposal of pesticides and pesticide containers; soil mechanics; boundary layer control in aircraft; aerial application of agricultural materials; design and development of experimental agricultural machinery; design construction, purchase, testing, installation of wine-processing equipment. *Mailing Add:* Dept of Agr & Biol Eng Miss State Univ PO Box 5465 Mississippi State MS 39762

SHUMAN, LARRY MYERS, b Harrisburg, Pa, Apr 3, 44; m 70; c 2. SOIL CHEMISTRY. *Educ:* Pa State Univ, BS, 66, MS, 68, PhD(agron), 70. *Prof Exp:* asst prof, 72-79, ASSOC PROF AGRON, UNIV GA, 79- *Mem:* Am Soc Agron; Soil Sci Soc Am; Soc Environ Geochem & Health. *Res:* Influence of soil properties on the retention and release of microelements to plants; chemical forms of microelements in soil. *Mailing Add:* Ga Exp Sta Experiment GA 30212

SHUMAN, MARK S, b Yakima, Wash, July 29, 36; m 63; c 3. ENVIRONMENTAL CHEMISTRY, ELECTROANALYTICAL CHEMISTRY. *Educ:* Wash State Univ, BS, 59; Univ Wis, PhD(chem), 66. *Prof Exp:* Asst prof chem, Tex Christian Univ, 66-69 & Whitman Col, 69-70; asst prof, 70-75, assoc prof, 75-80, PROF ENVIRON SCI & ENG, UNIV NC, CHAPEL HILL, 80- *Mem:* Am Chem Soc; Electrochem Soc. *Res:* Transport of trace inorganics in natural water systems; trace metal-organic associations in natural water; electroanalytical chemistry. *Mailing Add:* Dept of Environ Sci Univ of NC Chapel Hill NC 27514

SHUMARD, RAYMOND FRED, parasitology, see previous edition

SHUMATE, KENNETH MCCLELLAN, b Houston, Tex, Nov 9, 36; m 66; c 2. ORGANIC CHEMISTRY, SCIENCE EDUCATION. *Educ:* Baylor Univ, BS, 58, MS, 63; Univ Tex, PhD(org chem), 66. *Prof Exp:* Res chemist, Petro-Tex Chem Corp, 66-67; from asst prof to assoc prof, 67-75, PROF CHEM, SAN ANTONIO COL, 75-, CHMN DEPT, 73- *Mem:* Am Chem Soc. *Res:* Thermal and photochemical reactions of conjugated medium ring dienes; low molecular weight polymers of butadiene. *Mailing Add:* 11006 Whispering Wind San Antonio TX 78230

SHUMATE, MICHAEL S, electrical engineering, see previous edition

SHUMATE, PAUL WILLIAM, JR, b Philadelphia, Pa, July 15, 41; m 64; c 1. SOLID STATE PHYSICS. *Educ:* Col William & Mary, BS, 63; Univ Va, PhD(physics), 68. *Prof Exp:* Asst prof physics, Univ Va, 67-69; mem tech staff, 69-75, SUPVR, BELL LABS, 75- *Concurrent Pos:* Ed-in-chief, Transactions on Magnetics, Inst Elec & Electronics Engrs, 74- *Mem:* Am Phys Soc; Inst Elec & Electronics Engrs. *Res:* Magnetics; magnetic bubble domain materials and device applications; solid-state electronics and integrated circuits; semiconductor lasers and optical fibers. *Mailing Add:* Bell Labs Rm 2D343 Murray Hill NJ 07974

SHUMATE, STARLING EVERETT, II, b Martinsville, Va, Aug 20, 47. BIOCHEMICAL ENGINEERING. *Educ:* Va Polytech Inst & State Univ, BS, 70; Univ Tenn, MS, 74, PhD(chem eng), 75. *Prof Exp:* Res engr bioeng, 74-76, leader bioeng res group, 76-81, MGR BIOTECHNOL & ENVIRON PROF, OAK RIDGE NAT LAB, 81- *Concurrent Pos:* Lectr, Dept Chem, Metall & Polymer Engr, Univ Tenn, 80- *Mem:* Am Inst Chem Engrs; Am Chem Soc; Sigma Xi. *Res:* Bioengineering; chemical engineering science, especially reaction kinetics and mass transfer; separation processes; chemical and biochemical reactor design. *Mailing Add:* Oak Ridge Nat Lab PO Box X Oak Ridge TN 37830

SHUMRICK, DONALD A, b Newark, NJ, Mar 8, 25; m; c 10. OTORHINOLARYNGOLOGY. *Educ:* Seton Hall Univ, BS, 49; Univ Minn, Minneapolis, MS, 52, MD, 57; Am Bd Otolaryngol, dipl, 63. *Prof Exp:* Teaching asst physiol, Univ Minn, Minneapolis, 52-57; intern surg, San Francisco City & County Hosp, 57-58; resident gen surg, 58-59; resident, instr otolaryngol & NIH fel, Washington Univ, 59-63; asst prof, Univ Iowa, 63-66; PROF OTOLARYNGOL & MAXILLOFACIAL SURG & DIR DEPT, MED CTR, UNIV CINCINNATI, 66- *Concurrent Pos:* Consult, Study Sect, NIH, 70- *Mem:* Soc Univ Otolaryngol (secy, 70-); Am Col Surg; Am Soc Head & Neck Surgeons; Am Acad Ophthal & Otolaryngol; Pan Am Asn Oto-Rhino-Laryngol & Broncho-Esophagol. *Res:* Head and neck cancer; maxillofacial surgery. *Mailing Add:* Dept of Otolaryngol & Maxillofacial Surg Univ of Cincinnati Med Ctr Cincinnati OH 45267

SHUMWAY, CLARE NELSON, (JR), b Painted Post, NY, Oct 28, 25; m 55; c 2. PEDIATRICS, HEMATOLOGY. *Educ:* Univ Buffalo, MD, 48; Am Bd Pediat, dipl, 53, cert pediat hemat-oncol, 74. *Prof Exp:* Intern med, Buffalo Gen Hosp, 48-49; resident pediat, Buffalo Children's Hosp, 49-52; instr, Sch Med & Dent, Univ Rochester, 52-57; assoc prof, Sch Med, Univ Buffalo, 57-64; prof pediat, Med Col Va, 64-72; dir pediat, Harrisburg Polyclin Hosp, 72-77; DIR HEALTH SERV, GETTYSBURG COL, 77- *Concurrent Pos:* Am Cancer Soc fel, Univ Rochester, 52-53, USPHS res fel, 55-57; dir hemat, Buffalo Children's Hosp, 57-64; spec res fel, Univ Wash, 69-70. *Mem:* AAAS; Am Acad Pediat; Am Pediat Soc; NY Acad Sci; Am Soc Hemat. *Res:* The role of bacterial hemolysin in the pathogenesis of pneumococcal infections. *Mailing Add:* Health Serv Gettysburg Col Gettysburg PA 17325

SHUMWAY, LEWIS KAY, b Salt Lake City, Utah, Dec 3, 34; m 58; c 6. PLANT GENETICS. *Educ:* Brigham Young Univ, BS, 60, MS, 62; Purdue Univ, PhD(plant genetics), 65. *Prof Exp:* Res botanist, Univ Calif, Davis, 65-66; asst res botanist, Univ Calif, Berkeley, 66-67; from asst prof to assoc prof genetics & bot, Wash State Univ, 67-77; CHMN INSTRNL SERV, SAN JUAN CTR, COL EASTERN UTAH, 77- *Mem:* AAAS. *Res:* Plant cell ultrastructure; chloroplast inheritance, development and ultrastructure; protoplasts. *Mailing Add:* San Juan Ctr Col Eastern Utah Box 729 Blanding UT 84511

SHUMWAY, RICHARD PHIL, b Taylor, Ariz, Aug 21, 21; m 43; c 6. ANIMAL PHYSIOLOGY. *Educ:* Utah State Univ, BS, 47, PhD, 59; Univ Minn, MS, 49. *Prof Exp:* Asst prof agr, Utah State Univ, 47-48; from asst prof to assoc prof, 49-63, PROF ANIMAL SCI, BRIGHAM YOUNG UNIV, 63- *Concurrent Pos:* Chmn dept animal sci, Brigham Young Univ, 63-72. *Mem:* Am Soc Animal Sci. *Mailing Add:* Dept of Animal Sci Brigham Young Univ Provo UT 84602

SHUNG, K KIRK, b China, June 2, 45; US citizen; m 71; c 2. BIOMEDICAL ULTRASOUND, BIOINSTRUMENTATION. *Educ:* Nat Cheng-Kung Univ, Taiwan, BSEE, 68; Univ Mo, MSEE, 70; Univ Wash, PhD(elec eng), 75. *Prof Exp:* Res assoc, Ctr Bioeng, Univ Wash, 70-75; res fel, Providence Med Ctr, Seattle, Wash, 75-76, res engr, 76-79; ASST PROF BIOENG, PA STATE UNIV, 79- *Concurrent Pos:* Prin investr NSF, 77- & NIH, 79- *Mem:* Inst Elec & Electronics Engrs; Am Inst Ultrasound Med; assoc mem Acoust Soc Am. *Res:* Characterizing biological tissues in terms of their ultrasonic properties, such as velocity, absorption, attenuation and scattering for the purpose of assisting clinicians in making a correct diagnosis. *Mailing Add:* 254 Hammond Bldg Pa State Univ University Park PA 16802

SHUPE, DEAN STANLEY, b Clarion, Iowa, July 7, 37; m 62; c 2. MECHANICAL ENGINEERING, INDUSTRIAL ENGINEERING. *Educ:* Iowa State Univ, BS, 60; Stanford Univ, MS, 61; Mass Inst Technol, ScD(mech eng), 69. *Prof Exp:* Process engr, Procter & Gamble Co, 61-62; from instr to assoc prof mech eng, 63-77, PROF MECH & INDUST ENG, UNIV CINCINNATI, 77- *Concurrent Pos:* Prin, Eng & Mgt Assocs, 77- *Honors & Awards:* Ralph R Teetor Award, Soc Automotive Engrs, 80. *Mem:* Am Soc Mech Engrs; Am Soc Eng Educ; Am Inst Indust Engrs. *Res:* Thermodynamics and energy sciences; water utility and solid waste management. *Mailing Add:* Dept of Mech & Indust Eng Univ of Cincinnati Cincinnati OH 45221

SHUPE, JAMES LEGRANDE, b Ogden, Utah, Nov 5, 18; m 57; c 2. VETERINARY MEDICINE. *Educ:* Utah State Univ, BS, 48; Cornell Univ, DVM, 52. *Prof Exp:* From asst prof to prof vet med, Utah State Univ, 52-61; res vet animal dis & parasite res div, Agr Res Serv, USDA, 61-66; head Dept Vet Sci, 73-76, prof vet med, 66-80, PROF ANIMAL DAIRY & VET SCI, UTAH STATE UNIV, 80- *Concurrent Pos:* Resident path, Armed Forces Inst Path, Walter Reed Med Ctr, 57-58; chmn subcomt fluorosis, Nat Res Coun. *Mem:* Am Vet Med Asn; Am Col Vet Toxicol (pres, 72); Am Acad Clin Toxicol; Pan-Am Med Asn; Int Acad Path. *Res:* Toxicology; pathology. *Mailing Add:* 296 S 250 E Hyde Park UT 84318

SHUPE, JOHN W(ALLACE), b Liberal, Kans, Mar 30, 24; m 44; c 4. CIVIL ENGINEERING, RENEWABLE ENERGY. *Educ:* Kans State Univ, BS, 48; Univ Calif, MS, 51; Purdue Univ, PhD(civil eng), 58. *Prof Exp:* Instr appl mech, Kans State Univ, 48-49, asst prof, 51-53; lectr civil eng, Univ Calif, 49-51; struct engr, Convair Div, Gen Dynamics Corp, 53-54; assoc prof appl mech, Kans State Univ, 54-65, assoc dean eng, 60-65; dean eng, 65-80, DIR HAWAII NATURAL ENERGY INST, UNIV HAWAII, 80- *Concurrent Pos:* Mem environ coun, State of Hawaii; dir, Hawaii Geothermal Proj; chmn, Governor's Comt Alt Energy; sci adv to asst secy for energy technol, US Dept of Energy, 77-78. *Honors & Awards:* Templin Award, Am Soc Testing & Mat, 60. *Mem:* Am Soc Civil Engrs; Am Soc Eng Educ; Nat Soc Prof Engrs; Inst Solar Energy Soc; Geothermal Resources Coun. *Res:* Geothermal and solar energy. *Mailing Add:* Hawaii Natural Energy Inst Univ Hawaii 2540 Dole St Honolulu HI 96822

SHUPE, ROBERT EUGENE, b Sparks, Kans, Sept 6, 34; m 57; c 3. RADIATION PHYSICS, RADIOBIOLOGY. *Educ:* Wayne State Col, BS, 62; Purdue Univ, West Lafayette, MS, 67, PhD(radiol physics), 70. *Prof Exp:* Instr radiol physics, Southwestern Radiol Health Lab, USPHS, Las Vegas, 69-70; ASST PROF RADIATION BIOL, MED CTR, IND UNIV, INDIANAPOLIS, 70- *Concurrent Pos:* Mem, Mid-West Radiation Protection, Inc, 71-; consult radiation physics. *Mem:* AAAS; Radiation Res Soc. *Res:* Hyperthermia research combined with ionizing radiation and chemotherapy in the treatment of malignant diseases. *Mailing Add:* Dept of Radiation Ther Ind Univ Med Ctr Indianapolis IN 46202

SHUPE, RUSSELL DWAYNE, b Arkansas City, Kans, Jan 14, 43; m 71. ORGANIC CHEMISTRY. *Educ:* Okla State Univ, BS, 65, MS, 67, PhD(org chem), 69. *Prof Exp:* res chemist, Texaco, Inc, Houston, 69-78; RES CHEMIST, TEXACO, INC, BELLAIRE, 69- *Res:* Isotopic labeling of triphenylmethyl compounds and CONTINENTAL OIL CO, PONCA CITY, 78- when treated with aryl Grignard reagents; mass spectral analyses of isotopically labeled triphenylmethyl compounds; use of surfactants in enhanced oil recovery techniques; kinetic studies of the degradation of water soluble polymers used in enhanced oil recovery techniques. *Mailing Add:* Texaco Chemical Co PO Box 430 Bellaire TX 77401

SHUR, BARRY DAVID, b Elizabeth, NJ, Jan 3, 50; m 71; c 1. DEVELOPMENTAL BIOLOGY. *Educ:* Marietta Col, BS, 71; Johns Hopkins Univ, PhD(biol), 76. *Prof Exp:* Fel develop genetics, Mem Sloan-Kettering Cancer Ctr, 76-78; ASST PROF ANAT, HEALTH CTR, UNIV CONN, 78- *Concurrent Pos:* Helen Hay Whitney Found fel, 76-78. *Mem:* Am Soc Zoologists; Am Soc Anatomists; AAAS. *Res:* Cell surface biochemistry of normal and mutant morphogenesis. *Mailing Add:* Dept of Anat Univ of Conn Farmington CT 06032

SHURBET, DESKIN HUNT, JR, b Lockney, Tex, Aug 27, 25; m 58; c 3. SEISMOLOGY. *Educ:* Univ Tex, BS, 50, MA, 51. *Prof Exp:* Dir Bermuda-Columbia Seismograph Sta, Lamont Geol Observ, 51-56; PROF GEOL & DIR SEISMOL OBSERV, TEX TECH UNIV, 56- *Mem:* Fel AAAS; Seismol Soc Am; Am Geophys Union; Soc Explor Geophys; NY Acad Sci. *Res:* Earthquake seismology. *Mailing Add:* Dept Geosci Tex Tech Univ Lubbock TX 79409

SHURE, DONALD JOSEPH, b Washington, DC, July 21, 39; m 65; c 2. ECOSYSTEMS PROCESSES. *Educ:* Western Md Col, BA, 61; Rutgers Univ, MS, 66, PhD(zool), 69. *Prof Exp:* Teaching asst zool, Rutgers Univ, 64-67, NSF fel ecol, 68-69; asst prof, 69-74, ASSOC PROF BIOL, EMORY UNIV, 74- *Concurrent Pos:* Consult, Allied Gen Nuclear Serv, 70-80; dir grad studies, Dept Biol, Emory Univ, 78-81. *Mem:* Ecol Soc Am; Am Soc Mammalogists; Am Inst Biol Sci; AAAS. *Res:* Perturbation effects on ecosystem structure and function; nutrient cycling, decomposition, consumer dynamics and plant-animal interactions in systems undergoing natural succession. *Mailing Add:* Dept Biol Emory Univ Atlanta GA 30322

SHURE, FRED C(HARLES), b New York, NY, Feb 26, 34; m 63; c 3. PHYSICS, NUCLEAR ENGINEERING. *Educ:* Harvard Col, AB, 55; Univ Mich, MS, 57, PhD(physics), 61. *Prof Exp:* Instr physics, Univ Mich, 59-61; assoc res physicist, Conductron Corp, 61-62; from lectr to asst prof, 62-65, ASSOC PROF NUCLEAR ENG, UNIV MICH, ANN ARBOR, 65- *Concurrent Pos:* Physicist plasma physics lab, Princeton Univ, 63-64; pres ESZ Assocs, Inc. *Mem:* Am Phys Soc; Am Nuclear Soc. *Res:* Transport theory; reactor theory; plasma physics; applied mathematics. *Mailing Add:* 1127 Brooks Ann Arbor MI 48103

SHURE, KALMAN, b Brooklyn, NY, Mar 14, 25; m 51; c 2. NUCLEAR SCIENCE. *Educ:* Brooklyn Col, AB, 45; Mass Inst Technol, PhD(physics), 51. *Prof Exp:* Gen phys scientist, US Air Force Cambridge Res Ctr, 49; sr scientist, Bettis Atomic Power Div, 51-54, supvry scientist, 54-65, adv scientist, 65-73, CONSULT, BETTIS ATOMIC POWER LAB, WESTINGHOUSE ELEC CORP, 73- *Mem:* Am Phys Soc; fel Am Nuclear Soc. *Res:* Shielding, penetration of gamma rays and neutrons in materials; decay energies of radioactive isotopes. *Mailing Add:* Bettis Atomic Power Lab Westinghouse Elec Corp Box 79 West Mifflin PA 15122

SHURMAN, MICHAEL MENDELSOHN, b St Louis, Mo, Aug 4, 21. ASTRONOMY. *Educ:* Univ Wis, BA, 43, MA, 46, PhD(physics), 51. *Prof Exp:* Instr physics, Exten, Univ Wis, 46-48; physicist, Los Alamos Sci Lab, 52-55; from asst prof to assoc prof physics, 55-61, assoc dean sci, 62-65, PROF PHYSICS, UNIV WIS-MILWAUKEE, 61- *Mem:* Am Asn Physics Teachers. *Mailing Add:* Dept of Physics Univ of Wis Milwaukee WI 53201

SHURTLEFF, DAVID B, b Fall River, Mass, July 1, 30; m 52; c 3. PEDIATRICS. *Educ:* Tufts Univ, MD, 55. *Prof Exp:* Intern pediat, Mass Gen Hosp, Boston, 55-56, asst resident, 56-57; chief resident, Children's Orthop Hosp, Seattle, Wash, 57-58; from instr to assoc prof, 60-71, PROF PEDIAT, SCH MED, UNIV WASH, 71- *Concurrent Pos:* Teaching fel, Harvard Med Sch, 55-57; assoc, Sch Med, Univ Wash, 57-58; sr consult, US Army, Madigan Hosp, 61-; Nat Found March of Dimes fel, Welsh Nat Sch Med, Univ Wales, 69-70, vis prof & consult, 69-71. *Mem:* Am Acad Pediat; Soc Pediat Res; Am Pediat Soc. *Res:* Congenital defects; clinical study of epidemiology and cerebrospinal fluid dynamics and ecology of children with hydrocephalus and meningomyelocele. *Mailing Add:* Dept Pediat RD 20 Univ Wash Sch Med Seattle WA 98105

SHURTLEFF, MALCOLM C, JR, b Fall River, Mass, June 24, 22; m 50; c 3. PHYTOPATHOLOGY. *Educ:* Univ RI, BS, 43; Univ Minn, MS, 50, PhD(plant path), 53. *Prof Exp:* Asst, Univ Minn, 47-50; instr bot, Univ RI, 50-51, asst res prof plant path & asst exten prof plant path & entom, 51-54; asst prof plant path & exten plant pathologist, Iowa State Univ, 54-58, assoc prof bot & plant path, 58-61; assoc prof plant path, 61-65, PROF PLANT PATH, UNIV ILL, URBANA, 65-, EXTEN PLANT PATHOLOGIST, 61- *Concurrent Pos:* Chmn exten comt, Int Soc Plant Path, 78-80; chief ed, Plant Dis, 79-82. *Mem:* AAAS; fel Am Phytopath Soc; Bot Soc Am. *Res:* Fungicides; turf, field crop and ornamental diseases. *Mailing Add:* Dept of Plant Path N-533 Turner Hall Univ of Ill Urbana IL 61801

SHURVELL, HERBERT FRANCIS, b London, Eng, Sept 3, 34; m 60; c 3. SPECTROCHEMISTRY. *Educ:* Univ Exeter, BSc, 59; Univ BC, MSc, 62, PhD(chem), 64. *Hon Degrees:* DSc, Univ Exeter, 81. *Prof Exp:* Res attache, Nat Ctr Sci Res, Fac Sci, Marseille, France, 64-65; from asst prof to assoc prof chem, 65-77, PROF CHEM, QUEEN'S UNIV, ONT, 77- *Concurrent Pos:* Res fel, Univ Queensland, 72-73; vis prof, Sao Paulo, Brazil, 79, Univ Queensland, 78 & 81. *Mem:* Fel Chem Inst Can; Spectros Soc Can (pres, 78-79); Royal Soc Chem. *Res:* Infrared and Raman spectroscopy. *Mailing Add:* Dept of Chem Queen's Univ Kingston ON K7L 3N6 Can

SHUSHAN, SAM, b Bronx, NY, July 6, 22; m 46; c 3. LICHENOLOGY, MYCOLOGY. *Educ:* City Col New York, BS, 43; Rutgers Univ, MS, 47, PhD(bot), 49. *Prof Exp:* From instr to assoc prof, 49-72, PROF BOT, UNIV COLO, BOULDER, 72- *Mem:* AAAS; Bot Soc Am; Am Bryol & Lichenological Soc; Mycol Soc Am; Phycol Soc Am. *Res:* Developmental plant anatomy; lichen taxonomy. *Mailing Add:* Biol Dept Campus Box 334 EPO Univ of Colo Boulder CO 80309

SHUSKUS, ALEXANDER J, b Hartford, Conn, June 15, 29; m 55; c 3. SOLID STATE PHYSICS. *Educ:* Univ Conn, BA, 50; Univ Ala, MS, 57; Univ Conn, PhD(physics), 61. *Prof Exp:* Engr, Hart Mfg Co, 50-51; engr, Pratt & Whitney Aircraft Div, United Aircraft Corp, 53-55, physicist, Res Labs, 61-65, group leader microwave physics, 65-68, mgr microelectronics lab, 68-71, SR RES CONSULT, RES CTR, UNITED TECHNOLOGIES CORP, 71- *Mem:* Inst Elec & Electronics Engrs; Am Phys Soc. *Res:* Electron spin resonance studies; radiation effects in solids; microwave properties of solids; semiconductor physics; thin films; photovoltaics; ion implantation. *Mailing Add:* United Technologies Corp Res Ctr Silver Lane East Hartford CT 06108

SHUSMAN, T(EVIS), b Bristol, RI, May 7, 20; m 44; c 2. CHEMICAL ENGINEERING, POLYMER CHEMISTRY. *Educ:* Univ RI, BS, 42. *Prof Exp:* Res chemist, res group & sr group leader, 46-54, mfg specialist & tech supt, 54-66, TECHNOL MGR, MONSANTO CO, 66- *Concurrent Pos:* Int consult, Springborn Labs, Conn, 77-82. *Res:* Polymer catalysis, process and product development, safety, productivity and economic performance; polymer projects in North and South America, Europe, Asia and Australia; styrenic, olefinic and vinyl polymer developments. *Mailing Add:* 10 Chestnut St Apt 3204 Springfield MA 01103

SHUSTER, CARL NATHANIEL, JR, b Randolph, Vt, Nov 16, 19; m 44; c 5. AQUATIC ECOLOGY, INVERTEBRATE ZOOLOGY. *Educ:* Rutgers Univ, BSc, 42, MSc, 48; NY Univ, PhD(biol), 55. *Prof Exp:* Instr zool, Rutgers Univ, 49-54, lectr & demonstr sci, Univ Col, 53-55, lectr zool, 54-55; asst prof biol sci & dir marine labs, Univ Del, 55-63; dir Northeast Marine Health Serv Lab, USPHS, 63-69, ecologist, Bur Water Hyg, 69-71; br chief water progs, Environ Protection Agency, 71-72; asst adv environ qual, Ecol Systs Anal, 72-74, actg adv environ qual, 74-75, ECOL SYSTS ANALYST, FED ENERGY REGULATORY COMN, 75- *Concurrent Pos:* Mem, US Nat Mus Smithsonian-Bredin Caribbean exped, 58; adj prof zool & oceanogr, Univ RI, 63-70. *Mem:* Fel AAAS; Am Soc Limnol & Oceanog; Ecol Soc Am; fel NY Acad Sci; Am Soc Zoologists. *Res:* Limulidae; estuarine ecology, especially of arthropods and mollusks; evaluation of environmental impacts on aquatic ecosystems from federal actions, particularly interrelations within river basins, electrical power systems and water use management; evaluation of endangered species regulations and state coastal management programs on energy systems. *Mailing Add:* 3733 North 25th St Arlington VA 22207

SHUSTER, JOSEPH, b Montreal, Que, Jan 29, 37; m 64; c 2. CANCER, IMMUNOLOGY. *Educ:* McGill Univ, BS, 58; Univ Alta, MD, 62; Univ Calif, PhD(immunol), 68. *Prof Exp:* From asst prof to assoc prof med, 68-78, PROF MED & ASSOC DIR, MCGILL CANCER CTR, MCGILL UNIV, 78-; SCI DIR, MONTREAL GEN HOSP RES INST, 81- *Concurrent Pos:* Med Res Coun Can scholar, 68-73; from asst phys to assoc phys, Montreal Gen Hosp, 68-77, sr physician, 77-, dir, Div Clin Immunol & Allergy, 80-; clin res assoc, Nat Cancer Inst Can, 74- *Mem:* NY Acad Sci; Can Soc Immunol; Can Soc Oncol; Can Soc Clin Invest. *Res:* Identification and characterization of human tumor antigens, particularly alpha fetoprotein, carcinoembryonic antigen and tumor modified histocompatibility antigens. *Mailing Add:* Div of Clin Immunol & Allergy Mont Gen Hosp 1650 Cedar Ave Montreal PQ H3G 1A4 Can

SHUSTER, KENNETH ASHTON, b Trenton, NJ, Apr 3, 46; m 69; c 1. ENVIRONMENTAL SYSTEMS & TECHNOLOGY, OPERATIONS ANALYSIS. *Educ:* Rutgers Univ, BS & BA, 69; Xavier Univ, MBA, 72. *Prof Exp:* Staff engr solid waste collection, Dept HEW, USPHS, 69-70; staff engr, 70-71, sect chief solid waste systs, 71-74, PROG MGR LAND DISPOSAL, US ENVIRON PROTECTION AGENCY, 74- *Concurrent Pos:* Staff comt safety standards solid waste equip, Am Nat Standards Inst, 74-77; adv staff task force solid waste, Nat Comn Prod, 72-73; chmn, Environ Protection Agency Disposal Regs Work Group, 76-79. *Honors & Awards:* Bronze Medal, US Environ Protection Agency, 77, Silver Medal, 79. *Mem:* Am Pub Works Asn. *Res:* Environmental and economic analyses technologies and regulations of solid waste management systems, particularly land disposal of hazardous and non-hazardous wastes, resource conservation and recovery and waste storage and collection systems. *Mailing Add:* Off of Solid Waste WH-564 US Environ Protection Agency Washington DC 20460

SHUSTER, LOUIS, b Wysock, Poland, Apr 17, 29; nat US; m 59; c 2. PHARMACOLOGY, NEUROCHEMISTRY. *Educ:* Univ BC, BA, 50; Johns Hopkins Univ, PhD(biochem), 54. *Prof Exp:* Nat Res Coun Can overseas fel, Nat Inst Med Res, Eng, 54-55; vis scientist, Nat Cancer Inst, 55-58; from asst prof to assoc prof pharmacol, 58-70, assoc prof biochem, 67-70, PROF BIOCHEM & PHARMACOL, SCH MED, TUFTS UNIV, 70- *Mem:* Am Chem Soc; Am Soc Biol Chemists; Brit Biochem Soc; Am Soc Pharmacol & Exp Therapeut; Soc Neurosci. *Res:* Mechanisms of drug action; liver damage from drugs; addiction to narcotics and stimulants; pharmacogenetics. *Mailing Add:* Dept of Biochem & Pharmacol Tufts Univ Sch of Med Boston MA 02111

SHUSTER, ROBERT C, b Brooklyn, NY, Dec 15, 32; m 58; c 2. BIOCHEMISTRY, MICROBIOLOGY. *Educ:* Brooklyn Col, BA, 53; Purdue Univ, MS, 59; Albany Med Col, PhD(biochem), 63. *Prof Exp:* Res assoc biochem, Sch Med, Yale Univ, 63-66; staff fel, NIH, 66-68; asst prof, 68-74, ASSOC PROF BIOCHEM, EMORY UNIV, 74- *Mem:* Am Soc Biol Chemists. *Res:* Replication and development of temperate bacteriophages. *Mailing Add:* Dept of Biochem Emory Univ Atlanta GA 30322

SHUTE, EVAN VERE, obstetrics & gynecology, deceased

SHUTER, ELI RONALD, b New York, NY, June 16, 35; m 58; c 4. NEUROLOGY, NEUROCHEMISTRY. *Educ:* Cornell Univ, AB, 56; Wash Univ, MD, 60; Am Bd Psychiat & Neurol, dipl, 71. *Prof Exp:* Intern med, NY Hosp, 60-61; asst resident neurol, Mass Gen Hosp, 61-62; resident neurol, Cleveland Metrop Gen Hosp, 64-65 & neuropath, 65-66; Nat Inst Neurol Dis & Stroke spec res fel, Wash Univ, 66-69; asst prof neurol, Sch Med, St Louis Univ, 69-75, asst clin prof, 75-79; ASST PROF CLIN NEUROL, SCH MED, WASHINGTON UNIV, 79- *Concurrent Pos:* Teaching fel, Harvard Univ, 61-62; consult, Vet Admin Hosps, St Louis, 70-77; USPHS res grant, St Louis Univ, 70-75; mem active staff, Christian Hosp Northeast-Northwest, 75-; asst neurologist, Barnes Hosp, 79-; consult staff, St Anthony's Hosp, 80- & Alton Mem Hosp, 81- *Mem:* Asn Res Nerv & Ment Dis; Am Acad Neurol; Soc Neurosci; Am Asn Study Headache; NY Acad Sci. *Res:* Biochemical changes in neuropathologic conditions; biochemical changes during development of the central nervous system; metabolism of gangliosides; hexosaminidases in the nervous system; pseudobulbar palsy; headache. *Mailing Add:* 11155 Dunn Rd St Louis MO 63136

SHUTER, WILLIAM LESLIE HAZLEWOOD, b Rangoon, Burma, Jan 17, 36; m 63; c 2. RADIO ASTRONOMY. *Educ:* Rhodes Univ, SAfrica, BSc, 57, MSc, 59; Univ Manchester, PhD(physics), 63. *Prof Exp:* Lectr physics, Rhodes Univ, SAfrica, 63-65; asst prof, 65-68, assoc prof, 68-79, PROF PHYSICS, UNIV BC, 79- *Mem:* Can Astron Soc. *Res:* Millimeter wave astronomy; interstellar gas; radio astronomical spectroscopy; galactic structure. *Mailing Add:* Dept of Physics Univ of BC Vancouver BC V6T 1W5 Can

SHUTZE, JOHN V, b Hale, Colo, Apr 21, 24; m 47; c 2. POULTRY NUTRITION. *Educ:* Colo State Univ, BS, 55, MS, 57; Wash State Univ, PhD(poultry nutrit), 64. *Prof Exp:* Rancher, Imperial, Nebr, 49-52; instr poultry sci, Wash State Univ, 57-63; exten poultryman, Pa State Univ, 63-65; exten poultryman & assoc poultry scientist, Colo State Univ, 65-70; HEAD EXTEN POULTRY SCI DEPT & EXTEN POULTRY SCIENTIST, UNIV GA, 70- *Mem:* AAAS; Poultry Sci Asn; World Poultry Sci Asn. *Res:* Effect of pesticides on growth and reproduction; effect of polychlorinated biphenyls on hatchability and tissue residue; effect of calcium sources and additives on eggshell quality; effect of calorie protein ratio and energy sources on the thiamine requirement in chicks; fatty acid metabolism in laying hens. *Mailing Add:* Exten Poultry Sci Dept Univ of Ga Athens GA 30601

SHUVAL, HILLEL ISAIAH, b Washington, DC, July 16, 26; m 52; c 3. ENVIRONMENTAL ENGINEERING, PUBLIC HEALTH. *Educ:* Univ Mo, BSCE, 48; Univ Mich, MPH, 52. *Prof Exp:* Sanit engr, Ministry Health, Israel, 49-57, chief sanit engr, 58-65; assoc prof, 65-75, PROF ENVIRON HEALTH, HEBREW UNIV JERUSALEM, 76- *Concurrent Pos:* Design engr, Metcalf & Eddy Consult Eng, 55-56; Nat Water Coun, Ministry Agr, Israel, 57-68; Expert Adv Panel, Environ Health Div, WHO, 60-; vis prof, Sch Pub Health, Univ Mich, 61-62 & 78-79; Sci Adv Bd, WAPORA-Environ Consult Engrs, 74-; Reactor Safety Comn, Israel AEC, Environ Eng Consult, World Bank & Consult WHO, United Nations Environ Prog, 76- *Honors & Awards:* Distinguished Foreign Lectr, Asn Environ Eng Profs, 74; Presidential Citation, US Nat Asn Environ Health, 62. *Mem:* Int Asn Water Pollution Res (vpres, 68-70); fel Am Pub Health Asn; Am Soc Civil Engrs; Int Acad Environ Safety; Water Pollution Control Fedn. *Res:* Environmental engineering and health; water quality management; wastewater renovation and reuse; viruses in water; marine pollution; water microbiology; waste treatment. *Mailing Add:* Dir Div of Human Environ Sci Hebrew Univ Jerusalem Israel

SHUYLER, HARLAN R, economic zoology, medical zoology, see previous edition

SHWACHMAN, HARRY, b Boston, Mass, Mar 19, 10; m 44; c 3. MEDICINE. *Educ:* Mass Inst Technol, BS, 32; Johns Hopkins Univ, MD, 36. *Prof Exp:* Asst, 39-46, instr, 46-48, assoc, 48-51, asst prof, 51-57, from assoc clin prof to clin prof, 57-72, prof pediat, 72-77, EMER PROF PEDIAT, HARVARD MED SCH, 77- *Concurrent Pos:* Chief div clin labs, Children's Hosp Med Ctr, 46-71, chief clin nutrit div, 47-72, consult cystic fibrosis, 72-; mem med adv comt & educ comt, Nat Cystic Fibrosis Found, 55-; vis prof, Univ PR, 59. *Honors & Awards:* Mead-Johnson Award, 49; Borden Award, 76. *Mem:* Fel Am Pediat Soc; Soc Pediat Res; AMA; Am Acad Pediat. *Res:* Diseases affecting infants and children, especially nutritional diseases with emphasis on cystic fibrosis. *Mailing Add:* Dept of Pediat Harvard Med Sch Boston MA 02115

SHWARTZ, JOSEF, b Turka, Poland, Jan 15, 39; m 69; c 3. ENGINEERING SCIENCES, APPLIED PHYSICS. *Educ:* Israel Inst Technol, BSc, 61; Mass Inst Technol, MSc, 66, PhD(mech eng), 68. *Prof Exp:* Lectr aerodynamics, Ethiopian Air Acad, 62-64; sr res scientist, Hydronautics Inc, 68-70; from sr lectr to assoc prof, Israel Inst Technol, 70-78; staff engr, 78-80, SR STAFF SCIENTIST LASERS, TRW DEFENSE & SPACE SYSTS GROUP, 80- *Concurrent Pos:* Consult, AVCO, 71-74 & Laser Industs, Israel, 73-75; mem tech staff, TRW, 75-77. *Mem:* Sigma Xi; Am Inst Aeronaut & Astronaut. *Res:* Fluid mechanics and laser physics. *Mailing Add:* 3228 Barry Ave Los Angeles CA 90066

SHWE, HLA, b Rangoon, Burma, May 2, 34; US citizen; m 62; c 3. HIGH ENERGY PHYSICS, NUCLEAR PHYSICS. *Educ:* Univ Calif, Berkeley, AB, 58, MA, 59, PhD(physics), 62. *Prof Exp:* US AEC fel, Lawrence Radiation Lab, 62; from asst prof to assoc prof physics, Ripon Col, 63-69; chmn dept, 69-74, dean fac sci, 74-79, PROF PHYSICS, EAST STROUDSBURG STATE COL, 69-, DEAN, SCH ARTS & SCI, 79- *Concurrent Pos:* US AEC & Assoc Cols Midwest fel, Argonne Nat Lab, 66-67; consult, Argonne Nat Lab, 68-72, Oak Ridge Nat Lab, 70-72 & Lawrence Berkeley Lab, 72-76. *Mem:* Am Asn Univ Prof; Am Asn Higher Educ; AAAS; Am Phys Soc; Am Asn Physics Teachers. *Res:* Particle physics, especially meson and strange particle detection in nuclear emulsion and bubble chamber; neutron physics, especially in the area of cross section work; heavy-ion nuclear physics; high-energy heavy ions. *Mailing Add:* Dean Sch Arts & Sci East Stroudsburg State Col East Stroudsburg PA 18301

SHY, CARL MICHAEL, medicine, epidemiology, see previous edition

SHYKIND, EDWIN B, b Los Angeles, Calif, Oct 10, 31; m 57; c 3. MARINE GEOLOGY. *Educ:* Northwestern Univ, BS, 53; Univ Chicago, SM, 55, PhD(geol), 56. *Prof Exp:* Instr geol, Wright Jr Col, 54-55; res engr, Montaine Corp, Ill, 56-57; asst prof earth sci, Northern Ill Univ, 57-62; chief earth sci br & spec asst to dir sci inform exchange, Smithsonian Inst, 62-64; assoc staff dir interagency comt oceanog, Fed Coun Sci & Technol, Exec Off of Pres, 64-67, actg exec secy, 67, exec secy interagency comt marine res educ & fac, Nat Coun Marine Resources & Eng Develop, 67-69; staff dir marine sci affairs staff, Off Oceanogr, Dept Navy, 69; sr staff mem, Nat Coun Marine Resources & Eng Develop, Exec Off of Pres, 69-71; dir, Environ Affairs Div, 71-77, dir, Off Bus & Policy Anal, Bus Domestic Com, 71-79, SR TECH ADV, OFF REGULATORY POLICY, US DEPT COM, 79- *Mem:* AAAS; Am Asn Petrol Geol. *Res:* Sedimentation; hydrodynamics; scientific information; ocean engineering; environmental affairs. *Mailing Add:* Off Regulatory Policy Bur Domestic Com US Dept Com Washington DC 20903

SHYNE, J(OHN) C(ORNELIUS), b Detroit, Mich, Nov 26, 25; m 47; c 5. METALLURGY. *Educ:* Univ Mich, BS(math) & BS(metall), 51, MS, 52, PhD(metall), 58. *Prof Exp:* Res engr, Ford Motor Co, 52-59; proj dir mat res, Mueller Brass Co, 59-60; from asst prof to assoc prof mat sci, 60-66, chmn dept mat sci & eng, 71-75, PROF MAT SCI, STANFORD UNIV, 66- *Concurrent Pos:* Head, Metall & Mat Sect, NSF, 75-77. *Mem:* Am Soc

Metals; Am Inst Mining, Metall & Petrol Engrs. *Res:* Internal friction, crystalline defects and phase transformations in metals; relation of structure to properties in metals; metallurgical failure analysis; acoustic NDE. *Mailing Add:* Dept of Mat Sci & Eng Stanford Univ Stanford CA 94305

SHYSH, ALEC, b Vilna, Alta, Apr 2, 36; m 61; c 1. BIONUCLEONICS. *Educ:* Univ Alta, BSc, 58, MSc, 68, PhD(bionucleonics), 70. *Prof Exp:* Teaching asst pharm, 65-70, asst prof bionucleonics, 70-75, ASSOC PROF BIONUCLEONICS & RADIOPHARM, UNIV ALTA, 75- *Mem:* Can Pharmaceut Asn; Soc Nuclear Med. *Res:* Development, quality control and application of radiopharmaceuticals as diagnostic scanning agents. *Mailing Add:* Fac of Pharm & Pharmaceut Sci Univ of Alta Edmonton AB T6G 2N8 Can

SIAKOTOS, ARISTOTLE N, b Dedham, Mass, July 19, 28; m 72; c 4. BIOCHEMISTRY. *Educ:* Univ Mass, BS, 52, MS, 54; Cornell Univ, PhD(entom), 58. *Prof Exp:* Res asst entom, Cornell Univ, 54-56; entomologist, Med Res Labs, US Army Chem Ctr, 58-62, biochemist, 62-68; from asst prof to assoc prof path, 68-78, PROF PATH, MED CTR, IND UNIV, INDIANAPOLIS, 78- *Concurrent Pos:* Nat Retinitis Pigmentosa sr res fel, 74-76. *Mem:* Am Chem Soc; Am Oil Chem Soc; Am Soc Neurochem; Am Soc Neurosci; Am Soc Exp Path. *Res:* Subcellular particulates of the central nervous system; drug induced changes in brain; lipid composition and metabolism in subcellular particles; retinal degeneration; biochemistry of the eye; vision; ophthalmology; biochemical pathology; atypical slow virus diseases; lipopigments. *Mailing Add:* Dept of Path Ind Univ Med Ctr Indianapolis IN 46202

SIANO, DONALD BRUCE, b Sewickley, Pa, June 30, 42; m 72. PHYSICAL CHEMISTRY, BIOPHYSICS. *Educ:* Kent State Univ, BS, 60; Iowa State Univ, MS, 68, PhD(biophys), 78. *Prof Exp:* Res assoc chem, Columbia Univ, 76-78; RES PHYSICIST EMULSION SCI, EXXON RES & ENG CO, 78- *Mem:* AAAS; Am Chem Soc. *Res:* Rayleigh and dynamic light scattering; biopolymers; microemulsions; enhanced oil recovery. *Mailing Add:* Exxon Res & Eng Co Box 45 Linden NJ 07036

SIAS, CHARLES B, b Denver, Colo, Jan 26, 19; m 42; c 4. CHEMICAL ENGINEERING. *Educ:* Univ Denver, BS, 40, MS, 41. *Prof Exp:* Chem engr, 41-48, tech serv dir reinforced plastics, 49-73, labeling coordinator, 73-82, CONSULT, PPG INDUSTS, INC, 82- *Mem:* Am Chem Soc; Am Inst Chem Engrs; Soc Plastics Engrs. *Res:* Reinforced plastics. *Mailing Add:* 1820 Ferguson Rd Alison Park PA 15101

SIAU, JOHN FINN, b Detroit, Mich, Mar 30, 21; m 57; c 2. WOOD SCIENCE, CHEMICAL ENGINEERING. *Educ:* Mich State Univ, BS, 43; State Univ NY Col Environ Sci & Forestry, MS, 66, PhD(wood sci), 68. *Prof Exp:* Engr loudspeaker mfr, Utah Radio Prod Div, Newport Steel Corp, 46-48; mfg & designing engr vacuum tube, Gen Elec Co, 48-58; physics teacher, Paul Smiths Col, 58-68; assoc prof, 68-78, PROF WOOD SCI, STATE UNIV NY COL ENVIRON SCI & FORESTRY, 78- *Concurrent Pos:* Proj dir, NSF, 69-77. *Honors & Awards:* Wood Award, Forest Prod Res Soc, 68. *Mem:* Forest Prod Res Soc; Soc Wood Sci & Technol; Am Wood Preservers' Asn. *Res:* Flow of liquids and gases through wood; non-isothermal moisture movement in wood; wood drying; wood preservation. *Mailing Add:* State Univ NY Col Environ Sci & Forestry Syracuse NY 13210

SIBAL, LOUIS RICHARD, b Chicago, Ill, Aug 6, 27; m 64; c 2. MICROBIOLOGY. *Educ:* Univ Ill, BS, 49; Univ Colo, MS, 54, PhD(microbiol), 57. *Prof Exp:* Assoc prof microbiol, Col Med, Univ Ill, 57-65; spec fel, Nat Cancer Inst, 65-66, res microbiologist, 66-71, dep assoc dir, 71-76, actg assoc dir viral oncol, 76-80, ASSOC DIR, DIV CANCER CAUSE & PREV, NAT CANCER INST, 80- *Mem:* AAAS; Am Asn Cancer Res; Am Soc Microbiol; Am Asn Immunol. *Res:* Viral oncology; immunologic aspects of virus-induced cancer of animals and man. *Mailing Add:* Viral Oncol Div Nat Cancer Inst Bldg 31 Rm 11A05 NIH Bethesda MD 20014

SIBBALD, IAN RAMSAY, b Eng, Sept 20, 31; nat Can; m 55; c 4. NUTRITION. *Educ:* Univ Leeds, BSc, 53; Univ Alta, MSc, 55, PhD(animal nutrit), 57. *Prof Exp:* Asst nutrit, Macdonald Col, McGill Univ, 57; asst prof, Ont Agr Col, 57-63; group leader, Animal Prod Res, John Labatt Ltd, 63-70, mgr food res sect, 70-72; PRIN RES SCIENTIST, ANIMAL RES CTR, AGR CAN, OTTAWA, 72- *Honors & Awards:* Borden Award, Nutrit Soc Can, 60; Tom Newman Mem Int Award, 77; Am Feed Mfgs Award, Poultry Sci Asn, 79. *Mem:* Poultry Sci Asn; World's Poultry Sci Asn; Animal Nutrit Res Coun; Nutrit Soc Can. *Res:* Utilization of energy and nitrogen by monogastrics; various aspects of poultry nutrition. *Mailing Add:* Animal Res Inst Cent Exp Farm Ottawa ON K1A 0C6 Can

SIBBETT, DONALD JOSEPH, physical chemistry, biophysics, see previous edition

SIBBITT, W(ILMER) L(AWRENCE), b Greencastle, Ind, June 6, 14; m 47; c 6. SOLAR ENERGY, GEOTHERMAL ENERGY. *Educ:* Purdue Univ, BS, 37, MS, 41, PhD(chem eng), 42. *Prof Exp:* Res chemist, E I du Pont de Nemours & Co, NY, 37-38; asst chem, Univ Ill, 38-39; asst chem, Eng Lab, Purdue Univ, 40, from instr to prof mech eng, 41-55; sr chem engr, Phillips Petrol Co, Okla, 45-46; sr engr & group leader, Monsanto Chem Co, Clinton Lab & Carbide & Carbon Chem Corp, Oak Ridge Nat Lab, 46-48; mem staff, Ramo-Wooldridge Corp, Calif, 55-56; mem staff nuclear propulsion, 57-72 & geothermal energy, 73-77, staff mem solar energy, 77-80, STAFF MEM TECH ENG SUPPORT, LOS ALAMOS NAT LAB, 81- *Mem:* Am Soc Mech Engrs. *Res:* Heat transmission; thermodynamics; fluid flow; materials. *Mailing Add:* 939 Tewa Loop Los Alamos NM 87544

SIBENER, STEVEN JAY, b Brooklyn, NY, Apr, 3, 54. SURFACE CHEMISTRY, MOLECULAR BEAM SCATTERING. *Educ:* Univ Rochester, BA & ScB, 75; Univ Calif, Berkeley, MS, 77, PhD(chem), 79. *Prof Exp:* Res fel, Bell Labs, 79-80; ASST PROF CHEM, DEPT CHEM & JAMES FRANCK INST, UNIV CHICAGO, 80- *Mem:* Am Phys Soc; Royal Soc Chem; Sigma Xi. *Res:* Molecular beam, laser spectroscopic, and ultra-high vacuum surface characterization techniques; gas-surface interaction potentials; chemisorption; physisorption; heterogeneous catalysis; two-dimensional phase transitions; surface structure; surface phonons; semiconductor reconstruction; epitaxial film growth. *Mailing Add:* James Franck Inst Univ Chicago 5640 S Ellis Ave Chicago IL 60637

SIBERT, ELBERT ERNEST, b DeQueen, Ark, Oct 7, 41; m 63; c 2. COMPUTER SCIENCE, MATHEMATICS. *Educ:* Rice Univ, BA, 63, PhD(math), 67. *Prof Exp:* Asst prof comput sci, Rice Univ, 67-70; assoc prof comput & info sci, 70-77, PROF COMPUT & INFO SCI, SYRACUSE UNIV, 77- *Concurrent Pos:* Develop engr, Schlumberger Well Serv, 69-70, consult, 68- *Mem:* Asn Comput Mach; Comput Soc. *Res:* Mechanical theorem proving; numerical techniques for digital computation; organization of digital computers. *Mailing Add:* Dept Comput & Info Sci 313 Link Hall Syracuse Univ Syracuse NY 13201

SIBERT, JOHN RICKARD, b Glendale, Calif, Dec 3, 40; Can citizen. MARINE ECOLOGY, STATISTICS. *Educ:* Univ Pac, BA, 62; Columbia Univ, PhD(zool), 68. *Prof Exp:* Fel oceanog, Univ BC, 68-69, teaching fel bot, 69-70; RES SCIENTIST MARINE ECOL, PAC BIOL STA, 70- *Mem:* AAAS; Am Soc Limnol & Oceanog. *Res:* Sources and fates of detritus in aquatic ecosystems; productivity of estuarine meiofauna; mathematical modelling of estuarine ecosystems; statistical descriptions of community structure. *Mailing Add:* RR2 Parksville BC V0R 2S0 Can

SIBILA, KENNETH FRANCIS, b Canton, Ohio, Dec 2, 11; m 40; c 3. ELECTRICAL ENGINEERING. *Educ:* Case Inst Technol, BSEE, 35, MSEE, 37. *Prof Exp:* Engr, Ohio Crankshaft Co, 37-40; from instr to assoc prof elec eng, 40-47, prof & head dept, 47-68, dir electronic systs eng, 68-77, EMER PROF ELEC ENG, UNIV AKRON, 77- *Mem:* Am Soc Eng Educ; sr mem Inst Elec & Electronics Engrs; Nat Asn Educ Broadcasters. *Res:* Electronic systems used in educational TV instruction. *Mailing Add:* 1929 Silver Lake Ave Akron OH 44309

SIBILIA, JOHN PHILIP, b Newark, NJ, Mar 12, 33; m 58; c 3. CHEMICAL PHYSICS. *Educ:* Rutgers Univ, BA, 53; Univ Md, PhD(chem), 58. *Prof Exp:* Res chemist, US Rubber Co, 59-61; res chemist, 61-62, group leader, 62-67, res supvr, 67-77, MGR CHEM PHYSICS DEPT, ALLIED CHEM CORP, 77- *Concurrent Pos:* Lectr spectros & molecular workshop, Fairleigh Dickinson Univ, 65-66, instr polymer sci, 72-78. *Mem:* Am Chem Soc; Am Soc Testing & Mat; Soc Appl Spectros. *Res:* Molecular structure of organic compounds, morphology of polymers; analysis of materials through spectroscopic; x-ray diffration; microscopy, nuclear magnetic resonance and thermal analytical techniques; material structure-property relationships and pollution analysis. *Mailing Add:* 12 Balmoral Dr Livingston NJ 07039

SIBLEY, CAROL HOPKINS, b Freeport, NY, Oct 9, 43; m 66; c 2. DEVELOPMENTAL GENETICS, IMMUNOGENETICS. *Educ:* Univ Rochester, BA, 65, MS, 69; Univ Calif, San Francisco, PhD(biochem), 74. *Prof Exp:* Fel, Calif Inst Technol, 74-76; ASST PROF GENETICS, UNIV WASH, 76- *Concurrent Pos:* Vis prof, Calif Inst Technol, 81. *Mem:* Am Asn Immunologists; AAAS; Asn Women Sci. *Res:* Control of B lymphocyte development using transcription, processing and synthesis of the antibody genes as a model for control of developmental processes. *Mailing Add:* SK-50 Dept Genetics Univ Wash Seattle WA 98195

SIBLEY, CHARLES GALD, b Fresno, Calif, Aug 7, 17; m 42; c 3. SYSTEMATIC ZOOLOGY, ORNITHOLOGY. *Educ:* Univ Calif, PhD(zool), 48. *Prof Exp:* Asst prof zool, Univ Kans, 48-49 & San Jose State Col, 49-53; assoc prof ornith, Cornell Univ, 53-59, prof zool, 59-65; dir, Peabody Mus Natural Hist, 70-76, PROF BIOL & DIR DIV VERT ZOOL, YALE UNIV, 65- *Concurrent Pos:* Guggenheim fel, 59-60; secy gen, Int Ornith Cong, 62. *Honors & Awards:* Brewster Mem Award, Am Ornith Union, 71. *Mem:* AAAS; Soc Syst Zool; Am Soc Naturalists; Am Ornith Union (treas, 53-62); Am Soc Zoologists. *Res:* DNA hybridization and protein structure as source of taxonomic information; egg white proteins; interspecific hybridization and speciation in birds; geographic variation and distribution; isolating mechanisms; fossil birds. *Mailing Add:* Peabody Mus of Natural Hist Yale Univ New Haven CT 06520

SIBLEY, DUNCAN FAWCETT, b Newton, Mass, Mar 9, 46; m 68. SEDIMENTARY PETROLOGY. *Educ:* Lafayette Col, BA, 68; Rutgers Univ, MS, 71; Univ Okla, PhD(geol), 75. *Prof Exp:* Asst prof, 74-80, ASSOC PROF GEOL, MICH STATE UNIV, 80- *Mem:* Soc Econ Paleontologists & Mineralogists. *Res:* Understanding of diagenesis in sandstone and carbonate rocks with specific interest in the origin and evolution of porosity. *Mailing Add:* Dept of Geol Mich State Univ East Lansing MI 48824

SIBLEY, WILLIAM ARTHUR, b Ft Worth, Tex, Nov 22, 32; m 57; c 3. SOLID STATE PHYSICS. *Educ:* Univ Okla, BS, 56, MS, 58, PhD(physics), 60. *Prof Exp:* Res physicist, Nuclear Res Estab, Julich & Inst Metal Physics, Aachen Tech Univ, 60-61; res physicist, Oak Ridge Nat Lab, 61-70; chmn dept physics, 70-78, PROF PHYSICS, OKLA STATE UNIV, 70-, ASST V PRES RES, 78- *Mem:* Fel Am Phys Soc; Sigma Xi. *Res:* Optical and mechanical properties of both irradiated and unirradiated single crystals; light scattering; optical absorption and luminescence of laser materials. *Mailing Add:* Off of Asst Vpres for Res Okla State Univ Stillwater OK 74074

SIBLEY, WILLIAM AUSTIN, b Miami, Okla, Jan 25, 25; m 54; c 4. NEUROLOGY. *Educ:* Yale Univ, BS, 45, MD, 48. *Prof Exp:* Asst resident neurologist, Presby Hosp, New York, 51 & 53-55, resident neurologist, 56; asst neurol, Col Physicians & Surgeons, Columbia Univ, 55-56; from asst prof to assoc prof, Sch Med, Western Reserve Univ, 56-67, actg dir div, 59-61; PROF NEUROL & DIR DEPT, COL MED, UNIV ARIZ, 67- *Concurrent Pos:* Consult neurologist, Vet Admin & Benjamin Rose Hosps, Cleveland, 58-; physician-in-chg neurol, Univ Hosps, 59-61. *Mem:* Am Neurol Asn; fel Am Acad Neurol; Asn Res Nerv & Ment Dis. *Mailing Add:* Dept of Neurol Univ of Ariz Health Sci Ctr Tucson AZ 85724

SIBOO, RUSSELL, b Trinidad, Wis, Mar 21, 30; Can citizen; m 66; c 2. IMMUNOLOGY, MICROBIOLOGY. *Educ:* McMaster Univ, BA, 58; Univ Toronto, MSc, 62; McGill Univ, PhD(immunol), 64. *Prof Exp:* Med Res Coun Can fel immunol, Univ Lund, 64-65; asst prof, Univ Sask, 65-67; asst prof, Univ Ottawa, 67-69; asst prof, 69-73, ASSOC PROF IMMUNOL, McGILL UNIV, 73- *Mem:* Can Soc Immunol; Can Soc Microbiol. *Res:* Complement synthesis; gene expression of hybridized Ig producing cells. *Mailing Add:* Dept of Microbiol & Immunol McGill Univ Montreal PQ H3A 2B4 Can

SIBUL, LEON HENRY, b Voru, Estonia, Aug 30, 32; US citizen; m 61; c 2. APPLIED MATHEMATICS, UNDERWATER ACOUSTICS. *Educ:* George Washington Univ, BEE, 60; NY Univ, MEE, 63; Pa State Univ, PhD(appl math & elec eng), 68. *Prof Exp:* Mem tech staff syst design, Bell Tel Labs, 60-64; SR RES ASSOC STOCHASTIC PROCESSES, ADAPTIVE SYSTS, APPL RES LAB, PA STATE UNIV, UNIVERSITY PARK, 64- *Concurrent Pos:* Consult, Nat Acad Sci, Nat Res Coun, 72-73. *Mem:* Soc Indust & Appl Math; Inst Elec & Electronic Engrs. *Res:* Adaptive systems and application of adaptive algorithms to array processing with applications to sonar, radar and seismic signal processing; broadband ambiguity function and signal design; system optimization theory. *Mailing Add:* Appl Res Lab Pa State Univ PO Box 30 University Park PA 16802

SIBULKIN, MERWIN, b New York, NY, Aug 20, 26; m 49; c 2. FLUID DYNAMICS. *Educ:* NY Univ, AB; Univ Md, MS, 53; Calif Inst Technol, AeroE, 56. *Prof Exp:* Aeronaut res scientist, Nat Adv Comt Aeronaut, 48-51; res engr, US Naval Ord Lab, 51-53; res engr, Jet Propulsion Lab, Calif Inst Technol, 53-56; staff scientist, Sci Res Lab, Convair Div, Gen Dynamics Corp, 56-63; assoc prof eng, 63-66, PROF ENG, BROWN UNIV, 66- *Mem:* Am Phys Soc; Am Inst Aeronaut & Astronaut; Combustion Inst. *Res:* Combustion and fire research; heat transfer; viscous flow. *Mailing Add:* Div of Eng Brown Univ Providence RI 02912

SIBUYA, YASUTAKA, b Maizuru, Japan, Oct 16, 30; m 62; c 4. MATHEMATICS. *Educ:* Univ Tokyo, BS, 53, MS, 55; Univ Calif, Los Angeles, PhD(math), 59; Univ Tokyo, DS(math), 61. *Prof Exp:* Res assoc, Mass Inst Technol, 59-60; temp mem, Courant Inst, NY Univ, 60-61; asst prof math, Ochanomizu Univ, Tokyo, 62-63; assoc prof, 63-65, PROF MATH, UNIV MINN, 65- *Concurrent Pos:* Vis prof, Math Res Ctr, Univ Wis-Madison, 72-73. *Mem:* Math Soc Japan; Am Math Soc; Soc Indust & Appl Math. *Res:* Field of analytic theory of ordinary differential equations. *Mailing Add:* Sch of Math Univ of Minn Minneapolis MN 55455

SICA, ALBERT JOSEPH, b New York, NY, Oct 9, 15; m 44; c 6. PHARMACY. *Educ:* Fordham Univ, BS, 37, MS, 41, PhD(biochem), 48. *Prof Exp:* Asst chem, Fordham Univ, 37-40; pharmaceut chemist, Centaur Co, NJ, 40-42; pharmaceut chemist, Burroughs Wellcome Co, 42; from instr to prof pharm, Fordham Univ, 42-70, chmn dept, 52, assoc dean, 54-56, dean, 56-70; mem, 62-70, pres, 66-67, EXEC SECY, NY STATE BD PHARM, 70- *Res:* Nutrition in the rat; pharmaceutical chemical problems; pharmaceutical development; relation of diet to reproduction and lactation in the rat. *Mailing Add:* NY State Bd of Pharm Cult Educ Ctr Rm 3035 Albany NY 12230

SICA, LOUIS, b Miami, Fla, June 14, 35; m 78. OPTICAL PHYSICS. *Educ:* Fla State Univ, BA, 58; Johns Hopkins Univ, PhD(physics), 66. *Prof Exp:* Res asst infrared spectros, Lab Astrophys & Phys Meteorol, Johns Hopkins Univ, 63-67; RES PHYSICIST OPTICAL PHYSICS, NAVAL RES LAB, 67- *Concurrent Pos:* Surveyor res topics mod optics, Off Naval Res, 75-76. *Mem:* Optical Soc Am. *Res:* Optical coherence effects; nonlinear propagation; interferometry; unconventional imaging; space variant imaging, image-sharpness inertia. *Mailing Add:* Code 6530 Naval Res Lab Washington DC 20375

SICARD, RAYMOND EDWARD, b Lawrence, Mass, Apr 18, 48; m 77. DEVELOPMENTAL PHYSIOLOGY. *Educ:* Merrimack Col, AB, 69; Univ RI, MS, 72, PhD(biol sci), 75. *Prof Exp:* Jr bacteriologist anal, Mass Dept Pub Health, 69; hemat tech anal, New Eng Deaconess Hosp, 70-73; res assoc, Dept Biol, Amherst Col, 74; res fel, Shriners Burns Inst, Mass Gen Hosp & Harvard Med Sch, 75-76; ASST PROF, DEPT BIOL, BOSTON COL, 76- *Concurrent Pos:* Grad teaching asst, Dept Zool, Univ RI, 69-71 & 73-74; lectr, Div Pharm & Allied Health, Northeastern Univ, 75-76. *Mem:* Am Inst Biol Sci; Am Soc Cell Biol; Int Soc Develop & Comp Immunol; Int Soc Develop Biologists; Soc Develop Biol. *Res:* Nature of physiological (neural, endocrine, and immunological) regulation of the developmental events occurring during the process of forelimb regeneration in amphibians. *Mailing Add:* Dept Biol Boston Col 140 Commonwealth Ave Chestnut Hill MA 02167

SICCAMA, THOMAS G, b Philadelphia, Pa, July 6, 36; m 62; c 1. ECOLOGY. *Educ:* Univ Vt, BS, 62, MS, 63, PhD(bot), 68. *Prof Exp:* Assoc in res ecol, Yale Univ, 67-69; lectr forest ecol, 77-80. *Mem:* AAAS; Ecol Soc Am; Torrey Bot Club. *Res:* Ecosystem analysis; computer applications in ecology; heavy metals cycling in natural ecosystems. *Mailing Add:* 37 Martin Rd East Haven CT 06512

SICE, JEAN, b Paris, France, Oct 13, 19; nat US; m 43; c 3. PHARMACOLOGY. *Educ:* Univ Aix-Marseille, BA & BS, 37, PhD(pharmacol), 43, BM & MS, 45. *Prof Exp:* Asst pharmacol, Fac Med, Univ Aix-Marseille, 43-45, lectr, 45-48; instr surg, Sch Med, Univ Chicago, 48-51, asst prof cancer res, 51-53; from asst prof to prof pharmacol, Chicago Med Sch, 53-74; head pharmacol, Quincy Res Ctr, 76-80. *Concurrent Pos:* USPHS career develop award, 58-63; consult clin pharmacol, Div Med, Cook County Hosp, 69-73; lectr, Cook County Grad Sch Med, 71-73; mem spec comn on internal pollution, Cambridge, Eng, 73-76. *Honors & Awards:* Perron Award, French Nat Acad Med, 45; Sang Award, Univ Health Sci, 73. *Mem:* Am Chem Soc; Am Soc Pharmacol & Exp Therapeut; AAAS. *Res:* Distribution, metabolic transformations and behavioral effects of drugs; design of controlled trials; determinants of drug utilization. *Mailing Add:* 866 Adams Denver CO 80206

SICHEL, ELSA KEIL, b New Rochelle, NY, Mar 2, 06; m 37; c 1. ZOOLOGY. *Educ:* Elmira Col, BS, 27; Brown Univ, MA, 29. *Prof Exp:* Asst zool, Brown Univ, 27-29; from instr to asst prof, Douglass Col, Rutgers Univ, 29-39; head dept sci, Johnson State Col, 39-43; prof biol, St Michael's Col, 43-44; prof, 43-73, EMER PROF BIOL, TRINITY COL, VT, 73- *Concurrent Pos:* Sloan Found res investr, Univ Vt, 45-46; lectr, Univ, 58-59; lectr, Champlain Col, 66-73; mem corp, Marine Biol Lab, Woods Hole; chairperson, Woods Hole Hist Collection Mus, 73- *Mem:* AAAS; Am Soc Zoologists; Sigma Xi. *Res:* Regeneration in flatworms; effect of cations on regeneration and growth; micrurgical studies on invertebrate and vertebrate muscles. *Mailing Add:* 4 Whitman Rd Woods Hole MA 02543

SICHEL, ENID KEIL, b Burlington, Vt, May 14, 46. PHYSICS. *Educ:* Smith Col, Mass, AB, 67; Rutgers Univ, New Brunswick, PhD(physics), 71. *Prof Exp:* Vis scientist, Nat Magnet Lab, Mass Inst Technol, 70-71; res assoc, Rutgers Univ, New Brunswick, 71-73; mem tech staff, David Sarnoff Res Ctr, RCA Labs, 73-80; MEM STAFF, GTE ADVAN TECHNOL LAB, 80- *Mem:* AAAS; Am Phys Soc. *Res:* Low temperature physics; thermophysical properties; transport and optical properties of thin solid films. *Mailing Add:* 40 Sylvan Rd Waltham MA 02254

SICHEL, JOHN MARTIN, b Montreal, Que, Dec 2, 43; m 67; c 3. QUANTUM CHEMISTRY. *Educ:* McGill Univ, BS, 64, PhD(quantum chem), 68. *Prof Exp:* Fel theoret chem, Univ Bristol, 67-69; res assoc chem & physics, Ctr Res Atoms Molecules, Laval Univ, 69-70, asst prof physics, 70-72; asst prof, 72-76, ASSOC PROF CHEM, UNIV MONCTON, 76- *Mem:* Chem Inst Can; Can Asn Physicists; Fr Can Asn Advan Sci. *Res:* Quantum calculation of autoionizing levels in atoms and molecules; quantum theory of chemisorption. *Mailing Add:* Dept of Chem Univ of Moncton Moncton NB E1A 3E9 Can

SICHEL, MARTIN, b Stuttgart, Ger, Sept 1, 28; m 52; c 3. AEROSPACE ENGINEERING, FLUID DYNAMICS. *Educ:* Rensselaer Polytech Inst, BME, 50, MME, 51; Princeton Univ, PhD(aerospace eng), 61. *Prof Exp:* Develop engr thermal power, Gen Elec Co, 51-54; res aide aerospace, Princeton Univ, 58-61; from asst prof to assoc prof aerospace eng, 61-68, PROF AEROSPACE ENG, UNIV MICH, ANN ARBOR, 68- *Mem:* Am Phys Soc; Am Inst Aeronaut & Astronaut. *Res:* Fluid dynamics; shock wave structure; boundary layer theory; flow with chemical reactions; hypersonic flow; detonations. *Mailing Add:* Dept of Aerospace Eng Univ of Mich Ann Arbor MI 48109

SICHLER, JIRI JAN, b Prague, Czech, Dec 30, 41; m 68. MATHEMATICS. *Educ:* Charles Univ Prague, MSc, 66, PhD(math), 68. *Prof Exp:* Nat Res Coun Can fel, 69-70, asst prof math, 70-75, PROF MATH, UNIV MAN, 75- *Concurrent Pos:* Nat Res Coun Can grants, 70, 71, 72-75 & 76-78. *Mem:* Am Math Soc. *Res:* Algebra; general mathematical systems; category theory. *Mailing Add:* Dept of Math Univ of Man Winnipeg MB R3T 2N2 Can

SICILIAN, JAMES MICHAEL, b Bronx, NY, May 25, 47. NUMERICAL ANALYSIS. *Educ:* Mass Inst Technol, BS, 69; Stanford Univ, MS, 70, PhD(nuclear eng), 73. *Prof Exp:* Res analyst, Savannah River Lab, 73-76; asst group leader, Los Alamos Sci Lab, 76-80; SR SCIENTIST, FLOW SCI INC, 80- *Mem:* Sigma Xi; AAAS. *Res:* Application of numerical simulation methods to the analysis and solution of problems in hydrodynamics with emphasis on the development of convenient, efficient programs. *Mailing Add:* Flow Sci Inc PO Box 933 Los Alamos NM 87544

SICILIANO, ARTHUR ANTHONY, b Boston, Mass, Jan 9, 43. PHARMACEUTICAL CHEMISTRY. *Educ:* Mass Col Pharm, BS, 65; Univ Conn, MS, 67, PhD(chem), 69; Babson Col, MBA, 75. *Prof Exp:* Sr chemist prod res, Toiletries Div, Gillette Co, South Boston, 69-73; dir res, Kolmar Labs, Inc, 73-75; TECH DIR, REHEIS CHEM CO, DIV ARMOUR PHARMACEUT CO, 75- *Mem:* Soc Cosmetic Chem; Am Chem Soc; Am Pharmaceut Asn. *Res:* Pharmaceutical technology; research and product development in cosmetic chemistry; applied and basic research, skin and hair care; bulk pharmaceutical chemicals. *Mailing Add:* 14 Avondale RD Denville NJ 07834

SICILIANO, EDWARD RONALD, b Brooklyn, NY, Aug, 13, 48; m 75. NUCLEAR SCATTERING THEORY, REACTION THEORY. *Educ:* Univ Conn, BA, 70; Ind Univ, MS, 73, PhD(physics), 76. *Prof Exp:* Fel, Dept Physics, Case Western Reserve Univ, 76-78 & Meson Physics Div, Los Alamos Nat Lab, 78-80; ASST PROF PHYSICS, UNIV COLO, 80- *Concurrent Pos:* Vis staff mem, Meson Physics Div, Los Alamos Nat Lab, 80- *Mem:* Am Phys Soc; Am Asn Physics Teachers; Sigma Xi. *Res:* Nuclear structure, scattering and reaction theories; electron, pion, proton, and kaon induced reactions. *Mailing Add:* Nuclear Physics Lab Box 446 Univ Colo Boulder CO 80309

SICILIANO, MICHAEL J, b Brooklyn, NY, May 12, 37; m 61; c 3. BIOCHEMICAL GENETICS. *Educ:* St Peter's Col, BS, 59; Long Island Univ, MS, 62; NY Univ, PhD(biol), 70. *Prof Exp:* From instr to assoc prof biol, Long Island Univ, 61-72; asst prof, 72-76, ASSOC PROF BIOL & HEAD, DEPT GENETICS, UNIV TEX SYST CANCER CTR, M D ANDERSON HOSP & TUMOR INST, 76- *Concurrent Pos:* Fel, Dept Biol, M D Anderson Hosp & Tumor Inst, 70-72; consult, Tex Epidemiol Studies Prog, 77- *Mem:* Genetics Soc Am; Am Soc Cell Biol; Am Soc Ichthyologists & Herpatologists; Environ Mutagen Soc. *Res:* Control of gene expression in normal and neoplastic cells; somatic cell, animal model and human tissue materials used to study the genetics of the control of enzyme phenotypes. *Mailing Add:* Univ of Tex Syst Cancer Ctr M D Anderson Hosp & Tumor Inst Houston TX 77030

SICILIO, FRED, b Italy, Aug 10, 20; nat US; m 44; c 4. INORGANIC CHEMISTRY, RADIOCHEMISTRY. *Educ:* Centenary Col, BS, 51; Vanderbilt Univ, MA, 53, PhD(chem), 56. *Prof Exp:* Asst chemist, Springhill Paper Co, 49-51; asst, Vanderbilt Univ, 53-56; sr nuclear engr, Convair Div,

Gen Dynamics Corp, Tex, 56-58; res assoc prof chem, assoc prof chem eng & head, Radioisotopes Lab, Ga Inst Technol, 58-61; assoc prof, 61-67, PROF CHEM, TEX A&M UNIV, 67- *Mem:* Am Chem Soc. *Res:* Radioisotope separations and purifications; radiation chemistry of organic substances; studies on free radicals in solution. *Mailing Add:* Dept of Chem Tex A&M Univ College Station TX 77843

SICK, LOWELL VICTOR, b Elmira, NY, Apr 28, 44; m 72. ORGANOMETALLIC CHEMISTRY. *Educ:* Univ Conn, BS, 65; NC State Univ, PhD(zool biochem), 70. *Prof Exp:* Res asst zool, Nat Marine Fisheries Serv, 66-67; res assoc zool, Duke Univ, 69-70; asst prof zool nutrit, Univ Ga, Skidaway Inst, 70-75; asst prof, 75-80, ADJ ASST PROF ZOOL BIOCHEM, UNIV DEL, 80- *Concurrent Pos:* Res fel, Univ Del, 76. *Mem:* Am Soc Limnol & Oceanog; Am Chem Soc; Atlantic Estuarine Res Soc; World Mariculture Soc. *Res:* Nutritional and biochemical studies of crustacea and mollusks; specific interest in trace metal physiology. *Mailing Add:* Col of Marine Studies Univ of Del Lewes DE 19958

SICKA, RICHARD WALTER, b Cleveland, Ohio, May 28, 38. PHYSICAL CHEMISTRY, POLYMER SCIENCE. *Educ:* Case Inst Technol, BS, 59, MS, 61. *Prof Exp:* Sr res assoc, Horizons Inc, 64-66, proj supYr, 66-69, group leader, 69-74; CONSULT, R SICKA & ASSOCS, 74-; sr res scientist, 76-81, ASSOC SCIENTIST, CENT RES, FIRESTONE TIRE & RUBBER CO, 81- *Mem:* AAAS; Am Chem Soc; Soc Rheology; Am Soc Testing & Mat. *Res:* Applied physical chemistry; polymer structure property relationships; biomedical applications of polymers; inorganic polymers; polyphosphazene polymers; composite materials; polymer processing; rheology; mixing and extrusion. *Mailing Add:* 3207 Boston Rd Brecksville OH 44141

SICKAFUS, EDWARD N, b St Louis, Mo, Mar 7, 31; m 53; c 2. SOLID STATE PHYSICS. *Educ:* Mo Sch Mines, BS, 55, MS, 56; Univ Va, PhD(physics), 60. *Prof Exp:* Vis lectr, Sweet Briar Col, 59-60; res physicist, Denver Res Inst, Univ Denver, 60-67, actg head physics div, 61-62, from asst prof to assoc prof physics, Univ Denver, 62-67; prin res scientist surface sci, 67-80, MGR, ADVAN COMPONENTS & ENERGY SYSTS DEPT, FORD SCI LAB, 80- *Concurrent Pos:* Instr sign lang, Madonna Col, 75-76. *Mem:* Am Phys Soc; Am Vacuum Soc. *Res:* Electron spectroscopy and crystal physics related to surface physics; secondary cascade theory; auger electron spectroscopy; low energy electron diffraction; crystal defect state and growth; dynamic transmission analysis of x-rays and electrons; theoretical calculations of interstitial geometry. *Mailing Add:* Ford Sci Lab PO Box 2053 Dearborn MI 48121

SICKEL, SHARON RAE, b Indianapolis, Ind, May 5, 46. COMPUTER SCIENCE. *Educ:* Univ Wash, BA, 67, MS, 71, PhD(comput sci), 73. *Prof Exp:* Assoc engr comput, Boeing Co, 68-70; consult, Comput Ctr, Univ Wash, 70-71, res assoc comput sci, 71-73; comput ctr dir, Univ Calif, Santa Cruz, 74-75, sr preceptor acad affairs, Crown Col, 75-77, asst prof comput sci, 73-80. *Concurrent Pos:* Off of Naval Res grant, 76- *Mem:* Asn Comput Mach; Inst Elec & Electronics Engrs. *Res:* Automatic theorem proving. *Mailing Add:* 26 Moreno Dr Santa Cruz CA 96060

SICKELS, MARGARET HINES, zoology, see previous edition

SICKO-GOAD, LINDA MAY, b Highland Park, Mich, Sept 21, 48; m 74. CELL BIOLOGY, ALGOLOGY. *Educ:* Wayne State Univ, BS, 70; Univ New York, PhD(biol), 74. *Prof Exp:* Technician elec micros, Mich Cancer Found, 69-70; adj lectr biol, Herbert H Lehman Col, City Univ New York, 70-72 & Bronx Community Col, 72, lab technician elec micros, Herbert H Lehman Col, 72-74; res assoc cell biol, 74-76, asst res scientist, 76-78, ASSOC RES SCIENTIST, GREAT LAKES RES DIV, UNIV MICH, 78- *Mem:* Am Soc Cell Biol; Phycol Soc Am; Electron Micros Soc Am; Can Soc Microbiol. *Res:* Algae ultrastructure, phosphate metabolism in phytoplankton and x-ray analysis application in ecology. *Mailing Add:* Great Lakes Res Div Inst Sci & Technol Bldg Univ Mich Ann Arbor MI 48109

SICOTTE, YVON, b Montreal, Que, Oct 12, 30; m 59; c 2. PHYSICAL CHEMISTRY. *Educ:* Univ Montreal, BSc, 54, MS, 56, PhD(chem), 59. *Prof Exp:* From asst prof to assoc prof, 58-74, PROF CHEM, UNIV MONTREAL, 74- *Concurrent Pos:* NATO fel, Res Ctr Macromolecules, Strasbourg, France, 59-60; guest prof phys chem, Univ Bordeaux, 66-67. *Mem:* Chem Inst Can; Fr-Can Asn Advan Sci. *Res:* Light scattering by pure liquids and solutions; molecualr anisotropy and dielectric polarization at optical frequencies, correlations of molecular orientations in liquids; polymer chemistry and polymer characterization in solution. *Mailing Add:* Dept of Chem Fac of Sci Univ of Montreal Montreal PQ H3C 3J7 Can

SICULAR, GEORGE M, b New York, NY, Aug 15, 21; m 48; c 2. HYDRAULICS. *Educ:* Cooper Union, BS, 49; Columbia Univ, MS, 53; Stanford Univ, Engr, 71. *Prof Exp:* Lectr civil eng, City Col, 49-54; PROF CIVIL ENG, SAN JOSE STATE UNIV, 54- *Concurrent Pos:* Consult, 55-; vis prof, Univ Roorkee, 63-64; Ford Found-Univ Wis adv, Univ Singapore, 67-69. *Mem:* Am Soc Civil Engrs; Am Geophys Union. *Res:* Hydraulics; planning in water resources. *Mailing Add:* 18 Peralta Ave Los Gatos CA 95030

SIDA, DEREK WILLIAM, b Barking, Eng, Nov 4, 26; m 54; c 3. APPLIED MATHEMATICS, ASTRONOMY. *Educ:* Univ London, BSc, 51, MSc, 52, PhD(math), 55. *Prof Exp:* Asst lectr math, Univ Leeds, 55-57, lectr, 57-59; sr lectr, Univ Otago, NZ, 59-62; assoc prof, 62-71, chmn dept, 69-71, dean fac arts, St Patricks Col, 71-73, PROF MATH, CARLETON UNIV, 68- *Mem:* Royal Astron Soc London; Royal Astron Soc Can; Int Astron Union. *Res:* Stellar dynamics; cosmology; history of astronomy; population dynamics in biology. *Mailing Add:* Dept of Math Carleton Univ Ottawa ON K1S 5B6 Can

SIDBURY, JAMES BUREN, JR, b Wilmington, NC, Jan 13, 22; m 53; c 5. PEDIATRICS. *Educ:* Yale Univ, BS, 44; Columbia Univ, MD, 47. *Prof Exp:* Intern med, Roosevelt Hosp, NY, 47-48; asst resident, 48-49; intern pediat, Johns Hopkins Hosp, 49-50; asst resident, Univ Hosps Cleveland, Ohio, 50-51; asst & instr, Sch Med, Emory Univ, 51-53; from instr to asst prof, Johns Hopkins Univ, 54-61; assoc prof, 61-68, prof & dir clin res unit, Sch Med, Duke Univ, 68-75; SCI DIR, NAT INST CHILD HEALTH & HUMAN DEVELOP, NIH, 75- *Concurrent Pos:* Fel, Sch Med, Johns Hopkins Univ, 54-57. *Mem:* AAAS; Soc Pediat Res; Am Pediat Soc; Am Soc Human Genetics; Am Acad Pediat. *Res:* Biochemical genetics. *Mailing Add:* Bldg 31, Rm 2A-50 NIH Bethesda MD 20014

SIDDALL, JOHN BRIAN, bio-organic chemistry, deceased

SIDDALL, THOMAS HENRY, III, b Sumter, SC, Oct 4, 22. CHEMISTRY. *Educ:* Univ NC, AB, 42; Univ Chicago, MS, 48; Duke Univ, PhD(chem), 51. *Prof Exp:* Chemist, E I Du Pont De Nemours & Co, 50-54, res supvr chem, 54-63, res assoc, 63-69; PROF CHEM, UNIV NEW ORLEANS, 69- *Mem:* Am Chem Soc. *Res:* Chemistry of actinide elements and fission products; role of structure in determining behavior of organic extractants toward actinides and fission products; molecular dynamics; isomerism; nuclear magnetic resonance. *Mailing Add:* Dept Chem Univ New Orleans New Orleans LA 70122

SIDDIQEE, MUHAMMAD WAHEEDUDDIN, b Pakistan, Aug 23, 31; US citizen; m 61; c 2. TRANSPORTATION SYSTEMS. *Educ:* Panjab Univ, BA, 51, BSc, 55; Univ Tenn, MS, 60; Univ Minn, PhD(control sci), 67. *Prof Exp:* Elec engr, Siemens Pakistan, 55-56 & Siemens Schuckertwerke, WGer, 56-58; sr elec engr, Siemens Pakistan, 58-59, exec engr, 60-62; res engr, 67-69, sr res engr, 69-74, STAFF SCIENTIST & MGR TRANSP, SRI INT, 74- *Mem:* Inst Elec Engrs, Pakistan. *Res:* Advanced transportation systems; air traffic analysis; railroad analysis; urban transportation systems and electric power systems. *Mailing Add:* SRI Int Menlo Park CA 94025

SIDDIQUE, IRTAZA H, b Budaun, India, July 4, 29; m 54; c 2. VETERINARY MEDICINE, MICROBIOLOGY & PUBLIC HEALTH. *Educ:* Bilhar Vet Col, Patna, GBVC, 50; Univ Minn, St Paul, MS, 61, PhD(vet med), 63; Univ Ala, Birmingham, MPH, 78. *Prof Exp:* Vet, Govt Uttar Pradesh, India, 50-59; from asst prof to assoc prof, 64-71, PROF MICROBIOL, SCH VET MED, TUSKEGEE INST, 71-, PROF PUB HEALTH, 78- *Concurrent Pos:* Assoc proj dir, USPHS grant, 64-69, proj dir, 69-; dir, NSF grant, 65-75; dir, USDA-Coop State Res Serv grant, 74-; chmn S-92 tech comt, Southern Regional Proj, 77-78. *Mem:* Conf Res Workers Animal Dis; Am Vet Med Asn; Am Soc Microbiol; NY Acad Sci; Sigma Xi. *Res:* Listeriosis; immunofluorescent techniques and electron microscopy; cattle abortion and bacterial infections and pathogenesis. *Mailing Add:* Sch of Vet Med Tuskegee Inst Tuskegee AL 36088

SIDDIQUI, ASLAM RASHEED, b British India, Dec 12, 46; US citizen; m 73; c 3. NUCLEAR MEDICINE. *Educ:* Chittagong Med Col, EPakistan, MD, 69. *Prof Exp:* Asst prof, 76-80, ASSOC PROF RADIOL, SCH MED, IND UNIV, 80- *Concurrent Pos:* Consult radiol, Vet Admin Hosp, Indianapolis & staff physician radiol, Wishard Mem Hosp, Indianapolis, 76- *Mem:* Soc Nuclear Med; Am Fedn Clin Res; Radiol Soc NAm; Am Col Physicians; AAAS. *Res:* Bone marrow imaging in children; nuclear medicine studies in pediatric oncology; nuclear thyroidology. *Mailing Add:* Div of Nuclear Med Ind Univ Sch of Med Indianapolis IN 46223

SIDDIQUI, IQBAL RAFAT, b India, Jan 28, 31; m 56. ORGANIC CHEMISTRY. *Educ:* Univ Sind, Pakistan, BSc, 48, MSc, 50; Univ Birmingham, PhD(chem), 57, DSc(org chem), 69. *Prof Exp:* Lectr chem, Govt Col, Lahore, Pakistan, 51-52; Sugar Res Found fel, Univ London, 57-58; Nat Res Coun Can fel, 58-60; Harold Hibbert Mem fels, McGill Univ, 61-62; GROUP LEADER FOOD CARBOHYDRATES, FOOD RES INST, CAN DEPT AGR, 62- *Mem:* Fel Royal Inst Chem. *Res:* Structural, synthetic and analytical studies of carbohydrates. *Mailing Add:* Cent Exp Farm Can Dept of Agr Food Res Inst Ottawa ON Can

SIDDIQUI, MOHAMMED MOINUDDIN, b Hyderabad, India, Apr 19, 28; m 57; c 5. MATHEMATICAL STATISTICS. *Educ:* Univ Osmania, India, MA, 48; Am Univ, MA, 54; Univ NC, PhD(math, statist), 57. *Prof Exp:* Lectr statist, Univ Panjab, Pakistan, 49-53, sr lectr, 58-59; res asst, Univ NC, 54-57; math statistician, Nat Bur Standards, 57-58 & 59-64; PROF MATH STATIST, COLO STATE UNIV, 64- *Mem:* Fel AAAS; Am Statist Asn; Inst Math Statist; Am Geog Soc. *Res:* Distribution theory; stationary time series; order statistics and stochastic processes. *Mailing Add:* Dept Statist Colo State Univ Ft Collins CO 80523

SIDDIQUI, WAHEED HASAN, b Bijnor, India, Feb 8, 39; Can citizen; m 69; c 2. TERATOLOGY, PHARMACOKENETICS. *Educ:* Agra Univ, India, BSc, 60; Sind Univ, Pakistan, MSc, 64; Carleton Univ, Ont, PhD(biol), 71; Univ Western Ont, MEng, 77. *Prof Exp:* Sr biologist, Environ Control Consult, Ltd & Natural Mus Nat Sci, Can, 72-76; res scientist toxicol, Health Protection Br, Dept Health & Welfare, Govt Can, 77-79; SR RES TOXICOLOGIST, DOW CORNING CORP, MICH, 79- *Mem:* Soc Toxicol; Soc Toxicol Can; Sigma Xi. *Res:* Safety evaluation of new chemicals; long and short-term effects of chemicals in animal models; risk assessment for human exposure. *Mailing Add:* Dow Corning Corp 2200 W Saltzburg Rd Midland MI 48640

SIDDIQUI, WASI MOHAMMAD, b Saharanpur, India, Jan 1, 39; m 62; c 3. PLANT PATHOLOGY, MICROBIOLOGY. *Educ:* Univ Lucknow, BS, 56; Aligarh Muslim Univ, India, MS, 59; Rutgers Univ, New Brunswick, PhD(plant path), 67. *Prof Exp:* Asst prof bot, Aligarh Muslim Univ, India, 59-65; res fel plant path, Rutgers Univ, New Brunswick, 65-67; USDA res assoc, 67; assoc prof, 67-70, PROF LIFE SCI, BISHOP COL, 70- *Concurrent Pos:* Clin assoc microbiol, Southweserm Med Sch, Dallas, 68-; consult city parks dept, Dallas, 70-71; regional group, Comn Undergrad Educ Biol Sci,

70-71. *Mem:* Am Phytopath Soc; Am Soc Microbiol. *Res:* Root rot diseases; plant viruses; yeast and smut genetics; virus interferons and their sensitivities; air pollution and plant diseases. *Mailing Add:* 1623 Aurora Dr Dallas TX 75217

SIDDIQUI, WASIM A, b India, May 10, 34; m 65; c 1. PARASITOLOGY, TROPICAL MEDICINE. *Educ:* Aligarh Muslim Univ, India, BSc, 52, MSc, 54; Univ Calif, Berkeley, PhD(zool), 61. *Prof Exp:* Lectr zool, Aligarh Muslim Univ, 54-57; res asst, Univ Calif, Berkeley, 57-61; lectr, Aligarh Muslim Univ, 61-62; NIH res fel parasitol, Rockefeller Univ, 62-65; instr trop med, Sch Med, Stanford Univ, 65-69; assoc prof, 69-73, PROF TROP MED & MICROBIOL, SCH MED, UNIV HAWAII, MANOA, 73- *Mem:* Soc Protozool; Am Soc Parasitol; Am Soc Trop Med & Hyg. *Res:* Protozoa, especially parasitic protozoans; amoebiasis and malaria. *Mailing Add:* Dept of Med Microbiol & Trop Med Univ of Hawaii Sch of Med Honolulu HI 96822

SIDDOWAY, FRANCIS H, b Rexburg, Idaho, Nov 10, 22; m 52; c 4. SOIL SCIENCE. *Educ:* Univ Idaho, BS, 47, MS, 51; Kans State Univ, PhD, 65. *Prof Exp:* Soil conservationist, Soil Conserv Serv, USDA, 49-53, soil scientist, Agr Res Serv, 53-80; CONSULT, SOIL & WATER MGT, 80- *Mem:* Soil Sci Soc Am; Am Soc Agron; Soil Conserv Soc Am; Soc Range Mgt. *Res:* Wind erosion control and dryland soil management research. *Mailing Add:* 716 9th Ave SW Sidney MT 59270

SIDEBOTTOM, OMAR M(ARION), b Forest City, Ill, Mar 13, 19; m 59; c 2. MECHANICS. *Educ:* Univ Ill, BS, 42, MS, 43. *Prof Exp:* Asst, Univ Ill, Urbana, 41-44, res assoc, 44-46, from instr to assoc prof, 46-57, prof theoret & appl mech, 57-82; RETIRED. *Mem:* Am Soc Mech Engrs; Am Soc Eng Educ; Am Soc Testing & Mat; Soc Exp Stress Anal. *Res:* Creep analysis of load carrying members; creep buckling of columns; multiaxial creep; inelasticity; load carrying capacity of members which have been inelastically deformed; experimental evaluation of assumptions made in theory. *Mailing Add:* 601 S Race Urbana IL 61801

SIDEL, VICTOR WILLIAM, b Trenton, NJ, July 7, 31; m 56; c 2. COMMUNITY HEALTH, PREVENTIVE MEDICINE. *Educ:* Princeton Univ, AB, 53; Harvard Med Sch, MD, 57. *Prof Exp:* From intern to jr asst resident med, Peter Bent Brigham Hosp, 57-59; clin assoc, Nat Heart Inst, 59-61; sr asst res, Peter Bent Brigham Hosp, 61-62; instr biophys, Harvard Med Sch, 62-64, assoc prev med, 64-68, asst prof med, 68-69; PROF COMMUNITY HEALTH, ALBERT EINSTEIN COL MED, 69-, CHMN DEPT SOCIAL MED, MONTEFIORE HOSP & MED CTR, 69- *Concurrent Pos:* Am Heart Asn advan res fel, 62-64; consult physician, Child Health Div, Children's Hosp Med Ctr, Boston, 63-67; Med Found, Inc res fel, 64-68; asst med & chief prev & community med units, Mass Gen Hosp, 64-69; Milbank Mem Fund fac fel, 64-71; consult, USPHS, 64-70, WHO, 69, 74 & 77 & Int J Health Serv, 71-79; vis prof community health & social med, City Col New York, 73-; vis prof, Scand Sch Pub Health, 75-81; attend physician, NCent Bronx Hosp, 76- *Mem:* Am Pub Health Asn; Am Col Prev Med; Int Epidemiol Asn; NY Acad Med; Asn Teachers Prev Med. *Res:* International health care comparisons; health care delivery; medical ethics; health policy. *Mailing Add:* Montefiore Hosp & Med Ctr 111 E 210th St Bronx NY 10467

SIDELL, BRUCE DAVID, b Manchester, NH, Mar 20, 48; m 70; c 2. COMPARATIVE PHYSIOLOGY, FISH BIOLOGY. *Educ:* Boston Univ, AB, 70; Univ Ill, MS, 72, PhD(physiol), 75. *Prof Exp:* Asst res scientist aquatic biol, Chesapeake Bay Inst, Johns Hopkins Univ, 75-77; ASST PROF ZOOL, UNIV MAINE, 77- *Concurrent Pos:* Mem coord comt, Migratory Fish Res Inst, Univ Maine, 77-, chmn, 78-79. *Mem:* Am Soc Zoologists; Am Inst Biol Sci; Sigma Xi. *Res:* Physiological and biochemical adaptations of aquatic ectotherms; physiology of fishes. *Mailing Add:* Dept of Zool Univ of Maine Orono ME 04469

SIDEROPOULOS, ARIS S, b Thessaloniki, Greece, Jan 30, 37; US citizen. PHOTOBIOLOGY, ENVIRONMENTAL POLLUTANTS. *Educ:* Concordia Col, Minn, BS, 60; NDak State Univ, MS, 62; Univ Kans, PhD(molecular genetics), 67. *Prof Exp:* Fel microbiol genetics, Palo Alto Res Found, 67-70; res assoc, Univ Tex, Austin, 70-71; asst prof, Med Col Pa, 71-75; ASSOC PROF MICROBIOL, DUQUESNE UNIV, 75- *Concurrent Pos:* Chief, Microbiol Lab, Fairmont Dairy Co, Minn & instr bacteriol, NDak State Univ, 62-63. *Mem:* Am Soc Microbiol; Sigma Xi; AAAS. *Res:* Cellular repair of potentially mutogenic damage to establish and utilize an experimental method in evolution of mutogenic effects of chemicals on ultraviolet irradiated living cells. *Mailing Add:* Dept Biol Sci Duquesne Univ Pittsburgh PA 15219

SIDES, GARY DONALD, b Tuscaloosa, Ala, Oct 5, 47; c 3. INSTRUMENT DEVELOPMENT, ENVIRONMENTAL MONITORING. *Educ:* Univ Ala, BS, 69; Univ Fla, MS, 71, PhD(phys chem), 75. *Prof Exp:* Res scientist, Aerospace Res Labs, 71-75; res assoc prof, Wright State Univ, 75-77; sr scientist, 77-78, HEAD, PHYS CHEM SECT, SOUTHERN RES INST, 78- *Mem:* Am Soc Mass Spectrometry; Am Chem Soc. *Res:* Automated analytical instruments for the detection of nanogram levels of toxic organophophorus and organosulfur compounds. *Mailing Add:* Southern Res Inst PO Box 3307-A Birmingham AL 35255

SIDHU, BHAG SINGH, b Ludhiana, India, Apr 30, 29; m 54; c 2. PLANT GENETICS, PLANT SCIENCE. *Educ:* Punjab Univ, India, BSc, 51, MSc, 53; Cornell Univ, PhD(genetics, plant sci), 60. *Prof Exp:* Chmn dept bot, Govt Col, Rupar, India, 54-57; chmn dept agr & biol, Govt Col, Faridkot, India, 61-62, prin-pres, 63; Nat Res Coun Can fel, McGill Univ, 64-65; assoc prof biol, Winston-Salem State Col, 65-66; UN adv agron & biol, UNESCO, UN Develop Prog, Manila, P I, 66-68; PROF BIOL, WINSTON-SALEM STATE UNIV, 69- *Concurrent Pos:* Res award, Asn Cols Agr, Philippines, 67; NSF fel, NC State Univ, 70. *Mem:* AAAS; Am Inst Biol Sci; Am Soc Agron; Crop Sci Soc Am. *Res:* Biosystematics and germ plasm screening of international field food crops materials; radiation genetics and international seed production and distribution. *Mailing Add:* Dept of Biol Winston-Salem State Univ Winston-Salem NC 27102

SIDHU, DEEPINDER PAL, b Chachrari, India, May 13, 44; m 69; c 4. THEORETICAL PHYSICS, COMPUTER SCIENCE. *Educ:* Univ Kans, BE, 66; State Univ NY Stony Brook, PhD(theoret physics), 73, MS, 79. *Prof Exp:* Res assoc physics, Rutgers Univ, New Brunswick, 73-75; asst physicist, Brookhaven Nat Lab, 75-77, assoc physicist, 77-80; MEM TECH STAFF, MITRE CORP, 80- *Res:* Unified gauge theories of strong, electromagnetic and weak interactions; computer communication networks. *Mailing Add:* Mitre Corp MS B332 PO Box 208 Bedford MA 01730

SIDHU, GURMEL SINGH, b Pasla, India, May 23, 40; Can citizen; m 79; c 2. GENETICS, PLANT PATHOLOGY. *Educ:* Punjab Univ, BSc, 58, MSc, 60; Univ BC, PhD(genetics), 72. *Prof Exp:* Res assoc plant genetics, Punjab Agr Univ, 62-64, lectr genetics cytogenetics, 64-66; res assoc plant sci, Univ BC, 66-67; fel, Simon Fraser Univ, 72-76, res scientist genetics & path, 76-80; ASST PROF PLANT PATHOL, UNIV NEBR, 80- *Concurrent Pos:* Vis prof, Punjab Agr Univ, 76-77; Genetics Soc Am travel grant, 78; assoc ed, Phytopath, 82-86. *Mem:* Genetics Soc Can; Genetics Soc Am; Am Soc Phytopath; Can Phytopath Soc; Indian Soc Crop Improvement. *Res:* Genetics of host-parasite interactions; genetics of plant disease complexes; breeding for disease resistance; fungal genetics. *Mailing Add:* Dept Plant Path 406 Plant Sci Hall Univ Nebraska Lincoln NE 68583 Can

SIDHU, KIRPAL S, b India, Sept 12, 38; US citizen; m 62; c 2. ENVIRONMENTAL TOXICOLOGY, NUTRITIONAL BIOCHEMISTRY. *Educ:* Panjab Univ, DVM, 59; Univ Mo, MS, 66; Okla State Univ, PhD(animal nutrit & biochem), 69; Am Registry Cert Animal Sci, cert, 76. *Prof Exp:* Res instr biochem, Res Inst Endocrine Lab, Univ Miami, 72-74; LAB SCIENTIST, MICH DEPT PUB HEALTH, 74- *Concurrent Pos:* Res scientist, Dept Pharmacol & Toxicol, Mich State Univ, 75-78. *Mem:* AAAS; Soc Toxicol; Am Dairy Sci Asn; Am Soc Animal Sci; Sigma Xi. *Res:* Endocrine and nutritional regulation of metabolic processes; environmental toxicology. *Mailing Add:* Mich Dept Pub Health PO Box 3505 Lansing MI 48909

SIDI, HENRI, b Provadia, Bulgaria, Mar 13, 19; US citizen; m 56; c 2. ORGANIC CHEMISTRY, POLYMER CHEMISTRY. *Educ:* Univ Toulouse, ChE, 41, PhD(org chem), 48. *Prof Exp:* Asst anal chem, Univ Toulouse, 46-47; sr chemist, Poudrerie Nationale, Toulouse, France, 47-48; asst dir dyestuffs, Francolor, Oissel, 48-50; fel, Rutgers Univ, 50-51; sr chemist, Heyden Chem Corp, 51-61; group leader, Heyden Div, Garfield, 61-71, SR SCIENTIST, INTERMEDIATES DIV, TENNECO CHEM, INC, PISCATAWAY, 71- *Mem:* AAAS; Am Chem Soc; Chem Soc France. *Res:* Polymerization of formaldehyde; fire retardant chemicals; amino-alcohols; pesticides. *Mailing Add:* 156 Victoria Ave Paramus NJ 07652

SIDIE, JAMES MICHAEL, b Elizabeth, NJ, May 22, 41; m 66; c 1. NEUROETHOLOGY, COMPARATIVE PHYSIOLOGY. *Educ:* Univ Notre Dame, BS, 64, MS, 67, PhD(biol), 70. *Prof Exp:* Pub Health Serv fel, Ind Univ, 69-71; vis lectr, Princeton Univ, 71-72; res assoc, Univ Ore, 72-74, vis asst prof, 74-76; ASST PROF PHYSIOL/NEUROBIOL, STATE UNIV NY, BUFFALO, 76- *Concurrent Pos:* NSF fel, Woods Hole, 71. *Mem:* AAAS; Am Soc Zoologists; Animal Behav Soc; Sigma Xi. *Res:* Neuroethological studies of communication in honeybees, Apis mellifera; computer assisted analyses of neural spike trains in nerve/muscle systems. *Mailing Add:* Dept Biol Sci State Univ NY Buffalo NY 14260

SIDKY, YOUNAN ABDEL MALIK, b Khartoum, Sudan, Feb 9, 28; m 64; c 2. IMMUNOLOGY, TUMOR BIOLOGY. *Educ:* Cairo Univ, BSc, 50, MSc, 55; Univ Marburg, DrPhil(zool), 56. *Prof Exp:* Demonstr zool, Cairo Univ, 50-59, lectr, 59-65; res assoc, Univ Wis-Madison, 65-69; fel, Univ Alta, 69-72; proj res assoc, 72-76, ASSOC SCIENTIST, UNIV WIS-MADISON, 76- *Mem:* Am Asn Immunologists. *Res:* Parathyroid glands in reptiles; effect of steroids on mouse thymus development; development of immunity in turtles; hibernation and immunity in hamsters; inhibitory effect of brown fat on the immune response; tumor and lymphocyt-induced angiogenesis. *Mailing Add:* Zool Res Bldg Univ of Wis-Madison 1117 W Johnson St Madison WI 53706

SIDLER, JACK D, b Rochester, Pa, Sept 19, 39; m 58; c 3. ORGANIC CHEMISTRY. *Educ:* Geneva Col, BS, 61; State Univ NY Buffalo, PhD(chem), 66. *Prof Exp:* Teaching asst, State Univ NY Buffalo, 61-62; asst prof chem, Geneva Col, 65-67; assoc prof, 67-72, PROF CHEM, MANSFIELD STATE COL, 72- *Mem:* Am Chem Soc. *Res:* Organic synthesis; organolithium chemistry; organic reaction mechanisms. *Mailing Add:* Dept of Chem Mansfield State Col Mansfield PA 16933

SIDLES, PAUL HOWARD, b Centerville, Iowa, Sept 5, 21; m 44; c 2. EXPERIMENTAL SOLID STATE PHYSICS, SOLAR PHYSICS. *Educ:* Iowa Wesleyan Col, BA, 48; Iowa State Col, MS, 51. *Prof Exp:* Res assoc, Iowa State Univ, 51-59, assoc physicist, 59-62; prof, Univ Sao Paulo, 62-64; ASSOC PHYSICIST, IOWA STATE UNIV, 64- *Mem:* AAAS; Am Vacuum Soc; Am Phys Soc; Int Solar Energy Soc. *Res:* Amorphous semiconductors; transport properties in metals and semiconductors; single crystal growth; non-stoichiometric compounds; high vacuum technology; solar energy utilization. *Mailing Add:* Ames Lab-DOE Iowa State Univ Ames IA 50011

SIDMAN, RICHARD LEON, b Boston, Mass, Sept 19, 28; m 50 & 74; c 2. NEUROPATHOLOGY. *Educ:* Harvard Univ, AB, 49, MD, 53. *Prof Exp:* Intern med, Boston City Hosp, Mass, 53-54; Moseley traveling fel, Strangeways Res Lab, Cambridge Univ & Dept Human Anat, Oxford Univ, 54-55; asst resident neurol, Mass Gen Hosp, Boston, 55-56; assoc, 59-63, from asst prof to prof, 63-68, BULLARD PROF NEUROPATH, HARVARD MED SCH, 69-; CHIEF DEPT NEUROSCI, CHILDREN'S HOSP MED CTR, BOSTON, 72- *Concurrent Pos:* Stearns mem lectr, Albert Einstein Col Med, 58; asst, Mass Gen Hosp, 59-69; consult, Nat Inst Neurol Dis & Blindness, 59- *Mem:* Histochem Soc; Am Asn Anat; Tissue Cult Asn (secy, 64-70); Am Asn Neuropath; Soc Neurosci. *Res:* Embryological development of the normal and diseased mammalian brain. *Mailing Add:* Dept of Neurosci 300 Longwood Ave Boston MA 02115

SIDMAN, ROBERT DAVID, b Troy, NY. MATHEMATICS. *Educ:* Harvard Univ, AB, 61; Rensselaer Polytech Inst, MS, 63, PhD(math), 68. *Prof Exp:* Asst prof, Univ Conn, 67-74; assoc prof math, Univ Southwestern La, 74-80; RES ASSOC, INST LIVING, 80- *Concurrent Pos:* Vis assoc prof, Rensselaer Polytech Inst, 81. *Mem:* AAAS; Am Math Soc; Soc Indust & Applied Math; assoc mem Am Electroencephalog Soc; Soc Indust & Applied Math. *Res:* biomathematics; applied mathematics; petroleum engineering; bioengineering. *Mailing Add:* 63 Hartford Ave Old Saybrook CT 06475

SIDNEY, STUART JAY, b New Haven, Conn, June 8, 41; m 65; c 4. MATHEMATICAL ANAYLSIS. *Educ:* Yale Univ, BA, 62; Harvard Univ, MA, 63, PhD(math), 66. *Prof Exp:* Instr math, Yale Univ, 66-68, asst prof, 68-71; assoc prof, 71-80, PROF, UNIV CONN, 80- *Concurrent Pos:* Vis prof, Univ Grenoble, 71-72 & 78-79. *Mem:* Am Math Soc; Math Asn Am. *Res:* Analysis, especially uniform algebras and Banach spaces; geometry. *Mailing Add:* Dept of Math Univ of Conn Storrs CT 06268

SIDRAN, MIRIAM, b Washington, DC, May 25, 20. SOLID STATE PHYSICS. *Educ:* Brooklyn Col, BA, 42; Columbia Univ, MA, 49; NY Univ, PhD(physics), 56. *Prof Exp:* Instr physics & chem, Brothers Col, Drew Univ, 46-47; instr physics, Adelphi Col, 47-49; asst solid state physics, NY Univ, 50-55, Nat Carbon Co fel, 55-58; sr physicist, Balco Res Labs, NJ, 55; asst prof chem & physics, Staten Island Community Col, State Univ NY, 58-59; res scientist, Grumman Aircraft Eng Corp, 59-67; prof physics & dep chmn dept, NY Inst Technol, New York Campus, 67-72; PROF PHYSICS, BARUCH COL, 72- *Concurrent Pos:* NSF sci fac fel, Nat Marine Fisheries Serv, Nat Oceanic & Atmospheric Admin, 71-72. *Honors & Awards:* NY Univ Founder's Day Award, 56. *Mem:* Assoc fel Am Inst Aeronaut & Astronaut; NY Acad Sci; Soc Women Engrs; Sigma Xi; Am Asn Physics Teachers. *Res:* Microwave spectrometry; optical spectrometry; infrared astronomy; lunar luminescence; lunar surface studies; radiation dosimetry; rotational energy levels of asymmetric molecules; remote sensing of sea surface temperature. *Mailing Add:* Dept Physics Baruch College New York NY 10010

SIDRANSKY, HERSCHEL, b Pensacola, Fla, Oct 17, 25; m 52; c 2. PATHOLOGY. *Educ:* Tulane Univ, BS, 48, MD, 53, MS, 58; Am Bd Path, dipl, 58. *Prof Exp:* Intern, Charity Hosp La, New Orleans, 53-54, vis asst pathologist, 54-58; instr path, Tulane Univ, 54-58; med officer, Nat Cancer Inst, 58-61; prof path, Sch Med, Univ Pittsburgh, 61-72; prof path & chmn dept, Col Med, Univ SFla, 72-77; PROF PATH & CHMN DEPT, GEORGE WASHINGTON UNIV MED CTR, 77- *Concurrent Pos:* Consult, Div Biologics, Stand Contract Comt, NIH, 66-67, mem path study sect res grants rev br, Div Res Grants, 68-72, mem nutrit study sect, 73-77; vis scientist, Weizmann Inst Sci, 67-68, Eleanor Roosevelt Int Cancer fel travel award & USPHS spec res fel, 67-68; mem bd reviewers fedn proceedings, 72-74; mem bd, Am Registry Path, 79- *Mem:* Soc Exp Biol & Med; Am Inst Nutrit; Sigma Xi; AAAS; Int Acad Path. *Res:* Chemical pathology of nutritional deficiencies; experimental liver tumor igenesis. *Mailing Add:* Dept Path 2300 Eye St NW Washington DC 20037

SIDWELL, ROBERT WILLIAM, b Huntington Park, Calif, Mar 17, 37; m 57; c 5. VIROLOGY. *Educ:* Brigham Young Univ, BS, 58; Univ Utah, MS, 61, PhD(microbiol), 63. *Prof Exp:* Head serol & rickettsial res, Univ Utah, 58-63; head virus research, Univ Utah & Dugway Proving Grounds, 63; sr virologist, Chemother Dept, Southern Res Inst, 63-66, head virus sect, 66-69; head dept virol, 69-72, chemother div, 72-75, dir, ICN Pharmaceut Nucleic Acid Res Inst, 75-77; RES PROF, DEPTS BIOL & ANIMAL, DAIRY & VET SCI, UTAH STATE UNIV, 77- *Mem:* AAAS; Am Asn Immunologists; Soc Exp Biol & Med; Am Soc Microbiol; Pan Am Med Asn. *Res:* Basic and applied research on viral disease chemotherapy, nutritional factors on viral diseases. *Mailing Add:* Dept of Animal Dairy & Vet Sci UMC 56 Utah State Univ Logan UT 84322

SIDWELL, VIRGINIA DECECCO, b Erie, Pa, Feb 3, 09; m 51. FISHERIES, NUTRITION. *Educ:* Col Wooster, AB, 31; Pa State Univ, BS, 41, MS, 46; Iowa State Univ, PhD(human nutrit), 54. *Prof Exp:* Teacher pub sch, Pa, 35-43; res assoc nutrit, Pa State Univ, 45-47 & Iowa State Univ, 47-54; prof, Univ Md, 57-60; human nutritionist, Nat Marine Fishery, Nat Oceanic & Atmospheric Admin, 60-71, food technologist, Nat Marine Fisheries Serv, 71-78, prog leader fishery develop, Southeast Res Utilization Ctr, 75-78; RETIRED. *Honors & Awards:* Achievement Award, US Dept Interior, 67 & 72. *Mem:* Am Inst Chemists. *Res:* Development of food products fortified with fish protein concentrate and chemical and nutritive composition of fish and fishery products. *Mailing Add:* Nat Marine Fisheries Serv 3300 White Haven St NW Washington DC 20235

SIE, CHARLES H, b Shanghai, China, Sept 12, 34; US citizen; m 58; c 3. ELECTRICAL ENGINEERING, MATERIAL SCIENCE. *Educ:* Manhattan Col, BS, 57; Drexel Univ, MS, 60; Iowa State Univ, PhD(elec eng), 69. *Prof Exp:* Elec engr, Radio Corp Am, NJ, 57-63; mem res staff, Watson Res Ctr, IBM Corp, NY, 66-69; mgr, Memory Device Develop, Energy Conversion Devices, Inc, 69-74; mgr, Component Lab, Burroughs Corp, 74-77; MGR COMPONENT & PACKAGING TECHNOL, XEROX CORP, 77- *Mem:* Inst Elec & Electronics Engrs; Am Phys Soc. *Res:* Semiconductor and ferromagnetic memory devices; amorphous chalcogenide semiconductor; electrical circuit design; component and reliability engineering. *Mailing Add:* Xerox Corp 701 S Aviation Blvd El Segundo CA 90245

SIE, EDWARD HSIEN CHOH, b Shanghai, China, Jan 17, 25; US citizen; wid; c 1. BIOCHEMISTRY. *Educ:* Univ Nanking, BS, 46; Ill Inst Technol, MS, 51; Princeton Univ, PhD(biochem), 57. *Prof Exp:* Int trainee, Joseph E Seagram & Sons, Inc, Ky, 47-48; biochemist trainee, E R Squibb & Sons, Inc, NY, 51-52; jr biochemist, Ethicon Inc, 52-54; res assoc biochem, Princeton Univ, 57-59; res assoc microbial chem, Mt Sinai Hosp, New York, 59-62; sr chemist, Space Div, NAm Aviation, Inc, 62-63; res specialist, 63-66, sr tech specialist, Autonetics Div, NAm Rockwell Corp, 66-68; res supvr, Biomed Div, Gillette Res Inst, 68-70; SR DEVELOP SCIENTIST, MICROBICS OPERS, BECKMAN INSTRUMENTS, INC, 70- *Mem:* AAAS; Am Chem Soc. *Res:* Industrial enzymology and fermentation; chemistry of bioluminescence and its application; growth and nutrition of thermophilic bacteria; keratin of hair and skin; action of keratinase; clinical enzymology and diagnostic reagents. *Mailing Add:* Microbics Opers Beckman Instrum 6200 El Camino Real Carlsbad CA 92008

SIEBEL, M(ATHIAS) P(AUL) L, b Witten, Ger, Mar 6, 24; nat US; m 60. MECHANICAL ENGINEERING. *Educ:* Bristol Univ, BS, 49, PhD, 52. *Prof Exp:* In charge res & develop & asst works mgr, Tube Investments, Ltd, Eng, 53-57; res assoc, Columbia Univ, 58-59; gen mgr, Pressure Equip Div, Pall Corp, 59-64; vpres & mgr opers, Radiation Dynamics, Inc, NY, 64-65; dep dir mfg eng lab, 65-68, dir process eng lab, 68-74, staff scientist, Marshall Space Flight Ctr, 74-79, MGR, MICHOUD ASSEMBLY FACIL, NASA, 79- *Mem:* Sigma Xi. *Res:* Industrial and research management; strength of materials; space sciences. *Mailing Add:* Michoud Assembly Facil NASA PO Box 29300 New Orleans LA 70189

SIEBELING, RONALD JON, b Oostburg, Wis, Nov 10, 37; m 59; c 4. MICROBIOLOGY. *Educ:* Hope Col, AB, 60; Univ Ariz, MS, 62, PhD(microbiol), 66. *Prof Exp:* Asst prof, 66-74, ASSOC PROF MICROBIOL, LA STATE UNIV, BATON ROUGE, 74- *Mem:* Am Soc Microbiol. *Res:* Immunobiology; immune suppression and antigenic competition. *Mailing Add:* Dept of Microbiol La State Univ Baton Rouge LA 70803

SIEBENS, ARTHUR ALEXANDRE, b Atlanta, Ga, July 13, 21; m 48; c 6. PHYSIOLOGY, REHABILITATION MEDICINE. *Educ:* Oberlin Col AB, 43; Johns Hopkins Univ, MD, 47. *Prof Exp:* Asst physiol, Sch Med, Johns Hopkins Univ, 45-48; asst prof physiol & pharmacol, Long Island Col Med, State Univ NY Downstate Med Ctr, 48-52, from assoc prof physiol to prof, 54-58; prof physiol, Sch Med & dir respiratory & rehab ctr, Hosps, Univ Wis-Madison, 58-71; prof rehab med & surg, 71-76, RICHARD BENNETT DARNALL PROF REHAB MED & PROF SURG, JOHNS HOPKINS UNIV, 77-, CHIEF DIV REHAB MED, UNIV & DIR REHAB MED, HOSP, 71- *Concurrent Pos:* Mem physiol study sect, USPHS, 49-64 & prog-proj comt, Nat Heart Inst, 65-69; dir dept rehab med, Good Samaritan Hosp, Baltimore, Md, 71-; consult, Vet Admin Hosp, Madison, Wis. *Mem:* AAAS; Am Physiol Soc; Am Thoracic Soc; Am Cong Rehab Med. *Res:* Respiratory, cardiovascular and nervous system physiology. *Mailing Add:* Dept of Rehab Med Johns Hopkins Univ Med Ctr Baltimore MD 21205

SIEBENTRITT, CARL R, JR, b Jersey City, NJ, Aug 14, 22; m 57; c 5. HEALTH PHYSICS. *Educ:* Univ Cincinnati, BSME, 47, MS, 49. *Prof Exp:* Physicist, Instrument Div, Keleket X-ray Corp, 49-51; supvr nuclear instrument develop, Cincinnati Div, Bendix Corp, 51-62; dir, Nucleonics Div, Defense Civil Preparedness Agency, Dept Defense, 62-73, staff dir, Detection & Countermeasures Div, 73-79; CHIEF, LOGISTICS SUPPORT BR & CHMN INTERAGENCY SUBCOMT OFFSITE EMERGENCY INSTRUMENTATION, FED EMERGENCY MGT AGENCY, 79- *Concurrent Pos:* Chmn, Interagency Task Force Training & Exercise for Radiol Emergencies Involving Fixed Nuclear Facil, 73- *Mem:* Health Physics Soc; Am Nuclear Soc. *Res:* Instrumentation and systems for detection and measurement of radioactivity; nuclear instrumentation for radiological emergency response; radiation damage to insulators. *Mailing Add:* Fed Emergency Mgt Agency Washington DC 20472

SIEBER, JAMES LEO, b New Glasgow, NS, Nov 3, 36; US citizen. MATHEMATICS. *Educ:* Shippensburg State Col, BS, 58; Pa State Univ, MA, 61, PhD(math), 63. *Prof Exp:* From asst prof to assoc prof, 63-67, PROF MATH & COMPUT SCI, SHIPPENSBURG STATE COL, 67-, CHMN DEPT, 64- *Concurrent Pos:* Actg dir comput ctr, Shippensburg State Col, 67-68; dir, NSF Inst, 69-71. *Mem:* Math Asn Am; Asn Comput Mach. *Res:* Abstract spaces in general topology, syntopogenous spaces, quasi-uniform spaces and quasi-proximity spaces; computer science and mathematics administration. *Mailing Add:* Dept of Math & Comput Sci Shippensburg State Col Shippensburg PA 17257

SIEBER-FABRO, SUSAN M, b Hattiesburg, Miss, May 18, 42; m 71. PHARMACOLOGY. *Educ:* Univ Va, BS, 64; George Washington Univ, MS, 69, PhD(pharmacol), 70. *Prof Exp:* Staff fel pharmacol, 71-76, PHARMACOLOGIST, LAB CHEM PHARMACOL, NAT CANCER INST, 76- *Mem:* Am Asn Cancer Res; Teratology Soc; AAAS. *Res:* Developmental pharmacology; drug disposition; cancer chemotherapy; toxicology. *Mailing Add:* Lab of Chem Pharmacol Nat Cancer Inst Bethesda MD 20014

SIEBERT, ALAN ROGER, b Cleveland, Ohio, July 16, 30; m 54; c 3. PHYSICAL CHEMISTRY, POLYMER CHEMISTRY. *Educ:* Fenn Col, BChemEng, 53; Western Reserve Univ, MS, 54, PhD(chem), 57. *Prof Exp:* Sr res chemist, Res Ctr, 56-68, res assoc, 68-69, sect leader specialty elastomer, 69-73, proj tech mgr, Res & Develop Ctr, 73-77, prod mgr reactive liquid polymers, 77-78, sr prod mgr new prod, Chem Div, 78-80, MKT MGR & RES & DEVELOP MGR, REACTIVE LIQUID POLYMERS, CHEM GROUP, B F GOODRICH CO, 80- *Mem:* Am Chem Soc; Soc Aerospace Mat & Process Engrs. *Res:* Relation between structure and properties of polymers; emulsion and solution polymerization; polymerization and characterization of reactive liquid polymers; polymerization and characterization of rubber and plastic latexes; impact resistant; thermo setting and thermoplastic resins. *Mailing Add:* Res & Develop Ctr B F Goodrich 9921 Brecksville Rd Brecksville OH 44141

SIEBERT, DONALD ROBERT, b Oak Ridge, Tenn, July 6, 46; m 68; c 2. ENGINEERING PHYSICS, OPTICS. *Educ:* Union Col, NY, BS, 68; Columbia Univ, New York, PhD(phys chem), 73. *Prof Exp:* Asst prof chem, Drew Univ, Madison, NJ, 74-78; res chemist, Photon Chem Dept, 78-79, res physicist electrooptical prod, 80-81, PROJ ENGR ELECTROOPTICAL

PROD, ALLIED CORP, 81- *Concurrent Pos:* Asst prof chem, Drew Univ, 79-80. *Mem:* Am Chem Soc; Am Phys Soc; Fedn Am Scientists; Optical Soc Am. *Res:* Design and development of scientific solid state lasers and laser systems; molecular spectroscopy; thermal lensing; applications of lasers to chemical, physical and environmental problems. *Mailing Add:* Allied Chem Corp PO Box 1021A Morristown NJ 07960

SIEBERT, ELEANOR DANTZLER, b Birmingham, Ala, July 18, 41; m 67; c 2. PHYSICAL CHEMISTRY, SCIENCE EDUCATION. *Educ:* Duke Univ, BA, 63; Univ Calif, Los Angeles, PhD(chem), 69. *Prof Exp:* Res chemist, Allied Chem Corp, 63-65; mem fac, Dept Chem, Univ Calif, Los Angeles, 70-71; mem fac, Dept Phys Sci, Westlake Sch, 71-73; ASSOC PROF PHYS SCI, MT ST MARY'S COL, 74- *Concurrent Pos:* Proj dir, NSF CAUSE Prog, 76-79. *Mem:* AAAS; Am Chem Soc; Sigma Xi. *Res:* Equation of state data; corresponding states; thermodynamic measurements; molecular potentials; individualized learning. *Mailing Add:* Mt St Mary's Col 12001 Chalon Rd Los Angeles CA 90049

SIEBERT, JEROME BERNARD, b Fresno, Calif, Dec 12, 38; m 60; c 2. AGRICULTURAL ECONOMICS. *Educ:* Univ Calif, Davis, BS, 60; Univ Calif, Berkeley, PhD(agr econ), 64. *Prof Exp:* Asst undersecy admin, USDA, 69-70, exec asst admin, Consumer & Mkt Serv, 70-71, asst secy, 71-72; economist agr econ, 66-69, ASSOC DIR ADMIN, UNIV CALIF COOP EXTEN, 72- *Concurrent Pos:* Consult to dir, Calif Dept Food & Agr, 67-69; alt, Walnut Control Bd, USDA, 67-69, mem, Joint USDA & Nat Asn State Univ & Land Grant Cols Comt Educ & chmn, Independent Study & Exten Educ Comt, USDA Grad Sch, 71-72; dir, Tri Valley Growers Inc, 72-75; mem, Blue Ribbon Comt Agr, State Calif, Lt Gov Off, 73-74. *Mem:* Am Agr Econ Asn; Am Econ Asn. *Mailing Add:* 11 Wandel Dr Moraga CA 94556

SIEBERT, JOHN, b Aurora, Ill, Mar 12, 40; m 61; c 2. ORGANIC CHEMISTRY, BUSINESS ADMINISTRATION. *Educ:* Procopius Col, BS, 62; Wichita State Univ, MS, 63; Univ Mo, PhD(org chem), 67. *Prof Exp:* Res chemist, Procter & Gamble Co, 67-70; dir household prod res & develop, Merck-Calgon Consumer Prod Div, 70-74; dir new prod develop, Gillette Toiletries Div, 74-77; DIR RES & DEVELOP, AMWAY CORP, 77- *Mem:* Am Chem Soc; Indust Res Inst; Sigma Xi; Soc Cosmetic Chemists. *Res:* Novel steroid chemistry; synthesis and nuclear magnetic resonance analysis of sterically hindered alkyl and aromatic quaternary carbon olefins. *Mailing Add:* Amway Corp 7575 E Fulton Rd Ada MI 49355

SIEBERT, KARL JOSEPH, b Harrisburg, Pa, Oct 29, 45; m 70; c 2. BREWING CHEMISTRY, LABORATORY AUTOMATION. *Educ:* Pa State Univ, BS, 67, MS, 68, PhD(biochem), 70. *Prof Exp:* Synthetic chemist, Appl Sci Labs, Inc, 70; res assoc, 71, head res & develop sect, 71-76, MGR RES DEVELOP LAB, STROH BREWERY CO, 76- *Mem:* Am Chem Soc; Am Soc Brewing Chemists. *Res:* Beer flavor; chemistry of hop compounds; process monitoring and controlling instrumentation; computer programming; laboratory automation. *Mailing Add:* Stroh Brewery Co 1 Stroh Dr Detroit MI 48226

SIEBERT, W(ILLIAM) M(CCONWAY), b Pittsburgh, Pa, Nov 19, 25; m 49; c 4. COMMUNICATIONS. *Educ:* Mass Inst Technol, SB, 46, ScD, 52. *Prof Exp:* Jr res engr, Res Labs, Westinghouse Elec Corp, 46-47; asst & instr elec eng, 47, from asst prof to assoc prof, 52-63, mem staff & group leader, Lincoln Lab, 53-55, PROF ELEC ENG, MASS INST TECHNOL, 63- *Concurrent Pos:* Mem, security resources panel, Gaither Comt, 56. *Mem:* Fel Inst Elec & Electronics Engrs; Acoust Soc Am. *Res:* Statistical communication theory; radar theory; electrical communications; communications biophysics. *Mailing Add:* Dept of Elec Eng & Comput Sci Mass Inst Technol Cambridge MA 02139

SIEBRAND, WILLEM, b IJsselmuiden, Netherlands, Aug 12, 32; m 61; c 2. CHEMICAL PHYSICS, THEORETICAL CHEMISTRY. *Educ:* Univ Amsterdam, Drs, 60, Dr(phys chem), 63. *Prof Exp:* From asst res officer to assoc res officer, 63-72, SR RES OFFICER THEORET CHEM, NAT RES COUN CAN, 72- *Mem:* Am Phys Soc. *Res:* Electronic and spectroscopic properties of molecular crystals; vibrational-electronic coupling in molecules; radiationless transitions. *Mailing Add:* Div of Chem Nat Res Coun of Can Ottawa ON K1A 0R6 Can

SIEBRING, BARTELD RICHARD, b George, Iowa, Sept 24, 24. INORGANIC CHEMISTRY. *Educ:* Macalester Col, BA, 47; Univ Minn, BS, 48, MS, 49; Syracuse Univ, PhD, 53. *Prof Exp:* Instr chem, Worthington Jr Col, 48-50; prof, Jamestown Col, 53; from asst prof to assoc prof, 53-62, PROF CHEM, UNIV WIS-MILWAUKEE, 62- *Mem:* Am Chem Soc; Hist Sci Soc; Nat Asn Res Sci Teaching. *Res:* History of chemistry; coordination compounds; identification and description of areas of excellence in the training of scientists, especially the study of institutions and professors; modern trends and issues of chemical education; identification of personal attributes of leading personalities in the history of chemistry, with emphasis on possibly common characteristics. *Mailing Add:* Dept Chem Univ Wis-Milwaukee Milwaukee WI 53201

SIEBURTH, JOHN MCNEILL, b Calgary, Alta, Sept 1, 27; nat US; m 50; c 5. MARINE MICROBIOLOGY, OCEANOGRAPHY. *Educ:* Univ BC, BSA, 49; Wash State Univ, MS, 51; Univ Minn, PhD(bact), 54. *Prof Exp:* Assoc prof vet sci, Va Polytech Inst & State Univ, 55-60; researcher biol oceanog, 60-61, PROF OCEANOG, UNIV RI, 66-, PROF MICROBIOL, 68- *Concurrent Pos:* Vis prof, Marine Biol Lab, Woods Hole, Mass, 73-74 & Norweg Inst Seaweed Res, Trondheim, 66-67; antarctic microbiologist, Int Geophys Yr, Arg Navy, 57-59. *Mem:* Am Soc Microbiol; Am Soc Limnol & Oceanog; Phycol Soc Am. *Res:* Role of bacteria microalgae and protozoa in planktonic ecosystems; development of methodology for measurements of in-situ growth rates in natural and artificial microcosms. *Mailing Add:* Grad Sch of Oceanog Univ Rhode Island Bay Campus Narragansett RI 02882

SIECK, L WAYNE, physical chemistry, see previous edition

SIECKHAUS, JOHN FRANCIS, b St Louis, Mo, Sept 23, 39; m 63; c 3. INDUSTRIAL CHEMISTRY. *Educ:* Rockhurst Col, AB, 61; St Louis Univ, MS, 65, PhD(chem), 67. *Prof Exp:* Sr chemist & group leader, 66-80, MGR, LIFE SCI RES & DEVELOP DEPT, OLIN CORP, 80- *Honors & Awards:* IR-100 Award, Indust Res Mag, 71. *Mem:* Am Chem Soc; Sigma Xi. *Res:* Biotechnology development related to agriculture, energy and chemical production. *Mailing Add:* Olin Corp PO Box 30-275 New Haven CT 06511

SIECKMANN, EVERETT FREDERICK, b Tobias, Nebr, Dec 31, 28; m 51; c 2. THEORETICAL PHYSICS, EXPERIMENTAL SOLID STATE PHYSICS. *Educ:* Doane Col, BA, 50; Fla State Univ, MS, 52; Cornell Univ, PhD(theoret solid state physics), 60. *Prof Exp:* Asst chem, Fla State Univ, 50-52; asst physics, Cornell Univ, 52-57; asst prof, Univ Ky, 57-62; assoc prof, 62-67, PROF PHYSICS, UNIV IDAHO, 67- *Concurrent Pos:* Consult, Librascope Div, Gen Precision, Inc, Calif, 61 & US Air Force, Holloman AFB, NMex, 62-63; vis prof physics, Univ Calif, Berkeley, Jet Propulsion Lab, 80. *Mem:* Am Asn Physics Teachers; Am Phys Soc. *Res:* Impurity states in ionic crystals; single crystals of alkaline earth oxides; electrochemistry; applied mathematics; theoretical calculations on electron hole drops in Ge; optical dispersion of crystals containing color centers; heat storage by alkaliflourides. *Mailing Add:* Dept Physics Univ Idaho Moscow ID 83843

SIEDLE, ALLEN R, b Pittsburgh, Pa. INORGANIC CHEMISTRY. *Educ:* Ind Univ, PhD(chem), 73. *Prof Exp:* Fel chem, Nat Bur Standards, 73-75, res chemist, 75-77; RES CHEMIST, SCI RES LAB, 3M CENT RES LAB, 77- *Res:* Synthetic inorganic chemistry; bioinorganic and surface chemistry. *Mailing Add:* Sci Res Lab 3M Cent Res Lab St Paul MN 55101

SIEDLER, ARTHUR JAMES, b Milwaukee, Wis, Mar 17, 27; m 76; c 3. FOOD SCIENCE, NUTRITION. *Educ:* Univ Wis, BS, 51; Univ Chicago, MS, 56, PhD(biochem), 59. *Prof Exp:* Asst biochem, Am Meat Inst Found, 51-53, from asst biochemist to biochemist, 53-64, chief, Div Biochem & Nutrit, 59-64; group leader spec biol, Norwich Pharmacal Co, 64-65, chief physiol, 65-69, biochem, 69-72; PROF FOOD SCI & HEAD DEPT, UNIV ILL, URBANA, 72- *Concurrent Pos:* Instr & asst prof, Univ Chicago, 59-64. *Mem:* AAAS; Inst Food Technologists; Am Chem Soc; Am Inst Nutrit; Am Heart Asn. *Res:* Heme chemistry; amino acids and fats; chemotherapeutic agents; food science. *Mailing Add:* Dept Food Sci Univ Ill Urbana IL 61801

SIEDSCHLAG, KARL GLENN, JR, b Akron, Ohio, Oct 28, 20; m 41; c 1. ORGANIC CHEMISTRY. *Educ:* Western Reserve Univ, BS, 46, MS, 48, PhD(chem), 49. *Prof Exp:* Asst prof chem, Univ WVa, 49-51; res chemist, Benger Lab, E I DuPont de Nemours & Co, 51-54, res chemist, Patent Div, Textile Fibers Dept, 54-74, patent assoc, 74-79; RETIRED. *Mem:* Am Chem Soc; Sigma Xi. *Res:* Condensation polymer fibers; inorganic fibers. *Mailing Add:* Box 78 Wineburg OH 44690

SIEFKEN, HUGH EDWARD, b Warsaw, Ind, Apr 13, 40; US citizen; m 62; c 2. EXPERIMENTAL NUCLEAR PHYSICS. *Educ:* Greenville Col, BA, 62; Univ Kans, MS, 65, PhD(physics), 68. *Prof Exp:* Res fel nuclear physics, Univ BC, 68-69; from asst prof to assoc prof, 69-77, PROF PHYSICS, GREENVILLE COL, 77- *Concurrent Pos:* Vis scientist, Nuclear Res Ctr, Univ Alta, 76-77. *Mem:* Am Phys Soc; Sigma Xi; Am Asn Physics Teachers. *Res:* low energy nuclear physics; gamma ray spectroscopy and ion bombardment of solids. *Mailing Add:* 414 Eastern Ave Greenville IL 62246

SIEFKEN, MARK WILLIAM, b Hankinson, NDak, Oct 3, 39; m 61; c 3. ORGANIC POLYMER CHEMISTRY. *Educ:* NDak State Univ, BS, 61; Univ Wis-Madison, PhD(org chem), 67. *Prof Exp:* Capt chem, Med Res Lab, Edgewood Arsenal, Md, 67-69; sr chemist, Cent Res Lab, 3M Co, 69-73, res scientist recreation & athletic prod, 73-74, supvr res & develop indust mineral prod div, Minn, 74-77; res mgr metals, detergents, surfactants, cleaning & sanitizing compounds, Diversey Chem, 77-78; TECH V PRES, THE DIVERSEY CORP, 78- *Mem:* Am Chem Soc. *Res:* Tricyclic hydrocarbon rearrangements; polymer synthesis and development; new product research and development. *Mailing Add:* 20217 Ward Bend Dr Northville MI 48167

SIEFKER, JOSEPH ROY, b Brownstown, Ind, Mar 14, 33; m 56; c 2. ANALYTICAL CHEMISTRY, INORGANIC CHEMISTRY. *Educ:* Wabash Col, AB, 55; Univ NDak, MS, 57; Ind Univ, PhD(chem), 60. *Prof Exp:* Res chemist, E I du Pont de Nemours & Co, 57; instr chem, St Louis Univ, 60-62; from asst prof to assoc prof, 62-71, PROF CHEM, IND STATE UNIV, TERRE HAUTE, 71- *Concurrent Pos:* Consult, Sporlan Valve Co, St Louis, 61 & OA Labs, Indianapolis, 70-; vis asst prof, Ind Univ, 62 & 64. *Mem:* Am Chem Soc; Sigma Xi. *Res:* Water pollution; coordination compounds and complex ions; spectrophotometry; polarography; non-aqueous solvents; redox titrants; electroanalytical chemistry. *Mailing Add:* Dept Chem Ind State Univ Terre Haute IN 47809

SIEG, ALBERT LOUIS, b Chicago, Ill, Mar 25, 30; m 55; c 3. ORGANIC CHEMISTRY. *Educ:* Univ Ill, BS, 51; Univ Rochester, PhD, 55; Harvard Grad Sch Bus, PMD, 72. *Prof Exp:* Anal chemist, 54-55, develop engr, 55-59, sr develop engr, 59-66, supvr chem testing, Paper Div, 67-69, supvr process develop, 69-71, supvr emulsion control, 71-72, corp coordr instant photog, 72-76, asst dir, 74-76, dir, Paper Serv Div, 76-78, asst mgr paper mfg, 78-80, mgr, 80-81, DIR PHOTOG STRATEGIC PLANNING, EASTMAN KODAK CO, 81-, VPRES, 82- *Concurrent Pos:* Lectr, Univ Rochester, 59-65, sr lectr, 65-69. *Mem:* AAAS; fel Am Inst Chemists; Am Chem Soc; Soc Photog Sci & Eng. *Res:* Synthesis of natural products; photographic chemistry; chemistry of gelatins; lithographic chemistry. *Mailing Add:* 159 Hillhurst Lane Rochester NY 14617

SIEGAL, BERNARD, b Brooklyn, NY, Nov 11, 24; m 48; c 3. PHARMACEUTICAL SCIENCES. *Educ:* Yeshiva Univ, BA, 45; Rutgers Univ, PhD(pharmaceut), 68. *Prof Exp:* Chemist, Estro Chem Co, 49-53; from chemist to lab dir, Prod Div, Bristol Meyers, 53-69; dir res & develop, Toiletries Div, Gillette Co, 69-77; DIR RES & DEVELOP, H V SHUSTER, INC, 77- *Mem:* Am Chem Soc; Am Pharmaceut Asn; Acad Pharmaceut Sci;

Soc Cosmetic Chem. *Res:* Over-the-counter pharmacy, health aids and allied products; product research and development; safety and claim substantiation; regulatory compliance. *Mailing Add:* H V Shuster Inc 5 Hayward St Quincy MA 02171

SIEGAL, FREDERICK PAUL, b New York, NY, Sept 24, 39; m 66; c 2. IMMUNOLOGY, INTERNAL MEDICINE. *Educ:* Cornell Univ, AB, 61; Columbia Univ, MD, 65. *Prof Exp:* From intern to resident internal med, Mt Sinai Hosp, New York, 65-67; asst prev med officer, Walter Reed Army Med Ctr, 67-69; resident internal med, Mt Sinai Hosp, New York, 69-70, clin asst physician, 70-73; assoc immunol, Mem Sloan-Kettering Cancer Ctr, 73-79, assoc mem, 77-78, head, Lab Human Lymphocyte Differentiation, Sloan-Kettering Inst, 75-78; asst prof med, Cornell Univ Col Med, 75-78; ASSOC PROF MED & DIR, DIV CLIN IMMUNOL, MT SINAI SCH MED, NEW YORK, 78- *Concurrent Pos:* Helen Hay Whitney Found fel, Rockefeller Univ, 70-73; asst res physician, Rockefeller Univ Hosp, 70-73; vis assoc physician, 73-74; adj asst prof, Rockefeller Univ, 73-74; asst attend physician, Mem Hosp, New York, 73-78; asst prof biol, Sloan-Kettering Div, Cornell Univ, 74-78; assoc sci, Mem Sloan-Kettering Cancer Ctr, 78- *Mem:* AAAS; Am Asn Immunologists; Am Fedn Clin Res; NY Acad Sci. *Res:* Clinical immunology; immunodeficiency diseases; development of lymphoid cells; cell surfaces. *Mailing Add:* Dept Med 100th St & Fifth Ave New York NY 10029

SIEGART, WILLIAM RAYMOND, b Paterson, NJ, July 28, 31; m 55; c 3. ORGANIC CHEMISTRY. *Educ:* Gettysburg Col, BA, 53; Univ Pa, MS, 55, PhD(org chem), 57. *Prof Exp:* Asst instr chem, Univ Pa, 53-54, res assoc org chem, 54-56; chemist, 58-59, sr chemist, 59-62, res chemist, 62-67, group leader, 67-69, asst supvr petrochem res, 69-71, sr technologist, Mfg Div, Res & Technol Dept, 71-72, sr technologist prog planning & coord, 72-76, staff coordr, 76-78, sr staff coordr, Strategic Planning Dept, Res & Technol Dept, 78-80, SR COORDR, ALTERNATE ENERGY DEPT, TEXACO, INC, 80- *Mem:* Am Chem Soc; Sigma Xi. *Res:* Petrochemicals; products and processes; lubricant additives and products; long range research planning; coal gasification; corporate planning; alternate energy. *Mailing Add:* Texaco Inc 2000 Westchester Ave White Plains NY 10650

SIEGEL, ALBERT, b New York, NY, Aug 20, 24; m 47; c 4. MOLECULAR GENETICS, PLANT VIROLOGY. *Educ:* Cornell Univ, BA, 47; Calif Inst Technol, PhD(genetics), 51. *Prof Exp:* USPHS fel, Univ Calif, Los Angeles, 51-53, res assoc bot, 53-59; prof agr biochem, Univ Ariz, 59-72; chmn dept, 72-74, PROF BIOL, WAYNE STATE UNIV, 72- *Concurrent Pos:* NSF fel, 65-66, prog dir, 67-68; fel award, Am Phytopath Soc, 78. *Mem:* AAAS; Am Soc Cell Biol; Am Soc Microbiol; Genetics Soc Am; Am Phytopath Soc. *Res:* Nucleic acids; mechanism of plant virus replication; organization of plant nuclear and organelle genomes. *Mailing Add:* Dept of Biol Wayne State Univ Detroit MI 48202

SIEGEL, ALLAN, b New York, NY, June 18, 39. NEUROBIOLOGY, NEUROANATOMY. *Educ:* City Col New York, BS, 61; State Univ NY Buffalo, PhD(psychol), 66. *Prof Exp:* USPHS fel, Sch Med, Yale Univ, 65-67; instr anat, 67-69, asst prof, 69-73, assoc prof anat & neurosci, 73-77, PROF NEUROSCI, NJ MED SCH, 77- *Concurrent Pos:* Consult neurol & res, East Orange Vet Admin Hosp, 72- *Mem:* AAAS; Am Asn Anat; Soc Neurosci. *Res:* Experimental psychology; anatomy and neurophysiology of limbic system; biology of aggressive behavior. *Mailing Add:* Dept of Neurosci NJ Med Sch Newark NJ 07103

SIEGEL, ALVIN, b New York, NY, Aug 29, 31; m 59; c 4. CHEMICAL OCEANOGRAPHY. *Educ:* City Col New York, BS, 53; Rutgers Univ, PhD(phys chem), 62. *Prof Exp:* Asst scientist, Woods Hole Oceanog Inst, 61-67; assoc prof, 67-71, PROF CHEM, SOUTHAMPTON COL, LONG ISLAND UNIV, 71-, DIR, MARINE SCI PROG, 73-, PROF MARINE SCI, 75-, DIR, NATURAL SCI DIV, 80- *Mem:* AAAS; Am Soc Limnol & Oceanog; Am Chem Soc. *Res:* Polyelectrolytes; speciation of metal ions in natural waters; organic bonding to metal ions; extraction of polar organics from sea water. *Mailing Add:* Dept of Chem Southampton Col LI Univ Southampton NY 11968

SIEGEL, ANDREW FRANCIS, b Cambridge, Mass, Jan 6, 50. GEOMETRICAL PROBABILITY, BIOSTATISTICS. *Educ:* Boston Univ, AB, 73; Stanford Univ, MS, 75, PhD(statist), 77. *Prof Exp:* Asst prof, Univ Wis-Madison, 77-79; ASST PROF STATIST, PRINCETON UNIV, 79- *Concurrent Pos:* Vis res assoc, Dept Paleobiol, Smithsonian Inst, 78; res fel, Dept Biostatist, Harvard Univ, 78-79; vis staff mem, Statist Group, Los Alamos Nat Lab, 79; consult, Statist Group, Bell Telephone Labs, 79-80; co-prin investr, US Army Res Off, 79-; vis scholar, Dept Statist, Stanfor Univ, 80, Univ Wash, Seattle, 81. *Mem:* Am Statist Asn; Inst Math Statist; Biomet Soc; Royal Statist Soc; AAAS. *Res:* Geometric probability; statistical robustness; pattern matching; morphology; probability distributions; biological and medical applications of statistics. *Mailing Add:* Dept Statist Fine Hall PO Box 37 Princeton Univ Princeton NJ 08544

SIEGEL, ARMAND, b New York, NY, Oct 10, 14; m 43; c 3. STATISTICAL MECHANICS, BIOMATHEMATICS. *Educ:* NY Univ, AB, 36; Univ Pa, AM, 44; Mass Inst Technol, PhD(physics), 49. *Prof Exp:* Asst physics, Univ Pa, 42-43, instr, 43-44; instr elec commun, Radar Sch, Mass Inst Technol, 44-45, res assoc physics, 52-53; instr, Worcester Polytech Inst, 49-50; from instr to prof, 50-80, EMER PROF PHYSICS, BOSTON UNIV, 80-, PROF PSYCHIAT PHYSICS, SCH MED, 75- *Concurrent Pos:* Guggenheim fel, Univ Mich, 57-58. *Mem:* Am Phys Soc. *Res:* Relativistic nucleon-nucleon interactions; differential space formulation of quantum mechanics; kinetic theory; stochastic processes; mathematical theory of turbulence; electroencephalography of petit-mal epilepsy; stochastic aspects of the origin of the electroencephalogram. *Mailing Add:* Dept Physics Boston Univ Boston MA 02215

SIEGEL, ARTHUR D, b Montclair, NJ, Jan 22, 30; m 56; c 4. MECHANICAL ENGINEERING. *Educ:* Newark Col Eng, BS, 52; Stevens Inst Technol, MS, 61. *Prof Exp:* Test engr, Curtiss-Wright Corp, 52-54; develop engr, Walter Kidde Co, 57-58 & Picatinny Arsenal, US Dept Army, 58-60; develop engr, Uniroyal Res Ctr, NJ, 60-66, group leader fiber res, 66-69, sr res engr, Uniroyal Mgt & Res Ctr, Conn, 69-78; SR RES ENGR, FARREL CO DIV, EMHART CORP, 78- *Res:* Process development for synthetic fibers; melt spinning; drawing; texturizing; filament cross-sectional modifications; bicomponent fibers; effect of fiber structure on dyeability; relation of fiber properties to fabric performance; radial tire development; computer simulation of feed screws; mixing and devolatilization of polymer melts. *Mailing Add:* Farrel Co Div Emhart Corp Ansonia CT 06401

SIEGEL, BARBARA ZENZ, b Detroit, Mich, July 22, 31; m 50; c 4. BIOLOGY. *Educ:* Univ Chicago, AB, 60; Columbia Univ, MA, 63; Yale Univ, PhD(biol), 66. *Prof Exp:* Purchasing liaison, Army Chem Corp, Ft Detrick, Md, 50-52; res assoc human genetics, Sch Med, NY Univ, 62-63; res staff mem biol, Yale Univ, 66-67; from asst prof to assoc prof microbiol, 67-75, dir biol prog, 71-75, researcher Biomed Res Ctr & assoc prof Current Res & Develop, 75-76, RES PROF PAC BIOMED RES CTR, UNIV HAWAII, 76- *Concurrent Pos:* Mem, Boston Univ-NASA exped, Iceland & Surtsey, 70 & Nat Geog Soc-Hawaii Found & Cottrell Found expeds, Iceland & Surtsey, 72; Fulbright-Hays sr res scholar, Univ Belgrade, Marine Sta, Montenegro, Yugoslavia & Univ Heidelberg, 73-74; sr NATO fel, Nordic Volcanol Inst, Iceland, 75; res assoc, Volcani Agr Ctr, Israel; proj leader, US Antarctic Res Prog, NSF, McMurdo, Antarctic, 78- *Mem:* Am Chem Soc; Am Genetic Asn; Genetics Soc Am; Am Soc Plant Physiologists; Am Inst Biol Sci. *Res:* Biochemical control mechanisms in growth and development; biological oxidations, biochemical interactions in eco-systems; volcanic gas emissions on biological systems; ecology of heavy metals. *Mailing Add:* 210 Snyder Univ of Hawaii Honolulu HI 96822

SIEGEL, BARRY ALAN, b Nashville, Tenn, Dec 30, 44; div; c 2. NUCLEAR MEDICINE, RADIOLOGY. *Educ:* Washington Univ, AB, 66, MD, 69. *Prof Exp:* Intern med, Barnes Hosp, St Louis, 69-70; resident nuclear med & radiol, Edward Mallinckrodt Inst Radiol, 70-73; asst prof, 73-76, assoc prof, 76-79, PROF RADIOL, SCH MED, WASHINGTON UNIV, 79-, ASSOC PROF MED, 80-, DIR NUCLEAR MED, EDWARD MALLINCKRODT INST RADIOL, 73- *Concurrent Pos:* asst prof radiol, Sch Med, Johns Hopkins Univ, 74-76; chief, Radiol Sci Div, Armed Forces Radiobiol Res Inst, Defense Nuclear Agency, 74-76; mem radioactive pharmaceut adv comt, Food & Drug Admin, 74-77 & 81- & task force short-lived radionuclides appln nuclear med, 75-76; mem task force nuclear med, Energy Res & Develop Admin, 75-76; mem adv panel radiopharmaceut, US Pharmacopeia, 76-; consult ed bd, J Nuclear Med, 76-81; mem adv comt on med radioisotopes, Los Alamos Sci Lab, 76-79; assoc ed, Radiol, 80- *Mem:* Fel Am Col Nuclear Physicians; fel Am Col Radiol; Radiol Soc NAm; fel Am Col Physicians; Soc Nuclear Med. *Res:* Clinical research with positron-emitting radionuclides and coincidence axial tomographic detection systems; radioisotopic detection of vascular thrombosis; radioisotopic evaluation of myocardial infarction. *Mailing Add:* Edward Mallinckrodt Inst Radiol 510 S Kingshwy Blvd St Louis MO 63110

SIEGEL, BENJAMIN MORTON, b Superior, Wis, Mar 26, 16; m 44; c 3. ION BEAMS, IMAGE PROCESSING. *Educ:* Mass Inst Technol, BS, 38, PhD(phys chem), 40. *Prof Exp:* Vis fel, Calif Inst Technol, 40-41; res assoc, Heat Res Lab, Nat Defense Res Comt Proj, Mass Inst Technol, 41-42 & 44-46, US Bur Ships Proj, 48-49; Nat Defense Res Comt Proj, Harvard Univ, 42-44; Weizmann Inst Sci assoc & chg electron micros lab, Polytech Inst Brooklyn, 46-48; assoc prof, 49-59, PROF APPL & ENG PHYSICS, CORNELL UNIV, 59- *Concurrent Pos:* Vis prof, Hebrew Univ, Israel, 62-63; vis fel, Salk Inst Biol Sci, 71. *Mem:* AAAS; Sigma Xi; Am Vacuum Soc; Am Phys Soc; Electron Micros Soc Am (pres, 73). *Res:* High brightness field ionization sources; electron and ion optics; field ion probe systems for nanometer ion beam lithography; computer image processing of high resolution electron microscope images. *Mailing Add:* Clark Hall Cornell Univ Ithaca NY 14853

SIEGEL, BENJAMIN VINCENT, b New York, NY, Dec 14, 13; m 43; c 3. VIROLOGY. *Educ:* Univ Ga, BS, 34; Columbia Univ, MA, 37; Stanford Univ, PhD(bact, exp path), 50; Am Bd Microbiol, dipl. *Prof Exp:* Teacher pub schs, Calif, 39-42; chmn biol & phys sci high sch, 46-48; asst bact physiol, Stanford Univ, 49-50; instr bact & exp path, 50-52, Nat Found Infantile Paralysis fel, 52-53; fel med phys & virol, Univ Calif, Berkeley, 53-54, asst res virologist, 54-56; assoc res virologist, Sch Med, San Francisco & res microbiologist, Donner Radiation Lab, Berkeley, 56-61, lectr microbiol, 59-60; PROF PATH, MED SCH, UNIV ORE, PORTLAND, 61- *Mem:* Fel Am Acad Microbiol; fel NY Acad Sci; Am Soc Exp Path; Int Acad Path; fel AAAS. *Res:* Tumor virology; experimental pathology; immunology. *Mailing Add:* 3900 SW Pendleton St Portland OR 97221

SIEGEL, BERNARD, b New York, NY, Oct 14, 28; m 54; c 2. PHYSICAL CHEMISTRY, INORGANIC CHEMISTRY. *Educ:* Brooklyn Col, BS, 48; Polytech Inst Brooklyn, PhD(phys chem), 53. *Prof Exp:* Res chemist, Shell Oil Co, 52-55; head phys chem br, Naval Propellant Plant, US Off Naval Res, 55-58; res chemist, Gen Corp, 58-61; sect head propellant chem, Aerospace Corp, Calif, 61-70; CONSULT, 70- *Mem:* Am Chem Soc; NY Acad Sci; The Chem Soc. *Res:* High temperature chemistry, chemistry; inorganic syntheses, especially hydrides and fluorides; energetics of chemical propellants. *Mailing Add:* 1079 Redstone Pl Hayward CA 94542

SIEGEL, BERNARD BARRY, b New York, NY, Apr 29, 18; m 49; c 2. ALLERGY, IMMUNOLOGY. *Educ:* Univ Mich, Ann Arbor, AB, 39; Long Island Col Med, MD, 43. *Prof Exp:* Co-chief allergy clin, King's County Hosp, Brooklyn, NY, 51-63; CO-DIR DIV ALLERGY, JEWISH HOSP & MED CTR BROOKLYN, 68-; CLIN ASSOC PROF MED, STATE UNIV NY DOWNSTATE MED CTR, 76- *Concurrent Pos:* NIH-USPHS res grant, 59-64; co-chief allergy clin, King's County Hosp, Brooklyn, 76- *Honors &*

Awards: Distinguished Serv Award, Am Acad Allergy, 72. *Mem:* Fel Am Acad Allergy; fel Am Col Allergists; Am Asn Immunologists. *Res:* Penicillin hypersensitiveness; aerobiology, pollen surveys. *Mailing Add:* 360 Central Ave Lawrence NY 11559

SIEGEL, BROCK MARTIN, b Binghamton, NY, Aug 25, 47; m 78. ORGANIC CHEMISTRY, BIOORGANIC CHEMISTRY. *Educ:* Syracuse Univ, BS, 69; Univ Ill, PhD(chem), 74. *Prof Exp:* NIH fel, Columbia Univ, 74-76; asst prof chem, Univ Minn, Minneapolis, 76-80; RES MGR, HEENKEL CORP, 80- *Concurrent Pos:* DuPont fac fel, Univ Minn, 76-77, NIH grant, 78-79. *Mem:* AAAS; Am Chem Soc; NY Acad Sci; Sigma Xi. *Res:* Kinetics mechnisms; synthetic and physical-ortanic chemistry; liquid ion exchange chelating reagents; tocopherols and vitamine E; phytosterols and steroidal derivatives; aromatic substitution chemistry; biomimetic catalysts. *Mailing Add:* 2010 E Hennepin Ave Henkel Corp Minneapolis MN 55413

SIEGEL, CAROLE ETHEL, b US, Sept 29, 36; m 57; c 2. BIOSTATISTICS. *Educ:* NY Univ, BA, 57, MS, 59, PhD(math), 63. *Prof Exp:* prin res scientist math, 65-73, HEAD RES EVAL METHODICAL UNIT, ROCKLAND RES INST, 73- *Concurrent Pos:* Adj asst prof math, NY Univ, 65-68 & 69, res assoc prof, Dept Psychiat, 79-; adj prof, Fairleigh Dickinson Univ, 68; consult, Rev Comt Statist Anal & Qual Control, Cancer Data Ctr, Nat Cancer Inst, 75-76; prin investr, Nat Inst Alchol Abuse & Alcoholism, 78-81 & Nat Ctr Health Serv Res, 79-81. *Mem:* Inst Math Statist; Asn Women Math. *Res:* Mental health evaluation methodology; mathematical and statistical approaches to mental health data; epidemiology. *Mailing Add:* Info Sci Div Rockland Res Inst Orangeburg NY 10962

SIEGEL, CHARLES DAVID, b New York, NY, Sept 28, 30. BIOLOGY. *Educ:* NY Univ, BA, 53, MS, 55, PhD(biol), 60. *Prof Exp:* Instr biol sci, Sch Com, NY Univ, 56-59; from instr to assoc prof, 59-77, PROF BIOL, WASH SQUARE COL, 77-, ASST DEAN, 70- *Mem:* AAAS; Am Asn Anat; Am Soc Zoologists; Am Soc Hemat; fel NY Acad Sci. *Res:* Physiologic hematology; mechanism involved in the formation and destruction of blood and bone marrow cellular elements. *Mailing Add:* Dept of Biol Washington Square Col New York NY 10003

SIEGEL, CLIFFORD M(YRON), b Apple River, Ill, Apr 15, 21; m 46; c 4. ELECTRICAL NETWORK THEORY, COMPUTER AIDED INSTRUCTION. *Educ:* Marquette Univ, BEE, 47; Univ NH, MSEE, 49; Univ Wis, PhD(elec eng), 51. *Prof Exp:* Engr, Wis Elec Power Co, 41-43; instr elec eng, Marquette Univ, 47; asst, Univ NH, 47-48, instr, 48-49; asst, Univ Wis, 49-51; from asst prof to assoc prof, 51-62, acting chmn dept, 67-69, PROF ELEC ENG, UNIV VA, 62- *Mem:* Am Soc Eng Educ; Inst Elec & Electronics Engrs. *Res:* Methods for electrical engineering education; computer-assisted instruction; gallium arsenide semi-conductor devices technology. *Mailing Add:* Dept of Elec Eng Univ of Va Charlottesville VA 22901

SIEGEL, EDWARD, b New York, NY, Aug 1, 19; m 44. BIOPHYSICS. *Educ:* City Col New York, BS, 41; Univ Calif, Berkeley, PhD(biophys), 66. *Prof Exp:* Physicist-in-chg optical res, Universal Camera Corp, NY, 41-44; physicist, Frankford Arsenal, US Dept Army, 45, biophysicist, Aero-Med Lab, Wright Field, 45-46; res assoc, Col Eng, Rutgers Univ, 47-48; physicist-in-chg, Med Physics Lab, Montefiore Hosp, 48-62; assoc prof radiol physics, Sch Med, Stanford Univ, 66-70; actg dir nuclear med sect, Sch Med, Univ Mo-Columbia, 71-73, prof radiol sci & med, 70-76, prof biol sci, 75-76, dir nuclear med sect, 73-76; PROF RADIOL & RADIATION SCI & DIR, RADIATION BIOL SECT, SCH MED, VANDERBILT UNIV, 76-, PROF PHYSICS, COL ARTS & SCI, 79- *Concurrent Pos:* Consult physicist, Radioisotope Dept, Newark Beth Israel Hosp, NJ, 50-55 & Radioisotope Dept, Lebanon Hosp, NY, 53-62; guest scientist, Donner Lab, Univ Calif, 66-70; consult physicist, Palo Alto Vet Admin Hosp, 67-70; consult adv comt human uses radioactive mat, Bur Radiol Health, State of Calif, 67-70; consult physicist, USPHS Hosp, San Francisco, 68-70 & Vet Admin Hosp, Columbia, Mo, 72-76; ed, Med Physics, 79- *Mem:* Endocrine Soc; Tissue Culture Asn; Radiation Res Soc; Radiol Soc NAm; Brit Hosp Physicists Asn. *Res:* Applications of radioisotopes to biology and medicine; radiation physics; thyroid physiology and thyroid cancer; cell culture; radiation dosimetry; nuclear medicine; high resolution radioautography; radiation biology; biological effects of radiation and ultrasound. *Mailing Add:* Med Sch Dept of Radiol & Radiation Sci Vanderbilt Univ Nashville TN 37232

SIEGEL, EDWARD T, b Lawrence, Mass, Aug 3, 34; m 59; c 3. VETERINARY ENDOCRINOLOGY. *Educ:* Univ Pa, VMD, 58; Jefferson Med Col, PhD(physiol), 64. *Prof Exp:* Scientist, Worcester Found Exp Biol, 61-63; asst prof biochem in med, 63-68, assoc prof med, 68-73, PROF MED, UNIV PA, 73- *Concurrent Pos:* NIH res fel, 60-63, res grant, 64-66; Inst Coop Res grants, Univ Pa & Am Cancer Soc, 63-64; Seeing Eye, Inc grant, 68-71. *Mem:* Am Vet Med Asn; Am Col Vet Internal Med. *Res:* Hormonal synthesis in the canine Sertoli cell tumor; steroid biosynthesis and catabolism in domestic animals; clinical endocrinology in domestic animals. *Mailing Add:* 2071 E Pacific Philadelphia PA 19134

SIEGEL, ELI CHARLES, b Newark, NJ, July 25, 38; m 68; c 1. MICROBIAL GENETICS. *Educ:* Rutgers Univ, BA, 60, PhD(microbiol), 66. *Prof Exp:* Fel biochem, Albert Einstein Col Med, 66-68; asst prof, 68-74, ASSOC PROF BIOL, TUFTS UNIV, 74- *Concurrent Pos:* USPHS fel, 67-68. *Mem:* AAAS; Am Soc Microbiol; Genetics Soc Am. *Res:* Mutator genes; DNA repair; bacterial genetics. *Mailing Add:* Dept of Biol Tufts Univ Medford MA 02155

SIEGEL, ELLIOT ROBERT, b New York, NY, May 31, 42; m 67; c 2. COMMUNICATIONS SCIENCE, INFORMATION SCIENCE. *Educ:* Brooklyn Col, BA, 64; Mich State Univ, MA, 66, PhD(commun), 69. *Prof Exp:* Res scientist commun, Human Sci Res, Inc, 69-70; res assoc commun & info sci, Off Commun, Am Psychol Asn, 70-72, mgr & exec ed, 72-74 & sci affairs officer, 75-76; INFO SCIENTIST COMMUN, LISTER HILL NAT CTR BIOMED COMMUN, NAT LIBR MED, 76- *Concurrent Pos:* Mem adv panel, Comt Instnl Coop, Acad Contemp Prob, 72-73; mem adv comt, NSF, Ind Univ, 74-75; assoc ed, Am Psychologist J, 75-76; mem dissemination comt, Fed Coun Educ Res & Develop, 78-; consult, Nat Inst Educ, 79- *Mem:* AAAS; Am Soc Info Sci; Am Psychol Asn; Int Commun Asn. *Res:* Information transfer and knowledge utilization in the health sciences; information systems development; scientific and technical communication processes; interpersonal communication processes; science policy research. *Mailing Add:* Lister Hill Nat Ctr for Nat Libr of Med Bethesda MD 20014

SIEGEL, ELSIE P, b New York, NY, Aug 29, 23; m 44. CELL BIOLOGY, ENDOCRINOLOGY. *Educ:* Brooklyn Col, BS, 44; NY Univ, MS, 52. *Prof Exp:* Asst corneal physiol, Col Physicians & Surgeons, Columbia Univ, 49-51; asst muscle physiol, Dept Biol, NY Univ, 51-52; lit researcher, E R Squibb & Sons, 52-54; biologist, Div Neoplastic Dis, Montefiore Hosp, New York, 54-59, Med Physics Lab, 59-62; res asst cell biol, Univ Calif, Berkeley, 62-67; res assoc, Sch Med, Stanford Univ, 68-70; res assoc, Sch Med, Univ Mo-Columbia, 70-76; RES ASSOC, DEPT RADIOL & RADIOL SCI, SCH MED, VANDERBILT UNIV, 76- *Mem:* Am Chem Soc; NY Acad Sci. *Res:* Metabolism of rare earth strontium chelates; yttrium-90 intracavitary therapy; nucleic acid and protein synthesis during cell cycle; high resolution radioautography; electron microscopy; thyroid hormone metabolism in cultured cells. *Mailing Add:* Dept of Radiol & Radiation Sci Sch of Med Vanderbilt Univ Nashville TN 37232

SIEGEL, FRANK LEONARD, b Brooklyn, NY, Apr 15, 31; m 62. BIOCHEMISTRY. *Educ:* Reed Col, BA, 53; Univ Tex, PhD(chem), 60. *Prof Exp:* Asst chem, Univ Tex, 54, Clayton Found fel biochem, 60-64; from instr to asst prof, 64-71, assoc prof pediat & physiol chem, Sch Med, 71-75, PROF PEDIAT & PHYSIOL CHEM, NEUROCHEM SECT, WAISMAN CTR, UNIV WIS-MADISON, 75- *Concurrent Pos:* Res scientist, NIMH Develop Comt. *Mem:* AAAS; Am Chem Soc; Am Soc Biol Chemists; Am Soc Neurochem; Soc Neurosci. *Res:* Molecular pathology of aminoacidopathies; cyclic nucleotides and calcium-binding proteins in brain; effects of perinatal hyperthermia on central nervous system development; protein methylation. *Mailing Add:* Neurochem Sect Waisman Ctr Univ Wis Madison WI 53706

SIEGEL, FREDERIC RICHARD, b Chelsea, Mass, Feb 8, 32; m 62; c 2. GEOLOGY. *Educ:* Harvard Univ, BA, 54; Univ Kans, MS, 58, PhD(geol), 61. *Prof Exp:* Prof & researcher geochem & sedimentology, Inst Miguel Lillo, Nat Univ Tucuman, 61-63; div head geochem, Kans Geol Surv, 63-65, res assoc, 64-65; assoc prof, 65-69, PROF GEOCHEM, GEORGE WASHINGTON UNIV, 69-, CHMN GEOL DEPT, 76- *Concurrent Pos:* Vis prof, Univ Buenos Aires, 63; lectr, Univ Kans, 65; res assoc, Smithsonian Inst, 67-; Fulbright scholar, Facultad de Minas, Medellin, Colombia, 70; consult, World Bank, 79 & UN Develop Prog, 80. *Mem:* AAAS; Asn Explor Geochem; Geochem Soc; Soc Econ Paleont & Mineral; Soc Environ Geochem & Health. *Res:* Trace element distribution in modern marine sediments; geochemical prospecting; clay mineralogy of marine units; suspended sediment mineralogy and geochemistry; environmental geology and geochemistry; carbonate geochemistry; geological hazards in land-use planning. *Mailing Add:* Dept of Geol George Washington Univ Washington DC 20052

SIEGEL, GEORGE JACOB, b Bronx, NY, Aug 6, 36; m 57; c 3. NEUROLOGY, NEUROBIOLOGY. *Educ:* Yeshiva Col, BA, 57; Univ Miami, MD, 61. *Prof Exp:* Resident neurol, Mt Sinai Hosp, New York, 62-65; res assoc neurochem, Nat Inst Neurol Dis & Stroke, 65-68; from asst prof to assoc prof physiol & neurol, Mt Sinai Sch Med, 68-73; assoc prof, 73-75, PROF NEUROL, MED SCH, UNIV MICH, ANN ATBOR, 75-, CHIEF NEUROL CHEM LAB, 73- *Concurrent Pos:* Assoc attend neurologist, Mt Sinai Hosp & chmn neurosci integrated curric comt. *Mem:* Am Neurol Asn; Int Soc Neurochem; Am Asn Neuropath; Am Acad Neurol; Harvey Soc. *Res:* Enzymology of active transport in the nervous system. *Mailing Add:* Dept Neurol Med Sch Univ Mich Ann Arbor MI 48109

SIEGEL, GEORGES GIOVANNI, b Port-au-Prince, Haiti, Oct 11, 30; US citizen; m 64; c 3. PHYSICAL CHEMISTRY. *Educ:* Rensselaer Polytech Inst, BChE, 53; Yale Univ, MS, 60, PhD(chem), 65. *Prof Exp:* Asst chem, Rensselaer Polytech Inst, 53-55; asst prof, Univ PR, 55-59; res asst, Yale Univ, 59-65; sr res engr, US Steel Corp, 65-71; from asst to assoc prof, 71-76, PROF CHEM, UNIV PR, MAYAGUEZ, 76- *Mem:* AAAS; Am Chem Soc. *Res:* Change of volume for ionic reactions in solution; compressibilities of electrolyte solutions. *Mailing Add:* Dept of Chem Univ of PR Mayaguez PR 00708

SIEGEL, HENRY, b New York, NY, Oct 16, 10; m 34; c 2. PATHOLOGY. *Educ:* City Col New York, BS, 33; NY Univ, MD, 37; Am Bd Path, dipl. *Hon Degrees:* ScD, Mercy Col, 78. *Prof Exp:* Asst to toxicologist, Off Chief Med Examr, New York, 28-33; asst med examr, 47-50; assoc prof path, Col Med, State Univ NY Downstate Med Ctr, 50-55; from asst med exam to exec dep chief, Off Chief Med Examr, NY, 55-70; PROF PATH, NY MED COL, 70- *Concurrent Pos:* Res pathologist, Merck Inst Therapeut Res, NJ, 41-43; assoc med, Long Island Col Med, 43-44; asst pathologist, Lenox Hill Hosp, 48-50; chief pathologist, Kings County Hosp, 50-55; assoc prof, Albert Einstein Col Med, 55-58; pathologist, Bronx Munic Hosp Ctr, 55-58; pathologist & dir labs, Grand Cent Hosp, 58-63; res specialist, Rutgers Univ, 58; pathologist-med examr, Westchester County, NY, 70-78, consult, Labs & Res Dept, 78- *Mem:* Fel Am Soc Clin Path; Am Asn Path & Bact; fel Col Am Path; NY Acad Sci. *Res:* Toxicology; morphologic effects of chemical compounds; forensic and experimental pathology. *Mailing Add:* Off of Med Examr Grasslands Valhalla NY 10595

SIEGEL, HERBERT, b New York, NY, Apr 23, 25; m 56; c 2. INFORMATION SCIENCE, ORGANIC CHEMISTRY. *Educ:* Ind Univ, BS, 47; WVa Univ, PhD(org chem), 56. *Prof Exp:* Chemist, Ohio-Apex, Inc, WVa, 48-50; from asst prof to assoc prof chem, Waynesburg Col, 55-58; asst ed, Chem Abstr Serv, 59-61, asst dept head appl org ed, 62-63, dept head, 64-

66, spec projs mgr, 66-69, mgr org ed anal dept, 69-72, asst mgr chem technol dept, 72-73, asst mgr org chem dept, 73-75; info chemist, 75-79, HEAD, INT OCCUP SAFETY & HEALTH INFO CTR, INT LABOR OFF, 80- *Concurrent Pos:* Res fel & lectr, Bedford Col, Univ London, 58-59. *Mem:* Am Chem Soc; Am Soc Info Sci; Royla Soc Chem. *Res:* Biphenyl stereochemistry; chemical information storage and retrieval; abstracting and indexing. *Mailing Add:* CIS Int Labor Off 1211 Geneva 22 Switzerland

SIEGEL, HERBERT S, b Mt Vernon, NY, Aug 29, 26; m 48; c 3. PHYSIOLOGY. *Educ:* Pa State Univ, BS, 50, MS, 57, PhD, 59. *Prof Exp:* Asst poultry husb, Pa State Univ, 55-57; from asst prof to assoc prof, Va Polytech Inst & State Univ, 58-64; RES PHYSIOLOGIST, AGR RES SERV, USDA, 64- *Concurrent Pos:* Adj mem grad fac vet physiol & pharmacol, Univ Ga, 66-; Fulbright-Hays res award, Neth, 80-81. *Honors & Awards:* Res Award, Poultry Sci Asn, 61. *Mem:* AAAS; Am Soc Zoologists; Poultry Sci Asn; NY Acad Sci. *Res:* Avian physiology; environmental physiology, stress, adrenals and the immune systems; pesticide residues. *Mailing Add:* SE Poultry Res Lab USDA ARS 934 College Station Rd PO Box 5677 Athens GA 30601

SIEGEL, HOWARD JAY, b Newark, NJ, Jan 16, 50; m 72. COMPUTER ARCHITECTURE. *Educ:* Mass Inst Technol, BS(mgt) & BS(elec eng), 72; Princeton Univ, MA, 74, MSE, 74, PhD(elec eng), 77. *Prof Exp:* Researcher compiler design, Mass Inst Technol, 70, info systs, 71; researcher & teaching asst elec eng & comput sci, Princeton Univ, 72-76; asst prof, 76-81, ASSOC PROF ELEC ENG, PURDUE UNIV, 81- *Mem:* Asn Comput Mach. *Res:* Development of large-scale parallel and distributed multimicrocomputer systems for image and speech processing, including system hardware and software and study of parallel algorithms; design and analysis of interconnection networks for parallel machines; modeling of distributed processing systems. *Mailing Add:* Sch Elec Eng Purdue Univ West Lafayette IN 47907

SIEGEL, IRVING, b Brooklyn, NY, June 15, 24; m 50; c 2. SOLID STATE PHYSICS, CHEMICAL PHYSICS. *Educ:* Univ Iowa, BA, 50; Ill Inst Technol, MS, 61; Univ Toledo, PhD, 70. *Prof Exp:* Physicist, Semiconductor Div, Battelle Mem Inst, 51-55, Physics Res Div, IIT Res Inst, 55-59 & Semiconductor & Mat Div, RCA, 59-60; res physicist fundamental res sect, Owens-Ill Tech Ctr, Ohio, 60-70; asst prof physics, Calif Polytech State Univ, 71-76; RES PHYSICIST, NORTHROP CORP, 79- *Concurrent Pos:* Adj lectr, Univ Toledo, 61-70. *Mem:* Am Phys Soc; Inst Elec & Electronics Engrs; Magnetics Soc. *Res:* Electron paramagnetic resonance; ferromagnetic resonance; magnetic materials and magnetism; teaching. *Mailing Add:* 2071 Hope St San Luis Obispo CA 93401

SIEGEL, IRWIN MICHAEL, b New York, NY, Apr 18, 30; m 56; c 1. PHYSIOLOGY, GENETICS. *Educ:* City Col New York, BS, 51; Columbia Univ, MS, 54, MA, 58, PhD(vision), 60. *Prof Exp:* From asst prof to assoc prof, 60-73, PROF EXP OPHTHAL, MED CTR, NY UNIV, 73- *Mem:* AAAS; Asn Res Vision & Ophthal. *Res:* Vision physiology; ophthalmic genetics. *Mailing Add:* Dept Ophthal 550 First Ave New York NY 10016

SIEGEL, IVENS AARON, b Bay Shore, NY, Jan 28, 32; m 59; c 3. PHARMACOLOGY, ORAL BIOLOGY. *Educ:* Columbus Univ, BS, 53; Univ Kans, MS, 58; Univ Cincinnati, PhD(pharmacol), 62. *Prof Exp:* From instr to asst prof pharmacol, State Univ NY Buffalo, 62-68; assoc prof pharmacol & oral biol, Univ Wash, 68-72, prof, 72-79, chmn, Dept Oral Biol, 76-79; PROF & CHMN PHARMACOL, UNIV ILL-URBANA, 79- *Mem:* Int Asn Dent Res; Am Soc Pharmacol & Exp Therapeut. *Res:* Ion transport, transport in salivary glands; physiology and pharmacology of salivary glands; drug transport across the oral mucosa. *Mailing Add:* 190 Med Sci Bldg 506 S Matthews Ave Urbana IL 61801

SIEGEL, JACK MORTON, b Sioux City, Iowa, June 11, 22; m 46; c 3. BIOCHEMISTRY. *Educ:* Univ Calif, Los Angeles, AB, 44; Washington Univ, PhD(chem), 50. *Prof Exp:* Assoc chemist radiochem, Oak Ridge Nat Lab, 44-46; asst chem, Washington Univ, 46-48, instr, Univ Col, 49-50; asst prof biochem, Sch Med, Univ Ark, 50-55; tech dir, 55-70, vpres, 70-80, SR VPRES, P-L BIOCHEM, INC, PABST BREWING CO, 80- *Mem:* Am Chem Soc; AAAS. *Res:* Uranium fission products; photosynthetic bacteria, nucleotides and coenzymes. *Mailing Add:* 8815 N Rexleigh Dr Milwaukee WI 53217

SIEGEL, JEFFRY A, b New York, NY. NUCLEAR MEDICINE. *Educ:* Univ Cincinnati, BS, 73, MS(chem), 76, MS(radiol physics), 77; Univ Calif, Los Angeles, PhD(med physics), 81. *Prof Exp:* ASST PROF NUCLEAR MED PHYSICS, TEMPLE UNIV HOSP, 81- *Mem:* Soc Nuclear Med; Asn Physicists Med; Inst Elec & Electronics Engrs. *Res:* Quantitative nuclear medicine; nuclear cardiology; image processing of digital data. *Mailing Add:* Dept Nuclear Med Temple Univ Hosp 3401 Broad St Philadelphia PA 19140

SIEGEL, JOHN H, b Baltimore, Md, Dec 12, 32; m 56; c 3. SURGERY, PHYSIOLOGY. *Educ:* Cornell Univ, BA, 53; Johns Hopkins Univ, MD, 57; Am Bd Surg, dipl, 66. *Prof Exp:* Intern surg, Grace-New Haven Community Hosp, 57-58; Cardiovasc fel, Dept Surg, Yale Univ, 58-59 & Lab Cardiovasc Physiol, Nat Heart Inst, 59-61; dir cardiovasc physiol lab, Dept Surg, Sch Med, Univ Mich, 62-65; instr surg, Albert Einstein Col Med, 65-66, assoc, 66-67, from asst prof to assoc prof, 67-72; PROF SURG & BIOPHYS, STATE UNIV NY BUFFALO, 72- *Concurrent Pos:* USPHS trainee acad surg, Dept Surg, Sch Med, Univ Mich, 62-65; Health Res Coun City of New York career scientist award, 66-71; prin investr, Nat Heart Inst grants, 62-65, 66-70, 66-72 & Nat Inst Gen Med Sci grant, 69-71; dir renal transplantation serv & assoc dir clin res ctr-acute, Albert Einstein Col Med, 67-72; asst vis surgeon, Bronx Munic Hosp, 65-67, from assoc attend surgeon to attend surgeon, 67-72; attend, Hosp, Albert Einstein Col Med, 66-72; chief dept surg, Buffalo Gen Hosp, 72-82; prof surg, Univ Md, 82-; dir, Md Inst Emergency Med Serv Systs & dep dir, 82- *Mem:* Am Physiol Soc; fel Am Col Surgeons; Am Asn Surg of Traums; Am Surg Asn; Int Cardiovasc Soc. *Res:* General and vascular surgery; computer science; physiologic evaluation of the critically ill. *Mailing Add:* Buffalo Gen Hosp 100 High St Buffalo NY 14203

SIEGEL, LAURANE GEARY, neurochemistry, enzymology, see previous edition

SIEGEL, LAWRENCE SHELDON, b Fargo, NDak, Oct 13, 10; m 42; c 1. MEDICINE. *Educ:* Univ NDak, BS, 33; Rush Med Col, MD, 36. *Prof Exp:* From asst prof to prof, 54-70, EMER PROF PEDIAT, SCH MED, LOMA LINDA UNIV, 70-; ASSOC PROF, SCH MED, UNIV SOUTHERN CALIF, 64- *Concurrent Pos:* Sr attend pediatrician, Los Angeles City Hosp, 50-; from assoc attend pediatrician to attend pediatrician, Cedars of Lebanon Hosp, 50-67, sr attend pediatrician, 69- *Mem:* AMA; Am Acad Pediatricians. *Res:* Pediatrics. *Mailing Add:* 6010 Wilshire Blvd Los Angeles CA 90036

SIEGEL, LEAH JAMIESON, b Trenton, NJ, Aug 27, 49; m 72. SPEECH PROCESSING, PARALLEL PROCESSING. *Educ:* Mass Inst Technol, SB, 72; Princeton Univ, MA & MSE, 74, PhD(elec eng & comput sci), 77. *Prof Exp:* Researcher ins comput systs, Prudential Ins Co, 69 & info systs, Mass Inst Technol, 70; res teaching asst elec eng & comput sci, Princeton Univ, 72-76; asst prof, 76-82, ASSOC PROF ELEC ENG, PURDUE UNIV, 82- *Concurrent Pos:* Int assoc chairperson, Distrib Comput Systs, Inst Elec & Electronics Engrs, 81-82. *Mem:* Inst Elec & Electronics Engrs; Asn Comput Mach. *Res:* Computer analysis and recognition of speech; design of parallel processing algorithms for digital speech, signal and image processing, including parallel languages and modelling of parallel and distributed computing. *Mailing Add:* Sch Elec Eng Purdue Univ West Lafayette IN 47907

SIEGEL, LESTER AARON, b New York, NY, Sept 25, 25. PHYSICS. *Educ:* Mass Inst Technol, SB, 45, PhD(physics), 48. *Prof Exp:* Instr physics, Mass Inst Technol, 48-50; from res physicist to sr res physicist, 50-61, group leader, 61-69, SR RES PHYSICIST, AM CYANAMID CO, 69- *Mem:* Am Phys Soc; Am Chem Soc; Am Crystallog Asn. *Res:* X-ray diffraction. *Mailing Add:* Am Cyanamid Co 1937 W Main St Stamford CT 06904

SIEGEL, LEWIS MELVIN, b Baltimore, Md, Aug 7, 41; m 60; c 3. BIOCHEMISTRY. *Educ:* Johns Hopkins Univ, BA, 61, PhD(biol), 65. *Prof Exp:* Res assoc biol, Brookhaven Nat Lab, 65; res assoc, 66-68, ASSOC PROF BIOCHEM, SCH MED, DUKE UNIV, 68- *Concurrent Pos:* Res chemist, Vet Admin Hosp, Durham, 68- *Mem:* Am Soc Biol Chemists. *Res:* Mechanisms of electron transport in metalloflavoproteins; multi-electron reductions; sulfur and nitrogen metabolism. *Mailing Add:* Dept of Biochem Duke Univ Sch of Med Durham NC 27706

SIEGEL, MALCOLM RICHARD, b New Haven, Conn, Nov 5, 32; m 62. PLANT PATHOLOGY, TOXICOLOGY. *Educ:* Univ Conn, BS, 55; Univ Del, MS, 59; Univ Md, PhD(bot), 63. *Prof Exp:* NIH res grant bot, Univ Md, 63-66; from asst prof to assoc prof, 66-73, PROF PLANT PATH, UNIV KY, 73- *Concurrent Pos:* Nat Inst Environ Health Sci res grant, 67-73; assoc ed, Phytopathology, 73-76; assoc ed, Pesticide Biochem & Physiol, 78-83; sabbatical, Inst Org Chem, 75; mem staff, USDA, 79. *Mem:* Am Phytopath Soc; Sigma Xi. *Res:* Action and metabolic fate of fungicides; mechanisms of fungal risistance to fungicides. *Mailing Add:* Dept of Plant Path Univ of Ky Lexington KY 40506

SIEGEL, MARTHA J, b New York, NY, Nov 5, 39; m 62; c 2. MATHEMATICS. *Educ:* Russell Sage Col, BA, 60; Univ Rochester, MA, 63, PhD(math), 69. *Prof Exp:* Asst prof math, Goucher Col, 66-71; PROF MATH, TOWSON STATE UNIV, 71- *Concurrent Pos:* Fel, Sch Hyg & Pub Health, Johns Hopkins Univ, 77-78. *Mem:* Math Asn Am; Am Math Soc. *Res:* Birth and death processes. *Mailing Add:* Dept of Math Towson State Univ Towson MD 21204

SIEGEL, MAURICE L, b New York, NY, Aug 7, 27; m 59. ORGANIC CHEMISTRY. *Educ:* City Col New York, BS, 49; NY Univ, MS, 51, PhD, 58. *Prof Exp:* Dir res, Caryl Richards Co, 57-67; vpres, 67-78, EXEC VPRES, FABERGE, INC, 78-, DIR RES, 67- *Concurrent Pos:* Adj asst prof, NY Univ, 59-67. *Mem:* AAAS; Soc Cosmetic Chem; Am Chem Soc. *Res:* Hair technology. *Mailing Add:* 15 Sierra Ct Hillsdale NJ 07642

SIEGEL, MELVIN WALTER, b New York, NY, May 26, 41; m 68. MASS SPECTROMETRY, ION PHYSICS. *Educ:* Cornell Univ, BA, 62; Univ Colo, MS, 67, PhD(physics), 70. *Prof Exp:* Instr physics & math, Achimota Col, Ghana, 62-64; res assoc physics, Joint Inst Lab Astrophysics, Univ Colo, 70; sr scientist, Univ Va, 70-72, lectr, 71-72; asst prof physics, State Univ NY Buffalo, 72-74; PHYSICIST, EXTRANUCLEAR LABS, INC, 74-, DIR, RES & DEVELOP, 78- *Honors & Awards:* IR-100 Awards, 78 & 79. *Mem:* AAAS; Am Phys Soc; Am Soc Mass Spectros; NY Acad Sci. *Res:* Ionization phenomena; mass spectrometry; laser photodetachment; photoelectron spectroscopy; negative ion structure; high pressure ionization; ion eptics; instrumentation. *Mailing Add:* Extranuclear Labs Inc PO Box 11512 Pittsburgh PA 15238

SIEGEL, MICHAEL ELLIOT, b New York, NY, May 13, 42; m 66; c 2. NUCLEAR MEDICINE, RADIOLOGY. *Educ:* Cornell Univ, BA, 64; Chicago Med Sch, MD, 68. *Prof Exp:* NIH fel diag radiol, Temple Univ Med Ctr, 70-71; NIH fel nuclear med, Johns Hopkins Univ, 71-73, asst prof radiol & environ health, 73-76; asst clin prof radiol, George Washington Univ, 75-77; ASSOC PROF RADIOPHARM, SCH PHARM & ASSOC PROF RADIOL & MED, SCH MED, UNIV SOUTHERN CALIF, 76- *Concurrent Pos:* Radiologist, Johns Hopkins Univ, 71-76; consult nuclear med, Ann Arundel Hosp, Annapolis, Md, 74-76; dir, Dept Nuclear Med, Orthop Hosp, Los Angeles, 76-; dir, Dept Nuclear Med & attend physician, Los Angeles County-Univ Southern Calif Med Ctr, 76- *Honors & Awards:* Silver Medal, Soc Nuclear Med, 74 & 75. *Mem:* Soc Nuclear Med; Am Col Nuclear Physicians; Radiol Soc NAm; Asn Univ Radiologists; Am Col Nuclear Med. *Res:* Development of new applications of radioisotopes for prognostic and diagnostic evaluation of vascular disease, both cardiac and peripheral; diagnosis and therapy of malignancies. *Mailing Add:* Los Angeles County-Univ Southern Calif Med Ctr 1200 N State St Los Angeles CA 90033

SIEGEL, MICHAEL IAN, b Brooklyn, NY, Nov 24, 42. PHYSICAL ANTHROPOLOGY, PRIMATOLOGY. *Educ:* Queens Col, NY, BA, 67; City Univ, New York, PhD(phys anthrop), 71. *Prof Exp:* Lectr phys anthrop, Hunter Col, 67-69; instr, Adelphi Univ, 69-71; from asst prof, to assoc prof phys anthrop, 71-76, orthod, Col Dent, 75-76, asst prof, 76-78, assoc prof anat & cell biol, 78-80, ASSOC PROF PHYS ANTHROP, SCH MED, UNIV PITTSBURGH, 75- *Concurrent Pos:* Vis scientist, Lab Exp Med & Surg Primates, 70-; adj lectr prev dent, NY Univ, 70-; sr res, Cleff Palate Ctr, 75-, NIH grants, 77 & 80. *Mem:* Fel AAAS; fel Am Anthrop Asn; Am Asn Phys Anthropologists; NY Acad Sci. *Res:* Experimental morphology and functional anatomy; growth and development; cleft palate models. *Mailing Add:* Dept of Anthrop Univ of Pittsburgh Pittsburgh PA 15213

SIEGEL, MORRIS, b US, Mar 2, 04; m 33; c 2. PREVENTIVE MEDICINE, EPIDEMIOLOGY. *Educ:* City Col New York, BA, 24; NY Univ, MD, 28; Johns Hopkins Univ, MPH, 39. *Prof Exp:* Intern, Bellevue Hosp, New York, 29 & 31; resident physician, Sea View Hosp, 32-34; res assoc, New York Health Dept, 35-41; assoc, Pub Health Res Inst New York, 41-47; health officer, New York Health Dept, 47-52, chief poliomeylitis div, 49-50; from assoc prof to prof, 52-74, EMER PROF PREV MED, STATE UNIV NY DOWNSTATE MED CTR, 74- *Concurrent Pos:* Vis lectr, Sch Pub Health, Harvard Univ, 59-65. *Mem:* Harvey Soc; Epidemiol Soc; Ny Acad Med; Sigma Xi. *Res:* Public health, prevnetive medicine and epidemiology of acute and chronic diseases. *Mailing Add:* 345 E 69th St New York NY 10021

SIEGEL, PAMELA JEAN, b Port Jefferson, NY, Aug 15, 45; m 68; c 1. MOLECULAR BIOLOGY, VIROLOGY. *Educ:* State Univ NY Stony Brook, BS, 68; Med Sch, Tufts Univ, PhD(molecular biol), 75. *Prof Exp:* Spec reviewer, Am Soc Microbiol, 73; Helen Hay Whitney Found fel, 76-79, RES ASSOC, HARVARD MED SCH & SIDNEY FARBER CANCER INST, 79- *Concurrent Pos:* Vis scientist, Univ Southern Calif & Tufts Univ, 81. *Mem:* Am Soc Microbiol; AAAS. *Res:* DNA metabolism of Epstein-Barr virus; repticaton proceeds via an open circular form during productive infection; restriction studies of circular and small species. *Mailing Add:* 1 Belknap St #8 Arlington MA 02174

SIEGEL, PAUL BENJAMIN, b Hartford, Conn, Nov 19, 32; m 57; c 3. GENETICS. *Educ:* Univ Conn, BS, 53; Kans State Univ, MS, 54, PhD(genetics), 57. *Prof Exp:* From asst prof to prof, 57-75, UNIV DISTINGUISHED PROF POULTRY SCI, VA POLYTECH INST & STATE UNIV, 75- *Mem:* AAAS; Ecol Soc Am; Animal Behav Soc; Am Genetic Asn; Poultry Sci Asn. *Res:* Genetic aspects of behavior; population genetics. *Mailing Add:* Dept of Poultry Sci Va Polytech Inst & State Univ Blacksburg VA 24061

SIEGEL, RICHARD DAVID, b Hammond, Ind, Apr 16, 42; m 66. CHEMICAL & AIR POLLUTION CONTROL. *Educ:* Tufts Univ, BS, 64, MS, 66; Lehigh Univ, PhD(chem eng), 69. *Prof Exp:* Sr engr appl sci, Northern Res & Eng Corp, 69-72; prin engr & mgr admin, Walden Div, Abcor Inc, 72-77; CONSULT ENVIRON ENG DIV, STONE & WEBSTER ENG CORP, 77- *Concurrent Pos:* Lectr chem eng, Northeastern Univ, 70-71; prog mgr & prin investr to numerous govt agencies and private industs environ control studies. *Mem:* AAAS; Sigma Xi; Am Chem Soc; NY Acad Sci; Air Pollution Cont Asn. *Res:* Air pollution control; diffusion through polymer films; heat transfer, especially boiling and combustion; computer applications to chemical engineering; air pollution impact from stationary and mobile sources; ambient monitoring; dispersion analysis techniques. *Mailing Add:* Stone & Webster Eng Corp 245 Summer St PO Box 2325 Boston MA 02107

SIEGEL, RICHARD W(HITE), b Cambridge. Mass, May 21, 37; m 62; c 2. MATERIALS SCIENCE, METAL PHYSICS. *Educ:* Williams Col, AB, 58; Univ Ill, Urbana, MS, 60, PhD(phys metall), 65. *Prof Exp:* Res assoc , Dept Mats Sci & Eng, Cornell Univ, 64-66; from asst prof to assoc prof, Dept Mat Sci, State Univ NY, Stony Brook, 66-75; GROUP LEADER METAL PHYSICS, MAT SCI DIV, ARGONNE NAT LAB, 74- *Concurrent Pos:* Guest prof, Max Planck Inst for Metal Res, Stuttgart, Ger, 72-73; adj prof, Dept Mat Sci, State Univ NY Stony Brook, 75-76; vis prof, Mat Eng Dept, Ben-Gurion Univ Negev, Beer-Sheva, Israel, 80-81; assoc ed, Mat Letters, 81- *Mem:* Am Phys Soc; Metall Soc; Inst Physics; AAAS. *Res:* Properties and interactions of atomic defects in metals diffusion; electron microscopy; positron annihilation spectroscopy. *Mailing Add:* Mat Sci Div Argonne Nat Lab Argonne IL 60439

SIEGEL, RICHARD WEIL, b New York, NY, Jan 30, 24; m 62; c 4. GENETICS. *Educ:* Univ Conn, BS, 47; Ind Univ, PhD(zool), 52. *Prof Exp:* Res assoc, Univ Pa, 52-54; instr biol, Reed Col, 54-56; from asst prof to prof zool, 56-74, PROF BIOL, UNIV CALIF, LOS ANGELES, 74- *Concurrent Pos:* Prog dir develop biol, NSF, 70-72. *Res:* Developmental genetics. *Mailing Add:* Dept of Biol Univ of Calif Los Angeles CA 90024

SIEGEL, ROBERT, b Cleveland, Ohio, July 10, 27; m 51; c 2. MECHANICAL ENGINEERING, HEAT TRANSFER. *Educ:* Case Inst Technol, BS, 50, MS, 51; Mass Inst Technol, ScD(mech eng), 53. *Prof Exp:* Asst mech eng, Case Inst Technol, 50-51; fluid dynamics, Mass Inst Technol, 52-53; res engr, Gen Eng Lab, Gen Elec Co, 53-54, res engr, Knolls Atomic Power Lab, 54-55; RES ENGR, NASA, 55- *Concurrent Pos:* Assoc tech ed, J Heat Transfer, 73- *Honors & Awards:* Heat Transfer Mem Award, Am Soc Mech Engrs, 70. *Mem:* Fel Am Soc Mech Engrs. *Res:* Heat transfer and fluid dynamics theory; forced and free convection; transient fluid flow and heat convection; thermal radiation exchange and boiling. *Mailing Add:* Fluid Mech & Acoust Div NASA Lewis Res Ctr Cleveland OH 44135

SIEGEL, ROBERT TED, b Springfield, Mass, June 10, 28; m 51; c 4. PARTICLE PHYSICS. *Educ:* Carnegie Inst Technol, BS, 48, MS, 50, DSc, 52. *Prof Exp:* Resident physicist, Carnegie Inst Technol, 52-54, from asst prof to assoc prof physics, 54-63; dean grad studies, 64-67, dir, Space Radiation Effects Lab, Newport News, Va, 67-78, prof physics, 63-69, W F C FERGISON PROF PHYSICS, COL WILLIAM & MARY, 79- *Mem:* fel Am Phys Soc. *Res:* Elementary particle physics; weak interactions; muon physics. *Mailing Add:* Dept of Physics Col of William & Mary Williamsburg PA 23185

SIEGEL, SAMUEL, b Lake Mills, Wis, Feb 15, 17; m 48; c 2. ORGANIC CHEMISTRY. *Educ:* Univ Calif, BS, 38; Univ Calif, Los Angeles, MA, 40, PhD(chem), 42. *Prof Exp:* Res assoc, Northwestern Univ, 42-43; res assoc chem warfare agents & insect repellants, Nat Defense Res Comt Proj, Harvard Univ, 43-45; asst prof chem, Ill Inst Technol, 46-51; assoc prof, 51-57, chmn dept, 57-63, PROF CHEM, UNIV ARK, FAYETTEVILLE, 57- *Concurrent Pos:* Consult, Universal Oil Prod Co, 56-62; Am Chem Soc-Petrol Res Fund Int fac award, 63-64; vis prof, Queen's Univ, Belfast, 63-64; vis prof, Res Inst Catalysis, Hokkaido Univ, Japan, 78. *Mem:* AAAS; Am Chem Soc; Royal Soc Chem. *Res:* Stereochemistry; quantitative structure-reactivity relationships; mechanism of heterogeneous and homogeneous catalytic hydrogenation. *Mailing Add:* Dept of Chem Univ of Ark Fayetteville AR 72701

SIEGEL, SANFORD MARVIN, b Kansas City, Mo, Sept 3, 28; m 50; c 4. ENVIRONMENTAL CHEMISTRY, BIOGEOCHEMISTRY. *Educ:* Univ Chicago, SM, 50, PhD(biol), 53. *Prof Exp:* Asst bot, Univ Chicago, 49-50; biochemist, Chem Corps Biol Lab, US Dept Army, Md, 50-52; Am Cancer Soc res fel, Calif Inst Technol, 53-54; asst prof biol & instr phys sci, Univ Tampa, 54-55; asst prof biol, Univ Rochester, 55-58; group leader phys biochem, Union Carbide Res Inst, 58-67; PROF BOT, UNIV HAWAII, 67-, CHMN DEPT, 80- *Concurrent Pos:* Guggenheim fel, 57-58; NASA grants, 63-67, 67-76, 67-74; mem, Environ Biol Adv Panel, NASA, 68-71; Res Corp Cottrell res grant toxic volcanic emissions, Iceland & Hawaii, 72-73, Nat Geog Soc grant, 72; sr fel, Weizmann Inst Sci, 74; pub responsibility officer, Am Inst Biol Sci, State Hawaii, 72-76; mem staff, Hawaii Natural Energy Inst, 78- *Mem:* AAAS; Am Chem Soc; Scand Soc Plant Physiologists; Phytochem Soc; NY Acad Sci. *Res:* Planetary biology and biogeochemistry of mercury and other heavy elements; physiology of stress; biology of extreme environments; exobiology; salinity and salt tolerance; membrane physiology; planetary biology; environmental impacts of energy development. *Mailing Add:* Dept of Bot Univ of Hawaii Honolulu HI 96822

SIEGEL, SEYMOUR, b New York, NY, Oct 19, 32; m 55; c 2. CHEMICAL PHYSICS. *Educ:* Brooklyn Col, BS, 54; Harvard Univ, MA, 56, PhD(phys chem), 59. *Prof Exp:* Mem sr staff, Appl Physics Lab, Johns Hopkins Univ, 58-59; chem physicist, Aerojet-Gen Corp, Gen Tire & Rubber Co, 59-61; head chem physics dept, Mat Sci Lab, Aerospace Corp, 61-73, dir, Chem & Phys Lab, 73-80. *Mem:* Am Phys Soc; Am Chem Soc. *Res:* Free radical and excited molecule reactions; space environmental effects on materials; forensic material analysis; thin film chemistry and physics; photochemistry; surface kinetics and catalysis. *Mailing Add:* 11432 Bolas St Los Angeles CA 90049

SIEGEL, SHELDON, b New York, NY, May 10, 32; m 54; c 3. PHARMACEUTICAL CHEMISTRY. *Educ:* Long Island Univ, BS, 53; Columbia Univ, MS, 57; Fairleigh Dickinson Univ, MBA, 69. *Prof Exp:* Teaching asst, Columbia Univ, 55-57; sr chemist, Merck & Co, 57-63; mgr res planning, 63-69, prod mgr mkt, 69-70, dir, Am Chicle Develop, 70-72, vpres res & develop, Am Chicle, 72-79, vpres, Res & Develop Consumer Prod, 79-81, VPRES WORLDWIDE TECHNOL, CONSUMER PROD, WARNER-LAMBERT CO, 81- *Concurrent Pos:* Mem bd dir, Nat Confectioners Asn US; mem, Exec Comt, Nat Asn Chewing Gum Mfg. *Mem:* Nat Asn Chewing Gum Mfrs; Am Pharmaceut Asn; Am Chem Soc; Int Food Technologists. *Res:* Areas of confectionery products and proprietary drugs. *Mailing Add:* 201 Tabor Rd Morris Plains NJ 07950

SIEGEL, SIDNEY, b New York, NY, Jan 10, 12; m 37; c 4. PHYSICS. *Educ:* Columbia Univ, AB, 32, PhD(physics), 36. *Prof Exp:* Asst physics, Columbia Univ, 33-38; res engr, Res Labs, Westinghouse Elec Corp, 38-44, sect mgr, 44-46, mgr, Physics Dept, Atomic Power Div, 49-50; chief physicist, Oak Ridge Nat Lab, 46-49; assoc dir, Atomic Res Dept, NAm Aviation, Inc, 50-55, tech dir, Atomic Int Div, 55-60, vpres, Atomic Int Div, NAm Rockwell Corp, 60-72; dep assoc dir, Oak Ridge Nat Lab, 72-74; CONSULT ADVAN ENERGY SYSTS, 74- *Concurrent Pos:* Lectr, Univ Pittsburgh, 38-40; res assoc, Calif Inst Technol, 51. *Mem:* Fel Am Nuclear Soc (vpres, 65, pres, 66); fel Am Phys Soc. *Res:* Solid state physics; ferromagnetism; radiation effects; nuclear reactor development. *Mailing Add:* 722 Jacon Way Pacific Palisades CA 90272

SIEGEL, STANLEY, b Waterloo, Iowa, Feb 5, 15; m 40. CRYSTALLOGRAPHY. *Educ:* Univ Chicago, BS, 36, MS, 38, PhD(physics), 41. *Prof Exp:* Asst, Univ Chicago, 39-40 & Duke Univ, 40-41; assoc physicist, Nat Bur Standards, 41-44; physicist, Armour Res Found, 44-50; PHYSICIST, ARGONNE NAT LAB, 50- *Mem:* Am Phys Soc; Am Crystallog Asn. *Res:* X-ray diffraction; crystallography; crystal physics. *Mailing Add:* Argonne Nat Lab 9700 S Cass Ave Argonne IL 60439

SIEGEL, WILLIAM CARL, b Eau Claire, Wis, Sept 11, 32; m 62; c 5. RESOURCE ECONOMICS. *Educ:* Mich State Univ, BS, 54, MS, 57; Loyola Univ, La, LLB, 65, JD, 68. *Prof Exp:* Timber mgt asst, Sam Houston Nat Forest, US Forest Serv, 58, asst economist, Southern Forest & Range Exp Sta, 58-60, assoc economist, 60-66, economist, 66-68, PRIN ECONOMIST, SOUTHERN FOREST & RANGE EXP STA, US FOREST SERV, 68-, PROJ LEADER, 77- *Mem:* Soc Am Foresters; Nat Tax Asn; Am Bar Asn. *Res:* Forestry economics, especially forest taxation, insurance, and credit with emphasis on the relationship between law and economics. *Mailing Add:* Southern For & Rng Exp Sta USFS 10210 Fed Bldg 701 Loyola Ave New Orleans LA 70113

SIEGELMAN, HAROLD WILLIAM, b Los Angeles, Calif, Feb 1, 20; m 47; c 2. PLANT BIOCHEMISTRY. *Educ:* Univ Calif, BS, 42; Univ Calif, Los Angeles, MS, 47, PhD, 51. *Prof Exp:* Horticulturist, Bur Plant Indust, Soils & Agr Eng, Plant Indust Sta, USDA, Wash, 51-53, Hort Crops Res Br, Agr Res Serv, 53-57, plant physiologist, Crops Res Div, 57-65; plant biochemist, 65-69, chmn dept biol, 69-74, SR PLANT BIOCHEMIST, BROOKHAVEN NAT LAB, 74- *Concurrent Pos:* Instr exp marine bot, Marine Biol Lab, Woods Hole, Mass, 68, instr-in-chg, 69-70. *Mem:* Am Soc Plant Physiologists; Am Chem Soc; Am Soc Biol Chemists; Biochem Soc; Am Acad Arts & Sci. *Res:* Effect of light on biochemistry of plants; algal toxins. *Mailing Add:* Dept of Biol Brookhaven Nat Lab Upton NY 11973

SIEGENTHALER, BRUCE MONROE, b Fremont, Ohio, Aug 29, 21; m 47; c 3. SPEECH PATHOLOGY, AUDIOLOGY. *Educ:* Bowling Green State Univ, BS, 43; Univ Mich, Ann Arbor, MA, 48, PhD, 51. *Prof Exp:* Clin asst speech improv, Nat Speech Improv Camp, Univ Mich, 47-50, sr clinician, 50-51, maj clinician, 51; from asst prof to assoc prof clin speech, 51-62, dir speech & hearing clin & in-chg speech path & audiol prog, 62-79, PROF CLIN SPEECH & PATH, PA STATE UNIV, UNIVERSITY PARK, 62-, MEM GRAD FAC, 53-, RES PROF, 79- *Concurrent Pos:* Prof coordr, Harmony Hall Hearing Prog, 52-73; sr engr, HRB-Singer, 56; speech & hearing consult, Camp Easter Seal, Pa Soc Crippled Children & Adults, 56-58; mem, Lib Arts Comt Res, Pa State Univ, 57-58, chmn speech dept res comt, 60-61; mem, Fac Res Comt, US Dept Educ, 58-59; sr engr, Haller, Raymond & Brown, Inc, 58-64; mem, Adv Comt Audiol, Pa Bur Voc Rehab, 60-, Comt Handicapped Children, Pa Health Coun, 60-, Audiol-otol Adv Comt, Pa Dept Health, 61-; co-chmn, Sect Serv Needed, Pa Sch Serv Task Force, 64-65; mem, Prof Adv Comt, Rehab Serv Agency, 67-, training prog consult, 67-70; consult speech & hearing, Pa Rehab Ctr & Pa Bur Voc Rehab, 69- *Mem:* Acoust Soc Am; fel Am Speech & Hearing Asn; Acad Rehab Audiol; Int Soc Audiol; Nat Rehab Asn. *Res:* Relationship between measured hearing loss and intelligibility of selected words; diagnostic word test of hearing. *Mailing Add:* Commun Disorders Prog Pa State Univ University Park PA 16802

SIEGER, JOHN S(YLVESTER), b Pittsburgh, Pa, Oct 3, 25; m 51; c 4. CHEMICAL ENGINEERING. *Educ:* Carnegie Inst Technol, BS, 45; Columbia Univ, MS, 47, PhD(chem eng), 50. *Prof Exp:* Res engr, Pittsburgh Coke & Chem Co, 45-47; fel, Mellon Inst, 50-56; group leader, Pittsburgh Plate Glass Co, 56-59, head surfacing res dept, 59-64, SR RES ASSOC, GLASS RES LABS, PPG INDUST INC, 64- *Mem:* Am Ceramic Soc; Am Chem Soc; Am Inst Chem Engrs. *Res:* Research and development on the production and properties of flat glass. *Mailing Add:* Glass Res Lab PPG Indust Inc Creighton PA 15030

SIEGERT, ARNOLD JOHN FREDERICK, b Dresden, Ger, Jan 1, 11; nat US; m 44; c 1. STATISTICAL PHYSICS. *Educ:* Univ Leipzig, PhD(theoret physics), 34. *Prof Exp:* Lorentz Funds fel, Univ Leiden, Holland, 34-36; asst physics, Stanford Univ, 36-39; physicist, Tex Co, 39-42, Nat Geophys Co, 42, Stanolind Oil & Gas Co, Okla, 42 & radiaiton lab, Mass Inst Technol, 42-46; assoc prof physics, Syracuse Univ, 46-47; prof physics, Northwestern Univ, Evanston, 47-79. *Concurrent Pos:* Consult, Pan-Am Petrol Corp, 42-66, Rand Corp, 50-57, Lockheed Aircraft Corp, 58-61 & Argonne Nat Lab, 65-71; Guggenheim fel, Inst Adv Study, 53-54; NSF sr fels, Inst Theoret Physics, Amsterdam, Neth, 62-63 & Weizmann Inst, Israel, 63-64; vis prof, Univ Utrecht, Neth, 71-72 & 79-80, Kramers prof, 80. *Mem:* Fel Am Phys Soc. *Res:* Theoretical physics; quantum theory; random processes; exploration geophysics; gravity and magnetic methods; statistical mechanics. *Mailing Add:* 2347 Lake Ave Wilmette IL 60091

SIEGESMUND, KENNETH A, b Milwaukee, Wis, Nov 28, 32; m 59; c 4. CYTOLOGY. *Educ:* Univ Wis, BS, 55, PhD(bot), 60. *Prof Exp:* Res assoc bot, 60-62, ASSOC PROF ANAT, MED COL WIS, 62- *Concurrent Pos:* Consult, Vet Admin Hosp, 62- & Milwaukee County Hosp, 62-65. *Mem:* Am Asn Anat; Electron Micros Soc Am; Neuroelec Soc; Am Asn Forensic Sci. *Res:* Ultrastructure of the nervous system; applications of electron microscopy in diagnostic pathology, diagnosis and pathogenesis of occupational lung disease; forensic sci. *Mailing Add:* Dept Anat Med Col Wis Milwaukee WI 53233

SIEGFRIED, JOHN BARTON, b Philadelphia, Pa, Mar 19, 38. VISUAL PHYSIOLOGY, ELECTROPHYSIOLOGY. *Educ:* Univ Rochester, BA, 60; Brown Univ, MS, 62, PhD(physiol psychol), 67. *Prof Exp:* From asst prof to assoc prof psychol, Univ Houston, 66-73; PROF PHYSIOL OPTICS & COORDR, NEURO-VISUAL SCI TRACT, PA COL OPTOM, 73- *Concurrent Pos:* Asst prof, Dept Neural Sci, Grad Sch Biomed Sci, Univ Tex, Houston, 67-70; consult, US Army Human Eng Labs, Aberdeen Proving Ground, 67-; asst prof, Dept Ophthal, Baylor Col Med, 68-70; lectr, Dept Psychol, Univ Tex, Austin, 73; mem vision comt, Nat Acad Sci-Nat Res Coun, 73-; adj assoc prof psychol, Lehigh Univ, 73-80; NSF res grant, 73, Nat Eye Inst & NIH res develop grant, 80; consult, Retina Dept, Wills Eye Hosp, Philadelphia, 76-80 & Ophthal Dept, St Christopher's Hosp for Children, Philadelphia, 78- *Mem:* AAAS; Asn Res Vision & Ophthal; Psychonomic Soc; Soc Neurosci. *Res:* Processing of information by the human visual cortex as measured by the visual evoked cortical potential; the relation between electrophysiological measures and perception; color vision; electro-diagnostic procedures. *Mailing Add:* Neuro-visual Sci Tract Pa Col Optom 1200 W Godfrey Ave Philadelphia PA 19141

SIEGFRIED, ROBERT, b Columbus, Ohio, Jan 18, 21; m 46; c 4. HISTORY OF SCIENCE, CHEMISTRY. *Educ:* Marietta Col, BA, 42; Univ Wis, PhD(chem, hist sci), 52. *Prof Exp:* Asst prof sci, Col Gen Educ, Boston Univ, 52-54; asst prof chem, Univ Ark, 54-58; from asst prof to assoc prof div gen studies, Univ Ill, 58-63; assoc prof, 63-65, chmn dept, 64-73, PROF HIST SCI, UNIV WIS-MADISON, 65- *Concurrent Pos:* NSF fel, Royal Inst London, 67-68. *Mem:* AAAS; Hist Sci Soc. *Res:* History of chemistry, and the structure of matter, 1700-1850; chemical revolution. *Mailing Add:* 410 South Hall Univ of Wis Madison WI 53706

SIEGFRIED, ROBERT WAYNE, II, b Elmhurst, Ill, July 1, 50; m 78. APPLIED PHYSICS, GEOPHYSICS. *Educ:* Calif Inst Technol, BS, 72; Mass Inst Technol, PhD(geophys), 77. *Prof Exp:* sr scientist geophys, Corning Glass Works, 77-80; SCIENTIST, ATLANTIC RICHIELD CO, 80- *Mem:* Am Geophys Union; Am Ceramic Soc. *Res:* Vapor phase deposition processes; effect of microstructure on the physical properties of materials. *Mailing Add:* PO Box 2819 Dallas TX 75221

SIEGL, WALTER OTTO, b Rochester, NY, Mar 7, 42; m 69; c 1. ORGANOMETALLIC CHEMISTRY, ORGANIC CHEMISTRY. *Educ:* Ohio Wesleyan Univ, BA, 63; Emory Univ, MS, 66; Wayne State Univ, PhD(org chem), 69. *Prof Exp:* Fel chem, Stanford Univ, 69-72; RES SCIENTIST CHEM, FORD MOTOR CO, 72- *Mem:* Am Chem Soc. *Res:* Synthesis of transition metal complexes with unusual properties; chemistry of fuel and lubricant additives. *Mailing Add:* 11 Brookline Lane Dearborn MI 48120

SIEGLAFF, CHARLES LEWIS, b Waterloo, Iowa, Sept 30, 27; m 50; c 2. POLYMER CHEMISTRY, COLLOID CHEMISTRY. *Educ:* Univ Iowa, BS, 50, PhD(chem), 56; Univ Cincinnati, MS, 53. *Prof Exp:* Res chemist, Corn Prod Refining Co, 53 & Polymer Res Lab, Dow Chem Co, 55-60; res assoc, 60-73, sr res assoc, 73-76, RES FEL DIAMOND SHAMROCK CORP, 76- *Concurrent Pos:* Chmn, Gordon Res Conf Polymers, 74-75. *Mem:* Soc Rheol; Am Chem Soc; Japanese Soc Polymer Sci; Royal Soc Chem; NY Acad Sci. *Res:* Electrochemistry and transport phenomena; physical chemistry of polymer solutions; surface and polymer flow properties; colloid chemistry of latex systems; catalytic surface chemistry; rheology of polymers and dispersions. *Mailing Add:* T R Evans Res Ctr Diamond Shamrock Corp PO Box 348 Painesville OH 44077

SIEGLER, EDOUARD HORACE, JR, b Sandy Springs, Md, Apr 27, 25; m 49; c 3. PHYSICS. *Educ:* Johns Hopkins Univ, AB, 45, PhD(physics), 53. *Prof Exp:* Eng mgr, 70-74, SR ENG MGR, INSTRUMENT DIV, PERKIN-ELMER CORP, 74- *Mem:* Optical Soc Am. *Res:* Spectroscopy; scientific instruments. *Mailing Add:* 7 Maywood Ct Darien CT 06820

SIEGLER, PETER EMERY, b Budapest, Hungary, Feb 3, 24; m 57. INTERNAL MEDICINE, ALLERGY. *Educ:* Eotvos Lorand Univ, Budapest, MD, 51. *Prof Exp:* Instr path, Med Univ Budapest, 48-51, from instr to asst prof med, 51-56; instr, Hahnemann Med Col, 59-61, assoc, 61-63, assoc prof, 63-68, dir clin pharmacol, 66-68. Am Soc Pharmacol & Exp Therapeur; Am Soc Clin Pharmacol & Therapeut; Am Fedn Clin Res; Am Acad Allergy; Am Col Allergists. *Res:* Clinical pharmacology; allergy. *Mailing Add:* Stacy Rd & Wynne Lane Penn Valley Narberth PA 19072

SIEGMAN, A(NTHONY) E(DWARD), b Detroit, Mich, Nov 23, 31; m 56, 74; c 3. ELECTRICAL ENGINEERING. *Educ:* Harvard Univ, AB, 52; Univ Calif, Los Angeles, MS, 54; Stanford Univ, PhD(elec eng), 57. *Prof Exp:* Mem tech staff, Hughes Aircraft Co, 52-54; asst, Electronics Lab, 54-56, from asst prof to assoc prof elec eng, 56-65, PROF ELEC ENG, STANFORD UNIV, 65-, DIR, EDWARD L GINZTON LAB, 78- *Concurrent Pos:* Vis prof appl physics, Harvard Univ, 65; consult, GTE Sylvania, United Technol & others; Guggenheim fel, Univ Zurich, 69-70; mem, Air Force Sci Adv Bd. *Honors & Awards:* W R G Baker Award, Inst Elec & Electronics Engrs, 72, J J Ebers Award, 77. *Mem:* Nat Acad Eng; Am Phys Soc; fel Inst Elec & Electronics Engrs; fel Optical Soc Am; Am Soc Eng Educ. *Res:* Lasers; quantum electronics; optics. *Mailing Add:* Ginzton Lab Stanford Univ Stanford CA 94305

SIEGMAN, FRED STEPHEN, b Brooklyn, NY, Apr 15, 46. BIOCHEMISTRY. *Educ:* Brooklyn Col, BS, 67; Ind Univ, Bloomington, PhD(biochem), 75. *Prof Exp:* ASST BIOCHEMIST, EVANSVILLE CTR MED EDUC, 73-; APPL SPECIALIST, MILLIPORE CORP, 76- & ULTRAFICATION PROD MGR, 81- *Mem:* Parenteral Drug Asn. *Res:* The study of nucleic acid and protein synthesis and its controls in bacteriophage T4-infected E coli; metabolism of rat liver cells in in vitro cell suspensions, specifically the effect of alcohol on metabolism. *Mailing Add:* Evansville Ctr for Med Educ 8600 University Blvd Evansville IN 47732

SIEGMAN, MARION JOYCE, b Brooklyn, NY, Sept 7, 33. PHARMACOLOGY, PHYSIOLOGY. *Educ:* Tulane Univ, BA, 54; State Univ NY, PhD(pharmacol), 66. *Prof Exp:* Teaching asst pharmacol, State Univ NY Downstate Med Ctr, 61-66, res assoc, 66-67; from instr to assoc prof, 67-77, PROF PHYSIOL, JEFFERSON MED COL, 77- *Concurrent Pos:* NIH res grants, 68-84; mem panel regulatory biol, NSF, 78-79; mem physiol study sect, NIH, 79-83. *Mem:* Biophys Soc; Soc Exp Med Biol; Am Physiol Soc; Soc Gen Physiol; Sigma Xi. *Res:* Mechanical properties of smooth muscle; energetics of contraction; excitation-contraction coupling; cation transport and metabolism of uterine smooth muscle; electron microscopy. *Mailing Add:* Dept Physiol Jefferson Med Col Thomas Jefferson Univ Philadelphia PA 19107

SIEGMANN, WILLIAM LEWIS, b Pittsburgh, Pa, Sept 14, 43; m 65; c 6. UNDERWATER ACOUSTICS, GEOPHYSICAL FLUID DYNAMICS. *Educ:* Mass Inst Technol, BS, 64, MS, 67, PhD(appl math), 68. *Prof Exp:* Fel & res assoc mech, Johns Hopkins Univ, 68-70; from asst prof to assoc prof, 70-82, PROF MATH SCI, RENSSELAER POLYTECH INST, 82- *Concurrent Pos:* Prin investr, Off Naval Res, 77- *Mem:* Acoust Soc Am; Soc Indust & Appl Math; Am Phys Soc; Am Meteorol Soc. *Res:* Oceanic sound transmission and reception; geophysical fluid dynamics; asymptotic and numerical methods. *Mailing Add:* Dept Math Sci Rensselaer Polytech Inst Troy NY 12181

SIEGMUND, DAVID O, b St Louis, Mo, Nov 15, 41; m 62; c 2. MATHEMATICAL STATISTICS. *Educ:* Southern Methodist Univ, BA, 63; Columbia Univ, PhD(statist), 66. *Prof Exp:* Asst prof statist, Columbia Univ, 66-67 & Stanford Univ, 67-69; assoc prof statist, Columbia Univ, 69-71, prof, 71-76; PROF STATIST, STANFORD UNIV, 76- *Concurrent Pos:* NSF fel, 71-72; Guggenheim fel, 74-75; Humboldt award, 80-81. *Mem:* Inst Math Statist; Berndulli Soc Math Statist & Probability. *Res:* Probability theory. *Mailing Add:* Dept Statist Stanford Univ Stanford CA 94305

SIEGMUND, OTTO HANNS, b Gross Neudorf, Ger, Aug 25, 20; nat US; m 50. VETERINARY MEDICINE. *Educ:* Mich State Col, DVM, 44. *Prof Exp:* Asst animal path, Univ Ill, 45-46; pharmacologist, Sterling-Winthrop Res Inst, 46-49; pathologist, Chem Corps, US Dept Army, 49-50; lectr vet therapeut, Univ Calif, 50-51; DIR VET PUBL, ANIMAL SCI RES, MERCK, SHARP & DOHME RES LABS, 51- *Mem:* Fel AAAS; Sigma Xi; Am Soc Mammal; Am Vet Med Asn; NY Acad Sci. *Res:* Veterinary pharmaceuticals and literature. *Mailing Add:* Animal Sci Res Labs Merck Sharp & Dohme Rahway NJ 07065

SIEGRIST, JACOB C, b Oella, Md, June 11, 19; m 40. VETERINARY MEDICINE, DAIRY HUSBANDRY. *Educ:* Univ Md, BS, Cornell Univ, DVM, 50. *Prof Exp:* Pvt pract, Md, 50-51 & NJ 52-53; assoc prof vet path, Univ Md, 51-52; staff vet, Div, Schering Corp, 53-56, vet med dir, 56-62; vet dir, Inst Clin Med, Syntex Corp, 62-65, animal dir, Syntex Agribus, Inc, 65-71, vpres, Far East Opers, 71-75, VPRES INT ANIMAL HEALTH, SYNTEX, USA, INC, 75- *Mem:* Am Vet Med Asn; Indust Vet As (pres, 56); US Animal Health Asn; NY Acad Sci. *Res:* Ma control; reproduction physiology; endocrinology; uses of corticoids. *Mailing Add:* 3401 Hillview Ave Palo Alto CA 94304

SIEGWARTH, JAMES DAVID, b Chehalis, Wash, June 22, 34; m 62; c 1. SOLID STATE PHYSICS. *Educ:* Univ Wash, 57, PhD(physics), 66. *Prof Exp:* Reactor physicist, Atomic Energy Div, Phillips Petrol Co, 57-60; res asst physics, Univ Wash, 61-66, sr res assoc ceramic eng, 66-67; PHYSICIST, NAT BUR STANDARDS, 67- *Mem:* Am Phys Soc. *Res:* Behavior of antiferromagnetic materials as a function of temperature using the Mossauer effect. *Mailing Add:* Nat Bur of Standards 325 Broadway Boulder CO 80302

SIEH, DAVID HENRY, b Columbus, Nebr, Aug 21, 47; m 78. PHARMACEUTICAL CHEMISTRY. *Educ:* Unvi Nebr-Lincoln, BA, 69, PhD(chem), 79. *Prof Exp:* Scientist, Frederick Cancer Res Facil, 78-81; RES INVESTR, E R SQUIBB & SONS, INC, 81- *Mem:* Am Chem Soc. *Res:* Trialkyltriazenes, including the carcinogenic and tumor inhibiting properties; develop analytical methods, emphasizing ultraviolet-visible derivative spectrophotometry. *Mailing Add:* 15-08 Deer Creek Dr Plainsboro NJ 08536

SIEH, KERRY EDWARD, b Waterloo, Iowa, Oct 11, 50; m 76; c 2. GEOLOGY. *Educ:* Univ Calif, Riverside, AB, 72; Stanford Univ, PhD(geol), 77. *Prof Exp:* ASST PROF GEOL, CALIF INST TECHNOL, 77- *Honors & Awards:* E B Burwell Jr Mem Award, Geol Soc Am, 80. *Mem:* Am Geophys Union; Geol Soc Am; Seismol Soc Am. *Res:* Historic and prehistoric behavior of the San Andreas fault of California using geomorphologic and stratigraphic methods; neotectonics of southern China, Alaska and western coastal Mexico. *Mailing Add:* Calif Inst Technol Pasadena CA 91125

SIEHR, DONALD JOSEPH, b Milwaukee, Wis, Nov 13, 28; m 56; c 2. BIOCHEMISTRY. *Educ:* Univ Wis, PhD(biochem), 57. *Prof Exp:* Res biochemist, Abbott Labs, 57-61; assoc prof, 61-69, PROF CHEM, UNIV MO-ROLLA, 69- *Concurrent Pos:* NIH sr fel, 68-69. *Mem:* AAAS; Am Chem Soc; Brit Biochem Soc; Mycol Soc Am; Brit Mycol Soc. *Res:* Differentiation in Basidiomycetes; plant growth substances; chemical transformations in biological systems; microbial chemistry and technology. *Mailing Add:* Dept Chem Univ Mo Rolla MO 65401

SIEKANOWICZ, WIESLAW WOJCIECH, electrical engineering, see previous edition

SIEKER, HERBERT OTTO, b Maplewood, Mo, Mar 20, 24; m 48; c 1. MEDICINE. *Educ:* Washington Univ, MD, 48; Am Bd Internal Med, dipl. *Prof Exp:* Intern med, 48-49, asst resident, 49-50, res fel, Sch Med, 50-51, sr asst resident, 53-54, instr & Life Ins Med Res Fund fel, 54-55, assoc, 55-56, from asst prof to assoc prof, 56-60, PROF MED, SCH MED, DUKE UNIV, 61-, CHIEF PULMONARY-ALLERGY DIV, 70- *Concurrent Pos:* Chief pulmonary dis sect, Vet Admin Hosp, 55-56, asst chief med serv, 56-57, consult, 58, Durham & Fayetteville, 59-; consult, US Army Hosp, Ft Bragg, NC, 59- *Mem:* Asn Am Physicians; Soc Exp Biol & Med; Am Thoracic Soc; Am Soc Clin Invest; Am Fedn Clin Res. *Res:* Cardiorespiratory physiology and disease; allergic and immunologic disorders. *Mailing Add:* Pulmonary-Allergy Div Sch of Med PO Box 3822 Durham NC 27710

SIEKER, LARRY CHARLES, b Great Bend, Kans, Feb 22, 31; c 2. PROTEIN CRYSTALLOGRAPHY, BIOCHEMISTRY. *Educ:* Pac Lutheran Univ, BA, 54. *Prof Exp:* Technician biochem, Univ Wash, 59-62 & Univ Calif, San Diego, 62-64; physicist, 64-71, RES ASSOC BIOL STRUCT, UNIV WASH, 71- *Concurrent Pos:* Res assoc, Nat Ctr Sci Res, Marseille, France, 78-79. *Mem:* Am Crystallog Asn. *Res:* Determination of structure and function of biological macromolecules by x-ray crystal analysis. *Mailing Add:* Dept Biol Struct Univ Wash Seattle WA 98195

SIEKERT, ROBERT GEORGE, b Milwaukee, Wis, July 23, 24; m 51; c 3. NEUROLOGY. *Educ:* Northwestern Univ, BS, 45, MS, 47, MD, 48. *Prof Exp:* Instr anat, Sch Med, Univ Pa, 48-49; fel neurol, Mayo Grad Sch Med, 50 & 53-54, from instr to assoc prof, 55-73, PROF NEUROL, MAYO MED SCH, 69-, CONSULT, MAYO CLIN, 54- *Concurrent Pos:* Head A sect neurol, Mayo Clin, 66-76, assoc bd govs, 73-80; mem bd trustees, Mayo Found, 74-81; ed-in-chief, Mayo Clin Proc, 82- *Mem:* AAAS; Am Neurol Asn; AMA; fel Am Acad Neurol. *Res:* Cerebrovascular disease; descriptions of transient ischemic episodes and investigation of therapeutic programs. *Mailing Add:* Dept of Neurol Mayo Clin 200 First Ave SW Rochester MN 55901

SIEKEVITZ, PHILIP, b Philadelphia, Pa, Feb 25, 18; m 49; c 2. BIOCHEMISTRY. *Educ:* Philadelphia Col Pharm, BS, 42; Univ Calif, PhD(biochem), 49. *Prof Exp:* USPHS res fel biochem, Harvard Univ, 49-51; fel oncol, Univ Wis, 51-54; asst, 54-59, assoc prof, 59-66, PROF BIOCHEM, ROCKEFELLER UNIV, 66- *Mem:* Nat Acad Sci; Am Soc Biol Chemists; Am Soc Cell Biol (pres, 66-67). *Res:* Protein synthesis; oxidative phosphorylation; cytochemistry. *Mailing Add:* Rockefeller Univ New York Ave & 66th St New York NY 10021

SIELKEN, ROBERT LEWIS, JR, b Little Rock, Ark, July 10, 44; m 68. MATHEMATICAL STATISTICS, OPERATIONS RESEARCH. *Educ:* DePauw Univ, BA, 66; Fla State Univ, MS, 68, PhD(statist), 71. *Prof Exp:* Asst prof, 71-76, ASSOC PROF STATIST, TEX A&M UNIV, 76- *Mem:* Inst Math Statist; Am Statist Asn; Biomet Soc; Opers Res Soc Am; Math Prog Soc. *Res:* Optimization theory; risk estimation; mathematical programming; stochastic approximation methods. *Mailing Add:* Inst of Statist Tex A&M Univ College Station TX 77843

SIEM, ROBERT ARTHUR, b Clark, SDak, Jan 2, 24. MICROBIOLOGY. *Educ:* Univ Minn, BA, 46, MS, 49; Univ Colo, PhD(microbiol, biochem), 55. *Prof Exp:* Microbiologist, Rocky Mountain Spotted Fever Labs, USPHS, 49-50; virologist, Upjohn Co, Mich, 50-52; asst res microbiologist, Univ Calif, Los Angeles, 56-60; virologist, Commun Dis Ctr, USPHS, Ariz, 60-65 & Int Ctr Med Res & Training, San Jose, Costa Rica, 65-66; VIROLOGIST, MINN STATE DEPT HEALTH, 67- *Mem:* Am Soc Microbiol; Sigma Xi. *Res:* Virology; biochemistry; biophysics. *Mailing Add:* Minn State Dept of Health 717 Delaware St SE Minneapolis MN 55440

SIEMANKOWSKI, FRANCIS THEODORE, b Buffalo, NY, Nov 12, 14; m 42; c 2. GEOLOGY, SCIENCE EDUCATION. *Educ:* State Col Teachers, BS, 39; Univ Buffalo, MEd, 50; State Univ NY Buffalo, EdD(sci educ), 70. *Prof Exp:* Teacher pub schs, NY, 39-41 & 45-49, prin & adult educ dir, 49-51, teacher, 51-54; assoc prof phys sci, 64-71, PROF GEOSCI & SCI EDUC, STATE UNIV NY BUFFALO, 71- *Concurrent Pos:* Consult, Teacher Corps, Peace Corps Spec Prog, Afghanistan, 71-74. *Mem:* AAAS; Nat Asn Geol Teachers; Geol Soc Am; Nat Asn Res Sci Teaching; Nat Sci Teachers Asn. *Res:* Individualizing the teaching of science in geology and other physical sciences. *Mailing Add:* Dept of Phys/Geosci/Interdisc Sci State Univ of NY Col at Buffalo Buffalo NY 14222

SIEMANKOWSKI, RAYMOND FRANCIS, b Buffalo, NY, Feb 18, 45; m 65; c 1. BIOPHYSICS, BIOCHEMISTRY. *Educ:* State Univ NY Buffalo, BA, 66, MA, 71, PhD(biol), 72. *Prof Exp:* Fel biophys & med, State Univ NY Downstate Med Ctr, 72-77, instr med, 77-79; res assoc nutrit & food sci, 79-81, RES ASST PROF BIOCHEM, UNIV ARIZ, 81- *Mem:* Biophys Soc; Harvey Soc; AAAS. *Res:* Molecular mechanisms involved in muscle contraction and cell motility ave investigated using structural and enzymological approaches of purified and reconstituted contractile proteins. *Mailing Add:* Dept Biochem Biosci West Bldg Univ Ariz Tucson AZ 85721

SIEMANN, DIETMAR W, b Hanover, WGer, Jan 11, 50; Can citizen; m 72. CANCER RESEARCH, MEDICAL BIOPHYSICS. *Educ:* Univ Man, BSc, 72; Univ Toronto, MSc, 75, PhD(med biophysics), 77. *Prof Exp:* Res assoc, 77-78, sr instr, 78-79, ASST PROF RADIATION ONCOL RADIOL, CANCER CTR, SCH MED & DENT, UNIV ROCHESTER, 80-, ASST PROF RADIATION BIOL & BIOPHYSICS, 81- *Concurrent Pos:* Travel grants, Radiation Res Soc, 77 & 79; co-prin investr grant, NIH, 82- *Mem:* Radiation Res Soc. *Res:* Response to antitumor agents assessed in cell cultures, multicell spheroids and in solid tumors and normal tissue in the laboratory as models for clinical cancer therapy; multi-modality therapies with chemotherapeutic agents, radiation, sensitizers and protectors. *Mailing Add:* Exp Therapeut Div Cancer Ctr Box 704 Univ Rochester 601 E Elmwood Ave Rochester NY 14642

SIEMANN, ROBERT HERMAN, b Englewood, NJ, Dec 3, 42; m 64; c 4. HIGH ENERGY PHYSICS. *Educ:* Brown Univ, ScB, 64; Cornell Univ, PhD(physics), 69. *Prof Exp:* Res assoc, Stanford Linear Accelerator Ctr, 69-72; assoc physicist, Brookhaven Nat Lab, 72-73; asst prof, 73-78, ASSOC PROF PHYSICS, CORNELL UNIV, 78- *Mem:* AAAS; Am Physical Soc. *Res:* Electron-positron colliding beam physics; accelerator design and construction; electron scattering; photoproduction. *Mailing Add:* Lab of Nuclear Studies Cornell Univ Ithaca NY 14853

SIEMENS, ALBERT JOHN, b Winnipeg, Man, Dec 7, 43; m 65; c 2. PHARMACOLOGY. *Educ:* Univ Man, BSc, 66, MSc, 69; Univ Toronto, PhD(pharmacol), 73. *Prof Exp:* sr res scientist alcoholism & drug abuse, Res Inst Alcoholism, NY State Dept Ment Hyg, 73-80; ASST DIR, NEW DRUG DEVELOP, PFIZER, INC, 80- *Concurrent Pos:* Adj asst prof biochem pharmacol, Sch Pharm, State Univ NY Buffalo, 74- *Mem:* Can Pharmaceut Asn; Res Soc Alcoholism; NY Acad Sci; Am Soc Pharmacol & Exp Therapeut. *Res:* Drug metabolism; drug interactions; pharmacology of marihuana; biochemical pharmacology of drug tolerance, dependence and addiction; alcoholism. *Mailing Add:* 235 E 42nd St New York NY 10017

SIEMENS, JOHN CORNELIUS, b Shafter, Calif, Feb 22, 34; m 61; c 3. AGRICULTURAL ENGINEERING. *Educ:* Univ Calif, BS, 57; Univ Ill, MS, 58, PhD(soil mech), 63. *Prof Exp:* Instr agr eng, Univ Ill, 58-63; asst prof, Cornell Univ, 63-68; assoc prof, 68-76, PROF AGR ENG, UNIV ILL, URBANA, 76- *Mem:* Am Soc Agr Engrs. *Res:* Power and machinery area of agricultural engineering. *Mailing Add:* Dept Agr Eng Univ Ill Urbana IL 61801

SIEMENS, PHILIP JOHN, b Elgin, Ill, Nov 13, 43. NUCLEAR PHYSICS. *Educ:* Mass Inst Technol, BSc, 65; Cornell Univ, PhD(physics), 70. *Prof Exp:* Actg Amanuensis, Niels Bohr Inst, 70-71; NATO fel, Univ Copenhagen, 71-72, univ fel, 72-73, lectr, 74-81; PROF PHYSICS, TEX A&M UNIV, 80- *Concurrent Pos:* Vis assoc prof, Univ Ill, 77; vis scientist, Lawrence Bekeley Lab, Univ Calif, 78-79. *Mem:* Am Phys Soc. *Res:* Theoretical nuclear and many-body physics. *Mailing Add:* Physics Dept Tex A&M Univ College Station TX 77843

SIEMER, EUGENE GLEN, b Cincinnati, Ohio, Jan 3, 26; m 49; c 3. PLANT MORPHOLOGY, AGRONOMY. *Educ:* Colo State Univ, BS, 50, MS, 61; Univ Ill, PhD(plant morphol), 64. *Prof Exp:* From instr to asst prof, 54-58, assoc prof, 64-77, PROF AGRON & SUPT MOUNTAIN MEADOW RES CTR, COLO STATE UNIV, 77- *Concurrent Pos:* Asst scientist, Univ Tenn-AEC Agr Res Lab, 68-69. *Mem:* Am Soc Agron; Am Forage & Grassland Coun; Sigma Xi; Crop Sci Soc Am. *Res:* Mountain meadow forage production and utilization; root vascular anatomy; progressive morphological development of maize, small grains, forage grasses and legumes; water management; climatology; information retrieval; radiobotany. *Mailing Add:* Colo Agr Exp Sta PO Box 598 Gunnison CO 81230

SIEMERS, CHARLES T, b Lodi, Calif, Aug 30, 44. GEOLOGY, OCEANOGRAPHY. *Educ:* Ore State Univ, BS, 66; Ind Univ, AM, 68, PhD(geol), 71. *Prof Exp:* Asst prof geol, Ind Univ, NW Campus, 70-71; asst prof, Univ NMex, 71-75; RES GEOLOGIST SEDIMENTOL, RES CTR, CITIES SERV CO, 75- *Concurrent Pos:* Ed, Trace Fossil Newsletter, 73-77. *Honors & Awards:* A I Levorsen Award, Am Asn Petrol Geologists, 78. *Mem:* Soc Econ Paleontologists & Mineralogists; Am Asn Petrol Geologists; Geol Soc Am; Sigma Xi. *Res:* Sedimentology; stratigraphy; sedimentary petrology; paleoecology and interpretation of depositional paleoenvironments. *Mailing Add:* Res Ctr Box 50408 Tulsa OK 74150

SIEMS, NORMAN EDWARD, b St Louis, Mo, Feb 28, 44; m 66; c 2. NUCLEAR SCIENCE. *Educ:* Rensselaer Polytechnic Inst, BS, 66; Johns Hopkins Univ, MS, 70; Cornell Univ, PhD(nuclear sci), 76. *Prof Exp:* Instr math, physics & reactor prin, US Naval Nuclear Power Sch, Bainbridge, Md, 66-70; instr, Quincy Col, 73-75, asst prof physics, 75-80, chmn dept, 77-80; asst prof, 80-81, ASSOC PROF PHYSICS, JUNIATA COL, 81- *Mem:* Am Asn Physics Teachers. *Res:* Investigation of the low-lying first excited state of Silver-110. *Mailing Add:* Dept Physics Juniata Col Huntingdon PA 16652

SIEMS, PETER LAURENCE, b London, Eng, Jan 26, 32; m 57; c 4. GEOLOGY. *Educ:* Univ London, BSc, 57; Colo Sch Mines, DSc(geol), 67. *Prof Exp:* Geologist, Anglo Am Corp S Africa, 57-61; from asst prof to assoc prof, 65-72, PROF GEOL, UNIV IDAHO, 72- *Concurrent Pos:* Vis prof, Fed Univ Bahia, Brazil, 70-71. *Mem:* Soc Econ Geol; Asn Explor Geochem; Am Inst Mining, Metall & Petrol Eng; Brit Inst Mining & Metall; Geol Soc Am. *Res:* Origin of mineral deposits; geochemical exploration for mineral deposits. *Mailing Add:* Dept of Geol Univ of Idaho Moscow ID 83843

SIEMSEN, JAN KARL, b Duisburg, Ger, May 24, 24; US citizen; m 55; c 4. NUCLEAR & INTERNAL MEDICINE. *Educ:* Univ Duesseldorf, MD, 48, Univ Basel, MD, 50; Am Bd Internal Med, dipl, 63; Am Bd Nuclear Med, dipl, 72. *Prof Exp:* Resident physician, Univ Basel, 50-52; med dir pulmonary dis, Park Sanitorium, Arosa, Switz, 52-54; resident physician, Laurel Heights Hosp, Shelton, Conn, 55-57; intern physician, Virginia Mason Hosp, Seattle, 59-60; resident physician, Vet Admin Hosp, Long Beach, Calif, 60-61, asst chief med & radioisotope serv, 62-65; assoc prof radiol & med, Sch Med, 65-75, assoc prof biomed chem, Sch Pharm, 68-75, PROF RADIOL & MED, SCH MED, UNIV SOUTHERN CALIF, 75- PROF BIOMED CHEM, SCH PHARM, 75-; DIR DEPT NUCLEAR MED, LOS ANGELES COUNTY-UNIV SOUTHERN CALIF MED CTR, 65- *Concurrent Pos:* Consult nuclear med, Vet Admin Hosp Long Beach, US Naval Hosp, Long Beach, Orthopaedic Hosp, Los Angeles & Intercommunity Hosp, Covina, 65- *Mem:* Fel Am Col Physicians; Am Col Nuclear Physicians; Asn Univ Radiologists; European Soc Nuclear Med; Radiol Soc NAm. *Res:* Development and evaluation of radiopharmaceuticals in medicine; in vivo kinetics studies of metabolic processes; modalities of radiotherapy with internally administered radionuclides; radiopharmacokinetics; image processing. *Mailing Add:* Dept of Nuclear Med LAC-USC Med Ctr Los Angeles CA 90033

SIENIEWICZ, DAVID JAMES, b Halifax, NS, Nov 15, 24; m 54; c 3. RADIOLOGY. *Educ:* Univ NB, BA, 45; Dalhousie Univ, MD, CM, 50; Royal Col Physicians & Surgeons Can, cert specialist diag & therapeut radiol, 54; Am Bd Radiol, dipl, 54. *Prof Exp:* Asst radiologist, Montreal Gen Hosp, 55-56, assoc radiologist, 56-58, radiologist-in-chief, 58-68, sr radiologist, 68-71; RADIOLOGIST, ST MICHAEL'S HOSP, TORONTO, 71-; ASSOC PROF, DEPT RADIOL, UNIV TORONTO, 71- *Concurrent Pos:* From asst prof to assoc prof radiol, McGill Univ, 55-71; vis fel, Stockholm, 68-69; consult staff, Montreal Gen Hosp, 71-; gov & mem bd gov, Toronto Inst Med Technol, 77-; chancellor, Am Col Radiol, 79- *Mem:* Fel Am Col Radiol; Am Roentgen Ray Soc; Can Med Asn; Can Asn Radiologists (hon secy-treas, 63-65, pres, 75-76); Asn Univ Radiologists. *Res:* Diagnostic and therapeutic radiology. *Mailing Add:* Dept Radiol St Michael's Hosp 37 Glenview Ave Toronto ON M4R 1P5 Can

SIENKO, MICHELL JOSEPH, b Bloomfield, NJ, May 15, 23; m 46; c 1. PHYSICAL INORGANIC CHEMISTRY. *Educ:* Cornell Univ, AB, 43; Univ Calif, PhD(phys chem), 46. *Prof Exp:* Asst chem, Cornell Univ, 42-43; asst, Univ Calif, 44-46, instr, 46; res assoc, Off Naval Res, Stanford Univ, 46-47; from instr to assoc prof, 47-59, PROF CHEM, CORNELL UNIV, 59- *Concurrent Pos:* Fulbright lectr, Univ Toulouse, 56-57; vis prof, Am Col, Paris, 63-64; Guggenheim fel, Univ Grenoble, 70-71; guest prof, Inst Phys Chem, Univ Vienna, 74-75; vis fel, Cambridge Univ, 78-79. *Mem:* Am Chem Soc; Am Phys Soc. *Res:* Solid state magnetism; liquid ammonia; catalysis; photoelectrodes. *Mailing Add:* Dept of Chem Cornell Univ Ithaca NY 14853

SIERAKOWSKI, ROBERT L, b Vernon, Conn, Apr 11, 37; m 75; c 2. ENGINEERING MECHANICS, MATERIALS SCIENCE. *Educ:* Brown Univ, BSc, 58; Yale Univ, MS, 60, PhD(eng mech), 64. *Prof Exp:* Sr engr mech, Sikorsky Aircraft Div, United Technol Corp, 58-60; res asst, Yale Univ, 60-63; sr res scientist, United Technol Res Labs, 63-67; PROF ENG SCI, UNIV FLA, 67- *Concurrent Pos:* Adj asst prof eng mech, Rensselaer Polytech Inst, 64-67; Nat Res Coun fel, 72-73. *Mem:* Am Soc Mech Engrs; Am Inst Aeronaut & Astronaut; Soc Exp Stress Anal; Soc Advan Mat & Processing Eng; Am Soc Eng Educ. *Res:* Advanced structural composites; structural vibrations; biomechanics. *Mailing Add:* Univ Fla Gainesville FL 32611

SIEREN, DAVID JOSEPH, b Ashland, Wis, May 10, 41; m 72. TAXONOMIC BOTANY. *Educ:* Northland Col, AB, 63; Univ Ill, Urbana, MS, 65, PhD(bot), 70. *Prof Exp:* Asst prof, 69-74, chmn dept, 73-78, ASSOC PROF BIOL, UNIV NC, WILMINGTON, 74-, DIR HERBARIUM, 69- *Mem:* Am Soc Plant Taxonomists. *Res:* Taxonomy of Bryophytes and vascular plants. *Mailing Add:* Dept of Biol Univ of NC Wilmington NC 28403

SIERK, ARNOLD JOHN, b Batavia, NY, Nov 10, 46; m 68; c 3. NUCLEAR PHYSICS. *Educ:* Cornell Univ, BS, 68; Calif Inst Technol, PhD(nuclear physics), 73. *Prof Exp:* Fel theoret nuclear physics, Los Alamos Sci Lab, Univ Calif, 72-74; asst prof nuclear physics, Calif Inst Technol, 74-77; STAFF MEM, THEORET DIV, LOS ALAMOS NAT LAB, 77- *Concurrent Pos:* Vis staff mem, Los Alamos Sci Lab, Univ Calif, 74-77; fel, Alfred P Sloan Found, 75-77. *Mem:* Am Phys Soc; Sigma Xi. *Res:* Models of fission and heavy-ion fusion reactions; low-energy light-particle reactions; heavy-ion accelerators. *Mailing Add:* T-9 MS452 Los Alamos Nat Lab Los Alamos NM 87545

SIERS, DAVID GARD, b Parkersburg, WVa, Sept 17, 41; m 62; c 3. POPULATION GENETICS. *Educ:* Ohio State Univ, BSc, 63; Iowa State Univ, MSc, 66, PhD(animal breeding), 68. *Prof Exp:* Instr animal sci, Iowa State Univ, 67-68; fel, Res Inst, Ohio State Univ, 68-69; asst prof, Iowa State Univ, 69-73; LEADER GROWTH PROD DEVELOP, BIOL SCI RES, SHELL DEVELOP CO, 73- *Mem:* Am Soc Animal Sci. *Res:* Drug development, efficacy and safety testing of potential animal growth promotants; intracellular physiology and genetic control of protein synthesis and energy production; efficiency of protein production in domestic animals. *Mailing Add:* Shell Develop Co Stoddard Rd Modesto CA 95350

SIERVOGEL, ROGER M, b Phoenix, Ariz, Dec 17, 44; m 64; c 2. HUMAN GENETICS, CARDIOVASCULAR DISEASE. *Educ:* Ariz State Univ, BS, 67, MS, 68; Univ Ore, PhD(genetics), 71. *Prof Exp:* NIH fel human genetics, Sch Pub Health, Univ NC, 71-73, vis asst prof, Dept Biostatist, 73-74; res scientist human genetics, Fels Res Inst, 74-77, fels asst prof, 77-78, FELS ASSOC PROF PEDIAT, SCH MED, WRIGHT STATE UNIV, 79-, SR SCIENTIST HUMAN GENETICS, FELS RES INST, 78- *Concurrent Pos:* Prin investr grants, Nat Heart, Lung & Blood Inst, 76-77, 77-79 & 79-82, Am Heart Asn, Miami Valley Chap, 77-78 & 78-79; mem, High Blood Pressure Res Coun & Epidemiol Couns, Am Heart Asn. *Mem:* Am Soc Human Genetics; Am Heart Asn; Am Dermatoglyphics Asn; fel Human Biol Coun (secy-treas, 80). *Res:* Genetics of multifactorial traits, major gene effects, and genetic linkage in humans, especially quantitative traits related to hypertension, body composition and growth. *Mailing Add:* Dept of Pediat Fels Res Inst Wright State Univ Sch of Med Yellow Springs OH 45387

SIESHOLTZ, HERBERT WILLIAM, b Newark, NJ, June 21, 15; m 43; c 4. INDUSTRIAL CHEMISTRY. *Educ:* Cooper Union Inst Technol, BS, 38. *Prof Exp:* Chemist pigments, Witco Chem Co, NY, 38-39; inspector ammunitions & explosives, Picatinny Arsenal, NJ, 39-40; chemist, Witco Chem Co, 40-41 & 45-48; coatings chemist, Aberdeen Proving Ground, Md, 48-52; tech dir, Crown Paint Co, 53-76; DIR, FLAMINGO RES LABS, 76- *Mem:* Fedn Coatings Technol; Am Chem Soc. *Res:* Formulation of paints and lacquers; corrosion prevention through organic coatings and metal treatments; metal cleaners; pigment properties; specialty coatings. *Mailing Add:* Flamingo Res Labs 2619 SW 37th Ave Miami FL 33133

SIESS, CHESTER P(AUL), b Alexandria, La, July 28, 16; m 41; c 1. STRUCTURAL ENGINEERING. *Educ:* La State Univ, BS, 36; Univ Ill, MS, 39, PhD(struct eng), 48. *Prof Exp:* With State Hwy Dept, La, 36-37; asst, Univ Ill, 37-39; testing engr, Dept Subways, Chicago, 39-41; engr, NY Cent Rwy, Ill, 41; spec res assoc struct eng, 41-45, from res asst prof to res assoc prof, 45-55, prof, 55-78, head dept civil eng, 73-78, EMER PROF CIVIL ENG, UNIV ILL, URBANA, 78- *Concurrent Pos:* Mem adv comn reactor safeguards, Nuclear Regulatory Comn, 68-, chmn, 72. *Honors & Awards:* Wason Medal, Am Concrete Inst, 49, Turner Medal, 64; Award, Concrete Reinforcing Steel Inst, 56; Huber Award, Am Soc Civil Engrs, 56, Howard Award, 68, Reese Award, 70. *Mem:* Nat Acad Eng; hom mem Am Soc Civil Engrs; Int Asn Bridge & Struct Engrs; hon mem Am Concrete Inst (pres, 73-74). *Res:* Reinforced and prestressed concrete. *Mailing Add:* 3110 Newmark Lab Univ Ill 208 N Romine Urbana IL 61801

SIEVEKING, WILLIAM EARL, agronomy, plant breeding, see previous edition

SIEVER, RAYMOND, b Chicago, Ill, Sept 14, 23; m 45; c 2. SEDIMENTARY PETROLOGY, GEOCHEMISTRY. *Educ:* Univ Chicago, BS, 43, MS, 47, PhD(geol), 50. *Hon Degrees:* MA, Harvard Univ, 60. *Prof Exp:* Asst, Ill Geol Surv, 43-44, from asst geologist to geologist, 47-57; NSF sr fel & res assoc, 56-57, from asst prof to assoc prof, 57-65, chmn dept geol sci, 68-71 & 76-81, PROF GEOL, HARVARD UNIV, 65- *Concurrent Pos:* Res assoc, Oceanog Inst, Woods Hole, Mass, 57-70; vis scholar, Scripps Inst Oceanog, 81-82; Guggenheim fel, 81-82; fel, Japan Soc Prom Sci, Univ Tokyo, 81. *Honors & Awards:* Am Asn Petrol Geologists Award, 52; Soc Econ Paleont & Mineral Award, 59. *Mem:* Fel Am Acad Arts & Sci; fel Geol Soc Am; Soc Econ Paleont & Mineral; Geochem Soc; Am Geophys Union. *Res:* Stratigraphy and sedimentation; origin of coal; silica in sediments; cementation of sandstones; marine sediments; plate tectonics and sediment formation; evolution of atmosphere and oceans. *Mailing Add:* Hoffman Lab Harvard Univ Cambridge MA 02138

SIEVERS, ALBERT JOHN, III, b Oakland, Calif, June 28, 33; m 59; c 4. SOLID STATE PHYSICS. *Educ:* Univ Calif, Berkeley, AB, 58, PhD(physics), 62. *Prof Exp:* Model maker microwave tubes, Varian Assocs, 51-54; res asst solid state physics, Univ Calif, Berkeley, 59-62; res assoc, 62-63, from instr to assoc prof, 63-71, PROF SOLID STATE PHYSICS, CORNELL UNIV, 71- *Concurrent Pos:* Consult, Lockheed Res & Develop, 66-67, Los Alamos Sci Lab, 68-69 & 78-, Nat Acad Sci, 75 & Gen Motors Corp, 78- mem, Mat Res Coun, Advan Res Projs Agency, 69-; Erskine fel, Univ Canterbury, NZ, 75; vis scientist, IBM, 81- *Mem:* Fel Am Phys Soc; Optical Soc Am. *Res:* Infrared spectroscopy of condensed matter in both time and frequency domain; surfaces superconductivity; semi-metals; semiconductors; lattice vibrations; far infrared spectroscopy of biological molecules; impurity modes; interfaces; selective surfaces. *Mailing Add:* 518 Clark Hall Dept of Physics Cornell Univ Ithaca NY 14850

SIEVERS, DENNIS MORLINE, b Fremont, Nebr, June 15, 44; m 64; c 1. ENVIRONMENTAL ENGINEERING, AGRICULTURAL ENGINEERING. *Educ:* Univ Nebr, BS, 67; Univ Mo-Columbia, MS, 69, PhD(sanit eng), 71. *Prof Exp:* Res asst agr eng, 67-69, Environ Protection Agency fel, 69-71, asst prof, 72-79, ASSOC PROF AGR ENG, UNIV MO-COLUMBIA, 79- *Mem:* Am Soc Agr Engrs; Water Pollution Control Fedn; Sigma Xi. *Res:* Water quality; aquatic ecology; waste treatment for agriculture. *Mailing Add:* Dept of Agr Eng Univ of Mo Columbia MO 65211

SIEVERS, GERALD LESTER, b Winona, Minn, July 15, 40; m 67. MATHEMATICAL STATISTICS. *Educ:* St Mary's Col, Minn, BA, 62; Univ Iowa, MS & PhD(statist), 67. *Prof Exp:* Assoc prof, 67-77, PROF MATH, WESTERN MICH UNIV, 77- *Mem:* Inst Math Statist; Am Statist Asn. *Res:* Nonparametric statistics; exact bahadur efficiency. *Mailing Add:* Dept of Math Western Mich Univ Kalamazoo MI 49008

SIEVERS, ROBERT EUGENE, b Anthony, Kans, Mar 28, 35; m 61; c 2. ANALYTICAL CHEMISTRY, INORGANIC CHEMISTRY. *Educ:* Univ Tulsa, BChem, 56; Univ Ill, MS, 58, PhD(inorg chem), 60. *Prof Exp:* Res chemist, Monsanto Chem Co, Mo, 60; res chemist, Aerospace Res Labs, Wright-Patterson AFB, 60-63, group leader anal & inorg chem, 63-69, sr scientist & dir inorg & anal chem, 69-75; PROF CHEM & CHMN DEPT, UNIV COLO, BOULDER, 75- *Concurrent Pos:* Vis prof, Univ Tubingen, 68-69; adj prof, Wright State Univ, 69-75. *Honors & Awards:* Res & Develop Award, US Air Force, 62, Tech Achievement Award, 71. *Mem:* Am Chem Soc; Royal Soc Chem; Soc Environ Geochem & Health. *Res:* Trace analysis, environmental analytical chemistry; chromatography, highly volatile and soluble metal chelates, lanthanide Nuclear Magnetic Resonance shift reagents; inorganic stereochemistry, gas chromatography and mass spectrometry of metal chelates; fuel additives; trace analysis of anions. *Mailing Add:* Dept of Chem Univ of Colo Boulder CO 80309

SIEVERS, SALLY RIEDEL, b Butte, Mont, Dec 23, 41. MATHEMATICAL STATISTICS. *Educ:* Stanford Univ, BS, 63; Cornell Univ, PhD(math), 72. *Prof Exp:* Res assoc social psychol, Cornell Univ, 68-69; instr math, Ithaca Col, 69-72; res assoc math statist, Cornell Univ, 72-73, lectr math, 72-74; LECTR MATH, WELLS COL, 77- *Concurrent Pos:* Statist consult, Environ Protection Agency & Energy Dept Studies, Tech Empirics Corp, 78- *Mem:* Inst Math Statist; Am Math Soc; Am Statist Asn. *Res:* Theory of Ranking procedures; applied statistics. *Mailing Add:* 406 Cayuga Heights Rd Ithaca NY 14850

SIEVERT, CARL FRANK, b Blue Island, Ill, Oct 25, 20; m 43; c 3. CHEMISTRY. *Educ:* Capital Univ, BS, 42; Univ Ill, PhD(biochem), 47. *Prof Exp:* Asst chem, Univ Ill, 42-44 & 46-47; from asst to assoc prof, Franklin & Marshall Col, 47-57; prof & head dept, Catawba Col, 57-59; PROF CHEM, CAPITAL UNIV, 59-, CHMN DEPT, 63- *Concurrent Pos:* With Armstrong Cork Co, Pa, 48. *Mem:* AAAS; Am Chem Soc. *Res:* Fatty acid metabolism; omega oxidation of fatty acids. *Mailing Add:* Dept of Chem Capital Univ Columbus OH 43209

SIEVERT, HERMAN WILLIAM, b Aurora, Ill, Sept 19, 28; m 53; c 2. BIOCHEMISTRY. *Educ:* NCent Col, Ill, BA, 50; Univ Wis, MS, 52, PhD(biochem), 58. *Prof Exp:* Biochemist, 58-70, head dept molecular biol, 70-74, mgr planning & admin, 74-77, MGR RES QUAL ASSURANCE, PHARM PROD, ABBOTT LABS, 77- *Mem:* AAAS; Am Chem Soc. *Mailing Add:* Dept 44F Abbott Labs North Chicago IL 60064

SIEVERT, RICHARD CARL, b Brooklyn, NY, Nov 27, 37; m 59; c 3. PLANT PATHOLOGY. *Educ:* Cornell Univ, BS, 58; Univ Wis, PhD(plant path), 63. *Prof Exp:* Plant pathologist, US Army Biol Labs, 63-65; res plant pathologist, USDA, 65-78. *Concurrent Pos:* Asst prof agr biol, Univ Tenn, 65-74 & plant path, NC State Univ, 74-78. *Mem:* AAAS; Am Phytopath Soc; Am Inst Biol Sci; Sigma Xi. *Res:* Tobacco diseases; virology; nutrition of microorganisms; soil microbiology. *Mailing Add:* 102 Tranquil Circle Oxford NC 27565

SIEWERT, CHARLES EDWARD, b Richmond, Va, Oct 20, 37. NUCLEAR ENGINEERING, ASTROPHYSICS. *Educ:* NC State Univ, BS, 60, MS, 62; Univ Mich, PhD(nuclear eng), 65. *Prof Exp:* Teaching asst physics, NC State Univ, 60-62 & Mid East Tech Univ, Ankara, 64-65; asst prof nuclear eng, 65-69, ASSOC PROF NUCLEAR ENG, NC STATE UNIV, 69- *Mem:* Am Nuclear Soc; Am Phys Soc. *Res:* Neutron transport theory and radiative transfer. *Mailing Add:* Dept of Nuclear Eng NC State Univ Raleigh NC 27607

SIEWIOREK, DANIEL PAUL, b Cleveland, Ohio, June 2, 46; m 72; c 1. ELECTRICAL ENGINEERING, COMPUTER SCIENCE. *Educ:* Univ Mich, BSEE, 68; Stanford Univ, MSEE, 69, PhD(elec eng), 72. *Prof Exp:* assoc prof, 72-80, PROF ELEC ENG & COMPUT SCI, CARNEGIE-MELLON UNIV, 80- *Concurrent Pos:* Consult engr, Digital Equip Corp, 72-; assoc ed, Comput Systs, Asn Comput Mach, 72-78; mem bd dirs, Spec Interest Group Comput Archit, 75-79; consult, Naval Res Lab, 75-77, Res Triangle Inst, 78- & United Technol, 78- *Mem:* Fel Inst Elec & Electronics Engrs; Asn Comput Mach. *Res:* Computer architecture; multiprocessors; reliability; fault tolerant computing; design automation. *Mailing Add:* Dept of Comput Sci & Elec Eng Carnegie-Mellon Univ Pittsburgh PA 15213

SIFFERMAN, THOMAS RAYMOND, b Chicago, Ill, July 28, 41; m 68; c 3. FLUID MECHANICS, RHEOLOGY. *Educ:* Marquette Univ, BME, 64; Purdue Univ, MSME, 66, PhD(fluid mech), 70. *Prof Exp:* Co-op student, Allis-Chalmers, 61-64; res & teaching asst, Purdue Univ, 68-70; SR RES SCIENTIST FLUID FLOW, RES & DEVELOP, CONOCO, INC, 70- *Concurrent Pos:* Vis assoc prof petrol eng, Univ Tulsa, 81- *Mem:* Soc Petrol Engrs; Soc Rheology; Am Soc Mech Engrs; Sigma Xi. *Res:* Rheology of non-Newtonian fluids including fracturing fluids, heavy and waxy crudes, drilling muds, and sand control. *Mailing Add:* 1308 Cookson Dr Ponca City OK 74601

SIFFERT, ROBERT S, b NY, June 16, 18; m 41; c 2. ORTHOPEDIC SURGERY. *Educ:* NY Univ, BA, 39, MD, 43. *Prof Exp:* PROF ORTHOP & CHMN DEPT, MT SINAI SCH MED, 66- *Concurrent Pos:* Dir dept orthop, Mt Sinai Hosp, 60- & City Hosp at Elmhurst, 63-; mem bd, Care-Medico, 72. *Mem:* Am Orthop Asn; Am Acad Orthop Surg; Asn Bone & Joint Surg; Am Col Sugeons; NY Acad Med. *Res:* Clinical and laboratory research in problems relating to growth and deformity; community research. *Mailing Add:* Dept of Orthop Mt Sinai Sch of Med New York NY 10029

SIFFORD, BRUCE M, communications engineering, see previous edition

SIFFORD, DEWEY H, b La Grange, Ark, Sept 9, 30; m 58; c 6. ORGANIC CHEMISTRY. *Educ:* Ark State Univ, BS, 52; Univ Okla, PhD(org chem), 62. *Prof Exp:* From asst prof to assoc prof, 61-65, actg chmn div, 68-69, PROF CHEM, ARK STATE UNIV, 65- CHMN DIV PHYS SCI, 70-, ACTG DEAN, COL SCI, 80- *Mem:* Sigma Xi; Am Chem Soc. *Res:* Terpenes; venoms. *Mailing Add:* Div of Phys Sci Ark State Univ State University AR 72467

SIFNEOS, PETER E, b Greece, Oct 22, 20; nat US; div; c 3. MEDICINE. *Educ:* Sorbonne, cert, 40; Harvard Univ, MD, 46. *Prof Exp:* Teaching fel psychiat, Harvard Univ, 52-53, res fel ment health, 53-54, asst psychiat, 54-55, instr, 55-58, assoc, 58-64, asst prof, 64-68; assoc clin prof, 68-71, assoc prof, 71-74, PROF PSYCHIAT, HARVARD MED SCH, 74-; ASSOC DIR PSYCHIAT DEPT, BETH ISRAEL HOSP, 68- *Concurrent Pos:* Asst, Mass Gen Hosp, 53-55; from asst psychiatrist to assoc psychiatrist, 55-64, psychiatrist, 64-, dir inpatient & outpatient psychiat serv, 65-68; vis prof, Med Sch, Univ Oslo, 71-; ed-in-chief, Psychother & Psychososm, 75-; vpres, Int Fedn Med Psychother, 73-; vis prof psychiat, McGill Univ, 75-79. *Mem:* AAAS; AMA; Am Psychiat Asn; Am Psychosom Soc; Royal Soc Med. *Res:* Psychophysiological correlations of psychosomatic symptoms; neurophysiological, neurochemical and psychological correlations of emotions; manipulative suicide attempts; short-term dynamic psychotherapy; teaching of psychiatry. *Mailing Add:* Beth Israel Hosp Psychiat Serv 330 Brookline Ave Boston MA 02115

SIFNIADES, STYLIANOS, b Piraeus, Greece, Dec 22, 35; US citizen; m 80; c 2. PHYSICAL CHEMISTRY, ORGANIC CHEMISTRY. *Educ:* Univ Athens, Dipl, 57; Univ BC, MSc, 62, PhD(chem), 65. *Prof Exp:* Sr res chemist, 65-67, res group leader, 67-71, res assoc, 71-76, res tech supvr, 76-80, RES SCIENTIST RES & DEVELOP, ALLIED CORP, 80- *Mem:* Am Chem Soc. *Res:* kinetic methods of optical resolution and asymmetric transformation; ion exchange processes; liquid membranes and extraction; kinetics and mechanism of polycondensation reactions; catalytic processes. *Mailing Add:* Allied Corp Box 1021R Morristown NJ 07960

SIFONTES, JOSE E, b Arecibo, PR, Oct 17, 26; US citizen; m 52; c 7. PEDIATRICS, PULMONARY. *Educ:* Syracuse Univ, MD, 48; Am Bd Pediat, dipl, 54. *Prof Exp:* Chief pediat, A Ruiz Soler Tuberc Hosp, 52-56; med officer in chg, Tuberc Res Ctr, USPHS, 56-58; assoc prof, Tuberc Res Ctr, USPHS, 58-66; dean, Sch Med, 66-71, chmn dept, 74-77, PROF PEDIAT, SCH MED, UNIV PR, SAN JUAN, 66- *Concurrent Pos:* Spec consult, USPHS, 58-66; comt, Int Child Health, Am Acad Pediat, 76-80. *Mem:* Am Thoracic Soc; Am Acad Pediat; Am Med Asn; Am Pediat Soc; AAAS. *Res:* Pediatric pulmonary diseases tuberculosis; medical education. *Mailing Add:* Dept Pediat Sch Med Univ PR GPO Box 5067 San Juan PR 00936

SIFRE, RAMON ALBERTO, b Vega Alta, PR, May 15, 24; m 47; c 6. INTERNAL MEDICINE, GASTROENTEROLOGY. *Educ:* Univ Louisville, MD, 46; Univ PR, BS, 47; Am Bd Internal Med, dipl, 54 & 77; Am Bd Gastroenterol, dipl, 57, 77. *Prof Exp:* Intern, Grad Hosp, Univ Pa, 47-48, post grad student internal med, Grad Sch Med, 48-49, resident, Grad Hosp, 49-50, resident gastroenterol, 50-51; chief gastroenterol sect, Fitzsimons Army Hosp, 51-53; asst prof, 53-57, ASSOC PROF CLIN MED, MED SCH, UNIV PR, SAN JUAN, 57- *Concurrent Pos:* Asst attend physician, San Juan City Hosp, 54-57, assoc attend, 57-; asst attend physician, Presby Hosp, San Juan, 54-57, consult, 57-; consult, Mimiya Hosp, 54-; attend, Doctors' Hosp, 58-; chief gastroenterol sect, Univ Hosp, 59-62. *Mem:* Fel Am Col Physicians. *Mailing Add:* Cacique 2070 Ocean Park Santurce PR 00911

SIFTON, HAROLD BOYD, botany, deceased

SIGAFOOS, ROBERT SUMNER, b Akron, Ohio, June 4, 20; m 74; c 3. PLANT ECOLOGY. *Educ:* Ohio State Univ, BS, 42, MSc, 43; Harvard Univ, MA, 48, PhD(biol), 51. *Prof Exp:* Assoc bot, Ohio State Univ, 42-43; botanist, Mil Geol Br, 48-57, botanist & proj hydrologist, Gen Hydrol Br, 57-66, RES BOTANIST, WATER RESOURCES DIV, US GEOL SURV, 66- *Concurrent Pos:* Assoc prof lectr, George Washington Univ, 58-70, prof lectr, 70-76. *Mem:* Fel AAAS; fel Arctic Inst NAm. *Res:* Relationship of drainage basin vegetation to streamflow; effects of flooding upon flood-plain forests; tree growth in natural environments; botanical evidence of alpine glacier history; effects of high natural sulfur and carbon dioxide emissions upon wild plants. *Mailing Add:* US Geol Surv MS 461 Reston VA 22092

SIGAFUS, ROY EDWARD, b Warren, Ill, Nov 15, 20; m 43; c 4. AGRICULTURE. *Educ:* Univ Mass, BS, 48, MS, 49; Cornell Univ, PhD(crops), 51. *Prof Exp:* Teacher elem sch, Ill, 40-42; asst forage crops, Cornell Univ, 48-50; asst agronomist, 50-52, asst prof crops, 52-53, assoc prof, 53-61, PROF AGRON, UNIV KY, 61- *Concurrent Pos:* Mem, Univ Ky-US Agency Int Develop contract team, Agr Univ Develop, Indonesia, 64-66 & Agr Res Sta Develop, Thailand, 66-69; mem comt forage crop variety eval, 69- *Mem:* Am Soc Agron; Crop Sci Soc Am. *Res:* Forage crop variety evaluation. *Mailing Add:* Dept of Agron Univ of Ky Lexington KY 40506

SIGAI, ANDREW GARY, b Baltimore, Md, Dec 3, 44; m 69. HIGH TEMPERATURE CHEMISTRY. *Educ:* Rensselaer Polytech Inst, BS, 65, MS, 68, PhD(chem), 70. *Prof Exp:* Mem tech staff vapor phase crystal growth & characterization, RCA Labs, David Sarnoff Res Ctr, RCA Corp, 69-72; scientist photoreceptor technol, Joseph C Wilson Ctr Technol, Xerox Corp, 72-80; SCIENTIST, GTE LABS, 80- *Mem:* Am Chem Soc; Electrochem Soc; Am Vacuum Soc. *Res:* High temperature thermodynamics; vapor-phase crystal growth; xerography and photoreceptor technology; investigation of the evaporation properties of selenium alloys for xerographic applications; electroluminescence and lasers; III-V compound semiconductor technology. *Mailing Add:* 40 Sylvan Rd Waltham MA 02154

SIGAL, RICHARD FREDERICK, b Cleveland, Ohio, Mar 19, 43; m 79; c 1. EXPLORATION GEOPHYSICS, THEORETICAL PHYSICS. *Educ:* Case Inst Technol, BS, 65; Yeshiva Univ, MA, 67, PhD(physics), 71. *Prof Exp:* Adj asst prof physics, Hunter Col City Univ New York, 71-72; fel physics, Univ Alta, 72-74, res assoc, 74-75, vis asst prof physics, 75-76, res assoc instr, 76-78; SR RES SCIENTIST, AMOCO PROD CO, 78- *Mem:* Am Phys Soc; Am Geophys Union; AAAS; Soc Exp Geophysicists. *Res:* The use of various electrical and electro-magnetic methods in geophysical exploration. *Mailing Add:* Amoco Prod Co Box 591 Tulsa OK 74102

SIGEL, BERNARD, b Wilno, Poland, May 14, 30; US citizen; m 56; c 5. SURGERY. *Educ:* Univ Tex, MD, 53. *Prof Exp:* Staff mem surg, Vet Admin Hosp, Coral Gables, Fla, 59-60; from asst prof to prof surg, Med Col Pa, 60-74; dean, 74-78, PROF SURG, ABRAHAM LINCOLN SCH MED, UNIV ILL COL MED, 74- *Concurrent Pos:* Mem coun thrombosis, Am Heart Asn; USPHS res career develop award, 63- *Mem:* Soc Univ Surgeons; Am Gastroenterol Asn; Am Col Surgeons; Am Asn Pathologists. *Mailing Add:* Lincoln Sch of Med Univ of Ill Col of Med Chicago IL 60612

SIGEL, CARL WILLIAM, b Skokie, Ill, Apr 10, 42; m 69. ORGANIC CHEMISTRY. *Educ:* Univ Ill, Urbana, BS, 63; Ind Univ, Bloomington, PhD(org chem), 67. *Prof Exp:* NIH fel, Univ Wis-Madison, 67-69; NIH fel, Univ Va, 69, res assoc cancer, 69-71; GROUP LEADER DRUG METABOLISM, BURROUGHS-WELLCOME & CO, 71- *Mem:* Am Chem Soc. *Res:* Drug metabolism and pharmacokinetics, isolation, structural elucidation and synthesis of biologically active molecules. *Mailing Add:* Room 0227 Med Biochem Burroughs-Wellcome & Co Research Triangle Park NC 27709

SIGEL, M(OLA) MICHAEL, b Nieswiez, Poland, June 24, 20; nat US; m 41; c 5. VIROLOGY, IMMUNOLOGY. *Educ:* Univ Tex, AB, 41; Ohio State Univ, PhD(bact), 44; Am Bd Microbiol, dipl. *Prof Exp:* Asst bact, Univ Tex, 39-41; asst, Ohio State Univ, 41-43; assoc virologist, Sch Med, Univ Pa, 46-50, asst prof, 50-53; chief reference diag & res unit, Virol & Rickettsial Sect, Commun Dis Ctr, USPHS, 53-55; assoc prof bact, Sch Med, Univ Miami, 55-58, prof microbiol & oncol, 58-78; PROF MICROBIOL & IMMUNOL & CHMN DEPT, SCH MED, UNIV SC, 78- *Concurrent Pos:* Vis prof, Univ Ala, 53; dir virus lab, Variety Children's Res Found, 55-60, res dir, Found, 60-70; consult, WHO, 56; vis prof, Univ WI; Res assoc, Lerner Marine Lab, Am Mus Natural Hist, Bimini; consult, Vet Admin Comt Infectious Dis. *Mem:* Fel Am Acad Microbiol; Soc Exp Biol & Med; Am Asn Immunol; Am Asn Cancer Res; fel NY Acad Sci. *Res:* Myxoviruses and interferon; psittacosis; tumor virology; basic immunology; tumor immunology; phylogeny of immunity; regulation of immune responses by chemical agents. *Mailing Add:* Dept of Microbiol & Immunol Univ of SC Sch of Med Columbia SC 29208

SIGELL, LEONARD, b Portland, Ore, Dec 28, 38. PHARMACOLOGY. *Educ:* Ore State Univ, BS, 61; Univ Ore, PhD(pharmacol), 64. *Prof Exp:* Instr pharmacol, 64-66, instr clin pharmacol & exp med, 66-68, asst prof pharmacol & instr med, 68-72, DIR DRUG & POISON INFO CTR, UNIV CINCINNATI, 72-, FROM ASSOC TO PROF PHARMACOL & ASSOC PROF EXP MED, COL MED, 81-; DIR DRUG & POISON INFO CTR, CINCINNATI GEN HOSP, 72- *Concurrent Pos:* Dir drug info, Cincinnati Gen Hosp, 66-72. *Mem:* Am Fedn Clin Res. *Res:* Information science; cardiovascular and behavioral pharmacology; clinical pharmacology-drug epidemiology. *Mailing Add:* Drug & Poison Info 7701 Bridge Col Med Univ Cincinnati Cincinnati OH 45267

SIGG, ERNEST BEAT, b Basel, Switz, June 7, 24; m 62; c 2. PHYSIOLOGY. *Educ:* Univ Basel, MD, 49. *Prof Exp:* Resident surg & obstet, Gen Hosp, Davos, Switz, 49-51; res assoc neurophysiol, Univ Minn, 52-53; res assoc, Neuropsychiat Inst, Univ Ill, 53-55; sr physiologist, Ciba Pharmaceut Prod, Inc, 55-57; dir dept pharmacol, Res Labs, Geigy Chem Corp, 57-66; sect head pharmacol, Hoffmann-La Roche Inc, 67-80; DIR, DEPT PHARMACOL, WYETH LABS, 80- *Concurrent Pos:* Adj prof pharmacol, NY Med Col, Valhalla, NY, 74- *Mem:* fel Am Col Neuropsychopharmacol; Am Soc Pharmacol & Exp Therapeut. *Res:* Neuropharmacol; neurophysiology; central autonomic nervous system; hypertension; stress. *Mailing Add:* 453 W Saddle River Rd Upper Saddle River NJ 07458

SIGGIA, ERIC DEAN, b Easton, Pa, Nov 24, 49. STATISTICAL MECHANICS. *Educ:* Harvard Univ, AB & AM, 71, PhD(physics), 72. *Prof Exp:* Asst prof physics, Univ Pa, 75-77; asst prof, 77-80, ASSOC PROF PHYSICS, CORNELL UNIV, 80- *Concurrent Pos:* Soc Fel jr fel, Harvard Univ, 71-75; Sloan Found grant, 81-83. *Mem:* Am Phys Soc. *Res:* Theory of fluid turbulence and dynamics of phase transitions. *Mailing Add:* Dept Physics Cornell Univ Ithaca NY 14853

SIGGIA, SIDNEY, b New York, NY, June 22, 20; m 44; c 2. ANALYTICAL CHEMISTRY. *Educ:* Queens Col, NY, BS, 42; Polytech Inst Brooklyn, MS, 43, PhD(org chem), 44. *Prof Exp:* From res analyst to mgr, Anal Dept, Gen Aniline & Film Corp, Pa, 44-58; dir anal res & serv, Res Lab, Olin Mathieson Chem Corp, 58-66; PROF CHEM, UNIV MASS, AMHERST, 66- *Honors & Awards:* Anachem Soc Award, 69; Fisher Award, Am Chem Soc, 75. *Mem:* AAAS; Sigma Xi; Am Chem Soc. *Res:* Organic and functional group analysis; analysis of mixtures, surface active agents and polymers; analytical separation; establishment of specifications; chemical kinetics; management of analytical chemical facilities. *Mailing Add:* Dept of Chem Univ of Mass Amherst MA 01003

SIGGINS, GEORGE ROBERT, b Miami, Okla, Dec 29, 37; m 78; c 1. NEUROSCIENCES, NEUROPHARMACOLOGY. *Educ:* Harvard Univ, AB, 60; Boston Univ, AB, 63, PhD(biol & physiol), 67. *Prof Exp:* Fel vascular physiol, Boston Univ, 67-68; fel pharmacol, NIH/NIMH, 68-70; res scientist, Lab Neuropharmacol, St Elizabeth's Hosp, 70-72, sect chief, 72-76, actg lab chief, 75-76; ASSOC DIR NEUROBIOL, A V DAVIS CTR, SALK INST, 76- *Honors & Awards:* A E Bennett Award, Soc Biol Psychiat, 71; A Cressy

Morrison Award, NY Acad Sci, 71; Sr US Scientist Award, Alexander von Humboldt Found, 78. *Mem:* Am Soc Pharmacol & Exp Therapy; Soc Neurosci. *Res:* Neurophysiology; psychopharmacology; autonomic physiology; microcirculation; neuronal cytochemistry; tissue cultures. *Mailing Add:* A V Davis Ctr Salk Inst Box 1809 San Diego CA 92114

SIGGINS, JAMES ERNEST, b Salt Lake City, Utah, Oct 14, 28; m 58; c 2. MEDICINAL CHEMISTRY. *Educ:* Amherst Col, BA, 52; Univ Chicago, MS, 57, PhD(chem), 59. *Prof Exp:* Chemist, Res Ctr, Lever Bros Co, 52-54; RES ASSOC SYNTHETIC ORG CHEM, STERLING-WINTHROP RES INST, 59- *Mem:* Am Chem Soc. *Res:* Heterocyclics; synthetic organic medicinals; radiopaque contrast agents. *Mailing Add:* 3015 Delware Ave #219 Kenmore NY 14217

SIGILLITO, VINCENT GEORGE, b Washington, DC, Feb 20, 37; m 58; c 2. APPLIED MATHEMATICS. *Educ:* Univ Md, College Park, BS, 58, MA, 62, PhD(math), 65. *Prof Exp:* Assoc chemist, 58-62, assoc mathematician, 62-65, sr staff mathematician, 65-76, PRIN STAFF MATHEMATICIAN, APPL PHYSICS LAB, JOHNS HOPKINS UNIV, 76-, GROUP SUPVR, APPL MATH GROUP, 81- *Concurrent Pos:* Instr eve col grad prog, NIH, 65-68; instr, Johns Hopkins Univ, 66-; reviewer, Zentralblatt für Mathematik, 66-, Math Reviews, 68- & Computing Reviews, 71-; Parsons vis prof, Dept Math Sci, Johns Hopkins Univ, 78-79. *Mem:* Soc Indust & Appl Math. *Res:* Approximate solutions of partial differential equations and eigenvalue problems. *Mailing Add:* Appl Physics Lab Johns Hopkins Univ Laurel MD 20810

SIGLER, JOHN WILLIAM, b Ames, Iowa, Dec, 20, 46; m 76; c 3. ECOLOGICAL & ENVIRONMENTAL ASSESSMENTS. *Educ:* Utah State Univ, BS, 69, MS, 72; Univ Idaho, PhD(fisheries mgt), 81. *Prof Exp:* Res asst, Utah State Univ, 69-72; proj scientist environ protection team, Armament Lab, 72-73, Weapons Lab, US Air Force, 73-75; NSF res asst, Res Appl Nat Needs, Univ NM, 74-76, Univ Idaho, 76-81; CONSULT BIOLOGIST, W F SIGLER & ASSOCS INC, 81- *Mem:* Am Fisheries Soc; Am Inst Fishery Res Biologists; Wildlife Soc; Ecol Soc Am; Am Soc Limnol & Oceanog. *Res:* Effects of chronic exposure of anadromous salmonids to turbidity, and its effect on growth and social behavior; toxic effects of unique Air Force wastes on aquatic life; utilization of adenosine triphosphate as an indicator of ecosystem condition in a large reservoir; production-biomass relationships in a large reservoir. *Mailing Add:* PO Box 1268 Logan UT 84322

SIGLER, JULIUS ALFRED, JR, b Kissimmee, Fla, Dec 22, 40; m 65; c 3. SOLID STATE PHYSICS. *Educ:* Lynchburg Col, BS, 62; Univ Va, MS, 66, PhD(physics), 67. *Prof Exp:* Assoc prof, 67-71, PROF PHYSICS & CHMN DEPT, LYNCHBURG COL & DIR GRAD SCI PROGS, 71- *Concurrent Pos:* Consult, Oak Ridge Assoc Univs, 73-74; vis prof physics, Ind State Univ & re-write ed, NSF Physics Technol Proj, 74-75; consult, Solar Tech Proj, NSF, 80. *Mem:* Am Asn Physics Teachers; Soc Physics Students; Nat Rwy Hist Soc. *Res:* Theoretical calculations of relative energies of various defects in quenched face centered cubic metals; variation of mechanical density of gold wires with tensile strains; development of physics curricula and teaching strategies. *Mailing Add:* Dept of Physics Lynchburg Col Lynchburg VA 24504

SIGLER, LAURENCE EDWARD, b Tulsa, Okla, Aug 26, 28; m 64; c 2. MATHEMATICS. *Educ:* Okla State Univ, ScB, 50; Columbia Univ, AM, 54, PhD(math), 63. *Prof Exp:* Instr math, Columbia Univ, 56-59; asst prof, Hunter Col, 61-65 & Hofstra Univ, 65-67; assoc prof, 67-72, PROF MATH, BUCKNELL UNIV, 72- *Mem:* Am Math Soc; Math Asn Am; Ital Math Union. *Res:* Asymptotic theory of ordinary differential equations; set theory. *Mailing Add:* Dept of Math Bucknell Univ Lewisburg PA 17837

SIGLER, MILES HAROLD, b Buffalo, NY, Feb 11, 29; m 54; c 3. NEPHROLOGY. *Educ:* Univ Rochester, BA, 51; Cornell Univ, MD, 55. *Prof Exp:* Intern med, State Univ NY Syracuse, 55-56; resident, Col Med, Thomas Jefferson Univ, 56-58; NIH fel nephrol, Hosp Univ Pa, 60-62; assoc med, Jefferson Med Col Hosp, 62-64; assoc med, 64-69, CHIEF DEPT NEPHROL, LANKENAU HOSP, 69- *Concurrent Pos:* Clin prof med, Col Med, Thomas Jefferson Univ, 72- *Mem:* Am Fedn Clin Res; Am Soc Nephrol; fel Am Col Physicians; Int Soc Nephrol; Am Heart Asn. *Res:* Renal mechanisms controlling fluid and electrolyte excretion during fasting; mechanism of the sodium diuresis of fasting; mechanism of the phosphateuresis of fasting; energy metabolism in uremia. *Mailing Add:* 416 Haywood Rd Merion Station PA 19066

SIGLER, PAUL BENJAMIN, b Richmond, Va, Feb 19, 34; m 58; c 5. BIOCHEMISTRY. *Educ:* Princeton Univ, AB, 55; Columbia Univ, MD, 59; Cambridge Univ, PhD(biochem), 68. *Prof Exp:* Intern & resident med, Col Physicians & Surgeons, Columbia Univ, 59-61; res assoc protein crystallog, Nat Inst Arthritis & Metab Dis, 61-63, mem staff, 63-64; fel protein crystallog, Lab Molecular Biol, Med Res Coun, Eng, 64-67; assoc prof, 67-74, PROF BIOPHYS & THEORET BIOL, UNIV CHICAGO, 74- *Mem:* AAAS; Am Chem Soc; Am Crystallog Soc. *Res:* X-ray diffraction; protein crystallography; membrane interactive proteins; genetic control of protein: nuclei acid interactions; transfer ribonucleic acid; protein synthesis. *Mailing Add:* Dept Biophys & Theoret Biol 920 E 58th St Chicago IL 60637

SIGLER, WILLIAM FRANKLIN, b LeRoy, Ill, Feb 17, 09; m 36; c 2. FISHERIES. *Educ:* Iowa State Univ, BS, 40, MS, 41, PhD(zool), 47. *Prof Exp:* Soil conservationist, Soil Conserv Serv, USDA, 35-37; consult, Cent Eng Co, Iowa, 40-41; res assoc fisheries, Iowa State Col, 41-42; asst prof fisheries & limnol, Utah State Univ, 47-50, prof wildlife sci & head dept, 50-74; PRES & CHMN BD DIRS, W F SIGLER & ASSOCS, INC, 74- *Concurrent Pos:* Mem, Utah Water Pollution Control Bd, 57-65, chmn, 63-65; consult, US Surgeon Gen, 63-67; adv, Int Fish & Game Law Enforcement Asn. *Mem:* Fel AAAS; fel Int Acad Fishery Sci; Wildlife Soc; Am Fisheries Soc; Ecol Soc Am. *Res:* Basic stream productivity; fishery biology; wildlife law enforcement. *Mailing Add:* 309 E 200 S Logan UT 84321

SIGMAN, DAVID STEPHAN, b New York, NY, June 14, 39; m 63; c 2. BIOCHEMISTRY. *Educ:* Oberlin Col, AB, 60; Harvard Univ, AM, 62, PhD(chem), 65. *Prof Exp:* NIH res fel biochem, Sch Med, Harvard Univ, 65-67, instr, 67-68; asst prof, 68-73, assoc prof, 73-79, PROF BIOCHEM, SCH MED, UNIV CALIF, LOS ANGELES, 79- *Concurrent Pos:* Alfred P Sloan fel, 72-74. *Mem:* Am Soc Biol Chem; Am Chem Soc; Molecular Biol Inst. *Res:* Mechanism of enzyme action; role of metal ions in biological systems; structure of nucleic acids. *Mailing Add:* Dept Biol Chem Univ Calif Sch Med Los Angeles CA 90024

SIGMAR, DIETER JOSEPH, b Vienna, Austria, 1935; c 3. PLASMA PHYSICS, NUCLEAR ENGINEERING. *Educ:* Tech Univ Vienna, MS, 60, ScD(theoret physics), 65. *Prof Exp:* Asst prof theoret physics, Tech Univ, Vienna, Austria, 65-66; res staff plasma physics & thermonuclear fusion, Oak Ridge Nat Lab, Tenn, 66-70; res staff plasma physics, Res Lab Electronics, 70-72, Mass Inst Technol, 70-72, assoc prof nuclear eng & aeronaut & astronaut, 72-78; SR SCIENTIST, FUSION ENERGY DIV, OAK RIDGE NAT LAB, 78- *Concurrent Pos:* Consult, Fusion Energy Div, Oak Ridge Nat Lab, 70-76 & Argonne Nat Lab, 74-76; vis fac mem, Los Alamos Sci Lab, 74 & 75; lectr plasma physics, Tech Univ, Vienna, 73-; adj prof nuclear eng, Mass Inst Technol, 78- *Mem:* Am Phys Soc; Am Nuclear Soc; Austrian Phys Soc. *Res:* Theoretical plasma physics; controlled thermonuclear fusion research; fudamental transport theory of magnetically confined fully ionized gases and its application to toroidal fusion reactors. *Mailing Add:* 136 Westlook Circle Oak Ridge TN 37830

SIGMON, KERMIT NEAL, b Lincoln Co, NC, Apr 18, 36; m 60; c 1. MATHEMATICS. *Educ:* Appalachian State Univ, BS, 58; Univ NC, Chapel Hill, MEd, 59; Univ Fla, PhD(math), 66. *Prof Exp:* Teacher, Charlotte-Mecklenburg Schs, NC, 59-63; asst prof math, 66-81, ASSOC PROF MATH, UNIV FLA, 81- *Concurrent Pos:* Ger Res Asn study grant, Hannover Tech Univ, 72-73. *Mem:* Am Math Soc; Math Asn Am; Sigma Xi. *Res:* Topological algebra; algebraic topology. *Mailing Add:* Dept of Math Univ of Fla Gainesville FL 32611

SIGNELL, PETER STUART, b Lima, Ohio, June 29, 28; m 52; c 2. THEORETICAL PHYSICS, SCIENCE EDUCATION. *Educ:* Antioch Col, BS, 52; Univ Rochester, MS, 54, PhD, 58. *Prof Exp:* From instr to asst prof physics, Bucknell Univ, 57-59; from asst prof to assoc prof, Pa State Univ, 59-64; assoc prof, 64-65, PROF PHYSICS, MICH STATE UNIV, 65- *Res:* Nuclear forces; research and development for independent study instruction. *Mailing Add:* Dept of Physics Mich State Univ East Lansing MI 48824

SIGNER, ETHAN ROYAL, b Brooklyn, NY, Apr 3, 37. MOLECULAR BIOLOGY. *Educ:* Yale Univ, BS, 58; Mass Inst Technol, PhD(biophys), 63. *Prof Exp:* NSF fel, Med Res Coun Lab Molecular Biol, Eng, 62-64; Am Cancer Soc fel, Pasteur Inst, Paris, 64-65, Jane Coffin Childs Mem Fund fel, 65-66; from asst prof to assoc prof microbiol, 66-72, PROF BIOL, MASS INST TECHNOL, 72- *Honors & Awards:* Distinguished Martin vis lectr, NY Law Sch, 79-80; Philips distinguished vis, Harverford Col, 78. *Mem:* AAAS; Am Soc Microbiol; NY Acad Sci. *Res:* Genetics; microbiology; genetics of nodulation and nitrogen-fixation by root nodule bacteria of leguminous plants. *Mailing Add:* Dept of Biol Mass Inst of Technol Cambridge MA 02139

SIGNORINO, CHARLES ANTHONY, b Beaverdale, Pa, July 28, 32; m 54; c 8. ORGANIC CHEMISTRY, PHYSICAL CHEMISTRY. *Educ:* Pa State Univ, BS, 54; Univ Pa, MS, 56, PhD, 59; Westminster Theol Seminary, MAR, 78. *Prof Exp:* Asst instr chem, Univ Pa, 54-58; res chemist, Atlantic Refining Co, 58-62; assoc prof chem, Eastern Baptist Col, 62-68; dir tech serv, 66-68, vpres, 68-72, MEM BD DIRS, COLORCON, INC, 72- *Concurrent Pos:* Vis prof, Eastern Baptist Col, 68-69. *Mem:* Am Chem Soc; Am Pharmaceut Asn; Acad Pharmaceut Sci. *Res:* New processes for monomer synthesis; polymerization kinetics; radiation induced polymerization; selective oxidation of hydrocarbons, especially olefins; patented lake manufacturing processes; patented special tablet coatings. *Mailing Add:* 300 Lincoln Rd King of Prussia PA 19406

SIGSBEE, RAYMOND A(RTHUR), metallurgy, see previous edition

SIGUEL, EDUARDO, biostatistics, operations research, see previous edition

SIGURDSSON, HARALDUR, b Iceland, May 31, 39; div; c 2. PETROLOGY, VOLCANOLOGY. *Educ:* Queen's Univ, Belfast, BSc, 65; Durham Univ, Eng, PhD(geol), 70. *Prof Exp:* Res fel geol, Univ W Indes, Trinidad, 70-73; assoc prof oceanog, 74-80, PROF OCEANOG, UNIV RI, 80- *Mem:* Am Geophys Union; Geochem Soc. *Res:* Petrology of ocean ridge basalts; volcanic geology of Iceland and the Lesser Antilles Island Arc. *Mailing Add:* Grad Sch of Oceanog Univ of RI Kingston RI 02881

SIH, CHARLES JOHN, b Shanghai, China; nat US; m 59. BIO-ORGANIC CHEMISTRY. *Educ:* Carroll Col, Mont, AB, 53; Mont State Col, MS, 55; Univ Wis, PhD(bact), 58. *Prof Exp:* Sr res microbiologist, Squibb Inst Med Res, 58-60; assoc prof, 60-66, prof, 66-77, F B POWER PROF PHARMACEUT CHEM, UNIV WIS-MADISON, 77- *Concurrent Pos:* Sci adv, Eastman Kodak. *Honors & Awards:* Ernest Volwiler Award, 77; Roussel Prize, 80. *Mem:* Am Soc Microbiol; Am Soc Biol Chemists; Acad Pharmaceut Sci; Am Chem Soc. *Res:* Chemical syntheses using enymes; enymatic mechanism of sterol side chain degradation; suicide inhibitors; slow-reacting substance of anaphylaxis; natural products chemistry. *Mailing Add:* 6322 Landfall Dr Madison WI 53705

SIIROLA, JEFFREY JOHN, b Patuxent River, Md, July 17, 45; m 71; c 2. CHEMICAL PROCESS SYNTHESIS. *Educ:* Univ Utah, BS, 67; Univ Wis-Madison, PhD, 70. *Prof Exp:* Res engr, 72-74, sr res engr, Tenn Eastman Co, 74-80, RES ASSOC, EASTMAN KODAK CO, 80- *Concurrent Pos:* dir, Comput & Systs Technol Div, Am Inst Chem Engrs, 80- *Mem:* Am Inst Chem Engrs; Am Chem Soc. *Res:* Computer-aided chemical process design synthesis, analysis and optimization; energy conservation; non-numeric programming; artificial intelligence; technology assessment. *Mailing Add:* ECD Res Labs Eastman Kodak Co Kingsport TN 37662

SIITERI, PENTTI KASPER, b Finland, Oct 20, 26; US citizen; m 50; c 5. BIOCHEMISTRY. *Educ:* Dartmouth Col, AB, 48; Univ NH, MS, 50; Columbia Univ, PhD(biochem), 63. *Prof Exp:* Res scientist, Lederle Labs, Am Cyanamid Co, 53-59; from assoc prof to prof obstet, gynec & biochem, Univ Tex Southwestern Med Br, Dallas, 62-73; PROF OBSTET & GYNEC, UNIV CALIF, SAN FRANCISCO, 73- *Concurrent Pos:* Mem, Endocrinol Sect, NIH, 69-75, chmn, 75-77; NIH res grant, 73- *Mem:* AAAS; Am Soc Biol Chem; Endocrine Soc; Soc Gynec Invest. *Res:* Mechanism of estrogen action; hormones in reproduction and cancer. *Mailing Add:* Dept of Obstet & Gynec Univ of Calif San Francisco CA 94143

SIJ, JOHN WILLIAM, b St Louis, Mo, June 21, 43; m 65; c 2. PLANT PHYSIOLOGY. *Educ:* Eastern Ill Univ, BSEd, 65; Ohio State Univ, MS, 67, PhD(plant physiol), 71. *Prof Exp:* Res assoc, Evapotranspiration Lab, Kans State Univ, 71-72; asst prof, 72-77, ASSOC PROF, AGR RES & EXTEN CTR, TEX A&M UNIV, 77- *Mem:* Am Asn Plant Physiologists; Crop Sci Soc Am; Am Soc Agron. *Res:* Soybean physiology and management. *Mailing Add:* Res & Exten Ctr Tex A&M Univ Rte 7 Box 999 Beaumont TX 77706

SIKAND, RAJINDER S, b Barnala, India. PHYSIOLOGY, MEDICINE. *Educ:* King Edward Med Col, Lahore, Punjab, MB, BS, 46. *Prof Exp:* Res fel physiol, Sch Med, Yale Univ, 49-52; med officer, West Middlesex Hosp, UK, 53-54; med registr, King George V Hosp, Godalming, UK, 54-56; res fel physiol, Sch Med, Univ Md, Baltimore City, 61-63; res assoc, State Univ NY Buffalo, 63-64; res assoc, Max Planck Inst Med Res, Gottingen, 64-65; assoc clin prof internal med, Sch Med, Yale Univ, 65-75; CO-DIR, SECT PULMONARY DIS, DEPT MED, ST RAPHAEL'S HOSP, NEW HAVEN, CT, 75- *Mem:* Am Physiol Soc; fel Am Col Physicians; fel Am Col Chest Physicians; Am Thoracic Soc; Am Fedn Clin Res. *Res:* Cardiopulmonary physiology. *Mailing Add:* St Raphael's Hosp Sect Pulmon Dis 1450 Chapel St New Haven CT 06511

SIKARSKIE, DAVID L(AWRENCE), b Marquette, Mich, Aug 3, 37; m 57; c 3. ENGINEERING MECHANICS. *Educ:* Univ Pa, BS, 59; Columbia Univ, MS, 60, ScD(eng mech), 64. *Prof Exp:* Res asst solid mech, Columbia Univ, 62-63; mem tech staff, Ingersoll Rand Res Ctr, 63-66; from asst prof to assoc prof aerospace eng, Univ Mich, Ann Arbor, 66-72, prof aerospace eng, 72-80. *Concurrent Pos:* Vis lectr, Princeton Univ, 65-66. *Mem:* Am Soc Mech Engrs. *Res:* Brittle fracture; rock mechanics; elasticity; nonlinear structural mechanics. *Mailing Add:* 4824 Buttercup Lane Okemos MI 48864

SIKDAR, DHIRENDRA N, b India, Nov 1, 30; m 61; c 2. PHYSICS, METEOROLOGY. *Educ:* Univ Calcutta, BSc, 49, MSc, 51; Univ Wis-Madison, PhD(meteorol), 69. *Prof Exp:* Asst Meteorol Dept, Govt India, 61-69; asst scientist, Space Sci & Eng Ctr, Univ Wis-Madison, 69-70, assoc scientist, 70-74; PROF ATMOS SCI, UNIV WIS-MILWAUKEE, 74- *Concurrent Pos:* NSF res grants, 70- *Mem:* Am Geophys Union; Sigma Xi; Am Meteorol Soc. *Res:* Satellite meteorology; severe storm circulations and energetics; Great Lake research; urban meteorology. *Mailing Add:* Dept Geol Sci Univ Wis Milwaukee WI 53201

SIKES, JAMES KLINGMAN, b Henderson, Tenn, Apr 12, 24; m 50; c 2. ANALYTICAL CHEMISTRY, PHYSIOLOGY. *Educ:* Abilene Christian Col, BS, 47; Tex Technol Col, MS, 51; Tex Tech Univ, MS, 67. *Prof Exp:* Supvr lab, Paymaster Oil Mills, Anderson Clayton Co, 47-54; chief chemist res, Plains Coop Oil Mill, 54-65; partner, Plains Lab, 65-73; dept head lab, Brookside Farms Lab Asn, 73-75; PRES, SCAN, INC, 75- *Concurrent Pos:* Mem res comt, Nat Cottonseed Prods Asn, 60-62. *Mem:* Am Oil Chemists Soc; Am Inst Chemists; AAAS; Am Soc Animal Sci; Asn Consult Chemists & Chem Engrs. *Res:* Cottonseed oil processing and refining; laboratory methodology; water quality; insecticides; herbicides; animal feeds; animal nutrition; soil and crop improvement. *Mailing Add:* Scan Inc PO Box 3968 Lubbock TX 79452

SIKLOSI, MICHAEL PETER, b Akron, Ohio, Sept 8, 48; m 71. ORGANIC CHEMISTRY. *Educ:* Montclair State Col, BA, 70; Purdue Univ, MS, 72, PhD(chem), 77. *Prof Exp:* RESEARCHER CHEM, PROCTER & GAMBLE CO, 77- *Mem:* Am Chem Soc. *Res:* Peroxyacids; reactivity; decomposition mechanisms, reaction mechanisms; organometallic chemistry; reactions of allylic Grignard reagents. *Mailing Add:* Procter & Gamble Co 11520 Reed Hartman Hwy Cincinnati OH 45241

SIKLOSSY, LAURENT, b Budapest, Hungary; US citizen. COMPUTER SCIENCE. *Educ:* Yale Univ, BA, 63; Harvard Univ, MA, 64; Carnegie-Mellon Univ, PhD(comput sci), 68. *Prof Exp:* Proj scientist comput sci, Carnegie-Mellon Univ, 65-68; asst prof info & comput sci, Univ Calif, Irvine, 68-70; asst prof comput sci, Univ Tex, Austin, 71-74, assoc prof, 74-78; dir grad studies, Dept Info Eng, 79-80, PROF, DEPT INFO ENG, UNIV ILL, CHICAGO, 78- *Concurrent Pos:* Regents grant, Univ Calif, Irvine, 69-70; consult, Hughes Aircraft Corp, Calif, 70; lectr & consult, US Dept State, Repub of Cameroun & Algeria, 70-71; vis titular prof, Univ Sao Paulo, 72; Univ Res Inst grant, Univ Tex, Austin, 70-75, NSF grants, 71-75; Arts & Sci Found grant, 72-75; Orgn Am States vis prof, Univ Tech Fed Santa Maria, Valparaiso, 74 & 75; Nat Acad Sci grant, 75; vis prof, Univ Paris, 76 & 81; consult, Jelmoli AG, Zurich, Switz, 77. *Mem:* Asn Comput Mach; Sigma Xi; Am Phys Soc. *Res:* Artificial intelligence; robotics; problem-solving; intelligent computer tutors; information structures; list processing; management information systems; use of computers in developing countries; speech processing by computer; author or coauthor of over 50 publications. *Mailing Add:* Dept Info Eng Box 4348 Univ Ill Chicago IL 60680

SIKORA, JEROME PAUL, b Cleveland, Ohio, Apr 9, 47; m 71; c 2. STRUCTURAL MECHANICS, PHOTOMECHANICS. *Educ:* Univ Detroit, BS, 69. *Prof Exp:* PHYSICIST, D TAYLOR NAVAL SHIP RES & DEVELOP CTR, 69- *Mem:* Sigma Xi. *Res:* Optical methods such as holography, speckle, moire and photoelasticity to measure displacements, stresses, vibrations, and contour mapping of hard structures. *Mailing Add:* D Taylor Naval Ship Res & Develop Ctr Code 1730.5 Bethesda MD 20084

SIKORSKA, MARIANNA, b Wilkolaz, Poland, Jan 20, 44. NEUROCHEMISTRY, NEUROPHYSIOLOGY. *Educ:* Polytech Univ, Warsaw, BChemE, 72; Polish Acad Sci, PhD(biochem), 78. *Prof Exp:* Res asst neurochem, Med Res Ctr, Polish Acad Sci, Warsaw, 69-78; RES ASSOC CELL PHYSIOL, DIV BIOL, NAT RES COUN, CAN, 78- *Res:* Role of nuclear protein kinesas in changes in chrometin structure. *Mailing Add:* Nat Res Coun Can Div Biol M-54 Montreal Rd Ottawa ON K1A 0R6 Can

SIKORSKI, JAMES ALAN, b Stevens Pt, Wis, Nov 9, 48; m 77; c 1. HETEROCYCLIC CHEMISTRY, ORGANOPHOSPHORUS CHEMISTRY. *Educ:* Northeast La State Col, BS, 70; Purdue Univ, MS, 76, PhD(org chem), 81. *Prof Exp:* Res chemist II, 76-78, sr res chemist, 78-82, RES SPECIALIST, MONSANTO AGR PROD CO, 82- *Concurrent Pos:* Instr org chem, St Louis Community Col, Florisant Valley, 77-78. *Mem:* Am Chem Soc. *Res:* Synthetic applications of organoborane reagents; heterocycle synthesis; organophosphorus chemistry; herbicide and plant growth regulator synthesis. *Mailing Add:* Monsanto Agr Prod Co 800 N Lindbergh Blvd St Louis MO 63166

SIKOV, MELVIN RICHARD, b Detroit, Mich, July 8, 28; m 52; c 3. RADIATION BIOLOGY. *Educ:* Wayne State Univ, BS, 51; Univ Rochester, PhD(radiation biol), 55. *Prof Exp:* Res assoc radiation biol, Univ Rochester, 52-55; asst prof radiobiol, Col Med, Wayne State Univ, 55-61, assoc prof, 61-65; sr res scientist, 65-68, res assoc, 68-78, mgr develop toxicol, 78-81, SR STAFF SCIENTIST, PAC NORTHWEST LABS, BATTELLE MEM INST, 81- *Mem:* Radiation Res Soc; Health Physics Soc; Am Asn Pathologists; Soc Toxicol; Teratology Soc. *Res:* Age and environmental factors in isotope metabolism and toxicity; effects of radiation and chemicals on embryonic and postnatal development; radiation and other agents affecting tumor biology. *Mailing Add:* Dept of Biol Pac Northwest Labs Battelle Mem Inst Richland WA 99352

SILAGI, SELMA, b Sept 5, 16; US citizen; m 36; c 2. GENETICS, CANCER. *Educ:* Hunter Col, AB, 36; Columbia Univ, MA, 38, PhD(genetics), 61. *Prof Exp:* Teacher pub schs, NY, 38-50; lectr biol, Queens Col, 57-59; NIH fel, 61-62; res assoc biochem genetics, Rockefeller Univ, 62-65; from asst prof to assoc prof, 65-74, PROF GENETICS, MED COL, CORNELL UNIV, 74- *Concurrent Pos:* Guest investr, Rockefeller Univ & vis investr, Sloan-Kettering Inst Cancer Res, 65-66. *Mem:* AAAS; Genetics Soc Am; Am Soc Cell Biol; Harvey Soc; Tissue Cult Asn. *Res:* Cellular differentiation and gene action in mammalian cells in tissue culture; reversible suppression of malignancy by 5-bromodeoxyuridine; cancer immunology; cell hybridization and somatic cell genetics; mechanism of action of bomodeoxyuridine. *Mailing Add:* Dept of Obstet & Gynec Cornell Univ Med Col New York NY 10021

SILANDER, JOHN AUGUST, JR, b Highland Park, Ill, Mar 1, 45; m 71; c 2. PLANT ECOLOGY, EVOLUTION. *Educ:* Pomona Col, BA, 67; Univ Mich, MA, 69; Duke Univ, PhD(bot), 76. *Prof Exp:* Teaching fel bot, Univ Mich, 67-69; instr biol, Peace Corps Prog, Kpandu Sec Sch, Ghana, 69-71; res asst fel ecol genetics, Duke Univ, 71-72; trainee fel, NIH, 72-76; ASST PROF BIOL SCI, UNIV CONN, 76- *Concurrent Pos:* Collabr ecol, Nat Park Serv, US Dept Interior, 72-76; Fulbright-Hayes fel & univ fel, Australian Nat Univ, 77-78. *Mem:* Ecol Soc Am; Soc Study Evolution; Soc Int de Plantorum Demog; Sigma Xi; Brit Ecol Soc. *Res:* Population, genetic, evolutionary and community aspects of plant ecology; biogeography, pollination ecology, salt marsh and sand dune ecology. *Mailing Add:* Biol Sci Group Univ of Conn Storrs CT 06268

SILBAR, RICHARD R(OBERT), b Milwaukee, Wis, Jan 19, 37; m 63. PHYSICS. *Educ:* Univ Mich, BS, 59, MS, 60, PhD(physics), 63. *Prof Exp:* Res assoc & instr physics, Johns Hopkins Univ, 63-65; res asst prof, Cath Univ Am, 65-67; group leader, 75-78, STAFF PHYSICIST, MEDIUM ENERGY NUCLEAR PHYSICS THEORY, LOS ALAMOS NAT LAB, 67- *Concurrent Pos:* Vis scientist, Swiss Inst Nuclear Res, 73-74; vis prof, State Univ NY, 76-77; longterm acad sci exchange, Inst Nuclear Res, Moscow, USSR, 78-; detaillee, Div Nuclear Physics, Dept Energy, 81-82. *Mem:* Am Phys Soc. *Res:* Particle and nuclear physics theory; medium energy physics. *Mailing Add:* Los Alamos Nat Lab Los Alamos NM 87544

SILBER, HERBERT BRUCE, b New York, NY, Apr 3, 41; m 66; c 2. INORGANIC CHEMISTRY. *Educ:* Lehigh Univ, BS, 62, MS, 64; Univ Calif, Davis, PhD(inorg chem), 67. *Prof Exp:* Swedish Govt fel & Fulbright-Hays travel grant, Royal Inst Technol, Stockholm, 67-68 & Univ Md, College Park, 68-69; asst prof chem, Univ Md, Baltimore County, 69-75; ASSOC PROF CHEM, UNIV TEX, SAN ANTONIO, 75- *Mem:* Am Chem Soc; Royal Soc Chem; Sigma Xi. *Res:* Lanthanide chemistry; metal ion complexation chemistry; solvation; relaxation kinetics; phosphate chemistry; ultrasonic absorption in cellular systems. *Mailing Add:* Div of Earth & Phys Sci Univ of Tex San Antonio TX 78085

SILBER, ROBERT, b Vienna, Austria, Jan 4, 31; US citizen; m 54; c 4. INTERNAL MEDICINE, HEMATOLOGY. *Educ:* NY Univ, BA, 50; State Univ NY, MD, 54. *Prof Exp:* From intern to resident med, Third Med Div, Bellevue Hosp, New York, 54-58; instr & USPHS spec fel biochem, Univ Wash, 60-62; asst prof, 62-66, ASSOC PROF MED, SCH MED, NY UNIV, 66-, DIR DIV HEMAT, 68- *Concurrent Pos:* Nat Cancer Inst clin fel, Col Med, Univ Utah, 56-57; Guggenheim Mem Found fel, 71-72. *Mem:* Am Soc Clin Invest; Am Soc Biol Chem; Am Fedn Clin Res; Soc Hemat; Harvey Soc. *Res:* Leukocyte enzymology; folic acid metabolism; disorders of the red cell membrane; biochemistry. *Mailing Add:* NY Univ Sch of Med 550 First Ave New York NY 10016

SILBER, ROBERT, b Montgomery, WVa, Nov 8, 37; m 64; c 2. MATHEMATICS. *Educ:* Vanderbilt Univ, BA, 57; Univ Ala, MA, 63; Clemson Univ, PhD(math), 68. *Prof Exp:* Aerospace technologist, NASA, 58-63; asst prof math, 68-81, ASSOC PROF MATH, NC STATE UNIV, 81- *Mem:* Am Math Soc; Math Asn Am. *Res:* Optimization theory; functional analysis. *Mailing Add:* Dept of Math NC State Univ Raleigh NC 27607

SILBERBERG, DONALD H, b Washington, DC, Mar 2, 34; m 59; c 2. NEUROLOGY. *Educ:* Univ Mich, MD, 58. *Prof Exp:* Resident neurol, NIH, 59-61; Fulbright fel neurol & Neuro-ophthal, Nat Hosp, London, Eng, 61-62; USPHS spec fel neuro-ophthal, Sch Med, Wash Univ, 62-63; assoc neurol, 63-65, from asst prof to assoc prof neurol & ophthal, 65-71, PROF NEUROL & OPHTHAL, SCH MED, UNIV PA, 71-, VCHMN NEUROL DEPT, 74- *Concurrent Pos:* Consult, Philadelphia Vet Admin Hosp, 66- & Childrens Hosp Philadelphia, 67- *Mem:* Am Acad Neurol; Am Neurol Asn; Am Asn Neuropath; Am Soc Neurochem; Soc Neurosci. *Res:* Tissue culture studies of myelination; demyelinating diseases. *Mailing Add:* Dept of Neurol Hosp of the Univ of Pa Philadelphia PA 19104

SILBERBERG, I(RWIN) HAROLD, b Austin, Tex, Feb 25, 26; m 49; c 4. CHEMICAL ENGINEERING. *Educ:* Univ Tex, BS, 47, MS, 51, PhD(chem eng), 58. *Prof Exp:* Sr res technologist, Field Res Lab, Socony Mobil Oil Co, 57-60; ASST DIR, UNIV DIV, TEX PETROL RES COMT, UNIV TEX, AUSTIN, 60- *Mem:* Am Chem Soc; Am Inst Chem Engrs; Am Soc Petrol Engrs; Am Inst Chemists; Nat Soc Prof Engrs. *Res:* Volumetric and phase behavior of fluids, particularly hydrocarbons; petroleum production and reservoir engineering; thermodynamics. *Mailing Add:* Tex Petrol Res Comt Univ of Tex Austin TX 78712

SILBERBERG, REIN, b Tallinn, Estonia, Jan 15, 32; US citizen; m 65; c 2. COSMIC RAY PHYSICS. *Educ:* Univ Calif, Berkeley, AB, 55, MA, 56, PhD(physics), 60. *Prof Exp:* Res asst physics, Univ Calif, 56-60; Nat Acad Sci-Nat Res Coun res assoc, 60-62, RES PHYSICIST, US NAVAL RES LAB, 62-, ACTG CHIEF SCIENTIST, LAB COSMIC RAY PHYSICS, 81- *Concurrent Pos:* Assoc Dir, Int Sch Cosmic Ray Astrophysics, Enice, Italy, 78- *Mem:* Am Geophys Union; Radiation Res Soc. Fel Am Phys Soc; Am Astron Soc; Sigma Xi. *Res:* Cosmic ray effects on microelectronics; acceleration of cosmic rays in accretion disks of ultra-massive black holes; isotopic and elementary composition of cosmic rays; solar modulation and transformation of cosmic ray composition in space; spallation and fission reactions; neutrino astronomy; radiobiological effects of heavy cosmic ray nuclei. *Mailing Add:* Code 4028 US Naval Res Lab Washington DC 20375

SILBERBERG, RUTH, b Kassel, Ger, Mar 20, 06; nat US; m 33. PATHOLOGY. *Educ:* Breslau Univ, MD, 31. *Prof Exp:* Asst, Path Inst, Breslau Univ, 30-33; pathologist, Jewish Hosp, 33; vol res path, Dalhousie Univ, 34-36 & Wash Univ, 37-41; asst, NY Univ, 41-44; from instr to prof, 45-74, emer prof path, Sch Med, Wash Univ, 74-76; VIS SCIENTIST, HEBREW HADASSAH UNIV, 76- *Concurrent Pos:* Dean fel, NY Univ, 41-44; actg pathologist, Jewish Hosp, St Louis, 45-46; pathologist, Barnard Free Skin & Cancer Hosp, 47; sr pathologist, Hosp Div, City of St Louis, 47-59. *Mem:* Am Soc Exp Path; Soc Exp Biol & Med; Soc Develop Biol; Am Asn Path & Bact; Am Asn Cancer Res. *Res:* Experimental pathology; skeletal growth and aging; hormonal carcinogenesis; developmental potencies of the lymphocyte; pathogenesis of osteoarthrosis. *Mailing Add:* Dept of Path Box 1172 Jerusalem Israel

SILBERFELD, MICHEL, b Paris, France, Feb 15, 46; Can citizen. PSYCHIATRY, EPIDEMIOLOGY. *Educ:* McGill Univ, BSc, 66, MDCM, 70; Univ Toronto, MSc, 73. *Prof Exp:* ASST PROF EPIDEMIOL & PSYCHIAT, UNIV TORONTO, 76-; STAFF PSYCHIATRIST, WELLESLEY HOSP, 78- *Concurrent Pos:* Consult & res scientist psychiat & epidemiol, Addiction Res Found, 76-78; consult, Princess Margaret Hosp, 78-, mem staff, 79- *Res:* Social psychiatry. *Mailing Add:* Wellesley Hosp 160 Wellesley St E Toronto ON M4Y 1J3 Can

SILBERG, STANLEY LOUIS, b Kansas City, Mo, Dec 27, 27; m 56; c 2. EPIDEMIOLOGY, BACTERIOLOGY. *Educ:* Univ Kans, AB, 51, MA, 52; Univ Minn, MPH, 59, PhD(epidemiol), 65. *Prof Exp:* Res asst mycol, Kans State Health Dept, 52-53 & Sch Med, Univ Kans, 53-54; res fel epidemiol, Univ Minn, 57-61; asst prof, Sch Med, Univ Mo-Columbia, 61-69, assoc prof biostatist & epidemiol, 69-72, actg chmn, 78-81 PROF BIOSTATIST & EPIDEMIOL, SCH PUB HEALTH, HEALTH SCI CTR, UNIV OKLA, 72-, VCHMN, 81- *Concurrent Pos:* Mo Div Health grant, 63-65; USPHS grant, 65-; consult, USPHS Commun Dis Ctr, Ga, 66- *Res:* Infectious disease epidemiology. *Mailing Add:* Univ Okla Health Sci Ctr Col Health Bldg PO Box 26901 Oklahoma City OK 73190

SILBERGELD, ELLEN K, b Washington, DC, 1945. TOXICOLOGY, NEUROSCIENCES. *Educ:* Vassar Col, AB, 67; Johns Hopkins Univ, PhD(eng), 72. *Prof Exp:* Fel neurosci, Johns Hopkins Sch Hyg, 72-75; staff fel neuropharm, Nat Inst Neurol & Commun Disorders & Stroke, NIH, 75-79, sect chief neurotoxicol, 79-81; CHIEF SCIENTIST TOXICOL, ENVIRON DEFENSE FUND, 82- *Concurrent Pos:* Dele, US & USSR Environ Health Exchange, 77-78; mem, US Dept Human Health Serv, 77-81; lectr continuing med, educ environ & occup med, 78-80; adv, Hyperkinesis & Diet, Nutrit Found, 75- *Mem:* Soc Neurosci; Int Brain Res Orgn; Am Soc Pharmacol & Exp Therapeut; Am Soc Neurochem; Soc Occup & Environ Health. *Res:* Neurotoxicology and environmental toxicology; adverse effects of chemicals and drugs on nervous system function; lead poisoning; developmental neurosciences. *Mailing Add:* Environ Defense Fund 1525 18th St NW Washington DC 20036

SILBERGELD, MAE DRISCOLL, b Bowersville, Ohio, Nov 23, 23; m 52; c 4. SPACE PHYSICS, COMPUTER SCIENCES. *Educ:* Univ Dayton, BS, 45; Univ Ill, MS, 46. *Prof Exp:* Instr physics, Univ Ill, 46-52 & NC State Univ, 52-54; res physicist, Robert A Taft Sanit Eng Ctr, USPHS, 54-56 & Stanford Univ, 66-68; lead programmer, Thomas A Larson Assocs, 69-70; sr analyst, 70-71, task leader, 71-73, mgr space physics sect, 73-76, mgr, Appl Physics Dept, 76-79, DEP DIR SCI & APPLICATIONS, COMPUT SCI CORP, 79- *Mem:* Asn Comput Mach; Am Geophys Union. *Res:* Radio astronomy; solar physics; magnetic and electric field phenomena in magnetosphere and ionosphere; x-ray and gamma ray spectroscopy; stratospheric modeling; atmospheric and particle physics. *Mailing Add:* 10704 Clermont Ave Garrett Park MD 20766

SILBERGELD, SAM, b Wengrow, Poland, Mar 1, 18; US citizen; m 52; c 4. PSYCHIATRY. *Educ:* Blackburn Col, AA, 38; Univ Chicago, BS, 39; Univ Ill, MS, 41, PhD(biochem), 43; Duke Univ, MD, 54. *Prof Exp:* Instr biochem, Mayo Found, 44-45; instr, Ill Neuropsychiat Inst, Univ Ill Med Sch, 45, asst prof chem, Chicago Undergrad Div, Univ Ill, 46-52; intern med, Cincinnati Gen Hosp, 54-55, resident internal med, 56; MED DIR, USPHS, 56- *Concurrent Pos:* Staff asst to dir, Div Biol Stand, Nat Inst Ment Health, NIH, 56-59, res grants specialist, Div Gen Med Sci, 59-61, chief gen clin res ctr br, Div Res Facil & Resources, 61-64, res grants specialist, Nat Inst Ment Health, 64 & Ment Health Career Develop Prog, 64-, res psychiatrist, Ment Health Study Ctr, 70-, actg dir, Div Intramural Res, Nat Inst Alcohol Abuse & Alcoholism, 76-77; USPHS ment health career develop award, 64-70; resident psychiat, Sch Med, Stanford Univ, 64-67, res assoc, 67-68, res psychiatrist, Lab Clin Sci, 68-70; physician's recognition award, AMA, 77-82. *Mem:* Am Psychiat Asn; NY Acad Sci; Am Chem Soc. *Res:* Clinical, community and psychobiochemical research, especially the metabolic and behavioral aspects of stress. *Mailing Add:* 10704 Clermont Ave Garrett Park MD 20766

SILBERGER, ALLAN JOSEPH, b York, Pa, Aug 24, 33; m 57; c 4. MATHEMATICS. *Educ:* Univ Rochester, AB, 55; Johns Hopkins Univ, MA, 62, PhD(math), 66. *Prof Exp:* Assoc math, Appl Physics Lab, Johns Hopkins Univ, 58-64, instr, Univ, 64-66; asst prof, Bowdoin Col, 66-71; mem, Inst Advan Study, 71-73; guest prof, Math Inst, Univ Bonn, WGer, 73-74; vis assoc prof, Univ Mass, 74-75; assoc prof, 75-80, PROF MATH, CLEVELAND STATE UNIV, 80- *Mem:* Am Math Soc; Math Asn Am. *Res:* Representation theory; group theory. *Mailing Add:* Dept Math Cleveland State Univ Cleveland OH 44115

SILBERGER, DONALD MORISON, b York, Pa, Feb 26, 30; m 80; c 4. MATHEMATICS. *Educ:* Harvard Univ, BA, 53; Univ Wash, MS, 61, PhD(math), 73. *Prof Exp:* High sch instr, Ohio, 56-58; NSF res asst, 62-63; instr math, Idaho State Univ, 63-65; assoc prof, Butler Univ, 65-67; lectr, Western Wash State Col, 67-68; from asst prof to assoc prof, Tougaloo Southern Christian Col, 68-74 & 76-77; spec asst prof math, Univ Colo, Boulder, 74-76; PROF POST GRAD MATH, FED UNIV SANTA CATARINA, 76- *Mem:* AAAS; Am Math Soc; Asn Symbolic Logic; Math Asn Am. *Res:* Finite combinatorics; algebraic theory of semigroups; theory of regular finite simple hypergraphs; logic; universal terms. *Mailing Add:* Prog Postgrad Math Fed Univ Santa Catarina 88000 Florianopolis SC Brazil

SILBERGLEIT, ALLEN, b Springfield, Mass, Mar 8, 28; m 56; c 3. SURGERY, PHYSIOLOGY. *Educ:* Univ Mass, BA, 49, MS, 51; Univ Cincinnati, MD, 55; Wayne State Univ, PhD(physiol), 65; Am Bd Surg, dipl, 61; Bd Thoracic Surg, dipl, 65. *Prof Exp:* From intern to resident surg, Univ Minn, 55-60; chief surg serv, Sheppard AFB Hosp, Tex, 60-62; instr surg, 62-65, ASSOC PROF PHYSIOL, SCH MED, WAYNE STATE UNIV, 65-, ASSOC SURG, 66- *Concurrent Pos:* Mich Heart Asn res grants; resident thoracic surg & clin investr, Allen Park Vet Admin Hosp, Detroit, 62-65; surgeon, Detroit Gen Hosp, 62-, Hutzel Hosp, Detroit, 66- & St Joseph Mercy Hosp, Pontiac, 66-; consult, Mayor's Comt Human Resources Develop, Detroit, 66- & Pontiac Motor Div, Gen Motors Corp, 66- *Mem:* Fel Am Col Surgeons; Soc Thoracic Surg; Am Heart Asn; Am Physiol Soc; Sigma Xi. *Res:* Cardiopulmonary, vascular and gastrointestinal problems; surgical physiology. *Mailing Add:* Dept of Physiol Wayne State Univ Sch Med Detroit MI 48201

SILBERGLIED, ROBERT ELLIOT, entomology, animal behavior, deceased

SILBERGLITT, RICHARD STEPHEN, b Brooklyn, NY, Mar 9, 42; m 66; c 2. SOLID STATE PHYSICS. *Educ:* Stevens Inst Technol, BS, 63; Univ Pa, MS, 64, PhD(physics), 68. *Prof Exp:* Res assoc theoret solid state physics, Univ Pa, 68; lectr physics, Univ Calif, Santa Barbara, 68-69; res assoc solid state physics, Brookhaven Nat Lab, 69-71; asst prog dir theoret physics, Physics Sect, NSF, 71, asst prog dir solid state & low temperature physics, Div Mat Res, 71-72, assoc prog dir solid state physics, 72-75; mem energy study staff, Nat Acad Sci, 76-80; MEM STAFF, DHR, INC, 80- *Mem:* Am Phys Soc. *Res:* Effect of spin wave and spin-phonon interactions on dynamical properties; inelastic neutron scattering; unique properties of systems with layered structure of displaying soft modes; lattic instabilities in nonstoichiometric materials. *Mailing Add:* 1055 Thomas Jefferson St Washington DC 20007

SILBERHORN, GENE MICHAEL, b Lenawee Co, Mich, Apr 30, 38; m 60; c 2. MARINE BOTANY. *Educ:* Eastern Mich Univ, BS, 63; WVa Univ, MS, 65; Kent State Univ, PhD(bot), 70. *Prof Exp:* Teaching asst gen bot & gen biol, WVa Univ, 63-65, NSF teaching fel, 65; asst prof ecol & Plant ecol, Radford Col, 65-67; NSF trainee gen bot, Kent State Univ, 67-70; Killian fel & instr, Univ Alta, 70-72; sect head, Wetlands Res Sect, 72-80, DEPT HEAD, WETLANDS ECOLOGY DEPT, VA INST MARINE SCI, 80-; ASSOC PROF, SCH MARINE SCI, COL WILLIAM & MARY, 80- *Mem:* Coastal Soc; Sigma Xi. *Res:* Inventory and evaluation of tidal wetlands of Virginia; community structure of tidal freshwater marshes; monitoring of coastal habitats. *Mailing Add:* Wetlands Res Sect Va Inst Marine Sci Gloucester Point VA 23062

SILBERLING, NORMAN JOHN, b Oakland, Calif, Nov 28, 28; m; c 2. STRATIGRAPHY. *Educ:* Stanford Univ, BS, 50, MS, 53, PhD(geol), 57. *Prof Exp:* Geologist, US Geol Surv, 50-66; from assoc prof to prof geol, Stanford Univ, 66-75; GEOLOGIST, US GEOL SURV, 75- *Mem:* AAAS; Geol Soc Am; Am Asn Petrol Geologists. *Res:* Pre-Tertiary stratigraphy and tectonics of western North America; paleontology and biostratigraphy of Triassic marine invertebrates. *Mailing Add:* US Geol Surv Denver Fed Ctr Denver CO 80225

SILBERMAN, EDWARD, b Minneapolis, Minn, Feb 8, 14; m 41; c 4. FLUID MECHANICS, WATER RESOURCES MANAGEMENT. *Educ:* Univ Minn, BCE, 35, MS, 36. *Prof Exp:* Water technician, State Planning Bd, Minn, 36; jr engr, flood control, Tenn Valley Authority, 37; jr engr construct, Minneapolis Dredging Co, 38; engr construct, US Civil Aeronaut Admin, 38-41 & 46; from res assoc to assoc prof civil eng, 46-63, dir St Anthony Falls Hydraul Lab, 63-74, prof, 63-81, EMER PROF CIVIL ENG, UNIV MINN, MINNEAPOLIS, 82- *Concurrent Pos:* Comnr, Bassett Creek Flood Control Comn, Hennepin County, Minn, 72- *Mem:* Am Soc Civil Engrs; Am Acad Mech; Soc Am Mil Engrs; Am Water Resources Asn (pres, 69); Int Asn Hydraul Res. *Res:* Water resources management; model studies of hydraulic and fluid flow phenomena, supercavitating flows; boundary layers; turbulence; air-water mixtures; flow losses in closed and open conduits; underwater acoustics. *Mailing Add:* 2325 Brookridge Ave Minneapolis MN 55422

SILBERMAN, ENRIQUE, b Buenos Aires, Arg, Dec 9, 21; m 49; c 2. MOLECULAR SPECTROSCOPY. *Educ:* Univ Buenos Aires, PhD(eng), 45. *Prof Exp:* Investr physics, Arg Atomic Energy Comn, 53-58, head dept, 58-63; prof, Univ Buenos Aires, 63-66; PROF PHYSICS, FISK UNIV, 66- *Concurrent Pos:* Guest prof, Univ Notre Dame, 63; consult, Arg Nat Coun Sci Res, 64; vis prof, Vanderbilt Univ, 67- *Mem:* AAAS; Am Asn Physics Teachers; Am Phys Soc; Arg Physics Asn. *Res:* Infrared and Raman spectroscopy; normal coordinates analysis; inorganic ions in solid solutions; vibrational determination of crystal structures; ferroelectrics. *Mailing Add:* Dept Physics Fisk Univ Nashville TN 37203

SILBERMAN, MILES LOUIS, b New York, NY, Sept 25, 40; m 61; c 1. GEOCHEMISTRY. *Educ:* City Univ New York, BS, 63; Univ Rochester, MS, 67, PhD(geol), 71. *Prof Exp:* Geologist, Pac Mineral Resources Br, 67-75, geologist, Alaskan Geol Br, 76-81, GEOLOGIST, MARINE GEOL, US GEOL SURV, 81- *Mem:* Geol Soc Am; Mineral Asn Can; Geochem Soc; Soc Econ Geologists. *Res:* Geochronology and geochemistry of igneous rocks and their associated ore deposits using chemical, isotopic and geol mapping techniques; exploration for precious and base metal deposits; regional and structural controls on localization of ore deposits. *Mailing Add:* US Geol Surv 345 Middlefield Rd Menlo Park CA 94025

SILBERMAN, ROBERT G, b New York, NY, Aug 20, 39; m 61; c 2. ORGANIC CHEMISTRY, CHEMICAL EDUCATION. *Educ:* Brooklyn Col, BS, 60; Cornell Univ, MS, 63, PhD(org chem), 65. *Prof Exp:* Asst prof, 65-69, ASSOC PROF CHEM, STATE UNIV NY COL, CORTLAND, 69- *Mem:* Am Chem Soc; Nat Sci Teachers Asn; Sigma Xi. *Res:* Organic analysis; insect pheromones; natural products chemistry; chemical education; laboratory programs. *Mailing Add:* Dept of Chem State Univ of NY Col Cortland NY 13045

SILBERMAN, RONALD, b Jackson, Mich, July 31, 32; m 55; c 3. CLINICAL MICROBIOLOGY, IMMUNOLOGY. *Educ:* Temple Univ, BA, 58; Hahnemann Med Col, MS, 60; Univ Md, Baltimore City, PhD(microbiol), 70. *Prof Exp:* Asst prof microbiol & immunol, 69-74, asst prof path, 71-74, ASSOC PROF PATH, SCH MED, MED CTR, LA STATE UNIV, SHREVEPORT, 74- *Concurrent Pos:* Chief microbiologist, Lab Serv, Vet Admin Med Ctr, Shreveport, 71-; dir microbiol, Clin Lab, Med Ctr, La State Univ Hosp, Shreveport, 71-, asst dir, Sch Med Technol, 72-; clin prof microbiol, Med Technol, La Tech Univ, Ruston, 81- *Mem:* Am Soc Microbiol; Asn Practrs in Infection Control. *Res:* Rickettsiology. *Mailing Add:* Dept of Path Med Ctr La State Univ PO Box 33932 Shreveport LA 71130

SILBERNAGEL, BERNARD GEORGE, b Wausau, Wis, Dec 13, 40; m 65; c 2. PHYSICS. *Educ:* Yale Univ, BS, 62; Univ Calif, San Diego, MS, 64, PhD(physics), 66. *Prof Exp:* Lectr physics, Univ Calif, Santa Barbara, 66-68, asst prof, 68-72; mem staff, 72-81, SR RES ASSOC, EXXON RES & ENG CO, 81- *Mem:* AAAS; Am Phys Soc; Am Chem Soc. *Res:* Magnetic resonance; solid state physics; superconductivity; magnetism. *Mailing Add:* Exxon Res & Eng Co PO Box 45 Linden NJ 07036

SILBERNAGEL, MATT JOSEPH, b Hague, NDak, May 13, 33; m 55; c 5. PLANT PATHOLOGY, PLANT BREEDING. *Educ:* Univ Wash, BS, 57; Wash State Univ, PhD(plant path), 61. *Prof Exp:* PLANT PATHOLOGIST, CROPS RES DIV, AGR RES SERV, USDA, 61- *Concurrent Pos:* AID consult, Brazil, 70, India-Pakistan, 77, Cent Int de Agr Trop Workshops, 75 & 81 & AID Title XII Tanzanian-Wash State Univ Bean Collabr Res Support Prog, 80-85. *Mem:* Am Phytopath Soc. *Res:* Breeding snap beans for disease resistance, environmental stress tolerance and seed quality; study of bean-disease-environment interactions; improvement of beans for direct mechanical harvesting. *Mailing Add:* Irrig Agr Res & Exten Ctr USDA PO Box 30 Prosser WA 99350

SILBERSCHATZ, ABRAHAM, b Haifa, Israel, May 1, 47; m 68; c 2. OPERATING SYSTEMS, DATABASE SYSTEMS. *Educ:* State Univ NY, Stony Brook, PhD(comput sci), 76. *Prof Exp:* Asst prof, 76-79, ASSOC PROF COMPUT SCI, UNIV TEX, AUSTIN, 79- *Mem:* Asn Comput Mach; Inst Elec & Electronics Engrs. *Res:* Operating systems; language design; distributed systems; database systems and protection. *Mailing Add:* Dept Comput Sci Univ Tex Austin TX 78712

SILBERSTEIN, EDWARD B, b Cincinnati, Ohio, Sept 3, 36; m 62; c 2. NUCLEAR MEDICINE, ONCOLOGY. *Educ:* Yale Univ, BS, 58; Harvard Univ, MD, 62; Am Bd Internal Med, cert, 69, recert, 80, cert hemat, 72, cert oncol, 82; Am Bd Nuclear Med, cert, 72. *Prof Exp:* Resident internal med, Cincinnati Gen Hosp, 63-64 & Univ Hosps of Cleveland, 66-67; trainee hemat, New Eng Med Ctr Hosps, 67-68; asst prof med, Univ Cincinnati, 70-75, assoc prof radiol, 72-77; ASSOC DIR NUCLEAR MED, RADIOISOTOPE LAB, CINCINNATI GEN HOSP, 68-; ASSOC PROF MED, UNIV CINCINNATI, 75-, PROF RADIOL, 77- *Concurrent Pos:* Am Cancer Soc res grants, 72 & 74; mem adv panel radiopharmaceut, US

Pharmacopoeia, 80. *Mem:* AAAS; Am Col Physicians; Radiation Res Soc; Am Soc Hemat; fel Royal Soc Health. *Res:* Marrow transplantation; effect of radiation on chromosomes; biological indicators of radiation damage; diagnosis of tumors with radiopharmaceuticals. *Mailing Add:* Radioisotope Lab Cincinnati Gen Hosp Cincinnati OH 45267

SILBERSTEIN, OTMAR OTTO, b Graz, Austria, Apr 18, 21; US citizen; m 47; c 2. FOOD SCIENCE. *Educ:* Mich State Univ, BS, 49, MS, 50; Cornell Univ, PhD(veg crops), 53. *Prof Exp:* Res asst, US Plant, Soil & Nutrit Lab, NY, 53-54; res chemist, Welch Grape Juice Co, 54-58; head dept food technol, Wallerstein Labs Div Baxter Labs, 58-63; dir res & develop, Gilroy Foods, Inc, 63-80; DIR EXPLOR TECHNOL, MCCORMICK & CO, INC, 80- *Mem:* Am Chem Soc; Inst Food Technologists; Am Soc Bakery Eng; Am Asn Cereal Chemists. *Res:* Food enzymology and flavor chemistry; dehydration of vegetables. *Mailing Add:* McCormick & Co 11350 McCormick Rd Hunt Valley MD 21031

SILBERT, DAVID FREDERICK, b Cambridge, Mass. BIOCHEMISTRY. *Educ:* Harvard Univ, AB, 58, MD, 62. *Prof Exp:* Intern & resident med, Sch Med, Washington Univ, 62-64; res assoc microbial genetics, Nat Inst Arthritis & Metab Dis, 64-66; Am Cancer Soc fel biol chem, Sch Med, 66-68, from asst prof to assoc prof, 68-77, PROF BIOL CHEM, SCH MED, WASHINGTON UNIV, 77- *Concurrent Pos:* NIH res grant, 68-; res grant, Am Chem Soc, 75-; mem microbiol chem study sect, NIH, 75- *Mem:* Am Soc Biol Chem; Am Soc Microbiol. *Res:* Biochemical genetics; membrane chemistry. *Mailing Add:* Dept of Biol Chem Washington Univ Sch of Med St Louis MO 63110

SILBERT, LEONARD STANTON, b Philadelphia, Pa, Dec 16, 20. PHYSICAL CHEMISTRY, ORGANIC CHEMISTRY. *Educ:* Philadelphia Col Pharm, BSc, 43; Univ Pittsburgh, PhD(chem), 53. *Prof Exp:* Jr prof asst, Eastern Regional Res Labs, 46-47, Nat Renderers Asn res fel, Eastern Utilization Res Br, 53-56, RES CHEMIST, EASTERN REGIONAL RES CTR, USDA, 56- *Mem:* AAAS; Am Chem Soc; Am Oil Chemists Soc. *Res:* Synthesis of lipid compounds and their physical properties; syntheses; structural determinations and applications of peroxide chemistry; organic thiocyanations; isopropesoylation chemistry; free radical studies; food irradiation; carbonian chemistry. *Mailing Add:* Apt 105 Pastorius Bldg 7800 C Stenton Ave Philadelphia PA 19118

SILBEY, ROBERT JAMES, b Brooklyn, NY, Oct 19, 40; m 62. PHYSICAL CHEMISTRY. *Educ:* Brooklyn Col, BS, 61; Univ Chicago, PhD(chem), 65. *Prof Exp:* Nat Acad Sci-Nat Res Coun-Air Force Off Sci Res fel, Univ Wis, 65-66; asst prof, 66-69, assoc prof, 69-76, PROF CHEM, MASS INST TECHNOL, 77- *Concurrent Pos:* Sloan Found res fel, 68-70; Camille & Henry Dreyfus Found teacher scholar, 71-76; vis prof, Inst Theoret Physics, Univ Utrecht, 72-73; Guggenheim Found fel, 72-73. *Mem:* Am Phys Soc. *Res:* Quantum chemistry; theory of excited states of solids. *Mailing Add:* Dept of Chem Mass Inst of Technol Cambridge MA 02139

SILCOX, JOHN, b Saltash, Eng, May 26, 35; m 60; c 3. PHYSICS. *Educ:* Bristol Univ, BSc, 57; Cambridge Univ, PhD(physics), 61. *Prof Exp:* From asst prof to assoc prof eng physics, 61-70, actg chmn dept appl physics, 70-71, dir sch appl & eng physics, 71-74, PROF ENG PHYSICS, CORNELL UNIV, 70-, DIR, SCH APPL & ENG PHYSICS, 79- *Concurrent Pos:* Guggenheim Found fel, 67-68; mem solid state sci comt, Nat Res Coun, Nat Acad Sci, chmn-elect, 81- *Mem:* Fel Am Phys Soc; Electron Micros Soc Am(pres, 79). *Res:* Transmission electron microscopy; defects in crystals; inelastic electron scattering. *Mailing Add:* 210 Clark Hall Cornell Univ Ithaca NY 14853

SILEN, WILLIAM, b San Francisco, Calif, Sept 13, 27; m 47; c 3. SURGERY. *Educ:* Univ Calif, Berkeley, BA, 46; Univ Calif, San Francisco, MD, 49; Am Bd Surg, dipl, 58. *Hon Degrees:* MA, Harvard Univ, 66. *Prof Exp:* Intern, Univ Calif Hosp, San Francisco, 49-50, asst resident gen surg, 50; ward surgeon, Travis AFB, 50-52; asst resident gen surg, Univ Calif Hosp, San Francisco, 52-56, chief resident, 56-57; from instr to asst prof surg, Sch Med, Univ Colo, 57-60; from asst prof to assoc prof, Sch Med, Univ Calif, San Francisco, 60-66; PROF SURG, HARVARD MED SCH, 66-; SURGEON-IN-CHIEF, BETH ISRAEL HOSP, BOSTON, 66- *Concurrent Pos:* Asst chief surg, Denver Vet Admin Hosp, 57-59, chief, 59-60; asst chief, San Francisco Gen Hosp, 60-61, chief, 61-66; consult, Children's Hosp Med Ctr, Boston, 68-; secy depts surg, Harvard Med Sch, 70-73; mem, Am Bd Surg, 70-73, sr mem, 73-; ed, Year Book Surg, 70; mem surg B study sect, NIH, 72-76; Guggenheim fel, 73-74. *Mem:* Soc Clin Surgeons; Soc Univ Surgeons; Am Col Surgeons; Asn Acad Surg; Am Surg Asn. *Res:* Gastrointestinal physiology. *Mailing Add:* Beth Israel Hosp 330 Brookline Ave Boston MA 02215

SILER, WILLIAM MACDOWELL, b Houston, Tex, Aug 5, 20; m 74; c 3. BIOMATHEMATICS, THEORETICAL BIOLOGY. *Educ:* Stevens Inst Technol, MS, 49; City Univ New York, PhD(biol), 72. *Prof Exp:* Proj engr, Exp Towing Tank, Stevens Inst Technol, 47-49; physicist radiol physics, Mem Sloan-Kettering Cancer Ctr, Mem Hosp, New York, 59-65; assoc prof & chmn med comput sci prog, Downstate Med Ctr, Brooklyn, 65-72; prof biomath, Univ Ala, Birmingham, 72-80, chmn dept, 72-75; DIR BIOMATH, CARRAWAY CTR, BIRMINGHAM, 80- *Concurrent Pos:* Mem, Study Sect Comput & Biomath Res, NIH, 69-73, consult to var study sects, 66- *Mem:* Am Asn Physicists Med; Biomed Eng Soc; Sigma Xi; Inst Elec & Electronics Engrs. *Res:* Computer applications in biology and medicine; modelling biological systems; radiological physics; computers in cardiology. *Mailing Add:* 417 22 Ave S Birmingham AL 35205

SILER-KHODR, THERESA M, b Pomona, Calif, June 17, 52; m 74; c 2. REPRODUCTIVE ENDOCRINOLOGY. *Educ:* Immaculate Heart Col, BA, 68; Univ Hawaii, PhD(biochem), 71. *Prof Exp:* Teaching asst biochem, Univ Hawaii, 68-71; asst prof obstet & gynec, Am Univ Beirut, 74-76; ASSOC PROF PHYSIOL, OBSTET & GYNEC, UNIV TEX, SAN ANTONIO, 76- *Concurrent Pos:* NIH prin investr, 81-83. *Mem:* Am Endocrine Soc; Soc Gynec Invest; Am Fertil Soc; Sigma Xi. *Res:* The nature and function of human chorionic gonadotropin releasing hormone in the human placenta. *Mailing Add:* 9130 Powhatun San Antonio TX 78230

SILFLOW, CAROLYN DOROTHY, b Kendvick, Idaho, Jan 8, 50; m 81. CELL BIOLOGY. *Educ:* Pac Lutheran Univ, BS, 72; Univ Ga, PhD(bot), 77. *Prof Exp:* Fel, Dept Biol, Yale Univ, 77-81; ASST PROF CELL & DEVELOP BIOL, DEPT GENETICS & CELL BIOL, UNIV MINN, 82- *Mem:* Am Soc Cell Biol; Soc Develop Biol. *Res:* Regulation of flagellar gene expression following removal of flagella in Chlamydomonas; tubulin gene structure and expression; molecular basis for microtubule heterogeneity. *Mailing Add:* Dept Genetics & Cell Biol Univ Minn 250 Biosci Ctr St Paul MN 55108

SILFVAST, WILLIAM THOMAS, b Salt Lake City, Utah, June 7, 37; m 59; c 3. PHYSICS. *Educ:* Univ Utah, BS(math) & BS(physics), 61, PhD(physics), 65. *Prof Exp:* Res assoc physics, Univ Utah, 65-66; NATO fel, Oxford Univ, 66-67; MEM TECH STAFF, BELL TEL LABS, 67- *Concurrent Pos:* NATO fel. *Mem:* Am Phys Soc; Optical Soc Am. *Res:* Lasers and plasma physics, with specific interest in gaseous and metal vapor lasers; recombination lasers and laser-produced plasmas. *Mailing Add:* Bell Tel Labs Holmdel NJ 07733

SILHA, ROBERT EMMETT, b Burlington, Iowa, July 24, 21; m 45. DENTISTRY. *Educ:* Univ Minn, BS, 52, DDS, 53, Univ Iowa, MS, 57. *Prof Exp:* Asst oral diag, resident oral surg, Col Dent, Univ Iowa, 53-55, from instr to asst prof, 55-62; ED DENT RADIOG & PHOTOG, EASTMAN KODAK CO, 62-; CLIN ASSOC PROF DENT & DENT RADIOL, SCH MED & DENT, UNIV ROCHESTER, 67- *Concurrent Pos:* Consult, Kodak Off Med Dept, 62-; secy oral radiol sect, Am Asn Dent Sch, 72-73, chmn, 74-75. *Mem:* Fel Am Acad Dent Radiol; fel Int Col Dentists; Int Dent Fedn; Am Dent Asn; Am Acad Dent Radiol (pres, 70-71, secy Am Acad Oral Roentgenol, 66-68). *Res:* Clinical dental radiology. *Mailing Add:* 343 State St Rochester NY 14650

SILHACEK, DONALD LE ROY, b Norfolk, Nebr, Nov 9, 37; m 60; c 2. BIOCHEMISTRY, ENTOMOLOGY. *Educ:* Univ Nebr, Lincoln, BSc, 58, MSc, 61; Univ Wis-Madison, PhD(biochem, entom), 66. *Prof Exp:* RES CHEMIST, INSECT ATTRACTANTS LAB, AGR RES SERV, USDA, 65- *Concurrent Pos:* Instr, Armstrong State Col, 66-68; asst prof, Univ Fla, 70-80, prof, 80- *Mem:* Am Chem Soc; Am Soc Zoologists. *Res:* Endogenous mechanisms controlling intermediary metabolism in insects; hormonal mechanisms controlling development of insects. *Mailing Add:* Insect Attractants Lab USDA PO Box 14565 Gainesville FL 32604

SILJAK, DRAGOSLAV (D), b Beograd, Yugoslavia, Sept, 10, 33; m 67; c 2. ELECTRICAL ENGINEERING. *Educ:* Univ Belgrade, Dipl Ing, 58, MSEE, 61, DrSci(elec eng), 63. *Prof Exp:* Docent prof elec eng, Univ Belgrade, 60-64; PROF ELEC ENG & COMPUT SCI, UNIV SANTA CLARA, 64- *Concurrent Pos:* NASA res grant, Univ Santa Clara, 65-77, NSF grant, 68-69 & Dept Energy contract, 77- *Mem:* Inst Elec & Electronics Engrs. *Res:* Large scale dynamic systems. *Mailing Add:* Dept of Elec Eng Univ of Santa Clara Santa Clara CA 95053

SILK, JOHN KEVIN, b Cambridge, Mass, May 6, 38; m 60; c 2. SOLAR PHYSICS, X-RAY OPTICS. *Educ:* Harvard Univ, AB, 60; Mass Inst Technol, PhD(physics), 69. *Prof Exp:* Scientist asst, Raytheon Co, 60-64, consult, 64-68; SR STAFF SCIENTIST, AM SCI & ENG CO, 69- *Concurrent Pos:* Res asst plasma physics, Mass Inst Technol, 66-69. *Honors & Awards:* Skylab Achievement Award, NASA, 74 & Solar Physics Group Award, 75. *Mem:* Am Astron Soc. *Res:* X-ray telescope on skylab; x-ray imaging systems; x-ray diagnostics of laboratory fusion plasmas; x-ray lithography. *Mailing Add:* Am Sci & Eng Co 955 Massachusetts Ave Cambridge MA 02142

SILK, MARGARET WENDY KUHN, b Baltimore, Md, Nov 16, 46; m 68; c 2. QUANTITATIVE BOTANY, AGRICULTURE. *Educ:* Harvard Univ, BA, 68; Univ Calif, Berkeley, PhD(bot), 75. *Prof Exp:* Teaching asst, Univ Calif, Berkeley, 70-75; res fel biol, Univ Pa, 75-76; ASST RES SCIENTIST, AGR EXP STA & ASST PROF QUANT PLANT SCI, UNIV CALIF, DAVIS, 76- *Mem:* Am Soc Plant Physiol; Bot Soc Am; Soc Develop Biol. *Res:* Quantitative aspects of plant development, morphogenesis, physiology and plant-water-environment interactions. *Mailing Add:* Dept of LAWR Univ of Calif Davis CA 95616

SILKER, THEODORE HENRY, b Marion, Iowa, Apr 11, 14; m 37; c 3. FOREST ECOLOGY, SOILS. *Educ:* Iowa State Univ, BS, 40, MS, 41; Okla State Univ, PhD(agron, soils), 75. *Prof Exp:* Forestry aide, Mich State Civilian Conserv Corps, 40; teaching asst mensuration, Iowa State Univ, 40-41; forester, Tenn Valley Authority, 41-45, eastern dist head, 45-48; res technician, Tex Forest Serv, 48-49, asst silviculturist, Tex Forest Serv & Tex Agr Exp Sta, 49-54, assoc silviculturist, 54-61; from asst prof to assoc prof, 61-76, PROF SILVICULT, OKLA STATE UNIV, 76- *Mem:* Soc Am Foresters; Soil Sci Soc Am; Am Soc Agron; Sigma Xi. *Res:* Plant control with prescribed burning and aerial silvicides; site amendment related to reforestation and direct seeding; site classification; surface geology-soil-site relationships; forest management; wildlife habitat. *Mailing Add:* Dept Forestry Okla State Univ Stillwater OK 74074

SILKER, WYATT BURDETTE, radiochemistry, physical chemistry, see previous edition

SILL, ARTHUR DEWITT, b Akron, Ohio, Dec 1, 21; m 47; c 3. ORGANIC CHEMISTRY. *Educ:* Ohio State Univ, BS, 48; Univ Cincinnati, MS, 61, PhD(org chem), 64. *Prof Exp:* Prin chemist, Battelle Mem Inst, 49-55; res asst org prod res, 55-64, proj leader org res dept, 64-71, org chemist, Anal Res Dept, Merrell-Nat Labs Div, Richardson-Merrell, Inc, 71-80, SR ANAL CHEMIST, MERRELL DOW PHARMACEUTICALS, INC, 80- *Mem:* Am Chem Soc. *Res:* Study of structure of organic substances, including metabolites, via spectroscopic methods, including mass spectrometry and nuclear magnetic resonance; organic synthesis; development of analytical methods for drug substances; identification of impurities and other organic substances. *Mailing Add:* Anal Res Dept Merrell Dow Pharmaceuticals Inc Cincinnati OH 45215

SILL, CLAUDE WOODROW, b Layton, Utah, Oct 29, 18; m 55; c 3. ANALYTICAL CHEMISTRY. *Educ:* Univ Utah, AB, 39, MA, 41. *Prof Exp:* Researcher, Iowa State Col, 41-42; chemist, US Bur Mines, 42-51; chief anal chem br, AEC, 51-75; chief anal chem br, Health Serv Lab, Energy Res & Develop Admin, 75-77; sr scientist, Radiol & Environ Sci Lab, Dept Energy, 77-80; SR SCIENTIST, EG&G IDAHO, INC, 80- *Res:* Synthesis of organo-uranium compounds: analytical methods. *Mailing Add:* EG&G Idaho Inc PO Box 1625 Idaho Falls ID 83415

SILL, LARRY R, b Fairmont, Minn, Sept 10, 37; m 59; c 2. MAGNETISM, LOW TEMPERATURE SOLID STATE PHYSICS. *Educ:* Carleton Col, BA, 59; Iowa State Univ, PhD(physics), 64. *Prof Exp:* From instr to prof, 64-78, actg head dept, 66-68, assoc dean, Col Lib Arts & Sci, 69-80, PROF PHYSICS, NORTHERN ILL UNIV, 78- *Mem:* AAAS; Am Phys Soc; Am Asn Physics Teachers; Sigma Xi. *Res:* Measurements of the low temperature transport and magnetic properties of rare earth compounds and alloys. *Mailing Add:* Dept Physics Northern Ill Univ De Kalb IL 60015

SILL, RICHARD CLEMENTS, b Lincoln, Nebr, Oct 6, 22; m 49. PHYSICS. *Educ:* Univ Nebr, AB, 45, MA, 50, PhD(physics), 54. *Prof Exp:* Res engr jet propulsion lab, Calif Inst Technol, 45-46; asst, Lick Observ, Univ Calif, 48-49; instr physics, Univ Nebr, 50-53; physicist, Stanford Res Inst, 53-56; asst prof physics, NMex Inst Min & Technol, 56-59; from asst prof to assoc prof, 59-74, PROF PHYSICS, UNIV NEV, RENO, 74- *Concurrent Pos:* Consult & res assoc, Desert Res Inst, Univ Nev, Reno, 61-64. *Mem:* AAAS; Am Phys Soc; Fedn Am Sci. *Res:* Solid state surface physics; capillarity; theory of liquid state, melting; photometry; applications of physics to ecological problems, especially wilderness; physiological optics; instrumental electronics; systems analysis; thermodynamics; large systems hydrology; intermolecular correlations. *Mailing Add:* Dept of Physics Univ of Nev Reno NV 89557

SILL, WEBSTER HARRISON, JR, b Wheeling, WVa, Dec 4, 16; m 43; c 3. PLANT PATHOLOGY, ENVIRONMENTAL BIOLOGY. *Educ:* WVa Wesleyan Col, BS, 39; Boston Univ, MA, 47; Pa State Univ, MS, 48; Univ Wis, PhD(plant path), 51. *Prof Exp:* Asst biol, Boston Univ, 40; instr, WVa Wesleyan Col, 46-47; asst biol, Boston Univ, 47; asst plant path & bot, Pa State Univ, 47-48; asst plant path, Univ Wis, 48-51, res assoc, 51-52; from asst prof to prof bot & plant path, Kans State Univ, 52-69; PROF BIOL & CHMN DEPT, UNIV SDAK, 69- *Concurrent Pos:* Guest prof, Univ Giessen, 60, Int Symp Plant Viruses, Scotland, 60 & Int Symp Plant Path, India, 67; consult, Gen Foods Corp, Frontier Chem Co, Vulcan Chem Co, Int Rice Res Inst, Philippines, 62-63, Food & Agr Orgn, UN Italy, 62-63, Joint Comn Rural Reconstruct, Taiwan, 63, H J Heinz Co & State Planning Agency SDak, 70-; agr res adv, Kans State Univ-AID, India, 66-68; chmn, Nat Comt Virus Dis Small Grains & Grasses, 69; chmn bd dirs, Black Hills Natural Sci Field Sta, 69-; chmn & dir ctr environ studies, Univ SDak, 69-; sr fel, Food Inst, East-West Ctr, Honolulu, 74-75; govt fel, Am Coun Educ, 76-77; res specialist, Nat Sci Coun, Taiwan, 80-81. *Mem:* AAAS; Am Soc Pub Admin; Am Phytopath Soc; Mycol Soc Am. *Res:* Plant virology; viruses of small grains and grasses; international agricultural development. *Mailing Add:* Dept of Biol Univ of SDak Vermillion SD 57069

SILL, WILLIAM ROBERT, b Cleveland, Ohio, Oct 14, 37; m 63; c 2. GEOPHYSICS. *Educ:* Mich State Univ, BS, 60; Mass Inst Technol, MS, 63, PhD(geophys), 68. *Prof Exp:* Mem tech staff, Bellcomm Inc, Washington, DC, 67-72; assoc res prof, 72-81, RES PROF GEOPHYS, UNIV UTAH, 81- *Mem:* AAAS; Am Geophys Union. *Res:* Electrical properties of rocks and planetary interiors; solar wind-planetary interactions; lunar geophysics; mineral exploration. *Mailing Add:* Dept of Geol & Geophys Sci Univ of Utah Salt Lake City UT 84112

SILLA, HARRY, b Jersey City, NJ, Dec 7, 29; m 57; c 3. CHEMICAL ENGINEERING. *Educ:* City Col New York, BChE, 54; Stevens Inst Technol, MS, 61, PhD(chem eng), 70. *Prof Exp:* Proj engr, Eng Ctr, Columbia Univ, 54 & 56-57; chem engr, Stevens Inst Technol, 57-59; proj leader, Aerochem Res Labs, Sybron Corp, 59-64; asst prof chem eng, 64-78, PROF CHEM ENG, STEVENS INST TECHNOL, 78- *Mem:* Combustion Inst; Am Chem Soc; Am Inst Chem Engrs. *Res:* Combustion; electrical properties of flames. *Mailing Add:* Stevens Inst of Technol Castel Point Sta Hoboken NJ 07030

SILLECK, CLARENCE FREDERICK, b Brooklyn, NY, Nov 12, 09; m 34; c 1. CHEMISTRY, PIGMENT DISPERSION. *Educ:* Polytech Inst Brooklyn, BS, 32, MS, 36. *Hon Degrees:* DSc, Polytech Inst NY, 79. *Prof Exp:* Tech dir, C J Osborn Co, 32-68, pres, 68-69; VPRES, C J OSBORN CHEM, INC, PENNSAUKEN, NJ, 69- *Concurrent Pos:* Trustee, Polytech Inst New York. *Mem:* AAAS; Am Chem Soc; fel Am Inst Chemists; Am Soc Testing & Mat; Fedn Socs Coatings Technol. *Res:* Synthetic resins and pigment dispersions for protective coatings; colloidal dispersion of carbon black in cellulose nitrate; dispersion of carbon black in alkyd resins; specialty finishes. *Mailing Add:* 186-20 Henley Rd Jamaica NY 11432

SILLIKER, JOHN HAROLD, b Ayer's Cliff, Que, June 20, 22; nat US; m 79; c 2. MICROBIOLOGY. *Educ:* Univ Southern Calif, AB, 47, MS, 48, PhD(bact), 50; Am Bd Med Microbiol, dipl. *Prof Exp:* USPHS fel bact, Hopkins Marine Sta, Stanford Univ, 50-51; asst prof, Sch Med, Univ Rochester, 51-52; bacteriologist, George W Gooch Labs, Ltd, Calif, 52-53; chief bacteriologist & assoc dir res, Swift & Co, Ill, 53-61; res assoc & consult, Dept Path, St James Hosp, Chicago Heights, Ill, 61-67; PRES, SILLIKER LABS, 67- *Concurrent Pos:* Mem res coun, Inst Am Poultry Industs & Am Meat Inst Found, 53-61; lectr, Meat Hyg Training Ctr, USDA, 61-; mem, Comt on Salmonella Sampling & Methodology in Egg Prod, 64-; vis prof food sci, Univ Ill, 65; mem comt salmonella, Nat Res Coun-Nat Acad Sci, 67-68; consult, Int Comn Microbiol Specifications for Foods, 70-74, mem, 74. *Honors & Awards:* Sci Award, Am Pub Health Asn, 63. *Mem:* Fel Am Pub Health Asn; Inst Food Technologists; fel Am Acad Microbiol; Soc Appl Microbiol; Royal Soc Health. *Res:* Fatty acid oxidation by bacteria; enteric and food bacteriology; microbiological methods for examination of foods, particularly Salmonella and other enteric organisms. *Mailing Add:* 1139 E Dominguez St Suite I Carson CA 90746

SILLIMAN, RALPH PARKS, b Seattle, Wash, June 26, 13; m 37; c 2. FISH BIOLOGY. *Educ:* Univ Wash, BS, 36. *Prof Exp:* Tech asst Pac halibut res, Int Fish Comn, 36-37; aquatic biologist Pac sardine res, US Fish & Wildlife Serv, 38-45, aquatic biologist, Pac salmon res, 45-49, adminr anadromous & inland fishery res, 49-63, fish pop res, US Bur Commercial Fisheries, 64-69 & Nat Marine Fisheries Serv, 70-73; CONSULT FISHERY BIOLOGIST, 73- *Mem:* Am Fisheries Soc; Am Inst Fishery Res Biol (pres, 64-66). *Res:* Population dynamics; mathematical population models. *Mailing Add:* 4135 Baker NW Seattle WA 98107

SILLMAN, EMMANUEL I, b Philadelphia, Pa, Dec 7, 15. PARASITOLOGY, INVERTEBRATE ZOOLOGY. *Educ:* Univ Mich, PhD(zool), 54. *Prof Exp:* Lectr & asst prof zool, Ont Agr Col, 53-58; asst prof, Univ Man, 58-60; assoc prof, 60-68, PROF BIOL, DUQUESNE UNIV, 68- *Mem:* AAAS; Am Soc Zoologists; Am Soc Parasitologists; Soc Syst Zool; Am Micros Soc. *Res:* Life histories of digenetic trematodes and warble flies; disease and parasites of fish; biology and ecology of protozoa, flatworms and gastropods. *Mailing Add:* Dept of Biol Sci Duquesne Univ Pittsburgh PA 15219

SILLS, JOE FRED, public health, see previous edition

SILLS, RONALD ALAN, chemical engineering, see previous edition

SILSBEE, HENRY BRIGGS, b Washington, DC, Jan 15, 23; m 56. PHYSICS. *Educ:* Harvard Univ, BS, 43, MA, 47, PhD(physics), 51. *Prof Exp:* Asst, Carnegie Inst Dept Terrestrial Magnetism, 41; jr physicist, Nat Bur Standards, 43-44; jr scientist Manhattan proj, Los Alamos Sci Lab, 44-46; asst prof physics, Univ Calif, Berkeley, 51-58; assoc prof, Univ Wash, Seattle, 58-63; mem staff, Brookhaven Nat Lab, 63-64; assoc prof, 64-67, PROF PHYSICS, STATE UNIV NY, STONY BROOK, 67- *Res:* Molecular beams; solid state physics; low temperature physics. *Mailing Add:* Dept of Physics State Univ of NY Stony Brook NY 11790

SILSBEE, ROBERT HERMAN, b Washington, DC, Feb 24, 29; m 50; c 3. SOLID STATE PHYSICS, MAGNETIC RESONANCE. *Educ:* Harvard Univ, AB, 50, MA, 51, PhD(physics), 56. *Prof Exp:* Mem staff, Solid State Div, Oak Ridge Nat Lab, 56-57; from instr to assoc prof, 57-65, PROF PHYSICS, CORNELL UNIV, 65- *Concurrent Pos:* Sloan res fel, 58-60; NSF sr fel, 65-66; Guggenheim Found fel, 73-74. *Mem:* Am Phys Soc. *Res:* Solid state physics; magnetic resonance; radiation damage; optical properties. *Mailing Add:* Dept of Physics Cornell Univ Ithaca NY 14853

SILVA, ARMAND JOSEPH, b Waterbury, Conn, June 1, 31; m 54, 68; c 3. OCEAN & CIVIL ENGINEERING. *Educ:* Univ Conn, BSE, 54, MS, 56, PhD(civil eng), 65. *Prof Exp:* Instr civil eng, Univ Conn, 55-56; soils engr, Thompson & Lichtner Co, 56-58; from instr to prof civil eng, Worcester Polytech Inst, 58-76, head dept, 71-76; PROF OCEAN & CIVIL ENG, UNIV RI, 76-, DIR, MARINE GEOMECH RES GROUP, 81- *Concurrent Pos:* Consult, 58-; pres & treas, Geotechnics, Inc, 56-67; grants, NSF, Worcester Polytech Inst, 66-67 & 71-72, Shell Develop Co, 71 & Off Naval Res, 72-; res contract, Dept Energy, 74-; NSF grant, 78- *Mem:* Am Soc Civil Engrs; Inst Soc Soil Mech & Found Engrs; Am Geophys Union; Marine Technol Soc; AAAS. *Res:* Ocean engineering; soil mechanics; geotechnical properties of ocean sediments; marine sediment processes; sediment coring technology; soil-structure interaction; marine geomechanics. *Mailing Add:* Dept of Ocean Eng Univ of RI Narragansett RI 02882

SILVA, JAMES ANTHONY, b Kilauea, Hawaii, Sept 4, 30; m 67; c 2. SOIL FERTILITY. *Educ:* Univ Hawaii, BS, 51, MS, 59; Iowa State Univ, PhD(soil biochem), 64. *Prof Exp:* Asst-in-training sugar cane, Exp Sta, Hawaiian Sugar Planter's Asn, 51-53, asst agronomist, 53-59; asst soil biochem, Iowa State Univ, 59-64; asst prof soil sci, 64-70, assoc prof soil sci & sta statistician, 70-76, PROF SOIL SCI, COL TROP AGR, UNIV HAWAII, HONOLULU, 76- *Concurrent Pos:* NSF fel, 64-66; sabbatical, Cornell Univ, 71-72; prin investr int proj, Benchmark Soils Proj, AID, 76- *Mem:* Soil Sci Soc Am; Am Soc Agron; Int Soc Soil Sci. *Res:* Nutrient availability and uptake by plants, especially nitrogen, phosphorus, silicon and zinc; soil and plant tissue testing for nutrient requirements of tropical soils and crops, especially maize and sugarcane; transfer of agrotechnology based on the soil family of soil taxonomy. *Mailing Add:* Dept of Agron & Soil Sci Univ of Hawaii Honolulu HI 96822

SILVA, OMEGA LOGAN, b Dec 14, 36; US citizen; m 58; c 1. INTERNAL MEDICINE, ENDOCRINOLOGY. *Educ:* Howard Univ, BS, 58, MD, 67; Am Bd Internal Med, dipl, 74. *Prof Exp:* Chemist, NIMH, 58-63; from intern to resident internal med, Vet Admin Hosp, 67-70, res assoc endocrinol, 71-74, clin investr, 74-77; asst prof, 74-80, ASSOC PROF MED, GEORGE WASHINGTON UNIV, 80- *Concurrent Pos:* Fel endocrinol, Vet Admin Hosp, Washington, DC, 70-71; adj assoc prof oncol, Howard Univ, 77- *Mem:* AAAS; Am Chem Soc; Am Med Women's Asn; Am Fedn Clin Res; Endocrine Soc. *Res:* Calcium metabolism; function of human calcitonin. *Mailing Add:* 354 N St SW Washington DC 20024

SILVA, PATRICIO, b Santiago, Chile, July 7, 39; c 3. NEPHROLOGY. *Educ:* Cath Univ Chile, BS, 59, MD, 64. *Prof Exp:* Resident, Clin Hosp, Univ Chile, 64-67; staff physician & consult nephrol, Regional Hosp Talca, Chile, 67-69; prof nutrit, Univ Chile, 68, prof pathophysiol, Cent Univ Talca, 69; res assoc pharmacol, Dartmouth Med Sch, 69-70; fel, Yale Univ Sch Med, 70-71, res assoc, 72; instr, 72-74, asst prof, 74-79, ASSOC PROF MED, HARVARD MED SCH, 79-; ASSOC DIR, RENAL UNIT & ASST PHYSICIAN BETH ISRAEL HOSP, 75- *Concurrent Pos:* Fel, Nat Kidney Found, 70 & Conn Heart Asn, 71; clin asst, Boston City Hosp, 72-74; investr, Am Heart Asn, 77. *Mem:* Am Fedn Clin Res; Am Soc Nephrol; Am Physiol Soc; Am Soc Exp Biol & Med; AAAS. *Mailing Add:* Dept Med 330 Brookline Ave Boston MA 02215

SILVA, PAUL CLAUDE, b San Diego, Calif, Oct 31, 22. BOTANY. *Educ:* Univ Southern Calif, BA, 46; Stanford Univ, MA, 48; Univ Calif, PhD(bot), 51. *Prof Exp:* Res fel bot, Univ Calif, 51-52; from instr to assoc prof, Univ Ill, 52-61, sr herbarium botanist, 61-67, RES BOTANIST, UNIV CALIF, BERKELEY, 67- *Concurrent Pos:* Guggenheim fel, 58-59; ed, Phycologia 61-69. *Honors & Awards:* Darbaker Award, Bot Soc Am, 58. *Mem:* Bot Soc Am; Am Soc Plant Taxonomists; Phycol Soc Am (secy, 54-57, vpres, 57, pres, 58); Int Asn Plant Taxon; Int Phycol Soc (pres, 65). *Res:* Morphology, taxonomy and ecology of marine algae. *Mailing Add:* Dept of Bot Univ of Calif Berkeley CA 94720

SILVA, RICARDO, b Hong Kong, Nov 20, 31; US citizen; m 63; c 4. ORGANIC CHEMISTRY. *Educ:* Univ Sydney, BS, 53; Univ Calif, Los Angeles, PhD(chem), 61. *Prof Exp:* NIH fel, Imp Col, Univ London, 61-62; from asst prof to assoc prof, 62-70, chmn dept, 73-76, PROF CHEM, CALIF STATE UNIV, NORTHRIDGE, 70- *Concurrent Pos:* NSF inst grants, 62-63 & 64-65, fel, 66-67; NIH res grant, 64-65; Calif Inst Technol Pres Fund grant, 72-73. *Mem:* Am Chem Soc; Royal Soc Chem. *Res:* Nuclear magnetic resonance; polycyclic compounds; natural products; structure and reactivity; biogenetic origins; photochemical reactions of naturally occurring compounds; synthesis of indole alkaloids. *Mailing Add:* Dept of Chem Calif State Univ Northridge CA 91330

SILVA, ROBERT JOSEPH, b Oakland, Calif, Feb 16, 27; m 50; c 3. NUCLEAR CHEMISTRY. *Educ:* Univ Ore, BS, 51; Univ Calif, Berkeley, PhD(chem), 59. *Prof Exp:* Chem engr, Kaiser Aluminum Corp, Calif, 50-51; health physicist, Radiation Lab, Univ Calif, 51-54, lab technician, 54-57, res asst, 57-59; chemist, Oak Ridge Nat Lab, 59-66; nuclear chemist, Lawrence Radiation Lab, Univ Calif, 66-68; res scientist, Spec Training Div, Oak Ridge Assoc Univs, 68-70; mem staff, Oak Ridge Nat Lab, 70-77; STAFF SCIENTIST, LAWRENCE BERKELEY LAB, UNIV CALIF, 77- *Mem:* Am Phys Soc; Am Chem Soc; Sigma Xi. *Res:* Low energy nuclear reactions and scattering; nuclear spectroscopy; nuclear instruments; transuranium nuclear research; transuranium chemical research. *Mailing Add:* Lawrence Berkeley Lab PO Box X Berkeley CA 94720

SILVA-HUTNER, MARGARITA, b Rio Piedras, PR, Nov 28, 15; m 56; c 1. MYCOLOGY, MICROBIOLOGY. *Educ:* Univ PR, BA, 36; Harvard Univ, AM, 45, PhD, 52; Am Bd Med Microbiol, dipl. *Prof Exp:* Instr mycol & dermat, Sch Trop Med, PR, 36-45, assoc, 45-49, asst mycol, Dept Dermat, Col Physicians & Surgeons, NY, 50-53, res assoc, 53-56, asst prof mycol & head mycol lab, 56-63, ASSOC PROF DERMAT, COL PHYSICIANS & SURGEONS, COLUMBIA UNIV, 63- *Concurrent Pos:* Teaching asst, Boston Univ, 47 & 49; consult, Communicable Dis Ctr, USPHS, 52-53 & Squibb Inst Med Res, 54-55; mem standards & exam comt pub health & med Lab mycol, Am Bd Med Microbiol; mem tech adv comt, Am Type Cult Collection; dir mycol lab, Presby Hosp, New York, 56-; consult, USPHS Hosp in Stapleton, Staten Island, NY, 63-79; mycologist dermat serv, Presby Hosp, New York, 76- *Mem:* AAAS; fel Am Acad Microbiol; Am Soc Microbiol; Med Mycol Soc of the Americas (pres, 78-79); hon mem Soc Brasileira Dermat. *Res:* Morphology, taxonomy and biology of pathogenic fungi. *Mailing Add:* Dept of Dermat Columbia Univ New York NY 10032

SILVEGGIO, PETER MICHAEL, b Syracuse, NY, July 24, 47; m 77. ASTROPHYSICS, PHYSICS. *Educ:* Syracuse Univ, BS, 69; Cornell Univ, MS, 75, PhD(physics), 77. *Prof Exp:* Res assoc physics, Nat Acad Sci, Nat Res Coun, NASA, 77-79; PHYSICIST, LAWRENCE LIVERMORE NAT LAB, 79- *Concurrent Pos:* Asst prof physics, San Jose State Univ, 79-80; dir res, Craig Res & Technol, Inc, 79- *Res:* Net flux radiometer on Galileo Mission to Jupiter; infrared spectroscopy; planetary atmospheric modeling; systems analysis on military effectiveness of strategic weapon systems; net flux radiometer experiment on Galileo Mission to pepifer infrared spectroscopy; planetary atmospheric modeling. *Mailing Add:* 776 Flume Ct Milpitas CA 95035

SILVEIRA, AUGUSTINE, JR, b New Bedford, Mass, July 17, 34; m 60; c 2. ORGANIC CHEMISTRY. *Educ:* Southeastern Mass Univ, BS, 57; Univ Mass, PhD(chem), 62. *Hon Degrees:* ScD, Southeastern Mass Univ, 75. *Prof Exp:* Teaching fel chem, Univ Mass, 57-58, teaching assoc, 58-60, instr, 60-62; asst prof, Rutgers Univ, 62-63; assoc prof chem, 63-64, mem patent policy bd, 71, prof chem, 64-76, DISTINGUISHED TEACHING PROF, STATE UNIV NY COL OSWEGO, 76- CHMN DEPT, 67-, EVALUATOR GRAD PROGS, 68- *Concurrent Pos:* Dir res, NIH res grant, 62-63; State Univ NY fac res fel, 64 & 67, res grant in aid, 64-65 & 67-69; dir, NSF Undergrad Sci Equip grant, 65-67 & 77-78, partic grant org mech, NSF Conf, Vt, 66; Am Coun Educ fel, Univ Calif, Irvine, 69-70; indust consult, 70-; mem comn higher educ, Mid States Asn Cols & Sec Schs, 71-; dir, NSF res grants, 73-74, 77-78 & 79-82; consult, NY State Educ Dept, 75; vis prof, Univ Calif, Irvine & Calif State Univ, Long Beach, 76-77; res corp grant, State Univ NY, 77-78, fac grant, 78-79, fac grant undergrad instr, 77-79 & 80-82; grant, Eastern Col Sci Conf, 78; NSF res grant, 79-82; mem optom bd, State NY, 80-85; mem optom bd, State NY, 80-85; State Univ NY fac exchange scholar, 81- *Mem:* AAAS; Am Chem Soc; fel Am Inst Chemists; Sigma Xi. *Res:* Structure, synthesis and reactions of organonitrogen and organometallic chemistry; study of polynuclear hydrocarbons. *Mailing Add:* 2021 Benson Ave Minetto NY 13115

SILVEIRA, MILTON ANTHONY, b Mattapoisett, Mass, May 4, 29; m; c 4. MECHANICAL ENGINEERING. *Educ:* Univ Vt, BSME, 51; Univ Va, MSAE, 60. *Hon Degrees:* Dr, Univ Vt, 77. *Prof Exp:* Res intern, Dynamic Loads Div, Langley Field, 51 & studies on helicopter vibration & dynamic probs, Vibration & Flutter Br, 55-61, actg head loads sect, Struct Br, Space Task Group, 61-63, from asst br chief to dep chief, Aerodyn Br, Spacecraft Res Div, 63-65, from tech mgr to prog mgr, Little Joe II Launch Vehicle, 64-65, head, Flight Performance & Dynamics Br, 65-67, asst to dir eng & develop for spec proj, 67-68, chief, Eng Anal Off, 68-69, mgr, Space Shuttle Eng Off, 69-73, dep prog, Space Orbiter Proj, Johnson Spacecraft Ctr, 73-81, ASST TO DEP ADMINR, HQ, NASA, 81- *Honors & Awards:* Sustained Superior Performance Award, NASA, 65 & 69, Except Serv Medal, 69. *Mem:* Am Inst Aeronaut & Astronaut. *Res:* Engineering systems analysis; engineering of the space shuttle systems and directing in-house design and analysis efforts. *Mailing Add:* NASA Houston TX 77058

SILVER, ALENE FREUDENHEIM, b New York, NY, Oct 31, 16; div; c 3. DEVELOPMENTAL BIOLOGY, DERMATOLOGY. *Educ:* Columbia Univ, BA, 38; Univ Ill, PhD(physiol), 47. *Prof Exp:* Res asst circulatory physiol, Col Med, Univ Ill, 42-46; res assoc, Michael Reese Hosp, Chicago, 46-47; res assoc wound healing, Johns Hopkins Hosp, Baltimore, 48-49; res assoc skin physiol, Brown Univ, 61-64, res assoc develop genetics, 65-70, res asst prof, 69-70; assoc prof biol, 70-75, PROF BIOL, RI COL, 76- *Concurrent Pos:* USPHS biomed sci support grant, 66-68; assoc mem, Inst Life Sci, Brown Univ, 70-75; sr investr biol & med, Brown Univ, 75- *Mem:* Int Pigment Cell Soc; Sigma Xi; Am Soc Cell Biol; Am Soc Zoologists; Soc Develop Biol. *Res:* Physiology of skin; developmental genetics of hair regeneration; phenotypic modulation of hair germ melanocytes during hair cycle; development of the eye in mutant and normal mice. *Mailing Add:* Dept of Biol RI Col Providence RI 02908

SILVER, ARNOLD HERBERT, b Brooklyn, NY, Sept 27, 31; m 52; c 5. SOLID STATE PHYSICS. *Educ:* Rensselaer Polytech Inst, BS, 52, MS, 54, PhD(physics), 58. *Prof Exp:* Asst physics, Rensselaer Polytech Inst, 52-55 & Brown Univ, 55-57; res engr, Sci Lab, Ford Motor Co, 57-62, sr res scientist, 62-64, prin res scientist assoc, 64-65, staff scientist, 65-69; dir, Electronics Res Lab, Aerospace Corp, 69-80; SR SCIENTIST, TRW INC, 80- *Mem:* AAAS; fel Am Phys Soc; Inst Elec & Electronics Engrs. *Res:* Nuclear and electron magnetic resonance; radio frequency spectroscopy; superconductivity; quantum effects in superconductors; electronic techniques and instrumentation; superconducting and cryogenic devices. *Mailing Add:* TRW-DSSG RI/1086 One Space Park Redondo Beach CA 90278

SILVER, BURTON BARNEY, b Montreal, Que, Apr 3, 28. PHYSIOLOGY, ELECTRON MICROSCOPY. *Educ:* Upsala Col, BA, 51; Rutgers Univ, MS, 61, PhD(physiol, biochem), 66. *Prof Exp:* Bacteriologist, Bellevue Hosp, New York, 51; teacher, High Sch, 53-62; asst prof physiol, Montclair State Col, 62-63; instr physiol, Rutgers Univ, 63-66; asst prof med & dent physiol, 66-67, ASST PROF PHYSIOL & BIOPHYS, SCH MED, UNIV LOUISVILLE, 67- *Concurrent Pos:* Res assoc, Merck Inst Biol Res, 55 & Air Reduction Labs, 56-60; assoc lectr, Upsala Col, 65-; NIH res grant metab dis; SKF & Eli Lilly res grants. *Mem:* AAAS; Electron Micros Soc Am. *Res:* Cellular energetics and metabolism electron microscopy; correlation of cellular structure with metabolic function as associated with endocrine deficiencies; structural studies of rejection phenomena in cardiac and kidney transplants. *Mailing Add:* Dept of Physiol Univ of Louisville Sch of Med Louisville KY 40208

SILVER, DAVID MARTIN, b Chicago, Ill, Sept 25, 41; m 63; c 1. THEORETICAL CHEMISTRY. *Educ:* Ill Inst Technol, BS, 62; Johns Hopkins Univ, MA, 64; Iowa State Univ, PhD(chem), 68. *Prof Exp:* NSF fel chem, Harvard Univ, 68-69; vis scientist, Europ Ctr Atomic & Molecular Calculations, Orsay, France, 70; CHEMIST, APPL PHYSICS LAB, JOHNS HOPKINS UNIV, 70-, PRIN STAFF, 76-, SUPVR CHEM PHYSICS RES, 77- *Mem:* AAAS; Am Chem Soc; Am Phys Soc. *Res:* Molecular physics; electron correlation and electronic structure of atoms and molecules; chemical reaction dynamics; chemical kinetics; molecular interactions; mathematical analysis; submarine oxygen systems. *Mailing Add:* Appl Physics Lab Johns Hopkins Univ Laurel MD 20707

SILVER, DONALD, b New York, NY, Oct 19, 29; m 58; c 4. CARDIOVASCULAR SURGERY, THORACIC SURGERY. *Educ:* Duke Univ, AB, 50, BS & MD, 55. *Prof Exp:* Asst prof surg, Med Ctr, Duke Univ, 64-66, assoc prof surg & dir vascular clin, 66-72, prof, 72-75; PROF SURG & CHMN DEPT, UNIV MO MED CTR, 75- *Concurrent Pos:* Attend physician, Vet Admin Hosp, Durham, 65-75; consult, Watts Hosp, Durham, 65-75; consult, Harry S Truman Vet Admin Hosp, Columbia, Mo, 75; mem bd sci adv, Cancer Res Ctr, Columbia, Mo, 75. *Mem:* Aerospace Med Asn; fel Am Col Surgeons; Int Cardiovasc Soc; Soc Univ Surgeons; Am Surg Asn. *Res:* Thromboembolic phenomena with special emphasis on the vascular and fibrinolytic systems. *Mailing Add:* Dept of Surg Univ of Mo Med Ctr Columbia MO 65212

SILVER, EDWARD A, b Mt Vernon, NY, Aug 20, 48; m 71; c 1. MATHEMATICS, MATHEMATICS EDUCATION. *Educ:* Iona Col, BA, 70; Columbia Univ, MA, 73, MS & EDD(math educ), 77. *Prof Exp:* asst prof math, Northern Ill Univ, 77-79; asst prof, 79-81, ASSOC PROF MATH, SAN DIEGO STATE UNIV, 81- *Mem:* Math Asn Am; Am Educ Res Asn; Nat Coun Teachers Math; Cognitive Sci Soc. *Res:* Study of mathematical cognition, especially mathematical problem solving, using an eclectic approach that leans heavily on techniques drawn from artificial intelligence, cognitive psychology, and mathematics education. *Mailing Add:* Dept Math Sci San Diego State Univ San Diego CA 92182

SILVER, EDWARD ALLAN, b Montreal, Que, June 13, 37; m 66; c 3. OPERATIONS RESEARCH, INDUSTRIAL ENGINEERING. *Educ:* McGill Univ, BEng, 59; Mass Inst Technol, ScD(opers res), 63. *Prof Exp:* Prof staff mem, Opers Res Group, Arthur D Little, Inc, Mass, 63-67; assoc prof bus admin, Boston Univ, 67-69; assoc prof mgt sci, Univ Waterloo, 69-72, prof, 72-81; PROF MGT SCI, UNIV CALGARY, 81- *Concurrent Pos:* Lectr, Mass Inst Technol, 65-67; consult, Arthur D Little Inc, Bell Can, US Army Inventory Res Off, Defence Res Bd Can, Can Ctr Remote Sensing, Can Gen Tower, Am Optical, Uniroyal & Standard Oil Ind; vis prof, Ecole Polytech Federale de Lausanne, Switz, 76-77. *Mem:* Can Oper Res Soc (pres, 80-81); Opers Res Soc Am; Inst Mgt Sci; Am Production & Inventory Control Soc; Am Inst Indust Engrs. *Res:* Applications of approximate solutions to complex problems in operations research and industrial engineering with particular emphasis in areas of production planning and inventory control. *Mailing Add:* Fac Mgt Univ Calgary Calgary AB T2N 1N4 Can

SILVER, ERNEST GERARD, b Munich, Ger, Dec 26, 29; US citizen; m 54; c 1. EXPERIMENTAL PHYSICS. *Educ:* Boston Univ, BA, 52; Harvard Univ Grad Sch, MS, 54; Oak Ridge Sch Reactor Technol, dipl, 55; Univ Tenn, Knoxville, PhD(physics), 65. *Prof Exp:* Staff physicist reactor physics & neutron physics, Oak Ridge Nat Lab, 55-74; staff mem, Inst Energy Anal, 74-75, exec officer, 75-77, asst mgr, Breeder Reactor Proj, 77-79, ASST MGR, NUCLEAR STANDARDS MGT CTR, OAK RIDGE NAT LAB, 79- *Mem:* Am Nuclear Soc; Am Phys Soc; AAAS. *Res:* Energy policy; relation of energy use to national economy; neutron cross section for reactor application; time-dependent neutron diffusion. *Mailing Add:* 107 Lehigh Lane Oak Ridge TN 37830

SILVER, FRANK MORRIS, b Eden, NC, Aug 30, 43; m 69; c 2. POLYMER CHEMISTRY, ORGANIC CHEMISTRY. *Educ:* Univ NC, Chapel Hill, BS, 65; Univ Wis-Madison, PhD(org chem), 70. *Prof Exp:* Sr res chemist, 70-74, res specialist, 74-78, GROUP LEADER, MONSANTO CO, 78- *Mem:* Am Chem Soc. *Res:* Organic and polymer reaction mechanisms; solution and melt polymerization of novel polymers; organic and polymer characterization; fiber spinning, characterization and end use application of novel polymers; rubber-plastic blends; injection molding. *Mailing Add:* 260 Springside Dr Akron OH 44313

SILVER, GARY LEE, b Columbus, Ga, Nov, 22, 36; m 68; c 1. ANALYTICAL CHEMISTRY. *Educ:* Mass Inst Technol, BS, 59; Univ NC, PhD(anal chem), 63. *Prof Exp:* Sr chemist, 63-80, MONSANTO FEL, MOUND LAB, MONSANTO RES CORP, 80- *Mem:* Am Chem Soc. *Res:* Inorganic chemistry: lanthanides and actinides, particularly plutonium; radioactive materials and radioactive waste treatment; numerical methods for study of equilibrium state. *Mailing Add:* Mound Lab Monsanto Res Corp Miamisburg OH 45342

SILVER, GEORGE ALBERT, b Philadelphia, Pa, Dec 23, 13; m 37; c 3. MEDICINE, PUBLIC HEALTH. *Educ:* Univ Pa, BA, 34; Jefferson Med Col, MD, 38; Johns Hopkins Univ, MPH, 48. *Hon Degrees:* MA, Yale Univ, 70. *Prof Exp:* Asst demonstr bact, Jefferson Med Col, 39-42; asst prof pub health admin, Sch Hyg & Pub Health, Johns Hopkins Univ, 48-51; asst prof admin med, Col Physicians & Surgeons, Columbia Univ, 53-59; prof social med, Albert Einstein Col Med, 59-65; dep asst secy health, US Dept Health, Educ & Welfare, Weashington, DC, 66-68, exec urban coalition, Health Prog, 68-70; PROF PUB HEALTH, SCH MED, YALE UNIV, 69- *Concurrent Pos:* Regional med officer, US Dept Agr Migrant Prog, 47-48; health officer, Eastern Health Dist, City Dept Health, Baltimore, Md, 48-51; chief dept social med, Montefiore Hosp, 51-65; consult, WHO, 68- mem tech bd, Milbank Mem Fund, 63-76. *Mem:* Sr mem Inst Med-Nat Acad Sci; Am Pub Health Asn; Sigma Xi; AAAS. *Res:* Social medicine; medical care organization and administration; health policy. *Mailing Add:* Dept of Pub Health Yale Univ Sch of Med New Haven CT 06510

SILVER, HENRY K, b Philadelphia, Pa, Apr 22, 18; m 41; c 2. PEDIATRICS. *Educ:* Univ Calif, AB, 38, MD, 42. *Prof Exp:* Intern pediat, Univ Hosp, Univ Calif, 41-42, clin asst, Med Sch, 44-45, from instr to asst prof, 46-52; assoc prof, Sch Med, Yale Univ, 52-57; PROF PEDIAT, SCH MED, UNIV COLO, DENVER, 57-, CLIN PROF NURSING, SCH NURSING, 76-, ASSOC DEAN ADMISSIONS, SCH MED, 77- *Concurrent Pos:* Rosenberg Found fel, 45-47; vis prof, Children's Hosp, Hawaii, 61; clin prof nursing, assoc dean & consult, Fitzsimons Gen Hosp, Denver. *Mem:* Inst Med-Nat Acad Sci; Soc Pediat; Am Pediat Soc; Am Acad Pediat. *Res:* Health manpower; pediatric endocrinology; syndromes with short stature; deprivation dwarfism. *Mailing Add:* Univ Colo Sch Med 4200 E Ninth Ave Denver CO 80262

SILVER, HERBERT GRAHAM, b Somerset, Eng, Sept 10, 38, US citizen; wid. PHYSICAL CHEMISTRY, ELECTROCHEMISTRY. *Educ:* Univ London, BSc & ARCS, 60, PhD(phys chem), 63; Imp Col, Univ London, dipl, 63. *Prof Exp:* NIH grant & Fulbright scholar, Harvard Univ, 63-65; mem tech staff chem, Bell Tel Labs, Inc, 65-67 & Gen Tel & Electronics Labs, Inc, 67-72, eng specialist, GTE Sylvania Inc, 72-75; chief lamp engr & mgr linear lamps, Canrad-Hanovia, Inc Div, Canrad Precision Industs Inc, 75-77; mgr, Filter Performance & Contamination Labs, Pall Corp, 78-81; SR SCIENTIST, ADVAN DEVELOP, COMPONENTS DIV, BUNDY CORP, 81- *Mem:* AAAS; fel Royal Soc Chem; Sigma Xi; NY Acad Sci. *Res:* Gas discharges; materials research; electrochemistry; electroplating; development of high-efficiency gas discharge lamps for lighting, photochemical processes, medical therapeutics; filters and fluid clarification devices. *Mailing Add:* 14 Gay Dr Kings Point NY 11024

SILVER, HOWARD FINDLAY, b Denver, Colo, Sept 16, 30; m 61; c 3. CHEMICAL ENGINEERING. *Educ:* Univ Mich, MSc, 57, PhD(chem eng), 61. *Prof Exp:* Chem engr, E I du Pont de Nemours & Co, 52-53 & 55; res engr, Calif Res Corp Div, Standard Oil Co Calif, 57-58 & 61-64; assoc prof chem eng, 64-68, PROF CHEM ENG, UNIV WYO, 68- *Concurrent Pos:* Prog mgr supporting res, Fossil Fuels & Advan Systs Dept, Elec Power Res Inst, 74-75, consult, Clean Liquid & Solid Fuels Dept, 75- *Mem:* Am Inst Chem Engrs; Am Chem Soc. *Res:* Conversion of coal and shale oil to synthetic liquid hydrocarbon products by means of hydrogenation and cracking reactions. *Mailing Add:* Dept Mineral Eng Univ Wyo Laramie WY 82071

SILVER, HOWARD I(RA), b New York, NY, June 2, 39; m 62; c 2. ELECTRICAL ENGINEERING. *Educ:* City Col New York, BEE, 61; NY Univ, MEE, 64, PhD(elec eng), 68. *Prof Exp:* Eng trainee, Missile & Space Div, Gen Elec Co, 61-62; engr, Fed Labs, Int Tel & Tel Corp, 62-64; assoc engr, Sperry Gyroscope Co, 64-66; instr elec eng, NY Univ, 66-68; from asst prof to assoc prof, 68-76, chmn dept, 71-76, PROF ELEC ENG, FAIRLEIGH DICKINSON UNIV, 76- *Concurrent Pos:* Consult, Devenco Res Lab, 69; instr & consult, Bell Tel Labs, 71- *Mem:* Am Asn Univ Professors; Am Soc Eng Educ. *Res:* Microprocessor system design; digital signal processing; logic design. *Mailing Add:* Dept of Elec Eng Fairleigh Dickinson Univ Teaneck NJ 07666

SILVER, LAWRENCE, b New York, NY, Apr 15, 21; m 52; c 3. MEDICINE. *Educ:* Queens Col, BS, 41; Univ Idaho, MS, 42; NY Univ, MD, 50. *Prof Exp:* Intern, Beth Israel Hosp, New York, 50-51; asst resident internal med, Vet Admin Hosp, Bronz, NY, 51-52; fel, Mayo Found, Univ Minn, 52-53; asst physician & vis investr hypertension, Hosp, Rockefeller Inst, 53-54; assoc scientist, Med Res Ctr, Brookhaven Nat Lab, 56-58; assoc med dir, Dept Clin Invest, Chas Pfizer & Co, 58-59; res assoc hypertension, Brookhaven Nat Lab, 59-61; assoc med dir, Dept Clin Infest, Chas Pfizer & Co, 61-64; PHYSICIAN-IN-CHG, DEPT NUCLEAR MED, QUEENS HOSP CTR, 64- *Mem:* AAAS; Am Physiol Soc; Soc Exp Biol & Med. *Res:* Relationship of salt to hypertensive disease states; influence and mechanism of action of hormones on movement of salt and water in normals and hypertensives. *Mailing Add:* Nuclear Med Queens Hosp Ctr 82-68 164th St Jamaica NY 11432

SILVER, LEE MERRILL, b Philadelphia, Pa, Apr 27, 52; m 74. DEVELOPMENTAL GENETICS, MOLECULAR BIOLOGY. *Educ:* Univ Pa, BA & MS, 73; Harvard Univ, PhD(biophys), 78. *Prof Exp:* Res fel genetics, Sloan Kettering Cancer Inst, 77-79, assoc, 79-80; SR STAFF INVESTR, COLD SPRING HARBOR LAB, 80- *Concurrent Pos:* Fel, Pop Coun, 77-78 & NIH, 78-79; asst prof genetics, Med Sch, Cornell Univ, 79-80 & State Univ NY Stony Brook, 80-; vis asst prof genetics, Albert Einstein Col Med, 80. *Mem:* Am Soc Cell Biol; AAAS; Int Soc Differentiation. *Res:* Molecular embryology; molecular biology of spermatogenesis; the mouse T/t complex; chromosomal proteins; cell surface proteins. *Mailing Add:* Cold Spring Harbor Lab PO Box 100 Cold Spring Harbor NY 11724

SILVER, LEON THEODORE, b Monticello, NY, Apr 9, 25; m 47; c 2. PETROLOGY, GEOCHEMISTRY. *Educ:* Univ Colo, BSc, 45; NMex Univ, MS, 48; Calif Inst Technol, PhD(petrol, geochem), 55. *Prof Exp:* Jr geologist, 47-65, GEOLOGIST, US GEOL SURV, 65-; PROF GEOL, CALIF INST TECHNOL, 65- *Concurrent Pos:* From asst prof to assoc prof geol, Calif Inst Technol, 55-65; Guggenheim fel, 64-65; mem subcomn geochronology, Int Union Geol Sci, 70-; consult, NASA, 71-; counr, Am Geol Soc, 74-76. *Honors & Awards:* Exceptional Sci Achievement Medal, NASA, 71. *Mem:* Nat Acad Sci; fel Geol Soc Am (vpres, 78, pres 79); fel Mineral Soc Am; Geochem Soc; Am Geophys Union. *Res:* Igneous and metamorphic petrology; geochemistry of uranium, thorium and lead; geochronology; regional geology of southwestern United States; tectonic history of North America; mineralogy and petrology of meteorites and lunar materials. *Mailing Add:* Div of Geol & Planetary Sci Calif Inst of Technol Pasadena CA 91125

SILVER, LEONARD, b Bridgeport, Conn, Apr 16, 24; m 51; c 2. CHEMICAL ENGINEERING. *Educ:* Yale Univ, BEng, 44, MEng, 50. *Prof Exp:* Chem engr, Manhattan Dist Proj, 44-46; chem engr, 47-51, sr engr, 51-56, sect leader process develop, 56-62, mgr eng develop, 62-64, mgr res & develop eng serv, 64-68, AUTOMATION & CONTROL MGR, MERCK & CO, INC, 68- *Mem:* Am Inst Chem Engrs; Am Chem Soc; Instrument Soc Am. *Res:* Development and scale-up of chemical processes; experimental methods for process hazard evaluation; computer aided process cost and capital estimation methods; process control computers; simulation techniques; multivariable optimization. *Mailing Add:* Merck & Co Inc PO Box 2000 Rahway NJ 07065

SILVER, MALCOLM DAVID, b Adelaide, SAustralia, Apr 29, 33; m 57; c 3. PATHOLOGY. *Educ:* Univ Adelaide, MB, BS, 57, MD, 72; McGill Univ, MSc, 61, PhD(path), 63; Am Bd Path, dipl, 63; FRACP, 64; FRCP(C), 75. *Prof Exp:* Resident med officer, Royal Adelaide Hosp, Australia, 57-58; resident path, Royal Victoria Hosp, Montreal, 58-63; res fel exp path, John Curtin Sch Med Res, Australian Nat Univ, 63-65; from asst prof to assoc prof, 65-74, PROF PATH, BANTING INST, UNIV TORONTO, 74- *Concurrent Pos:* Resident path, Path Inst, McGill Univ, 58-63; staff pathologist, Toronto Gen Hosp, 65-72, sr staff pathologist, 72- *Mem:* Am Asn Path & Bact; Am Heart Asn; Can Asn Path; Can Cardiovasc Soc; Int Acad Path. *Res:* Cardiovascular pathology. *Mailing Add:* Dept of Path Banting Inst Univ of Toronto Toronto ON M5S 2R8 Can

SILVER, MARC STAMM, b Philadelphia, Pa, Jan 5, 34; m 61; c 3. BIO-ORGANIC CHEMISTRY. *Educ:* Harvard Univ, AB, 55; Calif Inst Technol, PhD(chem, physics), 59. *Hon Degrees:* MA, Amherst Col, 69. *Prof Exp:* From instr to assoc prof, 58-69, PROF CHEM, AMHERST COL, 69- *Concurrent Pos:* NSF fels, Northwestern Univ, 61-62 & Weizmann Inst, 66-67; vis prof, Yale Univ, 77-78; res fel, Oxford Univ, 71 & Imp Col, 81-82. *Mem:* AAAS; Am Soc Biol Chemists; Am Chem Soc. *Res:* Organic reaction mechanisms; mechanism of enzyme action. *Mailing Add:* Dept of Chem Amherst Col Amherst MA 01002

SILVER, MARSHALL LAWRENCE, b Los Angeles, Calif, Nov 26, 42; m 69. CIVIL ENGINEERING. *Educ:* Univ Colo, Boulder, BS, 65; Univ Calif, Berkeley, MS, 67, PhD(civil eng), 69. *Prof Exp:* Civil engr, John P Elliott-Consult Engr, Colo, 66-67; res engr, Inst Traffic & Transp Eng, Univ Calif, Berkeley, 67-69; PROF SOIL MECH, UNIV ILL, CHICAGO CIRCLE, 69- *Concurrent Pos:* Vis prof, Cent Univ, Caracas, 76 & Univ Tokyo, 77; Terzaghi fel, 81. *Mem:* Am Soc Civil Engrs; Am Railway Eng Asn; Am Soc Testing & Mat; Int Soc Soil Mech & Found Eng. *Res:* Dynamic behavior of soil materials; ground born and industrial vibrations; earthquake engineering. *Mailing Add:* Dept of Mat Eng Box 4348 Chicago IL 60680

SILVER, MARVIN, b New York, NY, Oct 22, 24; m 51; c 1. SOLID STATE PHYSICS. *Educ:* Rensselaer Polytech Inst, BEE, 45; NY Univ, MS, 51, PhD(physics), 59. *Prof Exp:* Electronic engr, Radio Corp, Am, 47-48 & Franklin Inst, 48-49; res physicist, Chatham Electronics Co, 52-55; instr, Hunter Col, 56-57; chief solid state br, US Res Off, NC, 58-67; assoc prof, 67-70, PROF PHYSICS, UNIV NC, CHAPEL HILL, 70- *Concurrent Pos:* From vis asst prof to adj prof, Univ NC, Chapel Hill, 59-67; consult, Kuthe Labs, 56-57. *Mem:* Am Phys Soc. *Res:* Electronic conductivity in organic solids; breakdown phenomena in gaseous electrical discharges. *Mailing Add:* Dept of Physics Univ of NC Chapel Hill NC 27514

SILVER, MARY WILCOX, b San Francisco, Calif, July 13, 41; m 67. BIOLOGICAL OCEANOGRAPHY, MARINE ECOLOGY. *Educ:* Univ Calif, Berkeley, AB, 63; Scripps Inst Oceanog, Univ Calif, San Diego, PhD(oceanog), 71. *Prof Exp:* Lectr marine biol, Moss Landing Marine Labs, Moss Landing, Calif, 70-71; asst prof marine biol, San Francisco State Univ, 71-72; ASST PROF MARINE SCI, UNIV CALIF, SANTA CRUZ, 72- *Mem:* Am Soc Limnol & Oceanog; Ecol Soc Am; Phycol Soc Am; AAAS; Am Soc Naturalists. *Res:* Coastal oceanography: includes phytoplankton productivity and distribution and the general ecology of the neritic pelagic zone; the ecology of planktonic tunicates; ecology of suspended particulates (marine snow). *Mailing Add:* Ctr for Coastal Marine Studies Univ of Calif Santa Cruz CA 95064

SILVER, MELVIN JOEL, b Philadelphia, Pa, June 22, 20; m 55; c 1. BIOCHEMISTRY, PHARMACOLOGY. *Educ:* Temple Univ, AB, 41; Philadelphia Col Pharm, MSc, 43, DSc(bact), 53. *Prof Exp:* Res biochemist, 53-57, assoc prof pharmacol, 59-72, PROF PHARMACOL, JEFFERSON MED COL, THOMAS JEFFERSON UNIV, 72-, ASSOC, CARDEZA FOUND, 57-, SR MEM, 72- *Concurrent Pos:* Wellcome Trust res fel, Royal Col Surgeons Eng, 70-71. *Mem:* Am Soc Pharmacol & Exp Therapeut; Am Chem Soc; NY Acad Sci; Int Soc Thrombosis & Haemostasis. *Res:* Role of prostaglandin synthesis, phospholipids and platelets in hemostasis. *Mailing Add:* Dept Pharmacol Jefferson Med Col Cardeza Found 1015 Walnut St Philadelphia PA 19107

SILVER, MEYER, b New York, NY, Sept 12, 26; m 47; c 3. QUANTUM ELECTRONICS, LASERS. *Educ:* Brooklyn Col, BA, 49; Rensselaer Polytech Inst, MS, 57; Univ Notre Dame, PhD, 60. *Prof Exp:* Physicist, US Naval Ord Test Sta, 52-55, 60-62 & TRW Systs, Inc, Calif, 62-67; mem tech staff, Aerospace Corp, 67-70; chief laser systs sect, Martin-Marietta Corp, Fla, 70-71; div chief mil progs, Zenith Radio Res Corp, Calif, 71-72; dir advan eng, Appl Technol Div, Itek Corp, 72-75; mgr advan technol dept, Lockheed Missiles & Space Corp, 75-77; asst mgr, Optics Dept, TRW Defense, 77-80, MGR, OPTICAL COMPONENTS DEPT, SPACE SYSTS GROUP, TRW, INC, 80- *Mem:* Am Phys Soc; Sigma Xi; Res Soc Am; Optical Soc Am. *Res:* Acousto-optics-electronics; laser research; gas discharges; atomic physics; multiple photon processes. *Mailing Add:* TRW Defense & Space Systs Group One Space Park Redondo Beach CA 90278

SILVER, RICHARD N, b Bridgeport, Conn, July 18, 45; m 69; c 4. THEORETICAL SOLID STATE PHYSICS. *Educ:* Calif Inst Technol, BS, 66, PhD(theoret physics), 71. *Prof Exp:* Res assoc elem particle physics, Brown Univ, 71-72; res assoc solid state physics, Calif Inst Technol, 72-74; staff mem solid state physics, 74-79, GROUP LEADER CONDENSED MATTER PHYSICS, LOS ALAMOS NAT LAB, 79- *Concurrent Pos:* IBM fel, Calif Inst Technol, 72-74. *Mem:* Am Phys Soc. *Res:* High excitation conditions in semiconductors; solid state lasers; statistical mechanics of phase transitions; neutron scattering experiments with pulsed spallation neutron sources. *Mailing Add:* MS 805 Group P-8 Los Alamos Nat Lab Los Alamos NM 87544

SILVER, RICHARD TOBIAS, b New York, NY, Jan 18, 29; m 63; c 1. MEDICINE. *Educ:* Cornell Univ, AB, 50, State Univ NY, MD, 53; Am Bd Internal Med, dipl, 62, cert med oncol, 73. *Prof Exp:* Intern med, NY Hosp-Cornell Med Ctr, 53-54, resident physician, 56-58; clin assoc, Gen Med Br, Nat Cancer Inst, 54-56; from instr to assoc prof, 58-73, PROF CLIN MED, MED COL, CORNELL UNIV, 73, CHIEF ONCOL SERV, NEW YORK HOSP-CORNELL MED CTR, 77- *Concurrent Pos:* Vis Fulbright lectr, res scholar & vis prof, Sch Med, Univ Bahia, 58-59; physician outpatients, New York Hosp, 58-62, from asst attend physician to assoc attend physician, 62-73, attend physician, 73-; hematologist & consult, Gracie Sq Gen Hosp, 59-; asst vis physician, 2nd Cornell Div, Bellevue Hosp, 62-68; consult leukemia & mem, Leukemia-Myeloma Task Force, NIH, 65-69, mem polycythemia study group, 67-; dir chemother serv, Div Hemat & Oncol, Cornell Med Ctr, 67-75; consult & attend hematologist, Englewood Hosp, NJ & Manhattan Eye, Ear & Throat Hosp; prin investr, Clin Chemother Prog, Cancer Control, 73-80; group vchmn, Cancer & Leukemia Group B, 76-; mem, Comt Pub Affairs, Am Soc Clin Oncol, 81. *Mem:* Am Soc Hemat; Harvey Soc; Am Fedn Clin Res; fel Am Col Physicians; Am Soc Clin Oncol. *Res:* Hematology and oncology, especially leukemia and oncology chemotherapy; over 75 publications and articles. *Mailing Add:* New York Hosp-Cornell Med Ctr 525 E 68th St New York NY 10021

SILVER, ROBERT, b Detroit, Mich, Aug 3, 21; m 47; c 2. PHYSICS. *Educ:* Wayne State Univ, BS, 48; Univ Calif, Berkeley, PhD(physics), 58. *Prof Exp:* Physicist, Lawrence Radiation Lab, Univ Calif, 51-57; sr res physicist, Gen Motors Res Labs, 57-66; assoc prof, 66-71, PROF PHYSICS & ASTRON, EASTERN MICH UNIV, 71-, CHMN DEPT, 74- *Concurrent Pos:* Instr, Wayne State Univ, 59-61 & Univ Detroit, 63-66. *Mem:* Am Phys Soc; Am Asn Physics Teachers. *Res:* Low energy paricle scattering; nuclear reactors and neutron moderation; thermionic conversion; traffic dynamics; electrooptics; Mossbauer effect. *Mailing Add:* Dept of Physics & Astron Eastern Mich Univ Ypsilanti MI 48197

SILVER, SCOTT ALBERT, b San Antonio, Tex, June 30, 45; m 68; c 2. IMMUNOLOGY, CLINICAL BACTERIOLOGY. *Educ:* Ariz State Univ, BS, 67; Univ Ariz, MS, 73, PhD(microbiol), 76. *Prof Exp:* Fel microbiol, Univ Dayton, 76-77; asst prof, 77-81, ASSOC PROF MICROBIOL, OKLA COL OSTEOP MED, 81- *Concurrent Pos:* Adj prof microbiol, Okla State Univ, 80- *Mem:* Am Soc Microbiol; Sigma Xi. *Res:* Pathogenesis of chronic pseudomonas lung infections in patients with cystic fibrosis. *Mailing Add:* Okla Col Osteop Med PO Box 2280 Tulsa OK 74101

SILVER, SIMON DAVID, b Detroit, Mich, June 22, 36; m 58; c 2. MOLECULAR BIOLOGY, MICROBIAL PHYSIOLOGY. *Educ:* Univ Mich, BA, 57; Mass Inst Technol, PhD(biophys), 62. *Prof Exp:* NSF fel, Med Res Coun-Microbial Genetics Res Unit, Hammersmith Hosp, London, 62-64; asst res biophysicist, Virus Lab, Univ Calif, Berkeley, 64-66; from asst prof to assoc prof, 66-76, PROF BIOL & MICROBIOL, WASHINGTON UNIV, 76- *Concurrent Pos:* Vis fel, Dept Biochem, John Curtin Sch Med Res, Australian Nat Univ, 74-75 & 79-80; ed-in-chief, J Bacteriol, 78-; mem metabolic biol panel, NSF, 80- *Mem:* Am Soc Microbiol; Genetics Soc Am; Biophys Soc; Am Soc Biol Chemists; Soc Gen Microbiol. *Res:* Bacterial physiology; molecular genetics. *Mailing Add:* Dept of Biol Washington Univ St Louis MO 63130

SILVER, SYLVIA, b Chicago, Ill, Dec 11, 42; m 63; c 1. MEDICAL TECHNOLOGY, MICROBIOLOGY. *Educ:* Drake Univ, BA, 65; Cath Univ Am, MTS, 75, DA(med technol), 77. *Prof Exp:* Res asst biochem & vet physiol, Iowa State Univ, 66-68; res asst surg res, Harvard Med Sch, 68-69; instr med technol, Sch Med, Univ Md, 71-73; lectr, Montgomery Col, 75-78; ASST PROF MED TECHNOL IN PATH & DIR MED TECHNOL PROG, SCH MED & HEALTH SCI, GEORGE WASHINGTON UNIV, 78- *Concurrent Pos:* Consult, Dept Health & Human Serv, health professions, 79-81. *Mem:* Am Soc Microbiol; Am Soc Clin Pathologists; Am Soc Med Technol; Am Soc Allied Health Professions; Sigma Xi. *Res:* Isolation and identification of anaerobic bacteria; micro-methods in identification of bacteria; structure of hepatitis virus; clinical microbiology; laboratory medicine; computer assisted instruction. *Mailing Add:* George Washington Univ Med Ctr 2300 Eye St NW Washington DC 20037

SILVER, WARREN SEYMOUR, b New York, NY, Nov 14, 24; m 50; c 4. MICROBIOLOGY. *Educ:* Univ Md, BS, 49, MS, 50; Johns Hopkins Univ, PhD(biochem), 53. *Prof Exp:* Jr instr biol, Johns Hopkins Univ, 50-53; res scientist, Upjohn Co, 53-54; Nat Cancer Inst fel, Inst Microbiol, Rutgers Univ, 54-56; from asst prof to prof bact, Univ Fla, 56-67; prof life sci & chmn dept, Ind State Univ, 67-70; PROF BIOL, UNIV S FLA, 70- *Concurrent Pos:* Prog mgr, Competitive Res Grants Off, USDA, 79-80. *Mem:* AAAS; Asn Trop Biol; Am Soc Microbiol; Brit Soc Gen Microbiol; fel Am Acad Microbiol. *Res:* Bacterial nutrition; inorganic nitrogen metabolism by microorganisms; autotophic bacteria; respiratory enzymes; plant-microbe symbiosis; biological nitrogen fixation. *Mailing Add:* Dept of Biol Univ of S Fla Tampa FL 33620

SILVERA, ISAAC F, b San Diego, Calif, Mar 25, 37; m 61; c 4. SOLID STATE PHYSICS. *Educ:* Univ Calif, Berkeley, AB, 59, PhD(physics), 65. *Prof Exp:* Franco-Am exchange fel, Lab Electrostatics & Physics of Metal, 65-66; mem tech staff, Sci Ctr, NAm Rockwell Corp, 66-71; PROF EXP PHYSICS, PHYSICS LAB, UNIV AMSTERDAM, 71- *Mem:* Am Phys Soc. *Res:* Far infrared spectroscopy of solids at low temperatures; critical phenomena, especially in ordered magnetic systems; light scattering in quantum solids and molecular beams; atomic hydrogen in the condensed phase. *Mailing Add:* Physics Lab Univ of Amsterdam Valckenierstraat 65 Amsterdam Netherlands

SILVERBERG, STEVEN GEORGE, b New York, NY, Nov 30, 38; m 68. SURGICAL PATHOLOGY. *Educ:* Brooklyn Col, AB, 58; Johns Hopkins Univ, MD, 62. *Prof Exp:* Intern med, Bellevue Hosp, 62-63; resident path, Yale Univ-Grace New Haven Hosp, 63-65; fel path, Mem Hosp for Cancer & Allied Dis, 65-66; from asst prof to assoc prof surg path, Med Col Va, 68-72; assoc prof path, Sch Med, Univ Colo, Denver, 72-78, prof, 78-81; PROF PATH & DIR ANAT PATH, GEORGE WASHINGTON UNIV, MED CTR, 81- *Concurrent Pos:* Exec dir, Colo Regional Cancer Ctr, 76-79. *Mem:* Am Soc Clin Path; Int Acad Path; Soc Gynec Oncol; Am Soc Cytol; James Ewing Soc. *Res:* Natural history and histogenesis of neoplasms; ultrastructure in surgical pathology; gynecologic pathology. *Mailing Add:* Geo Washington Univ Med Ctr 2300 Eye St NW Washington DC 20037

SILVERBORG, SAVEL BENHARD, b Gardner, Mass, Jan 20, 13; m 43. FORESTRY. *Educ:* UNiv Idaho, BS, 36; Univ Minn, PhD(forest path), 48. *Prof Exp:* Asst, Univ Minn, 40-42; prin procurement inspector, US Dept Army Air Force, Ill, 42-43; forest pathologist, 47-60, assoc prof, 60-66, prof, 66-77, EMER PROF FOREST PATH & FOREST BOT, 77- *Mem:* AAAS; Soc Am Foresters; Am Phytopath Soc. *Res:* Diseases of Hevea brasiliensis; wood decay in buildings in New York; factors affecting the growth and survival of phytophthora palmivora; estimating cull in northern hardwoods; forest plantation diseases. *Mailing Add:* Dept of Forest Bot & Path Col of Environ Sci & Forestry Syracuse NY 13210

SILVERMAN, ALBERT, b Boston, Mass, Oct 29, 19; m 41; c 2. NUCLEAR PHYSICS. *Educ:* Univ Calif, PhD(physics), 50. *Prof Exp:* Res assoc physics, 50-52, from asst prof to assoc prof, 52-60, PROF PHYSICS, CORNELL UNIV, 60-, MEM STAFF, LAB NUCLEAR STUDIES, 77- *Concurrent Pos:* Guggenheim & Fulbright fels, 59-60. *Mem:* Am Phys Soc. *Res:* High energy physics. *Mailing Add:* Lab Atomic & Solid State Physics Clark Hall Ithaca NY 14853

SILVERMAN, ALBERT JACK, b Montreal, Que, Jan 27, 25; nat US; m 47; c 2. PSYCHIATRY, PSYCHOPHYSIOLOGY. *Educ:* McGill Univ, BSc, 47, MD & CM, 49; Am Bd Psychiat & Neurol, dipl, 55; Washington Psychoanal Inst, grad, 64. *Prof Exp:* Intern, Jewish Gen Hosp, Montreal, 49-50; resident psychiat, Med Ctr, Univ Colo, 50-53, instr, 53; instr, Sch Med, Duke Univ, 53-54, assoc, 54-56, from asst prof to assoc prof, 56-63; prof & chmn dept, Med Sch, Rutgers Univ, 63-70; chmn dept, 70-81, PROF PSYCHIAT, MED CTR, UNIV MICH, ANN ARBOR, 70- *Concurrent Pos:* Chief stress-fatigue sect, Aeromed Lab, Wright-Patterson AFB, 56-57; attend psychiatrist, Durham Vet Admin Hosp, 57-60, consult, 60-63; consult, Watts Hosp, 59-63, Lyons Vet Admin Hosp, 63-70, Fitkin Mem Hosp & Carrier Clin, 64-70, Ann Arbor Vet Admin Hosp, 70- & Dept of Defense, 70-; mem comt biol sci, Nat Inst Ment Health, 64-69, chmn, 68-69, mem res scientist develop comt, 70-74, chmn, 72-74; mem, Merit Rev Bd Behav Sci, Vet Admin, 75-78, chmn, 77-78. *Mem:* Soc Biol Psychiat; Am Psychosom Soc (pres, 76-77); Am Psychiat Asn; Am Col Psychiat; Am Acad Psychoanal. *Res:* Psychosomatic medicine; psycho-endocrinology. *Mailing Add:* 19 Regent Dr Ann Arbor MI 48104

SILVERMAN, ANN JUDITH, b Providence, RI, Nov 4, 46. NEUROENDOCRINOLOGY. *Educ:* Univ Calif, Los Angeles, BA, 67, PhD(zool), 70. *Prof Exp:* Fel, Dept Anat, Sch Med, Univ Rochester, 70-72, Dept Biol, Univ Calif, Los Angeles, 72-74; asst scientist, Wis Regional Primate Res Ctr, Univ Wis, 74-76; asst prof, 76-81, ASSOC PROF ANAT & CELL BIOL, COL PHYSICIANS & SURGEONS, COLUMBIA UNIV, 81- *Concurrent Pos:* Prin investr grant, Nat Inst Child Health & Human Develop, US PHS, 75-, co-prin investr, Nat Inst Arthritis, Metabolic & Digestive Dis, 77-; fel, Alfred P Sloan Founc, 76; Career Scientist Award, Irma T Hirschl Trust, 77; mem, Molecular Cell Neurobiol Panel, NSF, 81- *Mem:* AAAS; Soc Neurosci; Am Soc Anatomists. *Res:* Distribution and function of neurosecretory neurons related to reproductive function and water balance. *Mailing Add:* Dept Anat Col Physicians & Surgeons Columbia Univ 630 W 168th St New York NY 10032

SILVERMAN, BENJAMIN DAVID, b New York, NY, Mar 14, 31; m 67; c 2. SOLID STATE PHYSICS. *Educ:* Brooklyn Col, BA, 53; Univ Rochester, MA, 55; Rutgers Univ, PhD, 59. *Prof Exp:* Prin res scientist, Raytheon Co, 59-66 & Electronics Res Ctr, NASA, 66-69; PRIN RES SCIENTIST, IBM CORP, 69- *Mem:* Fel Am Phys Soc. *Res:* Solid state theory; dielectrics; ferroelectrics; lattice dynamics; organic solids. *Mailing Add:* T J Watson Lab IBM Corp PO Box 218 Yorktown Heights NY 10598

SILVERMAN, BERNARD, b Richmond, Va, Aug 15, 22; m 57; c 2. ELECTRICAL ENGINEERING. *Educ:* Va Polytech Inst, BS, 42; Univ Ill, MS, 47, PhD(elec eng), 54. *Prof Exp:* Instr elec eng, Univ Ill, 47-53; engr, Gen Elec Co, 53-58; ASSOC PROF ELEC ENG, SYRACUSE UNIV, 58- *Mem:* Sr mem Inst Elec & Electronics Engrs. *Res:* Nonlinear analysis; stability; communications; magnetic and dielectric devices. *Mailing Add:* Dept of Elec Eng Link Hall Syracuse Univ Syracuse NY 13210

SILVERMAN, BERNARD ALLEN, b New York, NY, May 1, 32; m 58; c 4. ATMOSPHERIC PHYSICS, METEOROLOGY. *Educ:* City Col New York, BS, 53; Univ Chicago, MS, 58, PhD(geophys sci), 72. *Prof Exp:* Res physicist, Air Force Cambridge Res Labs, 56-69, chief stratiform cloud physics br, Meteorol Lab, 69-74; CHIEF RES & DEVELOP BR, DIV ATMOSPHERIC WATER RESOURCES MGT, BUR RECLAMATION, 74- *Concurrent Pos:* Mem spec panel weather modification, Interdept Comt Atmospheric Sci, 64-65; mem adv panel weather modification, NSF/RANN, 75- *Mem:* AAAS; Am Meteorol Soc; Royal Meteorol Soc; Weather Modification Asn. *Res:* Cloud and precipitation physics; weather modification; development of a scientifically and socially acceptable technology for precipitation management to serve the nation's water resources needs. *Mailing Add:* 7038 E Peakview Pl Denver CO 80202

SILVERMAN, BERNARD BENNETT, b Torrington, Conn, Apr 3, 26; m 52; c 2. SYSTEMS ANALYSIS. *Educ:* NY Univ, BS, 49; Univ Conn, MS, 57. *Prof Exp:* Sr res engr, 52-67, chief laser systs anal, 67-81, MGR ELECTROMAGNETICS SYSTS RES, UNITED TECHNOL RES CTR, 81- *Mem:* Am Inst Aeronaut & Astronaut. *Res:* Lasers, laser radars and fiber optics sensors. *Mailing Add:* United Technol Res Ctr 400 Main St East Hartford CT 06108

SILVERMAN, CHARLOTTE, b New York, NY, May 21, 13. EPIDEMIOLOGY, RADIATION. *Educ:* Brooklyn Col, BA, 33; Med Col Pa, MD, 38; Johns Hopkins Univ, MPH, 42, DrPH, 48; Am Bd Prev Med, dipl, 49. *Prof Exp:* Field analyst, US Children's Bur, DC, 42-43; field researcher, Tuberc Control Div, USPHS, 43-45; from asst dir to dir bur tuberc, Baltimore City Health Dept, 46-56; chief div epidemiol, State Dept Health, Md, 56-59 & Off Planning & Res, 59-62; consult, Nat Inst Ment Health, 62-64, asst chief social psychiat sect, 65-66, chief epidemiol studies br, 66-67, chief pop studies prog, Nat Ctr Radiol Health, 68-70, DEP DIR DIV BIOL EFFECTS, BUR RADIOL HEALTH, FOOD & DRUG ADMIN, 71- *Concurrent Pos:* Lectr prev med, Sch Med, Johns Hopkins Univ, 47-52, lectr epidemiol, Sch Hyg & Pub Health, 54-56 & 66-, asst prof, 56-64. *Honors & Awards:* Award of Merit, Food & Drug Admin, 74. *Mem:* AAAS; fel Am Col Prev Med; fel Am Orthopsychiat Asn; Soc Epidemiol Res; fel Am Col Epidemiol. *Res:* Epidemiology of chronic conditions, including ionizing and nonionizing radiation. *Mailing Add:* FDA-Bur of Radiol Health 5600 Fishers Lane Rockville MD 20857

SILVERMAN, DAVID J, b Summerville, SC, July 13, 43; m 66; c 2. MICROBIOLOGY, CELL BIOLOGY. *Educ:* Muhlenberg Col, BS, 65; Univ Tenn, Knoxville, MS, 67; WVa Univ, PhD(med microbiol), 70. *Prof Exp:* Res assoc microbiol, Dartmouth Med Sch, 71-73, instr, 73; ASST PROF MICROBIOL, SCH MED, UNIV MD, 73- *Concurrent Pos:* Nat Cancer Inst fel, Dartmouth Med Sch, 71-73. *Mem:* Am Soc Microbiol; Electron Micros Soc Am. *Res:* Structure and function of ribosomes in bacterial and mammalian systems and intracellular bacterial parasites, especially Rickettsia. *Mailing Add:* Dept of Microbiol Univ of MD Sch of Med Baltimore MD 21201

SILVERMAN, DAVID NORMAN, b South Bend, Ind, July 22, 42; m 66; c 2. PHARMACOLOGY, BIOPHYSICS. *Educ:* Mich State Univ, BS, 64; Columbia Univ, MA, 66, PhD(phys chem), 68. *Prof Exp:* NIH fel, Cornell Univ, 69-71; asst prof, 71-76, assoc prof, 76-80, PROF PHARMACOL & BIOCHEM, COL MED, UNIV FLA, 80- *Concurrent Pos:* Fogartay fel, Umea Univ, Sweden, 78; mem adv bd, Molecular Pharmacol, 78- *Mem:* Am Soc Biol Chemist; Am Chem Soc; Am Soc Pharmacol & Exp Therapeut. *Res:* Stable isotopes in pharmacology and biochemistry; magnetic resonance; mass spectrometry. *Mailing Add:* Dept of Pharmacol Univ of Fla Col of Med Gainesville FL 32610

SILVERMAN, DENNIS JOSEPH, b Long Beach, Calif, Oct 7, 41; m 65; c 1. ELEMENTARY PARTICLE PHYSICS. *Educ:* Univ Calif, Los Angeles, BA, 63; Stanford Univ, MS, 64, PhD(physics), 68. *Prof Exp:* Res assoc, Princeton Univ, 68-69, instr, 69-70; res assoc, Univ Calif, San Diego, 70-71; asst prof, 71-74, ASSOC PROF PHYSICS, UNIV CALIF, IRVINE, 74- *Mem:* Am Phys Soc. *Res:* Quark models of elementary particle structure and interactions. *Mailing Add:* Dept of Physics Univ of Calif Irvine CA 92717

SILVERMAN, DONALD A, b Chicago, Ill, May 12, 38; m 65; c 1. BIOCHEMISTRY. *Educ:* Oberlin Col, BA, 60; Univ Chicago, PhD(biochem), 65. *Prof Exp:* RES ASSOC BIOCHEM, HEKTOEN INST MED RES, 66- *Concurrent Pos:* USPHS fel pharmacol, Johns Hopkins Univ, 65-66. *Mem:* Am Asn Clin Chem. *Res:* Biochemistry of amino acid and lipid metabolism in liver disease. *Mailing Add:* Biochem Hektoen Int of Med Res 627 S Wood St Chicago IL 60612

SILVERMAN, EDWARD, b Minneapolis, Minn, Nov 23, 17; m 61; c 2. MATHEMATICS. *Educ:* Univ Calif, AB, 38, MA, 39, PhD(math), 48. *Prof Exp:* Asst math, Univ Calif, 46-48; Off Naval Res fel, Inst Adv Study, 48-49; asst prof math, Kenyon Col, 49-51; mem staff, Sandia Corp, 51-54; asst prof math, Mich State Univ, 54-57; assoc prof, 57-61, PROF MATH, PURDUE UNIV, LAFAYETTE, 61- *Mem:* Am Math Soc; Math Asn Am. *Res:* Multiple integral problems in the calculus of variations. *Mailing Add:* Div of Math Sci Purdue Univ Lafayette IN 47907

SILVERMAN, ELLEN-MARIE, b Milwaukee, Wis, Oct 12, 42; div; c 1. SPEECH PATHOLOGY, OTOLARYNGOLOGY. *Educ:* Univ Wis-Milwaukee, BS, 64; Univ Iowa, MA, 67, PhD(speech path), 70. *Prof Exp:* Speech clinician, Curative Workshop Milwaukee, 64-65; res assoc commun, Univ Ill, Urbana, 70-71; asst prof, Marquette Univ, 73-79; ASSOC PROF SPEECH PATH, MARQUETTE UNIV, 79-; ASSOC CLIN PROF OTOLARYNGOL, MED COL WIS, 79- *Concurrent Pos:* Nat Inst Dent Res fel, 69-71; asst prof otolaryngol, Med Col Wis, 75-79. *Mem:* Int Transactional Anal Asn; Acoust Soc Am; Am Cleft Palate Asn; Am Speech & Hearing Asn; Sigma Xi. *Res:* Speech pathology, especially stuttering and voice disorders; voice disorders associated with otolaryngology. *Mailing Add:* Col of Speech Marquette Univ Milwaukee WI 53233

SILVERMAN, FRANKLIN HAROLD, b Providence, RI, Aug 16, 33; c 1. SPEECH PATHOLOGY, APPLIED STATISTICS. *Educ:* Emerson Col, BS, 60; Northwestern Univ, MA, 61; Univ Iowa, PhD(speech path), 66. *Prof Exp:* Res assoc stuttering, Univ Iowa, 65-68; asst prof speech path, Univ Ill, Urbana-Champaign, 68-71; assoc prof, 71-77, PROF SPEECH PATH, MARQUETTE UNIV, 77-; CLIN PROF REHABILITATION MED, MED COL WIS, 80- *Mem:* Fel Am Speech Language Hearing Asn; Psychomet Soc; Sigma Xi. *Res:* Stuttering in elementary-school children; assessment of the impacts of stuttering therapy methods; research design in speech pathology and audiology; nonspeech communication modes for the speechless. *Mailing Add:* Col of Speech Marquette Univ Milwaukee WI 53233

SILVERMAN, GERALD, b New York, NY, Aug 18, 25; m 63. MICROBIOLOGY, FOOD SCIENCE. *Educ:* Cornell Univ, BS, 50, PhD, 54. *Prof Exp:* Chemist, Gen Foods Corp, 54-58; assoc prof microbiol, Mass Inst Technol, 58-69; MICROBIOLOGIST, FOOD SCI LAB, US ARMY NATICK LABS, 69- *Concurrent Pos:* Adj prof, Univ RI, 69-; ed, J Food Serv Syst & J Food Safety; mem, Device Good Mfg Practices Adv Comt, Food & Drug Admin. *Mem:* Fel AAAS; Am Soc Microbiol; Inst Food Technologists; Soc Indust Microbiol. *Res:* Food safety; microbial toxins; thermal and irradiation sterilization; taxonomy; dehydration; public health; epidemiology. *Mailing Add:* Food Microbiol Group/SATL DRDNA-YMN Labs US Army Natick Res & Develop Command Natick MA 01760

SILVERMAN, GERALD BURTON, mathematics, see previous edition

SILVERMAN, GORDON, b Brooklyn, NY, Mar 4, 34; m 57; c 3. ELECTRONICS. *Educ:* Columbia Col, AB, 55, BS, 56, MS, 57; Polytech Inst Brooklyn, PhD(syst sci), 72. *Prof Exp:* Sr engr, Int Tel & Tel Corp, 57-61; proj engr, Loral Electronics Corp, 61-64; affiliate, 64-80, SR RES ASSOC ELEC ENG, ROCKEFELLER UNIV, 80- *Concurrent Pos:* Mem adj fac, Fairleigh Dickinson Univ, 58- & Polytech Inst Brooklyn, 65-68. *Mem:* Inst Elec & Electronics Engrs. *Res:* Application of electronic instrumentation to the study of biological systems; analysis and simulation of human learning. *Mailing Add:* Electronics Lab Rockefeller Univ New York NY 10021

SILVERMAN, HAROLD I, b Lawrence, Mass, Apr 27, 28; m 51; c 2. PHARMACY. *Educ:* Philadelphia Col Pharm & Sci, BSc, 51, MSc, 52, DSc, 56. *Prof Exp:* Instr pharmacog, Philadelphia Col Pharm & Sci, 52-56; asst prof pharm, Brooklyn Col Pharm & Long Island Univ, 56-59, assoc prof pharm & dir aerosol res lab, 59-64; vpres & sci dir, Knoll Pharmaceut Co, NJ, 64-68; chmn dept pharm, 68-73, PROF PHARM & ASSOC DEAN, MASS COL PHARM, 68-, DIR DIV APPL SCI, 73- *Concurrent Pos:* Sr scientist pharmaceut prod res & develop, Warner Lambert Res Inst, NJ, 58-61; lectr, New Eng Col Optom, 71- & Sch Med, Boston Univ, 71-; consult, Malmstrom Chem Corp, Warner Lambert Res Inst, J T Baker Chem Co, Gallard & Schlessinger Co, Thompson Med Co, Topps Chewing Gum, Inc, Cooper Labs, Inc, H V Shuster, Inc, Gillette Co, Corneal Sci, Inc, Arthur D Little, Inc, NJ Bd Pharm, Mass Bd Pharm, Boston Mus of Sci & R I Bd Optom; partic, US Pharmacopea, Nat Formulary Rev, 68-; mem human subjects comt, Peter Bent Brigham Hosp, Boston Univ Med Ctr, 74-; sci ed, Pharm Lett, 74-; contrib ed, Apothecary, 74-; grants from Smith, Kline & French, S B Penick, Baker Castor Oil Co & Pfeiffer Found. *Honors & Awards:* Newcomb Award, 56; Am Cyanamid Co Lederle res awards, 62, 63; Distinguished Serv Award, Am Optom Asn, 74. *Mem:* Am Pharmaceut Asn; AAAS; Am Chem Soc; Soc Pharmacists in Indust; fel Soc Cosmetic Chemists. *Res:* Pharmaceutical chemistry and drug development; drug stabilization; methods of analysis; pharmacokinetics. *Mailing Add:* Div Appl Sci Mass Col of Pharm 179 Longwood Ave Boston MA 02115

SILVERMAN, HERBERT PHILIP, b Brooklyn, NY, Sept 8, 24; m 49; c 3. ELECTROCHEMISTRY. *Educ:* City Col New York, BS, 48; Stanford Univ, PhD(chem), 57. *Prof Exp:* Actg instr anal chem, Stanford Univ, 55; res chemist, Kaiser Aluminum & Chem Co, 55-58; sr scientist, Lockheed Missiles & Space Co, 58-61; group leader electrochem, Magna Corp, TRW, Inc, Anaheim, 61-62, dept mgr phys chem, 62-64, div mgr res & develop, 64-65, assoc mgr chem sci, TRW Systs, 65-66, mgr biosci, 66-78; group leader electrochem res, 78-79, HEAD MEMBRANE RES, OCCIDENTAL RES

CORP, 79- *Concurrent Pos:* Lectr, Univ Southern Calif. *Mem:* AAAS; Am Chem Soc; Electrochem Soc; Sigma Xi; Sigma Xi. *Res:* Electrochemical processes; electrobiochemistry; photochemical influence on electrochemical reactions; biochemical influence on electrochemical reactions; nonaqueous electrochemistry; ion exchange membranes. *Mailing Add:* Occidental Res Corp PO Box 19601 Irvine CA 92713

SILVERMAN, HOWARD L, instrumentation, see previous edition

SILVERMAN, JACOB, b Brooklyn, NY, May 11, 23; m 51; c 2. PHYSICAL CHEMISTRY, SCIENCE ADMINISTRATION. *Educ:* Wayne State Univ, BSc, 43, PhD(phys chem), 49. *Prof Exp:* Lectr & res assoc chem, Univ Southern Calif, 49-51; radiol chemist, US Naval Radiol Defense Lab, 51-53; res chemist, Aerojet Gen Corp Div, Gen Tire & Rubber Co, 53-54; mgr chem & mat sci, Rocketdyne Div, NAm Rockwell, Inc, 54-75, dir energy systs, Rocketdyne Div, 75-78, DIR, FOSSIL ENERGY SYSTS, ENERGY SYSTS GROUP, ROCKWELL INT CORP, 78- *Mem:* AAAS; Am Chem Soc; Sigma Xi. *Res:* Technical management; research administration; fuel technology; physical chem. *Mailing Add:* Energy Syst Group Rockwell Int Corp 8900 De Soto Ave Canoga Park CA 91304

SILVERMAN, JERALD, b Brooklyn, NY, Mar 23, 42; m 67; c 2. BIOASSAY PERFORMANCE. *Educ:* Cornell Univ, BS, 64, DVM, 66; Am Col Lab Animal Med, dipl, 81. *Prof Exp:* Staff vet, Humane Soc NY, 66-67; pvt vet pract, Brooklyn, NY, 68-69 & Pearl River, NY, 70-75; DIR, RES ANIMAL FACIL, NAYLOR DANA INST DIS PREV, AM HEALTH FOUND, 75-; RES ASST PROF PATH, NY MED COL, 76- *Concurrent Pos:* Assoc ed, Lab Animal, 79-, Lab Animal Sci, 82-; consult, Revlon Health Care Group, Inc, 80- *Mem:* Am Vet Med Asn; Am Asn Lab Animal Sci; Am Soc Lab Animal Practitioners; Am Col Lab Animal Med. *Res:* Nutritional aspects of cancer prevention, especially dietary fat and vitamins; bioassay methodology; diseases of laboratory animals. *Mailing Add:* Am Health Found Naylor Dana Inst Dis Prev Dana Rd Valhalla NY 10595

SILVERMAN, JEREMIAH NORDAU, b New York, NY, Apr 18, 20; m 64; c 2. QUANTUM MECHANICS. *Educ:* Yale Univ, BS, 41; Univ Berne, PhD(chem), 56. *Prof Exp:* Welch Found fel crystallog, Univ Tex, 56-58, fel quantum mech, 58-60, instr physics, 60-61; res physicist, Nat Bur Standards, DC, 61-63; res physicist, Ft Worth Div, Gen Dynamics Corp, 63-74; prof physics, Pahlavi Univ, Iran, 74-80; MEM FAC, INST RADIOCHEM, MAX PLANCK INST COAL RES, 80- *Concurrent Pos:* Sr vis res fel, Battelle Advan Studies Ctr, Switz, sabbatical archaeol studies, Greece, 72-74. *Mem:* Am Asn Physics Teachers; Am Crystallog Asn; Am Phys Soc. *Res:* Perturbational-variational methods for obtaining accurate perturbed eigenfunctions in astrophysics, chemical physics and nuclear physics; quantum mechanical calculation of properties of atomic molecular and nuclear systems; general application of perturbational-variational methods in physical sciences. *Mailing Add:* Max Planck Inst Coal Res Stiftstrasse 34-36 D-4330 Mulheim West Germany

SILVERMAN, JOSEPH, b New York, NY, Nov 5, 22; m 51; c 2. RADIATION CHEMISTRY, POLYMER CHEMISTRY. *Educ:* Brooklyn Col, BA, 44; Columbia Univ, AM, 48, PhD(chem), 51. *Prof Exp:* Staff phys chemist, Atomic Energy Div, H K Ferguson Co, NY, 51-52; res dir nuclear labs, Walter Kidde & Co, 52-55; vpres & lab dir, Radiation Appln, Inc, 55-58; assoc prof chem, State Univ NY, 58-59; assoc prof, 60-63, PROF CHEM & NUCLEAR ENG, UNIV MD, COLLEGE PARK, 63-, DIR, INST PHYS SCI & TECHNOL, 77- *Concurrent Pos:* Guggenheim fel, 66-67; consult, Danish Atomic Energy Comn, 67-76; guest scientist, Atomic Energy Res Estab, Denmark; vis prof, Royal Mil Co Sci, Eng; ed, Int J Appl Radiation & Isotopes, 73-78; consult, Indust Res Inst, Japan, 73-; vis prof, Univ Tokyo, 74; mem, UN Develop Prog, 76- *Honors & Awards:* Radiation Indust Award, Am Nuclear Soc, 75. *Mem:* Am Chem Soc; fel Am Nuclear Soc; fel Am Phys Soc. *Res:* Pure and applied polymer and radiation chemistry; radiation source technology. *Mailing Add:* Inst for Phys Sci & Technol Univ of Md College Park MD 20742

SILVERMAN, MELVIN PHILIP, microbiology, geochemistry, deceased

SILVERMAN, MEYER DAVID, b New York, NY, Jan 8, 15; m 40; c 1. PHYSICAL INORGANIC CHEMISTRY. *Educ:* Yale Univ, BChE, 34; George Washington Univ, MA, 42; Univ Tenn, PhD(phys chem), 50. *Prof Exp:* Sci aide, Food & Drug Admin, USDA, Washington, DC, 38, sci aide, Cotton Mkt Div, 39-41; jr chem engr, Edgewood Arsenal, Md, 41-42; res chem engr, Permutit Water Conditioning Corp, NY, 42-43; assoc chem engr, Oak Ridge Nat Lab, 43-46, chemist, 47-52, sr res chemist, 52-75, res staff mem chem eng, 75-81. *Concurrent Pos:* Fel, Oak Ridge Inst Nuclear Studies. *Mem:* Am Chem Soc; Sigma Xi. *Res:* Chemical potentials; ion exchange; reactor chemistry; radiation-induced corrosion; aerosol physics; nuclear reactor safety; coal conversion processes and plant equipment; high temperature energy storage; mineral recovery from eastern oil shales. *Mailing Add:* 397 East Dr Oak Ridge TN 37830

SILVERMAN, MICHAEL ROBERT, b Ft Collins, Colo, Oct 7, 43; m 64; c 2. MOLECULAR & MICROBIAL GENETICS. *Educ:* Univ Nebr, BS, 66, MS, 68; Univ Calif, San Diego, PhD(biol), 72. *Prof Exp:* USPHS trainee tumor virol, Med Sch, Univ Colo, 73-75; ASST RES BIOLOGIST MOLECULAR GENETICS, UNIV CALIF, SAN DIEGO, 75- *Mem:* Am Soc Microbiol. *Res:* Regulation of gene expression, particularly of genes which determine components of the flagellar organelle of Escherichia coli. *Mailing Add:* Dept of Biol Univ of Calif San Diego La Jolla CA 92093

SILVERMAN, MORRIS, b Brooklyn, NY, June 19, 26; m 55; c 2. BIOCHEMISTRY, BACTERIOLOGY. *Educ:* NY Univ, BA, 49; Univ Mich, MS, 51; Yale Univ, PhD(biochem), 60. *Prof Exp:* USPHS fel biochem, Pub Health Res Inst New York, 59-61; instr, 61-63, ASST PROF BIOCHEM, COL MED, STATE UNIV NY DOWNSTATE MED CTR, 63- *Mem:* AAAS; Am Chem Soc. *Res:* Carbohydrate metabolism; oxidative phosphorylation; oxidative enzymes; microbial metabolism. *Mailing Add:* Dept of Biochem State Univ NY Downstate Med Ctr Brooklyn NY 11203

SILVERMAN, MORRIS BERNARD, b Roxbury, Mass, June 28, 24; m 56. INORGANIC CHEMISTRY. *Educ:* Boston Univ, AB, 48; Univ Washington, Seattle, PhD(chem), 56. *Prof Exp:* Radiochemist, Tracerlab, Inc, 49-50; draftsman, Johnson Fare Box Co, 51; develop chemist, Armour & Co, 52-53; fel organometallics, Univ Wash, Seattle, 56-57; chemist, Calif Res Corp, Standard Oil Co Calif, 57-59; ASSOC PROF CHEM, PORTLAND STATE UNIV, 59- *Mem:* Am Chem Soc; Soc Cosmetic Chemists. *Mailing Add:* Dept of Chem Portland State Univ Box 751 Portland OR 97201

SILVERMAN, MYRON SIMEON, b New York, NY, Aug 2, 15. BACTERIOLOGY, IMMUNOLOGY. *Educ:* Cornell Univ, BS, 37, MS, 38; Univ Calif, PhD, 50; Am Bd Microbiol, dipl. *Prof Exp:* Lab technician, Div Lab & Res, NY State Dept Health, 39-41; asst bact, Univ Calif, 48-50; supvry bacteriologist, US Naval Radiol Defense Lab, 50-62, head microbiol & immunol br, 62-69; res microbiologist, Naval Med Res Unit 1, Calif, 69-70; assoc dean, Grad Sch, 79-81, PROF ORAL BIOL & BACT, DENT RES CTR & SCH MED, UNIV NC, CHAPEL HILL, 70-, SPEC ASST TO DEAN, GRAD SCH, 81- *Concurrent Pos:* Nat Cancer Inst res fel, Guy's Hosp, Med Sch, Univ London, 60-61; Naval Radiol Defense Lab fel, Brookhaven Nat Lab, 68-69; res assoc, Univ Calif, Berkeley, 50-59, lectr, 58-68; mem comn radiation & infection & comn epidemiol surv, Armed Forces Epidemiol Bd. *Mem:* AAAS; Am Soc Microbiol; Radiation Res Soc; Soc Exp Biol & Med; Am Asn Immunol. *Res:* Induction of immune response; cellular interactions in the immune response; immunological aspects of oral disease. *Mailing Add:* Dent Res Ctr Univ of NC Chapel Hill NC 27514

SILVERMAN, PAUL HYMAN, b Minneapolis, Minn, Oct 8, 24; m 45; c 2. PARASITOLOGY, IMMUNOLOGY. *Educ:* Roosevelt Univ, BS, 49; Northwestern Univ, MS, 51; Univ Liverpool, PhD(parasitol), 55. *Hon Degrees:* DSc, Univ Liverpool, 68. *Prof Exp:* Sr sci officer, Dept Parasitol, Moredun Inst, Edinburgh, Scotland, 56-59; head dept immunoparasitol, Allen & Hansburys, Ltd, Ware, Eng, 60-62; prof zool, vet path & hyg, Univ Ill, Urbana, 63-72, chmn dept zool, 64-65, head, 65-69; chmn dept biol, Univ NMex, 72-73, actg vpres res & grad affairs, 73-74, vpres res & grad affairs, 74-77; provost res & grad studies, State Univ NY Albany, 77-79, pres res found, 79-80; PRES, UNIV MAINE, 80- *Concurrent Pos:* Consult-examr, NCent Asn, Comn Cols & Univs; prof & head natural sci div, Temple Buell Col, 70-71; adj prof, Univ Colo, Boulder, 70-72; consult comn malaria, Armed Forces Epidemiol Bd, 71-; mem bd dirs, NCent Asn Cols & Sec Schs, 71-, vchmn comn on insts of higher educ, 72-74, chmn, 74- *Mem:* Am Soc Parasitologists; Am Asn Immunol; Am Soc Trop Med & Hyg; Am Mosquito Control Asn; Am Soc Animal Sci. *Res:* Nature of host-parasite of relationship, particularly on immunological phenomena; in vitro culture of metazoan parasite. *Mailing Add:* Univ Maine Orono ME 04469

SILVERMAN, PHILIP MICHAEL, b Chicago, Ill, Oct 21, 42; div; c 2. BIOCHEMISTRY, MOLECULAR BIOLOGY. *Educ:* Univ Ill, Urbana, BS, 64; Univ Calif, Berkeley, PhD(biochem), 68. *Prof Exp:* Asst prof, 71-75, ASSOC PROF MOLECULAR BIOL, ALBERT EINSTEIN COL MED, 75- *Concurrent Pos:* Damon Runyon Mem Fund Cancer Res fel, Albert Einstein Col Med, 69-71; estab investr, Am Heart Asn, 75-80; Irma T Hirschl career scientist, 81-; mem adv panel genetic biol, NSF, 81- *Mem:* Am Soc Biol Chemists; Am Soc Microbiol. *Res:* Biochemistry and genetics of bacterial conjugations; synthesis and function of membrane proteins. *Mailing Add:* Dept of Molecular Biol Albert Einstein Col of Med Bronx NY 10461

SILVERMAN, ROBERT, b Cleveland, Ohio, Oct 23, 28; m 48 & 71; c 4. MATHEMATICS. *Educ:* Ohio State Univ, BSc, 51, MA, 54, PhD(math), 58. *Prof Exp:* Instr math, Ohio State Univ, 59; Nat Acad Sci-Nat Res Coun res assoc, Nat Bur Standards, 59-60; asst prof math, Syracuse Univ, 60-65; assoc prof, 65-80, PROF MATH, WRIGHT STATE UNIV, 80- *Concurrent Pos:* Res assoc, Univ Western Ont, 80. *Mem:* Math Asn Am; Am Math Soc; fel Nat Sci Found; Sigma Xi. *Res:* Combinatorial analysis; algebra. *Mailing Add:* Box 291 Yellow Springs OH 45387

SILVERMAN, ROBERT ANDREW, b New York, NY, Oct 16, 39; m 60; c 3. PHOTOGRAPHIC CHEMISTRY. *Educ:* Cornell Univ, BA, 60; Univ Rochester, MS, 63. *Prof Exp:* Chemist org chem, 62-68, SR CHEMIST PHOTOG CHEM, EASTMAN KODAK CO RES LABS, 68- *Mem:* Soc Photog Scientists & Engrs. *Res:* Photographic developers and films. *Mailing Add:* Eastman Kodak Co 343 State St Rochester NY 14650

SILVERMAN, ROBERT HUGH, b Houston, Tex, Nov 24, 48. PATHOLOGY, INTERFERON. *Educ:* Mich State Univ, BSc, 70; Iowa State Univ, PhD(molecular biol), 77. *Prof Exp:* Fel, Roche Inst Molecular Biol, 77-79; mem sci staff, Nat Inst Med Res, Mill Hill, London, 79-80, Imperial Cancer Res Fund Labs, London, 80-81; ASST PROF PATH, UNIFORMED SERV, UNIV HEALTH SCI, 82- *Res:* Biochemical mechanism of action of interferons, in particular the role of the unusual oligonucleotide series known as 2-5A . *Mailing Add:* Dept Path Uniformed Serv Univ Health Sci 4301 Jones Bridge Rd Bethesda MD 20814

SILVERMAN, SAM M, b New York. NY, Nov 16, 25; m 48, 66; c 5. GEOPHYSICS, PHYSICAL CHEMISTRY. *Educ:* City Col New York, BChE, 45; Ohio State Univ, PhD(phys chem), 52; Suffolk Univ Law Sch, JD, 82. *Prof Exp:* Res assoc phys chem, Ohio State Univ, 52-55; asst prof silicate chem, Univ Toledo, 55-57; chief, Polar Atmospheric Processes Br & dir, Geopole Observ, Air Force Cambridge Res Labs, 63-74, res physicsist, 57-80; CONSULT, 80-; SR RES PHYSICIST, PHYSICS DEPT, BOSTON COL, 81- *Concurrent Pos:* Vis res assoc, Queens Univ, Belfast, 63-64; adv bd, Inst Space & Atmospheric Studies, Univ Sask, 65-69; abstractor & reviewer psychohist, Am J Psychother, 75. *Mem:* Fel Am Phys Soc; Am Geophys Union; Sigma Xi; fel Explorers Club. *Res:* Polar cap upper atmosphere; aurora, airglow and related fields of upper atmosphere physics; law. *Mailing Add:* 18 Ingleside Rd Lexington MA 02173

SILVERMAN, SIDNEY JOSEPH, b New York, NY, Aug 2, 15. BACTERIOLOGY. *Educ:* Cornell Univ, BS, 37, MS, 38; Univ Calif, PhD(bact), 49; Am Bd Med Microbiol, cert. *Prof Exp:* Med bacteriologist, Chem Corps Biol Labs, US Dept Army, Ft Detrick, 49-54, immunochemist, Med Serv Grad Sch, Walter Reed Army Med Ctr, 54-55 & Biol Labs, Ft Detrick, 55-71; microbiologist, Nat Cancer Inst, 71-75; ASSOC PROF BIOL, HOOD COL, 75- *Concurrent Pos:* Secy Army fel, Clin Lavoro, Univ Milan, 62-63. *Mem:* AAAS; Am Soc Microbiol; Am Asn Immunol: Sigma Xi; fel Am Acad Microbiol. *Res:* Immunology; medical bacteriology. *Mailing Add:* 1201 Beechwood Dr Frederick MD 21701

SILVERMAN, SOL ROBERT, b New York, NY, Nov 5, 18; m 51; c 3. ORGANIC GEOCHEMISTRY. *Educ:* NY Univ, BA, 40; Univ Chicago, MS & PhD(geol), 50. *Prof Exp:* Chemist, Chem Warfare Serv, US War Dept, 42-44 & Mat Lab, US Dept Navy, 46-47; geochemist, US Geol Surv, 50-51; res assoc, Calif Res Corp, 51-63, SR RES ASSOC, CHEVRON OIL FIELD RES CO, 63- *Concurrent Pos:* Lectr petrol geol, Calif State Polytech Univ, 76- *Mem:* Fel AAAS; Am Chem Soc; Geochem Soc; Am Asn Petrol Geologists. *Res:* Distribution of stable isotopes in nature; petroleum geochemistry; biogeochemistry. *Mailing Add:* Chevron Oil Field Res Co PO Box 446 La Habra CA 90631

SILVERMAN, WILLIAM BERNARD, b New York, NY, Mar 3, 32. PLANT PATHOLOGY. *Educ:* City Col New York, BSc, 53; Univ Minn, MSc, 56, PhD(plant path, bot), 58. *Prof Exp:* Asst plant path & bot, Univ Minn, 53-58; res assoc polyacetylenes, NY Bot Garden, 58-59; from asst prof to assoc prof, 59-74, PROF BIOL, COL ST THOMAS, 74- *Res:* Histology-cytology; microbiology. *Mailing Add:* Dept of Biol Col of St Thomas St Paul MN 55105

SILVERNAIL, WALTER LAWRENCE, b St Louis, Mo, Sept 8, 21; m 44; c 3. INDUSTRIAL CHEMISTRY. *Educ:* Park Col, AB, 47; Univ Mo, AM, 49, PhD(chem), 54. *Prof Exp:* From assoc prof to prof chem, Ill Col, 49-56; assoc prof, Ferris Inst, 56-57; res chemist, Lindsay Chem Div, Am Potash & Chem Corp, 57-64, mgr tech serv, Kerr-McGee Chem Corp, West Chicago Plant, 64-73; CONSULT, 74- *Res:* Rare earth and thorium chemistry; ion exchange; glass polishing; chemical education. *Mailing Add:* 140 E Stimmel St West Chicago IL 60185

SILVERS, J(OHN) P(HILLIP), b Chicago, Ill, Jan 23, 20; m 45; c 3. THERMODYNAMICS. *Educ:* Purdue Univ, BS, 44, MS, 46, PhD(heat transfer, thermodyn), 51. *Prof Exp:* Asst heat transfer & vibration anal, Eng Exp Sta, Purdue Univ, 44-47, instr & admin asst to head dept thermodyn & heat transfer, 47-50; assoc scientist, Argonne Nat Lab, 50-55; assoc mgr dept appl res, Res & Adv Develop Div, Avco Corp, 55-57, tech asst to vpres res, 57-60, head adv prog undersea technol, 60-65, mgr marine technol dept, 65-66, mgr prog planning, Avco Space Systs Div, 66-68, asst dir eng, Avco Systs Div, 68-71; exec dir, Mass Sci & Technol Found, 72-77; ENERGY CONSULT, 77- *Mem:* Marine Technol Soc; Sigma Xi. *Res:* Nuclear reactor development; heat transfer; numerical analysis; marine technology; environmental science. *Mailing Add:* 327 Salem St Wilmington MA 01887

SILVERS, WILLYS KENT, b New York, NY, Jan 12, 29; m 56; c 2. GENETICS. *Educ:* Johns Hopkins Univ, BA, 50; Univ Chicago, PhD(zool), 54. *Prof Exp:* Assoc staff scientist, Jackson Lab, Bar Harbor, 57; assoc mem, Wistar Inst, Philadelphia, 57-65; assoc prof med genetics, 65-67, PROF HUMAN GENETICS, SCH MED, UNIV PA, 67-, PROF PATH, 69- *Concurrent Pos:* USPHS fel, Brown Univ, 55-56 & Jackson Lab, Bar Harbor, Maine, 56; NIH career develop award, 64-71; mem allergy & immunol study sect, NIH, 62-66; assoc ed, J Exp Zool, 65-70 & 82-; mem primate res ctr adv comt, NIH, 68-71; sect ed, Immunogenetics & Transplantation, J Immunol, 73-77; mem comt cancer immunobiol, Nat Cancer Inst, 74-77. *Mem:* AAAS; Genetics Soc Am; Am Genetic Asn; Am Soc Human Genetics; Soc Study Evolution. *Res:* Mammalian genetics, with particular reference to the genetics of coat-color determinant and immunogenetics; biology and immunology of tissue transplantation; biology of skin. *Mailing Add:* Dept of Human Genetics Univ of Pa Sch of Med Philadelphia PA 19104

SILVERSMITH, ERNEST FRANK, b Nuernberg, Ger, Oct 3, 30; nat US; m 53; c 4. ORGANIC CHEMISTRY. *Educ:* Harvard Univ, AB, 52; Univ Wis, PhD(chem), 55. *Prof Exp:* Res fel chem, Calif Inst Technol, 55-56; asst prof, Mt Holyoke Col, 56-58; res chemist, E I du Pont de Nemours & Co, 58-67; PROF CHEM, MORGAN STATE UNIV, 67- *Mem:* Am Chem Soc. *Res:* Kinetics and mechanisms of organic reactions; photochemistry; spectroscopy. *Mailing Add:* Dept of Chem Morgan State Univ Baltimore MD 21239

SILVERSTEIN, ABE, b Terre Haute, Ind, Sept 15, 08; m 50; c 3. MECHANICAL ENGINEERING. *Educ:* Rose Polytech Inst, BS, 29, MechEng, 34. *Hon Degrees:* ScD, Rose Polytech Inst, 59; DEng, Case Western Reserve Univ, 58; LHD, Yeshiva Univ, 60; DAS, Fenn Col, 64. *Prof Exp:* Aerodynamic res engr, Langley Res Ctr, Nat Adv Comt Aeronaut, Va, 29-40, head full scale wind tunnel, 40-43, chief engine installation res div, Lewis Flight Propulsion Lab, Ohio, 43-45, chief wind tunnel & flight res div, 45-49, chief res, 49-52, assoc dir, 52-58, dir off space flight progs, NASA, Washington, DC, 58-61, dir, Lewis Res Ctr, 61-70; DIR ENVIRON PLANNING, REPUB STEEL CORP, 70-; CONSULT, 76- *Mem:* Nat Acad Eng; fel Am Astronaut Soc; fel Am Inst Aeronaut & Astronaut; fel Royal Aeronaut Soc; Int Acad Astronaut. *Res:* Aerodynamic and propulsion aspects of aeronautical research; propulsion and power generation aspects of space; design and construction of facilities for space research. *Mailing Add:* 21160 Seabury Ave Fairview Park OH 44126

SILVERSTEIN, ALEXANDER, b Russia, Aug 7, 00; nat US; m 29; c 2. NEUROLOGY, PSYCHIATRY. *Educ:* Temple Univ, MD, 25; Am Bd Psychiat & Neurol, dipl, 41. *Prof Exp:* Asst neurol psychiat & neuropath, 27-32, from asst prof to assoc prof neurol, 40-60, prof clin neurol, 60-75, EMER PROF CLIN NEUROL, MED SCH, TEMPLE UNIV, 75- *Concurrent Pos:* Asst, Philadelphia Gen Hosp, 27-41, chief neurol, 41-; consult, Induction Ctr, US Armed Forces, 42-45; chief psychiat & chmn staff, Philadelphia Psychiat Ctr, 59-61; neurologist, Health & Sci Ctr, Temple Univ; consult neurol & psychiat, Northeastern Hosp, 50-; chief neurol & psychiat, Ctr City Hosp. *Mem:* Fel Am Psychiat Asn; AMA; fel Am Acad Neurol; Am Neurol Asn; Asn Res Nerv & Ment Dis. *Res:* Cerebral localization; trophic function of the parietal lobe; cerebral fat embolism; vascular lesions in distribution of basilar artery; clinical and pathological correlation of vascular lesions in the brain stem; Pontine infarction; Pontine hemorrhage. *Mailing Add:* 1901 JFK Bldg Apt 2206 Philadelphia PA 19103

SILVERSTEIN, CALVIN C(ARLTON), b Newark, NJ, Jan 31, 29; m 59; c 3. MECHANICAL ENGINEERING, NUCLEAR ENGINEERING. *Educ:* Newark Col Eng, BS, 50; Princeton Univ, MSE, 51. *Prof Exp:* Res engr, Bendix Aviation Corp Res Labs, 52-54; asst proj engr, Martin Co, 55-57; proj eng, Bell Aircraft Corp, 57; prin mech engr, Cornell Aeronaut Lab, Inc, 57-61; res specialist, Atomics Int Div, N Am Aviation, Inc, 61-62; chief anal & sr staff analyst, Hittman Assoc, Inc, 63-65; eng consult, 65-73; mgr prog develop, Westinghouse Elec Corp, 73-81; PRES, CCS ASSOCS, 81- *Mem:* Am Soc Mech Engrs. *Res:* Heat transfer; energy conversion; energy storage; power generation; heat pipe technology and applications; capillary-pumped heat transfer loops; hydrogen production and applications; fluidized beds; solar energy. *Mailing Add:* PO Box 563 Bethel Park PA 15102

SILVERSTEIN, EDWARD ALLEN, b Washington, DC, Aug 25, 30; m 56; c 3. NUCLEAR MEDICINE, NUCLEAR PHYSICS. *Educ:* Univ Chicago, BA, 50, MS, 53; Univ Wis, PhD(physics), 60. *Prof Exp:* Res asst nuclear physics, Univ Padua, 61-63; instr & res assoc, Univ Wis, 63-64; asst prof, Case Western Reserve Univ, 64-69; sr staff scientist, Bendix Aerospace Systs Div, 69-70; asst prof radiol, Med Col Wis, 70-75; radiation physicist & assoc dir sch nuclear med, Milwaukee County Gen Hosp, 70-75; group leader nuclear med physics, Sect Med Radiation Physics & asst prof, Rush Med Col, 75-81; PHYSICIST NUCLEAR MED, NORTHWESTERN MEM HOSP, 81-; ASST PROF, MED SCH, NORTHWESTERN UNIV, 81- *Mem:* AAAS; Soc Nuclear Med; Am Asn Physicists Med. *Res:* Application of digital computer to nuclear medicine. *Mailing Add:* Dept Med Northwestern Mem Hosp 1753 West Congress Pkwy Chicago IL 60611

SILVERSTEIN, ELLIOT MORTON, b Chicago, Ill, Jan 2, 28; m 57; c 3. ELECTROOPTICS, INFRARED SYSTEMS. *Educ:* Univ Chicago, BA, 50, MS, 53, PhD(physics), 58. *Prof Exp:* Mem tech staff, Opers Anal Group, Hughes Aircraft Co, Calif, 58-61, group head, Surveyor Spacecraft Lab, 61-64, sr proj engr, Surveyor Lab, 64-65, sr staff physicist, 66-68; prin engr/scientist, Avionics Control & Info Systs Div, McDonnell Dougals Astronaut Co, Huntington Beach, 68-81; SR MEM TECH STAFF, DEFENSE DEVELOP DIV, AEROSPACE CORP, CALIF, 81- *Concurrent Pos:* Mem, Standards Comt, Optical Soc Am, 82- *Mem:* AAAS; Am Phys Soc; Optical Soc Am; Sigma Xi; Inst Elec & Electronics Engrs. *Res:* Theoretical and experimental studies in infrared and optical physics and in optical and electrooptical imaging, image processing, detection, communications and radar; design and analysis of spacecraft instrumentation. *Mailing Add:* 8004 El Manor Ave Los Angeles CA 90045

SILVERSTEIN, EMANUEL, b New York, NY, Feb 14, 30; m 65; c 2. BIOCHEMISTRY, GENETICS. *Educ:* City Col New York, BS, 50; State Univ NY Downstate Med Ctr, MD, 54; Univ Minn, PhD(biochem), 63. *Prof Exp:* Intern med, Med Sch, Univ Minn, 54-55; intern path, Sch Med, Yale Univ, 55-56; res assoc exp path, Nat Inst Arthritis & Metab Dis, 56-58; resident med, Med Sch, Univ Minn, 58-59; from asst prof to assoc prof med, 70-77, PROF MED & BIOCHEM, STATE UNIV NY DOWNSTATE MED CTR, 77- *Concurrent Pos:* Fel molecular biol, Mass Inst Technol, 63-64; vis scientist, Weizmann Inst Sci, 71. *Mem:* AAAS; Am Asn Path; Am Soc Biol Chem; Am Soc Microbiol; Genetics Soc Am. *Res:* Enzyme mechanism and regulation; medical and molecular genetics; protein synthesis; hormone receptors; cell differentiation; porphyrins and oxidative enzymes; chemical diagnosis and therapy of disease. *Mailing Add:* Dept of Med State Univ NY Downstate Med Ctr Brooklyn NY 11203

SILVERSTEIN, MARTIN ELLIOT, b New York, NY, Sept 6, 22; m 62. MEDICAL SCIENCE, HEALTH SCIENCES. *Educ:* Columbia Univ, AB, 45; NY Med Col, MD, 48. *Prof Exp:* Asst res surg, Flower & Fifth Ave Hosps, 49-50, chief res, 51-52, instr bact & surg, NY Med Col, 53-57, assoc prof surg & assoc dean, 57-63; chmn exp surg, Menorah Inst Med Educ & Res, 63-66, chmn dept exp surg & exec dir, Menorah Med Ctr, 63-66, gen dir, 66; dir grad med educ, Bronx-Lebanon Hosp Ctr, 67-69; chief surg, Grand Canyon Hosp, 69-70; pres, Health Anal Inc, 70-73; ASSOC PROF SURG & CHIEF, SURG OF TRAUMA SECT, COL MED, UNIV ARIZ, 74- *Concurrent Pos:* Asst res, Metrop Hosp, New York, 50, chief res surg, 52-53, res investr, Col Burn Study, 52-54, mem staff, Res Unit, 54-55, vis surgeon, 55-63; asst surgeon & asst vis surgeon, Flower & Fifth Ave Hosps, 53-57, vis surgeon, 57-63; Dazian Found fel, 54-55; vis surgeon, Bird S Coler Hosp & Hebrew Home for Aged; trustee, Midwest Res Inst, 64-66, mem exec comt, Bd Trustees, 65-66; pres, Claudia Gips Found, 67-; dir med systs, Resource & Mgt Systs Corp, DC; NSF vis scientist, Auburn Univ; lectr, UNIVAC Int Exec Ctr, Italy, 69-70; Gov & dep secy gen, Int Coun Comput Commun, 74-; consult, US Arms Control & Disarmament Agency, 76; vis scholar, Ctr Strategic & Int Studies, 81-82. *Mem:* Am Fedn Clin Res; Am Asn Surg Trauma; Harvey Soc; NY Acad Sci; fel Am Col Nuclear Med. *Res:* Control of hemodynamics and neurovascular syndromes in man; physiology of body water; burns; shock; metabolism of trauma; surgical physiology; curriculum design; man-machine systems; bioinstrumentation; operations research; computer applications; shock and hemodynamics; biological sensing; processing and telecommunications; emergency medical systems; societal impact of disasters. *Mailing Add:* Dept of Surg Univ of Ariz Med Ctr Tucson AZ 85724

SILVERSTEIN, RICHARD, b Boston, Mass, Aug 9, 39; m 62; c 3. BIOCHEMISTRY. *Educ:* Brandeis Univ, BA, 60; Fla State Univ, PhD(chem), 65. *Prof Exp:* Staff scientist, Charles F Kettering Res Lab, 68-69; asst prof, 69-77, ASSOC PROF BIOCHEM, UNIV KANS MED CTR, 69-

Mem: Am Soc Biol Chem; Am Chem Soc; NY Acad Sci. *Res:* enzymes; protein turnover; oligonucleotide synthesis and applicaton to recombinant DNA studies. *Mailing Add:* Dept Biochem Univ Kans Med Ctr Kansas City KS 66103

SILVERSTEIN, ROBERT MILTON, b Baltimore, Md, Mar 26, 16; m 43; c 3. NATURAL PRODUCTS CHEMISTRY. *Educ:* Univ Pa, BS, 37; NY Univ, PhD, 49. *Prof Exp:* Asst, NY Univ, 46-48; sr org chemist, Stanford Res Inst, 48-64, res fel, 64-69; PROF CHEM, STATE UNIV NY COL FORESTRY, SYRACUSE UNIV, 69- *Mem:* Am Chem Soc; Sigma Xi; Entom Soc Am. *Res:* Organic synthesis; mechanisms and isolation and structure elucidation of natural products; application of spectrometry to organic chemistry. *Mailing Add:* Dept of Chem State Univ of NY Col of Forestry Syracuse Univ Syracuse NY 13210

SILVERSTEIN, SAUL JAY, b Brooklyn, NY, Aug 23, 46; m 76; c 1. MOLECULAR BIOLOGY, GENE EXPRESSION. *Educ:* Cornell Univ, BS, 68; Univ Fla, PhD(microbiol), 71. *Prof Exp:* Asst prof, 74-80, ASSOC PROF MICROBIOL, COLUMBIA UNIV, 80- *Concurrent Pos:* Fel virol, Univ Chicago, 71; career develop award, Nat Cancer Inst, 78; ed, Somatic Cell Genetics, 80-; mem, Exp Virol Study Sect, 82- *Mem:* Harvey Soc; Am Soc Microbiol; Am Soc Virol. *Res:* Gene regulation, particularly applied to eukaryotic virus-host cell interactions. *Mailing Add:* Dept Microbiol Columbia Univ 701 W 168th St New York NY 10032

SILVERSTONE, HARRIS JULIAN, b New York, NY, Sept 18, 39; m 60; c 4. QUANTUM CHEMISTRY. *Educ:* Harvard Univ, AB, 60; Calif Inst Technol, PhD(chem), 64. *Prof Exp:* NSF fel, Yale Univ, 64; from asst prof to assoc prof, 65-71, PROF CHEM, JOHNS HOPKINS UNIV, 71- *Concurrent Pos:* Sloan Found fel, 69. *Mem:* Am Phys Soc; Am Chem Soc. *Res:* Application of quantum mechanics to chemistry. *Mailing Add:* Dept Chem Johns Hopkins Univ Baltimore MD 21218

SILVERT, WILLIAM LAWRENCE, b New York, NY, Dec 11, 37; m 68; c 2. MARINE ECOLOGY, BIOECONOMICS. *Educ:* Brown Univ, ScB, 58, PhD(physics), 65. *Prof Exp:* Res assoc physics, Mich State Univ, 64-66; asst prof, Case Western Reserve Univ, 66-69; asst prof physics & astron, Univ Kans, 69-72; assoc prof physics, 72-75, dir, E Coast Fisheries Mgt Proj, Inst Environ Studies, Dalhousie Univ, 75-78; RES SCIENTIST, MARINE ECOL LAB, BEDFORD INST OCEANOG, 78- *Concurrent Pos:* Lectr, Univ Mich, 65-66; consult, Bendix Corp, 66; Nat Acad Sci exchange scholar, Inst Physics Probs, Moscow, 66-67. *Res:* Theoretical marine ecology; systems analysis; resource management; bioeconomics; trophodynamics. *Mailing Add:* 6113 Oakland Rd Halifax NS B3H 1P1 Can

SILVERTHORN, SAIDEE UNGLAUB, b New Orleans, La, Dec 3, 48; m 72. INVERTEBRATE PHYSIOLOGY. *Educ:* Tulane Univ, BS, 70; Univ SC, PhD(marine sci), 73. *Prof Exp:* Res assoc biochem, Med Univ SC, 73-74; from instr to asst prof physiol, 74-77; asst prof physiol & biophys, Univ Tex Med Br, Galveston, 78-80. *Concurrent Pos:* Vis asst prof biol, Univ Houston, 77-78. *Mem:* Am Inst Biol Sci; Am Soc Zoologists; Am Physiol Soc; Int Oceanog Found; Sigma Xi. *Res:* Endocrinology and physiology of thermal acclimation and osmoregulation in crustaceans; biochemistry and physiology of osmoregulation in crustaceans. *Mailing Add:* 2603 Thomas Dr Austin TX 78703

SILVERTON, JAMES VINCENT, b Seaton Delaval, Eng, May 10, 34; m 64; c 2. PHYSICAL CHEMISTRY, CRYSTALLOGRAPHY. *Educ:* Glasgow Univ, BSc, 55, PhD(chem), 63. *Prof Exp:* Res assoc chem, Cornell Univ, 58-61; sr res fel solid state physics, UK Atomic Energy Authority, Eng, 61-62; asst lectr chem, Glasgow Univ, 62-63; asst prof, Georgetown Univ, 63-70; SCIENTIST, NIH, 70- *Concurrent Pos:* Petrol Res Fund starter grant, 63-65; prog dir, Nat Inst Dent Res training grant x-ray crystallog, 65-70. *Mem:* Am Chem Soc; Am Crystallog Asn; Royal Soc Chem; Sigma Xi. *Res:* Structures of complex inorganic and organic compounds by x-ray crystallographic techniques. *Mailing Add:* NIH Bethesda MD 20014

SILVESTER, JOHN ANDREW, b Kent, Eng, Apr 26, 50; m 80. PERFORMANCE MODELING, COMPUTER COMMUNICATION. *Educ:* Cambridge Univ, BA, 71, MA, 75; WVa Univ, MS, 73; Univ Calif, Los Angeles, PhD(comput sci), 80. *Prof Exp:* Mem staff comput sci, Univ Calif, Los Angeles, 73-78; ASST PROF COMPUT SCI, DEPT ELEC ENG SYST, UNIV SOUTHERN CALIF, 79- *Concurrent Pos:* Consult, 79- *Mem:* Inst Elec & Electronics Engrs; Asn Comput Mach. *Res:* Performance modelling of computer systems and networks, especially computer communications and multiple access techniques. *Mailing Add:* PHE 418 Dept Elec Eng Syst Univ Southern Calif Los Angeles CA 90007

SILVESTER, PETER PEET, b Jan 25, 35; Can citizen; m 58. ELECTRICAL ENGINEERING. *Educ:* Carnegie Inst Technol, BS, 56; Univ Toronto, MASc, 58; McGill Univ, PhD(elec eng), 64. *Prof Exp:* Lectr elec eng, 58-61; asst, 61-65; assoc prof, 65-72, PROF ELEC ENG, McGILL UNIV, 72- *Concurrent Pos:* Acad vis, Imp Col, Univ London, 67-68 & 80-81. *Mem:* Inst Elec & Electronics Engrs; Soc Indust & Appl Math. *Res:* Numerical analysis of electromagnetic field problems. *Mailing Add:* Dept of Elec Eng McGill Univ 3480 University St Montreal PQ H3A 2A7 Can

SILVESTON, PETER LEWIS, b New York, NY, Mar 10, 31; m; c 3. CHEMICAL ENGINEERING. *Educ:* Mass Inst Technol, SB, 51, SM, 53; Munich Tech Univ, Dr Ing, 57. *Prof Exp:* Chem engr, Esso Res & Eng Co, 57-59; res engr, Res Div, Am Standard Corp, 59-61; asst prof chem eng, Univ BC, 61-63; assoc prof, 63-69, PROF CHEM ENG, UNIV WATERLOO, 69- *Mem:* Am Chem Soc; Chem Inst Can; Am Inst Chem Engrs. *Res:* Reactor design; kinetics; catalysis; waste treatment. *Mailing Add:* 121 Allen W Waterloo ON N2J 1J5 Can

SILVESTRI, ANTHONY JOHN, b Glassboro, NJ, Mar 14, 36; m 60; c 2. PETROLEUM CHEMISTRY. *Educ:* Villanova Univ, BS, 58; Pa State Univ, PhD(chem), 61. *Prof Exp:* Res chemist, 61-63, sr res chemist, 63-68, res assoc, 68-73, mgr, Anal & Spec Technol Group, 73-75, mgr, Catalysis Res Sect, 75-77, mgr, Process Res & Develop Sect, 77-79, mgr planning & eval, 79-80, MGR, PROCESS RES & TECH SERV DIV, MOBIL RES & DEVELOP CORP, 80- *Mem:* Am Inst Chem Engrs; Am Chem Soc; Sigma Xi. *Res:* Heterogeneous catalysis and chemical kinetics. *Mailing Add:* Mobil Res & Develop Corp Billingsport Rd Paulsboro NJ 08066

SILVEY, J K GWYNN, b Clarendon, Tex, Mar 31, 07; m 37, 71; c 3. LIMNOLOGY. *Educ:* Southern Methodist Univ, BS, 27; Univ Mich, MA, 28. PhD(zool), 32. *Prof Exp:* Instr biol, Southern Methodist Univ, 28-29; instr zool, Univ Mich, 29-32; prof biol, McMurry Col, 32-35; from assoc prof to prof biol, 35-72, chmn dept biol sci & dir inst environ studies, 35-75, actg dir dept basic health sci, 73-75, distinguished prof, 72-77, EMER DISTINGUISHED PROF BIOL, N TEX STATE UNIV, 77- *Concurrent Pos:* Chmn bd dirs, Tex Water & Sanit Res Found; founding dir, Inst Environ Studies, N Tex State Univ, 73-; assoc dean basic health sci, Tex Col Osteop Med, 75-76. *Mem:* Fel AAAS; Am Soc Limnol & Oceanog; fel Am Soc Civil Engrs; Soc Indust Microbiol; Am Water Works Asn. *Res:* Limnology of reservoirs; actinomycetes in fresh-water reservoirs; taste and odor in surface waters; water purification techniques; water pollution research. *Mailing Add:* 1811 Locksley Lane Denton TX 76201

SILVIDI, ANTHONY ALFRED, b Steubenville, Ohio, Jan 17, 20; m 47; c 4. BIOPHYSICS. *Educ:* Ohio Univ, BS, 43, MS, 45; Ohio State Univ, PhD(physics), 49. *Prof Exp:* Assoc prof physics & head dept, Col Steubenville, 49-51; res physicist, Cornell Aeronaut Lab, Inc, 51-52; from asst prof to assoc prof, 52-63, res assoc, 52-59, coord grad progs, 68-73, PROF PHYSICS, KENT STATE UNIV, 63- *Concurrent Pos:* Res physicist, Goodyear Aircraft Corp, 52-58; consult, Biochem Dept, Children's Hosp of Akron, Ohio, 70- *Mem:* Am Phys Soc; Biophys Soc. *Res:* Nuclear magnetic resonance; biophysics; application of physical techniques for solutions of biological problems. *Mailing Add:* Biophys Lab Dept of Physics Kent State Univ Kent OH 44242

SILVIS, SAL J(OHN), b Brooklyn, NY, Aug 18, 22; m 56; c 2. CHEMICAL ENGINEERING. *Educ:* Polytech Inst Brooklyn, BChE, 44, MChE, 47, DChE, 51. *Prof Exp:* Proj engr, S A M Labs, Manhattan Proj, Columbia Univ, 43-44; eng supvr, Garfield Div, Houdaille-Hershey Corp, 44-45; instr chem eng, Polytech Inst Brooklyn, 47-51; group leader, Colgate-Palmolive Int Co, 49-56, tech supvr detergent opers, 56-63; consult to int detergent indust, 63-70; exec vpres, Darrill Indust Inc, 70-75; CHEM ENG CONSULT, 75- *Mem:* Am Chem Soc; Am Inst Chem Engrs. *Res:* Vapor-liquid equilibria; sulfonation; spray drying. *Mailing Add:* 140 Douglas Rd Staten Island NY 10304

SILVIUS, JOHN EDWARD, b Dover, Ohio, May 9, 47; m 69; c 2. PLANT PHYSIOLOGY, BOTANY. *Educ:* Malone Col, BA, 69; WVa Univ, PhD(plant physiol), 74. *Prof Exp:* Teacher biol, Dover Pub Schs, 69-71; vis lectr bot, Univ Ill, Champaign-Urbana, 74-75; res assoc agron, 75-76; plant physiologist, Sci & Educ Admin-Agr Res, USDA, 76-80; MEM FAC, SCI DEPT, CEDARVILLE COL, OHIO, 80- *Mem:* Am Soc Plant Physiologist; Am Soc Agron; Sigma Xi. *Res:* Physiological and biochemical mechanisms which regulate the photosynthetic production, partitioning and translocation of carbon assimilates in plants. *Mailing Add:* Sci Dept Cedarville Col Cedarville OH 45314

SILZARS, ARIS, b Riga, Latvia, June 22, 40; m 65; c 2. ELECTRICAL ENGINEERING, PHYSICS. *Educ:* Reed Col, 63; Univ Utah, MA, 65, PhD(elec eng), 69. *Prof Exp:* Teaching asst, Univ Utah, 63-65; res asst, NASA, 65-68; mem tech staff, Watkins-Johnson Co, 69-73; sect head, EBS Devices, 73-74; mgr display devices, 74-77, dir, Component Develop Group, 77-79, DIR, SOLID STATE GROUP, TEKTRONIX INC, 79- *Concurrent Pos:* Consult, Dept Chem, Univ Utah, 68-70; adj assoc prof, Ore State Univ, 75- *Mem:* Inst Elec & Electronics Engrs; Soc Info Display. *Res:* Semiconductor devices; hybrids; display devices. *Mailing Add:* Tektronix Inc PO Box 500 MS 50-479 Beaverton OR 97077

SIM, STEPHEN KAHSUN, b Singapore, June 15, 17; Can citizen; m 57; c 2. PHARMACOGNOSY. *Educ:* Univ Wash, BS, 49, MS, 51, PhD(pharmacog), 55. *Prof Exp:* Asst, Col Pharm, Univ Wash, 49-54, instr pharmacog, 54-55; instr, Univ BC, 55-57, asst prof, 57-59; asst prof, 59-65, assoc prof, 65-79, PROF PHARMACOG, UNIV TORONTO, 79- *Honors & Awards:* Newcomb Award, Am Found Pharmaceut Educ, 56. *Mem:* AAAS; Am Pharmaceut Asn; Can Pharmaceut Asn; Can Soc Plant Physiol; Sigma Xi. *Res:* Biochemical aspects of medicinal substances from plants and microorganisms; antibiotics. *Mailing Add:* Fac Pharm Univ Toronto Toronto ON M5S 1A1 Can

SIMAAN, MARWAN, b Jerusalem, July 23, 46; US citizen. ELECTRICAL ENGINEERING, GEOPHYSICS. *Educ:* Am Univ Beirut, BS, 68; Univ Pittsburgh, MS, 70; Univ Ill, PhD(elec eng), 72. *Prof Exp:* Vis asst prof elec eng, Univ Ill, 73-74; res engr geophys, Shell Develop Co, 74-75; ASSOC PROF ELEC ENG, UNIV PITTSBURGH, 76- *Concurrent Pos:* Res assoc, Coord Sci Lab, Univ Ill, 72-73; reviewer, Zentralblatt fur Math, 73 & Math Reviews, 78-; consult, Gulf Res & Develop Co, 78- *Mem:* Sr mem Inst Elec & Electronics Engrs; Sigma Xi; NY Acad Sci; Soc Explor Geophysicists. *Res:* Theory of optimization and optimal control; large scale systems theory; operations research and dynamic socio-economic systems; digital signal processing and geophysical applications. *Mailing Add:* Dept of Elec Eng Univ of Pittsburgh Pittsburgh PA 15261

SIMANEK, EUGEN, b Prague, Czech, July 15, 33; m 55, 69; c 1. PHYSICS. *Educ:* Prague Tech Univ, MEE, 56; Czech Acad Sci, Cand Sci, 63. *Prof Exp:* Res physicist, Inst Physics, Czech Acad Sci, 56-68; theoret physicist, IBM Res Lab, Switz, 68-69; PROF PHYSICS, UNIV CALIF, RIVERSIDE, 69-

Concurrent Pos: Vis assoc prof, Univ Calif, Los Angeles, 65-67; Energy Res & Develop Admin contract theory of superconductivity, 75. *Res:* Theoretical solid state physics; quantum theory of metals; many body problem; critical phenomena; low temperature physics. *Mailing Add:* Dept of Physics Univ of Calif Riverside CA 92521

SIMANTEL, GERALD M, b Huron, SDak, Oct 12, 34; m 55; c 3. PLANT BREEDING. *Educ:* Ore State Univ, BS, 59; SDak State Univ, PhD(agron), 63. *Prof Exp:* PLANT BREEDER, RES DEPT, AMALGAMATED SUGAR CO, 63- *Mem:* Am Soc Agron; Crop Sci Soc Am; Am Soc Sugar Beet Technologists. *Res:* Development of more productive sugar beets. *Mailing Add:* Res Dept Amalgamated Sugar Co PO Box 1766 Nyssa OR 97913

SIMARD, ALBERT JOSEPH, b Hartford, Conn, July 11, 42. FOREST FIRE SCIENCE, SYSTEMS ANALYSIS. *Educ:* Univ Conn, BS, 63; Univ Calif, Berkeley, MSc, 68; Univ Wash, PhD(fire sci), 78. *Prof Exp:* Res scientist, Forest Fire Res Inst, Can Forest Serv, 67-79; PROJ LEADER, NCENT FOREST EXP STA, US FOREST SERV, 79- *Concurrent Pos:* Adj prof, Mich State Univ, 80- *Mem:* Soc Am Foresters. *Res:* Forest fire research in the Northeastern United States; fire danger rating, fire management systems, fire weather, fire economics, fire ecology and fire prevention. *Mailing Add:* US Forest Serv 1407 S Harrison Rd East Lansing MI 48823

SIMARD, GERALD LIONEL, b Lewiston, Maine, May 11, 12; m 46; c 5. PHYSICAL CHEMISTRY. *Educ:* Bates Col, BS, 33; Mass Inst Technol, PhD(phys chem), 37. *Prof Exp:* Res chemist, Atlantic Refining Co, 37-38; indust fel, Battelle Mem Inst, 39, res engr, 39-43; group leader, Am Cyanamid Co, 43-53; sect leader, Schlumberger Well Surv Corp, Conn, 53-60, res mgr, 60-67; assoc prof, 67-77, EMER PROF CHEM ENG, UNIV MAINE, ORONO, 77- *Mem:* Am Chem Soc; Am Inst Chem Engrs; Sigma Xi. *Res:* Thermodynamics; surface chemistry; kinetics, catalysis; electrochemistry; instrumental analysis; pulp and paper technology; environmental chemistry. *Mailing Add:* Dept of Chem Eng Univ of Maine Orono ME 04469

SIMARD, RENE, b Montreal, Que, Oct 4, 35; m 69; c 3. CELL BIOLOGY, MOLECULAR BIOLOGY. *Educ:* Univ Montreal, BA, 56, MD, 62; Univ Paris, DSc, 68, FRCP, 76. *Prof Exp:* Resident path, Mt Sinai Sch Med, 65; asst prof path, Univ Montreal, 68-69; from asst prof to assoc prof & dir cell biol, Sch Med, Univ Sherbrooke, 69-75; PROF PATH & DIR MONTREAL CANCER INST, UNIV MONTREAL, 75- *Concurrent Pos:* Med Res Coun Can fel, Inst Cancer Res, Villejuif, France, 65-68 & scholar, Univ Sherbrooke, 68-; mem grants comt anat & path, Med Res Coun Can, 70-77; mem res adv group & grants chmn, Nat Cancer Inst Can, 72-77; chmn, Quebec Health Res Coun, 75-78; pres, Med Res Coun, 78-81. *Mem:* AAAS; Am Soc Cell Biol; Inst Soc Cell Biol; Fr Soc Electron Micros; Can Soc Oncol (pres, 82-83). *Res:* Regulation of nucleic acids synthesis in eukaryotic cells; herpes viruses and cancer of the cervix. *Mailing Add:* Montreal Cancer Inst Univ Montreal 1560 E Sherbrook St Montreal PQ H2L 4M1 Can

SIMARD, RONALD E, b Aug 8, 39; Can citizen; m 66; c 1. MICROBIOLOGY. *Educ:* Univ Montreal, BSc, 62; McGill Univ, MSc, 65, PhD(microbiol), 70. *Prof Exp:* Microbiologist & indust scholar yeast res, J E Seagram & Sons, Inc, 62-65; microbiologist, Fed Dept Fisheries, 65-67; prof microbiol, Laval Univ, 70-75; prof microbiol, Univ Sherbrooke, 75-77; MEM FAC, DEPT VIRUSES, UNIV LAVAL, 77- *Mem:* Can Soc Microbiol; Am Soc Microbiol; Can Inst Food Sci & Technol; Am Soc Enol. *Res:* Applied microbiology in fermentation; pollution; biological treatment of domestic wastes. *Mailing Add:* 727 Dalquier Ste-Foy PQ G1S 2K4 Can

SIMARD, RONALD LEE, b Portland, Maine, Dec 21, 41; m 65; c 2. ENERGY ANALYSIS. *Educ:* Univ Bridgeport, BA, 67; Brown Univ, MS, 73, PhD(physics), 75. *Prof Exp:* Analyst nuclear safety, United Engrs, Philadelphia, 74-76; STAFF SCIENTIST ENERGY TECHNOL, OAK RIDGE NAT LAB, 76- *Mem:* AAAS; Am Nuclear Soc; Atomic Indust Forum; Sigma Xi. *Res:* Energy technology; powerplant performance; energy supply/demand forecasting. *Mailing Add:* Oak Ridge Nat Lab Bldg 9104-1 Oak Ridge TN 37830

SIMARD, THERESE GABRIELLE, b St-Lambert, Que, Mar 3, 28. ANATOMY. *Educ:* Univ Montreal, BA, 56, BSc, 62; Univ Mich, MSc, 64; Queen's Univ, Ont, PhD(anat), 66. *Prof Exp:* Prof anat, Univ Mich, 64 & Queen's Univ, Ont, 65-66; asst prof, 66-71, ASSOC PROF ANAT, UNIV MONTREAL, 71- *Honors & Awards:* Gold Medal, Int Soc Phys Med & Rehab, 72. *Mem:* Biofeedback Res Soc; Can Asn Anat; Am Asn Anat; Can Asn Phys Med & Rehab; Int Soc Electrophysiol Kinesiology (treas, 73-). *Res:* Electromyographic studies on the kinesiology of muscles and developmental method of studies; training of the neuromuscular action potential. *Mailing Add:* Dept Anat Univ Montreal Fac Med Montreal PQ H3T 1J4 Can

SIMARD-SAVOIE, SOLANGE, pharmacology, see previous edition

SIMBERLOFF, DANIEL S, b Easton, Pa, Apr 7, 42. ECOLOGY, MATHEMATICAL BIOLOGY. *Educ:* Harvard Univ, AB, 64, PhD(biol), 69. *Prof Exp:* From asst prof to assoc prof biol, 68-78, NSF grants ecol, 69-82, PROF BIOL, FLA STATE UNIV, 78- *Honors & Awards:* Mercer Award, Ecol Soc Am, 71. *Mem:* Ecol Soc Am; Soc Study Evolution; Brit Ecol Soc; Japanese Soc Pop Ecol; Soc Syst Zool. *Res:* Biogeography; evolution. *Mailing Add:* Dept of Biol Sci Fla State Univ Tallahassee FL 32306

SIMCO, BILL AL, b Mountainburg, Ark, July 14, 38; m 60. ICHTHYOLOGY. *Educ:* Col of Ozarks, BS, 60; Univ Kans, MA, 62, PhD(zool), 66. *Prof Exp:* Kettering intern biol, Kenyon Col, 65-66; from asst prof to assoc prof, 66-77, PROF BIOL, MEMPHIS STATE UNIV, 77- *Mem:* AAAS; Am Inst Biol Sci; Am Fisheries Soc; Am Soc Ichthyologists & Herpetologists; Sigma Xi. *Res:* Nutritional studies on production of channel catfish in ponds and raceways; systematic survey of fishes of western Tennessee; culture of catfish in recirculating raceways. *Mailing Add:* Dept of Biol Memphis State Univ Memphis TN 38152

SIME, DAVID GILBERT, b Glasgow, Scotland, July 4, 48. SOLAR CORONA, INTERPLANETARY MEDIUM. *Educ:* Univ Edinburgh, BSc Hons, 70; Univ Calif, San Diego, PhD(appl physics), 76. *Prof Exp:* Res asst, Univ Calif, San Diego, 70-76; res assoc, Swiss Fed Inst Technol, Zurich, 76-77; vis scientist, 77-78, staff scientist I, 78-80, STAFF SCIENTIST II, HIGH ALTITUDE OBSERV, BOULDER, 80- *Mem:* Am Geophys Union; Am Astron Soc; Swiss Soc Astron & Astrophys. *Res:* Three dimensional structure of the solar corona and the interplanetary medium; instrument development and data processing, especially as applied to the sun. *Mailing Add:* High Altitude Observ PO Box 3000 Boulder CO 80307

SIME, RODNEY J, b Madison, Wis, July 3, 31; m 55; c 2. PHYSICAL CHEMISTRY. *Educ:* Univ Wis, BS, 57; Univ Wash, PhD(chem), 59. *Prof Exp:* From asst prof to assoc prof, 59-67, PROF CHEM, CALIF STATE UNIV, SACRAMENTO, 67- *Honors & Awards:* Alexander von Humboldt fel, Univ Tübingen, 64-66; guest prof, Swiss Fed Inst Technol, 74-75. *Res:* High temperature chemistry and vaporization processes of transition element halides; x-ray diffraction studies of crystal and molecular structure. *Mailing Add:* 609 Shangri Lane Sacramento CA 95825

SIME, RUTH LEWIN, b New York, NY, July 2, 39; m 68; c 2. PHYSICAL CHEMISTRY. *Educ:* Columbia Univ, BA, 60; Radcliffe Col, MA, 61; Harvard Univ, PhD(chem), 65. *Prof Exp:* Asst prof chem, Calif State Col, Long Beach, 64-65, Sacramento State Col, 65-67 & Hunter Col, 67-68; INSTR CHEM, SACRAMENTO CITY COL, 68- *Mem:* AAAS; Am Crystallog Asn. *Res:* X-ray crystallography. *Mailing Add:* 609 Shangri Lane Sacramento CA 95825

SIMENSTAD, CHARLES ARTHUR, b Yakima, Wash, Feb 22, 47. MARINE ECOLOGY, FISHERIES BIOLOGY. *Educ:* Univ Wash, BS, 69, MS, 71. *Prof Exp:* FISHERIES BIOLOGIST MARINE BIOL, FISHERIES RES INST, UNIV WASH, 71- *Mem:* AAAS; Sigma Xi; Am Inst Fisheries Res Biologists; Ecol Soc Am. *Res:* Community and trophic ecology of nearshore marine communities; ecology of epibenthic zooplankton; food web structure and feeding ecology of marine fish assemblages; early marine life history of Pacific salmon. *Mailing Add:* Fisheries Res Inst Univ of Wash Seattle WA 98195

SIMEON, GEORGE JOHN, b New York, NY, July 21, 34; m 65; c 3. MEDICAL ANTHROPOLOGY. *Educ:* Univ Hawaii, BA, 62, MPH, 77; Univ Southern Calif, PhD 68. *Prof Exp:* Fel & researcher med anthrop, Org Am States, 68-69; researcher anthrop, US Fulbright Comn, 70-71 & Macquarie Univ, 72-74; researcher med anthrop, Nat Geog Soc & Wenner-Gren Found, 74; med data analyst, Dept Health Educ & Welfare, Kaiser Found Hosps, 75; researcher med anthrop, Cross-Cult res fel, Univ Hawaii & Indonesia Schs Pub Health, 76; researcher, Nat Museum Man, 79-80; FEL, NAT INST ALCOHOL ABUSE & ALCOHOLISM, BROWN UNIV, 80-81. *Concurrent Pos:* Vis lectr, Ohio State Univ, 79. *Mem:* Am Pub Health Asn; Am Anthrop Asn. *Res:* Ethnomedicine and medical anthropology in reference to the acquisition and analysis of field data with a view towards developing an ethnomedical theory; traditional terrestrial and sea navigational systems. *Mailing Add:* PO Box 68 Kauai Waimea HI 96796

SIMEONE, FIORINDO ANTHONY, b St Ambrose, Italy, Jan 20, 08; nat US; m 41; c 5. SURGERY. *Educ:* Brown Univ, AB, 29, ScM, 30; Harvard Univ, MD, 34; Am Bd Surg & Bd Thoracic Surg, dipl. *Hon Degrees:* ScD, Brown Univ, 54. *Prof Exp:* House officer surg, Mass Gen Hosp, 34-36, res surg, 38-39; asst surg, Harvard Med Sch, 38-40, asst genito-urinary surg, 40, instr, 40-41, assoc, 41-42, asst prof surg, 46-50; prof, Sch Med, Western Reserve Univ, 50-67; prof, 67-76, EMER PROF MED SCI, BROWN UNIV, 76- *Concurrent Pos:* Nat Res Coun fel & teaching fel physiol, Harvard Med Sch, 36-38; fel, Peter Bent Brigham Hosp, 39-41, surgeon-in-chief, 59; asst, Mass Gen Hosp, 41-42, asst vis surgeon, 46-50, consult, 50-; consult, Mass Eye & Ear Infirmary & surg gen, US Army, 46-50; dir surg, Cleveland Metrop Gen Hosp, 50-67; chief of surg, Miriam Hosp, RI, 67-; hon prof, Med Schs & hon dir prof units, St Bartholomew's & St Thomas Hosps, London, Eng, 56; lectr, Harvard Med Sch, 59; prof, Am Univ, Beirut & chief surg, Hosp, 60; mem subcomt cardiovasc syst & mem subcomt on shock, Nat Res Coun; mem subcomt metab in trauma, Adv Comt Metab, US Armed Forces & mem surg study sect, USPHS. *Honors & Awards:* Hon Perpetual Student, St Bartholomew's Hosp. *Mem:* AAAS; Am Cancer Soc; Soc Univ Surg; Soc Vascular Surg; AMA. *Res:* Physiology of the autonomic nervous system and its effectors; surgery and physiology of the cardiovascular system; physiology of trauma. *Mailing Add:* 104 Olney Ave N Providence RI 02911

SIMEONE, JOHN BABTISTA, b Providence, RI, Nov 20, 19; m 45. FOREST ENTOMOLOGY. *Educ:* Univ RI, BS, 42; Yale Univ, MF, 48; Cornell Univ, PhD(entom), 60. *Prof Exp:* Asst entom, 48-56, from asst prof to assoc prof, 56-64, chmn dept entom, 62-77, chmn dept environ & forest biol, 77-81, PROF FOREST ENTOM, STATE UNIV NY COL ENVIRON SCI & FORESTRY, SYRACUSE, 64- *Concurrent Pos:* Co-ed, J Chem Ecol, 75- *Mem:* AAAS; Entom Soc Am; Soc Am Foresters; Ecol Soc Am; NY Acad Sci. *Res:* Biology of insects causing deterioration of wood; chemical ecology; chemical ecology of forest insects. *Mailing Add:* State Univ NY Col Environ Sci & Forestry Syracuse NY 13210

SIMERAL, WILLIAM GOODRICH, b Portland, Ore, May 22, 26; m 49; c 4. MANAGEMENT. *Educ:* Franklin & Marshall Col, BS, 48; Univ Mich, MS, 50, PhD(physics), 53. *Prof Exp:* Res physicist, 53-56, res supvr, 56-57, sr res supvr, 57-64, res mgr, 64-66, asst dir res & develop div, Plastics Dept, 66-68, dir commercial resins div, 68-71, asst dir cent res dept, 71-74, asst gen mgr, Plastics Dept, 74, vpres & gen mgr, 74-77, sr vpres, 77-81, DIR, PLASTICS DEPT, E I DU PONT DE NEMOURS & CO, INC, 77-, EXEC VPRES, 81- *Mem:* Am Phys Soc; Am Chem Soc. *Res:* Physics of high polymers. *Mailing Add:* Box 3934 Greenville DE 19807

SIMERL, L(INTON) E(ARL), b Chillicothe, Ohio, Dec 2, 11; m 41; c 4. CHEMICAL ENGINEERING. *Educ:* Ohio State Univ, BChE, 35; Lawrence Col, MS, 37, PhD(chem eng), 39. *Prof Exp:* Develop engr, Mead Corp, Ohio, 39-41; supvr mat eng lab, Mfg Eng Dept, Marathon Corp, Wis, 46-53; chief develop sect, Res & Develop Dept, Film Div, Olin Industs, Inc, 53-56, dir res & develop, Film Div, Olin Mathieson Chem Corp, 56-62, dir packaging opers, Int Div, 62-65; vpres res & develop, Oxford Paper Co, 65-70; gen mgr, C H Dexter Div, Dexter Corp, Scotland, 71-73; CONSULT, 73- *Concurrent Pos:* Vol consult, Int Exec Serv Corps, 73- *Mem:* Am Chem Soc; Tech Asn Pulp & Paper Indust; Inst Food Technol. *Res:* Cellulose and lignin chemistry; protective packaging; design and construction of chemical plants; pulp; paper; cellophane; high polymers; chemical warfare agents. *Mailing Add:* 15 Richmond Hill Rd Greenwich CT 06830

SIMHA, ROBERT, b Vienna, Austria, Aug 4, 12; nat US; m 41. MACROMOLECULAR SYSTEMS. *Educ:* Univ Vienna, PhD(physics), 35. *Prof Exp:* Res assoc, Univ Vienna, 35-38; vis fel, Columbia Univ, 39-40, res assoc, 40-41; lectr, Polytech Inst Brooklyn, 41-42; asst prof, Howard Univ, 42-45; lectr, Nat Bur Standards Grad Sch, 44-45, consult & coordr polymer res, 45-51, lectr, 47-48; prof chem eng, NY Univ, 51-59; prof chem, Univ Southern Calif, 59-67; PROF MACROMOLECULAR SCI, CASE WESTERN RESERVE UNIV, 68- *Concurrent Pos:* Lectr, Grad Div, Brooklyn Col, 40-42; vis prof, Univ Southern Calif, 58-59; chmn, First Winter Gordon Res Conf, 63; John F Kennedy Mem Found sr fel, Weizmann Inst, 66-67; sr vis res fel, Univ Manchester, 67-68. *Honors & Awards:* Lalor Award, 40; Award, US Dept Com, 48; Award, Wash Acad Sci, 46; Morrison Prize, NY Acad Sci, 48; Nat Bur Standards Award, 49; Bingham Medal, Soc Rheol, 73; High Polymer Physics Prize, Am Phys Soc, 81. *Mem:* Fel AAAS; fel Am Phys Soc; Am Chem Soc; fel Am Inst Chemists; fel NY Acad Sci. *Res:* Hydrodamics of colloidal solutions; viscosity of liquids and macromolecular solutions; physical and thermodynamic properties of polymers; polymerization and depolymerization processes, including biological macromolecules. *Mailing Add:* Dept Macromolecular Sci Case Western Reserve Univ Cleveland OH 44106

SIMINOFF, PAUL, b Brooklyn, NY, May 8, 23; m 51; c 3. VIROLOGY, IMMUNOBIOLOGY. *Educ:* Mich State Col, BS, 48; Univ Ill, MS, 49, PhD, 51. *Prof Exp:* Microbiologist, S B Penick & Co, NJ, 51-54 & Upjohn Co, Mich, 54-58; MICROBIOLOGIST, BRISTOL LABS, INC, 58- *Mem:* AAAS; Am Soc Microbiol. *Res:* Fermentation of antibiotics and vitamins; application of tissue culture to virus and cancer research; immunology and cancer; interferon induction; drug research in allergic and immune complex diseases. *Mailing Add:* 705 Sycamore Terr Syracuse NY 13214

SIMINOVITCH, LOUIS, b Montreal, Que, May 1, 20; m 44; c 3. BIOPHYSICS, MICROBIOLOGY. *Educ:* McGill Univ, BSc, 41, PhD(phys chem), 44. *Prof Exp:* Res phys chemist, Nat Res Coun Can, 44-47; Royal Soc Can fel biochem & microbiol, Pasteur Inst, Paris, 47-49, microbiol, Nat Ctr Sci Res, 49-53; Nat Cancer Inst Can fel, Connaught Med Res Lab, 53-56, assoc prof, 56-60, assoc prof med biophys, 58-60, prof microbiol, 60-67, PROF MED BIOPHYS, UNIV TORONTO, 60-, CHMN DEPT MED CELL BIOL, 66-, MEM RES 69-, MEM CANCER RES UNIT, 77- *Concurrent Pos:* Del, Int Cong Cell Biol, Scotland, 57; head subdiv microbiol div biol res, Ont Cancer Inst, 57-63, head div, 63-69; ed, Virology, 60-; Louis Rapkine Mem lectr, Pasteur Inst, Paris, 64; mem coun, Sch Grad Studies, Univ Toronto, 65-68; mem panel sect, Nat Cancer Inst Can, 65-69, res adv group, 68-, chmn, 70-; Major G Seelig lectr, Washington Univ, 66; mem virol & rickettsiology study sect, NIH, 66-68; mem grant comt cellular biol & genetics, Nat Res Coun Can, 66-69, mem long-range planning comt, 66-; mem health res comt, Ont Coun Health, 66-; mem grants comt cancer, growth & differentiation, Med Res Coun Can, 67-, chmn, 70-, mem ad hoc comt aminocentesis, 71, mem genetics comt, 71-; head study basic biol in Can, Kenneth C Fisher Study Group, Biol Coun Can, 68-; ed, Bact Rev, 69-; mem reconstituted comt health res, Ont Coun Health, 69-; convenor panel V, Int Cell Res Orgn, UNESCO, 70-71; geneticist-in-chief, Hosp Sick Children, Toronto, 70-; chmn ad hoc comt activities of Can Commun Dis Ctr, Ottawa, 71; partic adv group somatic cell genetics, Nat Cancer Inst, 72; vis prof, Col France, 72. *Mem:* Am Asn Cancer Res; Royal Soc Can; Genetics Soc Can; Can Soc Cell Biol(pres-elect, 66, pres, 67). *Res:* Differentiation in haemopoietic tissues in mice; biochemical and physiological genetics of bacteriophages; tumor viruses. *Mailing Add:* Dept of Biophys Univ of Toronto Toronto ON M5S 2R8 Can

SIMITSES, GEORGE JOHN, b Athens, Greece, July 31, 32; US citizen; m 60; c 3. ENGINEERING & STRUCTURAL MECHANICS. *Educ:* Ga Inst Technol, BS, 55, MS, 56; Stanford Univ, PhD(aeronaut & astronaut), 65. *Prof Exp:* Instr struct, 56-59, proj engr, Eng Exp Sta, 58-61, asst prof struct & design, 59-66, assoc prof spacecraft struct, 66-68, assoc prof eng sci & mech, 68-74, PROF ENG SCI & MECH, GA INST TECHNOL, 74- *Concurrent Pos:* Consult to numerous industs & co, 66- *Mem:* Am Soc Eng Educ; assoc fel Am Inst Aeronaut & Astronaut; Am Soc Mech Engrs; Am Acad Mech; Sigma Xi. *Res:* Stability theory; optimization of basic structural elements such as beams, columns, plates; snapping of low arches of uniform and non-uniform geometry under static and dynamic loads; stability of stiffened plates and shells; structural stability; structural optimization; mechanics of composite materials. *Mailing Add:* Sch of Eng Sci & Mech Ga Inst of Technol Atlanta GA 30332

SIMIU, EMIL, b Bucharest, Romania, Apr 8, 34; US citizen; m 70; c 2. STRUCTURAL ENGINEERING. *Educ:* Inst Civil Eng, Bucharest, Dipl Ing, 56; Polytech Inst Brooklyn, MS, 68; Princeton Univ, PhD(civil eng), 71. *Prof Exp:* Design engr struct eng, Bucharest Design Inst, 56-62, Bechtel Corp, 63-65, Lev Zetlin & Assocs, 65-66 & Ammann & Whitney, Inc, 66-68; res asst civil eng, Princeton Univ, 68-71; RES ENGR STRUCT ENG, NAT BUR STANDARDS, 71- *Concurrent Pos:* Res assoc, Nat Bur Standards, 71-73. *Mem:* Am Soc Civil Engrs; Sigma Xi. *Res:* Dynamic loads on structures induced by wind, earthquake, and ocean waves; dynamic and aeroelastic response of slender structures. *Mailing Add:* Ctr for Bldg Technol Nat Bur of Standards Washington DC 20234

SIMKIN, BENJAMIN, b Philadelphia, Pa, Apr 17, 21; m 47; c 2. ENDOCRINOLOGY. *Educ:* Univ Southern Calif, AB, 41, MD, 44. *Prof Exp:* Intern, Los Angeles County Hosp, 43-44; resident med, Cedars of Lebanon Hosp, 44-46; instr, 49-66, ASST CLIN PROF, SCH MED, UNIV SOUTHERN CALIF, 66-; clin chief endocrinol, 60-73, ATTEND PHYSICIAN, CEDARS-SINAI MED CTR, 69- *Concurrent Pos:* Beaumont res fel med, Cedars of Lebanon Hosp, 46-47; fel, Michael Reese Hosp, 47-48; res fel, May Inst, Jewish Hosp, Cincinnati, 48-49; jr attend physician, Los Angeles County Hosp, 49-65, attend physician, 65-; asst adj, Cedars of Lebanon Hosp, 52-58, assoc attend physician, 58-60, attend physician & chief endocrine clin, 61-69. *Mem:* AAAS; Soc Exp Biol & Med; Endocrine Soc; Am Diabetes Asn; AMA. *Res:* Pituitary hormones; obesity; clinical endocrinology. *Mailing Add:* 6200 Wilshire Blvd Los Angeles CA 90048

SIMKIN, DONALD JULES, b Brooklyn, NY, Sept 5, 25; m 53; c 3. AEROSPACE ENGINEERING & TECHNOLOGY. *Educ:* Univ Calif, Berkeley, BS, 45, MS, 49. *Prof Exp:* Engr, Shell Develop Co, 49-57; sr engr, Marquardt Corp, 57-58, supvr rocket propulsion, 58-60; dept head, Astropower Lab, Douglas Aircraft Co, 60-62; supvr spacecraft propulsion, Space & Info Div, Downey, 62, chief, 62-66, mgr, 66-67, sr proj engr advan systs dept, 67-69, MGR MISSION & OPERS ANAL, SPACE SHUTTLE PROJ, ROCKWELL INT CORP, 69- *Concurrent Pos:* Lectr, Space Technol Series, Univ Calif, Los Angeles, 58-68. *Mem:* Assoc fel Am Inst Aeronaut & Astronaut; Am Chem Soc; Am Inst Chem Engrs; Combustion Inst. *Res:* Spacecraft propulsion systems; thermodynamics of propellants; combustion phenomena; chemical kinetics; fluid dynamics; unit operations of chemical engineering; spacecraft design; space shuttle mission planning and operations. *Mailing Add:* 3 Morena Irvine CA 92715

SIMKIN, SUSAN MARGUERITE, b Detroit, Mich, July 26, 40; m 61; c 2. ASTRONOMY. *Educ:* Earlham Col, BA, 62; Univ Wis, PhD(astron), 67. *Prof Exp:* Res assoc & lectr astron, Columbia Univ, 66-73; res assoc, 74-75, asst prof astron, 76-79, ASSOC PROF PHYSICS & ASTRON, MICH STATE UNIV, 79- *Concurrent Pos:* NATO fel, Kapteyn Lab, 75-76; sr res fel, Mt Stromlo Observ, 76-80, vis fel, 80-81. *Mem:* AAAS; Int Astron Union; Am Astron Soc. *Res:* Astronomical photometry; spectroscopy; structure of galaxies; radio galaxies. *Mailing Add:* Dept Physics & Astron Mich State Univ East Lansing MI 48824

SIMKIN, THOMAS EDWARD, b Auburn, NY, Nov 11, 33; m 65; c 1. GEOLOGY, VOLCANOLOGY. *Educ:* Swarthmore Col, BS, 55; Princeton Univ, MSE, 60, PhD(geol), 65. *Prof Exp:* Indust engr, Proctor & Gamble Co, 55-56; hydrographer, US Coast & Geodetic Surv, 56-58; instr geol, State Univ NY Binghamton, 64-65; res assoc geophys sci, Univ Chicago, 65-67; supvr geol, Smithsonian Oceanog Sorting Ctr & res assoc, Petrol Div, Smithsonian Inst, 67-72, CUR PETROLOGY & VOLCANOLOGY, SMITHSONIAN INST, 72- *Concurrent Pos:* Secy for Americas, Charles Darwin Found for Galapagos Isles, 70- *Mem:* Mineral Soc Am; Am Geophys Union; Int Asn Volcanology & Chem Earth's Interior; AAAS. *Res:* Volcanology, particularly oceanic volcano evolution, processes, calderas and contemporary volcanism; petrology of differentiated and olivine-rich rocks in Galapagos Islands and Scottish Tertiary Province. *Mailing Add:* NHB Stop 119 Smithsonian Inst Washington DC 20560

SIMKINS, CHARLES ABRAHAM, b Reading, Kans, Nov 3, 23; m 45; c 6. SOIL FERTILITY, AGRONOMY. *Educ:* Kans State Univ, BS(biol sci) & BS(agr), 48, MS, 50, PhD(soil), 58; Oak Ridge Inst Nuclear Studies, DRIP, 51. *Hon Degrees:* Dr, Univ Hungary, 73. *Prof Exp:* Res asst soils, Kans State Univ, 46-48, asst prof, 49; asst prof, Univ Idaho, 50-52; res asst, Kans State Univ, 52-53; assoc prof, Univ Minn, 53-58; chief soils, Develop & Res Corp, Iran, 58-63; soil scientist, Food & Agr Orgn, UN, Cyprus, 63-64; chief of party agr develop, Chile Proj, 64-70, PROF SOILS, UNIV MINN, ST PAUL, 70-, EXTEN SPECIALIST, AGR EXTEN, 74- *Concurrent Pos:* Consult, Govt Saudi Arabia, 60 & Govt Hungary, 71-72; proj mgr, UN Drug Fund, Lebanon, 73-74. *Mem:* Am Soc Agron; Soil Sci Soc Am. *Res:* Nutrition of wheat plant; pasture fertility research; potato fertility; land use. *Mailing Add:* Dept of Soils Univ of Minn St Paul MN 55101

SIMKINS, KARL LEROY, JR, b Aldine, NJ, July 2, 39; m 61; c 3. ANIMAL SCIENCE. *Educ:* Rutgers Univ, BS, 61; Univ Wis, MS, 62, PhD(animal nutrit & biochem), 65. *Prof Exp:* Res asst dairy sci, Univ Wis, 61-62, res asst dairy sci & biochem, 62-65; res nutritionist, 65-70, group leader, Clin Develop Lab, 70-77, MGR, ANIMAL INDUST DEVELOP, AGR RES CTR, AM CYANAMID CO, PRINCETON, NJ, 77- *Mem:* Am Soc Animal Sci; Am Dairy Sci Asn. *Res:* Appetite and growth regulation in domestic animals; evaluation of nitrogen and phosphorus sources for ruminants; efficacy and safety of antibacterials, anthelmintics, coccidiostats and pesticides; evaluation of compounds which alter rumen fermentation. *Mailing Add:* Agr Res Ctr Am Cyanamid Co PO Box 400 Princeton NJ 08540

SIMKINS, RONALD ALLEN, biochemistry, see previous edition

SIMKOVER, HAROLD GEORGE, b Montreal, Que, Mar 27, 23; nat US; m 47; c 2. ENTOMOLOGY. *Educ:* McGill Univ, BSc, 47; Univ Wis, MS, 48, PhD(entom), 51. *Prof Exp:* Jr entomologist & instr, Wash State Univ, 51-53; entomologist, Shell Develop Co, 53-63, patent agt, 63-66, sr field rep, Shell Chem Co, 66-69, SR FIELD REP, BIOL SCI RES CTR, SHELL DEVELOP CO, 69- *Mem:* AAAS; Entom Soc Am. *Res:* Economic entomology; pesticides. *Mailing Add:* Shell Develop Co Biol Sci Res Ctr Modesto CA 95352

SIMKOVICH, GEORGE, b Smithton, Pa, Apr 19, 28; m 63; c 3. MATERIAL SCIENCES, METALLURGY. *Educ:* Pa State Univ, BS, 52, MS, 55, PhD(metall), 59. *Prof Exp:* Res asst mineral prep, Pa State Univ, 52-55, asst, 55; res assoc metall, Yale Univ, 58-60; Nat Sci Found res fel, 60-61; res fel, Max Planck Inst Phys Chem, 61-62; scientist, Fundamental Res Lab, US Steel Corp, 62-64; assoc prof, 64-71, PROF METALL, PA STATE UNIV, UNIVERSITY PARK, 71- *Mem:* Am Inst Mining, Metall & Petrol Engrs;

Am Soc Metals; Nat Asn Corrosion Engrs; Electrochem Soc. *Res:* Physical chemistry of metallurgy; physical chemistry of materials; high-temperature studies; oxidation; point defects in solids. *Mailing Add:* 206 Steidle Bldg Pa State Univ University Park PA 16802

SIMMANG, C(LIFFORD) M(AX), b San Antonio, Tex, Feb 14, 12; m 42; c 1. MECHANICAL ENGINEERING. *Educ:* Agr & Mech Col Tex, BS, 36, MS, 38; Univ Tex, PhD(mech eng), 52. *Prof Exp:* Jr engr petrol, Humble Oil Co, 36-37; from instr to prof mech eng, 38-77, head dept, 57-77, EMER PROF MECH ENG, TEX A&M UNIV, 77- *Honors & Awards:* Charles W Crawford Award, Eng, 79. *Mem:* Am Soc Mech Engrs; Soc Am Mil Engrs; Sigma Xi. *Res:* Heat transfer and coefficients in regenerative air heater; fluid flow, loss in tubing elbows and bends. *Mailing Add:* Dept of Mech Eng Tex A&M Univ College Station TX 77843

SIMMEL, EDWARD CLEMENS, b Berlin, Ger, Jan 30, 32; US citizen; div; c 3. BEHAVIORAL GENETICS, ANIMAL BEHAVIOR. *Educ:* Univ Calif, Berkeley, AB, 55; Wash State Univ, PhD(exp psychol), 60. *Prof Exp:* Res trainee, Vet Admin Hosp, American Lake, Wash, 60; asst prof psychol, Western Wash State Col, 60-62 & Calif State Univ, Los Angeles, 62-65; from asst prof to assoc prof, 65-71, PROF PSYCHOL, MIAMI UNIV, 71-, DIR BEHAV GENETICS LAB, 77- *Mem:* Am Soc Zoologists; Animal Behav Soc; Behav Genetics Asn; Psychonomic Soc; Int Soc Develop Psychobiol. *Res:* Developmental and social psychobiology. *Mailing Add:* Dept of Psychol Miami Univ Oxford OH 45056

SIMMER, ROBERT LLOYD, b Pontiac, Mich, June 16, 48; m 81. CELL BIOLOGY, PROTEIN CHEMISTRY. *Educ:* Oakland Univ, BS, 71; Univ Chicago, MS, 73; Univ Calif, Irvine, PhD(biol), 80. *Prof Exp:* Res fel, City Hope Res Inst, 80-81; cancer res fel, Ladies Auxilliary Vet Foreign Wars, 80-81; RES FEL II, CITY HOPE RES INST, CALIF, 81- *Res:* Relationships between the cell membrane and cellular events as they apply to the control of cell division; molecular cloning of tumor markers and the analysis of the relationship between their expression and various disease states. *Mailing Add:* Div Immunol City Hope Res Inst 1450 E Duarte Rd Duarte CA 91010

SIMMON, VINCENT FOWLER, b Los Angeles, Calif, Aug 9, 43; div; c 1. MICROBIOLOGY. *Educ:* Amherst Col, Mass, BA, 64; Univ Toledo, MS, 67; Brown Univ, RI, PhD(molecular biol), 72. *Prof Exp:* Res & develop chemist thermoplastics, Textileather Div, Gen Tire & Rubber Co, 64-65; fel microbiol, Stanford Univ, Stanford, Calif, 71-73; microbiologist, Stanford Res Inst, 73-75, mgr microbial genetics, 75-77, asst dir dept toxicol, SRI Int, 77-79; dir tech opers, 79-80, vpres mkt, 80-81, VPRES INT DEVELOP, GENEX CORP, 82- *Concurrent Pos:* Vis asst prof, Dept Anesthesiol, Stanford Med Sch, 77-79; mem, Comt Chem & Environ Mutagens, Nat Res Coun, 79- *Mem:* Am Environ Mutagen Soc; Am Soc Microbiol; AAAS; Sigma Xi; NY Acad Sci. *Res:* The use and development of microbial systems for the detection of mutagenic chemicals in particular carcinogens, which may be harmful to man or the environment. *Mailing Add:* Genex Corp 6110 Executive Blvd Rockville MD 20852

SIMMONDS, RICHARD CARROLL, b Baltimore, Md, Aug 22, 40. LABORATORY ANIMAL SCIENCE, RESEARCH ADMINISTRATION. *Educ:* Univ Ga, DVM, 64; Tex A&M Univ, MS, 73. *Prof Exp:* US Air Force, 64-, res vet, Arctic Aeromed Lab, 64-67 & Arctic Med Res Lab, Alaska, 67-68; staff vet & resident, Lab Animal Med, Sch Aerospace Med, 68-70; area test dir, Lunar Quarantine Prog & staff vet, Air Force Detailee, Johnson Space Ctr, 70-73; staff vet & mgr, Joint US/USSR Biol Satellite Proj, Air Force Detailee, Ames Res Ctr, NASA, 73-76; DIR DEPT LAB ANIMAL MED, SCH MED, UNIFORMED SERV UNIV HEALTH SCI, 76- *Honors & Awards:* Commendation Medal, US Air Force & US Army, 68; Meritorious Serv Medal, US Air Force, 74; Meritorious Serv Medal, NASA, 76. *Mem:* Am Vet Med Asn; Am Asn Lab Animal Sci; Am Col Lab Animal Med; AAAS; Am Soc Mammal. *Res:* Biomedical effects of altered geophysical environments; laboratory animal science and mammalian thermal regulation. *Mailing Add:* Dept of Lab Animal Med Uniformed Serv Univ Health Sci Bethesda MD 20014

SIMMONDS, ROBERT T, b Hackensack, NJ, Aug 2, 32; m 57. PALEOBIOLOGY. *Educ:* Columbia Univ, BS, 54; Syracuse Univ, MS, 58; Univ Ill, PhD(geol), 61. *Prof Exp:* Instr geol, Denison Univ, 61; assoc prof, 61-65, PROF EARTH SCI, STATE UNIV NY COL ONEONTA, 65- *Mem:* AAAS; Nat Asn Geol Teachers. *Res:* Paleoecology, evolution, geotectonics. *Mailing Add:* Dept of Geol State Univ of NY Col Oneonta NY 13820

SIMMONDS, SIDNEY HERBERT, b Winnipeg, Man, Aug 29, 31; m 55; c 3. CIVIL ENGINEERING. *Educ:* Univ Alta, BSc, 54, MSc, 56; Univ Ill, PhD, 62. *Prof Exp:* Assoc prof, 57-70, PROF CIVIL ENG, UNIV ALTA, 70- *Mem:* Am Concrete Inst; Am Soc Civil Engrs; Int Asn Shell Struct. *Res:* Structural analysis and design. *Mailing Add:* 11311 Malmo Rd Edmonton AB T6H 4M3 Can

SIMMONDS, SOFIA, b New York, July 31, 17; m 36. BIOCHEMISTRY. *Educ:* Columbia Univ, BA, 38; Cornell Univ, PhD(biochem), 42. *Prof Exp:* Asst biochem, Med Col, Cornell Univ, 41-42, res assoc, 42-45; instr physiol chem, 45-46, from instr to asst prof microbiol, 46-50, from asst prof to assoc prof biochem & microbiol, 50-62, assoc prof biochem, 62-69, assoc prof molecular biophys & biochem, 69-75, PROF MOLECULAR BIOPHYS & BIOCHEM, 75-, DIR UNDERGRAD STUDIES, DEPT MOLECULAR BIOPHYS & BIOCHEM, SCH MED, YALE UNIV, 73- *Honors & Awards:* Garvan Medal, Am Chem Soc, 69. *Mem:* Am Soc Biol Chem; Am Chem Soc. *Res:* Amino acid metabolism; transmethylation in animals; amino acid and protein metabolism in micro-organisms. *Mailing Add:* Molecular Biophys & Biochem Sch Med Yale Univ PO Box 3333 New Haven CT 06510

SIMMONDS, WALTER HENRY CLIVE, b London, Eng, Sept 24, 17; Can citizen; m 50; c 2. CHEMISTRY, CHEMICAL ENGINEERING. *Educ:* Oxford Univ, BSc, 40, MA, 43; Sir George Williams Univ, BA, 71. *Prof Exp:* From res chemist to chem engr, Lever Bros & Unilever Ltd, 40-47; sr lectr chem eng, Univ Durham, 47-52; asst to dir res, Dom Tar & Chem Co, 52-56; develop engr, Can Industs Ltd, 56-64; consult, Expo 67, 64-65; corp planner, Can Industs Ltd, 65-70; SR RES OFFICER INDUST POLICY & ANAL, NAT RES COUN CAN, 70- *Mem:* NY Acad Sci; Soc Gen Systs Anal; Inst Chem Eng; Can Sociol & Anthrop Asn; Am Sociol Asn. *Res:* Value, funding of research and development programs; classification and analysis of industrial behavior; technology; innovation; economic and social forecasting and assessment; futures research. *Mailing Add:* Nat Res Coun Can Montreal Rd Ottawa ON K1A 0R6 Can

SIMMONS, ALAN J(AY), b New York, NY, Oct 14, 24; m 47; c 5. ELECTRICAL ENGINEERING. *Educ:* Harvard Univ, BS, 45; Mass Inst Technol, MS, 48; Univ Md, PhD(elec eng), 57. *Prof Exp:* Electronic scientist, US Naval Res Lab, 48-57; head, Microwave Dept, TRG, Inc, 57-71; ASSOC GROUP LEADER, LINCOLN LAB, MASS INST TECHNOL, 71- *Mem:* AAAS; fel Inst Elec & Electronics Engrs. *Res:* Microwave antennas, waveguides and components; electromagnetic theory; communication satellites. *Mailing Add:* 9 Cliff St Winchester MA 01890

SIMMONS, CHARLES EDWARD, b Oklahoma City, Okla, Apr 5, 27; m 53; c 2. PSYCHIATRY. *Educ:* Univ Okla, BS, 50, MD, 54. *Prof Exp:* Intern, Gorgas Hosp, Ancon, Panama, CZ, 54-55; resident psychiat, Griffith Mem Hosp, Norman, Okla, 55-57; resident, Parkland Hosp, Dallas, Tex, 57-58; from instr to asst prof, Univ Tex Southwest Med Sch Dallas, 58-60; mem staff, Chestnut Lodge, Md, 62-63; PROF PSYCHIAT, UNIV TEX MED SCH SAN ANTONIO, 67- *Concurrent Pos:* NIMH teaching fel psychiat, Univ Tex Southwest Med Sch Dallas, 57-58; consult, Wilford Hall Air Force Hosp, San Antonio, Tex, 67- *Mem:* AMA; Am Psychiat Asn; Am Psychoanal Asn. *Res:* Psychoanalysis. *Mailing Add:* Dept of Psychiat Univ of Tex Med Sch San Antonio TX 78284

SIMMONS, CHARLES FERDINAND, b Andalusia, Ala, May 17, 10; m 40; c 1. AGRONOMY, SOIL SCIENCE. *Educ:* Auburn Univ, BS, 32, MS, 34; Ohio State Univ, PhD(soils), 37. *Prof Exp:* Exten agronomist, Univ Ark, 37-44; assoc agronomist, Exp Sta, La State Univ, 44-46; head, Dept Agron, 46-51, assoc dir, Exp Sta, 51-55, assoc dean, Sch Agr, 51-80, asst dir, Exp Sta, 55-80, EMER DEAN, SCH AGR, AUBURN UNIV, 80- *Mem:* Am Soc Agron; Soil Sci Soc Am; Am Inst Biol Sci. *Res:* Soil chemistry and fertility; effect of carbon dioxide pressure upon equilibrium of calcium carbonate soil systems. *Mailing Add:* 357 S Gay St Auburn AL 36830

SIMMONS, DANIEL HAROLD, b New York, NY, June 22, 19; m 42; c 2. INTERNAL MEDICINE, PHYSIOLOGY. *Educ:* Univ Calif, Los Angeles, BA, 41; Univ Southern Calif, MD, 48; Univ Minn, PhD(physiol), 53. *Prof Exp:* Instr math, Univ Calif, Los Angeles, 43; asst prof med, 53-55, from asst prof to assoc prof med & physiol, 55-65, prof physiol, 65-81, PROF MED, UNIV CALIF, LOS ANGELES, 65- *Concurrent Pos:* Nat Heart Inst trainee, Univ Minn, 51-53; sect chief, Vet Admin Ctr, Los Angeles, 53-61; dir res & assoc dir div med, Mt Sinai Hosp, 61-64, dir med res inst, Cedars-Sinai Med Ctr, 64-66. *Mem:* Am Physiol Soc; Am Fedn Clin Res; Am Col Chest Physicians; fel Am Thoracic Soc. *Res:* Animal research on mechanisms of clinically-related problems in respiration physiology. *Mailing Add:* Dept Med Univ Calif Sch Med Los Angeles CA 90024

SIMMONS, DAVID J, b Jamaica Plain, Mass, Mar 10, 31; m 57; c 1. PHYSIOLOGY, ENDOCRINOLOGY. *Educ:* Boston Univ, BA, 54; Clark Univ, MA, 56; Univ Chicago, PhD(paleozool), 59. *Prof Exp:* Instr biol, Wright Jr Col, 59-60; res assoc physiol, Univ Chicago, 59-62; from asst physiologist to assoc physiologist, Radiol Physics Div, Argonne Nat Lab, 62-72; asst prof orthop surg, 72-7S, ASSOC PROF RES ORTHOP SURG, SCH MED, WASH UNIV, 75- *Concurrent Pos:* NIH fel, Univ Chicago, 60-62. *Mem:* AAAS; Am Asn Anatomists; Int Soc Chronobiol; Soc Vert Paleont; Orthop Res Soc. *Res:* Skeletal development; collagen formation; cell population dynamics. *Mailing Add:* Dept of Orthop Surg Wash Univ Sch of Med St Louis MO 63130

SIMMONS, DAVID RAE, b Oklahoma City, Okla, May 4, 40; m 61; c 3. MATHEMATICS. *Educ:* Centenary Col La, BS, 62; Univ Ark, MS, 66, PhD(math), 69. *Prof Exp:* Asst prof math, Centenary Col La, 69-74, actg chmn dept, 70-72; ASST PROF MATH & CHMN DEPT MATH & PHYSICS, LA COL, 74- *Mem:* Am Math Soc; Asn Comput Mach; Math Asn Am. *Res:* Category theory; universal algebra, computer studies of semigroups of relations. *Mailing Add:* Dept of Math & Physics La Col Pineville LA 71360

SIMMONS, DICK BEDFORD, b Houston, Tex, Dec 24, 37; m 59; c 3. COMPUTER & INFORMATION SCIENCES. *Educ:* Tex A&M Univ, BS, 59; Univ Pa, MS, 61, PhD(comput & info sci), 68. *Prof Exp:* Design engr, Radio Corp Am, 59-61; mem tech staff, Bell Tel Labs, 63-69, supvr comput lang & systs, 69-70; assoc prof, 71-81, PROF COMPUT SCI, TEX A&M UNIV, 81-, DIR COMPUT CTR, 72- *Concurrent Pos:* Consult, Tex A&M Univ, 70-71 & Datamaster Div, Am Chain & Cable Co, 72-; prin investr, Unitech Oper Systs Proj, 71-72 & NASA Automated Doc Study, 72. *Mem:* Asn Comput Mach; Inst Elec & Electronics Engrs; Asn Educ Data Systs; Am Soc Eng Educ. *Res:* Automatic documentation; computer languages; programmer productivity; computer architecture. *Mailing Add:* Data Processing Ctr Tex A&M Univ College Station TX 77843

SIMMONS, DONALD GLICK, b Waynesboro, Va, Sept 6, 38. VETERINARY MICROBIOLOGY. *Educ:* Bridgewater Col, BA, 62; Univ Ga, DVM, 67, MS, 69, PhD(vet microbiol), 71. *Prof Exp:* NIH spec fel vet med microbiol, Univ Ga, 67-71; from asst prof to assoc prof, 71-78, prof vet med microbiol, 78-80, PROF MICROBIOL, PATH & PARASITOL, NC STATE UNIV, 80- *Honors & Awards:* P P Levine Award, 80. *Mem:* Sigma Xi; Am Vet Med Asn; Am Col Vet Microbiologists; Am Soc Microbiol; Am Asn Avian Pathologists. *Res:* Veterinary medical microbiology; avian medicine; respiratory and enteric viruses of poultry; respiratory bacteria of poultry. *Mailing Add:* Sch Vet Med NC State Univ Raleigh NC 27650

SIMMONS, EMORY GUY, b Ind, Apr 12, 20. MYCOLOGY. *Educ:* Wabash Col, AB, 41; DePauw Univ, AM, 46; Univ Mich, PhD(bot), 50. *Prof Exp:* Instr bact & bot, DePauw, 46-47; asst prof bot, Dartmouth Col, 50-53; mycologist, US Army Natick Labs, 53-58, head mycol lab, 58-74, prin investr, Develop Ctr Cult Collection of Fungi, 74-77; prof bot, 74-77, PROF MICROBIOL, UNIV MASS, AMHERST, 77- *Concurrent Pos:* Chmn adv comt fungi, Am Type Cult Collection; US rep, Expert Group on Fungus Taxon, Orgn Econ Coop & Develop; Secy Army res fel, Thailand, Indonesia, 68-69; adj prof, Univ RI, 72-74; mem exec bd, US Fedn Cult Collections, 74-76, pres, 76-78; pres & chmn bd, Second Int Mycol Cong, Inc, 75-78; mem adv comt cult collections, UN Environ Prog/UNESCO/Int Cell Res Orgn, 77- *Mem:* Fel AAAS; Mycol Soc Am (secy-treas, 63-65, vpres, 66, pres, 68); Brit Mycol Soc; Am Soc Microbiol; Int Asn Plant Taxonomists. *Res:* Taxonomic mycology; taxonomy of Fungi imperfecti; taxonomy and cultural characteristics of Ascomycetes. *Mailing Add:* Dept of Microbiol Univ of Mass Amherst MA 01003

SIMMONS, ERIC LESLIE, b Santo Domingo, Dom Repub, Feb 11, 17; nat US; m 43; c 4. BIOLOGY. *Educ:* Swarthmore Col, AB, 38; Ind Univ, PhD(zool), 44. *Prof Exp:* Res assoc, Metall Lab, 43-46, from instr to asst prof biol sci, 46-55, premed adv, 48-52, asst dean students, 52-54, assoc prof med, 55-78, PROF MED, SCH MED, UNIV CHICAGO, 78- *Mem:* Sigma Xi; assoc Am Soc Zoologists; Radiation Res Soc; Am Asn Lab Animal Sci; Int Soc Exp Hemat. *Res:* Radiobiology; effect of radiation on the hemopoietic system; cancer induction. *Mailing Add:* Franklin McLean Mem Res Inst Univ of Chicago Chicago IL 60637

SIMMONS, EUGENE LYNN, physical chemistry, see previous edition

SIMMONS, FRANCIS BLAIR, b Los Angeles, Calif, Nov 15, 30; m 71; c 4. PHYSIOLOGY. *Educ:* Transylvania Col, AB, 52; Univ Louisville, MD, 56. *Prof Exp:* Intern med, Madigan Army Hosp, 56-57; res physiologist, Walter Reed Army Inst Res, 58-59; resident physician & res assoc otolaryngol, 59-62, assoc prof, 65-71, PROF OTOLARYNGOL, SCH MED, STANFORD UNIV, 71-, CHIEF DEPT, 65- *Res:* Auditory physiology and psychophysics; neurophysiology. *Mailing Add:* Stanford Univ Med Ctr Stanford CA 94305

SIMMONS, FREDERICK CHARLES, b Waverly, NY, Oct 27, 05; m 29, 64; c 2. FOREST PRODUCTS. *Educ:* Cornell Univ, BS, 28; Yale Univ, MF, 31. *Prof Exp:* Timber cruiser, Int Paper Co, NY, 28 & J D Lacey Co, La, 29; instr forestry, Pa State Col, 31-32; mgt asst, Allegheny Nat Forest, US Forest Serv, 33-34, mgt asst, Eastern Region, Washington, DC, 35-45, technologist, Northeastern Forest Exp Sta, 45-62; UN Food & Agr Orgn adv, Chile, 63-64; sr ed, Northern Logger & Timber Processor Mag & exec secy, Northeastern Loggers' Asn, 64-77; CONSULT, FOREST PROD INDUSTS, 77- LOGGERS' ASN, 65- *Concurrent Pos:* Adv, Forestry Eng Panel, Food & Agr Orgn, UN. *Honors & Awards:* Heiberg Mem Award, NY Forest Owners, 79. *Mem:* Soc Am Foresters; Forest Prod Res Soc; Int Union Forest Res Orgns. *Res:* Timber harvesting and forest management; saw milling; manufacture of veneer, pulp, charcoal and other wood products; author of approximately 200 publications. *Mailing Add:* PO Box 409 Old Forge NY 13420

SIMMONS, GARY ADAIR, b Dothan, Ala, Aug 7, 44; m 69; c 2. FOREST ENTOMOLOGY. *Educ:* Mich Tech Univ, BS, 66, MS, 68; Univ Mich, PhD(forestry), 72. *Prof Exp:* Res assoc, Univ Maine, Orono, 72-73, res asst prof, 73-74, asst prof forest entom & biomet, Dept Entom & Sch Forest Resources, 74-77; mem fac, 77-81, ASSOC PROF, DEPT ENTOM, MICH STATE UNIV, 81- *Concurrent Pos:* Prin investr, Dept Conserv, State Maine, 74-76, Thomson-Hayward Chem Co & Sumitomo Chem Co, Ltd, 75-76; prin & co-prin investr, US Forest Serv, USDA, Northeast Forest Exp Sta, 75-76. *Mem:* AAAS; Am Inst Biol Sci; Can Entom Soc; Entom Soc Am; Soc Am Foresters. *Res:* Biometrics and environmental impact of forest insect pest management practices. *Mailing Add:* Dept of Entom Mich State Univ East Lansing MI 48824

SIMMONS, GARY WAYNE, b Parsons, WVa, June 17, 39; m 64; c 1. PHYSICAL CHEMISTRY, SURFACE CHEMISTRY. *Educ:* WVa Univ, BS, 61; Univ Va, PhD(chem), 67. *Prof Exp:* Fel physics, Ga Inst Technol, 66-67, res chemist, 67-70; asst prof, 70-74, assoc prof, 74-79, PROF CHEM, LEHIGH UNIV, 79- *Honors & Awards:* Melvin Romanoff Award, Nat Asn Corrosion Engrs, 74; Henry Marion Howe Medal, Am Soc Metals, 79. *Mem:* Am Chem Soc. *Res:* Fundamental properties of the solid-gas and solid-liquid interface and application of these properties to practical problems of catalysis, corrosion, stress corrosion cracking and corrosion fatigue; low energy electron diffraction, Auger electron spectroscopy, Mossbauer spectroscopy, x-ray photoelectron spectroscopy and electron microscopy. *Mailing Add:* Ctr Surface & Coatings Res Lehigh Univ Bethlehem PA 18015

SIMMONS, GENE, b Dallas, Tex, May 15, 29; div; c 4. GEOPHYSICS. *Educ:* Tex A&M Univ, BS, 49; Southern Methodist Univ, MS, 58; Harvard Univ, PhD(geophys), 62. *Prof Exp:* Petrol engr, Humble Oil & Refining Co, 49-51; partner, Simmons Gravel Co, 53-62; asst prof geol, Southern Methodist Univ, 62-65; PROF GEOPHYS, MASS INST TECHNOL, 65- *Concurrent Pos:* Mem var adv groups, NASA, 65-; chief scientist, Manned Spacecraft Ctr, 69-71. *Honors & Awards:* Except Sci Achievement Medal, NASA, 71. *Mem:* AAAS; fel Am Geophys Union; Soc Explor Geophys; fel Geol Soc Am; Seismol Soc Am. *Res:* Thermal measurements of earth, moon and planets; physical properties of rocks at high pressures and temperatures; application of geophysical techniques to geological problems. *Mailing Add:* 9 Edgehill Rd Winchester MA 01890

SIMMONS, GEORGE FINLAY, b Austin, Tex, Mar 3, 25; m 54; c 1. MATHEMATICS. *Educ:* Calif Inst Technol, BS, 46; Univ Chicago, MS, 48; Yale Univ, PhD(math), 57. *Prof Exp:* Instr math, Univ Col, Univ Chicago, 47-50, Univ Maine, 50-52 & Yale Univ, 52-56; asst prof, Univ RI, 56-58 & Williams Col, 58-62; assoc prof, 62-65, PROF MATH, COLO COL, 65- *Mem:* Math Asn Am. *Res:* Topology; abstract algebra; analysis. *Mailing Add:* Dept of Math Colo Col Colorado Springs CO 80903

SIMMONS, GEORGE MATTHEW, JR, b Charleston, SC, Dec 25, 42; m 63; c 1. LIMNOLOGY. *Educ:* Appalachian State Univ, BS, 64; Va Polytech Inst & State Univ, PhD(zool), 68. *Prof Exp:* Asst prof biol & ecol, Va Commonwealth Univ, 68-71; from asst prof to assoc prof limnol, 71-78, ASSOC PROF ZOOL, VA POLYTECHNIC INST & STATE UNIV, 78- *Mem:* Int Soc Theoret Appl Limnol; Am Soc Limnol & Oceanog. *Res:* Limnological studies of reservoir ecosystems; origin and role of freshwater benthic communities in antarctic lakes; productivity of tropical marine sand flats. *Mailing Add:* Dept of Biol Va Polytechnic Inst & State Univ Blacksburg VA 24061

SIMMONS, GUSTAVUS JAMES, b Ansted, WVa, Oct 27, 30; m 50; c 1. INFORMATION THEORY, CRYPTOGRAPHY. *Educ:* NMex Highlands Univ, BS, 55; Univ Okla, MS, 58; Univ NMex, PhD(math), 69. *Prof Exp:* Res assoc, Sandia Corp, 54-55, physicist, Nuclear Test Dept, 58-60; res scientist res staff, Lockheed Aircraft Corp, 55-56; sr group engr, Adv Electronics Div, McDonnell Aircraft Corp, 60-61; chief electronic engr, Electronic & Res Div, Fairbanks Morse & Co, 61; div supvr advan systs res, Sandia Corp, 62-70; dir res, Rolamite, 70-71; MGR MATH DEPT, SANDIA CORP, 71- *Concurrent Pos:* Mem subcomt facil, Gov Tech Excellence Comt. *Mem:* Math Asn Am; Am Math Soc. *Res:* Digital message authentication theory; nuclear weapon system, especially the control and engineered use of such systems; combinatorial mathematics and graph theory; algorithms for high speed computation; cryptography. *Mailing Add:* Math Dept Sandia Labs Albuquerque NM 87115

SIMMONS, GUY HELD, b Lafayette, Tenn, Oct 9, 36; m 59; c 5. NUCLEAR MEDICINE. *Educ:* Western Ky Univ, BS, 61; Univ NC, MS, 64; Univ Cincinnati, PhD(nuclear eng), 72. *Prof Exp:* Instr physics, Western Ky Univ, 61; physicist radiation physics, USPHS, 61-72; ASSOC PROF RADIATION MED, UNIV KY, 72-; ASST CHIEF NUCLEAR MED, VET ADMIN HOSP, LEXINGTON, 72- *Concurrent Pos:* KY Heart Asn grant, Univ Ky, 74-, Nat Cancer Inst grant, 75-; Vet Admin grant, 78; instr radiol, Med Ctr, Univ Cincinnati, 66-72. *Mem:* Soc Nuclear Med; Am Asn Physicists Med. *Res:* Nuclear medicine instrumentation development and evaluation; digital image processing for clinical applications. *Mailing Add:* Nuclear Med Serv Vet Admin Hosp Lexington KY 40507

SIMMONS, HAROLD FRANKLYN, mathematics, see previous edition

SIMMONS, HARRY DADY, JR, b Chicago, Ill, June 10, 38. MEDICINAL CHEMISTRY, ONCOLOGY. *Educ:* Univ Ill, BS, 60; Mass Inst Technol, PhD(chem), 66. *Prof Exp:* NIH fels inorg chem, Munich Inst Technol, 66-67; NIH fel chem, Brandeis Univ, 67-69; res chemist, Allied Chem Corp, 69-71; lab supvr, Kingsbrook Jewish Med Ctr, 71-74; med resident, Berkshire Med Ctr, 77-78, path resident, 78-80; res fel molecular biol, Albany Med Col, 80-81; RES FEL MED ENG, POLYTECH INST, TROY, NY, 81- *Mem:* Am Chem Soc; NY Acad Sci; AMA; Am Meteorol Soc; Sigma Xi. *Res:* Synthetic organometallic chemistry of mercury, chromium, iron, group IV A metals; coordination compounds and complexes as catalysts; biomedical engineering; applications of scanning electron microscopy. *Mailing Add:* 369 Washington Ave Albany NY 12206

SIMMONS, HOWARD ENSIGN, JR, b Norfolk, Va, June 17, 29; m 51; c 2. ORGANIC CHEMISTRY. *Educ:* Mass Inst Technol, BS, 51, PhD(org chem), 54. *Prof Exp:* Res chemist, 54-59, res supvr, 59-70, assoc dir res, 70-74, dir res, 74-79, DIR, CENT RES & DEVELOP DEPT, E I DU PONT DE NEMOURS & CO, INC, 79- *Concurrent Pos:* Sloan vis prof, Harvard Univ, 68; Kharasch vis prof, Univ Chicago, 78; adj prof, Univ Del, 70- *Mem:* Nat Acad Sci; fel AAAS; Am Chem Soc; Sigma Xi; Am Acad Arts & Sci. *Res:* Physical organic chemistry; reaction mechanisms; small ring chemistry; theoretical chemistry; chemistry of large molecules. *Mailing Add:* Cent Res & Develop Dept Exp Sta E I du Pont de Nemours & Co Inc Wilmington DE 19898

SIMMONS, IVOR LAWRENCE, b London, Eng, July 17, 24; nat US; m 45; c 2. PHYSICAL CHEMISTRY, ANALYTICAL CHEMISTRY. *Educ:* Univ London, BSc, 52; Stevens Inst Technol, MS, 57. *Prof Exp:* Res chemist, 52-60, supvr phys chem, 61-63, from asst supvr to supvr instrumental anal, 63-67, mgr cent anal dept, 67-75, DIR CENT ANAL DEPT, M&T CHEM INC, 75- *Concurrent Pos:* Asst ed, Appl Spectros, Soc Appl Spectros, 60-68. *Mem:* AAAS; Am Chem Soc; The Chem Soc; NY Acad Sci; Soc Appl Spectros. *Res:* Absorption and emission spectroscopy; instrumental methods of analysis; gas chromatography; x-ray fluorescence. *Mailing Add:* Cent Anal Dept M&T Chem Inc PO Box 1104 Rahway NJ 07065

SIMMONS, JAMES E, b Chicago, Ill, Sept 16, 25; m 48; c 2. EXPERIMENTAL NUCLEAR PHYSICS. *Educ:* Univ Calif, BS, 49, MA, 54, PhD(physics), 57; Univ Paris, dipl, 52. *Prof Exp:* PHYSICIST, LOS ALAMOS NAT LAB, UNIV CALIF, 57- *Concurrent Pos:* Vis scientist, Cen-Saclay Synchrutron, France, 80. *Mem:* Am Phys Soc. *Res:* Low energy nuclear physics with neutron beams; medium energy experiments on spin dependence of nuclear forces using polarized targets and polarized nucleon beams at lampf accelerator; development of cryogenic instrumentation for nuclear physics. *Mailing Add:* Physics Div MS 456 Los Alamos Nat Lab Los Alamos NM 87545

SIMMONS, JAMES EDWIN, b Toledo, Ohio, July 13, 23; m 72; c 7. CHILD PSYCHIATRY. *Educ:* Toledo Univ, BS, 45; Ohio State Univ, MD, 47; Am Bd Psychiat & Neurol, dipl, 54, cert child psychiat, 60. *Prof Exp:* Intern, St Vincent's Hosp, Toledo, Ohio, 47-48; psychiat resident, Menninger Found, Kans, 48-51; from instr to assoc prof psychiat, 53-62, coordr child psychiat serv, 62-74, actg chmn dept psychiat, 74-75, PROF PSYCHIAT, SCH MED, IND UNIV, INDIANAPOLIS, 62-, DIR CHILD PSYCHIAT SERV, 75- *Concurrent Pos:* Psychiatrist-dir, Child Guid Clin Marion County, Inc, Indianapolis, 53-57; fel child psychiat, Univ Louisville, 57-58; consult, La Rue D Carter Hosp, Indianapolis, 58; ed newslett, Am Asn Psychiat Serv Children, 70-74. *Mem:* Fel Am Acad Child Psychiat; fel Am Orthopsychiat Asn; fel Am Psychiat Asn. *Res:* Human neonatal behavior; follow-up of psychiatric hospitalization of children. *Mailing Add:* 1100 W Michigan St Indianapolis IN 46202

SIMMONS, JAMES QUIMBY, III, b Philadelphia, Pa, Apr 16, 25; m 54; c 4. PSYCHIATRY. *Educ:* Rutgers Univ, BS, 48; Bowman Gray Sch Med, Wake Forest Univ, MD, 52. *Prof Exp:* Intern, Walter Reed Army Med Ctr, 52-53; chief inpatient child psychiat, 62-68, assoc clin prof psychiat & assoc prog dir ment retardation, 68-72, PROF PSYCHIAT IN RESIDENCE & ASSOC CHIEF MENT RETARDATION, NEUROPSYCHIAT INST, CTR FOR HEALTH SCI, UNIV CALIF, LOS ANGELES, 72- *Concurrent Pos:* Asst prof in residence psychiat, Neuropsychiat Inst, Ctr for Health Sci, Univ Calif, Los Angeles, 64-68; atten psychiatrist, Vet Admin Ctr, Los Angeles, 65- *Mem:* AAAS; fel Am Psychiat Asn. *Res:* Behavior modification in schizophrenic and retarded children utilizing reinforcement principles; language in autistic children. *Mailing Add:* Neuropsychiat Inst Univ of Calif Ctr for Health Sci 760 Westwood Plaza Los Angeles CA 90024

SIMMONS, JAMES WOOD, b Chase City, Va, Sept 20, 16; m 41; c 3. MOLECULAR SPECTROSCOPY. *Educ:* Hampden-Sydney Col, BS, 37; Va Polytech Inst, MS, 39; Duke Univ, PhD(physics), 48. *Prof Exp:* Instr physics, Va Polytech Inst, 39-41, asst prof, 46; from asst prof to assoc prof, 48-59, chmn dept, 58-63, PROF PHYSICS, EMORY UNIV, 59- *Concurrent Pos:* Consult, Eng Exp Sta, Ga Inst Technol, 65-75. *Mem:* Am Phys Soc; Am Asn Physics Teachers. *Res:* Determination of molecular and nuclear properties by microwave spectroscopy; electronics instrumentation. *Mailing Add:* Dept of Physics Emory Univ Atlanta GA 30322

SIMMONS, JEAN ELIZABETH MARGARET, b Cleveland, Ohio, Jan 20. 14; m 35; c 3. ORGANIC CHEMISTRY, BIOCHEMISTRY. *Educ:* Western Reserve Univ, BA, 33; Univ Chicago, PhD(org chem), 38. *Prof Exp:* From instr to prof chem & chmn dept, Barat Col, 38-58; chmn dept chem, 65-71, 74 & 76-81 chmn div natural sci, 66-69, asst to the pres, 69-73, PROF CHEM, UPSALA COL, 59- *Concurrent Pos:* Instr, Univ Chicago, 38-41; coordr basic sci, Sch Nursing, Evangelical Hosp, 43-47; chmn comt study sci div of Upsala Col, Lutheran Church Am grant, 65-68; pres & trustee, Va Gildersleeve Int Fund Univ Women, Inc; dir & officer, NJ Educ Comput Ctr, 69-72; pres, Grad Women in Sci, 70-71, Fedn Orgns Prof Women, 74-75; consult fund raising, Higher Educ, 72-; vis fel, Hist of Sci, Princeton Univ, 77; consult to pres, Upsala Col, 76- *Honors & Awards:* Citation, Surgeon Gen US, 45; Award, Lindback Found, 64. *Mem:* Fel AAAS; Am Chem Soc; Am Asn Univ Women; fel Am Inst Chemists; fel Sigma Xi. *Res:* Biuret reactions of polypeptides; respiratory pigments; protein chemistry; women in science. *Mailing Add:* Dept of Chem Upsala Col East Orange NJ 07019

SIMMONS, JOE DENTON, b Elberton, Ga, Jan 14, 38; m 63; c 2. PHYSICAL CHEMISTRY, MOLECULAR SPECTROSCOPY. *Educ:* David Lipscomb Col, BA, 59; Vanderbilt Univ, PhD(phys chem), 63. *Prof Exp:* Nat Acad Sci-Nat Res Coun res fel spectros, 63-65, PHYSICIST, NAT BUR STAND, 65- *Mem:* Am Phys Soc; AAAS; Optical Soc Am; Sigma Xi. *Res:* Molecular spectroscopy and structure. *Mailing Add:* Nat Bur Standards Washington DC 20234

SIMMONS, JOHN ARTHUR, b Santa Monica, Calif, Jan 25, 32; m; c 4. THEORETICAL MECHANICS, MATERIALS SCIENCE. *Educ:* Univ Calif, Berkeley, BA, 53, MA, 56, PhD(appl math), 62. *Prof Exp:* Res mathematician, Inst Eng Res, Univ Calif, Berkeley, 57-60, mathematician, Lawrence Radiation Lab, 60-61; fel, Miller Inst Basic Res Sci, 61-62; RES MATHEMATICIAN, NAT BUR STANDARDS, 62- *Concurrent Pos:* Com, sci & technol fel, Staff of Congressman J W Symington, 72-73. *Mem:* Am Soch Mech Engrs; Am Phys Soc; Soc Indust & Appl Math; Am Inst Mech Eng; Am Soc Testing & Mat. *Res:* Dislocation theory; elastodynamics; plastic flow and fracture; acoustic emission and ultrasonics; residual and internal stresses. *Mailing Add:* A125 Mat Bldg Nat Bur Standards Washington DC 20234

SIMMONS, JOHN ROBERT, b Cokeville, Wyo, May 28, 28; m 52; c 4. BIOCHEMISTRY, GENETICS. *Educ:* Utah State Univ, BS, 55, MS, 56; Calif Inst Technol, PhD(biochem), 59. *Prof Exp:* USPHS fel biochem, Sch Med, Stanford Univ, 59-61; from asst prof to prof zool, 61-74, PROF BIOL, UTAH STATE UNIV, 74- *Res:* Proteins and nucleic acids in genetic function; genetic studies of plant tissues in vitro. *Mailing Add:* Dept of Biol UMC53 Utah State Univ Logan UT 84322

SIMMONS, JOSEPH HABIB, b Marrakech, Morocco, Feb 19, 41; US citizen; m 62; c 2. SOLID STATE PHYSICS. *Educ:* Univ Md, College Park, BS, 62; John Carroll Univ, MS, 66; Cath Univ Am, PhD(physics), 69. *Prof Exp:* Res physicist, Lewis Res Ctr, NASA, 62-66; sr scientist solid state physics, Inorg Mat Div, Nat Bur Stand, 66-74; ADJ ASSOC PROF PHYSICS, CATH UNIV AM, 74- *Concurrent Pos:* Consult inorg mat div, Nat Bur Stand, 74- *Honors & Awards:* Superior Accomplishment Award, Nat Bur Stand, 71. *Mem:* Am Ceramic Soc; Am Phys Soc. *Res:* Phase transitions in glasses; thermodynamics and kinetics of liquid state; relaxation processes; optical fiber transmission lines. *Mailing Add:* Vitreous State Lab Cath Univ of Am Washington DC 20064

SIMMONS, KENNETH ROGERS, b Flushing, NY, Aug 27, 26; m 53; c 4. REPRODUCTIVE PHYSIOLOGY. *Educ:* Univ Maine, BS, 52; Cornell Univ, MS, 61, PhD(physiol, endocrinol), 63. *Prof Exp:* Teaching asst animal sci, Cornell Univ, 58-63; asst prof, 63-67, ASSOC PROF ENDOCRINOL & PHYSIOL OF REPROD, UNIV VT, 67- *Mem:* Am Dairy Sci Asn; Am Soc Animal Sci; Soc Study Reproduction. *Res:* Reproductive physiology, especially estrous cycle regulation; reproductive behavior; pheromones. *Mailing Add:* Dept Animal Sci Univ Vt Burlington VT 05401

SIMMONS, LEONARD MICAJAH, JR, b Hattiesburg, Miss, Nov 23, 37; m 59; c 3. THEORETICAL PHYSICS. *Educ:* Rice Univ, BA, 59; La State Univ, Baton Rouge, MS, 61; Cornell Univ, PhD(theoret), 65. *Prof Exp:* Res assoc physics, Univ Minn, 65-67 & Univ Wis-Madison, 67-69; asst prof, Univ Tex, Austin, 69-71; vis asst prof, Univ NH, 71-73; asst theoret div leader, 74-76, assoc theoret div leader, 76-81, STAFF MEM, LOS ALAMOS NAT LAB, 73-, DEP ASSOC DIR PHYSICS & MATH, 81- *Concurrent Pos:* Trustee, Aspen Ctr for Physics, 76-, asst treas, 76-79, treas, 79-82; vis prof physics, Wash Univ, 80-81; co-ed, Los Alamos Series Basil & Appl Sci, Univ Calif Press, 78- *Mem:* AAAS; Am Phys Soc; NY Acad Sci. *Res:* Theory of elementary particles; coherent states; mathematical physics, properties of special functions. *Mailing Add:* Los Alamos Nat Lab Los Alamos NM 87545

SIMMONS, MELVIN KURT, b Susanville, Calif, Oct 17, 43. EXPERIMENTAL ATOMIC PHYSICS. *Educ:* Univ Calif, Berkeley, BS, 65, MA, 67, PhD(physics), 72. *Prof Exp:* Fel physics, Univ Calif, Berkeley, 72-73; researcher solar energy, Lawrence Berkeley Lab, 73-75, dep head, Energy Environ Div, 75-77; ASST DIR, ANAL & ASSESSMENT DIV, SOLAR ENERGY RES INST, 77- *Mem:* AAAS; Fedn Am Scientists. *Res:* Energy policy analysis; solar cooling of buildings. *Mailing Add:* Anal Assessment Div Solar Energy Inst 1536 Cole Blvd Golden CO 80401

SIMMONS, MICHAEL PATRICK, b New York, NY, Feb 10, 37; m 65; c 2. ARCHAEOLOGY, PHYSICAL ANTHROPOLOGY. *Educ:* Columbia Univ, BS, 62; Univ Ariz, MA, 66, PhD(anthrop), 70. *Prof Exp:* Sr ceramist, Mid Am Res Inst, Tulane Univ, 68-71; asst prof, 71-77, ASSOC PROF ANTHROP, CALIF STATE COL, SAN BERNARDINO, 77-, CHMN DEPT, 74- *Mem:* Soc Am Archaeol. *Res:* Archaeology and ceramic analysis; Mesoamerican archaeology. *Mailing Add:* Dept of Anthrop Calif State Col San Bernardino CA 92407

SIMMONS, NOEL, biochemistry, see previous edition

SIMMONS, PAUL C, b Jerome, Ariz, July 14, 32; m 52; c 3. METALLURGY, MATERIALS ENGINEERING. *Educ:* Univ Ariz, BS, 54, MS, 61, PhD(metall), 67. *Hon Degrees:* Prof Eng, Univ Ariz, 70. *Prof Exp:* Metallurgist, Guided Missile Mfg Div, 54-59, supvr metall eng, 59-63, process engr, 63-65, group head mat & processes, Missile Systs Div, 66-67 & Res & Develop Div, 67-68, sr tech staff asst mat & processes & prod effectiveness, 68-71, sect head prod anal & develop, 71-74, SR SCIENTIST & MGR, MISSILE DEVELOP DIV, HUGHES AIRCRAFT CO, 74- *Res:* High strength wire; precipitation hardening; fracture dynamics; short arc lamp technology; rocket motor and pressure vessel design; missile finish systems; long term storage of missiles; guidance unit technology; management principles; standardization; producibility. *Mailing Add:* 652 S Del Valle Tucson AZ 85711

SIMMONS, RALPH OLIVER, b Kensington, Kans, Feb 19, 28; m 52; c 4. PHYSICS. *Educ:* Univ Kans, BA, 50; Oxford Univ, BA, 53; Univ Ill, PhD(physics), 57. *Prof Exp:* Asst, 54-55, res assoc, 57-59, from asst prof to assoc prof, 59-65, PROF PHYSICS, UNIV ILL, URBANA-CHAMPAIGN, 65-, HEAD DEPT, 70- *Concurrent Pos:* NSF sr fel, Ctr Study Nuclear Energy, Mol, Belg, 65; mem, Int Adv Bd, J of Physics C: Solid State Physics, 70-76; chmn, Div of Solid State Physics, Am Phys Soc, 76-77, Off of Phys Sci, Nat Res Coun, Nat Acad Sci, 78-; mem assembly math & phys sci, Nat Res Coun-Nat Acad Sci, 78-81; consult, Argonne Nat Lab, 78-; trustee, Argonne Univs Asn, 79- *Mem:* AAAS; fel Am Phys Soc; Am Crystallog Asn; Am Asn Physics Teachers; Sigma Xi. *Res:* Lattice defects in solid helium metals, semiconductors and ionic crystals; irradiation damage of solids; thermal, elastic and defect properties of noble gas crystals and other molecular solids. *Mailing Add:* 209 Loomis Lab Physics Univ Ill at Urbana-Champaign Urbana IL 61801

SIMMONS, RICHARD LAWRENCE, b Boston, Mass, Feb 23, 34; m 58; c 2. SURGERY, IMMUNOLOGY. *Educ:* Harvard Univ, AB, 55; Boston Univ, MD, 59. *Prof Exp:* Asst surg, Columbia Univ, 63-64, instr, 64-68; from asst prof to assoc prof, 68-72, PROF SURG & MICROBIOL, UNIV MINN, MINNEAPOLIS, 72- *Concurrent Pos:* NIH fel, Columbia Univ, 60-61, Am Cancer Soc clin fel, 63-64; Markle Found scholar acad med, 69-75; consult, Vet Admin Hosp, Minneapolis, 71- *Honors & Awards:* Found Award, Am Asn Obstet & Gynec. *Mem:* Am Asn Immunol; Soc Univ Surg; Am Soc Nephrol; Transplantation Soc. *Res:* Transplantation biology; immunology of cancer. *Mailing Add:* Box 185 Univ of Minn Hosp Minneapolis MN 55455

SIMMONS, THOMAS CARL, b Williamsport, Pa, Nov 14, 20; m 52. ORGANIC CHEMISTRY. *Educ:* Pa State Univ, BS, 45, MS, 50, PhD(biochem), 52. *Prof Exp:* Asst biochem, Pa State Col, 45-52; org res chemist, 52-68, CHIEF, ORG CHEM SECT, US ARMY CHEM SYSTS LAB, 68- *Mem:* AAAS; Am Chem Soc; Sigma Xi; Am Defense Preparedness Asn; NY Acad Sci. *Res:* Physiological, fluorine, natural product and medicinal chemistry; chemistry of organo-phosphorus compounds and chemical warfare agents. *Mailing Add:* 2706 Bynum Hills Circle Bel Air MD 21014

SIMMONS, WILLIAM BRUCE, JR, b Bay City, Tex, Nov 5, 43; m 66; c 2. MINERALOGY, PETROLOGY. *Educ:* Duke Univ, BS, 66; Univ Ga, MS, 68; Univ Mich, Ann Arbor, PhD(mineral), 72. *Prof Exp:* Field geologist, Owens Ill Glass Co, 68; from instr to asst prof, 72-75, ASSOC PROF EARTH SCI, UNIV NEW ORLEANS, 75- *Mem:* AAAS; Mineral Soc Am; Geol Soc Am; Am Inst Mining; Am Inst Mining, Metall & Petrol Engrs. *Res:* Mineralogy, petrology and geochemistry of pegmatite systems; mineralogical applications of laser microscopy. *Mailing Add:* Dept Earth Sci Univ New Orleans New Orleans LA 70122

SIMMONS, WILLIAM FREDERICK, b Philadelphia, Pa, Nov 14, 38. OCEANOGRAPHY. *Educ:* Lehigh Univ, BS, 60; Pa State Univ, MS, 62; Johns Hopkins Univ, PhD(mech), 67. *Prof Exp:* Instr mech, Johns Hopkins Univ, 63-66, res asst, 66-67; res assoc, Mass Inst Technol, 67-69; asst scientist oceanog, Woods Hole Oceanog Inst, 69-71, assoc scientist, 71-74; mode exec officer, 74-77, polymode exec officer, Mass Inst Technol, 74-75, polymode exec scientist, 76-77; first global exper prog officer, Global Atmospheric Res Prog Off, World Meteorol Orgn, 77-80. *Mem:* AAAS; Am Geophys Union; Sigma Xi (secy). *Res:* Wave motions and nonlinear processes; thermo-mechanical coupling at the air-sea interface; theoretical and experimental studies of resonant interactions of internal waves; oceanic Mesoscale; equatorial phenomena. *Mailing Add:* Box 412 Woods Hole MA 02543

SIMMONS, WILLIAM W, b Chicago, Ill, Apr 24, 32; m 54; c 3. PHYSICS, ELECTRONICS ENGINEERING. *Educ:* Carleton Col, BA, 53; Univ Ill, Urbana, MS, 55, PhD(physics), 60. *Prof Exp:* Staff scientist physics, Space Technol Labs, 59-62 & Gen Technol Corp, 62; sr scientist appl physics, TRW Systs Group, 63-71; sr engr appl physics & elec eng, 72-74, proj mgr & tech dir appl physics, 75-76, proj engr, 76-78, div leader elec eng, 78-80, ENG MGR, LAWRENCE LIVERMORE NAT LABS, 79- *Concurrent Pos:* Assoc prof elec eng, Univ Calif, Los Angeles, 68-71. *Mem:* Optical Soc Am; Inst Elec & Electronic Engrs; Laser Inst Am. *Res:* Laser-plasma interactions; inertial confinement fusion; nonlinear optical propagation phenomena; electrooptic techniques and devices; signal analysis and pattern recognition; acoustic surface wave propagation; nuclear resonance; antiferomagnetism. *Mailing Add:* Lawrence Livermore Nat Labs L-463 Univ Calif Livermore CA 94550

SIMMS, HORACE RIDGLY, b Racine, Wis, June 15, 21; m 52; c 1. MYCOLOGY. *Educ:* Univ NMex, BS, 55, MS, 62; Univ Colo, PhD(bot), 65. *Prof Exp:* Teacher high sch, NMex, 55-61; prof biol, Adams State Col, 65-66; PROF BIOL, EASTERN WASH UNIV, 66-, COORD NATURAL SCI EDUC, 81- *Mem:* AAAS; Mycol Soc Am; Bot Soc Am. *Res:* Fungi of subalpine forests; morphology and anatomy of basidiomycetes; occurrence and distribution of lichens of eastern Washington. *Mailing Add:* Dept of Biol Eastern Wash State Univ Cheney WA 99004

SIMMS, JOHN ALVIN, b Cleveland, Ohio, Apr 2, 31; m 55; c 2. ORGANIC POLYMER CHEMISTRY. *Educ:* NGa Col, BS, 51; Purdue Univ, MS, 53, PhD(org chem), 56. *Prof Exp:* RES FEL, FABRICS & FINISHES DEPT, E I DU PONT DE NEMOURS & CO, INC, 55- *Mem:* Am Chem Soc. *Res:* Synthesis of monomers a polymers; free radical polymerization; adhesives; elastoplastic film formers with superior photooxidative stability; isocyanate functional oligomers. *Mailing Add:* Du Pont Exp Sta Bldg 174/308 Wilmington DE 19899

SIMMS, NATHAN FRANK, JR, b Winston-Salem, NC, Oct 20, 32; m 59; c 3. PURE MATHEMATICS. *Educ:* NC Cent Univ, BS, 54, MS, 59; Lehigh Univ, PhD(math), 70. *Prof Exp:* Instr math, Fla A&M Univ, 59-60 & NC Cent Univ, 60-62; from asst prof to assoc prof, 64-72, PROF MATH, WINSTON-SALEM UNIV, 72- *Concurrent Pos:* Consult, Regional Educ Lab Carolinas & Va, 70-72, Math Asn Am Minority Insts, 72-73 & Metric Educ Prog Winston-Salem/Forsyth Schs, 74-; NSF res grant, 73; dir, Div of Lib Arts & Sci. *Mem:* Math Asn Am; Sigma Xi; Am Math Soc. *Res:* Category theory and homological algebra; frobenius categories and spectral sequences. *Mailing Add:* Winston-Salem State Univ PO Box 13115 Winston-Salem NC 27102

SIMMS, PAUL C, b Jackson, Tenn, Nov 10, 32; m 59; c 2. NUCLEAR PHYSICS. *Educ:* NGa Col, BS, 53; Purdue Univ, PhD(physics), 58. *Prof Exp:* Res assoc physics, Columbia Univ, 59-60, asst prof, 60-64; assoc prof, 64-73, PROF PHYSICS, PURDUE UNIV, LAFAYETTE, 73- *Mem:* Am Phys Soc. *Res:* Nuclear structure. *Mailing Add:* Dept of Physics Purdue Univ Lafayette IN 47907

SIMNAD, MASSOUD T, b Teheran, Iran, Mar 11, 20; nat US; m 54; c 2. MATERIALS SCIENCE. *Educ:* Univ London, BS, 41; Cambridge Univ, PhD(phys chem), 45. *Prof Exp:* Res assoc, Imp Col, Univ London, 41-42 & Cambridge Univ, 45-48; Am Electrochem Soc Weston fel, Carnegie Inst Technol, 48, mem staff, Metals Res Lab, 49-56; head chem & metall II div, Gen Atomic Div, Gen Dynamics Corp, Calif, 56-60, asst chmn metall dept, 60-69; sr res adv, Gen Atomic Co, Inc, 69-73, sr tech adv, 73-81. *Concurrent Pos:* Vis prof, Mass Inst Technol, 62-63; mem rev comt, Argonne Nat Lab, 74-80; vis lectr nuclear energy, Univ Calif, San Diego, 78-, adj prof, 82- *Honors & Awards:* Cert of Merit, Am Nuclear Soc, 65. *Mem:* Fel AAAS; Am Inst Aeronaut & Astronaut; fel Am Soc Metals; Am Inst Mining, Metall & Petrol Engrs; fel Am Nuclear Soc. *Res:* Nuclear reactor materials and fuels research and development; materials science and technology; energy conversion and utilization. *Mailing Add:* 9342 La Jolla Farms Rd La Jolla CA 92037

SIMON, ALBERT, b New York, NY, Dec 27, 24; m 72; c 3. PLASMA PHYSICS, CONTROLLED FUSION REACTORS. *Educ:* City Col New York, BS, 47; Univ Rochester, PhD(physics), 50. *Prof Exp:* Physicist, Oak Ridge Nat Lab, 50-55, assoc dir neutron physics div, 55-61; head plasma physics div, Gen Atomic Div, Gen Dynamics Corp, 61-66; PROF MECH & ENG, UNIV ROCHESTER, 66-, PROF PHYSICS, 67-, CHMN DEPT MECH & ENG, 77- *Concurrent Pos:* Guggenheim fel, 64-65; mem inst advan study, 74-75; sr vis fel, UK Sci Res Coun, Oxford Univ, 75. *Mem:* Fel Physics Soc; Am Nuclear Soc; Am Asn Mech Engrs; AAAS; Am Soc Eng Educ. *Res:* Controlled thermonuclear reactor research. *Mailing Add:* Dept Mech Eng Univ Rochester Rochester NY 14627

SIMON, ALEXANDER, b New York, NY, Oct 13, 06; m 34; c 1. PSYCHIATRY. *Educ:* Columbia Univ, BA, 26, MD, 30; Am Bd Psychiat & Neurol, dipl, 38; Am Psychiat Asn, cert ment hosp adminr, 54. *Prof Exp:* Intern, St Joseph's Hosp, Paterson, NJ, 30-31; resident psychiat, St Elizabeth's Hosp, Washington, DC, 31-34; assoc neurol, Med Sch, George Washington Univ, 35-43; lectr, 43-45, from assoc prof to prof, 45-74, EMER PROF PSYCHIAT, SCH MED, UNIV CALIF, SAN FRANCISCO, 74- *Concurrent Pos:* Consult, Dept Army & Letterman Army Hosp, San Francisco, 46-, Vet Admin Hosp, Palo Alto, 49-58, Parks AFB, 53-56, Surgeon Gen, US Air Force, 53-59 & Travis AFB, 59-63; chmn dept psychiat, Univ Calif, San Francisco, 56-74; consult, Mayor's Comt, White House Conf on Aging, 59, Calif deleg, 61 & 71; consult, San Francisco Comt on Aging, USPHS, 60 & Gov Citizens Adv Comt on Aging; asst med supt, Langley Porter Neuropsychiat Inst, 43-56, med dir, 56-74; lectr, Sch Social Welfare, Univ Calif, Berkeley, 49-66; mem training study sect, Nat Inst Ment Health, 56-60 & ment health prog-proj comt, 61-65, chmn, 64-6S, consult res utilization br, 63-65; mem Gov Interdept Comt Probs of Aging, 60-66; mem, Dept Ment Hyg Comt on Aging, 61-69, chmn, 64-69; mem adv comt housing for sr citizens, Housing & Home Finance Agency, Fed Housing Admin, 62-63; mem med adv bd, Nat Asn Prev Addiction to Narcotics, 64-69; trustee, Pac Inst Living, San Francisco, 64-70; mem med adv bd, Nat Aid to Visually Handicapped, 68-; comnr, Calif Comn on Aging, 76-79; psychiatrist to geriat serv unit, SE Community Ment Health, San Francisco, 74- *Honors & Awards:* Outstanding Civilian Serv Medal, US Army, 67; J Elliott Royer Award, 68; Outstanding Serv Award & Western Geront Soc Award, 77. *Mem:* AMA; fel Am Psychiat Asn; Am Psychopath Asn; Am Acad Neurol; Geront Soc. *Res:* Geriatric mental illness. *Mailing Add:* Dept of Psychiat Univ of Calif Sch of Med San Francisco CA 94143

SIMON, ALLAN LESTER, b Boston, Mass, Mar 18, 34; m 55; c 3. MEDICINE, RADIOLOGY. *Educ:* Boston Univ, AB, 55; Tufts Univ, MD, 59. *Prof Exp:* Intern med, Univ Md, 59-60; resident radiol, Beth Israel Hosp, Boston, 60-63; instr radiol, Yale-New Haven Med Ctr, 65-66; sr surgeon, NIH, 66-68; assoc prof radiol, Johns Hopkins Univ, 68-69; assoc prof, Univ Calif, San Diego, 69-72; prof diag radiol, Sch Med, Yale Univ, 72-75; CLIN PROF RADIOL, UNIV CALIF, SAN DIEGO, 75- *Concurrent Pos:* Nat Cancer Inst trainee radiol, 61-62; USPHS res fel cardiovasc radiol, Yale-New Haven Med Ctr, 63-65; consult, Nat Heart & Lung Inst & Clin Ctr, NIH, 68- *Res:* Diagnostic methods in cardiovascular disease; electronic processing of radiographic images. *Mailing Add:* Dept Radiol Alvarado Community Hosp San Diego CA 92120

SIMON, ANDREW L, b Kisujszallas, Hungary, Dec 1, 30; m 61; c 2. CIVIL ENGINEERING. *Educ:* Budapest Tech Univ, Dipl Ing, 54; Purdue Univ, PhD(fluid mech), 62. *Prof Exp:* Hydraul design engr, Eng Design Bur, State of Hungary, 54-56; stress analyst, Babcock & Wilcox Co, Ohio, 56-58; asst civil eng, Purdue Univ, 58-61; prof & head dept, WVa Inst Technol, 61-65; PROF CIVIL ENG & HEAD DEPT, UNIV AKRON, 65-, DIR, INST TECH ASSISTANCE, 77- *Concurrent Pos:* Lectr, Kanawha Valley Grad Ctr, WVa Univ, 63-64. *Mem:* Am Soc Civil Engrs; Am Soc Eng Educ. *Res:* Hydraulics; ground water seepage; two phase flows potential theory. *Mailing Add:* Dept of Civil Eng Univ of Akron Akron OH 44325

SIMON, ARTHUR BERNARD, b New York, NY, Jan 17, 27; m 51; c 2. MATHEMATICS. *Educ:* St Louis Univ, BS, 49; Univ Miami, MS, 54; Tulane Univ, PhD, 57. *Prof Exp:* Instr math, Yale Univ, 57-59; from asst prof to prof math, Northwestern Univ, 59-72; chmn dept, 72-80, PROF MATH, CALIF STATE UNIV, HAYWARD, 72- *Mem:* Am Math Soc. *Res:* Mathematical analysis; Banach algebras. *Mailing Add:* Dept of Math Calif State Univ Hayward CA 95420

SIMON, BARRY MARTIN, b Brooklyn, NY, Apr 16, 46; m 71; c 3. MATHEMATICAL PHYSICS. *Educ:* Harvard Univ, BA, 66; Princeton Univ, PhD(physics), 70. *Prof Exp:* Instr math, Princeton Univ, 69-70, from asst prof to assoc prof math & physics, 70-76, prof, 76-81; PROF MATH & THEORET PHYSICS, CALIF INST TECHNOL, 81- *Concurrent Pos:* Sloan fel, Princeton Univ, 71-73; assoc ed, J Operator Theory, 78-, J Math Physics & J Statist Physics, 79-81 & Commun Math Physics & Duke Math J, 81-; Sherman B Fairchild distinguished vis scholar, Calif Inst Technol, 80-81. *Mem:* Am Math Soc; Am Phys Soc. *Res:* Applications of rigorous mathematics to theoretical physics, especially to quantum physics; atomic and molecular physics; nonrelativistic quantum mechanics; quantum field theory; statistical mechanics. *Mailing Add:* Dept Math & Theoret Physics Mail Code 253-37 Calif Inst Technol Pasadena CA 91125

SIMON, CARL PAUL, b Chicago, Ill, Feb 7, 45; m 66; c 2. MATHEMATICS. *Educ:* Univ Chicago, BS, 66; Northwestern Univ, MS, 67, PhD(math), 70. *Prof Exp:* Instr math, Univ Calif, Berkeley, 70-72; asst prof math, 72-78, ASSOC PROF MATH & ECON, UNIV MICH, 78- *Concurrent Pos:* Vis asst prof math, Northwestern Univ, 75; assoc prof math & econ, Univ NC, 78-80. *Mem:* Am Math Soc; Soc Indust & Appl Math; Economet Soc; Sigma Xi. *Res:* Stability of dynamical systems; index of fixed points and singularities; symplectic geometry; mathematical economics. *Mailing Add:* Dept of Math Univ Mich Ann Arbor MI 48109

SIMON, CHRISTINE MAE, b Memphis, Tenn, Oct 14, 49. EVOLUTIONARY BIOLOGY, SYSTEMATICS. *Educ:* Univ Fla, BS, 71, MS, 74; State Univ NY, Stony Brook, PhD(ecol & evolution), 79. *Prof Exp:* Res assoc evolutionary systs, Univ Chicago, 78-79; RES ASSOC, ZOOL DEPT, UNIV HAWAII, 80-, ASSOC ENTOMOLOGIST, BERNICE P BISHOP MUS, 81- *Concurrent Pos:* T Roosevelt Mem Fund grant, 76-77. *Mem:* Sigma Xi; Soc Study Evolution; Soc Syst Zool; Ecol Soc Am. *Res:* Geographic variation and its relationship to speciation; rates of evolution; interaction between ecology and genetics; macroevolution; phylogenetic systematics; history of evolutionary biology; periodical cicadas, Toxorhynchites mosquitos, Hawaiian Drosophila. *Mailing Add:* Dept Zool Univ Hawaii Honolulu HI 96822

SIMON, DAVID ZVI, b Montreal, Que, May 16, 29; m 48; c 4. MEDICINAL CHEMISTRY. *Educ:* Univ Montreal, BPh, 54, PhD(med chem), 65. *Prof Exp:* Nat Res Coun France fel, 66-67; asst prof, 67-71, ASSOC PROF MED CHEM, FAC PHARM, UNIV MONTREAL, 71- *Concurrent Pos:* Prof, Health Sci Centre & Res & Develop Inst, 3en-Gurion Univ, 74-75. *Res:* The role of the acetylenic bond in drug molecules. *Mailing Add:* 6985 Victoria Ave Montreal PQ H3W 2T5 Can

SIMON, DOROTHY MARTIN, b Harwood, Mo, Sept 18, 19; m 46. PHYSICAL CHEMISTRY. *Educ:* Southwest Mo State Col, AB, 40; Univ Ill, PhD(chem), 45. *Hon Degrees:* DSc, Worcester Polytech Inst, 71; DE, Lehigh Univ, 78. *Prof Exp:* Asst chem, Univ Ill, 41-45; res chemist, E I du Pont de Nemours & Co, NY, 45-46; chemist, Clinton Lab, Tenn, 47; assoc chemist, Argonne Nat Lab, 48-49; aeronaut res scientist, Lewis Lab, Nat Adv Comt Aeronaut, 49-53, asst chief chem br, 54-55; Rockefeller fel, Cambridge Univ, 53-54; group leader combustion, Magnolia Petrol Co, Tex, 55-56; prin scientist & tech asst to pres res & advan develop div, 56-62, dir corp res, 62-64, vpres defense & indust prod group, 64-68, CORP VPRES & DIR RES, AVCO CORP, 68- *Concurrent Pos:* Fel, Univ Ill, 45; Marie Curie lectr, Pa

State Univ, 62; dir, Econ Systs Corp, 66-72; mem comt sponsored res, Mass Inst Technol, 72-, Harvard Bd of Overseers Comt for Appl Res & NASA Space Systs & Technol Adv Comt, 78-; trustee, Worchester Polytech Inst, 73-; dir, Crown Zellerbach Corp & Conn Nat Bank, 78-; dir, Warner Lambert Co, 80 & The Charles Stark Draper Lab, 81; trustee, NEastern Univ, 80-; mem, Nat Mats Adv Bd, Nat Res Coun/Nat Acad Sci, 81; mem, President's Comt, Nat Medal Sci, 78-81; Chmn bd, Guggenheim Medal Award, 79-82. *Honors & Awards:* Rockefeller Pub Serv Award, 53; Achievement Award, Soc of Women Engrs, 56. *Mem:* AAAS; Am Chem Soc; fel Am Inst Aeronaut & Astronaut; Combustion Int; fel Am Inst Chemists. *Res:* Combustion; aerothermo chemistry; research management and strategic planning. *Mailing Add:* Avco Corp 1275 King St Greenwich CT 06830

SIMON, EDWARD, b Bradley Beach, NJ, Sept 24, 27; m 50; c 5. SOLID STATE SCIENCE. *Educ:* Rutgers Univ, BS, 50; Purdue Univ, MS, 52, PhD(physics), 55. *Prof Exp:* Res engr, Transitron, Inc, 54-58; vpres & founder, Solid State Prod, Inc, 58-67, VPRES, UNITRODE CORP, 67- *Mem:* AAAS; Am Phys Soc; Electrochem Soc; Inst Elec & Electronics Engrs. *Res:* Semiconductor devices, design, research and development. *Mailing Add:* Moses Hill Rd Manchester MA 01944

SIMON, EDWARD HARVEY, b Elizabeth, NJ, June 25, 34; m 56; c 4. VIROLOGY. *Educ:* Rutgers Univ, BS, 56; Calif Inst Technol, PhD(biol), 60. *Prof Exp:* USPHS fel genetics, Carnegie Inst, 59-60; from asst prof to assoc prof, 60-70, PROF BIOL, PURDUE UNIV, LAFAYETTE, 70- *Concurrent Pos:* NSF sr res fel, Weizmann Inst. 66; vis prof, Hebrew Univ, Israel, 73 & Weizmann Inst, 79. *Mem:* AAAS; Am Soc Microbiol. *Res:* Genetics of animal viruses; mode of action and induction of interferon; production in interferon from single cells. *Mailing Add:* Dept of Biol Sci Purdue Univ Lafayette IN 47907

SIMON, ELIOT MORTON, physics, chemistry, see previous edition

SIMON, ELLEN MCMURTRIE, b Norristown, Pa, Mar 29, 19; m 54; c 1. PROTOZOOLOGY, CRYOBIOLOGY. *Educ:* Ursinus Col, AB, 40; Univ Wis, MS, 52, PhD, 55. *Prof Exp:* Res assoc bact, Univ Wis, 55-58; res assoc zool, 63-64, asst prof, 64-76; RES SCIENTIST GENETICS & DEVELOP, UNIV ILL, URBANA, 77- *Concurrent Pos:* Vis asst prof microbiol, Univ Ill, 75 & 76, vis assoc prof, 77, 78 & 79; mem exec bd, US Fedn for Cult Collections, 76- *Mem:* Am Soc Microbiol; Soc Protozoologists; Soc Cryobiol; Soc Indust Microbiol. *Res:* Genetics; variants of Salmonella and Brucella; preservation of protozoa in liquid nitrogen; genetics and aging of ciliated protozoa. *Mailing Add:* Dept Gentics & Develop Univ Ill 515 Morrill Hall 505 S Goodwin Urbana IL 61801

SIMON, ERIC, b Egelsbach, Ger, Jan 8, 20; US citizen; m 51; c 3. CHEMICAL ENGINEERING, CHEMISTRY. *Educ:* City Col NY, BChE, 45. *Prof Exp:* Prof supvr, Harmon Color Works, 46-48; group leader res, Sun Chem Corp, 48-53; tech dir chem prod, Pigmentos y Oxidos, 54-74; OWNER, E S CONSULT ENG CO, 74- *Concurrent Pos:* Lectr, Cent Patronal de Nuevo Leon, 70-74. *Mem:* Asn Consult Chemists & Engrs; AAAS; Am Chem Soc; Inst Ingenieros Quimicos Mex. *Res:* Development of appropriate technology for developing countries. *Mailing Add:* E S Consult Eng Co 15 Charleston Park Suite 904 Houston TX 77025

SIMON, ERIC JACOB, b Wiesbaden, Ger, June 2, 24; US citizen; m 47; c 3. NEUROCHEMISTRY, PHARMACOLOGY. *Educ:* Case Inst Technol, BS, 44; Univ Chicago, MS, 47, PhD(org chem), 51. *Prof Exp:* Res assoc muscular dystrophy, Med Col, Cornell Univ, 53-59; from asst prof to assoc prof, 59-72, prof exp med, 72-80, PROF PSYCHIAT & PHARMACOL, MED SCH, NY UNIV, 80- *Concurrent Pos:* Nat Found Infantile Paralysis fel biochem, Col Physicians & Surgeons, Columbia Univ, 51-53; lectr chem, City Col of New York, 53-59. *Honors & Awards:* Res Pacesetter Award, Nat Inst on Drug Abuse, 79; Louis & Bert Freedman Found Award, NY Acad Sci, 80. *Mem:* Fel AAAS; Am Chem Soc; Am Soc Pharmacol & Exp Therapeut; Am Soc Neurochem; Am Soc Biol Chem. *Res:* Study of opiate receptors and biochemical action; metabolism of vitamin E; neurochemical studies in nerve cells in culture. *Mailing Add:* Dept Psychiat NY Univ Med Ctr New York NY 10016

SIMON, FREDERICK OTTO, b New York, NY, Dec 11, 39. GEOCHEMISTRY, ANALYTICAL CHEMISTRY. *Educ:* Am Univ, BS, 61, MS, 63; Univ Md, PhD(chem), 72. *Prof Exp:* Chemist, 61-73, proj leader, 73-75, supvr chemist anal chem & geochem, 75-79, RES CHEMIST, US GEOL SURV, 79- *Concurrent Pos:* Ed, Geochem Int J, Am Geol Inst, 72-76. *Mem:* Am Chem Soc; Geochem Soc; Geol Soc Am. *Res:* Inorganic geochemistry of coal; coal quality; application of analytical, inorganic and physical chemistry to problems in earth science; analysis of rarer elements in geologic materials. *Mailing Add:* US Geol Surv Nat Ctr 923 Reston VA 22092

SIMON, FREDERICK TYLER, b Pittsburgh, Pa, May 9, 17; m 46; c 2. PHYSICAL CHEMISTRY, COLOR SCIENCE. *Educ:* Morris Harvey Col, 3S, 55; Marshall Univ, MS, 57. *Prof Exp:* Asst colorist, Am Cyanamid Co, 38-40; head res lab, Philadelphia Qm Corps, US Army, 40-44; head spectros lab, Sidney Blumenthal & Co, 44-48; head qual control, Peerless Woolen Mills, 49-53; dir textiles, Good Housekeeping Inst, 53-54; res specialist, Union Carbide Corp, 54-68; J E SIRRINE PROF TEXTILE SCI, CLEMSON UNIV, 68- *Concurrent Pos:* Consult, Burlington Industs, Inc, 70-, Cherokee Finishing Corp, 70-, Sandoz Wander Inc, 71- & Diano Corp, 74-; deleg, Comt Colorimetry, Int Comn Illum, 71; chairholder, Color Mkt Group; mem, The Colour Group, Gt Brit. *Mem:* Am Chem Soc; Am Asn Textile Chem & Colorists; Intersoc Color Coun; Optical Soc Am; Sigma Xi. *Res:* Color science, including dyeing and coloration chemistry of dyes and pigments; polymer morphology, including microscopy, x-ray diffraction, crystallization kinetics, neutron scattering and general textile processing and fiber manufacture; computer color matching and industrial color toleracnces as well as fluorescent colorants. *Mailing Add:* Sirrine lHall Clemson Univ Clemson SC 29631

SIMON, GARY ALBERT, b Wilkes-Barre, Pa, Apr 24, 45. STATISTICS, APPLIED STATISTICS. *Educ:* Carnegie-Mellon Univ, BS, 66; Stanford Univ, PhD(statist), 72. *Prof Exp:* Asst prof statist, Princeton Univ, 71-75; ASSOC PROF, DEPT APPL MATH & STATIST, STATE UNIV NY STONY BROOK, 75- *Mem:* Am Statist Asn. *Res:* Analysis of categorical data and nonparametric statistics. *Mailing Add:* Dept of Appl Math & Statist State Univ of NY Stony Brook NY 11794

SIMON, GEORGE WARREN, b Frankfurt, Ger, Apr 22, 34; US citizen; m 58; c 3. ASTROPHYSICS. *Educ:* Grinnell Col, AB, 55; Calif Inst Technol, MS, 61, PhD(physics), 63; Univ Utah, MBA, 76. *Prof Exp:* Jr scientist, Atomic Power Div, Westinghouse Elec Corp, 55-56, assoc scientist, 58; mem tech staff radiation effects, Hughes Res Labs, 58-61 & Space Technol Labs, 61-63; dir comput lab, 69-76, dep dir observ, 75-76, RES ASTROPHYSICIST, SACRAMENTO PEAK OBSERV, 63-, CHIEF SOLAR RES BR, AIR FORCE GEOPHYS LAB, 76-; SPACE SHUTTLE ASTRONAUT, 78- *Concurrent Pos:* Physicist, Max Planck Inst Physics & Astrophys, 65-66 & 77; consult, NASA, 67-; vis assoc, Harvard Col Observ, 69-70. *Mem:* Am Astron Soc; Am Phys Soc; Int Astron Union. *Res:* Magnetic and velocity fields and other inhomogeneities in the solar atmosphere; solar physics; nuclear reactor physics; radiation effects in semiconductors; space physics. *Mailing Add:* Sacramento Peak Observ Sunspot NM 88349

SIMON, GERARD THEODOR, pathology, electron microscopy, see previous edition

SIMON, GEZA, b Budapest, Hungary, Mar 6, 41; US citizen; m 65; c 2. CARDIOVASCULAR DISEASES, INTERNAL MEDICINE. *Educ:* NY Univ, BA, 64; State Univ NY Downstate Med Ctr, MD, 68; Mich State Univ, PhD(physiol), 74; Am Bd Internal Med, dipl, 73. *Prof Exp:* From intern to resident med, NY Univ-Bellevue Hosp, 68-70; med officer, US Army, 70-72; fel physiol & clin instr med, Mich State Univ, 72-74; NIH res fel med, Univ Mich Med Ctr, 74-75, res scientist, 75-76; ASST PROF MED, UNIV MINN, MINNEAPOLIS, 76- *Concurrent Pos:* Fel, Am Heart Asn. *Mem:* Soc Exp Biol Med; Am Fedn Clin Res. *Res:* Human and experimental hypertension with emphasis on unidentified vasoactive humoral agents in volume-expanded hypertension. *Mailing Add:* Vet Admin Med Ctr 111C2 54th St & 48th Ave S Minneapolis MN 55417

SIMON, HAROLD A, b Durban, SAfrica, Mar 30, 25; US citizen; m 56; c 3. HEAT TRANSFER, FLUID MECHANICS. *Educ:* Univ Witwatersrand, BSc, 45, MS, 60; Univ Minn, PhD(mech eng), 61; Col Aeronaut, Eng, dipl CAe, 51. *Prof Exp:* Aerodynamicist, Bristol Aircraft Co, Eng, 51-53; sr lectr mech eng, Univ Witwatersrand, SAfrica, 53-59 & 62-63; assoc prof, Univ Del, 63-65; assoc prof, 65-71, PROF ENERGY ENG, UNIV ILL, 71- *Concurrent Pos:* Prin investr, NSF grants, 65-66, 73-74, 77-78. *Mem:* Am Soc Mech Engrs; Sigma Xi. *Res:* Heat transfer in curved tubes with pulsatile flow; solar energy systems and performance. *Mailing Add:* Energy Eng Univ of Ill Box 4348 Chicago IL 60680

SIMON, HAROLD J, b Karlsruhe, Ger, Jan 22, 28; US citizen; m 49; c 3. MEDICINE. *Educ:* Harvard Med Sch, MD, 53; Rockefeller Inst, PhD(microbiol), 59. *Prof Exp:* Intern med, NY Hosp-Cornell Med Ctr, 53-54, asst resident, 54-56; asst prof med, Sch Med, Stanford Univ, 59-66; asst dean, Sch Med, 66-69, assoc dean educ & student affairs, 69-78, PROF MED & COMMUNITY MED, SCH MED, UNIV CALIF, SAN DIEGO, 66- *Concurrent Pos:* Arthritis Found fel, 59-61; USPHS grant, 59-78 & career develop award, 62-65; asst, Med Col, Cornell Univ, 54-56; asst physician, Hosp, Rockefeller Inst, 56-59; physician outpatients, NY Hosp-Cornell Med Ctr, 56-59; mem study sect commun dis, USPHS, 66-71; panelist & chmn sect III, Pac Intersci Cong, Japan, 66; convener, Panel Coccal Infections, Int Cong Chemother, Austria, 67; mem comt manned probs space flight, Nat Acad Sci, 68-; vis sr scholar, Div Int Health, Inst Med, Nat Acad Sci, 78-79. *Mem:* AAAS; Infectious Dis Soc Am; Am Col Physicians; Am Soc Clin Pharmacol & Therapeut; Am Fedn Clin Res. *Res:* Studies in host-parasite interactions; clinical pharmacology of antimicrobial agents; prevention of hospital-acquired infections; international medicine and epidemiology; medical education; student affairs. *Mailing Add:* Sch Med Univ Calif San Diego La Jolla CA 92037

SIMON, HENRY JOHN, b London, Eng, May 4, 39; US citizen; m 60; c 4. SOLID STATE PHYSICS. *Educ:* Tufts Univ, BSEE, 60; Harvard Univ, MA, 65, PhD(appl physics), 69. *Prof Exp:* Sr res scientist, United Aircraft Res Lab, East Hartford, 69-70; asst prof physics, Worcester Polytech Inst, 70-72; asst prof, 72-81, PROF PHYSICS, UNIV TOLEDO, 81- *Mem:* Am Phys Soc. *Res:* Interaction of intense light with matter; nonlinear optics; harmonic generation of light; surface plasmons. *Mailing Add:* Dept Physics & Astron Univ Toledo Toledo OH 43606

SIMON, HOWARD ELLIOTT, b San Francisco, Calif, May 6, 47. MEDICAL SCIENCES. *Educ:* Univ Calif, Berkeley, BS, 70; Univ Calif, San Diego, MS, 74, PhD(chem), 75. *Prof Exp:* Res assoc, Dept Chem, State Univ NY, Stony Brook, 75-81; SR STAFF ASSOC NUCLEAR MAGNETIC RESONANCE, RADIOL DEPT, HEALTH SCI DIV, COLUMBIA UNIV, 82- *Concurrent Pos:* Lectr, Dept Chem, State Univ NY, Stony Brook, 75-76. *Res:* Developing nuclear magnetic resonance imaging for use in clincial diagnostic radiology; use of hydrogen, sodium and phosphorous, utilizing their magnetic relaxation properties to aid in image contrast and tissue identification. *Mailing Add:* Neurol Inst Box 55 710 W 168th St New York NY 10032

SIMON, JACK AARON, b Champaign, Ill, June 17, 19. COAL GEOLOGY. *Educ:* Univ Ill, BA, 41, MS, 46. *Hon Degrees:* DSc, Univ Ill, 81. *Prof Exp:* From asst geologist to assoc geologist, 46-53, geologist & head coal div, 53-67, prin geologist, 67-73, asst chief, 73-74, chief, 74-81, PRIN SCIENTIST, ILL STATE GEOL SURV, 81-; PROF METALL & MINING, UNIV ILL, 80- *Concurrent Pos:* Assoc prof metall & mining, Univ Ill, 67-74, prof, 74-77, adj prof geol; consult, state & fed comts. *Honors & Awards:* Gilbert H Cady

Award, Geol Soc Am, 75; Percy W Nicholls Award, Am Inst Mining, Metall & Petrol Engrs. *Mem:* AAAS; Geol Soc Am; Am Asn Petrol Geol; Am Inst Mining, Metall & Petrol Engrs; Asn Prof Geol Scientists (vpres, 80-81). *Res:* Coal resources; coal mining geology; Pennsylvanian stratigraphy. *Mailing Add:* Ill State Geol Surv 615 East Peabody Dr Champaign IL 61820

SIMON, JEROME BARNET, b Regina, Sask, Aug 21, 39; m 63; c 2. GASTROENTEROLOGY. *Educ:* Queens Univ, Can, MD, 62; Royal Col Physicians & Surgeons, FRCP(C), 67; Am Bd Internal Med, dipl, 69. *Prof Exp:* House officer med, Montreal Gen Hosp, McGill Univ, 62-65, training resident gastroenterol, 65-66; fel, Liver Study Unit, Yale Univ, 66-69; from lectr to asst prof gastroenterol, 69-74, ASSOC PROF, DIV GASTROENTEROL, DEPT MED, QUEENS UNIV, 74- *Concurrent Pos:* Attend staff, Kingston Gen Hosp, Ont, 69-, head, Div Gastroenterol, 75-; consult staff, Hotel Dieu, Can Forces & St Marys Hosp, 69-; mem, Med Adv Bd, Can Hepatic Found, 72-75; vis prof, Univ Alta, 72, Univ Toronto, 73, 77, 79 & 81, Dalhousie Univ, 75, Univ Conn & Mem Univ, 76, Univ Calgary, 77, McMaster Univ, 78; mem, Prog Grants Comt, Med Res Coun Can, 75-76, Clin Invest Comt, 77-79; res comts, Can Asn Gastroenterol, 76-81. *Mem:* Am Fedn Clin Res; Am Asn Study Liver Dis; Am Gastroenterol Asn; AAAS; Can Med Asn. *Res:* Lipid metabolism in liver disease. *Mailing Add:* Dept of Med Queens Univ Kingston ON K7L 2V6 Can

SIMON, JIMMY L, b San Francisco, Calif, Dec 27, 30; m 53; c 2. MEDICINE. *Educ:* Univ Calif, Berkeley, AB, 52; Univ Calif, San Francisco, MD, 55. *Prof Exp:* Intern, Hosp, Univ Calif, 55-56; asst resident pediat, Grace-New Haven Hosp, 56-57; sr resident, Children's Hosp, Boston, Mass, 57-58; from instr to asst prof, Sch Med, Univ Okla, 60-64; dir, Kern County Gen Hosp, Bakersfield, Calif, 65-66; from assoc prof to prof pediat, Univ Tex Med Br Galveston & dep chmn dept, 66-74; PROF PEDIAT & CHMN DEPT, BOWMAN GRAY SCH MED, 74- *Mem:* Am Pediat Soc; Am Acad Pediat. *Res:* Clinical pediatrics; ambulatory medical care. *Mailing Add:* Dept of Pediat Bowman Gray Sch of Med Winston-Salem NC 27103

SIMON, JOHN ANTONY, clinical biochemistry, see previous edition

SIMON, JOSEPH, b Pittsfield, Mass, Sept 17, 18; m 54; c 1. VETERINARY PATHOLOGY. *Educ:* Cornell Univ, BS, 40; Agr & Mech Col, Tex, MS, 42; Kans State Col, DVM, 46; Univ Wis, PhD(vet path, vet bact), 51. *Prof Exp:* From instr to asst prof vet sci, Univ Wis, 48-58; res assoc prof cancer res, Univ Fla, 58-60; prof hyg & vet res, 60-79, PROF PATH, UNIV ILL, URBANA, 60- *Mem:* AAAS; Am Vet Med Asn; Int Acad Path; Fedn Biol Soc; Am Col Vet Path. *Res:* Pathology and microbiology of bovine mastitis; reproductive diseases; carcinogenesis; enteric and pulmonary diseases of swine. *Mailing Add:* Dept Path Univ Ill 1101 W Peabody Urbana IL 61801

SIMON, JOSEPH LESLIE, b Everett, Mass, Mar 16, 37. ZOOLOGY. *Educ:* Tufts Univ, BS, 58; Univ NH, MS, 60, PhD(zool), 63. *Prof Exp:* From instr to assoc prof, 63-78, PROF ZOOL, UNIV S FLA, 78- *Concurrent Pos:* Fel, Systs Ecol Prog, Marine 3iol Lab, Woods Hole, Mass, 65-67. *Mem:* AAAS; Am Soc Zool; Soc Syst Zool; Ecol Soc Am; Am Soc Limnol & Oceanog. *Res:* Systematics of and reproduction and development of Polychaetous Annelids; ecology of marine benthic communities. *Mailing Add:* Dept of 3iol Univ of SFla 4202 Fowler Ave Tampa FL 33620

SIMON, JOSEPH MATTHEW, b Reading, Pa, July 14, 41; m 67. ANALYTICAL CHEMISTRY. *Educ:* Albright Col, BS, 63; Univ Pittsburgh, PhD(chem), 69. *Prof Exp:* Asst prof, 69-74, assoc prof, 74-81, PROF CHEM, POINT PARK COL, 81-, CHMN DEPT NATURAL SCI & TECHNOL, 74- *Mem:* AAAS; Am Chem Soc. *Res:* Medium effects and nonaqueous solutions; electrochemistry; polarography. *Mailing Add:* Dept of Chem Point Park Col Pittsburgh PA 15222

SIMON, LEE WILL, b Evanston, Ill, Feb 18, 40; m 66; c 3. ASTRONOMY. *Educ:* Northwestern Univ, Evanston, BA, 62, MS, 64, PhD(astron), 72. *Prof Exp:* Staff astronomer & prog supvr, Adler Planetarium, 69-77; PLANETARIUM DIR, MORRISON PLANETARIUM, CALIF ACAD SCI, GOLDEN GATE PARK, SAN FRANCISCO, 77- *Mem:* AAAS; Am Astron Soc; Royal Astron Soc; Int Planetarium Soc. *Res:* Stellar spectroscopy. *Mailing Add:* 600 Cedarberry Lane San Rafael CA 94903

SIMON, LESLIE EARL, b Memphis, Tenn, Aug 11, 00; m 30; c 2. STATISTICS, ENGINEERING. *Educ:* US Mil Acad, BS, 24; Mass Inst Technol, BS, 29. *Prof Exp:* Mem coast artil, US Army, 24-27, ord property officer, Field Artil Sch, 29-33, chief metal shops, Picatinny Arsenal, 33, asst-chief mfg & planning div, 34-36, officer in charge qual control, 36-37, asst dir, Ballistic Res Labs, Aberdeen Proving Ground, Md, 37-40, dir, 40-49, asst chief ord res & develop, 49-56, dir res & develop, Carborundum Co, 56-57, vpres & dir res & develop, 57-59, staff dir res & develop, 60-61; consult sci & mgt, 60-77; RETIRED. *Concurrent Pos:* Lectr, US Army Ord Sch, 37-39, USDA Grad Sch, 38, Air War Col, 39, US Naval Postgrad Sch, 41-42 & Cornell Univ, 58; trustee, Ill Inst Technol & Armour Res Found, 56-58; dir, Canadair Ltd, 56-63 & Electro-tec Corp, 64-; mem sci adv comts & panels & consult, univs, indust, govt agencies, NASA & US Army, 56-; hon prof, Rutgers Univ, 58-; US deleg, Tripartite Armaments, Explosives & Propellants Res Conf, Can, 59. *Honors & Awards:* Shewhart Medal, Am Soc Qual Control; Samuel S Wilks Award, Am Statist Asn, 66; Gold Medal, Am Ord Asn, 69; Harold T Dodge Award, Am Soc Testing & Mat, 81. *Mem:* AAAS; fel Am Acad Arts & Sci; Am Statist Asn; Am Soc Qual Control; Am Ord Asn. *Res:* Quality control; statistical methods for economical inspection techniques and procurement specifications; proof-testing and surveillance of munitions; exterior ballistics of projectiles launched from aircraft; engineering of guns and mechanisms; reliability of complex systems. *Mailing Add:* 1761 Pine Tree Rd Winter Park FL 32789

SIMON, MARCIA LEE MIELKE, neuropharmacology, see previous edition

SIMON, MARK ROBERT, b New York, NY, July 26, 41; m 78. ANATOMY, PHYSICAL ANTHROPOLOGY. *Educ:* City Univ NY, BA, 66, PhD(anthrop), 74. *Prof Exp:* ASST PROF VET ANAT, UNIV ILL SCH VET MED, 77- *Mem:* Am Asn Vet Anatomists. *Res:* Experimental morphology; gross anatomy; craniofacial morphogenesis; mechanical and electric factors in bone and cartilage development; biomechanics; implant-host reactions. *Mailing Add:* Dept of Vet Biosci Univ of Ill Urbana IL 61801

SIMON, MARTHA NICHOLS, b New York, NY, Dec 31, 40; m 63; c 1. BIOCHEMISTRY, MOLECULAR BIOLOGY. *Educ:* Radcliffe, Col, AB, 62; Cornell Univ, PhD(chem), 68. *Prof Exp:* Res fel chem, Calif Inst Technol, 67-69; res assoc biochem, State Univ NY, Stony Brook, 69-72; sr res assoc biol, 72-75, res biologist, 75-77, ASSOC BIOLOGIST, BROOKHAVEN NAT LAB, 77- *Concurrent Pos:* Spec fel, NIH, 71-72, co-investr, 75-77, investr, 77- *Mem:* AAAS; Biophys Soc. *Res:* Structure and funtion of nucleis acids; molecular details involved in DNA metabolism. *Mailing Add:* Dept of Biol Brookhaven Nat Lab Upton NY 11973

SIMON, MARVIN KENNETH, b New York, NY, Sept 10, 39; m 66; c 2. ELECTRICAL ENGINEERING. *Educ:* City Col New York, BEE, 60; Princeton Univ, MSEE, 61; NY Univ, PhD(elec eng), 66. *Prof Exp:* Mem tech staff commun, Bell Tel Labs, 61-63; instr elec eng, NY Univ, 63-66; mem tech staff commun, Bell Tel Labs, 66-68; mem tech staff commun, 68-80, SR RES ENGR, JET PROPULSION LAB, 80- *Concurrent Pos:* Instr elec eng, West Coast Univ, 69; consult, LinCom Corp, 73-76 & Axiomatix Corp, 76-; ed Communications, Inst Elec & Electronic Engrs, 74-76, chmn commun theory workshop, 75, chmn commun theory comt, 77-, fel grade, 78; lectr elec eng, Calif Inst Technol, 78, vis prof, 79. *Honors & Awards:* Tech Paper Award, NASA, 74. *Mem:* Sigma Xi; Inst Elec & Electronic Engrs. *Res:* Digital communications as applied to space and satellite communication systems; modulation theory; synchronization techniques. *Mailing Add:* Jet Propulsion Lab 4800 Oak Grove Dr Pasadena CA 91103

SIMON, MEREDITH ANN, b Cincinnati, Ohio, Apr 23, 46. IMMUNOLOGY, OPHTHALMOLOGY. *Educ:* Smith Col, AB, 67; Univ Wis-Madison, MS, 70. *Prof Exp:* Asst bact, Univ Wis, 67-70; res assoc biochem, Harvard Univ, 70-71; res asst diabetic retinopathy, Eye Res Inst, Retina Found, 71-72; sr res asst energy prod mitochondria, Boston Biomed Res Inst, 72-74; SR RES ASST OCULAR IMMUNOL, EYE RES INST, RETINA FOUND, 75- *Res:* Morphology and immunopathology of the conjunctiva in normal human subjects and various diseases. *Mailing Add:* Retina Found 20 Staniford St Boston MA 02114

SIMON, MICHAEL RICHARD, b New York, Oct 12, 43; m 70; c 2. IMMUNOLOGY, INTERNAL MEDICINE. *Educ:* State Univ NY, Binghamton, BA, 65; NY Univ, MD, 69; Stanford Univ, MA, 73. *Prof Exp:* Intern internal med, Kings County Hosp-Downstate Med Ctr, Brooklyn, 69-70; gen med officer, Indian Hosp, USPHS, San Carlos, Ariz, 70-72; resident internal med, Affil Intern-Resident Phys Prog, Wayne State Univ, 73-75; fel allergy & immunol, Med Ctr, Univ Mich, 75-77; ASST PROF INTERNAL MED, SCH MED, WAYNE STATE UNIV, 77-; CO-CHIEF ALLERGY-IMMUNOL SECT, VET ADMIN MED CTR, ALLEN PARK, 77- *Concurrent Pos:* Tuberc control officer, Indian Hosp, USPHS, San Carlos, Ariz, 71-72; Allergy Found Am fel clin allergy & immunol res, 76-77. *Mem:* Fel Am Col Physicians; Am Acad Allergy; Am Fedn Clin Res. *Res:* Immunology of infectious diseases; clinical allergy. *Mailing Add:* Allergy & Immunol Sect 111F Vet Admin Hosp Allen Park MI 48101

SIMON, MICHAL, b Prague, Czech, Sept 28, 40; US citizen; div; c 1. ASTRONOMY. *Educ:* Harvard Univ, AB, 62; Cornell Univ, PhD(astrophys), 67. *Prof Exp:* Res fel astron, Calif Inst Technol, 67-69; from asst prof to assoc prof, 69-74, PROF ASTRON, STATE UNIV NY STONY BROOK, 74-, CHMN, DEPT EARTH & SPACE SCI, 80- *Mem:* AAAS; Am Astron Soc; Int Astron Union. *Res:* Infrared astronomy; solar radio astronomy; physics of strong radio sources. *Mailing Add:* Dept of Earth & Space Sci State Univ of New York Stony Brook NY 11794

SIMON, MORRIS ARTHUR, pathology, deceased

SIMON, MYRON SYDNEY, b Burlington, Vt, Sept 23, 26; m 50; c 3. ORGANIC CHEMISTRY. *Educ:* Harvard Univ, AB, 46, AM, 48, PhD(chem), 49. *Prof Exp:* Res chemist, 49-55, group leader, 55-59, from asst mgr to mgr, Org Chem Res Dept, 59-73, asst dir, 74-80, ASSOC DIR, ORGANIC CHEM RES DIV, POLAROID CORP, 81- *Mem:* Am Chem Soc. *Res:* Photographic materials; monomers; organic synthesis; diffusion transfer color photographic research. *Mailing Add:* Polaroid Corp Res Div 730 Main St Cambridge MA 02139

SIMON, NANCY JANE, b Pittsburgh, Pa, June 1, 39. LOW TEMPERATURE PHYSICS. *Educ:* Univ Chicago, BS, 60; Radcliffe Col, AM, 61; Harvard Univ, PhD(physics), 68. *Prof Exp:* PHYSICIST, NAT MEASUREMENT LAB, NAT BUR STAND, 68- *Mem:* Sigma Xi. *Res:* Mossbauer effect; Kapitza coefficient; low temperature physics and engineering; cryogenic information retrieval; properties of structural materials at cryogenic temperatures. *Mailing Add:* Fracture & Deformation Div 562 Nat Bur Standards Boulder CO 80303

SIMON, NORMAN M, b Chicago, Ill, Mar 30, 29; m 57; c 3. MEDICINE. *Educ:* Harvard Univ, BA, 50; Yale Univ, MS, 51; Northwestern Univ, MD, 55; Am Bd Internal Med, dipl, 63; Sub-Comt Nephrology, dipl, 76. *Prof Exp:* Instr, 63-64, assoc, 64-66, asst prof, 66-70, ASSOC PROF MED, NORTHWESTERN UNIV, 70- *Concurrent Pos:* Nat Heart Inst res fel, Michael Reese Hosp, 56-57; fel med, Med Sch, Northwestern Univ, 61-63; assoc chief med, Passavant Mem Hosp, Chicago, 72-73; sr attending physician, Evanston Hosp, 79- *Mem:* AAAS; Int Soc Nephrology; Cent Soc Clin Res; fel Am Col Physicians; Am Soc Nephrology. *Res:* Renal hypertension; natural history of renal diseases; metabolism of uremia; chronic dialysis and renal transplantation. *Mailing Add:* Evanston Hosp 2650 Ridge Ave Evanston IL 60201

SIMON, NORMAN ROBERT, b New York, NY. ASTROPHYSICS. *Educ:* Syracuse Univ, BA, 59; City Col New York, MS, 64; Yeshiva Univ, PhD(physics), 68. *Prof Exp:* Fel astrophys, Nat Acad Sci-Nat Res Coun, 68-70; asst prof, 70-74, assoc prof, 74-79, PROF PHYSICS & ASTRON, UNIV NEBR, 79- *Mem:* Am Astron Soc; Int Astron Union. *Res:* Stellar interiors; pulsations of stars; stellar evolution; cepheid variable stars. *Mailing Add:* Behlen Lab of Physics & Astron Univ of Nebr Lincoln NE 68588

SIMON, RALPH, b Denver, Colo, Jan 1, 21; m 76; c 2. CHEMICAL & PETROLEUM ENGINEERING. *Educ:* Univ Mich, BS, 42. *Prof Exp:* Res engr, Tenn Valley Authority, 42-43; res engr, Calif Res Corp, 46-55, sr res engr, 55-63, SR ENG ASSOC, CHEVRON OIL FIELD RES CO, 63- *Mem:* Am Inst Chem Engrs; Soc Rheol; Soc Petrol Engrs. *Res:* Hydrocarbon phase behavior; non-Newtonian fluid behavior; fluid flow in porous media; petroleum refining process design and oil field operations technology. *Mailing Add:* Chevron Oil Field Res Co PO Box 446 La Habra CA 90631

SIMON, RALPH EMANUEL, b Passaic, NJ, Oct 20, 30; m 52; c 3. PHYSICS. *Educ:* Princeton Univ, BA, 52; Cornell Univ, PhD, 59. *Prof Exp:* Asst, Cornell Univ, 52-57; mem tech staff, Labs, RCA Corp, 59-68, dir, Conversion Devices Lab, David Sarnoff Res Ctr, 68-69, mgr advan technol, Electrooptics Oper, RCA Electronic Components, 69-70, mgr, Electrooptics Oper, 70-76, V PRES, ELECTRO-OPTICS DEVICES DIV, RCA ELECTRONIC COMPONENTS, 76- *Mem:* Am Phys Soc. *Res:* Solid state physics. *Mailing Add:* Electrooptics Oper RCA Electronic Components Lancaster PA 17604

SIMON, ROBERT DAVID, b Chicago, Ill, June 14, 45; m 67. MICROBIAL PHYSIOLOGY, DEVELOPMENTAL BIOLOGY. *Educ:* Univ Chicago, BS, 67; Mich State Univ, PhD(bot), 71. *Prof Exp:* ASSOC PROF BIOL, UNIV ROCHESTER, 71- *Mem:* Am Soc Microbiol. *Res:* Physiology and biochemistry of the cyanobacteria; plasmids in aquatic microorganisms; analysis of plant and microbial development. *Mailing Add:* Dept of Biol Univ of Rochester Rochester NY 14627

SIMON, ROBERT H, b Nashua, NH, July 10, 20; m 43; c 3. CHEMICAL ENGINEERING. *Educ:* Mass Inst Technol, SB & SM, 41; Ore State Univ, PhD(chem eng), 48. *Prof Exp:* Engr, Nat Defense Res Comt, Carnegie Inst Technol, 41-42; engr, Federated Metals Div, Am Smelting & Ref Co, 43-44; supvr nuclear fuel & waste processing, Knolls Atomic Power Lab, Gen Elec Co, 48-54, mgr naval nuclear reactor test loops, 55-59, proj engr, Gen Atomic Div, Gen Dynamics Corp, 59-61, mgr fuel fabrication eng, 62-63, proj mgr nuclear power reactors, 63-64, asst mgr eng, 64-66, asst mgr Wash rep power reactors, 67-69, proj mgr nuclear power reactors, Gulf Gen Atomic Co, 69-73, DIR GAS-COOLED FAST BREEDER REACTOR PROG, GEN ATOMIC CO, 73- *Concurrent Pos:* Mem radioactive waste processing comt, Atomic Energy Comn, 51-53. *Mem:* Am Inst Chem Engrs; Am Nuclear Soc. *Res:* Gas-cooled reactors; nuclear reactor test facilites and components; radioactive waste processing and fission product recovery. *Mailing Add:* Gen Atomic Co PO Box 81608 San Diego CA 92138

SIMON, ROBERT H(ERBERT) M(ELVIN), b New York, NY, Nov 11, 24; m 50; c 4. CHEMICAL ENGINEERING, POLYMER CHEMISTRY. *Educ:* Univ Del, BChE, 48; Yale Univ, DEng(chem eng), 57. *Prof Exp:* Develop engr, Gen Elec Co, 48-52; sr engr, 56-66, specialist process technol, 66-68, group supvr, 68-74, sr technol specialist, 74-80, MONSANTO FEL, MONSANTO CO, 80- *Mem:* Am Inst Chem Engrs; Am Chem Soc. *Res:* Polymer process development; extrusion; high pressure reactions. *Mailing Add:* 23 Caravelle Dr Longmeadow MA 01106

SIMON, RUTH B, b Philadelphia, Pa, Mar 29, 17; m 39; c 5. GEOPHYSICS. *Educ:* NY Univ, BA, 42; Univ Colo, enver, MA, 72. *Prof Exp:* Electroencephalographer var hosps, New York & Suffern, NY, 43-65; res assoc geophys, Colo Sch Mines, 66-78; geophysicist, Nat Earthquake Info Serv, Br Seismicity & Risk Anal, US Geol Serv, 74-78; PROJ SEISMOLOGIST, WOODWARD CLYDE CONSULT, 78- *Concurrent Pos:* Seismologist, Lamont Geol Observ Columbia, 56-66. *Mem:* Seismol Soc Am; Am Geophys Union; AAAS. *Res:* Historical seismicity; siting problems; research with animals and earthquake prediction. *Mailing Add:* Woodward Clyde Consult 3 Embarcadero Ctr Suite 700 San Francisco CA 94111

SIMON, SANFORD RALPH, b New York, NY, Nov 6, 42; m 64. BIOCHEMISTRY. *Educ:* Columbia Univ, AB, 63; Rockefeller Univ, PhD(biochem), 67. *Prof Exp:* Guest investr biochem, Rockefeller Univ, 67-69; asst prof, 69-75, ASSOC PROF BIOCHEM, STATE UNIV NY STONY BROOK, 75- *Concurrent Pos:* Nat Heart, Lung & Blood Inst grant & Am Heart Asn grant-in-aid, 70-; Alfred P Sloan Found res fel, 72; Nat Heart, Lung & Blood Inst career develop award, 75-80. *Mem:* Am Soc Biol Chem. *Res:* Structure-function relationships of normal and modified hemoglobins and metalloproteins; role of protein conformation in mechanisms of enzyme action; applications of physical biochemistry in protein research. *Mailing Add:* Dept of Biochem State Univ of NY Stony Brook NY 11790

SIMON, SELWYN, b Chicago, Ill, Mar 27, 25; m 51; c 2. MICROBIOLOGY. *Educ:* Purdue Univ, BS, 47, MS, 49; Ill Inst Technol, PhD, 56. *Prof Exp:* Res asst, Purdue Univ, 47-49; biochemist, 49-56, group leader, Food Lab, 56-62, asst mgr, 62-65, MGR FOOD SCI INST, FILMS-PACKAGING DIV, UNION CARBIDE CORP, 65- *Mem:* Am Soc Microbiol; Am Chem Soc; Am Meat Sci Asn. *Res:* Food technology; proteolytic enzymes; sausage and meat processing; texture; smoke process. *Mailing Add:* Films-Packaging Div Union Carbide Corp 6830 W 65th St Chicago IL 60638

SIMON, SHERIDAN ALAN, b Buffalo, NY, Apr 20, 47; m 70. ASTROPHYSICS. *Educ:* Univ Rochester, BS, 69, MA, 71, PhD(physics & astron), 78. *Prof Exp:* ASST PROF PHYSICS, GUILFORD COL, 74- *Concurrent Pos:* Kenan grant, Guilford Col, 76-78; Burroughs Wellcome Found grant, 78; res corp grant, 79-81. *Honors & Awards:* Stoddard Prize,

Univ Rochester, 69. *Mem:* Am Physical Soc; Sigma Xi. *Res:* Astrophysics of white dwarf stars; stellar evolution; computer simulation of stellar evolution in the presence of arbitrary rotation. *Mailing Add:* Dept of Physics Guilford Col Greensboro NC 27410

SIMON, SIDNEY, b New York, NY, Aug 6, 24; m 48; c 3. ALLERGY, IMMUNOLOGY. *Educ:* Philadelphia Col Osteop Med, DO, 50; Am Bd Allergy & Immunol, dipl. *Prof Exp:* DIR ALLERGY-IMMUNOL CLIN, NY OSTEOP HOSP, 76-; ASSOC CLIN PROF MED & CHMN DEPT ALLERGY & IMMUNOL, NY COL OSTEOPATHIC MED, NY INST TECHNOL, 78- *Concurrent Pos:* Pvt pract allergy-immunol, Family Physician Ctr, Bronx, NY, 53-; consult & assoc attend physician, St Barnabas Hosp, NY Orthopathic Hosp & Westchester Sq Hosp, 76-; lectr post-grad continuing med educ progs; consult ed, J Am Osteop Asn, Osteop Med & Osteop Annals, 76-; chief, Sect Allergy & Immunol, St Barnabas Hosp, Bronx. *Mem:* Fel Am Acad Allergy; fel Am Col Allergists; fel Am Col Chest Physicians; fel Am Osteop Col Allergy & Immunol (pres, 82-83); fel Am Asn Clin Immunol & Allergy. *Mailing Add:* 1846 Victor St Bronx NY 10462

SIMON, SIDNEY ARTHUR, b New York, NY, Feb 16, 43; m 71. PHYSICAL BIOLOGY. *Educ:* Ind Inst Technol, BS, 65; Ariz State Univ, MS, 68; Northwestern Univ, PhD(mat sci), 73. *Prof Exp:* Fel biol, Northwestern Univ, 73; fel physiol, 73-74, assoc anesthesiol, 74-80, asst prof physiol, 74-80, ASSOC PROF PHYSIOL & ASST PROF ANESTHESIOL, DUKE UNIV, 80- *Mem:* Biophys Soc; Soc Gen Physiologists. *Mailing Add:* Dept of Physiol Duke Univ Durham NC 27710

SIMON, TERRENCE WILLIAM, b Cottonwood, Idaho, Aug 16, 46; m 71; c 1. MECHANICAL ENGINEERING. *Educ:* Wash State Univ, BS, 68; Univ Calif, Berkeley, MS, 71; Stanford Univ, PhD(mech eng), 80. *Prof Exp:* Engr, Nuclear Energy Div, Gen Elec Co, 68-74, Stearns Roger, Inc, 74-76; ASST PROF THERMOSCI, MECH ENG DEPT, UNIV MINN, 80- *Concurrent Pos:* Consult, Stanford Linear Accelerator Ctr, 77-78, Hewlett-Packard Inc, 78-80. *Mem:* Am Soc Mech Engrs. *Res:* Experimental and analytical studies in the fundamentals of heat transfer and fluid mechanics. *Mailing Add:* Dept Mech Eng Univ Minn 111 Church St SE Minneapolis MN 55455

SIMON, THOMAS H, pharmacy, see previous edition

SIMON, VERNE A, b Woodville, Ohio, Apr 13, 31; m 58; c 4. PHYSICAL CHEMISTRY. *Educ:* Univ Toledo, BS, 53; Purdue Univ, MS, 56; Fla State Univ, PhD(chem), 62. *Prof Exp:* Asst prof chem, Rochester Inst Technol, 60-68; assoc prof & head dept chem, Morehead State Univ, 68-76, prof, 76-80. *Res:* Synthesis of several substituted tetra-aryl borons which have unique properties as analytical reagents; protolysis of tetraphenyl boron; study of donor acceptor properties by nuclear magnetic resonance. *Mailing Add:* 5173 N Willcrest Dr Toledo OH 43615

SIMON, WILBUR, b Geneva, Ill, July 5, 17; m 57; c 2. CHEMISTRY. *Educ:* Univ Ill, BS, 39; Univ Iowa, MS, 40, PhD(anal chem), 51. *Prof Exp:* Chem engr, Tenn Copper Co, 40-44; assoc chemist, Metall Lab, Univ Chicago, 44-45; jr res chemist, Carbide & Carbon Chem Corp, 45-49; head anal & stand br, US Naval Radiol Defense Lab, 51-53; res chemist, Princeton Radiation Chem Lab Inc, 53-55 & Morton Chem Co Ill, 55-61; assoc res coordr, Universal Oil Prod Co, 61-64; OWNER & DIR, SIMON RES LAB, 64- *Mem:* AAAS; Am Chem Soc. *Res:* Analytical development; application of nuclear magnetic resonance to organic chemistry; nuclear magnetic resonance spectroscopy; disposal of solid and liquid wastes; removal of contaminants from sewage; environmental problems; overflow and backup of sewers; corrosion; metal cleaning; adhesives. *Mailing Add:* 816 Murray Ave Elgin IL 60120

SIMON, WILLIAM, b Pittsburgh, Pa, May 27, 29. PHYSICS, BIOMATHEMATICS. *Educ:* Carnegie Inst Technol, BS, 50; Harvard Univ, MA, 52, PhD(appl physics), 58. *Prof Exp:* Instrument sect head elec eng, Spencer Kennedy Lab, Boston, Mass, 53-57; sr systs engr, Nat Radio Co, Malden, 57-59; chief physicist, Image Instruments, Inc, Newton, 59-60; mem staff comput, Lincoln Lab, Mass Inst Technol, 61-64; res assoc, Dept Physiol, Harvard Med Sch, 64-68; assoc prof, 68-77, PROF BIOMATH, ROCHESTER SCH MED & DENT, 77-, HEAD DIV, 68- *Concurrent Pos:* Vis assoc prof elec eng, Mass Inst Technol, 74-75. *Mailing Add:* Box 316 Div of Biomath Univ of Rochester Sch of Med & Dent Rochester NY 14642

SIMON, WILLIAM GEORGE, b Cleveland, Ohio, Apr 17, 31; m 60; c 2. NUCLEAR PHYSICS. *Educ:* Univ Calif, Berkeley, AB, 58, PhD(physics), 64. *Prof Exp:* ASSOC PROF PHYSICS, UNIV WYO, 64- *Concurrent Pos:* Res assoc, Univ Alta, 70-71. *Mem:* Am Phys Soc. *Res:* Penetration of charged particles through matter; fast neutron physics; low energy nuclear physics. *Mailing Add:* Dept of Physics Univ of Wyo Laramie WY 82070

SIMONAITIS, ROMUALDAS, b Lithuania, June 10, 34; US citizen; m 63; c 2. CHEMICAL KINETICS, PHOTOCHEMISTRY. *Educ:* Ill Inst Technol, BS, 58; Univ Calif, Los Angeles, MS, 64; Univ Calif, Riverside, PhD(phys chem), 68. *Prof Exp:* Chemist, Douglas Aircraft Co, 62-63; actg instr chem, Univ Wis-Milwaukee, 63-64; fel, 68-70, res assoc, 70-80, SR RES ASSOC PHYS CHEM, IONOSPHERE RES LAB, PA STATE UNIV, 80- *Mem:* Am Chem Soc; Sigma Xi. *Res:* Photochemistry of atmospheric molecules; atom and free radical reactions important in planetary atmospheres. *Mailing Add:* Ionosphere Res Lab 318 Elec Eng E Pa State Univ University Park PA 16802

SIMONDS, JOSEPHINE ABIGAIL, b Washington, DC, Mar 19, 21; m 43; c 4. BIOCHEMICAL GENETICS, MICROBIOLOGY. *Educ:* George Washington Univ, BSc, 41; Duke Univ, MA, 43; Univ Md, PhD(microbiol), 70. *Prof Exp:* STAFF FEL VIRAL CARCINOGENESIS, NAT CANCER INST, 70- *Mem:* AAAS; Am Soc Microbiol; Biophys Soc. *Res:* Genetics, biochemistry, virology, cell culture. *Mailing Add:* Nat Cancer Inst NIH Bethesda MD 20014

SIMONE, JOSEPH VINCENT, b Chicago, Ill, Sept 19, 35; m 60; c 3. HEMATOLOGY, PEDIATRICS. *Educ:* Loyola Univ, Chicago, MD, 60; Am Bd Internal Med & Am Bd Pediat, dipl, 67; Am Bd Pediat Hemat-Oncol, cert, 74. *Prof Exp:* Instr pediat, Col Med, Univ Ill, 66-67; from asst prof to assoc prof pediat, Univ Tenn Health Sci Ctr, 67-77; chief hemat & oncol, St Jude Children's Hosp, 73-77; prof pediat, Stanford Univ, 77-78; ASSOC DIR CLIN RES, ST JUDE CHILDREN'S RES HOSP, 78- *Concurrent Pos:* Trainee pediat hemat, Col Med, Univ Ill, 63-66; travel grant, Int Cong Blood Transfusion, Moscow, 69; chief hemat, St Jude Children's Hosp, 69-73. *Mem:* Fel Am Col Physicians; Am Soc Hemat; Soc Pediat Res; Am Asn Cancer Res; Am Pediat Soc. *Res:* Leukemia therapy; blood coagulation; blood platelet regulation. *Mailing Add:* St Jude Children's Res Hosp PO Box 318 Memphis TN 38101

SIMONE, LEO DANIEL, b New York, NY, Oct 6, 35. PLANT MORPHOLOGY, BRYOLOGY. *Educ:* Manhattan Col, BS, 57; Columbia Univ, MA, 59, PhD(bot), 67. *Prof Exp:* Teaching asst bot, Columbia Univ, 60-64, preceptor, 64-66; ASSOC PROF BIOL, STATE UNIV NY POTSDAM, 66- *Concurrent Pos:* NY State grant-in-aid, 68-69. *Mem:* AAAS; Am Soc Plant Physiol; Am Inst Biol Sci; Am Bryol & Lichenological Soc; Bot Soc Am. *Res:* Apogamy and apospory in the Hepaticae; experimental plant morphology and aseptic culture of liverworts. *Mailing Add:* Dept of Biol State Univ of NY Potsdam NY 13676

SIMONELLI, ANTHONY PETER, b Bridgeport, Conn, June 28, 24; m 56; c 3. DRUG DELIVERY SYSTEMS, CHEMICAL KINETICS. *Educ:* Univ Conn, BA & BS, 55; Univ Wis, MS, 58, PhD(pharm), 60. *Prof Exp:* From asst prof to assoc prof pharm, Med Col Va, 60-64; from asst prof to assoc prof, Univ Mich, Ann Arbor, 64-72; PROF PHARMACEUT & CHMN SECT, SCH PHARM, UNIV CONN, 72- *Concurrent Pos:* Consult, Eli Lilly Labs, 69, Pfizer Labs, 74-, Northeastern Univ, 75, Ortho Labs, 78, Ives Labs, 79- & SK&F Labs, 81-82; prin investr numerous grants, 64- *Mem:* AAAS; Am Chem Soc; fel Am Pharmaceut Asn Acad Pharmaceut Sci; Soc Rheology; NAm Thermal Anal Soc. *Res:* Biopharmaceutics; pharmacokinetics; biological calcification; amorphous-polymorphic drugs; solution drug interactions; transport phenomena; rheology; drug solubility and dissolution rates; biodegradable polymers as drug delivery systems; thermal analysis; drug formulations; solid state transformation kinetics; interfacial phenomena. *Mailing Add:* Sch Pharm Univ Conn Storrs CT 06268

SIMONEN, THOMAS CHARLES, b Munising, Mich, Aug 25, 38; m 64; c 2. PLASMA PHYSICS. *Educ:* Mich Technol Univ, BS, 60; Stanford Univ, MS, 64, PhD(elec eng), 66. *Prof Exp:* Mem tech staff elec eng, Hughes Aircraft Co, 60-62; res asst plasma physics, Garching, Ger, 67-68; res assoc plasma physics, Plasma Physics Lab, Princeton Univ, 68-69; EXP PHYS PROG LEADER, LAWRENCE LIVERMORE NAT LAB, 69- *Mem:* fel Am Phys Soc. *Res:* Plasma confinement of magnetic fusion plasmas. *Mailing Add:* Lawrence Livermore Nat Lab PO Box 808 Livermore CA 94550

SIMONET, DONALD EDWARD, b Orlando, Fla, Mar 26, 46; m 67; c 1. ENTOMOLOGY, AGRICULTURE. *Educ:* Emory & Henry Col, BA, 67; Va Polytech Inst & State Univ, MS, 75, PhD(entomol), 78. *Prof Exp:* asst prof entomol, Ohio Agr Res & Develop Ctr, 78-80; MEM FAC, DEPT ENTOMOL, VA POLYTECH INST & STATE UNIV, 80- *Mem:* Entomol Soc Am; Int Orgn Biol Control; Entomol Soc Can. *Res:* Integrated pest management of insect pests of vegetables. *Mailing Add:* Dept Entomol Va Polytech Inst & State Univ Blacksburg VA 24060

SIMONI, ROBERT DARIO, b San Jose, Calif, Aug 18, 39; m 61; c 3. BIOCHEMISTRY. *Educ:* San Jose State Col, BA, 62; Univ Calif, Davis, PhD(biochem), 66. *Prof Exp:* Fel biochem, Johns Hopkins Univ, 66-70; asst prof biol sci, 71-77, ASSOC PROF BIOL SCI, STANFORD UNIV, 77- *Mem:* AAAS; Am Soc Biol Chemists. *Res:* Structure and function of biological membranes; mechanisms of solute transport. *Mailing Add:* Dept of Biol Sci Stanford Univ Stanford CA 94305

SIMONIAN, VARTKES HOVANES, b Baghdad, Iraq, June 18, 11; nat US; m 44; c 3. PHARMACOGNOSY. *Educ:* Mass Col Pharm, MSc, 47; London Univ, PhD(med), 49. *Prof Exp:* Asst prof, Royal Col Pharm, Baghdad, 36-46, dir, 43-47; researcher, Mass Col Pharm, 48-49; assoc prof pharmacog, Univ Pittsburgh, 49-54; qual control chemist & consult, M G Shaghalians Corey Candies, 54-55; prof pharmacog, Univ Ariz, 55-76; RETIRED. *Concurrent Pos:* Controller chem, Ministry of Supply, Iraq, 43-46; consult & adv, Pharmaceut Importers, Iraq, 46. *Mem:* Fel AAAS; Am Pharmaceut Asn; Am Soc Pharmacog. *Res:* Vegetable constituents and diagnostic characters of natural products. *Mailing Add:* 1801 N Forgeus Ave Tucson AZ 85716

SIMONIS, GEORGE JEROME, b Wisconsin Rapids, Wis, Nov 9, 46; m 68. MILLIMETER WAVE MATERIALS, RED LASERS. *Educ:* Univ Wis-Platteville, BS, 68; Kans State Univ, PhD(physics), 73. *Prof Exp:* RES PHYSICIST LASER RES, HARRY DIAMOND LABS, DEPT ARMY, 72- *Mem:* Am Phys Soc; Optical Soc Am; Inst Elec & Electronics Engrs. *Res:* Infrared lasers; nonlinear optical interactions; diode lasers; near-millimeter waves. *Mailing Add:* 13609 Russett Terr Rockville MD 20853

SIMONOFF, ROBERT, b Baltimore, Md, Feb 27, 20; m 43; c 2. ORGANIC CHEMISTRY. *Educ:* Univ Md, BS, 40, MS, 42, PhD(chem), 45. *Prof Exp:* Asst biochem, Sch Dent, Univ Md, 41-45, fel pharmacol, Sch Med, 49-50; org chemist, Gen Elec Co, 45-49; res chemist, Nat Aniline Div, Allied Chem & Dye Corp, 50-51; chief chemist, William H Rorer, Inc, 51-54; sr res chemist, L Sonneborn Sons, Inc, 54-60, asst supt, Sulfonate Dept, Sonneborn Chem & Refining Corp, 60, supt, 60-65, dir sulfonate res, Sonneborn Div, Witco Chem Co, Inc, Pa, 65-68, tech dir, Sonneborn Div, 68-80, SR DIV SCIENTIST, SONNEBORN DIV, WITCO CHEM CORP, 80- *Mem:* Am Chem Soc; fel Am Inst Chemists. *Res:* Petroleum sulfonates; hydrogenations; synthetic medicinals. *Mailing Add:* Sonneborn Div Witco Chem Corp 100 Bauer Dr Oakland NJ 07436

SIMONS, ALLAN BARNARD, agronomy, see previous edition

SIMONS, DANIEL J, b Rochester, NY, Jan 17, 40; m 67. MICROBIOLOGY, INVERTEBRATE PHYSIOLOGY. *Educ:* Univ Rochester, AB, 61, MS, 63, PhD(biol), 68. *Prof Exp:* Res assoc biol, Univ Rochester, 68; sr res microbiologist, Biospherics, Inc, 68-69; from instr to assoc prof, 69-80, PROF ZOOL, MONTGOMERY COL, 80-, CHMN, DEPT BIOL, 80- *Mem:* AAAS; Am Soc Microbiol; Am Soc Zool. *Res:* Innovative learning experiences in teaching zoological sciences. *Mailing Add:* Dept of Zool Montgomery Col Rockville MD 20850

SIMONS, DARYL B, b Payson, Utah, Feb 12, 18; m 44; c 2. HYDRAULIC ENGINEERING. *Educ:* Utah State Univ, BS, 47, MS, 48; Colo State Univ, PhD(civil eng), 57. *Prof Exp:* Design engr, McGraw Constructors & Engrs, 48; prof civil eng, Univ Wyo, 49-57; proj chief fluid mech res, US Geol Surv, 57-63; sect chief eng, 63-65, assoc dean res, 65-77, PROF CIVIL ENG, COLO STATE UNIV, 63- *Concurrent Pos:* Consult, Int Boundary Water Comn, US Bur Pub Rds & Corps Engrs. *Mem:* Am Soc Civil Engrs; Int Asn Hydraul Res. *Res:* Water resources; fluid mechanics and hydraulics, especially river mechanics, sediment transport, resistance of flow in alluvial channels and design of stable channels. *Mailing Add:* Eng Res Ctr Colo State Univ Ft Collins CO 80523

SIMONS, DAVID STUART, mass spectrometry, see previous edition

SIMONS, E(UGENE) M(ORRIS), b Pittsburgh, Pa, Feb 23, 17; m 42; c 4. SCIENCE POLICY, MECHANICAL ENGINEERING. *Educ:* Inst Technol, BS, 37; Va Polytech Inst, MS, 41; Ohio State Univ, PhD(mech eng), 51. *Prof Exp:* Spec asst mech eng, Carnegie Inst Technol, 37-38; instr eng, Marshall Col, 38-40; asst prof mech eng, Va Polytech Inst, 40-43; res engr, Battelle Mem Inst, 43-51, asst chief eng mech, 51-57, consult, 57-64, fel, 64-72, coordr, 72-77, mgr, Scope Coord Off, 77-82; RETIRED. *Concurrent Pos:* Ed, Sci Policy Rev. *Mem:* Am Soc Mech Engrs. *Res:* Lubrication, friction and wear; heat transfer and fluid flow; engineering design and stress analysis; irradiation capsule experiment technology; molten metal heat-transfer media; science and public policy. *Mailing Add:* Battelle Mem Inst 505 King Ave Columbus OH 43201

SIMONS, EDWARD LOUIS, b New York, NY, May 9, 21; m 43; c 2. ENVIRONMENTAL CHEMISTRY. *Educ:* City Col New York, BS, 41; NY Univ, MS, 43, PhD(chem), 45. *Prof Exp:* Asst chem, NY Univ, 41-44; asst group leader, Kellex Corp, NJ, 44-45; res scientist, Carbide & Carbon Chem Corp, NY, 45-46; from instr to asst prof chem, Rutgers Univ, 46-51; res assoc, Gen Elec Res & Develop Ctr, 51-68, mgr fuel cells prog, 68-69, inorg chemist, 69-71, mgr environ info ctr, Gen Elec Co, 71-73, MGR ENVIRON PROTECTION OPER, GEN ELEC CO, 73- *Honors & Awards:* Award, Nat Asn Corrosion Engrs, 56. *Mem:* Am Chem Soc; AAAS. *Res:* Fuel cells; corrosion; phase equilibria. *Mailing Add:* Environ Protection Oper Gen Elec Co Schenectady NY 12345

SIMONS, ELIZABETH REIMAN, b Vienna, Austria, Sept 1, 29; nat US; m 51; c 2. BIOPHYSICAL CHEMISTRY. *Educ:* Cooper Union, BChE, 50; Yale Univ, MS, 51, PhD(phys chem), 54. *Prof Exp:* Asst, Biophys Div, Dept Physics, Yale Univ, 50-53; res chemist, Tech Opers, Inc, 53-54; instr chem, Wellesley Col, 54-57; from res asst to res assoc path, Children's Cancer Res Found, 57-63; res assoc biol chem, Harvard Med Sch, 63-65, lectr, 65-72; assoc prof biochem, 72-78, PROF BIOCHEM, SCH MED, BOSTON UNIV, 78- *Concurrent Pos:* Tutor, Harvard Univ, 71- *Mem:* Am Soc Biol Chemists; Am Chem Soc; Biophys Soc; Am Soc Hemat; Am Heart Asn. *Res:* Protein structure; sickle cell disease; hemostasis and platelet-collagen interactions; cell membrane biophysics. *Mailing Add:* 117 Chestnut St West Newton MA 02165

SIMONS, ELWYN LAVERNE, b Lawrence, Kans, July 14, 30; m 72; c 3. VERTEBRATE PALEONTOLOGY, PRIMATOLOGY. *Educ:* Rice Univ, AB, 53; Princeton Univ, MA, 55, PhD, 56; Oxford Univ, DPhil, 59; Yale Univ, MA, 67. *Prof Exp:* Lectr paleont, Princeton Univ, 58-59; asst prof zool, Univ Pa, 59-61; from asst prof to prof geol, Yale Univ, 61-77; PROF ANAT & ANTHROP, DUKE UNIV, 77-, DIR DUKE PRIMATE CTR, 77- *Concurrent Pos:* Res assoc, Am Mus Natural Hist; assoc cur, Peabody Mus, Yale Univ, 61-64, cur & dir div vert paleont, 64- *Honors & Awards:* Annadale Mem Medalist, Asiatic Soc, Calcutta, 73; Alexander Von Humboldt Medal, 75. *Mem:* Am Soc Zool; Am Asn Phys Anthrop; Brit Soc Study Human Biol. *Res:* Primatology; primate and human paleontology, early mammalian evolution and anatomy, particularly Pantodonta and related subungulates; primate husbandry and behavioral evolution of prosimians; fossil prosimians; paleocene of North America and Europe; earliest apes and monkeys of Africa; late Tertiary Old World apes, including human orgins. *Mailing Add:* Duke Primate Ctr 3705 Erwin Rd Durham NC 27705

SIMONS, GARY, b Brooklyn, NY, Jan 21, 46; m 70; c 2. CHEMISTRY, PHYSICS. *Educ:* Clarkson Col Technol, BS, 67; Johns Hopkins Univ, PhD(chem), 71. *Prof Exp:* Res assoc chem, Johns Hopkins Univ, 71-72; from asst prof to assoc prof chem, Wichita State Univ, 72-78; MEM TECH STAFF, E-SYSTS CTR ADVAN PLANNING & ANAL, 78- *Mem:* Am Phys Soc; Am Chem Soc; Int Solar Energy Soc. *Res:* Computational chemistry and physics; communications; defense electronics; technical analysis. *Mailing Add:* E-Systs Ctr Advan Planning & Anal 7900 West Park Dr suite 700 McLean VA 22102

SIMONS, GENE R, b Staten Island, NY, July 19, 36; m 61; c 4. MANAGEMENT SYSTEMS, MAINTENANCE PLANNING & CONTROL. *Educ:* Rensselaer Polytech Inst, BS, 57, PhD(mgt sci), 69; Stevens Inst Technol, MS, 61. *Prof Exp:* Planning engr indust eng, Western Elec Co, 57-61; mem staff indust eng, Am Cyanamid Co, 61-62; asst prof indust eng, New Haven Col, 62-64, chmn, 64-66; instr, 66-69, asst prof, 69-70, curriculum chmn mgt eng, 71-77, ASSOC PROF MGT ENG, RENSSELAER POLYTECH INST, 70-, DIR INDUST & MGT ENG, 77- *Concurrent Pos:* Curric chmn mgt eng, Rensselaer Polytech Inst, 71-77; Pres, Gene Simons, Inc, 80-; vpres, Workshops, Menands, NY, 81-83. *Mem:* Inst Indust Engrs (vpres, 82-83); Proj Mgt Inst; Am Soc Eng Educ; Sigma Xi. *Mailing Add:* Ctr Indust & Mgt Eng 7010 JEC Rensselaer Polytech Inst Troy NY 12181

SIMONS, HAROLD LEE, b New York, NY, Aug 25, 26; m 51; c 2. PHYSICAL CHEMISTRY. *Educ:* Princeton Univ, AB, 49; Yale Univ, MS, 51, PhD(chem), 53. *Prof Exp:* Res chemist, 53-70, group leader, 70-74, SR RES ASSOC, KENDALL CO, 75- *Concurrent Pos:* Lectr div continuing educ, Boston Univ, 62-65. *Mem:* Am Chem Soc; Soc Rheology; Am Phys Soc. *Res:* Characterization of polymers; physical properties of polymers. *Mailing Add:* 117 Chestnut St West Newton MA 02165

SIMONS, JOHN NORTON, b Lennox, SDak, Aug 13, 26; m 48; c 4. ENTOMOLOGY. *Educ:* Univ Calif, PhD(entom), 53. *Prof Exp:* Asst virologist, Everglades Exp Sta, Univ Fla, 53-59; sr entomologist, Stanford Res Inst, 59-70; sr scientist, Ciba-Geigy Corp, 70-77; PRES JMS FLOWER FARMS, INC, 77- *Concurrent Pos:* Vis prof entom, Univ Calif, Berkeley, 74-75. *Mem:* Entom Soc Am; Am Phytopath Soc. *Res:* Insect transmission of plant virus diseases; plant virus disease control. *Mailing Add:* 1105 25th Ave Vero Beach FL 32960

SIMONS, JOHN PETER, b Youngstown, Ohio, Apr 2, 45; m 68. PHYSICAL CHEMISTRY. *Educ:* Case Inst Technol, BS, 67; Univ Wis, PhD(chem), 70. *Prof Exp:* From asst prof to assoc prof, 71-79, PROF CHEM, UNIV UTAH, 79- *Concurrent Pos:* NSF fel, Mass Inst Technol, 70-71; Alfred P Sloan fel, Univ Utah, 73-77, Camille & Henry Dreyfus teaching fel, 75-80, David P Gardner fel, 79, 81; John Simon Gugenheim fel, 80-81. *Mem:* Am Chem Soc; Am Phys Soc; Sigma Xi; Asn Women Sci. *Res:* Quantum chemistry; statistical mechanics; molecular spectroscopy; negative molecular ions; solvation effects; molecular dynamics. *Mailing Add:* Dept Chem Univ Utah Salt Lake City UT 84112

SIMONS, MARR DIXON, b Murray, Utah, May 7, 25; m 50; c 2. PLANT PATHOLOGY. *Educ:* Iowa State Col, PhD(plant path, crop breeding), 52. *Prof Exp:* From asst prof to assoc prof bot & plant path, 52-59, PROF BOT & PLANT PATH, IOWA STATE UNIV, 60-; PLANT PATHOLOGIST, N CENT REGION, AGR RES SERV, USDA, 52- *Mem:* Am Phytopath Soc. *Res:* Diseases of oats; cereal rust diseases. *Mailing Add:* Dept Plant Path Iowa State Univ Ames IA 50011

SIMONS, MAYRANT, JR, b Charleston, SC, Aug 10, 36; m 59; c 3. ELECTRICAL ENGINEERING. *Educ:* Clemson Univ, BS, 58; Duke Univ, MS, 64, PhD(elec eng), 68. *Prof Exp:* Mem tech staff eng, Bell Tel Labs, NC, 61-66; supvr engr mat & device res, 66-80, SR ENGR, RES TRIANGLE INST, 80- *Res:* Investigation of nuclear radiation effects on semiconductor materials, devices and circuits; semiconductors. *Mailing Add:* 3 Winthrop Ct Durham NC 27709

SIMONS, ROGER ALAN, b Detroit, Mich, May 11, 43; m 74; c 2. COMPUTER ALGORITHMS. *Educ:* Univ Calif, Los Angeles, AB, 64; Univ Calif, Berkeley, MA, 66, PhD(math), 72. *Prof Exp:* From instr to assoc prof math, Univ Wis-Green Bay, 70-81; ASST PROF MATH & COMPUT SCI, RI COL, 81- *Concurrent Pos:* Vis asst prof, Univ Hawaii, 75, vis lectr, 77. *Mem:* Asn Comput Mach; Asn Symbolic Logic; Am Math Soc; Sigma Xi; NY Acad Sci. *Res:* Analysis of algorithms; boolean algebra and mathematical logic; applying mathematics to philosophical problems; theoretical aspects of computer design. *Mailing Add:* Dept Math RI Col Providence RI 02908

SIMONS, ROGER MAYFIELD, b Portland, Ore, Oct 11, 26; m 54; c 2. APPLIED MATHEMATICS. *Educ:* Stanford Univ, BS, 49; Mass Inst Technol, PhD(math), 55. *Prof Exp:* Appl sci rep, 55-59, staff mathematician, 59-60, mgr, Eng Comput Lab, 60-64, mgr eng & sci comput lab, 65-72, SR PROGRAMMER, IBM CORP, 72- *Concurrent Pos:* Asst prof, San Jose State Col, 60. *Mem:* Asn Comput Mach; Sigma Xi. *Res:* Digital computer applications and programming. *Mailing Add:* 20744 Scenic Vista Dr San Jose CA 95120

SIMONS, ROY KENNETH, b Kincheloe, WVa, Dec 26, 20; m 53; c 2. HORTICULTURE. *Educ:* Univ WVa, BS & MS, 47; Mich State Univ, PhD, 51. *Prof Exp:* Pomologist, Univ Del, 47-48; asst, Mich State Univ, 48-51; instr pomol, 51-53, asst prof, 53-58, assoc prof hort, 58-64, PROF HORT, UNIV ILL, URBANA, 64- *Concurrent Pos:* Ed, Fruit Varieties J, Am Pomol Soc. *Honors & Awards:* Stark Award, Am Soc Hort Sci, 67, Promotion Incentive Award, 77 & 78. *Mem:* Fel AAAS; fel Am Soc Hort Sci; Rootstock Res Found; Int Dwarf Fruit Tree Asn. *Res:* Nutrition of deciduous fruit trees; soil moisture conservation to maintain optimum production of quality fruit; morphological and anatomical development of deciduous fruits; orchard cultural management practices in relation to dwarfing rootstocks; growth and development of fruit. *Mailing Add:* Dept of Hort Univ of Ill Urbana IL 61801

SIMONS, SAMUEL STONEY, JR, b Philadelphia, Pa, Sept 13, 45; m 70; c 2. MOLECULAR ENDOCRINOLOGY, STEROID CHEMISTRY. *Educ:* Princeton Univ, AB, 67; Harvard Univ, MA, 69, PhD(chem), 72. *Prof Exp:* Fel molecular biol, Univ Calif, San Francisco, 72-75; staff fel, 75-78, sr staff fel, 78-80, RES CHEMIST ENDOCRINOL, NAT INST ARTHRITIS, DIABETES & DIGESTIVE & KIDNEY DIS, NIH, 80- *Mem:* Am Chem Soc. *Res:* Mechanism of action of steroid hormones; steroid-receptor interactions; affinity labelling of steroid receptors; fluorescence spectroscopy; synthetic organic chemistry; glucocorticoid steroids. *Mailing Add:* Nat Inst Arthritis Metab & Diabetes Digestive & Kidney Dis NIH Bldg 4 Rm 132 Bethesda MD 20014

SIMONS, SANFORD L(AWRENCE), b New York, NY, Apr 10, 22; m 47; c 5. METALLURGY. *Educ:* Univ Mo, BS, 44. *Prof Exp:* Res engr, Battelle Mem Inst, 44; jr scientist, Manhattan Dist Proj, Los Alamos Sci Lab, 44-46; consult engr, Alldredge & Simons Labs, 46-48; asst, US Army rocket prog, Denver, 48-50; consult engr, 50-53; design engr, Heckethorn Mfg Co, 53-55; chief develop engr, Metron Instrument Co, 56-57; consult engr, 57-66; dir med eng, 66-72, CONSULT MED ENGR, SCH MED, UNIV COLO, 72-; PRES, SIENCO, 72- *Mem:* Am Soc Metals; Am Soc Testing & Mat; Nat Soc Prof Engrs; Am Inst Mining, Metall & Petrol Engrs. *Res:* Metallurgy of copper-manganese systems and plutonium; development of rocketborne spectrographs; automatic perfusion apparatus; surgical prosthetics; medical and bio-engineering. *Mailing Add:* SIENCO 9188 S Turkey Creek Rd Morrison CO 80465

SIMONS, STEPHEN, b London, Eng, Aug 11, 38; m 63. MATHEMATICS. *Educ:* Cambridge Univ, BA, 59, PhD(math), 62. *Prof Exp:* Instr math, Univ BC, 62-63; res fel math, Peterhouse Col, Cambridge Univ, 63-64; asst prof, Univ BC, 64-65; from asst prof to assoc prof, 65-73, chmn dept, 75-77, PROF MATH, UNIV CALIF, SANTA BARBARA, 73- *Concurrent Pos:* NSF res grant, 65-76; mem bd dir, Calif Educ Comput Consortium, 74-75. *Mem:* Am Math Soc; Sigma Xi. *Res:* Functional analysis and numerical analysis. *Mailing Add:* Dept of Math Univ of Calif Santa Barbara CA 93106

SIMONS, THEODORE J, b Neth, Sept 5, 39. ATMOSPHERIC SCIENCES, OCEANOGRAPHY. *Educ:* Delft Univ, MS, 64; Colo State Univ, PhD(atmospheric sci), 70. *Prof Exp:* Res asst, Dutch Meteorol Inst, 63-64; RES SCIENTIST, CAN CTR INLAND WATERS, WATER MGT SERV, DEPT ENVIRON, 70- *Concurrent Pos:* Vis scientist, Inst Oceanog, Kiel, Ger, 75-76; head, Inst Meteorol & Oceanog, Univ Utrecht, Neth, 79-80. *Honors & Awards:* Chandler-Misener Award, Int Asn Great Lakes Res, 72, 73 & 76. *Mem:* Am Geophys Union; Am Meteorol Soc; Can Meteorol Soc. *Res:* Dynamics of atmosphere and oceans; physical limnology; numerical modeling; weather forecasting. *Mailing Add:* Can Ctr for Inland Waters PO Box 5050 Burlington ON L7P 4A6 Can

SIMONS, WILLIAM HADDOCK, b Vancouver, BC, Dec 2, 14; m 44; c 2. MATHEMATICS. *Educ:* Univ BC, BA, 35, MA, 37; Univ Calif, PhD(math), 47. *Prof Exp:* From asst prof to assoc prof math, Univ BC, 46-70; PROF MATH, ORE STATE UNIV, 70- *Concurrent Pos:* Lectr, Khaki Col Can, Eng; meteorologist, Can Meteorol Serv. *Mem:* Am Math Soc; Math Asn Am; Can Math Cong; London Math Soc. *Res:* Fourier coefficients of modular functions. *Mailing Add:* Dept of Math Ore State Univ Corvallis OR 97331

SIMONS, WILLIAM HARRIS, b Norwich, Conn, Apr 14, 38. MATHEMATICS. *Educ:* Carnegie-Mellon Univ, BS, 61, MS, 65, PhD(math), 69. *Prof Exp:* Asst prof, 69-74, assoc prof, 74-79, PROF MATH, WVA UNIV, 79- *Concurrent Pos:* Consult, US Bur Mines, 66-75 & US Dept Energy, 76-80. *Mem:* Soc Indust & Appl Math; Int Asn Math Modeling; Math Asn Am. *Res:* Disconjugacy of ordinary differential equations; magnetohydrodynamic generators and power plants; magnetic and electrostatic filtration; hydrogasification of coal to pipeline gas. *Mailing Add:* Dept of Math WVa Univ Morgantown WV 26506

SIMONSEN, DAVID RAYMOND, b Clay Co, Nebr, July 29, 16; m 47; c 5. PHYSICAL CHEMISTRY. *Educ:* Dana Col, BA, 38; Univ Nebr, MA, 43, PhD(chem), 44. *Prof Exp:* Prin & instr high schs, Nebr, 38-41; teaching asst, Univ Nebr, 41-44; res chemist, Eastman Kodak Co, 44-52, asst supvr, 52-64, supvr, 64-81; RETIRED. *Concurrent Pos:* Chmn int comt, Contamination Control Soc, 76-78. *Mem:* Am Chem Soc; Instrument Soc Am; Inst Environ Sci (liaison vpres, 73-76). *Res:* Contamination control; instrumental gas analysis. *Mailing Add:* 52 Oakridge Dr Rochester NY 14617

SIMONSEN, DONALD HOWARD, b Portland, Ore, June 12, 21; m 47; c 4. BIOCHEMISTRY. *Educ:* Reed Col, BA, 43; Ore State Col, MA, 45; Ind Univ, PhD(chem), 51. *Prof Exp:* Res assoc zool, Ind Univ, 47-50, fel, 51-52; res scientist virol, Upjohn Co, 52-56; from asst prof to assoc prof chem, 56-63, chmn dept phys sci & math, 60-6i, chmn dept chem, 61-64, assoc dean instr, 66-67, acad vpres, 67-69, actg pres, 69-70, PROF CHEM, CALIF STATE UNIV, LONG BEACH, 63- *Mem:* AAAS; Am Chem Soc; fel Am Inst Chem; Brit Biochem Soc; NY Acad Sci. *Res:* Growth factors for guinea pigs; tissue metabolism; salt and nitrogen metabolism in surgical patients; methods of blood volume determination; human plasma and plasma substitutes in treatment of clinical hypoproteinemia; biochemical genetics of Paramecia; microrespiration techniques; chemotherapy of virus disease. *Mailing Add:* Dept of Chem Calif State Univ 1250 Bellflower Blvd Long Beach CA 90840

SIMONSEN, STANLEY HAROLD, b Missoula, Mont, Aug 25, 18; m 43; c 4. CHEMISTRY. *Educ:* Iowa State Teachers Col, AB, 40; Univ Ill, MS, 47, PhD(chem), 49. *Prof Exp:* Anal chemist, Vanadium Corp Am, 40-44; asst anal chem, Univ Ill, 46-49; asst chem, 49-53, assoc prof, 53-63, dir, Anal Chem Res Lab, 51-52, PROF CHEM, UNIV TEX, AUSTIN, 63- *Concurrent Pos:* Instr, Pa State Col, 43-44. *Mem:* Am Chem Soc. *Res:* Structural investigations with x-rays; x-ray diffraction; instrumental analytical methods; investigation of metallo-organic compounds useful in analytical chemistry. *Mailing Add:* Dept of Chem Univ of Tex Austin TX 78712

SIMONSON, GERALD HERMAN, b Albert Lea, Minn, Nov 19, 27; m 52; c 3. SOIL SCIENCE, AGRONOMY. *Educ:* Univ Minn, BS, 51, MS, 53; Iowa State Univ, PhD(soils), 60. *Prof Exp:* Asst soil scientist, NDak State Univ, 53-55; res assoc soil surv, Iowa State Univ, 55-60; asst prof soil classification, Mont State Col, 60-61; from asst prof to prof soil classification & surv, 61-71, PROF SOIL SCI, ORE STATE UNIV, 71- *Mem:* Am Soc Agron. *Res:* Soil-landscape relationships in alluvial landscapes; nature of soil characteristics related to environment of formation; soil distribution patterns in Oregon. *Mailing Add:* Dept of Soils Ore State Univ Corvallis OR 97331

SIMONSON, LLOYD GRANT, b San Jose, Calif, Dec 1, 43; m 68. MICROBIOLOGY, BIOCHEMISTRY. *Educ:* Western Ill Univ, BA, 66; Ill State Univ, MS, 68, PhD(microbiol), 74. *Prof Exp:* Res microbiologist, 68-72, RES MICROBIOLOGIST DENT RES, NAVAL DENT RES INST, 74- *Concurrent Pos:* Consult, Chicago Med Sch, 77-80. *Mem:* Am Soc Microbiol; Int Asn Dent Res; Am Asn Dent Res. *Res:* Dental caries therapeutics; enzymology and molecular biology; cell mediated immunity and cancer; immobilized enzymes and intermolecular conjugation; bactertial adherence to surfaces and adherence-inhibition; surveys for microbial enzymes and fermentation. *Mailing Add:* 1115 Knollwood Rd Deerfield IL 60015

SIMONSON, SIMON CHRISTIAN, III, nuclear engineering, astronomy, see previous edition

SIMOONS, FREDERICK JOHN, b Philadelphia, Pa, Nov 2, 22; m 49. ZOOGEOGRAPHY, MEDICAL GEOGRAPHY. *Educ:* Rutgers Univ, BA, 49; Univ Calif, Berkeley, MA, 52, PhD(geog), 56. *Prof Exp:* Instr geog, Ohio State Univ, 56-57; asst prof, Univ Wis-Madison, 57-60, from assoc prof to prof, 60-66; prof, La State Univ, 66-67; prof, Univ Tex, Austin, 67-69; chmn dept, 73-77, PROF GEOG, UNIV CALIF, DAVIS, 69- *Concurrent Pos:* John Simon Guggenheim Mem Found fel, 63-64; consult, Nat Inst Child Health & Human Develop, NIH, 74-76; fac res lectr, Univ Calif, Davis, 80-81. *Res:* Human culture and food habits; domestic animals and human culture. *Mailing Add:* 140 Bartlett Ave Woodland CA 95695

SIMOPOULOS, ARTEMIS PANAGEOTIS, b Kampos-Avias, Greece, Apr 3, 33; US citizen; m 57; c 3. PEDIATRICS, ENDOCRINOLOGY. *Educ:* Barnard Col, Columbia Univ, BA, 52; Boston Univ, MD, 56; Am Bd Pediat, dipl, 64. *Prof Exp:* Spec lectr pediat, Sch Med, Ewha Woman's Univ, Seoul, Korea, 58-59; NIH fel hemat, 60-61; asst prof, Sch Med, George Washington Univ, 62-67; staff pediatrician, Nat Heart & Lung Inst, 68-71; prof assoc, Div Med Sci, Nat Acad Sci-Nat Res Coun, 71-74, actg exec secy, 74-75, exec secy, 75-76; chief develop biol & nutrit br, Nat Inst Child Health & Human Develop, 76-77, vchmn & exec secy nutrit coord comt, Off of Dir, 77-78, CHMN NAT COORD COMT & SPEC ASST FOR COORDR NUTRIT RES, OFF OF DIR, NIH, 78-; CO-CHMN & EXEC SECY, JOINT SUBCOMT, HUMAN NUTRIT RES, OFF SCI & TECHNOL POLICY, EXEC OFF OF THE PRESIDENT, 79- *Concurrent Pos:* Mem acad staff pediat, Children's Hosp of DC, 62-66, mem assoc staff, Nursery Serv, 66-; dir nurseries, George Washington Univ Hosp, 65-67; co-chmn perinatal comt, Working Party Biol Aspects Prev Ment Retardation for DC, 67-68; clin asst prof pediat, Sch Med, George Washington Univ, 67-; mem bd, Capitol Head Start, Inc, Washington, DC, 68-70; consult, Endocrinol Br, Nat Heart & Lung Inst, 71-78; liaison, Div Med Sci, Nat Acad Sci-Nat Res Coun to Am Acad Pediat Comt Drugs, 71-76; mem res adv comt, Maternity Ctr Assoc, New York, 72-; exec dir bd maternal, Child & Family Health Res, 74-76. *Mem:* Fel Am Acad Pediat; Soc Pediat Res; Endocrine Soc; Am Pediat Soc; Am Inst Nutrit. *Res:* Genetics of endocrine diseases and growth problems in children; clinical nutrition. *Mailing Add:* Nutrit Coord Comt Off of Dir NIH Bldg 31 Rm 4B59 Bethesda MD 20014

SIMOVICI, DAN, b Iassy, Romania, Feb 15, 43; US citizen; m 65; c 1. FORMAL LANGUAGES, AUTOMATA THEORY. *Educ:* Polytech Inst Iassy, Romania, MS, 65; Univ Iassy, MS, 70; Univ Bucharest, PhD(math), 74. *Prof Exp:* Asst prof comput sci, Univ Iassy, 71-78, assoc prof, 78-80; assoc prof comput sci, Univ Miami, 81-82; ASSOC PROF COMPUT SCI, UNIV MASS, 82- *Mem:* Am Math Soc; Asn Comput Mach. *Res:* Theoretical computer science and related areas; formal languages; automata theory; switching theory; boolean algebras; author or coauthor of over 40 publications. *Mailing Add:* Dept Math & Comput Sci Univ Mass Boston MA 02125

SIMPKINS, PETER G, b London, Eng, Nov 28, 34; m 59; c 3. AERONAUTICS, FLUID MECHANICS. *Educ:* Univ London, Dipl technol, 58, PhD(aeronaut), 64; Calif Inst Technol, MSc, 60. *Prof Exp:* Apprentice engr, Handley Page Co, Ltd, 53-57, mem res staff aerodyn, 57-58; res asst aeronaut, Imp Col, Univ London, 60-65; sr consult scientist, Avco Res & Tech Labs, 65-68; mem tech staff, Anal Mech Dept, 68-71 & Ocean Physics Res Dept, 71-74, MEM TECH STAFF, MAT RES LABS, BELL LABS, 74- *Concurrent Pos:* Sr res fel, Southampton Univ, Eng, 73-74; consult, Eng Mech Div, NSF, 75-; mem, Space Lab 3 Rev Bd, NASA, 78-79, Mat Processing in Space Panel, 80-81. *Mem:* Am Inst Physics. *Res:* Fluid mechanics, convection, gas dynamics, heat transfer and wave propagation in solids. *Mailing Add:* Bell Tel Labs Murray Hill NJ 07974

SIMPLICIO, JON, b Bronx, NY, Sept 18, 42; m 69. BIOCHEMISTRY, INORGANIC CHEMISTRY. *Educ:* State Univ NY Stony Brook, BS, 64; State Univ NY Buffalo, PhD(chem), 69. *Prof Exp:* Res assoc biochem, Cornell Univ, 68-69; asst prof chem, Univ Miami, 70-77; mem staff, Allied Chem Corp, 77-82; MEM STAFF, CELANESE CORP, 82- *Mem:* Am Chem Soc. *Res:* Fast reaction mechanisms and kinetics of enzymes; kinetics of metalloporphyrins with nucelophiles and their interactions with micelles. *Mailing Add:* Celanese Corp 1211 Ave Americas New York NY 10036

SIMPSON, ANTONY MICHAEL, b Leamington, Eng, May 8, 41; m 69. PHYSICS. *Educ:* Cambridge Univ, BA, 63; Dalhousie Univ, MSc, 65; PhD(physics), 69. *Prof Exp:* Asst prof, 68-76, ASSOC PROF PHYSICS, DALHOUSIE UNIV, 76- *Concurrent Pos:* Fel, Cambridge Univ, 71-72. *Mem:* Am Phys Soc; Can Asn Physicists. *Res:* Transport properties and ultrasonics in solids. *Mailing Add:* Dept of Physics Dalhousie Univ Halifax NS B3H 3J5 Can

SIMPSON, BERYL BRINTNALL, b Dallas, Tex, Apr 28, 42; div. BIOSYSTEMATICS. *Educ:* Radcliffe Col, BA, 64; Harvard Univ, MA & PhD(biol), 67. *Prof Exp:* Res botanist, Arnold Arboretum, Harvard Univ, 68, res fel bot, Gray Herbarium, 68-69, res assoc, 69-71; assoc cur dept bot, US Mus Natural Hist, Smithsonian Inst, 72-78; PROF BOT, UNIV TEX, AUSTIN, 78- *Mem:* Soc Study Evolution; Bot Soc Am; Am Soc Plant Taxon. *Res:* Speciation problems of Andean plant genera; systematics of Andean genera; reproductive systems of angiosperms; pollination biology. *Mailing Add:* Dept Bot Univ of Tex Austin TX 78712

SIMPSON, BILLY DOYLE, b Holdenville, Okla, Mar 12, 29; m 57; c 2. ORGANIC CHEMISTRY. *Educ:* Okla State Univ, BS, 51, MS, 53; Univ Kans, PhD(org chem), 57. *Prof Exp:* Res chemist, 57-66, adhesives develop & sales consult, 66-75, adhesive develop & lab coordr, 75-77, mkt segment mgr molded & extruded goods, 77-80, TECH SERV & DEVELOP MGR, PHILLIPS PETROL CO, 80- *Mem:* Am Chem Soc; Soc Petrol Engrs. *Res:* Nitrogen-containing compounds; petrochemicals; adhesives. *Mailing Add:* Phillips Petrol Co 1501 Commerce Dr Stow OH 44224

SIMPSON, CHARLES FLOYD, b East Orange, NJ, Jan 29, 19; m 47; c 2. VETERINARY PATHOLOGY. *Educ:* Rutgers Univ, BSc, 40; Cornell Univ, DVM, 44; Ohio State Univ, MSc, 55; Univ Minn, PhD, 61. *Prof Exp:* Pvt practice, 48-49; PROF VET SCI & PATHOLOGIST, DEPT VET SCI, INST FOOD & AGR SCI, UNIV FLA, 49-, ASST DEAN RES, COL VET MED, 75- *Concurrent Pos:* NIH spec fel, 58-60; Fogarty Int fel, 77. *Honors & Awards:* Vet Med Res Award, Am Feed Mfr Asn, 70. *Mem:* Am Vet Med Asn; Electron Micros Soc Am; Inst Acad Path. *Res:* Pathology of animal diseases, especially the cardiovascular system. *Mailing Add:* Col Vet Med BJ-136 JHMHC Univ of Fla Gainesville FL 32610

SIMPSON, DALE R, b Wilmar, Calif, Dec 29, 30; m 58; c 2. PETROLOGY, MINERALOGY. *Educ:* Pa State Univ, BS, 56; Calif Inst Technol, MS, 58, PhD(geol), 60. *Prof Exp:* From asst prof to assoc prof geol, 60-66, PROF GEOL, LEHIGH UNIV. 66- *Mem:* Mineral Soc Am; fel Geol Soc Am. *Res:* Synthesis, stability and chemical variants of phosphate minerals; petrology of granitic pegmatites; energy storage using latent heat; effect of saline waters on igneous rocks. *Mailing Add:* Dept of Geol Lehigh Univ Bethlehem PA 18015

SIMPSON, DAVID ALEXANDER, b Englewood, NJ, Mar 2, 43. PHYSICAL ORGANIC CHEMISTRY. *Educ:* Allegheny Col, BS, 65; Univ Ill, MS, 68, PhD(org chem), 69. *Prof Exp:* Res chemist, 69-74; SR RES CHEMIST, ORG & PHYS ORG CHEM, HERCULES, INC, 74- *Mem:* Am Chem Soc; Inter-Am Photochem Soc; Sigma Xi. *Res:* Photochemistry; photopolymerization; photooxidation; photo crosslinking and photodegradation of polymers; laser induced chemical and photochemical reactions. *Mailing Add:* Hercules Inc Res Ctr Wilmington DE 19899

SIMPSON, DAVID GORDON, b Belfast, Northern Ireland, Jan 24, 20; US citizen; m 56; c 4. INTERNAL MEDICINE. *Educ:* Queen's Univ, Belfast, MB, BCh & BAO, 42, MD, 50. *Prof Exp:* Sr registr med, Northern Ireland Hosps Authority, 49-52; from resident to chief resident chest serv, Bellevue Hosp, Columbia Univ Div, New York, 52-56, instr med, Col Physicians & Surgeons, Columbia Univ, 56-64; assoc prof med & head div pulmonary dis, 64-76, ASSOC PROF INTERNAL MED, SCH MED, UNIV MD, BALTIMORE, 76- *Concurrent Pos:* Consult, Vet Admin Hosp, Baltimore, 64-, Keswick Home, 64-, Md Gen Hosp, 64-, Mercy Hosp, 64- & Montebello State Hosp, 64- *Mem:* Am Thoracic Soc. *Res:* Pulmonary tuberculosis and other respiratory diseases. *Mailing Add:* Dept of Internal Med Univ of Md Sch of Med Baltimore MD 21201

SIMPSON, DAVID PATTEN, b Eugene, Ore, Mar 20, 30; m 56; c 4. NEPHROLOGY. *Educ:* Harvard Univ, AB, 52; McGill Univ, MD, 57. *Prof Exp:* Intern, Grace-New Haven Community Hosp, 57-58; resident med, Scripps Clin & Res Found, 58-60; vis scholar, Col Physicians & Surgeons, Columbia Univ, 60-65; from asst prof to assoc prof med, Univ Wash, 65-74; PROF MED & DIR NEPHROL PROG, UNIV WIS CTR HEALTH SCI, 74- *Concurrent Pos:* USPHS res fel, 60-62; NY Heart Asn sr res fel, 62-65; chief nephrology, USPHS Hosp, 70-74. *Res:* Relationships between intermediary metabolism in the kidney and renal physiology; regulation of organ growth. *Mailing Add:* H4/514 Univ Hosp 600 Highland Ave Madison WI 53792

SIMPSON, EUGENE SIDNEY, b Schenectady, NY, July 14, 17. HYDROLOGY. *Educ:* City Col New York, BS, 44; Columbia Univ, MA, 49, PhD(geol), 60. *Prof Exp:* Geologist, US Geol Surv, 46-63; PROF HYDROL, UNIV ARIZ, 63- *Mem:* Geol Soc Am; Am Soc Civil Eng; Am Geophys Union. *Res:* Dispersion of fluids in subsurface flow; ground water hydraulics and chemistry. *Mailing Add:* Dept of Hydrol & Water Resources Univ of Ariz Tucson AZ 85721

SIMPSON, EVERETT COY, b Maysville, NC, Feb 13, 25; m 51; c 4. ZOOLOGY, ENDOCRINOLOGY. *Educ:* Okla State Univ, BS, 50; Univ Ky, MS, 52, PhD(genetics), 60. *Prof Exp:* Res asst animal sci, Univ Ky, 51-52 & genetics, 56-60; asst prof biol, Memphis State Univ, 60-61; assoc prof, 61-64, assoc dir dept, 71, PROF BIOL, E CAROLINA UNIV, 64- *Concurrent Pos:* Res grants, 63-65 & 66-68; NSF inserv Inst Awards, 65-67; dir three inserv insts, 66, 67 & 68. *Mem:* AAAS; Am Genetic Asn. *Res:* Endocrinology, especially the physiology of reproduction. *Mailing Add:* Dept of Biol ECarolina Univ Greenville NC 27834

SIMPSON, FRANK MARTIN, JR, analytical chemistry, physical chemistry, see previous edition

SIMPSON, FREDERICK JAMES, b Regina, Sask, June 8, 22; m; c 5. BACTERIOLOGY, SCIENCE ADMINISTRATION. *Educ:* Univ Alta, BSc, 44, MSc, 46; Univ Wis, PhD(bact), 52. *Prof Exp:* Jr res officer div appl biol, 46-48, asst res officer bact, Prairie Regional Lab, 52-57, from assoc res officer to sr res officer, 58-70, head physiol & biochem of bacteria, 58-70, asst dir, Atlantic Regional Lab, 70-73, DIR ATLANTIC REGIONAL LAB, NAT RES COUN CAN, 73- *Concurrent Pos:* Chmn, Atlantic Coun Provinces Coun Sci, 81- *Mem:* Am Soc Biol Chem; Am Soc Microbiol; Can Soc Microbiol. *Res:* Metabolism of sugars; enzymic degradation of hemicelluloses and aromatic compounds; marine phycology. *Mailing Add:* Atlantic Regional Lab Nat Res Coun 1411 Oxford Halifax NS B3H 3Z1 Can

SIMPSON, GEDDES WILSON, b Scranton, Pa, Aug 15, 08; m 33; c 4. ENTOMOLOGY. *Educ:* Bucknell Univ, AB, 29; Cornell Univ, AM, 31, PhD(econ entom), 35. *Prof Exp:* Asst entom, State Univ NY Col Agr, Cornell Univ, 30-31; asst entomologist, Exp Sta, 31-44, chg roguing serv, 38-46, chg Fla test plot, 39-59, assoc entomologist, 44-52, entomologist, 52-74, prof entom & chmn dept, Univ, 54-74; EMER PROF ENTOM, UNIV MAINE, ORONO, 74- *Concurrent Pos:* Ed-in-chief, Am Potato J, 75-; asst to dir, Maine Agr Exp Sta, 76- *Mem:* Fel AAAS; Entom Soc Am; Potato Asn Am. *Res:* Insect transmission of plant virus diseases; biology and control of aphids affecting potatoes. *Mailing Add:* 1 Winslow Hall Univ of Maine Orono ME 04469

SIMPSON, GEORGE GAYLORD, b Chicago, Ill, June 16, 02; m 23, 38; c 4. VERTEBRATE PALEONTOLOGY, GEOLOGY. *Educ:* Yale Univ, PhB, 23, PhD(geol), 26. *Hon Degrees:* ScD, Yale Univ, 46, Princeton Univ, 47, Durham Univ, 51, Oxford Univ, 51, Univ NMex, 54, Univ Chicago, 59, Cambridge Univ, 65, York Univ, 66, Kenyon Col & Univ Colo, 68; LLD, Glasgow Univ, 51; Dr, Univ Paris, 65, Univ LaPlata, 77. *Prof Exp:* Field asst, Am Mus Natural Hist, 24, from asst cur to assoc cur vert paleont, 27-42, cur fossil mammals & birds & chmn dept paleont & geol, 44-59; Nat Res Coun fel biol sci, Brit Mus Natural Hist, 26-27; Agassiz prof vert paleont, Harvard Univ, 59-70; PROF GEOSCI, UNIV ARIZ, 67- *Concurrent Pos:* Prof, Columbia Univ, 45-59; lectr, Univs; mem, Am Mus Natural Hist Exped, western US, 24, 29, 32, 35, 36, 46-50 & 52-54, southeastern US, 29-30, Arg, 30-31 & 33-34, & Brazil, 54-56. *Honors & Awards:* Thompson Medal, Nat Acad Sci, 43, Elliott Medal, 44 & 61; Lewis Prize, Am Philos Soc, 42; Gaudry Medal, Geol Soc France, 47; Hayden Medal, Philadelphia Acad Sci, 50; Penrose Medal, Geol Soc Am, 52; Du Mont Medal, Geol Soc Belg, 53; Darwin Wallace Medal, Linnean Soc London, 58, Linnean Gold Medal, 62; Darwin Medal, Royal Soc London, 62; Nat Medal Sci, 65; Verrill Medal, Yale Univ, 66; Distinguished Achievement Medal, Am Mus Nat Hist, 69; Cross Medal, Yale Grad Asn, 69; Paleont Soc Medal, 73; Int Award Distinguished Contrib Nat Hist, Smithsonian Inst, 76; Distinguished Serv Award, Am Inst Biol Sci, 78. *Mem:* Nat Acad Sci; Soc Vert Paleont (pres, 42); fel Am Philos Soc; fel Geol Soc Am; Soc Study Evolution (pres, 40). *Res:* Biology; recent and fossil mammals; stratigraphy, especially of early Tertiary of North and South America; penguins. *Mailing Add:* 5151 E Holmes St Tucson AZ 86711

SIMPSON, GEORGE M, b Pa, Sept 28, 26; m. PSYCHIATRY. *Educ:* Glasgow Univ, BSc, 48; Univ Liverpool, MB, ChB, 55. *Prof Exp:* Intern, Royal Southern Hosp, Liverpool, Eng, 55-56; asst resident psychiat, Allen Mem Inst, Royal Victoria Hosp, Montreal, Que, 56-57; resident, Rockland State Hosp, 57-58, sr psychiatrist, 58-61, supvry psychiatrist, 61-66, prin res scientist, Res Ctr, 67-77; PROF PSYCHIAT & BEHAV SCI, SCH MED, UNIV SOUTHERN CALIF, LOS ANGELES, 77-; DIR PSYCHOPHARMACOL SERV, METROP STATE HOSP, NORWALK, CALIF, 77- *Concurrent Pos:* Nat Inst Ment Health grants, 63-; vis prof, Menninger Clin; consult, Columbia Univ. *Mem:* Am Col Neuropsychopharmacol; AMA; Am Psychiat Asn; Am Soc Clin Pharmacol & Therapeut; NY Acad Sci. *Res:* Psychopharmacology; extrapyramidal disorder associated with phenothiazines and antidepressants in relation to side effects and treatment outcome. *Mailing Add:* 11400 Norwalk Blvd Norwalk CA 90650

SIMPSON, GRAHAM MILLER, b Wellington, NZ, Dec 21, 31; Can citizen; m 61; c 3. PLANT PHYSIOLOGY. *Educ:* Massey Univ, NZ, BAgrSc, 54, MAgrSc, 56; Univ London, PhD(plant physiol), 59. *Prof Exp:* Can Dept Agr fel crop sci, Univ Sask, 59-63; from asst prof to assoc prof plant physiol, 63-70, actg head crop sci dept, 68-69, dir crop develop ctr, 71-74, PROF CROP SCI, UNIV SASK, 70- *Concurrent Pos:* Vis fel plant physiol, Univ Col, Wales, 69-70, Int Agr Inst Develop Studies, Sussex Univ, 79-80. *Mem:* Agr Inst Can; Can Soc Plant Physiol. *Res:* Seed dormancy; plant growth regulators; growth analysis of cereals; drought physiology. *Mailing Add:* Dept of Crop Sci Univ of Sask Saskatoon SK S7N 0W0 Can

SIMPSON, HOWARD EDWIN, b Grand Forks, NDak, June 27, 17; m 43; c 4. GEOLOGY. *Educ:* Univ NDak, BA, 40; Univ Ill, MS, 42; Yale Univ, PhD(geol), 53. *Prof Exp:* Geologist, Eng Geol Br, US Geol Surv, 47-60, geologist, Regional Geol Br, 60-66, geologist, Eng Geol Br, 66-77, geologist, Spec Proj Br, 77-81; CONSULT GEOL & QUAL ASSURANCE ENG, 81- *Mem:* Asn Eng Geol; Am Inst Prof Geologists. *Res:* Application of geology to problems of urban development; geomorphology; Pleistocene geology. *Mailing Add:* 2020 Wash Ave Golden CO 80401

SIMPSON, JAMES EDWARD, b Chicago, Ill, July 6, 31; div; c 3. GRAPH THEORY, COMBINATORICS. *Educ:* Loyola Univ, Ill, BSEd, 53, MA, 56; Yale Univ, PhD(math), 61. *Prof Exp:* From instr to assoc prof math, Marquette Univ, 55-66; ASSOC PROF MATH, UNIV KY, 66- *Concurrent Pos:* NSF res grants, 63-66; vis Fulbright prof, Arya-Mehr Univ Technol, 68-70. *Mem:* Am Math Soc; Math Asn Am. *Res:* Functional analysis; spectral analysis of operators; graph theory; combinatorics; database management. *Mailing Add:* Dept of Math Univ of Ky Lexington KY 40506

SIMPSON, JAMES HENRY, JR, b Haledon, NJ, Oct 13, 29; m 61; c 3. PHYSICS. *Educ:* Rutgers Univ, BS, 51, PhD(physics), 58. *Prof Exp:* Asst prof physics, Univ Del, 57-58; PRIN SCIENTIST, KEARFOTT DIV, SINGER CO, 58- *Concurrent Pos:* Adj assoc prof, Fordham Univ, Lincoln Ctr, 70- *Mem:* Am Phys Soc; Inst Elec & Electronics Eng; Sigma Xi. *Res:* Magnetic resonance; atomic physics; ring laser gyroscopes; optically-pumped, magnetic-resonance gyroscopes. *Mailing Add:* Kearfott Div Singer Co 1225 McBride Ave Little Falls NJ 07424

SIMPSON, JAMES R(USSELL), b Passaic, NJ, Mar 22, 11; m 35; c 2. CIVIL ENGINEERING. *Educ:* Va Polytech Inst, BS, 34, MS, 42; Environ Engrs Intersoc, dipl, 56. *Prof Exp:* Indust hyg engr, USPHS, 35-36, sanit engr, 44-47; sanit engr, State Dept Health, Va, 36-37, pub health engr, 38-42; sanit engr, Fed Housing Admin, 43-44 & 47-56, chief sanit eng sect & spec asst tech studies prog, 56-59, chief standards & studies sect, 59-64, dep dir archit standards div, 64-67, dir off advan bldg technol, Dept Housing & Urban Develop, 67-70; HOUSING INDUST CONSULT, 70- *Mem:* AAAS; Am Pub Health Asn; Am Soc Civil Eng; Nat Soc Prof Eng; Inst Elec & Electronics Engrs. *Res:* Building research; application of microcomputers to residential construction, housing and telecommunications applications. *Mailing Add:* 7721 Weber Ct Annandale VA 22003

SIMPSON, JOANNE, b Boston, Mass, Mar 23, 23; m 48, 65; c 3. METEOROLOGY. *Educ:* Univ Chicago, PhD, 49. *Prof Exp:* Instr meteorol, NY Univ, 43-44; instr, Univ Chicago, 44-45; instr physics & meteorol, Ill Inst Technol, 46-49, asst prof, 49-51; meteorologist, Woods Hole Oceanog Inst, 51-60; prof meteorol, Univ Calif, Los Angeles, 60-65; head exp br atmospheric physics & chem lab, Environ Sci Serv Admin, 65-71, dir exp meteorol lab, Nat Oceanic & Atmospheric Admin, 71-74; prof environ sci & mem ctr advan studies, Univ Va, 74-76, W W Corcoran prof, 76-81. *Concurrent Pos:* Hon lectr, Imp Col, Univ London & Guggenheim fel, 54-55; counr, Am Meteorol Soc, 75-77 & 79-81; comnr, Sci Technol Activities, 82-84; chief scientist, Simpson Weather Assocs. *Honors & Awards:* Meisinger Award, Am Meteorol Soc, 62; Vincent J Schaefer Award, Weather Modification Asn, 79. *Mem:* Fel Am Meteorol Soc. *Res:* Convection in atmosphere; cumulus clouds; tropical meteorology; weather modification; satellite metorology. *Mailing Add:* Code 914 Severe Storms Br Goddard Space Flight Ctr Greenbelt MD 20771

SIMPSON, JOE LEIGH, b Birmingham, Ala, Apr 9, 43; m 78. HUMAN GENETICS, MEDICINE. *Educ:* Duke Univ, MD, 68; Am Bd Obstet & Gynec, dipl, 75. *Prof Exp:* Fel obstet & gynec, Cornell Med Col, 69-73; asst clin prof, Univ Tex, San Antonio, 73-75; chief, obstet serv, Brooke Army Med Ctr, 73-75; assoc prof, 75-79, PROF OBSTET & GYNEC & HEAD SECT HUMAN GENETICS, NORTHWESTERN UNIV, 79- *Concurrent Pos:* Clin assoc, NY Blook Ctr, 68-73; acad training fel, Cornell Med Col, 71-72; Am Col Obstet & Gynec rep, Am Acad Pediat Comt Genetics, 77- *Honors & Awards:* Upjohn lectr, Am Fertil Soc. *Mem:* Am Soc Human Genetics; fel Am Col Obstet & Gynec; Am Fertility Soc; Harvey Soc; Soc Gynecol Invest. *Res:* Human genetics, especially sex chromosomes and disorders of sex differentiation; antenatal diagnosis of genetic disorders; genetics of fetal wastage. *Mailing Add:* Printice Women's Hosp 333 E Superior St Chicago IL 60611

SIMPSON, JOHN ALEXANDER, b Portland, Ore, Nov 3, 16; m 46; c 2. PHYSICS. *Educ:* Reed Col, AB, 40; NY Univ, MS, 42, PhD(physics), 43. *Prof Exp:* Asst physics, NY Univ, 40-42, res assoc, Off Sci Res & Develop proj, 42-43; sci group leader, Manhattan Dist Proj, Metall Lab, 43-46, from instr to prof, 45-68, Edward L Ryerson distinguished serv prof, 68-74, ARTHUR H COMPTON DISTINGUISHED SERV PROF PHYSICS, UNIV CHICAGO & ENRICO FERMI INST NUCLEAR STUDIES, 74-, DIR, INST, 73- *Concurrent Pos:* Estab lab astrophys & space res in Enrico Fermi Inst, Univ Chicago, 64; fel, Ctr Policy Study, 66-; sci consult, Argonne Nat Lab, 46-54; chmn comt biophys, Univ Chicago, 51-52; mem spec int comt, Int Geophys Year, 54-60 & US nat comt & tech panel cosmic rays, 55-58; mem space sci bd, Nat Acad Sci, 58-66, consult, 66-; pres, Int Comn Cosmic Radiation, 64-67; mem astron missions bd, NASA. *Mem:* Nat Acad Sci; fel Am Phys Soc; fel Am Geophys Union; Am Astron Soc; Int Acad Astronaut. *Res:* Cosmic radiation origin; galactic, solar and magnetospheric acceleration of particles; experiments on nuclear composition, spectra, time variations of radiation with neutron monitors, satellite and space probes; interplanetary and solar magnetic fields deduced from particle propagation. *Mailing Add:* Enrico Fermi Inst Nuclear Studies & Dept of Physics Univ of Chicago Chicago IL 60637

SIMPSON, JOHN AROL, b Toronto, Ont, Mar 30, 23; nat US; m 48; c 1. PHYSICS, SCIENCE ADMINISTRATION. *Educ:* Lehigh Univ, BS, 46, MS, 48, PhD(physics), 53. *Prof Exp:* Physicist, 48-62, chief electron physics sect, 62-69, dep chief optical physics div, 69-75, chief mech div, 75-78, DIR CTR MECH ENG & PROCESS TECHNOL, NAT BUR STANDARDS, 78- *Concurrent Pos:* Asst, Lehigh Univ, 51-52. *Mem:* Am Phys Soc. *Res:* Metrology; optics. *Mailing Add:* 312 Riley St Falls Church VA 22046

SIMPSON, JOHN BARCLAY, b Oakland, Calif, June 8, 47; c 2. BEHAVIORAL PHYSIOLOGY. *Educ:* Univ Calif, Santa Barbara, BA, 69; Northwestern Univ, MA, 72, PhD(neurobiol & behav), 73. *Prof Exp:* Teaching asst psychol, Northwestern Univ, 69-70; instr, Col Gen Studies, Univ Pa, 74-75; asst prof, 75-78, ASSOC PROF PSYCHOL, UNIV WASH, 78- *Concurrent Pos:* Fel, Inst Neurol Sci, Univ Pa, 73-75; vis assoc prof physiol, Univ Calif, San Francisco, 76-80. *Mem:* AAAS; Soc Neurosci. *Res:* Neural involvement in body fluid regulation; neural control of ingestive behaviors. *Mailing Add:* Dept of Psychol NI-25 Univ of Wash Seattle WA 98195

SIMPSON, JOHN ERNEST, b Toledo, Ohio, Feb 10, 42; m 66; c 1. ORGANIC CHEMISTRY, ENOLOGY. *Educ:* Univ NMex, BS, 63, MS, 66, PhD(chem), 68. *Prof Exp:* Asst prof chem, Pomona Col, 67-68; assoc prof, 68-80, PROF CHEM, CALIF STATE POLYTECH UNIV, POMONA, 80- *Mem:* Am Chem Soc; AAAS; Sigma Xi; Am Soc Enologists. *Res:* Organic synthesis-crown ethers; bridged aromatics; C-13 labeled compounds; phenolics, isolation and identification in grapes and wines; nuclear magnetic resonance spectroscopy. *Mailing Add:* Chem Dept Calif State Polytech Univ Pomona CA 91768

SIMPSON, JOHN HAMILTON, b Montreal, Que, May 28, 15; m 53; c 2. THEORETICAL SOLID STATE PHYSICS, SOLID STATE ELECTRONICS. *Educ:* McGill Univ, BEng, 37; Bristol Univ, PhD(theoret physics), 50. *Prof Exp:* Test engr, Can Gen Elec Co, 37-38; res officer, Radio & Elec Eng Div, Nat Res Coun Can, 38-46, sr res officer, 48-61, prin res officer, Physics Div, 61-76, energy consult, 77-81; CONSULT PHOTOVOLTAICS, 81- *Concurrent Pos:* Lectr, Univ Ottawa; pres, Cosim Solar Res Ltd. *Mem:* Am Phys Soc; Can Asn Physicists; Inst Elec & Electronics Engrs. *Res:* Theory of optical-electrical properties of defects in ionic crystals; theory of semiconducting devices; theory of cooperative effects in dielectrics; direct current transmission line theory. *Mailing Add:* 2184 Braeside Ave Ottawa ON K1H 7J5 Can

SIMPSON, JOHN W(ISTAR), b Glenn Springs, SC, Sept 25, 14; m 48; c 4. ELECTRICAL ENGINEERING. *Educ:* US Naval Acad, BS, 37; Univ Pittsburgh, MS, 41. *Hon Degrees:* DSc, Seton Hill Col, 68. *Prof Exp:* Res engr, Westinghouse Elec Corp, 38-39, mgr, Navy & Marine Switchbd Sect, 39-46; mgr nuclear eng, Power Pile Div, Oak Ridge Nat Lab, 46-48; supv engr circuit breaker design, 48-49, asst eng mgr, Bettis Atomic Power Lab, 48-52, asst div mgr, 52-54, mgr pressurized water reactor proj, 54-55, div mgr, 55-58, vpres & gen mgr, 58-59, vpres & gen mgr, Atomic Power Div, 59-62, vpres eng & res, 62-63, vpres & gen mgr elec utility group, 63-69, PRES POWER SYSTS, WESTINGHOUSE ELEC CORP, 69- Concurrent Pos: Consult, US Navy, 45; mem US deleg, Int Conf Peaceful Uses Atomic Energy, 55 & 58. Honors & Awards: Edison Medal, 71. Mem: Nat Acad Eng; fel Inst Elec & Electronics Engrs; fel Am Soc Mech Engrs; Am Soc Naval Engrs; fel Am Nuclear Soc. Res: Design of nuclear reactors. Mailing Add: Westinghouse Elec Corp Westinghouse Bldg Gateway Ctr Pittsburgh PA 15222

SIMPSON, JOHN WAYNE, b Henryetta, Okla, Aug 17, 35; m 66. BIOCHEMISTRY. Educ: Phillips Univ, BA, 57; Rice Univ, MA, 59, PhD(biochem), 65. Prof Exp: Asst mem biochem, 67-71, ASSOC PROF BIOCHEM, UNIV TEX DENT SCI INST, HOUSTON, 71- Concurrent Pos: Fel, Rice Univ, 65-67. Mem: AAAS; Am Physiol Soc; Int Asn Dent Res. Res: Comparative aspects of free amino acid distribution; pathways of glucose degradation in invertebrates; intermediary metabolism in oral tissues. Mailing Add: Univ Tex Dent Sci Inst Houston TX 77025

SIMPSON, KARL WILLIAM, b Stamford, Conn, Feb 16, 45; m 74. FRESH WATER BIOLOGY, ENTOMOLOGY. Educ: Thiel Col, BA, 66; Univ Del, MS, 68; Cornell Univ, PhD(aquatic entom), 73. Prof Exp: RES SCIENTIST WATER POLLUTION BIOL, NY STATE DEPT HEALTH, 71- Concurrent Pos: Mem: Ecol Soc Am; Freshwater Biol Asn; NAm Benthol Asn; Sigma Xi. Res: Development of methods for utilizing aquatic macroinvertebrates in water quality evaluations and toxic substance monitoring; biology and immature stages of nonbiting midges (chironomidae) and shore flies (ephydridae). Mailing Add: Div of Labs & Res NY State Dept of Health Albany NY 12201

SIMPSON, KENNETH L, b Los Angeles, Calif, June 24, 31; m 57; c 3. FOOD SCIENCE. Educ: Univ Calif, Davis, BS, 54, MS, 60, PhD(agr chem), 63. Prof Exp: NSF fel biochem, Unv Col, Wales, 63-64; from asst prof to assoc prof agr chem, 64-69, assoc prof food & resource chem, 69-72, PROF FOOD SCI & TECHNOL, UNIV RI, 72- Concurrent Pos: NSF res grants, sea grant; NIH grants; Sci Res Coun vis fel, Univ Liverpool, 71-72. Mem: AAAS; Am Chem Soc; Inst Food Technol; NY Acad Sci; World Maericulture Soc. Res: Chemistry and biochemistry of carotenoids in microorganism plants and animals; fish nutrition; utilization of fish processing waste; provitamin A analysis in fruit and vegetables. Mailing Add: Dept of Food Sci & Technol Univ of RI Kingston RI 02881

SIMPSON, LARRY P, b Philadelphia, Pa, Oct 31, 40; m 68. CELL BIOLOGY, PROTOZOOLOGY. Educ: Princeton Univ, AB, 62; Rockefeller Univ, PhD(cell biol), 67. Prof Exp: Asst prof zool, 67-74, assoc prof cell biol, 74-75, PROF CELL BIOL, UNIV CALIF, LOS ANGELES, 75- Concurrent Pos: NATO fel sci, Univ Brussels, 67-68; Molecular Biol Inst. Honors & Awards: Hutner Award, Soc Protogeol, 80. Mem: Soc Protozool; Am Soc Cell Biol; Molecular Biol Inst. Res: Cell biology of parasitic protozoa, especially mitochondrial biogenesis. Mailing Add: Dept Biol Univ Calif Los Angeles CA 90024

SIMPSON, LEONARD, b Hale Center, Tex, Apr 25, 32; m 64. INVERTEBRATE ZOOLOGY. Educ: Univ Calif, Berkeley, AB, 55, MA, 62, PhD(zool), 68. Prof Exp: Instr biol, Diablo Valley Col, 61-66; asst prof, 68-72, ASSOC PROF BIOL, PORTLAND STATE UNIV, 72- Mem: AAAS; Am Soc Zool; Sigma Xi; Western Soc Naturalists. Res: Neurosecretion and neuroendocrinology of Mollusca; reproductive endocrinology of invertebrates. Mailing Add: Dept of Biol Portland State Univ PO Box 751 Portland OR 97207

SIMPSON, LEONARD ANGUS, b Vancouver, BC, Aug 1, 39; m 67; c 3. MATERIALS SCIENCE, FRACTURE MECHANICS. Educ: Univ BC, BSc, 61, MSc, 63; Univ Wales, PhD(metall), 68. Prof Exp: Metallurgist, Res Lab, Gen Elec Co, NY, 63-64; RES OFFICER, ATOMIC ENERGY CAN LTD, PINAWA, MAN, 68-- Concurrent Pos: Vis scientist, Mat Res Lab, Brown Univ, 78-80. Res: Fracture mechanics of metals and nonmetals elastic-plastic fracture criteria. Mailing Add: Whiteshell Nuclear Res Estab Atomic Energy of Can Ltd Pinawa MB R0E 1L0 Can

SIMPSON, MARGARET, b Hong Kong, Jan 19, 35; US citizen. INVERTEBRATE ZOOLOGY. Educ: Immaculate Heart Col, BA, 56; Cath Univ, MS, 59, PhD(zool), 61. Prof Exp: Technician sch med, Univ Southern Calif, 56-57; USPHS fel, St Francis Col, Maine, 63-67; asst prof, Adelphi Univ, 67-73; assoc prof, 73-80, PROF BIOL, SWEET BRIAR COL, 80- Concurrent Pos: Danforth assoc, 78-83. Mem: Sigma Xi; Am Inst Biol Sci; Marine Biol Asn UK; Am Soc Zoologists. Res: Biology of polychaetes, specifically family Glyceridae, especially histology, embryology and venom glands. Mailing Add: Dept of Biol Sweet Briar Col Sweet Briar VA 24595

SIMPSON, MARION EMMA, b Odenton, Md, Feb 3, 27. PLANT PHYSIOLOGY, BOTANY. Educ: Univ Md, BS, 52, MS, 59, PhD(plant physiol), 62. Prof Exp: Clerk, 44-46, sci aid, 46-58, plant pathologist, 58-60, res plant pathologist, Plant Indust Sta, Cotton Div, 60-77, MEM STAFF, BELTSVILLE AGR RES CTR, USDA, 77- Mem: Am Soc Plant Physiologists; Am Phytopath Soc; Mycol Soc Am; Soc Indust Microbiol. Res: Field deterioration of cotton fiber and physiology of organisms involved; cellulase production by fungi and characterization of this enzyme. Mailing Add: Beltsville Agr Res Ctr USDA Rm 219 Bldg 200 Beltsville MD 20705

SIMPSON, MAURICE H, environmental science & engineering, deceased

SIMPSON, MELVIN VERNON, b New York, NY, July 5, 21; m 76; c 3. BIOCHEMISTRY. Educ: City Col New York, BS, 42; Univ Calif, PhD(biochem), 49. Prof Exp: Physicist, Philadelphia Navy Yard, 42-44; physicist, US Naval Ord Lab, 44-45; instr physiol med sch, Tufts Col, 49-51; from asst prof to assoc prof biochem sch med, Yale Univ, 52-62; Am Cancer Soc prof, Dartmouth Med Sch, 62-66; chmn dept biochem, 66-75, AM CANCER SOC PROF BIOCHEM, STATE UNIV NY STONY BROOK, 76- Concurrent Pos: USPHS fel, Wash Univ, 51-52; mem fel review panel,

NIH, 66-70; mem adv comt nucleic acids & protein synthesis, Am Cancer Soc, 70-75; mem merit rev bd basic sci, US Vet Admin. Honors & Awards: Res Award, Union Carbide Co, 69 & 70. Mem: Am Soc Biol Chemists; Am Chem Soc; Am Soc Cell Biol; Biophys Soc. Res: Protein biosynthesis; ribosomes; mitochondria; DNA biosynthesis. Mailing Add: Dept of Biochem State Univ of NY Stony Brook NY 11794

SIMPSON, NANCY E, b Toronto, Ont, Oct 29, 24. HUMAN GENETICS. Educ: Univ Toronto, BPHE, 47, PhD, 59; Columbia Univ, MA, 51. Prof Exp: Res assoc human genetics, Hosp Sick Children, Toronto, 59-60; asst prof pharmacol, Univ Toronto, 61-65; from asst prof to assoc prof biol & pediat, 65-75, PROF MED GENETICS & CHMN DIV, DEPT PEDIAT, QUEEN'S UNIV, ONT, 75- Concurrent Pos: Res fel, Pop Genetics Res Unit, Oxford Univ, 60-61; Queen Elizabeth II scientist, 62-68; Med Res Coun Can fel & vis scientist, Galton Lab, Univ Col, Univ London, 72-73. Mem: Am Soc Human Genetics; Can Diabetic Asn; Genetics Soc Can; NY Acad Sci. Res: Diabetes; enzyme polymorphisms in man; human gene mapping; pharmacogenetics. Mailing Add: Dept of Pediat Queen's Univ Kingston ON K7L 3N6 Can

SIMPSON, PAUL GRAVIS, physical chemistry, see previous edition

SIMPSON, RICHARD ALLAN, b Portsmouth, NH, June 25, 45. RADAR ASTRONOMY. Educ: Mass Inst Technol, BS, 67; Stanford Univ, MS, 69, PhD(elec eng), 73. Prof Exp: Res assoc, 73-76, SR RES ASSOC RADAR ASTRON, STANFORD UNIV, 76- Concurrent Pos: Vis res assoc, Arecibo Observ, 75-76 & 78. Mem: Am Astron Soc; Am Geophys Union; Inst Elec & Electronics Engrs; AAAS. Res: Theoretical and experimental research on scattering of radio waves by planetary surfaces; inference of geophysical properties of surfaces from scattered waves. Mailing Add: Ctr for Radar Astron Stanford Univ Stanford CA 94305

SIMPSON, RICHARD S, b Pensacola, Fla, Sept 25, 35; m 59; c 3. ELECTRICAL ENGINEERING. Educ: Univ Fla, BSEE, 57, MSE, 58, PhD(elec eng), 61. Prof Exp: Res assoc elec eng, Univ Fla, 58-61; from asst prof to prof, Univ Ala, 61-69; PROF ELEC ENG, UNIV HOUSTON, 69- Mem: Inst Elec & Electronics Engrs; Am Soc Eng Educ. Res: Communication and telemetry systems; detection theory; video compression. Mailing Add: Dept of Elec Eng Univ of Houston Houston TX 77004

SIMPSON, ROBERT BLAKE, b US citizen. MOLECULAR BIOLOGY. Educ: Univ Ill, Urbana, BS,69; Harvard Univ, Cambridge, MA, 72, PhD(biophysics), 79. Prof Exp: Sr fel, Dept Microbiol, Univ Wash, Seattle, 79-81; RES SCIENTIST & GROUP LEADER, MOLECULAR BIOL GROUP, PLANT CELL RES INST, ATLANTIC RICHFIELD CO, CALIF, 81- Mem: Am Soc Microbiol; Plant Molecular Biol Asn. Res: The mechanism of Ti-plasmid DNA transfer from Agrobacteria to plant cells, resulting in crown gall tumors; to introducing useful genes into plants; regulation of gene expression in plants. Mailing Add: Plant Cell Res Inst Atlantic Richfield Co 6560 Trinity Ct Dublin CA 94566

SIMPSON, ROBERT E, b Minneapolis, Minn, May 12, 20; m 56; c 2. MICROBIOLOGY. Educ: Univ Iowa, BA, 48, MS, 50, PhD(zool), 66. Prof Exp: Instr biol, 56-57, from asst prof to assoc prof, 57-66, chmn dept, 63-68, PROF BIOL, UNIV WIS-STEVENS POINT, 66- Mem: Am Soc Microbiol; Nature Conservancy. Res: Cell division and cytodifferentiation in synchronized Tetrahymena pyriformis GL as influenced by high hydrostatic pressure; effects of herbicides on aquatic bacteria; incidence of Aeromonas in amphibians; Aerosol transmission of microorganisms. Mailing Add: Dept of Biol Univ of Wis Stevens Point WI 54481

SIMPSON, ROBERT GENE, b Neodesha, Kans, Aug 13, 25; m 51; c 2. ENTOMOLOGY. Educ: Colo Agr & Mech Col, BS, 50, MS, 53; Kans State Univ, PhD(entom), 59. Prof Exp: Sales rep, Calif Spray-Chem Corp, 52-53; entomologist, State Dept Agr, Colo, 53-56; asst entom, Kans State Univ, 56-59; asst exten entomologist, Univ Nebr, 59-60; asst prof entom, 60-67, assoc prof, 67-79, PROF ENTOM, COLO STATE UNIV, 79- Mem: Entom Soc Am; AAAS. Res: Biological control; life history and control of field crops and horticultural insects. Mailing Add: Dept Zool & Entom Colo State Univ Ft Collins CO 80523

SIMPSON, ROBERT JOHN, b Newburgh, NY, Feb 2, 27; m 52; c 4. ANIMAL PHYSIOLOGY. Educ: Houghton Col, BA, 50; Univ Ill, MS, 60, PhD(physiol), 63. Prof Exp: Biologist, Lederle Labs, Am Cyanamid Co, 52-58; teaching asst anat & physiol, Univ Ill, 58-62; asst prof biol & human & cell physiol, Muskingum Col, 62-65; asst prof human & animal physiol, 65-68, ASSOC PROF HUMAN & ANIMAL PHYSIOL & ENDOCRINOL, UNIV NORTHERN IOWA, 68- Mem: AAAS; Sigma Xi; Am Soc Zoologists. Res: Mechanisms in calcification of epiphyseal cartilage; vitamin D actions; factors in calciphylaxis; calcium metabolism and hormones; effects of estrogen and progesterone on cartilage calcification; mineral metabolism interrelations; normal and pathological calcium deposition. Mailing Add: Dept of Biol Univ of Northern Iowa Cedar Falls IA 50613

SIMPSON, ROBERT LEE, b San Francisco, Calif, Apr 3, 42; m 70; c 1. LIMNOLOGY, FRESHWATER WETLAND ECOLOGY. Educ: Fresno State Col, BA, 65, MA, 67; Cornell Univ, PhD(limnol), 71. Prof Exp: Teaching asst zool, Fresno State Col, 65-67; res asst limnol, Cornell Univ, 67-70; from asst prof to assoc prof, 70-79, chmn dept, 72-80, PROF BIOL, RIDER COL, 79- Concurrent Pos: Grants, Off Water Res & Technol, 75-78, 79-82, Environ Protection Agency, 76-77 & 78-81. Mem: Am Soc Limnol & Oceanog; Ecol Soc Am; Brit Ecol Soc; Estuarine Res Fedn; Am Inst Biol Sci. Res: Ecology of freshwater tidal and non-tidal wetlands including analysis of production, decomposition and nutrient cycling processes; impact of sewage and non-point source pollutants on freshwater wetlands. Mailing Add: Dept of Biol Rider Col Box 6400 Lawrenceville NJ 08648

SIMPSON, ROBERT TODD, b Chicago, Ill, June 28, 38; m 63; c 4. BIOCHEMISTRY. *Educ:* Swarthmore Col, BA, 59; Harvard Univ, MD, 63, PhD(biol chem), 69. *Prof Exp:* Intern med, Peter Bent Brigham Hosp, Boston, 63-64; teaching asst biol chem, Harvard Med Sch, 65-69; sr surgeon, 69-77, CHIEF SECT DEVELOP BIOCHEM, LAB NUTRIT & ENDOCRINOL, NAT INST ARTHRITIS, METAB & DIGESTIVE DIS, 73-; MED DIR, USPHS, 77-; CHIEF, LAB NUTRIT & ENDOCRINOL, NAT INST ARTHRITIS, DIABETES, DIGESTIVE & KIDNEY DIS, 80- *Mem:* Am Soc Biol Chem. *Res:* Chromatin structure; histone-DNA interactions; chemical basis for gene regulation in eucaryotic cells. *Mailing Add:* Bldg 6 Rm B1-38 Nat Insts of Health Bethesda MD 20014

SIMPSON, ROBERT WAYNE, b Providence, RI, Dec 28, 28; m 54; c 4. VIROLOGY. *Educ:* Univ RI, BS, 51; Brown Univ, MS, 56; Rutgers Univ, PhD(virol), 58. *Prof Exp:* Asst virol, Inst Microbiol, Rutgers Univ, 55-58; mem res staff, Dept Virol, Pub Health Res Inst New York, Inc, 58-68; assoc prof, 68-75, PROF VIROL, RUTGERS UNIV, NEW BRUNSWICK, 75- *Concurrent Pos:* Res asst prof path, Sch Med, NY Univ, 66-70; instr microbiol, Hunter Col, City Univ New York, 68; mem virol study sect, NIH, USPHS, 72-76. *Mem:* AAAS; Sigma Xi; Am Soc Microbiol; Brit Soc Gen Microbiol. *Res:* Animal RNA viruses; viral genetics; electron microscopy; viral persistence. *Mailing Add:* Waksman Inst Microbiol Rutgers Univ PO Box 759 Piscataway NJ 08854

SIMPSON, ROGER LYNDON, b Roanoke, Va, Oct 25, 42; m 64; c 1. FLUID MECHANICS, HEAT TRANSFER. *Educ:* Univ Va, BME, 64; Stanford Univ, MSME, 65, PhD(mech eng), 68. *Prof Exp:* Develop engr, Atomic Power Equip Dept, Gen Elec Co, Calif, 68; from asst prof to assoc prof thermal & fluid sci, 69-70, assoc prof civil & mech eng, 74-76, PROF CIVIL & MECH ENG, SOUTHERN METHODIST UNIV, 76- *Concurrent Pos:* Vis scientist, Max-Planck Inst fur Stroemungsforschung, W Ger, 75-76. *Mem:* Am Inst Aeronaut & Astronaut; Am Soc Mech Engrs; Sigma Xi. *Res:* Turbulent shear flows; structure of turbulent flows; laser anemometry; unsteady and separated flows; mass transfer; boundary layer control. *Mailing Add:* Dept of Civil & Mech Eng Southern Methodist Univ Dallas TX 75275

SIMPSON, RONALD P, materials science, metallurgy, see previous edition

SIMPSON, RUSSELL BRUCE, b Jersey City, NJ, Feb 15, 42; m 66; c 2. VETERINARY MICROBIOLOGY. *Educ:* Tex A&M Univ, BS, 65, DVM, 66, MS, 74; Am Col Vet Microbiologists, dipl, 75. *Prof Exp:* Lab officer microbiol, Vet Div, Walter Reed Army Inst Res, 66-68 & US Navy Prev Med Univ, DaNang, 68-69; instr & asst prof vet microbiol, 69-76, ASSOC PROF VET MICROBIOL & PARASITOL, COL VET MED, TEX A&M UNIV, 76- *Mem:* Am Asn Equine Practr; Am Asn Vet Lab Diagnosticians; Asn Am Vet Med Cols; Am Vet Med Asn. *Mailing Add:* Dept of Vet Microbiol Tex A&M Univ College Station TX 77843

SIMPSON, S(TEPHEN) H(ARBERT), JR, b Columbus, Tex, Mar 10, 07; m 59; c 4. ELECTRICAL ENGINEERING, COMMUNICATIONS. *Educ:* Agr & Mech Col Tex, BS, 28. *Prof Exp:* Mem staff, RCA Commun, Inc, 29-37, mgr, prog & radio- photo, 37-42, traffic engr, 46-53, asst vpres & dist mgr, 53; mgr commun res, Southwest Res Inst, 53-56, asst vpres, 56-58, asst to pres, 58-66; PRES, SOUTHWEST SOUND & ELECTRONICS INC, 66-, CHMN BD, 80- *Mem:* Inst Elec & Electronics Engrs; Sigma Xi; Audio Eng Soc. *Res:* International communications; special communications; program transmission; sound and closed circuit television hospital communications; industrial research adminstration; architectural acoustics and room equalization. *Mailing Add:* 2323 Loop 410 NW San Antonio TX 78230

SIMPSON, SIDNEY BURGESS, JR, b Russellville, Ark, Oct 8, 35; m 63; c 1. DEVELOPMENTAL BIOLOGY. *Educ:* Ark Polytech Col, BS, 57; Tulane Univ, MS, 62, PhD(zool), 63. *Prof Exp:* NIH fel, Case Western Reserve Univ, 64, sr instr anat, Sch Med, 64-65, asst prof, 65-71; assoc prof biol sci, 71-80, PROF DEPT BIOCHEM & MOLECULAR & CELL BIOL, NORTHWESTERN UNIV, 80- *Concurrent Pos:* NIH career develop award, 66- *Mem:* AAAS; Soc Develop Biol; Am Soc Zoologists. *Res:* Vertebrate and invertebrate regeneration. *Mailing Add:* Dept of Biol Sci Northwestern Univ Evanston IL 60201

SIMPSON, STEPHEN G, b Allentown, Pa, Sept 8, 45; m 73; c 2. MATHEMATICS, MATHEMATICAL LOGIC. *Educ:* Lehigh Univ, BA & MS, 66; Mass Inst Technol, PhD(math), 71. *Prof Exp:* Gibbs instr, Yale Univ, 71-72; lectr, Univ Calif, Berkeley, 72-74; res fel, Oxford Univ, 74-75; asst prof, 75-77, assoc prof, 77-80, PROF MATH, PA STATE UNIV, 81- *Concurrent Pos:* NSF res grants, 71-74 & 75-; res fel, Sci Res Coun, UK, 74-75; res fel Alfred P Sloan Found, 80-82; vis assoc prof, Univ Chicago, 78 & Univ Conn, 79-80; vis prof, Univ Paris, 81. *Mem:* Am Math Soc; Asn for Symbolic Logic. *Res:* Admissible recursion theory; degrees of unsolvability; model theory; set theory; foundations of mathematics. *Mailing Add:* Dept of Math Pa State Univ Univ Park PA 16802

SIMPSON, THEODORE B, b Orange, NJ, May 7, 25; m 61; c 3. CHEMICAL ENGINEERING. *Educ:* Yale Univ, BEng, 50; Cornell Univ, PhD(chem eng), 54. *Prof Exp:* Res & develop engr, Hooker Chem Co, 54-56; res & develop engr, Esso Res & Eng Co, 56-59; group supvr chem eng res & develop, Nat Distillers & Chem Co, 59-62; sect supvr, Am Agr Chem Co, 62-65; supt chem eng, Phosphate Div, Tex Gulf Sulphur Co, 65-68; sr res engr, Garrett Res & Develop Co, Occidental Petrol Co, 68-76; PROJ ENGR, US GOVT, 76- *Mem:* Am Inst Chem Engrs; Am Chem Soc. *Res:* Fertilizers; air pollution; fuel technology. *Mailing Add:* 7112 Benjamine St McLean VA 22101

SIMPSON, THOMAS A, b Adams, Mass, Oct 23, 25; m 54; c 2. MINING, GEOLOGY. *Educ:* Univ Mo-Rolla, BS, 51, EMines, 65; Univ Ala, MS, 59. *Prof Exp:* Geologist, US Geol Surv, 54-61; chief geologist, Econ Geol Div, Geol Surv Ala, 61-65, asst state geologist, planning sect, 65-75; actg head dept, 78-79, ASSOC PROF MINERAL ENG, UNIV ALA, 75-, RES ASSOC, MINERAL RESOURCES INST, 76- *Concurrent Pos:* Res assoc, Mus Natural Hist, Univ Ala, 63-, lectr univ, 65-75; mining geologist, Surinam, 64 & Venezuela, 67. *Mem:* Inst Mining, Metall & Petrol Engrs; fel Geol Soc Am; Asn Eng Geologists; Am Inst Prof Geologists; Am Asn Petrol Geol. *Res:* Economic geology; mining hydrology and hydrogeologic investigations; mine blasting studies; Southeast iron ore studies. *Mailing Add:* Dept Mineral Eng Univ Ala PO Box 1468 University AL 35486

SIMPSON, TRACY L, b New York, NY, July 12, 37. BIOLOGY, SPONGE BIOLOGY. *Educ:* Brown Univ, AB, 59; Yale Univ, PhD(biol), 65. *Prof Exp:* From instr to asst prof, Tufts Univ, 64-67; assoc prof biol, 67-76, PROF BIOL, UNIV HARTFORD, 76- *Concurrent Pos:* Asst proj dir, Undergrad Equip Grant, NSF, 65-67 & prin investr res grant, 65-68, 68-70 & 71-73; vis assoc prof, Dartmouth Col, 74; vis assoc prof, Health Ctr, Univ Conn & Res Found grant, 74-76; prin investr, Int Silicon Symposium, 77-78. *Mem:* AAAS; Am Soc Zool; Am Micros Soc; NY Acad Sci; Sigma Xi. *Res:* Cell biology of sponges; biology of silicon and silicification. *Mailing Add:* Dept Biol Univ Hartford West Hartford CT 06117

SIMPSON, WILBURN DWAIN, b Long Grove, Okla, Oct 4, 37; m 67. NUCLEAR PHYSICS. *Educ:* Univ Miss, BS, 59, MS, 61; Rice Univ, MA, 63, PhD(nuclear physics), 65. *Prof Exp:* Res assoc nuclear physics, Rice Univ, 65-67; asst physicist, Brookhaven Nat Lab, 67-69; vpres syst develop, Periphonics Corp, 69-80; VPRES TECHNOL, ALTA TECHNOL INC, 80-; PRES, AYENTKA CONSULT CORP, 80- *Mem:* AAAS; Am Phys Soc; NY Acad Sci. *Res:* Three-body systems in nuclear physics; intermediate energy nuclear physics; nuclear structure; nucleon-nucleon and nucleon-nucleus interactions; meson-nucleon interactions; computer controlled audio response; communication processors; electronic funds transfer terminals; computer controlled networks; automated fare collection. *Mailing Add:* 124 Catalpa Rd Wilton CT 06897

SIMPSON, WILLIAM HENRY, b Woodbury, NJ, Mar 24, 42; m 69; c 2. SOLID STATE CHEMISTRY, PHOTOGRAPHIC CHEMISTRY. *Educ:* Col William & Mary, BS, 63; Univ Pa, PhD(phys chem), 67. *Prof Exp:* Fel org solid state, Franklin Inst Res Labs, Pa, 67-70, res chemist, 70-71; scientist, 71-77, SR SCIENTIST, POLAROID CORP, 77- *Mem:* Am Chem Soc; Soc Photog Sci & Eng. *Res:* Photochemistry; radiation chemistry of organic materials; photographic science; silver halide photographic emulsions. *Mailing Add:* Polaroid Corp Bldg IV 1265 Main St Waltham MA 02154

SIMPSON, WILLIAM ROY, b Padernal, NMex, June 27, 24; m 47; c 3. PLANT PATHOLOGY. *Educ:* Univ Idaho, BS, 49, MS, 51. *Prof Exp:* Technician plant path, 47-49, from res asst to res assoc, 49-54, from jr plant pathologist to assoc plant pathologist, Br Exp Sta, 54-70, res plant pathologist, 54-80, RES PROF PLANT PATH, UNIV IDAHO, 70-, EXTEN PROF & EXTEN PLANT PATHOLOGIST, 80- *Mem:* Am Phytopath Soc. *Res:* Vegetable pathology, especially disease of tomatoes, beets, spinach, corn and onions; curly top virus disease of vegetable crops; stalk rot and head smut of corn; development of virus resistant tomato. *Mailing Add:* Res & Exten Ctr Univ of Idaho Parma ID 83660

SIMPSON, WILLIAM STEWART, b Edmonton, Alta, Apr 11, 24; US citizen; m 50; c 4. PSYCHIATRY, HOSPITAL ADMINISTRATION. *Educ:* Univ Alta, Edmonton, BS, 46, MD, 48. *Prof Exp:* Sect chief psychiat, C F Menninger Mem Hosp, 59-66; assoc dir psychiat, Menninger Sch Psychiat, Menninger Found, 66-68, dir field serv fund raising, 72-74; dir psychiat residency training & chief psychiat serv, Topeka Vet Admin Hosp, 74-77; SR PSYCHIATRIST & PSYCHOANALYST, ADULT OUTPATIENT DEPT, MENNINGER FOUND, 77- *Concurrent Pos:* Mem fac, Menninger Sch Psychiat, 53-, mem exec comt & mgt comt, 54-77; first pres, Topeka Alcoholism Info Ctr, 63-67; assoc ed, Bull Menninger Clin, 64-70; clin dir psychiat & hosp admin, Topeka State Hosp, 68-72; mem bd dirs, Nat Coun Alcoholism, 68-, vpres, 70-73, pres, 73-75; mem, Kans Citizens Adv Alcoholism, 73- *Honors & Awards:* Silver Key Award, Nat Coun Alcoholism, 75. *Mem:* Fel Am Psychiat Asn; Am Psychoanal Asn. *Mailing Add:* 834 Buchanan Topeka KS 66606

SIMPSON, WILLIAM TRACY, b Berkeley, Calif, Dec 7, 20; m 44, 61; c 5. CHEMISTRY. *Educ:* Univ Calif, AB, 43, PhD(chem), 48. *Prof Exp:* Asst chem, Univ Calif, 46-48; instr, Univ Wash, 48-49, from asst prof to assoc prof, 49-57, prof, 57-64; prof, 65-77, chmn dept, 72-75, EMER PROF CHEM, UNIV ORE, 77- *Concurrent Pos:* Vis lectr, Univ Calif; vis prof, Fla State Univ; chmn, Gordon Conf Theoret Chem, 66; Fulbright vis prof, Lima, Peru, 71; assoc ed, J Chem Physics, 66-69. *Mem:* Am Chem Soc; Am Phys Soc. *Res:* Theoretical and experimental study of molecular electronic spectra; vacuum ultraviolet spectroscopy; electronic spectra of thin films and molecular crystals. *Mailing Add:* 500 Fair Oaks Dr Eugene OR 97401

SIMPSON-HERREN, LINDA, b Birmingham, Ala, July 7, 27; m 63; c 1. CHEMOTHERAPY. *Educ:* Univ Ala, BS, 48. *Prof Exp:* Instr physics, Univ Ala, 48; assoc physicist, 48-57, res physicist, 57-69, sr physicist, 69-71, SECT HEAD CELL & TISSUE KINETICS, SOUTHERN RES INST, 71- *Concurrent Pos:* Am ed, Cell & Tissue Kinetics. *Mem:* Am Asn Cancer Res; Cell Kinetics Soc (vpres, 77-78, pres, 78-79); AAAS; Sigma Xi; Health Physics Soc. *Res:* Cell and tumor kinetics of experimental tumor systems to optimize scheduling of chemotherapy alone or in combination with surgery; radiation and drug effects. *Mailing Add:* Southern Res Inst 2000 Ninth Ave S Birmingham AL 35205

SIMRALL, HARRY C(HARLES) F(LEMING), b Memphis, Tenn, Oct 16, 12; m 36. ELECTRICAL & MECHANICAL ENGINEERING. *Educ:* Miss State Univ, BS, 34 & 35; Univ Ill, MS, 39. *Prof Exp:* Instr elec eng, Miss State Univ, 34-35, instr drawing, 35-37, from instr to assoc prof elec eng, 37-44; assoc prof, Cent Sta Eng, Indust Eng Dept, Westinghouse Elec Corp, 44-45; assoc prof elec eng, 45-47, prof elec eng & head dept, 47-57, dean col eng, 57-78, EMER DEAN COL ENG & EMER PROF ELEC ENG, MISS STATE UNIV, 78- *Mem:* Fel Inst Elec & Electronics Engrs; Am Soc Eng Educ; Illum Eng Soc; Am Soc Agr Engrs; Nat Soc Prof Engrs (vpres, 62-64, pres elect, 69-70, pres, 70-71). *Res:* Electric power. *Mailing Add:* 107 White Dr W Starkville MS 39759

SIMS, ASA C, JR, b Asheville, NC, Sept 30, 19; m 43; c 2. PLANT PATHOLOGY. *Educ:* Hampton Inst, BS, 40; Ohio State Univ, MS, 54, PhD, 56; Harvard Univ, dipl educ mgt, 73. *Prof Exp:* Instr hort, Fla Agr & Mech Col, 48-49; asst prof, SC State Col, 49-52; asst bot, Ohio State Univ, 53-56; from assoc prof to prof biol, Southern Univ, Baton Rouge, 56-68; prof, 68-70, chmn dept biol, 68-69, chmn div sci, 69-70, DEAN ACAD AFFAIRS, SOUTHERN UNIV, NEW ORLEANS, 70- *Concurrent Pos:* Sci fac fel, Univ Minn, 65-66. *Mem:* Am Phytopath Soc; Bot Soc Am. *Res:* Fungus physiology; nature of disease; radioisotopes. *Mailing Add:* 6400 Press Dr Southern Univ New Orleans LA 70126

SIMS, BENJAMIN TURNER, b Dec 11, 34; US citizen; m 64; c 1. MATHEMATICS. *Educ:* Univ Mo, AB, 56, MA, 59; Iowa State Univ, PhD(math), 62. *Prof Exp:* Asst prof math, San Jose State Univ, 62-64, Am Univ Beirut, 64-66 & San Jose State Univ, 66-67; assoc prof, 67-71, prof math, 71-80, PROF MATH & COMPUT SCI, EASTERN WASH UNIV, 80- *Res:* Point-set topology. *Mailing Add:* Dept of Math Eastern Wash Univ Cheney WA 99004

SIMS, BERNARD, pharmaceutical chemistry, physical chemistry, see previous edition

SIMS, CHESTER THOMAS, b Winchester, Mass, Dec 14, 23; m 49, 80; c 2. METALLURGICAL ENGINEERING. *Educ:* Northeastern Univ, BS, 47; Ohio State Univ, MS, 51. *Prof Exp:* Res engr, Battelle Mem Inst, 47-50 & 52-55, asst div chief, 55-58; mat engr, Knolls Atomic Power Lab, Gen Elec Co, 58-60, metallurgist, Mat & Processes Lab, 60-63, proj leader, 64-65; mgr high-temperature mat, 66-68, mgr alloy & joining metall, 68-71, mgr advan mat, Gas Turbine Div, 71-81, MGR, MAT INFO SERV, CORP RES & DEVELOP CTR, GEN ELEC CO, SCHENECTADY, NY, 81- *Concurrent Pos:* Lectr, Rensselaer Polytech Inst, 63-64; consult, Pac Northwest Labs, Battelle Mem Inst, 64-; chmn gas turbine panel, Am Soc Mech Engrs-Am Soc Testing & Mat. *Honors & Awards:* Distinguished Serv Award, Hudson-Mohawk Sect, Am Inst Mining, Metall & Petrol Engrs, 74; William Hunt Eisenman Award, Am Soc Metals, 76. *Mem:* fel Am Soc Metals; Am Welding Soc; Am Inst Mining, Metall & Petrol Engrs. *Res:* Physical metallurgy of superalloys, refractory and scarce metals; elevated temperature oxidation and corrosion; high-temperature alloy development and ceramics for gas turbines; materials for high-temperature reactors. *Mailing Add:* Mat Info Serv; Gen Elec Co 120 Erie Blvd Schenectady NY 12345

SIMS, ERNEST THEODORE, JR, b Atlanta, Ga, Aug 29, 32; m 63; c 2. HORTICULTURE, PLANT PHYSIOLOGY. *Educ:* Univ Ga, BSA, 54; Ohio State Univ, MSc, 59, PhD(hort), 62. *Prof Exp:* From asst prof to assoc prof, 62-72, PROF HORT, CLEMSON UNIV, 72-, ACTG HEAD, DEPT HORT, CLEMSON UNIV, 81. *Concurrent Pos:* Mem, Nat Coun Ther & Rehad Through Hort. *Mem:* Am Soc Hort Sci; Am Soc Plant Physiol; Produce Mkt Asn. *Res:* Characterizing and delaying ripening and senescence in peaches, nectarines and plums; effects of mechanical harvesting and handling on quality and marketability of hort crops. *Mailing Add:* Dept of Hort Clemson Univ Clemson SC 29631

SIMS, ETHAN ALLEN HITCHCOCK, b Newport, RI, Apr 22, 16; m 39; c 3. MEDICINE, BIOCHEMISTRY. *Educ:* Harvard Univ, BS, 38; Columbia Univ, MD, 42. *Prof Exp:* House officer, New Haven Hosp, Conn, 42-44; instr med, Sch Med, Yale Univ, 47-50; from asst prof to assoc prof med, 50-65, PROF MED, COL MED, UNIV VT, 66- *Concurrent Pos:* Brown res fel, New Haven Hosp, Conn, 46-47; Commonwealth fel, Sch Med, Case Western Reserve Univ, 64-65; assoc attend physician, Mary Fletcher & DeGoesbriand Mem Hosps, 50-64; dir metab unit, Dept Med, Univ Vt, 57-73; attend physician, Med Ctr, Hosp of Vt, 64-; vis prof med, Div Endocrinol, Sch Med, Tufts Univ, 74-75. *Mem:* Fel Am Col Physicians; Am Fedn Clin Res; Endocrine Soc; Am Diabetes Asn; Am Soc Clin Nutrit. *Res:* Metabolic diseases; diabetes and obesity. *Mailing Add:* Metab Unit Dept Med Given Bldg Univ of Vt Col of Med Burlington VT 05405

SIMS, JAMES JOSEPH, b Woodland, Calif, June 13, 37; div; c 2. ORGANIC CHEMISTRY. *Educ:* Ariz State Univ, BS, 59; Univ Calif, Los Angeles, PhD(org chem), 63. *Prof Exp:* NSF fel, Swiss Fed Inst Technol, 63-64; lectr chem, 64-65, asst chemist, 65-70, assoc prof, 70-74, PROF PLANT PATH & CHEM, UNIV CALIF, RIVERSIDE, 74- *Mem:* Am Chem Soc; The Chem Soc. *Res:* The chemistry of natural products; isolation; structure proof; synthesis. *Mailing Add:* Dept Plant Path Univ Calif Riverside CA 92521

SIMS, JAMES R(EDDING), b Macon, Ga, July 2, 18; m 46; c 3. CIVIL ENGINEERING. *Educ:* Rice Inst, BS, 41; Univ Ill, MS, 50, PhD(eng), 56. *Prof Exp:* Instr civil eng, 42-44 & 46-47, from asst prof to assoc prof, 47-58, chmn dept, 58-63, mgr campus bus affairs, 63-69, vpres, 69-70, dir campus bus, 70-74, PROF CIVIL ENG, RICE UNIV, 58-, HERMAN & GEORGE R BROWN CHAIR CIVIL ENG, 74- *Concurrent Pos:* Consult, Humble Oil & Refining Co, 53- *Mem:* Fel Am Soc Civil Engrs (vpres, 70-71, pres, 81-82); Am Soc Testing & Mat. *Res:* Structural materials, particularly steel and concrete; structures in open sea subject to storm loading; protective construction subject to blast loading. *Mailing Add:* Dept of Civil Eng Rice Univ PO Box 1892 Houston TX 77001

SIMS, JOHN DAVID, b Decatur, Ill, Dec 7, 39; c 2. SEDIMENTOLOGY, QUATERNARY GEOLOGY. *Educ:* Univ Ill, BS, 63; Univ Cincinnati, MS, 64; Northwestern Univ, PhD(geol), 67. *Prof Exp:* Res asst, Ill Geol Surv, 60-63; GEOLOGIST, US GEOL SURV, 67- *Concurrent Pos:* Consult, Yugoslavia post earthquake study, Nat Sci Found, 79. *Honors & Awards:* Meritorious Award, Am Planning Asn, 80 & 81. *Mem:* AAAS; Soc Econ Paleont & Mineral; Clay Minerals Soc; Sigma Xi; Geol Soc Am. *Res:* Lake Cenozoic stratigraphic and sedimentologic studies of lacustrine sediments; earthquake-induced deformation of soft sediments; pleistocene paleolimnology and paleoclimatology; detailed geologic studies in and near the San Andreas fault zone. *Mailing Add:* US Geol Surv 345 Middlefield Rd Menlo Park CA 94025

SIMS, JOHN LEONIDAS, b Sedalia, Ky, May 4, 30; m 51; c 4. AGRONOMY. *Educ:* Univ Ky, BS, 55, MS, 56; Iowa State Univ, PhD(soil microbiol), 60. *Prof Exp:* Asst soils, Univ Ky, 55-56 & Iowa State Univ, 56-60; asst prof agron, Univ Ark, 60-66; from asst prof to assoc prof, 66-75, PROF AGRON, UNIV KY, 75- *Concurrent Pos:* Vis assoc prof agron, La State Univ, 73-74. *Mem:* Am Soc Agron; Soil Sci Soc Am. *Res:* Soil plant relationships in the nitrogen nutrition of tobacco; microbial processes in soil as related to soil fertility and nitrogen fertilization of rice. *Mailing Add:* Dept of Agron Agr Sci Ctr Univ of Ky Lexington KY 40506

SIMS, JOHN LEROY, b Houston, Tex, Sept 21, 12; m 42; c 3. CLINICAL MEDICINE. *Educ:* Rice Inst, BA, 33; Univ Tex, MD, 37. *Prof Exp:* From intern to resident med, Wis Gen Hosp, 37-42; from instr to assoc prof, 46-56, PROF MED, MED SCH, UNIV WIS-MADISON, 56- *Concurrent Pos:* Mem staff, Wis Gen Hosp, 42- *Mem:* AAAS; fel AMA; Am Soc Internal Med; Am Heart Asn; fel Am Col Physicians. *Res:* Internal medicine; hepatic disease. *Mailing Add:* H6/512 Univ Hosp Univ of Wis Med Sch Madison WI 53792

SIMS, LESLIE BERL, b Royalton, Ill, Mar 21, 37; m 58; c 3. PHYSICAL CHEMISTRY. *Educ:* Southern Ill Univ, BA, 58; Univ Ill, MS, 61, PhD(chem), 67. *Prof Exp:* Asst prof chem, Mich State Univ, 64-67; asst prof, 67-70, assoc prof, 70-76, PROF CHEM, UNIV ARK, FAYETTEVILLE, 76-, CHMN DEPT, 79- *Mem:* Am Chem Soc; Sigma Xi. *Res:* Chemical kinetics; kinetic isotope effects; gas phase unimolecular reactions; theoretical kinetics; reaction dynamics; molecular vibrations. *Mailing Add:* Dept of Chem Univ of Ark Fayetteville AR 72701

SIMS, PAUL KIBLER, b Newton, Ill, Sept 8, 18; m 40; c 2. GEOLOGY. *Educ:* Univ Ill, AB, 40, MS, 42; Princeton Univ, PhD(geol), 50. *Prof Exp:* Asst, Univ Ill, 40-42; spec asst geologist, State Geol Surv, Ill, 42-43; geologist, US Geol Surv, 43-44 & 46-61; dir, Minn Geol Surv, 61-73; GEOLOGIST, US GEOL SURV, 73- *Concurrent Pos:* Asst, Princeton Univ, 46-47; pres, Econ Geol Publ Co. *Mem:* Geol Soc Am; Soc Econ Geol; Am Inst Mining, Metall & Petrol Engrs; Soc Econ Geologists (pres, 75-76). *Res:* Early crustal evolution in Lake Superior region; geology and magnetite iron ore deposits in New Jersey; geology and ore deposits of the Front Range, Colorado; Precambrian geology and ore deposits of Minnesota. *Mailing Add:* US Geol Surv Denver Fed Ctr Box 25046 MS 912 Denver CO 80225

SIMS, PHILIP LEON, b Mountain View, Okla, Apr 7, 40; m 62; c 1. RANGE SCIENCE. *Educ:* Okla State Univ, BS, 62, MS, 64; Utah State Univ, PhD(range sci), 67. *Prof Exp:* From asst prof to assoc prof range sci, Colo State Univ, 67-77; RES LEADER, US SOUTHERN GREAT PLAINS FIELD STA, SCI & EDUC ADMIN-AGR RES, USDA, 77- *Mem:* Soc Range Mgt; Am Soc Animal Sci; Brit Ecol Soc. *Res:* Range animal nutrition, management and improvements; dynamics of primary producer; grazing systems; secondary productivity of range ecosystems. *Mailing Add:* 2000 18th St Woodward OK 73801

SIMS, REX J, b Racine, Wis, July 1, 22; m 45; c 2. ORGANIC CHEMISTRY. *Educ:* Wabash Col, AB, 44; Northwestern Univ, PhD(org chem), 49. *Prof Exp:* Asst, Nat Defense Res Comt, Northwestern Univ, 43-45; res chemist, Swift & Co, Ill, 49-61; res scientist, 61-80, PRIN SCIENTIST, TECH CTR, GEN FOODS CORP, 80- *Honors & Awards:* Indust Achievement Award, Inst Food Technologists, 70. *Mem:* Am Chem Soc; Am Oil Chemists Soc. *Res:* Fats and oils; kojic acid and pyrones; fat oxidation; emulsification. *Mailing Add:* Gen Foods Tech Ctr White Plains NY 10640

SIMS, ROBERT ALAN, b Colorado Springs, Colo, Nov 1, 36; m 59; c 1. INSTRUMENTATION, COMPUTER SCIENCE. *Educ:* Colo Sch Mines, Engr, 58, MS, 61; Univ Okla, PhD(chem eng), 68. *Prof Exp:* Asst prof eng, Wright State Univ, 68-69; asst prof instrumentation, 69-80, ASSOC PROF ELECTRONICS & INSTRUMENTATION, GRAD INST TECHNOL, UNIV ARK, LITTLE ROCK, 80- *Mem:* Instrument Soc Am; Am Inst Chem Engrs. *Res:* Process control; computer simulation; water resources and land use management; control of waste treatment processes. *Mailing Add:* Grad Inst of Technol PO Box 3017 Little Rock AR 72203

SIMS, SAMUEL JOHN, b Los Angeles, Calif, Feb 20, 34; m 61; c 2. ECONOMIC GEOLOGY. *Educ:* Calif Inst Technol, BS, 55; Univ Tex, MA, 57; Stanford Univ, PhD(geol), 60. *Prof Exp:* Geologist, Soc des Mines de Fer de Mekambo, 60-62 & Companhia Minas de Jangada, 62-64, GEOLOGIST, DEPT GEOL, BETHLEHEM STEEL CORP, 64- *Mem:* Geol Soc Am; Soc Econ Geol; Am Inst Mining, Metall & Petrol Eng. *Res:* Geological exploration for economic mineral deposits. *Mailing Add:* Dept of Geol Bethlehem Steel Corp Bethlehem PA 18016

SIMS, WILLIAM LYNN, b Hazen, Ark, May 30, 24; m 51; c 3. VEGETABLE CROPS. *Educ:* Univ Wis, BS, 48, MS, 49, PhD, 54. *Prof Exp:* From asst prof to assoc prof hort, Tex Col Arts & Industs, 52-57; assoc agriculturist, 57-63, AGRICULTURIST, UNIV CALIF, DAVIS, 63- *Concurrent Pos:* Fulbright res scholar, NZ-US Educ Found, 74-75; assoc dir, Agr Develop Systs, Univ Calif/Egypt, US Agency for Int Develop, 81-82. *Mem:* fel Am Soc Hort Sci; fel AAAS. *Res:* Agricultural extension; variety evaluation and growth regulations. *Mailing Add:* Dept of Veg Crops Univ of Calif Davis CA 95616

SIMSON, JO ANNE V, b Chicago, Ill, Nov 19, 36; m 60; c 3. CELL BIOLOGY, CYTOCHEMISTRY. *Educ:* Kalamazoo Col, BA, 59; Univ Mich, MS, 61; State Univ NY, PhD(anat), 68. *Prof Exp:* Instr anat, State Univ NY Upstate Med Ctr, 67-68; Nat Cancer Inst fel cell biol, Fels Res Inst, Sch Med, Temple Univ, 68-70; asst prof path, 70-75, asst prof anat, 75-76, ASSOC PROF ANAT, MED UNIV SC, 76- *Mem:* AAAS; Am Asn Anat; Electron Micros Soc Am; Histochem Soc (secy, 79-); Sigma Xi. *Res:* Light and electron microscopic morphology and cytochemistry, especially of salivary glands; cellular ion localization and movement; secretion and stimulated cell replication; membrane alterations during both exocytosis and endocytosis. *Mailing Add:* Dept Anat Med Univ SC 80 Barre St Charleston SC 29401

SIMSON, JOSEPH MICHAEL, b New York, NY, Sept 17, 41; c 2. PHOTOGRAPHIC CHEMISTRY. *Educ:* City Col New York, BS, 62; Yale Univ, MS, 63, PhD(org chem), 67. *Prof Exp:* RES ASSOC PHOTOG RES, EASTMAN KODAK CO RES LABS, 67- *Concurrent Pos:* Assoc lectr, Univ Col, Univ Rochester, 70-; vis asst prof, Clarkson Col Technol, 72-73. *Mem:* Am Chem Soc; Soc Photog Scientists & Engrs. *Res:* Mechanism of spectral sensitization of silver halides and mechanism of infectious development in photographic systems; color photography. *Mailing Add:* Eastman Kodak Co Res Labs B-59 Kodak Park Rochester NY 14650

SINAI, JOHN JOSEPH, b Whiting, Ind, Oct 27, 30; m 57; c 5. PHYSICS. *Educ:* Miami Univ, BA, 53; Univ Ill, MS, 55; Purdue Univ, PhD(physics), 63. *Prof Exp:* Res assoc physics, Univ Chicago, 63-64; asst prof, 64-68, dir comput ctr, 66-70, assoc dean arts & sci, 70-74, actg chmn dept physics, 74-75, chmn dept, 75-78, assoc prof, 68-79, PROF PHYSICS, UNIV LOUISVILLE, 79- *Mem:* Am Phys Soc; Sigma Xi. *Res:* Vibrational spectra of disordered solids. *Mailing Add:* Dept of Physics Univ of Louisville Louisville KY 40208

SINANOGLU, OKTAY, b Bari, Italy, Feb 25, 35; Turkish citizen; m 63; c 2. THEORETICAL CHEMISTRY. *Educ:* Univ Calif, Berkeley, BS, 56, PhD(theoret chem), 59; Mass Inst Technol, MS, 57. *Prof Exp:* Chemist, Lawrence Radiation Lab, Univ Calif, Berkeley, 59-60; from asst prof to assoc prof chem, 60-63, PROF CHEM, YALE UNIV, 63-, PROF MOLECULAR BIOPHYS, 65- *Concurrent Pos:* Sloan fel, 61-64; vis prof, Middle East Tech Univ, Ankara, Turkey, 62-64, consult prof, 64-; consult prof, Bogazici Univ, Turkey, 73-; consult, Rocket Oxidizers Res Prog, Adv Res Projs Agency, 64 & Turkish Sci & Tech Res Coun, 73-; ed of biol & phys scientists, NIH, 64; mem Parr subcomt on theoret chem of Westheimer comt, Nat Acad Sci, 64-65; co-chmn elect, Gordon Res Conf physics & chem of biopolymers, 66; mem subpanel on atomic, molecular physics, Inst Defense Anal, 66; mem chem rev comt & consult, Argonne Univ Asn for Argonne Nat Lab, 67-70, consult, Nat Lab, 67-73. *Honors & Awards:* Turkish Sci Medal, 66; Alexander von Humboldt Award, 73. *Mem:* Am Inst Chem Engrs; Inst Am Chemists; Am Chem Soc; Am Phys Soc; Am Acad Arts & Sci. *Res:* Theoretical chemistry; quantum chemistry; theory of intermolecular forces; theory of solvent effects of biopolymer structure; biochemical reaction networks; many-electron theory of atoms and molecules. *Mailing Add:* Dept of Chem Yale Univ New Haven CT 06520

SINCIUS, JOSEPH ANTHONY, b Amsterdam, NY, Nov 30, 26; m 49; c 2. PHOTOGRAPHIC CHEMISTRY. *Educ:* Union Univ, NY, BS, 46; Canisius Col, MS, 56; Mich State Univ, PhD, 60. *Prof Exp:* Chemist, Hooker Chem Soc, NY, 47-54, group leader, 54-56; asst, Mich State Univ, 56-57, 59; res chemist, 59-64, sr res chemist, 64-67, res supvr, 67-73, res assoc, 73-81, RES FEL, PHOTO PROD DEPT, E I DU PONT DE NEMOURS & CO INC, PARLIN, NJ, 81- *Mem:* Soc Photog Sci & Eng. *Res:* Kinetics and reaction mechanisms; radioactive tracer techniques; photo and photographic chemistry; image forming systems. *Mailing Add:* 199 Pinckney Rd Little Silver NJ 07739

SINCLAIR, ALASTAIR JAMES, b Hamilton, Ont, Aug 1, 35; m 64; c 2. ECONOMIC GEOLOGY. *Educ:* Univ Toronto, BASc, 57, MASc, 58; Univ BC, PhD(geol), 64. *Prof Exp:* Asst prof geol, Univ Wash, 62-64; from asst prof to assoc prof, 64-74, PROF GEOL, UNIV BC, 74- *Concurrent Pos:* Consult, 64-; mem subcomt isotope studies & geochronology, Nat Res Coun Can, 66-69. *Mem:* Can Inst Mining & Metall; Asn Explor Geochemists; Soc Econ Geol; Mineral Asn Can; Geol Asn Can. *Res:* Origin of mineral deposits; isotope geology related to mineral depoists; temperature of mineral deposition; zoning applied to mineral exploration; geostatistics; mineral exploration data analysis. *Mailing Add:* Dept Geol Sci Univ BC Vancouver BC V6T 1W5 Can

SINCLAIR, ANNETTE, b Hale, Mo, Aug 14, 16. MATHEMATICS. *Educ:* Cent Mo State Col, BS, 40; Univ Ill, AM, 45, PhD(math), 49. *Prof Exp:* Teacher pub schs, Mo, 34-42; actuarial clerk, Gen Am Life Ins Co, 42-44; asst, Univ Ill, 44-49; instr, Univ Tenn, 49-52; from asst prof to assoc prof math, Southern Ill Univ, 52-57; asst prof, 57-67, ASSOC PROF MATH, PURDUE UNIV, WEST LAFAYETTE, 67- *Concurrent Pos:* Vis assoc prof, Univ Okla, 66-68. *Mem:* Am Math Soc; Math Asn Am. *Res:* Theory of approximation by analytic functions, especially topological methods; vector methods in analytic functions. *Mailing Add:* Dept of Math Purdue Univ West Lafayette IN 47907

SINCLAIR, CHARLES KENT, b Watertown, NY, Aug 9, 38. EXPERIMENTAL HIGH ENERGY PHYSICS. *Educ:* Rensselaer Polytech Inst, BS, 60; Cornell Univ, PhD(Physics), 67. *Prof Exp:* Res assoc physics, Tufts Univ, 66-68, asst prof, 68-69; STAFF PHYSICIST PHYSICS, STANFORD LINEAR ACCELERATOR CTR, 69- *Mem:* Am Phys Soc. *Res:* Experimental tests of quantum electrodynamics; single and multiple meson photoproduction; proton compton effect; research with polarized high energy electrons and gamma rays. *Mailing Add:* Stanford Linear Accelerator Ctr PO Box 4349 Stanford CA 94305

SINCLAIR, CLARENCE BRUCE, b Independence, Mo, Jan 28, 21; m 47; c 3. BOTANY. *Educ:* Univ Mo-Kansas City, Ba, 49, MA, 50, PhD(bot), 67. *Prof Exp:* Prof biol, Nat Col, 50-64; from asst prof to assoc prof, Univ Ark, Little Rock, 64-71, prof & dean, Col Sci, 71-80. *Concurrent Pos:* Lectr, Eve Div, Univ Mo, Kansas City, 63-64; Ark Power & Light Co grant, Dardanelle Reservoir, 68-78, Off Water Resources grant, 70-73; coun mem, Ark Regional Med Coun, 69- & Ark Manpower Coun, 71-; USPHS grant, Univ Ark, Little Rock, 70-72. *Mem:* Am Inst Biol Sci; Bot Soc Am; Int Asn Plant Taxon. *Res:* Water resources work on Dardanelle Reservoir prior to and following activation of Arkansas' first nuclear power plant; effects of thermal pollution on a reservoir; SEM investigations of plant structures. *Mailing Add:* 6827 Dahlia Dr Little Rock AR 72209

SINCLAIR, D G, b Rochester, NY, Nov 2, 33; Can citizen; m 58; c 2. ACADEMIC ADMINISTRATION. *Educ:* Univ Toronto, DVM, 58, MSA, 60; Queen's Univ, PhD(physiol), 63. *Prof Exp:* USPHS fel, Columbia Univ, 62-63; fel physiol & Meres sr scholar med res, St John's Col, Cambridge Univ, 63-65; from asst prof to assoc prof, 66-72, PROF PHYSIOL, QUEEN'S UNIV, ONT, 72-, DEAN FAC ARTS & SCI, 74- *Concurrent Pos:* Markle Scholar acad med, 66-71. *Mem:* Can Physiol Soc. *Res:* Gastrointestinal physiology. *Mailing Add:* Fac of Arts & Sci Queen's Univ Kingston ON K7L 3N6 Can

SINCLAIR, DONALD BELLAMY, b Winnipeg, Man, May 23, 10; nat US; m 32; c 4. ELECTRONICS. *Educ:* Mass Inst Technol, SB, 31, SM, 32, ScD(elec eng), 35. *Prof Exp:* Engr, NY Tel Co, 30, Bell Tel Labs, 30-31 & Western Elec Co, 31; mem staff, Dept Elec Eng, Mass Inst Technol, 32-36; from engr to chief engr, 36-54, vpres eng, 54-56, vpres & chief engr, 57-60, exec vpres & tech dir, 60-63, PRES, GEN RADIO CO, 63-, DIR, 55- *Concurrent Pos:* Engr, Gen Radio Co, 34-35; mem radio res lab, Harvard Univ, 42-45 & div 5, Nat Defense Res Coun, 43-45; tech rep, US Army Air Force, 43; rep, Indust Res Inst, 45-65; consult, US Dept Defense, 54-57 & 60; Inst Radio Engrs rep, Nat Res Coun, 60-63; dir, US Standards Inst, 65-68. *Honors & Awards:* Presidential Cert of Merit, 48. *Mem:* Nat Acad Eng; fel AAAS; fel Inst Elec & Electronics Engrs; Am Phys Soc; Instrument Soc Am. *Res:* Development and design of electrical testing equipment of laboratory grade in wide field; high-frequency electrical measurements. *Mailing Add:* Gen Radio Co 300 Baker Ave Concord MA 01742

SINCLAIR, DOUGLAS C, b Cambridge, Mass, July 13, 38; m 60; c 2. OPTICAL ENGINEERING. *Educ:* Mass Inst Technol, BS, 60; Univ Rochester, PhD(optics), 63. *Prof Exp:* Asst prof optics, Univ Rochester, 65-67; tech dir, Spectra-Physics, Calif, 67-69; assoc prof optics, Univ Rochester, 69-75, prof, 75-80; PRES, SINCLAIR OPTICS, NY, 80- *Concurrent Pos:* Lectr, Stanford Univ, 69; consult, Nat Acad Sci, 70; ed, Optical Eng, 72; ed, J Optical Soc Am, 76-78. *Honors & Awards:* Adolph Lomb Medal, Optical Soc Am, 68. *Mem:* AAAS; Optical Soc Am. *Res:* Design of optical systems; development of software for optical design. *Mailing Add:* Sinclair Optics Inc 20 North Main St Pittsford NY 14534

SINCLAIR, EDWARD ELLIOT, chemistry, see previous edition

SINCLAIR, GEORGE, b Hamilton, Ont, Nov 5, 12; m 51; c 3. ELECTRICAL ENGINEERING. *Educ:* Univ Alta, BSc, 33, MSc, 35; Ohio State Univ, PhD(elec eng), 46. *Hon Degrees:* DSc, Ohio State Univ, 73. *Prof Exp:* From asst prof to prof elec eng, Univ Toronto, 47-78; pres, 51-73, CHMN BD, SINCLAIR RADIO LABS LTD, 73- *Concurrent Pos:* Chmn, Can Comn, Int Sci Radio Union, 51-61, int chmn subcomn, 54-60; Guggenheim fel, 58. *Honors & Awards:* McNaughton Medal, Inst Elec & Electronics Engrs, 75. *Mem:* Fel Inst Elec & Electronics Engrs; Eng Inst Can; fel AAAS; fel Royal Soc Can. *Res:* Boundary-value problems of electromagnetic theory, particularly theory of slot antennas and applications of integral equation methods of solution. *Mailing Add:* Sinclair Radio Labs Ltd 120 Rayette Rd Concord ON L4K 1B6 Can

SINCLAIR, GEORGE M(ORTON), b Chicago, Ill, Mar 9, 22; m 43; c 2. MECHANICS, METALLURGY. *Educ:* Univ Ill, BS, 48, MS, 49. *Prof Exp:* Asst & res assoc, Univ Ill, 47-51, res asst prof, 51-52; res metallurgist, Res Labs, Westinghouse Elec Corp, 52-53; res assoc prof theoret & appl mech, 53-57, RES PROF THEORET & APPL MECH, UNIV ILL, URBANA, 57- *Concurrent Pos:* Consult, Mat Adv Bd, Nat Acad Sci-Nat Res Coun, Scott Paper Co, 64-, NSF, 64-66, ship hull mat panel, 65-68, US Naval Res Lab, 66, US Steel, 68 & Nat Acad Sci, 76- *Honors & Awards:* NADAI Award, Am Soc Mech Engrs, 75. *Mem:* Fel Am Soc Metals; Am Soc Testing & Mat; fel Am Soc Mech Engrs. *Res:* Fatigue of metals; mechanical properties of engineering materials. *Mailing Add:* Dept of Theoret & Appl Mech 216 Talbot Lab Univ Ill Urbana IL 69990

SINCLAIR, GLENN BRUCE, b Auckland, NZ, Mar 7, 46. SOLID MECHANICS. *Educ:* Univ Auckland, BSc, 67, BE, 69; Calif Inst Technol, PhD(appl mech), 72. *Prof Exp:* Res scientist, Dept Sci & Indust Res, Appl Math Div, Wellington, 68-69; J Willard Gibbs instr appl sci & eng, Yale Univ, 72-74; lectr appl mech, Univ Auckland, 74-77; asst prof, 77-80, assoc prof, 80-82, PROF MECH ENG, CARNEGIE-MELLON UNIV, 82- *Concurrent Pos:* Instr, Auckland Tech Inst, 64-66, 69, & 75-77; prof, Pratt & Whitney Aircraft Corp, Conn, 78, Fla, 79; vis prof, Dept Eng, Cambridge Univ, 81. *Mem:* Am Acad Mech; Am Soc Mech Engrs. *Res:* Modelling and analysis of engineering problems in solid and structural mechanics particularly as related to fatigue and fracture mechanics and contact problems; development of both analytical and numerical methods for such problems. *Mailing Add:* Dept Mech Eng Carnegie-Mellon Univ Pittsburgh PA 15213

SINCLAIR, HENRY BEALL, b St Louis, Mo, Jan 11, 30; m 55; c 2. ORGANIC CHEMISTRY. *Educ:* Univ Calif, Berkeley, BS, 52; Mass Inst Technol, PhD(org chem), 59. *Prof Exp:* Res chemist, Mallinckrodt Chem Works, 52-54 & Procter & Gamble Co, 58-63; res chemist, 63-69, PRIN CHEMIST, NORTHERN REGIONAL RES LAB, USDA, 69- *Mem:* Am Chem Soc; Royal Soc Chem; AAAS. *Res:* Amino acids; heterocyclics; opium alkaloids; carbohydrates and their derivatives. *Mailing Add:* USDA 1815 N University St Peoria IL 61604

SINCLAIR, JAMES BURTON, b Chicago, Ill, Dec 21, 27. PLANT PATHOLOGY. *Educ:* Lawrence Univ, BS, 51; Univ Wis, Madison, PhD(plant path), 55. *Prof Exp:* Res asst plant path, Univ Wis, Madison, 51-55, res assoc, 55-56; from asst prof to prof, La State Univ, Baton Rouge, 56-68, asst to chancellor, 66-68; PROF PLANT PATH, UNIV ILL, URBANA, 68- *Concurrent Pos:* Grants, Olin Mathieson Chem Corp, 60-66; Allied Chem Co, 64; Diamond Alkali Co, 66; E I du Pont de Nemours & Co, Inc, 66-68; US Rubber Co, 66-68; partic, Adv Virol Sem, Univ Md, 63; secy, Cotton Dis Coun, 63-64, chmn, 65-66; La State Univ Found res grants, 65-67, grad sch for travel grant, 68; partic conf seed & soil treatment, Am Phytopath Soc, 65-

67, chmn, 67, partic conf plant dis control & diag, 67; Conf Control Soil Fungi, Ariz, 68; Am Phytopath Soc for travel grant, 68; Agency Int Develop develop grant, 68-73; Int Cong Plant Path, London, 68, Minneapolis, 73 & Munich, 78; Indian Sci Cong, Kharapur, 70; Int Cong Plant Protection, Paris, 70; Sem Plant Protection Trop Food Crops, Ibadan, 71; Ford Found for travel grant, 71; campus coordr, Ill-Tehran Res Unit, 73-78. *Mem:* AAAS; Am Phytopath Soc; Am Inst Biol Sci. *Res:* Cotton seedling disease control and tolerance to fungicides; cytology and ultrastructure of Rhizoctonia; pathogenicity of Geotrichum; citrus fruit rots and viral diseases; seed and soil-borne diseases of soybean. *Mailing Add:* Dept Plant Path Univ Ill 1102 S Goodwin Ave Urbana IL 61801

SINCLAIR, JAMES DOUGLAS, b Evanston, Ill, Nov 23, 45; m 67; c 3. ANALYTICAL CHEMISTRY, CORROSION. *Educ:* Purdue Univ, BS, 67; Univ Wis, PhD(inorg chem), 72. *Prof Exp:* RES CHEMIST & SUPVR CONTAMINATION RES, BELL TEL LABS, 72- *Mem:* Am Chem Soc; AAAS; Electrochem Soc. *Res:* Atmospheric corrosion processes on silver, copper, aluminum and zinc, especially those involving attack by sulfur and chlorine containing gases and aerosols; the effect of light on corrosion processes; corrosion control; contamination research and control; development of analytical techniques for measuring ionic contaminants on surfaces. *Mailing Add:* Bell Tel Labs Holmdel NJ 07733

SINCLAIR, JOHN C, b Butte, Mont, Dec 19, 18; m 45; c 5. NEUROPHYSIOLOGY, BIOMEDICAL ENGINEERING. *Educ:* Univ Calif, Berkeley, AB, 48; Univ Calif, Los Angeles, MA, 56; Iowa State Univ, PhD(physiol), 66. *Prof Exp:* Res asst biochem, White Mem Hosp, Los Angeles, 48-52; res asst surg, Univ Calif, Los Angeles, 54-56 & anat, 56-57; res assoc physiol, Univ Calif, San Francisco, 60-61; assoc prof biol, Gordon Col, 62-63; assoc prof, Buena vista Col, 67-70; RES SCIENTIST, DIV NEURO-PHARMACOL, NJ NEUROPSYCHIAT INST, 70- *Concurrent Pos:* Res fel physiol, Univ Minn, 66-67; assoc prof psychol, Rider Col, 70-73. *Mem:* Am Chem Soc. *Res:* Instrumentation for cardiovascular physiology; neurophysiology of behavior and sensory integration; neurophysiological bases of mental health; diagnosis of mental illness. *Mailing Add:* Hillsboro Rd Five Oaks Belle Mead NJ 08502

SINCLAIR, JOHN HENRY, b Oakwood, Tex, Aug 14, 35; m 62; c 1. CELL BIOLOGY. *Educ:* Tex A&M Univ, BS, 58, MS, 59; Univ Chicago, PhD(zool), 66. *Prof Exp:* Res chemist, Coleman Instruments, Inc, 61-62; fel embryol, Carnegie Inst Technol, 66-68; from asst prof to assoc prof, 68-77, chmn dept, 73-77, PROF ZOOL, IND UNIV, BLOOMINGTON, 77- *Mem:* AAAS; Am Soc Cell Biol; Genetics Soc Am. *Res:* Chemical and physical characterization of nucleic acids of mitochondria and nucleoli; emphasis on zea mays; higher plants. *Mailing Add:* Dept of Biol Ind Univ Bloomington IN 47401

SINCLAIR, KENNETH F(RANCIS), b Kentfield, Calif, Jan 26, 25; m 53; c 6. ENGINEERING PHYSICS. *Educ:* Univ Calif, BS, 50. *Prof Exp:* Jr investr, Lab Instrumentation Prog, US Naval Radiol Defense Labs, 50-54, investr, 54-56, head radiac eng prog, 56-58, head radiation instrumentation br, 58-67; res scientist, Hq, NASA, Moffett Field, 67-72; PRES, XETEX, INC, MOUNTAIN VIEW, 72- *Mem:* Sr mem Inst Elec & Electronics Engrs; Health Physics Soc; Am Soc Nondestructive Testing. *Res:* Remote sensing; systems analysis; nuclear instrumentation; nondestructive testing; data handling and processing; radiation detectors. *Mailing Add:* 862 Russet Dr Sunnyvale CA 94087

SINCLAIR, MICHAEL MACKAY, b New Glasgow, NS, June 20, 44; m 70; c 1. FISHERIES MANAGEMENT, POPULATION BIOLOGY. *Educ:* Queen's Univ, Can, Bsc, 67; Southampton Univ, UK, MSc, 69; Univ Calif, San Diego, PhD(oceanog), 77. *Prof Exp:* Prof oceanog, Univ Que, Rimouski, 73-77, dir, MSc Oceanog Prog, 76-77; res scientist fisheries mgt, Bedford Inst Oceanog, 78-82, head, Pop Dynamics Sect, Marine Fish Div, 81-82; CHIEF, INVERT & MARINE PLANTS DIV, HALIFAX LAB, 82- *Concurrent Pos:* Vis reseacher, Sta Zoologique, Ville Frauche-sur-Mer, 78; chmn, Effects Freshwater Runoff in Marine Environ, Atlantic Dir Adv Comt, Dept Fisheries & Oceans, Can, 80-81. *Res:* Phytoplankton temporal and spatial distributions in relation to physical processes; maintenance and control of absolute abundance of relatively discrete infra specific populations of marine fish. *Mailing Add:* PO Box 1006 Dartmouth NS B2Y 4A2 Can

SINCLAIR, NICHOLAS RODERICK, b Bradford-on-Avon, Eng, Apr 20, 36; Can citizen; m 61, 76; c 6. IMMUNOLOGY, ONCOLOGY. *Educ:* Dalhousie Univ, BSc, 57, MD, 62, PhD(biochem), 65. *Prof Exp:* Vis scientist immunol, Chester Beatty Res Inst, Eng, 65-67; asst prof immunol, 67-73, assoc prof microbiol & immunol, 73-77, assoc prof med, 77-80, actg chmn, Dept Bact & Immunol, 74-76, asst dean res, Fac Med, 78-80, PROF MICROBIOL & IMMUNOL, UNIV WESTERN ONT, 79-, PROF MED, 80-, CHMN, DEPT MICROBIOL & IMMUNOL, 81-, ASSOC DIR, TRANSPLANT MONITORING LAB, DEPT NEPHROL, UNIV HOSP, 73- *Concurrent Pos:* Med Res Coun Can fel, 64-67 & scholar, 67-72. *Mem:* Can Soc Immunol (vpres, 81-); Am Asn Immunologists. *Res:* Immunobiology; tumour immunology. *Mailing Add:* Dept Microbiol & Immunol Univ Western Ont London ON N6A 5C1 Can

SINCLAIR, NORVAL A, b Sturgis, SDak, Sept 1, 35; m 58; c 2. MICROBIOLOGY. *Educ:* SDak State Univ, BS, 57, MS, 59; Wash State Univ, PhD(bact), 64. *Prof Exp:* Bacteriologist, Minn State Health Dept, 57-58; from instr to asst prof microbiol, Colo State Univ, 64-67; USPHS trainee, Hopkins Marine Sta, 67-68; from asst prof to assoc prof microbiol, 68-74, ASSOC PROF MICROBIOL & MED TECHNOL, UNIV ARIZ, 74- *Mem:* AAAS; Am Soc Microbiol. *Res:* Psychrophilic microbes; microbial physiology, growth and ecology. *Mailing Add:* Dept of Microbiol Univ of Ariz Tucson AZ 85721

SINCLAIR, PETER C, b Seattle, Wash, Feb 17, 29; m 60; c 4. ATMOSPHERIC PHYSICS. *Educ:* Univ Wash, BS, 52; Univ Calif, Los Angeles, MS, 58; Univ Ariz, PhD(atmospheric physics), 66. *Prof Exp:* Res asst meteorol, Univ Wash, 48-52; Univ Calif, Los Angeles, 57-60 & Univ Ariz, 60-65; asst prof, 65-68, ASSOC PROF ATMOSPHERIC SCI, COLO STATE UNIV, 69- *Concurrent Pos:* Mem bd dir, Waverly West Soaring Ranch, 68- *Mem:* AAAS; Am Meteorol Soc; Am Geophys Union. *Res:* Severe storms; atmospheric convection; airborne atmospheric instrumentation; weather modification. *Mailing Add:* Dept of Atmospheric Sci Colo State Univ Ft Collins CO 80521

SINCLAIR, RICHARD GLENN, II, b Parsons, Kans, Mar 10, 33; m 55; c 3. POLYMER CHEMISTRY. *Educ:* Univ Mo-Kansas City, BS, 60, PhD(polymer sci), 67. *Prof Exp:* Analyst, E I du Pont de Nemours & Co, 58-61; chemist, Chemagro Corp, 61-63; sr res chemist, 66-68, ASSOC SECT MGR, ORG & POLYMER CHEM SECT, BATTELLE MEM INST, 78- *Mem:* Am Chem Soc. *Res:* Discovery and development of novel high polymer systems; poly (lactic acid) controlled-release systems. *Mailing Add:* Battelle Mem Inst 505 King Ave Columbus OH 43201

SINCLAIR, ROBERT, b Liverpool, Eng, Feb 15, 47; m 69; c 2. MATERIALS SCIENCE, ELECTRON MICROSCOPY. *Educ:* Cambridge Univ, BA, 68, PhD(mat sci), 72. *Prof Exp:* Res assoc, Univ Newcastle, Tyne, 71-73; res engr, Univ Calif, Berkeley, 73-76; asst prof, 77-80, ASSOC PROF MAT SCI, STANFORD UNIV, 80- *Concurrent Pos:* Res consult, Xerox Corp, 78-; Alfred P Sloan Found fel, 79. *Honors & Awards:* Robert Lansing Hardy Gold Medal, Am Inst Mining, Metall & Petrol Engrs, 76; Eli Franklin Burton Award, Electron Micros Soc Am, 77. *Mem:* Am Inst Mining, Metall & Petrol Engrs; Electron Micros Soc Am. *Res:* Solid state phase transformations; high-resolution transmission electron microscopy; microstructure property relationships of materials; semiconductor interfaces. *Mailing Add:* Dept of Mat Sci & Eng Standford Univ Stanford CA 94305

SINCLAIR, ROLF MALCOLM, b New York, NY, Aug 15, 29; div; c 2. PHYSICS, ARCHAEOASTRONOMY. *Educ:* Calif Inst Technol, BS, 49; Rice Inst, MA, 51, PhD(exp physics), 54. *Prof Exp:* Res physicist, Westinghouse Res Labs, 53-56; res assoc nuclear physics, Nat Physics Inst, Univ Hamburg, 56-57; res asst, Univ Paris, 57-58; mem res staff, Plasma Physics Lab, Princeton Univ, 58-69; PROG DIR, PHYSICS DIV, NSF, 69- *Concurrent Pos:* Res assoc, UK Atomic Energy Auth, 65-66; Culham Lab, Eng; NSF rep, US Solar Eclipse Expedition, India, 80. *Mem:* Fel AAAS (secy physics sect, 72-); fel Am Phys Soc. *Res:* Atomic, plasma and nuclear physics; controlled thermonuclear power; administration of science. *Mailing Add:* Physics Div Nat Sci Found Washington DC 20550

SINCLAIR, RONALD, b Dungannon, NIreland, Oct 20, 31; m 57; c 3. CELL BIOLOGY, BIOCHEMISTRY. *Educ:* Queen's Univ, Belfast, BSc, 54, PhD(biochem), 58. *Prof Exp:* Res asst biochem, Queen's Univ, Belfast, 54-58; fel, Jackson Lab, 58-60; res fel chem biol unit, Univ Edinburgh, 60-65; ASSOC PROF BIOL, MCGILL UNIV, 65- *Mem:* AAAS; Tissue Cult Asn; Brit Biochem Soc; Brit Soc Cell Biol; Can Soc Cell Biol. *Res:* Cell growth. *Mailing Add:* Dept Biol McGill Univ 1205 McGregor Ave Montreal PQ H3A 1B1 Can

SINCLAIR, THOMAS FREDERICK, b Saskatoon, Sask, June 16, 45; m 81. VIROLOGY, CELL CULTURE. *Educ:* Univ Manitoba, BSc, 67, MSc, 72; Chicago Med Sch, PhD(virol), 77. *Prof Exp:* Lectr virol, Chicago Med Sch, 77-79, instr, 79-82; DIR ONCOL RES, VET ADMIN MED CTR, NORTH CHICAGO, 82- *Concurrent Pos:* Res assoc immunol, Vet Admin Med Ctr, North Chicago, 77-79, fel, 77-80, co-prin investr res & develop grant, 82-85; adj asst prof immunol, Chicago Med Sch, 82- *Mem:* AAAS; Sigma Xi. *Res:* Humoral and cellular immunology of patients who are immuno-suppressed due to malignant disease with emphasis on the relationship of plasma factors to inducer and suppressor T-lymphocytes. *Mailing Add:* Oncol Div Dept Med Rm 125 Bldg 50 Vet Admin Med Ctr North Chicago IL 60064

SINCLAIR, THOMAS RUSSELL, b Indianapolis, Ind, Aug 4, 44; m 67; c 3. AGRONOMY, PLANT PHYSIOLOGY. *Educ:* Purdue Univ, Lafayette, BS, 66, MS, 68; Cornell Univ, PhD(field crop sci), 71. *Prof Exp:* Mem staff, Nat Sci Found Int Biol Prog, Duke Univ, 71-74; plant physiologist, Microclimate Proj, Sci & Educ Admin-Agr Res, 74-79, PLANT PHYSIOLOGIST, ENVIRON PHYSIOL UNIT, AGR RES SERV, USDA, 80- *Concurrent Pos:* Vis scientist, State Agr Univ, Wageningen, Neth, 73-74; mem staff, Dept Agron, Cornell Univ, 74-79; adj prof, Dept Agron & Fruit Crops, Univ Fla, 80- *Mem:* Am Soc Agron; Crop Sci Soc Am; Am Soc Plant Physiol. *Res:* Experimental and computer simulation research on crop productivity, especially soybean, by improving carbon dioxide assimilation rates, nitrogen fixation rates, seed growth characteristics, use of vegetative stands. *Mailing Add:* Agron Physiol Lab Univ Fla Gainesville FL 32611

SINCLAIR, WARREN KEITH, b Dunedin, NZ, Mar 9, 24; nat US; m 48; c 2. BIOPHYSICS. *Educ:* Univ NZ, BSc, 44, MSc, 45; Univ London, PhD(physics), 50. *Prof Exp:* Physicist, Dept Sci & Indust Res, NZ Govt, 44-45; lectr radiol physics, Univ Otago & radiol physicist, Dunedin Pub Hosp, 45-47; teacher & lectr, Univ London & physicist, Royal Cancer Hosp, 47-54; prof physics, Postgrad Med Sch, Tex & chief physicist, MD Anderson Hosp & Tumor Inst, 54-60; dir div biol & med res, 70-74, assoc lab dir, 74-81, SR BIOPHYSICIST, DIV BIOL & MED, ARGONNE NAT LAB, 60-; PROF RADIOBIOL, UNIV CHICAGO, 64- *Concurrent Pos:* Consult, Humble Oil & Refining Co & Univ Tex MD Anderson Hosp & Tumor Inst; pres, Nat Coun Radiation Protection & Measurements, mem bd dirs & coun; mem, Int Comn Radiation Units; mem, Int Comn Radiation Protection; mem, US Nat Comt Pure & Appl Biophys & chmn, US Nat Comt Med Physics, 64-70; secy gen, Vth Int Cong Radiation Res, 74. *Honors & Awards:* Aurie lectr. *Mem:* Radiation Res Soc (pres, 78-79); Soc Nuclear Med; Asn Physicists in Med (pres, 60-61); Radiol Soc NAm; Brit Inst Radiol. *Res:* Radiation protection and radiological physics; radiation response in synchronized cell cultures; quantitative aspects of radiobiology; risk estimation. *Mailing Add:* OTD Bldg 202 Argonne Nat Lab Argonne IL 60439

SINCLAIR, WAYNE A, b Medford, Mass, Dec 15, 36; m 58; c 3. PLANT PATHOLOGY. *Educ:* Univ NH, BS, 58; Cornell Univ, PhD(plant path), 62. *Prof Exp:* From asst prof to assoc prof, 62-75, PROF PLANT PATH, CORNELL UNIV, 75- *Concurrent Pos:* Vis forest pathologist, Weyerhaeuser Co, Wash, 70. *Mem:* Am Phytopath Soc; Soc Am Foresters. *Res:* Forest pathology. *Mailing Add:* Dept of Plant Path Cornell Univ Ithaca NY 14853

SINCLAIR, WILLIAM ROBERT, b Chicago, Ill, Apr 30, 24; m 58; c 4. PHYSICAL INORGANIC CHEMISTRY. *Educ:* Univ Chicago, PhD(chem), 52. *Prof Exp:* Instr chem, Univ Minn, 50-51; MEM TECH STAFF, BELL TEL LABS, INC, 52- *Mem:* Electrochem Soc; Am Phys Soc. *Res:* Preparation and properties of glassy and crystalline inorganic films. *Mailing Add:* Bell Tel Labs Inc Murray Hill NJ 07974

SINCOVEC, RICHARD FRANK, b Pueblo, Colo, July 14, 42; c 2. APPLIED MATHEMATICS. *Educ:* Univ Colo, Boulder, BS, 64; Iowa State Univ, MS, 67, PhD(appl math), 68. *Prof Exp:* Instr math, Iowa State Univ, 64-68, jr mathematician, Ames Lab, 66-68; sr res mathematician, Esso Prod Res Co, 68-70; asst prof comput sci & math, Kans State Univ, 70-74, assoc prof comput sci, 74-77; mgr numerical anal, Boeing Comput Serv Co, 77-80; PROF COMPUT SCI, UNIV COLO, 80- *Concurrent Pos:* Am Chem Soc Petrol Res Fund fel, 71-74; consult, Lawrence Livermore Lab, 71-77. *Mem:* Soc Indust & Appl Math; Soc Petrol Eng; Asn Comput Mach. *Res:* Galerkin and collocation methods for solving ordinary and partial differential equations; numerical linear algebra; approximation with splines and hermite polynomials; petroleum reservoir simulation. *Mailing Add:* Dept Eng & Appl Sci Univ Colo Colorado Springs CO 80907

SINDEN, FRANK WILLIAM, b Aurora, Ill, Nov 30, 27; m 50; c 2. MATHEMATICS. *Educ:* Univ Chicago, BS, 48; Swiss Fed Inst Technol, DSc(math), 54. *Prof Exp:* RES MATHEMATICIAN, BELL TEL LABS, INC, 56- *Concurrent Pos:* Sr res scientist, Princeton Univ, 74- *Mem:* Am Math Soc; Soc Indust & Appl Math. *Res:* Linear algebra; eigenvalue problems; mathematical programming; econometrics; science and public policy; environment; energy. *Mailing Add:* Bell Tel Labs Inc Rm 2-C 283 Murray Hill NJ 07974

SINDEN, JAMES WHAPLES, b Oak Park, Ill, Nov 12, 02; m 26; c 2. PLANT PATHOLOGY. *Educ:* Univ Kans, AB, 24; Cornell Univ, PhD(plant path), 37. *Prof Exp:* Asst instr plant path, Cornell Univ, 24-25, instr, 25-30; from asst prof to prof, Pa State Univ, 30-52; CONSULT, 52- *Concurrent Pos:* Spec investr, Trop Deterioration Lab, US Army, 45-46. *Mem:* AAAS; Am Phytopath Soc; Mycol Soc Am; Bot Soc Am. *Res:* Physiology and pathology of the commercial mushroom; economic mycology. *Mailing Add:* Hauser Champignonkulturen AG Gossau Zurich 8625 Switzerland

SINDEN, STEPHEN LEE, b Bellefonte, Pa, Aug 7, 37; m 59; c 1. PLANT PATHOLOGY, PLANT PHYSIOLOGY. *Educ:* Cornell Univ, BS, 62; Univ Calif, Davis, PhD(plant path), 66. *Prof Exp:* Nat Acad Sci res assoc plant path, Univ Wis, 66-68; RES PLANT PHYSIOLOGIST, PLANT INDUST STA, USDA, 68- *Mem:* AAAS; Am Phytopath Soc. *Res:* Mode of action of toxins produced by phytopathogenic bacteria and the physiology of host-parasite interactions. *Mailing Add:* Agr Res Serv BARC Beltsville MD 20705

SINDERMANN, CARL JAMES, b North Adams, Mass, Aug 28, 22; m 43; c 5. MARINE BIOLOGY, PARASITOLOGY. *Educ:* Univ Mass, BS, 49; Harvard Univ, AM, 51, PhD(biol), 53. *Prof Exp:* Teaching fel biol, Harvard Univ, 50; parasitologist, Biol Surv, State Dept Conserv, Mass, 50; instr biol, Brandeis Univ, 51-53, asst prof, 53-56; res biologist, Bur Commercial Fisheries, US Fish & Wildlife Serv, 54-59, chief Atlantic herring invests, 59-62, prog coordr, Atlantic herring progs, 62-63, dir biol lab, Md, 63-68, dir, Trop Atlantic Biol Lab, Fla, 68-71; dir, Middle Atlantic Coastal Fisheries Ctr, Nat Marine Fisheries Serv, Nat Oceanic & Atmospheric Admin, 71-76; DIR, SANDY HOOK MARINE LAB, 76- *Concurrent Pos:* Asst, Harvard Med Sch, 52; marine biologist, State Dept Sea & Shore Fisheries, Maine, 52-54; vis lectr, Georgetown Univ, 66-68; adj prof, Div Fisheries Sci, Rosenstiel Sch Marine & Atmospheric Sci, Univ Miami, 69-72; adj prof biol, Lehigh Univ, 73-; adj prof vet microbiol, NY State Vet Col, Cornell Univ, 75-; vis prof, Ont Vet Col, Guelph, 78-79; sci ed, Fishery Bull, US Dept Com. *Mem:* Soc Invert Path; Am Soc Parasitol; Nat Shellfisheries Asn; World Maricult Soc. *Res:* Parasites and diseases of marine organisms; immune responses of marine invertebrates; marine pollution, ecology. *Mailing Add:* Sandy Hook Marine Lab Highlands NJ 07732

SINENSKY, MICHAEL, b New York, NY, July, 2, 45; m 74; c 1. BIOCHEMISTRY. *Educ:* Columbia Col, NY, BA, 66; Harvard Univ, PhD(biochem & molecular biol), 72. *Prof Exp:* Jr fel biochem, Soc Fels, Harvard Univ, 72-74; asst prof chem, Univ Pa, 74-75; SR FEL, ELEANOR ROOSEVELT INST CANCER RES, 75-; ASSOC PROF BIOCHEM, BIOPHYS & GENETICS, UNIV COLO HEALTH SCI CTR, 80- *Mem:* Am Soc Biol Chemists. *Res:* Mechanism of regulation of cholesterol biosynthesis. *Mailing Add:* Eleanor Roosevelt Inst Cancer Res 4200 E Ninth Ave Box B-129 Denver CO 80262

SINES, GEORGE, JR, b Salem, Ohio, July 12, 23; m 56; c 3. METALLURGY, CERAMICS. *Educ:* Ohio State Univ, BME, 43; Univ Calif, Los Angeles, MS, 49, PhD(metall), 53. *Prof Exp:* Design & test engr, Krouse Testing Mach Co, Ohio, 43-44; asst instr physics, San Diego State Col, 46-47; lectr & asst engr, Univ Calif, Los Angeles, 47-53; asst prof metall, Inst Study Metals, Univ Chicago, 53-56; assoc prof eng, 56-62, PROF MAT, UNIV CALIF, LOS ANGELES, 62- *Concurrent Pos:* Fulbright res prof, Tokyo Inst Technol, 58-59; consult, Japanese Atomic Energy Res Inst, 58-59 & Douglas Aircraft Co, Inc, 59-71; NSF sr fel, Ctr Nuclear Studies, Mol, Belg, 65-66; assoc ed, J Eng Mat & Technol, 73- *Honors & Awards:* Templin Award, Am Soc Testing & Mat, 78. *Mem:* Am Soc Testing & Mat; Am Soc Metals; Am Ceramic Soc; Am Soc Mech Engrs. *Res:* Fracture of solids; interactions between crystal defects; diffusion in solids; mechanical properties of ceramics. *Mailing Add:* Dept Mat Sch Eng Univ Calif Los Angeles CA 90024

SINEX, FRANCIS MAROTT, b Indianapolis, Ind, Jan 11, 23; c 2. BIOCHEMISTRY. *Educ:* DePauw Univ, AB, 44; Ind Univ, MA, 45; Harvard Univ, PhD, 51. *Prof Exp:* Jr biochemist, Brookhaven Nat Labs, 50-51, biochemist & exec officer, Biochem Div, 51-57; chmn dept, 57-77, PROF BIOCHEM, SCH MED, BOSTON UNIV, 57-, HEAD SECT BIOMED GERONT, 78- *Mem:* Geront Soc (pres, 69-70); Am Soc Biol Chem; Alzheimer's Dis & Related Dis Asn. *Mailing Add:* Dept Biochem Sch Med Boston Univ Boston MA 02118

SINFELT, JOHN HENRY, b Munson, Pa, Feb 18, 31; m 56; c 1. CHEMISTRY, CATALYSIS. *Educ:* Pa State Univ, BS, 51; Univ Ill, MS, 53, PhD(chem eng), 54. *Hon Degrees:* DSc, Univ Ill, 81. *Prof Exp:* Chem engr, 54-57, group leader, 57-62, res assoc, 62-68, sr res assoc, 68-72, sci adv, 72-79, SR SCI ADV, EXXON RES & ENG CO, 79- *Concurrent Pos:* Lacey lectr, Calif Inst Technol, 73; Reilley lectr, Notre Dame Univ, 74. *Honors & Awards:* Emmett Award, Catalysis Soc, 73; Petrol Chem Award, Am Chem Soc, 76; Dickson Prize lectr, Carnegie-Mellon Univ, 77; Dickson Prize Lectr, Carnegie-Mellon Univ, 77; Nat Medal Sci, 79, ; Gault lectr, Coun Europe Res Group Catalysis, 80; Chem Pioneer Award, Am Inst Chemists, 81; Welch lectr, Conf Chem Res, Robert A Welch Found, 81. *Mem:* Nat Acad Eng; Nat Acad Sci; Am Chem Soc; Catalysis Soc; Am Acad Arts & Sci. *Res:* Heterogeneous catalysis; chemical kinetics; surface science; petroleum chemistry. *Mailing Add:* Exxon Res & Eng Co PO Box 45 Linden NJ 07036

SING, CHARLES F, b Joliet, Ill, July 6, 36. HUMAN GENETICS, STATISTICS. *Educ:* Iowa State Univ, BS, 60; Kans State Univ, MS, 63; NC State Univ, PhD(statist genetics), 66. *Prof Exp:* Assoc prof, 72-76, PROF HUMAN GENETICS, MED SCH, UNIV MICH, ANN ARBOR, 76- *Mem:* Am Soc Human Genetics; Biometrics Soc; Genetics Soc; Sigma Xi. *Res:* Genetics of common diseases. *Mailing Add:* Dept of Human Genetics Univ of Mich Med Sch Ann Arbor MI 48108

SINGER, ALAN G, b Berkeley, Calif, Sept 28, 40; m 63; c 3. BIO-ORGANIC CHEMISTRY. *Educ:* Univ Calif, Berkeley, AB, 65; State Univ NY, PhD(chem), 74. *Prof Exp:* Technician protein chem, Univ Calif Space Sci, 65-66; instr chem, Cogswell Polytech Col, 67-69; res asst, Kaiser Found Res Inst, 68-69; res assoc, 73-76, ASST PROF ORG CHEM, ROCKEFELLER UNIV, 76- *Concurrent Pos:* Asst prof chem, Kingsborough Community Col, 74-75. *Mem:* AAAS; NY Acad Sci; Sigma Xi. *Res:* Chemistry of vertebrate pheromones. *Mailing Add:* 1230 York Ave Rockefeller Univ New York NY 10021

SINGER, ANITA LARKS, b Japan, Nov 9, 47; US citizen; m 73. DEVELOPMENTAL PHYSIOLOGY, ENZYMOLOGY. *Educ:* Univ Mo, Columbia, BA, 68; Univ Southern Calif, PhD(cellular & molecular biol), 74. *Prof Exp:* Teaching asst biochem & cell physiol, Dept Biol Sci, 68-73, USPHS fel biochem, 74-80, INSTR PATH, SCH MED, UNIV SOUTHERN CALIF, 80- *Concurrent Pos:* Res award, Interdept Cancer Res Comt, Los Angeles County-Univ Southern Calif, 74- *Mem:* Sigma Xi. *Res:* Hormonal control of development; cyclic nucleotide metabolism; lung endocrinology; molecular basis of disease; endocrine control of metabolism; biochemistry of neoplasia; enzyme purification and characterization. *Mailing Add:* Dept of Biochem Sch of Med Univ Southern Calif Med Ctr Los Angeles CA 90033

SINGER, ARNOLD J, b Paterson, NJ, Apr 7, 15; m 78; c 2. MEDICAL SCIENCES, GENERAL RESEARCH ADMINISTRATION. *Educ:* Rutgers Univ, BSc, 36, BS, 37; Cornell Univ, MS, 39, PhD(bact), 41. *Prof Exp:* Pharmacologist, State Dept Health, NJ, 40-43; dir res, Chatham Pharmaceut Inc, 46-48; dir res, Block Drug Co, 49-52; pres, Reed & Carnrick, 52-70, dir, Res Inst, 70-77, chmn bd, 70-80; VPRES, SIMBEC RES, 81- *Concurrent Pos:* Pres, Fesler Co, Inc, 61- *Mem:* AAAS; Am Chem Soc; NY Acad Sci. *Res:* Medicinal chemistry. *Mailing Add:* Simbec Res Inc 799 Bloomfield Ave Verona NJ 07044

SINGER, ARTHUR CHESTER, b Vienna, Austria, Aug 30, 36; US citizen; m 60; c 3. BIOSTATISTICS. *Educ:* Univ Ill, BS, 61, MS, 63, PhD(quantitative genetics), 67. *Prof Exp:* Asst prof genetics & statist, Ind State Univ, 67-70; SR STATISTICIAN, BIOSTATIST SECT, WYETH LABS, 70- *Mem:* Biomet Soc; Am Statist Asn. *Mailing Add:* Biostatist Sect Wyeth Labs Box 8299 Philadelphia PA 19101

SINGER, B, b San Francisco, Calif. MOLECULAR BIOLOGY. *Educ:* Univ Calif, Berkeley, BS, 42. *Prof Exp:* Jr chemist, Shell Develop Co, 42-43; jr chemist biochem, Western Regional Res Lab, USDA, 43-46; from staff res assoc molecular biol to assoc res biochemist, 46-79, RES PROF BIOCHEM, UNIV CALIF, BERKELEY, 79-, PRIN INVESTR MOLECULAR BIOL, 69- *Concurrent Pos:* Assoc ed, Cancer Res, 80-; vis prof, Univ Queensland, Australia, 82; sci writer. *Res:* Relationship of nucleic acid structure to function; effect of modification by mutagens and/or carcinogens on biological activity of viruses, viral nucleic acids and cells. *Mailing Add:* Dept Molecular Biol & Virus Lab Univ of Calif Stanley Hall Berkeley CA 94720

SINGER, BARRY M, b New York, NY, Feb 15, 40; m 64; c 2. DEVICE PHYSICS, SUB-SYSTEMS RESEARCH. *Educ:* Univ Colo, Boulder, BS, 61; NY Univ, MS, 64; Polytech Inst NY, PhD(electrophysics), 68. *Prof Exp:* Sr engr, Raytheon Co, 60-63, sect engr, 63-65, sect head, 65-69; sr prog leader component & device res, 69-79, group dir, 79-82, DEP DIR COMPONENT & DEVICE RES & MAT RES, PHILIPS LABS, NAM PHILIPS, 82- *Concurrent Pos:* Consult, Vita Corp. *Mem:* Inst Elec & Electronics Engrs; Sigma Xi. *Mailing Add:* Philips Labs 345 Scarborough Rd Briarcliff Manor NY 10510

SINGER, BURTON HERBERT, b Chicago, Ill, June 12, 38; m 71; c 1. STATISTICS. *Educ:* Case Inst Technol, BS, 59, MS, 61; Stanford Univ, PhD(statist), 67. *Prof Exp:* From asst prof to assoc prof statist, 67-77, PROF MATH STATIST, COLUMBIA UNIV, 77- *Concurrent Pos:* Statist consult, Rand Corp, 71-, Union Carbide Corp, 71- & US AEC, 72-75; res assoc statist, Princeton Univ, 72-73. *Mem:* AAAS; Am Statist Asn; Psychomet Soc. *Res:* Discrimination and identification of mathematical models in the social sciences; designs for observational studies; inverse problems. *Mailing Add:* Dept of Math Statist Columbia Univ New York NY 10027

SINGER, CLIFFORD EARLE, b Sept 8, 48; US citizen. PLASMA PHYSICS. *Educ:* Univ Ill, Urbana, BS, 66; Univ Calif, Berkeley, PhD(biochem), 71. *Prof Exp:* Fel molecular biol, Mass Inst Technol, 71-72; fel solar physics, Queen Mary Col, Univ London, 72-77; FEL PLASMA PHYSICS, PLASMA PHYSICS LAB, PRINCETON UNIV, 77- *Mem:* Brit Interplanetary Soc. *Res:* Controlled thermonuclear fusion; space physics; advanced space propulsion systems. *Mailing Add:* Plasma Physics Lab PO Box 451 Princeton NJ 08544

SINGER, DONALD ALLEN, b Ukiah, Calif, 43. APPLIED STATISTICS, MINERAL ECONOMICS. *Educ:* San Francisco State Univ, BA, 66; Pa State Univ, MS, 68, PhD(mineral & petrol), 71. *Prof Exp:* Syst analyst, Kennecott Copper Corp, 71-72; sr comput programmer, 72-73; GEOLOGIST, BR RESOURCE ANAL, US GEOL SURV, 73- *Mem:* Sigma Xi; Am Statist Asn; Int Asn Math Geol; Soc Mining Engrs. *Res:* Operational mineral resource classification; predicting the occurrence of mineral resources; modeling the search for mineral resources; mineral resource predictions for large regions. *Mailing Add:* US Geol Surv Mail Stop 84 345 Middlefield Rd Menlo Park CA 94025

SINGER, DONALD H, b New York, NY, Sept 27, 29; m 58; c 3. CARDIOLOGY. *Educ:* Cornell Univ, AB, 48; Stanford Univ, MA, 50; Northwestern Univ, MD, 54; Am Bd Internal Med, dipl, 63. *Prof Exp:* Intern, Michael Reese Hosp, Chicago, 54-55; asst resident med, Beth Israel Hosp, Boston, Mass, 57-58; chief med res & instr med, Sch Med, Georgetown Univ, 61-62; res assoc, Col Physicians & Surgeons, Columbia Univ, 62-63, asst prof pharmacol, 63-68; assoc prof, 68-77, PROF MED & PHARMACOL, SCH MED, NORTHWESTERN UNIV, 77-, DIR REINGOLD ELECTROCARDIOGRAPHY CTR, 68- *Concurrent Pos:* Nat Heart Inst trainee, Cardiovasc Dept, Michael Reese Hosp, Chicago, 55-57; fel cardiol, Georgetown Univ Hosp, 60-61; John Polachek Found fel, 63-66; estab investr, Am Heart Asn, 67-72, fel coun clin cardiol, 72-, mem coun circulation, 78-; attend physician, Passavant Mem Hosp & Northwestern Mem Hosp, 69- *Mem:* Fel Am Col Physicians; fel Am Col Cardiol; Cardiac Muscle Soc; Am Physiol Soc; Electrophysiol Soc. *Res:* Cardiology, electrocardiology and cardiac electrophysiology. *Mailing Add:* Reingold Electrocardiography Ctr Northwestern Univ Med Sch Chicago IL 60611

SINGER, EMANUEL, b New York, NY, July 1, 22; m 65; c 6. RELIABILITY, RISK & HAZARD ANALYSIS. *Educ:* Columbia Univ, BS, 43; Princeton Univ, MSE, 47, PhD(chem eng), 49. *Prof Exp:* Supvr develop, Shell Develop Co Div, Shell Oil Co, 49-61; dir prof serv, C-E-I-R, Inc, 61-62; pres, Mgt Decisions, Inc, 62-64; mgr comput appln, Sci Design Co, 64-66; consult mgt sci & comput appln, pvt pract, 66-72; sr staff mathematician, Bellaire Res Ctr, 72-80, RES ASSOC, WESTHOLLOW RES CTR, SHELL DEVELOP CO, 80- *Mem:* Am Inst Chem Engrs; Am Chem Soc; Opers Res Soc Am; NY Acad Sci; World Future Soc. *Res:* Industrial chemical kinetics; design and operations scheduling of chemical plants and oil refineries; information systems; operations research. *Mailing Add:* Westhollow Res Ctr Shell Develop Co PO Box 1380 Houston TX 77001

SINGER, EUGEN, b Levoca, Czech, Apr 1, 26; Can citizen; m 53; c 1. CHEMICAL ENGINEERING, INSTRUMENTATION. *Educ:* Prague Tech Univ, Dipl eng, 52, PhD(anal chem), 63. *Prof Exp:* Asst prof anal chem, Prague Tech Univ, 52-53; chief gas treatment div, Res Inst Inorganic Chem, Czech, 53-68; HEAD MONITORING & INSTRUMENTATION DEVELOP, MINISTRY ENVIRON ONT, 68- *Res:* Monitoring of ambient air pollutants, instrumentation development, acquisition, reduction and interpretation. *Mailing Add:* Ministry of Environ of Ont 880 Bay St Toronto ON M5S 1Z7 Can

SINGER, GEORGE, b Belgrade, Yugoslavia, Apr 23, 37; US citizen; m 60; c 2. ACAROLOGY. *Educ:* City Col New York, BSc, 59; Univ Kans, MS, 62; Ore State Univ, PhD(entom), 65. *Prof Exp:* Asst prof zool, Univ Mont, 65-68; fel entom, McGill Univ, 69-71; PROJ ASSOC ENTOM, UNIV WIS-MADISON, 71- *Res:* Biochemistry of chemoreception and repellency; sensory physiology; host parasite relationships; ecology and bionomics; systematics and evolution; pest control. *Mailing Add:* Dept Entom Univ Wis Madison WI 53706

SINGER, HOWARD JOSEPH, b Annapolis, Md, Mar 2, 44; m 73; c 2. SPACE PHYSICS, MAGNETOSPHERIC PHYSICS. *Educ:* Univ Md, BS, 67; Boston Univ, MA, 72; Univ Calif, Los Angeles, MS, 75, PhD(geophysics & space physics), 80. *Prof Exp:* Instr astron, Wellesley Col, 69-70; mathematician, Fed Systs Div, IBM, 70-72; staff res assoc, Inst Geophysics & Planetary Physics, Univ Calif, Los Angeles, 72-74, res assoc, 74-80; res assoc, 80-81, ASST RES PROF, DEPT ASTRON, BOSTON UNIV, 82- *Concurrent Pos:* Dep sta sci leader, S Pole Sta Antarctica, Inst Geophysics & Planetary Physics, Univ Calif, Los Angeles, 72-73. *Mem:* Am Geophys Union; AAAS; Am Asn Physics Teachers; Sigma Xi. *Res:* Analysis of hydromagnetic waves in the earth's magnetosphere; solar wind interaction with the magnetosphere; management and analysis of digital data. *Mailing Add:* Dept Astron Boston Univ Boston MA 02215

SINGER, IRWIN I, b New York, NY, Dec 20, 43; m 67; c 2. CELL BIOLOGY, VIROLOGY. *Educ:* City Col New York, BS, 65; NY Univ, MS, 67, PhD(biol), 70. *Prof Exp:* Instr biol, Mercy Col, 69-70; asst prof, St Louis Univ, 70-71; ASSOC INVESTR ELECTRON MICROS, INST MED RES, BENNINGTON, 71- *Mem:* Electron Micros Soc Am; Am Soc Cell Biol. *Res:* Ultrastructure and cytochemistry in regenerating Cnidaria; electron microscopy and pathobiology of the Parvoviruses. *Mailing Add:* Inst Med Res Bennington VT 05201

SINGER, ISADORE MANUAL, b Detroit, Mich, May 4, 24; m 44; c 3. PURE MATHEMATICS. *Educ:* Univ Mich, BS, 44; Univ Chicago, MS, 48, PhD(math), 50. *Prof Exp:* Moore instr math, Mass Inst Technol, 50-52; asst prof, Univ Calif, Los Angeles, 52-54; vis asst prof, Columbia Univ, 54-55; mem, Inst Advan Study, 55-56; from asst prof to prof math, Mass Inst

Technol, 56-77; VIS PROF MATH, UNIV CALIF, BERKELEY, 77- *Concurrent Pos:* Norbert Wiener prof, Mass Inst Technol, 70; Sloan fel, 59-62; Guggenheim fel, 68-69, 75-76. *Honors & Awards:* Bocher Prize, Am Math Soc, 69. *Mem:* Nat Acad Sci; Am Acad Arts & Sci; Am Math Soc. *Res:* Differential geometry; commutative Banach algebras; global analysis. *Mailing Add:* Dept of Math Evans Hall Univ of Calif Berkeley CA 94720

SINGER, JAMES ROBERT, low temperature physics, see previous edition

SINGER, JEROME RALPH, b Cleveland, Ohio, Oct 16, 21; m 56; c 2. BIOENGINEERING, BIOPHYSICS. *Educ:* Univ Ill, BS, 51; Northwestern Univ, MS, 53; Univ Conn, PhD(physics), 55. *Prof Exp:* Engr, Van de Graaff Proj, Northwestern Univ, 51-53; instr physics, Univ Conn, 53-55; physicist, Solid State Div, US Naval Ord Lab, 55-56; chief staff physicist, Nat Sci Labs, Inc, Washington, DC, 56-57; assoc prof elec eng, 57-77, PROF ENG SCI, UNIV CALIF, BERKELEY, 77- *Concurrent Pos:* Vis lectr, Catholic Univ, 55-56 & George Washington Univ, 56-57; proj engr, Sperry Corp, 54; sci consult, Missile Systs Div, Lockheed Aircraft Corp, 57-; Telemeter Magnetics, Inc, 57-58; Aeroneutronics, Inc div, Ford Motor Co, 58- *Mem:* AAAS; Am Phys Soc; Optical Soc Am; sr mem Inst Elec & Electronics Eng; Brit Inst Physics. *Res:* Electronics; magnetic phenomena; quantum mechanical amplifiers; magnetic resonance; blood studies; flow and magnetic properties of blood; rheological properties of body fluids. *Mailing Add:* Electronic Res Labs Univ of Calif Berkeley CA 94720

SINGER, LAWRENCE ALAN, b Chicago, Ill, June 7, 36; m 67; c 2. ORGANIC CHEMISTRY. *Educ:* Northwestern Univ, BA, 58; Univ Calif, Los Angeles, PhD(org chem), 62. *Prof Exp:* Fel, Harvard Univ, 62-64; asst prof chem, Univ Chicago, 64-67; assoc prof, 67-71, PROF CHEM, UNIV SOUTHERN CALIF, 73- *Concurrent Pos:* A P Sloan fel, 70-72. *Mem:* Am Chem Soc; Royal Soc Chem. *Res:* Organic photochemistry; laser spectroscopic studies; organic free radicals; photoinduced electron transfer reactions. *Mailing Add:* Dept of Chem Univ of Southern Calif Los Angeles CA 90007

SINGER, LEON, b Fla, Aug 15, 18; m 51; c 5. BIOCHEMISTRY. *Educ:* Univ Fla, BS, 40, MS, 42, PhD(biochem), 49. *Prof Exp:* Asst, Agr Exp Sta, Univ Fla, 46-49; from instr to assoc prof physiol chem, 49-62, Hill prof basic dent res, 60-70, PROF BIOCHEM, MED & DENT SCH, UNIV MINN, MINNEAPOLIS, 62- *Mem:* AAAS; Am Chem Soc; Am Soc Biol Chem; Int Asn Dent Res. *Res:* Biochemistry relative to mineral metabolism; minor element metabolism; calcium 45; phosphorus 32; metabolism of fluorine. *Mailing Add:* Dept of Biochem Univ of Minn Col of Med Sci Minneapolis MN 55455

SINGER, LEONARD SIDNEY, b Middletown, Pa, Oct 9, 23; m 48; c 3. PHYSICAL CHEMISTRY. *Educ:* Pa State Col, BS, 43; Univ Chicago, PhD(phys chem), 50. *Prof Exp:* Chem engr, Celanese Corp Am, 43-44; Du Pont fel chem, Cornell Univ, 50-51; phys chemist, US Naval Res Lab, 51-55; phys chemist, 55-75, CORP RES FEL, RES LAB, CARBON PROD DIV, UNION CARBIDE CORP, 75- *Honors & Awards:* Charles E Pettinos Award, Am Carbon Soc, 77. *Mem:* Am Chem Soc; Am Carbon Soc. *Res:* Magnetism; magnetic resonance; free radicals; carbon and graphite; carbon fibers. *Mailing Add:* Res Lab Carbon Prod Div Union Carbide Corp PO Box 6116 Cleveland OH 44101

SINGER, MARCUS, b Pittsburgh, Pa, Aug 28, 14; m 38; c 2. ANATOMY. *Educ:* Univ Pittsburgh, BS, 38; Harvard Univ, AM, 40, PhD(biol), 42. *Prof Exp:* Asst anat, Harvard Med Sch, 42-44, instr, 44-46, assoc, 46-48, asst prof, 48-51; from assoc prof to prof zool, Cornell Univ, 51-61; prof anat, 61-80, HENRY W PAYNE PROF ANAT, SCH MED, CASE WESTERN RESERVE UNIV, 80-, DIR DEPT, 61- *Concurrent Pos:* Guggenheim fel, 67; mem, Cell Biol Study Sect, NIH, 71-74 & Neurol B Study Sect, 76-79; mem, Int Brain Orgn, 78. *Mem:* AAAS; Am Soc Zool; Asn Res Nerv & Ment Dis; Am Asn Anat; fel Am Acad Arts & Sci. *Res:* Regeneration; histochemistry; experimental morphology; nerve regeneration; neuroanatomy. *Mailing Add:* Dept of Anat Case Western Reserve Univ Cleveland OH 44106

SINGER, MAXINE FRANK, b New York, NY, Feb 15, 31; m 52; c 4. BIOCHEMISTRY. *Educ:* Swarthmore Col, AB, 52, DSc, 78; Yale Univ, PhD(biochem), 57; Wesleyan Univ, DSc, 77. *Prof Exp:* USPHS fel, NIH, 57, biochemist, Nat Inst Arthritis & Metab Dis, 58-74, head sect nucleic acid enzymol, 74-79, CHIEF, LAB BIOCHEM, NAT CANCER INST, 79- *Concurrent Pos:* Guest scientist, Weizmann Inst Sci, 71-72; bd of trustees, Wesleyan Univ, Conn, 72-75; fel, Yale Corp, Yale Univ, 75- *Honors & Awards:* Iota Sig Sigma Pi Triennial Res Award, 63; Superior Serv Award, HEW, 75; NIH Dirs Award, 77. *Mem:* Inst Med-Nat Acad Sci; fel Am Acad Arts & Sci; Am Soc Biol Chem; Am Chem Soc; Am Soc Microbiol. *Res:* Nucleic acid chemistry and metabolism; biochemistry of animal viruses. *Mailing Add:* Bldg 37 Rm 4A-01 Nat Inst Health Bethesda MD 20014

SINGER, PHILIP C, b Brooklyn, NY, Sept 6, 42; m 65; c 4. ENVIRONMENTAL SCIENCES & ENGINEERING. *Educ:* Cooper Union, BCE, 63; Northwestern Univ, MS, 65; Harvard Univ, MS, 66, PhD, 69. *Prof Exp:* Asst prof civil eng, Univ Notre Dame, 69-73; assoc prof environ sci & eng, 73-78, PROF ENVIRON SCI & ENG, UNIV NC, 78-, DIR WATER RESOURCES ENG PROG, 79- *Concurrent Pos:* Guest prof, Swiss Fed Inst Water Res & Water Pollution Control, Dubendouf, Switz, 79. *Mem:* Am Soc Civil Engrs; Am Chem Soc; Am Water Works Asn; Water Pollution Control Fedn; Asn Environ Eng Prof. *Res:* Chemistry and control of pollution by acidic mine drainage; chemistry of eutrophication; chemical and physical processes for water quality management; aquatic chemistry; metal-organic interactions; control of trihalomethane formation; treatment and environmental impact assessment of coal conversion wastewaters; ozonation for water and wastewater treatment. *Mailing Add:* Dept of Environ Sci Eng Univ of NC Chapel Hill NC 27514

SINGER, RICHARD ALAN, b New York, NY, May 21, 45; m 71. EXPERIMENTAL HIGH ENERGY PHYSICS. *Educ:* Mass Inst Technol, BS, 67, PhD(physics), 72. *Prof Exp:* Fel, 72-75, ASST PHYSICIST, ARGONNE NAT LAB, 75- *Mem:* Am Phys Soc. *Res:* Analysis of bubble chamber experiments; study of strong interactions at both intermediate and high energies; weak interaction experiments using both neutrino and antineutrino beams. *Mailing Add:* Bldg 362 Rm E-213 Argonne Nat Lab Argonne IL 60439

SINGER, ROBERT MARK, b Brooklyn, NY, Nov 2, 43. CANCER, CELL BIOLOGY, ANATOMY. *Educ:* Long Island Univ, BA, 65; Hunter Col, MA, 67; Syracuse Univ, PhD(cell biol), 71. *Prof Exp:* Res fel cancer, Tufts Univ, 72-73, instr cancer, 73-74, asst prof cancer res, Dept Path, Sch Med, 75-78; mem staff, 78-80, CHMN DEPT ANAT, SCH DENT, FAIRLEIGH DICKINSON UNIV, 80- *Mem:* Am Soc Cell Biol. *Res:* Characterizing the role of tumor specific isoenzymes of alkaline phosphatase in cancer cells; glucocorticoid mediated alterations of isoenzyme profiles and the rate limiting effects of the cell cycle. *Mailing Add:* Sch of Dent 110 Fuller Place Hackensack NJ 07601

SINGER, ROLF, b Schliersee, Ger, June 23, 06; nat US; m; c 1. MYCOLOGY. *Educ:* Univ Vienna, PhD(bot), 31; Acad Sci, USSR, Dr Biol, 40. *Hon Degrees:* Dr Sc, Univ Lausanne, 77. *Prof Exp:* Asst cryptogams, Univ Barcelona, 34-35; sr sci specialist, Bot Inst, Acad Sci Leningrad, 35-40; res assoc, Farlow Herbarium, Harvard Univ, 41-44, asst cur, 44-48, actg dir, 46-48; prof extraordinary, Nat Univ Tucuman, 48-53; prof chem & head dept, Nebr Wesleyan Univ, 53-54; head dept bot, Inst M Lillo, Nat Univ Tucuman, 54-61; prof syst bot, Univ Buenos Aires, 61-68; vis res cur, 68-77, RES ASSOC, FIELD MUS NATURAL HIST, 77- *Concurrent Pos:* Oberlander Trust fel, 41-42; Guggenheim Mem Found fel, Subtrop Am, 42-43, 52-53; sci dir, Orgn for Flora Neotropica Inc, 54-68; mem sci mission, Caucasus Mts, Vienna Acad Sci, 28-29; Pyrenees, Coun Natural Sci, Spain, 34; Altai Mts, Acad Sci, USSR, 37; Brazil, Tierra del Fuego & Patagonia, Inst M Lillo, 50-66, Mex, 57-73; Yungas, NSF, 56; Peru, Philos Soc, 58; South Chile, 59-67; Columbia, 60, 68; Ecuador, NSF, 73; exchange scientist, Nat Acad Sci, 74; mem comt fungi, Int Bot Cong, 50-; Hon prof, Fed Univ Pernambuco & Univ Chile Pernambuco, Univ Chile & Univ Buenos Aires; vis prof biol sci, Univ Ill, Chicago Circle, 68-77; researcher, Nat Coun Sci & Technol Develop, Nat Res Inst Amazonia, 77-; vis prof bot, Univ Vienna, 76 & 79. *Mem:* Mycol Soc Am; Mycol Soc France; Mycol Soc Mex; Mycol Soc Ger; Mycol Soc Austria. *Res:* Taxonomy of the Basidiomycetes; especially of the Agaricales, commercial growing of mushrooms; antibiotics and psychotropic substances derived from Basidiomycetes; ecology of ectrophic mycorrhiza; antarctic fungi. *Mailing Add:* Field Mus of Natural Hist Roosevelt Rd & Lakeshore Dr Chicago IL 60605

SINGER, RONALD, b Cape Town, SAfrica, Aug 12, 24; m 50; c 4. ANATOMY, PHYSICAL ANTHROPOLOGY. *Educ:* Univ Cape Town, MB, ChB, 47, DSc(anat), 62. *Prof Exp:* Lectr anat, Univ Cape Town, 49-51, sr lectr, 51-60, assoc prof, 60-62; PROF ANAT, UNIV CHICAGO, 62-, R R BENSLEY PROF BIOL & MED SCI, 73- *Concurrent Pos:* Rotary Found & Johns Hopkins Univ fels, 51-52; vis prof, Univ Ill, 59-60, Robert J Terry lectr, 64; mem sci group pop genetics primitive pop, WHO, 62; consult, Nat Found, 65-; subcomt phys anthrop, Int Anat Nomenclature Comt, 71- *Honors & Awards:* Cornwall & York Prize, 50. *Mem:* Fel AAAS; fel Royal Soc SAfrica; SAfrican Asn Adv Sci (vpres, 58-62); SAfrican Archaeol Soc (pres, 61-62); Int Quaternary Asn. *Res:* Gross anatomy; paleoanthropology; genetics of African primitive populations. *Mailing Add:* Dept of Anat Univ of Chicago 1025 E 57th St Chicago IL 60637

SINGER, S(IEGFRIED) FRED, b Vienna, Austria, Sept 27, 24; nat US. GEOPHYSICS. *Educ:* Ohio State Univ, BEE, 43; Princeton Univ, AM, 44, PhD(physics), 48. *Hon Degrees:* DSc, Ohio State Univ, 70. *Prof Exp:* Instr physics, Princeton Univ, 43-44; mem staff electronic comput design, Naval Ord Lab, Md, 45-46; physicist, Appl Physics Lab, Johns Hopkins Univ, 46-50; sci liaison officer, Off Naval Attache, US Embassy, London, 50-53; from assoc prof to prof physics, Univ Md, 53-62; dir, Nat Weather Satellite Ctr, US Dept Com, 62-64; prof atmospheric sci & dean sch environ & planetary sci, Univ Miami, 64-67; dep asst secy sci progs, US Dept Interior, 67-70; dep asst adminr, Environ Protection Agency, 70-71; PROF ENVIRON SCI & MEM ENERGY POLICY STUDIES CTR, UNIV VA, 71- *Concurrent Pos:* Dir ctr atmospheric & space physics, Univ Md, 59-62; vis researcher, Jet Propulsion Lab, Calif Inst Technol, 61-62; fed exec fel, Brookings Inst, 71; mem Comn IV, Int Sci Radio Union, 54-; tech panels rockets & cosmic rays, US Nat Comt, Int Geophys Year, 57-58; head sci eval group & sci consult, Select Comt Astronaut & Space Explor, US House Rep, 58; chmn subcomt basic res, Comt Sci & Technol, US Chamber Com, 60-62 & mem environ pollution adv bd, 66-67; mem spacecraft oceanog adv group, Naval Oceanog Off, 66-67; chmn adv comt environ effects supersonic transport, Dept Transp, 71; consult, Inst Defense Anal, AEC & major industs; vchmn, Nat Adv Comt Oceans & Atmosphere, 81- *Honors & Awards:* President's Commendation Award, 58; 1st Astronaut Medal, Brit Interplanetary Soc, 62. *Mem:* Fel AAAS; fel Am Phys Soc; fel Am Inst Aeronaut & Astronaut; fel Brit Interplanetary Soc; fel Am Astronaut Soc. *Res:* Upper atmosphere, ionosphere currents, theory of magnetic storms, radiation belts; origin of meteorites, moon, solar system; environmental effects of pollution, especially on global climate; remote sensing, from earth satellites; pollution control techniques and economics; water and energy resources; effects of population growth. *Mailing Add:* Dept Environ Sci Univ Va Charlottesville VA 22903

SINGER, SAMUEL, b New York, NY, June 22, 27; m 57; c 3. MICROBIOLOGY. *Educ:* City Col New York, BS, 50; Univ Ky, MS, 52; NY Univ, PhD(protozool, physiol), 58. *Prof Exp:* Res microbiologist, Div Chemother, Burroughs Wellcome & Co, 52-62; sr res microbiologist, Dept Microbiol, Bioferm Div, Int Mineral & Chem Corp, Calif, 62-68; microbiologist, Brown & Williamson Tobacco Corp, Ky, 68-70; assoc prof, 70-75, PROF BIOL SCI, WESTERN ILL UNIV, 75- *Mem:* AAAS; Am Soc Microbiol; Soc Invert Path; Brit Soc Gen Microbiol; Sigma Xi. *Res:* Microbiol insecticides; fermentation of insecticidal bacillus; microbial nutrition; bacterial ecology. *Mailing Add:* Dept of Biol Sci Western Ill Univ Macomb IL 61455

SINGER, SANFORD SANDY, b Brooklyn, NY, Sept 14, 40; m 71. BIOCHEMISTRY. *Educ:* Brooklyn Col, BS, 62; Univ Mich, Ann Arbor, MS, 64, PhD(biochem), 67. *Prof Exp:* Fel, Albert Einstein Col Med, 67 & 68; fel, Fels Res Inst, Med Sch, Temple Univ, 68-72; asst prof chem, 72-78, ASSOC PROF CHEM, UNIV DAYTON, 78- *Concurrent Pos:* Am Cancer Soc fel, Albert Einstein Col Med, 67-69. *Res:* Studies of mechanism of action of adrenal glucocorticosteroids; studies of mechanism of carcinogenesis. *Mailing Add:* Dept of Chem Univ of Dayton Dayton OH 45409

SINGER, SEYMOUR JONATHAN, b New York, NY, May 23, 24; m 47; c 3. BIOLOGY. *Educ:* Columbia Univ, AB, 43, AM, 45; Polytech Inst Brooklyn, PhD(chem), 47. *Hon Degrees:* MA, Polytech Inst Brooklyn, 60. *Prof Exp:* Abbott fel, Calif Inst Technol, 47-48, USPHS fel, 48-50, sr res fel, 50-51; from asst prof to prof phys chem, Yale Univ, 51-61; PROF BIOL, UNIV CALIF, SAN DIEGO, 61- *Concurrent Pos:* Guggenheim fel, 59-60; mem adv panel molecular biol, NSF, 60-63; mem, Allergy & Immunol Study Sect, USPHS, 63-64; res prof, Am Cancer Soc, 76- *Mem:* Nat Acad Sci; Am Acad Arts & Sci; Am Chem Soc; Am Soc Biol Chem. *Res:* Molecular biology; physical chemistry of proteins; immunochemistry; membrane biology; chemical cytology. *Mailing Add:* Dept Biol PO Box 109 Univ Calif San Diego La Jolla CA 92037

SINGER, SOLOMON ELIAS, b Atlantic City, NJ, Aug 31, 19; m 44; c 3. CHEMISTRY, NUCLEAR PHYSICS. *Educ:* Rutgers Univ, BS, 41; Ohio State Univ, PhD, 53. *Prof Exp:* Res chemist, P J Schweitzer, Inc, NJ, 41-42; chemist, Edgewood Arsenal, Md, 42-43; radio engr, Trans World Airlines, 46-47; weather officer meteorol, US Air Force, 47-51, nuclear res officer, 54-65; consult scientist, Palo Alto, 65-74, CHIEF SCIENTIST MISSILE SYSTS DIV, LOCKHEED MISSILES & SPACE CO, SUNNYVALE, 74- *Mem:* Am Inst Aeronaut & Astronaut. *Res:* Nuclear weapons phenomena and effects. *Mailing Add:* Lockheed Missiles & Space Co 1111 Lockheed Way Box 504 Sunnyvale CA 94088

SINGER, STANLEY, b North Adams, Mass, Oct 2, 25. CHEMISTRY, PHYSICS. *Educ:* Univ Calif, Los Angeles, BS, 46, PhD(chem), 50. *Prof Exp:* Res assoc chem, Univ Calif, Los Angeles, 50-51; chemist, US Naval Ord Test Sta, 51-52, res assoc, 53, head properties sect, 54-55, liquid propellants & combustion br, 55-58; head phys & inorg chem, Hughes Tool Co, 58-59; head propulsion physics dept & assoc head chem dept, Rocket Power, 59-64; dir physics, Dynamic Sci Corp, 64-65; DIR, ATHENEX RES ASSOC, 65- *Concurrent Pos:* Engr in residence, Eng Socs Comn Energy, 81-82. *Mem:* AAAS; Am Chem Soc; Sigma Xi; Am Inst Aeronaut & Astronaut; Am Phys Soc. *Res:* Synthesis; polymers; combustion; rocket propellants; ion sources; arc-plasma chemistry; refractory metals; ion-molecule reactions; electric space propulsion; plasma-magnetic field interaction; fine particles; thunderstorm electrification; lightning; atmospheric particles; superconductivity; synthetic fuels. *Mailing Add:* 381 S Meridith Ave Pasadena CA 91106

SINGER, THOMAS PETER, b Budapest, Hungary, July 10, 20; nat US; m 62; c 2. BIOCHEMISTRY. *Educ:* Univ Chicago, SB, 41, SM, 43, PhD(biochem), 44. *Prof Exp:* Asst med, Off Sci Res & Develop & Comt Med Res Projs, Chicago, 42-44, res assoc, Manhattan Proj, 44-46; asst prof agr biochem, Univ Minn, 46-47; asst prof biochem, Sch Med, Western Reserve Univ, 47-51; mem, Inst Enzyme Res, Univ Wis, 52-54; chief div enzyme res, Edsel B Ford Inst Med Res, Henry Ford Hosp, Detroit, Mich, 54-65; prof biochem, 65-68, prof biochem & biophys, 68-70, ADJ PROF BIOCHEM & BIOPHYS, SCH MED, UNIV CALIF, SAN FRANCISCO, 70-; HEAD MOLECULAR BIOL DIV, VET ADMIN HOSP, 65- *Concurrent Pos:* Guggenheim fel, Univ Paris & Cambridge Univ, 51-52; Guggenheim fel, 59; Orgn Am States fel, 71; Fulbright fel, 72; estab investr, Am Heart Asn, 54-59. *Mem:* Am Soc Biol Chemists; Am Chem Soc. *Res:* Flavin and flavoenzyme structure; enzyme regulation; mechanism of action and regulation of enzymes of the respiratory chain, nonheme iron-sulfur roles in oxidizing enzymes; mitochondrial biogenesis. *Mailing Add:* Dept of Biochem & Biophys Univ of Calif Sch of Med San Francisco CA 94122

SINGER, WALTER, b Detroit, Mich, Oct 25, 17; m 40, 63; c 2. PHARMACEUTICAL CHEMISTRY. *Educ:* Univ Mich, AB, 39; Univ Calif, MA, 40; Union Univ, NY, BS, 48; Univ Calif, PhD(pharmaceut chem), 58. *Prof Exp:* Instr chem, Albany Col Pharm, Union Univ, NY, 48-53, asst prof, 53-54; asst prof pharm & pharmaceut chem, Sch Pharm, Univ Calif, San Francisco, 57-65, lectr & asst dean, 65-66; assoc dean, 66-67, PROF PHARM, ALBANY COL PHARM, 66-, PRES & DEAN, 80- *Mem:* Am Pharmaceut Asn. *Res:* Mechanism of drug action; insecticides and insect repellants. *Mailing Add:* Albany Col of Pharm 106 New Scotland Ave Albany NY 12208

SINGER, WILLIAM MERRILL, b New York, NY, Feb 26, 42. HOMOTOPY THEORY, HOMOLOGICAL ALGEBRA. *Educ:* Cornell Univ, BA, 63; Princeton Univ, MA, 65, PhD(math), 67. *Prof Exp:* Instr math, Mass Inst Technol, 67-69; asst prof, Boston Col, 69-74; ASSOC PROF MATH, FORDHAM UNIV, 74- *Concurrent Pos:* NSF res grant, Boston Col, 71-; NSF res grants, 73-74, 75-76, 76-77 & 81-83. *Mem:* Am Math Soc. *Res:* Algebraic topology; fiber spaces; Hopf algebras; homological algebra and its applications to homotopy theory; semi-simplicial methods. *Mailing Add:* Dept of Math Fordham Univ Bronx NY 10458

SINGEWALD, MARTIN LOUIS, b Baltimore, Md, May 10, 09; m 33; c 3. INTERNAL MEDICINE. *Educ:* Johns Hopkins Univ, BE, 30, MD, 38. *Prof Exp:* From asst prof to assoc prof, 55-74, EMER ASSOC PROF MED, SCH MED, JOHNS HOPKINS UNIV, 74- *Concurrent Pos:* Mem coun arteriosclerosis, Am Heart Asn. *Mem:* Am Soc Internal Med; AMA; fel Am Col Physicians; Am Clin & Climatological Asn. *Res:* Coronary artery diseases. *Mailing Add:* 11 E Chase St Baltimore MD 21202

SINGEWALD, QUENTIN DREYER, b Baltimore, Md, Sept 28, 02; m 52. ECONOMIC GEOLOGY. *Educ:* Johns Hopkins Univ, AB, 22, PhD(geol), 26. *Prof Exp:* Geologist, US Geol Surv, 21-23; geologist, State Geol Surv, Md, 23; geologist, Transcontinental Petrol Co, Mex, 26-27; asst prof geol, Colo Sch Mines, 27-29; from asst prof to assoc prof, Univ Rochester, 29-42; geologist, US Geol Surv, 42-48, asst chief mineral deposits br, 48-52, dist supvr, Mineral Deposits Northeastern Dist, 52-60, res geologist, 60-72; PVT RES, 72- *Concurrent Pos:* Mem, Hopkins Ellsworth Exped, SAm, 24; tech adv, Int Coop Admin, 60-62; foreign prof & adv, Inst Appl Geol, Univ Istanbul, 60-62. *Honors & Awards:* Legion of Honor, Am Inst Mech Engrs. *Mem:* Fel AAAS; fel Geol Soc Am; fel Am Mineral Soc; Soc Econ Geol; Am Asn Petrol Geol. *Res:* Economic geology and petrography of central Colorado, Mexico, Columbia, Peru and European countries; metamorphic geology; metamorphic complex and its thorium deposits in Custer County, Colorado. *Mailing Add:* 1900 Kimberly Rd Silver Spring MD 20903

SINGH, AJAIB, b Dholan Hithar, Pakistan, Jan 14, 35; m 64. PHYSICAL ORGANIC CHEMISTRY, POLYMER CHEMISTRY. *Educ:* Punjab Univ, India, BSc, 54, Hons, 56, MSc, 58; Univ Calif, Davis, PhD(phys org chem), 61. *Prof Exp:* Res fel chem, Harvard Univ, 61-62; res chemist, Am Cyanamid Co, 62-68, sr res chemist, Org Chem Div, 68-77, prin res chemist, Chem Res Div, 77-78; SR GROUP LEADER, UNIROYAL CHEM CO, UNIROYAL INC, 78- *Concurrent Pos:* Vis res fel, Queen Mary Col, Univ London, 68-69. *Mem:* Am Chem Soc. *Res:* Polymer structure properties, degradation kinetics and mechanisms; specialty, polyurethane elastomers. *Mailing Add:* 58 Autumn Ridge Rd Huntington CT 06484

SINGH, AJIT, b Indore, India, Oct 31, 32; m 55. RADIATION CHEMISTRY, PHOTOCHEMISTRY. *Educ:* Agra Univ, BSc, 50, MSc, 52; Univ Alta, PhD(radiation chem), 64. *Prof Exp:* Lectr chem, Holkar Col, Indore, 56-59; teaching asst, Univ Alta, 59-63; res assoc, Chem Div, Argonne Nat Lab, 63-65; asst res officer, 66-68, assoc res officer, 69-81, SR RES OFFICER, WHITESHELL NUCLEAR RES ESTAB, ATOMIC ENERGY CAN LTD, 81- *Concurrent Pos:* Ed, Int J Radiation Physics & Chem, 75. *Mem:* Chem Inst Can; The Chem Soc; Am Chem Soc; Am Soc Photobiol; Inter-Am Photochem Soc. *Res:* Mechanisms of reactions in radiation chemistry, radiation biology, photochemistry and photobiology; physical and chemical properties of transient molecular species by the pulse radiolysis and flash photolysis techniques. *Mailing Add:* Whiteshell Nuclear Res Atomic Energy of Can Ltd Pinawa MB R0E 1L0 Can

SINGH, ARJUN, b Gonda, India, Jan 27, 43; nat US; m 63; c 3. GENETICS. *Educ:* G V Pant Univ Agr & Technol, Pantnagar, India, BSc, 64; Univ Ill, Urbana, PhD(genetics), 69. *Prof Exp:* Res assoc, Sch Med, Case Western Reserve Univ, 69-70; asst specialist, Donner Lab, Univ Calif, Berkeley, 70-71; fel, Univ Rochester, 71-72, assoc, 73-74, instr, Sch Med, 74-76; res assoc, Univ Mass, 76-77; NIH trainee, Dept Biochem, Univ Wis-Madison, 77-78, res assoc, 78-80; WITH GENENTECH INC, 80- *Mem:* Genetics Soc Am; Am Soc Microbiol; Am Inst Biol Sci. *Res:* Maize genetics; cytoplasmic inheritance; yeast genetics. *Mailing Add:* Genentech Inc 460 Point San Bruno Blvd San Francisco CA 94080

SINGH, BALWANT, b Hasanpur, India, Jan 21, 34; US citizen; m 72. MICROBIOLOGY, EPIDEMIOLOGY. *Educ:* Aligarh Muslim Univ, India, BSc, 53; Agra Univ, BVSc & AH, 57; Univ Mo, MS, 62, PhD(microbiol), 65. *Prof Exp:* Vet officer, Uttar Pradesh State Animal Husb Dept, 57-61; res assoc epidemiol & microbiol, 66-70, asst res prof, 70-76, RES ASSOC PROF EPIDEMIOL & MICROBIOL, GRAD SCH PUB HEALTH, UNIV PITTSBURGH, 76- *Mem:* Am Soc Microbiol; Am Pub Health Asn; Int Epidemiol Asn; Soc Epidemiol Res; Am Venereal Dis Asn. *Res:* Venereal diseases; public health microbiology; uterine cancer; reproductive health. *Mailing Add:* Dept of Epidemiol & Microbiol Univ of Pittsburgh Pittsburgh PA 15261

SINGH, BHARAT, b Calcutta, India, Feb 21, 39; m 64; c 2. PLANT PHYSIOLOGY, FOOD SCIENCE. *Educ:* Banaras Hindu Univ, BSc, 58; Ranchi Univ, India, MSc, 61; Univ BC, PhD(bot), 64. *Prof Exp:* Lectr bot, St Columba's Col, Hazaribagh, India, 61-64; res fel, Univ BC, 64-68, Med Res Coun Can fel, 68-69; fel, Utah State Univ, 69-70, vis asst prof food sci, 70-72; assoc prof, 72-75, PROF FOOD SCI, ALA A&M UNIV, 75- *Honors & Awards:* Morrison-Evans Outstanding Scientist award, 80. *Mem:* Inst Food Technologists; Am Soc Agron; Crop Sci Soc Am; Am Asn Cereal Chemists. *Res:* Biochemical and functional characteristics of triticale; chemical regulation of growth and metabolism in plants; utilization of cellulosic biomass; toxicity of myristate. *Mailing Add:* Dept of Food Sci & Technol Ala A&M Univ Normal AL 35762

SINGH, DAULAT, b Dihwa, India, July 27, 39; m 54; c 3. SOIL CHEMISTRY, ANALYTICAL CHEMISTRY. *Educ:* Agra Univ, BSc, 57, MSc, 59; Univ Guelph, MSc, 65; Mich State Univ, PhD(soil chem), 69. *Prof Exp:* Res asst soil chem, Nat Sugar Inst, Kanpur, India, 60-63; res asst soil phosphorous, Macdonald Col, McGill Univ, 66; CHEMIST, ENVIRON, LAB DIV, MICH DEPT AGR, 69- *Mem:* Am Soc Agron; Int Soc Soil Sci; Indian Soil Sci Soc; Asn Off Anal Chem. *Res:* Mechanisms of soil-fertilizer interaction; soil phosphorous reaction products. *Mailing Add:* Lab Div Mich Dept Agr 1615 S Harrison Rd East Lansing MI 48823

SINGH, DILBAGH, b Partabpura, India, Oct 15, 34; m 54; c 3. PLANT PATHOLOGY. *Educ:* Govt Col, Ludhiana, India, BSc, 56; Panjab Univ, India, BSc, 59, MSc, 61; Univ Wis, Madison, PhD(plant path), 68. *Prof Exp:* Lectr biol, Sikh Nat Col, India, 61-62; res asst plant path, Univ Wis, 62-67; chmn, Div Natural Sci, 77-80, PROF BIOL, BLACKBURN COL, 67- *Concurrent Pos:* Vis scientist, Univ Mass, 74-76. *Mem:* Am Phytopath Soc; Bot Soc Am; Am Inst Biol Sci; Mycol Soc Am; Nat Geog Soc. *Res:* Vascular diseases of plants; effects of pathogenesis on the nitrogenous and carbohydrate contents of the xylem sap; seasonal variation in the xylem sap components; effects of water stress on growth and metabolism of wilt inducing fungi; effects of water stress on the flowering behavior of various ornamental plants, Begonia, Impaties and Cloeus. *Mailing Add:* Dept of Biol Blackburn Col Carlinville IL 62626

SINGH, GURDIAL, b Panjab, India, Aug 15, 34; m 60; c 3. ORGANOMETALLIC CHEMISTRY. *Educ:* Panjab Univ, India, BSc, 57, MSc, 59; Univ Cincinnati, PhD(chem), 64. *Prof Exp:* Demonstrator chem, Panjab Univ, India, 58, 59, jr fel, 59-60; teaching asst, Univ Cincinnati, 60-61, fel, 63-64; res assoc, Mass Inst Technol, 64-65; res chemist, 65-72, SR RES CHEMIST, TEXTILE FIBERS DEPT, EXP STA, E I DU PONT DE NEMOURS & CO, WILMINGTON, 72- *Mem:* Am Chem Soc. *Res:* Synthetic polymer chemistry; organophosphorus chemistry; applications of nuclear magnetic resonance spectroscopy in organometallic chemistry. *Mailing Add:* 215 King George Rd Greenville NC 27834

SINGH, HAKAM, b Bagh, WPakistan, Feb 11, 28; m 50; c 4. POLYMER CHEMISTRY, SURFACE CHEMISTRY. *Educ:* Univ Delhi, BSc, 52, MSc, 54, PhD(chem), 59. *Prof Exp:* Lectr chem, Univ Delhi, 57-60; res assoc & lectr, Univ Southern Calif, 60-62; lectr, Univ Delhi, 62-63; reader, Punjabi Univ, 63-65; asst prof, IIT, New Delhi, 65-68; vis assoc prof, Univ Southern Calif, 68; res supr, 68-81, MGR, POLYMER LABS, PROD RES & CHEM CORP, 81- *Concurrent Pos:* Nat fel polymer technol, Intra Sci Res Found, 70- *Mem:* NY Acad Sci; AAAS; Am Chem Soc. *Res:* Structural chemistry of clay minerals; electrochemistry of nerve impulse initiation; interactions of surfactants with metal ions; electrochemistry of crevice corrosion; design and development of protective coatings; development of high performing elastomers and their processing; synthesis of high temperature polysulfide polymers; development of cyanosilosane sealants for space shuttle. *Mailing Add:* Res & Develop Lab Prod Res & Chem Corp 2820 Empire Ave Burbank CA 91504

SINGH, HARBHAJAN, b Delhi, India, July 12, 41; m 71; c 1. CHEMISTRY, BIOCHEMISTRY. *Educ:* Univ Delhi, BS, 61, MS, 63, PhD(chem), 66. *Prof Exp:* Asst prof exp med, Sch Med, NY Univ, 66-77, adj assoc prof biochem, Sch Dent, 75-77; res specialist, 77-81, sr res specialist, 81, RES GROUP LEADER, DEPT ENVIRON SCI, MONSANTO AGR PROD CO, 81- *Concurrent Pos:* Coun Sci & Indust Res India sr res fel natural prod, Univ Delhi, 66-67; Med Res Coun Can fel, Univ Western Ont, 67-68; Hormel Inst fel, Univ Minn, 69; res biochemist, Lipid Metab Lab, Vet Admin Hosp, New York, 69-; adj asst prof biochem, Sch Dent, NY Univ, 72-74. *Mem:* Am Chem Soc; Int Soc Study Xenobiotics. *Res:* Chemistry and metabolism of myelin; bacterial lipid metabolism; spingolipids; chemistry of natural products; development of analytical methods; lipid metabolism; metabolic and environmental studies on pesticides. *Mailing Add:* Monsanto Agr Prod Co 800 N Lindbergh Blvd St Louis MO 63166

SINGH, HARPAL P, b India, Aug 16, 41; m 70; c 3. ENVIRONMENTAL HEALTH, TOXICOLOGY. *Educ:* Punjab Univ, India, BS, 60, MS, 62; Univ Tenn, Knoxville, PhD(biol), 70, MPH, 74. *Prof Exp:* Res asst zool, Punjab Agr Univ, Ludhiana, India, 62-64; asst prof biol, Bennett Col, Greensboro, NC, 69-70; assoc prof biol, Knox Col, Knoxville, 70-74; assoc prof & coordr allied health, 74-80, PROF BIOL & COORDR MED TECHNOL, SAVANNAH STATE COL, 80- *Concurrent Pos:* NIH grants, 77-82. *Mem:* Nat Sci Teachers Asn; Am Soc Allied Health Prof; AAAS. *Res:* Chemical and radiosensitivity of male germ cells. *Mailing Add:* Savannah State Col PO Box 20425 Savannah GA 31404

SINGH, HARWANT, b Amritsar, India, Nov 20, 34; m 55. BIOCHEMISTRY. *Educ:* Agra Univ, BSc, 55; Vikram Univ, India, MSc, 59; Univ Alta, PhD(biochem), 62. *Prof Exp:* NIH res fel biochem, Univ Alta, 62-63; res assoc, Med Sch, Northwestern Univ, 63-65; asst res officer, 66-68, ASSOC RES OFFICER BIOCHEM, WHITESHELL NUCLEAR RES ESTAB, ATOMIC ENERGY CAN LTD, 69- *Mem:* Am Soc Photobiol; Chem Inst Can; Can Biochem Soc. *Res:* Structure of oligonucleotides and nucleic acids; mechanisms involved in protein synt hesis; ribosome interactions; photo and radiation chemistry of ribosomes and their constituents. *Mailing Add:* Med Biophys Br Atomic Energy Can Pinawa MB R0E 1L0 Can

SINGH, INDER JIT, b India, Apr 28, 39. ANATOMY, DENTISTRY. *Educ:* Punjab Univ, India, BDS, 59; Univ Ore, PhD(anat), 69. *Prof Exp:* House surgeon, Govt Dent Col & Hosp, India, 59-60; asst pedodont, Dent Sch, Univ Ore, 61-65; res assoc med psychol, Med Sch, 68-69; asst res scientist, Inst Dent Res, 69-71, assoc res scientist, 71-78, asst prof, 72-74, assoc prof, 74-79, PROF ANAT, COL DENT & GRAD SCH ARTS & SCI, NY UNIV, 79-, ASSOC CHMN DEPT ANAT, 78- *Concurrent Pos:* Fel, Guggenheim Dent Clin, New York, 60-61; NIH spec res fel, Lab Cellular Res, Inst Dent Res, 71 & 72; adj asst prof, Fordham Univ, 70-71; assoc prof, City Univ New York, 71- *Mem:* AAAS; Am Asn Anat; fel Geront Soc; NY Acad Sci; Int Asn Dent Res. *Res:* Mammalian growth and development; experimental teratology; skeletal biology. *Mailing Add:* NY Univ Dent Ctr 342 E 24th St New York NY 10010

SINGH, INDERJIT, b Langrian, India, July 13, 43; US citizen; m 80. NEUROCHEMISTRY, NEUROBIOLOGY. *Educ:* Panjab Univ, India, BSc, 65, MSc, 67; Iowa State Univ, PhD(biochem), 74. *Prof Exp:* Res fel neurochem, Mass Gen Hosp, 75-76; res fel, 76-77, instr, 77-78, ASST PROF NEUROL, JOHNS HOPKINS SCH MED, 78- *Mem:* Am Soc Neurochem; Int Soc Neurochem; Am Soc Biol Chem. *Res:* Molecular mechanisms of the development of oligodendrocytes, myelinogenesis and the status of myelin in neuropathological disorders. *Mailing Add:* 707 N Broadway John F Kennedy Inst Baltimore MD 21205

SINGH, IQBAL, b Muzafaagarh, India, Feb 23, 26; nat US. ORTHOPEDIC SURGERY, IMMUNOLOGY. *Educ:* Punjab Univ, FSc, 42, MD, 49. *Prof Exp:* Instr physiol, Mission Med Col, India, 51; asst instr orthop, Univ Pa, 55-57; clin asst, Univ Calif, Los Angeles, 59-61; asst clin prof, Univ Calif, Irvine, 66-69; assoc prof orthop & chmn div, Dept Surg, 69-76, assoc prof, 76-80, PROF SURG, MED COL OHIO, 80- *Mem:* AMA; AAAS; Asn Clin Scientists; Can Orthop Asn; Am Asn Surg Trauma. *Res:* Cell mediated and humoral immunity; blocking factor; surgical extirpation supplemented with immunotherapy; horizontal and vertical transmission of immunity in patients; an animal model for human osteosarcoma. *Mailing Add:* Dept of Surg Med Col of Ohio PO Box 6190 Toledo OH 43614

SINGH, JAG JEET, b Rohtak, India, May 20, 26; c 1. PHYSICS, ASTRONOMY. *Educ:* Panjab Univ, BS, MS, 48; Liverpool Univ, PhD(nuclear physics), 56. *Prof Exp:* Lectr physics, Panjab Educ Serv, India, 50-53; res fel nuclear physics, Univ Liverpool, 56-57; prof physics, Panjab Govt Col, 57-58; USAEC res fel nuclear physics, Univ Kans, 58-59; asst prof physics, Mem Univ Nfld, 59-60; assoc prof, WVa State Col, 60-62 & Col William & Mary, 62-64; staff scientist aerospace sci, 64-80, CHIEF SCIENTIST, INSTRUMENT RES DIV, LANGLEY RES CTR, NASA, 80- *Concurrent Pos:* Adv Gov Va, William & Mary Repr, Govs Adv Coun, Va Assoc Res Ctr, 62-63; lectr-consult, NASA Langley Res Ctr, 62-64; adj prof physics & geophys sci, Old Dominion Univ & consult physicist, Col William & Mary, 74-; consult, Med Res Serv, Vet Admin Ctr, Hampton, 76- *Honors & Awards:* Appolo Achievement Award, NASA, 69, Technol Utilization Award, 77. *Mem:* Fel Brit Inst Physics; fel AAAS; assoc fel Am Inst Aeronaut & Astronaut; Am Phys Soc. *Res:* Materials science, environmental and optical physics relevant to NASA mission; specifically, Mossbauer spectroscopy and positron annihilation spectroscopy of structural alloys and aerosol characterization. *Mailing Add:* PO Box 2418 Williamsburg VA 23185

SINGH, JAGBIR, b Baraut, India, Jan 2, 40; m 68. PROBABILITY. *Educ:* Aligarh Muslim Univ, India, MS, 60; Fla State Univ, PhD(statist), 67. *Prof Exp:* Asst prof statist, J V Col, Baraut, India, 60-62; asst prof math, Ohio State Univ, 67-74; assoc prof, 74-78, PROF STATIST, TEMPLE UNIV, 78- *Concurrent Pos:* Sr prof, Indian Agr Res Sci Inst, New Delhi, 77-78. *Mem:* Inst Math Statist; Am Statist Asn; Biomet Soc. *Res:* Paired comparison model building; estimation; applied probability; sampling. *Mailing Add:* Dept of Statist Temple Univ Philadelphia PA 19122

SINGH, JASBIR, b Hong Kong, Feb 20, 45; Can citizen; m 70; c 2. BIOCHEMISTRY, PLANT PHYSIOLOGY. *Educ:* McGill Univ, BSc, 66, PhD(biochem), 71. *Prof Exp:* Res assoc biochem, Cornell Univ, 71-73 & Can Agr & Univ Ottawa, 73-76; RES SCIENTIST BIOCHEM AGR CAN, 76- *Concurrent Pos:* Nat Res Coun res fel, 73-75. *Mem:* Am Soc Plant Physiologists. *Res:* Cell biology and physiology of freezing; tolerance and injury in plant cells. *Mailing Add:* Chem & Biol Res Inst Res Br Agr Can Ottawa ON K1A 0C6 Can

SINGH, JASWANT, b Gunna Ur, WPanjab, Sept 29, 37; m 69. PLANT PATHOLOGY. *Educ:* Khalsa Col, India, BSc, 58; Panjab Univ, India, MSc, 60; Univ Ill, Urbana, PhD(plant path), 66. *Prof Exp:* Demonstr chem, Khalsa Col, India, 58-61; res assoc & asst prof bot & plant path, Sci Res Inst, Ore State Univ, 66-68; assoc prof, 68-69, PROF BIOL, MISS VALLEY STATE UNIV, 69-, HEAD DEPT, 77- *Mem:* AAAS. *Res:* Reproductive physiology; physiology and biochemistry of fungi. *Mailing Add:* Dept Biol Miss Valley State Univ Itta Bena MS 38941

SINGH, KANHAYA LAL, b Varanasi, India, Feb 15, 44; m 65; c 2. ANALYSIS, FUNCTIONAL ANALYSIS. *Educ:* Agra Univ, BSc, 62; Mem Univ, MA, 69; Tex A&M Univ, PhD(math), 80. *Prof Exp:* Fel, Lakehead Univ, 80-81; ASST PROF CALCULUS & DIFFERENTIAL EQUATIONS, UNIV MINN, DULUTH, 81- *Mem:* Am Math Soc; Math Asn Am. *Res:* Nonlinear functional analysis, fixed point theory, and approximation theory. *Mailing Add:* Dept Math Univ Minn Duluth MN 55812

SINGH, MADHO, b Mandha, India, Apr 25, 36. GENETICS, BIOMETRICS. *Educ:* Univ Rajasthan, BScAg, 54; Agra Univ, MScAg, 56; Univ Minn, PhD, 65. *Prof Exp:* Lectr animal genetics, SKN Col, Jobner, India, 56-60; res asst genetics, Univ Minn, 61-65; res assoc biol, Univ Chicago, 65-66; reader animal sci & head dept, Univ Udaipur, India, 66-68; res scientist zool, Univ Tex Austin, 68-69; asst prof, 69-71, ASSOC PROF BIOL, STATE UNIV NY COL ONEONTA, 71- *Concurrent Pos:* Vis prof genetics, Sch Med, Univ Hawaii, 74-75; vis fel, Cornell Univ, 76. *Mem:* NY Acad Sci; Genetics Soc Am; Biomet Soc; Soc Study Evolution; Am Soc Human Genetics. *Res:* Human genetics; biometrics; evolutionary biology; selection studies in mice; application of computers in genetic research; theoretical studies in population genetics. *Mailing Add:* Dept of Biol State Univ of NY Col Oneonta NY 13820

SINGH, MAHENDRA PAL, b India, Sept 20, 41; m 65; c 3. STRUCTURAL ANALYSIS & DESIGN. *Educ:* Univ Rookee, BE, 62, ME, 66; Univ Ill, PhD(civil eng), 72. *Prof Exp:* Asst engr civil eng, Western Railway, India, 63-68; sr engr structural design, Sargent & Lundy, Chicago, 72-76, supvr, 76-77; assoc prof, 77-82, PROF ENG MECH, VA POLYTECH INST & STATE UNIV, 82- *Concurrent Pos:* Consult, Sargent & Lundy, Chicago, 77-79, Woodward Clyde Consult, 79-80 & Stevenson & Assoc, Cleveland, 81-; engr, Lawrence Livermore Nat Lab, 79-80. *Mem:* Am Soc Civil Engrs; Earthquake Eng Res Inst; Seismol Soc Am; Indian Soc Earthquake Technol. *Res:* Structural engineering; structural reliability; soil dynamics; structural dynamics; earthquake and wind engineering. *Mailing Add:* Dept Eng Mech 227 Norris Hall Va Polytech Inst & State Univ Blacksburg VA 24061

SINGH, MANOHAR, b Panjab, India, Apr 13, 30; m 56; c 3. APPLIED MATHEMATICS, CONTINUUM MECHANICS. *Educ:* Panjab Univ, India, BA, 50, MA, 53; Brown Univ, MSc, 63, PhD(appl math), 65. *Prof Exp:* Lectr math, Govt Col, Panjab Univ, 53-61; asst prof, NC State Univ, 65-67; chmn dept, 78-81, PROF MATH, SIMON FRASER UNIV, 67- *Concurrent Pos:* Vis prof, Panjab Univ, 69-70. *Mem:* Can Math Cong; Can Appl Math Soc. *Mailing Add:* Dept Math Simon Fraser Univ Burnaby BC V5A 1S6 Can

SINGH, MANSA C, b Lyallpur, India, Oct 10, 28; m 63; c 3. ENGINEERING MECHANICS, STRUCTURAL ENGINEERING. *Educ:* Punjab Univ, India, BSc, 52; Univ Minn, MS, 56, PhD(struct & appl mech), 62. *Prof Exp:* Asst engr, Bhakra Dam Designs Directorate, 52-55; asst prof civil eng, Univ Kans, 61-63 & Punjab Eng Col, 63-64; asst prof eng mech, SDak State Univ, 64-68; ASSOC PROF MECH ENG, UNIV CALGARY, 68- *Mem:* AAAS; Am Soc Civil Engrs; Am Soc Eng Educ. *Res:* Viscoelastic behavior of surfaces of revolution under combined mechanical and thermal loads; thermoelastoplastic bending and stability of beam columns; application of group theory to problems of vibrations and wave propagation; impact of nonlinear viscoplastic and viscous rods; problem of notation in vector mechanics. *Mailing Add:* Dept of Mech Eng Univ of Calgary Calgary AB T2N 1N4 Can

SINGH, PARAM INDAR, b Ferozepore, India, Nov 27, 46; US citizen; m 69; c 1. FLUID DYNAMICS. *Educ:* Univ Colo, BS, 68, MS, 70, PhD(aerospace eng sci), 74. *Prof Exp:* Sr scientist, 74-76, PRIN RES SCIENTIST AEROPHYSICS, AVCO EVERETT RES LAB, 76- *Mem:* AAAS; Am Inst Aeronaut & Astronaut; Am Phys Soc. *Res:* Turbulent flows; high energy lasers; laser effects and propagation; acoustics; reentry physics; biological fluid mechanics. *Mailing Add:* 40 N Hancock St Lexington MA 02173

SINGH, PRITAM, b Okara, India, Mar 10, 29; Can citizen; m 63; c 3. BIOCHEMISTRY, PHARMACOLOGY. *Educ:* Panjab Univ, India, BSc, 49; Univ Saugar, MSc, 52; Univ Allahabad, PhD(chem), 55; Laval Univ, DSc(biochem), 65. *Prof Exp:* Res assoc chem, Univ Toronto, 56-57 & Laval Univ, 57-62; res biochem, Univ Montreal, 64-65; asst prof, 65-69, ASSOC PROF PHARMACOL, LAVAL UNIV, 69- *Mem:* Can Biochem Soc; Pharmacol Soc Can; Fr Soc Therapeut & Pharmacodyn. *Res:* Ontogenetic development of blood brain barrier; drug interactions in chronic multiple drug therapy. *Mailing Add:* Dept of Pharmacol Fac of Med Laval Univ Quebec PQ G1K 7P4 Can

SINGH, PRITHE PAUL, b Havialian, India, Sept 10, 30; m 59; c 2. NUCLEAR PHYSICS. *Educ:* Univ Agra, BSc, 51, MSc, 53; Univ BC, PhD(nuclear physics), 60. *Prof Exp:* Lectr physics, D C Jain Col, India, 53-54; res asst nuclear physics, Dept Atomic Energy, Govt of India, 54-55; Nat Res Coun Can fel, Atomic Energy Can, Ltd, 59-62; res assoc nuclear physics, Argonne Nat Lab, 62-64; from asst prof to assoc prof, 64-71, PROF PHYSICS, IND UNIV, BLOOMINGTON, 71- *Concurrent Pos:* Fac assoc, Argonne Nat Lab, 66-72; consult, US Naval Res Lab, 69- *Mem:* Fel Am Phys Soc. *Res:* Nuclear spectroscopy with neutrons and charged particles; inverse photodisintegration studies; nuclear reaction mechanism for alpha particle interaction with nuclei; statistical properties of nuclear cross sections; pion production; medium energy nuclear physics; heavy ion reactions. *Mailing Add:* Dept of Physics Swain Hall W Ind Univ Bloomington IN 47401

SINGH, PRITHIPAL, b Amritsar, India, Apr 6, 39; m 63; c 2. ORGANIC CHEMISTRY. *Educ:* Khalsa Col, India, BS, 59; Banaras Hindu Univ, MS, 61; Toronto Univ, PhD(org chem), 67. *Prof Exp:* Teacher chem, Khalsa Col, Delhi Univ, 61-68 & Banaras Hindu Univ, 68-69; res chemist, 70-73, group leader, 73-74, sect mgr chem, 74-77, asst dir, 77-81, VPRES, SYVA CORP, 81- *Concurrent Pos:* Fel, Southampton Univ & Brit Coun travel grant, 69-70. *Mem:* Am Chem Soc; fel The Chem Soc; Am Asn Clin Chem; Interam Soc Photochemists; Am Asn Photochem & Photobiol. *Res:* Synthetic, structural organic chemistry; immunochemistry; photochemistry. *Mailing Add:* Syva Corp 900 Arastradero Rd Palo Alto CA 94303

SINGH, RABINDAR NATH, b Ludhiana, India, Apr 10, 31; m 57; c 3. AGRONOMY, SOILS. *Educ:* Punjab Univ, India, BSc, 55; Univ Tenn, MS, 59; Va Polytech Inst & State Univ, PhD(agron), 65. *Prof Exp:* Res asst soil fertil, Va Polytech Inst & State Univ, 63-65, fel & res assoc, 65-66; res assoc soil chem & fertil, 66-69, res assoc clay mineral, 69-71, asst prof soil fertil & clay mineral, 71-75, assoc prof, 75-78, PROF AGRON & AGRONOMIST, WVA UNIV, 78- *Concurrent Pos:* Mem, Nat Task Force Sewage Sludge Crop Land, Coun Agr Sci & Technol, Environ Protection Agency. *Mem:* Am Soc Agron; Am Soc Soil Sci; Int Soc Soil Sci; Am Chem Soc. *Res:* Chemistry of soil phosphorus and micronutrients and their availability to crops; disposal of sewage sludge on agricultural land and mine sails; chemistry and mineralogy of coal overburden material; reclamation of strip mined land. *Mailing Add:* Dept Soil & Plant Sci WVa Univ Morgantown WV 26506

SINGH, RAGHBIR, b Punjab, India, Nov 1, 31; US citizen; m 66; c 1. AGRONOMY, PLANT PHYSIOLOGY. *Educ:* Punjab Univ, India, BSc, 52, MSc, 55; Univ Minn, PhD(agron), 64. *Prof Exp:* Res asst plant physiol, Ministry of Agr, India, 55-59; res fel, Univ Minn, 64-65; from asst prof to assoc prof biol, Chadron State Col, 65-67; PROF BIOL, BENEDICT COL, 67-, CHMN DIV SCI & MATH, 68- *Concurrent Pos:* NSF res grant, 66, undergrad equip, 67-69. *Res:* Nutrition, physiology and biochemistry of crop plants. *Mailing Add:* Dept of Biol Benedict Col Columbia SC 29204

SINGH, RAJINDER, b Adamke Cheema, WPakistan, Apr 1, 31; m 61; c 2. MATHEMATICAL STATISTICS. *Educ:* Panjab Univ, India, MA, 52; Univ Ill, Urbana, PhD(statist), 60. *Prof Exp:* Lectr statist, Panjab Univ, India, 52-56 & 60-62, reader, 62-64; asst prof math, Univ Ill, Urbana, 64-66; from asst prof to assoc prof, 66-75, PROF MATH, UNIV SASK, 75- *Res:* Estimation problems in statistics. *Mailing Add:* Dept Math Univ Sask Saskatoon SK S7N 0W0 Can

SINGH, RAMA SHANKAR, b Varanasi, India, Sept 27, 38; c 3. SOLID STATE PHYSICS. *Educ:* Banaras Hindu Univ, India, BSc, 59, MSc, 61; Univ RI, PhD(elec eng), 71. *Prof Exp:* Resident res asst solid state physics, US Army Munition Command & Nat Res Coun/Nat Acad Sci, 71-72; from asst prof to assoc prof physics, Univ PR, Mayaguez, 72-78; staff mem, Lincoln Lab, Mass Inst Technol, Lexington, 78-82; PROCESS ENGR, GEN ELEC CO, 82- *Concurrent Pos:* Scientist I, PR Nuclear Ctr, Mayaguez, 72-78. *Mem:* Soc Photo-Optical Instrumentation Engrs; Am Phys Soc; Inst Elec & Electronics Engrs. *Res:* Optical, thermal and mechanical properties of materials; lattice dynamics and phase transition; Raman and Brillouin scattering; solid state memory devices. *Mailing Add:* Gen Elec Co 206 French Rd Utica NY 02173

SINGH, RAMA SHANKAR, b Azamgarh, India, Mar 2, 45; m 76; c 2. POPULATION GENETICS, EVOLUTIONARY THEORY. *Educ:* Agra Univ, India, BSc, 65; Kanpur Univ, India, MSc, 67; Univ Calif, Davis, PhD(genetics), 72. *Prof Exp:* Lectr bot, Govt Agr Col Kanpur, 67-68; Ford Found fel biol, Univ Chicago, 72-73; fel zool, Harvard Univ, 73-75; asst prof,

75-80, ASSOC PROF BIOL, MCMASTER UNIV, 80- *Mem:* AAAS; Genetics Soc Am; Genetics Soc Can; Soc Study Evolution; Soc Am Naturalists. *Res:* Genetic variation and its role in adaptation and species formation; the role of sex in evolution; genetics of insecticide resistance. *Mailing Add:* Dept Biol McMaster Univ Hamilton ON L8S 4L8 Can

SINGH, RAMESHWAR, b Bihar, India, July 2, 37; m 54; c 4. HYDRAULICS, FLUID MECHANICS. *Educ:* Auburn Univ, BCE, 62, MS, 63; Stanford Univ, PhD(civil eng), 65. *Prof Exp:* Sectional officer design & construct, Irrig Dept, Govt Bihar, India, 56-60; asst prof civil eng, Univ BC, 65-67; assoc prof, 67-77, PROF CIVIL ENG, SAN JOSE STATE UNIV, 77- *Concurrent Pos:* Consult, Fraser River Flood Res, Can, 65-67 & Jennings, McDermitt & Heis Consult Firm, Calif, 68- *Mem:* Assoc mem Am Soc Civil Engrs; Am Geophys Union; Soil Conserv Soc Am. *Res:* Hydraulics; hydrology; fluid mechanics with application of applied mathematics and computers. *Mailing Add:* Dept of Civil Eng & Appl Mech 125 S Seventh St San Jose CA 95192

SINGH, RIPU DAMAN, b Patmau, Uttar Pradesh, India. PHYSICAL ANTHROPOLOGY, PRIMATOLOGY. *Educ:* Univ Lucknow, BA, 51, MA, 53; Univ Ore, MA, 69, PhD(anthrop), 71. *Prof Exp:* Asst prof anthrop, Univ Lucknow, 56-60; asst anthropologist, Anthrop Surv India, Govt India, 60-66; instr anthrop, Univ Ore, 66-70; asst prof anthrop, 70-72, ASSOC PROF ANTHROP, UNIV WINDSOR, 72- *Concurrent Pos:* Assoc anthrop. *Mem:* Am Asn Phys Anthrop; fel Royal Anthrop Inst Gt Brit & Ireland; Can Asn Phys Anthrop; Ethnog & Folk Cult Soc India; Int Dermatoglyphic Asn. *Res:* Human population variations; dermatoglyphic variations and genetic patterns in caste populations of India and Canada; primate behavior and comparative primatology; human evolution. *Mailing Add:* Dept of Sociol & Anthrop Univ of Windsor Windsor ON N9B 3P4 Can

SINGH, RODERICK PATAUDI, b Georgetown, Guyana, Feb 26, 35; Can citizen; m 61; c 3. ANATOMY. *Educ:* Univ Western Ont, BA, 61, MSc, 63, PhD(anat), 66. *Prof Exp:* Instr anat, Med Sch, Wayne State Univ, 66-67; from lectr to asst prof, 67-72, ASSOC PROF ANAT, UNIV WESTERN ONT, 72- *Concurrent Pos:* Cytogeneticist, Children's Psychiat Res Inst, London, Ont, 70-; consult, Depts Pediat & Obstet & Gynec, St Joseph's Hosp, London, Ont. *Honors & Awards:* Award, Soc Obstet & Gynec Can, 68. *Mem:* Am Asn Anat; Can Asn Anat; Am Asn Phys Anthrop; Soc Study Human Biol. *Res:* Cytogenetics of human abortuses; embryology and morphology of the human ovary. *Mailing Add:* Dept of Anat Univ of Western Ont London ON N6A 5B8 Can

SINGH, RUDRA PRASAD, b Sariya, India, Sept 1, 40; Can citizen; m 56; c 3. VIROLOGY. *Educ:* Agra Univ, India, BScAg, 59, MScAg, 61; NDak State Univ, Fargo, PhD(plant path), 66. *Prof Exp:* Sr res asst plant virol, Dept Agr, Uttar Pradesh, India, 61-62; fel, Nat Res Coun Can, 66-67; RES SCIENTIST PLANT VIROL, AGR CAN RES STA, 68- *Mem:* Am Phytopath Soc; Potato Asn Am; Can Phytopath Soc; Indian Potato Asn. *Res:* Isolation of different forms of infectious low molecular weight ribonucleic acid of potato spindle tuber disease; their purification, finger printing and nucleotide sequence analysis; virus indicator plants; determination of viroid strains and their interrelationship; viroid inhibitors. *Mailing Add:* Agr Can Res Sta PO Box 20280 Fredericton NB E3B 4Z7 Can

SINGH, SANKATHA PRASAD, b Varanasi, India, Jan 27, 37; m 59; c 2. MATHEMATICS. *Educ:* Agra Univ, BSc, 57; Benaras Hindu Univ, MSc, 59, PhD(math), 63. *Prof Exp:* Lectr math, Benaras Hindu Univ, 59-63; instr, Univ Ill, 63-64; asst prof, Wayne State Univ, 64-65; asst prof, Univ Windsor, 65-67; assoc prof, 67-72, PROF MATH, MEM UNIV NFLD, 72- *Concurrent Pos:* Nat Res Coun grant, 65- & NATO res grants, 80; foreign ed, Indian J Math. *Mem:* Am Math Soc; Math Asn Am; Can Math Cong; Indian Math Soc; Ind Sci Cong Asn. *Res:* Transform calculus; approximation theory; fixed point theory in tolopogy and functional analysis. *Mailing Add:* Dept Math Mem Univ Nfld St John's NF A1B 3X7 Can

SINGH, SANT PARKASH, b Anokh Singh Wala, India, Oct 2, 36; m 68. ENDOCRINOLOGY, PHYSIOLOGY. *Educ:* Punjab Univ, India, MBBS, 59; McGill Univ, MSc, 70; Am Bd Internal Med, dipl, 68; Am Bd Nuclear Med, dipl, 76; Am Bd Endocrinol & Metab, dipl, 77. *Prof Exp:* Intern med, Kingston Gen Hosp, Ont, 60-61; resident, Bergen Pines County Hosp, Paramus, NJ, 61-63; resident endocrinol, Philadelphia Gen Hosp, 63-64; resident med, Bergen Pines County Hosp, Paramus, NJ, 64-65; assoc endocrinologist, Brooklyn-Cumberland Med Ctr, 70-72, dir endocrinol sect, 72-73; asst prof med, State Univ NY Downstate Med Ctr, 71-73; assoc prof clin med, Northwestern Univ, Chicago, 73-74; assoc prof, 74-78, PROF MED, CHICAGO MED SCH, 78-; ASSOC CHIEF OF STAFF & CHIEF ENDOCRINE-METAB SECT, VET ADMIN HOSP, NORTH CHICAGO, 73-, DIR, DIV ENDOCRINOL & METAB, CHICAGO MED SCH, 74- *Concurrent Pos:* Fel, State Univ NY Downstate Med Ctr, 65-66; Med Res Coun Can fel, McGill Univ Clin Royal Victoria Hosp, Montreal, 66-70. *Mem:* Am Col Physicians; Endocrine Soc; Am Diabetes Asn; Am Fedn Clin Res. *Res:* Thyroid pathophysiology; carbohydrate metabolism. *Mailing Add:* Vet Admin Hosp North Chicago IL 60064

SINGH, SHIVA PUJAN, b Gonda, India, July 15, 47; US citizen; m 73; c 2. MICROBIOLOGY, BIOCHEMISTRY. *Educ:* Pant Univ Agr & Technol, India, BSc, 69, MSc, 71; Auburn Univ, PhD(microbiol), 76. *Prof Exp:* ASST PROF BIOL, ALA STATE UNIV, 76- *Mem:* AAAS; Am Inst Biol Sci; Am Soc Microbiol. *Res:* Bacterial physiology; serology, immnology and biochemistry of insect viruses. *Mailing Add:* Dept Biol Ala State Univ Montgomery AL 36195

SINGH, SHOBHA, b Delhi, India, July 15, 28; m 46; c 5. LASERS, SOLID STATE PHYSICS. *Educ:* Univ Delhi, BSc, 49, MSc, 51; Johns Hopkins Univ, PhD(physics), 57. *Prof Exp:* Res asst physics, Nat Phys Lab, India, 51-53; asst prof, Wilson Col, 57-59; res officer, Atomic Energy Estab, India, 59-61 & Nat Res Coun Can, 61-64; MEM TECH STAFF PHYSICS, BELL TEL LABS, 64- *Concurrent Pos:* Fel, Johns Hopkins Univ, 57-59; Nat Res Coun Can fel, 61-63. *Mem:* Am Phys Soc; fel Optical Soc Am. *Res:* Spectra of solids, Raman spectra, laser induced non-linear phenomena in solids, electrochromics and three to five compound semiconductors. *Mailing Add:* Bell Tel Labs Murray Hill NJ 07974

SINGH, SUKHJIT, b Ramidi, India, July 21, 41; US citizen. TOPOLOGY. *Educ:* Ariz State Univ, BA, 69; Pa State Univ, MA, 60, PhD(math), 73. *Prof Exp:* Asst, 70-73, asst prof, 73-80, ASSOC PROF MATH, PA STATE UNIV, 80- *Mem:* Am Math Soc. *Res:* Decomposition spaces and shape theory. *Mailing Add:* Pa State Univ Altoona Campus Altoona PA 16603

SINGH, SUMAN PRIYADARSHI NARAIN, b Ludhiana, India, June 23, 41; US citizen. FOSSIL ENERGY PROCESSES. *Educ:* Indian Inst Technol, Bombay, BTech, 64; Okla State Univ, MS, 67, PhD(chem eng), 73. *Prof Exp:* Process design engr natural gas liquids processing, Phillips Petrol Co, 66-69; engr petrol res, Exxon Res & Develop Labs, 74-75; from develop staff mem I to develop staff mem II coal processing, 76-81, TASK LEADER ENVIRON CONTROLS, OAK RIDGE NAT LAB, 81- *Concurrent Pos:* NSF fel, Okla State Univ, 76. *Mem:* Am Inst Chem Engrs; Sigma Xi. *Res:* Techno-economic assessment of environmental control processes applicable in fossil energy liquefaction and gasification processes. *Mailing Add:* Rm 226 Bldg 4500N PO Box X Oak Ridge Nat Lab Oak Ridge TN 37830

SINGH, SURESH PRATAP, b Pratapgarh, India, Sept 27, 37; m 62; c 2. POULTRY SCIENCE. *Educ:* Bihar Vet Col, India, BVSc, 59; Univ Vt, MS, 66; Va Polytech Inst, PhD(animal sci), 70. *Prof Exp:* Lectr animal sci, Animal Husbandry Sch, India, 59-60; asst vet sheep & poultry, Govt Vet Hosp, India, 60-63; res fel poultry sci, Univ Vt, 64-66; res asst, Va Polytech Inst, 66-69; res dir nutrit & lab div, Rockingham Poultry Mkt Coop, Inc, 70-78; DIR NUTRIT & RES DIV, MANDATA POULTRY CO, GETTYSBURG, 78- *Mem:* Poultry Sci Asn; World Poultry Sci Asn; Inst Food Technol; Animal Nutrit Res Coun. *Res:* Field research in broiler meat production regarding utilization of animal by-products; disease and nutrition relationship in broiler meat production; developing new food products from broiler meat. *Mailing Add:* PO Box 576 Gettysburg PA 17325

SINGH, SURINDER SHAH, b Kotshakir, India, Jan 5, 37. SOIL SCIENCE, SOIL CHEMISTRY. *Educ:* Panjab Univ, India, BSc, 57, MSc, 60; Indian Agr Res Inst, New Delhi, PhD(soil sci), 63. *Prof Exp:* Res asst saline soils, Indian Dept Agr, Ludhiana, 59-60; fel soil sci, Univ Uppsala, 63-64 & soil res inst, Nat Res Coun Can, 64-65; res officer, 65-67, res sci scientist res br, 67-77, MEM STAFF, LAND RESOURCE RES INST, CENT EXP FARM, CAN DEPT AGR, 77- *Mem:* Int Asn Study Clays; Am Soc Agron; Can Soc Soil Sci; Int Soc Soil Sci; Chem Inst Can. *Res:* Quality of irrigation waters; boron distribution in normal and saline-alkali soils; isolation and characterization of the reactions responsible for controlling the distribution of components among the different phases of a soil; reactions of metals and inorganic pollutants; solubility products of sparingly soluble substances; acidic precipitation and aluminum mobility. *Mailing Add:* Chemistry & Biol Res Inst Can Dept of Agr Ottawa ON K1A 0C6 Can

SINGH, SURJIT, b Roorkee, India, Oct 9, 31; m 64; c 1. PHYSICAL CHEMISTRY, ENVIRONMENTAL SAFETY. *Educ:* Khalsa Col, Amritsar, India, BSc, 52; Panjab Univ, India, MSc, 55; St Louis Univ, PhD(chem), 63. *Prof Exp:* Instr chem, Hindu Col, Amritsar, 52-53; asst prof, Khalsa Col, India, 55-56 & Govt Col, Gurdaspur, 56-59; asst, St Louis Univ, 59-63; from asst prof to assoc prof, Waynesburg Col, 63-67; assoc prof, 67-80, PROF CHEM, STATE UNIV NY BUFFALO, 80- *Concurrent Pos:* Res assoc, Centre Neurochimie, Strasbourg, 78. *Mem:* AAAS; Am Chem Soc; Am Inst Chem Eng. *Res:* Hazardous waste management and resource recovery; neurochemistry; toxicology; charge transfer spectra; fire safety of construction materials (thermodynamics and material properties); photochromism. *Mailing Add:* Dept Chem State Univ NY 1300 Elmwood Ave Buffalo NY 14222

SINGH, TEJA, b June 18, 28; Can citizen. FOREST HYDROLOGY, APPLIED STATISTICS. *Educ:* EPunjab Univ, India, BA, 49, Utah State Univ, Logan, MSc, 63, PhD(watershed mgt), 66. *Prof Exp:* Forestry aid res shelterbelts, US Forest Serv, Lincoln, Nebr, 59; asst res hydrol & ecol, Utah State Univ, Logan, 60-62; asst res watershed mgt, Eastern Rockies Forest Conserv Bd, Calgary, Alta, 63; res officer forest hydrol, Can Dept Forestry, Calgary, 65-66; res scientist, Calgary, 67-70, RES SCIENTIST FOREST HYDROL, NORTHERN FOREST RES CTR, CAN FORESTRY SERV, EDMONTON, ALTA, 71-; PRES, CANADA RESOURCES DEVELOP & MGT, LTD, 80- *Concurrent Pos:* Chief tech adv multidisciplinary hydrol res, Food & Agr Orgn Watershed Mgt & Coord Proj, Iran, 77-; consult environ impact, Food & Agr Orgn & UNESCO, Rome, 80. *Mem:* Sigma Xi; Can Wildlife Fedn; Am Geophys Union; Soc Range Mgt; Can Inst Forestry. *Res:* Energy from biomass; hydrologic research prarie provinces of Alberta, Saskatchewan and Manitoba; environmental quality, statistical procedures, biometrics, mathematical modeling and watershed hydrology. *Mailing Add:* N Forest Res Ctr Can Forest Serv Environ Can 5320-122 St Edmonton AB T6H 3S5 Can

SINGH, TRILOCHAN (HARDEEP), b Vehari, Pakistan, Dec 31, 37; m 64; c 2. MECHANICAL ENGINEERING. *Educ:* Punjab Eng Col, BSc, 61; Univ Calif, Berkeley, MS, 66, PhD(mech eng), 70. *Prof Exp:* Asst engr, Oil & Natural Gas Comn, Dehradum, India, 60-64; lectr mech eng, Thapar Col Eng, Patiala, 64-65; res asst, Univ Calif, Berkeley, 65-70; asst prof, 70-76, NSF res initiation grant, 72-74, ASSOC PROF MECH ENG SCI, WAYNE STATE UNIV, 76- *Mem:* Soc Automotive Engrs; Combustion Inst; Air Pollution Control Asn. *Res:* Basic combustion studies; pollutant species formation; eliminations and control in different types of combustion systems. *Mailing Add:* 664 Putnam Wayne State Univ Detroit MI 48202

SINGH, VIJAY PAL, b New Delhi, India, July 25, 47; US citizen; m 72; c 2. SOLAR CELLS-PHOTOVOLTAICS, INFRARED DETECTORS. *Educ:* Indian Inst Technol, Delhi, BTech, 68; Univ Minn, MS, 70, PhD(elec eng), 74. *Prof Exp:* Res asst prof, Inst Energy Conversion, Univ Del, 74-76; res engr, 76-80, sect head device res, 80-81, MGR MAT & DEVICE RES, PHOTON POWER INC, EL PASO, TEX, 81- *Mem:* Inst Elec & Electronics Engrs. *Res:* Low-noise infra-red detectors; solar cells; thin film. *Mailing Add:* Photon Power Inc 13 Founders El Paso TX 79906

SINGH, VIJENDRA KUMAR, b Moradabad, India, Aug 15, 47; m 74. NEUROIMMUNOLOGY, NEUROBIOLOGY. *Educ:* Lucknow Univ, India, BSc, 64, MSc, 66; Univ BC, PhD(biochem), 72. *Prof Exp:* Res asst biochem, Coun Sci & Indust Res, India, 66-68; fel, Univ BC, 72-74, res assoc neurosci, 74-78; mem staff, 78-81, DIR RES, DIV IMMUNOL, CHILDREN'S HOSP, 81-; ASST PROF, DEPT PATH, UNIV BC, 79- *Mem:* AAAS; Soc Neurosci. *Res:* Immunohistochemistry of cell surface markers; tissue culture study of nerve cells; immunochemical aspects of demyelinating diseases. *Mailing Add:* Div Immunol 250 W 59th Ave Vancouver BC V5X 1X2 Can

SINGHAL, AVINASH CHANDRA, b Aligarh, India, Nov 4, 41; m 67; c 2. CIVIL ENGINEERING, STRUCTURAL ENGINEERING. *Educ:* St Andrews Col, BSc, 60; Mass Inst Technol, SM, 61, ScD(civil eng), 64. *Prof Exp:* Prof civil eng, Laval Univ, Que, 65-69; asst prog mgr, TRW, 69-71; mgr systs eng, Gen Elec, 71-72 & Engrs India Ltd, 72-74; proj engr consult eng, Weidlinger Assoc, 74-77; ASSOC PROF CIVIL ENG, ARIZ STATE UNIV, 77- *Concurrent Pos:* Chmn Eng Mech Sub Task Comn, Am Soc Civil Eng, 68-70; mem Am Soc Civil Eng Comts, 69-73 & Tech Coun Lifeline Earthquake Eng, 78- *Honors & Awards:* First Prize, Int Asn Shell Struct, 61; Cert Merit, Inst Engrs, India, 69; Henry Adams Medal, Inst Struct Eng, London, 71. *Mem:* Am Soc Civil Engrs. *Res:* Earthquake engineering; soil engineering; blast and vibrations; pipelines; author of 152 publications. *Mailing Add:* Dept of Civil Eng Ariz State Univ Tempe AZ 85281

SINGHAL, RADHEY LAL, b Gulaothi, India, July 12, 40; m 61; c 3. PHARMACOLOGY. *Educ:* Univ Lucknow, BSc, 57, MSc, 59, PhD(pharmacol), 61. *Prof Exp:* Res assoc pharmacol, Ind Univ, 62-64, instr, 64-65; from asst prof to assoc prof, 66-72, actg chmn dept, 74-76, PROF PHARMACOL, UNIV OTTAWA, 72-, CHMN DEPT, 76- *Concurrent Pos:* Med Res Coun Can scholar, Univ Ottawa, 67-72. *Mem:* Endocrine Soc; Int Soc Neurochem; Soc Toxicol; Am Soc Pharmacol & Exp Therapeut; Am Soc Biol Chem. *Res:* Endocrine and biochemical pharmacology; neuroendocrinological approaches to the study of brain function; environmental toxicology. *Mailing Add:* Dept of Pharmacol Univ of Ottawa 275 Nicholas St Ottawa ON K1N 9A9 Can

SINGHAL, RAM P, b New Delhi, India, Aug 12, 39; US citizen; m 68; c 2. BIOCHEMISTRY, MOLECULAR BIOLOGY. *Educ:* Univ Lucknow, BS, 58, MS, 60; Univ Lille, Dipl, 64, PhD(biochem), 67. *Prof Exp:* Instr biochem, All-India Inst Med Sci, 60-62; researcher, Cancer Res Inst, Univ Lille, 62-67; scientist, Coun Sci & Indust Res, India, 67-68; USPHS fel, Wayne State Univ, 68-69; Univ Tenn-Oak Ridge Nat Lab fel, Oak Ridge Nat Lab, 70-71, res scientist, 72-74; vis scientist, Scripps Res Found, 74; asst prof, 74-79, ASSOC PROF BIOCHEM, WICHITA STATE UNIV, 79- *Concurrent Pos:* Nat Ctr Sci Res researcher, Univ Sci & Technol, Univ Lille, 64-67; NSF exchange 64-67. *Honors & Awards:* Cancer Res Award, Am Cancer Soc, 75. *Mem:* AAAS; Am Chem Soc; Am Soc Biol Chemists; Brit Biochem Soc; Biochem Soc India. *Res:* Relationship between biochemical functions and the chemical structure of nucleic acids; cancer, cause and cure; contemporary analytical tools. *Mailing Add:* Dept of Chem Wichita State Univ Wichita KS 67208

SINGHAL, SHARWAN KUMAR, b Oct 8, 39; Can citizen; m 64; c 2. IMMUNOLOGY. *Educ:* McGill Univ, PhD(immunol), 68. *Prof Exp:* Med Res Coun Can fel tumor biol, Karolinska Inst, Sweden, 68-70; assoc prof, 70-79, PROF IMMUNOL, UNIV WESTERN ONT, 80- *Mem:* Am Asn Immunol; Can Soc Immunol; Scand Soc Immunol. *Res:* Regulation of the immune response at the cellular level. *Mailing Add:* Dept Microbiol & Immunol Univ of Western Ont London ON N6A 5C1 Can

SINGHVI, SAMPAT MANAKCHAND, b Jodhpur, India, Oct 14, 47; m 71; c 2. BIOPHARMACEUTICS, PHARMACOKINETICS. *Educ:* BITS Pilani, Rajasthan, India, BPharm, 67; Philadelphia Col Pharm & Sci, MS, 70; State Univ NY, Buffalo, PhD(pharmaceut), 74. *Prof Exp:* Res sci, Wyeth Labs, Am Home Prod, 69, 70; teaching asst chem, Philadelphia Col Pharm & Sci, 69-70; res asst pharmaceut, State Univ NY, Buffalo, 70-73; res investr, 74-78, sr res investr, 78-79, RES GROUP LEADER DRUG METAB, E R SQUIBB & SONS, INC, 79- *Mem:* Am Soc Pharmacol & Exp Therapeut; Am Pharm Asn; Acad Pharmaceut Sci. *Res:* Drug metabolism in animals; bioavailability and pharmacokinetics of various new drugs in animals and man. *Mailing Add:* Squibb Inst for Med Res Georges Rd New Brunswick NJ 08903

SINGISER, ROBERT EUGENE, b Mechanicsburg, Pa, Aug 7, 30; m 54; c 2. RESEARCH ADMINISTRATION, PHARMACEUTICS. *Educ:* Temple Univ, BS, 52; Univ Fla, MS, 56; Univ Conn, PhD(pharm), 59. *Prof Exp:* Pharmaceut chemist, Merck & Co, Inc, 52-55; res pharmacist, 58-64, dept mgr, Pharmaceut Prod Res, 64-66, dir pharmaceut res & develop, 66-68, sci dir, Pharmaceut Prod Div, 68-70, VPRES SCI AFFAIRS, PHARMACEUT PROD DIV, ABBOTT LABS, 70- *Mem:* Am Chem Soc; Am Pharmaceut Asn; Am Soc Hosp Pharmacists; Int Pharmaceut Fedn; Acad Pharmaceut Sci. *Res:* Ultrasonic emulsification; thermo-stable ointment bases; air-suspension tablet coating techniques; non-sterile, human pharmaceutical dosage forms; biopharmaceutics. *Mailing Add:* Pharmaceut Prod Div Abbott Labs North Chicago IL 60064

SINGLER, ROBERT EDWARD, b Chicago, Ill, Mar 21, 41; m 70; c 2. POLYMER CHEMISTRY. *Educ:* Loyola Univ, BS, 63; Southern Ill Univ, MA, 65; Univ Calif, Los Angeles, PhD(chem), 70. *Prof Exp:* RES CHEMIST POLYMER RES, ARMY MAT & MECH RES CTR, 70- *Concurrent Pos:*

Army res fel, Univ Freiburg, WGer, 79-80. *Mem:* Am Chem Soc; Sigma Xi. *Res:* Synthesis, characterization and development of cyclic phosphazones and polyphosphazenes. *Mailing Add:* Army Mat & Mech Res Ctr Watertown MA 02172

SINGLETARY, CLYDE C, horticulture, see previous edition

SINGLETARY, JOHN BOON, b Houston, Tex, May 6, 28; m 55. NUCLEAR PHYSICS. *Educ:* Agr & Mech Col Tex, BS, 49, MS, 51; Northwestern Univ, PhD, 58. *Prof Exp:* Mem staff, Los Alamos Sci Lab, 57-59; res scientist, Lockheed Aircraft Co, 59-70; dept mgr, Braddock, Dunn & McDonald, 70-71; SR STAFF PHYSICIST, HUGHES AIRCRAFT CO, 71- *Mem:* Am Phys Soc. *Res:* Neutron and low energy nuclear physics; environmental effects on spacecraft materials; radiation effects on electronic components; electromagnetic pulse environment and effects on components and systems. *Mailing Add:* Hughes Aircraft Co Centinela Ave & Teale St Culver City CA 90230

SINGLETARY, LILLIAN DARLINGTON, b Chicago, Ill. NUCLEAR PHYSICS. *Educ:* Northwestern Univ, BS, PhD(exp neutron & charged particle physics), 62. *Prof Exp:* Res scientist, Lockheed Res Lab, 62-69; EMP sect head, Lockheed Missiles & Space Co, 69-70; dept mgr, EMP & Appl Nuclear Technol Dept, Braddock, Dunn & McDonald, Inc, NMex, 70-71; SECT HEAD ADV TECHNOL, VULNERABILITY & HARDNESS LAB, TRW SYSTS GROUP, 71- *Concurrent Pos:* Consult, Los Alamos Sci Lab, 69-73. *Mem:* Inst Elec & Electronic Engrs; Am Phys Soc; Sigma Xi. *Res:* Analytical and test programs investigating electromagnetic pulse generated by nuclear weapon and system generated electromagnetic pulse generated by nuclear weapon photons incident on systems. *Mailing Add:* 32759 Seagate Dr Rancho Palos Verdes CA 90274

SINGLETARY, ROBERT LOMBARD, b Atlanta, Ga, Mar 21, 41; m 64. MARINE ECOLOGY. *Educ:* Univ NC, AB, 63; Univ RI, MS, 67; Univ Miami, PhD(marine biol), 70. *Prof Exp:* ASSOC PROF BIOL, UNIV BRIDGEPORT, 70- *Mem:* Estuarine Res Fedn; Int Oceanog Found; Am Soc Limnol & Oceanog; AAAS. *Res:* Biology of Echinoderms; benthic and intertidal ecology. *Mailing Add:* Dept of Biol Univ of Bridgeport Bridgeport CT 06602

SINGLETARY, THOMAS ALEXANDER, b Cairo, Ga, Sept 17, 37; m 65; c 1. ELECTRONICS, TECHNOLOGY. *Educ:* Ga Southern Col, BS, 59; Stout Univ, MS, 60; Univ Mo-Columbia, EdD(indust educ), 68. *Prof Exp:* Assoc prof, 60-77, INSTR ELECTRONICS TECHNOL, GA SOUTHERN COL, 77- *Concurrent Pos:* Systs consult, Statesboro Telephone Inc, 60-; TV consult, Westinghouse Elec Corp, 62-65; tech instr, Rockwell Mfg Co, 64-; reviewing consult, Delmar Publs, 72- *Mem:* Am Indust Arts Asn. *Res:* Electrofinishing technology as applied to metals; photographic media as applied to education. *Mailing Add:* 303 Pitt-Moore Rd Statesboro GA 30458

SINGLETON, ALAN HERBERT, b Punxsutawney, Pa, Nov 28, 36; m 58; c 4. CHEMICAL ENGINEERING. *Educ:* Univ Md, College Park, BS, 58; Lehigh Univ, MS, 62, PhD(chem eng), 68. *Prof Exp:* Res engr, US Naval Propellant Plant, 58-59; mgr explor eng, Air Prod & Chem, Inc, 59-68; section mgr, Res Dept, Bethlehem Steel Corp, 68-77; prog mgr, UCG Opers, 77-81, DEPT MGR SYNTHETIC FUELS DEVELOP, GULF OIL CORP RES, 81- *Mem:* Am Inst Chem Eng; Am Chem Soc. *Res:* Synthetic fuels process development; underground coal gasification process development and operations; organic chemical product and process development; catalysis; cryogenic refrigeration, liquefaction, and containment system development. *Mailing Add:* Gulf Sci & Technol Co PO Drawer 2038 Pittsburgh PA 15230

SINGLETON, BERT, b New York, NY, July 13, 28; m 56; c 2. ANALYTICAL CHEMISTRY, ORGANIC CHEMISTRY. *Educ:* Cornell Univ, BChE, 50. *Prof Exp:* Res asst org fluorine chem, Cornell Univ, 51-53; process develop chemist, 55-57, foreign projs chemist, 57-59, sr develop chemist, 59-65, sect head, Process Controls Res, 65-69, mgr process controls, 69-80, ASSOC DIR ANAL RES, MERCK & CO, INC, 80- *Mem:* AAAS; Am Chem Soc; Sigma Xi. *Res:* Analytical methods; gas and liquid chromatography; ultraviolet and infrared spectrophotometry; microanalysis; automatic chemical and process control instrumentation; pharmaceuticals; steroids and vitamins; synthetic organic chemistry. *Mailing Add:* Merck Sharp & Dohme Res Labs PO Box 2000 Rahway NJ 07065

SINGLETON, CHLOE JOI, b Cleveland, Ohio, Dec 4, 43. MACROMOLECULAR SCIENCE. *Educ:* Case Inst Technol, BS, 67; Case Western Res Univ, MSE, 74, PhD(macromolecular sci), 75; Baldwin-Wallace Col, MBA, 81. *Prof Exp:* Physicist x-ray diffraction, 67-69, res physicist, 69-70, physicist res & develop electron micros, 74-78, sr physicist thermal anal polymers, Res & Develop Ctr, 78-79, SR RES & DEVELOP PHYSICIST / APPLICATIONS ENGR THERMOPLASTIC POLYURETHANES, B F GOODRICH TECH CTR, 78- *Mem:* Am Chem Soc; Am Phys Soc; NAm Thermal Anal Soc; Electron Micros Soc Am. *Res:* Morphological characterization of plastic and rubber materials, using the tools of thermal analysis; electron microscopy and x-ray diffraction; applications engineering of thermoplastic polyurethanes. *Mailing Add:* B F Goodrich Co Tech Ctr PO Box 122 Avon Lake OH 44012

SINGLETON, DAVID MICHAEL, b Poole, Eng, Nov 3, 39; m 62; c 2. ORGANIC CHEMISTRY, CATALYSIS. *Educ:* Univ London, BSc, 60; McMaster Univ, PhD(org chem), 65. *Prof Exp:* Res assoc reductive reactions of chromous ion, with J K Kochi, Case Western Reserve Univ, 65-67; chemist, Petrol Chem Dept, Shell Develop Co, Calif, 67-72, hydroprocessing dept, 72-74, SR RES CHEMIST, SHELL DEVELOP CO, 74-, DIR, CHEM RES & APPL DEPT, 77- *Concurrent Pos:* Shell exchange scientist, Shell Res & Develop Co, Amsterdam, 75-76. *Mem:* Am Chem Soc; Chem Inst Can; Royal Soc Chem; Southwest Catalysis Soc. *Res:* Free radical reactions; organic redox reactions by metal complexes; organometallic chemistry; catalysis of organic reactions by metal complexes; hydrocarbon chemistry; heterogeneous catalysis. *Mailing Add:* Westhollow Res Ctr Box 1380 Shell Develop Co Houston TX 77001

SINGLETON, DONALD LEE, b Lyons, Kans, Mar 26, 44; m 66; c 2. PHYSICAL CHEMISTRY. *Educ:* Univ Calif, Davis, BS, 66; Northwestern Univ, MS, 70, PhD(phys chem), 71. *Prof Exp:* Vis scientist atmospheric chem, Nat Ctr Atmospheric Res, 70-72; fel, 72-74, ASST RES OFFICER CHEM KINETICS, NAT RES COUN CAN, 74- *Mem:* Am Chem Soc; AAAS. *Res:* Kinetics and mechanisms of atomic and free radical reactions. *Mailing Add:* Div of Chem Nat Res Coun Ottawa ON Can

SINGLETON, EDGAR BRYSON, b Warren, Ohio, June 17, 26; m 53; c 3. MOLECULAR PHYSICS. *Educ:* Ohio Univ, BS, 49, MS, 51; Ohio State Univ, PhD(physics), 58. *Prof Exp:* Instr & res assoc physics, Ohio State Univ, 58-59; from asst prof to assoc prof, 59-72, PROF PHYSICS, BOWLING GREEN STATE UNIV, 72- *Mem:* Optical Soc Am; Am Asn Physics Teachers. *Res:* Molecular physics and infrared spectroscopy in absorption and emission of radiation. *Mailing Add:* Dept of Physics Bowling Green State Univ Bowling Green OH 43403

SINGLETON, GEORGE TERRELL, b Wichita Falls, Tex, Dec 16, 27; c 3. OTOLARYNGOLOGY. *Educ:* Midwestern Univ, BA & BS, 49; Baylor Univ, MD, 54; Am Bd Otolaryngol, dipl, 59. *Prof Exp:* Intern, Henry Ford Hosp, 54-55, asst resident, 55-57, sr resident, 57-58; assoc prof surg & head div otolaryngol, 61-68, chief otolaryngol, 68-75, asst dean clin affairs, 70-77, PROF SURG, UNIV FLA, 68- *Concurrent Pos:* NIH spec fel otolaryngol, Univ Chicago, 60-61; mem communicative dis res training comt, Nat Inst Neurol Dis & Stroke, 69-73; chief of staff, Shands Teaching Hosp & Clins, 72-76, actg hosp dir, 75-77. *Honors & Awards:* Award, Am Acad Ophthal & Otolaryngol, 60; Harris P Mosher Mem Award, Am Laryngol, Rhinol & Otol Soc. *Mem:* Am Acad Ophthal & Otolaryngol; Am Laryngol, Rhinol & Otol Soc; Soc Univ Otolaryngol; Am Otol Soc. *Res:* Computer analysis of caloric induced nystagmus responses with known central peripheral and vestibular lesions and histopathology of human temporal bones and related clinical neuro-otology. *Mailing Add:* Shands Teaching Hosp & Clins Box 264 Gainesville FL 32610

SINGLETON, JACK HOWARD, b Rawtenstall, Eng, Sept 27, 26; m 54; c 2. PHYSICAL CHEMISTRY. *Educ:* Univ London, BSc, 47, dipl & PhD, 50. *Prof Exp:* Asst phys chem, Aberdeen Univ, 49-52; res assoc, Univ Wash, 52-55; ENGR, RES LABS, WESTINGHOUSE ELEC CORP, 55- *Mem:* Am Chem Soc; Am Vacuum Soc (secy, 82). *Res:* Physical and chemi-sorption; catalysis on metals; ultrahigh vacuum. *Mailing Add:* Vacuum Lab Westinghouse Res Labs Pittsburgh PA 15235

SINGLETON, JAMES L, b Coya, Chile, Dec 4, 20; US citizen; m 45; c 3. ELECTRICAL ENGINEERING. *Educ:* Univ Colo, BSEE, 49; US Air Force Inst Technol, MS, 52. *Prof Exp:* Instr, Tech Training Command, US Air Force, 49-50, supvr teletype mech course, 50-51, instr eng, US Naval Acad, 52-56, asst prof elec eng, US Air Force Acad, 56-60, res & develop officer, Electronics Systs Div, Systs Command, 60-64, res & develop staff officer, Hq, Pentagon, 64-67; engr analyst, Command & Control Systs, Anal Serv, Inc, 68-76; engr analyst, Electrospace Systs, Inc, 76-82; ENG ANALYST, MITRE CORP, 82- *Mem:* Sr mem Inst Elec & Electronics Engrs. *Res:* Engineering education; electronics; avionics; communications. *Mailing Add:* Mitre Corp 1820 Dolly Madison Blvd McLean VA 22102

SINGLETON, JOHN BYRNE, b Troy, NY, May 16, 30; m 52; c 6. PHYSICS. *Educ:* Col of the Holy Cross, BS, 52; Univ RI, MS, 54. *Prof Exp:* Mem tech staff, 54-60, head, Integrated Circuits Dept, 60-70, head data & digital dept, 71-76, HEAD DIGITAL SYSTS DEPT, BELL TEL LABS, INC, 77- *Mem:* Sr mem Inst Elec & Electronics Engrs; Electrochem Soc. *Res:* Design and development of transmission lines and terminals. *Mailing Add:* Digital Systs Dept Bell Tel Labs Inc 1600 Osgood St North Andover MA 01845

SINGLETON, MARY CLYDE, b Enfield, NC, Mar 31, 12. ANATOMY, PHYSICAL MEDICINE & REHABILITATION. *Educ:* Univ NC, GreeGreensboro, BS, 32; Duke Univ, MA, 60, PhD(anat), 64. *Prof Exp:* Clin supvr phys ther, Med Ctr, Duke Univ, 40-54; coordr ther, Georgia Warm Springs Found, 54-58; asst prof phys ther & instr anat, 62-66, asst prof anat, 66-73, assoc prof phys ther, 69-74, assoc prof anat, 73-77, PROF PHYS THER, UNIV NC, CHAPEL HILL, 74-, PROF ANAT, 77- *Honors & Awards:* Golden Pen Award, Am Phys Ther Asn, 74, Lucy Blair Serv Award, 77. *Mem:* AAAS; Am Asn Anat; Am Phys Ther Asn (pres, 50-52). *Res:* Neuroanatomy; gross anatomy; physical therapy. *Mailing Add:* Dept of Anat Sch of Med Univ of NC Chapel Hill NC 27514

SINGLETON, PAUL C, b Provo, Utah, June 22, 19; m 42; c 3. SOIL CHEMISTRY, SOIL FERTILITY. *Educ:* Brigham Young Univ, BS, 50; Univ Wyo, MS, 57; Ore State Univ, PhD(soils), 66. *Prof Exp:* Soil scientist, Soil Conserv Serv, USDA, 51-55; from instr to asst prof, 55-65, ASSOC PROF SOILS, UNIV WYO, 65- *Mem:* Soil Sci Soc Am. *Res:* Soil fertility research; soils research with respect to surface and ground water hydrology and reclamation in strip mine areas; effect of clearcutting on nutrient status of forest soils. *Mailing Add:* Dept of Soil Sci Univ Wyo Laramie WY 82070

SINGLETON, RICHARD COLLOM, b Schenectady, NY, Feb 21, 28; m 50; c 6. MATHEMATICAL STATISTICS, INFORMATION SCIENCE. *Educ:* Mass Inst Technol, BS & MS, 50; Stanford Univ, MBA, 52, MS, 59, PhD(math statist), 60. *Prof Exp:* Economist, 52-54, res engr, 54-56, systs analyst, 56-59, res math statistician, 59-63, sr res math statistician, Dept Math, 63-72, STAFF SCIENTIST, DEPT MATH STATIST, URBAN & SOC SYSTS DIV, STANFORD RES INST, 72-, ASSOC ED, INFO SCI, 68- *Mem:* Inst Math Statist; Opers Res Soc Am; sr mem Inst Elec & Electronics Eng. *Res:* Design of experiments in the physical and biological sciences; time series analysis; statistical inference; theory of error-correcting codes; economics; litigation support statistical analysis. *Mailing Add:* Dept Math Statist Stanford Res Inst Menlo Park CA 94025

SINGLETON, RIVERS, JR, b New Orleans, La, Sept 2, 39; m 63; c 3. MICROBIAL PHYSIOLOGY. *Educ:* Trinity Univ, BS, 61; Mich State Univ, MS, 63; Univ Kans, PhD(biochem), 69. *Prof Exp:* Dir, Chem Div, First US Army Med Lab, 63-65; fel biochem, Case Western Reserve Univ, 69-72; res assoc biochem microbiol, Ames Res Ctr, NASA, 72-74; RES ASST PROF BIOETHICS & MICROBIOL, UNIV DEL, 74- *Concurrent Pos:* res assoc, Nat Acad Sci, 72. *Mem:* Sigma Xi; Am Soc Microbiol; fel Am Cancer Soc. *Res:* The evolutionary aspects and chemical mechanisms whereby microorganisms adapt to and grow under extreme environmental conditions. *Mailing Add:* Sch Life & Health Sci Univ Del Newark DE 19711

SINGLETON, ROBERT E(DMUND), fluid mechanics, see previous edition

SINGLETON, ROBERT RICHMOND, b Brooklyn, NY, Mar 23, 13; m 38; c 2. MATHEMATICS. *Educ:* Dartmouth Col, AB, 34; Brown Univ, MSc, 35; Princeton Univ, PhD(math), 62. *Prof Exp:* Clerk, Metrop Life Ins Co, 36-37; res asst govt, Princeton Univ, 37-39, res assoc, 39-42; res asst, Merrill Flood & Assoc, 42-46; dir develop, Aero Serv Corp, 46-52; res consult, self-employed, 52-56; res consult, Gen Elec Co, 56-62; lectr, 62-76, adj prof, 76-79, EMER ADJ PROF MATH, WESLEYAN UNIV, 79- *Concurrent Pos:* Consult, Gov, WVa, 38-40. *Mem:* Math Asn Am. *Res:* Management science; graph theory. *Mailing Add:* Dept Math Wesleyan Univ Middletown CT 06457

SINGLETON, SAMUEL WINSTON, b Blackpool, Eng, Nov 17, 28; US citizen; m 53; c 1. MEDICINE. *Educ:* Univ Manchester, Eng, MB & ChB, 52; Am Bd Pediat, dipl, 60. *Prof Exp:* Comn officer med, US Navy, 54-60; assoc physician, 60-71, dir clin res, 71-74, MED DIR, BURROUGHS WELLCOME CO, 74- *Concurrent Pos:* Intern, Chester Hosp, Pa, 53-54; resident pediat, US Naval Hosp, Oakland, Calif, 56-58. *Mem:* Am Acad Pediat; Am Soc Microbiol; Am Soc Clin Parmacol; Am Soc Nephrol; Am Acad Allergy. *Res:* Administrative interest in clinical pharmacology and clinical research; infectious diseases. *Mailing Add:* Burroughs Wellcome Co Res Labs 3030 Cornwallis Rd Research Triangle Park NC 27709

SINGLETON, TOMMY CLARK, b Lufkin, Tex, Oct 5, 28; m 58; c 3. ORGANIC CHEMISTRY. *Educ:* Stephen F Austin State Col, BS, 49; Rice Univ, PhD(chem), 54. *Prof Exp:* Chemist, Naval Stores Sta, USDA, 55-56; sr process chemist, Res Dept, 56-69, process specialist, Process Technol Dept, 69-75, SR PROCESS SPECIALIST, PROCESS TECHNOL DEPT, MONSANTO CO, 75- *Mem:* Am Chem Soc. *Res:* Carbonylation chemistry; plant process problems; syntheses of vinyl monomers. *Mailing Add:* Process Technol Dept Monsanto Co Box 1311 Texas City TX 77591

SINGLETON, VERNON LEROY, b Mill City, Ore, June 28, 23; m 47; c 3. NATURAL PRODUCTS CHEMISTRY, ENOLOGY. *Educ:* Purdue Univ, BSA, 47, MS, 49, PhD(biochem), 51. *Prof Exp:* Asst biochem, Purdue Univ, 47-49; res chemist, Lederle Labs, Am Cyanamid Co, 51-54; assoc biochemist, Pineapple Res Inst, Univ Hawaii, 54-58, biochemist, 58; asst enologist, 58-63, assoc enologist, 63-66, assoc chemist, 66-69, lectr, 59-69, PROF ENOL & CHEMIST, AGR EXP STA, UNIV CALIF, DAVIS, 69- *Concurrent Pos:* Assoc prof, Univ Hawaii, 56-58; consult, Pineapple Res Inst, 59; abstr ed, Am Soc Enol, 59-73; sr res fel, Inst Oenology & Viticulture, Univ Stellenbosch, SAfrica, 68-69; vis scientist Long Ashton Res Sta, Univ Bristol, UK, 75-76. *Honors & Awards:* Andre Simon Lit Prize, 65; Biennial Wine Res Award, Soc Med Friends Wine, 77. *Mem:* Am Chem Soc; Am Soc Enol (treas, 69-73, 2nd vpres, 73, 1st vpres, 74, pres, 75-76); Inst Food Technologists; Phytochem Soc NAm; Sigma Xi. *Res:* Chemistry of natural products, especially flavonoids, tannins, mold products, antibiotics and wines; food storage reactions; sensory analysis; biochemistry of fruits; chromatography. *Mailing Add:* Dept of Viticulture & Enology Univ of Calif Davis CA 95616

SINGLETON, WAYNE LOUIS, b Oaktown, Ind, Feb 2, 44; m 69. ANIMAL SCIENCE, REPRODUCTIVE PHYSIOLOGY. *Educ:* Purdue Univ, Lafayette, BS, 66; SDak State Univ, MS, 68, PhD(animal sci), 70. *Prof Exp:* Asst prof, 70-76, ASSOC PROF ANIMAL SCI, COOP EXTEN SERV, PURDUE UNIV, LAFAYETTE, 76- *Mem:* Soc Study Reproduction. *Res:* Swine and beef cattle artificial insemination; reproductive efficiency of beef cattle and swine. *Mailing Add:* Dept of Animal Sci Purdue Univ Lafayette IN 47907

SINGLEY, DONALD HEATH, mathematics, see previous edition

SINGLEY, JOHN EDWARD, b Wildwood, NJ, July 31, 24; m 50; c 4. WATER CHEMISTRY. *Educ:* Ga Inst Technol, BS, 50, MS, 52; Univ Fla, PhD(water chem), 66. *Prof Exp:* Asst chem, Ga Inst Technol, 49-50; phys chemist, US Army Ord Rocket Res Ctr, Redstone Arsenal, Ala, 50-51; chemist & group leader, Res & Develop Dept, Tenn Corp, 51-58, supvr tech serv, 58-65; instr chem, Ga State Col, 54-65, asst prof, 65-66, assoc prof, 66-67; assoc prof, 67-71, PROF WATER CHEM, UNIV FLA, 71- *Concurrent Pos:* Consult panel on public water supplies, Nat Acad Sci, 71-72 & President's Coun on Environ Qual, 74; sr staff consult, Environ Sci & Eng, Inc, Gainesville, 77-82, sr vpres res & develop, 82- *Honors & Awards:* Publication Award, Am Water Works Asn, 73, Ambassador Award. *Mem:* Am Water Works Asn; fel Am Inst Chem; Inter-Am Asn Sanit Eng. *Res:* Coagulation mechanisms; corrosion in portable water systems; color, iron and manganese in water supplies; water treatment processes. *Mailing Add:* Dept Environ Eng Sci Univ Fla Gainesville FL 32611

SINGLEY, MARK E(LDRIDGE), b Delano, Pa, Jan 25, 21; m 42; c 4. AGRICULTURAL ENGINEERING. *Educ:* Pa State Univ, BS, 42; Rutgers Univ, MS, 49. *Prof Exp:* From instr to assoc prof, 47-67, PROF AGR ENG, RUTGERS UNIV, 67- *Mem:* AAAS; Am Soc Agr Engrs. *Res:* Deep bed drying, pneumatic handling and characteristics of fibrous and granular farm crops; resource management; land use planning. *Mailing Add:* Dept Biol & Agr Eng PO Box 231 New Brunswick NJ 08903

SINGPURWALLA, NOZER DRABSHA, b Hubli, India, Apr 8, 39; m 69; c 1. OPERATIONS RESEARCH, STATISTICS. *Educ:* B V B Col Eng & Tech, India, BS, 59; Rutgers Univ, MS, 64; NY Univ, PhD(opers res). 68. *Prof Exp:* PROF OPERS RES, RES PROF STATIST & DIR, INST RELIABILITY & RISK ANAL, GEORGE WASHINGTON UNIV, 69- *Concurrent Pos:* Vis prof statist, Stanford Univ, 78-79. *Mem:* Int Asn Statist in Phys Sci; fel Am Statist Asn; Int Statist Inst. *Res:* Applications of statistics to reliability theory; development of statistical methodology. *Mailing Add:* Dept of Opers Res George Wash Univ Washington DC 20006

SINHA, AKHOURI ACHYUTANAND, b Churamanpur, Bihar, India, Dec 17, 33; US citizen. ZOOLOGY, ANATOMY. *Educ:* Univ Allahabad, BS, 54; Patna Univ, MS, 56; Univ Mo, Columbia, PhD(zool), 65. *Prof Exp:* Lectr zool, Ranchi Univ, India, 56-61; fel anat, Univ Wis, 65; asst prof biol, Wis State Univ, Wis Claire, 65-67; sr scientist, Univ Minn, Minneapolis, 67-69, assoc prof zool & vet anat, 69-76, assoc prof genetics & cell biol, 76-81; RES PHYSIOLOGIST, MED RES LAB, VET ADMIN HOSP, 69-; PROF GENETICS & CELL BIOL, UNIV MINN, ST PAUL, 81- *Mem:* Am Soc Zool; Am Asn Anat; Soc Study Reproduction; Am Soc Cell Biol; Indian Sci Cong Asn. *Res:* Reproductive physiology; mammalian placentation, corpus luteum and ultra structure; tissue culture; effect of steroids and chemotherapeutic agents on the prostatic carcinoma. *Mailing Add:* Bldg 49 Veterans Hosp Minneapolis MN 55417

SINHA, AKHOURI SURESH CHANDRA, b Churamanpur, India, Mar 14, 38; m 68. ELECTRICAL ENGINEERING. *Educ:* Bihar Univ, BS, 57; Banaras Hindu Univ, BS, 61; Univ Mo-Columbia, MS, 66, PhD(elec eng), 69. *Prof Exp:* Asst prof elec eng, Ind Inst Technol, 69-77; assoc prof, 77-80, PROF ELEC ENG & ACTG CHMN DIV ENG, IND UNIV-PURDUE UNIV, 80- *Res:* Control systems; stability theory; optimal control theory. *Mailing Add:* Div of Eng Ind Univ-Purdue Univ Indianapolis IN 46205

SINHA, AKHUARY KRISHNA, b Churamanpur, India, Jan 5, 41; m 70. GEOLOGY. *Educ:* Sci Col, Patna, BSc, 60; Patna Univ, MSc, 62; Univ Calif, Santa Barbara, PhD(geol), 69. *Prof Exp:* Lectr geol, Patna Univ, 63-65; Carnegie Inst fel, Dept Terrestrial Magnetism, Washington, DC, 69-71; asst prof, 71-76, ASSOC PROF GEOL, VA POLYTECH INST & STATE UNIV, 76- *Concurrent Pos:* NSF res grant, Va Polytech Inst & State Univ, 71- *Honors & Awards:* Cottrell Award, Res Corp, USA, 72. *Mem:* AAAS; Am Geophys Union; Geochem Soc; Geol Soc Am. *Res:* Common lead and strontium systematics, geochronology; trace element geochemistry; isotope geology; regional tectonics. *Mailing Add:* Dept Geol Va Polytech Inst & State Univ Blacksburg VA 24061

SINHA, ARABINDA KUMAR, b Kasiadanga, India, Mar 1, 33; m 62; c 1. PHYSIOLOGY, NEUROBIOLOGY. *Educ:* Calcutta Univ, BSc, 56, MSc, 61; Univ Calif, San Francisco, PhD(physiol), 69. *Prof Exp:* Demonstr & lectr physiol, Presidency Col, Calcutta, 61-62; actg asst prof, Univ Calif, Berkeley, 68; assoc physiol, Univ Calif, San Francisco, 68-69; asst prof, 72-78, ASSOC PROF PHYSIOL, RUTGERS MED SCH, COL MED & DENT NJ, 78- *Concurrent Pos:* Mem grad fac, Rutgers Univ, 72- *Mem:* Am Physiol Soc; Soc Neurosci. *Res:* Metabolic changes between sleep and wakefulness; biochemical mechanism of sleep induction. *Mailing Add:* Rutgers Med Sch Col of Med & Dent of NJ Piscataway NJ 08854

SINHA, ASRU KUMAR, b Tamluk, India, Aug 10, 43; m 69; c 1. HORMONAL REGULATION, THROMBOTIC DISORDERS. *Educ:* City Col Calcutta, BSC, 61; Univ Col Sci, Calcutta, MSC, 63; Calcutta Univ, DSc, 70. *Prof Exp:* Res assoc microbiol, Miami Univ, Oxford, Ohio, 69-72, Med Ctr, Kans Univ, 72-74; res investr med, Univ Pa, 74-78; ASST PROF, THROMBOSIS CTR, TEMPLE UNIV, 78- *Mem:* Am Soc Cell Biol; AAAS; Am Soc Biol Chem. *Res:* Hormonal control of cellular behaviors, particularly by prostaglandins through cyclic nucleotides dependent and independent pathways and the hormonal memories. *Mailing Add:* Thrombosis Res Ctr Temple Univ Philadelphia PA 19140

SINHA, BIDHU BHUSHAN PRASAD, b Mallehpur, India; Can citizen. PHYSICS, HISTORY & PHILOSOPHY OF SCIENCE. *Educ:* Patna Univ, India, MSc, 61; Mem Univ Nfld, MSc, 67; Univ Mass, PhD(nuclear physics), 71. *Prof Exp:* Lectr physics, Patna Univ, 62-64; instr physics & sci, Eastport Cent Sch, Nfld, 66-68; lectr & instr physics, Univ Guelph, Ont, 72-73; dir, Inst Sci & Math, 74-75; PROF PHYSICS & SCI, FANSHAWE COL APPL ARTS & TECHNOL, ONT, 78-; DIR, INST SCI & MATH, 79- *Concurrent Pos:* Lectr tech physics, Inst Technol, India, 61-64; teaching fel, Physics Dept, Mem Univ Nfld, 64-66; dir sports, Eastport Sch, Nfld, 66-68; fel physics, Univ Toronto, 71-72; vis prof, World Univ, Calif, 74-; vis student adminr, Grad Bus Sch, York Open Univ, 75-77. *Mem:* Am Phys Soc. *Res:* X-rays; molecular physics; nuclear accelerator physics; pioneering theoretical works in faster-than-light relativity; fundamental particles; parapsychophysics. *Mailing Add:* PO Box 892 Sta B London ON N6A 4Z3 Can

SINHA, BIRANDRA KUMAR, b Gaya, India, Jan 10, 45; US citizen; m 70. MEDICINAL CHEMISTRY, BIOPHYSICS. *Educ:* Ohio State Univ, PhD(med chem), 72. *Prof Exp:* Fel biochem, Ohio State Univ, 72-73; NIH fel molecular pharmacol, 74-75; sr investr med chem, Microbiol Assocs, 75-77; SR STAFF FEL BIOPHYSICS, NAT INST ENVIRON HEALTH SCI, 77- *Mem:* Am Chem Soc; Med Chem Soc; Sigma Xi; AAAS. *Res:* Binding of chemical carcinogens and antitumor agents to nucleic acids. *Mailing Add:* Nat Inst of Environ Health Sci PO Box 12233 Research Triangle Park NC 27709

SINHA, INDRANAND, b Bihar, India, July 3, 31; m 52; c 3. MATHEMATICS. *Educ:* Benares Hindu Univ, BSc, 51, MSc, 53; Univ Wis, PhD(algebra), 62. *Prof Exp:* Lectr math, Univ Bihar, 53-63; asst prof, Mich State Univ, 63-65; assoc prof, Indian Inst Technol, Kanpur, 65-68; assoc prof, 68-71, PROF MATH, MICH STATE UNIV, 71- *Res:* Linear algebra, Grour-rings, linear groups. *Mailing Add:* Dept of Math Mich State Univ East Lansing MI 48823

SINHA, KUMARES C, b Calcutta, India, July 12, 42; m 67; c 1. TRANSPORTATION ENGINEERING, URBAN SYSTEMS ENGINEERING. *Educ:* Jadavpur Univ, India, BCE, 61; Calcutta Univ, DTRP, 64; Univ Conn, MS, 66, PhD(civil eng), 68. *Prof Exp:* Jr lectr civil eng, Jadavpur Univ, India, 61-62; asst engr, Govt W Bengal, India, 62-64; res asst civil eng, Univ Conn, 64-68; asst prof civil eng, 68-72, assoc prof & dir urban transp prog, Marquette Univ, 72-74; assoc prof, 74-78, assoc dir, Ctr Pub Policy & Pub Admin, 78-80, PROF CIVIL ENG, PURDUE UNIV, 78- *Concurrent Pos:* Systs eng consult, Southeast Wis Regional Planning Comn, 69-72; mem, Nat Transp Res Bd. *Honors & Awards:* Fred Burggraf Award, Transp Res Bd, Nat Acad Sci, 72. *Mem:* Am Soc Civil Eng; Inst Transp Eng; Am Planning Asn; Am Inst Cert Planners. *Res:* Transportation systems analysis; urban and regional planning and policy analysis. *Mailing Add:* Purdue Univ Sch of Civil Eng West Lafayette IN 47907

SINHA, MAHENDRA KUMAR, b Kanpur, India, July 8, 31; m 57; c 2. SURFACE PHYSICS. *Educ:* Agra Univ, BSc, 49, MSc, 52; Pa State Univ, PhD(physics), 61. *Prof Exp:* Lectr physics, Christ Church Col, Kanpur, India, 52-57; res assoc, Pa State Univ, 61-62; sci officer, Atomic Energy Estab, Bombay, India, 62-64; fel physics, radio & elec eng div, Nat Res Coun Can, 64-66; from asst prof to assoc prof, 66-74, actg chmn dept, 77-78, PROF PHYSICS, N DAK STATE UNIV, 74- *Concurrent Pos:* Guest scientist, Max Planck Inst Plasma Phys, Ger, 75-76. *Mem:* Am Phys Soc. *Res:* Field ion and field ion microscopy; sputtering of solids by medium energy gas ions; high voltage breakdown in vacuum and insulators; entrapment and surface damage of solid due to kiloelectron volt gas ions. *Mailing Add:* Dept Physics NDak State Univ Fargo ND 58102

SINHA, NARESH KUMAR, b Gaya, India, July 25, 27; m 51; c 3. ELECTRICAL ENGINEERING. *Educ:* Benares Hindu Univ, BSc, 48; Manchester Univ, PhD(elec eng), 55. *Prof Exp:* From asst prof to assoc prof elec eng, Bihar Inst Technol, India, 50-61; asst res scientist, NY Univ, 61; assoc prof elec eng, Univ Tenn, 61-65; assoc prof, 65-71, PROF ELEC ENG, McMASTER UNIV, 71- *Concurrent Pos:* Res contract, NASA, Ala, 64-65; Nat Res Coun Can res grant, 66-; res contracts, Dept Commun, Ottawa, 73-76 & 77-78. *Mem:* Sr mem Inst Elec & Electronics Engrs; Eng Inst Can; fel Brit Inst Electronics and Radio Engrs; Can Soc Elec Eng. *Res:* Optimum nonlinear filtering of random signals embedded in noise; adaptive and learning control systems; optimal control theory; sensitivity of systems to variations in parameters; application of microcomputer to process control. *Mailing Add:* Dept of Elec Eng McMaster Univ Hamilton ON L8S 4K1 Can

SINHA, NAVIN KUMAR, b Patna, India, Oct 14, 45; m 71; c 2. MOLECULAR BIOLOGY. *Educ:* Patna Univ, BSc, 62, MSc, 64; Univ Minn, PhD(genetics), 72. *Prof Exp:* Res assoc biol, Mass Inst Technol, 72-73; fel biochem, Princeton Univ, 73-76; ASST PROF MICROBIOL, RUTGERS UNIV, 76- *Concurrent Pos:* NIH fel, Nat Cancer Inst, 74-76; prin investr, Nat Inst Gen Med Sci, 77- *Mem:* Am Soc Microbiol; Genetics Soc Am. *Res:* Mechanism of DNA replication; DNA protein interaction. *Mailing Add:* Waksman Inst of Microbiol Rutgers Univ Piscataway NJ 08854

SINHA, OM PRAKASH, b Faizabad, India; US citizen. THEORETICAL SOLID STATE PHYSICS. *Educ:* Allahabad Univ, India, BS, 46, MS, 48; Wayne State Univ, MA, 65; Yeshiva Univ, NY, PhD(physics), 69. *Prof Exp:* Lectr physics, Agra Univ, India, 50-58; instr physics, Marygrove Col, Detroit, 63-65; res physicist, Energy Conversion Devices Inc, Troy, Mich, 69-71; fel, Simon Fraser Univ & Nat Res Coun Can, 71-72; ASST PROF PHYSICS, CLARK COL, 73- *Concurrent Pos:* Cottrell Res Grant, Res Corp, 75. *Mem:* Am Asn Physics Teachers; Am Phys Soc; Nat Inst Sci. *Res:* Physics of semiconductors; charge and mass transport in solids; transport and relaxation processes in liquids; chemical physics. *Mailing Add:* Clark Col Atlanta GA

SINHA, RAJ P, b Pahsara, India, Nov 11, 34; Can citizen; m 58; c 3. MICROBIAL GENETICS, BIOCHEMICAL GENETICS. *Educ:* Bihar Univ, India, BSc, 57; Univ Wyo, Laramie, MS, 62; Univ Man, Winnipeg, PhD(genetics), 67. *Prof Exp:* Agr supvr, Dept Agr, Govt Bihar, India, 57-60; fel, Dept Biol, Carleton Univ, Ottawa, Ont, 68-72; RES SCIENTIST MICROBIAL GENETICS, CAN AGR, FOOD RES INST, CENT EXP FARM, OTTAWA, 72- *Mem:* Am Soc Microbiol; Can Soc Food Technol; Can Soc Microbiol. *Res:* Genetic organization and function in lactic acid bacteria; genetic recombination and repair mechanism; DNA replication, phage-host relation, modifications and restrictions. *Mailing Add:* Food Res Inst Cent Exp Farm Ottawa ON Can

SINHA, RAMANANDA, medicine, physiology, see previous edition

SINHA, RAMESH CHANDRA, b Bareilly, India, Feb 10, 34; Can citizen; m 57; c 2. PLANT PATHOLOGY. *Educ:* Agr Univ, India, BSc, 53; Lucknow Univ, India, MSc, 56; London Univ, Eng, PhD(plant virol), 60, DSc(plant virol & mycoplasma), 74. *Prof Exp:* Exp officer plant virol, Rothamsted Exp Sta, Eng, 59-60; res assoc plant virol, Univ Ill, Urbana, 60-65; res scientist, 65-76, PRIN RES SCIENTIST PLANT VIROL & MYCOPLASMA, AGR CAN, OTTAWA, 76- *Mem:* Can Phytopath Soc; Am Phytopath Soc; Indian Phytopath Soc; Int Orgn Mycoplasmologists. *Res:* Properties and insect transmission of plant viruses and mycoplasma. *Mailing Add:* Chem & Biol Res Inst Res Br Agr Can Ottawa ON K1A 0C6 Can

SINHA, RANENDRA NATH, b Calcutta, Ind, Jan 25, 30; Can citizen; m 63; c 2. INSECT ECOLOGY, ACAROLOGY. *Educ:* Univ Calcutta, BSc, 50; Univ Kans, PhD(entom, zool), 56. *Prof Exp:* Instr biol, St Xavier's Col, India, 51-52; res assoc zool, McGill Univ, 56-57; res scientist, 57-69, sr res scientist, 70-76, PRIN RES SCIENTIST, RES STA, CAN DEPT AGR, 76- *Concurrent Pos:* Nat Res Coun Can fel, 56-57; hon prof fac grad studies, Univ Manitoba, 61-; hon lectr entom, Kyoto Univ, 66-67. *Mem:* Entom Soc Am; Entom Soc Can; Japanese Soc Pop Ecol; Sigma Xi. *Res:* Ecology of stored grain and its products; ecosystem analysis by multivariate statistics; stored-product entomology and acarology; insect resistance to cereal varieties; arthropod-fungus interrelations. *Mailing Add:* Res Sta Can Dept Agr 195 Dafoe Rd Winnipeg MB R3T 2M9 Can

SINHA, SHYAMAL K, b Khulna, India, Mar 1, 27; US citizen; m 53; c 3. MEDICAL MICROBIOLOGY. *Educ:* Univ Philippines, DVM, 50; Univ Wis-Madison, MS, 52, PhD(microbiol), 57. *Prof Exp:* Dir biol res, Jensen Salsbery Lab, Richardson-Merrill Co, 57-60; AID adv to India & assoc prof, Zoonoses Res Ctr, Col Vet Med, Univ Ill, Urbana, 60-62; res microbiologist, Kansas City Field Sta, Ctr Dis Control, USPHS, 62-64; RES SCIENTIST, WIS STATE DIV MENT HYG, CENT COLONY, 64-; CLIN ASST PROF MED MICROBIOL, MED CTR, UNIV WIS-MADISON, 64- *Mem:* Am Soc Microbiol; Soc Exp Epidemiol. *Res:* Causes and prevention of prenatal and postnatal viral infections associated with mental retardation. *Mailing Add:* 317 Knutson Dr Madison WI 53704

SINHA, SNEHESH KUMAR, b Banaras, India; Can citizen; m 56; c 2. APPLIED STATISTICS. *Educ:* Patna Univ, BA, 46, MA, 49 & 54; Univ London, MSc, 59, PhD(statist), 72; Univ Chicago, AM, 68. *Prof Exp:* Lectr math, Jamshedpur Coop Col, Univ Bihar, 53-57; asst prof math & statist, St Mary's Univ, NS, 59-61; from asst prof to assoc prof, 61-72, PROF STATIST, UNIV MAN, 72- *Mem:* Fel Royal Statist Soc; Int Statist Inst. *Res:* Life testing and reliability estimation; bayesian inference; properties of associated distributions in the presence of an outlier observation. *Mailing Add:* Dept Statist Univ Man Winnipeg MB R3T 2N2 Can

SINHA, SUNIL K, b Calcutta, India, Sept 13, 39; m 62; c 2. SOLID STATE PHYSICS. *Educ:* Cambridge Univ, BA, 60, PhD(physics), 64. *Prof Exp:* Vis scientist, Atomic Energy Estab, Trombay, India, 64-65; assoc, 65-66, from asst prof to prof physics, Iowa State Univ, 66-75; SR SCIENTIST, ARGONNE NAT LAB, 75- *Concurrent Pos:* Vis fel, Japanese Soc Prom Sci, 77; adj prof physics, Northwestern Univ & Northern Ill Univ, 80- *Mem:* Am Phys Soc. *Res:* Experimental investigation of lattice dynamics of solids, magnetic structures and dynamics of magnetic systems by neutron scattering; theoretical studies of lattice dynamics, electron-phonon interactions and dielectric screening in solids; diffraction studies of adsorbed monolayers on surfaces. *Mailing Add:* Solid State Sci Div Argonne Nat Lab Argonne IL 60439

SINHA, VINOD T(ARKESHWAR), b Patna, India, June 10, 41; m 66; c 2. CHEMICAL ENGINEERING. *Educ:* Bombay Univ, BChemEng, 64; Univ Alta, MSc, 64; Univ Calif, Davis, PhD(chem eng), 67. *Prof Exp:* Res chem engr, 67-74, proj leader, 77-80, SR RES CHEM ENGR, AM CYANAMID CO, 74- *Mem:* Am Inst Chem Engrs; Am Chem Soc. *Res:* Fluid mechanics and hydrodynamic stability; heat and mass transfer; impact thermoplastics; extrusion. *Mailing Add:* 17 Diamond Crest Lane Stamford CT 06903

SINHA, YAGYA NAND, b Muzaffarpur, India, Oct 21, 36; m 58; c 4. ENDOCRINOLOGY. *Educ:* Bihar Univ, GBVC, 57; Mich State Univ, MS, 64, PhD(physiol), 67. *Prof Exp:* Vet asst surgeon, Govt Bihar, India, 57-59; res asst, Livestock Res Sta, Patna, India, 59-61; res assoc, Cornell Univ, 67-69; res assoc, Scripps Clin & Res Found, 69-81, MEM STAFF, WHITTIER INST DIABETES & ENDOCRINOL, SCRIPPS MEM HOSP, 82- *Mem:* AAAS; Soc Exp Biol & Med; Endocrine Soc. *Res:* Endocrinological and biochemical aspects of lactation, reproduction, carcinogenesis and growth. *Mailing Add:* Whittier Inst Diabetes & Endocrinol Scripps Mem Hosp 9894 Genesee Ave La Jolla CA 92037

SINIFF, DONALD BLAIR, b Bexley, Ohio, July 7, 35; m 59; c 3. ECOLOGY, BIOMETRY. *Educ:* Mich State Univ, BS, 57, MS, 58; Univ Minn, PhD(entom, fish & wildlife), 67. *Prof Exp:* Biometrician, Alaska Dept Fish & Game, 60-64; res fel, 64-67, assoc prof, 67-75, PROF ECOL, DEPT ECOL-BEHAV BIOL, 108 ZOOL BLDG, UNIV MINN, MINNEAPOLIS, 75- *Concurrent Pos:* Prin investr, NSF Off Polar Prog grant, 67-; comnr, Marine Mammal Comn, 75-81. *Mem:* Wildlife Soc; Ecol Soc. *Res:* Vertebrate ecology; statistical and computer applications in field studies. *Mailing Add:* Dept of Ecol & Behav Biol 108 Zool Bldg Univ of Minn Minneapolis MN 55108

SINK, DAVID SCOTT, b Findlay, Ohio, July 10, 50; m 73. INDUSTRIAL ENGINEERING. *Educ:* Ohio State Univ, BS, 73, MS, 77, PhD(indust eng), 78. *Prof Exp:* Serv systs engr, Eastman Kodak Corp, 73-75; res assoc, Ohio State Univ, 75-77, instr indust eng, 77-78; ASST PROF INDUST ENG & MGT, OKLA STATE UNIV, 78- *Concurrent Pos:* Res & develop dir, Okla Productivity Ctr, 78-; prin investr, Okla State Univ, 81- *Honors & Awards:* Halliburton Award, 81; Dow Award, 82. *Mem:* Inst Indust Engrs; Am Soc Eng Educ; Acad Mgt. *Res:* Methods and techniques for measuring and improving productivity in all aspects of organizations. *Mailing Add:* 322 Eng N Okla State Univ Stillwater OK 74078

SINK, DONALD WOODFIN, b Salisbury, NC, Nov 10, 37; m 60; c 3. INORGANIC CHEMISTRY. *Educ:* Catawba Col, AB, 59; Univ SC, PhD(inorg chem), 65. *Prof Exp:* Instr chem, Appalachian State Teachers Col, 60-61; asst prof, Lenoir-Rhyne Col, 65-67; asst prof, Northern Mich Univ, 67-68; from asst prof to assoc prof, 68-72, PROF CHEM, APPALACHIAN STATE UNIV, 72-, ASST DEAN ARTS & SCI, 75- *Mem:* Am Chem Soc; Sigma Xi. *Res:* Synthesis and study of cis-trans square planar isomers of palladium and platinum complexes; far infrared spectra of square planar complexes of palladium and platinum. *Mailing Add:* 101 Sanford Hall Appalachian State Univ Boone NC 28607

SINK, JOHN DAVIS, b Homer City, Pa, Dec 19, 34; m 64; c 2. BIOCHEMISTRY, BIOPHYSICS. *Educ:* Pa State Univ, BS, 56, MS, 60, PhD(biochem, animal sci), 62. *Prof Exp:* Admin officer, Pa Dept Agr, 62; asst prof animal sci, Pa State Univ, 62-66, assoc prof meat sci, 66-72, prof, 72-80; PROF & CHMN ANIMAL & VET SCI, WVA UNIV, 80- *Concurrent Pos:* NSF fel, 64-65; consult, Pa Dept Agr, 62-; joint staff officer, USDA, 79-80. *Honors & Awards:* Darbaker Prize, Pa Acad Sci, 67. *Mem:* AAAS; Am Meat Sci Asn (pres, 74-75); Am Chem Soc; Biophys Soc; Am Soc Animal Sci. *Res:* Lipid and steroid biochemistry; muscle biophysics and physiology; meat flavor chemistry. *Mailing Add:* G038 Agr Sci Bldg WVa Univ Morgantown WV 26506

SINK, KENNETH C, JR, b Altoona, Pa, Oct 7, 37. CELL GENETICS. *Educ:* Pa State Univ, BS, 59, MS, 61, PhD(genetics, plant breeding), 63. *Prof Exp:* From asst prof to assoc prof, 63-75, PROF, MICH STATE UNIV, 75- *Mem:* Am Soc Hort Sci; Am Genetic Asn. *Res:* Cell and protoplast culture and fusion. *Mailing Add:* Dept of Hort Mich State Univ East Lansing MI 48823

SINKE, CARL, b Moline, Mich, Oct 15, 28; m 56; c 4. MATHEMATICS. *Educ:* Calvin Col, AB, 49; Purdue Univ, MS, 51, PhD(math), 54. *Prof Exp:* Asst prof, 56-64, chmn dept, 64-74, PROF MATH, CALVIN COL, 64- *Concurrent Pos:* Consult, Hq, Ord Weapons Command, Ill, 56-57 & Off Ord Res, NC, 57-58. *Mem:* Am Math Soc; Math Asn Am. *Res:* Analysis; asymptotic series; operations research; optimization problems. *Mailing Add:* Dept of Math Calvin Col Grand Rapids MI 49506

SINKFORD, JEANNE C, b Washington, DC, Jan 30, 33; m 51; c 2. DENTISTRY, PHYSIOLOGY. *Educ:* Howard Univ, BS, 53, DDS, 58; Northwestern Univ, MS, 62, PhD(physiol), 63. *Prof Exp:* Res asst psychol, US Dept Health, Educ & Welfare, 53; instr dent, Col Dent, Howard Univ, 58-60; clin instr, Dent Sch, Northwestern Univ, 63-64; assoc prof & head dept, 64-74, assoc dean, 74-75, PROF PROSTHODONT COL DENT, HOWARD UNIV, 74-, DEAN, 75- *Concurrent Pos:* USPHS gen res & training grant, 65-; consult prosthodont, Freedmen's Hosp, Washington, DC, 64, res & prosthodont, Vet Admin Hosp, 65 & US Army grants, 65- *Mem:* Am Dent Asn; Int Asn Dent Res. *Res:* Endogenous anti-inflammatory substances; chemical healing agent; cyanoacrylates; gingival retraction agents; hereditary dental defects; oral endocrine effects; neuromuscular problems and temporomandibular joint. *Mailing Add:* Howard Univ Col of Dent 600 W St NW Washington DC 20059

SINKHORN, RICHARD DENNIS, mathematics, see previous edition

SINKINSON, KATHLEEN, b Philadelphia, Pa, Apr 23, 49. TOPOLOGY. *Educ:* Chestnut Hill Col, BS, 71; Temple Univ, MA, 73, PhD(math), 75. *Prof Exp:* Gibbs instr math, Yale Univ, 75-77; lectr, Mass Inst Technol, 77-78; ASST PROF MATH, BOSTON UNIV, 78- *Mem:* Am Math Soc. *Res:* Extraordinary chomology theories and stable homotopy theory. *Mailing Add:* Dept of Math Boston Univ Boston MA 02215

SINKOV, ABRAHAM, b Philadelphia, Pa, Aug 21, 07; m 42; c 1. MATHEMATICS. *Educ:* City Col New York, BS, 27; Columbia Univ, MA, 29; George Washington Univ, PhD(math), 33. *Prof Exp:* Teacher high schs, NY, 27-30; cryptanalyst, Dept Defense, 30-62; prof, 63-77, EMER PROF MATH, ARIZ STATE UNIV, 77- *Concurrent Pos:* Mem staff, Nat War Col, 54-55; lectr, Univ Md, 57-63; consult, Nat Security Agency; mem adv panel, Nat Bur Stand. *Honors & Awards:* Legion of Merit with Oak Leaf Cluster, Order of the Brit Empire. *Mem:* Math Asn Am; Am Math Soc. *Res:* Numerical analysis; group theory; cryptanalysis; computer programming. *Mailing Add:* Dept of Math Ariz State Univ Tempe AZ 85281

SINKOVIC, JELENA, b Celje, Yugoslavia, Aug 2, 24. ELECTROCHEMISTRY. *Educ:* Univ Ljubljana, PhD(eng chem), 66. *Prof Exp:* Res assoc eng chem, Metall Inst, Univ Ljubljana, 52-67; ASSOC SPECIALIST ELECTROCHEM, UNIV CALIF, BERKELEY, 68- *Mem:* Am Chem Soc. *Res:* Electrolytic isolation of inclusions from steel; current distribution on tall vertical electrodes; mass transfer in electrodialysis cell; ion exchange. *Mailing Add:* Univ Calif 1301 S 46th St Richmond CA 94804

SINKOVICS, JOSEPH, b Budapest, Hungary, June 17, 24; nat US. VIROLOGY, INTERNAL MEDICINE. *Educ:* Univ Budapest, MD, 48; Am Bd Med Microbiol, dipl, 62; Am Bd Internal Med, dipl, 65, recert, 80, cert infectious dis, 72, cert med oncol, 77. *Prof Exp:* Assoc prof med microbiol, Inst Microbiol, Univ Budapest, 48-50; sci investr virol, State Inst Pub Health, Hungary, 53-56; res assoc tumor virol, Hektoen Inst Med Res & resident physician internal med, Cook County Hosp, Chicago, Ill, 60-62; assoc prof, Univ Tex M D Anderson Hosp & Tumor Inst, 62-72, prof med, 72-79; VIS PROF VIROL, BAYLOR COL MED, 80- *Concurrent Pos:* Rockefeller fel, Inst Microbiol, Rutgers Univ, 57; Am Cancer Soc fel, Univ Tex M D Anderson Hosp & Tumor Inst, 59; specialist in lab diag, Univ Budapest, 54; prin investr, USPHS res grants; consult med oncol, Univ Tex M D Anderson Hosp & Tumor Inst, 80- *Mem:* AMA; Am Asn Cancer Res; Am Soc Microbiol; Am Soc Clin Oncol; Infectious Dis Soc Am. *Res:* Pleuropneumonia-like growth; influenza virus; pathogenicity, relationship, interference, neurotoxicity, incomplete form and carcinostatic activity of Newcastle disease virus; antibodies against lymphocytic choriomeningitis virus; mouse and human leukemia; immunology and immunotherapy of experimental and human tumors; life threatening infections; chemotherapy of human tumors. *Mailing Add:* 909 Frostwood Suite 153 Houston TX 77024

SINKS, LUCIUS FREDERICK, b Newburyport, Mass, Mar 14, 31; m 56; c 3. BIOPHYSICS, PEDIATRICS. *Educ:* Yale Univ, BS, 53; Jefferson Med Col, MD, 57; Ohio State Univ, MMSc, 63. *Prof Exp:* Assoc cancer res pediatrician, Roswell Park Mem Inst, 66-67, chief cancer res pediatrician, 67-76; prof pediat, Georgetown Univ, 76-81, chief, Div Pediat & Adolescent Oncol/Hemat, Vincent T Lombardi Cancer Res Ctr, 76-81; PROF PEDIAT, TUFTS UNIV, 81- *Concurrent Pos:* Nat Cancer Inst spec fel, Cambridge, Eng, 64-66; Nat Cancer Inst grant, Roswell Park Mem Inst, 66-74; Nat Cancer Inst Advan Clin Oncol Training Prog grant, 68-78; from asst res prof to assoc res prof pediat, State Univ NY, Buffalo, 66-69, res prof pediat, 69-; chief, Div Pediat & Adolescent Oncol & Hemat, New Eng Med Ctr Hosps, 81- *Mem:* Am Asn Cancer Res; Soc Pediat Res; Am Soc Clin Oncol. *Res:* Pediatric oncology; cell biology. *Mailing Add:* Dept Pediat Tufts Univ Medford MA 02155

SINKULA, ANTHONY ARTHUR, b Laona, Wis, Jan 2, 38; m 63; c 2. PHARMACEUTICAL CHEMISTRY, MEDICINAL CHEMISTRY. *Educ:* Univ Wis, BS, 59; Ohio State Univ, MS, 61, PhD(pharmaceut chem), 63; Western Mich Univ, MBA, 66. *Prof Exp:* Res assoc pharm, 63-68, sr res scientist, 68-76, res head, 76-78, MGR, RES PROG PLANNING, UPJOHN

CO, 78- *Mem:* Am Pharmaceut Asn; Acad Pharmaceut Sci. *Res:* Chemical modification of drugs; drug formulation research; prodrug chemistry research; research planning. *Mailing Add:* The Upjohn Co 301 Henrietta St Kalamazoo MI 49001

SINNETT, CARL E(ARL), b Wilkinsburg, Pa, Aug 26, 22; m 48; c 3. CHEMICAL ENGINEERING. *Educ:* Carnegie Inst Technol, BS, 46, MS, 47. *Prof Exp:* Asst tech man, B F Goodrich Co, Ohio, 46; chem engr, Standard Oil Co, Ind, 47-51; proj engr, Eval & Comput Div, Gulf Res & Develop Co, 51-68, sr proj engr, Econ & Comput Sci Div, 68-71 & Planning & Econ Div, 71-75, sr proj engr, Corp Res & Chem Div, Gulf Sci & Technol Co, 75-78, SR PROJ ENGR, CHEM & MINERALS DIV, GULF SCI & TECHNOL CO, 78- *Mem:* Am Inst Chem Engrs. *Res:* Process design and economic evaluation of petroleum refining and energy conversion processes. *Mailing Add:* Chem & Minerals Div Gulf Sci & Technol Co Box 2038 Pittsburgh PA 15230

SINNETTE, CALVIN HERMAN, pediatrics, see previous edition

SINNHUBER, RUSSELL OTTO, b Detroit, Mich, Apr 28, 17; m 42; c 3. FOOD SCIENCE, TOXICOLOGY. *Educ:* Mich State Univ, BS, 39; Ore State Univ, MS, 41. *Prof Exp:* From asst prof to assoc prof, 43-63, PROF FOOD SCI & TECHNOL, ORE STATE UNIV, 63- *Concurrent Pos:* Mem Agr Res Inst agr bd subcomt fish nutrit, Nat Acad Sci-Nat Res Coun. *Honors & Awards:* Conserv Serv Award, US Dept Interior, 66. *Mem:* Fel AAAS; Am Inst Nutrit; Am Oil Chem Soc; Inst Food Technol; Am Chem Soc. *Res:* Lipid chemistry and autoxidation; irradiation of seafoods; fish and shellfish nutrition; fatty acid metabolism; carcinogenesis; mycotoxins. *Mailing Add:* Dept of Food Sci Ore State Univ Corvallis OR 97331

SINNIS, JAMES CONSTANTINE, b Dover, NJ, May 31, 35; m 57; c 3. PLASMA PHYSICS. *Educ:* Stevens Inst Technol, ME, 57, MS, 59, PhD(physics), 63. *Prof Exp:* RES STAFF PLASMA PHYSICS LAB, PRINCETON UNIV, 63- *Mem:* Am Phys Soc; AAAS. *Res:* Plasma physics research with special interest in development of fusion power via the magnetic confinement approach. *Mailing Add:* Plasma Physics Lab Princeton Univ Princeton NJ 08540

SINNOCK, POMEROY, human genetics, see previous edition

SINNOTT, GEORGE, b St Louis, Mo, Mar 13, 32; m 57; c 3. MOLECULAR PHYSICS. *Educ:* Univ Chicago, AB, 53, MS, 57; Washington Univ, PhD(physics), 64. *Prof Exp:* Physicist, Argonne Nat Lab, 56-58, Lockheed-Palo Alto Labs, Calif, 64-68 & Joint Inst Lab Astrophys, Univ Colo, Boulder, 68-71; chief, Fire Physics & Dynamics Prog, Nat Bur Standards, 72-74; sci policy asst to Congressman Charles Mosher, 74-75; cong liaison officer, 75-78, ASSOC DIR TECH EVAL, NAT ENG LAB, NAT BUR STANDARDS, 78- *Mem:* Am Phys Soc; Sigma Xi. *Mailing Add:* Technol Bldg Rm B117 Nat Bur of Standards Washington DC 20234

SINNOTT, M(AURICE) J(OSEPH), b Detroit, Mich, Jan 19, 16; m 44; c 5. METALLURGICAL ENGINEERING. *Educ:* Univ Mich, BS, 38, MS, 41, ScD(metall eng), 46. *Prof Exp:* Plant metallurgist, Great Lakes Steel Corp, 38-40; res assoc, Eng Res Inst, Univ Mich, 40-43; sr develop engr, Goodyear Aircraft Corp, 43; instr chem & metall eng, 44-46, from asst prof to assoc prof, 46-54, PROF CHEM & METALL ENG, UNIV MICH, ANN ARBOR, 54-, ASSOC DEAN ENG, 73- *Mem:* Am Soc Metals; Am Inst Mining, Metall & Petrol Engrs; Brit Inst Metal. *Res:* Metal physics; grain boundary phenomena; x-ray analysis; nucleation; growth. *Mailing Add:* 438 W Eng Bldg Univ of Mich Ann Arbor MI 48109

SINOTTE, LOUIS PAUL, b Haverhill, Mass, June 12, 27; m 55; c 5. PHARMACEUTICAL CHEMISTRY, ORGANIC CHEMISTRY. *Educ:* Mass Col Pharm, BS, 50; Purdue Univ, MS, 52, PhD(pharmaceut chem), 54. *Prof Exp:* Tech asst to dir qual control, 54-55, mgr pharmaceut control, 55-61, DIR QUAL CONTROL, MERCK SHARP & DOHME DIV, MERCK & CO, INC, 61- *Concurrent Pos:* Mem trustee adv comt, Rutgers Col Pharm. *Mem:* Am Chem Soc; Soc Cosmetic Chemists; Am Soc Qual Control; Am Pharmaceut Asn; Pharmaceut Mfrs Asn. *Res:* Pharmaceutical and medicinal research; quality control; manufacturing pharmacy. *Mailing Add:* Merck Sharp & Dohme Div Merck & Co Inc West Point PA 19486

SINSHEIMER, JOSEPH EUGENE, b New York, NY, Dec 30, 22; m 54; c 3. MEDICINAL CHEMISTRY, PHARMACEUTICAL CHEMISTRY. *Educ:* Univ Mich, BS, 48, MS, 50, PhD(pharmaceut chem) 53. *Hon Degrees:* Dr, Univ Ghent, Belgium, 74. *Prof Exp:* Assoc technologist org chem, Gen Foods Corp, 53-57, proj leader, 57; from asst prof to assoc prof pharmaceut chem, Univ RI, 57-60; assoc prof, 60-68, PROF MED & PHARMACEUT CHEM, COL PHARM, UNIV MICH, ANN ARBOR, 68- *Concurrent Pos:* Consult, Labs Criminal Invest, Univ RI, 58-60; Am Found Pharmaceut Educ Pfeiffer Mem res fel, St Mary's Med Sch, London, 72; mem comt rev, US Pharmacopeia, 75-; fel, Belgium Nat Found Sci Res, Univ Ghent, 78-79. *Mem:* Am Chem Soc; Am Pharmaceut Asn; fel Acad Pharmaceut Sci. *Res:* Analytical medicinal chemistry; drug metabolism; natural product and flavor chemistry; toxicology of aliphatic epoxides. *Mailing Add:* Col of Pharm Univ of Mich Ann Arbor MI 48109

SINSHEIMER, ROBERT LOUIS, b Washington, DC, Feb 5, 20; c 3. BIOCHEMISTRY, BIOPHYSICS. *Educ:* Mass Inst Technol, SB, 41, SM, 42, PhD(biophys), 48. *Hon Degrees:* DSc, St Olaf Col, 74. *Prof Exp:* Res assoc biol, Mass Inst Technol, 48-49; from assoc prof to prof biophys, Iowa State Col, 49-57; prof biophys, Calif Inst Technol, 57-77, chmn div biol, 68-77; CHANCELLOR, UNIV CALIF, SANTA CRUZ, 77- *Concurrent Pos:* Chmn ed bd, Proc Nat Acad Sci, 72-80; mem bd sci adv, Jane Coffin Childs Fund Med Res, 73- *Honors & Awards:* Beijerinck Virol Medal, Royal Netherlands Acad Sci & Lett, 70. *Mem:* Nat' Acad Sci; Nat Inst Med; Am Acad Arts & Sci; Am Soc Biol Chem; Biophys Soc (pres, 70-71). *Res:* Physical and chemical properties of nucleic acids; replication of nucleic acids; bacterial viruses. *Mailing Add:* Off of Chancellor Univ of Calif Santa Cruz CA 95064

SINSKEY, ANTHONY J, b Highland, Ill, Apr 1, 40; m 69. FOOD SCIENCE, MICROBIOLOGY. *Educ:* Univ Ill, BSc, 62; Mass Inst Technol, ScD(food sci), 66. *Prof Exp:* Fel, Sch Pub Health, Harvard Univ, 66-67; from asst prof to assoc prof microbiol, 67-77, PROF APPL MICROBIOL, MASS INST TECHNOL, 77- *Honors & Awards:* Samuel Cate Prescott Award, 75. *Mem:* Fel Am Acad Microbiol; Am Chem Soc; Inst Food Technol; Brit Soc Appl Bact; Am Soc Microbiol. *Res:* Food and applied microbiology; radiation effects on microorganisms; single cell protein; recovery and characterization of injured microorganisms. *Mailing Add:* Dept of Nutrit & Food Sci Mass Inst of Technol Cambridge MA 02139

SINSKI, JAMES THOMAS, b Milwaukee, Wis, June 23, 27. MEDICAL MYCOLOGY. *Educ:* Marquette Univ, BS, 47, MS, 52; Purdue Univ, PhD(mycol), 55; Am Bd Med Microbiol, dipl, 69. *Prof Exp:* Instr biol, Spring Hill Col, 55-57; head chem anal lab sugar res, Am Sugar Refinery, New Orleans, 57-58; chief mycol sect, Fort Detrick, Frederick, Md, 60-66; ASSOC PROF MED MYCOL, UNIV ARIZ, 66- *Concurrent Pos:* US Dept Health, Educ & Welfare trainee med mycol, Tulane Univ, 58-60. *Mem:* Am Soc Microbiol; Med Mycol Soc of the Americas; Int Soc Human & Animal Mycol; fel Am Acad Microbiol. *Res:* Coccidioidomycosis; dermatomycosis. *Mailing Add:* Dept of Microbiol Univ of Ariz Tucson AZ 85721

SINSKY, JOEL A, physics, see previous edition

SINTES, JORGE LUIS, b San Juan, PR, Dec 8, 48. DENTISTRY, NUTRITIONAL BIOCHEMISTRY. *Educ:* Univ PR, BS, 68, DMD, 73, MS, 75; Mass Inst Technol, PhD(nutrit), 78. *Prof Exp:* Actg dir dent res, Dept Health, PR, 74-75; SCIENTIST & CARIOLOGIST, ORAL HEALTH RES CTR, FAIRLEIGH DICKINSON UNIV, 78- *Concurrent Pos:* Instr, Inter Am Univ, PR, 74-75; clin instr, Sch Dent, Tufts Univ, 75-78; Nat Inst Dent Res fel, Mass Inst Technol, 75-78; consult food stamp prog, Mass, 76-78; consult prev dent & nutrit, pvt pract, 74- & Native Am Consults Inc, 78- *Mem:* Am Dent Asn; AAAS; Am Pub Health Asn; Am Soc Prev Dent; Sigma Xi. *Res:* Basic and clinical sciences in dental education; public health dentistry; nutrition and preventive dentistry; applied nutrition in dentistry. *Mailing Add:* Oral Health Res Ctr Fairleigh Dickinson Univ Hackensack NJ 07601

SINTON, JOHN MAYNARD, b Bozeman, Mont, Apr 12, 46; div; c 2. GEOLOGY, PETROLOGY. *Educ:* Univ Calif, Santa Barbara, AB, 69; Univ Ore, MS, 71; Univ Otago, NZ, PhD(geol), 76. *Prof Exp:* Teaching fel geol, Univ Otago, NZ, 71-75; fel mineral sci, Smithsonian Inst, 76-77; asst prof, 77-81, ASSOC PROF GEOL, UNIV HAWAII, 81- *Mem:* Am Geophys Union. *Res:* Ophiolites; the oceanic crust; Hawaiian volcanic and plutonic rocks. *Mailing Add:* Hawaii Inst Geophysics 2525 Correa Rd Honolulu HI 96822

SINTON, STEVEN WILLIAMS, SOLID STATE PHYSICS. *Educ:* Univ Colo, Boulder, BS, 76; Univ Calif, Berkeley, PhD(chem), 81. *Prof Exp:* RES CHEMIST, EXXON PROD RES CO, 81- *Res:* Solid and liquid state coherent nuclear magnetic resonance spectroscopy; multiphoton processes; optical spectroscopy of surface active species. *Mailing Add:* PO Box 2189 Houston TX 77001

SINTON, WILLIAM MERZ, b Baltimore, Md, Apr 11, 25; m 60; c 3. ASTRONOMY. *Educ:* Johns Hopkins Univ, AB, 49, PhD(physics), 53. *Prof Exp:* Asst, Johns Hopkins Univ, 49-53, res staff, 53-54; res assoc, Harvard Univ, 54-56; astrophysicist, Smithsonian Inst, 56-57; astronr, Lowell Observ, Ariz, 57-66; PROF ASTRON, UNIV HAWAII, 66-, MEM, INST ASTRON, 67- *Honors & Awards:* Lomb Medal, Optical Soc Am, 54. *Mem:* Optical Soc Am; Am Astron Soc; Int Astron Union. *Res:* Infrared spectroscopy; temperatures of planets; infrared spectra of planets and stars. *Mailing Add:* Inst Astron Univ Hawaii Honolulu HI 96822

SIOMOS, KONSTADINOS, b Larissa, Greece, June 30, 47; m 75; c 2. LASER SPECTROSCOPY, LASER TECHNOLOGY. *Educ:* Ruprecht Carl Univ, WGer, dipl, 69, dipl(physics), 72; Univ Cologne, WGer, PhD(physics), 74. *Prof Exp:* Asst prof physics, Univ Cologne, WGer, 72-75; staff mem laser spectros, Nuclear Res Ctr, WGer, 75-76; STAFF MEM & PRIN INVESTR LASER SPECTROS, HEALTH & SAFETY RES DIV, OAK RIDGE NAT LAB, 76- *Concurrent Pos:* Asst prof, Univ Tenn, Knoxville, 80-81. *Mem:* Optical Soc Am; Ger Soc Physics; AAAS. *Res:* Laser atomic and molecular spectroscopy and dye laser technology; laser induced ionization processes of molecules and negative ions in the liquid and gaseous phase; non-linear laser spectroscopy of molecules in solution, energetics and kinetics of change separated states in liquids. *Mailing Add:* 102 Mohawk Rd Oak Ridge TN 37830

SION, MAURICE, b Skopje, Yugoslavia, Oct 17, 28; US citizen; m 57; c 3. MATHEMATICS. *Educ:* NY Univ, BA, 47, MS, 48; Univ Calif, PhD(math), 51. *Prof Exp:* Asst, Inst Math & Mech, NY Univ, 47-48; asst math, Univ Calif, Berkeley, 48-50, lectr, 50-51; mathematician, Nat Bur Standards, 51-52; mem, Inst Advan Study, 55-57; from asst prof to assoc prof, 60-64, PROF MATH, UNIV BC, 64- *Concurrent Pos:* Instr, Univ Calif, Berkeley, 52-53, asst prof, 57-60; mem, Inst Advan Study, 62; Can Coun fel, Univ Florence & Univ Pisa, 70-71; vis prof, Univ of Strasbourg, France, 74-76. *Mem:* Am Math Soc; Can Math Cong. *Res:* Measure theory. *Mailing Add:* Dept of Math Univ of BC Vancouver BC V6T 1W5 Can

SIOPES, THOMAS DAVID, b Bremerton, Wash, July 9, 39; m 62; c 2. AVIAN PHYSIOLOGY & BIOCHEMISTRY. *Educ:* Calif State Univ, Sacramento, BA, 64; Univ Calif, Davis, MS, 72, PhD(physiol), 78. *Prof Exp:* ASST PROF POULTRY SCI, NC STATE UNIV, 78- *Mem:* Poultry Sci Asn; Worlds Poultry Sci Asn; AAAS. *Res:* Environmental and reproductive physiology of birds: photo-periodism, biological rhythms and thermoregulation. *Mailing Add:* Dept Poultry Sci NC State Univ Raleigh NC 27650

SIOUI, RICHARD HENRY, b Brooklyn, NY, Sept 25, 37; m 62; c 6. CHEMICAL ENGINEERING. *Educ:* Northeastern Univ, BS, 64; Univ Mass, Amherst, MS, 67, PhD(chem eng), 68; Sch Indust Mgt, Worcester Polytech Inst, dipl, 76. *Prof Exp:* Sr res engr, Grinding Wheel Div, 68-71, res supvr, 71-78, TECH MGR, DIAMOND PROD DIV, NORTON CO, 78- *Mem:* Am Inst Chem Engrs. *Res:* Development of new products which utilize the superabrasives--diamond and cubic boron nitrides--for the grinding of hard materials much as carbides and tool steels and processes for their manufactors. *Mailing Add:* Avery Heights Dr Halden MA 01520

SIPE, HARRY CRAIG, b Flushing, Ohio, Nov 22, 17; m 46, 70. SCIENCE EDUCATION. *Educ:* Bethany Col, WVa, AB, 37; Univ Va, MA, 38; Peabody Col, PhD(sci educ), 52. *Prof Exp:* Teacher high sch, Va, 38-41; develop chemist, O'Sullivan Rubber Co, 41-42; instr physics, Bethany Col, WVa, 43-44; master, Woodberry Forest Sch, 44-46; asst prof, Mars Hill Col, 46-47; from asst prof to prof, Florence State Col, 47-54; phys scientist, Indian Springs Sch, 54-57; prof physics & sci ed, George Peabody Col, 57-67; PROF TECH EDUC, STATE UNIV NY ALBANY, 67- *Concurrent Pos:* Vis prof, Ohio State Univ, 66-67. *Mem:* AAAS; Am Chem Soc; Nat Asn Res Sci Teaching (pres, 66); Nat Sci Teachers Asn; Am Asn Physics Teachers. *Res:* Theory of science education; cognitive development; teacher education. *Mailing Add:* 1 Concord Rd Glenmont NY 12077

SIPE, HERBERT JAMES, JR, b Lewistown, Pa, Aug 17, 40. PHYSICAL CHEMISTRY. *Educ:* Juniata Col, BS, 62; Univ Wis-Madison, PhD(chem), 69. *Prof Exp:* Asst prof, 68-74, Res Corp grant, 69, chmn dept, 72-74, assoc prof, 74-81, PROF CHEM, HAMPDEN-SYDNEY COL, 81-, CHMN DEPT, 76- *Concurrent Pos:* NSF-Undergrad Res Partic grants, 72, 73, 77 & 78; NSF-ISEP grants, 73 & 78; vis prof, Univ Ala, 80-81. *Mem:* AAAS; Am Chem Soc. *Res:* Electron spin resonance spectroscopy of organo-metallic compounds and semiempirical molecular orbital calculations of bonding in organometallic compounds; endor spectroscopy. *Mailing Add:* Dept of Chem Hampden-Sydney Col Hampden-Sydney VA 23943

SIPE, JERRY EUGENE, b Hickory, NC, Sept 19, 42; m 63; c 3. BIOCHEMISTRY, MICROBIOLOGY. *Educ:* Lenoir-Rhyne Col, BS, 64; Wake Forest Univ, PhD(biochem), 69. *Prof Exp:* From instr biochem to asst prof, Bowman Gray Sch Med, Wake Forest Univ, 71-74; ASSOC PROF BIOL, ANDERSON COL, 74- *Concurrent Pos:* Dir teaching labs, Bowman Gray Sch Med, Wake Forest Univ, 69-74. *Mem:* AAAS; Am Soc Microbiol. *Res:* Nucleic acid methylation, especially ribosomal RNA methylation; methylation contributions to the growing cell. *Mailing Add:* Dept Biol Anderson Col Anderson IN 46011

SIPERSTEIN, MARVIN DAVID, b Minneapolis, Minn, Sept 21, 25; m 52; c 3. BIOCHEMISTRY, INTERNAL MEDICINE. *Educ:* Univ Minn, BS, 46, MB, 47, MD, 48; Univ Calif, PhD(physiol), 53. *Prof Exp:* From asst prof to prof internal med, Univ Tex Health Sci Ctr Dallas, 64-73; PROF MED, UNIV CALIF, SAN FRANCISCO, 73-; CHIEF METAB SECT, VET ADMIN HOSP, 73- *Concurrent Pos:* NIH res career award, 61-73. *Honors & Awards:* Marchman Award, 59; Lilly Award, Am Diabetes Asn, 59. *Mem:* AAAS; Am Soc Biol Chem; Am Soc Clin Invest; Soc Exp Biol & Med; Asn Am Physicians (pres, 79-80). *Res:* Control of isoprene synthesis in normal and cancer cells; diabetes. *Mailing Add:* Univ of Calif Med Serv Vet Admin Hosp San Francisco CA 94121

SIPES, IVAN GLENN, b Tarentum, Pa, July 26, 42. PHARMACOLOGY, TOXICOLOGY. *Educ:* Univ Cincinnati, BS, 65; Univ Pittsburgh, PhD(pharmacol), 69. *Prof Exp:* Staff fel pharmacol, Nat Heart, Lung & Blood Inst, 69-71, sr staff fel, 71-73; from asst prof to assoc prof, 73-81, PROF PHARMACOL & TOXICOL, COL MED, UNIV ARIZ, 81- *Concurrent Pos:* Spec lectr, George Wash Univ, 71-73; assoc ed, Life Sci J, 73-; fel Off Naval Res, 77-, Nat Inst Environ Health Sci, 77-79 & 78-83, Nat Cancer Inst, 77-80 & Int Union Pharmacol, Toxicol Sect. *Mem:* Soc Toxicol; Am Soc Pharmacol & Exp Therapeut; Western Pharmacol Soc; Asn Univ Anesthetists. *Res:* Role of biotransformation in drug or xenobiotic induced liver injury; organohalogen induced chemical carcinogenesis; pharmacokinetics of xenobiotics; disposition of polychlorinated biphenyls; halothane induced hepatitis. *Mailing Add:* Dept of Anesthesiol Ariz Health Sci Ctr Tuscon AZ 85724

SIPOS, FRANK, b Lucenec, Czech, July 13, 26; div; c 2. PEPTIDE CHEMISTRY. *Educ:* Charles Univ, Prague, Dr rer nat, 51; Czech Acad Sci, PhD(org chem), 56. *Prof Exp:* Teaching asst pharmaceut chem, Charles Univ, 48-51; scientist, Inst Org Chem & Biochem, Czech Acad Sci, 51-65; sr res chemist, Norwich Pharmacal Co, 66-70; SR RES INVESTR, SQUIBB INST MED RES, 70- *Honors & Awards:* Czech State Prize, 63. *Mem:* Am Chem Soc. *Res:* Reaction mechanism; stereochemistry; synthesis of polypeptides. *Mailing Add:* Squibb Inst Med Res Georges Rd New Brunswick NJ 08903

SIPOS, TIBOR, b Budapest, Hungary, May 13, 35; US citizen; m 59; c 3. BIOCHEMISTRY, MICROBIOLOGY. *Educ:* Lebanon Valley Col, BS, 64; Lehigh Univ, PhD(biochem), 68. *Prof Exp:* Sr res scientist enzymol, Wallerstein Co, 68-69; sr res scientist enzymol, 69-74, res assoc, Johnson & Johnson Res, 74-77, sr res assoc, 77-78, asst mgr, 78-79, MGR CONSUMER DENT CARE RES, JOHNSON & JOHNSON PROD INC, 80- *Concurrent Pos:* Adj asst prof med, Col Med & Dent, NJ Med Sch, 74- *Honors & Awards:* Philip B Hofmann Res Scientist Award, 78. *Mem:* AAAS; Am Chem Soc; Am Soc Microbiol; Int Asn Dent Res; NY Acad Sci. *Res:* Application of enzymes in the health care field; mechanism of action of anticoagulants; prevention of dental caries, gingivitis and periodontitis; development of a synthetic anticaries vaccine. *Mailing Add:* Johnson & Johnson Prod Inc 501 George St New Brunswick NJ 08903

SIPPEL, JOHN EDWARD, medical microbiology, see previous edition

SIPPEL, THEODORE OTTO, b West Englewood, NJ, Aug 19, 27; m 52; c 2. ANATOMY. *Educ:* Univ Rochester, AB, 48; Yale Univ, PhD(zool), 52. *Prof Exp:* From instr to asst prof biol, Johns Hopkins Univ, 52-57; sr instr anat, Sch Med, Western Reserve Univ, 57-59; from asst prof to assoc prof, 59-69, PROF ANAT, SCH MED, UNIV MICH, ANN ARBOR, 69- *Concurrent Pos:* Nat Eye Inst sr fel anat, Univ Dundee, 71-72; res assoc, Kresge Eye Inst, Mich, 64-65. *Honors & Awards:* Fight-for-Sight Citation, Asn Res Vis & Ophthal, 62. *Mem:* Asn Res Vision & Ophthal; Am Asn Anat; Histochem Soc. *Res:* Metabolism of the lens; histochemistry. *Mailing Add:* Dept of Anat Univ of Mich Ann Arbor MI 48109

SIPPEL, WILLIAM LAWRENCE, b Baltimore, Md, Mar 1, 15; m 46. VETERINARY PATHOLOGY. *Educ:* Univ Md, BS, 36; Univ Pa, VMD, 40; Cornell Univ, MS, 42; Tex A&M Univ, PhD(vet path), 55. *Prof Exp:* Jr vet, USDA, 40-41; instr vet clin med, Kans State Univ, 42-44; prof serv rep, Cutter Labs, Calif, 44-45; head animal dis dept, Coastal Plain Exp Sta, Univ Syst Ga, 45-56; dir labs, Fla Dept Agr, 56-68; prof vet med, Tex A&M Univ, 68-69; exec dir, Tex Vet Med Diag lab, 69-80; CONSULT, A DUDA & SONS, INC, OVIEDO, FLA, 80- *Mem:* Am Asn Vet Lab Diagnosticians (secy, 59, pres, 60); Am Vet Med Asn; US Animal Health Asn; Acad Vet Consults; Am Asn Bovine Practitioners. *Res:* Toxicology, nutrition and management. *Mailing Add:* 1103 Winter Springs Blvd Winter Springs FL 32708

SIPPELL, WILLIAM LLOYD, b Pembroke, Ont, Oct 21, 21; m 50; c 3. FOREST ENTOMOLOGY. *Educ:* Univ Western Ont, BSc, 50, MSc, 51; Univ Mich, PhD(forestry), 57. *Prof Exp:* Res scientist, Forest Insect Lab, Can Dept Forestry, 51-77, head forest insect & dis surv, 53-77, FORESTRY, 51-, HEAD FOREST INSECT & DIS SURV, GREAT LAKES FOREST RES CTR, RES MGR, ENTOMOL & PATH, GREAT LAKES FOREST RES CTR, CAN DEPT ENVIRON, 77- *Concurrent Pos:* Chmn, Cent Int Forest Insect & Dis Conf, 70 & 74; Ont deleg, Northeastern Forest Pest Coun, 74-77. *Mem:* Entom Soc Am; fel Entom Soc Can. *Res:* Insect and disease surveys; parasites of the forest tent caterpillar; strategies of spruce budworm control; impact of spruce budworm on forest resource. *Mailing Add:* 95 Parkdale Dr Sault Ste Marie ON P6A 4C7 Can

SIPSON, ROGER FREDRICK, b Buffalo, NY, Oct 7, 40; m 67. PHYSICS. *Educ:* Union Col, NY, BS, 62; Syracuse Univ, PhD(physics), 68. *Prof Exp:* Asst prof, 68-73, ASSOC PROF PHYSICS, MOORHEAD STATE UNIV, 73- *Mem:* Am Asn Physics Teachers. *Res:* Quantum theory of fields; mathematical physics. *Mailing Add:* Dept of Physics Moorhead State Univ Moorhead MN 56560

SIQUEIRA, EDIR BARROS, b Belo Horizonte, Brazil, Apr 4, 31. SURGERY. *Educ:* Univ Minas Gerais, MD, 55; Northwestern Univ, Chicago, 62, PhD(neuroanat), 70; Am Bd Neurol Surg, dipl, 64. *Prof Exp:* Intern, St Luke's Hosp, Chicago, 56, resident gen surg, 57-58, resident neurol surg, Chicago Wesley Mem Hosp, 58-61; clin asst surg, 63-64, instr, 64-65, assoc in surg, 65-66, asst prof, 66-71, ASSOC PROF SURG, MED SCH, NORTHWESTERN UNIV, CHICAGO, 71- *Concurrent Pos:* Fel surg, Med Sch, Northwestern Univ, Chicago, 61; fel neurosurg, Children's Mem Hosp, Chicago, 62; mem courtesy staff, Chicago Wesley Mem Hosp, 62-65, asst attend staff, 65-68, assoc attend staff, 68-70, attend staff, 71-; temporary asst attend neurosurgeon, Children's Mem Hosp, Chicago, 64-66, asst attend surgeon, 66-68, mem med staff, 69-; consult, Forkosh Mem, Grant, Augustana, St Elizabeth, St Mary of Nazareth, Chicago Osteopathic, St Joseph & Columbus Hosps, Chicago, 72- *Mem:* AMA; Cong Neurol Surg; Am Asn Neurol Surg; fel Am Col Surg; Am Neurol Asn. *Res:* Neuroanatomy. *Mailing Add:* 530 N Lake Shore Dr Chicago IL 60611

SIQUIG, RICHARD ANTHONY, b Gilroy, Calif, Feb 2, 42; m 74. UNDERWATER ACOUSTICS. *Educ:* Calif Inst Technol, BS, 66; Univ Colo, MS, 71, PhD(astrophys), 74. *Prof Exp:* Vis asst prof astron, Ohio State Univ, 74-75; vis asst prof, Univ Wis-Madison, 75-76; res assoc, Hamburg Observ, 76-77; vis scientist, Nat Ctr Atmospheric Res, 78-79; res assoc, Univ Colo, 79; SR TECH ASSOC, OCEAN DATA SYSTS, INC, 80- *Mem:* Am Geophys Union. *Res:* Stability of stellar models during their evolution; solar variability and climate; planetary atmosphere cooling rates. *Mailing Add:* Ocean Data Systs Inc 2600 Garden Rd Suite 202 Monterey CA 93940

SIRAGANIAN, REUBEN PAUL, b Aleppo, Syria, Feb 7, 40; US citizen; m 70; c 2. IMMUNOLOGY. *Educ:* Am Univ Beirut, BS, 59; State Univ NY Downstate Med Ctr, MD, 62; Johns Hopkins Univ, PhD(immunol), 68. *Prof Exp:* Assoc mem immunol, Pub Health Res Inst New York, 68-73; HEAD SECT CLIN IMMUNOL, LAB MICROBIOL & IMMUNOL, NAT INST DENT RES, NIH, 73- *Concurrent Pos:* Res career develop award, NIH, 70-73, mem immunobiol study sect, 74-78; asst prof med, NY Univ, 71-73. *Mem:* Am Asn Immunol; Am Acad Allergy; AAAS; Am Soc Clin Invest. *Res:* Inflammation; immediate hypersensitivity reactions. *Mailing Add:* Lab Microbiol & Immunol Nat Inst Develop Res NIH Bethesda MD 20205

SIRBASKU, DAVID ANDREW, b St Paul, Minn, Nov 25, 41; m 64; c 1. BIOCHEMISTRY, CELL BIOLOGY. *Educ:* Col St Thomas, BS, 63; Univ Ill, PhD(biochem), 67. *Prof Exp:* NIH fel, Mass Inst Technol, 67-70; NIH spec fel, Univ Calif, San Diego, 70-72; asst prof, 72-77, ASSOC PROF BIOCHEM, UNIV TEX MED SCH HOUSTON, 77- *Mem:* Am Soc Cell Biol; Endocrine Soc; Am Chem Soc; AAAS; Am Tissue Cult Asn. *Res:* Hormonal control of cell growth, tumor cell surface properties and induction of growth promoting serum factors. *Mailing Add:* Dept of Biochem Univ of Tex Med Sch Houston TX 77025

SIRCAR, ANIL KUMER, b Calcutta, India, Jan 1, 28; m 52; c 3. POLYMER CHEMISTRY. *Educ:* Univ Dacca, BS, 48, MS, 49; Univ Calcutta, DPhil(polymer chem), 55. *Prof Exp:* Chemist, Sindri Fertilizers & Chem Ltd, India, 51-52; res asst polymer chem, Indian Asn Cultivation Sci, 52-57; NSF fel emulsion polymerization, Univ Minn, 58; res officer rubber chem, Indian Asn Cultivation Sci, 58-59; sr sci officer, Indian Rubber Mfrs Res Asn, 60; sect mgr rubber lab, Nat Rubber Mfrs Ltd, 60-65; Nat Acad Sci res assoc cotton fiber, Southern Regional Res Lab, USDA, 65-67; res chemist, 67-81, SR SCIENTIST, J M HUBER CORP, 81- *Concurrent Pos:* Mem bd examrs, Univ Calcutta, Calcutta, India, 62-65 & Indian Inst Technol, Kharagpur, India, 75. *Mem:* NAm Thermal Anal Soc; Am Chem Soc; Soc Plastics Engrs. *Res:* Physical chemistry of polymers; reinforcement of rubber; thermal and thermomechanical analysis; cotton fiber; polyelectrolytes; polymer blends. *Mailing Add:* J M Huber Corp PO Box 2831 Borger TX 79007

SIRCAR, ILA, US citizen. SYNTHETIC ORGANIC CHEMISTRY, MEDICAL RESEARCH. *Educ:* Calcutta Univ, BS, 56, MS, 58, PhD(org chem), 64. *Prof Exp:* Lectr chem, Calcutta Univ, 64-65; assoc res prof photochem, Loyola Univ, La, 65; res chemist, Southern Regional Res Lab, New Orleans, USDA, 66-67; res assoc, Dept Chem, Stevens Inst Technol, Hoboken, NJ, 74-75; res assoc, Dept Physiol, Sch Med, Rutgers Univ, 75-77; scientist, 77-80, SR SCIENTIST, RES DIV, WARNER-LAMBERT CO, 80- *Concurrent Pos:* NIH res fel, Dept Chem, Univ New Orleans, 65-66; Nat Res Coun-Nat Acad Sci fel, USDA, New Orleans, 66-67. *Res:* Synthesis of sugar derivatives for photolabeling of biological receptor sites; cardiovascular agents; synthesis of heterocyclic compounds of medicinal interest, natural products, carbohydrates, steroids; study of reactions and their mechanism. *Mailing Add:* Res Div Warner-Lambert Co Ann Arbor MI 48105

SIRCAR, JAGADISH CHANDRA, b Calcutta, India, Dec 1, 35; m 63; c 2. ORGANIC CHEMISTRY. *Educ:* Univ Calcutta, BSc, 56, MSc, 58, PhD(org chem), 64. *Prof Exp:* Lectr chem, WBengal Jr Educ Serv, 60-64 & Kalyani Agr Univ, India, 64-65; NIH fel org chem, La State Univ, New Orleans, 65-67; res chemist, USDA, New Orleans, 67-69; scientist, 69-74, sr scientist, 74-79, RES ASSOC, WARNER-LAMBERT CO, 79- *Concurrent Pos:* Nat Acad Sci-Nat Res Coun resident res assoc Naval Stores Lab, USDA, Olustee, Fla, 67-69. *Mem:* Am Chem Soc; NY Acad Sci; AAAS; Int Soc Heterocyclic Chem. *Res:* Synthetic organic chemistry; steroids; natural products; photochemistry; medicinal chemistry; reactions and reaction mechanisms; heterocyclic chemistry; chemotherapy. *Mailing Add:* Chem Dept 2800 Plymouth Rd Ann Arbor MI 48105

SIREK, ANNA, b Velke Senkvice, Slovak, Jan 12, 21; Can citizen; m 46; c 4. PHYSIOLOGY, SURGERY. *Educ:* Univ Bratislava, MD, 46; Univ Toronto, MA, 55, PhD, 60. *Prof Exp:* Res assoc, Banting & Best Dept Med Res, 54-60, lectr, 60-63, from asst prof to assoc prof, 63-72, PROF PHYSIOL, UNIV TORONTO, 72-, DIR DEPT TEACHING LABS, 75- *Concurrent Pos:* Vis fel surg, Kronprinsessan Lovissas Barnsjukhus, Stockholm, Sweden, 47-50; fel, Hosp Sick Children, Toronto, Ont, 50-54; asst dir dept teaching labs, Univ Toronto, 69-75; vis prof, Dept Physiol, Sackler Sch Med, Univ Tel-Aviv, 78. *Honors & Awards:* Hoechst Centennial Medal, Frankfurt, Ger, 66; Starr Medal, Univ Toronto, 60. *Mem:* AAAS; Can Fedn Biol Socs; Int Diabetes Fedn; Can Endocrine Soc; Can Diabetic Asn. *Res:* Metabolic studies in animals deprived of endocrines by experimental surgery and the response of diabetic and Houssay animals to insulin and growth hormone. *Mailing Add:* Dept Teaching Labs Med Sci Bldg Univ Toronto Toronto ON M5S 1A8 Can

SIREK, OTAKAR VICTOR, b Bratislava, Slovak, Dec 1, 21; Can citizen; m 46; c 4. PHYSIOLOGY. *Educ:* Univ Bratislava, MD, 46; Univ Toronto, MA, 51, PhD(physiol), 54. *Prof Exp:* Res assoc, Banting & Best Dept Med Res, 50-57, from asst prof to assoc prof, 57-68, PROF PHYSIOL, FAC MED, UNIV TORONTO, 68- *Concurrent Pos:* Vis fel biochem, Wenner Gren Inst, 47-50; asst biochemist, Hosp Sick Children, Toronto, 55-57; vis scientist, La Rabida Inst, Univ Chicago, 62-63; vis prof, Univ Calif, Los Angeles, 67 & Univ Tel-Aviv, 78. *Honors & Awards:* Hoechst Centennial Medal, Frankfurt, Ger, 66; C H Best Prize, Can Workshops Diabetes, 75. *Mem:* Am Diabetes Asn; Am Physiol Soc; Endocrine Soc; Int Diabetes Fedn; Can Fedn Biol Soc. *Res:* Diabetes mellitus in humans and experimental animals; effect of hormones on vascular connective tissue. *Mailing Add:* Dept of Physiol Med Sci Bldg Univ of Toronto Toronto ON M5S 1A8 Can

SIREN, JAN CURTIS, b Pittsburgh, Pa, Nov 4, 42. ATMOSPHERIC PHYSICS. *Educ:* Carnegie-Mellon Univ, BS, 64; Stanford Univ, MS, 66, PhD(physics), 74. *Prof Exp:* Res assoc physics, Appl Physics & Info Sci Dept, Univ Calif, San Diego, 74-76; VIS ASST PROF PHYSICS, INST PHYS SCI & TECHNOL, UNIV MD, 77- *Concurrent Pos:* Consult, Maya Corp, 76-77. *Mem:* Am Geophys Union; AAAS. *Res:* Balloon and rocket borne studies of magnetospheric particle precipitation; riometer studies of the absorbing ionosphere; incoherent scatter radar studies of auroral ionosphere; ionospheric plasma physics. *Mailing Add:* Inst for Phys Sci & Technol Univ of Md College Park MD 20742

SIRIANNI, JOYCE E, b Niagara Falls, NY, Apr 27, 42. PHYSICAL ANTHROPOLOGY, DENTAL ANTHROPOLOGY. *Educ:* State Univ NY Buffalo, BA, 65, MA, 67; Univ Wash, PhD(phys anthrop), 74. *Prof Exp:* Asst prof, 72-78, ASSOC PROF PHYS ANTHROP, STATE UNIV NY, BUFFALO, 78- *Mem:* Am Asn Phys Anthropologists; Int Primatol Soc; Am Asn Anatomists; AAAS; Am Asn Dental Res. *Res:* Study of normal craniofacial growth and development in old world monkeys; study of the normal range of dental variability seen in old world monkeys. *Mailing Add:* Dept Anthrop State Univ NY Buffalo NY 14214

SIRICA, ALPHONSE EUGENE, b Waterbury, Conn, Jan 16, 44. CHEMICAL CARCINOGENESIS, LIVER CELL CULTURE. *Educ:* St Michaels Col, BA, 65; Fordham Univ, MS, 68; Univ Conn Health Ctr, PhD(biomed sci), 76. *Prof Exp:* Res assoc cancer chemother, Microbiol Assocs Cancer Chemother Res Lab, 69-71; fel trainee chem carcinogenesis, McArdle Lab Cancer Res, 76-79; ASST PROF ANAT & HEPATIC PATH, MED SCH, UNIV WIS, 79- *Concurrent Pos:* Prin investr, NIH Grant, 81-83 & 81-84. *Mem:* Am Asn Cancer Res; Am Soc Cell Biol; Tissue Culture Asn; AAAS; NY Acad Sci. *Res:* Pathobiology of hepatocarcinogenesis; regulatory mechanisms controlling hepatocyte differentiation, proliferation and drug metabolism; isolation and characterization of preneoplastic liver cell populations; hepatocyte cell culture. *Mailing Add:* Dept Anat Univ Wis Med Sch 1300 Univ Ave Madison WI 53706

SIRIGNANO, WILLIAM ALFONSO, b Bronx, NY, Apr 14, 38; m 77; c 2. COMBUSTION. *Educ:* Rensselaer Polytech Inst, BAEng, 59; Princeton Univ, MA, 62, PhD(aeronaut aerospace & mech sci), 64. *Prof Exp:* Mem res staff, Guggenheim Labs, Princeton Univ, 64-67, asst prof mech & aero eng, 67-69, assoc prof, 69-73, prof, 73-79; LADD PROF & HEAD MECH ENG, CARNEGIE-MELLON UNIV, 79- *Concurrent Pos:* Dir grad studies, Princeton Univ, 74-79; mem Emissions Control Panel, Nat Acad Sci, 71-73; assoc ed, Combustion Sci & Technol, 69-70; lectr & consult, aeronaut res & develop, NATO Adv Group, 67, 75 & 80. *Mem:* Combustion Inst; Am Inst Aeronaut & Astronaut; Soc Indust & Appl Math; Am Soc Mech Engrs; Soc Automotive Engrs. *Res:* Theoretical, computational and some experimental studies of turbulent reacting flows, spray combustion, fuel-droplet heating and vaporization, ignition, combustion of pulverized coal, combustion instability, and fire safety. *Mailing Add:* Mech Eng Dept Carnegie-Mellon Univ Pittsburgh PA 15213

SIRKEN, MONROE GILBERT, b New York, NY, Jan 11, 21; m 54; c 2. MATHEMATICAL STATISTICS, APPLIED STATISTICS. *Educ:* Univ Calif, Los Angeles, BA, 46, MA, 47; Univ Wash, PhD(sociol & math statist), 50. *Prof Exp:* Soc Sci Res Coun fel, Univ Calif, Berkeley, 50-51; math statistician & soc sci analyst, US Bur Census, 51-53; actuary, Nat Off Vital Statist, 53-55, chief, Actuarial Anal & Surv Methods Br, Vital Statist Div, 55-63; dir, Div Health Records Statist, 63-67, dir, Off Statist Methods, 67-73, chief math statistician & statist adv, 73-76, assoc dir math statist, 76-80, ASSOC DIR RES & METHODOLOGY, NAT CTR HEALTH STATIST, 80- *Concurrent Pos:* Lectr, Dept Prev Med, Sch Med, Univ Wash, 50; ed collabr, Am Statist Asn, 60-72; adj prof, Sch Pub Health, Univ NC, 68-70, mem fac, 68-; vis prof, Sch Pub Health, Univ Calif, Berkeley, 71; adv consult, Nat Inst Neurol & Communicative Disorders & Stroke, 75- *Mem:* AAAS; fel Am Statist Asn; Biomet Soc; Pop Asn Am; Am Sociol Asn. *Res:* Investigation of errors of measurement in population data systems and design of efficient sample surveys. *Mailing Add:* Nat Ctr for Health Statist 3700 East-West Hwy Hyattsville MD 20782

SIRKIN, LESLIE A, b Dover, Del, Sept 18, 33; m 59; c 3. GEOLOGY, PALYNOLOGY. *Educ:* Hamilton Col, BA, 54; Cornell Univ, MS, 57; NY Univ, PhD(geol), 65. *Prof Exp:* From asst prof to assoc prof, 62-72, chmn dept, 67-75, PROF EARTH SCI, ADELPHI UNIV, 72- *Mem:* AAAS; fel Geol Soc Am; Am Asn Stratig Palynologists; Int Asn Quaternary Res. *Res:* Mesozoic, Cenozoic stratigraphy; environmental geology. *Mailing Add:* Dept of Earth Sci Adelphi Univ Garden City NY 11530

SIRLIN, ALBERTO, b Buenos Aires, Arg, Nov 25, 30; m 63; c 2. THEORETICAL PHYSICS. *Educ:* Univ Buenos Aires, Dr(phys & math sci), 53; Cornell Univ, PhD(physics), 58. *Prof Exp:* Res assoc physics, Columbia Univ, 57-59; from asst to assoc prof, 59-68, PROF PHYSICS, NEW YORK UNIV, 68- *Concurrent Pos:* Vis scientist, Europ Orgn Nuclear Res, 60-61 & 67-68; vis prof, Univ Buenos Aires, 62-63; NSF res grant, 70- *Mem:* Am Phys Soc. *Res:* Theoretical particle physics; weak and electromagnetic interactions; unified gauge theories; solitons. *Mailing Add:* Dept of Physics New York Univ New York NY 10003

SIRLIN, JULIO LEO, b Buenos Aires, Argentina, Dec 18, 26; m 68; c 2. REPRODUCTIVE BIOLOGY, NEUROSCIENCES. *Educ:* Univ Buenos Aires, BSc, 50, DSc, 54. *Prof Exp:* Res fel genetics, Dept Biol, Univ Chile, 51-52; res assoc, Dept Animal Genetics, Univ Endinburgh, 53-59, mem staff, 60-67; assoc prof, 67-73, PROF, DEPT ANAT, MED COL, CORNELL UNIV, 73- *Mem:* Int Cell Res Orgn. *Res:* Fertilizing capacity of human spermatozoa: functional and structural correletes. *Mailing Add:* Dept Anat Med Col Cornell Univ 1300 York Ave New York NY 10021

SIROIS, DAVID LEON, b Skowhegan, Maine, Oct 15, 33; m 67; c 3. PLANT PHYSIOLOGY. *Educ:* Univ Maine, BS, 61, MS, 63; Iowa State Univ, PhD(plant physiol), 67. *Prof Exp:* Asst plant physiologist, 67-74, ASSOC PLANT PHYSIOLOGIST, BOYCE THOMPSON INST PLANT RES, CORNELL UNIV, 74- *Mem:* Plant Growth Regulator Soc Am; Weed Sci Soc Am; Sigma Xi. *Res:* Effects of exogenous chemical compounds on plant growth including herbicides and plant growth regulators with particular interest in chemicals with potential for enhancing crop yields. *Mailing Add:* Boyce Thompson Inst Tower Rd Ithaca NY 14853

SIROIS, JEAN CLAUDE, b Que, Nov 17, 21; m 49; c 4. PLANT PHYSIOLOGY. *Educ:* Laval Univ, BA, 41, BScA, 45, MSc, 48; Univ Wis, PhD, 51. *Prof Exp:* Res fel physiol, McGill Univ, 51-54; res officer, 54-77, RES SCIENTIST, CAN DEPT AGR, 77- *Mem:* Am Soc Plant Physiologists; Can Soc Plant Physiologists; Scand Soc Plant Physiologists. *Res:* Biochemistry, assay, mode of action and synthesis of plant growth substances. *Mailing Add:* Can Dept of Agr Res Br Chem Biol Res Inst Ottawa ON K1A 0C6 Can

SIROIS, PIERRE, b Que, Can, Dec 12, 45; m 73; c 1. IMMUNOPHARMACOLOGY. *Educ:* Univ Laval, Que, BA, 67; Univ Sherbrooke, BSc, 71, MSc, 72, PhD(pharmacol), 75. *Prof Exp:* Fel, Royal Col Surgeons, Eng, 75-77 & Hosp Sick Children, Toronto, 77-78; ASST PROF PHARMACOL, UNIV SHERBROOKE, 78- *Concurrent Pos:* Instr, Regionale L'estrie, Sherbrooke, 69-71 & Col Sherbrooke, 72-74; fel, Imperial Col Sci & Technol, 76-77. *Mem:* Brit Pharmacol Soc; Can Soc Clin Invest; Can Soc Immunologists; French-Can Asn Advan Sci. *Res:* Non-respiratory functions of lungs; mediators of hypersensitivity; leukotrienes; effects of asbestos on lung biochemistry and on macrophages. *Mailing Add:* Dept Pediat & Pharmacol Fac Med Univ Sherbrooke Sherbrooke PQ J1H 5N4 Can

SIROTNAK, FRANCIS MICHAEL, b Throop, Pa, Aug 10, 29. MOLECULAR PHARMACOLOGY, GENETICS. *Educ:* Univ Scranton, BS, 50; Univ NH, MS, 52; Univ Md, PhD(microbiol), 54. *Prof Exp:* Asst microbiol, Agr Exp Sta, Univ NH, 51-52; asst, Univ Md, 52-54; bacteriologist, US Army Chem Corps, 56-57; from asst prof to assoc prof, 63-76, PROF BIOL, SLOAN-KETTERING DIV, MED COL, CORNELL UNIV, 76-,

MEM, SLOAN KETTERING INST CANCER RES, 75-, LAB HEAD, 74- *Concurrent Pos:* Nat Cancer Inst career develop award, 66; res assoc, Sloan Kettering Inst Cancer Res, 57-59, assoc, 59-66, assoc mem, 66-75, sect head, 67-74; instr, Fairleigh-Dickinson Univ, 58-59; asst prof, Long Island Univ, 61- *Mem:* Am Soc Microbiol; Am Asn Cancer Res; NY Acad Sci. *Res:* Chemotherapy and drug resistance; biochemical genetics; biochemical control mechanisms; genetics of neoplastic transformation. *Mailing Add:* Sloan-Kettering Inst Cancer Res 1275 York Ave New York NY 10021

SIROVICH, LAWRENCE, b Brooklyn, NY, Mar 1, 33; m 60; c 2. APPLIED MATHEMATICS. *Educ:* Johns Hopkins Univ, AB, 56, PhD, 60; Brown Univ, MA, 65. *Prof Exp:* Res scientist appl math, Courant Inst Math Sci, NY Univ, 62-63; from asst prof to assoc prof, 63-67, PROF APPL MATH, BROWN UNIV, 67- *Concurrent Pos:* Fulbright fel, Free Univ Brussels, 61-62; prof, Inst Henri Poincare, Univ Paris, 68-69; vis prof, Rockefeller Univ, 71-72, adj prof, 72-; Guggenheim fel, 78-79; ed, Appl Math Sci, Quart Appl Math & Bull Sci Math; assoc managing ed, Soc Indust & Appl Math J. *Mem:* AAAS; Am Phys Soc; Am Math Soc. *Res:* Applied mathematics; kinetic theory of gases; fluid dynamics; biophysics; asymptotic analysis. *Mailing Add:* Div of Appl Math Brown Univ Providence RI 02912

SIRRIDGE, MARJORIE SPURRIER, b Kingman, Kans, Oct 6, 21; m 44; c 4. HEMATOLOGY, LABORATORY MEDICINE. *Educ:* Kans State Univ, BS, 42; Univ Kans, MD, 44. *Prof Exp:* Pvt pract hemat, 55-71; DOCENT & PROF INTERNAL MED & HEMAT, UNIV MOKANSAS CITY SCH MED, 71- *Concurrent Pos:* Consult, Providence-St Margaret's Health Ctr & Bethany Hosp, 60- *Mem:* Am Soc Hemat. *Res:* Antithrombin III; platelet function studies; monitoring heparin therapy; hypercoagulability. *Mailing Add:* Sch of Med Univ Mo 2411 Holmes Kansas City MO 64108

SIRY, JOSEPH WILLIAM, b New York, NY, Aug 7, 20; m 44; c 2. MATHEMATICS, PHYSICS. *Educ:* Rutgers Univ, BS, 41; Univ Md, MA, 47, PhD(math), 53. *Prof Exp:* Mem, Actuarial Div, Metrop Life Ins Co, 40-42; physicist, Naval Res Lab, 46-58, actg head theoret anal sect, Rocket-Sonde Res Br, 49-51, head, 51-53, lectr, 53, consult, 53-56, head theory & anal br, Proj Vanguard, 56-58, chmn, Vanguard Working Group on Orbits, 56-59; head theory & anal br, Vanguard Div, 58-59, head theory & planning staff, Beltsville Space Ctr, 59, CHIEF THEORY & ANAL STAFF & DIR TRACKING & DATA SYSTS DIRECTORATE, GODDARD SPACE FLIGHT CTR, NASA, 59- *Concurrent Pos:* Lectr grad math, Univ Md, 53-55; exec secy, Upper Atmosphere Rocket Res Panel, Spec Comt, Int Geophys Year, 54 & rep, US Nat Comt Spec Comt Meeting, Moscow, 58; lectr space technol, Univ Calif, 58; vis lectr, Univ Tex, 58; mem, Equatorial Range Comt, NASA, 59; vis lectr, NY Univ, 60; Am Geophys Union deleg, Gen Assembly Int Union Geodesy & Geophys, Helsinki, 60; mem comt high atmosphere, Int Asn Geomagnetism & Aeronomy. *Mem:* Am Math Soc; Am Astron Soc. *Res:* Chromatic polynomials; topology; compressible fluids; ionosphere; cosmic rays; orbit determination; flight mechanics; astrodynamics; upper atmosphere densities; space research, science and technology. *Mailing Add:* NASA Goddard Space Flight Ctr Tracking & Data Systs Directorate Greenbelt MD 20771

SIS, RAYMOND FRANCIS, b Munden, Kans, July 22, 31; m 53; c 5. VETERINARY ANATOMY. *Educ:* Kans State Univ, BS, 53, DVM & BS, 57; Iowa State Univ, MS, 62, PhD(vet anat), 65. *Prof Exp:* Asst vet clins, Iowa State Univ, 61-62, instr vet anat, 62-64, asst prof vet clin sci, 64-66; assoc prof, 66-68, PROF VET ANAT & HEAD DEPT, TEX A&M UNIV, 68- *Concurrent Pos:* Clin prof, Dent Inst, Univ Tex & prin investr biomed res. *Mem:* Am Vet Med Asn; Am Asn Vet Clinicians; Am Asn Vet Anat; World Asn Vet Anat. *Res:* Surgical anatomy; radiographic anatomy of the cat; feline anatomy and surgery; salivary glands of the cat; histology of marine fish and marine mammals. *Mailing Add:* Dept Vet Anat Tex A&M Univ College Station TX 77843

SISCOE, GEORGE L, b Lansing, Mich, June 13, 37; m 64. SPACE PHYSICS. *Educ:* Mass Inst Technol, BS, 60, PhD(physics), 64. *Prof Exp:* Res fel physics, Calif Inst Technol, 64-67; asst prof, Mass Inst Technol, 67-71; from assoc prof to prof meteorol, 71-77, PROF ATMOSPHERIC PHYSICS, UNIV CALIF, LOS ANGELES, 77- *Concurrent Pos:* Consult, McDonnell Douglas Corp, Ctr Space Res, Mass Inst Technol, TRW Inc, Jet Propulsion Lab & Boston Col; ed, J Geophys Res. *Mem:* Am Geophys Union; AAAS. *Res:* Space physics, especially the magnetosphere and the solar wind. *Mailing Add:* Dept Atmospheric Sci Univ Calif Los Angeles CA 90024

SISENWINE, SAMUEL FRED, b Philadelphia, Pa, Dec 30, 40; m 62; c 3. DRUG METABOLISM, ORGANIC CHEMISTRY. *Educ:* Philadelphia Col Pharm, BSc, 62; Univ Pa, PhD(chem), 66. *Prof Exp:* Sr chemist, 66-71, group leader, Metab Chem Sect, 71-78, MGR DRUG DISPOSITION SECT, WYETH LABS, 78-, CORP RADIATION HEALTH SAFETY OFFICER, 71- *Mem:* Am Soc Pharmacol & Exp Therapeut. *Res:* Absorption, distribution, excretion and biotransformation studies of antidepressants, steroids and other drugs; radiochemical methods of analysis. *Mailing Add:* Drug Disposition Sect Wyeth Labs Box 8299 Philadelphia PA 19101

SISK, DUDLEY BYRD, b Lexington, Ky, Jan 9, 38; m 61; c 2. VETERINARY PATHOLOGY. *Educ:* Auburn Univ, DVM, 62; Purdue Univ, MS, 67, PhD(vet physiol), 70. *Prof Exp:* Instr physiol, Purdue Univ, 65-70; asst prof vet physiol, Univ Mo-Columbia, 70-74; consult, 74; pathologist, Dept Vet Sci, Univ Ky, 74-80; PATHOLOGIST, VET DIAG LAB, 80- *Mem:* Am Vet Med Asn; Sigma Xi; Asn Am Vet Med Cols; Am Asn Vet Lab Diagnosticians. *Res:* Livestock diseases. *Mailing Add:* Vet Diag Lab PO Box 1389 Tifton GA 31794

SISKA, PETER EMIL, b Evergreen Park, Ill, Apr 11, 43; m 67; c 2. PHYSICAL CHEMISTRY, CHEMICAL PHYSICS. *Educ:* DePaul Univ, BS, 65; Harvard Univ, AM, 66, PhD(chem), 70. *Prof Exp:* Res assoc chem, James Franck Inst, Univ Chicago, 70-71; asst prof, 71-76, ASSOC PROF CHEM, UNIV PITTSBURGH, 76- *Concurrent Pos:* Alfred P Sloan Found res fel, 75. *Mem:* Am Chem Soc; Am Phys Soc. *Res:* Molecular dynamics of chemical reactions and energy transfer; intermolecular forces; crossed molecular beam studies; model calculations of collision dynamics and electronic structure. *Mailing Add:* Dept of Chem Univ of Pittsburgh Pittsburgh PA 15260

SISKEN, BETTY FLORIO, neurobiology, see previous edition

SISKEN, JESSE ERNEST, b Bridgeport, Conn, Dec 7, 30; m 54; c 3. CELL BIOLOGY. *Educ:* Syracuse Univ, AB, 52; Univ Conn, MS, 54; Columbia Univ, PhD(bot, cytochem), 57. *Prof Exp:* Asst bot, Univ Conn, 53-54; res asst bot & cytochem, Columbia Univ, 54-55; res assoc, City of Hope Med Ctr, 57-60, assoc res scientist, 60-66, scientist, 66-67; assoc prof, 67-75, PROF CELL BIOL, COL MED, UNIV KY, 75- *Mem:* Am Soc Cell Biol. *Res:* Nucleic acid and protein synthesis in the mitotic cycle; population kinetics of proliferating cells; regulation of cell metabolism related to cell division. *Mailing Add:* Dept of Path Univ of Ky Col of Med Lexington KY 40506

SISKIN, MILTON, b Cleveland, Tenn, May 14, 21; m 48. ORAL MEDICINE, ENDODONTICS. *Educ:* Univ Tenn, BA, 42, DDS, 45; Am Acad Oral Med, dipl; Am Bd Endodontics, dipl, 63. *Prof Exp:* From intern to resident, Walter G Zoller Mem Dent Clin, Billings Hosp, Univ Chicago, 46-47; from instr to assoc prof oral med & surg, 47-64, chief div oral med & surg & head dept oral med, 55-58, PROF ORAL MED & SURG, COL DENT, UNIV TENN, MEMPHIS, 64-, LECTR, GRAD SCH ORTHOD & DEPT GEN ANAT & EMBRYOL, 54- *Concurrent Pos:* Consult various orgns & hosps, 51-; Am Dent Asn del, Int Dent Cong, 62; asst ed, J Dent Med, 63; ed, Biol Human Dent Pulp, 73; ed endodontics sect, Clin Dent, 75 & Oral Surg, Oral Med & Oral Path, 75-; dir, Registry Periapical Lesions, Am Asn Endodontists, 65-66; mem rev bd, Am Asn Endodontists & Nat Med AV Ctr; mem bd, Am Bd Endodontics, 63-69 & 71-73; mem exec comt, Am Cancer Soc, 71-72, bd dirs, 71-72; dir, Am Col Stomatologic Surgeons; mem exec comt, Am Inst Oral Sci, 66-; mem, Coun Fed Dent Serv, Am Dent Asn, 71-; Am Dent Europe lectr, 62; lectr, Can Govt & Can Asn Endodontists, 70, Brit Dent Soc, 72, Royal Col Denmark, 74 & Int Dent Congress, 74. *Honors & Awards:* Hinman Medallion, 66. *Mem:* AAAS; fel Am Col Dent; fel Am Acad Oral Path; fel Am Asn Endodont; Am Acad Oral Med. *Res:* Oral diagnosis; pathology. *Mailing Add:* Col Dent Univ Tenn 847 Monroe Ave Memphis TN 38103

SISKIND, GREGORY WILLIAM, b New York, NY, Mar 3, 34. IMMUNOLOGY. *Educ:* Cornell Univ, BA, 55; NY Univ, MD, 59. *Prof Exp:* From instr to asst prof med, Med Ctr, NY Univ, 65-69; assoc prof, 69-76, PROF MED, MED SCH, CORNELL UNIV, 76-, HEAD DIV ALLERGY & IMMUNOL, 69- *Concurrent Pos:* Res fel microbiol, Sch Med, Wash Univ, 61-62; fel biol, Harvard Univ, 62-64; fel med, Med Ctr, NY Univ, 64-65. *Mem:* AAAS; Am Asn Immunol; Transplantation Soc; Am Acad Allergy; Am Soc Clin Invest. *Res:* Runting syndrome; immunologic tolerance; heterogeneity of antibody binding affinity and changes in antibody affinity during immunization; antigenic competition; idiopathic thrombocytopenic purpura; ontogeny of B-lymphocyte function; regulation of the immune response by auto-anti-idiotype antibody. *Mailing Add:* Dept of Med Cornell Univ Med Col New York NY 10021

SISLER, CHARLES CARLETON, b Oklahoma City, Okla, Jan 13, 22; m 57; c 3. CHEMICAL ENGINEERING. *Educ:* Mich State Univ, BS, 59, MS, 54. *Prof Exp:* Plant engr phosphates, 50-53, eng supvr, 53-64, eng mgr, 64-69, res mgr chem intermediates, 69-78, res mgr spec chem, 78-81, MGR PROCESS DEVELOP NUTRIT CHEM, MONSANTO CO, 81- *Mem:* Am Inst Chem Engrs; Am Chem Soc; Sci Res Soc Am. *Res:* Food and feed chemicals. *Mailing Add:* Monsanto Co 800 N Lindbergh Blvd St Louis MO 63167

SISLER, EDWARD C, b Friendsville, Md, Jan 25, 30. PLANT PHYSIOLOGY. *Educ:* Univ Md, BS, 54, MS, 55; NC State Col, PhD, 58. *Prof Exp:* Res assoc, Brookhaven Nat Lab, 58-59; biochemist, Smithsonian Inst, 59-61; asst prof, 61-64, assoc prof chem, 64-76, ASSOC PROF CROP SCI & BIOCHEM, NC STATE UNIV, 76- *Res:* Role of boron in plants; electron transport; citric acid and glyoxylate cycles in the purple sulfur bacteria; nucleotide phosphates levels as affected by visible radiation; alkaloid metabolism; ethylene action in plants. *Mailing Add:* Dept of Crop Sci NC State Univ Raleigh NC 27607

SISLER, GEORGE C, b Winnipeg, Man, Dec 28, 23; m 48; c 2. PSYCHIATRY. *Educ:* Univ Man, MD, 46; FRCP(C), 55. *Prof Exp:* Resident, Winnipeg Psychopath Hosp, 47-49 & Norton Mem Infirmary, 50-51; resident neurol, Louisville Gen Hosp, 51-52; lectr, 52-54, head dept, 54-75, PROF PSYCHIAT, FAC MED, UNIV MAN, 54-, PSYCHIATRIST, HEALTH SCI CTR, 75- *Concurrent Pos:* Clin instr, Univ Louisville, 50-52; clin dir, Winnipeg Psychopath Hosp, 52-54; chief psychiat, Winnipeg Gen Hosp, 54-75 & St Boniface Gen Hosps, 54-; Sandoz traveling prof, 64. *Mem:* Fel Am Psychiat Asn; Can Med Asn; Can Psychiat Asn; Am Acad Psychoanal. *Res:* Psychopathology of organic brain damage; teaching and learning process in psychiatry. *Mailing Add:* Fac Med Univ Man Winnipeg MB R3E 0W3 Can

SISLER, HUGH DELANE, b Friendsville, Md, Nov 4, 22; m 50; c 3. PLANT PATHOLOGY. *Educ:* Univ Md, BS, 49, PhD(bot), 53. *Prof Exp:* Asst, 53-55, from asst prof to assoc prof, 55-64, chem dept bot, 73-77, PROF PLANT PATH, UNIV MD, COLLEGE PARK, 64- . *Concurrent Pos:* Ed, Phytopath, Am Phytopath Soc, 60-63; mem fel rev panel, NIH, 61-; NIH spec fel, State Univ Utrecht, Neth, 66- *Mem:* AAAS; fel Am Phytopath Soc; AAAS; Pesticide Sci Soc Japan. *Res:* Fungicidal action; fungus physiology; viruses. *Mailing Add:* Dept of Bot Univ of Md College Park MD 20742

SISODIA, CHATURBHUJ SINGH, b Delhi, India, Apr 2, 34; m 57; c 2. VETERINARY PHARMACOLOGY, TOXICOLOGY. *Educ:* Agra Univ, BVSc & AH, 58; Mich State Univ, MS, 60; Univ Minn, PhD(vet pharmacol), 64; Am Bd Vet Toxicol, dipl. *Prof Exp:* Res assoc vet pharmacol, Univ Minn, 64; assoc prof, Punjab Agr Univ, India, 65; prof, Col Vet Sci & Animal Husb,

Mathura, India, 65-68; asst prof, 68-70, assoc prof, 70-75, PROF VET PHARMACOL & TOXICOL, UNIV SASK, 75- *Mem:* Am Soc Vet Physiol & Pharmacol; fel Am Col Vet Toxicol. *Res:* Pharmacokinetics, drug residues, poisonous plants and mycotoxins. *Mailing Add:* Western Col Vet Med Univ Sask Saskatoon SK S7N 0W0 Can

SISSENWINE, MICHAEL P, b Washington, DC, Feb 16, 47. BIOLOGICAL OCEANOGRAPHY, FISHERIES BIOLOGY. *Educ:* Univ Mass, BS, 69; Univ RI, PhD(oceanog), 75. *Prof Exp:* Res assoc oceanog, Univ RI, 73-75; OPERS RES ANALYST & CHIEF, FISHERIES SYSTS INVEST, NORTHEAST FISHERIES CTR, NAT MARINE FISHERIES SERV, 75-, DEP CHIEF, RESOURCE ASSESSMENT DIV, 80- *Concurrent Pos:* Consult, US Environ Protection Agency, 76-; US mem Demersal Fish Comt, Int Coun Explor Sea, Copenhagen, 77- *Mem:* Am Fisheries Soc; Int Estuarine Res Fedn. *Res:* Fish population dynamics; fisheries management systems; trophic interrelationships in marine ecosystems; biological systems models and simulations. *Mailing Add:* Northeast Fisheries Ctr Nat Marine Fisheries Serv Woods Hole MA 02543

SISSOM, LEIGHTON E(STEN), b Manchester, Tenn, Aug 26, 34; m 53; c 2. MECHANICAL ENGINEERING, ACCIDENT RECONSTRUCTION. *Educ:* Mid Tenn State Col, BS, 56; Tenn Polytech Inst, BSME, 62; Ga Inst Technol, MSME, 64, PhD(mech eng), 65. *Prof Exp:* Draftsman, Westinghouse Elec Corp, 53-57; mech designer, ARO, Inc, 57-58; instr eng sci, Tenn Polytech Inst, 58-61, instr mech eng, 61-62; prof mech eng & chmn dept, 65-79, DEAN ENG, TENN TECHNOL UNIV, 79- *Concurrent Pos:* Eng consult, industs, ins co, law firms & govt agencies, 55-; secy-treas, vpres & pres, Tenn Tech Eng Develop Found, Inc, 70-; evaluator, Southern Asn Cols & Schs & Accreditation Bd Eng & Technol, 72-; comnr, Eng Accreditation Comn, 79-; ed-in-chief, Mech Eng News, 77-80. *Mem:* Am Soc Mech Engrs; Am Soc Eng Educ; Soc Automotive Engrs; Syst Safety Soc; Nat Soc Prof Engrs. *Res:* Fluid handling; energy utilization; products liability; accident reconstruction; solar energy; heat and mass transfer; blood circulation; author or coauthor of over 40 publications. *Mailing Add:* Dean Eng Box 5005 Tech Technol Univ Cookeville TN 38501

SISSOM, STANLEY LEWIS, b Italy, Tex, June 19, 32; m 60; c 2. INVERTEBRATE ZOOLOGY, AQUATIC ECOLOGY. *Educ:* NTex State Univ, BS, 54, MS, 59; Tex A&M Univ, PhD(zool), 67. *Prof Exp:* Instr biol, NTex State Univ, 59-61, Lamar State Col, 61-63 & Tex A&M Univ, 65-67; asst prof, 67-70, assoc prof, 70-77, PROF BIOL, SOUTHWEST TEX STATE UNIV, 77- *Mem:* AAAS; Soc Syst Zool; Am Soc Limnol & Oceanog. *Res:* Taxonomy and ecology of phyllopod crustaceans; ecology of temporary ponds; limnology. *Mailing Add:* Dept of Biol Southwest Tex State Univ San Marcos TX 78666

SISSON, DONALD VICTOR, b East Chain, Minn, Apr 18, 34; m 60; c 4. APPLIED STATISTICS. *Educ:* Gustavus Adolphus Col, BS, 56; Iowa State Univ, MS, 58, PhD(entom & statist), 62. *Prof Exp:* Asst prof appl statist, Utah State Univ, 59-60 & 62-65, assoc prof, 65-66; biol statistician, Abbott Labs, Ill, 66; assoc prof, 66-76, PROF APPL STATIST & COMPUT SCI & ASST DEAN SCI, UTAH STATE UNIV, 76- ASST DEAN COL SCI, 71- *Concurrent Pos:* Vis assoc prof statist, NC State Univ, 75-76. *Mem:* Am Statist Asn; Biomet Soc. *Res:* Biological statistics; design and analysis of experiments. *Mailing Add:* Col of Sci Utah State Univ Logan UT 84322

SISSON, GEORGE ALLEN, b Minneapolis, Minn, May 11, 20; m 44; c 3. OTOLARYNGOLOGY. *Educ:* Syracuse Univ, AB, 42, MD, 45. *Prof Exp:* Clin instr otolaryngol, State Univ NY Upstate Med Ctr, 51-54, from clin instr to clin asst prof surg, 51-68, from clin asst prof to clin prof otolaryngol, 55-68; PROF OTOLARYNGOL & MAXILLOFACIAL SURG & CHMN DEPT, SCH MED, NORTHWESTERN UNIV, CHICAGO, 68- *Concurrent Pos:* Fel, Head & Neck Serv, Manhattan Eye, Ear & Throat Hosp, NY, 52-53; mem exec comt, Bd Dirs & Exam, Am Bd Otolaryngol; mem adv coun, Head & Neck Cancer Cadre, Nat Inst Neurol Dis & Stroke. *Mem:* Am Cancer Soc; Am Laryngol, Rhinol & Otol Soc; AMA; Am Col Surg; Am Acad Ophthal & Otolaryngol. *Res:* Cancer of the head and neck. *Mailing Add:* Otolaryngol & Maxillofac Surg Northwestern Univ Med Sch Chicago IL 60611

SISSON, GEORGE MAYNARD, b Boston, Mass, Feb 3, 22; m 52; c 3. PHYSIOLOGY, PHARMACOLOGY. *Educ:* Tufts Col, BS, 43; Univ Rochester, PhD(physiol), 52. *Prof Exp:* Asst, Univ Rochester, 48-49; jr physiologist, Brookhaven Nat Lab, 52; Nat Res Coun fel, Columbia Univ, 52-54; group leader pharmacol res, Am Cyanamid Co, 54-59; asst dir dept pharmacol, US Vitamin & Pharmaceut Corp, 59-61; dir pharmaceut prod info, 61-66, dir sci info & regulatory affairs, 66-77, dir dept, 77-79, DIR DRUG REGULATORY AFFAIRS, MEAD JOHNSON RES CTR, 79- *Mem:* AAAS; Drug Info Asn; NY Acad Sci; Am Thoracic Soc; Am Fedn Clin Res. *Res:* Regulatory activities; pharmacodynamics; clinical pharmacology; toxicology; chronic obstructive lung disease; normal and pathological renal function; peripheral and cerebral vascular disease. *Mailing Add:* Dept of Drug Reg Affairs Mead Johnson Res Ctr Evansville IN 47721

SISSON, HARRIET E, b Duluth, Minn, July 2, 16; m 41; c 2. PHARMACY. *Educ:* Univ Minn, BS, 37, MS, 39; Univ Ore, PhD, 78. *Prof Exp:* Pharmacist, Univ Hosps, Univ Minn, 37-41; from instr to asst prof, 46-67, ASSOC PROF PHARM, SCH PHARM, ORE STATE UNIV, 67- *Mem:* Am Pharmaceut Asn. *Res:* Pharmaceutical chemistry; measurement of pharmacy aptitude. *Mailing Add:* Sch of Pharm Ore State Univ Corvallis OR 97331

SISSON, JOSEPH A, b San Diego, Calif, Oct 24, 30; m 59; c 2. PATHOLOGY. *Educ:* San Diego Col, BA, 55; Wash Univ, MD, 60. *Prof Exp:* Res asst biochem, Scripps Clin, La Jolla, Calif, 55-56; intern path, Yale Univ New Haven Med Ctr, Conn, 60-61; resident, Albany Med Ctr, NY, 61-64; from instr to asst prof, Albany Med Col, 63-67; asst prof path, Creighton Univ, 68-69, chmn dept, 68-73, prof, 69-80; PROF PATH, EASTERN VA MED SCH, 80- *Concurrent Pos:* Fel, Albany New Med Col, 61-63; res grant, 65-67; asst attend pathologist, Albany Med Ctr Hosp, 65-67; attend

pathologist, Vet Admin Hosp, Albany, NY, 66-67; dir path, Creighton Mem St Joseph's Hosp, 68-72; consult radiologist, US Vet Admin Hosp, Omaha, 68- *Mem:* Am Asn Path & Bact; Am Soc Exp Path. *Res:* Amino acid and lipid metabolism in pregnancy; biochemical aspects of atherosclerosis and thrombosis. *Mailing Add:* Dept Path Eastern Va Med Sch Va Med Ctr Hampton VA 23667

SISSON, RAY L, b Pueblo, Colo, Apr 24, 34; m 52; c 3. ELECTRICAL ENGINEERING. *Educ:* Univ Colo, BSEE, 60; Colo State Univ, MS, 66; Univ Northern Colo, EdD(voc educ), 73. *Prof Exp:* Asst res engr, Univ Colo Exp Sta, 60; asst engr, Parker & Assoc, Consult Engrs, 61-62; prof eng, 60-63, HEAD DEPT ENG, UNIV SOUTHERN COLO, 63-, HEAD ELECTRONICS & INSTRUMENTATION, 68-, DIR ELEC AREA INSTR, 68-, DEAN APPL SCI & ENG TECHNOL, 73- *Mem:* Am Soc Eng Educ; Inst Elec & Electronics Engrs. *Res:* Electrical networks; computer science; feedback control; antenna studies research. *Mailing Add:* Univ of Southern Colo 2200 N Bonforte Blvd Pueblo CO 81001

SISSON, THOMAS RANDOLPH CLINTON, b Winnipeg, Man, Jan 22, 20; nat US; m 45; c 3. PEDIATRICS, OBSTETRICS. *Educ:* Colgate Univ, AB, 41; Temple Univ, MD, 44; Am Bd Pediat, dipl. *Prof Exp:* Asst resident pediat, Sch Med & Dent, Univ Rochester, 46-48, instr pediat, 52-54, instr pediat, obstet & gynec, 54-57, sr instr, 57-59; asst dir clin res, Ortho Res Found, 59-60, assoc clin prof pediat, Albert Einstein Col Med, 60-64; assoc prof pediat, Loma Linda Univ, 65-67; prof pediat, obstet & gynec & dir neonatal res, Sch Med, Temple Univ, 67-78; CLIN PROF PEDIAT, SCH MED, RUTGERS MED SCH, 78- *Concurrent Pos:* Res fel anat & pediat, Univ Rochester, 46-48; fel pediat hemat, Col Med, Cornell Univ, 48-50; Buswell fac fel, Sch Med & Dent, Univ Rochester, 58-60; mem US nat comt photobiol, Nat Acad Sci-Nat Res Coun; assoc dir clin res, Geigy Chem Corp, 60-64. *Mem:* AAAS; Soc Pediat Res; fel Am Acad Pediat; Am Inst Nutrit; Int Soc Hemat. *Res:* Iron metabolism of foetus; newborn; nutrition of the premature; chronobiology and photobiology of infants. *Mailing Add:* Dept of Pediat Perth Amboy Gen Hosp Perth Amboy NJ 08861

SISTEK, VLADIMIR, b Prague, Czech, Sept 22, 31; m 54; c 3. ANATOMY, SURGERY. *Educ:* Charles Univ, Prague, MD, 56, PhD(surg), 67. *Prof Exp:* Resident surg, Regional Hosp, Most, Czech, 56-59; mem staff, Charles Univ, Prague, 59-63, asst prof surg, 63-68; asst prof anat, 69-73, ASSOC PROF ANAT, UNIV OTTAWA, 73- *Mem:* Can Asn Anat; Can Fedn Biol Socs. *Res:* Surgical anatomy; gastroenterology; medical education. *Mailing Add:* Dept Anat Fac Med Univ Ottawa Ottawa ON K1N 9A9 Can

SISTERSON, JANET M, b Edinburgh, Scotland, July 7, 40; m 65; c 2. NUCLEAR & MEDICAL PHYSICS. *Educ:* Univ Durham, Eng, BSc, 61; Univ London, DIC & PhD(physics), 65. *Prof Exp:* Basic grade physicist, London Hosp, 65-66; sr physicist, Chelsea Hosp Women, London, 66-68; res fel physics, Cambridge Electronic Accelerator, 68-73; res fel, 73-79, RES ASSOC PHYSICS, CYCLOTRON LAB, HARVARD UNIV, 79- *Mem:* Am Phys Soc; Am Asn Physicist Med. *Res:* Proton activation analysis; medical application of proton beams. *Mailing Add:* Cyclotron Lab Harvard Univ Cambridge MA 02138

SISTI, ANTHONY JOSEPH, b Brooklyn, NY, Nov 9, 28; m 52; c 2. ORGANIC CHEMISTRY. *Educ:* City Col New York, BS, 50; Univ Mo, MA, 53; Univ Mich, PhD(chem), 59. *Prof Exp:* Assoc prof, 59-71, PROF CHEM, ADELPHI UNIV, 71- *Mem:* Royal Soc Chem. *Res:* Organic reaction mechanisms; field effects in the displacement reaction; transannular interactions in medium sized ring systems; ring enlargement. *Mailing Add:* Dept of Chem Adelphi Univ Garden City NY 11530

SISTO, FERNANDO, b Spain, Aug 2, 24; US citizen; m 46; c 3. AERONAUTICAL ENGINEERING, MECHANICAL ENGINEERING. *Educ:* US Naval Acad, BS, 46; Mass Inst Technol, ScD, 52. *Hon Degrees:* MEng, Stevens Inst Technol, 62. *Prof Exp:* Chief propulsion div, Res Div, Curtiss-Wright Corp, 52-58; assoc prof, 58-59, head dept, 66-79, prof, 59-79, GEORGE M BOND PROF MECH ENG, STEVENS INST TECHNOL, 79- *Concurrent Pos:* Consult, Curtiss-Wright Corp, NJ, 58-60, Gen Elec Co, Ohio, 59-63, Gen Motors, Ind, 66-70 & United Technol Corp, Conn, 73-79; UNESCO/United Nations Develop Prog consult, Nat Aeronat Lab, Bangalore, India, 78. *Mem:* Assoc fel Am Inst Aeronaut & Astronaut; Am Soc Mech Engrs. *Res:* Aeroelasticity of turbomachines; turbomachinery theory; aerodynamics; flight propulsion; applied mechanics. *Mailing Add:* Dept of Mech Eng Stevens Inst of Technol Castle Point Hoboken NJ 07030

SISTROM, WILLIAM R, b Los Angeles, Calif, Feb 15, 27; m 52; c 4. MICROBIOLOGY. *Educ:* Harvard Univ, AB, 50; Univ Calif, Berkeley, PhD(microbiol), 54. *Prof Exp:* USPHS fel, 55-57; instr microbiol, Sch Med, NY Univ, 57-58; asst prof biol, Harvard Univ, 58-63; assoc prof, 63-70, PROF BIOL, UNIV ORE, 70-, CHMN PREMEDICAL ADV COMT, 74- *Mem:* Am Soc Microbiol; Brit Soc Gen Microbiol. *Res:* Microbial physiology; bacterial photosynthesis. *Mailing Add:* Dept of Biol Univ of Ore Eugene OR 97403

SISTRUNK, THOMAS OLLOISE, b Sebastopol, Miss, Feb 24, 25; m 48; c 2. INORGANIC CHEMISTRY. *Educ:* Miss Southern Col, BS, 50; Tulane Univ, MS, 52, PhD(inorg chem), 53. *Prof Exp:* Asst chem, Tulane Univ, 50-52; inorg chemist, 53-60, rep, Com Develop Div, 60-65, prod mgr, La, 65-69, mgr com develop, 69-81, DIR COM DEVELOP, EUROPE, COM DEVELOP DIV, ETHYL CORP, 81- *Mem:* Chem Mkt Res Asn; Europ Ind Res Mgt Asn. *Res:* Complex metal ions and compounds; chemistry of organometallic compounds; simple and complex metal hydrides; propellant chemicals. *Mailing Add:* Ethyl Corp 1600 W Eight Mile Rd 1050 Brussels Belgium

SISTRUNK, WILLIAM ALLEN, b Mitchell, La, June 29, 19; m 45; c 5. FOOD TECHNOLOGY, BACTERIOLOGY. *Educ:* Southwestern La Inst, BS, 47; Ore State Col, MS, 49, PhD, 59. *Prof Exp:* Mkt specialist, USDA, 49-52; asst horticulturist, La State Univ, 52-56; from jr food technologist to asst food technologist, Ore State Col, 56-62; assoc horticulturist, 62-68, PROF HORT FOOD SCI, UNIV ARK, FAYETTEVILLE, 68- *Mem:* Am Soc Hort Sci; Inst Food Technol. *Res:* Biochemistry; new horticultural varieties; plant nutrition effects on processing quality; objective tests for measuring quality of fruits and vegetables. *Mailing Add:* Dept of Hort Food Sci Div of Agr Univ of Ark Fayetteville AR 72701

SIT, WILLIAM YU, b Hong Kong, Feb 18, 44; m 70. ALGEBRA. *Educ:* Univ Hong Kong, BA, 67; Columbia Univ, MA, 69, PhD(math), 72; City Col City Univ NY, MS, 78. *Prof Exp:* Lectr, 71-72, instr, 72-73, asst prof, 73-80, ASSOC PROF MATH, CITY COL CITY UNIV NEW YORK, 80- *Mem:* Math Asn Am; Am Math Soc. *Res:* Differential algebra; invariants of differential dimension polynominals. *Mailing Add:* Dept of Math City Col of New York Convent Ave & W 138th St New York NY 10031

SITAR, DANIEL SAMUEL, b Thunder Bay, Ont, May 1, 44; m 68; c 2. CLINICAL PHARMACOLOGY, PHARMACOLOGY. *Educ:* Univ Man, BSc, 66, MSc, 68, PhD(pharmacol), 72. *Prof Exp:* Assoc fel, Univ Minn Sch Med, 71-73; lectr, Fac Med, McGill Univ, 73-75, asst prof med, 74-78, asst prof pharmacol, 75-78; teaching fel pharmacol, Fac Med, Univ Man, 68-71; res asst, Div Clin Pharmacol, Montreal Gen Hosp Res Inst, 73-78; asst prof, 78-80, ASSOC PROF MED & PHARMACOL, FAC MED, UNIV MAN, 80- *Concurrent Pos:* Res grant, Nonmed Use Drugs Directorate, 74-79; Monat Scholar, McGill Univ, 75-78; sci staff, Health Sci Ctr, Univ Man & Dear Lodge Hosp, Winnipeg, 78-; Rho Inst grant, 80; K M Piafsky Young investr award, 81. *Mem:* Am Soc Pharmacol & Exp Therapeut; Can Soc Clin Invest; Soc Toxicol Can; Pharmacol Soc Can; Am Soc Clin Pharmacol & Therapeut. *Res:* Effects of development and disease on drug disposition and effect in man. *Mailing Add:* Dept of Pharmacol & Therapeut Univ of Man Winnipeg MB R3E 0W3 Can

SITES, JACK WALTER, JR, b Clarksville, Tenn, Aug 6, 51; m 73; c 1. FISH & WILDLIFE SCIENCES. *Educ:* Austin Peay State Univ, BS, 73, MS, 75; Tex A&M Univ, PhD(vertebrate zool), 80. *Prof Exp:* Asst prof biol, zool & ecol, Dept Biol, Tex A&M Univ, 80-82; ASST PROF BIOL, ZOOL & GENETICS, DEPT ZOOL, BRIGHAM YOUNG UNIV, 82- *Concurrent Pos:* Res zoologist, The Nature Conservancy, 75-76. *Mem:* AAAS; Soc Study Evolution; Soc Syst Zool; Am Soc Zoologists; Am Soc Icthyologists & Herpetologists. *Res:* Mechanisms of chromosomal evolution and speciation, rates of speciation; genetic structure of natural populations of vertebrates; basic ecology; evolutionary biology; systematics. *Mailing Add:* Dept Zool Brigham Young Univ Provo UT 84602

SITES, JAMES RUSSELL, b Manhattan, Kans, Nov 18, 43; m 64; c 3. SOLID STATE ELECTRONICS, LOW TEMPERATURE PHYSICS. *Educ:* Duke Univ, BS, 65; Cornell Univ, MS, 68, PhD(physics), 69. *Prof Exp:* Programmer, Union Carbide Corp, 62-64; NSF fel, 65-69; fel physics, Los Alamos Sci Lab, 69-71; from instr to asst prof, 71-77, ASSOC PROF PHYSICS, COLO STATE UNIV, 77- *Mem:* Am Vacuum Soc; Am Phys Soc. *Res:* Investigation of electronic properties of compound semiconductor surfaces and interfaces; studies of thermal transport mechanisms in solid helium three; development of heterojunction solar cells. *Mailing Add:* Dept of Physics Colo State Univ Ft Collins CO 80523

SITNEY, LAWRENCE RAYMOND, b Schenectady, NY, Oct 8, 23; m 56; c 2. PHYSICAL CHEMISTRY. *Educ:* Ohio State Univ, BS, 43, MS, 47, PhD(chem), 52. *Prof Exp:* Mem staff, Los Alamos Sci Lab, 52-59; staff scientist, Missiles & Space Div, Lockheed Aircraft Corp, Calif, 59-60; supvr adv nuclear systs appln, Rocketdyne Div, NAm Aviation, Inc, 60-61; tech mgr nuclear studies, Martin Co, Colo, 61-62; staff engr space power studies, 62-66, sr staff engr, 66-68, asst group dir, Advan Vehicle Systs Directorate, 68-70, assoc group dir, 70-75, dir, Advan Energy Systs, 75-81, SR ENGR PLANS & SYST ARCHIT, AEROSPACE CORP, EL SEGUNDO, 82- *Mem:* Am Phys Soc. *Res:* Chemical thermodynamics; high temperature chemistry; heat of sublimation of graphite; space power; reusable space transportation systems; advanced energy conversion systems; solar thermal power systems. *Mailing Add:* 240 Oceanaire Dr Rancho Palos Verdes CA 90274

SITRIN, ROBERT DAVID, b Utica, NY, July 24, 45; m 69; c 2. ORGANIC CHEMISTRY, ANALYTICAL CHEMISTRY. *Educ:* Mass Inst Technol, BS, 67; Harvard Univ, MS, 68, PhD(chem), 72. *Prof Exp:* Fel chem, Woodard Res Inst, Switz, 72-73; assoc sr investr chem, 73-77, SR INVESTR CHEM, SMITH KLINE & FRENCH LABS, 77- *Mem:* Am Chem Soc; AAAS. *Res:* Synthesis carbohydrate chemistry; amino slycoside antibiotics; natural product isolations; structure determination; natural products chemistry; high performance liquid chromatography; analytical biochemistry; instrumental analysis; laboratory automation antibiotic fermentation screen development. *Mailing Add:* Smith Kline & French Labs 709 Swedeland Rd Swedeland PA 19479

SITTEL, KARL, b Frankfurt am Main, Ger, Oct 10, 16; nat US; m 53; c 1. APPLIED PHYSICS. *Educ:* Goethe Univ, Ger, PhD(physics), 42. *Prof Exp:* Asst, Max Plank Inst Biophys, Ger, 39-40; chief, Radiosonde Lab, Aerological Instruments, Marine Observ, 41-45; res & develop physicist, Aeromed Equip Lab, Naval Air Exp Sta, 47-50; sr staff physicist, Labs Res & Develop, Franklin Inst, 50-59; sr systs engr, Radio Corp Am, 59-63, leader systs physics, 63-67; consult, Environ Sci Lab, Valley Forge Space Tech Ctr, Gen Elec Co, 67-73, staff engr res & develop, 73-81; CONSULT, 81- *Concurrent Pos:* Res assoc, Max Plank Inst Biophys, Ger, 46-47; consult, Jefferson Med Col, 53-56. *Mem:* NY Acad Sci; Am Phys Soc; Sigma Xi. *Res:* Radiosonde development; viscoelasticity; advanced systems; biomedical technology; nuclear effects engineering. *Mailing Add:* 916 Denston Dr Ambler PA 19002

SITTERLY, CHARLOTTE MOORE, b Ercildoun, Pa, Sept 24, 98; m 37. ASTRONOMY, ASTROPHYSICS. *Educ:* Swarthmore Col, AB, 20; Univ Calif, PhD(astron), 31. *Hon Degrees:* DSc, Swarthmore Col, 62; Dr, Univ Kiel, 68; DSc, Univ Mich, 71. *Prof Exp:* Computer, Princeton Observ, 20-25 & 28-29, res asst, 31-36, res assoc, 36-45; physicist, Atomic Physics Div, Nat Bur Standards, 45-68, Off Standard Ref Data, 68-70 & US Naval Res Lab, 71-78; RETIRED. *Concurrent Pos:* Mem comt line spectra of elements, Nat Res Coun; mem comn standard wavelengths & spectral tables, Int Astron Union, 50-64 & comn fundamental spectros data, 64, pres, 61-67; mem joint comn spectros, Int Coun Sci Unions, 50-58 & comt data sci & technol, 66-70; mem triple union comn spectros, Int Union Pure & Appl Physics, 60-65. *Honors & Awards:* Cannon Prize, Am Astron Soc, 37; Silver Medal, US Dept Com, 51, Gold Medal, 60; Fed Women's Award, 61; Cannon Centennial Medal, Wesley Col, 63; Nat Civil Serv League Career Serv Award, 66; William F Meggers Award, Optical Soc Am, 72. *Mem:* AAAS (vpres, Sect Astron, 52); fel Am Phys Soc; fel Optical Soc Am; Am Astron Soc (vpres, 58-60); hon mem Soc Appl Spectros. *Res:* Identification of lines in solar and sunspot spectra; analysis of atomic spectra; compilation of spectroscopic data derived from analyses of optical spectra; multiplet tables; atomic energy levels; solar spectrum. *Mailing Add:* 3711 Brandywine St NW Washington DC 20016

SITTERLY, WAYNE R, b Ashtabula, Ohio, Nov 18, 28; m 50; c 2. PLANT PATHOLOGY. *Educ:* Iowa State Col, BS, 52; Purdue Univ, MS, 54, PhD(plant path), 56. *Prof Exp:* From asst plant pathologist to assoc plant pathologist, 56-60, prof plant path, 65-74, PROF PLANT PATH & PHYSIOL, CLEMSON UNIV, 74-, SUPT, TRUCK EXP STA, 70- *Concurrent Pos:* Consult pvt chem companies & food prod indust. *Mem:* Weed Sci Soc Am; Am Phytopath Soc; Int Soc Plant Path. *Res:* Fungicides; fungus physiology; plant breeding; viruses; herbicides. *Mailing Add:* Clemson Univ Truck Exp Sta PO Box 30158 Charleston SC 29407

SITTLER, EDWARD CHARLES, JR, b Freeport, NY, Oct 4, 47; m 71; c 2. ASTROPHYSICS. *Educ:* Hofstra Univ, BS, 72; Mass Inst Technol, PhD(physics), 78. *Prof Exp:* Fel astrophysics, Nat Res Coun, 78-79, ASTROPHYSICIST, GODDARD SPACE FLIGHT CTR, NASA, 80- *Mem:* Am Geophys Union; Am Phys Soc. *Res:* Planetary magnetospheres of Jupiter and Saturn, including their respective novel satellites, Io and Titan; transport of energy by electrons in the solar wind, which may contribute to understanding the mechanisms driving the Sun's coronal expansion; development of plasma analyzer systems for future space applications. *Mailing Add:* 1723 Denton Ct Crofton MD 21114

SITTLER, ORVID DAYLE, physics, biophysics, deceased

SITZ, THOMAS O, b Newport, RI, Dec 9, 44; m 64; c 1. BIOCHEMISTRY. *Educ:* Va Polytech Inst, BS, 67, PhD(biochem), 71. *Prof Exp:* Fel pharmacol, Baylor Col Med, 71-73, instr, 73-74, res assoc cell biol, 74-75; asst prof, 75-81, ASSOC PROF CHEM, OLD DOMINION UNIV, 81- *Mem:* Am Chem Soc; Am Soc Microbiol; AAAS. *Res:* Secondary structure and methylation of 5.8S rRNA. *Mailing Add:* Dept of Chem Sci Old Dominion Univ Norfolk VA 23508

SIU, CHI-HUNG, b Hong Kong, July 29, 47. DEVELOPMENTAL BIOLOGY. *Educ:* Int Christian Univ, Tokyo, BA, 69; Univ Chicago, PhD, 74. *Prof Exp:* Fel sci res, Scripps Clin & Res Found, 74-76; ASST PROF, BANTING & BEST DEPT MED RES, UNIV TORONTO, 76- *Mem:* Am Soc Cell Biol; Can Biochem Soc. *Res:* Molecular mechanism of membrane biogenesis and the role of plasma membrane macromolecules in specific cell to cell recognition and cell differentiation. *Mailing Add:* C H Best Inst Univ of Toronto Toronto ON M5G 1L6 Can

SIU, TSUNPUI OSWALD, b Hong Kong, Dec 26, 45. EPIDEMIOLOGY. *Educ:* Univ Calif, Los Angeles, BS, 69; Yale Univ, MS, 73; Harvard Univ, MS, 75, DSc(biostatist), 78. *Prof Exp:* Teaching fel physics, Yale Univ, 70-73, res asst theoret studies atomic struct, 70-73; analyst epidemiol data mgt, Sch Pub Health, Harvard Univ, 73-74, sr analyst, 74-76; asst prof community health & epidemiol, Queen's Univ, Ont, 76-81; SR SCIENTIST EPIDEMIOL, ALTA CANCER HOSP BD, 81-; ASSOC PROF COMMUNITY HEALTH, UNIV CALGARY, 81- *Concurrent Pos:* Lab instr biostatist, Sch Pub Health, Harvard Univ, 74-76; Nat Health Sci scholar, Health & Welfare Can, 78-81. *Mem:* Am Statist Asn; Biomet Soc; Statist Soc Can; Am Col Epidemiol. *Res:* Statistics and computation of modelling of cross-tabulations, sample size allocation, reliability, preventive and harmful effects; epidemiology of automobile accident injuries; mass screening and treatment of breast cancer; epidemiology of cancer; mental health care planning; sociologic support for the elderly. *Mailing Add:* Tom Baker Cancer Ctr 1331 29th St NW Calgary AB T2N 4N2 Can

SIU, YUM-TONG, b Canton, China, May 6, 43; m 67. PURE MATHEMATICS. *Educ:* Univ Hong Kong, BA, 63; Univ Minn, MA, 64; Princeton Univ, PhD(math), 66. *Prof Exp:* Asst prof math, Purdue Univ, 66-67 & Univ Notre Dame, 67-70; assoc prof, 70-72, prof math, Yale Univ, 72-78; PROF MATH, STANFORD UNIV, 78- *Mem:* AAAS; Am Math Soc. *Res:* Cohomology groups of coherent analytic sheaves on complex analytic spaces; extension of coherent analytic sheaves. *Mailing Add:* Dept of Math Stanford Univ Stanford CA 94305

SIUKOLA, MATTI S(OLMU), electrical engineering, communications, deceased

SIUTA, GERALD JOSEPH, b Yonkers, NY, Apr 6, 47; m 69; c 1. ORGANIC CHEMISTRY, MEDICINAL CHEMISTRY. *Educ:* Lehman Col, BA, 69; Fordham Univ, PhD(org chem), 74. *Prof Exp:* res organic chemist, Med Res Div, 74-81, MGR, NEW PROD LICENSING, MED GROUP, LEDERLE LABS, AM CYNAMID CO, 81- *Concurrent Pos:* Lectr chem, Ladycliff Col, 76- *Mem:* Am Chem Soc; Sigma Xi. *Res:* Synthetic organic chemistry; prostaglandins; complement inhibitors; antidiabetic agents; anti-atherosclerotic agents. *Mailing Add:* Med Group Lederle Labs Am Cyanamid Co Pearl River NY 10965

SIVAK, ANDREW, b New Brunswick, NJ, May 31, 31; m 58; c 3. BIOCHEMISTRY, CELL BIOLOGY. *Educ:* Rutgers Univ, BS, 52, MS, 57, PhD(microbiol), 60. *Prof Exp:* USPHS fel, Univ Vienna, 60-61; biochemist Arthur D Little, Inc, 61-63; res dir, Bio-Dynamics, Inc, 63-64; res assoc, Med Ctr, NY Univ, 64-68, asst prof, 68-71, assoc prof environ med, 71-74; sr staff mem cell biol, 75-77, SECT MGR BIOMED SCI, ARTHUR D LITTLE, INC, 75-, VPRES, 77-; ADJ INSTR, MASS INST TECHNOL, 75- *Mem:* AAAS; Am Asn Cancer Res; Environ Mutagen Soc; Am Soc Cell Biol; Tissue Cult Asn. *Res:* Environmental toxicology; mechanisms of carcinogenesis and mutagenesis; cell membranes and control of cell division. *Mailing Add:* Arthur D Little Inc Acorn Park Cambridge MA 02140

SIVAK, JACOB GERSHON, b Montreal, Que, June 22, 44; m 67; c 2. COMPARATIVE PHYSIOLOGY, PHYSIOLOGICAL OPTICS. *Educ:* Univ Montreal, LScO, 67; Ind Univ, MS, 70; Cornell Univ, PhD(physiol), 72. *Prof Exp:* Asst prof, 72-75, assoc prof, 75-79, PROF OPTOM & BIOL, UNIV WATERLOO, 79- *Concurrent Pos:* Res assoc, Mote Marine Lab, Fla; fel, Am Acad Optom, 71-; Lady Davis vis prof, Technion-Israel Inst Technol, 78-79. *Mem:* Am Acad Optom; Asn Res Vision & Ophthal. *Res:* Comparative anatomy and physiology of the vertebrate eye with particular interest in the evolution of visual optics. *Mailing Add:* Lab of Comp Optom Univ of Waterloo Sch of Optom Waterloo ON N2L 3G1 Can

SIVASUBRAMANIAN, PAKKIRISAMY, b Andimadam, India, Aug 28, 39; m 67; c 3. DEVELOPMENTAL BIOLOGY. *Educ:* Annamalai Univ, India, BSc, 61; Univ Ill, MS, 71, PhD(physiol), 73. *Prof Exp:* Sci officer entom, Bhabha Atomic Res Ctr, India, 63-69; res fel insect develop, Biol Labs, Harvard Univ, 73-74; asst prof, 75-77, ASSOC PROF DEVELOP BIOL, UNIV NB, CAN, 78- *Mem:* Soc Develop Biol; Am Soc Zoologists. *Res:* Developmental neurobiology of insects; investigation of neuronal specificity and the mechanisms of establishment of neural networks in flies during metamorphosis by following the development of nerves in transplanted imaginal discs. *Mailing Add:* Dept of Biol Univ of NB Fredericton NB E3B 6E1 Can

SIVAZLIAN, BOGHOS D, b Cairo, Egypt, Feb 11, 36; US citizen; c 2. OPERATIONS RESEARCH, LOGISTICS. *Educ:* Cairo Univ, BSc, 59; Case Western Reserve Univ, MS, 62, PhD(opers res), 66. *Prof Exp:* Sr mgt sci assoc opers res, B F Goodrich Co, 62-65; from asst prof to assoc prof indust & systs eng, 66-72, PROF INDUST & SYSTS ENG, UNIV FLA, 72- *Concurrent Pos:* Consult, M&M Candies, Hackettstown, 61; consult scientist, Ft Belvoir, US Army, 68-69 & White Sands Missile Range, 70-76; Nat Acad Sci exchange scholar, Poland, 73-74; res partic, Inst Energy Anal, Oak Ridge Assoc Univs, 77-78; Fulbright scholar to USSR, 80. *Mem:* AAAS; Inst Mgt Sci; Soc Indust & Appl Math; Am Inst Indust Engrs; Opers Res Soc Am. *Res:* Inventory theory; replacement theory; logistics systems; applied stochastic process. *Mailing Add:* Dept of Indust & Systs Eng Univ of Fla Gainesville FL 32611

SIVER, PETER ALLAN, b Albany, NY, Dec 20, 53. PHYCOLOGY, LIMNOLOGY. *Educ:* State Univ NY Binghamton, BA, 74; Univ NH, MS, 76; Univ Conn, PhD(geol), 80. *Prof Exp:* Res asst biol, Univ NH, 74-76; res asst, Univ Conn, 76-78, teaching asst, 78-80; ASST PROF BIOL, WILKES COL, 80- *Mem:* Am Phycol Soc; Int Phycol Soc; Sigma Xi. *Res:* Vertical, horizontal and seasonal distribution of algal from a dual laboratory and field approach; algal polymorphism; limnology of aligotrophic lakes. *Mailing Add:* Dept Biol Wilkes Col Wilkes-Barnes PA 18766

SIVERS, DENNIS WAYNE, b Greeley, Colo, Jan 20, 44; m 66; c 2. HIGH ENERGY PHYSICS. *Educ:* Mass Inst Technol, BS, 66; Univ Calif, Berkeley, PhD(physics), 70. *Prof Exp:* Res assoc theoret physics, Argonne Nat Lab, 71-73 & Stanford Linear Accelerator, 73-75; vis scientist, Rutherford Lab, 75-76; asst physicist, 76-77, PHYSICIST THEORET PHYSICS, ARGONNE NAT LAB, 78- *Mem:* Am Phys Soc. *Res:* Theory and phenomenology of high energy physics. *Mailing Add:* High Energy Physics Div Argonne Nat Lab Argonne IL 60439

SIVIER, KENNETH R(OBERT), b Standish, Mich, Dec 10, 28; m 52; c 6. AEROSPACE ENGINEERING. *Educ:* Univ Mich, BSE(aeronaut eng) & BS(eng math), 51, PhD(aerospace eng), 67; Princeton Univ, MSE, 55. *Prof Exp:* Eng trainee, Naval Ord Lab, Aro, Inc, Tenn, 51-52; aeronaut eng, Aro, Inc, 52-53; res asst, Gas Dynamics Lab, Princeton Univ, 53-55; engr, McDonnell Aircraft Corp, 55-59, sr group engr, 59-62; res engr, Univ Mich, 62-67; ASSOC PROF AERONAUT & ASTRONAUT ENG, UNIV ILL, URBANA, 67- *Mem:* Am Inst Aeronaut & Astronaut. *Res:* Aerodynamic testing techniques and facilities; aerodynamic and aircraft design; aircraft flight mechanics; wind power; combustion of gases. *Mailing Add:* 105 Transportation Bldg Univ of Ill Urbana IL 61801

SIVINSKI, JACEK STEFAN, b Ashton, Nebr, June 23, 26; m 47; c 5. NUCLEAR BYPRODUCT UTILIZATION, FOOD IRRADIATION. *Educ:* Iowa State Univ, BS, 57. *Prof Exp:* Sect Supvr, Facil Eng Div, Sandia Corp, 57-64, mem adv systs res staff, 64-66, mgr, Planetary Quarantine Dept, 66-74, mgr, Appl Biol & Isotope Utilization Dept, Sandia Labs, 74-81; PROG DIR BENEFICIAL USES PROG, CH2M HILL, NMEX, 81- *Concurrent Pos:* Mem, Planetary Quarantine Adv Panel, NASA, 72-; mem, Comt Technol Transfer Develop Countries, Int Atomic Energy Agency. *Mem:* Am Inst Aeronaut & Astronaut; Am Asn Contamination Control; Europ Soc Nuclear Methods Agr. *Res:* Systems analysis for low level aircraft penetration; desalination, particularly brackish waters; systems analysis for re-entry vehicle systems, lunar and planetary quarantine, space environments; radiation biology; radiation treatment of agricultural commodities; beneficial uses of nuclear byproducts. *Mailing Add:* 9825 Hannett Pl NE Albuquerque NM 87112

SIVJEE, GULAMABAS GULAMHUSEN, b Zanzibar, Tanzania, Mar 11, 38; US citizen; m 59; c 3. AERONOMY. *Educ:* Univ London, BSc, 63; Johns Hopkins Univ, PhD(physics), 70. *Prof Exp:* Asst lectr physics, Makerere Col, Univ London, 63-65; res scientist physics, Stand Tel & Cables, Div Int Tel & Tel, 65-66; sr system analyst physics, Bendix Field Eng Corp, 70; fel physics, Johns Hopkins Univ, 71 & Space & Atmospheric Studies, Univ Sask, 71-72; asst prof, 72-76, ASSOC PROF GEOPHYS, GEOPHYS INST, UNIV ALASKA, 76- *Concurrent Pos:* Convener, Comt Airborne Studies Airglow, Auroral & Magnetospheric Physics, aboard NASA's Convair 990 Jet Aircraft, 73- *Mem:* Am Geophys Union. *Res:* Energy, flux and pitch angle distribution of magnetospheric particles and their interactions with atmospheric constituents; UV spectroscopy of Venus and Jupiter; minor constituents, including gaseous pollutants in terrestrial atmosphere. *Mailing Add:* Geophys Inst Univ of Alaska Fairbanks AK 99701

SIX, ERICH WALTHER, b Frankfurt, Ger, Sept 22, 26; m 57; c 1. BIOPHYSICS. *Educ:* Univ Frankfurt, Dr phil nat, 54. *Prof Exp:* Res fel radiobiol, Max Planck Inst Marine Biol, Ger, 54-56; res fel microbial genetics, Calif Inst Technol, 56-57; res assoc, Univ Southern Calif, 57, Max Planck Inst Biol, Ger, 58-59 & Univ Rochester, 59-60; from asst prof to assoc prof, 60-73, PROF MICROBIAL GENETICS, UNIV IOWA, 73- *Mem:* Am Soc Microbiol; Genetics Soc Am. *Res:* Microbial genetics; virology; molecular biology. *Mailing Add:* Dept of Microbiol Univ of Iowa Iowa City IA 52242

SIX, HOWARD RONALD, b Princeton, NJ, Jan 5, 42; m 64; c 2. VIRAL IMMUNOLOGY, IMMUNOCHEMISTRY. *Educ:* David Lipscomb Col, BA, 63; Vanderbilt Univ, PhD(microbiol), 72. *Prof Exp:* Fel, Sch Med, Washington Univ, 72-74; res assoc, Sch Med, Vanderbilt Univ, 74-75; ASST PROF, BAYLOR COL MED, 75- *Concurrent Pos:* Adj asst prof, Sch Biomed Sci, Univ Tex, Houston, 78- *Mem:* Am Soc Microbiol; Infectious Diseases Soc Am; Soc Exp Biol & Med; Am Asn Immunologists; Am Asn Virologists. *Res:* Mechanisms of adjuvant activity of liposomes; antigenic variation of influenza virus; immunity to respiratory viruses. *Mailing Add:* 5138 Karenbeth Houston TX

SIX, NORMAN FRANK, JR, b Tampa, Fla, July 24, 35; m 54; c 4. PHYSICS. *Educ:* Univ Fla, BS, 57, PhD(physics), 63; Univ Calif, Los Angeles, MS, 59. *Prof Exp:* Mem tech staff-physicist, Hughes Aircraft Co, Calif, 57-59; res asst astrophysics, Univ Fla, 59-63; mgr geo-astrophys lab, Sci Res Labs, Brown Eng Co, Ala, 63-66; prof physics, 66-74, PROF PHYSICS & ASTRON, WESTERN KY UNIV, 74-, HEAD DEPT, 66- *Concurrent Pos:* Res assoc, Univ Fla, 64-66; consult, Brown Eng Co, Ala, 66- *Mem:* AAAS; Am Phys Soc; Am Astron Soc; Am Geophys Union. *Res:* Analytical and experimental studies in planetary emissions; lunar and solar physics; electromagnetic wave propagation; space environment; radio astronomy experiments from earth satellites and from the moon. *Mailing Add:* Dept of Physics Western Ky Univ Bowling Green KY 42101

SIZE, WILLIAM BACHTRUP, b Chicago, Ill, June 8, 43; m 68; c 3. GEOLOGY. *Educ:* Northern Ill Univ, BS, 65, MS, 67; Univ Ill, Urbana, PhD(geol), 71. *Prof Exp:* Asst prof geol, Eastern Ill Univ, 70-71; geologist, Hawaii Inst Geophys, 71-72; asst prof, 73-78, ASSOC PROF GEOL, EMORY UNIV, 78- *Concurrent Pos:* Vis asst prof geol, Univ Hawaii, 71-72; corresp, Geodynamics Proj, Nat Acad Sci, 73-, Int Geol Correlation Prog, 77- *Mem:* Sigma Xi; Geol Soc Am. *Res:* Petrogenetic history of igneous rock textures; mechanics of igneous intrusions; origin of alkaline rocks; computer applications in petrology. *Mailing Add:* Dept of Geol Emory Univ Atlanta GA 30322

SIZEMORE, RONALD KELLY, b Farmville, Va, Feb 27, 47. MARINE MICROBIOLOGY. *Educ:* Wake Forest Univ, BS, 69; Univ SC, MS, 71; Univ Md, PhD(microbiol), 75. *Prof Exp:* Asst prof, Univ Houston, 75-81; ASST PROF MICROBIOL, UNIV NC, WILMINGTON, 81- *Concurrent Pos:* Vis res scientist, Galveston Lab, Nat Marine Fisheries Serv, 75-81. *Mem:* Sigma Xi; Am Soc Microbiol; AAAS. *Res:* Ecology, taxonomy and molecular biology of marine bacteria with emphasis on the members of the genus Vibrio. *Mailing Add:* Dept Biol Univ NC Wilmington NC 28406

SIZER, IRWIN WHITING, b Bridgewater, Mass, Apr 4, 10; m 35; c 1. BIOCHEMISTRY. *Educ:* Brown Univ, AB, 31; Rutgers Univ, PhD(physiol & biochem), 35. *Hon Degrees:* ScD, Brown Univ, 71. *Prof Exp:* Lab asst physiol, Rutgers Univ, 31-35; from instr to prof, 35-75, exec officer, 54-55, from actg head dept to head dept, 55-67, dean grad sch, 67-75, EMER PROF BIOCHEM, MASS INST TECHNOL, 75- *Concurrent Pos:* Mem comt physiol training, NIH, 48-64, chmn, 65, chmn comt gen res support, 65-69 & nat adv coun health res facilities, 70-72; consult, Johnson & Johnson Co, 49-; trustee, Rutgers Univ, 62-71, mem bd gov, 68-71; mem, Corp Lesley Col, 62-; trustee, Boston Mus Sci, 63-; mem adv comt, Inst Microbiol, 63-68; consult probs Latin Am, Ford Found, 65-67; dir, Leader Fed Savings & Loan Asn, Lexington, 67-; consult, Neurosci Res Prog, 67-; trustee, Boston Biomed Res Inst, 68-; mem adv comt grad educ, Mass State Bd Higher Educ, 68-75; consult resource develop, Mass Inst Technol, 75-; pres, Whitaker Health Sci Fund, Inc, 75- *Mem:* Am Chem Soc; fel Am Inst Chem; Am Soc Biol Chem; fel Am Acad Arts & Sci. *Res:* Chemical stimulation of animals; spectroscopy of biological materials; enzyme kinetics; action of oxidases on proteins; x-ray photography of insects; intermediary metabolism of sulfur; enzymes of oxidation and transanimation. *Mailing Add:* Rm 4-234 Mass Inst of Technol Cambridge MA 02139

SIZER, WALTER SCOTT, b Providence, RI, Aug 15, 47; m 77. LINEAR ALGEBRA. *Educ:* Dartmouth Col, AB, 69; Univ Mass, MA, 72; Univ London, PhD(math), 76. *Prof Exp:* Vis lectr math, Univ Mass, Amherst, 76-77; vis asst prof, Southern Ill Univ, 77-80; ASST PROF MATH, MOORHEAD STATE UNIV, 80- *Mem:* Am Math Soc; Math Asn Am; Asn Women Math. *Res:* Group retractions; similarity of matrices; representations of semigroup actions. *Mailing Add:* Dept Math Moorhead State Univ Moorhead MN 56560

SJOBLAD, ROY DAVID, b Worcester, Mass, Nov 22, 47; m 69; c 2. MICROBIOLOGY, BIOCHEMISTRY. *Educ:* Gordon Col, BS, 69; Univ Mass, MS, 71; Pa State Univ, PhD(agron), 76. *Prof Exp:* Res fel appl biol, Harvard Univ, 76-78; ASST PROF MICROBIOL, UNIV MD, 78- *Concurrent Pos:* Rockefeller Found fel, Harvard Univ, 76-77. *Mem:* Sigma Xi; Am Soc Microbiol; NY Acad Sci. *Res:* Microbial ecology; chemoreception in microorganisms; transformation of pesticides by microorganisms; fungal and algal enzymes. *Mailing Add:* Dept of Microbiol Univ of Md College Park MD 20742

SJODIN, RAYMOND ANDREW, b Salt Lake City, Utah, Oct 10, 27; m 54; c 2. BIOPHYSICS. *Educ:* Calif Inst Technol, BS, 51; Univ Calif, PhD(physiol), 55. *Prof Exp:* Asst physiol, Univ Calif, 51-55; res assoc biophys, Purdue Univ, 55-58; NIH fel, Univ Col, London, 58-59; res assoc physiol, Univ Uppsala, Sweden, 59-60; assoc prof, 60-66, PROF BIOPHYS, UNIV MD, BALTIMORE, 66- *Mem:* Fel AAAS; Soc Gen Physiol; Am Physiol Soc; Biophys Soc. *Res:* Physical chemistry of membranes, nerve excitation and conduction of nerve impulses; ion fluxes across cell membranes in relation to electrical events and transport problems. *Mailing Add:* Dept of Biophysics Univ of Md Baltimore MD 21201

SJOERDSMA, ALBERT, b Lansing, Ill, Aug 28, 24; m 50; c 4. EXPERIMENTAL MEDICINE, CLINICAL PHARMACOLOGY. *Educ:* Univ Chicago, BS, 45, PhD(pharmacol), 48, MD, 49; Am Bd Internal Med, dipl, 58. *Prof Exp:* Intern, Univ Hosp, Univ Mich, 49-50; resident, Cardiovasc Dept, Michael Reese Hosp, 51; resident med, USPHS Hosp, 51-53; clin investr, Nat Heart Inst, 53-58, chief exp therapeut br, 58-71; vpres & dir, Merrell Int Res Ctr, France, 71-76, sr vpres & dir, Merrell Nat Labs, Cincinnati & France, 76-78, vpres pharmaceut res & develop, Richardson-Merrell Inc, 78-81; VPRES PHARMACEUT RES, DOW CHEM CO, 81- *Concurrent Pos:* Nat Heart Inst res fel, Univ Chicago, 50-51; NIH fel, Malmo, Sweden, 59-60; spec lectr, George Washington Univ, 59-71; mem coun high blood pressure res, Am Heart Asn. *Honors & Awards:* Theobold Smith Award, AAAS, 58; Harry Gold Award, Am Soc Pharmacol & Exp Therapeut, 77; Oscar B Hunter Award, Am Soc Clin Pharmacol & Therapeut, 81. *Mem:* AAAS; Am Soc Pharmacol & Exp Therapeut; Am Soc Clin Invest; Asn Am Physicians; Am Soc Clin Pharmacol & Therapeut. *Res:* Metabolism of biogenic amines; collagen metabolism. *Mailing Add:* Merrell Dow Pharmaceut Inc Cincinnati OH 45215

SJOGREN, ROBERT ERIK, b Schenectady, NY, June 13, 31; m 72. MICROBIOLOGY, BIOCHEMISTRY. *Educ:* Cornell Univ, BS, 53; Univ Cincinnati, MS, 60, PhD(microbiol), 67. *Prof Exp:* Asst clin chemist, Ellis Hosp Lab, NY, 55-58; res assoc microbiol, Sterling Winthrop Res Inst, 60-64; ASSOC PROF MICROBIOL & BIOCHEM, UNIV VT, 67- *Concurrent Pos:* Hatch Act grant, Vt Agr Exp Sta, 68- *Mem:* Am Soc Microbiol; Sigma Xi. *Res:* Fungal metabolism; physical-chemical properties of protein; microbial ecology. *Mailing Add:* Dept of Micro & Biochem Hills Bldg Univ of Vt Burlington VT 05405

SJOLANDER, JOHN ROGERS, b LaCrosse, Wis, Aug 29, 24; m 45; c 3. ORGANIC CHEMISTRY. *Educ:* Univ Wis, BA, 46; Univ Minn, PhD(org chem), 50. *Prof Exp:* Res chemist, Merck & Co, Inc, 50-52; sr chemist, 52-54, proj coordr, 54-58, proj mgr, 58-61, tech & prod mgr, Film Dept, 61-63, tech dir, Film & Allied Prod Div, 63-69, dir corp tech planning & coord, 69-73, mgr agrichem proj, 73-77, TECH DIR, HOUSEHOLD & HARDWARE PRODS DIV, 3M CO, 77- *Mem:* Am Chem Soc. *Res:* Biaxially oriented plastic films; condensation polymers; food packaging; electrical insulating materials; research and development administration, appraisal and control; synthesis, screening and development of pesticides and growth regulators. *Mailing Add:* 3M Co 3M Ctr 251-2E St Paul MN 55144

SJOLANDER, NEWELL OSCAR, b LaCrosse, Wis, Mar 29, 12; m 43; c 3. INDUSTRIAL MICROBIOLOGY. *Educ:* Univ Wis, BS, 34, MS, 36, PhD(bact), 38. *Prof Exp:* Asst bacteriologist, Exp Sta, Univ Tenn, 38-41; asst, Alumni Res Found, Univ Wis, 41-42; res microbiologist, Heyden Chem Corp, 42-53; group leader, Fine Chem Div, Am Cyanamid Co, 53-55, group leader, Lederle Labs, 55-58, dept head, 58-77; RETIRED. *Mem:* Am Soc Microbiol; Am Chem Soc; NY Acad Sci. *Res:* Anaerobic bacteria; industrial fermentations; vitamins; enzymes; antibiotics; biosynthesis of tetracyclines; steroid conversions by microorganisms. *Mailing Add:* 11 Werimus Brook Rd Saddle River NJ 07458

SJOLUND, RICHARD DAVID, b Iron River, Mich, Dec 9, 39. BOTANY. *Educ:* Univ Wis-Milwaukee, BS, 63; Univ Calif, Davis, PhD(bot), 68. *Prof Exp:* Botanist, Ames Res Ctr, NASA, 63-64; from asst prof to assoc prof cytol, 68-73, ASSOC PROF BOT, UNIV IOWA, 73- *Mem:* Bot Soc Am; Am Soc Plant Physiol; Am Soc Cell Biol; Electron Micros Soc Am. *Res:* Electron microscopy of chloroplast development and cellular differentiation in plant tissue cultures; freeze-fracture of membranes; physiology. *Mailing Add:* Dept of Bot Univ of Iowa Iowa City IA 52242

SJÖSTRAND, FRITIOF S, b Stockholm, Sweden, Nov 5, 12; m. MOLECULAR BIOLOGY, NEUROANATOMY. *Educ:* Karolinska Inst, Sweden, MD, 41, PhD, 45. *Hon Degrees:* PhD(biol), Univ Siena, Italy, 74. *Prof Exp:* Asst prof anat, Karolinska Inst, Sweden, 45; Swedish Med Res Coun fel biol, Mass Inst Technol, 47-48; assoc prof anat, Karolinska Inst, Sweden, 49-60; vis prof, 59-60, PROF ZOOL, UNIV CALIF, LOS ANGELES, 60- *Concurrent Pos:* Mem exec comt, Int Fedn Electron Micros Socs, 54-62 & Int Brain Res Orgn; ed, J Ultrastruct Res, 57-; prof & head dept histol, Karolinska Inst, Sweden, 60-62, NSF spec fel, 65-66; sr consult, Vet Admin Radioisotope Serv, 61, 65 & 66. *Honors & Awards:* Swedish Med Asn Award, 59; Anders Retzius Gold Medal, 67; Paul Ehrlich & Ludwig Darmstaedter Prize, 71; Knight 1st Degree, Royal Swedish Order of the North Star, 74. *Mem:* Fel Am Acad Arts & Sci; Electron Micros Soc Am; Am Soc Cell Biol; hon mem Soc Electron Micros Japan; hon mem Scand Electron Micros Soc. *Res:* Ultrastructure of cells as related to function; molecular structure and functional significance of cellular membranes; neuronal circuitry of the retina. *Mailing Add:* Dept of Biol Univ of Calif Los Angeles CA 90024

SKAAR, PALMER DAVID, b Mishawaka, Ind, Mar 14, 23; m 47; c 3. GENETICS. *Educ:* Ind Univ, AB, 47, PhD(zool), 52. *Prof Exp:* Proj assoc genetics, Univ Wis, 51-53; geneticist, Biol Lab, Long Island Biol Asn, Cold Spring Harbor, NY, 53-57; from asst prof to assoc prof, 57-62, PROF GENETICS, MONT STATE UNIV, 62-, DIR GENETICS INST, 64- *Mem:* Genetics Soc Am. *Res:* Microbial genetics. *Mailing Add:* Genetics Inst Mont State Univ Bozeman MT 59715

SKADRON, GEORGE, b Vienna, Austria, July 1, 36; US citizen; m 65; c 1. PHYSICS, ASTROPHYSICS. *Educ:* Purdue Univ, BS, 57; Univ Rochester, MA, 60, PhD(physics), 65. *Prof Exp:* Res assoc physics, Univ Md, 65-67; Nat Acad Sci-Nat Res Coun res assoc, Res Labs, Environ Sci Serv Admin, 67-69; from asst prof to assoc prof, 69-75, PROF PHYSICS, DRAKE UNIV, 75- *Concurrent Pos:* Vis scientist, Max-Planck Inst Aeronomy, WGer, 75-76. *Mem:* Am Phys Soc; Am Geophys Union. *Res:* Cosmic radiation; plasma astrophysics; ionospheric physics. *Mailing Add:* Dept of Physics Drake Univ Des Moines IA 50311

SKADRON, PETER, b Vienna, Austria, Jan 19, 34; US citizen; m 63; c 1. SOLID STATE PHYSICS. *Educ:* Purdue Univ, BS, 54, MS, 57, PhD(physics), 65. *Prof Exp:* Res physicist, Res & Develop Lab, Sprague Elec Co, 64-67; asst prof, 67-71, assoc prof, 71-80, PROF PHYSICS, BUTLER UNIV, 80- *Mem:* AAAS; Am Phys Soc. *Res:* Electrical transport properties in metals and semiconductors. *Mailing Add:* Dept of Physics Butler Univ Indianapolis IN 46207

SKAFF, MICHAEL SAMUEL, b Boston, Mass, June 21, 36; m 64; c 3. MATHEMATICS. *Educ:* Univ Mich, BS, 58; Univ Ill, MS, 60; Univ Calif, Los Angeles, PhD(math), 68. *Prof Exp:* Comput engr, Douglas Aircraft Co, 62-63; sr staff mathematician, Hughes Aircraft Co, 63-68; PROF MATH, UNIV DETROIT, 68- *Concurrent Pos:* Adj prof, Lincoln Inst Land Policy, Harvard Univ, 80- *Mem:* Am Math Soc; Math Asn Am; Int Asn Assessing Officers. *Res:* Vector valued Orlicz spaces; computer simulation and modeling; calculus of variation and optimization; computer assited mass appraisal systems. *Mailing Add:* Dept of Math Univ of Detroit Detroit MI 48221

SKAGGS, LESTER S, b Trenton, Mo, Nov 21, 11; m 39; c 3. PHYSICS. *Educ:* Univ Mo, AB, 33, AM, 34; Univ Chicago, PhD(physics), 39. *Prof Exp:* Asst math, Univ Mo, 35; asst physics, Univ Chicago, 37-41; physicist, Michael Reese Hosp, 40-41, Carnegie Inst Technol, 41-43, Univ Mich, 43-44 & Univ Calif, 44-45; from asst prof to assoc prof, 48-56, prof med physics, 56-76, EMER PROF MED PHYSICS, UNIV CHICAGO, 76- *Concurrent Pos:* Physicist, Michael Reese Hosp, 45-49. *Mem:* Fel Am Phys Soc; AAAS; Am Col Radiol; Am Asn Physicists Med; Radiol Soc NAm. *Res:* High energy sources of radiation for therapy; dosimetry; computer modeling of biological systems. *Mailing Add:* Dept Radiol Box 442 Univ Chicago 950 E 59th St Chicago IL 60637

SKAGGS, ROBERT L, b St Louis, Mo, Apr 2, 32; m 61; c 3. METALLURGICAL ENGINEERING. *Educ:* Mo Sch Mines, BS, 55; Iowa State Univ, MS, 58, PhD(metall), 67. *Prof Exp:* Develop engr, Pigments Dept, E I du Pont de Nemours & Co, 55-56; mat engr, Standard Oil Co Calif, 58-61; sr mat engr, Aeronaut Div, Honeywell Corp, 62-64; asst prof metall eng, Univ Ky, 67-69; assoc prof eng, 69-72, chmn dept, 72-77, PROF ENG, UNIV NEV, LAS VEGAS, 72- *Mem:* Am Soc Metals; Am Inst Mining, Metall & Petrol Engrs; Am Soc Eng Educ; Am Ord Asn. *Res:* Thermodynamics; extractive metallurgy; metal joining; plastic deformation of alloys; corrosion. *Mailing Add:* Dept of Eng Univ of Nev Las Vegas NV 89109

SKAGGS, SAMUEL ROBERT, b Philipsburg, Pa, June 23, 36; m 58; c 5. MATERIALS SCIENCE. *Educ:* NMex State Univ, BS, 58; Univ NMex, MS, 67, PhD(mat sci), 72. *Prof Exp:* Asst mech engr, Argonne Nat Lab, 58-60; staff mem, Los Alamos Sci Lab, 60-61 & 62-67; physicist, US Air Force Spec Weapons Ctr, 67-68; STAFF MEM, LOS ALAMOS SCI LAB, 71- *Concurrent Pos:* Consult, US Air Force, 68-; sabbatical leave, Off Advan Res & Technol, Fossil Energy Div, US Dept Energy, 81-82. *Mem:* AAAS; Am Ceramic Soc; Mat Res Soc. *Res:* High temperature properties and behavior of nonferrous metals and ceramics; chemistry and ore processing using solar furnaces. *Mailing Add:* Los Alamos Sci Lab Box 1663/MS-348 Los Alamos NM 87545

SKALA, JAMES HERBERT, b Oak Park, Ill, July 27, 29; m 49. ANALYTICAL BIOCHEMISTRY, NUTRITION. *Educ:* Beloit Col, BS, 50; Univ Minn, MS, 57, PhD(poultry sci), 61. *Prof Exp:* Food chemist tech serv div, Am Can Co, 50-53; biochemist, Peru Surv, Interdept Comt Nutrit Nat Defense, 59; asst prof poultry prod technol, Univ Wis-Madison, 60-69; chief anal biochem br, Chem Div, US Army Med Res & Nutrit Lab, Denver, 69-74; chief, Anal Biochem Sect, Letterman Army Inst Res, 74-76, chief, Biochem Div, Dept Nutrit, 76-79; CHIEF, BIOANAL LABS, WESTERN HUMAN NUTRIT RES CTR, AGR RES SERV, USDA, 79- *Concurrent Pos:* Nutritionist, Uruguay Surv, Interdept Comt Nutrit Nat Defense, 62. *Mem:* Inst Food Technologists; Am Asn Clin Chem; Am Inst Nutrit; Poultry Sci Asn; Am Chem Soc. *Res:* Analytical biochemistry; clinical chemistry; human nutrition; especially biochemistry and dietary survey techniques; food chemistry; poultry meat and egg products. *Mailing Add:* Human Nutrit Res Ctr USDA Agr Res LR-3142 Lair Presidio San Francisco CA 94129

SKALAFURIS, ANGELO JAMES, b Pittsburgh, Pa, Dec 9, 31; m 67; c 1. APPLIED MATHEMATICS. *Educ:* Ill Inst Technol, BS, 54; Univ Chicago, MS, 58; Brandeis Univ, PhD(theoret physics), 63. *Prof Exp:* Harvard-Smithsonian Inst observator & res assoc, Harvard Univ, 59-63; Fulbright adv res lectr, Inst Advan Study Physics, Athens, 63-64 & Inst Astrophys, Paris, 64; Nat Acad Sci-Nat Res Coun resident res assoc, Inst Space Studies, NASA, 64-66; asst prof physics, City Col New York, 66-69; assoc prof theoret physics, Bartol Res Found, Franklin Inst, Pa, 69-72; sr res assoc theoret biol, State Univ NY, Albany, 72-74; HEAD MATH RES CTR, NAVAL RES LAB, 74- *Concurrent Pos:* Mem, Greek Bd Sci Adv Appln

Atomic Energy & Sci Res; fulbright assoc, Nat Acad Sci. *Mem:* Am Astron Soc; Am Phys Soc; Am Soc Mech Engrs. *Res:* Gas and radiation; plasmas and shockwaves; dense solid state; relativistic fluids; mathematical biology and physics; spermatazoa, flagella. *Mailing Add:* Math Res Ctr Naval Res Lab Washington DC 20375

SKALAK, RICHARD, b New York, NY, Feb 5, 23; m 53; c 4. CIVIL ENGINEERING, FLUID MECHANICS. *Educ:* Columbia Univ, BS, 43, CE, 46, PhD(civil eng), 54. *Prof Exp:* Instr struct anal & design, 46-54, from asst prof to assoc prof fluid mech, 54-64, PROF FLUID MECH, COLUMBIA UNIV, 64- *Concurrent Pos:* NSF fel, Cambridge Univ, 60-61; sr res fel, Gothenburg Univ, 67-68. *Mem:* AAAS; Am Soc Eng Educ; Am Soc Civil Engrs; Am Heart Asn; Int Asn Hydraul Res. *Res:* Surface waves, vibration and shock wave phenomena in liquids; fluid mechanics of biological systems; mechanics of blood flow. *Mailing Add:* Dept of Civil Eng & Eng Mech Columbia Univ New York NY 10027

SKALKA, ANNA MARIE, b New York, NY, July 2, 38; m 60; c 2. MOLECULAR BIOLOGY, VIROLOGY. *Educ:* Adelphi Univ, AB, 59; NY Univ, PhD(microbiol), 64. *Prof Exp:* Am Cancer Soc fel molecular biol, Carnegie Inst Genetics Res Unit, 64-66, fel, 66-69; asst mem, Dept Cell Biol, 69-71, assoc mem, 71-76, mem, 76-80, HEAD, LAB MOLECULAR & BIOCHEM GENETICS, ROCHE INST MOLECULAR BIOL, 80- *Concurrent Pos:* Vis prof, Dept Molecular Biol, Albert Einstein Col Med, 73- & Rockefeller Univ, 75. *Mem:* AAAS; Am Soc Microbiol; Am Soc Biol Chem; Sigma Xi; Asn Women Sci. *Res:* Structure and function of DNA; host and viral functions in the synthesis of viral DNA and RNA; phage DNA as a vehicle for the amplification and study of eukaryotic genes; molecular biology of avian retroviruses. *Mailing Add:* Dept of Cell Biol Roche Inst of Molecular Biol Nutley NJ 07110

SKALKO, RICHARD GALLANT, anatomy, see previous edition

SKALNIK, J(OHN) G(ORDON), b Medford, Okla, May 30, 23; m 47; c 2. ELECTRICAL ENGINEERING. *Educ:* Okla Agr & Mech Col, BS, 44; Yale Univ, ME, 46, DEng, 55. *Prof Exp:* Instr elec eng, Yale Univ, 44-49, from asst prof to assoc prof, 49-65; chmn dept, 68-71, dean, Col Eng, 71-76, PROF ELEC ENG, UNIV CALIF, SANTA BARBARA, 65- *Mem:* Sr mem Inst Elec & Electronics Engrs. *Res:* Splitanode magnetrons; signal-to-noise ratio study; solid-state devices and circuits. *Mailing Add:* Dept Elec Eng & Comput Sci Univ Calif Santa Barbara CA 93106

SKALNY, JAN PETER, b Bratislava, Czech, Mar 19, 35; m 65; c 2. SILICATE CHEMISTRY. *Educ:* Univ Chem Tech, Prague, Eng Chem, 58; Acad Mining & Metall, Cracow, PhD(silicate chem), 65. *Prof Exp:* Technologist, Pragocement, Prague, 58-60; asst prof bldg mat, Slovak Tech Univ, Bratislava, 60-66; vis res worker cement chem, Cement & Concrete Asn Res Sta, Slough, Eng, 67; res fel cement & surface chem, Clarkson Col, 68-69; group leader, Tech Ctr, Am Cement Corp, 69-71; mgr prod develop, Pac Southwest Region, 71-72; res scientist, Res Inst Advan Studies, 72-73, sr res scientist, 73-74, head cement dept, 74-78, ASSOC DIR, MARTIN MARIETTA LABS, 78- *Concurrent Pos:* Mem panel waste solidification, Comt Radioactive Waste Disposal, Nat Acad Sci, 76-77 & Comt Status of US Cement & Concrete Res & Develop, 77-78. mem Transp Res Bd. *Mem:* Am Ceramic Soc; Int Union Testing & Res Labs Mat & Structure; Am Soc Testing & Mat. *Res:* Building materials; cement production and hydration; admixture chemistry; research administration. *Mailing Add:* Martin Marietta Labs 1450 S Rolling Rd Baltimore MD 21227

SKALSKI, STANISLAUS, b Englewood, NJ, Feb 1, 34. SOLID STATE PHYSICS. *Educ:* Polytech Inst Brooklyn, BS, 58; Rutgers Univ, MS, 60, PhD(physics), 64. *Prof Exp:* Asst prof, 64-72, chmn dept, 72-78, ASSOC PROF PHYSICS, FORDHAM UNIV, 72- *Mem:* Am Phys Soc. *Res:* Ferromagnetism and superconductivity. *Mailing Add:* Dept of Physics Fordham Univ Bronx NY 10458

SKANDALAKIS, JOHN ELIAS, b Molai, Sparta, Greece, Jan 20, 20; nat US; m 50; c 3. SURGERY. *Educ:* Nat Univ, Athens, MD, 46; Emory Univ, MS, 50, PhD, 62. *Prof Exp:* Dir pediat surg, Temporary Hosp, Athens, Greece, 51; from instr to assoc prof, 56-63, PROF ANAT, SCH MED, EMORY UNIV, 63-, CHRIS CARLOS PROF SURG ANAT & TECHNIQUE, 77- *Concurrent Pos:* Fel surg, Grady Hosp, Atlanta, Ga, 51-52, from resident to chief resident, 54-57; dir surg training prog, Piedmont Hosp, 57-72, chmn dept postgrad educ, 73-77, sr attend surgeon, 77-; pvt pract. *Mem:* AMA; fel Am Col Surg; Greek Surg Soc; Am Asn Anat. *Res:* General and clinical surgery; surgical embryology; tumors of the neck. *Mailing Add:* 18 Woodruff Med Ctr Admin Bldg Emory Univ Sch Med Atlanta GA 30322

SKAPERDAS, GEORGE T(HEODORE), b New York, NY, Jan 25, 14; m 45; c 2. CHEMICAL ENGINEERING. *Educ:* McGill Univ, BEng, 36; Mass Inst Technol, SM, 38, ScD(chem eng), 40. *Prof Exp:* Lab chemist, British-Am Oil Co, Can, 36; test engr, Aluminum Co Can, Ltd, Que, 38; asst, Mass Inst Technol, 38-40; chem & process engr, M W Kellogg Co, New York, 40-51, assoc dir chem eng, 51-67, mgr develop, 67-73, mgr process eng, Pullman Kellogg, 73-74, dir coal develop, 74-75, sr consult, 75-79; CONSULT ENGR, 79- *Concurrent Pos:* Adj prof, NY Univ, 47-53. *Mem:* Am Chem Soc; fel Am Inst Chem Engrs. *Res:* Gas absorption; heat transfer; corrosion; process development engineering; oxychlorination; coal gasification; hydrogen recovery; synthetic chemicals; air separation; economic evaluation. *Mailing Add:* 14 Wychview Dr Westfield NJ 07090

SKARDA, R VENCIL, JR, b Los Angeles, Calif, May 22, 40; m 71. MATHEMATICS. *Educ:* Pomona Col, BA, 61; Calif Inst Technol, MS, 64, PhD(math), 66. *Prof Exp:* Asst prof, 65-71, ASSOC PROF MATH, BRIGHAM YOUNG UNIV, 71- *Mem:* Math Asn Am; Am Math Soc; London Math Soc. *Res:* Analytic number theory; functional analysis and functional iterations; combinatorics; inequalities in l-1-space; algebra manipulating on computers; control theory. *Mailing Add:* Dept of Math Brigham Young Univ Provo UT 84602

SKARLOS, LEONIDAS, b Manchester, NH, Apr 11, 41; m 70. CHEMISTRY, MATHEMATICS. *Educ:* Univ Vt, BA, 64; Univ NH, MS, 66; Boston Col, PhD(chem), 69. *Prof Exp:* Sr chemist, Richmond Res Labs, 74-79, PROJ CHEMIST, PORT ARTHUR RES LABS, TEXACO INC, 79- *Res:* Developing methods of determining pollution resulting from coal gasification. *Mailing Add:* Port Arthur Res Labs Texaco Inc Port Arthur TX 77640

SKARNES, ROBERT C, b Minneapolis, Minn, Aug 12, 24; m 56; c 4. BIOCHEMISTRY, IMMUNOLOGY. *Educ:* Univ Minn, PhD(bact), 56. *Prof Exp:* Chemist, NIH, 57-59, dir res, Pasteur Inst, Paris, 61-64, NATO sr investr, 64-65; assoc surg res, Beth Israel Hosp, Harvard Med Sch, 65-67; SR SCIENTIST, WORCESTER FOUND EXP BIOL, 67- *Concurrent Pos:* NIH spec fel immunol, Pasteur Inst, Paris, 59-60; asst prof bact, Med Sch, Univ Minn, 60-61. *Res:* Mechanisms of natural resistance to infectious disease. *Mailing Add:* Worcester Found for Exp Biol Shrewsbury MA 01545

SKARSAUNE, SANDRA KAYE, b Burlington, Iowa, Apr 16, 43; m 66; c 1. CEREAL & ANALYTICAL CHEMISTRY. *Educ:* Cornell Univ, BS, 65; NDak State Univ, PhD(cereal chem), 69. *Prof Exp:* Asst prof cereals, NDak State Univ, 69-73; lab chief, Centro Indust Exp Para Exportacion, 73-75; GROUP LEADER CHEM, KELLOGG CO, 75- *Mem:* Am Asn Cereal Chemists; Inst Food Technol; Am Chem Soc. *Mailing Add:* Kellogg Co 235 Porter St Battle Creek MI 49016

SKARSGARD, HARVEY MILTON, b Viscount, Sask, Feb 27, 29; m 59; c 3. PHYSICS. *Educ:* Univ Sask, MSc, 50; McGill Univ, PhD(physics), 55. *Prof Exp:* Seismic interpreter, Explor Dept, Imp Oil, Ltd, 51-53; Nat Res Coun fel nuclear physics, Atomic Energy Res Estab, Eng, 56-57; Nat Res Coun fel plasma physics, European Orgn Nuclear Res, Switz, 57-58; from asst prof to assoc prof, 58-69, PROF PHYSICS, UNIV SASK, 69- *Mem:* Am Phys Soc; Am Asn Physics Teachers; Can Asn Physicists; Can Asn Univ Teachers. *Res:* Plasma physics; beam-plasma interactions; current-generated wave instabilities in toroidal geometry; turbulent heating. *Mailing Add:* Dept of Physics Univ of Sask Saskatoon SK S7N 0N0 Can

SKARSGARD, LLOYD DONALD, b Viscount, Sask, Aug 16, 33; m 60; c 4. RADIATION BIOLOGY, BIOPHYSICS. *Educ:* Univ Sask, BE, 55, MSc, 56; Univ Toronto, PhD(radiation physics), 60. *Prof Exp:* Res assoc biophys, Yale Univ, 60-62, asst prof, 62-67; assoc prof physics, McMaster Univ, 67-72; head biophysics dept, BC Cancer Found, 72-78; HEAD, MED BIOPHYSICS UNIT, BC CANCER RES CTR, 78- *Concurrent Pos:* Consult physicist, Hartford Hosp, Conn, 61-67; head, Batho Biomed Facil, Tri-Univ Meson Facil, Univ BC, & hon prof physics & path, 72- *Mem:* AAAS; Radiation Res Soc; Biophys Soc; Can Asn Physicists. *Res:* X-ray and gamma-ray spectra; radiobiology of pi-mesons and heavy ions; radiation damage and repair; radiosensitization of anoxic cells. *Mailing Add:* BC Cancer Res Ctr 601 W 10th Ave Vancouver BC V5Z 1L3 Can

SKARSTEDT, MARK TEOFIL, b Washington, DC, Dec 5, 43; m 69; c 2. BIOCHEMISTRY. *Educ:* Univ Calif, Los Angeles, BSc, 65; Univ Miami, PhD(biochem), 71. *Prof Exp:* Fel biochem, Imp Col Sci & Technol, London, 71-73; instr med, State Univ NY, Downstate Med Ctr, 73-75; res scientist biochem, 75-77, RES SUPVR BIOCHEM, AMES DIV, MILES LABS, 77- *Mem:* Sigma Xi; AAAS. *Res:* Identification, purification and study of enzymes, chiefly from microbial sources, and development of their application to medical therapy and diagnosis. *Mailing Add:* Ames Div Miles Labs 1127 Myrtle St Elkhart IN 46515

SKARULIS, JOHN ANTHONY, b New Haven, Conn, Feb 18, 17; m 42; c 2. PHYSICAL CHEMISTRY. *Educ:* St John's Univ, NY, BS, 37, MS, 39; NY Univ, PhD(chem), 49. *Prof Exp:* Asst res chemist, Gen Chem Co, 40-42, res chemist, 44-45; supvr & explosive chemist, Gen Chem Defense Corp, 42-44; from instr to assoc prof, 45-54, PROF CHEM, ST JOHN'S UNIV, NY, 54- *Mem:* Am Chem Soc. *Res:* Phase rule studies; inorganic fluorine compounds. *Mailing Add:* Dept of Chem St John's Univ Grand Central & Utopia Pkwy Jamaica NY 11432

SKATRUD, THOMAS JOSEPH, b Manitowoc, Wis, Feb 27, 53. BIOENGINEERING. *Educ:* Univ Wis, Madison, BS, 75, PhD(biochem), 79. *Prof Exp:* Dir biochem, 79-80, VPRES, BIO-TECH RESOURCES, INC, 80- *Mem:* Am Chem Soc; Am Soc Plant Physiologists; AAAS. *Mailing Add:* Bio-Tech Resources, Inc 7th & Marshall Sts Manitowoc WI 54220

SKAU, EVALD LAURIDS, physical organic chemistry, deceased

SKAU, KENNETH ANTHONY, b Chicago, Ill, Apr 18, 47; m 72; c 1. PHARMACOLOGY. *Educ:* Ohio State Univ, BS, 70, PhD(pharm), 77. *Prof Exp:* Trainee pharmacol, May Grad Sch Med, 77-80; instr, 79-80; RES ASST PROF PHARMACOL, COL PHARM, UNIV UTAH, 80- *Mem:* Soc Neurosci; AAAS; Sigma Xi; NY Acad Sci. *Res:* Pharmacology, biochemistry and neurobiology of acetylcholinesterase molecular forms and pathological conditions related to aberrations of these forms; mechanisms of muscle and nerve diseases. *Mailing Add:* Col Pharm Univ Utah Salt Lake City UT 84112

SKAUEN, DONALD M, b Newton, Mass, May 14, 16; m 42; c 2. PHARMACY. *Educ:* Mass Col Pharm, BS, 38, MS, 42; Purdue Univ, PhD(pharm), 49. *Prof Exp:* Asst, Mass Col Pharm, 38-40; chief pharmacist, Children's Med Ctr, Boston, 40-46; asst, Purdue Univ, 46-48; from asst prof to assoc prof, 48-58, prof, 58-79, EMER PROF PHARM, UNIV CONN, 79- *Mem:* Am Soc Hosp Pharmacists; Am Pharmaceut Asn. *Res:* Ultrasound and radioisotopes in pharmacy research; pharmaceutical research and development. *Mailing Add:* 16 Storrs Heights Rd Storrs CT 06268

SKAVARIL, RUSSELL VINCENT, b Omaha, Nebr, Dec 6, 36; m 60; c 4. GENETICS. *Educ:* Univ Omaha, BA, 58; Creighton Univ, MT, 59; Ohio State Univ, MSc, 60, PhD(zool), 64. *Prof Exp:* Assoc prof, 64-77, PROF GENETICS, STATIST & COMPUT APPLN, OHIO STATE UNIV, 77- *Mem:* Am Genetic Asn; Biomet Soc. *Res:* Use of computers in biology. *Mailing Add:* Dept of Genetics Ohio State Univ 484 W 12th Ave Columbus OH 43210

SKAVDAHL, R(ICHARD) E(ARL), b Detroit, Mich, Nov 24, 34; m 59; c 3. NUCLEAR ENGINEERING. *Educ:* Mass Inst Technol, SB, 56, ScD(nuclear eng), 62; Univ Mich, MSE, 57. *Prof Exp:* Res engr, Am Metal Prod Co, Mich, 58-60; sr engr, Gen Elec Co, Wash, 62-64, mgr fuel element design & eval, 64-65; mgr fuel element design & eval, Pac Northwest Labs, Battelle Mem Inst, 65-66; proj engr, Fast Ceramic Reactor Develop Prog, 66-69, proj engr demonstration plant develop, 69-70, mgr develop & test progs, 70-73, mgr Clinch River proj, 73-78, mgr, Boiling Water Reactor 4 Proj, 78-79, MGR, BOILING WATER REACTOR 4 & 5 PROJS, GEN ELEC CO, 79- *Mem:* Am Nuclear Soc. *Res:* Nuclear power reactor design, development and project management. *Mailing Add:* Domestic BWR Proj Gen Elec Co 175 Curtner Ave San Jose CA 95125

SKAVENSKI, ALEXANDER ANTHONY, b East Liverpool, Ohio, Jan 27, 43; m 67; c 2. PSYCHOPHYSIOLOGY, NEUROPHYSIOLOGY. *Educ:* Univ Md, BS, 65, PhD(psychol), 70. *Prof Exp:* Fel biomed eng, Johns Hopkins Univ, 70-72; asst prof, 72-75, assoc prof, 75-80, PROF PSYCHOL, NORTHEASTERN UNIV, 80- *Concurrent Pos:* Vis scholar, Univ Calif, Berkeley, 78-79. *Mem:* AAAS; Asn Res Vision & Opthal; Soc Neurosci; Sigma Xi. *Res:* Eye movement control and the consequence of eye movement on vision and visual space perception. *Mailing Add:* Dept Psychol 282 NI Bldg Northeastern Univ 360 Huntington Ave Boston MA 02115

SKEAN, JAMES DAN, b Kenova, WVa, Feb 19, 32; m 55; c 4. MICROBIOLOGY. *Educ:* Berea Col, BS, 56; Univ Tenn, MS, 59, PhD(microbiol), 66. *Prof Exp:* Res asst dairying, Univ Tenn, 56-66; asst prof, 66-70, assoc prof, 70-80, PROF BIOL, WESTERN KY UNIV, 80- *Mem:* AAAS; Am Soc Microbiol. *Res:* Influence of psychophilic bacteria on quality of milk and dairy products; use of autogenous vaccines in control of staphylococcal bovine mastitis. *Mailing Add:* Dept of Biol Western Ky Univ Bowling Green KY 42101

SKEATH, J EDWARD, b Williamsport, Pa, June 12, 36; m 62; c 2. MATHEMATICS. *Educ:* Swarthmore Col, BA, 58; Univ Ill, MA, 60, PhD(math), 63. *Prof Exp:* Instr math, Cornell Univ, 63-65; asst prof, 65-71, from actg dean to dean men, 70-75, assoc prof, 71-78, PROF MATH, SWARTHMORE COL, 78-, CHMN MATH DEPT, 81- *Mem:* Am Math Soc; Math Asn Am. *Res:* Riemann surface theory; potential theory. *Mailing Add:* Dept of Math Swarthmore Col Swarthmore PA 19081

SKEELES, JOHN KIRKPATRICK, b Alexander, La, June 27, 45; m 67; c 4. VETERINARY MEDICINE, MICROBIOLOGY. *Educ:* Okla State Univ, BS, 67, DVM, 69; Univ Ga, MS, 77, PhD(microbiol), 78, Am Col Vet Microbiologists, dipl. *Prof Exp:* Vet, US Army, 69-75; vet med resident microbiol, Univ Ga, 75-78; ASST PROF POULTRY DIS, UNIV ARK, 78- *Mem:* Am Vet Med Asn; Am Asn Avian Pathologists; Sigma Xi; Am Col Vet Microbiologists. *Res:* Viral diseases of poultry. *Mailing Add:* Dept of Animal Sci Univ of Ark Fayetteville AR 72701

SKEEN, JAMES NORMAN, b Knoxville, Tenn, Feb 23, 42; m 66. FOREST ECOLOGY, TERRESTRIAL COMMUNITY ECOLOGY. *Educ:* Maryville Col, Tenn, BS, 64; Univ Ga, MS, 66, PhD(bot ecol), 69. *Prof Exp:* Asst prof biol, Mercer Univ, Atlanta, 69-70, actg chmn dept, 70-71; ECOLOGIST, FERNBANK SCI CTR, 72- *Concurrent Pos:* Consult, Environ Sci Div, Oak Ridge Nat Lab, 76-77; adj assoc prof, Dept Biol, Emory Univ, 78-; sci adv bd, Marshall Forest Nature Conserv, 80- *Mem:* Ecol Soc Am; Torrey Bot Club. *Res:* Community analysis and system maturity; regeneration dynamics; micrometeorology; selection and evaluation of biomass fuel species. *Mailing Add:* Fernbank Sci Ctr 156 Heaton Park Dr Atlanta GA 30307

SKEEN, LESLIE CARLISLE, b Dearborn, Mich, Feb 28, 42; m 63; c 3. NEUROANATOMY, COMPARATIVE NEUROLOGY. *Educ:* Fla State Univ, PhD(psychobiol), 72. *Prof Exp:* Fel anat, Duke Univ Med Ctr, 73-76, asst prof med res, 76-77; ASST PROF NEUROSCI & PSYCHOL, UNIV DEL, 77- *Concurrent Pos:* Prin investr, Brain Res Lab, Univ Del, 77- *Mem:* AAAS; Am Asn Anatomists; Soc Neurosci; Sigma Xi. *Res:* Evolutionary, developmental, and structural aspects of the vertebrate olfactory system, and its contributions to complex behavioral patterns. *Mailing Add:* Inst Neurosci Univ Del Newark DE 19711

SKEES, HUGH BENEDICT, b Elizabethtown, Ky, Sept 6, 27; m 56; c 7. APPLIED CHEMISTRY. *Educ:* St Louis Univ, BS, 54, MS, 63. *Prof Exp:* Chemist, Petrolite Corp, 56-62; proj engr explor res, Standard Register Co, 62-64, supvr, 64-67; tech dir, Wallace Bus Forms Inc, 67-70; appl res mgr, 70-80, PRINTING PROD RES MGR, STANDARD REGISTER CO, 80- *Mem:* AAAS; Am Chem Soc; Int Bus Forms Inst. *Res:* Petroleum waxes and derivatives; application of waxes in packaging, polishes and carbon paper; business forms technology; printing; carbon paper; adhesives; coating technology; chemical and instrumental analysis; physical testing; instrument design; test development. *Mailing Add:* Standard Regist Co LTB PO Box 1167 Dayton OH 45401

SKEGGS, LEONARD TUCKER, JR, b Fremont, Ohio, June 9, 18; m 41; c 3. BIOCHEMISTRY. *Educ:* Youngstown Univ, AB, 40; Western Reserve Univ, MS, 42, PhD(biochem), 48; Am Bd Clin Chem, dipl. *Hon Degrees:* DSc, Youngstown Univ, 60. *Prof Exp:* Res fel clin biochem, Case Western Reserve Univ, 48-49, from instr to sr instr biochem, 50-52, from asst prof to assoc prof, 52-69; chief, Biochem Sect & Hypertension Res Lab, 47-68, DIR HYPERTENSION RES LAB, VET ADMIN HOSP, CLEVELAND, 68-, MED INVESTR HYPERTENSION, 76-; PROF BIOCHEM, CASE WESTERN RESERVE UNIV, 69- *Honors & Awards:* Flemming Award, 57; Van Slyke Medal, 63; Am Chem Soc Award, 66; Ames Award, 66; Middleton Award, 68; Stouffer Award, 68; Bendetti-Pichler Award Microchem, 71; John Scott Award, 72; Cleveland Award Artificial Organs, 78. *Mem:* Am Chem Soc; Am Soc Biol Chem; fel Am Asn Clin Chem; fel NY Acad Sci. *Res:* Hypertension; automatic chemical analysis; multiple automatic analysis. *Mailing Add:* Hypertension Res Lab Vet Admin Hosp Cleveland OH 44106

SKEHAN, JAMES WILLIAM, b Houlton, Maine, Apr 25, 23. GEOLOGY, TECTONICS. *Educ:* Boston Col, AB, 46, AM, 47; Weston Col, PhL, 47, STB, 54, STL, 55; Harvard Univ, AM, 51, PhD(geol), 53. *Hon Degrees:* DHumL, St Joseph's Col, 78. *Prof Exp:* Asst prof geophys, 56-61, from asst dir to assoc dir, Weston Observ, 56-72, actg dir, 73-74, chmn dept geol, 58-68, assoc prof geophys & geol, 62-68, chmn dept geol & geophys, 68-70, dir environ ctr, 70-72, PROF GEOPHYS & GEOL, BOSTON COL, 68-, DIR WESTON OBSERV, ENERGY RES CTR, 73- *Concurrent Pos:* Chmn, Eng Geol Div, Geol Soc Am, 75; dir & proj mgr, Narragansett Basin Coal Proj, 76- *Mem:* AAAS; Geol Soc Am; Nat Asn Geol Teachers (pres, 71-72); Am Geophys Union; Geol Soc London. *Res:* Geotectonics, origin and development of the earth's crust with special reference to the origin of mountains of Eastern North America and Western Europe; origin and evolution of metamorphic coal basins. *Mailing Add:* Weston Observ Energy Res Ctr Concord Rd Weston MA 02193

SKEIST, IRVING, b Worcester, Mass, Apr 9, 15; m 39; c 4. POLYMER CHEMISTRY. *Educ:* Worcester Polytech Inst, BS, 35; Polytech Inst Brooklyn, MS, 43, PhD(polymer chem), 49. *Prof Exp:* Res chemist, Celanese Corp Am, 37-51; tech dir, Newark Paraffine Paper Co, 51-53 & Am Molding Powder, 53; mkt specialist, Gering Prod, Inc, 53-54; CONSULT & PRES, SKEIST LABS, INC, 54- *Mem:* Am Chem Soc; Soc Plastics Indust; Soc Plastics Engrs; Com Develop Asn; Chem Mkt Res Asn. *Res:* Epoxy resins; polymers; plastics; adhesives; coatings; fibers. *Mailing Add:* Skeist Labs Inc 112 Naylon Ave Livingston NJ 07039

SKELCEY, JAMES STANLEY, b Saginaw, Mich, Sept 26, 33; m 55; c 3. INORGANIC CHEMISTRY. *Educ:* Univ Detroit, BS, 56; Mich State Univ, PhD(chem), 61. *Prof Exp:* Proj leader, 61-72, res specialist, 72-79, RES LEADER, INORG RES & SEMIPLANTS, DOW CHEM CO, 79- *Mem:* Am Chem Soc; Sigma Xi. *Res:* Brine chemicals; transition metals; inorganic fluids and polymers; metal-organic compounds; metal hydrides. *Mailing Add:* 6015 Sturgeon Creek Pkwy Midland MI 48640

SKELL, PHILIP S, b New York, NY, Dec 30, 18; m 48; c 4. ORGANIC CHEMISTRY. *Educ:* City Col, BS, 38; Columbia Univ, MA, 41; Duke Univ, PhD(chem), 42; Lewis Col, LLD, 65. *Prof Exp:* Instr chem, City Col, 38-39; asst, North Regional Res Lab, USDA, Ill, 42-43; res assoc antibiotics, Univ Ill, 43-46; instr chem, Univ Chicago, 46-47; asst prof, Univ Portland, 47-52; from asst prof to prof, 52-74, EVAN PUGH PROF CHEM, PA STATE UNIV, 74- *Concurrent Pos:* Committeeman, Nat Res Coun; NSF Sr Scientist Award, 61; Guggenheim fel, 68; Alexander von Humboldt Found Sr Scientist award, 74-75. *Mem:* Nat Acad Sci; NY Acd Sci; Am Chem Soc; Royal Soc Chem. *Res:* Free radicals; carbenes; methylenes; carbonium ions; nonmetal atomic chemistry; ground and excited states; transition metal atomic chemistry. *Mailing Add:* 220 Whitmore Lab Chem Dept Pa State Univ University Park PA 16802

SKELLEY, DEAN SUTHERLAND, b Melrose, Mass, Mar 27, 38; m 66; c 4. ENDOCRINOLOGY, CLINICAL CHEMISTRY. *Educ:* Bates Col, BS, 60; Ohio State Univ, MS, 65, PhD(physiol), 68. *Prof Exp:* Dir steroid lab, Col Vet Med, Ohio State Univ, 68-70; asst prof obstet & gynec & assoc dir reprod res lab, Baylor Col Med, 70-77; CLIN BIOCHEMIST, DEPT PATH, MEM HOSP SYST, HOUSTON, 77-, CONSULT RADIOIMMUNOASSAY, 74- *Concurrent Pos:* Consult biol diag prod, AMF, Inc, 73-; consult, Ctr Dis Control, 74-76; exec ed, Ligand Rev, 79-; pres, Tech & Prof Serv, Inc, 79- *Mem:* Am Asn Clin Chem. *Res:* Radioimmunoassay of steroids, polypeptide hormones and pharmacological agents; competitive protein binding and radioreceptor assays; ligand assays. *Mailing Add:* Dept Path Mem Hosp 7600 Beechnut Houston TX 77074

SKELLEY, GEORGE CALVIN, JR, b Boise City, Okla, Jan 28, 37; m 58; c 2. ANIMAL SCIENCE. *Educ:* Panhandle Agr & Mech Col, BS, 58; Univ Ky, MS, 60, PhD(meats), 63. *Prof Exp:* Res asst meats, Univ Ky, 58-62; from asst prof to assoc prof, 62-72, PROF ANIMAL SCI, CLEMSON UNIV, 72- *Mem:* Am Meat Sci Asn; Sigma Xi; Am Soc Animal Sci; Inst Food Technol. *Res:* Evaluation of and effect of nutrition on beef and pork carcasses; studies on meat tenderness. *Mailing Add:* Dept of Animal Sci Clemson Univ Clemson SC 29631

SKELLY, DAVID W, b Buffalo, NY, Dec 9, 38; m 62; c 4. THIN FILM TECHNOLOGY, VACUUM DEPOSITION TECHNIQUES. *Educ:* Canisius Col, BS, 60; Univ Notre Dame, PhD(phys chem), 65. *Prof Exp:* PHYS CHEMIST, GEN ELEC RES & DEVELOP LAB, 65- *Concurrent Pos:* Fel, Univ Notre Dame, 65. *Res:* Thin film deposition processes; sensor technology; liquid crystal display technology; electroluminescent displays; radiation effects in condensed matter. *Mailing Add:* Gen Elec Res & Develop Lab PO Box 8 Schenectady NY 12301

SKELLY, JEROME PHILIP, SR, b Vermillion Twp, Ill, Dec 15, 32; m 57; c 3. BIOPHARMACEUTICS. *Educ:* Wayne State Univ, BS, 64, MS, 66, PhD(chem), 69. *Prof Exp:* Res assoc coated abrasives, Mich Abrasive Co, 58-59, head lab, 59-63; res asst connective tissue res, Wayne State Univ, 63-68; chemist, Bur Med, Food & Drug Admin, 68-72, dir clin res br, Bur Drugs, 72-74, chmn bioavailability comt, 73-74; scholar, Sch Pharm, Univ Calif, 74-75; chief, Pharmacokinetics & Biopharmaceut Br, 75-79, DEP DIR, DIV BIOPHARMACEUT, BUR DRUGS, FOOD & DRUG ADMIN, 79- *Mem:* Sigma Xi; Am Soc Clin Pharmacol & Therapeut; Acad Pharmaceut Sci; Am Chem Soc; NY Acad Sci. *Res:* Drug bioavailability, absorption, disposition, metabolism, elimination; drug dosage regimen; analysis of drug in physiological fluids; kinetic data analysis, especially in toxicity and special populations. *Mailing Add:* Pharmacokinetics & Biopharmaceut 5600 Fishers Lane Rockville MD 20857

SKELLY, NORMAN EDWARD, b Minneapolis, Minn, Nov 27, 28; m 53; c 6. ANALYTICAL CHEMISTRY, PHYSICAL CHEMISTRY. *Educ:* Col St Thomas, BS, 51; Univ Iowa, MS, 53, PhD, 55. *Prof Exp:* ASSOC SCIENTIST, DOW CHEM CO, 55- *Mem:* Am Chem Soc; Sigma Xi. *Res:* Liquid chromatography. *Mailing Add:* 2007 Sharon Ct Midland MI 48640

SKELSEY, JAMES JEREMIAH, b Los Angeles, Calif, Feb 18, 35; m 60; c 2. ENTOMOLOGY. *Educ:* Calif State Polytech Col, BS, 56; Univ Calif, Davis, MS, 59; Cornell Univ, PhD(entom), 68. *Prof Exp:* Tech serv to sales rep insecticide develop, Niagara Chem Div, FMC Corp, 60-65; ENTOMOLOGIST, BIOL SCI RES CTR, SHELL DEVELOP CO, 68- *Mem:* Entom Soc Am. *Res:* Discovery and development of agricultural pesticides. *Mailing Add:* Shell Develop Co PO Box 4248 Modesto CA 95352

SKELTON, BOBBY JOE, b Clemson, SC, Feb 11, 35; m 56; c 4. HORTICULTURE, PLANT PHYSIOLOGY. *Educ:* Clemson Univ, BS, 57, MS, 60; Va Polytech Inst, PhD(plant physiol), 66. *Prof Exp:* From instr to assoc prof, 57-75, PROF HORT, CLEMSON UNIV, 75- *Mem:* Am Soc Plant Physiol; Am Soc Hort Sci. *Res:* Mineral nutrition of horticultural crops; pomology. *Mailing Add:* Dept of Hort Clemson Univ Clemson SC 29631

SKELTON, EARL FRANKLIN, b Hackensack, NJ, Apr 8, 40; m 62; c 2. SOLID STATE PHYSICS. *Educ:* Fairleigh Dickinson Univ, BS, 62; Rensselaer Polytech Inst, PhD(physics), 67. *Prof Exp:* Nat Acad Sci-Nat Res Coun res assoc solid state physics, Solid State Div, 67-68, res physicist, 68-76, HEAD, PHASE TRANSFORMATION SECT, US NAVAL RES LAB, 76- *Concurrent Pos:* Lectr, Prince George's Community Col, 68-74; assoc prof lectr, George Washington Univ, 74-79; prof lectr, 79-; lectr, Univ Md, 75-; liaison scientist, Off Naval Res, Tokyo, 78; vis scholar, Stanford Univ, 80-81. *Mem:* Fel Am Phys Soc; Am Crystallog Asn; Am Asn Physics Teachers; Sigma Xi; Am Asn Univ Professors. *Res:* Theoretical and experimental investigation of response of materials to conditions of extreme pressure and temperature; high technitium superconductors; selected III-V and II-VI compounds; phase transformation toughening mechanisms in ceramics; conventional x-ray scattering techniques and synchrotron produced radiation for very rapid in situ measurements. *Mailing Add:* US Naval Res Lab Code 6683 Overlook Ave SE Washington DC 20375

SKELTON, J(ESSE) D, b Wichita, Kans, Apr 24, 23; m 44; c 3. ELECTRICAL ENGINEERING. *Educ:* Kans State Univ, BS, 48; Okla State Univ, MS, 54. *Prof Exp:* Res engr, Carter Oil Co, Standard Oil Co, NJ, 48-58; sect head interpretation res, Jersey Prod Res Co, 58-60, div mgr geophys, 60-63, vpres explor, 63-64; vpres explor, Esso Prod Res Co, 64-67; asst mgr, Eastern Marine Div, Humble Oil & Refining Co, 67-69; MGR EXPLOR DATA PROCESSING CTR, EXXON CO, USA, 69- *Mem:* Soc Explor Geophysicists (pres, 74-75); Am Asn Petrol Geol; European Asn Explor Geophysicists; Asn Prof Geol Scientists; Am Geol Inst (pres, 75-76). *Res:* Petroleum exploration seismic methods and equipment; management and operation of large digital computers for analysis of exploration data. *Mailing Add:* Explor Data Processing Ctr Exxon Co USA PO Box 2180 Houston TX 77001

SKELTON, MARILYN MAE, b Coffeyville, Kans, May 3, 36; m 58; c 3. FOOD SCIENCE, BIOCHEMISTRY. *Educ:* Kans State Univ, BS, 57, MS, 58; Univ Wyo, PhD(biochem), 70. *Prof Exp:* Instr res foods & nutrit, Dept Foods & Nutrit, Kans State Univ, 59-62; asst prof foods & nutrit, Div Home Econ, Univ Wyo, 62-69; teacher sci & math, Army Educ Ctr, US Army, Ger, 71-72, educ counsr couns & admin, 72-74; asst prof foods & nutrit, Kans State Univ, 75-77; ASST PROF HOTEL & RESTAURANT MGT, UNIV DENVER, 78- *Mem:* Inst Food Technologists. *Res:* Relationship of chemical composition and histology to meat tenderness; alkaline degradation of pectin; relationship of chemical and physical properties of fruits and vegetables to palatability. *Mailing Add:* Sch of Hotel & Restaurant Mgt Univ of Denver Denver CO 80208

SKELTON, THOMAS EUGENE, b Six Mile, SC, Dec 15, 30; m 53; c 3. ENTOMOLOGY. *Educ:* Clemson Univ, BS, 53, MS, 56; Univ Ga, PhD(entom), 69. *Prof Exp:* Asst entomologist, 56-60, from asst prof to assoc prof entom, 69-76, PROF ENTOM, CLEMSON UNIV, 76- *Mem:* Entom Soc Am; Sigma Xi. *Res:* Economic entomology; insects affecting apples, peaches and vegetables. *Mailing Add:* Dept of Entom Clemson Univ Clemson SC 29631

SKEWIS, JOHN DAVID, b Lancaster, Pa, Dec 18, 32; m 57; c 3. PHYSICAL CHEMISTRY. *Educ:* Pa State Univ, BA, 54; Lehigh Univ, MS, 57, PhD(chem), 59. *Prof Exp:* Asst chem, Lehigh Univ, 54-56; fel, Univ Southern Calif, 59-60; res chemist, Res Ctr, US Rubber Co, NJ, 60-68, sr res scientist, 68-72, mgr polymer physics res, 72-78, MGR CORP TIRE RES, RES CTR, UNIROYAL, INC, 78- *Mem:* Am Chem Soc. *Res:* Surface and colloid chemistry. *Mailing Add:* Res Ctr Uniroyal Inc Middlebury CT 06749

SKIBBE, MARTIN OTTO, b Danzig, Ger, Apr 24, 23; US citizen; m 63; c 1. PHARMACEUTICAL CHEMISTRY. *Educ:* Mass Col Pharm, BS, 55; Purdue Univ, MS, 57, PhD(pharmaceut chem), 59. *Prof Exp:* Sr res chemist, Armour Pharmaceut Co, 59-79; ASSOC RES FEL, REVLON HEALTH CARE GROUP, 79- *Mem:* Am Chem Soc. *Res:* Peptide chemistry; anti-inflammatory agents; phospholipids; hormones. *Mailing Add:* Revlon Health Care Group Scarsdale Rd Tuckahoe NY 10530

SKIBINSKY, MORRIS, b New York, NY, Aug 3, 25; m 51; c 2. MATHEMATICAL STATISTICS. *Educ:* City Col, BS, 48; Univ NC, MA, 51, PhD(math statist), 54. *Prof Exp:* Asst prof math & statist, Purdue Univ, 54-55; vis asst prof math statist, Mich State Univ, 56; from asst prof to assoc prof math & statist, Purdue Univ, 57-62; vis assoc prof statist, Univ Minn, Minneapolis, 62-63; mathematician, Brookhaven Nat Lab, 63-68; PROF STATIST, UNIV MASS, AMHERST, 68- *Concurrent Pos:* Vis lectr, Univ Calif, 61-62; vis prof statist, Fla State Univ, 81-82. *Mem:* Math Asn Am; Inst Math Statist. *Res:* Probability; decision theory; theory of moment spaces. *Mailing Add:* Dept of Math & Statist Univ of Mass Amherst MA 01002

SKIDMORE, DUANE R(ICHARD), b Seattle, Wash, Mar 5, 27; m 62; c 4. CHEMICAL ENGINEERING, PHYSICAL CHEMISTRY. *Educ:* Univ NDak, BS, 49; Univ Ill, Urbana, MS, 51; St Louis Univ, PhL, 56; Fordham Univ, PhD(phys chem), 60. *Prof Exp:* AEC asst chem eng, Univ Ill, Urbana, 51; instr, Creighton Prep, Nebr, 60; Petrol Res Fund/AEC fel, Fordham Univ, 60; res chemist, E I du Pont de Nemours & Co, 61-64; from asst prof to assoc prof chem eng, Univ NDak, 64-72, actg dean, Col Eng, 68-69; prof, Sch Mines, WVa Univ, 72-78; PROF CHEM ENG, OHIO STATE UNIV, 78- *Concurrent Pos:* Consult coal utilization & environ qual control & sanit chem. *Mem:* AAAS; Am Chem Soc; Am Inst Chem Engrs. *Res:* Kinetics of gas-phase reactions; reactor design; coal utilization. *Mailing Add:* Dept of Chem Eng Ohio State Univ Columbus OH 43210

SKIDMORE, EDWARD LYMAN, b Delta, Utah, Jan 21, 33; m 53; c 6. SOIL CONSERVATION, AGRONOMY. *Educ:* Utah State Univ, BS, 58; Okla State Univ, PhD(soil sci), 63. *Prof Exp:* Assoc prof, 70-75, PROF AGRON, KANS STATE UNIV, 75-; RES SOIL SCIENTIST, WIND EROSION LAB, SCI & EDUC ADMIN-AGR RES, USDA, 63- *Mem:* Am Soc Agron; Soil Sci Soc Am; Int Soc Soil Sci; Soil Conserv Soc Am. *Res:* Soil plant water relations; soil physics; wind erosion; agricultural micrometeorology. *Mailing Add:* Dept of Agron Kans State Univ Manhattan KS 66506

SKIDMORE, WESLEY DEAN, b Pocatello, Idaho, Jan 18, 31; m 52; c 5. BIOCHEMISTRY, RADIOBIOLOGY. *Educ:* Univ Utah, BS, 53; George Washington Univ, MS, 58; Univ Calif, San Francisco, PhD(biochem), 65. *Prof Exp:* Prin investr radiobiol, Armed Forces Radiobiol Res Inst, 65-69, proj dir, 70-74; CHEMIST, BUR FOODS, FOOD & DRUG ADMIN, 74- *Mem:* Am Chem Soc; Radiation Res Soc. *Mailing Add:* Bur Foods Food & Drug Admin 200 C St SW Washington DC 20204

SKIFF, PETER DUANE, b Pittsburgh, Pa, Dec 16, 38; m 65. PHYSICS. *Educ:* Univ Calif, Berkeley, AB, 59; Univ Houston, MS, 61; La State Univ, PhD(physics), 66. *Prof Exp:* Instr, La State Univ, 63-65; from asst prof to assoc prof, 65-75, PROF PHYSICS, BARD COL, 75- *Concurrent Pos:* Vis instr, Marist Col, 67-68. *Mem:* Am Phys Soc; Am Asn Physics Teachers; History Sci Soc; Archaeol Inst Am. *Res:* Foundations of quantum theory; quantum statistical mechanics; archaeometry; history of science; philosophy of science; quantum field theory. *Mailing Add:* Bard Col Annandale on Hudson NY 12504

SKILES, JAMES J(EAN), b St Louis, Mo, Oct 16, 28; m 48; c 3. ELECTRICAL ENGINEERING. *Educ:* Washington Univ, BSEE, 48; Mo Sch Mines, MSEE, 51; Univ Wis, PhD, 54. *Prof Exp:* Engr, Union Elec Co, Mo, 48-49; instr elec eng, Mo Sch Mines, 49-51; instr, 51-54, from asst prof to assoc prof, 54-62, assoc chmn dept, 63-67, chmn dept, 67-72, dir, Univ-Indust Res Prog, 72-75, PROF ELEC ENG, UNIV WIS-MADISON, 62-, DIR, ENERGY RES CTR, 75-, WIS ELEC UTILITIES RES FOUND PROF ENERGY ENG, 75- *Concurrent Pos:* Consult, Allis-Chalmers Mfg Co, 56-62, Space Technol Labs, Inc, 60-63 & Astronaut Corp Am, Wis, 66-69. *Mem:* Am Soc Eng Educ; Inst Elec & Electronics Engrs; Am Inst Navig; Arctic Inst NAm; Nat Soc Prof Engrs. *Res:* Computer applications; power systems analysis; energy conservation and systems. *Mailing Add:* Dept of Elec & Comput Eng Univ Wis-Madison 1415 Johnson Dr Madison WI 53706

SKILLING, DARROLL DEAN, b Carson City, Mich, June 18, 31; m 51; c 3. PLANT PATHOLOGY, FORESTRY. *Educ:* Univ Mich, BS, 53, MFor, 54; Univ Minn, PhD(plant path), 68. *Prof Exp:* Res forester, Lake States Forest Exp Sta, 54-61, RES PLANT PATHOLOGIST, NCENT FOREST EXP STA, US FOREST SERV, 61- *Concurrent Pos:* Assoc prof, Dept Plant Path, Univ Minn, 69- *Mem:* Am Phytopath Soc. *Res:* Epidemiology of conifer tree diseases; fungicide screening and control of foliage tree diseases; Scleroderris canker, Lophodermium needlecast, brown spot disease and Cylindrocladium root rot. *Mailing Add:* NCent Forest Exp Sta US Forest Serv Folwell Ave St Paul MN 55108

SKILLING, HUGH, b San Diego, Calif, Sept 2, 05; m 32; c 1. ELECTRICAL ENGINEERING. *Educ:* Stanford Univ, AB, 26, PhD(elec eng), 31; Mass Inst Technol, SM, 30. *Prof Exp:* Engr, Southern Calif Edison Co, 27-29; instr elec mach, 29, from instr to assoc prof elec eng, 31-42, actg head dept, 41-44, exec head dept, 44-64, actg dean eng, 44-46, PROF ELEC ENG, STANFORD UNIV, 42- *Concurrent Pos:* Consult, US Secy War, Bikini, 46, Dartmouth Col & Univ Hawaii, 57, Univ Alaska, 64 & Univ Wash, 66; vis prof, Cambridge Univ, 51-52 & 65; lectr, Coun Higher Sci Invests, Madrid, 52 & Univ Chile, 57. *Honors & Awards:* Nat Award & Teaching Medal, Inst Elec & Electronics Engrs, 65. *Mem:* AAAS; fel Inst Elec & Electronics Engrs. *Res:* Electric circuits; electric power transmission; transient electric currents; fundamentals of electric waves; preparation of doctoral students for engineering teaching. *Mailing Add:* Dept of Elec Eng Stanford Univ Stanford CA 94305

SKILLING, JOHN BOWER, b Los Angeles, Calif, Oct 8, 21; m 43; c 3. STRUCTURAL ENGINEERING. *Educ:* Univ Wash, BS, 47. *Prof Exp:* Design engr, W H Witt Co, 47-54; SR PARTNER STRUCT & CIVIL ENG, SKILLING, HELLE, CHRISTIANSEN, ROBERTSON, 54- *Concurrent Pos:* Mem adv comt, Am Inst Steel Construct, 67-68; mem bldg res adv bd, Nat Acad Eng, 65-; mem Seismic Design Comt, Nat Acad Eng & Nat Res Coun. *Mem:* Nat Acad Eng; fel Am Soc Civil Engrs; Int Asn Bridge & Struct Eng; Int Asn Shell Struct. *Mailing Add:* Skilling Helle Christiansen Robertson 1215 Fourth Ave Suite 2200 Seattle WA 98161

SKILLMAN, ROBERT ALLEN, b Peoria, Ill, Aug 21, 41. FISHERIES MANAGEMENT, POPULATION ECOLOGY. *Educ:* Bradley Univ, BA, 63; Iowa State Univ, MS, 65; Univ Calif, Davis, PhD(zool), 69. *Prof Exp:* Fishery biologist, Nat Marine Fisheries Serv, Honolulu Lab, 69-79; tuna specialist, UN Food & Agr Orgn, 79-80; FISHERY BIOLOGIST, NAT MARINE FISHERIES SERV, HONOLULU LAB, 81- *Mem:* Am Fisheries Soc; Ecol Soc Am. *Res:* Quantitative analysis of the population dynamics of marine fishes, including but not limited to production model analysis and the estimation of population parameters for growth, mortality, and recruitment. *Mailing Add:* Nat Marine Fisheries Serv Lab PO Box 3830 Honolulu HI 96812

SKILLMAN, THOMAS G, b Cincinnati, Ohio, Jan 7, 25; m 47; c 2. MEDICINE. *Educ:* Baldwin-Wallace Col, BS, 46; Univ Cincinnati, MD, 49. *Prof Exp:* Instr med, Univ Cincinnati, 54-57; asst prof, Ohio State Univ, 57-61; from assoc prof to prof, Creighton Univ, 61-67; PROF MED, OHIO STATE UNIV, 67-, KURTZ PROF ENDOCRINOL, 74- *Mem:* Am Diabetes Asn; Am Fedn Clin Res. *Res:* Clinical diabetes. *Mailing Add:* Ohio State Univ Hosp Clin 456 Clinic Dr Columbus OH 43210

SKINNER, BRIAN JOHN, b Wallaroo, SAustralia, Dec 15, 28; nat US; m 54; c 3. GEOCHEMISTRY, ECONOMIC GEOLOGY. *Educ:* Univ Adelaide, BSc, 50; Harvard Univ, AM, 52, PhD, 55. *Prof Exp:* Lectr crystallog, Univ Adelaide, 55-58; res geologist, US Geol Surv, 58-62, chief, Br Exp Geochem & Mineral, 62-66; prof geol, 66-72, chmn dept geol & geophys, 67-72, EUGENE HIGGINS PROF, YALE UNIV, 72- *Concurrent Pos:* Ed, Econ Geol, 70-; chmn comt mineral resources & the environ, Nat Acad Sci-Nat Res Coun, 73-75. *Honors & Awards:* McKinsley Mem lectr, Harvard Univ, 78; DuToit Mem lectr, SAfrica, 79; Medal, Soc Econ Geologists, 81. *Mem:* Mineral Soc Am; Geochem Soc (pres, 73); Soc Econ Geologists; Geol Soc Am. *Res:* Phase equilibria in systems containing sulfur; geochemistry of ore deposits. *Mailing Add:* Dept Geol & Geophys Yale Univ New Haven CT 06520

SKINNER, CHARLES GORDON, b Dallas, Tex, Apr 23, 23; m 44; c 2. ORGANIC CHEMISTRY, BIOCHEMISTRY. *Educ:* NTex State Univ, BS, 44, MS, 47; Univ Tex, PhD(org chem), 53. *Prof Exp:* Res chemist, Celanese Corp Am, 49-50; Lilly fel, Univ Tex, 53-54; res scientist, Clayton Found Biochem Inst, 55-64; chmn dept, 69-74, PROF CHEM, NTEX STATE UNIV, 64-, CHMN, DEPT BASIC HEALTH SCI, 79-; asst dean basic sci, 75-79, PROF BIOCHEM, TEX COL OSTEOP MED, 72-, DIR RES, 79- *Concurrent Pos:* Consult eng, AID, Dallas. *Honors & Awards:* Daugherty Award, Am Chem Soc, 78. *Mem:* Am Chem Soc; Am Soc Biol Chem; Sigma Xi; Am Inst Chem. *Res:* Synthesis and biological activity of metabolite antagonists; vitamins; purine and pyrimidines; antitumor agents. *Mailing Add:* Tex Col Osteop Med Camp Bowie at Montgomery Ft Worth TX 76107

SKINNER, DALE DEAN, b Payette, Idaho, July 23, 31; m 56; c 4. UNDERWATER ACOUSTICS, ELECTRICAL ENGINEERING. *Educ:* Univ Idaho, BSEE, 53. *Prof Exp:* Jr engr, 53-54, intermediate res engr, Res Labs, 54-61, res engr, 61-63, fel engr, 63-69, mgr ultrasonic technol, Underwater Acoust, 69-73, FEL ENGR, OCEAN RES & ENERGY CTR, WESTINGHOUSE ELEC CORP, 74- *Mem:* Inst Elec & Electronics Engrs. *Res:* Underwater sound scattering; sonar system and transducer designs; use of ultrasonics for medical diagnostics and nondestructive testing. *Mailing Add:* Ocean Res & Energy Ctr Westinghouse Elec Corp Annapolis MD 21404

SKINNER, DAVID BERNT, b Joliet, Ill, Apr 28, 35; m 56; c 4. SURGERY. *Educ:* Univ Rochester, BA, 58; Yale Univ, MD, 59. *Hon Degrees:* ScD, Univ Rochester, 80. *Prof Exp:* Intern, Mass Gen Hosp, Boston, 59-60, asst resident, 60-64, resident, 65; clin asst prof surg, Univ Tex Med Sch, San Antonio, 66-68; from asst prof to prof, Johns Hopkins Univ, 68-72; DALLAS B PHEMISTER PROF SURG & CHMN DEPT, PRITZKER SCH MED, UNIV CHICAGO, 72- *Concurrent Pos:* Am Cancer Soc fel, Harvard Med Sch, 65, teaching fel, 65; NIH res grants, Johns Hopkins Univ, 68-72, Markle Scholar, 69-74; NIH res grant, Univ Chicago, 72-; sr registr, Frenchay Hosp, Britol, Eng, 63-64; asst chief exp surg, US Air Force Sch Aerospace Med, San Antonio, 66-68; consult surg, Robert B Green Hosp, San Antonio, 66-68, Loch Raven Vet Admin Hosp, 68-72, Good Samaritan Hosp, 68-72, USPHS Hosp, Baltimore, 69-72 & US Naval Med Ctr, Bethesda, 70-72; ed, Current Topics Surg Res, 69-71 & J Surg Res, 72-; dir, Am Bd Surg, 74-80. *Mem:* Am Surg Asn; Soc Univ Surgeons (pres, 79); Soc Surg Chmn (pres, 80-82); Am Asn Thoracic Surg; Soc Vascular Surg. *Res:* Esophageal and upper gastrointestinal physiology and disorders; pulmonary disorders; cardiovascular physiology and artificial circulation. *Mailing Add:* Univ of Chicago Hosps & Clins 950 E 59th St Chicago IL 60637

SKINNER, DOROTHY M, b Newton, Mass, May 22, 30; m 65. MOLECULAR BIOLOGY. *Educ:* Tufts Univ, BS, 52; Harvard Univ, PhD(biol), 58. *Prof Exp:* Asst dir admis, Jackson Col, Tufts Univ, 52-54; USPHS fel, Yale Univ & Brandeis Univ, 58-62; asst prof physiol & biophys, Med Ctr, NY Univ, 62-66; res partic, Oak Ridge Inst Nuclear Studies, 66-68; SR SCIENTIST, OAK RIDGE NAT LAB, 68-; PROF, OAK RIDGE GRAD SCH BIOMED SCI, UNIV TENN, 68- *Concurrent Pos:* Mem molecular biol study sect, NIH, 72-76; assoc ed, Growth, 79-83. *Mem:* Soc Gen Physiol (treas, 73-75); fel AAAS; Am Soc Cell Biol; Am Soc Biol Chem; Soc Develop Biol. *Res:* Macromolecular changes associated with growth and development in Crustacea; satellite DNAs, structure and functions. *Mailing Add:* Biol Div Oak Ridge Nat Lab PO Box Y Oak Ridge TN 37830

SKINNER, G(EORGE) M(ACGILLIVRAY), b Buffalo, NY, Aug 26, 09; m 38; c 1. ENGINEERING PHYSICS. *Educ:* Univ Mich, BS, 33, MS, 34. *Prof Exp:* Res engr, Linde Air Prod Co, Union Carbide & Carbon Corp, 34-40, group leader, 40-48, sect head, 48-56, res supvr, Linde Div, Union Carbide Corp, 56-62, head, Develop Lab Div, 62-69, mgr admin, Linde Div Lab, Tarrytown Tech Ctr, Union Carbide Corp, 69-79; RETIRED. *Mem:* Am Welding Soc; Inst Elec & Electronics Engrs; Am Inst Aeronaut & Astronaut. *Res:* High temperature technique; high frequency dielectrics; metallurgy; method of oxyacetylene cutting; welding arc and gaseous conduction; fluid dynamics; magnetohydrodynamics; high intensity, high pressure arc research. *Mailing Add:* 2100 S Ocean Lane Apt 410 Ft Lauderdale FL 33316

SKINNER, GEORGE T, b Dundee, Scotland, July 22, 23; US citizen; m 52; c 2. ATMOSPHERE DYNAMICS, COMPUTER HARDWARE SYSTEMS. *Educ:* St Andrews Univ, BS, 48; Calif Inst Technol, MS, 49, AE, 51, PhD(aeronaut), 55. *Prof Exp:* Asst res officer aerodyn, Nat Res Coun Can, 51; res engr, 58-63, PRIN AERONAUT ENGR, CALSPAN CORP, 63- *Mem:* Am Phys Soc. *Res:* Atmospheric boundary layer flows; molecular beam research using shock tubes as gas source; radiation from collisionally excited molecules; contained airflow in automobile tires. *Mailing Add:* Calspan Advan Technol Ctr PO Box 400 Buffalo NY 14225

SKINNER, GORDON BANNATYNE, b Winnipeg, Man, Jan 7, 26; nat US; m 52; c 3. PHYSICAL CHEMISTRY. *Educ:* Univ Man, BSc, 47, MSc, 49; Ohio State Univ, PhD(phys chem), 51. *Prof Exp:* Chemist, Monsanto Co, 51-64; assoc prof, 64-67, PROF CHEM, WRIGHT STATE UNIV, 67- *Mem:* Combustion Inst; Am Chem Soc; AAAS. *Res:* Thermodynamic studies of zirconium and titanium; kinetics of gas reactions at high temperatures; application of kinetics to problems in combustion and detonation; computer simulation of complex systems. *Mailing Add:* Dept of Chem Wright State Univ Dayton OH 45435

SKINNER, H CATHERINE W, b Brooklyn, NY, Jan 25, 31; m 54; c 3. MINERALOGY, BIOINORGANIC CHEMISTRY. *Educ:* Mt Holyoke Col, BA, 52; Radcliffe Col, MA, 54; Univ Adelaide, PhD(mineral), 59. *Prof Exp:* Mineralogist crystallog, Harvard Med Sch, 54-55; mineralogist, Nat Inst Arthritis & Metab Dis, 61-65 & Nat Inst Dent Res, 65-66; res assoc molecular biophys & geol, 67-68, res assoc molecular biophys & biochem & surg, 68-72, sr res assoc & lectr surg, 72-75, ASSOC PROF BIOCHEM IN SURG, YALE UNIV, 78-, MASTER, JONATHAN EDWARDS COL, 77- *Concurrent Pos:* Mem insts & spec progs comt, Nat Inst Dent Res, 71-75; mem publ comt, Yale Univ Press, 74-76; Agassiz vis lectr biol, Harvard Univ, 76-77; assoc ed, Am Mineral & counr, Mineral Soc Am, 78-81; co-chmn panel geochemistry of fibrous materials related to health risks, Nat Acad Sci, 79-; vis prof, Biol Dept, Cornell Univ, 81. *Mem:* Fel Mineral Soc Am; Am Crystallog Asn; NY Acad Sci; Int Asn Dental Res; Orthopaedic Res Soc. *Res:* Phase equilibria studies of calcium phosphates; crystal chemistry of the mineral portion of calcified tissues; teeth, bone and invertebrate hard tissues; mineral metabolism; sedimentary carbonate deposits; geochemistry. *Mailing Add:* Jonathan Edwards Col Yale Univ New Haven CT 06520

SKINNER, HENRY THOMAS, b East Sutton, Eng, Sept 24, 07; nat US; m 51; c 1. HORTICULTURE, BOTANY. *Educ:* Cornell Univ, BS, 36, MS, 38; Univ Pa, PhD(bot), 52. *Prof Exp:* Asst propagation, Hiller Nurseries, Eng, 27-29; asst, Arnold Arboretum, Harvard Univ, 29-31; propagator & instr ornamental hort, Cornell Univ, 31-40; cur, Morris Arboretum, Univ Pa, 40-43 & 45-52; dir, US Nat Arboretum, DC, 52-72, collabr, 73-80. *Concurrent Pos:* Lectr, Hort Sch, Barnes Found, Pa, 43 & 48; vpres, Am Hort Coun, 58-59; consult, Morris Arboretum, Univ Pa, 73-79; mem bd trustees, Henry F du Pont Winterthur Mus, 75-80 & corp dir, 80- *Honors & Awards:* Jackson Dawson Medal, Mass Hort Soc, 43; Am Home Achievement Medal, 61; Arthur Hoyt Scott Award, 63; Gold Medal, Am Rhododendron Soc, 65; Colman Res Award, Am Asn Nurserymen, 68; Silver Seal Award, Nat Coun State Garden Clubs, 69; Liberty Hyde Bailey Medal, Am Hort Soc, 72; Gold Medal, Mass Hort Soc, 73. *Mem:* Am Hort Soc (pres, 62); Am Asn Bot Gardens & Arboreta (pres, 47); Am Rodoendron Soc; Royal Hort Soc (vpres, 72-). *Res:* Propagation, hybridization and genetics of azaleas and rhododendrons; distribution and taxonomy of native azaleas; regulatory factors in hardiness of woody temperate plants; environmental biology. *Mailing Add:* 929 Toxaway Dr Hendersonville NC 28739

SKINNER, HUBERT CLAYTON, b Tulsa, Okla, Oct 3, 29; m 58; c 3. GEOLOGY. *Educ:* Univ Okla, BS, 51, MS, 53, PhD(geol), 54. *Prof Exp:* Mus technician, Univ Okla, 51-52, asst geol, 52-53, instr, 53-54; from asst prof to assoc prof, 54-62, PROF GEOL, TULANE UNIV, 62- *Concurrent Pos:* Supvr paleo lab, La Div, Texaco, 54-57; ed, Tulane Studies Geol & Paleont, 62- *Mem:* Fel Geol Soc London; Paleont Soc; Geol Soc Am; Am Asn Petrol Geologists; Brit Palaeont Asn. *Res:* Paleontology; stratigraphy; Cretaceous and Tertiary micropaleontology, paleoecology and stratigraphy of the Gulf Coast; history of geology. *Mailing Add:* 3737 Napoleon Ave New Orleans LA 70125

SKINNER, JAMES ERNEST, b Okmulgee, Okla, Apr 15, 40. NEUROSCIENCES. *Educ:* Pomona Col, BA, 62; Univ Calif, Los Angeles, MA, 64, PhD(physiol), 67. *Prof Exp:* Res physiologist, Univ Calif, Los Angeles & Brain Res Inst, 66-67, asst res physiologist, Ment Health Training Prog grant, 67-68; asst prof, 68-76, ASSOC PROF NEUROL, BAYLOR COL MED, 76- *Concurrent Pos:* Mem, Basic Psychopharmacol/Neuropsychol Res Rev Comt, NIMH. *Mem:* Soc Neurosci; Am EEG Soc. *Res:* Brain mechanisms and behavior. *Mailing Add:* Neurophysiol Sect Dept Neurol Baylor Col of Med MS F 603 Houston TX 77030

SKINNER, JAMES F, b St John, NB, July 19, 40; m 65; c 1. PHYSICAL INORGANIC CHEMISTRY. *Educ:* Williams Col, BA, 61; Yale Univ, MS, 62, PhD(chem), 64. *Prof Exp:* Nat Res Coun Can fel, 65-66; asst prof, 66-74, assoc prof, 74-78, PROF CHEM, WILLIAMS COL, 78- *Concurrent Pos:* Ramsay Mem fel, Univ Col, London, 65-66. *Mem:* Am Chem Soc. *Res:* Properties of electrolytic solutions, especially those involving hydrogen-bonded solvents; preparation and characterization of transition metal complexes of nitrogen-containing heterocylic ligands. *Mailing Add:* Dept of Chem Williams Col Williamstown MA 01267

SKINNER, JAMES STANFORD, b Lucedale, Miss, Sept 22, 36; m 63; c 2. PHYSIOLOGY. *Educ:* Univ Ill, Urbana, BS, 58, MS, 60, PhD(phys educ & physiol), 63. *Prof Exp:* Assoc physiol, Sch Med, George Washington Univ, 64, asst prof lectr, 64-65; res assoc cardiol, Sch Med, Univ Wash, Seattle, 65-66; asst prof, Lab Human Performance Res, Pa State Univ, University Park, 66-70; res assoc, Med Clin, Univ Freiburg, Ger, 70-71; assoc prof phys educ, Univ Montreal & res assoc, Inst Cardiol, 71-77; prof phys educ, Univ Western Ont, 77-82; PROF PHYS EDUC, ARIZ STATE UNIV, 82- *Mem:* Fel Am Col Sports Med (pres-elect, 78-79, pres, 79-80); Can Asn Sports Sci (secy, 76-78); Am Asn Health, Phys Educ & Recreation; fel Am Heart Asn; Am Acad Phys Educ. *Res:* Physiology of exercise, especially pertaining to cardiovascular system; effects of increased physical activity on the course and severity of cardiovascular disorders. *Mailing Add:* Fac of Phys Educ Univ of Western Ont London ON N6A 3K7 Can

SKINNER, JOHN TAYLOR, b Whitesville, Ky, Jan 1, 03; m 26; c 3. CHEMISTRY. *Educ:* Western Ky State Teachers Col, BS, 26; Univ Wis, MS, 28, PhD(agr chem), 32. *Prof Exp:* From instr to asst prof chem, Western Ky State Teachers Col, 26-29; asst agr chem, Univ Wis, 29-32; assoc prof chem, Western Ky State Teachers Col, 32-42; asst chemist, Exp Sta, Univ Ky, 42-45; chief chemist, Grapette Co, 45-55; from asst prof to prof, 55-73, EMER PROF CHEM, TENN TECHNOL UNIV, 73- *Mem:* Am Biol Chem; Am Chem Soc. *Res:* Manganese and arsenic in animal metabolism; determination of benzedrine; biological values of fats and proteins; role of manganese in animal nutrition. *Mailing Add:* 218 E 12th St Cookeville TN 38501

SKINNER, JOSEPH L, b Bartlesville, Okla, Dec 2, 31; m 54; c 2. CHEMICAL ENGINEERING. *Educ:* Okla Baptist Univ, AB, 53; Univ Okla, BS, 56, MS, 58, PhD(chem eng), 62. *Prof Exp:* Res engr, 62-64, sr res engr, 64-66, res group leader, 66-72, STAFF ENGR, CHEM RES, CONTINENTAL OIL CO, 72- *Res:* Aluminum alkyl chemistry; chemical reactor design; high pressure equipment; chemical kinetics; crystallization; sulfation-sulfonation reaction; process development studies; research in production of alcohols and olefins. *Mailing Add:* Chem Res Continental Oil Co Ponca City OK 74601

SKINNER, LINDSAY A, b Chicago, Ill, Mar 28, 38; m 62; c 3. APPLIED MATHEMATICS. *Educ:* Northwestern Univ, BS, 60, PhD, 63. *Prof Exp:* Mem res staff, Int Bus Mach Corp, Calif, 63-64; asst prof math, Purdue Univ, Lafayette, 64-69; chmn dept, 75-78, ASSOC PROF MATH, UNIV WIS-MILWAUKEE, 69- *Mem:* Soc Indust & Appl Math. *Res:* Perturbation theory and asymptotic expansions. *Mailing Add:* Dept of Math Univ of Wis Milwaukee WI 53201

SKINNER, LOREN COURTLAND, II, b Borger, Tex, Aug 16, 40; m 65; c 3. PHYSICS, METALLURGY. *Educ:* Mass Inst Technol, SB, 62, SM, 64, PhD(metall), 65. *Prof Exp:* Res assoc metall, Mass Inst Technol, 65-66; physicist, Integrated Circuits Ctr, Motorola, Inc, 66-70; dept mgr res & develop, Microprod Div, Am Micro-Systs Inc, 70-72, M O S Mgr, Data Gen Semiconductor Div, 72-76; mem tech staff, Advan Microdevices, Inc, 76-78; MGR, SOLID STATE TECHNOL CTR, NAT SEMICONDUCTOR CORP, SANTA CLARA, 78- *Mem:* Am Inst Mining, Metall & Petrol Engrs; Am Phys Soc; Am Vacuum Soc; Electrochem Soc. *Res:* Metal oxide semiconductor integrated circuit processing; electronic materials research, including device behavior, thin film deposition and patterning; circuit application development. *Mailing Add:* 19379 Dehavilland Dr Saratoga CA 95070

SKINNER, MARGARET SHEPPARD, b Jamaica, NY, May 8, 38; m 69; c 2. PATHOLOGY. *Educ:* Emory Univ, MD, 62. *Prof Exp:* From instr to assoc prof path, Sch Med, Tulane Univ, 65-73; PATHOLOGIST, CEDARS OF LEBANON HOSP, MIAMI, 73- *Concurrent Pos:* NIH fel path, Tulane Univ, 65-68; asst vis pathologist, Charity Hosp, New Orleans, 65-68, vis pathologist, 68-73; consult staff, Lallie Kemp Charity Hosp, 72-73; clin assoc prof path, Univ Miami, 77- *Mem:* Am Asn Pathologists; Am Soc Microbiol; AMA. *Res:* Experimental cell pathology; surgical pathology. *Mailing Add:* Dept Path Cedars of Lebanon Hosp 1400 NW 12th Ave Miami FL 33136

SKINNER, MORRIS FREDRICK, b Springview, Nebr, Sept 14, 06; m 30; c 2. GEOLOGY, PALEONTOLOGY. *Educ:* Univ Nebr, BSc, 32. *Hon Degrees:* DSc, Univ Nebr, 78. *Prof Exp:* Field assoc fossil collecting, geol res & pub bison & Pleis cave fauna, 33-54, asst cur, 54-66, assoc cur, 69-73, EMER CUR DEPT VERT PALEONT, FRICK LAB, AM MUS NATURAL HIST, 73- *Mem:* Soc Vertebrate Paleont; fel Geol Soc Am; fel AAAS. *Res:* Extinct and living horses of the world, mainly those from North and South America, Eurasia, and Africa; geologic and paleontologic study of late Cenozoic rocks, particularly the northern Great Plains and Texas. *Mailing Add:* PO Box 294 Ainsworth NE 69210

SKINNER, NEWMAN SHELDON, JR, b Gadsden, Ala, Nov 13, 34; m 55; c 3. MEDICINE, PHYSIOLOGY. *Educ:* Auburn Univ, BS, 55; Med Col Ala, MD, 60. *Prof Exp:* Med intern, Med Ctr, Yale Univ, 60-61; res assoc cardiovasc physiol, Lab Cardiovasc Physiol, Nat Heart Inst, 61-63 & 64-66; asst prof physiol & med, Univ Tex, Southwestern Med Sch, 66-68; from assoc prof to prof med, Sch Med, Emory Univ, 68-72, dir div clin physiol, 69-72; prof physiol & med & chmn dept physiol, 72-74, PROF MED, & PROF PHYSIOL, BOWMAN GRAY SCH MED, WAKE FOREST UNIV, 74- *Concurrent Pos:* Res assoc med res, Med Col Ala, 63-64. *Mem:* Am Fedn Clin Res; Am Physiol Soc; Soc Exp Biol & Med; Microcirculatory Soc. *Res:* Regulation of peripheral blood flow, particularly skeletal muscle and adipose tissue blood flow; general cardiovascular physiology. *Mailing Add:* Dept Med Bowman Gray Sch Med Wake Forest Univ Winston-Salem NC 27103

SKINNER, (ORVILLE) RAY, b Oshawa, Ont, Oct 25, 27; m 79. THEORETICAL PHYSICS. *Educ:* Univ Toronto, BA, 50; Carnegie Inst Technol, MSc & PhD(math), 52. *Prof Exp:* Res assoc, Math Inst, NY Univ, 52-53; Nat Res Coun Can fel, 53-54; Nat Res Coun Can fel, 54-56, from asst prof to assoc prof, 56-68, PROF PHYSICS, UNIV SASK, 68- *Mem:* AAAS; Can Asn Physicists; Am Phys Soc; Am Asn Physics Teachers. *Res:* Teaching of physics; relativity. *Mailing Add:* Dept of Physics Univ of Sask Saskatoon SK S7H 0W0 Can

SKINNER, RICHARD EMERY, b Anderson, Ind, Feb 15, 34; m 54; c 2. ENGINEERING PHYSICS, MATHEMATICS. *Educ:* Reed Col, BA, 55; Calif Inst Technol, MS, 57. *Prof Exp:* Physicist, Atomics Int Div, NAm Aviation, Inc, 55 & 56-59, consult, 55-56; physicist, Radio Corp Am, 59-64; supvry physicist, Electromagnetic Res Inc, 64-65; tech dir, Manst Corp, 66-68; vpres & gen mgr, Parzen Res Div, Ovitron, 68-69; pres, Skinner Industs, Inc, 69-70, INDEPENDENT CONSULT & PRES, R E SKINNER & ASSOCS, 70- *Mem:* Am Phys Soc; Am Nuclear Soc; Nat Soc Prof Engrs. *Res:* Electronics; electrical, mechanical and structural engineering; land surveying and communications; plasma physics; nuclear reactor dynamics theory. *Mailing Add:* R E Skinner & Assocs 1731 SE 55th Ave Portland OR 97215

SKINNER, ROBERT DOWELL, b Waxahachie, Tex, Nov 23, 42; m 66; c 4. NEUROSCIENCES. *Educ:* Univ Tex, Arlington, BS, 65; Univ Tex Southwestern Med Sch, Dallas, PhD(biophysics), 69. *Prof Exp:* Instr, 70-71, asst prof, 71-80, ASSOC PROF ANAT, COL MED, UNIV ARK MED SCI CAMPUS, LITTLE ROCK, 80- *Concurrent Pos:* NIH fel, Harvard Med Sch, 69-70. *Mem:* Am Asn Anat; Soc Neurosci. *Res:* Motor system; spinal cord physiology; motor units. *Mailing Add:* Dept of Anat Univ of Ark Med Sci Campus Little Rock AR 72201

SKINNER, ROBERT L, b Salt Lake City, Utah, Nov 6, 30; m 53; c 4. ELECTRICAL ENGINEERING. *Educ:* Univ Utah, BS, 54, MS, 55. *Prof Exp:* Res dir, Ensco, Inc, 54-68; PRES, ENTEC INC, 68- *Concurrent Pos:* Instr, Univ Utah, 55-56. *Mem:* Inst Elec & Electronics Engrs. *Res:* Specialized systems and instrumentation used in medical research. *Mailing Add:* 8456 S 1430 E Sandy Salt Lake City UT 84119

SKINNER, WALTER SWART, b Middletown, NY, Oct 13, 21; m 50; c 2. EARTH SCIENCE. *Educ:* Monmouth Col, Ill, BS, 43; Lehigh Univ, MS, 48. *Prof Exp:* Instr geol, Lehigh Univ, 46-48; deep well geologist, S Penn Oil Co, 48-54; staff geologist, Sun Oil Co, 54-59, dist geologist, 59-65; assoc prof phys sci, 65-66, assoc prof earth sci, 66-72, actg chmn dept physics, 72-73, PROF EARTH SCI, DUQUESNE UNIV, 72-, CHMN DEPT PHYSICS, 73- *Concurrent Pos:* Consult, Hard Rock Mining Co, 58-59. *Honors & Awards:* Outstanding Serv to Profession Award, Pittsburgh Geol Soc, Inc, 74. *Mem:* Am Asn Petrol Geol; Geol Soc Am; Am Inst Prof Geol; fel Explorers Club. *Res:* Stratigraphy, structure and sedimentation of the New York, Pennsylvania and West Virginia areas; regional stratigraphy and sedimentation of eastern United States. *Mailing Add:* Dept of Physics Duquesne Univ Pittsburgh PA 15282

SKINNER, WILFRED AUBREY, JR, b Monroe, La, Dec 24, 23; m 45; c 6. ORGANIC CHEMISTRY. *Educ:* Univ Calif, Los Angeles, BS, 48; Univ Okla, MS, 50; Univ Tex, PhD(chem), 52. *Prof Exp:* Asst, Univ Okla, 48-50; res scientist, Basic Cotton Res Lab, 50-52; res chemist, Aerojet Gen Corp, Gen Tire & Rubber Co, 52-53 & Celanese Corp Am, 53-55; exec dir life sci res, 55-80, VPRES, LIFE SCI DIV, SRI INT, 80- *Mem:* Am Chem Soc; Sigma Xi. *Res:* Oxidation products of vitamin E; biphenyl compound syntheses; initiators for polymerizations; physical properties of polymers; high vacuum investigations with metal hydrides; solid propellants; metal alkyl syntheses; synthesis of medicinals; biosynthetic studies; insect repellants; drug metabolism; natural products chemistry. *Mailing Add:* SRI Int 333 Ravenswood Ave Menlo Park CA 94025

SKINNER, WILLIAM CAREY, b Calvert City, Ky, Apr 4, 20; m 45; c 3. PHYSICS. *Educ:* Western Ky State Col, BS, 41; Vanderbilt Univ, MS, 42, PhD(physics), 50. *Prof Exp:* Res assoc, Div War Res, Columbia Univ, 43-45; res physicist, Field Res Labs, Mobil Oil Corp, 45-49, sr res physicist, 49-57, sect supvr, 57-65, mgr tech serv, 65-69, mgr opers, Cent Res Div, Mobil Res & Develop Corp, 69-71, MGR PROD RES, EXPLOR & PROD DIV, MOBIL RES & DEVELOP CORP, MOBIL OIL CORP, 71- *Mem:* Am Phys Soc; Am Inst Mining, Metall & Petrol Eng. *Res:* Fluid flow through porus media; electron microscopy; metallography; petroleum reservoir behavior; research management. *Mailing Add:* Explor & Prod Div Mobil Res & Develop Corp PO Box 900 Dallas TX 75221

SKINNER, WILLIAM ROBERT, b Tampa, Fla, Jan 1, 30; m 57; c 4. PETROLOGY, STRUCTURAL GEOLOGY. *Educ:* Univ Tex, BS, 53; Columbia Univ, PhD(geol), 66. *Prof Exp:* Inspector construct, Pittsburgh Testing Lab, 57-59; asst prof, 66-71, ASSOC PROF GEOL, OBERLIN COL, 71-, CHMN DEPT, 74- *Mem:* Geol Soc Am. *Res:* Structure and petrogenesis of Precambrian metamorphic terranes; petrology and geochemistry of Alpine-type and stratiform igneous complexes. *Mailing Add:* Dept of Geol Oberlin Col Oberlin OH 44074

SKINNIDER, LEO F, b Paisley, Scotland, Oct 2, 29; Can citizen; c 8. PATHOLOGY, HEMATOLOGY. *Educ:* Univ Glasgow, MB, ChB, 51; FRCP(C), 68. *Prof Exp:* Assoc prof, 69-73, PROF PATH, UNIV SASK, SASKATOON, 73- *Concurrent Pos:* Consult, Can Tumor Reference Ctr, 72-; Nat Cancer Inst Can grant, 74-; deleg, Col Am Pathologists, 70-78. *Mem:* Am Soc Clin Pathologists; Can Asn Pathologists; Col Am Pathologists; Can Soc Hematol; Can Health Res. *Res:* Ultrastructure and agar-culture characteristics of cells of lymphomas and leukemias; effect of retinol and its analogies on the proliferation of lymphoid cells. *Mailing Add:* B418 Health Sci Bldg Univ of Sask Saskatoon SK S7H 0W0 Can

SKIPSKI, VLAIDIMIR P(AVLOVICH), b Urgojedy, Ukraine, Russia, Oct 18, 13; nat US; div; c 1. BIOCHEMISTRY. *Educ:* Kiev State Univ, USSR, MS, 38; Inst Exp Biol & Path, Kiev, PhD, 41; Univ Southern Calif, PhD(biochem), 56. *Prof Exp:* Mem res staff, Inst for Exp Biol & Path, USSR, 41-43; res assoc, Kaviar Inst, Calif, 49-51 & Univ Southern Calif, 56; res assoc, 56-59, assoc, 59-69, ASSOC MEM, SLOAN-KETTERING INST CANCER RES, 69-, HEAD, LAB LIPIDS & LIPID COMPLEXES, 79- *Concurrent Pos:* Asst prof biochem, Sloan-Kettering Div, Grad Sch Med Sci, Cornell Univ, 61-70, assoc prof, 70- *Mem:* Am Soc Biol Chemists; Am Physiol Soc; Soc Gen Physiol; Brit Biochem Soc; Am Asn Cancer Res. *Res:* Biochemistry of lipids; lipid-protein complexes, including lipoproteins and proteolipids; chemical and structural characteristics of biological membranes, mechanism of metastasis formation; lipids and cancer; chromatography of lipids; glycosphingolipids. *Mailing Add:* Sloan-Kettering Inst Cancer Res 145 Boston Post Rd Rye NY 10580

SKIRVIN, ROBERT MICHAEL, b Burlington, Wash, Oct 27, 47; m 73; c 1. PLANT BREEDING, PLANT PHYSIOLOGY. *Educ:* Southern Ill Univ, BS, 69, MS, 71; Purdue Univ, PhD(hort), 75. *Prof Exp:* Lab & field asst, Fruit Res Sta, 68-69; res asst grape physiol, Southern Ill Univ, 69-71; David Ross fel hort, Purdue Univ, 71-73, res asst, 73-74, from instr to asst prof, 74-76; ASST PROF HORT, UNIV ILL, 76- *Honors & Awards:* Commendation Award, NAm Strawberry Growers Asn, 77. *Mem:* Am Soc Hort Sci; Am

Pomol Soc; Int Asn Plant Tissue Cult; Sigma Xi. *Res:* Development of methods to utilize tissue culture techniques for the improvement of asexually propagated crops; breeding and genetic studies of small fruits with a particular interest in thornless blackberries. *Mailing Add:* Dept of Hort Univ of Ill Urbana IL 61801

SKITEK, GABRIEL G(EORGE), b St Joseph, Mo, Oct 25, 19; m 43; c 2. ELECTRONICS, ENGINEERING. *Educ:* Univ Mo, BS, 43, MS, 49. *Prof Exp:* PROF ELEC ENG, UNIV MO-ROLLA, 46- *Mem:* Am Soc Eng Educ; Inst Elec & Electronics Engrs. *Res:* Microwaves and antennas. *Mailing Add:* Dept of Elec Eng Univ of Mo Rolla MO 65401

SKJEGSTAD, KENNETH, b Henning, Minn, Oct 18, 31. BOTANY. *Educ:* Moorhead State Col, BS, 53; Univ Calif, Los Angeles, PhD(bot), 60. *Prof Exp:* Assoc biol, Univ Calif, 58-60; from instr to assoc prof bot, Univ Minn, Minneapolis, 60-66; assoc prof, 66-69, PROF BIOL, MOORHEAD STATE UNIV, 69- *Mem:* AAAS; Bot Soc Am; Am Soc Plant Physiol. *Res:* Physiology of plant growth and development; plant genetics. *Mailing Add:* Dept of Biol Moorhead State Univ Moorhead MN 56560

SKJELBREIA, LARS, b Shedsmo, Norway, May 27, 23; nat US; m 50; c 4. CIVIL ENGINEERING. *Educ:* Bucknell Univ, BS, 48; Univ Wash, MS, 49; Calif Inst Technol, PhD(civil eng), 53. *Prof Exp:* Instr civil eng, Bucknell Univ, 48; design engr, State Water Conserv, Mont, 49-50; design engr & consult, Sandberg & Serrell Corp, Calif, 51-54; sr res engr, Calif Res Corp, Standard Oil Co, Calif, 54-58, group supvr, 58-59; vpres, Nat Eng Sci Co, 59-64; gen mgr, 64-74, PRES, SCI ENG ASSOC, 75- *Concurrent Pos:* Mem, Coun Wave Res, Eng Found. *Mem:* Am Soc Mech Engrs; Am Soc Civil Engrs; Am Geophys Union. *Res:* Overall design and construction of various large concrete platforms installed in the North Sea; Ekofisk oil storage tank; wave force calculations, model studies, duties of liaison and monitoring of platform design; design and procurement of sensors and data acquisition equipment for the platform instrumentation system. *Mailing Add:* 2111 W Crescent Ave Anaheim CA 92801

SKJOLD, ARTHUR CHRISTOPHER, b Minneapolis, Minn, Dec 20, 43; m 72. BIOCHEMISTRY, MICROBIAL GENETICS. *Educ:* Macalester Col, BA, 66; Kans State Univ, PhD(biochem), 70. *Prof Exp:* Res assoc microbiol genetics, Albert Einstein Med Ctr, 70-73; asst dir res immunodiag, Kallestad Labs Inc, 73-77; SR RES SCIENTIST, URINE CHEM LAB, AMES DIV, MILES LABS, 77- *Res:* Nucleic acids; microbial genetics; regulation of RNA and protein synthesis; immunochemistry; protein purification; urinalysis; regulation of bacterial growth. *Mailing Add:* Ames Div Miles Labs PO Box 70 Elkhart IN 46515

SKJONSBY, HAROLD SAMUEL, b Sisseton, SDak, July 6, 37; m 61; c 3. HISTOLOGY, ANATOMY. *Educ:* Concordia Col, BA, 59; Univ NDak, MS, 62, PhD(anat), 64. *Prof Exp:* From asst prof to assoc prof, 64-74, PROF HISTOL & CHMN DEPT, UNIV TEX DENT BR HOUSTON, 74- *Res:* Histochemistry of tooth development; structure of bone and connective tissue. *Mailing Add:* Dept of Histol Univ of Tex Dent Br Houston TX 77025

SKLANSKY, J(ACK), b Brooklyn, NY, Nov 15, 28; m 57; c 3. ELECTRICAL ENGINEERING, COMPUTER SCIENCE. *Educ:* City Col New York, BEE, 50; Purdue Univ, MSEE, 52; Columbia Univ, DSc(eng), 55. *Prof Exp:* Res engr, Electronics Res Labs, Columbia Univ, 54-55 & RCA Labs, NJ, 55-65; head systs res sect, Nat Cash Register Co, Ohio, 65-66; assoc prof elec eng, 66-69, chmn dept, 78-80, PROF ELEC ENG, INFO & COMUT SCI & RADIOL SCI, UNIV CALIF, IRVINE, 69- *Concurrent Pos:* Res grants, Nat Inst Gen Med Sci & NSF. *Mem:* Asn Comput Mach; fel Inst Elec & Electronics Engrs; Comput Soc. *Res:* automatic pattern classifiers; image processing by computer; medical imaging; biomedical engineering; digital system theory. *Mailing Add:* Sch of Eng Univ of Calif Irvine CA 92717

SKLAR, ABRAHAM, b Chicago, Ill, Nov 17, 25. MATHEMATICS. *Educ:* Calif Inst Technol, PhD(math), 56. *Prof Exp:* From instr to assoc prof, 56-70, PROF MATH, ILL INST TECHNOL, 70- *Mem:* AAAS; Am Math Soc; Am Geog Soc; Fedn Am Sci; Math Asn Am. *Res:* Analytic number theory; probabilistic geometry; applications of mathematics to linguistics and scientific methodology. *Mailing Add:* Dept of Math Ill Inst of Technol Chicago IL 60616

SKLAR, STANLEY, b Bronx, NY, July 12, 37; m 63; c 2. PHARMACEUTICS. *Educ:* Philadelphia Col Pharm & Sci, BS, 59; Purdue Univ, Lafayette, MS, 61; Univ Conn, PhD(pharm), 65. *Prof Exp:* Res pharmacist, Bristol Labs, 65-67; res pharmacist, Radnor, 67-72, unit supvr, 72-73, unit supvr, Pilot Plant, 73-80, QUAL ASSURANCE MGR, WYETH LABS, WEST CHESTER, 80- *Concurrent Pos:* Secy, Parenteral Drug Asn, 80-81. *Mem:* Am Pharmaceut Asn; Acad Pharmaceut Sci; Am Chem Soc. *Res:* Quality assurance and quality control functions, including parenteral dosage forms, fermentation production and a fine chemical facility. *Mailing Add:* 4 Selwyn Dr Broomall PA 19008

SKLAREW, DEBORAH S, b New York, NY, Apr 6, 50; m 77. ORGANIC GEOCHEMISTRY, ANALYTICAL CHEMISTRY. *Educ:* City Col NY, BS, 70; Univ Calif, Berkeley, MS, 72; Univ Ariz, PhD(geosci), 78. *Prof Exp:* RES SCIENTIST GEOCHEM, BATTELLE PAC NORTHWEST LABS, 78- *Mem:* Geochem Soc; Am Chem Soc. *Res:* Kerogen analysis in Precambrian and recent sedimentary rocks; characterization of fossil fuel effluents; sulfur and nitrogen gas analysis in oil shale retorts. *Mailing Add:* Battelle Pac Northwest Labs Box 999 Richland WA 99352

SKLAREW, RALPH C, b Yonkers, NY, Mar 22, 44; m 68; c 1. PHYSICS, SCIENCE PLANNING. *Educ:* San Fernando Valley State Col, BS, 64; Univ Calif, Riverside, MS, 67, PhD(physics), 68. *Prof Exp:* Dir air qual studies, Systs, Sci & Software, Inc, 68-72; mem staff environ modeling, Div Meteorol, Environ Protection Agency, 72-73; mgr geophys fluid dynamics div, Sci Applns, Inc, 74-77; PRES, FORM & SUBSTANCE, INC, 77- *Mem:* AAAS; Am Inst Aeronaut & Astronaut; Am Meteorol Soc; Air Pollution Control Asn; Am Phys Soc. *Res:* Mathematical and environmental modeling; air and water pollution control; microcomputer applications and long range planning for space industrialization. *Mailing Add:* Form & Substance Inc 875 Westlake Blvd 212 Westlake Village CA 91361

SKOBBA, JOSEPH STANLEY, b Nanticoke, Pa, Oct 24, 04; m 40; c 1. PSYCHIATRY. *Educ:* Ind Univ, BS, 28, MD, 30. *Prof Exp:* From asst prof to assoc prof psychiat, Sch Med, Ind Univ, 37-41; assoc, 41-48, from asst prof to assoc prof clin psychiat, 48-56, assoc prof psychiat & actg chmn dept, 56-58, clin prof, 58-68, prof, 68-73, EMER PROF PSYCHIAT, SCH MED, EMORY UNIV, 73- *Concurrent Pos:* Lectr, Sch Soc Work, Atlanta Univ, 46-50; regional consult, Vet Admin, Ga, 46-47; consult, Vet Admin Hosp, 48-56; Surgeon Gen, US Third Army, 46-; actg dir, Ga Ment Health Inst, 69-71. *Mem:* AAAS; AMA; fel Am Psychiat Asn; Am Col Psychiat. *Res:* Changes in spinal fluid protein in mental illness. *Mailing Add:* Dept Psychiat Sch Med Emory Univ Atlanta GA 30322

SKOBE, ZIEDOMIS, b Riga, Latvia, Apr 29, 41; US citizen; m 63; c 4. CELL BIOLOGY. *Educ:* Boston Univ, BA, 63, PhD(biol), 72; Clark Univ, MA, 67. *Prof Exp:* DEPT HEAD ELECTRON MICROSCOPY, FORSYTH DENT CTR, 72- *Concurrent Pos:* Lectr, Boston Univ, 75- *Mem:* Am Asn Dent Res; Int Asn Dent Res; Am Soc Cell Biol. *Res:* Structure of tooth enamel and the ultrastructure of the cells involved in amelogenesis in several mammals using both scanning and transmission electron microscopy. *Mailing Add:* Forsyth Dent Ctr 140 Fenway Boston MA 02115

SKOCHDOPOLE, RICHARD E, b Ravenna, Nebr, Dec 11, 27; m 53; c 4. PHYSICAL CHEMISTRY, POLYMER CHEMISTRY. *Educ:* Univ Nebr, BSc, 49; Iowa State Univ, PhD(phys chem), 54. *Prof Exp:* Fel, Ames Lab, AEC, 54-55; res chemist, Phys Res Lab, 56-63, sr res chemist, 63-64, assoc scientist, 64-68, dir converted plastics lab, 68, res mgr designed plastics res, 68-70, res mgr foam prod res, 70-73, assoc scientist foam prods res, 73-76, ASSOC SCIENTIST CHEM PROD LAB, DOW CHEM CO, 76- *Mem:* Am Chem Soc; Sigma Xi; Am Soc Heating & Refrig Engrs. *Res:* Preparation and characterization of cellular plastics, particularly thermal properties; physical chemistry of polymers and polymer solutions; preparation and characterization of polymers. *Mailing Add:* Chem Prod Lab 1776 Bldg Dow Chem Co Midland MI 48640

SKOFRONICK, JAMES GUST, b Merrill, Wis, Oct 11, 31; m 59; c 4. CHEMICAL PHYSICS, SURFACE PHYSICS. *Educ:* Univ Wis, BS, 59, MS, 61, PhD(nuclear physics), 64. *Prof Exp:* Res asst physics, Univ Wis, 59-64; from asst prof to assoc prof, 64-74, PROF PHYSICS, FLA STATE UNIV, 74- *Concurrent Pos:* Mem staff, Max Planck Inst Aerodyn, 79 & 80. *Mem:* Am Phys Soc; Sigma Xi. *Res:* Studies of the microscopic properties of neutral atoms and molecules by the use of colliding beam methods; studies of the properties of surfaces by colliding neutral atoms and molecules with surfaces; medical physics. *Mailing Add:* Dept Physics Fla State Univ Tallahassee FL 32306

SKOG, LAURENCE EDGAR, b Duluth, Minn, Apr 9, 43; m 68. PLANT TAXONOMY. *Educ:* Univ Minn, BS, 65; Univ Conn, MS, 68; Cornell Univ, PhD(bot), 72. *Prof Exp:* Fel, Royal Bot Garden, Edinburgh, 68-69; res asst bot, Cornell Univ, 69-72; asst ed, Flora NAm Prog, 72-73, ASSOC CUR BOT, SMITHSONIAN INST, 73- *Concurrent Pos:* Adj prof biol, George Mason Univ, 80- *Mem:* Bot Soc Am; Am Soc Plant Taxonomists; Int Asn Plant Taxon; Asn Trop Biol; Bot Soc Am. *Res:* Taxonomy and floristics of neotropical Gesneriaceae, Coriariaceae; pollination biology. *Mailing Add:* Dept Bot Nat Mus Natural Hist Smithsonian Inst Washington DC 20560

SKOGEN, HAVEN SHERMAN, b Rochester, Minn, May 8, 27; m 49; c 1. ANALYTICAL & PETROLEUM CHEMISTRY. *Educ:* Iowa State Univ, BS, 50; Rutgers Univ, New Brunswick, MS, 54, PhD(ceramics), 55; Univ Chicago, MBA, 70. *Prof Exp:* Res engr, E I du Pont de Nemours & Co, 55-56; prof chem, Elmhurst Col, 56-57; asst chief engr, Stackpole Carbon Co, 58-62; asst plant mgr, Manatronics, Inc, 62-65; mgr, Allen-Bradley Co, 65-70; pres, Haven S Skogen & Assocs, 70-74; CHIEF CHEMIST, OCCIDENTAL OIL SHALE INC, 74- *Mem:* AAAS; Am Ceramic Soc; Nat Inst Ceramic Engrs; Am Soc Prof Engrs. *Res:* Shale oil production and control including environmental impact and economics. *Mailing Add:* 3152 Primrose Grand Junction CO 81501

SKOGERBOE, GAYLORD VINCENT, b Cresco, Iowa, Apr 1, 35; m 58; c 2. AGRICULTURAL ENGINEERING, CIVIL ENGINEERING. *Educ:* Univ Utah, BS, 58, MS, 59. *Prof Exp:* Hydraulic engr, Utah Water & Power Bd, 60-63; res proj engr hydraulics, Utah Water Res Lab, Utah State Univ, 63-68; PROF IRRIGATION & DRAINAGE, COLO STATE UNIV, 68- *Mem:* Am Soc Agr Engrs; Am Soc Civil Engrs; Int Soc Ecol Modelling; Int Water Resources Asn. *Res:* Interdisciplinary research involving physical and social scientists on topics related to agricultural development and environmental problems of irrigated agriculture. *Mailing Add:* Dept of Agr & Chem Eng Colo State Univ Ft Collins CO 80523

SKOGERBOE, RODNEY K, b Blue Earth, Minn, June 25, 31; m 58; c 4. ANALYTICAL CHEMISTRY. *Educ:* Mankato State Col, BA, 58; Mont State Univ, PhD(chem), 63. *Prof Exp:* Jr chemist, Ames Lab, US AEC, 58-60; asst prof chem, SDak Sch Mines & Technol, 63-64; res mgr, Cornell Univ, 64-69; from asst prof to assoc prof chem, 69-73, PROF CHEM & ATMOSPHERIC SCI, COLO STATE UNIV, 73-, CHMN, DEPT CHEM, 80- *Mem:* Am Chem Soc; Soc Appl Spectros (pres, 72). *Res:* Spectrochemical and radiochemical methods of trace analysis; application of statistics to chemical problems. *Mailing Add:* Dept of Chem Colo State Univ Ft Collins CO 80523

SKOGERSON, LAWRENCE EUGENE, b Ft Collins, Colo, Aug 19, 42; m 69; c 3. BIOCHEMISTRY. *Educ:* Grinnell Col, AB, 64; Univ Pittsburgh, PhD(biochem), 68. *Prof Exp:* Asst prof biochem, Col Physicians & Surgeons, Columbia Univ, 70-77; ASSOC PROF BIOCHEM, MED COL WIS, 77- *Concurrent Pos:* Am Cancer Soc fel, NIH, Bethesda, 68-70; USPHS res grant, Columbia Univ, 71-78, Am Cancer Soc fac res award, 72-77. *Mem:* Am Soc Biol Chemists; Harvey Soc. *Res:* Regulation of RNA and protein synthesis. *Mailing Add:* Dept of Biochem Med Col of Wis PO Box 26509 Milwaukee WI 53226

SKOGLEY, CONRAD RICHARD, b Deer Lodge, Mont, Nov 9, 24; m 48; c 3. AGRONOMY. *Educ:* Univ RI, BS, 50, MS, 52; Rutgers Univ, PhD, 57. *Prof Exp:* Asst agronomist, Univ RI, 51-53; asst & res assoc, Rutgers Univ, 53-56, exten assoc, 56-57, asst exten specialist, 57-59, assoc exten specialist, 59-60; assoc prof agron, 60-70, PROF PLANT & SOIL SCI, UNIV RI, 70- *Mem:* Am Soc Agron; Crop Sci Soc Am. *Res:* Turfgrass management; establishment and maintenance of fine turf grasses. *Mailing Add:* Dept of Plant & Soil Sci Univ of RI Kingston RI 02881

SKOGLEY, EARL O, b Mott, NDak, Mar 18, 33; m 55; c 3. SOIL FERTILITY, PLANT NUTRITION. *Educ:* NDak State Univ, BS, 55, MS, 57; NC State Univ, PhD(soil fertility), 62. *Prof Exp:* Instr soils, NC State Univ, 57-62; res assoc soil fertil, Cornell Univ, 62-63; from asst prof to assoc prof, 63-71, PROF SOIL FERTIL, MONT STATE UNIV, 71- *Concurrent Pos:* Res adv, USAID, Brazil, 67 & 68 & on contract with IRI Res Inst, Inc, NY; consult/team mem develop transmission environ report proposed twin 500 Kv power lines Mont, 77-78. *Mem:* AAAS; Soil Sci Soc Am; Am Soc Agron; Int Soil Sci Soc. *Res:* Development of synthetic growth media for plant nutrition studies; investigation of plant nutrient relations in soils and plants. *Mailing Add:* Dept of Plant & Soil Sci Mont State Univ Bozeman MT 59715

SKOGLUND, WINTHROP CHARLES, b Lynn, Mass, Dec 7, 16; m 41; c 1. POULTRY HUSBANDRY. *Educ:* Univ NH, BS, 38; Pa State Col, MS, 40, PhD, 58. *Prof Exp:* Asst, Pa State Col, 38-40; instr poultry indust & asst res poultryman, Univ Del, 40-42, exten poultry specialist, 42-46, from asst prof to assoc prof poultry indust, 46-50, dir agr short course, 49-50; prof poultry husb & chmn dept, Univ NH, 50-81; RETIRED. *Res:* Nutrition; breeding; hatching; egg production. *Mailing Add:* Dept of Animal Sci Univ of NH Durham NH 03824

SKOK, JOHN, b Rumania, Nov 18, 09; nat US; m 38; c 1. PLANT PHYSIOLOGY. *Educ:* Northern Ill State Teachers Col, BEd, 35; Univ Chicago, SM, 37, PhD(plant physiol), 41. *Prof Exp:* Asst plant physiol, Univ Chicago, 40-41; assoc veg crops, Univ Ill, 42-43, asst chief, 43-47, asst prof hort, Exp Sta, 47-50; plant physiologist, Argonne Nat Lab, 50-62; dean col lib arts & sci, prof biol sci, 65-75, EMER PROF, NORTHERN ILL UNIV, 75- *Mem:* AAAS; Am Soc Plant Physiologists; Bot Soc Am; Am Soc Hort Sci. *Res:* Plant nutrition; photoperiodism; radiobiology. *Mailing Add:* 1200 Loren Dr De Kalb IL 60115

SKOK, RICHARD ARNOLD, b St Paul, Minn, June 19, 28; m; c 2. FOREST ECONOMICS. *Educ:* Univ Minn, BS, 50, MF, 54, PhD, 60. *Prof Exp:* Asst prof forest econ, Sch Forestry, Mont State Univ, 58-59; from instr to assoc prof, Univ Minn, 59-65, asst dir sch forestry, 67-71, assoc dean forestry, 71-74, PROF FOREST ECON, UNIV MINN, ST PAUL, 65-, DEAN COL FORESTRY, 74- *Concurrent Pos:* Mem, Joint Coun Food & Agr Sci. *Mem:* Fel Soc Am Foresters; Forest Prods Res Soc. *Res:* Forest resource development economics and policy. *Mailing Add:* Col of Forestry 110G Green Hall Univ of Minn St Paul MN 55108

SKOLD, LAURENCE NELSON, b Haxtun, Colo, Apr 11, 17; m 40; c 1. AGRONOMY. *Educ:* Colo Agr & Mech Col, BS, 38; Kans State Col, MS, 40. *Prof Exp:* Asst, Kans State Col, 38-40; from asst agronomist to assoc agronomist, Ga Agr Exp Sta, 40-46; from asst prof to assoc prof agron, Univ Tenn, Knoxville, 47-56, prof & head dept, 56-60, agron adv, India Agr Prog, 61-66, prof plant & soil sci, 67-82; RETIRED. *Mem:* Am Soc Agron. *Res:* Field crops, culture and improvement. *Mailing Add:* Dept of Plant & Soil Sci Univ of Tenn Knoxville TN 37996

SKOLIL, LESTER L, b Crete, Nebr, Mar 22, 13; m 37. PHYSICS. *Educ:* Doane Col, AB, 35; Univ Nebr, MA, 37; Univ Calif, PhD, 51. *Hon Degrees:* DSc, Doane Col, 60. *Prof Exp:* Instr physics, Univ Nebr, 38-41; asst, Univ Calif, 42-44, assoc physics, 44-48, Davis, 48-50, instr & jr physicist, Exp Sta, 50-51; from asst prof to assoc prof, 51-57, chmn dept, 57-60, PROF PHYSICS, SAN DIEGO STATE UNIV, 57- *Concurrent Pos:* Vis physicist, NSF, 60-61; with Atomic Energy Comn, Oak Ridge & Nat Reactor Test Sta, 60-61. *Mem:* AAAS; Am Phys Soc; sr mem Inst Elec & Electronics Engrs; Am Nuclear Soc; Health Phys Soc. *Res:* Nuclear and radiological physics. *Mailing Add:* Dept of Physics San Diego State Univ San Diego CA 92182

SKOLMEN, ROGER GODFREY, b San Francisco, Calif, Dec 30, 29. TREE PHYSIOLOGY, FOREST PRODUCTS. *Educ:* Univ Calif, BS, 57, MS, 58, PhD, 77. *Prof Exp:* Asst chem, Shell Develop Co, 55; res asst forestry, Univ Calif, 56-59; soil scientist, Pac Southwest Forest Exp Sta, 59-60, wood scientist, Hawaii Res Ctr, 61-72, RES FORESTER, INST PAC ISLANDS FORESTRY, US FOREST SERV, 72- *Mem:* Forest Prod Res Soc; Soc Am Foresters; Plant Tissue Cult Asn. *Res:* Tissue culture propagation of trees; genetic tree improvement; eucalyptus biomass production; utilization of Hawaii-grown woods; tree, log, and wood quality; durability; preservation; seasoning; sawmilling; marketing; silviculture. *Mailing Add:* Inst of Pac Islands Forestry 1151 Punchbowl St Honolulu HI 96813

SKOLNICK, HERBERT, b Brooklyn, NY, Jan 15, 19; m 48; c 1. GEOLOGY. *Educ:* Brooklyn Col, BS, 47; Univ Okla, MS, 49; Univ Iowa, PhD(geol), 52. *Prof Exp:* Sedimentologist, Gulf Res & Develop Co, 52-53, supvr geol lab, Western Gulf Oil Co, 53-56, div stratigrapher, 56-60, chief stratigrapher & paleontologist, Spanish Gulf Oil Co, 60-64, supvr stratig lab, Nigerian Gulf Oil Co, 64-67; supvr stratig lab, Houston Tech Serv Ctr, 67-71, res assoc, 71-73, supvr geol sect, 73-77, SR RES ASSOC, GULF RES & DEVELOP CO, 77- *Mem:* Geol Soc Am; Am Asn Petrol Geologists; Soc Econ Paleontologists and Mineralogists; Sigma Xi. *Res:* Petrology, petrography and diagenesis of sedimentary rocks; evolution of subsurface fluid systems; plate tectonics; oceanography; geochemistry; stratigraphy and sedimentology; integration of listed disciplines as a tool for hydrocarbon exploration. *Mailing Add:* Gulf Res & Develop Co PO Drawer 2038 Pittsburgh PA 15230

SKOLNICK, JEFFREY, b Brooklyn, NY, June 27, 53. POLYMER DYNAMICS, BIOPHYSICS. *Educ:* Wash Univ, BA, 75; Yale Univ, MPhil, 77, PhD(chem), 78. *Prof Exp:* ASST PROF CHEM, LA STATE UNIV, 79- *Concurrent Pos:* Vis prof, Wash Univ, 81. *Mem:* Am Chem Soc; Am Phys Soc; Sigma Xi; NY Acad Sci. *Res:* Statistical mechanics of polymer solutions, glasses and melts with an emphasis on local main chain dynamics; stress strain behavior of polymer glasses, and conformational properties of biological macromolecules. *Mailing Add:* Dept Chem La State Univ Baton Rouge LA 70803

SKOLNICK, MALCOLM HARRIS, b Salt Lake City, Utah, Aug 11, 35; m 59; c 4. BIOPHYSICS. *Educ:* Univ Utah, BS, 56; Cornell Univ, MS, 59, PhD(theoret physics), 63. *Prof Exp:* Staff scientist elem sci study, Educ Develop Ctr, Mass, 62-63; mem, Sch Math, Inst Advan Study, Princeton Univ, 63-64; instr physics, Mass Inst Technol, 64-65; staff scientist elem sci study & dir Peace Corps Training & Support Serv, Educ Develop Ctr, Mass, 65-67; assoc prof physics, Health Sci Ctr, State Univ NY, Stony Brook, 67-70, assoc prof path, 70-71; PROF & CHMN DEPT BIOMED COMMUN, UNIV TEX MED SCH, HOUSTON, 71- *Concurrent Pos:* Dep dir, Instr Resources Ctr, State Univ NY, Stony Brook, 67-68, assoc prof health sci commun & dir dept, 68-71; consult, Educ Develop Ctr, Mass, Comn Col Physics, US Peace Corps, NSF & Nat Sci Teachers Asn; mem Asn Biomed Commun Dirs; chmn health care technol study sect, Nat Ctr Health Serv Res, 74-78. *Mem:* Inst Elec & Electronics Engrs. *Res:* Pattern recognition and automation of biomedical image processing; simulation and modeling in biophysical systems; application of media and computing technology to individualization of instruction, especially in health sciences education; health care technology assessment. *Mailing Add:* Dept of Biomed Commun Univ of Tex Med Sch Box 20708 Houston TX 70025

SKOLNICK, MARK HENRY, b Temple, Tex, Jan 28, 46; m 70; c 2. GENETICS, POPULATION GENETICS. *Educ:* Univ Calif, Berkeley, BA, 68; Stanford Univ, PhD(genetics), 75. *Prof Exp:* Res asst prof dept biol, 74-77; asst res prof, 74-76, ASST PROF DEPT MED BIOPHYSICS & COMPUT, UNIV UTAH, 76-, ADJ ASST PROF DEPT BIOL, 78- *Concurrent Pos:* NIH res grant, 74-81, 76-80, 77-80 & 79-; Pub Health grant, 76-81; mem Int Union Sci Study of Pop, 76-; dir, Div Health, Utah State Dept Soc Serv, 77-; mem epidemiol comn, Nat Cancer Inst, NIH, 78- *Mem:* Am Soc Human Genetics. *Res:* Genetic epidemiological studies of Mormon genealogies; historical and genetic demography; computerized genealogical data bases, human chromosome mapping, relationship of HLA to disease; preventive medicine and screening for genetic diseases. *Mailing Add:* Dept of Med Biophys & Comput Latter Day Saints Hosp Salt Lake City UT 84143

SKOLNICK, PHIL, b New York, NY, Feb 26, 47. PHARMACOLOGY. *Educ:* Long Island Univ, BSc, 68; George Washington Univ, PhD(pharmacol), 72. *Prof Exp:* Staff fel, 72-75, sr staff fel pharmacol, NIH, 75-77; pharmacologist, Nat Inst Alcohol Abuse, Alcoholism, Alcohol, Drug Abuse & Ment Health Admin, 77-78; SR INVESTR & PHARMACOLOGIST, NAT INST HEALTH, 78- *Honors & Awards:* A E Bennett Award, 80. *Mem:* Am Soc Pharmacol & Exp Therapeut; Int Soc Neurochem; Soc Biol Psychiat. *Res:* Neuropharmacology; neuroendocrinology; neurochemical correlates of behavior. *Mailing Add:* Lab Bioorgan Chem NIH Bldg 4 Rm 212 Bethesda MD 20205

SKOLNIK, HERMAN, b Harrisburg, Pa, Mar 22, 14; c 2. ORGANIC CHEMISTRY, INFORMATION SCIENCE. *Educ:* Pa State Univ, BS, 37; Univ Pa, MS, 41, PhD(org chem), 43. *Prof Exp:* Chemist, Roosevelt Oil Co, Mich, 37-38, testing labs, State Hwy Dept, Pa, 38-39 & Barrett Div, Allied Chem & Dye Corp, Pa, 39-42; res chemist, Hercules Inc, 42-53, mgr, Tech Info Div, 53-79; CONSULT, 79- *Concurrent Pos:* Grants, Univ Pa; ed, Jour Chem Doc, Terpene Chem-Chem Abstracts. *Honors & Awards:* Austin M Patterson Award Chem Doc, 69, Chem Info Sci Award, Am Chem Soc, 76. *Mem:* Am Soc Info Sci; Am Chem Soc; Tech Asn Pulp & Paper Indust. *Res:* Chemical documentation; history of science; terpenes; heterocyclics; azeotropy. *Mailing Add:* 239 Waverly Rd Wilmington DE 19803

SKOLNIK, LYN HOWARD, optics, see previous edition

SKOLNIK, MERRILL I, b Baltimore, Md, Nov 6, 27; m; c 4. ELECTRICAL ENGINEERING. *Educ:* Johns Hopkins Univ, BE, 47, MSE, 49, DrEng, 51. *Prof Exp:* Res asst elec eng, Johns Hopkins Univ, 47-50, res assoc, Radiation Lab, 50-53; eng specialist, Sylvania Elec Prod Co, 54; staff mem, Lincoln Lab, Mass Inst Technol, 54-59; res mgr, Electronic Commun Inc, 59-64; staff mem, Inst Defense Anal, 64-65; SUPT RADAR DIV, US NAVAL RES LAB, 65- *Concurrent Pos:* Lectr, Eve Div, Northeastern Univ, 56-59; adj prof, Drexel Inst Technol, 60-66 & Eve Div, Johns Hopkins Univ, 70- *Honors & Awards:* Heinrich Hertz Premium, Brit Inst Electronic & Radio Engrs, 65. *Mem:* Fel Inst Elec & Electronics Engrs; Soc Scholars. *Res:* Radar; antennas; electronic systems; electronic countermeasures; electric arc discharges. *Mailing Add:* Code 5300 US Naval Res Lab Washington DC 20375

SKOMAL, EDWARD N, b Kansas City, Mo, Apr 15, 26; m 51; c 3. RADIO SYSTEMS. *Educ:* Rice Univ, BA, 47, MA, 49. *Prof Exp:* Physicist, Socony-Mobil Field Res Lab, 49-51; supvry physicist, Nat Bur Standards, 51-56; adv develop engr, Sylvania Elec Microwave Physics Lab, 56-59; chief appl engr, Solid State Electronics Div, Motorola, Inc, 59-63; sr develop engr & physicist, 63-67, staff scientist, 67-80, SR ENG SPECIALIST, OFF CHIEF ENGR, AEROSPACE CORP, EL SEGUNDO, 80- *Concurrent Pos:* Mem,

Presidential Joint Tech Adv Comt Electromagnetic Compatibility, 65-; mem Comn, US Nat Comt, Int Union Radio Sci, 72- *Honors & Awards:* Inst Elec & Electronics Engrs Cert Achievement, 71; Richar S Stoddart Award, Inst Elec & Electronics Engrs, 80. *Mem:* Am Phys Soc; fel Inst Elec & Electronics Engrs. *Res:* Electromagnetism; microwave physics and interaction with solids; radio wave propagation; electromagnetic interference processes; stochastic progresses; radio scattering; guided wave propagation; cryogenics; automatic vehicle locating systems. *Mailing Add:* 1831 Valle Vista Dr Redlands CA 92373

SKOOG, DOUGLAS ARVID, b Willmar, Minn, May 4, 18; m 42; c 2. CHEMISTRY. *Educ:* Ore State Col, BS, 40; Univ Ill, PhD(anal chem), 43. *Prof Exp:* Res chemist, Calif Res Corp, Standard Oil Co Calif, 43-47; from asst prof to prof, 47-76, assoc exec head dept chem, 61-76, EMER PROF CHEM, STANFORD UNIV, 76- *Mem:* Am Chem Soc; AAAS; Sigma Xi. *Res:* Instrumental analysis; spectrophotometry; organic reagents; complex ions. *Mailing Add:* Dept of Chem Stanford Univ Stanford CA 94305

SKOOG, FOLKE, b Fjäras, Sweden, July 15, 08; nat US; m 49. PLANT PHYSIOLOGY. *Educ:* Calif Inst Technol, BS, 32, PhD(biol), 36. *Hon Degrees:* Dr, Univ Lund, 56. *Prof Exp:* Nat Res Coun fel bot, Univ Calif, 36-37; instr & res assoc, Harvard Univ, 37-41; assoc prof bot, Johns Hopkins Univ, 41-44; biochemist, Off Qm Gen, Washington, DC, Eng, Scand, Ger & Austria, 44-46; lectr, Washington Univ, 46; assoc prof, 47-49, prof, 49-79, EMER PROF BOT, UNIV WIS-MADISON, 79- *Concurrent Pos:* Vis physiologist, Exp Sta, Pineapple Res Inst & Univ Hawaii, 38-39; assoc physiologist, NIH, 43; vpres physiol sect, Int Bot Cong, France, 54, Edinburgh, 64, Leningrad, 75, mem comt algal cult, 54-; mem study sect genetics & morphol, NIH, 56-60; mem panel regulatory biol, NSF, 56-60; mem surv comt sci & technol educ, Brazil, Nat Acad Sci, 60. *Honors & Awards:* Hales Prize, 54, Barnes Life Mem Award, Am Soc Plant Physiol; Cert of Merit, Bot Soc Am. *Mem:* Nat Acad Sci; Int Plant Growth Subst Asn (vpres, 76-79, pres, 79-82); foreign mem Swed Nat Acad Sci; Deutsch Akademie de Naturforscher Leopoldina; Am Acad Arts & Sci. *Res:* Plant growth and development; cytokinins. *Mailing Add:* Dept Bot Univ Wis Madison WI 53706

SKOOG, IVAN HOOGLUND, b Kewanee, Ill, July 26, 28; m 55; c 2. ORGANIC CHEMISTRY. *Educ:* Univ Ill, BS, 50; Northwestern Univ, MS, 52, PhD, 55. CHEMIST, MINN MINING & MFG CO, 54- *Mem:* Am Chem Soc; Soc Photog Sci & Eng. *Res:* Organic synthesis; photography. *Mailing Add:* Photog Prods Div 209-2S 3M Center 3M Co St Paul MN 55144

SKOOG, WILLIAM ARTHUR, b Culver City, Calif, Apr 10, 25; m 49; c 4. INTERNAL MEDICINE. *Educ:* Stanford Univ, AB, 46, MD, 49; Am Bd Internal Med, dipl, 57. *Prof Exp:* Intern med, Univ Hosp, Stanford Univ, 48-49, asst resident, 49-50; asst resident med, NY Hosp-Cornell Med Ctr & asst in med col, 50-51; sr resident, Wadsworth Vet Admin Hosp, Los Angeles, Calif, 51; jr resident physician, Atomic Energy Proj, Univ Calif, Los Angeles, 54-55, from instr to asst prof med, Sch Med, 55-59, jr resident physician, 55-56, asst res physician & co-dir metab res unit, Ctr for Health Sci, 56-59; asst clin prof med & assoc res physician oncol, Sch Med & assoc staff, Health Sci, Univ Calif, San Francisco, 59-61; lectr, 61, co-dir, Health Sci Clin Res Ctr, 65-67, dir health sci clin res ctr, 67-72, assoc prof, 62-73, ASSOC CLIN PROF MED, SCH MED, UNIV CALIF, LOS ANGELES, 73- *Concurrent Pos:* Clin assoc hemat, Vet Admin Ctr, Los Angeles, 56-59; clin instr, Sch Med, Stanford Univ, 59-61; mem staff, Palo Alto-Stanford Hosp Ctr, 59-61; attend specialist, Wadsworth Vet Admin Hosp, Los Angeles, 62-68; vis physician, Harbor Gen Hosp, Torrance, 62-65, attend physician, 65-77; consult, Clin Lab, Univ Calif, Los Angeles Hosp, 63-68; mem affiliate consult staff, St John's Hosp, Santa Monica, 64-71, courtesy staff, 71-72; active staff, St Bernardine Hosp, San Bernardino, 72-; active staff San Bernardino Community Hosp, 72-; consult staff, Redlands Community Hosp, 72-; chief, Oncol Sect, San Bernardino County Med Ctr, 72-76. *Mem:* AMA; fel Am Col Physicians; Am Soc Clin Oncol; Am Fedn Clin Res; Western Soc Clin Res. *Res:* Hematology; hematologic malignancies, especially multiple myeloma; cancer chemotherapy. *Mailing Add:* 399 E Highland Ave Suite 201 San Bernardino CA 92404

SKOP, RICHARD ALLEN, b Baltimore, Md, Mar 12, 43; m 64; c 3. APPLIED MECHANICS. *Educ:* Wash Univ, St Louis, BA, 64; Univ Rochester, PhD(appl mech), 68. *Prof Exp:* Res engr appl mech, 67-71, head fluid mech sect, 71-78, HEAD APPL MECH BR, US NAVAL RES LAB, 78- *Mem:* Am Soc Mech Engrs; Marine Technol Soc; Sigma Xi. *Res:* Fluid and structure interaction problems; wake dynamics; computational fluid dynamics. *Mailing Add:* Code 8440 US Naval Res Lab Washington DC 20375

SKOPEK, JERRY, b Berwyn, Ill, June 16, 20. BACTERIOLOGY. *Educ:* Univ Conn, BS, 42, MS, 50; Univ Md, PhD(bact), 55. *Prof Exp:* Asst, Nat Res Coun, 51-54; asst dir, St Louis Pub Health Labs, 54-56; consult microbiologist, St Mary's Mercy Hosp, Gary, Ind, 56-57; dir labs, J J McCook Mem Hosp, Hartford, 57-68; DIR LABS, HARTFORD HEALTH DEPT, 57- *Mem:* Am Soc Microbiol; Am Pub Health Asn. *Res:* Microbiological and biochemical problems relating to public health and clinical diagnosis. *Mailing Add:* 4 Skopek Rd Union Stafford Springs CT 06076

SKOPIK, STEVEN D, b Detroit, Mich, Dec 9, 40; m 60; c 3. PHYSIOLOGY. *Educ:* Defiance Col, BS, 62; Princeton Univ, MA, 64, PhD, 66. *Prof Exp:* From instr to lectr biol, Princeton Univ, 65-67; asst prof, 67-71, assoc chairperson dept biol sci, 73-76, ASSOC PROF BIOL, UNIV DEL, 71-, COODR PHYSIOL SECT, 76- *Mem:* AAAS; Entom Soc Am. *Res:* Role of biological clocks in the development of insects; role of clock systems in insect photoperiodism. *Mailing Add:* Sch of Life & Health Sci Univ of Del Newark DE 19711

SKOPP, JOSEPH MICHAEL, b Long Beach, Calif, Nov 24, 49; m 77; c 2. SOIL PHYSICS. *Educ:* Univ Calif, Davis, BS, 71; Univ Ariz, MS, 75; Univ Wis, PhD(soils), 80. *Prof Exp:* ASST PROF SOIL PHYSICS, UNIV NEBR, 80- *Mem:* Soil Sci Soc Am; Am Geophys Union; Am Phys Soc; Am Chem Soc; AAAS. *Res:* Measurement and description of solute (plant nutrients, pollutants or microorganisms) movement in soils; physical processes, particularly oxygen and nutrient transport, limiting microbiol activity in soil. *Mailing Add:* Dept Agron Unvi Nebr Lincoln NE 68583

SKORCZ, JOSEPH ANTHONY, b Milwaukee, Wis, May 25, 36; m 60; c 3. INDUSTRIAL ORGANIC CHEMISTRY. *Educ:* Marquette Univ, BS, 57; Univ Wis, MS, 59; Brown Univ, PhD(org chem), 62. *Prof Exp:* Sr res chemist, Lakeside Labs Div Colgate-Palmolive Co, 62-67, admin asst to dir res, 67-70, dir chem mfg & environ control, 70-74, dir mfg, 74-75; asst vpres mfg, Merrell-National Labs Div, 75-76, dir chem synthesis opers, Richardson-Merrell, Inc, 76-81, TECH MGR, MERRELL DOW PHARMACEUT INC, 81- *Mem:* Am Chem Soc. *Res:* Production scale synthetic organic chemistry; pharmaceutical manufacturing technology. *Mailing Add:* Merrell Dow Pharmaceut Inc Cincinnati OH 45215

SKORINKO, GEORGE, b Palmerton, Pa, Sept 25, 30; m 60; c 2. PHYSICS. *Educ:* Lehigh Univ, BS, 52; Boston Univ, MA, 53; Pa State Univ, PhD(physics), 60. *Prof Exp:* Physicist, Westinghouse Res Lab, 60-62; assoc prof, 62-74, PROF PHYSICS, BROOKLYN COL, 74- *Mem:* Optical Soc Am. *Res:* Infrared spectroscopy of molecules; extreme ultraviolet spectroscopy; solid state physics. *Mailing Add:* Dept of Physics Brooklyn Col Brooklyn NY 11210

SKOROPAD, WILLIAM PETER, b Alta, Can, May 23, 18; m 45; c 4. PLANT PATHOLOGY. *Educ:* Univ Alta, BSc & MSc, 50; Univ Wis, PhD(plant path), 55. *Prof Exp:* Agr res off, Fed Lab Plant Path, Alta, 52-59; from asst prof to assoc prof, 59-67, PROF PLANT PATH, UNIV ALTA, 67- *Mem:* Am Phytopath Soc; Can Phytopath Soc; Agr Inst Can. *Res:* Disease of rape crops, and foliage diseases of barley. *Mailing Add:* Dept of Plant Sci Univ of Alta Edmonton AB T6G 2P5 Can

SKORYNA, STANLEY C, b Warsaw, Poland, Sept 4, 20; Can citizen; m 70; c 1. GASTROENTEROLOGY, EXPERIMENTAL SURGERY. *Educ:* Univ Vienna, MD, 43, PhD(biol), 62; McGill Univ, MSc, 50. *Prof Exp:* Lectr, 55-59, asst prof, 59-62, ASSOC PROF SURG, MCGILL UNIV, 62-, DIR GASTROINTESTINAL RES LAB, 59-, DIR, RIDEAU INST, 69- *Concurrent Pos:* Res fel cancer, McGill Univ, 47-49; res fel, Nat Cancer Inst Can, 49-51; sr res fel, 51-54; dir, Can Med Exped to Easter Island, 64-65; deleg, Biol Coun Can, 67. *Honors & Awards:* Medal Surg, Royal Col Physicians & Surgeons, Can, 57. *Mem:* Am Asn Cancer Res; Am Gastroenterol Asn; Am Col Surgeons; Nutrit Soc Can. *Res:* Experimental carcinogenesis; pathophysiology of peptic ulcer; intestinal absorption of the metal ions, strontium and calcium; mucolytic action of amides; growth curve studies on Coelenterata. *Mailing Add:* Gastrointestinal Res Lab 740 Ave Dr Penfield Montreal ON H3A 1A4 Can

SKOSEY, JOHN LYLE, b Gillespie, Ill, Jan 19, 36; m 60; c 3. MEDICINE, PHYSIOLOGY. *Educ:* Univ Southern Ill, BA, 57; Univ Chicago, MD, 61, PhD(physiol), 64. *Prof Exp:* Intern, Univ Chicago Hosp, 61-62, jr asst resident med, Univ Chicago, 62-63; clin assoc, Endocrinol Br, Nat Cancer Inst, 63-65; sr res resident med, 65-66, resident, 66-67, instr, 67-69, asst prof, 69-74, ASSOC PROF MED, UNIV CHICAGO, 74- *Concurrent Pos:* USPHS trainee physiol, Univ Chicago, 62-63, USPHS clin trainee, 65-67; Arthritis Found fel, 68-71. *Mem:* Am Fedn Clin Res; Am Physiol Soc; Am Rheumatism Asn; Sigma Xi. *Res:* Cell physiology and pathophysiology. *Mailing Add:* Dept of Med Univ of Chicago Chicago IL 60637

SKOUG, DAVID L, b Rice Lake, Wis, Dec 31, 37; m 61; c 2. MATHEMATICAL ANALYSIS. *Educ:* Wis State Univ, River Falls, BA, 60; Univ Minn, PhD(math), 66. *Prof Exp:* From asst prof to assoc prof, 66-75, CHMN MATH, UNIV NEBR, LINCOLN, 75- *Mem:* Am Math Soc; Math Asn Am. *Res:* Mathematical research in the areas of integration in function space, Wener space and integrals, Feynman integrals. *Mailing Add:* Math Dept 809 Oldfather Hall Univ of Nebr Lincoln NE 68588

SKOUGSTAD, MARVIN WILMER, b Beloit, Wis, July 4, 18; m 43; c 2. ANALYTICAL CHEMISTRY. *Educ:* Univ Wis, BS, 39, PhD(chem), 49. *Prof Exp:* Chemist, Washburn Co, 39-41 & Fairbanks-Morse Co, 41-46; assoc prof chem, St Olaf Col, 49-58; chemist, Water Resources Div, US Geol Surv, 58-80; RETIRED. *Mem:* Am Chem Soc; Soc Appl Spectros; Am Soc Test & Mat. *Res:* Water analysis; spectroscopy. *Mailing Add:* 1000 Alkire St Golden CO 80401

SKOULTCHI, ARTHUR, b New York, NY, Aug 8, 40; m 65; c 2. CELL BIOLOGY. *Educ:* Princeton Univ, AB, 62; Yale Univ, MS, 65, PhD(molecular biophys & biochem), 69. *Prof Exp:* Fel biochem, Yale Univ, 69-70, spec fel, 72-73; fel biol, Mass Inst Technol, 70-72; ASST PROF CELL BIOL, ALBERT EINSTEIN COL MED, 73- *Concurrent Pos:* Fac res award, Am Cancer Soc, 74. *Mem:* Sigma Xi; Am Soc Cell Biol. *Res:* Mechanisms for controlling gene expression during differentiation of mammalian cells; somatic cell genetics of differentiation; messenger RNA biosynthesis in animal cells. *Mailing Add:* Dept of Cell Biol Albert Einstein Col of Med Bronx NY 10461

SKOULTCHI, MARTIN MILTON, b New York, NY, Oct 27, 33; m 60; c 3. ORGANIC CHEMISTRY, POLYMER CHEMISTRY. *Educ:* NY Univ, BA, 54, MS, 57, PhD(org chem), 60. *Prof Exp:* Assoc chemist organometallic chem, Res Div, Col Eng, NY Univ, 55-60; SR RES ASSOC, NAT STARCH & CHEM CORP, 60- *Mem:* Am Chem Soc; Soc Photog Sci & Eng. *Res:* Synthesis of speciality monomers and polymers; chemical reactions of and on polymers; photochemistry. *Mailing Add:* 6 Lilac Lane Somerset NJ 08873

SKOV, CHARLES E, b Kearney, Nebr, June 29, 33; m 54; c 3. SOLID STATE PHYSICS. *Educ:* Nebr State Col, Kearney, BA, 54; Univ Nebr, PhD(physics), 63. *Prof Exp:* Assoc prof, 63-73, PROF PHYSICS, MONMOUTH COL, ILL, 73- *Mem:* Am Phys Soc; Am Optical Soc; Am Asn Physics Teachers; Sigma Xi. *Res:* Electrical and optical properties of insulating crystals. *Mailing Add:* Dept of Physics Monmouth Col Monmouth IL 61462

SKOV, NIELS A, b Ribe, Denmark, Nov 6, 19; US citizen; m 53; c 2. PHYSICAL OCEANOGRAPHY, HISTORY OF SCIENCE. *Educ:* Technol Denmark, BS, 47; Ore State Univ, MS, 65, PhD(phys oceanog), 67. *Prof Exp:* PROF OCEANOG, EVERGREEN STATE COL, 72- *Mem:* AAAS. *Mailing Add:* Evergreen State Col Olympia WA 98505

SKOVE, MALCOLM JOHN, b Cleveland, Ohio, Mar 3, 31; m 56; c 2. SOLID STATE PHYSICS. *Educ:* Clemson Univ, BS, 56; Univ Va, PhD(physics), 60. *Prof Exp:* Asst prof physics, Ill State Univ, 60-61 & Univ PR, 61; from asst prof to assoc prof, 61-68, PROF PHYSICS, CLEMSON UNIV, 68- *Concurrent Pos:* Fulbright lectr, Haile Selassie Univ, 66-67; vis prof, Swiss Fed Inst Technol, 74-75. *Mem:* AAAS; Am Phys Soc; Am Asn Physics Teachers. *Res:* Effect of elastic strain on electrical properties of metals. *Mailing Add:* Dept of Physics Clemson Univ Clemson SC 29631

SKOVLIN, JON MATTHEW, b Colfax, Wash, Oct 31, 30; m 52; c 4. RANGE SCIENCE, WILDLIFE BIOLOGY. *Educ:* Ore State Univ, BS, 52; Univ Idaho, MS, 59. *Prof Exp:* Range scientist, Res Br, US Forest Serv, Ore, 56-68; ecologist, UN Food & Agr Orgn, Nairobi, Kenya, 68-71; res biologist wildlife habitat res, Range & Wildlife Habitat Lab, 71-76, RANGE SCIENTIST/PROJ LEADER, USDA FOREST SERV, ORE, 76- *Concurrent Pos:* Consult, EAfrica natural resources & environ, 77, 78 & 80; prin investr, EAfrica rangeland invest, Kenya; cert rangeland consult, Soc Range Mgt; cert wildlife biologist, Wildlife Soc. *Mem:* Soc Range Mgt; Soc Am Foresters; EAfrican Wildlife Soc; Wildlife Soc; Int Soc Trop Foresters. *Res:* Investigations of levels, seasons and systems of livestock grazing and interactions on related resources throughout semi-arid zones of western North America and arid zones of East Africa; numerous scientific publications. *Mailing Add:* Range & Wildlife Habitat Lab Rte 2 Box 2315 La Grande OR 97850

SKOVRONEK, HERBERT SAMUEL, b Brooklyn, NY, Apr 19, 36; m 60; c 2. ORGANIC CHEMISTRY, ENVIRONMENTAL ENGINEERING. *Educ:* Brooklyn Col, BS, 56; Pa State Univ, PhD(carbenes), 61. *Prof Exp:* From chemist to sr chemist, Texaco, Inc, 61-62; res chemist, Rayonier, Inc, 62-67; res chemist, J P Stevens & Co, Inc, 67, group leader, 67-71; res chemist, Indust Waste Technol Br, 71-74, tech adv, Indust Waste Treatment Res Lab, 74-75, tech adv, Indust Environ Res Lab, US Environ Protection Agency, 75-78; mgr environ control, Semet-Solvay Div, 78-79, ENVIRON SPECIALIST, ALLIED CHEM CORP, 79- *Mem:* Water Pollution Control Fedn; Am Inst Chemists; Am Chem Soc. *Res:* Pollution abatement technology for metal finishing, pharmaceuticals, paints and organic chemicals manufacturing; environmental impacts of industrial energy conservation practices. *Mailing Add:* 88 Moraine Rd Morris Plains NJ 07950

SKOW, LOREN CURTIS, b Gainesville, Tex, Sept 4, 46; m 74. GENETICS, BIOCHEMISTRY. *Educ:* Abilene Christian Col, BSEd, 69, MS, 71; Tex A&M Univ, PhD(fisheries sci), 76. *Prof Exp:* Res assoc mammalian genetics, Oak Ridge Nat Lab, 78-79, staff scientist mammalian mutagenesis, 79-81; SR STAFF FEL GENETICS, NAT INST ENVIRON HEALTH SCI, 81- *Concurrent Pos:* NIH fel, Jackson Lab, 76-78; cystic fibrosis consult, NIH, 78- *Mem:* Genetics Soc Am; AAAS. *Res:* Comparative vertebrate genetics; gene mapping; organization of genes controlling rodent salivary secretions; genetics of rodent lens crystallins. *Mailing Add:* Genetics Lab Nat Inst Environ Health Sci Research Triangle Park NC 27709

SKOWRONSKI, RAYMUND PAUL, b Detroit, Mich, Feb 7, 48; m 70. PHYSICAL CHEMISTRY, ORGANIC CHEMISTRY. *Educ:* Univ Mich, BS, 69; Tex A&M Univ, PhD(chem), 75. *Prof Exp:* Teaching asst chem, Tex A&M Univ, 69-70, instr, 70-72; RES CHEMIST, ROCKWELL INT, 75- *Mem:* Am Chem Soc; Sigma Xi. *Res:* Catalysis; synthetic fuels; isotopic tracer research; coal liquefaction; molten salt chemistry; nuclear chemistry. *Mailing Add:* Energy Systs Group 8900 De Soto Ave Canoga Park CA 91304

SKRABEK, EMANUEL ANDREW, b Baltimore, Md, Mar 3, 34; m 72; c 1. ENERGY CONVERSION, PHYSICAL CHEMISTRY. *Educ:* Univ Md, BS, 56; Univ Wis, MS, 58; Univ Pittsburgh, PhD(phys chem), 62. *Prof Exp:* Sr res scientist energy conversion, Martin-Marietta Corp, 62-69; sr scientist heat pipe mat, Dynatherm Corp, 69-72; MGR RES THERMOELEC, TELEDYNE ENERGY SYSTS, 72- *Mem:* Am Chem Soc; AAAS; Am Soc Testing & Mat; Sigma Xi. *Res:* Thermoelectric materials development and testing; heat pipe materials compatibility; wetting of surfaces; thermal conductivity of insulators; thermodynamic compatibility of materials at 1000 C and above. *Mailing Add:* Teledyne Energy Systs 110 W Timonium Rd Timonium MD 21093

SKRABLE, KENNETH WILLIAM, b Teaneck, NJ, Oct 10, 35; m 57; c 2. PHYSICS, RADIOLOGICAL HEALTH. *Educ:* Moravian Col, BS, 58; Vanderbilt Univ, MS, 63; Rutgers Univ, PhD(environ sci), 70. *Prof Exp:* Health physics supvr, Indust Reactor Lab, Inc, 59-63; radiation safety officer & lectr radiation sci, Rutgers Univ, 63-68; prof & chmn radiological sci dept, Lowell Technol Inst, 68-74; PROF RADIOLOGICAL SCI, UNIV LOWELL, 74- *Concurrent Pos:* Chmn, New Eng Consortium on Environ Protection, 71-72; consult, Yankee Atomic Elec Co, 75-76, US Nuclear Regulatory Comn, 80- *Mem:* Health Physics Soc; Am Nuclear Soc; Sigma Xi. *Res:* Air pollution, aerosols; naturally occurring and man-made radioactive aerosols; measurement and control of air pollutants and radioactivity; internal and external radiation dosimetry. *Mailing Add:* 6 Ruthellen Rd Chelmsford MA 01824

SKRAMSTAD, HAROLD KENNETH, b Tacoma, Wash, July 26, 08; m 40; c 4. PHYSICS. *Educ:* Univ Puget Sound, BS, 30; Univ Wash, Seattle, PhD(physics), 35. *Prof Exp:* Teacher high sch, Wash, 30-31; physicist, Nat Bur Stand, 35-46, chief, Guided Missiles Sect, 46-50, asst chief, Missile Develop Div, 50-53; chief, Missile Systs Div, US Naval Ord Lab, 53-54; asst chief systs, Data Processing Systs Div, Nat Bur Stand, 54-61; assoc tech dir, US Naval Ord Lab, 61-67; prof indust eng & sci dir comput ctr, 67-74, EMER PROF MGT SCI & EMER ADJ PROF MATH, UNIV MIAMI, 74-; ADJ PROF, FLA INST TECHNOL, 76- *Concurrent Pos:* Life mem, Simulation Coun. *Honors & Awards:* Reed Award, Am Inst Aeronaut & Astronaut, 47. *Mem:* Am Phys Soc; assoc fel Am Inst Aeronaut & Astronaut; sr mem Inst Elec & Electronics Engrs; Asn Comput Mach. *Res:* Primary ionization of gases; wind tunnel turbulence; boundary layer flow; development of guided missiles; aerodynamics; computers; simulators; automatic control. *Mailing Add:* 8045 S A1A Hwy Melbourne Beach FL 32951

SKRDLA, WILLIS HOWARD, b DeWitt, Nebr, Feb 22, 20; m 42; c 3. AGRONOMY. *Educ:* Univ Nebr, BSc, 41; Purdue Univ, PhD(agron), 49. *Prof Exp:* Asst, Purdue Univ, 46-49; assoc prof agron, Va Agr Exp Sta, Va Polytech Inst, 49-53; agronomist airport turfing, US Dept Air Force, 53-57; PROF AGRON, IOWA STATE UNIV & AGRONOMIST RES LEADER & COORDR, N CENT REGIONAL PLANT INTROD STA, US DEPT AGR, 57- *Mem:* AAAS; Sigma Xi; Soc Econ Bot; Am Soc Agron. *Res:* Plant introduction; seed increase, distribution, evaluation and permanent storage of world collections of agronomic and horticultural crops; coordinate regional program in 13 states; field crop, forage and turf investigations. *Mailing Add:* 2136 Duff Ave Ames IA 50010

SKREINER, KLAUS MICHAEL, b Berlin, Ger, May 4, 41; Australian citizen. MECHANICAL ENGINEERING, EARTHQUAKE ENGINEERING. *Educ:* Univ Western Australia, BME, 64; Univ Sydney, PhD(mech eng), 68. *Prof Exp:* Sr res engr, 67-71, mgr mech eng, 71-77, mgr appl physics & mech eng, 77-80, MGR, ENG DEVELOP LAB, GEN ELEC CO, 80- *Concurrent Pos:* Consult & lectr nuclear qualifications, Inst Elec & Electronics Engrs, 78- *Honors & Awards:* Edward J Noyes Prize, Inst Engrs, Australia, 68. *Mem:* Am Soc Mech Engrs; Inst Elec & Electronics Engrs. *Res:* Kinematics and dynamics of linkage mechanisms; transient mechanical behavior of systems; seismic qualification of class 1E equipment for nuclear power generating stations. *Mailing Add:* Gen Elec Co 6901 Elmwood Ave Philadelphia PA 19142

SKRINAR, GARY STEPHEN, b Teaneck, NJ, Aug 28, 42; c 1. EXERCISE PHYSIOLOGY. *Educ:* Oklahoma City Univ, BA, 64; Univ Ill, MS, 65; Univ Pittsburgh, PhD(exercise phys motor learning), 78. *Prof Exp:* Instr phys educ, Midland Mich Pub Schs, 65-68, Oklahoma City Univ, 68-70 & Ore Sta Univ, 70-71; asst prof, Brookdale Community Col, 71-74; ASST PROF HEALTH SCI, BOSTON UNIV, 78- *Concurrent Pos:* Exercise tech, exercise leader, Univ Pittsburgh Cardiac Rehab Prog, 74-78; exercise prog dir, Am Col Sports Med, 78. *Mem:* Am Col Sports Med; Am Alliance for Health, Phys Educ & Recreation; NAm Soc for Psychol Sport & Phys Activ. *Res:* Exercise physiology; cardiac rehabilitation; acquisition and maintenance of physical fitness. *Mailing Add:* Dept of Health Sci 36 Cummington St Boston MA 02215

SKRINDE, ROLF T, b Stanwood, Wash, Sept 1, 28; m 58; c 3. CIVIL & ENVIRONMENTAL ENGINEERING. *Educ:* Wash State Univ, SB & CE, 51; Mass Inst Technol, SM, 52, SanE, 56, PhD(sanit eng), 59. *Prof Exp:* Sanit eng adv, Ministry Health, Saudi Arabia & Thailand, 53-55; asst sanit eng, Mass Inst Technol, 55-58; asst prof civil eng, Wash State Univ, 58-60, assoc prof, 60-61; assoc prof, Wash Univ, 61-64, chmn dept civil eng, 64-65; dir res, SEATO Grad Sch Eng, Bangkok, 65-67; prof civil eng, Univ Mass, Amherst, 67-69; prof & chmn dept civil eng, Univ Iowa, 69-77; MEM STAFF, OLYMPIC ASSOCS CO, 77- *Mem:* Am Soc Civil Eng; Water Pollution Control Fedn; Am Water Works Asn; Nat Soc Prof Engrs. *Res:* Corrosion control in potable water systems; stream pollution; waste water treatment; determination of public health effects of agricultural use on return irrigation waters; pesticide residues; reverse osmosis water treatment; metal plating waste treatment. *Mailing Add:* 16327 Inglewood Place NE Bothell WA 98011

SKRIVAN, J(OSEPH) F(RANCIS), b Baltimore, Md, Oct 25, 31; m 54; c 6. CHEMICAL ENGINEERING. *Educ:* Johns Hopkins Univ, BE, 53, MS, 56, DEng, 58. *Prof Exp:* Res engr, 58-63, sr res engr, 64-66, group leader eng res, 66-72, res mgr, 72-75, tech dir, 75-78, mgr mfg catalyst dept, 78-81, RES DIR, AM CYANAMID CO, 81- *Mem:* Am Inst Chem Engrs; Sigma Xi. *Res:* Kinetics; heat transfer; high temperature processing and plasma technology; process development; auto exhaust catalysts. *Mailing Add:* 154 Berrian Rd Stamford CT 06905

SKROCH, WALTER ARTHUR, b Arcadia, Wis, July 1, 37; m 63; c 2. WEED SCIENCE. *Educ:* Wis State Univ, River Falls, BS, 59; Univ Wis, Madison, MS, 61, PhD(hort), 65. *Prof Exp:* Assoc prof, 68-73, PROF HORT SCI, N C STATE UNIV, 73- *Mem:* Am Pomol Soc; Weed Sci Soc Am; Am Soc Hort Sci. *Res:* Herbicide activity, tree fruits, ornamental, Christmas trees, landscape and broadrange fumigation as preplant treatment of horticultural crops. *Mailing Add:* Dept of Hort Sci 166 Kilgore N C State Univ Raleigh NC 27607

SKROMME, LAWRENCE H, b Roland, Iowa, Aug 26, 13; m 39; c 3. AGRICULTURAL ENGINEERING. *Educ:* Iowa State Univ, BSc, 37. *Prof Exp:* From draftsman to design engr, Goodyear Tire & Rubber Co, 37-41; from proj engr to asst chief engr, Harry Ferguson, Inc, 41-51; chief engr, 51-61, V PRES ENG, SPERRY NEW HOLLAND, SPERRY RAND CORP, 61- *Concurrent Pos:* Mem, Farm Resources & Facilities Res Adv Comt, USDA, 65; mem, Int Rels Comt & Nat Medal of Sci Comt, Engrs Joint Coun; mem, Gov Comt Preserv Agr Land; vpres, Farm & Home Found, Lancaster County, Pa; mem div eng, Nat Res Coun; power & mach rep, Int Comn Agr Eng; vpres, bd mem & pres, Agr Mach Sect, Comn Int Genie Rurale, 73-

Mem: Nat Acad Eng; fel Am Soc Agr Engrs (vpres, 52-55, pres, 59-60); Am Soc Eng Educ; Nat Soc Prof Engrs; Soc Automotive Engrs. *Res:* Development of efficient farm machines to reduce labor and improve productivity. *Mailing Add:* 2150 Landis Valley Rd Lancaster PA 17601

SKRYPA, MICHAEL JOHN, b Woonsocket, RI, Sept 26, 27; m 53; c 3. COMMERCIALIZATION OF RESEARCH DISCOVERIES. *Educ:* Brown Univ, BSc, 50; Clark Univ, PhD(org chem), 54. *Prof Exp:* Res chemist, Solvay Process Div, Allied Chem Corp, 53-61, assoc res supvr, 61-62, res supvr, 62-63, mgr appl res, 63-67, mgr new polymer applns develop, Plastics Div, res consult, Corp Res Ctr, 72-76, mgr com develop, Venture Mgt Div, 76-79, MGR MKT DEVELOP, NEW VENTURES GROUP, ALLIED CORP, 79- *Mem:* Soc Plastics Eng; Com Develop Asn; Am Chem Soc; Am Soc Metals. *Res:* Organic syntheses; polymerizations; physical chemistry of polymers; physical chemistry of metals; development of applications for chemicals, polymers and metals; direction and management of research organizations. *Mailing Add:* Corp Res Ctr Allied Chem Corp Morristown NJ 07960

SKUBIC, PATRICK LOUIS, b Eveleth, Minn, Sept 9, 47. ELEMENTARY PARTICLE PHYSICS. *Educ:* SDak State Univ, BS, 69; Univ Mich, MS, 70, PhD(physics), 77. *Prof Exp:* Fel, Rutgers Univ, 77-80; ASST PROF, UNIV OKLA, 81- *Mem:* Am Phys Soc; Sigma Xi. *Res:* Experimental elementary particle physics; precise measurement of neutral hyperon polarization and magnetic moments in high energy neutral hyperon beams; evidence for production of particles containing heavy quarks in electron-positron collisions. *Mailing Add:* Dept Physics & Astron Univ Okla 440 W Brooks St Norman OK 73019

SKUCAS, JOVITAS, b Klaipeda, Lithuania, Sept 21, 36; US citizen; m 65; c 3. RADIOLOGY. *Educ:* Newark Col Eng, BS, 58, MS, 64; Hahnemann Med Col, MD, 68. *Prof Exp:* Intern med, St Vincent's Hosp, New York, 68-69, resident radiol, 69-72; instr, Univ Ind, 72-73; asst prof, 73-76, ASSOC PROF RADIOL, UNIV ROCHESTER, 76- *Concurrent Pos:* Vis radiologist, Isaac Gordon Ctr Digestive Dis, Genesee Hosp, NY, 75- *Mem:* Radiol Soc NAm; Inst Elec & Electronics Engrs; Asn Univ Radiologists; Roentgen Ray Soc; Am Gastroenterol Asn. *Res:* Application of engineering to radiological science; gastro-intestinal radiology. *Mailing Add:* Dept of Radiol Sch of Med Univ of Rochester Rochester NY 14642

SKUD, BERNARD EINAR, b Ironwood, Mich, Jan 31, 27; m 50; c 3. MARINE BIOLOGY, FISHERIES. *Educ:* Univ Mich, BS, 49, MS, 50; Princeton Univ, cert pub affairs, 68. *Prof Exp:* Asst freshwater fishes, Univ Mich, 49-50; fishery res biologist, Alaska salmon & herring, 50-56, supv fishery res biologist, 56-58, asst lab dir, Gulf of Mex fisheries, 58-61, lab dir, Biol Lab, Boothbay Harbor, 61-70, dir invests, Int Pac Halibut Comn, Seattle, 70-78; DIR INVESTS, US NAT MARINE FISHERIES SERV, US BUR COMMERCIAL FISHERIES, US FISH & WILDLIFE SERV, 78- *Concurrent Pos:* Chmn, herring & pelagic fish subcomt, Int N Atlantic Fisheries Comn; affil prof, Univ Wash, 71-78; adj prof, Univ RI. *Mem:* Am Fisheries Soc; Am Soc Limnol & Oceanog; Am Soc Ichthyol & Herpet; Am Inst Fisheries Res Biol (pres, 81-83). *Res:* Pacific salmon; Pacific and Atlantic herring population dynamics; age and growth studies; biological oceanography; estuaries; off-shore lobsters; Pacific halibut; marine ecosystems. *Mailing Add:* Nat Marine Fisheries Serv South Ferry Rd Narragansett RI 02882

SKUJINS, JOHN JANIS, b Latvia, Apr 13, 26; US citizen; div; c 2. SOIL BIOCHEMISTRY, SOIL MICROBIOLOGY. *Educ:* Univ Calif, Berkeley, BA, 57, PhD(agr chem), 63. *Prof Exp:* Fel soil microbiol, Cornell Univ, 62-64; res biochemist, Univ Calif, Berkeley, 64-69; assoc prof, 69-76, PROF BIOL & SOIL SCI, UTAH STATE UNIV, 76- *Concurrent Pos:* NSF study grant soil microbiol, US Int Biol Prog; chmn, Int Symp Environ Biogeochem Inc, 73-; vis staff mem Helsinki Univ, 77; consult, US Environ Protection Agency, 74-78; mem, Int Comt Microbial Ecol, 78-; assoc ed, Geomicrobiol J, 78- *Mem:* Am Chem Soc; Am Soc Microbiol; Soil Sci Soc Am; fel Am Inst Chemists; Int Soil Sci Soc. *Res:* Ecology of arid lands; nitrogen fixation and cycling; soil enzymology; microbial ecology; enzymatic and microbial activities in adverse environmental conditions; ecology of forest soils. *Mailing Add:* Dept Biol Utah State Univ Logan UT 84322

SKULAN, THOMAS WILLIAM, b Milwaukee, Wis, Feb 12, 32; m 52; c 3. PHARMACOLOGY, PHYSIOLOGY. *Educ:* Univ Wis-Madison, BS, 58, PhD(pharmacol), 62. *Prof Exp:* NIH fel, Univ Fla, 62-63; GROUP LEADER DIURETICS, STERLING-WINTHROP RES INST, 66-, HEAD CARDIOVASC SECT, 69- *Res:* Renal pharmacology, hypertension. *Mailing Add:* Dept of Pharmacol Sterling-Winthrop Res Inst Rensselaer NY 12144

SKULTETY, FRANCIS MILES, b Rochester, NY, June 6, 22; m 45; c 3. MEDICINE. *Educ:* Univ Rochester, BS, 44, MD, 46; Univ Iowa, PhD(anat), 58; Am Bd Neurol Surg, dipl, 54. *Prof Exp:* Intern, Worcester City Hosp, Mass, 46-47; asst resident neurol, Cushing Vet Admin Hosp, 49-50; sr resident neurosurg, Univ Iowa Hosps, 51-52, instr surg, 52-53, assoc, 53-54, from asst prof to prof, 54-66; interim dean, Col Med, 78-79, SHAKLEFORD PROF NEUROSURG & NEUROANAT, COL MED, UNIV NEBR, OMAHA, 66-, ASSOC DEAN CLIN AFFAIRS, 74-78, 79-, PROF & CHMN DEPT NEUROSURG, 75- *Concurrent Pos:* Fel neurosurg, Lahey Clin, 50-51; clin traineeship Nat Inst Neurol Dis & Stroke, Dept Physiol, Oxford Univ, 57-58. *Mem:* AMA; Am Asn Neurol Surg; fel Am Col Surg; Am Neurol Asn; Soc Neurosci. *Res:* Neuroanatomy; neurophysiology; neural regulation of intake. *Mailing Add:* Dept of Neurosurg Univ of Nebr Col of Med Omaha NE 68105

SKUMANICH, ANDREW, b Wilkes-Barre, Pa, Oct 5, 29; m 55; c 3. ASTROPHYSICS. *Educ:* Pa State Univ, BS, 51; Princeton Univ, PhD(astrophys), 54. *Prof Exp:* Staff mem, Los Alamos Sci Lab, Univ Calif, 54-60; asst prof & res assoc physics & astron, Univ Rochester, 60-61; MEM SR STAFF, HIGH ALTITUDE OBSERV, NAT CTR ATMOSPHERIC RES, 61-; PROF ADJOINT, UNIV COLO, 69- *Concurrent Pos:* Consult, Los Alamos Sci Lab, 61-73; lectr, Univ Colo, 61-69; vis scientist, Lab Stellar & Planetary Physics, 73-74; consult, NASA, 74- *Mem:* Am Phys Soc; Am Astron Soc; Int Astron Union. *Res:* Thermodynamics and hydrodynamics of high temperature plasma; visible, ultraviolet and x-ray spectroscopy; radiative processes; atomic and electronic collision phenomena; solar, atmospheric and chromospheric physics. *Mailing Add:* High Altitude Observ Nat Ctr for Atmospheric Res Boulder CO 80302

SKUTNIK, BOLESH JOSEPH, b Passaic, NJ, Aug 19, 41; m 67; c 2. PHYSICAL CHEMISTRY. *Educ:* Seton Hall Univ, BS, 62; Yale Univ, MS, 64, PhD(theoret phys chem), 67. *Prof Exp:* Res assoc phys chem, Brandeis Univ, 67-69; sr res scientist, Firestone Radiation Res Div, Firestone Tire & Rubber Co, 69-73; asst prof chem, Fairfield Univ, 73-80; WITH E B INDUST, 80- *Concurrent Pos:* Lectr, Brandeis Univ, 68-69; abstractor, Chem Abstr Serv, 69-; consult, Acad Press, Inc, 74-76. *Mem:* Am Phys Soc; Am Chem Soc. *Res:* Effects of radiation on matter, theoretical and applied; characterization and physical properties of irradiated polymers; electronic structure of atoms and molecules; inter- and intra-molecular energy transfer. *Mailing Add:* E B Indust 660 Hopmeadow St Simsbury CT 06070

SKYE, GEORGE ERI, II, biochemistry, see previous edition

SKY-PECK, HOWARD H, b London, Eng, July 24, 23; nat US; m 52; c 3. BIOCHEMISTRY. *Educ:* Univ Southern Calif, BS, 49, PhD, 56. *Prof Exp:* Lab instr biochem, Univ Southern Calif, 50-52; res assoc, Presby Hosp, Chicago, 55; from instr to assoc prof, Col Med, 55-67, assoc prof, Grad Sch, 58-67, PROF BIOCHEM, GRAD SCH, UNIV ILL, 67- *Concurrent Pos:* Asst attend biochemist, Presby-St Lukes Hosp, 58-62, sr attend biochemist, 62-, dir, Clin Chem Lab, 67-75; mem biochem comt, Nat Cancer Chemother Serv Ctr, NIH, 60; actg chmn dept, Rush Med Col, 70-71, prof biochem & chmn dept, 71-80. *Mem:* AAAS; Am Chem Soc; Am Cancer Soc; Am Asn Clin Chem; Am Asn Cancer Res. *Res:* Amino acid metabolism in mouse brains; biochemical comparison between normal and neoplastic human cancer tissues and use of biochemical techniques in evaluation of chemotherapeutic agents in cancer. *Mailing Add:* Dept of Biochem Rush-Presby-St Luke's Med Ctr Chicago IL 60612

SKYPEK, DORA HELEN, b Noma, Fla, Sept 18, 15; m 44; c 2. MATHEMATICS EDUCATION, MATHEMATICS. *Educ:* Fla State Univ, BA, 37; Emory Univ, MA, 61; Univ Wis, PhD(math educ), 66. *Prof Exp:* Teacher math, Fla Pub High Schs, 37-44 & St John's Country Day Sch, Fla, 54-58; from asst prof to assoc prof math & math educ, 63-77, PROF MATH & MATH EDUC, EMORY UNIV, 77- *Concurrent Pos:* Dir, Experienced Teacher Fel Prog, US Off Educ, 68-69; dir res proj, NSF, 74-76; co-dir women sci career workshop, NSF, 80; coordr working group women math, IV Int Cong Math Educ, 80. *Mem:* Nat Coun Teachers Math; Math Asn Am; Am Educ Res Asn. *Res:* The teaching and learning of mathematics; related Piagetian theory; factors that support and inhibit women in science careers. *Mailing Add:* Div of Educ Studies Emory Univ Atlanta GA 30322

SLABAUGH, WENDELL HARTMAN, colloid chemistry, deceased

SLABY, HAROLD THEODORE, b Traverse City, Mich, Oct 11, 20; m 51; c 1. ALGEBRA. *Educ:* Wayne State Univ, AB, 46, MA, 48; Univ Wis, PhD(math), 53. *Prof Exp:* From instr to asst prof, 53-63, ASSOC PROF MATH, WAYNE STATE UNIV, 64- *Concurrent Pos:* Mem consult bur, Math Asn Am, 68- *Mem:* Am Math Soc; Math Asn Am. *Res:* Projective geometry; non associative algebra. *Mailing Add:* Dept Math Wayne State Univ Detroit MI 48202

SLABYJ, BOHDAN M, b Chernivci, Ukraine, Dec 3, 31; US citizen; m 63; c 2. FOOD SCIENCE. *Educ:* Univ Alta, BSc, 58, MSc, 60; Univ Wash, PhD(food sci), 68. *Prof Exp:* Instr bact, Univ Alta, 60-62; asst microbiologist, Univ Wash, 62-67; asst prof microbiol, Duquesne Univ, 67-69; fel, Albert Einstein Med Ctr, 69-72, ASST PROF FOOD SCI, UNIV MAINE, 72- *Mem:* Am Soc Microbiol; Inst Food Technol; Soc Appl Bacteriol. *Res:* Seafood processing, quality, and safety. *Mailing Add:* Food Sci Dept Univ of Maine Orono ME 04469

SLACK, DERALD ALLEN, b Cedar City, Utah, Dec 22, 24; m 45; c 2. PHYTOPATHOLOGY, NEMATOLOGY. *Educ:* Utah State Agr Col, BS, 48, MS, 49; Univ Wis, PhD, 53. *Prof Exp:* Asst res & collabr, US Dept Agr, Utah State Agr Col, 46-47, asst, 47-49; asst, Univ Wis, 49-52; from asst prof to assoc prof, 52-60, PROF PLANT PATH, UNIV ARK, FAYETTEVILLE, 60-, HEAD DEPT, 64- *Concurrent Pos:* Mem & secy, Ark State Plant Bd, 64- *Mem:* Am Phytopath Soc (secy, 78-80); Soc Nematol; Int Soc Plant Path. *Res:* Fruit diseases; plant parasitic nematodes. *Mailing Add:* Dept of Plant Path Univ of Ark Fayetteville AR 72701

SLACK, GLEN ALFRED, b Rochester, NY, Sept 29, 28; m 51; c 3. SOLID STATE PHYSICS. *Educ:* Rensselaer Polytech Inst, BS, 50; Cornell Univ, PhD, 56. *Prof Exp:* PHYSICIST, GEN ELEC RES & DEVELOP CTR, 56- *Concurrent Pos:* Guggenheim Mem fel, Oxford Univ, 66-67. *Mem:* Fel Am Phys Soc; Sigma Xi. *Res:* Thermal properties and heat transport in solids; preparation and chemistry of crystals; properties of semiconductors; ultrasonic phonon propagation in solids. *Mailing Add:* Gen Elec Res & Develop Ctr Schenectady NY 12345

SLACK, JIM MARSHALL, b Irving, Tex, Mar 11, 31; m 65; c 3. PHYSIOLOGY. *Educ:* Sam Houston State Col, BS, 52; Sam Houston State Univ, MA, 66; Tex A&M Univ, PhD(zool), 71. *Prof Exp:* Res assoc biochem, Radiation Res Assocs, 62-65; asst prof biol, Hardin-Simmons Univ, 66-67; assoc prof, Howard Payne Col, 70-73; asst prof physiol, Auburn Univ, 73-77, asst prof zool-entomol, 77-79; MEM STAFF DEPT PHYSIOL & CHEM, TEX CHIROPRACTIC COL, 79- *Mem:* Am Soc Zoologists; Sigma Xi. *Res:* Physiology of trauma and stress, with particular interest in the action of Prostaglandin, following ionizing radiation. *Mailing Add:* Dept Physiol & Chem Tex Chiropractic Col Pasadena TX 77505

SLACK, JOHN MADISON, b Polson, Mont, Mar 9, 14; m 40; c 1. MEDICAL BACTERIOLOGY. *Educ:* Univ Minn, AB, 36, MS, 37, PhD(bact), 40; Am Bd Microbiol, dipl, 62. *Prof Exp:* Asst bact, Univ Minn, 38-40; instr path & bact, Col Med, Univ Nebr, 40-42; bacteriologist, US Army Chem Warfare Labs, Ft Detrick, Md, 46; prof, 46-77, EMER PROF MICROBIOL, MED CTR, W VA UNIV, 77- *Mem:* AAAS; Am Soc Microbiol; fel Am Pub Health Asn. *Res:* Identification and classification of Actinomyces; fluorescent antibody techniques; nocardin; food poisoning. *Mailing Add:* 1513 Flamingo Lane Sun City FL 33570

SLACK, KEITH VOLLMER, b Louisville, Ky, May 20, 24; m 62; c 4. STREAM LIMNOLOGY, BIOLOGICAL WATER QUALITY. *Educ:* Univ Ky, BS, 49, MS, 50; Ind Univ, PhD(zool), 54. *Prof Exp:* Asst zool, Univ Ky, 49-50, State Lake & Stream Surv, Ind Univ, 50-52 & Ind Univ, 52-53; oceanogr, US Navy Oceanog, 53-60; RES LIMNOLOGIST, US GEOL SURV, 60- *Concurrent Pos:* Res adv ecol, Water Resources Div, US Geol Surv, 74-76 & 78- *Mem:* Am Inst Biol Sci; Ecol Soc Am; Am Soc Limnol & Oceanog; Int Asn Theoret & Appl Limnol; NAm Benthological Soc. *Res:* Interrelations between aquatic organisms and their environment; stream limnology; arctic and alpine limnology; biological controls on water quality; limnological methods. *Mailing Add:* Water Resources Div US Geol Surv 345 Middlefield Rd Menlo Park CA 94025

SLACK, LEWIS, b Philadelphia, Pa, Apr 15, 24; m 48; c 3. NUCLEAR PHYSICS. *Educ:* Harvard Univ, SB, 44; Wash Univ, PhD(physics), 50. *Prof Exp:* Asst physics, Wash Univ, 46-50; physicist, US Naval Res Lab, 50-54; from assoc prof to prof physics, George Washington Univ, 54-62, actg head dept, 57-60; asst exec secy div phys sci, Nat Acad Sci-Nat Res Coun, 62-67, ASSOC DIR, AM INST PHYSICS, 67- *Concurrent Pos:* Secy comt nuclear sci, Nat Res Coun, 62-67; secy, US Nat Comt for Int Union Pure & Appl Physics, 74-; mem, Sci Manpower Comn, 68-, pres, 74-76. *Mem:* AAAS; Am Phys Soc; Am Asn Physics Teachers. *Res:* Beta ray and gamma ray spectroscopy; angular correlation; science administration. *Mailing Add:* Am Inst Physics 335 E 45th St New York NY 10017

SLACK, LYLE HOWARD, b Wellsville, NY, Jan 6, 37; m 54; c 4. CERAMICS. *Educ:* Alfred Univ, BS, 58, PhD(ceramic sci), 65. *Prof Exp:* Res engr, Hommel Co, Pa, 58-60 & Lexington Labs, Mass, 60-61; mem tech staff thin film electronics, Bell Tel Labs, 65-67; asst prof ceramic eng, Va Polytech Inst & State Univ, 67-71, assoc prof, 71-80; SR RES CHEMIST, E I DU PONT DE NEMOURS & CO, INC, NY, 80- *Concurrent Pos:* Consult, Naval Res Labs, 69-81. *Mem:* Fel Am Ceramic Soc; Nat Inst Ceramic Engrs; Am Soc Eng Educ; Electrochem Soc; Int Soc Hybrid Microelectronics. *Res:* Structure and electric properties of semiconducting glasses; structure and electronic conduction in oxide thin films; solar photovoltaic materials; solar thermal coatings; thick film resistors; thick film dielectrics. *Mailing Add:* Elec Mat Div E I du Pont de Nemours & Co Inc Niagara Falls NY 14302

SLACK, NANCY G, b New York, NY, Aug 12, 30; m 51; c 3. PLANT ECOLOGY. *Educ:* Cornell Univ, BS, 52, MS, 54; State Univ NY, Albany, PhD(ecol), 71. *Prof Exp:* Demonstr bot & evolution, Bot Sch, Oxford Univ, Eng, 66-67; lectr bot, State Univ NY, Albany, 69; asst prof, 71-75, ASSOC PROF BIOL, RUSSELL SAGE COL, TROY, NY, 75-, CHMN DEPT, 78- *Concurrent Pos:* Consult, Environ Impact Studies, Environ-One Corp, 73-, Environ Assessment Study, Dunn Geosci, 74-, Environ Impact Studies, Environmed Inc, 75-; trustee & ecol consult land acquisition, The Nature Conserv, 73-; consult col sci progs, NY State Educ Dept, 75-76, 78 & 82; Am Asn Univ Professors fel, 79. *Honors & Awards:* Donald Richards Fund Award, NY Bot Garden, 74, Diamond Award, 75. *Mem:* Ecol Soc Am; Am Bryol & Lichenol Soc; Int Bryol Asn; AAAS; Sigma Xi. *Res:* Community ecology of bryophytes and vascular plants including Sphagnum bog ecology; species diversity and community structure in bryophytes; ecology of epiphytic bryophytes in North America; island biogeography and vegetation changes on islands due to human disturbance; bryophytes in relation to ecological niche theory. *Mailing Add:* Dept of Biol Russell Sage Col Troy NY 12180

SLACK, NELSON HOSKING, b Burlington, Vt, Feb 7, 35; m 60; c 3. BIOSTATISTICS. *Educ:* Univ Vt, BS, 57; Rutgers Univ, MS, 63, PhD(dairy sci), 64. *Prof Exp:* Res asst dairy sci, Rutgers Univ, 63-64; assoc cancer res scientist biostatist, 64-77, DEP DIR CLIN TRIALS, NAT PROSTATIC CANCER PROJ, ROSWELL PARK MEM INST, 77- *Concurrent Pos:* Res prof, Niagara Univ; asst res prof, State Univ NY Buffalo. *Mem:* AAAS; Am Asn Cancer Res; Am Statist Asn. *Res:* Cancer research; authored or coauthored 70 articles in scientific journals. *Mailing Add:* Nat Prostatic Cancer Proj Roswell Park Mem Inst 666 Elm St Buffalo NY 14263

SLACK, SAMUEL THOMAS, b Sykesville, Md, Apr 6, 18; m 45; c 1. NUTRITION, PHYSIOLOGY. *Educ:* Univ Md, BS, 47; Cornell Univ, MS, 49, PhD(animal sci), 51. *Prof Exp:* PROF ANIMAL SCI, NY STATE COL AGR & LIFE SCI, CORNELL UNIV, 51- *Concurrent Pos:* Consult, Columbian Proj, Rockefeller Found, 63-64. *Mem:* Am Dairy Sci Asn. *Res:* Nutritional adequacy of forages and grain for livestock production with particular interest in milk production. *Mailing Add:* Dept Animal Sci NY State Col Agr & Life Sci Cornell Univ Ithaca NY 14850

SLACK, STEVEN ALLEN, b Logan, Utah, May 6, 47; m 70. PLANT PATHOLOGY, PLANT VIROLOGY. *Educ:* Univ Ark, BSA, 69, MS, 71; Univ Calif, Davis, PhD(plant path), 74. *Prof Exp:* Asst prof, 75-79, ASSOC PROF PLANT PATH, UNIV WIS-MADISON, 79- *Mem:* Am Phytopath Soc; Potato Asn Am; AAAS. *Res:* Characterization and serology of plant viruses, epidemiology and control of plant virus diseases, potato diseases. *Mailing Add:* Dept of Plant Path Col of Agr & Life Sci Univ of Wis Madison WI 53706

SLACK, WARNER VINCENT, b East Orange, NJ, June 10, 33; m 56; c 3. COMPUTER SCIENCE, PATIENT-COMPUTER DIALOGUE. *Educ:* Princeton Univ, AB, 55; Columbia Univ, MD, 59. *Prof Exp:* Intern med, Univ Wis Hosps, 59-60, resident, 60-61, instr, Univ, 65-66, from asst prof to assoc prof med & comput sci, 66-70; asst prof, 70-73, ASSOC PROF MED, HARVARD MED SCH, 73-; ASSOC MED, BETH ISRAEL HOSP, 70- *Concurrent Pos:* Alumni Res Found fel, Univ Wis Hosps, 61 & 64-65, NIH spec res fel, 65-66; lectr, Univ Philippines, 63-64; co-dir, Div Comput Med, Beth Israel Hosp & Brigham & Women's Hosp, 80- *Res:* Application of computer techniques to clinical medicine, specifically the use of computers to interview and counsel patients regarding their medical problems and to help patients to make their own medical decisions. *Mailing Add:* Havard Med Sch 25 Shattuck St Boston MA 02115

SLADE, ARTHUR LAIRD, b Aiken, SC, Oct 21, 37; m 78; c 2. POLYMER CHEMISTRY, ELECTROCHEMISTRY. *Educ:* Duke Univ, AB, 59; Univ NC, PhD(phys chem), 64. *Prof Exp:* Res chemist, Marshall Res & Develop Lab, 64-69, staff chemist, 69, res supvr, 69-72, sr financial analyst, 72-73, distrib mgr, 73-75, prin consult corp planning, 75-78, mgr planning & financial commun, 78-80, PUB AFFAIRS MGR, TEXTILE FIBERS, E I DU PONT DE NEMOURS & CO, INC, 80- *Mem:* Sigma Xi; Am Chem Soc. *Res:* Electrolyte solutions; electrochemistry; polymer coatings; automotive specialty products; man made textile fibers. *Mailing Add:* Pub Affairs Dept E I du Pont de Nemours & Co Inc Wilmington DE 19898

SLADE, BERNARD NEWTON, b Sioux City, Iowa, Dec 21, 23; m 46; c 2. ELECTRICAL ENGINEERING. *Educ:* Univ Wis, BS, 48; Stevens Inst Technol, MS, 54. *Prof Exp:* Advan develop engr, Tube Div, Radio Corp Am, NJ, 48-53, mgr advan develop, 53-55, res engr labs, 55-56; mgr semiconductor develop, 56-60, mgr components prod opers, 60-65, dir advan mfg tech, 65-66, dir mfg planning & controls, 66-69, dir mfg eng & technol, 69-81, ADV, MFG TECHNOL, IBM CORP, HOPEWELL JCT, NY, 81- *Concurrent Pos:* Adj instr, Pace Univ, 77-79. *Mem:* Sr mem Inst Elec & Electronics Engrs. *Res:* Development and design of solid state components, including transistors, diodes and other semiconductor devices. *Mailing Add:* Merry Hill Rd Poughkeepsie NY 12603

SLADE, H CLYDE, b Millestown, Nfld, July 2, 18; m 44; c 4. INTERNAL MEDICINE, PSYCHIATRY. *Educ:* Dalhousie Univ, MD & CM, 49; FRCPS(C), 49. *Prof Exp:* Assoc prof health care & epidemiol, 68-71, assoc prof primary health care & dir div, 71-77, HON ASSOC PROF PSYCHIAT, UNIV BC 68- *Concurrent Pos:* Assoc med, Vancouver Gen Hosp, 50-; consult, Shaughnessy Hosp, 52- *Mem:* Can Med Asn; Can Psychiat Asn. *Res:* Psychosomatic medicine; rheumatology. *Mailing Add:* Div of Primary Health Care Fac of Med Univ of BC Vancouver BC V6T 1W5 Can

SLADE, JOEL S, b Brooklyn, NY, Jan 1, 47; m 78. HETEROCYCLIC CHEMISTRY, ASYMMETRIC SYNTHESIS. *Educ:* Lowell Tech Inst, BS, 68, MS, 74; Colo State Univ, PhD(chem), 79. *Prof Exp:* Fel org chem res, Univ Pa, 79-80; SR RES CHEMIST MED CHEM, CIBA-GEIGY CORP, 80- *Mem:* Am Chem Soc. *Res:* Preparation of biologically interesting molecules which have the potential to become new therapeutic agents. *Mailing Add:* Rd 1 Crafts Rd Carmel NY 10512

SLADE, LANDRY THOMAS, b Medford, Mass, Oct 23, 31; m 57; c 3. UNIVERSITY ADMINISTRATION. *Educ:* Mass Inst Technol, BS, 53; Univ Va, MS, 58, PhD(org chem), 60. *Prof Exp:* Asst prof, 60-65, ASSOC PROF ORG CHEM, AM UNIV BEIRUT, 65-, ASSOC DEAN FAC ART & SCI, 74- *Concurrent Pos:* Fel steroid chem training prog, Worcester Found Exp Biol, 66-67; res assoc, Worcester Found Exp Biol, 73-74. *Mem:* Am Chem Soc; Sigma Xi. *Mailing Add:* Dept of Chem Am Univ of Beirut Beirut Lebanon

SLADE, LARRY MALCOM, b Durango, Colo, Feb 20, 36; m 62; c 4. ANIMAL HUSBANDRY, NUTRITION. *Educ:* Brigham Young Univ, BS, 62; Va Polytech Inst, MS, 65; Univ Calif, Davis, PhD(animal nutrit), 71. *Prof Exp:* Teacher high sch, Calif, 65-66; asst prof animal sci, Calif State Polytech Col, 70-72; assoc prof animal sci, Colo State Univ, 71-78; ASST PROF ANIMAL SCI, UTAH STATE UNIV, 78- *Mem:* Am Soc Animal Sci; Equine Nutrit & Physiol Soc. *Res:* Nutrient requirements of horses; conformation and performance of horses. *Mailing Add:* Dept of Animal Dairy & Vet Sci Utah State Univ Logan UT 84322

SLADE, MARTIN ALPHONSE, III, b Dunedin, Fla. CELESTIAL MECHANICS, RADIO ASTRONOMY. *Educ:* Mass Inst Technol, SB, 64, SM, 67, PhD(planetary sci), 71. *Prof Exp:* RESEARCHER, EARTH & LUNAR PHYSICS APPLN GROUP, JET PROPULSION LAB, CALIF INST TECHNOL, 71- *Concurrent Pos:* Mem, Lunar Sci Review Panel, Lunar Sci Inst, Houston, 75- *Mem:* Am Astron Soc; Am Geophys Union. *Res:* Rotational dynamics of the moon; very long baseline interferometry; analysis of lunar laser ranging data; testing gravitational theories. *Mailing Add:* 264-720 4800 Oak Grove Dr Pasadena CA 91103

SLADE, NORMAN ANDREW, b Wichita, Kans, Oct 14, 43; m 64; c 3. POPULATION ECOLOGY. *Educ:* Kans State Univ, BS, 65; Utah State Univ, MS, 69, PhD(ecol), 72. *Prof Exp:* Res assoc statist ecol, San Diego State Univ, 71-72; asst prof, 72-76, assoc prof, 76-81, PROF SYST & ECOL, UNIV KANS, 81- *Concurrent Pos:* Vis scientist pop ecol, Unit Behav Syst, Nat Inst Mental Health, 76. *Mem:* Ecol Soc Am; Am Soc Mammalogists; Biometric Soc; AAAS; Am Soc Naturalists. *Res:* Mammalian population dynamics, interspecific competition and computer simulation models of ecological systems; biostatistics. *Mailing Add:* Mus of Natural Hist Dept of Syst & Ecol Univ of Kans Lawrence KS 66045

SLADE, PHILIP EARL, JR, b Hatiesburg, Miss, Sept 2, 29; m 65; c 4. POLYMER CHEMISTRY. *Educ:* Miss Southern Col, BA, 51; Tulane Univ, MS, 53, PhD(chem), 55. *Prof Exp:* Res chemist, Chemstrand Corp, Ala, 55; assoc chem, George Washington Univ, 56-57; assoc prof, Miss Southern Col, 57-60; sr res chemist, Chemstrand Res Ctr, Inc, 60-67; group supvr, 67-74, SUPVR, NYLON TECH CTR, MONSANTO TEXTILES CO, 74- *Mem:* Am Chem Soc; Fiber Soc; Textured Yarn Asn. *Res:* Polymer characterization; polymer solution properties; thermal analysis; fiber characterization; fiber finish analysis. *Mailing Add:* Tech Ctr Monsanto Textiles Co PO Box 12830 Pensacola FL 32575

SLADEK, CELIA DAVIS, b Denver, Colo, Mar 25, 44; m 70; c 3. MEDICAL NEUROENDOCRINOLOGY. *Educ:* Hastings Col, BA, 66; Northwestern Univ, Chicago, MS, 69, PhD(physiol), 70. *Prof Exp:* Asst prof physiol, Univ Ill Med Ctr, 70-73; res assoc prof neuroendocrinol, 74-76, asst prof, 76-80, ASSOC PROF NEUROL & ANAT, MED SCH, UNIV ROCHESTER, 80- *Concurrent Pos:* Am Cancer Soc grant, Univ Ill Med Ctr, 71-72; Am Diabetes Asn grant, 74-75; Nat Inst Arthritis, Metab & Digestive Dis grant, 77-82, NIH res develop career award, 77-82 & Nat Heart Lung Blood Inst, 82-85; NSF equipment grant, 80-; ed, Brain Res Bulletin, 80- *Mem:* Soc Neurosci; Am Asn Anatomists; NY Acad Sci. *Res:* Regulation of vasopressin and oxytocin secretion; clinical abnormalities associated with inappropriate vasopressin secretion; hypertension; development and aging of the neurohypophyseal system. *Mailing Add:* Dept of Anat Univ of Rochester Med Sch Rochester NY 14642

SLADEK, JOHN RICHARD, JR, b Chicago, Ill, Feb 6, 43; m 70; c 3. NUROSCIENCE, AGING & DEVELOPMENT. *Educ:* Carthage Col, BA, 65; Northwestern Univ, MS, 68; Univ Health Sci, PhD(anat), 71. *Prof Exp:* Asst prof, 73-77, ASSOC PROF ANAT, SCH MED, UNIV ROCHESTER, 77-, ASSOC PROF, CTR BRAIN RES, 79- *Concurrent Pos:* Consult, Nat Inst Aging, Nat Inst Neurol & Commun Dis & Stroke & NSF, 80; ed, Brain Res Bull, ANKHO Int Press, 80; mem, Biol Neurosci Study Sect, NIMH, 80-84. *Mem:* Am Asn Anatomists; Histochem Soc; NY Acad Sci; Soc Neurosci; Geront Soc. *Res:* Neuron interactions of aminergic and peptidergic neurons during development, aging and following transplantation; neuroendocrinology of the hypothalamo-neurohypophyseal system of vasopressin and oxytocin neurons. *Mailing Add:* 6499 Lake Rd Bergen NY 14416

SLADEK, KARL JOSEF, III, b St Louis, Mo, July 31, 40; m 61; c 1. CHEMICAL ENGINEERING. *Educ:* Mass Inst Technol, BS, 62, MS, 63, ScD(chem eng), 67. *Prof Exp:* Instr chem eng, Mass Inst Technol, 64; res engr, Abcor, Inc, Mass, 67; asst prof, Univ Tex, Austin, 67-72; res mgr, Millipore Corp, 72-78; ASSOC PROF CHEM ENG, UNIV LOWELL, 78- *Mem:* Am Chem Soc; Am Inst Chem Engrs; Electrochem Soc. *Res:* Surface chemistry; environmental monitoring; on-site waste treatment. *Mailing Add:* Dept of Chem Eng Univ of Lowell Lowell MA 01854

SLADEK, NORMAN ELMER, b Montgomery, Minn, Aug 20, 39; m 64; c 3. PHARMACOLOGY. *Educ:* Univ Minn, Minneapolis, BS, 62, PhD(pharmacol), 66. *Prof Exp:* NIH fel, Univ Wis-Madison, 66-68; asst prof, 68-74, assoc prof, 74-79, PROF PHARMACOL, MED SCH, UNIV MINN, MINNEAPOLIS, 79- *Concurrent Pos:* NIH res career develop award, 72-77. *Mem:* AAAS; Am Asn Cancer Res; Am Soc Pharmacol & Exp Therapeut. *Res:* Cancer chemotherapy; drug interactions; drug metabolism; carcinogenesis. *Mailing Add:* Dept Pharmacol 3-260 Millard Hall Univ of Minn Minneapolis MN 55455

SLADEK, RONALD JOHN, b Chicago, Ill, Sept 19, 26; m 53; c 6. SOLID STATE PHYSICS. *Educ:* Univ Chicago, PhD(physics), 54. *Prof Exp:* Res physicist, Westinghouse Elec Corp, 53-61; assoc prof, 61-66, actg head dept, 69-71, PROF PHYSICS, PURDUE UNIV, 66-, ASSOC DEAN SCI, 74- *Mem:* Fel Am Phys Soc; Sigma Xi. *Res:* Ultrasonic and electrical properties and thermal expansion of solids, especially crystalline solids exhibiting a phase transition and chalcogenide glasses; effects of low temperatures, stress, and magnetic fields thereon. *Mailing Add:* Dept of Physics Purdue Univ West Lafayette IN 47907

SLAGA, THOMAS JOSEPH, b Smithfield, Ohio, Dec 15, 41; m 66; c 2. BIOCHEMICAL PHARMACOLOGY. *Educ:* Col Steubenville, BA, 64; Univ Ark, PhD(physiol biophys), 69. *Prof Exp:* Fel, McArdle Lab Cancer Res, Univ Wis-Madison, 68-71; res investr chem carcinogenesis, Pac Northwest Res Ctr, 71-73; asst mem, Fred Hutchinson Cancer Res Ctr, 73-76; staff mem, E Tenn Cancer Res Ctr, 76-78, SR STAFF MEM CANCER & TOXICOL, BIOL DIV, OAK RIDGE NAT LAB, 76- *Concurrent Pos:* Asst prof pharmacol, Sch Med, Univ Wash, 74-76. *Mem:* Am Asn Cancer Res; Am Soc Invest Dermatol; Sigma Xi. *Res:* Mechanism of chemical carcinogenesis in both in vivo and in vitro; in particular, the early molecular events after the application of chemical carcinogens and tumor promoters, mechanism of action of the antitumor agents of the skin. *Mailing Add:* Cancer & Toxicol Prog Biol Div Oak Ridge Nat Lab Oak Ridge TN 37830

SLAGAN, PETER MICHAEL, b Scranton, Pa, Feb 16, 39; m 61; c 1. INDUSTRIAL ORGANIC CHEMISTRY. *Educ:* Univ Scranton, BS, 60; Univ NC, Chapel Hill, PhD(organometallic chem), 67. *Prof Exp:* Chemist, 60-62, RES CHEMIST, AM CYANAMID CO, 67-, ELASTOMERS TECH PROJ LEADER, 67- *Mem:* Am Chem Soc. *Res:* Organic synthesis. *Mailing Add:* Am Cyanamid Co Bound Brook NJ 08805

SLAGEL, DONALD E, b Louisville, Ky, Sept 30, 30; m 57; c 3. BIOCHEMISTRY, NEUROBIOLOGY. *Educ:* Univ Ky, BS, 54; Univ Wis, MS, 56, PhD(biochem, phys chem), 61. *Prof Exp:* ASSOC PROF SURG, UNIV KY, 64- *Concurrent Pos:* NIH fel neuropath, Univ Wis, 61-63 & neurobiol, Gothenburg Univ, 63-64. *Mem:* Am Chem Soc; Am Soc Cell Biol; Am Asn Neuropath; Am Soc Neurochem; Soc Neurosci. *Res:* Chemistry and ultrastructure of the nervous system; use of athymic mouse-human tumor xenograft in experimental studies, including combined modality treatment studies; study of DNA damage and repair using DNA alkaline elution technique. *Mailing Add:* Dept of Surg Div of Neurosurg Univ of Ky Med Ctr Lexington KY 40536

SLAGEL, ROBERT CLAYTON, b Sabetha, Kans, Jan 4, 37; m 61; c 2. ORGANIC CHEMISTRY. *Educ:* Western Mich Univ, BS, 58; Univ Ill, PhD(sesquiterpenoids), 62. *Prof Exp:* Res chemist, Archer Daniels Midland Co, 62-64; sr res chemist, 64-67; group leader basic res, ADM Chem Div, Ashland Oil & Refining Co, 67-68; group leader polymer synthesis, Calgon Corp, Subsid Merck & Co Inc, 68-69; sect leader specialty chem res, 69-71, mgr polymer res, 71-77, asst dir res & develop, 77-78, dir specialty chem res,

78-79; TECH DIR, CHEM PROD DIV, UNION CAMP CORP, 79- *Mem:* Am Chem Soc; Tech Asn Pulp & Paper Indust; Am Inst Mining Engrs; Am Oil Chemists Soc. *Res:* Monomers and polymers, chiefly polyelectrolytes; organonitrogen chemistry; ozonization of organic compounds; carbenes, chiefly halocarbenes; rosin based resins; fatty acid derivatives; tall oil distillation. *Mailing Add:* Union Camp Corp PO Box 2668 Savannah GA 31402

SLAGER, URSULA TRAUGOTT, b Frankfurt, Ger, Sept 15, 25; nat US; m 49. PATHOLOGY. *Educ:* Wellesley Col, BA, 48; Univ Md, MD, 52; Am Bd Path, dipl, 58. *Prof Exp:* Instr path, Sch Med, Univ Md, 54-55, assoc, 56-57; pathologist, Los Alamos Med Ctr, 57-59 & Res Dept, Martin Co, 59-60; assoc clin prof, 61-67, ASSOC PROF PATH, UNIV SOUTHERN CALIF, 67-; PATHOLOGIST, RANCHO LOS AMIGOS HOSP, 68- *Concurrent Pos:* Hitchcock fel neuropath, Univ Md, 53-55; assoc pathologist, Orange County Gen Hosp, 61-65, actg dir path serv, 65-67; mem staff, Los Angeles County Gen Hosp, 67- *Mem:* AMA; Am Col Path; Int Acad Path; Am Soc Clin Path; Am Soc Neuropath. *Res:* Neuropathology; radiation damage. *Mailing Add:* 7705 Goloudrinas Downey CA 90242

SLAGG, NORMAN, b New York, NY, Jan 8, 31; m 57; c 2. PHYSICAL CHEMISTRY, CHEMICAL KINETICS. *Educ:* Brooklyn Col, BS, 52; Polytech Inst Brooklyn, PhD(chem), 60. *Prof Exp:* Res chemist, Reaction Motors Div, Thiokol Chem Corp, 60-62; sr res engr, Lamp Div, Westinghouse Elec Corp, 62-67; instr phys chem, Fairleigh Dickinson Univ, 65-67; lectr, Rutgers Univ, 67-75; HEAD FAST REACTION SECT, EXPLOSIVE LAB, PICATINNY ARSENAL, 67- *Mem:* Am Chem Soc; Am Phys Soc; Sigma Xi. *Res:* Kinetics; mechanism of chemical reactions; photochemistry; reactions of molten salts with glasses and ceramics; shock tube techniques; time resolved spectroscopy; explosive phenomena. *Mailing Add:* 22 Marlton Dr Wayne NJ 07470

SLAGLE, JAMES R, b Brooklyn, NY, Mar 1, 34; m 58; c 5. COMPUTER SCIENCE, MATHEMATICS. *Educ:* St John's Univ, BS, 55; Mass Inst Technol, MS, 57, PhD(math), 61. *Prof Exp:* Staff mathematician, Lincoln Lab, Mass Inst Technol, 55-63; group leader, Lawrence Radiation Lab, Univ Calif, 63-67; chief, Heuristics Lab, NIH, 67-74; head, Comput Sci Lab, 74-80, SPECIAL ASST, NAVY CTR APPL RES ARTIFICIAL INTELLIGENCE, NAVAL RES LAB, 80- *Concurrent Pos:* Teacher elec eng, Mass Inst Technol, 62-63 & Univ Calif, Berkeley, 63-67; teacher comput sci, Johns Hopkins Univ, 67-73. *Mem:* Asn Comput Mach. *Res:* Artificial intelligence; automatic pattern recognition; automatic theorem proving; automatic expert consultant systems. *Mailing Add:* Code 7510 Naval Res Lab Washington DC 20375

SLAGLE, OTIS DANIEL, b New Bethlehem, Pa, Dec 22, 39; m 61; c 2. MATERIALS SCIENCE. *Educ:* Pa State Univ, BS, 61, PhD(solid state technol), 65. *Prof Exp:* Sr res scientist mat sci, Battelle-Northwest, 65-70; SR RES SCIENTIST MAT SCI, WESTINGHOUSE HANFORD CO, 70- *Mem:* Am Ceramic Soc. *Res:* Property measurement and gas release studies of irradiated and un-irradiated nuclear fuel materials at temperatures near melting. *Mailing Add:* Box 1970 Westinghouse Hanford Co Richland WA 99352

SLAGLE, WAYNE GREY, b Monkstown, Tex, Nov 23, 34; m 57. PARASITOLOGY. *Educ:* Tex A&M Univ, BS, 63, MS, 66, PhD(zool), 70. *Prof Exp:* Asst biol, Tex A&M Univ, 63-66, instr, 66-70; asst prof 70-77, ASSOC PROF BIOL, STEPHEN F AUSTIN STATE UNIV, 77- *Mem:* Am Soc Parasitol. *Res:* Biological control of helminth parasites which cause human disease. *Mailing Add:* Dept of Biol Stephen F Austin State Univ Nacogdoches TX 75961

SLAGOWSKI, EUGENE LOUIS, b Sharon, Wis, Aug 9, 38; m 66; c 2. POLYMER PHYSICS. *Educ:* Univ Wis-Madison, BS, 60; Univ Akron, PhD(polymer sci), 72. *Prof Exp:* Chemist polymer characterization, Gen Tire & Rubber Co, 66-68; sr res chemist polymer physics, Hooker Chem & Plastics Corp, 72-74, group leader polymer characterization, 74-75, sect leader polymer physics, 75-77, support mgr plastics res & develop, 77-80; WITH PARKER SEAL CO, 80- *Mem:* Soc Plastics Engrs; Am Chem Soc. *Res:* Dilute solution characterization of polymers; application of techniques to block, graft and semi crystalline polymers; rheological and dynamic mechanical investigations of polymer blends and composite systems. *Mailing Add:* Parker Seal Co PO Box 11751 Lexington KY 40512

SLAKEY, LINDA LOUISE, b Oakland, Calif, Jan 2, 39. BIOCHEMISTRY. *Educ:* Siena Heights Col, BS, 62; Univ Mich, PhD(biochem), 67. *Prof Exp:* Instr chem, St Dominic's Col, 67-69; fel biochem, Univ Wis, 70-73; asst prof, 73-79, ASSOC PROF BIOCHEM, UNIV MASS, 79- *Mem:* AAAS; Tissue Culture Asn; Am Soc Biol Chemists. *Res:* Metabolism of arterial wall; lipid structure and metabolism; regulation of metabolism in cultured arterial cells; interaction of vascular endothelium with blood components; regulation of plasma membrane protein turnover. *Mailing Add:* Dept Biochem Univ Mass Amherst MA 01003

SLAMA, FRANCIS J, b St Louis, Mo, Apr 17, 39; m 63; c 2. CHEMISTRY. *Educ:* St Louis Univ, AB, 62, PhD(chem), 69. *Prof Exp:* Chemist, Commercial Div, Calgon Corp, 62-66; res chemist, 69-75, RES SUPVR, AMOCO CHEM CORP, STANDARD OIL CO IND, 75- *Concurrent Pos:* Instr, Col of DuPage, 70-73; instr, Waybonsee Community Col, 74- *Mem:* Am Chem Soc. *Res:* Plastics; polymer structure and properties. *Mailing Add:* Amoco Chem Corp Naperville IL 60540

SLAMECKA, VLADIMIR, b Brno, Czech, May 8, 28; US citizen; m 62; c 2. INFORMATION SCIENCE, COMPUTER SCIENCE. *Educ:* Columbia Univ, MS, 58, DLS, 62. *Prof Exp:* Chemist, Brookvale Brewery, 52-54; assoc ed, Mid-Europ Press, Inc, 56-57; head chem libr, Columbia Univ, 58-60, proj investr sci orgn, 60-62; mgr info systs design, Document, Inc, Md, 62-64; PROF INFO & COMPUT SCI, GA INST TECHNOL, 64-; CLIN PROF

MED, EMORY UNIV, 80- *Concurrent Pos:* NSF grant, Sci Orgn Eastern Europe, 60-62; Fulbright prof, 63-64; consult, NSF, 65- & NIH, 70-; vchmn comt int sci & technol prog, Nat Acad Sci, 74-; chmn, US Nat Comt FID, 74-; vchmn US Nat Comt, UNESCO/Proj Group Inc, 78- *Mem:* AAAS; Am Soc Info Sci; Asn Comput Mach; Sigma Xi. *Res:* Medical information systems; national and international information systems; education in information and computer science. *Mailing Add:* Sch of Info & Comput Sci Ga Inst of Technol Atlanta GA 30332

SLANA, LAURENCE JOSEPH, botany, plant pathology, see previous edition

SLANETZ, LAWRENCE WILLIAM, b Islip, NY, Apr 14, 08; m 28; c 3. MICROBIOLOGY. *Educ:* Univ Conn, BS, 29; Yale Univ, PhD(bact), 32. *Prof Exp:* Asst serologist, Conn State Dept Health, 31; asst instr, Yale Univ, 31-32; from instr to assoc prof bact, 32-48, dean, Sch Health Studies, 69-73, prof & head dept, 48-77, EMER PROF MICROBIOL, UNIV NH, 77- *Concurrent Pos:* Bacteriologist, Exp Sta, Univ NH, 41-69; mem, Environ Sci & Eng Study Sect, NIH, 58-; lectr, Sch Pub Health, Harvard Univ, 61. *Mem:* Am Soc Microbiol; Am Pub Health Asn; Am Water Works Asn; Am Acad Microbiol; Royal Soc Health. *Res:* Bovine mastitis; oral bacteria and disinfectants; fusiform bacteria; streptococci; staphylococci; Staphylococcus bacteriophage; fecal streptococci and water bacteriology; microbiology of estuarine and shellfish pollution. *Mailing Add:* Dept of Microbiol Univ of NH Durham NH 03824

SLANGER, TOM GEORGE, b Vienna, Austria, Apr 30, 35; US citizen; m 60; c 2. CHEMICAL KINETICS, ATMOSPHERIC CHEMISTRY. *Educ:* Calif Inst Technol, BS, 56, MS, 57; Univ Calif, Los Angeles, PhD(chem), 65. *Prof Exp:* Chemical engr, Stauffer Chem Co, 57-58; chemist, Int Rectifier Corp, 59-60; from teaching asst to res asst chem, Univ Calif, Los Angeles, 60-65; fel photochem, Comn Atomic Energy, France, 65-66; SR PHYSICIST, SRI INT, 66- *Mem:* AAAS. *Res:* Studies of spectroscopy, kinetics and products of reactions involving atoms and molecules of interest in terrestrial and planetary atmospheres; techniques include resonance fluorescence and absorption and vacuum ultraviolet photochemistry. *Mailing Add:* Molecular Physics Lab PS 091 SRI Int Menlo Park CA 94025

SLANSKY, CYRIL METHOD, b Albuquerque, NMex, July 8, 13; m 39; c 3. CHEMISTRY. *Educ:* Col of Idaho, BS, 36; Univ Calif, PhD(chem), 40. *Prof Exp:* Asst chem, Univ Calif, 37-39; res chemist, Dow Chem Co, Mich, 40-44 & Calif, 44-47; chemist, Hanford Works, Gen Elec Co, 47-52; chief, Works Lab, Am Cyanamid Co, 52-53; chem develop, Atomic Energy Div, Phillips Petrol Co, 53, sect head, 53-60, mgr, Chem Develop Br, 60-62, mem staff nuclear & chem tech, 62-66; mem staff nuclear & chem tech, 66-71; sr tech adv, Allied Chem Corp, 71-78, nuclear consult, Chem Progs, 78; NUCLEAR CONSULT, 78- *Concurrent Pos:* Mem radioactive waste mgt, Int Atomic Energy Agency, 69-71. *Mem:* AAAS; Am Chem Soc; Am Nuclear Soc; Am Inst Chem Eng. *Res:* Chemistry and technology of inorganic compounds and compounds from calcined dolomite; electrolytic production of magnesium; separations processes; nuclear fuel cycle; radioactive waste disposal; applications of nuclear heat. *Mailing Add:* 2815 Holly Place Idaho Falls ID 83401

SLANSKY, RICHARD CYRIL, b Oakland, Calif, Apr 3, 40; c 2. THEORETICAL HIGH ENERGY PHYSICS. *Educ:* Harvard Univ, BA, 62; Univ Calif, Berkeley, PhD(physics), 67. *Proi Exp:* Res fel physics, Calif Inst Technol, 67-69; from instr to asst prof, Yale Univ, 69-74; MEM STAFF, LOS ALAMOS SCI LAB, 74- *Res:* Elementary particle physics. *Mailing Add:* 3025 Arizona Ave Los Alamos NM 87544

SLAPIKOFF, SAUL ABRAHAM, b Bronx, NY, Nov 5, 31; m 56; c 2. BIOCHEMISTRY. *Educ:* Brooklyn Col, BA, 52; Tufts Univ, PhD(biochem), 64. *Prof Exp:* USPHS fel biochem, Sch Med, Stanford Univ, 64-66; asst prof, 66-72, ASSOC PROF BIOL, TUFTS UNIV, 72- *Concurrent Pos:* NRS fel genetic toxicol, 76-77; vis scientist, Mass Inst Technol, 77-78. *Mem:* AAAS; Am Chem Soc; Am Soc Microbiol; Sigma Xi. *Res:* DNA repair; biochemistry of environmental toxins; environmental toxicology. *Mailing Add:* Dept Biol Tufts Univ Medford MA 02155

SLATE, FLOYD OWEN, b Carroll Co, Ind, July 26, 20; m 39; c 3. APPLIED CHEMISTRY. *Educ:* Purdue Univ, BS, 41, MS, 42, PhD(anal chem), 44. *Prof Exp:* Chemist, Purdue Univ, 41-44, chemist & asst prof hwy eng, 46-49; lab supvr, Manhattan Dist Proj, Columbia Univ, 44; asst chief chemist, Garfield Div, Houdaille-Hershey, Ill, 44-46; PROF ENG MAT, CORNELL UNIV, 49- *Concurrent Pos:* Adv, Int Coop Admin, Pakistan, 56; vpres res & develop & mem bd, Geotech & Resources, Inc, White Plains, NY, 59-63; consult, Pure Waters Prog, 69- *Honors & Awards:* Wason Medal, Am Concrete Inst, 57, 65 & 74. *Mem:* Am Chem Soc; Am Soc Test & Mat; Am Concrete Inst; Am Inst Chem; Am Soc Civil Eng. *Res:* Low cost housing; concrete; engineering materials; soils; chemistry applied to engineering problems. *Mailing Add:* Sch of Civil Eng Cornell Univ Ithaca NY 14850

SLATER, CARL DAVID, b Moundsville, WVa, Oct 26, 33; m 65; c 2. ORGANIC CHEMISTRY. *Educ:* Univ WVa, BS, 55; Ohio State Univ, PhD(org chem), 60. *Prof Exp:* Res assoc org chem, Mass Inst Technol, 60-61; proj chemist, Chem Div, Union Carbide Corp, 61-62; from asst prof to assoc prof org chem, NDak State Univ, 62-67; assoc prof org chem, Memphis State Univ, 67-80; PROF & CHMN DEPT PHYS SCI, NORTHERN KY UNIV, 80- *Mem:* Am Chem Soc. *Res:* Mechanism of electrocyclic processes; synthesis and reactions of aminothiophene derivatives; kinetics and mechanism of reactions of halogen-containing nitro compounds; quantum chemical calculations of molecular properties. *Mailing Add:* Phys Sci Dept Northern Ky Univ Highland Heights KY 41076

SLATER, DONALD CARLIN, b Pensacola, Fla, July 27, 45; m 75; c 1. EXPERIMENTAL PHYSICS. *Educ:* Stanford Univ, BS, 67; Mass Inst Technol, PhD(physics), 71. *Prof Exp:* Res assoc physics, Stanford Univ, 71-74 & Univ Va, 74-76; res scientist, 76-78, MGR, KMS FUSION, INC, 79- *Mem:* Am Phys Soc. *Res:* Experimental inertial confinement fusion; laser-plasma interaction; diagnostic instrumentation. *Mailing Add:* KMS Fusion Inc PO Box 1567 Ann Arbor MI 48106

SLATER, GEORGE E(DWARD), b Warren, Pa, Mar 1, 41; m 65; c 3. PETROLEUM ENGINEERING. *Educ:* Pa State Univ, BA, 63, MS, 68, PhD(petrol & natural gas eng), 69. *Prof Exp:* Foreman, Pa Gas Co, 64-66; res engr, Gulf Res & Develop Co, 69-70; from asst prof to assoc prof petrol & natural gas eng, Pa State Univ, University Park, 70-76; dir reservoir appln, Gulf Res & Develop Co, Houston, 76-78, res assoc, Denver, 79-80. *Mem:* Soc Petrol Engrs; Can Inst Mining & Metall. *Res:* Numerical reservoir simulation development and application; operations research methods applied to petroleum industry; solution mining of uranium; underground coal gasification. *Mailing Add:* 339 Granding Iron Houston TX 77060

SLATER, GEORGE P, b Findochty, Scotland, Mar 11, 32; m 56; c 2. GAS CHROMATOGRAPHY. *Educ:* Aberdeen Univ, BSc, 54; Univ Sask, MSc, 57; Queen's Univ, Belfast, PhD(chem), 61. *Prof Exp:* Anal chemist, Swift Canadian Co, 54-55; res asst chem, Univ Sask, 57-58; chemist, Polymer Corp, Can, 58; Nat Res Coun Can fel chem, Univ Sask, 61-62; SR RES OFFICER, NAT RES COUN CAN, 62- *Mem:* Chem Inst Can. *Res:* Water pollution; analysis of pulp mill effluent; gas chromotography-mass spectroscopy. *Mailing Add:* Nat Res Coun Can Prairie Regional Lab Saskatoon SK S7N 0W9 Can

SLATER, GRANT GAY, b Rochester, NY, Jan 6, 18; m 57; c 2. NUTRITION, MEDICAL RESEARCH. *Educ:* Univ Miami, BS, 40, MS, 50; Univ Southern Calif, PhD(biochem), 54. *Prof Exp:* Biochemist, Res Inst, Cedars Lebanon Hosp, Los Angeles, 54-55; res physiol chemist, Univ Calif, Los Angeles, 55-58; res specialist, State Dept Mental Hyg, 58-61; biochemist, Vet Admin Ctr, 61-68; res biochemist, Gateways Hosp, 68-72; RESEARCHER I, DIV ENVIRON & NUTRIT SCI, SCH PUB HEALTH, UNIV CALIF, LOS ANGELES, 72- *Concurrent Pos:* Vis instr, Univ Southern Calif, 55-57, vis asst prof, 58-59; mem fac, Dept Psychiat, Univ Calif, Los Angeles, 58- & Brain Res Inst, 61-; study grants, Anti-trypsin in Lung Dis from Air Pollution, Div Lung Dis, NIH, 74-75. *Mem:* Am Chem Soc; Am Inst Chem; Am Physiol Soc; Endocrine Soc; Soc Neurosci. *Res:* Basic methodological research on plasma proteins and studies on the relationship of plasma proteins in humans to lung and brain disease; nutritional studies relating dietary and plasma cholesterol in humans. *Mailing Add:* Div Environ & Nutrit Sci Univ Calif Sch Pub Health Los Angeles CA 90024

SLATER, JAMES ALEXANDER, b Belvidere, Ill, Jan 10, 20; m 43; c 4. ENTOMOLOGY, SYSTEMATICS. *Educ:* Univ Ill, BA, 42, MS, 47; Iowa State Col, PhD(entom), 50. *Prof Exp:* From instr to assoc prof, 54-60, head dept zool, entom & biochem, 64-67, head syst & evolutionary biol sect, 70-80, PROF ENTOM, UNIV CONN, 60- *Concurrent Pos:* Comnr, Conn Geol & Natural Hist Surv & state ornithologist, 63-72; panelist, Sci Div, NSF, 63-66; res assoc, Nat Insect Col Pretoria, SAfrica, 67-68; res assoc, Am Mus Natural Hist, 76- *Mem:* Entom Soc Am; Soc Syst Zool (pres, 81-83); Royal Entom Soc; SAfrican Entom Soc. *Res:* Systematics and bionomics of Hemiptera, Lygaeidae and Miridae. *Mailing Add:* Biol Sci Group U-43 Univ of Conn Storrs CT 06268

SLATER, JAMES LOUIS, b Grand Rapids, Mich, Dec 2, 44; c 2. INORGANIC CHEMISTRY. *Educ:* Mich State Univ, BS, 67; Fla State Univ, PhD(inorg chem), 71. *Prof Exp:* Fel inorg chem, Ames Lab, US AEC, Iowa State Univ, 71-73; instr inorg chem, Univ Va, 73-74; asst prof inorg chem, 74-77, ASST PROF CHEM, COL STEUBENVILLE, 77- *Mem:* Am Chem Soc. *Res:* Chemical studies of the metal carbonyls. *Mailing Add:* Dept of Chem Col of Steubenville Steubenville OH 43952

SLATER, JAMES MUNRO, b Salt Lake City, Utah, Jan 7, 29; m 48; c 5. RADIOTHERAPY. *Educ:* Univ Utah & Utah State, BS, 54; Sch Med, Loma Linda Univ, MD, 63. *Prof Exp:* Instr radiother, 67-68, asst clin prof radiol radiother, 68-70, from asst prof to assoc prof, 70-74, PROF RADIOL RADIOTHER, SCH MED, LOMA LINDA UNIV, 75- *Concurrent Pos:* Fel, White Mem Med Ctr, 67-68 & Univ Tex, M D Anderson Hosp & Tumor Inst, 68-69; dir radiation oncol, Sch Med, Loma Linda Univ, 70-, dir nuclear med, 75-, interim chmn dept radiol sci, 78-; mem prof educ comt, Am Cancer Soc, 75-76, chmn, 76-77, vpres, 78-79. *Honors & Awards:* Physician's Recognition Award, AMA, 69, 72 & 75; First Place Award, Div Radiation Oncol, Europ Asn Radiol, 75; First Place Award Sci Exhibit, Am Soc Therapeut Radiologists, 78. *Mem:* Am Soc Therapeut Radiologists; Am Soc Clin Oncol; AAAS; Am Cancer Soc; Am Radium Soc. *Res:* Cancer immunology, emphasizing the effect of ionizing radiation on the human immune system; computerized dosimetry for radiation therapy planning; treatment of malignant disease using ionizing irradiation. *Mailing Add:* Radiation Oncol Med Ctr Loma Linda Univ Loma Linda CA 92350

SLATER, JOHN VERNON, b Eng, Aug 3, 20; nat US; m 51; c 4. RADIATION BIOLOGY, COMPARATIVE PHYSIOLOGY. *Educ:* Wayne State Univ, BS, 47, MS, 48; Univ Mich, PhD(zool), 51. *Prof Exp:* Asst biol, Wayne State Univ, 38-39, 46-47; instr anat & physiol, Sch Nursing, St Mary's Hosp, 49; asst zool, Univ Mich, 50; res assoc protozoan physiol, Marine Biol Lab, Woods Hole, 51; from instr to asst prof biol, Univ Fla, 52-55; asst prof, Univ Buffalo, 55-57; assoc prof, Univ Ariz, 57-60; res biophysicist, Biophys Group, Donner Lab Nuclear & Med Physics, Univ Calif, Berkeley, 60-68, assoc prof pub health, Univ, 66-68; prof biol sci & head dept, Mich Technol Univ, 68-70; prof biol, State Univ NY, New Paltz, 70-79; prof biol & chmn dept, Sch Med, King Faisal Univ, Saudi Arabia, 79-80; PROF BIOL, STATE UNIV NY, NEW PALTZ, 80- *Concurrent Pos:* Asst limnol, Cranbrook Inst Sci, 49; mem panel, NSF, 58-60; consult, Tucson Med Ctr, Univ Ariz, 59-60; fac exchange scholar, State Univ NY, 75. *Mem:* Soc

Protozool; Am Soc Zool; Am Micros Soc. *Res:* Ion accumulation in protozoans; comparative effects of x-rays and accelerated ions on development; comparative accumulation of radioisotopes in desert organisms. *Mailing Add:* Dept of Biol State Univ of NY New Paltz NY 12561

SLATER, KEITH, b Oldham, Eng, Dec 20, 35; m 59; c 3. TEXTILES. *Educ:* Univ Leeds, BSc, 56, MSc, 58, PhD(textiles), 65. *Prof Exp:* Asst master, Leeds Cent High Sch, Eng, 60-65; from asst prof to assoc prof, 65-75, PROF TEXTILES, UNIV GUELPH, 75- *Concurrent Pos:* Nat Res Coun grant, Univ Guelph, 66-, Defence Res Bd grant, 68-; consult, Wool Bur Can, 69-70, Hart Chem Ltd, 69-71 & Harding Carpets Ltd, 70- *Mem:* Inst Textile Sci (pres, 72-73); fel Textile Inst (vpres, 74-78); Textile Fedn Can (pres, 79-81). *Res:* Yarn irregularity; yarn hairiness; acoustic properties of textiles; comfort of textiles; textile drying behavior; progressive deterioration of textiles. *Mailing Add:* Textile Sci Div Univ of Guelph Guelph ON N1G 2W1 Can

SLATER, PETER JOHN, b Mt Vernon, NY, Sept 30, 46; m 70. MATHEMATICS, OPERATIONS RESEARCH. *Educ:* Iona Col, BS, 68; Univ Iowa, MS, 72, PhD(math), 73. *Prof Exp:* Asst prof math, Cleveland State Univ, 74; res assoc, Nat Bur Stand, 74-75; mathematician, Sandia Labs, 75-81; ASSOC PROF MATH, UNIV ALA, 81- *Mem:* Am Math Soc; Opers Res Soc Am. *Res:* The field of graph theory with particular emphasis on problems of N-connectivity, geodesics and facility location; network modelling of facilities. *Mailing Add:* Math Dept Univ Ala Huntsville AL 35899

SLATER, PHILIP NICHOLAS, b London, Eng, Feb 9, 32; US citizen; m 58; c 3. OPTICS, REMOTE SENSING. *Educ:* Univ London, BS, 55, PhD(appl optics) & dipl, Imp Col, 58. *Prof Exp:* Res physicist, Optics Res Sect, IIT Res Inst, 58-62, sect mgr, 62-66; PROF OPTICAL SCI, UNIV ARIZ, 66-, CHMN, REMOTE SENSING COMT, 76- *Mem:* fel Optical Soc Am; Am Soc Photogram & Remote Sensing; Soc Photog Sci & Engrs. *Res:* Remote sensing physics and sensor systems; photographic science and microdensitometry. *Mailing Add:* Optical Sci Ctr Univ of Ariz Tucson AZ 85721

SLATER, RICHARD CRAIG, b Jersey City, NJ, Nov 16, 46; m 73; c 1. PHYSICAL CHEMISTRY. *Educ:* Stevens Inst Technol, BS, 68; Columbia Univ, PhD(chem), 73. *Prof Exp:* Fel chem, Dept Chem, Columbia Univ, 73-76; RES SCIENTIST, AVCO EVERETT RES LAB, 76- *Mem:* Am Chem Soc; Am Phys Soc; Sigma Xi. *Res:* Laser applications in chemistry; chemical kinetics; vibrational energy transfer. *Mailing Add:* 2385 Revere Beach Pkwy Everett MA 02149

SLATER, ROBERT LEE, b Denver, Colo, Apr 4, 39; m 62; c 2. VETERINARY PARASITOLOGY. *Educ:* Colo State Univ, BS, 62, MS, 64; Utah State Univ, PhD(zool), 69. *Prof Exp:* Res asst fish pesticides, Bur Sport Fisheries & Wildlife, 62; asst prof biol, Minot State Col, 64-66; asst prof vet med, Univ Ill, 68-70; sr res parasitologist, 70-74, RES FEL, MERCK INST THERAPEUT RES, MERCK, SHARP & DOHME, INC, 74- *Concurrent Pos:* NIH grant, Univ Ill, Urbana, 68-70. *Mem:* AAAS; Wildlife Dis Asn. *Res:* Avian and mammalian coccidiosis in vitro cultivation host parasite relationship parasite physiology and immunology chemotherapy. *Mailing Add:* Basic Animal Sci Res Merck Inst Merck & Co Inc Rahway NJ 07065

SLATER, SCHUYLER G, b New Haven, Conn, Feb 22, 23. ORGANIC CHEMISTRY, NATURAL PRODUCTS CHEMISTRY. *Educ:* Univ Conn, BS, 44, MS, 47; Boston Univ, EdD(sci educ), 65. *Prof Exp:* Instr chem, Univ Conn, 46-49; instr sci, Boston Univ, 50-54 & Cent Conn State Col, 54-55; assoc prof, Univ Maine, 54-56; PROF CHEM, SALEM STATE COL, 56-, CHMN DEPT, 80- *Concurrent Pos:* Observer, Brit Open Univ, 71-72. *Mem:* Am Chem Soc. *Res:* Curriculum development. *Mailing Add:* Dept Chem Salem State Col Salem MA 01970

SLATER, WILLIAM E, b Springfield, Ohio, July 16, 31; m 58. EXPERIMENTAL HIGH ENERGY PHYSICS. *Prof Exp:* Fel, 60-62, from asst prof to assoc prof, 62-73, PROF PHYSICS, UNIV CALIF, LOS ANGELES, 73- *Mem:* Am Phys Soc. *Res:* Track chamber and counter experiments. *Mailing Add:* Dept of Physics Univ of Calif Los Angeles CA 90024

SLATES, HARRY LOVELL, b Canton, Ohio, Feb 7, 23; m 51; c 1. ORGANIC CHEMISTRY. *Educ:* Mt Union Col, BSc, 44; Ohio State Univ, MSc, 48. *Prof Exp:* Chemist qual control, Goodyear Tire & Rubber Co, 45; asst chem, Ohio State Univ, 47-48; SR RES CHEMIST, MERCK & CO, INC, 48- *Mem:* AAAS; Am Chem Soc; Am Inst Chem; Royal Soc Chem; Swiss Chem Soc. *Res:* Steroid sapogenins; organic synthesis and structure determination. *Mailing Add:* 601 S Chestnut St Westfield NJ 07090

SLATKIN, DANIEL NATHAN, b Montreal, Que, Aug 5, 34. PATHOLOGY. *Educ:* McGill Univ, BSc, 55, MD, 59. *Prof Exp:* Intern, Mt Sinai Hosp, New York, 59-60; res assoc med, Brookhaven Nat Lab, 60-61; resident path, Montefiore Hosp, New York, 61-63 & neuropath, 63-64; resident pediat path, Presby Hosp, New York, 64-65; registr, Hammersmith Hosp, London, Eng, 65-66; assoc pathologist, McKellar Gen Hosp, Thunder Bay, Ont, 68-69; from instr to asst prof path, State Univ NY Stony Brook, 69-72; PATHOLOGIST, HOSP MED RES CTR & SCIENTIST, MED DEPT, BROOKHAVEN NAT LAB, 72- *Concurrent Pos:* Anna Fuller Found fel, Inst Sci Res Cancer, Villejuif, France, 66-67; asst prof path, State Univ NY Stony Brook, 72-; consult path, Vet Admin Hosp, Northport, NY, 72- *Mem:* Harvey Soc; NY Acad Sci; Am Asn Pathologists. *Res:* Stable isotope tracers; deoxyribonucleoside metabolism; neutron-boron capture therapy of gliomas; coal-workers' pneumoconiosis. *Mailing Add:* Med Dept Brookhaven Nat Lab Upton NY 11973

SLATKIN, MONTGOMERY WILSON, b Toronto, Ont, June 29, 45; US citizen. APPLIED MATHEMATICS, POPULATION BIOLOGY. *Educ:* Mass Inst Technol, SB, 66; Harvard Univ, PhD(appl math), 70. *Prof Exp:* Res assoc biol, Univ Chicago, 70-71, asst prof theoret biol, biophys & biol, 71-76, assoc prof, 76-77; ASSOC PROF ZOOL, UNIV WASH, 77- *Concurrent Pos:* Vis staff mem, Los Alamos Sci Labs, 70- *Res:* Mathematical population genetics and population ecology. *Mailing Add:* Dept of Zool Univ of Wash Seattle WA 98195

SLATON, JACK H(AMILTON), b Riverside, Ill, Mar 9, 25; m 54. ELECTRICAL ENGINEERING. *Educ:* Ill Inst Technol, BS, 45; Calif Inst Technol, MS, 47; Univ Calif, Los Angeles, PhD(eng), 72. *Prof Exp:* Engr, Dayton Acme Co, Ohio, 45-46; asst prof eng res, Ord Res Lab, Pa State Col, 47-50; res scientist, Mil Physics Res Lab, Univ Tex, 50-51; res engr, NAm Aviation, Inc, 51-53; ELECTRONIC ENGR, NAVAL OCEAN SYSTS CTR, SAN DIEGO, 53- *Honors & Awards:* L T E Thompson Award, 62. *Res:* Underwater acoustics; development of underwater ordnance; electronic circuit design. *Mailing Add:* 1659 Calle Candela La Jolla CA 92037

SLATT, ROGER MALCOLM, sedimentology, see previous edition

SLATTERY, CHARLES WILBUR, b LaJunta, Colo, Nov 18, 37; m 58; c 2. PHYSICAL CHEMISTRY. *Educ:* Union Col, Nebr, BA, 59; Univ Nebr, MS, 61, PhD(phys chem), 65. *Prof Exp:* From asst prof to assoc prof chem, Atlantic Union Col, 63-69; res assoc, Mass Inst Technol, 69-70; from asst prof to assoc prof, 70-78, PROF BIOCHEM, SCH MED, LOMA LINDA UNIV, 78-, PROF PEDIAT, 80- *Mem:* Sigma Xi; Am Soc Biol Chemists; AAAS; Am Chem Soc. *Res:* Ultracentrifuge theory with computer application to the problem of sedimentation in multicomponent systems; physical chemistry of macromolecules, principally on the structure and interactions of the bovine and human caseins; enzyme complexes in blood coagulation. *Mailing Add:* Dept of Biochem Loma Linda Univ Sch of Med Loma Linda CA 92354

SLATTERY, JOHN C, b St Louis, Mo, July 20, 32; m 56; c 5. CHEMICAL ENGINEERING. *Educ:* Washington Univ, St Louis, BS, 54; Univ Wis, MS, 55, PhD(chem eng), 59. *Prof Exp:* From asst prof to assoc prof, 59-67, PROF CHEM ENG, NORTHWESTERN UNIV, EVANSTON, 67- *Mem:* Am Inst Chem Engrs; Soc Rheol; Am Chem Soc; Soc Natural Philos. *Res:* Interfacial phenomena; multiphase flows; fluid mechanics; continuum mechanics. *Mailing Add:* Dept of Chem Eng Northwestern Univ Evanston IL 60201

SLATTERY, LOUIS R, b Ft Leavenworth, Kans, Oct 16, 08; m 44; c 2. SURGERY. *Educ:* Columbia Univ, AB, 29, MD, 33; Am Bd Surg, dipl, 40. *Prof Exp:* PROF CLIN SURG, MED CTR, NY UNIV, 50- *Concurrent Pos:* Consult, Inst Rehab & Phys Med, 48- & St Francis Hosp, Port Jervis, 50-; vis surgeon, Bellevue Univ & Doctors Hosps, 50-; consult surgeon, Lenox Hill Hosp, 68 & Vet Admin Hosp, 68. *Mem:* AMA; Am Col Surg. *Mailing Add:* Dept of Surg NY Univ Med Ctr New York NY 10016

SLATTERY, PAUL FRANCIS, b Hartford, Conn, July 21, 40; m 64; c 1. HIGH ENERGY PHYSICS. *Educ:* Univ Notre Dame, BS, 62; Yale Univ, MS, 63, PhD(physics), 67. *Prof Exp:* Atomic Energy Comn fel, 67-69, asst prof, 69-73, assoc prof, 73-78, PROF PHYSICS, UNIV ROCHESTER, 78- *Honors & Awards:* Leigh Page Mem Prize, 63. *Mem:* Am Phys Soc. *Res:* Experimental high energy physics; study of hadron induced reactions via electronic techniques. *Mailing Add:* Dept Physics & Astron Univ Rochester Rochester NY 14627

SLATTERY, RICHARD ERICK, physics, see previous edition

SLAUGHTER, CHARLES WESLEY, b Baker, Ore, Oct 28, 41; m 62; c 3. FOREST HYDROLOGY. *Educ:* Wash State Univ, BS, 62; Colo State Univ, PhD(watershed mgt), 68. *Prof Exp:* res hydrologist, US Army Cold Regions Res & Eng Lab, 68-76, PRIN WATERSHED SCIENTIST, INST NORTHERN FORESTRY, US FOREST SERV, 76- *Concurrent Pos:* Assoc prof, Univ Alaska, 69-76 & adj prof water resources, 76-; chmn res coord subcomt, Inter-Agency Tech Comt, Alaska, 69- *Mem:* Soc Am Foresters; Soil Conserv Soc Am; Am Geophys Union. *Res:* Wildland and snow hydrology; watershed management; permafrost hydrology. *Mailing Add:* Inst of Northern Forestry US Forest Serv College AK 99701

SLAUGHTER, FRANK GILL, JR, b Jacksonville, Fla, May 15, 40; m 59; c 2. MATHEMATICS. *Educ:* Harvard Univ, BA, 61; Duke Univ, PhD(math), 66. *Prof Exp:* Asst prof, 66-70, ASSOC PROF MATH & STATIST, UNIV PITTSBURGH, 71- *Mem:* Am Math Soc; Math Asn Am. *Res:* General topology; generalizations of metric spaces. *Mailing Add:* Dept of Math Univ of Pittsburgh Pittsburgh PA 15260

SLAUGHTER, JOHN BROOKS, b Topeka, Kans, Mar 16, 34; m 56; c 2. COMPUTER SCIENCES. *Educ:* Kans State Univ, BS, 56; Univ Calif, Los Angeles, MS, 61; Univ Calif, San Diego, PhD(eng sci), 71. *Prof Exp:* Engr simulation, Convair Div, Gen Dynamics Corp, 56-60; phys sci admin info systs, Naval Electronics Lab Ctr, 60-75; dir appl physics lab, Univ Wash, 75-77; ASST DIR, NSF, 77- *Concurrent Pos:* Ed, J Comput & Elec Eng Pergamon Press, 72- *Honors & Awards:* Community Serv Award, Inst Elec & Electronics Engrs, 72. *Mem:* Fel AAAS; Inst Elec & Electronics Engrs. *Res:* Development of computer algorithms for system optimization and discrete signal processing with emphasis on application to ocean and environmental system problems. *Mailing Add:* Nat Sci Found Washington DC 20550

SLAUGHTER, JOHN SIM, b Muskagee, Okla, Aug 2, 43; m 73. PSYCHOPHYSIOLOGY, EXPERIMENTAL PSYCHOLOGY. *Educ:* Lynchburg Col, BA, 67; Univ Denver, MA, 70, PhD(exp psychol), 71. *Prof Exp:* Instr psychol, Lynchburg Col, 67-68; res asst, Univ Denver, 68-71; instr, Fitzsimmons Army Hosp, 69-70; asst prof, 71-76, ASSOC PROF PSYCHOL, STATE UNIV NY COL, FREDONIA, 76- *Concurrent Pos:* Res grants, State Univ NY, 72-74. *Honors & Awards:* RACET, NY State Exemplary Media Award, 75. *Mem:* Am Psychol Asn; Soc Psychophysiol Res. *Res:* Role of peripheral autonomic responses in determining emotional development. *Mailing Add:* Dept of Psychol State Univ NY Col Fredonia NY 14063

SLAUGHTER, MAYNARD, b Athens, Ohio, Jan 13, 34; m 53; c 5. CRYSTALLOGRAPHY. *Educ:* Ohio Univ, BS, 55; Univ Mo-Columbia, AM, 57; Univ Pittsburg, PhD, 61. *Prof Exp:* Chem mineralogist, Gulf Res & Develop Co, 57-60; asst prof x-ray crystallog, Univ Mo-Columbia, 60-69; PROF GEOCHEM, COLO SCH MINES, 69- *Concurrent Pos:* Chief scientist, Crystal Res Lab, Golden, Colo. *Mem:* fel Mineral Soc Am; Am Crystallog Asn; Geol Soc Am. *Res:* Crystalline structure of minerals clay mineralogy, methods of rock analysis, theoretical mineralogy. *Mailing Add:* Dept of Chem & Geochem Colo Sch of Mines Golden CO 80401

SLAUNWHITE, WILSON ROY, JR, b Waltham, Mass, Sept 25, 19; m 42; c 4. BIOCHEMISTRY. *Educ:* Mass Inst Technol, BS & MS, 42, PhD(org chem), 48. *Prof Exp:* Res assoc, Radiation Lab, Mass Inst Technol, 42-45 & Naval Res Lab, 45-46; res fel med, Mass Gen Hosp, 48-52; Damon Runyon fel, Med Sch, Univ Utah, 52-53; sr cancer res scientist, Roswell Park Mem Inst, 53-55, assoc scientist cancer res, 55-60, prin cancer res scientist, 60-67; res dir, Med Found Buffalo, 67-69; dir endocrine labs, Children's Hosp, 69-73; PROF BIOCHEM & ASSOC RES PROF PEDIAT, STATE UNIV NY BUFFALO, 70- *Concurrent Pos:* From asst res prof to assoc res prof biochem, State Univ NY Buffalo, 56-63, res prof, Roswell Park Grad Div, 63-70, chmn dept, 63-67; consult, Med Found Buffalo, 58-67; ed, Steroids, 64- & J Clin Endocrinol & Metab, Endocrine Soc, 68-70; consult, Roswell Park Mem Inst, 70- *Mem:* Endocrine Soc; Am Soc Biol Chem; Soc Study Reproduction. *Res:* Steroid and thyroid endocrinology; glycoprotein structure. *Mailing Add:* Dept Biochem 3435 Main St Buffalo NY 14214

SLAUTTERBACK, DAVID BUELL, b Indianapolis, Ind, July 15, 26; m 52; c 4. CELL BIOLOGY. *Educ:* Univ Mich, BS, 48, MS, 49; Cornell Univ, PhD(anat), 52. *Prof Exp:* Instr anat, Med Sch, NY Univ, 54-55; instr, Med Col, Cornell Univ, 55-59; from asst prof to assoc prof, 59-67, PROF ANAT & CHMN DEPT, MED SCH, UNIV WIS-MADISON, 67- *Concurrent Pos:* Am Cancer Soc res fel, Med Sch, NY Univ, 52-54; Nat Cancer Inst fel, 54-55. *Mem:* AAAS; Am Soc Cell Biol; Am Asn Anatomists. *Res:* Cell differentiation; fine structure and function of cytoplasmic organelles; biomembranes and coated vesilles. *Mailing Add:* Dept of Anat Univ of Wis-Madison Madison WI 53706

SLAVEN, ROBERT WALTER, b Salem, Mass, Mar 8, 48; m 69; c 2. ORGANIC CHEMISTRY, ANALYTICAL CHEMISTRY. *Educ:* Univ Lowell, BSc, 69; Univ Wis, PhD(org chem), 74. *Prof Exp:* Fel, Northeastern Univ, 74-76; RES CHEMIST ORG CHEM, LORILLARD RES CTR, 76- *Mem:* Am Chem Soc; Sigma Xi. *Res:* Organometallic chemistry; oxidative coupling catalysts and the chemistry of metal-metal multiple bonds; nuclear magnetic resonance; structure elucidation especially of natural products. *Mailing Add:* Lorillard Res Ctr 420 English St Greensboro NC 27410

SLAVIK, NELSON SIGMAN, b St Louis, Mo, Feb 28, 48; m 70. BIOLOGICAL SAFETY, OCCUPATIONAL HEALTH & SAFETY. *Educ:* Kalamazoo Col, BA, 70; Univ Ill, Urbana, MS, 72, PhD(microbiol), 75. *Prof Exp:* Res assoc plant tissue culture, 75-77, BIOL SAFETY OFFICER, UNIV ILL, URBANA, 77-, ASST PROF, OCCUP HEALTH & SAFETY, 81- *Concurrent Pos:* Asst dir, Div Environ Health & Safety, Univ Ill, Urbana, 78-81. *Mem:* Sigma Xi. *Mailing Add:* Dept Health & Safety Univ Ill 1206 S Fourth Champaign IL 61820

SLAVIN, BERNARD GEOFFREY, b San Francisco, Calif, Oct 18, 36; m 60; c 2. ANATOMY. *Educ:* Univ Calif, Berkeley, BA, 59; Univ Calif, San Francisco, MA, 62, PhD(anat), 67. *Prof Exp:* Teaching fel anat, Univ Calif, 64-65, res asst, 65-66, lectr, 66-67; NIH fel, Yale Univ, 67-69; asst prof, 69-74, ASSOC PROF ANAT, UNIV SOUTHERN CALIF, 74- *Concurrent Pos:* NIH res grant, 75. *Mem:* AAAS; Am Asn Naturalists; Electron Micros Soc Am. *Res:* Hormonal influence on adipose tissue in vitro; histochemistry and electron microscopy of adipose cells; innervation of adipose tissue. *Mailing Add:* Dept of Anat Univ of Southern Calif Med Sch Los Angeles CA 90033

SLAVIN, OVID, b Romania, Dec 20, 21; US citizen; m 45. DENTISTRY, BIOLOGY. *Educ:* Washington Univ, AB, 42, DDS, 45. *Prof Exp:* Intern, Guggenheim Dent Clin, NY, 45-46; instr pedodont, Sch Dent & Oral Surg, Columbia Univ, 52-58; asst prof, Seton Hall Col Med & Dent, 58-62, asst dir prototype prog handicapped children, 61-62; prof biomed eng, NY Inst Technol, 64-65, prof life sci & chmn dept, 65-67, dean admin, Long Island Ctr, 64-66; chief dentist, Brookdale Hosp Ctr, Brooklyn, NY, 67-71, asst dir, Comprehensive Child Care Prog, 68-71; regional dent consult, Maternal & Child Health Serv, Health Serv & Ment Health Admin, Dept Health, Educ & Welfare, Philadelphia, 71-77; ASSOC PROF, SCH DENT, TEMPLE UNIV, 77- *Concurrent Pos:* Chief pedodont sect, Long Island Jewish Hosp, NY, 53-55; chief pedodont serv, Jewish Chronic Dis Hosp, NY, 53-62. *Mem:* Am Asn Pub Health Dentists; Am Acad Pedodont; Am Dent Asn; Am Soc Dent Children. *Res:* Dentistry for handicapped children; biomedical engineering, particularly its application to clinical procedures; pedodontics. *Mailing Add:* 703 W Mt Airy Ave Philadelphia PA 19119

SLAVIN, RAYMOND GRANAM, b Cleveland, Ohio, June 29, 30; m 53; c 4. INTERNAL MEDICINE, ALLERGY. *Educ:* Univ Mich, AB, 52; St Louis Univ, MD, 56; Northwestern Univ, Chicago, MS, 63. *Prof Exp:* Resident internal med, Sch Med, St Louis Univ, 59-61; asst internal med, Northwestern Univ, 64-65; from asst prof to assoc prof, 65-73, PROF INTERNAL MED, SCH MED, ST LOUIS UNIV, 73- *Concurrent Pos:* NIH training grant allergy & immunol, Northwestern Univ, 61-64; bd dirs, Am Bd Allergy & Immunol; chmn, Med Adv Coun, Asthma & Allergy Found Am. *Mem:* fel Am Acad Allergy; fel Am Col Physicians; Am Asn Immunologists. *Res:* Immunology, clinical allergy; allergic bronchopulmonary aspergillosis and other pulmonary hypersensitivity syndromes; delayed hypersensitivity-clinical states in which delayed hypersensitivity is suppressed; health effects of air pollution. *Mailing Add:* 1402 S Grand St St Louis MO 63104

SLAVKIN, HAROLD CHARLES, b Chicago, Ill, Mar 20, 38. DEVELOPMENTAL BIOLOGY, CELL BIOLOGY. *Educ:* Univ Southern Calif, BA, 63, DDS, 65. *Prof Exp:* Fel, Dept Anat, Sch Med, Univ Calif, Los Angeles, 65-66; fel, Dept Biochem, Univ Southern Calif, 66-68, asst prof, Sch Dent, 68-70, fac, gerontol, Gerontol Inst, 69-70, assoc prof, 71-73, PROF BIOCHEM & NUTRIT, SCH DENT, UNIV SOUTHERN CALIF, 74- *Concurrent Pos:* Res Career Develop Award, US Pub Health Serv, 68-72; prin investr, Southern Calif State Dent Asn grants, 69-70, NIH, Prog Proj grants, 69-, Intercellular Commun grants, 72-80, Training grants, 69-85 & NIH grants, 81-84; vis scientist, Intramural Prog, Nat Inst Dent Res, NIH, 75-76; co-ed, J Craniogacial Genetics & Develop Biol, 80-, co-managing ed, Differentiation, 80-81; consult, NIH, 67-, NSF, 73-75, Med Res Coun, Australia, Can, & Gt Brit, 72-, Bd Sci Dirs, Nat Inst Dent Res, NIH, 76-80, Human Biol Series, US News & World Report, 81-85 & Oral Biol & Med Study Sect, NIH, 81-85. *Mem:* AAAS; Am Soc Cell Biol; Int Asn Dent Res; Int Soc Develop Biol; NY Acad Sci. *Res:* Epithelial-mesenchymal interactions during vertebrate epidermal organ development; induction of epithelial-specific gene products such as enamel proteins during tooth morphogenesis; immunogenetic studies of drug-induced craniofacial malformations in murine and human embryogenesis. *Mailing Add:* Andrus Gerontol Ctr Rm 314 Univ Southern Calif PO Box 77912 Los Angeles CA 90007

SLAWSON, PETER (ROBERT), b Toronto, Ont, July 10, 39; m 62; c 3. AIR POLLUTION, MECHANICAL ENGINEERING. *Educ:* Univ Waterloo, BASc, 64, MASc, 66, PhD(mech eng), 67. *Prof Exp:* Res assoc air pollution, 67-69, asst prof mech eng, 69-74, ASSOC PROF MECH ENG, UNIV WATERLOO, 74- *Res:* Diffusion; atmospheric dynamics as applied to the dispersal of air pollutants. *Mailing Add:* 20 Braeburn Pl Waterloo ON N2L 5A9 Can

SLAWSON, WILLIAM FRANCIS, b Ann Arbor, Mich, July 4, 29; m 56; c 3. GEOCHEMISTRY. *Educ:* Univ Mich, BS, 52; Univ Utah, PhD(geol eng), 58. *Prof Exp:* Res fel physics, Univ Toronto, 58-61; from asst prof to assoc prof physics, Univ BC, 61-70, prof, 70-80; WITH US GEOL SURV, 80- *Mem:* Geochem Soc; Am Geophys Union; Can Geophys Union. *Res:* Isotope geology; trace element distribution. *Mailing Add:* US Geol Surv MS/77 345 Middlefield Rd Menlo Park CA 94025

SLAYDEN, SUZANNE WEEMS, b Heidelberg, Ger, Aug 11, 48; US citizen. ORGANIC CHEMISTRY. *Educ:* Univ Tenn, BS, 70, PhD(org chem), 76. *Prof Exp:* ASST PROF CHEM, GEORGE MASON UNIV, 76- *Mem:* Am Chem Soc. *Res:* Mechanisms of organoborate rearrangements. *Mailing Add:* Chem Dept George Mason Univ Fairfax VA 22030

SLAYMAN, CAROLYN WALCH, b Portland, Maine, Mar 11, 37; m 59; c 2. GENETICS. *Educ:* Swarthmore Col, BA, 58; Rockefeller Univ, PhD(biochem genetics), 63. *Prof Exp:* Instr biol, Western Reserve Univ, 64-65, asst prof, 65-67; asst prof microbiol & physiol, 67-70, assoc prof, 70-72, assoc prof human genetics and physiol, 72-77, PROF HUMAN GENETICS & PHYSIOL, SCH MED, YALE UNIV, 77- *Concurrent Pos:* NSF fel, Cambridge Univ, 63-64; consult, Adv Panel Genetic Biol, NSF, 74-77; assoc ed, Genetics, 77-; mem bd overseers, Bowdoin Col, 77- *Res:* Genetic control of membrane transport. *Mailing Add:* Dept Human Genetics Sch Med Yale Univ New Haven CT 06510

SLAYMAN, CLIFFORD L, b Mt Vernon, Ohio, July 7, 36; m 59; c 2. PHYSIOLOGY. *Educ:* Kenyon Col, AB, 58; Rockefeller Univ, PhD(physiol), 63. *Prof Exp:* NSF fel physiol, Cambridge Univ, 63-64; asst prof, Sch Med, Western Reserve Univ, 64-67; asst prof, 67-70, ASSOC PROF PHYSIOL, SCH MED, YALE UNIV, 70- *Concurrent Pos:* NIH res grants, 65, 68, 73 & 78, res career develop award, 69. *Mem:* Am Physiol Soc; Am Soc Microbiol; Soc Gen Physiologists; Am Soc Plant Physiologists; AAAS. *Res:* Membrane biophysics; transport, energy-coupling, and electrogenesis in microorganisms. *Mailing Add:* Dept of Physiol Yale Univ Sch of Med New Haven CT 06510

SLEATOR, WILLIAM WARNER, JR, b Ann Arbor, Mich, Apr 5, 17; m 40; c 4. BIOPHYSICS, PHYSIOLOGY. *Educ:* Univ Mich, AB, 38, MS, 39, PhD(physics), 46. *Prof Exp:* Physicist, Ballistic Res Lab, Aberdeen Proving Ground, Md, 42-45; res assoc physics, Univ Minn, 46-49; from asst prof biophys to assoc prof physiol, Sch Med, Wash Univ, St Louis, 49-64, prof physiol & biophys, 64-69, actg chmn dept, 66-68; head dept, 69-76, PROF PHYSIOL & BIOPHYSICS, UNIV ILL, URBANA, 69- *Concurrent Pos:* Mem, Physiol Study Sect, NIH, 76-80. *Mem:* Fel Am Phys Soc; Am Physiol Soc; Biophys Soc (secy, 62-67). *Res:* Scattering of elementary particles and light nuclei; light scattering and absorption by living muscle and muscle proteins; fundamental cellular processes in heart, skeletal and smooth muscle; ionic conductance changes during cardiac action potential; mechanism of contraction process and of coupling between excitation and contraction. *Mailing Add:* Dept of Physiol & Biophysics Univ of Ill Urbana IL 61801

SLECHTA, ROBERT FRANK, b New York, NY, June 4, 28; m 53; c 1. REPRODUCTIVE PHYSIOLOGY. *Educ:* Clark Univ, AB, 49, MA, 51; Boston Univ, PhD(biol), 55. *Prof Exp:* Asst physiol, Worcester Found Exp Biol, 52-53; res assoc & instr, Tufts Univ, 55-58; from asst prof to assoc prof, 58-65, assoc dean, Grad Sch, 67-79, PROF BIOL, BOSTON UNIV, 65- *Mem:* AAAS; Soc Study Reproduction. *Res:* Reproductive and microcirculatory physiology. *Mailing Add:* 101 Wilson Rd Bedford MA 01730

SLEDD, MARVIN BANKS, b Greensboro, Ala, Aug 24, 12; m 40; c 1. MATHEMATICS. *Educ:* Emory Univ, AB, 35, MS, 36; Mass Inst Technol, MS, 47, PhD, 54. *Prof Exp:* Elec engr, Gen Elec Co, 37-40; from asst to instr elec eng, Mass Inst Technol, 41-43, asst prof, 46-47; asst prof math, Emory Univ, 46, 48-49, assoc prof, 49-50; Atomic Energy Comn fel, Mass Inst Technol, 50-51; from assoc prof to prof math, Ga Inst Technol, 51-68, Regents prof, 68-81; RETIRED. *Mem:* Soc Indust & Appl Math. *Res:* Electrical engineering; infinite systems of ordinary differential equations with attention to applications in the natural sciences and technology. *Mailing Add:* 306 Kenilworth Circle Stone Mountain GA 30083

SLEDD, WILLIAM T, b Murray, Ky, Aug 25, 35; m 58; c 2. MATHEMATICS. *Educ:* Murray State Col, BA, 56; Univ Ky, MA, 59, PhD(math), 61. *Prof Exp:* Asst math, Univ Ky, 56-60; from asst prof to assoc prof, 61-69, PROF MATH, MICH STATE UNIV, 69- *Mem:* Math Asn Am; Am Math Soc. *Res:* Summability theory; Fourier analysis. *Mailing Add:* Dept of Math Mich State Univ East Lansing MI 48823

SLEDGE, EUGENE BONDURANT, b Mobile, Ala, Nov 4, 23; m 52; c 2. BIOLOGY. *Educ:* Auburn Univ, BS, 49, MS, 55; Univ Fla, PhD(biol), 60. *Prof Exp:* Res asst, Auburn Univ, 53-55; asst, Univ Fla, 56-59; nematologist, Div Plant Indust, Fla State Dept Agr, 59-62; asst prof biol, Ala Col, 62-70; chmn dept, 70-72, PROF BIOL, UNIV MONTEVALLO, 70- *Mem:* Am Ornith Union; Wilson Ornith Soc. *Res:* Ornithology, particularly avian myology. *Mailing Add:* Dept of Biol Univ of Montevallo Montevallo AL 35115

SLEE, FREDERICK WATFORD, b Spokane, Wash, Mar 16, 37. NUCLEAR PHYSICS. *Educ:* Univ Wash, BS, 59, MS, 60, PhD(physics), 66. *Prof Exp:* ASSOC PROF PHYSICS, UNIV PUGET SOUND, 66-, CHMN PHYSICS, 80- *Mem:* Am Phys Soc; AAAS. *Res:* Electronic instrumentation applied to physics, geophysics and biophysics. *Mailing Add:* Dept of Physics Univ of Puget Sound Tacoma WA 98416

SLEEMAN, HARRY KENNETH, b Eckhart, Md, Mar 25, 20; m 42; c 5. BIOCHEMISTRY. *Educ:* State Teachers Col, Frostburg, BS, 42; Univ Md, BS, 50; Georgetown Univ, MS, 56, PhD(biochem), 60. *Prof Exp:* Biochemist, Walter Reed Army Inst Res, 50-56, immunochemist, 56-62, supvry res biochemist, 62-66, dept chief surg metab, 66-71, dept chief appl biochem, 71-81; RETIRED. *Mem:* Am Chem Soc; Soc Exp Biol & Med. *Res:* Biochemical analyses and metabolic pathways; parasitic antigens; biochemical alterations in shock; drug effects and metabolism. *Mailing Add:* Div of Biochem Walter Reed Army Inst of Res Washington DC 20012

SLEEMAN, LYLE HERMAN, JR, geology, see previous edition

SLEEMAN, RICHARD ALEXANDER, b Bennington, Vt, Sept 15, 26; m 50. CHEMISTRY. *Educ:* Fordham Univ, BS, 49; NY Univ, MA, 51, EdD(phys sci), 55. *Prof Exp:* Instr phys sci, Vt State Teachers Col, Castleton, 49-54 & NY Univ, 54-55; asst prof chem, Kent State Univ, 56-60; PROF CHEM, NORTH ADAMS STATE COL, 70-, MEM FAC DEPT EDUC, 76- *Mem:* AAAS; Nat Asn Res Sci Teaching. *Res:* Physics; quantum mechanics and black body radiation. *Mailing Add:* Dept of Educ North Adams State Col North Adams MA 01247

SLEEPER, DAVID ALLANBROOK, b Exeter, NH, Feb 1, 22; m 49; c 1. BIOLOGY, ENTOMOLOGY. *Educ:* Univ NH, BS, 43; Cornell Univ, PhD(entom), 63. *Prof Exp:* Entomologist, Alaska Insect Proj, USDA, 48 & Arctic Health Res Ctr, USPHS, 49-54; instr biol, Cornell Univ, 61-63; asst prof, Elmira Col, 63-65; asst prof, 65-71, assoc prof, 71-81, PROF BIOL, HOBART & WILLIAM SMITH COLS, 81- *Mem:* Ecol Soc Am; Soc Syst Zool; Animal Behav Soc. *Res:* Ecology, taxonomy, and physiology of biting diptera, especially blackflies of the family Simuliidae. *Mailing Add:* Dept of Biol Hobart Col Geneva NY 14456

SLEEPER, ELBERT LAUNEE, b Newton, Iowa, July 27, 27; m 49; c 3. ENTOMOLOGY. *Educ:* Ohio State Univ, BS, 50, MS, 51, PhD(entom), 56. *Prof Exp:* Asst, Ohio Biol Surv, Ohio State Univ, 53-56; from asst prof to assoc prof, 57-66, PROF ENTOM, CALIF STATE UNIV, LONG BEACH, 66- *Concurrent Pos:* Collabr, US Nat Park Serv, 57-; consult lab nuclear med & radiation biol, Univ Calif, Los Angeles, 70- *Mem:* AAAS; Ecol Soc Am; Am Entom Soc; Am Forestry Soc; Entom Soc Am. *Res:* Systematics of the Curculionoidea excluding the Scolytidae; dynamics of desert insect populations; systematics, zoogeography and ecological distribution of Curculionoidea of the new world. *Mailing Add:* Dept of Biol Calif State Univ Long Beach CA 90840

SLEETH, BAILEY, b Linn, WVa, Nov 1, 00; m 33; c 2. PLANT PATHOLOGY. *Educ:* Univ WVa, BS, 27, MS, 28, PhD(plant path), 32. *Prof Exp:* Teacher high sch, WVa, 27-30; asst plant path, Univ WVa, 32-33, asst exten plant pathologist, 42; asst forest pathologist, Bur Plant Indust, US Dept Agr, 33-41, assoc plant pathologist, Rubber Plant Invests, 42-46, pathologist, Div Soil Mgt & Irrig, 46-51; plant pathologist, 51-66, EMER PLANT PATHOLOGIST, TEX AGR EXP STA, TEX A&M UNIV, 66-; AGR CONSULT, 66- *Mem:* Am Phytopath Soc; Mycol Soc Am; Am Inst Biol Sci. *Res:* Forest tree diseases in eastern United States; guayule seedling diseases in California and Texas; citrus diseases. *Mailing Add:* 307 Nebraska Weslaco TX 78596

SLEETH, RHULE BAILEY, b Linn, WVa, Feb 6, 29; m 53; c 2. FOOD TECHNOLOGY, ANIMAL NUTRITION. *Educ:* WVa Univ, BS, 51; Univ Fla, MS, 53; Univ Mo, PhD(meat & food technol), 59. *Prof Exp:* Instr meat technol, Univ Mo, 55-59; food technologist, 59-63, sect head fresh meat develop, 63-64, asst mgr, Food Res Div, 64-68, asst dir, Food Res Div, 68-78, dir food res & develop, 78-80, VPRES FOODS RES & DEVELOP, ARMOUR & CO, 81- *Concurrent Pos:* Mem prog comt, Meat Indust Res Conf, 65-66, chmn, 67; chmn, Reciprocal Meat Conf, 68; contact, Europ Meeting Meat Res Workers. *Honors & Awards:* Signal Serv Award, Reciprocal Meat Conf, 71. *Mem:* Fel Inst Food Technologists; Am Soc Animal Sci; Am Meat Sci Asn (pres, 73-74); Soc Advan Food Serv Res. *Res:* Sausage and cured meat development; sterile and refrigerated canned meats; food service research; food chemistry; dairy, poultry and food oils; packaging research. *Mailing Add:* Armour Res Ctr 15101 N Scottsdale Rd Scottsdale AZ 85260

SLEEZER, PAUL DAVID, b Chicago, Ill, Jan 26, 36; m 63. ORGANIC CHEMISTRY. *Educ:* Univ Rochester, BS, 58; Univ Calif, Los Angeles, PhD(chem), 63. *Prof Exp:* Sr res chemist, Solvay Process Div, Allied Chem Corp, NY, 63-66; sr develop chemist, Bristol Labs, 66-72, DEPT HEAD

ORG SYNTHESIS LABS, INDUST DIV, BRISTOL-MYERS CO, 72- *Mem:* Am Chem Soc. *Res:* Exploratory organic research; synthesis and process development; process analysis and control; organic reaction mechanisms; physical-organic; organometallics. *Mailing Add:* Bristol-Myers Co PO Box 657 Syracuse NY 13201

SLEICHER, CHARLES A, b Albany, NY, Aug 15, 24; m 53; c 2. CHEMICAL ENGINEERING. *Educ:* Brown Univ, ScB, 46; Mass Inst Technol, MS, 49; Univ Mich, PhD(chem eng), 55. *Prof Exp:* Res engr, Shell Develop Co, 55-59; NSF fel, Cambridge Univ, 59-60; assoc prof chem eng, 60-66, PROF CHEM ENG, UNIV WASH, 66-, CHMN DEPT, 77- *Concurrent Pos:* Grants, Am Chem Soc, 60-64, NSF, 61- & Chevron Res Found, 64-67; consult, Westinghouse-Hanford Co, 73- *Mem:* AAAS; Am Chem Soc; Am Inst Chem Engrs; Am Soc Enologists. *Res:* Turbulent diffusion, heat transfer; heat transfer with variable fluid properties; dispersion of toxins in the environment; aerosol deposition in the lung. *Mailing Add:* Dept Chem Eng BF-10 Univ Wash Seattle WA 98195

SLEIGHT, ARTHUR WILLIAM, b Ballston Spa, NY, Apr 1, 39; m 63; c 3. SOLID STATE CHEMISTRY, HETEROGENEOUS CATALYSIS. *Educ:* Hamilton Col, BA, 60; Univ Conn, PhD(inorg chem), 63. *Prof Exp:* Fel crystallog, Univ Stockholm, 63-64; res chemist solid state chem, 64-79, res supvr, 79-81, RES MGR, E I DU PONT DE NEMOURS & CO, 81- *Concurrent Pos:* Assoc ed, Mat Res Bull, 76- & Inorg Chem Rev, 79-; adj prof, Univ Del, 78- *Mem:* Am Chem Soc. *Res:* Heterogeneous catalysis, molybdate, supported metal and zeolite catalysts, partial oxidation catalysis; solid state chemistry, structure-property relationships for inorganic solids, especially oxides and sulfides, superconductivity, ionic conductivity, defects; crystal growth; crystallography; structural chemistry; heterogeneous catalysis; electrical, magnetic and optical properties. *Mailing Add:* Cent Res & Develop Dept Exp Sta E I du Pont De Nemours & Co Wilmington DE 19898

SLEIGHT, STUART DUANE, b Lansing, Mich, Oct 19, 27; m 50; c 4. VETERINARY PATHOLOGY. *Educ:* Mich State Univ, DVM, 51, MS, 59, PhD(vet path), 61. *Prof Exp:* Vet, Columbus Vet Hosp, Wis, 51-58; from asst prof to assoc prof, 61-68, PROF PATH, MICH STATE UNIV, 68- *Mem:* Am Col Vet Path; Conf Res Workers Animal Dis; Am Vet Med Asn; AAAS; Soc Toxicol. *Res:* Toxicopathology of nitrates, heavy metals and pesticides; toxicity and carcinogenicity of brominated biphenyls. *Mailing Add:* 522 E Fee Hall Dept of Path Mich State Univ East Lansing MI 48824

SLEIGHT, THOMAS PERRY, b Glens Falls, NY, May 15, 43; m 66; c 4. COMPUTER SCIENCE. *Educ:* Ohio Univ, BS(chem) & BS(math), 65; State Univ NY Buffalo, PhD(chem), 69. *Prof Exp:* Sci Res Coun fel, Univ Leicester, 68-69; PRIN STAFF, APPL PHYSICS LAB, JOHNS HOPKINS UNIV, 69-, ADVAN SYSTS DESIGN SUPVR, 80- *Mem:* Am Chem Soc; Int Elec & Electronics Engrs Comput Soc. *Res:* Advanced computer systems; software engineering; navy computer systems; real time software. *Mailing Add:* Appl Physics Lab Johns Hopkins Univ Johns Hopkins Rd Laurel MD 20707

SLEIN, MILTON WILBUR, b St Louis, Mo, Jan 26, 19; m 50; c 3. BIOCHEMISTRY. *Educ:* washington Univ, AB, 40, MS, 43, PhD(biochem), 49. *Prof Exp:* Asst biochem, Wash Univ, 42-49; biochemist, US Army Biol Ctr, Ft Detrick, 49-71 & Edgewood Arsenal, 71-72; BIOCHEMIST, FREDERICK CANCER RES CTR, 72- *Mem:* Am Soc Biol Chemists. *Res:* Enzymology; microbiological biochemistry. *Mailing Add:* 16 Kline Blvd Frederick MD 21701

SLEISENGER, MARVIN HERBERT, b Pittsburgh, Pa, June 3, 24; m 48; c 1. MEDICINE. *Educ:* Harvard Med Sch, MD, 47; Am Bd Internal Med, dipl, 54. *Prof Exp:* Intern med, Beth Israel Hosp, Boston, Mass, 47-48, chief resident, 49-50; intern, Beth Israel Hosp, Newark, NJ, 48-49; resident gastroenterol, Hosp Univ Pa, 50-51; instr med, Med Col, Cornell Univ, 52-53, from asst prof to assoc prof clin med, 54-65, prof med, 65-68; PROF MED & VCHMN DEPT, MED CTR, UNIV CALIF, SAN FRANCISCO, 68- *Concurrent Pos:* Fel gastroenterol, Hosp, Univ Pa, 50-51; fel med, Med Col, Cornell Univ, 51-52; assoc, Harvard Med Sch, 49-50; instr, Sch Med, Tufts Univ, 49-50; asst physician, out-patient clin, New York Hosp, 51-54, physician, 54-56, chief gastrointestinal clin, 54-68, from asst attend physician to attend physician, 56-68; consult, Rockefeller Inst Hosp, New York & aerospace prog, US Air Force, 64-; chief med serv, Ft Miley Vet Admin Hosp, San Francisco, Calif, 68- *Mem:* AAAS; Am Soc Clin Invest; Harvey Soc; Am Gastroenterol Asn; Am Fedn Clin Res. *Res:* Intestinal absorption; esophageal motility; fractionation of gastric juice mucoproteins; experimental ulcerative colitis; measurement of enzymes. *Mailing Add:* Univ Calif Serv Vet Admin Hosp 4150 Clement St San Francisco CA 94121

SLEMMONS, DAVID BURTON, b Alameda, Calif, Dec 31, 22; m 46; c 2. GEOLOGY, GEOPHYSICS. *Educ:* Univ Calif, BS, 47, PhD(geol), 53. *Prof Exp:* Asst geol, Univ Calif, 49-51; from asst prof to assoc prof, 51-63, dir seismog sta, 52-64, chmn dept geol & geog, 66-70, PROF GEOL & GEOPHYS, UNIV NEV, RENO, 63- *Concurrent Pos:* prog dir geophys, Earth Sci Div, NSF, 70-71; del, 2nd & 3rd US-Japan Conf Earthquake Prediction; mem, Nat Res Coun; mem, Earthquake Eng Res Inst. *Honors & Awards:* G K Gilbert Award, Carnegie Inst. *Mem:* Geol Soc Am; Seismol Soc Am; Soc Econ Geol; Am Inst Mining, Metall & Petrol Eng. *Res:* Geology, geomorphology, seismology and volcanology, basin and range and Sierra Nevada area; petrography; universal stage determination of plagioclase; surface faulting; seismicity, faulting mechanics, earthquake hazards, seismic risk for engineering structures, seismicity of crustal structures of North America; safety of dams. *Mailing Add:* Dept Geol Sci Mackay Sch Mines Univ Nev Reno NV 89557

SLEMON, CLARKE EDWARD, synthetic organic chemistry, medicinal chemistry, see previous edition

SLEMON, GORDON R(ICHARD), b Bowmanville, Ont, Aug 15, 24; m 49; c 4. ELECTRICAL ENGINEERING. *Educ:* Univ Toronto, BASc, 46, MASc, 48; Univ London, DIC & PhD(eng), 52, DSc, 68. *Prof Exp:* Lectr, Imp Col, Univ London, 49-53; prof elec eng, NS Tech Col, 53-55; head dept, 66-76, PROF ELEC ENG, UNIV TORONTO, 55-, DEAN, FAC APPL SCI & ENG, 79- *Concurrent Pos:* Pres, Elec Eng Consociates, 76-79; chmn bd, Innovation Found, 80- *Honors & Awards:* Western Elec Award, Am Soc Eng Educ, 65. *Mem:* Am Soc Eng Educ; fel Inst Elec & Electronics Engrs; fel Inst Elec Engrs UK; fel Eng Inst Can; Can Soc Elec Eng. *Res:* Power systems; electric propulsion; rotating machines; magnetics. *Mailing Add:* Dept of Elec Eng Univ of Toronto Toronto ON M5S 1A4 Can

SLENTZ, LOREN WILLIAM, b Great Bend, Kans, Sept 21, 24; m 44; c 6. GEOCHEMISTRY. *Educ:* Stanford Univ, BS, 48, MS, 50; Univ Utah, PhD(geol, mineral), 55. *Prof Exp:* Instr chem, Southern Ill Univ, 50-53; instr, Westminster Col, 53-55, actg head dept, 53-54; SR RES ASSOC, CHEVRON OILFIELD RES CO, STANDARD OIL CO CALIF, 55-, LIAISON & COORDR TECH SERV, OVERSEAS OFF, 73-, SUPVR STRATIG & SPEC STUDIES, ARAMCO OVEREAS CO, CROYDON, ENG, 80- *Concurrent Pos:* Asst, Univ Utah, 54-55; instr eve sch, Long Beach City Col & Fullerton Jr Col, 55-74. *Mem:* Am Asn Petrol Geol. *Res:* Stratigraphy and sedimentation of Tertiary deposits of the western interior; organic and inorganic geochemistry, particularly origin and migration of oils, gases and formation waters; general relationship of gas, oil and water composition to geologic framework. *Mailing Add:* Chevron Oilfield Res Co PO Box 446 La Habra CA 90631

SLEPECKY, RALPH ANDREW, b Nanticoke, Pa, Oct 8, 24; m 67; c 2. MICROBIOLOGY. *Educ:* Franklin & Marshall Col, BS, 48; Pa State Univ, MS, 50; Univ Md, PhD(bact), 53. *Prof Exp:* Asst bact, Pa State Univ, 48-50 & Univ Md, 50-53; asst prof biol, Franklin & Marshall Col, 53-56; res scientist, Univ Tex, 56-58; asst prof biol, Northwestern Univ, 58-63; assoc prof microbiol, 63-68, adminr biol res labs, 64-70, PROF MICROBIOL, SYRACUSE UNIV, 68- *Concurrent Pos:* Instr, Montgomery Jr Col, 52; bacteriologist, Stand Brands, Inc, 52; Found Microbiol lectr, 71-72. *Mem:* AAAS; Am Soc Microbiol; Am Chem Soc. *Res:* Morphogenesis and differentiation of bacterial spores. *Mailing Add:* Dept of Biol Syracuse Univ Syracuse NY 13210

SLEPER, DAVID ALLEN, b Buffalo Ctr, Iowa, Aug 25, 45; m 65; c 2. PLANT BREEDING. *Educ:* Iowa State Univ, BS, 67, MS, 69; Univ Wis, PhD(plant breeding, genetics), 73. *Prof Exp:* Asst prof agron, Univ Fla, 73-74; asst prof, 74-76, ASSOC PROF AGRON, UNIV MO, 76- *Mem:* Am Soc Agron; Genetics Soc Can; Crop Sci Soc Am; Am Forage & Grass Coun. *Res:* Investigations on the breeding and genetics of Festuca arundinacea and Dactylis glomerata. *Mailing Add:* Dept of Agron Rm 16 Waters Hall Univ of Mo Columbia MO 65211

SLEPETYS, RICHARD ALGIMANTAS, b Ukmerge, Lithuania, Apr 4, 28; US citizen; m 54; c 1. PHYSICAL CHEMISTRY, INORGANIC CHEMISTRY. *Educ:* Univ Detroit, BChE, 54; Newark Col Eng, MSChE, 57; Rutgers Univ, PhD(chem), 67. *Prof Exp:* Jr technologist, NL Industs, Inc, 54-59, technologist, 59-66, sr technologist, 66-72, res & develop sect mgr, 72-78; res group leader, Englehard Minerals & Chem Corp, 78-80, RES GROUP LEADER, ENGLEHARD CORP, 80- *Mem:* AAAS; Am Chem Soc; Am Inst Chem. *Res:* Titanium dioxide pigment technology; lattice energies; crystal structure; kaolin extenders; light scattering. *Mailing Add:* Engelhard Corp M & C Div Menlo Park Edison NJ 08817

SLEPIAN, DAVID, b Pittsburgh, Pa, June 30, 23; m 50; c 3. MATHEMATICS, ELECTRICAL ENGINEERING. *Educ:* Harvard Univ, PhD(physics), 49. *Prof Exp:* Parker fel, Harvard Univ, 49-50; RES MATHEMATICIAN, BELL TEL LABS INC, 50-; PROF ELEC ENG, UNIV HAWAII, 70- *Concurrent Pos:* Vis Mackay prof, Univ Calif, Berkeley, 58-59; prof elec eng, Univ Hawaii, 70-81. *Honors & Awards:* Alexander Graham Bell Medal, Inst Elec & Electronics Engrs, 81. *Mem:* Nat Acad Sci; Nat Acad Eng; AAAS; Inst Elec & Electronics Engrs; Soc Indust & Appl Math. *Res:* Communication theory; applied mathematics. *Mailing Add:* 212 Summit Ave Summit NJ 07901

SLEPIAN, PAUL, b Boston, Mass, Mar 26, 23; m 49; c 2. MATHEMATICS. *Educ:* Mass Inst Technol, SB, 50; Brown Univ, PhD(math), 56. *Prof Exp:* Instr math, Brown Univ, 54-56; mathematician, Ramo-Wooldridge Corp, Calif, 56 & Hughes Aircraft Co, 56-60; assoc prof math, Univ Ariz, 60-62; from assoc prof to prof, Rensselaer Polytech Inst, 62-69; chmn dept, Bucknell Univ, 69-70; PROF MATH, HOWARD UNIV, 70- *Concurrent Pos:* Lectr, Univ Southern Calif, 56-60. *Mem:* Am Math Soc; Soc Indust & Appl Math; Math Asn Am; Inst Elec & Electronics Eng. *Res:* Surface area; applications of mathematics to circuit theory; general topology. *Mailing Add:* 9200 Edwards Way #218 Adelphi MD 20783

SÖLER, FRANCOIS, differential geometry, relativity, see previous edition

SLESNICK, IRWIN LEONARD, b Canton, Ohio, Aug 5, 26; m 47; c 5. SCIENCE EDUCATION. *Educ:* Bowling Green State Univ, BA & BS, 49; Univ Mich, MS, 53; Ohio State Univ, PhD(zool), 62. *Prof Exp:* Instr high sch, Ohio, 49-55; instr unified sci, Ohio State Univ, 56-63; assoc prof, 63-66, coordr sci educ, 71-73, PROF BIOL, WESTERN WASH UNIV, 66-, COORDR SCI EDUC, 80- *Concurrent Pos:* Consult, AID, India, 66-67; sci educ adv, 67-70; consult, UNESCO, 71-; consult, Biol Sci Curric Study, Scott, Foresman & Co, 72-76, ed adv, 77- *Mem:* Nat Sci Teachers Asn. *Res:* Population education; curriculum development in interdisciplinary studies. *Mailing Add:* 518 Highland Dr Bellingham WA 98225

SLESNICK, WILLIAM ELLIS, b Oklahoma City, Okla, Feb 24, 25. MATHEMATICS. *Educ:* US Naval Acad, BS, 45; Univ Okla, BA, 48; Oxford Univ, BA, 50, MA, 54; Harvard Univ, AM, 52. *Hon Degrees:* AM, Dartmouth Col, 72. *Prof Exp:* Teacher, St Paul's Sch, NH, 52-62; from asst

prof to assoc prof, 62-71, vis instr, 58-59, asst dir educ uses, Kiewit Comput Ctr, 66-69, PROF MATH, DARTMOUTH COL, 71- *Concurrent Pos:* Mem, advan placement exam comt math, Col Entrance Exam Bd, 67-71; Nat Humanities Fac, 72- *Mem:* Nat Coun Teachers of Math; Math Asn Am. *Mailing Add:* Dept of Math Dartmouth Col Hanover NH 03755

SLESSOR, KEITH NORMAN, b Comox, BC, Nov 4, 38; m 60. ORGANIC CHEMISTRY. *Educ:* Univ BC, BSc, 60, PhD(org chem), 64. *Prof Exp:* Nat Res Coun Can fels, Royal Free Hosp Med Sch, Univ London, 64-65 & Inst Org Chem, Univ Stockholm, 65-66; asst prof, 66-71, ASSOC PROF ORG BIOCHEM, SIMON FRASER UNIV, 71- *Res:* Carbohydrate chemistry and pheromone determination, structure and synthesis. *Mailing Add:* Dept of Chem Simon Fraser Univ Burnaby BC V5A 1S6 Can

SLETTEBAK, ARNE, b Danzig, Aug 8, 25; nat US; m 49; c 2. ASTROPHYSICS. *Educ:* Univ Chicago, SB, 45, PhD(astron), 49. *Prof Exp:* Asst, Yerkes Observ, Univ Chicago, 45-49; from instr to assoc prof, 49-59, dir, Perkins Observ, 59-78, chmn dept, 62-78, PROF ASTRON OHIO STATE UNIV, 59- *Concurrent Pos:* Fulbright res fel, Hamburg Observ, Ger, 55-56; mem bd dirs, Asn Univs for Res Astron, 61-79, steering comt earth sci curric proj, 65-68, chmn sci comt, 70-73; comt astron, Nat Res Coun; adv, Off Naval Res, 63-66; mem, Adv Panel Astron, NSF, 68-71; Fulbright lectr & guest prof, Univ Vienna Observ, Austria, 74-75 & 81. *Mem:* Am Astron Soc; Int Astron Union. *Res:* Stellar rotation; spectroscopic investigations of normal and peculiar stars. *Mailing Add:* Dept of Astron Ohio State Univ Columbus OH 43210

SLETTEN, ANDREAS M(OE), b Ogndal, Norway, Sept 22, 26; m 57. ELECTRICAL ENGINEERING, GAS PHYSICS. *Educ:* Norweg Inst Technol, MSc, 50; Univ London, PhD(elec eng), 60. *Prof Exp:* Engr, Standard Telefon og Kabelfabrik A/S, Norway, 51-57; sr engr, 60-65, MGR, WESTINGHOUSE RES & DEVELOP CTR, 65- *Concurrent Pos:* Ed conf elec insulation & dielectric phenomena, Nat Acad Sci-Nat Res Coun, 65, prog chmn, 68. *Mem:* Inst Elec & Electronic Engrs. *Res:* High voltage technology; insulation. *Mailing Add:* Westinghouse Res & Develop Ctr Beulah Rd Pittsburgh PA 15235

SLETZINGER, MEYER, b New York, NY, Sept 15, 14; m 46; c 3. ORGANIC CHEMISTRY. *Educ:* City Col New York, BS, 39; Columbia Univ, MA, 46, PhD(chem), 47. *Prof Exp:* Asst chemist, Merck & Co, Inc, 37-41, sr res chemist, 41-52, res assoc, 52-58, group leader, 58-60, mgr develop res, 60-70, DIR DEVELOP RES, MERCK SHARP & DOHME, RAHWAY, 70- *Concurrent Pos:* Statutory asst org chem, Columbia Univ, 43. *Mem:* Am Chem Soc. *Res:* Sulfa drugs; tropine alkaloids; vitamin B; morphine substitutes; nicotinic acid; antibiotics from streptomycin; streptothricin; structure of alkenyl side chain of monophenolic component of cashew nut shell liquid; vitamin A; folic acid; synthesis of B-Lactam actibiotics such as penicillius, cephamycins and cephelosporius. *Mailing Add:* 135 Rockview Ave North Plainfield NJ 07060

SLEZAK, FRANK BIER, b Manhasset, NY, Nov 19, 28; m 51; c 2. ORGANIC CHEMISTRY. *Educ:* Antioch Col, BS, 51; Okla State Univ, MS, 53, PhD(org chem), 55. *Prof Exp:* Org res chemist, Diamond Alkali Co, 54-59, group leader condensation polymers, 59-63; group leader chem res & develop, Union Camp Corp, NJ, 63-69; assoc prof, 69-74, chmn dept biol & chem, 71-77, PROF CHEM, MERCER COUNTY COMMUNITY COL, 74- *Mem:* AAAS; Am Chem Soc. *Res:* Tree based chemicals; synthetic organic chemistry related to biological activity; heterocyclics; condensation polymerization. *Mailing Add:* 9 Pine Knoll Dr Lawrenceville NJ 08648

SLEZAK, JANE ANN, b Amsterdam, NY. BIOMEDICAL ENGINEERING. *Educ:* State Univ NY, Albany, BS, MS; Rensselaer Polytech Inst, PhD(chem). *Prof Exp:* Res assoc chem, Univ Pittsburgh & Syracuse Univ; lectr chem, State Univ NY; asst prof chem, Schenectady Community Col; RES ASSOC BIOMED ENG, RENSSELAER POLYTECH INST, 79- *Concurrent Pos:* Fel, AEC, NSF, Gen Elec, & NIH. *Mem:* Am Phys Soc; Sigma Xi; Am Chem Soc. *Res:* Materials properties of biological and calcified tissues using spectroscopy, magnetic resonance and physical chemistry; analyses of composite behavior and methods of failure of biological specimens. *Mailing Add:* 191 Church St Amsterdam NY 12012

SLICHTER, CHARLES PENCE, b Ithaca, NY, Jan 21, 24; m 80; c 4. SOLID STATE PHYSICS. *Educ:* Harvard Univ, AB, 45, AM, 47, PhD(physics), 49. *Prof Exp:* From instr to assoc prof, 49-55, PROF PHYSICS, UNIV ILL, URBANA-CHAMPAIGN, 55-, CTR ADVAN STUDY, 68- *Concurrent Pos:* Morris Loeb lectr, Harvard Univ, 61; mem sci adv comt, Off of the President, 65-69, comt nat medal sci, 69-74; Harvard Corp, 70-; dir, Polaroid Corp; former trustee & mem corp, Woods Hole Oceanog Inst. *Honors & Awards:* Langmuir Prize, Am Phys Soc, 69. *Mem:* Nat Acad Sci; fel AAAS; Am Acad Arts & Sci; Am Philos Soc; fel Am Phys Soc. *Res:* Nuclear magnetic resonance in solids. *Mailing Add:* Dept Physics Univ Ill 1110 W Green St Urbana IL 61801

SLICHTER, WILLIAM PENCE, b Ithaca, NY, Mar 31, 22; m 50; c 4. PHYSICAL CHEMISTRY. *Educ:* Harvard Univ, AB, 44, AM, 49, PhD(chem physics), 50. *Prof Exp:* Mem tech staff, 50-58, head chem physics res dept, 58-67, chem dir, 67-73, EXEC DIR RES, MATS SCI & ENG DIV, BELL LABS, 73- *Honors & Awards:* High Polymer Physics Award, Am Phys Soc, 70. *Mem:* Nat Acad Eng; fel AAAS; fel Am Phys Soc; Am Chem Soc; Sigma Xi. *Res:* Physical chemistry of high polymers; nuclear magnetic resonance spectroscopy. *Mailing Add:* Bell Labs Murray Hill NJ 07974

SLIDER, HARTZEL C, b Paden City, WVa, June 26, 24; m 46; c 2. PETROLEUM ENGINEERING. *Educ:* Ohio State Univ, BEM & MS, 49. *Prof Exp:* Exploitation engr, Shell Oil Co, 49-50, reservoir engr, 51-52, div reservoir engr, 53-56; PROF PETROL ENG, OHIO STATE UNIV, 56- *Concurrent Pos:* Consult, Shell Oil Co, 56, Humble Oil Co, 57 & 65, Esso Prod Res, Jersey Prod Res & Carter Prod Res Co, 58-65, Ins Co Am, 62-63

& 65-66, Texaco Inc, 66-, Petroleos del Peru, 70-71, Schlumberger, 69 & 72, Off Technol Assessment, US Cong, 76, Japan Petroleum Develop Co, 77, Caltex, Indonesia, 79, Aramed, Saudi Arabia, Texaco, Angola & Nigeria, & Texaco Prod Serv, Eng, 80; vis prof, Univ Indust de Santander, Colombia, 77 & Tech Univ Clausthal, Ger, 78; distinguished lectr, Soc Petroleum Eng, 78-79. *Mem:* Am Inst Mining, Metall & Petrol Engrs; Am Inst Chem Engrs; Am Soc Eng Educ; Am Arbit Asn. *Res:* Porous media fluid flow and fluid displacement technology; gas well deliverability; water-flooding; decline curve analysis; oil and gas well transient pressure analysis. *Mailing Add:* Ohio State Univ Dept Chem Eng 140 W 19th Ave Columbus OH 43210

SLIEMERS, FRANCIS ANTHONY, JR, b Lima, Ohio, June 28, 29; m 52; c 8. POLYMER CHEMISTRY. *Educ:* Univ Notre Dame, BS, 51; Ohio State Univ, MSc, 54. *Prof Exp:* Res assoc chem, Ohio State Univ, 54-56; prin chemist, 56-62, sr res chemist, 62-71 & 73-79, assoc chief, 71-73, ASSOC SECT MGR, BATTELLE MEM INST, 79- *Mem:* Am Chem Soc. *Res:* Physical characterization of polymers; plasma polymerization. *Mailing Add:* Dept of Chem Battelle Mem Inst 505 King Ave Columbus OH 43201

SLIEPCEVICH, CEDOMIR M, b Anaconda, Mont, Oct 4, 20; m 55. CHEMICAL ENGINEERING. *Educ:* Univ Mich, BS, 41, MS, 42, PhD(chem eng), 48. *Prof Exp:* Asst, Univ Mich, 41-46, from instr to assoc prof chem & metall eng, 46-55; prof chem eng & mat sci, 55-63, assoc dean col eng, 56-63, chmn sch gen eng, 58-63, RES PROF CHEM ENG, UNIV OKLA, 63- *Concurrent Pos:* Consult, 43-; sr chem engr, Monsanto Chem Co, 52-53; dir res & eng, Constock Liquid Methane Corp, NY, 55-60. *Honors & Awards:* McGraw Award, 58; Ipatieff Award, Am Chem Soc, 59; Westinghouse Award, Am Soc Eng Educ, 64. *Mem:* Nat Acad Eng; AAAS; Am Chem Soc; Am Soc Eng Educ; Am Inst Chem Engrs. *Res:* High pressure equipment design; chemical reaction kinetics; process control and dynamic analysis; energy scattering; cryogenics; thermodynamics; flame dynamics; liquefaction; ocean transport and storage of natural gas; fundamental behavior of flames and combustion; desalination. *Mailing Add:* Dept of Chem Eng Univ of Okla Norman OK 73019

SLIFE, FRED WARREN, b Milford, Ill, Nov 6, 23; m 47; c 4. AGRONOMY. *Educ:* Univ Ill, BS, 47, MS, 48, PhD, 52. *Prof Exp:* From instr to assoc prof, 47-60, prof agron, 60-77, PROF CROP PROD, UNIV ILL, URBANA, 77- *Mem:* Am Soc Agron; Weed Sci Soc Am. *Res:* Weed control, especially penetration and translocation; metabolism of herbicides in plants. *Mailing Add:* Dept of Agron Univ of Ill Urbana IL 61801

SLIFKIN, LAWRENCE, b Bluefield, WVa, Sept 29, 25; m 48; c 4. SOLID STATE PHYSICS. *Educ:* NY Univ, BA, 47; Princeton Univ, PhD(phys chem), 50. *Prof Exp:* Res assoc physics, Univ Ill, 50-52, res asst prof, 52-54; asst prof, Univ Minn, 54-55; from asst prof to assoc prof, 55-63, PROF PHYSICS, UNIV NC, CHAPEL HILL, 63-, BOWMAN GRAY PROF UNDERGRAD TEACHING, 79- *Concurrent Pos:* NSF sr fel, Clarendon Lab, Oxford Univ, 62-63; foreign collabr, Centre d'Etudes Nucleaires, Saclay, France, 75-76. *Mem:* Am Phys Soc. *Res:* Diffusion in solids; defects in ionic crystals; the photographic process. *Mailing Add:* Dept of Physics Univ of N C Chapel Hill NC 27515

SLIFKIN, MALCOLM, b Newark, NJ, Nov 9, 33; m 66; c 2. MEDICAL MICROBIOLOGY, VIROLOGY. *Educ:* Furman Univ, BS, 55; Univ NC, MSPH, 56, MS, 59; Rutgers Univ, PhD(serol), 62; Am Bd Med Microbiol, dipl. *Prof Exp:* Instr parasitol, Sch Med, Yale Univ, 6264; microbiologist, 65-71, HEAD SECT MICROBIOL, DEPT LAB MED, ALLEGHENY GEN HOSP, 71-; CLIN ASST PROF PATH, SCH MED, UNIV PITTSBURGH, 75- *Concurrent Pos:* Fel microbiol, Sch Med, Yale Univ, 62-64; adj asst prof, Pa State Univ, 65-71, adj assoc prof, 71- *Mem:* AAAS; Am Soc Cell Biol; Am Soc Microbiol; fel Am Acad Microbiol; NY Acad Sci. *Res:* Oncogenic simian adenoviruses; tissue culture of chemically induced liver cancer and preneoplastic liver; microcolony varients of Staphylococcus aureus; rapid niacin tests for Mycobacterium tuberculosis; applied clinical microbiology; choriogonadotropin-like antigens in bacteria and cancer cells; rapid identification of bacteria. *Mailing Add:* Microbiol Sect Dept Lab Med Allegheny Gen Hosp Pittsburgh PA 15212

SLIFKIN, SAM CHARLES, b Milwaukee, Wis, July 28, 18; m 56; c 3. ORGANIC CHEMISTRY. *Educ:* Univ Wis, BS, 42. *Prof Exp:* Develop chemist, Ozalid Div, Gen Aniline & Film Corp, 42-43, supvr control & develop, 43-44, dir res & mgr qual control, 42-49; vpres & tech dir, Tecnifax Corp, 49-51; consult, 51-70; pres, Specialty Coatings, Inc, 63-72; consult, Ozalid Group Holdings, LTD, 72-78; PRES, SLIFKIN CO, ANN ARBOR, MICH, 75- *Concurrent Pos:* Dir, Kalvar Corp, New Orleans & Diazo Specialty Co, Beltsville, Md. *Mem:* Am Chem Soc; Photog Soc Am; Soc Photog Scientists & Engrs; Tech Asn Pulp & Paper Indust; fel Am Inst Chemists. *Res:* Photosensitive duplicating processes, especially diazotype. *Mailing Add:* PO Box 7450 Ann Arbor MI 48107

SLIGAR, STEPHEN GARY, b Inglewood, Calif, Mar 19, 48; m 75. BIOCHEMISTRY. *Educ:* Drexel Univ, BS, 70; Univ Ill, Urbana, MS, 71, PhD(physics, biochem), 75. *Prof Exp:* Physicist, Naval Air Propulsion Test Ctr, Aeronaut Engine Lab, Philadelphia, 66-69; res student physics, Drexel Univ, 68-70; resident, Cent States Univ Honors Prog, Argonne Nat Lab, 70, guest assoc molecular biol, Div Biol & Med Res, 71-73; res asst, Univ Ill, Urbana, 72-75, res assoc biochem, 75-77; ASST PROF, DEPT MOLECULAR BIOPHYS & BIOCHEM, YALE UNIV, 77- *Mem:* Biophys Soc; Am Soc Biol Chemists; Am Chem Soc; Am Phys Soc; AAAS. *Res:* Physical biochemistry, mechanisms of energy transfer and oxygenation reactions; thermodynamics of regulation and control in biological catalysis; kinetic and equilibrium description of multi-protein systems and complexes; biochemical pharmacology. *Mailing Add:* Dept of Molecular Biophys & Biochem Yale Univ New Haven CT 96520

SLIGER, WILBURN ANDREW, b Oklahoma City, Okla, Jan 21, 40; m 58; c 2. FISH BIOLOGY, FRESH WATER BIOLOGY. *Educ:* Cent State Univ, Okla, BS, 64; Okla State Univ, Stillwater, MS, 67, PhD(zool), 75. *Prof Exp:* Instr, 66-72, asst prof, 72-76, ASSOC PROF BIOL, UNIV TENN, MARTIN, 76- *Concurrent Pos:* Vis prof biol, Murray State Univ, Ky, 76-77. *Mem:* Am Fisheries Soc; Sigma Xi (secy, 75-79); Am Soc Ichthyologists & Herpetologists. *Res:* Effects of water pollutants on the physiology of fish. *Mailing Add:* Dept of Biol Univ of Tenn Martin TN 38238

SLIKER, ALAN, b Cleveland, Ohio, June 7, 27; m 56; c 3. WOOD TECHNOLOGY. *Educ:* Duke Univ, BS, 51, MF, 52; NY Col Forestry, Syracuse Univ, PhD, 58. *Prof Exp:* Packaging engr, US Forest Prod Lab, Wis, 52-53; from instr to assoc prof forest prod, 55-74, PROF FORESTRY, MICH STATE UNIV, 74- *Mem:* Forest Prod Res Soc; Soc Am Foresters; Sigma Xi; Soc Wood Sci & Technol; Soc Exp Stress Anal. *Res:* Mechanical properties of wood, particularly those properties concerned with structural use of wood. *Mailing Add:* Dept of Forestry Mich State Univ East Lansing MI 48824

SLIKER, TODD RICHARD, b Rochester, NY, Feb 9, 36; m 63; c 2. SOLID STATE PHYSICS. *Educ:* Univ Wis, BS, 55; Cornell Univ, PhD(physics), 62; Harvard Univ, MBA, 70. *Prof Exp:* Res assoc physics, Cornell Univ, 62; sr staff physicist, Electronic Res Div, Clevite Corp, 62-65, head appl physics sect, 65-68; asst to pres, Granville-Phillips Co, 70; vpres & gen mgr, McDowell Electronics, Inc, 70-71; pres, CA Compton Inc, 71-77; chief acct, 77-80, VPRES FINANCE, C&S INC, 80- *Res:* Nuclear magnetic and electron paramagnetic resonance of solids; photolysis of silver chloride; linear electro-optic effects and devices; low frequency piezoelectric tuning fork filters; high frequency resonators and acoustic delay lines. *Mailing Add:* 1658 Bear Mountain Dr Boulder CO 80303

SLINEY, DAVID H, b Washington, DC, Feb 21, 41; m 66; c 3. HEALTH PHYSICS. *Educ:* Va Polytech Inst, BS, 63; Emory Univ, MS, 65. *Prof Exp:* CHIEF LASER BR, US ARMY ENVIRON HYG AGENCY, 65- *Concurrent Pos:* Consult, WHO, 65-; mem Army-Indust Comt Laser Safety, 67; consult laser hazards, NASA, 67-; US Coast & Geod Surv, 68-; mem comt laser safety, Am Nat Standards Inst, 68-; ed, Health Physics J, 76-; Hayes-Fulbright fel, Yugoslavia, 76; US chief deleg, Comt TC76, Lasers of Int Electrotech Comm, 77-; mem, Nat Acad Sci/Nat Res Coun Panel, Health Aspects Video Viewing, 80-82. *Mem:* AAAS; Optical Soc Am; Health Physics Soc; Am Conf Govt Indust Hygienists; Soc Photo-Optical Instrument Eng. *Res:* Criteria for laser hazard analysis; standards for laser exposure; optical radiation hazards; non-ionizing radiation; co-author of 1000 publications. *Mailing Add:* US Army Environ Hyg Agency Aberdeen Proving Ground MD 21010

SLINGER, STANLEY JAMES, b Ont, Nov 20, 14; m 44; c 3. ANIMAL NUTRITION. *Educ:* Univ Toronto, BSA, 37, MSA, 41; Cornell Univ, PhD(poultry nutrit), 50. *Prof Exp:* From lectr to assoc prof, Ont Agr Col, 38-53, chmn dept, 64-74, prof, 53-79, EMER PROF NUTRIT, COL BIOL SCI, UNIV GUELPH, 80- *Concurrent Pos:* Res award, Poultry Nutrit, Am Feed Mfrs, 56; res award nutrit, Agradex Int, 74-; mem, Comt Coldwater Fish, US Nat Res Ctr, 79. *Honors & Awards:* Golden Award, Can Feed Indust Asn, 79. *Mem:* Am Inst Nutrit; Nutrit Soc Can; Soc Nutrit Educ; Am Inst Biol Sci; Can Fedn Biol Socs. *Res:* Comparative nutrition; energy metabolism. *Mailing Add:* Dept of Nutrit Univ of Guelph Col of Biol Sci Guelph ON N1G 2W1 Can

SLINGERLAND, RUDY LYNN, b Troy, Pa, Apr 7, 47. GEOLOGY, SEDIMENTOLOGY. *Educ:* Dickinson Col, BS, 69; Pa State Univ, MS, 73, PhD(geol), 77. *Prof Exp:* ASST PROF GEOL, PA STATE UNIV, 77- *Concurrent Pos:* Consult sedimentary brain analysis. *Mem:* Geol Soc Am; Am Geophys Union; Sigma Xi; Soc Econ Paleontologists & Mineralogists; Int Asn Sedimentologists. *Res:* Sedimentalogy; coal geology; coastal geology; flurial geomorphology. *Mailing Add:* 303 Deike Bldg University Park PA 16802

SLINKARD, ALFRED EUGENE, b Rockford, Wash, Apr 5, 31; m 51; c 4. AGRONOMY. *Educ:* Wash State Univ, BS, 52, MS, 54; Univ Minn, PhD(plant genetics), 57. *Prof Exp:* Asst prof agron & asst agronomist, Univ Idaho, 57-66, assoc prof agron & assoc agronomist, 66-72; SR RES SCIENTIST, UNIV SASK, 72- *Mem:* AAAS; Crop Sci Soc Am; Am Soc Agron; Genetics Soc Am; Genetics Soc Can. *Res:* Genetics and breeding of peas and lentils; establishment of lentils as a commercial crop in Western Canada, including development of a package of agronomic practices and the licensing of two cultivars, Laird and Eston. *Mailing Add:* Dept of Crop Sci Univ of Sask Saskatoon SK S7N 0W0 Can

SLINKARD, WILLIAM EARL, b Omaha, Nebr, May 14, 43; m 65; c 2. INORGANIC CHEMISTRY. *Educ:* Trinity Univ, Tex, BS, 65; Ohio State Univ, PhD(inorg chem), 69. *Prof Exp:* RES CHEMIST, CELANESE CHEM CO, 69- *Mem:* Am Chem Soc; Catalysis Soc. *Res:* Coordination properties and reactions of phosphines and phosphine chalcogenides; synthesis and characteriation of supported metals and metal oxides; catlytic vapor phase oxidation of hydrocarbons, methanol synthesis, steam reforming of methane and methanol homologation reactions; methanol synthesis; homogeneous catalysis and hydroformylation reactions. *Mailing Add:* Tech Ctr Celanese Chem Co Box 9077 Corpus Christi TX 78408

SLIVA, PHILIP OSCAR, b Yonkers, NY, Apr 22, 38; m 61; c 2. SOLID STATE PHYSICS. *Educ:* Clarkson Col Technol, BS, 60; Purdue Univ, PhD(solid state physics), 67. *Prof Exp:* Assoc scientist, Solid State Res Br, 67-68, scientist, Exp Physics Br, 68-73, sr scientist, Explor Photoconductor Physics Area, 73-76, MGR PHOTOCONDUCTOR CHARACTERIZATION AREA, XEROX CORP, 76- *Mem:* Am Phys Soc. *Res:* Acoustoelectric effects in III-IV semiconductors; solid state switching and memory devices in amorphous and polycrystalline materials; charge generation and transport in photoconductors. *Mailing Add:* Res Labs Xerox Corp Xerox Square W114 PO Box 1540 Rochester NY 14603

SLIVINSKY, CHARLES R, b St Clair, Pa, May 20, 41; m 63; c 2. ELECTRICAL ENGINEERING, COMPUTER SCIENCE. *Educ:* Princeton Univ, BSE, 63; Univ Ariz, MS, 65, PhD(elec eng), 69. *Prof Exp:* From asst prof to assoc prof, 68-77, PROF ELEC ENG, UNIV MO-COLUMBIA, 77- *Concurrent Pos:* NSF sci equip grant, 69-71, res initiation grant, 71-72, solid state power control stability anal grant, 72-74, res equip grant, 77-79; consult, Air Force Flight Dynamics Lab, 75-; US Air Force Off Sci Res grant, 76-79. *Mem:* AAAS; Inst Elec & Electronics Engrs; Am Soc Eng Educ. *Res:* Automatic control; computer control and signal processing; redundancy in digital systems. *Mailing Add:* Dept of Elec Eng Univ of Mo Columbia MO 65201

SLIVINSKY, SANDRA HARRIET, b New York, NY. HIGH TEMPERATURE TECHNOLOGY, LASER PROCESSING. *Educ:* Alfred Univ, BA, 62; Pa State Univ, MS(physics), 66; Univ Calif, Davis-Livermore, MS(appl sci), 73. *Prof Exp:* Res assoc, Dikewood Corp, 66-68; physicist, Lawrence Livermore Lab, 68-73; sr res engr, Lockheed Missiles & Space Co, 73-76; ENGR, GEN ELEC CO, 76- *Mem:* Am Physics Soc; Soc Women Engrs; Inst Elec & Electronics Engrs; Nat Soc Prof Engrs; Sigma Xi. *Res:* development of a laser processing methods for skiving plastics over metal substrates; nitrogen-nitride equilibria in molten tin alloys, particularly for uranium and thorium metals using a modified sieverts apparatus. *Mailing Add:* M/C 173 Gen Elec Co 175 Curtner Ave San Jose CA 95125

SÖLL, DIETER GERHARD, b Stuttgart, Ger, Apr 19, 35; US citizen; m 64; c 3. MOLECULAR BIOLOGY. *Educ:* Stuttgart Tech Univ, MSc, 60; PhD(chem), 62. *Prof Exp:* Fel, Inst Enzyme Res, Univ Wis, Madison, 62-65, from asst prof to assoc prof, 65-76, PROF MOLECULAR BIOPHYS, YALE UNIV, 76- *Concurrent Pos:* Guggenheim Found fel, 72-73. *Mem:* Am Soc Microbiol; AAAS; Am Soc Biol Chem; Am Chem Soc. *Res:* Nucleic acid chemistry and biochemistry. *Mailing Add:* Dept Molecular Biophys & Biochem Yale Univ New Haven CT 06511

SLOAN, ALAN DAVID, b New York, NY, July 5, 45; m 69. APPLIED MATHEMATICS. *Educ:* Mass Inst Technol, BS, 67; Cornell Univ, PhD(math), 71. *Prof Exp:* Fel, Carnegie-Mellon Univ, 71-72; vis asst prof physics, Princeton Univ, 74-75; from instr to asst prof, 72-77, ASSOC PROF MATH, GA INST TECHNOL, 77- *Mem:* Am Math Soc; Soc Indust & Appl Math; Math Asn Am; Sigma Xi. *Res:* Applications of functional analysis and nonstandard analysis to mathematical physics especailly to the area of quantum theory. *Mailing Add:* Sch of Math Ga Inst of Technol Atlanta GA 30332

SLOAN, BEN LEROY, zoology, see previous edition

SLOAN, BERNARD JOSEPH, b Detroit, Mich, Oct 29, 25; m 55; c 4. MEDICAL MICROBIOLOGY. *Educ:* St Mary's Col, Minn, BS, 50; Univ Detroit, MS, 52; Mich State Univ, PhD(bot), 57. *Prof Exp:* Asst, Univ Detroit, 50-52; asst, Mich State Univ, 52-56, asst prof res, 57; mycologist, Med Res Labs, Chas Pfizer & Co, 57-60; mycologist, 60-70, SR RES MICROBIOLOGIST, PARKE DAVIS & CO, WARNER-LAMBERT CO, 70- *Mem:* Mycol Soc Am; Soc Indust Microbiol; Am Soc Microbiol. *Res:* New antibiotics; fermentations; microbial genetics; virus chemotherapy; medical mycology; virus and medical mycology chemotherapy; new anticancer antibiotic and synthetic drug; new drug acquisitions. *Mailing Add:* Res Div Parke Davis & Co Warner-Lambert Co PO Box 118 Detroit MI 48232

SLOAN, DONALD LEROY, JR, b Denver, Colo, Sept 27, 44. BIOCHEMISTRY. *Educ:* Northern Colo Univ, BA, 66; Purdue Univ, MS, 69; Univ Utah, PhD(biochem), 72. *Prof Exp:* Res assoc biochem, Inst Cancer Res, 72-75; asst prof, 75-80, ASSOC PROF CHEM, CITY COL NEW YORK, 81- *Mem:* Biophys Soc; Am Chem Soc; AAAS; Am Soc Biol Chemists. *Res:* Studies of the conformations of enzyme-bound nucleotides and enzyme-metal complexes using nuclear magnetic and electron paramagnetic resonance techniques; phosphoribosyltransferase-catalyzed reactions. *Mailing Add:* Dept Chem City Col New York New York NY 10031

SLOAN, GILBERT JACOB, b Elizabeth, NJ, July 25, 28; m 57; c 2. PHYSICAL ORGANIC CHEMISTRY. *Educ:* Mich Col Mining & Technol, BS, 48; Univ Mich, PhD(chem), 54. *Prof Exp:* Res chemist, 53-73, supvr, 73-80, RES MGR CENT RES & DEVELOP DEPT, E I DU PONT DE NEMOURS & CO, INC, 80- *Concurrent Pos:* Assoc ed, J Crystal Growth, 67- *Mem:* Am Chem Soc; Sigma Xi. *Res:* Stable free radicals; purification of organic compounds; crystal growth. *Mailing Add:* Cent Res & Develop Dept E I du Pont de Nemours & Co Wilmington DE 19898

SLOAN, HERBERT, b Clarksburg, WVa, Oct 10, 14; m 43; c 5. THORACIC SURGERY. *Educ:* Washington & Lee Univ, AB, 36; Johns Hopkins Univ, MD, 40. *Prof Exp:* Assoc prof, 53-62, PROF SURG, UNIV MICH, ANN ARBOR, 62, HEAD SECT THORACIC SURG, 70- *Concurrent Pos:* Assoc ed, Ann Thoracic Surg, 6468, ed, 69-; mem, Am Bd Thoracic Surg, 66-71, vchmn, 71-72, chmn credentials comt, 69-, vchmn nominating comt, 71-72, secy, 73-; mem, Residency Rev Comt Thoracic Surg, 72-; mem, Adv Group Cardiac Surg, Vet Admin, 71-; mem, Surg Study Group, Inter-Soc Comn Heart Dis Resources, 71-, Cardiac Surg Rev Panel, 73-; liaison mem, Am Bd Thoracic Surg to Inter-Soc Comn Heart Dis Resources, 73; mem, Adv Comt, Second Henry Ford Hosp Int Symp Cardiac Surg, 73-75, assoc ed, Proc Symp, 75; prog chmn, Adv Comt Thoracic Surg, Am Col Surgeons, 75-78. *Mem:* Am Surg Asn; Am Col Surgeons; Am Heart Asn; Soc Thoracic Surgeons (vpres, 73-74, pres, 74-75); Am Asn Thoracic Surg (vpres, 78-79). *Res:* Cardiac surgery. *Mailing Add:* Univ Hosp Box 32 C7079 Ann Arbor MI 48109

SLOAN, MARTIN FRANK, b St Louis, Mo, Oct 9, 34; m 60; c 2. INDUSTRIAL ORGANIC CHEMISTRY. *Educ:* Wash Univ, BA, 56; Univ Wis, PhD, 60. *Prof Exp:* Res chemist, 60-69, res supvr, 69-74, supvr mkt develop, 74-76, DEVELOP MGR, HERCULES INC, 76- *Mem:* Am Chem Soc. *Mailing Add:* Hercules Inc Develop Dept Wilmington DE 19899

SLOAN, MINER JOE, entomology, see previous edition

SLOAN, NORMAN F, b Hillsdale, Mich, Nov 11, 34; m 69. FOREST ENTOMOLOGY, WILDLIFE ECOLOGY. *Educ:* Mich Technol Univ, BS, 57; Univ Wis, MS, 61, PhD(entom, wildlife), 65. *Prof Exp:* Forester, US Bur Land Mgt, 57-59; land appraiser, US Fish & Wildlife Serv, 59-60; res asst, Univ Wis, 60-65; from asst prof to assoc prof, 65-74, PROF FORESTRY, MICH TECHNOL UNIV, 74- *Concurrent Pos:* NSF grant, 66-68. *Mem:* Am Ornith Union; Wilson Ornith Soc. *Res:* Regulation of forest insect through the manipulation of bird population; biological factors in the control of forest insect population; peregrin falcon reintroduction efforts in the upper peninsula of Michigan; study of the barred owl; population dynamics of common raven and white pelican; effect of controlled burning on the song bird and small mammal populations in a grassland community. *Mailing Add:* Dept of Forestry Mich Technol Univ Houghton MI 49931

SLOAN, NORMAN GRADY, b Oklahoma City, Okla, May 8, 37; m 74; c 2. ENGINEERING. *Educ:* Univ Okla, BS, 60; Univ Tulsa, MS, 71. *Prof Exp:* Mech engr air conditioning design, US Corps Engrs, 60-61; PROJ ENGR NATURAL GAS PROCESSING PLANTS, DRESSER ENG CO, 61- *Mem:* Am Soc Mech Engrs. *Res:* Design of natural gas processing plants. *Mailing Add:* 4241 S Norfolk Tulsa OK 74105

SLOAN, ROBERT DYE, b Clarksburg, WVa, Feb 17, 18; m 46; c 2. MEDICINE. *Educ:* Washington & Lee Univ, AB, 39; Johns Hopkins Univ, MD, 43. *Prof Exp:* From instr to assoc prof radiol, Johns Hopkins Univ, 48-55; PROF RADIOL & CHMN DEPT, MED CTR, UNIV MISS, 55- *Concurrent Pos:* Consult, Vet Admin Hosp, 55- *Mem:* Am Roentgen Ray Soc; Radiol Soc NAm. *Res:* Diagnostic radiology; intestinal obstruction. *Mailing Add:* Dept of Radiol Univ of Miss Med Ctr Jackson MS 39216

SLOAN, ROBERT EVAN, b Champaign, Ill, July 17, 29; m 53; c 2. STRATIGRAPHY, PALEONTOLOGY. *Educ:* Univ Chicago, PhB, 48, SB, 50, SM, 52, PhD(geol), 53. *Prof Exp:* Asst prof, 53-63, assoc prof, 64-71, PROF GEOL, UNIV MINN, MINNEAPOLIS, 71- *Mem:* Soc Econ Paleont & Mineral; Soc Vert Paleont; Soc Study Evolution; Geol Soc Am; Soc Syst Zool. *Res:* Mesozoic and Paleocene mammals; Multituberculata; terrestrial vertebrate paleoecology; Cretaceous and Paleocene stratigraphy of western North America. *Mailing Add:* Dept of Geol & Geophysics Univ of Minn Minneapolis MN 55455

SLOAN, ROBERT W, b Rankin, Ill, July 18, 24; m 49; c 2. MATHEMATICS. *Educ:* US Naval Acad, BS, 46; Univ Ill, MS, 51, PhD(math), 55. *Prof Exp:* Asst prof math, Univ NH, 55-56; asst prof, Carleton Col, 56-59; prof, State Univ NY Col Oswego, 59-65; chmn dept, 65-76, PROF MATH, ALFRED UNIV, 65- *Mem:* Math Asn Am. *Res:* Analysis and numerical analysis. *Mailing Add:* Dept of Math Alfred Univ Alfred NY 14802

SLOAN, WILLIAM COOPER, b Asheville, NC, Aug 26, 27; m 51; c 2. BIOLOGY. *Educ:* Univ Fla, BS, 52, MS, 54, PhD(biol), 58. *Prof Exp:* Asst biol, Univ Fla, 52-54 & 55-58; entom, Univ Minn, 54-55; instr biol, Vanderbilt Univ, 58-60; NIH fel, Univ Calif, 60-61; asst prof zool, 61-65, assoc prof biol, 65-68, PROF BIOL, SAN DIEGO STATE UNIV, 68- *Mem:* AAAS. *Res:* Comparative physiology; nitrogen metabolism and excretion in invertebrates. *Mailing Add:* Dept of Biol San Diego State Univ San Diego CA 92182

SLOANE, CHRISTINE SCHEID, b Washington, DC, May 1, 45; m 69; c 2. ATMOSPHERIC DYNAMICS. *Educ:* Col William & Mary, BS, 67; Mass Inst Technol, PhD(chem physics), 71. *Prof Exp:* Res assoc phys chem, Univ Calif, Berkeley, 72-73; asst prof chem, Oakland Univ, 74-78; assoc sr res scientist, 78-80, STAFF RES SCIENTIST ENVIRON SCI, GEN MOTORS RES LABS, 80- *Mem:* Am Chem Soc; Am Phys Soc; AAAS; Am Meteorol Soc. *Res:* Atmospheric chemistry and physics; chemical kinetics; reaction dynamics; light scattering from molecules and aerosols. *Mailing Add:* Gen Motors Res Labs Warren MI 48090

SLOANE, HOWARD J, b New York, NY, May 9, 31; m 57; c 2. SPECTROCHEMISTRY. *Educ:* Trinity Col, BS, 53; Wesleyan Univ, MA, 55. *Prof Exp:* Infrared spectroscopist, Dow Chem Co, 55-60; chief chemist, Beckman Instruments, Inc, 60-67; dir appln res, Cary Instruments Div, Varian Assocs, 67-72; sr scientist, Beckman Instruments, Inc, 72-74, mgr appln res, Sci Instruments Div, 74-77; PRES, SAVANT, SLOANE AV ANAL & TRAINING, 77- *Concurrent Pos:* Lectr, Raman Inst & Workshop, Univ Md, 68-72 & absorption spectros, Ariz State Univ, 60- *Mem:* Am Chem Soc; Soc Appl Spectros; Coblentz Soc (treas, 72-); Sci Apparatus Makers Asn; NY Acad Sci. *Res:* Instrumentation and applications of spectroscopy, especially vibrational and atomic. *Mailing Add:* Savant Sloane AV Anal Training PO Box 3670 Fullerton CA 92634

SLOANE, NATHAN HOWARD, b Boston, Mass, Sept 15, 17; m 46; c 2. BIOCHEMISTRY. *Educ:* Mass Col Pharm, BS, 39; Mass Inst Technol, MPH, 43; Harvard Univ, PhD, 50. *Prof Exp:* Chemist, Lederle Labs, Am Cyanamid Co, 43-45; group leader biochem, 51-56; biochemist, Ciba Pharmaceut Prod, Inc, 49-51; biochemist, Nat Drug Co, Vick Chem Co, 56-58; biochemist & sr fel, Mellon Inst, 58-64; PROF BIOCHEM, COL MED, UNIV TENN, MEMPHIS, 64- *Res:* Biochemistry of microorganisms; microbial nutrition; mechanism of biochemical hydroxylation; chemical carcinogenesis. *Mailing Add:* Dept of Biochem Univ of Tenn Med Units Memphis TN 38103

SLOANE, NEIL JAMES ALEXANDER, b Beaumaris, Wales, Oct 10, 39. MATHEMATICS, ELECTRICAL ENGINEERING. *Educ:* Univ Melbourne, BEE, 59, BA, 60; Cornell Univ, MS, 64, PhD(elec eng), 67. *Prof Exp:* Asst prof elec eng, Cornell Univ, 67-69; MEM TECH STAFF, MATH DEPT, BELL TEL LABS, 69- *Honors & Awards:* Chauvenet Prize, Math Asn Am, 79. *Mem:* Am Math Soc; Math Asn Am; fel Inst Elec & Electronics Engrs. *Res:* Coding theory; communication theory; combinatorial mathematics; graph theory. *Mailing Add:* Rm 2C-363 Bell Tel Labs Murray Hill NJ 07974

SLOANE, ROBERT BRUCE, b Harrogate, Eng, Mar 28, 23; US citizen; m 46; c 6. PSYCHIATRY. *Educ:* Univ London, MB, BS, 45, MD, 50, dipl psychol med, 51; FRCP(C), 74, cert psychiat, 57; Am Bd Psychiat & Neurol, dipl, 63; FRCP, 74. *Prof Exp:* House physician, London Hosp, 45-46; asst registr, Nat Hosp Nerv Dis, London, 49; registr neurol, Guy's Hosp Med Sch, 50; resigstr, sr registr & chief asst, Maudsley Hosp, 50-52, chief asst psychiat, 54-55; resident & chief resident, Mass Gen Hosp, Boston, 53, Milton res fel, 53-54; asst psychiatrist, Allan Mem Inst, McGill Univ, 55-57; prof psychiat & head dept, Queen's Univ, Ont, 57-64; prof & chmn dept, Health Sci Ctr, Temple Univ, 64-72; prof, 72-80, FRANZ ALEXANDER PROF PSYCHIAT, MED SCH, UNIV SOUTHERN CALIF, 81-, CHMN DEPT, 72- *Honors & Awards:* Res Award, Soc Psychotherapy, 80. *Mem:* Am Psychiat Asn; Am Col Neuropsychopharmacology. *Res:* Research and writing in psychotherapy, depression and aging. *Mailing Add:* Dept of Psychiat Psychiat Hosp LAC-USC Med Ctr Los Angeles CA 90033

SLOANE, THOMPSON MILTON, b Baltimore, Md, Aug 30, 45. PHYSICAL CHEMISTRY. *Educ:* Univ Ariz, BS, 67; Mass Inst Technol, PhD(phys chem), 72. *Prof Exp:* Chemist, Lawrence Berkeley Lab, Univ Calif, 72-73; assoc sr res chemist, 73-77, SR RES SCIENTIST, RES LABS, GEN MOTORS CORP, 77- *Mem:* Am Chem Soc; Sigma Xi; Combustion Inst. *Res:* Dynamics of elementary chemical reactions; combustion chemistry. *Mailing Add:* Phys Chem Dept Res Labs Gen Motors Tech Ctr Warren MI 48090

SLOBODA, ADOLPH EDWARD, b New York, NY, Jan 17, 28; m 54; c 4. CELL PHYSIOLOGY, PHARMACOLOGY. *Educ:* Champlain Col, AB, 52; NY Univ, MS, 57, PhD(cytophysiol), 61. *Prof Exp:* Biologist, 52-56, biostatistician, 57, res biologist, 58-65, SR RES BIOLOGIST & GROUP LEADER INFLAMMATION & IMMUNOSUPPRESSION, LEDERLE LABS, AM CYANAMID CO, 66- *Mem:* Am Soc Pharmacol & Exp Therapeut. *Res:* Drug effects on various aspects of inflammation and the immune system; relationship of immunosuppression and cancer. *Mailing Add:* Metab Dis Ther Lederle Labs Am Cyanamid Co Pearl River NY 10965

SLOBODA, ROGER D, b Troy, NY, May 18, 48; m 70; c 2. BIOLOGY, BIOCHEMISTRY. *Educ:* State Univ NY, BS, 70; Rensselaer Polytech Inst, PhD(develop biol), 74. *Prof Exp:* Fel biol, Yale Univ, 74-77; ASST PROF BIOL, DARTMOUTH COL, 77- *Concurrent Pos:* Instr, Physiol Course, Marine Biol Lab, 81-82. *Mem:* Am Soc Cell Biol; AAAS; Sigma Xi. *Res:* Biochemistry of assembly and function of microtubules with specific interests in their roles in cell division and the maintenance of cell form. *Mailing Add:* Dept Biol Sci Dartmouth Col Hanover NH 03755

SLOBODCHIKOFF, CONSTANTINE NICHOLAS, b Shanghai, China, Apr 23, 44; US citizen; m 71; c 2. EVOLUTIONARY BIOLOGY, BEHAVIORAL ECOLOGY. *Educ:* Univ Calif, Berkeley, BS, 66, PhD(entom), 71. *Prof Exp:* asst prof, 71-78, ASSOC PROF BIOL, NORTHERN ARIZ UNIV, 78- *Mem:* Ecol Soc Am; Soc Study Evolution; Soc Syst Zool; AAAS; Animal Behavior Soc. *Res:* Evolutionary biology and behavior of herbivores and social animal systems; mimicry, and models of predator-prey interactions in mimetic situations; communication in animal systems. *Mailing Add:* Dept of Biol Sci Northern Ariz Univ Flagstaff AZ 86011

SLOBODKIN, LAWRENCE BASIL, b New York, NY, June 22, 28; m 52; c 3. ECOLOGY. *Educ:* Bethany Col, WVa, BS, 47; Yale Univ, PhD(zool), 51. *Prof Exp:* Chief invests, US Fish & Wildlife Serv, 51-52, fisheries res biologist, 52-53; vis investr, Bingham Oceanog Lab, 53; res assoc, Univ Mich, Ann Arbor, 53-54, instr zool, 53-57, from asst prof to prof, 57-68; chmn prog ecol & evolution, 69-74, PROF BIOL, STATE UNIV NY STONY BROOK, 68- *Concurrent Pos:* Guggenheim fel, 61; vis prof, Tel Aviv Univ, 65-66. *Honors & Awards:* Russel Award, 61. *Mem:* AAAS; Am Soc Limnol & Oceanog; Ecol Soc Am; Am Soc Nat; Brit Ecol Soc. *Res:* Theoretical and experimental population ecology; evolutionary strategy; ecological planning and decision making with reference to environmental management. *Mailing Add:* Dept of Ecol & Evolution State Univ of NY Stony Brook NY 11794

SLOBODRIAN, RODOLFO JOSE, b Buenos Aires, Arg, Jan 1, 30; m 59; c 3. PHYSICS. *Educ:* Univ Buenos Aires, Bachelor, 48, LicSc, 53, DSc (physics), 55. *Prof Exp:* Investr nuclear physics, Arg Nat AEC, 53-63; prof physics, Nat Univ La Plata, 58-63; physicist, Lawrence Radiation Lab, Univ Calif, 63-68; PROF PHYSICS, LAVAL UNIV, 68- *Concurrent Pos:* Asst to chair theoret physics, Univ Buenos Aires, 54-55, head lab spec physics, 57-58; Arg Nat AEC study mission, Radiation Lab, Univ Calif, 55-57. *Mem:* Am Phys Soc; NY Acad Sci; Can Asn Physicists. *Res:* Nuclear reactions; nucleon-nucleon interactions, final state interactions, polarization phenomens, multibody channels and nucleon transfer reactions. *Mailing Add:* Dept of Physics Laval Univ Quebec PQ C1K 7P4 Can

SLOCOMBE, JOSEPH OWEN DOUGLAS, b Port-of-Spain, Trinidad, July 27, 31; m 63; c 3. PARASITOLOGY, VETERINARY MEDICINE. *Educ:* Univ West Indies, dipl, 55; Univ Toronto, DVM, 61; Cornell Univ, PhD(parasitol), 69. *Prof Exp:* Asst to plant pathologist, Cent Exp Sta, Govt Trinidad & Tobago, 55-56, vet, Tobago, 61-65; asst parasitol, NY State Vet Col, Cornell Univ, 65-69; from asst prof to assoc prof, 69-76, PROF PARASITOL, ONT VET COL, UNIV GUELPH, 76- *Concurrent Pos:* Ont Racing Comn grant, Univ Guelph, 70-78; Nat Res Coun Can grant, 71-80; res grants, Ont Ministry Agr & Food, 74-78, E P Taylor res fund, 76-78, Can Vet res fund, 77-79 & Can Dept Agr, 78-79. *Mem:* Am Soc Parasitol. *Res:* Parameters associated with the growth, development and ecdysis of Strongylata in domestic animals and host reaction to parasite excretions and secretions; strongyles in horses; heartworm in dogs; Bouvine parasitism; surveillance for parasitisms in domestic animals. *Mailing Add:* 29 Oak St Guelph ON N1G 2N1 Can

SLOCOMBE, ROBERT JACKSON, b Peabody, Kans, May 22, 17; m 46; c 2. ORGANIC POLYMER CHEMISTRY. *Educ:* Univ Kans, AB, 39, MA, 41, PhD(org chem), 43. *Prof Exp:* Asst instr chem, Univ Kans, 40-43; res chemist, Monsanto Co, 43-45; res group leader, Ala, 45-50, Ohio, 50-61, Mo, 61-69; sr res specialist, 69-79; CONSULT, 79- *Mem:* AAAS; Am Chem Soc; Am Inst Chem Eng. *Res:* Preparation and production of isocyanates; reactions of phosgene; synthesis and stabilization of high polymers; multicomponent copolymerization; protein fractionation; reactive copolymers; epoxy matrix resins in composites; electrostatic printing inks; photopolymers; cellular plastics; bio-medical polymer systems. *Mailing Add:* 7825 Stanford Ave St Louis MO 63130

SLOCUM, DONALD WARREN, b Rochester, NY, May 1, 33; div; c 2. ORGANOMETALLIC CHEMISTRY, ORGANIC CHEMISTRY. *Educ:* Univ Rochester, BS & BA, 56; NY Univ, PhD(chem), 63. *Prof Exp:* Res chemist, Am Cyanamid Co, 56-60; res assoc & fel chem, Duke Univ, 63-64; asst prof, Carnegie Inst Technol, 64-65; from asst prof to assoc prof, Southern Ill Univ, Carbondale, 65-72, prof chem, 72-79; SR RES CHEMIST, GULF RES & DEVELOP CO, PITTSBURGH, PA, 80- *Mem:* Am Chem Soc; Royal Soc Chem. *Res:* Organometallic and ferrocene chemistry; homogeneous catalysis; coal chemistry; stereochemistry; instrumental analysis. *Mailing Add:* Gulf Res & Develop Co Pittsburgh PA 15230

SLOCUM, EDGAR WINFRED, b New Bedford, Mass, Oct 21, 28; m 53; c 2. CHEMICAL ENGINEERING. *Educ:* Worcester Polytech Inst, BS, 52; Yale Univ, DEng, 57. *Prof Exp:* Sr res engr, 56-73, SR RES ASSOC, ENG TECH LAB, E I DU PONT DE NEMOURS & CO, INC, 73- *Res:* Thermodynamics of phase equilibria; coal hydropyrolysis. *Mailing Add:* E I du Pont Exp Sta 304 Wilmington DE 19898

SLOCUM, HARRY KIM, b Buffalo, NY, June 8, 47; m 74; c 1. BIOCHEMISTRY, BIOLOGY. *Educ:* State Univ NY, Buffalo, BA, 69, PhD(chem), 74. *Prof Exp:* Res assoc immunol, Scripps Clin & Res Found, 74-76; cancer res scientist I, 76-77, SCIENTIST II PHARMACOL, ROSWELL PARK MEM INST, 77- *Mem:* Tissue Cult Asn; Am Asn Cancer Res. *Res:* Characterization of cells comprising human solid tumors, including determinants of drug action, cellular interactions and mechanism of metastases. *Mailing Add:* Grace Cancer Drug Ctr Roswell Park Mem Inst Buffalo NY 14263

SLOCUM, RICHARD WILLIAM, b Bryn Mawr, Pa, May 16, 34; c 5. ENGINEERING. *Educ:* Mass Inst Technol, BS, 55, PhD(nuclear physics), 59. *Prof Exp:* Scientist, Raytheon Co, 58-61; sect head, Aerospace Corp, 61-69; spec asst to dir, Advan Res Proj Agency, US Govt, 69-71; DIR RES & DEVELOP, AIR LOGISTICS CORP, 72- *Concurrent Pos:* Instr, Calif State Univ, Long Beach, 62-64; Marymount Col, 62-65; Univ Calif, Los Angeles, 63; Univ Southern Calif, 63-64. *Mem:* Soc Naval Architects & Engrs; Inst Elec & Electronics Engrs; Am Phys Soc; Arctic Inst NAm. *Res:* Arctic operations; ships and platforms; undersea vehicles and systems; air cushion vehicles; meteorological and surveillance satellites and systems. *Mailing Add:* 2138 Kinnelon Canyon Rd Pasadena CA 91107

SLOCUM, ROBERT EARLE, b El Reno, Okla, Nov 28, 38; m 67. PHYSICS. *Educ:* Univ Okla, BA, 60, MEP, 63; Univ Tex, Austin, PhD(physics), 68. *Prof Exp:* Res engr, Tex Instruments Inc, 60-63; res engr, Boeing Co, 63-64; mem tech staff atomic physics, Equip Res & Develop Lab, 66-73, MGR, ADVAN MAGNETICS PROGS, TEX INSTRUMENTS INC, PLANO, 74- *Mem:* AAAS; Am Phys Soc; Optical Soc Am. *Res:* Optical pumping with application to magnetometers for space and geophysical applications; thin film Hertzian polarizers; application of superconducting thin films to magnetometry. *Mailing Add:* 307 Arborcrest Richardson TX 74080

SLOCUM, ROBERT RICHARD, b Traverse City, Mich, June 21, 31; m 60; c 2. SOLID STATE PHYSICS, RADIOLOGICAL PHYSICS. *Educ:* Berea Col, AB, 52; Mich State Univ, MS, 56; Col William & Mary, PhD(physics), 69. *Prof Exp:* Instr physics, Colgate Univ, 56-57, 58-59; res physicist, Airborne Instruments Labs, NY, 59-60; from asst prof to assoc prof physics, Old Dom Col, 60-69; ASSOC PROF PHYSICS, CENT MICH UNIV, 69- *Concurrent Pos:* NSF sci fac fel, 66-67. *Mem:* Am Asn Physics Teachers; Am Phys Soc. *Res:* Semiconductor devices; nuclear magnetic resonance in metals. *Mailing Add:* Dept of Physics Cent Mich Univ Mt Pleasant MI 48858

SLOCUMB, CHARLES HENRY, b Plainview, Minn, Aug 28, 05; m 33; c 4. INTERNAL MEDICINE. *Educ:* Univ Minn, BS, 27, MB, 28, MD, 29, MS, 30. *Prof Exp:* Intern, Ancker Hosp, Minn, 30-31; intern internal med, 31-35, assoc prof, 36-54, consult, Mayo Clin, 36-73, PROF MED, MAYO GRAD SCH MED, UNIV MINN, 54-, EMER CONSULT, MAYO CLIN, 73- *Honors & Awards:* Am Rheumatism Asn Award, 51 & 73; Gold Medal, WLondon Med & Surg Soc, 51. *Mem:* Am Rheumatism Asn (pres, 51); hon mem Span Rheumatism Soc; AMA. *Res:* Fibrositis; gout; bacterial allergies; Lupus Eryhtematosus; vitamin toxicity; rheumatic fever; rheumatoid arthritis and relation to endocrines. *Mailing Add:* Mayo Clin 200 First St SW Rochester MN 55901

SLODKI, MOREY ELI, b Chicago, Ill, June 16, 28; m 67; c 2. BIOCHEMISTRY. *Educ:* Univ Ill, BS, 48; Univ Iowa, PhD, 55. *Prof Exp:* RES LEADER MICROBIAL BIOCHEM RES, FERMENTATION LAB, NORTHERN REGIONAL RES CTR, SCI & EDUC AGR RES SERV, USDA, 55- *Mem:* Am Chem Soc; Am Soc Microbiol; Soc Indust Microbiol. *Res:* Microbial enzymes; biological nitrogen fixation; exocellular microbial polysaccharides. *Mailing Add:* Northern Regional Res Ctr USDA Sci & Educ Admin-Agr Res Peoria IL 61604

SLODOWSKI, THOMAS R, b Jersey City, NJ, Dec 21, 26; m 52; c 2. EXPLORATION GEOLOGY. *Educ:* Calif Inst Technol, BS, 53; Princeton Univ, PhD(geol), 56. *Prof Exp:* Geologist, Am Overseas Petrol Ltd, 56-70; geologist, Explor Dept, Standard Oil Co Calif, 70-74; geologist, Geothermal Div, Union Oil Co Calif, 74-80; SR STAFF EXPLORATIONIST, TEX EASTERN CORP, 80- *Mem:* Fel Geol Soc Am; Am Asn Petrol Geol. *Res:* Regional and field geology. *Mailing Add:* 2418 S Voss Rd #L122 Houston TX 77057

SLOGER, CHARLES, b Albany, NY, Dec 22, 38; m 67; c 2. PLANT PHYSIOLOGY. *Educ:* State Univ NY Albany, BS, 61, MS, 63; Univ Fla, PhD(bot), 68. *Prof Exp:* PLANT PHYSIOLOGIST, PLANT PHYSIOL INST, CELL CULT & NITROGEN FIXATION LAB, NORTHEASTERN REGION, SCI & EDUC ADMIN-AGR RES, USDA, 68- *Mem:* Am Soc Plant Physiol; Am Soc Microbiol. *Res:* Physiology of symbiotic nitrogen fixation; mineral nutrition. *Mailing Add:* Agr Res Serv NE Region USDA Beltsville Agr Res Ctr-West Beltsville MD 20705

SLOMA, LEONARD VINCENT, b Chicago, Ill, June 28, 20; m 46; c 2. ENGINEERING PHYSICS. *Educ:* Northwestern Univ, BS, 42, PhD, 51; Mass Inst Technol, SM, 48. *Prof Exp:* Consult, Arthur D Little, Inc, 46-48; instr mech eng, Northwestern Univ, 48-51; res engr, Autonetics Div, NAm Aviation, Inc, 51-53, supvr systs anal, 53-55, staff specialist, 55-56; scientist, 56-57, sect mgr, 57-59, ASSOC DIR & HEAD PHYSICS & ELECTRONICS DEPT, ROY C INGERSOLL RES CTR, BORG-WARNER CORP, 59- *Mem:* Sigma Xi; Soc Photo-optical Instrumentation Engrs. *Res:* Applied and fluid mechanics; heat transfer; refrigeration; air conditioning; acoustics; electronics; solid state circuitry; solid state physics; electrochemical physics; servo controls; systems analysis. *Mailing Add:* Ingersoll Res Ctr Borg-Warner Corp Wolf & Algonquin Rds Des Plaines IL 60018

SLOMP, GEORGE, b Grand Rapids, Mich, Feb 15, 22; m 51; c 4. PHYSICAL CHEMISTRY. *Educ:* Calvin Col, AB, 42; Ohio State Univ, PhD(chem), 49. *Prof Exp:* Lab asst chem, Calvin Col, 41-42; asst inorg chem, Ohio State Univ, 42-43, org chem, 46-49; asst org synthesis, Am Petrol Inst, 43-44; res chemist, Am Oil Co, Tex, 44-46; SR SCIENTIST, UPJOHN CO, 49- *Res:* Synthesis and reactions of steroidal hormones and natural products; reaction mechanisms; ozonolysis; catalytic hydrogenation; Grignard reactions; nuclear magnetic resonance spectroscopy; molecular structure determination; computer programming. *Mailing Add:* Spectros Sect Upjohn Co Kalamazoo MI 49001

SLONCZEWSKI, JOHN CASIMIR, b New York, NY, July 26, 29; m 55; c 3. SOLID STATE PHYSICS. *Educ:* Worcester Polytech Inst, BS, 50; Rutgers Univ, PhD(physics), 55. *Prof Exp:* RES STAFF MEM, WATSON RES CTR, IBM CORP, 55- *Mem:* Fel Am Phys Soc. *Res:* Theories of ferromagnetism; magnetic domain phenomena; structural phase transitions and electron-lattice interactions. *Mailing Add:* IBM Res Ctr Box 218 Yorktown Heights NY 10598

SLONECKER, CHARLES EDWARD, b Gig Harbor, Wash, Nov 30, 38; m 61; c 3. ANATOMY. *Educ:* Univ Wash, DDS, 65, PhD(biol struct), 67. *Prof Exp:* Sci asst path, Int Path, Univ Bern, 67-68; from asst prof to assoc prof, 68-76, PROF ANAT, UNIV BC, 76-, HEAD DEPT, 81- *Concurrent Pos:* Nat Inst Allergy & Infectious Dis fels, Univ Wash, 65-67; Swiss Nat Fund grant, 67-69; BC Med Res Found grant, 68-69; Med Res Coun grant, 70-75; res grants, G&F Heighway Fund, 75- & Muscular Dystrophy of Can, 78- *Mem:* Am Asn Anatomists; Can Asn Anatomists. *Res:* Lymphocytic tissue morphology and physiology; cellular immunology; radiobiology; hematology and radioautography. *Mailing Add:* Dept Anat Fac Med Univ BC Vancouver BC V6T 1W5 Can

SLONIM, ARNOLD ROBERT, b Springfield, Mass, Feb 15, 26; m 51; c 3. BIOCHEMISTRY, PHYSIOLOGY. *Educ:* Tufts Col, BS, 47; Boston Univ, AM, 48; Johns Hopkins Univ, PhD(biol), 53. *Prof Exp:* Res asst nutrit, Sterling-Winthrop Res Inst, 48-49; res asst pharmacol, George Washington Univ, 49-50; res asst & jr instr biol, Johns Hopkins Univ, 50-53; res assoc chemother, Children's Cancer Res Found, 53-54; head chem lab, Lynn Hosp, Mass, 55-56, res physiologist, 56-60, chief appl ecol sect, 60-62, res biochemist/group leader biotechnol & environ pollution, 62-77, asst chief, Biodyn Effects Br, 77-80, ASST CHIEF, BIODYN & BIOENG DIV, AEROSPACE MED RES LAB, WRIGHT-PATTERSON AFB, 80- *Concurrent Pos:* Lectr, Mass Sch Physiother, 55-56; mem life support group, Int Bioastronaut Comt, Int Astronaut Fedn, 67-70; mem comt biol handbooks, Fedn Am Socs Exp Biol, 67-71; mem carcinogen waste disposal proj, Int Agency Res Cancer, WHO, 81- *Mem:* AAAS; Sigma Xi; Am Soc Biol Chemists; NY Acad Sci; Aerospace Med Asn. *Res:* Aerospace physiology and biochemistry; applied ecology; bioastronautics; biotechnology; environmental pollution. *Mailing Add:* Aerospace Med Res Lab Wright-Patterson AFB OH 45433

SLONKA, GERALD FRANCIS, b Kansas City, Kans, Oct 6, 40. PARASITOLOGY. *Educ:* Rockhurst Col, AB, 63; Kans State Univ, BS, 67, MS, DVM, 69, PhD(parasitol), 72. *Prof Exp:* Instr parasitol & infectious dis, Col Vet Med, Kans State Univ, 69-72; epidemic intel serv officer epidemiol, Ctr Dis Control, USPHS, 72-74; asst prof parasitol, Dept Vet Microbiol, Sch Vet Med, Univ Calif, Davis, 74-76; MEM STAFF, BELTSVILLE AGR RES CTR, MPI-USDA, 76- *Mem:* Am Asn Vet Parasitologists; Am Vet Med Asn. *Res:* Invitro cultivation of parasites; epidemiology of parasites; experimental chemotherapy of parasitisms; host-parasite relationships. *Mailing Add:* Beltsville Agr Res Ctr-East Bldg 318C Beltsville MD 20705

SLOOPE, BILLY WARREN, b Clifton Forge, Va, Jan 4, 24; m 51; c 2. PHYSICS, THIN FILMS. *Educ:* Univ Richmond, BS, 49; Univ Va, MS, 51, PhD(physics), 53. *Prof Exp:* Asst prof physics, Clemson Col, 53-55; from asst prof to assoc prof, Univ Richmond, 55-61, adj assoc prof, 61-68; head dept, 68-79, PROF PHYSICS, VA COMMONWEALTH UNIV, 68- *Concurrent Pos:* Sr res physicist, Va Inst Sci Res, 56-68, head physics div, 61-68; Horsley res award, Va Acad Sci, 61. *Mem:* Am Vacuum Soc; Am Asn Physics Teachers. *Res:* Epitaxial thin films and their properties. *Mailing Add:* 8718 Avalon Dr Richmond VA 23229

SLOSS, LAURENCE LOUIS, b Mountain View, Calif, Aug 26, 13; m 37; c 2. GEOLOGY. *Educ:* Stanford Univ, BA, 33; Univ Chicago, PhD(geol), 37. *Prof Exp:* From instr to assoc prof geol, Mont Sch Mines, 37-46; from lectr to assoc prof, 47-54, prof, 54-77, William Deering prof, 77-81, EMER PROF GEOL, NORTHWESTERN UNIV, EVANSTON, 81- *Concurrent Pos:* Geologist, State Bur Mines & Geol, Mont, 37-46. *Honors & Awards:* Twenhofel Medal, Soc Econ Paleont & Mineral, 80. *Mem:* Hon mem Am Asn Petrol Geologists (pres, 79-80); Am Geophys Union; fel Geol Soc Am; Paleont Soc; hom mem Soc Econ Paleont & Mineral (pres, 62). *Res:* Sedimentary petrology; stratigraphic analysis; regional sedimentary tectonics. *Mailing Add:* Dept Geol Sci Northwestern Univ Evanston IL 60201

SLOSS, PETER WILLIAM, b Butte, Mont, May 11, 42; m 66; c 3. GEOLOGY, OCEANOGRAPHY. *Educ:* Northwestern Univ, BS, 64; Univ Chicago, MS, 66; Rice Univ, PhD(geol), 72. *Prof Exp:* Sr res technician meteorol, Univ Chicago, 67-68; assoc researcher, Inst Storm Res, Houston, 68-69; vis asst prof geol, Mich State Univ, 72-73; phys scientist oceanog, 73-78, GEOLOGIST, NAT OCEANIC & ATMOSPHERIC ADMIN, 78-, CHIEF DATA SYSTEMS & PROD, MARINE GEOL & GEOPHYSICS DIV, NAT GEOPHYSICAL & SOLAR-TERRESTRIAL DATA CTR, 81- *Honors & Awards:* Spec Achievement Award, Nat Oceanic & Atmospheric Admin, 77. *Mem:* Am Meteorol Soc; Am Geophys Union; AAAS; Geol Soc Am; Sigma Xi. *Res:* Interdisciplinary studies spanning geology, meteorology and oceanography; management of data from such studies. *Mailing Add:* Nat Oceanic & Atmospheric Admin Code D64 325 Broadway Boulder CO 80303

SLOSSER, JEFFREY ERIC, b Winslow, Ariz, Dec 1, 43; m 68; c 2. ENTOMOLOGY. *Educ:* Ariz State Univ, BS, 66; Univ Ariz, MS, 68, PhD(entom), 71. *Prof Exp:* Res assoc entom, Univ Ariz, 68-70 & Univ Ark, 72-75; asst prof, 75-79, ASSOC PROF ENTOM, TEX A&M UNIV, 79- *Mem:* Entom Soc Am; Sigma Xi. *Res:* Integrated control and population dynamics of cotton and wheat insect pests in the rolling plains of Texas. *Mailing Add:* Tex Agr Exp Sta PO Box 1658 Vernon TX 76384

SLOSSON, JAMES E, b Van Nuys, Calif, Apr 12, 23; m 47; c 2. GEOLOGY. *Educ:* Univ Southern Calif, BA, 49, MS, 50, PhD(geol), 58. *Prof Exp:* Prof geol, Los Angeles Valley Col, 50-79; CONSULT ENG GEOLOGIST, 60- *Concurrent Pos:* Geologist, US Geol Surv, 49-50; res geologist, Gulf Oil Corp, 52-56; NSF grant mineralogy & geol, Univ Ill, 57; consult eng geologist for various projs, 58-73; chief eng geol, James E Slosson & Assoc, 60-73 & 75-; mem, Eng Geologists Qual Bd, City of Los Angeles, 61-76, County of Los Angeles, 66-68 & 81-, chmn, Eng Geol Rev & Appeals Bd, 72; mem, Gov Earthquake Coun, 73-74, Am Asn State Geologists, 73-75 & Nat Acad Sci panel on mudslides, 74; state geologist, Calif Div Mines & Geol, 73-75; comnr, Seismic Safety Comn, 75-; lectr, Environ Mgt Inst, Sch Pub Admin, Univ Southern Calif, 74-; mem adv comt for socioecon & polit consequences of earthquake prediction, Univ Colo, NSF Study, 75-76; prof geol, Los Angeles Valley Col, 75-; mem, Calif Earthquake Prediction Eval Coun, 75-; guest lectr, Harvard Univ Grad Sch, Calif State Northridge, Occidental Col, Univ Nev & Univ Calif, Los Angeles, Berkeley, Irvine & Davis. *Mem:* Am Asn Petrol Geol; fel Earthquake Eng Res Inst; Am Soc Civil Eng; Asn Eng Geol; fel Geol Soc Am. *Res:* Engineering geology; seismic research. *Mailing Add:* 15373 Valley Vista Blvd Sherman Oaks CA 91403

SLOTA, PETER JOHN, JR, b Cleveland, Ohio, July 11, 24; m 59. CHEMISTRY. *Educ:* Hiram Col, BA, 46; Temple Univ, MA, 49, PhD(chem), 54. *Prof Exp:* Instr chem, Hiram Col, 46-47, instr night sch, Drexel Inst, 51-53; res assoc chem, Univ Southern Calif, 54-57; Alexander von Humboldt stipend, Res Inorg Chem, Univ Munich, 57-59; res chemist & head organometallics br, US Naval Ord Lab, 59-70; assoc dir archaeol res unit, Dry Lands Res Inst, 72-74, ASSOC RES CHEMIST, RADIOCARBON DATING & RES LAB, UNIV CALIF, RIVERSIDE, 74- *Mem:* Am Chem Soc; Am Inst Chemists. *Res:* Organometallic and phosphorus chemistry; radiocarbon-14; chemistry of the environment; archaeological dating and ecological research. *Mailing Add:* 2903 Ivy St Riverside CA 92506

SLOTE, LAWRENCE, b New York, NY, May 23, 24; m 60; c 1. OCCUPATIONAL SAFETY & HEALTH, HUMAN FACTORS. *Educ:* Univ RI, BSME, 47; NY Univ, MME, 48, EngScD(civil eng), 61. *Prof Exp:* Sr res scientist, Res Div, Sch Eng & Sci, NY Univ, 48-63; environ engr, Pollution Control & Life Support, Advan Civil Systs, Grumman Aerospace Corp, 63-73; sr environ engr & scientist, Bradford Comput & Systs, Inc, 73-74; assoc prof allied health sci, York Col, City Univ New York, 74-75; dir res, Ctr for Safety, 75-78, PROF OCCUP HEALTH & SAFETY, NY UNIV, 75-, CHMN DEPT, 78-, DIR, CTR FOR SAFETY, 78- *Concurrent Pos:* Adj prof, Dept Indust Eng, Sch Eng & Sci, NY Univ, 61-67 & Dept Grad Mgt Eng, C W Post Col, Long Island Univ, 65-75; mem, US Nat Comt Eng in Med & Biol, Nat Acad Eng, 66-69; mem bd adminrs, North Shore Jr Sci Mus, 70-71. *Mem:* Syst Safety Soc; Sigma Xi; fel NY Acad Sci; assoc fel NY Acad Med. *Res:* Environmental control of closed ecological systems; biological waste treatment systems; biomedical and biomechanical engineering; cryptobioclimatology; mathematical modeling of environmental pollution; immobilized enzymes and wastewater treatment; human factors; safety sciences. *Mailing Add:* 333 East Shore Rd Kings Point NY 11023

SLOTKIN, THEODORE ALAN, b Brooklyn, NY, Feb 17, 47; m 67. PHARMACOLOGY. *Educ:* Brooklyn Col, BS, 67; Univ Rochester, PhD(pharmacol), 70. *Prof Exp:* NIMH trainee biochem, 70-71, asst prof, 71-75, assoc prof, 75-79, PROF PHARMACOL, DUKE UNIV, 79- *Mem:* Am Soc Pharmacol & Exp Therapeut; Am Soc Neurochem; Soc Neurosci. *Res:* Neuropharmacology; neurochemistry; developmental neurobiology; drug abuse. *Mailing Add:* Dept of Pharmacol Duke Univ Durham NC 27710

SLOTKOFF, LAWRENCE M, b Brooklyn, NY, Nov 14, 30; m 62; c 3. PHYSIOLOGY, INTERNAL MEDICINE. *Educ:* NY Univ, BA, 50; Univ Berne, MD, 55; Georgetown Univ, PhD(physiol), 68. *Prof Exp:* Intern & resident med, Beth El Hosp, Brooklyn, NY, 56-68; asst resident neurol, NY Univ-Bellevue Med Ctr, 58-59; asst cardiol, Nat Inst Cardiol, Mex, 59-60; instr med & physiol, 62-65, asst prof med, 65-70, assoc prof med & dir hypertension clin, 70-75, PROF MED & PHYSICS, GEORGETOWN UNIV, 76- *Concurrent Pos:* Fel, Georgetown Univ, 61-62; Am Heart Asn advan res fel, 65-67. *Mem:* AAAS; Am Fedn Clin Res; Am Heart Asn; Am Physiol Soc; fel Am Col Physicians. *Res:* Renal and cardiovascular physiology; hypertension. *Mailing Add:* Georgetown Univ Sch of Med Washington DC 20007

SLOTNICK, DANIEL LEONID, b New York, NY, Nov 12, 31; m 52; c 2. COMPUTER SCIENCES, HARDWARE SYSTEMS. *Educ:* Columbia Univ, BS, 51, MA, 52; NY Univ, PhD, 56. *Prof Exp:* Lectr math, Columbia Univ, 51-52; mathematician, Elec Comput Proj, Inst Advan Study, 52-54; res asst, Inst Math Sci, NY Univ, 54-56; res assoc, Differential Equations Proj, Princeton Univ, 56-57; adv engr, Int Bus Mach Corp, 57-61 & Air Arm Div, Westinghouse Elec Corp, 61-65; dir ctr advan comput, 70-74, PROF COMPUT SCI, UNIV ILL, URBANA, 65- *Concurrent Pos:* Instr, Rutgers Univ, 56-57; consult, indust & govt, 57-; assoc, Ctr Advan Study, Univ Ill, 80. *Honors & Awards:* Mellon lectr, Carnegie Mellon Univ, 67. *Mem:* Fel Inst Elec & Electronics Engrs. *Res:* Digital systems design and applications. *Mailing Add:* 283 Digital Comput Lab 1304 W Springfield Ave Urbana IL 61801

SLOTNICK, HERBERT, b Malden, Mass, Oct 6, 28; m 53; c 2. CHEMICAL ENGINEERING, PHYSICAL CHEMISTRY. *Educ:* Northeastern Univ, BS, 51; Worcester Polytech Inst, MS, 53; Mass Inst Technol, SM, 55; Univ Conn, PhD(eng), 64. *Prof Exp:* Proj chemist, Pratt & Whitney Aircraft, United Aircraft Corp, 54-67; PROF CHEM, CENT CONN STATE COL, 67- *Concurrent Pos:* Res partic, NSF Acad Year Exten, Cent Conn State Col, 70-72. *Mem:* Am Chem Soc; Am Inst Chem Engrs; Sigma Xi. *Res:* Active nitrogen reactions; air-water pollution; materials; high vacuum, inert gas, liquid metal technology; materials related to biomedical science. *Mailing Add:* 134 Hyde Rd West Hartford CT 06117

SLOTNICK, IRVING JAMES, b Springfield, Mass, Aug 3, 21; m 53; c 3. BACTERIOLOGY. *Educ:* Univ Mass, BS, 42; Univ Southern Calif, PhD(bact), 54; Am Soc Microbiol, dipl, 65. *Prof Exp:* Res chemist, Ammecco Chem Corp, 42-43; asst biochem, Univ Rochester, 43-45; chief technician & bacteriologist, Norwalk Hosp, 47-50; asst & instr, Univ Pa, 54; sr cancer res asst, Roswell Park Mem Inst, 54-56; asst prof microbiol, Roswell Park Mem Inst Grad Div, Buffalo, 56-59; asst prof microbiol & dir clin microbiol labs, Univ Fla, 5966; CHIEF MICROBIOLOGIST, CEDARS-SINAI MED CTR, 66- *Mem:* Am Soc Microbiol; Am Acad Microbiol. *Res:* Bacterial metabolism; chemotherapy; drug resistance; genital tract microbiology; host-parasite relationships. *Mailing Add:* Div of Labs Beverly Blvd 8700 Los Angeles CA 90048

SLOTNICK, VICTOR BERNARD, b Chicago, Ill, Oct 27, 31; m 60; c 3. MICROBIOLOGY, MEDICINE. *Educ:* Roosevelt Univ, BS, 53; Univ Chicago, MS, 55; Hahnemann Med Col, PhD(microbiol), 60; Jefferson Med Col, MD, 65; Am Bd Family Pract, dipl, 77. *Prof Exp:* Assoc microbiol, Univ Chicago, 54; res assoc, Virus Lab, Ill State Dept Pub Health, 54-55; assoc microbiol, Hahnemann Med Col, 57-60; sr virologist, Merck Inst, 60-61; intern, Albert Einstein Med Ctr, 65-66; asst dir, 66-68, assoc dir, 68-75, dir clin res, McNeil Labs Inc, 75-81, CLIN RES FEL, MCNEIL PHARMACEUT, 81- *Concurrent Pos:* NIH res fel, Jefferson Med Col, 64-65, clin instr, Dept Family Med, 75- *Mem:* Am Soc Microbiol; AMA; NY Acad Sci; Am Col Neuropsychopharmacol. *Res:* Virology; immunology; antiviral chemotherapy; cytology; biochemistry; experimental teratology; psychopharmacology. *Mailing Add:* McNeil Pharmaceut Spring House PA 19477

SLOTSKY, MYRON NORTON, b Portland, Maine, Apr 30, 35; m 62; c 2. INDUSTRIAL PHARMACY. *Educ:* Mass Col Pharm, BS, 57, MS, 59, PhD(pharm), 67. *Prof Exp:* Chemist, Res Dept, Gillette Safety Razor Co, 59-62, sr cosmetic chemist, Toiletries Develop Sect, 62-64, chem & biol sect, 64; sr pharmaceut chemist, Colgate-Palmolive Co, 66-68; dir prod develop, 68-75, spec develop proj analyst, 75-80, MGR PILOT OPERS, MARION LABS, INC, 80- *Mem:* Am Chem Soc; Am Pharmaceut Asn; Acad Pharmaceut Sci; Soc Cosmetic Chem. *Res:* Tablet and capsule formulation, suspension and solution technology; emulsion and aerosol technology; problems related to stabilization, preservation and production scale-up of cosmetics and pharmaceuticals; dandruff; acne; processes development. *Mailing Add:* Marion Labs Inc 10236 Bunker Ridge Rd Kansas City MO 64137

SLOTTA, KARL HEINRICH, b Breslau, Ger, May 12, 95; nat US; m 27; c 2. BIOCHEMISTRY. *Educ:* Breslau Univ, PhD(biochem), 23. *Hon Degrees:* DrSci, Univ Bonn, 65. *Prof Exp:* Prof org chem, Breslau Univ, 24-35; chmn chem, Butantan Inst, Brazil, 35-38; sci dir, Industria Farmaceutica Endochimica, 38-55; res prof, 56-77, EMER PROF BIOCHEM, SCH MED, UNIV MIAMI, 77-, CONSULT, 77- *Mem:* Am Chem Soc; Am Soc Biol Chemists; Brazilian Acad Sci; Ger Chem Asn; Geront Soc. *Res:* Progesterone; snake venoms; phospholipids; blood coagulation; growth factor; cancer research. *Mailing Add:* 5740 SW 52 Terr Miami FL 33155

SLOTTA, LARRY STEWART, b Billings, Mont, Aug 20, 34; m 58; c 3. CIVIL ENGINEERING, HYDRAULICS. *Educ:* Univ Wyo, BS, 56, MS, 59; Univ Wis, PhD(civil eng), 62. *Prof Exp:* Mem fac, Univ Wyo, 57-58 & Univ Wis, 58-61; from asst prof to assoc prof civil eng, 62-77, PROF CIVIL ENG, ORE STATE UNIV, 77-, DIR OCEAN ENG PROGS, SCH ENG, 71- *Concurrent Pos:* Consult, Reed Col, 65; vis prof, Thayer Sch Eng, Dartmouth Col, 66; Am Soc Eng Educ-Ford Found Prog prin scientist, Hydronautics Inc, Md, 69-70; dir res dredge spoil distribution & estuarine effects, NSF-Res Appl to Nations Needs; counr, Pac Chapter, World Dredging Asn. *Mem:* Am Soc Eng Educ; Am Soc Civl Engrs; Int Asn Hydraul Res. *Res:* Fluid mechanics; systems engineering; computer applications; dredge spoil distribution and estuarine effects. *Mailing Add:* Ocean Eng Progs Sch of Eng Ore State Univ Corvallis OR 97331

SLOTTER, RICHARD ARDEN, b Souderton, Pa, Mar 3, 32; m 54; c 3. INORGANIC CHEMISTRY. *Educ:* Bluffton Col, BS, 54; Univ Mich, MS, 57, PhD(chem), 60. *Prof Exp:* From asst prof to assoc prof chem, Bluffton Col, 58-64; assoc prof, Robert Col, Istanbul, 64-67, prof, 67-71, chmn dept, 66-71; vis assoc prof, Bucknell Univ, 71-72; ASST CHMN DEPT CHEM, NORTHWESTERN UNIV, EVANSTON, 72-, LECTR, 72- *Mem:* AAAS; Am Chem Soc. *Res:* Polarography; coordination complexes; electrochemical kinetics. *Mailing Add:* Dept of Chem Northwestern Univ Evanston IL 60201

SLOTTERBECK-BAKER, OBERTA ANN, b Cincinnati, Ohio, July 3, 36; m 70. SYMBOLIC ALGEBRA. *Educ:* Ohio State Univ, BS, 58; Univ Tex, Austin, MA, 66, PhD(math), 69. *Prof Exp:* Teacher, Columbus Pub Schs, Ohio, 58-60 & Union County Regional Schs, NJ, 60-64; asst math, Univ Tex, Austin, 65-69; res fel, Univ Fla, 69-70, asst prof, 70-74; ASSOC PROF MATH, HIRAM COL, 74- *Mem:* Am Math Soc; Asn Comput Mach; Math Asn Am. *Res:* Symbolic/algebraic computing algorithms; macsyma development work on the VAX 111780. *Mailing Add:* Dept Math Sci Hiram Col Hiram OH 44234

SLOVACEK, RUDOLF EDWARD, b Bloomington, Ind, Jan 4, 48; m 70; c 2. BIOCHEMISTRY, BIOENERGETICS. *Educ:* Univ Rochester, BA, 70, MS, 72, PhD(biol), 75. *Prof Exp:* Res assoc marine biol, Nat Res Coun, 75-76; res assoc, Brookhaven Nat Lab, 76-78, asst biophysicist biol, 78-80; SR SCIENTIST BIOL, CORNING GLASS WORKS, 80- *Mem:* Am Soc Plant Physiologists; Am Soc Photobiol; AAAS; NY Acad Sci. *Res:* Physical and chemical studies of the photosynthetic energy conversion process and its regulatory mechanisms in the chloroplast membrane organelles of higher plants and phytoplankton. *Mailing Add:* Corning Glass Works Sullivan Park FR-64 Corning NY 14831

SLOVITER, HENRY ALLAN, b Philadelphia, Pa, June 16, 14. PHYSIOLOGICAL CHEMISTRY. *Educ:* Temple Univ, AB, 35, AM, 36; Univ Pa, PhD(org chem), 42, MD, 49. *Prof Exp:* Chemist, US Navy Yard, Philadelphia, 36-45; chemist, Harrison Dept Surg Res, Sch Med, Univ Pa, 45-49, intern, Hosp, 49-50; res fel, Nat Inst Med Res, London, 50-52; asst prof physiol chem & res asst prof surg, 52-57, res assoc prof neurosurg, 57-66, res prof neurosurg, 66-75, PROF BIOCHEM, SCH MED, UNIV PA, 66-, PROF SURG RES & PROF BIOPHYS, 75- *Concurrent Pos:* Vis scientist, Univ Tokyo, 63; US-USSR health exchange scientist, Sechenov Inst Physiol, Moscow, 65, Inst Biol & Med Chem Moscow, 71; US-India exchange scientist, Christian Med Col, Vellore, India, 67; proj officer award to Inst for Biol Res, Fogarty Int Ctr, NIH, Belgrade, Yugoslavia, 72-75, fel, Med Res Coun Exp Haemat Unit, St Mary's Hosp Med Sch, London, 78. *Honors & Awards:* Glycerine Res Award, 54. *Mem:* AAAS; Am Physiol Soc; Am Soc Biol Chem; Int Soc Neurochem. *Res:* Brain metabolism; erythrocyte lipids and metabolism; erythrocyte substitutes. *Mailing Add:* Sch of Med Univ of Pa Philadelphia PA 19104

SLOWEY, JACK WILLIAM, b Wauwatosa, Wis, Mar 19, 32; m 52; c 4. AERONOMY. *Educ:* Univ Wis, BS, 55, MS, 56. *Prof Exp:* Physicist, 56-59, ASTRONOMER, SATELLITE TRACKING PROG, ASTROPHYS OBSERV, SMITHSONIAN INST, 59- *Concurrent Pos:* Lectr, Harvard Col, 57-60 & Boston Univ, 68-69; consult, IBM Corp, 62-75 & Boston Col, 75- *Mem:* Am Geophys Union; Am Astron Soc. *Res:* Artificial earth satellite orbits; structure and variations of earth's upper atmosphere. *Mailing Add:* Smithsonian Astrophys Observ 60 Garden St Cambridge MA 02138

SLOWIK, JOHN HENRY, b Hastings, Nebr, Sept 12, 45; m 72. SOLID STATE PHYSICS. *Educ:* Manhattan Col, BS, 67; Univ Ill, MS, 71, PhD(solid state physics), 73. *Prof Exp:* Scanner nuclear physics, Johns Hopkins Univ, 67; asst physics, Univ Ill, 68-73; assoc scientist, 73-74, SCIENTIST SOLID STATE PHYSICS, XEROX CORP, 75- *Mem:* Am Inst Physics; Sigma Xi. *Res:* Extreme-ultraviolet spectroscopy; charge transport in disordered solids; thermally stimulated phenomena; contact and interfacial charge transport phenomena. *Mailing Add:* Xerox Webster Res Ctr 800 Phillips Rd W-114 Webster NY 14580

SLOWINSKI, EMIL J, JR, b Newark, NJ, Oct 12, 22; m 51; c 5. PHYSICAL CHEMISTRY. *Educ:* Mass State Col, BS, 46; Mass Inst Technol, PhD(phys chem), 49. *Prof Exp:* Instr chem, Swarthmore Col, 49-52; from instr to assoc prof, Univ Conn, 53-64; PROF CHEM, MACALESTER COL, 64- *Concurrent Pos:* Indust fel, Monsanto Chem Co, 53-54; NSF fel, 60-61; Nat Acad Sci exchange prof, 68-69. *Mem:* Am Chem Soc. *Res:* Mathematical preparation for general chemistry; qualitative analysis and the properties of ions in aqueous solution. *Mailing Add:* Dept of Chem Macalester Col St Paul MN 55105

SLOYAN, MARY STEPHANIE, b New York, NY, Apr 18, 18. MATHEMATICS. *Educ:* Georgian Court Col, AB, 45; Catholic Univ, MA, 49, PhD(math), 52. *Prof Exp:* from asst prof to assoc prof math, 52-59, pres, 68-74, PROF MATH, GEORGIAN COURT COL, 59- *Concurrent Pos:* Vis lectr math, Cath Univ Am, 60- *Mem:* Am Math Soc; Math Asn Am. *Res:* Metric geometry; application of complex variables to geometry. *Mailing Add:* Dept Math Georgian Court Col Lakewood NJ 08701

SLOYER, CLIFFORD W, JR, b Easton, Pa, Apr 30, 34; m 62; c 4. TOPOLOGY. *Educ:* Lehigh Univ, BA, 56, MS, 58, PhD(math), 64. *Prof Exp:* Instr math, Lehigh Univ, 58-64; from asst prof to assoc prof, 64-74, asst chmn dept, 69-78, PROF MATH, UNIV DEL, 74- *Concurrent Pos:* Vis lectr pub schs, Pa, 65-66 & Del, 66-67. *Mem:* Math Asn Am; Nat Coun Teachers Math; Sch Sci & Math Assoc. *Res:* Several complex variables; continuation of meromorphic functions on complex analytic manifolds; secondary programs for gifted students. *Mailing Add:* Dept of Math Univ of Del Newark DE 19711

SLUDER, EARL RAY, b Newland, NC, Nov 9, 30; m 57; c 3. FORESTRY, GENETICS. *Educ:* NC State Univ, BS, 56, MS, 60, PhD(forestry, genetics), 70. *Prof Exp:* Forester, Container Corp Am, 56-57; res forester timber mgt, 57-66, RES FORESTER TREE IMPROV, SOUTHEASTERN FOREST EXP STA, USDA FOREST SERV, 66- *Mem:* Soc Am Foresters. *Res:* Genetic improvement of the southern yellow pines; tree breeding southern pines. *Mailing Add:* 742 Forest Lake Dr N Macon GA 31210

SLUSARCHYK, WILLIAM ALLEN, b Port Jefferson, NY, June 6, 40; m 68. ORGANIC CHEMISTRY. *Educ:* Brown Univ, BS, 61; Pa State Univ, PhD(org chem), 65. *Prof Exp:* SR RES CHEMIST, SQUIBB INST MED RES, NEW BRUNSWICK, 65- *Mem:* Am Chem Soc; NY Acad Sci. *Res:*

Semi-synthetic antibiotics, monobactams, penicillins and cephalosporins; isolation, synthesis and structural elucidation of antibiotics; synthesis and structural elucidation of alkaloids. *Mailing Add:* Sunset Rd Belle Mead NJ 08502

SLUSARCZUK, GEORGE MARCELIUS JAREMIAS, b Stanyslaviv, Ukraine, Jan 14, 32; US citizen; m 64; c 1. ORGANIC CHEMISTRY, ENVIRONMENTAL ANALYSIS. *Educ:* Wayne State Univ, BS, 60, MS, 62; Univ Pa, PhD(org chem), 67. *Prof Exp:* Chemist, Res & Develop Ctr, Gen Elec Corp, 62-64, mem staff res & develop, 67-76; spectroscopist, Univ Pa, 65-67; SR RES ASSOC, CORP RES CTR, INT PAPER CORP, 76- *Mem:* Am Chem Soc; Am Indust Hyg Asn; Shevchenko Sci Soc. *Res:* Environmental organic trace pollutants; pollutants of the working place. *Mailing Add:* Corp Res Ctr PO Box 797 Tuxedo Park NY 10987

SLUSAREK, LIDIA, b Poland; US citizen; m 70; c 1. ANALYTICAL CHEMISTRY. *Educ:* Polytech Inst, Poland, MS, 69; Columbia Univ, PhD(chem), 76. *Prof Exp:* Res asst med chem, Albert Einstein Col Med, 69-71; res investr anal chem, Squibb Inst Med Res, 76-78; sect head mat control, E R Squibb & Sons, 78-79; GROUP LEADER, INDUST LAB DIV, EASTMAN KODAK CO, 79- *Mem:* Am Chem Soc. *Res:* Development assays for drugs and impurities in formulations, bulk materials and body fluids; electrochemical analysis. *Mailing Add:* Eastman Kodak Co Kodak Park Bldg 129 Rochester NY 14650

SLUSHER, RICHART ELLIOTT, b Higginsville, Mo, May 20, 38; m 61; c 3. PHYSICS. *Educ:* Univ Mo-Rolla, BS, 60; Univ Calif, Berkeley, PhD(physics), 66. *Prof Exp:* MEM TECH STAFF, BELL TEL LABS, 65- *Mem:* Am Phys Soc. *Res:* Laser scattering from plasmas, solids and liquids; nonlinear optics of resonant coherent pulses; nuclear double resonance; astrophysics. *Mailing Add:* Interface Electronics Res Dept Bell Tel Labs Murray Hill NJ 07974

SLUSKY, SUSAN E G, b New York, NY, Dec 6, 49; m 71; c 2. SOLID STATE PHYSICS, APPLIED PHYSICS. *Educ:* Brown Univ, AB, 71; Univ Pa, MS, 72; Princeton Univ, PhD(physics), 78. *Prof Exp:* MEM TECH STAFF PHYSICS, BELL LABS, 78- *Mem:* Am Phys Soc. *Res:* Magnetic materials; superconducting electronics. *Mailing Add:* Bell Labs Crawford Hill Lab Box 400 Holmdel NJ 07733

SLUSS, ROBERT REGINALD, b Louisville, Ohio, July 18, 28; m 71; c 1. ENTOMOLOGY, ECOLOGY. *Educ:* Colo Col, BS, 53; Colo State Univ, MS, 55; Univ Calif, Berkeley, PhD(entom), 66. *Prof Exp:* Microbiologist, Pink Bollworm Res Ctr, USDA, 55-59; res assoc entom, Gill Tract, Univ Calif, 59-66; from asst to assoc biol, San Jose State Col, 66-69; assoc prof, State Univ NY Col Old Westbury, 69-70; PROF BIOL, EVERGREEN STATE COL, 70- *Mem:* Ecol Soc Am. *Res:* Insect pathology; insect population ecology; insect physiology; nematology. *Mailing Add:* Dept of Biol Evergreen State Col Olympia WA 98505

SLUSSER, M(ARION) L(ILES), b Memphis, Tenn, May 9, 19; m 46; c 4. CHEMICAL ENGINEERING. *Educ:* Univ Okla, BS, 48; Univ Colo, MS, 49. *Prof Exp:* Res engr, 49-55, sr res engr, 55-67, ENGR ASSOC, FIELD RES LAB, MOBIL RES & DEVELOP CORP, 67- *Mem:* Sigma Xi. *Res:* Well completion and oil production problems; oil well stimulation; thermal recovery methods for recovery of oil from oil shale by in-place methods; oil well stimulation by fracturing and acidizing. *Mailing Add:* Field Res Lab Mobil R&D Corp PO Box 900 Dallas TX 75221

SLUTSKY, HERBERT L, b Chicago, Ill, Nov 6, 25; m 55; c 2. EPIDEMIOLOGY. *Educ:* Univ Ill, BS, 50, MS, 51, PhD(geog, physiol), 59. *Prof Exp:* Vis lectr geog, Univ Ill, 58; assoc prof, 59-67, PROF GEOG, ROOSEVELT UNIV, 67-, HEAD DEPT, 59- *Mem:* Am Geog Soc; Asn Am Geog; Int Soc Biometeorol; Am Pub Health Asn. *Res:* Physiology; geographical distribution of disease; ecological studies of protein, malnutrition and kwashiorkor; pediatric lead poisoning; tubercullosis; salmenella. *Mailing Add:* Dept of Geog Roosevelt Univ 430 S Michigan Ave Chicago IL 60605

SLUTSKY, JOEL, organic chemistry, see previous edition

SLUTSKY, LEON JUDAH, b New York, NY, Oct 9, 32. PHYSICAL CHEMISTRY. *Educ:* Cornell Univ, BA, 53; Mass Inst Technol, PhD, 57. *Prof Exp:* Instr chem, Univ Tex, 57-59, asst prof, 59-61; asst prof, 61-69, PROF CHEM, UNIV WASH, 69- *Mem:* Am Phys Soc. *Res:* Lattice dynamics; mechanical properties of solids; surface chemistry. *Mailing Add:* Dept of Chem Univ of Wash Seattle WA 98195

SLUTSKY, MARK SENDER, theoretical physics, quantum optics, see previous edition

SLUTZ, RALPH JEFFERY, b Cleveland, Ohio, May 18, 17; m 46; c 4. NUMERICAL ANALYSIS. *Educ:* Mass Inst Technol, BS & MS, 39; Princeton Univ, PhD(theoret physics), 46. *Prof Exp:* Asst, Mass Inst Technol, 37-38; asst, Princeton Univ, 39-42, instr, 41-42; tech aide, Nat Defense Res Comt, 42-45; comput design engr, Inst Adv Study, 46-48; physicist, Nat Bur Standards, 48-49, asst chief electronic comput sect, 49-53, consult comput & math, 53-54, asst chief cent radio propagation lab, 54, chief radio propagation physics div, 54-60; guest worker magnetosphere res, Max-Planck Inst Physics & Astrophys, 60-61; sr scientist & consult upper atmosphere & space physics div, Nat Bur Standards, 61-65; sr scientist space disturbances lab, Environ Sci Serv Admin, 65-69, actg dir space environ lab, Nat Oceanic & Atmospheric Admin, 69-70, chief numerical anal & comput techniques group, 70-73, SR SCIENTIST ENVIRON RES LABS, NAT OCEANIC & ATMOSPHERIC ADMIN, 73- *Concurrent Pos:* Mem, US nat comt, Int Sci Radio Union, 56-59; consult, President's Sci Adv Comt, 64-67; mem study group IV, US preparatory comt, Int Radio Consult Comt; vis lectr, Univ Col, 70-72, adj prof elec eng, 72- *Honors & Awards:* Gold Medal, Dept Commerce, 52. *Mem:* Am Phys Soc; Inst Elec & Electronics Eng; Am Geophys Union; Int Asn Geomag & Aeronomy. *Res:* Numerical analysis; numerical forecasting; computer techniques. *Mailing Add:* Nat Oceanic & Atmospheric Admin 325 Broadway Boulder CO 80303

SLY, PETER G, b Sidcup, Eng, Feb 11, 39; m 64; c 2. MARINE GEOLOGY. *Educ:* Univ London, BSc, 60; Univ Liverpool, PhD(geol), 67. *Prof Exp:* head process res, 72-79, RES SCIENTIST, CAN CENTRE INLAND WATERS, 79- *Concurrent Pos:* Tech adv, Geonautics Ltd, 78- *Mem:* Soc Econ Paleont & Mineral; Int Asn Great Lakes Res; Geol Asn Can. *Res:* Marine geology of England; giology and benthic fauna of large lake sediments, fish habitat and substrate analyses; develoment and testing of equipment; application of submersible and diver usable techniques. *Mailing Add:* Can Centre for Inland Waters PO Box 5050 Burlington ON L7R 4A6 Can

SLY, RIDGE MICHAEL, b Seattle, Wash, Nov 3, 33; m 57; c 2. MEDICINE. *Educ:* Kenyon Col, AB, 56; Washington Univ, MD, 60; Am Bd Pediat, dipl, 65, cert allergy, 67. *Prof Exp:* NIH fel pediat allergy & immunol, Med Sch, Univ Calif, Los Angeles, 65-67; from asst prof to prof pediat, La State Univ Sch Med, New Orleans, 67-78; PROF CHILD HEALTH & DEVELOP, GEORGE WASHINGTON UNIV SCH MED & HEALTH SCI & DIR ALLERGY & IMMUNOL, CHILDREN'S HOSP NAT MED CTR, 78- *Concurrent Pos:* Vis physician, Charity Hosp, New Orleans, 67-78. *Mem:* Am Acad Allergy; Am Acad Pediat; Am Col Allergists; Am Thoracic Soc; Asn for the Care of Asthma (pres, 80-81). *Res:* Pulmonary physiology and pharmacology of asthma; exercise induced asthma. *Mailing Add:* Children's Hosp Nat Med Ctr 111 Michigan Ave NW Washington DC 20010

SLY, WILLIAM GLENN, b Arcara, Calif, June 15, 22. PHYSICAL CHEMISTRY. *Educ:* San Diego State Col, BS, 51; Calif Inst Technol, PhD(chem), 55. *Prof Exp:* NSF fel, Calif Inst Technol, 55-56, Hale fel, 56-57; fel, Mass Inst Technol, 57-58; from asst prof to assoc prof, 58-66, PROF CHEM, HARVEY MUDD COL, 66- *Concurrent Pos:* Res assoc, Calif Inst Technol, 59-61, sr res fel, 61-62; NSF sr fel, Swiss Fed Inst Technol, 65-66; guest prof, Ore State Univ, Corvallis, 72-73; vis scholar, Univ Calif, San Diego, 80. *Mem:* Am Chem Soc; Am Crystallog Asn; Inst Elec & Electronics Eng; Am Inst Physics. *Res:* Molecular structure; x-ray crystallography; application of high speed computers to structural analysis; metal complexes; organic molecules. *Mailing Add:* Dept Chem Harvey Mudd Col Claremont CA 91711

SLY, WILLIAM S, b East St Louis, Ill, Oct 19, 32; m 60; c 7. MEDICAL GENETICS. *Educ:* St Louis Univ, MD, 57. *Prof Exp:* Intern med, Washington Univ, 57-58, resident, 58-59; clin assoc & res biochemist, Nat Heart Inst, 59-63; from asst prof to assoc prof, 64-74, PROF PEDIAT, SCH MED, WASHINGTON UNIV, 74- *Concurrent Pos:* Am Cancer Soc fel, Lab Enzymol, Nat Ctr Sci Res, Gif-sur-Yvette, France, 63 & Dept Biochem & Genetics, Univ Wis, 63-64. *Mem:* AMA; Soc Pediat Res; Am Soc Human Genetics; Am Soc Clin Invest; Am Chem Soc. *Res:* Biochemical regulation; enveloped viruses as membrane probes in human diseases; lysosomal enzyme replacement in storage diseases; somatic cell genetics. *Mailing Add:* Div of Med Genetics St Louis Children's Hosp St Louis MO 63110

SLYE, JOHN MARSHALL, b Boulder, Colo, Nov 27, 23. PURE MATHEMATICS. *Educ:* Calif Inst Technol, BS, 45; Univ Tex, PhD(pure math), 53. *Prof Exp:* Technician physics cyclotron oper, Los Alamos Sci Lab, Calif, 46-48; instr pure math, Univ Tex, 50-53; from instr to assoc prof math, Univ Minn, Minneapolis, 53-69; ASSOC PROF MATH, UNIV HOUSTON, 69- *Mem:* AAAS; Am Math Soc; Am Phys Soc. *Res:* Two dimensional spaces; point set theory. *Mailing Add:* Dept of Math Univ of Houston Houston TX 77004

SLYH, JOHN A(LLEN), b Columbus, Ohio, July 24, 13; m 37, 51; c 2. CERAMICS ENGINEERING. *Educ:* Ohio State Univ, BCerE, 35. *Prof Exp:* Chem engr, Nat Carbon Co Div, Union Carbide & Carbon Corp, 35-46; res engr, Battelle Mem Inst, 46-48, asst supvr, 49-54; head res, Denver Fire Clay Co, Colo, 48-49; dir res, 54-61, vpres res & develop, 61-81, VPRES CONSULT, AM OLEAN TILE CO, INC, 81- *Mem:* Fel Am Ceramic Soc; Nat Inst Ceramic Engrs; Am Concrete Inst. *Res:* Development of activated carbon; special carbon and graphite; unusual concrete; whitewares; non-metallic minerals. *Mailing Add:* Am Olean Tile Co Inc 1000 N Cannon Ave Lansdale PA 19446

SLYKHUIS, JOHN TIMOTHY, b Carlyle, Sask, May 7, 20; m 46; c 5. PLANT PATHOLOGY. *Educ:* Univ Sask, BSA, 42, MSC, 43; Univ Toronto, PhD(plant path), 47. *Prof Exp:* Res plant pathologist, Sci Serv Lab, Can Dept Agr, Ont, 47-49; asst plant pathologist, SDak State Col, 49-52; plant pathologist, Sci Serv Lab, Can Dept Agr, Alta, 52-57, head plant virol sect, Plant Res Inst, 57-67, cereal virologist, Cent Exp Farm, Ottawa Res Sta, 67-76, PLANT PATHOLOGIST, RES STA, AGR CAN, SUMMERLAND, BC, 76- *Mem:* fel Am Phytopath Soc; fel Royal Soc Can; Can Phytopath Soc; Agr Inst Can. *Res:* Virus diseases of Gramineae; virus disease of fruit trees; replant diseases of apples. *Mailing Add:* Res Sta Agr Can Summerland BC V0H 1Z0 Can

SLYSH, ANTON ROMAN, b Kornicz, Ukraine, Apr 28, 21; nat US; m 64; c 2. BOTANY, MICROBIOLOGY. *Educ:* Univ Munich, BS, 50; Syracuse Univ, MS, 56; State Univ NY, PhD(mycol), 59. *Prof Exp:* Asst forest bot, State Univ NY Col Forestry, 56-58, asst mycol, 58-59; instr, Paul Smith's Col, 59-61; asst prof bot, Univ Tenn, 61-64; assoc prof, 64-69, PROF BOT, SHIPPENSBURG STATE COL, 69- *Mem:* Sigma Xi; NY Acad Sci; AAAS; Mycol Soc Am; Torrey Bot Club. *Res:* General botany; taxonomy of Thelephoraceae. *Mailing Add:* Dept of Biol Shippensburg State Col Shippensburg PA 17257

SLYSH, ROMAN STEPHAN, b Ukraine, June 11, 26; US citizen; m 54; c 4. POLYMER CHEMISTRY. *Educ:* Williams Col, BA, 53; Union Col, MS, 55; Pa State Univ, PhD(fuel sci, chem), 60. *Prof Exp:* Res asst chem, Pa State Univ, 55-59; from res chemist to sr res chemist, Esso Res & Eng Co, 59-70; sr scientist, 70-72, RES ASSOC, AMP, INC, 72- *Mem:* Am Chem Soc; Soc Plastics Eng. *Res:* Polymer modification; crosslinking; characterization and compounding; polymer composition; adhesives and sealants; adhesion to metals and plastics. *Mailing Add:* Res Div AMP Inc Harrisburg PA 17105

SLYTER, ARTHUR LOWELL, b Havre, Mont, Oct 23, 41; m 64; c 2. REPRODUCTIVE PHYSIOLOGY, ANIMAL SCIENCE. *Educ:* Kans State Univ, BS, 64, PhD(reproductive physiol), 69; Univ Nebr, Lincoln, MS, 66. *Prof Exp:* PROF ANIMAL SCI & LIVESTOCK RES, S DAK STATE UNIV, 70- *Mem:* Am Soc Animal Sci; Soc Study Reproduction. *Res:* Reproductive physiology and efficiency in beef cattle and sheep. *Mailing Add:* Dept of Animal Sci SDak State Univ Brookings SD 57007

SLYTER, LEONARD L, b Fontana, Kans, Nov 13, 33; m 48; c 2. MICROBIOLOGY, NUTRITION. *Educ:* Kans State Univ, BS, 55; Univ Mo, MS, 49; NC State Univ, PhD(animal nutrit), 63. *Prof Exp:* Res assoc bacteriol, Univ Ill, 62-64; res chemist animal sci, Res Div, USDA, 64-72, nutrit microbiol lab, Nutrit Inst, Agr Res Serv, 72-75, res chemist feed energy conserve lab, Animal Phys Genetics Inst, 75-78, RES MICROBIOL, RUMINAL NUTRIT LAB, ANIMAL SCI INST, AGR RES SERV, USDA, 79- *Mem:* Am Soc Microbiol; Am Soc Animal Sci. *Res:* Nutritional requirements, ecology and biochemical processes of microorganisms, particularly those involving ruminal bacteria and protozoa, pure and mixed cultures and continuous culture techniques. *Mailing Add:* Ruminal Nutrit Agr Res Serv USDA Animal Sci Inst Beltsville MD 20705

SLYWKA, GERALD WILLIAM ALEXANDER, b Hafford, Sask, Apr 23, 39; m 65; c 4. ANALYTICAL CHEMISTRY, TOXICOLOGY. *Educ:* Univ Sask, BSP, 61, MSc, 63; Univ Alta, PhD(pharmaceut chem), 69; Univ Tenn, BS, 76; Cent Mich Univ, MA, 78. *Prof Exp:* Res chemist, Food & Drug Directorate, Ottawa, Ont, 63-64; lectr pharm, Univ Sask, 64-65; toxicologist, Crime Detection Lab, Royal Can Mounted Police, Regina, Sask, 69-71, head toxicol sect, Vancouver, BC, 71-72; asst prof med chem & head anal sect, Col Pharm, Univ Tenn Ctr Health Sci, Memphis, 72-75; ASSOC PROF MED CHEM, SCH PHARM, FERRIS STATE COL, 75- *Mem:* Int Asn Forensic Toxicologists; Am Asn Cols Pharm; Am Asn Poison Control Ctrs. *Res:* Bioavailability; instrumentation; drug metabolism; drug abuse. *Mailing Add:* Sch of Pharm Ferris State Col Big Rapids MI 49307

SMAGORINSKY, JOSEPH, b New York, NY, Jan 29, 24; m 48; c 5. DYNAMIC METEOROLOGY. *Educ:* NY Univ, BS, 47, MS, 48, PhD(meteorol), 53. *Hon Degrees:* DSc, Univ Munich, 72. *Prof Exp:* Res & instr meteorol, NY Univ, 46-48; res meteorologist, US Weather Bur, 48-50; res meteorologist, Inst Adv Study, 50-53; head numerical weather prediction unit, Nat Weather Serv, 53-54, chief comput sect, Joint Numerical Weather Prediction Unit, 54-55, chief gen circulation res lab, 55-63, dir geophys fluid dynamics lab & dep dir meteorol res, 64-65, actg dir inst atmospheric sci, 65-66, DIR GEOPHYS FLUID DYNAMICS LAB, ENVIRON RES LABS, NAT OCEANIC & ATMOSPHERIC ADMIN, 65- *Concurrent Pos:* Mem comt atmospheric sci, panel weather & climate modification, Nat Acad Sci, 63, interdept comt comput tech, 64, panel on pollution, Presidential Sci Adv Comt, 65; vis prof, Princeton Univ, 68-; officer, Int Joint Organizing Comt Global Atmospheric Res Prog, 68-, chmn, Int Joint Sci Comt World Climate Res Prog, 80-81; vchmn, Nat Acad Sci-US Comt Global Atmospheric Res Prog, 67-73 & 80-, officer, 74-77, mem, Climate Bd, 77-, chmn, Climate Res Comt, 81- *Honors & Awards:* Gold Medal, US Dept Commerce, 66; Environ Sci Serv Admin Award, 70; Meisinger Award, Am Meteorol Soc, 67, Carl-Gustaf Rossby Res Medal, 72; Buvs Ballot Medal, Royal Netherlands Acad Arts & Sci, 73; Int Meteorol Orgn Prize, World Meteorol Orgn, 74; Symons Mem Award, Royal Meteorol Soc, 81. *Mem:* Fel Am Meteorol Soc; Royal Meteorol Soc. *Res:* Geophysical fluid dynamics and thermodynamics; geophysical applications of high speed computers; atmospheric general circulation and theory of climate; atmospheric predictability. *Mailing Add:* Geophys Fluid Dynamics Lab NOAA PO Box 308 Princeton NJ 08540

SMAIL, JAMES RICHARD, b Youngstown, Ohio, Dec 6, 34; m 58; c 2. EMBRYOLOGY, MARINE BIOLOGY. *Educ:* Oberlin Col, AB, 57; Univ Ill, PhD(zool), 65. *Prof Exp:* Instr, 63-65, asst prof, 65-72, ASSOC PROF BIOL, MACALESTER COL, 72- *Mem:* AAAS; Am Inst Biol Sci; Int Oceanog Found. *Res:* Mechanism of hatching in birds, especially the role of the musculus complexus in the hatching process; changes in surface ultrastructure of sea urchin eggs during cleavage; ecology of coral. *Mailing Add:* Dept of Biol Macalester Col St Paul MN 55105

SMALE, STEPHEN, b Flint, Mich, July 15, 30; m 54; c 2. MATHEMATICS. *Educ:* Univ Mich, BS, 52, MS, 53, PhD(math), 56. *Prof Exp:* Instr math, Univ Chicago, 56-58; mem Inst Adv Study, 58-60; assoc prof, Univ Calif, Berkeley, 60-61; prof, Columbia Univ, 61-64; PROF UNIV CALIF, BERKELEY, 64- *Honors & Awards:* Fields Medal, Int Union Math, 66; Veblen Prize, Am Math Soc, 66. *Mem:* Nat Acad Sci; Am Acad Arts & Sci; Int Union Math; Am Math Soc. *Res:* Differential topology; global analysis. *Mailing Add:* Dept of Math Univ of Calif Berkeley CA 94720

SMALL, ARNOLD MCCOLLUM, JR, b Springfield, Mo, Sept 16, 29; div; c 5. PSYCHOACOUSTICS. *Educ:* San Diego State Col, BA, 51; Univ Wis, MS, 53, PhD(psychol), 54. *Prof Exp:* Res assoc, Mass Inst Technol, 51; asst psychol, Univ Wis-Madison, 51-54; asst prof psychol & dir bioelec lab, Lehigh Univ, 54-58; from asst prof to assoc prof, 58-64, PROF SPEECH PATH, AUDIOL & PSYCHOL, UNIV IOWA, 64- *Concurrent Pos:* NIH fel, 54 & res grants, 56-58 & 68-73; NSF Res grants, 54-56, 60-66 & 77-80; Off Naval Res res grant, 54-58; vis scholar, Stanford Univ, 76-77; consult, Vet Admin, 63-, Radio Corp Am, 66 & Cent Inst Deaf, 78-; assoc ed, J Speech & Hearing Res, 58-64 & J Acoust Soc Am, 70-77. *Mem:* Fel AAAS; fel Am Speech & Hearing Asn; fel Acoust Soc Am; sr mem Inst Elec & Electronics Eng; Psychonomic Soc. *Res:* Psycho-acoustics and physiological acoustics; psychological and physiological aspects of sensory processes; audition; computer science. *Mailing Add:* Dept of Psychol Univ of Iowa 127C SHC Iowa City IA 52240

SMALL, DONALD BRIDGHAM, b Philadelphia, Pa, May 25, 35; m 60; c 3. MATHEMATICS. *Educ:* Middlebury Col, BA, 57; Univ Kans, MA, 59; Univ Conn, PhD(math), 68. *Prof Exp:* Instr math, Univ Conn, 60-67; asst prof, Eastern Conn State Col, 67-68; asst prof, 68-74, ASSOC PROF MATH, COLBY COL, 74-, CHMN DIV NAT SCI, 76- *Concurrent Pos:* Dir, Maine High Sch Lect Prog. *Mem:* Am Math Soc; Math Asn Am. *Res:* Number theory, especially continued fractions; graph theory. *Mailing Add:* Dept of Math Colby Col Waterville ME 04901

SMALL, ERNEST, b Ottawa, Ont, Mar 10, 40. BIOSYSTEMATICS. *Educ:* Carleton Univ, BA, 63, BSc, 65, MSc, 66; Univ Calif, Los Angeles, PhD(bot), 69. *Prof Exp:* RES BIOLOGIST & HEAD VASCULAR PLANT SECT, CAN DEPT AGR, 69- *Honors & Awards:* G M Cooley Award, Am Soc Plant Taxon, 74. *Mem:* Am Soc Plant Taxon; Int Asn Plant Taxon. *Res:* Systematics of cultivated plants. *Mailing Add:* 12 Gervin Nepean ON K2G 0J8 Can

SMALL, ERNEST WILLIAM, b Perth, Scotland, Apr 7, 20; m 45; c 4. ORAL SURGERY, MAXILLOFACIAL SURGERY. *Educ:* Univ Minn, BA, 43, DDS, 45; Am Bd Oral Surg, dipl, 64; Old Dom Univ, MS, 70. *Prof Exp:* Chief dent serv, Naval Hosp, Portsmouth, Va, 67-69; chief oral surg, Nat Naval Med Ctr, 69-72; PROF ORAL SURG & CHMN DEPT, DENT SCH, UNIV NC, CHAPEL HILL, 72-, PROF SURG, MED SCH, 72- *Concurrent Pos:* Oral surg consult, Surgeon Gen, US Navy, 69-72, Naval Grad Dent Sch, 72-74, Naval Hosp, Camp Lejeune, NC, 72-74 & Vet Hosp, Fayetteville, NC, 72-74; prof lectr, Georgetown Univ, 70-72 & George Washington Univ, 71-72. *Mem:* Fel Am Col Dent; fel Int Asn Oral Surgeons; fel Am Trauma Soc; Am Dent Asn; Am Soc Oral Surg. *Res:* Bone grafting; temporomandibular joint pain and dysfunction; facial pain. *Mailing Add:* Dept of Oral Surg Univ NC Sch of Dent Chapel Hill NC 27514

SMALL, ERWIN, b Boston, Mass, Nov 28, 24. VETERINARY MEDICINE. *Educ:* Univ Ill, BS, 55, DVM, 57, MS, 65. *Prof Exp:* Intern, Angell Mem Hosp, Boston, Mass, 57-58; from instr to assoc prof, 58-67, PROF VET CLIN MED, UNIV ILL, URBANA, 67-, HEAD SMALL ANIMAL MED, COL VET MED, 70-, ASSOC DEAN ALUMNI & PUB AFFAIRS, 78- *Concurrent Pos:* Fel, Nat Heart Inst, 65 & Morris Animal Found, 67-68. *Mem:* NY Acad Sci; Sigma Xi; Am Col Vet Dermat (pres, 79-82). *Res:* Serodiagnostic and immunologic approaches to the study of hemotrophic parasites. *Mailing Add:* Col of Vet Med Univ Ill 1008 W Hazelwood Urbana IL 61801

SMALL, EUGENE BEACH, b Reed City, Mich, Jan 7, 31; m 65; c 4. PROTISTOLOGY, MICROBIAL ECOLOGY. *Educ:* Wayne State Univ, BS, 53, MS, 56; Univ Calif, Los Angeles, PhD(zool), 64. *Prof Exp:* Asst prof zool, Univ Ill, 64-70; ASSOC PROF ZOOL, UNIV MD, COLLEGE PARK, 70- *Mem:* Soc Prototozoologists (treas, 62-64); Am Micros Soc; AAAS; Soc Evolutionary Protistologists; Sigma Xi. *Res:* Protistan organisms: their morphology, morphogenesis, ecology, and evolutionary history; development of electron microscopical techniques applicable to the study of unicellular organisms; systematics of the phylum ciliophora. *Mailing Add:* Dept Zool Univ Md College Park MD 20742

SMALL, GARY D, b Atkinson, Nebr, Oct 17, 37; m 64; c 2. BIOCHEMISTRY. *Educ:* Nebr State Col, BS, 59; Western Reserve Univ, PhD(biochem), 65. *Prof Exp:* Nat Cancer Inst feldept biochem, Univ Wash, 65-67; asst prof, 67-73, assoc prof, 73-76, PROF BIOCHEM, UNIV S DAK, 76- *Concurrent Pos:* Vis biochemist, Nat Cancer Inst fel, Brookhaven Nat Lab, 74-75. *Mem:* AAAS; Am Chem Soc; Am Soc Biol Chemists; Am Soc Photobiol. *Res:* Enzymology of nucleases; effects of ultraviolet radiation on nucleic acids; biological repair of nucleic acid damage. *Mailing Add:* Dept of Biochem Univ of SDak Vermillion SD 57069

SMALL, HAMISH, b Antrim, Northern Ireland, Oct 5, 29; US citizen; m 54; c 2. PHYSICAL CHEMISTRY, ANALYTICAL CHEMISTRY. *Educ:* Queen's Univ, Belfast, BSc, 49, MSc, 52. *Prof Exp:* Chemist phys chem, Atomic Energy Res Estab, Eng, 49-55; chemist, 55-62, sr res chemist, 62-63, assoc scientist, 63-74, RES SCIENTIST PHYS CHEM, DOW CHEM CO, 74- *Honors & Awards:* Appl Anal Chem Award, Soc Anal Chemists Pittsburgh, 77; Albert F Sperry Medal, Instrument Soc Am, 78. *Mem:* Sigma Xi; Am Chem Soc. *Res:* Separation science; liquid chromatography; hydrodynamic chromatography; ion chromatography. *Mailing Add:* 3810 Moorland Dr Midland MI 48640

SMALL, IVER FRANCIS, b Sask, Can, Sept 19, 23; US citizen; m 54; c 4. PSYCHIATRY. *Educ:* Univ Sask, BA, 51; Univ Man, MD, 54; Univ Mich, MS, 60. *Prof Exp:* Asst prof psychiat, Med Sch & dir inserv psychiat, Hosp, Univ Ore, 60-62; dir inpatient serv psychiat, Malcolm Bliss Ment Health Ctr, 62-65; assoc prof, 65-69, PROF PSYCHIAT, SCH MED, IND UNIV, INDIANAPOLIS, 69-; ASST SUPT PSYCHIAT, LARUE D CARTER MEM HOSP, 65- *Concurrent Pos:* Asst prof psychiat, Sch Med, Washington Univ, 62-65; vis physician, Unit I, St Louis City Hosp, 6265. *Mem:* AMA; Soc Biol Psychiat (secy-treas, 70-); Am Psychiat Asn. *Res:* Work in clinical psychiatry; follow-up studies; the convulsive therapies; and the neuropsychology of mental illness. *Mailing Add:* Larue D Carter Mem Hosp 1315 W Tenth St Indianapolis IN 46202

SMALL, JAMES DAVID, b Oak Park, Ill, Aug 19, 37. VETERINARY MEDICINE, MICROBIOLOGY. *Educ:* Elmhurst Col, BS, 59; Southern Ill Univ, Carbondale, MA, 60; Univ Ill, Champaign, DVM, 64; Johns Hopkins Univ, MPH, 70; Am Col Lab Animal Med, dipl. *Prof Exp:* Vet, Nat Heart Inst, USPHS, 64-66, vet-pharmacologist, Food & Drug Admin, 66-68, vet-scientist, Nat Inst Dent Res, 68-73, vet, Vet Resources Br, 73-81, HEAD, DIAG & RES LAB, NAT INST ENVIRON HEALTH SCI, NIH, USPHS, 81- *Concurrent Pos:* USPHS fel, Johns Hopkins Univ, 68-71. *Mem:* AAAS; NY Acad Sci; Am Vet Med Asn; Am Asn Lab Animal Sci. *Res:* Immunology; host-parasite relationships; endotoxin; diseases and management of laboratory animals, especially rodents and rabbits. *Mailing Add:* Nat Inst Environ Health Sci PO Box 12233 Research Triangle Park NC 27709

SMALL, JAMES GRAYDON, b Seattle, Wash, Feb 10, 45; m 75. QUANTUM OPTICS, MEDICAL ULTRASOUND. *Educ:* Mass Inst Technol, BS, 67, PhD(physics), 74. *Prof Exp:* Lectr, Univ Ariz, 74-75, asst prof optical sci, 75-80, adj asst prof surg, 79-80; ASSOC PROF PHYSICS & ASSOC DIR, INST MODGAN OPTICS, UNIV NMEX, 80- *Mem:* Optical Soc Am. *Res:* Applications of stable lasers; special relativity; aids for blind. *Mailing Add:* Dept Physics & Astron Univ NMex Albuquerque NM 87131

SMALL, JOHN, JR, b Hartford, Conn, May 28, 31; m 78; c 4. GEOLOGY, GEOPHYSICS. *Educ:* Mass Inst Technol, BS, 52; Univ Colo, PhD(geol), 62. *Prof Exp:* Geol observer, Calif Co, Standard Oil Co Calif, La, 52-54; field & compilation geologist, Richmond Petrol Co, Colombia, 56-58, regional geologist, Calif Ecuador Petrol Co, 58-60, geophysicist, Calif Co, La, 60-61, regional geologist, Dom Oil Ltd, WI, 61-62, lead geologist, 62-65, subsurface geologist, Standard Oil Co Tex, 65, lead regional geologist, Am Overseas Petrol Ltd, The Hague, Netherlands, 65-69, sr geologist, Madrid, Spain, 69-71, geol supvr, 71-73, proj leader-staff geologist, Chevron Overseas Petrol, Inc, 73-76; explor mgr, 76-80, MGR, NEW FOREIGN VENTURES, NORSK HYDRO, 81- *Mem:* Am Asn Petrol Geol; Norwegian Geol Soc. *Res:* Exploration petroleum geology and geophysics in North Sea. *Mailing Add:* Norsk Hydro PO Box 2594 Solli Oslo 2 Norway

SMALL, JOYCE G, b Edmonton, Alta, June 12, 31; US citizen; m 54; c 4. PSYCHIATRY. *Educ:* Univ Sask, BA, 51; Univ Man, MD, 56; Univ Mich, MS, 59; Am Bd Psychiat & Neurol, dipl, 61. *Prof Exp:* Intern, Winnipeg Gen Hosp, Man, 5556; resident psychiat, Ypsilanti State Hosp, Mich, 56-59; instr, Neuropsychiat Inst, Univ Mich, 59-60; from instr to asst prof, Sch Med, Univ Ore, 60-62; clin dir, Malcolm Bliss Ment Health Ctr, 62-65; asst prof psychiat, Sch Med, Washington Univ, 62-65; assoc prof, 65-69, PROF PSYCHIAT, SCH MED, IND UNIV, INDIANAPOLIS, 69-; CLIN DIR, LARUE D CARTER MEM HOSP, 65- *Concurrent Pos:* Teaching fel biochem, Univ Man, 55-56; res assoc neurol & psychiat consult, Crippled Children's Div, Med Sch, Univ Ore, 60-62; vis physician, St Louis City Hosps, 62-65; attend staff mem, Vet Admin Hosp, Indianapolis, 65-69. *Mem:* AAAS; fel Am Psychiat Asn; Soc Neurosci; Am Electroencephalog Soc; Soc Biol Psychiat. *Res:* Clinical psychiatry; electroencephalography; neurophysiology; computers. *Mailing Add:* Larue D Carter Mem Hosp Indianapolis IN 46202

SMALL, LAVERNE DOREYN, b Black Earth, Wis, Dec 22, 16; m 38; c 2. MEDICINAL CHEMISTRY. *Educ:* Univ Minn, BS, 38, MS, 43, PhD(pharmaceut chem), 45. *Prof Exp:* Pharmacist, Walgreen Drug Co, Minn, 38-40; pharmacist, Johnson Co, Minn, 40-42; res chemist, Sterling-Winthrop Res Inst, 45-48; assoc prof pharmaceut chem, 48-54, prof & chmn pharm & pharmaceut chem, 54-73, prof med chem & pharmacog, 73-80, PROF BIOMED CHEM, COL PHARM, UNIV NEBR, 80- *Mem:* Am Chem Soc; Am Pharmaceut Asn. *Res:* cardiac drugs and organic sulfur compounds. *Mailing Add:* 1540 Sunburst Lane Lincoln NE 68506

SMALL, LAWRENCE FREDERICK, b St Louis, Mo, Feb 16, 34; m 63; c 3. BIOLOGICAL OCEANOGRAPHY. *Educ:* Univ Mo, AB, 55; Iowa State Univ, MS, 59, PhD(zool), 61. *Prof Exp:* Instr limnol, Iowa State Univ, 60-61; from asst prof to assoc prof, 61-72, PROF BIOL OCEANOG, ORE STATE UNIV, 72- *Concurrent Pos:* NSF fels, 61-64 & 70-72, res grant, 73-79; AEC fel, 63-66; USPHS training grant, 63-, fel, 64-67; EPA res grant, 77-79; Int AEC spec serv res award, Monaco, 70-71 & 77-78; Nat Acad Sci res grant, Yugoslavia, 72; res grant sea grant, Nat Oceanic & Atmospheric Asn, 72; res contract, US Army Corps of Engrs, 74. *Mem:* AAAS; Am Soc Limnol & Oceanog; Sigma Xi; Phycological Soc. *Res:* Phytoplankton ecology and physiology; energy and material transfer in lower marine trophic levels. *Mailing Add:* Ore State Univ Sch of Oceanog Corvallis OR 97331

SMALL, PARKER ADAMS, JR, b Cincinnati, Ohio, July 5, 32; m 56; c 3. IMMUNOLOGY, MEDICINE. *Educ:* Univ Cincinnati, MD, 57. *Prof Exp:* Intern med, Univ Pa Hosp, Philadelphia, 57-58; res assoc immunol, USPHS, 58-60, surgeon, NIMH, 61-64, sr surgeon, Sect Phys Chem, 64-66; chmn dept, 66-76, PROF IMMUNOL & MED MICROBIOL, COL MED, UNIV FLA, 66- *Concurrent Pos:* USPHS res fel, 55 & spec fel, 60; res fel, Wright-Fleming Inst Microbiol, St Mary's Hosp Med Sch, 60-61; vis prof immunol, Univ Lausanne, 72; vis scholar, Asn Am Med Cols, 73; consult, Med Scientist Training Comt, Nat Inst Gen Med Sci & WHO. *Mem:* AAAS; Fedn Am Scientists; Am Asn Immunologists. *Res:* Host defense against influenza; medical education. *Mailing Add:* Dept of Immunol & Med Microbiol Univ of Fla Col of Med Box 266 Gainesville FL 32610

SMALL, ROBERT JAMES, b Philadelphia, Pa, Nov 23, 38; m 63; c 2. ORGANIC CHEMISTRY, PHOTOCHEMISTRY. *Educ:* Norwich Univ, BS, 61; Tex Tech Univ, MS, 64; Univ Ariz, PhD(org chem), 71. *Prof Exp:* Fel org chem, Univ Ky, 72-73; res chemist, Celanese Chem Co, 73-74; sr res chemist org chem, Ashland Chem Co, 74-80; PROJ LEADER, CIBA-GEIGY CORP, 80- *Mem:* Am Chem Soc; Royal Soc Chemists; Am Inst Chemists; Sigma Xi. *Res:* Heterogenous and homogenous catalytic oxidation of olefins and heterogenous oxidative dehydrogenation of aliphatic systems; process development of reductive methylation of amines and hydrazine derivatives; photochemistry of oximes. *Mailing Add:* Ciba-Geigy Corp Box 113 McIntosh AL 36553

SMALL, SAUL MOUCHLY, b New York, NY, Oct 11, 13; m 37; c 4. PSYCHIATRY. *Educ:* City Col New York, BS, 33; Cornell Univ, MD, 37; Am Bd Psychiat & Neurol, dipl. *Prof Exp:* Asst psychiat, Med Col & asst res psychiat, Inst Human Rels, Yale Univ, 38-39; from asst resident to resident psychiatrist, Payne Whitney Clin, Cornell Univ, 39-43, instr psychiat, Univ, 40-43; asst med dir & psychiat consult, Nat Hosp Speech Dis, 43-47; lectr psychiat, Columbia Univ, 48-51, prof psychiat & chmn dept, Sch Med, State Univ NY, Buffalo, 51-78; head psychiat, Buffalo Gen Hosp, 63-78. *Concurrent Pos:* Consult, Vassar Col, 43-47; psychiatrist, Rehab Ctr, NY Hosp, 44-46; from adj attend psychiatrist to assoc attend psychiatrist, Mt Sinai Hosp, 46-51, Clarence P Oberndorf vis psychiatrist, 66; consult to Surgeon Gen, US Army, 47-; consult, Buffalo Gen Hosp, 51-; dir psychiat, E J Meyer Mem Hosp, Buffalo, 51-68 & 74-78 med coordr, Dept Psychiat, 68-74; consult & lectr, US Vet Admin, chief consult & mem, Dean's Comt, Vet Admin Hosp, Buffalo, 52-; examr, US Info Agency, 59-62; chmn, Part III Comt, Patient Mgt Problems, Nat Bd Med Examrs, 60-; univ chief, dept Psychiat, Buffalo Children's Hosp, 68-; chmn, Sci Adv Coun, Muscular Dystrophy Asn, Inc; mem corp, Am Col Psychiatrists, Bd Regents; dir, Am Bd Psychiat & Neurol, mem, Part I Exam Comt; pres, Muscular Dystrophy Asn Inc, 80- *Honors & Awards:* Stockton Kimbell Fac Award, 65. *Mem:* AMA; Am Psychoanal Asn; Asn Am Med Cols; Am Psychosom Soc; life fel Am Psychiat Asn. *Res:* Anorexia nervosa; psychology of chemical warfare; unconscious determination of vocational choice; stuttering; physiological validation of psychoanalytic theory; psychodynamic factors in surgery; psychopathology of alcoholism; hyperbaric oxygen effect on cognition and behavior in the aged; continuing medical education for psychiatrists; evaluation, self-assessment. *Mailing Add:* Erie County Med Ctr 462 Grider St Buffalo NY 14215

SMALL, TIMOTHY MICHAEL, b Muncie, Ind, Sept 29, 40; m 75; c 4. RESEARCH ADMINISTRATION, TECHNICAL MANAGEMENT. *Educ:* Ind Univ, BS, 63, MS, 64, PhD(physics), 68. *Prof Exp:* Teaching assoc, Ind Univ, 63-64, from res asst to res assoc physics, 64-68; res physicist, US Army Nuclear Effects Lab, Edgewood Arsenal, 68-70; actg mgr proj eng, Gen Elec Mgt & Tech Serv Dept, NASA Miss Test Facil, 70-71; res physicist, 71-78, develop proj officer, 78-81, TECH ASST, MOBILITY EQUIP RES & DEVELOP COMMAND, US ARMY, 81- *Mem:* Am Phys Soc; AAAS; Sigma Xi. *Res:* Applications of nuclear physics to detection of objects; nuclear interactions and activation; x-ray fluorescence and backscatter; radiation transport; nuclear instrumentation; detection statistics and high energy physics. *Mailing Add:* DRDME-N Mobility Equip Res & Develop Command Ft Belvoir VA 22060

SMALL, WILLIAM ANDREW, b Cobleskill, NY, Oct 16, 14; m 39; c 1. MATHEMATICS. *Educ:* US Naval Acad, BS, 36; Univ Rochester, AB, 50, AM, 52, PhD(math), 58. *Prof Exp:* Instr math, DeVeaux Sch, NY, 45-48; instr Univ Rochester, 51-55; asst prof, Alfred Univ, 55-56; asst prof, Grinnell Col, 56-58, assoc prof & chmn dept, 58-60; prof, Tenn Polytech Inst, 60-62; chmn dept, 62-68, PROF MATH, STATE UNIV NY COL GENESEO, 62- *Concurrent Pos:* Fulbright-Hays lectr, Univ Aleppo, 64-65; assoc ed, Philosophia Mathematica. *Mem:* Math Asn Am. *Res:* Mathematical theory of probability; philosophy and history of mathematics; mathematical statistics. *Mailing Add:* 28 Court St Geneseo NY 14454

SMALLEY, ALFRED EVANS, b Chester, Pa, Feb 29, 28; div; c 2. ECOLOGY. *Educ:* Pa State Univ, BS, 50, MS, 52; Univ Ga, PhD(zool), 59. *Prof Exp:* Instr biol, Univ Ky, 58-59; from instr to assoc prof, 59-75, PROF BIOL, TULANE UNIV LA, 75- *Mem:* Am Soc Limnol & Oceanog; Soc Syst Zool; Ecol Soc Am; Am Ornith Union. *Res:* Ecology of aquatic ecosystems; marine invertebrate zoology; taxonomy of decapod crustacea. *Mailing Add:* Dept Biol Tulane Univ New Orleans LA 70118

SMALLEY, ARNOLD WINFRED, b Shreveport, La, Aug 2, 33; m 66. ORGANIC CHEMISTRY. *Educ:* Wiley Col, BS, 59; Univ Kans, MS, 62; Univ Mass, PhD(org chem), 65. *Prof Exp:* ASSOC PROF CHEM, SOUTHERN UNIV, BATON ROUGE, 65- *Mem:* Am Chem Soc. *Res:* Stabilities of metallocenyl substituted cations; electrophilic substitution reactions of metallocenes; quaternary phosphonium hydroxide decompositions; organic pollutants in municipal water supplies. *Mailing Add:* Dept of Chem Southern Univ Baton Rouge LA 70813

SMALLEY, EDMUND WALTER, b Ottawa, Ill, Apr 27, 28; m 57; c 2. INORGANIC CHEMISTRY. *Educ:* Univ Utah, BS, 52; Univ Pittsburgh, PhD(inorg chem), 64. *Prof Exp:* Anal chemist atomic energy div, Nat Reactor Testing Sta, Am Cyanamid Co, Idaho, 53, anal chemist pilot plant W, Cent Res Div, Conn, 53-56, anal chemist, Stamford Res Lab, 56-59; sr chemist, Indust Chem Div, Allied Chem Corp, Syracuse, 64-80, SR RES CHEMIST, ALLIED CHEMICAL, BUFFALO, 80- *Mem:* Am Chem Soc. *Res:* Chemistry of organo-metallic compounds; electrochemistry. *Mailing Add:* Allied Chemical 20 Peabody St Buffalo NY 14210

SMALLEY, EUGENE BYRON, b Los Angeles, Calif, July 11, 26; m 55; c 5. PLANT PATHOLOGY. *Educ:* Univ Calif, Los Angeles, BS, 49, Univ Calif, MS, 53, PhD(plant path), 57. *Prof Exp:* Asst plant path, Univ Calif, 53-56; asst prof plant path & forestry, 57-64, assoc prof plant path, 64-69, PROF PLANT PATH, UNIV WIS-MADISON, 69- *Mem:* Am Phytopath Soc. *Res:* Forest pathology; vascular wilts of woody plants; diseases of garlic; mycotoxins; dutch elm disease. *Mailing Add:* Dept Plant Path Univ Wis 1630 Linden Dr Madison WI 53706

SMALLEY, GLENDON WILLIAM, b Bridgeton, NJ, Jan 23, 28; m 54; c 2. FOREST SOILS, SILVICULTURE. *Educ:* Mich State Univ, BS, 52, MS, 56; Univ Tenn, PhD, 75. *Prof Exp:* Forester, Sam Houston Nat Forest, Southern Region, US Forest Serv, 53-55, forester & asst dist ranger, Ouachita Nat Forest, 55-56, res forester, Southern Forest Exp Sta, Birmingham Res Ctr, 56-63, Silvicult Lab, 63-74, RES SOIL SCIENTIST SILVICULT LAB, SOUTHERN FOREST EXP STA, USDA FOREST SERV, SEWANEE, TENN, 74- *Mem:* Soc Am Foresters; Soil Sci Soc Am; Am Soc Agron; Ecol Soc Am. *Res:* Detailed planning, conducting, supervising and evaluating fundamental and applied research in forest soils for Cumberland Plateau and Highland Rim regions of Tennessee and Alabama. *Mailing Add:* Silvicult Lab US Forest Serv SPO Box 1290 Sewanee TN 37375

SMALLEY, HARRY EDWIN, b Brooklyn, NY, Oct 23, 24; m 61; c 2. VETERINARY TOXICOLOGY. *Educ:* Trinity Univ, BS, 51, MS, 55; Tex A&M Univ, DVM, 59; Am Bd Vet Toxicol, dipl. *Prof Exp:* Biologist, Tex State Dept Health, Austin, 51-52; sanitarian, San Antonio Health Dept, 52-53; parasitologist, Grad Sch Med, Baylor Univ, 53-55; vet agr res serv, USDA, DC, 59-61, inspector chg, 61-63; res vet pharmacol div, US Food & Drug Admin, 64-66; vet toxicol & entom res lab, 66-73, RES LEADER VET

TOXICOL RES GROUP, AGR RES SERV, USDA, 73-, LAB DIR VET TOXICOL & ENTOM RES LAB, 74- *Concurrent Pos:* Area consult, Vector Control Surv, WHO-Pan-Am Sanit Bur, 52-53; panel mem, US Civil Serv Bd Exam Lab Animal Officers, 64-; tech adv agr res serv, USDA, 74-; consult ed, J Environ Qual, 75- *Mem:* Am Bd Vet Toxicol (secy-treas, pres, 73-76); AAAS; Am Col Vet Toxicol; Soc Toxicol; Am Vet Med Asn. *Res:* Action of pesticides and drugs on reproduction and teratology; comparative toxicology; ectoparasite pathology; disease vectors identification and control; research administration; toxicology of insect growth regulators. *Mailing Add:* Vet Toxicol & Entom Res Lab PO Box GE College Station TX 77840

SMALLEY, LARRY L, b Grand Island, Nebr, Aug 7, 37; m 57; c 3. GENERAL RELATIVITY. *Educ:* Univ Nebr, BS, 59, MS, 64, PhD, 67. *Prof Exp:* Instr physics, US Naval Nuclear Power Sch, Conn, 61-62; asst prof, 67-73, assoc prof, 73-80, CHMN DEPT, UNIV ALA, HUNTSVILLE, 73-, PROF, 80- *Concurrent Pos:* Asst reactor engr, Hallam Nuclear Power Fac, Nebr, 65; res physicist, Phys Sci Lab, Army Missile Command, Redstone Arsenel, 68; Nat Acad Sci/Nat Res Coun sr fel, NASA, 74-75; Humboldt fel, Univ Colgne, 76-77 & 80. *Mem:* Am Phys Soc; Sigma Xi. *Res:* Theoretical physics, especially gravitational physics and discrete spacetime. *Mailing Add:* Dept Physics Univ Ala Huntsville AL 35807

SMALLEY, RALPH RAY, b Starkey, NY, Aug 26, 19; m 46; c 3. AGRONOMY. *Educ:* Cornell Univ, BS, 50, MS, 51; Univ Fla, PhD(soil fertil), 61. *Prof Exp:* Asst prof soils & crops, State Univ NY Agr & Tech Col Farmingdale, 51-58; res asst turfgrass, Univ Fla, 58-61, turf technologist, 61-62; PROF SOILS & TURFGRASS, STATE UNIV NY AGR & TECH COL COBLESKILL, 62- *Mem:* Am Soc Agron. *Res:* Effect of amendments on the physical and chemical properties of soil; turfgrass production and management. *Mailing Add:* State Univ of NY Agr & Tech Col Cobleskill NY 12043

SMALLEY, RICHARD ERRETT, b Akron, Ohio, June 6, 43; m 68; c 1. CHEMICAL PHYSICS. *Educ:* Univ Mich, BS, 65; Princeton Univ, MA, 71, PhD(chem), 73. *Prof Exp:* Res chemist, Shell Chem Co, 65-69; res assoc chem, Univ Chicago, 73-76; ASST PROF CHEM, RICE UNIV, 76- *Mem:* Am Phys Soc; Am Inst Physics; Am Chem Soc. *Res:* Spectroscopic study of the unperturbed gas-phase structure and elementary chemical and photophysical processes of polyatomic molecules, radicals, and ions, including simple clusters of these with each other and with atoms. *Mailing Add:* Dept of Chem Rice Univ Houston TX 77001

SMALLEY, ROBERT GORDON, b Chicago, Ill, June 1, 21; m 46; c 2. GEOLOGY, GEOCHEMISTRY. *Educ:* Univ Chicago, SB, 42, MS, 43, PhD, 48. *Prof Exp:* Geologist, US Geol Surv, 43-44; geologist, Stand Oil Co, Calif, 48-49, res geologist, La Habra Lab, Calif Res Corp, 49-59, sr res geologist, 59-66, SR RES ASSOC GEOCHEM, CHEVRON RES CO, 66- *Mem:* Geol Soc Am; Geochem Soc; Soc Appl Spectros. *Res:* Geochemistry of sediments and sedimentary rocks, carbonates and natural waters; petrology; igneous and metamorphic rocks; economic and petroleum geology. *Mailing Add:* Chevron Oil Field Res Co PO Box 446 La Habra CA 90631

SMALLEY, ROBERT LEE, b Mt Auburn, Iowa, Sept 30, 31; m 59; c 2. BIOCHEMISTRY. *Educ:* Grinnell Col, BA, 53; Univ Iowa, MS, 60, PhD(biochem), 63. *Prof Exp:* Fel biochem, Univ Iowa, 63-64; PROF CHEM, EMPORIA STATE UNIV, 64- *Mem:* AAAS; Am Chem Soc; Am Oil Chem Soc. *Res:* Ontogeny of brown and white fats; ultrastructure of pathological tissues; metabolic adaptations in recovering alcoholics; metabolism of developing hereditarily obese mice; cold adaptation of invertebrates. *Mailing Add:* Dept Chem Emporia State Univ Emporia KS 66801

SMALLWOOD, CHARLES, JR, b Philadelphia, Pa, May 20, 20; m 44; c 3. SANITARY ENGINEERING. *Educ:* Case Western Reserve Univ, BS, 42; Harvard Univ, SM, 48. *Prof Exp:* Jr engr, Utilities Installation, US Eng Dept, Mich, 42-43; jr engr, Havens & Emerson, Consult Engrs, 46; asst, Harvard Univ, 46-48; asst prof civil eng, 50-52, assoc prof, 52-58, grad adminr, 58-77, PROF CIVIL ENG, NC STATE UNIV, 58- *Concurrent Pos:* Consult, Charles T Main, Inc, NC, 50- & J Harwood Beebe, SC, 56- *Mem:* Am Soc Civil Engrs; Am Water Works Asn; Water Pollution Control Fedn. *Res:* Biological treatment of wastes; hydrology; hydraulics; analysis of industrial wastes; radioactive wastes. *Mailing Add:* Dept of Civil Eng NC State Univ Ralcigh NC 27607

SMALLWOOD, RICHARD DALE, b Portsmouth, Ohio, Oct 9, 35; m 59; c 3. OPERATIONS RESEARCH, SYSTEMS ANALYSIS. *Educ:* Mass Inst Technol, SB, 57, SM, 58, ScD(elec eng), 62. *Prof Exp:* Lectr opers res, Mass Inst Technol, 62-64; asst prof eng-econ systs, Stanford Univ, 64-67, assoc prof, 67-73; res scientist anal res, Xerox Palo Alto Res Ctr, 73-79; PRES, APPL DECISION ANAL, INC, 79- *Concurrent Pos:* Consult prof, Dept Eng-Econ Systs, Stanford Univ, 73-; consult var govt & indust orgn. *Mem:* Inst Mgt Sci; Opers Res Soc Am; Inst Elec & Electronics Engrs. *Res:* Decision analysis; market analysis systems; modeling; man-machine systems; analysis of health care systems. *Mailing Add:* 1795 Hamilton Ave Palo Alto CA 94303

SMALTZ, JACOB JAY, b Fulton, Ill, June 14, 17; m 35; c 2. ENGINEERING COMPUTING. *Educ:* Bradley Univ, BS, 39; Kans State Univ, MS, 46. *Prof Exp:* Instr mach shop, 40-46, asst prof motion & time study safety, 46-49, assoc prof, 49-52, dir ctr occup safety & health, 77-79, PROF INDUST ENG, KANS STATE UNIV, 52-, DIR, ENG COMPUT CTR, 63- *Mem:* Inst Indust Engrs; Am Soc Eng Educ; Am Soc Safety Engrs; Asn Comput Mach; Am Conf Govt Indust Hygienists. *Res:* Computers; occupational safety and health; manufacturing processes. *Mailing Add:* Dept of Indust Eng Kans State Univ Manhattan KS 66506

SMARDZEWSKI, RICHARD ROMAN, b Nanticoke, Pa, July 4, 42. SURFACE CHEMISTRY. *Educ:* King's Col, Pa, BS, 64; Iowa State Univ, Ames, PhD(inorg chem), 69. *Prof Exp:* Sci Res Coun fel inorg chem, Univ Leicester, Eng, 69-70; NSF fel phys chem, Univ Va, Charlottesville, 71-72;

Nat Res Coun res assoc, 72-74, res chemist inorg chem, 74-79, HEAD, ADVAN SURFACE SPECTROSCOPY SECT, NAVAL RES LAB, WASHINGTON, DC, 79- *Concurrent Pos:* Adv, Nat Res Coun, Washington, DC. *Mem:* Am Chem Soc; Am Inst Chemists; Sigma Xi; Am Vacuum Soc. *Res:* Surface spectroscopy and analysis. *Mailing Add:* Naval Res Lab Code 6170 4555 Overlook Ave SW Washington DC 20375

SMARR, LARRY LEE, b Columbia, Mo, Oct 16, 48; m 73; c 1. BLACK HOLES, RADIO JETS. *Educ:* Univ Mo, BA & MS, 70; Stanford Univ, MS, 72; Univ Tex, Austin, PhD(physics), 75. *Prof Exp:* Lectr astrophysics, Dept Astrophysical Sci, Princeton Univ, 74-75, res asst, Observ, 75-76; res affil, Dept Physics, Yale Univ, 78-79; jr fel physics, Dept Physics & Astron, Harvard Soc Fellows, 76-79; asst prof, 79-81, ASSOC PROF ASTROPHYSICS, DEPT ASTRON & PHYSICS, UNIV ILL, 81- *Concurrent Pos:* B Div, Lawrence Livermore Nat Lab, 76-79, consult, 76-; vis fel, Cambridge Univ, 78; assoc ed, J Comput Physic, 77-80; consult, Smithsonian Astrophys Observ, 79-; mem, Subcomt Comput Facil Theoret Physics, NSF, 81. *Mem:* Am Phys Soc; Am Astron Soc; Int Soc Gen Relativity & Gravitation. *Res:* Relativistic astrophysics; radio galaxies; numerical relativity; numerical hydrodynamics. *Mailing Add:* 314 Astron Bldg Univ Ill 1011 W Springfield Ave Urbana IL 61801

SMART, BRUCE EDMUND, b Philadelphia, Pa, Oct 9, 45; m 69. PHYSICAL ORGANIC CHEMISTRY. *Educ:* Univ Mo-Kansas City, BS(chem) & BS(math), 67; Univ Calif, Berkeley, PhD(chem), 70. *Prof Exp:* RES SUPVR, E I DU PONT DE NEMOURS & CO, INC, 70- *Mem:* Am Chem Soc (secy-treas, 78-79). *Res:* Organofluorine chemistry; small ring systems; carbonium ion chemistry; molecular rearrangements. *Mailing Add:* Cent Res Dept Exp Sta E I du Pont de Nemours & Co Wilmington DE 19898

SMART, CHARLES WILLIAM, organic chemistry, deceased

SMART, G N RUSSELL, b Montreal, Que, May 28, 21; m 46; c 3. ORGANIC CHEMISTRY. *Educ:* McGill Univ, BSc, 42, PhD(org chem), 45. *Prof Exp:* Asst, McGill Univ, 42-44; lectr chem, 44-45; Nat Res Coun Can fel, Univ Toronto, 45-46; res fel, Iowa State Univ, 46-47; from asst prof to assoc prof, 47-58, PROF CHEM, MUHLENBERG COL, 58-, HEAD DEPT, 62- *Concurrent Pos:* Indust consult; exec dir, Tuition Exchange, Inc. *Honors & Awards:* Lindback Distinguished Teaching Award, 61. *Mem:* Sigma Xi; Am Asn Univ Prof; Am Chem Soc. *Res:* Stereochemistry; conformational analysis; organometallic and organosilicon chemistry; explosives. *Mailing Add:* Dept of Chem Muhlenburg Col Allentown PA 18104

SMART, GROVER CLEVELAND, JR, b Stuart, Va, Nov 6, 29; m 57; c 2. AGRICULTURE, NEMATOLOGY. *Educ:* Univ Va, BA, 57; Univ Wis, PhD(plant path), 60. *Prof Exp:* Asst biol, Univ Va, 56-57; res asst plant path, Univ Wis, 57-60; asst prof plant path & physiol, Tidewater Res Sta, Va, Agr Exp Sta, Va Polytech Inst, 60-64; from asst prof to assoc prof, 64-73, asst chmn, 76-79, actg chmn, 79-80, PROF NEMATOL, INST FOOD & AGR SCI, UNIV FLA, 73-, ASST CHMN, DEPT ENTOMOL & NEMATOL, 80- *Mem:* Soc Nematologists; Sigma Xi; Soc Europ Nematol; Orgn Trop Am Nematol. *Res:* Biological control of plant parasitic nematodes; morphology of nematodes. *Mailing Add:* Dept Entom & Nematol 3103 McCarty Hall Univ of Fla Inst Food & Agr Sci Gainesville FL 32611

SMART, JAMES BLAIR, b Des Moines, Iowa, Oct 6, 36; m 63; c 3. PHYSICAL INORGANIC CHEMISTRY, CLINICAL CHEMISTRY. *Educ:* Carroll Col (Mont), BA, 59; Univ Detroit, MS, 62; Wayne State Univ, PhD(inorg chem), 66. *Prof Exp:* Res assoc, Mich State Univ, 66-67; asst prof chem, Xavier Univ, 67-74; dir mfg, 74-78, dir tech opers, 78-81, DIR PROD DEVELOP, NUCLEAR DIAG, INC, 81- *Concurrent Pos:* Res Corp grant, 68-70. *Mem:* Am Chem Soc; Royal Soc Chem; Am Soc Qual Control; Soc Appl Spectros; Am Asn Clin Chemists. *Res:* Spectroscopic investigations of the effects on chemical and physical properties of through-space interactions between pi-systems and sigma-bonded organometallic compounds; applications of magnetic resonance spectroscopy; radioimmunoassay. *Mailing Add:* Nuclear Diag 575 Robbins Dr Troy MI 48084

SMART, JAMES CONRAD, b Caribou, Maine, Mar 8, 45; m 73; c 2. INORGANIC CHEMISTRY. *Educ:* Univ Calif, Riverside, BS, 68; Mass Inst Technol, PhD(inorg chem), 73. *Prof Exp:* Asst prof chem, Univ Calif, Berkeley, 73-78; sr scientist, 78-80, TASK LEADER, SOLAR ENERGY RES INST, 80-, ASSOC PROF ADJ CHEM, COLO SCH MINES, GOLDEN, 80- *Mem:* AAAS; Am Chem Soc. *Res:* Inorganic and organometallic synthesis; structure and reactivity of transition metal complexes, homogenous and heterogenous, catalysis, photocatalysis, photoelectrochemistry. *Mailing Add:* Solar Energy Res Inst 1617 Cole Blvd Golden CO 80401

SMART, JAMES SAMUEL, b New Bloomfield, Mo, Aug 31, 19; m 42. PHYSICS. *Educ:* Westminster Col, Mo, AB, 39; La State Univ, MS, 41; Univ Minn, PhD(physics), 48. *Prof Exp:* Instr aviation cadet eng, US Army Air Force, 41-43; physicist, Bur Ships, US Dept Navy, 43-46; asst physics, Univ Minn, 46-48; physicist, US Naval Ord Lab, 48-55; sci liaison officer, US Off Naval Res, Eng, 55-57, Wash, DC, 58-60; vis physicist, Brookhaven Nat Lab, 57-58; mem sr staff, Res Ctr, Int Business Mach Corp, 60-80; RETIRED. *Concurrent Pos:* Consult, US Off Naval Res, 58; mem, Nat Res Coun, 63-66; secy, Int Cong Magnetism, 67. *Honors & Awards:* Distinguished Civilian Serv Award, US Navy, 50. *Mem:* Am Phys Soc; Am Asn Physics Teachers; Brit Inst Physics; Am Geophys Union. *Res:* Origin of chemical elements; magnetism; solid state physics; hydrology. *Mailing Add:* 71 Mt Airy Rd Croton-on-Hudson NY 10520

SMART, JOHN RODERICK, b Laramie, Wyo, Sept 16, 34; m 59; c 5. NUMBER THEORY. *Educ:* San Jose State Col, AB, 56; Mich State Univ, MS, 58, PhD(math), 61. *Prof Exp:* From asst prof to assoc prof, 62-71, PROF MATH, UNIV WIS-MADISON, 71- *Concurrent Pos:* NSF fel, Courant Inst

Math Sci, NY Univ, 61-62 & Glasgow Univ, 65-66. *Mem:* Am Math Soc; Math Asn Am; London Math Soc. *Res:* Analytic number theory; automorphic and modular functions; discontinuous groups. *Mailing Add:* Dept of Math Univ of Wis Madison WI 53706

SMART, KATHRYN MARILYN, b Boston, Mass, May 28, 24. MICROBIOLOGY, VIROLOGY. *Educ:* Univ Mich, BS, 45; Columbia Univ, MA, 51; Cornell Univ, PhD(virol), 61. *Prof Exp:* Ress assoc pub health, Med Col, Cornell Univ, 61-62, res fel, 62-63, instr, 63-64; asst prof, 64-68, ASSOC PROF BIOL, ALDELPHI UNIV, 68- *Concurrent Pos:* USPHS fel, 61-64. *Mem:* Am Soc Microbiol; Tissue Cult Asn; Am Inst Biol Sci. *Res:* Bacteriophage infection in spore-forming bacteria; influence of cortisol on viral infection and interference. *Mailing Add:* Dept of Biol Adelphi Univ Garden City NY 11530

SMART, KEITH LORENZO, immunobiology, deceased

SMART, LEWIS ISAAC, b Nowata, Okla, Apr 1, 36; m 56; c 2. ANIMAL NUTRITION. *Educ:* Okla State Univ, BS, 60; Univ Ill, Urbana, MS, 62; Kans State Univ, PhD, 70. *Prof Exp:* Asst, Univ Ill, Urbana, 60-62; asst prof, Southern State Col Ark, 62-67; mem staff, Kans State Univ, 67-69; asst prof, 69-71, assoc prof, 71-77, PROF ANIMAL SCI, LA STATE UNIV, BATON ROUGE, 77- *Mem:* Am Soc Animal Sci. *Res:* Beef cattle nutrition and basic nutrition as related to animals. *Mailing Add:* Dept of Animal Sci La State Univ Baton Rouge LA 70803

SMART, WESLEY MITCHELL, b San Francisco, Calif, Dec 12, 38; div; c 1. HIGH ENERGY PHYSICS. *Educ:* Univ Calif, Berkeley, BA, 61, MA, 65, PhD(high energy physics), 67. *Prof Exp:* Technician bubble chambers/high energy physics, Lawrence Berkeley Lab, Univ of Calif, 56-67; physicist bubble chambers/high energy physics, Stanford Linear Accelerator Ctr, Stanford Univ, 67-71; PHYSICIST BUBBLE CHAMBERS/HIGH ENERGY PHYSICS, FERMI NAT ACCELERATOR LAB, 71- *Mem:* Am Phys Soc. *Res:* Design, construction, and operation of the Fermi Lab bubble chamber and high energy physics experiments using bubble chambers. *Mailing Add:* Fermi Nat Accelerator Lab PO Box 500 Batavia IL 60510

SMART, WILLIAM DONALD, b Waukegan, Ill, Jan 26, 27; m 53; c 5. ORGANIC CHEMISTRY. *Educ:* Northwestern Univ, BS, 51; Univ Ill, MS, 53; Univ Chicago, MBA, 64. *Prof Exp:* Chemist, 53-60, group leader chem develop, 60-63, sect head, 63-64, dir chem mfg, 64-67, vpres hosp equip mfg, 69-72, vpres, Mkt Hosp Prod Div, 72-75, vpres & gen mgr, Agr & Vet Prods Div, 75-76, exec vpres, 76-80, PRES, ROSS LABS DIV & VPRES, ABBOTT LABS, NORTH CHICAGO, 80- *Mem:* Am Chem Soc. *Mailing Add:* 1930 Walnut Hill Park Dr Columbus OH 43227

SMARTT, RICHARD ALLEN, b Omaha, Nebr, Apr 23, 48; m 68; c 2. POPULATION ECOLOGY. *Educ:* Univ Tex, El Paso, BA, 70, MS, 72; Univ NMex, PhD(biol), 75. *Prof Exp:* Res assoc ecol, Nat Fishery & Wildlife Lab, US Fishery & Wildlife Serv, 75-77; LECTR ECOL, UNIV TEX, 77- *Mem:* Am Soc Mammalogists; Ecol Soc Am; Am Soc Naturalists. *Res:* Morphological and trophic structure of animal communities. *Mailing Add:* Dept of Biol Sci Univ of Tex El Paso TX 79968

SMAT, ROBERT JOSEPH, b Chicago, Ill, June 24, 38; m 61; c 2. ORGANIC CHEMISTRY. *Educ:* St Joseph's Col, Ind, BS, 60; Iowa State Univ, MS, 62; Ill Inst Technol, PhD(org chem), 66. *Prof Exp:* Res chemist, Chems, Dyes & Pigments Dept, Org Chem Div, Jackson Lab, 66-72, patent chemist, 72-78, sr patent chemist, Elastomer Chem Dept, 78-80, PATENTS CONSULT, PROD DEPT, E I DU PONT DE NEMOURS & CO, INC, 80- *Mem:* Am Chem Soc; The Chem Soc. *Res:* Synthesis and stereochemistry of small ring heterocyclic compounds; textile dyes and polymer finishes; thermoplastic film-forming polymers. *Mailing Add:* Polymer Prod Dept E I du Pont de Nemours & Co Inc Wilmington DE 19898

SMATHERS, GARRETT ARTHUR, b Canton, NC, Mar 15, 26; m 56; c 2. PLANT ECOLOGY, SCIENCE ADMINISTRATION. *Educ:* Univ NC, Asheville, dipl, 50; Furman Univ, BS, 52; Western Carolina Univ, MA, 55; Univ Hawaii, PhD(plant ecol), 72. *Prof Exp:* Chemist, Taylor Colquitt Co, 52-53, Am Enka Corp, 54-55; high sch teacher sci, Waynesville, NC, 53-54, 55-59, actg prin, 55-59; supvry park naturalist & res, Nat Park Serv, 59-66; res asst plant ecol, Univ Hawaii, 66-67; res biologist, Hawaii Volcanoes Nat Park, 67-70, instr, Mather & Albright Training Ctrs, 70-71, regional chief scientist, Univ Wash, Pac Northwest Region, 70-73, chief scientist, Res Sci Admin, Nat Park Serv Sci Ctr, 73-77, SR RES SCIENTIST, NAT PARK SERV COOP PARK STUDIES UNIT, WESTERN CAROLINA UNIV, 77-, ADJ PROF BIOL, 80- *Concurrent Pos:* Mem, Adv Coun, Dept Forestry, Miss State Univ, 74-; prof B-1 coordr, Mem Org Preserves US-USSR Bilateral Agreement, Nat Park Serv, 75- *Mem:* Am Ecol Soc; Am Inst Biol Sci. *Res:* Study of the invasion, succession and recovery of vegetation on volcanic substrates; preparation of ecological atlases of present and proposed national parks. *Mailing Add:* Biol Dept NPS/CPSU Western Carolina Univ Cullowhee NC 28723

SMATHERS, JAMES BURTON, nuclear engineering, bioengineering, see previous edition

SMAY, TERRY A, b Oakland, Iowa, Aug 30, 35; m 54; c 3. ELECTRICAL ENGINEERING. *Educ:* Iowa State Univ, BS, 57, MS, 59, PhD(elec eng), 62. *Prof Exp:* Elec engr, Remington Rand Univac Div, Sperry Rand Corp, 57-58; from instr to asst prof elec eng, Iowa State Univ, 58-62; sr res scientist, Res Div, Control Data Corp, 62-65; supvr govt systs div, 65-66, dept mgr thin film memory develop, 66-70; assoc prof, 70-76, PROF ELEC ENG, IOWA STATE UNIV, 76- *Concurrent Pos:* Lectr, Univ Minn, 62-64. *Mem:* Inst Elec & Electronics Engrs. *Res:* Magnetic film memory development; high speed memory components. *Mailing Add:* Dept of Elec Eng Iowa State Univ Ames IA 50011

SMAYDA, THEODORE JOHN, b Peckville, Pa, Aug 28, 31; m 56; c 2. BIOLOGICAL OCEANOGRAPHY. *Educ:* Tufts Univ, BS, 53; Univ RI, MS, 55; Univ Oslo, Dr Philos, 67. *Prof Exp:* Asst biol oceanog, 59-61, asst prof biol oceanog, 61-66, assoc prof oceanog, 66-70, PROF OCEANOG & BOT, GRAD SCH OCEANOG, UNIV RI, 70- *Concurrent Pos:* Mem working panel phytoplankton methods, comt oceanog, Nat Acad Sci, 65-69; adv comt algae, Smithsonian Oceanog Sorting Ctr, 71- *Mem:* Fel AAAS; Am Soc Limnol & Oceanog; Phycol Soc Am; Int Phycol Soc; Marine Biol Asn. *Res:* Ecology and physiology of marine phytoplankton; estuarine and coastal ecology; tropical and upwelling ecology. *Mailing Add:* Grad Sch of Oceanog Univ of RI Kingston RI 02881

SMEACH, STEPHEN CHARLES, b Hanover, Pa, Feb 25, 45; m 65; c 2. BIOMATHEMATICS. *Educ:* Univ Del, BS, 67; NC State Univ, MA, 70, PhD(biomath), 73. *Prof Exp:* NIH fel biomath, Biomath Prog, NC State Univ, 67-73; asst prof math, Univ South Fla, 73-80; WITH DEPT SCI EVAL, G D SEARLE & CO, 80- *Mem:* Soc Math Biol; Biomet Soc; Am Statist Asn; Sigma Xi. *Res:* Mathematical modeling of biological phenomenon, specifically statistical and stochastic approaches to include time series studies of population density behavior and stochastic models for drug concentration changes in the blood plasma. *Mailing Add:* Dept Sci Eval G D Searle & Co PO Box 1045 Skokie IL 60076

SMEAL, PAUL LESTER, b Clearfield, Pa, June 11, 32; m 54; c 3. ORNAMENTAL HORTICULTURE. *Educ:* Pa State Univ, BS, 54; Univ Md, MS, 59, PhD(hort), 61. *Prof Exp:* Res asst hort, Univ Md, 59-60; from asst prof to assoc prof, 60-67, PROF HORT, VA POLYTECH INST & STATE UNIV, 67- *Concurrent Pos:* Instr, Flower Show Sch, Nat Coun State Garden Clubs. *Mem:* Am Soc Hort Sci; Am Hort Soc; Int Plant Propagators Soc. *Res:* Ornamentals; plant propagation; nursery management; production of nursery stock, greenhouse flowers and bedding plants produced by nurserymen and flower growers; work with county extension personnel, nurserymen, flower growers, professional grounds management personnel, garden clubs and civic groups. *Mailing Add:* Dept of Hort Va Polytech Inst & State Univ Blacksburg VA 24061

SMEBY, ROBERT RUDOLPH, b Chicago, Ill, Dec 24, 26; m 50; c 4. BIOCHEMISTRY. *Educ:* Univ Ill, BS, 50; Univ Wis, MS, 52, PhD(biochem), 54. *Prof Exp:* Biochemist, R J Reynolds Tobacco Co, 54-56; biochemist, Miles-Ames Res Lab, Miles Labs, Inc, 56-59; BIOCHEMIST CLEVELAND CLIN, 59- *Concurrent Pos:* Adj prof, John Carroll Univ, 65-70 & Cleveland State Univ, 70- *Mem:* AAAS; Am Chem Soc; Am Physiol Soc. *Res:* Synthesis of peptides; isolation of substances from natural products with biological activity. *Mailing Add:* Res Div Cleveland Clin 9500 Euclid Ave Cleveland OH 44106

SMECK, NEIL EDWARD, b Lancaster, Ohio, July 9, 41; m 65; c 3. AGRONOMY. *Educ:* Ohio State Univ, BS, 63, MS, 66; Univ Ill, PhD(agron), 70. *Prof Exp:* Soil scientist soil surv, Soil Conserv Serv, 63-66; asst prof agron, NDak State Univ, 69-71; ASSOC PROF AGRON, OHIO STATE UNIV-OHIO AGR RES & DEVELOP CTR, 71- *Mem:* Am Soc Agron; Soil Sci Soc Am; Soil Conserv Soc Am. *Res:* Soil genesis, morphology, and classification; sediment chemistry and mineralogy; weathering strip mine spoils. *Mailing Add:* Dept of Agron Ohio State Univ 1885 Neil Ave Columbus OH 43210

SMEDES, HARRY WYNN, b Spokane, Wash, Sept 11, 26; m 45; c 4. GEOLOGY, RESOURCE MANAGEMENT. *Educ:* Univ Wash, BS, 48, PhD(geol), 59. *Prof Exp:* Instr geol, Kans State Col, 51-53; geologist, Mineral Deposits Br, US Geol Surv, 53-61, Northern Rocky Mountains Br, 61-69 & Rocky Mountain Br Environ Geol, Colo, 69-75, staff geologist, Dept Interior Resource & Land Invest, 72-76, proj chief & coordr, 76-80; WITH OFF WASTE ISOLATION, DEPT ENERGY, 80- *Concurrent Pos:* Mem, Boulder Batholith Proj, 53-72; chief area pub unit, US Geol Surv, 64-66, chief Absaroka volcanics proj, Yellowstone Nat Park, 66-70, chief geol mapping res proj, Rocky Mountain Br Environ Geol & remote sensing studies for Landsat & Skylab Prog, 69-75; mem geol verification team for US-Russian Peaceful Nuclear Explosives Treaty, 76- *Honors & Awards:* AIL Award, Am Soc Photogram, 75. *Mem:* Fel Geol Soc Am. *Res:* Mapping techniques; automated cartography. *Mailing Add:* Off Waste Isolation Dept Energy MSB-107 Germantown Bldg Washington DC 20545

SMEDFJELD, JOHN B, b Oslo, Norway, Apr 18, 35; US citizen; m 58; c 2. AEROELASTICITY, STRUCTURAL DYNAMICS. *Educ:* Pratt Inst, BME, 55, MS, 59. *Prof Exp:* Res engr, 55-57, dynamic anal engr, 57-63, adv develop group leader dynamics, 63-65, aeroelasticity methods group leader, 65-72, head dynamic structural methods group, 72-77, TECH SPECIALIST STRUCT MECH, GRUMMAN AEROSPACE CORP, BETHPAGE, 77- *Mem:* Am Inst Aeornaut & Astronaut. *Res:* Gust response analysis; flutter analysis; unsteady aerodynamics; applied leads; structural optimization. *Mailing Add:* 9 Darrell St East Northport NY 11731

SMEDLEY, WILLIAM MICHAEL, b Chicago, Ill, Aug 2, 16; m 43; c 1. ORGANIC CHEMISTRY. *Educ:* Northwestern Univ, BS, 38, MS, 40. *Prof Exp:* Instr chem & physics, 40-47, from asst prof to assoc prof chem, 48-59, PROF CHEM, US NAVAL ACAD, 60- *Concurrent Pos:* Asst prof, Univ Md, 56-58, NSF fac fel, 64-65; dir res & vpres, Appl Sci & Chem Corp, Md & Am Chem Co, dir & vpres, Everett Factories, Mass. *Mem:* AAAS; Am Chem Soc. *Res:* Chlorination dioxanes; 2, 5-diphenyl dioxane, 2, 5-dichlorodioxane and derivatives; heterocyclics; derivatives of quinoline-quinone; chemistry of explosives. *Mailing Add:* Dept Chem US Naval Acad Annapolis MD 21402

SMEDSKJAER, LARS CHRISTIAN, b Copenhagen, Denmark, Oct 3, 44; m 75. EXPERIMENTAL PHYSICS, METALLURGY. *Educ:* Tech Univ Denmark, Cand Polyt, 69, PhD(exp physics), 72. *Prof Exp:* Amanvensis physics, Tech Univ Denmark, 72-74, assoc prof, 74; PHYSICIST METALL, ARGONNE NAT LAB, 74- *Mem:* Danish Soc Engrs. *Res:* Metal physics; positron physics. *Mailing Add:* Argonne Nat Lab MSD 212 9700 Case Ave Argonne IL 60439

SMEINS, FRED E, b Luverne, Minn, Feb 14, 41; m 60; c 1. PLANT ECOLOGY. *Educ:* Augustana Col, SDak, 63; Univ Sask, MA, 65, PhD(plant ecol), 67. *Prof Exp:* Asst prof biol, Univ NDak, 67-69; asst prof, 69-73, assoc prof, 73-80, PROF RANGE SCI, TEX A&M UNIV, 80- *Res:* Ecology of wetland and grassland vegetation. *Mailing Add:* Dept of Range Sci Texas A&M Univ College Station TX 77843

SMELLIE, ROBERT HENDERSON, JR, b Glasgow, Scotland, June 2, 20; US citizen; m 45; c 3. PHYSICAL CHEMISTRY. *Educ:* Trinity Col, Conn, BS, 42, MS, 44; Columbia Univ, PhD(phys chem), 51. *Prof Exp:* Instr chem, Trinity Col, Conn, 43-44; anal foreman & supvr, Tenn Eastman Corp, 44-46; asst chem, Columbia Univ, 47-48; from instr to prof, 48-64, chmn dept, 63-71, SCOVILL PROF CHEM, TRINITY COL, CONN, 64- *Mem:* Am Chem Soc. *Res:* Kinetics of nitrile reactions; analytical chemistry of uranium; chemistry and electrokinetics of sulfur sols; flocculation of suspensions; combustion chemistry. *Mailing Add:* Dept of chem Trinity Col Hartford CT 06106

SMELT, RONALD, b Durham, Eng, Dec 4, 13; nat US; m 39, 65; c 1. AERODYNAMICS. *Educ:* Cambridge Univ, BA, 35, MA, 39; Stanford Univ, PhD, 61. *Prof Exp:* Engr aerodyn, Royal Aircraft Estab, Eng, 35-41, chief, High Speed Flight, 41-45, Gas Dynamics, 45-47 & Guided Missiles, 47-48; chief hyperballistics div, Aeroballistic Res Dept, US Naval Ord Lab, 48-50; chief gas dynamics facil, ARO, Inc, 50-57; dir new design off, Missiles & Space Div, Lockheed Aircraft Corp, 57-58, chief res, 58-59, mgr satellite systs, 59-60, chief scientist, 60-62, vpres & gen mgr, Space Prog Div, 63, vpres & chief scientist, Corp Off, 63-78; RETIRED. *Concurrent Pos:* Mem subcomt, High-Speed Aerodyn, NASA, 58-59, res adv comt, Missile & Space Vehicle Aerodyn, 59-60, chmn res adv comt space vehicle aerodyn, 65-66; mem res & develop adv comt, Nat Security Indust Asn, 65-66; Guggenheim lectr, Int Cong Aeronaut Sci, 78. *Mem:* Nat Acad Eng; hon fel Am Inst Aeronaut & Astronaut (pres, 69-71); Am Phys Soc; fel Royal Aeronaut Soc. *Res:* Highspeed aerodynamics; jet and rocket propulsion. *Mailing Add:* Lockheed Aircraft Corp PO Box 551 Burbank CA 91520

SMELTZER, DALE GARDNER, b Carlyle, Mont, Apr 19, 20; m 51; c 3. RESEARCH SYSTEMS, AGRICULTURAL DEVELOPMENT. *Educ:* Mont State Col, BS, 43, MS, 47; Univ Calif, PhD(genetics), 50. *Prof Exp:* Asst agron, Mont State Col, 46-47, asst prof, 47-48; asst, Univ Calif, Davis, 48-50, asst specialist, 50, instr, 50-52, asst prof, 52-64, assoc specialist, 64-69; AGRONOMIST, ROCKEFELLER FOUND, BANGKOK, 69- *Concurrent Pos:* Vis prof, Cornell Univ, 79-81. *Mem:* Am Soc Agron; Genetics Soc Am. *Res:* Production and breeding of zeamays and sorghum bicolor. *Mailing Add:* Rockefeller Found GPO Box 2453 Bangkok Thailand

SMELTZER, RICHARD HOMER, b Sapulpa, Okla, Aug 14, 40; m 63; c 3. PLANT MORPHOGENESIS. *Educ:* Okla State Univ, BS, 62; Stephen F Austin State Univ, MF, 70; Lawrence Univ, MS, 72, PhD(paper chem), 75. *Prof Exp:* Inspector lumber, Southern Pine Inspection Bur, 62-65; asst qual control supt, Temple Indust, Inc, 65-68; RES ASSOC PLANT MORPHOGENESIS, INT PAPER CO, 75- *Mem:* Am Soc Plant Physiologists; Int Asn Plant Tissue Cult. *Res:* Asexual propagation of trees through tissue culture and related biochemistry; evaluation of vegetative propagules. *Mailing Add:* Int Paper Co 495 Greenfield Rd Natchez MS 39120

SMELTZER, WALTER WILLIAM, b Moose Jaw, Sask, Dec 4, 24; m 60. METALLURGY, MATERIALS SCIENCE. *Educ:* Queen's Univ, Ont, BSc, 48; Univ Toronto, PhD(phys chem), 53. *Hon Degrees:* Dr, Univ Dijon, 81. *Prof Exp:* Res chemist, Nat Res Coun Can, 48-50; res chem engr, Aluminum Co, Ltd, 53-55; res metall engr, Metals Res Lab, Carnegie Inst Technol, 56-59; from asst prof to assoc prof, 59-65, PROF METALL, MCMASTER UNIV, 65- *Concurrent Pos:* Sr fel, Brit Res Coun, 76 & NATO, 79-80. *Honors & Awards:* Centennial Medal for Serv to the Nation, Govt Can, 68. *Mem:* Nat Asn Corrosion Engrs; Electrochem Soc; fel Am Soc Metals; Can Inst Mining & Metall; fel Royal Soc Can. *Res:* Adsorption and oxidation kinetics of metals; thermodynamic properties of solids; lattice defect structures of solid metal oxides and their influence on mass and thermal transport properties. *Mailing Add:* Dept Metall & Mat Sci McMaster Univ Hamilton ON L85 4L8 Can

SMERAGE, GLEN H, b Topsfield, Mass, May 3, 37; m 60; c 2. SYSTEMS ENGINEERING. *Educ:* Worcester Polytech Inst, BS, 59; San Jose State Col, MS, 63; Stanford Univ, PhD(elec eng), 67. *Prof Exp:* Res asst & test engr, Instrumentation Labs, Mass Inst Technol, 59-60; jr engr, Western Develop Labs, Philco Corp, 60-61; engr, Electronic Defense Labs, Sylvania Electronics Systs, 62-67; asst prof elec eng, Utah State Univ, 67-76; ASSOC PROF AGR ENG, UNIV FLA, 76- *Mem:* Inst Elec & Electronics Engrs. *Res:* Modeling and analysis of systems; current emphasis on human social systems and their interaction with the physical and biological environment. *Mailing Add:* Dept of Agr Eng Univ of Fla Gainesville FL 32611

SMERDON, ERNEST THOMAS, b Ritchey, Mo, Jan 19, 30; m 51; c 3. CIVIL & AGRICULTURAL ENGINEERING. *Educ:* Univ Mo, BS, 51, MS, 56, PhD(agr eng), 59. *Prof Exp:* Res engr, Univ Mo, 56-57, instr civil eng, 57-58, instr agr eng, 58-59; from assoc prof to prof, Tex A&M Univ, 59-68, prof civil eng & dir, Water Res Inst, 64-68; prof agr eng & chmn dept, Univ Fla, 68-74, asst dean res, 74-76; vchancellor acad affairs, Univ Tex Syst, 76-82, PROF CIVIL ENG & DIR, CTR RES WATER RESOURCES, UNIV TEX, AUSTIN, 82- *Concurrent Pos:* Inst Int Educ & Ohio State Univ consult, Punjab Agr Univ, India, 65; consult govt of SVietnam, Guyana & El Salvador, 71; Bahamas, Peru & Brazil, 76 & USAID, Pakistan, 81; chmn, Univ Coun Water Resources, 72-74. *Mem:* Fel AAAS; Am Soc Agr Engrs; Am Soc Civil Engrs; Am Geophys Union; Am Asn Higher Educ. *Res:* Water resources development and irrigation; energy use and conservation; research administration. *Mailing Add:* Civil Eng Dept Univ Tex Austin TX 78712

SMERIGLIO, ALFRED JOHN, b Port Chester, NY, May 17, 37; m 65. BIOLOGY, COMPARATIVE ANATOMY. *Educ:* NY Univ, BS, 59, MA, 60, EdD(biol), 64. *Prof Exp:* from instr to asst prof biol, NY Univ, 59-66; asst prof, Jersey City State Col, 66-67; from asst prof to assoc prof, 67-70, PROF BIOL, NASSAU COMMUNITY COL, 75-, CHMN DEPT ALLIED HEALTH SCI, 70- *Concurrent Pos:* Asst res scientist biophys res lab, NY Univ, 65- *Mem:* AAAS; Nat Sci Teachers Asn. *Res:* Mammalian biology; physiological patterns of behavior in the Albino rat; piezoelectric properties of mineralized tissue. *Mailing Add:* Dept of Allied Health Sci Nassau Community Col Garden City NY 11530

SMETANA, ALES, b Hradec, Kralove, Czech, Apr 4, 31; m 57; c 3. ENTOMOLOGY, ZOOGEOGRAPHY. *Educ:* Charles Univ, Prague, MD, 56; Czech Acad Sci, CSc(systs Anoplura), 60. *Prof Exp:* Res scientist, Inst Parasitol, Czech Acad Sci, 56-70; res scientist, Nat Mus, Prague, 70-71; RES SCIENTIST, BIOSYSTS RES INST, CAN DEPT AGR, 71- *Concurrent Pos:* Nat Res Coun Can fel, Entom Res Inst, Ottawa, 67-69. *Mem:* NY Acad Sci; Entom Soc Can; Entom Soc Am. *Res:* Systematics of the insect order Coleoptera, especially aquatic Coleoptera and the family Staphylinidae; zoogeography, particularly the holarctic distribution of Coleoptera. *Mailing Add:* Biosysts Res Inst Ottawa ON K1A 0C6 Can

SMETANA, FREDERICK OTTO, b Philadelphia, Pa, Nov 29, 28; m 52; c 4. MECHANICAL ENGINEERING, AEROSPACE ENGINEERING. *Educ:* NC State Col, BME, 50, MSME, 53; Univ Southern Calif, PhD(eng), 61. *Prof Exp:* Vpres, Philcord Corp, NC, 50-51; flight test analyst, Douglas Aircraft Co, Calif, 51-52; teaching asst mech eng, NC State Col, 52-53; res scientist, Eng Ctr, Univ Southern Calif, 55-62; assoc prof mech eng, 62-65, PROF MECH ENG, NC STATE UNIV, 65- *Concurrent Pos:* Asst dir, NC Sci & Technol Res Ctr, 66-; past consult, Pneumafil Corp, Litton Systs, Inc, Corning Glass Works, State King Corp & Servomechanisms, Inc; consult, US Army Armament Res & Develop Command, 76-79. *Mem:* Am Inst Aeronaut & Astronaut; Am Vacuum Soc. *Res:* Vehicle design; air data instrumentation; dynamic response flight testing; flight data systems identification; Rankine cycle solar electric power generation. *Mailing Add:* Dept Mech & Aerospace Eng NC State Univ Raleigh NC 27650

SMETANA, JOHN A(LBERT), b Baltimore, Md, Sept 21, 29; m 50; c 5. MECHANICAL ENGINEERING. *Educ:* NC State Col, BME, 50; Wash State Univ, MS, 52. *Prof Exp:* Asst theoret & appl mech, Wash State Univ, 50-52; res engr, Guided Missile Div, Lockheed Aircraft Corp, 52-53; res mech engr, NMex Inst Mining & Technol, 53-55; ASSOC PROF MECH ENG, WASH STATE UNIV, 55- *Concurrent Pos:* Consult, Pratt & Whitney Aircraft Div, United Aircraft Corp, 57, Boeing Aircraft Co, 58, Granville-Phillips Co, 60-62, Off Mining Res, 61-62 & NSF, 61-, assoc prog dir, 62-63. *Mem:* Am Soc Eng Educ; Soc Eng Sci. *Res:* Theoretical and applied mechanics. *Mailing Add:* Dept of Mech Eng Wash State Univ Pullman WA 99163

SMETHIE, WILLIAM MASSIE, JR, b Rocky Mount, NC, Mar 29, 45; m 69; c 1. CHEMICAL OCEANOGRAPHY, ESTURINE OCEANOGRAPHY. *Educ:* Wofford Col, BS, 67; San Jose State Univ, MA, 73; Univ Wash, PhD(oceanog), 79. *Prof Exp:* Sr oceanographer, Univ Wash, 78-79; res scientist, 79-80, RES ASSOC, LAMONT-DOHERTY GEOL OBSERV, 80- *Mem:* Am Geophys Union; AAAS. *Res:* Measuring the distribution of natural and man made radioactive compounds in the ocean and other marine systems for use in investigating mixing and circulation processes. *Mailing Add:* Lamont-Doherty Geol Observ Palisades NY 10964

SMIALEK, ROBERT LOUIS, b Mineral Wells, Tex, Feb 4, 44; m 65; c 3. PHYSICAL METALLURGY. *Educ:* Case Western Reserve Univ, BS, 65, MS, 67, PhD(metall), 70. *Prof Exp:* Res metallurgist, Lighting Res Lab, Gen Elec Co, 69-77; res metallurgist, 77-79, MGR MFG, REFRACTORY METALS DEPT, LEWIS RES CTR, NASA, 79- *Mem:* Am Inst Mining, Metall & Petrol Engrs. *Res:* Physical metallurgy of the refractory metals; mechanical properties of body centered cubic metals; high temperature reactions. *Mailing Add:* Gen Elec 21800 Tungsten Rd Euclid OH 44117

SMIBERT, ROBERT MERRALL, II, b New Haven, Conn, Dec 9, 30; m 61; c 2. MICROBIOLOGY. *Educ:* Univ Conn, BA, 52; Univ Md, MS, 57, PhD(microbiol), 59. *Prof Exp:* Instr microbiol, Sch Med, Temple Univ, 59-60; assoc prof vet sci, 60-65, prof microbiol, 68-78, prof bact, Anaerobe Lab, 78-80, PROF MICROBIOL, DEPT ANAEROBIC MICROBIOL, VA POLYTECH INST & STATE UNIV, 80- *Mem:* AAAS; Am Soc Microbiol; Soc Gen Microbiol; Am Venereal Dis Asn. *Res:* Microbial physiology and nutrition; taxonomy of bacteria; Mycoplasma; vibrios; campylobacter; leptospirosis; Treponemas; Borrelias. *Mailing Add:* Dept Anaerobic Microbiol Va Polytech Inst & State Univ Blacksburg VA 24061

SMID, JOHANNES, b Amsterdam, Netherlands, Jan 18, 31; m 56; c 4. PHYSICAL CHEMISTRY, POLYMER CHEMISTRY. *Educ:* Free Univ, Amsterdam, BSc, 52, MSc, 54; State Univ NY, PhD(phys chem), 57. *Prof Exp:* Res assoc polymer chem, 59-63, from asst prof to assoc prof, 63-70, PROF POLYMER CHEM, STATE UNIV NY COL ENVIRON SCI & FORESTRY, 70- *Concurrent Pos:* NSF fel, 59-61; vis prof, Roman Cath Univ Nijmegen, 69-70 & Louis Pasteur Univ, Strasbourg, 77-78. *Mem:* AAAS; Am Chem Soc. *Res:* Organometallic chemistry; solvent-solute interactions; ion pair structures; ion-binding to macromolecules; mechanism of ionic polymerization. *Mailing Add:* Dept of Chem State Univ of NY Col of Environ Sci & Forestry Syracuse NY 13210

SMID, ROBERT JOHN, b US. CERAMICS ENGINEERING. *Educ:* Univ Ill, BS, 62, MS, 65, PhD(ceramics eng), 68. *Prof Exp:* Sr engr, 68-74, prin engr, 74-80, ADV SCIENTIST, BETTIS ATOMIC POWER LAB, WESTINGHOUSE ELEC CORP, 80- *Mem:* Am Ceramic Soc. *Res:* Advanced naval nuclear fuel systems. *Mailing Add:* Westinghouse/Bettis PO Box 79 West Mifflin PA 15122

SMIDT, FRED AUGUST, JR, b Sioux City, Iowa, July 19, 32; m 56; c 3. METALLURGY, RESEARCH ADMINISTRATION. *Educ:* Univ Nebr, BSc, 54; Iowa State Univ, PhD(phys chem), 62. *Prof Exp:* Sr engr, Hanford Lab, Gen Elec Co, 62-65; sr res scientist, Pac Northwest Labs, Battelle Mem Inst, 65-69; res metallurgist, Reactor Mat Br, Metall Div, Naval Res Lab, 69-71, sect head, 71-77; prog monitor, Reactor Res & Technol Div, US Dept Energy, 77-78; SECT HEAD, REACTOR MAT BR, METALL DIV, NAVAL RES LAB, 78- *Concurrent Pos:* Special prog coordr, Mat Sci & Components Directorate, 80- *Honors & Awards:* Dudley Medal, Am Soc Testing & Mat, 79. *Mem:* Am Soc Metals; Am Inst Mining, Metall & Petrol Engrs; Am Soc Testing & Mat; Sigma Xi. *Res:* Irradiation damage to metals; electron microscopy; fast breeder and controlled thermonuclear reactor materials; ion implantation for materials processing. *Mailing Add:* Thermostruct Mat Br Naval Res Lab Code 6390 Washington DC 20375

SMIKA, DARRYL EUGENE, b Hill City, Kans, July 1, 33; m 56; c 4. SOIL CHEMISTRY. *Educ:* Kans State Univ, BS & MS, 56, PhD(soil chem), 69. *Prof Exp:* Soil conservationist, Soil Conserv Serv, USDA, Kans, 56-57, soil scientist, Soil & Water Conserv Res Div, Agr Res Serv, NDak, 57-61, res soil scientist, Exp Sta, Nebr, 61-73, RES SOIL SCIENTIST, CENT GREAT PLAINS RES STA, SOIL & WATER CONSERV RES DIV, AGR RES SERV, USDA, 73- *Mem:* Fel Am Inst Chemists; Soil Conserv Soc Am; Am Soc Agron; Soil Sci Soc Am; Can Soil Sci Soc. *Res:* Soil moisture and fertility under dryland conditions with present emphasis on stubble mulch tillage. *Mailing Add:* Cent Great Plains Res Sta PO Box K Akron CO 80720

SMILEN, LOWELL I, b New York, NY, Apr 18, 31; m 63; c 2. ELECTRICAL ENGINEERING. *Educ:* Cooper Union, BSEE, 52; Univ Calif, Los Angeles, MS, 56; Polytech Inst Brooklyn, PhD(elec eng), 62. *Prof Exp:* Res engr, Hughes Aircraft Co, Calif, 52-56; sr res assoc, Polytech Inst Brooklyn, 56-62, asst prof electrophys, 62-64; res sect head, Sperry Gyroscope Co, 64-67; asst chief engr res, Loral Electronic Systs, Bronx, 67-70; leader advan microwave technol, Missile & Surface Radar Div, RCA Corp, NJ, 70-72; vpres eng, Laser Link Corp, 72-74; VPRES ENG, ALMAC/STROUM ELECTRONICS CORP, DIV KDM ELECTRONICS CORP, 74- *Concurrent Pos:* Adj prof, Polytech Inst Brooklyn; mem eng sci dept, Hofstra Univ, 65. *Mem:* Sr mem Inst Elec & Electronics Engrs; Am Inst Physics; Optical Soc Am; Am Soc Eng Educ. *Res:* Network theory and synthesis; microwave components and systems; antenna feed systems; solid state phased array antennas and radars; applied information theory and coding; applications of microprocessors and microcomputers. *Mailing Add:* Almac/Stroum Electronics Corp 14310 SE Eastgate Way Bellevue WA 98007

SMILES, KENNETH ALBERT, b Elizabeth, NJ, Aug 5, 44; m 66; c 2. DERMATOLOGY, ENVIRONMENTAL PHYSIOLOGY. *Educ:* Denison Univ, BS, 66; Ind Univ, PhD(physiol), 70. *Prof Exp:* Res assoc physiol, Ind Univ, 70; res physiologist, Aerospace Med Res Lab, US Air Force, 70-72, actg chief environ physiol br, 72-74; group leader dermat group antiperspirant res, Carter Prods Res, Div Carter-Wallace, Inc, 74-76; sr med res assoc, 76-80, ASST DIR DERMAT, SCHERING CORP, 80- *Honors & Awards:* Sci Achievement Award, Systs Command, US Air Force, 72. *Mem:* Am Acad Dermat; Soc Invest Dermat; AAAS. *Res:* Mechanisms of anhydrosis and dermatological testing. *Mailing Add:* 44 Hawthorne Lane East Windsor NJ 08520

SMILEY, HARRY M, b Cynthiana, Ky, Oct 6, 33; m 56; c 3. PHYSICAL CHEMISTRY. *Educ:* Eastern Ky State Col, BS, 55; Univ Ky, MS, 57, PhD(chem), 60. *Prof Exp:* Asst chem, Univ Ky, 55-60; res chemist, Union Carbide Corp, 60-67; assoc prof, 67-70, PROF CHEM & CHMN DEPT, EASTERN KY UNIV, 70- *Mem:* Am Chem Soc. *Res:* Physical and thermodynamic properties of non-ideal solutions, especially activity coefficients and heats of mixing. *Mailing Add:* Dept of Chem Eastern Ky Univ Richmond KY 40475

SMILEY, JAMES DONALD, b Lubbock, Tex, Dec 6, 30; m 57; c 5. IMMUNOLOGY, MEDICINE. *Educ:* Tex Tech Col, BS, 52; Johns Hopkins Univ, MD, 56. *Prof Exp:* Intern & resident med, Columbia-Presby Hosp, 56-58; res assoc biochem, Nat Inst Arthritis & Metab Dis, 58-60; from instr to assoc prof, 60-70, PROF MED, UNIV TEX HEALTH SCI CTR, 70- *Concurrent Pos:* USPHS spec res fel, 60-63; USPHS career develop award, 68-73; sr investr, Arthritis Found, 63-68; mem, Rheumatol Comt, Am Bd Internal Med, 70-73. *Mem:* Am Rheumatism Asn; Am Soc Clin Invest; Am Asn Immunologists. *Res:* Connective tissue biochemistry; clinical immunology related to research in rheumatoid arthritis. *Mailing Add:* Univ of Tex Health Sci Ctr 5323 Harry Hines Blvd Dallas TX 75235

SMILEY, JAMES RICHARD, b Montreal, Que, June 22, 51; c 1. MOLECULAR BIOLOGY. *Educ:* McGill Univ, BSc, 72; McMaster Univ, PhD(biol), 77. *Prof Exp:* Fel biol, Yale Univ, 77-78, fel virol, 78-79; ASST PROF PATH, MCMASTER UNIV, 79- *Res:* Control of the expression of herpes simplex viral genes; mechanism of viral DNA replication. *Mailing Add:* Dept Path McMaster Univ 1200 Main St W Hamilton ON L8N 3Z5 Can

SMILEY, JAMES WATSON, b Charleston, WVa, Feb 17, 40; m 61; c 2. PHYSIOLOGY. *Educ:* Univ SC, BS, 62, MS, 65, PhD, 68. *Prof Exp:* Instr biol, Univ SC, 65-68; asst prof, Northeast La Univ, 68-71; assoc prof, 71-77, PROF BIOL, COL CHARLESTON, 77-, CHMN DEPT, 78- *Mem:* AAAS. *Res:* Endocrine control of molting in Crustacea. *Mailing Add:* Dept of Biol Col of Charleston Charleston SC 29401

SMILEY, JONES HAZELWOOD, b Casey Co, Ky, Apr 23, 33; m 53; c 1. AGRONOMY, PLANT PATHOLOGY. *Educ:* Univ Ky, BS, 59, MS, 60; Univ Wis-Madison, PhD(genetics), 63. *Prof Exp:* Res asst plant path, Univ Ky, 58-60; res asst genetics, Univ Wis-Madison, 60-63; asst prof agron, 63-68, assoc prof, 68-72, prof agron & plant path, 72-80, EXT PROF, DEPT AGRON, UNIV KY, 80- *Mem:* Am Soc Agron. *Res:* Tobacco breeding, management and diseases. *Mailing Add:* Dept of Agron Agr Sci Ctr Univ of Ky Lexington KY 40506

SMILEY, MALCOLM FINLAY, b Monmouth, Ill, Dec 15, 12; m 41. MATHEMATICS. *Educ:* Univ Chicago, BS, 34, MS, 35, PhD(math), 37. *Prof Exp:* Asst math, Univ Chicago, 35; grant-in-aid, Sch Math, Inst Adv Study, 37-38; from instr to asst prof math, Lehigh Univ, 38-42; instr math & mech, Postgrad Sch, US Naval Acad, 42-45; assoc prof math, Lehigh Univ, 46 & Northwestern Univ, 46-48; prof, Univ Iowa, 48-60 & Univ Calif, Riverside, 60-67; prof math, State Univ NY, Albany, 67-81, assoc dean sci & math, 71-72. *Concurrent Pos:* Fund Advan Educ fac fel, 54-55. *Mem:* Am Math Soc; Math Asn Am. *Res:* Lattice theory; matric algebra; theory of rings. *Mailing Add:* 42 W Bayberry Rd Glenmont NY 12077

SMILEY, RICHARD WAYNE, b Paso Robles, Calif, Aug 17, 43; m 67; c 1. PLANT PATHOLOGY, SOIL MICROBIOLOGY. *Educ:* Calif State Polytech Univ, BS, 65; Wash State Univ, MS, 69, PhD(plant path), 72. *Prof Exp:* Soil scientist fertility res, USDA Agr Res Serv, 66-69; res asst root dis, Dept Plant Path, Wash State Univ, 69-72; NATO fel, Commonwealth Sci & Indust Res Orgn, Soils Div, Adelaide, SAustralia, 72, vis res scientist soil microbiol, 73; asst prof, 73-80, ASSOC PROF PLANT PATH, CORNELL UNIV, 80- *Concurrent Pos:* Vis scientist, Victoria Dept Agr, Melbourne, Australia, 81-82. *Mem:* Am Phytopath Soc; Am Soc Agron; Int Soc Plant Path; Int Turfgrass Soc. *Res:* Disease control investigations on turfgrasses and cereal grains; with emphasis on biological control of wheat root diseases, and on fungicidal, cultural or integrated chemical-biological control of turfgrass diseases. *Mailing Add:* 403 Plant Sci Bldg Dept of Plant Path Cornell Univ Ithaca NY 14853

SMILEY, ROBERT ARTHUR, b Cleveland, Ohio, Mar 14, 25; m 49; c 10. ORGANIC CHEMISTRY. *Educ:* Case Inst Technol, BS, 50; Purdue Univ, PhD(org chem), 54. *Prof Exp:* From res chemist to sr res chemist, Explosives Dept, 54-69, tech asst, 69-70, mgr polymer intermediates dept, 70-74, res assoc, 74-81, RES FEL, PETROCHEM DEPT, E I DU PONT DE NEMOURS & CO, INC, 81- *Mem:* Am Chem Soc; Catalysis Soc. *Res:* Preparation and reactions of aliphatic nitro compounds; reactions of nitric acid and nitrogen oxides with organic compounds; heterogeneous catalysis; preparation and reactions of nitriles. *Mailing Add:* Exp Sta Bldg 336 E I du Pont de Nemours & Co Inc Wilmington DE 19898

SMILEY, SEYMOUR HOWARD, chemistry, deceased

SMILEY, TERAH LEROY, b Clay Co, Kans, Aug 21, 14; m; c 5. GEOCHRONOLOGY. *Educ:* Univ Ariz, BA, 46, MA, 49. *Prof Exp:* Ranger naturalist & actg custodian, Nat Park Serv, 39-41; asst dendrochronologist, 46-51, asst archaeol, 51-54, geochronologist, Lab Tree Ring Res, 54-57, actg dir, 58-60, dir geochronology labs, 56-67, prof geochronology & head dept, 67-70, assoc head dept geosci & chief res labs, 70-74, PROF GEOSCI, UNIV ARIZ, 74- *Concurrent Pos:* Res fel, Clare Col, Cambridge Univ, 69; vis prof geol inst, Univ Uppsala, Sweden, 69-70. *Mem:* fel Geol Soc Am; Am Meteorol Soc; Am Quaternary Asn. *Res:* Arid lands studies, paleoclimatology of Southwest United States. *Mailing Add:* Dept of Geosci Univ of Ariz Tucson AZ 85721

SMILEY, VERN NEWTON, b Goshen, Ind, Sept 7, 30; m 56. OPTICS, ATMOSPHERIC PHYSICS. *Educ:* Univ Wis, BS, 55, MS, 56; Univ Colo, PhD(physics), 59. *Prof Exp:* Sr engr, Gen Dynamics/Convair, 59-61; resident res assoc, US Navy Electronics Lab Ctr, 61-62, res physicist, 62-71; prof physics, Univ Nev, Reno, 71-80, res prof atmospheric optics, Desert Res Inst, 71-80; SECT HEAD, ENERGY MEASUREMENT GROUP, EG&G, INC, 80- *Concurrent Pos:* Consult, Gen Dynamics/Convair, 61-63; US Navy res fel & vis scientist, York, Eng, 66-67; lectr appl physics & info sci dept, Univ Calif, San Diego, 71; liaison scientist, Off Naval Res, London, 77-79. *Mem:* AAAS; Am Phys Soc; Optical Soc Am; Sigma Xi. *Res:* Multi-layer thin films; infrared radiometers; gas phase lasers; scanning active interferometers; laser amplifiers; air pollution; atmospheric remote sensing with optical instrumentation; solar energy research; electro-optics and fiber optics research and development. *Mailing Add:* EG&G Inc 680 E Sunset Rd MS D-31 Las Vegas NV 89101

SMILLIE, LAWRENCE BRUCE, b Galt, Ont, July 5, 28; m 56; c 4. BIOCHEMISTRY. *Educ:* McMaster Univ, BSc, 50; Univ Toronto, MA, 52, PhD(biochem), 55. *Prof Exp:* Asst prof biochem, Univ Alta, 55-57; Nat Acad Sci-Nat Res Coun Donner fel med res, Univ Wash, 57-58; assoc prof, 58-67, PROF BIOCHEM, UNIV ALTA, 67- *Prof Exp:* Vis scientist, Lab Molecular Biol, Cambridge Univ, 63-64; vis scientist, Dept Biochem, Univ Birmingham, 71-72. *Mem:* Can Biochem Soc; Am Soc Biol Chemists; Brit Biochem Soc; fel Royal Soc Can. *Res:* Structure and function of enzymes; chemistry and functional role of the proteins of muscle and contractile systems. *Mailing Add:* Dept of Biochem Univ of Alta Edmonton AB T6G 2G7 Can

SMILOWITZ, BERNARD, b Philadelphia, Pa. APPLIED PHYSICS, ELECTRICAL ENGINEERING. *Educ:* Temple Univ, AB, 55; Univ Pittsburgh, PhD(physics), 63. *Prof Exp:* Instr physics, Temple Univ, 63-66; res scientist, AIL Div, Cutler Hammer Inc, 66-77, sr res scientist appl physics, AIL Div, Eaton Corp, 77-80. *Mem:* Am Phys Soc; Math Asn Am; Sigma Xi; Inst Elec & Electronics Engrs. *Res:* Applied physics and material science research associated with the development of microwave solid state devices. *Mailing Add:* AIL Div Walt Whitman Rd Melville NY 11746

SMILOWITZ, HENRY MARTIN, b Brooklyn, NY, Sept 25, 46. NEUROBIOLOGY, CELL BIOLOGY. *Educ:* Reed Col, AB, 68; Mass Inst Technol, PhD(biochem), 72. *Prof Exp:* Fel microbiol, Med Sch, Tufts Univ, 72-73, neurobiol, Harvard Med Sch, 73-76; ASST PROF PHARMACOL, HEALTH CTR, UNIV CONN, 76- *Mem:* Am Soc Cell Biol; Soc Neurosci; NY Acad Sci; Int Soc Neurosci; AAAS. *Res:* Regulation and development of neuromuscular junction function post-synaptic mechanisms; acetylcholine receptor and esterase: development, intracellular transport and localization; phosphorylation; role of calcium and calmodulin in maintenance and function; pharmacologic dissection of the acelyloholine receptor channel. *Mailing Add:* Dept Pharmacol Health Ctr Univ Conn Farmington CT 06032

SMILOWITZ, ZANE, b New York, NY, Sept 13, 33; m 59; c 3. ENTOMOLOGY. *Educ:* Univ Ga, BS, 61; Cornell Univ, MS, 65, PhD(entom), 67. *Prof Exp:* ASSOC PROF ENTOM, PA STATE UNIV, 67- *Mem:* AAAS; Entom Soc Am; Can Entom Soc. *Res:* Biological control; research and development of integrated pest management systems for potatoe pest; field effects; finding, acceptance and discrimination, suitability and parasitoid regulation of host development. *Mailing Add:* Dept Entom Pa State Univ University Park PA 16802

SMIT, CHRISTIAN JACOBUS BESTER, b Piet Retief, SAfrica, Jan 10, 27; m 52, 68; c 4. FOOD SCIENCE, AGRICULTURAL CHEMISTRY. *Educ:* Univ Pretoria, BS, 47, HED, 48; Univ Calif, Berkeley, PhD, 53. *Prof Exp:* Tech asst chem, SAfrican Dept Agr, 44-46; asst prof officer, Agr Res Inst, Univ Pretoria, 48-49; prof officer, Fruit & Food Technol Res Inst, SAfrica, 53-58, first prof officer & chief food technol sect, 58-60; prof food sci & head dept, Stellenbosch, 60-63; res food scientist, Sunkist Growers Inc, 63-68; head dept & chmn div, 73-80, actg dean, Col Agr, 80-81, PROF FOOD SCI, UNIV GA, 68-, ASSOC DEAN & DIR RESIDENT INSTRUCTION, COL AGR, 81- *Concurrent Pos:* Consult, Nat Nutrit Res Inst, SAfrica, 60-63. *Mem:* AAAS; Am Chem Soc; Inst Food Technol; hon mem SAfrican Asn Food Sci & Technol. *Res:* Fruit and vegetable chemistry and processing; occurrence, manufacture and use of pectic substances. *Mailing Add:* Rm 102 Conner Hall Col Agr Univ Ga Athens GA 30602

SMIT, DAVID ERNST, b Beloit, Wis, Sept 1, 42; m 67; c 3. SEDIMENTARY GEOLOGY, STRATIGRAPHY. *Educ:* Augustana Col, AB, 64; Univ Iowa, MS, 67, PhD(geol), 71. *Prof Exp:* Teaching asst geol, Univ Iowa, 65-67, res asst, 67-70; from instr to asst prof, Univ Wis-Stevens Point, 70-74; asst prof geol, Wichita State Univ, 74-78, res assoc, 78-80; SR GEOLOGIST, ENERGY RESERVES GROUP, 80- *Concurrent Pos:* Res assoc, Univ Iowa, 71; pres, Quad Resources Inc, 79-; co-dir NURE prog, Wichita State Univ, 79-80. *Mem:* Geol Soc Am; Soc Econ Paleontologists & Mineralogists; Int Asn Sedimentologists; Int Geol Cong. *Res:* Depositional environments and diagenesis of shallow marine-platform sedimentary rocks; comparative sedimentology of recent limestones and the equivalent ancient rocks; location and mode of occurence of uranium in sedimentary rocks. *Mailing Add:* 221 Timber Ridge Court Edmond OK 73034

SMIT, JAN, b Midwoud, Netherlands, Aug 30, 21; m 48; c 2. SOLID STATE PHYSICS. *Educ:* Delft Univ Technol, Ingenieur, 48; State Univ Leiden, PhD(physics), 56. *Prof Exp:* Engr, Philips, Endhoven, Netherlands, 41-45, physicist, 48-63; prof solid state magnetism, 63-74, PROF MAT SCI, UNIV SOUTHERN CALIF, 74- *Concurrent Pos:* Consult, Ampex Corp, 64- *Mem:* Am Phys Soc. *Mailing Add:* Dept of Elec Eng Sch of Eng Univ of Southern Calif Los Angeles CA 90007

SMITH, A(LBERT) LEE, b Omaha, Nebr, Apr 11, 24; m 48; c 6. PHYSICAL CHEMISTRY. *Educ:* Iowa State Univ, BS, 46; Ohio State Univ, PhD(phys chem), 50. *Prof Exp:* Res assoc, Res Found, Ohio State Univ, 50-51; supvr spectros lab, 51-69, mgr anal dept, 69-80, SCIENTIST, DOW CORNING CORP, 80- *Mem:* Am Chem Soc; Soc Appl Spectros; Coblentz Soc. *Res:* Infrared spectra of organosilicon compounds. *Mailing Add:* 400 Rollcrest Ct Midland MI 48640

SMITH, A(POLLO) M(ILTON) O(LIN), b Columbia, Mo, July 2, 11; m 43; c 3. AERONAUTICAL ENGINEERING. *Educ:* Calif Inst Technol, MS, 38. *Hon Degrees:* DSc, Univ Colo, 75. *Prof Exp:* Aerodynamicist, Douglas Aircraft Co, 38-42; chief engr rocket propulsion, Aerojet Eng Corp, 42-44; asst chief aerodynamicist, Douglas Aircraft Co, Long Beach, McDonnell Douglas Corp, 44-48; supvr design res, 48-54, supvr aerodyn res, 54-69, chief aerodyn eng res, 69-75; CONSULT, 75- *Concurrent Pos:* Mem subcomt internal flow, Nat Adv Comt Aeronaut, 48-51; mem, US Naval Tech Mission, Europe, 45; lectr, Univ Calif, Los Angeles, 54-58, adj prof, 75-80; Am ed, J Comput Methods Appl Mech & Eng, 72-77; consult, McDonnell Douglass Corp, 75-, Dynamics Technol, Inc, 77-80 & Bolt, Beranek & Newman, 78-; lectr, Peking Inst Aeronaut & Astronaut, 79; mem, Aeronaut Adv Comn, NASA, 80- *Honors & Awards:* Goddard Award, Am Inst Aeronaut & Astronaut, 54; co-winner Casey Baldwin Award, Can Aeronaut & Space Inst, 71; Wright Bros lectr, Am Inst Aeronaut & Astronaut, 74. *Mem:* Am Phys Soc; fel Am Inst Aeronaut & Astronaut; Am Soc Mech Engrs; AAAS. *Res:* Aerodynamic and applied mechanics, especially boundary layer and heat transfer; inviscid flow theory. *Mailing Add:* 2245 Ashbourne Dr San Marino CA 91108

SMITH, A(LLEN) N(ATHAN), b New Orleans, La, Oct 24, 21. CHEMICAL ENGINEERING. *Educ:* Tulane Univ, BS, 41; Ga Inst Technol, MS, 43; Ore State Univ, PhD(chem eng), 48. *Prof Exp:* With J E Sirrine & Co, Engrs, SC, 41; chem engr, Aberdeen Proving Ground, Md, 41-42; technologist, Shell Oil Co, 43-45; chem engr, Union Oil Co, 45-56; assoc prof chem eng, Univ Louisville, 48-52; from assoc prof to prof, 52-63, CHMN DEPT CHEM ENG, SAN JOSE STATE UNIV, 63- *Mem:* Am Soc Eng Educ; fel Am Inst Chem Engrs. *Res:* Dialysis; fluid flow; heat and mass transfer. *Mailing Add:* Dept of Chem Eng San Jose State Univ San Jose CA 95192

SMITH, ADOLPH E, biophysics, see previous edition

SMITH, ALAN B, b Chicago, Ill, Dec 19, 24; m 43; c 1. NUCLEAR PHYSICS. *Educ:* Beloit Col, BA, 49; Ind Univ, MS, 50, PhD(nuclear physics), 53. *Prof Exp:* Assoc physicist, Argonne Nat Lab, 53-58, head, Appl Nuclear Physics Sect, Appl Physics Div, 58-61, SR PHYSICIST, APPL NUCLEAR PHYSICS SECT, APPL PHYSICS DIV, ARGONNE NAT LAB, 61- *Mem:* Fel Am Phys Soc. *Res:* Neutron and fission physics. *Mailing Add:* Bldg 208 Argonne Nat Lab 9700 S Cass Ave Argonne IL 60439

SMITH, ALAN BRADFORD, b Karuizawa, Japan, July 28, 32; US citizen; m 57; c 2. MAGNETISM. *Educ:* Swarthmore Col, BS, 53; Rensselaer Polytech Inst, MEE, 59; Harvard Univ, MA, 60, PhD(appl physics), 66. *Prof Exp:* Engr, Sprague Elec Co, 53-59; res asst appl physics, Harvard Univ, 61-65;

MEM RES STAFF, SPERRY RAND RES CTR, 65- *Concurrent Pos:* Ed-in-chief, Transactions on Magnetics, Inst Elec & Electronics Engrs, 79-81. *Mem:* AAAS; Am Phys Soc; Inst Elec & Electronics Engrs. *Res:* Magneto-optics; magnetic-domain memory devices; magnetoacoustic interactions in solids; ferromagnetic resonance; microwave ultrasonics. *Mailing Add:* Stonehedge Lincoln MA 01773

SMITH, ALAN JERRARD, b London, Eng, May 8, 29; m 58; c 2. PHARMACOLOGY. *Educ:* Univ London, BSc, 50, PhD(chem), 56. *Prof Exp:* Asst, Univ Col, Exeter, Eng, 53-54; res chemist, Admiralty Mat Lab, Eng, 54-57; group leader res, Rohm and Haas Co, 57-63, regulatory liaison, 63-64; asst mgr anal develop, 64-70, mgr qual control tech serv, 70-78, mgr, 78-79, ASST DIR, CORP QUAL ASSURANCE, AYERST LABS INC, 79- *Concurrent Pos:* mem, Comt Quality Systs, Am Soc Testing & Mat, 78- *Mem:* Am Soc Qual Control; Am Chem Soc. *Res:* Pharmaceutical quality assurance and control; stability of pharmaceuticals; analytical methods for pharmaceuticals; ion exchange; redox polymers; chemistry of transition metals. *Mailing Add:* Ayerst Labs Rouses Point NY 12979

SMITH, ALAN LYLE, b Bartley, Nebr, June 27, 41; m 61; c 2. PLANT ECOLOGY. *Educ:* Kearney State Col, BS, 64; Univ Nebr, MS, 68; Tex A&M Univ, PhD(ecol), 71. *Prof Exp:* Instr chem, Cozad High Sch, Nebr, 64-65; range scientist veg control, Tex Trans Inst, 72; plant ecologist, Dames & Moore, 72-80. *Concurrent Pos:* Proj ecologist, Prep Environ Report, Seadock Inc, 73-74; ecol consult, Environ Report LOOP Inc, 73-75; proj mgr, site selection petrochem facil Int Consortium, 74. *Mem:* Bot Soc Am; Soc Range Mgt. *Res:* Impact of crude oil on coastal marshes and problems associated with establishing vegetation on problem soils, especially related to strip mining reclamation. *Mailing Add:* 11626 Crystalwood Houston TX 77013

SMITH, ALAN PAUL, b Morristown, NJ, Mar 31, 45. PLANT ECOLOGY. *Educ:* Earlham Col, BA, 67; Duke Univ, MA, 70, PhD(bot), 74. *Prof Exp:* Asst prof biol, Univ Pa, Philadelphia, 74-80; BIOLOGIST ECOL, SMITHSONIAN TROP RES INST, BALBOA, CZ, 74-; ASSOC PROF BIOL, UNIV MIAMI, CORAL GABLES, 82- *Mem:* Sigma Xi; Torrey Bot Club; Ecol Soc Am; Asn Trop Biol. *Res:* Ecological and evolutionary significance of latitudinal gradients in plant form; plant ecology of tropical alpine zones of the world; population ecology of early successional communities in eastern US. *Mailing Add:* Smithsonian Trop Res Inst Box 2072 Balboa CZ

SMITH, ALAN REID, b Sacramento, Calif, July 14, 43; m 66; c 2. BOTANY. *Educ:* Kans State Univ, BS, 65; Iowa State Univ, PhD(bot), 69. *Prof Exp:* Asst res botanist, 69-77, ASSOC RES BOTANIST, UNIV CALIF, BERKELEY, 77- *Concurrent Pos:* Ed, Pteridologia, 78- *Mem:* Am Soc Plant Taxon; Am Fern Soc; Brit Pteridological Soc. *Res:* Taxonomy of ferns; Thelypteris; pteridophytes of Chiapas, Mexico. *Mailing Add:* Dept of Bot Univ of Calif Berkeley CA 94720

SMITH, ALAN WAYNE, b Alameda, Calif, Sept 18, 24; m 49; c 1. PHYSICAL CHEMISTRY. *Educ:* Univ Calif, BS, 47; Princeton Univ, PhD(phys chem), 50. *Prof Exp:* Instr chem, City Col San Francisco, 47; instr Princeton Univ, 50-52; sr res engr, NAm Aviation, Inc, 52-55; sr res chemist, Union Carbide Corp, 55-64; staff mem, Boeing Sci Res Lab, 64-73, process engr, 73-81, SUPVR, BOEING AEROSPACE CO, 81- *Mailing Add:* 1654 Interlaken Pl E Seattle WA 98112

SMITH, ALBERT CARL, b Los Angeles, Calif, Sept 13, 34; m 67; c 2. PATHOBIOLOGY, PATHOLOGY. *Educ:* Univ Calif, Los Angeles, BA, 56; Univ Calif, Irvine, PhD(biol sci), 67; Univ Hawaii, MD, 75, Am Bd Path, cert, 79. *Prof Exp:* Asst to sr scientists, Univ Hawaii, 59; res scientist, Calif Dept Fish & Game, 61-63, 65-66 & 70-71; lab technician, Allergan Pharmaceut, 63; lab technician, Orange County Gen Hosp, 64; lab technician, Univ Calif, Irvine, 64-65, res asst organismic biol, 66, res assoc & instr pop & environ biol, 66-67; from asst prof to assoc prof biol, Univ Hawaii, Hilo, 67-73, mem grad fac zool, Univ Hawaii, Honolulu, 68-77, mem staff, Oceanic Inst, Hawaii, 77-; Dir, Medical Labs Hawaii, Inc, 79-80; CHIEF CLIN LAB, VET ADMIN MED CTR, 80-; ASST PROF PATH, COL MED & VET MED, UNIV FLA, GAINESVILLE, 80- *Concurrent Pos:* Res assoc from dept pop & environ & pop environ biol, Univ Calif, Irvine, 67-; res grants, Bur Nat Marine Fisheries Serv, US Dept Commerce, 68-69; res grant Univ Hawaii, 68-72, sea grant, 71-73; consult dir genetics lab, Calif State Fisheries Lab, Long Beach, 69-; prog dir path, Aquatic Sci, Inc, Fla, 69-70, consult, 70-; Marine Biol Consults, Inc, Calif, 70-; grant Am Found Oceanog, 69-77, 77 & 78; with Calif Dept Fish & Game, 70-71; chief consult, Hawaii BioMarine, 70-; res assoc & consult, Oceanic Inst, 71-; sr sci staff consult pathobiol, Pan Pac Inst Ocean Sci, 73-; grants, US Energy Res & Develop Admin, 71-72, NIH, 72-73, NSF, 72-74 & Puerto Rico Int Undersea Lab, 73, USAID, 76-, Rockefeller Found, 78-79 & Engelhard Found, 78-79; res fel path, Univ Hawaii, 75-76; clin path residency, St Francis Hosp, Honolulu, 77-78 & Queens Med Ctr, 78-79; marine affairs coordr, State Hawaii, 78; consult, Astromarine, Kuai, Hawaii, Hawaiian Elec Comp, Honolulu, State Univ Syst Fla, 81, Sea Grant, 80, clin path, Sunland Ctr, Gainesville, Fla; res fac, Univ Fla, 81. *Mem:* Hawaiian Acad Sci (pres-elect, 68-69); AAAS; Soc Invert Path; NY Acad Sci; Am Fisheries Soc. *Res:* Evolution; experimental taxonomy; electrophoretic technique; diving and deep sea biology; pathobiology; proteins of the eye lens; immunobiology and serology; chemical phylogenetics. *Mailing Add:* Lab Serv Vet Admin Med Ctr Archer Rd Gainesville FL 32602

SMITH, ALBERT CHARLES, b Springfield, Mass, Apr 5, 06; m 35, 60, 66; c 2. BOTANY. *Educ:* Columbia Univ, AB, 26, PhD(bot), 33. *Prof Exp:* From asst cur to assoc cur, NY Bot Garden, 28-40; cur herbarium, Arnold Arboretum, Harvard Univ, 40-48, ed j, 41-48, cur div phanerogams, Dept Bot, Smithsonian Inst, 48-56; prog dir syst biol, NSF, 56-58; dir, Mus Natural Hist, US Nat Mus, 58-62, asst secy, Smithsonian Inst, 62-63; dir res & prof bot, Univ Hawaii, 63-65, Wilder prof, 65-70; Torrey prof bot, Univ Mass, Amherst, 70-76; ED CONSULT, PAC TROP BOT GARDEN, 77- *Concurrent Pos:* Mem bot expeds, Colombia, Peru, Brazil, Fiji, Brit Guiana

& W Indies, 26-69; fel, Bishop Mus, Yale Univ, 33-34; Guggenheim fel, 46-47; Ed, Brittonia, 35-40, J Arnold Arboretum, 41-48, Sargentia, 42-48 & Allertonia, 77- *Honors & Awards:* Robert Allerton Award, 79. *Mem:* Nat Acad Sci; fel Am Acad Arts & Sci; Linnean Soc London; Asn Trop Biol (pres, 67-68); Int Asn Plant Taxon (vpres, 59-64). *Res:* Taxonomy and phytogeography of flowering plants, especially of tropical America and southwest Pacific. *Mailing Add:* Dept of Bot Univ of Hawaii Honolulu HI 96822

SMITH, ALBERT ERNEST, b Ransom, Kans, Dec 4, 38; m 60; c 2. PLANT PHYSIOLOGY. *Educ:* Ft Hays Kans State Col, BSc, 64; Tex A&M Univ, PhD(range sci), 69. *Prof Exp:* Assoc prof, 69-80, PROF AGRON, UNIV GA, 80- *Mem:* Am Soc Plant Physiol; Am Soc Agron; Weed Sci Soc Am; Am Soc Range Mgt. *Res:* Research on the plant physiology and biochemistry of the modes of actions of herbicides. *Mailing Add:* Dept of Agron Univ of Ga Exp Sta Experiment GA 30212

SMITH, ALBERT ERNEST, b Windham, Vt, Nov 1, 27; m 50; c 2. PHYSICS. *Educ:* Atlantic Union Col, BA, 49; Mich State Univ, MS, 51, PhD(physics), 54. *Prof Exp:* Instr physics, Mich State Univ, 53-54; asst prof, Union Col, Nebr, 54-57; res physicist, Radio Corp Am, NJ, 57-59; prof, Atlantic Union Col, 59-69, dean, 67-69; assoc dir phys sci, Tech Opers Inc, 69-71; PROF PHYSICS, LOMA LINDA UNIV, LA SIERRA CAMPUS, 71- *Mem:* Optical Soc Am. *Res:* Physical optics; image theory; photographic methods; optical instrumentation. *Mailing Add:* Dept of Physics Loma Linda Univ La Sierra Campus Riverside CA 92505

SMITH, ALBERT GOODIN, b Charleston, Mo, Aug 26, 24; m 53. PATHOLOGY. *Educ:* Washington Univ, MD, 47. *Prof Exp:* Intern, St Luke's Hosp, St Louis, 47-48; asst resident & resident path, Hosp, Univ Ark, 48-50; vol asst surg path, Col Physicians & Surgeons, Columbia Univ, 50; asst resident, resident & instr path, Sch Med, Duke Univ, 5051, assoc, 52-55, from asst prof to assoc prof, 55-66; prof path & dep chmn dept, Col Med, Univ Tenn & dir labs, City Memphis Hosps, 66-70; PROF PATH & HEAD DEPT, SCH MED, LA STATE UNIV, SHREVEPORT, 70- *Concurrent Pos:* Chief lab serv, Vet Admin Hosp, Shreveport, La, 70-; chief path serv, Confederate Mem Med Ctr, Shreveport, 71- *Mem:* AAAS; Am Soc Clin Path; Am Soc Exp Path; AMA; Am Asn Pathologists & Bacteriologists. *Res:* Surgical pathology; tissue culture; nucleic acid tissue effects; teratology. *Mailing Add:* Dept of Path La State Univ Sch of Med Shreveport LA 71130

SMITH, ALBERT MATTHEWS, b Bangor, Maine, Dec 25, 27; m 50; c 2. ANIMAL NUTRITION. *Educ:* Univ Maine, BS, 52; Cornell Univ, MS, 54, PhD(animal nutrit), 56. *Prof Exp:* From instr to asst prof animal husb, Cornell Univ, 55-57; from asst prof to assoc prof, 57-64, chmn dept animal sci, 63-79, PROF ANIMAL NUTRIT, UNIV VT, 64-, ANIMAL NUTRITIONIST, 61-, ASSOC DEAN, COL AGR & ASSOC DIR, VT STATE AGR EXP STA, 75- *Mem:* Am Dairy Sci Asn; Am Soc Animal Sci; Sigma Xi; AAAS. *Res:* Dairy cattle nutrition; forage evaluation, especially role of forages in summer and winter feeding regimes; mineral metabolism. *Mailing Add:* Off Dean Col Agr Morill Hall Univ of Vt Burlington VT 05401

SMITH, ALDEN ERNEST, b Lockport, NY, Apr 25, 23. SCIENCE EDUCATION, AQUATIC BIOLOGY. *Educ:* Univ Colo, Boulder, BA, 50; Univ Buffalo, EdM, 60; Syracuse Univ, MS, 64; State Univ NY Buffalo, EdD(sci educ), 71. *Prof Exp:* Lab asst bot, Brookhaven Nat Lab, 54-56; teacher jr high sch, Lockport Bd Educ, NY, 56-59, high sch, 59-65; assoc prof, 65-80, PROF BIOL, STATE UNIV NY COL BUFFALO, 80- *Mem:* AAAS; Am Inst Biol Sci; Nat Asn Biol Teachers; Nat Sci Teachers Asn. *Res:* Methods of teaching biology at the college level; aquatic plants; biology of organisms in fresh water environments; wild and cultivated poisonous plants. *Mailing Add:* Dept of Biol State Univ Col 1300 Elmwood Ave Buffalo NY 14222

SMITH, ALEXANDER GOUDY, b Clarksburg, WVa, Aug 12, 19; m 42; c 2. ASTROPHYSICS. *Educ:* Mass Inst Technol, SB, 43; Duke Univ, PhD(physics), 49. *Prof Exp:* Mem staff radiation lab, Mass Inst Technol, 42-46; instr & asst Duke Univ, 46-68; from asst prof to prof physics, 48-56, asst dean grad sch, 61-69, chmn dept astron, 62-71, actg dean grad sch, 71-73, PROF ASTRON & PHYSICS, UNIV FLA, 56-, DISTINGUISHED ALUMNI ASSOC PROF, 81- *Concurrent Pos:* Consult, US Air Force, 54-65; mem bd dirs, Assoc Univ for Res in Astron, 60-63, consult, 64-69; mem users' comt, Nat Radio Astron Observ, 66-78, vis comt, 68-71; mem comt astron, Nat Res Coun, 66-69, chmn, 68-69; adv panel astron, NSF, 69-72; ed, Am Astron Soc Photo Bull, 75- *Honors & Awards:* Medal, Fla Acad Sci, 65. *Mem:* Fel AAAS; fel Am Phys Soc; fel Optical Soc Am; Am Astron Soc; Int Sci Radio Union. *Res:* Magnetron design; microwave molecular spectroscopy; atmospheric optics; radio astronomy; planetary radio astronomy; optical and radio variations of quasars; photographic techniques in astronomy. *Mailing Add:* Dept Astron Univ of Fla 211 Space Sci Bldg Gainesville FL 32611

SMITH, ALICE LORRAINE, b Trinity, Tex. PATHOLOGY. *Educ:* Univ Tex, BA, 40, MD, 46; Am Bd Path, dipl, 51. *Prof Exp:* Asst prof path, Univ Tex Southwestern Med Sch, 50-54; asst pathologist, Univ Hosp, Baylor Univ, 54-55; from asst prof to assoc prof path, Col Med, 55-57, prof, Res Inst & assoc prof, Col Dent, 57-61; assoc prof, 62-76, PROF PATH, UNIV TEX HEALTH SCI CTR, DALLAS, 76-; DIR, DIV DIAG CYTOL & DIR, SCH CYTOTECHNOL, PARKLAND MEM HOSP, 62- *Concurrent Pos:* Pathologist, Wadley Res Inst & Blood Bank, 57-61, clin assoc, Univ Tex Health Sci Ctr, Dallas, 58-62. *Mem:* Fel Am Col Physicians; fel Am Soc Clin Path; fel Am Col Path; AMA. *Mailing Add:* Dept Path Univ Tex Health Sci Ctr Dallas TX 75235

SMITH, ALLAN EDWARD, b Hull, Eng, June 2, 37; m 70. AGRICULTURE, ORGANIC CHEMISTRY. *Educ:* Univ Liverpool, BSc, 59, PhD(org chem), 63. *Prof Exp:* Fel radiol sci, Johns Hopkins Hosp, 63-65; res chemist, Agr Div, Imp Chem Industs, 65-67; RES CHEMIST, CAN DEPT AGR, 67- *Mem:* Europ Weed Res Soc; fel Chem Inst Can; The Chem Soc; Weed Sci Soc Am. *Res:* Fate of herbicides after application, their biological and chemical degradation and their uptake into plants and metabolism. *Mailing Add:* Can Dept Agr Box 440 Regina SK S4P 3A2 Can

SMITH, ALLAN LASLETT, b Newark, NJ, June 21, 38; m 60; c 2. PHYSICAL CHEMISTRY. *Educ:* Harvard Univ, BA, 60; Mass Inst Technol, PhD(phys chem), 65. *Prof Exp:* Nat Acad Sci-Nat Res Coun fel, Nat Bur Standards, 65-66; from asst prof to assoc prof chem, Yale Univ, 66-74; head dept math, Daycroft Sch, Rock Ridge, Conn, 75; ASSOC PROF CHEM, DREXEL UNIV, 75- *Concurrent Pos:* Alfred P Sloan Found fel, 70; NATO sr fel, Phys Chem Lab, Oxford Univ, 71. *Mem:* Am Phys Soc; Am Chem Soc; Inst Elec & Electronic Engrs Comput Sci. *Res:* Molecular spectroscopy; gas phase electronic spectroscopy; laser fluroescence and flash photolysis of transient species; photochemical kinetics; computers in chemistry (simulations, graphics). *Mailing Add:* Dept Chem Drexel Univ Philadelphia PA 19104

SMITH, ALLEN ANDERSON, b Boston, Mass. DEVELOPMENTAL BIOLOGY, HISTOCHEMISTRY. *Educ:* Brown Univ, AB, 61; Univ Ore, PhD(anat), 69. *Prof Exp:* Instr anat, Hahnemann Med Col, 69-70; instr zool, Tel Aviv Univ, 70-71; res asst, Temple Univ, 71-74; asst prof, 74-78, ASSOC PROF BIOL, WIDENER COL, 78- *Concurrent Pos:* Vis scientist, Dept Org Chem, Weizmann Inst, 81. *Mem:* Am Inst Biol Sci; Soc Develop Biol; Histochem Soc. *Res:* Sweat glands; epithelio-mesenchymal interactions; pharmacology of rotaxanes. *Mailing Add:* Div of Sci Widener Col Chester PA 19013

SMITH, ALLIE MAITLAND, b Lumberton, NC, June 9, 34; m 57; c 3. MECHANICAL & AEROSPACE ENGINEERING. *Educ:* NC State Univ, BSME, 56, MS, 61, PhD(thermal radiation), 66. *Prof Exp:* Assoc engr, Martin Co, 56-57; develop engr, Western Elec Co, 57-58; instr eng, NC State Col, 58-60; mem tech staff, Bell Tel Labs, 60-62; res engr, Res Triangle Inst, 62-66; supvr res, Aro, Inc, 66-80; PROF MECH ENG & DEAN, SCH ENG, UNIV MISS, 80- *Concurrent Pos:* Asst prof mech eng, Exten Div, NC State Col, 61-62; part-time assoc prof aerospace eng, Space Inst, Univ Tenn, 67- *Mem:* Am Inst Aeronaut & Astronaut. *Res:* Thermal radiative characteristics of cryodeposits and surfaces; effects of space environment on thermal control materials; space simulation; radiation gas dynamics; solid state diffusion; heat transfer; fluid mechanics; cryogenics; vacuum. *Mailing Add:* Dept Eng Univ Miss University MS 38677

SMITH, ALTON HUTCHISON, b Long Beach, Calif, July 28, 30. TOPOLOGY. *Educ:* Pepperdine Col, BA, 51; Univ Southern Calif, MA, 52, PhD(math), 56. *Prof Exp:* Res mathematician, Ramo-Wooldridge Corp, 56-57; from asst prof to assoc prof 57-65, PROF MATH, CALIF STATE UNIV, LONG BEACH, 65- *Concurrent Pos:* Consult, Ramo-Wooldridge Corp, 57-58. *Mem:* Am Math Soc; Math Asn Am. *Res:* Algebraic topology; spaces with operators. *Mailing Add:* Dept of Math Calif State Univ Long Beach CA 90840

SMITH, ALVIN WINFRED, laboratory animal medicine, marine virology, see previous edition

SMITH, ALVIN WINFRED, b Kooskia, Idaho, Sept 25, 33; m 58; c 4. MARINE VIROLOGY. *Educ:* Wash State Univ, BA, 55, DVM, 57; Tex A&M Univ, MS, 67; Univ Calif, Berkeley, PhD(comp path), 75. *Prof Exp:* Chief, Res Animal Br, Sch Aerospace Med, 67-69, Res Animal Div, Naval Biosci Lab, 69-78, virol, Naval Ocean Syst Ctr, 78-80; res veterinarian, 80-81, DIR RES, SCH VET MED, ORE STATE UNIV, 81- *Concurrent Pos:* chief, Marine Mammal Res Div, Naval Biosci Lab, 74-78, Virol Sect, San Diego Zoo, 78-80. *Mem:* Am Vet Med Asn; Am Col Lab Animal Med; Int Asn Aquatic Animal Med. *Res:* Mechanisms of transmission and survival of infectious disease agents in nature. *Mailing Add:* Sch Vet Med Ore State Univ Corvallis OR 97331

SMITH, AMELIA LILLIAN, b Phila, Pa, Mar 25, 24; m 50; c 2. PHYSIOLOGY. *Educ:* Ursinus Col, BS, 48; Rutgers Univ, MS, 62, PhD(physiol), 72. *Prof Exp:* Res assoc physiol, Merck Inst Therapeut Res, 50-54; instr radiation physics, Lyons Inst, 54-58; biophysicist, Rutgers Univ, NB, 63-64; assoc prof, 66-76, prof physiol, 76-80, PROF BIOL SCI, KEAN COL NJ, 80- *Concurrent Pos:* Researcher, Rutgers Univ, NB, 67-72. *Res:* Cardiac muscle tissue; electron-microscopy, electrolytic and biochemical assays including acid hydrolases as well as isolation and characterization of acid, neutral and alkaline proteases and study of effects of stress models on these enzymes; radiation science. *Mailing Add:* Dept of Biol Kean Col of NJ Union NJ 07083

SMITH, ANDERSON DODD, b Richmond, Va, May 3, 44; m 66; c 2. GERONTOLOGY, EXPERIMENTAL PSYCHOLOGY. *Educ:* Washington & Lee Univ, BA, 66; Univ Va, MA, 69, PhD(exp psychol), 70. *Prof Exp:* Asst prof, 70-75, assoc prof, 75-81, PROF PSYCHOL, GA INST TECHNOL, 81- *Concurrent Pos:* NIH res grant, Nat Inst Aging, 72-, NIMH grant, 81; ed psychol sci, J Gerontol, 81-; affil scientist, Yerkes Regional Primate Ctr, 81- *Mem:* Sigma Xi; fel Am Psychol Asn; Psychonomic Soc; fel Gerontol Soc. *Res:* Experimental psychology of human memory; age-related differences in encoding, storage and retrieval processes. *Mailing Add:* Sch of Psychol Ga Inst of Technol Atlanta GA 30332

SMITH, ANDREW GEORGE, b Williamsport, Pa, July 11, 18; m 45; c 2. MICROBIOLOGY, MEDICAL MYCOLOGY. *Educ:* Pa State Univ, BS, 40; Univ Pa, MS, 47, PhD, 50; Am Bd Med Microbiol, dipl, 71. *Prof Exp:* From asst prof to assoc prof microbiol, Sch Med, Univ Md, 50-66; dir bact prod div, BBL Div, BioQuest, Md, 66-69; from assoc prof to prof microbiol, Sch Med, Univ Vt, 69-72; assoc prof, 72-75, PROF PATH, SCH MED, UNIV MD, BALTIMORE CITY & DIR MICROBIOL LAB, HOSP, 72-, ASSOC PROF MED IN DERMATOL, 77- *Concurrent Pos:* Consult, Vet Admin Hosp, Baltimore, 67-69 & 73. *Honors & Awards:* Lederle Med Fac Award, 55; Barnett L Cohem Award, Am Soc Microbiol, 76. *Mem:* Fel Am Acad Microbiol; AAAS; Am Soc Microbiol; Med Mycol Soc Ams. *Res:* Bacterial cytology; applied and clinical mcirobiology; medical mycology. *Mailing Add:* Dept of Clin Path Univ of Md Sch of Med Baltimore MD 21201

SMITH, ANDREW PHILIP, b Rochester, NY, Mar 6, 45. MEMBRANE BIOCHEMISTRY, NEUROCHEMISTRY. *Educ:* Dartmouth Col, AB, 66; Stanford Univ, PhD(neurosci), 71. *Prof Exp:* Lab asst, 71-72, fel, 72-73, RES PHARMACOLOGIST, MED CTR, UNIV CALIF, SAN FRANCISCO, 74- *Res:* Structure and function of biological membranes; isolation and characterization of neurotransmitter receptors. *Mailing Add:* Dept Pharmacol Med Ctr Univ Calif San Francisco CA 94137

SMITH, ANDREW THOMAS, b Glendale, Calif, Mar 14, 46. ECOLOGY. *Educ:* Univ Calif, Berkeley, AB, 68; Univ Calif, Los Angeles, PhD(biol), 73. *Prof Exp:* Lectr zool, Univ Alta, 73-74; asst prof biol, Univ Miami, 74-78; ASST PROF ZOOL, ARIZ STATE UNIV, 78- *Concurrent Pos:* Prin investr, US Nat Park Serv, 78-79; hon consult, Int Union Conserv Nature, 78- *Mem:* AAAS; Am Soc Mammalogists; Ecol Soc Am; Soc Study of Evolution; Wildlife Soc. *Res:* Wildlife ecology; population and community ecology; dispersal; biogeography; mammalogy; reproductive strategies. *Mailing Add:* Dept of Zool Ariz State Univ Tempe AZ 85281

SMITH, ANTHONY JAMES, b Kansas City, Mo, Aug 19, 18; m 43; c 4. ELECTROCHEMISTRY. *Educ:* Univ Mo, AB, 42. *Prof Exp:* res chemist, Nat Fertilizer Develop Ctr, Tenn Valley Authority, 42-81; RETIRED. *Mem:* Am Chem Soc; Int Asn Hydrogen Energy; Nat Mgt Asn. *Res:* Electrolytic production of hydrogen; corrosion; microwave dielectric properties, density, pH, specific gravity, vapor pressure, viscoscity of phosphatic solutions; electrolytic production of potassium phosphates; purification of phosphoric acid. *Mailing Add:* 710 Prospect St Florence AL 35630

SMITH, ARCHIBALD WILLIAM, b Edmonton, Alta, Jan 6, 30; m 53; c 3. LASERS. *Educ:* Univ Alta, BSc, 52, MSc, 53; Univ Toronto, PhD(physics), 55. *Prof Exp:* Staff mem, Defense Res Bd, Can, 56-61; staff mem, Thomas J Watson Res Ctr, IBM Corp, 62-76, sr adv engr, 77-80; WITH DISCOVISION, 80- *Mem:* Am Phys Soc; Inst Elec & Electronics Eng. *Res:* Laser and semiconductor physics. *Mailing Add:* Discovision 3300 Hyland Ave Costa Mesa CA 92626

SMITH, ARCHIE LEE, b Washington, DC, Aug 24, 32; m 53; c 1. BIOCHEMISTRY. *Educ:* George Washington Univ, BS, 55, MS, 57, PhD(biochem), 60. *Prof Exp:* Water chemist, US Geol Surv, 51-55; instr biochem, George Washington Univ, 56-59; trainee, Inst Enzyme Res, Univ Wis, 59-61, asst prof enzyme chem, 61-64; vis scholar zool, Columbia Univ, 64-65; assoc prof biochem, Sloan-Kettering Inst Cancer Res, 65-67; sr scientist res div, Shulton Inc, NJ, 67-72; consult biochem, Lab Animal Supplies & Toxicol, Riverside, Conn, 72-74; ASSOC PROF BIOCHEM, NY COL PODIATRIC MED, 74- *Concurrent Pos:* Estab investr, Am Heart Assn, 64-69. *Mem:* AAAS; Am Soc Biol Chemists. *Res:* Role of lipids in mitochondrial electron transport and oxidative phosphorylation; lipid interaction in enzyme catalysis. *Mailing Add:* Dept of Biochem NY Col of Podiatric Med New York NY 10035

SMITH, ARLO IRVING, b Ft Smith, Ark, July 23, 11; m 37; c 3. BIOLOGY. *Educ:* Hendrix Col, AB, 32; Northwestern Univ, MS, 35; Univ Wash, PhD(bot), 38. *Prof Exp:* Prof biol, McMurry Col, 38-39; instr, Tex Tech Col, 39-42, asst prof bot, 45-46; from assoc prof to prof biol, 46-77, EMER PROF BIOL, SOUTHWESTERN AT MEMPHIS, 77- *Concurrent Pos:* Dir, Southwestern Arboretum, 55- *Mem:* Fel AAAS; Am Inst Biol Sci; Ecol Soc Am; Bot Soc Am. *Res:* Systematic botany; ecology; science education; wild flowers of south central United States, including some common trees, vines, shrubs and ferns. *Mailing Add:* 3724 Oakley Ave Memphis TN 38111

SMITH, ARMAND VERNE, JR, mathematics, statistics, see previous edition

SMITH, ARNOLD CHAUNCEY, b Barton, Vt, Sept 25, 20; m 47; c 3. DAIRY INDUSTRY. *Educ:* Univ Vt, BS, 42; Pa State Univ, MS, 48, PhD, 50. *Prof Exp:* Asst, Pa State Univ, 46-50; asst prof animal indust, Okla Agr & Mech Col, 50-52; asst prof, 52-58, assoc prof, 58-68, prof animal indust, 68-77, PROF DAIRY MGT, UNIV CONN, 77- *Mem:* Dairy Sci Asn. *Res:* Dairy manufacturing relating to market milk adulteration; cream viscosity and storage; off-flavors in milk and quality milk production; vacuum processing of fluid milk; laboratory procedures related to quality control. *Mailing Add:* Dept of Animal Indust Univ of Conn Storrs CT 06268

SMITH, ARTHUR CLARKE, b Bartlesville, Okla, Sept 23, 29; m 55; c 3. SOLID STATE PHYSICS. *Educ:* Univ Kans, BS, 51; Harvard Univ, MA, 54, PhD(appl physics), 58. *Prof Exp:* Res fel & instr appl physics, Harvard Univ, 58-59; from asst prof to assoc prof elec eng, 59-68, PROF ELEC ENG, MASS INST TECHNOL, 68- *Mem:* Am Asn Physics Teachers; Am Phys Soc. *Mailing Add:* Dept of Elec Eng & Comput Sci Mass Inst Technol Cambridge MA 02139

SMITH, ARTHUR GERALD, b Newton, Kans, Jan 12, 29; m 49; c 1. ELECTROCHEMISTRY, ACCELERATED CORROSION. *Educ:* Phillips Univ, AB, 50; Iowa State Univ, MS, 53. *Prof Exp:* Chemist, Standard Oil Co, 53-58; res scientist, 58-68, sr res scientist, 68-76, PRIN RES SCIENTIST ASSOC, FORD MOTOR CO, 76- *Mem:* Am Chem Soc; Electrochem Soc. *Res:* Paint adhesion failure mechanism studies; development of novel paints and paint application techniques; corrosion studies of single and multimetal systems; development of accelerated corrosion tests. *Mailing Add:* 9257 California Livonia MI 48150

SMITH, ARTHUR HAMILTON, b Santa Barbara, Calif, Mar 28, 16; m 39; c 2. PHYSIOLOGY. *Educ:* Univ Calif, AB, 38, PhD(comp physiol), 48. *Prof Exp:* Asst animal husb, Univ Calif, Davis, 37-41 & 46-47, sr biochemist, 48; physiologist, Radiation Lab, Univ Calif, Berkeley, 48, AEC fel med sci, 48-50; lectr poultry husb, 50-51, asst prof, 51-55, assoc prof & assoc physiologist, Agr Exp Sta, 55-62, prof poultry husb & physiologist, 62-64, PROF PHYSIOL & PHYSIOLOGIST, AGR EXP STA, UNIV CALIF, DAVIS, 76- *Mem:* Aerospace Med Soc; Soc Exp Biol & Med; Am Phys Soc; Biophys Soc; Poultry Sci Asn. *Res:* Environmental physiology; gravitational physiology. *Mailing Add:* Dept of Animal Physiol Univ of Calif Davis CA 95616

SMITH, ARTHUR JOHN STEWART, b Victoria, BC, June 28, 38; m 66; c 2. EXPERIMENTAL HIGH ENERGY PHYSICS. *Educ:* Univ BC, BA, 59, MSc, 61; Princeton Univ, PhD(physics), 66. *Prof Exp:* Volkswagen Found fel physics, Deutsches Elektronen-Synchrotron, Hamburg, WGer, 66-67; from instr to assoc prof, 67-78, PROF PHYSICS, PRINCETON UNIV, 78- *Concurrent Pos:* Vis scientist, Brookhaven Nat Lab & Fern Lab. *Mem:* Am Phys Soc. *Res:* Experimental high energy particle physics; electromagnetic and weak interactions. *Mailing Add:* Joseph Henry Labs Princeton Univ Princeton NJ 08540

SMITH, ARTHUR R, b Pittsburgh, Pa, Feb 9, 31; m 53; c 3. ECONOMIC GEOLOGY. *Educ:* Pa State Univ, BS, 52; Univ Calif, Berkeley, MS, 58, MBA, 70. *Prof Exp:* Explor geologist, Phelps Dodge Corp, 58-63; geologist, Calif Div Mines & Geol, 63-70; SR RES GEOLOGIST, MINERAL EXPLOR & DEVELOP DEPT, UTAH INT INC, SAN FRANCISCO, 70- *Mem:* Am Inst Mining, Metall & Petrol Eng. *Res:* Regional geology; mineral economic studies; geochemical exploration methods. *Mailing Add:* Utah Int Inc Explor Div 550 California St San Francisco CA 94104

SMITH, B(LANCHARD) D(RAKE), JR, b New Orleans, La, Aug 22, 25; m 45; c 4. ELECTRICAL ENGINEERING. *Educ:* Ga Inst Technol, BS, 45; Mass Inst Technol, MS, 48. *Prof Exp:* Asst elec eng, Mass Inst Technol, 46-48; from engr to mgr transp systs ctr, Melpar, Inc, Westinghouse Air Brake Co, 48-68; vpres & tech dir, Appl Systs Technol, Inc, 68-78; consult, 78-80; CONSULT, ADVAN DEVELOP STAFF, MELPAR DIV, ENG SYSTS, 80- *Honors & Awards:* Thompson Award, Inst Elec & Electronics Engrs, 55. *Mem:* Inst Elec & Electronics Engrs. *Res:* Electronic systems. *Mailing Add:* 2509 Ryegate Lane Alexandria VA 22308

SMITH, BARRY THOMAS STURT, b Toronto, Ont, Apr 18, 45; m 69; c 2. NEONATOLOGY, PNEUMOLOGY. *Educ:* Queen's Univ, Ont, MD, 69; FRCP(C), 72. *Prof Exp:* Res fel endocrinol, Dept Exp Med, McGill Univ, 72-75; ASST PROF, DIV NEONATOL, DEPT PAEDIAT, QUEEN'S UNIV, ONT, 75- *Concurrent Pos:* Fel, Med Res Coun Can, 73-75, med res scholar, 75-; asst prof, Dept Oncol & Gynec & Dept Physiol, Queen's Univ 78-; mem adj fac, W Alton Jones Cell Sci Ctr, 78-79. *Mem:* Can Thoracic Soc; Can Soc Clin Invest; Soc Pediat Res; Soc Obstetricians & Gynecologists Can; Can Paediat Soc. *Res:* Hormonal control of pulmonary surfactant synthesis by the fetal lung; cellular interactions in fetal lung development; cholinergic control of surfactant secretion by cultured alveolar cells. *Mailing Add:* Dept of Paediat Queen's Univ Kingston ON K7L 3N6 Can

SMITH, BENJAMIN HARPER, JR, organic chemistry, see previous edition

SMITH, BENJAMIN WARFIELD, b Hampden-Sydney, Va, Mar 29, 13; m 40; c 2. PLANT CYTOLOGY, GENETICS. *Educ:* Univ Va, BA, 34, MA, 36; Univ Wis, PhD(genetics), 39. *Prof Exp:* Asst genetics, Univ Wis, 36-39; asst agronomist, Exp Sta, 39-44; asst prof agron, 41-44, assoc prof, 44-52, assoc prof genetics, 52-59, prof, 59-80, EMER PROF GENETICS & BOT, NC STATE UNIV, 80- *Mem:* AAAS; Genetics Soc Am; Bot Soc Am; Soc Study Evolution; Am Genetic Asn. *Res:* Quantitative inheritance in maize; cytogenetics of forage grasses; reproductive morphology of Arachis; sex chromosomes and sex determination in Rumex; evolution. *Mailing Add:* Dept Genetics NC State Univ Raleigh NC 27607

SMITH, BENJAMIN WILLIAMS, b Falls Church, Va, Aug 9, 18; m 40; c 5. BIOCHEMISTRY. *Educ:* Va Polytech Inst, BS, 40; George Washington Univ, MS, 47, PhD(biochem), 51. *Prof Exp:* From instr to assoc prof, 49-69, PROF BIOCHEM, MED SCH, GEORGE WASHINGTON UNIV, 69- *Mem:* AAAS; Asn Am Med Cols. *Res:* Enzymes; amylase; carbohydrate metabolism. *Mailing Add:* Dept of Biochem George Washington Univ Washington DC 20005

SMITH, BENNETT LAWRENCE, b Whitby, Ont, 1910; m 37; c 4. GEOLOGY. *Educ:* Univ Toronto, BA, 36; Syracuse Univ, MS, 50, PhD, 54. *Prof Exp:* Mine geologist, Sylvanite Gold Mines, Ltd, 39-46; geologist & consult, Can, 46-49; instr, Syracuse Univ, 49-51; lectr, 51-54, from asst prof to prof, 54-74, chmn dept, 66-67, asst dean, 67-71, assoc dean, 71-74, EMER PROF GEOL, RUTGERS UNIV, NEW BRUNSWICK, 74- *Concurrent Pos:* Geologist, Nfld Dept Mines, 42 & Ont Dept Mines, 49-51; consult, NJ Power & Light Co, Jersey Cent Power & Light Co, Ebasco Serv, Inc, Jersey Cent Power & Light Co, Fed Power Comn Greece & other utilities, Ebasco Serv, Inc, TAMS, other eng co & US Army Corps Engrs. *Mem:* Fel Geol Soc Am; Am Inst Mining, Metall & Petrol Engrs; Asn Eng Geologists; Can Inst Mining & Metall; Am Inst Prof Geologists. *Res:* Engineering geology of hydroelectric pumped storage projects; mining geology and minerals exploration; use of underground space; problems of Precambrian geology, including restudy of the New Jersey Highlands. *Mailing Add:* 27 Sagebrush Lane Don Mills ON MCA 1K4 Can

SMITH, BERNARD, b New York, NY, Aug 11, 27. PHYSICS, COMPUTER SCIENCE. *Educ:* City Col New York, BS, 48; Columbia Univ, AM, 51, PhD(physics), 54. *Prof Exp:* Lectr elec eng & physics, City Col New York, 48-54; mem tech staff, Bel Tel Labs, Inc, 54-59; staff consult, Gen Tel & Electronics Labs, Inc, 59-61, mgr, 61-63, sr scientist & mgr, 63-70; chief scientist, 70-71, VPRES & CHIEF SCIENTIST, MARCOM, INC, 71- *Mem:* AAAS; Asn Comput Mach; Am Phys Soc; sr mem Inst Elec & Electronics Engrs; Soc Indust & Appl Math. *Res:* Cryophysics; superfluidity; liquid helium II; telecommunication systems; psychoacoustics; quantized signals; statistical communication theory; operations research; semiconductors; solid state electronics; computer science. *Mailing Add:* Marcom Inc 175 Great Neck Rd Great Neck NY 11021

SMITH, BERNARD H, b Peterculter, Scotland, Nov 22, 17; US citizen; m. NEUROLOGY. *Educ:* Aberdeen Univ, MB, ChB, 40, MD, 56, Univ London, DPM, 50; FRCP, 65; FRCP(C), 72; FRCPsychiat, 73. *Prof Exp:* Intern med & surg, Aberdeen Royal Infirmary, Scotland, 40-41, registr path & med,

46-47; consult nutrit, UNRRA, 46; registr neurol & psychiat, Nat & Maudsley Hosps, London, Eng, 47-50; lectr neurol, McGill Univ & Montreal Neurol Inst, 51-53; HEAD DEPT NEUROL, E J MEYER MEM HOSP, 53-; PROF NEUROL, STATE UNIV NY BUFFALO, 55- Concurrent Pos: Fel med & psychiat, Cincinnati Gen Hosp, 50-51; fel neurol, McGill Univ & Montreal Neurol Inst, 51-53; consult, Vet Admin Hosp, Buffalo, 54-, Gowanda State Hosp, Helmuth, 57-, Craig Colony & Hosp, Sonyea, 58-, Millard Fillmore Hosp, 60-, Mem Hosp, Niagara Falls & Brooks Mem Hosp, Dunkirk, 61- Mem: Am Acad Neurol; Asn Res Nerv & Ment Dis; Am Epilepsy Soc; Can Neurol Soc. Res: Nutrition; epilepsy; cerebrovascular disease; cervical spondylosis. Mailing Add: 244 High Park Blvd Buffalo NY 14226

SMITH, BERTRAM BRYAN, JR, b Fort Jackson, SC, Sept 20, 42; m 72. SCIENCE POLICY. Educ: Univ Ala, BS, 64; Purdue Univ, PhD(chem), 70. Prof Exp: Gen phys scientist, Foreign Sci Technol Ctr, 70-79, GEN PHYS SCIENTIST, OFF OF ASST CHIEF OF STAFF FOR INTELL, DEPT ARMY, 79- Mem: Am Chem Soc; Am Phys Soc; AAAS. Res: Liquid theory; scattering theory. Mailing Add: 9543 Hunt Square Ct Springfield VA 22153

SMITH, BETTY F, b Magnolia, Ark, June 29, 30. TEXTILE CHEMISTRY, CARBOHYDRATE CHEMISTRY. Educ: Univ Ark, BS, 51; Univ Tenn, MS, 57; Univ Minn, PhD(textile), 60, PhD(biochem), 65. Prof Exp: Home agent home econ, Ark Agr Exten Serv, 51-56; assoc prof textiles, Cornell Univ, 65-70, chmn, Dept Textiles & Clothing, 68-69; PROF & HEAD DEPT, DEPT TEXTILES & CONSUMER ECON, UNIV MD, 70- Mem: Am Chem Soc; Am Asn Textile Chemists & Colorists; fel Textile Inst; Am Asn Textile Technol. Res: Burning characteristics of seams; the effects of environmental pollutants on the flammability properties of textiles; flammability of polyester cotton blends and flammability test methods. Mailing Add: Rm 3107 Turner Lab Univ Md College Park MD 20742

SMITH, BILL ROSS, b Stamford, Tex, Sept 22, 41; m 61. SOIL SCIENCE. Educ: Tex Tech Univ, BS, 64; Univ Ariz, MS, 66; NC State Univ, PhD(soil sci), 70. Prof Exp: Soil scientist, Soil Conserv Serv, USDA, 63 & Wake County Health Dept, NC, 70-73; asst prof, 73-77, ASSOC PROF AGRON & SOILS, CLEMSON UNIV, 77- Res: Soil genesis and classification; evaluation of soils for different kinds of land use; soil mineralogy. Mailing Add: Dept of Agron & Soils Clemson Univ Clemson SC 29631

SMITH, BOB HUGH, electrical engineering, physics, see previous edition

SMITH, BOB L(EE), b Topeka, Kans, Jan 26, 26; m; c 2. CIVIL ENGINEERING. Educ: Kans State Univ, BS, 48, MS, 53; Purdue Univ, PhD, 64. Prof Exp: From instr to assoc prof, 48-65, PROF CIVIL ENG, KANS STATE UNIV, 65- Concurrent Pos: Mem motorist info systs, bicycling & bicycle facil & oper effects of geometrics comts, Transp Res Bd, Nat Acad Sci-Nat Res Coun. Mem: Am Soc Civil Engrs; Nat Soc Prof Engrs; Inst Transp Engrs. Res: Trip generation and distribution; economic analysis as related to transportation systems; traffic engineering; geometric design of highways; traffic assignment; highway safety design. Mailing Add: Dept of Civil Eng Kans State Univ Manhattan KS 66506

SMITH, BRADFORD ADELBERT, b Cambridge, Mass, Sept 22, 31; m 54; c 4. ASTRONOMY. Educ: Northeastern Univ, BS, 54. Prof Exp: Res engr, Williamson Develop Co, 54-55; assoc astronr, Res Ctr, NMex State Univ, 57-64, dir observ, 64-69, dir planetary progs, 69-74; ASSOC PROF LUNAR & PLANETARY LAB & ASSOC ASTRONOMER, STEWARD OBSERV, UNIV ARIZ, 74- Mem: Am Astron Soc; Int Astron Union. Res: Planetary and lunar astronomy; image aberration electromechanical optical servo systems. Mailing Add: Dept Planetary Sci Univ of Ariz Tucson AZ 85721

SMITH, BRADLEY EDGERTON, b Cedar-Vale, Kans, Jan 4, 33; m 53; c 2. ANESTHESIOLOGY. Educ: Tulsa Univ, BSc, 54; Okla Univ, MS, 57. Prof Exp: Res fel obstet anesthesiol, Columbia Univ, 60-61; instr anesthesiol, Yale Univ, 62-63; assoc prof, Univ Miami, 63-69; PROF ANESTHESIOL & CHMN DEPT, VANDERBILT UNIV, 69- Concurrent Pos: Consult, FDA, 68-74 & 75-76, mem adv coun anesthetic & respiratory drugs, 70-72; assoc examr, Nat Bd Respiratory Ther, 69- & Am Bd Anesthesiologists, 77-; consult, Vet Admin, 69-; mem comt anesthetic toxicity, Nat Res Coun-Nat Acad Sci, 72-74; fac Sen, Vanderbilt Univ, 72-76. Mem: Am Col Chest Physicians; Asn Univ Anesthetists; Am Soc Anesthesiologists; assoc fel Am Col Obstet & Gynec; Soc Obstet Anesthesia & Perinatology (pres, 70-71). Res: Obstetric anesthesia; anesthetic toxicity; developmental pharmacology and teratology; perinatal physiolosy; resuscitation of the newborn. Mailing Add: Dept of Anesthesiol 21st Ave S Nashville TN 37232

SMITH, BRIAN THOMAS, b Toronto, Ont, Apr 20, 42; m 65; c 2. NUMERICAL ANALYSIS. Educ: Univ Toronto, BS, 65, MS, 67, PhD(comput sci), 69. Prof Exp: Res asst appl math, Swiss Fed Inst Technol, 69; asst scientist, 70-75, SCIENTIST COMPUT SCI, ARGONNE NAT LAB, 76- Concurrent Pos: Mem numerical software work group, Int Fedn Info Processing; mem, Fortran Standards Comt, Am Nat Standards Inst. Mem: Soc Indust & Appl Math; Asn Comput Mach. Res: Numerical software; computational aspects related to study of nonassociative algebras; automated reasoning; proving claims about programs; Fortran standardization. Mailing Add: Appl Math Div Argonne Nat Lab 9700 S Cass Ave Argonne IL 60439

SMITH, BRUCE BARTON, b Poplar Bluff, Mo, Sept 28, 41; m 63; c 2. PLANT MORPHOLOGY. Educ: Ark State Univ, BS, 63; Univ Miss, MS, 66; Univ SC, PhD(biol), 71. Prof Exp: Instr biol, Parsons Col, 66-67; asst prof, Atlantic Christian Col, 67-68; instr, Univ SC, 69-71; asst prof, 71-74, assoc prof, 74-81, PROF BIOL, YORK COL PA, 81-, CHMN DEPT, 81- Concurrent Pos: Sigma Xi res grant-in-aid, York Col Pa, 71- Mem: Bot Soc Am; Am Inst Biol Sci. Res: Angiosperm embryology and its use in phylogenetic studies of flowering plants. Mailing Add: Dept of Biol York Col of Pa York PA 17405

SMITH, BRUCE DYFRIG, geophysics, see previous edition

SMITH, BRUCE H, b New York, NY, Feb 16, 19; m 43; c 4. MEDICINE. Educ: Syracuse Univ, AB, 40, MD, 43. Prof Exp: Med Corps, US Navy, 43-71, resident path, US Naval Hosp, Brooklyn, NY, 45-47; resident, Long Island Col Hosp, 47-49, dir labs, US Naval Hosp, Mare Island, Calif, 50-55, Philadelphia, 55-63, dep dir, Armed Forces Inst Path, 63-67, dir, 67-71; PROF PATH, SCH MED, GEORGE WASHINGTON UNIV, 71- Concurrent Pos: Fel path, Harvard Univ, 49-50; vis prof, Sch Med, Temple Univ, 57-64; clin prof, Georgetown Univ, 67-71. Mem: Fel Am Col Physicians; Int Acad Path; NY Acad Sci; AAAS; Am Asn Pathologists. Res: Pathology. Mailing Add: Dept Path Sch Med George Washington Univ Washington DC 20006

SMITH, BRUCE NEPHI, b Logan, Utah, Apr 3, 34; m 59; c 6. PLANT PHYSIOLOGY. Educ: Univ Utah, BS, 59, MS, 62; Univ Wash, PhD(bot), 64. Prof Exp: Asst bot, Univ Utah, 58-60; asst, Univ Wash, 60-62, actg instr, 62-63, asst, 63-64; res fel plant physiol, Univ Calif, Los Angeles, 64-65; res fel geochem, Calif Inst Technol, 65-68; asst prof bot, Univ Tex, Austin, 68-74; assoc prof, 74-79, chmn bot & range sci, 76-79, PROF BOT, BRIGHAM YOUNG UNIV, 79-, DEAN, COL LIFE SCI, 82- Mem: AAAS; Am Soc Plant Physiol; Bot Soc Am; Geochem Soc; Soc Environ Geochem & Health. Res: Carbon, hydrogen, oxygen and nitrogen cycles followed by fractionation of natural abundance ratios of the stable isotopes; plant volatiles; trace metals in plants. Mailing Add: Dept of Bot & Range Sci Brigham Young Univ Provo UT 84602

SMITH, BRYCE EVERTON, b Lotumbe, Belgian Congo, Oct 21, 30; US citizen; m 52; c 3. ECOLOGY. Educ: Univ Mich, BSF, 52, AM, 57; Univ Wis, PhD(bot), 65. Prof Exp: Forester, Bowaters Southern Paper Corp, 54-55; teacher, High Schs, 57-60; asst prof biol sci, Western Ill Univ, 65-67; assoc prof biol, Eastern Conn State Col, 67-70; chmn dept biol sci, 70-76, assoc prof biol, 70-76, PROF BIOL, LAKE SUPERIOR STATE COL, 76- Mem: AAAS; Am Inst Biol Sci; Ecol Soc Am. Res: Interrelationships of higher plants in forest communities. Mailing Add: Dept Biol Sci Lake Superior State Col Sault Ste Marie MI 49783

SMITH, BUFORD DON, b Omega, Okla, Feb 18, 25; m 47; c 2. CHEMICAL ENGINEERING. Educ: Okla State Univ, BS, 50, MS, 51; Univ Mich, PhD(chem eng), 54. Prof Exp: Chem engr, Humble Oil & Refining Co, 54-58; assoc prof chem eng, Purdue Univ, 58-65; PROF CHEM ENG & DIR THERMODYNTHERMODYNAMICS RES LAB, WASH UNIV, 65- Concurrent Pos: Consult, Allison Div, Gen Motors Corp, 63, Sun Oil Co, 65 & Monsanto Co & Am Oil Co, 66. Mem: Am Inst Chem Engrs; Am Chem Soc. Res: Design of vapor-liquid separation processes; thermodynamics of liquid mixtures. Mailing Add: Dept of Chem Eng Box 1144 Wash Univ St Louis MO 63130

SMITH, BURTON JORDAN, b Chapel Hill, NC, Mar 21, 41; m 66 66; c 2. COMPUTER & ELECTRICAL ENGINEERING. Educ: Univ NMex, BSEE, 67; Mass Inst Technol, MSEE, 68, EE, 69, ScD(elec eng), 72. Prof Exp: Teaching asst elec eng, Mass Inst Technol, 67-70, instr, 70-72; asst prof, 72-78, ASSOC PROF ELEC ENG, UNIV COLO, DENVER, 78- Concurrent Pos: Consult, Hendrix Electronics, Inc, 67-72 & Denelcor, Inc, 74-; dir, Sci Electronics Corp, 68-70. Mem: Inst Elec & Electronics Engrs; Asn Comput Mach. Res: Architecture of parellel computers; interface between hardware and software. Mailing Add: Univ of Colo 1100 14th St Denver CO 80202

SMITH, BYRON COLMAN, b Crawfordsville, Ind, Apr 14, 24; m 71. COMPARATIVE ANATOMY. Educ: Ind State Univ, BS, 48; DePauw Univ, MA, 52; Univ Ga, PhD(zool), 58. Prof Exp: Asst prof zool, Univ SC, 58-64; assoc prof, 64-71, PROF BIOL, UNIV SOUTHERN MISS, 71- Mem: AAAS. Res: Acarology; ecology of the desert spider mite; Tetranychus desertorium banks on cotton; micro-fauna population of soils in the Sand Hill region of South Carolina and areas of the Piedmont and Coastal Plains. Mailing Add: Dept Biol Box 8444 Univ Southern Miss Hattiesburg MS 39401

SMITH, C(HARLES) WILLIAM, b Va, Jan 1, 26; m 50; c 2. ENGINEERING MECHANICS. Educ: VaPolytech Inst, BS, 46, MS, 49. Prof Exp: From instr to assoc prof, 47-58, prof, 58-81, DISTINGUISHED PROF APPL MECH, VA POLYTECH INST & STATE UNIV, 81- Concurrent Pos: Instr, Exten, Univ Va, 57-58; lectr grad eng training progs, Western Elec Co & Gen Elec Co, 63-64; consult, Brunswick Corp, 65, Masonite Corp, 70, Polysci Corp, 71, US Army Missile Command, 71-72 & Kollmorgen Corp, 74-72; proj dir, NASA grants, 71-75; prin investr, NSF, 73-78, proj dir, 73-; proj dir, Delft Univ Technol, 75-76, Flight Dynamics Lab, US Air Force, 75-77 & Oak Ridge Nat Lab, 75-78; ed, Fracture Mechanics, 78. Mem: Int Asn Struct Mech in Reactor Technol; fel Soc Exp Stress Anal; Am Soc Testing & Mat; Am Soc Mech Engrs; Soc Eng Sci. Res: Theoretical and experimental continuum solid mechanics, especially fracture mechanics and experimental stress analysis. Mailing Add: Dept of Eng Sci & Mech Va Polytech Inst & State Univ Blacksburg VA 24061

SMITH, CALVIN ALBERT, b Troy, NH, Mar 11, 35; m 57; c 2. BOTANY. Educ: Wheaton Col, Ill, BS, 57; Miami Univ, MA, 60; Rutgers Univ, PhD(bot), 63. Prof Exp: From asst prof to assoc prof, 63-75, PROF BIOL, BALDWIN-WALLACE COL, 75- Mem: Bot Soc Am; Sigma Xi; Am Inst Biol Sci. Res: Shoot apices in the family Moraceae. Mailing Add: Dept Biol Baldwin-Wallace Col Berea OH 44017

SMITH, CARL HUGH, b New York, NY, Nov 18, 34; m 69; c 2. PERINATAL RESEARCH, CLINICAL CHEMISTRY. Educ: Swarthmore Col, BA, 55; Yale Univ, MD, 59. Prof Exp: Instr pathol, 65-67, asst prof pathol, 67-72, asst prof, 72-74, ASSOC PROF PATHOL & PEDIAT, SCH MED, WASHINGTON UNIV, 74- Concurrent Pos: Mem, Human Embryol & Develop Study Sect, NIH, 77-79. Honors & Awards: Borden Res Award, 59. Mem: Perinatal Res Soc; Soc Pediat Res; Am Physiol Soc; Soc Gynecol Invest; Am Asn Clin Chemists. Res: Transfer of amino acids and glucose by placenta, structure and function of its plasma membranes. Mailing Add: Dept Pediat Washington Univ Children's Hosp 500 S Kingshighway Blvd St Louis MO 63178

SMITH, CARL WALTER, b Salem, Mass, Dec 15, 37; m 61. PHYSICS. *Educ:* Earlham Col, BA, 60; Brown Univ, ScM, 63, PhD(physics), 66. *Prof Exp:* 75; PHYSICIST, SANDIA LABS, 76- *Mem:* AAAS; Acoust Soc Am; Am Geophys Union. *Res:* Mechanical wave propagation. *Mailing Add:* Div 1111 Sandia Labs Albuquerque NM 94025

SMITH, CARL WALTER, JR, b Lamont, Okla, Mar 20, 27; m 55; c 2. NUCLEAR MEDICINE, ENDOCRINOLOGY. *Educ:* Univ Okla, BA & MD, 53; Am Bd Nuclear Med, dipl; Am Bd Internal Med, dipl. *Prof Exp:* Asst prof med, 59-63, asst prof med & radiol, 63-65, dir outpatient clins, 60-65, ASSOC PROF MED, PROF RADIOL SCI & DIR DIV NUCLEAR MED, COL MED, UNIV OKLA, 65- *Mem:* AAAS; Am Fedn Clin Res; Am Soc Nuclear Med; Endocrine Soc. *Res:* Medical education; endocrinological diseases; nuclear medicine, including methodology, development of radiopharmaceuticals and clinical investigation related to nuclear medicine. *Mailing Add:* Univ Hosps & Clins Nuclear Med PO Box 25606 Oklahoma City OK 73190

SMITH, CARLTON G, b Kitchener, Ont, Nov 8, 05; m 76. NEUROLOGY. *Educ:* Univ Toronto, BA, 28, MD, 35, PhD(biol), 36; Univ Western Ont, MSc, 30. *Prof Exp:* Instr anat, Univ Western Ont, 28-31; demonstr physiol, 35-37, lectr, 3740, from asst prof to assoc prof, 40-50, prof anat, 50-72, EMER PROF ANAT, UNIV TORONTO, 72- *Concurrent Pos:* Spec lectr, Univ Toronto, 73-79; vis prof, Uniformed Serv Univ Health Sci, 79- *Honors & Awards:* Reeve Prize, Univ Toronto, 38. *Mem:* Am Asn Anatomists; Can Physiol Soc; Can Asn Anat. *Res:* Olfactory mucosa atrophy and regeneration; changes in brain with age; distortion of central nervous system with body movements; blood supply of visual sensory cortex in relation to visual field defects. *Mailing Add:* Dept Anat Med Sci Bldg Univ Toronto Toronto ON M5S 1A8 Can

SMITH, CAROL MCDONALD, b Birmingham, Ala, May 9, 43; m 67. TOPOLOGY. *Educ:* Birmingham-Southern Col, BS, 65; Univ Ga, MA, 68; Univ Ala, Tuscaloosa, PhD(math), 75. *Prof Exp:* asst prof, 67-77, ASSOC PROF MATH, BIRMINGHAM SOUTHERN COL, 77- *Mem:* Math Asn Am; Asn Women Math; Sigma Xi. *Res:* Hereditarily unicoherent continua; fixed point theory. *Mailing Add:* Birmingham Southern Col 800 8th Ave W Birmingham AL 35204

SMITH, CAROL PRICE, b Lansing, Mich, Oct 15, 41. PROTEIN CHEMISTRY. *Educ:* Albion Col, AB, 63; Univ Vt, PhD(physiol), 72. *Prof Exp:* res assoc med, 72-76, RES ASST PROF MED, COL MED, UNIV VT, 76- *Concurrent Pos:* Dir, Vt Alpha-Fetoprotein Prenatal Screening Prog, 81- *Mem:* Sigma Xi; Int Soc Oncodevelop Biol & Med. *Res:* Investigation of the physicochemistry and metabolism of the carcino-embryonic protein alpha-fetoprotein and its molecular variants in sera of fetal and hepatoma-bearing rats and also in human maternal serum and amniotic fluid in the presence of fetal malformations. *Mailing Add:* Dept of Med Given Bldg C-342 Col of Med Univ of Vt Burlington VT 05401

SMITH, CAROLYN JEAN, b Fitzgerald, Ga; m 75. CHEMISTRY. *Educ:* Mercer Univ, AB, 59; Emory Univ, PhD(org chem), 62. *Prof Exp:* Teaching asst chem, Emory Univ, 59-60; res chemist, E I du Pont de Nemours & Co, Inc, 62-71; asst prof, Lincoln Univ, 72-73; instr chem, Del Tech & Community Col, 73-75; lectr, Wilmington Col, 75-76; ASSOC PROF, CHEYNEY STATE COL, 76- *Concurrent Pos:* Instr, Oxford Col, Emory Univ, 62; vis assoc prof, Lincoln Univ, 77. *Mem:* Am Inst Chemists; Am Chem Soc; Am Asn Univ Professors. *Mailing Add:* 8 Pinecrest Dr Wilmington DE 19810

SMITH, CARROLL N, b Menlo, Iowa, Nov 5, 09; m 37; c 1. MEDICAL ENTOMOLOGY. *Educ:* George Washington Univ, AB, 32, MA, 34, PhD(med entom), 41; Am Regist Prof Entomologists, cert. *Prof Exp:* Jr entomologist, USDA, Washington, DC, 35-37, asst entomologist, Mass, 37-41, assoc entomologist, Ga, 41-46, entomologist, Fla, 46-63, dir insect attractants behav & basic biol res lab, 63-69; consult-dir, Res Unit Genetic Control Mosquitoes, WHO, New Delhi, 70; ED, annual rev entom, Annual Rev Inc, 71-77. *Concurrent Pos:* Courtesy prof entom, Univ Fla, Gainesville, 63-69; mem, WHO Expert Panel Insecticides & Food & Agr Orgn expert panel on tick-borne dis of livestock; assoc mem, Rickettsial Dis Comn & Malaria Comn Armed Forces Epidemiol Bd; consult, S C Johnson & Son, 74-75. *Honors & Awards:* Medal of Honor, Am Mosquito Control Asn, 76. *Mem:* Hon mem Entom Soc Am (pres, 64); Am Mosquito Control Asn. *Res:* Biology, behavior and control of arthropods affecting man and animals. *Mailing Add:* 317 NW 32nd St Gainesville FL 32607

SMITH, CARROLL WARD, b Abilene, Tex, Dec 24, 27; m 55; c 4. BIOCHEMISTRY, ENVIRONMENTAL HEALTH. *Educ:* Univ Okla, BS, 58, MS, 59, PhD(environ health), 68. *Prof Exp:* Res chemist, Samuel Roberts Noble Found, Okla, 59-64; res biochemist, Civil Aeromed Res Inst, Fed Aviation Agency, Oklahoma City, 64-65; asst prof chem, 68-74, assoc prof, 74-81, PROF CHEM, HARDING COL, 81-, RES ASSOC PHYSIOL OF EXERCISE, 68- *Mem:* Am Chem Soc; Nat Speleol Soc. *Res:* Biochemistry and physiology of exercise with emphasis on preventive and rehabilitative medicine. *Mailing Add:* Dept of Chem Box 682 Harding Col Searcy AR 72143

SMITH, CARTER RILEY, b Columbus, Ohio, July 12, 20; m 44; c 1. HORTICULTURE, POMOLOGY. *Educ:* Ohio Univ, BS, 48, MS, 51; Rutgers Univ, PhD(hort), 57. *Prof Exp:* Orchardist, Citrus Exp Sta, Riverside, Calif, 48-49; res asst pomol, Wash State Univ, 49-51, jr horticulturist, 51-53; from instr to assoc prof pomol, 53-69, asst vpres acad affairs, 72-76, PROF POMOL, RUTGERS UNIV, NEW BRUNSWICK, 69-, ASSOC PROVOST, 76- *Mem:* Am Soc Hort Sci; Am Hort Soc. *Res:* Physiology and culture of small fruits. *Mailing Add:* Provost Off Rutgers Univ New Brunswick NJ 08903

SMITH, CASSANDRA LYNN, b New York, NY, May 25, 47. MOLECULAR BIOLOGY. *Educ:* WVa Univ, AB, 67, MS, 71; Tex A&M Univ, PhD(genetics), 74. *Prof Exp:* Res asst med microbiol, Med Sch, WVa Univ, 68-70; res assoc cardiovasc surg, Presby Hosp, San Francisco, 71-72; teaching asst biol, Tex A&M Univ, 72-73; fel & res asst biochem, Baylor Col Med, Tex, 73-74; NIH fel genetics, Pub Health Res Inst, New York, 74-80; MEM STAFF HUMAN GENETICS & DEVELOP, COL PHYSICIANS, COLUMBIA UNIV & SURGEONS, 80- *Mem:* Am Soc Microbiol; Genetics Soc Am. *Res:* DNA replication, repair, and recombination and prophage induction. *Mailing Add:* Human Genetics Rm 1602 Hammer Heath Bldg Columbia Col Physicians & Surgeons New York NY 10032

SMITH, CATHERINE AGNES, b St Louis, Mo, Jan 5, 14. OTOLOGY, ANATOMY. *Educ:* Washington Univ, PhD(anat), 51. *Prof Exp:* Asst otolaryngol, Med Sch, Washington Univ, 48-54, res associ clin otolaryngol, 54-59, from res asst prof to res prof otolaryngol, 58-69; prof, 69-79, EMER PROF OTOLARYNGOL, MED SCH, UNIV ORE, 79- *Concurrent Pos:* Inst, Washington Univ, 53-54; res assoc, Cent Inst Deaf, 54-62, res collabr, 62-69. *Honors & Awards:* Shambaugh Prize in Otology, 77. *Mem:* Am Asn Anatomists; Am Otol Soc; Am Soc Cell Biol; Col Otorhinolaryngol Amicitiae Sacrum. *Res:* Ultrastructure and histology of the ear; neurophysiology of the inner ear. *Mailing Add:* Dept of Otolaryngol Univ of Ore Med Sch Portland OR 97201

SMITH, CECIL RANDOLPH, JR, b Denver, Colo, May 31, 24; m 54; c 3. NATURAL PRODUCTS CHEMISTRY, LIPID CHEMISTRY. *Educ:* Univ Colo, BA, 46, MS, 48; Wayne State Univ, PhD(org chem), 55. *Prof Exp:* Asst chem, Univ Colo, 46-47; org chemist, US Bur Mines, Wyo, 47-51, Julius Hyman & Co, Colo, 51-52 & Northern Regional Res Lab, USDA, 56-62; asst prof chem, Western Mich Univ, 62-63; ORG CHEMIST, NORTHERN REGIONAL RES CTR, USDA, 63-, RES LEADER, 73- *Concurrent Pos:* Res fel, Nat Heart Inst, Glasgow, 55-56. *Mem:* Am Chem Soc; Am Oil Chem Soc; Sigma Xi; Am Soc Pharmacognosy; Soc Economic Bot. *Res:* Shale oil; alkaloids; fatty acids; natural products; medicinal chemistry. *Mailing Add:* 1815 N University Peoria IL 61604

SMITH, CEDRIC MARTIN, b Stillwater, Okla, Feb 1, 27; m 48; c 3. PHARMACOLOGY, NEUROPHARMACOLOGY. *Educ:* Okla Agr & Mech Col, BS, 49; Univ Ill, BS, 50, MS & MD, 53. *Prof Exp:* Asst pharmacol, Col Med, Univ Ill, 55-58; intern, Philadelphia Gen Hosp, 53-54; from instr to prof pharmacol, Col Med, Univ Ill, 54-66, actg head dept, 65-66; chmn dept, 66-73, PROF PHARMACOL & THERAPEUT, SCH MED, STATE UNIV NY BUFFALO, 66- *Concurrent Pos:* USPHS spec fel, Univ Göttingen, 61-62; staff scientist, Inst Defense Anal, 64-65; consult neuropharmacol adv comt, Food & Drug Admin, 71-76, Neurol Sci Res Training B Comt, Nat Inst Neurol Dis & Stroke, 68-72; dir, Res Inst Alcoholism, NY State, 70-79. *Mem:* AAAS; Am Soc Pharmacol & Exp Therapeut; Am Soc Clin Pharmacol & Therapeut; Am Med Soc Alcoholism; Int Brain Res Orgn. *Res:* Neuropharmacology of spinal cord, nerve, muscle and sensory rececreptors; pharmacological methodology; non-medical drug use; alcohol and nutrition; alcoholism, sleep & drug treatment in geriatrics. *Mailing Add:* Dept Pharmacol & Therapeut 127 Farber Hall State Univ NY Buffalo NY 14214

SMITH, CHARLES ALLEN, b Lexington, Ky, Aug 4, 44; m 75. MOLECULAR BIOLOGY. *Educ:* Mass Inst Technol, SB, 66; Calif Inst Technol, PhD(biophys), 71. *Prof Exp:* Fel, 72-75, SR RES ASSOC BIOPHYS, STANFORD UNIV, 75- *Mem:* Biophys Soc; Sigma Xi. *Res:* Mechanisms for replication, repair, and function of eukaryotic DNA; organization of DNA in chromosomes; function of mitochondrial DNA. *Mailing Add:* Dept of Biol Stanford Univ Stanford CA 94305

SMITH, CHARLES ALOYSIUS, b Minneapolis, Minn, Aug 18, 39; m 70; c 1. ANALYTICAL CHEMISTRY, PHARMACEUTICAL CHEMISTRY. *Educ:* Col St Thomas, BS, 61; Kans State Univ, PhD(chem), 66. *Prof Exp:* Chemist, McDonnell-Douglas Corp, Santa Monica, 65-75; chemist, Dept Entom, Univ Calif, Riverside, 75-78; mgr qual assurance methods, McGaw Labs, Irvine, Ca, 78-80. *Mem:* Am Chem Soc. *Res:* Analytical chemical methods development and applications. *Mailing Add:* 17669 San Vicente Fountain Valley CA 92708

SMITH, CHARLES E, b Omaha, Nebr, Nov 16, 17; m 41; c 2. PSYCHIATRY. *Educ:* George Washington Univ, AB, 39, MD, 41. *Prof Exp:* Intern, USPHS Hosp, Baltimore, Md, 41-42; staff psychiatrist, Vet Admin Hosp, Northport, NY, 45-49; chief med officer, Fed Correction Inst, Ky, 49-50; resident psychiatrist, USPHS Hosp, Staten Island, NY, 50-51; chief psychiat serv, Med Ctr Fed Prisoners, Mo, 51-55; asst med dir, Fed Bur Prisons, 56-62, med dir, 62-66; chief serv, West Side Div, St Elizabeth's Hosp, DC, 66-67; assoc prof, 67-74, PROF PSYCHIAT, SCH MED, UNIV NC, CHAPEL HILL, 74-; DIR MENT HEALTH SERV, NC DEPT CORRECTIONS, 74- *Concurrent Pos:* Mem, Bd Dirs, Washington DC Area Coun Alcoholism, 61-67; mem, Prof Coun, Nat Coun Crime & Delinquency, 65-; consult, NC Dept Corrections, 67- *Mem:* Fel AAAS; fel Am Psychiat Asn. *Res:* Legal aspects of psychiatry; correctional treatment of the mentally ill offender. *Mailing Add:* Dept of Psychiat Univ of NC Sch of Med Chapel Hill NC 27514

SMITH, CHARLES EDWARD, b Clayton, Ala, June 8, 34; m 60; c 3. ELECTRICAL ENGINEERING. *Educ:* Auburn Univ, BEE, 59, MS, 63, PhD(elec eng), 68. *Prof Exp:* Res engr, Auburn Res Found, 59-68; assoc prof, 68-76, PROF ELEC ENG, UNIV MISS, 77-, CHMN DEPT, 76- *Mem:* Inst Elec & Electronics Engrs; Am Soc Eng Educ. *Res:* Antennas; microwave circuits; communication systems. *Mailing Add:* Dept Elec Eng Univ Miss University MS 38677

SMITH, CHARLES EDWARD, JR, b Sharpsburg, Ky, Oct 26, 27; m 49. LIMNOLOGY, PHYCOLOGY. *Educ:* Eastern Ky Univ, BS, 54; Univ Ky, MS, 56; Univ Louisville, PhD(biol), 63. *Prof Exp:* Mat testing engr, Dept Hwy, Frankfort, Ky, 49-50; off engr, 50-51; asst zool, Univ Ky, 54-56; teacher,

High Sch, Ky, 56-61; res asst algal physiol, Potamological Inst, Univ Louisville, 61-63; from asst prof to assoc prof biol, 63-71, admin asst, 67-68, assoc dir, 68-69, PROF BIOL, BALL STATE UNIV, 71-, DIR OFF RES, 69- *Mem:* AAAS; Am Soc Limnol & Oceanog; Am Phycol Soc; Int Asn Theoret & Appl Limnol. *Res:* Physiology and ecology of phytoplankton, especially members of the cyanophyta. *Mailing Add:* Off of Res Ball State Univ Muncie IN 47306

SMITH, CHARLES EUGENE, b Atlanta, Ga, June 22, 50; m 75; c 1. NEUROBIOLOGY. *Educ:* Mass Inst Technol, BS, 72; Univ Chicago, MS, 73, PhD(biophysics), 79. *Prof Exp:* Fel, 79-80, ASST PROF BIOMET, MED UNIV SC, 80- *Concurrent Pos:* Co-dir, Cardiomet Scientist Training Prog, 81-82. *Mem:* Acoust Soc Am; Inst Elec & Electronics Engrs; Biomet Soc; Am Statist Asn. *Res:* Applied stochastic processes. *Mailing Add:* Biomet Dept Med Univ SC 171 Ashley Ave Charleston SC 29425

SMITH, CHARLES FRANCIS, JR, b Casper, Wyo, Aug 8, 36; m 60; c 3. RADIOCHEMISTRY, ENVIRONMENTAL CHEMISTRY. *Educ:* Purdue Univ, BS, 58, MS, 61; Univ Calif, Berkeley, PhD(nuclear chem), 65. *Prof Exp:* CHEMIST, LAWRENCE LIVERMORE NAT LAB, UNIV CALIF, 65-, PROJ LEADER, 74- *Concurrent Pos:* Staff mem anal geochem, Nat Uranium Resources Eval Prog. *Mem:* AAAS. *Res:* Radiochemistry and chemistry of gaseous products and fission product gases; analytical geochemistry; neutron activation analyses. *Mailing Add:* Lawrence Livermore Nat Lab L-232 Box 808 Livermore CA 94551

SMITH, CHARLES HADDON, b Dartmouth, NS, Sept 3, 26; m 49; c 4. GEOLOGY. *Educ:* Dalhousie Univ, BSc, 46, MSc, 48; Yale Univ, MS, 51, PhD(geol), 52. *Prof Exp:* Instr eng, Dalhousie Univ, 46-48; geologist, Cerro de Pasco Copper Corp, Peru, 49; geologist, Geol Surv Can, 51-64, chief petrol sci div, 64-67 & crustal geol div, 67-68; sci adv, Sci Coun Can, 68-70; dir planning, 70-71, asst dep minister sci & technol, 72-75, SR ASST DEP MINISTER, CAN DEPT ENERGY, MINES & RESOURCES, 75- *Concurrent Pos:* Dep secy gen, Int Upper Mantle Comt, chmn Can Upper Mantle Comn. *Mem:* Can Inst Mining & Metall; Mineral Soc Am; Soc Econ Geol; Geol Asn Can; fel Royal Soc Can. *Res:* Petrology and economic geology; study of ultrabasic rocks. *Mailing Add:* 2056 Thistle Crescent Ottawa ON K1H 5P5 Can

SMITH, CHARLES HENRY, forensic science, see previous edition

SMITH, CHARLES HOOPER, b Winnfield, La, July 24, 17; m 45; c 3. CHEMISTRY. *Educ:* La Polytech Inst, BS, 38; La State Univ, MS, 40, PhD(phys chem), 47. *Prof Exp:* Asst prof chem, La Polytech Inst, 40-42; chemist, US Rubber Co, Mich, 42-45; asst & Am Chem Soc fel chem, La State Univ, 47-48; from assoc prof to prof chem, La Tech Univ, 48-80, head dept chem, 54-78; fel, Univ Col NWales, 80-81; RETIRED. *Mem:* Am Chem Soc. *Res:* Spectra of deuterated toluenes and deuterated formamide; analysis of blood, particularly of mental patients. *Mailing Add:* 1600 Cooktown Rd Ruston LA 71270

SMITH, CHARLES IRVEL, b Baltimore, Md, Aug 22, 23; c 3. MEDICINAL CHEMISTRY. *Educ:* Univ Md, BS, 44, PhD(pharm chem), 50. *Prof Exp:* Asst, Dent Sch, Univ Md, 46-50; from sr res asst to instr physiol chem, Johns Hopkins Univ, 50-52; sr res scientist, Squibb Inst Med Res, 52-60; assoc prof med chem, 60-74, PROF MED CHEM, COL PHARM, UNIV RI, 74- CHMN DEPT, 75- *Mem:* Fel AAAS; Am Chem Soc; Sigma Xi; Am Asn Cols Pharm. *Res:* Drug Assay; radiopharmaceuticals; drug metabolism; drug design and synthesis. *Mailing Add:* Dept Med Chem Col Pharm Univ RI Kingston RI 02881

SMITH, CHARLES ISAAC, b Hearne, Tex, Feb 9, 31. GEOLOGY. *Educ:* Baylor Univ, BS, 52; La State Univ, MS, 55; Univ Mich, PhD, 66. *Prof Exp:* Geologist, Shell Develop Co, 55-65; from asst prof to assoc prof, 65-72, prof geol & mineral, Univ Mich, Ann Arbor, 72-77, chmn dept, 71-77; PROF GEOL, UNIV TEX, ARLINGTON, 77-, CHMN DEPT, 77- *Mem:* Geol Soc Am; Am Asn Petrol Geol. *Res:* Stratigraphy; sedimentation. *Mailing Add:* Dept of Geol Univ of Tex Arlington TX 76019

SMITH, CHARLES JAMES, b Buffalo, NY, Sept 29, 25. NEUROPSYCHOLOGY. *Educ:* Univ Buffalo, BA, 48; McGill Univ, MA, 51, PhD, 54. *Prof Exp:* Instr psychol, Univ Mich, 53-61; ASSOC PROF PSYCHOL, STATE UNIV NY BUFFALO, 61- *Concurrent Pos:* Vis res fel physiol, John Curtin Sch Med Res, Australian Nat Univ, 67-68. *Mem:* Soc Neurosci; Int Brain Res Orgn; Sigma Xi. *Res:* Brain function; psychophysiology of vision. *Mailing Add:* Dept of Psychol State Univ of NY Buffalo NY 14226

SMITH, CHARLES LEA, b Alto, Tex, Mar 8, 18; m 46; c 2. CHEMISTRY. *Educ:* Stephen F Austin State Col, BA, 38. *Prof Exp:* Teacher, High Sch, 38-41; chemist, Trojan Powder Co, Pa, 42-44 & Standard Oil Co, NJ, 44-46; mat engr, Naval Air Exp Sta, Pa, 46-47; res engr, Battelle Mem Inst, 47-50, prin chemist, 50-57; mgr proj develop, Southern Res Inst, 57-60; RES ADMINR, WYETH LABS, INC, 60- *Mem:* Am Chem Soc. *Res:* Alkyd resins; lacquers; drying oils; polyhydric alcohols; preservation and protection of materials; rubber and rubber-like materials; leather. *Mailing Add:* Wyeth Labs Inc PO Box 8299 Philadelphia PA 19101

SMITH, CHARLES O(LIVER), b Clinton, Mass, May 28, 20; m 46; c 7. METALLURGY. *Educ:* Worcester Polytech Inst, BS, 41; Mass Inst Technol, MS, 47, ScD, 51. *Prof Exp:* Engr, Blake Mfg Co, 40-43; instr mech eng, Worcester Polytech Inst, 41-43; instr metall, Mass Inst Technol, 46-47, from instr mech eng to asst prof, 47-51; res engr, Mech Testing Div, Res Labs, Aluminum Co Am, 51-54; eng consult, E I du Pont de Nemours & Co, 55; lectr reactor mat, Oak Ridge Nat Lab, 55-65; prof eng, Univ Detroit, 65-76, chmn dept, 65-68; prof eng, Univ Nebr, 76-81; PROF ENG, ROSE-HULMAN INST TECHNOL, 81- *Honors & Awards:* Fred Merryfield Design Award, 81. *Mem:* Am Soc Metals; Am Soc Eng Educ; Sigma Xi; Systs Safety Soc; Am Soc Mech Engrs. *Res:* Materials and their application with special reference to design; author of over 100 publications in engineering. *Mailing Add:* 1920 College Ave Terre Haute IN 47803

SMITH, CHARLES R, b Campti, La, Sept 11, 36; m 59; c 2. MATHEMATICS. *Educ:* Northwestern State Univ, BS, 57; Okla State Univ, MS, 64, EdD(math), 66. *Prof Exp:* Teacher, La, 59-63; asst prof, 66-69, ASSOC PROF MATH, NORTHEAST LA UNIV, 69- *Concurrent Pos:* NSF sci faculty fel, Univ Wash, 70-71. *Mem:* Math Asn Am. *Res:* Convexity; combinatorial geometry; functional analysis. *Mailing Add:* Dept of Math Northeast La Univ Monroe LA 71209

SMITH, CHARLES RAY, b Fayetteville, Tenn, May 15, 33; m 58; c 2. THEORETICAL PHYSICS. *Educ:* Vanderbilt Univ, BA, 55, MS, 62; Univ Colo, PhD(physics), 67. *Prof Exp:* Teaching asst physics, Univ Wis, 57-58; from physicist to aero-res engr, Redstone Arsenal, Ala, 58-61; physicist, Nat Bur Stand, Colo, 61-64; asst prof, 64-72, ASSOC PROF PHYSICS, UNIV WYO, 72- *Mem:* Am Asn Physics Teachers. *Res:* Many-body physics; quantum electrodynamics; laser-plasma interactions. *Mailing Add:* Dept of Physics Univ of Wyo Laramie WY 82071

SMITH, CHARLES ROGER, b Hartville, Ohio, Mar 31, 18; m 46; c 3. VETERINARY PHYSIOLOGY. *Educ:* Ohio State Univ, DVM, 44, MSc, 46, PhD(vet physiol), 53. *Prof Exp:* From instr to prof, 44-69, chmn dept, 58-72, dean Col Vet Med, 72-80, RES PROF VET PHYSIOL & PHARMACOL, OHIO STATE UNIV, 69-, EMER DEAN COL VET MED, 80- *Concurrent Pos:* Mem, Div Med Sci, Nat Acad Sci-Nat Res Coun, 65-68, Am Vet Med Asn rep, Nat Acad Sci, 66-68; mem adv bd, Morris Animal Found, 65-68; mem vet med rev comt, Bur Health Professions Educ & Manpower Training, NIH, 70-74; mem nat adv coun, Bur Vet Med, Food & Drug Admin, Dept Health, Educ & Welfare; dipl in cardiol, Am Col Vet Internal Med; mem NCent res rev & adv comt, Am Heart Asn, 76-81, chmn Ohio affil, 76-78. *Mem:* Am Soc Vet Physiol & Pharmacol (secy, 57); Am Vet Med Asn; Am Physiol Soc; Acad Vet Cardiol (pres, 69-71); fel Am Col Vet Pharmacol & Therapeut. *Res:* Comparative mammalian cardiology; electrocardiography. *Mailing Add:* Ohio State Univ Col Vet Med 1900 Coffey Rd Columbus OH 43210

SMITH, CHARLES SYDNEY, JR, b Lorain, Ohio, Apr 29, 16; m 40; c 3. PHYSICS. *Educ:* Case Inst Technol, BS, 37; Mass Inst Technol, ScD(physics), 40. *Prof Exp:* Instr physics, Univ Pittsburgh, 40-42; from instr to prof, Case Inst Technol, 42-68; distinguished prof, 68-81, EMER PROF PHYSICS & DIR MAT RES CTR, UNIV NC, CHAPEL HILL, 81- *Concurrent Pos:* With Bell Tel Labs, 52-53; consult, Union Carbide Corp. *Mem:* Fel Am Phys Soc. *Res:* Solid state physics. *Mailing Add:* Dept of Physics Univ of NC Chapel Hill NC 27514

SMITH, CHARLES T, b San Diego, Calif, Mar 22, 14; m 35; c 2. CHEMISTRY, DENTISTRY. *Educ:* Pac Union Col, AB, 35; Col Physicians & Surgeons, San Francisco, DDS, 40. *Prof Exp:* Instr restorative dent, 57-60, from asst prof to prof periodont, 60-71, dean, Col Dent, 60-71, EMER DEAN COL DENT, LOMA LINDA UNIV, 71-; PROF DENT, SCH DENT, UNIV TEX HEALTH SCI CTR, SAN ANTONIO, 73-, ACTG CHMN COMMUNITY DENT, 77- *Concurrent Pos:* Prog coordr, Div Physician Health Prof Educ, Bur Health Manpower Educ, NIH, 71-73. *Mem:* Am Dent Asn; fel Am Col Dent; Am Acad Periodont. *Res:* Pathology of periodontal disease; periodontology. *Mailing Add:* 5515 King Richard San Antonio TX 78229

SMITH, CHARLES WELSTEAD, b Asheville, NC, Aug 21, 27; m 50; c 4. PHYSIOLOGY. *Educ:* Wheaton Col, BS, 48; Univ Mich, MS, 49, MS, 53, PhD(physiol), 55. *Prof Exp:* Instr physiol, Sch Med, Univ Mich, 55-56; from instr to assoc prof, NJ Col Med & Dent, 56-64; assoc prof, 64-69, PROF PHYSIOL, COL MED, OHIO STATE UNIV, 69- *Mem:* AAAS; Am Physiol Soc; Soc Exp Biol & Med. *Res:* Respiration; oxygen toxicity; blood gases; cardiac output; pulmonary blood flow; coronary blood flow. *Mailing Add:* Dept of Physiol Ohio State Univ Col of Med Columbus OH 43210

SMITH, CHARLES WILLIAM, JR, b Greensburg, Pa, May 13, 40; m 64; c 1. LOW TEMPERATURE PHYSICS. *Educ:* Allegheny Col, BS, 62; Ohio Univ, PhD(physics), 68. *Prof Exp:* From asst prof to assoc prof, 68-80, PROF PHYSICS, UNIV MAINE, ORONO, 80-, COOP ASSOC PROF ENERGY & SCI, 77- *Mem:* Sigma Xi; Am Phys Soc. *Res:* Low temperature condensed matter physics; superconductivity; liquid helium . *Mailing Add:* Dept Physics Bennett Hall Univ Maine Orono ME 04469

SMITH, CHARLINE GALLOWAY, b Louisiana, Mo, Apr 9, 25; div; c 2. PHYSICAL ANTHROPOLOGY. *Educ:* Univ Utah, BS, 65, PhD(anthrop), 70. *Prof Exp:* Staff nurse surg, Barnes Hosp, St Louis, Mo, 46-47; staff nurse, Am Hosp, Chicago, 48-49; staff nurse, Lutheran Hosp, Los Angeles, 49-54; specialist thoracic intensive care, LDS Hosp, Salt Lake City, 62-63; instr anthrop, Div Continuing Educ, Univ Utah, 66-68, assoc ed, 66-70, teaching asst, 70; asst prof, 70-77, ASSOC PROF PHYS ANTHROP, UNIV MONT, 77- *Mem:* AAAS; Am Asn Phys Anthrop; Am Anthrop Asn; Am Diabetes Asn; Am Ethnol Soc. *Res:* Diabetes Mellitus among American Indians; medical ethnobotany; sex ratios among primitive groups; cerebral dominance and handedness. *Mailing Add:* Dept of Anthrop Univ of Mont Missoula MT 59801

SMITH, CHARLOTTE DAMRON, b Columbus, Ohio, Nov 13, 19; m 57. BIOCHEMISTRY. *Educ:* Wellesley Col, BA, 40; Rutgers Univ, MS, 42; George Washington Univ, PhD(biochem), 51. *Prof Exp:* Asst chem, Rutgers Univ, 40-42; res chemist, E I du Pont de Nemours & Co, 44-47; asst biochem, George Washington Univ, 47-51; res fel, Nat Cancer Inst, 51-54; res assoc environ med, Sch Hyg, Johns Hopkins Univ, 53-55; assoc sci info exchange, Smithsonian Inst, 55-81; RETIRED. *Res:* Metabolism of ascorbic acid in the guinea pig and of carcinogen 2-acetylamino fluorene in the rat; mode of action of chromium compounds in causing human lung cancer. *Mailing Add:* 3708 Manor Rd Chevy Chase MD 20815

SMITH, CHESTER MARTIN, JR, b Randolph, Vt, Sept 8, 35; m 58; c 2. COMPUTER SCIENCE. *Educ:* Univ Vt, BA, 57; Pa State Univ, MS, 59, PhD(mineral), 64. *Prof Exp:* Res asst comput sci, 61-62, ASST PROF COMPUT SCI, PA STATE UNIV, 63- *Concurrent Pos:* Chmn, Share Inc, 67-69, mgr, 69-70, dir, 70-71, secy, 71-72; chmn, Fortran Data Base Comt, Conf Data Systs Lang, 74-79. *Mem:* Asn Comput Mach. *Res:* Programming languages; compiler construction; information retrieval; data base management and standards; historical place name data bases; micro-computers. *Mailing Add:* Comput Bldg Pa State Univ University Park PA 16802

SMITH, CHRISTOPHER CARLISLE, b Boston, Mass, June 18, 38; m 60; c 3. EVOLUTIONARY ECOLOGY. *Educ:* Univ Colo, BA, 60; Univ Wash, MA, 63, PhD(ecol), 65. *Prof Exp:* Asst prof biol, Fisk Univ, 65-67; res assoc ecol, Smithsonian Trop Res Inst, 67-68; asst prof zool, Univ Mo-Columbia, 68-70; assoc prof, 70-81, PROF ZOOL, KANS STATE UNIV, 81- *Mem:* AAAS; Ecol Soc Am; Soc Study Evolution; Am Soc Mammal; Am Soc Naturalists. *Res:* relationship between mammalian social organization and ecology; relationship between animals and the fruiting pattern in forest trees; ecology of wind pollination. *Mailing Add:* Div of Biol Kans State Univ Manhattan KS 66506

SMITH, CLAIBOURNE DAVIS, b Memphis, Tenn, Jan 6, 38; m 59; c 2. ORGANIC CHEMISTRY. *Educ:* Univ Denver, BS, 59, MS, 61; Univ Ore, PhD(org chem), 64. *Prof Exp:* Res asst org chem, Denver Res Inst, Univ Denver, 59-61; res chemist, Cent Res Dept, 64-71, tech prog mgr, Fabrics & Finishes Dept, 71-73, sales mgr, 73-74, TECH MGR, INDUST PROD DIV, FABRIC & FINISHES DEPT, E I DU PONT DE NEMOURS & CO, INC, 74- *Mem:* Am Chem Soc. *Res:* Organic synthesis of polynitrafluoro aromatics; polymeric binders and thermal stable organic polymers; non-benzoid aromatic hydrocarbons and strained small ring compounds. *Mailing Add:* 114 Somerset Rd Alapocas Wilmington DE 19803

SMITH, CLAIRE LEROY, b Atlantic, Iowa, May 1, 23; m 53; c 4. MICROBIOLOGY. *Educ:* Univ Omaha, BS, 53; Univ Iowa, MS, 55. *Prof Exp:* BACTERIOLOGIST, GRAIN PROCESSING CORP, 55- *Mem:* Soc Indust Microbiol; Am Soc Microbiol; Am Inst Biol Sci. *Res:* Industrial fermentations; brewing; vitamins; amino acids; antibiotics; enzymes. *Mailing Add:* Grain Processing Corp PO Box 349 Muscatine IA 52761

SMITH, CLARENCE LAVETT, b Hamburg, NY, Dec 19, 27; m 54; c 2. ZOOLOGY. *Educ:* Cornell Univ, BS, 49; Tulane Univ, MS, 51; Univ Mich, PhD, 59. *Prof Exp:* CUR DEPT ICHTHYOL, AM MUS NATURAL HIST, 62-, CHMN, 75- *Concurrent Pos:* Vis prof, Univ Okla, 49, Ohio State Univ, 59, 63 & 71 & Univ Mich, 76, 78 & 80; assoc prof, Col Guam, 60-61 & Univ Hawaii, 61-62; scientist, Aquanaut Proj, Tektile II, 70; adj prof, City Col New York, 70- *Mem:* Ecol Soc Am; Am Soc Ichthyol & Herpet; Am Fisheries Soc; Am Soc Limnol & Oceanog. *Res:* Ichthyology; taxonomy, ecology, morphology and distribution of Recent fishes; ecology of coral reef fishes. *Mailing Add:* Am Mus Nat Hist Dept Ichthyol Central Park W at 79th New York NY 10024

SMITH, CLAUDE EARLE, JR, b Boston, Mass, Mar 8, 22; m 48; c 4. SYSTEMATIC BOTANY. *Educ:* Harvard Univ, AB, 49, PhD, 53. *Prof Exp:* Instr biol, Cambridge Jr Col, 51-52; curator, Dept Bot, Acad Natural Sci Philadelphia, 53-58; curator vascular plants, Chicago Natural Hist Mus, 59-61; res botanist, New Crops Res Br, Crops Res Div, Agr Res Serv, USDA, 62-69; PROF ANTHROP & BIOL, UNIV ALA, TUSCALOOSA, 70- *Mem:* Am Soc Plant Taxon; Soc Econ Bot; Soc Am Archaeol; Int Asn Plant Taxon. *Res:* Interpretation of plant remains from excavations in Peru, Venezuela, Panama, Oaxaca and Amazon Valleys, Mexico and Southeast United States. *Mailing Add:* Dept of Anthrop Univ of Ala Tuscaloosa University AL 35486

SMITH, CLAY TAYLOR, b Omaha, Nebr, June 30, 17; m 40; c 2. GEOLOGY. *Educ:* Calif Inst Technol, BS, 38, MS, 40, PhD(geo), 43. *Prof Exp:* Recorder, US Geol Surv, 38, 39, jr geologist, 40-42; geol field engr, Consol Mining & Smelting Co Can, 43; asst geologist, Union Mines Develop Corp, NY, 43-46; field geologist, US Vanadium Corp, 46-47; asst prof eng, 47, assoc prof geol, 51-56, head dept, 52-66, dean student & admissions, 67-68, PROF GEOL, N MEX INST MINING & TECHNOL, 56- *Concurrent Pos:* Consult raw mat resource eval, 50- *Mem:* AAAS; Soc Econ Geol; Geol Soc Am; Nat Asn Geol Teachers; Am Inst Prof Geologists. *Res:* Secondary earth science education; raw material resources of New Mexico; mining geophysics; geology of chromite deposits; origin of sedimentary type uranium ores; geology of ferroalloy elements. *Mailing Add:* Dept Geosci NMex Inst Mining & Technol Socorro NM 87801

SMITH, CLAYTON ALBERT, JR, b Champaign, Ill, June 10, 34. POSITIONAL ASTRONOMY. *Educ:* Univ Chicago, BA, 56, BS, 57; Georgetown Univ, PhD(astron), 69. *Prof Exp:* ASTRONOMER ASTROMETRY, NAVAL OBSERV, 59-, CHIEF, CATALOGING BR, 80- *Concurrent Pos:* Resident dir, Yale-Columbia Southern Observ, Arg, 68-70. *Mem:* Am Astron Soc; Astron Soc Pac; Sigma Xi; AAAS; Int Astron Union. *Res:* Formulation of catalogs of differential and fundamental systems of stellar positions and proper motions. *Mailing Add:* Transit Circle Div Naval Observ Washington DC 20390

SMITH, CLIFFORD JAMES, b Brooklyn, NY, Oct 30, 38; m 59; c 4. ANIMAL PHYSIOLOGY. *Educ:* Cornell Univ, BS, 60; Univ Md, PhD(physiol, biochem), 64. *Prof Exp:* Res asst physiol, Univ Md, 60-64; NIH fel anat, Univ Vt, 64-65; from asst prof to assoc prof biol, 65-75, PROF BIOL, UNIV TOLEDO, 75-, CHMN DEPT, 70- *Mem:* AAAS; Am Soc Zool; Poultry Sci Asn. *Res:* Physiological control of hunger and appetite. *Mailing Add:* Dept Biol Univ Toledo Col Arts & Sci Toledo OH 43606

SMITH, CLOYD VIRGIL, JR, b Seminole, Okla, Dec 2, 36; m 60; c 3. SOLID MECHANICS. *Educ:* Ga Inst Technol, BCE, 58; Stanford Univ, MSCE, 59; Mass Inst Technol, ScD(civil eng), 62. *Prof Exp:* Res engr, Jet Propulsion Lab, Calif Inst Technol, 63-64; ASSOC PROF AEROSPACE ENG, GA INST TECHNOL, 64- *Mem:* Am Inst Aeronaut & Astronaut. *Res:* Elastic stability; matrix methods of structural analysis; nonlinear elasticity; structural dynamics. *Mailing Add:* Sch of Aerospace Eng Ga Inst of Technol Atlanta GA 30332

SMITH, CLYDE F, b Riverdale, Idaho, Aug 10, 13; m 36; c 3. ENTOMOLOGY. *Educ:* Utah State Agr Col, BS, 35, MS, 37; Ohio State Univ, PhD(entom), 39. *Prof Exp:* Asst entom, Utah State Agr Col, 34-36 & 37; asst, Ohio State Univ, 36-38, asst, Exten, 38 & 39; from asst entomologist to res prof entom, 39-50, head dept, 50-64, prof, 64-78, EMER PROF ENTOM, NC STATE UNIV, 78- *Mem:* AAAS; Entom Soc Am; Soc Syst Zool. *Res:* Biology; entomology, ecology and control of fruit insects; taxonomy of Aphididae (Homoptera) and Aphidiinae (Hymenoptera). *Mailing Add:* Dept Entom NC State Univ Box 5215 Raleigh NC 27607

SMITH, CLYDE KONRAD, b Sturgeon Bay, Wis, Dec 9, 25; m 47. VETERINARY MICROBIOLOGY. *Educ:* Mich State Univ, BS, 47, DVM, 51, MS, 53; Univ Notre Dame, PhD, 66; Am Col Vet Microbiologists, dipl. *Prof Exp:* Instr bact, Mich State Univ, 51, asst prof, 56-66; assoc prof vet sci, 66-72, PROF VET SCI, OHIO AGR RES & DEVELOP CTR, 72- *Mem:* AAAS; Am Soc Microbiol; Am Vet Med Asn; Am Asn Bovine Practr; Conf Res Workers Animal Dis. *Res:* Ruminant nutrition and physiology and germfree ruminants; respiratory and enteric diseases of sheep, feeder calves and dairy calves. *Mailing Add:* Dept of Vet Sci Ohio Agr Res & Develop Ctr Wooster OH 44691

SMITH, COLIN MCPHERSON, b Edinburgh, Scotland, Mar 14, 27; Can citizen; m 62; c 4. PSYCHIATRY, GERIATRIC MEDICINE. *Educ:* Univ Glasgow, MB, ChB, 49, MD, 59; FRCP(C), 56; Univ Sask, MD, 63; FRCP sychiat, 72. *Prof Exp:* Res asst psychol, Univ London, 58-59; dep dir psychiat res, 56-66, dir psychiat training psychiat, 66-67; dir psychiat servs, 67-76, CONSULT MENT HEALTH SERV TO ELDERLY, SASK DEPT HEALTH, 76- *Concurrent Pos:* Mem, Alcohol Comn Sask, 68-80; clin prof psychiat, Univ Sask, 71-; head psychiat, Plains Health Ctr, 78-81; consult, Univ Hosp, 75- & Staff Plains Health Ctr, 81-; ed, Can Phychiat Asn Bull, 80- *Honors & Awards:* Ment Health Res Award, Can Ment Health Asn, 62. *Mem:* Can Psychiat Asn (pres, 74-75); fel Am Geriat Soc; fel Am Psychiat Asn. *Res:* Geriatric psychiatry; social psychiatry, alcoholism; gerontology; research design. *Mailing Add:* 4437 Castle Rd Regina SK S4S 4W4 Can

SMITH, COLLEEN MARY, b Minneapolis, Minn, Oct 4, 43. BIOCHEMISTRY. *Educ:* Univ Minn, BA, 63; Univ Utah, PhD(biochem), 69. *Prof Exp:* Instr, 72-74, ASST PROF BIOCHEM, SCH MED, TEMPLE UNIV, 74- *Concurrent Pos:* NIH fel, Johnson Res Found, Univ Pa, 70-72. *Mem:* AAAS; Am Chem Soc; Biophys Soc; Fedn Am Soc Exp Biol. *Res:* Metabolic regulation; co-factor biosynthesis; enzymology. *Mailing Add:* Heath Sci Ctr Dept Biochem Temple Univ Sch of Med Philadelphia PA 19104

SMITH, CORNELIA MARSCHALL, b Llano, Tex, Oct 15, 95; wid. MORPHOLOGY. *Educ:* Baylor Univ, BA, 18; Univ Chicago, MA, 23; Johns Hopkins Univ, PhD(biol), 28. *Prof Exp:* From instr to asst prof bot, Baylor Univ, 28-35; prof biol & head dept, Stetson Univ, 35-40; prof, 40-67, chmn dept, 43-67, dir, Strecker Mus, 45-67, Piper prof, 67-80, EMER PROF BIOL, BAYLOR UNIV, 80- *Concurrent Pos:* Secy, Tex Bd Exam Basic Sci, 49-67. *Mem:* AAAS; Bot Soc Am; Modern Lang Asn Am; Sigma Xi. *Res:* Morphology of Dionaea; toxicity of Polistes venom; electrophoretic comparison of six species of Yucca and Hesperaloe. *Mailing Add:* F E Box 141 Baylor Univ Waco TX 76798

SMITH, CRAIG LA SALLE, b Miami Beach, Fla, Mar 29, 43; m 67. ORGANIC CHEMISTRY, MARINE SCIENCE. *Educ:* Johns Hopkins Univ, BA, 64; Univ Fla, PhD(chem), 68. *Prof Exp:* Fel, Ga Inst Technol, 67-70; ASSOC MARINE SCIENTIST, VA INST MARINE SCI, 70-; ASST PROF MARINE SCI, COL WILLIAM & MARY, 70-; ASST PROF MARINE SCI, UNIV VA, 70- *Mem:* Am Chem Soc. *Res:* Heterocyclic organic chemistry; carbanion chemistry; mass spectroscopy; oil pollution; organic geochemistry. *Mailing Add:* Va Inst of Marine Sci Gloucester Point VA 23062

SMITH, CURTIS ALAN, b Long Beach, Calif, Sept 8, 48. PHYSIOLOGY. *Educ:* Calif State Col, Fullerton, BA, 70; Univ Calif, San Francisco, PhD(physiol), 78. *Prof Exp:* FEL PHYSIOL, DEPT PREV MED, UNIV WIS-MADISON, 78- *Mem:* Assoc Am Physiol Soc. *Res:* Control of breathing. *Mailing Add:* Dept of Prev Med Univ of Wis Madison WI 53706

SMITH, CURTIS GRIFFIN, b Milwaukee, Wis, Nov 14, 23; m 47; c 3. PHYSIOLOGY. *Educ:* Univ Chicago, AB, 47, PhD, 54. *Prof Exp:* Instr biophys, Sch Med, Univ Calif, Los Angeles, 54-55; from instr to assoc prof physiol, 55-69, PROF PHYSIOL, MT HOLYOKE COL, 69- *Concurrent Pos:* Vis prof, Univ EAnglia, 69-70. *Mem:* Am Soc Biol Chem; Am Chem Soc; Brit Soc Gen Microbiol. *Res:* Biochemical genetics; molecular biophysics; biochemistry and physiology of neurotransmitters; neurophysiology. *Mailing Add:* Dept of Biol Sci Mt Holyoke Col South Hadley MA 01075

SMITH, CURTIS PAGE, b Long Prairie, Minn, Dec 25, 38; m 60; c 2. ORGANIC CHEMISTRY. *Educ:* Univ Mich, BSch, 61; State Univ NY, PhD(chem), 67. *Prof Exp:* Fel chem, State Univ NY Stony Brook, 66-68; sr res chemist, Olin Res Ctr, 68-69; STAFF SCIENTIST, D S GILMORE RES LAB, THE UPJOHN CO, 69- *Mem:* Am Chem Soc; Sigma Xi. *Res:* Organo phosphorus chemistry; mechanism of organic reactions. *Mailing Add:* The Upjohn Co 410 Sackett Point Rd North Haven CT 06473

SMITH, CURTIS R, b Mineola, Tex, Nov 12, 36; m 58; c 3. AUDIOLOGY. *Educ:* Univ Southern Miss, BS, 60, MS, 61, PhD(audiol), 65. *Prof Exp:* Chief audiol, Brooke Gen Hosp, Ft Sam Houston, Tex, 65-66; dir grad training audiol, Our Lady of the Lake Col, 66-69; ASSOC PROF SPEECH COMMUN, AUBURN UNIV & DIR SPEECH & HEARING CLIN, 69-*Concurrent Pos:* Chief clin audiologist, Harry Jersig Speech & Hearing Ctr, 66-69. *Mem:* Am Speech & Hearing Asn. *Res:* Hearing mechanism and vestibular system. *Mailing Add:* Dept of Speech Commun Auburn Univ Auburn AL 36830

SMITH, CURTIS WILLIAM, b Omaha, Ill, Jan 14, 18; m 42; c 5. ORGANIC CHEMISTRY. *Educ:* Southern Ill Univ, BEd, 40; Univ Ill, PhD(org chem), 43. *Prof Exp:* Chemist, Res & Develop, Shell Develop Co, 43-52, mem staff mgt, 52-63, di71-77, 63-65, mgr, Ind Chem Div, Shell Chem Co, 65-71, asst to pres, Shell Develop Co, 71-77, SR CONSULT, CHEM INDUST REGULATIONS, SHELL OIL CO, 77- *Mem:* Sigma Xi; Am Chem Soc. *Res:* Develop synthesis of tryptophan using quaternary ammonium akylation; penicillin; chemistry of acroleim. *Mailing Add:* 163 Stoney Creek Houston TX 77024

SMITH, CYRIL BEVERLEY, b Winnipeg, Man, Feb 21, 21; m 52. PLANT NUTRITION. *Educ:* Univ Man, BSA, 42, MSc, 45; Pa State Univ, PhD(hort), 50. *Prof Exp:* From instr to assoc prof, 47-65, PROF PLANT NUTRIT, PA STATE UNIV, UNIVERSITY PARK, 65- *Mem:* Am Soc Hort Sci; Am Soc Plant Physiol; Am Chem Soc; Soc Appl Spectros. *Res:* Use of plant analysis in studying nutritional status of plants. *Mailing Add:* 101 Tyson Bldg Dept Hort Pa State Univ University Park PA 16802

SMITH, CYRIL STANLEY, b Birmingham, Eng, Oct 4, 03; US citizen; m 31; c 2. METALLURGY. *Educ:* Univ Birmingham, BSc, 24; Mass Inst Technol, DSc(metall), 26. *Hon Degrees:* DLitt, Case Inst Technol, 65; ScD, Univ Pa, 74, Univ Mass, 79. *Prof Exp:* Res metallurgist, Am Brass Co, 27-42; assoc div leader, Los Alamos Sci Lab, 43-46; dir, Inst Study Metals, Univ Chicago, 46-61; inst prof, 61-69, EMER INST PROF, MASS INST TECHNOL, 69-*Concurrent Pos:* Mem gen adv comt, US AEC, 46-52; Guggenheim Found fels, 55-56 & 78-79; mem, President's Sci Adv Comt, 59; mem coun, Smithsonian Inst, 66-76. *Honors & Awards:* Gold Medal, Am Soc Metals, 61; Douglas Gold Medal, Inst Mining & Metall Engrs, 63; Platinum Medal, Inst Metals, London, 70; Dexter Award, Am Chem Soc, 81. *Mem:* Nat Acad Sci; Am Philos Soc; Am Soc Metals; Hist Technol Soc (pres, 63-65); Metall Soc. *Res:* General theory of structure as heirarchy; history of technology and science and their relations to art; author or coauthor of numerous publications. *Mailing Add:* 31 Madison St Cambridge MA 02138

SMITH, DALE, b Fairmont, Nebr, Apr 13, 15; m 40; c 2. AGRONOMY. *Educ:* Univ Nebr, BSc, 38; Univ Wis, MSc, 40, PhD(agron, plant physiol), 47. *Prof Exp:* From asst prof to assoc prof, 46-56, prof agron, 56-77, EMER PROF AGRON, UNIV WIS-MADISON, 77- *Concurrent Pos:* NATO fel, Eng, 64; Haight travel award, Asia, Australia & NZ, 70; mem, Acad Quest, Swiss Inst Technol, Zurich, 79; adj prof plant sci, Univ Ariz, Tucson, 79-*Honors & Awards:* Crop Sci Award, Am Soc Agron, 63. *Mem:* Fel AAAS; fel Am Soc Agron. *Res:* Forage management; chemical composition; growth responses and food reserves in forage plants. *Mailing Add:* Dept of Plant Sci Univ Ariz Tucson AZ 85721

SMITH, DALE METZ, b Portland, Ind, Dec 23, 28; m 50; c 2. SYSTEMATIC BOTANY. *Educ:* Ind Univ, BS, 50, PhD(bot), 57; Purdue Univ, MS, 52. *Prof Exp:* Instr bot, Univ Ariz, 52-53; from instr to assoc prof, Univ Ky, 55-61; assoc prof, Univ Ill, 61-64; assoc prof, 64-71, PROF BOT, UNIV CALIF, SANTA BARBARA, 71- *Honors & Awards:* Cooley Award, Am Soc Plant Taxon, 63. *Mem:* AAAS; Bot Soc Am; Am Soc Plant Taxon; Am Fern Soc. *Res:* Biosystematics of Phlox; cytotaxonomy and chemotaxonomy. *Mailing Add:* Dept of Biol Sci Univ of Calif Santa Barbara CA 93106

SMITH, DALLAS GLEN, JR, b Gainesboro, Tenn, June 25, 40; m 61; c 3. ENGINEERING MECHANICS. *Educ:* Tenn Polytech Inst, BS, 63; Tenn Technol Univ, MS, 66; Va Polytech Inst, PhD(eng mech), 69. *Prof Exp:* Bridge design engr, Bridge Div, Tenn Dept Hwy, 63-65; asst prof eng mech, Va Polytech Inst, 69-70; asst prof eng sci, 70-74, assoc prof, 74-79, PROF ENG SCI & MECH, TENN TECHNOL UNIV, 79- *Concurrent Pos:* Consult, US Army Missile Command, Redstone Arsenal, 71- *Mem:* Am Soc Testing & Mat; Soc Exp Stress Anal; Am Soc Eng Educ. *Res:* Brittle fracture mechanics; fiber-reinforced composite materials; experimental mechanics. *Mailing Add:* Dept Eng Sci & Mech Tenn Technol Univ Cookeville TN 38501

SMITH, DANIEL JAMES, b Rochester, NY, June 17, 44; m 67; c 3. IMMUNOLOGY, ORAL BIOLOGY. *Educ:* Houghton Col, BS, 66; NY Med Col, PhD(immunol), 72. *Prof Exp:* Staff assoc, Forsyth Dent Ctr, 72-74, asst mem staff immunol, 74-76; clin instr, 76-79, Harvard Sch Dent Med, Harvard Univ, assoc clin prof, 79-82; ASSOC MEM STAFF, FORSYTH DENT CTR, 79- *Mem:* Am Asn Immunologists; Int Asn Dent Res. *Res:* Nature and function of secretory immune system, role of immunity in diseases of oral cavity, oral microbiology, and autoimmune mechanisms. *Mailing Add:* Forsyth Dental Ctr 140 Fenway Boston MA 02115

SMITH, DANIEL JOHN, b Horicon, Wis, Apr 19, 46. BIOCHEMISTRY, ORGANIC CHEMISTRY. *Educ:* Wis State Univ, BS, 68; Univ Calif, Berkeley, PhD(org chem), 74. *Prof Exp:* Fel biochem, Univ Calif, Los Angeles, 74-76; vis scientist, Syva Res Inst, 76-77; ASST PROF BIOCHEM, UNIV AKRON, 77- *Mem:* Am Chem Soc; Control Release Soc. *Res:* Mechanism of photophosphorylation and oxidative phosphorylation; mechanism of control release organotin compounds as molluscicides. *Mailing Add:* Dept of Chem Univ of Akron Akron OH 44325

SMITH, DANIEL MONTAGUE, b Gainesville, Tex, Oct 17, 32; m 53; c 3. PHYSICS. *Educ:* NTex State Col, BA, 52, MS, 53; Univ Tex, PhD(physics), 59. *Prof Exp:* Lab asst, NTex State Col, 50-52; asst, Univ Tex, 55-58, scientist, 57-58; physicist, Oak Ridge Nat Lab, 58-61; mem tech staff, Tex Instruments Inc, Tex, 61-75; mgr device technol, Nitron Div, McDonnell Douglas, 75-80. *Mem:* Am Phys Soc; Inst Elec & Electronics Engrs. *Res:* Medium energy experimental nuclear physics; semiconductor device design and development. *Mailing Add:* 5904 Burnhill Austin TX 78745

SMITH, DANIEL NEWTON, JR, poultry nutrition, see previous edition

SMITH, DARRELL WAYNE, b Long Beach, Calif, July 31, 37; m 58; c 3. MATERIALS SCIENCE, PHYSICAL METALLURGY. *Educ:* Mich Technol Univ, BS, 59; Case Western Reserve Univ, MS, 65, PhD(phys metall), 69. *Prof Exp:* Metallurgist, Babcock & Wilcox Co, 59-62 & Gen Elec Co, 62-68; res assoc, Case Western Reserve Univ, 68-69; res metallurgist, Gen Elec Co, 69-70; asst prof, 70-75, assoc prof, 75-81, PROF METALL ENG, MICH TECHNOL UNIV, 81- *Mem:* Am Soc Metals; Am Powder Metall Inst; Am Soc Testing Mat. *Res:* Fracture behavior of ceramics; powder metallurgy. *Mailing Add:* Dept of Metall Eng Mich Technol Univ Houghton MI 49931

SMITH, DARRYL LYLE, b Minneapolis, Minn, July 30, 46. SOLID STATE PHYSICS. *Educ:* St Mary's Col, Minn, BA, 68; Univ Ill, MS, 71, PhD(physics), 74. *Prof Exp:* INSTR APPL PHYSICS, CALIF INST TECHNOL, 74- *Mem:* Am Phys Soc; Sigma Xi. *Res:* Optical properties of solids. *Mailing Add:* 116-81 Calif Inst of Technol Pasadena CA 91125

SMITH, DARWIN WALDRON, b Los Angeles, Calif, Mar 25, 31; m 52; c 3. PHYSICAL CHEMISTRY. *Educ:* Univ Calif, Los Angeles, BS, 53; Calif Inst Technol, PhD(chem), 59. *Prof Exp:* NSF fel chem, Math Inst, Oxford Univ, 59; from asst prof to assoc prof chem, Univ Fla, 60-68; ASSOC PROF CHEM, UNIV GA, 68- *Mem:* Am Phys Soc; Am Chem Soc. *Res:* Quantum chemistry; theory of molecular structure. *Mailing Add:* Dept of Chem Univ of Ga Athens GA 30602

SMITH, DAVID, b Fall River, Mass, Nov 7, 39; m 67; c 6. PHYSICAL CHEMISTRY. *Educ:* Providence Col, BS, 61; Mass Inst Technol, PhD(chem), 65. *Prof Exp:* Instr chem, Brooklyn Col, 65-68; asst prof, 68-76, ASSOC PROF CHEM, PA STATE UNIV, HAZLETON, 76- *Mem:* Am Chem Soc; Am Phys Soc. *Res:* Low temperature heat capacities; hindered rotation in solids; quantum chemistry program exchange. *Mailing Add:* Dept of Chem Pa State Univ Hazleton PA 18201

SMITH, DAVID ALEXANDER, b New York, NY, Jan 6, 38; m 58; c 4. MATHEMATICS. *Educ:* Trinity Col, Conn, BS, 58; Yale Univ, PhD(math), 63. *Prof Exp:* Asst prof math, 62-68, dir grad studies, 68-71, ASSOC PROF MATH, DUKE UNIV, 68- *Concurrent Pos:* Vis assoc prof, Case Western Reserve Univ, 75-76; series ed math, Proj Conduit, 75-; calculus proj adv, DC Heath & Co, 76-79; assoc ed, Math Mag, 81-85. *Mem:* Soc Indust & Appl Math; AAAS; Am Math Soc; Math Asn Am; Asn Develop Comput-Based Instructional Systs. *Res:* Abstract algebra; arithmetic functions; algorithmic algebra; combinatorial theory; numerical analysis; uses of computers in mathematics; application in social and biological sciences. *Mailing Add:* Dept of Math Duke Univ Durham NC 27706

SMITH, DAVID ALLEN, b Osceola, Nebr, Feb 25, 33; div; c 3. MOLECULAR BIOLOGY, RADIOBIOLOGY. *Educ:* Dana Col, BA, 59; Univ Southern Calif, PhD(biochem), 64. *Prof Exp:* Biochemist, Biomed Res Group, Los Alamos Sci Lab, Univ Calif, 64-77; MOLECULAR BIOLOGIST, OFF HEALTH & ENVIRON RES, DEPT ENERGY, 77-, ACTG DEP DIR, HEALTH EFFECTS RES DIV, 79- *Mem:* AAAS; Biophys Soc; Am Chem Soc; Am Soc Biol Chemists. *Res:* Effects of radiation and other environmental pollutants on genetic information transfer; nucleic acids and nucleic acid enzymology. *Mailing Add:* Off of Health & Environ Res Dept of Energy Washington DC 20545

SMITH, DAVID BEACH, b Newton, NJ, Dec 3, 11; m 42; c 4. SYSTEMS ENGINEERING, ELECTRICAL ENGINEERING. *Educ:* Mass Inst Technol, BS, 33, MS, 34. *Prof Exp:* Engr, Philco Corp, 34-45, vpres res, 45-58, vpres tech affairs, 58-61, vpres res & eng, Philco-Ford, 61-64; prof systs eng, Moore Sch, Univ Pa, 64-67; pres, HRB Singer, Inc, 67-69; vis lectr, Univ Pa, 69-72; prof & dir grad prog eng mgt, 72-78, EMER PROF, DREXEL UNIV, 78- *Concurrent Pos:* Mem, Nat TV Syst Comt, 40-41; mem bd dirs, Philco Corp, 46-56; vchmn, Second Nat TV Syst Comt, 50-53; mem adv comt, Signal Corp, US Army, 53-56; mem bd dirs, Narco Sci, 65-; mem, Sci & Arts Comt, Franklin Inst, 68-, chmn, 81. *Mem:* AAAS; Am Soc Eng Educ; fel Inst Elec & Electronics Engrs. *Res:* Research and development management. *Mailing Add:* 1642 Graham Rd Meadowbrook PA 19046

SMITH, DAVID BURRARD, b Kidderminster, Eng, Dec 6, 16; Can citizen; m 42; c 3. BIOCHEMISTRY. *Educ:* Univ BC, BA, 39, MA, 41; Univ Toronto, PhD(biochem), 50. *Prof Exp:* Res officer, Div Biosci, Nat Res Coun Can, 50-66; PROF BIOCHEM, UNIV WESTERN ONT, 66- *Mem:* AAAS; Can Soc Cell Biol; Am Soc Biol Chem; Can Biochem Soc. *Res:* Physical chemistry of proteins, especially hemoglobin; amino acid sequence and oxygen equilibrium of hemoglobin; hemoglobin haptoglobin complex; cross-linking proteins with bifunctional reagents. *Mailing Add:* Dept of Biochem Univ of Western Ont London ON N6A 5C1 Can

SMITH, DAVID CLEMENT, IV, b Midland, Tex, Apr 26, 51. PHYSICAL OCEANOGRAPHY, OCEAN NUMERICAL MODELS. *Educ:* Univ Houston, BS, 73; Tex A&M Univ, MS, 75, PhD(oceanog), 80. *Prof Exp:* Assoc, Mesoscale Air Sea Interaction Group, Fla State Univ, 80-81; ADJ RES PROF, DEPT OCEANOG, NAVAL POSTGRAD SCH, 81- *Mem:* Am Meteorol Soc. *Res:* Physical oceanographic research in ocean mesoscale dynamics through the use of regional ocean numerical models. *Mailing Add:* Code 68 Dept Oceanog Naval Postgrad Sch Monterey CA 93940

SMITH, DAVID EDMUND, b Brentford, Eng, Nov 3, 34; m 61; c 4. SATELLITE GEODESY, CELESTIAL MECHANICS. *Educ:* Univ Durham, Eng, BSc, 58; Univ London, MSc, 62, PhD(satellite geod), 66. *Prof Exp:* Sci officer math, Radio & Space Res Sta, 58-68; sr scientist geod, EG&G, Wolf Res & Develop Corp, 68-69; staff scientist geophys, 69-71, HEAD GEODYNAMICS BR, NASA GODDARD SPACE FLIGHT CTR, 71- *Concurrent Pos:* Mem working group 1 satellite geod & geodynamics, Comt Space Res, 67-; mem comn satellite geod, Joint Comt Space Res & Int Union Geod & Geophys, 71-; mem study group fundamental geod constants, Int Asn Geod, 74-; mem study group ref systs geod & geodynamics, 76-; mem working group measurement earth rotation, Int Astron Union, 78-; proj scientist, Crustal Dynamics Proj, NASA, 80- *Honors & Awards:* Except Sci Achievement Medal, NASA, 74; John C Lindsay Mem Award, Goddard Space Flight Ctr, 78. *Mem:* Royal Astron Soc; Am Geophys Union. *Res:* Determination of shape and size of earth, its tectonics, gravity field, internal structure, rotations and tides; motion of artificial satellites and their perturbation. *Mailing Add:* Geodynamics Br Code 921 Goddard Space Flight Ctr Greenbelt MD 20771

SMITH, DAVID ENGLISH, b San Francisco, Calif, June 9, 20; m 48; c 3. PATHOLOGY. *Educ:* Cent Col, Mo, AB, 41; Washington Univ, MD, 44; Am Bd Path, dipl, 50. *Prof Exp:* Intern & resident path, Barnes Hosp, St Louis, Mo, 44-46; from instr to assoc prof path, Sch Med, Washington Univ, 48-55, asst head dept, 53-54; prof, Sch Med, Univ Va, 55-73, chmn dept, 58-73, dir cancer ctr, 72-73; prof path, Northwestern Univ, Evanston, 74-75; prof path, Univ Pa, Philadelphia, 76-80; PROF PATH & ASSOC DEAN, TULANE UNIV, 80- *Concurrent Pos:* Mem, Exec Comt, Nat Bd Med Examrs, 70-80, vpres & dir undergrad div, 75-80, secy, 77-80; trustee, Am Bd Path, 66-73; assoc dir, Am Bd Med Specialists, 74-75. *Mem:* Am Soc Clin Path; Am Asn Pathologists & Bacteriologists; AMA; Am Acad Neurol; Int Acad Path (pres, 64-65). *Res:* Neuropathology; quantitative histochemistry; evaluation of medical education. *Mailing Add:* Off Dean Tulane Univ Sch Med 1430 Tulane Ave New Orleans LA 70112

SMITH, DAVID FRANCIS, marine ecology, microbial ecology, see previous edition

SMITH, DAVID HARRISON, JR, b Hibbing, Minn, Mar 7, 26; div; c 2. GERMPLASM RESOURCES, PLANT BREEDING. *Educ:* Hamline Univ, BS, 50; Univ Minn, MS, 55; Mich State Univ, PhD(crop sci), 63. *Prof Exp:* Instr, High Sch, 55-56; instr bot & zool, Brainerd Jr Col, 56-59; asst prof crop sci, Mich State Univ, 63-65; res geneticist, Plant Sci Res Div, 65-80, CUR, USDA SMALL GRAINS COLLECTION, 80- *Mem:* Am Soc Agron; Crop Sci Soc Am; Am Genetic Asn. *Res:* Isolation and incorporation of resistance to the Cereal Leaf Beetle into adapted wheat, barley and oat germ-plasm; collection, maintenance and distribution of cereal germplasm. *Mailing Add:* USDA ARS NER BARC-W B046 Beltsville MD 20705

SMITH, DAVID HIBBARD, b Springfield, Mo, July 29, 41; m 66. ORGANIC CHEMISTRY. *Educ:* Univ Notre Dame, BS, 63; Univ Mo-Columbia, PhD(org chem), 71. *Prof Exp:* Asst prof, 70-78, ASSOC PROF CHEM, DOANE COL, 78-, CHMN, NAT SCI DIV, 79- *Concurrent Pos:* Mem, Environ Control Coun, State Nebr, 74-79. *Mem:* Am Chem Soc. *Res:* Nitrosamines; azirdines; identification of polysaccharides in molasses; proteins in seminal fluid and sperm. *Mailing Add:* Dept of Chem Doane Col Crete NE 68333

SMITH, DAVID HUSTON, b Seattle, Wash, July 14, 37; m 58; c 2. CHEMISTRY. *Educ:* Whitman Col, BA, 59; Cornell Univ, MS, 62; Univ Tenn, Knoxville, PhD(anal chem), 70. *Prof Exp:* CHEMIST, OAK RIDGE NAT LAB, UNION CARBIDE NUCLEAR CO, 62- *Res:* Applications of mass spectrometry to safeguards; mass spectrometric research and development; design and development of computer programs for mass spectrometric data. *Mailing Add:* Analytical Chem Div Oak Ridge Nat Lab Oak Ridge TN 37830

SMITH, DAVID JOSEPH, b Parkersburg, WVa, Dec 17, 43; m 64; c 2. PHARMACOLOGY. *Educ:* Bethany Col, BS, 65; WVa Univ, PhD(pharmacol), 69. *Prof Exp:* Fel, Univ Iowa, 69-71; asst prof, 71-74, assoc prof, 71-81, PROF ANESTHESIOL & PHARMACOL, WVA UNIV, 81-, DIR, ANESTHESIOL RES LAB, 74- *Mem:* Am Soc Pharmacol & Exp Therapeut; Am Soc Anesthesiologists; AAAS; Sigma Xi; Soc Neurosci. *Res:* Neuropharmacological and cytological research of drug action on neurochemical processes of neurotransmitter metabolism; behavioral correlation of metabolic changes in transmitter metabolism with alterations in central nervous system function. *Mailing Add:* Dept Anesthesiol Med Ctr WVa Univ Morgantown WV 26506

SMITH, DAVID JOSEPH, b New York, NY, Aug 8, 21; m 44; c 3. BIOCHEMISTRY. *Educ:* Columbia Univ, DDS, 44, MPhil, 74. *Prof Exp:* Assoc res dentist, NY State Dept Health, 53-63; from asst prof to assoc prof biochem, Columbia Univ, 63-74, assoc prof oral biol, 71-74; PROF BIOCHEM & CHMN DEPT, FAIRLEIGH DICKINSON UNIV, 74. *Concurrent Pos:* USPHS fel, 48-51 & career develop award, 6370. *Mem:* Am Brit Biochem Soc; Am Chem Soc; Int Asn Dent Res. *Res:* Biochemistry of connective tissue. *Mailing Add:* Dept of Biochem Fairleigh Dickinson Univ Hackensack NJ 07601

SMITH, DAVID KENT, b Oakland, Calif, Oct 19, 46; m 69. BOTANY, BRYOLOGY. *Educ:* Humboldt State Col, BA, 69, MA, 70; Univ Tenn, Knoxville, PhD(bot), 74. *Prof Exp:* ASST PROF BOT, UNIV TENN, KNOXVILLE, 74- *Mem:* Bot Soc Am; Am Bryol & Lichenol Soc; Sigma Xi. *Res:* Floristic and taxonomic studies of bryophytes in North America, including Mexico; floristic and phytogeographic studies of the Aleutian and Arctic Alaskan bryophyte floras. *Mailing Add:* Dept of Bot Univ of Tenn Knoxville TN 37916

SMITH, DAVID LAWRENCE THOMSON, b Regina, Sask, Apr 18, 14; m 43; c 3. VETERINARY PATHOLOGY. *Educ:* Ont Vet Col, DVM, 43; Cornell Univ, PhD(vet path), 55. *Prof Exp:* Assoc prof path, Ont Vet Col, 47-51; prof vet path, Cornell Univ, 52-53; prof vet path & head dept path & bact, Ont Vet Col, 54-63, dean, Western Col Vet Med, 63-74, PROF PATH, UNIV SASK, 74- *Concurrent Pos:* Can Int Develop Agency expert & prof path, Fac Vet Med, Univ Pertanian, Malaysia, 74- *Mem:* Am Col Vet Pathologists (pres, 65-66); Am & Can Vet Med Asn. *Mailing Add:* 11 Kirk Crescent Saskatoon SK 57H 3B1 Can

SMITH, DAVID LEE, b June 7, 44; US citizen; m 67; c 2. GAS CHROMATOGRAPHY, MASS SPECTOMETRY. *Educ:* Univ Kans, BS, 66, PhD(chem), 69. *Prof Exp:* Instr chem, 69-76, RES ASST PROF MED CHEM, UNIV UTAH, 76- *Concurrent Pos:* NATO sr res scientist fel, 74. *Mem:* Am Chem Soc; Am Soc Mass Spectros. *Res:* Ion-molecule reactions and fundamental processes of atoms and molecules in the gas phase; biomedical applications of mass spectrometry and gas chromatography. *Mailing Add:* Dept of Med Chem Univ of Utah Salt Lake City UT 84112

SMITH, DAVID MARSHALL, b Gary, Ind, July 22, 43. PATHOLOGY, IMMUNOLOGY. *Educ:* Colo State Univ, DVM, 68; Mass Inst Technol, PhD(biochem & path), 74. *Prof Exp:* Intern vet med, Angell Mem Animal Hosp, 68-69; res fel path, Harvard Med Sch, 69-70 & Mass Inst Technol, 70-73; veterinarian, Mass Inst Technol, 73-74; EXP PATHOLOGIST & ASST GROUP LEADER, LOS ALAMOS SCI LAB, UNIV CALIF, 74- *Concurrent Pos:* Res affil, Forsyth Dent Ctr, 72-74. *Mem:* Am Vet Med Asn; Am Acad Clin Toxicol; Reticuloendothelial Soc; Hamster Soc; Am Animal Hosp Asn. *Res:* Immunology of carcinogenesis; lung cancer; radiation-induced carcinogenesis; toxicology. *Mailing Add:* Los Alamos Sci Lab MS 880 Univ of Calif Los Alamos NM 87545

SMITH, DAVID MARTYN, b Bryan, Tex, Mar 10, 21; m 51; c 2. SILVICULTURE, FOREST ECOLOGY. *Educ:* Univ RI, BS, 41; Yale Univ, MF, 46, PhD, 50. *Prof Exp:* Instr silvicult, 46-47 & 48-51, from asst prof to prof, 51-67, asst dean sch, 53-58, MORRIS K JESUP PROF SILVICULT, SCH FORESTRY & ENVIRON STUDIES, YALE UNIV, 67- *Concurrent Pos:* Vis prof, Univ Munich, 81. *Mem:* Ecol Soc Am; fel Soc Am Foresters. *Res:* Silviculture; regeneration and manipulation of forest vegetation, especially stratified mixtures. *Mailing Add:* Sch Forestry & Environ Studies Yale Univ New Haven CT 06520

SMITH, DAVID R(ICHARD), b London, Eng, July 29, 36; m 61; c 3. ELECTRICAL ENGINEERING. *Educ:* Univ London, BS, 57; Univ Wis, PhD(elec eng), 61. *Prof Exp:* Res fel, Nat Phys Lab, Teddington, Eng, 61-63; asst prof bioeng, Case Inst Technol, 63-66; assoc prof elec sci, 66-71, PROF COMPUT SCI, STATE UNIV NY STONY BROOK, 72- *Mem:* Inst Elec & Electronics Engrs. *Res:* Computer architecture and digital systems design. *Mailing Add:* Dept of Comput Sci State Univ of NY Stony Brook NY 11794

SMITH, DAVID REEDER, b Murray, Utah, Nov 1, 38; m 63; c 3. SOLID STATE PHYSICS. *Educ:* Univ Utah, BS, 63; Purdue Univ, West Lafayette, MS, 66, PhD(physics), 69. *Prof Exp:* Asst prof, 69-78, ASSOC PROF PHYSICS, S DAK SCH MINES & TECHNOL, 78- *Mem:* AAAS; Sigma Xi; Am Asn Physics Teachers. *Res:* Low temperature solid state physics; cryogenics; heat transfer. *Mailing Add:* Dept of Physics SDak Sch Mines & Technol Rapid City SD 57701

SMITH, DAVID ROLLINS, b Rockford, Ill, July 27, 37; m 67; c 2. SYSTEMATICS, ENTOMOLOGY. *Educ:* Ore State Univ, BA, 60, PhD(entom), 67. *Prof Exp:* RES ENTOMOLOGIST, SYST ENTOM LAB, AGR RES SERV, USDA, 65- *Honors & Awards:* Cert of Merit, USDA, 68. *Mem:* Entom Soc Am; Soc Syst Zool; Am Entom Soc. *Res:* Systematics of sawflies and ants. *Mailing Add:* Syst Entom Lab c/o US Nat Museum Washington DC 20560

SMITH, DAVID S, b Ipswich, Mass, June 29, 21; m 47; c 3. PEDIATRICS. *Educ:* Dartmouth Col, AB, 42; Univ Pa, MD, 44; Am Bd Pediat, dipl, 50. *Prof Exp:* PROF PEDIAT, SCH MED, TEMPLE UNIV, 68- *Concurrent Pos:* Consult, Nazareth Hosp, Philadelphia, 66-; prin investr, Clin Res Ctr, 76-; dir impatient serv, St Christophers Hosp Children, 66-76, actg chmn, Dept Pediat, 76- *Honors & Awards:* Arthur Dannenberg MD lectr, Albert Einstein Med Ctr, 79. *Mem:* Am Acad Pediat; AMA. *Res:* Infectious disease. *Mailing Add:* St Christopher's Hosp for Children 2600 N Lawrence Philadelphia PA 19133

SMITH, DAVID SPENCER, b London, Eng, Apr 10, 34; m 64. CELL BIOLOGY. *Educ:* Cambridge Univ, BA, 55, MA & PhD(zool), 58. *Prof Exp:* Fel cell biol, Rockefeller Univ, 58-59, res assoc, 59-61; res fel zool, Cambridge Univ, 61-63; asst prof biol, Univ Va, 63-66; assoc prof med, anat & biol, 66-70, PROF MED & PHARMACOL, UNIV MIAMI, 70- *Concurrent Pos:* USPHS fel, 59; NSF res grant, 63-66; external dir res, Int Ctr Insect Physiol & Ecol, 70, dir res, Nairobi, Kenya; NIH res grants, 71-; Hope prof entom (zool), Univ Oxford, 80. *Mem:* Am Soc Cell Biol; Royal Entom Soc London. *Res:* Electron microscopic studies on vertebrate and invertebrate animal tissues, especially muscle fibers and central and peripheral nervous systems; studies on structure and function of cellular membranes. *Mailing Add:* Dept Med Sch Med Univ Miami PO Box 520875 Miami FL 33152

SMITH, DAVID VARLEY, b Memphis, Tenn, Apr 21, 43; m 65; c 3. NEUROSCIENCE, PSYCHOLOGY. *Educ:* Univ Tenn, BS, 65, MA, 67; Univ Pittsburgh, PhD(psychobiol), 69. *Prof Exp:* Res assoc, Rockefeller UniY, 69-71; asst prof, 71-75, assoc prof, 75-80, PROF PSYCHOL, UNIV WYO, 80- *Concurrent Pos:* Adj asst prof psychol, Hunter Col, City Univ New York, 70-71; Nat Inst Neurol Commun Dis & Stroke res career develop award, 76-82; asst prog dir, NSF, 77-78. *Mem:* AAAS; Soc Neurosci; Europ Chemoreception Res Orgn; Asn Chemoreceptor Sci. *Res:* Gustatory physiology and behaYior; taste quality coding; neurophysiology. *Mailing Add:* Dept of Psychol Box 3415 University Sta Laramie WY 82071

SMITH, DAVID W, b Oakland, Calif, Sept 24, 21; m 50; c 4. PEDIATRICS. *Educ:* Univ Calif, AB, 46; Johns Hopkins Univ, MD, 50. *Prof Exp:* Clin instr pediat endocrinol, Johns Hopkins Hosp, 55-56; from instr to asst prof pediat, Med Sch, Univ Wis, 57-66; assoc prof, 66-67, PROF PEDIAT, SCH MED, UNIV WASH, 67- *Res:* Pediatric endocrinology. *Mailing Add:* Dept of Pediat Univ of Wash Sch of Med Seattle WA 98195

SMITH, DAVID WALDO EDWARD, b Fargo, NDak, Apr 3, 34; m 60. PATHOLOGY, MOLECULAR BIOLOGY. *Educ:* Swarthmore Col, BA, 56; Yale Univ, MD, 60. *Prof Exp:* From intern to asst resident, Yale-New Haven Med Ctr, 60-62; res assoc, Molecular Biol Lab, Nat Inst Arthritis & Metab Dis, 62-64, investr, Lab Exp Path, 64-67; assoc prof path & microbiol, Ind Univ, Bloomington, 67-69; PROF PATH, MED SCH, NORTHWESTERN UNIV, CHICAGO, 69- *Concurrent Pos:* Res fel, Yale-New Haven Med Ctr, 60-62; res career develop award, Nat Inst Gen Med Sci, 68-69; mem, Pathobiological Chem Study Sect, NIH, 75-79. *Mem:* AAAS; Am Asn Pathologist; Am Soc Hematol; Am Soc Biol Chemists. *Res:* Transfer RNA; genetic control of protein synthesis; regulation of hemoglobin synthesis; hemoglobinopathies. *Mailing Add:* Dept of Path Northwestern Univ Med Sch Chicago IL 60611

SMITH, DAVID WARREN, b Garden Prairie, Ill, Jan 28, 39; m 62; c 3. ANALYTICAL CHEMISTRY. *Educ:* Northern Ill Univ, BS, 61; Iowa State Univ, PhD(anal chem), 68. *Prof Exp:* Teacher, High Sch, Ill, 61-63; sr chemist, Mallinckrodt, Inc, 68-70, sr res assoc, 70-73, group leader, 73-78, mgr res & develop, 78-79; GROUP LEADER PROCESS RES & DEVELOP, EDWIN COOPER, INC, 79- *Mem:* Am Chem Soc. *Res:* Analytical chemistry of alkaloids; analytical chromatography; process research and development of natural products. *Mailing Add:* Monsanto Ave Edwin Cooper Div Ethyl Corp Sauget IL 62201

SMITH, DAVID WILLIAM, b Wisconsin Rapids, Wis, June 16, 38; m 77; c 2. FORESTRY. *Educ:* Iowa State Univ, BS, 60, MS, 68, PhD(forest biol), 70. *Prof Exp:* Exten forester, Iowa State Univ & Coop Exten Serv, Iowa, 66-67; asst prof forest technol & chmn, Glenville State Col, 70-72; asst prof forestry, 72-78, ASSOC PROF FOREST SOILS & SILVICULT & CHMN FOREST BIOL SECT, VA POLYTECH INST & STATE UNIV, 78- *Mem:* Soil Sci Soc Am; Soc Am Foresters. *Res:* Nutrient cycling in forest systems, specifically the effects of silvicultural practices on site productivity through changes in soil physical and chemical properties. *Mailing Add:* Sch of Forestry & Wildlife Resources Va Polytech Inst & Sta Univ Blacksburg VA 24061

SMITH, DAVID WILLIAM, b Edson, Alta, Jan 18, 33; m 56; c 3. PLANT ECOLOGY. *Educ:* Univ Alta, BSc, 56, MSc, 59; Univ Toronto, PhD(ecol), 67. *Prof Exp:* Res officer host, Res Br, Can Dept Agr, 58-67; asst prof ecol, 67-72, asst prof, 72-77, ASSOC PROF BOT, UNIV GUELPH, 77- *Concurrent Pos:* Grants, Ont Dept Lands & Forests, Univ Guelph, 70-73 & Nat Res Coun Can, 71-80; Indian & Northern Affairs contract, 77-82. *Mem:* Can Bot Asn; Ecol Soc Am. *Res:* Vegetation dynamics and productivity of natural systems. *Mailing Add:* Dept of Bot Univ of Guelph Guelph ON N1G 2W1 Can

SMITH, DAVID WILLIAM, b Dayton, Ohio, March 17, 48; m 69; c 2. MICROBIAL ECOLOGY, PHYSIOLOGICAL ECOLOGY. *Educ:* Univ Calif, San Diego, BA, 69; Ind Univ, MA, 71; Univ Wis, PhD(bacteriol), 72. *Prof Exp:* Fel, Dept Bacteriol, Univ Calif, Los Angeles, 73-74; asst prof, 75-81, ASSOC PROF MICROBIOL, UNIV DEL, 81- *Concurrent Pos:* Prin investr res grants, Sea Grant Off, Nat Oceanic & Atmospheric Admin, 77- *Mem:* Am Soc Microbiol; AAAS; Fedn Am Scientists; Soc Gen Microbiol. *Res:* Sulfur and nitrogen cycle activities in salt marsh sediments as related to physical and chemical factors. *Mailing Add:* Sch Life & Health Sci Univ Del Newark DE 19711

SMITH, DAVID YOUNG, b Schenectady, NY, July 24, 34; m 63; c 2. SOLID STATE PHYSICS, OPTICAL PHYSICS. *Educ:* Rensselaer Polytech Inst, BS, 56; Univ Rochester, PhD(physics), 62. *Prof Exp:* Asst physics, Univ Rochester, 60-62; res assoc, Univ Ill, 62-63, res asst prof, 63-66; NSF fel, Physics Inst, Univ Stuttgart, 66-67; PHYSICIST, SOLID STATE SCI DIV, ARGONNE NAT LAB, 67-, ASST DIV DIR, 74- *Concurrent Pos:* Vis assoc prof, Mich State Univ, 71-72; Ger Acad Exchange Serv res fel, Physics Inst, Univ Stuttgart, 75-76; guest prof, Physics Inst, Univ Stuttgart & Max Planck Inst, Stuttgart, 79-80. *Mem:* Am Phys Soc. *Res:* Theoretical solid state physics especially the electronic states and optical properties of pure crystals and of defects. *Mailing Add:* Solid State Sci Div Argonne Nat Lab Argonne IL 60439

SMITH, DEAN FRANCIS, b Los Angeles, Calif, July 25, 42; m 67; c 2. ASTROPHYSICS. *Educ:* Mass Inst Technol, BS, 64; Stanford Univ, MS, 66, PhD(astrophys), 69. *Prof Exp:* Vis scientist, High Altitude Observ, Nat Ctr Atmospheric Res, 70-72, scientist, 72-78; SR RES ASSOC, DEPT ASTRO-GEOPHYSICS, UNIV COLO, 78- *Concurrent Pos:* US-USSR, Cultural Exchange fel, Shternberg Astron Inst, Moscow, 69-70; lectr, Univ Colo, 71- *Mem:* Int Astron Union; Am Phys Soc; Am Astron Soc; Astron Soc Australia; Int Union Radio Sci. *Res:* Plasma astrophysics; theory of solar radio bursts; theory of flares and particle acceleration on the sun; theory of reconnection; theory of pulsar magnetospheres. *Mailing Add:* Dept of Astro-Geophysics Univ of Colo Boulder CO 80309

SMITH, DEAN HARLEY, b Dayton, Wash, May 4, 22; m 45; c 2. VETERINARY MEDICINE, CLINICAL PATHOLOGY. *Educ:* Wash State Univ, BS, 44, DVM, 49; Ore State Univ, MS, 59. *Prof Exp:* Vet, Button Vet Hosp, Tacoma, Wash, 49-50 & Dayton, 50-52 & 54-56; res asst, Ore State Univ, 56-59, from asst prof to prof vet med, 59-76; SUPVR FED-STATE PROGS, ORE DEPT AGR, 76- *Concurrent Pos:* Fulbright lectr, Col Vet Med, Cairo Univ, 65-66. *Mem:* Am Vet Med Asn; US Livestock Sanit Asn; Am Pub Health Asn. *Res:* Animal disease diagnosis with special emphasis on sheep and cattle. *Mailing Add:* Animal Health Div Agr Bldg Salem OR 97310

SMITH, DEAN ORREN, b Colorado Springs, Colo, May 28, 44; m 65; c 2. NEUROPHYSIOLOGY. *Educ:* Harvard Univ, BA, 67; Stanford Univ, AM, 69, PhD(biol sci), 71. *Prof Exp:* Fel physiol, Univ Göteborg, 71-72; fel, Tech Univ München, 72-74, Wissen Angestellter, 74-75; actg asst prof biol, Univ Calif, Los Angeles, 75-76; asst prof, 76-80, ASSOC PROF PHYSIOL, UNIV WIS-MADISON, 80- *Concurrent Pos:* Helen Hay Whitney Found fels, Univ Göteborg, 71-72 & Tech Univ, München, 72-74; A P Sloan res fel, Univ Wis-Madison, 78-80, res career develop award, 79-83. *Mem:* Soc Neurosci; Am Physiol Soc. *Res:* Integration in the nervous system at the level of the axon and the synapse; changes in synaptic mechanisms during aging. *Mailing Add:* Dept of Physiol Univ of Wis Madison WI 53706

SMITH, DEANE KINGSLEY, JR, b Berkeley, Calif, Nov 8, 30; m 53; c 5. MINERALOGY, CRYSTALLOGRAPHY. *Educ:* Calif Inst Technol, BS, 52; Univ Minn, PhD(geol), 56. *Prof Exp:* Instr field geol, Univ Minn, 56; Portland Cement Asn fel, Nat Bur Standards, 56-60; chemist, Lawrence Livermore Lab, Univ Calif, 60-68; assoc prof mineral, 68-71, PROF MINERAL, PA STATE UNIV, UNIVERSITY PARK, 71- *Concurrent Pos:* Chmn, Joint Comt Powder Diffraction Standards, Int Ctr Diffraction Data, 78- *Mem:* Fel Geol Soc Am; Am Soc Testing & Mat; fel Mineral Soc Am; Am Crystallog Asn (secy, 76-78); Mineral Asn Can. *Res:* Defects in crystals and crystal structures of inorganics and minerals; uranium and nuclear waste management; applications of powder-x-ray diffractometry. *Mailing Add:* Dept Geosci 239 Deike Bldg Pa State Univ University Park PA 16802

SMITH, DELMONT K, b Pocatello, Idaho, June 9, 27; m 46; c 5. ORGANIC CHEMISTRY. *Educ:* Utah State Univ, BS, 49, MS, 55; Purdue Univ, PhD(org chem), 54. *Prof Exp:* Res chemist, Rayonier, Inc, 54-56, sect supvr, 56-59, asst res mgr, 59, div mgr, 59-61; res supvr, 61-66, dir woven prod res, 66-70, DIR TECHNOL PLANNING, CHICOPEE MFG CO, 70- *Mem:* Am Chem Soc; Tech Asn Pulp & Paper Indust; Am Asn Textile Chemists & Colorists; Int Nonwovens & Disposables Asn. *Res:* Organic halogen compounds; high polymers; cellulose and cellulose derivatives; textile technology; nonwoven technology. *Mailing Add:* Chicopee 317 George St New Brunswick NJ 08901

SMITH, DENNIS CLIFFORD, b Lincoln, Eng, Mar 24, 28; m 55; c 6. BIOMATERIALS. *Educ:* Univ London, BSc, 50, MSc, 53; Univ Manchester, PhD(chem), 57. *Prof Exp:* Asst lectr dent mat, Univ Manchester, 52-69, reader, 69; PROF BIOMAT, UNIV TORONTO, 69- *Concurrent Pos:* Vis assoc prof, Northwestern Univ, 60-61. *Res:* Polymer chemistry; tissue reaction to materials; physical properties of materials. *Mailing Add:* Faculty of Dent Univ of Toronto 124 Edward St Toronto ON M5S 2R8 Can

SMITH, DENNISON A, b Newton, Mass, June 19, 43; m 69. NEUROSCIENCES. *Educ:* Colgate Univ, AB, 65; Univ Mass, MS, 67, PhD(psychol), 70. *Prof Exp:* Asst prof, 69-75, ASSOC PROF PSYCHOL, OBERLIN COL, 75-, CHMN DEPT, 78-, CHMN PSYCHOBIOL PROG, 76- *Mem:* AAAS; Soc Neurosci; Sigma Xi. *Res:* Biological aspects of aggressive and sexual behavior. *Mailing Add:* Dept of Psychol Oberlin Col Oberlin OH 44074

SMITH, DIANE ELIZABETH, b New York, NY, Nov 15, 37. NEUROANATOMY. *Educ:* Bucknell Univ, BS, 59; Am Univ, MS, 65; Univ Pa, PhD(anat), 68. *Prof Exp:* Res biologist, Clin Neuropath Sect, Surg Neurol Br, Nat Inst Neurol Dis & Blindness, 62-65; asst prof anat, Daniel Baugh Inst Anat, Jefferson Med Col, Thomas Jefferson Univ, 69-75, assoc prof, 75; assoc prof, 75-80, PROF ANAT, LA STATE UNIV SCH MED, 80- *Concurrent Pos:* NIH res fel anat, Harvard Med Sch, 68-69; NIH res grant, Thomas Jefferson Univ, 70-73 & 75-; NSF res grant, 73-75; NIH res grant, La State Univ Sch Med, 75-84; DISCUS res grant, 80-81. *Mem:* AAAS; Soc Neurosci; Am Asn Anatomists. *Res:* Effect of alterations in the environmental milieu on the postnatal development of the spinocerebellar system. *Mailing Add:* Dept Anat Med Ed Bldg LSU Med Ctr 1901 Perdido St New Orleans LA 70112

SMITH, DON WILEY, b Weinert, Tex, Nov 11, 36; m 58; c 4. AGRONOMY, PLANT PHYSIOLOGY. *Educ:* Tex Tech Col, BS, 58; Univ Wis, MS, 60, PhD(agron), 63. *Prof Exp:* Res assoc agron, Univ Wis, 62-63; asst prof bot, Colo State Univ, 65-67; ASST PROF BIOL, N TEX STATE UNIV, 67- *Mem:* Am Soc Plant Physiol; Weed Sci Soc Am; Am Inst Biol Sci. *Res:* Chemical inhibition of plant transpiration; physiology of weedy species; mechanics of action of herbicides; effects of microwaves on plants. *Mailing Add:* Dept of Biol Sci N Tex State Univ Denton TX 76203

SMITH, DONALD ALAN, b Toronto, Ont, Aug 29, 30; m 53; c 5. VERTEBRATE ZOOLOGY. *Educ:* Univ Toronto, BA, 52, MA, 53, PhD(exp biol), 57. *Prof Exp:* Lectr, 57-58, asst prof, 58-63, ASSOC PROF BIOL, CARLETON UNIV, 63-, CUR, CARLETON UNIV MUS ZOOL, 73- *Concurrent Pos:* Vis prof, Makerere Univ, Uganda, 66-67; asst to ed, Can Field-Naturalist, 72-81. *Mem:* Can Soc Environ Biologists; Am Soc Mammal; Can Soc Zool. *Res:* Ecology, distribution, taxonomy, conservation, behavior and environmental physiology of vertebrates, especially rodents, bats and insectivores; reproductive biology; ectoparasites of mammals, especially fleas. *Mailing Add:* Dept of Biol Carleton Univ Ottawa ON K1S 5B6 Can

SMITH, DONALD ARTHUR, b Can, Feb 2, 26; nat US; m 49; c 4. POLYMER CHEMISTRY. *Educ:* Univ BC, BA, 48; Univ Toronto, PhD(chem), 51. *Prof Exp:* Res assoc, Kodak Park Works, 51-77, sr lab head, 68-77, ASST DIR CHEM DIV, RES LABS, EASTMAN KODAK CO, 77- *Mem:* Am Chem Soc. *Res:* Sterochemistry; high polymers; synthesis of hydrophilic monomers and polymers. *Mailing Add:* Bldg 82 Kodak Park Works Eastman Kodak Co Rochester NY 14650

SMITH, DONALD C, preventive medicine, maternal & child health, see previous edition

SMITH, DONALD E, b Pittsburgh, Pa, Jan 12, 36; m 57; c 5. PHYSICAL CHEMISTRY, ANALYTICAL CHEMISTRY. *Educ:* Allegheny Col, BS, 58; Columbia Univ, MA, 59, PhD(chem), 61. *Prof Exp:* From instr to assoc prof, 61-71, chmn dept, 75-77, PROF CHEM, NORTHWESTERN UNIV, EVANSTON, 71- *Concurrent Pos:* Chmn, Electrochem Gordon Res Conf, 80. *Mem:* AAAS; Am Chem Soc; fel Am Asn Univ Professors. *Res:* Kinetics and mechanisms of electrode reactions; nonaqueous electrochemistry; chemical instrumentation. *Mailing Add:* Dept of Chem Northwestern Univ Evanston IL 60201

SMITH, DONALD EDGAR, biochemistry, see previous edition

SMITH, DONALD EUGENE, b Tunkhannock, Pa, Jan 26, 34; m 58; c 3. REPRODUCTIVE PHYSIOLOGY, ENDOCRINOLOGY. *Educ:* Bloomsburg State Col, BScEd, 55; Ohio State Univ, MSc, 58, PhD(physiol, zool), 62. *Prof Exp:* Pub sch teacher, Pa, 55-56; asst zool, Ohio State Univ, 56-59, instr, 59-60; from instr to asst prof, Ohio Wesleyan Univ, 60-66; assoc prof, 67-72, PROF ZOOL, NC STATE UNIV, 72- *Concurrent Pos:* NSF res partic, Univ Ill, 65, vis asst prof, 66-67; vis prof, Duke Univ Med Ctr, 81. *Mem:* AAAS; Am Soc Zool; Sigma Xi; Soc for Study of Reproduction. *Res:* Mechanisms of hormone action; effects of estrogen on uterine glucose metabolism; effects of copper on uterine steroid hormone receptors. *Mailing Add:* Dept of Zool NC State Univ Raleigh NC 27650

SMITH, DONALD EUGENE, b Alice, Tex, Sept 29, 44; m 65; c 1. PHYSICAL CHEMISTRY, MATERIALS SCIENCE. *Educ:* Okla State Univ, BS, 66, PhD(phys chem), 71. *Prof Exp:* Res engr, 70-73, sr res engr, 73-75, supv res engr, 75-78, GEN SUPV RES ENGR STEEL RES, INLAND STEEL CO, 78- *Mem:* Nat Coil Coaters Asn; Am Soc Testing & Mat; Nat Asn Corrosion Engrs. *Res:* Corrosion; organic coatings for metals; surface structure and characterization; vibrational spectroscopy. *Mailing Add:* Inland Steel Co 30 W Monroe St Chicago IL 60603

SMITH, DONALD FOSS, b Athens, Tenn, Feb 14, 13; m 40; c 2. PHYSICAL CHEMISTRY. *Educ:* Univ Chattanooga, BS, 34; Univ Tenn, MS, 36; Univ Va, PhD(chem), 39. *Prof Exp:* Asst prof chem, Judson Col, 39-40 & The Citadel, 40-43; assoc explosives chemist, US Bur Mines, 43-44; asst prof chem, Pa Col Women, 44-45; from asst prof to assoc prof, Univ Vt, 45-51; assoc prof, 51-56, PROF & ASSOC CHMN CHEM, UNIV ALA, TUSCALOOSA, 56- *Mem:* Am Chem Soc; Am Inst Chem. *Res:* Heat capacity determinations at high temperatures; solubility determinations; cryoscopic determinations in fused salt systems; conductance in fused salts; heat capacities at low temperatures. *Mailing Add:* Dept of Chem Univ of Ala at Tuscaloosa University AL 35486

SMITH, DONALD FREDERICK, b Picton, Ont, Nov 25, 49; m 74; c 1. VETERINARY SURGERY. *Educ:* Univ Guelph, DVM, 74; Am Col Vet Surgeons, dipl. *Prof Exp:* Intern vet med, Univ Pa, 74-75, resident vet surg, 75-77; ASST PROF LARGE ANIMAL SURG, NY STATE COL VET MED, CORNELL UNIV, 77- *Mem:* Comp Gastroenterol Soc. *Res:* General large animal gastroenterology; surgery of the gastrointestinal tract. *Mailing Add:* Dept Clin Sci Cornell Univ Ithaca NY 14853

SMITH, DONALD HENRY, b Ogden, Utah, Feb 15, 18; m 40; c 2. SOIL CHEMISTRY. *Educ:* Brigham Young Univ, BS, 39; Iowa State Col, MS, 49, PhD(soil bact), 51. *Prof Exp:* Jr soil surveyor & asst soil technol, Soil Conserv Serv, USDA, 40-43, soil scientist, 45-47, soil scientist, Bur Plant Indust, Soils & Agr Eng, 51-52; soil chemist, Pineapple Res Inst, 53-63; agr res dir & res mgr, Philippine Packing Corp, 63-73; AGR RES MGR, CA DIV, DEL MONTE CORP, 73- *Mem:* AAAS; Am Soc Agron. *Res:* Improvement in yield and quality of food crops. *Mailing Add:* Del Monte Corp 111 Civic Dr Walnut Creek CA 94596

SMITH, DONALD LARNED, b White Plains, NY, June 8, 40; m 67; c 1. NUCLEAR PHYSICS. *Educ:* Ga Inst Technol, BS, 62; Mass Inst Technol, PhD(physics), 67. *Prof Exp:* Asst physicist, 69-73, PHYSICIST, APPL PHYSICS DIV, ARGONNE NAT LAB, 73- *Mem:* Am Phys Soc; Am Nuclear Soc. *Res:* Nuclear measurement techniques; gamma-ray spectroscopy and associated correlations; radiation interaction with matter; neutron cross sections and neutron scattering phenomena. *Mailing Add:* Argonne Nat Lab Appl Physics Div 9700 S Cass Ave Argonne IL 60439

SMITH, DONALD LEONARD, b Boston, Mass, Feb 1, 44. EXPERIMENTAL SOLID STATE PHYSICS. *Educ:* Mass Inst Technol, BS, 65; Univ Calif, Berkeley, PhD(chem eng), 69. *Prof Exp:* Asst prof chem eng, Berkeley, 66-69; asst prof chem eng, Mass Inst Technol, 69-70; SR RES SCIENTIST, CORP RES DEPT, PERKIN-ELMER CORP, 70- *Mem:* Am Vacuum Soc; Electrochem Soc. *Res:* Vacuum and plasma deposition of thin films for electro-optic applications, especially solar cells; plasma etching and other surface chemistry. *Mailing Add:* Optical Group Mail Sta 283 Perkin-Elmer Corp Main Ave Norwalk CT 06856

SMITH, DONALD LUKE, mathematics, see previous edition

SMITH, DONALD RAY, b Seminole, Okla, Jan 23, 39; m 64; c 2. MATHEMATICS. *Educ:* Auburn Univ, BS, 61; Stanford Univ, PhD(math), 65. *Prof Exp:* Vis mem, Courant Inst Math Sci, NY Univ, 65-66; asst prof, 66-71, assoc prof, 71-80, PROF MATH, UNIV CALIF, SAN DIEGO, 80- *Concurrent Pos:* NSF res grant, 67-69. *Mem:* Am Math Soc; Soc Indust & Appl Math. *Res:* Ordinary and partial differential equations. *Mailing Add:* Dept of Math Univ of Calif at San Diego La Jolla CA 92093

SMITH, DONALD REED, b Hamilton, Ont, Sept 3, 36; m 60; c 3. PHYSICAL CHEMISTRY. *Educ:* McMaster Univ, BSc, 58; Univ Leeds, PhD(radiation chem), 61. *Prof Exp:* Demonstr phys chem, Univ Leeds, 58-61; from asst res off to assoc res off, 61-70, SR RES OFF, CHALK RIVER NUCLEAR LAB, ATOMIC ENERGY CAN LTD, 70-, HEAD, PHYS CHEM BR, 69- *Concurrent Pos:* Emmanuel Col vis fel, Univ Cambridge, Eng, 75-76. *Mem:* Fel Chem Inst Can. *Res:* Electron spin resonance and laser magnetic resonance spectroscopy; radiation chemistry; isotope separation. *Mailing Add:* Atomic Energy Can Ltd Chalk River ON K0J 1J0 Can

SMITH, DONALD ROSS, b Indianapolis, Ind, Jan 24, 40; m 63; c 2. POLYMER CHEMISTRY, ORGANIC CHEMISTRY. *Educ:* Tufts Univ, BS, 62; Northeastern Univ, PhD(polymer chem), 72. *Prof Exp:* Sr chemist, 71-78, RES ASSOC, DENNISON MFG CO, 79- *Mem:* Soc Glass Decorators; Royal Soc Arts; Am Chem Soc. *Res:* Thermosetting label systems comprising release, protective lacquers, inks and adhesive lacquers; water repellant coatings for paper. *Mailing Add:* Dennison Mfg Co Framingham MA 01701

SMITH, DONALD STANLEY, b New Westminster, BC, Dec 23, 26; US citizen; m 48; c 1. MECHANICAL ENGINEERING. *Educ:* Univ Calif, Berkeley, BS, 50, MS, 66, PhD(mech eng), 69. *Prof Exp:* Engr, Procter & Gamble Co, 50-54; mgt consult, McKinsey & Co, 54-58; asst vpres eng, Hallamore Electronics Co, 58-59; independent consult, 59-60; asst vpres eng, Aircraft Div, Hughes Tool Co, 60-64; res engr, Univ Calif, 64-69; assoc prof, 69-72, PROF & CHMN DEPT MECH ENG, CALIF STATE UNIV, CHICO, 72- *Mem:* Combustion Inst. *Res:* Engine generated air pollution. *Mailing Add:* 2 Canterbury Circle Chico CA 95926

SMITH, DONALD W(ANAMAKER), b Bethlehem, Pa, Aug 30, 23; m 46; c 2. CHEMICAL ENGINEERING. *Educ:* US Naval Acad, BS, 45. *Prof Exp:* Engr chem, 47-56, tech supt, 56-59, staff mem, Develop Dept, 61-76, ADMIN ASST, OFF ENVIRON AFFAIRS, E I DU PONT DE NEMOURS & CO, INC, 76- *Mem:* Am Inst Chem Engrs. *Res:* Corporate environmental management. *Mailing Add:* RD 3 Box 250 C4I Hockessin DE 19707

SMITH, DONALD WARD, b Flint, Mich, Jan 23, 26; m 45; c 5. MICROBIOLOGY, IMMUNOLOGY. *Educ:* Mich Col Mining & Technol, BS, 48; Univ Mich, MS, 50, PhD(bact), 51. *Prof Exp:* Instr bact, Univ Mich, 52-54; from asst prof to assoc prof, 54-65, PROF MED MICROBIOL, UNIV WIS-MADISON, 65- *Concurrent Pos:* USPHS fel, Univ Mich, 51-52; consult, Tuberc Div Commun Dis, WHO; mem tuberc panel, US-Japan Coop Med Sci Prog, NIH, 65-69; mem, Tuberc-Leprosy Spec Study Sect, Nat Inst Allergy & Infectious Dis, 67-69. *Mailing Add:* Dept of Med Microbiol Univ of Wis-Madison Madison WI 53706

SMITH, DONN LEROY, b Denver, Colo, Nov 1, 15; m 37; c 2. PHARMACOLOGY. *Educ:* Univ Denver, AB, 39, MS, 41; Univ Colo, PhD(physiol, pharmacol), 48, MD, 58. *Prof Exp:* Asst prof physiol, Univ Denver, 48-50; from asst prof to assoc prof pharmacol, Med Sch, Univ Colo, 50-60, assoc dean, 60-63; dean sch med & prof physiol, Univ Louisville, 63-69; dir med ctr & dean col med, 69-76, PROF PHARMACOL & THERAPEUT, UNIV S FLA, 76- *Mem:* AAAS; AMA; Am Soc Pharmacol & Exp Therapeut; Soc Exp Biol & Med; Am Col Clin Pharmacol. *Res:* Analgesia; traumatic shock; experimental hypertension. *Mailing Add:* 5212 E 127th Ave Tampa FL 33617

SMITH, DORIAN GLEN WHITNEY, b London, Eng, Oct 11, 34; m 59; c 3. GEOLOGY, MINERALOGY. *Educ:* Univ London, BSc, 59; Univ Alta, MSc, 60; Cambridge Univ, PhD(petrol), 63; Oxford Univ, MA, 64. *Prof Exp:* Demonstr mineral, Oxford Univ, 63-66; from asst prof to assoc prof geol, 66-74, PROF GEOL & CUR MINERALS, UNIV ALTA, 74- *Concurrent Pos:* Nuffield Found Travel Award mineral & petrol, Cambridge Univ, 71. *Mem:* Fel Geol Soc London; Mineral Soc London; Geo Asn Can; Mineral Soc Am; Geochem Soc. *Res:* High temperature thermal metamorphism; electron microprobe applications in mineralogy and petrology; study of bonding in minerals by soft x-ray spectroscopy; energy dispersive electron microprobe analysis. *Mailing Add:* Dept Geol Univ Alta Edmonton AB T6G 2G7 Can

SMITH, DOROTHY GORDON, b Barbados, BWI, Mar 5, 18; US citizen. MICROBIOLOGY. *Educ:* Queen's Univ, BA, 40; Rutgers Univ, PhD(microbiol), 47; Am Bd Microbiol, dipl. *Prof Exp:* Technician epidemiol, Meningitis Comn, Johns Hopkins Univ, 41-43; asst chemother, Merck Inst, 43-46; bacteriologist, Biol Labs, US Army, 47-62, microbiologist & biol sci adminr, Ft Detrick, 62-70; Infection Surveillance Officer, Frederick Mem Hosp, 71-76; RETIRED. *Mem:* Fel AAAS; Am Soc Microbiol; Am Acad Microbiol; Soc Exp Biol & Med; Am Asn Contamination Control. *Res:* Arbovirus relationships; virus vaccines; immunology; environmental balance and imbalance; ecological control; infection control in the community hospital. *Mailing Add:* Brooklawn Apts Frederick MD 21701

SMITH, DOROTHY POND, nutrition, see previous edition

SMITH, DOUGLAS, b St Joseph, Mo, 1940; m 66. GEOLOGY. *Educ:* Calif Inst Technol, BS, 62, PhD(geol), 69; Harvard Univ, Am, 63. *Prof Exp:* Fel, Washington Geophys Lab, Carnegie Inst, 68-71; asst prof, 71-77, ASSOC PROF GEOL, UNIV TEX, AUSTIN, 77- *Mem:* Mineral Soc Am; Geol Soc Am; Am Geophys Union. *Res:* Igneous and metamorphic petrology; experimental studies of phase equilibria; physical conditions and chemistry of rock-forming processes. *Mailing Add:* Dept Geol Univ Tex Austin TX 78712

SMITH, DOUGLAS B, chemical engineering, see previous edition

SMITH, DOUGLAS CALVIN, b Kokomo, Ind, Aug 5, 49. PSYCHOBIOLOGY, NEUROPHYSIOLOGY. *Educ:* Tex A&M Univ, BS, 71, MS, 73; Kans State Univ, PhD(psychol), 77. *Prof Exp:* Fel physiol & psychol, Univ Ill, 77-79; ASST PROF PSYCHOBIOL, SOUTHERN ILL UNIV, 79- *Concurrent Pos:* Lectr, Med Sch, Univ Ill, 77-79; prin investr, Visual Suppression NSF grant, 80-82. *Mem:* Soc Neurosci; Asn Res Vision & Opthal. *Res:* Electrophysiological and behavioral investigation of the effects of abnormalities in the development of the visual system of mammals with binocular vision, as well as the neural basis of memory. *Mailing Add:* Dept Psychol Southern Ill Univ Carbondale IL 62901

SMITH, DOUGLAS GRAHAM, animal behavior, see previous edition

SMITH, DOUGLAS LEE, b St Louis, Mo, Sept 22, 43; m 65; c 2. GEOLOGY. *Educ:* Univ Ill, BS, 65; Univ Minn, PhD(geophys), 72. *Prof Exp:* Asst prof, 72-76, ASSOC PROF GEOL, UNIV FLA, 76- *Mem:* Am Geophys Union; Soc Explor Geophysicists; Geol Soc Am. *Res:* Geothermal conditions and their implications for energy resources; tectonic conditions; nature of earth's crust. *Mailing Add:* Dept Geol Univ Fla Gainesville FL 32611

SMITH, DOUGLAS LEE, b Staten Island, NY, Nov 16, 37; m 59; c 3. X-RAY CRYSTALLOGRAPHY. *Educ:* Dartmouth Col, AB, 58; Univ Wis, PhD(phys chem), 62. *Prof Exp:* Res chemist, Sandia Corp, NMex, 62-65; sr res chemist, 65-70, RES ASSOC, EASTMAN KODAK CO, 70- *Honors & Awards:* Journal Award-Sci, Soc Photog Scientists & Engr, 75. *Mem:* Soc Photog Scientists & Engr; Am Crystallog Asn; Am Chem Soc. *Res:* X-ray crystal structure determinations of compounds of photographic interest; x-ray powder diffraction; applied crystallography. *Mailing Add:* Eastman Kodak Res Labs Kodak Park Bldg 82 Rochester NY 14650

SMITH, DOUGLAS LEE, b San Diego, Calif, June 22, 30; m 51; c 6. OCCUPATIONAL HEALTH, TOXICOLOGY. *Educ:* Univ Utah, BS, 51, PhD(pharmacog & pharmacol), 56. *Prof Exp:* Supvr pharmacol, Aerospace Med Lab, Wright Patterson AFB, 58-59; from instr to assoc prof physiol, US Air Force Acad, 59-66; criteria mgr health standards develop, 71-74, asst br chief, 74-76, toxicologist, Western Area Lab, 76, sr review pharmacologist, 76-80, br chief, Priorities & Res Anal, 80, SR SCI ADVR TO DIR, NAT INST OCCUP SAFETY & HEALTH, 81- *Concurrent Pos:* Res assoc neurophysiol, Dept Sci Res, US Air Force Acad, 63; Nat Inst Occup Safety & Health rep occup health to Environ Protection Agency for Dept Health, Educ & Welfare, 72-74; liaison rep, Dept Labor, 74- *Honors & Awards:* Achievement Award, Nat Inst Occup Safety & Health, USPHS, 76. *Mem:* Am Conf Govt Indust Hygienists; Am Indust Hyg Asn; Comn Officers Asn Pub Health Serv; Asn Mil Surgeons, US. *Res:* Toxicological research; industrial hygiene evaluation; criteria development for occupational health standards; evaluations for scientific merit. *Mailing Add:* NIOSH-Off Dir 5600 Fishers Lane Rm 8A-53 Rockville MD 20857

SMITH, DOUGLAS ROANE, b St Louis, Mo, Nov 8, 30; m 53; c 1. BOTANY. *Educ:* Ill State Univ, BS, 53; Univ Ill, Urbana, MS, 57; Wash State Univ, PhD(bot), 69. *Prof Exp:* Instr biol, Lincoln Col, 57-60; field rep, Hosp Labs, Aloe Sci, 60-61; instr biol, Millikin Univ, 61-63; asst prof, Col Guam, 63-65; assoc bot, Miami Univ, 65-67; res asst, Wash State Univ, 67-68; assoc prof, 68-72, PROF BOT, UNIV GUAM, 72- *Mem:* AAAS; Am Bryol & Lichenological Soc; Bot Soc Am; Am Inst Biol Sci; Int Asn Plant Taxon. *Res:* Phytogeography of mosses of Hawaiian Islands and Micronesia; solar energy conversion of sea water to drinking water; bryology of the western Pacific. *Mailing Add:* Dept of Biol Univ of Guam PO Box 1784 Agana GU 96910

SMITH, DOUGLAS STEWART, b Fargo, NDak, Nov 26, 24; m 49; c 5. ORGANIC CHEMISTRY, RESEARCH ADMINISTRATION. *Educ:* NDak State Univ, BS, 49; Mass Inst Technol, PhD, 52. *Prof Exp:* Res chemist, G D Searle & Co, 52-55; dir res & develop, J B Williams Co, 55-58; tech dir, Vick Mfg Div, 58-61, dir explor res, Vick Div Res & Develop, 61-64, assoc dir, Cent Sci Servs Dept, 64-69, spec proj mgr, Vick Div Res & Develop, 69-71, asst dir develop, 71-72, DIR DRUG (COLDS) PROD, VICK DIV RES & DEVELOP, RICHARDSON-VICKS, INC, 72- *Mem:* AAAS; Am Chem Soc. *Res:* Pharmaceutical development and production. *Mailing Add:* Vick Div Res & Develop Richardson-Vicks Inc Mt Vernon NY 10553

SMITH, DOUGLAS WEMP, b Los Angeles, Calif, July 13, 38; m 75; c 3. MOLECULAR BIOLOGY, GENETICS. *Educ:* Stanford Univ, BS, 60, PhD(biophys), 67; Univ Ill, Urbana, MS, 62. *Prof Exp:* NIH fel, Max Planck Inst Virus Res, Tübingen, Ger, 67-69; asst prof, 69-77, ASSOC PROF BIOL, UNIV CALIF, SAN DIEGO, 77- *Concurrent Pos:* Acad res grant, Univ Calif, 70-71, Cancer Res Coord Comt grants, 70-72, 74-75, 78-79 & 81-82; Am Cancer Soc grants, 70-75; NIH grants, 76-81. *Mem:* AAAS; Biophys Soc; Am Soc Biol Chemists; NY Acad Sci; Am Soc Microbiol. *Res:* Biochemistry; microbiology; recombinant DNA research; DNA replication and repair in prokaryotes; structure and function of bacterial origins; DNA metabolism in mycoplasmas; atomic physics; optical pumping and hyperfine structure. *Mailing Add:* Dept of Biol C-016 Univ Calif San Diego La Jolla CA 92093

SMITH, DUDLEY COZBY, physical chemistry, glass technology, deceased

SMITH, DUDLEY TEMPLETON, b Washington, DC, June 8, 40; m 65. WEED SCIENCE, RESEARCH MANAGEMENT & ADMINISTRATION. *Educ:* Univ Md, College Park, BS, 63, MS, 65; Mich State Univ, PhD(crop sci), 68. *Prof Exp:* Asst prof crop sci, 68-72, assoc prof, 72-73, asst dir, 73-79, ASSOC DIR, TEX AGR EXP STA, TEX A&M UNIV, 79- *Concurrent Pos:* Chmn, Bd Dirs Title XII Sorghum/Millet Consortium. *Mem:* Weed Sci Soc Am; Am Soc Agron; Coun Agr Sci & Technol. *Res:* Herbicide behavior, residues and movement in soil and water; weed control in crops; growth, phenology and competition of perennial and annual weeds; international agricultural research. *Mailing Add:* Tex Agr Exp Sta Tex A&M Univ College Station TX 77843

SMITH, DUNGAN, b Attleboro, Mass, May 24, 39; m 59; c 3. PHYSICAL OCEANOGRAPHY, GEOLOGICAL OCEANOGRAPHY. *Educ:* Brown Univ, BA, 62, MS, 63; Univ Chicago, PhD(geophys), 68. *Prof Exp:* From actg asst prof to assoc prof, 67-77, PROF, DEPT OCEANOG & GEOPHYS PROG & ADJ PROF GEOL SCI, UNIV WASH, 77-, CHMN GEOPHYS PROG, 80- *Mem:* AAAS; Am Geophys Union; Sigma Xi; Int Asn Hydraul Res. *Res:* Coastal oceanography; mechanics of turbulent boundary layers; erosion and sediment transport; fluvial geomorphology; geophysical fluid mechanics. *Mailing Add:* Dept of Oceanog WB-10 Univ of Wash Seattle WA 98195

SMITH, DURWARD A, b Raymond, Wash, Jan 4, 47. FOOD SCIENCE, ENGINEERING. *Educ:* Univ Wash, BA, 70; Univ Idaho, BS, 72; La State Univ, MS, 73, PhD(food sci), 76. *Prof Exp:* ASST PROF FOOD SCI, DEPT HORT, AUBURN UNIV, 76- *Mem:* Inst Food Technologists; Am Hort Soc. *Res:* Food engineering and science. *Mailing Add:* Dept of Hort Auburn Univ Auburn AL 36830

SMITH, DWIGHT GLENN, b Binghampton, NY, Apr 15, 43; m 68; c 2. POPULATION ECOLOGY. *Educ:* Elizabethtown Col, BS, 66; Brigham Young Univ, MS, 68, PhD(zool), 71. *Prof Exp:* Asst prof, 70-77, ASSOC PROF BIOL, SOUTHERN CONN STATE COL, 77- *Concurrent Pos:* Ecol consult, Environ Pop Educ Asn, 74-; mem sci staff referee Condor, Cooper Ornith Soc, 75- *Mem:* Am Ornithologists Union; Cooper Ornith Soc. *Res:* Investigations of vertebrate predator and prey relationships with emphasis on mathematical models of habitat partitioning. *Mailing Add:* Dept of Biol Southern Conn State Col New Haven CT 06515

SMITH, DWIGHT MORRELL, b Hudson, NY, Oct 10, 31; m 55; c 3. PHYSICAL CHEMISTRY, ANALYTICAL CHEMISTRY. *Educ:* Cent Col, Iowa, BA, 53; Pa State Univ, PhD(chem), 57. *Prof Exp:* Instr chem, Calif Inst Technol, 57-59; sr chemist, Texaco, Inc, 59-61; asst prof chem, Wesleyan Univ, 61-66; from assoc prof to prof, Hope Col, 66-72; PROF CHEM & CHMN DEPT, UNIV DENVER, 72- *Concurrent Pos:* NSF fac fel, Scripps Inst Oceanog, 71-72. *Mem:* Catalysis Soc; Am Chem Soc; AAAS. *Res:* Catalysis; infrared spectroscopy; kinetics; electrochemistry; surface chemistry. *Mailing Add:* Dept of Chem Univ of Denver Denver CO 80208

SMITH, DWIGHT RAYMOND, b Sanders, Idaho, July 28, 21; m 44; c 2. FISH & WILDLIFE SCIENCES. *Educ:* Univ Idaho, BS, 49, MS, 51; Utah State Univ, PhD(ecol), 71. *Prof Exp:* Res biologist, Idaho Fish & Game Dept, 50-52, area big game mgr, 53-56; range scientist, US Forest Serv, 56-61, wildlife res biologist, 62-65; asst prof big game mgt ecol, 65-70, assoc prof wildlife habitat mgt, 71-75, PROF ENVIRON LAW, COLO STATE UNIV, 76- *Mem:* The Wildlife Soc; Soc Range Mgt. *Res:* Large terrestrial ungulates and relationships to habitat; inventory procedures and ecological concepts related to wildlife planning; environmental law as a tool of natural resources management. *Mailing Add:* Dept Fishery & Wildlife Biol Colo State Univ Ft Collins CO 80523

SMITH, E(ASTMAN), b Springfield, Mass, Apr 2, 97; m 33. MECHANICS, OPHTHALMOLOGY INSTRUMENTATION. *Educ:* Mass Inst Technol, BS, 22, MS, 31, ScD, 34. *Prof Exp:* Machinist, Wright Aero Corp, 22-23; in chg prod schedule control, Gilbert Clock Co, 23; in chg res, Mack Trucks, 23-25; tech writer, 25-26; engr, Advert Dept, Johns-Manville Corp, 26-27; instr & lectr sci, NY Univ, 27-29; from asst prof to assoc prof physics, Newark Col Eng, 33-39; consult engr, Shaw-Porter Automatic Transmission, 39-41; optical & mech engr, Pioneer Div, Bendix Aviation Corp, 41-42; consult engr, Perfex Corp, 42-43; dir res & develop, Milwaukee Gas Specialty Co, 43-44; res engr, Woods Hole Oceanog Inst, 44-45; res assoc prof mech eng, Univ Mo, 45-63; dir, Optone Instruments, 63-82. *Mem:* Fel AAAS; Am Soc Mech Engrs; emer mem Optical Soc Am. *Res:* Mechanical engineering; vibration measurement; sound control in musical instrument structures; eyesight instruments. *Mailing Add:* Optone Instruments Cranfield Circle RR 4 Box 460 Mountain Home AR 72653

SMITH, EARL COOPER, b Bridgeport, Ill, Apr 20, 06; m 38; c 2. ANALYTICAL CHEMISTRY. *Educ:* Univ Ill, BS, 30, MS, 31; Cornell Univ, PhD(anal chem), 39. *Prof Exp:* Res asst chem, NY State Agr Exp Sta, 31-35; asst chemist, NMex State Agr Exp Sta, 39-42; from assoc prof to prof chem, Trinity Univ, Tex, 46-59; from assoc prof to prof, 59-72, EMER PROF CHEM, IND STATE UNIV, TERRE HAUTE, 72- *Concurrent Pos:* Consult, Southwest Found Res & Educ, Tex, 52-56. *Honors & Awards:* Piper Prof Award, 58; Caleb Mills Award, 70. *Mem:* Am Chem Soc; NY Acad Sci. *Res:* Analytical methods. *Mailing Add:* 35 S 24th St Terre Haute IN 47803

SMITH, EDDIE CAROL, b Lexington, KY, Apr 13, 37; m 61; c 3. BIOCHEMISTRY. *Educ:* Univ Ky, BS, 59; Iowa State Univ, PhD(biochem), 63. *Prof Exp:* Asst biochem, Iowa State Univ, 59-63, NIH res assoc, 63-64; scholar, Univ Calif, Los Angeles, 64-65; from asst prof to assoc prof, 65-74, prof biochem, 74-80, DAVID ROSS BOYD CHEM, UNIV OKLA, 80-, ASSOC DEAN, GRAD COL, 81- *Concurrent Pos:* Am Cancer Soc grant, 66-67; NSF res grant, 69-74. *Mem:* AAAS; Am Chem Soc; Am Soc Biol Chemists; NY Acad Sci. *Res:* Enzymic studies of alcoholic animals; regulation of metabolism; metabolic role of plant peroxidases. *Mailing Add:* 620 Parrington Oval Univ Okla Norman OK 73019

SMITH, EDGAR CLARENCE, JR, b Los Angeles, Calif, July 20, 26; m 48; c 3. COMPUTER SCIENCE. *Educ:* Stanford Univ, BS, 49, MS, 50; Brown Univ, PhD(math), 55. *Prof Exp:* Instr math, Univ Ore, 53-54; asst prof, Univ Utah, 54-55; appl sci rep, 55-58, univ rep, 58-60, mgr univ prog, 60-61, systs anal mgr, 61-65, large sci acct support, 66-68, mgr sci mkt, 68-71, mgr prog develop, 71-74, SYSTS & PROG CONSULT, IBM CORP, 74- *Concurrent Pos:* Teacher, Exten Div, Univ Calif, 57-58. *Mem:* Am Math Soc; Asn Comput Mach. *Res:* Boolean algebra; numerical analysis; applications of digital computers. *Mailing Add:* IBM E/ME/A CORP 360 Hamilton Ave White Plains NY 10601

SMITH, EDGAR DUMONT, b New Orleans, La, May 16, 18; m 43; c 1. ORGANIC CHEMISTRY. *Educ:* Tulane Univ, BS, 39, MS, 41; La State Univ, PhD(chem), 48. *Prof Exp:* Chemist, Tenn Coal & RR, Ala, 41, Dow Chem Co, Tex, 41-44, Ethyl Corp, La, 46, US Off Naval Res, La, 48-50 & Buckeye Cotton Oil Co, 50-52; group leader dyeing res, Chemstrand Corp, 52-58, group leader nylon intermediates, 58-60; assoc prof org chem, Univ Ark, Little Rock, 60-66, prof, 66-80; RETIRED. *Concurrent Pos:* NIH res grant, 62-69. *Honors & Awards:* A Cressy Morrison Award, NY Acad Sci, 67. *Mem:* Am Chem Soc; Sigma Xi. *Res:* Organic synthesis; theoretical organic chemistry; chromatography. *Mailing Add:* 4725 Glenmere Rd North Little Rock AR 72116

SMITH, EDGAR EUGENE, b Hollandale, Miss, Aug 6, 34; m 55; c 4. BIOCHEMISTRY. *Educ:* Tougaloo Col, BS, 55; Purdue Univ, MS, 57, PhD(biochem), 60. *Prof Exp:* Res fel surg-biochem, Harvard Med Sch, 59-61, res assoc, 61-68; asst prof biochem & surg, Sch Med, Boston Univ, 68-71, assoc prof biochem & surg & asst dean student affairs, 71-74; ASSOC PROF BIOCHEM & PROVOST ACAD AFFAIRS, UNIV MASS MED SCH,

WORCESTER, 74- *Concurrent Pos:* NIH res grant, 66-69; assoc surg res, Beth Israel Hosp, Boston, 59-68; Robert Wood Johnson Health Policy Fel, 77-78. *Mem:* AAAS; Am Soc Biol Chemists; Am Chem Soc; NY Acad Sci; fel Am Inst Chemists. *Res:* Usefulness of certain enzymes in the development of new techniques for cancer diagnosis and prognosis; pyrimidine biosynthesis in normal and neoplastic human tissue; biochemistry of cell division; sickle cell anemia. *Mailing Add:* Off of Provost Univ of Mass Med Sch Worcester MA 01605

SMITH, EDGAR FITZHUGH, b Rattan, Tex, Dec 13, 19; m 45; c 2. ANIMAL HUSBANDRY. *Educ:* Agr & Mech Col, Tex, BS, 41, PhD(range mgt), 56; Kans State Univ, MS, 47. *Prof Exp:* Asst prof animal husb, Ark State Col, 47-48; asst prof, 48-53, assoc prof, 53-61, prof, 61-70, PROF ANIMAL SCI & INDUST, KANS STATE UNIV & ANIMAL SCIENTIST, AGR EXTEN STA, 70- *Mem:* Am Soc Animal Sci; Soc Range Mgt. *Res:* Beef cattle production and grazing. *Mailing Add:* Dept of Animal Sci & Indust Kans State Univ Manhattan KS 66502

SMITH, EDITH LUCILE, b Jackson, Miss, Sept 9, 13. BIOCHEMISTRY, MICROBIOLOGY. *Educ:* Tulane Univ, BS, 35, MS, 37; Univ Rochester, PhD(biochem), 50. *Prof Exp:* Lab asst chem, Newcomb Col, Tulane Univ, 35-36, from lab asst to assoc instr biochem, Tulane Univ, 36-47; asst prof biophys, Univ Pa, 55-58; from assoc prof to prof, 58-78, EMER PROF BIOCHEM, DARTMOUTH MED SCH, 78- *Concurrent Pos:* Fel biophys, Univ Pa, 50-54; Brit & Am Cancer Socs exchange fel, Cambridge Univ, 54-55. *Mem:* AAAS; Am Soc Biol Chemists; Am Soc Microbiol; Am Chem Soc. *Res:* Oxidative enzymes, particularly cytochrome pigments; respiratory chain systems of mammalian tissues and microorganisms; oxidative enzyme systems of photosynthetic bacteria. *Mailing Add:* Dept Biochem Dartmouth Med Sch Hanover NH 03755

SMITH, EDMUND HOBART, b Oakland, Calif, Jan 4, 35; m 61; c 3. MARINE ZOOLOGY. *Educ:* Occidental Col, AB, 57; Univ Pac, MA, 59; Glasgow Univ, PhD(zool), 64. *Prof Exp:* NIH fel, Marine Biol Lab, Woods Hole, 64-65; PROF BIOL SCI, UNIV PAC, 70-, DIR, PAC MARINE STA, 65- *Concurrent Pos:* Mem bd, Calif Water Quality Bd, 70-75. *Mem:* Soc Study Evolution; Ecol Soc Am; Marine Biol Asn UK; Scottish Marine Biol Asn; Conchol Soc Gt Brit & Ireland. *Res:* Functional morphology of marine mollusks, particularly the gastropod group Turridae and bivalve groups which are involved in boring into calcareous substrates. *Mailing Add:* Pac Marine Sta Dillon Beach CA 94929

SMITH, EDWARD, b Liberty, NY, Aug 26, 34; m 65; c 3. PHARMACEUTICAL CHEMISTRY. *Educ:* Long Island Univ, BSPharm, 55; Univ Mich, MS, 58, PhD(pharmaceut chem), 62. *Prof Exp:* Anal chemist, 62-65, res chemist, Div Pharmaceut Chem, Bur Sci, 65-70, RES CHEMIST, DIV DRUG CHEM, OFF PHARMACEUT RES & TESTING, BUR DRUGS, US FOOD & DRUG ADMIN, 70- *Mem:* Am Pharmaceut Asn; Am Chem Soc; Acad Pharmaceut Sci; Asn Off Anal Chem. *Res:* Analysis of pharmaceuticals and their active constituents and possible degradation products using chromatographic techniques; electrometric methods and nuclear chemical techniques; structure proof using spectrophotometric techniques. *Mailing Add:* Div of Drug Chem USFDA Off Pharmaceut Res & Test Washington DC 20204

SMITH, EDWARD HOLMAN, b Abbeville, SC, Sept 2, 15; m 47; c 4. ECONOMIC ENTOMOLOGY. *Educ:* Clemson Univ, BS, 38; Cornell Univ, MS, 40, PhD, 47. *Prof Exp:* Asst prof entom, Exp Sta, State Univ NY Col Agr, Cornell Univ, 47-50, from assoc prof to prof, 55-64; head dept, NC State Univ, 64-67; prof entom & dir coop exten, Cornell Univ, 67-72, chmn dept entom, 72-81. *Mem:* Entom Soc Am; AAAS. *Res:* Fruit insects; insect biology and control; mode of ovicidal action. *Mailing Add:* Col of Agr & Life Sci Cornell Univ 162 Comstock Hall Ithaca NY 14853

SMITH, EDWARD J(OSEPH), b New York, NY, Dec 12, 20; m 54; c 2. ELECTRICAL ENGINEERING. *Educ:* Cooper Union, BEE, 45; Polytech Inst Brooklyn, MEE, 48, PhD(elec eng), 51. *Prof Exp:* Res engr, Remington Rand Co, Conn, 45-47; instr elec eng, NY Univ, 47-48; res assoc, 50-53, res assoc prof, 53-57, assoc prof, 57-59, dir comput ctr, 59-63, head dept elec eng, 67-71, head dept elec eng & comput sci, 78-81, PROF ELEC ENG, POLYTECH INST BROOKLYN, 59- *Concurrent Pos:* Vis prof, Eindhoven Technol Univ, 63-64. *Mem:* Asn Comput Mach; Inst Elec & Electronics Engrs; Am Soc Eng Educ; NY Acad Sci; AAAS. *Res:* Computers; logic design; computer architecture; switching and automata theory; nonlinear magnetics. *Mailing Add:* Dept Elec Eng & Comput Sci Polytech Inst NY Brooklyn NY 11201

SMITH, EDWARD JOHN, b Dravosburg, Pa, Sept 21, 27; m 53; c 4. PHYSICS, SPACE MAGNETISM. *Educ:* Univ Calif, Los Angeles, BA, 51, MS, 52, PhD(physics), 60. *Prof Exp:* Res geophysicist, Inst Geophys, Univ Calif, Los Angeles, 55-59; mem tech staff, Space Tech Labs, 59-61; MEM TECH STAFF, JET PROPULSION LAB, 61- *Honors & Awards:* Medal Exceptional Sci Achievement, NASA. *Mem:* AAAS; Sigma Xi; Int Sci Radio Union; Am Geophys Union. *Res:* Planetary magnetism; space physics; interplanetary physics; wave-particle interactions in plasmas; propagation of electromagnetic waves; solar-terrestrial relations. *Mailing Add:* 2536 Boulder Rd Altadena CA 91001

SMITH, EDWARD LEE, b Apache, Okla, June 6, 32; m 58; c 2. PLANT GENETICS, FIELD CROPS. *Educ:* Okla State Univ, BS, 54, MS, 59; Univ Minn, PhD(plant genetics), 62. *Prof Exp:* Instr agron, Okla State Univ, 57-58; asst prof, Univ Tenn, 62-63; asst prof, Okla State Univ-Ethiopian Contract, 63-65; asst prof, Univ Ill, 65-66; assoc prof, 66-71, PROF AGRON, OKLA STATE UNIV, 71- *Mem:* AAAS; Crop Sci Soc Am; Am Soc Agron; Genetics Soc Am. *Res:* Wheat breeding and genetics; milling and baking quality in wheat; disease and insect resistance in small grains; heterosis, cytoplasmic male sterility and fertility restoration in wheat. *Mailing Add:* Dept of Agron Okla State Univ Stillwater OK 74074

SMITH, EDWARD M(ANSON), b Sharpsburg, Ga, Feb 16, 25; m 46; c 4. AGRICULTURAL ENGINEERING. *Educ:* Univ Ga, BS, 49; Kans State Univ, MS, 50. *Prof Exp:* Asst prof, Southwest Tex State Col, 50-52; assoc prof agr eng & assoc agr engr, USDA & Okla State Univ, 52-57; ASSOC PROF AGR ENG & ASSOC AGR ENGR, EXP STA, UNIV KY, 57- *Mem:* Am Soc Agr Engrs. *Res:* Farm machinery. *Mailing Add:* Dept of Agr Eng Univ of Ky Lexington KY 40506

SMITH, EDWARD RUSSELL, b Knoxville, Tenn, May 18, 44; m 69; c 5. BIOCHEMISTRY. *Educ:* Univ Louisville, AB, 66, PhD(biochem), 71. *Prof Exp:* Instr biochem, obstet & gynec, Col Med, Univ Nebr, Omaha, 71, res asst prof, 71-75; asst prof, 75-80, ASSOC PROF OBSTET & GYNEC, UNIV TEX MED BR GALVESTON, 80- *Mem:* AAAS; Am Chem Soc; Sigma Xi; Geront Soc; Soc Study Reproduction. *Res:* Mechanism of reproductive senescence; regulation of protein synthesis and degradation; hormone action upon target tissues. *Mailing Add:* Dept of Obstet & Gynec Univ of Tex Med Br Galveston TX 77550

SMITH, EDWIN BARKLEY, JR, biochemistry, nutrition, see previous edition

SMITH, EDWIN BURNELL, b Wellington, Kans, Dec 1, 36; m 58; c 3. PLANT TAXONOMY, BIOSYSTEMATICS. *Educ:* Univ Kans, BS, 61, MA, 63, PhD(bot), 65. *Prof Exp:* Asst prof bot, Rutgers Univ, 65-66; vis cytologist, Brookhaven Nat Lab, 66; from asst prof to assoc prof, 66-76, chmn, Dept Bot & Bact, 78-81, PROF BOT, UNIV ARK, FAYETTEVILLE, 76- *Concurrent Pos:* Consult, Brookhaven Nat Lab, 66. *Mem:* Bot Soc Am; Am Soc Plant Taxon; Int Asn Plant Taxon; Int Asn Plant Biosystematists. *Res:* Flora of Arkansas; biosystematics of flowering plants, especially Compositae; taxonomy of Coreopsis of the world. *Mailing Add:* Dept Bot & Bact Univ Ark Fayetteville AR 72701

SMITH, EDWIN E(ARLE), b Sugarcreek, Ohio, Jan 18, 23; m 44; c 3. CHEMICAL ENGINEERING. *Educ:* Ohio State Univ, BChE, 44, MS, 47, PhD(chem eng), 49. *Prof Exp:* Asst prof fuels res, 49-56, assoc prof chem eng, 56-66, PROF CHEM ENG, OHIO STATE UNIV, 66-, DIR CHEM RES, 56- *Mem:* Am Inst Chem Engrs. *Res:* Industrial water pollution; combustibility of materials; chemical reaction kinetics; phase equilibrium studies. *Mailing Add:* 551 Brevoort Rd Columbus OH 43214

SMITH, EDWIN LAMAR, JR, b San Marcos, Tex, Aug 13, 36; m 66; c 1. RANGE MANAGEMENT. *Educ:* Colo State Univ, BS, 58, MS, 64, PhD(soil sci), 66. *Prof Exp:* Instr range mgt, Colo State Univ, 61-64, instr forestry, 65-66; range adv, Brazil Contract, 66-69, from asst prof to assoc prof watershed mgt, 69-72, chief of party agr, Brazil Contract, 72-73, ASSOC PROF RANGE MGT, SCH RENEWABLE NATURAL RESOURCES, UNIV ARIZ, 74-, ASSOC RES SPECIALIST, AGR EXP STA, 76- *Mem:* AAAS; Soc Range Mgt; Soil Sci Soc Am. *Res:* Range ecology; soil-geomorphology-vegetation relationships; remote sensing. *Mailing Add:* Sch Renewable Natural Resources Univ of Ariz Tucson AZ 85721

SMITH, EDWIN LEE, b Shelton, Nebr, Aug 12, 07; m 33; c 2. PHYSIOLOGY. *Educ:* Univ Nebr, BS, 35, MS, 38; Univ Chicago, PhD(physiol), 41. *Prof Exp:* Instr physiol, Col Med, Univ Ill, 41-43; asst prof, Med Col Va, 43-47; PROF PHYSIOL, UNIV TEX DENT BR HOUSTON, 47- *Mem:* AAAS; Am Physiol Soc; Soc Exp Biol & Med; Int Asn Dent Res. *Res:* Bioassay; pharmacology and physiology of circulation; renal physiology; maximum capacity of the vascular system; experimental renal hypertension; digitalis assay; barbiturates. *Mailing Add:* Univ of Tex Dent Br PO Box 20068 Houston TX 77025

SMITH, EDWIN MARK, b Grand Rapids, Mich, Apr 10, 27; m 40; c 2. MEDICINE. *Educ:* Univ Mich, BS, 50, MD, 53. *Prof Exp:* Intern, Univ Hosp, Univ Mich, Ann Arbor, 53-54, resident phys med & rehab, 54-57, res assoc, Univ, 57-59, from asst prof to prof phys med & rehab, Sch Med, 59-78; PVT PRACT, FLINT, MICH, 78- *Mem:* AMA; Asn Electromyog & Electrodiag; Cong Rehab Med; Am Acad Phys Med & Rehab. *Res:* Physical medicine and rehabilitation; mechanics of deformity formation in rheumatoid arthritis; design and development of orthetic devices. *Mailing Add:* G5067 W Bristol Rd Flint MI 48507

SMITH, EILEEN PATRICIA, b Trenton, NJ, Mar 20, 41. PHYSICAL ORGANIC CHEMISTRY. *Educ:* Univ Pa, BSChem, 62, PhD(org chem), 67. *Prof Exp:* Instr chem, Mercer County Community Col, 67-68; asst prof, 68-72, ASSOC PROF CHEM, TRENTON STATE COL, 72- *Mem:* Sigma Xi; NY Acad Sci; Am Chem Soc; Am Inst Chemists. *Res:* Mass spectral studies; organic laboratory experiments; liquid crystal studies. *Mailing Add:* Dept Chem Trenton State Col Trenton NJ 08625

SMITH, ELBERT GEORGE, b Eugene, Ore, July 18, 13. CHEMISTRY. *Educ:* Ore State Col, BA, 36; Iowa State Col, PhD(physiol & nutrit chem), Iowa State Col, 43. *Prof Exp:* From asst to instr chem, Iowa State Col, 36-43; asst prof, Hamline Univ, 43-46 & Univ Denver, 46-47; from asst prof to assoc prof, Univ Hawaii, 47-58; from assoc prof to prof, 58-78, EMER PROF CHEM, MILLS COL, 78- *Concurrent Pos:* Staff mem surv chem notation systs, Nat Res Coun, 61-64, mem comt mod methods handling chem info, 64-70. *Mem:* Fel AAAS; Chem Notation Asn (pres, 72); Am Chem Soc. *Res:* Nutritional biochemistry; chemical structure information retrieval; Wiswesser notation. *Mailing Add:* 6360 Melville Dr Oakland CA 94611

SMITH, ELDON RAYMOND, b Halifax, Can, May 21, 39; m 64; c 2. CARDIOLOGY. *Educ:* Dalhousie Univ, MD, 67; FRCP(C), 72. *Prof Exp:* Lectr, Dalhousie Univ, 73-74, asst prof, 74-75, assoc prof, 75-80; PROF MED, ASSOC PROF PHYSIOL & HEAD, CARDIOL DIV, UNIV CALGARY, 80-; HEAD, CARDIOL DIV, FOOTHILLS GEN HOSP, 80- *Concurrent Pos:* Mem coun circulation, Am Heart Asn. *Honors & Awards:* Nat Res Award, Can Cardiovasc Soc, 73. *Mem:* Am Fedn Clin Res; Can Soc Clin Invest; Can Cardiovasc Soc; Royal Col Physicians & Surgeons Can; fel Am Heart Asn. *Res:* Echocardiography; body-surface electrocardiographic mapping; circulatory physiology. *Mailing Add:* Cardiol Div Foothills Hosp 1403 29th St Northwest Calgary AB T2N 2T9 Can

SMITH, ELIZABETH KNAPP, b Coraopolis, Pa, Dec 15, 17; m 51. CLINICAL BIOCHEMISTRY, PEDIATRIC ENDOCRINOLOGY. *Educ:* Fla State Col Women, BS, 38; Univ Mich, MS, 39; Univ Iowa, PhD(biochem), 43. *Prof Exp:* Asst pediat, Univ Iowa, 39-43, res assoc, 44-47, res asst prof, 47-50; asst, Rackham Arthritis Res Unit, Univ Mich, 43-44; from asst prof to assoc prof obstet & gynec, 50-58, RES ASSOC PROF PEDIAT, SCH MED, UNIV WASH, 58-, RES ASSOC PROF, LAB MED, 71- *Concurrent Pos:* Clin chemist, Children's Orthop Hosp, 58- *Mem:* AAAS; Am Chem Soc; Endocrine Soc; Am Asn Clin Chemists; Lawson Wilkins Pediat Endocrine Soc. *Res:* Endocrine and metabolic disorders in children; metabolism of adrenocortical hormones in infancy and childhood. *Mailing Add:* Chem Lab Children's Orthop Hosp & Med Ctr PO Box C-5371 Seattle WA 98105

SMITH, ELIZABETH MELVA, b Regina, Sask, Nov 4, 43. STEROID CHEMISTRY, SYNTHETIC ORGANIC CHEMISTRY. *Educ:* Univ Sask, Saskatoon, BSP, 65, PhD(pharmaceut chem), 69. *Prof Exp:* Fel chem, La State Univ, New Orleans, 69-70 & Wayne State Univ, Detroit, 70; res assoc, Dept Chem, Univ Ala, 70-72; fel, 73, sr scientist, 74-77, PRIN SCIENTIST CHEM, SCHERING CORP, 77- *Concurrent Pos:* Med Res Coun Can fel, 69 & 70. *Mem:* Am Chem Soc. *Res:* Steroid synthesis; synthesis and chemistry of heterocyclic compounds. *Mailing Add:* Schering Corp 60 Orange St Bloomfield NJ 07003

SMITH, ELMER ROBERT, b Adams, Wis, Nov 14, 23; m 57; c 2. CHEMICAL ENGINEERING, BIOPHYSICS. *Educ:* Univ Wis, BS, 44. *Prof Exp:* Asst biophys, Univ Calif, 51-54 & Sloan-Kettering Inst, 54-56; instr, Med Col, Cornell Univ, 56; sr scientist, Bettis Atomic Power Lab, Westinghouse Elec Corp, 57-61; supvr radiochem, Hazleton Nuclear Sci Corp, 61-64; mgr chem & tech servs, 64-72, staff consult, 72-73, prin engr, 73-75, consult engr, 75-78, EXEC ENGR, ENVIRON SYSTS DIV, NUS CORP, 78- *Mem:* AAAS; Am Chem Soc; Sigma Xi. *Res:* Industry; air pollution; nuclear reactor safeguards and siting; radiochemistry; analytical methods in chemistry and radiochemistry; meteorology; reactor chemistry; environmental monitoring; low and high level radioactive solid waste disposal; environmental impact assessment; project management; pollution control; risk assessment. *Mailing Add:* 11206 Healy St Silver Spring MD 20902

SMITH, ELSKE VAN PANHUYS, b Monte Carlo, Monaco, Nov 9, 29; nat US; m 50; c 2. ASTRONOMY. *Educ:* Radcliffe Col, BA, 50, MA, 51, PhD(astron), 56. *Prof Exp:* Harvard res fel solar physics, Sacramento Peak Observ, 55-62; vis fel, Joint Inst Lab Astrophys, Colo, 62-63; assoc prof astron, Univ Md, College Park, 63-75, asst provost, Div Math & Phys Sci & Eng, 73-78, actg dir astron prog, 75, prof, 75-80, asst vchancellor acad affairs, 78-80; DEAN, COL HUMANITIES & SCI & PROF PHYSICS, VA COMMONWEALTH UNIV, RICHMOND, 80- *Concurrent Pos:* Res assoc, Lowell Observ, 56-57; consult, Goddard Space Flight Ctr, NASA, 63-65; counr, Am Astron Soc, 77-80; chmn, US Nat Comt, Int Astron Union, 78-80. *Mem:* Fel AAAS; Int Astron Union; Am Astron Soc. *Res:* Active regions on the sun, especially flares and plages; solar chromosphere; interstellar polarization; solar physics. *Mailing Add:* Col Humanities & Sci Va Commonwealth Univ Richmond VA 23284

SMITH, EMIL L, b New York, NY, July 5, 11; m 34; c 2. BIOCHEMISTRY, BIOPHYSICS. *Educ:* Columbia Univ, BS, 31, PhD(biophys), 37. *Prof Exp:* Asst zool, Columbia Univ, 31-34; asst biophys, 34-36, instr, 36-38; res assoc, Rockefeller Inst, 40-42; biophysicist, Biol Lab, E R Squibb & Sons, 42-46; assoc res prof biochem & physiol, Col Med, Univ Utah, 46-47, from assoc prof to prof biochem & from assoc res prof to res prof med, 47-63; prof biol chem & chmn dept, 63-79, EMER PROF, SCH MED, UNIV CALIF, LOS ANGELES, 79- *Concurrent Pos:* Guggenheim fel, Cambridge Univ, 38-40; hon fel, Yale Univ, 40; mem, Panel Comt Growth, Nat Res Coun, 49-53; mem, Sect Arthritis & Metab, USPHS, 49-50, biochem, 50-54, Adv Comt Biochem, US Off Naval Res, 57-60, US Nat Comt Biochem, 58-62, chmn, 59-62; Reynolds lectr, Univ Utah, 58, Bloor lectr, Univ Rochester, 59, Hanna lectr, Western Reserve Univ, 66 & Alexander Agassiz lectr, Harvard Univ, 68; mem, Comt Int Orgn & Prog, Nat Acad Sci, 62-72, chmn, 64-68; mem, Bd Trustees, Calif Found Biochem Res, 64-, Adv Coun, Life Ins Med Res Fund, 66-70 & Sci Adv Panel, Ciba Found, 67-79; vis prof, Col France, 68; mem, Vis Comt, Dept Biol Chem, Harvard Med Sch, 68-71; mem, Comt Scholarly Commun with People's Repub China, 70-76, chmn, 72-75; mem, Bd Int Sci Exchange, Nat Res Coun-Nat Acad Sci, 73-77, Exec Comt Assembly Life Sci, 73-75 & Comn Int Relations, 78- *Honors & Awards:* Annual Lectr & Medalist, Ciba Found, 68. *Mem:* Nat Acad Sci; Am Chem Soc; Am Acad Art & Sci; Am Philos Soc; Am Soc Biol Chemists. *Res:* Chemistry of proteins; milk proteins; amino acids; proteolytic enzymes; peptides; enzymology; histones; cytochromes; dehydrogenses; biochemical evolution. *Mailing Add:* Dept of Biol Chem Univ of Calif Sch of Med Los Angeles CA 90024

SMITH, EMIL RICHARD, b Bridgewater, Mass, July 25, 31; m 56; c 5. PHARMACOLOGY. *Educ:* Northeastern Univ, BS, 54; Tufts Univ, MS, 56, PhD(pharmacol), 58. *Prof Exp:* Assoc res pharmacologist, Sterling-Winthrop Res Inst, 60-62; res pharmacologist, Mason Res Inst, Worcester, Mass, 62-67; sect head gen pharmacol & toxicol, Res Labs, Astra Pharmaceut Prod, Inc, 67-72; sect head chem carcinogenesis, Mason Res Inst, 72-75; ASSOC PROF PHARMACOL, UNIV MASS MED SCH, WORCESTER, 75- *Concurrent Pos:* USPHS res fel pharmacol, Sch Med, Univ Buffalo, 58-60; lectr, Albany Med Col, 61-62, res pharmacologist, St Vincent Hosp, 63-; asst prof, Sch Med, Tufts Univ, 69-73; lectr pharmacol, Sch Med, Univ Mass, 74-75. *Mem:* Am Soc Pharmacol & Exp Therapeut; Soc Toxicol. *Res:* Cardiovascular and autonomic pharmacology; toxicology. *Mailing Add:* Dept of Pharmacol Univ of Mass Med Sch Worcester MA 01605

SMITH, ERIC HOWARD, b Cincinnati, Ohio, July 4, 43. SYSTEMATIC ENTOMOLOGY. *Educ:* Miami Univ, Ohio, BA, 66; Purdue Univ, MS, 70; Ohio State Univ, PhD(entom), 73. *Prof Exp:* collection mgr, Div Insects, Field Mus Natural Hist, 75-80; TECH DIR, ORKIN NAT SERV DEPT, 81-

Mem: Coleopterists Soc; Entom Soc Am; Soc Syst Zool. *Res:* Primarily the systematics, but also all other aspects of the Chrysomelidae (Insecta: Coleoptera) with emphasis on the subfamily Alticinae or flea beetles. *Mailing Add:* Orkin-Nat Serv Dept 2170 Piedmmont Rd N E Atlanta GA 30324

SMITH, ERLA RING, b Colma, Calif, Feb 18, 38; m 60; c 2. NEUROENDOCRINOLOGY, ANATOMY. *Educ:* Univ Wash, BA, 59, PhD(biol struct), 65. *Prof Exp:* Teaching asst biol struct, Univ Wash, 59-64; res assoc, 68-80, SR RES ASSOC NEUROENDOCRINOL, STANFORD UNIV, 80- *Concurrent Pos:* Nat Inst Arthritis & Metab Dis fel neuroendocrinol, Stanford Univ, 65-68. *Mem:* AAAS; Endocrine Soc; Am Physiol Soc; Soc Neurosci. *Res:* Reproductive physiology; endocrinology; sex behavior. *Mailing Add:* Dept of Physiol Stanford Univ Sch of Med Stanford CA 94305

SMITH, ERNEST KETCHAM, b Peking, China, May 31, 22; US citizen; m 50; c 3. RADIO PHYSICS, TELECOMMUNICATIONS. *Educ:* Swarthmore Col, BA, 44; Cornell Univ, MS, 51, PhD(radio wave propagation), 56. *Prof Exp:* Asst radio engr, Mutual Broadcasting Syst, 46-47, chief plans & allocations div, 47-49; res asst, Cornell Univ, 50-51; proj leader, Nat Bur Stand, 51-52; res asst, Cornell Univ, 52-54; proj leader, Nat Bur Stand, 54-57, asst chief ionosphere res sect, Boulder Labs, 57, chief sect, 57-60, chief ionosphere res & propagation div, 60-62, chief upper atmosphere & space physics div, 62-65, chief aeronomy div, 65; dir aeronomy lab, Inst Telecommun Sci & Aeronomy, Environ Sci Serv Admin, 65-67, actg dir, Inst Telecommun Sci, 67-68, actg dir off univ rels, Res Labs, 68-70; assoc dir, Inst Telecommun Sci, 70-72, Consult to dir, Inst Telecommun Sci, Off Telecommun, US Dept Com, 72-76; MEM TECH STAFF, CALIF INST TECHNOL, JET PROPULSION LAB, 76- *Concurrent Pos:* Int vchmn study group six, Int Telecommun Union, Consultative Comt Int Radio, Dept State, 59-70, chmn US study group six, US Nat Comt, 70-76; vis prof, Colo State Univ, 63, affil prof, 64-69; assoc, Harvard Col Observ, 66-75; adj prof, Univ Colo, Boulder, 69-78. *Mem:* Fel AAAS; fel Inst Elec & Electronics Engrs; Sigma Xi; Int Union Radio Sci; Am Geophys Union. *Res:* Sporadic-E region of the ionosphere; radio scattering from the ionospheric F-region; radio refractive index of the nonionized atmosphere; very high frequency propagation via the ionosphere; natural noise; earthspace propagation. *Mailing Add:* 5019 Merita Place La Canada CA 91011

SMITH, ERNEST LEE, JR, b Nashville, Tenn, Aug 3, 34; m 60; c 2. OPERATIONS RESEARCH. *Educ:* Vanderbilt Univ, BA, 58. *Prof Exp:* Mathematician, US Army, 58-60 & Defense Atomic Support Agency, 60-63; br chief anal syst, 63-65, div chief appl prog div, 65-70, dep chief oper, 71-74, chief, Syst Planning & Eng Off, Nat Mil Command Syst Support Ctr, 74-76; chief plans div, 76-79, tech adv to dep dir, plans prog & mgt, 79-80, CHIEF, HARDWARE SYSTS DIV, COMMAND & CONTROL TECH CTR, 80- *Concurrent Pos:* Rep, Defense Commun Agency-Advan Airborne Command Post Software Develop Team, 73. *Mem:* Asn Comput Mach. *Res:* CCTC ADP/Communication program planning, budgeting and contracting; directing studies, analyses and engineering necessary to examine alternative approaches and to insure new technology is being planned to future ADP/ Communication capabilities. *Mailing Add:* Command & Control Tech Ctr Rm BE685 Pentagon Washington DC 20301

SMITH, ERVIN PAUL, b Bozeman, Mont, May 15, 22; m 45; c 5. ANIMAL SCIENCE. *Educ:* Mont State Col, BS, 47, MS, 51; State Col Wash, PhD(animal sci), 54. *Prof Exp:* Instr high sch, Mont, 46-48; asst prof dairy indust, 48-55, assoc prof animal prod, 55-60, statistician, Agr Exp Sta, 66-81, PROF ANIMAL PHYSIOL, MONT STATE UNIV, 60-, ASSOC DEAN AGR, 81- *Concurrent Pos:* Vis assoc prof, Iowa State Univ, 60-61; vis prof, W Pakistan Agr Univ, 64-66. *Res:* Animal physiology and nutrition; statistics. *Mailing Add:* Dept Animal Sci Mont State Univ Bozeman MT 59715

SMITH, EUCLID O'NEAL, b Jackson, Miss, May 27, 47; m 77. PHYSICAL ANTHROPOLOGY. *Educ:* Miss State Univ, BA, 69; Univ Ga, MA, 72; Ohio State Univ, PhD(anthropol), 77. *Prof Exp:* ASST PROF ANTHROPOL, EMORY UNIV, 76-, ASST RES PROF, YERKES REGIONAL PRIMATE RES CTR, 77- *Mem:* Am Anthropol Asn; Am Asn Phys Anthropologists; Am Soc Primatologists; Animal Behav Soc; Int Primatol Soc. *Res:* Primate social behavior; sociopharmacology; developmental sociobiology. *Mailing Add:* Dept of Anthropol Emory Univ Atlanta GA 30322

SMITH, EUGENE IRWIN, b Buffalo, NY, Mar 4, 44; m 73. PETROLOGY, PLANETARY GEOLOGY. *Educ:* Wayne State Univ, BS, 65; Univ NMex, MS, 68, PhD(geol), 70. *Prof Exp:* Geologist, US Geol Surv, Ctr Astrogeol, 66-68; res assoc geol, Univ NMex, 70-72; asst prof, Univ Wis-Parkside, 72-76, ASSOC PROF GEOL, 76-80; assoc prof geol, UNIV NEV, LAS VEGAS, 80- *Concurrent Pos:* Vis assoc prof geol, Univ Nev, Las Vegas, 78-79. *Mem:* Geol Soc Am; Am Geophys Union; AAAS. *Res:* Geological, petrographic and geochemical study of teritiary volcanic rocks in southern Nevada and Precambrian volcanic and plutonic rocks in central Wisconsin; volcanological and crater studies of Mars, Mercury and the Moon. *Mailing Add:* Dept Geosci Univ Nev Las Vegas NV 89154

SMITH, EUGENE JOSEPH, b New York, NY, Jan 26, 29; m 56; c 3. BIOCHEMISTRY. *Educ:* Queens Col, NY, BS, 51; Univ Conn, MS, 55; Duke Univ, PhD(biochem), 59. *Prof Exp:* Arthritis & Rheumatism Found fel, 59-61; asst prof biochem, Schs Med & Dent, Georgetown Univ, 61-68; res chemist, Food & Drug Admin, 68-69; RES CHEMIST, INST GENETICS & PHYSIOL, SCI & EDUC ADMIN-AGR RES, USDA, 69- *Concurrent Pos:* Consult, Walter Reed Armed Forces Inst Dent Res, 63-67. *Mem:* AAAS; Am Soc Biochemists. *Res:* Microbial metabolism and polysaccharides; nucleotides and amino-sugars; nucleic acid metabolism; avian tumor-virus research. *Mailing Add:* USDA Regional Poultry Res Lab East Lansing MI 48823

SMITH, EUGENE WILLIAM, b West Bend, Wis, Aug 11, 23; m 47, 65; c 2. BOTANY, MICROBIOLOGY. *Educ:* Marquette Univ, BS, 50, MS, 51; Cornell Univ, cert, 57; Colo State Univ, cert, 64. *Prof Exp:* Asst bot, Marquette Univ, 48-51; from instr to asst prof, 51-61, ASSOC PROF BOT, AQUINAS COL, 61- *Mem:* Bot Soc Am; Mycol Soc Am. *Res:* Mycology; bacteriology; genetics; microorganisms on blueberries. *Mailing Add:* Dept of Biol Aquinas Col Grand Rapids MI 49506

SMITH, F(REDERICK) DOW(SWELL), b Winnipeg, Man, Jan 2, 21; nat US; m 49; c 4. OPTICS. *Educ:* Queen's Univ, Ont, BA, 47, MA, 48; Univ Rochester, PhD(optics), 51. *Prof Exp:* Asst optics, Univ Rochester, 48-51; instr physics, Phys Res Lab, Boston Univ, 51-52; from asst prof to assoc prof, 52-55, chmn dept physics, 53-58, dir lab, 55-58; mgr advan tech div, Itek Corp, 58-67, vpres & corp scientist, 67-74; CONSULT, 75-; PRES, NEW ENG COL OPTOM, 79- *Concurrent Pos:* Asst, Res Coun, Ont, 47-48 & Bausch & Lomb Optical Co, NY, 49-50; mem vision comt, Nat Res Coun-US Armed Forces, 57-, chmn, 78; mem US comt, Int Comn Optics, 58-61 & 67-, vpres, 75-81. *Mem:* Fel AAAS; fel Optical Soc Am (pres, 74); fel Am Acad Optom. *Res:* Physical and geometrical optics; interferometry; aerial photography; physiological and ophthalmic optics. *Mailing Add:* 39 Gray Cliff Rd Newton Center MA 02159

SMITH, F HARRELL, b Auburn, WVa, June 28, 18; m 46; c 4. ANIMAL SCIENCE, AGRICULTURAL MECHANICS. *Educ:* WVa Univ, BS, 42, MS, 49; Va Polytech Inst, 50; Pa State Univ, EdD(agr educ & mech), 58. *Prof Exp:* High sch teacher, 42; teacher agr, Potomac State Col, WVa Univ, 46-54, head dept, 54-60; PROF AGR & HEAD DEPT, UNIV MD EASTERN SHORE, 60- *Res:* Dairy and animal husbandry; herdsmanship and farm management; agricultural uses for Loblolly pine bark. *Mailing Add:* Rte 1 Box 390 Princess Anne MD 21853

SMITH, FELIX TEISSEIRE, b San Francisco, Calif, Aug 19, 20. ATOMIC PHYSICS. *Educ:* Williams Col, Mass, BA, 42; Harvard Univ, LLB, 49, MS, 53, PhD(chem), 56. *Prof Exp:* PHYSICIST, SRI INT, 56-, DIR MOLECULAR PHYSICS LAB, 74- *Concurrent Pos:* Mem comt atomic & molecular physics, Nat Acad Sci-Nat Res Coun, 71; chmn comt atomic & molecular physics, Nat Acad Sci, 73-75; chmn, Int Conf Physics Electronic & Atomic Collisions, 75-77. *Mem:* Fel Am Phys Soc; Am Chem Soc; Brit Inst Physics. *Res:* Quantum and semiclassical collision theory of electrons, atoms, ions and small molecules; differential scattering and collision spectroscopy; three-body processes. *Mailing Add:* Molecular Physics Lab SRI Int Menlo Park CA 94025

SMITH, FINLEY W(OODWARD), b Dunbar, Pa, Sept 11, 04; m 47; c 1. ELECTRICAL ENGINEERING. *Educ:* Pa State Col, BS, 27; Lafayette Col, MS, 32. *Prof Exp:* Asst supvr substa operators, Western Pa Power Co, 27-28; from instr to assoc prof elec eng, Lafayette Col, 28-44; engr, Res Lab, Gen Elec Co, 44-46; from assoc prof to prof, 46-70, EMER PROF ELEC ENG, LAFAYETTE COL, 70- *Mem:* Sr mem Inst Elec & Electronics Engrs; Am Soc Eng Educ; Nat Soc Prof Engrs. *Res:* Frequency stability, modulation magnetrons; ultra-high frequency circuits. *Mailing Add:* 321 Porter St Easton PA 18042

SMITH, FLOYD FRANKLIN, b Brunswick, Ohio, July 27, 00; m 23; c 2. ENTOMOLOGY. *Educ:* Ohio State Univ, BSc, 23, MSc, 24, PhD(entom, zool), 29. *Prof Exp:* Asst econ entom, Ohio State Univ, 23-24; nursery inspector, State Dept Agr, Pa, 24-29; assoc entomologist, Div Cereal & Forage Insects, Bur Entom & Plant Quarantine, USDA, 29-31, entomologist, Insects Affecting Ornamentals, Div Truck Crops & Garden Insects, 31-44, sr entomologist & leader proj, 44-53, prin entomologist, Entom Res Br, 53-57, head truck crop & garden insects sect, Fruit & Veg Insects Br, Entom Res Div, 57-59, invests leader, 59-70; consult scientist, AID Prog, El Salvador, Cent Am, 70-73; COLLABR & RES SCIENTIST, PLANT GENETICS & GERMPLASM INST, SCI & EDUC ADMIN-AGR RES, USDA, 73- *Mem:* Fel & hon mem Entom Soc Am; Am Phytopath Soc. *Res:* Cyclamen and spider mites; black vine weevil; insect transmission of virus diseases of lilies, carnations, chrysanthemums and other ornamentals; insecticidal aerosols for control of pests of greenhouse and field crops; insect attractants; insect sterility; plant resistance to insect attack. *Mailing Add:* 9022 Fairview Rd Silver Spring MD 20910

SMITH, FLOYD W, b Limon, Colo, May 31, 20; m 50; c 3. SOIL FERTILITY, SOIL CHEMISTRY. *Educ:* Kans State Univ, BS, 42; Mich State Univ, MS, 46, PhD(soil sci), 49. *Prof Exp:* From asst prof to assoc prof, 46-50, actg head dept agron, 64-65, assoc dir exp sta, 65, PROF SOIL SCI, KANS STATE UNIV, 50-, DIR, KANS AGR EXP STA, 65- *Concurrent Pos:* Guest lectr, Mich State Univ, 63. *Mem:* Am Soc Agron; Soil Sci Soc Am; Crop Sci Soc Am; Soil Conserv Soc Am; fel Am Inst Chem. *Res:* Fertilizer research with corn, grain sorghum and wheat; productivity indexes for principal soil types in Kansas. *Mailing Add:* Kans Agr Exp Sta Kans State Univ Manhattan KS 66506

SMITH, FRANCIS MARION, b Columbus, Kans, Nov 16, 23; m 45; c 3. NUCLEAR CHEMISTRY. *Educ:* Kans State Univ, BS, 44, MS, 48. *Prof Exp:* Instr chem, Kans State Univ, 45-49; chemist anal res & asphalt rheol, Stand Oil Co, Ind, 49-56; chemist emission spectros, Hanford Labs, Gen Elec Co, 56-65; res scientist, Battelle-Northwest Labs, 65-70; advan scientist, 70-80, SR SCIENTIST, WESTINGHOUSE HANFORD CO, 80- *Res:* Emission spectroscopy; radiometallurgy; nuclear safeguards; calorimetry; hazardous materials shipping. *Mailing Add:* 9013 Franklin Rd Pasco WA 99301

SMITH, FRANCIS WHITE, b Capetown, SAfrica, July 20, 31; m 56; c 3. PHYSICAL CHEMISTRY, ANALYTICAL CHEMISTRY. *Educ:* Univ Cape Town, 52, Hons, 54, PhD(phys anal chem), 67. *Prof Exp:* Chemist, Metal Box Co, SAfrica, 52-54 & Schweppes Ltd, Eng, 55-56; res chemist, B F Goodrich Res Ctr, Ohio, 56-59; chemist, Geol Surv Dept, Uganda, 59-66; from asst prof to assoc prof, 67-80, PROF CHEM, YOUNGSTOWN STATE UNIV, 80- *Mem:* Am Chem Soc; Royal Inst Chem. *Res:* Ion-exchange; chemistry of niobium and tantalum in alkaline solution; organometallic compounds; spectrographic analysis. *Mailing Add:* Dept of Chem Youngstown State Univ Youngstown OH 44555

SMITH, FRANCIS XAVIER, b Chelsea, Mass, Aug 28, 45; m 71. ORGANIC CHEMISTRY. *Educ:* Lowell Technol Inst, BS, 67, MS, 69; Tufts Univ, PhD(chem), 72. *Prof Exp:* Postdoctoral assoc org chem, Univ Va, 72-74; ASST PROF CHEM, KINGS COL, 74- *Mem:* Am Chem Soc; Sigma Xi. *Res:* Synthesis of organic compounds; chemistry of nitrogen heterocycles; investigation of reaction mechanisms. *Mailing Add:* Dept of Chem Kings Col Wilkes-Barre PA 18711

SMITH, FRANK A, b New York, NY, Jan 19, 37; m 65. MATHEMATICS. *Educ:* Brooklyn Col, BA, 58; Purdue Univ, MS, 60, PhD(math), 65. *Prof Exp:* Asst prof math, Ohio State Univ, 64-66 & Univ Fla, 66-67; lectr, Univ Leicester, 67-68; fel, Carnegie-Mellon Univ, 68-69; ASSOC PROF MATH, KENT STATE UNIV, 69- *Concurrent Pos:* Vis prof, Pitzer Col, 80-81. *Mem:* NY Acad Sci; Am Math Soc; Math Asn Am. *Res:* Structure of ordered semigroups and semirings and extensions of such orders; embeddings of subspaces of topological spaces with certain extension properties. *Mailing Add:* Dept Math Kent State Univ Kent OH 44242

SMITH, FRANK ACKROYD, b Winnipeg, Man, Feb 14, 19; m 44; c 2. PHYSIOLOGICAL CHEMISTRY. *Educ:* Ohio State Univ, BA, 40, MSc, 41, PhD(physiol chem), 44; Am Bd Clin Chem, dipl. *Prof Exp:* Assoc scientist, Atomic Energy Proj, 44, from instr to asst prof toxicol, Sch Med & Dent, 46-58, asst prof radiation biol & toxicol, 58-60, ASSOC PROF RADIATION BIOL & TOXICOL, SCH MED & DENT, UNIV ROCHESTER, 60- *Concurrent Pos:* Mem fluoride panel, Comt Biol Effects of Air Pollutants, Nat Acad Sci-Nat Res Coun; dent study sect, Div Res Grants, NIH, 69- *Honors & Awards:* Adolph G Kammer Merit in Authorship Award, Am Occup Med Asn, 78. *Mem:* Am Chem Soc; Am Indust Hyg Asn; Soc Toxicol; Am Soc Pharmacol & Exp Therapeut; Sigma Xi. *Res:* Absorption, distribution and excretion of toxic materials, especially fluorides; mechanism of action of toxic agents; clinical chemistry as criterion of toxicity in industrial hygiene. *Mailing Add:* Dept of Radiation Biol & Biophys Univ Rochester Sch of Med & Dent Rochester NY 14642

SMITH, FRANK E, b Edmonton, Alta, Aug 5, 36; m 63; c 2. ONCOLOGY, CHEMOTHERAPY. *Educ:* Univ Alta, MD, 60. *Prof Exp:* Intern, Edmonton Gen Hosp, Alta, 60-61; resident med, 61-64, instr pharmacol & med, 66-69, asst prof, 69-76, ASSOC, PROF PHARMACOL & MED, BAYLOR COL MED, 76- *Concurrent Pos:* Fel cancer chemother, Baylor Col Med, 64-66; attend physician & consult chemother, Vet Admin Hosp; asst, Ben Taub Hosp; assoc physician, Methodist Hosp. *Mem:* Am Col Clin Pharmacol & Chemother; Am Soc Clin Oncol; Am Col Physicians. *Res:* Internal medicine; clinical oncology and pharmacology; cancer chemotherapy. *Mailing Add:* Baylor Col of Med 1200 Moursund Ave Houston TX 77025

SMITH, FRANK ENGELBERT, b Paterson, NJ, July 14, 03. MATHEMATICS. *Educ:* Cornell Univ, AB, 24; Cath Univ Am, AM, 25, PhD, 28. *Prof Exp:* Instr math, Cath Univ Am, 26-28; tutor, City Col New York, 28-31; instr, Brooklyn Col, 31-35, from asst prof to assoc prof, 35-73; adj prof math, Molloy Col, 73-78; RETIRED. *Concurrent Pos:* Chmn dept math, Molloy Col, 55-73. *Honors & Awards:* Citation, Medal, Distinguished Serv & Pioneer Award, Molloy Col, 75. *Mem:* Math Asn Am. *Res:* Projective geometry; triangles in and circumscribed to plane rational curves. *Mailing Add:* RD 1 Box 704 Westtown NY 10998

SMITH, FRANK ROYLANCE, b London, Eng, Mar 20, 32; m 61; c 2. PHYSICAL CHEMISTRY, ELECTROCHEMISTRY. *Educ:* Univ London, BSc, 56, PhD(chem), 64. *Prof Exp:* Lab asst, Distillers Co, 51-55; sr chemist, Mullard Res Labs, 60-64; fel, La State Univ, 64-65; from asst prof to assoc prof chem, 65-74, PROF CHEM, MEM UNIV NFLD, 74- *Concurrent Pos:* Consult, Bell Northern Res Ltd, Ottawa, 77-79 & Instrumar, St John's, Nfld, 80. *Mem:* The Chem Soc; Chem Inst Can; Can Asn Physicists. *Res:* Electrochemical kinetics of electrolytic hydrogen evolution; redox reactions; solar photoelectrolysis of water with semiconductor electrodes; lead-acid batteries; metal deposition; diffusion of hydrogen isotopes through metals; catalysis and electrocatalysis. *Mailing Add:* Dept of Chem Mem Univ of Nfld St John's NF A1B 3X7 Can

SMITH, FRANK W(ILLIAM), b Philadelphia, Pa, Dec 1, 19; m 49; c 2. CHEMICAL ENGINEERING. *Educ:* Villanova Col, BChE, 41; Ill Inst Technol, MS, 42; Mass Inst Technol, ScD, 49. *Prof Exp:* Asst chem eng, Ill Inst Technol, 41-42; res assoc combustion, Mass Inst Technol, 42-49 & US Bur Mines, 49-55; asst tech dir, Abex Corp, 55-60, dir chem res, 60-63; DIR RES & ENG, MINE SAFETY APPLIANCES CO, 63-, VPRES, 67- *Concurrent Pos:* Mem Gov Sci Adv Comn. *Mem:* Am Chem Soc; Soc Automotive Engrs; Am Inst Chem Engrs; Am Inst Chemists; Am Inst Mining, Metall & Petrol Engrs. *Res:* Coal chemistry; combustion; polymers; sintered metals; safety equipment; process instrumentation; research planning and management. *Mailing Add:* Mine Safety Appliances Co 201 N Braddock Ave Pittsburgh PA 15208

SMITH, FRED GEORGE, JR, b Calif, Jan 1, 28; m 51; c 3. PEDIATRICS, NEPHROLOGY. *Educ:* Univ Calif, Los Angeles, BS, 51, MD, 55. *Prof Exp:* Intern pediat, Ctr Health Sci, Univ Calif, Los Angeles, 55-56; resident, Univ Minn Hosps, 56-57; chief resident, Ctr Health Sci, Univ Calif, Los Angeles, 57-58, from asst prof to prof, Sch Med, 60-73; PROF PEDIAT & CHMN DEPT, COL MED, UNIV IOWA, 73- *Concurrent Pos:* USPHS fel, St Mary's Hosp Med Sch, London, Eng, 68-69, grant, Univ Calif, Los Angeles, 71-73. *Mem:* Soc Pediat Res; Am Soc Pediat Nephrology; Am Pediat Soc. *Res:* Developmental and fetal renal physiology. *Mailing Add:* Dept of Pediat Univ of Iowa Col of Med Iowa City IA 52240

SMITH, FREDERICK ADAIR, JR, b Trinity, Tex, Dec 8, 21; m 49; c 2. THEORETICAL MECHANICS, APPLIED MECHANICS. *Educ:* US Mil Acad, BS, 44; Johns Hopkins Univ, MS, 49; George Washington Univ, MBA, 63; Univ Ill, PhD(theoret & appl mech), 68. *Prof Exp:* US Army, 44-, asst prof physics, US Mil Acad, 49-52, instr, Army Command & Gen Staff Col, 55-58, gen staff officer, 59-62, infantry comdr, Seventh Army, Europe, 63-65, prof mech, US Mil Acad, 65-74, head dept, 69-74, DEAN ACAD BD, US MIL ACAD, 74-, TRUSTEE, ASN GRAD, 75- *Concurrent Pos:* Trustee, Asn Grad, US Mil Acad. *Mem:* Am Acad Mech. *Res:* Elasticity; materials science. *Mailing Add:* Acad Bd US Mil Acad West Point NY 10996

SMITH, FREDERICK ALBERT, b Janesville, Wis, Sept 11, 11; m 35; c 2. PHYSICAL CHEMISTRY, ORGANIC CHEMISTRY. *Educ:* Univ Wis, BS, 34. *Prof Exp:* Control chemist, Nat Aniline Div, Allied Chem & Dye Corp, 34-39; res chemist, Linde Air Prod Co Div, Union Carbide Corp, 39-49, sales develop, 49-55, chemist, Silicones Div, 55-65, sr scientist, 65-76; RETIRED. *Concurrent Pos:* Consult, Lawrence Livermore Lab, Univ Calif, 76-81. *Mem:* Am Chem Soc. *Res:* Chemistry of high polymers; metal-organic compounds; silicones; silicone elastomers and resins. *Mailing Add:* 60 Stonecrest Rd Ridgefield CT 06877

SMITH, FREDERICK EDWARD, b Springfield, Mass, July 23, 20; m 45; c 3. THEORETICAL ECOLOGY, LANDSCAPE ECOLOGY. *Educ:* Univ Mass, BS, 41; Yale Univ, PhD(zool), 50. *Prof Exp:* From instr to prof zool, Univ Mich, 50-66, prof natural resources, 66-69; PROF ADVAN ENVIRON STUDIES IN RESOURCES & ECOL, GRAD SCH DESIGN, HARVARD UNIV, 69-, CHMN, LANDSCAPE ARCHIT, 81- *Concurrent Pos:* Mem, Nat Sci Bd, 68-74. *Mem:* Ecol Soc Am (pres, 73-74). *Res:* Form of population growth and population interactions; community studies; ecosystem science; landscape ecology; computer modeling. *Mailing Add:* Harvard Univ Grad Sch of Design Cambridge MA 02138

SMITH, FREDERICK GEORGE, b Oak Park, Ill, Aug 16, 17; m 43; c 1. BIOCHEMISTRY. *Educ:* Univ Chicago, BS, 39; Univ Wis, MS, 41, PhD(biochem), 43. *Prof Exp:* Asst biochem & plant path, Univ Wis, 39-43, res assoc, 43-44; asst prof chem, State Univ NY Col Agr, Cornell Univ, 44-47; res assoc biochem, Univ Rochester, 47-48; assoc prof bot, 48-56, head dept bot & plant path, 64-79, PROF BOT & BIOCHEM, IOWA STATE UNIV, 56- *Mem:* AAAS; Am Soc Biol Chemists; Am Soc Plant Physiol. *Res:* Fungus physiology; biochemistry of plant disease resistance; respiratory enzymes. *Mailing Add:* Dept of Bot & Plant Path Iowa State Univ Ames IA 50010

SMITH, FREDERICK GEORGE WALTON, b Bristol, Eng, Jan 28, 09; nat US; m 39; c 1. MARINE ZOOLOGY. *Educ:* Univ London, BSc, 31, PhD(invert embryol), 34. *Hon Degrees:* DSc, Mem Univ Nfld, 67 & Univ Miami, 74. *Prof Exp:* Commonwealth fel, Princeton Univ, US Fisheries Lab, NC & Hopkins Marine Sta, Stanford, 34-36; biologist sponge fishery invests, Govt Bahamas, 36-40; from asst prof to prof zool, 40-73, dir inst marine sci, 43-73, dean, Rosenstiel Sch Marine & Atmospheric Sci, 69-73, EMER DEAN, ROSENSTIEL SCH MARINE & ATMOSPHERIC SCI & EMER PROF ZOOL, UNIV MIAMI, 73- *Concurrent Pos:* Coordr war training serv, Civil Aeronaut Admin, 42-45; spec collabr, US Fish & Wildlife Serv; mem, Bermuda Biol Sta, 43-; biologist in-chg, Trop Field Sta, Oceanog Inst, Woods Hole, 43-45; consult, Govt Bahamas, 44-; tech adv, Atlantic States Marine Fisheries Comn & Gulf States Marine Fisheries Comn; ed, Sea Frontiers; chmn, Gulf & Caribbean Fisheries Inst; mem, Fla Nuclear & Space Comn & Fla Comn Marine Sci & Technol; chmn exec comt, Joint Oceanog Insts Deep Earth Sampling, 67-68, mem, 68-73; pres, Int Oceanog Found, 63-, dir, Planet Ocean, 74- *Mem:* Am Soc Limnol & Oceanog; Am Soc Zool; fel Am Geog Soc; Am Geophys Union; Marine Biol Asn UK. *Res:* Embryology of marine invertebrates; problems incommercial fisheries; tropical oceanography. *Mailing Add:* Int Oceanog Found 3979 Rickenbacker Causeway Va Key Miami FL 33149

SMITH, FREDERICK GORDON, b Toronto, Ont, Mar 27, 14; m 42; c 6. GEOCHEMISTRY. *Educ:* Univ Man, BSc, 37, MSc, 39; Univ Toronto, PhD(geol), 42. *Prof Exp:* Res testing engr, Res Lab, Int Nickel Co, Can, 42-43; phys chemist, Geophys Lab, Washington, DC, 43-44; from asst prof to assoc prof geol sci, 44-65, prof, 65-79, EMER PROF GEOL, UNIV TORONTO, 79- *Res:* Physical geochemistry; geothermometry; applied mathematics and computing; computer-assisted instruction; information storage and retrieval. *Mailing Add:* 201 Mason Dr Whitby ON L1N 2B2 Can

SMITH, FREDERICK T(UCKER), b Waltham, Mass, Nov 24, 20; m 49; c 1. SYSTEMS ENGINEERING, SOFTWARE ENGINEERING. *Educ:* Tufts Univ, BS, 43; Mass Inst Technol, MS, 48; Univ Calif, Los Angeles, PhD, 65. *Prof Exp:* Flight test engr, Instrumentation Lab, Mass Inst Technol, 48-51; systs engr, NAm Aviation, Inc, 51-54; res engr, Rand Corp, 54-65; SR STAFF ENGR, SYSTS ENG, SINGER-LIBRASCOPE, 65- *Res:* Anti-submarine warfare systems; computer science; applied mathematics. *Mailing Add:* Singer-Librascope 833 Sonora Ave Glendale CA 91201

SMITH, FREDERICK W(ILSON), b Lansdowne, Pa, Mar 15, 17; m 42; c 4. CHEMICAL ENGINEERING. *Educ:* Univ Mich, BSE, 38, MSE, 39. *Prof Exp:* Chem engr, E I du Pont de Nemours & Co, Del & WVa, 39-44; from head sect to supvr, Chem Eng Dept, BASF Wyandotte Corp, 44-58, mgr chem eng res & semicommercial chem, 58-62, res staff consult, Res Div, 62-79; RETIRED. *Mem:* Am Chem Soc; Am Inst Chem Engrs. *Res:* Organic and inorganic synthesis; polyethylene; synthetic detergents; sodium carboxymethylcellulose; pilot plant research and semicommercial chemicals production supervision; research project and economic evaluations. *Mailing Add:* 7814 Park Ave Allen Park MI 48101

SMITH, FREDERICK WILLIAM, b Albany, NY, Aug 2, 42; m 65; c 2. EXPERIMENTAL SOLID STATE PHYSICS. *Educ:* Lehigh Univ, BA, 64; Brown Univ, PhD(physics), 69. *Prof Exp:* Res fel, Rutgers Univ, New Brunswick, 68-70; asst prof, 70-77, assoc prof, 77-81, PROF PHYSICS, CITY COL NEW YORK, 81- *Concurrent Pos:* Alexander von Humboldt fel, Max-Planck Inst, 77-78. *Mem:* Am Phys Soc. *Res:* surface reactions on semiconductors; magnetic properties of disordered systems; epitaxial growth of thin films; amorphous semiconductor films. *Mailing Add:* Dept of Physics City Col of New York New York NY 10031

SMITH, FREDERICK WILLIAMS, b Mooresville, Ala, Sept 6, 22; m 46; c 2. SURGERY. *Educ:* Vanderbilt Univ, BA, 42, MD, 44; Am Bd Surg, dipl. *Prof Exp:* Intern surg, Duke Univ Hosp, 44-45; from jr resident to sr chief resident, Jefferson Hillman Hosp, 47-50; from instr to assoc prof surg, Med Col, Univ Ala, Birmingham, 64-73; mem clin fac, 73-81, ASSOC PROF SURG, SCH PRIMARY MED CARE, UNIV ALA, HUNTSVILLE, 81-; PATHOLOGIST, JEFFERSON HILLMAN HOSP, 47- *Concurrent Pos:* Consult, Tuberc Sanitorium, Flint, Ala, 50-52; chief surg, Huntsville Hosp, 62-63; chief staff, 66-67; chief surg, Crestwood Hosp, 66. *Mem:* Fel Am Col Surgeons. *Mailing Add:* 2500 Vista Dr SE Huntsville AL 35803

SMITH, FREDERICK WILLIS, b Seattle, Wash, Apr 28, 38; m 60; c 2. MECHANICAL ENGINEERING. *Educ:* Univ Wash, BS, 61, MS, 63, PhD(mech eng), 66. *Prof Exp:* From asst prof to assoc prof mech eng, Colo State Univ, 65-77; MGR, SEMICONDUCTOR PROD DIV, MOTOROLA INC, 77- *Concurrent Pos:* Consult fracture mech. *Mem:* Am Soc Mech Engrs. *Res:* Fracture mechanics; elasticity; snow mechanics. *Mailing Add:* Motorola Inc 5005 E McDowell Rd Phoenix AZ 85008

SMITH, G(EORGE) V, b Clarksburg, WVa, Apr 7, 16; m 49; c 1. METALLURGY. *Educ:* Carnegie Inst Technol, BS, 37, ScD(metall), 41. *Prof Exp:* Asst metall, Metals Res Lab, Carnegie Inst Technol, 37-39; metallurgist, Res Lab, US Steel Corp, 41-55; Francis Norwood Bard prof metall eng, Cornell Univ, 55-70; CONSULT ENGR, 70- *Concurrent Pos:* Adj prof, Polytech Inst Brooklyn, 48-55; asst dir, Sch Chem & Metall Eng, Cornell Univ, 57-62; consult, US Steel Corp, Socony Mobil Oil Co, Babcock & Wilcox Co, Gulf Gen Atomic & Metal Properties Coun, Atomic Energy Comn. *Honors & Awards:* Award, Am Soc Testing & Mat. *Mem:* Am Soc Metals; fel Am Soc Testing & Mat; Am Inst Mining, Metall & Petrol Engrs; Am Soc Mech Engrs. *Res:* Plastic deformation of metals; elevated temperature properties. *Mailing Add:* 104 Berkshire Rd Ithaca NY 14850

SMITH, GAIL PRESTON, b Unionville, Pa, Jan 25, 15; m 37; c 2. APPLIED PHYSICS. *Educ:* Geneva Col, BS, 34; Syracuse Univ, MS, 36; Univ Mich, PhD(physics), 41. *Prof Exp:* Instr physics, Battle Creek Col, 36; instr math & physics, Geneva Col, 36-37; asst physics, Univ Mich, 37-41; res physicist, Corning Glass Works, 41-50, sr res assoc, 50-61, mgr gen prod develop, 61-66, mgr int res, 66-70, dir tech staff serv, 70-78, dir int res, 78-80; CONSULT, 80- *Mem:* Fel AAAS; fel Brit Inst Physics; fel Am Ceramic Soc; Am Phys Soc; Europ Phys Soc. *Res:* Beta-ray spectroscopy; density and expansivity of glasses; dielectric properties of glasses and glass electronic components; optical properties and applications of glasses and coatings; structural application of glasses and glass-ceramics. *Mailing Add:* 75 Caton Rd Corning NY 14830

SMITH, GALE EUGENE, b Van Wert, Ohio, Feb 11, 33. PHOTOGRAPHIC CHEMISTRY, GRAPHIC ARTS RESEARCH. *Educ:* Bowling Green State Univ, BA, 55; Mich State Univ, PhD, 63. *Prof Exp:* Res asst phys chem, Mich State Univ, 60-63; RES CHEMIST, RES LABS, EASTMAN KODAK CO, 63- *Mem:* Am Chem Soc; Soc Photog Sci & Eng; Tech Asn Graphic Arts. *Res:* Offset lithography; electrochemistry of photographic developers; reaction mechanisms in photographic systems. *Mailing Add:* Res Labs Eastman Kodak Co Rochester NY 14650

SMITH, GARDNER WATKINS, b Boston, Mass, July 2, 31; m 58; c 3. SURGERY. *Educ:* Princeton Univ, AB, 69; Harvard Med Sch, MD, 56; Am Bd Surg, dipl, 64; Am Bd Thoracic Surg, dipl, 65. *Prof Exp:* From instr to assoc prof surg, Sch Med, Univ Va, 63-70; PROF SURG, SCH MED, JOHNS HOPKINS UNIV, 70-; PROF SURG, SCH MED, UNIV MD, BALTIMORE CITY, 70-; surgeon-in-chief, Baltimore City Hosps, 70-78; DEP DIR, DEPT SURG, JOHNS HOPKINS HOSP, 78- *Concurrent Pos:* Fel surg, Sch Med, Johns Hopkins Univ, 57-58; consult, Vet Admin Hosps, Salem, Va, 68-70 & Baltimore, 71- & Greater Baltimore Med Ctr, 71- *Mem:* Am Col Surgeons; Am Surg Asn; Soc Univ Surgeons; Soc Vascular Surg; Soc Surg Alimentary Tract. *Res:* Physiology of portal hypertension; clinical research in gastrointestinal and vascular surgery. *Mailing Add:* Johns Hopkins Hosp 601 N Broadway Baltimore MD 21205

SMITH, GARMOND STANLEY, b Wayne, WVa, July 9, 32; m 53; c 6. ANIMAL NUTRITION. *Educ:* WVa Univ, BS, 53, MS, 57, PhD(agr biochem), 59. *Prof Exp:* Asst agr biochem, WVa Univ, 57-59; res assoc animal sci, Univ Ill, 59-60, asst prof, 60-65; instr biol, sci & relig, Lincoln Christian Col, 65-68; PROF ANIMAL NUTRIT, NMEX STATE UNIV, 68- *Concurrent Pos:* Consult, SAfrica, Inter-Am Educ Asn & Food & Agr Orgn, Vienna, 81. *Mem:* AAAS; Am Inst Nutrit; Am Soc Animal Sci; Am Inst Biol Sci; Am Nutrition Res Coun. *Res:* Nonprotein nitrogen, ruminants; metabolic changes in starvation and refeeding; vitamin A nutrition; nitrate toxicity; potassium-40 as an index of lean body mass; silica in animal metabolism; recycling of nutrients in agricultural and municipal wastes. *Mailing Add:* Dept Animal Sci NMex State Univ Las Cruces NM 88003

SMITH, GARRY AUSTIN, b Alta, Can, Sept 25, 40; m 63; c 2. PLANT GENETICS. *Educ:* NMex State Univ, BS, 64, MS, 66; Ore State Univ, PhD(genetics), 68. *Prof Exp:* Res asst, NMex State Univ, 64-66, Ore State Univ, 66-68; res geneticist, USDA Agr Res Serv, Canal Pt, Fla, 68-69; SUPVR RES GENETICIST, SCI & EDUC ADMIN-AGR RES, USDA, CROPS RES LAB, 69- *Concurrent Pos:* Acad fac affil, Colo State Univ, 69-, grad fac, 70; assoc ed, Crop Sci, Crops Sci Soc Am, 77-80. *Mem:* Am Genetic Asn; Am Soc Agron; Am Soc Sugar Beet Technologists; Western Soc Crop Sci; Crops Sci Soc Am. *Res:* Quantitative plant genetics; inheritance of disease resistance. *Mailing Add:* Sci & Educ Admin-Agr Res USDA Colo State Univ Ft Collins CO 80523

SMITH, GARY CHESTER, b Ft Cobb, Okla, Oct 25, 38; m 65; c 4. MEAT SCIENCE. *Educ:* Calif State Univ, Fresno, BS, 60; Wash State Univ, MS, 62; Tex A&M Univ, PhD(meat sci), 68. *Prof Exp:* Mgt trainee, Armour & Co, Wash, 62; instr animal sci, Wash State Univ, 62-65, asst prof meat sci, 68-69, assoc prof, 69-75, PROF MEAT SCI, TEX A&M UNIV, 75- *Honors &*

Awards: Distinguished Res Award, Am Soc Animal Sci, 74. *Mem:* Am Soc Animal Sci; Am Meat Sci Asn; Inst Food Technologists. *Res:* Meat packaging, muscle properties chemical, physical and histological as related to palatability; quantitative and qualitative evaluation of beef, pork, lamb and goat carcasses. *Mailing Add:* Meats & Meat Chem Sect Tex A&M Univ Dept Animal Sci College Station TX 77843

SMITH, GARY E, b Ontario, Ore, Apr 18, 40; m 61; c 3. ANIMAL NUTRITION, BIOCHEMISTRY. *Educ:* Ore State Univ, BS, 62, MS, 64; Purdue Univ, PhD(animal nutrit & biochem), 66. *Prof Exp:* Wildlife res aid, Ore State Game Comn, 62-63; asst prof animal nutrit, Univ Wyo, 66-70; animal nutritionist, Animal Husb Lab, 70-74, dir vet physiol & path lab, 74-75, DIR ANIMAL NUTRIT & PHYSIOL, MERCK, SHARP & DOHME RES LAB, 75- *Mem:* Am Soc Animal Sci; Am Dairy Sci Asn. *Res:* Sheep and cattle metabolism with emphasis on drug metabolism and protein and lipid synthesis in the ruminant. *Mailing Add:* Animal Nutrit & Physiol Merck Sharp & Dohme Res Lab Rahway NJ 07065

SMITH, GARY LANE, b Dexter, Iowa, Dec 3, 39; m 61; c 2. BOTANY. *Educ:* Univ Iowa, BA, 62, MS, 64; Columbia Univ, PhD(bot), 69. *Prof Exp:* Adj asst prof biol sci, Herbert H Lehman Col, 71-76; ASSOC CUR, NEW YORK BOT GARDEN, 69- *Mem:* Am Bryol & Lichenol Soc; Brit Bryol Soc; Int Asn Plant Taxon; Torrey Bot Club; Nordic Bryol Asn. *Res:* Taxonomy and geography of bryophytes; Polytrichaceae; Sphagnaceae. *Mailing Add:* New York Bot Garden Bronx Park Bronx NY 10458

SMITH, GARY LEE, b Rock Springs, Wyo, May 27, 47; m 67; c 1. VIROLOGY. *Educ:* Univ Wyo, BS, 69; Kans State Univ, PhD(microbiol), 72. *Prof Exp:* Fel oncol, Leukemia Soc Am, Univ Wis, 73-74; asst prof, 74-77, ASSOC PROF MICROBIOL, UNIV NEBR, 77- *Mem:* Am Soc Cell Biol; Sigma Xi; Am Soc Microbiol; AAAS. *Res:* Control of cellular proliferation by growth factors; endocrinology of cellular growth and development. *Mailing Add:* Sch Life Sci Univ Nebr Lincoln NE 68508

SMITH, GARY LEROY, b Mitchell, SDak, Nov 30, 35; m 59; c 4. NUCLEAR PHYSICS, SYSTEMS ANALYSIS. *Educ:* Univ Calif, Davis, BS, 63, MA, 65, PhD(physics), 69. *Prof Exp:* Nat Res Coun Res assoc, US Naval Res Lab, 69-70; PHYSICIST, APPL PHYSICS LAB, JOHNS HOPKINS UNIV, 70- *Mem:* Am Phys Soc. *Res:* Resonance-neutron capture gamma-ray spectroscopy on rare-earth nuclei; underwater acoustics. *Mailing Add:* Johns Hopkins Appl Physics Lab Johns Hopkins Rd Laurel MD 20810

SMITH, GARY RICHARD, b Palo Alto, Calif, Nov 15, 48. THEORETICAL PLASMA PHYSICS. *Educ:* Oberlin Col, BA, 70; Univ Calif, Berkeley, PhD(physics), 77. *Prof Exp:* PHYSICIST, LAWRENCE LIVERMORE NAT LAB, 77- *Concurrent Pos:* Lectr, Univ Calif, Davis, 80-81. *Mem:* Am Phys Soc; Sigma Xi. *Res:* Physics of magnetic-mirror plasma-confinement devices. *Mailing Add:* Lawrence Livermore Nat Lab Univ of Calif Livermore CA 94550

SMITH, GASTON, b Poplarville, Miss, Apr 7, 27; m 50; c 2. MATHEMATICS. *Educ:* Univ Southern Miss, BS, 49; Univ Ala, MA, 55 & 57, PhD(math), 63. *Prof Exp:* Instr high sch, Miss, 51-52; instr math, Sunflower Jr Col, 52-56; asst prof, Univ Southern Miss, 57-60; instr, Univ Ala, 60-63; prof, Univ Southern Miss, 63-67; PROF & CHMN DEPT MATH, WILLIAM CAREY COL, 67- *Mem:* Am Math Soc; Math Asn Am; Can Math Cong. *Res:* Summability. *Mailing Add:* Dept of Math William Carey Col Hattiesburg MS 39401

SMITH, GENE E, b Fulton Co, Ohio, June 6, 36; m 58; c 5. MECHANICAL ENGINEERING. *Educ:* Univ Mich, BSME, 59, MSME, 60, PhD(mech eng), 63. *Prof Exp:* Asst prof, 63-68, assoc prof, 68-81, PROF MECH ENG, UNIV MICH, ANN ARBOR, 81- *Concurrent Pos:* Develop engr, Gen Motors Corp, 65-66. *Mem:* Soc Automotive Engrs; Am Inst Chem Engrs; Am Soc Eng Educ; Am Soc Mech Engrs. *Res:* Thermodynamics; heat transfer; phase equilibrium at low temperatures; direct energy conversion. *Mailing Add:* 2420 Bunker Hill Ann Arbor MI 48105

SMITH, GEOFFREY W, b Boston, Mass, Sept 29, 39; m 65; c 1. GEOLOGY. *Educ:* Tufts Univ, BS, 61; Univ Maine, MS, 64; Ohio State Univ, PhD(geol), 69. *Prof Exp:* Instr geol, Colby Col, 68-69; asst prof, 69-74, chmn dept, 74-80, ASSOC PROF GEOL, OHIO UNIV, 74- *Mem:* Am Quaternary Asn; Nat Asn Geol Teachers; AAAS; Geol Soc Am; Soc Econ Paleont & Mineral. *Res:* Glacial geology; geomorphology; quaternary stratigraphy; deglaciation studies and quaternary stratigraphy in Maine, British Columbia and Southeastern Ohio. *Mailing Add:* Dept Geol Ohio Univ Athens OH 45701

SMITH, GEORGE ALLAN, b Denver, Colo, Aug 25, 16; m 47; c 2. ELECTRICAL ENGINEERING. *Educ:* Univ Colo, BS, 38; Yale Univ, PhD(elec eng), 41; Stanford Univ, MS, 56. *Prof Exp:* Engr, Gen Elec Co, 41-45; res engr, Nat Adv Comt Aeronaut, 46-58; RES SCIENTIST & BR CHIEF SPACE CRAFT GUID, AMES RES CTR, NASA, 58- *Concurrent Pos:* Vis scientist, Instrumentation Lab, Mass Inst Technol, 49-51; asst prof & lectr, Stanford Univ, 51-58. *Mem:* Inst Elec & Electronics Engrs; Am Inst Aeronaut & Astronaut. *Res:* Aircraft and spacecraft guidance and control; aircraft instrumentation; servomechanisms; digital autopilots; digital automatic control of aircraft. *Mailing Add:* NASA Ames Res Ctr Moffett Field CA 94035

SMITH, GEORGE BYRON, b Pittsburgh, Pa, Apr 18, 33; m 55; c 6. PHYSICAL CHEMISTRY. *Educ:* Univ Pittsburgh, BS, 54, PhD(phys chem), 59. *Prof Exp:* Sr chemist, 59-67, SECT LEADER, ANAL & PHYS RES DEPT, MERCK, SHARP & DOHME RES LABS, 67- *Res:* Physical analytical chemistry; chemical kinetics. *Mailing Add:* Anal & Phys Res Dept Merck Sharp & Dohme Res Labs Rahway NJ 07065

SMITH, GEORGE C, b West Unity, Ohio, May 23, 35. PHYSICS, COMPUTERS. *Educ:* Cornell Univ, AB, 57, MS, 62, PhD(eng physics), 65; Univ NMex, JD(law), 73. *Prof Exp:* Physicist solid state, Sandia Labs, 66-70; sr scientist computing, Opers Res Inc, 75-76; PHYSICIST SYSTS, LAWRENCE LIVERMORE LAB, 77- *Concurrent Pos:* Mem, Telluride Asn, 55-56; foreign scientist, Alexander von Humboldt Found, 65-66; consult, Opers Res Inc, 76-77. *Mem:* Am Phys Soc; Inst Elec & Electronic Engrs; Am Inst Aeronaut & Astronaut; Sigma Xi. *Res:* Systems optimization; computer graphics; strategic studies; modeling of military conflicts; advanced energy concepts; fast computer algorithms. *Mailing Add:* Lawrence Livermore Lab L-7 PO Box 808 Livermore CA 94550

SMITH, GEORGE C(UNNINGHAM), b Pittsburgh, Pa, Feb 16, 26; m 53; c 3. CHEMICAL ENGINEERING, ENVIRONMENTAL SCIENCE. *Educ:* Univ Pittsburgh, BSChE, 48, MS, 50; Carnegie Inst Technol, PhD(chem eng), 56. *Prof Exp:* Process engr, Gen Elec Co, 50-52; res engr, E I du Pont de Nemours & Co, 56-60; sr res engr, 60-63, res assoc process metall, 63-69, staff engr, 69-70, TECH COORDR ENVIRON CONTROL, JONES & LAUGHLIN STEEL CORP, 70- *Mem:* Am Inst Chem Engrs; Am Chem Soc; Am Inst Mining, Metall & Petrol Engrs; Air Pollution Control Asn. *Res:* Waste water treatment and air cleaning in iron and steel industry; solid waste and toxic materials management; steelmaking processes, especially fluid mechanics of basic oxygen processes; fluid mechanics. *Mailing Add:* 866 Foxland Dr Pittsburgh PA 15243

SMITH, GEORGE DAVID, b Youngstown, Ohio, Aug 24, 41; m 63; c 2. PHYSICAL CHEMISTRY, X-RAY CRYSTALLOGRAPHY. *Educ:* Westminster Col, BA, BS, 63; Ohio Univ, PhD(chem), 68. *Prof Exp:* Res assoc, Mont State Univ, 68-74; RES SCIENTIST, MED FOUND BUFFALO, 74- *Mem:* Am Chem Soc; Am Crystallog Asn. *Res:* X-ray crystal structures of organophosphate esters, ionophores, antibiotics and polypeptides; correlation of structure to function; protein crystallography. *Mailing Add:* Med Found of Buffalo 73 High St Buffalo NY 14203

SMITH, GEORGE ELWOOD, b White Plains, NY, May 10, 30; Wid; c 3. SOLID STATE ELECTRONICS. *Educ:* Univ Pa, BS, 55; Univ Chicago, MS, 56, PhD(physics), 59. *Prof Exp:* Mem staff, 59-64, HEAD MOS DEVICE DEPT, BELL LABS, 64- *Honors & Awards:* Ballantine Medal, Franklin Inst, 73; Liebmann Award, Inst Elec & Electronics Engrs, 74. *Mem:* Fel Am Phys Soc; fel Inst Elec & Electronics Engrs. *Res:* Band structure of semimetals; thermoelectric effects; electronic transport phenomena; optical properties of semiconductors; optoelectronic devices; electrical conduction in metal oxides; semiconductor devices; charge coupled devices; integrated circuits. *Mailing Add:* MOS Device Dept Bell Labs Murray Hill NJ 07974

SMITH, GEORGE FOSTER, b Franklin, Ind, May 9, 22; m 50; c 3. PHYSICS, ELECTRONICS. *Educ:* Calif Inst Technol, BS, 44, MS, 48, PhD(physics), 52. *Prof Exp:* Asst, Calif Inst Technol, 47-50, res assoc, 48-50; res physicist, 52-57, dept mgr, 57-62, assoc dir, 62-69, vpres, 65-81, DIR RES LABS, HUGHES AIRCRAFT CO, 69-, SR VPRES, 81- *Concurrent Pos:* Res engr, Eng Res Assocs, 46-48; adj assoc prof, Univ Southern Calif, 60-62; consult, Army Sci Adv Panel, 75-78. *Mem:* AAAS; fel Am Phys Soc; fel Inst Elec & Electronics Engrs; Sigma Xi. *Res:* Research management; electron devices; lasers; microelectronics; displays; physical electronics. *Mailing Add:* Hughes Aircraft Co Res Labs 3011 Malibu Canyon Rd Malibu CA 90265

SMITH, GEORGE IRVING, b Waterville, Maine, May 20, 27; c 2. QUATERNARY GEOLOGY. *Educ:* Colby Col, AB, 49; Calif Inst Technol, MS, 51, PhD(geol), 56. *Prof Exp:* Mem staff geol, Occidental Col, 51-52; geologist, 52-66, chief light metals & indust minerals br, 66-69, geologist, 69-78, coordr climate prog, 78-81, GEOLOGIST, US GEOL SURV, 81- *Concurrent Pos:* Fulbright scholar grant, Australia, 81. *Mem:* Geol Soc Am; Geochem Soc; Mineral Soc Am; Soc Econ Geol; Sigma Xi. *Res:* Structure and stratigraphy of Mojave Desert area; Quaternary deposits and climates; evaporite deposits; volcanic petrology. *Mailing Add:* US Geol Surv 345 Middlefield Rd Menlo Park CA 94025

SMITH, GEORGE LEONARD, JR, b State College, Pa, Sept 6, 35. INDUSTRIAL ENGINEERING. *Educ:* Pa State Univ, BS, 57; Lehigh Univ, MS, 58 & 67; Okla State Univ, PhD(indust eng), 69. *Prof Exp:* Grad asst indust eng, Lehigh Univ, 57-58; instr, Prod Tech, Pa State Univ, York Campus, 58-59 & indust eng, Lehigh Univ, 59-67; grad res asst, Okla State Univ, 67-68; PROF INDUST ENG, OHIO STATE UNIV, 68- *Concurrent Pos:* Labor arbitrator, Fed Mediation & Conciliation Serv, 70-; consult, Amalgamated Meat Cutters & Butcher Workmen, 78-; dir, Ergonomics Div, Am Inst Indust Engrs, 76-78; ed, Human Factors, 80- *Mem:* Am Inst Indust Eng; Human Factors Soc; Soc Gen Syst Res; Am Soc Eng Educ. *Res:* Man and machine systems analysis and design, human performance; design methods with particular emphasis on design of work and workspaces. *Mailing Add:* Dept of Indust & Systs Eng Ohio State Univ Columbus OH 43210

SMITH, GEORGE PEDRO, b Norfolk, Va, Oct 26, 23; m 45; c 3. PHYSICAL CHEMISTRY. *Educ:* Univ Va, BS, 44, PhD(chem), 50. *Prof Exp:* GROUP LEADER, OAK RIDGE NAT LAB, 50- *Concurrent Pos:* Lectr, Univ Tenn, Knoxville, 52-63, prof, 64-78; prof, Tech Univ Denmark, 72-73; ed, Advan in Molten Salt Chem, 71-76; lectr, Norwegian Inst Technol, 78. *Mem:* Royal Soc Chem; AAAS; Am Chem Soc; Am Phys Soc. *Res:* Mechanisms and reaction intermediates in molten salt catalysis with emphasis on radical cations, carbonium ions and unusual oxidation states of metal ions. *Mailing Add:* Oak Ridge Nat Lab PO Box X Oak Ridge TN 37830

SMITH, GEORGE THOMAS, b Evansville, Ind, Oct 19, 31; m 64; c 5. PATHOLOGY. *Educ:* Univ Md, BS, 52, MD, 56; Vienna Acad Med, cert, 58; Mass Inst Technol, MS, 76. *Prof Exp:* Intern, Royal Victoria Hosp, Montreal, 56-57; resident path, Peter Bent Brigham Hosp, 59-60, sr asst resident, 61-62; asst resident, Children's Hosp, Boston, 62; chief resident, Peter Bent Brigham Hosp, 63, assoc pathologist, Hosp & Harvard Med Sch, 63-64; res prof path, Desert Res Inst, 65-70; actg dean sch med, 67-70, dean sch med sci & prof path, Univ Nev, Reno, 70-77; dir labs environ pathophysiol, 65-77; assoc chief staff & educ, Boston Vet Admin Hosp, 77-78; PROF PATH & ASSOC DEAN, UNIV ALA, 79-; DIR, SOUTHEASTERN REGIONAL MED EDUC CTR, 79- *Concurrent Pos:* Nat Heart Inst res trainee, Peter Bent Brigham Hosp, 61-62; res fel path, Harvard Med Sch, 60-61; fel, Free Hosp Women, 62-63; trainee, Congenital Heart Dis Training & Res Ctr, Chicago, 62; NIH career develop award cardiovasc path, 64; mem, Regional Adv Bd Heart Dis, Cancer & Stroke, Utah, 65 & Nev Heart Dis, Cancer & Stroke Adv Bd, 66; prof path, Sch Med, Tufts Univ & Boston Univ, 77-78. *Mem:* AAAS; AMA; Am Fedn Clin Res; Am Soc Exp Path; Int Acad Path. *Res:* Cardiovascular and pulmonary disease. *Mailing Add:* Southeastern Regional Med Educ Ctr 1717 11th Ave S Birmingham AL 35205

SMITH, GEORGE WOLFRAM, b Des Plaines, Ill, Sept 19, 32; m 56; c 2. CHEMICAL PHYSICS. *Educ:* Knox Col, AB, 54; Rice Univ, MA, 56, PhD(physics), 58. *Prof Exp:* Welch Found fel physics, Rice Univ, 58-59; sr res physicist, 59-76, DEPT RES SCIENTIST GEN MOTORS RES LABS, 76- *Concurrent Pos:* Instr, Lawrence Inst Technol, 63-65; lectr, Cranbrook Inst Sci, 63-; coun, Gordon Res Conf, 78. *Mem:* Fel Am Phys Soc; Sigma Xi; Am Carbon Soc; Combustion Inst. *Res:* Low temperature physics; nuclear magnetic resonance; molecular structures and motions in solid and liquid states; internal friction; liquid crystals; thermomagnetic gas torque; particulate carbon; phase transformations in solids. *Mailing Add:* Dept Physics Gen Motors Res Labs Warren MI 48090

SMITH, GERALD A, b Akron, Ohio, Jan 8, 36; m 58; c 2. HIGH ENERGY PHYSICS. *Educ:* Miami Univ, BA, 57; Yale Univ, MS, 58, PhD(physics), 61. *Prof Exp:* Physicist, Lawrence Radiation Lab, 61-67; PROF PHYSICS, MICH STATE UNIV, 67- *Concurrent Pos:* From lectr to asst prof, Univ Calif, Berkeley, 63-67; consult, Argonne Nat Lab, 68-72, Argonne Univs Asn, 71-73 & NSF, 73-76; mem, Bd Trustees, Argonne Univs Asn, 76-78; assoc lab dir high energy physics, Argonne Nat Lab, 78; mem, High Energy Discussion Group Exec Comt, Brookhaven Nat Lab, 81- *Mem:* Fel Am Phys Soc; AAAS; Sigma Xi. *Res:* High energy particle physics; electronic detectors; analysis. *Mailing Add:* Dept of Physics Mich State Univ East Lansing MI 48823

SMITH, GERALD DUANE, b Cass City, Mich, Aug 31, 42; m 67; c 1. PHYSICAL CHEMISTRY, HEALTH PHYSICS. *Educ:* Huntington Col, BS, 64; Purdue Univ, PhD(health physics), 72. *Prof Exp:* AEC fel trainee, Battelle Northwest Labs, 64-65; instr chem, Owosso Col, 65-67; PROF CHEM, HUNTINGTON COL, 67- *Concurrent Pos:* Consult, Ind Radiation Emergency Response Team, 74- *Mem:* Am Chem Soc; Health Physics Soc; Sigma Xi; Am Asn Physics Teachers. *Res:* Radiation dosimetry; crystal growth; reaction kinetics. *Mailing Add:* Dept of Chem Huntington Col Huntington IN 46750

SMITH, GERALD FLOYD, b Louisville, Ky, Jan 4, 42; m 65; c 2. BIO-ORGANIC CHEMISTRY, MOLECULAR BIOL. *Educ:* Univ Louisville, BS, 63, MS, 65, PhD(chem), 68. *Prof Exp:* NIH training grant molecular path, Sch Med, Univ Louisville, 68-71; Eli Lilly sr res fel, Eli Lilly Res Clin, 71-72, SR SCIENTIST, ELI LILLY RES LABS, 73- *Mem:* Sigma Xi; AAAS; Am Chem Soc. *Res:* Fibrinogen-fibrin chemistry; blood coagulation-thrombosis; inflammation; proteases-inhibitors; disease mechanisms; heparin; therapeutic agents; drug receptors. *Mailing Add:* Eli Lilly Res Labs Indianapolis IN 46285

SMITH, GERALD FRANCIS, b Buffalo, NY, Oct 17, 28; m 56. APPLIED MATHEMATICS, MECHANICS. *Educ:* Univ Buffalo, BS, 52; Brown Univ, PhD(appl math), 56. *Prof Exp:* Res assoc appl math, Brown Univ, 56; mathematician, Calif Res Crop Div, Stand Oil Co Calif, 56-58; asst prof mech, Lehigh Univ, 58-60; asst prof eng & appl sci, Yale Univ, 60-64; assoc prof math, Univ Wis, Milwaukee, 64-65; prof, 65-80, DIR, CTR APPLN MATH, LEHIGH UNIV, 80- *Concurrent Pos:* NSF study grants, 61-64 & 66-68. *Mem:* Am Math Soc. *Res:* Theory of invariants and continuum mechanics. *Mailing Add:* Ctr Appln Math Lehigh Univ Bethlehem PA 18015

SMITH, GERALD LYNN, b Seminole, Okla, Feb 3, 34; m 65. ELECTRICAL ENGINEERING, MATHEMATICS. *Educ:* Univ Okla, BSME & BSEE, 57, MSEE, 59, PhD(plasma dynamics), 66. *Prof Exp:* Assoc res engr, Cities Serv Res Co, 57-58; design engr, Douglas Aircraft Co, 59-60; instr elec eng, Univ Okla, 60-63; instr col eng, Okla State Univ, 63-64; head dept, 64-70, ASSOC PROF ELEC ENG, UNIV TULSA, 64- *Mem:* AAAS; Am Soc Mech Engrs; Am Inst Mining, Metall & Petrol Engrs; Am Soc Eng Educ; Inst Elec & Electronics Engrs (secy, 67-68). *Res:* Electrodynamics; plasmadynamics; digital electronics; systems analysis and design. *Mailing Add:* Dept of Elec Eng Univ of Tulsa Tulsa OK 74104

SMITH, GERALD M(AX), b Osborne, Kans, Jan 2, 20; m 41; c 3. ENGINEERING. *Educ:* Kans State Univ, BS, 48, MS, 51. *Prof Exp:* Res engr, Kans State Univ, 48-50; asst prof appl mech, 50-53; assoc prof, 53-61, PROF ENG MECH, UNIV NEBR-LINCOLN, 61-, CHMN DEPT, 72- *Honors & Awards:* Wasson Medal, Am Concrete Inst, 53 & 65. *Mem:* Am Concrete Inst. *Res:* Mechanics of deformable bodies; vibrations; dynamics computers and numerical methods. *Mailing Add:* Univ of Nebr Dept of Eng Mech Lincoln NE 68588

SMITH, GERALD NELSON, JR, physiology, developmental biology, see previous edition

SMITH, GERALD RALPH, b Vandalia, Ill, Feb 19, 44. MOLECULAR BIOLOGY. *Educ:* Cornell Univ, BS, 66; Mass Inst Technol, PhD(biol), 70. *Prof Exp:* Fel, Dept Biochem, Univ Calif, Berkeley, 70-72 & Dept Molecular Biol, Univ Geneva, 72-75; asst prof, 75-80, ASSOC PROF MOLECULAR BIOL, UNIV ORE, 80- *Concurrent Pos:* Helen Hay Whitney Found fel, 70-73; Swiss NSF int fel, 73-74. *Mem:* Am Soc Microbiol; AAAS. *Res:* Regulation of gene expression in bacteria and bacteriophage; molecular mechanisms of genetic recombination. *Mailing Add:* Dept Biol Univ Ore Eugene OR 97403

SMITH, GERALD RAY, b Los Angeles, Calif, Mar 20, 35; m 55; c 3. ZOOLOGY. *Educ:* Univ Utah, BS, 57, MS, 59; Univ Mich, PhD(zool), 65. *Prof Exp:* Asst prof zool & geol, Univ, 69-72, assoc cur, Mus Paleont, 69-72, assoc prof, Univ, 72-81, dir, Mus Paleont, 74-81, PROF ZOOL & GEOL, UNIV MICH, ANN ARBOR, 81-, CUR FISHES, MUS PALEONT, 69-, CUR LOWER VERT PALEONT, 72- *Mem:* AAAS; Soc Study Evolution; Soc Syst Zool; Am Soc Ichthyologists & Herpetologists; Soc Vertebrate Paleont. *Res:* Evolution of western North American freshwater fishes. *Mailing Add:* Mus Zool Univ Mich Ann Arbor MI 48109

SMITH, GERALD RAY, b Prattville, Ala, May 12, 52; m 77. LEGUME BREEDING, FORAGE MANAGEMENT. *Educ:* Auburn Univ, BS, 75, MS, 77; Miss State Univ, PhD(agron), 81. *Prof Exp:* Plant breeder, Northrup King Co, 77-78; ASST PROF, TEX A&M UNIV, 81- *Mem:* Am Soc Agron; Crop Sci Soc Am. *Res:* Plant genetic control of legumes-rhizobia dinitrogen fixation; improvement of forage legumes through breeding and selection for increased dinitrogen fixation; pest resistance and improved reseeding. *Mailing Add:* PO Drawer E Overton TX 75684

SMITH, GERALD WAVERN, b Des Moines, Iowa, Dec 1, 29; m 58; c 1. ENGINEERING ECONOMICS, INDUSTRIAL ENGINEERING. *Educ:* Iowa State Univ, BS, 52, MS, 58, PhD(eng), 61. *Prof Exp:* From instr to assoc prof, 56-67, Alcoa prof, 68-71, PROF INDUST ENG, IOWA STATE UNIV, 67- *Mem:* Am Inst Indust Engrs; Am Soc Eng Educ. *Res:* Engineering economy; engineering valuation; management of capital expenditures by public and private organizations; capital expenditures by public and private organizations; capital expenditure decisions for public utilities. *Mailing Add:* Dept of Indust Eng Iowa State Univ Ames IA 50011

SMITH, GERARD PETER, b Philadelphia, Pa, Mar 24, 35; m 62; c 4. PHYSIOLOGY, PSYCHIATRY. *Educ:* St Joseph's Univ, BS, 56; Univ Pa, MD, 60. *Prof Exp:* Assoc physiol, Sch Med, Univ Pa, 64-65, asst prof, 65-68; from asst prof to assoc prof, 68-73, PROF PSYCHIAT, MED COL, CORNELL UNIV, 73-, HEAD, DIV BEHAV SCI, 69- *Concurrent Pos:* Dir, Edward W Bourne Behav Res Lab, NY Hosp-Cornell Med Ctr, 69- *Mem:* Am Physiol Soc; Endocrine Soc; Soc Neurosci; Asn Res Nerv & Ment Dis. *Res:* Physiological psychology of feeding. *Mailing Add:* E W Bourne Behav Res Lab 21 Bloomingdale Rd White Plains NY 10605

SMITH, GERARD VINTON, b Delano, Calif, Oct 14, 31; m 56; c 3. PHYSICAL ORGANIC CHEMISTRY. *Educ:* Col of the Pac, BA, 53, MS, 56; Univ Ark, PhD(phys org chem), 59. *Prof Exp:* Res assoc, Northwestern Univ, 59-60; instr chem, 60-61; asst prof, Ill Inst Technol, 61-66; assoc prof, 66-73, PROF CHEM, SOUTHERN ILL UNIV, 73-, CHMN MOLECULAR SCI PROG, 78- *Concurrent Pos:* Mem, Int Cong Catalysis; chmn, Gordon Res Conf, 78. *Mem:* AAAS; Am Chem Soc; Catalysis Soc (treas, 76-78); Org Reactions Catalysis Soc. *Res:* Mechanisms of heterogeneous catalysis; hydrogenation and exchange; oxidation ; stereochemistry; asymmetric induction; hydrodesulfurization; substituent effects; nuclear magnetic resonance; mass spectrometry; gas-liquid chromatography. *Mailing Add:* Dept Chem & Biochem Southern Ill Univ Carbondale IL 62901

SMITH, GERRIT JOSEPH, b Syracuse, NY, Dec 18, 38. THEORETICAL PHYSICS, PHILOSOPHY OF SCIENCE. *Educ:* LeMoyne Col, BS, 60, Boston Col, MS, 62; Syracuse Univ, PhD(physics), 71. *Prof Exp:* Instr physics, Regis High Sch, New York, 70-71; res, Syracuse Univ, 71-72; asst prof, 72-80, ASSOC PROF PHILOS SCI, FORDHAM UNIV, 80- *Mem:* Am Phys Soc. *Res:* Measurability analysis of the gravitational field as part of the quantization of general relativity; relativistic conservation laws and the dimensionality of space-time; role of relativity principles in theory change. *Mailing Add:* Dept Philos Fordham Univ Bronx NY 10458

SMITH, GILBERT EDWIN, b Nelsonville, Ohio, Oct 26, 22; m 51. GEOLOGY. *Educ:* Ohio Univ, BS, 50; WVa Univ, MS, 51. *Prof Exp:* Geologist, Ohio Div Geol Surv, 51-53; coal geologist, 53-56; geologist, Aluminum Co Am, 56-61; consult, 61-63; coal geologist, Ky Geol Surv, 63-66, geologist & head coal sect, 66-78; geologist & head coal sect, 78-80, ASSOC DIR, INST MINING & MINERALS RES, UNIV KY, 78- *Mem:* Am Inst Mining Metall & Petrol Engrs; Fel Geol Soc Am; Am Asn Stratig Palynologists; Mine Inspectors Inst Am. *Res:* Coal geology; mapping; resources; Pennsylvanian stratigraphy; reclamation; mining geology. *Mailing Add:* Inst for Mining & Minerals Res Univ of Ky KCER Lab PO Box 13015 Lexington KY 40512

SMITH, GILBERT HOWLETT, b Cornwall, NY, July 25, 38; m 61; c 5. CELL BIOLOGY, MOLECULAR BIOLOGY. *Educ:* Hartwick Col, AB, 59; Brown Univ, ScM, 63, PhD(biol), 65. *Prof Exp:* Staff fel, 65-67, head, Ultrastruct Res Sect, 67-70, sr staff scientist, Lab Biol, 70-75, SR STAFF SCIENTIST CANCER RES, LAB MOLECULARBIOL, NAT CANCER INST, NIH, 76- *Mem:* Am Asn Cancer Res; Am Soc Cell Biol; Am Soc Microbiol; Sigma Xi. *Res:* Genetic, molecular and cellular mechanisms by which mammary epithelial cells functionally differentiate and the relationship of these mechanisms to malignant transformation of mammary cells by various carcinogenic stimuli. *Mailing Add:* Lab Molecular Biol Bldg 37 Rm 2E20 Nat Cancer Inst Bethesda MD 20205

SMITH, GLEN CHARLES, chemical engineering, see previous edition

SMITH, GLENN EDWARD, b Charleston, WVa, Mar 26, 23; m 54; c 4. PLANT PATHOLOGY. *Educ:* Morris Harvey Col, BS, 52; Ohio State Univ, MS, 54, PhD(bot & plant path), 60. *Prof Exp:* Asst prof bot & plant path, Ohio State Univ, 57-67; PROF BIOL, MORRIS HARVEY COL, 67- *Mem:* Am Phytopath Soc; Soc Nematol. *Res:* Phytonematology. *Mailing Add:* Dept of Biol Morris Harvey Col Charleston WV 25304

SMITH, GLENN SANBORN, b Antler, NDak, Dec 21, 07; m 30; c 3. PLANT BREEDING. *Educ:* NDak Agr Col, BS, 29; Kans State Univ, MS, 31; Univ Minn, PhD(plant breeding, genetics), 47. *Prof Exp:* Jr agronomist, Bur Plant Indust, USDA, 29-35, asst agronomist, 35-42, from assoc agronomist to agronomist, Bur Plant Indust, Soils & Agr Eng, 42-47; assoc dean sch agr & assoc dir exp sta, 47-51, chief div plant indust, Exp Sta, 51-54, dean grad sch, 54-73, fac lectr, 65, prof, 47-78, EMER PROF AGRON, NDAK STATE UNIV, 78- *Concurrent Pos:* Consult wheat breeding, Ministry Agr, Repub Uruguay, 77-78 & agron curriculum, Fac Agr, Univ Repub, Uruguay, 79. *Mem:* Sigma Xi; Crop Sci Soc Am; fel Am Soc Agron. *Res:* Durum, hard red spring wheat, and oat breeding and genetics; pathology and quality problems. *Mailing Add:* 1115 N 14th St Fargo ND 58102

SMITH, GORDON MEADE, b Alva, Okla, June 21, 30; m 52; c 5. PHYSICAL CHEMISTRY. *Educ:* Okla State Univ, BS, 53, MS, 55; Univ Fla, PhD(chem), 58. *Prof Exp:* Asst chem, Univ Fla, 56-58; MEM STAFF, LOS ALAMOS SCI LAB, 58- *Res:* Ionospheric and atmospheric chemistry; active modification of the ionosphere. *Mailing Add:* 415 Estante Way Los Alamos NM 87544

SMITH, GORDON ROBERT, b Twin Falls, Idaho, Apr 16, 28; m 52; c 4. CHEMICAL ENGINEERING. *Educ:* Seattle Univ, BS, 53; Mont State Univ, MS, 54. *Prof Exp:* Chem engr, Minn Mining & Mfg Co, 54-58, sr chem engr, 58-62, res specialist, 62-65, lab mgr new bus ventures, 67-69, res mgr magnetic prod, 69-77; MEM STAFF, CELITE DIV, JOHNS MANVILLE CORP, 77- *Mem:* Am Chem Soc. *Res:* Research management; free radical chemistry; polymer processing; polymer film adhesion; gas discharge reactions; ceramic processing; combustion processes; magnetic materials; magnetic tapes and recording. *Mailing Add:* Johns Manville Corp PO Box 5108 Denver CO 80217

SMITH, GORDON STUART, b St Louis, Mo; m 54; c 2. X-RAY CRYSTALLOGRAPHY. *Educ:* Washington Univ, AB, 52; Cornell Univ, PhD(phys chem), 57. *Prof Exp:* Fel, Cornell Univ, 57-58 & Mellon Inst, 58-63; STAFF SCIENTIST, LAWRENCE LIVERMORE NAT LAB, UNIV CALIF, 63- *Mem:* Am Crystallog Asn. *Res:* X-ray diffraction applications in materials science; crystal structures; phase equilibria; computer applications; instrumentation. *Mailing Add:* Dept Chem Lawrence Livermore Nat Lab Livermore CA 94550

SMITH, GRAHAM MONRO, b Bayshore, NY, Nov 11, 47; m 71; c 2. COMPUTER GRAPHICS. *Educ:* Adelphi Univ, BA, 69; Univ Buffalo, PhD(chem), 74. *Prof Exp:* Fel theoret chem, Princeton Univ, 74-75; fel theoret chem, Univ Calif, Santa Cruz, 75-76; RES FEL THEORET CHEM, MERCK SHARP & DOHMS RES LABS, 76- *Mem:* Am Chem Soc; AAAS; Asn Comput Mach. *Res:* Developing computational tools, including real time computing graphics, and applying them to structural problems in organic and medicinal chemistry. *Mailing Add:* Merck Sharp & Dohme Res Labs R80-101M PO Box 2000 Rahway NJ 07065

SMITH, GRAHME J C, b Kapuda, SAustralia, Feb 16, 42. INSECT ECOLOGY. *Educ:* Univ Adelaide, BS, 62; Cornell Univ, MS, 65, PhD(insect ecol), 67. *Prof Exp:* From instr to asst prof ecol, Brown Univ, 67-72; ASSOC PROF ECOL, BOSTON UNIV, 72-, ASST DEAN COL LIB ARTS, 75- *Mem:* Ecol Soc Am. *Res:* Behavior of insect parasitoids on different host species and factors which affect this behavior, particularly interactions with other individuals of the same parasitoid species. *Mailing Add:* 132 Mt Vernon St Arlington MA 02174

SMITH, GRANT GILL, b Fielding, Utah, Sept 25, 21; m 46; c 6. ORGANIC CHEMISTRY. *Educ:* Univ Utah, BA, 43; Univ Minn, PhD(org chem), 49. *Prof Exp:* Asst chem, Univ Minn, 43-44, 46-48, actg instr, 48-49; from instr to assoc prof, Wash State Univ, 49-61; assoc prof, 61-63, faculty honors lectr, 67, PROF CHEM, UTAH STATE UNIV, 63- *Concurrent Pos:* Researcher, Univ London, 57-58; NIH sr fel, Stanford Univ, 69-70. *Honors & Awards:* Utah Award, Am Chem Soc, 77. *Mem:* AAAS; Am Chem Soc; Royal Soc Chem; Int Soc for Study Origin Life. *Res:* Physical organic chemistry; mechanisms of gas phase reactions; proximity effects in organic reactions; organic mass spectroscopy; organic geochemistry. *Mailing Add:* Dept Chem 03 Utah State Univ Logan UT 84322

SMITH, GRANT WARREN, physical chemistry, analytical chemistry, deceased

SMITH, GRANT WARREN, II, b Kansas City, Mo, Jan 21, 41; m 62; c 1. ORGANIC CHEMISTRY. *Educ:* Grinnell Col, BA, 62; Cornell Univ, PhD(chem), 66. *Prof Exp:* Asst chem, Grinnell Col, 62; teaching asst, Cornell Univ, 62-63, asst prof, 66-68; head dept chem, Univ Alaska, Fairbanks, 68-73, actg head dept gen sci, 72-73, assoc prof chem, 68-77, prof 77-78; DEAN, SCH SCI & TECHNOL & PROF CHEM, UNIV HOUSTON, CLEAR LAKE CITY, 78- *Concurrent Pos:* Du Pont fel, Cornell Univ, 67; mem, Asn William Pengelly Cave Res Ctr, Eng; vis prof, Cornell Univ, 73-74; Am Coun Educ fel, Acad Admin Internship Prog, 73-74; pres, Univ Assembly, Univ Alaska Syst, 76-77. *Mem:* AAAS; Am Chem Soc; Am Asn Higher Educ; Fedn Am Scientists; Soc Econ Bot. *Res:* Organic photochemistry of unsaturated molecules and arctic water pollutants; chemistry and uses of arctic natural products. *Mailing Add:* Univ Houston 2700 Bay Area Blvd Houston TX 77058

SMITH, HADLEY J(AMES), b Detroit, Mich, May 5, 18; m 52; c 6. ENGINEERING MECHANICS. *Educ:* Univ Mich, BS, 40, PhD(eng mech), 57. *Prof Exp:* Jr engr, Res Lab, Detroit Edison Co, 40-41; prod engr, Com Res Labs, Inc, 46-51; res engr, Res Inst, 52-55, from instr to assoc prof, 55-62, PROF ENG MECH, UNIV MICH, ANN ARBOR, 62- *Concurrent Pos:* Fac res fel, Rackham Sch Grad Studies, 58; NSF fel, Harvard Univ, 59; guest scientist, Los Alamos Sci Lab, 74. *Mem:* Am Phys Soc; Am Soc Mech Engrs. *Res:* Mathematical physics; hydraulics; hydrodynamics; thermodynamics; kinetic theory; statistical mechanics; heat and mass transfer. *Mailing Add:* Dept Eng Mech Univ Mich Ann Arbor MI 48104

SMITH, HAL LESLIE, b Cedar Rapids, Iowa, Mar 18, 47; m 70. MATHEMATICS. *Educ:* Univ Iowa, BA, 69, PhD(math), 76. *Prof Exp:* Instr math, Univ Utah, 76-79; ASST PROF, ARIZ STATE UNIV, 79- *Mem:* Am Math Soc; Soc Indust & Appl Math; AAAS. *Res:* Differential equations; biomathematics. *Mailing Add:* Dept Math Ariz State Univ Tempe AZ 85281

SMITH, HAMILTON OTHANEL, b New York, NY, Aug 23, 31; m 57; c 5. MICROBIAL GENETICS. *Educ:* Univ Calif, Berkeley, AB, 52; Johns Hopkins Univ, MD, 56. *Prof Exp:* Intern, Barnes Hosp, St Louis, 56-57; res, Henry Ford Hosp, Detroit, 59-62; USPHS res fel microbial genetics, Univ Mich, 62-64, res assoc, 64-67; from asst prof to assoc prof microbiol, 67-73, prof, 73-81, PROF MOLECULAR BIOL & GENETICS, SCH MED, JOHNS HOPKINS UNIV, 81- *Concurrent Pos:* Guggenheim fel, 75-76; ed, Gene, 76- *Honors & Awards:* Nobel Prize Med, 78. *Mem:* Nat Acad Sci; Am Soc Microbiol; Am Soc Biol Chemists; AAAS; fel Am Acad Arts & Sci. *Res:* Genetic recombination; biochemistry of DNA recombination and DNA methylation and restriction. *Mailing Add:* Dept Microbiol Sch Med Johns Hopkins Univ Baltimore MD 21205

SMITH, HARLAN EUGENE, plant pathology, see previous edition

SMITH, HARLAN J, b Wheeling, WVa, Aug 25, 24; m 50; c 4. ASTRONOMY. *Educ:* Harvard Univ, BA, 49, MA, 51, PhD(astron), 55. *Hon Degrees:* Dr, Nicholas Copernicus Univ, Torun, Poland, 73. *Prof Exp:* Instr astron, Observ, Yale Univ, 53-57, from asst prof to assoc prof, 57-63; chmn dept, 63-78, PROF ASTRON & DIR McDONALD OBSERV, UNIV TEX, AUSTIN, 63- *Concurrent Pos:* Mem space sci bd, Nat Res Coun, 77-80, chmn comt astron & astrophysics, space sci bd; Astron Union & Int Sci Radio Union; co-ed, Astron J, Am Astron Soc, 58-63; chmn bd dirs, Assoc Univs Res Astron, 80-82. *Mem:* Am Astron Soc (actg secy, 61-62, vpres, 77-80); Am Geophys Union; Royal Astron Soc. *Res:* Variable stars; planets; quasars. *Mailing Add:* Dept of Astron Univ of Tex Austin TX 78712

SMITH, HARLAN MILLARD, b Iowa City, Iowa, Sept 2, 21; m 54; c 3. PHYSICAL CHEMISTRY. *Educ:* Carroll Col, BA, 42; Univ Chicago, PhD(phys chem), 49. *Prof Exp:* From res chemist to head fertilizer res sect, Exxon Res & Eng Co, 49-65, proj develop adv, 65-79, SR RES ASSOC, EXXON CHEM CO, 79- *Mem:* Am Chem Soc. *Res:* Raman spectra of aqueous sulfuric acid solutions; lubricating oil additives; industrial lubricants; fertilizers; pesticides. *Mailing Add:* 66 Cray Terr Fanwood NJ 07023

SMITH, HAROLD CARTER, b Statesboro, Ga, Aug 13, 20; m 49; c 2. BIOCHEMISTRY. *Educ:* Ga Southern Col, BS, 60; Univ NC, PhD(biochem), 64. *Prof Exp:* Dir labs, Evans County Heart Res Proj, Claxton, Ga, 59-60; res fel, McArdle Lab Cancer Res, Sch Med, Univ Wis, 64-67; dir biochem sect, Surg Biol Lab & asst prof biochem, Sch Med, Univ NC, Chapel Hill, 67-69; chemist, Res Dept, R J Reynolds Tobacco Co, 69-70; ASST PROF SURG & BIOCHEM, SCH MED, UNIV NC, CHAPEL HILL, 70- *Mem:* AAAS; Am Chem Soc; NY Acad Sci. *Res:* Chemical carcinogenesis; enzymes and steroids in breast and thyroid cancer; iodoamino acids; biochemistry of wound healing. *Mailing Add:* Dept of Surg Univ of NC Sch of Med Chapel Hill NC 27514

SMITH, HAROLD GLENN, b Lafayette, La, July 3, 27; m 50; c 3. LATTICE DYNAMICS, SUPERCONDUCTIVITY. *Educ:* Univ Southwestern La, BS, 49; Tulane Univ, MS, 51; Iowa State Univ, PhD(physics), 57. *Prof Exp:* Jr res assoc physics, Iowa State Univ, 51-54, asst, 54-57; PHYSICIST, OAK RIDGE NAT LAB, 57- *Mem:* Fel Am Phys Soc; Sigma Xi; Am Crystallog Asn. *Res:* Neutron diffraction; x-ray crystallography; atomic, molecular, and solid state physics. *Mailing Add:* Oak Ridge Nat Lab PO Box X Oak Ridge TN 37830

SMITH, HAROLD GREGORY, b Healdsburg, Calif, Sept 12, 54. CLIMATOLOGY, COMPUTER MAPPING & GRAPHICS. *Educ:* Ore State Univ, BA, 76, PhD(phys geog & statist), 82; Univ Calif, Berkeley, MA, 78. *Prof Exp:* Res asst & geographer, Univ Calif, Berkeley, 77-78, fel, 78-79; asst scientist, Ore State Univ, 79-81; SCIENTIST, LOCKHEED ENG & MGT SERV CO, INC, 81- *Mem:* Am Soc Photogrammetry; Asn Am Geographers. *Res:* Inventory and evaluation of earth resources through the use of data gathered by aerial and space-borne platforms. *Mailing Add:* #79 18290 Upper Bay Rd Houston TX 77058

SMITH, HAROLD HILL, b Arlington, NJ, Apr 24, 10; m 39; c 4. GENETICS. *Educ:* Rutgers Univ, BS, 31; Harvard Univ, AM, 34, PhD(genetics), 36. *Prof Exp:* Asst, Dept Genetics, Carnegie Inst, 31-32; asst bot, Harvard Univ, 34-35; asst geneticist, Bur Plant Indust, USDA, 35-43; from assoc prof to prof plant genetics, Cornell Univ, 46-57; sr geneticist, Brookhaven Nat Lab, 55-78; RETIRED. *Concurrent Pos:* Chem Corps, US Dept Army, Md, 47-50; Guggenheim fel, 52; Fulbright lectr, Amsterdam, 53; sr scientist, Int Atomic Energy Agency, Vienna, 58-59; vis prof, Univ Calif, Berkeley, 66 & Univ Buenos Aires, 66; hon res assoc, Univ Col, London, 66; acad sci exchange, Romania, 70; adj prof, NY Univ, 77-; consult, Brookhaven Nat Lab, 78. *Mem:* AAAS; Genetics Soc Am; Bot Soc Am; Tissue Cult Asn; Soc Develop Biol. *Res:* Plant cytogenetics; experimental evolution; mutagenesis; radiation genetics; plant tumors; genetic control of differentiation; isozymes; plant cell genetics. *Mailing Add:* Dept of Biol Brookhaven Nat Lab Upton NY 11973

SMITH, HAROLD LINWOOD, b Richmond, Va, Dec 7, 27; m 49; c 2. PHYSICAL PHARMACY, BIOPHARMACEUTICS. *Educ:* Med Col Va, BS, 56, PhD(pharm chem), 62. *Prof Exp:* Lederle fel, Univ Mich, 61-63; chemist, Lederle Labs, Am Cyanamid, 63-64, proj leader, 64-68, group leader, 68; asst prof, 68-76, ASSOC PROF PHARM, MED COL VA, VA COMMONWEALTH UNIV, 76- *Honors & Awards:* Lunsford Richardson Pharm Award, Merrell-Nat Labs, Richardson-Merrell Inc, 60. *Mem:* Am Pharmaceut Asn; Acad Pharmaceut Sci. *Res:* Rheology of pharmaceutical and biological systems; protein binding; solution theory; solid dissolution rate studies; pharmaceutic dosage form studies. *Mailing Add:* Med Col of Va Sch of Pharm Va Commonwealth Univ Richmond VA 23295

SMITH, HAROLD W(OOD), b Brookfield, Mo, Feb 8, 23; m 42; c 1. ELECTRICAL ENGINEERING. *Educ:* Univ Tex, BS, 44, MS, 49, PhD(elec eng), 54. *Prof Exp:* Asst prof, 46-58, PROF ELEC ENG, UNIV TEX, AUSTIN, 58-, DIR GEOMAGNETICS LAB, 66- *Mem:* Inst Elec & Electronics Engrs; Am Geophys Union. *Res:* Geomagnetics; electrical geoscience; information science. *Mailing Add:* ENS 623 Univ of Tex Austin TX 78712

SMITH, HAROLD WARREN, b Wyandotte, Mich, June 26, 38; m 61; c 3. STRUCTURAL CHEMISTRY. *Educ:* Albion Col, BA, 60; Harvard Univ, PhD(chem), 66. *Prof Exp:* Asst prof chem, Tuskegee Inst, 65-67; from asst prof to assoc prof, Earlham Col, 67-74; RES ASSOC CHEM, SCH MED, UNIV WASH, 74- *Mem:* Am Chem Soc; Am Crystallog Asn. *Res:* Determination by x-ray crystallography the molecular structure of anticancer drugs and of metal complexes. *Mailing Add:* Div of Neurol RG-20 Univ of Wash Seattle WA 98195

SMITH, HAROLD WILLIAM, b Toronto, Ont, Aug 15, 28; m 50; c 2. CONTROL ENGINEERING. *Educ:* Univ Toronto, BASc, 50; Mass Inst Technol, ScD(instrumentation), 61. *Prof Exp:* Assoc prof, 66-69, PROF ELEC ENG, UNIV TORONTO, 69- *Concurrent Pos:* Mem assoc comt automatic control, Nat Res Coun Can, 64-, chmn, 70-; consult, Falconbridge Nickel Mines Ltd, 67-; mem reactor control comt, Atomic Energy Control Bd Can, 72- *Res:* Modeling and control of industrial processes; multivariable systems; metallurgical applications. *Mailing Add:* Dept of Elec Eng Univ of Toronto Toronto ON M5S 2R8 Can

SMITH, HARRIETT ELIZABETH, b Guntersville, Ala, Jan 5, 44; m 82. ULTRASTRUCTURE, ELECTRON MICROSCOPY. *Educ:* Univ Ala, BS, 66; Univ Tex, Austin, PhD(biol sci), 70. *Prof Exp:* Fel biophysics, Univ Chicago, 70-72, res assoc physiol, 73-76; asst prof, 76-80, ASSOC PROF CELL BIOL ULTRASTRUCT, DEPT BIOL, UNIV ALA, 80- *Concurrent Pos:* Teaching assoc biol, Dept Biol, Univ SFla, 73; vis asst prof, Dept Biol Sci, Univ Ill, 74-76. *Mem:* Am Soc Cell Biol; Soc Protozoologists; Am Micros Soc; AAAS; Sigma Xi. *Res:* Oral apparatus structure, food vacuole formation and membrane recycling in Tetrahymena Vorax; cell motility; microtubules; microfilaments; microfilament-membrane interactions. *Mailing Add:* Dept Biol Univ Ala PO Box 1927 University AL 35486

SMITH, HARRY ANDREW, b Grand Rapids, Mich, Aug 29, 33; m 56; c 3. ORGANIC CHEMISTRY, POLYMER CHEMISTRY. *Educ:* Univ Mich, BS, 55, MS, 57, PhD(org chem), 60. *Prof Exp:* Chemist, Polymer Res Lab, 60-62, res chemist, 62-66, Sci Proj Lab, 66-68, sr res chemist, Chem Lab, 68-71 & Org Chem Prod Res Lab, 71-74, res specialist II, Org Chem Res Lab, 74-76, RES ASSOC DEPTS POLYMERS & CHEM LAB, DOW CHEM CO, 76- *Mem:* AAAS; Am Chem Soc; Sigma Xi. *Res:* Condensation and ring opening polymerization, including preparation and characterization of phenylene sulfide polymers, carbonyl polymers, carbonyl-epoxide copolymers, phenolic resins, solvents and solvency. *Mailing Add:* 4608 James Dr Midland MI 48640

SMITH, HARRY FRANCIS, b Sioux City, Iowa, Mar 29, 41; m 65; c 4. ALGEBRA. *Educ:* Univ Calif, Berkeley, BA, 67; Univ Iowa, MS, 69, PhD(math), 72. *Prof Exp:* Asst prof math, Univ Iowa, 72-73; asst prof math, Madison Col, 73-77; asst prof, 77-80, ASSOC PROF MATH, IOWA STATE UNIV, 80- *Mem:* Am Math Soc; Math Asn Am. *Res:* Nonassociative algebra, alternative rings and their generalizations. *Mailing Add:* Dept of Math Iowa State Univ Ames IA 50011

SMITH, HARRY JOHN, b Arundel, Quebec, Sept 3, 27; m 59; c 2. VETERINARY PARASITOLOGY, MEDICAL ENTOMOLOGY. *Educ:* McGill Univ, BSc, 54; Ont Vet Col, DVM, 58; Univ Toronto, MVSc, 60. *Prof Exp:* Res officer, 58-62, vet, 62-65, RES SCIENTIST PARASITOL, AGR CAN, 65- *Concurrent Pos:* Hon lectr, Mt Allison Univ, 72-77. *Mem:* Entom Soc Ont; Am Asn Vet Parasitologist; World Asn Advan Vet Parasitol; Wildlife Dis Asn. *Res:* Epidemiology and ecology of livestock gastrointestinal helminths with special emphasis on parasitic gastroenteritis. *Mailing Add:* 5 West Ave PO Box 1410 Sackville NB E0A 3C0 Can

SMITH, HARRY LOGAN, JR, b Philadelphia, Pa, June 4, 30; m 53; c 5. MICROBIOLOGY. *Educ:* Temple Univ, AB, 52; Jefferson Med Col, MS, 54, PhD, 57. *Prof Exp:* Asst, 53-57, from instr to assoc prof, 57-74, PROF MICROBIOL, JEFFERSON MED COL, 74- *Concurrent Pos:* NIH res career develop award, 62-66; consult cholera, WHO, 66. *Mem:* Am Soc Microbiol. *Res:* Vibrios; cholera. *Mailing Add:* Jefferson Med Col Philadelphia PA 19107

SMITH, HARVEY ALVIN, b Easton, Pa, Jan 30, 32; m 55; c 3. MATHEMATICS, PHYSICS. *Educ:* Lehigh Univ, BS, 52; Univ Pa, MS, 55, AM, 58, PhD(math), 64. *Prof Exp:* Physicist, Opers Res Div, Fire Control Instrument Group, Frankford Arsenal, 52-54; engr, Radio Corp Am, 54-57; sr systs analyst, Remington Rand Univac Div, Sperry Rand Corp, 57-58; mem tech staff, Auerbach Electronics Corp, 58-59; instr math, Drexel Inst, 59-60, asst prof, 60-64; NSF sci fel, Univ Pa, 64-65; mem tech staff weapons systs eval group, Inst Defense Anal, DC, 65-66; from assoc prof to prof math, Oakland Univ, 66-77; PROF MATH & CHMN DEPT, ARIZ STATE UNIV, 77- *Concurrent Pos:* Consult, Ford Found proj measurement of delinquency, Dept Sociol, Univ Pa, 63-64, US Army Security Agency, 67-68 & Inst Defense Anal, 67-69; consult, Exec Off of President, 68-73, dep chief systs eval, Off Emergency Preparedness; consult, US Arms Control & Disarmament Agency, 73-79 & Los Alamos Nat Lab, 80- *Honors & Awards:* Exec Off of President Meritorious Serv Award. *Mem:* Am Math Soc; Soc Indust & Appl Math; Sigma Xi. *Res:* Functional analysis; applied mathematics; systems analysis; operations research; representations of locally compact groups; strategic policy studies; twisted group algebras; integral operators. *Mailing Add:* Dept of Math Ariz State Univ Tempe AZ 85281

SMITH, HASTINGS ALEXANDER, JR, b Lexington, Ky, Apr 20, 43; m 65; c 2. NUCLEAR PHYSICS. *Educ:* Purdue Univ, BS, 65, MS, 67, PhD(nuclear physics), 70. *Prof Exp:* Appointee nuclear physics, Los Alamos Sci Lab, Univ Calif, 70-72; from asst prof to assoc prof physics, Ind Univ, 72-78; STAFF SCIENTIST, LOS ALAMOS SCI LAB, UNIV CALIF, 78- *Mem:* Am Phys Soc; AAAS; Am Asn Physics Teachers. *Res:* Intermediate and low-energy nuclear physics; gamma-ray and beta-ray spectroscopy; nuclear reactions; nuclei far from stability; non-destructive assay of special nuclear materials. *Mailing Add:* Los Alamos Sci Lab PO Box 1663 Los Alamos NM 87544

SMITH, HAYWOOD CLARK, JR, b Raleigh, NC, Oct 11, 45; m 69; c 2. ASTROPHYSICS, ASTRONOMY. *Educ:* Univ NC, Chapel Hill, AB, 67; Univ Va, MA, 69, PhD(astron), 72. *Prof Exp:* Vis asst prof, 72-78, asst prof, 78-79, ASSOC PROF ASTRON, UNIV SOUTH FLA, 79- *Mem:* Int Astron Union; Am Astron Soc. *Res:* Dynamical evolution of clusters of stars and galaxies; satellite orbital evolution from tidal friction. *Mailing Add:* Dept of Astron 211 Space Sci Res Bldg Univ Fla Gainesville FL 32611

SMITH, HELENE SHEILA, b Philadelphia, Pa, Feb 13, 41; m 62; c 1. MOLECULAR BIOLOGY. *Educ:* Univ Pa, BS, 62, PhD(microbiol), 67. *Prof Exp:* Asst res prof virol, Univ Calif, Berkeley, 71-75, assoc res prof, 75-77; STAFF RESEARCHER BIOL, DONNER LAB, LAWRENCE BERKELEY LAB, 77-; ASST DIR, PERALTA CANCER RES INST, 80- *Concurrent Pos:* Mem, Grad Group Genetics, Univ Calif, Berkeley, 79-, Cell Biol Panel, NSF, 80- *Mem:* Am Asn Cancer Res; Am Asn Cell Biol; Tissue Cult Asn. *Res:* Biology of human mammary epithelial cells in culture, and the use of these cells to study radiation induced survival and carcinogenesis, chemotherapeutic drug sensitivity, and tumor heterogeneity. *Mailing Add:* Peralta Cancer Res Inst 3023 Summit St Oakland CA 94609

SMITH, HERBERT L, b Mayport, Pa, June 28, 29; m 52; c 4. INORGANIC CHEMISTRY. *Educ:* Univ Pittsburgh, BSEd, 53, MLitt, 57, PhD(inorg chem), 65. *Prof Exp:* Jr fel glass sci, Mellon Inst, 54-65; PROF CHEM, SLIPPERY ROCK STATE COL, 65-, CHMN DEPT, 71- *Mem:* Am Chem Soc; Sigma Xi. *Res:* Effects of irradiation on glasses and crystals; effects of electrolytes on the circular dichroism of coordination compounds. *Mailing Add:* Dept Chem Slippery Rock State Col Slippery Rock PA 16057

SMITH, HILTON ALBERT, b Plymouth, NY, Sept 4, 08; m 33, 74; c 5. PHYSICAL CHEMISTRY. *Educ:* Oberlin Col, AB, 30; Harvard Univ, AM, 32, PhD(chem), 34. *Prof Exp:* Asst chem, Harvard Univ, 30-33 & 34-35; instr, Lehigh Univ, 35-39, asst prof, 39-41; prof, 41-61, dean grad sch & coordr res, 61-66, vpres grad studies & res, 66-68, vchancellor, 68-77, EMER VCHANCELLOR GRAD STUDIES & RES, UNIV TENN, KNOXVILLE, 77- *Concurrent Pos:* Dir fels, Hercules Powder Co, 43-48; consult, Union Carbide Nuclear Co, 50-, Ethyl Corp & Houdry Process Co; counr, Oak Ridge Inst Nuclear Studies, 57-69; dir, Oak Ridge Assoc Univs, 69-76; dir, Maryville Col, 72-78, Knoxville Col, 79- *Honors & Awards:* Oak Ridge Inst Nuclear Studies Award, 49; Southern Chemist Award, 67; Honor Scroll, Tenn Inst Chemists, 74. *Mem:* Am Chem Soc; The Chem Soc; Am Inst Chemists. *Res:* Photochemistry; calorimetry; phase diagrams; chemical kinetics; catalysis; physical organic chemistry; adsorption; isotope studies. *Mailing Add:* Rm 404 Andy Holt Tower Univ of Tenn Knoxville TN 37916

SMITH, HOBART MUIR, b Stanwood, Iowa, Sept 26, 12; m 38; c 2. VERTEBRATE ZOOLOGY. *Educ:* Kans State Col, BS, 32; Univ Kans, AM, 33, PhD(zool), 36. *Prof Exp:* Nat Res Coun fel biol, Univ Mich, 36-37; asst, Chicago Acad Sci, 37-38 & Chicago Mus Natural Hist, 38; Bacon traveling scholar, Smithsonian Inst, 38-41; instr zool, Univ Rochester, 41-45; asst prof comp anat, Univ Kans, 45-46; assoc prof, Agr & Mech Col, Tex, 46-47; from asst prof to prof comp anat & herpet, Univ Ill, Urbana, 47-68; chmn dept environ, pop & organismic biol, 70-74 & 78-79, PROF ENVIRON, POP & ORGANISMIC BIOL, UNIV COLO, BOULDER, 68- *Mem:* Am Soc Ichthyologists & Herpetologists (vpres, 37); Soc Study Amphibians & Reptiles; Soc Syst Zool (pres, 65); Ger Herpet Soc; Brit Herpet Soc. *Res:* Herpetology; principles of taxonomy; zoogeography; comparative anatomy. *Mailing Add:* Dept of Environ Pop & Org Biol Univ of Colo Boulder CO 80309

SMITH, HOMER ALVIN, JR, b Houston, Tex, Feb 23, 32; m 59; c 2. ORGANOMETALLIC CHEMISTRY, MEDICINAL CHEMISTRY. *Educ:* Rice Univ, BA, 53; Okla State Univ, PhD(chem), 61. *Prof Exp:* Asst prof chem, Tarkio Col, 61-64; assoc prof, 64-67, chmn dept, 66-68, 74-76 & 80-81, PROF CHEM, HAMPDEN-SYDNEY COL, 67- *Concurrent Pos:* NSF sci fac fel, Duke Univ, 68-69 & Ind Univ, 76-78. *Mem:* Am Chem Soc; Royal Soc Chem. *Res:* syntheses involving organometallic intermediates and strong base systems; preparation of sulfur heterocycles; synthesis of potential medicinals. *Mailing Add:* Dept of Chem Hampden-Sydney Col Hampden-Sydney VA 23943

SMITH, HORACE VERNON, JR, b Rockford, Ill, July 23, 42; m 64; c 1. ION SOURCE PHYSICS, ACCELERATOR PHYSICS. *Educ:* Univ Tex, Austin, BES, 64; Univ Ill, Urbana, MS, 65; Univ Wis-Madison, PhD(physics), 71. *Prof Exp:* Asst prof physics, Prairie View Agr & Mech Col, 70-71; res assoc, 71-74, asst scientist nuclear eng & physics, Univ Wis-Madison, 74-78; STAFF MEM, LOS ALAMOS NAT LAB, 78- *Mem:* Am Phys Soc; Inst Elec & Electronics Engrs. *Res:* Ion source and accelerating column development. *Mailing Add:* Los Alamos Nat Lab AT-2 MS 818 Los Alamos NM 87545

SMITH, HOWARD DUANE, b Fillmore, Utah, June 25, 41; m 61; c 1. MAMMALOGY, ECOLOGY. *Educ:* Brigham Young Univ, BS, 63, MS, 66; Univ Ill, Urbana, PhD(vert ecol), 69. *Prof Exp:* Instr biol, Univ Ill, 68-69; from asst prof to assoc prof, 69-80, PROF ZOOL, BRIGHAM YOUNG UNIV, 81- *Concurrent Pos:* Collabr, Intermountain Forest & Range Exp Sta, US Forest Serv, 65-; NSF fels, Brigham Young Univ, 69-; consult, Wilderness Assocs, 74-; mem, Am Mus Natural Hist; consult terrestrial wildlife. *Mem:* AAAS; Am Soc Mammal; Wildlife Soc; Ecol Soc Am. *Res:* Small mammal populations; demography; bioenergetics; environmental impact studies on man; environmental impact of coal generating power plants or pesticide applications on the biota; wildlife biology. *Mailing Add:* 163 Widtsoe Bldg Brigham Young Univ Provo UT 84602

SMITH, HOWARD E, b San Francisco, Calif, Aug 1, 25; m 60; c 3. ORGANIC CHEMISTRY. *Educ:* Univ Calif, BS, 51; Stanford Univ, MS, 54, PhD(chem), 57. *Prof Exp:* Asst res chemist, Calif Res Corp, Stand Oil Co, Calif, 51-52; res assoc, Stanford Univ, 56; USPHS fel, Wayne State Univ, 56-58; fel, Swiss Fed Inst Technol, Zurich, 58-59; from asst prof to assoc prof chem, 59-71, PROF CHEM, VANDERBILT UNIV, 71- *Mem:* AAAS; Am Chem Soc; The Chem Soc. *Res:* Natural products; stereochemistry. *Mailing Add:* Dept Chem Vanderbilt Univ Nashville TN 37235

SMITH, HOWARD EDWIN, b Dayton, Ohio, Nov 9, 23; m 46; c 2. MECHANICAL ENGINEERING, AEROSPACE ENGINEERING. *Educ:* Univ Dayton, BME, 51; Univ Cincinnati, MS, 61, PhD, 69. *Prof Exp:* Tool designer, Master Elec Co, 41-43, 46-47, process engr, 51-57; from instr to assoc prof, 57-70, PROF MECH ENG, UNIV DAYTON, 70-, CHMN DEPT, 66- *Concurrent Pos:* Consult, Aerospace Res Labs, Wright Patterson AFB, 64-66. *Mem:* Am Soc Mech Engrs; Am Inst Aeronaut & Astronaut; Am Soc Eng Educ. *Res:* Experimental and theoretical analysis of the flow field and heat transfer downstream of a rearward-facing step in supersonic flow of air. *Mailing Add:* Dept of Mech Eng Univ of Dayton Dayton OH 45469

SMITH, HOWARD JOHN TREWEEK, b Hornchurch, Eng, June 21, 37; m 63; c 2. LOW TEMPERATURE PHYSICS. *Educ:* Univ London, BSc, 58, PhD(physics), 61. *Prof Exp:* Res physicist, Petrocarbon Develop Ltd, Eng, 61-64; res physicist, Ferranti Electronics Ltd, Ont, 64; asst prof, 64-69, ASSOC PROF PHYSICS, UNIV WATERLOO, 69- *Mem:* Brit Inst Physics; Can Asn Physicists. *Res:* Superconductivity tunneling; far infrared spectroscopy; low temperature heat engines. *Mailing Add:* Dept of Physics Univ of Waterloo Waterloo ON N2L 3G1 Can

SMITH, HOWARD LEROY, b Eldorado, Kans, Nov 12, 24; m 47; c 5. ORGANIC CHEMISTRY. *Educ:* Univ Calif, BS, 48; Mass Inst Technol, PhD, 51. *Prof Exp:* Org chemist, Jackson Lab, 51-55, div head, 55-59, asst lab dir, 59-60, res dir, 60-65, asst gen supt process dept, Chambers Works, 65-66, supt miscellaneous intermediates area, 66-67, asst gen supt dyes & chem dept, 67-68, asst works mgr, 68-70, works mgr, 70-71, dir mfg serv, Org Chem Dept, 71-75, dir mfg, 75-76, DIR, EQUIP & MAGNETIC PROD, PHOTO PROD DEPT, E I DU PONT DE NEMOURS & CO, INC, 76- *Mem:* Am Chem Soc. *Res:* Dyes and textile chemicals; fluorocarbon chemistry; petroleum chemicals. *Mailing Add:* Photo Prod Dept E I du Pont de Nemours & Co Inc Wilmington DE 19898

SMITH, HOWARD MICHAEL, optics, see previous edition

SMITH, HOWARD WESLEY, b New York, NY, Nov 24, 29; m; c 7. AEROSPACE ENGINEERING. *Educ:* Wichita State Univ, BS, 51, MS, 58; Okla State Univ, PhD(aerospace eng), 68. *Prof Exp:* Jr engr, Boeing Co, Kans, 50-51, stress analyst, 52-55, struct engr, 56-58, group supvr, 59-63, struct res mgr, 65-68, mem hq staff, Washington, DC, 69-70; PROF AEROSPACE STRUCT, UNIV KANS, 70- *Mem:* Am Inst Aeronaut & Astronaut; Soc Exp Stress Anal; Am Soc Eng Educ; Soc Am Military Engrs; Soc Advan Mat & Process Eng. *Res:* Aircraft loads; stresses; flutter and materials; composites; crashworthiness; computing; optimization; teaching methods; biomechanics of bone. *Mailing Add:* Dept of Aerospace Eng 2003 Learned Hall Univ of Kans Lawrence KS 66045

SMITH, HUGO DUNLAP, b Natick, Mass, Nov 28, 23; m 49; c 5. PEDIATRICS. *Educ:* Yale Univ, BS, 44; Harvard Univ, MD, 47; Am Bd Pediat, dipl, 52. *Prof Exp:* Intern, Children's Hosp, Boston, 47-48; resident, Hosp Univ Pa, 48-49; resident & chief resident, Children's Hosp, Cincinnati, 49-52, asst chief staff & med dir clins, 54-69; PROF PEDIAT & ASSOC DEAN CURRIC, SCH MED, TEMPLE UNIV, 70- *Concurrent Pos:* From instr to prof pediat, Univ Cincinnati, 50-69; consult, US Air Force Hosp, Wright Patterson AFB, 58-66; ed, Am J Dis Children, 63-72. *Mem:* Am Pediat Soc; Am Diabetes Asn; Am Acad Pediat; Ambulatory Pediat Asn. *Res:* Medical education, curricula and teaching methodology; clinical and emotional aspects of juvenile diabetes mellitus. *Mailing Add:* Off of the Dean Temple Univ Sch of Med Philadelphia PA 19140

SMITH, IAN CORMACK PALMER, b Winnipeg, Man, Sept 23, 39; m 65; c 4. BIOPHYSICS. *Educ:* Univ Manitoba, BSc, 61, MSc, 62; Cambridge Univ, PhD(theoret chem), 65. *Prof Exp:* NATO fel, Stanford Univ, 65-66; mem res staff, Bell Tel Labs, 66-67; RES OFFICER, NAT RES COUN CAN, 67- *Concurrent Pos:* Consult, Bell Tel Labs, 68-70, CPC Int, 75- & Smith, Kline & French, 79-; adj prof chem, Carleton Univ, 73-; adj prof biophys, Univ Ill, Chicago, 75-80; adj prof chem, Univ Ottawa, 77- *Honors & Awards:* Merck, Sharp & Dohme Award, Chem Inst Can; Ayerst Award, Can Biochem Soc; Barringer Award, Can Spectros Soc. *Mem:* AAAS; fel Chem Inst Can; Am Chem Soc; Biophys Soc; Can Biochem Soc. *Res:* Electron spin resonance; nuclear magnetic resonance; optical spectroscopy; infrared spectroscopy application of these techniques to problems in molecular biology, especially biological membranes and microbial metabolism. *Mailing Add:* Div Biol Sci Nat Res Coun Can Ottawa ON K1A 0R6 Can

SMITH, IAN MACLEAN, b Glasgow, Scotland, May 21, 22; nat US; m 48; c 5. INFECTIOUS DISEASES, GERIATRICS INTERNAL MEDICINE. *Educ:* Glasgow Univ, MB, ChB, 44, MD, 57; FRCPSG, 49; FRCPath, 76. *Prof Exp:* House physician internal med, Stobhill Hosp, Scotland, 4445; clin asst, Royal infirmary, 47; registr path, Post-grad Med Sch, London, 47-48, house physician internal med, 48; tutor med path, Royal Hosp & Univ Sheffield, 48-49; fel internal med, Johns Hopkins Hosp, 49-51; asst resident, Washington Univ & Barnes Hosp, 51-53; asst prof, Rockefeller Inst & asst physician, Hosp, 53-55; from asst prof to assoc prof internal med, Col Med, Univ Iowa, 55-65, chief infectious dis lab, Univ Hosps, 55-74, prof internal med, 65-76; prof & chmn dept, Col Med, East Tenn State Univ, 76-78; PROF INTERNAL MED, COL MED, UNIV IOWA, 78- *Concurrent Pos:* Consult, Iowa State Dept Health, 58-76. *Mem:* Am Soc Microbiol; Am Thoracic Soc; Soc Exp Biol & Med; AMA; Am Geriatric Soc. *Res:* Epidemiology and treatment of infectious diseases; epidemiology of elderly patients in acute care hospital. *Mailing Add:* Dept of Med Univ of Iowa Hosp & Clin Iowa City IA 52242

SMITH, IEUAN TREVOR, b Bromley, Eng, Jan 11, 33; m 58; c 3. CHEMISTRY. *Educ:* Univ London, BSc, 54, MSc, 60. *Prof Exp:* Res chemist, Cray Valley Prod Ltd, Eng, 57-61; sr res officer, Paint Res Sta, 61-64; tech mgr, Epoxlite Ltd, 64-66; sr res chemist, Toni Co Div, 66-67, res supvr, 67-69, res supvr, 69-77, prin res assoc, 78-80, GROUP LEADER, GILLETTE RES INST, GILLETTE CO, 80- *Mem:* Fiber Soc; Soc Appl Spectros; Microbeam Anal Soc. *Res:* Properties and structure of polymers; polyelectrolyte behavior; surface and colloid chemistry; infrared spectroscopy, especially of surface species and proteins; keratin fibers, structure and properties. *Mailing Add:* Gillette Res Inst 1413 Research Blvd Rockville MD 20850

SMITH, ISAAC LITTON, b Russellville, Ala. ANALYTICAL CHEMISTRY. *Educ:* Florence State Univ, Ala, 61; Univ Ala, PhD(anal chem), 74. *Prof Exp:* Chemist, Reynolds Metals Co, 68-70; ANAL CHEMIST, ETHYL CORP, 74- *Concurrent Pos:* Mem res comt, Water Pollution Control Fedn, 74. *Mem:* Am Chem Soc; Water Pollution Control Fedn; Sigma Xi. *Res:* Analytical methods development; investigation of plant production problems; development and design of continuous monitor instrumentation. *Mailing Add:* Ethyl Corp PO Box 341 Baton Rouge LA 70821

SMITH, ISSAR, b New York, NY, Dec 4, 33; m 55; c 2. MOLECULAR BIOLOGY. *Educ:* City Col New York, BA, 55; Columbia Univ, MA, 57, PhD(biol), 61. *Prof Exp:* Fel, Sloan-Kettering Inst Cancer Res, 61-62; fel microbiol, Sch Med, NY Univ, 62-63; fel molecular biol, Albert Einstein Col Med, 63-64, res asst prof path, 64-67; assoc microbiol, 67-74, assoc mem, 74-79, MEM, PUB HEALTH RES INST CITY NEW YORK, 79-; RES PROF, SCH MED, NY UNIV, 79- *Concurrent Pos:* USPHS fel, 61-62, trainee, 62-63; Am Cancer Soc fel, 63-64, res grant, 65-; NIH career develop award, 71-, res grant, 72- *Mem:* AAAS; Am Soc Microbiol. *Res:* Genetics and physiology of ribosomes; evolutionary interrelationships between bacteria; nucleic acids; prokaryote differentiation and regulation. *Mailing Add:* 605 Water New York NY 10002

SMITH, IVAN C, environmental chemistry, physical inorganic chemistry, see previous edition

SMITH, J C, b Hudson, NC, Apr 19, 33; m 55; c 2. CIVIL ENGINEERING. *Educ:* NC State Univ, BCE, 55, MS, 60; Purdue Univ, PhD(civil eng), 66. *Prof Exp:* Teaching asst, 55-56 & 58-60, from instr to asst prof, 60-74, ASSOC PROF CIVIL ENG, NC STATE UNIV, 74- *Mem:* Am Soc Civil Engrs. *Res:* Structural mechanics and design; closed form solutions of bridge floor systems; dynamic analysis of grids; numerical methods in structural engineering. *Mailing Add:* Dept of Civil Eng NC State Univ Raleigh NC 27650

SMITH, JACK, b Morristown, NJ, Nov 28, 27; m 54; c 3. ELECTRICAL ENGINEERING, AERONOMY. *Educ:* Univ Ariz, BS, 52, MS, 58, PhD(elec eng), 64. *Prof Exp:* Test engr, Gen Elec Co, 52-53, engr, 53-56; instr elec eng, Univ Ariz, 57-64, asst prof, 64, res assoc, Appl Res Lab, 57-64; assoc prof, 64-73, PROF ELEC ENG, UNIV TEX, EL PASO, 73-, DEAN, COL ENG, 76- *Concurrent Pos:* NSF sci fac fel, 61-62; consult, Atmospheric Sci Lab, US Army, 71- *Mem:* Inst Elec & Electronics Engrs; Am Geophys Union. *Res:* Atmospheric effects on high frequency electromagnetic wave propagation; lightning; upper atmosphere and ionospheric ionization characteristics and variations. *Mailing Add:* Dept of Elec Eng Univ of Tex El Paso TX 79968

SMITH, JACK CARLTON, b Kansas City, Mo, May 8, 13; m 57. POLYMER PHYSICS. *Educ:* Ohio State Univ, BEngPhysics, 35, MSc, 36; Calif Inst Technol, PhD(physics), 42. *Prof Exp:* Asst physics, Ohio State Univ, 36-37; physicist, US Dept Navy, 41-44; res physicist, Los Alamos Sci Lab, Univ Calif, 44-45; pioneering res div, Textile Fibers Dept, E I du Pont de Nemours & Co, 46-54; PHYSICIST, POLYMERS DIV, NAT BUR STAND, 54- *Mem:* Am Phys Soc; Soc Rheology. *Res:* High polymer physics; physical properties of textile yarns; mechanical properties of composite materials. *Mailing Add:* 3708 Manor Rd Chevy Chase MD 20815

SMITH, JACK HOWARD, b Middletown, NY, Nov 8, 21; m 49; c 3. THEORETICAL PHYSICS. *Educ:* Cornell Univ, AB, 43, PhD(theoret physics), 51. *Prof Exp:* Asst, Cornell Univ, 43-44; jr scientist, Theoret Div, Los Alamos Sci Lab, 44-46; asst, Cornell Univ, 46-49; mem staff, Theoret Div, Los Alamos Sci Lab, 49-51; res assoc theoret physics, Knolls Atomic Power Lab, Gen Elec Co, 51-63; PROF PHYSICS, STATE UNIV NY ALBANY, 63- *Mem:* AAAS; Am Asn Physics Teachers; Acoust Soc Am; Am Phys Soc. *Res:* Electromagnetic scattering; nuclear scattering of high energy electrons; neutron diffusion; reactor physics; reactor shielding; musical acoustics. *Mailing Add:* 1030 Atateka Rd Schenectady NY 12309

SMITH, JACK LOUIS, b Huntington, WVa, July 15, 34; m 61; c 2. BIOCHEMISTRY, NUTRITION. *Educ:* Univ Cincinnati, BS, 56, PhD(biochem), 62. *Prof Exp:* NIH trainee animal nutrit, Univ Ill, 61-63; Muscular Dystrophy Asn Am fel, Stanford Res Inst, 64; from asst prof to assoc prof biochem, Sch Med, Tulane Univ, 65-74, from asst prof to assoc prof biochem-nutrit, Sch Pub Health & Trop Med, 68-74, adj prof biochem, Sch Pub Health & Trop Med, 74-79; SWANSON ASSOC PROF BIOCHEM, 74- *Concurrent Pos:* Prin investr biochem, Touro Res Inst, 69-74. *Mem:* AAAS; Am Chem Soc; Am Inst Nutrit; Am Soc Clin Nutrit; Am Bd Nutrit; Am Dietetic Asn. *Res:* Nutritional biochemistry; nutritional assessment. *Mailing Add:* Dept of Biochem Univ of Nebr Med Ctr Omaha NE 68105

SMITH, JACK R(EGINALD), b Carrington, NDak, June 16, 35; m 59; c 3. ELECTRICAL ENGINEERING. *Educ:* Univ Southern Calif, BS, 58, MS, 60, PhD(elec eng), 64. *Prof Exp:* Mem tech staff, Hughes Aircraft Co, 58-59; res engr, Jet Propulsion Lab, 61; res assoc elec eng, Univ Southern Calif, 63-64; from asst prof to assoc prof, 64-70, PROF ELEC ENG, UNIV FLA, 70- *Mem:* Inst Elec & Electronics Engrs; Int Fedn Med Electronics & Biol Eng. *Res:* Biomedical engineering. *Mailing Add:* Dept of Elec Eng Univ of Fla Gainesville FL 32601

SMITH, JACKSON BRUCE, b Mt Holly, NJ, Mar 2, 38; m 63; c 2. INTERNAL MEDICINE, IMMUNOLOGY. *Educ:* Wake Forest Col, BS, 60, MD, 65. *Prof Exp:* Clin res fel, Inst Cancer Res, 67-69; fel, Univ Col, London, Eng, 72-74; clin assoc med, Univ Pa, 75-78; res physician, Inst Cancer Res, 74-81; ASSOC PROF MED, JEFFERSON MED COL, 81- *Concurrent Pos:* Clin assoc med, Pa Hosp, 76-81; grant, Am Cancer Soc, 78-80; adj asst prof med, Univ Pa Sch Med, 78-81. *Mem:* AAAS; Am Col Physicians; Am Fedn Clin Res; Am Asn Immunologists; Am Asn Cancer Res. *Res:* Immune system regulatory mechanisms in normal individuals and in patients and laboratory animals with lymphoproliferative and autoimmune disorders; effects of temperature variation on immune responses in vitro. *Mailing Add:* Div Rheumatol Jefferson Med Col 1015 Walnut St Rm 613 Philadelphia PA 19107

SMITH, JAMES ALAN, b Detroit, Mich, Nov 19, 42; m 65; c 2. REMOTE SENSING, SCENE RADIATION MODELING. *Educ:* Univ Mich, BS, 63, MS, 65, PhD(physics), 70. *Prof Exp:* Res asst, Willow Run Labs, Univ Mich, 64-66, from res asst to assoc, Dept Physics, 66-70; asst prof remote sensing, Dept Earth Resources, 70-74, assoc prof, 74-78, PROF REMOTE SENSING & COMPUT APPL, DEPT FORESTRY, COLO STATE UNIV, 78- *Concurrent Pos:* Assoc dir, Comput Ctr, Colo State Univ, 74-76; consult, numerous Fed Agencies & Indust; prin investr, NASA, Army Res Off, US Forest Serv, US Geol Surv, Corp Engrs, & US Fish & Wildlife Serv. *Res:* Modeling of optical reflective and thermal radiation patterns from earth surface features and the application of such models to remote sensing. *Mailing Add:* 2913 Eagle Dr Ft Collins CO 80526

SMITH, JAMES ALLBEE, b Detroit, Mich, Oct 20, 37; m 58; c 2. ANALYTICAL CHEMISTRY. *Educ:* Univ Mich, Ann Arbor, BS, 59; Ohio State Univ, PhD(org chem), 64. *Prof Exp:* Res chemist, Res & Develop Dept, Union Carbide Corp, 64-67, proj scientist catalysis, 67-68; res assoc coordr chem, Case Western Reserve Univ, 68-70; sr res chemist, Eng Develop Ctr, C E Lummus Co, 70-73; chemist, WVa Dept Agr, 73-78, asst dir, 78-81; MGR, TECH TESTING LABS, 81- *Mem:* Am Chem Soc; Asn Off Anal Chemists. *Res:* Development of methodology for residue analysis. *Mailing Add:* Tech Testing Labs Charleston WV 25305

SMITH, JAMES CECIL, b Little Orleans, Md, Jan 17, 34; m 61; c 3. PHYSIOLOGY, BIOCHEMISTRY. *Educ:* Univ Md, BS, 56, MS, 59, PhD(animal nutrit), 64. *Prof Exp:* Health serv officer, NIH, 59-61; biol chemist, Univ Calif, Los Angeles, 64-65; res physiologist, Vet Admin Hosp, Long Beach, Calif, 65-66; res biochemist, Vet Admin Hosp, Washington, DC, 66-77, chief, Trace Element Res Lab, 71-77; CHIEF VITAMIN & MINERAL NUTRIT LAB, USDA, 77-, ELEMENT RES LAB, 71- *Concurrent Pos:* Lectr, George Washington Univ. *Mem:* Am Inst Nutrit. *Res:* Trace element metabolism such as zinc and copper. *Mailing Add:* Nutrit Inst US Dept Agr Beltsville MD 20705

SMITH, JAMES CLARENCE, JR, b Martinsville, Va, Aug 16, 39; m 62; c 2. MATHEMATICS. *Educ:* Davidson Col, BS, 61; Col William & Mary, MS, 64; Duke Univ, PhD(math), 67. *Prof Exp:* Aerospace technologist, Langley Res Ctr, NASA, 61-67; asst prof, 67-71, ASSOC PROF MATH, VA POLYTECH INST & STATE UNIV, 71- *Concurrent Pos:* Consult, Langley Res Ctr, NASA, 68 & 69. *Mem:* Am Math Soc; Math Asn Am; Soc Indust & Appl Math. *Res:* Topology; dimension theory. *Mailing Add:* Dept of Math Va Polytech Inst & State Univ Blacksburg VA 24061

SMITH, JAMES DARRELL, b Albuquerque, NMex, Apr 13, 40; m 65; c 1. NEUROPHYSIOLOGY. *Educ:* Univ Okla, BS, 63; Med Ctr, Univ Ill, PhD(physiol), 71. *Prof Exp:* Instr human physiol, Dept Biomed Eng, Univ Ill, 67-69, attend asst & biomed engr, 68-69; res assoc, Dept Biomed Eng, Univ Southern Calif, 69-73; res assoc physiol optics, Univ Calif, 73-77; res assoc exercise physiol, Synanon Res Inst, 77-79, mem staff, 78-80; vis asst prof physiol, Sch Optom, Univ Calif, 81; NAT RES COUN SR RES FEL, AMES RES CTR, NASA, 82- *Concurrent Pos:* Core fac chem & behav/brain & behav, Calif Sch Prof Psychol, 73-75. *Mem:* AAAS; Int Brain Res Orgn; Sigma Xi. *Res:* Visual system neurophysiology; human eye movements; perception and decision processes. *Mailing Add:* NASA Man Vehicle Syst Ames Res Ctr Moffett Field CA 94035

SMITH, JAMES DAVID BLACKHALL, b Peterhead, Scotland, Apr 25, 40. POLYMER CHEMISTRY. *Educ:* Aberdeen Univ, BSc, 62, PhD(polymer chem), 65. *Prof Exp:* NSF res grant, Polymer Res Ctr, State Univ NY, 65-66; sr chemist, Laporte Industs Ltd, Luton, Eng, 67-68; MGR INSULATION SYSTS, RES & DEVELOP CTR, WESTINGHOUSE ELEC CORP, 68- *Mem:* Am Chem Soc; Royal Soc Chem. *Res:* Polymerization kinetics; electroinitiated polymerization reactions; polyester and epoxy resin technology; flame retardants; insulation and dielectric properties of polymers. *Mailing Add:* Insulation Dept Westinghouse Elec Corp R&D Ctr Churchill Boro PA 15235

SMITH, JAMES DOUGLAS, b Paullina, Iowa, Dec 14, 27; m 55; c 2. GENETICS, STATISTICS. *Educ:* Iowa State Univ, BS, 50, MS, 56, PhD(genetics), 60. *Prof Exp:* Plant breeder, United-Hagie Hybrids, Inc, 53, consult, 53-59; from asst prof to assoc prof, 59-70, PROF GENETICS, TEX A&M UNIV, 70- *Mem:* Am Genetics Asn; Genetics Soc Can. *Res:* Quantitative genetic studies of corn and sorghum; mutagenic and cytogenetic effects of fluorides and genetic regulation in higher plants. *Mailing Add:* Genetics Sect Plant Sci Dept Tex A&M Univ College Station TX 77843

SMITH, JAMES DOYLE, b Charlottesville, Va, Jan 27, 21; m 44; c 2. ORGANIC CHEMISTRY. *Educ:* Univ Va, BS, 42, MS, 44, PhD(chem), 46. *Prof Exp:* Asst, Med Col Va, Va Commonwealth Univ, 46-48, asst prof chem, 48-51, assoc prof, 51-62, prof, 62-81, actg chmn, 61, chmn dept, 62-74, actg chmn, Dept Pharmaceut Chem, 76-77; RETIRED. *Mem:* AAAS; Am Chem Soc; Am Pharmaceut Asn. *Res:* Synthetic organic and medicinal chemistry; amino acids; antimalarials; anti-tumor agents. *Mailing Add:* Sch of Pharm Med Col of Va Va Commonwealth Univ Richmond VA 23298

SMITH, JAMES EDWARD, b Atlanta, Ga, Apr 7, 35; m 62; c 2. GEOCHEMISTRY, GEOPHYSICS. *Educ:* Univ of the South, BS, 58; Rochester Univ, PhD(statist, mech), 65. *Prof Exp:* Phys chemist, Union Carbide Res Inst, NY, 63-64; NIH fel chem, Ill Inst Technol, 64-65; PHYS CHEMIST, CHEM LAB, PHILLIPS PETROL CO, 65- *Mem:* Am Chem Soc; Soc Petrol Eng; Sigma Xi (secy, 74-75, vpres, 75-76, pres, 76-77); Geochem Soc. *Res:* Relative abundance and isotopic composition of alkanes in sediments; petroleum migration, accumulation and dissipation in the earth; petroleum geochemistry; shale compaction over geologic time and geopressures; transport phenomena in the earth; salinity changes accompanying shale compaction; theoretical interpretation of electric logs; synthetic seismograms. *Mailing Add:* 1209 Harris Dr Bartlesville OK 74003

SMITH, JAMES EDWARD, JR, b Cincinnati, Ohio, Dec 5, 41; m 69; c 4. TECHNOLOGY TRANSFER. *Educ:* Univ Cincinnati, BS, 63, MS, 66; Wash Univ, DSc, 69. *Prof Exp:* Res sanitary engr, Advan Waste Treatment Lab, 68-71, sanitary engr, 71-76, head municipal technol transfer staff, 76-77, ENVIRON ENGR, CTR ENVIRON INFO, US ENVIRON PROTECTION AGENCY, 77- *Mem:* Am Soc Civil Engrs; Water Pollution Control Fedn; Int Asn Water Pollution Res. *Res:* Land application of sludge; sludge dewatering; drinking water treatment; definition of the effects and control of non-ionizing radiation. *Mailing Add:* 5821 Marlborough Dr Cincinnati OH 45230

SMITH, JAMES ELDON, b Ft Wayne, Ind, June 9, 28; m 51; c 5. MICROBIOLOGY. *Educ:* DePauw Univ, BA, 50; Purdue Univ, MS, 52, PhD, 55. *Prof Exp:* Fel, Am Cancer Soc, Purdue Univ, 55-56, Life Ins Med Res Fund, 56-57; from res asst prof to asst prof bact, 57-70, ASSOC PROF MICROBIOL, SYRACUSE UNIV, 70- *Mem:* Am Soc Microbiol; Electron Micros Soc Am. *Res:* Virology and microbial genetics; physiology of virus reproduction; mycology and plant pathology; germfree animal physiology. *Mailing Add:* Dept of Biol Syracuse Univ Syracuse NY 13210

SMITH, JAMES F, b Syracuse, NY, Apr 26, 30. MATHEMATICAL ANALYSIS. *Educ:* Bellarmine Col, NY, AB, 54; Cath Univ Am, MS, 57, PhD(math), 59; Woodstock Col, Md, STL. *Prof Exp:* From instr to assoc prof, 64-74, PROF MATH, LE MOYNE COL, NY, 74- *Mem:* Am Math Soc; Math Asn Am. *Res:* Banach algebras; Hilbert space; structure and spectral theory. *Mailing Add:* Dept of Math Le Moyne Col Syracuse NY 13214

SMITH, JAMES G(ILBERT), b Benton, Ill, May 1, 30; m 55; c 1. ELECTRICAL ENGINEERING. *Educ:* Univ Mo, BSEE, 57, MSEE, 59, PhD(eng physics), 66. *Prof Exp:* Instr elec eng, Sch Mines, Univ Mo-Rolla, 57-59 & 61-66, asst prof, 59-61; asst prof, Sch Technol, 66-69, assoc prof, 69-72, chmn, Dept Elec Sci & Systs Eng, 71-80, PROF ELEC ENG, SCH ENG & TECHNOL, SOUTHERN ILL UNIV, 72-, DIR, LIGHTNING RES LAB, 80- *Mem:* Am Soc Eng Educ; Inst Elec & Electronics Engrs. *Res:* electromagnetics and antennas, lightning, lightning protection and electrical properties of materials. *Mailing Add:* Dept of Elec Sci & Systs Eng Southern Ill Univ Carbondale IL 62901

SMITH, JAMES GRAHAM, b Toronto, Ont, July 23, 28; m 51; c 2. ORGANIC CHEMISTRY. *Educ:* Univ Toronto, BA, 50, MA, 51, PhD(org chem), 53. *Prof Exp:* Sr res chemist, Tenn Eastman Co, Eastman Kodak Co, 53-64; group leader organometallic & oxidation chem, Dow Chem Can, 64-67; assoc prof org chem, 67-74, prof chem, 74-81, ASSOC DEAN, GRAD STUDIES & SCI FAC, 81- *Concurrent Pos:* Invited lectr, Emory Univ, 62-63; consult, Thomson Res Assocs, Toronto, 68- *Mem:* AAAS; Am Chem Soc; Chem Inst Can. *Res:* Condensation polymers; synthesis and chemistry of organometallic compounds; reactions of hydroperoxides; environmental chemistry. *Mailing Add:* Dept of Chem Univ of Waterloo Waterloo ON N2L 3G1 Can

SMITH, JAMES GRAHAM, JR, b Burlington, Wash, June 5, 30; m 52; c 3. ANALYTICAL CHEMISTRY. *Educ:* Univ Wash, BA, 52, PhD(chem), 60. *Prof Exp:* Sr res chemist, Pennsalt Chem Corp, 60-63, proj leader mass spectrometry & gas chromatography, 63-65, GROUP LEADER INSTRUMENTAL ANAL, PENNWALT CORP, 65- *Mem:* Am Chem Soc. *Res:* Laboratory and process instrumentation, including mass spectrometry, gas chromatography, infrared, nuclear magnetic resonance, Raman, and computer automation. *Mailing Add:* Pennwalt Corp Anal Dept 900 First Ave King of Prussia PA 19406

SMITH, JAMES H, b Oneida, Tenn, Feb 28, 34; c 3. PHYSICS, MATHEMATICS. *Educ:* Eastern Ky Univ, BS, 60; Univ Tenn, MS, 71. *Prof Exp:* Technician electronics, US Navy Airforce, 52-55; technician commun, Am Tel & Tel Co, 55-58; instr physics, Eastern Ky Univ, 60-61; assoc physicist phys tests, 62-68, PHYSICIST NONDESTRUCTIVE TESTING, NUCLEAR DIV, UNION CARBIDE CORP, OAK RIDGE NAT LAB, 68- *Concurrent Pos:* Instr, Univ Tenn. *Honors & Awards:* Achievement Award, Am Soc Nondestructive Testing, 76. *Mem:* Fel Am Soc Nondestructive Testing; Am Welding Soc; Soc Exp Stress Anal. *Res:* Nondestructive testing, specifically ultrasonics and eddy currents. *Mailing Add:* Oak Ridge Nat Lab PO Box X Oak Ridge TN 37830

SMITH, JAMES H(ENRY), electrical engineering, deceased

SMITH, JAMES HAMMOND, b Colorado Springs, Colo, Feb 2, 25; m 50, 55; c 4. NUCLEAR PHYSICS. *Educ:* Stanford Univ, AB, 45; Harvard Univ, AM, 47, PhD(physics), 52. *Prof Exp:* Jr lab technician, Oak Ridge Nat Lab, 50-51; instr physics, 51, from asst prof to assoc prof, 53-60, assoc head dept, 72-80, PROF PHYSICS, UNIV ILL, URBANA, 60- *Concurrent Pos:* Guggenheim fel, 66. *Mem:* Fel Am Phys Soc. *Res:* Photonuclear reactions; K meson decays; high energy nuclear reactions. *Mailing Add:* Dept of Physics 1110 W Green St Univ Ill Urbana IL 61801

SMITH, JAMES HART, b North Plainfield, NJ, Jan 20, 42. ENVIRONMENTAL CHEMISTRY. *Educ:* Yale Univ, BSci, 63; Univ Calif, Berkeley, PhD(chem), 67. *Prof Exp:* Fel, Calif Inst Technol, 67-70; DIR, DEPT PHYS CHEM, SRI INT, 70- *Mem:* Am Chem Soc. *Res:* Prediction of the environmental fate of chemicals; collection and analysis of environmental samples; measurement of physical properties of chemicals. *Mailing Add:* SRI Int 333 Ravenswood Ave Menlo Park CA 94025

SMITH, JAMES JOHN, b St Paul, Minn, Jan 28, 14; div; c 4. PHYSIOLOGY. *Educ:* St Louis Univ, BS, 35, MD, 37; Northwestern Univ, MS, 40, PhD(physiol), 46. *Prof Exp:* Intern, Ancker Hosp, Minn, 37-38; asst path, Cook County Hosp, Chicago, Ill, 38-39; assoc prof physiol & dean, Sch Med, Loyola Univ Chicago, 46-50; chief, Med Educ Div, Cent Off, US Vet Admin, DC, 50-52; chmn dept, 52-78, PROF PHYSIOL, MED COL WIS, 52-, PROF MED, 78-; DEP DIR, CARDIOPULMONARY REHAB CTR, VET ADMIN MED CTR, WOOD, WIS, 78- *Concurrent Pos:* Fulbright res scholar, Heidelberg, 59-60; dep dir, Cardiopulmonary Rehab Ctr, Vet Admin Ctr, Wood, Wis, 78- *Mem:* Soc Exp Biol & Med; Am Physiol Soc; Reticuloendothelial Soc; Sigma Xi. *Res:* Cardiovascular physiology, particularly effect of aging and circulatory disease on autonomic response of circulatory system to non-exercise and exercise stress; cardiovascular evaluation; peripheral circulation; circulatory control, aging, stress response. *Mailing Add:* Dept Physiol Med Col Wis Milwaukee WI 53233

SMITH, JAMES L, b Lackawanna, NY, Aug 5, 29; m 54; c 4. MATHEMATICS. *Educ:* Univ Louisville, BA, 51; Univ Pittsburgh, MS, 55; Okla State Univ, EdD(found in geom), 63. *Prof Exp:* Asst math, Univ Pittsburgh, 54-56; instr, Westminster Col, Pa, 56-61; asst, Okla State Univ, 61-63; assoc prof, 63-75, chmn dept, 65-71, PROF MATH & COMPUT SCI, MUSKINGUM COL, 75-, CHMN DEPT, 76- *Concurrent Pos:* Vis lectr, NSF summer insts, Southwestern State Col, Okla, 63 & Northeast Mo State Col, 64; dir & instr, Teacher Oriented Insts, 65-66; NSF sci fac fel, Wash State Univ, 67-68; vis assoc prof, Univ NH, 71-72; assoc dir, NSF Pre-Col Teacher Develop Proj, 77-78, dir, NSF CAUSE Comput Lit Proj, 77- *Mem:* Math Asn Am; Am Math Soc. *Res:* Geometry; psychometric analysis of underachievers in mathematics. *Mailing Add:* Dept of Math Muskingum Col New Concord OH 43762

SMITH, JAMES LAWRENCE, b Detroit, Mich, Sept 3, 43; m 65; c 2. MAGNETISM, SUPERCONDUCTIVITY. *Educ:* Wayne State Univ, BS, 65; Brown Univ, PhD(physics), 74. *Prof Exp:* staff mem physics, 73-82, FEL, LOS ALAMOS NAT LAB, UNIV CALIF, 82- *Mem:* Am Phys Soc; AAAS. *Res:* Study of electronic behavior of actinides; occurence of superconductivity and magnetism in transition metals. *Mailing Add:* Group CMB-5 MS 730 Los Alamos Nat Lab Los Alamos NM 87545

SMITH, JAMES LEE, b Clinton Co, Ind, Dec 23, 28. MICROBIOLOGY. *Educ:* Ind Univ, AB, 52, MA, 54, PhD(bact), 62. *Prof Exp:* Med bacteriologist, US Army, Ft Detrick, Md, 54-59; USPHS fel microbiol, Univ Chicago, 61-63; RES MICROBIOLOGIST, EASTERN MKT & NUTRIT RES DIV, USDA, 63- *Mem:* AAAS; Am Soc Microbiol; Am Chem Soc; Brit Soc Gen Microbiol. *Res:* Bacterial physiology and nutrition. *Mailing Add:* Meat Lab USDA 600 E Mermaid Lane Philadelphia PA 19118

SMITH, JAMES LEE, b Thayer, Kans, Feb 27, 35; m 68; c 2. BIOLOGY. *Educ:* San Francisco State Col, BA, 58; Univ Calif, Berkeley, PhD(bot), 63. *Prof Exp:* Asst prof biol, Chico State Col, 63-64 & Univ Colo, Boulder, 64-69; asst prof, 69-74, ASSOC PROF BIOL, CENT MO STATE UNIV, 74- *Mem:* AAAS; Bot Soc Am; Am Bryol & Lichenological Soc. *Res:* Phytoplankton ecology. *Mailing Add:* Dept of Biol Cent Mo State Univ Warrensburg MO 64093

SMITH, JAMES LEROY, watershed management, see previous edition

SMITH, JAMES LUTHER, b Terre Haute, Ind, Jan 18, 24; m 48; c 4. ORGANIC CHEMISTRY. *Educ:* Univ Fla, BS, 46, PhD(org chem), 57. *Prof Exp:* From chemist to sr chemist, Fiber Develop Div, 51-58, lab supvr, Qual & Stand Dept, Acetate Yarn Div, 58-61, sr chemist, Plastic Develop Dept, 61-62, supt develop & qual control, Acetate Yarn Div, 62-72, CHIEF CHEMIST FIBER DEVELOP, TENN EASTMAN CO, 72- *Res:* Synthetic fibers. *Mailing Add:* Tenn Eastman Co Kingsport TN 37660

SMITH, JAMES LYNN, b Columbia, Miss, Sept 15, 40; m 65. SOLID STATE PHYSICS, OPTICAL PHYSICS. *Educ:* Univ Southern Miss, BS, 62; Auburn Univ, MS, 65, PhD(physics), 68. *Prof Exp:* RES PHYSICIST, PHYS SCI LAB, US ARMY MISSILE COMMAND, 68- *Mem:* Am Optical Soc; Am Phys Soc. Sigma Xi. *Res:* Ultra high vacuum techniques; Hall effect in thin metal films; dielectric breakdown in evaporated films; gallium arsenide injection lasers; laser material degradation; optical data processing; laser radar. *Mailing Add:* Res Directorate US Army Missile Res & Develop Command Redstone Arsenal AL 35809

SMITH, JAMES M(ARTYN), JR, b Hoboken, NJ, Oct 15, 20; m 67. ENGINEERING, HEALTH PHYSICS. *Educ:* Stevens Inst Technol, ME, 41; Am Bd Health Physics, Cert, 60. *Prof Exp:* Qual control engr, Remington Arms Div, E I du Pont de Nemours & Co, 41-44, supvr radiation protection, Hanford Atomic Prod Opers, 44-46; supvr radiation protection, 46-52, mgr radiol eng, 52-55, radiol engr, 55-64, CONSULT RADIOL ENGR, NUCLEAR POWER SYSTS DIV, GEN ELEC CO, 64- *Mem:* Am Soc Mech Engrs; Am Nuclear Soc; Health Phys Soc. *Res:* Nuclear power reactor safety and radiation protection; reactor site evaluation; reactor licensing; radioactive waste disposal criteria. *Mailing Add:* 14651 Golf Links Dr Los Gatos CA 95030

SMITH, JAMES PAYNE, JR, b Oklahoma City, Okla, Apr 13, 41. PLANT TAXONOMY, AGROSTOLOGY. *Educ:* Tulsa Univ, BA & BS, 63; Iowa State Univ, PhD(bot), 68. *Prof Exp:* Vis lectr bot, Iowa State Univ, 68-69; asst prof, 69-73, assoc prof, 73-78, PROF BOT, HUMBOLDT STATE UNIV, 78-

Mem: Am Soc Plant Taxon; Bot Soc Am; Soc Study Evolution; Soc Econ Bot; Int Asn Plant Taxonomists. *Res:* Taxonomy of flowering plants; flowering plants of northern California; grasses of the US, especially California. *Mailing Add:* Dept of Biol Humboldt State Univ Arcata CA 95521

SMITH, JAMES R, b Springfield, Mo, Apr 28, 41; m 75; c 2. CELL BIOLOGY. *Educ:* Univ Mo, BS, 63; Univ Ariz, BS, 66; Yale Univ, MPh, 68, PhD(molecular biophys), 70. *Prof Exp:* Teaching asst, Biophys Lab, Yale Univ, 68-69; res assoc microbiol, Stanford Univ, 70-72; res physiologist, Vet Admin Hosp, Martinez, Calif, 72-75; assoc scientist, 75-80, SR SCIENTIST, W ALTON JONES CELL SCI CTR, 80- *Concurrent Pos:* Vis asst res physiologist, Univ Calif, Berkeley, 72-75; adj prof, Dept Biol Sci, State Univ NY Plattsburgh & Biol Dept, North Country Community Col, NY, Saranac Lake; adj assoc prof, Dept Molecular Pharmacol, Univ RI, Kingston & Dept Med Microbiol, Univ Vt, Burlington; adj affil assoc prof life sci, Worcester Polytech Inst, Mass. *Mem:* Tissue Cult Asn; Am Soc Cell Biol; Gerontol Soc. *Res:* Cellular aging; control of cell proliferation. *Mailing Add:* W Alton Jones Cell Sci Ctr Old Barn Rd Lake Placid NY 12946

SMITH, JAMES REAVES, b Columbia, SC, June 6, 42; m 64; c 2. ALGEBRA. *Educ:* Univ SC, BS, 63, PhD(math), 68. *Prof Exp:* Asst prof, 68-72, assoc prof, 72-78, PROF MATH, APPALACHIAN STATE UNIV, 78- *Mem:* Am Math Soc; Math Asn Am; Nat Coun Teachers Math. *Res:* Study of regular modules, those whose submodules are all pure; also projective simple modules. *Mailing Add:* Dept of Math Sci Appalachian State Univ Boone NC 28608

SMITH, JAMES ROSS, b Kingsport, Tenn, Nov 15, 43; m 63; c 2. QUALITY CONTROL, OPERATIONS RESEARCH. *Educ:* Va Polytech Inst & State Univ, BS, 65, MS, 67, PhD(indust eng & opers res), 71. *Prof Exp:* Indust engr, Holston Defense Corp, 66-69; grad asst indust eng, Va Polytech Inst & State Univ, 69-71; asst prof, 71-74, ASSOC PROF INDUST ENG, TENN TECHNOL UNIV, 74- *Mem:* Am Inst Indust Engrs; Am Soc Qual Control. *Res:* Applied statistics and applied operations research. *Mailing Add:* Dept Indust Eng Tenn Technol Univ Cookville TN 38501

SMITH, JAMES S(TERRETT), b Pittsburgh, Pa, Aug 21, 17; m 43; c 5. METALLURGY, CHEMISTRY. *Educ:* Yale Univ, BS, 40, PhD(phys chem), 43. *Prof Exp:* Chemist, Off Sci Res & Develop, Yale Univ, 42; res chemist, Manhattan Proj, Columbia Univ, 43-45 & Carbide & Carbon Chems Corp, NY, 45; res chemist, E I du Pont de Nemours & Co, 45-50, res supvr, 51; sect head, 52-54, res mgr, 54-65, eng mgr metall, 65-77, CONSULT METALL, GTE SYLVANIA, 77- *Mem:* Am Chem Soc; Am Phys Soc. *Res:* Physical and process powder metallurgy of ceramics, molybdenum and wolfram. *Mailing Add:* GTE Sylvania Div Eng Towanda PA 18848

SMITH, JAMES STANLEY, b Ithaca, NY, Apr 7, 39. ENVIRONMENTAL ANALYTICAL CHEMISTRY. *Educ:* Williams Col, AB, 60; Iowa State Univ, PhD(org chem), 64. *Prof Exp:* Fel org chem, Univ Ill, 64-65; asst prof, Eastern Mich Univ, 66-68; fel mass spectros, Cornell Univ, 68-69; supvr anal chem, Allied Corp, 69-81; DIR, ANAL LAB, ROY F WESTON, INC, 81- *Concurrent Pos:* Vis lectr org chem, Univ Ill, 66-69. *Mem:* Am Soc Testing Mat; Am Soc Mass Spectrometry; Am Chem Soc. *Res:* Analysis of drinking water, waste water, air and hazardous chemical waste; development of methodologies to determine environmental pollutants. *Mailing Add:* Roy F Weston, Inc Weston Way West Chester PA 19380

SMITH, JAMES THOMAS, b Springfield, Ohio, Nov 8, 39; m 63; c 1. MATHEMATICS. *Educ:* Harvard Univ, BA, 61; San Francisco State Col, MA, 64; Stanford Univ, MS, 66; Univ Sask, PhD(math), 70. *Prof Exp:* Mathematician, US Naval Radiological Defense Lab, 62-67; instr math, San Francisco State Col, 66-67 & Univ Sask, Regina Campus, 68; assoc prof, 69-77, PROF MATH, SAN FRANCISCO STATE UNIV, 77-, CHMN DEPT, 75- *Mem:* Ger Math Asn; Math Asn Am. *Res:* Foundations of geometry. *Mailing Add:* Dept of Math San Francisco State Univ San Francisco CA 94132

SMITH, JAMES W(ILMARTH), b Charleston, WVa, July 7, 39; m 63; c 2. MATERIALS SCIENCE. *Educ:* Pa State Univ, BS, 61, MS, 63, PhD(solid state sci), 67. *Prof Exp:* Sr physicist, Corning Glass Works, 67-77; MEM STAFF, GTE SYLVANIA, 77- *Mem:* Am Ceramic Soc. *Res:* Ferroelectric materials and devices, including single crystals; sintered and hot-pressed ceramics. *Mailing Add:* GTE Prod Corp RR 25 Federal Rd Kezar Falls ME 04047

SMITH, JAMES W, dairy science, see previous edition

SMITH, JAMES W(ILMER), b Kamloops, BC, June 13, 31; m 58; c 3. CHEMICAL ENGINEERING. *Educ:* Univ BC, BASc, 54, MASc, 55; PhD(chem eng London, PhD(chem eng), 60. *Prof Exp:* Process engr, Du Pont Can, Ont, 55-57; fel chem eng, Univ BC, 61-62; from asst prof to assoc prof, 62-70, PROF CHEM ENG, UNIV TORONTO, 70-, ASSOC CHMN CHEM ENG, 75-, PRES, CHEM ENG RES CONSULTS LTD, 75- *Concurrent Pos:* Consult, Polar Gas Proj, Toronto, 74- *Mem:* Chem Inst Can; Can Soc Chem Eng; Air Pollution Control Asn; Am Indust Hygiene Asn. *Res:* Heat transfer, fluid flow and chemical reaction; properties of particulate systems; industrial hygiene. *Mailing Add:* Dept of Chem Eng Univ of Toronto Toronto ON M5S 1A4 Can

SMITH, JAMES WARREN, b Logan, Utah, July 5, 34; m 58; c 2. CLINICAL PATHOLOGY. *Educ:* Univ Iowa, BA, 56, MD, 59. *Prof Exp:* Resident path, Univ Iowa Hosp, 60-65; pathologist, US Naval Hosp, Chelsea, Mass, 65-67; asst prof, Med Col, Univ Vt, 67-70; PROF PATH, IND UNIV MED CTR, INDIANAPOLIS, 70- *Mem:* Am Soc Clin Path; Col Am Path; Am Soc Microbiol; AMA; Infectious Dis Soc Am. *Res:* Clinical microbiology. *Mailing Add:* Ind Univ Med Ctr Indianapolis IN 46223

SMITH, JAMES WILLIAM, bacteriology, see previous edition

SMITH, JAMES WILLIE, JR, b Jackson, Miss, Mar 17, 44; m 69. ENTOMOLOGY. *Educ:* Miss State Univ, BS, 66; Univ Calif, Riverside, PhD(entom), 70. *Prof Exp:* Res asst entom, Univ Calif, Riverside, 66-69; asst prof, 70-74, ASSOC PROF ENTOM, TEX A&M UNIV, 74- *Mem:* AAAS; Entom Soc Am. *Res:* Insect pest management of field crops; population ecology; resistant plant varieties; biological control. *Mailing Add:* Dept of Entom Tex A&M Univ College Station TX 77843

SMITH, JAMES WINFRED, b Greenwood, Miss, Jan 27, 43; m 66; c 2. ENTOMOLOGY, ECOLOGY. *Educ:* Miss State Univ, BS, 65; La State Univ, MS, 67, PhD(entomol), 70. *Prof Exp:* Asst prof biol, Motlow State Community Col, 70-71; RES ENTOMOLOGIST, BIOENVIRON INSECT RES LAB, SCI & EDUC ADMIN-AGR RES, USDA, 71- *Concurrent Pos:* Assoc, Dept Entomol, Miss State Univ, 74- *Mem:* Entomol Soc Am; Acarological Soc Am; Sigma Xi. *Res:* Field research on the ecology, population dynamics, and control of insect pests by bioenvironmental methods. *Mailing Add:* Bioenviron Insect Res Lab Sci & Educ Admin-Agr Res USDA Stoneville MS 38776

SMITH, JAN D, b Pretoria, SAfrica, Feb 6, 39; m 62; c 3. PULMONARY DISEASES, ANESTHESIOLOGY. *Educ:* Univ Pretoria, MB ChB, 62; Royal Col Physicians UK, MRCP, 73; Am Bd Anesthesiol, dipl, 69; Am Bd Internal Med, dipl, 80. *Prof Exp:* Resident anesthesiol, Sch Med, Harvard Univ, Peter Bent Brigham Hosp, 64-66; fel, Sch Med, Univ Pittsburgh, 66-69, resident, 71; resident int med, Groote Schuur Hosp, Univ Cape Town, 70-71; asst prof int med, Sch Med, Univ Iowa, 74-76; asst prof, 76-80, ASSOC PROF, ANESTHESIOL & INT MED, HEALTH SCI CTR, UNIV TEX, 80- *Mem:* Am Fedn Clin Res; Am Col Chest Physicians; Am Col Physicians; Am Soc Anesthesiol; Am Thoracic Soc. *Res:* Pathogenesis of Shock Lung; carbon dioxide physiology. *Mailing Add:* Univ Tex Health Sci Ctr 7703 Floyd Curl Dr San Antonio TX 78284

SMITH, JAN G, b Yoe, Pa, Sept 25, 38; m 60; c 1. GEOLOGY. *Educ:* Pa State Univ, BS, 60, MS, 61; Univ Tasmania, PhD(geol), 64. *Prof Exp:* Geologist, Continental Oil Co Australia, Ltd, 64-66; res geologist, 66-68, SUPV GEOLOGIST, GULF RES & DEVELOP CO, 68- *Mem:* Geol Soc Am; Am Asn Petrol Geologists; Am Geophys Union. *Res:* Tectonics. *Mailing Add:* Gulf Res & Develop Co PO Box 36506 Houston TX 77036

SMITH, JANICE MINERVA, b Osco, Ill, Oct 13, 06. NUTRITION. *Educ:* Univ Ill, AB, 30, MS, 32, PhD(biochem), 37. *Prof Exp:* Asst nutrit, Univ Ill, 30-36; assoc prof human nutrit res, Pa State Col, 37-43; nutritionist, War Food Admin, USDA, 43-44; prof nutrit, 44-71, head dept home econ, 50-71, EMER PROF NUTRIT, UNIV ILL, URBANA, 71- *Concurrent Pos:* Mem community-family consumer work group, USDA, 63-64; mem, Nat Adv Comn Food & Fiber, 65-67. *Mem:* AAAS; Am Home Econ Asn; Am Dietetic Asn; Am Inst Nutrit; NY Acad Sci. *Res:* Protein requirements of adults; calcium requirements of adolescents and preschool children; nutritional status of selected population in Pennsylvania and Illinois; riboflavin and thiamine needs of preadolescents; energy and dietary needs of aging. *Mailing Add:* 1112 S Pine St Champaign IL 61820

SMITH, JAY ALFRED, b Vincennes, Ind, Sept 21, 13; m 39; c 2. PHYSIOLOGY. *Educ:* DePauw Univ, AB, 36; Johns Hopkins Univ, MA, 38, PhD(physiol), 39. *Prof Exp:* Asst, Johns Hopkins Univ, 36-39; head dept biol, Springfield Col, 39-40; from instr to assoc prof physiol, 40-59, PROF PHYSIOL, CHICAGO MED SCH, 59-, DIR, DEPT MED COMMUN, UNIV HEALTH SCI, 70- *Res:* Sex inversion in molluscs; effects of temperature on growth of protozoa; toxicity of thiamine; basic mechanism of action of digitalis. *Mailing Add:* Univ of Health Sci Chicago Med Sch Chicago IL 60612

SMITH, JAY HAMILTON, b Rexburg, Idaho, June 5, 27; m 49; c 5. SOIL MICROBIOLOGY. *Educ:* Brigham Young Univ, BS, 51; Utah State Univ, MS, 53; Cornell Univ, PhD(soil microbiol), 55. *Prof Exp:* Soil microbiologist, Soil & Water Conserv Res Div, US Dept Agr, SC, 55-58, soil scientist, Soils Lab, Agr Res Serv, Md, 58-64, SOIL SCIENTIST, SNAKE RIVER CONSERV RES CTR, AGR RES SERV, USDA, 64- *Concurrent Pos:* Soil scientist, Clemson Col, 55-58; prof, Utah State Univ, 64- & Univ Idaho, 68- *Mem:* AAAS; Soil Sci Soc Am; Soil Conserv Soc Am; Am Soc Agron. *Res:* Instrumentation of soil organic matter and nitrogen; chemistry of soil nitrogen; microbiology of irrigation water and drainage; land disposal of food processing wastes. *Mailing Add:* Snake River Conserv Res Ctr USDA Rte 1 Box 186 Kimberly ID 83341

SMITH, JEAN BLAIR, b Detroit, Mich, Sept 23, 42; m 67; c 2. CLINICAL CHEMISTRY. *Educ:* WVa Univ, BA, 65; Univ Kans, PhD(anal chem), 68. *Prof Exp:* Staff electrochemist, Artificial Eye Proj, Univ Utah, 72-76, res instr, Bioeng Dept, 76-77; res chemist, Vet Admin Hosp, 77-81; RES ASST PROF, DEPT PATH, MED CTR, UNIV UTAH, 81- *Mem:* Am Asn Clin Chemists. *Res:* Role of prostaglandins in platelet aggregation; ion transport mechanisms of erythrocytes. *Mailing Add:* Dept Path Med Ctr Univ Utah 50 N Medical Dr Salt Lake City UT 84132

SMITH, JEAN E, b Buffalo, NY, Jan 15, 32; m 65. ANIMAL ECOLOGY. *Educ:* Ohio Univ, BS, 54, MS, 56, PhD(zool), 62. *Prof Exp:* Instr biol, Alderson-Broaddus Col, 56-57; asst prof, Adams State Col, 62-66; assoc prof, Metrop State Col, 66-69; assoc prof, 69-80, PROF BIOL SCI, CARROLL COL, MONT, 80-, CHMN DEPT, 78- *Mem:* AAAS; Ecol Soc Am; Am Ornith Union; Cooper Ornith Soc; Am Inst Biol Sci. *Res:* Vertebrate ecology; population dynamics; community energy relations; animal behavior; niche segregation. *Mailing Add:* Dept of Biol Carroll Col Helena MT 59601

SMITH, JEFFREY DREW, b Wearhead, Durham, Eng, Aug 2, 22; m 50; c 2. PLANT PATHOLOGY, MYCOLOGY. *Educ:* Univ Durham, BSc, 46, MSc, 57. *Prof Exp:* Demonstr agr bot, King's Col, Univ Durham, 46-48, jr lectr plant path, 48-51; res plant pathologist, Sports Turf Res Inst, Eng, 51-58; exten plant pathologist, NScotland Col Agr, Aberdeen, 58-60; prin sci officer,

Res Div, NZ Dept Agr, 60-64; RES SCIENTIST, RES BR, CAN DEPT AGR, 65- *Concurrent Pos:* NZ Dept Agr overseas res grant, Rothamsted Exp Sta, Eng, 62; vis scientist, Ore State Univ, 70 & Norweg Plant Protection Inst, 74-75. *Mem:* Can Phytopath Soc; Brit Inst Biol; Brit Mycol Soc. *Res:* Epidemiology and control of diseases of forage, range and turf grasses; psychophilic fungi and mycotoxicology. *Mailing Add:* 306 Egbert Saskatoon SK S7N 1X1 Can

SMITH, JEROME ALLAN, b Lansing, Mich, Apr 17, 40; m 62; c 2. AERONAUTICAL ENGINEERING, FLUID MECHANICS. *Educ:* Univ Mich, BSE, 62, Calif Inst Technol, MS, 63, PhD, 67. *Prof Exp:* From asst prof to assoc prof aerospace & mech sci, Princeton Univ, 67-78, prof, 78-79; TECH DIR, OFF NAVAL RES, 79- *Concurrent Pos:* Mem, Lab Adv Bd Surface Weapons, US Navy, 73-78, chmn, 75-78; consult, McDonnell Douglas Res Labs, 74-79. *Mem:* Am Phys Soc; AAAS; Sigma Xi. *Res:* Experimental investigation of high speed flow-shock tubes and hypersonic wind tunnels. *Mailing Add:* Off Tech Dir Off Naval Res Arlington VA 22217

SMITH, JEROME PAUL, b Ft Wayne, Ind, Apr 18, 46. ANALYTICAL CHEMISTRY, OCCUPATIONAL HEALTH. *Educ:* Col St Thomas, BA, 69; Univ Colo, PhD(anal chem), 73. *Prof Exp:* Asst res chemist, Univ Calif, Riverside, 73-77; AEROSOL RES SPECIALIST, NAT INST OCCUP SAFETY & HEALTH, 78- *Res:* Analytical chemistry applied to the measurement of contaminants in the workplace; health assessment for contaminants in the workplace. *Mailing Add:* Nat Inst for Occup Safety & Health Cincinnati OH 45226

SMITH, JERRY HOWARD, b Mobile, Ala, Jan 28, 44; m 67. ORGANIC CHEMISTRY, BIO-ORGANIC CHEMISTRY. *Educ:* Auburn Univ, BS, 66; Emory Univ, PhD(org chem), 70. *Prof Exp:* Fel, Univ Chicago, 70-72, NIH fel, 71-72; asst prof chem, Marquette Univ, 72-76; RES CHEMIST, ICI AMERICAS, 77- *Mem:* AAAS; Am Chem Soc. *Res:* Mechanistic organic chemistry; enzyme mechanisms. *Mailing Add:* Corp Res Dept ICI United States Inc Wilmington DE 19897

SMITH, JERRY JOSEPH, b Oblong, Ill, Feb 8, 39; m 55; c 4. PHYSICAL INORGANIC CHEMISTRY. *Educ:* Univ Ill, BS, 61; Univ Calif, Berkeley, PhD(inorg chem), 65. *Prof Exp:* Instr inorg chem & sr res assoc, Univ Wash, 66-70; asst prof chem, Drexel Univ, 70-76; chemist, Chicago Off Naval Res, 76-78; CHEMIST, ARLINGTON OFF NAVAL RES, 78- *Mem:* Electrochem Soc; Am Chem Soc. *Res:* Electrochemistry; surface science; interfacial processes. *Mailing Add:* Off Naval Res Arlington VA 22217

SMITH, JERRY MORGAN, b Winchester, Va, Mar 13, 34; m 57; c 2. PHARMACOLOGY, TOXICOLOGY. *Educ:* The Citadel, BS, 56; Med Col SC, MS, 59; Univ Kans, PhD(pharmacol), 64. *Prof Exp:* Fel pharmacol, Emory Univ, 63-65; NIH fel, 64-65; res pharmacologist, Lederle Labs, Am Cyanamid Co, 65-69; sect head toxicol, Wellcome Res Labs, Burroughs Wellcome & Co, 69-70; dir toxicity, Biodynamics, Inc, 70-73; CHIEF TOXICOLOGIST & MGR TOXICOL RES, ROHM AND HAAS CO, 73- *Res:* Renal and biochemical pharmacology; teratology; toxicology, especially pharmaceutical, pesticide, food and chemical. *Mailing Add:* Rohm and Haas Co Norristown & Mckean Rds Spring House PA 19477

SMITH, JERRY WARREN, b Welch, WVa, Oct 8, 42; m 67; c 1. VIROLOGY, IMMUNOLOGY. *Educ:* Marshall Univ, BS, 64; Ohio Univ, MS, 66; Univ Iowa, PhD(microbiol), 70. *Prof Exp:* NIH fel, Baylor Col Med, 70-72; asst prof, 72-77, ASSOC PROF MICROBIOL, LA STATE UNIV MED CTR, NEW ORLEANS, 77- *Mem:* Am Soc Microbiol. *Res:* Immunological interactions between viruses and hosts; relationship between herpes viruses and human cancers. *Mailing Add:* Dept of Microbiol La State Univ Med Ctr New Orleans LA 70112

SMITH, JESSE GRAHAM, JR, b Winston-Salem, NC, Nov 22, 28; m 50; c 3. DERMATOLOGY, GERONTOLOGY. *Educ:* Duke Univ, MD, 51. *Prof Exp:* From asst resident to resident dermat, Duke Univ Hosp, 54-56 & Jackson Mem Hosp, 5657; from instr to asst prof, Univ Miami, 57-60; from assoc prof to prof, Sch Med, Duke Univ, 60-67; actg chmn dept path, 73-75, PROF DERMAT & MED & CHMN DEPT DERMAT, MED COL GA, 67- *Concurrent Pos:* Nat Inst Arthritis & Metab Dis fel, 57-60; mem, Gen Med A Study Sect, NIH, 64-69, chmn, 68-69, mem, Dermat Training Grants Comt, 69-73 & Adv Coun, Nat Inst Arthritis, Metab & Digestive Dis, 75-79; chief staff, Eugene Talmadge Mem Hosp, 70-72; mem & dir, Am Bd Dermat, 74-; ed, Jour Am Acad Dermatol, 78- *Honors & Awards:* Am Dermat Asn Award, 59 & 60; Clyde L Cummer Gold Award, Am Acad Dermat, 63. *Mem:* Soc Invest Dermat (pres, 78-79); AMA; Am Dermat Asn (secy, 76-81, pres, 81-82); fel Am Col Physicians; Am Fedn Clin Res. *Res:* Aging of the skin. *Mailing Add:* Dept of Dermat Med Col of Ga Augusta GA 30902

SMITH, JOE K, b Burlington, Ky, Feb 5, 30; m 60. MATHEMATICS. *Educ:* Eastern Ky State Col, BS, 52; Fla State Univ, MS, 57, EdD(math), 67. *Prof Exp:* Instr math, Cent Fla Jr Col, 58-60; instr, Miami Dade Jr Col, 60-63, assoc prof, 64-65; teacher high sch, Fla, 65-66; asst prof, Western Ky Univ, 66-69, assoc prof, 69-71; ASSOC PROF MATH, NORTHERN KY UNIV COL, 71- *Mem:* Math Asn Am; Am Meteorol Soc; Nat Coun Teachers Math. *Res:* Mathematics education. *Mailing Add:* Dept of Math Northern Ky Univ Highland Heights KY 41076

SMITH, JOE M(AUK), b Sterling, Colo, Feb 14, 16; m 43; c 2. CHEMICAL ENGINEERING. *Educ:* Calif Inst Technol, BS, 37; Mass Inst Technol, ScD(chem eng), 43. *Prof Exp:* Design engr, Tex Co, NY, 37-38; res engr, Stand Oil Co, Calif, 38-41; asst, Nat Defense Res Comt, Mass Inst Technol, 42-43, instr chem eng, 43; asst prof, Univ Md, 43-44; proj engr, Publicker Com Alcohol Co, Pa, 44-45; from asst prof to prof chem eng, Purdue Univ, 45-57, asst dir eng exp sta, 54-57; dean col technol, Univ NH, 57; prof chem eng & chmn dept, Northwestern Univ, 57-60, Walter P Murphy distinguished prof, 59-61; PROF CHEM ENG & CHMN DEPT, UNIV CALIF, DAVIS, 61- *Concurrent Pos:* Res Corp grant, 46-48; Guggenheim fel & Fulbright res scholar, Delft Univ Technol, 53-54; Ford Found scholar, Argentina, 61; hon prof, Univ Buenos Aires, 63-; Fulbright awards, Argentina, 63, 66 & Spain, 65. *Honors & Awards:* Walker Award, Am Inst Chem Engrs, 60. *Mem:* Nat Acad Eng; Am Chem Soc; Am Soc Eng Educ; Am Inst Chem Engrs. *Res:* Interaction of physical and chemical processes in heterogeneous reactions; heat transfer combined with chemical reaction; applied chemical kinetics and reactor design. *Mailing Add:* Dept of Chem Eng Univ of Calif Davis CA 95616

SMITH, JOE NELSON, JR, b Washington, DC, June 24, 32; m 52; c 3. SURFACE PHYSICS, SOLID STATE PHYSICS. *Educ:* Calif Inst Technol, BS, 58, MS, 59; Nat Univ Leiden, PhD, 70. *Prof Exp:* Staff mem atomic physics, Gen Atomic Div, Gen Dynamics Corp, 59-69; vis scientist, FOM Inst Atomic & Molecular Physics, Neth, 69-70; sr staff physicist, Gulf Radiation Technol Div, Gulf Energy & Environ Systs Co, 70-72; sr staff physicist, IRT Corp, 72-74; STAFF SURFACE PHYSICIST, GEN ATOMIC CO, 74- *Mem:* Am Phys Soc; Am Vacuum Soc; Am Nuclear Soc. *Res:* Experimental research in particle-surface interactions including momentum and energy transfer, chemical reaction and catalysis, surface ionization; sputtering, radiation damage in surface region of solids, secondary ion mass spectrometry and auger electron spectroscopy. *Mailing Add:* RFD 1 Box 138F-3 Del Mar CA 92014

SMITH, JOHN, b Selkirk, Scotland, May 4, 38. PHYSICS. *Educ:* Univ Edinburgh, BS, 60, MS, 61, PhD, 63. *Prof Exp:* Joint Inst Nuclear Res, Dubna, Russia, 63; NATO res fel, Niels Bohr Inst, Copenhagen, Denmark, 64-65; Rothman res fel, Univ Adelaide, 66-67; res assoc, 67-69, asst prof, 69-74, assoc prof, 74-78, PROF PHYSICS, INST THEORET PHYSICS, STATE UNIV NY STONY BROOK, 78- *Mem:* Edinburgh Math Soc; Am Inst Physics. *Res:* Elementary particle physics. *Mailing Add:* Dept of Physics Inst Theoret Phys State Univ NY Stony Brook NY 11794

SMITH, JOHN COLE, b Anniston, Ala, Jan 26, 35; m 59; c 2. ENTOMOLOGY. *Educ:* Auburn Univ, BS, 57, MS, 61; La State Univ, PhD(entom), 65. *Prof Exp:* Asst prof entom, 65-71, ASSOC PROF ENTOM, VA POLYTECH INST & STATE UNIV, 71- *Mem:* Entom Soc Am. *Res:* Research on insects affecting peanuts and soybeans, primarily through chemical and biological control with major emphasis on resistant plant lines. *Mailing Add:* Tidewater Res & Cont Educ Ctr Holland Sta Suffolk VA 23437

SMITH, JOHN EDGAR, b West Alexander, Pa, June 14, 39. NUTRITIONAL BIOCHEMISTRY. *Educ:* WLiberty State Col, BS, 61; WVa Univ, MS, 65; Univ Nebr, Lincoln, PhD(nutrit), 70. *Prof Exp:* Teacher high sch, Ohio, 61-62; trainee med, Columbia Univ, 69-72, res assoc, 72-80; MEM FAC NUTRIT PROG, COL HUMAN DEVELOP, PA STATE UNIV, 80- *Mem:* AAAS; Am Chem Soc; Am Soc Animal Sci; Am Inst Nutrit. *Res:* Fat-soluble vitamin transport in blood. *Mailing Add:* Nutrit Prog Col Human Develop Pa State Univ University Park PA 16802

SMITH, JOHN ELVANS, b Washington, DC, Sept 6, 29; m 62; c 3. ANALYTICAL CHEMISTRY. *Educ:* Univ Colo, BA, 52, PhD(anal chem), 60. *Prof Exp:* Res chemist, US Naval Res Lab, DC, 60-62; asst prof chem, Pueblo Col, 62-64, assoc prof, Southern Colo State Col, 64-70, PROF CHEM, UNIV SOUTHERN COLO, 70-, HEAD DEPT, 64- *Mem:* Am Chem Soc. *Res:* Energy conservation; gas chromatography; electroanalytical chemistry; spectrographic and spectrophotometric analysis. *Mailing Add:* Dept of Chem Univ of Southern Colo Pueblo CO 81001

SMITH, JOHN ERNEST, JR, b Glassport, Pa, Apr 26, 39. SOLID STATE PHYSICS. *Educ:* Mass Inst Technol, SB, 61; Univ Ill, Urbana, MS, 63, PhD(physics), 67. *Prof Exp:* Asst physics, Univ Ill, Urbana, 61-67; res staff mem semiconductor physics, Thomas J Watson Res Ctr, 67-78, MEM CORP TECH COMT STAFF, IBM CORP HQ, IBM CORP, 78- *Mem:* Am Phys Soc. *Res:* Raman scattering and optical properties of solids; low temperature physics and superconductivity; semiconductor physics; high field transport in semiconductors; chemical vapor deposition systems. *Mailing Add:* IBM Corp Headquarters Old Orchard Rd Armonk NY 10504

SMITH, JOHN F(RANCIS), b Kansas City, Kans, May 9, 23; m 47; c 2. METALLURGY, PHYSICAL CHEMISTRY. *Educ:* Univ Mo-Kansas City, BA, 48; Iowa State Univ, PhD(phys chem), 53. *Prof Exp:* Assoc prof, 54-63, chmn dept, 66-70, div chief, Inst Atomic Res, 66-70, chemist & metallurgist, 53-66, PROF MAT SCI & ENG, IOWA STATE UNIV, 63-, SR METALLURGIST & SECT CHIEF, AMES LAB, DEPT ENERGY, 70- *Concurrent Pos:* Mem, World Metall Cong, Chicago, 57; consult, Tex Instruments, 58-63, Argonne Nat Lab, 64-70 & Iowa Hwy Comn, 73- *Mem:* Fel Am Inst Chemists; Am Soc Metals; Am Crystallog Asn; Metall Soc; Am Inst Mining, Metall & Petrol Engrs. *Res:* Crystal structures and thermodynamics of alloys and intermetallic compounds; relationships between energetics, crystal structures, and physical properties. *Mailing Add:* Dept Mat Sci & Eng 124 Metall Bldg Iowa State Univ Ames IA 50011

SMITH, JOHN FREDERICK, b London, Eng, May 11, 22; nat US; m 48; c 3. POLYMER CHEMISTRY. *Educ:* Univ London, BSc, 49, PhD, 51. *Prof Exp:* Res chemist, Imp Chem Industs, Ltd, 51-52 & BC Res Coun, Can, 52-54; RES CHEMIST, E I DU PONT DE NEMOURS & CO, INC, 54- *Mem:* Am Chem Soc. *Res:* Chemistry and technology of production and application of natural and synthetic elastomers; technology of adhesives. *Mailing Add:* Exp Sta E I du Pont de Nemours & Co Inc Wilmington DE 19898

SMITH, JOHN HARRY GILBERT, b Kamloops, BC, May 28, 25; m 53; c 3. FORESTRY. *Educ:* Univ BC, BSF, 49; Yale Univ, MF, 50, PhD, 55. *Prof Exp:* Instr forest mensuration, 50-51, asst prof mensuration, photogram & statist, 52-60, assoc prof mensuration photogram & statist, 60-63, PROF FOREST LAND & TIMBER MGT, UNIV BC, 63- *Concurrent Pos:* Study group leader forest resources res, Sci Coun Can; UN Develop Prog & Food & Agr Orgn assignments in forestry, Turkey, Taiwan, Ecuador & Dominican Repub; ed, Forestry Chronicle, 60-66. *Mem:* Soc Am Foresters; Am Soc Photogram; Can Inst Forestry; Biomet Soc. *Res:* Forest management, mensuration, economics and silviculture; tree form and taper, yield tables, dendochronology; economics, objectives and methods of forest resources management. *Mailing Add:* Fac of Forestry Univ of BC Vancouver BC V6T 1W5 Can

SMITH, JOHN HENRY, b Gilman, Iowa, July 18, 04; m 36. STATISTICS. *Educ:* Iowa State Teachers Col, BA, 35; Univ Chicago, MBA, 39, PhD(bus), 41. *Prof Exp:* Instr statist, Univ Chicago, 40-42; statistician, US Bur Labor Statist, 42-47; prof statist, 47-73, EMER PROF STATIST, AM UNIV, 73- *Mailing Add:* 4803 Westway Dr Bethesda MD 20816

SMITH, JOHN HENRY, b Rome, NY, July 3, 37. PHYSICAL METALLURGY. *Educ:* Lafayette Col, AB & BS, 58; Mo Sch Mines, MS, 59; Mass Inst Technol, ScD(metall), 64. *Prof Exp:* Res asst metall, Mass Inst Technol, 59-64; aerospace scientist, NASA Lewis Res Ctr, 64-66; sr res engr, Res Ctr, US Steel Corp, 66-75; METALLURGIST, NAT BUR STANDARDS, 75- *Concurrent Pos:* Dept Commerce sci & technol fel, 80-81. *Mem:* AAAS; Am Soc Metals; Am Inst Mining, Metall & Petrol Eng; Am Welding Soc; Am Soc Mech Engrs. *Res:* Mechanical metallurgy; fracture mechanics; stress corrosion; fatigue; corrosion fatigue; welding. *Mailing Add:* A-113 Mat Bldg Nat Bur Standards Washington DC 20234

SMITH, JOHN HOWARD, b Ithaca, NY, Jan 21, 37. MATHEMATICS. *Educ:* Cornell Univ, AB, 58; Mass Inst Technol, PhD(math), 63. *Prof Exp:* Instr math, Univ Mich, 63-65, asst prof, 65-66; vis lectr, Mass Inst Technol, 66-67; asst prof, 67-69, ASSOC PROF MATH, BOSTON COL, 69- *Mem:* Am Math Soc; Math Asn Am. *Res:* Algebraic number theory. *Mailing Add:* Dept of Math Boston Col Chestnut Hill MA 02167

SMITH, JOHN KELLY, infectious diseases, immunology, see previous edition

SMITH, JOHN LESLIE, JR, b Waco, Tex, Dec 2, 24; m 64. MEDICINE. *Educ:* Tulane Univ, MD, 48; Am Bd Path, dipl, 55. *Prof Exp:* Asst pathologist, Armed Forces Inst Path, 55-57; from asst pathologist to assoc pathologist, Univ Tex M D Anderson Hosp & Tumor Inst Houston, 57-74; from asst prof to assoc prof, 57-74, PROF PATH, UNIV TEX GRAD SCH BIOMED SCI HOUSTON, 74-, PATHOLOGIST, UNIV TEX M D ANDERSON HOSP & TUMOR INST HOUSTON, 74- *Mem:* Int Acad Path; Am Soc Clin Path; Am Acad Dermat; Am Soc Dermatopath; AMA. *Res:* Pathology; neoplastic diseases. *Mailing Add:* Dept of Path M D Anderson Hosp & Tumor Inst Houston TX 77025

SMITH, JOHN M, b Indianapolis, Ind, May 20, 22; m 48; c 3. ECONOMIC GEOLOGY, CLAY MINERALOGY. *Educ:* Ind Univ, BS, 52, MA, 54. *Prof Exp:* Geologist, Ind Geol Surv, 54-57; geologist, 57-67, CHIEF GEOLOGIST & DIR, GA KAOLIN CO INC, 67- *Concurrent Pos:* Mem, State Bd Regist Prof Geologists, Ga, 75-81. *Mem:* Fel Geol Soc Am; Clay Minerals Soc; Am Inst Mining, Metall & Petrol Engrs. *Res:* Evaluation of United States and foreign nonmetallic mineral deposits; direction of exploration and development of nonmetallics; research and development of clay minerals, especially kaolinite. *Mailing Add:* Ga Kaolin Co Dry Branch GA 31020

SMITH, JOHN MELVIN, b Washington, DC, Apr 16, 37; m 59; c 4. MATHEMATICS EDUCATION. *Educ:* Univ Richmond, BS, 59; Univ Md, MA, 61, PhD(math, educ), 70. *Prof Exp:* Instr math, Georgetown Univ, 62-66; from instr to assoc prof, 66-75, PROF MATH EDUC, GEORGE MASON UNIV, 75- *Concurrent Pos:* Mathematician, Nat Bur Standards, 57- *Mem:* Am Math Soc; Math Asn Am; Nat Coun Teachers Math. *Res:* Matrix theory; computer applications; elementary school mathematics. *Mailing Add:* Dept of Gen Studies George Mason Univ Fairfax VA 22030

SMITH, JOHN ROBERT, b Salt Lake City, Utah, Oct 1, 40; m 62; c 2. THEORETICAL SOLID STATE PHYSICS. *Educ:* Toledo Univ, BS, 62; Ohio State Univ, PhD(physics), 68. *Prof Exp:* Aerospace engr surface physics, Lewis Res Ctr, NASA, 65-68, fel solid state theory, Univ Calif, San Diego, 70-72; sr res physicist & head, Surface & Interface Physics Group, 72-80, ST STAFF SCIENTIST & HEAD, SOLID STATE PHYSICS GROUP, GEN MOTORS, 80- *Concurrent Pos:* Air Force Off Sci Res & Nat Res Coun fel, Univ Calif, 70-72. *Mem:* Fel Am Phys Soc; Am Vacuum Soc; Sigma Xi. *Res:* Theory of solid surfaces, electronic properties, spectroscopy and chemisorption; nonlinear optics; adhesion, metal contact electronic structure; defects in solids. *Mailing Add:* Physics Dept Gen Motors Res Warren MI 48090

SMITH, JOHN ROBERT, b Los Angeles, Calif, Apr 17, 48. PHARMACOLOGY. *Educ:* Loyola Univ, Calif, BS, 70; Ore State Univ, MS, 74, PhD(pharmacol), 76. *Prof Exp:* Fel pharmacol, Sch Med, Univ Wash, 75-77; asst prof, Sch Dent Med, Southern Ill Univ, 77-79; ASST PROF & SR RESEARCHER COMP PHARMACOL, MARINE SCI CTR, ORE STATE UNIV, 79- *Mem:* AAAS; Am Asn Dent Schs. *Res:* Comparative neuropharmacology and toxicology. *Mailing Add:* Marine Sci Ctr Marine Sci Dr Newport OR 91365

SMITH, JOHN THURMOND, b Mo, May 29, 25; m 55. BIOCHEMISTRY. *Educ:* Culver-Stockton Col, BA, 51; Univ Mo, MS, 53, PhD(agr chem), 55. *Prof Exp:* Asst agr chem, Univ Mo, 52-55, res assoc biochem, 55; res assoc biochem, Univ Tenn, Memphis, 56-58, from instr to assoc prof nutrit, 58-65, PROF NUTRIT, UNIV TENN, KNOXVILLE, 65- *Mem:* Am Inst Nutrit; Am Chem Soc. *Res:* Chemistry of sulfur compounds and sulphatases; dietary sulfur and xenobiotic metabolism; enzyme chemistry; food phosphates; importance of inorganic sulfate, enzymes, metabolic obesity. *Mailing Add:* Dept Nutrit & Food Sci Food Systs Admin Univ of Tenn Knoxville TN 37996

SMITH, JOHN W(ARREN), b De Soto, Mo, Nov 18, 43; m 64; c 3. ENVIRONMENTAL ENGINEERING, CIVIL ENGINEERING. *Educ:* Mo Sch Mines & Metall, BS, 65; Univ Mo-Rolla, MS, 67, PhD(civil eng), 68. *Prof Exp:* Instr civil eng & res asst environ eng, Univ Mo-Rolla, 65-68; proj engr, Esso Res & Eng Co, 68-70; from asst prof to assoc prof environ eng, 70-75, actg dir, Ctr Alluvial Valley Studies, 77-79, PROF CIVIL ENG, MEMPHIS STATE UNIV, 75- *Concurrent Pos:* Mem bd consults, Ryckman, Edgerly, Tomlinson & Assocs, 71-72; actg dep city engr, City of Memphis, 73-74. *Mem:* Water Pollution Control Fedn; Am Water Works Asn. *Res:* Industrial and municipal waste treatment; water resources; biological wastewater treatment using fixed film reactors, hazardous waste analysis and management, water reuse; kinetics of fixed film reactors and low energy treatment systems. *Mailing Add:* Dept Civil Eng Memphis State Univ Memphis TN 38152

SMITH, JOHN WESLEY, b Paducah, Ky, July 14, 32; m 55; c 2. CHEMICAL ENGINEERING. *Educ:* Vanderbilt Univ, BE, 55. *Prof Exp:* Process engr, 55-60, sect head, 60-69, mgr new prod develop, 69-70, MGR PROD RES DEPT, BUCKEYE CELLULOSE CORP, PROCTER & GAMBLE CO, 70- *Mem:* Tech Asn Pulp & Paper Indust; Am Inst Chem Engrs. *Mailing Add:* 2899 Jackson Ave Memphis TN 38108

SMITH, JOHN WOLFGANG, b Vienna, Austria, Feb 18, 30; US citizen. MATHEMATICS. *Educ:* Cornell Univ, AB, 48; Purdue Univ, MS, 50; Columbia Univ, PhD(math), 57. *Prof Exp:* Aerodynamicist, Bell Aircraft Corp, 50-53; C L E Moore instr math, Mass Inst Technol, 58-61; asst prof, Univ Calif, Los Angeles, 61-64; assoc prof, 64-67, PROF MATH, ORE STATE UNIV, 67- *Mem:* Am Math Soc. *Res:* Differential geometry; algebraic topology. *Mailing Add:* Dept of Math Ore State Univ Corvallis OR 97331

SMITH, JONATHAN JEREMY BERKELEY, b Leicester, Eng, Dec 26, 40; m 67, 81. ZOOLOGY. *Educ:* Cambridge Univ, BA, 62, PhD(zool), 65, MA, 66. *Prof Exp:* Asst prof zool, 65-71, ASSOC PROF ZOOL, UNIV TORONTO, 71- *Mem:* AAAS; Brit Soc Exp Biol; Can Soc Zool; Can Entom Soc; NY Acad Sci. *Res:* Sensory physiology; chemoreception and feeding in insects, particularly blood-feeders; hearing mechanisms in lower vertebrates. *Mailing Add:* Dept Zool Univ Toronto Toronto ON M5S 1A1 Can

SMITH, JOSEPH COLLINS, b Knoxville, Tenn, Oct 26, 28; m 53; c 1. ENGINEERING, ASTRONOMY. *Educ:* US Naval Acad, BS, 53; George Washington Univ, MA, 64. *Prof Exp:* Mem staff opers of Comdr Submarines Pac, 64-66; commanding officer submarines, USS Odax (55-484), 66-68; mem staff opers & plans submarines of Chief Naval Opers, 68-71; asst chief staff opers of Comdr Antisubmarine Warfare Forces, US Sixth Fleet, 71-74; prof & head dept naval sci, Iowa State Univ, 74-76; supt-in-chg time & navig, US Naval Observ, 76-79; CONSULT, 79- *Concurrent Pos:* Mem bd, Coast Guard Adv Bd, 76- *Honors & Awards:* Secy Navy Commendation, 61. *Mem:* Naval Inst; Inst Navig. *Res:* Astrometric instrumentation; timing; fundamental positioning; global navigational equipment; systems improvements; radio interferometry. *Mailing Add:* 6806 Northfield Dr Annandale VA 22003

SMITH, JOSEPH DONALD, b New Brunswick, NJ, Sept 18, 43. BIOCHEMISTRY. *Educ:* Columbia Univ, AB, 65; Univ Chicago, PhD(biochem), 69. *Prof Exp:* Res molecular biol, Albert Einstein Col Med, 70-74; res scientist neurosci, NY State Psychiat Inst, 74-75; ASST PROF CHEM, MIAMI UNIV, 75- *Concurrent Pos:* Asst prof biochem, Sch Med, Wright State Univ, 75-77. *Mem:* Am Chem Soc; AAAS; Am Soc Microbiol; NY Acad Sci; Am Soc Biol Chem. *Mailing Add:* Dept of Chem Miami Univ Oxford OH 45056

SMITH, JOSEPH EMMITT, b Big Spring, Tex, Jan 24, 38; m 60; c 2. CLINICAL PATHOLOGY, PHYSIOLOGY. *Educ:* Tex A&M Univ, BS, 59, DVM, 61; Univ Calif, Davis, PhD(comp path), 64. *Prof Exp:* Lab asst vet anat, Tex A&M Univ, 58-59, NSF res trainee reproduction physiol, 59-61; USPHS trainee metab & hemat dis, Univ Calif, Davis, 61-64; assoc res scientist, City of Hope Med Ctr, Duarte, Calif, 64-66; from asst prof to assoc prof path, Okla State Univ, 66-69; PROF PATH, COL VET MED, KANS STATE UNIV, 69- *Concurrent Pos:* USPHS res grant, 65-; career develop awardee, NIH. *Mem:* Am Vet Med Asn; Am Asn Clin Chemists; Am Soc Vet Clin Path; Soc Exp Biol & Med; Am Col Vet Path. *Res:* Inherited metabolic errors of animals which serve as models of human disorders, particularly those of erythrocyte metabolism; clinical enzymology. *Mailing Add:* Col of Vet Med Kans State Univ Manhattan KS 66502

SMITH, JOSEPH H, JR, b Moscow, Pa, July 9, 25. ELECTRICAL ENGINEERING. *Educ:* Rensselaer Polytech Inst, BEE, 45, MEE, 54. *Prof Exp:* From instr to asst prof, 45-59, asst dept head, 59-60, exec officer dept elec eng, 60-69, ASSOC PROF ELEC ENG, RENSSELAER POLYTECH INST, 60-, ASST DEAN ENG FOR PRE-ENG CURRIC, 69- *Mem:* AAAS; Am Soc Eng Educ. *Res:* Electromechanical energy conversion, especially recent developments in speed control of alternating current saturistor motors; transmission or transfer of power in a multimachine system. *Mailing Add:* Sch of Eng 102 Sage Rensselaer Polytech Inst Troy NY 12181

SMITH, JOSEPH HAROLD, b Fielding, Utah, Oct 5, 14; m 40; c 5. PHYSICAL CHEMISTRY, INORGANIC CHEMISTRY. *Educ:* Univ Utah, BS, 36, MA, 38; Univ Wis, PhD(phys chem), 41. *Prof Exp:* Asst chem, Univ Utah, 36-38; asst, Univ Wis, 38-41; instr, Univ Ill, 41-43; assoc prof, 43-47, PROF CHEM, UNIV MASS, AMHERST, 47- *Concurrent Pos:* Consult, Chicopee Mfg Corp, 51-; indust consult, Johnson & Johnson. *Mem:* Am Chem Soc. *Res:* Chemical kinetics; coordination complexes; spectrophotometrics of complex ions; gas phase kinetics of nitrogen oxides; carbon dioxide absorption rates in alkaline solutions. *Mailing Add:* Dept of Chem Univ of Mass Amherst MA 01002

SMITH, JOSEPH JAMES, b New York, NY, Apr 6, 21; m 46; c 7. CHEMISTRY, RESEARCH ADMINISTRATION. *Educ:* Fordham Univ BS, 43. *Hon Degrees:* DS, WVa State Col, 75. *Prof Exp:* Res chemist, Bakelite Co Div, Union Carbide & Carbon Corp, 43-51, proj leader, 51-53, group leader, 53-56, sect head, Union Carbide Plastics Co, 56-64, asst dir, 64-66, tech mgr polyolefins & asst dir res & develop, Chem Div, 66-67, DIR CHEM & PLASTICS DIV, UNION CARBIDE CORP, 67- *Honors & Awards:* Medal, Am Inst Chemists, 43. *Mem:* Am Chem Soc. *Res:* Surface chemistry; corrosion and protective coatings; infrared and ultraviolet spectrophotometry; chemistry of organic high polymers; catalysis; organometallic compounds; polyolefins; electron irradiation; program management of research and development organizations. *Mailing Add:* Chem & Plastics Div Union Carbide Corp Charleston WV 25303

SMITH, JOSEPH JAY, b Cementon, NY, Feb 13, 15; m 62; c 3. OBSTETRICS & GYNECOLOGY. *Educ:* Cornell Univ, AB, 36; Long Island Col Med, Cornell Univ, MD, 41. *Prof Exp:* Intern, Montefiore Hosp, New York, 41-42 & Fordham Hosp, 42-43, resident path, 45-46; intern obstet & gynec, Long Island Col Hosp, 46-47; from asst resident to resident, Greenpoint Hosp, Brooklyn, 47-50; clin instr, Col Med, State Univ NY Downstate Med Ctr, 50-54; from clin asst prof to clin assoc prof, 55-66, dir dept gynec & obstet, Lincoln Hosp, 63-70, assoc prof, 66-73, PROF GYNEC & OBSTET, ALBERT EINSTEIN COL MED, 73- *Concurrent Pos:* Attend obstetrician, Bronx Munic Hosp Ctr, 57- *Mem:* Fel Am Col Surgeons; fel Am Col Obstet & Gynec. *Res:* Resident and student training in obstetrics and gynecology. *Mailing Add:* 1 Hen Hawk Rd Kings Point NY 11024

SMITH, JOSEPH LAWTON, ophthalmology, see previous edition

SMITH, JOSEPH LECONTE, JR, b Macon, Ga, Sept 4, 29; m 53; c 3. MECHANICAL & CRYOGENIC ENGINEERING. *Educ:* Ga Inst Technol, BME, 52, MS, 54; Mass Inst Technol, DSc(mech eng), 59. *Prof Exp:* Res asst, 55-56, from instr to assoc prof, 56-69, PROF MECH ENG, MASS INST TECHNOL, 69-, PROF IN CHG CRYOGENIC ENG LAB, 64- *Concurrent Pos:* Consult, Los Alamos Sci Lab, 58-66, Cambridge Electron Accelerator, Harvard Univ, 59-65, Arthur D Little, Inc, 69-71 & Westinghouse Res Lab, 70- *Mem:* Am Soc Mech Engrs. *Res:* Thermodynamics; heat transfer; fluid mechanics. *Mailing Add:* Dept of Mech Eng Mass Inst of Technol Cambridge MA 02139

SMITH, JOSEPH PATRICK, b Lackawanna, NY, July 9, 51; m 79. SPECTROSCOPY, SURFACE & COLLOID SCIENCE. *Educ:* Univ Rochester, BS, 72; Univ Calif, Berkeley, PhD(phys chem), 78. *Prof Exp:* NSF Nat Needs Res fel, Dept Biochem, Univ Wis-Madison, 78-79; fel, Chem Div, Argonne Nat Lab, 79-81; SR RES CHEMIST, LONG RANGE RES DIV, EXXON PROD RES CO, 81- *Mem:* Am Chem Soc. *Res:* Physico-chemical phenomena associated with petroleum production; radiation chemistry; nitrogen fixation and spectroscopy: (magnetic resonance, fluorescence and x-ray absorption). *Mailing Add:* Exxon Prod Res Co PO Box 2189 Houston TX 77001

SMITH, JOSEPH VICTOR, b Eng, July 30, 28; m 51; c 2. MINERALOGY. *Educ:* Cambridge Univ, BA, 48, MA & PhD(physics), 51. *Prof Exp:* Fel crystallog, Geophys Lab, Carnegie Inst, 51-54; demonstr mineral & petrol, Cambridge Univ, 54-56; from instr to assoc prof mineral, Pa State Univ, 56-60; prof mineral & crystallog, 60-76, LOUIS BLOCK PROF PHYS SCI, UNIV CHICAGO, 76- *Concurrent Pos:* Consult, Linde Div, Union Carbide Corp, 56-; ed, X-ray Powder Data File, Am Soc Testing & Mat, 58-68. *Honors & Awards:* Mineral Soc Am Award, 61; Murchison Medal, 80; Roebling Medal, 81. *Mem:* Fel Mineral Soc Am (pres, 72-73); fel Geol Soc Am; fel Royal Soc; fel Am Geophys Union; fel Am Acad Arts & Sci. *Res:* Mineralogy applied to petrology, geochemistry and industrial chemistry. *Mailing Add:* Dept of Geophys Sci Univ of Chicago Chicago IL 60637

SMITH, JOSEPHINE REIST, b Altoona, Pa, Nov 26, 29; m 51; c 3. MEDICAL MICROBIOLOGY. *Educ:* Pa State Univ, BS, 52; Temple Univ, MS, 71, PhD(pharm chem), 76. *Prof Exp:* Technician immunol, Protein Found, Dept Phys Chem, Harvard Univ, 53-54; res asst, Dept Biol, Haverford Col, 64-69; INSTR MICROBIOL, DEPT BIOL, MONTGOMERY COUNTY COMMUNITY COL, 75- *Mem:* Am Soc Microbiol; Sigma Xi; AAAS. *Res:* Application of pharmacokinetics to the study of immune responses. *Mailing Add:* Dept of Biol Montgomery Co Community Col Blue Bell PA 19422

SMITH, JUDITH TERRY, b New York, NY, Mar 4, 40; m 69; c 3. PALEONTOLOGY. *Educ:* Barnard Col, Columbia Univ, AB, 62; Stanford Univ, MS, 64, PhD(geol), 68. *Prof Exp:* Curatorial asst, 68-69, RES ASSOC PALEONT, DEPT GEOL, STANFORD UNIV, 69-; GEOLOGIST, US GEOL SURV, 70 & 72- *Concurrent Pos:* Res assoc, US Geol Surv, 72-73. *Mem:* Geol Soc Am; Paleont Soc; Paleont Res Inst. *Res:* Cenozoic molluscan paleontology; biostratigraphy and paleoecology, especially zonation and distribution problems involving pectinids; Tethyan and related faunas. *Mailing Add:* Paleont & Stratig Br US Geol Surv 345 Middlefield Rd Menlo Park CA 94025

SMITH, JULIAN CLEVELAND, b Westmount, Que, Mar 10, 19; US citizen; m 46; c 3. CHEMICAL ENGINEERING. *Educ:* Cornell Univ, BChem, 41, ChemE, 42. *Prof Exp:* Engr chem eng, E I du Pont de Nemours & Co, 42-46; from asst prof to assoc prof, 46-53, assoc dir, 73-75, PROF CHEM ENG, CORNELL UNIV, 53-, DIR, 75- *Concurrent Pos:* Prof engr, NY State Educ Dept, 57-; consult, E I du Pont de Nemours & Co, 55-, US Army Corps Engrs, 57-65, Atlantic Richfield Hanford Co, 71-77 & Rockwell Int Co, 77- *Mem:* fel Am Inst Chem Engrs; Am Chem Soc; Soc Chem Indust. *Res:* Mixing of liquids and pastes; flow of granular solids. *Mailing Add:* Sch Chem Eng Cornell Univ Ithaca NY 14853

SMITH, KATHLEEN, b Fayetteville, Ark, Oct 9, 22. PSYCHIATRY. *Educ:* Univ Ark, BS, 44; Wash Univ, MD, 49; Am Bd Psychiat & Neurol, dipl, 56. *Prof Exp:* Intern, St Louis City Hosp, 49-50; resident psychiat, Barnes & McMillan Hosps, 50-52 & Malcolm Bliss Psychiat Hosp, 52-53; from instr to assoc prof, 53-72, PROF PSYCHIAT, SCH MED, WASHINGTON UNIV, 72- *Concurrent Pos:* USPHS fel, 52-53; physician, Malcolm Bliss Ment Health Ctr, 53-, dir inpatient serv, 57-60, dir training, 60-64, med supt, 64-; vis physician, St Louis City Hosp, 56-, consult, Nurses Infirmary, 55-57. *Mem:* AMA; Am Psychiat Asn. *Res:* Odor of schizophrenic sweat; gas chromatography; multihospital studies of tranquilizers and antidepressants. *Mailing Add:* Dept Psychiat Sch Med Washington Univ St Louis MO 63110

SMITH, KEITH DAVIS, b Portsmouth, Ohio, Dec 14, 30; m 58; c 3. ENDOCRINOLOGY, INTERNAL MEDICINE. *Educ:* Pa State Univ, BS, 52; Sch Med, Univ Pittsburgh, MD, 59. *Prof Exp:* Chief div endocrinol, Mercy Hosp, Pittsburgh, 64-67; asst prof med, Sch Med, Temple Univ, 68-71; assoc prof reproductive med, 71-75, PROF REPRODUCTIVE MED, UNIV TEX MED SCH HOUSTON, 75- *Concurrent Pos:* USPHS fel, Albert Einstein Med Ctr, Philadelphia, 62-64; assoc mem div endocrinol, 68-71; clin instr med, Sch Med, Univ Pittsburgh, 65-67; prin investr contract endocrine changes vasectomized men, NIH, 72-79, co-investr prog proj multidisciplinary approach control male reproduction, 74-83; co-investr grant develop contraceptive agents human male, Ford Found, 74-78. *Mem:* Am Fertil Soc; Am Psychosomatic Soc; Endocrine Soc; Soc Study Reproduction; Am Soc Andrology. *Res:* Ovarian and testicular function; control by the pituitary and hypothalamus; effects of various physical, emotional and chemical stimuli on the hypothalamo-pituitary-gonadal axis. *Mailing Add:* Dept Reproductive Med & Biol PO Box 20708 Houston TX 77025

SMITH, KEITH JAMES, b Cedar Rapids, Iowa, Mar 16, 37; m; c 2. ANIMAL NUTRITION. *Educ:* Iowa State Univ, BS, 59, PhD(ruminant nutrit), 63. *Prof Exp:* Asst prof basic nutrit, Iowa State Univ, 63; asst dir res & educ, Nat Cotton Seed Prod Asn, Inc, 66-75; animal nutritionist, 75-77, DIR RES, AM SOYBEAN ASN, 77- *Mem:* Am Inst Nutrit; Am Soc Animal Sci; Am Asn Food Technologists. *Res:* Oilseed protein feed product utilization. *Mailing Add:* Am Soybean Asn Box 27300 777 Craig Rd St Louis MO 63141

SMITH, KENDALL O, b Wilson, NC, Sept 5, 28; m 49; c 1. MICROBIOLOGY, VIROLOGY. *Educ:* George Washington Univ, BA, 51; Univ NC, MS, 57, PhD(microbiol), 59. *Prof Exp:* Fel biophys, Univ NC, 59-60; from instr to assoc prof virol, Col Med, Baylor Univ, 60-65; res microbiologist, Div Biol Stand, NIH, 65-69; PROF MICROBIOL, UNIV TEX MED SCH SAN ANTONIO, 69- *Concurrent Pos:* Res fel, NIH, Baylor Univ, 61-62, res career develop award, 63. *Mem:* Am Soc Microbiol; Am Asn Immunol; Electron Micros Soc Am. *Res:* Correlation of physical and biological properties of viruses; viruses associated with chronic, degenerative diseases of man; chemotherapy of herpes infections; detection of viral antigens and antibodies by radioimmunoassay, enzyme linked immunosorbent assay. *Mailing Add:* Dept of Microbiol Univ of Tex Med Sch San Antonio TX 78229

SMITH, KENDRIC CHARLES, b Oakwood, Ill, Oct 13, 26; m 55; c 2. PHOTOBIOLOGY, RADIATION BIOLOGY. *Educ:* Stanford Univ, BS, 47; Univ Calif, PhD(biochem), 52. *Prof Exp:* Res asst radiol, Med Sch, Univ Calif, 54-56; res assoc, 56-62, from asst prof to assoc prof, 62-73; PROF RADIOL, SCH MED, STANFORD UNIV, 73- *Concurrent Pos:* USPHS fel, Univ Calif, 52-54; USPHS career develop award, Stanford Univ, 66-71; mem, Comt Photobiol, Nat Acad Sci-Nat Res Coun, 64-74, chmn, 70-74; exec ed, Photochem & Photobiol, 66-72 & Photochem Photobiol Rev, 76-; mem, US Nat Comt, Int Union Biol Sci, 67-73 & secy, 71-73; mem, Radiation Bioeffects & epidemiol Adv Comt, Food & Drug Admin, 74-75. *Mem:* Am Inst Biol Chemists (vpres, 81-82, pres, 82-83, past pres, 83-84); Am Soc Biol Chemists; Am Chem Soc; Brit Photobiol Soc; Am Soc Photobiol (pres, 71-72). *Res:* Chemistry and function of nucleic acids; photochemical and radiation chemical reactions of nucleic acids; genetic control and biochemical mechanisms for repair of radiation damage; the molecular mechanisms of mutagenesis. *Mailing Add:* 927 Mears Ct Stanford CA 94305

SMITH, KENNAN TAYLOR, b Green Bay, Wis, July 17, 26; m 48; c 2. MATHEMATICS. *Educ:* Bowling Green State Univ, BA, 47; Harvard Univ, MA, 48; Univ Wis, PhD(math), 51. *Prof Exp:* Asst prof math, Univ Kans, 52-59; from assoc prof to prof, Univ Wis-Madison, 59-68; PROF MATH, ORE STATE UNIV, 68- *Concurrent Pos:* Fulbright scholar, France, 51-52. *Mem:* Am Math Soc. *Res:* Linear topological spaces; Hilbert spaces. *Mailing Add:* Dept of Math Ore State Univ Corvallis OR 97331

SMITH, KENNETH CARLESS, b Toronto, Ont, May 8, 32; m 59; c 2. MAN-MACHINE INTERFACE, SPECIAL PURPOSE PROCESSORS. *Educ:* Univ Toronto, BASc, 54, MASc, 56, PhD(physics), 60. *Prof Exp:* Transmission engr tel, Can Nat Tel, 54-55; res engr digital electronics, Univ Toronto, 56-58, asst prof electronics, 60-61; res asst prof comput design, Dept Elec Eng, Univ Ill, 61-64, assoc prof, 64-65; assoc prof, 65-70, chmn dept, 76-81, PROF ELEC & COMPUT, DEPT ELEC ENG, UNIV TORONTO, 70-; PROF INFO SCI, FACIL LIBERAL SCI, 81- *Concurrent Pos:* Res engr, Comput Ctr, Univ Toronto, 60-61; chief engr & prin investr, Digital Comput Lab, Univ Ill, 61-65, eng consult, Training Res Lab, 62-64; consult, Pattern Processor Proj, 65-70; dir & founder, Consociates, Ltd, 68-76; mem, Ont Task Force Microelectronic Technol, 80-81; vpres, Owl Instruments, Ltd, Med Instrument Mfg, 70-; dir, several small US & Can co, 68-; assoc, Inst Biomed Eng, Univ Toronto, 74- *Mem:* fel Inst Elec & Electronics Engrs; Can Soc Elec Eng; Can Info Process Soc. *Res:* Linear and digital circuits and systems including multivalued logic, parallel and other special-purpose processors, the man-machine interface and input and output systems with application in industry, education, medicine and music. *Mailing Add:* Dept Elec Eng Univ Toronto 34 St George St Toronto ON M5S 1A4 Can

SMITH, KENNETH EDWARD, b Milwaukee, Wis, Dec 29, 43; m 66; c 2. ANALYTICAL CHEMISTRY, SPECTROSCOPY. *Educ:* Univ Wis-Milwaukee, BS, 66; Univ Iowa, PhD(anal chem), 71. *Prof Exp:* NSF fel, Kans State Univ, 70-72; asst prof chem, Eastern Ill Univ, 72-73; assoc chemist, Wildlife Res Sect, Ill Natural Hist Surv, 73-80; MGR ANAL CHEM, INST GAS TECHNOL, 80- *Concurrent Pos:* Instr, Kans State Univ. *Mem:* Am Chem Soc; Soc Appl Spectros; Am Soc Testing & Mat. *Res:* Analytical atomic spectroscopy; non-flame absorption systems; low-pressure plasmas in spectroscopy; temperature effects in plasmas; environmental metal analysis as contaminants. *Mailing Add:* Inst Gas Technol 3424 S State St Chicago IL 60616

SMITH, KENNETH JUDSON, JR, b Raleigh, NC, Sept 4, 30; m 54; c 2. PHYSICAL CHEMISTRY, POLYMER PHYSICS. *Educ:* ECarolina Col, AB, 57; Duke Univ, MA, 59, PhD(phys chem), 62. *Prof Exp:* From res chemist to sr res chemist, Chemstrand Res Ctr, Inc, 61-68; from asst prof to assoc prof, 68-72, PROF CHEM & CHMN DEPT, COL ENVIRON SCI & FORESTRY, STATE UNIV NY, 72-, ASST DIR POLYMER RES CTR, 71- *Concurrent Pos:* Dir org mat sci prog, Col Environ Sci & Forestry, State Univ NY, 71-74. *Mem:* AAAS. *Res:* Mechanical behavior of polymers; rubber elasticity; statistical mechanics of rubber networks at large deformations; stress induced crystallization in polymer networks; elastic behavior of composite and interpenetrating networks; thermoelastic behavior of polyelectrolyte networks. *Mailing Add:* Dept Chem SUNY Col Environ Sci & Forestry Syracuse NY 13210

SMITH, KENNETH LARRY, b Minerva, Ohio, Apr 30, 41; m 67; c 2. DAIRY SCIENCE, IMMUNOBIOLOGY. *Educ:* NMex State Univ, BS, 64; Ohio State Univ, MS, 66, PhD(dairy sci), 70. *Prof Exp:* Res assoc dairy sci, Ohio State Univ, 64-70, asst prof, Ohio Agr Res & Develop Ctr, 70-75, ASSOC PROF DAIRY SCI, OHIO AGR RES & DEVELOP CTR & OHIO STATE UNIV, 75- *Mem:* Am Dairy Sci Asn; Nat Mastitis Coun. *Res:* Specific and nonspecific resistance to infection of the bovine mammary gland; hormonal control of colostrum formation and lactogenesis in the bovine. *Mailing Add:* Dept of Dairy Sci Ohio Agr Res & Develop Ctr Wooster OH 44691

SMITH, KENNETH LEROY, b Holly, Colo, Oct 15, 31; m 60. DAIRY MICROBIOLOGY. *Educ:* Univ Mo, BS, 53, MS, 56, PhD(dairy microbiol), 60. *Prof Exp:* Instr dairy mfg, Univ Mo, 57-60, asst prof, 60; from asst prof to assoc prof dairy sci, 60-77, MICROBIOLOGIST, INST FOOD & AGR SERV, UNIV FLA, 66- & ASSOC PROF MICROBIOL & CELL SCI, 77- *Mem:* AAAS; Am Soc Microbiol; Am Dairy Sci Asn. *Res:* Application of microbial physiology and taxonomy in dairy science, especially in mastitis, the microbial flora and antibiotic residues in dairy products. *Mailing Add:* Dept of Microbiol & Cell Sci Univ of Fla Gainesville FL 32611

SMITH, KENNETH MCGREGOR, b Wheeling, WVa, Mar 24, 23; m 43, 76; c 3. PHYSICAL CHEMISTRY. *Educ:* Ohio Wesleyan Univ, BA, 47; Ohio State Univ, MSc, 50, PhD(chem), 55. *Prof Exp:* Res chemist, 55-61, tech serv rep, 61-68, tech specialist, 68-76, TECH ASSOC, E I DU PONT DE NEMOURS & CO, INC, 76- *Concurrent Pos:* Chmn comt photog processing, Nat Standards Inst; US deleg, Int Standards Orgn. *Mem:* Am Chem Soc; Soc Photog Scientists & Engrs; Nat Micrographics Asn. *Res:* Chemical kinetics; photographic chemistry; photographic pollution abatement. *Mailing Add:* Photo Prod Dept Chestnut Run E I du Pont de Nemours & Co Inc Wilmington DE 19898

SMITH, KENNETH RUPERT, JR, b St Louis, Mo, Sept 23, 32; m 56; c 7. NEUROSURGERY. *Educ:* Washington Univ, MD, 57. *Prof Exp:* Trainee anat, Washington Univ, 59-60 & 62, instr neurosurg, 63-66, instr anat, 64-66; from asst prof to assoc prof neurosurg, 6671, PROF NEUROSURG, SCH MED, ST LOUIS UNIV, 71-, CHMN SECT, 68- *Concurrent Pos:* Nat Inst Neurol Dis & Blindness spec fel, Washington Univ, 64-65 & Oxford Univ, 65-66. *Mem:* AAAS; AMA; Cong Neurol Surg; Am Asn Anatomists; Am Asn Neurol Surg. *Res:* Electron microscopy of the nervous system; neurophysiology of sensory receptors; clinical evaluation of cerebral circulation. *Mailing Add:* Dept of Surg 1325 S Grand St Louis MO 63104

SMITH, KENT FARRELL, b Fish Haven, Idaho, June 26, 35; m 57; c 5. INTEGRATED CIRCUITS. *Educ:* Utah State Univ, BS, 57, MS, 58; Univ Utah, PhD(elec eng), 82. *Prof Exp:* Res engr, Stanford Res Inst, 59-61; electronic specialist, Phillips Petrol Co, 61-66; tech dir, Res & Develop Ctr, Gen Instrument, 66-72; scientist, Res Inst, 72-78, ASSOC PROF COMPUT SCI, UNIV UTAH, 78- *Concurrent Pos:* VPres, LSI Testing, 67-72; consult, Gen Instrument Corp, 72- *Res:* Design methodology for the implementation of very large scale integrated circuits, using path programmable logic. *Mailing Add:* Dept Comput Sci 3160 MEB Univ Utah Salt Lake City UT 84112

SMITH, KEVIN MALCOLM, b Birmingham, Eng, Mar 15, 42; m 65; c 2. ORGANIC CHEMISTRY, BIOLOGICAL CHEMISTRY. *Educ:* Univ Liverpool, Eng, BSc, 64, PhD(chem), 67, DSc, 77; FRIC, 77. *Prof Exp:* Fel chem, Harvard Univ, 67-69; lectr chem, Univ Liverpool, Eng, 69-77; PROF CHEM, UNIV CALIF, DAVIS, 77- *Concurrent Pos:* Fulbright travel grant, 67-69; org chem consult, Palmer Res Labs, 74-77. *Honors & Awards:*

Leverhulme Prize, Soc Chem Indust, Eng, 64; Parke-Davis Prize, Parke-Davis & Co, 67; Corday-Morgan Medal & Prize, Chem Soc, 78. *Mem:* Am Chem Soc; Royal Soc Chem; Sigma Xi. *Res:* Chemistry, biochemistry and spectroscopy of porphyrins, chlorophylls, bile pigments and their diverse metal complexes. *Mailing Add:* Dept of Chem Univ of Calif Davis CA 95616

SMITH, KIRBY CAMPBELL, b Dallas, Tex, Feb 7, 40. MATHEMATICS. *Educ:* Southern Methodist Univ, BA, 62; Univ Wis, MS, 64, PhD(algebra), 69. *Prof Exp:* Asst prof math, Univ Miss, 68-70; asst prof math, Univ Okla, 70-75; ASSOC PROF MATH, TEX A&M UNIV, 75- *Mem:* Math Asn Am; Am Math Soc. *Res:* Noncommutative ring theory. *Mailing Add:* Dept of Math Tex A&M Univ College Station TX 77843

SMITH, KIRK ROBERT, energy, environmental science, see previous edition

SMITH, L(EROY) H(ARRINGTON), JR, b Baltimore, Md, Nov 3, 28; m 51; c 3. MECHANICAL ENGINEERING. *Educ:* Johns Hopkins Univ, BE, 49, MS, 51, DEng, 54. *Prof Exp:* Compressor aerodynamicist gas turbines, Flight Propulsion Div, 54-61, supvr turbomach develop, 61-67, mgr compressor aerodyn develop unit, 67-69, mgr compressor & fan design tech opers, 69-71, mgr adv fan & compressor aerodyn, 71-74, mgr adv turbomach aerodyn, 75-80, MGR ADV TURBOMACH AERODYN & ACOUST OPERS, AIRCRAFT ENGINE GROUP, ENG DIV, GEN ELEC CO, 80- *Mem:* Fel Am Soc Mech Engrs. *Res:* Fluid mechanics; turbomachinery. *Mailing Add:* Aircraft Engine Group Eng Div Gen Elec Co Mail Drop H4 Cincinnati OH 45215

SMITH, LARRY, b Hughes Springs, Tex, June 26, 44; m 66; c 2. COLLOID CHEMISTRY. *Educ:* NTex State Univ, BA, 68, PhD(phys chem, org chem), 70. *Prof Exp:* Res chemist, Corp Res, Am Hoechst Corp, 71-72; RES CHEMIST, SUN OIL CO, 73- *Concurrent Pos:* Res assoc, Univ Tex, Dallas, 72-73. *Mem:* Am Chem Soc; Soc Petrol Engrs; AAAS. *Res:* Surfactant, polymer and caustic flooding as methods of enhancing oil recovery. *Mailing Add:* Sun Oil Co 503 N Central Expressway Richardson TX 75080

SMITH, LARRY, b New York, NY, May 13, 42; m 64. MATHEMATICS. *Educ:* Brooklyn Col, BS, 62; Yale Univ, PhD(math), 66. *Prof Exp:* Actg instr math, Yale Univ, 65-66; instr, Princeton Univ, 66-68, asst prof, 68-69; assoc prof math, Univ Va, 69-77; INSTR MATH, CALIF STATE UNIV, LONG BEACH & CHAPMAN COL, 77- *Concurrent Pos:* Air Force Off Sci Res fel math, Inst Advan Sci Study, France, 68-69. *Mem:* Am Math Soc. *Res:* Algebraic topology. *Mailing Add:* 19622 Canberra Ln Huntington Beach CA 92646

SMITH, LAURA LEE WEISBRODT, b Georgetown, Ohio, July 16, 03; m; c 2. FOOD CHEMISTRY. *Educ:* Miami Univ, BS, 25; Iowa State Col, MS, 27; Univ Calif, PhD(nutrit), 30. *Prof Exp:* Asst, Iowa State Col, 25-27; Smith Incubator Co fel, Cornell Univ, 30-31, instr home econ, 37-42; teacher pub schs, NY, 42-45; consult, Inter-Am Inst Agr Sci, 47-55; from asst prof to prof food chem, Sch Hotel Admin, 55-72, EMER PROF FOOD CHEM, CORNELL UNIV, 72- *Mem:* Am Chem Soc; Inst Food Technologists; fel Am Inst Chemists; NY Acad Sci. *Res:* Use of modified starches in ready food programs; evaluation of frozen sauces; methods of detecting breakdown of fats; nutrition; science education. *Mailing Add:* 1707 Slaterville Rd Ithaca NY 14850

SMITH, LAWRENCE HUBERT, b Jackson, Mich, Apr 2, 30; m 50; c 5. PLANT PHYSIOLOGY. *Educ:* Mich State Univ, PhD(crops), 59. *Prof Exp:* Instr pub schs, Mich, 55-57; asst, Mich State Univ, 57-59; from asst prof to assoc prof, 59-68, PROF AGRON & PLANT GENETICS, UNIV MINN, ST PAUL, 68- *Mem:* Am Soc Agron; Am Soc Plant Physiol. *Res:* Physiological genetics; crop physiology. *Mailing Add:* Dept of Agron Univ of Minn St Paul MN 55101

SMITH, LAWRIE BOOTH, b Oakville, Ont, June 6, 30; m 61; c 3. BIOLOGY, ENTOMOLOGY. *Educ:* McMaster Univ, BSc, 52; Univ Toronto, MSA, 55; Univ Nottingham, PhD(ecol), 60. *Prof Exp:* RES SCIENTIST ENTOM, CAN DEPT AGR, 55- *Concurrent Pos:* Hon prof, Univ Man; hon adj prof, Simon Fraser Univ. *Mem:* Entom Soc Am; Entom Soc Can; Brit Ecol Soc; Ecol Soc Am; Sigma Xi. *Res:* Ecology and population dynamics of stored grain insects; insect acclimation to low temperature; sampling stored grain insects. *Mailing Add:* Can Agr Res Sta 195 Dafoe Rd Winnipeg MB R3T 2M9 Can

SMITH, LAWTON HARCOURT, b Poughkeepsie, NY, Nov 15, 24; m 46; c 1. RADIOBIOLOGY. *Educ:* Univ Conn, BA, 50; Syracuse Univ, MS, 53, PhD(zool), 54. *Prof Exp:* BIOLOGIST, OAK RIDGE NAT LAB, 54- *Concurrent Pos:* NSF sr fel, 60. *Mem:* Radiation Res Soc; Am Physiol Soc; Soc Exp Biol & Med. *Res:* Radiation injury, protection and recovery in mammals. *Mailing Add:* Biol Div Oak Ridge Nat Lab Oak Ridge TN 37830

SMITH, LEE ANDERSON, micropaleontology, biostratigraphy, see previous edition

SMITH, LEHI TINGEN, b Oakley, Idaho, Nov 29, 27; m 56; c 4. MATHEMATICS. *Educ:* Ariz State Univ, BS, 48, MA, 55; Stanford Univ, EdD, 59. *Prof Exp:* Teacher high schs, Ariz, 53-54 & 55-57; asst math, Brigham Young Univ, 54; from asst prof to assoc prof, 59-70, PROF MATH, ARIZ STATE UNIV, 70- *Mem:* Math Asn Am; Nat Coun Teachers Math. *Res:* Cultural influence on mathematical perceptions; design and appraisal of improved curricula for preparation of prospective mathematics teachers. *Mailing Add:* Dept of Math Ariz State Univ Tempe AZ 85281

SMITH, LELAND LEROY, b Bradenton, Fla, May 14, 26; m 53; c 4. ORGANIC CHEMISTRY, BIOCHEMISTRY. *Educ:* Univ Tex, BA, 46, MA, 48, PhD(chem), 50. *Prof Exp:* Res assoc chem, Columbia Univ, 50-51; res chemist, Southwest Found Res & Educ, 52-54; group leader, Lederle Labs,

Inc, Am Cyanamid Co, 54-60 & Wyeth Labs, Inc, 60-64; assoc prof biochem, 64-68, PROF BIOCHEM, UNIV TEX MED BR GALVESTON, 68- *Concurrent Pos:* Vis scientist, Worcester Found Exp Biol, 51-52 & Oak Ridge Inst Nuclear Studies, 53. *Mem:* Am Chem Soc; Am Soc Biol Chemists. *Res:* Steroid chemistry and biochemistry; steroid analysis, synthesis and biosynthesis; microbiological transformations of steroids; natural products chemistry. *Mailing Add:* Univ of Tex Med Br Galveston TX 77550

SMITH, LEO ANTHONY, b Waycross, Ga, May 22, 40; m 62; c 3. INDUSTRIAL ENGINEERING. *Educ:* Ga Inst Technol, BS, 62, MS, 64; Purdue Univ, PhD(indust eng), 69. *Prof Exp:* Asst prof, 69-73, ASSOC PROF INDUST ENG, AUBURN UNIV, 73- *Mem:* Am Inst Indust Engrs; Human Factors Soc; Ergonomics Soc; Am Indust Hyg Asn. *Res:* Evaluation of physiological and psychological aspects of human performance in man-machine systems; design of man-machine systems. *Mailing Add:* Dept of Indust Eng Auburn Univ Auburn AL 36830

SMITH, LEONARD CHARLES, b Spokane, Wash, Jan 31, 21; m 45; c 5. BIOCHEMISTRY. *Educ:* Univ Mont, AB, 43; Univ Ill, PhD(chem), 49. *Prof Exp:* Asst, Univ Ill, 43-49; res biochemist, Hines Vet Admin Hosp, Ill, 49-56; from asst prof to prof biochem, Sch Med, Univ SDak, 56-66; PROF CHEM, IND STATE UNIV, TERRE HAUTE, 66- *Concurrent Pos:* Instr biochem, Med Sch, Northwestern Univ, 49-56; consult, Northern States Power Co, 59-66; vis lectr, Univ Glasgow, 61-62; prof biochem, Med Sch, Ind Univ, 71-80. *Mem:* Am Chem Soc; Soc Exp Biol & Med; spec affil AMA; The Chem Soc. *Res:* Metabolic effects of vitamin E deficiency; free amino acids of tissues. *Mailing Add:* 422 Bluebird Dr Terre Haute IN 47803

SMITH, LESLIE E, b New York, NY, Jan 6, 41; m 63; c 2. PHYSICAL CHEMISTRY. *Educ:* Case Inst Technol, BSc, 62; Cath Univ Am, PhD(chem), 70. *Prof Exp:* Phys chemist, Polymers Div, 64-66 & 69-74, CHIEF POLYMER STABILITY & STANDARDS, NAT BUR STANDARDS, 74- *Mem:* AAAS; Am Chem Soc. *Res:* Interfacial phenomena; optical properties of surfaces; ellipsometry; adsorption of polymers; polymer decomposition; diffusion and transport through polymers. *Mailing Add:* Polymers Div Nat Bur Standards Washington DC 20234

SMITH, LESLIE GARRETT, b Rotherham, Eng, Nov 14, 27; nat US; m 55; c 2. IONOSPHERE, ATMOSPHERIC ELECTRICITY. *Educ:* Cambridge Univ, BA, 48, PhD(physics), 51. *Prof Exp:* Res assoc meteorol, Univ Chicago, 51-52; res geophysicist, Univ Calif, Los Angeles, 52-53; physicist geophys res directorate, Air Force Cambridge Res Ctr, 53-58; dir space sci lab, Tech Div, GCA Corp, 58-72; prin res scientist, Dept Elec Eng, 72-75, PROF ELEC ENG, UNIV ILL, URBANA-CHAMPAIGN, 75- *Concurrent Pos:* UNESCO consult to India, 81. *Honors & Awards:* Darton Prize, Royal Meteorol Soc, 54. *Mem:* Am Geophys Union; Int Sci Radio Union; Inst Elec & Electronics Engrs. *Res:* Atmospheric physics; atmospheric electricity; ionospheric physics; sounding rockets; satellites. *Mailing Add:* 2305 Southmoor Dr Champaign IL 61820

SMITH, LESTER, b McGehee, Ark, Oct 27, 41; m 73; c 2. BIOCHEMISTRY. *Educ:* Univ Calif, BS, 63; Howard Univ, MS, 66; Univ Calif, PhD(biochem), 69. *Prof Exp:* Biochemist, Vet Admin Hosp, 69-71; health scientist adminr biochem of aging, 71-77, CHIEF MOLECULAR & BIOCHEM AGING PROG, NAT INST AGING, NIH, 77- *Concurrent Pos:* Vis instr mitochondrial physiol, Univ Calif, 69-71; consult, Biol Div, AEC, 73-74. *Mem:* AAAS; Am Inst Biol Sci; fel Geront Soc. *Res:* Lipid chemistry; lipoproteins; mitochondrial structure and function; biochemistry of aging; immunology; pharmacology. *Mailing Add:* NIH Nat Inst on Aging 9000 Rockville Pike Bethesda MD 20014

SMITH, LESTER ANAH, b Birchwood, Tenn, Oct 15, 17; m 40; c 1. NUCLEAR PHYSICS. *Educ:* Carson-Newman Col, BS, 38. *Prof Exp:* Teacher, Tenn, 40-42; catalyst lab operator & oxidation plant supvr, Hercules Powder Co, 42-44; chief operator, SAM Labs, Columbia Univ, 44; lab dept head, 45-80, SR STAFF ASSOC, OAK RIDGE GASEOUS DIFFUSION PLANT, NUCLEAR DIV, UNION CARBIDE CORP, 81- *Mem:* Am Chem Soc; Am Soc Mass Spectrometry. *Res:* Mass spectrometry; administration of scientific personnel and activities; radioanalysis; health physics. *Mailing Add:* Union Carbide Corp Nuclear Div PO Box P MS 431 Oak Ridge TN 37830

SMITH, LEVERETT RALPH, b Oakland, Calif, Feb 24, 49; m 78. SCIENCE EDITING. *Educ:* Univ Calif, Santa Cruz, BA, 70; Cornell Univ, MS, 74, PhD(chem), 76. *Prof Exp:* Teacher chem & math, Techiman Sec Sch, Ghana, 70-72; fel chem, Dept Entomol, Cornell Univ, 76-77; assoc fel chem, Col Environ Sci & Forestry, State Univ NY, 77-78; asst prof chem, Oberlin Col, 78-81. *Concurrent Pos:* Chem ed, Acad Press, 81- *Mem:* Am Chem Soc; Sigma Xi. *Res:* Exploratory organic chemistry; chemical ecology. *Mailing Add:* Acad Press 1001 Polk St San Francisco CA 94109

SMITH, LEVERING, b Joplin, Mo, Mar 5, 10; m 33. ORDNANCE. *Educ:* US Naval Acad, BS, 32; NMex State Univ, LLD, 61. *Prof Exp:* Sect head, Res Div, Bur Ord, US Navy, 44-47, dep head explosives dept, Ord Test Sta, 47-49, head, Rockets & Explosives Dept, 49-51; assoc tech dir, 51-54, commanding officer, Ord Missile Test Facil, 54-56; br head & dep tech dir, Polaris Proj, 56-57, tech dir, 57-65, dir, 65-71, dir strategic systs projs, 71-77; RETIRED. *Concurrent Pos:* Indust consult, 77- *Honors & Awards:* Hickman Award, Rocket Soc, Am Inst Aeronaut & Astronaut, 56; US Navy League Parsons Award, 61; Gold Medal, Am Soc Naval Engrs, 61; Conrad Award, 66; Knight Comdr, Order Brit Empire, 72; James Forrestal Award, Nat Security Indust Asn, 78. *Mem:* Nat Acad Engrs; fel Am Inst Aeronaut & Astronaut; Am Soc Naval Engrs. *Res:* Technology of propellants and high explosives; interior ballistics of rockets; statistical analysis; operations research. *Mailing Add:* 1462 Waggaman Circle McLean VA 22101

SMITH, LEWIS DENNIS, b Muncie, Ind, Jan 18, 38; m 61; c 2. DEVELOPMENTAL BIOLOGY. *Educ:* Ind Univ, Bloomington, AB, 59, PhD(exp embryol), 63. *Prof Exp:* Res assoc, Ind Univ, 63-64; asst embryologist, Argonne Nat Lab, 64-67, assoc biologist, 67-69; assoc prof, 69-73, assoc head, 79-80, PROF BIOL & DEVELOP BIOL, PURDUE UNIV, 73-, HEAD BIOL, 81- *Concurrent Pos:* Instr embryol, Woods Hole Marine Biol Lab, 72, 73 & 74; assoc ed, Develop Biol, 74-, Wilhelm Roax's Archiv Develop Biol, 75-78; mem, Cell Biol Study Sect, NIH, 71-75, chmn, 77-79; mem, Am Inst Biol sci, Space Biol Panel, NASA, 80- *Mem:* Soc Develop Biol; Int Soc Develop Biol; AAAS. *Res:* Mechanism of steroid action in induction of oocyte maturation; regulation of cell cycle; regulation of RNA and protein synthesis during oogenesis and oocyte maturation; role of germinal plasm in formation and migration of primordial germ cells. *Mailing Add:* Dept Biol Sci Purdue Univ West Lafayette IN 47907

SMITH, LEWIS OLIVER, JR, b Eckley, Colo, Nov 20, 22; div; c 2. ORGANIC CHEMISTRY. *Educ:* Grove City Col, BS, 44; Univ Rochester, PhD(org chem), 47. *Prof Exp:* Asst chem, Univ Rochester, 44-46; head dept, Polytech Inst PR, 47-48; instr, Wilson Col, 48-50, asst prof, 50-52; asst prof, 52-59, assoc prof, 59-66, chmn dept, 59-61 & 63-65, PROF CHEM, VALPARAISO UNIV, 66- *Mem:* Am Chem Soc. *Res:* Yield studies in organic chemical reactions; molecular analogies; synthesis and comparison of properties; matrix catalysis. *Mailing Add:* Dept of Chem Valparaiso Univ Valparaiso IN 46383

SMITH, LEWIS TAYLOR, b Seal Beach, Calif, Nov 2, 25; m 50; c 2. RADIATION PHYSICS. *Educ:* Univ Calif, Los Angeles, BS, 57, MS, 59, PhD(physics), 66. *Prof Exp:* Mem tech staff physics, Ground Systs Div, Hughes Aircraft Co, 65-71; scientist, Aerospace Div, Martin Marietta Corp, 72-74; sr physicist, Space Div, Gen Elec Co, 74-76; SR SCIENTIST PHYSICS, ELECTRONICS DIV, NORTHROP CORP, 76- *Mem:* Am Phys Soc. *Res:* Effects of nuclear weapon radiation upon materials and electronics, parts, circuits and systems. *Mailing Add:* 6426 Danette St Simi Valley CA 93063

SMITH, LEWIS TURNER, b Providence, RI, Mar 30, 26; m 47; c 2. ANIMAL SCIENCE, STATISTICS. *Educ:* Univ RI, BS, 50; NC State Col, MS, 53; Iowa State Univ, PhD, 61. *Prof Exp:* Asst animal husb, NC State Col, 52-53; asst poultry husb, Univ RI, 53-56; res assoc, Iowa State Univ, 56-61; asst prof poultry sci, Kans State Univ, 61-63; assoc prof, 63-71, Chmn Dept, 71-76, prof animal sci, 71-80, PROF AQUACULT SCI & PATH, UNIV RI, 71-, STATISTICIAN, 63- *Res:* Genetics. *Mailing Add:* Dept Aquacult Sci & Path Univ of RI Kingston RI 02881

SMITH, LINDA LOU, b Orlando, Fla, Oct 7, 33. PHYSICAL BIOCHEMISTRY. *Educ:* Univ SC, BS, 54, MS, 56, PhD(chem), 59. *Prof Exp:* Instr biochem & oncol, Med Col of Ga, 59-60; chemist, E I du Pont de Nemours & Co, 60-64; asst res prof biochem, 64-71, asst prof cell & molecular biol & med, 71-72, asst prof med, 72-76, ASSOC PROF CELL & MOLECULAR BIOL, MED COL GA, ASSOC RES PROF MED, 76-, NIH RES GRANT, 66- *Mem:* AAAS; Am Chem Soc; Am Inst Chem. *Res:* Subunit dissociation of normal and abnormal hemoglobins; physicochemical and immunological characterization of pathological immunoglobulins; physical chemistry of biological macromolecules. *Mailing Add:* Dept of Cell & Molecular Biol Med Col of Ga Augusta GA 30902

SMITH, LLOYD HOLLINGWORTH, JR, b Easley, SC, May 27, 24; m 54; c 6. MEDICINE. *Educ:* Washington & Lee Univ, AB, 44; Harvard Med Sch, MD, 48; Am Bd Internal Med, dipl, 59. *Prof Exp:* Intern & asst resident med, Mass Gen Hosp, 48-50; chief med resident, 56, chief endocrine & metab unit, 58-63; vis investr, Oxford Univ, 63-64; PROF MED & CHMN DEPT, SCH MED, UNIV CALIF, SAN FRANCISCO, 64. *Concurrent Pos:* Harvard Soc Fels fel biochem, Harvard Univ & Pub Health Res Inst New York, Inc, 52-54; USPHS res fel, Karolinska Inst, Sweden, 54-55; res fel biochem, Huntington Labs, 57-58; counr, Nat Heart Inst; mem, President's Sci Adv Comt, 70-74; mem, Bd Overseers, Harvard Univ, 74-80. *Mem:* Am Soc Clin Invest; Endocrine Soc; Am Fedn Clin Res; Am Soc Biol Chemists; Asn Am Physicians. *Res:* Medical research, particularly areas of inherited metabolic diseases. *Mailing Add:* Univ of Calif Sch of Med San Francisco Med Ctr San Francisco CA 94143

SMITH, LLOYD MUIR, b Calgary, Alta, Feb 20, 17; nat US; m 48; c 2. FOOD CHEMISTRY. *Educ:* Univ Alta, BSc, 43, MSc, 49; Univ Calif, PhD(agr chem), 53. *Prof Exp:* Instr dairy indust, Univ Alta, 46-49, lectr, 49-50; asst dairy indust, Univ Calif, Davis, 50-52; asst prof dairying, Univ Alta, 52-54; from asst prof dairy indust to assoc prof food sci & technol, 54-67, PROF FOOD SCI & TECHNOL, UNIV CALIF, DAVIS, 67-, CHEMIST, 67- *Concurrent Pos:* Sr Fulbright res scholar, Dept Sci & Indust Res, NZ, 61-62. *Mem:* Am Chem Soc; Am Oil Chem Soc; Am Dairy Sci Asn; Nutrition Today Soc; Inst Food Technologists. *Res:* Chemistry of fats and other lipids; composition, structure and deterioration of lipids in foods; technology of edible fats, oils and emulsions; chemistry of milk; food quality assurance. *Mailing Add:* Dept of Food Sci & Technol 3471 Chem Annex Univ Calif Davis CA 95616

SMITH, LLOYD P, b Reno, Nev, Nov 6, 03; m 28, 71; c 2. PHYSICS, ENGINEERING. *Educ:* Univ Nev, BS, 25; Cornell Univ, PhD(exp physics), 30. *Hon Degrees:* DSc, Univ Nev, 61. *Prof Exp:* Res engr, Gen Elec Co, 25-26; instr physics, Cornell Univ, 27-30; Nat Res Coun fel, Calif Inst Technol, 30-31; int fel, Univs Munich & Utrecht, 31-32; asst prof, Cornell Univ, 32-36, prof, 36-56, dir dept eng physics & chmn dept physics, 46-56; pres, Res & Advan Develop Div, Avco Corp, 56-58; res dir, Aeronutronic Div, Ford Motor, 59-64; vpres res, Philco Corp, 64-65; vpres physics & appl sci, Stanford Res Inst, 65-69, sr sci adv, 69-72; ASSOC, LLOYD P SMITH & ASSOCS, 72- *Concurrent Pos:* Mem staff, Manhattan Proj, RCA Labs, 41-46, assoc dir res, 45-46; consult to indust & govt, 42-; dir & vpres, Avco Mfg Corp, 54-59; off sci personnel, Nat Acad Sci-Nat Res Coun, 66-; mem solid state panel, Nat Res Coun; mem comt physics & eng educ, Am Inst Physics;

mem adv coun Eng Col, Cornell Univ, 56-57; mem bd dirs, Knox Glass, Inc, NY, 65-68; pres, Desert Res Inst, Univ Nev Syst, 75-80; pres, Wright Energy Nev Corp, 80-81. *Mem:* AAAS; Am Ord Asn; fel NY Acad Sci. *Res:* Theoretical, experimental, solid state and plasma physics; electrodynamics; quantum theory; electronics; mass spectroscopy; isotope separation; electron and ion thermionic emission; magnetohydrodynamics; technological forecasting; techno-economics. *Mailing Add:* 565 Woodside Dr Woodside CA 94062

SMITH, LOIS C, b Hawthorne, NJ, Jan 14, 35; m 60; c 4. ORGANIC CHEMISTRY. *Educ:* Rutgers Univ, BA, 55, PhD(chem), 60; Univ Ill, MA, 57. *Prof Exp:* Jr chemist, Hoffmann-La Roche, Inc, 57; from asst prof to assoc prof, 64-71, dean fac, 73-77, chmn dept, 69-73, PROF CHEM, RUSSELL SAGE COL, 71-, ACAD DEAN, 77- *Mem:* AAAS; Nat Sci Teachers Asn; Am Asn Higher Educ; Sigma Xi; Am Chem Soc. *Res:* Synthetic organic chemistry, especially the preparation and reactions of organophosphorous compounds; elucidation of organic reaction mechanisms; preparation and reactions of organoarsenic compounds. *Mailing Add:* Russell Sage Col Troy NY 12180

SMITH, LORRAINE CATHERINE, b Toronto, Ont, May 8, 31; m 53; c 5. VERTEBRATE ZOOLOGY. *Educ:* Univ Toronto, BA, 53, MA, 54; Univ Ottawa, PhD(biol), 63. *Prof Exp:* Res asst physiol, Univ Toronto, 54-55; defence res sci officer, Defence Res Med Labs, Defence Res Bd Can, 55-57; res assoc physiol biol, Univ Ottawa, 63-65; res assoc zool biol, Carleton Univ, 70-75, res fel, 75-77; ASST ED, CAN J FISHERIES & AQUATIC SCI, SCI INFO & PUBL BR, DEPT FISHERIES & OCEANS CAN, 76- *Concurrent Pos:* Ed, Canadian Field-Naturalist, 72-81. *Mem:* Coun Biol Ed; Can Soc Zoologists; Can Soc Environ Biologists. *Res:* Scientific editing; physiology and ecology of small mammals, especially population dynamics and reproductive biology; general natural history and urban wildlife studies. *Mailing Add:* Regional Rd 5 RR 3 Stittsville ON K0A 3G0 Can

SMITH, LOUIS C, b Hobbs, NMex, Nov 24, 37; m 60; c 3. BIOCHEMISTRY. *Educ:* Abilene Christian Col, BS, 59; Univ Tex, Austin, PhD(biochem), 63. *Prof Exp:* Res assoc biochem, Mass Inst Technol, 63-66, instr, 64-66; asst prof, 66-74, assoc prof biochem, 74-77, assoc prof, 77-79, PROF EXP MED & BIOCHEM, BAYLOR COL MED, 79- *Concurrent Pos:* NIH fel, Mass Inst Technol, 63-65; estab investr, Am Heart Asn, 72-77; mem study sect, Nat Heart, Lung & Blood Inst, NIH, 75-81. *Mem:* AAAS; Am Chem Soc; Biochem Soc; NY Acad Sci; Am Soc Biol Chemists. *Res:* Lipoprotein structure, metabolism and transport of lipids and xenobiotics. *Mailing Add:* Dept of Med Alkek A601 Baylor Col of Med Houston TX 77030

SMITH, LOUIS CHARLES, b Rochester, NY, Sept 16, 18; m 41; c 2. PHYSICAL ORGANIC CHEMISTRY. *Educ:* Univ Rochester, BS, 40; Columbia Univ, PhD(chem), 44. *Prof Exp:* Instr chem, Univ Vt, 43-44; sr res assoc, Nat Defense Res Comt, Carnegie Inst Technol, 44-45; res chemist, Gen Elec Co, 45-46; sect chief, US Naval Ord Lab, 46-49; group leader, Los Alamos Sci Lab, 49-74, assoc group leader 74-79; RETIRED. *Mem:* Am Chem Soc; Am Phys Soc. *Res:* Development of military high explosives; properties of military explosives and propellants. *Mailing Add:* 27 Allegheny Irvine CA 92714

SMITH, LOUIS DE SPAIN, b Odessa, Wash, Oct 12, 10; m 36; c 3. MICROBIOLOGY. *Educ:* Univ Idaho, BS, 32, MS, 35; Univ Wash, PhD(microbiol), 48; Am Bd Med Microbiol, dipl. *Hon Degrees:* ScD, Univ Idaho, 71, Mont State Univ, 76. *Prof Exp:* Cytologist inst cancer res, Univ Pa, 35-40; bacteriologist biochem res found, Franklin Inst, 40-42 & 47-49; from assoc prof to prof bact, Vet Res Lab, Exp Sta, Mont State Univ, 50-67; PROF MICROBIOL, VA POLYTECH INST & STATE UNIV, 67- *Concurrent Pos:* Head dept bot & bact, Mont State Univ, 57-64, dean grad sch, 64-67. *Mem:* AAAS; hon mem Am Soc Microbiol; Am Acad Microbiol. *Res:* Pathogenic anaerobic bacteria. *Mailing Add:* Va Polytech Inst & State Univ Blacksburg VA 24061

SMITH, LOUIS LIVINGSTON, b College Place, Wash, May 19, 25; c 1. SURGERY. *Educ:* Walla Walla Col, BA, 48; Loma Linda Univ, MD, 48. *Prof Exp:* From intern to sr resident, Los Angeles County Gen Hosp, 48-57; from instr to assoc prof surg, 56-69, PROF SURG, LOMA LINDA UNIV, 69-, DIR SURG RES LAB, 59-, CHIEF PERIPHERAL VASCULAR SURG SERV, MED CTR, 71- *Concurrent Pos:* NIH res fel, Peter Bent Brigham Hosp & Harvard Univ, 57-59; Harvey Cushing res fel, 58-59. *Mem:* AMA; fel Am Col Surgeons; Am Surg Asn; Int Cardiovasc Soc; Int Soc Surg. *Res:* Surgical metabolism; shock; surgical trauma. *Mailing Add:* Dept of Surg Loma Linda Univ Loma Linda CA 92354

SMITH, LOWELL R, b Minneapolis, Minn, Nov 21, 33; m 60; c 2. ORGANIC CHEMISTRY. *Educ:* Univ Minn, BA, 55, PhD(org chem), 60. *Prof Exp:* Chemist, Russell-Miller Milling Co, 55-56; sr res chemist, 60-63, sr res specialist org chem, 63-75, SCI FEL, MONSANTO CO, 75- *Mem:* Am Chem Soc. *Res:* Indole, organophosphorus and heterocyclic chemistry; chemistry of oxalyl chloride; reaction mechanisms; chemical processing; amino acids; isocyanates. *Mailing Add:* Monsanto Co T-408 800 N Lindbergh Blvd St Louis MO 63166

SMITH, LOWELL SCOTT, b Akron, Ohio, July 20, 50. SOLID STATE PHYSICS. *Educ:* Univ Rochester, BS, 72; Univ Pa, PhD(physics), 76. *Prof Exp:* PHYSICIST, GEN ELEC CORP RES & DEVELOP, 76- *Mem:* Am Phys Soc. *Res:* Ultrasonic imaging; transducer design; physical acoustics; magnetism; magnetic resonance. *Mailing Add:* Gen Elec Corp Res & Develop PO Box 8 Schenectady NY 12301

SMITH, LUCIAN ANDERSON, b Mayfield, Ky, Nov 17, 10; m 37; c 5. MEDICINE. *Educ:* Wabash Col, AB, 30; Rush Med Col, MD, 35; Am Bd Internal Med, dipl, 43; Am Bd Gastroenterol, dipl. *Prof Exp:* Intern, Presby Hosp, Chicago, 34-35; first asst internal med & neurol, 39-43, head sect internal med, 47-70, assoc prof, 47-77, SR CONSULT, SECT MED, MAYO CLIN, 70-, EMER PROF MED, MAYO GRAD SCH MED, UNIV MINN, 77- *Concurrent Pos:* Fel internal med, Mayo Clin, 36-39. *Mem:* Am Gastroenterol Asn; AMA; fel Am Col Physicians; Am Osteop Asn; Sigma Xi. *Mailing Add:* 3801 Valleyview Rd SW Rochester MN 55901

SMITH, LUTHER W, b Greenfield, Mass, Apr 26, 32. PHYSICS, MATHEMATICS. *Educ:* Univ Mass, BA, 53; Univ Kans, MS, 56. *Prof Exp:* Res physicist, Res Ctr, 58-82; OPTICAL ENGR, AO INSTRUMENT GROUP, WARNER-LAMBERT, 82- *Mem:* Optical Soc Am. *Res:* Diffraction theory of image formation; phase microscopy; surface guided waves. *Mailing Add:* AO Instrument Group Warner Lambert Keene NH 03431

SMITH, LYLE W, b Normal, Ill, Feb 20, 20; m 42; c 2. PHYSICS. *Educ:* Univ Ill, BS, 42, MS, 43, PhD(physics), 48. *Prof Exp:* Asst physics, Univ Ill, 43-44 & 46-47, asst chem, 44-46, assoc physics, 47-48; physicist, 48-61, SR PHYSICIST, BROOKHAVEN NAT LAB, 61- *Mem:* AAAS; fel Am Phys Soc; NY Acad Sci; Sigma Xi. *Res:* High energy particle accelerators; high energy elementary particle physics. *Mailing Add:* Accelerator Dept Brookhaven Nat Lab Upton NY 11973

SMITH, LYNWOOD S, b Snohomish, Wash, Nov 15, 28; m 51; c 3. FISH PHYSIOLOGY. *Educ:* Univ Wash, BS, 52, MS, 55, PhD(zool), 62. *Prof Exp:* Teacher high sch, Wash, 52-53; instr biol & zool, Olympic Col, 55-60; asst prof zool, Univ Victoria, 62-65; from asst prof to assoc prof, Col Fisheries, 65-74, PROF FISHERIES, COL FISHERIES, UNIV WASH, 74- *Mem:* AAAS; Am Fisheries Soc; Am Soc Zoologists. *Res:* Osmoregulation and blood circulation, effects of pollutants, general environmental physiology and functional anatomy in teleost fish; effects of stress and exercise on salmonids particularly during smolting. *Mailing Add:* Sch Fisheries Univ of Wash Seattle WA 98195

SMITH, M SUSAN, b Detroit, Mich, July 18, 42. NEUROENDOCRINOLOGY, REPRODUCTIVE PHYSIOLOGY. *Educ:* NTex State Univ, BA, 64; Fla State Univ, MS, 69; Univ Ga, PhD(physiol), 72. *Prof Exp:* Fel physiol, Emory Univ, 71-73, instr, 73-74; asst prof, Med Sch, Univ Mass, 74-77, assoc prof, 77-79; res assoc prof, 79-81, ASSOC PROF PHYSIOL, SCH MED, PITTSBURGH UNIV, 82- *Concurrent Pos:* Vis lectr, Med Sch, New York Univ, 78; NIH Career Develop Award, Nat Inst Child Health & Human Develop, 78. *Mem:* Endocrine Soc; Soc Study Reprod; Am Physiol Soc; AAAS. *Res:* Regulation of pituitary gonadotropin and prolactine secretion by the hypothalamic-pituitary-ovarian axis. *Mailing Add:* Dept Physiol Sch Med Univ Pittsburgh Pittsburgh PA 15261

SMITH, MALCOLM (KINMONTH), b Morristown, NJ, Dec 19, 19; m 60; c 3. PHYSICS, INSTRUMENTATION. *Educ:* Haverford Col, BS, 41; Columbia Univ, MA, 54. *Prof Exp:* Teacher, Gow Sch, NY, 48-52 & Putney Sch, Vt, 52-56; engr, Woods Hole Oceanog Inst, 56-58; ed, Phys Sci Study Comt, 58-60; exec officer physics, Sci Teaching Ctr, Mass Inst Technol, 60-66; assoc prof, Lowell Technol Inst, 66-72, PROF PHYSICS & APPL PHYSICS, UNIV LOWELL, 72- *Concurrent Pos:* Consult, Educ Develop Ctr, Newton, Mass, 57-68, Inst Serv to Educ, DC, 67-69 & Tech Educ Res Ctr, Cambridge, Mass, 70-80. *Mem:* Inst Elec & Electronics Eng; Am Asn Physics Teachers. *Mailing Add:* Dept Physics & Appl Physics Univ Lowell Lowell MA 01854

SMITH, MALCOLM CRAWFORD, JR, b Kingsville, Tex, Jan 2, 36; m 61; c 2. VETERINARY MEDICINE, NUTRITION. *Educ:* Tex A&M Univ, DVM, 59; Purdue Univ, MS, 65. *Prof Exp:* Base vet, US Air Force, Holloman AFB, NMex, 59-62; chief vet serv, Sidi Slimane Air Base, Morocco, 62-63; Toul Rosieres Air Base, France, 63-65; CHIEF FOOD & NUTRIT BR, BIOMED RES DIV, 5D-3, JOHNSON SPACE CTR, NASA, 66- *Mem:* Am Vet Med Asn; Asn Military Surg US; Inst Food Technol. *Res:* Food technology; nutrition; aerospace life support systems; public health; veterinary medicine. *Mailing Add:* NASA-Johnson Space Ctr Mail Code 5D-3 Houston TX 77058

SMITH, MANIS JAMES, JR, b Memphis, Tenn, Sept 26, 40. CARDIOVASCULAR ENDOCRINOLOGY. *Educ:* Memphis State Univ, BS, 62; Palmer Col Chiropractic, DC, 65; La State Univ Med Ctr, PhD(physiol), 74. *Prof Exp:* Fel, 75-77, ASST PROF, DEPT PHYSIOL & BIOPHYSICS, UNIV MISS MED CTR, 77- *Concurrent Pos:* Prin investr, Miss Heart Asn, 78-83. *Mem:* AAAS. *Res:* Control of adrenal steroidogenesis; radioimmunoassay development. *Mailing Add:* Dept Physiol & Biophysics Univ Miss Med Ctr Jackson MS 39216

SMITH, MARCIA SUE, b Greenfield, Mass, Feb 22, 51. SCIENCE POLICY. *Educ:* Syracuse Univ, BA, 72. *Prof Exp:* Corresp & admin asst space, Am Inst Aeronaut & Astronaut, 73-75; analyst aerospace & energy technol, 75-80, SPECIALIST, AEROSPACE & ENERGY SYSTS, SCI POLICY RES DIV, CONG RES SERV, LIBR CONG, 80- *Mem:* AAAS; Am Inst Aeronaut & Astronaut; assoc fel Brit Interplanetary Soc; Sigma Xi; NY Acad Sci. *Res:* Space science. *Mailing Add:* Sci Policy Res Div 10 First St SE Washington DC 20540

SMITH, MARIAN JOSE, b Hoboken, NJ, Oct 24, 15. BIOCHEMISTRY. *Educ:* Col St Elizabeth, AB, 36; Fordham Univ, MS, 54, PhD(biochem), 60. *Prof Exp:* Chemist, Reed & Carnrick, 37-45; teacher parochial schs, 45-47; from instr to assoc prof chem, 48-69, PROF CHEM, COL ST ELIZABETH, 69-, CHMN CHEM DEPT, 76- *Concurrent Pos:* AEC equip grant, 61-62; NSF travel grant, Int Symp, Göttingen, Ger, 61; Ciba Corp res grant, Univ Glasgow, 62; USPHS grant, 65-66; NSF res partic grant, 68; NSF grant for sci educ workshops, 80 & 81. *Mem:* Am Chem Soc; fel Am Inst Chemists. *Res:* Activity of enzymes related to nucleic acid metabolism in tumor-bearing rats; biochemistry of aging. *Mailing Add:* Dept of Chem Col of St Elizabeth Convent Station NJ 07961

SMITH, MARIANNE (RUTH) FREUNDLICH, b Karlsruhe, Ger, June 11, 22; US citizen; c 4. MATHEMATICS. *Educ:* Queens Col, BS, 43; Univ Ill, MS, 44, PhD(math), 47. *Prof Exp:* Asst physics, Univ Ill, 43-44, asst math, 46-47; lectr, Univ Calif, Berkeley, 47-49, instr, 49-50; vis prof physics, Univ Pittsburgh, 51-52; lectr math, Univ Calif, Berkeley, 57-58; from asst prof to assoc prof, Calif State Col Hayward, 63-73, PROF MATH, CALIF STATE UNIV, HAYWARD, 73- *Mem:* Am Math Soc; Math Asn Am; Am Asn Univ Prof. *Res:* Normed rings; duality theorems; functional analyses, differential equations. *Mailing Add:* Dept Math Calif State Univ Hayward CA 94542

SMITH, MARION BUSH, JR, b Ferriday, La, Feb 25, 29. MATHEMATICS. *Educ:* La State Univ, BS, 49, MS, 51; Univ NC, PhD(math), 57. *Prof Exp:* Instr math, Univ NC, 53-57; asst prof, Fla State Univ, 57-58 & Univ Utah, 58-61; vis assoc prof, Univ Wis-Madison, 61-63, assoc prof & chmn dept exten div, 63-64; assoc prof math, Univ Wis-Baraboo/Sauk County Campus, 64-72, vchancellor ctr syst, 64-68, chmn dept math, 68-72, 74-77; PROF MATH, CALIF, STATE COL, BAKERSFIELD, 72- *Mem:* Am Math Soc; Math Asn Am. *Res:* History of mathematics; abstract topological spaces; foundations of geometry. *Mailing Add:* Calif State Col Dept Math 9001 Stockdale Hwy Bakersfield CA 93309

SMITH, MARION EDMONDS, b Susanville, Calif, July 13, 26; m 55; c 2. BIOCHEMISTRY. *Educ:* Univ Calif, BA, 52, MA, 54, PhD(biochem), 56. *Prof Exp:* Asst, Univ Calif, 53-56; res assoc med, Sch Med, Stanford Univ, 56-63, instr, 63-71, sr scientist med, 71-74; NEUROCHEMIST, VET ADMIN HOSP, PALO ALTO, 62- *Concurrent Pos:* Adj prof neurol, Stanford Univ, 74- *Mem:* AAAS; Int Soc Neurochem; Am Soc Neurochem (secy, 81-83); Soc Neurosci; Am Soc Biol Chemists. *Res:* Lipid and protein metabolism in nervous system; biochemistry of demyelinating diseases; myelin metabolism and function. *Mailing Add:* Neurol Serv Vet Admin Hosp Palo Alto CA 94304

SMITH, MARION L(EROY), b Sharon, Pa, June 3, 23; m 44; c 3. MECHANICAL ENGINEERING. *Educ:* La State Univ, BS, 44; Ohio State Univ, MS, 48. *Prof Exp:* From instr to assoc prof, 47-58, PROF MECH ENG & ASSOC DEAN COL ENG, OHIO STATE UNIV, 58- *Concurrent Pos:* Mem staff year-in-indust prog, Eng Dept, E I du Pont de Nemours & Co, 56-57; mem, State Bd Regist Prof Engrs & Surveyors, 75-80; mem, Uniform Exam Comt, Nat Coun Eng Examrs, 76, chmn, 81- *Mem:* fel Am Soc Mech Engrs; fel Am Soc Eng Educ; fel Soc Automotive Eng; fel Nat Soc Prof Engrs; fel Nat Coun Eng Examrs. *Res:* Fundamentals of fuels and combustion; mechanism of oxidation of hydrocarbons, particularly pre-combustion reactions; dual fuel diesel engines; characteristics of miniature engine generator sets; methods of heat dissipation from aircraft compartments; gas turbines. *Mailing Add:* Col of Eng Ohio State Univ 2070 Neil Ave Columbus OH 43210

SMITH, MARK ANDREW, b East Brady, Pa, Nov 24, 47; m 69; c 2. MATHEMATICS, FUNCTIONAL ANALYSIS. *Educ:* Indiana Univ Pa, BS, 69; Univ Ill, Urbana, MS, 70, PhD(math), 75. *Prof Exp:* Asst prof, Lake Forest Col, 75-77; asst prof, 77-79, ASSOC PROF MATH, MIAMI UNIV, 79- *Mem:* Am Math Soc; Sigma Xi. *Res:* Geometry of Banach spaces. *Mailing Add:* Dept of Math Miami Univ Oxford OH 45056

SMITH, MARK WILLIAM, b La Crosse, Wis, Apr 21, 35; m 59; c 3. COMPUTER SCIENCE, STATISTICS. *Educ:* Univ Minn, Minneapolis, BS, 57, MS, 59; Southern Methodist Univ, PhD(statist), 69. *Prof Exp:* Mem tech staff, Cent Res Lab, 59-61, mem equip group, Res & Develop Lab, 61-68, mem tech staff equip group, 68-80, sr mem tech staff, 80, PROG MGR, MISSILE & ORD SYSTS DEPT, TEX INSTRUMENTS INC, 80- *Mem:* Inst Elec & Electronics Engrs. *Res:* Computer simulation of complex systems. *Mailing Add:* 5319 W University Blvd Dallas TX 75209

SMITH, MARTHA KATHLEEN, b Detroit, Mich, Mar 14, 44. MATHEMATICS. *Educ:* Univ Mich, Ann Arbor, BA, 65; Univ Chicago, MS, 67, PhD(math), 70. *Prof Exp:* G C Evans instr math, Rice Univ, 70-72; asst prof, Wash Univ, 72-73; asst prof math, 73-76, ASSOC PROF MATH, UNIV TEX, AUSTIN, 76- *Mem:* Am Math Soc; Math Asn Am; Asn Women Math. *Res:* Ring theory. *Mailing Add:* Dept of Math Univ of Tex Austin TX 78712

SMITH, MARTIN BRISTOW, b Owatonna, Minn, Feb 18, 16; m 45; c 2. PHYSICAL CHEMISTRY. *Educ:* Univ Chicago, BS, 36, PhD(phys chem), 42. *Prof Exp:* Jr chemist, Universal Oil Prod, Ill, 36-38; rubber chemist, US Rubber Co, Mich, 42-46; chemist, Consol Vultee Co, 46-47; phys chemist, Ethyl Corp, 47-62, res assoc, 62-77; RETIRED. *Mem:* Fel Am Chem Soc. *Res:* Micro-calorimetry; heats of mixing of strong electrolytes; physical property measurements; thermody- namic calculations; monomer-dimer equilibria of aluminum alkyls; heats of formation of aluminum alkyls and related compounds. *Mailing Add:* 1742 Carl Ave Baton Rouge LA 70808

SMITH, MARY ANN HARVEY, b Camden, Ark, Jan 29, 40; m 71. NUTRITION, MENTAL RETARDATION. *Educ:* Henderson State Col, BSE, 60; Univ Tenn, MS, 62, PhD(food sci, nutrit), 65. *Prof Exp:* Instr food sci, Univ Ala, 61-62; therapeut dietitian, Ft Sanders Hosp, 64-65; asst prof foods & nutrit, Mid Tenn State Univ, 65-67; asst prof, 67-70, assoc prof, 70-77, PROF NUTRIT, CHILD DEVELOP CTR, UNIV TENN MED UNITS, MEMPHIS, 77-, CHIEF DEPT, 67- *Concurrent Pos:* Adj prof nutrit, Col Home Econ, Univ Tenn, 67-, Sch Home Econ, Univ Ark, 70- & Dept Home Econ, Col Educ, Univ Miss, 79- *Mem:* Am Dietetic Asn; Soc Nutrit Educ; Am Asn Ment Deficiency; Nutrit Today Soc. *Res:* Nutrition as related to mental retardation, including nutritional status of the retarded, feeding techniques and management of inborn errors of metabolism. *Mailing Add:* Child Develop Ctr Nutrit Dept 711 Jefferson Ave Memphis TN 38105

SMITH, MARY ELIZABETH, b Presque Isle, Maine, Mar 29, 25. LABORATORY ANIMAL MEDICINE, ONCOLOGY. *Educ:* Univ Maine, Orono, BA, 46, MS, 50; Mich State Univ, DVM, 58. *Prof Exp:* Res asst animal behav, Jackson Lab, 49-54; assoc vet, Portland Vet Hosp, 59-69;

res asst med res, Life Sci Res Labs, Life Sci Inc, 73-81, res assoc path & oncol, 73-81; RES ASSOC, RES INST BIOMED, SHOWA UNIV, 81- Mem: Am Vet Med Asn; Am Soc Microbiol; AAAS. Res: Investigation of the basic mechanisms in viral oncogenesis, specifically the involvement of avian herpesviruses and oncornaviruses in viral transformation and oncogenesis. Mailing Add: Inst Biomed Showa Univ 2900 72nd St N Clearwater FL 33520

SMITH, MAURICE JOHN VERNON, b London, Eng, Aug 11, 29; nat US; c 5. UROLOGY. Educ: Cambridge Univ, BA, 55, MB, BChir, 56; Columbia Univ, PhD(anat), 65. Prof Exp: Intern & sr house officer, St Thomas Hosp, London, 56-58; resident gen surg, Univ Hosp, Saskatoon, Sask, 58-59; resident urol, Col Physicians & Surgeons, Columbia Univ, 59-60, asst anat, 60-64, assoc urol, 64-66; resident, Bowman Gray Sch Med, 66-68; from asst prof to assoc prof, 68-75, PROF UROL, MED COL VA, VA COMMONWEALTH UNIV, 75- Concurrent Pos: Consult, McGuire Vet Hosp, Richmond, Va, 69- & Portsmouth Naval Hosp, 69- Mem: Am Urol Asn; Soc Univ Urologists; fel Am Col Surgeons. Res: Renal calculi; renal and prostatic cancer. Mailing Add: Div of Urol Med Col of Va Richmond VA 23298

SMITH, MAURICE VERNON, b Toronto, Ont, June 4, 20; m 48; c 4. APICULTURE. Educ: Univ Toronto, BSA, 42, MSA, 54; Cornell Univ, PhD, 57. Prof Exp: From asst to ASSOC PROF ENVIRON BIOL, UNIV GUELPH, 49- Mem: Entom Soc Am. Res: Honeybee behavior and pollination; bee breeding; insect photography. Mailing Add: Dept of Environ Biol Univ of Guelph Guelph ON N1G 2W1 Can

SMITH, MAYNARD E, b Boston, Mass, Nov 29, 16; m 41; c 2. ANALYTICAL CHEMISTRY. Educ: Mass Inst Technol, PhD(chem), 49. Prof Exp: Asst chem, Mass Inst Technol, 41-49; anal chemist, 49-72, SECT LEADER, LOS ALAMOS NAT LAB, 72- Mem: Am Chem Soc; Am Inst Chemists. Res: Gases in metals; mass spectrometry; gas chromatography. Mailing Add: 75 Mesa Verde Dr Los Alamos NM 87544

SMITH, MELVIN I, b New York, NY, July 21, 24; m 46; c 4. MECHANICAL & CHEMICAL ENGINEERING. Educ: City Col New York, BChE, 44; Columbia Univ, MS, 47, EngScD, 55. Prof Exp: Res technologist, Res Dept, Socony Mobil Oil Co, Inc, 47-58, supv technologist, 58-72, MGR LUBRICANTS, TECH SERV DEPT, MOBIL OIL CORP, 72- Mem: Am Soc Lubrication Engrs; Am Soc Mech Engrs. Res: Application problems and formulation of lubricating, hydraulic and metal processing fluids. Mailing Add: Tech Serv Lab Mobil Oil Corp PO Box 1027 Princeton NJ 08540

SMITH, MEREDITH FORD, b Milwaukee, Wis; c 2. INTERNATIONAL NUTRITION, COMMUNITY NUTRITION. Educ: Trinity Univ, Tex, BS, 70; Va Polytech Inst, PhD(human nutrit), 78. Prof Exp: Home economist, Consumer & Food Econ Inst, USDA, 71-75; teaching asst foods & nutrit, Va Polytech Inst & State Univ, 74-77; instr, Human Develop & Consumer Sci Dept, Univ Houston, 77-78; asst prof, 78-81; ASST PROF COMMUNITY NUTRIT & INT NUTRIT, DEPT FOODS & NUTRIT, KANS STATE UNIV, 81- Concurrent Pos: Food serv proj assoc, Coord Vocational Acad Educ Workshop, Univ Houston, 79; nutrit consult, Tex Dept Human Resources, 78-79 & Cath Univ, Santiago, 79, Off Int Coop & Develop, USDA, 80; tech advisor, Off Nutrit, USAID, 80; prin investr, Analysis of Indigenous Food Patterns in Low-Income Families, USDA. Mem: Soc Nutrit Educ; Am Pub Health Asn; Am Home Econ Asn; Sigma Xi. Res: Nutritional assessment of at-risk populations in US and developing countries; factors influencing nutritional states and food behavior; evaluation of domestic and international community nutrition programs. Mailing Add: Dept Foods & Nutrit Kans State Univ Manhattan KS 66506

SMITH, MICHAEL, b London, Eng, Dec 18, 32; m 61. PHYSICAL CHEMISTRY. Educ: Univ Southampton, BSc, 54, PhD(phys chem), 58. Prof Exp: Asst lectr radiation chem, Kings Col, Univ Durham, 57-60; sr chemist, Am Cyanamid Co, 60-62; assoc scientist, 62-63, scientist, 63-65, sr scientist, 65-67, systs photoconductors, 67-69, lab mgr xerography, 69-71, process sect mgr, Webster, 71-73, mgr, Xerographic Technol Dept, 73-75, vpres, Info Technol Group, 74-76, group dir, Rank Xerox Eng, 76-78, vpres, Reprod Technol Group, 78-81, GEN MGR, SUPPLIES & MAT BUS UNIT, XEROX CORP, 81- Concurrent Pos: Atomic Energy Res Estab fel, 57-60. Mem: Am Chem Soc; Royal Soc Chem; Am Inst Chem. Res: Radiation chemistry; organic semiconductors; xerography; imaging technologies and systems. Mailing Add: 7 Duxbury Way Rochester NY 14618

SMITH, MICHAEL, b Blackpool, Eng, Apr 26, 32; Can citizen; m 60; c 3. ORGANIC CHEMISTRY, BIOCHEMISTRY. Educ: Univ Man, BSc, 53, PhD(chem), 56. Prof Exp: Fel, BC Res Coun, 56-60; res assoc, Inst Enzyme Res, Univ Wis, 60-61; head chem sect, Vancouver Lab, Fisheries Res Bd Can, 61-66; assoc prof, 66-70, PROF BIOCHEM, UNIV BC, 70- Concurrent Pos: Med res assoc, Med Res Coun Can, 66- Mem: Fel Chem Inst Can; Royal Soc Chem. Res: Nucleic acid and nucleotide chemistry and biochemistry; endocrinology of fish. Mailing Add: Dept Biochem Univ BC Vancouver BC V6T 1W5 Can

SMITH, MICHAEL CLAUDE, b Winston-Salem, NC, May 31, 49; m 70; c 2. INDUSTRIAL & MANUFACTURING ENGINEERING. Educ: Univ Tenn, Knoxville, BSIE, 71, MSIE, 74; Univ Mo-Columbia, PhD(indust eng), 77. Prof Exp: Indust engr, Buckeye Cellulose Corp, 71-72, St Mary's Med Ctr, Knoxville, Tenn, 72-74; asst prof, Ore State Univ, 77-79; ASST PROF INDUST ENG, UNIV MO-COLUMBIA, 79- Concurrent Pos: Consult, Pharm Serv, Vet Admin, 78-; Univ Mo Hosp & Clin, 79-; prin investr & dir mgr sci, Air Force Logistic Command, 81-82. Mem: Sr mem Am Inst Indust Eng; Operations Res Soc Am. Res: Analysis of alternative maintenance policy for systems involving life-limited components; analysis of health care delivery systems and alternative strategies for designing and delivering health care systems. Mailing Add: 1008 Westport Dr Columbia MO 65201

SMITH, MICHAEL HOWARD, b San Pedro, Calif, Aug 30, 38; m 58; c 2. ECOLOGY, EVOLUTION. Educ: San Diego State Col, AB, 60, MA, 62; Univ Fla, PhD(zool), 66. Prof Exp: Res assoc zool, Inst Ecol, Univ Ga, 66-67, asst prof, 67-71; assoc prof, Univ Tex, 70-71; assoc prof, 70-77, ADJ PROF ZOOL, UNIV GA, 77-, RES ASSOC, 77-; DIR SAVANNAH RIVER ECOLOGY LAB, 77- Concurrent Pos: NSF res grant, 66-68; AEC Comn grants, 67-; dir, Savannah River Ecol Lab, Aiken, SC, 74- Mem: AAAS; Am Soc Mammal; Soc Study Evolution; Ecol Soc Am; Animal Behav Soc. Res: Behavior; various biological aspects of vertebrates as they relate to the study of speciation and population ecology. Mailing Add: Dept of Zool Univ of Ga Athens GA 30602

SMITH, MICHAEL JAMES, b East St Louis, Ill, Feb 18, 45; m 67; c 2. ANALYTICAL CHEMISTRY, ENVIRONMENTAL CHEMISTRY. Educ: Southern Ill Univ, BA, 67; Univ Mo, Columbia, MA, 69, PhD(anal chem), 72. Prof Exp: Asst prof anal chem & environ chem, Wright State Univ, 72-76, assoc prof, 76-77, assoc dir, Brehm Lab, 74-77; mgr, Chem Sci Lab, 77-79, mgr engineered barriers group & proj, 79-80, MGR, WASTE PACKAGE STUDIES DEPT & PROG, ROCKWELL HANFORD OPERS, 80- Concurrent Pos: Consult, Monsanto Res Corp, Am Nuclear Soc; Nat Mgt NSF & Inst Environ Educ, 74; mem proposal rev panel, NSF Off Exp Prog, 74-77; consult, Miami Conservancy Dist, 75-76; consult, Atlantic Richfield Hanford Co, 76-77. Honors & Awards: Award, Am Bicentennial Comn, 75. Mem: Am Chem Soc; AAAS; Am Water Works Asn; Am Nuclear Soc. Res: The environmental chemistry of air, water and solid waste systems, including nuclear waste chemistry; acid mine drainage treatment; heavy metal studies, pesticides analyses, photochemical oxidants measurements and chelate analyses. Mailing Add: Rockwell Hanford Opers 2101-M Bldg 200 E Area Richland WA 99352

SMITH, MICHAEL JOSEPH, b Bay City, Mich, Jan 20, 39; m 78; c 1. DEVELOPMENTAL & MOLECULAR BIOLOGY. Educ: St Mary's Col, Calif, BS, 63; Univ BC, PhD(zool), 69. Prof Exp: Asst prof zool, Univ Nebr, Lincoln, 69-71; res fel biol, Calif Inst Technol, 71-73, sr res fel, 73-76; asst prof, 76-78, ASSOC PROF BIOL, SIMON FRAZER UNIV, 78- Concurrent Pos: Spec res fel, USPHS, Calif Inst Technol, 71-73; res grant, Nat Res Coun Can, Simon Fraser Univ, 77-83 & Brit Columbia Health Care Res Found grant, 78-82. Mem: Can Soc Cell Biologist. Res: Molecular biology of eukaryote development; phylogeny and evolution of genomic DNA sequence arrangement. Mailing Add: Dept Biol Sci Simon Fraser Univ Burnaby BC V5A 1S6 Can

SMITH, MICHAEL LEW, b Ashland, Kans. ENDOCRINOLOGY, HUMAN PHYSIOLOGY. Educ: Emporia Kans State Univ, BA, 70; Purdue Univ, PhD(chem), 74. Prof Exp: Biochemist, Madigan Army Med Ctr, 75-77, chief, Res Lab, 77-80; ASST CHIEF, DEPT CLIN RES, WILLIAM BEAUMONT ARMY MED CTR, 80- Mem: Endocrine Soc; Am Asn Clin Chemists. Res: Functions of prolactin in male mammals. Mailing Add: Dept Clin Invest William Beaumont Army Med Ctr El Paso TX 79920

SMITH, MICKE JOE, b Memphis, Tenn, Oct 16, 47; m 72; c 1. COMPARATIVE PHYSIOLOGY, ZOOLOGY. Educ: Memphis State Univ, BS, 70, MS, 75; Va Polytech Inst & State Univ, PhD(zool), 78. Prof Exp: Grad teaching asst zool, Memphis State Univ, 70-73; teacher chem, Lausanne Sch, 73-75; res asst, Va Polytech Inst & State Univ, 75-76, teaching asst physiol, 77-78; ASST PROF BIOL, MILLSAPS COL, 78- Mem: Sigma Xi; Asn Southeastern Biologists; Am Soc Zoologists. Res: Study of biochemical and physiological adaptation to hypoxia by fish using tolerant species (carp and catfish) as compared to sensitive species (trout). Mailing Add: Dept of Biol Millsaps Col Jackson MS 39210

SMITH, MILTON LOUIS, b Childress, Tex, May 30, 39; m 66; c 2. INDUSTRIAL ENGINEERING. Educ: Tex Tech Univ, BS, 61, MS, 66, PhD(indust eng), 68. Prof Exp: Asst, 65-68, assoc prof, 68-78, PROF INDUST ENG, TEX TECH UNIV, 78- Mem: Am Inst Indust Engrs; Am Soc Eng Educ; Am Soc Testing & Mat. Res: Job sequencing; application of systems analysis to cotton production and processing; economic evaluation of agricultural systems; hail damage to solar collectors/reflectors. Mailing Add: Dept of Indust Eng Tex Tech Univ Lubbock TX 79409

SMITH, MILTON REYNOLDS, b Chicago, Ill, Mar 15, 34; m 55; c 1. BIOCHEMISTRY, PHYSIOLOGY. Educ: Knox Col, BA, 56; Univ Ariz, MS, 58, PhD(biochem), 63. Prof Exp: Res assoc biochem, Univ Ariz, 58-63; sr biochemist, Eli Lilly & Co, 63-80; TECH DIR, HEPAR INDUSTS, 80- Concurrent Pos: Instr, Ind Cent Col, 67-71; career consult, Knox Col, 72. Mem: AAAS; Am Chem Soc; Am Inst Chemists; NY Acad Sci. Res: Isolation research in the fields of lipids, proteins and enzymes; protein chemistry and endocrinology. Mailing Add: Hepar Industs Inc 160 Industrial Dr Franklin OH 45005

SMITH, MORGAN SCOTT, b Laconia, NH, July 7, 49; m 74; c 1. SOIL SCIENCE, MICROBIOLOGY. Educ: Cornell Univ, BA, 71, MS, 75; Mich State Univ, Ph(crop & soil sci), 78. Prof Exp: ASST PROF SOIL MICROBIOL, DEPT AGRON, UNIV KY, 78- Mem: Am Soc Microbiol; Am Soc Agron; Soil Sci Soc Am. Res: Soil microbiology, especially microbial transformations of soil nitrogen and plant-microbe interactions. Mailing Add: Dept of Agron Univ of Ky Lexington KY 40506

SMITH, MORRIS WADE, b Baytown, Tex, Aug 1, 38; m 62; c 2. HORTICULTURE, PLANT PHYSIOLOGY. Educ: Tex Technol Univ, BS, 64; Tex A&M Univ, MS, 72, PhD(hort), 77. Prof Exp: Technician II, Dept Hort, Tex A&M Univ, 65-78; RES HORTICULTURIST, SCI & EDUC ADMIN-AGR RES, USDA, COASTAL PLAIN EXP STA, 78- Mem: Am Soc Hort Sci. Res: Nutrition concerning container-grown ornamental plants; irrigation; herbicide and plant growth regulator research. Mailing Add: Sci & Educ Admin-Agr Res USDA Coastal Plain Exp Sta Tifton GA 31794

SMITH, MORTON C(HARLES), b Selby, SDak, Sept 15, 17; m 45; c 4. GEOTHERMAL ENGINEERING, MATERIALS SCIENCE. *Educ:* SDak Sch Mines & Technol, BS, 38, MetE, 44; Lehigh Univ, MS, 39. *Prof Exp:* Instr metall, Univ Alaska, 39-42; asst prof & actg head dept, Mont Sch Mines, 42-45; metallurgist, Black, Sivalls & Bryson, Inc, Mo, 45-46; asst prof metall & actg head dept, NMex Inst Mining & Technol, 46-47; prof metall eng, Colo Sch Mines, 47-54; alt group leader phys metall, 54-73, group leader geothermal energy, 73-76, MEM GEOTHERMAL STAFF, LOS ALAMOS NAT LAB, 76- *Concurrent Pos:* Consult, 40-; lead partic, CCMS Pilot Study Geothermal Energy, NATO, 73-77; mem US Org Comt, 2nd UN Symposium Geothermal Energy, 73-77; proj leader, US-Italy Agreement Geothermal Res & Develop, 75-; mem supply & delivery panel, NRC Comt Nuclear & Alternative Energy Systs, 75-77. *Mem:* Fel Am Soc Metals. *Res:* Geothermal energy; graphite technology; physical metallurgy; materials science. *Mailing Add:* Los Alamos Nat Lab Los Alamos NM 87544

SMITH, NAT E, b Bartow, Fla, Nov 29, 22; m 53; c 7. MEDICINE. *Educ:* Erskine Col, AB, 43; Med Col Ga, MD, 49. *Prof Exp:* Intern, Gorgas Hosp, Ancon, CZ, 49-50; med resident, DC Gen Hosp & George Washington Univ, Hosp, 52-54; staff physician, Vet Admin, 55-57; from instr to assoc prof med, Col Med, Univ Ill, 57-69, assoc dean, 62-75, prof med, 69-75; dean sch med, Mercer Univ, 74-76; ASSOC DEAN & PROF MED, BOWMAN GRAY SCH MED, WAKE FOREST UNIV, 76- *Mem:* Am Rheumatism Asn. *Res:* Rheumatic diseases; methods and evaluation of medical education. *Mailing Add:* Bowman Gray Sch Med Wake Forest Univ Winston-Salem NC 27103

SMITH, NATHAN ELBERT, b Avon, NY, Apr 30, 36; m 58; c 2. ANIMAL SCIENCE. *Educ:* Cornell Univ, BS, 67; Univ Calif, Davis, PhD(nutrit), 70. *Prof Exp:* Res nutritionist, Univ Calif, Davis, 70-71; asst prof animal sci, Cornell Univ, 71-74; ASST PROF ANIMAL SCI, UNIV CALIF, DAVIS, 74- *Mem:* Am Dairy Sci Asn; Am Soc Animal Sci. *Res:* Animal nutrition with emphasis on dairy nutrition, animal metabolism, mathematical and computer modeling of animal metabolism and animal production systems. *Mailing Add:* Dept of Animal Sci Univ of Calif Davis CA 95616

SMITH, NATHAN JAMES, b Cuba City, Wis, Oct 12, 21; m 46; c 3. PEDIATRICS. *Educ:* Univ Wis, BA, 43, MD, 45. *Prof Exp:* Fulbright scholar, Univ Paris, 50; instr pediat, Sch Med, Temple Univ, 51-53; from asst prof to assoc prof, Univ Calif, Los Angeles, 54-56; prof & chmn dept, Sch Med, Univ Wis, 57-65; PROF PEDIAT, SCH MED, UNIV WASH, 65-; PEDIATRICIAN-IN-CHIEF, KING COUNTY HOSP, 65- *Concurrent Pos:* Mem hemat training grant comt, NIH, 60-; spec asst nutrit progs to Secy Health, Educ & Welfare, 70-71. *Mem:* Am Soc Hemat; Soc Pediat Res; Am Pediat Soc; Soc Exp Biol & Med; Am Acad Pediat. *Res:* Nutrition as applied to pediatrics; sports and nutrition; sports and children. *Mailing Add:* Univ of Wash GB 15 Seattle WA 98195

SMITH, NATHAN LEWIS, III, b Baltimore, Md, May 12, 43; m 65; c 2. ENZYMOLOGY, IMMUNOCHEMISTRY. *Educ:* Univ Miami, BS, 66; Univ Calif, Irvine, PhD(biol), 72. *Prof Exp:* Jr specialist biochem, Univ Calif, Irvine, 71-72, asst res biologist, 72-74; group leader diag, Nelson Res & Develop Co, 73-74; STAFF IMMUNOLOGIST, CORDIS CORP, 75- *Mem:* Am Chem Soc. *Res:* Design and development of clinical diagnostic test procedures especially enzyme tagged immunoassays. *Mailing Add:* Cordis Labs 2190 N Miami Ave Miami FL 33127

SMITH, NATHAN MCKAY, b Wendell, Idaho, Apr 22, 35; m 53; c 5. ZOOLOGY. *Educ:* Eastern Ore Col, BS, 61; Ore State Univ, MS, 64; Brigham Young Univ, MLS, 69, PhD(zool), 72. *Prof Exp:* Teacher, The Dalles, Ore, 61-63 & La Grande, 65-66; ASSOC PROF LIBR INFO SCI, BRIGHAM YOUNG UNIV, 70- *Mem:* Soc Study Amphibians & Reptiles. *Res:* Reptilian taxonomy, comparative anatomy and natural history. *Mailing Add:* 5042 Harold B Lee Libr Brigham Young Univ Provo UT 84602

SMITH, NEAL A(USTIN), b Norwich, Ohio, Feb 10, 19; m 42. ELECTRICAL ENGINEERING. *Educ:* Ohio State Univ, BEE, 41, MSc, 47. *Prof Exp:* Elec engr, Fed Mach & Welder Co, 41-44; from instr to assoc prof, 47-65, PROF ELEC ENG, OHIO STATE UNIV, 65- *Concurrent Pos:* From res asst to res assoc, Res Found, 47-53; elec engr, Columbus & Southern Ohio Elec Co, 54-58; consult engr, 51-76. *Mem:* Inst Elec & Electronics Engrs; Am Soc Eng Educ. *Res:* Electrical circuits, machines and power system operation; high voltage power transmission. *Mailing Add:* Dept Elec Eng Ohio State Univ 2015 Neil Ave Columbus OH 43210

SMITH, NED PHILIP, b Beaver Dam, Wis, Dec 3, 42. PHYSICAL OCEANOGRAPHY. *Educ:* Univ Wis-Madison, BS, 65, MS, 67, PhD(limnol & oceanog), 72. *Prof Exp:* Asst prof phys oceanog, Univ Tex, Austin, 72-77; ASSOC RES SCIENTIST, HARBOR BR FOUND, INC, FT PIERCE, FLA, 77- *Mem:* Am Meteorol Soc; Gulf Estuarine Res Soc (secy-treas, 80-83); Am Soc Limnol & Oceanog; Am Geophys Union. *Res:* Descriptive physical oceanography, including continental shelf circulation and intracoastal tides; heat budget of estuaries. *Mailing Add:* Harbor Br Found Inc RR 1 Box 196 Ft Pierce FL 33450

SMITH, NELSON S(TUART), JR, b Weirton, WVa, Aug 9, 29; m 51; c 3. ELECTRICAL ENGINEERING. *Educ:* Univ WVa, BSEE, 56, MSEE, 58; Univ Pittsburgh, DSc(electrets), 62. *Prof Exp:* From instr to assoc prof, 56-70, PROF ELEC ENG, W VA UNIV, 70- *Concurrent Pos:* NSF res grant, 63-66; elec engr, Morgantown Energy Technol Ctr, 65- *Mem:* Am Soc Eng Educ; Inst Elec & Electronics Engrs. *Res:* Dielectric absorption currents; electrets; electrogasdynamics; solid state gas sensors. *Mailing Add:* Dept of Elec Eng WVa Univ Morgantown WV 26506

SMITH, NEVILLE VINCENT, b Leeds, Eng, Apr 21, 42; m 70; c 2. PHYSICS. *Educ:* Queens' Col, Cambridge Univ, BA, 63, MA & PhD(physics), 67. *Prof Exp:* Res assoc physics, Stanford Univ, 66-69; MEM STAFF, BELL LABS, 69- *Concurrent Pos:* Res head, Condensed State Physics Dept, Bell Labs, 78-81. *Mem:* Fel Am Phys Soc. *Res:* Optical properties and band structures of metals; photoemission and electronic structure of solids and surfaces; synchrotron radiation spectroscopies. *Mailing Add:* Bell Labs 600 Mountain Ave Murray Hill NJ 07974

SMITH, NORMAN DWIGHT, b Natural Bridge, NY, Jan 26, 41; m 67; c 2. SEDIMENTOLOGY. *Educ:* St Lawrence Univ, BS, 62; Brown Univ, MS, 64, PhD(geol), 67. *Prof Exp:* Asst prof geol, 67-72, assoc prof, 72-78, PROF GEOL, UNIV ILL, CHICAGO CIRCLE, 78- *Concurrent Pos:* Vis assoc prof geol, Univ Alta, 74-75; consult geologist, Anglo-Am Corp of South Africa, 78-; Indo-Am fel, 82. *Mem:* Soc Econ Paleontologists & Mineralogists; Geol Soc Am; Int Asn Sedimentologists; Nat Asn Geol Teachers. *Res:* Fluvial sedimentology; stratigraphy and sedimentology of clastic rocks; limnology and lacustrine sedimentology; origin of placers. *Mailing Add:* Dept Geol Sci Univ Ill Chicago Circle Chicago IL 60680

SMITH, NORMAN H, organic chemistry, see previous edition

SMITH, NORMAN L(EE), b St John, Kans, Sept 24, 22; m 57; c 1. CHEMICAL ENGINEERING. *Educ:* Univ Ark, BS, 43; Univ Minn, PhD(chem eng), 50. *Prof Exp:* Chem engr, Linde Air Prod Co, 43-46; process engr, Tex Co, 46-47; assoc prof chem eng, Mo Sch Mines, 50-54; sr engr, Chemstrand Corp, 54-59; mgr, Develop Div, United Carbon Co, Tex, 59-69; MGR CARBON BLACK RES & DEVELOP, ASHLAND CHEM CO, 69- *Mem:* Am Inst Chem Engrs; Am Chem Soc. *Res:* Chemical engineering kinetics; process development. *Mailing Add:* Ashland Chem Co Columbus OH 43216

SMITH, NORMAN OBED, b Winnipeg, Man, Jan 23, 14; nat US; m 44; c 3. PHYSICAL CHEMISTRY. *Educ:* Univ Man, BSc, 35, MSc, 36; NY Univ, PhD(phys chem), 39. *Prof Exp:* Asst chem, Univ Man, 39-40, lectr, 40-46, from asst prof to assoc prof, 46-50; assoc prof, 50-65, res assoc, Air Force contract, 50-51, chmn dept, 74-78, PROF CHEM, FORDHAM UNIV, 65- *Mem:* Sr mem Am Chem Soc; fel Chem Inst Can. *Res:* Heterogeneous equilibria; hydrates; solid solutions; clathrates; solubility of gases; author or coauthor of over 40 publications. *Mailing Add:* Dept Chem Fordham Univ Bronx NY 10458

SMITH, NORMAN SHERRILL, b Roseburg, Ore, May 22, 32; m 57; c 2. WILDLIFE ECOLOGY. *Educ:* Ore State Univ, BSc, 58; Univ Mont, MSc, 62; Wash State Univ, PhD(zool), 69. *Prof Exp:* Lab technician II, Hopland Field Sta, Univ Calif, Davis, 60-62; res biologist, EAfrica Agr Forest Res Orgn, Kenya, 62-64; ASST UNIT LEADER WILDLIFE RES, ARIZ COOP WILDLIFE RES UNIT, UNIV ARIZ, 68- *Concurrent Pos:* Fulbright Sr res scholar, 62-63; Rockefeller Res grant, 63-64. *Mem:* Wildlife Soc; Am Soc Mammal. *Res:* Ecology of big game animals; reproduction physiology of wild mammals; metabolism and water requirements of game mammals. *Mailing Add:* 214 Biol Sci Bldg E Univ of Ariz Tucson AZ 85721

SMITH, NORMAN TY, b Ft Madison, Iowa, May 5, 32; m 58. ANESTHESIOLOGY, PHARMACOLOGY. *Educ:* Harvard Med Sch, MD, 57; Am Bd Anesthesiol, dipl, 63. *Prof Exp:* Intern pediat, Children's Med Ctr, Boston, Mass, 57-58; resident anesthesia, Mass Gen Hosp, 58-60; from instr to asst prof, Sch Med, Stanford Univ, 62-72; assoc prof, 72-74, vchmn dept, 72-77, PROF, DEPT ANESTHESIA, UNIV CALIF, SAN DIEGO, 74- *Concurrent Pos:* NIH career develop award, 66-71; actg chief anesthesia, Vet Admin Hosp, Palo Alto, 62-64; vis scientist, Univ Wash, 67; vis prof, Inst Med Physics, Utrecht, Holland, 70-71; chief anesthesia, Vet Admin Hosp, San Diego, 72-77; dir anesthesia res, Univ Calif & US Naval Hosps, 75-77. *Honors & Awards:* Detur Award, 53. *Mem:* AAAS; fel Am Col Anesthesiol; Ballistocardiographic Res Soc (pres, 73-76); Am Heart Asn; Am Soc Pharmacol & Exp Therapeut. *Res:* Cardiovascular pharmacology and physiology; ballistocardiography; control systems theory; control systems; analog and digital computation; on-line data processing; multiple drug interaction. *Mailing Add:* 225 Dickenson San Diego CA 92103

SMITH, OLIN DAIL, b Tonkawa, Okla, Dec 15, 31; m 51; c 3. PLANT BREEDING. *Educ:* Okla State Univ, BS, 54, MS, 61; Univ Minn, PhD(agron), 69. *Prof Exp:* Supt, Wheatland Conserv, Exp Sta, Okla State Univ, 57-58; univ instr agron, 58-62; asst secy-mgr, Okla Crop Improv Asn, 62-65; res fel, Univ Minn, 65-70; asst prof agron, 70-75, ASSOC PROF SOIL & CROP SCI, TEX A&M UNIV, 75- *Mem:* Am Soc Agron; Crop Sci Soc Am; Am Peanut Res & Educ Asn (pres, 72-73). *Res:* Plant breeding and genetics; inheritance by Arachis Hypogaea; peanut variety improvement; breeding peanuts for disease and insect resistance. *Mailing Add:* Dept Soil & Crop Sci Tex A&M Univ College Station TX 77843

SMITH, OLIVER HUGH, b Rochester, NY, Sept 13, 29; m 68. MOLECULAR GENETICS. *Educ:* St Louis Univ, BS, 51; Syracuse Univ, MS, 53; Stanford Univ, PhD(biochem genetics), 61. *Prof Exp:* USPHS trainee, Stanford Univ, 58-61; Nat Found fel, Biol Div, Oak Ridge Nat Labs, 61-63; asst prof biol, 63-67, assoc prof, 67-75, PROF BIOL, MARQUETTE UNIV, 76- *Concurrent Pos:* NIH spec fel & vis scientist, Lab Chem Biol, Nat Insts Arthritis & Metab Dis, 72; vis scientist, Serv de Biochimie Cellulaire, Inst Pasteur, 76; vis scientist, Div Biol Energy Res, Dept Energy, Washington, DC, 81. *Mem:* AAAS; Am Soc Microbiol; Genetics Soc Am. *Res:* Genetic alteration of protein structure; gene-enzyme relationships in bacteria. *Mailing Add:* Dept of Biol Marquette Univ Milwaukee WI 53233

SMITH, OLIVER KING, b Atlanta, Ga, Dec 25, 17; m 50; c 4. MATHEMATICS, COMPUTER SCIENCE. *Educ:* Mass Inst Technol, BS, 40, MS, 41; Princeton Univ, PhD(math), 55. *Prof Exp:* Aerodynamicist, Northrop Aircraft Corp, 46-51; asst math, Princeton Univ, 51-55; mem tech staff, Space Tech Labs, Inc, 55-61; mgr appl math dept, 61-70, SR STAFF MATHEMATICIAN, TRW DEFENSE & SPACE SYSTS GROUP, 70- *Mem:* Am Math Soc; Soc Indust & Appl Math; Asn Comput Mach. *Res:* Scientific applications of digital computers; numerical analysis; nonlinear ordinary differential equations. *Mailing Add:* TRW Defense & Space Systs Group 1 Space Park Redondo Beach CA 90278

SMITH, OLIVER WENDELL, organic polymer chemistry, see previous edition

SMITH, OMAR EWING, JR, b Memphis, Tenn, Oct 21, 31; m 55; c 3. ECONOMIC ENTOMOLOGY, MEDICAL ENTOMOLOGY. *Educ:* Memphis State Univ, BS, 54; Iowa State Univ, MS, 58, PhD, 61. *Prof Exp:* Instr entom, Iowa State Univ, 60-61; from asst prof to assoc prof, 61-77, PROF BIOL, MEMPHIS STATE UNIV, 77- *Concurrent Pos:* Univ grant, 65-67. *Mem:* Entom Soc Am. *Res:* Mosquito and arthropod research; agricultural pests and insecticides; taxonomy of insects; extension entomology and related fields. *Mailing Add:* Dept of Biol Memphis State Univ Memphis TN 38152

SMITH, ORA, b Freeburg, Ill, Apr 13, 00; m 27; c 2. PLANT & FOOD SCIENCE. *Educ:* Univ Ill, BS, 23; Iowa State Univ, MS, 24; Univ Calif, PhD(plant physiol), 29. *Prof Exp:* Instr hort, Iowa State Univ, 24-27; res asst vegetable crops, Univ Calif, 27-29; asst prof hort, Okla State Univ, 29-30; from asst prof to prof, 30-67, EMER PROF VEGETABLE CROPS, CORNELL UNIV, 67- *Concurrent Pos:* Hort rep, Farm Credit Admin, 34-35; collabr, USDA, 31-39; consult indust waste comt, Nat Tech Task, 52-56; fel, Cornell Univ, 38-39; consult, US Army Quartermaster Gen Off, 44-45; prof, Interam Inst Agr Sci, 46-47; consult, Standard Oil Develop Co, 47-49; res dir, Potato Chip Inst Int, 49-76. *Mem:* Potato Asn Am (pres, 38-39); Inst Food Technol; Europ Asn Potato Res; Can Inst Food Sci & Technol; Am Oil Chem Soc. *Res:* Quality improvement of all forms of processed potatoes, including color, flavor, odor, texture and maintenance of high quality in storage. *Mailing Add:* 1707 Slaterville Rd Ithaca NY 14850

SMITH, ORA KINGSLEY, b Orange, NJ, Mar 9, 27; m 53; c 4. PHYSIOLOGY, MEDICINE. *Educ:* Wellesley Col, BA, 49; Yale Univ, MD, 53. *Prof Exp:* Intern, Yale-New Haven Hosp, 53-54; from res asst to res assoc physiol, 56-67, res assoc med, 67-70, RES ASSOC EPIDEMIOL & PUB HEALTH, SCH MED, YALE UNIV, 70- *Concurrent Pos:* Fel med, Georgetown Univ, 54-56; asst fel, John B Pierce Found, 70-72, assoc fel, 72- *Mem:* Endocrine Soc; Am Diabetic Asn; Brit Diabetic Asn; Am Physiol Soc; Sigma Xi. *Res:* Endocrinology and metabolism as involved in environmental adaptation. *Mailing Add:* John B Pierce Found Lab 290 Congress Ave New Haven CT 06519

SMITH, ORRIN ERNEST, b Albany, Ore, Nov 20, 35; m 56; c 2. HORTICULTURE, PLANT PHYSIOLOGY. *Educ:* Ore State Univ, BS, 57; Univ Calif, Davis, PhD(plant physiol), 62. *Prof Exp:* Res plant physiologist cotton br, Crops Res Div, Agr Res Serv, USDA, 62-66; asst plant physiologist, Univ Calif, Riverside, 66-70, assoc prof plant physiol, assoc plant physiologist & vchmn dept plant sci, 70-75; chmn, Dept Hort, Wash State Univ, 75-80; ASSOC DEAN & DIR RESIDENT INSTR, ORE STATE UNIV, 80- *Concurrent Pos:* Fulbright sr res scholarship, 72; review ed, Am Soc Hort Sci, 74-78. *Mem:* Fel Am Soc Hort Sci; Japanese Soc Plant Physiol; Scand Soc Plant Physiol; Am Soc Plant Physiol. *Res:* Hormonal regulation of plant growth and development; physiology of dormancy and germination; seed vigor. *Mailing Add:* Sch Agr Ore State Univ Corvallis OR 97331

SMITH, ORVILLE AUVERNE, JR, b Nogales, Ariz, June 16, 27; m 53; c 2. NEUROPHYSIOLOGY. *Educ:* Univ Ariz, BA, 49; Mich State Univ, MA, 50, PhD, 53. *Prof Exp:* Instr psychol, Mich State Univ, 51-54; fel neuroanat, Univ Pa, 54-56; fel neurophysiol, Sch Med, Univ Wash, 56-58; from instr to asst prof anat & physiol, 58-59, from asst prof to assoc prof physiol & biophys, 62-67, from asst dir to assoc dir ctr, 62-71, DIR REGIONAL PRIMATE RES CTR, SCH MED, UNIV WASH, 71-, PROF PHYSIOL & BIOPHYS, 67- *Mem:* Am Physiol Soc; Am Asn Anatomists. *Res:* Physiological basis of behavior; cardiovascular control; neuroanatomy. *Mailing Add:* Dept of Physiol & Biophys Univ of Wash Seattle WA 98195

SMITH, ORVILLE L, nuclear physics, see previous edition

SMITH, OTTO J(OSEPH) M(ITCHELL), b Urbana, Ill, Aug 6, 17; m 41; c 4. LARGE SYSTEMS, SOLAR ENERGY. *Educ:* Univ Okla, BS, 38; Stanford Univ, PhD(elec eng), 41. *Prof Exp:* Asst, Stanford Univ, 38-41; instr power & high voltage, Tufts Col, 41-43; asst prof commun, Univ Denver, 43-44; res engr, Electronics Dept, Westinghouse Elec Corp, Pa, 44-45; chief elec engr, Summit Corp, 45-47; from lectr to assoc prof control & large systs, 47-58, PROF CONTROL & LARGE SYSTS, UNIV CALIF, BERKELEY, 58- *Concurrent Pos:* Vis prof, Inst Tech Aeronaut, Brazil, 54-56; Guggenheim fel, Tech Hochsch Univ, Darmstadt, Ger, 60; vis lectr, Kiev Inst Electrotech, Polytech Mus & Inst Electromech, USSR, 60; deleg, Cong Int Fedn Automatic Control, Moscow, 60; vis sr res fel, Monash Univ, Australia, 66-67; vis lectr, Fed Sch Eng, Itajuba, Brazil, 71; mem rev comt, Solar Thermal Test Facil, Users Asn, 77-78; NSF appointee, Adac Econ Studies & Inst Power Designs, Romania, 73; Vis prof, Tech Univ Eindhover, Neth, 74; prof, Escola Fed Engenharia Itajuba, Brasil, 74. *Mem:* Fel AAAS; fel Inst Elec & Electronics Engrs; Am Soc Eng Educ; Instrument Soc Am; Int Solar Energy Soc. *Res:* Electronics; feedback systems; servomechanisms; statistical and nonlinear synthesis; economic analogs; cybernetics; optimal economic planning; construction of digital computer programs for optimizing the use of government resources for maximum economic growth; solar-thermal-electric power system design; wind-electric systems. *Mailing Add:* 612 Euclid Ave Berkeley CA 94708

SMITH, P GENE, b Jackson, Mo, July 17, 21; m 48; c 5. ELECTRICAL ENGINEERING, COMMUNICATIONS. *Educ:* Univ Mo, Rolla, BS, 44; Mass Inst Technol, MS, 48, EE, 51. *Prof Exp:* Res asst microwave systs, Mass Inst Technol, 46-48, elec eng, 50-51; proj engr radar develop, Sperry Gyroscope Co, 48-50, res engr radar systs, 51-56, res sect head, Sperry Phoenix Co, 57-61, mem tech staff, Commun Sci, Sperry Rand Res Ctr, 61-63; dir radiation systs lab, Res Triangle Inst, 63-67; MEM TECH STAFF, GEN RES CORP, 67- *Concurrent Pos:* Adj prof, NC State Univ, 64-67; mem Int Radio Consult Comt, 65-67. *Mem:* Sr mem Inst Elec & Electronics Engrs. *Res:* Microwaves and antennas; radar systems; communications sciences; large antenna systems; guidance and control systems. *Mailing Add:* Sci & Technol Div Gen Res Corp 5383 Nollister Box 6770 Santa Barbara CA 93105

SMITH, P SCOTT, b Richmond, Va, Dec 22, 22. PHYSICS. *Educ:* Cornell Univ, PhD, 51. *Prof Exp:* Asst physics, US Naval Res Lab, 43-45 & Cornell Univ, 46-50; asst prof, Kans State Col, 51-53; assoc prof, 53-71, PROF PHYSICS, EASTERN ILL UNIV, 71- *Mem:* Am Phys Soc; Am Asn Physics Teachers. *Res:* Nuclear, space and radiological physics; quantification of nuclear shell structure; rocketry and celestial mechanics; nuclear weapons. *Mailing Add:* Dept of Physics Eastern Ill Univ Charleston IL 61920

SMITH, PATRICIA ANNE, b Rockwood, Tenn, Sept 1, 35. DEVELOPMENTAL GENETICS. *Educ:* Carson-Newman Col, BS, 58; Northwestern Univ, MS, 65, PhD(genetics), 66. *Prof Exp:* Res asst genetics, Oak Ridge Nat Lab, 57-59; teacher jr high sch, Tenn, 59-61; res asst biochem, NMex Highlands Univ, 61; res assoc develop genetics, Northwestern Univ, 66-68; asst prof, 68-71, assoc prof, 71-79, PROF GENETICS, NORTHEASTERN ILL UNIV, 79- *Concurrent Pos:* Lectr eve div, Northwestern Univ, 65-72, NIH fel, 66-67. *Mem:* AAAS; Genetics Soc Am; Am Soc Zoologists. *Res:* Control of cell division and differentiation in the ovaries of Drosophila melanogaster; genetic control of synaptonemal complex formation. *Mailing Add:* Dept Biol Northeastern Ill Univ Chicago IL 60625

SMITH, PATRICIA LEE, b Houston, Tex, Sept 16, 46. STATISTICS. *Educ:* Southwestern Univ, BA, 68; Purdue Univ, MS, 70; Tex A&M Univ, PhD(statist), 75. *Prof Exp:* Instr math, Purdue Univ, 70-72; asst prof statist, Tex A&M Univ, 76-80; ASST PROF STATIST, OLD DOMINION UNIV, 80- *Mem:* Am Statist Asn; Biometric Soc. *Res:* Linear models with emphasis on applications of splines to design of experiments, regression and time series. *Mailing Add:* Dept Math Sci Old Dominion Univ Norfolk VA 23508

SMITH, PATRICK JOHN, metallurgy, see previous edition

SMITH, PAUL ALTHAUS, mathematics, deceased

SMITH, PAUL CLAY, b Gray Hawk, Ky, Apr 3, 34; m 57; c 3. VETERINARY VIROLOGY, VETERINARY PATHOLOGY. *Educ:* Auburn Univ, DVM, 59; Ohio State Univ, MS, 66; Iowa State Univ, PhD, 77. *Prof Exp:* Chief rabies diag, SEATO Med Res Labs, Walter Reed Army Inst Res, 66-69, asst chief diag lab, 69-70; vet med officer virol invests, Nat Animal Dis Lab, USDA, 70-77; mem staff, Col Vet Med, Univ Tenn, 77-80; HEAD, DEPT MICROBIOL, SCH VET MED, AUBURN UNIV, 80- *Mem:* Wildlife Dis Asn; Conf Res Workers Animal Dis. *Res:* Bovine herpesviruses and respiratory disease of cattle; pseudorabies in swine; veterinary immunology. *Mailing Add:* Dept Microbiol Sch Vet Med Auburn Univ Auburn AL 36830

SMITH, PAUL DAVID, electronic engineering, control systems, see previous edition

SMITH, PAUL DENNIS, b Baltimore, Md, Nov 14, 42. GENETICS. *Educ:* Loyola Col, BS, 64; Univ NC, PhD(zool), 68. *Prof Exp:* NIH fel, Univ Conn, 68-70; asst prof biol, 70-74, ASSOC PROF BIOL, EMORY UNIV, 74- *Concurrent Pos:* NIH res grant, 71-, res career develop award, Gen Med Sci, 74-79. *Mem:* Environ Mutagen Soc; AAAS; Genetics Soc Am. *Res:* DNA repair and mutagenesis in Drosophila. *Mailing Add:* Dept of Biol Emory Univ Atlanta GA 30322

SMITH, PAUL E, JR, b Elizabeth, NJ, May 16, 23; m 47; c 3. ELECTRICAL ENGINEERING. *Educ:* Rensselaer Polytech Inst, BEE, 47; Mass Inst Technol, EE, 53. *Prof Exp:* Instr elec eng, Mass Inst Technol, 50-53, asst prof, 53-57; engr, Conval Corp, 57-58; chief engr, Feedback Controls, Inc, Mass, 58-68; sr eng specialist, GTE Sylvania Electronics Systs-East Div, 68-71; sr engr, Ikor, Inc, Burlington, 71-77, New Ikor Inc, Omniwave Electronics Corp, Gloucester, 77-80; ENGR, WINCOM CORP, 80- *Mem:* Inst Elec & Electronics Engrs. *Res:* Process control; servomechanics. *Mailing Add:* Wincom Corp PO Box 329 Lawrence MA 01842

SMITH, PAUL EDWARD, b Emmetsburg, Iowa, May 24, 33; m 57; c 5. ECOLOGY, FISH BIOLOGY. *Educ:* State Col Iowa, BA, 56; Univ Iowa, PhD(zool), 62. *Prof Exp:* Sverdrup fel plankton behav, Scripps Inst, Univ Calif, 62-63; RES BIOLOGIST & GROUP LEADER, LA JOLLA LAB, SOUTHWEST FISHERY CTR, NAT MARINE FISHERIES SERV, 63- *Mem:* Ecol Soc Am; Am Soc Limnol & Oceanog. *Res:* Zooplankton ecology and fish larva biology in marine environments, especially as influenced by temporal and spatial variations in small scale distribution; development of field and statistical methods for economical and concise descriptions of small scale distribution. *Mailing Add:* Southwest Fishery Ctr PO Box 271 La Jolla CA 92037

SMITH, PAUL FRANCIS, b Brookville, Pa, Apr 3, 27; m 51; c 4. MICROBIOLOGY. *Educ:* Pa State Univ, BS, 49; Univ Pa, MS, 50, PhD(bact), 51. *Prof Exp:* Asst instr bact, Univ Pa, 49-51; res microbiologist, Merck & Co, Inc, NJ, 51-52; from instr med microbiol to asst prof microbiol, Sch Med, Univ Pa, 52-61, res microbiologist, Inst Coop Res, 52-58; PROF & CHMN DEPT, SCH MED, UNIV SDAK, 61- *Concurrent Pos:* Vis scientist, Univ Utrecht, 70; treas, Int Orgn Mycoplasmology, 81-85. *Honors & Awards:* Lederle Med Fac Award, 60. *Mem:* AAAS; fel Am Soc Microbiol; Am Chem Soc; fel Am Pub Health Asn. *Res:* Biochemistry and physiology of mycoplasmas; lipid biochemistry. *Mailing Add:* Dept of Microbiol Univ of SDak Vermillion SD 57069

SMITH, PAUL FREDERICK, b Copeland, Kans, Dec 17, 16; m 40; c 2. PHYSIOLOGY, HORTICULTURE. *Educ:* Univ Okla, BS, 38, MS, 40; Univ Calif, PhD(physiol), 44. *Prof Exp:* Asst bot, Univ Okla, 38-39; asst plant physiol, Univ Calif, 40-42; asst physiologist, 43-47, assoc physiologist, 48-49, physiologist, 50-55, sr physiologist, 56-58, prin physiologist, Agr Res Serv, 59-71, head physiologist, 71-75, WORLD CITRUS CONSULT, AGR RES SERV, USDA, 75- *Mem:* Bot Soc Am; fel Am Soc Hort Sci; Am Inst Biol Scientists; Am Soc Plant Physiol. *Res:* Pollen tube growth; bud dormancy and inhibition; vegetative propagation; mineral nutrition of citrus. *Mailing Add:* Rt 3 Box 408-C Orlando FL 32811

SMITH, PAUL GORDON, b Fair Oaks, Calif, Mar 19, 15; m 37; c 3. VEGETABLE CROPS. *Educ:* Univ Calif, BS, 37; Univ Wis, PhD(plant path), 41. *Prof Exp:* Asst plant path & agron, Univ Wis, 37-43; instr, 41-44, asst prof truck crops, 44-52, assoc prof veg crops, 52-59, from asst olericulturist to assoc olericulturist, 44-59, prof, 59-80, olericulturist, Exp Sta, 59-80, EMER PROF VEG CROPS, UNIV CALIF, DAVIS, 80- *Concurrent Pos:* Specialist, Foreign Econ Admin, 42-44. *Mem:* Am Soc Hort Sci; Am Phytopath Soc; Soc Econ Botanists; Am Genetics Asn. *Res:* Breeding for disease resistance in vegetable crops. *Mailing Add:* Dept of Veg Crops Univ of Calif Davis CA 95616

SMITH, PAUL HOWARD, b Akron, Ohio, Sept 26, 24; m 50; c 2. BACTERIOLOGY. *Educ:* Va Polytech Inst, BS, 53, MS, 55; Univ Calif, PhD(microbiol), 59. *Prof Exp:* Res bacteriologist, Univ Calif, 57-59; from asst prof to assoc prof biol sci, Univ Fla, 59-69; vis prof civil eng, Stanford Univ, 69-70; PROF MICROBIOL & CELL SCI, UNIV FLA, 70-, CHAIRPERSON DEPT, 71-, MICROBIOLOGIST, 74- *Res:* Microbiology of domestic sewage sludge; rumen fermentation; methane evolution; degradation of cellulose. *Mailing Add:* Dept of Microbiol Univ of Fla Gainesville FL 32611

SMITH, PAUL JAMES, b Warrington, Eng, Mar 1, 53; m 75; c 2. CELLULAR RADIOBIOLOGY, PHOTOBIOLOGY. *Educ:* Univ Bristol, BSc, 74; Victoria Univ Manchester, PhD(cellular biol), 77. *Prof Exp:* Fel, 77-80, RES ASSOC, CHALK RIVER NUCLEAR LABS, ATOMIC ENERGY CAN LTD, 80- *Concurrent Pos:* Vis fel, Nat Res Coun Can, 77-79. *Mem:* Radiation Res Soc. *Res:* Molecular biology and somatic cell genetics of DNA repair processes in cultured human cells; role of defective DNA repair in human syndromes showing predisposition to cancer and developmental abnormalities. *Mailing Add:* Biol & Health Physics Div Chalk River Nuclear Labs Chalk River ON K0J 1J0 Can

SMITH, PAUL JOHN, b Philadelphia, Pa, Jan 6, 43; m 70. STATISTICS, MATHEMATICS. *Educ:* Drexel Univ, BS, 65; Case Western Reserve Univ, MS, 67, PhD(math), 69. *Prof Exp:* Asst prof math, Wayne State Univ, 69, Ind Univ, 69-71; asst prof, 71-76, ASSOC PROF MATH, UNIV MD, 76- *Concurrent Pos:* Statist consults, US Selective Serv Syst, 73, Sci Educ Systs, Inc, 73-74, US Consumer Prod Safety Comn, 76-77 & Nat Inst Mental Health, 77- *Mem:* Inst Math Statist; Am Statist Soc. *Res:* Nonparametric and multivariate statistical inference. *Mailing Add:* Dept of Math Univ of Md College Park MD 20742

SMITH, PAUL KENT, b Woodbury, NJ, July 12, 35; m 61; c 2. PHYSICAL CHEMISTRY. *Educ:* Univ Va, BS, 57; Univ Kans, PhD(chem), 64. *Prof Exp:* Fel, Univ Kans, 64; res chemist, Savannah River Lab, 64-71, sr res supvr, 71-75, RES STAFF SCIENTIST, SAVANNAH RIVER LAB, E I DU PONT DE NEMOURS & CO, INC, 76- *Mem:* Fel Am Inst Chemists; Am Ceramic Soc; Am Chem Soc; Am Nuclear Soc. *Res:* High temperature chemistry of refractory materials; vaporization processes; phase equilibria; thermodynamics; x-ray crystallography; nuclear materials; mass spectrometry; ceramics; isotopic heat sources. *Mailing Add:* Savannah River Lab E I du Pont de Nemours & Co Inc Aiken SC 29802

SMITH, PAUL L, b London, Eng, Oct 12, 50; m 72. SURASSIC BIOCHRONOLOGY. *Educ:* Univ London, BSc, 72; Portland State Univ, MS, 76; McMaster Univ, PhD(geol), 81. *Prof Exp:* ASST PROF GEOL, UNIV BC, 80- *Concurrent Pos:* Consult, Petrocan Ltd, 81-, Anaconda Mines Ltd, 82; cochmn, Sect H, Proj 171, Int Geol Correlation Prog, 81- *Mem:* Geologists Asn London; Paleontol Asn; fel Geol Asn Can; Paleontol Res Inst. *Res:* Stratigraphy biochronology and basin analysis of the surassic of western North America. *Mailing Add:* Dept Geol Sci Univ BC 6339 Stores Rd Vancouver BC V6T 2B4 Can

SMITH, PAUL LETTON, JR, b Columbia, Mo, Dec 16, 32; m 54; c 5. ATMOSPHERIC PHYSICS, ELECTRICAL ENGINEERING. *Educ:* Carnegie Inst Technol, BS, 55, MS, 57, PhD(elec eng), 60. *Prof Exp:* From instr to asst prof elec eng, Carnegie Inst Technol, 55-63; sr engr, Midwest Res Inst, 63-66; res engr & assoc prof meteorol, 66-68, assoc prof meteorol & elec eng, 68-73, head eng group, Inst Atmospheric Sci, 68-75, sr scientist & head data acquistition & anal group, 76-81, RES PROF METEOROL & ELEC ENG, SDAK SCH MINES & TECHNOL, INST ATMOSPHERIC SCI, 73-, DIR, INST ATMOSPHERIC SCI, 81- *Concurrent Pos:* NSF fel meteorol, McGill Univ, 64, vis prof, 69-70; chief scientist, Hq, US Air Force Air Weather Serv, 74-75; actg dir, Inst Atmospheric Sci, 76-77. *Mem:* Am Meteorol Soc; Am Soc Eng Educ; Inst Elec & Electronics Engrs; Sigma Xi. *Res:* Radar meteorology; weather radar data systems; weather modification; remote sensing; meteorological instrumentation; electrostatic precipitation; propagation and scattering of electromagnetic and acoustic waves in the atmosphere; cloud and precipitation physics. *Mailing Add:* Inst Atmospheric Sci SDak Sch of Mines & Technol Rapid City SD 57701

SMITH, PAUL VERGON, JR, b Lima, Ohio, Apr 25, 21; m 45; c 4. CHEMISTRY. *Educ:* Miami Univ, AB, 42; Univ Ill, MS, 43, PhD(org chem), 45. *Prof Exp:* Instr, Miami Univ, 42; asst, Univ Ill, 42-43; from asst to res chemist, Off Rubber Reserve, 43-46; res chemist & group leader, Esso Res & Eng Co, 46-54, sci liaison, Esso Res, Ltd, Eng, 55-57, asst dir, Chem Res Div, NJ, 57-60, asst dir, Cent Basic Res Lab, 60-66, asst dir, Res Dept, Esso Petrol Co Ltd, Eng, 66-67, dir, Chem Dept, Esso Res SA, Belg, 67-71, head educ & sci rels, Esso Res & Eng Co, 71-73, mgr educ & sci rels, 73-78, mgr pub affairs, 78-81, MGR EDUC & PROF SOC RELS, PUB AFFAIRS, EXXON RES & ENG CO, 81- *Concurrent Pos:* Mem adv bd, Petrol Res Fund, 65-66. *Honors & Awards:* President's Award, Am Asn Petrol Geologists, 55. *Mem:* AAAS; Am Soc Eng Educ (pres, 80-); Am Inst Chem Eng; Am Chem Soc; NY Acad Sci. *Res:* Synthetic rubber; detergents; physical separation of organic compounds; oil additives and synthetic lubricants; geochemistry; origin of petroleum; oxo process; plasticizers; polypropylene. *Mailing Add:* Exxon Res & Eng Co PO Box 101 Florham Park NJ 07932

SMITH, PERCY LEIGHTON, b Dunbar, WVa, July 23, 19; m 39; c 2. CHEMISTRY. *Educ:* Morris Harvey Col, BSc, 50. *Prof Exp:* Lab asst, 39-47, res chemist, 47-66, group leader, 66-74, ASSOC DIR RES & DEVELOP, UNION CARBIDE CORP, 74- *Mem:* Am Chem Soc. *Res:* Analytical and organophosphorus chemistry; epoxy and polyester resins; polyurethanes. *Mailing Add:* 1508 Meyers Ave Dunbar WV 25064

SMITH, PERRIN GARY, b Bowie, Tex, Sept 3, 12; m 37; c 1. ORGANIC CHEMISTRY. *Educ:* Austin Col, BS, 34; Northwestern Univ, PhD(org chem), 38. *Prof Exp:* Abbott Labs fel, Northwestern Univ, 38-40; chemist res dept, Sharples Chem Inc, Mich, 40-44, chemist develop dept, Pa, 44-54, asst to pres, 54-56; asst to gen mgr, Indust Div, Pennwalt Corp, Philadelphia, 56-65, proj evaluator, Eng Dept, King of Prussia, 65-77; RETIRED. *Mem:* Am Chem Soc. *Res:* Amines; rubber chemicals; pharmaceutical intermediates; sulfer chemicals; process development. *Mailing Add:* Black Horse Hill RD 2 Chester Springs PA 19425

SMITH, PETER, b Sale, Eng, Sept 7, 24; m 51; c 4. PHYSICAL CHEMISTRY. *Educ:* Cambridge Univ, BA, 46, MA, 49, PhD(phys chem), 53. *Prof Exp:* Jr sci officer, Chem Dept, Royal Aircraft Estab, Eng, 43-46; demonstr phys & inorg chem, Univ Leeds, 50-51; asst prof chem, Purdue Univ, 54-59; from asst prof to assoc prof, 59-70, PROF CHEM, DUKE UNIV, 70- *Mem:* Am Chem Soc; Am Phys Soc; The Chem Soc. *Res:* Application of electron paramagnetic resonance spectroscopy to kinetic and structural problems; chemical kinetics, especially solution processes; biophysical chemistry. *Mailing Add:* Dept Chem Paul M Gross Chem Lab Duke Univ Durham NC 27706

SMITH, PETER ALAN SOMERVAIL, b Erskine Hill, Eng, Apr 16, 20; nat US; m 52; c 2. HETEROCYCLIC CHEMISTRY, COAL CHEMISTRY. *Educ:* Univ Calif, BSc, 41; Univ Mich, PhD(inorg chem), 44. *Prof Exp:* Res assoc chem, 44-45; from instr to assoc prof, 45-59, PROF CHEM, UNIV MICH, ANN ARBOR, 59- *Concurrent Pos:* Fulbright res scholar, Univ Auckland, 51; mem, Am Chem Soc Adv Comt, Chem Corps, US Army, 55-60, mem sch & training comt, Chem Corps Adv Coun, 58-64; consult, Parke, Davis/Warner-Lambert Co, 57-; chmn comt nomenclature, Div Chem & Chem Technol, Nat Acad Sci-Nat Res Coun, 60-68; guest res prof, Inst Org Chem, Stuttgart Tech Univ, 61-62; bk rev ed, J Am Chem Soc, 70- *Mem:* Am Chem Soc. *Res:* Heterocyclic chemistry; carbenes and nitrenes; organic nitrogen compounds; azides; hydrazines; hydroxylamines; coal asphaltenes. *Mailing Add:* Dept of Chem Univ of Mich Ann Arbor MI 48104

SMITH, PETER BYRD, b Warrenton, Va, Feb 6, 29; m 53; c 2. MEDICAL BACTERIOLOGY. *Educ:* Univ Richmond, BS, 49; Univ Tenn, MS, 51; Univ Wis, PhD(bact), 59. *Prof Exp:* Bacteriologist, Ctr Dis Control, 55-57, res microbiologist, 59-62, asst chief staphylococci & streptococci unit, 62-68, chief clin bact unit, 68-73, CHIEF CLIN BACT BR, CTR DIS CONTROL, USPHS, 73- *Concurrent Pos:* Ed, J Clin Microbiol, 79- *Honors & Awards:* Commendation Medal, USPHS, 71. *Mem:* Fel Am Acad Microbiol; Am Soc Microbiol; Am Pub Health Asn. *Res:* Staphylococcal disease, diagnosis; phage typing of staphylococci; identification of pathogenic bacteria with bacteriophages; clinical bacteriology; diagnostic products and methodology; hospital infections; automation. *Mailing Add:* Ctr for Dis Control USPHS 1600 Clifton Rd Atlanta GA 30333

SMITH, PETER DAVID, b Providence, RI, Oct 25, 38; c 3. MATHEMATICS, COMPUTER SCIENCE. *Educ:* Col Holy Cross, AB, 60; Naval Postgrad Sch, MS, 64; Univ Wis, PhD(math), 68; Mich State Univ, MS, 75. *Prof Exp:* Instr math & comput sci, US Naval Postgrad Sch, 62-64, Xavier Univ La, 68-69; ASSOC PROF MATH & COMPUT SCI, ST MARY'S COL, IND, 69- *Concurrent Pos:* Consult, St Mary's Bus Off, 81. *Mem:* Asn Educ Data Systs. *Mailing Add:* St Mary's Col Notre Dame IN 46556

SMITH, PETER JAMES, physical organic chemistry, see previous edition

SMITH, PETER LLOYD, b Victoria, BC, Apr 28, 44; m 68. ATOMIC & MOLECULAR SPECTROSCOPY, SOLAR PHYSICS. *Educ:* Univ BC, BS, 65; Calif Inst Technol, PhD(physics), 72. *Prof Exp:* Res fel physics, Calif Inst Technol, 72; asst prof, Harvey Mudd Col, 72-73; res fel, 73-75, RES ASSOC PHYSICS, CTR ASTROPHYS, HARVARD COL OBSERV, 75- *Mem:* Am Phys Soc; Optical Soc Am; Am Astron Soc; Int Astron Union. *Res:* visible and visible ultraviolet spectroscopy of atoms, ions and molecules; astrophysical applications include interstellar clouds, the sun, comets and plasmas; atmospheric chemistry; transitions probabilities; photon and electron cross sections for allowed and forbidden transitions. *Mailing Add:* Ctr for Astrophys Harvard Col Observ 60 Garden St Cambridge MA 02138

SMITH, PETER WILLIAM, b London, Eng, Nov 3, 37; Can citizen. PHYSICS, ELECTRICAL ENGINEERING. *Educ:* McGill Univ, BSc, 58, MSc, 61, PhD(physics), 64. *Prof Exp:* Engr, Can Marconi Co, 58-59; MEM TECH STAFF LASER RES, BELL TEL LABS, 63- *Concurrent Pos:* Vis Mackay lectr, Univ Calif, Berkeley, 70-71; vis scientist, Lab d'Optique, Ecole Polytech, Palaiseau, France, 78-79. *Mem:* Am Phys Soc; fel Optical Soc Am; fel Inst Elec & Electronics Engrs. *Res:* Quantum electronics; atomic physics; gas lasers and laser devices. *Mailing Add:* Bell Tel Labs Rm 4B-409 Holmdel NJ 07733

SMITH, PHILIP EDWARD, b Johnson Co, Ill, Dec 25, 16; m 42; c 4. PARASITOLOGY. *Educ:* Southern Ill Univ, BEd, 40; Univ Ill, MS, 42; Johns Hopkins Univ, ScD(parasitol), 49. *Prof Exp:* Mus technician, Southern Ill Univ, 36-39, asst zool, 39-40; asst zool, Univ Ill, 40-42; asst parasitol, Sch Hyg & Pub Health, Johns Hopkins Univ, 47-49; asst prof zool, Okla Agr & Mech Col, 49-52; from asst prof to prof prev med & pub health, 52-70, assoc dean grad col med, Med Ctr, 56-70, assoc dean student affairs, 60-70, PROF PARASITOL, SCH HEALTH, UNIV OKLA HEALTH SCI CTR, 70-, DEAN, SCH HEALTH RELATED PROFESSIONS, 70- *Mem:* Am Soc Parasitol; Am Soc Trop Med & Hyg; Micros Soc Am. *Res:* Morphology, life history and host-parasite relations of nematodes. *Mailing Add:* Univ Okla Health Sci Ctr PO Box 26901 Oklahoma City OK 73190

SMITH, PHILIP WAYNE, b Neoga, Ill, Dec 2, 21; m 42; c 1. VERTEBRATE ZOOLOGY. *Educ:* Univ Ill, BS, 48, MS, 49, PhD(zool), 53. *Prof Exp:* Asst zool, Ill Natural Hist Surv, 42, lab asst, 47-52, asst taxonomist, 52-55, assoc taxonomist, 55-63, taxonomist, 63-69, head, Faunistics Sect, 69-79; prof zool, Univ Ill, Urbana, 66-79. *Mem:* Am Soc Ichthyologists & Herpetologists (vpres, 66, pres, 66-67). *Res:* Systematics and ecology of freshwater fishes, amphibians and reptiles; taxonomy; zoogeography; ichthyology; herpetology. *Mailing Add:* Ill Natural Hist Surv Natural Resources Bldg 172 Urbana IL 61801

SMITH, PHILLIP J, b Muncie, Ind, Oct 2, 38; m 60; c 3. METEOROLOGY. *Educ:* Ball State Univ, BS, 60; Univ Wis, MS, 64, PhD(meteorol), 67. *Prof Exp:* Res asst meteorol, Univ Wis, 63-67; asst prof, 67-70, assoc prof, 70-81, PROF METEOROL, PURDUE UNIV, WEST LAFAYETTE, 81- *Concurrent Pos:* Sr fel, Nat Ctr Atmospheric Res, 72-73. *Mem:* Am Meteorol Soc; Am Geophys Union. *Res:* Atmospheric energy processes and their application to synoptic scale systems. *Mailing Add:* Dept of Geosci Purdue Univ West Lafayette IN 47907

SMITH, PIERRE FRANK, b North Tonawanda, NY, Aug 17, 20. PHARMACY, MEDICINAL CHEMISTRY. *Educ:* Univ Buffalo, BS, 41; Univ Md, PhD(pharmaceut chem), 47. *Prof Exp:* Asst chem, Univ Md, 41-44; asst prof pharmaceut chem, Western Reserve Univ, 47-49; assoc prof, Rutgers Univ, 49-57; prof & chmn dept, Col Pharm, Univ RI, 57-65; chmn dept, 65-77, PROF, COL PHARM, NORTHEASTERN UNIV, 65- *Mem:* Am Chem Soc; Am Pharmaceut Asn; Am Inst Hist Pharm; Am Acad Pharmaceut Sci. *Res:* Organic synthesis; analytical chemistry; synthesis and study of tranquilizers and central nervous systems depressants; physical pharmacy. *Mailing Add:* Northeastern Univ Col of Pharm 360 Huntington Ave Boston MA 02115

SMITH, QUENTON TERRILL, b Ames, Iowa, Jan 6, 29. BIOCHEMISTRY, ORAL BIOLOGY. *Educ:* Iowa State Univ, BS, 51, MS, 52; Univ Minn, PhD(physiol chem), 59. *Prof Exp:* Res assoc dermat, 59-69, from lectr to asst prof biochem, 59-69, assoc prof oral biol & biochem, 69-73, PROF ORAL BIOL, SCH DENT, UNIV MINN, MINNEAPOLIS, 73- *Concurrent Pos:* USPHS spec fel, Argonne Nat Lab, 68-69; adj prof biochem & med sci, Univ Minn, Minneapolis, 73- *Mem:* Am Soc Biol Chemists; AAAS; Soc Exp Biol & Med; Int Asn Dent Res. *Res:* Biochemistry of oral fluids, especially fractionation of salivary proteins and the relationship of salivary composition to oral and systemic disease; connective tissue biochemistry. *Mailing Add:* 17-226C Health Sci Unit A Univ Minn Minneapolis MN 55455

SMITH, R JAY, b Flint, Mich, July 26, 22. ZOOLOGY. *Educ:* Alma Col, AB, 47; Univ Mich, MS, 49, PhD(zool, parasitol), 53. *Prof Exp:* Instr biol, Marquette Univ, 48-49; asst prof, Dubuque Univ, 53-55 & Col William & Mary, 55-56; asst prof zool, Univ Miami, 56-57; asst prof, 57-80, ASSOC PROF BIOL, UNIV DETROIT, 80- *Concurrent Pos:* USPHS fel parasitol, Univ PR, 59. *Mem:* Am Soc Parasitologists; Am Micros Soc; Am Soc Zoologists. *Res:* Invertebrate zoology; helminthology; trematodes as hosts to ancylid snails; water pollution biology; indicators of pollution, especially coliforms and invertebrates. *Mailing Add:* Dept of Biol Univ of Detroit Detroit MI 48221

SMITH, R L, b Rigby, Idaho, Jan 13, 24; m 44; c 5. SOIL CHEMISTRY. *Educ:* Utah State Univ, BS, 51, MS, 52; Univ Calif, Los Angeles, PhD(plant sci), 55. *Prof Exp:* Asst soils, Utah State Univ, 51-52; asst plant sci, Univ Calif, Los Angeles, 52-54; asst pomologist, Univ Calif, 54-55; asst prof soils & asst soil chemist, 55-59, assoc prof & assoc soil chemist, 59-64, prof soils & soil chemist, 73-80, head Dept Soil Sci & Biometeorol, 73-80, PROF SOIL SCI & BIOMETEOROL, UTAH STATE UNIV, 80- *Mem:* Am Soc Agron; Soil Sci Soc Am; Am Soc Plant Physiol; Am Soc Hort Sci. *Res:* Soil chemistry of micro-nutrient elements in soils; lime-induced chlorosis; nitrogen interchanges in soil; soil and plant root relationships. *Mailing Add:* Dept Soil Sci & Biometeorol Utah State Univ Logan UT 84322

SMITH, RALPH CARLISLE, b West New York, NJ, May 24, 10; m 54. CHEMICAL ENGINEERING. *Educ:* Rensselaer Polytech Inst, ChE, 31; George Washington Univ, JD, 39; Univ NMex, PhD, 62. *Prof Exp:* Chemist org, E I du Pont de Nemours & Co, 31-36; patent examr, US Patent Off, 36-38; chem engr org, Colgate Palmolive Co, 39-42; Lt Col nuclear, US Army Engrs, Manhattan Proj, 42-47; asst dir, Los Alamos Sci Lab, 47-57; asst to pres, Nuclear Div, ACF Industs, 57-60; dean & pres, NMex Highlands Univ, 61-72, grad dean, 72-77; PROF, COLUMBIA COL, 78- *Mem:* Am Inst chemists; Am Inst Chem Engrs; Am Nuclear Soc. *Mailing Add:* 838 Arguello Blvd San Francisco CA 94118

SMITH, RALPH E(DWARD), b Porterdale, Ga, May 6, 23; m 48; c 3. AGRICULTURAL ENGINEERING. *Educ:* Univ Ga, BS, 48, MS, 61; Okla State Univ, PhD(agr eng), 66. *Prof Exp:* Instr agr, Polk County Bd Educ, Ga, 48-54; instr physics & agr eng, Abraham Baldwin Agr Col, 54-56; from instr to asst prof, 56-70, ASSOC PROF AGR ENG, UNIV GA, 70- *Concurrent Pos:* Vis prof, Okla State Univ, 65-66. *Mem:* Am Soc Agr Engrs; Am Soc Eng Educ; Am Soc Heating, Refrig & Air-Conditioning Engrs; Sigma Xi. *Res:* Environmental control engineering for livestock; farm electrification engineering; process engineering for agricultural engineering; processes of transient conduction heat transfer. *Mailing Add:* Dept of Agr Eng Univ of Ga Athens GA 30602

SMITH, RALPH EARL, b Yuma, Colo, May 10, 40; m 61; c 1. VIROLOGY, ONCOLOGY. *Educ:* Colo State Univ, BS, 61; Univ Colo, Denver, PhD(microbiol), 68. *Prof Exp:* NIH fel, 68-70, asst prof, 70-74, assoc prof viral oncol, microbiol & immunol 74-80, PROF, DEPT MICROBIOL & IMMUNOL, DUKE UNIV MED CTR, NC, 80- *Concurrent Pos:* Assoc prof, Dept Microbiol & Immunol, Duke Univ Med Ctr, NC, 74-80; Sabbatical leave, Dept Exp Immunobiol, Wellcome Res Found, Eng, 78-79; mem, Duke Univ Cancer Ctr, 74- *Mem:* Am Soc Microbiol; NY Acad Sci. *Res:* RNA tumor virus structure; mechanisms of transformation of avian cells; pathogenesis of avian leukosis viruses in vivo; methods of preventing virus-induced neoplasms; establishing the total spectrum of avian retrovirus-induced disorders. *Mailing Add:* Dept Microbiol & Immunol Box 3020 Duke Univ Med Ctr Durham NC 27710

SMITH, RALPH EMERSON, b Vayland, SDak, Nov 7, 14; m 40; c 4. AGRICULTURAL ECONOMICS. *Educ:* Univ Minn, BS, 40, MS, 55. *Prof Exp:* Coop supvr, Farm Security Admin, 40-44; training officer, Vet Admin, 46-49; from instr to assoc prof agr econ, 49-73, PROF AGR ECON, WEST CENT EXP STA, UNIV MINN, MORRIS, 73-, SUPT, 61- *Mem:* Am Agr Econ Asn. *Res:* Economic analysis of selected research data and the application of farm management research to livestock and crop production. *Mailing Add:* West Cent Exp Sta Univ of Minn Morris MN 56267

SMITH, RALPH EMERSON, b Beckley, WVa, Jan 13, 16; m 50; c 2. GROUNDWATER GEOLOGY. *Educ:* Tex Christian Univ, AB, 37, MS, 39. *Prof Exp:* Asst, Tex Christian Univ, 37-39 & Univ Okla, 39-42; assoc prof geol & geog, Drury Col, 46-47; geologist geol div, Fuels Br, US Geol Surv, 47-48, geologist water res div, Ground Water Br, 49-75, geologist, Pub Lands Hydrol Prog, 64-75; CONSULT, 75- *Concurrent Pos:* Supvr water well drilling, Indonesia, 80. *Res:* Water supply for stock and camp sites; relation of geology, weather and vegetation to water on public domains in the western mountain states; area studies; evaluate the possibility for additional ground water. *Mailing Add:* 1417 S Yank St Lakewood CO 80228

SMITH, RALPH G, b St John, NB, Jan 11, 20; nat; m 42; c 6. INDUSTRIAL HYGIENE, ANALYTICAL CHEMISTRY. *Educ:* Wayne State Univ, BS, 42, MS, 49, PhD(chem), 53. *Prof Exp:* Chemist, Rotary Elec Steel Co, Mich, 40-42; assoc indust hygienist & chief chemist, Bur Indust Hyg, Detroit Dept Health, Mich, 46-55; assoc prof indust med & hyg, Sch Med, Wayne State Univ, 55-63, prof occup & environ health, 63-70; PROF ENVIRON & INDUST HEALTH, SCH PUB HEALTH, UNIV MICH, ANN ARBOR, 70- *Mem:* AAAS; Am Conf Govt Indust Hygienists; Am Indust Hyg Asn; Air Pollution Control Asn; Am Chem Soc. *Res:* Chemistry and toxicology; air analysis; analysis of biological samples for toxic substances; analytical chemistry of beryllium, ozone, mercury and lead; toxicity of air pollutants; mercury and chlorine. *Mailing Add:* Dept of Environ & Indust Health Univ of Mich Sch of Pub Health Ann Arbor MI 48104

SMITH, RALPH GRAFTON, b Oxford Co, Ont, Mar 15, 00; nat US; m 74; c 4. PHARMACOLOGY. *Educ:* Univ Toronto, BA, 21, MA, 22, MD, 25; Univ Chicago, PhD(pharmacol), 28. *Prof Exp:* Asst biochem, Univ Toronto, 21-22 & Connaught Labs, 23-25; intern, Toronto Gen Hosp, 25-26; Nat Res Coun fels, Washington Univ, 26-27 & Univ Chicago, 27-28; from instr to assoc prof pharmacol, Univ Mich, 28-43, asst secy med sch, 42-43; prof pharmacol, Tulane Univ, 43-50; from chief new drug br to dir div new drugs, Bur Med, US Food & Drug Admin, 50-66, actg dir, Bur Med, 62-64, asst to dir bur med for Nat Acad Liaison, 66-68, dir off med support, 68-70; consult div med sci, Nat Acad Sci-Nat Res Coun, 70-73; RETIRED. *Concurrent Pos:* Ed pharmacol sect, Biol Abstr, 40-67. *Mem:* AAAS; Am Soc Pharmacol & Exp Therapeut; Sigma Xi; Pan Am Med Asn. *Res:* Alveolar airarterial blood equilibrium; respiratory stimulants; cyanide poisoning and sulfur metabolism; diffusible calcium of blood serum; ergot; antimony metabolism; new drugs. *Mailing Add:* 1026 Noyes Dr Silver Spring MD 20910

SMITH, RALPH INGRAM, b Cambridge, Mass, July 3, 16; m 40; c 5. ZOOLOGY. *Educ:* Harvard Univ, BA, 38, MA, 40, PhD(zool), 42. *Prof Exp:* From instr to assoc prof zool, 46-59, PROF ZOOL, UNIV CALIF, BERKELEY, 59- *Concurrent Pos:* Fulbright lectr, Univ Glasgow, 53-54; Fulbright vis prof, Univ Turku, 61-62; Guggenheim fel, Univ Newcastle, 68-69. *Mem:* Fel AAAS; Soc Exp Biol; cor mem Finnish Zool Bot Soc; Am Soc Zoologists. *Res:* Invertebrate zoology and comparative physiology. *Mailing Add:* Dept of Zool Univ of Calif Berkeley CA 94720

SMITH, RALPH J(UDSON), b Herman, Nebr, June 5, 16; m 38; c 4. ELECTRICAL ENGINEERING. *Educ:* Univ Calif, BS, 38, MS, 40, EE, 42; Stanford Univ, PhD(elec eng), 45. *Prof Exp:* Jr engr, Stand Oil Co, Calif, 38-40; instr eng, San Jose State Col, 40-42, head dept, 45-52, chmn div eng, math & aeronaut, 52-57; adv electronics, Repub of Philippines, 57-58; instr, 42-45, PROF ELEC ENG, STANFORD UNIV, 58- *Concurrent Pos:* Consult, State Dept Educ, Calif, 60. *Mem:* Am Soc Eng Educ; fel Inst Elec & Electronics Engrs. *Res:* Orientation and motivation of engineering. *Mailing Add:* Dept of Elec Eng Stanford Univ Stanford CA 94305

SMITH, RANDALL BRUCE, b Oakland, Calif, Sept 25, 51; m 80; c 1. HIGH ENERGY THEORY. *Educ:* Univ Calif, Davis, BS, 74; Univ Calif, San Diego, PhD(physics), 81. *Prof Exp:* LECTR PHYSICS, UNIV CALIF, DAVIS, 81- *Mem:* Am Phys Soc. *Res:* Constructing mathematical models which may describe quark confinement inside subatomic particles. *Mailing Add:* 415 Layo Pl Davis CA 95616

SMITH, RAPHAEL FORD, b Wilson, NC, Jan 22, 33; m 58; c 4. MEDICINE, CARDIOLOGY. *Educ:* Vanderbilt Univ, BA, 55; Harvard Med Sch, MD, 60; FACP, 68; FACC, 69. *Prof Exp:* Intern, Mass Gen Hosp, 60-61, asst resident, 61-62; res asst aviation med, US Naval Sch Aviation Med, 62-65; resident, Mass Gen Hosp, 65-66; chief, Cardiol Br, Naval Aerospace Med Inst, 66-69; asst prof, 69-74, ASSOC PROF MED, SCH MED, VANDERBILT UNIV, 74-, SCH ENG, 76-; CHIEF, CARDIOL SECT, NASHVILLE VET ADMIN HOSP, 75- *Concurrent Pos:* Consult, US Naval Hosp, 67-69 & NIH, Specialized Ctrs Res, 74-77. *Honors & Awards:* Skylab Achievement Award, NASA, 74. *Mem:* Am Heart Asn; Southern Soc Clin Invest. *Res:* Cardiac electrophysiology; aerospace medical research. *Mailing Add:* Cardiol Sect Vet Admin Hosp Nashville TN 37203

SMITH, RAY FRED, b Los Angeles, Calif, Jan 20, 19; m 40; c 3. ENTOMOLOGY. *Educ:* Univ Calif, BS, 40, MS, 41, PhD(entom), 46. *Hon Degrees:* DAgrSc, Landbouwhogesch, Wageningen, 76. *Prof Exp:* Field entomologist, Balfour-Guthrie Investment Co, 40; field & lab asst entom, 40-45, assoc, Exp Sta, 45-46, instr & jr entomologist, 46-48, asst prof & asst entomologist, 48-54, assoc prof & assoc entomologist, 54-60, chmn dept entom & parasitol, 59-63, PROF ENTOM & ENTOMOLOGIST, EXP STA, UNIV CALIF, 60-, EXEC DIR, CONSORTIUM INT CROP PROTECTION, 79- *Concurrent Pos:* Guggenheim fel, 50; consult, Food & Agr Orgn, UN. *Honors & Awards:* C W Woodworth Award, 71. *Mem:* Fel AAAS; fel Entom Soc Am (pres, 76); Entom Soc Am; Entom Soc Can; Brit Ecol Soc. *Mailing Add:* 2288 Fulton St Suite 310 Univ of Calif Berkeley CA 94704

SMITH, RAYMOND CALVIN, b Glendale, Calif, Nov 17, 34; m 56; c 2. PHYSICAL OCEANOGRAPHY. *Educ:* Mass Inst Technol, SB, 56; Stanford Univ, PhD(physics), 61. *Prof Exp:* Res fel, Cambridge Electron Accelerator, Harvard Univ, 61-63; asst res physicist, 63-69, assoc res physicist, 69-73, res physicist, 73-80, ASSOC RES BIOLOGIST, SCRIPPS INST OCEANOG, UNIV CALIF, SAN DIEGO, 80- *Mem:* AAAS; Optical Soc Am; Am Acad Polit & Soc Sci; Am Soc Limnol & Oceanog. *Res:* High energy nuclear physics; environmental radio activity; environmental optics; primary productivity; remote sensing. *Mailing Add:* Scripps Inst of Oceanog Univ of Calif San Diego La Jolla CA 92093

SMITH, RAYMOND DALE, b Ambridge, Pa, July 1, 14; m 39; c 7. ANATOMY. *Educ:* Univ Pittsburgh, BS, 36, MS, 38, PhD(biol), 39. *Prof Exp:* Asst physiol, Univ Pittsburgh, 36-37, asst anat, 37-39; instr biol & head dept premed, Gonzaga Univ, 39-40, prof biol & head dept, 43-46; prof, Col of Our Lady of the Elms, 40-43; from asst prof to assoc prof gross anat, Sch Med, Univ Md, 46-50; prof anat & chmn dept, Sch Med, Creighton Univ, 50-69, asst dean sch med, 59-65; PROF ANAT & CHMN DEPT, SCH DENT MED, SOUTHERN ILL UNIV, EDWARDSVILLE, 69- *Mem:* AAAS; Am Asn Anatomists; Am Asn Phys Anthrop; Int Asn Dent Res. *Res:* Oral proprioception and muscles of mastication. *Mailing Add:* Sch of Dent Med Southern Ill Univ Edwardsville IL 62026

SMITH, RAYMOND JAMES, b Manchester, NH, July 16, 24. CIVIL ENGINEERING, GEOLOGY. *Educ:* Calif Inst Technol, BS, 45, MS, 48; Princeton Univ, MA, 50, PhD, 51. *Prof Exp:* Investr for Princeton, Caribbean, 48-54; asst prof, La State Univ, 54-57; res engr & geologist, NY Explor Co, 57-61; civil engr-geologist, US Naval Civil Eng Lab, Calif, 61-68; prof oceanog, Naval Postgrad Sch, 68-71; CONSULT CIVIL ENGR & GEOLOGIST, 71- *Mem:* Geol Soc Am; Am Soc Civil Engrs; Soc Econ Geologists; Am Geophys Union. *Res:* Application of geology to civil engineering. *Mailing Add:* 791 Via Ondulando Ventura CA 93003

SMITH, RAYMOND V(IRGIL), b Esbon, Kans, Nov 17, 19; m 48; c 5. MECHANICAL ENGINEERING. *Educ:* Univ Colo, BS, 48, MS, 51; Univ Utah, MS, 57; Oxford Univ, DPhil, 68. *Prof Exp:* Design engr, Boeing Airplane Co, 41-44 & 48; instr mech eng, Colo Sch Mines, 49-52; res engr, Sandia Corp, 52-53; asst prof mech eng, NMex State Univ, 53-54; assoc prof, Univ Utah, 54-57 & Colo State Univ, 57-61; mech engr, Cryogenic Eng Lab, Nat Bur Standards, 58-71; PROF MECH ENG, WICHITA STATE UNIV, 71- *Concurrent Pos:* With UK Atomic Energy Res Estab, 66-67, 78 & 81. *Mem:* Am Soc Mech Engrs; Am Soc Eng Educ; India Inst Sci. *Res:* Fuel combustion mechanism; two-phase flow cryogenic studies of heat transfer, thermodynamics and fluid mechanics; technology assessement. *Mailing Add:* Dept Mech Eng Wichita State Univ Wichita KS 67208

SMITH, REX L, b Beaver, Utah, June 7, 29; m; c 4. PLANT GENETICS, PLANT BREEDING. *Educ:* Utah State Univ, BS, 63; Iowa State Univ, PhD(plant breeding & genetics), 67. *Prof Exp:* Asst prof agron, Univ Ark, 67-68; from asst prof to assoc prof, 68-78, PROF AGRON, UNIV FLA, 78- *Mem:* AAAS; Am Soc Agron; Am Soc Plant Physiol; Am Genetic Asn. *Res:* Biochemical genetics; genetics and breeding tropical grasses; nitrogen fixation, especially in grasses. *Mailing Add:* Dept Agron Univ Fla Gainesville FL 32611

SMITH, RICHARD ALAN, b Moscow, Idaho, Aug 6, 40; m 67; c 2. BIOCHEMISTRY. *Educ:* Whitman Col, BA, 62; Univ Minn, St Paul, PhD(biochem), 67. *Prof Exp:* Res assoc biochem, Univ Hawaii, 67-69; asst prof, 69-78, ASSOC PROF CHEM, STATE UNIV COL ARTS & SCI, 78- *Mem:* AAAS; Am Chem Soc; Sigma Xi. *Res:* Structure-function relationships in enzymes; amine oxidases; aminoacyl-tRNA synthetases. *Mailing Add:* Dept of Chem State Univ Col of Arts & Sci Geneseo NY 14454

SMITH, RICHARD ANDREW, b Buffalo, NY, Aug 9, 50; m 74. HEMATOLOGY, ANATOMY. *Educ:* Canisius Col, BA, 72; State Univ NY, Buffalo, MA, 76, PhD(anat), 78. *Prof Exp:* Grad asst, 74-77, CLIN INSTR ANAT, STATE UNIV KY, BUFFALO, 78- *Mem:* AAAS; Am Soc Zoologists; Sigma Xi. *Res:* Morphological hematology; origin of the hemopoietic stem cell in mammalian embryos; endocrine control of hemopoiesis. *Mailing Add:* Dept of Anat Sci State Univ of NY Buffalo NY 14214

SMITH, RICHARD AVERY, b Long Beach, Calif, July 22, 24; m 47; c 4. GEOLOGY, SCIENCE EDUCATION. *Educ:* Stanford Univ, BS, 49, EdD(teacher educ), 56; Univ Northern Colo, MA, 50. *Prof Exp:* Instr, Menlo Sch & Col, 49-50; teacher high sch, Calif, 51-55; asst prof, 55-80, chmn, Dept Natural Sci, 68-82, PROF PHYS SCI & SCI EDUC, SAN JOSE STATE UNIV, 80- *Concurrent Pos:* Sci consult, Peace Corps, Philippines, 64-66; chmn adv comt sci educ, Calif State Bd Educ. *Mem:* AAAS; Nat Sci Teachers Asn; Nat Asn Res Sci Teaching; Nat Asn Geol Teachers. *Res:* Improvement of science teaching. *Mailing Add:* Dept Geol San Jose State Univ San Jose CA 95192

SMITH, RICHARD BARRIE, b Vernon, BC, Apr 18, 34; m 59; c 2. FOREST PATHOLOGY, FOREST ECOLOGY. *Educ:* Univ BC, BSF, 57, PhD(forest ecol), 63; Yale Univ, MF, 58. *Prof Exp:* Res officer forest path, Can Dept Agr, 59-63; res officer, 63-65, RES SCIENTIST FOREST PATH, PAC FOREST RES CTR, CAN FORESTRY SERV, 65- *Mem:* Ecol Soc Am; Can Inst Forestry; Can Phytopath Soc; Can Bot Soc; Can Soc Soil Sci. *Res:* Edaphotopes of forest ecosystems; epidemiology and taxonomy of dwarf mistletoes on western North American conifers; environmental impact of forest management practices. *Mailing Add:* Pac Forest Res Centre 506 W Burnside Rd Victoria BC V8W 2Y2 Can

SMITH, RICHARD CARPER, b Jacksonville, Fla, May 9, 38; m 66; c 2. OPTICS. *Educ:* Davidson Col, BS, 60; Lehigh Univ, MS, 62, PhD(physics), 66. *Prof Exp:* Res physicist, Nat Security Agency, 67-68; asst prof physics, 68-71, ASSOC PROF PHYSICS, UNIV W FLA, 71- *Mem:* Am Asn Physics Teachers; Am Phys Soc; Optical Soc Am. *Res:* Use of coherent optical processing systems for image storage and enhancement. *Mailing Add:* Dept of Physics Omega Col Univ of WFla Pensacola FL 32504

SMITH, RICHARD CECIL, b Sydney, Australia, Feb 21, 70; US citizen; m 63; c 2. APPLIED NUCLEAR PHYSICS, COMPUTER SCIENCE. *Educ:* Princeton Univ, AB, 62; Univ Md, College Park, PhD(physics), 70. *Prof Exp:* Res asst high energy physics, Dept Physics & Astron, Univ Md, 65-70; sr physicist, 70-78, FEL PHYSICIST, RES & DEVELOP CTR, WESTINGHOUSE ELEC CORP, 78- *Concurrent Pos:* Mem, Westinghouse Res & Develop Planning, 78. *Mem:* Am Phys Soc; Sigma Xi. *Res:* Electron beam technology; gas discharge excitation; elementary particles; applied nuclear physics; neutron activation; DFN uranium exploration; oil well logging instrumentation; neutron generators; ion implantation; nuclear power instrumentation. *Mailing Add:* Westinghouse Res & Develop Ctr 1310 Beulah Rd Pittsburgh PA 15235

SMITH, RICHARD CHANDLER, b St Paul, Minn, Sept 10, 13; m 44; c 1. FOREST ECONOMICS. *Educ:* Univ Minn, BS, 37; Duke Univ, MF, 47, DF, 50. *Prof Exp:* Field asst & jr forester, Forest Serv, USDA, 33-39; forester, Am Creosoting Co, 40-42; PROF FORESTRY & ASST DIR, UNIV MO-COLUMBIA, 47- *Concurrent Pos:* Res forester, Forest Serv, USDA, 62-63. *Honors & Awards:* Forest Conserv Award, Mo Conserv Fedn, 71. *Mem:* Fel Soc Am Foresters; Int Union Forest Res Orgn. *Res:* Forest economics and management; economics of timber production and multiple-use forestry. *Mailing Add:* Sch Forestry Fishery & Wildlife Univ of Mo Columbia MO 65201

SMITH, RICHARD CLARK, b Salem, Ind, Apr 17, 27; m 57; c 1. PLANT PHYSIOLOGY. *Educ:* Vanderbilt Univ, AB, 49; Duke Univ, AM, 52, PhD(bot), 57. *Prof Exp:* Instr bot, Univ Tenn, 56-58 & Miami Univ, 58-59; from instr to asst prof, Rutgers Univ, 59-62; plant physiologist, Univ Calif, Davis, 62-64; from asst prof to assoc prof bot, 64-77, PROF BOT, UNIV FLA, 77- *Concurrent Pos:* Consult, Univ Ill, 72. *Mem:* AAAS; Bot Soc Am; Am Soc Plant Physiol; Scand Soc Plant Physiol. *Res:* Absorption and translocation of mineral ions in plants; metabolic activities of roots; plant growth. *Mailing Add:* Dept of Bot Univ of Fla Gainesville FL 32611

SMITH, RICHARD DEAN, b Amarillo, Tex, July 10, 22; m 44; c 2. CHEMICAL ENGINEERING. *Educ:* Univ Tex, BS, 42. *Prof Exp:* Chem engr, B F Goodrich Chem Co, 42-45, develop engr chem processes, 45-49, sr develop engr, 49-51, develop supvr, 51-58, mgr synthetic fiber develop, 58-61; asst tech dir, Celanese Fibers Co, 61-64; plant mgr nylon mfg, Fiber Industs, Inc, Charlotte, NC, 64-67, dir res & develop, 67-71, vpres & prod dir, 71-73; pres, Celanese Fibers Co, 73-74, Celanese Fibers Mkt Co, 74-78 & Fiber Indust Inc, 78-81; RETIRED. *Concurrent Pos:* Trustee, Philadelphia Col Textiles & Sci, 79- *Mem:* Am Chem Soc; Fiber Soc; Am Inst Chem Engrs. *Res:* Process development and manufacture of synthetic fibers, polymers and organic chemicals; nylon manufacture. *Mailing Add:* 918 Cherokee Rd Charlotte NC 28207

SMITH, RICHARD ELBRIDGE, b Keene, NH, May 30, 32; m 63; c 2. GEOLOGY, GEOCHEMISTRY. *Educ:* Univ NH, BA, 59; Univ Ill, Urbana, MS, 60; Pa State Univ, PhD(petrol), 66. *Prof Exp:* Res oceanogr, Ocean Sci Dept, 66-70, ACTG HEAD MARINE CHEM BR, RES & DEVELOP DEPT, US NAVAL OCEANOG OFF, 70- *Mem:* AAAS; Am Geophys Union; Geol Soc Am; Soc Econ Paleontologists & Mineralogists. *Res:* Geochemistry of coastal marine sediments; trace metal concentrations in coastal marine sediments and seawater; chemical pollution of sediments; nutrients in seawater and harbors; uptake of trace metals by clay minerals. *Mailing Add:* 7829 Willowbrook Rd Fairfax Station VA 22039

SMITH, RICHARD FREDERICK, b Lockport, NY, Jan 31, 29; m 51; c 3. ORGANIC CHEMISTRY. *Educ:* Allegheny Col, BS, 50; Univ Rochester, PhD(chem), 54. *Prof Exp:* Res chemist, Monsanto Chem Co, 53-55; res assoc, Sterling-Winthrop Res Inst, 55-57; from assoc prof to prof chem, State Univ NY Albany, 57-65; chmn dept chem, 65-68, prof 65-74, DISTINGUISHED TEACHING PROF, STATE UNIV NY COL GENESEO, 74- *Concurrent Pos:* NSF fac fel, Univ Calif, Los Angeles, 62-63; vis prof, Dartmouth Col, 81. *Mem:* Am Chem Soc; Royal Soc Chem. *Res:* Heterocycles; amine-imides; organic hydrazine derivatives. *Mailing Add:* Dept of Chem State Univ of NY Col Geneseo NY 14454

SMITH, RICHARD G(RANT), b Flint, Mich, Jan 19, 37; c 3. APPLIED PHYSICS, ELECTRICAL ENGINEERING. *Educ:* Stanford Univ, BS, 58, MS, 59, PhD(elec eng, appl physics), 63. *Prof Exp:* Mem tech staff, 63-68, SUPVR, BELL TEL LABS, 68- *Concurrent Pos:* Chmn, Conf Laser & Electro-optical Systs, 80- & Coun Legal Educ Opportunity, 81. *Mem:* Am Phys Soc; fel Inst Elec & Electronics Engrs. *Res:* Quantum theory of nonlinear effects; nonlinear optics; lasers; optical fiber communications. *Mailing Add:* Solid State Device Lab Bell Tel Labs Murray Hill NJ 07974

SMITH, RICHARD HARRISON, b Ellenville, NY, Nov 28, 20; m 46; c 2. FOREST ENTOMOLOGY. *Educ:* State Univ NY, BS, 42, MS, 47; Univ Calif, PhD(entom), 61. *Prof Exp:* Forest entomologist, Bur Entom & Plant Quarantine, USDA, 46-52, FOREST ENTOMOLOGIST, FOREST SERV, USDA, 53- *Mem:* Entom Soc Am; Am Inst Biol Scientists. *Res:* Biology and control of Lyctus and Dendroctonus terebrans; resistance of pines to bark beetles and the pine reproduction weevil; monoterpenes of pine xylem resin; forest insect research; residual insecticides for bark beetles. *Mailing Add:* Pac SW Forest & Range Exp Sta Box 245 Berkeley CA 94701

SMITH, RICHARD JAMES, b Lansing, Mich, Jan 31, 47; m 70; c 2. SOLID STATE PHYSICS. *Educ:* St Mary's Col, Minn, BA, 69; Iowa State Univ, PhD(solid state physics), 75. *Prof Exp:* Res assoc physics, Mont State Univ, 75-77; asst scientist, Brookhaven Nat Lab, 77-80; MEM FAC PHYS DEPT, MONT STATE UNIV, 80- *Mem:* Am Phys Soc. *Res:* Electronic and structural studies of surfaces of condensed matter. *Mailing Add:* Phys Dept Mont State Univ Bozeman MT 59717

SMITH, RICHARD JAY, b Brooklyn, NY, Aug 10, 48; m 70; c 2. CRANIOFACIAL BIOLOGY, HOMINOID EVOLUTION. *Educ:* Brooklyn Col, BA, 69; Tufts Univ, MS & DMD, 73; Yale Univ, PhD(anthrop), 80. *Prof Exp:* Resident orthodonists, Health Ctr, Univ Conn, 73-76, asst clin prof, 76-79; asst prof, 79-81, ASSOC PROF ORTHOD, DENT SCH, UNIV MD, 81- *Concurrent Pos:* Dir, Postgrad Prog, Dept Orthod, Dent Sch, Univ Md, 80-; vis assoc prof, Dept Cell Biol, Med Sch, Johns Hopkins Univ, 81-; ed-in-chief, J Baltimore Col Dent Surg, 81- *Mem:* Am Asn Orthodonists; Int Asn Dent Res; Am Asn Phys Anthropologists; Soc Syst Zool. *Res:* Functional morphology of craniofacial variation in mammals, particularly primates; biomechanical modeling correlates; paleontology. *Mailing Add:* Dept Orthod Dent Sch Univ Md 666 W Baltimore St Baltimore MD 21201

SMITH, RICHARD LAWRENCE, b Los Angeles, Calif, Mar 14, 39. PHYCOLOGY. *Educ:* Univ Calif, Davis, AB, 61; Univ Tex, Austin, PhD(bot), 65; Registry Med Technol, cert, 62. *Prof Exp:* From asst prof to assoc prof, 65-77, PROF BOT, EASTERN ILL UNIV, 77- *Concurrent Pos:* Consult, Phytoplankton Anal, Wapora, Inc, 72-75; ed-in-chief, The Biologist, 80- *Mem:* Int Phycol Soc; Bot Soc Am; Phycol Soc Am; Am Inst Biol Scientists; Am Soc Clin Path. *Res:* Morphology and physiology of certain Chlorococcalean algae; nutrition of certain green algae; extramorphological criteria as taxonomic tools in phycology. *Mailing Add:* Dept Bot Eastern Ill Univ Charleston IL 61920

SMITH, RICHARD LLOYD, b Binghamton, NY, Oct 15, 45; m 68; c 1. ASTROPHYSICS. *Educ:* Rensselaer Polytech Inst, BS, 67; Mass Inst Technol, PhD(physics), 71. *Prof Exp:* Res fel physics, Calif Inst Technol, 71-72; asst prof physics, Rensselaer Polytech Inst, 72-77; STAFF MEM, SYST SCI DIV, COMPUT SCI CORP, 77- *Mem:* Am Astron Soc. *Res:* Orbit determination. *Mailing Add:* Syst Sci Div Colesville Rd Silver Spring MD 20910

SMITH, RICHARD MERRILL, b South Bend, Ind, Nov 3, 42; m 64; c 2. PHYSIOLOGY. *Educ:* Ind Univ, Bloomington, AB, 64, PhD(physiol), 69. *Prof Exp:* Rockefeller Found vis prof physiol, Mahidol Univ, Thailand, 69-71; asst prof, 71-80, ASSOC PROF PHYSIOL, SCH MED, UNIV HAWAII, 80- *Res:* Environmental and comparative physiology; hypobarism and hyperbarism; cardiopulmonary physiology. *Mailing Add:* Dept of Physiol Univ of Hawaii Sch of Med Honolulu HI 96822

SMITH, RICHARD NEILSON, b Springfield, Mass, May 20, 18; m 37. PHYSICAL CHEMISTRY, ELECTROCHEMISTRY. *Educ:* Univ Mass, BS, 41; Univ Del, MS, 50, PhD(phys chem), 56. *Prof Exp:* Sr res chemist, Gen Chem Co Div, Allied Chem Corp, 41-55; sect mgr, Am Mach & Foundry Co, 55-71; mgr, Spec Proj Lab, Sybron Corp, 71-78; SR CHEMIST, SOUTHERN RES INST, 78- *Mem:* Am Chem Soc; Sigma Xi (secy, Sci Res Soc Am, 63). *Res:* Permselective membranes; electrodialysis processes; process and equipment development; specialty and heavy chemicals; plastics; film forming and processing. *Mailing Add:* 3545 Stoneheng pl Birmingham AL 35205

SMITH, RICHARD PAUL, b Omaha, Nebr, Jan 31, 43; m 63; c 2. SUPERCONDUCTING MAGNET TECHNOLOGY, EXPERIMENTAL HIGH ENERGY PHYSICS. *Educ:* Univ Nebr, BS, 65; Syracuse Univ, MS, 67, PhD(physics), 72. *Prof Exp:* Res physics, 72-79, group leader superconducting magnets, 79, PRIN INVESTR ACCELERATOR FACIL RES & DEVELOP, ARGONNE NAT LAB, 80- *Mem:* Am Phys Soc; Sigma Xi. *Res:* High energy particle physics, weak interactions; computer controlled film scanning; superconducting magnet design. *Mailing Add:* 360-C137 Argonne Nat Lab 9700 Cass Ave S Argonne IL 60439

SMITH, RICHARD PEARSON, b Garland, Utah, Mar 4, 26. PHYSICAL CHEMISTRY. *Educ:* Univ Utah, BA, 48, PhD(phys chem), 51. *Prof Exp:* Jr fel, Harvard Univ, 51-53; from asst prof to assoc prof chem, Univ Utah, 53-61; MEM STAFF, EXXON RES & ENG CO, 61- *Mem:* Am Chem Soc; Am Phys Soc. *Res:* Electronic structure of molecules; polarizabilities; dipole moments; substituent effects on rates and equilibria; polymer structure and property relationships; computer applications in chemistry. *Mailing Add:* Exxon Res & Eng Co PO Box 45 Linden NJ 07036

SMITH, RICHARD R, b Mendota, Ill, Aug 7, 36; m 59; c 4. PLANT BREEDING, PLANT GENETICS. *Educ:* Univ Ill, BSAgr, 62, MS, 63; Iowa State Univ, PhD(plant breeding), 66. *Prof Exp:* Asst prof agron, 66-72, ASSOC PROF AGRON, UNIV WIS-MADISON, 72-, RES GENETICIST, AGR RES SERV, USDA, 66- *Mem:* Crop Sci Soc Am; Am Soc Agron. *Res:* Quantitative genetics; statistics; agronomy; plant pathology. *Mailing Add:* Dept of Agron Univ of Wis Madison WI 53706

SMITH, RICHARD S, JR, b Somerville, NJ, Mar 2, 30; m 56; c 4. PLANT PATHOLOGY. *Educ:* Utah State Univ, BS, 58; Univ Calif, Berkeley, PhD(plant path), 63. *Prof Exp:* Lab technician plant path, Univ Calif, Berkeley, 60-61; plant pathologist, Pac Southwest Forest & Range Exp Sta, USDA, 61-76; SUPVRY PLANT PATHOLOGIST, PAC SOUTHWEST REGION, FOREST SERV, USDA, SAN FRANCISCO, CALIF, 76- *Mem:* Am Phytopath Soc. *Res:* Epidemiology; control of diseases of forest tree seedlings; root diseases of mature western forest trees; management of forest disease problems; diseases of semi-tropical forest trees. *Mailing Add:* Forest Pest Mgt Forest Serv 630 Sansome St San Francisco CA 94111

SMITH, RICHARD SCOTT, b San Francisco, Calif, Aug 7, 39; m 79; c 2. IMMUNOLOGY, IMMUNOCHEMISTRY. *Educ:* Northwestern Univ, BA, 62; Ariz State Univ, MS, 65, PhD(immunol), 67. *Prof Exp:* Res scientist immunol, Children's Asthma Res Inst & Hosp, 69-73; sr res scientist, Hyland Labs, 74-76; MGR CLIN RES & DEVELOP IMMUNOL, BECTON DICKINSON IMMUNODIAG, 76- *Concurrent Pos:* Res fel, Scripps Clin & Res Found, 67-69. *Mem:* Am Asn Immunologists; Am Acad Allergy. *Res:* Development of new protein radioimmunoassays for hormones and tumor antigens. *Mailing Add:* Becton Dickinson Immunodiag 180 W 2950 S Salt Lake City UT 84115

SMITH, RICHARD SIDNEY, b Eng, May 22, 33; Can citizen; m 59; c 4. PHYSIOLOGY. *Educ:* Univ Alta, BSc, 59, MD, 61; Karolinska Inst, MD, 64. *Prof Exp:* Docent neurophysiol, Karolinska Inst, Sweden, 64-66; from asst prof to assoc prof surg, 66-75, PROF SURG & MED RES COUN CAN ASSOC, UNIV ALTA, 75- *Concurrent Pos:* Med Res Coun Can scholar, Univ Alta, 66-69. *Mem:* Can Physiol Soc; Neurosci Soc. *Res:* Neuromuscular physiology; function of sense organs in muscle; axoplasmic transport. *Mailing Add:* Neurophysiol Lab Dept of Surg Univ of Alta Edmonton AB T6G 2G5 Can

SMITH, RICHARD THOMAS, b Oklahoma City, Okla, Apr 15, 24; m 46; c 5. PEDIATRICS, PATHOLOGY. *Educ:* Univ Tex, BA, 44; Tulane Univ, MD, 50; Am Bd Pediat, dipl; Am Bd Allergy & Immunol, dipl. *Prof Exp:* Intern pediat, Univ Minn Hosps, 50-51, resident, Med Sch, 51-52, asst prof pediat, 55-56; assoc prof, Southwestern Med Sch, Univ Tex, 57-58; prof pediat & head dept, Col Med & chief pediat, Hosp & Clin, 58-67, PROF PATH & CHMN DEPT, COL MED, UNIV FLA, 67-, C A STETSON PROF EXP MED, 81- *Concurrent Pos:* Nat Res Coun fel med sci, Med Sch, Univ Minn, 52-53, Helen Hay Whitney Found res fel rheumatic fever & allied dis, 53-55; sr investr, Arthritis & Rheumatism Found, 55-58. *Mem:* AAAS; Am Pediat Soc; Soc Pediat Res; Soc Exp Biol & Med; Am Soc Path. *Res:* General and clinical immunology; tumor immunobiology. *Mailing Add:* Dept of Path Univ of Fla Col of Med Gainesville FL 32601

SMITH, RICHARD THOMAS, b Allentown, Pa, June 15, 25; m 56; c 2. NONDESTRUCTIVE EVALUATION, OCEAN ENGINEERING. *Educ:* Lehigh Univ, BS, 46, MS, 47; Ill Inst Technol, PhD(elec eng), 55. *Prof Exp:* Engr, Radio Corp Am, 47; instr elec eng, Lehigh Univ, 47-50; asst, Ill Inst Technol, 50-52; design engr, Gen Elec Co, 52-55, eng analyst, Anal Eng Sect, 55-58; assoc prof elec eng, Univ Tex, 58-61; Westinghouse prof, Va Polytech Inst, 61; proj dir, Tracor, Inc, 62-64; asst dir, Dept Electronics & Elec Eng, Southwest Res Inst, 64-65, dir dept instrumentation res, 65-66; Okla Gas & Elec Prof elec eng, Univ Okla, 66-68; prof elec mach, Rensselaer Polytech Inst, 68-70; Alcoa Found Distinguished Prof elec eng, Univ Mo-Rolla, 70-73; INST ENGR, SOUTHWEST RES INST, 73- *Concurrent Pos:* Consult, Jack & Heintz & Lear Inc, 59, Southwest Res Inst, 61 & 70-73 & Gen Elec Co, 69-70; ed, Trans on Power Apparatus & Systs, Inst Elec & Electronics Engrs, 66-68; NSF fel, Univ Colo, 70; adv, Int Electrotech Comn; adj prof, Univ Tex, 73- & St Mary's Univ, 77- *Mem:* Sr mem Inst Elec & Electronics Engrs; fel Brit Inst Engrs; assoc fel Am Inst Aeronaut & Astronaut; NY Acad Sci; Am Soc Testing & Mat. *Mailing Add:* Box 28510 San Antonio TX 78284

SMITH, ROBBIN PEGGY PIETY, biochemistry, see previous edition

SMITH, ROBERT, b Dublin, Ireland, Apr 2, 21; m 47; c 4. FAMILY MEDICINE. *Educ:* Univ Dublin, BA, 44, MB, BCh & BAO, 45, MA, 54, MD, 57. *Prof Exp:* Asst prof physiol, Trinity Col, Dublin, 44-46; physician, Royal Army Med Corps, 46-48; practitioner family med, Nat Health Serv Brit, 48-63; sr lectr, Guy's Hosp Med Sch, Univ London, 63-68; assoc prof prev med, 68-70, prof family med & chmn dept, Univ NC, Chapel Hill, 70-75; PROF FAMILY MED & DIR DEPT, UNIV CINCINNATI, 75- *Concurrent Pos:* Vchmn, NC Regional Med Prog, 70-72; Wander lectr, Royal Soc Med, 70; vpres, NC Health Coun, 73-74; pres elect, 74-75; mem, US Pharmacopeia Adv Panel Family Pract. *Honors & Awards:* Hawthorne Prize, Brit Med Asn, 58; Int Prize, Royal Col Gen Practitioners, 59. *Mem:* Fel Royal Col Gen Practitioners; Am Acad Family Physicians; Royal Soc Med; Soc Teachers Family Med. *Res:* Pain threshold and its relationship to patient behavior; role of family in health and disease; behavioral and social factors and their interaction with pathophysiology of disease. *Mailing Add:* Dept of Family Med Univ of Cincinnati Cincinnati OH 45267

SMITH, ROBERT, b Cumberland, Md, Nov 25, 21; m 48; c 1. OPERATIONS RESEARCH, MECHANICAL & SANITARY ENGINEERING. *Educ:* Tri-State Col, BSME, 43; Univ Cincinnati, MS, 67. *Prof Exp:* Mech engr supersonic wind tunnel, Ballistic Res Lab, Aberdeen Proving Ground, Md, 46-47, chief terminal ballistic info sect, 48-52, chief air blast sect, 52-56; cycle anal specialist, Jet Engine Dept, Gen Elec Co, Ohio, 56-60; sr staff engr, AVCO-Crosley, Ohio, 60-61; chief eng anal unit, Robert A Taft Sanit Eng Ctr, 61-64; oper res analyst, 64-68; chief, Systs & Econ Anal Sect, Munic Environ Res Lab, Wastewater Res Div, Environ Protection Agency, 68-81; ASSOC PROF, UNIV CENT FLA, 81- *Mem:* Water Pollution Control Fedn; Int Asn Water Pollution Res. *Res:* Ballistics; thermodynamics; economic analysis; mathematical models of environmental problems. *Mailing Add:* PO Box 552 Goldenrod FL 32733

SMITH, ROBERT ALAN, b Glendale, Calif, Oct 30, 39; m 61; c 2. BORON CHEMISTRY. *Educ:* Univ Calif, Los Angeles, BS, 62; State Univ NY Buffalo, PhD(org chem), 68. *Prof Exp:* Sr res chemist petrochem, Atlantic Richfield Co, 68-69; fel, Calif Inst Technol, 69-70; SR RES CHEMIST BORON CHEM, US BORAX RES CORP, SUBSID RIO TINTO ZINC, LTD, 70- *Mem:* Am Chem Soc; Sigma Xi. *Res:* Inorganic and organic borate chemistry. *Mailing Add:* 2521 Gelid Ave Anaheim CA 92806

SMITH, ROBERT ARNOLD, b Los Angeles, Calif, Jan 23, 37; m 63; c 2. NUMBER THEORY. *Educ:* Sacramento State Univ, BA, 60, MSc, 61; Univ Colo, Boulder, PhD(math), 65. *Prof Exp:* Lectr, 64-65, asst prof, 65-71, ASSOC PROF MATH, UNIV TORONTO, 71- *Mem:* Am Math Soc; Can Math Cong. *Res:* Algebraic and analytical number theory. *Mailing Add:* Dept of Math Univ of Toronto Toronto ON M5S 2R8 Can

SMITH, ROBERT BAER, b Logan, Utah, Oct 6, 38; m 60; c 2. GEOPHYSICS, GEOLOGY. *Educ:* Utah State Univ, BS, 60, MS, 65; Univ Utah, PhD(geophys), 67. *Prof Exp:* Am exchange scientist, Brit Antarctic Surv, 62-63; res asst seismol, 64-67, from asst prof, to assoc prof geophys, 67-76, PROF GEOL & GEOPHYS, UNIV UTAH, 76-, DIR SEISMOG STAS, 80- *Concurrent Pos:* Consult geophys surv groups, 67- *Honors & Awards:* Antarctic Serv Medal, 63. *Mem:* AAAS; Soc Explor Geophys; Am Geophys Union; Geol Soc Am; Seismol Soc Am. *Res:* Earthquake seismology; micro-earthquakes; focal mechanisms; computer graphics; earthquake prediction; crust-mantle refraction studies; seismic profiling; geophysics as applied to regional tectonics; exploration seismology. *Mailing Add:* Dept of Geophys Univ of Utah Salt Lake City UT 84112

SMITH, ROBERT BRUCE, b Philadelphia, Pa, July 8, 37; m 59; c 3. ORGANIC CHEMISTRY, ACADEMIC ADMINISTRATION. *Educ:* Wheaton Col, Ill, BS, 58; Univ Calif, Berkeley, PhD(org chem), 62. *Prof Exp:* Asst prof chem, Nev Southern Univ, 61-66, assoc prof chem & chmn dept phys sci, 66-67, chmn dept chem, 67-68; PROF CHEM & DEAN COL SCI MATH & ENG, UNIV NEV, LAS VEGAS, 68- *Mem:* AAAS; Am Chem Soc. *Res:* Humanistic strategies in science teaching. *Mailing Add:* Col of Sci Math & Eng Univ of Nev Las Vegas NV 89154

SMITH, ROBERT C, b Chicago, Ill, Sept 15, 32; m 57; c 3. BIOCHEMISTRY. *Educ:* Elmhurst Col, BS, 54; Univ Ill, MS, 58, PhD(biochem), 60. *Prof Exp:* USPHS res fel, 59-61; from asst prof to assoc prof, 61-68, alumni assoc prof, 68-69, ALUMNI PROF ANIMAL SCI, AUBURN UNIV, 69- *Mem:* Am Soc Microbiol; Am Soc Biol Chemists; Am Soc Animal Sci; Soc Exp Biol & Med. *Res:* Nucleic acids; nucleotides; uric acid; 3-ribosyluric acid. *Mailing Add:* Dept of Animal & Dairy Sci Auburn Univ Auburn AL 36830

SMITH, ROBERT C(HARLES), b Davis, WVa, Feb 6, 24; m 46; c 3. ENGINEERING MECHANICS, MATERIALS SCIENCE. *Educ:* Univ WVa, BS, 48, MS, 50. *Prof Exp:* Asst prof eng mech, Univ WVa, 48-50 & 52-54; eng scientist, US Naval Res Lab, 54-60; assoc prof, 60-66, prof eng mech, 66-80, PROF CIVIL ENG, MONT STATE UNIV, 80- *Mem:* Am Soc Civil Engrs. *Res:* Metallic solids, concrete and wood. *Mailing Add:* Dept of Civil Eng & Eng Mech Mont State Univ Bozeman MT 59715

SMITH, ROBERT CLINTON, b St Thomas, Ont, Mar 11, 32; m 55; c 2. THEORETICAL PHYSICS. *Educ:* Univ Western Ont, BSc, 54; McGill Univ, MSc, 56, PhD(theoret physics), 60. *Prof Exp:* Lectr, 58-60, asst prof, 60-66, ASSOC PROF PHYSICS, UNIV OTTAWA, 66-, SECY, FAC SCI & ENG, 78- *Mem:* Am Asn Physics Teachers; Can Asn Physicists; Can Asn Univ Teachers. *Mailing Add:* Dept Physics Univ Ottawa Ottawa ON K1N 9B4 Can

SMITH, ROBERT EARL, b Indianapolis, Ind, Sept 13, 23; m 47; c 4. AERONOMY. *Educ:* Fla State Univ, BS, 59, MS, 60; Univ Mich, PhD(atmospheric sci), 74. *Prof Exp:* DEP CHIEF ATMOSPHERIC SCI DIV, GEORGE C MARSHALL SPACE FLIGHT CTR, 63- *Mem:* Am Meteorol Soc. *Res:* Temperature and dynamic structure of the upper atmosphere from 6300 angstrom units; atomic oxygen airglow emissions. *Mailing Add:* Code ES81 Marshall Space Flight Ctr Marshall Space Flight Center AL 35812

SMITH, ROBERT EDWARD, b Winnipeg, Man, Oct 4, 29; m 56; c 4. PEDOLOGY. *Educ:* Univ Man, BA, 52, 55. *Prof Exp:* Pedologist, Man Dept Agr, 56-63; pedologist, 63-68, HEAD PEDOLOGY SECT, LAND RESOURCE RES INST, CAN DEPT AGR, 68-, MEM STAFF, MAN SOIL SURV UNIT, 73- *Concurrent Pos:* Adj prof soil sci, Univ Man, 74- *Mem:* Agr Inst Can; Can Soc Soil Sci; Int Soc Soil Sci. *Res:* Soil characterization, genesis and classification. *Mailing Add:* Man Soil Surv Unit Univ of Man Winnipeg MB R3T 2N2 Can

SMITH, ROBERT ELIJAH, b Pittsburgh, Pa, Aug 14, 11; m 38; c 4. COMPUTER SCIENCE, STATISTICS. *Educ:* State Univ Iowa, BA, 34; Univ Pittsburgh, PhD(statist, educ), 51. *Prof Exp:* Teacher, Iowa, Pa & NJ, 34-44; prof math & head dept, Duquesne Univ, 44-57; analyst computer, Univac Div, Sperry Rand Corp, Minn, 57-58; prin consult, Control Data Corp, Minneapolis, 58-80; RETIRED. *Mem:* Am Math Soc. *Res:* Computer programming projects. *Mailing Add:* 6912 Creston Rd Edina MN 55435

SMITH, ROBERT ELPHIN, b Pasadena, Calif, Sept 26, 29; m 59; c 2. PHYSIOLOGY, BIOMEDICAL ENGINEERING. *Educ:* Calif Inst Technol, BS, 51; Univ Wash, PhD(physiol, biophys), 62. *Prof Exp:* Civil engr, CZ Govt, 51-52; design engr, Lockheed Aircraft Corp, 52-53, tech writer, 53-54; civil engr, Daniel, Mann, Johnson & Mendenhall, 54; res asst physiol, Univ Wash, 57-58; asst prof physiol & biophys, Univ Ky, 62-68; asst prof human physiol, 68-70, ASSOC PROF HUMAN PHYSIOL, SCH MED, UNIV CALIF, DAVIS, 70- *Concurrent Pos:* US Air Force contract grant, 64-67; NASA grant, 64-68; NIH fel, 64-66, grant, 67-69. *Mem:* AAAS; Biophys Soc; Inst Elec & Electronics Eng; Arctic Inst NAm; Int Primatol Soc. *Res:* Physiological control systems; temperature regulation; circadian rhythms; menstrual cycles; peripheral circulation. *Mailing Add:* Dept of Human Physiol Univ of Calif Sch of Med Davis CA 95616

SMITH, ROBERT EMERY, b Jacksonville, Fla, Feb 2, 42; m 63; c 2. ENGINEERING PHYSICS. *Educ:* Duke Univ, BS, 63; Washington Univ, MA, 65, PhD(physics), 69. *Prof Exp:* RES SCIENTIST, CARBON PROD DIV, UNION CARBIDE CORP, 69- *Mem:* Am Phys Soc. *Res:* Mathematical models of industrial products and processes, principally by finite element analysis; stress and heat transfer models; physical properties of graphite. *Mailing Add:* Parma Tech Ctr Union Carbide Corp Parma OH 44130

SMITH, ROBERT EWING, b Montreal, Que, Sept 20, 34; m 59; c 4. NUTRITION. *Educ:* McGill Univ, BSc, 55, MSc, 57; Univ Ill, PhD(animal sci), 63. *Prof Exp:* Res scientist, Animal Res Inst, Can Dept Agr, 57-60 & 63-67; mgr poultry res, Quaker Oats Co, 67-69, mgr nutrit res, 69-73, dir qual assurance, 73-77, vpres foods res & develop, 77-79; VPRES RES & DEVELOP, SWIFT CO, 79- *Concurrent Pos:* Indust liaison, Food & Nutrit Bd, Am Acad Pediat; panel chmn nutrit comt, Am Corn Millers Fedn. *Mem:* Poultry Sci Asn; Am Inst Nutrit; Nutrit Soc Can; Am Acad Pediat; Soc Nutrit Educ. *Res:* Nutritional quality of human and pet foods; proteins and amino acid requirements and interrelationships. *Mailing Add:* Swift & Co 1919 Swift Dr Oak Brook IL 60521

SMITH, ROBERT JOHNSON, b Blodgett, Mo, July 23, 16; m 48; c 3. ORGANIC CHEMISTRY. *Educ:* Southeast Mo State Col, BS, 36; Univ Iowa, PhD(chem), 50. *Prof Exp:* Instr high schs, Mo, 36-42; from asst prof to prof chem, Southeast Mo State Col, 46-55; asst, Univ Iowa, 49-50; assoc prof, 55-60, PROF CHEM, EASTERN ILL UNIV, 60- *Mem:* Am Chem Soc. *Res:* Mechanism and rate of addition of bromine to olefins in carbon tetrachloride solution; preparation and reactions of mercurials derived from olefins. *Mailing Add:* Dept of Chem Eastern Ill Univ Charleston IL 61920

SMITH, ROBERT KINGSTON, b Melrose, Mass, May 15, 24; m 78; c 1. INORGANIC CHEMISTRY. *Educ:* Univ Mass, BS & MS, 50; Univ Wyo, PhD(chem), 66. *Prof Exp:* Tech asst food technol, Mass Inst Technol, 54-56; instr chem, Univ Wyo, 56-63, asst, 63-66; asst prof chem, 66-68, asst dean col arts & sci, 68-70, actg dean, 70-71, ASSOC PROF CHEM, YOUNGSTOWN STATE UNIV, 68-, ASST DEAN COL ARTS & SCI, 71- *Mem:* Am Chem Soc. *Res:* Complexes of group VA elements, especially those of the antimony halides. *Mailing Add:* Off of the Dean Col Arts & Sci Youngstown State Univ Youngstown OH 44503

SMITH, ROBERT LAWRENCE, b Albemarle, NC, Aug 29, 39; m 62; c 2. ORGANIC CHEMISTRY, MEDICINAL CHEMISTRY. *Educ:* Univ NC, BS, 61; Univ Maine, MS, 63, PhD(org chem), 65. *Prof Exp:* NIH res fel org chem, Univ NC, 65-67; sr res chemist, 67-74, res fel, 74-75, asst dir, 75-77, assoc dir, 77-79, DIR, MERCK SHARP & DOHME RES LABS, 79- *Mem:* AAAS; Am Chem Soc. *Res:* General organic synthesis; synthesis of medicinals. *Mailing Add:* Merck Sharp & Dohme Res Labs West Point PA 19486

SMITH, ROBERT LEE, b Schaller, Iowa, Oct 31, 23; m 47; c 3. CIVIL ENGINEERING. *Educ:* Univ Iowa, BS, 47, MS, 48. *Prof Exp:* Asst prof hydraul, Univ Kans, 48-52; exec dir, Iowa Natural Resources Coun, 52-55; exec secy & chief engr, Kans Water Resources Bd, 55-62; Parker prof water resources, 62-66, prof civil eng, chmn dept & dir water resources inst, 66-72, DEANE ACKERS PROF CIVIL ENG, UNIV KANS, 70- *Concurrent Pos:* Chmn, Interstate Conf Water Probs, 61 & Inter-Agency Comt Water Resources Res, 66-; tech asst, Off Sci & Technol, Exec Off President, 66-; mem ex officio, US Nat Comt, Int Hydrol Decade, 66-, mem, 68-71. *Mem:* Nat Acad Eng; fel Am Soc Civil Engrs; Nat Soc Prof Engrs; Am Water Works Asn; Am Geophys Union. *Res:* Hydrology; water resources planning; Midwestern water problems; water policy. *Mailing Add:* 2915 Harvard Rd Lawrence KS 66045

SMITH, ROBERT LELAND, b Sacramento, Calif, June 30, 20; m 52; c 3. VOLCANOLOGY, RARE METAL GEOCHEMISTRY. *Educ:* Univ Nev, BS, 42. *Prof Exp:* From jr geologist to prin geologist, 43-60, chief field geochem & petrol br, 60-66, RES GEOLOGIST, US GEOL SURV, 66- *Concurrent Pos:* Mem earth sci div, Nat Res Coun, 62-65; mem, US-Japan Sci Coop Volcano Res, 63-65; mem preliminary exam team, First Lunar Samples, Apollo 11 & 12, NASA, 69. *Mem:* Fel Geol Soc Am; fel Mineral Soc Am; Geochem Soc; Am Ornithologists Union; fel AAAS. *Res:* Mineralogy; petrology; geochemistry; pyroclastic rocks; volcanic glasses; rhyolitic volcanism; volcano tectonics, calderas and eruption cycles; geology of the Valles Mountains of New Mexico; geothermal resources; rare metals in igneous rocks; volcano hazards. *Mailing Add:* 10116 Lloyd Rd Potomac MD 20854

SMITH, ROBERT LEO, b Brookville, Pa, Mar 23, 25; m 52; c 4. WILDLIFE MANAGEMENT, ECOLOGY. *Educ:* Pa State Univ, BS, 49, MS, 54; Cornell Univ, PhD(wildlife mgt, ecol, soils), 56. *Prof Exp:* Instr agr, Jefferson County Bd Educ, Pa, 49-50; asst, Cornell Univ, 54-56; asst prof biol, State Univ NY Col Plattsburgh, 56-58; PROF WILDLIFE MGT, WVA UNIV, 58-, WILDLIFE BIOLOGIST, 74- *Concurrent Pos:* Mem task forces, Nat Res Coun, 81. *Mem:* Wildlife Soc; Ecol Soc Am; Cooper Ornith Soc; Am Soc Mammalogists; Am Ornithologists Union. *Res:* Habitat selection; structure of forest bird communities; ecology of highly disturbed lands; succession. *Mailing Add:* Div of Forestry WVa Univ Morgantown WV 26506

SMITH, ROBERT LEONARD, b New Orleans, La, Jan 19, 44; m 66; c 1. ANALYTICAL CHEMISTRY, INDUSTRIAL HYGIENE CHEMISTRY. *Educ:* La State Univ, New Orleans, BS, 65, PhD(chem), 70. *Prof Exp:* Res chemist, Res & Develop Lab, 70-77, environ chemist, 77-79, SUPVR, TOXICOL & INDUST HYGIENE LAB, ETHYL CORP, 79- *Mem:* Am Chem Soc; Am Soc Mass Spectrometry; Am Indust Hygiene Asn. *Res:* Absorption spectroscopy; photochemistry. *Mailing Add:* Toxicol & Indust Hygene Lab Ethyl Corp 8000 GSRI Ave Baton Rouge LA 70808

SMITH, ROBERT LEWIS, b Ranger, Tex, June 22, 38; m 60; c 4. BIOCHEMISTRY. *Educ:* Abilene Christian Col, BS, 61; Univ Tenn, Memphis, MS, 62, PhD(biochem), 66. *Prof Exp:* Vis lectr chem, Queens Col, NC, 62-63; res assoc protein chem & enzym, Biol Dept, Brookhaven Nat Lab, 66-68; asst prof biochem, 68-71, ASSOC PROF BIOCHEM, LA STATE UNIV, SHREVEPORT, 71- *Concurrent Pos:* Res chemist, Vet Admin Hosp, Shreveport, La, 69-77. *Mem:* Sigma Xi; Am Chem Soc. *Res:* Protein chemistry; enzymology; blood coagulation; membrane transport of amino acids and peptides. *Mailing Add:* Dept Biochem Sch Med La State Univ Box 33932 Shreveport LA 71130

SMITH, ROBERT LLOYD, b Chicago, Ill, Dec 10, 35; div; c 3. PHYSICAL OCEANOGRAPHY. *Educ:* Reed Col, BA, 57; Univ Ore, MA, 59; Ore State Univ, PhD(oceanog), 64. *Prof Exp:* From instr to assoc prof, 62-75, PROF PHYS OCEANOG, ORE STATE UNIV, 75- *Concurrent Pos:* NATO fel, Nat Inst Oceanog, Eng, 65-66; sci officer, Off Naval Res, 69-71; vis prof, Inst Meerekunde, Univ Kiel, Ger, 79. *Mem:* AAAS; Am Geophys Union; Am Soc Limnol & Oceanog; Am Meteorol Soc. *Res:* General physical oceanography, currents, upwelling, coastal oceanography, underwater sound. *Mailing Add:* Sch of Oceanog Ore State Univ Corvallis OR 97331

SMITH, ROBERT LLOYD, b Spirit Lake, Iowa, July 25, 41; m 74; c 1. ENTOMOLOGY, ZOOLOGY. *Educ:* NMex State Univ, BS, 68, MS, 71; Ariz State Univ, PhD(zool), 75. *Prof Exp:* Entomologist, USDA, Agr Res Serv, Western Cotton Res Lab, 75-77; res assoc, Dept Zool, Ariz State Univ, 77-78; ASST PROF, DEPT ENTOMOL, UNIV ARIZ, 77- *Concurrent Pos:* NSF grant, 77-80. *Mem:* AAAS; Am Inst Biol Sci; Am Soc Naturalists; Animal Behav Soc; Entomol Soc Am. *Res:* Insect behavior; evolutionary ecology; aquatic entomology; urban entomology. *Mailing Add:* Dept of Entomol Univ of Ariz Tucson AZ 85721

SMITH, ROBERT NELSON, b Long Beach, Calif, Sept 25, 16; m 38; c 3. PHYSICAL CHEMISTRY. *Educ:* Pomona Col, BA, 38; Stanford Univ, MA, 40, PhD(chem), 42. *Prof Exp:* Instr chem, Stanford Univ, 41-42, res chemist, Nat Defense Res Comt Proj, 42; instr chem, Mo Sch Mines, 42-44; res chemist, Manhattan Proj, Univ Chicago, 44 & E I du Pont de Nemours & Co, Wash, 44-45; from asst prof to assoc prof, 45-54, chmn dept, 53-72, PROF CHEM, POMONA COL, 54- *Concurrent Pos:* Guggenheim res fel, Bristol Univ, 51-52; Petrol Res Found fel, Cambridge & Bristol Univs, 58-59; mem adv comt grants, Res Corp, 61-68, fel, Univ Munich, 65-66; consult, Col Chem Consult Serv, 68-76; vis prof, Brandeis Univ, 72-73. *Honors & Awards:* Mfg Chem Asn Award, 61. *Mem:* Am Chem Soc; Royal Soc Chem. *Res:* Adsorption of gases on solids; kinetics of photochemical reactions; microanalytical methods of analysis; heterogeneous catalysis; hydrophobic interaction of small molecules with macromolecules. *Mailing Add:* Seaver Chem Lab Dept of Chem Pomona Col Claremont CA 91711

SMITH, ROBERT OWENS, b Elizabethton, Tenn, May 13, 37; m 61; c 2. EXPERIMENTAL SOLID STATE PHYSICS, ENVIRONMENTAL PHYSICS. *Educ:* Univ Colo, BS, 62; Rutgers Univ, MS, 64, PhD(physics), 69. *Prof Exp:* Mem tech staff explor develop, Bell Labs, 62-64; res fel solid state physics, Rutgers Univ, 64-69; PROF PHYSICS, MONMOUTH COL, 69-, CHMN DEPT, 74- *Mem:* Am Phys Soc; Am Asn Physics Teachers. *Res:* Solar energy conversion. *Mailing Add:* Dept of Physics Monmouth Col West Long Branch NJ 07764

SMITH, ROBERT PAUL, b St Lucas, Iowa, Sept 9, 42; m 69; c 2. MATHEMATICS, STATISTICS. *Educ:* Loras Col, BS, 64; Univ Ariz, MA, 66, PhD(math), 71. *Prof Exp:* ASST PROF MATH, ARK STATE UNIV, 69- *Mem:* Inst Math Statist. *Res:* Statistical inference and hypothesis testing for continuous time parameter stochastic processes. *Mailing Add:* Dept of Math Ark State Univ State University AR 72467

SMITH, ROBERT SEFTON, b Baltimore, Md, Aug 16, 41. MATHEMATICS. *Educ:* Morgan State Col, BS, 63; Pa State Univ, MA, 67, PhD(math), 69. *Prof Exp:* asst prof math, 69-77, ASSOC PROF MATH & STATIST, MIAMI UNIV, 77- *Mem:* Am Math Soc. *Res:* Groupoids; lattice theory. *Mailing Add:* Dept of Math Miami Univ Oxford OH 45056

SMITH, ROBERT VICTOR, b Brooklyn, NY, Feb 16, 42; m 66; c 2. PHARMACEUTICAL CHEMISTRY, ANALYTICAL CHEMISTRY. *Educ:* St John's Univ, NY, BS, 63; Univ Mich, Ann Arbor, MS, 64, PhD(pharmaceut chem), 68. *Prof Exp:* From asst prof to assoc prof med chem, Col Pharm, Univ Iowa, 68-74; assoc prof & asst dir, 77-78, assoc dir, 77-78, PROF, DRUG DYNAMICS INST, COL PHARM, UNIV TEX, AUSTIN, 77-, DIR, 78- *Concurrent Pos:* NIH award, 74, 76 & 79; mem rev comt, US Pharmacopoeia, 75-80. *Mem:* Am Chem Soc; fel Acad Pharmaceut Sci. *Res:* Drug metabolism; analysis of drugs alone and in dosage forms; analysis of drugs in biological fluids. *Mailing Add:* Drug Dynamics Inst Col Pharm Univ Tex Austin TX 78712

SMITH, ROBERT WILLIAM, b Ft Worth, Tex, Apr 14, 39; m 58; c 2. MICROBIOLOGY, BIOCHEMISTRY. *Educ:* N Tex State Univ, BA, 60; Okla State Univ, PhD(microbiol), 65. *Prof Exp:* Fel, 64-65, res assoc, 65-67, asst prof microbiol, 67-74, EXEC OFFICER, DEPT BIOL SCI, PURDUE UNIV, WEST LAFAYETTE, 74- *Mem:* Am Soc Microbiol. *Res:* Microbial physiology; structure genetics; protein chemistry; nature of self-associating protein systems; thermophily. *Mailing Add:* Dept Biol Sci Purdue Univ West Lafayette IN 47907

SMITH, ROBERT WILLIAM, b Chelsea, Mass, Mar 21, 43; m 68; c 1. ECOLOGY, STATISTICS. *Educ:* Univ Calif, Berkeley, BA, 65; Univ Wash, BS, 69; Univ Southern Calif, PhD(biol), 76. *Prof Exp:* Instr ecol, Univ Southern Calif, 76-77; CONSULTS DATA ANAL, SOUTHERN CALIF EDISON, SCI APPL, INC, WOODWARD-CLYDE CONSULTS, INC, HARBORS ENVIRON PROJ, INST MARINE & COASTAL STUDIES, UNIV SOUTHERN CALIF, LA CO SANITATION DIST, 77- & LOCKHEED AIRCRAFT SERV, MARINE BIOL CONSULTS, 78- *Mem:*

AAAS; Am Soc Naturalists; Ecol Soc Am; Am Statist Asn. *Res:* Development of analytical techniques for ecological-survey data; development of computer software for data analysis. *Mailing Add:* 1151 Avila Dr Ojai CA 93023

SMITH, ROBERTA HAWKINS, b Tulare, Calif, May 3, 45; m 69. PLANT PHYSIOLOGY, PLANT SCIENCE. *Educ:* Univ Calif, Riverside, BA, 67, MS, 68, PhD(plant sci & physiol), 70. *Prof Exp:* Asst prof biol, Sam Houston State Univ, 73-74; asst prof, 74-80, ASSOC PROF PLANT SCI, TEX A&M UNIV, 80- *Mem:* Am Soc Plant Physiol; Am Soc Bot; Am Soc Plant Physiol; Int Asn Plant Tissue Cult; Tissue Cult Asn. *Res:* Plant morphology; plant tissue culture; crop improvement. *Mailing Add:* Dept of Plant Sci Tex A&M Univ College Station TX 77843

SMITH, ROBERTS ANGUS, b Vancouver, BC, Dec 22, 28; nat US; m 53; c 4. BIOCHEMISTRY. *Educ:* Univ BC, BSA, 52, MSc, 53; Univ Ill, PhD(biochem), 57. *Prof Exp:* Instr chem, Univ Ill, 57-58; from asst prof to assoc prof, 58-68, PROF CHEM, UNIV CALIF, LOS ANGELES, 68- *Concurrent Pos:* Dir, ICN Pharmaceut Inc, 61-; Guggenheim fel, Cambridge Univ, 63; pres, VIRATEK Inc, 80- *Mem:* Am Chem Soc; Am Soc Biol Chemists; Brit Biochem Soc. *Res:* Biological phosphoryl transfer reactions; chromosomal protein modification. *Mailing Add:* Dept Chem Univ Calif Los Angeles CA 90024

SMITH, RODERICK MACDOWELL, b Boston, Mass, Mar 15, 44; m 66; c 3. FISHERIES. *Educ:* Earlham Col, BA, 65; Univ Mass, MS, 69, PhD(fisheries), 72. *Prof Exp:* Consult, Mass Div Fisheries & Game, 71; asst prof marine sci, Stockton State Col, 71-74; asst prof zool, 74-81, ADJ ASST PROF ZOOL, UNIV NH, 81- *Concurrent Pos:* Mem, Acad Adv Coun Study Comn, 73; consult biologist, Wetlands Inst, Lehigh Univ, 73-74. *Mem:* Am Fisheries Soc. *Res:* The reestablishing of anadromous fish runs in New England coastal plain rivers, including Pacific salmon introductions; biocide effects on larval marine fishes. *Mailing Add:* Dept of Zool Spaulding Bldg Univ of NH Durham NH 03824

SMITH, RODGER CHAPMAN, b South Hadley, Mass, July 18, 15; m 40; c 3. INORGANIC CHEMISTRY. *Educ:* Univ Mass, BS, 38. *Prof Exp:* Asst head fertilizer res, Eastern States Farmers' Exchange, Inc, 46-54, head fertilizer res, 55-62; mgr agr technol serv, Southwest Potash Corp, NY, 62-66, mgr mkt develop, 66-71; DIR MKT DEVELOP, AMAX CHEM CORP, 71- *Mem:* Am Chem Soc; Am Soc Hort Sci; Am Inst Chemists; Am Soc Agron. *Res:* Administration of market development for potash, phosphate rock and heavy chemicals in the United States and other countries; coordination with industry and governmental agencies; processes for mixed fertilizer granulation. *Mailing Add:* Amax Chem Corp 35 Mason St Greenwich CT 06830

SMITH, ROGER ALAN, b Pomona, Calif, July 16, 47; m 69; c 1. THEORETICAL PHYSICS. *Educ:* Oberlin Col, BA, 68; Stanford Univ, MS, 69, PhD(physics), 73. *Prof Exp:* Res assoc physics, Univ Ill, Urbana-Champaign, 73-75; Res assoc physics, State Univ NY Stony Brook, 75-77, lectr, Inst Theoret Physics, 77-79, res assoc physics, 79-81; ASST PROF PHYSICS, TEXAS A&M UNIV, 81- *Mem:* Am Phys Soc. *Res:* Properties of the nucleon-nucleon interaction; techniques for many-body calculations; structure of neutron stars. *Mailing Add:* Dept of Physics Texas A&M Univ College Station TX 77843

SMITH, ROGER BRUCE, b New Bethlehem, Pa, Sept 12, 47; m 67; c 3. TOXICOLOGY. *Educ:* Philadelphia Col Pharm & Sci, BS, 70, MS, 73, PhD(pharmacol), 79. *Prof Exp:* Res scientist, 77-79, sr scientist, 79-82, PRIN SCIENTIST, MCNEIL PHARMACEUT, JOHNSON & JOHNSON, 82- *Mem:* Am Col Toxicol; Mid-Atlantic Soc Toxicol; Sigma Xi. *Res:* Elucidation of mechanisms of drug toxicity to develop antidotes or supportive techniques for clinical overdosage; assessing appropriateness of existing animal models for toxicity studies and establishing reliable new predictive models where routine systems have failed. *Mailing Add:* Toxicol Res Unit McNeil Pharmaceut McKean Rd Spring House PA 19477

SMITH, ROGER DEAN, b New York, NY, Oct 6, 32; m 57; c 4. PATHOLOGY, VIROLOGY. *Educ:* Cornell Univ, AB, 54; NY Med Col, MD, 58. *Prof Exp:* Resident surg, Detroit Receiving Hosp, Mich, 59-60; instr path, Col Med, Univ Ill, Chicago, 62-66, from asst prof to assoc prof, 66-72, asst dean col med, 70-72; PROF PATH & DIR DEPT, UNIV CINCINNATI, 72- *Concurrent Pos:* USPHS grant, 62-65; Nat Cancer Inst spec fel, 65-66; resident, Presby-St Luke's Hosp, Chicago, 62-66, consult; co-investr, Ill Div, Am Cancer Soc grant, 65-66; asst attend pathologist, Res & Educ Hosp, 66-; consult, Vet Admin Hosp, Chicago; prin investr, NIH grants, 67-72 & 76-79. *Mem:* Int Acad Path; Am Asn Path; Soc Exp Biol & Med; Am Soc Nephrology; Am Soc Clin Path . *Res:* Virus pathology and virus-cell relationships; renal and virus pathology; experimental renal disease; persistent virus infections and possible relation to glomerulonephritis. *Mailing Add:* Dept of Path Univ of Cincinnati Col of Med Cincinnati OH 45229

SMITH, ROGER ELTON, b Stillwater, Okla, Apr 16, 41. CIVIL ENGINEERING, HYDROLOGY. *Educ:* Tex Tech Univ, BSc, 63; Stanford Univ, MSc, 64; Colo State Univ, PhD(civil eng), 70. *Prof Exp:* Design engr, Metcalf & Eddy Engrs, Calif, 64-65; engr, Peace Corps, Pakistan, 65-67; res hydraul engr, Southwest Watershed Res Ctr, Agr Res Serv, 70-76, RES HYDRAULIC ENGR, FED RES, SCI EDUC ADMIN, USDA, 76- *Mem:* Am Soc Civil Engrs; Am Geophys Union. *Res:* Soil infiltration from rainfall; watershed response in relation to physical features; stochastic rainfall models; hydraulics of alluvial streams, including measuring techniques and unsteady flow phenomena. *Mailing Add:* Feg Bldg 301 S Howes PO Box E Ft Collins CO 80521

SMITH / 833

SMITH, ROGER FRANCIS COOPER, b Kapunda, South Australia, Mar 6, 40; m 73. ZOOLOGY, ECOLOGY. *Educ:* Univ Adelaide, BSc, 62; Australian Nat Univ, MSc, 66; Univ Alta, PhD(zool), 73. *Prof Exp:* Exp officer, Commonwealth Sci & Insust Res Orgn, Div Wildlife Res, 63-64; res asst physiol, Dept Zool, Australian Nat Univ, 66, res assoc, Dept Zool, Univ Alta, 72-73; asst prof, 73-79, ASSOC PROF, DEPT ZOOL, BRANDON UNIV, 79- *Mem:* Brit Ecol Soc; Australian & NZ AAS; Wildlife Soc; Can Soc Zoologists; Am Mammal Soc. *Mailing Add:* Dept of Zool Brandon Univ Brandon MB R7A 6A9 Can

SMITH, ROGER M, b Winnipeg, Man, Sept 12, 18; m 47; c 4. RESEARCH ADMINISTRATION. *Educ:* Univ Man, BSc, 40. *Prof Exp:* Sr supvr reactor opers, Chalk River Nuclear Labs, Atomic Energy Can Ltd, 46-52, supt prod planning & control, 53-58; dir div safeguards, Int Atomic Energy Agency, 58-60; MGR ADMIN DIV, WHITESHELL NUCLEAR RES ESTAB & SAFEGUARDS COORDR, ATOMIC ENERGY CAN LTD, 60- *Mem:* Can Asn Physicists; Inst Nuclear Mat Mgt. *Res:* Technical administration and planning; development of safeguard techniques. *Mailing Add:* Whiteshell Nuclear Res Estab Pinawa MB R0E 1L0 Can

SMITH, ROGER POWELL, b Hokuchin, Korea, July 16, 32; US citizen; m 56; c 3. TOXICOLOGY. *Educ:* Purdue Univ, BS, 53, MS, 55, PhD(pharmaceut chem), 57. *Prof Exp:* From instr to assoc prof, 60-73, PROF TOXICOL, DARTMOUTH MED SCH, 73-, CHMN DEPT PHARMACOL & TOXICOL, 76- *Concurrent Pos:* Consult, Vet Admin Ctr, White River Junction, Vt, 65-; assoc staff mem, Mary Hitchcock Mem Hosp, 68-; mem toxicol study sect, NIH, 68-72; assoc ed, Toxicol & Appl Pharmacol, 72-78; mem pharmacol toxicol prog comt, Nat Inst Gen Med Sci, 72-79; mem comt med & biol effects environ pollutants, Div Med Sci, Nat Res Coun, 75-77; adj prof, Vt Law Sch, 81- *Mem:* Fel AAAS; Soc Exp Biol & Med; Soc Toxicol; Am Soc Pharmacol & Exp Therapeut; Sigma Xi. *Res:* Experimental toxicology; red cell metabolism; vasodilator drugs; abnormal blood pigments. *Mailing Add:* Dept of Pharmacol & Toxicol Dartmouth Med Sch Hanover NH 03755

SMITH, ROGER STANLEY, b London, Eng, Sept 21, 32; Can citizen; m 54; c 2. WOOD PRODUCTS. *Educ:* Univ London, Eng, BSc Hons, 57, PhD(plant pathol), 60; Imp Col Sci & Technol, London, DIC, 60. *Prof Exp:* Res scientist, Forest Prod Res Lab, 60-64; SECT HEAD, WOOD PROTECTION, WESTERN FOREST PROD LAB, CAN, 64- *Mem:* Brit Mycol Soc; Mycol Soc Am; Am Wood Preservers Asn; Int Res Group Wood Preservation; Can Stand Asn. *Res:* Biodeterioration and protection of wood products; preservation methods; techniques; standards; biology of wood-destroying fungi and wood inhabiting microorganisms. *Mailing Add:* Western Forest Products Ltd 1111 W Georgia Vancouver BC V6E 3G7 Can

SMITH, ROLAND F, b Kittery, Maine, June 27, 21; m 47; c 2. ZOOLOGY. *Educ:* Univ NH, BS, 43, MS, 47; Rutgers Univ, PhD(zool), 60. *Prof Exp:* From fishery biologist to prin fishery biologist, NJ Div Fish & Game, 51-60, asst chief bur fisheries mgt, 60-63; asst chief br marine fisheries, Div Biol Res, Bur Commercial Fisheries, US Fish & Wildlife Serv, US Dept Interior, 63-64; chief br shell fisheries, 64-66; asst dir biol res, 66-69, asst dir marine resources, 69-77; actg dir, 78-81, DEP DIR, OFF RESOURCE CONSERV MGT, NAT MARINE FISHERIES SERV, NAT OCEANIC & ATMOSPHERIC ADMIN, 81-, CHIEF, OFF LIVING RESOURCES, OFF MARINE RESOURCES, 77-; ACTG DIR RESOURCE CONSERV & MGT, NAT MARINE FISHERIES SERV, 78- *Concurrent Pos:* NSF lectr, High Sch Sci Teachers, Glassboro State Col, 62; consult, Ga Game & Fish Comn Rev State Marine Sport & Commercial Fisheries Progs, 63; mem, Gov Comt Power Plants & Environ for Chesapeake Bay, Md, 70-; mem resolutions comt, Food & Agr Orgn Tech Conf Marine Pollution, Rome, Italy, 70; deleg, Int Conf & Negotiations, Int Whaling Comn, 72, UNESCO Conf Man & Biosphere, 74 & FAO Conf on Aquacult, 76. *Mem:* Am Fisheries Soc. *Res:* Fishery biology, especially estuarine fisheries. *Mailing Add:* Nat Marine Fisheries Serv Nat Oceanic & Atmospheric Admin Rockville MD 20852

SMITH, RONALD DUANE, b Washington, Ill, July 5, 43; m 69; c 2. PHARMACOLOGY. *Educ:* St Louis Col Pharm, BS, 66; Univ Tenn, MS, 68, PhD(pharmacol), 71. *Prof Exp:* NIH fel pharmacol, Div Cardiol, Univ NC, 71-72, res assoc, Biol Sci Res Ctr, 72-73; res assoc, Parke Davis & Co, 73-80; WITH CARDIOVASC SEC, REVLON HEALTH CARE GROUP, 80- *Mem:* Am Soc Pharmacol & Exp Therapeuts. *Res:* The physiology and pharmacology of the cardiovascular system in man and animals; specifically the physiology and pharmacology of hypertension, models of experimental hypertension and anti-hypertensive drugs. *Mailing Add:* Cardiovasc Sec Revlon Health Care Group Tuckahoe NY 10707

SMITH, RONALD E, b Beeville, Tex, Mar 30, 36; m 57; c 3. PHYSICS. *Educ:* Tex A&M Univ, BS, 58, MS, 59, PhD(physics), 66. *Prof Exp:* Instr physics, Tex A&M Univ, 60-66; assoc prof, 66-70, PROF PHYSICS, NORTHEAST LA UNIV, 70-, HEAD DEPT, 77- *Mem:* Am Phys Soc; Am Asn Physics Teachers. *Res:* Nuclear magnetic resonance; electron spin resonance; solid state. *Mailing Add:* Dept of Physics Northeast La Univ Monroe LA 71209

SMITH, RONALD EARL, vertebrate zoology, see previous edition

SMITH, RONALD GENE, b Woodland, Wash, Jan 24, 44; m 70; c 2. ORGANIC CHEMISTRY, ANALYTICAL PHARMACOLOGY. *Educ:* Whitworth Col, BS, 66; Purdue Univ, PhD(org chem), 72. *Prof Exp:* Res assoc org chem, Ore Grad Ctr, 72-74, instr, 74-77; asst prof org chem, 77-80, ASSOC PROF ORG CHEM, UNIV TEX M D ANDERSON HOSP & TUMOR INST, HOUSTON, 80- *Concurrent Pos:* Asst prof, Grad Sch Biomed Sci, Univ Tex Health Sci Ctr, 78-80, fac mem, 80- *Mem:* Am Asn Cancer Res; Am Chem Soc; Am Soc Mass Spectrometry. *Res:* Application of mass spectrometry to the pharmacology of antitumor agents; identification of drug metabolites; pharmacokinetics; mechanism of drug action. *Mailing Add:* Dept of Develop Therapeut M D Anderson Hosp & Tumor Inst Houston TX 77030

SMITH, RONALD W, b June 15, 36; m 60; c 3. PHYSICAL CHEMISTRY, CHEMICAL ENGINEERING. *Educ:* Pa State Univ, BS, 58; Univ Del, PhD, 65. *Prof Exp:* Res chemist, Hercules, Inc, 64-69, tech develop rep, 69-70, develop supvr, 70-72, tech mgr, 72-75; asst gen mgr, Haveg Industs, Inc, 75-80; PROD MGR, HERCULES INC, 81- *Mem:* Am Chem Soc; Am Inst Chem Engrs. *Res:* Surface chemistry; environmental science, pollution control. *Mailing Add:* 27D Walnut Hill Rd Hockessin DE 19707

SMITH, ROSE MARIE, b Beaumont, Tex, Mar 3, 34; m 55; c 3. MATHEMATICS. *Educ:* Lamar Univ, BS, 55; Tex Woman's Univ, MA, 68; Okla State Univ, EdD, 75. *Prof Exp:* Teacher math & music, Grapevine Pub Schs, Grapevine, Tex, 55-66; PROF MATH, TEX WOMAN'S UNIV, 66- *Mem:* Nat Coun Teachers Math; Math Asn Am. *Res:* Mathematical education. *Mailing Add:* Dept of Math & Physics Tex Woman's Univ Denton TX 76204

SMITH, ROSS W, b Turlock, Calif, Dec 11, 27; m 55; c 3. MINERAL ENGINEERING, SURFACE CHEMISTRY. *Educ:* Univ Nev, BS, 50; Mass Inst Technol, SM, 55; Stanford Univ, PhD(mineral eng), 69. *Prof Exp:* Jr mining engr, Consol Coppermines Corp, Nev, 50; res asst metall, Mass Inst Technol, 53-55; assoc mfg process engr, Portland Cement Asn, 55-57; proj engr, Res Found, Colo Sch Mines, 58-60; assoc prof metall, SDak Sch Mines & Technol, 60-66; actg instr mineral eng, Stanford Univ, 66-68; assoc prof metall, 68-69, PROF METALL & CHMN DEPT CHEM & METALL ENG, UNIV NEV, RENO, 69- *Concurrent Pos:* Dept Health, Educ & Welfare grant, 64-66. *Mem:* Am Inst Mining, Metall & Petrol Engrs; Am Chem Soc; Am Inst Chem Engrs. *Res:* Comminution; pipeline flow of liquid-solid slurries; flotation; surface chemistry. *Mailing Add:* Dept of Chem & Metall Eng Univ of Nev Reno NV 89557

SMITH, ROY E, b Chippewa Falls, Wis, Apr 28, 26; m 47; c 3. SCIENCE EDUCATION, PHYSICS. *Educ:* Wis State Univ-Eau Claire, BS, 50; Univ Wis, MS, 57; Ohio State Univ, PhD(sci educ), 66. *Prof Exp:* Jr high sch teacher, Ill, 50-51; pub sch teacher, Wis, 51-56; from asst prof to assoc prof, 57-65, PROF PHYSICS & HEAD DEPT, UNIV WIS-PLATTEVILLE, 66- *Concurrent Pos:* Consult, Wis Mold & Tool Co, 57-63. *Mem:* Am Asn Physics Teachers; Nat Sci Teachers Asn. *Res:* Use of unit operators and dimensional methods as a vehicle for teaching fundamental quantitative physical science. *Mailing Add:* Dept of Physics Univ of Wis Platteville WI 53818

SMITH, ROY JEFFERSON, JR, b Covington, La, Nov 25, 29; m 52; c 2. WEED SCIENCE. *Educ:* Miss State Univ, BS, 51, MS, 52; Univ Ill, PhD(weed sci), 55. *Prof Exp:* RES AGRONOMIST WEED SCI, AGR RES SERV, USDA, 55- *Concurrent Pos:* Mem grad staff, Univ Ark, 55-; adv, Rockefeller Found, Int Rice Res Inst, Philippines, 64; adv, Inst Tech Interchange, East-West Ctr, 67-69; coop scientist, US Dept Army, 68-70; coop scientist for pest mgt proj in Pakistan & for biol control weeds with Univ Ark, USDA, 73-; res award, Ark Asn Coop Exten Specialist, 81. *Mem:* Weed Sci Soc Am; Int Weed Sci Soc; Sigma Xi; Rice Tech Working Group. *Res:* Biology and interference of weeds in agronomic crops; integrated weed management systems for rice and potato crops; biological control of weed with plant pathogens. *Mailing Add:* Rice Res & Exten Ctr USDA Agr Res Serv Stuttgart AR 72160

SMITH, ROY MARTIN, b Alamo, Tenn, Oct 21, 27; m 48; c 2. DENTISTRY, ORAL PATHOLOGY. *Educ:* Univ Tenn, DDS, 51, MS, 63. *Prof Exp:* Pvt pract, 53-58; asst prof oral med & surg, 58-62, assoc prof oral diag & chmn dept, 62-64, PROF ORAL DIAG, COL DENT, UNIV TENN, MEMPHIS, 64-, ASSOC PROF PATH, 63- *Concurrent Pos:* Consult, Vet Admin Hosp, Memphis, Tenn. *Mem:* Am Dent Asn; Am Acad Oral Path; Am Col Dent. *Res:* Transplantation of intraoral tissues; oral carcinogenesis; pharmacologic effects of eugenol. *Mailing Add:* Dept of Oral Diag Univ of Tenn Memphis TN 38103

SMITH, RUFUS ALBERT, JR, b Shreveport, La, Jan 29, 32; m 60; c 2. HORTICULTURE. *Educ:* La State Univ, BS, 56, MS, 58; Wash State Univ, PhD(hort), 67. *Prof Exp:* Instr hort, Western Ill Univ, 61-63; asst prof, Ore State Univ, 67-73; assoc prof, 73-79, PROF HORT, UNIV TENN, MARTIN, 81- *Mem:* Am Soc Hort Sci; Am Hort Soc. *Mailing Add:* Sch of Agr Univ of Tenn Martin TN 38238

SMITH, RUSSELL AUBREY, b Little Rock, Ark, June 8, 36; m 60; c 3. MECHANICAL ENGINEERING, MOTOR VEHICLE SAFETY. *Educ:* Rice Univ, BA & BSME, 58; Cath Univ Am, MME, 64, PhD(mech eng), 69. *Prof Exp:* Mem fac, Mech Eng Dept, Cath Univ Am, 66-76, chmn dept, 73-76; head advan technol, Accident Invest Div, 76-80, DIR, NAT ACCIDENT SAMPLING SYST, NAT HWY TRAFFIC SAFETY ADMIN, 80- *Concurrent Pos:* Adj prof, Cath Univ Am, 78- *Mem:* Am Soc Mech Engrs; Am Inst Aeronaut & Astronaut; Soc Automotive Engrs. *Res:* Engineering mechanics; vehicle collision mechanics. *Mailing Add:* Accident Invest Div Nat Hwy Traffic Safety Admin Washington DC 20590

SMITH, S(HALER) GORDON, JR, b Rockford, Ill, Dec 1, 23; m 53; c 1. POLYMER CHEMISTRY, INFORMATION SCIENCE. *Educ:* Mass Inst Technol, SB, 45; Lehigh Univ, MS, 49; Univ Ill, PhD(chem), 55. *Prof Exp:* Res chemist, Ill Water Treatment Co, 46-47; asst synthetic org chem, Nat Lead Co, Lehigh, 47-49; asst org chem, Univ Ill, 49-51 & 53-54; RES ASSOC, E I DU PONT DE NEMOURS & CO, INC, 54- *Mem:* Am Chem Soc. *Res:* Polymeric coating materials; organic chemistry. *Mailing Add:* E I du Pont de Nemours & Co Inc PO Box 3886 Philadelphia PA 19146

SMITH, SAM CORRY, b Enid, Okla, July 3, 22; m 45; c 3. NUTRITION. *Educ:* Univ Okla, BS, 47, MS, 48; Univ Wis, PhD(biochem), 51. *Prof Exp:* Spec instr chem, Univ Okla, 47-48, asst prof biochem, Sch Med, 51-54, assoc prof, 54-55; secy, Williams-Waterman Fund, Res Corp, NY, 55-67, assoc dir grants, 57-65, dir, 65-68, chmn, Williams-Waterman Prog Comt & chmn adv comt grants, 67-75, vpres grants, 68-75; EXEC DIR, M J MURDOCK CHARITABLE TRUST, 75- *Concurrent Pos:* Pub trustee, Nutrit Found, 76-;

mem bd councilors, Sch Med, Univ Southern Calif, 77- *Mem:* AAAS; Am Chem Soc; Am Inst Biol Sci; Am Inst Nutrit. *Res:* Human nutrition; amino acid and vitamin metabolism; international nutrition. *Mailing Add:* M J Murdock Charitable Trust PO Box 1618 Vancouver WA 98668

SMITH, SAMUEL, b Bronx, NY, Sept 13, 27; m 51; c 5. POLYMER CHEMISTRY. *Educ:* City Col New York, BS, 48; Univ Mich, MS, 49. *Prof Exp:* Chemist, Inst Paper Chem, 49-51; sr chemist, Cent Res, 51-57, sr chemist, Chem Div, 57-61, supvr polymer res, 61-67, res assoc, 67-75, CORP SCIENTIST, CENT RES LABS, MINN MINING & MFG CO, 75- *Honors & Awards:* Henry Millson Award, 80. *Mem:* AAAS; Am Chem Soc; Am Asn Textile Chemists & Colorists. *Res:* Ring-opening polymerization; elastomeric resins; surface chemistry relating to adhesion and desorption processes; fluorochemical polymers and textile finishes. *Mailing Add:* Cent Res Labs Minn Mining & Mfg Co St Paul MN 55144

SMITH, SAMUEL COOPER, b Lock Haven, Pa, Sept 21, 34; m 55; c 2. BIOCHEMISTRY. *Educ:* Pa State Univ, BS, 55, MS, 59, PhD(biochem), 62. *Prof Exp:* From asst prof to assoc prof, 61-74, PROF ANIMAL SCI & BIOCHEM, UNIV NH, 74- *Mem:* AAAS; Am Chem Soc; Am Oil Chem Soc. *Res:* Lipid biochemistry in tissue culture systems. *Mailing Add:* Animal Sci 407 Kendall Hall Univ of NH Durham NH 03824

SMITH, SAMUEL H, b Salinas, Calif, Feb 4, 40; m 60; c 2. PLANT PATHOLOGY, PLANT VIROLOGY. *Educ:* Univ Calif, Berkeley, BS, 61, PhD(plant path), 64. *Prof Exp:* NATO fel plant path, Glasshouse Crops Res Inst, Eng, 64-65; asst prof, Univ Calif, Berkeley, 65-69; assoc prof, Fruit Res Lab, 69-71 & Buckhout Lab, 71-74, head dept, 76-81, PROF PLANT PATH, BUCKOUT LAB, PA STATE UNIV, UNIVERSITY PARK, 74-, HEAD DEPT, 76-, DEAN, COL AGR & DIR PA AGR EXP STA & PA COOP EXTEN SERV, 81- *Mem:* Am Phytopath Soc; Brit Asn Appl Biol. *Mailing Add:* Dept Plant Path Pa State Univ University Park PA 16802

SMITH, SELWYN MICHAEL, b Sydney, Australia, Aug 12, 42; Can citizen; c 2. FORENSIC PSYCHIATRY. *Educ:* Sydney Univ, MB & BS, 66; London Univ, DPM, 69; Birmingham Med Inst, Eng, MD, 74; Royal Col Physicians & Surgeons, Can, FRCP (C), 76; Royal Col Psychiatrists, FRCP, 80. *Prof Exp:* House physician & house surgeon, Sydney Hosp, 67; registrar psychiat, All Saints Hosp, Birmingham, Eng, 68-70; hon res fel psychiat, United Birmingham Hosp, 70-72, hon sr registrar, 71-75; dir forensic psychiat, Royal Ottawa Hosp, 75-80; PROF PSYCHIAT, UNIV OTTAWA, 80- *Concurrent Pos:* Consult psychiat, Ottawa Gen Hosp & Brockville Hosp, 76-; vis prof, Dept Psychol, Carleton Univ, 77-; chmn, Forensic Serv Comt, Region Ottawa-Carleton & Eastern Ont, 77-; mem, Task Force, Acceptable Lead Levels in Blood, Fed/Provincial Sub-comt Environ Health, Health & Welfare, Can, 77-, Secure Serv Adv Comt Adolescent Serv, Ont Ministry Community & Social Serv, 80-, Sci Prog Comt, Second World Congress Prison Health Care, Fed Govt Can, 81-; psychiatrist-in-chief, Royal Ottawa Hosp, 78- *Honors & Awards:* Cloake Medal, Birmingham Med Inst, Eng, 73; Bronze Medal, Royal Col Psychiatrists, 74. *Mem:* Royal Col Psychiatrists; Am Acad Psychiat & Law; Am Col Psychiatrists; Can Psychiat Asn; Can Asn Treatment Offenders. *Res:* Child abuse; forensic and legal issues. *Mailing Add:* 1145 Carling Ave Ottawa ON K1Z 7K4 Can

SMITH, SHARON LOUISE, b Denver, Colo, June 14, 45. OCEANOGRAPHY. *Educ:* Colo Col, BA, 67; Univ Auckland, NZ, MSc, 69; Duke Univ, PhD(zool), 75. *Prof Exp:* Biologist, Raytheon Corp, 69-71; fel, Dalhousie Univ, 75-78; asst oceanographer, 78-81, ASSOC OCEANOGRAPHER, BROOKHAVEN NAT LAB, 81- *Concurrent Pos:* Adj asst prof, State Univ NY, Stony Brook, 79-, Univ Wash, 80- *Mem:* AAAS; Am Soc Limnol & Oceanog. *Mailing Add:* Brookhaven Nat Lab Bldg 318 Upton NY 11973

SMITH, SHARRON WILLIAMS, b Ashland, Ky, Apr 3, 41; m 64; c 2. BIOCHEMISTRY. *Educ:* Transylvania Col, BA, 63; Univ Ky, PhD(biochem), 74. *Prof Exp:* Chemist, Charles Pfizer Pharmaceut Co, 63 & Procter & Gamble, 63-64; teacher sci, Lexington Pub Schs, Ky, 64-67; chemist biol membranes, Lab Cell Biol, Nat Heart & Lung Inst, 74-75; ASST PROF CHEM, HOOD COL, 75- *Mem:* AAAS. *Res:* Membrane biochemistry, proteins, phospholipids, phosphonoglycans. *Mailing Add:* Dept of Chem Hood Col Frederick MD 21702

SMITH, SHELBY DEAN, b Macomb, Ill, Nov 25, 23; m 45; c 2. MATHEMATICS. *Educ:* Western Ill Univ, BS & MS, 50; Univ Ill, PhD, 66. *Prof Exp:* High sch teacher, Ill, 50-54; from asst prof to assoc prof, 56-70, PROF MATH SCI, BALL STATE UNIV, 70- *Res:* Mathematics education. *Mailing Add:* Dept of Math Lab Sch Ball State Univ Muncie IN 47306

SMITH, SIDNEY R, JR, b New Orleans, La, Oct 5, 35; m 58; c 4. ZOOLOGY, BIOCHEMISTRY. *Educ:* Univ Conn, BA, 57; Howard Univ, MS, 59, PhD, 63. *Prof Exp:* Fel endocrinol, Univ Wis, 63-64; asst prof biol, Morehouse Col, 64-66; NIH fel biochem, Univ Conn, 66-68; sr res scientist, 68-71; head sect immunol, 71-73, SR RES SCIENTIST, SCHERING CORP, 73- *Mem:* AAAS; Am Asn Immunol; Am Inst Chem; NY Acad Sci. *Res:* Embryology; endocrinology; immunology. *Mailing Add:* Schering Corp 60 Orange St Bloomfield NJ 07003

SMITH, SIDNEY RUVEN, b Hamilton, Ont, Aug 25, 20; m 53; c 6. PHYSICAL CHEMISTRY. *Educ:* McMaster Univ, BSc, 42, MSc, 43; Ohio State Univ, PhD(phys chem), 52. *Prof Exp:* Jr res chemist, Nat Res Coun Can, 43-46; phys chemist, US Naval Ord Test Sta, Calif, 52-60; from asst prof to assoc prof, 60-74, PROF CHEM, UNIV CONN, 74- *Mem:* Am Chem Soc; Am Phys Soc. *Res:* Mass spectrometry; kinetics; stable isotopes. *Mailing Add:* 31 Lynwood Rd Storrs CT 06268

SMITH, SPENCER B, b Ottawa, Ont, Jan 31, 27; m 54. OPERATIONS RESEARCH. *Educ:* McGill Univ, BE, 49; Columbia Univ, MS, 50, EngScD(indust eng), 58. *Prof Exp:* Instr indust eng, Columbia Univ, 50-58; admin engr, Mergenthaler Linotype Co, 53-58; mgr opers res, Semiconductor Div, Raytheon Co, 58-61 & Montgomery Ward & Co, 61-66; assoc prof, 66-71, chmn grad comt, 66-77, actg chmn dept indust eng, 70-71, prof & chmn dept indust eng, 71-77, PROF MGT SCI & DIR OFF RES OF STUART SCH MGT & FINANCE, ILL INST TECHNOL, 77- *Concurrent Pos:* Consult, UN, 57, Chicago Mercantile Exchange, 74 & Inst Gas Technol, 76; Harris Trust & Savings Bank res grant, 68-70; Ill Law Enforcement Comn res grant, 72-73; res grant, Am Prod & Inventory Control Soc, 80; res grant, US Army Corps Engrs, 81. *Mem:* Am Inst Indust Engrs; Am Statist Asn; Am Soc Mech Engrs; Opers Res Soc Am; Inst Mgt Sci. *Res:* Mathematical programming; inventory theory; forecasting; production planning; simulation; information systems; law enforcement; planning of energy production and distribution systems. *Mailing Add:* Dept of Mgt Sci Ill Inst of Technol Chicago IL 60616

SMITH, SPURGEON EUGENE, b San Marcos, Tex, July 17, 25; m 48; c 2. TOPOLOGY. *Prof Exp:* Southwest Tex State Col, BS, 46. *Prof Exp:* Res mathematician, Defense Res Lab, Tex, 51-57; vpres & dir res, Textran Corp, 57-62; prin scientist & dir, 62-69, VPRES & DIR ADVAN RES SCI & SYSTS GROUP, TRACOR INC, 69- *Mem:* Am Math Soc; Acoust Soc Am. *Res:* Functions of a complex variable; probability; decision theory; complex group decision maps. *Mailing Add:* 1305 Bradwood Rd Austin TX 78722

SMITH, STAMFORD DENNIS, b San Jose, Calif, Feb 27, 39; m 63; c 2. ENTOMOLOGY, HYDROBIOLOGY. *Educ:* San Jose State Col, BA, 61; Univ Idaho, MA, 64; PhD(entom), 67. *Prof Exp:* Asst prof biol, Kans State Col Pittsburg, 66-68; asst prof, 68-72, assoc prof, 72-80, PROF BIOL, CENT WASH UNIV, 80- *Mem:* Entom Soc Am; Soc Syst Zool. *Res:* Ecology and systematics of Trichoptera; biology of aquatic insects. *Mailing Add:* Dept Biol Sci Cent Wash Univ Ellensburg WA 98926

SMITH, STANFORD HENRY, b Twin Falls, Idaho, June 25, 20; m 42; c 2. FISH BIOLOGY. *Educ:* Ore State Col, BS, 43; Univ Mich, AM, 51, PhD(zool), 54. *Prof Exp:* Aquatic biologist, US Fish & Wildlife Serv, 44-49, fishery res biologist, 49-67, sr investr, 67-71, sr scientist, 72; fishery res biologist, Nat Marine Fisheries Serv, 72-77. *Concurrent Pos:* Res assoc, Univ Mich, Ann Arbor, 68-71, adj prof, Sch Natural Resources, 72- *Mem:* Am Fisheries Soc; Am Inst Fishery Res Biol; Int Asn Gt Lakes. *Res:* Coregonids of northeast America; fishery ecology of the Great Lakes. *Mailing Add:* 924 Northwood St Ann Arbor MI 48103

SMITH, STANFORD LEE, b Detroit, Mich, June 3, 35; m 58, 77; c 2. ORGANIC CHEMISTRY. *Educ:* Albion Col, BA, 57; Iowa State Univ, PhD(org chem), 61. *Prof Exp:* Res assoc & instr chem, Iowa State Univ, 61-62; asst prof, 62-68, ASSOC PROF CHEM, UNIV KY, 68- *Concurrent Pos:* UN consult, Cent Testing Lab, Pakistan, 75; fac consult, Varian Workshops, 81 & 82. *Mem:* AAAS; Am Chem Soc; Am Asn Univ Professors. *Res:* High resolution nuclear magnetic resonance spectroscopy; biochemical structure studies; molecular structure and associations. *Mailing Add:* Dept Chem Univ Ky Lexington KY 40506

SMITH, STANLEY GALEN, b Laramie, Wyo, Mar 25, 26; m 50; c 3. SYSTEMATIC BOTANY, AQUATIC ECOLOGY. *Educ:* Univ Calif, Berkeley, BA, 49, MS, 51, PhD(bot), 61. *Prof Exp:* Asst prof bot, Iowa State Univ, 60-65; assoc prof, 65-76, PROF BIOL, UNIV WIS-WHITEWATER, 76- *Concurrent Pos:* Univ res grants, 66-68, Wis Dept Natural Resources, 67-68 & US Off Water Resources, 68-69. *Mem:* Am Inst Biol Scientists; Ecol Soc Am; Asn Aquatic Vascular Plant Biologists; Sigma Xi. *Res:* Vascular plant biosystematics, especially aquatics, Typha and Scirpus; ecology; natural area conservation. *Mailing Add:* Dept of Biol Univ of Wis Whitewater WI 53190

SMITH, STANLEY GLEN, b Glendale, Calif, June 20, 31; m 65. ORGANIC CHEMISTRY. *Educ:* Univ Calif, Berkeley, BS, 53; Univ Calif, Los Angeles, PhD(chem), 59. *Prof Exp:* From instr to assoc prof, 60-73, PROF CHEM, UNIV ILL, URBANA, 73- *Concurrent Pos:* Sloan fel, 64-66. *Mem:* Am Chem Soc. *Res:* Physical organic chemistry; reaction kinetics; computer-based teaching. *Mailing Add:* Dept of Chem Univ of Ill Urbana IL 61801

SMITH, STEPHEN ALLEN, b Marietta, Ohio, Sept 7, 42; m 75. OPERATIONS RESEARCH. *Educ:* Univ Cincinnati, BS, 65; Stevens Inst Technol, MS, 67; Stanford Univ, PhD(eng econ), 72. *Prof Exp:* Mem tech staff opers res, Bell Tel Labs, 65-68; RES SCIENTIST OPERS RES, XEROX PALO ALTO RES CTR, 72- *Mem:* Inst Mgt Sci; Inst Elec & Electronics Engrs. *Res:* Inventory control, queueing theory, and office systems. *Mailing Add:* Xerox Palo Alto Res Ctr 3333 Coyote Hill Rd Palo Alto CA 94304

SMITH, STEPHEN D, b Philadelphia, Pa, Jan 15, 39; m 61; c 2. ANATOMY, EMBRYOLOGY. *Educ:* Wesleyan Univ, AB, 61; Tulane Univ, PhD(anat), 65. *Prof Exp:* Instr anat & ophthal, Tulane Univ, 64-65; from instr to asst prof anat, 65-71, ASSOC PROF ANAT, UNIV KY, 71- *Mem:* AAAS; Am Asn Anatomists; Soc Develop Biol; Am Soc Zoologists; NY Acad Sci. *Res:* Control of regeneration and differentiation-growth-limiting mechanisms; effects of physical stress and electrical currents on development. *Mailing Add:* Dept Anat Chandler Med Ctr Univ Ky Lexington KY 40506

SMITH, STEPHEN JUDSON, b Fairfield, Iowa, June 14, 24; m 51; c 5. LASER SPECTROSCOPY. *Educ:* Kalamazoo Col, BA, 49; Harvard Univ, MA, 50, PhD(physics), 54. *Prof Exp:* Asst physics, Harvard Univ, 53-54; PHYSICIST, NAT BUR STANDARDS, 54- *Concurrent Pos:* Fel, Joint Inst Lab Astrophys, Univ Colo, Boulder, 62-, lectr, Univ, 62-66, adj prof, 66-; Dept of Com sci & technol fel, 75-76; NSF prog dir, 75-76; Alexander von Humboldt Found sr US scientist award, Univ Munich, 78-79. *Mem:* AAAS; Am Phys Soc. *Res:* Multi-photon ionization including angular distributions, absolute cross sections; effects of laser field fluctuations on nonlinear atoms absorption; molecular structure measurements by stimulated Raman gain method. *Mailing Add:* Joint Inst for Lab Astrophys Univ Colo Boulder CO 80302

SMITH, STEPHEN ROGER, b Fayette, Ala, Nov 21, 39; m 66; c 2. PHYSICS. *Educ:* Mass Inst Technol, SB, 62, PhD(physics), 69. *Prof Exp:* Instr physics, Princeton Univ, 69-72; asst prof physics, Bryn Mawr Col, 72-78, assoc prof, 78-79; sr staff scientist, 79-80, DIR RES & ENG, EMR PHOTOELECTRIC, PRINCETON, NJ, 80- *Mem:* Am Phys Soc; Am Asn Physics Teachers. *Res:* Quantum optics; photodetectors. *Mailing Add:* 27 Dunbar Dr Rural Rte 4 Trenton NJ 08691

SMITH, STEVEN JOEL, b Everett, Mass, Aug 4, 40; m 64; c 2. PHARMACOLOGY, BIOCHEMISTRY. *Educ:* Univ Mass, BA, 62; Baylor Col Med, MS, 64, PhD(pharmacol), 69. *Prof Exp:* Instr, 69-70, ASST PROF PHARMACOL, HERSHEY MED CTR, PA STATE UNIV, 70- *Mem:* AAAS; Sigma Xi; Soc Neurosci; Am Soc Pharmacol & Exp Therapeut. *Res:* Effects of xenobiotics and endogenous compounds on nucleolar RNA synthesis and processing of 45S RNA in normal and neoplastic tissues; nuclear RNA of brain and liver; isolation of subcellular organelles. *Mailing Add:* Dept of Pharmacol Hershey Med Ctr Pa State Univ 500 Univ St Hershey PA 17033

SMITH, STEVEN PATRICK DECLAND, b Tampa, Fla, July 12, 39; m 63; c 2. AEROSPACE ENGINEERING, NUCLEAR PHYSICS. *Educ:* Univ Fla, BSME, 62, MSE, 63, PhD(nuclear sci), 67. *Prof Exp:* RES AEROSPACE ENGR, US ARMY MISSILE RES & DEVELOP COMMAND, 67- *Mailing Add:* 827 Tannahill Dr S E Huntsville AL 35802

SMITH, STEWARRT EDWARD, b Baltimore, Md, Oct 5, 37; m 62; c 2. COAL SCIENCE, CHEMICAL KINETICS. *Educ:* Howard Univ, Wash, BS, 60; Onio State Univ, PhD(chem), 69. *Prof Exp:* Chemist, E I Du Pont de Nemours & Co, 63-64; teaching asst & phys chem, Ohio State Univ, 64-69; chemist, Sun Oil Co, 69-71; chemist, E I Du Pont de Nemours & Co, 72-74, tech serv rep, 74-78; chemist, 78-81, GROUP HEAD, EXXON RES & ENG CO, 81- *Mem:* Am Chem Soc; AAAS; Sigma Xi; Combustion Inst. *Res:* Gas-phase hydrocarbon oxidation kinetics; heterogeneous catalysis; polymer chemistry; coal science incluuding coal characterization, liquifaction and combustion. *Mailing Add:* Exxon Res & Eng Co PO Box 4255 Baytown TX 77520

SMITH, STEWART W, b Minneapolis, Minn, Sept 15, 32; m 56; c 3. GEOPHYSICS. *Educ:* Mass Inst Technol, SB, 54; Calif Inst Technol, MS, 58, PhD(geophys), 61. *Prof Exp:* Seismologist, Shell Oil Co, 54-57; from asst prof to assoc prof geophys, Calif Inst Technol, 61-70; chmn geophys prog, 70-80, PROF GEOPHYS, UNIV WASH, 70- *Mem:* Am Geophys Union; Seismol Soc Am; Earthquake Eng Res Inst. *Res:* Seismology; free oscillations of the earth; instrumentation for long period seismic waves; elastic strain accumulation in the earth's crust; earthquake risk assessment. *Mailing Add:* Geophys Prog Univ Wash Seattle WA 98195

SMITH, STUART D, b Montreal, Que, Jan 9, 41:; m 41, 63; c 2. OCEANOGRAPHY. *Educ:* McGill Univ, BEng, 62; Univ BC, PhD(oceanog & physics) ,66. *Prof Exp:* Sci officer oceanog, 62-66, RES SCIENTIST OCEANOG, ATLANTIC OCEANOG LAB, BEDFORD INST, 66- *Mem:* Can Meteorol Soc; Am Geophys Union. *Res:* Wind stress; heat flux; evaporation; carbon dioxide exchange and boundary-layer turbulence over the open ocean and over drifting sea ice; surface wave generation; dynamics of iceberg drift. *Mailing Add:* Atlantic Oceanog Lab Bedford Inst Dartmouth NS B2Y 4A2 Can

SMITH, STUART WERNER, anatomy, deceased

SMITH, SUSAN MAY, b Winnipeg, Man, Jan 14, 42. ECOLOGY, ANIMAL BEHAVIOR. *Educ:* Univ BC, BSc, 63, MSc, 65; Univ Wash, PhD(zool), 69. *Prof Exp:* Asst prof biol, Wellesley Col, 69-73; mem fac, Dept Biol, Univ Costa Rica, 73-77; asst prof biol, Adelphi Univ, 77-79; ASST PROF BIOL, MT HOLYOKE COL, 79- *Mem:* AAAS; Asn Study Animal Behav; Cooper Ornith Soc; Wilson Ornith Soc; Am Ornith Union. *Res:* Territoriality, social dominance and population regulation; animal communication; behavior of predators and the reactions of their prey; interspecific competition and niche overlap. *Mailing Add:* Dept of Biol Sci Mt Holyoke Col South Hadley MA 01075

SMITH, SUSAN T, b Detroit, Mich, Nov 22, 37; m 64; c 2. BIOCHEMISTRY, CLINICAL CHEMISTRY. *Educ:* Univ Mich, BS, 59; Duke Univ, PhD(biochem), 67. *Prof Exp:* Asst prof chem, ECarolina Univ, 67-69; teaching supvr med lab asst prog, Beaufort County Tech Inst, 69-71; CHAIRPERSON DEPT MED TECHNOL, SCH ALLIED HEALTH & SOCIAL PROFESSIONS, ECAROLINA UNIV, 72- *Mem:* AAAS; Am Soc Med Technol. *Res:* Mechanism of action of flavoproteins, especially xanthine oxidase and related enzymes. *Mailing Add:* Sch Allied Hlth & Soc Profsns ECarolina Univ Greenville NC 27834

SMITH, SUSAN TRUSSELL, b Iowa City, Iowa, Dec 14, 39; m 64; c 1. ANIMAL BEHAVIOR. *Educ:* Oberlin Col, AB, 61; Harvard Univ, MA, 63, PhD(biol), 68. *Prof Exp:* RES INVESTR BIOL, UNIV PA, 68- *Res:* Information encoded in communication signals of animals; patterned communication of birds which sing continuously. *Mailing Add:* Dept of Biol Univ of Pa Philadelphia PA 19174

SMITH, TERENCE E, b Penarth, UK, Mar 11, 36; m 62; c 2. PETROLOGY, GEOCHEMISTRY. *Educ:* Univ Wales, BSc, 59, PhD(geol), 63. *Prof Exp:* Sci off, Geol Surv Gt Brit, 62-65; lectr geol, Sunderland Tech Col, Eng, 65-67 & Univ WI, 67-69; from asst prof to assoc prof, 69-76, PROF GEOL, UNIV WINDSOR, 76- *Res:* Metamorphic petrology and structural geology of the Scottish Highlands; clastic sedimentation and structure in British Lower Paleozoic and West Indian Tertiary sediments; petrology and geochemistry of Nova Scotia granitic batholith; coast complex of british Columbia, Pennsula Rouges batholith of Southern California and tertiary volcanoes in Jamaica. *Mailing Add:* Dept of Geol Univ of Windsor Windsor ON N9B 3P4 Can

SMITH, TERRY DOUGLAS, b Bethel Springs, Tenn, Nov 20, 42. MEDICINAL CHEMISTRY. *Educ:* Univ Tenn, Memphis, BS, 64; Univ Mich, MS, 65, PhD(med chem), 68. *Prof Exp:* Res investr radiopharmaceut, E R Squibb & Sons, Inc, NJ, 69-70; asst prof pharmaceut, radiol & nuclear med, Col Pharm, Univ Tenn, Memphis, 70-72; assoc chemist, Brookhaven Nat Lab, 73-75; sr radio pharm chemist, Mallinckrodt, Inc, 75-80; DIR, RES & DEVELOP NUCLEAR DIV, SYNCOR INT CORP, 80- *Res:* Design and preparation of radiolabeled compounds for diagnosis of selected pathological conditions by external body scanning techniques. *Mailing Add:* Syncor Int Corp 12847 Arroyo St Sylmar CA 91342

SMITH, TERRY EDWARD, b Evansville, Ind, Aug 23, 40; m 62; c 3. POLYMER CHEMISTRY. *Educ:* David Lipscomb Col, BA, 62; Ga Inst Technol, PhD(phys chem), 67. *Prof Exp:* Res chemist, Am Cyanamid Co, 67-72; res specialist, 72-76, group leader, 76-79, MGR, GAF CORP, 79- *Mem:* Am Chem Soc. *Res:* Polymer solutions and blends; light scattering; polymer characterization; fire retardation. *Mailing Add:* Anal Dept GAF Corp 1361 Alps Rd Wayne NJ 07470

SMITH, THEODORE BEATON, b Columbus, Ohio, Feb 14, 18; m 47. METEOROLOGY. *Educ:* Ohio State Univ, BA, 38; Calif Inst Technol, MS, 40 & 42, PhD(meteorol), 49. *Prof Exp:* Instr meteorol, Calif Inst Technol, 42-44 & 47-48; res meteorologist, Am Inst Aerologic Res, 48-55; res meteorologist, 55-70, vpres res, 70-78, PRES, METEOROL RES, INC, 78- *Mem:* AAAS; fel Am Meteorol Soc. *Res:* Cloud physics; turbulent diffusion. *Mailing Add:* Meteorol Res Inc Box 637 Altadena CA 91001

SMITH, THEODORE CRAIG, b Mansfield, Ohio, Sept 18, 30; m 52; c 4. ANESTHESIOLOGY, PHARMACOLOGY. *Educ:* Ohio Wesleyan Univ, BA, 52; Univ Wis, MS, 60; Univ Cincinnati, MD, 56; Univ Pa, BBA, 78. *Prof Exp:* Intern & resident, Univ Wis, Hosps, 56-60; from asst prof to assoc prof anesthesia, Univ Pa, 62-72, prof, 72-80; MEM FAC DEPT ANESTHESIOL, STRITCH SCH MED, LOYOLA UNIV, 80- *Concurrent Pos:* chief anesthesiol, Vet Admin Hosp, Philadelphia, 78-80. *Mem:* Am Physiol Soc; Asn Univ Anesthetists; Am Soc Anesthesiol. *Res:* Respiratory physiology and pharmacology and their applications to anesthesiology. *Mailing Add:* Dept Anesthesiol Stritch Sch Med Loyola Univ Maywood IL 60153

SMITH, THEODORE G, b Baltimore, Md, Aug 12, 34; m 65; c 2. CHEMICAL ENGINEERING. *Educ:* Johns Hopkins Univ, BEngSci, 56, MS, 58; Washington Univ, DSc(chem eng), 60. *Prof Exp:* Chem engr, Res Div, E I du Pont de Nemours & Co, Del, 60-62, WVa, 62-63; from asst prof to assoc prof, 63-68, PROF CHEM ENG, UNIV MD, COLLEGE PARK, 71- *Mem:* AAAS; Am Inst Chem Engrs; Am Chem Soc. *Res:* Polymer plastics; fractionation, crystallization and solubility; diffusion through polymers; large scale chromatography; control of chemical processes; rheology; reactor design; kinetics. *Mailing Add:* Dept of Chem Eng Univ of Md College Park MD 20742

SMITH, THEODORE ISAAC JOGUES, b Brooklyn, NY, Jan 13, 45; m 68; c 1. AQUACULTURE, MARINE SCIENCE. *Educ:* Cornell Univ, BS, 66; C W Post Col, MS, 68; Univ Miami, PhD(marine sci), 73. *Prof Exp:* ASST MARINE SCIENTIST AQUACULT, SC WILDLIFE & MARINE RESOURCES DEPT, 73- *Concurrent Pos:* Contrib ed, World Maricult Soc, 75- *Mem:* World Mariculture Soc; Southeastern Estuarine Res Soc. *Res:* Determination of biological requirements for commercially important species; development of applicable techniques for use in mariculture; technical and advisory services for mariculture and related industries. *Mailing Add:* 850 Targave Rd James Island SC 29412

SMITH, THOMAS CALDWELL, b Charleston, WVa, Feb 20, 41; m 65; c 2. PHYSIOLOGY, BIOPHYSICS. *Educ:* Univ Richmond, BS, 63, MS, 65; Med Col Va, PhD(physiol), 69. *Prof Exp:* Instr physiol, Med Col Va, 68-69; asst prof, 69-76, ASSOC PROF PHYSIOL, UNIV TEX MED SCH SAN ANTONIO, 76- *Mem:* Biophys Soc; Am Physiol Soc; Soc Gen Physiol. *Res:* Active ion transport in epithelium and biomembranes. *Mailing Add:* Dept Physiol Med Sch Univ Tex San Antonio TX 78284

SMITH, THOMAS CHARLES, b Elyria, Ohio, Dec 6, 25. PHARMACOLOGY. *Educ:* Oberlin Col, AB, 47; Harvard Univ, MA, 49, PhD, 52; Northwestern Univ, MD, 62. *Prof Exp:* Lab asst, Oberlin Col, 44-47; asst bot, Cambridge Jr Col, 48; teaching fel gen physiol, Harvard Univ, 49, teaching fel zool, 50 & endocrinol, 51; from instr to asst prof pharmacol, Sch Med, Boston Univ, 53-58; asst prof, Med Sch, Northwestern Univ, 59-62; intern, Univ Chicago Hosps, 62-63; asst prof gynec, obstet & pharmacol, Sch Med, Marquette Univ, 63-65; from asst dir to assoc dir div clin res, Ortho Res Found, 65-66, dir div pharmacol, 66-68; dir clin pharmacol, Parke, Davis & Co, 68-81; MED DIR & ATTEND STAFF, CLIN INVEST UNIT, BRONSON METHODIST HOSP, 81- *Concurrent Pos:* Assoc attend staff, Milwaukee County Hosp, Wis, 63-65, head gynec-endocrine lab & family planning clin, 64-65; vis lectr, Sch Med, Marquette Univ, 66-; spec attend staff, Somerset Hosp, Somerville, NJ, 67-68; lectr, Rutgers Univ, 67-68 & Univ Mich, 69-; attend staff, Chelsea Med Clin, Mich, 70- *Mem:* Am Soc Pharmacol & Exp Therapeut; Am Soc Clin Pharmacol & Therapeut. *Res:* Physiology of reproduction; mammary gland function; hormones affecting metabolism and tumor growth; drugs and adipose tissue; endocrine and clinical pharmacology. *Mailing Add:* 2412 Bronson Blvd Kalamazoo MI 49008

SMITH, THOMAS DAVID, b Eng, Nov 25, 23; m 47. PHYSICAL CHEMISTRY. *Educ:* Univ London, BSc, 44, PhD(chem), 47. *Prof Exp:* Chemist, C A Parsons & Co, Ltd, Eng, 39-44; res assoc, Brit Coke Res Asn, 44-47; res assoc, Univ Southern Calif, 48-49; res chemist, Union Oil Co, Calif, 49-50; res fel, Cambridge Univ, 50-51; res supvr, 51-57, res mgr, 57-64, lab dir, 64-65, asst plant mgr, 65-68, lab dir, 66-68, asst dir res & develop, Photo Prod Dept, 68-72, DIR RES, E I DU PONT DE NEMOURS & CO, INC, 72- *Mem:* Am Chem Soc; Soc Photog Sci & Eng; Royal Photog Soc Gt Brit. *Res:* Physical and colloid chemistry, especially in photographic systems. *Mailing Add:* PO Box 3951 Wilmington DE 19807

SMITH, THOMAS ELIJAH, b North Augusta, SC, Apr 11, 33; m 53; c 2. BIOCHEMISTRY. *Educ:* Benedict Col, BS, 53; George Washington Univ, MS, 59, PhD(biochem), 62. *Prof Exp:* Chemist, Lab Exp Med & Clin Therapeut, Nat Heart Inst, 53-54, biochemist, Lab Clin Biochem, 56-62; NIH fel enzyme mech, Wash Univ, 62-63; sr biochemist, Biol & Med Div, Melpar, Inc, 63-65; sr biochemist, Lawrence Livermore Lab, Univ Calif, 65-74; assoc prof biochem, Univ Tex Health Sci Ctr Dallas, 74-80; PROF & CHMN, DEPT BIOCHEM, COL MED, HOWARD UNIV, 80- *Mem:* AAAS; Am Chem Soc; Am Soc Biol Chemists; Sigma Xi. *Res:* Enzyme mechanisms. *Mailing Add:* Dept Biochem Howard Univ Col Med Washington DC 20059

SMITH, THOMAS GRAVES, JR, b Winnsboro, SC, Mar 22, 31; m 56. NEUROPHYSIOLOGY. *Educ:* Emory Univ, BA, 53; Oxford Univ, BA & MA, 56; Columbia Univ, MD, 60. *Prof Exp:* Intern, Bronx Munic Hosp, New York, 60-61; vis res assoc biol, Mass Inst Technol, 64-66; res med officer physiol, 64-68, CHIEF SECT SENSORY PHYSIOL, LAB NEUROPHYSIOL, NAT INST NEUROL COMMUN & NEUROL DIS & STROKE, 68- *Mem:* AAAS. *Res:* Neurophysiology and biophysics of excitable membranes, of synaptic transmission between nerve cells and of the transduction of energy in photoreceptors. *Mailing Add:* Bldg 36 Rm 2C02 Nat Inst Neurol & Commun Dis & Stroke Bethesda MD 20205

SMITH, THOMAS HADWICK, b Boise, Idaho, Dec 5, 40; m 65; c 2. MECHANICAL & CHEMICAL ENGINEERING. *Educ:* Johns Hopkins Univ, BES, 63; Univ Utah, PhD(mech eng), 69. *Prof Exp:* LAB SCIENTIST & SPECIALIST NUCLEAR ANAL & SAFETY, DONALD W DOUGLAS LABS, McDONNELL DOUGLAS CORP, 68- *Res:* Turbulent boundary layers; nuclear heat source analysis and safety; energy conversion engineering. *Mailing Add:* McDonnell Douglas Astronaut Co 1100 Sproute Rd Richland WA 99352

SMITH, THOMAS HARRY FRANCIS, b Paterson, NJ, Feb 15, 28; m 51. TOXICOLOGY. *Educ:* Fordham Univ, BS, 47; Philadelphia Col Pharm, MSc, 56, PhD(pharmacol), 61. *Prof Exp:* Asst pharmacologist, Hoffmann-La Roche, Inc, 49-51 & Wallace Labs, 51-52; bacteriologist, Children's Hosp Philadelphia, 54-55; asst zool & bot & res pharmacologist, Philadelphia Col Pharm, 56-57, admin asst, 57-59; res pharmacologist & parasitologist, Vet Sch, Univ Pa, 57-58, lectr anat, physiol & microbiol, Sch Nursing, 58-61; exp pharmacologist & toxicologist, Wyeth Labs, Inc, 61-64; tech info coordr, Avon Prod Inc, NJ, 64-67; dir sci serv, Lehn & Fink Div, Sterling Drug Inc, 67-71; dir qual assurance, Lanvin Charles of the Ritz, 71-76; dir prod integrity, Naval Ocean Res & Develop Activity, 76-80; CORP TOXICOLOGIST, IBM CORP, 81- *Concurrent Pos:* Instr, Misericordia Hosp, 57-59. *Mem:* Am Acad Clin Toxicol; Am Acad Dermat; Am Soc Law & Med; Soc Cosmetic Chem; fel Royal Soc Chem. *Res:* Cosmetic chemistry; dermatotoxicology; psychopharmacology. *Mailing Add:* IBM Corp One Barker Ave White Plains NY 10601

SMITH, THOMAS HENRY, b Lackawanna, NY, Aug 14, 47; m 77. ORGANIC CHEMISTRY. *Educ:* Niagara Univ, BS, 69; Ariz State Univ, PhD(org chem), 74. *Prof Exp:* Res asst org chem, Ariz State Univ, 69-74; fel, Stanford Res Inst, 74-75; ORG CHEMIST, SRI INT, 75- *Mem:* AAAS; Am Chem Soc. *Res:* Synthetic organic chemistry; synthesis of biologically active compounds; drug design. *Mailing Add:* Dept of Bio-Org Chem SRI Int Menlo Park CA 94025

SMITH, THOMAS JEFFERSON, b Atlanta, Ga, June 12, 30; m 57; c 1. GEOPHYSICS, MATHEMATICS. *Educ:* Emory Univ, BA, 51; Univ Wis, MS, 57, PhD(math), 61. *Prof Exp:* Asst prof math, Kalamazoo Col, 61-62; mem staff geophys, Carnegie Inst Wash, assoc prof, 70-74, PROF MATH, KALAMAZOO COL, 74- *Mem:* Am Math Soc; Seismol Soc Am. *Res:* Minkowskian and Finsler geometries; convex sets; explosion seismology. *Mailing Add:* Dept of Math Kalamazoo Col Kalamazoo MI 49001

SMITH, THOMAS MARION, biochemistry, parasitology, see previous edition

SMITH, THOMAS PATRICK, b San Diego, Calif, Aug 21, 49; m 75. ZOOLOGY. *Educ:* St Mary's Col, Calif, BS, 71; Univ Southern Calif, PhD(biol), 81. *Prof Exp:* Res asst, Marine Educ Prog, NSF, Univ Southern Calif, 77-78; lectr, Chapman Col, 79-81; LECTR BIOL, CALIF STATE UNIV, LOS ANGELES, 80- *Mem:* Soc Protozoologists; Am Micros Soc; Ecol Soc Am; Int Asn Meioenthologists; Sigma Xi. *Res:* Systematics and ecology of free-living ciliated protozoa; role of ciliates in detrital food chains; systematics of chonotrich ciliates and relationship to crustacean hosts; systematics of mammalian gut ciliates. *Mailing Add:* Dept Biol Sci Univ Southern Calif Los Angeles CA 90007

SMITH, THOMAS STEVENSON, b Hubbard, Ohio, Feb 8, 21; m 44; c 3. SOLID STATE PHYSICS. *Educ:* Kenyon Col, AB, 47; Ohio State Univ, PhD(physics), 52. *Hon Degrees:* LHD, Kenyon Col, 70, Cardinal Stritch Col, 80; DSc, Ripon Col, 71; LLD, Lawrence Univ, 80. *Prof Exp:* Instr physics, Kenyon Col, 46-47; asst, Ohio State Univ, 47-51, res fel, 51-52; from asst prof to prof, Ohio Univ, 52-69, asst to pres, 61-62, vpres acad affairs, 62-67, provost, 67-69; pres, Lawrence Univ, 69-79. *Concurrent Pos:* Chmn, Great Lakes Dist Selection Rhodes Scholar; educ consult-examr, Comn Cols & Univs, NCent Asn Cols & Sec Schs. *Mem:* Am Phys Soc; AAAS; Sigma Xi; Am Asn Physics Teachers. *Res:* Cryogenics; superconductivity; nuclear magnetic resonance; x-ray powder diffraction; vapor pressures at high temperature. *Mailing Add:* Rte 1 Pine River WI 54965

SMITH, THOMAS WOODS, b Portsmouth, Ohio, Dec 16, 43; m 68; c 2. ORGANIC POLYMER CHEMISTRY. *Educ:* John Carroll Univ, BS, 69; Univ Mich, PhD(org chem), 73. *Prof Exp:* Chemist, Lubrizol Corp, 63-70; assoc scientist, 73-75, SCIENTIST, WEBSTER RES CTR, XEROX CORP, 75- *Concurrent Pos:* Consult, Environ Res Inst Mich, 72-73. *Mem:* Am Chem Soc; Sigma Xi. *Res:* The synthesis of functional polymers; the mechanism of polymerization processes and the utilization of macromolecules as catalysts for chemical processes. *Mailing Add:* Xerox Corp Xerox Sq W-114 Rochester NY 14644

SMITH, THOR LOWE, b Zion, Ill, June 11, 20; m 49; c 2. POLYMER SCIENCE. *Educ:* Wheaton Col, BS, 42; Ill Inst Technol, MS, 44; Univ Wis, PhD(chem), 48. *Prof Exp:* Res chemist, Hercules Powder Co, 48-54; sr res engr, Jet Propulsion Lab, Calif Inst Technol, 54-56, chief solid propellant chem sect, 56-59; chmn propulsion dept, Stanford Res Inst, 59-61, dir propulsion sci div, 61-64, sci fel, 64-68; prof chem, Tex A&M Univ, 68-69; RES STAFF MEM, IBM RES LAB, 69- *Concurrent Pos:* Mem, Nat Acad Sci Eval Panel, Nat Bur Standards, 74-77; mem bd trustees, Gordon Res Conf, 78-, chmn, 81-82; mem, Nat Adv Bd Comts, 71-72 & 78-80. *Honors & Awards:* Bingham Medal, Soc Rheol, 78; Centennial scholars lectr, Case Western Reserve Univ, 80. *Mem:* Am Chem Soc; Soc Rheol; Brit Soc Rheol; fel Am Phys Soc. *Res:* Mechanical electro-optical and other physical properties of polymer systems; polymer physical chemistry; deformation and fracture of polymeric materials; rheology of dispersions and polymers. *Mailing Add:* IBM Res Lab K42-282 5600 Cottle Rd San Jose CA 95193

SMITH, TIM DENIS, b Eugene, Ore, Dec 30, 46; m 67; c 1. BIOLOGY, STATISTICS. *Educ:* Pac Lutheran Univ, BA, 69; Univ Wash, PhD(biomath), 73. *Prof Exp:* Res assoc oceanog, Univ Wash, 72-73; fisheries biologist, Nat Marine Fisheries Serv, 73-75; asst prof zool, Univ Hawaii, 75-78; FISHERIES BIOLOGIST, NAT MARINE FISHERIES SERV, 78- *Concurrent Pos:* Mem sci comt, Int Whaling Comn, 74-; mem, Comt Sci Adv, US Marine Mammal Comn, 76-79; mem, Sci & Statist Comt, Western Pac Regional Fisheris Mgt Coun, 77-78. *Mem:* Am Inst Fishery Res Biologists. *Res:* Applied and theoretical population biology, especially of large mammals; management of living resources. *Mailing Add:* Southwest Fisheries Ctr 8604 La Jolla Shores Dr La Jolla CA 92038

SMITH, TODD IVERSEN, b Mobile, Ala, June 11, 40; m 70. PHYSICS. *Educ:* Cornell Univ, BA, 61; Rice Univ, MA, 63, PhD(physics), 65. *Prof Exp:* Res assoc physics, Stanford Univ, 65-68; asst prof physics & elec eng, Univ Southern Calif, 68-74; RES PHYSICIST, HANSEN LAB, STANFORD UNIV, 74- *Mem:* AAAS; Am Phys Soc; Inst Elec & Electronics Engrs. *Res:* Superconducting microwave cavities; Josephson tunneling between superconductors; fluctuation effects and flux flow effects in thin superconducting films; instrumentation using Josephson junctions as sensors. *Mailing Add:* Hansen Lab Stanford Univ Stanford CA 94305

SMITH, TOWNSEND JACKSON, b West Union, WVa, Oct 15, 10; m 41; c 1. AGRONOMY. *Educ:* WVa Univ, BSA, 36; Ohio State Univ, PhD(agron), 40. *Prof Exp:* Agt, USDA & asst, Ohio Agr Exp Sta, 36-40; instr, Univ & asst agronomist, Exp Sta, Univ Ariz, 40-41, asst prof & asst agronomist, 41-46; assoc agronomist, Exp Sta, 46-48, prof, 48-78, EMER PROF AGRON, VA POLYTECH INST & STATE UNIV, 78- *Mem:* Am Soc Agron. *Res:* Physiology of cotton fibers; forage crops breeding; soybean breeding, culture and physiology; use of ionizing radiation in alfalfa improvement. *Mailing Add:* 1014 Allendale Ct SW Blacksburg VA 24060

SMITH, TRUDY ENZER, b Eger, Czech, May 23, 24; nat US; m 53; c 6. PHYSICAL CHEMISTRY. *Educ:* Greensboro Col, AB, 44; Ohio State Univ, PhD(chem), 57. *Prof Exp:* Asst, Ohio State Univ, 45-50; res chemist, Aerojet Gen Corp, Gen Tire & Rubber Co, Calif, 51-53; phys chemist, US Naval Ord Test Sta, 53-60; instr chem, Univ Conn, 60-62; from asst prof to assoc prof, 62-77, PROF CHEM, CONN COL, 77- *Mem:* Am Chem Soc; Sigma Xi. *Res:* Chemical kinetics; mass spectrometry. *Mailing Add:* Dept of Chem Conn Col New London CT 06320

SMITH, VANN ELLIOTT, b Pensacola, Fla, June 28, 40; m 69; c 2. MARINE BIOLOGY. *Educ:* Fla State Univ, BS, 62, MS, 64; Scripps Inst Oceanog, PhD(marine biol), 68. *Prof Exp:* COORDR LAKE & MARINE RES, CRANBROOK INST, 71- *Concurrent Pos:* Edison scholar, Cranbrook Inst Sci, 71-72. *Mem:* Marine Technol Soc; Sigma Xi; Int Asn Great Lakes Res. *Res:* Water chemistry in the Great Lakes; comparative marine biochemistry; heavy metals and pesticides in lake ecosystems; remote sensing of lakes, lake watersheds and coral reef systems. *Mailing Add:* Cranbrook Inst Sci 500 Lone Pine Rd PO Box 801 Bloomfield Hills MI 48013

SMITH, VEARL ROBERT, agriculture, see previous edition

SMITH, VELMA MERRILINE, b San Bernardino, Calif, Mar 11, 40; m 61. ALGEBRA. *Educ:* Calif State Col, San Bernardino, BA, 67; Univ Calif, Riverside, MA, 69, PhD(math), 72. *Prof Exp:* asst prof, 72-77, assoc prof, 77-81, PROF MATH, CALIF STATE POLYTECH UNIV, 81- *Mem:* Am Math Soc; Math Asn Am. *Res:* Commutative algebra, especially ideal and ring theory. *Mailing Add:* Dept of Math Calif State Polytech Univ Pomona CA 91768

SMITH, VICTOR HERBERT, b Lewistown, Mont, Aug 1, 25; m 50; c 5. HOSPITAL ADMINISTRATION, ENVIRONMENTAL HEALTH. *Educ:* Mont State Col, BS, 50; Ore State Col, PhD(chem), 55. *Prof Exp:* Biol scientist, Hanford Atomic Prod Oper, Gen Elec Co, 54-65; sr res scientist, Pac Northwest Labs, Battelle Mem' Inst, 65-81; MGR, KENNEWICK PRIMARY CLINIC, 82- *Concurrent Pos:* AEC fel radiation chem & biophys, Univ Minn, 59-61; mem SC-37, Nat Comt Radiation Protection, 73- *Mem:* AAAS; Am Chem Soc; Radiation Res Soc; Health Physics Soc; Soc Exp Biol & Med. *Res:* Heterocyclics; radiation induced reactions and effects on organics and biological systems; radiation protection; removal of radioactive emitters; chelation therapy; effects and treatment of incorporated radionuclides, toxic metals, organometallics and combined insults. *Mailing Add:* Kennewick Primary Clin 203 W 8th Kennewick WA 99336

SMITH, VINCENT C, b Albany, NY, Nov 4, 14; m 40; c 4. FLORICULTURE, MARKETING. *Educ:* Cornell Univ, BS, 37; NY Univ, MS, 47. *Prof Exp:* Teacher, Rockland County Voc Educ & Exten Bd, 40-47; asst prof floricult, 48-55, head dept, 56-75, prof ornamental hort, 56-80, EMER PROF, STATE UNIV NY AGR & TECH COL, 80- *Mem:* Am Soc Hort Sci. *Res:* Problems involved in marketing floral and ornamental horticulture crops. *Mailing Add:* Dept of Ornamental Hort SUNY Agr & Tech Col Alfred NY 14802

SMITH, VINCENT FRANCIS, JR, physical organic chemistry, see previous edition

SMITH, VIRGIL KIRKLAND, JR, b Indianola, Miss, Aug 23, 19; m 41; c 3. ENTOMOLOGY. *Educ:* Miss State Univ, BS, 54, MS, 56. *Prof Exp:* Entomologist, Forest Insect Lab, 56-71, proj leader Wood Prod Insect Lab, 71-73, mem staff, Forest Insect Lab, 73-80, CONSULT, STRUCTURAL PEST ORGANISMS, EVERGREEN STA, US FOREST SERV, 80- *Mem:* Entom Soc Am. *Res:* Termites and forest products insects. *Mailing Add:* Forest Sci Lab Box 2008 GMF Sta US Forest Serv Gulfport MS 39501

SMITH, VIVIAN SWEIBEL, b New York, NY, Oct 29, 20; m 42; c 4. HEALTH SCIENCES. *Educ:* Hunter Col, AB, 40; Univ Ill, AM, 41, PhD(zool), 44. *Prof Exp:* Asst prof biol, Miss Southern Col, 45; parasitol technician, Johns Hopkins Hosp, 46-48; consult asst prof, 53-58, ADJ ASSOC PROF PARASITOL, COL MED, UNIV OKLA, 59- & COL HEALTH, 67-, ADJ ASSOC PROF ALLIED HEALTH EDUC, HEALTH SCI CTR, 72- *Concurrent Pos:* Instr, Oklahoma City Univ, 54-70; coordr health manpower educ progs, Okla Regional Med Prog, 70-72; coordr, Okla Interagency Task Force Health Manpower Data, 75- *Mem:* AAAS; Am Soc Parasitologists; Am Soc Allied Health Professions; Am Pub Health Asn. *Res:* Health manpower planning; factors relevant to decision making; role of licensure of health personnel. *Mailing Add:* Univ of Okla Health Sci Ctr PO Box 26901 Oklahoma City OK 73190

SMITH, VIVIANNE CAMERON, b Woodford, Eng, July 7, 38; US citizen; m 65; c 2. PSYCHOPHYSIOLOGY. *Educ:* Columbia Univ, BS, 62, MA, 64, PhD(psychol), 67. *Prof Exp:* From instr to assoc prof, 68-79, PROF OPHTHAL, UNIV CHICAGO, 79- *Concurrent Pos:* Mem, Inst Res Group Colour Vision Deficiencies. *Mem:* Fel Optical Soc Am; Asn Res Vision & Ophthal. *Res:* Mechanism of color vision in humans; theories of color vision; spatial and temporal factors in vision. *Mailing Add:* Eye Res Lab EB-24 Univ of Chicago Chicago IL 60637

SMITH, W JOHN, b Toronto, Ont, Dec 20, 34; m 64; c 1. BIOLOGY, ANIMAL BEHAVIOR. *Educ:* Carleton Univ, Can, BSc, 57; Univ Mich, MS, 58; Harvard Univ, PhD(biol), 61. *Prof Exp:* Asst prof zool, 63-68, assoc prof, 68-76, PROF BIOL & PSYCHOL, UNIV PA, 76- MEM, INST NEUROL SCI, 67- *Concurrent Pos:* Res assoc, Mus Comp Zool, Harvard Univ, 61-64; consult, Penrose Res Lab, Philadelphia Zool Soc, 65-; res assoc, Smithsonian Trop Res Inst, 66-; res assoc, Acad Natural Sci, Pa, 67- *Mem:* Am Ornithologists Union. *Res:* Animal communication and social behavior; ecology; systematics; evolutionary theory. *Mailing Add:* Leidy Labs Univ of Pa Philadelphia PA 19104

SMITH, W(ILLIAM) P(AYNE), b Superior, Wis, Jan 5, 15; m 42; c 3. ELECTRICAL ENGINEERING. *Educ:* Univ Minn, BEE, 36, MS, 37; Univ Tex, PhD, 50. *Prof Exp:* Engr, Commonwealth Edison Co, Ill, 37-39; asst prof, Chicago Tech Col, 39-41; dean, Sampson Col, 46-50; prof elec eng, Univ Kans, 50-80, chmn, Dept Elec eng, Sch Eng & Archit, 55-56, dean, 65-80. *Concurrent Pos:* Lectr, Univ Tex, 48-50. *Mem:* Am Soc Eng Educ; Inst Elec & Electronics Engrs. *Mailing Add:* 1107 West Campus Rd Lawrence KS 66045

SMITH, WADE KILGORE, b Paterson, NJ, Sept 7, 37; m 63; c 2. HEMATOLOGY, IMMUNOLOGY. *Educ:* Oberlin Col, AB, 59; Sch Med, Johns Hopkins Univ, MD, 63. *Prof Exp:* Intern, Mt Sinai Hosp, New York, 63-64, resident, 64-68, chief res, 68-69, fel hematol, 69; res asst immunol, Med Ctr, Duke Univ, 70-71, instr, 71-72, assoc med & immunol, 72-74; asst prof, 75-80, ASSOC PROF MED, MED COL VA, 75-; CHIEF, HEMAT/ONCOL SECT, VET ADMIN MED CTR, RICHMOND, 81- *Concurrent Pos:* Instr med, Mt Sinai Sch Med, 68-69; Nat Cancer Inst Spec fel, Med Ctr, Duke Univ, 70-72; mem chemotherapy comt, Nat Bladder Cancer Collaborative Group A, 77-; mem, Med Col Va/Va Commonwealth Univ Cancer Ctr, 76- *Mem:* Am Asn Clin Histocompatibility Testing; Am Soc Hematol; Am Soc Microbiol; Int Soc Hematol; NY Acad Sci. *Res:* Leukocyte antigens and immune destruction of leukocytes; humoral factors suppressing immune responses in tumor bearing or normal graft bearing hosts; clinical cancer chemotherapy trials. *Mailing Add:* Med Col of Va Med Col Va Sta Richmond VA 23298

SMITH, WALDO E(DWARD), b New Hampton, Iowa, Aug 20, 00; m 27; c 2. HYDRAULIC ENGINEERING, GEOPHYSICS. *Educ:* Univ Iowa, BS, 23, MS, 24. *Prof Exp:* Asst engr, Burns & McDonnell Eng Co, Mo, 24-26 & Black & Veatch, 26-27; instr theoret & appl mech, Univ Ill, 27-28; assoc prof civil eng & actg head dept, Robert Col, Istanbul, 28-31; asst prof, N Dak State Univ, 31-35; hydraul engr, Muskingum Watershed Conserv Dist, Ohio, 35-39; mem staff flood control, US Eng Off, WVa, 39-40; soil conserv serv, USDA, 40-41, head sect hydrol land use, Hydrol Div, Off Res, 41-43; hydraul engr, US Pub Rd Admin, Washington, DC, 43-44; exec secy & ed, Transactions, Am Geophys Union, 44-70, ed, Geophys Monograph Series, 58-70, EMER EXEC DIR, AM GEOPHYS UNION, 70-; *Concurrent Pos:* Asst to pres, Nat Grad Univ, 70 - 78; Collabr, Soil Conserv Serv, USDA, 37-40; prof lectr, George Washington Univ, 46-61; specialist, Res & Develop Bd, US Dept Defense, DC, 47-53; US del, Int Union Geod & Geophys, Oslo, 48, Brussels, 51, Rome, 54, Toronto, 57, Helsinki, 60, Berkeley, 63, Switz, 68, Moscow, 72 & Canberra, 79. *Mem:* Fel AAAS; Am Soc Civil Engrs; Am Geophys Union. *Res:* Geophysical education; hydrology; environmental and natural resources problems. *Mailing Add:* 3907 Jocelyn St NW Washington DC 20015

SMITH, WALKER O, JR, b Buffalo, NY, Nov 21, 50. BIOLOGICAL OCEANOGRAPHY, PHYCOLOGY. *Educ:* Univ Rochester, BS, 72; Duke Univ, PhD(bot), 76. *Prof Exp:* Res asst oceanog, Duke Univ, 72-76; ASST PROF BOT, UNIV TENN, 76- *Mem:* AAAS; Phycol Soc Am; Am Soc Limnol & Oceanog; Sigma Xi. *Res:* Flux of carbon in marine systems; dissolved organic carbon excretion and its heterotrophic utilization; respiration; upwelling ecosystems and seagrass communities. *Mailing Add:* Dept Bot Univ Tenn Knoxville TN 37916

SMITH, WALLACE BRITTON, b Parrish, Ala, Jan 21, 41; m 60; c 2. APPLIED PHYSICS. *Educ:* Jacksonville State Univ, BS, 67; Auburn Univ, MS, 69, PhD(physics), 72. *Prof Exp:* Asst prof physics, Appalachian State Univ, 72-73; res physicist, 73-74; head physics sect, 74-77, HEAD PHYSICS DIV, SOUTHERN RES INST, 77- *Mem:* Inst Elec & Electronic Engrs; Sigma Xi. *Res:* Electrical breakdown in insulators and semiconductors; particle sizing techniques and instruments; physics of the electrostatic precipitation; fabric filtration processes. *Mailing Add:* Southern Res Inst PO Box 3307-A Birmingham AL 35255

SMITH, WALTER LAWS, b London, Eng, Nov 12, 26; m 50; c 2. MATHEMATICAL STATISTICS. *Educ:* Cambridge Univ, BA, 47, MA, 50, PhD(math statist), 53. *Prof Exp:* Statistician, Med Sch, Cambridge Univ, 53-54, lectr math, 56-58; from asst prof to assoc prof, 53-62, PROF STATIST, UNIV NC, CHAPEL HILL, 62- *Mem:* Am Math Soc; fel Am Statist Asn; fel Inst Math Statist; fel Royal Statist Soc; Int Statist Inst. *Res:* Probability theory; operations research. *Mailing Add:* Dept Statist 318 Phillips Hall Univ of NC Chapel Hill NC 27514

SMITH, WALTER LEE, b Siler City, NC, Nov 12, 48; m 72. PHYSICS. *Educ:* NC State Univ, BS, 71; Harvard Univ, PhD(appl physics), 76. *Prof Exp:* PHYSICIST OPTICAL & MAT PHYSICS, LAWRENCE LIVERMORE LAB, 76- *Mem:* Am Inst Physics. *Res:* Nonlinear optics; laser physics; ultraviolet materials properties; absolute measurement techniques; laser-induced breakdown physics. *Mailing Add:* Lawrence Livermore Lab PO Box 5508 L-470 Livermore CA 94550

SMITH, WALTER THOMAS, JR, b Havana, Ill, Feb 28, 22; m 45; c 2. ORGANIC CHEMISTRY. *Educ:* Univ Ill, BS, 43; Ind Univ, PhD(chem), 46. *Prof Exp:* Chemist, Mallinckrodt Chem Works, Mo, 43; Fels Fund fel, Univ Chicago, 46-47; from instr to asst prof chem, Univ Iowa, 47-53; assoc prof, 53-57, PROF CHEM, UNIV KY, 57- *Concurrent Pos:* Fulbright-Hays vis prof, Univ Libya, 63-64 & Am Univ Beirut, 65-66. *Mem:* AAAS; Am Chem Soc. *Res:* Organic synthesis; agricultural and pharmaceutical chemicals; pyrolysis; natural products; enzymes in nonaqueous solvents. *Mailing Add:* Dept of Chem Univ of Ky Lexington KY 40506

SMITH, WALTON RAMSAY, b Asheville, NC, Apr 26, 48. WOOD SCIENCE & TECHNOLOGY, WOOD PHYSICS. *Educ:* NC State Univ, BS, 71; Univ Calif, Berkeley, MS, 75, PhD(wood sci & technol), 81. *Prof Exp:* Consult, Walton R Smith Consult, 71-73; res asst, Univ Calif, Berkeley, 73-77; researcher, Ctr Technique du Bois, Paris, 77-78; ASSOC PROF WOOD PHYSICS, UNIV WASH, 78- *Concurrent Pos:* Consult, Dept Wood Physics, Ctr Technique du Bois, Paris, 81. *Mem:* Forest Prod Res Soc; Soc Woods Sci & Technol; Int Union Forestry Res Orgn; Am Soc Testing & Mat; Am Forestry Asn. *Res:* Wood moisture relationships; biomass fuel characterization; working properties of wood as a material; lumber, veneer and wood fuel drying characteristics; thermal properties of wood; dimensional stability of wood and wood products. *Mailing Add:* AR-10 Col Forest Resources Univ Wash Seattle WA 98195

SMITH, WARD ARDEN, b Dixon, Ill, Nov 14, 23; m 45; c 4. CHEMISTRY. *Educ:* Knox Col, AB, 48. *Prof Exp:* Chief chemist, Smith-Douglas Co, Ill, 48-52; res chemist, Cent Res Labs, Firestone Tire & Rubber Co, 52-62; mgr compound develop, Mohawk Rubber Co, 62-65; group leader, 65-67, div mgr, 67-69, ASST DIR, CENT RES LABS, FIRESTONE TIRE & RUBBER CO, 69- *Mem:* Am Chem Soc. *Res:* Rubber chemistry; tire technology. *Mailing Add:* Cent Res Labs Firestone Tire & Rubber Co Akron OH 44317

SMITH, WARREN EDWARD, b Cardston, Alta, June 4, 19; m; c 6. GENETICS, PLANT BREEDING. *Educ:* Univ Alta, BSc, 41, MSc, 47; Univ Nebr, PhD(genetics), 59. *Prof Exp:* Instr agr exten, Univ Alta, 41-42; feed technician, Can Packers, 42-43; seed buyer, Can West Grain, 45-47; from instr to assoc prof plant sci, 47-61, assoc prof genetics, 61-66, PROF GENETICS, UNIV ALTA, 66- *Concurrent Pos:* Consult, Food & Agr Orgn, UN & Near East Plant Breeding, 62-63. *Mem:* Agr Inst Can; Genetics Soc Can; Can Soc Agron. *Res:* Genetical studies in genus linum; varietal breeding in cereal crops. *Mailing Add:* Dept of Genetics Univ of Alta Edmonton AB T6G 2E1 Can

SMITH, WARREN HARVEY, b Brooklyn, NY, Oct 6, 35; m 60; c 3. PHYSICAL CHEMISTRY. *Educ:* City Col New York, BS, 58; Syracuse Univ, PhD(phys chem, kinetics), 64. *Prof Exp:* Sr res chemist, 64-67, group leader plutonium chem, 67-69, plutonium fuels develop mgr, 69-71, isotope separation mgr, 71-73, APPLIED PHYSICS MGR, MOUND LAB, MONSANTO RES CORP, MIAMISBURG, 73- *Mem:* Am Chem Soc; Am Inst Chemists. *Res:* Gas phase kinetics; physical-inorganic chemistry of the actinide elements; use of plutonium-238 as a fuel for heat sources. *Mailing Add:* 5413 Coppermill Pl Dayton OH 45429

SMITH, WARREN LAVERNE, b Wayne, Nebr, July 6, 24; m 48; c 5. PHYSICS, ELECTRICAL ENGINEERING. *Educ:* Univ Wis, BSEE, 45. *Prof Exp:* Staff mem, 54-62, SUPVR ENG, BELL TEL LABS, INC, 62- *Mem:* Fel Inst Elec & Electronics Engrs. *Res:* Development and design of precision frequency standards, quartz crystal units and monolithic crystal filters. *Mailing Add:* Bell Tel Labs Inc 555 Union Blvd Allentown PA 18103

SMITH, WAYNE EARL, b Franklin, Ind, Jan 7, 27; m 53; c 3. MATHEMATICS. *Educ:* Pomona Col, BA, 49; Univ Calif, Los Angeles, MA, 53, PhD(math), 58. *Prof Exp:* Asst math, Univ Calif, Los Angeles, 50-53, assoc math & jr res mathematician, 54-58; asst prof math, Occidental Col, 58-62; asst prof appl math, Univ Calif, 62-63; vis asst prof biostatist, 63-65, lectr biostatist & asst res statistician, 65-68, analyst, 68-80, ADMINISTRATIVE ANALYST, UNIV CALIF, LOS ANGELES, 80- *Mem:* Math Asn Am; Asn Instnl Res. *Res:* Numerical analysis; probability and statistics; simulation of university processes. *Mailing Add:* Planning Off Univ Calif Los Angeles CA 90024

SMITH, WAYNE H, b Marianna, Fla, Aug 10, 38; m 62. FORESTRY. *Educ:* Univ Fla, BSA, 60; Miss State Univ, MS, 62, PhD(soils), 65. *Prof Exp:* Asst soils, Miss State Univ, 63-64; asst prof, 64-70, assoc prof forestry & asst dir res, 70-81, PROF FOREST RESOURSES & CONSERV & DIR ENVIRON & NATURAL SCI PROGS, UNIV FLA, 81- *Concurrent Pos:* Fac develop leave, Coop State Res Serv, USDA, Washington, DC, 73-74. *Mem:* Soc Am Foresters; Am Soc Agron. *Res:* Nutritional problems of forest trees, particularly nitrogen metabolism and forest soil-plant relationships. *Mailing Add:* Sch Forest Resources & Conserv Univ of Fla Gainesville FL 32611

SMITH, WAYNE HOWARD, b Pittsburgh, Pa, July 18, 46; m 65; c 3. ELECTROCHEMISTRY. *Educ:* Univ Pittsburgh, BS, 71; Univ Tex, Austin, PhD(chem), 74. *Prof Exp:* Fel, Calif Inst Technol, 74-76; ASST PROF CHEM, TEX TECH UNIV, 76- *Concurrent Pos:* Consult, Monogram Indust, 75-76, Westvaco, 79- & Mikro Environ Lab, 80- *Mem:* Am Chem Soc; Electrochem Soc. *Res:* Electroorganic synthesis; homogeneous transition metal catalysis via electrochemically generated organometallic; kinetics and mechanisms of reactions initiated electrochemically. *Mailing Add:* Dept Chem Tex Tech Univ PO Box 4260 Lubbock TX 79409

SMITH, WAYNE LEE, b Oneonta, NY, Jan 29, 36; m 59; c 3. INORGANIC CHEMISTRY, PHYSICAL CHEMISTRY. *Educ:* Hartwick Col, BA, 57; Pa State Univ, PhD(chem), 63. *Prof Exp:* Res assoc chem, Univ Mich, 63-64; res chemist, Allied Chem Corp, 64-66; asst prof chem, Carnegie-Mellon Univ, 66-67; asst prof, 67-76, ASSOC PROF CHEM, COLBY COL, 76- *Concurrent Pos:* Vis prof, Univ Mich, Ann Arbor, 74-75. *Mem:* Am Chem Soc; Royal Soc Chem. *Res:* Coordination compounds of the nontransition metal elements; organometallics; heteroborane chemistry; chemical education. *Mailing Add:* Dept of Chem Colby Col Waterville ME 04901

SMITH, WENDELL R(OY), physics, electrical engineering, deceased

SMITH, WENDELL VANDERVORT, b Caldwell, Idaho, Apr 16, 12; m 38; c 3. PHYSICAL CHEMISTRY. *Educ:* Col Idaho, BS, 33; Univ Calif, PhD(phys chem), 37. *Prof Exp:* Res chemist, Gen Labs, US Rubber Co, 37-59 & Res Ctr, 59-72; res chemist corp res & develop, Oxford Mgt & Res Ctr, Uniroyal Inc, 72-77. *Mem:* Am Chem Soc. *Res:* Ionic entropies; new rubber products; theory of emulsion polymerization; physical properties of rubbers; radiation chemistry of polymers. *Mailing Add:* 3 Nettleton Ave Newton CT 06470

SMITH, WESLEY EARL, organic chemistry, see previous edition

SMITH, WESLEY R, b Allentown, Pa, Nov 5, 28; m 55; c 6. FLUID PHYSICS, MOLECULAR PHYSICS. *Educ:* Lehigh Univ, BS, 50, MS, 51; Princeton Univ, PhD(physics), 57. *Prof Exp:* Instr, Princeton Univ, 56-58; from asst prof to assoc prof, 58-74, PROF PHYSICS, LEHIGH UNIV, 74- *Mem:* AAAS; Am Phys Soc. *Res:* Application of shock tubes to measurements of chemical and physical properties of gases, liquids and solids; application of Vande Graaff particle beams to the study of thin films and solid surfaces. *Mailing Add:* Dept of Physics Lehigh Univ Bethlehem PA 18015

SMITH, WILLARD NEWELL, b Wellington, Kans, Jan 27, 26. CELL PHYSIOLOGY. *Educ:* Univ Md, BS, 50, MS, 53, PhD, 66. *Prof Exp:* Asst parasitologist, Ga Exp Sta, 54-57; parasitologist, Animal Dis & Parasite Res Div, USDA, 57-62 & Sch Dent, Univ Md, 62-66; ASSOC PROF DENT, UNIV TEX DENT SCI INST HOUSTON, 66- *Concurrent Pos:* Nat Inst Dent Res spec fel, Univ Tex Dent Br Houston, 67-70. *Mem:* Int Asn Dent Res; Am Soc Parasitol; Am Soc Microbiol. *Res:* Isolation and characterization of virus-like particles from oral microorganisms; parasites of South American primates. *Mailing Add:* Univ of Tex Dent Sci Inst Box 20068 Houston TX 77025

SMITH, WILLIAM ADAMS, JR, b Parkersburg, WV, July 13, 29; m 51; c 5. INDUSTRIAL ENGINEERING. *Educ:* Naval Acad, BS, 51; Lehigh Univ, MS, 57; NY Univ, DEngSc, 66. *Prof Exp:* Instr indust eng, Lehigh Univ, 55-57, dir, Comput Lab, 57-67, prof indust eng, 67-73; prof & head, Dept Indust Eng, 73-82, DIR, PRODUCTIVITY RES & EXTENSION PROG, NC STATE UNIV, 82- *Concurrent Pos:* Alcoa Professorship, Lehigh Univ, 68-69; Ford Found residency eng, Am Soc Eng Educ, Smith Kline Corp, 69-70; consult, IBM, Air Prod, Western Elec Co & Gen Elec; Am Asn Coop Eng & Bd Eng Coop; fel Am Inst Indust Engrs (pres, 75-76); Sigma Xi; Inst Mgt Sci; Am Soc Eng Educ. *Res:* Management systems engineering; source data automation. *Mailing Add:* 1620 Hunting Ridge Rd Raleigh NC 27609

SMITH, WILLIAM ALLEN, b Ashland, Ky, June 26, 40; m 66; c 2. MATHEMATICS. *Educ:* Mass Inst Technol, BS, 62, PhD(math), 66. *Prof Exp:* Asst prof math, Univ SC, 66-70; ASSOC PROF MATH, GA STATE UNIV, 70- *Mem:* Math Asn Am. *Res:* Differential equations; difference equations; numerical analysis. *Mailing Add:* Dept of Math Ga State Univ Atlanta GA 30303

SMITH, WILLIAM BOYCE, b Port Arthur, Tex, Sept 7, 38; m 63; c 3. MATHEMATICAL STATISTICS. *Educ:* Lamar Univ, BS, 59; Tex A&M Univ, MS, 60, PhD(statist), 67. *Prof Exp:* Asst prof math, Lamar State Col, 62-64; from asst prof to assoc prof, 66-73, asst dean col sci, 72-77, PROF STATIST, TEX A&M UNIV, 73-, DIR INST STATIST, 77- *Concurrent Pos:* Vis prof, Southern Methodist Univ, 70 & Nat Agr Exp Sta, Argentina, 77; vis scholar, Japanese Soc for Prom Sci, 80. *Mem:* Biomet Soc; Am Statist Asn; Math Asn Am. *Res:* Statistical estimation theory with incomplete observation vectors; applications of numerical solutions to partial differential equations to stochastic processes; multivariate analysis. *Mailing Add:* 1040 Rose Circle College Station TX 77840

SMITH, WILLIAM BRIDGES, b Washington, DC, Feb 13, 44; m 65; c 2. COMPUTER SCIENCE, ELECTRICAL ENGINEERING. *Educ:* Univ Md, BS, 62; Princeton Univ, MS, 63; Univ Pa, PhD(elec eng), 67. *Prof Exp:* Mem tech staff, Prog Design, 62-67, supvr number 4, Electronic Switching

Syst, 67-70, dept head toll studies, 70-74, dir, Oper, Opers Systs, 74-77 & Local Electronic Switching Syst Appln, 77-78, exec dir, Toll Electronic Switching & Oper Serv Div, Bell Tel Labs, 78-79, EXEC DIR, LOCAL DIGITAL SWITCHING DIV, BELL LABS, 79- *Concurrent Pos:* Instr, Ill Inst Technol, 68-70; bd of overseers, Armor Col Eng, Ill Inst Technol, 80- *Mem:* Inst Elec & Electronics Engrs. *Res:* Management of large software and hardware development; telecommunications. *Mailing Add:* 819 Golf Lane Wheaton IL 60187

SMITH, WILLIAM BURTON, b Muncie, Ind, Dec 13, 27; m 53; c 2. ORGANIC CHEMISTRY. *Educ:* Kalamazoo Col, BA, 49; Brown Univ, PhD(chem), 54. *Prof Exp:* Res assoc chem, Fla State Univ, 53-54 & Univ Chicago, 54-55; from asst prof to assoc prof, Ohio Univ, 55-61; prof chem & chmn dept, Tex Christian Univ, 61-81. *Concurrent Pos:* Partic fel, Oak Ridge Assoc Univs, 55-; Welch vis scientist, Tex Christian Univ, 60-61; vis prof, Univ Sussex, UK, 81. *Mem:* Am Chem Soc. *Res:* Physical organic chemistry of carbonium ions and free radicals; nuclear magnetic resonance; biosynthesis and action of steroid hormones. *Mailing Add:* Dept of Chem Tex Christian Univ Ft Worth TX 76129

SMITH, WILLIAM CONRAD, b Cisco, Tex, May 20, 37; m 59; c 2. PHYSICS. *Educ:* NTex State Univ, BS, 60, MS, 62; Iowa State Univ, PhD(physics), 71. *Prof Exp:* Instr physics & math, Decatur Baptist Col, 61-62; asst prof physics, Howard Payne Col, 62-64 & Mankato State Col, 70-73; asst prof, 73-77, ASSOC PROF PHYSICS, TEX WOMANS UNIV, 77- *Mem:* Am Asn Physicists in Med; Am Phys Soc; Am Asn Physics Teachers. *Res:* Hyperfine fields in magnetic metallic compounds; nuclear magnetic resonance; effect of magnetic fields on axon signals; design of microprocessor-based instruments. *Mailing Add:* Dept Math & Physics Tex Womans Univ Box 22865 Denton TX 76204

SMITH, WILLIAM DAVID, JR, chemical engineering, see previous edition

SMITH, WILLIAM EDGAR, b Baltimore, Md, Feb 14, 14; m; c 2. EXPERIMENTAL PATHOLOGY. *Educ:* Princeton Univ, AB, 34; Johns Hopkins Univ, MD, 38. *Prof Exp:* Fel bact, Harvard Med Sch, 38-39 & 41-42; fel med, Mass Gen Hosp, 40-41; asst bact, Harvard Med Sch, 42-43; asst path, Rockefeller Inst Med Res, 43-47; assoc, Sloan Kettering Inst Cancer Res, 47-49; from asst prof to assoc prof indust med, NY Univ-Bellevue Med Ctr, 49-56; prof health educ, 57-68, DIR HEALTH RES INST, FAIRLEIGH DICKINSON UNIV, 60- *Concurrent Pos:* Mem comts, Int Union Against Cancer, Belg, 52, Brazil, 54, Eng, 58, Japan, 60, Nat Lung Cancer Confs, 52-53, Lung Tumors, Italy, 65, Conf Biol Effects Asbestos, Dresden, 68 & WHO/Int Agency Res Cancer, Conf Biol Effects Mineral Fibers, France, 79; asst clin prof community med, Mt Sinai Sch Med & consult, Environ Sci Lab, 66-73. *Mem:* Am Asn Cancer Res; Am Asn Path & Bact; Am Indust Hyg Asn. *Res:* Animal tests for chemical carcinogens, tumor viruses. *Mailing Add:* Health Res Inst Fairleigh Dickinson Univ Madison NJ 07940

SMITH, WILLIAM EDMOND, b Wilmington, NC, Nov 16, 39; m 67; c 3. PULP CHEMISTRY, PAPER CHEMISTRY. *Educ:* NC State Univ, MS, 65, PhD(wood & paper sci), 69. *Prof Exp:* Res forest prod technologist, US Forest Prod Lab, 64-69; sr res chemist, Res Lab, 69-72, DIR TECH SERV, PAPER DIV, SONOCO PROD CO, 72- *Mem:* Tech Asn Pulp & Paper Indust; Soc Wood Sci & Technol. *Res:* Product development; stress analysis of structures produced from paper and plastics; basic failure criteria of materials; process control. *Mailing Add:* Paper Div Sonoco Prod Co Hartsville SC 29550

SMITH, WILLIAM EDWARD, b Philadelphia, Pa, May 30, 38; m 63; c 2. INDUSTRIAL ORGANIC CHEMISTRY, CHEMICAL ENGINEERING. *Educ:* La Salle Col, BS, 65; Purdue Univ, Lafayette, PhD(chem), 69. *Prof Exp:* NIH fel, Mass Inst Technol, 69-70; res chemist, 70-74, mgr, Catalytic Processes Unit, 74-79, MGR, CHEM ENG BR, GEN ELEC RES & DEVELOP CTR, 79- *Mem:* Am Chem Soc; Catalysis Soc. *Res:* Process research and development; homogeneous and heterogeneous catalysis; monomer synthesis. *Mailing Add:* Gen Elec Res & Develop Ctr Schenectady NY 12345

SMITH, WILLIAM FORTUNE, b Vancouver, BC, Oct 11, 31; US citizen; m 58; c 3. MATERIALS SCIENCE, PHYSICAL METALLURGY. *Educ:* Univ BC, BA, 52; Purdue Univ, MS, 55; Mass Inst Technol, ScD(phys metall), 68. *Prof Exp:* Res engr, Metall Res Labs, Reynolds Metals Co, Va, 57-62; res engr, Metall Res Labs, Kaiser Aluminum Co, Washington, 65-67; assoc prof, 68-71, PROF ENG, FLA TECHNOL UNIV, 71- *Mem:* Am Soc Metals; Am Inst Mining, Metall & Petrol Engrs. *Res:* Precipitation reactions in the solid state; physical metallurgy of aluminum alloys; stress corrosion cracking. *Mailing Add:* Col of Eng PO Box 25000 Orlando FL 32816

SMITH, WILLIAM GRADY, b Dover, Ark, Mar 29, 37; m 59; c 3. BIOCHEMISTRY. *Educ:* Univ Ark, BS, 59, MS, 60; Okla State Univ, PhD(biochem), 64. *Prof Exp:* Asst prof biochem & path, 64-66, from asst prof to assoc prof biochem, 66-77, PROF BIOCHEM, SCH MED, UNIV ARK, LITTLE ROCK, 77- *Concurrent Pos:* Fel biochem, Univ Minn, 63-64; res grants, NSF, 65-75 & NIH, 67-70; Lederle med fac award, 68-71. *Mem:* Am Soc Biol Chem. *Res:* Amino acid metabolism; metabolic control. *Mailing Add:* Dept of Biochem Univ of Ark Med Sch Little Rock AR 72201

SMITH, WILLIAM HAROLD, b Kingston, Okla, Jan 25, 29; m 54; c 2. ANIMAL SCIENCE. *Educ:* Okla State Univ, BS, 56; Purdue Univ, MS, 57, PhD(animal nutrit), 59. *Prof Exp:* Prof animal nutrit & mgt, Purdue Univ, West Lafayette, 59-76; RESIDENT DIR RES, TEX A&M UNIV, 76- *Concurrent Pos:* Sabbatical, Univ Calif, Davis, 66. *Mem:* Am Soc Animal Sci; Sigma Xi; Am Soc Agron. *Res:* Nutrient requirements of beef cows; value of cornstalks; methods of preventing grass tetany; value of liquid supplements; total digestible nutrients for heifers; value of forage quality. *Mailing Add:* Tex A&M Univ Overton TX 75689

SMITH, WILLIAM HAYDEN, b Paducah, Ky, Oct 19, 40; m 65. ASTRONOMY. *Educ:* Univ Ky, BS, 62; Princeton Univ, MA, 63, PhD(phys chem), 66. *Prof Exp:* Res assoc chem physics, Princeton Univ, 66; res assoc surface physics, Univ Ky, 66-67; res assoc astrophys, 68, res staff, 69-73, res astronr, Princeton Univ Observ, 73-76; PROF DEPTS CHEM & EARTH & PLANETARY SCI, WASH UNIV, 76- *Concurrent Pos:* NATO sr fel, Inst Physics, Stockholm, 71; NSF res grant, Princeton Univ Observ, 71-; NATO sr fel, 75; vis prof, Inst Astron, Univ Hawaii, 75-76; fel, McDonnell Ctr Space Sci, 75- *Mem:* Am Chem Soc; Am Phys Soc; Am Astron Soc; Int Astron Union. *Res:* Planetary atmospheres; atomic and molecular physics. *Mailing Add:* Wash Univ Dept Chem St Louis MO 63130

SMITH, WILLIAM HULSE, b Trenton, NJ, May 9, 39; m 63; c 2. PLANT PATHOLOGY. *Educ:* Rutgers Univ, BS, 61, PhD(plant path), 65; Yale Univ, MF, 63. *Prof Exp:* Asst prof forestry, Rutgers Univ, 64-66; asst prof, 66-72, asst dean, 71-78, assoc prof forest path, 72-78, assoc dean, Sch Forestry & Environ Studies, 78-81, PROF FOREST PATH, YALE UNIV, 79-, ACTG DEAN, 81- *Mem:* AAAS; Am Phytopath Soc; Ecol Soc Am; Soc Am Foresters; Sigma Xi. *Res:* Chemistry and biological significance of materials released from tree roots; influence of gaseous and particulate air contaminants on woody plant health. *Mailing Add:* Sch Forestry & Environ Studies Yale Univ New Haven CT 06511

SMITH, WILLIAM K, b Danville, Pa, Mar 8, 20; m 47; c 2. MATHEMATICS. *Educ:* Bucknell Univ, AB, 41, MA, 46; Univ Mich, PhD(math), 53. *Prof Exp:* Instr math, Bucknell Univ, 41-42 & 46-47, asst prof, 51-56; assoc prof, Antioch Col, 56-57; prof, Bucknell Univ, 57-64, New Col, 64-66 & Hobart & William Smith Cols, 66-67; prof math, New Col, Fla, 67-76; PROF MATH & CHMN DEPT, ILL WESLEYAN UNIV, 76- *Mem:* Am Math Soc; Math Asn Am. *Res:* Functional analysis. *Mailing Add:* Dept of Math Ill Wesleyan Univ Bloomington IL 61701

SMITH, WILLIAM KIRBY, b Greensboro, NC, Mar 6, 47; m 80; c 2. BIOPHYSICAL ECOLOGY, ENVIRONMENTAL PHYSIOLOGY. *Educ:* San Diego State Col, BS, 67, MS, 71; Univ Calif, Los Angeles, PhD, 77. *Prof Exp:* ASST PROF, UNIV WYO, 77- *Mem:* Am Soc Plant Physiologists; Ecol Soc Am; AAAS; Am Inst Biol Sci; Bot Soc Am. *Res:* Biophysical and physiological ecology; plant and animal adaptations in harsh or unusual environments; photosynthesis, water relations and growth physiology. *Mailing Add:* Dept Bot Univ Wyo Laramie NY 82071

SMITH, WILLIAM LEE, b Providence, RI, June 3, 22; m 57; c 3. EXPLORATION GEOLOGY, REMOTE SENSING. *Educ:* Columbia Univ, AB, 49; Rutgers Univ, MS, 51. *Prof Exp:* Petrologist, US Geol Surv, Washington, DC, 52-56; prin geologist, Battelle Mem Inst, 56-67; geologist, Bellcomm, Inc, Washington, DC, 67-72; geologist, Syst Planning Corp, 72-75 & ERIM, Washington, DC, 75-78; VPRES, SPECTRAL DATA CORP, 78- *Honors & Awards:* NASA Apollo Achievement Award, 69; Am Tel & Tel Cert Recognition, 69. *Mem:* Am Inst Prof Geologists; fel Geol Soc Am; Am Soc Photogram. *Res:* Mineralogy of ores of radioactive and rarer elements; economic geology; remote sensing for mineral deposits; systems analysis and planning for earth resources observation from satellites. *Mailing Add:* Spectral Data Corp Suite 1000 1901 N Moore St Arlington VA 22209

SMITH, WILLIAM LEE, b Tulsa, Okla, Oct 28, 45; m 68; c 3. BIOCHEMISTRY. *Educ:* Univ Colo, Boulder, BA, 67; Univ Mich, Ann Arbor, PhD(biol chem), 71. *Prof Exp:* NIH fel biochem, Univ Calif, Berkeley, 71-74; sr scientist biochem, Mead Johnson & Co, Bristol-Myers Co, 74-75; asst prof, 75-79, PROF BIOCHEM, MICH STATE UNIV, 79- *Concurrent Pos:* Estab investr, Am Heart Asn. *Mem:* AAAS; Am Soc Biol Chemists. *Res:* Regulation of prostaglandin metabolism; mechanism of luteolysis; platelet aggregation; biochemistry of anti-inflammatory drugs. *Mailing Add:* Dept Biochem Mich State Univ East Lansing MI 48824

SMITH, WILLIAM MAYO, JR, b Fredericksburg, Va, Nov 30, 17; m 40; c 4. ORGANIC POLYMER CHEMISTRY. *Educ:* Va Mil Inst, BS, 38; Univ Ala, MS, 41; Univ Md, PhD(org chem), 46. *Prof Exp:* Cellulose chemist, Sylvania Indust Corp, Va, 38-43; instr chem, Univ Md, 43-46; sr res chemist, Firestone Tire & Rubber Co, 47-54, group leader, Defense Res Div, 54-56; asst dir res & develop, Escambia Chem Corp, Conn, 56-58, vpres & dir res, 58-67; vpres, Air Reduction Co, Inc, NY, 67-69; tech dir polymers & plastics, Air Prod & Chem, Inc, 69-71, group res & develop coordr, Chem Group, 71-79, dir sci affairs, 79-81; CONSULT CHEM & PLASTICS, 81- *Mem:* Am Chem Soc; Soc Plastics Indust; Soc Plastics Engrs; Am Mgt Asn; Chem Mfg Asn. *Res:* Plastics; polymerizations; petrochemicals; organic reactions; chemical carcinogens and toxic substances; industrial research management. *Mailing Add:* 20 Painted Bunting Amelia Island Plantation FL 32034

SMITH, WILLIAM NOVIS, JR, b Chicago, Ill, May 21, 37; m 58. ORGANIC CHEMISTRY, INORGANIC CHEMISTRY. *Educ:* Mass Inst Technol, BS, 59; Univ Calif, Berkeley, PhD(org chem), 68. *Prof Exp:* Res chemist, Org Chem Dept, E I du Pont de Nemours & Co, 62-64; res assoc chem, Foote Mineral Co, 64-71, mgr chem res, 72-74; asst to dir, Eastern Res Ctr, Stauffer Chem Co, 74-76; asst dir corp res, Air Prod, 76-77, asst dir contract res, 77-79; mgr develop progs, Reentry Systs Div, Gen Elec Co, 80-82; CONSULT. *Mem:* Am Chem Soc; Royal Soc Chem; Inst Elec & Electronics Engrs. *Res:* Catalysis, inorganic and organic lithium chemistry; organometallic chemistry; extractive metallurgy, catalysts, polymers, anionic polymerization; polyolefin catalysts. *Mailing Add:* 135 S 18th St Philadelphia PA 19103

SMITH, WILLIAM OGG, b Shawnee, Okla, July 17, 25; m 48; c 3. MEDICINE. *Educ:* Harvard Med Sch, MD, 49. *Prof Exp:* Intern, Univ Chicago, 49-50; resident med, Vet Admin Hosps, Boston, 52-54 & Oklahoma City, 54-55; chief resident & clin asst med, 55-56, from instr to assoc prof, 56-66, vchmn dept med, 67-75, PROF MED, MED SCH, UNIV OKLA, 66- *Concurrent Pos:* Asst dir radioisotope serv, Vet Admin Hosp, Oklahoma City, 56-60, from assoc chief to chief med serv, 60-71. *Mem:* Fel Am Col Physicians; Soc Exp Biol & Med; Am Soc Nephrol. *Res:* Renal and electrolyte physiology; magnesium metabolism. *Mailing Add:* Dept of Med Univ of Okla Oklahoma City OK 73104

SMITH, WILLIAM OWEN, b Louisville, Ky, Sept 2, 41; m 64; c 2. PHOTOBIOLOGY. *Educ:* Univ Ky, BS, 67, PhD(plant physiol), 75. *Prof Exp:* PLANT PHYSIOLOGIST, RADIATION BIOL LAB, SMITHSONIAN INST, 75- *Mem:* Am Soc Plant Physiologists; Am Soc Photobiol. *Res:* Molecular aspects of plant photomorphogenesis; biochemistry of phytochrome. *Mailing Add:* Radiation Biol Lab Smithsonian Inst 12441 Parklawn Dr Rockville MD 20852

SMITH, WILLIAM R, b Lyman, Okla, June 26, 25. BIOPHYSICS, MATHEMATICS. *Educ:* Bethany Nazarene Col, BA, 48; Wichita State Univ, MA, 50; Univ Calif, Los Angeles, PhD(biophys), 67. *Prof Exp:* Engr, Beech Aircraft Corp, 51-53; sr group engr, McDonnell Aircraft Corp, 53-60; asst prof math & physics, Pasadena Col, 60-62; sr engr, Lockheed Aircraft Corp, 62-63; sr engr-scientist, McDonnell Douglas Aircraft Corp, 66-71; teacher math, Glendale Col, Calif, 72; asst prof math & physics, Mount St Mary's Col, 72-73; TECH STAFF, ROCKWELL INT CORP, 73- *Mem:* AAAS; Sigma Xi; Aerospace Med Asn; Aerospace Industs Asn Am. *Res:* Mathematical analysis of the electrical activity of the brain; mathematical modeling; time series analysis; engineering dynamics; digital signal processing; image processing. *Mailing Add:* 2405 Roscomare Rd Los Angeles CA 90024

SMITH, WILLIAM ROBERT, b San Antonio, Tex, Jan 11, 35; m 63. NUCLEAR PHYSICS. *Educ:* Univ Tex, BS, 57, BA, 58, PhD(physics), 63. *Prof Exp:* Res assoc nuclear physics, Nuclear Physics Lab, Univ Tex, 63 & Neutron Physics Div, Oak Ridge Nat Lab, 63-65; sr res officer, Nuclear Physics Lab, Oxford Univ, 65-66; res assoc nuclear physics, Nuclear Physics Lab, Univ Southern Calif, 66; ASSOC PROF PHYSICS, TRINITY UNIV, TEX, 67- *Concurrent Pos:* Ed low energy nuclear physics, Comput Physics Commun, 68- *Mem:* Am Phys Soc. *Res:* Low energy nuclear reaction theory. *Mailing Add:* Dept of Physics Trinity Univ San Antonio TX 78284

SMITH, WILLIAM RUSSELL, b Denton, Tex, Jan 13, 17; m 39; c 2. MICROBIOLOGY. *Educ:* NTex State Univ, BS, 37, MS, 38; Univ Tex, PhD(bact), 55. *Prof Exp:* From asst prof to prof, 46-73, REGENTS PROF BIOL, LAMAR UNIV, 73- *Concurrent Pos:* Res scientist, Univ Tex, 51-53. *Mem:* Am Soc Microbiol; Sigma Xi; NY Acad Sci. *Res:* Chemical and heat activation of bacterial spores; bacteriology of foods; medical bacteriology; general, food and medical microbiology. *Mailing Add:* Dept of Biol Lamar Univ Beaumont TX 77710

SMITH, WILLIAM RUTHVEN, III, b Breaux Bridge, La, June 27, 35; m 61; c 3. MICROCOMPUTER SYSTEMS. *Educ:* Trinity Col, Conn, BS, 56; George Washington Univ, BEE, 58, MSE, 59; Univ Conn, PhD(eng, phys electronics), 69. *Prof Exp:* Instr eng, Trinity Col, Conn, 61-64; instr math, Univ Conn, 64-68; asst prof elec eng, Univ Bridgeport, 68-78; sr systs programmer, Intec Corp, 77-78; sr engr, Systs Design, Spec Purpose Comput Ctr, Gen Elec Co, 78-80; partner, Microwave Assocs, 78-80; WITH SOFTWARE DEVELOPMENT, INTEC CORP, 80- *Mem:* Math Asn Am; Inst Elec & Electronics Engrs. *Res:* Microprocessor systems; software; operating systems; switching theory; matrix methods, multi-valued logic. *Mailing Add:* Software Development Intec Corp Trumbull CT 06611

SMITH, WILLIAM S, b Greenwich, Conn, July 29, 18; m; c 4. ORTHOPEDIC SURGERY. *Educ:* Univ Mich, AB, 40, MD, 43; Am Bd Orthop Surg, dipl, 53. *Prof Exp:* Instr orthop surg, Univ Mich, 50; from instr to prof, Ohio State Univ, 52-63; PROF ORTHOP SURG, UNIV MICH, ANN ARBOR, 63- *Concurrent Pos:* Res grants, Easter Seal Found, 56-59, Orthop Res & Educ Found, 60 & NIH, 61-63. *Mem:* Fel Am Acad Orthop Surg; Orthop Res Soc; Clin Orthop Soc; Am Orthop Asn; Am Asn Surg of Trauma. *Res:* Congenital dislocation of the hip. *Mailing Add:* Dept of Orthop Surg Univ of Mich Med Ctr Ann Arbor MI 48109

SMITH, WILLIAM WALKER, b Duncan, Okla, Sept 26, 40; m 59; c 3. MATHEMATICS. *Educ:* Southeastern State Col, BS, 61; La State Univ, MS, 63, PhD(math), 65. *Prof Exp:* Asst prof, 65-71, chmn dept, 76-81, assoc prof, 71-79, PROF MATH, UNIV NC, CHAPEL HILL, 79- *Mem:* Math Asn Am; Am Math Soc; Nat Coun Teachers Math. *Res:* Algebra; commutative ring and ideal theory; mathematics education. *Mailing Add:* Dept of Math Univ of NC Chapel Hill NC 27514

SMITH, WILLIAM WARD, b Greenfield, Tenn, July 7, 14; m 40; c 2. MEDICAL ENTOMOLOGY, ECONOMIC ENTOMOLOGY. *Educ:* Univ Tenn, AB, 36; Cornell Univ, MA, 37; Tulane Univ, PhD(med entom), 52. *Prof Exp:* Asst entom, Univ Mo, 37-43; med entomologist, USPHS, Miss, 43-51, vector control rep, Region X, 51-52, scientist, Newton Field Sta, 52-57; asst res prof, 57-62, assoc res prof, 62-72, EMER ASSOC PROF MED ENTOM & PUB HEALTH, UNIV FLA, 72- *Mem:* Entom Soc Am; Sigma Xi; Am Mosquito Control Asn. *Res:* Mosquito and fly control; taxonomy and control of rodent ectoparasites. *Mailing Add:* 1948 NW 31st Terrace Gainesville FL 32605

SMITH, WILLIS DEAN, b Ipava, Ill, Aug 5, 42; m 66. SOLID STATE PHYSICS. *Educ:* Bradley Univ, BS, 64; Washington Univ, MA, 66, PhD(physics), 70. *Prof Exp:* Tech staff mem physics, Sandia Labs, NMex, 70-75; sci staff mem, Comt Sci & Technol, US House Rep, 75-77; PROF STAFF MEM, COMT ON ENERGY & NATURAL RESOURCES, US SENATE, 77- *Concurrent Pos:* Energy consult, Comt Interior & Insular Affairs, US Sen, 74-75; Inst Elec & Electronics Engrs cong sci fel, 74-75. *Mem:* AAAS; Inst Elec & Electronics Engrs. *Res:* Ultrasonics; electron-phonon interactions; surface waves; ferroelectric ceramics; information processing and display; photoconductors; electrooptics and photovoltaic materials and devices; solar energy. *Mailing Add:* US Senate Comt on Energy & Natural Resources Rm 3106 Dirksen Senate Off Bldg Washington DC 20510

SMITH, WILLY, b Dec 7, 25. NUCLEAR ENGINEERING, PHYSICS. *Educ:* Univ of the Repub, Uruguay, BSE, 53; Univ Mich, MSE, 55, PhD, 64. *Prof Exp:* Design engr, Ford Motor Co, 56-58; teaching fel, Univ Mich, Ann Arbor, 58-61, res asst, 61-64; lectr physics, Univ Mich, Dearborn, 64, vis asst prof, 65; res assoc nuclear eng, Univ Mich, Ann Arbor, 65; assoc prof, Univ PR, 65; chief scientist, PR Nuclear Ctr, 65; ASSOC PROF PHYSICS, LYCOMING COL, 66-, CHMN DEPT ASTRON & PHYSICS, 76- *Concurrent Pos:* Lectr, Univ Mich, 61-70; vis prof, Inst Corpuscular Radiation, Fac Sci, Univ Valencia, Spain, 73-74, chmn dept astron & physics, 74-77. *Mem:* Am Asn Physics Teachers; Sigma Xi. *Res:* Natural convection; cavitation; nuclear instrumentation; gamma spectroscopy; UFOs. *Mailing Add:* Dept Physics Lycoming Col Williamsport PA 17701

SMITH, WILSON LEVERING, JR, plant pathology, deceased

SMITH, WINFIELD SCOTT, b Detroit, Mich, Nov 1, 41; m 63. OPTICS. *Educ:* Oakland Univ, BA, 63; Univ Ariz, MS, 67, PhD(physics), 70. *Prof Exp:* Asst prof physics, Univ Nev, Reno, 70-71; res assoc, Univ Ariz, 70 & 71, prog mgr, Optical Sci Ctr, 72-79; PROD MGR, CONTRAVES-GOERZ CORP, PITTSBURGH, 79- *Mem:* Am Phys Soc; Optical Soc Am. *Res:* Atmospheric optics; optical testing and fabrication. *Mailing Add:* 727 Old Mill Rd Pittsburgh PA 15238

SMITH, WINTHROP WARE, b New York, NY, Aug 4, 36; m 65; c 1. EXPERIMENTAL ATOMIC PHYSICS. *Educ:* Amherst Col, BA, 58; Mass Inst Technol, PhD(physics), 63. *Prof Exp:* Nat Acad Sci-Nat Res Coun res assoc physics, Nat Bur Standards, 63-65; instr, Columbia Univ, 65-66, asst prof, 66-69; assoc prof, 69-75, PROF PHYSICS, UNIV CONN, 75- *Concurrent Pos:* Mem, Joint Inst Lab Astrophys, Boulder, Colo, 63-65, vis fel, 75-76; lectr physics, Univ Colo, 64-65; res partic, Oak Ridge Nat Lab, 69- *Mem:* AAAS; fel Am Phys Soc. *Res:* Beam-foil spectroscopy; low energy nuclear physics; atomic physics and collisions; atomic hyperfine structure and lifetimes of excited states; laser spectroscopy. *Mailing Add:* Dept of Physics Univ of Conn Storrs CT 06268

SMITH, WIRT WILSEY, b Colorado Springs, Colo, Nov 2, 20; m 50; c 2. MEDICINE. *Educ:* Rice Inst, BA, 42; Univ Tex, MD, 51. *Prof Exp:* Anal chemist, Dow Chem Co, 42-44; intern, Univ Wis Hosps, 51-52; resident path, Univ Tex M D Anderson Hosp & Tumor Inst, 52-56; assoc exp surg, 58-59, asst prof, 59-65, ASSOC PROF EXP SURG, SCH MED, DUKE UNIV, 65- *Concurrent Pos:* Hite fel, Univ Tex M D Anderson Hosp & Tumor Inst, 53-56; USPHS fel, Sch Med, Duke Univ, 56-57; Nat Inst Neurol Dis & Blindness clin trainee, 57-58; mem, hyperbaric prog proj, Duke Univ, Med Ctr, 63- *Mem:* AAAS; Am Fedn Clin Res. *Res:* Hyperbaric oxygenation and physiology. *Mailing Add:* Dept of Surg Duke Univ Med Ctr Box 3823 Durham NC 27706

SMITH, WRAY, b Los Angeles, Calif, Oct 11, 24; m 64; c 5. OPERATIONS RESEARCH, STATISTICS. *Educ:* George Washington Univ, BA, 48, DSc, 80; Univ Mich, MS, 58. *Prof Exp:* Physicist, Nat Bur Standards, 48-53; sci asst, Naval Ord Lab, Calif, 53-54; assoc res engr & inst asst dir, Univ Mich, 55-62; dep assoc dir & sr training officer, Peace Corps, 62-63; exec dir, Consumers Union Us, Inc, 63-64; assoc Job Corps dir & spec asst, Off Econ Opportunity, Washington, DC, 65-67; prin opers res analyst, 67-73; dir tech planning & eval, Dept Health, Educ & Welfare, 73-80; ASST ADMINR & DIR ENERGY MARKETS & END USE, ENERGY INFO ADMIN, 80- *Concurrent Pos:* Tutor, St John's Col, Md, 50-51; tech adv, US Cong, 61-62. *Mem:* Inst Mgt Sci; Opers Res Soc Am; Am Statist Asn; Inst Math Statist; Economet Soc. *Res:* Quanitative methods in economic dynamics and policy research; applied probability models; statistical forecasting techniques; survey planning and data analysis; operations research problems in public programs; mathematical demography; energy model development. *Mailing Add:* PO Box 70065 Washington DC 20088

SMITHBERG, EUGENE H, b New York, NY, June 3, 22; m 53; c 2. MECHANICAL ENGINEERING. *Educ:* City Col New York, BSME, 43; Brooklyn Poltech Inst, MME, 49; NY Univ, DEngSc, 61. *Prof Exp:* Proj engr, Va Lincoln Corp, Va, 43-44; from instr to assoc prof, 50-61, assoc dean grad div, 64-67, actg vpres acad affairs, 76-80, PROF MECH ENG, NJ INST TECHNOL, 61-, DEAN GRAD DIV, 67- *Concurrent Pos:* Consult, Liquid Rocket Propulsion Lab, Picatinny Arsenal, 63- *Mem:* AAAS; Am Soc Mech Engrs. *Res:* Heat transfer; fluid flow. *Mailing Add:* Grad Div 323 High St Newark NJ 07102

SMITHBERG, MORRIS, b Brooklyn, NY, Aug 28, 24; m 54; c 3. EMBRYOLOGY, NEUROANATOMY. *Educ:* Univ Rochester, PhD(zool), 53. *Prof Exp:* Asst biol, Univ Rochester, 48-52; fel, Jackson Mem Lab, 52-57; asst prof anat, Univ Fla, 57-60; from asst prof to assoc prof, 60-69, actg head dept, 75-77, PROF ANAT, UNIV MINN, MINNEAPOLIS, 69- *Mem:* Am Asn Anat. *Res:* Development in frogs; pregnancy in prepuberal mice; teratology in mice and fish. *Mailing Add:* Dept of Anat Univ of Minn Minneapolis MN 55455

SMITHCORS, JAMES FREDERICK, b Camden, NJ, Mar 27, 20; wid; c 4. VETERINARY MEDICINE. *Educ:* Rutgers Univ, BS, 41; Cornell Univ, MS, 43; State Univ NY, DVM, 45; Mich State Univ, PhD, 51. *Prof Exp:* From asst prof to assoc prof anat, Mich State Univ, 45-61; assoc ed, 61-70, ED, AM VET PUBL, 71- *Mem:* Am Vet Med Asn; Am Asn Hist Med; Am Soc Animal Sci; Am Vet Hist Soc. *Res:* History of veterinary medicine. *Mailing Add:* 553 Scenic Dr Santa Barbara CA 93103

SMITHER, ROBERT KARL, b Buffalo, NY, July 18, 29; m 55; c 3. EXPERIMENTAL NUCLEAR PHYSICS, RADIATION DAMAGE. *Educ:* Univ Buffalo, BA, 51; Yale Univ, MS, 52, PhD(physics), 56. *Prof Exp:* Instr physics, Yale Univ, 55-56; PHYSICIST, ARGONNE NAT LAB, 56- *Mem:* Am Phys Soc; AAAS; Sigma Xi; Am Archaeol Soc. *Res:* The study of nuclear structure of medium to heavy nuclei with neutron captive gamma ray experiments and charge particle experiments with special emphasis on high spin states made through heavy ion reactions. *Mailing Add:* Argonne Nat Lab Physics Div 9700 S Cass Ave Argonne IL 60439

SMITHERMAN, RENFORD ONEAL, b Randolph, Ala, Aug 26, 37; m 59; c 1. FISH BIOLOGY. *Educ:* Auburn Univ, BS, 59, PhD(fisheries), 64; NC State Col, MS, 61. *Prof Exp:* Asst fish cult, Auburn Univ, 61-64; leader, La Coop Fishery Unit, US Bur Sportfish & Wildlife, 64-67; coordr fisheries res, 67-72, assoc prof fisheries & allied aquacult, 72-77, PROF AQUACULT, AUBURN UNIV, 77- *Concurrent Pos:* Chief party, AID-Auburn-Univ-Repub of Panama Aquacult Proj, 72-73. *Mem:* World Maricult Soc; Catfish Farmers of Am; Am Fisheries Soc. *Res:* Fish genetics, hybridization, pathology and ecology; biological weed control with fishes; crawfish ecology; polyculture of fishes; aquaculture. *Mailing Add:* Dept of Fisheries & Allied Aquacult Auburn Univ Auburn AL 36830

SMITH-EVERNDEN, ROBERTA KATHERINE, b Los Angeles, Calif. MICROPALEONTOLOGY. *Educ:* Univ Alaska, BA, 57; Univ Calif, Berkeley, MA, 60; Univ BC, PhD(geol), 66. *Prof Exp:* Geologist, Smithsonian Inst, 65-73; asst prof lectr, George Washington Univ, 67-68; asst prof, Howard Univ, 68-70; RES ASSOC, UNIV CALIF, SANTA CRUZ, 75-, CONSULT RES GEOLOGIST, 77- *Mem:* Paleont Soc; Soc Woman Geogrs; Sigma Xi. *Res:* Distribution and ecology of living benthonic and planktonic Foraminifera; Tertiary biostratigraphy; environmental geology. *Mailing Add:* Earth Sci Bd Univ of Calif Santa Cruz CA 95060

SMITH-GILL, SANDRA JOYCE, b Chicago, Ill, Jan 8, 44; m 67. DEVELOPMENTAL BIOLOGY, ENDOCRINOLOGY. *Educ:* Univ Mich, BS, 65, MS, 66, PhD(zool), 71. *Prof Exp:* Asst prof biol, Swarthmore Col, 71-74; asst prof biol, George Washington Univ, 74-76; vis asst prof, 76-77, ASSOC PROF ZOOL, UNIV MD, 77- *Concurrent Pos:* Biologist, Nat Cancer Inst, 80-82. *Mem:* Int Soc Develop Biol; Soc Develop Biol; Int Pigment Cell Soc; Am Soc Zoologists; Tissue Cult Asn. *Res:* Hormonal regulation of morphogenesis; genetic and structural basis of antibody recognition of protein antigens. *Mailing Add:* Dept Zool Univ of Md College Park MD 20742

SMITHIES, OLIVER, b July 23, 25; US citizen. GENETICS. *Educ:* Oxford Univ, Eng, PhD(biochem), 51. *Prof Exp:* LEON J COLE PROF GENETICS & MED GENETICS, UNIV WIS-MADISON, 60- *Mem:* Nat Acad Sci. *Mailing Add:* Lab of Genetics Univ of Wis Madison WI 53706

SMITH-JOHANNSEN, HEIDI, b Schenectady, NY, Dec 14, 45; m 73. MOLECULAR BIOLOGY. *Educ:* McGill Univ, BSc, 67, MSc, 71, PhD(biol), 76. *Prof Exp:* Fel transport proteins, Lady Davis Inst, Jewish Gen Hosp, 76-78; FEL INTERFERON, DIV MED BIOCHEM, UNIV CALGARY, 78- *Mem:* Sigma Xi; Am Soc Microbiol. *Res:* Interferons, a class of anti-viral glycoproteins, which have potential as an anti-tumor agent; induction and purification of these molecules and how they work. *Mailing Add:* 3727 Silver Springs Dr Univ Calgary Calgary AB T3B 4N3 Can

SMITH-LEWIS, MARGARET J, pharmacology, see previous edition

SMITHSON, GEORGE RAYMOND, JR, b New Vienna, Ohio, Mar 2, 26; m 50; c 3. INORGANIC CHEMISTRY. *Educ:* Wilmington Col, BS, 49; Miami Univ, MS, 50. *Prof Exp:* Asst chem, Miami Univ, 49-50; prof phys sci, Rio Grande Col, 50-52; prin chemist extractive metall div, 52-60, proj leader, 60-61, sr scientist, 61-65, assoc chief minerals & metall waste technol div, 68-70, chief waste control & process technol div, 70-71, asst mgr environ systs & processes dept, 71-74, mgr environ technol prog off, Environ Energy Res Dept, 74-80, MGR ENVIRON PROGS OFF, CHEM DEPT, BATTELLE-COLUMBUS LABS, BATTELLE MEM INST, 80- *Mem:* Fel AAAS; fel Am Inst Chem; Sigma Xi. *Res:* Waste management and control; process technology; fluidized-bed technology; thermodynamics of extractive metallurgical systems; electrowinning; electrodialysis; sorption technology. *Mailing Add:* 3068 Kingston Ave Grove City OH 43123

SMITHSON, JANET ELEANOR, histology, cytology, see previous edition

SMITHSON, SCOTT BUSBY, b Oak Park, Ill, Oct 28, 30; m 53; c 2. GEOPHYSICS, PETROLOGY. *Educ:* Univ Okla, BS, 54; Univ Wyo, MA, 59; Univ Oslo, DSc(petrol geophys), 63. *Prof Exp:* Asst seismologist, Shell Oil Co, 54-57; analyst, Geotech Corp, 57-58; Royal Norweg Coun Sci & Indust Res fel, 63-64; from asst prof to prof geophys, 64-77, PROF GEOL, UNIV WYO, 77- *Mem:* Geol Soc Am; Soc Explor Geophys; Am Geophys Union; Mineral Soc Am; Norweg Geol Soc. *Res:* Solid earth geophysics and petrology; structure and composition of the continental crust of the earth. *Mailing Add:* Dept of Geol Univ of Wyo Laramie WY 82070

SMITH-SONNEBORN, JOAN, b Albany, NY, Nov 5, 35; div; c 2. CELL BIOLOGY. *Educ:* Bryn Mawr Col, BA, 57; Ind Univ, PhD(zool, biochem), 62. *Prof Exp:* Fel biochem, Brandeis Univ, 61-62; fel virol & microbiol, Univ Calif, Berkeley, 62-64; res assoc zool, Univ Wis-Madison, 64-71; ASSOC PROF ZOOL, UNIV WYO, 71- *Mem:* Am Soc Cell Biol; fel Gerontol Soc Am; NY Acad Sci; AAAS. *Res:* Extranuclear DNA of organelles; mutagenesis and repair; cellular aging; interaction of cell components and external environment on the determination of modulation of gene expression during development and aging as well as genotoxicology. *Mailing Add:* Dept of Zool Univ of Wyo Laramie WY 82070

SMITH-THOMAS, BARBARA, b Palo Alto, Calif, Oct 2, 42; c 1. CRYPTOGRAPHIC PROTOCOLS, CRYPTOGRAPHY. *Educ:* Reed Col, BA, 64; Carnegie-Mellon Univ, MS, 70, PhD(math), 73; Ga Inst Technol, MS, 82. *Prof Exp:* Mellon fel, Univ Pittsburgh, 72-73; asst prof math, Memphis State Univ, 73-78, assoc prof, 78-79; vis assoc prof math, Univ Ala, Birmingham, 79-80. *Mem:* Am Math Soc; Math Asn Am; Asn Women Math; Asn Comput Mach. *Res:* Security of cryptographic protocols; complexity of cryptographic systems; protocols for concurrency control in distributed systems, especially distributed data bases. *Mailing Add:* Sch Info Comput Sci Ga Inst Technol Atlanta GA 30332

SMITHWICK, ELIZABETH MARY, b Casco, Wis, Jan 20, 26. PEDIATRICS, IMMUNOLOGY. *Educ:* Univ Wis, BS, 48, MD, 55; Am Bd Allergy & Immunol, dipl, 77. *Prof Exp:* Intern, Kings Co Hosp, NY, 55-56 & Bellevue Hosp, 56-57; resident pediat, Metrop Hosp & Babies Hosp, 57-58; sr house officer, Queen Charlotte's Hosp, London, Eng, 59-60; from instr to assoc prof, State Univ NY Downstate Med Ctr, 60-73; ASSOC MEM & ASSOC PROF PEDIAT, SLOAN-KETTERING INST CANCER RES, CORNELL UNIV, 73- *Concurrent Pos:* USPHS grant, Southwestern Med Sch, Univ Tex Dallas, 63-64. *Mem:* AAAS; Soc Pediat Res; Am Acad Pediat; Am Rheumatism Asn. *Res:* Immune deficiency diseases; neutrophil and monocyte function. *Mailing Add:* Sloan-Kettering Inst 1275 York Ave New York NY 10021

SMITS, FRIEDOLF M, b Stuttgart, Ger, Nov 10, 24; US citizen; m 55; c 3. PHYSICS. *Educ:* Univ Freiburg, PhD(physics), 50. *Prof Exp:* Res assoc physics, Univ Freiburg, 50-54; mem tech staff device develop, Bell Tel Labs, 54-62; mgr dept radiation physics, Sandia Corp, 62-65; dept head, Device Develop, 65-68, Dir, Semi-nuclear Device Lab, 68-71, DIR MOS TECH & MEMORY LAB, BELL TEL LABS, 71- *Mem:* Am Phys Soc; Inst Elec & Electronics Eng. *Res:* Geological age determinations; physics of semiconductor devices; physics of radiation damage in semiconductors; ultrasonic and optical memories. *Mailing Add:* 2079 Greenwood Rd Allentown PA 18103

SMITS, TALIVALDIS I(VARS), b Riga, Latvia, Sept 18, 36; US citizen; m 67. COMMUNICATIONS ENGINEERING, ENGINEERING STATISTICS. *Educ:* Univ Minn, BS, 58, MSEE, 62, PhD(elec eng), 66. *Prof Exp:* Res asst elec eng, Univ Minn, 58-62, res assoc, 66-67, asst prof, 66-68; assoc prof, 68-78, LECTR ELEC ENG, CATH UNIV AM, 78-; MEM TECH STAFF, TRW, 77- *Concurrent Pos:* Assoc ed, J Acoust Soc Am, 74-; consult, Anal Adv Group, McLean, Va, 73-75, Undersea Res Corp, Falls Church, Va, 75-76 & Planning Systs Inc, 76. *Mem:* Acoust Soc Am; Inst Elec & Electronics Engrs; Am Sci Affil; Creation Res Soc. *Res:* Random signal processing; passive and active sonar-radar detection and estimation; statistical communication theory; pattern recognition; statistical methods in system analysis; non-Gaussian random processes. *Mailing Add:* TRW DSSG Washington Opers 7600 Calshire Dr McLean VA 22102

SMITTLE, BURRELL JOE, b Paola, Kans, July 13, 34; m 55; c 2. ENTOMOLOGY. *Educ:* Univ Ark, BS, 55, MS, 56; Rutgers Univ, PhD(entom), 64. *Prof Exp:* MED ENTOMOLOGIST, INSECTS AFFECTING MAN & ANIMAL RES LAB, AGR RES SERV, USDA, 59- *Concurrent Pos:* Courtesy prof entom, Univ Fla, 65- *Mem:* Entom Soc Am; Am Mosquito Control Asn. *Res:* Radiation and radioisotopes in medical entomology. *Mailing Add:* 1605 NW 71st St Gainesville FL 32605

SMITTLE, DOYLE ALLEN, b Bradley, Ark, Feb 27, 39; m 57; c 2. OLERICULTURE, PLANT PHYSIOLOGY. *Educ:* Univ Ark, BS, 61 & MS, 65; Univ Md, PhD(hort), 69. *Prof Exp:* Res asst hort, Univ Ark, 61-66; asst prof, Wash State Univ, 68-73; asst prof, 73-76, ASSOC PROF HORT, UNIV GA, 76- *Mem:* Sigma Xi; Am Soc Hort Sci; Potato Asn Am. *Res:* Soil-plant-water relations and post-harvest handling of cucurbits and edible legumes. *Mailing Add:* Coastal Plain Exp Sta Univ of Ga Tifton GA 31794

SMITTLE, RICHARD BAIRD, food microbiology, see previous edition

SMOAKE, JAMES ALVIN, b Langdale, Ala, Oct 5, 42. PHYSIOLOGY, BIOCHEMISTRY. *Educ:* Jacksonville State Univ, BA, 65; Univ Tenn, Knoxville, MS, 66, PhD(zool), 69. *Prof Exp:* Nat Cancer Inst spec cancer res trainee biochem, St Jude Children's Res Hosp, 72-73; MEM FAC BIOL, N MEX INST MINING & TECHNOL, 73- *Concurrent Pos:* Sabbatical leave, Endocrine & Metab Sect, Vet Admin Med Ctr, Memphis, 79-80. *Mem:* AAAS; Sigma Xi. *Res:* Action of insulin on liver cells. *Mailing Add:* Dept Biol NMex Inst Mining & Technol Socorro NM 87801

SMOCK, DALE OWEN, b Cochranton, Pa, Feb 13, 15; m 42. ELECTRICAL ENGINEERING. *Educ:* Grove City Col, BS, 42; Carnegie-Mellon Univ, BS, 48; Purdue Univ, MS, 62. *Prof Exp:* Instr pre-radar, US Naval Training Sch, Grove City Col, 42-45; jr engr, Westinghouse Elec Corp, Md, 45; instr eng, Grove City Col, 45-49, from asst prof to assoc prof, 49-56, actg head, Eng Dept, 72-77, prof elec eng, 56-80, chmn, Eng Dept, 77-80; RETIRED. *Mem:* Am Soc Eng Educ; Inst Elec & Electronics Engrs. *Res:* Electronics; electromagnetic theory; transmission circuits; electrical measurements; linear systems. *Mailing Add:* Dept of Eng Grove City Col Grove City PA 16127

SMOCK, ROBERT MUMFORD, b Erie, Pa, Oct 21, 08; m 32; c 3. POMOLOGY. *Educ:* Muskingum Col, BS, 30; Ohio State Univ, BSAgr, 31, MS, 32, PhD(pomol), 34. *Prof Exp:* Asst & jr pomologist, Univ Calif, 34-37; asst prof pomol, 37-44, prof, 44-74, EMER PROF POMOL, CORNELL UNIV, 74- *Concurrent Pos:* Cornell Univ grant, Cambridge, 38; Rockefeller res grant, India, 57; Fulbright res grant, New Zealand, 58; lectr, AID, Israel, 61; Ford Found res & teaching, Univ Philippines, 66-67. *Mem:* Am Soc Hort Sci. *Res:* Storage of fresh fruits. *Mailing Add:* Dept of Pomol Cornell Univ Ithaca NY 14850

SMOKE, MARY E, b Charlestown, WVa, Sept 30, 31; m 65. MATHEMATICAL STATISTICS. *Educ:* Am Univ, B3, 55; Stanford Univ, MS, 58, PhD(math statist), 64. *Prof Exp:* Asst biostatistician, Med Ctr, Univ Calif, San Francisco, 61-65; asst prof, 65-68, ASSOC PROF MATH, CALIF STATE UNIV, LONG BEACH, 68- *Mem:* Inst Math Statist; Am Statist Asn. *Res:* Non-parametric inference. *Mailing Add:* Dept of Math Calif State Univ Long Beach CA 90840

SMOKE, WILLIAM HENRY, b Battle Creek, Mich, Nov 7, 28; m 65. MATHEMATICS. *Educ:* Univ Mich, BA, 58, MA, 60; Univ Calif, Berkeley, PhD(math), 66. *Prof Exp:* Asst prof, 65-74, ASSOC PROF MATH, UNIV CALIF, IRVINE, 74- *Mem:* Am Math Soc. *Res:* Algebra. *Mailing Add:* Dept of Math Univ of Calif Irvine CA 92664

SMOKER, WILLIAM ALEXANDER, b Ishpeming, Mich, July 28, 15; m 41; c 3. FISHERIES, FORESTRY. *Educ:* Univ Calif, BS, 38; Univ Wash, PhD, 55. *Prof Exp:* Asst fisheries lab, Univ Wash, 46-47; fisheries biologist, Wash Dept Fish, 47-51, asst supvr res, 51-56; sr biologist, Alaska Dept Fish & Game, 56-59, chief biol res div, 59-60; asst lab dir, Auke Bay Biol Lab, Bur Com Fisheries, US Fish & Wildlife Serv, 61-67, lab dir, Auke Bay Fisheries Lab, Nat Marine Fisheries Serv, 67-82; RETIRED. *Mem:* AAAS; Am Fisheries Soc; Am Inst Fishery Res Biol. *Res:* Ecological factors determining abundance of fresh water and marine fishes in Alaska. *Mailing Add:* Auke Bay Fisheries Lab Box 155 Nat Marine Fisheries Serv Auke Bay AK 99821

SMOKER, WILLIAM WILLIAMS, b Washington, DC, Sept 6, 45; m 75; c 1. FISH & WILDLIFE SCI. *Educ:* Carleton Col, BA, 67; Ore State Univ, MS, 70, PhD(fisheries), 82. *Prof Exp:* ASST PROF FISHERIES, SCH FISHERIES, UNIV ALASKA, JUNEAU, 78- *Concurrent Pos:* Assoc dir, Alaska Sea Grant Prog, 82- *Mem:* Am Fisheries Soc; Genetics Soc Am; Am Soc Limnol & Oceanog; Am Inst Fisheries Res Biologists. *Res:* Quantitative genetics of Pacific salmon, particularly as applied to culture of their early stages; technology of the culture of Pacific salmon. *Mailing Add:* Sch Fisheries Univ Alaska 11120 Glacier Hwy Juneau AK 99801

SMOLEN, VICTOR FRANK, b Chicago, Ill, Aug 25, 39; m 62; c 1. PHARMACOLOGY, BIOENGINEERING. *Educ:* Univ Ill, BS, 61, PhD(pharm), 65. *Prof Exp:* USPHS fel molecular biol, Univ Pa, 65-66; asst prof phys pharm & biopharmaceut, 66-71, assoc prof, 71-76, PROF PHYS PHARM & BIOPHARMACEUT, PURDUE UNIV, LAFAYETTE, 76-; DIR INTERDISCIPLINARY DRUG ENG & ASSESSMENT LAB, 78- *Concurrent Pos:* Coordr interdisciplinary drug eng & assessment lab, 75-78; spec appointment, Food & Drug Admin, 77; consult to drug indust. *Mem:* Am Pharmaceut Asn; Am Acad Pharmaceut Sci; Am Chem Soc; NY Acad Sci. *Res:* Pharmacokinetics; bioavailability effected time optimal drug delivery systems and control of multiple drug effects; solute transport and mechanisms of water and drug interaction with biological structures and their models; automated drug administration devices; optimally predictive in-vitro drug bioavailability testing methods; biomedical engineering. *Mailing Add:* Sch of Pharm & Pharmaceut Sci Purdue Univ Lafayette IN 47907

SMOLENSKY, MICHAEL HALE, b Chicago, Ill, May 10, 42; m 63; c 1. ENVIRONMENTAL PHYSIOLOGY, OCCUPATIONAL HEALTH. *Educ:* Univ Ill, Urbana-Champaign, BS, 64, MS, 66, PhD(physiol), 71. *Prof Exp:* Asst prof, 70-74, ASSOC PROF ENVIRON PHYSIOL, UNIV TEX HEALTH SCI CTR, HOUSTON, 74- *Concurrent Pos:* Res dir, Tex Allergy Res Found, 71- & McGovern Allergy Clin, Houston, 71- *Mem:* AAAS; Int Soc Study Chronobiol. *Res:* Shift work, occupational health; pharmacology; toxicology; chronobiology; public health; allergy. *Mailing Add:* Sch Pub Health Univ Tex Health Ctr Houston TX 77025

SMOLIAR, STEPHEN WILLIAM, b Philadelphia, Pa, July 8, 46. INFORMATION SCIENCE. *Educ:* Mass Inst Technol, BS, 67, PhD(appl math), 71. *Prof Exp:* Instr comput sci, Israel Inst Technol, 71-73; asst prof comput & info sci, Univ Pa, 73-78; MEM TECH STAFF, GEN RES CORP, 78- *Mem:* Asn Comput Mach; Inst Elec & Electronics Engrs. *Res:* Distributed data processing. *Mailing Add:* Gen Res Corp PO Box 6770 Santa Barbara CA 93111

SMOLIK, JAMES DARRELL, b Rapid City, SDak, Mar 28, 42. PLANT NEMATOLOGY. *Educ:* SDak State Univ, BS, 65, MS, 69, PhD(plant path), 73. *Prof Exp:* Foreman pest control, M L Warne Chem & Equip Co, 66; asst plant path, 67-69, from res asst to res assoc, 70-75, ASST PROF PLANT NEMATOL, SDAK STATE UNIV, 75- *Mem:* Sigma Xi; Soc Nematologists. *Res:* Effect of nematodes on productivity of row, field and legume crops; nematode ecology studies in native range. *Mailing Add:* Plant Sci Bldg SDak State Univ Brookings SD 57006

SMOLINSKY, GERALD, b Philadelphia, Pa, Feb 25, 33; m 79; c 2. ORGANIC CHEMISTRY, PLASMA ETCHING. *Educ:* Drexel Inst, BS, 55; Univ Calif, Berkeley, PhD(org chem), 58. *Prof Exp:* Fel, Columbia Univ, 58-59; MEM TECH STAFF, BELL LABS, 59- *Mem:* AAAS; Am Chem Soc. *Res:* Reactions of organic compounds in cold plasmas; plasma polymerization and etching studies. *Mailing Add:* Bell Tel Labs Murray Hill NJ 07974

SMOLKER, ROBERT ELIOT, b Cambridge, Mass, Feb 28, 23; m 50; c 3. ECOLOGY. *Educ:* Bates Col, BS, 47; Boston Univ, AM, 49; Univ Chicago, PhD(zool), 59. *Prof Exp:* Instr biol, George Williams Col, 49-50; instr anat & genetics, Univ Ill, 54-55; instr natural sci, Mich State Univ, 55-59; ASSOC PROF BIOL, STATE UNIV NY STONY BROOK, 59- *Concurrent Pos:* Grant, Res Found State Univ NY, 59; panelist comn undergrad educ biol sci, NSF & consult, 65-66; mem exec comt, Environ Defense Fund. *Mem:* Am Soc Zool; Soc Study Evolution; Am Ornith Union. *Res:* General ecology; ecology in public policy; Sigma Xi. Res: General ecology; ecology in public policy; environmental impact analysis. *Mailing Add:* Dept of Ecol & Evolution State Univ of NY Stony Brook NY 11790

SMOLLER, JOEL A, b New York, NY, Jan 2, 39; m 60. MATHEMATICS. *Educ:* Brooklyn Col, BS, 57; Ohio Univ, MS, 58; Purdue Univ, PhD(math), 63. *Prof Exp:* Instr math, Univ Mich, 63-64; vis mem, Courant Inst Math Sci, NY Univ, 64-65; from asst prof to assoc prof, Univ Mich, Ann Arbor, 65-69; vis mem, Courant Inst Math Sci, NY Univ, 69-70; PROF, UNIV MICH, ANN ARBOR, 70- *Concurrent Pos:* Vis prof, Math Res Ctr, 72-73. *Mem:* Am Math Soc. *Res:* Partial differential equations; functional analysis. *Mailing Add:* Dept of Math Univ of Mich Ann Arbor MI 48109

SMOLLER, SYLVIA WASSERTHEIL, b Poland, Feb 24, 32; US citizen; m 71; c 2. BIOSTATISTICS, EPIDEMIOLOGY. *Educ:* Syracuse Univ, BS, 53, MA, 55; NY Univ, PhD(statist), 69. *Prof Exp:* Engr human factors, IBM, 58-61; statistician ment health, Astor Home Children, 62-64; asst prof math, State Univ NY Col New Paltz, 64-69; ASSOC PROF COMMUNITY HEALTH, ALBERT EINSTEIN COL MED, 69- *Concurrent Pos:* Consult,

Int Proj, Asn Vol Sterilization, 72-; fel coun epidemiol, Am Heart Asn, 76. *Mem:* Am Pub Health Asn; Soc Epidemiol Res; Am Statist Asn; fel NY Acad Sci. *Res:* Epidemiological studies of hypertension, diabetes, abortion, cervical cancer, computer applications. *Mailing Add:* Dept of Community Health Albert Einstein Col of Med Bronx NY 10461

SMOLUCHOWSKI, ROMAN, b Zakopane, Austria, Aug 31, 10; nat US; m 51; c 2. SOLID STATE PHYSICS, ASTROPHYSICS. *Educ:* Univ Warsaw, MA, 33; Univ Groningen, PhD(physics), 35. *Prof Exp:* Mem, Inst Adv Study, 35-36; res assoc, Univ Warsaw & head physics sect, inst metals, Warsaw Inst Technol, 36-39; instr & res assoc, Princeton Univ, 40-41; res physicist, Gen Elec Co, 41-46; assoc prof & mem staff metals res lab, Carnegie Inst Technol, 46-50, prof physics & metall, 50-56, prof physics, 56-60; prof solid state sci & dir solid state lab, Princeton Univ, 60-78; PROF ASTRON & PHYSICS, UNIV TEX, AUSTIN, 78- *Concurrent Pos:* Mem solid state panel, Res & Develop Bd, US Dept Defense, 49, tech adv bd aircraft nuclear propulsion, 50; secy solid state sci adv panel, Nat Res Coun, 50-61, chmn comt solids, 61-67, chmn div phys sci, 69-75, mem exec comt assembly math & phys sci, 74-75; chmn adv comt magnetism, Off Naval Res, 52-56; Fulbright prof, Univ Paris, 55-56, exchange prof, 65-66; lectr, Univ Liege, Belg, 56; vis prof, Nat Res Coun Brazil, 58-59 & Tech Univ Munich, Ger, 74; mem adv comt metall, Oak Ridge Nat Lab, 60-62; mem physics surv comt, Nat Acad Sci, 64-66 & 70-72, space sci bd, 69-75, comt planetary and lunar expl, 80-; chmn bd trustees, Simon's Rock Col; John Simon Guggenheim Mem Fel, 74. *Mem:* Fel Am Phys Soc; Am Astron Soc; Am Crystallog Asn; fel Am Acad Arts & Sci; AAAS. *Res:* Condensed matter in astrophysics; lattice imperfections; radiation effects; phase transformation; magnetism. *Mailing Add:* Dept Astron & Physics Univ Tex Austin TX 78712

SMOOK, MALCOLM ANDREW, b Seattle, Wash, Aug 22, 24; m 45; c 2. ORGANIC CHEMISTRY. *Educ:* Univ Calif, BS, 45; Ohio State Univ, PhD(chem), 49. *Prof Exp:* Chemist, 49-52, res supvr, 52-53, div head, 53-58, from asst lab dir to lab dir, 58-63, asst dir res & develop div, Elastomers Dept, 63-68, asst dir res & develop div, Plastics Dept, 68-76, gen lab dir, Plastics Prod & Resins Dept, 76-80, MGR PATENTS & REGULATORY AFFAIRS, POLYMER PROD DEPT, E I DU PONT DE NEMOURS & CO, INC, 80- *Concurrent Pos:* Mem res & technol adv comt, Materials & Structures, NASA, 75-78. *Mem:* Am Chem Soc; Sigma Xi; Soc Rheol. *Res:* Organic fluorine chemistry; polymer and rubber chemistry. *Mailing Add:* 107 Walnut Ridge Rd Wilmington DE 19807

SMOOT, CHARLES RICHARD, b Marmet, WVa, Nov 15, 28; m 51; c 6. PHYSICAL CHEMISTRY. *Educ:* Morris Harvey Col, BS, 51; Purdue Univ, PhD(phys chem), 55. *Prof Exp:* Chemist, FMC Co, 47-51; chemist, 55-59, from res supvr to sr res supvr, 59-72, LAB SUPT, E I DU PONT DE NEMOURS & CO, INC, 72- *Concurrent Pos:* Asst prof, WVa Univ Br, Parkersburg, 61-63. *Mem:* Am Chem Soc. *Res:* Applied research on polymers; research administration. *Mailing Add:* Plastic Prod & Resins Dept Exp Sta Bldg 323 Wilmington DE 19898

SMOOT, GEORGE FITZGERALD, b Wetumpka, Ala, Jan 16, 22; m 43; c 2. HYDROLOGY, INSTRUMENTATION. *Educ:* Auburn Univ, BS, 50. *Prof Exp:* Eng technician, Ala, 48-50, hydraul engr, 50-52, hydraul engr, Alaska, 52-56 & Ohio, 56-62, res hydrologist, Wash, DC, 62-66, COORDR RES ON INSTRUMENTATION, WASH, DC, US GEOL SURV, 66- *Concurrent Pos:* Chmn working group tech comt, Int Orgn Standardization & mem hydrometry comt, Int Asn Sci Hydrol, 68-; mem, Interagency Adv Comt Nat Oceanog Instrumentation Ctr; chmn, Task Group Velocity Measurements, Am Soc Testing & Mats. *Mem:* Am Soc Civil Eng; Am Soc Testing & Mats; Am Geophys Union. *Res:* Research, design and development of instrumentation for use in hydrologic investigations. *Mailing Add:* Box 870 Star Rte B Orange Beach AL 36561

SMOOT, GEORGE FITZGERALD, III, b Yukon, Fla, Feb 20, 45; m 69. ASTROPHYSICS, COSMIC RAY PHYSICS. *Educ:* Mass Inst Technol, BS(math) & BS(physics), 66, PhD(physics), 70. *Prof Exp:* Res physicist, Mass Inst Technol, 70; RES PHYSICIST, UNIV CALIF, BERKELEY, 71-, RES PHYSICIST, LAWRENCE BERKELEY LAB, 74- *Mem:* Am Phys Soc; Am Astron Soc; Sigma Xi. *Res:* Microwave experiments using cosmic black body radiation as a probe of the homogeneity and isotropy of the universe; balloon-borne superconducting magnetic spectrometer experiments on the charged cosmic rays. *Mailing Add:* 10 Panoramic Way Berkeley CA 94704

SMOOT, JOHN JONES, b Parkton, Md, Aug 10, 21; m 47; c 3. PLANT PATHOLOGY. *Educ:* Univ Md, BS, 42, MS, 48, PhD(plant path), 51. *Prof Exp:* Asst, Univ Md, 46-51; plant pathologist, Biol Warfare Labs, US Dept Army, Ft Detrick, Md, 51-57; plant pathologist, Agr Mkt Serv, 57-64, RES PLANT PATHOLOGIST, SCI & EDUC ADMIN-AGR RES, USDA, 64- *Mem:* Am Phytopath Soc. *Res:* Epidemiology of plant diseases; post-harvest diseases of fruits and vegetables. *Mailing Add:* 2120 Camden Rd Orlando FL 32803

SMOOT, LEON DOUGLAS, b Provo, Utah, July 26, 34; m 53; c 4. CHEMICAL ENGINEERING. *Educ:* Brigham Young Univ, BS & BEngS, 57; Univ Wash, MS, 58, PhD(chem eng), 60. *Prof Exp:* Lab asst chem, Brigham Young Univ, 54-55, instr math, 55-56, res asst chem eng, 56-57; consult engr heat transfer, 58-59; asst chem eng, Univ Wash, 57-60; asst prof, Brigham Young Univ, 60-63; sr tech specialist res & develop, Lockheed Propulsion Co, 63-67; assoc prof, 67-70, chmn dept, 70-77, PROF CHEM ENG, BRIGHAM YOUNG UNIV, 70-, DEAN ENG SCI & TECHNOL, 77- *Concurrent Pos:* Vis asst prof, Calif Inst Technol, 66-67; Indust partic, US-UK-Can Tech Coop Prog, 64-72; chmn ad hoc hybrid combustion comt, Int Agency Chem Rocket Propulsion Group, 66; consult, several companies and agencies in the US & Europe, 70- *Mem:* Am Inst Chem Engrs; Am Inst Aeronaut & Astronaut; Sigma Xi; Am Soc Eng Educ; Int Combustion Inst. *Res:* Combustion; energy; fossil fuels. *Mailing Add:* 270 CB Brigham Young Univ Provo UT 84602

SMOSNA, RICHARD ALLAN, b Chicago, Ill, Nov 3, 45; m 67; c 2. STRATIGRAPHY. *Educ:* Mich State Univ, BS, 67; Univ Ill, MS, 70, PhD(geol), 73. *Prof Exp:* Instr geol, Hanover Col, 71-72; PETROL GEOLOGIST, WVA GEOL SURV, 72- *Concurrent Pos:* Adj asst prof, WVa Univ, 74- *Honors & Awards:* Levorsen Award, Am Asn Petrol Geologist, 74; Distinguished Tech Commun Award, Soc Tech Commun, 75. *Res:* Determination of paleoenvironments, paleoecology, stratigraphy and petroleum potential of Silurian-aged carbonate rocks of central Appalachians. *Mailing Add:* WVa Geol Surv PO Box 879 Morgantown WV 26505

SMOTHERS, JAMES LLEWELLYN, b Jackson, Tenn, Aug 30, 30; m 64. ANIMAL PHYSIOLOGY. *Educ:* Lambuth Col, BS, 52; Univ Tenn, MS, 53, PhD(zool), 61. *Prof Exp:* Nat Heart Found fel marine biol, Inst Marine Sci, Univ Miami, 61-62; from asst prof to assoc prof, 62-71, PROF BIOL, UNIV LOUISVILLE, 71- *Mem:* Am Soc Zoologists. *Res:* Effects of dietary and hormonal factors on mitochondrial structure and funtion, mechanisms of actions of hormones; comparative physiology of respiratory enzyme activities and respiration of animals and tissues. *Mailing Add:* Dept of Biol Univ of Louisville Louisville KY 40208

SMOTHERS, WILLIAM JOSEPH, b Poplar Bluff, Mo, Mar 17, 19; m 43; c 2. ENGINEERING. *Educ:* Univ Mo, BS, 40, MS, 42, PhD(ceramic eng), 44. *Prof Exp:* Chem analyst, Mo Portland Cement Co, 39; lab asst physics, Mo Sch Mines, 40-42; engr, Mo Exp Sta, Rolla, 42-44; res engr, Bowes Elec Ceramic Corp, 44-50; assoc prof, Inst Sci & Technol, Univ Ark, 50-53; dir ceramic res, Ohio Brass Co, 54-63; SECT MGR REFRACTORIES, HOMER RES LABS, BETHLEHEM STEEL CORP, 63- *Concurrent Pos:* Ed, Am Ceramic Soc, 72- *Honors & Awards:* Toledo Glass & Ceramic Award, Am Ceramic Soc, 75. *Mem:* Fel AAAS; fel Am Ceramic Soc (vpres, 64-65, pres, 71-72); Am Chem Soc. *Res:* Refractories research; differential thermal analysis; solid state; ceramic materials. *Mailing Add:* Homer Res Labs Bethlehem Steel Corp Bethlehem PA 18016

SMOUSE, PETER EDGAR, b Long Beach, Calif, Apr 17, 42. HUMAN GENETICS, STATISTICS. *Educ:* Univ Calif, Berkeley, BS, 65; NC State Univ, PhD(genetics), 70. *Prof Exp:* NSF grant, Univ Tex, Austin, 70-72; asst prof, 72-76, ASSOC PROF HUMAN GENETICS, UNIV MICH, ANN ARBOR, 76- *Concurrent Pos:* Mem, Comt Quant Genetics & Common Dis, Nat Inst Gen Med Sci, NIH, 78, study sect mammalian genetics, 81; assoc ed, Theoret Pop Biol, 79-81; mem rev panel, Pop Biol & Physiol Ecol, NSF, 80-82. *Mem:* Int Soc Genetics; Soc Study Evolution; Genetics Soc Am; Am Soc Human Genetics; Am Soc Naturalists. *Res:* Biometry; genetics; ecology; demography; epidemiology; anthropology; taxonomy. *Mailing Add:* Dept of Human Genetics Univ of Mich Ann Arbor MI 48109

SMOUSE, THOMAS HADLEY, b Cumberland, Md, July 10, 36; m 59; c 3. FOOD SCIENCE, BIOCHEMISTRY. *Educ:* Pa State Univ, BS, 58; Rutgers Univ, MS, 64, PhD(food sci), 65. *Prof Exp:* Anal chemist, Nabisco Res Ctr, 58-61; res fel fats & oils, Rutgers Univ, 61-65; sr res chemist, Campbell's Inst Food Res, 65-67; res assoc, Anderson Clayton Foods, 67-77; MGR LIPID SCI, RALSTON PURINA CO, 77- *Mem:* Sigma Xi; Am Oil Chemists Soc; Am Chem Soc; Inst Food Technol. *Res:* Exploratory and applied research in fat and oil constituents and their interactions with foods to produce flavor effects. *Mailing Add:* Venture Mgt Res & Develop Checkerboard Sq St Louis MO 63188

SMUCKER, ARTHUR ALLAN, b Dhamtari, India, Nov 27, 23; US citizen; m 48; c 6. BIOCHEMISTRY, COMPUTER-INSTRUMENT INTERFACING. *Educ:* Goshen Col, BA, 49; Univ Ill, MS, 51, PhD(chem), 54. *Prof Exp:* From asst to instr chem, Univ Ill, 49-53; from instr to assoc prof, 54-74, PROF CHEM, GOSHEN COL, 74- *Concurrent Pos:* Consult, Miles Labs, Inc, 59-; fels, Nat Inst Arthrities & Metab Dis, Univ Calif, Berkeley, 63-64 & Univ Iowa, 72-73. *Mem:* Am Chem Soc. *Res:* Enzyme purification, kinetics and structure. *Mailing Add:* Dept Chem Goshen Col Goshen IN 46526

SMUCKER, SILAS JONATHAN, b Goshen, Ind, Dec 31, 04; m 35; c 2. SOIL CONSERVATION. *Educ:* Goshen Col, AB, 30; Purdue Univ, MS, 32. *Prof Exp:* Asst plant pathologist, Div Forest Path, USDA, 34-44, soil conservationist, Soil Conserv Serv, 45-62; agriculturist, AID, 62-69; CONSULT AGR SERV, 70- *Mem:* Am Phytopath Soc; Soil Conserv Soc Am. *Res:* Elm tree diseases; wood decay fungi and wood preservatives; soil and water conservation; wildlife biology; tropical agriculture. *Mailing Add:* 1304 S 14th St Goshen IN 46526

SMUCKLER, EDWARD AARON, b New York, NY, Feb 10, 31; m 54; c 5. EXPERIMENTAL PATHOLOGY, BIOCHEMISTRY. *Educ:* Dartmouth Col, AB, 52; Tufts Univ, MD, 56; Univ Wash, PhD(path), 63. *Prof Exp:* Lab instr elem zool, Dartmouth Col, 51-52, lab instr & examr chem, 51-52; from instr to prof path, Univ Wash, 61-76; PROF & CHMN DEPT PATH, UNIV CALIF, SAN FRANCISCO, 76- *Concurrent Pos:* Attend physician, Univ Wash Hosp, 61-76; consult, Northern State Hosp, Sedro Woolley, 61-63 & Vet Admin Hosp, Seattle, 63-76; NSF sr fel, Wenner-Gren Inst, Sweden; Europ Molecular Biol Orgn spec fel, Royal Vet Col, London, 66; Guggenheim fel, Nat Inst Med Res, Eng, 70-71; WHO travelling fel, Weizmann Inst Sci, Israel. *Mem:* AAAS; Am Chem Soc; Am Asn Path & Bact; Am Soc Exp Path; Brit Biochem Soc; Am Soc Biol Chem. *Res:* Cellular alteration in disease. *Mailing Add:* Dept of Path Univ of Calif Sch of Med San Francisco CA 94143

SMUDSKI, JAMES W, b Greensburg, Pa, Oct 31, 25; m 49; c 3. PHARMACOLOGY, DENTISTRY. *Educ:* Univ Pittsburgh, BS, 50, DDS, 52, Univ Calif, San Francisco, MS, 61, PhD(pharmacol), 65. *Prof Exp:* Pvt pract dent, 52-58; asst prof pharmacol, 63-64, assoc prof & head dept, 64-67, dir div grad & post grad educ, 70-73, prof pharmacol & physiol & head dept, Sch Dent, Univ Pittsburgh, 67-76; DEAN SCH DENT, UNIV DETROIT, 76- *Concurrent Pos:* Nat Inst Dent Res res-teacher trainee, 58-62 & career develop award, 62-64; consult, Oakland Vet Admin Hosp, Pittsburgh, Pa, 64-76; consult, Nat Bd Dent Exam, 65-75. *Mem:* AAAS; Am Dent Asn; Am Inst Oral Biol; NY Acad Sci; Int Asn Dent Res. *Res:* Pharmacology of agents affecting the central, autonomic and peripheral nervous systems. *Mailing Add:* 712 Berkshire Rd Grosse Point Park MI 48230

SMUK, JOHN MICHAEL, b Biwabik, Minn, Aug 16, 32; m 56; c 2. CHEMICAL ENGINEERING. *Educ:* Univ Wis, MS, 56, PhD(chem eng), 60. *Prof Exp:* Res engr, Forest Prod Lab, USDA, 60-64, proj leader, 64-66; consult engr waste treatment, Ruble-Miller Assocs, 66-69; SR RES ENGR, POTLATCH FOREST INDUSTS, 69-, MGR PROCESS ENG, 81- *Concurrent Pos:* Consult indust develop orgn prod of furfural from bagasse, UN, 67. *Mem:* Am Chem Soc; Am Inst Chem Engrs; Tech Asn Pulp & Paper Indust; Instrument Soc Am. *Res:* Furfural plant and process design; acid decomposition of simple sugars; kinetic studies; chemistry of wood; process control; secondary fiber process design; oxygen bleaching; computer applications; pulp and paper plant design. *Mailing Add:* 321 E Faribault Duluth MN 55803

SMULDERS, ANTHONY PETER, b Oss, Netherlands, July 6, 42. PHYSIOLOGY. *Educ:* Loyola Univ, Los Angeles, BS, 66; Univ Calif, Los Angeles, PhD(physiol), 70. *Prof Exp:* Asst prof, 70-77, assoc prof, 77-81, PROF BIOL, LOYOLA MARYMOUNT UNIV, 81-, ASSOC DEAN SCI & ENG, 72- *Concurrent Pos:* Res physiologist, Univ Calif, Los Angeles, 70-; comnr, Los Angeles County Narcotics and Dangerous Drugs Comn, 73- *Mem:* AAAS; Sigma Xi; Biophys Soc; Nat Asn Adv Health Prof. *Res:* Transport phenomena, the movement of ions and non-electrolytes across biological and artificial membranes; improvemnt of university science teaching; drug abuse and prevention. *Mailing Add:* Col of Sci & Eng Loyola Marymount Univ Los Angeles CA 90045

SMULLIN, LOUIS DIJOUR, b Detroit, Mich, Feb 5, 16; m 39; c 4. ELECTRICAL ENGINEERING. *Educ:* Univ Mich, BSE, 36; Mass Inst Technol, SM, 39. *Prof Exp:* Draftsman, Swift Elec Welder Co, Mich, 36; engr, Ohio Brass Co, 36-38, Farnsworth TV Corp, 39-40 & Scintilla Magneto Div, Bendix Aviation Corp, 40-51; sect head radiation lab, Mass Inst Technol, 41-46; head microwave tube lab, Fed Telecommun Labs Div, Int Tel & Tel Corp, NJ, 46-48; head tube lab, Res Lab Electronics, 48-50, div head, Lincoln Lab, 50-55, from assoc prof to prof, 55-76, DUGALD CALEB JACKSON PROF ELEC ENG, MASS INST TECHNOL, 76-, CHMN DEPT, 67- *Concurrent Pos:* Mem steering comt, Kanpur Indo-Am Prog, 61-65; vis prof, Indian Inst Technol, Kanpur, 65-66; NSF Working Group Sci & Eng Instr, India; mem comt telecommun, Nat Acad Eng; bd govs, Israel Inst Technol. *Mem:* Nat Acad Eng; Am Phys Soc; fel Inst Elec & Electronics Engrs; fel Am Acad Arts & Sci. *Res:* Plasma physics; technology assessment. *Mailing Add:* Dept of Elec Eng Mass Inst of Technol 38-294 Cambridge MA 02139

SMULOW, JEROME B, b New York, NY, July 29, 30; m 68; c 1. ORAL PATHOLOGY, PERIODONTOLOGY. *Educ:* NY Univ, AB, 51, DDS, 55; Tufts Univ, MS, 61, cert, 64. *Prof Exp:* From instr to assoc prof, 60-68, PROF PERIODONT, SCH DENT MED, TUFTS UNIV, 69- *Concurrent Pos:* Fulbright-Hays fel, Iran, 72-73. *Mem:* AAAS; Tissue Cult Asn; Am Dent Asn; Int Asn Dent Res. *Res:* Histopathology; tissue cultures. *Mailing Add:* 673 Boylston Brookline MA 02146

SMULSON, MARK ELLIOTT, b Baltimore, Md, Mar 25, 36; m 66; c 2. BIOCHEMISTRY. *Educ:* Washington & Lee Univ, AB, 58; Cornell Univ, MNS, 61, PhD(biochem), 71. *Prof Exp:* Fel biochem, Albert Einstein Med Ctr, 64-65; USPHS fel, Nat Cancer Inst, 65-67; from asst prof to assoc prof, 67-78, PROF BIOCHEM, SCHS MED & DENT, GEORGETOWN UNIV, 78- *Mem:* Am Asn Cancer Res; Am Soc Biol Chemists. *Res:* Molecular biology; poly adenosine diphosphoribose polymerase in control of DNA replication and in nucleosomal structure of chromatin; carcinogens interaction with nucleosomes. *Mailing Add:* Dept Biochem Schs Med & Dent Georgetown Univ Washington DC 20007

SMULYAN, HAROLD, b Philadelphia, Pa, Jan 2, 29; m 52; c 3. INTERNAL MEDICINE, CARDIOLOGY. *Educ:* Univ Pa, AB, 49; Univ Buffalo, MD, 53. *Prof Exp:* From instr to assoc prof, 59-72, PROF MED, STATE UNIV NY UPSTATE MED CTR, 71-; CHIEF CARDIOL, VET ADMIN MED CTR HOSP, SYRACUSE, 78- *Mem:* Am Fedn Clin Res; NY Acad Sci; Am Heart Asn. *Res:* Hypertension; circulatory control; exercise physiology. *Mailing Add:* Dept Med State Univ NY Upstate Med Ctr Syracuse NY 13210

SMURA, BRONISLAW BERNARD, b Solvay, NY, Aug 9, 30; m 52; c 3. CHEMICAL ENGINEERING. *Educ:* Syracuse Univ, BChE, 52, MChE, 54, PhD(chem eng), 68. *Prof Exp:* Res engr, Indust Chem Div, Allied Chem Corp, 57-79; MGR PROCESS ENG, LINDEN CHEM & PLASTICS CORP, 80- *Mem:* Am Inst Chem Engrs. *Res:* Industrial inorganic chemicals with recent major emphasis on electrolytic production of chlorine and caustic soda. *Mailing Add:* Indust Chem Div PO Box 6 Solvay NY 13209

SMUTNY, EDGAR JOSEF, b New York, NY, Apr 20, 28. ORGANIC CHEMISTRY. *Educ:* Univ Colo, BA, 48; Univ Minn, PhD(chem), 53. *Prof Exp:* Mem staff, Allied Chem & Dye Corp, 48-49; asst org chem, Univ Minn, 50-52; res fel, Calif Inst Technol, 53-55; res chemist, 55-68, res supvr, 68-72, SR STAFF CHEMIST, SHELL DEVELOP CO, 72- *Mem:* Am Chem Soc; The Chem Soc. *Res:* Small ring compounds; strain energy; photochemistry; free radical chemistry; heterocyclic chemistry; organometallic chemistry; sulfur compounds; homogeneous palladium catalysis; heterogeneous catalysis; fuels and lubricant research. *Mailing Add:* Chem Dept Shell Develop Co Houston TX 77001

SMUTS, MARY ELIZABETH, b Waterbury, Conn, Mar 15, 48; m 72. DEVELOPMENTAL BIOLOGY. *Educ:* Albertus Magnus Col, BA, 70; Temple Univ, PhD(develop biol), 75. *Prof Exp:* Res fel, Lab Develop Biol & Anomalies, Nat Inst Dent Res, NIH, 74-76; asst prof develop biol, Cath Univ Am, 76-78; ASST PROF BIOL, WHEATON COL, 78- *Mem:* Soc Develop Biol; Am Soc Cell Biol; Am Soc Zoologist; Sigma Xi. *Res:* Cranio-facial development, concentrating on two stages of primary palate development; the initiation of the nasal placode and closure of the primary palate. *Mailing Add:* Wheaton Col Dept of Biol Norton MA 02766

SMUTZ, MORTON, b Twin Falls, Idaho, Jan 10, 18; m 45, 70. CHEMICAL ENGINEERING. *Educ:* Kans State Col, BS, 40, MS, 41; Univ Wis, PhD(chem eng), 50. *Prof Exp:* Chem engr, Monsanto Chem Co, 41; asst prof chem eng, Bucknell Univ, 49-51; assoc prof, Iowa State Univ, 51-55, prof & head dept, 55-61; asst dir, Ames Lab, US Atomic Energy Comn, 55-64, dep dir, 64-69; chmn, Coastal & Oceanog Eng Dept, Col Eng, Univ Fla, 75-78, assoc dean eng res & prof chem eng, 69-79; SR PROJ ENGR, NAT OCEANIC & ATMOSPHERIC ADMIN, 79- *Mem:* Am Chem Soc; Am Soc Eng Educ; Am Inst Chem Engrs; Am Nuclear Soc; Coastal Soc (secy, 77). *Res:* Solvent extraction; coastal engineering; ocean engineering. *Mailing Add:* N-1302 12000 Old Georgetown Rd Rockville MD 20852

SMYLIE, DOUGLAS EDWIN, b New Liskeard, Ont, June 22, 36; wid; c 3. GEOPHYSICS. *Educ:* Queen's Univ, Ont, BSc, 58; Univ Toronto, MA, 59, PhD(physics), 63. *Prof Exp:* Fel geophys, Univ Toronto, 64; asst prof, Univ Western Ont, 64-68; from asst prof to assoc prof, Univ BC, 68-72; PROF EARTH SCI & DIR EARTH & ENVIRON SCI PROG, YORK UNIV, 72- *Concurrent Pos:* Nat Res Coun Can operating grant, 65- *Mem:* Seismol Soc Am; Soc Exp Geophys; Am Geophys Union; fel Royal Astron Soc. *Res:* Rotation of the earth; Chandler wobble; main magnetic field; elasticity theory of dislocations; dynamics of the earth's core. *Mailing Add:* Dept Physics York Univ Downsview ON M3J 2R3 Can

SMYLIE, ROBERT EDWIN, b Lincoln Co, Miss, Dec 25, 29; m; c 3. MECHANICAL ENGINEERING. *Educ:* Miss State Univ, BSc, 52, MSc, 56; Mass Inst Technol, MSc, 67. *Prof Exp:* Indust engr, Ethyl Corp, Tex, 52-54; instr mech eng, Miss State Univ, 54-56; lead engr, Skybolt Missile Syst Thermo-Conditioning Systs, Douglas Aircraft Co, Calif, 56-62; chief, Apollo Support Off, Crew Systs Div, Manned Spacecraft Ctr, 62-66, asst chief div, 67-68, actg chief, 68-70, chief, Crew Systs Div, 70-76, DEP DIR, GODDARD SPACE FLIGHT CTR, NASA, 76- *Concurrent Pos:* Mem US deleg engaged in discussions with USSR to establish common docking systems for spacecraft of the two countries. *Honors & Awards:* Except Serv Medal, NASA, 69; Victor Prather Award, 71. *Mem:* Am Inst Aeronaut & Astronaut. *Res:* Analyses, design and development in specific advanced system areas such as space suits, extravehicular activity support hardware and environmental and thermal control subsystems. *Mailing Add:* NASA Goddard Space Flight Ctr Code 100 Greenbelt MD 20771

SMYRL, WILLIAM HIRAM, b Brownfield, Tex, Dec 12, 38; m 64; c 2. PHYSICAL CHEMISTRY, ELECTROCHEMISTRY. *Educ:* Tex Tech, BS, 61; Univ Calif, Berkeley, PhD(chem), 66. *Prof Exp:* Asst prof pharmaceut chem, Univ Calif, San Francisco, 66-68; mem tech staff, Boeing Sci Res Labs, 68-72; MEM TECH STAFF, SANDIA LABS, 72- *Mem:* Electrochem Soc; Sigma Xi. *Res:* Molten salts; corrosion science; modeling of corrosion and electrochemical processes; photoelectrochemistry; digital measurement of Faradaic impedance of electrochemical and corrosion reactions. *Mailing Add:* Sandia Labs Div 5841 Albuquerque NM 87125

SMYRNIOTIS, PAULINE ZOE, b Williamsport, Pa, Mar 21, 24. BIOCHEMISTRY. *Educ:* George Washington Univ, BS, 48, MS, 53; Georgetown Univ, PhD, 56. *Prof Exp:* BIOCHEMIST, NIH, 49- *Mem:* Am Chem Soc; Am Soc Microbiol; Soc Exp Biol & Med. *Res:* Intermediary metabolism; enzymology. *Mailing Add:* Lab of Biochem Nat Heart Lung & Blood Inst NIH Bethesda MD 20014

SMYTH, CHARLES PHELPS, b Clinton, NY, Feb 10, 95; m 55. PHYSICAL CHEMISTRY, ATOMIC & MOLECULAR PHYSICS. *Educ:* Princeton Univ, AB, 16, AM, 17; Harvard Univ, PhD(chem), 21. *Hon Degrees:* DSc, Univ Salford, 70. *Prof Exp:* Asst chemist, Nat Bur Stand, 17; from instr to prof chem, 20-58, chemist, Manhattan Dist Proj, 43-45, David B Jones prof, 58-63, EMER DAVID B JONES PROF, PRINCETON UNIV, 63- *Concurrent Pos:* Coop expert, Int Critical Tables, 24; expert consult, Europ Theater of Oper, US Army, 45; chmn Fulbright fel adv comt chem & fel bd, NSF, 50-54; consult, Off Naval Res, 63-69 & 71-78, liaison scientist, London Off, Off Naval Res, 69-70; vis prof, Japan, 65 & Univ Salford, Eng, 74-76. *Honors & Awards:* Medal of Freedom, US Army, 47; Nichols Medal, Am Chem Soc, 54. *Mem:* Nat Acad Sci; Am Chem Soc; fel Am Phys Soc; Am Philos Soc; Royal Soc Chem. *Res:* Electromotive forces of amalgams; vapor pressures; refraction; heat capacities; dipole moment and molecular structure; molecular rotation in solids; microwave absorption in liquids; dielectric constant and loss; molecular relaxation times. *Mailing Add:* Frick Chem Lab Princeton Univ Princeton NJ 08540

SMYTH, DONALD MORGAN, b Bangor, Maine, Mar 20, 30; m 51; c 2. SOLID STATE CHEMISTRY. *Educ:* Univ Maine, BS, 51; Mass Inst Technol, PhD(inorg chem), 54. *Prof Exp:* Sr engr, Sprague Elec Co, 54-61, head solid state res, 61-71; assoc prof metall, mat eng & chem, 71-73, PROF METALL, MAT ENG & CHEM, LEHIGH UNIV, 73-, DIR MAT RES CTR, 71- *Concurrent Pos:* Vis instr, Williams Col, 59-61. *Honors & Awards:* Battery Div Res Award, Electrochem Soc, 60. *Mem:* Am Chem Soc; Electrochem Soc; Am Inst Chem; Am Ceramic Soc. *Res:* Defect structure of inorganic solids; nonstoichiometry, impurity effects and electrical conductivity of ternary oxides. *Mailing Add:* Mat Res Ctr Bldg 32 Lehigh Univ Bethlehem PA 18015

SMYTH, HAROLD THOMAS, b Lisburn, Northern Ireland, Feb 7, 10; nat US; m 37, 60; c 5. CERAMICS. *Educ:* Queen's Univ, Ireland, BSc, 31, MSc, 32; Mass Inst Technol, PhD(physics), 36. *Prof Exp:* Jr demonstr physics, Queen's Univ, Ireland, 31-32; res physicist, Corhart Refractories Co, Ky, 36-45, dir res, 45-48; res physicist, Appl Physics Lab, Johns Hopkins Univ, 48-49; res specialist, 49-56, prof, 56-79, EMER PROF CERAMICS, RUTGERS UNIV, NEW BRUNSWICK, 79- *Concurrent Pos:* Physicist, Silver Spring Lab, Kellex Corp, 48-49. *Mem:* AAAS; fel Am Ceramic Soc. *Res:* Spectroscopy; refractories; intensity measurements in arc spectrum of copper; structure of glass; mechanical properties of ceramic materials. *Mailing Add:* Dept of Ceramic Eng Rutgers Univ New Brunswick NJ 08903

SMYTH, HENRY DE WOLF, b Clinton, NY, May 1, 98; wid. PHYSICS. *Educ:* Princeton Univ, AB, 18, PhD(physics), 21; Cambridge Univ, PhD(physics), 23. *Hon Degrees:* DSc, Drexel Univ, 50, Case Western Reserve Univ, 53, Hamilton, 65, Princeton Univ, 77; LLD, Rutgers Univ, 68. *Prof Exp:* From instr to prof, 24-66, EMER PROF PHYSICS, PRINCETON UNIV, 66. *Concurrent Pos:* Consult atomic energy, Nuclear Res Coun & Off Sci Res & Develop, 40-45; comnr, US Atomic Energy Comn, 49-54; US Ambassador Int Atomic Energy Agency, US Dept State, 61-70. *Honors & Awards:* Atomic Energy Comn Citation, 67; Atoms Peace Award, 68; Distinguished Honor Award, Dept State, 70; 1st Henry De Wolf Smyth Nuclear Statesman Award, Atomic Indust Forum & Am Nuclear Soc, 72; Spec Award, Int Atomic Energy Agency, 77. *Mem:* Am Phys Soc (vpres, 56, pres, 57). *Mailing Add:* Dept of Physics PO Box 708 Princeton NJ 08540

SMYTH, HENRY FIELD, JR, b Philadelphia, Pa, June 5, 03; m 29; c 2. INDUSTRIAL TOXICOLOGY. *Educ:* Univ Pa, BS, 25, PhD(med sci), 34. *Prof Exp:* Spec investr, State Dept Labor & Indust, Pa, 25-26; consult, 26-28; instr sanit chem, Univ Pa, 28-37; fel, Mellon Inst, 37-40, sr fel, 40-47, admin fel, 47-67; lectr, Med Sch & Grad Sch Pub Health, Univ Pittsburgh, 51-67. *Concurrent Pos:* Partner, Smyth Lab, Pa, 26-37; secy-treas, Am Bd Indust Hyg, 60-67; Mellon Inst award, 76; adj prof Grad Sch Pub Health, 67-82; adv fel, Mellon Inst, 67-69. *Honors & Awards:* Donald E Cummings Mem Award, Am Indust Hyg Asn, 56; Merit Award, Soc Toxicol, 66. *Mem:* AAAS; Am Chem Soc; Am Indust Hyg Asn (dir, 46-49, exec secy, 47-54, pres, 53-54); Soc Toxicol. *Res:* Toxicity of organic industrial chemicals. *Mailing Add:* 41 Bel Aire Rd Delmont PA 15626

SMYTH, JAY RUSSELL, b Trenton, NJ, Apr 24, 39; c 3. CERAMICS SCIENCE, MATERIALS SCIENCE. *Educ:* Rutgers Univ, BS, 61, MS, 63; Pa State Univ, PhD(ceramics sci), 74. *Prof Exp:* Develop engr, Western Elec, Inc, 63-66; supvr prod eng, Mitronic, Inc, 66-68; eng mgr, Nat Berylia Corp, 68-71; from asst prof to assoc prof, Iowa State Univ, 74-81; SR MAT ENGR, GERRETT TURBINE ENGINE CO, 81- *Mem:* Am Ceramic Soc; Nat Inst Ceramic Engrs; Ceramic Educ Coun; Am Soc Metals. *Res:* Mechanics properties of materials including fracture and deformation; fracture mechanics of brittle materials; microkacking in brittle materials; ceramics for turbine engine applications. *Mailing Add:* Garrett Turbine Engine Co 111 S 34th St Phoenix AZ 85010

SMYTH, JOHN BRIDGES, b Pembroke, Ga, June 8, 14; m 38; c 4. PHYSICS. *Educ:* Univ Ga, BS, 34, MS, 37; Brown Univ, PhD(physics), 42. *Prof Exp:* Teacher high sch, Ga, 34-35; asst physics, Univ Ga, 35-37; physicist, Tenn Eastman Corp, 37-38; asst physics, Brown Univ, 38-42; from assoc physicist to physicist, US Navy Electronics Lab, 42-55; PRES & TECH DIR, SMYTH RES ASSOCS, 55- *Concurrent Pos:* Mem int comn II, Int Sci Radio Union. *Mem:* AAAS; Am Phys Soc; Acoust Soc Am; fel Inst Elec & Electronics Eng. *Res:* Galvanomagnetic effects; electromagnetics; atmospheric physics; thermal physics. *Mailing Add:* 5011 Helix Terr La Mesa CA 92041

SMYTH, JOSEPH RICHARD, b Louisville, Ky, Oct 10, 44. GEOLOGY, MINERALOGY. *Educ:* Va Polytech Inst, BS, 66; Univ Chicago, SM, 68, PhD(mineral), 70. *Prof Exp:* Res fel geol, Harvard Univ, 70-72; vis fel, Lunar Sci Inst, 72-74, res scientist, 74-76; MEM STAFF, LOS ALAMOS SCI LAB, 76- *Concurrent Pos:* Vis sr lectr, Univ Cape Town, 75. *Mem:* Mineral Soc Am; Mineral Soc Japan; Am Geophys Union; Meteoritical Soc; Geol Soc Am. *Res:* Crystal chemistry of rock-forming silicates; igneous petrology; radioactive waste isolation. *Mailing Add:* Mail Stop 978 Los Alamos Sci Lab Los Alamos NM 87545

SMYTH, MICHAEL P(AUL), b Albany, NY, Oct 2, 34; m 77; c 1. ELECTRICAL ENGINEERING, SYSTEMS ANALYSIS. *Educ:* Syracuse Univ, BS, 57, MS, 59; Univ Pa, PhD(elec eng), 63. *Prof Exp:* Elec engr, Gen Elec Co, 57; res asst, Radar Display, Syracuse Univ, 57-59; from instr to asst prof elec eng, Univ Pa, 59-67; assoc prof, 67-71; dir eng, 71-74, PROF, WIDENER UNIV, 71- *Concurrent Pos:* Ed consult, Bell Tel Co, Pa, 61-; mem, Franklin Inst, 62-; consult, Gen Elec Co, 65-67 & Philadelphia Elec Co, 74. *Honors & Awards:* Ralph R Tetor Award, Soc Automotive Engrs, 74. *Mem:* Inst Elec & Electronics Engrs; Am Soc Eng Educ; Soc Automative Engrs. *Res:* Methods of systems analysis; industrial educational methods. *Mailing Add:* Sch of Eng Widener Univ Chester PA 19013

SMYTH, NICHOLAS PATRICK DILLON, b Dublin, Ireland, Apr 1, 24; nat US; m 55; c 5. SURGERY. *Educ:* Nat Univ Ireland, BSc, 46, MSc, 48, MB, BCh, 49; Univ Mich, MS, 54. *Prof Exp:* From instr to assoc prof, 58-68, ASSOC CLIN PROF SURG, SCH MED, GEORGE WASHINGTON UNIV, 68-; DIR SURG RES, WASHINGTON HOSP CTR, 68-, CONSULT, 70- *Concurrent Pos:* Chief surg, St Elizabeth's Hosp, 60-63, consult, 63-; consult, DC Gen Hosp, 60- & NIH, 70-; chmn dept surg, Washington Hosp Ctr, 63-68; consult thoracic surg, NIH & Walter Reed Army Med Ctr. *Mem:* Am Heart Asn; Am Col Surgeons; Am Asn Thoracic Surg; Am Col Chest Physicians; Am Fedn Clin Res. *Res:* Thoracic and cardiovascular surgery. *Mailing Add:* 106 Irving St NW Washington DC 20010

SMYTH, REX W(ILFRED), b Masontown, WVa, Apr 8, 26; m 48; c 5. CHEMICAL ENGINEERING. *Educ:* Carnegie Inst Technol, BS, 50, MS, 55. *Prof Exp:* Develop engr, Pennsalt Chem Co, Pa, 50-52; engr, Gulf Res & Develop Co, 52-55; group leader, 55-59; develop engr, Petrochem Dept, Gulf Oil Corp, 59-64, develop sect supvr, Gulf Res & Develop Co, 64-75, STAFF ENGR, GULF RES & DEVELOP CO, 75- *Mem:* Am Inst Chem Engrs. *Res:* Petrochemical processes and products; commercialization of petrochemical processes. *Mailing Add:* Gulf Res & Develop Co PO Drawer 2038 Pittsburgh PA 15230

SMYTH, THOMAS, JR, b Binghamton, NY, May 12, 27. INSECT PHYSIOLOGY. *Educ:* Princeton Univ, AB, 48; Johns Hopkins Univ, PhD(biol), 52. *Prof Exp:* Res assoc & instr biol, Tufts Univ, 52-55; from asst prof to assoc prof entom 55-73, PROF ENTOM, PA STATE UNIV, 73- *Mem:* AAAS; Biophys Soc; Am Soc Zool; Entom Soc Am; Animal Behav Soc. *Res:* Neuromuscular and sensory physiology of arthropods. *Mailing Add:* Dept of Entom Pa State Univ University Park PA 16802

SMYTHE, CHEVES MCCORD, b Charleston, SC, May 25, 24; m 49; c 6. MEDICINE. *Educ:* Harvard Univ, MD, 47. *Prof Exp:* From asst prof to assoc prof, Med Col SC, 57-66, dean sch med, 62-64; dir, Asn Am Med Cols, 66-70; dean, Univ Tex Med Sch Houston, 70-75; PROF MED, UNIV TEX MED SCH HOUSTON, 76- *Concurrent Pos:* Teaching fels med, Harvard Univ, 48-49 & 54-55; teaching fel, Columbia Univ, 50-52, Am Col Physicians & Life Ins Med Res Fund fels, 51-52; Markle fel med, 55-60; dir gen commissary & opers & prof med, Aga Khan Hosp & Med Col, Karshi, Pakistan, 82. *Mem:* AMA; Am Fedn Clin Res; Am Col Physicians. *Res:* Hypertension; renal disease; medical education. *Mailing Add:* 6431 Fannin St Houston TX 77030

SMYTHE, RICHARD VINCENT, b Philadelphia, Pa, June 27, 39; m 62; c 2. ENTOMOLOGY. *Educ:* Col Wooster, BA, 61; Univ Wis-Madison, MS, 63, PhD(entom), 66. *Prof Exp:* Entomologist, Southern Forest, Exp Sta, 66-69, proj leader entom, 69-74, staff entomologist, Forest Serv, USDA, 74-76, staff asst dep chief res, 76-77; ASST DIR CONTINUING RES, N CENT FOREST EXP STA, FOREST SERV, USDA, 77- *Concurrent Pos:* Consult, Nat Pest Control Asn, 71-76. *Mem:* AAAS; Entom Soc Am. *Res:* Feeding behavior, physiology and ecology of wood products insects, chiefly subterranean termites. *Mailing Add:* N Cent Forest Exp Sta 1992 Folwell Ave St Paul MN 55108

SMYTHE, ROBERT C, b Orlando, Fla. CIRCUIT THEORY. *Educ:* Rice Univ, BA, 52, BS, 53; Univ Fla, MS, 57. *Prof Exp:* Asst vpres, Syst, Inc, 62-65; VPRES, PIEZO TECHNOL INC, 65- *Mem:* Inst Elec & Electronics Engrs; AAAS; Acoust Soc Am. *Res:* Linear and nonlinear theory of piezoelectric resonators and filters especially monolithic filters; precision resonator measurement. *Mailing Add:* Piezo Technol Inc PO Box 7859 Orlando FL 32854

SMYTHE, WILLIAM RODMAN, b Calif, Jan 6, 30; m 54; c 4. PHYSICS. *Educ:* Calif Inst Technol, BS, 51, MS, 52, PhD(physics), 57. *Prof Exp:* Engr, Microwave Lab, Gen Elec Co, 56-57; res assoc physics, 57-58, from asst prof to assoc prof, 58-67, chmn nuclear physics lab, 67-69, PROF PHYSICS, UNIV COLO, BOULDER, 67- *Mem:* Am Phys Soc. *Res:* Nuclear physics and applications of nuclear physics techniques to medical and environmental problems. *Mailing Add:* Dept of Physics & Astrophys Univ of Colo Boulder CO 80302

SNAPER, ALVIN ALLYN, b Hudson Co, NJ, Sept 9, 27; m 49; c 3. RESEARCH ADMINISTRATION. *Educ:* McGill Univ, BS, 49. *Prof Exp:* Sr chemist, Bakelite Div, Union Carbide Corp, 50-52; chief chemist, McGraw Colorgraph Co, 52-55; vpres, Marcal Electro-Sonics Co, 55-61 & Houston Fearless Corp, 61-63; consult, Marquardt Corp, 63-64; dir res, Fed Res & Develop Corp, 64-66; vpres, Advan Patent Technol, Inc, 69-80; CONSULT, AEROSPACE CORP, 66-; PRES, NICOA CORP, 81- *Concurrent Pos:* Consult, US Libr Cong, 67- & US Air Force Missile Command, 68-; corp staff consult, Telecommunications Industs Inc, 72- *Mem:* Sr mem AAAS; sr mem Am Ord Asn; sr mem Soc Photo-Optical Instrument Eng; sr mem Instrument Soc Am. *Res:* Basic research in ultrasonics for environmental waste treatment and biological effects on bacteria and virus. *Mailing Add:* 2800 Cameo Circle Las Vegas NV 89107

SNAPP, OLIVER IRVIN, SR, b Winchester, Va, Aug 1, 95; m 28; c 3. ECONOMIC ENTOMOLOGY. *Educ:* Va Polytech Inst, BS, 16; Miss State Univ, MS, 25. *Prof Exp:* Soil surveyor, Del Agr Exp Sta, 15; supt agr sch, Va, 16-17; soil surveyor, Ohio Agr Exp Sta, 17; entomologist, Entom Res Div, Agr Res Serv, USDA, 17-64, in chg, Peach Insect Sta, 20-64; CONSULT, 65- *Concurrent Pos:* Consult & tech adv, Woolfolk Chem Works, Ltd, 69-71. *Mem:* Hon mem Entom Soc Am (vpres, 40). *Res:* Plant pathology; soil surveying; pressure regulation for unit spraying; picking up peach drops. *Mailing Add:* PO Box 932 Ft Valley GA 31030

SNAPP, THOMAS CARTER, JR, b Suffolk, Va, Aug 23, 38; m 60; c 1. ORGANIC CHEMISTRY, ANALYTICAL CHEMISTRY. *Educ:* E Tenn State Col, BS, 59; Univ Miss, PhD(org & anal chem), 64. *Prof Exp:* Develop assoc, 74-78, dept head, 70-81, CHEMIST, TEX EASTMAN CO, 63-, ASST DIV HEAD, 81- *Mem:* Catalysis Soc; Am Chem Soc. *Res:* Cyclodehydrogenation; organic syntheses by heterogenious catalytic vapor phase reactions; surface catalysis; epoxidation and organic peracid chemistry; chemistry of lactones. *Mailing Add:* 713 Kay Dr Box 7444 Longview TX 75601

SNAPPER, ERNST, b Groningen, Neth, Dec 2, 13; nat US; m 41; c 2. MATHEMATICAL LOGIC. *Educ:* Princeton Univ, MA, 39, PhD(math), 41. *Prof Exp:* Instr math, Princeton Univ, 41-45; from asst prof to prof, Univ Southern Calif, 45-55; Andrew Jackson Buckingham prof, Miami Univ, 55-58; prof, Ind Univ, 58-63; prof, 63-71, B P CHENEY PROF MATH, DARTMOUTH COL, 71- *Concurrent Pos:* Vis assoc prof, Princeton Univ, 49-50, vis prof, 54-55; NSF fel, Harvard Univ, 53-54. *Honors & Awards:* Carl B Allendoerfer Award, Math Asn Am, 80. *Mem:* AAAS; Am Math Soc; Math Asn Am; Can Math Cong. *Res:* Algebra; geometry; combinatorial theory; philosophy of mathematics. *Mailing Add:* Dept of Math Dartmouth Col Hanover NH 03755

SNARE, LEROY EARL, b Garden City, Mo, Nov 6, 31; m 60; c 3. AERONAUTICS, ASTRONAUTICS. *Educ:* Univ Mo-Kansas City, BA, 53, MS, 59; Mass Inst Technol, MS, 62. *Prof Exp:* Gen res physicist, Appl Res Div 820, 59-62, chief, Dynamic Anal & Simulation Br, 62-72, res physicist, 72-76, dir, Appl Res Div 820, 76-80, DEP DIR, APPL RES DEPT, NAVAL

AVIONICS CTR, 80- *Mem:* Nat Soc Unmanned Vehicles. *Res:* Alignment of inertial navigation systems; design, development and testing of alignment and filtering programs for airborne computers; auxiliary equipment for aligning inertial navigation systems aboard ships; analysis and conceptual design of air-to-surface missile systems and electronic intelligence systems. *Mailing Add:* Naval Avionics Ctr Code 801 Indianapolis IN 46218

SNARR, JOHN FREDERIC, b Cincinnati, Ohio, Jan 3, 39; m 60; c 2. PHYSIOLOGY. *Educ:* Univ Cincinnati, EE, 61; Drexel Inst, MS, 62; Northwestern Univ, PhD(physiol), 67. *Prof Exp:* Asst prof, 67-73, ASSOC PROF PHYSIOL, MED SCH, NORTHWESTERN UNIV, 73-, ASSOC DEAN STUDENT AFFAIRS, 77- *Mem:* AAAS; Soc Exp Biol & Med. *Res:* Quantification of nutrient supply system operation and regulation. *Mailing Add:* Dept Physiol Med Sch Northwestern Univ Chicago IL 60611

SNAVELY, BENJAMIN BRENEMAN, b Lancaster, Pa, Jan 6, 36; m 61; c 2. QUANTUM ELECTRONICS, SOLID STATE PHYSICS. *Educ:* Swarthmore Col, BS, 57; Princeton Univ, MSE, 59; Cornell Univ, PhD(eng physics), 62. *Prof Exp:* Sr res physicist, Eastman Kodak Co, 62-65, res assoc solid state physics, Res Labs, 65-69, head solid state & molecular physics lab, 69-73; assoc div leader, Laser Div, Lawrence Livermore Lab, 73-75; asst dir, Physics Div, 75-81, TECH ASST TO DIR RES, RES LABS, EASTMAN KODAK CO, 81- *Concurrent Pos:* Vis prof, Phys-Chem Inst, Univ Marburg, 68-69; assoc prof, Inst Optics, Univ Rochester. *Mem:* Am Phys Soc; fel Optical Soc Am; Europ Phys Soc. *Res:* Photoconductivity in silver halides and II-VI compounds; electronic and optical properties of thin films; electroluminescence; organic dye lasers; tunable lasers; laser induced photochemistry. *Mailing Add:* Res Labs Eastman Kodak Co Rochester NY 14650

SNAVELY, CLOYD A(RTEN), b Massillon, Ohio, May 8, 17; m 41; c 3. CHEMICAL & METALLURGICAL ENGINEERING. *Educ:* Columbia Univ, BA, 39, BS, 40, MS, 41; Ohio State Univ, PhD(metall eng), 47. *Prof Exp:* Metall observer, Republic Steel Corp, Ohio, 40; res engr, Battelle Mem Inst, 47-49, asst div chief, 49-54, asst mgr, Chem Eng Dept, 54-60; gen mgr Sifco Metachem, Steel Improv & Forge Co, 60-61; tech adv, Battelle Mem Inst, 61-63, tech admin, Battelle Develop Corp, 63-66, mgr develop dept, 66-69; pres, Technovation Mgt, Inc & Develop Eng, Inc, 69-70; tech consult, Nat Standard Co, 70-72, res projs mgr, 72-80; PRES, TECHNOVATION ADV SERV, INC, 80- *Mem:* Am Soc Metals; Electrochem Soc; Am Inst Mining, Metall & Petrol Engrs. *Res:* Metallurgical processes, materials technology; industrial waste treatment; invention development; patents; coal gasification. *Mailing Add:* 3342 Henderson Rd Columbus OH 43220

SNAVELY, EARL SAMUEL, JR, b Brackettville, Tex, Apr 10, 27; m 53; c 1. PHYSICAL CHEMISTRY. *Educ:* Agr & Mech Col, Tex, BS, 47; Univ Tex, MA, 50, PhD, 58. *Prof Exp:* Chemist, Oyster Mortality Proj, Res Found, Agr & Mech Col, Tex, 47-48; chemist, Southern Alkali Corp, 50-51; res scientist, Defense Res Lab, Univ Tex, 51-58; chemist, Oak Ridge Nat Lab, 58-60; dir chem res, Tracor, Inc, 60-66; sr res chemist, Mobile Oil Corp, Tex, 66-68, res assoc, Field Res Lab, 68-80, ENG CONSULT, MOBIL RES & DEVELOP CORP, 80- *Concurrent Pos:* Ed corrosion div, J Electrochem Soc. *Mem:* Am Chem Soc; Electrochem Soc; Nat Asn Corrosion Eng. *Res:* Electrochemistry; corrosion; surface chemistry; environmental science. *Mailing Add:* Field Res Lab PO Box 900 Mobil Res & Develop Corp Dallas TX 75221

SNAVELY, FRED ALLEN, b Lititz, Pa, Feb 27, 19; m 46; c 2. INORGANIC CHEMISTRY. *Educ:* Franklin & Marshall Col, BS, 49; Pa State Univ, PhD(chem), 52. *Prof Exp:* From asst prof to assoc prof, 52-63, PROF CHEM, FRANKLIN & MARSHALL COL, 63- *Concurrent Pos:* Fulbright lectr, Col Sci, Univ Baghdad, 64-65. *Mem:* AAAS; Am Chem Soc. *Res:* Chelating tendencies of ortho-substituted azo dyes with various metal ions. *Mailing Add:* Dept of Chem Franklin & Marshall Col Lancaster PA 17604

SNAVELY, PARKE DETWEILER, JR, b Yakima, Wash, Apr 7, 19; m 42; c 3. GEOLOGY. *Educ:* Univ Calif, Los Angeles, BA, 41, MA, 51. *Prof Exp:* From jr geologist to supvry geologist, 42-53, supvr, Pac Region, 53-59, res geologist, 59-60, chief, Pac Coast Br, 60-66, chief, Off Marine Geol & Hydrol, 66-69, asst chief geologist, 69-71, SR RES GEOLOGIST, OFF MARINE GEOL, US GEOL SURV, 71- *Concurrent Pos:* Chmn marine geol panel, US-Japan Coop Prog Natural Resources, 70-; res assoc, Univ Calif, Santa Barbara, 69-76. *Honors & Awards:* Distinguished Serv Award, Dept of Interior. *Mem:* Fel Geol Soc Am; Am Asn Petrol Geologists. *Res:* Tertiary geology and mineral resource potential of western Oregon and Washington and adjacent continental shelf; relation of plate tectonics to structural, stratigraphic, and igneous history of Pacific coast states. *Mailing Add:* Off Marine Geol US Geol Surv 345 Middlefield Rd Menlo Park CA 94025

SNAZELLE, THEODORE EDWARD, b Richmond, Ind, Aug 30, 41; m 61; c 2. MICROBIOLOGY. *Educ:* Belmont Col, BS, 65; Purdue Univ, MS, 68, PhD(plant path), 70. *Prof Exp:* Instr biol, Rock Valley Col, Rockford, Ill, 70-72; asst prof biol, Univ Tenn, Nashville, 72-74, assoc prof,74-79, coordr, 75-79, prof, 79; prof biol, Tenn State Univ, 79-80; PROF BIOL, MISS COL, CLINTON, 80- *Concurrent Pos:* Vis reaseacher, Gulf Coast Res Lab, Ocean Springs, Miss, 75. *Mem:* Am Phytopath Soc; Int Soc Plant Path; Am Soc Microbiol; AAAS; Sigma Xi. *Res:* Pigment production in Bacillus cereus; Narcissus diseases and pests. *Mailing Add:* Dept Biol Sci Box 4045 Miss Col Clinton MS 39058

SNEAD, CLARENCE LEWIS, JR, b Richmond, Va, Sept 25, 36; m 60; c 3. SOLID STATE PHYSICS. *Educ:* Univ Richmond, BS, 59; Univ NC, PhD(physics), 65. *Prof Exp:* Res assoc physics, Univ NC, 65; res assoc mat sci, Northwestern Univ, 65-67; from asst physicist to assoc physicist, 67-71, ed, Sect A, Phys Rev & Res Collabr, 71-74, assoc physicist, 74-80, PHYSICIST, MAT SCI DEPT, BROOKHAVEN NAT LAB, 80- *Concurrent Pos:* Consult ed, Phys Rev, 74- *Mem:* Am Phys Soc; Am Inst Mech Engrs; Metall Soc. *Res:* Radiation effects, especially in type II superconductors and metals; position annihilation studies in defects in metals; internal-friction studies of defects. *Mailing Add:* Mat Sci Dept Brookhaven Nat Lab Upton NY 11973

SNECK, HENRY JAMES, (JR), b Schenectady, NY, Nov 9, 26; m 52; c 3. MECHANICAL ENGINEERING. *Educ:* Rensselaer Polytech Inst, BME, 51, PhD(mech eng), 63; Yale Univ, MEng, 52. *Prof Exp:* Jr engr, Eastman Kodak Co, 51; test engr, Gen Elec Co, 52-53; from instr to assoc prof, 53-76, PROF MECH ENG, RENSSELAER POLYTECH INST, 76- *Concurrent Pos:* Consult, Corp Res & Develop Ctr, Gen Elec Co, 53- *Mem:* AAAS; Am Soc Mech Engrs. *Res:* Bearings, seals, lubrication, atmospheric thermal pollution. *Mailing Add:* Dept of Mech Eng Rensselaer Polytech Inst Troy NY 12181

SNECKENBERGER, JOHN EDWARD, b Hagerstown, Md, Aug 17, 37; m 68; c 1. MECHANICAL ENGINEERING. *Educ:* WVa Univ, BS, 64, MS, 66, PhD(eng), 69. *Prof Exp:* Asst prof mech eng, 70-74, assoc prof, 74-81, PROF MECH ENG, WVA UNIV, 81- *Concurrent Pos:* NSF initiation res grant, 71-72; lectr, Hagerstown Jr Col, Md, 72; mem res adv bd, Nelson Industs, Inc, Wis, 78- *Mem:* Am Soc Mech Engrs; Am Soc Eng Educ; Soc Automotive Engrs. *Res:* Engineering systems analysis involving vibration and noise reduction; coal mechanics research in conversion processes. *Mailing Add:* Mech Eng & Mech WVa Univ Morgantown WV 26506

SNEDAKER, SAMUEL CURRY, b Long Beach, Calif, May 22, 38; m 68; c 3. ECOLOGY. *Educ:* Univ Fla, BSA & BSF, 61, MS, 63, PhD(ecol), 70. *Prof Exp:* Res assoc ecol, 68-69, asst prof, 70-73, asst prof ecol & environ eng sci, Resource Mgt Systs Prog, 73-74, asst prof aquatic sci, Univ Fla, 71-74, asst prof ecol, Inst Food & Agr Sci, 74-75; PROF BIOL & LIVING RESOURCES, UNIV MIAMI, 75- *Concurrent Pos:* Res fel, East-West Ctr, Honolulu, Hawaii. *Mem:* AAAS; Am Inst Biol Sci; Asn Trop Biol; Ecol Soc Am. *Res:* Structure and function of tropical lowland and coastal ecosystems with respect to their relationship to man. *Mailing Add:* Sch Marine & Atmospheric Sci 4600 Rickenbacker Causeway Miami FL 33149

SNEDECOR, JAMES GEORGE, b Ames, Iowa, June 9, 17; m 44; c 2. PHYSIOLOGY. *Educ:* Iowa State Univ, BS, 39; Ind Univ, PhD(zool), 47. *Prof Exp:* Asst prof zool, La State Univ, 47-48; from asst prof to assoc prof, 48-57, PROF PHYSIOL, UNIV MASS, AMHERST, 57- *Concurrent Pos:* NIH sr res fel, 55-56. *Mem:* Endocrine Soc; Am Soc Zoologists; Am Physiol Soc. *Res:* Carbohydrate metabolism; avian thyroid physiology. *Mailing Add:* Dept of Zool Univ of Mass Amherst MA 01003

SNEDEGAR, WILLIAM H, JR, b Ward, WVa, Aug 31, 26; m 48; c 2. NUCLEAR PHYSICS. *Educ:* WVa Univ, AB, 48, MS, 49; Univ Ky, PhD(physics), 58. *Prof Exp:* Physicist, Nat Bur Stand, 49-52; instr physics, Wis Col, Superior, 52-53; asst prof, Univ Ky Aid Prog to Univ Indonesia, 57-61; assoc prof physics, Eastern Ky State Col, 61-63; prof & chmn dept, Parsons Col, 63-67; PROF PHYSICS & CHMN DEPT, CLARION STATE COL, 67- *Mem:* Am Asn Physics Teachers. *Mailing Add:* Dept of Physics Clarion State Col Clarion PA 16214

SNEDEKER, ROBERT A(UDLEY), b New York, NY, Aug 3, 28; m 52; c 3. CHEMICAL ENGINEERING. *Educ:* Mass Inst Technol, SB, 50, SM, 51; Princeton Univ, PhD, 56. *Prof Exp:* Engr, Photo Prod Dept, E I du Pont de Nemours & Co, 55-58, res supvr, 58-67; tech dir, Scott Paper Co, 67-70; V PRES MFG, MERRIMAC PAPER CO, 70- *Mem:* Am Chem Soc; Am Inst Chem Engrs. *Res:* Polymer fabrication; photopolymerization; coating and drying; papermaking techniques; pollution control. *Mailing Add:* Merrimac Paper Co Box 9 Lawrence MA 01842

SNEE, RONALD D, b Washington, Pa, Dec 11, 41; m 67; c 2. STATISTICS. *Educ:* Wash & Jefferson Col, BA, 63; Rutgers Univ, MS, 65, PhD(statist), 67. *Prof Exp:* Asst prof statist, Rutgers Univ, 66-68; statistician, 68-71, sr statistician, 71-75, consult, 75-76, CONSULT SUPVR STATIST, DEPT ENG, DUPONT CO, 76- *Concurrent Pos:* Statistics fac, Univ Del, 70-75. *Honors & Awards:* Brumbaugh Award, Am Soc Qual Control, 71, Shewell Prize, 72, Wilcoxon Prize, 72 & 75, Youden Prize, 74 & 77, Ellis R Ott Award, 80. *Mem:* Fel Am Statist Asn; Am Soc Qual Control; Biometrics Soc; Air Pollution Control Asn. *Res:* Design and analysis of experiments; data analysis; graphical methods; mixture experiments; model building; analysis of variance; scientific problem solving. *Mailing Add:* Dept of Eng Dupont Co Wilmington DE 19898

SNEED, RICHARD J, electrooptics, solid state science, deceased

SNEEN, RICHARD ALLEN, b Menomonie, Wis, July 19, 30. ORGANIC CHEMISTRY. *Educ:* St Olaf Col, BA, 52; Univ Ill, PhD(chem), 55. *Prof Exp:* Fel & res asst, Univ Calif, Loa Angeles, 55-56; from instr to assoc prof chem, 56-72, PROF CHEM, PURDUE UNIV, LAFAYETTE, 72- *Mem:* Am Chem Soc; Royal Soc Chem. *Res:* Physical organic chemistry; reaction mechanisms; kinetics; stereochemistry; solvolysis reactions; ion-pair intermediates. *Mailing Add:* Dept of Chem Purdue Univ West Lafayette IN 47907

SNEIDER, ROBERT MORTON, b Asbury Park, NJ, Mar 2, 29; m 56; c 3. PETROLEUM. *Educ:* Rutgers Univ, BS, 51; Univ Wis, PhD(geol), 62. *Prof Exp:* Res geologist, Shell Develop Co, 57-65, res assoc, 65-66, from staff prod geologist to sr staff prod geologist, 66-71, res sect leader geol eng, Shell Develop Co, 71-74; pres, Sneider & Meckel Assocs, Inc, 74-81; PRES, ROBERT M SNEIDER EXPLOR INC, 81- *Concurrent Pos:* Distinguished lectr, Soc Petrol Engrs, 77-78. *Mem:* AAAS; Am Geol Inst; Am Asn Petrol Geol; Soc Econ Paleontologists & Mineralogists; Can Well Logging Soc. *Res:* Exploration and reservoir geology and petrophysics of petroleum reservoirs in the Gulf Coast, California, Wyoming and Canadian Rocky Mountains. *Mailing Add:* Robert M Sneider Explor, Inc 419 Wycliffe Dr Houston TX 77079

SNEIDER, THOMAS W, b Fremont, Ohio, Apr 19, 38; m 65; c 3. BIOCHEMISTRY, MOLECULAR BIOLOGY. *Educ:* Univ Detroit, BSc, 61; Marquette Univ, MSc, 63, PhD(physiol), 65. *Prof Exp:* Instr oncol, Univ Wis-Madison, 67-69; from asst prof to assoc prof pharmacol, Baylor Col Med, 69-75; assoc prof, 75-81, PROF BIOCHEM, COLO STATE UNIV, 81-

Concurrent Pos: NSF fel biochem & oncol, McArdle Lab, Univ Wis-Madison, 65-67; NIH res career develop award, 73-78; chmn, Grad Facil Cellular & Molecular Biol, Colo State Univ, 78-80. *Mem:* AAAS; Am Soc Biol Chemists; Am Asn Cancer Res. *Res:* The control mechanisms of pyrimidine biosynthesis and liver regeneration; mechanisms and functions of eukaryotic DNA modifications; control of cellular differentiation. *Mailing Add:* Dept of Biochem Colo State Univ Ft Collins CO 80523

SNELGROVE, JAMES ARTHUR, b Toronto, Ont, Aug 19, 22; m 46; c 4. POLYMER CHEMISTRY. *Educ:* Univ Toronto, BA, 49, PhD(phys chem), 52. *Prof Exp:* Asst chem, Univ Toronto, 49-50; res chemist, 52-56, group leader, 56-79, TECH MGR, RES DEPT, MONSANTO CO, 79- *Mem:* Am Chem Soc; NY Acad Sci. *Res:* Physical chemistry of polymers; surface chemistry; adhesion; polymer solutions; polymerization kinetics; colloid chemistry; surface coatings; electrical insulation; glazing. *Mailing Add:* Res Dept Monsanto Co 190 Grochmal Ave Indian Orchard MA 01051

SNELGROVE, JAMES LEWIS, b Cookeville, Tenn, Jan 9, 42; m 65; c 2. REACTOR PHYSICS, REACTOR FUEL TESTING. *Educ:* Tenn Polytech Inst, BS, 64; Mich State Univ, MS, 66, PhD(physics), 68. *Prof Exp:* PHYSICIST, ARGONNE NAT LAB, 68- *Mem:* Am Phys Soc; Am Nuclear Soc; Sigma Xi. *Res:* Use of reduced-enrichment fuel in research and test reactors, including design of reactor cores and testing of new high-density fuels. *Mailing Add:* Appl Physics Div Argonne Nat Lab 9700 S Cass Ave Argonne IL 60439

SNELL, A(BSALOM) W(EST), b Parler, SC, Apr 29, 24; m 51; c 4. AGRICULTURAL ENGINEERING. *Educ:* Clemson Univ, BS, 49; Iowa State Univ, MS, 52; NC State Univ, PhD(agr eng), 64. *Prof Exp:* Asst prof agr eng, Clemson Univ, 49-51; instr & res fel, Iowa State Univ, 51-52; from asst prof to prof & head dept, 52-75, chmn directorate, Water Resources Res Inst, 64-75, ASSOC DIR, SC AGR EXP STA, CLEMSON UNIV, 75- *Mem:* Am Soc Agr Engrs; Am Soc Eng Educ; Am Geophys Union. *Res:* Water resources engineering; irrigation; drainage; water movement in soils; agricultural research. *Mailing Add:* 104 Barre Hall Clemson Univ Clemson SC 29631

SNELL, ARTHUR HAWLEY, b Montreal, Que, Mar 10, 09; nat US; m 37, 41; c 3. NUCLEAR PHYSICS, ATOMIC PHYSICS. *Educ:* Univ Toronto, BA, 30; McGill Univ, MSc, 31, PhD(physics), 33. *Prof Exp:* Res assoc, McGill Univ, 33-34; 1851 Exhib scholar, Univ Calif, 34-37, res assoc, Radiation Lab, 37-38; res instr physics, Univ Chicago, 38-42, sr physicist & chief cyclotron sect, Metall Lab, 40-44; chief physicist & sect chief group leader, 44-48, dir physics div, 48-57, from asst dir to assoc dir lab, 57-73, dir thermonuclear div, 58-67, CONSULT, OAK RIDGE NAT LAB, 73- *Concurrent Pos:* Chmn subcomt nuclear instruments & tech, Nat Acad Sci-Nat Res Coun, 54-61; mem bd dirs, Oak Ridge Inst Nuclear Studies, 59-62. *Mem:* Fel AAAS; fel Am Phys Soc; fel Royal Soc Arts; Sigma Xi. *Res:* Fast-neutron effect in nuclear chain reaction; delayed neutrons for control of chain reaction; indentification of delayed neutron emitters; radioactive decay of the neutron; neutrino recoil spectrometry; atomic vacancy caseades by charge spectrometry; plutonium project history. *Mailing Add:* Rt 4 Box 222 Kingston TN 37763

SNELL, CHARLES MURRELL, b Johnson City, Tenn, Aug 19, 46. COMPUTATIONAL PHYSICS, GEOPHYSICS. *Educ:* Vanderbilt Univ, BA, 67; Univ Ariz, MS, 69. *Prof Exp:* Physicist explosives eng, Explosive Excavation Res Off, US Army Engr Waterways Exp Sta, 71-73; physicist comput physics, Lawrence Livermore Lab, 73-78; physicist comput physics & geophys, 78-80, PHYSICIST, PARTICLE-IN-CELL NUMERICAL MODELING, LOS ALAMOS NAT LAB, 80- *Res:* Physical properties of solid materials; constitutive relations of rocks and soils; material equations of state; underground and underwater explosions; computer modeling of material dynamics; particle-in-cell numerical modeling; simulation of intense charged-particle beams. *Mailing Add:* Los Alamos Nat Lab MS-608 PO Box 1663 Los Alamos NM 87545

SNELL, ESMOND EMERSON, b Salt Lake City, Utah, Sept 22, 14; m 41; c 4. BIOCHEMISTRY. *Educ:* Brigham Young Univ, BA, 35; Univ Wis, MA, 36, PhD(biochem), 38. *Prof Exp:* Res assoc chem, Univ Tex, 39-41, from asst prof to prof, 41-56; from assoc prof to prof biochem, Univ Wis, 45-51; prof biochem, Univ Calif, Berkeley, 56-76; prof & chmn, Dept Microbiol, 76-80, ASHBEL SMITH PROF MICROBIOL & CHEM, UNIV TEX, AUSTIN, 80- *Concurrent Pos:* Ed, Ann Rev Biochem, Ann Rev, Inc, 69-, pres, 72-76; Guggenheim fels, 54, 62, 70. *Honors & Awards:* Lilly Award, Am Soc Bacteriologists, 45; Mead Johnson Award, Am Inst Nutrit, 46 & Osborne Mendel Award, 51; Kenneth A Spencer Awar, Am Chem Soc, 74. *Mem:* Nat Acad Sci; AAAS; Am Soc Microbiol; Am Soc Biol Chem (pres, 61-62); Am Chem Soc. *Res:* Metabolism and mechanism of action of vitamin B6; vitamin metabolism and transport; pyruvoyl enzymes. *Mailing Add:* Dept of Microbiol Univ of Tex Austin TX 78712

SNELL, FRED MANGET, b Soochow, China, Nov 11, 21; m 46; c 3. BIOPHYSICS. *Educ:* Maryville Col, Tenn, AB, 42; Harvard Univ, MD, 45; Mass Inst Technol, PhD(biochem), 52. *Prof Exp:* Intern pediat, Children's Hosp, 45-46, from jr asst resident to asst resident, 48-49; res assoc biol, Mass Inst Technol, 52-54; assoc biochem, Harvard Med Sch, 54-57, asst prof, 57-59; prof biophys & chmn dept, 59-70, dean grad sch, 67-69, master, Col A, 68-71, PROF BIOPHYS SCI, SCH MED, STATE UNIV NY BUFFALO, 70- *Concurrent Pos:* Nat Found Infantile Paralysis fel, Mass Inst Technol, 52-54; Nat Found Infantile Paralysis fel, Children's Med Ctr, 52-54; Palmer sr fel, Harvard Med Sch, 54-57; US Navy rep & mem atomic bomb casualty comn, Comt Atomic Casualties, Nat Res Coun; mem biophys sci training comt, Nat Inst Gen Med Sci, 62-66, chmn, 65-66; mem biophys panel, President's NIH Study Comt, 64; mem interdisciplinary panel, Comn Undergrad Educ Biol Sci, 65; comn biomath subpanel, 66-68; consult, Comn Undergrad Progs in Math, 65-68; mem adv comt on NIH training progs, Nat Acad Sci-Nat Res Coun; ed, Biophys J, 66-69. *Mem:* AAAS; Biophys Soc (pres, 71); Am Chem Soc; Am Physiol Soc; NY Acad Sci. *Res:* Biophysical aspects of transport processes including selective ionic accumulation and diffusion; membrane processes; global thermodynamics. *Mailing Add:* Dept Biophys Sci Sch Med State Univ NY Buffalo NY 14214

SNELL, GEORGE DAVIS, b Bradford, Mass, Dec 19, 03; m 37; c 3. GENETICS, TISSUE TRANSPLANTATION. *Educ:* Dartmouth Col, BS, 26; Harvard Univ, MS, 28, ScD(genetics), 30. *Hon Degrees:* MD, Charles Univ, Prague, 68; ScD, Dartmouth Col, 74 & Univ Maine & Gustavus Aldolphus Col, 81. *Prof Exp:* Instr zool, Dartmouth Col, 29-30 & Brown Univ, 30-31; Nat Res Coun fel, Univ Tex, 31-33; asst prof, Wash Univ, 33-34; res assoc, Jackson Lab, 35-56, sci adminstr, 49-50, sr staff scientist, 57-68, retired assoc, 69, emer sr staff scientist, 69-73; RETIRED. *Concurrent Pos:* Guggenheim fel, Univ Tex, 53-54; mem allergy & immunol study sect, NIH, 58-62. *Honors & Awards:* Corecipient, Nobel Prize in Physiol & Med, 80; Gairdner Found Award, 76; Wolf Prize Med Res, 78. *Mem:* Nat Acad Sci; AAAS; Am Acad Arts & Sci; Am Soc Nat; foreign assoc Fr Acad Sci. *Res:* Genetics of the house mouse; radiation genetics; genetics and immunology of tissue transplantation; immunogenetics. *Mailing Add:* 21 Atlantic Ave Bar Harbor ME 04609

SNELL, JAMES LAURIE, b Wheaton, Ill, Jan 15, 25; m 52; c 2. PROBABILITY. *Educ:* Univ Ill, BS, 47, MA, 48, PhD(math), 51. *Prof Exp:* Fine instr, Princeton Univ, 51-54; from asst prof to assoc prof, 54-62, PROF MATH, DARTMOUTH COL, 62- *Mem:* Am Math Soc; Math Asn Am. *Res:* Probability theory. *Mailing Add:* Dept of Math Dartmouth Col Hanover NH 03755

SNELL, JOHN B, b Waterbury, Conn, May 10, 36; m 66. PLASTICS CHEMISTRY. *Educ:* Univ Wis, BSChE, 59; Inst Paper Chem, PhD(phys chem), 64. *Prof Exp:* Sr chemist, Tape Div, 64-68, res supvr, 68-71, RES SPECIALIST, INDUST SPEC DIV, 3M CO, 71- *Mem:* Am Chem Soc. *Res:* Epoxy resins and curing agents for reinforced plastics and advanced composites; polymers for vibration dampening. *Mailing Add:* Indust Spec Div Bldg 230-1 3M Ctr St Paul MN 55144

SNELL, JUNIUS FIELDING, b Lovell, Wyo, Feb 6, 21; m 45; c 2. BIOCHEMISTRY. *Educ:* Univ Tex, BS, 43; Univ Wis, MS, 44, PhD(biochem), 49. *Prof Exp:* Res scientist, Chas Pfizer & Co, Inc, 45-46, dir radiobiochem lab, 52-61; actg chmn dept biochem, 66-67, PROF BIOCHEM, BIOPHYS & MICROBIOL, OHIO STATE UNIV, 61- *Concurrent Pos:* Dir, Pfizer Therapeut Inst, 55-61. *Mem:* Soc Nuclear Med; Am Soc Microbiol; NY Acad Sci. *Res:* Phosphorous metabolism; yeast growth; antibiotic fermentations; mode of action of antibiotics; non-specific immunity; reticuloendothelial system. *Mailing Add:* Dept of Biochem Vivian Hall Ohio State Univ 464 W 12th St Columbus OH 43210

SNELL, RICHARD SAXON, b Richmond, Eng, May 3, 25; m 49; c 5. ANATOMY. *Educ:* Univ London, MB, BS, 49, PhD(med), 55, MD, 61. *Prof Exp:* House surgeon, King's Col Hosp, London, 48-49; jr lectr anat, King's Col, London, 49-53, lectr anat & hist, 53-59; lectr anat, Univ Durham, 59-63; from asst prof to assoc prof, Yale Univ, 63-67; prof & chmn dept, NJ Col Med & Dent, 67-69; vis prof, Yale Univ, 69 & Harvard Univ, 70-71; prof, Univ Ariz, 70-72; PROF ANAT & CHMN DEPT, MED SCH, GEORGE WASHINGTON UNIV, 72- *Mem:* Am Asn Anatomists; Anat Soc Gt Brit & Ireland. *Res:* Pigmentation of mammalian skin and its control; light and electron microscopic appearances of the skin; histochemistry of cholinesterase in the peripheral and central parts of the nervous system. *Mailing Add:* Dept Anat George Washington Univ Sch Med Washington DC 20037

SNELL, ROBERT ISAAC, b Hancock, Mich, Mar 16, 37; m 65; c 1. MATHEMATICS. *Educ:* Northern Mich Univ, BS, 59; Univ Mich, MS, 60; Univ Colo, PhD(appl math), 68. *Prof Exp:* Instr math, Mich Tech Univ, 60-64; asst prof math, Univ Puget Sound, 68-73, assoc prof, 73-80. *Mem:* Math Asn Am; Soc Indust & Appl Math. *Res:* Continued fractions; real and complex analysis; differential equations. *Mailing Add:* 112 Bon Bluff Rd Fox Island WA 98333

SNELL, ROBERT L, b El Dorado Springs, Mo, Jan 28, 25; m 55; c 2. ORGANIC CHEMISTRY. *Educ:* Drury Col, BS, 48; Mo Sch Mines, MS, 52; Tex Tech Col, PhD(chem), 59. *Prof Exp:* Chemist, Dowell, Inc, 54-55; from asst prof to assoc prof, 59-66, PROF CHEM, E TENN STATE UNIV, 66- *Concurrent Pos:* Adj prof pharmacol, Quillen-Dishner Col Med. *Mem:* Am Chem Soc; Sigma Xi. *Mailing Add:* Dept Chem E Tenn State Univ Johnson City TN 37601

SNELL, ROBERT ROSS, b St John, Kans, Apr 17, 32; m 52; c 2. CIVIL ENGINEERING. *Educ:* Kans State Univ, BS, 54, MS, 60; Purdue Univ, Lafayette, PhD(civil eng struct), 63. *Prof Exp:* Civil engr, Kans State Hwy Comn, 54-55; from instr to assoc prof civil eng, Kans State Univ, 57-67; Ford Found resident, Rust Eng Co, Pa, 67-68; PROF CIVIL ENG, KANS STATE UNIV, 68-, HEAD DEPT, 72- *Mem:* Am Soc Eng Educ; Am Soc Civil Engrs. *Res:* Structural analysis and design; systems optimization; structural modeling. *Mailing Add:* Dept of Civil Eng Seaton Hall Kans State Univ Manhattan KS 66506

SNELL, RONALD LEE, b Salina, Kans, May 15, 51; m 78. ASTRONOMY. *Educ:* Univ Kans, BA, 73; Univ Tex at Austin, MA, 75, PhD(astron), 79. *Prof Exp:* Teaching asst astron, Univ Kans, 72-73; teaching asst & res asst, Univ Tex, 73-79, instr 76-79; RES ASSOC, UNIV MASS, 79- *Mem:* Am Astron Soc. *Res:* Interstellar medium and the formation of stars by radio frequency observations of spectral lines emitted by atoms and molecules in interstellar clouds. *Mailing Add:* GRC Tower B Five Col Radio Astron Observ Univ Mass Amherst MA 01003

SNELLING, CHRISTOPHER, b Hartford, Conn, Nov 8, 35; m 59; c 1. ELECTRICAL ENGINEERING, APPLIED MATHEMATICS. *Educ:* Union Col, NY, BEE, 57; Univ Rochester, MS, 64. *Prof Exp:* Assoc physicist, Haloid Corp, 57-60, physicist, Haloid-Xerox, 60-62, sr physicist, Xerox Corp, 62-65, scientist, 65-68; proj engr, Hamco Mach & Electronics Corp, 68-72; scientist, 72-76, tech specialist/proj mgr I, 76-80, MEM RES STAFF, XEROX CORP, 81- *Mem:* Inst Elec & Electronics Engrs; Soc Photographic Scientists & Engrs; Sigma Xi. *Res:* Measurement and analysis of xerographic photoreceptors; xerographic process studies; electrostatics; photoconductivity; radiometry; direct current instrumentation; development of Czochralski silicon crystal growing furnaces for semiconductor production. *Mailing Add:* 5 High Meadow Dr Penfield NY 14526

SNELLINGS, WILLIAM MORAN, b Norfolk, Va, May 7, 47; m 70; c 2. TOXICOLOGY, INHALATION TOXICOLOGY. *Educ:* Va Polytech Inst, BS, 69; Univ Mich, PhD(toxicol), 76. *Prof Exp:* Sr technician, Hazelton Labs, 69-71; toxicologist, Carnegie-Mellon Inst Res, 76-80; MGR INHALATION TOXICOL, BUSHY RUN RES CTR, 80- *Concurrent Pos:* Prin investr Ethylene Oxide Toxicity Prog worldwide consortium Ethylene Oxide Toxicity producers, 76-81. *Res:* Toxicity evaluation of various industrial chemicals; assessment of the oncogenic, teratogenic and mutagenic potential of test chemicals; inhalation chambers, vapor generators, aerosol generators, and atmospheric sampling systems. *Mailing Add:* Bushy Run Res Ctr RD #4 Mellon Rd Export PA 15632

SNELLMAN, LEONARD W, b Lansford, Pa, June 27, 20; m 48; c 4. METEOROLOGY. *Educ:* Kenyon Col, AB, 43. *Prof Exp:* Forecaster, US Weather Bur, 46-51; civilian consult meteorol, US Air Force-Hq Air Weather Serv, 53-65; CHIEF SCI SERV DIV, NAT WEATHER SERV, OCEANIC & ATMOSPHERIC ADMIN, 65- *Concurrent Pos:* Lectr, Univ Utah, 66-68, adj asst prof, 68- *Honors & Awards:* Silver Medal, Dept of Commerce, 69. *Mem:* Fel Am Meteorol Soc. *Res:* Synoptic and satellite meteorology especially weather forecasting. *Mailing Add:* 4278 South 2700 East Salt Lake City UT 84109

SNELSIRE, ROBERT W, b Pittsburgh, Pa, May 8, 33; m 57; c 3. ELECTRICAL ENGINEERING. *Educ:* Bethany Col, BA, 56; Carnegie Inst Technol, BS, 56, MS, 58, PhD(elec eng), 64. *Prof Exp:* Instr elec eng, Carnegie Inst Technol, 58-63; sr engr, Westinghouse Defense Ctr, 63-64; asst prof elec eng, State Univ NY Buffalo, 64-67; ASSOC PROF ELEC ENG, CLEMSON UNIV, 67- *Concurrent Pos:* Consult, Bell Aerosysts Co, 66-67 & Wachovia Bank & Trust Co, 66- *Mem:* Inst Elec & Electronics Engrs; Am Soc Eng Educ. *Res:* Computer science; simulation of human behavior. *Mailing Add:* Dept of Elec & Comput Eng Clemson Univ Clemson SC 29631

SNELSON, ALAN, b Manchester, Eng, Oct 17, 34; m 77; c 1. PHYSICAL CHEMISTRY, THERMODYNAMICS. *Educ:* Univ Manchester, Eng, BSc, 57, MSc, 58, PhD(chem), 60. *Prof Exp:* Fel chem, Univ Calif, Berkeley, 60-62; SR CHEMIST, IIT RES INST, 62- *Concurrent Pos:* Lectr, Ill Inst Technol, 67- *Mem:* Am Chem Soc. *Res:* Thermochemistry; spectroscopy; kinetics; cryogenics atmospheric chemistry. *Mailing Add:* IIT Res Inst 10 W 35th St Chicago IL 60616

SNELSON, FRANKLIN F, JR, b Richmond, Va, June 13, 43; c 1. ICHTHYOLOGY. *Educ:* NC State Univ, BS, 65; Cornell Univ, PhD(vert zool), 70. *Prof Exp:* Asst prof, 70-74, ASSOC PROF BIOL SCI, FLA TECHNOL UNIV, 74- *Concurrent Pos:* Soc Sigma Xi grant, 70-71, NASA grant, 72-75 & 76-79; prof staff mem, Inst Fresh Water Ecol, 70- *Mem:* Am Soc Ichthyologists & Herpetologists; Am Inst Biol Sci; Am Fisheries Soc; Soc Syst Zool; Am Inst Fishery Res Biologists. *Res:* Systematics and ecology of fishes. *Mailing Add:* Dept of Biol Sci Fla Technol Univ Orlando FL 32816

SNELSON, SIGMUND, b Santa Paula, Calif, June 22, 32; m 60; c 2. GEOLOGY. *Educ:* Univ Redlands, BS, 53; Univ Wash, MS, 55, PhD(geol), 57. *Prof Exp:* Fulbright fel, Univ Graz, 57-58; geologist, Shell Oil Co, 59-66, sr geologist, 66-69, staff geologist, Shell Develop Co, 69-70 & Shell Oil Co, 70-74, SR STAFF GEOL SUPVR, GLOBAL GEOL SECT, SHELL DEVELOP CO, 75- *Honors & Awards:* A I Levorsen Mem Award, Am Asn Petrol Geologists, 72. *Mem:* Geol Soc Am; Am Asn Petrol Geologists. *Res:* Large-scale thrusting and migrating Cretaceous foredeeps in North Alaska; structural evolution of California; oil accumulations in coastal California; Appalachian geology; South American and Caribbean geology; evolution of continental margins. *Mailing Add:* Shell Develop Co PO Box 481 Houston TX 77024

SNETSINGER, DAVID CLARENCE, b Barrington, Ill, Apr 22, 30; m 53; c 4. POULTRY NUTRITION. *Educ:* Univ Ill, BS, 52, MS, 57, PhD(poultry nutrit), 59. *Prof Exp:* Asst poultry, Univ Ill, 55-59; from asst prof to assoc prof poultry sci, Univ Minn, St Paul, 59-68; mgr com layer res div, 68-70, mgr com egg & breeder res div, 70-72, mgr gen poultry res div, 72-76, DIR POULTRY RES & MKT DEPT, RALSTON PURINA CO, 76- *Mem:* Poultry Sci Asn; Am Inst Nutrit; World Poultry Sci Asn. *Res:* Amino acid and mineral nutrition and metabolism. *Mailing Add:* Poultry Res Dept 2RS Ralston Purina Co 835 S Eighth St St Louis MO 63199

SNETSINGER, KENNETH GEORGE, b San Francisco, Calif, Feb 21, 39; m 78. GEOCHEMISTRY, MINERALOGY. *Educ:* Stanford Univ, BS, 61, MS, 62, PhD(mineral), 66. *Prof Exp:* Nat Acad Sci-Nat Res Coun resident res assoc, 66-69, RES SCIENTIST, NASA AMES RES CTR, 69- *Mem:* Mineral Soc Am; Mineral Soc Can. *Res:* Mineralogy and geochemistry of meteorites, lunar samples, platinum metals; composition and minerology of atmospheric aerosols. *Mailing Add:* NASA Ames Res Ctr Moffett Field CA 94035

SNETSINGER, ROBERT J, b Diamond Lake, Ill, Mar 6, 28; m 60; c 2. ECOMONIC ENTOMOLOGY, ARACHNOLOGY. *Educ:* Univ Ill, Urbana, BS, 52, MS, 53, PhD(entom), 60. *Prof Exp:* Asst econ entom, Ill Nat Hist Surv, 55-60; from asst prof to assoc prof entom, 60-71, PROF ENTOM, PA STATE UNIV, UNIVERSITY PARK, 71- *Concurrent Pos:* Ed, Int Mushroom Cong, 62, Entom Soc Pa, 64- & Pa Pest Control Quart, 67-75. *Mem:* Entom Soc Am; Entom Soc Can. *Res:* Biology and control of animal pests of horticultural crops including mushrooms; professional pest control and urban ecology; biology and control of arachnids. *Mailing Add:* Dept of Entom 106 Patterson Pa State Univ University Park PA 16802

SNIDER, ALBERT MONROE, JR, b Hoffman, NC; m 66; c 2. POLYMERS, ANALYTICAL CHEMISTRY. *Educ:* Univ NC, Chapel Hill, BA, 59, MEd, 62; Appalachian State Univ, MA, 69; Univ Pittsburgh, PhD(chem), 74. *Prof Exp:* Teaching asst chem, Appalachian State Univ, 67-69; chemist, Mellon Inst, 70; instr, Community Col Allegheny County, 75; res asst, Dept Chem, Sch Eng, Univ Pittsburgh, 69-74, res assoc polymer sci, 75-76; lab dir, K Tator Assocs, 76-77; group leader, Spectros Lab, Carnegie-Mellon Inst Res, 78-79; group leader polymer characteriation, Merck & Co, 79-81; MGR, CHEM & NONMETALS LAB, GEN ELEC CO, 81- *Mem:* Am Chem Soc; Soc Appl Spectros; Coblentz Soc; Sigma Xi. *Res:* Molecular spectroscopy and polymer science particularly utilizing infrared, raman, nuclear magnetic resonance, photoelectron, and mass spectroscopies, x-ray diffraction and electron microscopy. *Mailing Add:* Gen Elec Co 2901 E Lake Rd Erie PA 16531

SNIDER, ARTHUR DAVID, b Richmond, Va, Oct 7, 40. MATHEMATICS. *Educ:* Mass Inst Technol, BS, 62; Boston Univ, MA, 66; NY Univ, PhD(math), 71. *Prof Exp:* Analyst, Instrumentation Lab, Mass Inst Technol, 62-66; asst prof, 70-77, ASSOC PROF MATH, UNIV S FLA, 77- *Concurrent Pos:* Math consult, Honeywell Aerospace Corp, 74. *Mem:* Soc Indust & Appl Math; Am Math Soc; Math Asn Am. *Res:* Applied mathematics; numerical analysis; differential equations; plasmas. *Mailing Add:* Dept of Math Univ of SFla Tampa FL 33620

SNIDER, BILL CARL F, b Cedar Rapids, Iowa, July 11, 20; m 54; c 1. STATISTICS. *Educ:* Univ Wichita, BA, 42, MA, 51; Univ Iowa, PhD, 55. *Prof Exp:* Res assoc prev ment health, Child Welfare Res Sta, Univ Iowa, 56-65, res assoc comput ctr, 62-65, asst prof statist, Col Educ & Comput Ctr, 65-69, assoc prof educ, 69-77, PROF EDUC, PSYCHOL, MEASUREMENT & STATIST, UNIV IOWA, 77- STATIST CONSULT, COMPUT CTR, 73- *Mem:* Am Educ Res Asn; Am Psychol Asn; Asn Comput Mach; Am Statist Asn. *Res:* Mental health; statistics and preventive mental health. *Mailing Add:* Col Educ & Univ Comput Ctr Univ of Iowa Iowa City IA 52242

SNIDER, DALE REYNOLDS, b Cincinnati, Ohio, Mar 21, 38; m 61; c 2. HIGH ENERGY PHYSICS. *Educ:* Ohio State Univ, BS & MS, 61; Univ Calif, San Diego, PhD(physics), 68. *Prof Exp:* Instr nuclear eng, US Navy Nuclear Power Sch, Calif, 61-65; theoret physicist, Lawrence Radiation Lab, Univ Calif, Berkeley, 68-70; asst prof, 70-77, ASSOC PROF PHYSICS, UNIV WIS-MILWAUKEE, 77- *Concurrent Pos:* Vis prof physics, Univ Ill, Urbana, 74-75. *Mem:* Am Phys Soc. *Res:* Theoretical high energy physics; strong interaction theory. *Mailing Add:* Dept of Physics Univ of Wis-Milwaukee Milwaukee WI 53201

SNIDER, DIXIE EDWARD, JR, b Frankfort, Ky, Jan 16, 43; m 66; c 2. MEDICINE. *Educ:* Western Ky State Col, BS, 65; Univ Louisville, MD, 69. *Prof Exp:* Intern internal med, Barnes Hosp, 69-70, resident, 70-71; resident, Vanderbilt Univ, 71-72; fel allergy & clin immunol, Washington Univ, 72-73; med officer tuberc, USPHS, 73-74; CHIEF RES & DEVELOP BR, TUBERC CONTROL DIV, BUR STATE SERV, CTR DIS CONTROL, USPHS, 74- *Concurrent Pos:* Fel allergy & clin immunol, Washington Univ, 75-76. *Mem:* Am Thoracic Soc; Int Union Against Tuberc; Am Col Physicians; Am Acad Allergy; Am Pub Health Asn. *Res:* Tuberculin skin testing; mycobacterial drug resistance; preventive therapy of tuberculosis; treatment of tuberculosis; prostaglandins and asthma; lymphocyte cyclic nucleotide metabolism. *Mailing Add:* 1600 Clifton Rd Atlanta GA 30333

SNIDER, DONALD EDWARD, b Lakewood, Ohio, Sept 12, 44; m 78. ATMOSPHERIC PHYSICS. *Educ:* Ohio State Univ, BS, 66, MS, 68, PhD(physics), 71. *Prof Exp:* RES PHYSICIST, BALLISTIC RES LABS, 71-, ATMOSPHERIC SCI LAB, 76- *Mem:* Optical Soc Am; Am Meteorol Soc. *Res:* Investigations of atmospheric effects on electro optical systems; attenuation by atmospheric gases; attenuation and scattering by natural and man made aerosols; refraction and scintillation due to turbulance; atmospheric optics; propagation of electro-magnetic energy. *Mailing Add:* Atmospheric Sci Lab White Sands Missile Range NM 88002

SNIDER, GORDON LLOYD, b Toronto, Ont, Apr 11, 22; US citizen; m 45; c 3. PULMONARY DISEASES. *Educ:* Univ Toronto, MD, 44; Am Bd Internal Med, dipl, 53; Am Bd Pulmonary Dis, dipl, 58. *Prof Exp:* Intern, Toronto Gen Hosp, 44-45; resident med, Bronx Hosp, New York, 46-47, resident path, Mass Mem Hosp, Boston, 47-48; fel med, Lahey Clinic, Boston, 48-49; resident pulmonary med, Trudeau Sanitarium, NY, 49-50; asst dir chest dept, Michael Reese Hosp, 50-61; chief div thoracic med, Mt Sinai Hosp, 61-66, actg chmn dept med, 65-66; chief pulmonary dis sect, Wood Vet Admin Hosp, 66-68; prof med, Sch Med & head respiratory sect, Univ Hosp, Boston Univ, 68-76; CHIEF PULMONARY DIS SECT, BOSTON VET ADMIN HOSP, 68- *Concurrent Pos:* Attend physician, Winfield Hosp, Ill, 52-61; consult physician & dir pulmonary function lab, Munic Tuberc Sanitarium, Chicago, 52-68; med consult, Social Security Admin, 58-66; from asst prof to prof med, Chicago Med Sch, 58-66, actg chmn dept, 65-66; consult, West Side Vet Admin Hosp, Chicago, 64-66; prof, Sch Med, Marquette Univ, 66-68; attend physician, Milwaukee County Gen Hosp & med consult, Mt Sinai Hosp, Milwaukee, 66-68; mem respiratory dis comt, Tuberc Inst Chicago & Cook County; mem med adv bds, Suburban Cook County Tuberc Sanitarium Dis & Asthma & Allergy Res Found, Greater Chicago; mem med adv comt, Chicago Chap, Cystic Fibrosis Res Found; consult comt, Div Sanatoria & Tuberc Control, Mass Dept Pub Health; mem pulmonary dis adv comt, Nat Heart, Lung & Blood Inst, 80- *Mem:* Fel Am Col Chest Physicians; fel Am Col Physicians; Am Fedn Clin Res; Am Thoracic Soc. *Res:* Clinical pulmonary disease and physiology; experimental pulmonary diseases. *Mailing Add:* Boston Vet Admin Hosp 130 S Huntington Ave Boston MA 02130

SNIDER, JERRY ALLEN, b Danville, Ill, Feb 17, 37; m 67; c 1. BRYOLOGY, CYTOLOGY. *Educ:* Southern Ill Univ, BA, 67; Univ NC, Chapel Hill, MA, 70; Duke Univ, PhD(bot), 74. *Prof Exp:* Asst prof biol, Baylor Univ, 73-74; asst prof, 74-80, HERBARIUM CUR, DEPT BIOL SCI, UNIV CINCINNATI, 74-, ASSOC PROF, 80- *Mem:* Am Bryol & Lichenological Soc; Sigma Xi; British Bryol Soc; Int Asn Plant Taxon; Int Asn Bryol. *Res:* Cytology and taxonomy of bryophytes; morphological development in bryophytes. *Mailing Add:* Dept of Biol Sci Univ of Cincinnati Cincinnati OH 45221

SNIDER, JOHN WILLIAM, b Middleport, Ohio, Sept 13, 24; m 49; c 1. PHYSICS. *Educ:* Miami Univ, AB, 49, MA, 51; Ohio State Univ, PhD, 57. *Prof Exp:* Res assoc, Ohio State Univ, 57-59; from asst prof to assoc prof, 53-73, PROF PHYSICS, MIAMI UNIV, 73- *Concurrent Pos:* Sr res physicist, Mound Lab, Monsanto Chem Co, 58-69; consult, Ohio River Div, Army Corps Engrs, 63-65. *Mem:* Am Asn Physics Teachers. *Res:* Low temperature physics, especially superconductivity and thermal transpiration; calorimetry. *Mailing Add:* Dept of Physics Miami Univ Oxford OH 45056

SNIDER, JOSEPH LYONS, b Boston, Mass, June 10, 34. ATOMIC PHYSICS, ASTROPHYSICS. *Educ:* Amherst Col, BA, 56; Princeton Univ, PhD(physics), 61. *Prof Exp:* Instr & res fel physics, Harvard Univ, 61-64, asst prof, 64-69; assoc prof, 69-75, PROF PHYSICS, OBERLIN COL, 75- *Mem:* Am Phys Soc; Am Astron Soc; Am Asn Physics Teachers. *Res:* Solar physics; atomic physics; relativity and gravitation. *Mailing Add:* Dept of Physics Oberlin Col Oberlin OH 44074

SNIDER, NEIL STANLEY, b Schenectady, NY, May 25, 38. THEORETICAL CHEMISTRY. *Educ:* Purdue Univ, BSc, 59; Princeton Univ, MA, 61, PhD(chem), 64. *Prof Exp:* NSF fel, 64-65; res assoc chem, Cornell Univ, 65 & Yale Univ, 65-66; asst prof, 66-72, ASSOC PROF CHEM, QUEEN'S UNIV, ONT, 72- *Mem:* Am Chem Soc; Can Asn Physicists; Chem Inst Can. *Res:* Theory of rates of homogeneous gas phase reactions; statistical mechanics of classical fluids. *Mailing Add:* Dept of Chem Queen's Univ Kingston ON K7L 3N6 Can

SNIDER, PHILIP JOSEPH, b Richmond, VA, Apr 5, 29; m 52; c 2. GENETICS. *Educ:* Richmond Univ, BS, 52; Harvard Univ, AM, 55, PhD, 57. *Prof Exp:* Res assoc biol div, Genetics Sect, Oak Ridge Nat Lab, 58-59; asst prof bot, Univ Calif, Berkeley, 59-63; dir univ honors prog, 65-70, ASSOC PROF BIOL, UNIV HOUSTON, 63- *Concurrent Pos:* Consult mem, Biol Sci Curriculum Studies, 64-70. *Mem:* AAAS. *Res:* Microbial and molecular genetics, especially regulatory genetics of reproductive processes. *Mailing Add:* 5312 Clarewood Houston TX 77081

SNIDER, ROBERT FOLINSBEE, b Calgary, Alta, Nov 22, 31; m 58; c 4. THEORETICAL CHEMISTRY. *Educ:* Univ Alta, BSc, 53; Univ Wis, PhD(theoret chem), 58; FRSC; FCIC. *Prof Exp:* Fel appl chem, Nat Res Coun Can, 58; from instr to assoc prof chem, 58-69, PROF CHEM, UNIV BC, 69- *Mem:* Can Asn Physicists; Am Inst Phys; Chem Inst Can. *Res:* Statistical mechanics; transport properties of gases; collisions of non-spherical molecules. *Mailing Add:* Dept Chem 2036 Main Mall Vancouver BC V6T 1Y6 Can

SNIECKUS, VICTOR A, b Kaunas, Lithuania, Aug 1, 37; Can citizen; m 66; c 2. ORGANIC CHEMISTRY. *Educ:* Univ Alta, BSc, 59; Univ Calif, Berkeley, MS, 61; Univ Ore, PhD(chem), 65; FCIC, 78. *Prof Exp:* Nat Res Coun Can fel chem, 65-66; asst prof, 66-71, fel, 66-67, ASSOC PROF CHEM, UNIV WATERLOO, 71- *Concurrent Pos:* H C Orsted Found Fel, Univ Copenhagen, Denmark, 73; vis prof, Univ Geneva, Switzerland, 76-77; Can-Japan exchange fel, 81. *Mem:* Am Chem Soc; Chem Inst Can; The Chem Soc; Int Soc Heterocyclic Chem. *Res:* Synthetic organic chemistry, especially anthraquinones, anthracyclinones, indole and benzylisoquinoline alkaloids; chemistry of 1, 2 diazepines; general methodology, especially stereoselective synthesis; biosynthesis of serotonin lithiated aromatic and aliphatic amides; antibodies of indole alkylamines. *Mailing Add:* Dept of Chem Univ of Waterloo Waterloo ON N2L 3G1 Can

SNIPES, CHARLES ANDREW, b Tampa, Fla, Nov 1, 36. PHYSIOLOGY. *Educ:* Western Carolina Univ, BA, 57; Duke Univ, PhD(physiol, pharmacol), 67. *Prof Exp:* From instr to asst prof pediat, Johns Hopkins Univ, 62-68, asst dir res training prog pediat endocrinol, 62-68; asst prof physiol, 68-71, ASSOC PROF PHYSIOL, HAHNEMANN MED COL, 71- *Mem:* AAAS; Endocrine Soc; Am Physiol Soc; Lawson Wilkins Pediat Endocrine Soc. *Res:* Neuroendocrinology; metabolism of steroid hormones; growth hormone and insulin on amino acid accumulation; control of development. *Mailing Add:* Dept of Physiol & Biophys Hahnemann Med Col Philadelphia PA 19102

SNIPES, DAVID STRANGE, b Hartsville, SC, Apr 16, 28; m 53; c 4. GEOLOGY. *Educ:* Wake Forest Col, BS, 50; Univ NC, PhD(geol), 65. *Prof Exp:* Geologist, Stand Oil Co Calif, 56-59; assoc prof geol, Furman Univ, 63-68; assoc prof, 68-81, PROF GEOL, CLEMSON UNIV, 81- *Res:* X-ray analysis of clay minerals; application of digital computer methods to solution of geological problems. *Mailing Add:* Dept of Geol Clemson Univ Clemson SC 29631

SNIPES, MORRIS BURTON, b Clovis, NMex, Oct 29, 40; m 58; c 1. RADIATION BIOLOGY. *Educ:* Univ NMex, BS, 67, MS, 68; Cornell Univ, PhD(phys biol), 71. *Prof Exp:* ASSOC SCIENTIST RADIOBIOL, INHALATION TOXICOL RES INST, 71- *Mem:* Sigma Xi; Radiation Res Soc; Health Physics Soc. *Res:* Metabolism of radionuclides and radiation dosimetry. *Mailing Add:* Radiobiol Dept Lovelace Found PO Box 5890 Albuquerque NM 87185

SNIPES, WALLACE CLAYTON, b Graham, NC, Oct 11, 37; m 60; c 1. BIOPHYSICS. *Educ:* Wake Forest Col, BS, 60; Duke Univ, PhD(phsics), 64. *Prof Exp:* From asst prof to assoc prof, 64-72, PROF BIOPHYS, PA STATE UNIV, UNIVERSITY PARK, 72- *Concurrent Pos:* Vis prof, Univ Calif, Berkeley, 69 & Univ Calif, Santa Cruz, 74-75. *Mem:* Am Phys Soc; Radiation Res Soc; Biophys Soc. *Res:* Molecular genetics; viral membrane assembly. *Mailing Add:* Dept of Biophys Pa State Univ University Park PA 16802

SNIPP, ROBERT LEO, b Omaha, Nebr, Aug 13, 36; m 63; c 2. PHYSICAL CHEMISTRY. *Educ:* Creighton Univ, BS, 58, MS, 60; Univ Iowa, PhD(phys chem), 65. *Prof Exp:* Asst prof, 64-71, chmn dept, 74-77, ASSOC PROF CHEM, CREIGHTON UNIV, 71- *Mem:* Am Chem Soc. *Res:* Physical chemistry of macromolecules, particularly polyelectrolytes in solution. *Mailing Add:* Dept of Chem Creighton Univ Omaha NE 68178

SNITGEN, DONALD ALBERT, b St John's, Mich, Feb 25, 36; m 59; c 3. BIOLOGY, SCIENCE EDUCATION. *Educ:* Cent Mich Univ, BS, 60; Mich State Univ, MS, 64, PhD(sci educ), 71. *Prof Exp:* Teacher high sch, Mich, 62-66; from instr to assoc prof, 66-79, PROF BIOL, NORTHERN MICH UNIV, 79- *Res:* Distribution of stream bottom fauna, especially insects; preservice elementary school teachers' attitudes toward biological science; development of audio-tutorial program for non-majors in biological science; feasibility study to develop a regional environmental education center in Upper Peninsula of Michigan. *Mailing Add:* Dept of Biol Northern Mich Univ Marquette MI 49855

SNITZER, ELIAS, b Lynn, Mass, Feb 27, 25; m 50; c 5. PHYSICS. *Educ:* Tufts Univ, BS, 45; Univ Chicago, MS, 50, PhD(physics), 53. *Prof Exp:* Res physicist, Minneapolis-Honeywell Regulator Co, 54-56; assoc prof electronics eng, Lowell Tech Inst, 56-58; res assoc, Mass Inst Technol, 59; res physicist, Am Optical Corp, 59-68, dir basic res, 68-75, dir corp res, 75-77, mgr tech planning, Res Ctr, 77-79, MGR APPLIED PHYSICS LAB, UNITED TECHNOLOGIES CORP, 79- *Honors & Awards:* George W Morey Award, Am Ceramic Soc, 71; Quantum Electronics Award, Inst Elec & Electronics Engrs, 79. *Mem:* Nat Acad Eng; Am Phys Soc; Optical Soc Am; Am Ceramic Soc. *Res:* Physical optics; glass technology; solid state physics; materials and instrument research in optics. *Mailing Add:* United Technologies Corp Res Ctr Silver Lane East Hartford CT 06108

SNIVELY, LESLIE O, b Laramie, Wyo, Mar 11, 53; m 75. MAGNETIC INTERACTIONS. *Educ:* Colo State Univ, BS, 75; Mont State Univ, MS, 77, PhD(physics), 81. *Prof Exp:* RES ASSOC, MONT STATE UNIV, 81- *Mem:* Am Phys Soc. *Res:* Experimental and theoretical investigation of supererchange interaction in magnetically lower-dimentsional metal-halide compounds using magnetic susceptibility and magnetization measurement. *Mailing Add:* Dept Physics Mont State Univ Bozeman MT 59717

SNOBLE, JOSEPH JERRY, b Center Point, Iowa, Feb 11, 31; m 55; c 2. PHYSICS, SCIENCE EDUCATION. *Educ:* Iowa State Teachers Col, BA, 57, MA, 61; State Univ Iowa, PhD(sci educ), 67. *Prof Exp:* Teacher sci, Kingsley Pub Sch, 57-59; instr, State Univ Iowa, 61-67; PROF PHYSICS, CENT MO STATE UNIV, 67- *Mem:* Nat Sci Teachers Asn; Sch Sci & Math Asn; Am Asn Physics Teachers; Sigma Xi. *Res:* Teacher education in science, especially elementary, secondary and collegiate teaching procedures and methods; meaningful demonstration and laboratory activities and experiments. *Mailing Add:* Dept Physics Cent Mo State Univ Warrensburg MO 64093

SNODDON, W(ILLIAM) J(OHN), b Port Huron, Mich, Sept 25, 22; m 49; c 3. CHEMICAL ENGINEERING. *Educ:* Univ Mich, BS, 47, MS, 48, MS, 51, PhD(chem eng), 53. *Prof Exp:* Chemist, Minn Mining & Mfg Co, 48-49, res chemist, 52-53, tech serv supvr, 53-54, sr res chemist, 54-56; DIR RES, YALE RUBBER MFG CO, 56- *Mem:* Am Chem Soc; Am Soc Testing & Mat. *Res:* Mechanical properties of paint films; oxidation of drying oils; oil resistant sealing materials and elastomers; elastomer-to-metal bonding. *Mailing Add:* Yale Rubber Mfg Co Sandusky MI 48471

SNODDY, EDWARD L, b Kelso, Tenn, Mar 6, 33; m 52; c 2. MEDICAL ENTOMOLOGY, ECOLOGY. *Educ:* Mid Tenn State Univ, BS, 62; Auburn Univ, PhD(med entom), 66. *Prof Exp:* NDEA fel med entom, Auburn Univ, 62-65; prof med entom, Coastal Plain Exp Sta, Univ Ga, 65-76; MED ENTOMOLOGIST, WATER QUALITY & ECOL BR, TENN VALLEY AUTHORITY, ALA, 76- *Concurrent Pos:* Consult, US Air Force Hosp, Robins AFB, Warner Robins, Ga, 69-76; mem sci adv panel, WHO, 74-; secy-treas, Ga Mosquito Control Asn, 75-; Ga dir, Mid-Atlantic Mosquito Control Asn, 75-; consult, Armed Forces Pest Mgt Bd, Dept Defense, 76-; mem Fed Interagency Comt, Forest Integrated Pest Mgt, 81- *Mem:* Entom Soc Am; Ecol Soc Am; Am Mosquito Control Asn. *Res:* Ecology and taxonomy of medically important arthropods; attractants and repellents for insects of medical importance, particularly Simuliidae, Tabanidae, Ceratopogonidae and Ixodidae. *Mailing Add:* Water Control & Ecol Br Tenn Valley Authority Mussel Shoals AL 35660

SNODGRASS, HERSCHEL ROY, b Lebanon, Ore, May 31, 13; m 37; c 5. PHYSICS. *Educ:* Univ NMex, BA & MS, 41; Univ Calif, Berkeley, PhD(physics), 53. *Prof Exp:* Asst prof meteorol, Univ Chicago, 41-43; asst prof physics, Univ NMex, 43-45; assoc, Univ Calif, Berkeley, 46-53, asst prof, 53-54; from asst prof to assoc prof, San Diego State Col, 54-59; staff mem, Gen Atomic Div, Gen Dynamics Corp, Calif, 59-67; prof, 67-80, EMER PROF PHYSICS, SAN DIEGO STATE UNIV, 80- *Concurrent Pos:* Asst res physicist & consult, Visibility Lab, Scripps Inst, Calif, 55-59. *Mem:* AAAS; Am Phys Soc; Am Asn Physics Teachers; Soc Explor Geophys. *Res:* Atmospheric electricity and optics; upper atmospheric instrumentation; meteorology; cosmic ray and solid state physics; superconductivity; geophysical seismic prospecting. *Mailing Add:* Dept of Physics San Diego State Univ San Diego CA 92182

SNODGRASS, MICHAEL JENS, b Portland, Ore, July 1, 41; m 62; c 5. MICROSCOPIC ANATOMY. *Educ:* Cascade Col, BA, 65; Univ NDak, MS, 66, PhD(anat), 69. *Prof Exp:* Investr, Oak Ridge Nat Lab, Tenn, 69-71, res assoc immunol of carcinogenesis, 71-73; asst prof anat, 73-76, ASSOC PROF ANAT, MED COL VA, 76- *Mem:* Am Asn Anatomists; AAAS; Am Asn Immunologists; Am Asn Cancer Res; Sigma Xi. *Res:* Reticuloendothelial system in tumor immunity; macrophage activation with Mycobacterium bovis, Corynebacterium parvum and pyran copolymer; interaction between activated macrophages and tumor cells in vivo and in vitro; cytostasis and cytotoxicity. *Mailing Add:* Dept of Anat Box 906 Med Col of Va Richmond VA 23298

SNODGRASS, REX JACKSON, b St Louis, Mo, Feb 24, 34. ALTERNATIVE ENERGY, INFORMATION SCIENCE. *Educ:* Harvard Univ, AB, 56; Univ Md, MS, 60, PhD(physics), 63. *Prof Exp:* Physicist, Harry Diamond Labs, 53-59; physicist, Nat Bur Stand, 60-66; fel, Inst Mat Sci & mem fac physics, Univ Conn, 66-72, mgr tech serv, New Eng Res Appl Ctr, 72-80; WITH ENVIRON SCI INFO CTR, NAT OCEANIC & ATMOSPHERIC ADMIN, 80- *Concurrent Pos:* Nat Bur Stand training fel, Univ Paris, 63-64. *Mem:* Am Phys Soc; AAAS; Am Soc Info Sci. *Res:* Information management; energy related problems, especially solar energy research; energy conservation efficiencies. *Mailing Add:* Environ Sci Info Ctr D 8 Rm 678 11400 Rockville Pike Rockville MD 20852

SNOEYENBOS, GLENN HOWARD, b Glenwood City, Wis, Sept 16, 22; m 49; c 3. VETERINARY MEDICINE. *Educ:* Mich State Col, DVM, 45. *Prof Exp:* Sta vet, Univ Minn, 45-46; PROF VET MED, UNIV MASS, AMHERST, 47- *Concurrent Pos:* Grants, USPHS, 65-68, Fats & Proteins Res Found, 66-69 & USDA, 66-71. *Mem:* Am Vet Med Asn; Am Asn Avian Path (secy treas, 61-70); Poultry Sci Asn; Conf Res Workers Animal Dis. *Res:* Infectious diseases of poultry; methods of preventing salmonellosis as a public health problem. *Mailing Add:* Paige Lab Dept Vet Sci Univ of Mass Amherst MA 01002

SNOEYINK, VERNON LEROY, b Kent Co, Mich, Oct 10, 40; m 64; c 2. ENVIRONMENTAL ENGINEERING. *Educ:* Univ Mich, BS, 64, MS, 66, PhD(water resources eng), 68. *Prof Exp:* Engr, Metcalf & Eddy Engrs, 68-69; from asst prof to assoc prof sanit eng, Dept of Civil Eng, 69-77, PROF ENVIRON ENG, DEPT CIVIL ENG, UNIV ILL, 77- *Mem:* Am Soc Civil Engrs; Am Water Works Asn; Water Pollution Control Fedn; Asn Environ Eng Prof. *Res:* Water purification using adsorption processes; water chemistry; drinking water purification. *Mailing Add:* Dept Civil Eng Univ Ill Urbana IL 61801

SNOKE, ARTHUR WILMOT, b Baltimore, Md, Oct 5, 45; m 66; c 2. GEOLOGY, PETROLOGY. *Educ:* Franklin & Marshall Col, AB, 67; Stanford Univ, PhD(geol), 72. *Prof Exp:* Nat Res Coun assoc, US Geol Surv, 71-73; asst prof, 74-78, ASSOC PROF GEOL, UNIV SC, 78- *Concurrent Pos:* Lectr, Humboldt State Univ, 74. *Mem:* Geol Soc Am. *Res:* Genesis of metamorphic rocks in regard to the evolution of orogenic belts; origin and emplacement of ophiolite; structural petrology and analysis of deformed rocks. *Mailing Add:* Dept of Geol Univ of SC Columbia SC 29208

SNOKE, J ARTHUR, b Rochester, NY, Mar 3, 40; m 64; c 2. SEISMOLOGY. *Educ:* Stanford Univ, BS, 63; Yale Univ, MS, 64, PhD(physics), 69. *Prof Exp:* Asst prof physics, Mid East Tech Univ, Turkey, 69-72; res fel seismol, Dept Terrestrial Magnetism, Carnegie Inst, Washington, DC, 72-77; asst prof, 77-80, ASSOC PROF GEOPHYSICS, VA POLYTECH INST & STATE UNIV, BLACKSBURG, 80- *Mem:* Am Geophys Union; Seismol Soc Am; AAAS. *Res:* Earthquake source models, the dynamics and kinematics of the earth's mantle; measurement of earth strain, other topics in theoretical and observational seismology. *Mailing Add:* Dept of Geol Sci Va Polytech Inst & State Univ Blacksburg VA 24061

SNOKE, JOHN EDWARD, b Buffalo, NY, May 17, 21; m 46; c 3. BIOCHEMISTRY. *Educ:* Univ Ill, BS, 46; Duke Univ, PhD(biochem), 49. *Prof Exp:* USPHS fel biochem, Duke Univ, 49-50; res assoc, Univ Chicago, 50-54; asst prof, 54-58, ASSOC PROF BIOCHEM, SCH MED, UNIV CALIF, LOS ANGELES, 58- *Mem:* Am Soc Biol Chemists. *Res:* Enzymes; synthesis and hydrolysis of peptides; polypeptide antibiotics. *Mailing Add:* Dept of Biol Chem Univ of Calif Sch of Med Los Angeles CA 90024

SNOKE, LLOYD RANDOLPH, b Philadelphia, Pa, Apr 10, 23; m 47; c 3. FORESTRY. *Educ:* Pa State Univ, BS, 48. *Prof Exp:* Mem tech staff, Bell Tel Labs, Inc, 48-58, head mat eng protection & testing dept, 58-67, tech rels mgr, 67-74, DIR, TECH RELS INFO CTR, BELL LABS, INC, 74- *Concurrent Pos:* Mem tech panel miscellaneous mat, Mat Adv Pd Int, US Dept Defense Res & Develop Prog, 57; mem steering comt & co-chmn microbiol deterioration conf, Gordon Res Conf, 57 & 58. *Mem:* AAAS; Soc Indust Microbiol. *Res:* Microbiological deterioration of materials; corrosion; materials engineering; preservation of organic materials. *Mailing Add:* Bell Labs Inc Murray Hill NJ 07971

SNOKE, ROY EUGENE, b Shippensburg, Pa, Aug 6, 43; m 67; c 2. ENZYMOLOGY. *Educ:* Shippensburg State Col, BS, 65; Univ NDak, MS, 67, PhD(biochem), 70. *Prof Exp:* NIH fel, Inst Enzyme Res, Univ Wis-Madison, 70-72, asst prof biochem, 72; sr res chemist, 72-79, RES ASSOC, EASTMAN KODAK CO, 79- *Mem:* Am Soc Microbiol; Am Chem Soc. *Res:* Regulation of gluconeogenesis; enzyme mechanisms and adaptations involved in biological control, specifically phosphoenolpyruvate carboxykinase; microbial enzyme isolation and characterization; use of enzymes for biotransformation; design of enzyme analytical systems; clinical diagnostic analysis systems. *Mailing Add:* Res Labs Eastman Kodak Co Rochester NY 14650

SNOOK, JAMES RONALD, b Seattle, Wash, Oct 2, 30; m 52; c 4. GEOLOGY. *Educ:* Ore State Univ, BS, 52, MS, 57; Univ Wash, PhD(geol), 62. *Prof Exp:* From instr to asst prof geol, Ore State Univ, 59-62; res geologist, Humble Oil & Ref Co, 62-64, prod geologist, 64-65; explor geologist, Stauffer Chem Co, 65-67; from asst prof to assoc prof geol, 67-72, chmn dept, 68-71, PROF GEOL, EASTERN WASH UNIV, 72- *Concurrent Pos:* Consult, US Borax, 77- *Mem:* AAAS; Am Inst Mining, Metall & Petrol Eng; Am Inst Prof Geol; fel Geol Soc Am; Am Asn Petrol Geol. *Res:* Igneous and metamorphic petrology; economic geology. *Mailing Add:* Dept of Geol Eastern Wash Univ Cheney WA 99004

SNOOK, THEODORE, b Titusville, NJ, Apr 14, 07; m 33; c 1. HISTOLOGY, EMBRYOLOGY. *Educ:* Rutgers Univ, BSc, 29, MSc, 30; Cornell Univ, PhD(histol), 33. *Prof Exp:* Asst zool, Rutgers Univ, 29-30; instr histol & embryol, Cornell Univ, 30-34; from instr histol & embryol to asst prof anat,

Col Med, Syracuse Univ, 34-46; asst prof, Tulane Univ, 46-49; assoc prof, Sch Med, Univ Pittsburgh, 49-53; chmn dept, 67-72, from assoc prof to prof, 53-77, EMER PROF ANAT, SCH MED, UNIV NDAK, 77- *Mem:* AAAS; Am Asn Anatomists; Biol Photog Asn; Microcirc Soc; Sigma Xi. *Res:* Development of pharyngeal tonsil; spleen vascular connections and lymphatics; comparative mammalian spleen morphology. *Mailing Add:* 343 Sheridan Rd Racine WI 53403

SNOPE, ANDREW JOHN, b Paterson, NJ, Jan 19, 39; m 57; c 3. GENETICS, CYTOGENETICS. *Educ:* Del Valley Col, BS, 60; Rutgers Univ, MS, 62; Ind Univ, PhD, 66. *Prof Exp:* Asst prof biol, Univ Md, Baltimore, 66-70; assoc prof, 70-77, PROF BIOL & CHMN DEPT, ESSEX COMMUNITY COL, 77- *Mem:* AAAS; Am Inst Biol Sci. *Res:* Chromosome structure and behavior; human cytogenetics; instructional methods in college biology teaching. *Mailing Add:* Dept Biol Essex Community Col Baltimore MD 21237

SNOPKO, ROSE MARIE C ZABINSKI, clinical chemistry, biochemistry, see previous edition

SNOVER, JAMES EDWARD, b Troy, NY, Nov 23, 20; m 42; c 4. MATHEMATICS. *Educ:* State Univ NY, BA, 41; Syracuse Univ, MA, 50, PhD, 55. *Prof Exp:* Asst prof math, Assoc Cols Upper NY, 46-49; asst prof, 54-71, ASSOC PROF MATH, FLA STATE UNIV, 71- *Mem:* Am Math Soc; Math Asn Am. *Res:* Analysis. *Mailing Add:* Dept of Math Fla State Univ Tallahassee FL 32306

SNOVER, KURT ALBERT, b Albany, NY, Apr 26, 43; m 64; c 1. PHYSICS. *Educ:* Fla State Univ, BS, 64; Stanford Univ, MS, 68, PhD(physics), 69. *Prof Exp:* Res assoc nuclear physics, State Univ NY Stony Brook, 69-71, asst prof physics, 71-72; SR RES ASSOC NUCLEAR PHYSICS, UNIV WASH, 72-, RES ASST PROF PHYSICS, 77- *Mem:* Am Phys Soc. *Res:* Low energy nuclear physics. *Mailing Add:* Dept of Physics Univ of Wash Seattle WA 98195

SNOW, ADOLPH ISAAC, b Providence, RI, Oct 8, 21; m 44; c 2. CHEMISTRY. *Educ:* Brown Univ, ScB, 43; Iowa State Col, PhD(chem), 50. *Prof Exp:* From asst to res assoc inst atomic res, Iowa State Col, 43-50; instr inst study metals, Univ Chicago, 50-52; head phys chem sect, Sinclair Res, Inc, 52-56, dir radiation lab, 56-59, radiation div, 59-66 & radiation & instrumentation div, 66-69; mgr phys res, 69-72, mgr phys & environ res, 72-78, SR CONSULT, ATLANTIC RICHFIELD CO, 78- *Concurrent Pos:* Consult air & water qual control, Alyeska Pipeline Serv Co, 72- *Mem:* Am Chem Soc; Am Soc Metals; Am Crystallog Asn. *Res:* X-ray crystallography; uranium and thorium alloy phase diagrams; metallurgy of thorium and alloys; neutron diffraction; bonding in solids; physical properties of catalysts; radiation and tracer chemistry; petroleum processing and instrumentation; environment; fate of oil in water; air and water pollution. *Mailing Add:* Harvey Tech Ctr 400 E Sibley Blvd Atlantic Richfield Co Harvey IL 60426

SNOW, ANNE EVELYN, b Spokane, Wash, Apr 9, 43; m 80. PHYSIOLOGY. *Educ:* Univ Ore, BA, 66; Univ Wash, PhD(pharmacol), 77. *Prof Exp:* Res technician pharmacol, Univ Wash, 66-73, res asst, 73-74, NIH traniee, 74-77; res assoc pharmacol, 77-80, RES ASSOC PHYSIOL, MED COL VA, VA COMMONWEALTH UNIV, 80- *Concurrent Pos:* Consult, A H Robins Pharmaceut Co, 79-80. *Mem:* Soc Neurosci; AAAS; Intersci Res Found. *Res:* Mechanisms by which stress produces anti-nociception; effect of stress in altering responses to pharmacologic agents; effects of opiates and endogenous peptides on serotonergic systems; role of calcium in excitation-contraction coupling 5; role of calcium in fertilization and cell division. *Mailing Add:* Dept Physiol Box 551 Med Col Va Richmond VA 23298

SNOW, BEATRICE LEE, b Boston, Mass, June 9, 41. MAMMALIAN GENETICS, MICROCOMPUTERS. *Educ:* Suffolk Univ, AB, 62; Univ NH, MS, 64, PhD(zool), 71. *Prof Exp:* From instr to assoc prof biol, 65-74, actg chmn dept, 72-73, chmn dept biol, 73-78, COORD MED TECHNOL PROG, SUFFOLK UNIV, 68-, PROF BIOL, 74- *Concurrent Pos:* Allied health adv, Brookline Pub Schs, 68-70; dir, Marine Sci Prog, NH Col & Univ Coun, 75-76; coordr, Biol-Comput Prog, Suffolk Univ, 81- *Mem:* Am Soc Human Genetics; Am Genetic Asn; Am Inst Biol Sci; Am Soc Med Technol; Am Soc Zool. *Res:* Alkaline phosphatase activity and siren mutation expressivity in the mouse. *Mailing Add:* Dept of Biol Suffolk Univ Beacon Hill Boston MA 02108

SNOW, CLYDE COLLINS, b Ft Worth, Tex, Jan 7, 28; m 55; c 5. PHYSICAL ANTHROPOLOGY, FORENSIC ANTHROPOLOGY. *Educ:* Eastern NMex Univ, BS, 50; Tex Tech Col, MS, 55; Univ Ariz, PhD, 67; Am Bd Forensic Anthrop, dipl. *Prof Exp:* Res asst anat, Med Col SC, 60-61; res anthropologist, 61-65; chief appl biol sect, Civil Aeromed Inst, Fed Aviation Agency, 65-69, chief phys anthrop res, 69-79; FORENSIC ANTHROP CONSULT, 79- *Concurrent Pos:* Adj instr, Univ Okla, 62-67, adj asst prof, 67-80, adj prof anthrop, 80-, res assoc, Sch Med, 64-; trustee, Forensic Sci Found, 73-79; forensic anthrop consult, Okla State Med Examr, 78- & Med Examr, Cook County, Ill, 79-; consult, Select Comt Assassinations, US House Representatives, 78-79; pres, Forensic Sci Educ, Inc, 82- *Mem:* Am Acad Forensic Sci (vpres, 78-79); Am Anthrop Asn; Am Asn Phys Anthrop; Soc Study Human Biol; Am Soc Forensic Odontol. *Res:* Forensic anthropology; study of human skeletal remains to establish personal identification and cause of death. *Mailing Add:* Forensic Anthrop Assocs 2230 Blue Creek Pkwy Norman OK 73071

SNOW, DAVID BAKER, b Albuquerque, NMex, Nov 15, 41; m 70; c 2. MATERIALS SCIENCE. *Educ:* Mass Inst Technol, BS, 63, ScD(metall), 71. *Prof Exp:* Res metallurgist, Dept Refractory Metals Prod, Gen Elec Co, 70-77; RES SCIENTIST MAT, UNITED TECHNOL RES CTR, 77- *Mem:* Am Soc Metals; Metall Soc; Electron Microscopy Soc Am; Sigma Xi. *Res:* Physical metallurgy of rapidly-solidified metals and alloys; development of advanced nickel-based alloys; recovery and recrystallization; applications of electron microscopy to materials science. *Mailing Add:* United Technol Res Ctr Silver Lane East Hartford CT 06108

SNOW, DAVID T(UNISON), b Worcester, Mass, July 11, 30; m 52, 77; c 6. GEOLOGICAL ENGINEERING, GROUNDWATER HYDROLOGY. *Educ:* Harvard Univ, AB, 51; Univ Calif, Berkeley, MA, 57, PhD(eng sci), 65. *Prof Exp:* Civil engr, Cerro de Pasco Corp, 57-58, geol engr, 58-59; from asst prof to assoc prof geol, Colo Sch Mines, 65-78; CONSULT, 77- *Concurrent Pos:* Faculty, Univ Oriente, Venezuela, 68; consult geol engr, Hazleton-Nuclear Sci Corp & Isotopes, Inc, 64-71, Am Cyanamid Corp, 65-66, Martin-Marietta Corp, 66-67, Am Cement Co, 67-69, Woodward-Clyde Consult, 73-, Dames & Moore, Inc, 75-77, Fugro, Inc, 74, Wyo Mineral Co, 76, Corps of Eng, 76-77, Homestake Mining Co, 76-77, Lawrence Berkeley Labs, 77-78, Rockwell Hanford Operations, 78-81, Amax Inc, 80-82 & Steffen-Robertson & Kirsten, 80-81. *Mem:* Asn Eng Geol. *Res:* Foundations of hydraulic structures, rock mechanics and groundwater hydrology; hydraulic properties of fractures media; applications to civil and mining engineering; grouting; dispersion; waste disposal; seismic reservoir mechanisms. *Mailing Add:* 6235 Turret Dr Colorado Springs CO 80907

SNOW, DONALD L(OESCH), b Cleveland, Ohio, Apr 10, 17; m 48; c 3. ENVIRONMENTAL HEALTH ENGINEERING. *Educ:* Case Western Reserve Univ, BS, 39; Univ Wis, MS, 41; Environ Engrs Intersoc, dipl. *Prof Exp:* Sanit engr, Pan-Am Sanit Bur, USPHS, 43-48, sr sanit engr, 48-51, chief res facilities planning br, 51-54, chief sanit eng br, 54-60, lab design documentation proj, NIH, 61-62, ed radiol health data, 62-64, chief radiation surveillance ctr, Bur Radiol Health, 64-67 & Standards & Intel Br, 68-69, dir, Off Criteria & Standards, 69-71; DIR, NAT CTR TOXICOL RES PROG OFF, UNIV ARK, 71- *Concurrent Pos:* Ed, J Inter-Am Asn Sanit Eng, 46-48; pres, Fed Conf Sanit Engrs, 64; sanit eng dir, USPHS, 43-52. *Honors & Awards:* Hemispheric Award, Inter-Am Asn Sanit Engrs, 54. *Mem:* Am Soc Civil Engrs; Am Acad Environ Engrs; fel Am Pub Health Asn; Inter-Am Asn Sanit Eng (secy, 46-48); AAAS. *Res:* Medical research facilities planning; environmental health engineering; radiological health data program management; radiation standards; environmental standards. *Mailing Add:* 13723 Rivercrest Dr Little Rock AR 72212

SNOW, DONALD RAY, b Los Angeles, Calif, Mar 19, 31; m 58; c 6. MATHEMATICS. *Educ:* Univ Utah, BSME & BA, 59; Stanford Univ, MSME, 60, MS, 62, PhD(math), 65. *Prof Exp:* Res asst comput ctr, Stanford Univ, 61-62; res engr res labs, Lockheed Missiles & Space Co, 62-64; res assoc math, Univ Minn, Minneapolis, 64-66; asst prof, Univ Colo, Boulder, 66-69; assoc prof, 69-74, PROF MATH, BRIGHAM YOUNG UNIV, 74- *Concurrent Pos:* Vis prof, Fulbright-Hayes sr lectureship to Peru, 74 & vis res prof, Dept Appl Math, Univ Waterloo, Ontario, 76-77; chmn bd dir, Rocky Mountain Math Consortium, 77-78; lectr math, Asn Am, 78-; Atomic Energy Comn fel, Stanford Univ. *Honors & Awards:* Hamilton Watch Award. *Mem:* AAAS; Am Math Soc; Math Asn Am; Soc Indust & Appl Math; Nat Coun Teachers Math. *Res:* Calculus of variations and optimal control theory; functional equations; combinatorics; partial and ordinary differential and integral equations and inequalities; history of math; computers in math instruction and research. *Mailing Add:* Dept of Math Brigham Young Univ Provo UT 84602

SNOW, DOUGLAS OSCAR, b Port Maitland, NS, Nov 27, 17; m 51. MATHEMATICS. *Educ:* Acadia Univ, BSc, 43, MA, 46; Brown Univ, MSc, 52; Queen's Univ, Can, PhD(math), 56. *Prof Exp:* Asst prof math, Mt Allison Univ, 46-47; from asst prof to assoc prof, 47-56, PROF MATH, ACADIA UNIV, 56- *Mem:* Am Math Soc; Math Asn Am; Can Math Cong. *Res:* Analysis; integration in abstract spaces. *Mailing Add:* Dept of Math Acadia Univ Wolfville NS B0P 1X0 Can

SNOW, EDWARD HUNTER, b St George, Utah, June 26, 36; m 56; c 3. SOLID STATE PHYSICS. *Educ:* Univ Utah, BA, 58, PhD(physics), 63. *Prof Exp:* Mem tech staff, Physics Dept Res & Develop Lab, Semiconductor Div, Fairchild Camera & Instrument Corp, 63-68, mgr, Physics Dept, 68-71; VPRES & DIR OPERS, RETICON CORP, 71- *Concurrent Pos:* Lectr, Univ Santa Clara. *Honors & Awards:* Cert of Merit, Franklin Inst, 75. *Mem:* Fel Inst Elec & Electronics Engrs; Am Phys Soc. *Res:* Optoelectronics; electrical properties of insulators and semiconductors; semiconductor device physics; properties of interfaces between metals; insulators. *Mailing Add:* Reticon Corp 345 Potrero Ave Sunnyvale CA 94086

SNOW, GEORGE ABRAHAM, b New York, NY, Aug 24, 26; m 48; c 3. PHYSICS. *Educ:* City Col, BS, 45; Princeton Univ, MS, 47, PhD(physics), 49. *Prof Exp:* Jr physicist, Brookhaven Nat Lab, 48-51, assoc physicist, 51-55; physicist, US Naval Res Lab, 55-58; assoc prof physics, 58-61, actg chmn dept physics & astron, 70-71, PROF PHYSICS, UNIV MD, COLLEGE PARK, 61- *Concurrent Pos:* Mem, Inst Advan Study, 52-53; vis lectr, Univ Wis, 55; NSF sr fel, Europ Orgn Nuclear Res, Geneva, 61-62; sci assoc, 80; John S Guggenheim fel & Fulbright res scholar, Univ Rome, 65-66; vis prof, Univ Paris, 72-73 & Tohoku Univ, 79; consult, Argonne Nat Lab, Fermilab, Brookhaven Nat Lab & Prentice Hall Publ Co; mem bd trustees, Univ Res Asn, 73-78, vchmn, 74, chmn Sci Comt, 75-77; vchmn div particles & fields, Am Phys Soc, 75, chmn, 76. *Mem:* AAAS; Am Asn Physics Teachers; fel Am Phys Soc; Fedn Am Sci; NY Acad Sci. *Res:* Experimental and theoretical high energy physics; neutrino interactions; e-plus e-minus and muon interactions. *Mailing Add:* Dept Physics & Astron Univ Md College Park MD 20742

SNOW, JAMES BYRON, JR, b Oklahoma City, Okla, Mar 12, 32; m 54; c 3. OTOLARYNGOLOGY. *Educ:* Univ Okla, BS, 53; Harvard Univ, MD, 56. *Prof Exp:* Asst prof otorhinolaryngol, Med Ctr, Univ Okla, 62-64, prof & head dept, 64-72; PROF OTORHINOLARYNGOL & CHMN DEPT, SCH MED, UNIV PA, 72- *Mem:* Am Acad Ophthal & Otolaryngol; Am Col Surgeons; Soc Univ Otolaryngol; Am Otol Soc; Am Laryngol Asn. *Res:* Pathophysiology of the inner ear. *Mailing Add:* Dept of Otorhinolaryngol Univ of Pa Philadelphia PA 19104

SNOW, JEAN ANTHONY, b Richmond, Ind, Apr 18, 32; m 62; c 2. MYCOLOGY, AEROBIOLOGY. *Educ:* DePauw Univ, AB, 54; Pa State Univ, PhD(plant path, genetics), 64. *Prof Exp:* Asst prof plant path, Univ Mass, 63-67; chief plant pathologist, Standard Fruit Co, 67-70; res assoc, Ctr Air Environ Studies, Pa State Univ, University Park, 70-77; CONSULT, 77- *Mem:* AAAS; Am Phytopath Soc; Am Inst Biol Sci; Int Soc Plant Path; Int Asn Aerobiol. *Res:* Epidemiology and biometeorology of fungal diseases of plants; aerobiology, especially occurrence and dispersal of fungus air spora and aeroallergens. *Mailing Add:* 720E West Beaver Ave State College PA 16801

SNOW, JOHN ELBRIDGE, b Marion, Ohio, June 4, 15; m 41; c 3. ORGANIC CHEMISTRY. *Educ:* Oberlin Col, AB, 38; Cornell Univ, MS, 40, PhD(org chem), 42. *Prof Exp:* Group leader org synthesis res dept, Heyden Chem Corp, 42-56; mgr chem & plastics res, Res Div, Curtiss-Wright Corp, 56-61; res dir, Rap-in-Wax Co, 61-65; mgr process & prod develop, Packages Co Div, Champion Papers Co Div, US Plywood Champion Papers Co, 65-70, dir appl res, Champion Packages Co, Div Champion Int, 70-80; CONSULT FLEXIBLE PACKAGING, 80- *Concurrent Pos:* Lectr, Dept Food Sci, Univ Minn, 70-, vis prof, 72. *Mem:* Am Chem Soc; Packaging Inst. *Res:* Organic chemicals; pentaerythritols; resins and plastics; flexible packaging meterials; films; extrusion coating and laminating; adhesives; paper technology; adhesion; coextrusion coating; surface chemistry. *Mailing Add:* 4750 Dona Lane Minneapolis MN 55422

SNOW, JOHN THOMAS, b St Petersburg, Fla, Dec 29, 43; m 66. ORGANIC CHEMISTRY. *Educ:* Earlham Col, AB, 65; Middlebury Col, MS, 67; Univ Calif, Davis, PhD(chem), 70. *Prof Exp:* Res assoc chem, Univ Calif, Davis, 70-71; chief chemist, US Sugar Corp, 71-74; Nat Res Coun assoc, USDA, Western Regional Res Lab, Berkeley, Calif, 74-75; res scientist, 75-76, MGR BIOCHEM, MKT DEPT, CALBIOCHEM-BEHRING CORP, LA JOLLA, CALIF, 77- *Mem:* Am Chem Soc; Sigma Xi; Int Food Technologists. *Res:* Mechanistic and synthetic organic chemistry. *Mailing Add:* Biochem Mkt Dept 10933 N Torrey Pines Rd La Jolla CA 92037

SNOW, JOHN THOMAS, b St Louis, Mo, Dec 14, 45; m 69. MESO-METEOROLOGY, GEOPHYSICAL FLUID DYNAMICS. *Educ:* Rose Polytech Inst, BS, 68, MS, 69; Purdue Univ, PhD(atmospheric sci), 74. *Prof Exp:* ASST PROF ATMOSPHERIC SCI, DEPT GEOSCI, PURDUE UNIV, 77- *Mem:* Sigma Xi; Am Meteorol Soc. *Res:* Fluid dynamics of mesoscale meteorological phenomena; severe local storms; tornadoes and other geophysical vortices; gravity waves; lake and sea breeze circulations. *Mailing Add:* Dept Geosci Purdue West Lafayette IN 47907

SNOW, JOHNNIE PARK, b Abilene, Tex, July 12, 42; m 68; c 1. PLANT PATHOLOGY. *Educ:* McMurry Col, BA, 65; Univ Ark, MS, 67; Tex A&M Univ, PhD(plant path), 70. *Prof Exp:* Fel plant path, NC State Univ, 70-72; from asst prof to assoc prof, 72-81, PROF PLANT PATH, LA STATE UNIV, BATON ROUGE, 81- *Mem:* Sigma Xi; Am Phytopath Soc. *Res:* Basic and applied research on cotton diseases. *Mailing Add:* Dept of Plant Path La State Univ Baton Rouge LA 70803

SNOW, JOSEPH WILLIAM, b Scarborough, Maine, Apr 3, 39. WIND & SOLAR ENERGY. *Educ:* Boston Col, BS, 61; Univ Utah, BS, 64; Univ Wis, Madison, MS, 75; Univ Va, PhD(environ sci), 81. *Prof Exp:* Weather officer, Air Weather Serv, US Air Force, 62-67; proj mgr, E G & G Inc, 68-69; supvr meteorologist, Panama Canal Co, Balboa, 70-71; res assoc, Dept Environ Sci, Univ Va, 80-81; ASST PROF METEOROL, LYNDON STATE COL, 81- *Mem:* Am Meteorol Soc; Am Geophys Union; Am Inst Aeronaut & Astronaut. *Res:* Analytical explanation of area climates and the modifications effected by man; coastal wind power and wind shear within the atmospheric boundary layer. *Mailing Add:* 146 Pine Point Rd ME 04074

SNOW, LOUDELL FROMME, b Kansas City, Mo, July 17, 33; m 60; c 1. MEDICAL ANTHROPOLOGY. *Educ:* Univ Colo, BA, 59; Univ Ariz, MA, 70, PhD(anthrop), 71. *Prof Exp:* Mem fac, Col Human Med & asst prof anthrop, 71-73 & community med, 74-78, ASSOC PROF ANTHROP, MICH STATE UNIV, 78- *Mem:* AAAS; Am Anthrop Asn; Soc Med Anthrop; Sigma Xi; Am Folklore Soc. *Res:* Folk medical systems; folk practitioners as psychotherapists; witchcraft beliefs; behavioral science in the medical school curriculum; spirit possession and trance states; impact of cultural background on beliefs and attitudes concerning female reproductive cycle. *Mailing Add:* Dept of Anthrop Mich State Univ East Lansing MI 48824

SNOW, MICHAEL DENNIS, b Sacramento, Calif, Nov 9, 42; m 66; c 2. PHYTOPATHOLOGY, MICROBIAL ECOLOGY. *Educ:* Sacramento State Col, BA, 65; Wash State Univ, PhD(phytopath), 74. *Prof Exp:* asst prof, 70-75, chmn dept phys & life sci, 77-80, ASSOC PROF BIOL, UNIV PORTLAND, 75-; RES ASSOC, CORVALLIS ENVIRON RES LAB, 81- *Concurrent Pos:* NSF fac develop fel, 81. *Mem:* Bot Soc Am; AAAS; Am Phytopath Soc; Sigma Xi. *Res:* Ecology and pathology of rust fungal diseases of grasses and cereals in the Pacific Northwest; moisture stress physiology. *Mailing Add:* Corvallis Environ Res Lab 200 SW 35th St Corvallis OR 97330

SNOW, MIKEL HENRY, b Three Rivers, Mich, Sept 18, 44. MUSCLE REGENERATION, MUSCLE PLASTICITY. *Educ:* Olivet Col, BA, 66; Univ Mich, PhD(anat), 71. *Prof Exp:* Instr anat, Sch Med, Univ Miami, 71-72, asst prof, 72-75; asst prof, 75-79, ASSOC PROF ANAT, UNIV SOUTHERN CALIF, 79- *Concurrent Pos:* Vis prof, Sch Med, Univ Miami, 80; ed, Anat Record, 81- *Mem:* Am Asn Anatomists; Develop Biol. *Res:* The role of satellite cells in muscle regeneration and denervation; muscle adaptation to chronic and acute exercise in mammals. *Mailing Add:* Dept Anat Sch Med Univ Southern Calif Los Angeles CA 90033

SNOW, MILTON LEONARD, b Providence, RI, Feb 16, 30; m 58; c 4. PHYSICAL CHEMISTRY. *Educ:* Brown Univ, ScB, 51; Princeton Univ, MA, 53, PhD(phys chem), 56. *Prof Exp:* Chemist, Davison Chem Co, WR Grace Co, 56-59; proj supvr, 76, SR CHEMIST, APPL PHYSICS LAB, JOHNS HOPKINS UNIV, 59- *Res:* Heterogeneous catalysis; gas phase reaction kinetics; supersonic ramjet performance analysis and prediction; hypersonic ramjet design; air pollution analysis; chemical anti-submarine warfare. *Mailing Add:* 1329 Winding Way Lane Wheaton MD 20902

SNOW, PHILIP ANTHONY, b Baltimore, Md, July 19, 51. HYDROLOGY, MINERALOGY. *Educ:* Univ Md, BS, 73, MS, 77, PhD(soil, mineral), 81. *Prof Exp:* Res asst soil chem, 73-77, soil & mineral, 78-81, lectr soil physics, 81-82, RES ASSOC SOIL MINERAL, UNIV MD, 82- *Mem:* Am Soc Agron; Soil Sci Soc Am. *Res:* Rectification of domestic and industrial waste waters by land application; reclamation of acid mine and dredge spoil materials; development of x-ray spectroscopy techniques for the analysis of soil and geologic materials. *Mailing Add:* Box 53 Henderson MD 21640

SNOW, RICHARD HUNTLEY, b Worcester, Mass, Apr 26, 28; m 52; c 3. CHEMICAL ENGINEERING. *Educ:* Harvard Univ, AB, 50; Va Polytech Inst, MS, 52; Ill Inst Technol, PhD(chem eng), 56. *Prof Exp:* Res fel chem eng, 52-56, res engr, 56-63, sr engr, 63-73, ENG ADV, IIT RES INST, 73-, MGR CHEM ENG RES, 77- *Mem:* AAAS; fel Am Inst Chem Engrs; Am Chem Soc; Soc Mining Engrs; Am Inst Mining, Metall & Petrol Engrs. *Res:* Applications of computers; comminution; chemical kinetics; thermodynamics; paper drying; odor control; particle-fluid separation; oil shale processing. *Mailing Add:* IIT Res Inst 10 W 35th St Chicago IL 60616

SNOW, RICHARD L, b Salt Lake City, Utah, Jan 27, 30. PHYSICAL CHEMISTRY. *Educ:* Univ Utah, BS, 53, PhD(phys chem), 57. *Prof Exp:* From asst prof to assoc prof, 57-66, PROF CHEM, BRIGHAM YOUNG UNIV, 66- *Concurrent Pos:* NSF sci fac fel, Brown Univ, 63-64; Oak Ridge Assoc Univs fel, Savannah River Lab, E I du Pont de Nemours & Co, Inc, 71-72. *Mem:* Sigma Xi; Am Chem Soc. *Res:* Quantum chemistry; theory of liquids. *Mailing Add:* Dept of Chem Brigham Young Univ Provo UT 84601

SNOW, ROBERT E, b New Britain, Conn, Oct 4, 34; m 61; c 2. HISTORY OF TECHNOLOGY. *Educ:* Rensselaer Polytech Inst, BMetE, 56; Ind Univ, MA, 65, PhD(hist sci), 67. *Prof Exp:* Lectr natural sci, York Univ, 66-67, asst prof, 67-70; from asst prof to assoc prof, 70-78, prof natural sci, Lyman Briggs Col, Mich State Univ, 78-81; PROF SCI & TECHNOL STUDIES, STATE UNIV COL ARTS & SCI, NY, 81. *Mem:* AAAS; Soc Hist of Technol; Popular Cult Asn; Am Sci Affil. *Res:* Technical change; technology and values; American studies. *Mailing Add:* Lyman Briggs Col Mich State Univ East Lansing MI 48824

SNOW, SIDNEY RICHARD, b Los Angeles, Calif, June 22, 29. GENETICS. *Educ:* Univ Calif, Los Angeles, BS, 54, PhD(bot), 58. *Prof Exp:* From instr to assoc prof, 57-70, PROF GENETICS, UNIV CALIF, DAVIS, 70- *Mem:* AAAS; Genetics Soc Am; Bot Soc Am; Am Soc Microbiol. *Res:* Genetics of fungi, especially yeast; genetic recombination; microbial genetics; cyto-genetics. *Mailing Add:* Dept of Genetics Univ of Calif Davis CA 95616

SNOW, THEODORE PECK, JR, b Seattle, Wash, Jan 30, 47; m 69. ASTRONOMY. *Educ:* Yale Univ, BA, 69; Univ Wash, MS, 70, PhD(astron), 73. *Prof Exp:* Res assoc astrophys sci, Princeton Univ Observ, 73-76, mem res staff, 76-77; asst prof physics & astrophys & fel, 77-80, ASSOC PROF ASTROPHYS & FEL, LAB ATMOSPHERIC & SPACE PHYSICS, UNIV COLO, 80- *Concurrent Pos:* Mem, Users Comt, Int Ultraviolet Explorer, NASA Satellite, 77-79 & Working Group Shuttle Aston, 78-81. *Mem:* Int Astron Union; Am Astron Soc. *Res:* Visible wave length and ultraviolet space-borne spectroscopy of hot stars, stellar winds and interstellar gas and dust. *Mailing Add:* Lab Atmospheric & Space Physics Univ Colo Boulder CO 80309

SNOW, THOMAS RUSSELL, b Danville, Va, Mar 29, 44. CARDIOVASCULAR PHYSIOLOGY. *Educ:* Carnegie-Mellon Univ, BS, 65; Duke Univ, PhD(physics), 71. *Prof Exp:* Instr biomed eng, Baylor Col Med, 71-73; res assoc physics, 69-71, NIH FEL PHYSIOL, DUKE UNIV, 73-, ASST PROF. *Mem:* Biophysical Soc; Int Soc Heart Res. *Res:* Determination of the relevant factors controlling contractility and metabolism in mammalian myocardium. *Mailing Add:* Dept of Physiol Box 3709 Duke Univ Med Ctr Durham NC 27710

SNOW, WILLIAM ROSEBROOK, b New York, NY, Jan 6, 30; m 51; c 2. ATOMIC PHYSICS, MOLECULAR PHYSICS. *Educ:* Stanford Univ, BS, 52; Univ Wash, MS, 65, PhD(physics), 66. *Prof Exp:* Rotational trainee reactor physics, Hanford Atomic Prod Oper, Gen Elec Corp, 52-54; physicist, Precision Technol, Inc, 54-58; staff assoc afterglows & atomic beams, Gen Atomic, 58-62; mem res staff satellite mass spectrometry, Aerospace Corp, 66-68; asst prof physics, Univ Mo-Rolla, 68-73, assoc prof, 73-80; MEM STAFF, PAC WESTERN SYST, INC, 80- *Mem:* Am Phys So. *Res:* Ion-neutral reactions in plasmas and afterglows; negative ion charge transfer; ionosphere reactions; mass spectrometry; molecular scattering. *Mailing Add:* 505 E Evelyn Ave Pac Western Syst Inc Mountain CA 94041

SNOW, WOLFE, b New York, NY, May 17, 38; m 60; c 3. MATHEMATICS. *Educ:* Brooklyn Col, BS, 59; NY Univ, MS, 61, PhD(math), 64. *Prof Exp:* Instr, 64-65, ASST PROF MATH, BROOKLYN COL, 65- *Mem:* Soc Actuaries; Math Asn Am. *Res:* Stability for differential-difference equations. *Mailing Add:* Dept of Math Brooklyn Col Brooklyn NY 11210

SNOWDEN, DONALD PHILIP, b Los Angeles, Calif, Sept 9, 31. SOLID STATE PHYSICS. *Educ:* Calif Inst Technol, BS, 53; Univ Calif, Berkeley, MA, 55, PhD(physics), 59. *Prof Exp:* Staff mem, Gen Atomic Div, Gen Dynamics Corp, 59-67; staff mem, Gulf Gen Atomic, 67-73; PRIN PHYSICIST, IRT CORP, 73- *Mem:* Am Phys Soc. *Res:* Application of high

current superconductors; semiconductor and device radiation effects; physical and electrical surface characterization; new materials development; vacuum vapor deposition; photovoltaic solar cells; nuclear fuel reprocessing; fiber optics communications. *Mailing Add:* IRT Corp PO Box 80817 San Diego CA 92138

SNOWDEN, F(RANKLIN) CURTIS, b Trenton, NJ, Mar 4, 21; m 41, 64; c 4. ELECTRONIC ENGINEERING, CHEMICAL INSTRUMENTATION. *Educ:* Lafayette Col, BS, 42; Roosevelt Univ, PhD, 80. *Prof Exp:* Electronics engr, Off Sci Res & Develop, Johns Hopkins Univ, 42-43; instr math, Lafayette Col, 43-44; electronics engr, Cent Res Lab, Gen Aniline & Film Corp, 46-51; sr res technologist, Leeds & Northrup Co, 52-56, sr application engr, 56-60, group chief prod eng, 60-63, sect head eng, 63-68, gen mgr, Anal Equip Div, 68-72; dir res develop & eng, Milton Roy Co, 72-75; eng mgr anal instrumentation, Bailey Meter Co, 75-76; ENG MGR INDUST PROD, COULTER ELECTRONICS INC, 77- *Mem:* Am Chem Soc; Fel Am Inst Chemist. *Res:* Development of new analytical chemical instruments and methods; gas analysis instrumentation; particle size analysis and distribution instruments. *Mailing Add:* Coulter Electronics Inc 590 W 20th St Hialeah FL 33010

SNOWDEN, JESSE OTHO, b McComb, Miss, Oct 19, 37; m 57; c 2. CLAY MINERALOGY. *Educ:* Millsaps Col, BS, 59; Univ Mo, AM, 61, PhD(geol), 66. *Prof Exp:* Instr geol, Millsaps Col, 62-63; asst prof, Miss State Univ, 64-66; assoc prof, Millsaps Col, 66-69; asst prof earth sci, La State Univ, New Orleans, 69-72; assoc prof, 72-79, PROF, UNIV NEW ORLEANS, 79- *Mem:* AAAS; Am Asn Petrol Geol; Geol Soc Am; Clay Minerals Soc; Mineral Soc Am. *Res:* Geochemistry of estuaries; clay petrology of sediments; environmental geology. *Mailing Add:* Dept Earth Sci Univ New Orleans Lake Front New Orleans LA 70148

SNOWDEN, WILLIAM EDWARD, b Hornell, NY, Apr 19, 47; m 70; c 1. MATERIALS SCIENCE. *Educ:* Alfred Univ, BS, 69; Univ Calif, Berkeley, MS, 71, PhD(mat sci), 76. *Prof Exp:* Res ceramist, Corning Glass Works, 75-76; res ceramist, Gen Elec Co, 76-79; MAT SCIENTIST, LAWRENCE LIVERMORE NAT LAB, 79- *Mem:* Am Ceramic Soc; Nat Inst Ceramic Engrs. *Res:* Mechanical behavior of non-metallic materials; creep; fracture mechanics; thermal shock; impact; processing and properties relations; magnetic ceramics. *Mailing Add:* Lawrence Livermore Nat Lab PO Box 808 L-369 Livermore CA 94550

SNOWDON, CHARLES THOMAS, b Pittsburgh, Pa, Aug 8, 41. ANIMAL BEHAVIOR, PHYSIOLOGICAL PSYCHOLOGY. *Educ:* Oberlin Col, BA, 63; Univ Pa, MA, 64, PhD(psychol), 68. *Prof Exp:* Fel, Inst Neurol Sci, Univ Pa, 68-69; asst prof psychol, 69-74, assoc prof, 74-79, PROF PSYCHOL, UNIV WIS-MADISON, 79- *Concurrent Pos:* Affil scientist, Wis Regional Primate Res Ctr, 72; fac fel, NSF, 75-76; res scientist develop award, Nat Inst Mental Health, 77-82. *Mem:* AAAS; Animal Behav Soc; Am Soc Zool; Psychonomics Soc. *Res:* Communication and social behavior; evolution of language; social development and parental care; reproductive physiology and communication of reproductive status. *Mailing Add:* Dept of Psychol Univ of Wis-Madison Madison WI 53706

SNOWDON, JOHN COLIN, applied mechanics, acoustics, deceased

SNUDDEN, BIRDELL HARRY, b Elkhorn, Wis, Nov 20, 35; m 64; c 2. BACTERIOLOGY, FOOD SCIENCE. *Educ:* Univ Wis, BS, 57, MS, 61, PhD(bact, food sci), 64. *Prof Exp:* Fel food sci, Mich State Univ, 64-66; from asst prof to assoc prof, 66-80, PROF BIOL, UNIV WIS-EAU CLAIRE, 80- *Mem:* Am Soc Microbiol; Int Asn Milk, Food & Environ Sanitarians. *Res:* Aquatic microbiology; food and water borne diseases. *Mailing Add:* Dept of Biol Univ of Wis Eau Claire WI 54701

SNUSTAD, DONALD PETER, b Bemidji, Minn, Apr 6, 40; m 64; c 1. GENETICS. *Educ:* Univ Minn, BS, 62; Univ Calif, Davis, MS, 63, PhD(genetics), 65. *Prof Exp:* From asst prof to assoc prof genetics, 65-74, PROF GENETICS & CELL BIOL, UNIV MINN, ST PAUL, 74- *Mem:* Genetics Soc Am; Am Genetic Asn; Am Soc Microbiol; Am Inst Biol Sci. *Res:* Replication recombination and morphogenesis of bacteriophage T-4; virus-host cell interactions. *Mailing Add:* Dept Genetics & Cell Biol Col Biol Sci Univ Minn St Paul MN 55101

SNYDER, ANDREW KAGEY, b Philadelphia, Pa, May 19, 37; m 59; c 2. MATHEMATICS. *Educ:* Swarthmore Col, BA, 59; Univ Colo, MA, 61; Lehigh Univ, PhD(math), 65. *Prof Exp:* Instr math, Lehigh Univ, 64-65 & Mass Inst Technol, 65-67; asst prof, 67-69, ASSOC PROF MATH, LEHIGH UNIV, 69- *Mem:* Am Math Soc; Math Asn Am. *Res:* Functional analysis; sequence spaces; summability. *Mailing Add:* Dept of Math Lehigh Univ Bethlehem PA 18015

SNYDER, ANN KNABB, b West Reading, Pa, Aug 1, 44; m 65; c 1. MEDICAL RESEARCH, ENDOCRINOLOGY & METABOLISM. *Educ:* Pa State Univ, BS, 65; Univ Ill, MS, 68, PhD(physiol), 71. *Prof Exp:* Med technologist, Pediat Immunol Lab, Duke Univ Med Ctr, 70-71; Dept Immunol, Rush-Presby-St Lukes Med Ctr, 71-73; MED TECHNOLOGIST ENDOCRINOL, MED RES PROG, VET ADMIN MED CTR, NORTH CHICAGO, 74-; RES ASST PROF, DEPT MED, CHICAGO MED SCH, NORTH CHICAGO, ILL, 81- *Mem:* Sigma Xi; AAAS. *Res:* Influence of ethanol on carbohydrate metabolism in mammals, especially in respect to its interaction with the effects of thyroxine and insulin. *Mailing Add:* Endocrin & Metab Res 151A Vet Admin Med Ctr North Chicago IL 60064

SNYDER, ARNOLD LEE, JR, b Washington, DC, Oct 12, 37; m 63; c 3. SPACE PHYSICS, AURORAL & IONOSPHERIC PHYSICS. *Educ:* George Washington Univ, BCE, 60; Univ Colo, MS, 66; Univ Alaska, PhD(geophysics), 72. *Prof Exp:* Weather officer, Detachment 15, 1st Weather Wing, US Air Force, 61-62, weather officer, NY Air Defense Sector, 62-65, solar forecaster, Space Environ Support Ctr, 66-69, sect chief, Global

Weather Cent, 72-76, br chief, Geophysics Lab, 76-80, test dir, 80-81, PROG DIR, ELECTRONIC SYSTS DIV, US AIR FORCE, 81- *Concurrent Pos:* Lectr, Western New Eng Col, 78-79; US Air Force Res & Develop Award, 81. *Mem:* Am Geophys Union; Am Meteorol Soc; Sigma Xi; Int Test & Evaluation Asn. *Res:* Development and test of a continental United States over-the-horizon backscatter radar for tactical warning of a bomber attack on North America. *Mailing Add:* 13 Gary Rd Chelmsford MA 01824

SNYDER, BENJAMIN WILLARD, b Albion, Mich, July 5, 39; m 65; c 1. ENDOCRINOLOGY, DEVELOPMENTAL BIOLOGY. *Educ:* Albion Col, BA, 62; Univ Mich, MS, 67, PhD(zool), 70. *Prof Exp:* Fel reproduct biol, Sch Hygiene & Pub Health, Johns Hopkins Univ, 70-71 & Harvard Med Sch, 72-73; assoc prof biol, Swarthmore Col, 73-80; SR RES BIOL, STERLING-WINTHROP RES INST, 80- *Mem:* Sigma Xi; Am Soc Zoologists. *Res:* Reproductive biology; regulation of gonadotropin secretion in primates; maintainence of pregnancy in primates. *Mailing Add:* Dept Endocrinol Sterling-Winthrop Res Inst Rensselaer NY 12144

SNYDER, CARL EDWARD, b Akron, Ohio, Aug 13, 21; m 43; c 2. CHEMISTRY. *Educ:* Univ Akron, BS, 42; Case Univ, PhD, 49; Northwestern Univ, AMP, 72; Harvard Univ, AMP, 77. *Prof Exp:* Res chemist rubber, Barrett Div, Allied Chem Co, 42-46; rubber consult, Carl Prutton & Assoc, 48-50; high polymer res chemist, 50-57, head condensation polymer res sect, 57-68, mgr tires & spec prod res, 68-69, mgr new prod res, 69-74, assoc dir res, 74-76, dir projs & mat coord, 76-78, dir elastomer & chem res, 78-79, VPRES RES, GOODYEAR TIRE & RUBBER CO, 79- *Res:* Rubber chemistry; high polymers; aerospace materials; tire and textiles; carbon composites. *Mailing Add:* 1144 E Market St Goodyear Tire & Rubber Co Akron OH 44316

SNYDER, CARL HENRY, b Pittsburgh, Pa, Sept 18, 31; m 53; c 2. ORGANIC CHEMISTRY. *Educ:* Univ Pittsburgh, BS, 53; Ohio State Univ, PhD(org chem), 58. *Prof Exp:* Res chemist, Eastman Kodak Co, 58-59; res asst chem, Purdue Univ, 59-61; from asst prof to assoc prof, 61-74, PROF CHEM, UNIV MIAMI, 74- *Mem:* Am Chem Soc. *Res:* Reactions in dipolar, aprotic solvents; stereochemistry of carbonyl reductions; biomolecular eliminations; organoborane chemistry. *Mailing Add:* Dept of Chem Univ of Miami Coral Gables FL 33124

SNYDER, CHARLES THEODORE, b Powell, Wyo, July 19, 12; m 73; c 2. HYDROLOGY. *Educ:* Univ Ariz, BSc, 48. *Prof Exp:* Geologist, 46, 48-59, hydrologist, 59-66, res hydrologist, 66-75, CONSULT, US GEOL SURV, 75- *Mem:* AAAS; Arctic Inst NAm. *Res:* Hydrology and climate of Ice Age lakes in western United States; stream environmental studies; high altitude, cold weather or arid zone field operations safety and survival; sand dune morphology. *Mailing Add:* 552-17 Bean Creek Rd Scotts Valley CA 95066

SNYDER, CHARLES THOMAS, b Belle Plaine, Kans, July 2, 38; m 60; c 4. AERONAUTICAL ENGINEERING, GUIDANCE & CONTROL. *Educ:* Univ Wichita, BS, 62; Stanford Univ, MS, 69, Engr, 76. *Prof Exp:* Aerospace eng flight dynamics, Flight & Systs Simulation Br, 62-65, proj engr, 65-70, group leader, 70-74, div chief flight systs, Res Div, 74-80, DIR AERONAUT & FLIGHT SYSTS, AMES RES CTR, NASA, 80- *Concurrent Pos:* Dryden mem fel, Nat Space Club, 72; mem, NASA Adv Subcomt Aviation Safety & Oper Systs, 75-77 & Adv Subcomt Avionics & Controls, 77-80; assoc dir, Stanford/Ames Joint Inst Aeronaut & Acoust, 77-80. *Honors & Awards:* Sustained Super Performance, NASA, 70. *Mem:* Am Inst Aeronaut & Astronaut; Am Helicopter Soc. *Res:* Flight mechanics; stability and control; handling qualities; guidance and navigation; avionics systems; aerodynamics; aircraft operating problems; simulation technology. *Mailing Add:* NASA-Ames Res Ctr Mail Stop 200-3 Moffett Field CA 94035

SNYDER, CLIFFORD CHARLES, b Ft Worth, Tex, Feb 16, 16; m 39; c 1. PLASTIC SURGERY. *Educ:* Univ Tenn, BS, 40, MD, 44; Am Bd Surg, dipl; Am Bd Plastic Surg, dipl. *Prof Exp:* Asst prof surg, Sch Med, Univ Tex, 52-54; from asst prof to assoc prof, Sch Med, Univ Miami, 54-67; PROF SURG & CHMN DIV PLASTIC SURG, COL MED, UNIV UTAH, 67-; CHIEF SURG, SALT LAKE CITY VET ADMIN HOSP, 67- *Concurrent Pos:* Attend physician, Jackson Mem, Doctor's & Cedars of Lebanon Hosps; consult, Vet Admin Hosp, 54-67 & Nat Surg Consult, 69-; chief staff, Variety Children's Hosp, 58-67; mem, Am Bd Plastic Surg, 63-69; abstr ed, J Plastic & Reconstruct Surg, 67-73, co-ed, 73-; mem, Vet Admin Nat Adv Comt, 74-; spec ed, Small Animal Clinician. *Mem:* Am Soc Plastic & Reconstruct Surg (asst secy, 59-60, vpres, 66-67); Am Soc Surg of Hand; Am Asn Plastic Surg (pres-elect, 74); Am Col Surgeons; hon mem Am Col Vet Surgeons. *Res:* Plastic and reconstructive surgery; transplantation of organs; snake bite; regeneration of nerves; wound healing. *Mailing Add:* Div of Plastic Surg Univ of Utah Col of Med Salt Lake City UT 84112

SNYDER, CONWAY WILSON, b Kirksville, Mo, Jan 24, 18; m 43; c 3. PHYSICS. *Educ:* Univ Redlands, AB, 39, DSc, 68; Univ Iowa, MS, 41; Calif Inst Technol, PhD(physics), 48. *Prof Exp:* Jr physicist, US Naval Ord Lab, Washington, DC, 41-42; mem staff, Off Naval Res, Washington, DC, 48-49; with Fairchild Engine & Airplane Corp Nuclear Engine Propulsion Aircraft Proj, Ky, 49-51; Oak Ridge Nat Lab, 51-54; asst prof physics, Fla State Univ, 54-56; sr res engr, 56-59, scientist specialist, 59-63, staff scientist, 63-69, Viking orbiter scientist, 69-77, Viking proj scientist, 77-80, ASST PROJ MGR SCI, INFRARED ASTRON SATELLITE PROJ, JET PROPULSION LAB, CALIF INST TECHNOL, 81- *Mem:* Am Geophys Union; Am Phys Soc; Sigma Xi. *Mailing Add:* 4409 Lowell Ave La Crescenta CA 91214

SNYDER, DANA PAUL, b Winnipeg, Man, Apr 29, 22; nat US; m 52; c 4. ECOLOGY. *Educ:* Univ Ill, BS, 47, MS, 48; Univ Mich, PhD(zool), 51. *Prof Exp:* Instr biol, Pa Col Women, 52-53; res mammalogist, Carnegie Mus, 51-55; vis lectr, Smith Col, 56; from instr to asst prof, 55-65, ASSOC PROF ZOOL, UNIV MASS, AMHERST, 65- *Mem:* Am Soc Mammal; Ecol Soc Am; Soc Syst Zool; Wildlife Soc; Wilson Ornith Soc. *Res:* Systematics and ecology of mammals, especially Tamias striatus; geographic variation; population biology. *Mailing Add:* Dept of Zool Univ of Mass Amherst MA 01003

SNYDER, DANIEL RAPHAEL, b Detroit, Mich, July 5, 40; m 61; c 2. NEUROPSYCHOLOGY, PRIMATOLOGY. *Educ:* Wayne State Univ, BS, 62; Univ Mich, Ann Arbor, MS, 64, PhD(physiol psychol), 70. *Prof Exp:* Res assoc psychiat, 69-70, NIMH Biol Sci Training Prog fel biol psychiat, 70-71, asst prof lab animal sci, 71-73 & comp med & anthrop, 73-76, ASSOC PROF COMP MED & ANTHROP, SCH MED, YALE UNIV, 76-, HEAD NEUROBEHAV & PRIMATE RES FAC, 74- *Concurrent Pos:* Consult, Am Asn Accreditation Lab Animal Care, 74-; sci adv, Inst Biol Sci, Univ Islamabad, Pakistan, 75-; vet neurologist, Comp Med Referral Clin, Sch Med, Yale Univ, 76- *Mem:* Soc Neurosci; Psychonomic Soc; Int Primatol Soc; AAAS; Animal Behav Soc. *Res:* Neural mechanisms of social and emotional behavior; biomedical primatology & primate behavior; neuropsychology; behavioral & neurotoxicology. affective behavior; behavioral toxicology. *Mailing Add:* Neurobehav Lab & Primate Res Facil 333 Cedar St New Haven CT 06510

SNYDER, DAVID HILTON, b Giles Co, Va, June 24, 38; m 54; c 5. VERTEBRATE BIOLOGY, ETHOLOGY. *Educ:* Univ Mo-Columbia, BA, 58, MA, 62; Univ Notre Dame, PhD(biol), 71. *Prof Exp:* Teacher, Berkeley Pub Schs, Mo, 58-59; from instr to assoc prof, 62-77, PROF BIOL, AUSTIN PEAY STATE UNIV, 77- *Mem:* Am Soc Ichthyologists & Herpetologists; Soc Study Amphibians & Reptiles; Am Soc Zoologists; Ecol Soc Am; Am Soc Mammal. *Res:* Reproductive behavior of amphibians; taxonomy of American amphibians and reptiles. *Mailing Add:* Dept of Biol Austin Peay State Univ Clarksville TN 37040

SNYDER, DEXTER DEAN, b Toledo, Ohio, Feb 6, 42; m 68; c 3. PHYSICAL CHEMISTRY, ELECTROCHEMISTRY. *Educ:* Wabash Col, AB, 64; Mass Inst Technol, PhD(phys chem), 68. *Prof Exp:* Prof staff phys chem, Arthur D Little, Inc, 68-71; mem staff, Bendix Res Labs, 71-72; sr assoc res chem, 72-75, sr res chemist, 75-80, STAFF RES SCIENTIST, GEN MOTORS RES LABS, 80- *Mem:* Am Chem Soc; Electrochem Soc; Sigma Xi; Am Inst Chem Engrs. *Res:* Thermodynamics of solids; high temperature, high pressure solid state chemistry; cooperative and membrane phenomena; air and water pollution control research; resource recovery technology; electrochemical power source research and development. *Mailing Add:* Gen Motors Res Labs Gen Motors Corp Warren MI 48089

SNYDER, DONALD BENJAMIN, b North Manchester, Ind, Oct 6, 35; m 65; c 2. ORNITHOLOGY. *Educ:* Manchester Col, BS, 57; Ohio State Univ, MS, 59, PhD(zool), 63. *Prof Exp:* Asst prof biol, Cent Wesleyan Col, 63-64; asst prof, Geneva Col, 64-69; PROF BIOL, EDINBORO STATE COL, 69- *Mem:* Wildlife Soc; Wilson Ornith Soc. *Res:* Animal behavior; wildlife ecology. *Mailing Add:* Dept Biol Edinboro State Col Edinboro PA 16444

SNYDER, DONALD DUWAYNE, b Mich, Apr 11, 28; m 51; c 2. PHYSICS. *Educ:* Andrews Univ, BA, 48; Mich State Univ, PhD(physis), 57. *Prof Exp:* Asst physics, Mich State Univ, 54-56, lectr, 57; sr res physicist labs, Gen Motors Corp, 57-59; from assoc prof to prof physics, Andrews Univ, 59-67, chmn dept, 59-67; assoc prof, 67-70, chmn div arts & sci, 68-78, PROF PHYSICS, IND UNIV, SOUTH BEND, 70-, CHMN, 81- *Mem:* Int Solar Energy Soc; Sigma Xi; Am Asn Physics Teachers. *Res:* Solid state and metal physics; compound semiconductors. *Mailing Add:* Dept Physics Ind Univ South Bend IN 46615

SNYDER, DONALD LEE, b Bridgeport, Ohio, Sept 3, 43; m 67; c 3. ELECTROCHEMISTRY. *Educ:* Cleveland State Univ, BES, 66; Case Western Reserve Univ, MS, 68, PhD(phys chem), 70. *Prof Exp:* RES ASSOC METAL FINISHING, HARSHAW CHEM CO, 70-, GROUP LEADER, 73-, RES & DEVELOP MGR, 82- *Mem:* Am Chem Soc; Am Electroplaters Soc; Electrochem Soc; Am Soc Testing & Mat. *Res:* Electrochemical research primarily on the deposition of metals and the study of corrosion. *Mailing Add:* 1945 E 97th St Harshaw Chem Co Cleveland OH 44106

SNYDER, EVAN SAMUEL, b Lehighton, Pa, Aug 24, 23; m 48; c 3. NUCLEAR PHYSICS. *Educ:* Ursinus Col, BS, 44; Univ Pa, MS, 51, PhD(physics), 57. *Prof Exp:* From instr to assoc prof, 46-69, PROF PHYSICS & DEPT CHMN, URSINUS COL, 69- *Concurrent Pos:* Vis prof, NSF Inst, NMex State Univ, 59, 64-69; res partic, Oak Ridge Nat Lab, 60, 62; NSF sci fac fel, Princeton Univ, 68-69. *Mem:* Am Phys Soc; Am Asn Physics Teachers. *Res:* Low energy nuclear physics. *Mailing Add:* 80 Linfield Rd Trappe Collegeville PA 19426

SNYDER, FRED CALVIN, b Valley View, Pa, Apr 9, 16; m 42. AGRICULTURE. *Educ:* Pa State Univ, BS, 39, MS, 47, PhD(agr ed), 55. *Prof Exp:* Teacher pub schs, Pa, 39-41, 46-47; actg dir short courses, 56-58, dir short courses & chmn corresp agr & home econ, Pa State Univ, 58-79; RETIRED. *Mem:* AAAS. *Mailing Add:* Main St Boalsburg PA 16827

SNYDER, FRED LEONARD, b New Ulm, Minn, Nov 22, 31; m 55; c 3. BIOCHEMISTRY. *Educ:* St Cloud State Col, BS, 53; Univ NDak, MS, 55, PhD(biochem), 58. *Prof Exp:* From res scientist to chief scientist, 58-79, asst chmn, 75-79, ASSOC CHMN, MED & HEALTH SCI DIV, OAK RIDGE ASSOC UNIVS, 79- *Concurrent Pos:* Prof biochem, Med Units, Univ Tenn, Memphis, 64-; assoc prof biochem, Univ Tenn, Memphis, 66-70; prof med & chem, Univ NC, Chapel Hill, 66- *Mem:* Soc Exp Biol & Med; Sigma Xi; Am Soc Biol Chemists; Am Asn Cancer Res. *Res:* Metabolism and chemistry of lipids; cancer and pulmonary disorders; membranes; bioactive phopholipids; separation techniques. *Mailing Add:* Med & Health Sci Div Oak Ridge Assoc Univs PO Box 117 Oak Ridge TN 37830

SNYDER, FREEMAN WOODROW, b Philadelphia, Pa, Dec 6, 17; m 38; c 2. PLANT PHYSIOLOGY. *Educ:* Univ Idaho, BS, 38; Cornell Univ, PhD(plant physiol), 50. *Prof Exp:* Eng aide, Soil Conserv Serv, USDA, 42-43, agr engr, 46-47; asst bot, Cornell Univ, 48-50; asst agronomist, Univ Ark, 50-53; plant physiologist, Sugar Beet Invests, Plant Sci Res Div, 53-64, res plant physiologist, 64-68, plant physiologist, North Cent Region, 68-75, plant physiologist, Northeastern Region, 75-78, MEM STAFF, SCI & EDUC

ADMIN, AGR RES SERV, USDA, 78- *Concurrent Pos:* Adj assoc prof, Crop & Soil Sci, Mich State Univ, 70-75; actg lab chief, Light & Plant Growth Lab, Beltsville Agr Res Ctr, 81; coordr, Photosynthesis Prog, Org Econ Coop & Develop, 80- *Mem:* AAAS; Bot Soc Am; Am Soc Plant Physiol; Soc Sugar Beet Technol; Am Soc Agron. *Res:* Role of environmental and genetic factors in growth, development and yield of crop plants. *Mailing Add:* Light & Plant Growth Lab Bldg 046A Agr Res Ctr-West Beltsville MD 20705

SNYDER, GARY DEAN, b New Castle, Pa, Aug 22, 47; m 72; c 2. BIOCHEMICAL ENDOCRINOLOGY, MEMBRANE RECEPTORS. *Educ:* Pa State Univ, BS, 69, MS, 72, PhD(biol), 75. *Prof Exp:* Fel endocrinol, Univ Ill Col Med, 75-77; fel endocrinol, 77-79, ASST PROF PHYSIOL, UNIV TEX HEALTH SCI CTR, DALLAS, 79- *Res:* Biochemical mechanism of action of hypothalamic releasing hormones on the anterior pituitary; regulation of hormone secretion from the anterior pituitary. *Mailing Add:* Dept Physiol Univ Tex Health Sci Ctr 5323 Harry Hines Blvd Dallas TX 75235

SNYDER, GEORGE HEFT, b Evanston, Ill, July 19, 39; m 69. AGRONOMY, SOIL CHEMISTRY. *Educ:* Ohio State Univ, BS, 62, MS, 64, PhD(agron), 67. *Prof Exp:* Asst instr agron, Ohio State Univ, 63-64; asst prof, 67-73, assoc prof, 73-79, PROF SOILS, AGR RES & EDUC CTR, UNIV FLA, 79- *Mem:* Am Soc Agron. *Res:* Soil chemistry; nutrient uptake by plants; sand soil fertilization; wetload agriculture; nutrient leaching. *Mailing Add:* Agr Res & Educ Ctr Univ of Fla Belle Glade FL 33430

SNYDER, GLENN J(ACOB), b Akron, Ohio, Aug 1, 23; m 51; c 4. MECHANICAL ENGINEERING. *Educ:* Ohio Univ, BSME, 49. *Prof Exp:* Tool designer, Gun Mount Div, Firestone Tire & Rubber Co, 42-43; engr, Ohio Boxboard Co, 49-51; sr engr, Aerospace Div, Goodyear Tire & Rubber Co, 51-55; sr engr, Nuclear Power Div, 55-60, supvr reactor vessel, internals & control rod drives, 60-77, PRIN ENGR, NUCLEAR POWER GENERATION DIV, BABCOCK & WILCOX CO, 77- *Mem:* Nat Soc Prof Engrs; Am Soc Mech Engrs; Soc Mfg Engrs. *Mailing Add:* Babcock & Wilcox Co PO Box 1260 Lynchburg VA 24505

SNYDER, HAROLD LEE, b Denver, Colo, Dec 30, 52; m 77; c 2. POLYMER BLENDS, PHASE TRANSITIONS. *Educ:* Lewis & Clark Col, BS, 75; Univ Calif, Santa Barbara, PhD(phys chem), 80. *Prof Exp:* STAFF SCIENTIST, E I DU PONT DE NEMOURS & CO, INC, 80- *Concurrent Pos:* Lectr, Morgan State Univ, 81-82. *Res:* Dynamical aspects of chemilumenescent reactions in crossed molecular beams; dynamical aspects of phase transitions in polymer blends. *Mailing Add:* Exp Sta E I du Pont De Nemours & Co Inc Wilmington DE 19808

SNYDER, HARRY E, b Peoria, Ill, Jan 14, 30; m 52; c 3. FOOD SCIENCE, BIOCHEMISTRY. *Educ:* Univ Calif, Berkeley, AB, 51; Univ Calif, Davis, PhD(microbiol), 59. *Prof Exp:* From asst prof to assoc prof food technol, Iowa State Univ, 59-68, prof, 68-79; PROF FOOD SCI, UNIV ARK, 79- *Mem:* AAAS; Inst Food Technologists; Am Chem Soc; Am Asn Cereal Chemists; Am Soc Biol Chemists. *Res:* Biochemistry of soybean lipoxygenase as related to off flavors in soy protein products; world food problems; possibility of making use of soy protein in human diets. *Mailing Add:* Dept Hort Food Sci Univ Ark Fayetteville AR 72701

SNYDER, HARRY RAYMOND, JR, b Lawrence, Mass, Jan 19, 24; m 49; c 2. ORGANIC CHEMISTRY, MEDICINAL CHEMISTRY. *Educ:* Brown Univ, ScB, 49; Boston Univ, MA, 52, PhD(org chem), 58. *Prof Exp:* Res chemist, R J Reynolds Tobacco Co, 54-56; sr res chemist, 56-61, unit leader org chem, 61-73, SCI ASSOC, NORWICH-EATON PHARMACEUT DIV, MORTON-NORWICH PROD, INC, 73- *Mem:* Am Chem Soc; NY Acad Sci. *Res:* Synthesis of nitrofurans and other heterocycles for possible medicinal uses. *Mailing Add:* PO Box 371 Norwich NY 13815

SNYDER, HERBERT HOWARD, b Ravenswood, WVa, Feb 26, 27; m 66; c 1. APPLIED MATHEMATICS, MATHEMATICAL PHYSICS. *Educ:* Marietta Col, AB, 49; Lehigh Univ, MA, 51, PhD(math), 65; Univ SAfrica, PhD(appl math), 71. *Prof Exp:* Instr math, Lehigh Univ, 49-53; develop engr, ITT Fed Labs Div, Int Tel & Tel Corp, 53-63; instr math, Newark Col Eng, 63-64; instr math, Lehigh Univ, 64-65; asst prof, Drexel Inst, 65-66; assoc prof, 66-72, PROF MATH, SOUTHERN ILL UNIV, CARBONDALE, 72- *Concurrent Pos:* Vis assoc prof, Univ Ariz, 71-72; ed-in-chief, Handbuch der Electrotechnic; trustee, Ind Technol Univ. *Mem:* Am Math Soc; Ger Math Asn. *Res:* Function-theory on linear algebras; partial differential equations; electromagnetic theory; guided wave propagation and non-linear electron-wave interactions. *Mailing Add:* Dept Math Southern Ill Univ Carbondale IL 80303

SNYDER, HOWARD ARTHUR, b Lehighton, Pa, Mar 7, 30; m 75. FLUIDS, SOLID STATE PHYSICS. *Educ:* Rensselaer Polytech Inst, BS, 52; Univ Chicago, SM, 56, PhD(physics), 61. *Prof Exp:* Asst prof physics, Brown Univ, 61-68; ASSOC PROF AEROSPACE ENG SCI, UNIV COLO, BOULDER, 68- *Concurrent Pos:* NSF res grants. *Mem:* Am Phys Soc; Am Geophys Union. *Res:* Hydrodynamics and acoustics of liquid helium; laboratory modeling experiments of the atmosphere and the oceans; stability of fluid flow; finite amplitude waves in fluids. *Mailing Add:* Aerospace Box 429 Univ of Colo Boulder CO 80309

SNYDER, HUGH DONALD, b Norwalk, Conn, Sept 2, 23; m 52, 66, 69; c 3. PAPER INDUSTRY, MICROBIOLOGY. *Educ:* Rutgers Univ, BS, 48, PhD(plant path), 59. *Prof Exp:* Mycologist, Nuodex Prod Co, Inc, 49-54; chief microbiol lab, Troy Chem Co, 56-61; vpres & tech dir, Cosan Chem Corp, 62-66; tech dir indust biocides, Velsicol Chem Corp, 66-69; tech rep, Merck Chem Div, Merck & Co, Inc, 70-74; MGR TECH SERV, VININGS CHEM CO, 74- *Mem:* Am Phytopath Soc; Soc Indust Microbiol; Bot Soc Am; Am Soc Microbiol; Tech Asn Pulp & Paper Indust. *Res:* Industrial microbiology and biocides; paper slime and deposit control methods. *Mailing Add:* 6140 Blackwood Circle Norcross GA 30093

SNYDER, JACK AUSTIN, b Lansing, Mich, Oct 21, 27; m 49; c 2. BIOCHEMISTRY. *Educ:* Mich State Univ, BS, 49; Univ Wis, MS, 51, PhD(biochem), 53. *Prof Exp:* From res scientist to res assoc, 58-66, res supvr, 66-71, res assoc, 71-73, tech serv mgr, Pharmaceut Div, Biochem Dept, 73-81, CONSULT PHARMACEUT RES, E I DU PONT DE NEMOURS & CO, INC, 81- *Mem:* Am Chem Soc. *Res:* Synthesis; structure in relation to activity; process development; drug candidate evaluation. *Mailing Add:* Rd 3 Box 250 B5C Hockessin DE 19707

SNYDER, JACK RUSSELL, b Levels, WVa, Jan 31, 26; m 45; c 4. ZOOLOGY. *Educ:* Frostburg State Col, BS, 52; Pa State Univ, MEd, 54, DEd, 60. *Prof Exp:* Teacher pub schs, Md, 51-56; assoc prof biol, West Chester State Col, 56-58; PROF BIOL, FROSTBURG STATE COL, 58-, DIR GRAD STUDIES, 65- *Mem:* AAAS. *Mailing Add:* Dept of Biol Frostburg State Col Frostburg MD 21532

SNYDER, JACK WILLARD, biology, deceased

SNYDER, JAMES NEWTON, b Akron, Ohio, Feb 17, 23; m 44; c 1. PHYSICS, COMPUTER SCIENCE. *Educ:* Harvard Univ, BS, 45, AM, 47, PhD(physics), 49. *Prof Exp:* Instr physics, Allegheny Col, 43-44; from asst to assoc prof physics, 44-58, assoc head dept, 64-70, PROF PHYSICS & COMPUT SCI, UNIV ILL, URBANA, 58-, HEAD DEPT COMPUT SCI, 70- *Mem:* AAAS; Am Phys Soc; Am Soc Eng Educ; Asn Comput Mach; Inst Elec & Electronics Engrs. *Res:* Quantum theory; physical applications of high speed digital computers; data analysis in high energy physics. *Mailing Add:* Dept of Comput Sci Univ of Ill Urbana IL 61801

SNYDER, JOHN CRAYTON, b Salt Lake City, Utah, May 24, 10; m 42; c 3. MICROBIOLOGY, POPULATION POLICY. *Educ:* Stanford Univ, AB, 31; Harvard Univ, MD, 35; dipl, Am Bd Prev Med, 49. *Hon Degrees:* LLD, Harvard Univ, 64. *Prof Exp:* Fel surg, Harvard Med Sch, 36-37; Soc Fels jr fel, Harvard Univ, 39-40; mem staff, Int Health Div, Rockefeller Found, 40-46; prof pub health bact, Harvard Univ, 46-50 & microbiol, 50-61, dean fac, 54-71, Henry Pickering Walcott prof, 61-71, prof pop & pub health & med dir, Ctr Pop Studies, Sch Pub Health, 71-76; chief, Div Pop Policy, Pathfinder Fund, 78; LECTR, MASS INST TECHNOL & ASSOC DIR, INT POP INITIATIVES, 79- *Concurrent Pos:* Consult, Univ Assocs for Int Health, 74- & Med in Pub Interest, 76- virus dis, 63- & Pathfinder Fund, pop control, 70- *Mem:* Am Pub Health Asn; Am Soc Trop Med & Hyg; Am Epidemiol Soc; Asn Am Physicians; Am Acad Arts & Sci. *Res:* Typhus fever and other rickettsial diseases; chemotherapy and immunology; trachoma and related diseases of the eye; human fertility control and population problems. *Mailing Add:* 112 Hugh Cargill Rd Concord MA 01742

SNYDER, JOHN L, b Lansing, Mich, June 23, 30; m 65. PHYSICAL GEOLOGY. *Educ:* Mich State Univ, BS, 51; Dartmouth Univ, AM, 53; Northwestern Univ, PhD(geol), 57. *Prof Exp:* Instr geol, Univ Tex, 57, asst prof, 57-62; dir educ, Am Geol Inst, 62-69; assoc prog dir undergrad educ div, 69-72, prog mgr, Div Higher Educ in Sci, 72-78, PROF DIR, LOCAL COURSE IMPROV PROG, NSF, 78- *Concurrent Pos:* Mem steering comt, Geo-Study & mem steering comt & adv bd, Earth Sci Curriculum Proj; vis prof, Dept Geol, Univ Mo-Columbia, 79. *Mem:* Geol Soc Am; Geochem Soc; Nat Asn Geol Teachers. *Res:* Igneous petrology; science education. *Mailing Add:* Nat Sci Found 1800 G St NW Washington DC 20550

SNYDER, JOHN MARSHALL, b Lawrenceville, Ill, Feb 17, 23; m 43; c 1. ANIMAL SCIENCE. *Educ:* Univ Ill, BS, 47, MS, 52, PhD(animal sci), 55; St Louis Univ, MBA, 73. *Prof Exp:* Teacher high sch, Ill, 47-51; asst animal sci, Univ Ill, 52-54; poultry specialist, Beacon Milling Co Div, Spencer Kellogg & Sons, Inc, 54-58, dir poultry res, 59-61, dir res, 61-63; coord res, Int Div, 63-65, DIR RES, RALSTON PURINA INT, RALSTON PURINA CO, 65- *Mem:* AAAS; Poultry Sci Asn; Am Soc Animal Sci. *Res:* Poultry nutrition and management; research administration; formulation of feeds and foods. *Mailing Add:* Ralston Purina Co Checkerboard Sq St Louis MO 63188

SNYDER, JOHN WILLIAM, b Oakhill, WVa, May 12, 40. PHYSICAL OPTICS, SPECTROSCOPY. *Educ:* Ohio State Univ, BS, 63, MS, 64, PhD(physics), 68. *Prof Exp:* Mem fac, 68-77, ASSOC PROF PHYSICS, SOUTHERN CONN STATE COL, 81-, CHMN DEPT, PHYSICS, 77- *Mem:* Am Asn Physics Teachers; Am Optical Soc. *Res:* Fourier transform spectroscopy; microprocessors. *Mailing Add:* Dept of Physics 501 Crescent St New Haven CT 06515

SNYDER, JOSEPH QUINCY, b Joplin, Mo, Aug 7, 20; m 42; c 4. CHEMISTRY. *Educ:* Univ Okla, BS, 42, MS, 51, PhD(chem, chem eng), 54. *Prof Exp:* Org chemist & asst dir res, Samuel Roberts Noble Found, Okla, 48-51; instr chem, Univ Okla, 51-52 & 53-54; instr chem eng, 54-55; dir res, DanCu Chem Co, 55-56; sr res chemist, 56-64, res group leader, 64-70, RES SPECIALIST, MONSANTO CO, 71- *Mem:* Am Chem Soc. *Res:* Free radical copolymerizations; hydrocarbon reactions; catalytic conversions of olefins. *Mailing Add:* 1151 Tomkins St Charles MO 63301

SNYDER, JUDITH ARMSTRONG, b Washington, DC, Nov 11, 46; m 72. CELL BIOLOGY. *Educ:* Univ Calif, Berkeley, AB, 68, PhD(bot), 73. *Prof Exp:* Res asst bot, Univ Calif, Berkeley, 72; res assoc cell biol, Univ Colo, Boulder, 73-78; ASST PROF BIOL SCI, UNIV DENVER, 78- *Concurrent Pos:* Res assoc, NIH fel, 75-78. *Mem:* AAAS; Am Soc Plant Physiologists; Am Soc Cell Biol. *Res:* Isolation and characterization of the intact mitotic apparatus from mammalian tissue culture cells and investigation of factors controlling mitotic spindle assembly. *Mailing Add:* Dept of Biol Sci Univ of Denver Denver CO 80208

SNYDER, LAWRENCE CLEMENT, b Ridley Park, Pa, Apr 16, 32; m 58; c 3. CHEMICAL PHYSICS. *Educ:* Univ Calif, Berkeley, BS, 53; Carnegie Inst Technol, MS, 54, PhD(chem), 59. *Prof Exp:* Mem tech staff, Bell Labs, 59-80; PROF & CHMN, CHEM DEPT, STATE UNIV NY ALBANY, 80- *Concurrent Pos:* Lectr chem, Columbia Univ, 65-67; lectureship in chem,

Robert A Welch Found, 71. *Mem:* AAAS; Am Chem Soc; fel Am Phys Soc; fel Am Inst Chem. *Res:* Electronic structure of molecules; structure and thermochemistry of silicon hydrides; silicon crystal surface reconstruction; structure of borate glasses; theory of molecular Compton profiles. *Mailing Add:* Chem Dept State Univ NY Albany NY 12222

SNYDER, LEE RICHMOND GIRTON, b Sioux Falls, SDak, Jan 5, 46. GENETICS, POPULATION BIOLOGY. *Educ:* Harvard Univ, AB, 70; Stanford Univ, PhD(biol), 77. *Prof Exp:* ASST PROF BIOL, UNIV CALIF, RIVERSIDE, 76- *Mem:* Soc Study Evolution; Genetics Soc Am; AAAS. *Res:* Genetic variation in natural populations; hemoglobins; genetic adapatation to high altitudes. *Mailing Add:* Dept of Biol Univ of Calif Riverside CA 92521

SNYDER, LEON ALLEN, b Oakland, Calif, July 31, 20; m 44; c 2. GENETICS. *Educ:* Univ Calif, BS, 42, PhD(genetics), 49. *Prof Exp:* Asst prof, Univ Okla, 49-52; plant geneticist, USDA, PR, 52-54; res assoc, 54-55, asst prof agron & plant genetics, 55-58, assoc prof, 58-61, PROF GENETICS & CELL BIOL, UNIV MINN, ST PAUL, 61- *Mem:* AAAS; Genetics Soc Am; Bot Soc Am; Am Soc Naturalists. *Res:* Mutagenesis and developmental genetics. *Mailing Add:* Dept of Genetics & Cell Biol Univ of Minn St Paul MN 55101

SNYDER, LEWIS EMIL, b Ft Wayne, Ind, Nov 26, 39; m 62; c 2. ASTROPHYSICS, MOLECULAR PHYSICS. *Educ:* Ind State Univ, BS, 61; Southern Ill Univ, MA, 64; Mich State Univ, PhD(physics), 67. *Prof Exp:* Res assoc astrophys, Nat Radio Astron Observ, 67-69; from asst prof to assoc prof astron, Univ Va, 69-75; PROF ASTRON, UNIV ILL, 75- *Concurrent Pos:* Mem, Ctr Advan Studies, Univ Va, 69-75; mem radio & radar astron comn, Int Sci Radio Union, 69-; mem radio astron subcomt, Comt Radio Frequencies, Nat Res Coun, 71-74; vis fel, Joint Inst Lab Astrophys, Boulder, Colo, 73-74. *Mem:* Sigma Xi; Am Phys Soc; Am Astron Soc; Int Astron Union. *Res:* Spectral line radio astronomy and chemical composition of the interstellar medium. *Mailing Add:* 341 Astron Bldg Univ Ill 1011 W Springfield Ave Urbana IL 61801

SNYDER, LLOYD ROBERT, b Sacramento, Calif, July 30, 31; m 52; c 4. CLINICAL CHEMISTRY. *Educ:* Univ Calif, BS, 52, PhD, 54. *Prof Exp:* Res chemist, Shell Oil Co, 54-56 & Technicolor Corp, 56-57; from sr res chemist to sr res assoc, Union Oil Co Calif, 57-71; dir separations res, 71-72, VPRES CLINICAL CHEM, TECHNICON CORP, 72- *Honors & Awards:* Petrol Chem Award, Am Chem Soc, 70. *Mem:* Am Chem Soc. *Res:* Automated analysis; high speed liquid chromatography; adsorption and adsorption chromatography; analytical separations; biomedical chemistry. *Mailing Add:* Technicon Corp 511 Benedict Ave Tarrytown NY 10591

SNYDER, LOREN RUSSELL, b Milwaukee, Wis, June 19, 41; div; c 2. MOLECULAR BIOLOGY. *Educ:* Univ Minn, Duluth, BA, 63; Univ Chicago, PhD(biophys), 68. *Prof Exp:* Jane Coffin Childs Mem Fund Med Res fel, Int Lab Genetics & Biophys, Naples, 68-69, fac sci, Univ Paris, 69-70; from asst prof to assoc prof, 70-79, PROF MICROBIOL, MICH STATE UNIV, 79- *Concurrent Pos:* NIH res grants, 74-77 & 80-83; NSF res grants, 78-80 & 80-83. *Res:* Molecular basis for control of gene expression in bacteria. *Mailing Add:* Dept of Microbiol Mich State Univ East Lansing MI 48823

SNYDER, LOUIS MICHAEL, b Boston, Mass, May 10, 35; m 58; c 3. HEMATOLOGY. *Educ:* Brown Univ, AB, 57; Chicago Med Sch, MD, 62; Am Bd Internal Med, Hematol Bd, dipl. *Prof Exp:* NIH grant hemat, Mass Gen Hosp, 65-66; DIR DIV HEMAT, ST VINCENT HOSP, 68-; PROF INTERNAL MED & PEDIAT, MED SCH, UNIV MASS, 79- *Concurrent Pos:* mem med adv bd, New Eng Hemophilia Asn, 72-; chmn med adv bd, Cent Mass, Leukemia Soc of Am, 73-78. *Mem:* Am Fedn Clin Res; Am Soc Hemat; fel Am Col Physicians; NY Acad Sci. *Res:* Red cell metabolism; interaction of organic phosphates and hemoglobin; red cell membrane structure and function. *Mailing Add:* Div of Hemat St Vincent Hosp Worcester MA 01610

SNYDER, LYNN SEBESTYEN, speech pathology, see previous edition

SNYDER, MELVIN H(ENRY), JR, b Pittsburgh, Pa, Sept 22, 21; m 46, 59; c 6. THERMODYNAMICS. *Educ:* Carnegie Inst Technol, BS, 46; Wichita State Univ, MS, 50; Okla State Univ, PhD, 67. *Prof Exp:* From instr to assoc prof aeronaut eng, 46-58, head dept, 51-58, asst dean, 58-67, PROF AERONAUT ENG, WICHITA STATE UNIV, 58-, CHAIRPERSON DEPT, 77- *Concurrent Pos:* Consult, 51-; vis prof, Von Karman Inst Fluid Dynamics, Belg, 70-71. *Mem:* Am Inst Aeronaut & Astronaut. *Res:* Drag of bodies in sheared-flow fields; lift, drag and pitching moment of delta wings; use of power to aerothermodynamics. *Mailing Add:* Dept of Aeronaut Eng Wichita State Univ Wichita KS 67208

SNYDER, MERRILL J, b McKeesport, Pa, May 25, 19; m 42; c 3. CLINICAL MICROBIOLOGY. *Educ:* Univ Pittsburgh, BS, 40; Univ Md, MS, 50, PhD(bact), 53; Am Bd Med Microbiol, dipl. *Prof Exp:* Clin chemist, McKeesport Hosp, Pa, 38-41; med bacteriologist, Dept Virus & Rickettsial Dis, US Army Med Ctr, DC, 45-49; instr bact & med, 49-53, asst prof med in clin bact, 53-57, from asst prof to assoc prof microbiol, 55-65, assoc dir div infectious dis, 57-74, assoc prof med in clin microbiol, 59-76, PROF MED CLIN MICROBIOL, SCH MED, UNIV MD, BALTIMORE CITY, 76- *Concurrent Pos:* Head diag microbiol & serol, Univ Md Hosp, 59-71, hosp epidemiologist, 73-77. *Mem:* Am Soc Microbiol; Infectious Dis Soc Am. *Res:* Infectious diseases. *Mailing Add:* Dept of Med Univ of Md Sch Med Baltimore MD 21201

SNYDER, MILTON JACK, b Columbus, Ohio, Oct 12, 21; m 44; c 2. CHEMISTRY, CONSTRUCTION MATERIALS. *Educ:* Ohio State Univ, BSc, 43. *Prof Exp:* Res engr, 43-50, from asst div chief to div chief, 50-70, sect mgr inorg mat, 70-73, dept mgr, 73-74, 74-75, mgr, Energy Conserv Mat Prog Off, 75-76, mgr, Mat Develop Sect, 76-79, MGR, CONSTRUCT & GEOMAT PROG OFF, COLUMBUS LABS, BATTELLE MEM INST, 79- *Honors & Awards:* Wason Medal, Am Concrete Inst, 71. *Mem:* Am Chem Soc; Am Concrete Inst; fel Am Ceramic Soc; Nat Inst Ceramic Eng; Sigma Xi. *Res:* Surface chemistry and physics; materials utilization; nuclear energy. *Mailing Add:* Battelle Mem Inst Inorg Mat Sect 505 King Ave Columbus OH 43201

SNYDER, MITCHELL, b Philadelphia, Pa, Nov 4, 38; m 63; c 5. STATISTICS. *Educ:* Yeshiva Univ, BA & BHL, 60; NY Univ, MS, 62; Univ Chicago, PhD(statist), 66. *Prof Exp:* Consult, Biol Sci Comput Ctr, Univ Chicago, 62-65; mem tech staff, Bell Tel Labs, 65-68; LECTR MATH, BAR-ILAN UNIV, ISRAEL, 68-, SCI DIR COMPUT CTR, 69- *Concurrent Pos:* Lectr, Roosevelt Univ, 64-65. *Mem:* Inst Math Statist; Am Statist Asn; Asn Comput Mach; Israel Statist Asn; Info Processing Asn Israel. *Res:* Multivariate analysis; robust data analysis; computer applications in data analysis. *Mailing Add:* Dept Math Bar-Ilan Univ Ramat Gan Israel

SNYDER, NATHAN W(ILLIAM), b Montreal, Que, Apr 21, 18; nat US; m 44; c 2. ENERGY CONVERSION, HEAT & MASS TRANSFER. *Educ:* Univ Calif, Berkeley, BS, 41, MS, 44, PhD(mech eng, math), 47. *Prof Exp:* Instr & res scientist, Univ Calif, Berkeley, 42-47, asst prof mech eng, 47-53, assoc prof process eng & chmn dept nuclear eng, 53-57, prof nuclear eng & chmn dept, 57-58; sr staff scientist in space technol, chmn, Space Power & Energy Conversion Panel & adv, Propulsion Panel, Inst Defense Anal, 58-61; vpres res & eng, Royal Res Corp, 61-62; chief scientist, Kaiser Aerospace & Electronics Corp, 62-64; Neely Prof nuclear eng, Ga Inst Technol, 64-66, Neely Prof aerospace eng, 66-68; asst sr vpres res & eng, N Am Rockwell Corp, 68-71; pres, N W Snyder Assocs, 71-72; chief scientist, 72-78, tech dir, 78-80, MGR TECHNOL DEPT, RALPH M PARSONS CO, 81- *Concurrent Pos:* Consult various govt agencies and pvt industs, 44-; mem adv comt nuclear systs in space, NASA, 59-61, biotechnol & human res adv comt, 69-71 & life sci comt, 71-74; sci adv to Air Force, 62-70, mem, Air Force Sci Adv Bd, 67-70; mem space technol panel, President's Sci Adv Comt, 64-67; mem adv comt isotopes & radiation develop, Atomic Energy Comn, 66-67; mem, Environ Impacts Panel, Am Inst Biol Sci, 74-78; chmn transp comt, Calif Intersoc Legis Adv Comn, 77-; chmn tech comt, Dept Energy Strategic Petrol Reserve Prog, 78- *Honors & Awards:* George Washington Award & Engr of Year, Inst Advan Eng, 77. *Mem:* Am Phys Soc; Am Inst Aeronaut & Astronaut; Am Nuclear Soc; Acoust Soc Am; Am Inst Chem Engrs. *Res:* Energy conversion; physics of fluids and heat; mass transfer; space technology; nuclear power; space power; acoustics; physics of boiling; thin film thermal instruments; sea water conversion; nuclear and electric propulsion; environmental control and life support; solid waste conversion and resource recovery. *Mailing Add:* Ralph M Parsons Co Pasadena CA 91124

SNYDER, RICHARD GERALD, b Northampton, Mass, Feb 14, 28; m 49; c 6. AEROSPACE MEDICINE, ANTHROPOLOGY. *Educ:* Univ Ariz, BA, 56, MA, 57, PhD(phys anthrop), 59. *Prof Exp:* Asst anthrop, Univ Ariz, 57-59, from assoc res engr to res phys anthropologist, Appl Res Lab, 59-60; chief phys anthrop, Civil Aeromed Res Inst, Fed Aviation Agency, 60-66; mgr biomech dept, Automotive Safety Res Off, Ford Motor Co, Mich, 66; assoc prof anthrop, Mich State Univ, 66-68; assoc prof, 68-73, PROF ANTHROP, UNIV MICH, ANN ARBOR, 73-, HEAD BIOMED DEPT & RES SCIENTIST, HWY SAFETY RES INST, INST SCI & TECHNOL, 69- *Concurrent Pos:* Mem staff, Ariz Transp & Traffic Inst, 59-60; assoc prof syst eng, Univ Ariz, 60; adj assoc prof, Univ Okla, 61-66; res assoc, Univ Chicago, 63-66; consult, US Air Force, US Navy, NASA, US Dept Transp, Southwest Res Inst, US Army, Dept Health, Educ & Welfare & Am Inst Biol Scientists; mem biodynamics comt aerospace med panel, Adv Group Aeronaut Res & Develop-NATO, 63-, planning comt, Int Meeting on Impact, Portugal, 71, adv comt, Stapp Car Crash Conf, Harvard Univ, 69 & Univ Mich, 70 & 74, adv panel grad prog systs safety eng, NC State Univ, 69-; mem comt on hearing, bioacoust & biomech, Nat Acad Sci-Nat Res Coun, 70-72, mem exec coun, 73-75; mem fac, Bioeng Prog, Univ Mich, Ann Arbor, 70-; mem med adv bd, Prof Race Pilots Asn, 74- *Honors & Awards:* Nat Safety Coun Metrop Life Award, 70; Arch T Colwell Merit Award, Soc Automotive Engrs, 73. *Mem:* Fel AAAS; fel Am Anthrop Asn; Aerospace Indust Life Sci Asn (vpres, 74); fel Aerospace Med Asn; fel Am Acad Forensic Sci. *Res:* Human biology; aviation and automotive medicine; biomedical sciences; human tolerances to impact trauma; occupant restraint systems; dental morphology; forensic medicine. *Mailing Add:* Dept of Anthrop Univ of Mich Ann Arbor MI 48109

SNYDER, ROBERT, b Brooklyn, NY, Jan 17, 35; m 57; c 1. BIOCHEMICAL PHARMACOLOGY. *Educ:* Queens Col, NY, BS, 57; State Univ NY, PhD(biochem), 61. *Prof Exp:* Trainee pharmacol, Col Med, Univ Ill, 61-63; assoc prof, 63-76, PROF PHARMACOL, JEFFERSON MED COL, THOMAS JEFFERSON UNIV, 76- *Mem:* AAAS; NY Acad Sci; Am Soc Pharmacol & Exp Therapeut; Soc Toxicol; Int Soc Biochem Pharmacol. *Res:* Control of enzyme activity; drug enzyme interactions and metabolism; relationship of metabolism of xenobiotics to toxicological activity, cytochrome P450, drug metabolism. *Mailing Add:* Dept of Pharmacol Jefferson Med Col Philadelphia PA 19107

SNYDER, ROBERT DOUGLAS, b Lancaster, Pa, Apr 15, 34; m 55; c 3. ENGINEERING MECHANICS, APPLIED MATHEMATICS. *Educ:* Ind Inst Technol, BSME, 55; Clemson Univ, MSME, 59; WVa Univ, PhD(theoret & appl mech), 65. *Prof Exp:* Servo engr, Bell Aircraft Corp, 55; instr mech eng, Ind Inst Technol, 55-57; from instr to asst prof mech, Clemson Univ, 57-60; from instr to prof, WVa Univ, 62-75; chmn, Dept Eng Sci, Mech & Mat, 75-76, DEAN ENG, UNIV NC, CHARLOTTE, 76- *Mem:* Nat Soc Prof Engrs; Am Soc Mech Engrs; Sigma Xi; Soc Nat Philos; Am Acad Mech. *Res:* Continuum mechanics. *Mailing Add:* Col of Eng Univ NC Charlotte NC 28223

SNYDER, ROBERT GENE, b Boise, Idaho, July 4, 29; m 53; c 2. MOLECULAR SPECTROSCOPY. *Educ:* Ore State Univ, BA, 51, MA, 53, PhD(chem), 55. *Prof Exp:* Fel vibrational spectros, Univ Minn, 55-56; chemist, Shell Develop Co, 56-63; res fel, Polytech Inst Indust Chem, Milan,

Italy, 63-64; chemist, Shell Develop Co, 64-72; res chemist, Western Regional Res Lab, 72-75; res scientist, Midland Macromolecular Inst, 75-77; RES FEL, DEPT CHEM, UNIV CALIF, BERKELEY, 77- *Honors & Awards:* Coblentz Mem Award, Coblentz Soc, 65. *Mem:* Am Phys Soc; Am Chem Soc; Soc Appl Spectros; Biophys Soc. *Res:* Vibrational spectroscopy; spectra and structure of chain molecules and polymers. *Mailing Add:* Dept Chem Univ Calif Berkeley CA 94720

SNYDER, ROBERT L(EON), b Albion, NY, Sept 3, 34; m 60; c 2. MATERIALS SCIENCE, ENGINEERING. *Educ:* Rochester Inst Technol, BS, 56; Iowa State Univ, PhD(metall), 60. *Prof Exp:* Res engr, Metall, Res & Eng Ctr, Ford Motor Co, 60-65; res scientist, Res Div, Am Standard, Inc, 65-67; assoc prof mat, 67-70, PROF MECH ENG, ROCHESTER INST TECHNOL, 70- *Mem:* Am Soc Metals; Am Soc Eng Educ; Am Soc Mech Engrs. *Mailing Add:* Dept Mech Eng Rochester Inst Technol 1 Lomb Memorial Dr Rochester NY 14623

SNYDER, ROBERT LEROY, b Ellwood City, Pa, Apr 24, 26; m 49; c 4. COMPARATIVE PATHOLOGY, VERTEBRATE ECOLOGY. *Educ:* Pa State Univ, BS, 50, MS, 52; Johns Hopkins Univ, ScD(hyg), 60. *Prof Exp:* Res aide wildlife ecol, US Fish & Wildlife Serv, 50-52; biologist, Pa State Game Comn, 52-56; res asst vert ecol, Johns Hopkins Univ, 56-59; from res assoc to assoc dir, Penrose Res Lab, Zool Soc Philadelphia, 59-69; asst instr path, 61-62, assoc comp path, 62-66, asst prof, 66-70, ASSOC PROF PATH, DIV GRAD MED, UNIV PA, 70-, DIR, PENROSE RES LAB, ZOOL SOC PHILADELPHIA, 69- *Mem:* Am Asn Lab Animal Sci; Am Asn Zool Parks & Aquariums; Wildlife Dis Assoc. *Res:* Comparative pathology, viral hepatitis and population ecology; study of chronic viral diseases and their role in the development of cancer; woodchuck hepatitis virus and similar agents of importance in cancer research. *Mailing Add:* Penrose Res Lab Zool Soc Phila 34th St & Girard Ave Philadelphia PA 19104

SNYDER, RUTH EVELYN, b Canadian, Tex, May 21, 11; m 42; c 3. MEDICINE, RADIOLOGY. *Educ:* Park Col, BA, 32; Univ Tex, MD, 36; Am Bd Radiol, cert, 43. *Prof Exp:* Intern, NY Infirmary, Women & Child, 36-37; fel, Strang Clinic, 37-38; clin fel radiation ther, Mem Hosp, 39-42; asst radiologist, NY Hosp, 42-45; asst roentgenologist, Mem Hosp, 42-45; assoc roentgenologist & radiation ther, Hosp Spec Surg, 44-47; roentgenologist, Strang Clinic, Mem Hosp, 48-51; asst roentgenologist, 51-52; assoc roentgenologist, Mem Hosp, 52-77; CONSULT RADIOL, NY INFIRMARY, 54-; attend roentgenologist & sr staff, 77-81, CONSULT, MEM SLOAN-KETTERING CTR, 81- *Concurrent Pos:* Instr radiol, Cornell Univ Med Col, 52-61, clin instr, 61-63, clin asst prof, 64- *Mem:* AMA; Am Women's Med Asn; Radiol Soc NAm; Soc Surg Oncol; Asn Women Sci; Am Col Radiol. *Res:* Mammography. *Mailing Add:* 222 E 68th St New York NY 10021

SNYDER, SOLOMON H, b Washington, DC, Dec 26, 38; m 62. NEUROPHARMACOLOGY. *Educ:* Georgetown Univ, MD, 62. *Hon Degrees:* DSc, Northwestern Univ, 81. *Prof Exp:* Intern med, Kaiser Found Hosp, 62-63; res assoc pharmacol, NIMH, 63-65; from asst prof pharmacol to prof psychiat & pharmacol, 66-77, DISTINGUISHED SERV PROF PSYCHIAT & PHARMACOL, MED SCH, JOHNS HOPKINS UNIV, 77-, DIR DEPT NEUROSCI, 80- *Concurrent Pos:* Asst resident psychiat, Johns Hopkins Hosp, 65-68. *Honors & Awards:* John Jacob Abel Award, Am Soc Pharmacol & Exp Therapeut, 70; A E Bennett Award, Soc Biol Psychiat, 70; Hofheimer Prize, Am Psychiat Asn, 72; Gaddum Prize, Brit Pharmacol Soc, 74; Francis O Schmitt Award, 74; Daniel Efron Award, Am Col Neuropsychopharmacol, 74; Salmon Award, 78; Lasker Prize, 78. *Mem:* Nat Acad Sci; Am Col Neuropsychopharmacol; Am Soc Pharmacol & Exp Therapeut; assoc Neurosci Res Prog; Int Soc Neurochem. *Res:* Neurotransmitters; mechanism of action of psychotropic drugs. *Mailing Add:* Dept Neurosci Med Sch Johns Hopkins Univ 725 N Wolfe St Baltimore MD 21205

SNYDER, STANLEY PAUL, b Rifle, Colo, Sept 11, 42; m 66; c 2. VETERINARY PATHOLOGY, ONCOLOGY. *Educ:* Colo State Univ, DVM, 66, MS, 67; Univ Calif, Davis, PhD(comp path), 71. *Prof Exp:* Am Cancer Soc fel, Univ Calif, Davis, 71-72; asst prof vet med, Ore State Univ, 72-74; asst prof path, 74-78, ASSOC PROF PATH, COLO STATE UNIV, 78- *Mem:* Am Vet Med Asn; Am Col Vet Path; Am Asn Cancer Res; Vet Cancer Soc. *Res:* Viral and comparative oncology; pathogenesis of viral diseases; leprology. *Mailing Add:* Dept of Path Col of Vet Med Colo State Univ Ft Collins CO 80523

SNYDER, STEPHEN LAURIE, b Herkimer, NY, Oct 2, 42; m 66; c 2. BIOLOGICAL CHEMISTRY. *Educ:* Hobart Col, BS, 64; State Univ NY Binghamton, MA, 67; Univ Vt, PhD(chem), 70. *Prof Exp:* Res assoc biochem, Univ Colo, Boulder, 70-72; Nat Res Coun fel, Agr Res Serv, New Orleans, La, 72-75; biochemist, Armed Forces Radiobiol Res Inst, Bethesda, Md, 75-78; mem fac, Dept Chem, US Naval Acad, Annapolis, Md, 78-81; MEM STAFF, NAVAL MED RES INST, 81- *Mem:* Am Chem Soc. *Res:* Reaction mechanisms; enzymology; charge-transfer complexes; radiation biology; pathophysiology of endotoxins; role of lysosomal hydrolases in inflammation. *Mailing Add:* Naval Med Res Inst Bethesda MD 20014

SNYDER, THOMA MEES, b Baltimore, Md, May 21, 16; m 58; c 2. PHYSICS. *Educ:* Johns Hopkins Univ, PhD(physics), 40. *Prof Exp:* Instr physics, Princeton Univ, 40-42, res assoc, Off Sci Res & Develop contract, 42-43; res assoc, Los Alamos Sci Lab, 43-45; res assoc, Res Lab, Gen Elec Co, 46-47, proj head preliminary pile assembly & mem intermediate breeder reactor staff, Knolls Atomic Power Lab, 47-49, asst mgr, physics sect, 49-52, mgr reactor sect, 52-54, mgr phys sect, 54-56, mgr res oper, 56-57, mgr phys sect, Vallecitos Atomic Lab, 57-64, consult, Res & Eng Prog, 64-69, CONSULT SCIENTIST, NUCLEAR ENERGY DIV, GEN ELEC CO, 70- *Concurrent Pos:* Mem cross sect adv group, US AEC, 48-56, secy, 48, mem adv comt reactor physics, 50-72, chmn, 54; tech adv, US AEC, Geneva Conf Peaceful Uses of Atomic Energy, 55 & 58; mem, Mission Atomic Energy, Eng & Belg, 56. *Mem:* Fel Am Nuclear Soc; fel Am Phys Soc. *Res:* Nuclear energy technology; processes and materials; nuclear and reactor physics; solid state and plasma physics; radiation effects. *Mailing Add:* Nuclear Energy Div Gen Elec Co M/C 179 175 Curtner Ave San Jose CA 95114

SNYDER, VIRGIL W(ARD), b Midland, Mich, Mar 4, 34; m 58; c 2. STRUCTURAL DYNAMICS, FINITE ELEMENTS. *Educ:* Mich Technol Univ, BSCE, 56, MSCE, 62; Univ Ariz, PhD(aerospace eng), 68. *Prof Exp:* Stress engr, Northrup Aircraft, Inc, 56-58; struct engr, NAm Aviation, Inc, 58-60; instr eng mech, Mich Technol Univ, 60-62; consult, Kitt Peak Nat Observ, Univ Ariz, 63-65; PROF ENG MECH, MICH TECHNOL UNIV, 65- *Mem:* Am Soc Eng Educ; Soc Mining Engrs; Am Soc Civil Engrs; Am Acad Mech. *Res:* Vibrations, dynamics, finite elements and rock mechanics. *Mailing Add:* Dept of Mech Eng-Eng Mech Mich Technol Univ Houghton MI 49931

SNYDER, WALTER STANLEY, b Oakland, Calif, Jan 17, 49; m 76. GEOLOGY. *Educ:* Stanford Univ, BS, 72, MS, 73, PhD(geol), 77. *Prof Exp:* Fel, 77-78, res assoc geol, Lamont-Doherty Geol Observ, Columbia Univ, 78-81; RES GEOL, PHILLIPS PETROL, 81- *Mem:* Geol Soc Am; Am Inst Mining Engrs. *Res:* Stratigraphy, tectonics and mineral resources. *Mailing Add:* Res & Develop Phillips Petrol Co Bartlesville OK 10964

SNYDER, WARREN EDWARD, b Hutchinson, Kans, Feb 24, 22; m 43; c 3. MECHANICAL ENGINEERING. *Educ:* Univ Kans, BS, 43; Univ Minn, MS, 48, PhD(mech eng), 50. *Prof Exp:* Mech engr, US Naval Res Lab, 43-46; instr mech eng & asst head, Univ Minn, 46-50; assoc prof & head, Univ Kans, 50-52; sr res engr, Res Labs, Gen Motors Corp, 52-57; dir eng div, Midwest Res Inst, 57-62; vpres eng, Cummins Eng Co, Ind, 62-66; vpres eng & res div, Am Bosch Arma Corp, Mass, 66-70; VPRES ENG, WAUKESHA ENG DIV, DRESSER INDUST, INC, 70- *Mem:* Am Soc Mech Engrs; Am Soc Eng Educ; Soc Automotive Engrs. *Res:* Design; analysis; mathematics; management. *Mailing Add:* 32903 Hwy G Dousman WI 53118

SNYDER, WESLEY EDWIN, b Orlando, Fla, Nov 11, 46; m 68; c 3. ELECTRICAL ENGINEERING. *Educ:* NC State Univ, BS, 68; Univ Ill, Urbana-Champaign, MS, 70, PhD(elec eng), 75. *Prof Exp:* Vis asst prof elec eng, Univ Ill, Urbana-Champaign, 75; asst prof, 76-81, ASSOC PROF ELEC ENG, NC STATE UNIV, 81- *Concurrent Pos:* Fel, Langley Res Ctr, NASA, 76; consult, UN, 75 & 77, IBM, Westinghouse, Gen Elec, & Res Triangle Inst; vis scientist, WGer Space Agency, 79. *Mem:* Sr mem Inst Elec & Electronics Engrs; Soc Mech Engrs; Asn Comput Mach; Robotics Inst Am. *Res:* Computer image analysis; machine vision; robotics. *Mailing Add:* 3603 Octavia St Raleigh NC 27606

SNYDER, WILBERT FRANK, b Marion, Ohio, Apr 19, 04; m 33, 76; c 2. PHYSICS, HISTORY OF SCIENCE. *Educ:* NCent Col, BA, 26; Univ Ill, AM, 27. *Prof Exp:* From jr physicist to physicist, 27-46, asst chief, Microwave Stand Sect, 46-54, asst to chief, Radio Stand Div, 54-56, asst chief, Electronic Calibration Ctr, 56-62, coord calibration serv, Radio Stand Eng Div, 62-68, guest worker, Electromagnetics Div, 72-77, GUEST WORKER, PROG INFO OFF, NAT BUR STANDARDS, 78- *Mem:* Fel Acoust Soc Am; Sigma Xi; sr mem Inst Elec & Electronics Eng; sr mem Instrument Soc Am. *Res:* Acoustics of buildings and sound; standards and testing of hearing aids, audiometers and sixteen millimeter sound motion picture projectors; radar countermeasures; microwave standardization; calibration of electronic standards; radio history. *Mailing Add:* Nat Bur Standards Boulder CO 80302

SNYDER, WILLARD MONROE, b Lehighton, Pa, Sept 29, 18; m 48. HYDROLOGY. *Educ:* Ursinus Col, BS, 40; Mass Inst Technol, MS, 48. *Prof Exp:* Engr hydrol, Fed-State Flood Forecasting Serv, Pa, 47-50; engr hydrol, Hydraul Data Br, Tenn Valley Authority, 50-55, head statist anal unit, Hydrol Sect, 55-57, head hydrol sect, Hydraul Data Br, 57-60, staff res hydrologist, Off Tributary Area Develop, 60-62; prof hydrol, Ga Inst Technol, 63-69; res hydrol engr, Sci & Educ Admin-Agr Res, USDA, 69-75, res invest leader watershed eng, 70-73, res leader watershed hydrol, Southeast Watershed Res Ctr, Athens area, 74-80; RETIRED. *Concurrent Pos:* Consult, Oak Ridge Nat Lab, 67; consult hydrol, 80- *Mem:* Am Soc Civil Eng; Am Geophys Union; Am Water Resources Asn; Sigma Xi. *Res:* Formulation and evaluation of hydrologic models based on statistical analysis and on explicit and implicit solution of watershed process equations. *Mailing Add:* 275 Gatewood Circle Athens GA 30606

SNYDER, WILLIAM, b San Francisco, Calif, Feb 2, 21. ELECTRICAL ENGINEERING. *Educ:* Calif Inst Technol, BS, 43, MS, 46; Stanford Univ, PhD(elec eng), 55. *Prof Exp:* Jr engr, Westinghouse Elec & Mfg Co, 42; electronics engr, Hughes Aircraft Co, 46-49; sr res engr, Electronics Sect, Res Dept, Detroit Controls Corp, 53-56, group leader, 56-57, head sect, 57-59; mgr space systs dept, Adv Tech Labs, 59-61, sr scientist, 61-66; assoc prof elec eng, 66-71, PROF ELEC ENG, SAN JOSE STATE UNIV, 71- *Concurrent Pos:* Asst, Stanford Univ, 49-55; exten lectr, Univ Calif, 58. *Mem:* AAAS; Instrument Soc Am; Inst Elec & Electronics Engrs; Am Inst Navig. *Res:* Theory of ionospheric radio propagation; design of instruments and control systems for space navigation; magnetic amplifiers; electro-optical and electromechanical devices; electrical circuits; solid state electronic devices. *Mailing Add:* Dept of Elec Eng San Jose State Univ San Jose CA 95114

SNYDER, WILLIAM H, b Northampton, Pa, Aug 11, 29; m 52; c 3. ADHESIVES, POLYMERIC COATINGS. *Educ:* Temple Univ, AB, 52; Univ Pa, PhD(chem), 61. *Prof Exp:* Chemist, Rohm and Haas Co, Pa, 54-58; instr chem, Brooklyn Col, 61-63; from asst prof to assoc prof, 63-71, PROF CHEM, NJ INST TECHNOL, 71- *Concurrent Pos:* Proj dir, NSF Instrnl Sci Equip Prog grant, 78-81; prin investr, NIH Nat Inst Dent Res grant, 79- *Mem:* Am Chem Soc; Sigma Xi; Int Asn Dent Res. *Res:* Preparation and characterization of adhesives; cis effect in substituted vinylethers; anionic polymerization; base-initiated elimination reactions; the preparation and characterization of new polymers; polymeric coatings; blocked isocyanates; dentin adhesives; material properties. *Mailing Add:* Dept of Chem Eng & Chem NJ Inst Technol Newark NJ 07102

SNYDER, WILLIAM JAMES, b Altoona, Pa, Nov 4, 41; m 64; c 1. CHEMICAL ENGINEERING. *Educ:* Pa State Univ, BS, 63, MS, 65, PhD(chem eng), 67. *Prof Exp:* Fel, Lehigh Univ, 67-68; asst prof chem eng, 68-74, assoc prof, 74-80, PROF CHEM ENG, BUCKNELL UNIV, 80- *Mem:* AAAS; Am Inst Chem Engrs; Am Chem Soc; Am Soc Eng Educ. *Res:* Thermodynamic properties of solutions; heterogeneous catalysis; differential thermal analysis; polymers in solution; application of computers to chemical engineering plant design; mathematical modeling and simulation. *Mailing Add:* Dept of Chem Eng Bucknell Univ Lewisburg PA 17837

SNYDER, WILLIAM RICHARD, b Brooklyn, NY, Jan 24, 47; m 69; c 3. ORGANIC CHEMISTRY, POLYMER CHEMISTRY. *Educ:* Hamline Univ, BA, 69; Northwestern Univ, MS, 70, PhD(org chem), 74. *Prof Exp:* RES SPECIALIST, 3M CO, 76- *Concurrent Pos:* Res fel, Calif Inst Technol, 74-76. *Mem:* Am Chem Soc. *Res:* Organic synthesis of biologically active molecules. *Mailing Add:* 3M Co 270-3N-03 St Paul MN 55144

SNYDER, WILLIAM ROBERT, b Youngstown, Ohio, Mar 11, 46; m 77. NEUROCHEMISTRY, MEMBRANE ENZYMOLOGY. *Educ:* Ohio State Univ, BS, 68; Univ Chicago, PhD(biochem), 72. *Prof Exp:* Res fel chem, Harvard Univ, 72-74; sr res scientist biochem, Armour Pharmaceut, 74-77; res fel neuropath, Ohio State Univ, 77-78; vis asst prof chem, Univ Ill, Chicago, 78-81; ASST PROF CHEM, NORTHERN ILL UNIV, 81- *Mem:* Am Chem Soc; AAAS; Sigma Xi. *Res:* Properties of enzymes involved in lipid metabolism; relationship of lipid hydrolypis to the structure and function of biological membranes; involvement of membrane alteration in synaptic transmission. *Mailing Add:* Dept Chem Northern Ill Univ De Kalb IL 60115

SNYDER, WILLIAM THOMAS, b Knoxville, Tenn, Oct 18, 31; m 56; c 3. ENGINEERING MECHANICS. *Educ:* Univ Tenn, BS, 54; Northwestern Univ, MS, 56, PhD(mech eng), 58. *Prof Exp:* Asst prof mech eng, NC State Univ, 58-61; assoc prof thermal sci, State Univ NY, Stony Brook, 61-64; assoc prof aerospace eng, Space Inst, Univ Tenn, Tullahoma, 64-70; PROF ENG SCI & MECH & HEAD DEPT, UNIV TENN, KNOXVILLE, 70- *Mem:* Am Soc Eng Educ; Am Soc Heating, Refrig & Air Conditioning Engrs; Am Acad Mech; Energy Conserv Soc; Asn Energy Engrs. *Res:* Combustion; lubrication; magnetohydrodynamics; energy conservation. *Mailing Add:* Dept of Eng Sci & Mech Univ of Tenn Knoxville TN 37916

SNYDERMAN, RALPH, b New York, NY, Mar 13, 40; m 67. INTERNAL MEDICINE, RHEUMATOLOGY. *Educ:* Washington Col, BS, 61; State Univ NY, MD, 65. *Prof Exp:* Intern med, Med Ctr, Duke Univ, 65-66; resident, 66-67; res assoc immunol, Lab Microbiol, Nat Inst Dent Res, 67-69, sr investr, 69-72; assoc prof med, 72-77, assoc prof immunol, 72-79, PROF MED, DUKE UNIV MED CTR, 77-, CHIEF RHEUMATIC & GENETIC DIS, 75-, PROF IMMUNOL, 79-; CHIEF RHEUMATOLOGY, DURHAM VET HOSP, 72- *Concurrent Pos:* Howard Hughes med investr. *Mem:* Am Asn Clin Investr; Am Asn Immunol; Am Acad Allergy; Am Rheumatism Asn; Am Fedn Clin Res. *Res:* Investigation of the biological effectors of inflammation. *Mailing Add:* Dept of Med Duke Univ Med Ctr Durham NC 27710

SNYDERMAN, SELMA ELEANORE, b Philadelphia, Pa, July 22, 16; m 39; c 2. PEDIATRICS, MEDICINE. *Educ:* Univ Pa, AB, 37, MD, 40. *Prof Exp:* Fel pediat, 44-46, from instr to assoc prof, 46-47, PROF PEDIAT, SCH MED, NY UNIV, 67- *Concurrent Pos:* Assoc attend physician, NY Univ Hosp, 52-60, attend pediatrician, 60-; attend physician, Bellevue Hosp, 58-; career scientist, Health Res Coun, City of New York, 61-; mem nutrit study sect, NIH. *Honors & Awards:* Borden Award, Am Acad Pediat, 75. *Mem:* Soc Pediat Res; Am Pediat Soc; Am Acad Pediat; Am Inst Nutrit; Am Soc Clin Nutrit. *Res:* Pediatric nutrition, especially amino acid metabolism and requirements. *Mailing Add:* Dept of Pediat NY Univ Sch of Med New York NY 10016

SNYGG, JOHN MORROW, b Oswego, NY, Dec 2, 37; m 65; c 3. APPLIED MATHEMATICS. *Educ:* Harvard Univ, BA, 59; NY Univ, MA, 62, PhD(math), 67. *Prof Exp:* Lectr math, Hunter Col, 64-67; asst prof, 67-76, ASSOC PROF MATH, UPSALA COL, 76- *Res:* Clifford algebra; quantum mechanics; population growth. *Mailing Add:* Dept of Math & Physics Upsala Col East Orange NJ 07019

SO, ANTERO GO, b Davao City, Philippines, Jan 3, 32; US citizen; m 65; c 2. INTERNAL MEDICINE, HEMATOLOGY. *Educ:* Univ Santo Tomas, MD, 56; Univ Wash, PhD(biochem), 65. *Prof Exp:* USPHS fel, Western Reserve Univ, 60-62; USPHS trainee, Univ Wash, 62-65; Helen Hay Whitney Found res fel, Univ Geneva, 66-67; res instr biochem, Univ Wash, 67-68; asst prof biochem, 68-73, assoc prof med, 68-74, ASSOC PROF BIOCHEM, UNIV MIAMI, 73-, PROF MED, 74- *Concurrent Pos:* Estab investr, Am Heart Asn, 69, mem coun basic sci, 70; investr, Howard Hughes Med Inst, 74. *Mem:* Am Soc Clin Invest; Am Soc Biol Chemists. *Res:* Regulation of DNA and RNA synthesis in mammalian tissues. *Mailing Add:* Univ of Miami Sch of Med Miami FL 33152

SO, RONALD MING CHO, b Hong Kong, Nov 26, 39; US citizen; m 68; c 2. MECHANICAL ENGINEERING, AERONAUTICAL SCIENCES. *Educ:* Univ Hong Kong, BSc, 62; McGill Univ, MEng, 66; Princeton Univ, MA, 68, PhD(mech sci), 71. *Prof Exp:* Exec trainee, Shell Co, Hong Kong, 62-63; instr mech eng, Univ Hong Kong, 63-64; res scientist paper sci, Union Camp Corp, Res & Develop, 70-72; asst prof mech eng, Rutgers Univ, 72-76; mech engr res & develop, Gen Elec Corp, 76-81; ASSOC PROF, ARIZ STATE UNIV, 81- *Concurrent Pos:* Fluid physics consult, Res Cottrell Corp, 74-76; adj asst prof, Fairleigh Dickinson Univ, 74-76; adj assoc prof, Union Col, 77-78 & Union Col, 79-81. *Mem:* Am Soc Mech Engrs; Am Phys Soc; Am Inst Aeronaut & Astronaut. *Res:* Fluid dynamics; energy and power generation research; wind power systems; combustion; nuclear reactors and gas turbines; flow induced vibrations; turbulent flows; heat transfer; atmospheric surface layers. *Mailing Add:* Dept Mech & Energy Systs Eng Ariz State Univ Tempe AZ 85281

SOARE, ROBERT I, b Orange, NJ, Dec 22, 40; m 66; c 1. MATHEMATICS. *Educ:* Princeton Univ, AB, 63; Cornell Univ, PhD(math), 67. *Prof Exp:* From asst prof to prof math, Univ Ill, Chicago Circle, 67-75; PROF MATH, UNIV CHICAGO, 75- *Concurrent Pos:* NSF grant recursive anal, 68-70; prin investr, NSF grant recursive function theory, 70-; sr fel, Grad Col, Univ Ill, Chicago Circle, 71; assoc ed, Proc Am Math Soc, 71-74. *Mem:* Asn Comput Mach; Am Math Soc; Asn Symbolic Logic. *Res:* Mathematical logic, particularly recursive functions. *Mailing Add:* Dept of Math Univ of Chicago Chicago IL 60637

SOARES, EUGENE ROBBINS, b New Bedford, Mass, Nov 22, 45; m 71. MAMMALIAN GENETICS. *Educ:* Univ RI, BS, 67, PhD(biol sci), 72. *Prof Exp:* NIH trainee, Jackson Lab, 72-73; staff fel, Nat Inst Environ Health Sci, 75-77; MAMMALIAN GENETICIST, CHEM INDUST INST TOXICOL, 76- *Mem:* AAAS; Environ Mutagen Soc; Genetics Soc Am; Am Genetic Asn. *Res:* Mammalian genetics; the genetic effects of chemical mutagens and electromagnetic radiation in mice; studies of chromosomal aberrations biochemical mutations, dominant and recessive lethal mutations and polygenic mutations in mice. *Mailing Add:* Chem Indust Inst of Technol PO Box 12137 Research Triangle Park NC 27709

SOARES, JOSEPH HENRY, JR, b Fall River, Mass, July 30, 41; m 62; c 2. ANIMAL NUTRITION, BIOCHEMISTRY. *Educ:* Univ Md, BS, 64, MS, 66, PhD(animal sci), 69. *Prof Exp:* Animal husbandman, Bur Com Fisheries, US Dept Interior, 68-69; res animal husbandman, Nat Marine Fisheries Serv, US Dept Com, 69-72; from asst prof to assoc prof, 72-79, PROF NUTRIT, UNIV MD, COLLEGE PARK, 79- *Concurrent Pos:* Am Feed Mfrs res award, 77; vis prof, Human Nutrit Inst, USDA, 82; assoc ed, Poultry Sci, 76- *Mem:* AAAS; Am Inst Nutrit; Poultry Sci Asn; Animal Nutrit Res Coun. *Res:* Gnotobiology; interactions of heavy metals and their effects on essential nutrients; trace mineral and vitamin nutrition; avian nutrition; calcification and vitamin D hormones. *Mailing Add:* Dept Poultry Sci Univ Md College Park MD 20740

SOBCZYK, ANDREW, b Duluth, Minn, May 4, 15; m 40; c 5. MATHEMATICS. *Educ:* Univ Minn, AB, 35, MA, 36; Princeton Univ, PhD(math), 39. *Prof Exp:* Instr math, Princeton Univ, 38-39; from instr to assoc prof, Ore State Univ, 39-46; mem staff, Radiation Lab, Mass Inst Technol, 42-46; assoc prof, Boston Univ, 46-51; mem staff, Los Alamos Sci Lab, Univ Calif, 51-56; prof math, Univ Fla, 56-60 & Univ Miami, 60-65; SAMUEL MANER MARTIN PROF MATH, CLEMSON UNIV, 65- *Concurrent Pos:* Deleg, Int Cong Math, Harvard Univ, 50 & Moscow, Prague, 66; deleg, Int Conf Group Theory & Physics, Austin, Tex, 78. *Mem:* Am Math Soc; Math Asn Am; Swiss Math Soc; Math Soc Belg. *Res:* Servomechanisms and smoothing filters; topology; algebra; convex regions and projections; functional analysis; combinatorial geometry; applications of octonionic systems; Lie and Jordan algebras; fibre-bundles; groups and representations; analysis on differentiable manifolds, and other topics, in physics. *Mailing Add:* Dept of Math Clemson Univ Clemson SC 29631

SOBEL, ALAN, b New York, NY, Feb 23, 28; m 52; c 2. ELECTRONIC ENGINEERING, PHYSICS. *Educ:* Columbia Univ, BS, 47, MS, 49; Polytech Inst Brooklyn, PhD(physics), 64. *Prof Exp:* Engr, Telectro Indust Corp, NY, 49-50; asst chief engr, Electronic Workshop, Inc, 50-51; electronic engr, Freed Radio Corp, 51-53; chief electronics dept, Freed Electronics & Controls Corp, 53-55, head functional eng dept, Fairchild Controls Corp, 55-56; proj engr, Skiatron Electronics & TV Corp, 56-57; teaching fel physics, Polytech Inst Brooklyn, 57-59, from res asst to instr, 61-64; physicist, Zenith Radio Corp, 64-77; V PRES, LUCITRON, INC, 78- *Concurrent Pos:* Assoc ed, IEEE Transactions Electron Devices, 70-77. *Mem:* Sr mem Inst Elec & Electronics Engrs; Am Phys Soc; fel Soc Info Display. *Res:* Flat-panel displays; display systems & devices; gas discharges; electronic devices and circuits. *Mailing Add:* Lucitron Inc 1918 Raymond Dr Northbrook IL 60062

SOBEL, EDNA H, b New York, NY, Nov 2, 18. MEDICINE, PEDIATRICS. *Educ:* Univ Wis, BA, 39, MA, 40; Boston Univ, MD, 43; Am Bd Pediat, dipl, 54. *Prof Exp:* Intern, Montefiore Hosp, New York, 44; clin fel pediat, Harvard Med Sch & Mass Gen Hosp, 44-47, res fel, Harvard Med Sch, 47-49, res assoc, 55-56, clin & res fel, Mass Gen Hosp, 48-49; instr, Col Med, Univ Cincinnati, 50-53; from asst prof to assoc prof, 56-68, PROF PEDIAT, ALBERT EINSTEIN COL MED, 68- *Concurrent Pos:* Commonwealth Fund fel advan med, Mass Gen Hosp, 49-50; Commonwealth Fund fel, 63-64; asst, Sch Pub Health, Harvard Univ, 44-46; vis physician, Children's Hosp, Cincinnati, Ohio, 50-53, asst physician, 55-56; res assoc, Children's Cancer Res Found, 53-56; asst vis pediatrician, Bronx Munic Hosp, Cent Res, 53-60, assoc vis pediatrician, 60-68, vis pediatrician, 68-; asst prof, Antioch Col & res assoc, Fels Res Inst, 51-53; consult, Misericordia Hosp, New York, 58-59; attend pediatrician, Lincoln Hosp, 59-70. *Mem:* AAAS; Am Pediat Soc; Endocrine Soc; Europ Soc Paediatric Endocrinol; Lawson Wilkins Pediat Endocrine Soc. *Res:* Endocrine function of normal and abnormal children. *Mailing Add:* Dept of Pediat Albert Einstein Col of Med Bronx NY 10461

SOBEL, HENRY WAYNE, b Philadelphia, Pa. PARTICLE PHYSICS, COSMIC RAY PHYSICS. *Educ:* Rensselaer Polytech Inst, BS, 62; Case Inst Technol, PhD(physics), 69. *Prof Exp:* Asst res physicist, 69-74, assoc res physicist, 74-80, RES PHYSICIST, UNIV CALIF, 80- *Res:* Neutrino physics; fission. *Mailing Add:* Physics Dept Univ of Calif Irvine CA 92717

SOBEL, JAEL SABINA, b Israel, Nov 29, 35. CANCER RESEARCH, CELL MOTILITY. *Educ:* Cornell Univ, BA, 57; Columbia Univ, MA, 62; Univ Wis-Madison, PhD(zool), 66. *Prof Exp:* Fel cancer res, Sloan-Kettering Inst, 68-70; lectr embryol, Med Sch, Tel-Aviv Univ, 72-76; res fel, Lab Radiobiol, Univ Calif, San Francisco, 77-79; ASST PROF EMBRYOL & HISTOL, STATE UNIV NY BUFFALO, 79- *Concurrent Pos:* Consult, Lab Human Reproduction & Fetal Develop, Tel-Aviv Univ, 72-76. *Honors & Awards:* Rothschild Prize, Israel, 73. *Mem:* AAAS; Am Soc Cell Biol; Am Asn Anatomists. *Res:* Cell motility and characterization of cytoskeletal proteins during normal embryonic development and in developmental mutants; development of the trophoblast with emphasis on the regulation of invasive behavior. *Mailing Add:* Dept Anat State Univ NY Buffalo NY 14214

SOBEL, KENNETH MARK, b Brooklyn, NY, Oct 3, 54. MULTIVARIABLE CONTROL, ADAPTIVE CONTROL. *Educ:* City Col New York, BSEE, 76; Rensselaer Polytech Inst, MEng, 78, PhD(comput & syst eng), 80. *Prof Exp:* Res asst, Rensselaer Polytech Inst, 76-79, instr syst eng, 79-80; RES SCIENTIST, LOCKHEED CALIF CO, 80- *Concurrent Pos:* Adj asst prof, Calif State Univ, Northridge, 81. *Mem:* Inst Elec & Electronics Engrs; Sigma Xi. *Res:* Optimal output feedback; robust multivariable control; adaptive control; linear and nonlinear filtering; parameter identification. *Mailing Add:* Lockheed Calif Co Burbank CA 91520

SOBEL, MICHAEL I, b Brooklyn, NY, Feb 5, 39; m 59; c 2. THEORETICAL PHYSICS. *Educ:* Swarthmore Col, BA, 59; Harvard Univ, MA, 61, PhD(physics), 64. *Prof Exp:* Res assoc physics, Northeastern Univ, 64; from asst prof to assoc prof, 64-72, PROF PHYSICS, BROOKLYN COL, 72- *Concurrent Pos:* NSF res grant, 65-72; res assoc, Harwell, Eng, 67-68; NATO fel, 73 & sr fel, 75. *Mem:* AAAS; Am Phys Soc; Am Asn Physics Teachers; NY Acad Sci. *Res:* Nucleon-nucleon interactions; heavy ion reactions. *Mailing Add:* Dept Physics Brooklyn Col Brooklyn NY 11210

SOBEL, ROBERT EDWARD, b New York, NY, Aug 8, 41; m 63; c 1. CLINICAL CHEMISTRY, BIOCHEMISTRY. *Educ:* Columbia Col, BA, 62; George Washington Univ, MS, 66, PhD(biochem), 69. *Prof Exp:* NIH fel path, Col Med, Univ Fla, 69-71; asst prof cell & molecular biol, Med Col Ga, 71-78, dir clin chem, Clin Path Labs, 71-79, assoc prof cell & molecular biol, Dept Path, 78-79; TECH DIR, NAT HEALTH LABS, VIENNA, VA, 79- *Mem:* AAAS; Am Chem Soc; Am Asn Clin Chem; Sigma Xi. *Res:* Methods in clinical chemistry; correlation of laboratory results with clinical findings; lipid metabolism; trace metals. *Mailing Add:* Nat Health Labs 1007 Electric Ave Vienna VA 22180

SOBELL, HENRY MARTINIQUE, b Los Angeles, Calif, Nov 7, 35; m 58; c 5. MOLECULAR BIOLOGY, X-RAY CRYSTALLOGRAPHY. *Educ:* Columbia Col, AB, 56; Med Sch, Univ Va, MD, 60. *Prof Exp:* Instr, genetics & develop biol, Mass Inst Technol, 60-61, res assoc, 61-65; assoc prof, dept chem, Col Arts & Sci, 65-73 & dept radiation biol & biophysics, Sch Med & Dent, 68-73, PROF DEPT RADIATION BIOL & BIOPHYSICS, SCH MED & DENT, UNIV ROCHESTER & DEPT CHEM, COL ARTS & SCI, 73- *Concurrent Pos:* Helen Hay Whitney fel, 61-65; NIH award, 66-71; vis investr & lectr, Rockefeller Univ, 67-68; vis prof pharmacol, Stanford Med Sch, 72-73. *Mem:* AMA; Am Crystallog Asn; AAAS; Am Chem Soc; Am Biophys Soc. *Res:* Drug-nucleic acid crystallography; actinomycin D-DNA binding; protein-nucleic acid interactions; wave phenomena in the DNA double-helix. *Mailing Add:* Dept of Chem Univ of Rochester Rochester NY 14627

SOBER, DANIEL ISAAC, b New York, NY, Sept 5, 42; m 73; c 1. EXPERIMENTAL NUCLEAR PHYSICS, ELEMENTARY PARTICLE PHYSICS. *Educ:* Swarthmore Col, AB, 63; Cornell Univ, PhD(physics), 69. *Prof Exp:* Res asst physics, Princeton-Pa Accelerator, Princeton Univ, 68-70; adj asst prof, Univ Calif, Los Angeles, 70-75; ASST PROF PHYSICS, CATH UNIV AM, 75- *Mem:* Am Phys Soc. *Res:* Electromagnetic and weak interactions of elementary particles and nuclei; particle detectors; accelerators. *Mailing Add:* Dept of Physics Cath Univ Am Washington DC 20064

SOBERMAN, ROBERT K, b New York, NY, Apr 8, 30; m 54; c 2. ENVIRONMENTAL PHYSICS. *Educ:* City Col New York, BS, 50; NY Univ, MS, 52, PhD(physics), 56; Temple Univ, MBA, 72. *Prof Exp:* Res physicist, Vallecitos Atomic Lab, Gen Elec Co, 55-57; sr scientist res & advan develop div, Avco Corp, 57-59; assoc prof elec eng, Northeastern Univ, 59-60; chief meteor physics br, Air Force Cambridge Res Labs, 60-66; mgr environ progs, Gen Elec Space Sci Lab, 66-76; vpres progs, Univ City Sci Ctr, 76-78; DIR, PROCESS TECHNOL DEPT, FRANKLIN INST, 78- *Concurrent Pos:* Adj assoc prof, Northeastern Univ, 60-64; adj prof, Drexel Univ, 68-; mem, Post Apollo Sci Eval Comt, 65-; vchmn comn 22B, Int Astron Union; sect noctilucent cloud subcomn, Int Union Geod & Geophys & mem Cosmic Dust Panel, Comt Space Res, Int Coun Sci Unions; lectr astron, Univ Pa, 74- *Mem:* AAAS; Am Astron Soc; Am Geophys Union. *Res:* Micrometeoroid flux and composition; rocket sampling of noctilucent clouds and cosmic dust; artificial meteors; recoverable and nonrecoverable satellite studies of meteoroids. *Mailing Add:* Franklin Inst 20th & Ben Franklin Pkwy Philadelphia PA 19103

SOBERON, GUILLERMO, b Iguala, Mex, Dec 29, 25; m 52; c 6. BIOCHEMISTRY. *Educ:* Nat Univ Mex, BS, 41, MD, 49; Univ Wis, PhD(biochem), 56. *Hon Degrees:* DSc, Univ Wis, 76 & Univ Oviedo, 79. *Prof Exp:* Intern internal med, Nat Inst Nutrit, Mex, 50, resident, 51, head biochem dept, 56-58; prof biochem, Sch Med, 58-63, dir inst biomed res, 65-71, coordr sci, 71-73, rector, 73-81, PROF BIOCHEM, SCH CHEM, NAT UNIV MEX, 63-, HEALTH SECT COORDR, 81- *Honors & Awards:* Sourasky Sci Award, 69; Elizondo Sci Award, 74. *Mem:* Am Soc Biol Chemists; Mex Soc Biochem (1st pres, 57-59); Mex Soc Physiol Sci; Mex Acad Sci Res (pres, 66-67); Brit Biochem Soc. *Res:* Nitrogen intermediary metabolism, particularly ureotelism. *Mailing Add:* Nat Univ of Mex PO Box 70228 Mexico DF Mexico

SOBEY, ARTHUR EDWARD, JR, b Shawnee, Kans, May 28, 24; m 48; c 4. PHYSICS, MATHEMATICS. *Educ:* Univ Tex, BS, 49, MA, 51, PhD(physics), 58. *Prof Exp:* Res scientist, Defense Res Lab, Univ Tex, 50-58; eng specialist, Chance Vought Aircraft Co, Tex, 58-59; mem tech staff, 59-66, mgr marine sci progs, 66-68, mgr signal processing progs, 69-71, mgr antisubmarine warfare surveillance progs, Tex Instruments Inc, 72-73; prog mgr, Electronic Sci, 73-76, mgr electronics & optics res, 77-80, ENG PROJ MGR, VOUGHT CORP ADV TECHNOL CTR, INC, 80- *Res:* Underwater acoustics, including propagation and ambient noise; acoustic signal processing; space-time signal processing; infrared sensors and systems; electrooptic devices and subsystems; noise-cancelling microphones; atmospheric research. *Mailing Add:* 914 Northlake Dr Richardson TX 75080

SOBIESKI, JAMES FULTON, b Berlin, Wis, Mar 18, 40. CHEMISTRY. *Educ:* Univ Wis-Madison, BS, 61; Lawrence Univ, MS, 63, PhD(chem), 67. *Prof Exp:* SR RES CHEMIST, MICROFILM PROD LAB, 3M CO, ST PAUL, 68- *Mem:* Am Chem Soc; Soc Photog Sci & Eng. *Res:* Applications of photoconductors to imaging systems; imaging systems. *Mailing Add:* 225 Hickory St Mahtomedi MN 55115

SOBIESZCZANSKI-SOBIESKI, JAROSLAW, b Wilno, Poland, Mar 11, 34; nat US; m 58; c 2. APPLIED MECHANICS, OPTIMIZATION METHODS. *Educ:* Warsaw Tech Univ, dipl aeronaut, 55, MS, 57, Dr Tech Sci(theory of thin shells), 64. *Prof Exp:* Asst aeronaut struct, Warsaw Tech Univ, 55-57, sr asst, 57 & 60-64, adj prof, 64-66; designer cranes & steel struct, Design Off Heavy Mach, Poland, 58-59; res fel, Inst Aeronaut, Norweg Inst Technol, 66; from asst prof to assoc prof aerospace eng, Parks Col Aeronaut Tech, St Louis, 66-71; Nat Acad Sci sr res fel, 70-71, aerospace engr, 71-73, sr res scientist, Struct Div, 73-80, BR HEAD MULTIDISCIPLINARY ANAL & OPTIMIZATION & STRUCT DIR, LANGLEY RES CTR, NASA, 80- *Concurrent Pos:* Cert expert stress & vibration, Polish Eng Asn, 62-64; Norweg Govt fel, Inst Aeronaut, Norweg Inst Technol, 64-65; NASA res grant nonlinear struct anal, 68-70; consult, Polish Aviation Indust, 61-64; assoc prof lectr, George Washington Univ, 71-80, prof lectr, 80- *Honors & Awards:* Awards, Polish Soc Theoret & Appl Mech, 63-65. *Mem:* Assoc fel Am Inst Aeronaut & Astronaut; assoc fel Royal Aeronaut Soc. *Res:* Experimental and numerical stress analysis; development of finite element methods for analysis of nonlinear structures; development of automated methods for interdisciplinary systems analysis and design; optimization of structures. *Mailing Add:* 518 Elizabeth Lake Dr Hampton VA 23669

SOBIN, LESLIE HOWARD, b New York, NY, Feb 10, 34; m 62; c 1. PATHOLOGY. *Educ:* Union Col, NY, BS, 55; State Univ NY, MD, 59; Am Bd Path, dipl anat path, 64. *Prof Exp:* Res fel, Inst Cell Res, Karolinska Inst, Sweden, 58; asst path, Med Col, Cornell Univ, 60-62, from instr to asst prof, 62-66; prof, WHO, 65-68; assoc prof, Med Col, Cornell Univ, 68-70; pathologist, WHO, 70-81; PATHOLOGIST, ARMED FORCES INST PATH, 81- *Concurrent Pos:* Vis prof, Fac Med, Kabul, Afghanistan, 65-68; mem, WHO Expert Adv Panel Cancer. *Mem:* Am Asn Path; Int Acad Path; fel Royal Col Pathologists. *Res:* Histological classification of tumors; geographical pathology. *Mailing Add:* Dept Gastrointestinal Path Armed Forces Inst Path Washington DC 20306

SOBIN, SIDNEY S, b Bayonne, NJ, Jan 1, 14; m 43; c 2. PHYSIOLOGY. *Educ:* Univ Mich, BS, 35, MA, 36, PhD(physiol), 38, MD, 41. *Prof Exp:* Asst physiol, Univ Mich, 34-38; resident med, Barnes Hosp, St Louis, Mo, 42-44; Nat Res Coun fel physiol, Harvard Med Sch, 44-46; assoc, Univ Southern Calif, 47-56, dir cardiovasc lab, Childrens Hosp, 49-56; res prof med, Sch Med, Loma Linda Univ, 56-66; PROF PHYSIOL, SCH MED, UNIV SOUTHERN CALIF, 66- *Mem:* Microcirc Soc; Soc Exp Biol & Med; Am Physiol Soc. *Res:* Micro and peripheral circulation; hypertension. *Mailing Add:* Cardiovasc Res Lab 1200 N State St Box 1800 Los Angeles CA 90033

SOBKOWICZ, HANNA MARIA, b Warsaw, Poland, Jan 1, 31; m 72. NEUROLOGY. *Educ:* Med Acad, Warsaw, MD, 54, cert bd neurol, 59, PhD(med sci), 62. *Prof Exp:* From jr asst to sr asst neurol, Med Acad, Warsaw, 59-63; Nat Multiple Sclerosis Soc res fel tissue cult, Mt Sinai Hosp, 63-65; vis fel, Columbia Univ, 65-66; from asst prof to assoc prof, 66-79, PROF NEUROL, MED SCH, UNIV WIS-MADISON, 79- *Mem:* Soc Neurosci; Int Brain Res Orgn; Asn Res Otolaryngol. *Res:* Development of nervous system in culture; organ of Corti. *Mailing Add:* Dept of Neurol Univ of Wis Med Sch Madison WI 53706

SOBOCINSKI, PHILIP ZYGMUND, b Salem, Mass, Oct 29, 34; m 58; c 2. BIOCHEMISTRY, RADIATION BIOLOGY. *Educ:* Tufts Univ, BS, 56; City Univ New York, MA, 64; Univ Rochester, Sch Med, PhD(radiation biol), 70. *Prof Exp:* Chief, clin lab, US Army Hosp, 59-61; asst dir biochem, First US Army Area Med Lab, 61-62; chief biochem, SEATO Med Res Lab, Bangkok, 63-65 & Armed Forces Radiobiol Res Inst, 70-74; chief phys sci, US Army Med Res Inst Infectious Dis, 74-80, DIR RES PROGS, US ARMY MED RES & DEVELOP COMMAND, 80- *Concurrent Pos:* Consult biochem to USA Surg Gen, 81- *Mem:* Sigma Xi; Soc Exp Biol & Med; Asn Mil Surgeons US; NY Acad Sci. *Res:* Biological effects of ionizing radiation; host metabolic responses to infectious diseases; trace metal metabolism; leukocyte physiology and function. *Mailing Add:* US Army Ft Detrick Med Res & Develop Command Frederick MD 21701

SOBOCZENSKI, EDWARD JOHN, b Exeter, NH, July 2, 29; m 53; c 2. INSECT TOXICOLOGY. *Educ:* Univ NH, BS, 52, MS, 54; Ohio State Univ, PhD(chem), 56. *Prof Exp:* Res chemist, 56-65, patent liason chem & law, 65-70, res biologist, 70, RES SUPVR INSECTICIDES, EXP STA, E I DU PONT DE NEMOURS & CO, 70- *Mem:* Am Chem Soc. *Res:* Discovery and development of agricultural chemicals; inventor of Venzar R herbicide sold for control of weeds in sugarbeets in Europe and Demosan R soil fungicide. *Mailing Add:* Exp Sta E I du Pont de Nemours & Co Wilmington DE 19898

SOBOL, BRUCE J, b June 10, 23; US citizen; m 51; c 2. MEDICINE, PHYSIOLOGY. *Educ:* Swarthmore Col, BS, 47; NY Univ, MD, 50; Am Bd Internal Med, dipl. *Prof Exp:* Intern med, Third Med Div, Bellevue Hosp, New York, 50-51, asst resident, 51-52; resident cardiol, Vet Admin Hosp, Boston, 52-53; dir, Cardiopulmonary Lab, Westchester County Med Ctr, 59-78; RES PROF MED, NY MED COL, 77-, DIR MED RES, 81-; DIR CLIN RES, BOEHRINGER INGELHEIM LTD, 78- *Concurrent Pos:* Prof med, New York Med Col, 70-77. *Mem:* Am Physiol Soc; fel Am Col Physicians; fel Am Col Chest Physicians; Am Heart Asn. *Res:* Cardiac and pulmonary physiology. *Mailing Add:* Boehringer Ingelheim Ltd PO Box 368 Ridgefield CT 06877

SOBOL, HAROLD, b Brooklyn, NY, June 21, 30; m 57; c 4. PHYSICAL ELECTRONICS, COMMUNICATIONS. *Educ:* City Col New York, BS, 52; Univ Mich, MSE, 55, PhD(elec eng), 60. *Prof Exp:* Res assoc radar, Willow Run Labs, Univ Mich, 52-55, res assoc phys electronics, Electron Physics Lab, 56-60; mem tech staff, Watson Res Ctr, Int Bus Mach Corp, 60-62; mem tech staff & group head, RCA Labs, 62-68, mgr microwave electronics, RCA Solid State Div, 68-70, mem, RCA Corp Res & Eng Staff, 70-72, group head, Commun Technol Res, RCA Labs, 72-73; DIR PROD DEVELOP, COLLINS TRANSMISSION SYSTS DIV, ROCKWELL INT, 73- *Concurrent Pos:* Nat lectr, Inst Elec & Electronics Engrs, 70. *Mem:* Am Physics Soc; fel Inst Elec & Electronics Engrs; Sigma Xi. *Res:* Radar propagation studies; electron devices; microwaves; superconductivity; plasmas; communications. *Mailing Add:* Rockwell Int PO Box 10462 Dallas TX 75207

SOBOL, STANLEY PAUL, b Boston, Mass, Oct 8, 37; m 63; c 2. FORENSIC SCIENCE, RESEARCH ADMINISTRATION. *Educ:* Tufts Univ, BS, 59. *Prof Exp:* Biochemist, Pharmacol Dept, Arthur D Little Inc, 59-61; from chemist to res coordr, US Food & Drug Admin, Boston Dist, 61-69; forensic chemist, Bur Narcotics & Dangerous Drugs, Lab Div, 69-70, chief chemist, 70-73; LAB DIR CHEM, DRUG ENFORCEMENT ADMIN, SPEC TESTING & RES LAB, 73- *Concurrent Pos:* Consult, UN Div Narcotics, 73-; mem forensic subcomt, Joint Comt on Powder Diffraction Stand & Org Subcomt, 75- *Honors & Awards:* Spec Achievement Award, Bur Narcotics & Dangerous Drugs, 73; Exceptional Serv Award, Drug Enforcement Admin, 75, Excellence of Performance Award, 77. *Mem:* Am Acad Forensic Sci; Int Asn Toxicologists; Am Mgt Asn; Soc Advan Mgt; Asn Off Anal Chemists. *Res:* Identification of trace contaminants in illicit drug preparations; computer assisted correlations of drug exhibits and establishment of data base. *Mailing Add:* 7704 Old Springhouse Rd McLean VA 22101

SOBOLEV, IGOR, b Zlin, Czech, July 31, 31; nat US; m 53; c 2. ORGANIC CHEMISTRY. *Educ:* State Univ NY Col Forestry, Syracuse, BS, 54, MS, 55, PhD(org chem), 58. *Prof Exp:* Res chemist, Olympic Res Div, Rayonier, Inc, Wash, 58-61; chemist, Shell Develop Co, 61-64, sr technologist, Indust Chem Div, Shell Chem Co, NY, 64-66, chemist, 66-67, res supvr, Shell Develop Co, Calif, 67-70; SECT HEAD, CHEM, KAISER ALUMINUM & CHEM CORP, 70- *Mem:* Am Chem Soc; Tech Asn Pulp & Paper Indust. *Res:* Chemical process and product research and development involving raw materials and intermediates in alumium production; reduction cell technology, organic polymers, fluorocarbons, atmospheric science, heterogeneous catalysis and flame retardants; fluorine chemistry. *Mailing Add:* Kaiser Aluminum & Chem Corp Ctr for Technol PO Box 870 Pleasanton CA 94566

SOBOTA, ANTHONY E, b Bradenville, Pa, May 29, 38; m 62; c 1. BACTERIOLOGY. *Educ:* Ind Univ Pa, BSEd, 60; Univ Pittsbur- gh, MS, 63, PhD(biol), 66. *Prof Exp:* NIH fel, Purdue Univ, 66-67; USDA grant, 67-68; assoc prof, 68-77, PROF BIOL SCI, YOUNGSTOWN STATE UNIV, 77- *Mem:* Am Inst Biol Sci; Am Soc Microbiologists. *Res:* Importance of adherence in urinary tract infections. *Mailing Add:* Dept Biol Sci Youngstown State Univ Youngstown OH 44555

SOBOTKA, THOMAS JOSEPH, b Baltimore, Md, Aug 16, 42; m 64; c 2. NEUROBEHAVIORAL TOXICOLOGY, BEHAVIORAL TERATOLOGY. *Educ:* Loyola Col, BS, 64; Loyola Stritch Sch Med, MS, 67, PhD(pharmacol), 69. *Prof Exp:* Res pharmacologist, 69-78, actg chief, Whole Animal Toxicol Br, 81, SUPVRY PHARMACOLOGIST, FOOD & DRUG ADMIN, 78- *Concurrent Pos:* Mem organizing comt, Conf Nutrit & Behav, Franklin Res Found, 79-80; exec secy, Interagency Collab Group Hyperkinesis, Dept Health & Human Serv, 81- *Mem:* Am Soc Pharmacol & Exp Therapeut; Soc Neurosci; Behav Pharmacol Soc; Neurobehav Toxicol Soc. *Res:* Neurobehavioral methodology which may be used in the safety evaluation of chemicals found in foods; effects of chemicals on the developing nervous system. *Mailing Add:* Neurobehav Toxicol Team/HFF-162 Bur Foods/Food & Drug Admin Washington DC 20204

SOBOTTKA, STANLEY EARL, b Plum City, Wis, Dec 20, 30. PHYSICS. *Educ:* Univ Wis, BS, 55; Stanford Univ, MS, 57, PhD(physics), 60. *Prof Exp:* Mem tech staff, Sci Res Labs, Boeing Airplane Co, 59-60 & Watkins-Johnson Co, 60-63; assoc prof, 64-71, PROF PHYSICS, UNIV VA, 71- *Mem:* Am Phys Soc. *Res:* High energy electron scattering; electron beam-plasma interactions; lasers; pion and muon interactions with nuclei; nuclear particle detectors; x-ray diffraction. *Mailing Add:* Dept of Physics Univ of Va Charlottesville VA 22901

SOBSEY, MARK DAVID, b Lakewood, NJ, Sept 5, 43; m 65; c 2. MICROBIOLOGY, ENVIRONMENTAL HEALTH. *Educ:* Univ Pittsburgh, BS, 65, MS, 67; Univ Calif, Berkeley, PhD(environ health sci), 71. *Prof Exp:* Fel, Baylor Col Med, 71-72, from instr to asst prof, 72-74; ASST PROF ENVIRON MICROBIOL, SCH PUB HEALTH, UNIV NC, CHAPEL HILL, 74- *Mem:* Am Pub Health Asn; Am Soc Microbiol; Water Pollution Control Fedn; AAAS. *Res:* Environmental microbiology; public health aspects of water pollution; environmental virology. *Mailing Add:* Dept Environ Sci & Eng Univ NC Sch Pub Health Chapel Hill NC 27514

SOCHA, WLADYSLAW WOJCIECH, b Paris, France, July 3, 26; m 56. IMMUNOLOGY, PATHOLOGY. *Educ:* Jagiellonian Univ, MD, 52; Cracow Acad Med, Poland, DMedS(genetics), 59. *Prof Exp:* Assoc path, Inst Oncol, Warsaw, Gliwice & Cracow, 52-61; asst prof forensic med, Cracow Acad Med, Poland, 55-64, dir inst pediat, 65-68; RES PROF FORENSIC MED, LAB EXP MED & SURG PRIMATES, SCH MED, NY UNIV, 69-; assoc dir, 77-80, DIR, PRIMATE BLOOD GROUP REF LAB & WHO COLLAB CTR HAEMATOL PRIMATE ANIMALS, 80- *Concurrent Pos:* Fr Asn Study Cancer fel, Regional Anticancer Ctr, Univ Montpellier, 59-60; US AID fel, 66; Fr Nat Inst Med Res fel, Ctr Hemotypology, Nat Ctr Sci Res, Toulouse, France, 71; mem comt human genetics, Polish Acad Sci, 65-68; vis scientist, Nat Inst Health & Med Res, Toulouse, France, 72; assoc ed, J Med

Primatol, 73-77, ed, 77-; mem rev bd, J Human Evolution, 78- *Honors & Awards:* Polish Med Asn Award, 60; Polish Surg Asn Award, 60; Polish Acad Sci Award, 66. *Res:* Blood and serum groups; comparative serology; seroprimatology; population genetics; pathology of tumors; pathology of nonhuman primates; forensic pathology and serology. *Mailing Add:* Dept Forensic Med NY Univ Med Ctr New York NY 10016

SOCHER, SUSAN HELEN, b Chicago, Ill, June 19, 44. CELL BIOLOGY. *Educ:* Mt Mary Col, BS, 66; Case Western Reserve Univ, PhD(cell biol), 70. *Prof Exp:* Univ res fel & NIH trainee, Sch Med, Vanderbilt Univ, 70-72, res assoc cell biol, 72; ASST PROF CELL BIOL, BAYLOR COL MED, 72- *Mem:* AAAS; Am Soc Cell Biol; Develop Biol Soc. *Res:* Hormonal regulation of gene expression during mammary gland development and in mammary cancer; chromatin biochemistry. *Mailing Add:* Dept of Cell Biol Baylor Col of Med Houston TX 77030

SOCOLAR, SIDNEY JOSEPH, b Baltimore, Md, Feb 10, 24; m 51; c 2. MEMBRANE PHYSIOLOGY, BIOPHYSICS. *Educ:* Johns Hopkins Univ, AB, 43, AM, 44, PhD(chem), 45. *Prof Exp:* Jr instr chem, Johns Hopkins Univ, 43-44, res chemist, 44-46; instr chem, Univ Ill, 47-48; from instr to asst prof phys sci, Univ Chicago, 50-57; math physicist, Heat & Mass Flow Analyzer Lab, Columbia Univ, 57-59, res assoc physiol, Col Physicians & Surgeons, 59-69, asst prof, 69-71; asst prof physiol & biophys, 71-72, ASSOC PROF PHYSIOL & BIOPHYS, SCH MED, UNIV MIAMI, 72- *Concurrent Pos:* Phillips fel, Pa State Col, 46-47. *Mem:* AAAS; Biophys Soc. *Res:* Cell-to-cell membrane channels: Assembly kinetics, permeability and permeability regulation; electrophysiology; membrane physiology. *Mailing Add:* Univ of Miami Sch of Med PO Box 016430 Miami FL 33101

SOCOLOFSKY, JOHN FREDERICK, chemistry, see previous edition

SOCOLOFSKY, MARION DAVID, b Marion, Kans, Sept 23, 31; m 53; c 2. MICROBIOLOGY. *Educ:* Kans State Univ, BS, 53; Univ Tex, MA, 55, PhD(bact), 61. *Prof Exp:* From asst prof to assoc prof, 61-68, PROF BACT, LA STATE UNIV, BATON ROUGE, 68-, CHMN DEPT, 66- *Mem:* AAAS; Am Soc Microbiol; Electron Micros Soc Am; Brit Soc Gen Microbiol. *Res:* Electron microscopy; bacterial ultrastructure. *Mailing Add:* Dept of Microbiol La State Univ Baton Rouge LA 70803

SOCOLOW, ARTHUR A, b New York, NY, Mar 23, 21; m 49; c 3. ECONOMIC GEOLOGY. *Educ:* Rutgers Univ, BS, 42; Columbia Univ, MA, 47, PhD(econ geol), 55. *Prof Exp:* Asst field geologist, State Geol Surv, Va, 42; photogram engr, US Geol Surv, 42 & 46, geologist, 52 & Eagle Picher Mex, 47; asst econ geol, Columbia Univ, 47-48; instr geol & dir geol field camp in Colo, Southern Methodist Univ, 48-50; from instr to asst prof geol, Boston Univ, 50-55; from asst prof to prof geol, Univ Mass, 55-57; econ geologist, 57-61, STATE GEOLOGIST & DIR, PA GEOL SURV, 61- *Concurrent Pos:* Geologist, Defense Minerals Explor Authority, 52; geol adv, Boston Mus Sci, 55-57; lectr, 56; lectr, Pa State Univ, 59-73; mem, NSF Earth Sci Conf, 59; dir annual field conf Pa Geol, 61-; gov rep & past chmn, Res Comt & Environ Protection Comt, Interstate Oil Compact Comn, 72-; mem & past chmn, Am Comn Stratig Nomenclature; chmn, Pa Water Resources Coord Comt. *Mem:* AAAS; fel Mineral Soc Am; Am Geophys Union; Sigma Xi; Nat Asn Geol Teachers. *Res:* Genesis and structural control of ore deposits; regional structure interpretation; alteration effects related to igneous rocks and ore deposits; geologic interpretation of aeromagnetic data; geologic impact on man's environment. *Mailing Add:* 420 Larry Dr Harrisburg PA 17109

SOCOLOW, ROBERT H(ARRY), b New York, NY, Dec 27, 37; m 62; c 2. ENERGY POLICY, ENVIRONMENTAL SCIENCES. *Educ:* Harvard Univ, BA, 59, MA, 61, PhD(physics), 64. *Prof Exp:* Asst prof physics, Yale Univ, 66-71; jr fac fel, 70-71; assoc prof environ sci, 71-77, PROF ENVIRON SCI, PRINCETON UNIV, 77-, DIR, CTR ENVIRON STUDIES, 78- *Concurrent Pos:* NSF fel, 64-66; mem, Inst Advan Studies, 71; Guggenheim & Ger Marshall Fund fels, Energy Res Group, Cavendish Lab, Univ Cambridge, 77-78. *Mem:* Am Phys Soc; Fedn Am Sci. *Res:* Energy utilization; regional and global constraints on growth. *Mailing Add:* Ctr for Environ Studies Princeton Univ Princeton NJ 08540

SODANO, CHARLES STANLEY, b Newark, NJ, Nov 13, 39; c 5. NATURAL PRODUCTS CHEMISTRY. *Educ:* Seton Hall Univ, BS, 61, MS, 63; Ariz State Univ, PhD(org chem), 67. *Prof Exp:* Res chemist cancer res, Pfizer Inc, 66-69; res chemist, 69-75, MGR ANAL SYSTS RES, NABISCO BRANDS INC, 75- *Mem:* Am Chem Soc. *Res:* Structure elucidation of anti-tumor agents; fabricated foods development; catalytic hydrogenation; development of new analytical methods for food analysis; process control. *Mailing Add:* Nabisco Inc 2111 Rte 208 Fair Lawn NJ 07410

SODD, VINCENT J, b Toledo, Ohio, Nov 20, 34; m 56; c 4. NUCLEAR CHEMISTRY, NUCLEAR MEDICINE. *Educ:* Xavier Univ, Ohio, BS, 56, MS, 58; Univ Pittsburgh, PhD(nuclear chem), 64. *Prof Exp:* Asst chem, Xavier Univ, Ohio, 56-58; res chemist, Robert A Taft Sanit Eng Ctr, 58-60, nuclear chemist, 64-66, dep chief nuclear med lab, 66-71, CHIEF NUCLEAR MED LAB & CHIEF RADIOPHARMACEUT DEVELOP SECT, USPHS, 71- *Concurrent Pos:* Asst clin prof, Col Med, Univ Cincinnati, 68-74, assoc prof, 74-77, prof, 77- *Mem:* Sigma Xi; Am Chem Soc. *Res:* Nuclear medicine investigations involving clinic practice, radiation exposure reduction, dosimetry and instrumentation development; radiopharmaceutical production; cyclotron and linear accelerator research; activation analysis; semiconductor theory and use; development of analytical procedures for radionuclides regarded as being hazardous to our environment. *Mailing Add:* 5987 Turpin Hills Dr Cincinnati OH 45244

SODERBERG, C(ARL) RICHARD, engineering, deceased

SODERBERG, ROGER HAMILTON, b Congress Park, Ill, June 19, 36; m 59; c 2. INORGANIC CHEMISTRY. *Educ:* Grinnell Col, AB, 58; Mass Inst Technol, PhD(coord chem), 63. *Prof Exp:* From instr to assoc prof, 62-75, PROF CHEM, DARTMOUTH COL, 75- *Mem:* Am Chem Soc; AAAS. *Res:* Inorganic chemistry of transition metals. *Mailing Add:* Dept of Chem Dartmouth Col Hanover NH 03755

SODERBLOM, LAURENCE ALBERT, b Denver, Colo, July 17, 44; m 68; c 3. PLANETARY GEOLOGY. *Educ:* NMex Inst Mining & Technol, BS(geol) & BS(physics), 66; Calif Inst Technol, PhD(planetary sci & geophysics), 70. *Prof Exp:* Geophysicist, 70-78, SUPVR PHYS SCIENTIST, US GEOL SURV, 78- *Concurrent Pos:* Assoc ed, J Geophys Res, 71-73; dep team leader, Voyager Imaging Sci Team, NASA, 72-, Comt Lunar & Planetary Explor, Space Sci Bd, 73-77, Viking Orbiter Imaging Team, 76-78, Galileo Near Infrared Mapping Spectrometer Team, 77- & Space Sci Adv Comt, 80- *Mem:* Am Geophys Union. *Res:* Global geologic histories of planets and satellites of the solar system employing earth-based and spacecraft remote-sensing data; established timescales for planetary evolution; computerized image processing. *Mailing Add:* US Geol Surv 2255 N Gemini Dr Flagstaff AZ 86001

SODERHOLM, SIDNEY CASE, b Auburn, NY, Oct 11, 49; m 72; c 2. AEROSOL SCIENCE, INHALATION TOXICOLOGY. *Educ:* Clarkson Col Technol, BS, 71; Univ Rochester, MA, 73, PhD(physics), 79. *Prof Exp:* assoc sr res scientist, 77-80, SR RES SCIENTIST BIOMED SCI, GEN MOTORS RES LABS, 80- *Res:* Aerosol science; inhalation toxicology. *Mailing Add:* Dept of Biomed Sci Gen Motors Res Labs Warren MI 48090

SODERLING, THOMAS RICHARD, b Bonners Ferry, Idaho, May 25, 44; m 65; c 2. PHYSIOLOGY, BIOCHEMISTRY. *Educ:* Univ Idaho, BS, 66; Univ Wash, PhD(biochem), 70. *Prof Exp:* NIH fel, Vanderbilt Univ, 71-72, Am Diabetes Asn fel, 72-73, asst prof physiol, 73-78, ASSOC PROF PHYSIOL, MED SCH, VANDERBILT UNIV, 78- *Concurrent Pos:* Investr, Howard Hughes Med Inst, 76- *Honors & Awards:* Andrew Mellon Found Scientist-Educr Award, 74. *Mem:* Am Soc Biol Chemists. *Res:* Regulation of glycogen metabolism; mechanism of action of insulin. *Mailing Add:* Dept Physiol Vanderbilt Univ Nashville TN 37203

SODERLUND, DAVID MATTHEW, b Oakland, Calif, Oct 1, 50; m 72. ENTOMOLOGY, BIOCHEMICAL TOXICOLOGY. *Educ:* Pac Lutheran Univ, BS, 71; Univ Calif, Berkeley, PhD(entomol), 76. *Prof Exp:* Vis res fel, insecticide biochem, Rothamsted Exp Sta, Harpenden, Eng, 76-77; ASST PROF, DEPT ENTOMOL, NY STATE AGR EXP STA, CORNELL UNIV, 78- *Concurrent Pos:* Rockefeller Found fel, 76-77; consult, Crop Chem Res & Develop, Mobil Chem Co, 78-81. *Mem:* Am Chem Soc; Entomol Soc Am. *Res:* Biochemical and physiological interactions of insecticide chemicals and insect growth regulators in insects and mammals. *Mailing Add:* Dept of Entomol NY State Agr Exp Sta Geneva NY 14456

SODERMAN, J WILLIAM, b Helsinki, Finland, Oct 31, 35; US citizen; m 56; c 3. GEOLOGY. *Educ:* Columbia Univ, BA, 57; Univ Ill, MS, 60, PhD(geol), 62. *Prof Exp:* Geologist, Texaco Inc, 62-72, supvr geol res, 72-74, asst div geologist, 74-78; chief geologist, 78-79, DIR DOMESTIC EXPLOR, MONSANTO OIL & GAS, 79- *Mem:* Geol Soc Am; Am Asn Petrol Geol; Soc Econ Paleont & Mineral. *Res:* Geology of sedimentary rocks. *Mailing Add:* Rte 1 Box 239-A Wallis TX 77485

SODERQUIST, DAVID RICHARD, b Idaho Falls, Idaho, June 26, 36; m 62; c 3. PSYCHOACOUSTICS. *Educ:* Utah State Univ, BS, 61, MS, 63; Vanderbilt Univ, PhD(psychol), 68. *Prof Exp:* Sr human factors specialist, Syst Develop Corp, 63-65; asst prof, 68-72, ASSOC PROF PSYCHOL, UNIV NC, GREENSBORO, 72- *Mem:* Acoust Soc Am; Soc Neurosci. *Res:* Psychological acoustics; signal detection; pitch perception and temporal masking. *Mailing Add:* Dept of Psychol Univ of NC Greensboro NC 27412

SODERSTROM, EDWIN LOREN, b Riverside, Calif, Feb 8, 31; m 60; c 3. ENTOMOLOGY. *Educ:* Calif State Polytech Col, BS, 57; Kans State Univ, MS, 59, PhD(entom), 62. *Prof Exp:* Asst res entom, Kans State Univ, 61-62; RES ENTOMOLOGIST, AGR RES SERV, USDA, 62- *Mem:* Entom Soc Am. *Res:* Entomological research on geographical populations of rice weevils; response of stored product insects to light; effects of pesticides on populations of dried fruit and tree nut insects; controlled atmosphere fumigation; insect attractants and repellents. *Mailing Add:* Stored Prod Insects Lab USDA 5578 Air Terminal Dr Fresno CA 93727

SODERSTROM, KENNETH G(UNNAR), b Red Bank, NJ, Apr 21, 36; m 62; c 2. MECHANICAL ENGINEERING, SOLAR ENERGY. *Educ:* Univ Fla, BME, 58, MSE, 59, PhD(mech eng), 72. *Prof Exp:* From asst prof to assoc prof mech eng, 61-76, chmn dept, 63-68, PROF MECH ENG, DEPT MECH ENG, UNIV PR, MAYAGUEZ, 76-, SR SCIENTIST, CTR ENERGY & ENVIRON RES, 73-, ASSOC DIR, 79- *Concurrent Pos:* Res assoc, PR Nuclear Ctr, Univ PR, 62- *Mem:* Int Solar Energy Soc; Am Soc Mech Engrs. *Res:* Nuclear engineering in fields of irradiation effects on emissivity of materials and convection heat transfer; solar energy, particularly experimental and analytical system studies; solar data measurements and modeling. *Mailing Add:* Dept Mech Eng Univ PR Mayaguez PR 00708

SODERWALL, ARNOLD LARSON, b Portland, Ore, Nov 13, 14; m 38; c 2. ENDOCRINOLOGY. *Educ:* Linfield Col, AB, 36; Univ Ill, AM, 38; Brown Univ, PhD(endocrinol), 41. *Prof Exp:* Asst zool, Univ Ill, 36-38; from instr to assoc prof zool, Univ Ore, 41-61, prof, 61-77, prof biol, 77-80; RETIRED. *Concurrent Pos:* AEC fel; vis prof, Cornell Univ, 54-55 & 65-66 & Univ Hawaii Sch Med, 72-73. *Mem:* Soc Study Reproduction; Am Asn Anat. *Res:* Gerontological studies related to reproductive capacities in rodents; x-irradiation effects on simulated aging; electrophoretic studies of blood gonadotropins; nature of litter size loss in senescent hamsters; preimplantation death in older females; induction of decidual cell response by air injections in young and senescent female hamsters. *Mailing Add:* 2943 Harris Eugene OR 97405

SODICKSON, LESTER A, b New York, NY, Oct 23, 37; m 63; c 3. PHYSICS, BIOMEDICAL ENGINEERING. *Educ:* Mass Inst Technol, BS, 58, PhD(physics), 63. *Prof Exp:* Sr scientist & dir new prod, Am Sci & Eng Inc, 63-70, pres, Biotech Diag, 70-71; prog mgr, 71-72, vpres, Res & Eng Div, 72-74, VPRES RES & DEVELOP, IEC DIV, DAMON CORP, 75- *Mem:* AAAS; Am Phys Soc. *Res:* Electromagnetic sensing of molecular species for clinical chemistry; environmental pollution; infrared and optical physics; computer science. *Mailing Add:* 263 Waban Ave Waban MA 02168

SODICOFF, MARVIN, b Brooklyn, NY, June 12, 37; m 60; c 3. ANATOMY. *Educ:* Brooklyn Col, BS, 59; Univ Cincinnati, PhD(anat), 66. *Prof Exp:* From instr to asst prof, 66-74, ASSOC PROF ANAT, MED SCH, TEMPLE UNIV, 74- *Mem:* AAAS; Reticuloendothelial Soc; Am Asn Anatomists. *Res:* Experimental hematology; radiation biology; oral biology; electron microscopy. *Mailing Add:* Dept of Anat Temple Univ Med Sch Philadelphia PA 19140

SOECHTING, JOHN F, b Sept 27, 43; US citizen. NEUROPHYSIOLOGY. *Educ:* Lehigh Univ, BS, 65; Cornell Univ, PhD(mech), 69. *Prof Exp:* Res assoc biomech, Brown Univ, 69-72; assoc, 72-74, lectr, 74-75, asst prof, 75-79, ASSOC PROF NEUROPHYSIOL, UNIV MINN, MINNEAPOLIS, 79- *Concurrent Pos:* NIH spec fel, 75-76. *Mem:* Soc Neurosci; Sigma Xi. *Res:* Motor control. *Mailing Add:* Dept of Physiol Univ of Minn Minneapolis MN 55455

SOEDEL, WERNER, b Prague, Czech, Apr 24, 36; US citizen; m 61; c 4. MECHANICS, ENGINEERING MECHANICS. *Educ:* Frankfurt State Inst Eng, Ing Grad, 57; Purdue Univ, MSME, 65, PhD(mech eng), 67. *Prof Exp:* Proj engr mech eng, Adam Opel AG, 57-63; from asst prof to assoc prof, 67-75, PROF MECH ENG, PURDUE UNIV, 75- *Mem:* Soc Exp Stress Analysis; Am Soc Mech Engrs; Am Acoustical Soc. *Res:* Vibrations of shell structures; dynamic interactions of solids and fluids; gas dynamics; acoustics; hydrodynamics; probability. *Mailing Add:* Ray W Herrick Labs Purdue Univ West Lafayette IN 47407

SOEDER, ROBERT W, b Philadelphia, Pa, Oct 5, 35; m 59. ORGANIC CHEMISTRY. *Educ:* Ursinus Col, BS, 57; Univ Del, MS, 59, PhD(org chem), 62. *Prof Exp:* Fel org chem, Univ Minn, 61-62; from asst prof to assoc prof, Wilkes Col, 62-67; assoc prof, 67-72, PROF CHEM, APPALACHIAN STATE UNIV, 72- *Res:* Synthesis and reactions of heterocyclic compounds; reactions of B-diketones; chemical constituents of ferns. *Mailing Add:* Dept of Chem Appalachian State Univ Boone NC 28608

SOEIRO, RUY, b Boston, Mass, May 28, 32; m 66. INFECTIOUS DISEASES, CELL BIOLOGY. *Educ:* Harvard Univ, AB, 54; Tufts Univ, MD, 58. *Prof Exp:* From instr biochem to asst prof med, 67-73, assoc prof med & cell biol, 73-76, assoc prof immunol, 73-78, PROF MED & IMMUNOL, ALBERT EINSTEIN COL MED, 78-, CO-DIR DIV INFECTIOUS DIS, 73- *Concurrent Pos:* USPHS trainee bact, Harvard Med Sch, 62-65; USPHS spec fel biochem, Albert Einstein Col Med, 66-67; City New York career res scientist award, 68-73. *Mailing Add:* Dept of Med Albert Einstein Col of Med Bronx NY 10461

SOERENS, DAVE ALLEN, b Sheboygan, Wis, Aug 26, 52; m 72; c 2. PRESSURE-SENSITIVE ADHESIVES, NONWOVENS. *Educ:* Calvin Col, BS, 74; Univ Wis-Milwaukee, PhD(chem), 78. *Prof Exp:* SR RES CHEMIST, 3M CO, 78- *Mem:* Am Chem Soc; NAm Thermal Anal Soc. *Res:* Adhesives research and development; thermal analysis; nonwovens. *Mailing Add:* 3975 Lakewood Ave White Bear Lake MN 55110

SOERGEL, KONRAD H, b Coburg, Ger, July 27, 29; US citizen; m 55; c 4. INTERNAL MEDICINE, GASTROENTEROLOGY. *Educ:* Univ Erlangen, MD, 54, DrMedSci, 57. *Prof Exp:* Res fel gastroenterol, Sch Med, Boston Univ, 58-60; instr med, 60-61; from asst prof to assoc prof, 61-69, PROF MED, MED COL WIS, 69-, CHIEF DEPT GASTROENTEROL, 61- *Concurrent Pos:* Consult gastroenterologist, Wood Vet Admin Hosp, 67; consult, Vet Admin Res Serv Rev Bd, 69-71 & 72-74; mem gen med A study sect, NIH, 76-80. *Mem:* Am Fedn Clin Res; Am Gastroenterol Asn; Am Soc Clin Invest. *Res:* Absorption of water, electrolyte and sugar from the human small intestine. *Mailing Add:* Milwaukee County Gen Hosp 8700 W Wisconsin Ave Milwaukee WI 53226

SOFER, SAMIR SALIM, b Teheran, Iran, Oct 10, 45. CHEMICAL ENGINEERING. *Educ:* Univ Utah, BS, 69; Tex A&M Univ, ME, 71; Univ Tex, PhD(chem eng), 74. *Prof Exp:* Process design engr, Celanese Chem Co, 69-72; res assoc, Univ Tex, 73-74; from asst prof to assoc prof, 74-80, PROF CHEM ENG, UNIV OKLA, 80-, DIR, SCH CHEM ENG & MAT SCI, 75- *Concurrent Pos:* Fel, Clayton Found Biochem Inst, 74-75. *Honors & Awards:* First place, SCORE (Student Contest on Relevant Eng), 75. *Mem:* Am Inst Chem Engrs; AAAS; Am Soc Eng Educ. *Res:* Insolubilized enzyme technology and biochemical reactor design; reaction kinetics; process design. *Mailing Add:* Sch of Chem Eng & Mat Sci Univ of Okla Norman OK 73019

SOFER, WILLIAM HOWARD, b Brooklyn, NY, Jan 14, 41; m 64; c 2. MOLECULAR GENETICS. *Educ:* Brooklyn Col, BS, 61; Univ Miami, PhD(cell physiol), 67. *Prof Exp:* NIH fel, Johns Hopkins Univ, 67-69, NSF fel, 69-71; asst prof biol, 69-75, assoc prof, 75-80; MEM FAC, WAKSMAN INST MICROBIOL, RUGTERS STATE UNIV, 80- *Concurrent Pos:* NIH grant, 71-; Nat Inst Environ Health Sci grant, 77-; Dept of Energy contract, 76- *Mem:* AAAS; Genetics Soc Am. *Res:* Regulation of the activity of alcohol dehydrogenase in Drosophila; mechanisms of mutagenesis; aging. *Mailing Add:* Waksman Inst Microbiol Rutgers Univ Piscataway NJ 08854

SOFFEN, GERALD A(LAN), b Cleveland, Ohio, Feb 7, 26; m 79. BIOLOGY. *Educ:* Univ Calif, Los Angeles, BA, 49; Univ Southern Calif, MS, 56; Princeton Univ, PhD(biol), 60. *Prof Exp:* USPHS fel biol, Sch Med, NY Univ, 60-61; sr space scientist, Jet Propulsion Lab, Calif Inst Technol, 61-69; proj scientist, Viking, Langley Res Ctr, 69-78, DIR LIFE SCI, HQ, NASA,

78- *Mem:* AAAS. *Res:* Physiology; biochemistry; growth, metabolism and physiology of the cell; effects of ultraviolet light; transport mechanisms; exobiology; muscle biochemistry; science administration. *Mailing Add:* 617 4th Place SW Washington DC 20024

SOFFER, ALFRED, b South Bend, Ind, May 5, 22; m 56; c 3. MEDICINE. *Educ:* Univ Wis, BA, 42, MD, 45; Am Bd Internal Med, dipl. *Prof Exp:* Electrocardiographer, Genesee Hosp, NY, 51-58; dir cardiopulmonary lab, Rochester Gen Hosp, 59-62; assoc med, Northwestern Univ, 63-64; clin asst prof, 64-65, assoc prof, 65-68, PROF MED, CHICAGO MED SCH/UNIV HEALTH SCI, 68- *Concurrent Pos:* Sr ed jour, AMA, 62-67; ed-in-chief, Dis of the Chest, 68-; exec dir, Am Col Chest Physicians, 69-; consult on med jours to secy, Dept Health, Educ & Welfare, DC, 71-; ed, Heart & Lung, J Total Care, 72. *Mem:* Fel Am Col Physicians; fel Am Col Chest Physicians; fel Am Col Cardiol; fel Am Med Writers' Asn; Am Fedn Clin Res. *Res:* Medical administration; cardiology. *Mailing Add:* 911 Busse Hwy Park Ridge IL 60068

SOFFER, BERNARD HAROLD, b Brooklyn, NY, Mar 2, 31; m 56; c 1. PHYSICS. *Educ:* Brooklyn Col, BS, 53; Mass Inst Technol, MS, 58. *Prof Exp:* Staff mem, Lab Insulation Res, Mass Inst Technol, 58-59; res physicist, Hughes Res Lab, Calif, 59-61; res physicist, Appl Physics Lab, Quantatron Inc, 61-62, sr scientist, Optical Physics Div, Korad Corp, Union Carbide Corp, Calif, 62-69; mem tech staff, 69-80, SR STAFF PHYSICIST, HUGHES RES LABS, 80- *Mem:* Am Phys Soc; Optical Soc Am; sr mem Inst Elec & Electronics Eng; fel Optical Soc Am. *Res:* Optical, infrared and spin resonance spectroscopy of solids; laser physics and laser materials; optical physics; image and information processing. *Mailing Add:* 665 Bienveneda Ave Pacific Palisades CA 90272

SOFFER, IRVING HERBERT, b Brooklyn, NY, Dec 11, 26; m 52; c 2. PHYSICAL CHEMISTRY. *Educ:* Brooklyn Col, BS, 48; Purdue Univ, MS, 50, PhD(phys chem), 52. *Prof Exp:* Asst, Purdue Univ, 48-51; res chemist, Textile Fibers Dept, E I du Pont de Nemours & Co, 52-54; develop chemist, 54-78, GROUP LEADER, DYES TECH, AM CYANAMID CO, 78- *Mem:* Am Chem Soc. *Res:* Dipole moments and structure of organosilicon compounds; dielectric constants of adsorbed vapors; thermometric standards; fiber and fabric properties; pigment dispersions; dyes; physical properties of surfactants; crystal structure; particle size reduction. *Mailing Add:* Am Cyanamid Co Bound Brook NJ 08805

SOFFER, MILTON DAVID, b New York, NY, Dec 11, 14; m 45; c 3. SYNTHETIC ORGANIC CHEMISTRY, NATURAL PRODUCTS CHEMISTRY. *Educ:* Univ Ark, BS, 37; Harvard Univ, AM, 39, PhD(org chem), 42. *Prof Exp:* Indust chemist, Wm R Rogers, Inc, NY, 37; from instr to prof, 42-70, SOPHIA SMITH PROF CHEM, SMITH COL, 70- *Concurrent Pos:* Res grant, Res Corp, 45-52; Guggenheim fel, Oxford Univ, 50-51; NSF grant, 52-; NSF sr fel, Harvard Univ, 58-59; vis prof, Univ Mass, 62 & Hollins Col, 63; consult, Tex Co, 43-47. *Mem:* AAAS; Am Chem Soc; NY Acad Sci; Sigma Xi. *Res:* Synthetic and structural investigations of natural products; terpenes and alkaloids; porphyrins and chlorins; synthesis of high molecular weight and cyclic compounds. *Mailing Add:* Dept of Chem Smith Col Northampton MA 01063

SOFFER, RICHARD LUBER, b Baltimore, Md, Oct 1, 32; m 68; c 2. BIOCHEMISTRY. *Educ:* Amherst Col, BA, 54; Harvard Univ, MD, 58. *Prof Exp:* Asst resident med, Sch Med, NY Univ, 61-62, resident, 64-65; fel biochem, Pasteur Inst, Paris, 62-64; asst mem enzymol, Inst Muscle Dis, New York, 65-67; from asst prof to assoc prof molecular biol, Albert Einstein Col Med, 72-76; PROF MED & BIOCHEM, MED COL, CORNELL UNIV, 76- *Concurrent Pos:* Career develop award, Nat Inst Arthritis & Metab Dis, 68; fac res award, Am Cancer Soc, 73. *Mem:* Am Soc Biol Chemists. *Res:* Post-translational protein modification catalyzed by aminoacyl-t RNA-protein transferases; angiotensin-converting enzyme and regulation of vasoactive peptides; enzymes involved in the metabolism of thyroid hormones by target cells. *Mailing Add:* Dept of Biochem & Med Cornell Univ Med Col New York NY 10021

SOFIA, R DUANE, b Ellwood City, Pa, Oct 8, 42; m 65; c 4. PHARMACOLOGY. *Educ:* Geneva Col, BS, 64; Fairleigh-Dickinson Univ, MS, 69; Univ Pittsburgh, PhD(pharmacol), 71. *Prof Exp:* Res biologist, Lederle Labs, NY, 64-67; res assoc pharmacol, Union Carbide Corp, 67-69; sr pharmacologist, Pharmakon Labs, Pa, 69; sr res pharmacologist, 71-73, dir, Dept Pharmacol & Toxicol, 73-76, vpres biol res, 76-80, VPRES RES & DEVELOP, WALLACE LABS, CRANBURY, 80- *Concurrent Pos:* Consult, Pharmakon Labs, 69-71. *Mem:* Am Soc Pharmacol & Exp Therapeut; Soc Toxicol; Soc Neurosci; Int Soc Study Pain; Am Rheumatism Asn. *Res:* Pharmacology and toxicology of various constituents of marihuana; development of new drugs for inflammatory diseases and pain relief. *Mailing Add:* 11 Endwell Lane Willingboro NJ 08046

SOFIA, SABATINO, b Episcopia, Italy, May 14, 39; m 63; c 2. ASTROPHYSICS. *Educ:* Yale Univ, BS, 63, MS, 65, PhD(astrophys), 66. *Prof Exp:* Nat Acad Sci-Nat Res Coun res assoc astrophys, Goddard Inst Space Studies, NASA, 66-67; from assoc prof to prof astron, Univ SFla, 67-73; vis fel, Joint Inst Lab Astrophys, 73-74; sr res assoc, Univ Rochester, 74-75; staff scientist, Hq, 75-77, Nat Acad Sci-Nat Res Coun sr res assoc solar phys, 77-79, SPACE SCIENTIST, GODDARD SPACE FLIGHT CTR, NASA, 79- *Concurrent Pos:* Adj prof astron, Univ Fla, 75- *Mem:* Am Astron Soc; Int Astron Union; Am Geophys Union. *Res:* Solar physics, variability and evolution; stellar evolution; interstellar matter. *Mailing Add:* Goddard Space Flight Ctr Code 961 Greenbelt MD 20771

SOGAH, DOTSEVI YAO, b Ghana, West Africa, April, 19, 45; m 73; c 3. HOST-GUEST CHEMISTRY. *Educ:* Univ Ghana, BSc, 70, Hons, 71; Univ Calif, Los Angeles, MS, 74, PhD(chem), 75. *Prof Exp:* Fel chem, Univ Calif, Santa Barbara, 75-77; asst res chemist, Univ Calif, Los Angeles, 78-79, asst prof bio-org chem, 79-80; RES CHEMIST POLYMER CHEM, E I DU PONT DE NEMOURS & CO, INC, 81- *Mem:* Am Chem Soc; Ghana Sci Asn. *Res:* Synthesis and complexation of crown ethers; liquid-solid interface chemistry; chromatographic resolution of amino acids by immobilized crown ethers; kinetics and mechanisms of reaction of nitrogen heterocycles-acridines, flavins and flavoproteins; asymmetric inductions and catalysis of Michael addition reactions; synthesis of optically active polymers. *Mailing Add:* E I du Pont de Nemours & Co Inc Cent Res & Develop Dept Exp Sta Wilmington DE 19898

SOGANDARES-BERNAL, FRANKLIN, b Panama, CZ, May 12, 31; div; c 3. PARASITOLOGY. *Educ:* Tulane Univ, BS, 54; Univ Nebr, MS, 55, PhD(zool), 58. *Prof Exp:* Parasitologist, Marine Lab, State Bd Conserv, Fla, 58-59; from instr to prof zool, Tulane Univ, La, 59-71, mem grad fac, 61-71, exec officer biol, 62-65, univ coord sci planning, 65-67, dir lab parasitol, 67-71; prof zool & chmn dept, Univ Mont, 71-72, prof microbiol, 72-74; chmn dept, 74-77, PROF BIOL, SOUTHERN METHODIST UNIV, 74- *Concurrent Pos:* Guest investr, Lerner Marine Lab, Am Mus Natural Hist, 57 & 60; mem adv panel syst biol, Biomed Div, NSF, 63-66; mem bd sci adv, Saltwater Fish Div, Fla State Bd Conserv, 64-; consult in path, Dept Path, Baylor Univ Med Ctr, 75-, med staff affil, 77-; asst to dean, Div Continuing Educ, Univ Tex Health Sci Ctr, 77-80. *Honors & Awards:* Henry Baldwin Ward Medal, Am Soc Parasitol, 69. *Mem:* AAAS; Am Soc Zool; Am Soc Parasitol; Coun Biol Ed; Wildlife Dis Asn. *Res:* Evolutionary biology of parasitism immunopathology. *Mailing Add:* Dept Biol Southern Methodist Univ Dallas TX 75275

SOGIN, H(AROLD) H, b Chicago, Ill, Dec 14, 20; m 46; c 4. MECHANICAL ENGINEERING. *Educ:* Ill Inst Technol, BS, 43, MS, 50, PhD(mech eng), 52. *Prof Exp:* Asst prof mech eng, Ill Inst Technol, 53-55; from asst prof to assoc prof eng, Brown Univ, 55-60; PROF MECH ENG, TULANE UNIV, 60-, DEPT HEAD, 78- *Concurrent Pos:* Tulane Res Coun award, Inst Mech Statist Turbulence, Univ Marseille, 65-66; NSF res grants, 62-64, 69-71 & 72-75. *Mem:* Am Soc Mech Engrs; Sigma Xi. *Res:* Heat transfer; convection; thermal instability; measurements of thermal properties. *Mailing Add:* Dept Mech Eng Tulane Univ New Orleans LA 70118

SOGN, JOHN ALLEN, b Buffalo, NY, May 11, 46; m 69. IMMUNOLOGY, BIOCHEMISTRY. *Educ:* Brown Univ, AB, 68; Rockefeller Univ, PhD(biochem), 73. *Prof Exp:* Res assoc immunol & biochem, Rockefeller Univ, 73-76, asst prof, 76-77; sr staff fel, 77-78, RES CHEMIST, NAT INST ALLERGY & INFECTIOUS DIS, NIH, 78- *Mem:* Am Chem Soc; Harvey Soc; Am Asn Immunol; Sigma Xi. *Res:* Structural studies of immunologically relevant cell surface molecules from rabbits and humans; production of intraspecies and interspecies monoclonal antibodies as structural tools and genetic probes. *Mailing Add:* 9208 Cedarcrest Dr Bethesda MD 20814

SOGNEFEST, PETER WILLIAM, b Melrose Park, Ill, Feb 4, 41; m 64; c 3. GENERAL MANAGEMENT. *Educ:* Univ Ill, BSEE, 64, MS, 67. *Prof Exp:* Engr, Magnavox Co, 64-67; sr fel, Mellon Inst Sci, 67-71; gen mgr res & mfg, Essex Int Inc, 69-77; bus unit mgr, 77-80, VPRES & GEN MGR, MOTOROLA, INC, ILL, 80- *Concurrent Pos:* Vis fel, Mellon Inst Sci, 71- *Mem:* Inst Elec & Electronics Engrs. *Res:* Metal-Oxide-semiconductor integrated circuits as applied to automotive electrical systems; digital controls as applied to major appliances; microprocessor based instruments as applied to agriculture and construction equipment. *Mailing Add:* 4 Back Bay Rd Barrington IL 60010

SOGNNAES, REIDAR FAUSKE, b Bergen, Norway, Nov 6, 11; nat US; m 39; c 4. DENTISTRY, BIOLOGY. *Educ:* Univ Oslo, LDS, 36; Univ Rochester, PhD(path), 41; Harvard Univ, DMD, 51; Am Bd Forensic Odontol, dipl, 77. *Hon Degrees:* MA, Harvard Univ, 48; DrOdont, Univ Oslo, 61. *Prof Exp:* Dent investr, Norweg Sci Exped, Tristan da Cunha, 37-38; intern dent, Forsyth Dent Infirmary for Children, Boston, 38-39; from asst prof dent to assoc prof dent med, Sch Dent Med, Harvard Univ, 45-52, Charles A Brackett prof oral path & assoc dean sch, 52-60; dean sch dent, 60-69, PROF ORAL BIOL, SCH DENT, UNIV CALIF, LOS ANGELES, 60-, PROF ANAT, SCH MED, 63- *Concurrent Pos:* Mem, Unitarian Serv Comt Med Mission, Greece & Italy, 48, subcomt biol comt dent, Nat Res Coun, 51-56, sci comn dent res, Int Fedn Dentists, 58-61, Nat Adv Dent Res Coun, NIH, 64-68 & comt res & educ in Vet Admin Hosps, Nat Acad Sci, 66-67; chmn, Gordon Res Conf Bones & Teeth, 55-56; consult dent res adv comt, US Dept Army, 58-61. *Mem:* Sr fel Inst of Med of Nat Acad Sci; fel Am Acad Forensic Sci; Am Inst Oral Biol (pres, 64-72); Int Asn Dent Res (pres, 57-58); Int Soc Forensic Odont Stomatol (pres, 75-78). *Res:* Oral biology and pathology of the teeth; clinical and experimental caries; forensic science; application of radioactive isotopes, electron microscopy and histochemical methods for study of dental and osseous structures. *Mailing Add:* Ctr for Health Sci Univ of Calif Sch Dent Los Angeles CA 90024

SOGO, POWER BUNMEI, b San Diego, Calif, Feb 26, 25; div; c 3. PHYSICS. *Educ:* San Diego State Col, AB, 50; Univ Calif, PhD(physics), 55. *Prof Exp:* Physicist, Radiation Lab, Univ Calif, 55-59; asst prof physics, San Diego State Col, 59-62; from asst prof to assoc prof physics, Pomona Col, 62-66; from assoc prof to prof, Calif State Col San Bernardino, 66-71; PROF PHYSICS, UNIV HAWAII, HILO, 71-, CHMN, NATURAL SCI DIV, 78- *Mem:* Sigma Xi; Am Phys Soc. *Res:* Electron paramagnetic resonance. *Mailing Add:* Dept of Physics Univ Hawaii Hilo 1400 Kapiolani St Hilo HI 96720

SOH, SUNG KUK, b Korea, Mar 5, 51; m 80; c 1. POLYMER SCIENCE, POLYMER ENGINEERING. *Educ:* Seoul Nat Univ, BS, 73, MS, 76; Univ NH, PhD(chem eng), 81. *Prof Exp:* Chem engr, Res & Develop, Yuyu Indust Co, 73-74; ASST PROF CHEM ENG, MANHATTAN COL, 81- *Mem:* Am Inst Chem Engrs; Am Chem Soc; Sigma Xi. *Res:* Polymerization kinetics; emulsion polymerization and latex technology; polymer reactor modeling and control. *Mailing Add:* Apt 1F Thayer St New York NY 10040

SOHACKI, LEONARD PAUL, b Bay City, Mich, Aug 21, 33; m 60; c 5. LIMNOLOGY, ZOOLOGY. *Educ:* Mich State Univ, BS, 61, MS, 65, PhD(limnol), 68. *Prof Exp:* Asst prof, 68-71, ASSOC PROF BIOL, STATE UNIV NY COL ONEONTA, 71- *Mem:* Am Soc Limnol & Oceanog; Sigma Xi; Water Pollution Control Fedn. *Res:* Eutrophication and productivity. *Mailing Add:* Dept of Biol State Univ NY Col Oneonta Oneonta NY 13820

SOHAL, GURKIRPAL SINGH, b Punjab, India, Oct 1, 48; m 75; c 1. NEUROEMBRYOLOGY. *Educ:* Punjab Univ, BS, 69; La State Univ, PhD(anat), 73. *Prof Exp:* Asst prof anat, Fla Int Univ, 73-75; asst prof anat, Med Col Ga, 75-77, assoc prof, 77-80; MEM FAC, DEPT BIOL SCI, FLA INT UNIV, 80- *Concurrent Pos:* Res grant, Med Col Ga, 75; NIH res grant, 77- *Mem:* Am Asn Anatomists; AAAS; Soc Neurosci; Sigma Xi. *Res:* Factors responsible for cell death and cell differentiation in the developing brain. *Mailing Add:* Dept Biol Sci Fla Int Univ Miami FL 33199

SOHAL, MANOHAR SINGH, b Ludhiana, India, June 1, 43; US citizen; m 75; c 2. THERMOFLUIDS, HEAT TRANSFER. *Educ:* Birla Inst Technol & Sci, India, BE, 65, ME, 67; Univ Houston, PhD(mech eng), 72. *Prof Exp:* Lectr mech eng & heat transfer thermodynamics, Birla Inst Technol & Sci, India, 67-68; res fel, Eindhoven Univ Technol, Netherlands, 72-73 & Univ Strathclyde, Scotland, 73-74; spec res asst, Inst Sci & Technol, Univ Manchester, 75; res assoc, Solar Energy Lab, Univ Houston, 75-76; develop engr, Res & Develop Lab, Pullman Kellogg, Houston, Tex, 76-80; ENG SPECIALIST, IDAHO NAT ENG LAB, EG&G, IDAHO, INC, 80- *Concurrent Pos:* Lectr mech eng, Univ Houston, 76. *Mem:* Am Soc Mech Engrs; Sigma Xi. *Res:* Computer code development for transient thermohydraulic phenomena in both fission and fusion nuclear reactors; heat transfer, fluid flow and two-phase flow problems in energy related plants; safety problems in nuclear reactors. *Mailing Add:* EG&G Idaho Inc PO Box 1625 Idaho Falls ID 83415

SOHAL, RAJINDER SINGH, b Amritsar, India, July 1, 36; m 71. BIOLOGY. *Educ:* Panjab Univ, BS, 60, MS, 61; Tulane Univ, PhD(biol), 65. *Prof Exp:* Asst prof biol, Xavier Univ, 65-66; from instr to asst prof cardiovasc res, Sch Med, Tulane Univ, 66-69; asst prof, 69-71, assoc prof, 71-79, PROF BIOL, SOUTHERN METHODIST UNIV, 79- *Concurrent Pos:* Sr vis scholar, Cambridge Univ, 75 & 79. *Mem:* Am Soc Cell Biol; Am Soc Zoologists; Am Aging Asn; fel Geront Soc; Entom Soc Am. *Res:* Aging of cells; mitochondrial growth in flight muscles of insects; mechanisms of excretion in insects; relationship between life span and metabolic activity. *Mailing Add:* Dept Biol Southern Methodist Univ Dallas TX 75275

SOHL, CARY HUGH, b Pittsfield, Mass. ACOUSTICS. *Educ:* Rensselaer Polytech Inst, BS, 74; Northwestern Univ, MS, 76, PhD(physics), 79. *Prof Exp:* PHYSICIST, E I DU PONT DE NEMOUR & CO INC, 79- *Res:* Plant process monitoring. *Mailing Add:* Dupont Exp Sta 353 Bldg Wilmington DE 19898

SOHL, NORMAN FREDERICK, b Oak Park, Ill, July 14, 24; m 47; c 1. PALEONTOLOGY. *Educ:* Univ Ill, BS, 49, MS, 51, PhD(geol), 54. *Prof Exp:* Asst, State Geol Surv, Ill, 49-50; instr geol, Bryn Mawr Col, 52-53 & Univ Ill, 53-54; geologist, 54-68, chief br paleont & stratig, 68-73, RES PALEONTOLOGIST, US GEOL SURV, 73- *Concurrent Pos:* Pres bd dirs, Inst Malacol, 62-; vis prof, Univ Kans, 66; res assoc, Smithsonian Inst, 67-; mem bd overseers, Harvard Univ. *Honors & Awards:* Meritorious Serv Award, Dept Interior, 74. *Mem:* Soc Econ Paleont & Mineral; Soc Syst Zool; Soc Study Evolution; Paleont Soc Am. *Res:* Upper cretaceous gastropoda; mesozoic stratigraphy. *Mailing Add:* Rm E-501 US Nat Mus Washington DC 20242

SOHLER, ARTHUR, b New York, NY, Sept 23, 27; m 58; c 3. BIOCHEMISTRY, MICROBIOLOGY. *Educ:* City Col New York, BS, 51; St John's Univ, NY, MS, 54; Rutgers Univ, PhD(microbiol chem), 57. *Prof Exp:* Asst, St John's Univ, NY, 53-54; res assoc, Inst Microbiol, Rutgers Univ, 57-58, asst res specialist biochem, 58-59; biochemist, Bur Res in Neurol & Psychiat, NJ Neuropsychiat Inst, 58-73; BIOCHEMIST, BRAIN BIOCENTER, 73- *Mem:* AAAS; Am Chem Soc; Am Soc Microbiol. *Res:* Biochemistry of mental illness; clinical and microbial biochemistry; chemistry of natural products. *Mailing Add:* Princeton Brain Bio Ctr 862 Rte 518 Skillman NJ 08558

SOHLER, KATHERINE BERRIDGE, b Cambridge, Mass, May 31, 19; div; c 2. EPIDEMIOLOGY. *Educ:* Radcliffe Col, BA, 41; Yale Univ, PhD(int rels), 50, MPH, 61, DrPH(epidemiol), 66. *Prof Exp:* Res asst pub health statist, Yale Univ, 56-60; field off dir, Dutchess County Eval Studies, 61-63; res assoc med care, Yale Univ, 66-67; study dir, Community Health Info Ctr, Calif Dept Ment Hyg, 67-69; asst prof, 69-71, assoc prof, 71-81, EMER PROF MENT HEALTH EPIDEMIOL, UNIV OKLA, 81- *Concurrent Pos:* Res assoc psychiat, Columbia Univ, 61-63; consult, US Census Bur & Conn Dept Health, 67. *Mem:* AAAS; fel Am Pub Health Asn; Soc Epidemiol Res. *Res:* Epidemiology of mental disorders; schizophrenia; psychiatric service; methodology in demography and epidemiology. *Mailing Add:* 2106 N Indiana Oklahoma City OK 73106

SOHMER, BERNARD, b New York, NY, July 16, 29; m 52; c 2. MATHEMATICS. *Educ:* NY Univ, BA, 49, MS, 51, PhD(math), 58. *Prof Exp:* Mathematician, Army Signal Corps, 51-52; instr math, NY Univ, 52-53; lectr, City Col New York, 53-57; instr, NY Univ, 57-58; from asst prof to assoc prof, 58-69, from assoc dean to dean students, 68-75, PROF MATH, CITY COL NEW YORK, 69- *Mem:* AAAS; Am Math Soc; Math Asn Am. *Res:* Structure theory of groups; rings algebras. *Mailing Add:* City Col of New York 139th St & Convent Ave New York NY 10031

SOHMER, SEYMOUR H, b Bronx, NY, Feb 27, 41; m 67. SYSTEMATIC BOTANY. *Educ:* City Col New York, BS, 63; Univ Tenn, MS, 66; Univ Hawaii, PhD(bot), 71. *Prof Exp:* Dir herbarium & assoc prof bot, Univ Wis-LaCrosse, 67-80; CHMN DEPT BOT, BERNICE P BISHOP MUS, HONOLULU, 80- *Concurrent Pos:* Res fel, Smithsonian Inst, 75-76 & partic Flora of Ceylon proj, 73-74; NSF assignment to assess status basic res trop biol, 77-78. *Mem:* AAAS; Soc Study Evolution; Asn Trop Biol; Int Asn Plant Taxon; Am Soc Plant Taxon. *Res:* Systematic revisionary work with selected angiosperms. *Mailing Add:* Dept Bot Bernice P Bishop Mus PO Box 19000-A Honolulu HI 96819

SOHN, DAVID, b Far Rockaway, NY, Dec 5, 26; m 62; c 4. PATHOLOGY, TOXICOLOGY. *Educ:* Yeshiva Col, BA, 46; Columbia Univ, AM, 48; Polytech Inst Brooklyn, MA, 53; State Univ NY Downstate Med Ctr, MD, 57. *Prof Exp:* Asst attend path, Montefiore Hosp & Med Ctr, New York, 62-63; asst pathologist, Maimonides Hosp & Med Ctr, New York, 63-65; ATTEND PATH, CTR CHRONIC DIS & ASSOC PROF, NEW YORK MED COL, 65- *Concurrent Pos:* Mem comt alcohol & drug abuse, Nat Safety Coun, 72-; mem toxicol resource comt, Col Am Pathologists, 73-81, chmn, 74-80, mem surv comt, 74-81; assoc dean, New York Med Col, 73-, asst clin prof dermat, 74-; consult toxicol subcomt, Diag Devices Comt, US Food & Drug Admin, 75-, chmn, 80-81. *Mem:* Fel Col Am Pathologists; fel Am Soc Clin Pathologists; Am Asn Clin Chemists; fel Am Acad Forensic Sci; Am Chem Soc. *Res:* Methodology in the identification of drugs of abuse in biologic fluids, their quantitation and confirmed identification; quantitation of therapeutic drugs in body fluids. *Mailing Add:* 8 Muriel Ave Lawrence NY 11559

SOHN, HONG YONG, b Kaesung, Korea, Aug 21, 41; US citizen; m 71; c 1. EXTRACTIVE METALLURGY, REACTION ENGINEERING. *Educ:* Seoul Nat Univ, BS, 62; Univ NB, MSc, 66; Univ Calif, Berkeley, PhD(chem eng), 70. *Prof Exp:* Res engr chem eng, Cheil Sugar Co, 61-64 & I du Pont de Nemours & Co, 73-74; from asst prof to assoc prof, 74-80, PROF METALL ENG, UNIV UTAH, 80- *Concurrent Pos:* Res assoc, State Univ NY, Buffalo, 71-73; consult, Lawrence Livermore Lab, 75-; adj assoc prof fuels eng, Univ Utah, 78-80, adj prof, 80- *Mem:* Am Inst Mining, Metall & Petrol Engrs; Am Inst Chem Engrs; Am Chem Soc; Sigma Xi; NAm Thermal Analysis Soc. *Res:* Pyrometallurgy; hydrometallurgy; oil shale conversion; gas-solid reactions; combustion of solids. *Mailing Add:* Dept of Metall & Metall Eng Univ of Utah Salt Lake City UT 84112

SOHN, ISRAEL GREGORY, b Ukraine, Nov 12, 11; nat US; m 41; c 2. PALEONTOLOGY. *Educ:* City Col New York, BS, 35; Columbia Univ, AM, 38; Hebrew Univ, Israel, PhD, 66. *Prof Exp:* Preparator, 41-42, GEOLOGIST, US GEOL SURV, 42- *Concurrent Pos:* From assoc prof lectr to prof lectr, George Washington Univ, 58-68, adj prof, 69-; guest lectr, Hebrew Univ, Israel, 62-63 & academia sinica, Nanjing, Peoples Republic China, 79; res assoc, Smithsonian Inst, 68- *Mem:* Fel Geol Soc Am; Soc Econ Paleont & Mineral; Soc Syst Zool; Paleont Soc; Am Asn Petrol Geol. *Res:* Micropaleontology, especially post Devonian Ostracoda. *Mailing Add:* Rm E-501 Nat Mus of Natural Hist Washington DC 20560

SOHN, KENNETH S (KYU SUK), b Seoul, Korea, Aug 8, 33; m 62; c 2. ELECTRICAL ENGINEERING. *Educ:* Upsala Col, BS, 57; Stevens Inst Technol, MS, 59, ScD(elec eng), 67. *Prof Exp:* Instr elec eng, Stevens Inst Technol, 59-66; asst prof, 66-69, ASSOC PROF ELEC ENG, NJ INST TECHNOL, 69- *Concurrent Pos:* Consult, NY Tel Co, 67-73. *Mem:* Inst Elec & Electronics Engrs; Sigma Xi. *Res:* Determination of the electrical conductivity of semi-conductors by optical method; non-magnetic-DC-DC converters; ultrasonic array scanner for non-invasively visualizing blood vessels; medical instrumentation; investigation of planar edge-contact Josephson Junction radiation detector and mixer. *Mailing Add:* Box 33 Mountain Lakes NJ 07046

SOIFER, DAVID, b New York, NY, Sept 16, 37; m 60; c 2. CELL BIOLOGY. *Educ:* Columbia Univ, BS, 61; Cornell Univ, PhD(anat), 69. *Prof Exp:* AMA fel regulatory biol, Inst Biomed Res, 68-70; sr res scientist, 70-80, ASSOC RES SCIENTIST, INST BASIC RES DEVELOP DISABILITIES, 80- *Concurrent Pos:* Vis asst prof anat, Col Med & vis asst prof cell biol, Grad Sch Med Sci, Cornell Univ, 70-77; assoc prof anat cell biol, State Univ NY Downstate Med Ctr, 77- *Mem:* AAAS; Am Soc Cell Biol; Soc Neurosci; Am Soc Neurochem; Int Soc Neurochem. *Res:* Biology of microtubules; dynamics of neurofibrillary proteins; the molecular biology of neurofibrillary degeneration; function of cytoskeletal proteins in cells of the nervous system. *Mailing Add:* Inst for Basic Res Develop Disabilities 1050 Forest Hill Rd Staten Island NY 10314

SOINE, TAITO OLAF, medicinal chemistry, deceased

SOJKA, GARY ALLAN, b Cedar Rapids, Iowa, July 15, 40; m 62; c 2. MICROBIAL PHYSIOLOGY, GENETICS. *Educ:* Coe Col, BA, 62; Purdue Univ, MS, 65, PhD(microbiol), 67. *Prof Exp:* From res assoc to asst prof, 67-72, ASSOC PROF BIOL & ASSOC CHMN DEPT, IND UNIV, BLOOMINGTON, 72- *Mem:* AAAS; Am Soc Biol Chemists; Am Soc Microbiol. *Res:* Control of metabolism at a molecular level in photosynthetic bacteria. *Mailing Add:* Dept of Biol Ind Univ Bloomington IN 47401

SOJKA, STANLEY ANTHONY, b Buffalo, NY, Nov 6, 46; m 70; c 1. PHYSICAL ORGANIC CHEMISTRY. *Educ:* Canisius Col, BS, 68; Ind Univ, Bloomington, PhD(org chem), 72. *Prof Exp:* Res assoc spectros, Nat Res Coun, 72-74; res chemist, Naval Res Lab, 74-76; SR RES CHEMIST, HOOKER CHEM & PLASTICS CORP, 76- *Mem:* Am Chem Soc. *Res:* Using carbon-13 nuclear magnetic resonance spectroscopy to solve chemical problems; carbon-13 chemically induced dynamic nuclear polarization developed to gain knowledge about mechanism and kinetics of reactions. *Mailing Add:* Hooker Chem & Plastics Corp Res Ctr MPO Box 8 Niagara Falls NY 14302

SOKAL, JOSEPH EMANUEL, b Lwow, Poland, Apr 11, 17; nat US; m 47; c 2. INTERNAL MEDICINE, ONCOLOGY. *Educ:* Columbia Univ, BA, 36; Yale Univ, MD, 40; Am Bd Internal Med, cert med oncol. *Prof Exp:* Intern internal med, New Haven Hosp, 41-42, asst resident, 46-47; from instr to asst prof med, Sch Med, Yale Univ, 50-55; res prof physiol & med, Sch Med, State Univ NY Buffalo, 55-79; MED RES PROF, MED CTR, DUKE UNIV, 79- *Concurrent Pos:* Childs Mem Fund fel med res, Sch Med, Yale Univ, 47-50; Markle scholar med sci, 50-55; assoc physician, Univ Serv, Grace-New Haven Community Hosp, Conn, 50-55; attend physician, Vet Admin Hosp, West Haven, 53-55; chief cancer res internist, Roswell Park Mem Inst, 55-79, consult, 79- *Mem:* Soc Exp Biol & Med; Am Asn Cancer Res; Am Soc Clin Oncol; fel Am Col Physicians; Am Soc Hemat. *Res:* Oncology; lymphomas and leukemias; tumor immunology. *Mailing Add:* Box 3839 Duke Univ Med Ctr Durham NC 27710

SOKAL, ROBERT REUVEN, b Vienna, Austria, Jan 13, 26; nat US; m 48; c 2. POPULATION BIOLOGY, TAXONOMY. *Educ:* St John's Univ, China, BS, 47; Univ Chicago, PhD(zool), 52. *Prof Exp:* From instr to assoc prof entom, Univ Kans, 51-61, prof statist biol, 61-69; prof biol sci, 68-72, CHMN & DIR GRAD STUDIES, STATE UNIV NY STONY BROOK, 80-, ACTG VPROVOST RES GRAD STUDIES, 81- *Concurrent Pos:* Watkins scholar, Univ Ill, 56; NSF sr fel, Galton Lab, Univ Col, London, 59-60; Fulbright vis prof zool, Hebrew & Tel-Aviv Univs, Israel, 63-64; NIH career investr, 64-69; NATO sr fel, Cambridge Univ, 75; vis prof, Inst Advan Studies, Oeiras, Portugal, 71-80; vis distinguished scientist & Guggenheim Found fel, Univ Mich, 75-76; vis prof zool, Univ Vienna, 77 & 78. *Mem:* Soc Study Evolution (vpres, 67, pres, 77); hon fel Linnean Soc London; hon mem Soc Syst Zool; Am Soc Naturalists (ed, 69-74); Classification Soc (pres, 69-71). *Res:* Geographic variation analysis; numerical taxonomy; theory of systematics; spatial models. *Mailing Add:* Dept Ecol & Evolution State Univ NY Stony Brook NY 11794

SOKATCH, JOHN ROBERT, b Joliet, Ill, Dec 20, 28; m 57; c 3. BACTERIOLOGY. *Educ:* Univ Mich, BS, 50; Univ Ill, MS, 52, PhD(bact), 56. *Prof Exp:* Res assoc chem, Wash State Univ, 56-58; asst dean grad col, 70, from asst prof to assoc prof, Sch Med, 58-67, assoc dean grad col, 71-77, assoc dir res admin, 73-77, PROF MICROBIOL, SCH MED, UNIV OKLA, 67- *Concurrent Pos:* Fulbright sr res scholar, Sheffield, Eng, 63-64; USPHS res career develop award, 62-72; Fogarty sr int fel, Cambridge Univ, 79. *Mem:* Am Soc Microbiol; Am Soc Biol Chemists; Am Acad Microbiol. *Res:* Metabolism of branched chain amino acids by bacteria and regulation of catabolic pathways. *Mailing Add:* Univ Okla Health Sci Ctr PO Box 26901 Oklahoma City OK 73190

SOKOL, FRANTISEK, virology, biochemistry, deceased

SOKOL, HILDA WEYL, b St Louis, Mo, Dec 19, 28; m 51; c 3. NEUROENDOCRINOLOGY. *Educ:* Hunter Col, AB, 50; Radcliffe Col, AM, 51, PhD, 57. *Prof Exp:* Instr sci, Boston Univ, 54-55; instr zool, Wellesley Col, 55-58; res assoc physiol, Harvard Med Sch, 60-61; res assoc, 61-63, from instr to asst prof physiol, 63-75, ASSOC PROF PHYSIOL, DARTMOUTH MED SCH, 75- *Mem:* AAAS; Am Soc Zoologists; Endocrine Soc. *Res:* Comparative endocrinology; histology and physiology of the pituitary gland and hypothalamus; releasing factors, anterior and posterior pituitary hormones; diabetes insipidus. *Mailing Add:* Dept of Physiol Dartmouth Med Sch Hanover NH 03755

SOKOL, OTTO M, b Hattiesburg, Miss, Aug 10, 29; m 60. VERTEBRATE MORPHOLOGY. *Educ:* Stanford Univ, BA, 54; Univ Vienna, PhD(zool, paleont), 61. *Prof Exp:* NIH fel zool & paleont, Univ Vienna, 61-62; assoc biol, Univ Calif, Santa Barbara, 62-64; from asst prof to assoc prof zool, NDak State Univ, 64-72; actg asst prof anat, Stanford Univ, 72-77, lectr anat, 75-77; ASST PROF ANAT, COL MED, UNIV SOUTH ALA, 77- *Concurrent Pos:* NIH fel, 70-72; res assoc, Calif Acad Sci, 76- *Mem:* Am Asn Anatomists; Soc Study Evolution; Soc Syst Zool; Am Soc Ichthyologists & Herpetologists; Sigma Xi. *Res:* Evolution of ontogeny; vertebrate morphology and development. *Mailing Add:* Dept Anat Col Med Univ South Ala Mobile AL 36688

SOKOL, PHILLIP EDWARD, organic chemistry, polymer chemistry, deceased

SOKOL, ROBERT JAMES, b Rochester, NY, Nov 18, 41; m 64; c 3. OBSTETRICS & GYNECOLOGY, COMPUTER SCIENCE. *Educ:* Univ Rochester, BA, 63, MD, 66; Am Bd Obstet & Gynec, dipl, 72, cert maternal-fetal med, 75. *Prof Exp:* Intern & resident obstet & gynec, Barnes Hosp, Wash Univ, 66-70; from obstetrician & gynecologist to chief obstetrician & gynecologist, US Air Force Hosp, Ellsworth AFB, 70-72; asst prof obstet & gynec, Sch Med & Dent, Univ Rochester, 72-73; from asst prof to assoc prof, 73-81, PROF OBSTET & GYNEC, CASE WESTERN RESERVE UNIV, 81- *Concurrent Pos:* Buswell fel maternal-fetal med, Strong Mem Hosp, Sch Med & Dent, Univ Rochester, 72-73; asst prog dir, Perinatal Clin Res Ctr, Cleveland Metrop Gen Hosp, 73-78; fel maternal-fetal med, Cleveland Metrop Gen Hosp & Case Western Reserve Univ, 74-75; mem, Nat Inst Alcohol Abuse & Alcoholism, adv panel, Health Prof Educ Proj, 79-, ad hoc mem, intitial review group, Alcohol, Drug Abuse & Mental Health Admin, 78, 80 & 81; co-prog dir, Perinatal Clin Res Ctr, Cleveland Metrop Gen Hosp, 73-81, prog dir, 81-, assoc dir dept obstet & gynec, 81- *Mem:* Asn Prof Gynecol & Obstet; Royal Soc Med; AMA; Nat Coun Alcoholism; Cent Asn Obstet & Gynecologists. *Res:* Computer applications in perinatal medicine; substance use in pregnancy, including alcohol; programmed analysis of fetal monitoring (heart rate and intrauterine pressure); labor progress; risk for low birth weight; clinical research data management and statistics; fetal alcohol syndrome. *Mailing Add:* Perinatal Clin Res Ctr 3395 Scranton Rd Cleveland OH 44109

SOKOLOFF, ALEXANDER, b Tokyo, Japan, May 16, 20; nat US; m 56; c 3. GENETICS. *Educ:* Univ Calif, Los Angeles, AB, 48; Univ Chicago, PhD(ecol), 54. *Prof Exp:* Res assoc cancer, Univ Chicago, 54, instr biol, 55; from instr to asst prof biol, Hofstra Col, 55-58; geneticist, William H Miner Agr Res Inst, NY, 58-60; assoc res botanist, Univ Calif, Los Angeles, 60-61, assoc res geneticist, Univ Calif, Berkeley, 61-66; assoc prof natural sci div, 65-66, PROF BIOL, CALIF STATE COL, SAN BERNARDINO, 66- *Concurrent Pos:* NSF res grant, Cold Spring Harbor Lab Quant Biol, 58-60; ed, Tribolium Info Bull, 60-; USPHS res grant, 61; res geneticist, Univ Calif, Berkeley, 66-68; NSF res grants, 67-75; assoc ed, Evolution, 72-74; chmn subcomt on insect stocks, Comt for Maintenance of Genetic Stocks, Genetics Soc Am, 74-76; res grant, Army Res Off, 74-78. *Mem:* Am Inst Biol Sci; Am Soc Nat; Am Genetic Soc; Genetics Soc Am; Entom Soc Am. *Res:* Population ecological genetics of Tribolium; genetic control of flour beetles. *Mailing Add:* Dept of Biol Calif State Col San Bernardino CA 92407

SOKOLOFF, JACK, b New York, NY, July 28, 22; m 48; c 3. THEORETICAL PHYSICS. *Educ:* Univ Mich, BS, 48, MS, 49; Northwestern Univ, PhD(physics), 56. *Prof Exp:* Teaching asst physics, Univ Mich, 48-49; aerodynamicist, Bell Aircraft Corp, 49-50; teaching asst physics, Northwestern Univ, 52-54; student res assoc physics div, Argonne Nat Lab, 54-56; res scientist, Lockheed Palo Alto Res Lab, 56-68; PROF PHYSICS, YORK UNIV, 68- *Concurrent Pos:* Vis scientist, Lab Theoret Physics & Elem Particles, Univ Paris-SUD, Orsay, France, 75-76. *Mem:* Am Phys Soc. *Res:* Variation principles as applied to problems of atomic structure and atomic collisions. *Mailing Add:* Dept of Physics York Univ Toronto ON M3J 1P3 Can

SOKOLOFF, JEFFREY BRUCE, b New York, NY, Oct 7, 41; m 68; c 1. SOLID STATE PHYSICS. *Educ:* Queen's Col, NY, BS, 63; Mass Inst Technol, PhD(physics), 67. *Prof Exp:* Res assoc, Brookhaven Nat Lab, 67-69; ASSOC PROF PHYSICS, NORTHEASTERN UNIV, 69- *Concurrent Pos:* Vis mem staff, Weitzmann Inst, 79-80. *Mem:* Am Phys Soc. *Res:* Magnetic and transport properties of solids with itinerant electrons in narrow bands; theory of light scattering from nonmetallic systems undergoing an order-disorder transition; Frohlich conductivity in one-dimensional conductors; theory of ideal friction between sliding solid surfaces; excitations in crystals with two incommensurate periods. *Mailing Add:* Dept Physics Northeastern Univ Boston MA 02115

SOKOLOFF, LEON, b Brooklyn, NY, May 9, 19; m; c 2. PATHOLOGY. *Educ:* NY Univ, BA, 38, MD, 44. *Prof Exp:* Asst prof path, NY Univ, 50-52; chief sect rheumatic dis, Lab Exp Path, Nat Inst Arthritis, Metab & Digestive Dis, 53-73; PROF PATH, STATE UNIV NY STONY BROOK, 73- *Concurrent Pos:* Mem, path study sect, NIH, 56-60, gen med A, 78- *Mem:* AAAS; Harvey Soc; Am Asn Pathologists; Am Rheumatism Asn. *Res:* Pathology of rheumatic diseases. *Mailing Add:* 25 View Rd Setauket NY 11733

SOKOLOFF, LOUIS, b Philadelphia, Pa, Oct 14, 21; m 47; c 2. PHYSIOLOGY, BIOCHEMISTRY. *Educ:* Univ Pa, BA, 43, MD, 46. *Prof Exp:* Intern, Philadelphia Gen Hosp, 46-47; res fel physiol, Grad Sch Med, Univ Pa, 49-51, instr physiol, 51-54, assoc, 54-56; chief sect cerebral metab, 56-68, CHIEF LAB CEREBRAL METAB, NIMH, 68- *Concurrent Pos:* Assoc chief sect cerebral metab, NIMH, 53-56; Albert Lasker clin med res award, 81. *Honors & Awards:* F O Schmitt Award, 80. *Mem:* US Nat Acad Sci; Asn Res Nerv & Ment Dis; Am Soc Biol Chemists; Am Acad Neurol; Int Brain Res Orgn. *Res:* Cerebral circulation and metabolism; neurochemistry; biochemical basis of hormone actions; protein biosynthesis; thyroxine. *Mailing Add:* Lab of Cerebral Metab NIMH Bldg 36 Rm 1A-27 Bethesda MD 20014

SOKOLOFF, VLADIMIR P, b Tomsk, Siberia, Nov 8, 04; nat US; m 33; c 1. GEOCHEMISTRY. *Educ:* Univ Calif, PhD(soil sci), 37. *Prof Exp:* Jr chemist, Citrus Exp Sta & asst prof microbiol, Univ Calif, 37-43; soil scientist, US Geol Surv, 43-50; vis prof, Johns Hopkins Univ, 50-53; consult geochemist, Makhtsavei, Israel, 53-56; consult, US Geol Surv, 56 & Shell Oil Co, 57; eastern Europe specialist & phys scientist, US Bur Mines, DC, 58-66; trans rev ed, Am Geol Inst, 66, mem int geol rev staff, 66-74; RETIRED. *Concurrent Pos:* Consult geochemist, Zinc Corp, Pty, Ltd, Australia, 48, Western Mining Corp, 49 & Conzinc-Riotinto, 65. *Mem:* Fel AAAS; fel Am Geog Soc; fel Am Inst Chem; NY Acad Sci. *Res:* Applied geochemistry; physiology and parasitism of nitrate-reducing microorganisms; bacterial leaching of ores; soils physics in terrain intelligence. *Mailing Add:* PO Box 9724 Washington DC 20016

SOKOLOSKI, MARTIN MICHAEL, b Freeland, Pa, Sept 7, 37; m 62; c 3. CONDENSED MATTER PHYSICS, MATHEMATICS. *Educ:* Bucknell Univ, BS, 59, MS, 60; Catholic Univ Am, PhD(physics), 69. *Prof Exp:* Mathematician, Dept Defense, Nat Security Agency, 60-61; aerospace technician, NASA Goddard Space Flight Ctr, 61-63, aerospace engr, 63-66; res assoc, Catholic Univ Am, 70-71; mem staff, Harry Diamond Labs, 71-79; MGR ELECTRONICS, NASA, 79- *Mem:* Am Phys Soc; AAAS. *Res:* Determination of the nature of interface electronic states; theoretical studies of the static and dynamic properties of disordered systems; many body problems; basic research management. *Mailing Add:* 5526 Phelps Luck Dr Columbia MD 21045

SOKOLOSKI, THEODORE DANIEL, b Philadelphia, Pa, July 10, 33; m 61; c 3. PHARMACY, PHYSICAL CHEMISTRY. *Educ:* Temple Univ, BS, 55; Univ Wis, Madison, MS, 59, PhD(pharm), 61. *Prof Exp:* Asst prof pharm, Wash State Univ, 61-64; from asst prof to assoc prof pharm, 64-73, PROF PHARMACEUT & PHARMACEUT CHEM, OHIO STATE UNIV, 73- *Mem:* Am Chem Soc; Am Pharmaceut Asn; Acad Pharmaceut Sci. *Res:* Application of physical chemistry to pharmaceutical systems. *Mailing Add:* Col of Pharm Ohio State Univ Columbus OH 43210

SOKOLOVE, PHILIP GARY, b Los Angeles, Calif, Aug 24, 42; m 68; c 1. NEUROBIOLOGY, BIOPHYSICS. *Educ:* Univ Calif, Berkeley, AB, 64; Harvard Univ, PhD(biophysics), 69. *Prof Exp:* Actg asst prof neurobiol, Stanford Univ, 71-72; asst prof, 72-78, ASSOC PROF BIOL, UNIV MD BALTIMORE CO, 78- *Concurrent Pos:* Res assoc, Stanford Univ, 72-74; consult, SRI Int, 72-79. *Mem:* Am Soc Zoologists; Soc Gen Physiologists; Soc Neurosci; Am Physiol Soc; AAAS. *Res:* Biological circadian rhythms; reproductive neuroendocrinology in molluscs; behavioral neurobiology. *Mailing Add:* Dept Biol Sci Univ Md Baltimore Co Catonville MD 21228

SOKOLOW, MAURICE, b New York, NY, May 19, 11; wid; c 2. MEDICINE. *Educ:* Univ Calif, AB, 32, MD, 36; Am Bd Internal Med & Cardiovasc Dis, dipl. *Prof Exp:* Intern, San Francisco Hosp, Calif, 35-36; asst resident med, Univ Calif Hosp, 36-37; resident physician, New Eng Med Ctr, Boston, Mass, 37-38; researcher cardiovasc dis, Michael Reese Hosp, 38-39; clin instr med, 40-45, lectr, 45-46, from asst prof to prof, 46-78, chief, Electrocardiogram Dept, Univ Hosp, 46-78, chief cardiovasc serv, Univ Hosp, 58-74, EMER PROF MED, SCH MED, UNIV CALIF, SAN FRANCISCO, 78- *Concurrent Pos:* Res fel med, Sch Med, Univ Calif, San Francisco, 39-40, vis physician, 40-47; attend cardiologist, Langley Porter Clin, 46-; consult, Vet Admin Hosps, San Francisco & Oakland, Calif, 46-; researcher, Nat Heart Hosp, London, 53-54; mem coun arteriosclerosis, Am Heart Asn. *Mem:* Fel Am Col Physicians; Am Soc Clin Invest; Asn Univ Cardiologists; hon fel Am Col Cardiol; Am Fedn Clin Res (vpres, 49). *Res:* Rheumatic fever; electrocardiography; hypertension; cardiac arrhythmias; cardiac failure. *Mailing Add:* Rm 573 M Univ of Calif Sch of Med San Francisco CA 94143

SOKOLOWSKI, DANNY HALE, b Alton, Ill, June 1, 38; m 65; c 2. SOLID STATE PHYSICS. *Educ:* Southern Ill Univ, AB, 61; Univ Mo, Rolla, MS, 63; St Louis Univ, PhD(physics), 74. *Prof Exp:* Instr physics, Southern Ill Univ, 63-66, Marquette Univ, 69-71; ASSOC PROF PHYSICS, LEWIS & CLARK COMMUNITY COL, 71- *Mem:* Am Phys Soc; Sigma Xi; Am Asn Physics Teachers. *Res:* Electrical and thermoelectrical properties of semiconductors. *Mailing Add:* Dept of Physics Lewis & Clark Community Col Godfrey IL 62035

SOKOLOWSKI, HENRY ALFRED, b Hamtramck, Mich, Jan 21, 23; m 55; c 3. PHYSICS, MATHEMATICS. *Educ:* Univ Pa, AB, 57. *Prof Exp:* Physicist, 51-56, chief propellant physics, 56-61, chief ballistics lab, 61-71, chief test instrumentation div, 71-74, chief test & eval div, 74-76, DIR TECH SUPPORT DIRECTORATE, FRANKFORD ARSENAL, 77- *Mem:* Sigma Xi. *Res:* Ballistic, environmental materials test and evaluation utilizing the disciplines of physics, mathematics, metallurgy, chemistry, electrical engineering, mechanical engineering and associated specialized scientific fields. *Mailing Add:* 2731 Kirkbride St Philadelphia PA 19137

SOKOLSKI, WALTER THOMAS, b Newark, NJ, Oct 29, 16; m 47; c 2. MICROBIOLOGY. *Educ:* Ind Univ, AB, 48; Purdue Univ, MS, 53, PhD(bact), 55. *Prof Exp:* Serologist, Venereal Dis Res Lab, USPHS, 45-46; chemist, Parke, Davis & Co, 48-51; microbiologist, Upjohn Co, 54-59, head spec microbiol methods, Control Div, 59-67, head microbiol res, 67-70, mem staff infectious dis res, 70-78; RETIRED. *Concurrent Pos:* Consult antibiotic fermentation, Panlabs Taiwan Inc, Taiwan, 80-81. *Honors & Awards:* Award, Am Soc Microbiol, 52. *Mem:* Am Soc Microbiol; Am Soc Med Technol; Am Soc Clin Path; Soc Protozool; Soc Cryobiol. *Res:* Screening methods for new antibiotics; paper and column chromatography; microbiological assay for antibiotics; in vitro methodology in clinical research; environmental control. *Mailing Add:* 3304 Cranbrook Kalamazoo MI 49007

SOLAND, RICHARD MARTIN, b New York, NY, July 27, 40; div; c 5. OPERATIONS RESEARCH. *Educ:* Rensselaer Polytech Inst, BEE, 61; Mass Inst Technol, PhD(math), 64. *Prof Exp:* Mem tech staff, Advan Res Dept, Res Anal Corp, 64-71; assoc prof statist-opers res, Univ Tex, Austin, 71-76; assoc prof, Dept Indust Eng, Ecole Polytech, Univ Montreal, 76-78; PROF OPERS RES, GEORGE WASHINGTON UNIV, 78- *Concurrent Pos:* Asst prof lectr, Dept Bus Admin, George Washington Univ, 65-68, assoc prof lectr, Dept Eng Admin, 68-69; Fulbright lectr, Helsinki Sch Econ, Finland, 69-70; vis prof, Res Ctr, Inst d Admin des Enterprises, Univ Aix-Marseille, Aix-en-Provence, France, 73-74; vis prof, Carabobo Univ, Valencia, Venezuela, 75. *Mem:* Opers Res Soc Am; Inst Mgt Sci; Inst Elec & Electronics Engrs; Math Programming Soc; Can Opers Res Soc. *Res:* Multiple criteria decision making; branch-and-bound methods in mathematical programming; applications of mathematical programming; mathematical modeling; facility location; statistical decision analysis; Bayesian statistics. *Mailing Add:* Dept of Opers Res George Washington Univ Washington DC 20052

SOLANDT, OMOND McKILLOP, b Winnipeg, Man, Sept 2, 09; m 41, 72; c 3. PHYSIOLOGY. *Educ:* Univ Toronto, BA, 31, MA, 32, MD, 36; Cambridge Univ, MA, 39; FRCP, 64. *Hon Degrees:* Eleven from Can univs, 46-68. *Prof Exp:* Lectr physiol, Cambridge Univ, 39; dir, SW London Blood Supply Depot, 40; dir tank sect, Army Oper Res Group, 42, from dept supt to supt, 43-45; chmn, Defence Res Bd, Dept Nat Defence, 46-56; asst vpres res & develop, Can Nat Rwy, 56, vpres, 57-63; vpres res & planning, De Havilland Aircraft Can Ltd, 63-66; chmn, Sci Coun Can, 66-72; consult, Mitchell, Plummer & Co, Ltd, 72-75; SR CONSULT, INST ENVIRON STUDIES, UNIV TORONTO, 76- *Concurrent Pos:* Chancellor, Univ Toronto, 65-71; vchmn, Elec Reduction Co Can, Ltd, 66-70; chmn, Sci Adv Bd for Northwest Territories, 76-; pub gov, Toronto Stock Exchange; consult, Int Ctr Agr Res in Dry Areas, Syria, 76-81, Int Ctr Insect Physiol & Ecol, 77 & Int Ctr Diarrheal Dis Res, Bangladesh, 79. *Honors & Awards:* Companion, Order Can; Order Brit Empire, 46. *Mem:* Am Physiol Soc; Can Physiol Soc; Can Oper Res Soc (pres, 58-60); fel Royal Soc Can; fel Am Acad Arts & Sci. *Res:* Operational research. *Mailing Add:* RR 1 Bolton ON L0P 1A0 Can

SOLAR, SAMUEL LOUIS, b Boston, Mass, June 29, 19; m 43; c 1. ORGANIC CHEMISTRY. *Educ:* Mass Inst Technol, BS, 41; Rensselaer Polytech Inst, PhD(chem), 51. *Prof Exp:* Res chemist, J E Came Co, Mass, 41-42; asst polymers & inorg crystals, Mass Inst Technol, 42-43; res chemist, Celanese Corp Am, 43-44 & Cluett, Peabody & Co, 46-51; assoc chemist, Ethicon, Inc, 51-52; STAFF CHEMIST, RES LAB, IBM CORP, 52- *Mem:* AAAS; Am Chem Soc; Sigma Xi; The Chem Soc. *Res:* Synthetic organic chemistry; high polymers; stable free radicals. *Mailing Add:* 1714 Montemar Way San Jose CA 95125

SOLARZ, RICHARD WILLIAM, b Minneapolis, Minn, Dec 12, 47; m 68; c 1. CHEMICAL PHYSICS. *Educ:* Mass Inst Technol, SB, 69; Univ Chicago, PhD(chem physics), 74. *Prof Exp:* PHYSICIST LASER PHYSICS, LAWRENCE LIVERMORE LAB, 74- *Res:* Laser physics and photochemistry; spectroscopy of excited atoms and molecules; laser isotope separation. *Mailing Add:* Lawrence Livermore Lab L-468 Box 808 Livermore CA 94550

SOLBERG, JAMES J, b Toledo, Ohio, May 27, 42; m 66. INDUSTRIAL ENGINEERING, OPERATIONS RESEARCH. *Educ:* Harvard Col, BA, 64; Univ Mich, MA & MS, 67, PhD(indust eng), 69. *Prof Exp:* Asst prof indust eng, Univ Toledo, 68-72; assoc prof, 72-81, PROF INDUST ENG, PURDUE UNIV, 81- *Mem:* AAAS; Opers Res Soc Am; Inst Mgt Sci; Am Inst Indust Eng; Soc Mgf Eng. *Res:* Graph theory; queueing theory; scheduling; probability; computer aided manufacturing. *Mailing Add:* Sch of Indust Eng Purdue Univ West Lafayette IN 47907

SOLBERG, MYRON, b Boston, Mass, June 11, 31; m 56; c 3. FOOD SCIENCE, FOOD MICROBIOLOGY. *Educ:* Univ Mass, BS, 52; Mass Inst Technol, PhD(food technol), 60. *Prof Exp:* Res asst food technol, Mass Inst Technol, 54-60; qual control mgr, Colonial Provision Co, 60-64; from asst prof to assoc prof food sci, 64-70, PROF FOOD SCI, RUTGERS UNIV, NEW BRUNSWICK, 70- *Concurrent Pos:* Lectr, Meat Sci Inst, 65-; vis prof food eng & biotechnol, Israel Inst Technol, 73-74; co-ed, J Food Safety, 77- *Mem:* AAAS; Inst Food Technologists; Am Soc Qual Control; Am Soc Microbiol; Am Meat Sci Asn. *Res:* Mode of action of microbial inhibition by nitrite; microbial evaluation of protein quality; assurance of microbiological safety in mass-feeding; regulation of toxinogenesis in clostridium perfringens. *Mailing Add:* Dept of Food Sci Rutgers Univ New Brunswick NJ 08903

SOLBERG, RICHARD ALLEN, b Decorah, Iowa, Sept 21, 32; m 54; c 4. PLANT PATHOLOGY. *Educ:* Mont State Univ, BA, 54; Wash State Univ, MS, 56; Univ Calif, Los Angeles, PhD(bot), 61. *Prof Exp:* Asst air pollution, Inst Technol, Wash State Univ, 54-56; res botanist, Univ Calif, Los Angeles, 56-57, sr lab technician plant path, 57-61; assoc prof, 61-70, dir biol sta, 61-67, assoc dean, 67-69, PROF BOT, UNIV MONT, 70-, DEAN COL ARTS & SCI, 69- *Mem:* Bot Soc Am; Soc Develop Biol; Am Soc Limnol & Oceanog. *Res:* Plant anatomy and cytology; pathological cytology of virus infection; developmental anatomy; fine structure of cells; tissue differentiation and culture; phytotoxicants and virus cytology and their interrelationships. *Mailing Add:* Col Arts & Sci Univ of Mont Missoula MT 59801

SOLBERG, RUELL FLOYD, JR, b Norse, Tex, July 27, 39; m 59; c 2. MECHANICS, MECHANICAL ENGINEERING. *Educ:* Univ Tex, Austin, BS, 62, MS, 67; Trinity Univ, MBA, 77. *Prof Exp:* Res engr underwater acoustics div, Appl Res Labs, Univ Tex, 62-65, asst supvr mech eng sect, 65-67; res engr, 67-70, SR RES ENGR, DEPT OF ELECTROMAGNETIC ENG, SOUTHWEST RES INST, 70- *Concurrent Pos:* Tech Asst Appl Mech Rev, 80- *Honors & Awards:* Charles E Balleisen Award, Am Soc Mech Engrs, 76 & Centennial Medallion, 78. *Mem:* Sigma Xi; Am Soc Mech Engrs; Robot Inst Am; NY Acad Sci; Human Factors Soc. *Res:* Structural optimization; mechanical design; response of structures to periodic and impulsive loading; behavioral science; flexible automation; material fatigue; environmental effects; zero-gravity in space flight; oceanography; management science; human factors; corrosion; acoustics. *Mailing Add:* Dept of Electromagnetic Eng PO Drawer 28510 San Antonio TX 78284

SOLBRIG, OTTO THOMAS, b Buenos Aires, Arg, Dec 21, 30; US citizen; m 56; c 2. PLANT GENETICS. *Educ:* Univ Calif, Berkeley, PhD(bot), 59. *Hon Degrees:* MA, Harvard Univ, 69. *Prof Exp:* Botanist, Harvard Univ, 59-61, from asst cur to assoc cur, 61-66; from assoc prof to prof, Univ Mich, Ann Arbor & biosystematist, Bot Gardens, 66-69; PROF BIOL, HARVARD UNIV, 69-, DIR, GRAY HERBARIUM & SUPVR, BUSSEY INST, 78- *Concurrent Pos:* Hon travel fel, Univ Calif, Berkeley, 59-60; NSF & Am Acad Arts & Sci grants, 59-; lectr, Harvard Univ, 64-66; secy gen, Int Orgn Plant Biosysts, 64-69; mem, Int Orgn Biosysts & Orgn Trop Studies; dir, Struct Ecosystems Prog, US/IBP, 70-75; mem, IUBS Comt, Nat Acad Sci, 75-80. *Mem:* Bot Soc Am; Genetics Soc Am; Soc Study Evolution (secy, 73-78, pres, 81-82); Sigma Xi (secy-treas, 76-); fel Am Acad Arts & Sci. *Res:* Cytotaxonomical and cytogenetical studies of plant species; chemical and physiological studies of natural plant population; evolution of plants; plant population biology. *Mailing Add:* Gray Herbarium Harvard Univ 22 Divinity Ave Cambridge MA 02138

SOLC, KAREL, b Nachod, Czech, July 25, 33; m 57; c 2. PHYSICAL CHEMISTRY. *Educ:* Inst Chem Technol, Prague, Czech, MSc, 56; Czech Acad Sci, PhD(macromolecular chem), 61. *Prof Exp:* From scientist to sr scientist, Inst Macromolecular Chem, Czech Acad Sci, 61-68; res instr chem, Dartmouth Col, 71; res scientist, 71-74, SR RES SCIENTIST, MICH MOLECULAR INST, 74- *Concurrent Pos:* NSF vis fel, Dartmouth Col, 68-70; Mich Found Advan Res vis fel, 70-71. *Mem:* AAAS; Am Chem Soc; Am Phys Soc. *Res:* Physical chemistry of polymers; statistical mechanics and thermodynamics; chain statistics; chemical kinetics. *Mailing Add:* Midland Macromolecular Inst 1910 W St Andrews Dr Midland MI 48640

SOLDANO, BENNY A, b Utica, NY, Nov 17, 21; m 46; c 2. PHYSICAL CHEMISTRY. *Educ:* Alfred Univ, BS, 43; Univ Wis, PhD(phys chem), 49. *Prof Exp:* From chemist to sr chemist, Oak Ridge Nat Lab, Tenn, 49-71; prof chem, 71-77, PROF PHYSICS, FURMAN UNIV, 71- *Mem:* Am Chem Soc. *Res:* Ion exchange; thermodynamics; kinetics; solution chemistry. *Mailing Add:* Dept of Physics Furman Univ Greenville SC 26913

SOLDAT, JOSEPH KENNETH, b Chicago, Ill, May 4, 26; m 52; c 3. HEALTH PHYSICS, RADIOLOGICAL PHYSICS. *Educ:* Univ Colo, BS, 48; Am Bd Health Physics, cert. *Prof Exp:* Indust hyg engr, Med Ctr, Univ Colo, 48; from technician to sr engr, Gen Elec Co, Wash, 48-65; sr res scientist, 65-73, res assoc, 73-76, STAFF ENVIRON SCIENTIST, PAC

NORTHWEST LABS, BATTELLE MEM INST, 77- *Mem:* AAAS; Am Chem Soc; Health Physics Soc. *Res:* Human doses from environmental radiation sources; movement of radionuclides through the biosphere to man; radioactive waste management; surveillance of waste effluents and the environs for radioactive and nonradioactive materials. *Mailing Add:* Pac Northwest Labs Battelle Mem Inst PO Box 999 Richland WA 99352

SOLDATI, GIANLUIGI, b Bologna, Italy, Feb 17, 37; m 63; c 2. ORGANIC CHEMISTRY. *Educ:* Univ Bologna, PhD(org chem), 61. *Prof Exp:* Petrol Res Fund fel, Univ Mass, 62; lectr & res assoc org & anal chem, Univ Bologna, 63-64, phys & org chem, 64-65; sr res chemist, Agr Chem, Uniroyal, Inc, Conn, 65-70; sr synthetic chemist, 70-75, sr res chemist, 75-78, PROF LEADER, CARTER PROD RES DIV, CARTER-WALLACE, INC, 78- *Mem:* Soc Cosmetic Chemists; Am Inst Chemists; Am Chem Soc. *Res:* antihypertensive agents; inorganic antiperspirants; depilatory agents; polymers; synthesis of antiperspirant salts and complexes; synthesis and study of new anticalculus and anticaries materials; anticholinergics and antihypertensive agents; patent writing and liaison with Legal Department; surfactants; emulsion technology; product development cosmetics and toiletries. *Mailing Add:* Carter Prod Res Div of Carter-Wallace Inc Cranbury NJ 08512

SOLDO, ANTHONY THOMAS, b New York, NY, Sept 11, 27; m 51; c 3. BIOCHEMISTRY, NUTRITION. *Educ:* Brooklyn Col, BS, 50, MA, 53; Ind Univ, PhD(biochem), 60. *Prof Exp:* Biochemist, Schering Corp, NJ, 59-62; res assoc, Inst Muscle Dis Inc, NY, 62-64; asst prof, 65-72, assoc prof, 72-81, PROF BIOCHEM, SCH MED, UNIV MIAMI, 81- RES CHEMIST, VET ADMIN HOSP, 65- *Mem:* AAAS; Soc Protozool; NY Acad Sci; Am Inst Nutrit. *Res:* Nutrition and nucleic acid metabolism of Protozoa; biochemistry of endosymbiotes. *Mailing Add:* Vet Admin Hosp 1201 NW 16th St Miami FL 33125

SOLE, MICHAEL JOSEPH, b Timmins, Ont, Mar 5, 40; m 64; c 2. CARDIOLOGY, NEUROCHEMISTRY. *Educ:* Univ Toronto, BSc, 62, MD, 66; FRCP(C), 74. *Prof Exp:* Intern, Toronto Gen Hosp, 66-67, jr resident, 67-68, sr resident, 68-69; cardiol fel, Cardiovascular Res Inst, 69-71 & Peter Bent Brigham Hosp, 71-74; res assoc nutrit, Mass Inst Technol, 73-74; asst prof med, Univ Toronto, 74-78; STAFF CARDIOLOGIST & DIR CARDIOL RES, TORONTO GEN HOSP, 74-; ASSOC PROF & COORDR CARDIOL RES, UNIV TORONTO, 78- *Concurrent Pos:* Fels, Ont Heart Found, 73-80, res assoc, 80-, Med Review Comt, 78-; Sci Review Comt, Can Heart Found, 76-; fels, Coun Clin Cardiol & Am Col Cardiol, 76-; Hon secy-treas, Banting Res Found, 78-81; staff, Inst Med Sci, Univ Toronto, 77-; vchmn, Can Heart Found, 80-; rev comt, Gairdener Found, 80- *Honors & Awards:* Res Award, Can Cardiovascular Soc, 75; William Goldie Prize, 80. *Mem:* Am Heart Asn; Can Cardiovascular Soc; Am Fedn Clin Res; Int Soc Heart Res. *Res:* Central and peripheral biogenic amine metabolism in cardiovascular disease; studies of nuclear proteins in inherited heart disease. *Mailing Add:* Toronto Gen Hosp Rm 1-119 U W Toronto ON M5G 1L7 Can

SOLECKI, ROMAN, b Lwow, Poland, Apr 6, 25; US citizen; m 48. SOLID MECHANICS. *Educ:* Warsaw Polytech Inst, BS, 50, PhD(appl mech), 56; Inst Fund Technol Res, Warsaw, DSc, 60. *Prof Exp:* Asst prof civil eng, Warsaw Polytech Inst, 50-56, adj prof, 56-60; assoc prof continuum mech, Inst Fund Technol Res, Warsaw, 60-68; PROF MECH ENG, UNIV CONN, 68- *Concurrent Pos:* Royal Norwegian Coun Sci Res fels, 62- & 64-; NSF sr foreign sci fel, Univ Conn, 68- *Mem:* Am Soc Mech Engrs; Sigma Xi. *Res:* Wear; fracture mechanics. *Mailing Add:* Dept of Mech Eng PO Box U-139 Storrs CT 06268

SOLED, STUART, b New York, NY, May 11, 48. SOLID STATE CHEMISTRY. *Educ:* City Col New York, BS, 69; Brown Univ, PhD(chem), 73. *Prof Exp:* Res assoc chem res, Brown Univ, 73-77; res chemist, Allied Chem Co, 77-80; WITH EXXON RES & ENGR CO, 80- *Concurrent Pos:* Res assoc, Lab Inorg Chem, Univ Paris, 74-75. *Mem:* Am Chem Soc; Am Crystallog Asn. *Res:* Preparation, structure and properties of materials in solid state chemistry. *Mailing Add:* Exxon Res & Engr Co PO Box 45 Bldg 16 Linden NJ 07036

SOLEM, ALAN, b Chicago, Ill, July 21, 31; div; c 2. INVERTEBRATE ZOOLOGY. *Educ:* Haverford Col, BS, 52; Univ Mich, MA, 54, PhD(zool), 56. *Prof Exp:* Asst malacol, Univ Mich, 52-55; asst cur lower inverts, 57-58, cur lower invertebrates, 59-70, CUR INVERTEBRATES, FIELD MUS NATURAL HIST, 71- *Concurrent Pos:* Lectr, Comt Evolutionary Biol, Univ of Chicago; res assoc biol sci, Northwestern Univ. *Mem:* AAAS; Ecol Soc Am; Am Malacol Union (vpres, 69, pres, 70); Soc Syst Zool; Malacol Soc London. *Res:* Systematics, zoogeography, ecology and anatomy of mollusks, particularly non-marine taxa of the Indo-Pacific, Nearctic and Neo-tropical regions. *Mailing Add:* Dept Zool Field Mus Nat Hist Lake Shore & Roosevelt Chicago IL 60605

SOLEM, JOHNDALE CHRISTIAN, b Chicago, Ill, Nov 8, 41; m 65. LASERS, NUCLEAR EXPLOSIVE PHYSICS. *Educ:* Yale Univ, BS, 63, MS, 65, PhD(physics), 68, MPhil, 67. *Prof Exp:* Group leader, Thermonuclear Weapons Physics Group, 73-76, Neutron Physics Group, 77-79, High Power Density Group, 78, alt div leader, Physics Div, 78-80, ASST DIV LEADER, THEORET DIV, LOS ALAMOS NAT LAB, 80- *Concurrent Pos:* Mem, US Air Force Sci Adv Bd, 72-77 & Munitions & Armament Panel, 73-77. *Mem:* Am Phys Soc; AAAS; Am Nuclear Soc. *Res:* X-ray and gamma-ray lasers; laser-driven shockwaves; nuclear physics; transport theory; plasma physics; nuclear explosive physics; technical, political and military issues relating to tactical nuclear warfare. *Mailing Add:* Los Alamos Nat Lab MS-B210 Box 1663 Los Alamos NM 87545

SOLENBERGER, JOHN CARL, b San Diego, Calif, Apr 2, 41; m 71. INDUSTRIAL CHEMISTRY. *Educ:* Univ NMex, BS, 63; Wash Univ, PhD(chem), 69. *Prof Exp:* Sr res chemist, plastics dept, E I du Pont de Nemours & Co, Inc, 69-80. *Mem:* Am Chem Soc; Sigma Xi. *Res:* Development of membranes for use as separators on chlor-alkali cells, polymeric coatings and binders, and general industrial process research. *Mailing Add:* 100 Brighton Pl W Mt Prospect IL 60056

SOLER, ALAN I(SRAEL), b Philadelphia, Pa, Dec 9, 36; m 60; c 2. ENGINEERING MECHANICS. *Educ:* Univ Pa, BS, 58, PhD(mech eng), 62; Calif Inst Technol, MS, 59. *Prof Exp:* Res scientist, Dyna Struct, Inc, Pa, 61-64; mem tech staff, Ingersoll Rand Res Ctr, NJ, 64-65; from asst prof to assoc prof mech eng, 65-77, PROF MECH ENG, UNIV PA, 77- *Concurrent Pos:* Adj prof, Drexel Inst Technol, 64-65; consult, Ingersoll Rand Res Ctr, 65- *Mem:* Am Inst Aeronaut & Astronaut. *Res:* Viscoelasticity and thermoviscoelasticity; engineering theory of thick walled shells; buckling of deep beams; cable dynamics; transportation dynamics. *Mailing Add:* Dept of Mech Eng Univ of Pa Philadelphia PA 19104

SOLEZ, KIM, b Washington, DC, June 20, 46; m 72; c 1. PATHOLOGY, RENAL MEDICINE. *Educ:* Oberlin Col, BA, 68; Univ Rochester, MD, 72. *Prof Exp:* Nat Kidney Found fel, 76-77; ASST PROF PATH & MED, JOHNS HOPKINS UNIV, 77-; PATHOLOGIST, JOHNS HOPKINS HOSP, 77- *Mem:* Am Soc Clin Res; Am Soc Nephrology; Int Soc Nephrology. *Res:* Acute renal failure; renal circulation; glomerul- onephritis; atherosclerosis. *Mailing Add:* Dept of Path Johns Hopkins Hosp Baltimore MD 21205

SOLI, GIORGIO, b Rome, Italy, Feb 3, 20; nat US; m; c 3. MICROBIOLOGY. *Educ:* Univ Rome, DSc(microbiol), 47. *Prof Exp:* Res asst microbiol, Med Sch, Univ Calif, Los Angeles, 49-50; res asst petrol explor & develop, Gen Petrol Corp, Calif, 51-53; microbiologist & consult, Soli Microbiol Labs, 53-59; microbiologist, US Naval Ord Test Sta, China Lake, 59-62, res microbiologist, Res Dept, 62-68; staff scientist, Naval Undersea Ctr, Hawaii, 68-70; res microbiologist, Michelson Labs, China Lake, 70-73; SCI CONSULT, 73- *Concurrent Pos:* Guest scientist, Oceanog Mus, Monaco, 66-67; resident scientist, Oceanic Inst, Hawaii, 68-70. *Mem:* AAAS; Am Soc Microbiol; Am Soc Limnol & Oceanog; Sigma Xi; NY Acad Sci. *Res:* Marine microorganisms; bioluminescence; microbial degradation of petroleum; microbiology applied to diversified problems in marine pollution, petroleum technology and agriculture. *Mailing Add:* 16413 Akron St Pacific Palisades CA 90272

SOLIE, LELAND PETER, b Barron, Wis, July 19, 41; m 67; c 3. ACOUSTICS. *Educ:* Stanford Univ, BS, 64, MS, 67, PhD(appl physics), 71. *Prof Exp:* Res asst microwave acoust, Hansen Lab, Stanford Univ, 65-70; vis prof & res assoc, Norwegian Tech Inst, 71-72; MEM TECH STAFF MICROWAVE ACOUST, SPERRY RES CTR, 73- *Mem:* Sigma Xi; Inst Electronics & Elec Engrs. *Res:* Signal processing with surface acoustic wave devices; particular emphasis on band pass filters, convolvers, surface wave amplifiers and wave propagation in layered media. *Mailing Add:* 100 N Rd Sperry Res Ctr Div Sudbury MA 01776

SOLIE, THOMAS NORMAN, b Spring Grove, Minn, Sept 16, 31; m 59; c 2. PHYSICAL CHEMISTRY, BIOPHYSICS. *Educ:* Univ Minn, Minneapolis, BA, 59; Univ Ore, MA, 63, PhD(chem), 65. *Prof Exp:* Instr biophys, Med Ctr, Univ Colo, 65; USPHS fel, 65-66; res assoc molecular biol, Vanderbilt Univ, 66; asst prof chem, Luther Col, Iowa, 66-67; asst prof, 67-74, ASSOC PROF BIOPHYS & CHEM, COLO STATE UNIV, 74- *Mem:* AAAS; Am Chem Soc; Biophys Soc. *Res:* Physical chemistry of biological macromolecules; luminescence decay spectroscopy; membrane processes. *Mailing Add:* Dept of Physiol & Biophys Colo State Univ Ft Collins CO 80521

SOLIMAN, AFIFI HASSAN, b Cairo, Egypt, Feb 2, 31; m 62; c 4. TRANSPORTATION, PHOTOGRAMMETRY. *Educ:* Ain-Shams Univ, Cairo, BSc, 58; Ohio State Univ, MSc, 62, PhD(geod sci), 68. *Prof Exp:* Design engr, Suez Canal Authority, Egypt, 58-60; res asst geod sci, Res Ctr Found, Ohio State Univ, 62-64; sr engr, Brill Eng Inc, Ohio, 64-66; asst prof civil eng, McMaster Univ, 66-69; asst prof, 69-71, exec secy, Ctr Transp Studies, 71-73, ASSOC PROF CIVIL ENG, UNIV MAN, 71- *Concurrent Pos:* Nat Res Coun Can & Can Transp Comn grants, Ctr Transp Studies, Univ Man; mem, Hwy Res Bd, Nat Acad Sci-Nat Res Coun; Can Int Develop Agency vis prof, Univ West Indies, 75-77. *Mem:* Am Soc Photogram; Eng Inst Can; Can Roads & Transp Asn. *Res:* Transportation planning, especially public transportation in urban areas; transportation growth and demand; forecasting, methods and techniques for determining potential demand for highways; practical application of transportation system analysis on private and public transportations. *Mailing Add:* Dept of Civil Eng Univ of Man Winnipeg MB R3T 2N2 Can

SOLIMAN, KARAM FARAG ATTIA, b Cairo, Egypt, Oct 15, 44; US citizen; m 73; c 3. NEUROENDOCRINOLOGY, ENDOCRINOLOGY. *Educ:* Cairo Univ, BS, 64; Univ Ga, MS, 72, PhD(endocrinol), 72. *Prof Exp:* Res asst physiol, Univ Ga, 68-72; asst prof, Sch Vet Med, Tuskegee Inst, 72-75, assoc prof, 75-79; PROF PHYSIOL, SCH PHARM, FLA A&M UNIV, 79-, DIR BASIC SCI, 81- *Concurrent Pos:* Prin investr grants, NASA, 76- & NIH, 76-81. *Mem:* Am Physiol Soc; Endocrine Soc; Neurosci Soc; Chronobiol Soc. *Res:* Investigate the role of peripheral nervous system in the regulation of the endocrine gland function; elucidate the physiology and the pharmacology of the role of the antonomic nervous system in the regulation of adrenal cortex function. *Mailing Add:* Sch Pharm Fla A&M Univ Tallahassee FL 32307

SOLIN, STUART ALLAN, b Baltimore, Md, Sept 9, 42; m 64; c 1. SOLID STATE PHYSICS. *Educ:* Mass Inst Technol, BS, 63; Purdue Univ, MS, 66, PhD(physics), 69. *Prof Exp:* Asst physics, Purdue Univ, 64-69; asst prof physics, Univ Chicago, 69-74, assoc prof, 74-80; MEM FAC, DEPT PHYSICS, MICH STATE UNIV, 80- *Mem:* Am Phys Soc. *Res:* Solid state physics; laser Raman spectroscopy of solids; fundamental properties of lasers. *Mailing Add:* Dept Physics Mich State Univ E Lansing MI 48824

SOLIS-GAFFAR, MARIA CORAZON, b Tacloban City, Philippines, Dec 1, 39; m 70; c 1. BIOCHEMISTRY, MEDICINAL CHEMISTRY. *Educ:* Univ Santo Tomas, Manila, BS, 61; Mass Col Pharm, MS, 64, PhD(biochem), 67. *Prof Exp:* Qual control chemist, Inhelder Labs, 61; instr chem, Emmanuel Col, Mass, 64-67; SR RES CHEMIST, JOHNSON & JOHNSON RES CTR, COLGATE-PALMOLIVE CO, 67- *Mem:* Am Chem Soc; Am Pharmaceut

Asn; Am Asn Dent Res. *Res:* Structure-activity relationships; enzyme inhibition studies; pathological calcification; mouth odor studies; human clinical studies for evaluation of oral products in mouth odor reduction; biochemistry of sulfur metabolism in oral cavity; oral products and pharmaceutical product development. *Mailing Add:* Johnson & Johnson Res Ctr Colgate-Polmolive Co Rte 1 New Brunswick NJ 08902

SOLISH, GEORGE IRVING, b Providence, RI, Jan 7, 20; m 46; c 3. OBSTETRICS & GYNECOLOGY, HUMAN GENETICS. *Educ:* Providence Col, BS, 41; Tufts Univ, 48, MD, 50; Univ Mich, MS, 61, PhD(human genetics), 68. *Prof Exp:* From instr to asst prof, 57-68, assoc prof, 68-79, PROF OBSTET & GYNEC, STATE UNIV NY DOWNSTATE MED CTR, 79- *Concurrent Pos:* Res asst, Med Sch, Univ Mich, 60-63; consult, Margaret Sanger Res Bur, 64- *Mem:* Am Col Obstet & Gynec; Am Fertil Soc; Am Soc Human Genetics; Brit Eugenics Soc. *Res:* Population genetics; prezygotic selection and control of fertility including family planning techniques; infertility; reproduction. *Mailing Add:* Dept of Obstet & Gynec State Univ NY Downstate Med Ctr Brooklyn NY 11203

SOLL, DAVID RICHARD, b Philadelphia, Pa, Apr 29, 42; c 1. DEVELOPMENTAL BIOLOGY. *Educ:* Univ Wis, BA, 64, MA, 68, PhD(zool), 70. *Prof Exp:* Fel develop biol, Univ Wis, 69-70, Brandeis Univ, 71-72; asst prof, 72-77, ASSOC PROF ZOOL, UNIV IOWA, 77- *Concurrent Pos:* Res grants, NSF, 74 & 76 & NIH, 78, 79 & 81; mem, Cell Biol Study Sect, NIH, 78-83. *Mem:* Soc Develop Biol; AAAS. *Res:* An analysis of the molecular mechanisms controlling cell differentiation and muticellular morphogenesis. *Mailing Add:* Dept of Zool Univ of Iowa Iowa City IA 52242

SOLLBERGER, ARNE RUDOLPH, b Dresden, Ger, Mar 17, 24; m 54; c 2. BIOMETRY. *Educ:* Caroline Inst, Stockholm, Sweden, MB, 49, MD, 57. *Prof Exp:* From asst anat to assoc prof, Caroline Inst, Stockholm, Sweden, 48-62; prof pharmacol, Univ PR, 62-64; assoc med, Case Western Reserve Univ, 64-65; chief biomet, Eastern Res Supply Ctr, Vet Admin Hosp, West Haven, Conn, 65-67; assoc prof psychiat, Med Sch, Yale Univ, 68-72; PROF PHYSIOL & INFO PROCESSING, MED SCH, SOUTHERN ILL UNIV, 72- *Concurrent Pos:* Lectr anat & physiol, two nursing schs & Sch Indust Art, Stockholm, 57-62; asst ward physician, Hosp Swedish Diabetes Found, Stockholm, 54-62; lectr biometrics, Yale Univ, 66-72; ed-in-chief, J Interdiscplinary Cycle Res, 78-; chmn biol rhythms study group, Int Soc Biometeorol, 70; mem panel examr, Am Bd Prev Med, 73; bd mem, Found Study Cycles, 75, pres, 76- *Honors & Awards:* Award, Biometeorol Res Found, 75. *Mem:* AAAS; fel Royal Soc Health; Am Statist Asn; fel NY Acad Sci; hon mem Soc Biol Rhythm (secy, 55-67). *Res:* Cardiology and diabetes; biological rhythms, especially statistical problems; normal values in medicine; biomedical computer processing. *Mailing Add:* Lindegren Hall Southern Ill Univ Med Sch Carbondale IL 62901

SOLLBERGER, DWIGHT ELLSWORTH, b Sharpsburg, Pa, July 29, 08; m 35; c 1. BIOLOGY. *Educ:* Pa State Teachers Col, BS, 32; Cornell Univ, PhD(vert zool), 38. *Prof Exp:* Instr high sch, Pa, 32-35; instr biol, Ky State Teachers Col, Morehead, 38; instr biol & head dept, 38-70, coordr natural sci & math, 66-70, EMER PROF BIOL, IND UNIV, PA, 70- *Concurrent Pos:* Ed newsletter, Assoc Am Nature Study Soc. *Mem:* Assoc Am Nature Study Soc; Am Soc Mammal; Nat Asn Biol Teachers; Nat Sci Teachers Asn. *Res:* Life history of mammals and the small eastern flying squirrel. *Mailing Add:* 343 S 13th Indiana PA 15701

SOLLER, ARTHUR, b New York, NY, Aug 15, 36; m 65; c 2. INDUSTRIAL MICROBIOLOGY. *Educ:* City Col New York, BS, 57; Brandeis Univ, PhD(biol), 63. *Prof Exp:* NIH fel microbiol, Univ Milan, Italy, 63-64 & Int Lab Genetics & Biophys, Naples, 65-67; for consult genetics, 68-70; asst prof microbiol, Eppley Cancer Inst, Omaha, Nebr, 71 & Univ Ill, Chicago, 72; RES ASSOC, STAUFFER CHEM CO, 73- *Mem:* Am Soc Microbiologists. *Res:* Strain improvement of glutamic acid producing microorganisms via mutation and selection; development of phage resistant strains; investigation of microorganisms producing high yields of amino acids. *Mailing Add:* 1200 S 47th St Stauffer Chem Co Richmond CA 94804

SOLLER, ROGER WILLIAM, b Bronxville, NY, Nov 18, 46. PHARMACOLOGY, NEUROPHARMACOLOGY. *Educ:* Colby Col, BA, 68; Cornell Univ, PhD(neurobiol), 73. *Prof Exp:* Fel pharmacol, Sch Med, Univ Pa, 73-75, instr & res assoc, 75-77, asst prof, 77-79; sci assoc pharmacol, 79-81, VPRES DIR SCI AFFAIRS, GLENBROOK LABS, DIV STERLING DRUG INC, 81- *Concurrent Pos:* Pharmaceut Mfrs Asn fel, 74-76; Pa plan scholar, Univ Pa, 76-79. *Mem:* Soc Neurosci; Sigma Xi. *Res:* Mechanisms of action of analgesics, hormones and neurotransmitter substances; clinical pharmacology. *Mailing Add:* Glenbrook Labs Div 90 Park Ave New York NY 10016

SOLLERS-RIEDEL, HELEN, b Baltimore, Md, Sept 29, 11; wid. ENTOMOLOGY. *Educ:* Wilson Teachers Col, BS, 34. *Prof Exp:* With insect pest surv, Bur Entomol & Plant Quarantine, 37-43, jr entomologist, 43-47, asst entomologist, Insects Affecting Man and Animals, 46-53, entomologist, Plant Pest Control Div, Agr Res Serv, USDA, 53-71; MED ENTOMOLOGIST, NIH GRANT, 71- *Mem:* Am Mosquito Control Asn; Am Soc Parasitol; Am Soc Trop Med & Hyg; Entom Soc Am; Entom Soc Can. *Res:* Mosquito research and analysis. *Mailing Add:* PO Box 19009 Washington DC 20036

SOLLFREY, WILLIAM, b New York, NY, Mar 8, 25; m 49. PHYSICS. *Educ:* NY Univ, BA, 44, MS, 46, PhD(physics), 50. *Prof Exp:* Asst proj engr, Sperry Gyroscope Co, 44-47; res assoc, Math Res Group, NY Univ, 47-51; sr engr, W L Maxson Corp, 51-55; sr res engr, Chicago Midway Labs, 55-57; mgr syst anal, Mech Div, Gen Mills, Inc, 57-61; PHYS SCIENTIST, RAND CORP, 61- *Concurrent Pos:* Instr, Polytech Inst Brooklyn, 53-55. *Mem:* AAAS; Am Phys Soc. *Res:* Advanced analysis in military systems; mathematics; electrical engineering. *Mailing Add:* Rand Corp 1700 Main St Santa Monica CA 90406

SOLLID, JON ERIK, b Denver, Colo, Oct 1, 39; m 81; c 8. OPTICS. *Educ:* Univ Mich, Ann Arbor, BS, 61; NMex State Univ, MS, 65, PhD(physics), 67. *Prof Exp:* Physicist, White Sands Missile Range, 61-62; res assoc plasma physics, Los Alamos Sci Lab, 65-66; sr res scientist, Convair Aerospace Div, Gen Dynamics, 67-72 & Sci Res Lab, Ford Motor Co, 72-74; staff scientist, 74-81, PROJ LEADER, LOS ALAMOS NAT LAB, 81- *Concurrent Pos:* Adj prof, Texas Christian Univ, 70-72; prof, Northern NMex Community Col, 78-80; adj prof, Los Alamos Br, Univ NMex, 80- *Mem:* Am Phys Soc; Am Asn Physics Teachers; Optical Soc Am; Soc Photo-Optical Instrumentation Engrs; Sigma Xi. *Res:* Optical diagnostics; holographic interferometry and coherent optics; applications in experimental mechanics and plasma physics; laser fusion. *Mailing Add:* Mail Stop 533 Group P-5 Los Alamos Nat Lab Los Alamos NM 87545

SOLLMAN, PAUL BENJAMIN, b Ft Branch, Ind, May 2, 20; m 41; c 4. ORGANIC CHEMISTRY. *Educ:* Univ Ind, BS, 47; Univ Minn, PhD(org chem), 51. *Prof Exp:* res chemist, G D Searle Co, 51-80; RES CHEMIST, REGIS CHEM CO, 81- *Mem:* Am Chem Soc. *Res:* Organic synthesis; medicinal chemistry. *Mailing Add:* 2040 Glenview Rd Wilmette IL 60091

SOLLNER-WEBB, BARBARA THEA, b Washington, DC, Dec 21, 48; m 73. MOLECULAR BIOLOGY. *Educ:* Mass Inst Technol, BS, 70; Stanford Univ, PhD(biol), 76. *Prof Exp:* staff fel, Molecular Biol, Nat Inst Arthritis, Metab & Digestive Dis, NIH, 76-77; FEL, DEPT EMBRYOL, CARNEGIE INST, WASHINGTON, 77- *Res:* Structure and function of chromatin; nuclease protease and polymerase action on nucleoprotein and nuclei; ribosomal RNA transcriptional control regions of xenopus laevis; DNA sequencing. *Mailing Add:* Dept of Embryol 115 W University Pkwy Baltimore MD 21210

SOLLOTT, GILBERT PAUL, b Philadelphia, Pa, July 12, 27; m 54; c 2. ORGANIC CHEMISTRY. *Educ:* Univ Pa, BA, 49; Temple Univ, MA, 56, PhD(org chem), 62. *Prof Exp:* Chemist, R M Hollingshead Corp, 50-52 & Betz Labs, 52-53; org chemist, Pitman-Dunn Lab, Frankford Arsenal, 53-62, chief org chem br, 62-77; RES CHEMIST, US ARMY ARMAMENT RES & DEVELOP COMMAND, 77- *Honors & Awards:* Outstanding Achievement Award, US Dept Army, 64. *Mem:* AAAS; Am Chem Soc; Sigma Xi; NY Acad Sci; Royal Soc Chem. *Res:* Organic, organometallic and organometalloid chemistry including phosphorus, arsenic, boron, silicon and germanium; chemiluminescence research; new synthetic methods; mechanisms; ferrocene chemistry; polymers; nitrocompounds. *Mailing Add:* Energetic Mat Div US Army Armament Res & Develop Command Dover NJ 07801

SOLMAN, VICTOR EDWARD FRICK, b Toronto, Ont, May 24, 16; m 42; c 2. ZOOLOGY, ECOLOGY. *Educ:* Univ Toronto, BA, 38, MA, 39, PhD(biol), 42. *Prof Exp:* Asst zool, Univ Toronto, 36-42; limnologist, Nat Parks Bur, Dept Mines & Resources & Dom Wildlife Serv, 45-49, chief biologist, Dom Wildlife Serv, 49-50 & Can Wildlife Serv, 50-53, asst chief, 53-64, staff specialist, 64-81; RETIRED. *Honors & Awards:* Gold Medal, Prof Inst Pub Serv Can, 77. *Mem:* Fel AAAS. *Res:* Cladocera of Costello Creek, Algonquin Park, Ontario; ecological relations of waterfowl, especially predatory fish; ecology; wildlife research and management; reduction of bird hazards to aircraft. *Mailing Add:* 614 Denbury Ave Ottawa ON K2A 2P1 Can

SOLMON, DONALD CLYDE, b Fall River, Mass, Mar 28, 45; m 70; c 2. COMPUTED TOMOGRAPHY. *Educ:* Southeastern Mass Tech Inst, BS, 67; Ore State Univ, MS, 73, PhD(math), 74. *Prof Exp:* Vis asst prof math, Univ Ore, 74-75; George William Hill res instr, State Univ NY at Buffalo, 75-77; asst prof, 77-81, ASSOC PROF MATH, ORE STATE UNIV, 81- *Concurrent Pos:* Vis lectr math, Univ des Saarlandes, 81. *Mem:* Am Math Soc; Math Asn Am. *Res:* Applications of analysis and functional analysis to obtain a deeper understanding of problems in medical radiology especially computed tomography. *Mailing Add:* Dept Math Ore State Univ Corvallis OR 97331

SOLMSSEN, ULRICH VOLCKMAR, b Berlin, Ger, Oct 26, 09; US citizen; m 36; c 4. ORGANIC CHEMISTRY. *Educ:* Univ Zurich, PhD(chem), 35. *Prof Exp:* Sr res chemist, Hoffmann-La Roche, Inc, 38-46; asst dir res, Warner Inst Therapeut Res, 46-49, admin dir, 49-55, sci dir, Warner-Lambert Int, 56-62, vpres plants & opers, Warner-Lambert Res Inst, 62-63, exec vpres, 63-65, pres, Chem Div, Warner-Lambert Pharmaceut Co, NJ, 66-75. *Concurrent Pos:* Pres, Nepera Chem Co, Inc, 67-75; trustee, Mountainside Hosp. *Mem:* Fel NY Acad Sci. *Mailing Add:* 153 Oval Rd Essex Fells NJ 07021

SOLN, JOSIP ZVONIMIR, b Zagreb, Yugoslavia, Mar 31, 34; m 66. THEORETICAL PHYSICS. *Educ:* Univ Zagreb, BSc, 57, PhD(physics), 60. *Prof Exp:* Res assoc parity violation in mu decay, Rudjer Boskovic Inst, Zagreb, 57-61, researcher particle physics & field theory, 62-64; fel high energy physics, European Ctr Nuclear Res, Geneva, Switz, 61-62; res assoc broken symmetries, Univ Calif, Los Angeles, 64-65, asst prof in residence, 65-66; asst prof particle physics, Univ Wis, Milwaukee, 66-70; vis asst prof, Univ Ill, Chicago Circle, 70-71; res assoc, Inst Theoret Sci, Univ Ore, 71-72; PHYSICIST, NUCLEAR RADIATION EFFECTS LAB, HARRY DIAMOND LABS, 72- *Honors & Awards:* Scientific Achievement Award, Sigma Xi, 75. *Res:* Nonconservation of parity in weak decays; quantum field theory; soluble models; particle production in pion-proton collision; high energy behavior of the scattering amplitude; broken symmetries; solid state devices; cerenkov and stimulated radiations; free electron lasers; radiation propagation. *Mailing Add:* Harry Diamond Labs Nuclear Radiation Effects Lab Adelphi MD 20783

SOLO, ALAN JERE, b Philadelphia, Pa, Nov 7, 33; m 63; c 2. MEDICINAL CHEMISTRY, ORGANIC CHEMISTRY. *Educ:* Mass Inst Technol, SB, 55; Columbia Univ, AM, 56, PhD(chem), 59. *Prof Exp:* Res assoc org chem, Rockefeller Inst, 58-62; from asst prof to assoc prof, 62-70, PROF MED CHEM, STATE UNIV NY BUFFALO, 70-, CHMN DEPT, 69- *Concurrent Pos:* Consult, Westwood Pharmaceut Inc, 71- *Mem:* Am Chem Soc; Am

Pharmaceut Asn; Acad Pharm Sci. *Res:* Synthesis and structure-activity relationships of steroid hormones; investigations of mechanism of action of steroid hormones. *Mailing Add:* Dept of Med Chem Sch Pharm State Univ NY Buffalo NY 14260

SOLODAR, ARTHUR JOHN, b East Orange, NJ, Apr 18, 40; m 64; c 3. ORGANIC CHEMISTRY, CATALYSIS. *Educ:* Swarthmore Col, BA, 62; Yale Univ, MS, 63, PhD(chem), 67. *Prof Exp:* Nat Cancer Inst fel, Mass Inst Technol, 67-68; sr res chemist, 68-74, res specialist, 80-80, SR RES SPECIALIST, MONSANTO CO, 74- *Mem:* Sigma Xi; Am Chem Soc. *Res:* Homogeneous catalysis; asymmetric synthesis; phase-transfer catalysis; exploratory process research. *Mailing Add:* Monsanto Co 800 N Lindbergh St Louis MO 63167

SOLODAR, WARREN E, b New York, NY, Sept 29, 25; m 50; c 2. ORGANIC CHEMISTRY. *Educ:* NY Univ, AB, 48; Stevens Inst Technol, MS, 53. *Prof Exp:* Assoc chemist, Hoffmann-La Roche, Inc, 48-54; chemist, Polaroid Corp, 54-64; SCIENTIST, XEROX CORP, 64- *Concurrent Pos:* Res fel, Koor Chem Ltd, Beer Sheva, Israel, 74-75; vis prof, Hebrew Univ Jerusalem, 82. *Mem:* Am Chem Soc; Israel Chem Soc. *Res:* Pharmaceuticals; vitamins; hypertensive agents; analgesics; azo and anthraquinone dyes; photographic developers; organic photoconductors; pigments; photoelectrophoretic imaging materials. *Mailing Add:* Xerox Corp Joseph C Wilson Ctr for Technol Rochester NY 14644

SOLOFF, BERNARD LEROY, b New York, NY, June 21, 31; m 61; c 2. ANATOMY. *Educ:* Univ Cincinnati, BS, 53, MS, 56; Rice Univ, PhD(biol), 61. *Prof Exp:* Res asst trace metals, M D Anderson Hosp & Tumor Inst, 61; asst prof biol, Stephen F Austin State Col, 61-62; res assoc anat, Med Units, Univ Tenn, Memphis, 63-64; RES PHYSIOLOGIST, LITTLE ROCK HOSP DIV, VET ADMIN, 65- *Concurrent Pos:* Nat Heart Inst fel & training grant, Marine Lab, Inst Marine Sci, Univ Miami, 62-63; USPHS trainee, Med Units, Univ Tenn, Memphis, 64-65; instr, Med Ctr, Univ Ark, 65-70, asst prof, 70- *Mem:* NY Acad Sci; AAAS; Am Asn Anatomists; Tissue Culture Asn; Electron Micros Soc Am. *Res:* Ultrastructure of leukocytes; ultrastructure of hemoglobin interactions within erythrocytes; ultrastructure of lung; ultrastructure of bacteria and bacteriophage; ultrastructure of heart. *Mailing Add:* Gen Med Res Vet Admin Hosp Little Rock AR 72206

SOLOFF, LOUIS ALEXANDER, b Paris, France, Oct 2, 04; nat US; m 34; c 1. MEDICINE, CARDIOLOGY. *Educ:* Univ Chicago, MD, 30. *Prof Exp:* Chief labs, St Joseph's & St Vincent's Hosps & Eagleville Sanatorium, 34-45; chief dept cardiol, Episcopal Hosp, 50-56; chief div cardiol, Health Sci Ctr, 56-71, PROF MED, TEMPLE UNIV, 56-, BLANCHE P LEVY DISTINGUISHED SERV UNIV PROF, 71- *Mem:* Asn Univ Cardiol; Am Heart Asn; Am Col Physicians; Am Col Cardiol; Sigma Xi. *Res:* Diseases of the heart. *Mailing Add:* 340 N Broad St Philadelphia PA 19140

SOLOFF, MELVYN STANLEY, b Los Angeles, Calif, Oct 6, 38; m 68; c 2. ENDOCRINOLOGY. *Educ:* Univ Calif, Los Angeles, AB, 62, MA, 64, PhD(zool), 68. *Prof Exp:* Res fel, Univ Calif, Los Angeles, 68-69; assoc res biologist, Sterling-Winthrop Res Inst, 69-70; asst prof biochem, 70-74, assoc prof, 74-79, PROF BIOCHEM, MED COL OHIO, 79- *Mem:* Endocrine Soc; Am Soc Biol Chemists. *Res:* Hormone receptors; mechanisms of hormone action. *Mailing Add:* Dept Biochem Med Col Ohio Toledo OH 43699

SOLOMON, ALAN, b New York, NY, May 16, 33; m 59; c 2. HEMATOLOGY, ONCOLOGY. *Educ:* Bucknell Univ, BS, 53; Duke Univ, BSMed, 56, MD, 57; Am Bd Internal Med, dipl, 64. *Prof Exp:* Intern, Mt Sinai Hosp, New York, 57-58, asst resident med, 59-60; asst resident, Montefiore Hosp, 58-59; clin assoc, Nat Cancer Inst, 60-62; chief resident, Mt Sinai Hosp, 62-63, asst attend physician, 65-66; PROF RES, MEM RES CTR, UNIV TENN, KNOXVILLE, 66-, CLIN PROF MED, 72- *Concurrent Pos:* Res fel hemat, Mt Sinai Hosp, 63-65; Nat Inst Arthritis & Metab Dis spec fel, Rockefeller Inst, 63-65; USPHS res career develop award, 67-72; from asst physician to assoc physician, Rockefeller Inst, 63-66, guest investr, 63-66; prin investr, USPHS grant, 65-, mem review comt, Nat Cancer Inst, Clin Cancer Prog Proj. *Mem:* Am Soc Clin Invest; fel Am Col Physicians; Am Soc Clin Oncol; Am Asn Cancer Educ; Am Soc Hemat. *Res:* Internal medicine; cancer; immunoglobulins. *Mailing Add:* Univ of Tenn Mem Res Ctr 1924 Alcoa Hwy Knoxville TN 37920

SOLOMON, ALAN D, b New York, NY, Apr 6, 40; m 68. APPLIED MATHEMATICS, NUMERICAL ANALYSIS. *Educ:* City Col New York, BS, 59; NY Univ, MS, 60, PhD(math), 63. *Prof Exp:* Res asst math, NY Univ, 60-62, NSF fel, 62-63, asst res scientist, 63-65, asst prof, 65-67; sr lectr, Tel Aviv Univ, 67-70; sr lectr, Univ of the Negev, 70-74, assoc prof math & chmn dept, 74-77; MEM STAFF, UNION CARBIDE NUCLEAR DIV & COMPUT SCI DIV, 77- *Mem:* Am Math Soc; Soc Indust & Appl Math; Solar Energy Soc; NY Acad Sci; Israel Math Union. *Res:* Partial differential equations; minimal surfaces; calculus of variations; computer science; intelligent systems; robotics. *Mailing Add:* Union Carbide Nuclear Div Bldg 9704-1 PO Box Y Oak Ridge TN 37830

SOLOMON, ALLEN M, b Mt Clemens, Mich, Apr 29, 43; m 66; c 2. PLANT ECOLOGY, PALYNOLOGY. *Educ:* Univ Mich, Ann Arbor, BA, 65; Rutgers Univ, New Brunswick, PhD(bot), 70. *Prof Exp:* Res asst bot, Rutgers Univ, New Brunswick, 68-70; asst prof geosci, Univ Ariz, 70-76; res assoc, 76-81, MEM RES STAFF, OAK RIDGE NAT LAB, 81- *Concurrent Pos:* Ed, Amqua Newsletter, 79-; co-prin investr, Terrestrial Ecosysts, Climate & Global Carbon Cycle, NSF, 81-84. *Mem:* AAAS; Ecol Soc Am; Am Quaternary Asn; Am Inst Biol Sci; Int Asn Aerobiol. *Res:* Plant and desert ecology; biometeorology; ecological impacts of energy systems; quaternary palynology; plant geography; modelling paleoenvironmental reconstruction. *Mailing Add:* Environ Sci Div Oak Ridge Nat Lab PO Box X Oak Ridge TN 37830

SOLOMON, ALVIN ARNOLD, b Chicago, Ill, Aug 17, 37. MATERIALS SCIENCE. *Educ:* Univ Ill, BS, 59, MS, 61; Stanford Univ, PhD(mat sci), 68. *Prof Exp:* Develop engr, Advan Systs Develop Div, IBM Corp, 61-64; postdoctoral res, French Atomic Energy Comn, Saclay, 68-69; metallurgist, Argonne Nat Lab, 69-74; ASSOC PROF NUCLEAR ENG, PURDUE UNIV, 74- *Concurrent Pos:* Instr, San Jose State Col, 63-64; mem staff, Denver Res Inst, 66. *Honors & Awards:* Ceramographic Award, Am Ceramic Soc. *Mem:* Am Ceramic Soc. *Res:* Nuclear materials. *Mailing Add:* Purdue Univ Sch of Nuclear Eng West Lafayette IN 47907

SOLOMON, ARTHUR KASKEL, b Pittsburgh, Pa, Nov 26, 12; m; c 2. BIOPHYSICS. *Educ:* Princeton Univ, AB, 34; Harvard Univ, MA, 35, PhD(phys chem), 37; Cambridge Univ, PhD(physics), 47. *Hon Degrees:* ScD, Cambridge Univ, 64. *Prof Exp:* Res assoc physics & chem, Harvard Univ, 39-41, Exp Off, Brit Ministry Supply, 41-43 & Brit Admiralty, 43-45; mem staff, Radiation Lab, Mass Inst Technol, 45; asst prof physiol chem, 46-56, assoc prof biophys, 57-68, PROF BIOPHYS, HARVARD MED SCH, 68- *Concurrent Pos:* Assoc, Peter Bent Brigham Hosp, 50-72; mem ed bd, J Gen Physiol, 58-; chmn comt on higher degrees in biophys, Harvard Univ, 59-80; NIH radiation study sect, 60-63, biophys sci training comn, 63-68, chmn, 66-68; secy-gen, Int Union Pure & Appl Biophys, 61-72; mem bd, Int Orgn & Progs, Nat Res Coun, Nat Acad Sci, 67-80, chmn, 77-79; sci policy adv to Thai govt, UNESCO, 68-72, mem, US Nat Comt, 69-74. *Honors & Awards:* Order Andres Bello, Govt of Venezuela, 74. *Mem:* AAAS; Am Chem Soc; Am Physiol Soc; Biophys Soc; fel Am Acad Arts & Sci. *Res:* Permeability of cellular membranes and model systems. *Mailing Add:* Biophys Lab Harvard Med Sch 25 Shattuck St Boston MA 02115

SOLOMON, BARTON STEPHEN, analytical chemistry, physical chemistry, see previous edition

SOLOMON, DANIEL LESTER, b New York, NY, July 30, 41; m 67; c 3. BIOMETRICS, MATHEMATICAL STATISTICS. *Educ:* Fla State Univ, BS, 62, MS, 64, PhD(math statist), 68. *Prof Exp:* Instr statist, Fla State Univ, 67-68; from asst prof to prof biol statist, Biomet Unit, Cornell Univ, 68-80; PROF & HEAD, DEPT STATISTICS, NC STATE UNIV, 81- *Concurrent Pos:* Assoc ed, Biometrics, 75-79; mem comt statist, Southern Region Educ Bd. *Mem:* AAAS; Am Statist Asn; Biomet Soc; Inst Math Statist. *Res:* Bayesian statistical inference; mathematical models in biology. *Mailing Add:* Dept Statist NC State Univ Raleigh NC 27607

SOLOMON, DAVID EUGENE, b Milton, Pa, June 22, 31; m 50; c 3. RESEARCH ADMINISTRATION, MATERIALS SCIENCE. *Educ:* Susquehanna Univ, AB, 58; Bucknell Univ, MS, 60; Eastern Mich Univ, MBA, 75. *Prof Exp:* Sr engr, Electron Tube Lab, Westinghouse Elec Corp, Md, 59-65; sr res engr, Electron Physics Lab, Univ Mich, Ann Arbor, 65-67; chief engr, Electro Optics Div, Bendix Corp, Mich, 67-71, prog mgr Mars probe, Org Anal Spectrometer Prog, Bendix Aerospace Systs Div, 71-72; dir laser fusion mat, Div Mat Sci, 72-80, VPRES OPERS, KMS FUSION, INC, 80- *Mem:* Am Vacuum Soc; Inst Elec & Electronics Engrs; Am Ceramic Soc; Soc Mfg Engrs. *Res:* Broad research in the material sciences aimed at laser thermonuclear fuel pellets, encompassing glass synthesis and fabrication, polymers, copolymers, cryogenics, radiography, microdensitometry, active metals, vacuum deposition and others. *Mailing Add:* 3415 Woodlea Dr Ann Arbor MI 48103

SOLOMON, DAVID HARRIS, b Mass, Mar 7, 23; m 46; c 2. ENDOCRINOLOGY. *Educ:* Brown Univ, AB, 44; Harvard Med Sch, MD, 46. *Prof Exp:* House officer med, Peter Bent Brigham Hosp, 46-47, sr asst resident physician, 50-51; sr asst surgeon, NIH, 48-50; from instr to assoc prof med, 52-66, chmn dept med, 71-81, PROF MED & ENDOCRINOL, SCH MED, UNIV CALIF, LOS ANGELES, 66- *Concurrent Pos:* Res fel, Peter Bent Brigham Hosp, 47-48; fel endocrinol, New Eng Ctr Hosp, 51-52; attend physician, Harbor Gen Hosp, Torrance, 52-66, chief dept med, 66-71; attend physician, Vet Admin Ctr, 52- *Mem:* Am Asn Physicians; Endocrine Soc; Am Physiol Soc; Am Col Physicians; Inst of Med of Nat Acad Sci. *Res:* Action of thyrotropin on the thyroid gland; pathogenesis of Graves' disease; nature of thyroid-stimulating agents. *Mailing Add:* Dept of Med Univ of Calif Sch of Med Los Angeles CA 90024

SOLOMON, DONALD W, b Detroit, Mich, Feb 6, 41. ANALYTICAL MATHEMATICS. *Educ:* Wayne State Univ, BS, 61, MA, 63, PhD(math), 66. *Prof Exp:* From teaching asst to instr math, Wayne State Univ, 63-66; asst prof, 66-70, assoc chmn dept, 75-78, ASSOC PROF MATH, UNIV WIS-MILWAUKEE, 70-, CHMN, DIV NATURAL SCI, 76- *Concurrent Pos:* NSF res grants, 67-68 & 70-71; Univ Wis Grad Sch res grants, 69, 71-72 & 73-74. *Mem:* AAAS; Am Math Soc; Math Asn Am; Soc Indust & Appl Math; NY Acad Sci. *Res:* Measure, integration and differentiation. *Mailing Add:* Dept of Math Univ of Wis Milwaukee WI 53201

SOLOMON, EDWARD I, b New York, NY, Oct 20, 46. PHYSICAL INORGANIC CHEMISTRY, BIOINORGANIC CHEMISTRY. *Educ:* Rensselaer Polytech Inst, BS, 68; Princeton Univ, MA, 70, PhD(chem), 72. *Prof Exp:* Danish Nat Sci Found fel chem, H C Orsted Inst, Univ Copenhagen, 73-74; NIH fel, Noyes Lab, Calif Inst Technol, 74-75; A P Sloan res fel, 76; asst prof chem, Mass Inst Technol, 75-78, assoc prof, 79-80, prof, 81; PROF CHEM, STANFORD UNIV, 82- *Concurrent Pos:* Sloan fel, 76-78. *Mem:* Am Chem Soc; Am Phys Soc; Sigma Xi; Am Asn Univ Profs. *Res:* Inorganic spectroscopy and ligand field theory; spectral and magnetic studies on bioinorganic systems; interactions between metals in polynuclear complexes; spectroscopic studies of active sites in metalloprotein and heterogeneous catalysts. *Mailing Add:* Dept Chem Stanford Univ Stanford CA 94305

SOLOMON, FRANK I, b Denver, Colo, Oct 7, 24; m 48; c 3. ELECTROCHEMISTRY. *Educ:* City Col New York, BChE, 47. *Prof Exp:* Asst vpres & tech dir, Yardney Elec Corp, 49-71; tech dir, Molecular Energy Corp, 71-74; PRES, ELECTROMEDIA, INC, 74- *Mem:* Electrochem Soc. *Res:* Storage batteries, alkaline; gas diffusion electrodes. *Mailing Add:* 8 Hampton Ct Great Neck NY 11020

SOLOMON, GENE BARRY, zoology, parasitology, see previous edition

SOLOMON, GORDON CHARLES, b Salida, Colo, Dec 5, 24; m 49; c 6. ANATOMY, PATHOLOGY. *Educ:* Colo State Univ, BS, 49, MS, 51, DVM, 55, PhD(path), 63. *Prof Exp:* Vet epidemiologist, Commun Dis Ctr, USPHS, 55-58, lab dir, Southwest Rabies Invests, 58-60, vet pathologist, 64-66; ASSOC PROF ANAT, COLO STATE UNIV, 66- *Concurrent Pos:* USPHS fel, Colo State Univ, 63-64; consult, Southwest Radiol Health Lab, USPHS, 66-68. *Mem:* Am Asn Vet Anat; World Asn Vet Anat; Wildlife Dis Asn. *Res:* Bone and connective tissue; wildlife anatomy and diseases. *Mailing Add:* Dept of Anat Colo State Univ Ft Collins CO 80521

SOLOMON, HARVEY DONALD, b New York, NY, Dec 14, 41; m 66; c 2. METALLURGY, MATERIALS SCIENCE. *Educ:* NY Univ, BS, 63; Univ Pa, PhD(metall), 68. *Prof Exp:* METALLURGIST & MAT SCIENTIST, RES & DEVELOP CTR, GEN ELEC CO, 68- *Honors & Awards:* Joseph Vilella Award, Am Soc Testing & Mat, 79. *Mem:* Am Inst Mining, Metall & Petrol Engrs. *Res:* Physical and mechanical metallurgy; fatigue; fatigue crack propagation; creep-fatigue interactions; fatigue of solders; metallurgy of stainless steels; stress corrosion cracking; welding metallurgy; materials for advanced energy systems; superalloys. *Mailing Add:* Gen Elec Res & Develop Ctr PO Box 8 Schenectady NY 12345

SOLOMON, HERBERT, b New York, NY, Mar 13, 19; m 47; c 3. MATHEMATICAL STATISTICS. *Educ:* City Col New York, BS, 40; Columbia Univ, MA, 41; Stanford Univ, PhD(math statist), 50. *Prof Exp:* Asst res mathematician, Columbia Univ, 43-44, assoc math statistician, 44-46; instr, City Col New York, 46; asst prof math statist, Stanford Univ, 47; mathematician, Off Naval Intel, US Dept Navy, 48, Off Naval Res, DC, 49-52; prof math, Teachers Col, Columbia Univ, 52-59; PROF STATIST, STANFORD UNIV, 59- *Concurrent Pos:* Guggenheim fel, 58. *Honors & Awards:* Wilks Medalist, Am Statist Asn, 75; Townsend Harris Medalist, City College, NY, 77. *Mem:* Am Statist Asn; Inst Math Statist (pres, 65). *Res:* Psychometrics; engineering statistics; operations research. *Mailing Add:* Dept of Statist Stanford Univ Stanford CA 94305

SOLOMON, HOWARD FRED, b Jersey City, NJ, Nov 13, 48; m 71. RADIOBIOLOGY, CANCER BIOLOGY. *Educ:* Drew Univ, AB, 70; Rutgers Univ, PhD(zool), 76. *Prof Exp:* Res intern radiation biol, Rutgers Univ, 73-75; ASST PROF BIOL, LOYOLA COL, 75- *Concurrent Pos:* Dir, Preprof Prog, Med & Dent Schs, Loyola Col, 75-; consult, preprof adv, State Univ Syst Md, 78-; proj dir cell & tissue kinetics, NSF. *Mem:* AAAS. *Res:* Cell kinetics in the Mongolian gerbil; effects of chemotherapeutic drugs on same. *Mailing Add:* Loyola Col 4501 N Charles St Baltimore MD 21210

SOLOMON, IRVINE JEROME, organic chemistry, inorganic chemistry, see previous edition

SOLOMON, JACK, b Brooklyn, NY, July 26, 41; m 70; c 3. PHYSICAL CHEMISTRY. *Educ:* Mass Inst Technol, BS, 63; Columbia Univ, PhD(phys chem), 67. *Prof Exp:* Res scientist, 67-72, proj scientist, Linde Res Lab, Union Carbide Co, 72-74; sr proj engr, 74-77, supvr, Gas Prod Develop Lab, 77-80, PROCESS MGR, GAS PROD MKT DEVELOP, UNION CARBIDE CO, 80- *Mem:* Am Chem Soc; Sigma Xi. *Res:* Chemistry of oxygen in cryogenic, aqueous and other systems; atmospheres for carburizing; hardening and sintering; applications of oxygen in combustion. *Mailing Add:* Linde Gas Prods Develop Union Carbide Co Tarrytown NY 10591

SOLOMON, JAMES DOYLE, b Bee Branch, Ark, May 18, 34; m 61; c 1. FOREST ENTOMOLOGY. *Educ:* Univ Ark, BS, 56, MS, 60; Miss State Univ, PhD(entom), 71. *Prof Exp:* Res entomologist, Asheville, NC, 60-61 & Stoneville, Miss, 61-75, PRIN RES ENTOMOLOGIST, SOUTHERN FOREST EXP STA, STONEVILLE, MISS, 75- *Concurrent Pos:* Adj asst prof, Miss State Univ, 72-; mem, Interagency Task Force, Cross-Fla Barge Canal Environ Impact Statement, 72-73; mem, USDA task force, Long Range Forest Res Planning, Southern Region, 73-74. *Mem:* Entom Soc Am; Sigma Xi. *Res:* Hardwood insects with emphasis on the Cossid, Cerambycid and Sesiid Borers of living trees and shrubs. *Mailing Add:* US Forest Serv PO Box 227 Stoneville MS 38776

SOLOMON, JAY MURRIE, b Washington, DC, June 6, 36; m 59; c 3. COMPUTATION FLUID DYNAMICS, APPLIED MATHEMATICS. *Educ:* Univ Md, BS, 58, MS, 60, PhD(appl math), 68. *Prof Exp:* Res asst, Univ Md, 58-60; aerospace engr res viscous flows, 60-67, MATHEMATICIAN APPL MATH, WHITE OAK LAB, NAVAL SURFACE WEAPONS CTR, 67- *Mem:* Soc Indust & Appl Math; Am Inst Aeronaut & Astronaut. *Mailing Add:* White Oak Lab US Naval Surface Weapons Ctr Silver Spring MD 20910

SOLOMON, JEROME JAY, b Brooklyn, NY, Apr 23, 45. PHYSICAL CHEMISTRY, MASS SPECTROMETRY. *Educ:* Brooklyn Col, BS, 66; Cornell Univ, PhD(phys chem), 72. *Prof Exp:* Res assoc phys chem & ion-molecule reactions, Rockefeller Univ, 72-75; assoc res scientist, 75-77, ASST PROF, ENVIRON MED & MASS SPECTROMETRY, INST ENVIRON MED, NY UNIV MED CTR, 77- *Mem:* Am Soc Mass Spectrometry; Sigma Xi. *Res:* Development of the analytical capability of mass spectrometry for use in biomedical research; emphasis on metabolism of carcinogens and detection of trace pollutants in air and water. *Mailing Add:* Environ Med NY Univ Med Ctr Long Meadow Rd Tuxedo NY 10987

SOLOMON, JIMMY LLOYD, b Milan, Tenn, Oct 3, 41; m 64; c 2. MATHEMATICS. *Educ:* Univ Miss, BS, 64; Miss State Univ, MS, 66; Tex A&M Univ, PhD(math), 72. *Prof Exp:* Asst mathematician, Dept Aerophysics, Miss State Univ, 64-65, instr, 66-67; instr math, Tex A&M Univ, 71-72; asst prof, Tex A&I Univ, 72-75; ASSOC PROF MATH, MISS STATE UNIV, 75-, HEAD, DEPT MATH & STATIST, 81- *Concurrent Pos:* Consult. *Mem:* Am Math Soc. *Res:* Fixed point theory numerical analysis, and statistical pattern recognition. *Mailing Add:* Dept Math Drawer MA Miss State Univ Mississipi State MS 39759

SOLOMON, JOEL MARTIN, b Malden, Mass, Dec 25, 32; m 60; c 3. IMMUNOGENETICS, IMMUNOHEMATOLOGY. *Educ:* Boston Col, BS, 53; Johns Hopkins Univ, ScM, 57; Univ Wis, PhD(med genetics), 63. *Prof Exp:* Immunohematologist, NIH, 57-60; sr res assoc, Am Nat Red Cross, 63-64; sr res assoc & training dir, 64-67; dir blood bank, Brooklyn-Cumberland Med Ctr, 67-70; blood prod dir, E R Squibb & Sons, Inc, 70-73; dep dir, Div Blood & Blood Prod, Bur Biologics, Food & Drug Admin, 74-77, dir, 78-81; POLICY COORDR, OFF SECY, DEPT HEALTH & HUMAN SERV, 81- *Concurrent Pos:* Clin instr pediat, Calif Col Med, 63-64; mem fac genetics & fac microbiol & immunol, Grad Sch, NIH, 64-67 & 74-; lectr, Sch Med, George Washington Univ, 66-67; clin assoc prof path, Sch Med, State Univ NY Downstate Med Ctr, 67-73. *Mem:* AAAS; Am Soc Human Genetics. *Res:* Quantitative hemagglutination; genetics of human blood groups; immunochemistry of blood group antigens; parasite physiology. *Mailing Add:* Hubert H Humphrey Bldg Rm 631H 200 Independence Ave SW Washington DC 20201

SOLOMON, JOHN JUNIOR, b Mishawaka, Ind, July 20, 28; m 66; c 2. MICROBIOLOGY, BIOCHEMISTRY. *Educ:* Mich State Univ, BS, 52, MS, 56, PhD(microbiol, physiol), 61. *Prof Exp:* Bacteriologist, Mich Dept Health, 55-57; mem staff, Poultry Res Lab, USDA, 61-77; RETIRED. *Res:* Antibiotics screening and media development; studies on epidemiology of avian leukosis; tissue culture virus and antibody analyses. *Mailing Add:* 1719 Gay Lane Lansing MI 48912

SOLOMON, JOLANE BAUMGARTEN, b New York, NY, Sept 23, 27; m 57; c 3. PHYSIOLOGY, ENDOCRINOLOGY. *Educ:* Hunter Col, BS, 52; Radcliffe Col, MS, 55, PhD(physiol), 58. *Prof Exp:* Teaching fel, biol, Harvard Univ, 53-55, sci news writer, 55-57; teaching fel, anat, Harvard Med Sch, 57-59; res assoc nutrit, Harvard Sch Pub Health, 60-63; vis lectr, 63-72, assoc prof, 74-80, PROF BIOL, BOSTON COL, 80- *Concurrent Pos:* Dir, Off Resources, Boston Col, 70-72; Carnegie res fel, 72-74; grants, Nat Inst Drug Abuse, 75-76 & 76-78. *Mem:* AAAS; Am Diabetes Asn; Am Women Sci; Entomol Soc An; Endocrine Soc. *Res:* Effect of THC on reproduction in male and female rats; effect of lighting regimens on growth of the American cockroach, P Americana. *Mailing Add:* Dept Biol Boston Col 140 Commonwealth Ave Chestnut Hill MA 02167

SOLOMON, JOSEPH ALVIN, b New Kensington, Pa, July 25, 25; m 53; c 1. PHYSICAL CHEMISTRY. *Educ:* Westminster Col, BS, 49; Carnegie-Mellon Univ, MS, 58, PhD, 59. *Prof Exp:* Anal chemist, US Steel Corp, NJ, 51-54; analyst, Gulf Res & Develop Co, 54-55; prof chem, St Joseph Col, Md, 58-61 & Marietta Col, 61-62; coal res engr, WVa Univ, 62-63; prof chem, St Joseph Col, Md, 63-65; from asst prof to assoc prof, 65-70, PROF CHEM, PHILADELPHIA COL PHARM & SCI, 70- *Mem:* AAAS; Am Chem Soc. *Res:* Coal research, especially removal of sulfur both prior to and following combustion. *Mailing Add:* Dept of Chem Philadelphia Col Pharm & Sci Philadelphia PA 19104

SOLOMON, JULIUS, b Brooklyn, NY, Apr 14, 36; m 63; c 3. HIGH ENERGY PHYSICS. *Educ:* Columbia Univ, AB, 57; Univ Calif, Berkeley, PhD(physics), 63. *Prof Exp:* Res assoc, Lawrence Radiation Lab, Univ Calif, 63; instr, Princeton Univ, 63-66; asst prof, 66-70, ASSOC PROF PHYSICS, UNIV ILL, CHICAGO CIRCLE, 70- *Mem:* Am Phys Soc. *Res:* Experimental high energy physics; K zero meson decays; pion-proton scattering; neutron-proton scattering; k-zero regeneration; k-zero k-zero bar mass differences; high transverse momentum jets produce with Hadron beams. *Mailing Add:* Dept of Physics Univ Ill Chicago Circle Box 4348 Chicago IL 60680

SOLOMON, LAWRENCE MARVIN, b Montreal, Que, June 1, 31; m 59; c 2. DERMATOLOGY, MEDICAL EDUCATION. *Educ:* McGill Univ, BA, 53; Univ Geneva, MD, 59; FRCP(C), 64; Am Bd Dermat, dipl, 65. *Prof Exp:* Intern, Jewish Gen Hosp, Montreal, 59-60; resident med, Queen Mary Vet Hosp, 60-61; resident dermat, Grad Hosp, Univ Pa, 61-64; from asst prof to assoc prof, 66-74, actg dir, Univ Hosp, 69-70, assoc med educ, Ctr Educ Develop, 70-74, PROF DERMAT & HEAD DEPT, UNIV ILL MED CTR, 74-, PROF MED EDUC, 74- *Concurrent Pos:* Res fel, Jewish Gen Hosp, Montreal, 64-66; consult, Vet Admin Hosp, Hines, Ill, 66-, Dixon State Sch, Ill Dept Ment Health & Ill State Pediat Inst, 68- & West Side Vet Admin Hosp, 69-; mem, Nat Prog Dermat. *Honors & Awards:* Gold Award, Am Acad Dermat & Am Acad Allergy, 64. *Mem:* Am Acad Dermat; Soc Invest Dermat; Am Fedn Clin Res. *Res:* Biochemical and pharmacological studies in atopic dermatitis; pharmacogenetic changes in hereditary skin diseases; prostaglandins effect on skin; catecholamines; protein kinase in atopic dermatitis; congenital malformation of the skin; evaluation methodology in medical education. *Mailing Add:* Dept of Dermat Univ Ill Med Ctr PO Box 6998 Chicago IL 60680

SOLOMON, LOUIS, b New York, NY, June 20, 31; m 60; c 2. MATHEMATICS. *Educ:* Harvard Univ, AB, 51, AM, 52, PhD(math), 58. *Prof Exp:* Asst prof math, Bryn Mawr Col, 58-59 & Haverford Col, 59-62, 63-64; vis mem, Inst Advan Study, 62-63; asst prof, Rockefeller Univ, 64-65; from assoc prof to prof, NMex State Univ, 65-69; PROF MATH, UNIV WIS-MADISON, 69- *Concurrent Pos:* Vis prof, Univ London, 71-72. *Mem:* Am Math Soc; Math Asn Am. *Res:* Finite groups, especially groups generated by reflections and linear groups over finite fields. *Mailing Add:* Dept of Math Univ of Wis Madison WI 53706

SOLOMON, M MICHAEL, b Philadelphia, Pa, Sept 20, 24; m 48; c 2. ORGANIC CHEMISTRY, POLYMER CHEMISTRY. *Educ:* Temple Univ, BA, 45, MA, 47; Purdue Univ, PhD, 51. *Prof Exp:* Asst, Temple Univ, 45-47 & Purdue Univ, 47-48; res assoc endocrine chem, Worcester Found Exp Biol, 51-52; sr develop chemist, Silicone Prod Dept, 52-60, mgr liaison & info, Space Sci Lab, Missile & Space Div, 60-66, mgr eng mat & tech lab, Lab Oper, Power Transmission Div, Pa, 66-71, mgr metall & fabrication lab oper, Power Delivery Group, Group Tech Resources Oper, Pittsfield, Mass, 71-75; MGR SWITCHGEAR RESOURCES SUPPORT OPERS, SWITCHGEAR

DISTRIB TRANSFORMER DIV, TECH RESOURCES OPERATORS, GEN ELEC CO, PHILADELPHIA, 75- *Concurrent Pos:* mgr environ technol, Power Delivery Div, King of Prussia, Pa, 79- *Mem:* Am Chem Soc; Am Inst Aeronaut & Astronaut; Inst Elec & Electronics Eng; Sigma Xi. *Res:* Management; metals; metal fabrication and equipment development; ceramics; electrochemistry for use in power delivery equipment; composite materials; dielectrics; silicone chemistry; biological metabolism of adrenocorticotrophic hormone and cortisone; mechanical engineering; plasma physics and math. *Mailing Add:* 1871 Ambler Rd Abington PA 19001

SOLOMON, MALCOLM DAVID, b Swansea, Wales, Oct 16, 42. ORGANIC CHEMISTRY. *Educ:* Univ London, BSc, 64, PhD(org chem), 67. *Prof Exp:* Res chemist, Med Ctr, Univ Calif, San Francisco, 67-69; fel genetics, Med Ctr, Stanford Univ, 70-71; res chemist, Ultrachem Corp, Walnut Creek, 71-73, tech dir, Sci Res Info Serv Inc, San Francisco, 73-74; toxiologist, Hine Inc, San Francisco, 74-79. *Mem:* Am Chem Soc; Royal Soc Chem. *Res:* Synthesis and chemistry of natural products; mass spectrometry; gas-liquid chromatography; narcotics and dangerous drugs. *Mailing Add:* 350 Judah St San Francisco CA 94122

SOLOMON, MARVIN DAVID, b Hudson, NY, Nov 7, 16; m 46; c 2. BIOLOGY. *Educ:* Kans State Col, Pittsburgh, BS, 40, MS, 41; Mich State Univ, EdD, 51. *Prof Exp:* Head dept biol sci, El Dorado Jr Col, Kans, 42-43; asst prof biol, 46-52, from asst prof to assoc prof, 52-62, prof, 62-80, EMER PROF NATURAL SCI, MICH STATE UNIV, 80- *Concurrent Pos:* Adv sci teaching training, UNESCO Tech Assistance Prog, Govt Liberia, 53-54, chief mission, 56. *Mem:* AAAS; Am Asn Phys Anthrop; Soc Med Anthrop. *Res:* Science teaching; distribution human blood groups in Africa; sickle cell anemia; biology of race; assortative mating; bioecology of health. *Mailing Add:* 4651 N Van Atta Rd Okemos MI 48864

SOLOMON, MARVIN H, b Chicago, Ill, Mar 11, 49. OPERATING SYSTEMS, PROGRAMMING LANGUAGES. *Educ:* Univ Chicago, BS, 70; Cornell Univ, MS, 74, PhD(comput sci), 77. *Prof Exp:* Vis instr comput sci, Aarhus Univ, 75-76; instr, 76-77, asst prof, 77-82, ASSOC PROF COMPUT SCI, UNIV WIS-MADISON, 82- *Mem:* Asn Comput Mach; Inst Elec & Electronics Engrs. *Res:* Theory of programming languages; distributed operating systems; graph theory as applied to multiple-computer systems; computer networks; electronic mail. *Mailing Add:* 1210 W Dayton St Madison WI 53706

SOLOMON, NATHAN A, b Brooklyn, NY, Oct 31, 22; m 44; c 3. NUCLEAR MEDICINE. *Educ:* City Col New York, BS, 42; NY Univ, MS, 47, PhD(phys chem), 54; State Univ NY Downstate Med Ctr, MD, 59. *Prof Exp:* Chief chemist, Maimonides Med Ctr, 45-51, chief surg res, 51-55, chief nuclear med, 65-70; assoc prof, 70-80, PROF RADIOL, STATE UNIV NY DOWNSTATE MED CTR, 80-, CHIEF NUCLEAR MED, 70- *Concurrent Pos:* Nat Inst Neurol Dis & Blindness spec fel, 62-63; consult nuclear med, Maimonides Med Ctr, 70- *Honors & Awards:* A Cressy Morrison Award, NY Acad Sci, 54. *Mem:* AAAS; NY Acad Sci; Soc Nuclear Med; Am Asn Clin Chem. *Res:* Application of radioisotopes in the study of physiological and chemical processes with respect to mammals, especially human. *Mailing Add:* Dept Nuclear Med State Univ NY Downstate Med Ctr Brooklyn NY 11203

SOLOMON, NEIL, b Pittsburgh, Pa, Feb 27, 32; m 55; c 3. PHYSIOLOGY. *Educ:* Western Reserve Univ, AB, 54, MD & MS, 61; Univ Md, PhD(physiol), 65. *Prof Exp:* Instr, 63-68, ASST PROF PSYCHIAT, SCH MED, JOHNS HOPKINS UNIV, 63-; SECY, MD STATE DEPT HEALTH & MENT HYG, 69- *Concurrent Pos:* Am Heart Asn res fel, 65-67; intern med, Johns Hopkins Hosp, 61-62, asst resident, 62-63, asst, 63-64, instr, 64-69; vis physician & asst chief med, Baltimore City Hosp, 63-68; consult, Vet Admin Hosp, Perry Point, Md, 63-68; assoc prof physiol, Sch Med, Univ Md, Baltimore, 63-70; asst sr surgeon, Nat Inst Child Health & Human Develop, 64-65; vis physician, Univ Md Hosp, 65-68; clin prof pharmacol, Sch Med, Univ Miami, 78. *Mem:* Am Fedn Clin Res; Am Heart Asn; Am Physiol Soc; Fedn Am Socs Exp Biol; NY Acad Sci. *Res:* Aging and heart and endocrine function. *Mailing Add:* 1726 Reisterstown Rd Suite 213 Baltimore MD 21208

SOLOMON, PETER R, b New York, NY, Feb 19, 39; m 60, 75; c 3. SOLID STATE PHYSICS, COAL SCIENCE. *Educ:* City Col New York, BS, 60; Columbia Univ, MA, 63, PhD(physics), 65. *Prof Exp:* Res asst physics, Watson Lab, IBM Corp, 63-65; exp physicist, United Technol Res Ctr, 65-68, prin scientist, 68-71, asst to dir res progs & technol, 71-73, prin physicist, 73-80; WITH ADVANCED FUEL RES INC, 80- *Mem:* Am Phys Soc. *Res:* Low temperature physics; electrical instabilities in semiconductors; coal science; superconductivity; instabilities in solids. *Mailing Add:* Advanced Fuel Res Inc 87 Church St East Hartford CT 06108

SOLOMON, PHILIP M, b New York, NY, Mar 29, 39; m 58; c 1. ASTROPHYSICS, MOLECULAR PHYSICS. *Educ:* Univ Wis, BS, 59, MS, 61, PhD(astron), 64. *Prof Exp:* Res assoc astrophys, Princeton Univ, 64-66; lectr & sr res assoc astron, Columbia Univ, 66-70; assoc prof astrophysics, Univ Minn, Minneapolis, 71-74; PROF ASTRON, STATE UNIV NY STONY BROOK, 74- *Concurrent Pos:* Vis scientist, Inst Theoret Astron, Univ Cambridge, 67-72. *Mem:* Am Astron Soc. *Res:* Molecular opacities; interstellar matter; planetary atmospheres; interstellar chemistry; radioastronomy, masers; quasi stellar objects. *Mailing Add:* Dept of Earth & Space Sci State Univ of NY Stony Brook NY 11790

SOLOMON, ROBERT DOUGLAS, b Delavan, Wis, Aug 28, 17; m 43; c 4. PATHOLOGY. *Educ:* Johns Hopkins Univ, MD, 42. *Prof Exp:* Pathologist, Kankakee State Hosp, 49-50; assoc dir, Terre Haute Med Lab, 50-54; assoc pathologist, Sinai Hosp, Baltimore, Md, 55-58; asst prof path, Univ Md, 58-60; assoc pathologist, City of Hope Med Ctr, 60-63, dir path res, 63-67; dir labs, Doctors' Hosp San Leandro, Calif, 67-75; dir labs, Edgewater Hosp, Chicago, 75-76; ASSOC PATHOLOGIST, WILSON MEM HOSP, JOHNSON CITY, 78-; CLIN PROF PATH, STATE UNIV NY UPSTATE, 79- *Concurrent Pos:* Fel cancer res, Michael Reese Hosp, 47-49; trainee, Nat Cancer Inst, 58-60; consult, Regional Off US Vet Admin, Md, 58-60; assoc prof, Univ Southern Calif, 61-; fel coun arteriosclerosis, Am Heart Asn. *Mem:* Fel Royal Soc Med; Am Soc Clin Path; Am Chem Soc; Am Col Physicians; Col Am Path. *Res:* Urinary pigments; nutritional influences on carcinogenesis; leukoplakia and vitamin A; experimental arteriosclerosis; vascular surgery; mechanisms of aging. *Mailing Add:* Dept of Path 33 Harrison St Johnson City NY 13790

SOLOMON, SAMUEL, b Brest Litovsk, Poland, Dec 25, 25; Can citizen; m 53; c 3. BIOCHEMISTRY. *Educ:* McGill Univ, BSc, 47, MSc, 51, PhD(biochem), 53. *Prof Exp:* Res asst, McGill Univ, 51-53; from res asst to res assoc, Columbia Univ, 53-57, assoc biochem, 58-59, asst prof, 59-60; assoc prof biochem & exp med, 60-67, PROF BIOCHEM & EXP MED, MCGILL UNIV, 67-; DIR, ENDOCRINE LAB, ROYAL VICTORIA HOSP, 65- *Concurrent Pos:* Chem Inst Can fel, 65; Can Soc Clin Invest Schering traveling fel, 65. *Mem:* AAAS; Soc Gynec Invest; fel Royal Soc Can; Perinatal Res Soc (pres, 75-76); Am Chem Soc. *Res:* Hormones in pregnancy; endocrinology. *Mailing Add:* Endocrine Lab 687 Pine Ave W Montreal PQ H3A 1A1 Can

SOLOMON, SEAN CARL, b Los Angeles, Calif, Oct 24, 45; m 67; c 2. GEOPHYSICS. *Educ:* Calif Inst Technol, BS, 66; Mass Inst Technol, PhD(geophys), 71. *Prof Exp:* Fel, NSF, 71-72; asst prof, 72-77, ASSOC PROF GEOPHYS, MASS INST TECHNOL, 77- *Concurrent Pos:* Lunar Sample Anal Planning Team, NASA, 74-76, mem, Venus Orbital Imaging Radar Sci Working Group, 77-78, mem, Lunar and Planetary Rev Panel, 80-82; assoc ed, J Geophys Res, 76-78; Comt Planetary & Lunar exploration, Nat Acad Sci-Nat Res Coun, 76-79, mem, Space Sci Bd, 78-82, chmn comt Earth Sci, 79-82; Alfred P Sloan res fel, 77-81; mem, Lunar & Planetary Sci Coun, Univ Space Res Asn, 78-80; assoc ed, Eos Trans Am Geophhys Union, 78-81; mem, Working Group 1, Inter-Union Comn on the Lithosphere, 81-85. *Mem:* fel Am Geophys Union; Seismol Soc Am; AAAS; Sigma Xi. *Res:* Earthquake seismology; plate tectonics; planetary geology and geophysics. *Mailing Add:* 54-522 Mass Inst Technol Cambridge MA 02139

SOLOMON, SIDNEY, b Worcester, Mass, Feb 22, 23; m 47; c 2. PHYSIOLOGY. *Educ:* Univ Mass, BS, 48; Univ Chicago, PhD(physiol), 52. *Prof Exp:* From instr to assoc prof physiol, Med Col Va, 52-63; chmn dept, 63-78, PROF PHYSIOL, SCH MED, UNIV NMEX, 65- *Concurrent Pos:* Guggenheim fel, Berlin, Ger, 62-63; consult, Adv Panel Regulatory Biol, NSF, 65-67, consult metab biol, 80-; prof dir metab biol, NSF, 67-68; consult, Nat Bd Med Exam, 68-72; spec asst, Div Phys Molecular & Cell Biol, NSF, 78-79. *Mem:* Fel AAAS; Soc Exp Biol & Med; Biophys Soc; Am Physiol Soc; NY Acad Sci. *Res:* Renal and comparative physiology; active transport. *Mailing Add:* Dept of Physiol Univ of NMex Sch of Med Albuquerque NM 87106

SOLOMON, SOLOMON SIDNEY, b New York, NY, Dec 2, 36; m 62; c 2. MEDICINE, METABOLISM. *Educ:* Harvard Univ, AB, 58; Univ Rochester, MD, 62. *Prof Exp:* Intern internal med, Med Ctr, Tufts Univ, 62-63, resident, Univ & Boston City Hosp, 63-65; res & educ assoc, Vet Admin Hosp, Memphis, 69-71; from asst prof to assoc prof med, 69-77, PROF MED, UNIV TENN, MEMPHIS, 77- CHIEF ENDOCRINOL & METAB, VET ADMIN HOSP, MEMPHIS, 71-, HEAD SECT ENDOCRINOL, 81- *Concurrent Pos:* Vet Admin Hosp career develop award, Univ Tenn, Memphis, 69-71; attend physician, City of Memphis Hosp, 71-; reviewer, Journals & grants, NIH & Vet Admin Hosp. *Mem:* Am Soc Clin Invest; Am Fedn Clin Res; Am Diabetes Asn; Endocrine Soc. *Res:* Diabetes; intermediary metabolism; mechanism of action of insulin; role of second messenger's cyclic adenosine monophosphate in adipose tissue in normal and diabetes conditions; cyclic adenosine monophosphate phosphodiesterase lipolysis; hormonal receptors in fact. *Mailing Add:* Vet Admin Hosp 1030 Jefferson Ave Memphis TN 38104

SOLOMON, THOMAS ALLAN, b New Kensington, Pa, Apr 3, 41; m 68. PHARMACOLOGY, CARDIOVASCULAR PHYSIOLOGY. *Educ:* Westminster Col, Pa, BS, 64; WVa Univ, MA, 67; Univ Pittsburgh, PhD(pharmacol), 72. *Prof Exp:* From instr to asst prof psychiat & behav biol, Sch Med, 72-76, instr environ med, Sch Pub Health, 73-75, asst prof psychiat & behav biol, Sch Med, Johns Hopkins Univ, 74-76, instr environ med, Sch Pub Health, 73-75; head cardiovasc pharmacol, Pharmaceut Div, Sandoz, Inc, 74-80; WITH CLINICAL PHARMACOL, REVLON HEALTH CARE, 80- *Mem:* NY Acad Sci; Johns Hopkins Med Surg Soc; AAAS; Am Heart Asn. *Res:* Circulation; cardiovascular system and its regulation; control mechanisms involved in hypertension; cardiovascular pharmacology. *Mailing Add:* Revlon Health Care 1 Scarsdale Rd Tuckahoe NY 10707

SOLOMON, VASANTH BALAN, b Nagercoil, Madras, India, Aug 8, 35; US citizen; m 60; c 2. APPLIED STATISTICS. *Educ:* Univ Madras, BSc, 58, MSc, 61; Iowa State Univ, PhD(statist), 70. *Prof Exp:* Statistician, Rubber Res Inst Ceylon, 62-64; biometrician, Dept Fisheries & Forestry, Govt of Can, 67-69; ASSOC PROF STATIST, DRAKE UNIV, 70- *Mem:* Am Statist Asn. *Res:* Statistical research in epidemiological problems. *Mailing Add:* 1606 Amherst Dr Ames IA 50010

SOLOMONOW, MOSHE, b Tel-Aviv, Israel, Oct 24, 44; US & Israeli citizen. REHABILITATION ENGINEERING, NEUROSCIENCES. *Educ:* Calif State Univ, BS, 70, MS, 72; Univ Calif, Los Angeles, PhD(eng), 76. *Prof Exp:* Chief engr med eng, Calmag Electronics, 68-71; res engr neuromuscular eng, Rancho Los Amigos Hosp, 71-72; proj engr med eng, Clamag Electronics, 72-73; clin intern prosthetics, Child Amputee Clin, Univ Calif, Los Angeles, 75, res engr rehabilitative eng, 73-80; ASSOC PROF, DEPT BIOMED ENG, TULANE UNIV, 80- *Concurrent Pos:* Consult, Olivetti Am Inc, 74-75 & Child Amputee Clin, Univ Calif, Los Angeles, 75-76; prin engr, Bennett Respiration Prod Inc, 77; consult, Lida Inc, 75-, Perceptronics Inc, 75-76, Vet Admin Hosp, Brentwood, 77-78, Vet Admin Hosp, Sepulveda, 78-80 & Dept Health, La, 81- *Mem:* Biomed Eng Soc; AAAS; Sigma Xi; Inst Elec &

Electronics Engrs. *Res:* Research and development on sensory motor artificial organs for augmentation of losses in paralysis, amputations, blindness and deafness. *Mailing Add:* Dept Biomed Eng Tulane Univ New Orleans LA 70118

SOLOMONS, CLIVE (CHARLES), b Johannesburg, SAfrica, June 6, 31; m 56; c 3. BIOCHEMISTRY, PEDIATRICS. *Educ:* Univ Witwatersrand, BS, 52, PhD(biochem), 56. *Prof Exp:* Biochemist, SAfrican Inst Med Res, 52-55; biochemist, Dent Res Univ, Coun Sci & Indust Res & Univ Witwatersrand, 55-61; asst prof biochem, McGill Univ, 61-63; assoc prof pediat, 63-75, PROF ORTHOP, DIR ORTHOP RES & ASSOC PROF ANAESTHESIOL, UNIV COLO MED CTR, DENVER, 75- *Concurrent Pos:* Fel radiation biol, Univ Rochester, 58-59; Can Med Res Coun grant, 61-63; NIH grant, 64-; NSF grant; Cystic Fibrosis Res Found grant. *Res:* Application of analytical biochemistry to clinical and basic science investigation, especially on the metabolism of connective tissue disorders; metals in the environment, cystic fibrosis and renal disease, and anaesthetic risk; Reyes syndrome; orthopedics anaesthesiology. *Mailing Add:* Dept of Orthop Univ of Colo Med Ctr Denver CO 80262

SOLOMONS, GERALD, b London, Eng, Feb 22, 21; US citizen; m 55; c 2. PEDIATRICS, CHILD GROWTH. *Educ:* Royal Col Physicians & Surgeons, Edinburgh, LRCP, LRCS, 43; Royal Col Physicians & Surgeons Eng, dipl child health, 48; Am Bd Pediat, dipl, 52. *Prof Exp:* Asst supt, Charles V Chapin Hosp, Providence, RI, 52; pvt pract, 53-59; dep dir pediat, Inst Health Sci, Brown Univ, 59-62, asst mem, 60-62; from asst prof to assoc prof, 62-69, PROF PEDIAT, UNIV IOWA, 69-, DIR CHILD DEVELOP CLIN, 63-, ACTG HEAD, INST CHILD BEHAV & DEVELOP, 75- *Concurrent Pos:* Consult, NIH, 59-; prog dir, Regional Ctr Child Abuse & Neglect, 75- *Mem:* Fel Am Acad Pediat; fel Am Acad Cerebral Palsy (pres, 77-78); Am Asn Ment Deficiency. *Res:* Child abuse; minimal brain damage, its diagnosis, drug therapy and effect on learning. *Mailing Add:* Child Develop Clin Univ Hosp Sch Iowa City IA 52242

SOLOMONS, NOEL WILLIS, b Boston, Mass, Dec 31, 44. CLINICAL NUTRITION, GASTROENTEROLOGY. *Educ:* Harvard Univ, AB, 66; Harvard Med Sch, MD, 70. *Prof Exp:* Instr med, Univ Chicago, 75-76, res assoc gastroenterol, 77-79; asst prof, 77-80, ASSOC PROF CLIN NUTRIT, DEPT NUTRIT & FOOD SCI, MASS INST TECHNOL, 80- *Concurrent Pos:* Nutrit Found grant, 74-77; Josiah Macy Jr Found fac fel, 75-76; res assoc clin nutrit, Div Human Nutrit & Biol, Inst Nutrit Cent Am & Panama, 76-78, affil sci, 78-; mem, Comt Int Nutrit, Nat Acad Sci, 79-82. *Mem:* Am Gastroenterol Asn; Am Soc Clin Nutrit; Am Fedn Clin Res; Am Soc Nutrit; Latin Am Nutrit Soc. *Res:* Trace mineral nutrition; protein-energy malnutrition; trace mineral absorption, non-invasive and stable isotope technology in absorptive physiology. *Mailing Add:* Dept of Nutrit & Food Sci Mass Inst Technol Cambridge MA 02139

SOLOMONS, THOMAS WILLIAM GRAHAM, b Charleston, SC, Aug 30, 34. ORGANIC CHEMISTRY. *Educ:* The Citadel, BS, 55; Duke Univ, PhD(chem), 59. *Prof Exp:* Sloan Found fel, Univ Rochester, 59-60; instr, 60-61, from asst prof to assoc prof, 61-73, PROF CHEM, UNIV S FLA, 73- *Mem:* Am Chem Soc. *Res:* Synthesis and reactions of heterocyclic aromatic compounds. *Mailing Add:* Dept of Chem Univ of SFla Tampa FL 33620

SOLOMONS, WILLIAM EBENEZER, b Ridgeland, SC, Oct 2, 43; m 65; c 2. MEDICINAL CHEMISTRY, ORGANIC CHEMISTRY. *Educ:* Berry Col, BA, 65; Univ Miss, PhD(pharmaceut chem), 70. *Prof Exp:* Res asst prof, Ctr Health Sci, Univ Tenn, Memphis, 70-73, res assoc prof med chem, 73-76; ASSOC PROF CHEM, UNIV TENN, MARTIN, 76- *Mem:* Am Chem Soc; Sigma Xi. *Res:* Synthetic organic chemistry; organic synthesis and structure determination; the relationships between molecular structure and biological activity; synthesis of novel analgesic ankd antipsychotic agents. *Mailing Add:* Dept of Chem Univ of Tenn Martin TN 38238

SOLOMONSON, LARRY PAUL, b Scarville, Iowa, June 26, 41; m 68; c 2. BIOCHEMISTRY. *Educ:* Luther Col, BA, 63; Univ Chicago, PhD(biochem), 69. *Prof Exp:* Res chemist res & develop, Borden Chem Co, 63-64; amanuensis, Physiol Inst, Univ Aarhus, Denmark, 69-70; scientist, Max Planck Inst, Berlin, Ger, 70-74; vis asst prof, Col Med, Univ Iowa, 74-76; asst prof, 76-79, ASSOC PROF BIOCHEM, UNIV SOUTH FLA, 80- *Mem:* AAAS; Am Chem Soc; Am Soc Biol Chemists; Am Soc Plant Physiologists; Sigma Xi. *Res:* Mechanism and regulation of nitrate assimilation; molecular properties and functions of the sodium pump. *Mailing Add:* Dept Biochem Col Med Univ South Fla Tampa FL 33612

SOLON, LEONARD RAYMOND, b White Plains, NY, Sept 11, 25; m 46; c 3. RADIOLOGICAL PHYSICS. *Educ:* Hamilton Col, AB, 47; Rutgers Univ, MSc, 49; NY Univ, PhD(radiol health), 60. *Prof Exp:* Teaching asst physics, Rutgers Univ, 47-49; physicist, Nuclear Develop Assocs, 50-52; physicist radiation br, Health & Safety Lab, US Atomic Energy Comn, 52-54, asst chief, 54-59, chief, 59-60; dir appl nuclear tech, Tech Res Group, Inc, NY, 60-64; mgr res & develop, Del Electronics Corp, mem vpres & tech dir, Hadron Inc, Westbury, 67-75; DIR, BUR RADIATION CONTROL, DEPT OF HEALTH, CITY OF NEW YORK, 75- *Concurrent Pos:* Lectr, Med Center, NY Univ, 56-60, adj asst prof, 60-62, adj assoc prof, 62-; Mem tech consults panel, Div Mil Appln, US Atomic Energy Comn, 57-60, consult, Health & Safety Lab, 62-; prof health physics, US Merchant Marine Acad, 64. *Mem:* AAAS; Am Phys Soc; Am Asn Physics Teachers; Health Physics Soc; Am Nuclear Soc. *Res:* Radiation protection and health physics; reactor and accelerator shielding; environmental radiation measurements; laser physics and applications; biomedical instrumentation; radiation dosimetry; stratospheric sampling; application of lasers to thermonuclear fusion. *Mailing Add:* 28 Pilgrim Ave Yonkers NY 10710

SOLONCHE, DAVID JOSHUA, b New York, NY, Apr 10, 45; m 66; c 2. BIOMEDICAL ENGINEERING, BIOMEDICAL COMPUTING. *Educ:* Yeshiva Col, BA, 66; Worcester Polytech Inst, PhD(biomed eng), 71. *Prof Exp:* Res asst, 71-72, instr, 72-73, asst prof orthod, Sch Dent Med, 74-79, DIR BIOENG, HEALTH CTR, UNIV CONN, 79- *Concurrent Pos:* Consult eng, Trinity Col, 74; lectr biomed eng, Rensselaer Polytech Inst, 74. *Mem:* Inst Elec & Electronics Eng; Biomed Eng Soc; Instrument Soc Am. *Res:* Application of computers to biomedical research; biological signal processing; bioelectronics; automated orthondotic diagnosis. *Mailing Add:* Dir Bioeng Univ Conn Health Ctr Farmington CT 06032

SOLORZANO, ROBERT FRANCIS, b New York, NY, May 21, 29; div; c 3. VIROLOGY, MEDICAL MICROBIOLOGY. *Educ:* Georgetown Univ, BS, 51; Pa State Univ, MS, 56, PhD(bact), 62. *Prof Exp:* Bacteriologist, Montefiore Hosp Chronic Dis, New York, 53-54; res asst virol, Children's Hosp, Philadelphia, Pa, 56-58; asst, Pa State Univ, 58-62; asst virologist, Coastal Plain Exp Sta, Univ Ga, 62-68; assoc prof, 68-78, PROF VET MICROBIOL, COL VET MED & SR VIROLOGIST, VET MED DIAG LAB, UNIV MO-COLUMBIA, 78- *Concurrent Pos:* Mem, Am Asn & NCent Conf Vet Lab Diagnosticians. *Mem:* AAAS; Am Soc Microbiol. *Res:* Japanese B encephalitis ecology; effect of sonic vibrations on Newcastle virus; entero-cytopathogenic human orphan virus serology; fluorescent antibody test for hog cholera; serology for leptospirosis; ecology of hog cholera virus; enteric virus diseases of swine; diagnostic virology, and serology; pseudorabies. *Mailing Add:* Vet Med Diag Lab Col Vet Med Univ Mo Columbia MO 65211

SOLOTOROVSKY, MORRIS, b New York, NY, Oct 10, 13; m 45; c 4. BACTERIOLOGY. *Educ:* Univ Va, BS, 34; NY Univ, MS, 38; Columbia Univ, PhD(bact), 47. *Prof Exp:* Asst sanit sci, Col Physicians & Surgeons, Columbia Univ, 36-, instr epidemiol, 41-42; bacteriologist, Guggenheim Bros, NY, 40-41; res assoc chemotherapy, Merck Inst, 46-58; PROF BACT, RUTGERS UNIV, 58- *Mem:* AAAS; Am Soc Microbiol; Am Asn Immunol; fel Am Acad Microbiol. *Res:* Host-parasite interaction; chemotherapy of tuberculosis and fungus diseases; cell-mediated immunity; bacterial vaccines. *Mailing Add:* Dept Bact Rutgers Univ New Brunswick NJ 08903

SOLOW, DANIEL, b Washington, DC, Nov 19, 49; m 80. MATHEMATICAL PROGRAMMING. *Educ:* Carnegie-Mellon Univ, BS, 70; Univ Calif, Berkeley, MS, 72; Stanford Univ, PhD(opers res), 78. *Prof Exp:* ASST PROF OPERS RES, CASE WESTERN RESERVE UNIV, 78- *Mem:* Opers Res Soc; Math Prog Soc; Am Math Soc; Math Asn Am. *Res:* Development of computational algorithms for solving mathematical problems arising in combinatorial optimization, mathematical programming and operations research. *Mailing Add:* Dept Opers Res Case Western Reserve Univ Cleveland OH 44106

SOLOW, MAX, b Philadelphia, Pa, Nov 20, 16; m 41; c 2. PHYSICS, METALLURGY. *Educ:* George Washington Univ, BEE, 43, MS, 50; Catholic Univ, PhD(physics), 57. *Prof Exp:* Radio engr, Nat Bur Stand, 46-49, electronic scientist, 49-53; physicist, US Naval Ord Lab, 53-60; sr scientist, Martin Co, 60-64; res coordr physics, US Navy Marine Eng Lab, 64-68 & Naval Ship Res & Develop Ctr, Annapolis, 68-71, sr res scientist/tech consult, 71-80 ; MEM STAFF, UNIV MD, COLLEGE PARK, MD, 81- *Mem:* Am Phys Soc; AAAS; Am Soc Metals; Inst Elec & Electronics Engrs; Am Inst Mining, Metall & Petrol Engrs. *Res:* Solid state physics; metals; electrochemistry; corrosion, materials; vacancy and dislocation technique and theory; random noise; explosion hydrodynamics; lasers; holography. *Mailing Add:* 823 Painted Post Ct Baltimore MD 21208

SOLOWAY, ALBERT HERMAN, b Worcester, Mass, May 29, 25; m 53; c 3. MEDICINAL CHEMISTRY. *Educ:* Worcester Polytech Inst, BS, 48; Univ Rochester, PhD(org chem), 51. *Prof Exp:* USPHS fel, Sloan-Kettering Inst, 51-53; res chemist, Eastman Kodak Co, 53-56; res assoc surg, Harvard Med Sch, 56-63; asst chemist, Mass Gen Hosp, 56-61, assoc chemist, 61-73; assoc prof med chem, Northeastern Univ, 66-71, chmn dept med chem & pharmacol, Col Pharm & Allied Health Professions, 71-74, prof med chem & chem, 71-77, dir grad sch, Pharm & Allied Health Professions, 73-77, dean, Col Pharm & Allied Health Professions, 75-77; PROF MED CHEM & DEAN, COL PHARM, OHIO STATE UNIV, 77- *Mem:* Fel AAAS; Am Chem Soc; Am Asn Cols Pharm; Am Pharmaceut Asn; Am Asn Cancer Res. *Res:* Cancer therapy; development of drugs for chemoimmuno and chemoradiotherapy; use of Boron compounds in cancer. *Mailing Add:* Ohio State Univ Col of Pharm 500 W 12th Ave Columbus OH 43210

SOLOWAY, HAROLD, b New York, NY, June 15, 17; m 47; c 2. ORGANIC CHEMISTRY, MEDICINAL CHEMISTRY. *Educ:* Brooklyn Col, BA, 38; Polytech Inst Brooklyn, MS, 48. *Prof Exp:* Chemist, George Washington Coffee Div, Am Home Foods, Inc, 46-48; asst chemist, Sterling-Winthrop Res Inst, 49-52; chemist, US Vitamin & Pharmaceut Corp, 52-55, sr res chemist, 55-66; sr chemist, Endo Labs, Inc, 66-73, group leader, 73-76; GROUP LEADER, PHARM DIV, E I DU PONT DE NEMOURS & CO, INC, 76- *Mem:* NY Acad Sci; AAAS; Am Chem Soc. *Res:* Synthesis and reactions of organic heterocyclic compounds; synthesis of organic medicinals; alkaloid chemistry. *Mailing Add:* 31 DeWalt Rd Newark DE 19711

SOLOWAY, S BARNEY, b New York, NY, Jan 21, 15; m 38; c 2. ORGANIC CHEMISTRY. *Educ:* City Col New York, BS, 36; Univ Colo, PhD(chem), 55. *Prof Exp:* Chemist, Div Insecticide Invests, USDA, 41-47; chemist & asst dir, Julius Hyman & Co, 47-52; supvr org res, Agr Res Div, 52-64, head, Org Chem Div, Woodstock Agr Res Ctr, Shell Res Ltd, 64-67, mgr org chem, 67-72, head org chem, 67-80, DIR RES, AGR RES DIV, SHELL DEVELOP CO, 80- *Mem:* Am Chem Soc. *Res:* Synthesis; stereochemistry; agricultural chemicals. *Mailing Add:* Shell Develop Co Box 4248 Modesto CA 95352

SOLOWAY, SAUL, b New York, NY, Apr 12, 16; m 44; c 3. ORGANIC CHEMISTRY. *Educ:* City Col New York, BS, 36; Columbia Univ, AM, 38, PhD(chem), 42. *Prof Exp:* Hernschiem fel, Mt Sinai Hosp, New York, 40-41; mem staff, Nat Defense Res Comn, US Bur Mines, 41-43, Panel Chem Corp, 43-44 & Grosvenor Labs, 44-46; instr chem, City Col New York, 46-50, from asst prof to assoc prof, 50-73; CONSULT CHEMIST, 73- *Concurrent Pos:* Consult, Faberge, Inc, 56-, dir res, 58-; consult, Revlon, 60-64. *Mem:* Am Chem Soc; NY Acad Sci. *Res:* Chelation; cosmetics; perfume; encapsulation of liquids; lipids; organic analysis; polymerization; thermochromism. *Mailing Add:* 180 Broadview Ave New Rochelle NY 10804

SOLOYANIS, SUSAN CONSTANCE, b New York, NY, Jan 21, 52. GLACIAL GEOLOGY, PETROLEUM GEOLOGY. *Educ:* Smith Col, AB, 72; Univ Mass, Amherst, MS, 75, PhD(geol), 78. *Prof Exp:* Geologist environ geol, Conn Valley Urban Area Proj, US Geol Surv, 71-75; teaching asst geol & geog, Univ Mass, Amherst, 74-78; GEOLOGIST PETROL GEOL, AMOCO PROD CO, 78- *Concurrent Pos:* Teaching asst geol, Univ Ill, Urbana, 72-73. *Mem:* Geol Soc Am; Am Geophys Union; Sigma Xi; Soc Econ Paleontologists & Mineralogists; Am Asn Petrol Geologists. *Res:* Pleistocene paleomagnetic stratigraphy; magnetization of sediments glacial sedimentation; petroleum exploration. *Mailing Add:* Amoco Prod Co 7200 S Alton Way Englewood CO 80112

SOLSKY, JOSEPH FAY, b Corning, NY, June 9, 49; m 70. ANALYTICAL CHEMISTRY. *Educ:* State Univ NY, Buffalo, BA, 71, PhD(chem), 78. *Prof Exp:* ASST PROF CHEM, CREIGHTON UNIV, 76- *Mem:* Am Chem Soc. *Res:* Investigations of stationary phases used in chromatographic systems including liquid crystal and permanently bound types. *Mailing Add:* Dept of Chem Creighton Univ Omaha NE 68178

SOLTAN, HUBERT CONSTANTINE, b Wilno, Poland, Dec 16, 32; Can nat; m 62; c 3. MEDICAL GENETICS. *Educ:* Univ Toronto, BA, 55, PhD(human genetics), 59; Univ Western Ont, MD, 70. *Prof Exp:* Res fel genetics, Hosp Sick Children, Toronto, Ont, 55-58; asst prof biol, St Mary's Univ, NS, 58-61; asst prof human genetics, Fac Med, 61-66, assoc prof, 66-77, clin assoc prof pediat, 71-77, PROF HUMAN GENETICS, UNIV WESTERN ONT, 77- CLIN PROF PEDIAT, 77- *Mem:* Genetics Soc Can; Asn Genetic Counr Ont; Can Col Med Geneticists; Am Soc Human Genetics. *Mailing Add:* Dept of Anat Health Sci Ctr Univ of Western Ont London ON N6A 5C1 Can

SOLTANPOUR, PARVIZ NEIL, b Tehran, Iran, Mar 21, 37; m 60; c 4. SOIL FERTILITY, AGRONOMY. *Educ:* Am Univ Beirut, BS, 61, MS, 63; Univ Nebr, PhD(soil fertility), 66. *Prof Exp:* assoc prof, 66-80, PROF SOIL FERTILITY, COLO STATE UNIV, 80- *Concurrent Pos:* Consult, Egypt Water Mgt Proj, Asn Int Develop, Comn Int Develop & Colo State Univ; chmn elect, Coun on Soil Testing & Plant Anal, 83-84. *Mem:* Am Soc Agron; Soil Sci Soc Am; Int Soc Soil Sci; Soc Sigma Xi. *Res:* Methods of soil testing for fertilizer recommendations; soil fertility and plant nutrition. *Mailing Add:* Soil Testing Lab Colo State Univ Ft Collins CO 80523

SOLTER, DAVOR, b Zagreb, Yugoslavia, Mar 22, 41. DEVELOPMENTAL BIOLOGY. *Educ:* Univ Zagreb, MD, 65, MSc, 68, PhD(biol), 71. *Prof Exp:* Instr anat, Med Sch, Univ Zagreb, 66-68, instr biol, 68-72, asst prof, 72-73; assoc scientist, 73-75, assoc mem, 75-80, PROF, WISTAR INST, 81- *Concurrent Pos:* Europ Molecular Biol Orgn scholar, 71; Damon Runyon Mem Cancer Fund fel, 73; assoc ed, Develop Biol, 80-; mem study sect human embryol & develop, NIH, 81- *Mem:* Soc Develop Biol. *Res:* Development of early mouse embryo; role of membrane molecules in development of early mouse embryo; cross-reacting antigens on embryos and tumor cells; regulation and differentiation of embryo derived teratocarcinomas. *Mailing Add:* Wistar Inst 36th at Spruce Philadelphia PA 19104

SOLTERO, RAYMOND ARTHUR, b Milwaukee, Wis, July 20, 43; m 60; c 3. LIMNOLOGY, WATER POLLUTION. *Educ:* Mont State Univ, BS, 66, MS, 68, PhD(bot), 71. *Prof Exp:* asst prof, 71-80, PROF BIOL, EASTERN WASH UNIV, 80- *Mem:* Am Soc Limnol & Oceanog; Mem: Int Soc Limnol; Sigma Xi. *Res:* Eutrophication of lakes, streams and reservoirs; lake restoration. *Mailing Add:* Dept of Biol Eastern Wash Univ Cheney WA 99004

SOLTES, EDWARD JOHN, b Montreal, Que, Mar 25, 41; m 66; c 2. WOOD CHEMISTRY. *Educ:* McGill Univ, BSc, 61, PhD(carbohydrate chem), 65. *Prof Exp:* Fel, Ohio State Univ, 65-66, lectr, 66; sr res chemist, Tech Ctr, St Regis Paper Co, 66-76, asst to dir res & develop, 70-71, responsibility for Sylvachem Res & Develop, 73-75, responsibility for wood chem, 75-76; assoc prof forest sci, 76-81, PROF WOOD CHEM, AGR EXP STA, TEX A&M UNIV, 81- *Concurrent Pos:* Chmn, Div Cellulose, Paper & Textile Chem, Am Chem Soc, 79. *Mem:* Am Chem Soc; Am Forestry Asn; Soc Am Foresters; Tech Asn Pulp & Paper Indust. *Res:* Wood chemistry, utilization of agricultural and forestry residues, pyrolysis, gasification and naval stores. *Mailing Add:* Forest Sci Lab Tex A&M Univ College Station TX 77843

SOLTYSIK, EDWARD A, b Newark, NJ, Aug 23, 29; m 58; c 3. ATOMIC PHYSICS. *Educ:* Lafayette Col, BS, 50; Ind Univ, MS, 52, PhD(nuclear physics), 56. *Prof Exp:* Lectr physics, Univ Nev, 55-56; physicist, Lawrence Radiation Lab, 56-62; assoc prof, 62-71, PROF PHYSICS, UNIV MASS, AMHERST, 71- *Concurrent Pos:* Consult, Lawrence Radiation Lab, 62-65 & Air Force Off Sci Res grants, 63- *Res:* Nuclear decay, shake off process and inner Bremsstrahlung; atomic physics, polarization of collisional radiation, especially radiation resulting from the collisions of electrons and protons on atoms. *Mailing Add:* Dept of Physics Univ of Mass Amherst MA 01003

SOLTYSIK, SZCZESNY STEFAN, b Zakopane, Poland, Mar 27, 29; m 55; c 2. ANIMAL BEHAVIOR, NEUROPHYSIOLOGY. *Educ:* Jagiellonian Univ, Poland, MD, 53; Polish Acad Sci, PhD(behav sci), 60, Docent Sci, 65. *Prof Exp:* Asst prof human physiol, Sch Med, Jagiellonian Univ, 50-53; asst prof neurophysiol, Nencki Inst Exp Biol, 54-64, docent, 65-69; docent, Inst

Psychoneurol, Warsaw, 65-71; asst res anatomist, Brain Res Inst, 62-64, assoc res anatomist, Sch Med, 71-75, assoc prof, 75-76, PROF PSYCHIAT, DEPT PSYCHIAT & NEUROPSYCHIAT INST, UNIV CALIF, LOS ANGELES, 76- *Mem:* Int Brain Res Orgn; Psychonomic Soc. *Res:* Blocking of inhibitory conditioning: protection from extinction, behavioral role of nucleus accumbent; emotional behavior, classical and operant conditioning in normal and brain operated kittens at different ages. *Mailing Add:* Neuropsychiat Inst Rm 58-242 Univ of Calif 760 Westwood Plaza Los Angeles CA 90024

SOLTZ, DAVID LEE, b La Cross, Wis, Nov 7, 46; m 78; c 2. POPULATION ECOLOGY, ICHTHYOLOGY. *Educ:* Univ Calif, BA, 68, PhD(biol), 74. *Prof Exp:* Asst prof, 74-78, ASSOC PROF BIOL, CALIF STATE UNIV, 78-, CHMN DEPT, 81-79. *Concurrent Pos:* NSF grant, 77-79. *Mem:* AAAS; Am Soc Ichthyologists & Herpetologists; Ecol Soc Am; Soc Study Evolution. *Res:* Population biology; evolutionary and reproductive ecology of fish populations; community ecology of isolated freshwater habitats. *Mailing Add:* Dept Biol Calif State Univ Los Angeles CA 90032

SOLTZBERG, LEONARD JAY, b Wilmington, Del, July 10, 44. PHYSICAL CHEMISTRY, CRYSTALLOGRAPHY. *Educ:* Univ Del, BS, 65; Brandeis Univ, MA, 67, PhD(phys chem), 69. *Prof Exp:* Nat Res Coun res assoc, Air Force Cambridge Res Lab, 69; asst prof, 69-73, assoc prof, 73-79, PROF CHEM, SIMMONS COL, 79- *Mem:* Sigma Xi; Am Crystallog Asn; Am Chem Soc. *Res:* Chemical crystallography; optical and x-ray crystallography; phase transitions; microscopy; pedagogical computer application. *Mailing Add:* Dept of Chem Simmons Col 300 The Fenway Boston MA 02115

SOLURSH, MICHAEL, b Los Angeles, Calif, Dec 22, 42; m 64; c 1. DEVELOPMENTAL BIOLOGY, CELL BIOLOGY. *Educ:* Univ Calif, Los Angeles, BA, 64; Univ Wash, PhD(zool), 69. *Prof Exp:* Teaching asst zool, Univ Wash, 64-66; from asst prof to assoc prof, 69-79, PROF ZOOL, UNIV IOWA, 79- *Mem:* Am Soc Cell Biol; Am Soc Zool; Soc Develop Biol. *Res:* Extracellular materials in morphogenesis and migration of primary mesenchyme cell in sea urchin embryos; cartilage cell differentiation and limb morphogenesis (heterotypic and homotypic cell interaction during chondrogenesis). *Mailing Add:* Dept of Zool Univ of Iowa Iowa City IA 52242

SOLVIK, R S(VEN), b Fauske, Norway, Apr 24, 24; m 49; c 2. CHEMICAL ENGINEERING, CHEMISTRY. *Educ:* Tech Univ Norway, MS, 49. *Prof Exp:* Prod supvr, Mjondalen Rubber Factory, 50-52; engr, Technol Sect, E I du Pont de Nemours & Co, 52-57; group leader, Polymer Pilot Plant, US Indust Chem Co Div, Nat Distillers & Chem Corp, 57, res supvr polyolefin res, 57-59, asst mgr, 59-61, mgr, 61-66; DIR RES, CHEMPLEX CO, ROLLING MEADOWS, 66- *Mem:* Am Chem Soc; Soc Plastics Engrs. *Res:* Mechanical and industrial rubber goods and plastics; process development in high and low density polyehtylene, copolymers and polypropylene; catalyst and exploratory research in olefin polymerization; applications research, polymer development and technical service. *Mailing Add:* 190 C Pine Crest Circle Barrington IL 60010

SOM, PRANTIKA, b Silchar, Assam, India, Aug 31, 42; US citizen. NUCLEAR MEDICINE, VETERINARY MEDICINE. *Educ:* Univ Calcutta, ISc, 60, DVM, 65; Johns Hopkins Univ, ScM, 69. *Prof Exp:* Demonstr path, Bengal Vet Col, 65-66; investr, Marine Biol Lab, Wood's Hole, Mass, 67-68; asst pathobiol, Johns Hopkins Med Inst, 67-69, sr res fel, 73-74; from asst scientist to assoc scientist, 75-80, SCIENTIST, NUCLEAR MED, BROOKHAVEN NAT LAB, 80- *Concurrent Pos:* Reserve vet asst surgeon, Govt W Bengal, 65-66; jr res fel, Johns Hopkins Univ, 70-72, asst radiol, 73-74; mem vet serv comt, Brookhaven Nat Lab, 75-; mem educ comt, Soc Nuclear Med, 76-; res asst prof, State Univ NY, 79-; consult, Vet Admin Hosp, Nathpat, 81- *Mem:* Soc Nuclear Med; Am Vet Med Asn; Soc Invert Path. *Res:* Radiopharmaceutical development; evaluations and studies on their pharmacokinetics, metabolism and toxicology. *Mailing Add:* Dept Med Brookhaven Nat Lab Upton NY 11973

SOMA, LAWRENCE R, b New York, NY, Feb 2, 33; m 55; c 3. ANESTHESIOLOGY. *Educ:* Univ Pa, VMD, 57. *Prof Exp:* Intern vet med, Animal Med Ctr, NY, 57-58; fel anesthesiol, Sch Med, 60-62, instr, Sch Vet Med, 62-64, from asst prof to assoc prof, 64-72, PROF ANESTHESIOL, SCH VET MED, UNIV PA, 72-, CHMN DEPT CLIN STUDIES, 75- *Concurrent Pos:* NIH career develop award, 67-72, staff mem, Dept Anesthesiol, Sch Med, 71-; spec fel, Heart Lung Inst, 74-75. *Mem:* Am Vet Med Asn; AAAS; Am Soc Vet Physiologists & Pharmacologists; Am Thoracic Soc; Am Soc Anesthesiol. *Res:* Veterinary anesthesiology; anesthesia and pharmacology; effects of respiratory stimulants in the dog; cardiovascular effects of local anesthetics; effects of anesthetics on the fetus, pathophysiology of shock lung; physiology of bronchial circulation. *Mailing Add:* Dept Clin Studies-NBC Sch Vet Med Univ Pa Kenneth Square PA 19348

SOMANI, PITAMBAR, b Chirawah, India, Oct 31, 37; m 60; c 3. CLINICAL PHARMACOLOGY, MEDICINE. *Educ:* G R Med Col, Gwalior, India, MD, 60; Marquette Univ, PhD(pharmacol), 65. *Prof Exp:* Demonstr pharmacol, Indian Inst Med Sci, New Delhi, 60-62; from instr to asst prof, Sch Med, Marquette Univ, 65-69; assoc prof, Med Col Wis, 69-71, assoc clin prof, 71-74; prof pharmacol, Sch Med, Univ Miami, 74-80; DIR CLIN PHARMACOL, MED COL OHIO, 80- *Concurrent Pos:* Wis Heart Asn res grants, 65-71; NIH res grants, 66-72 & 74-78; Fla Heart Asn grant, 75 & 78; consult, Selvi & Co, Italy, 65-66, Abbott Labs, 74-76, Riker Labs, 77 & Dupont Labs, 78; mgr gen pharmacol dept, Abbott Labs, 71-74. *Mem:* AAAS; Am Soc Pharmacol & Exp Therapeut; Am Fedn Clin Res; fel Am Col Clin Pharmacol. *Res:* Cardiovascular and autonomic pharmacology; drug-design; clinical pharmacology. *Mailing Add:* Dept Pharmacol Med Col Ohio Toledo OH 43699

SOMANI, SATU M, b India, Mar 14, 37; m 66; c 1. PHARMACOLOGY, BIOCHEMICAL PHARMACOLOGY. *Educ:* Osmania Univ, BSc, 56; Univ Poona, MSc, 59; Duquesne Univ, MS, 64; Univ Liverpool, PhD(biochem pharmacol), 69. *Prof Exp:* Lectr chem, Vivek Vardhini Col, Osmania Univ, India, 59-61; scientist, Nuclear Sci & Eng Corp, Pa, 64-67; from instr to asst prof pharmacol, Univ Pittsburgh, 71-74; ASSOC PROF PHARMACOL & TOXICOL, SCH MED, SOUTHERN ILL UNIV, SPRINGFIELD, 74- *Concurrent Pos:* Health Res Serv Found grant, Univ Pittsburgh, 71. *Mem:* AAAS; Soc Toxicol; Am Soc Clin Pharmacol & Therapeut; Fedn Am Socs Exp Biol; NY Acad Sci. *Res:* Distribution, metabolism and excretion of drugs and pollutants in animal and man; competition of drugs for the plasma protein binding; biliary excretion of drugs; toxicology; analysis of water pollutants and mutagenicity. *Mailing Add:* 81 Interlacken Springfield IL 62704

SOMASUNDARAN, P(ONISSERIL), b Annallur, India, June 28, 39; m 66. SURFACE & COLLOID CHEMISTRY. *Educ:* Univ Kerala, BS, 58; Indian Inst Sci, Bangalore, BE, 61; Univ Calif, Berkeley, MS, 62, PhD(eng), 64. *Prof Exp:* Sr lab asst biochem, Nat Chem Lab, Univ Poona, India, 58-59; res asst metall & mat sci, Univ Calif, Berkeley, 61-64; sr mineral res engr, Int Minerals & Chem Corp, 64-67; sr res chemist, Res Dept-Basic Sci, R J Reynolds Industs Inc, 67-70; assoc prof, 70-78, PROF MINERAL ENG, HENRY KRUMB SCH MINES, COLUMBIA UNIV, 78- *Concurrent Pos:* NSF grants; Am Iron & Steel Inst grants; consult, NIH, 73, Ill Inst Technol Res Inst, 74-77, Amoco Prod Co, 74-77, Int Paper Co, 75, NSF, 77, B F Goodrich Co, 77-81, Exxon Corp, 77-, Occidental Res, 77, Am Cyanamid, 78, Proctor & Gamble, 78-79, Union Carbide, 79 & Colgate Palmolive, 79-; mem, Nat Acad Sci Comt Accessory Elements Phosphate, 76-78; ed-in-chief, Colloids & Surfaces; assoc ed, Int J Mineral Processing. *Mem:* Am Chem Soc; Am Inst Mining, Metall & Petrol Engrs (secy-treas, Mineral Processing Div, 78); Indian Inst Metals; Am Inst Chem Engrs; Int Asn Dent Res. *Res:* Surface and colloid chemistry; electrokinetics; flotation; flocculation; adsorption; mineral processing; enhanced oil recovery. *Mailing Add:* Sch Eng & Appl Sci Columbia Univ New York NY 10027

SOMBERG, ETHEL WEISS, b New York, NY, Jan 30, 20; m 42; c 3. BIOCHEMISTRY. *Educ:* Hunter Col, BA, 40; Rutgers Univ, MS, 62, PhD(biochem), 64. *Prof Exp:* Chemist, Venereal Dis Res Lab, USPHS, 44-46; asst biochem, Sloan Kettering Res Inst Cancer, 44-48; from asst prof to assoc prof, 63-79, PROF BIOCHEM, NEWARK COL ARTS & SCI, RUTGERS UNIV, 79- *Concurrent Pos:* Rutgers Res Coun grants, 64-; NSF grant, 68-70. *Mem:* Am Chem Soc; Am Soc Biol Chemists; Am Soc Microbiol; NY Acad Sci; Am Women Sci. *Res:* Synthesis, structure and function of cell membranes. *Mailing Add:* Newark Col Arts & Sci Rutgers Univ Newark NJ 07102

SOMEKH, GEORGE S, b Brussels, Belg, Apr 3, 35; US citizen; m 60; c 2. CHEMICAL ENGINEERING. *Educ:* Mass Inst Technol, BS, 56, MS, 57. *Prof Exp:* Proj engr, Plastics Div, 57-60, eng scientist, Chem Div, 60-77, RES ENGR, CHEM DIV, UNION CARBIDE CORP, 77- *Mem:* Am Inst Chem Engrs. *Res:* Separation and purification processes in petro-chemistry, petroleum refining and water pollution abatement; solvent extraction, azeotropic and extractive distillation; Rankine cycle fluids, lubricants and systems design. *Mailing Add:* Chem Div Union Carbide Corp 270 Park Ave New York NY 10017

SOMERO, GEORGE NICHOLLS, b Duluth, Minn, July 30, 40; m 68. BIOCHEMISTRY, PHYSIOLOGY. *Educ:* Carleton Col, BA, 62; Stanford Univ, PhD(biol), 67. *Prof Exp:* NSF fel, Univ BC, 67-69; I W Killam fel, 69-70; asst prof, 70-77, assoc prof, 77-80, PROF MARINE BIOL, SCRIPPS INST OCEANOG, UNIV CALIF, SAN DIEGO, 80- *Mem:* AAAS; Soc Cryobiol; Am Soc Zool. *Res:* Comparative biochemistry of environmental adaptation. *Mailing Add:* Dept of Marine Biol Scripps Inst of Oceanog La Jolla CA 92093

SOMERS, EDWARD V(INCENT), b Hazleton, Pa, July 1, 18; m 42; c 5. APPLIED MATHEMATICS, MECHANICAL ENGINEERING. *Educ:* Pa State Col, BS, 39; Univ Pittsburgh, MS, 46, PhD(math), 49. *Prof Exp:* Foundry engr, Westinghouse Elec Corp, 39-46, res engr, 46-50; res engr, Magnolia Petrol Co, 51-52; res engr, 52-57, mgr thermodyn activity, Res & Develop Ctr, 57-70, mgr heat transfer & flow res, Res Labs, 70-72, MGR ECOL SYSTS RES & CONSULT ENGR, RES LABS, WESTINGHOUSE ELEC CORP, 72- *Mem:* Am Soc Mech Engrs; Am Nuclear Soc. *Res:* Advanced energy conversion and utilization; thermal and mass transfer; fluid dynamics; power generation; air and water pollution and solid-waste disposal. *Mailing Add:* Energy Systs Div Res & Develop Ctr Westinghouse Elec Corp Pittsburgh PA 15235

SOMERS, EMMANUEL, b Leeds, Eng, July 3, 27; Can citizen; m 51; c 2. ENVIRONMENTAL TOXICOLOGY. *Educ:* Univ Leeds, BSc, 48, MSc, 50, DSc(chem), 69; Bristol Univ, PhD(chem), 56. *Prof Exp:* Prin sci off pesticide chem, Long Ashton Res Sta, Bristol Univ, 51-67; sect head food contaminants, Food & Drug Directorate, 67-68, chief food div, Health Protection Br, 68-72, dir, Food Res Labs, 72-74, DIR-GENERAL, ENVIRON HEALTH DIRECTORATE, CAN DEPT NAT HEALTH & WELFARE, 74- *Concurrent Pos:* Nat Res Coun fel, Pesticide Res Inst, London, Ont, 57-58; NSF grant, Conn Agr Exp Sta, 63-64; mgr, Int Prog Chem Safety, WHO Geneva, 80. *Mem:* Fel Chem Inst Can; fel Royal Soc Chem; Int Acad Environ Safety; Int Soc Toxicol & Environ Safety. *Res:* Mode of action of agricultural fungicides; analysis, metabolism and biochemistry of food contaminants and additives; research management; environmental health; risk assessment, science policy. *Mailing Add:* Health Protection Br Can Dept of Nat Health & Welfare Ottawa ON K1A 0L2 Can

SOMERS, GEORGE FREDRICK, JR, b Garland, Utah, July 9, 14; m 39; c 3. PLANT PHYSIOLOGY. *Educ:* Utah State Univ, BS, 35; Oxford Univ, BA, 38, BSc, 39; Cornell Univ, PhD(plant physiol), 42. *Prof Exp:* Instr biochem, Cornell Univ, 41-44, from asst prof to assoc prof, 44-51; assoc dir, Del Agr Exp Sta, 51-59, chmn dept agr biochem & food tech, 52-59, assoc dean, Sch

Agr, 54-59, chmn dept biol, 59-71, H Fletcher Brown prof, 62-81, EMER PROF BIOL, UNIV DEL, 81- *Concurrent Pos:* Plant physiologist, Plant, Soil & Nutrit Lab, USDA, 44-51, asst dir lab, 49-51; mem comt effects of atomic radiation on agr & food supplies, Nat Acad Sci-Nat Res Coun, 56-60; vis prof, Philippines, 58-59; ed, Gen Biochem Sect, Chem Abstr, 63-71; vis scientist, Brookhaven Nat Lab, 71; distinguished fac lectr, Univ Del, 80. *Mem:* Fel AAAS; Am Soc Plant Physiol; Bot Soc Am; Philippine Soc Adv Res. *Res:* Enzymes; cell wall chemistry; physiological ecology; halophytes as potential food plants. *Mailing Add:* Sch of Life & Health Sci Univ of Del Newark DE 19711

SOMERS, KENNETH DONALD, b Fremont, Mich, Mar 2, 38; m 61; c 3. MICROBIOLOGY. *Educ:* Univ Mich, BA, 60, MS, 62; Univ Chicago, PhD(microbiol), 69. *Prof Exp:* Res assoc virol, Ciba Pharmaceut Co, 63-65; res assoc biochem virol, Baylor Col Med, 69-70, asst prof, 70-74; ASSOC PROF MICROBIOL, EASTERN VA MED SCH, 74- *Mem:* AAAS; Am Soc Microbiol. *Res:* Oncogenic RNA viruses. *Mailing Add:* Microbiol Dept Eastern Va Med Sch PO Box 1980 Norfolk VA 23501

SOMERS, MICHAEL EUGENE, b Astoria, NY, Aug 11, 29; m 54; c 4. NEUROBIOLOGY, HISTOLOGY. *Educ:* Univ Bridgeport, BA, 51, MA, 55; Clark Univ, PhD(animal morphol), 67. *Prof Exp:* Instr, 55-59, asst prof, 60-67, assoc prof, 68-69, PROF BIOL & CHMN DEPT, UNIV BRIDGEPORT, 70- *Mem:* Am Soc Zool; Am Soc Ichthyol & Herpet; Am Micros Soc; Am Fisheries Soc. *Res:* Neuroanatomy of Crustacea; fine structure of invertebrate nervous systems; fish olfactory system. *Mailing Add:* Dept of Biol Univ of Bridgeport Bridgeport CT 06602

SOMERS, PERRIE DANIEL, b Winona, Minn, Oct 18, 18; m 42; c 4. BIOCHEMISTRY. *Educ:* Wabash Col, AB, 41; Purdue Univ, MS, 43, PhD(biochem), 46. *Prof Exp:* Res chemist, 46-51, GROUP LEADER, LAB TECH CTR, INT MULTIFOODS CORP, 51- *Mem:* Am Chem Soc; Am Asn Cereal Chemists. *Res:* Enzymic reactions; biological food chemistry; new food product development; food process design; food product patents; new cereal products. *Mailing Add:* 9912 Harriet Ave S Minneapolis MN 55420

SOMERSCALES, EUAN FRANCIS CUTHBERT, b London, Eng, Jan 23, 31; US citizen; m 64; c 2. HEAT TRANSFER, FLUID MECHANICS. *Educ:* Univ London, BSc, 53; Rensselaer Polytech Inst, MME, 61; Cornell Univ, PhD(heat transfer), 65. *Prof Exp:* Apprentice, NBrit Locomotive Co, 53-55; instr mech eng, 58-59, asst prof, 64-68, ASSOC PROF, RENSSELAER POLYTECH INST, 68- *Concurrent Pos:* Sr vis fel, Univ Manchester Inst Sci Technol, 75-76. *Mem:* Am Soc Mech Eng; Am Phys Soc. *Res:* Fluid mechanics and heat transfer with application to free convection and the fouling of heat transfer surfaces. *Mailing Add:* Rensselaer Polytechnic Inst Troy NY 12181

SOMERSET, JAMES H, b Philadelphia, Pa, Apr 19, 38; m 63; c 2. MECHANICAL & AEROSPACE ENGINEERING. *Educ:* Drexel Inst Technol, BS, 61; Syracuse Univ, MS, 63, PhD(mech & aerospace eng), 65. *Prof Exp:* Engr, Scott Paper Co, 58-61; asst prof mech & aerospace eng, 65-69, assoc prof, 69-80, PROF MECH & AEROSPACE ENG, COL ENG, SYRACUSE UNIV, 80- *Concurrent Pos:* NSF grant, 66-68; consult, Singer Publ Co, 66- *Mem:* Am Inst Aeronaut & Astronaut. *Res:* Stochastic response of structures; dynamic response of structures to periodic and impulse loads; dynamics; vibrations; stability of systems; plate and shell structures; biomechanics. *Mailing Add:* Dept of Mech Eng 129 Link Hall Syracuse NY 13210

SOMERSON, NORMAN L, b Philadelphia, Pa, Dec 17, 28; m 55; c 6. MEDICAL MICROBIOLOGY. *Educ:* Marietta Col, BS, 50; Univ Pa, MS, 52, PhD, 54. *Prof Exp:* Asst, Univ Pa, 53-54; asst prof, Bucknell Univ, 55; bacteriologist, Philadelphia Gen Hosp, 55; res microbiologist, Merck & Co, 56-62; sr scientist, Nat Inst Allergy & Infectious Dis, 62-66; assoc prof med microbiol, 66-69, assoc prof pediat, 67-70, PROF MED MICROBIOL, OHIO STATE UNIV, 69-, PROF PEDIAT, 70- *Concurrent Pos:* NIH grant pulmonary physiol in infection, 68-73; contract antigenicity of Mycoplasma pneumoniae, NIH, 66-72; mem, Int Subcomt Nomenclature of Mycoplasmas, 66-; consult, Ohio State Dept of Health, 75-81; distinguished vis prof biol, US Air Force Acad, 81-82. *Mem:* AAAS; Am Soc Microbiol; Soc Exp Biol Med. *Res:* Penicillin and glutamic acid fermentation process; microbial steroid conversions; mycoplasmas, including nucleic acid homology, serology, pathogenicity, vaccine process and lung changes in infection; male hybrid sterility in Drosophila. *Mailing Add:* Dept of Med Microbiol Ohio State Univ Col of Med Columbus OH 43210

SOMERVILLE, GEORGE R, US citizen. CHEMICAL ENGINEERING. *Educ:* Tex A&M Univ, BS, 42. *Prof Exp:* Plant engr, Chem Warfare Serv, US Army, 43-45; process engr, Neches Butane Prod Co, 46-53; assoc chem engr, 55-56, sr chem engr, 56-59, sr indust chemist, 59, asst mgr org & biol chem, 59-60, mgr encapsulation sect, 60-61, mgr spec projs, 61-64, actg dir, 64-65, asst dir, 65-74, dir, San Antonio Labs, Dept Chem & Chem Eng, 74-76, DIR DEPT APPL CHEM & CHEM ENG, SOUTHWEST RES INST, 76- *Mem:* Am Chem Soc; Sigma Xi. *Res:* Development of the process, materials and techniques for encapsulating various materails for commercial and military purposes. *Mailing Add:* Dept of Appl Chem & Chem Eng PO Drawer 28510 San Antonio TX 78284

SOMERVILLE, PAUL NOBLE, b Vulcan, Alta, May 7, 25; nat US; m 54; c 2. STATISTICS. *Educ:* Univ Alta, BSc, 49; Univ NC, PhD(statist), 53. *Prof Exp:* Teacher, Lethbridge Sch Div, Can, 42-44; assoc prof statist, Va Polytech Inst & assoc statistician exten serv, Agr Exp Sta, 53-55; vis prof math, Am Univ, 55-57; asst proj dir, C-E-I-R, Inc, Ariz, 58-61, mgr, Utah Off, 61-62; mgr tech eval, RCA Corp, Patrick AFB, 62-72; assoc prof, 72-80, PROF MATH & STATIST, UNIV CENT FLA, 80- *Concurrent Pos:* Guest scientist, Nat Bur Standards, 55-57; lectr, Univ Ariz, 58-61 & Brigham Young Univ, 62; chmn math dept, Fla Inst Technol, 63-72; adj prof, Univ Fla, Genesys, 68-72. *Mem:* Am Statist Asn; Am Meteorol Soc; Int Asn Statist Comput. *Res:* Statistics; climatology; education; computer simulation; model building; design of experiments; consulting. *Mailing Add:* Dept Math & Statist Univ Cent Fla Box 25000 Orlando FL 32816

SOMERVILLE, RICHARD CHAPIN JAMES, b Washington, DC, May 30, 41; m 65; c 2. METEOROLOGY, FLUID DYNAMICS. *Educ:* Pa State Univ, BS, 61; NY Univ, PhD(meteorol), 66. *Prof Exp:* Res meteorologist, Geophys Fluid Dynamics Lab, Environ Sci Serv Admin, 67-69; res scientist, Courant Inst Math Sci, NY Univ, 69-72; meteorologist, Inst Space Studies, Goddard Space Flight Ctr, NASA, 71-74; scientist, Nat Ctr Atmospheric Res, 74-79; PROF METEOROL & HEAD, CLIMATE RES GROUP, SCRIPPS INST OCEANOG, UNIV CALIF, SAN DIEGO, 79- *Concurrent Pos:* Fel, Nat Ctr Atmospheric Res, 66-67; fel geophys fluid dynamics prog, Woods Hole Oceanog Inst, 67, staff mem, 70, 76; adj assoc prof, NY Univ, 71-73 & Columbia Univ, 71-74. *Mem:* Am Meteorol Soc; Am Geophys Union. *Res:* Theoretical dynamic meteorology; numerical fluid dynamics; thermal convection; atmospheric general circulation; numerical weather prediction; parameterization of small-scale processes. *Mailing Add:* Dept Meteorol Scripps Inst Oceanog Mail Code A024 Univ Calif San Diego La Jolla CA 92093

SOMERVILLE, RONALD LAMONT, b Vancouver, BC, Feb 27, 35; nat US; m 55; c 5. BIOCHEMISTRY, BIOTECHNOLOGY. *Educ:* Univ BC, BA, 56, MSc, 57; Univ Mich, PhD, 61. *Prof Exp:* Res assoc biochem, Univ Mich, 60-61; asst prof, Univ Mich, Ann Arbor, 64-67; assoc prof, 67-77, PROF BIOCHEM, PURDUE UNIV, WEST LAFAYETTE, 77- *Concurrent Pos:* Fel biol sci, Stanford Univ, 61-64. *Mem:* Am Soc Biol Chemists; Genetics Soc Am. *Res:* Physico-chemical basis for specific interations between regulatory proteins and control sites in duplex DNA; genetic analysis; gene-splicing technology. *Mailing Add:* Dept of Biochem Purdue Univ West Lafayette IN 47907

SOMES, RALPH GILMORE, JR, b Melrose, Mass, Aug 15, 29; m 54; c 3. AVIAN GENETICS, HUMAN NUTRITION. *Educ:* Univ Mass, BS, 60, PhD(poultry genetics), 63. *Prof Exp:* From asst prof to assoc prof, 63-73, PROF NUTRIT & GENETICS, UNIV CONN, 73- *Mem:* Poultry Sci Asn; Am Genetic Asn; Genetics Soc Am; World Poultry Sci Asn. *Res:* Genetic investigations of feather pigment systems and new mutant traits in the domestic fowl; genetic-nutritional interaction; studies relating to fowl lines selected for transport of certain nutrients. *Mailing Add:* Dept of Nutrit Sci Box U-17 Univ of Conn Storrs CT 06268

SOMJEN, GEORGE G, b Budapest, Hungary, May 2, 29; c 4. PHYSIOLOGY, PHARMACOLOGY. *Educ:* Univ Amsterdam, MD, 56; Univ NZ, MD, 61. *Prof Exp:* Asst pharmacol, Univ Amsterdam, 53-56; lectr physiol, Univ Otago, NZ, 56-60, sr lectr, 61-62; res fel, Harvard Med Sch, 62-63; from asst prof to assoc prof, 63-71, PROF PHYSIOL, DUKE UNIV, 71- *Concurrent Pos:* Consult, Nat Inst Environ Health Sci, 71-75; invited speaker, XXVIIIth Int Cong Physiol, 81. *Mem:* AAAS; Am Electroencephalog Soc; Am Soc Pharmacol Exp Therapeut; Soc Neurosci; Am Physiol Soc. *Res:* Reflex function of spinal cord; mechanism of seizures; properties of motoneurons; effects of drugs and ions on central nervous system and on peripheral junctions; blood-brain barrier. *Mailing Add:* Dept of Physiol & Pharmacol Duke Univ Med Ctr Durham NC 27710

SOMKAITE, ROZALIJA, b Lithuania, Feb 10, 25; US citizen. PHARMACEUTICAL CHEMISTRY, ANALYTICAL CHEMISTRY. *Educ:* St John's Univ, NY, BS, 54; Univ Wis, MS, 56; Rutgers Univ, PhD(pharmaceut sci), 62. *Prof Exp:* Assoc scientist, Warner-Chillcot Pharmaceut Co, 56-58; teaching asst, Rutgers Univ, 58-59, NIH res fel anal, 61-62; sr scientist, Ethicon, Inc, 62-70; mgr anal res dept, 70-74, DIR ANAL SERV, REHEIS CHEM CO, 74- *Mem:* Am Pharmaceut Asn; Am Chem Soc; Am Microchem Soc; Soc Appl Spectros. *Res:* Analytical research applying multiple technique systems. *Mailing Add:* 386 Hillside Pl South Orange NJ 07079

SOMKUTI, GEORGE A, b Budapest, Hungary, Jan 6, 36; US citizen; m 59; c 2. FERMENTATION BIOCHEMISTRY, APPLIED GENETICS. *Educ:* Tufts Univ, MS, 59; Purdue Univ, MS, 63, PhD(microbiochem), 66. *Prof Exp:* NIH fel, Purdue Univ, 66-68; asst prof microbiochem & immunol, Duquesne Univ, 68-69; res assoc cell biol, Purdue Univ, 69-73; sr res scientist, Res & Develop, Lederle Labs, Am Cyanamid Co, 73-76; RES LEADER DEVELOP MICROBIOL & BIOCHEM, EASTERN REGIONAL RES CTR, USDA, 76- *Concurrent Pos:* Mem, NSF Curric Develop Comt Univ Tex, San Antonio, 74-75 & NIH Special Studies Sect, 76; ed, J Food Protection, 82- *Mem:* Am Soc Microbiol; Soc Indust Microbiol; NY Acad Sci. *Mailing Add:* Eastern Regional Res Ctr USDA 600 E Mermaid Lane Philadelphia PA 19118

SOMLYO, ANDREW PAUL, b Budapest, Hungary, Feb 25, 30; US citizen; m 61; c 1. PHYSIOLOGY, PATHOLOGY. *Educ:* Univ Ill, Chicago, BS, 54, MS & Md, 56; Drexel Inst Technol, MS, 63. *Prof Exp:* Intern, Philadelphia Gen Hosp, 56-57, resident, 57-58; asst resident med, Mt Sinai Hosp, New York, 58-59; sr asst resident, Bellevue Hosp, 59-60; asst physician, Columbia-Presby Med Ctr, 60-61; res assoc, Presby Hosp, 61-66; from asst prof to assoc prof, 64-71, PROF PATH, UNIV PA, 71- *Concurrent Pos:* Heart Asn Southeast Pa res fel, Philadelphia Gen Hosp, 57-58; NIH spec res fel, Presby Hosp, Philadelphia, 61-66; USPHS res career prog award, Presby-Univ Pa Med Ctr, 66-73; dir, Pa Muscle Inst; prof physiol & path, Univ of Pa Sch Med; sr res pathologist, Presby-Univ Pa Med Ctr, 67- *Mem:* Microbeam Anal Soc; AAAS; Soc Gen Physiol; Am Physiol Soc; Biophys Soc; Am Soc Cell Biol. *Res:* Development and application of quantitative electron optical techniques in biology including electron probe analysis and electron energy loss analysis; ultrastructure and cell physiology of vascular smooth muscle and skeletal muscle; pharmacology. *Mailing Add:* Sch Med B42 Anat Chem Bldg Penn Muscle Inst Univ Penn Philadelphia PA 19104

SOMLYO, AVRIL VIRGINIA, b Sask, Can, Apr 9, 39; m 61; c 1. CELL PHYSIOLOGY. *Educ:* Univ Sask, BA, 59, MSc, 61; Univ Pa, PhD, 76. *Prof Exp:* Co prin investr, 65-79, RES ASSOC PROF PHYSIOL, PRESBY UNIV PA MED CTR, 79- *Concurrent Pos:* Mem, Biol Instrumentation Panel, NSF, 79- & Pharmacol Study Sect, NIH, 79- *Mem:* Am Soc Pharmacol & Exp Therapeut; Biophys Soc; Sigma Xi; Soc Gen Physiologists. *Res:* Basic function and structure of striated and vascular smooth muscle, including excitation-contraction coupling, contractile proteins and the insitu distribution of elements using high spatial resolution electron probe analysis. *Mailing Add:* Pa Muscle Inst Univ Pa Sch Med B42 Anat-Chem Bldg G3 Philadelphia PA 19104

SOMMER, ALFRED HERMANN, b Frankfurt, Ger, Nov 19, 09; US citizen; m 38; c 3. ELECTRON EMISSION. *Educ:* Berlin Univ, Dr Phil(chem), 34. *Prof Exp:* Res engr photo multipliers, Baird TV Co, London, 36-46; res engr TV camera tubes, EMI-Res Lab, Eng, 46-53; res engr electron emission, RCA-Res Labs, Princeton, NJ, 53-74; RES ENGR, THERMO-ELECTRON CO, WALTHAM, MASS, 74- *Mem:* Am Phys Soc; fel Inst Elec & Electronics Engrs. *Res:* New photoemissive materials; secondary emission; thermionic emission; photo multipliers; television camera tubes; image intensifier tubes; thermionic energy conversion. *Mailing Add:* 16 Wildwood Circle Wellesley MA 02181

SOMMER, CHARLES JOHN, b New York, NY, Jan 12, 51. STATISTICS, BIOMETRICS. *Educ:* Manhattan Col, BS, 72; State Univ NY Buffalo, MA, 73, PhD(statist sci), 77. *Prof Exp:* Biostatistician, Sidney Farber Cancer Inst, 77-78; ASST PROF STATIST, TEMPLE UNIV, 78- *Mem:* Am Statist Asn. *Mailing Add:* Dept of Statist Temple Univ Philadelphia PA 19122

SOMMER, HARRY EDWARD, b Chatham, NY, July 25, 41; m 64; c 2. FOREST PHYSIOLOGY. *Educ:* Univ Vt, BSAgr, 63; Univ Maine, MS, 66; Ohio State Univ, PhD(bot), 72. *Prof Exp:* Res assoc tissue cult, Sch Forest Resources, Univ Ga, 72-74; scientist, Weyerhaauser Forestry Res Ctr, 74-76; ASST PROF TISSUE CULT, SCH FOREST RESOURCES, UNIV GA, 76- *Mem:* Bot Soc Am; Am Soc Plant Physiologists; Sigma Xi. *Res:* Tissue culture of trees. *Mailing Add:* Sch of Forest Resources Univ of Ga Athens GA 30602

SOMMER, HELMUT, b Ger, Aug 23, 22; nat US; m 46; c 6. ELECTRICAL ENGINEERING, ELECTRONICS. *Educ:* Agr & Mech Col, Tex, BS, 44, MS, 47, PhD, 50. *Prof Exp:* Electronic scientist, Nat Bur Stand, 49-53 & Diamond Ord Fuze Labs, US Dept Army, 53-57; res prof electronics, Univ Fla, 57-58; chief, Microwave Br, Diamond Ord Fuze Labs, US Dept Army, 58-62, chief, Systs Res Lab, Harry Diamond Labs, 62-66, assoc tech dir, Harry Diamond Labs, 66-80; CONSULT, 80- *Concurrent Pos:* Consult, Catholic Univ, 53-60. *Honors & Awards:* Meritorious Serv Award, US Dept Commerce, 52. *Mem:* Inst Elec & Electronics Engrs. *Res:* Radar; microwaves; military electronics; proximity fuzes. *Mailing Add:* 9502 Hollins Ct Bethesda MD 20817

SOMMER, HOLGER THOMAS, b Wittgendorf, Ger, June 18, 50; m 77. COMBUSTION, FLUID-THERMO SCIENCE. *Educ:* Tech Univ Aachen, dipl ing, 74, Imp Col Sci & Technol, London, MS, 77; Tech Univ Aachen, Dr Ing, 79. *Prof Exp:* Instr thermo-fluid, Tech Univ Aachen, 74-75; consult air conditioning, Behr Eng, Aachen, 76; res engr combustion, Imp Col London, 76-77; sr scientist combustion-mech fluid, Tech Univ Aachen, 77-80; prin investr solar energy, Ger Sci Found, Desert Res Inst, 80; ASST PROF COMBUSTION-FLUID MECH, CARNEGIE-MELLON UNIV, 81- *Concurrent Pos:* Consult engr, Forensic Consult & Engrs, 81-; fel, Lilly Endowment, 81. *Honors & Awards:* R R Teetor Award, Soc Automotive Engrs, 82. *Mem:* Am Soc Mech Engrs; Soc Automotive Engrs; Combustion Inst. *Res:* Fluid mechanics of combustion; ignition of combustible mixtures; development of optical diagnostic instrumentation; numerical modeling of combustion systems; spray formation; coal-energy conversion processes. *Mailing Add:* Dept Mech Eng Carnegie-Mellon Univ Pittsburgh PA 15213

SOMMER, JOACHIM RAINER, b Dresden, Ger, Apr 11, 24; nat US; m 51; c 2. PATHOLOGY. *Educ:* Univ Munich, MD, 50; Am Bd Path, dipl, 58, cert anat & clin path, 69. *Prof Exp:* Asst, Path Inst, Munich, Ger, 51-52; asst, Med Clin Munich, 52-53; intern, Garfield Mem Hosp, Washington, DC, 53-54; resident path, Garfield Mem & De Paul Hosps, 54-58; assoc, 58-59, from asst prof to assoc prof, 59-70, PROF PATH, MED CTR, DUKE UNIV, 70- *Res:* Histochemistry; cardiac ultrastructure and function. *Mailing Add:* Dept of Path Duke Univ Med Ctr Durham NC 27710

SOMMER, KATHLEEN RUTH, b Port Washington, Wis, June 2, 47. TOXICOLOGY. *Educ:* Ripon Col, BA, 69; Univ Iowa, PhD(biochem), 73; Am Bd Toxicol, dipl, 81. *Prof Exp:* Res assoc chem, Univ Wis-Milwaukee, 69; instr pharmacol, Baylor Col Med, 73-74; USPHS res fel, Baylor Col Med, 74-76; toxicologist, Shell Oil Co, 76-80; DIR RES, TOXICON CORP, 80- *Concurrent Pos:* Consult, Scientists Coop Indust, 72-76, Nat Adv Res Resources Coun, NIH, 74-78 & Div Res Resources, NIH, 78-; guest lectr, Med Sch, Univ Tex, 78- *Mem:* Am Col Toxicol; Am Indust Health Coun; Am Chem Soc; AAAS; Sigma Xi. *Res:* Drug metabolism and toxicity; pesticide toxicology; mass spectroscopy; effects of toxins on reproduction. *Mailing Add:* Shell Develop Co PO Box 4320 Houston TX 77210

SOMMER, LEO HARRY, b New York, NY, Sept 21, 17; m 44; c 3. ORGANIC CHEMISTRY. *Educ:* Pa State Univ, BS, MS, 42, PhD(org chem), 45. *Prof Exp:* Instr chem, Pa State Univ, 43-47, from asst prof to assoc prof, 47-60, prof, 60-65; PROF CHEM, UNIV CALIF, DAVIS, 65- *Concurrent Pos:* Res fel, Harvard Univ, 50-51; Guggenheim fel, 60-61; consult, Dow Corning Corp, 47- *Honors & Awards:* F S Kipping Award, Am Chem Soc, 63. *Mem:* Am Chem Soc; Royal Soc Chem. *Res:* Stereochemistry and reaction mechanisms of silicon centers in organosilicon compounds; chemistry of multiple-bonded unsaturated organosilicon compounds. *Mailing Add:* Dept of Chem Univ of Calif Davis CA 95616

SOMMER, LEONARD SAMUEL, b Springfield, Mass, July 3, 24; m; c 2. CARDIOLOGY. *Educ:* Yale Univ, BS, 44; Columbia Univ, MD, 47; Am Bd Internal Med, dipl, 57 & 77. *Prof Exp:* Intern med, Peter Bent Brigham Hosp, 47-48; instr med, Med Sch, Georgetown Univ, 51-52; resident med, Peter Bent Brigham Hosp, 48-49 & 53-54; res fel, Harvard Med Sch, 54-55, asst, 55-56; from asst prof to assoc prof, 56-74, PROF MED & PEDIAT, SCH

MED, UNIV MIAMI, 74- *Concurrent Pos:* Teaching fel, Harvard Med Sch, 48-49; Am Heart Asn res fel cardiol, Columbia-Presby Med Ctr & New York Hosp, Cornell Univ, 49-50; Nat Heart Inst res fel cardiol, Hammersmith Hosp, London, Eng, 52-53; fel cardiol, Cardiovasc Lab, Children's Med Ctr, Boston, 54-56; consult cardiologist, Adolescent Unit, Children's Med Ctr, Boston, Mass, 54-56; asst physician, Peter Bent Brigham Hosp, 54-56; investr, Howard Hughes Med Inst, 56-59; mem coun clin cardiol, Am Heart Asn; dir, Cardiovasc Lab, Jackson Mem Hosp, 56-75 & dir, Exercise Labs, 78- *Mem:* Am Heart Asn; fel Am Col Cardiol; fel Am Col Physicians; Am Fedn Clin Res. *Res:* Cardiovascular physiology and diseases. *Mailing Add:* Univ Miami Sch Med-D62 Div Cardiol PO Box 016960 Miami FL 33101

SOMMER, MICHAEL ANTHONY, II, geochemistry, see previous edition

SOMMER, NOEL FREDERICK, b Scio, Ore, Jan 21, 20; m 46; c 1. PLANT PHYSIOLOGY, PATHOLOGY. *Educ:* Ore State Col, BS, 41; Univ Calif, MS, 52, PhD(plant path), 55. *Prof Exp:* County agr exten agent, Ore State Col, 46-51; res asst, Univ Calif, 52-55; plant pathologist, USDA, 55-56; asst pomologist, 56-63, lectr & assoc pomologist, 63-67, lectr & pomologist, 67-75, chmn dept pomol, 75-81, LECTR POMOL & POSTHARVEST PATHOLOGIST, UNIV CALIF, DAVIS, 81- *Mem:* Am Phytopath Soc; Am Soc Hort Sci; Am Soc Microbiol; Mycol Soc Am. *Res:* Physiology and pathology of fruits and vegetables after harvest; mycotoxins. *Mailing Add:* Dept of Pomology Univ of Calif Davis CA 95616

SOMMER, SHELDON E, b New York, NY, Nov 3, 37; m 60. GEOCHEMISTRY. *Educ:* City Col New York, BS, 59; City Univ New York, MA, 61; Tex A&M, MS, 64; Pa State Univ, PhD(geochem), 69. *Prof Exp:* Sec sch teacher, Bd Ed, NY, 59-61; res asst geol, Kans Geol Surv, 61-62; oceanogr, Tex A&M, 62-63, res scientist, 63-64; asst geochem & mineral, Pa State Univ, 64-69; assoc prof geochem, 69-76, ASSOC PROF GEOL, UNIV MD, COLLEGE PARK, 76- *Mem:* AAAS; Geochem Soc; Mineral Soc Am; Soc Appl Spectros. *Res:* Geochemistry of marine sediments and sea water; low temperature mineral synthesis; study of geological materials by electron spectroscopy and electron microprobe spectroscopy. *Mailing Add:* Dept of Chem Univ of Md College Park MD 20742

SOMMERFELD, JUDE T, b Elmwood Place, Ohio, Feb 4, 36; m 58; c 4. CHEMICAL ENGINEERING. *Educ:* Univ Detroit, BChE, 58; Univ Mich, MSE, 60, PhD(chem eng), 63. *Prof Exp:* Sr systs engr, Monsanto Co, 63-65, eng specialist, 65-66; sr systs engr, Wyandotte Chem Corp, 66-67, mgr systs eng, 67-68, dir process eng, 68-70; assoc prof, 70-75, PROF CHEM ENG, GA INST TECHNOL, 75- *Mem:* Am Chem Soc; Instrument Soc Am; Am Inst Chem Engrs; Nat Soc Prof Engrs. *Res:* Energy conservation; digital and analog computer applications; applied mathematics; systems engineering; management science; thermodynamics; kinetics; catalysis. *Mailing Add:* 5057 Foxcreek Ct Atlanta GA 30360

SOMMERFELD, MILTON R, b Thorndale, Tex, Nov 24, 40; m 63. PHYCOLOGY. *Educ:* Southwest Tex State Col, BS, 62; Univ Wash, PhD(bot), 68. *Prof Exp:* Teaching asst biol, Southwest Tex State Col, 61-62; teaching asst bot, Univ Wash, 64-65, instr, 65; asst prof, 68-74, ASSOC PROF BOT, ARIZ STATE UNIV, 74- *Mem:* AAAS; Bot Soc Am; Phycol Soc Am; Int Phycol Soc. *Res:* Morphogenesis and development of the algae; systematics; morphogenesis; life cycles; ecology of the algae. *Mailing Add:* Dept Bot & Microbiol Ariz State Univ Tempe AZ 85281

SOMMERFELD, RICHARD ARTHUR, b Chicago, Ill, July 4, 33. GEOCHEMISTRY, GEOLOGY. *Educ:* Univ Chicago, PhD(geophys), 65. *Prof Exp:* Micrometeorologist, Univ Wash, 61-64; fel geochem, Univ Calif, Los Angeles, 65-67, inst geophys fel, 66-67; assoc geologist, 67-76, RES GEOLOGIST, ROCKY MOUNTAIN FOREST & RANGE EXP STA, US FOREST SERV, 77- *Concurrent Pos:* NSF fel, 65-66. *Mem:* Am Geophys Union. *Res:* Physical chemistry of mineral reactions, particularly the reactions of quartz and water; metamorphism and solid mechanics of snow; ice crystallization from vapor; acoustic properties of snow. *Mailing Add:* US Forest Serv 240 W Prospect St Ft Collins CO 80526

SOMMERFELDT, THERON G, b Cardston, Alta, Can, May 27, 23; m 48; c 5. SOIL SCIENCE, PHYSICAL CHEMISTRY. *Educ:* Univ Alta, BSc, 50; Utah State Univ, MS, 52, PhD(soil chem), 61. *Prof Exp:* Asst agronomist, Can Sugar Factories, 51-53; asst soil scientist, NDak State Univ, 53-60; self employed, 60-61; asst soil scientist, Univ Idaho, 61-65; SOIL SCIENTIST, CAN DEPT AGR, 65- *Mem:* Am Soc Agron; Agr Inst Can; Can Soc Soil Sci; Prof Inst Pub Serv Can; Can Soc Agr Engrs. *Res:* Reclamation and drainage of saline and alkali soils; soil and water pollution from fertilizers and animal wastes; investigations, management and reclamation of dryland salinity; animal waste disposal and utilization. *Mailing Add:* Res Sta Can Dept of Agr Lethbridge AB T1J 4B1 Can

SOMMERFIELD, CHARLES MICHAEL, b New York, NY, Oct 27, 33; m 69; c 2. THEORETICAL PHYSICS. *Educ:* Brooklyn Col, BS, 53; Harvard Univ, AM, 54, PhD(physics), 57. *Hon Degrees:* MA, Yale Univ, 67. *Prof Exp:* NSF fel physics, Univ Calif, 57-58, instr & jr res physicist, 58-59; res fel, Harvard Univ, 59-61, Corning lectr, 60-61; from asst prof to assoc prof, 61-67, PROF PHYSICS, YALE UNIV, 67- *Concurrent Pos:* Vis asst res mathematician, Univ Calif, 65. *Mem:* AAAS, Am Phys Soc. *Res:* Theories of quantized fields and elementary particle interactions. *Mailing Add:* Dept of Physics Yale Univ New Haven CT 06511

SOMMERMAN, KATHRYN MARTHA, b New Haven, Conn, Jan 11, 15. ENTOMOLOGY. *Educ:* Univ Conn, BS, 37; Univ Ill, MS, 41, PhD(entom), 45. *Prof Exp:* Artist entom, Univ Ill, 37-38, artist & asst entom, Ill Natural Hist Surv, 39-45; instr biol, Wells Col, 45; asst prof zool, Eastern Ill Col Educ, 46; entomologist, Army Med Dept Res & Grad Sch, Washington, DC, 46-51; entomologist bur entom & plant quarantine, USDA, 51-53, collabr, Sect Insect Identification, Entom Res Br, Agr Res Serv, Md, 53-58; res entomologist, Arctic Health Res Ctr, 55-73, chief entom unit, 60-73; RES CONSULT, 73- *Concurrent Pos:* Entomologist, Alaskan Insect Proj, US Dept Army, 48; fel, Univ Ill, Urbana, 49. *Mem:* Entom Soc Am; Ecol Soc Am; Am Inst Biol Sci; Am Mosquito Control Asn; Wilderness Soc. *Res:* Systematics and bionomics of Psocoptera and Alaskan biting flies. *Mailing Add:* PO Box 1144 Greenville ME 04441

SOMMERS, ARMIGER HENRY, b Clarksdale, Miss, June 15, 20; m 49; c 5. CHEMISTRY. *Educ:* Notre Dame Univ, BS, 42, MS, 43, PhD(org chem), 48. *Prof Exp:* Res chemist, Notre Dame Univ, 44-45 & Columbia Univ, 46; res chemist, 47-63, LICENSING LIAISON, ABBOTT LABS, 63- *Mem:* Am Chem Soc; Sigma Xi; AAAS. *Res:* Organic synthesis of nitrogen compounds for medicinal use; new drug information and licensing. *Mailing Add:* Abbott Labs North Chicago IL 60064

SOMMERS, ELLA BLANCHE, b Lahoma, Okla, Mar 12, 08. PHARMACY. *Educ:* Univ Okla, BS, 30, MS, 31; Ohio State Univ, PhD, 54. *Prof Exp:* From assoc prof to prof pharm, Univ Okla, 42-78, asst dean pharm, 71-78, consult, Col Pharm & Off Develop, 78- *Mem:* Am Chem Soc; Am Pharmaceut Asn. *Res:* Freeze drying. *Mailing Add:* Fac Exchange Univ Okla Norman OK 73069

SOMMERS, HENRY STERN, JR, b St Paul, Minn, Apr 21, 14; m 38; c 4. PHYSICS. *Educ:* Univ Minn, AB, 36; Harvard Univ, PhD(physics), 41. *Prof Exp:* Instr, Harvard Univ, 41-42; mem staff, Mass Inst Technol, 42-45; asst prof physics, Rutgers Univ, 46-49; mem staff, Los Alamos Sci Lab, NMex, 49-54; FEL, RCA LABS, RCA CORP, 54- *Concurrent Pos:* Fulbright lectr & Guggenheim fel, Hebrew Univ, Israel, 60-61. *Mem:* AAAS; fel Am Phys Soc; Fedn Am Sci. *Res:* Nuclear and semiconductor physics; instrumentation; cryogenics; photoconductivity; quantum electronics; experimental research on basic physics and control of power spectrum of injection lasers. *Mailing Add:* RCA Labs Princeton NJ 08540

SOMMERS, HERBERT M, b Colorado Springs, Colo, Sept 4, 25; m 55; c 4. PATHOLOGY. *Educ:* Northwestern Univ, BS, 49, MD, 52. *Prof Exp:* Instr, 59-61, assoc, 61-62, from asst prof to assoc prof, 62-71, PROF PATH, MED SCH, NORTHWESTERN UNIV, CHICAGO, 71-; DIR CLIN MICROBIOL, NORTHWESTERN MEM HOSP, 72- *Concurrent Pos:* Res fel path, Med Sch, Northwestern Univ, Chicago, 54-58; attend pathologist, Chicago Wesley Mem Hosp, 58-68, Passavant Mem Hosp, 68-73 & Northwestern Mem Hosp, 73-; consult, Vet Admin Res Hosp. *Mem:* Am Soc Clin Path; Am Asn Pathologists; Am Soc Microbiol; Am Thoracic Soc; Col Am Path. *Res:* Experimental pathology of ischemic myocardium and mechanisms of ventricular fibrillation; improvement of methods in clinical microbiology. *Mailing Add:* Dept of Path Northwestern Univ Med Sch Chicago IL 60611

SOMMERS, JAY RICHARD, b Brooklyn, NY, May 19, 39; m 61; c 3. ORGANIC CHEMISTRY. *Educ:* Brooklyn Col, BS, 61; Univ Pittsburgh, PhD(org chem), 66. *Prof Exp:* Res chemist, Org Chem Dept, E I du Pont de Nemours & Co, 65-69; asst mgr, Surg Specialty Div, Johnson & Johnson Co, 69-74, mgr surg apparel & fabrics develop, Res Div, 74-76, dir prod develop, Surgikos, 76-80, mgr fiber technol, 80-81; DIR PROD DEVELOP, INT PLAYTEX, INC, 81- *Mem:* Am Chem Soc; Asn Advan Med Instrumentation; Am Asn Textile Chem & Colorists; Sigma Xi; Asn Res Dirs. *Res:* Textile chemicals; nonwoven fabrics and finishes; disposable apparel; fabric flammability; medical/surgical products; biomedical devices; internal and external sanitary protection; health and beauty aids. *Mailing Add:* 30 Independence Dr Colonial Oaks East Brunswick NJ 08816

SOMMERS, LEE EDWIN, b Beloit, Wis, July 30, 44; m 66, 79; c 3. SOIL MICROBIOLOGY. *Educ:* Wis State Univ-Platteville, BS, 66; Univ Wis-Madison, MS, 68, PhD(soil sci), 70. *Prof Exp:* Assoc prof, 70-80, PROF SOIL MICROBIOL, PURDUE UNIV, 80- *Mem:* AAAS; Am Soc Agron; Soil Sci Soc Am. *Res:* Effect of soil chemical and physical properties on microbial growth; microbial transformations of heavy metals; role of soils and sediments in eutrophication; plant nutrient and metal transformations in soils amended with industrial and minicipal wastes. *Mailing Add:* Dept of Agron Purdue Univ West Lafayette IN 47907

SOMMERS, PAUL DANIEL, physics, mathematics, see previous edition

SOMMERS, RAYMOND A, b Marshfield, Wis, Nov 22, 31; m 54; c 14. ANALYTICAL CHEMISTRY, MICROCOMPUTERS. *Educ:* Univ Wis-Stevens Point, BS, 53; Lawrence Univ, MS, 59, PhD(chem), 63. *Prof Exp:* From asst prof to assoc prof, 62-76, PROF ANAL CHEM, UNIV WIS-STEVENS POINT, 76- *Concurrent Pos:* NSF sci faculty fel, Dept Chem, Mich State Univ, 68-69. *Mem:* Am Chem Soc. *Res:* microcomputers in teaching chemistry. *Mailing Add:* Dept of Chem Univ of Wis Stevens Point WI 54481

SOMMERS, SHELDON CHARLES, b Indianapolis, Ind, July 7, 16; m 43. PATHOLOGY. *Educ:* Harvard Univ, SB, 37, MD, 41. *Prof Exp:* Assoc prof path, Sch Med, Boston Univ, 53-61; clin prof, Univ Southern Calif, 62; from assoc prof path to prof, Columbia Univ, 63-68, clin prof path, Col Physicians & Surgeons, 68-81; pathologist & dir, Path Lab, Lenox Hill Hosp, 68-81; CONSULT PATH, 81- *Concurrent Pos:* Res assoc, Cancer Res Inst, New Eng Deaconess Hosp, 50-61; lectr, Harvard Med Sch, 53-61; pathologist, Mass Mem Hosps, 53-61, Scripps Hosp, 61-63 & Delafield Hosp, New York, 63-68; ed, Path Ann, 66- & Path Decenn, 66-75; dir, Coun Tobacco Res, 81- *Mem:* Am Soc Clin Path; Am Asn Path; Col Am Path. *Res:* Experimental pathology; intestinal disease; cancer; kidney disease; endocrine pathology. *Mailing Add:* Lenox Hill Hosp Dept Path 100 E 77th St New York NY 10021

SOMMERS, WILLIAM P(AUL), b Detroit, Mich, July 22, 33; m 56, 78; c 5. ENGINEERING, RESEARCH MANAGEMENT. *Educ:* Univ Mich, BSE, 55, MSE, 56, PhD(mech eng), 61. *Prof Exp:* Engr, Martin Co, 56-57, sr engr, 57-58; res asst aeronaut eng, Inst Sci & Technol, Univ Mich, 59-61; chief chem propulsion, Martin Co, 61-63; proj scientist mech & aeronaut eng, 63-

65, res dir eng & sci mgt, 65-67, vpres & dir NASA progs, 67-71, pres & mem bd dirs, 71-73, pres, Technol Mgt Group, 73-79, EXEC VPRES, BOOZ ALLEN & HAMILTON INC, 79- *Concurrent Pos:* Consult, Ethyl Corp, 60-61. *Mem:* Assoc fel Am Inst Aeronaut & Astronaut; sr mem Am Astron Soc; Sigma Xi. *Res:* Detonative combustion; fluid dynamics; heat transfer; propulsion and aerospace sciences. *Mailing Add:* Booz Allen & Hamilton Inc 4330 E West Hwy Bethesda MD 20814

SOMMESE, ANDREW JOHN, b New York, NY, May 3, 48; m 71. TRANSCENDENTAL ALGEBRAIC GEOMETRY. *Educ:* Fordham Univ, BA, 69; Princeton Univ, PhD(math), 73. *Prof Exp:* Gibbs instr, Yale Univ, 73-75; asst prof, Cornell Univ, 75-79; ASSOC PROF MATH, UNIV NOTRE DAME, 79- *Concurrent Pos:* Mem, Inst Advan Study, NJ, 75-76; guest prof, Univ Gottingen, WGer, 77 & Univ Bonn, WGer, 78-79; Sloan Fel, Alfred P Sloan Found, 79. *Mem:* Am Math Soc. *Res:* Holomorphic group actions; topology of algebraic varieties; Ampleness and hyperplane sections of projective manifolds. *Mailing Add:* Dept Math Univ Notre Dame Notre Dame IN 46556

SOMOANO, ROBERT BONNER, b Houston, Tex, Sept 2, 40; m 62; c 3. SOLID STATE PHYSICS. *Educ:* Tex A&M, BS, 62, MS, 64; Univ Tex, PhD(physics), 69. *Prof Exp:* MEM TECH STAFF, JET PROPULSION LABS, 69- *Mem:* Am Inst Physics; Am Phys Soc. *Res:* Liquid metals; polymer physics; superconductivity. *Mailing Add:* Jet Propulsion Lab Pasadena CA 91103

SOMOGYI, LASZLO P, b Budapest, Hungary, June 1, 31; US citizen; m 51; c 2. FOOD TECHNOLOGY. *Educ:* Univ Agr Sci Hungary, BS, 56; Rutgers Univ, MS, 60, PhD(hort), 62. *Prof Exp:* Lab technician plant physiol, Cornell Univ, 57-58; jr res pomologist, Univ Calif, Davis, 62-64; proj leader, Hunt-Wesson Foods, Inc, 64-70; dir res & develop, Vacu-Dry Co, 70-74; tech dir, Biophys Res & Develop Corp, 74-76; sr food scientist, SRI Int, 76-79; VPRES, FINN-CAL PROD, INC, 79- *Mem:* Inst Food Technologists; Am Soc Enologists. *Res:* Food processing and product development; food dehydration; technoeconomic market studies of food ingredients and additives; environmental impact of food processing operations; harvesting and storage of fruits and vegetables. *Mailing Add:* 12 Highgate Ct Kensington CA 94707

SOMORJAI, GABOR ARPAD, b Budapest, Hungary, May 4, 35; m 57. PHYSICAL CHEMISTRY. *Educ:* Budapest Tech Univ, ChE, 56; Univ Calif, PhD(chem), 60. *Prof Exp:* Mem res staff, Res Ctr, Int Bus Mach Corp, 60-64; from asst prof to prof, 64-77, MILLER PROF CHEM, UNIV CALIF, BERKELEY, 77-; PRIN INVESTR, MAT & MOLECULAR RES DIV, LAWRENCE BERKELEY LAB, 64- *Concurrent Pos:* Chmn, Int Conf Structure & Chem Solid Surfaces, 68; Guggenheim fel, 69-70; vis fel, Emmanuel Col, Cambridge, Eng, 69; Unilever vis prof, Bristol Univ, 71-72; chmn, Phys Electronics Conf, 73, Irvine Solid State Physics Conf, 74 & Div Colloid & Surface Chem, Am Chem Soc, 75; Baker lectr, Cornell Univ, 77. *Honors & Awards:* Emmett Award, Am Catalysis Soc, 77; Colloid & Surface Chem Award, Am Chem Soc, 81. *Mem:* Nat Acad Sci; fel Am Phys Soc; Am Chem Soc. *Res:* Chemistry of surfaces and solids; catalysis; surface science of energy conversion; mechanism of catalysis of hydrocarbon reactions by platinum and its alloys and catalysis of surface reactions involving nitrogen, carbon monoxide and hydrogen on iron surfaces; energy transfer during hydrogen atom recombination of platinum crystal surfaces; photodixoustion of water. *Mailing Add:* Dept of Chem Univ of Calif Berkeley CA 94720

SOMORJAI, RAJMUND LEWIS, b Budapest, Hungary, Jan 21, 37; Can citizen; m 70; c 2. THEORETICAL BIOLOGY, BIOMATHEMATICS. *Educ:* McGill Univ, BSc, 60; Princeton Univ, PhD(physics, phys chem), 63. *Prof Exp:* NATO sci fel, Cambridge Univ, 63-65; RES OFFICER, NAT RES COUN CAN, 65- *Concurrent Pos:* Adj prof, Dept Physiol & Biophys, Univ Ill Med Ctr, 75- *Mem:* Chem Inst Can; Am Phys Soc; Can Asn Physics. *Res:* Hydrogen bonds; approximation methods; calculation of the dynamics of protein folding and enzyme action; structure-function relationships in biology; properties of complex, hierarchical systems; nonequilibrium phenomena; nonlinear problems. *Mailing Add:* Div Chem Rm 1159 100 Sussex Dr Nat Res Coun Can Ottawa ON K1A 0R6 Can

SOMSEN, ROGER ALAN, b River Falls, Wis, May 4, 31; m 56; c 1. PULP CHEMISTRY. *Educ:* Univ Wis, BS, 53; Lawrence Col, Inst Paper Chem, MS, 55, PhD(pulp paper), 58. *Prof Exp:* Sr res chemist, Olin Mathieson Chem Corp, 58-59, asst supvr pulp & paper res, 59-60, supvr, 60-62, process eng res, 62-68, tech serv mgr, Pulp & Paper Div, 68-72, TECH SERV DIR, MANVILLE FOREST PROD CORP, INC, 72- *Mem:* Tech Asn Pulp & Paper Indust. *Res:* Improvement of old grades and development of new grades of paper, including pulping, bleaching and papermaking; product development in cartons, bags and corrugated containers. *Mailing Add:* Manville Forest Prods Corp PO Box 488 West Monroe LA 71291

SON, CHUNG HYUN, b Changyun, Korea, Mar 16, 17; m 39; c 3. FOOD SCIENCE, TECHNOLOGY. *Educ:* Rutgers Univ, BS, 56, MS, 57, PhD(food sci), 59. *Prof Exp:* FOOD TECHNOLOGIST, RES CTR, DEL MONTE CORP, 59- *Honors & Awards:* Kellog lectr, 79. *Mem:* Inst Food Technol. *Res:* Products development and processing research in the area of fruits, vegetables and fish. *Mailing Add:* Del Monte Corp Res Ctr 205 N Wiget Lane Walnut Creek CA 94598

SONAWANE, BABASAHEB R, b Nandgaon, India, April 5, 40; m 67; c 2. ENVIRONMENTAL TOXICOLOGY. *Educ:* Univ Peona, India, BS, 62, MS, 65; Univ Mo-Columbia, PhD(enthomol & toxicol), 71. *Prof Exp:* Lectr zool & entomol, Col Agr, Univ Peona, 63-67; res specialist toxicol & path, Univ Mo, Columbia, 71-72; fel environ & toxicol, Nat Inst Environ Health Sci, 72-75; sr res assoc pediat & pharm, Childrens Hosp, Philadelphia, 75-76; RES ASST PROF PEDIAT, UNIV PA, 76- *Concurrent Pos:* Vis fel, Nat Inst Environ Health Sci, 72-75. *Mem:* Teratology Soc Am; AAAS; Am Chem Soc; NY Acad Sci. *Res:* Developmental pharmacology-toxicology; mechanisms of xenobiotic toxicity and teratogenicity; regulation of drug metabolism and action during perinatal development and its modification by environmental factors such as nutrition, disease and exposure to chemicals. *Mailing Add:* 848 Meadowood Lane Warminster PA 18974

SONDAK, NORMAN EDWARD, b Cornwall, NY, Sept 1, 31; m 54; c 3. COMPUTER SCIENCE, INFORMATION SYSTEMS. *Educ:* City Col New York, BE, 53; Northwestern Univ, MS, 54; Yale Univ, DEng(eng), 58. *Prof Exp:* Sr technologist, Res Labs, Socony Mobil, 56-61; mgr data processing, Electronic Data Processing Div, RCA Corp, 61-63; vpres data processing, J Walter Thompson Co, NY, 63-68; prof comput sci & head dept, Worcester Polytech Inst, 68-78, dir comput ctr, 68-71; PROF & CHMN INFO SYSTS DEPT, SAN DIEGO STATE UNIV, 78- *Concurrent Pos:* Affil prof, Clark Univ, 69-78; mem coop staff, Worcester Found Exp Biol, 70-78; res prof, Med Sch, Univ Mass, 75-78; Kellog lectr, 79. *Mem:* Data Processing Mgt Asn; Soc Indust & Appl Math; Asn Comput Mach; Inst Elec & Electronics Engrs; Am Soc Info Sci. *Res:* Programming languages; compiler construction; operating systems; social implications of computing; computer architecture; computer science education; computer networks; structured systems design; world processing; microcomputer systems. *Mailing Add:* Info Systs Dept San Diego State Univ San Diego CA 92182

SONDEL, PAUL MARK, b Milwaukee, Wis, Aug 14, 50; m 73; c 2. TURMOR IMMUNOLOGY, IMMUNOGENETICS. *Educ:* Univ Wis-Madison, BS, 71, PhD(genetics), 75, Harvard Med Sch, MD, 77. *Prof Exp:* Res & teaching asst, Dept Genetics, Univ Wis-Madison, 71-72; res aide, Dept Immunol, Harvard Med Sch, 73-74; res assoc, Immunobiol Res Ctr, Univ Wis-Madison, 74-75; res fel tumor immunol, Sidney Farber Cancer Inst, 75-77; intern pediat, Univ Minn Hosp, 77-78; resident, Univ Wis Hosp, 78-80; ASST PROF PEDIAT & HUMAN ONCOL, UNIV WIS-MADISON, 80-, ASST PROF MED GENETICS, 81- *Mem:* Transplantation Soc; Am Asn Immunologists; Am Asn Clin Histocompatibility; Am Fedn Clin Res; Soc Pediat Res. *Res:* Tumor and transplantation immunogenetics: the in vitro responses of human lymphocytes to normal and abnormal cell populations to better define the role of human leucocyte antigen factors in immunoregulation. *Mailing Add:* Univ Wis Clin Sci Ctr 600 Highland Ave Rm K4-430 Madison WI 53792

SONDER, EDWARD, b Ger, May 1, 28; nat US; m 53; c 2. PHYSICS. *Educ:* Queens Col, BS, 50; Univ Ill, MS, 51, PhD(physics), 55. *Prof Exp:* Res assoc solid state physics, Iowa State Col, 55-56; PHYSICIST, OAK RIDGE NAT LAB, 56- *Concurrent Pos:* Vis prof physics, Okla State Univ, 74-75. *Mem:* Am Phys Soc; Am Ceramic Soc. *Res:* Imperfections in solids, particularly intermetallic diffusion, radiation effects in metals, and semiconductors; color centers in alkali halides. *Mailing Add:* Oak Ridge Nat Lab PO Box X Oak Ridge TN 37830

SONDEREGGER, THEO BROWN, b Brimingham, Ala, May 31, 25; m 47; c 3. MEDICAL PSYCHOLOGY. *Educ:* Fla State Univ, BS, 46; Univ Nebr, Lincoln, MA, 48 & 60, PhD(clin psychol), 65. *Prof Exp:* Teaching asst psychol, Univ Nebr, Lincoln, 59-62, instr med psychol, Med Ctr, 65-69; asst prof psychol, Nebr Wesleyan Univ, 65-68; asst prof, 69-72, assoc prof, 72-78, PROF MED PSYCHOL, MED CTR, UNIV NEBR, 78- *Concurrent Pos:* Vis scholar, Dept Neurosci, Northwestern Univ, Evanston, 73-74; vis assoc res anatomist, Med Sch, Univ Calif, Los Angeles, 74, vis res psychol, Dept Psychiat, 79-80; vis res assoc biol, Calif Inst Technol, 79-80; vis prof, Brain Res Inst, Univ Calif, Los Angeles, 80-81. *Mem:* Am Psychol Asn; Soc Neurosci; AAAS; Int Soc Develop Biol; Psychonomic Soc. *Res:* Neonatal narcotic addiction; fetal alcohol syndrome (animal model); intracranial self stimulation; catecholamines and the developing nervous system. *Mailing Add:* 1710 S 58th St Lincoln NE 68506

SONDERGAARD, NEAL ALBERT, b Schenectady, NY, Mar 20, 49; m 77. PHYSICAL CHEMISTRY, CHEMICAL PHYSICS. *Educ:* Marist Col, BA, 70; Brown Univ, MSc, 73, PhD(chem), 77. *Prof Exp:* Fel, Wash Univ, 77; fel phys chem, Johns Hopkins Univ, 77-80; CHEMIST, NAVAL SHIP RES & DEVELOP CTR, ANNAPOLIS, 80- *Concurrent Pos:* Fel, Johns Hopkins Univ, 80- *Mem:* Sigma Xi. *Res:* Physical and chemical phenamena of high current density sliding electric contacts; techniques include molecular beams, ion cyclotron resonance and mass spectroscopy. *Mailing Add:* Naval Ship Res & Develop Ctr DWTNSRDC Annapolis MD 21402

SONDERGELD, CARL HENDERSON, b Brooklyn, NY, Nov 4, 47; m 69; c 2. GEOPHYSICS, ROCK MECHANICS. *Educ:* Queen's Col, NY, BA, 69, MA, 73; Cornell Univ, PhD(geophysics), 77. *Prof Exp:* Res assoc geothermal energy, Cornell Univ, 77; vis fel, Nat Oceanic & Atmospheric Admin, Univ Colo, 77-78, res assoc rock mech, Coop Inst Res Environ Sic, 78-81; SR RES SCIENTIST, AMOCO PRODUCTION CO, 81- *Concurrent Pos:* Adj prof, Univ Colo, 80-; vis scientist, Los Alamos Nat Lab. *Mem:* Am Geophys Union; Am Ceramic Soc; Sigma Xi; Am Geol Inst; Coop Inst Res Environ Sci. *Res:* Acoustic emissions in rock; elasticity of rocks and poly crystals; geothermal energy-two-phase convection in porous media; sonic logging; acoustic magnetic and electrical properties of rock. *Mailing Add:* Amoco Prod Co PO Box 591 Tulsa OK 74102

SONDHAUS, CHARLES ANDERSON, b San Francisco, Calif, Oct 5, 24; m 55; c 3. BIOPHYSICS, RADIOBIOLOGY. *Educ:* Univ Calif, Berkeley, AB, 50, PhD(biophys), 58. *Prof Exp:* Radiol physicist, Naval Radiol Defense Lab, 51-55; res asst biophys, Lawrence Radiation Lab, Univ Calif, Berkeley, 56-58, biophysicist, Donner Lab, 59-64, asst prof, 65-66, ASSOC PROF RADIOL SCI, UNIV CALIF, IRVINE, 66- *Concurrent Pos:* Nat Acad Sci-Nat Res Coun Donner fel biophys, Karolinska Inst & Hosp, Stockholm, Sweden, 58-59; vis lectr, Mont State Univ, 60-62; lectr, Div Med Physics, Univ Calif, Berkeley, 60-65; res collabr, Med Dept, Brookhaven Nat Lab, 60-; consult radiol physicist, Off Civil Defense, US Air Force, NASA, 62-64, US Vet Admin & Fed Aviation Agency, 65-, Los Angeles County Gen Hosp, 65-68 & Orange County Med Ctr, 68-; mem subcomt rel biol effectiveness, Nat Coun Radiation Protection, 60-66, biol effects high altitude cosmic radiation,

Int Comn Radiol Protection, 63-65, high energy & space radiation dosimetry, Int Comn Radiation Units, 64- & space radiation study panel, Nat Acad Sci-Nat Res Coun, 64-68. *Mem:* Am Asn Physicists in Med; Am Phys Soc; Biophys Soc; Radiation Res Soc. *Res:* Applied nuclear & radiation physics, dosimetry; biophysical and optical microanalysis; cellular and mammalian radiobiology. *Mailing Add:* Dept of Radiol Sci Univ of Calif Irvine CA 92664

SONDHEIMER, NORMAN KEITH, computer sciences, see previous edition

SONENBERG, MARTIN, b New York, NY, Dec 1, 20; m 56; c 2. ENDOCRINOLOGY, BIOCHEMISTRY. *Educ:* Univ Pa, BA, 41; NY Univ, MD, 44, PhD(biochem), 52. *Prof Exp:* Intern, Beth Israel Hosp, 44-45; asst resident med, Goldwater Hosp, 45-46; from instr to assoc prof, 53-72, PROF MED, MED COL, CORNELL UNIV, 72-, PROF BIOCHEM, SLOANKETTERING DIV, GRAD SCH MED SCI, 66- *Concurrent Pos:* Am Cancer Soc fel, Mem Ctr Cancer & Allied Dis, 52-57; Guggenheim fel, Carlsberg Lab, Copenhagen Univ, 57-58; clin asst, Mem Ctr Cancer & Allied Dis, 51-; assoc, Sloan-Kettering Inst Cancer Res, 52-60, assoc mem, 60-66, mem, 66-; assoc attend physician, Mem & James Ewing Hosps, 59-; attend physician, Mem Hosp, 69- *Honors & Awards:* Van Meter award, Am Thyroid Asn, 52; Sloan Award, 68. *Mem:* AAAS; Biophys Soc; Am Soc Biol Chem; Am Soc Clin Invest; Am Thyroid Asn. *Res:* Chemistry and physiology of pituitary hormones; protein chemistry; mechanism of hormone action. *Mailing Add:* Mem Sloan-Kettering Cancer Ctr New York NY 10021

SONENSHEIN, ABRAHAM LINCOLN, b Paterson, NJ, Jan 13, 44; m 67. MICROBIOLOGY, MOLECULAR BIOLOGY. *Educ:* Princeton Univ, AB, 65; Mass Inst Technol, PhD(biol), 70. *Prof Exp:* Am Cancer Soc fel, Inst Microbiol, Univ Paris, 70-72; asst prof, 72-78, ASSOC PROF MOLECULAR BIOL & MICROBIOL, SCH MED, TUFTS UNIV, 78- *Concurrent Pos:* Nat Inst Gen Med Sci res support grant, 72-85; NSF res grant, 79-81. *Mem:* AAAS; Am Soc Microbiol; Fedn Am Sci. *Res:* Bacterial sporulation; control of transcription; RNA polymerase; genetics and physiology of Bacillus subtilis; phage infection of Bacillus subtilis. *Mailing Add:* Dept Molecular Biol & Microbiol Sch Med Tufts Univ Boston MA 02111

SONENSHINE, DANIEL E, b New York, NY, May 11, 33; m 57. ZOOLOGY. *Educ:* City Col New York, BA, 55; Univ MD, PhD(zool), 59. *Prof Exp:* Asst zool, Univ Md, 55-58, asst instr, 58-59; instr biol, Univ Akron, 59-61; mem staff, Old Dom Univ, 61-74; PROF MICROBIOL, EASTERN VA MED SCH, NORFOLK, 74- *Mem:* Am Soc Parasitol. *Res:* Acarology; parasitology; ecology and life history of ticks; physiology. *Mailing Add:* Dept of Biol Old Dominion Univ Norfolk VA 23508

SONETT, CHARLES PHILIP, b Pittsburgh, Pa, Jan 15, 24; m 48; c 2. PHYSICS. *Educ:* Univ Calif, Los Angeles, PhD(physics), 54. *Prof Exp:* Asst physics, Univ Calif, Los Angeles, 51-53, assoc, 53; mem tech staff & head range develop group, Ramo Wooldridge Corp, 54-57; mem sr staff & head space physics, Space Technol Labs, Inc, 57-60; chief sci, off lunar & planetary prog, NASA, 60-62, chief space sci div, Ames Res Ctr, 62-70, dep dir astronaut, 71-73; head dept & dir, Lunar & Planetary Lab, 73-77, PROF PLANETARY SCI, LUNAR & PLANETARY LAB, UNIV ARIZ, 73- *Concurrent Pos:* Lectr eng, Univ Calif, Los Angeles, 55-57; Guggenheim fel, Imp Col, Univ London, 68-69; ed, Cosmic Electrodynamics, 70-72; co-ed, Astrophys & Space Sci, 73-; mem, Space Sci Steering Comt, NASA, chmn subcomts lunar & planetary & interplanetary sci, 60-62, mem subcomts planetology, 62-65 & particles & fields, 62-63, mem outer planets sci adv group, 71-72, mem, Outer Planets Sci Working Group, Post-Apollo Sci Planning Conf & ad hoc working group on planetary remote sensing, 72; mem, Comn 17 & 49, Int Astron Union; consult, Jet Propulsion Lab & Rockwell Int; mem bd trustees, Univ Space Res Asn, 77-; co-ed, The Moon & Planets, 78- *Honors & Awards:* Space Sci Award, Am Inst Aeronaut & Astronaut, 69. *Mem:* Am Geophys Union; Sigma Xi; AAAS. *Res:* Planetary and interplanetary physics. *Mailing Add:* Dept of Planetary Sci Univ of Ariz Tucson AZ 85721

SONG, CHANG WON, b Chun Chon City, Korea, Apr 10, 32. RADIOBIOLOGY, IMMUNOLOGY. *Educ:* Seoul Nat Univ, BS, 57; Univ Korea, MS, 59; Univ Iowa, PhD(radiation biol), 64. *Prof Exp:* Res asst radiation biol, Univ Iowa, 60-64; asst mem, Res Labs, Albert Einstein Med Ctr, 64-69; asst prof, Med Col Va, 69-70; from asst prof to assoc prof, 70-78, PROF & DIR RADIATION BIOL, MED SCH, UNIV MINN, MINNEAPOLIS, 78- *Concurrent Pos:* Consult, Vet Admin. *Mem:* Cell Kinetic Soc; AAAS; Radiation Res Soc; Am Asn Cancer Res. *Res:* Relationship between vascular changes and curability of tumors by radiotherapy or hyperthermia; effect of radiation on immune system and feasibility of combination radio- and immuno-therapy for treatment of cancer. *Mailing Add:* Dept of Therapeut Radiol Univ of Minn Health Sci Ctr Minneapolis MN 55455

SONG, CHARLES CHIEH-SHYANG, b Taiwan, China, Jan 12, 31; m 55; c 3. CIVIL ENGINEERING, FLUID MECHANICS. *Educ:* Nat Taiwan Univ, BS, 53; Univ Iowa, MS, 56; Univ Minn, Minneapolis, PhD(civil eng), 60. *Prof Exp:* Asst prof, 61-63, assoc prof, 63-79, PROF CIVIL ENG, UNIV MINN, MINNEAPOLIS, 79- *Honors & Awards:* J C Stevens Award, 80. *Mem:* AAAS; Int Asn Hydraul Res; Soc Naval Archit & Marine Engrs; Am Soc Civil Engrs; Am Water Resources Asn. *Res:* Flows at low cavitation numbers; flutter of supercavitating bodies; non-Newtonian flows; wave motions and wave drag; hydraulic transient; sediment transport; variational principles. *Mailing Add:* St Anthony Falls Hydrology Lab Univ of Minn Minneapolis MN 55455

SONG, JOSEPH, b Seoul, Korea, May 11, 27; nat US; m 58. PATHOLOGY. *Educ:* Seoul Nat Univ, MD, 50; Univ Tenn, MS, 56; Univ Ark, MD, 65. *Prof Exp:* Instr path, Med Sch, Univ Tenn, 52-56; instr, Sch Med, Boston Univ, 56-61; assoc prof, Sch Med, Univ Ark, 61-65; DIR DEPT PATH, MERCY HOSP, 65- *Concurrent Pos:* Assoc dir, RI State Cancer Cytol Proj, 56-59; sr

instr, Med Sch, Tufts Univ, 59-61; assoc mem, Inst Health Sci, Brown Univ, 59-61; assoc pathologist, Providence Lying-In Hosp, 59-61; assoc med examr, State RI, 59-61; consult, St Joseph's Hosp, Providence, RI, 59-61 & Vet Admin Hosps, Little Rock & North Little Rock, Ark; clin prof, Sch Med, Creighton Univ. *Mem:* Fel Am Soc Clin Path; Am Asn Path & Bact; fel Am Col Path. *Res:* Hepatic pathology in sickle cell disease; exfoliative cytology in cancer of the cervix; splenic function and tumor growth, experimental cancer research. *Mailing Add:* Mercy Hosp Dept of Path Sixth & University Des Moines IA 50314

SONG, KONG-SOP, b Korea, 1934. SOLID STATE PHYSICS. *Educ:* Chunpuk Nat Univ, Korea, 56, MS, 57; Univ Paris, Dr 3e Cycle, 64; Univ Strasbourg, Dr es Sci(physics), 67. *Prof Exp:* Jr researcher, CNRS, France, 63-69; asst prof, 69-72, assoc prof, 72-80, PROF PHYSICS, UNIV OTTAWA, 80- *Concurrent Pos:* Instr, Univ Strasbourg, 65-69. *Mem:* Am Phys Soc; Can Asn Physics. *Res:* Electronic and optical properties of semiconductors and insulators. *Mailing Add:* Dept Physics Univ Ottawa Ottawa ON K1N 6N5 Can

SONG, PILL-SOON, b Osaka, Japan, Aug 5, 36; div; c 3. MOLECULAR BIOPHYSICS. *Educ:* Univ Seoul, BS, 58, MS, 60; Univ Calif, PhD(biochem), 64. *Prof Exp:* Res assoc biochem & biophys, Iowa State Univ, 64-65; from asst prof to prof, 65-75, PAUL W HORN PROF, TEX TECH UNIV, 75- *Concurrent Pos:* Robert A Welch Found grant photochem res, 66-, res grant, 72-75; NSF grant, 70-; Nat Cancer Inst grant, 72- *Mem:* Am Chem Soc; Biophys Soc; Am Soc Photobiol. *Res:* Electronic structure and photochemistry of biomolecules; electronic excited states of biomolecules; quantum biochemistry; molecular spectroscopy and photobiology of photoreceptor pigments, energy transduction, and quantum biology. *Mailing Add:* Dept of Chem Tex Tech Univ Lubbock TX 79409

SONG, SEH-HOON, b Seoul, Korea, June 29, 36; Can citizen; m 62; c 4. BIOPHYSICS, CARDIOPULMONARY PHYSIOLOGY. *Educ:* Yonsei Univ, MD, 60; State Univ NY Buffalo, MA, 69; Univ Western Ont, PhD(biophys), 72. *Prof Exp:* Instr physiol, Sch Med, Yonsei Univ, 60-62 & 66-67; res assoc, State Univ NY Buffalo, 67-69; lectr, 72-73, ASST PROF BIOPHYS, UNIV WESTERN ONT, 73- *Mem:* Biophys Soc; Am Physiol Soc; Can Physiol Soc. *Res:* Compartmentalization in the microcirculation of various organs, spleen, skeletal muscles and heart; transport of materials through the endothelial membranes. *Mailing Add:* Dept Biophys Fac Med Univ Western Ont London ON N6G 2C9 Can

SONG, SUN KYU, b Yonchon, Korea, May 15, 27; US citizen; m 56; c 3. NEUROPATHOLOGY. *Educ:* Yonsei Univ, Korea, MD, 49. *Prof Exp:* Asst prof, 65-71, ASSOC PROF NEUROPATH, MT SINAI SCH MED, 72- *Concurrent Pos:* USPHS spec fel, Mt Sinai Hosp, 59-63; asst attend neuropathologist, Mt Sinai Hosp, 63-; assoc attend physician, City Hosp Ctr, Elmhurst, NY, 64- *Mem:* Am Asn Neuropath; Histochem Soc; Am Asn Path & Bact; Am Soc Exp Path; Am Acad Neurol. *Res:* Histochemistry and electron microscopy of neuromuscular junction and pathology of neuromuscular diseases. *Mailing Add:* Dept of Neuropath Mt Sinai Sch of Med New York NY 10029

SONG, WON-RYUL, b Korea; US citizen; m 59; c 2. POLYMER CHEMISTRY. *Educ:* Yonsei Univ, Korea, BS, 52; McMaster Univ, MS, 58; Polytech Inst Brooklyn, PhD(polymer chem), 65. *Prof Exp:* Chemist, Am Cyanamide Co, 61-63; SR STAFF CHEMIST, EXXON CHEM CO, 65- *Mem:* Am Chem Soc. *Res:* Fundamental studies on polymeric lube oil additives. *Mailing Add:* 36 Dorset Lane Short Hills NJ 07078

SONG, YEONG-DU, b Busan, Korea; US citizen; c 3. ELECTRONICS ENGINEERING. *Educ:* Seoul Nat Univ, Korea, BS, 63; Univ Calif, Berkeley, PhD(eng sci), 71. *Prof Exp:* Fel physics, Simon Fraser Univ, BC, 71-73; res assoc, Univ Southern Calif, 73-75, instr, 75-77; MEM TECH STAFF DEVICES, AEROSPACE CORP, 77- *Concurrent Pos:* Lectr, Calif State Univ, Long Beach, 75-76; consult, Aerospace Corp, 76-77. *Mem:* Am Phys Soc; Electrochem Soc. *Res:* Radiation damage effects in semiconductor devices, especially silicon metal oxide semiconductor and bipolar transistors; very large scale integration processing induced defects in silicon oxides and silicon. *Mailing Add:* Aerospace Corp Ab 1443 PO Box 92957 Los Angeles CA 90009

SONG, YO TAIK, b Korea, Feb 23, 32; m 60; c 3. NUCLEAR ENGINEERING. *Educ:* Yonsei Univ, Korea, BE, 54; Univ Ill, Urbana, MS, 62, PhD(nuclear eng), 68. *Prof Exp:* Nuclear engr, Korean Atomic Energy Res Inst, 59-60; nuclear physicist, US Naval Civil Eng Lab, 63-67; asst prof nuclear eng, Univ Tenn, Knoxville, 68-69; nuclear engr, Tenn Valley Authority, 69-70; assoc dir, Prof Adv Serv Ctr, Univ Colo, 70-72; RES NUCLEAR ENGR, US NAVAL SURFACE WEAPONS CTR, WHITE OAK LAB, 72- *Mem:* Am Nuclear Soc. *Res:* Radiation shielding; fast reactor physics; fuel management; nuclear weapons; radiation, neutral and charged; transport through various media. *Mailing Add:* R-41 Naval Surface Weapons Ctr White Oak Lab Silver Spring MD 20910

SONGDAHL, JOHN HARALD, comparative physiology, marine biology, see previous edition

SONGER, JOSEPH RICHARD, b South Charleston, WVa, Dec 20, 26; m 48; c 7. MICROBIOLOGY. *Educ:* Eastern Nazarene Col, AB, 51; Iowa State Univ, MS, 65. *Prof Exp:* Bacteriologist, 51-60, VET MICROBIOLOGIST, NAT ANIMAL DIS CTR, SCI & EDUC ADMIN, AGR RES SERV, USDA, 60- *Mem:* Am Soc Microbiol; Am Soc Safety Eng; Am Indust Hyg Asn; Sigma Xi. *Res:* Biological laboratory safety, disinfection, sterilization, air filtration and airborne infection; animal disease research, vesicular diseases; hog cholera; equine infectious anemia; biological hazard assessment; contamination control and euthanasia. *Mailing Add:* Nat Animal Dis Ctr NCent Region Agr Res Serv USDA Ames IA 50010

SONGSTER, GERARD F(RANCIS), b Darby, Pa, Aug 29, 27; m 53; c 2. ELECTRICAL ENGINEERING. *Educ:* Drexel Inst Technol, BSEE, 51; Univ Pa, MSEE, 65, PhD(elec eng), 62. *Prof Exp:* Res engr, Philco Corp, 51-52; instr digital comput, Moore Sch Elec Eng, Univ Pa, 52-56; asst prof elec eng, Drexel Inst Technol, 56-62, assoc prof & actg dir biomed eng prog, 63; sr scientist, Res Div, Melpar Inc, 63-64; elec engr, US Naval Res Lab, 64-65; NIH spec fel, Mass Inst Technol, 65-67; physiol studies, NASA Electronics Res Ctr, 67-70; prof elec eng & chmn dept, Old Dominian Univ, 70-75; ELEC ENGR, NAVAL SHIP ENG CTR, 75- *Mem:* AAAS; Am Soc Eng Educ; Inst Elec & Electronics Engrs; Sigma Xi. *Res:* Electrophysiology of nerve tissue; switching theory; computer simulation of living systems; underwater acoustics; automated measurement. *Mailing Add:* 5426 Glenhaven Crescent Norfolk VA 23508

SONI, ATMARAM HARILAL, b Shihor, India, Oct 5, 35; m 64; c 3. MECHANICAL ENGINEERING. *Educ:* Univ Bombay, BSc, 57; Univ Mich, BS, 59, MS, 61; Okla State Univ, PhD(mech eng), 67. *Prof Exp:* Res asst comput prog, Univ Mich, 61-64; res asst mech eng, 64-67, from asst prof to assoc prof, 67-77, PROF MECH ENG, OKLA STATE UNIV, 77- *Concurrent Pos:* Prin investr, NSF grant, 68-69 & 70-72, dir appl mech conf, 69-71. *Mem:* Am Soc Mech Engrs; Am Soc Eng Educ. *Res:* Machine design; synthesis and analysis of mechanisms; fatigue; reliability. *Mailing Add:* Sch of Mech Eng Okla State Univ Stillwater OK 74074

SONI, KUSUM, b Hoshiarpur, India, Nov 14, 30; m 58; c 2. MATHEMATICAL ANALYSIS. *Educ:* Univ Panjab, India, BA, 49, MA, 51; Ore State Univ, PhD(math), 64. *Prof Exp:* Lectr math, Panjab Educ Serv, 52-59; asst prof, Ore State Univ, 66-67; asst prof, 67-70, ASSOC PROF MATH, UNIV TENN, KNOXVILLE, 70- *Mem:* Am Math Soc; Math Asn Am. *Res:* Classical analysis, asymptotic expansions and approximation. *Mailing Add:* Univ of Tenn Dept of Math Knoxville TN 37919

SONI, PREM SARITA, b Kisumu, Kenya, Nov 17, 48; Brit citizen; m 74. OPTOMETRY. *Educ:* Univ Manchester, BSc, 72; Ind Univ, OD, 75, MS, 79. *Prof Exp:* Optometrist, Eng, 72-75; lectr optom, 76-78, ASST PROF OPTOM, IND UNIV, 78- *Concurrent Pos:* Grant-in-aid, Ind Univ, 78-; Am Acad Optom grant, 78-; Wesley-Jassen, Inc grant, 78- *Mem:* Fel Brit Optical Asn; Am Acad Optom; Am Optom Asn; Contact Lens Educr Asn. *Res:* Corneal physiology and pathology with special reference to contact lens use. *Mailing Add:* Sch of Optom 800 E Atwater Bloomington IN 47401

SONIN, AIN A(NTS), b Tallinn, Estonia, Dec 24, 37; Can citizen; m 71. THERMO-FLUID SCIENCES. *Educ:* Univ Toronto, BASc, 60, MASc, 61, PhD(aerospace sci), 65. *Prof Exp:* From asst prof to assoc prof fluid mech, 65-74, PROF MECH ENG, MASS INST TECHNOL, 74- *Concurrent Pos:* Consult, Brookhaven Nat Lab & US Nuclear Regulatory Comn, 75-; sr scientist, Thermo Electron Corp, 81-82. *Mem:* AAAS; Am Phys Soc; Am Soc Mech Engrs; Am Nuclear Soc. *Res:* Fluid mechanics; thermodynamics; heat, mass and charge transport; thermal-hydraulic phenomena in nuclear reactors; electrochemistry. *Mailing Add:* Rm 3-256 Mass Inst of Technol Cambridge MA 02139

SONIS, MEYER, b Philadelphia, Pa, Jan 29, 19; m 44; c 3. PSYCHIATRY. *Educ:* Univ Pa, AB, 39; Hahnemann Med Col, MD, 43; Am Bd Psychiat & Neurol, dipl, 50, cert in child psychiat, 60. *Prof Exp:* Lectr psychiat, Sch Social Work, Univ Pa, 52-57, assoc, Sch Med, 52-61, instr, 55-61; assoc prof child psychiat, 61-69, PROF PSYCHIAT, 69-76, PROF CHILD PSYCHIAT, SCH MED, UNIV PITTSBURGH, 76-, CHILD DEVELOP & CARE, SCH HEALTH RELATED PROFESSIONS, 70-, CHIEF CHILD PSYCHIAT, SCH MED & EXEC DIR PITTSBURGH CHILD GUID CTR, 61-, CO-DIR POSTGRAD PEDIAT, 62- *Concurrent Pos:* Assoc physician, Children's Hosp Philadelphia, 51-61, sr physician & coordr child psychiat, 56-61; staff psychiatrist, Philadelphia Child Guid Clin, 51-61, supvr psychiat & sr psychiatrist, 54-61, coordr contract, Clin Eval Ctr, 57-61, dir training, 58-61, co-dir post-grad pediat, 60-62; vchmn sect content, Nat Conf Training Child Psychiat, 61-63; mem ad hoc comt outpatient studies, NIMH, 62-64, mem, Conf Planning Child Psychiat Serv, 64-66, mem planning comt, Conf Med Sch Child Psychiat, 65-66; mem bd examr, Am Bd Psychiat & Neurol, 62-66; mem, Joint Comn Ment Health for Children, 65-66; consult, Cath & Pub Schs, Pittsburgh, 65-66. *Mem:* AAAS; AMA; fel Am Psychiat Asn; fel Am Acad Child Psychiat; Asn Psychiat Clins for Children (pres, 65-67). *Mailing Add:* 3811 O'Hara St Dept Psychiatry Univ Pittsburgh Pittsburgh PA 15213

SONLEITNER, FRANK JOSEPH, b Chicago, Ill, Jan 23, 32; m 74; c 3. POPULATION ECOLOGY. *Educ:* Univ Chicago, AB, 51, SB, 56, PhD(zool), 59. *Prof Exp:* Fel, Dept Zool, Univ Sydney, 59-61; lectr, Univ Calif, Berkeley, 61-62; asst prof entom, Univ Kans, Lawrence, 62-65; asst prof, 65-69, ASSOC PROF, DEPT ZOOL, UNIV OKLA, NORMAN, 69- *Mem:* AAAS; Am Inst Biol Sci; Ecol Soc Am; Entom Soc Am; Sigma Xi. *Res:* Computer simulation models of population dynamics and ecogenetics (natural selection). *Mailing Add:* Dept Zool Univ Okla Norman OK 73019

SONN, JACK, mathematics, see previous edition

SONNEBORN, DAVID R, b Baltimore, Md, Oct 20, 36; m 62; c 2. DEVELOPMENTAL BIOLOGY, MICROBIOLOGY. *Educ:* Swarthmore Col, BA, 57; Brandeis Univ, PhD(biol), 62. *Prof Exp:* NIH fel virol, Univ Calif, Berkeley, 62-64; from asst prof to assoc prof, 64-72, PROF ZOOL, UNIV WIS-MADISON, 72- *Concurrent Pos:* Panel mem, Develop Biol Sect, NSF, 71-74. *Mem:* AAAS; Soc Develop Biol; Am Soc Microbiol. *Res:* Cell differentiation. *Mailing Add:* Zool Res Bldg Univ of Wis 1117 W Johnson St Madison WI 53706

SONNEBORN, LEE MEYERS, b Baltimore, Md, Dec 27, 31; m 55; c 2. MATHEMATICS. *Educ:* Oberlin Col, BA, 51; Calif Inst Technol, PhD(math), 56. *Prof Exp:* Asst math, Calif Inst Technol, 53-56; Fine instr, Princeton Univ, 56-58; from asst prof to assoc prof, Univ Kans, 58-67; PROF MATH, MICH STATE UNIV, 67-, DIR GRAD STUDIES, 70- *Concurrent Pos:* Math Asn Am vis lectr & NSF res grant, 65-67. *Mem:* Am Math Soc; Math Asn Am. *Res:* Group theory; differential equation; topology. *Mailing Add:* Dept of Math Mich State Univ East Lansing MI 48824

SONNEBORN, TRACY MORTON, genetics, deceased

SONNEMANN, GEORGE, b Munich, Ger, Feb 2, 26; nat US; m 54. ENGINEERING MECHANICS. *Educ:* NY Univ, BS, 47, MS, 49; Univ Mich, PhD(eng mech), 55. *Prof Exp:* Instr physics, Newark Col Eng, 47-48; instr eng mech, Univ Detroit, 48-49; asst prof aeronaut eng, Drexel Inst Tech, 49-52; res assoc, Univ Mich, 52-54; sr engr, Westinghouse Elec Corp, 54-55, Univ Pittsburgh-Westinghouse Elec Corp fel prog, 55-57; from assoc prof to prof mech eng, Univ Pittsburgh, 57-61, Westinghouse prof & dir grad studies mech eng, 57-61; dir staff eng & tech asst to gen mgr, Fecker Div, Am Optical Co, 61-63; chief adv design, United Aircraft Corp Systs Ctr, 63-66, mgr prod eng, 66-67, eng mgr, 67-69; mgr adv progs, Raytheon Co, Sudbury, 69-75; vpres-MIS, Com Union Assurance Co, 75-77; vpres, Conn Gen Life Ins Co, 77-78; V PRES PLANNING & MGT INFO, NATIONWIDE INS CO, 78- *Concurrent Pos:* Engr, Franklin Inst, 50; consult, Westinghouse Elec Corp, Am Optical Soc & Copes-Vulcan Div, Blaw-Knox Co. *Mem:* Am Soc Mech Engrs. *Res:* Thermal stress analysis and fluid flow problems in reactor engineering; continuum mechanics; structural analysis; heat conduction; optical instrumentation; guidance systems; computer peripherals; manufacturing systems; management information systems; data processing; planning. *Mailing Add:* 397 W Seventh Ave Columbus OH 43201

SONNENBERG, HARDY, b Schoensee, Ger, Apr 12, 39; Can citizen; m 64; c 2. EXPERIMENTAL PHYSICS, ENGINEERING PHYSICS. *Educ:* Univ Alta, BSc, 62; Stanford Univ, MS, 64, PhD(elec eng), 67. *Prof Exp:* Eng specialist, GTE Sylvania, 66-73; mgr res & develop, Optical Diodes, Inc, 73-74; mem sci staff, 75-78, MGR PHYSICS & ENG, XEROX RES CENTRE CAN, LTD, 78- *Concurrent Pos:* Referee, Am Inst Physics, 70-; proposal consult, US Govt, 74-; grant appl consult, Can Govt; mem, Task Force Univ/Indust, Can Mgt Asn, 81. *Honors & Awards:* Tech Brief Award, NASA, 72. *Mem:* Sigma Xi; Inst Elec & Electronics Engrs; Am Phys Soc. *Res:* Investigations of the physics and systems aspects of photoactive-pigment-electrography and the coupling of such systems to high-speed channels. *Mailing Add:* RR 3 Puslinch ON N0B 2J0 Can

SONNENBLICK, BENJAMIN PAUL, b New York, NY, May 31, 10; m 36; c 2. ENVIRONMENTAL BIOLOGY, RADIATION BIOLOGY. *Educ:* City Col New York, BS, 30; NY Univ, MSc, 34, PhD(biol), 38. *Prof Exp:* Res assoc & instr anat, Queens Col, NY, 38-41; Guggenheim fel, Columbia Univ & Carnegie Inst, 41-42; from asst prof to prof, 47-74, EMER PROF BIOL, RUTGERS UNIV, 74- *Concurrent Pos:* Ed, Protection in Diagnostic Radiol; mem, State Comn Radiation Protection, NJ, 58-; chmn, NJ State Adv Comt Licensing for Possession & Use Radioactive Isotopes; NJ State Adv Comt Nuclear Med; mem subcomt 3, Nat Comt Radiation Protection & Measurements, 61- *Mem:* Am Soc Nat; Environ Mutagen Soc; Am Soc Zool; Genetics Soc Am; Radiation Res Soc. *Res:* Genetics; radiation biology; human radiation protection; Drosophila development; cellular and organismic influences of chemical and physical agents, studied singly and in combinations. *Mailing Add:* Dept of Zool & Physiol Rutgers Univ 195 Univ Ave Newark NJ 07102

SONNENFELD, PETER, b Berlin, Ger, Jan 20, 22; Can citizen; m 59; c 2. GEOLOGY. *Educ:* Absolutorium, Univ Bratislava, 48; Dr rer nat(geol, geog), Charles Univ, Prague, 49. *Prof Exp:* Geologist, Falconbridge Nickel Mines, Nfld, 51-52; consult, Bennett & Burns, Sask, 52-53, Imp Oil Ltd, Alta, 53-58 & Shell Can Ltd, 58-63; asst prof geol & geog, Tex Col Arts & Indust, 63-66; assoc prof, 66-69, head dept, 68-73, PROF GEOL, UNIV WINDSOR, 69- *Mem:* Fel Geol Asn Can. *Res:* Sedimentology; genesis of sedimentary rocks; dolomitization; evaporite formation; petroleum geology. *Mailing Add:* Dept of Geol Univ of Windsor Windsor ON N9B 3P4 Can

SONNENFELD, RICHARD JOHN, b Britton, Okla, Apr 29, 19; m 42, 75; c 4. ORGANIC CHEMISTRY, SYNTHETIC INORGANIC CHEMISTRY. *Educ:* Univ Pittsburgh, BS, 41; Univ Okla, MS, 55, PhD(chem), 56. *Prof Exp:* Foreman, Weldon Spring Ord Works, 41-43; anal chemist Phillips Petrol Co, 46-49, rubber chemist, 49-53, sr group leader, 56-63, SECT MGR, PHILLIPS PETROL CO, 63- *Mem:* Am Chem Soc; AAAS. *Res:* Synthetic rubber by emulsion and stereospecific polymerization; chemicals from petroleum; free radicals; organo-metallic compounds. *Mailing Add:* 842 S E Concord Dr Bartlesville OK 74003

SONNENSCHEIN, RALPH ROBERT, b Chicago, Ill, Aug 14, 23; m 52; c 3. PHYSIOLOGY. *Educ:* Northwestern Univ, BS, 43, MS, 46, MD, 47; Univ Ill, PhD(physiol), 50. *Prof Exp:* Asst physiol, Northwestern Univ, 44-46; intern, Michael Reese Hosp, Chicago, Ill, 46-47; res asst psychiat, Univ Ill, 49-51, res assoc, 51; from asst prof to assoc prof physiol, 51-62, PROF PHYSIOL, UNIV CALIF, LOS ANGELES, 62- *Concurrent Pos:* USPHS res fel, 57-58; Swed Med Res Coun fel, 64-65; liaison scientist, Off Naval Res, London, 71-72. *Mem:* AAAS; Microcirc Soc; Am Physiol Soc; Soc Exp Biol & Med. *Res:* Peripheral circulation. *Mailing Add:* Dept of Physiol Univ of Calif Sch of Med Los Angeles CA 90024

SONNENWIRTH, ALEXANDER COLEMAN, b Oradea, Romania, Aug 12, 23; nat US; m 52; c 2. MEDICAL MICROBIOLOGY. *Educ:* Univ Nebr, AB, 50; Purdue Univ, MS, 53; Wash Univ, PhD(bact), 60; Am Bd Med Microbiol, dipl. *Prof Exp:* Instr, Sch Dent, 58-61, from asst prof to assoc prof, Sch Med, 62-77, PROF MICROBIOL & PATH, SCH MED, WASH UNIV, 77-; MICROBIOLOGIST, JEWISH HOSP, ST LOUIS, 53- *Mem:* Am Acad Microbiol; Infectious Dis Soc Am; Am Pub Health Asn; Am Soc Microbiol; Am Soc Clin Path. *Res:* Endogenous infections; antigens and taxonomy of Bacteroides; anaerobes; Yersinia; clinical microbiology. *Mailing Add:* Jewish Hosp Labs 216 S Kingshighway St Louis MO 63110

SONNER, JOHANN, b Munich, Ger, May 3, 24; nat US; m 57; c 2. MATHEMATICS. *Educ:* Univ Munich, Dr rer nat, 54. *Prof Exp:* Asst prof, State Sch Eng, Ger, 56-57; tech consult, Wright Air Develop Ctr, Ohio, 57-58; prof math, Univ SC, 58-67; PROF MATH, UNIV NC, CHAPEL HILL, 67- *Mem:* Am Math Soc; Math Asn Am; Ger Math Asn; Math Soc France. *Res:* Foundations of mathematics; general topology. *Mailing Add:* Dept of Math Univ of NC Chapel Hill NC 27514

SONNERUP, BENGT ULF ÖSTEN, b Malmö, Sweden, July 7, 31; m 55; c 3. SPACE PHYSICS, FLUID MECHANICS. *Educ:* Chalmers Inst Technol, Sweden, BME, 53; Cornell Univ, MAE, 60, PhD(fluid mech), 61. *Prof Exp:* Proj engr, Stal-Laval Steam Turbine Co, Sweden, 54-56; proj engr, Bofors Co, Sweden, 56-58; fel, Ctr Radiophys & Space Res, Cornell Univ, 61-62; fel, Inst Plasma Physics, Royal Inst Technol, Sweden, 62-64; assoc prof, 64-70, prof, 70-81, SYDNEY E JUNKINS PROF ENG SCI, DARTMOUTH COL, 81- *Concurrent Pos:* Lectr, Uppsala Univ, 63; Europ Space Res Orgn fel, Europ Space Res Inst, Italy, 70-71; vis scientist, Max Planck Inst Extraterrestrial Physics, Garching, Fed Repub Ger, 78-79; ed, J Geophys Res, 82-85. *Mem:* AAAS; Am Geophys Union; Am Inst Aeronaut & Astronaut. *Res:* Plasma physics and magnetohydrodynamics applied to problems in space physics, particularly the structure of the magnetopause current layer; magnetosphere and the nature of magnetic field merging. *Mailing Add:* Radiophysics Lab Dartmouth Col Hanover NH 03755

SONNESSA, ANTHONY J, b New York, NY, Mar 16, 26. PHYSICAL CHEMISTRY. *Educ:* Brooklyn Col, BS, 49; Purdue Univ, MS, 51; Wayne State Univ, PhD(chem), 61. *Prof Exp:* Group leader spectros, Interchem Corp, 51-57; asst prof, 60-65, ASSOC PROF CHEM, SETON HALL UNIV, 65- *Mem:* Am Chem Soc. *Res:* Physical methods of determining molecular structure; relationship between structure and the chemical and physical properties of matter. *Mailing Add:* Dept of Chem Seton Hall Univ South Orange NJ 07079

SONNET, PHILIP E, b New York, NY, Feb 6, 35; m 58; c 3. ORGANIC CHEMISTRY. *Educ:* Columbia Univ, AB, 56; Rutgers Univ, PhD(org chem), 63. *Prof Exp:* NIH fel org chem, Mass Inst Technol, 63-64; RES CHEMIST, AGR RES CTR, USDA, 64- *Concurrent Pos:* Instr, Univ Md, 72-76. *Mem:* Am Chem Soc; Entom Soc Am. *Res:* Insect pheremones; insect pheromenes, identification and syntheses; aliphatic synthesis. *Mailing Add:* PO Box 14565 Gainesville FL 32604

SONNICHSEN, GEORGE CARL, b Chicago, Ill, Nov 15, 41; m 70. CHEMISTRY. *Educ:* DePauw Univ, BS, 63; Mich State Univ, PhD(chem), 67. *Prof Exp:* NSF fel chem, Univ Calif, Berkeley, 67-68, lectr, 68-69; res chemist, 69-75, res supvr, 75-78, RES ASSOC, E I DU PONT DE NEMOURS & CO, 78- *Mem:* Am Chem Soc. *Res:* Heterogeneous and homogeneous catalysis. *Mailing Add:* E I du Pont de Nemours & Co Wilmington DE 19898

SONNICHSEN, HAROLD MARVIN, b Hancock, Minn, Apr 4, 12; m 39; c 2. ADHESIVES. *Educ:* Tex Col Mines, AB, 34; Harvard Univ, Phd(org chem), 39. *Prof Exp:* Res chemist, Electrochem Dept, E I du Pont de Nemours & Co, 39-40, supvr, Sales Res Sect, 40-43, plant supvr, 43-44; tech serv mgr, Permacel Tape Corp, 44-48, asst dir, 48-52, tech dir, 52-55, vpres, 55-60; dir fiber & saturant res, Dewey & Almy Chem Div, W R Grace & Co, 60-64, vpres, Precision Tech Prod, 65-75; PRES, H M SONNICHSEN & ASSOCS, 75- *Mem:* Am Chem Soc; fel Am Inst Chem. *Res:* Properties and applications of synthetic high polymers; pressure sensitive adhesives; structural adhesives; latex; paper; artificial leather; paper and nonwoven disposable products. *Mailing Add:* 37 Robin Hood Rd Arlington MA 02174

SONNINO, CARLO BENVENUTO, b Torino, Italy, May 12, 04; US citizen; m 49; c 3. ELECTROCHEMISTRY, ELECTROMETALLURGY. *Educ:* Univ Milano, PhD(chem eng), 27. *Prof Exp:* Dir res & mgr, Dept Flotation, Italian Aluminum Co, 28-33; mgr, Tonolli Co, 33-34; pres, LCI Consult, 34-39; mem bd & mgr, LAESA, 39-43; tech adv to bd dir, Boxal S A, Switzerland, 44-52; mgr & tech adv, Kreisler Co, 52-53; tech mgr, Alumacraft, St Louis, 53-56; MAT ENG MGR, EMERSON ELEC CO, ST LOUIS, 56-; PROF METALL ENG, UNIV MO, ROLLA, 68- *Concurrent Pos:* Prof metall & mat sci, Washington Univ, 60-67; tech adv, Thompson Brand, Paris & Rouen, 70-75; consult, Monsanto, Wagner Elec, & Amax, 75- *Honors & Awards:* Klixon Award, Am Soc Heating, Refrigeration, & Air Conditioning Engrs, 60; Knight Comdr, President Italian Repub, 77. *Mem:* Sigma Xi; Am Soc Testing Mat; fel Am Soc Metals; Soc Metal Engrs. *Res:* Synthetic cryolite; anodizing of aluminum alloys. *Mailing Add:* 7206 Kingsbury Blvd St Louis MO 63130

SONNTAG, NORMAN OSCAR VICTOR, b Brooklyn, NY, Sept 10, 19; m 47; c 2. ORGANIC CHEMISTRY, ANALYTICAL CHEMISTRY. *Educ:* Polytech Inst Brooklyn, PhD(chem), 51. *Prof Exp:* Res chemist, Polytech Inst Brooklyn, 49-51 & Colgate Palmolive Co, 51-55; chief chemist, Chem Div, Celanese Corp Am, 55-56; res chemist, Emery Industs, Inc, 56-59; assoc mgr, Res & Develop Div, Nat Dairy Prod Corp, Ill, 59-66; mgr process res, Glyco Chem, Inc, 66-68, dir res, 68-77; tech dir chem div, Southland Corp, 78-80; CONSULT, 80- *Mem:* Am Chem Soc; Am Oil Chem Soc (vpres, 78-79, pres, 79-80). *Res:* Reduction of highly arylated conjugated cyclic ketones; reactions of aliphatic acid chlorides; chemical utilization of fats; fatty chemicals; synthetic fatty acids; nitrogen derivatives; dibasic acids; hydantoin chemicals; agriculture and food chemistry. *Mailing Add:* 306 Shadowood Trail Red Oak TX 75154

SONNTAG, RICHARD E, b Chicago, Ill, Apr 17, 33; m 57; c 2. MECHANICAL ENGINEERING, THERMODYNAMICS. *Educ:* Univ Mich, BSE, 56, MSE, 57, PhD(mech eng), 61. *Prof Exp:* From asst prof to assoc prof, 60-67, PROF MECH ENG, UNIV MICH, ANN ARBOR, 67- *Mem:* Am Soc Mech Engrs; Am Soc Eng Educ. *Res:* Low temperature thermodynamics; phase equilibria; pressure-volume-temperature behavior. *Mailing Add:* Thermodynamics Lab 2204 GG Brown Lab Ann Arbor MI 48109

SONNTAG, ROY WINDHAM, b Cleburne, Tex, Nov 17, 29; m 53; c 4. ORGANIC CHEMISTRY. *Educ:* NTex State Col, BS, 53; Univ Tex, PhD(org chem), 59. *Prof Exp:* Res chemist, Monsanto Chem Co, 58 & Esso Res & Eng Co, 59-60; from asst prof to assoc prof, 60-69, PROF CHEM, MCMURRY COL, 69- *Mem:* Am Chem Soc. *Res:* Molecular rearrangements of organic systems; conformational analysis. *Mailing Add:* Dept of Chem McMurry Col McMurry Sta Abilene TX 79605

SONODA, RONALD MASAHIRO, b Hilo, Hawaii, June 4, 39; m 66; c 2. PLANT PATHOLOGY. *Educ:* Sacramento State Col, AB, 63; Univ Calif, Davis, MS, 65, PhD(plant path), 69. *Prof Exp:* From asst prof to assoc prof, 69-81, PROF, INST FOOD & AGR SCI, UNIV FLA, 81- *Concurrent Pos:* Fac develop grant, Univ Calif, Davis, 79-80. *Mem:* Am Phytopath Soc; Mycol Soc Am. *Res:* Control of soil-borne plant pathogens; diseases of tropical forage legumes and grasses; diseases of tomatoes. *Mailing Add:* Agr Res Ctr PO Box 248 Ft Pierce FL 33450

SONS, LINDA RUTH, b Chicago Heights, Ill, Oct 31, 39. MATHEMATICS. *Educ:* Ind Univ, AB, 61; Cornell Univ, MS, 63, PhD(math), 66. *Prof Exp:* from asst prof to assoc prof, 65-78, PROF MATH, NORTHERN ILL UNIV, 78- *Concurrent Pos:* NSF grant, 70-72 & 74-75. *Mem:* Math Asn Am; Am Math Soc. *Res:* Mathematical analysis, especially complex function theory. *Mailing Add:* Dept of Math Northern Ill Univ De Kalb IL 60115

SONSTEGARD, KAREN SUE, b Yankton, SDak, Dec 19, 43; m 65. DEVELOPMENTAL BIOLOGY, EXPERIMENTAL PATHOLOGY. *Educ:* Univ SDak, BA, 65; Ontario Vet Col, Univ Guelph, MA, 69, PhD(develop biol), 73. *Prof Exp:* Researcher path, Res Inst Hosp Sick Children & Univ Toronto, 74-76, res fel, 76-77, Am Lung Asn fel, 77-79; SR STAFF FEL PULMONARY BR, NAT INST ENVIRON HEALTH SCI, 79- *Concurrent Pos:* Nat Res Coun Can fel, 74-76; res assoc path, Hosp Sick Children & Univ Toronto; mem educ comt, Tissue Cult Asn, 76-80; Can Fedn Univ Women travel fel, 77; co-recipient grants, Ont Respiratory Dis Found, 78-79 & Can Lung Asn, 78-80. *Mem:* Sigma Xi; Am Thoracic Soc; Can Lung Asn; Tissue Cult Asn; Soc Cell Biol. *Res:* Lung cell biology; stem cells; mucous cells and neuro-endocrine cells of airway epithelium; isolated cell systems of lung; comparative studies of lung and intestinal neuro-endocrine cells. *Mailing Add:* Nat Inst Environ Health Sci Research Triangle Park NC 27709

SONSTEGARD, RONALD ARLYN, b Yankton, SDak, Feb 1, 41; m 65. CANCER, FISH PATHOLOGY. *Educ:* SDak State Univ, BS, 63, MS, 66; Univ Guelph, PhD(virol), 70. *Prof Exp:* Res assoc, Nat Cancer Inst Can, McMaster Univ, 70-73, res scholar cancer, Univ Guelph, 73-78, career develop award, 78-80; MEM FAC, DEPT MICROBIOL, UNIV GUELPH, 80- *Concurrent Pos:* Mem comt comp oncol, Int Union Against Cancer, 75-76. *Mem:* Sigma Xi; Am Soc Microbiol; Wildlife Dis Asn. *Res:* Investigations of the etiology and epizootiology of tumors in fishes, with particular reference to lymphoreticular neoplasia; utilization of fishes as indicator organisms for the early detection and identification of environmental carcinogens. *Mailing Add:* Dept Microbiol Univ Guelph Guelph ON N1G 2W1 Can

SONSTEIN, STEPHEN ALLEN, b Philadelphia, Pa, June 9, 42; m 66; c 2. MICROBIOLOGY. *Educ:* Rutgers Univ, BA, 64; Hahnemann Med Col, MS, 68, PhD(microbiol), 70. *Prof Exp:* Res assoc microbiol genetics, Univ Ga, 70-72; asst prof biol, Columbus Col, 72-74; asst prof & dir med technol biol, Univ Dayton, 74-76, asst prof biol, 76-80. *Mem:* Am Soc Microbiol; Am Soc Med Technol; Am Soc Allied Health Professions. *Res:* Mechanisms of virulence in Staphylococcus Aureus. *Mailing Add:* 1016 E Quarles Pl Fox Point WI 53217

SOO, SHAO-LEE, b Peiping, China, Mar 1, 22; US citizen; m 52; c 3. MECHANICAL ENGINEERING. *Educ:* Nat Chiaotung Univ, BS, 45; Ga Inst Technol, MS, 48; Harvard Univ, ScD(mech eng), 51. *Prof Exp:* Teaching fel appl physics, Harvard Univ, 51; instr mech eng, Princeton Univ, 51-52, lectr, 52-54, from asst prof to assoc prof, 54-59; PROF MECH ENG, UNIV ILL, URBANA, 59- *Concurrent Pos:* Indust consult, 51-; mem consult team Skylab I, Univ Space Res Assoc, NASA, 71-72; Agard lectr, NATO, 73; distinguished lectr, Fulbright-Hays Prog, Buenos Aires, Arg, 74; mem, Sci Adv Bd, US Environ Protection Agency, 76-78; adv energy transp, World Bank, 79; dir, S L Soo Assocs Inc, Urbana, 80- *Mem:* Fel Am Soc Mech Engrs; Am Soc Eng Educ; Combustion Inst; Sigma Xi; Int Powder Inst. *Res:* Basic formulation of nonequilibrium fluid dynamics; experimental research in two-phase flow; nonequilibrium ionized gases; gas-surface interaction; atmospheric transport of air pollutants and control by electrostatic precipitation; turbomachinery. *Mailing Add:* 123 Mech Eng Bldg Univ of Ill Urbana IL 61801

SOOD, MANMOHAN K, b Manpur Nagaria, India, Apr 17, 41; nat US; m 65; c 2. PETROLOGY, GEOCHEMISTRY. *Educ:* Panjab Univ, India, BSc, 60, MSc, 63; Univ Western Ont, MSc, 68, PhD(geol), 69. *Prof Exp:* Tech asst geol, Govt Punjab, 63-64; res assoc, Univ Western Ont, 69-70; asst prof earth sci, 70-73, assoc prof, 73-80, PROF EARTH SCI, NORTHEASTERN ILL UNIV, 80-, CHMN DEPT, 74- *Mem:* Mineral Soc Am; Int Asn Advancement Earth & Environ Sci(founding secy, 72-73). *Res:* Phase equilibrium related to alkaline igneous rocks; geochemical and crystallo-chemical studies of oxide and rare earth minerals, including the tantalite-columbite series; energy and mineral resources in the future. *Mailing Add:* Dept of Earth Sci Northeastern Ill Univ Chicago IL 60625

SOOD, SATYA P, b Abohar, Punjab, India, Feb 4, 23; m 57; c 1. PHYSICAL CHEMISTRY, POLYMER CHEMISTRY. *Educ:* Forman Christian Col, Punjab, BSc, 42; Acton Tech Col, London, API, 53; State Univ NY, MS, 56; Univ Hawaii, PhD(chem), 63. *Prof Exp:* Chemist various chem concerns, India, 42-49; tech asst, Indian High Comn, London, Eng, 50-53; teaching asst chem, State Univ NY, 53-55; res asst, Tex Tech Col, 55-57; asst, 57-62, res assoc physics, 62-63, from asst prof to assoc prof, 63-71, chmn div sci, 71-80,

PROF CHEM, UNIV HAWAII, HILO, 71- *Concurrent Pos:* Lectr, Bahawal Col, Pakistan, 46-47; res fel, McMaster Univ, 68-69. *Res:* Chemical kinetics; synthetic organic chemistry; ultraviolet spectroscopy; dipole moments; radiation chemistry. *Mailing Add:* Univ of Hawaii Hilo Campus Hilo HI 96720

SOOD, VIJAY KUMAR, b New Delhi, India, May 13, 51; m 80. AGRICULTURAL & FOOD CHEMISTRY. *Educ:* Nat Dairy Res Inst, India, BS, 70, MS, 72; Cornell Univ, PhD(food sci), 78. *Prof Exp:* Sr technologist, Punjab Dairy Develop Corp, India, 72-73; asst dairy technologist, Punjab Coop Dept, 73-74; SR SCIENTIST FOOD RES, UNIVERSAL FOODS CORP, 78- *Concurrent Pos:* Vis scientist, Nat Inst Agron Res, France, 78. *Mem:* Inst Food Technologists; Am Dairy Sci Asn. *Res:* Develop new food products and processes. *Mailing Add:* Tech Ctr Universal Foods Corp 6143 N 60th St Milwaukee WI 53218

SOODAK, MORRIS, biochemistry, see previous edition

SOODSMA, JAMES FRANKLIN, b Hull, Iowa, Feb 3, 38; m 64; c 2. COMBUSTION ENGINEERING. *Educ:* Univ SDak, BA, 63; Univ NDak, MS, 65, PhD(biochem), 68; Univ Tulsa, MS. *Prof Exp:* chief scientist, William K Warren Med Res Ctr, Inc, 71-77; TEST ENGR, JOHN ZINK CO, 77- *Concurrent Pos:* AEC fel, Med Div, Oak Ridge Assoc Univs, 68-71. *Mem:* Am Chem Soc. *Res:* Studies on rat kidney glucose-6-phosphatase and associated phosphotransferase activities; rat liver enzyme system which cleaves glyceryl ethers; mammalian newborn phospholipid and carbohydrate metabolism; pollution control. *Mailing Add:* 6301 E 56th Pl Tulsa OK 74135

SOOHOO, RONALD FRANKLIN, b Kwangtung, China, Sept 1, 28; US citizen; m 57; c 2. ELECTRICAL ENGINEERING, PHYSICS. *Educ:* Mass Inst Technol, SB, 48; Stanford Univ, MS, 52, PhD(elec eng, physics), 56. *Prof Exp:* Asst engr, Pac Gas & Elec Co, 48-51; dir res anal, Cascade Res Corp, 54-58; res physicist, Lincoln Lab, Mass Inst Technol, 58-61; assoc prof eng & appl sci, Calif Inst Technol, 61-64; chmn dept elec eng, 64-70, PROF ELEC ENG, UNIV CALIF, DAVIS, 64- *Concurrent Pos:* Consult, Space Technol Labs, 62-64, Ampex Corp, 62-64, Bunker-Ramo Corp, 62-64, E&M Labs, 67- & Lawrence Livermore Lab, 69-; NATO fel, Nat Ctr Sci Res, Bellevue, France, 70. *Mem:* Fel Inst Elec & Electronics Engrs; Am Inst Physics. *Res:* Magnetism and magnetic materials; solid state physics; microwave electronics; computer devices and systems; quantum electronics. *Mailing Add:* Dept of Elec Eng Univ of Calif Davis CA 95616

SOOKNE, ARNOLD MAURICE, b New York, NY, Oct 9, 15; m 39; c 2. CHEMISTRY. *Educ:* Brooklyn Col, BS, 35; George Washington Univ, MA, 42. *Prof Exp:* Res assoc, Am Asn Textile Chemists & Colorists, Washington, DC, 36-37, Nat Res Coun, 37-38 & Textile Found, Nat Bur Standards, 38-44; assoc dir, Harris Res Labs Div, Gillette Res Inst, Inc, 44-65, vpres labs, 65-68, vpres, Inst, 68-69; dir chem develop, res ctr, 69-77, ASST DIR CORP RES & DEVELOP, BURLINGTON INDUSTS, INC, 78- *Concurrent Pos:* Vis prof, Univ NC, Greensboro, 79- *Honors & Awards:* Olney medal, Am Asn Textile Chem & Colorists, 60; Harold DeWitt Smith Award, Am Soc Test & Mat, 71. *Mem:* Am Chem Soc; Am Asn Textile Chem & Colorists; Fiber Soc; Brit Textile Inst. *Res:* Physical chemistry of textiles; dyeing and finishing of textiles. *Mailing Add:* Corp Res & Develop Burlington Indust Inc PO Box 21327 Greensboro NC 27420

SOOKY, ATTILA A(RPAD), b Rakoscsaba, Hungary, Aug 22, 32; US citizen; m 64; c 3. FLUID MECHANICS. *Educ:* Budapest Tech Univ, BS, 55, MS, 56; Purdue Univ, PhD(fluid mech), 64. *Prof Exp:* Asst prof, 64-71, ASSOC PROF POLLUTION CONTROL, UNIV PITTSBURGH, 71- *Mem:* Am Soc Civil Engrs; Water Pollution Control Fedn. *Res:* Pollution control; fate of pollution in natural waters; health effects of pollutants. *Mailing Add:* Grad Sch of Pub Health Univ of Pittsburgh Pittsburgh PA 15261

SOONG, TSU-TEH, b Honan, China, Feb 10, 34; US citizen; m 59; c 3. CIVIL ENGINEERING, APPLIED MATHEMATICS. *Educ:* Univ Dayton, BS, 55; Purdue Univ, MS, 58, PhD(eng sci), 62. *Prof Exp:* Instr mech, Purdue Univ, 58-62; sr res engr, Jet Propulsion Lab, Calif Inst Technol, 62-63; from asst prof to assoc prof eng sci, 63-68, chmn dept, 70-80, PROF ENG & CIVIL ENG, STATE UNIV NY BUFFALO, 68- *Concurrent Pos:* Lectr, Univ Calif, Los Angeles, 62-63; res mathematician, Cornell Aeronaut Lab, 64-; NSF res grants, 64-, sci faculty fel, Delft Technol Univ, 66-67. *Mem:* Soc Indust & Appl Math. *Res:* Stochastic processes with applications to analysis of engineering systems; filtering and prediction; information theory; stochastic systems and bioengineering. *Mailing Add:* 218 MacArthur Dr Williamsville NY 14221

SOONG, YIN SHANG, b Shanghai, Repub of China, July 14, 47. PHYSICAL OCEANOGRAPHY. *Educ:* Nat Taiwan Univ, BS, 69; Fla State Univ, MS, 74, PhD(phys oceanog), 78. *Prof Exp:* ASST PROF OCEANOG, MILLERSVILLE STATE COL, 77- *Mem:* Am Meteorol Soc. *Res:* Geophysical fluid dynamics; inertial currents; mesoscale oceanic phenomenon. *Mailing Add:* Dept of Earth Sci Millersville State Col Millersville PA 17551

SOONPAA, HENN H, b Estonia, Mar 18, 30; nat US; m 59; c 2. SOLID STATE PHYSICS. *Educ:* Concordia Col, BA, 51; Univ Ore, MA, 53; Wayne State Univ, PhD(phys chem), 55. *Prof Exp:* Asst, Univ Ore, 51-52; res fel, Iowa State Univ, 56; sr scientist, Gen Mills, Inc, 57-58; assoc prof physics, Gustavus Adolphus Col, 58-59; sr & prin scientist, Gen Mills, Inc, 59-62 & Honeywell Corp Res Ctr, 62-66; assoc prof, 66-72, PROF PHYSICS, UNIV NDAK, 72- *Mem:* Am Phys Soc; Am Asn Physics Teachers; Am Vacuum Soc. *Res:* Solid state physics; transport phenomena; quantum size effects; two dimensional systems. *Mailing Add:* Dept of Physics Univ of ND Grand Forks ND 58202

SOOS, ZOLTAN GEZA, b Budapest, Hungary, July 31, 41; US citizen; m 66. PHYSICAL CHEMISTRY. *Educ:* Harvard Col, AB, 62; Calif Inst Technol, PhD(chem, physics), 65. *Prof Exp:* NSF fel, Stanford Univ, 65-66; from asst to assoc prof, 66-74, PROF CHEM, PRINCETON UNIV, 74- *Concurrent Pos:* Vis scientist, Sandia Corp, 71. *Res:* Theory of molecular excitons; many-body methods in para magnetic crystals. *Mailing Add:* Dept of Chem Princeton Univ Princeton NJ 08540

SOOST, ROBERT KENNETH, b Sacramento, Calif, Nov 13, 20; m 49; c 3. GENETICS. *Educ:* Univ Calif, PhD(genetics), 49. *Prof Exp:* From asst geneticist to assoc, 49-65, chmn, Dept Plant Sci, 69-75, GENETICIST, UNIV CALIF, RIVERSIDE, 65- *Mem:* AAAS; Genetics Soc Am; fel Am Soc Hort Sci. *Res:* Citrus genetics and breeding. *Mailing Add:* 2916 Las Palmas Ct Riverside CA 92506

SOOY, FRANCIS ADRIAN, b Coalinga, Calif, July 1, 15; m 44; c 5. OTOLARYNGOLOGY. *Educ:* Univ Calif, Berkeley, AB, 37; Univ Calif, San Francisco, MD, 41; Am Bd Otolaryngol, dipl, 44. *Prof Exp:* From clin instr to assoc clin prof, 46-61, actg chmn div, 56-58, chmn, 58-67, chmn dept otolaryngol, 67-73, PROF OTOLARYNGOL, MED CTR, UNIV CALIF, SAN FRANCISCO, 61-, DIR AUDIOL & SPEECH CLIN, 53- *Concurrent Pos:* Consult to Surgeon Gen, Otolaryngol Postgrad Training Comt, Nat Inst Neurol Dis & Blindness, 59-63, mem nat adv neurol dis & blindness coun, NIH, 64- *Mem:* AMA; Am Acad Ophthal & Otolaryngol; Am Col Surg; Am Laryngol, Rhinol & Otol Soc; Am Laryngol Asn. *Res:* Experimental surgery to improve present surgical otologic techniques; photography for experimental and surgical work. *Mailing Add:* Dept of Otolaryngol Univ of Calif Med Ctr San Francisco CA 94122

SOOY, WALTER RICHARD, b Boston, Mass, Dec 28, 32; div; c 2. PHYSICS. *Educ:* Mass Inst Technol, BS, 56; Univ Southern Calif, MS, 58; Univ Calif, Los Angeles, PhD(physics), 63. *Prof Exp:* Mem tech staff, Hughes Aircraft Co, 56-62, staff physicist, 62-64, sr staff physicist, 64-66, sr scientist, 66-70, dept mgr, 68-70; supt optical sci div, Naval Res Lab, 70-75; VPRES & CHIEF SCIENTIST, SCI APPLNS INC, 75- *Concurrent Pos:* Consult, Off of Secy Defense & Naval Mat Command, 75- *Mem:* AAAS; Optical Soc Am; Am Phys Soc. *Res:* Superconductivity; microwave oscillators; nuclear physics; optics; lasers; systems. *Mailing Add:* 8360 Greensboro Dr #3-201 McLean VA 22101

SOPER, DAVISON EUGENE, b Milwaukee, Wis, Mar 21, 43; m 71; c 2. THEORETICAL HIGH ENERGY PHYSICS. *Educ:* Amherst Col, AB, 65; Stanford Univ, PhD(physics), 71. *Prof Exp:* From instr to asst prof physics, Princeton Univ, 71-77; asst prof, 77-80, ASSOC PROF PHYSICS, UNIV ORE, 80- *Mem:* Am Phys Soc. *Res:* Quantum field theory and particle physics; classical field theory. *Mailing Add:* Inst of Theoret Sci Univ of Ore Eugene OR 97403

SOPER, GORDON KNOWLES, b Gunnison, Colo, July 25, 38; m 58; c 2. PLASMA PHYSICS. *Educ:* Univ Tenn, BS, 59, MS, 62, PhD(physics), 64. *Prof Exp:* From asst prof to assoc prof physics, US Air Force Inst Technol, 64-72; proj officer, HQ, 72-75, chief, Electronics Vulnerablity Div, 75-77, chief, Atmospheric Effects Div, 77-78, ASST TO DEP DIR SCI & TECHNOL EXP RES, DEFENSE NUCLEAR AGENCY, WASHINGTON, DC, 78- *Mem:* Am Phys Soc; Am Asn Physics Teachers. *Res:* Theoretical plasma physics, particularly stability theory. *Mailing Add:* HQ Defense Nuclear Agency Washington DC 20305

SOPER, JAMES HERBERT, b Hamilton, Ont, Apr 9, 16; m 46; c 4. BOTANY. *Educ:* McMaster Univ, BA, 38, MA, 39; Harvard Univ, PhD(biol), 43. *Prof Exp:* Botanist, Can Dept Agr, 45-46; spec lectr bot, Univ Toronto, 46-47, from asst prof to assoc prof, 47-66, prof, 66-67; chief botanist, 67-81, EMER CUR, BOT DIV, MUS NATURAL SCI, NAT MUS CAN, 81- *Concurrent Pos:* Curator, Herbarium Vascular Plants, Univ Toronto, 46-67. *Res:* Flora of Ontario; distribution of vascular plants of North America; data-processing and automated cartography. *Mailing Add:* Mus of Natural Sci Nat Mus of Can Ottawa ON K1A 0M8 Can

SOPER, JON ALLEN, b Wyandotte, Mich, Mar 7, 36; m 58; c 5. ELECTRICAL ENGINEERING. *Educ:* Mich Technol Univ, BS, 57, MS, 61; Univ Mich, Ann Arbor, PhD(elec eng), 69. *Prof Exp:* Instr elec eng, Mich Technol Univ, 57-60, asst prof, 60-63; design and develop engr, Raytheon Mfg Co, 63-64; asst prof elec eng, Mich Technol Univ, 64-65; asst res engr, Univ Mich, 67-68; asst prof, 68-70, assoc prof, 70-79, PROF ELEC ENG, MICH TECHNOL UNIV, 79- *Concurrent Pos:* Acting assoc dean, Mich Tech Univ, 78-79. *Mem:* Sr mem Inst Elec & Electronics Engrs; Am Soc Eng Educ. *Res:* Transient and steady state antenna behavior; microwave networks and special purpose digital computers; radar systems and navigation systems electromagnetic interactions with snow. *Mailing Add:* Dept Elec Eng Mich Technol Univ Houghton MI 49931

SOPER, QUENTIN FRANCIS, b Buhl, Minn, Dec 3, 19; m 46; c 4. CHEMISTRY. *Educ:* Univ Minn, BChem, 40; Univ Ill, PhD(org chem), 43. *Prof Exp:* Asst chem, Univ Ill, 40-43, spec asst, Nat Defense Res Comt Contract, 43-44; sr org chem, 44-65, head agr chem res, 65-72, agr sr assoc, 72-77, RES ADV, ELI LILLY & CO, 77- *Honors & Awards:* John Scott Award, Am Inst Chemists. *Mem:* Am Chem Soc; Weed Sci Soc Am; Am Inst Chemists. *Res:* Synthesis of new war gases; synthesis of new chemicals useful in the biosynthesis of new penicillins; quinoxaline formation and the ortho effect; hindrance at beta carbon atom; synthetic pharmaceuticals, herbicides and pesticides. *Mailing Add:* Eli Lilly & Co 307 E McCarty St Indianapolis IN 46285

SOPER, ROBERT JOSEPH, b Weston, Ont, Aug 25, 27; m 57. SOIL SCIENCE. *Educ:* Univ Sask, BA & BSA, 53, MSc, 55; McGill Univ, PhD(agr chem), 59. *Prof Exp:* From asst prof to assoc prof, 58-69, PROF SOILS, FAC AGR, UNIV MAN, 69- *Concurrent Pos:* App sr officer P-5 head, Soils, Irrigation & Crop Prod Sect, Atomic Energy Food & Agr, Vienna, Austria. *Mem:* Fel Can Soc Soil Sci; Agr Inst Can; Int Soc Soil Sci; Am Soc Agron. *Res:* Soil fertility, genesis and chemistry. *Mailing Add:* Dept of Soil Sci Univ of Man Fac of Agr Winnipeg MB R3T 2N2 Can

SOPER, ROBERT TUNNICLIFF, b Iowa City, Iowa, Sept 16, 25; m 51; c 6. MEDICINE. *Educ:* Cornell Col, BS, 49; Univ Iowa, MD, 52; Am Bd Surg, dipl, 59. *Prof Exp:* Intern med, Cleveland City Hosp, Ohio, 52-53; resident, 54-57, instr, 57-58, assoc, 58-59, from asst prof to assoc prof, 59-67, PROF SURG, UNIV IOWA HOSPS, 67- *Concurrent Pos:* Surg registr, Alder Hey Children's Hosp, Liverpool, Eng, 59-60. *Mem:* AMA; Am Col Surg; Brit Asn Pediat Surg; Am Pediat Surg Asn; Am Acad Pediat. *Res:* Clinical pediatric surgery. *Mailing Add:* Dept of Surg Univ of Iowa Hosps Iowa City IA 52242

SOPER, WILLIAM GALLAHAN, b Washington, DC, Aug 19, 30; m 56; c 1. ENGINEERING MECHANICS. *Educ:* Johns Hopkins Univ, BE, 52, MS, 53, PhD(eng mech), 56. *Prof Exp:* Staff mem stress & vibration anal, Los Alamos Sci Lab, 56-59; sr design engr, Aircraft Armaments, Inc, Md, 59-60; RES ASSOC, US NAVAL WEAPONS LAB, DAHLGREN, 60- *Res:* Similitude; dynamic properties of materials; plasticity; terminal ballistics; shock and vibration. *Mailing Add:* RR 1 Box 547 King George VA 22485

SOPHER, ROGER LOUIS, b Long Beach, Calif, Oct 7, 36; m 72. PATHOLOGY. *Educ:* St Mary'sCol, BS, 58; Johns Hopkins Univ, MD, 62. *Prof Exp:* Intern path, Med Ctr, Univ Calif, Los Angeles, 62-63, resident, 63-64; resident, 64-66, asst prof, 68-72, ASSOC PROF PATH, SCH MED, UNIV NMEX, 72-, VCHMN DEPT, 68-; CHIEF LAB SERV, ALBUQUERQUE VET ADMIN HOSP, 69- *Mem:* AAAS; Col Am Path; Am Soc Clin Path; Am Asn Pathologists & Bacteriologists. *Res:* Pulmonary effects of altered atmospheres; computerapplications to biomedicine. *Mailing Add:* Dept of Path Univ of NMex Sch of Med Albuquerque NM 87106

SOPHIANOPOULOS, ALKIS JOHN, b Athens, Greece, Aug 29, 25; US citizen; m 55; c 2. BIOCHEMISTRY, BIOPHYSICS. *Educ:* Drew Univ, AB, 53; Purdue Univ, MS, 57, PhD(chem), 60. *Prof Exp:* Trainee biophys, Dept Chem, Univ Ill, Urbana, 60-61; asst prof biochem, Univ Tenn Med Units, 61-68; ASSOC PROF BIOCHEM, EMORY UNIV, 68- *Honors & Awards:* Eli Lilly Med Fac Award, 65. *Mem:* Am Soc Biol Chemists; Biophys Soc; Am Chem Soc. *Res:* Physical chemistry of macromolecules; biophysical studies of relation of macromolecular structure to biological activity. *Mailing Add:* Dept of Biochem Emory Univ Atlanta GA 30322

SOPKA, KATHERINE RUSSELL, b Boston, Mass, May 11, 21; m 43; c 3. PHYSICAL SCIENCE, PHYSICS HISTORY. *Educ:* Radcliffe Col, AB, 42, AM, 48; Harvard Univ, PhD(hist sci & educ), 76. *Prof Exp:* Res asst physics, Dielectrics Lab, Mass Inst Technol, 42-43; lab instr, Army Specialized Training Prog, Colby Col, 43; res asst, Ballistics Lab, Princeton Univ, 44; asst prof physics & chem, Newark State Col, 58-59; instr phys sci, Div Integrated Studies, Univ Colo, 59-68; res asst proj physics, Harvard Univ, 69-70, res fel hist physics, 76-80; MEM FAC MATH DEPT, FT LEWIS COL, 80- *Mem:* Am Asn Physics Teachers; Hist Sci Soc; AAAS. *Res:* History of 19th and 20th century physics; growth of physics in the US; American women physicists. *Mailing Add:* Math Dept Ft Lewis Col Durango CO 81301

SOPP, SAMUEL WILLIAM, b Hammond, Ind, Aug 28, 34; m 63; c 2. INORGANIC CHEMISTRY, PHYSICAL CHEMISTRY. *Educ:* Ind State Univ, BS, 57; Ariz State Univ, MS, 62; Univ Ill, PhD(inorg chem), 65. *Prof Exp:* Prod develop assoc, 65-68, supvr & fel prod develop, 69-72, SR GROUP LEADER, MARINE PROD DEVELOP LABS, MERCK & CO, INC, 73- *Mem:* Am Chem Soc; Fine Particle Soc. *Res:* Characterization of transition metal complexes complexes using nuclear magnetic resonance; evaluation of new product concepts and characterizing physical properties of inorganic materials; development of novel coating materials for electrical steels. *Mailing Add:* 221 Shearwater Isle Foster City CA 94404

SOPPER, WILLIAM EDWARD, b Slatington, Pa, Aug 16, 28; m 51; c 3. FORESTRY. *Educ:* Pa State Univ, BS, 54, MF, 55; Yale Univ, PhD(forest hydrol), 60. *Prof Exp:* Asst forestry, 54-55, instr, 55-60, from asst prof to assoc prof, 60-68, PROF FOREST HYDROL, FOREST RES LAB, PA STATE UNIV, 68-, HYDROLOGIST, INST RES LAND & WATER RESOURCES, 69- *Concurrent Pos:* Mem forest influences & watershed mgt sect, Int Union Forestry Res Orgns, 64-66; Pa State del, Univs Coun Water Resources, 64-66. *Mem:* Soc Am Foresters; Am Geophys Union. *Res:* Forest hydrology; watershed management; forest influences; land application of wastewater, strip mine reclamation with sludge. *Mailing Add:* Inst Res Land & Water Res L & W Res Bldg Pa State Univ University Park PA 16802

SORAUF, JAMES E, b Milwaukee, Wis, May 19, 31; m 62; c 2. GEOLOGY. *Educ:* Univ Wis-Madison, BS, 54, MS, 55; Univ Kans, PhD(geol), 62. *Prof Exp:* From asst prof to assoc prof, 62-75, PROF GEOL, STATE UNIV NY BINGHAMTON, 75- *Mem:* Am Asn Petrol Geol; Geol Soc Am; Soc Econ Paleont & Mineral. *Res:* Petroleum geology; Permian stratigraphy; paleontology of Devonian corals. *Mailing Add:* Dept of Geol Sci State Univ of NY Binghamton NY 13901

SORBELLO, RICHARD SALVATORE, b New York, NY, Aug 10, 42. THEORETICAL SOLID STATE PHYSICS. *Educ:* Mass Inst Technol, BS, MS, 65; Stanford Univ, PhD(appl physics), 70. *Prof Exp:* Res assoc low temperature physics, Swiss Fed Inst, Zurich, 71-73; asst prof, 73-78, ASSOC PROF PHYSICS, UNIV WIS-MILWAUKEE, 78- *Concurrent Pos:* Vis prof, Vrije Univ, Amsterdam, 80. *Mem:* Am Phys Soc; AAAS. *Res:* Transport theory and atomic diffusion in solids; electromigration and thermomigration in metals; electronic structure of solids; dielectric response and transport properties of metallic microstructures. *Mailing Add:* Dept of Physics Univ of Wis Milwaukee WI 53201

SORBER, CHARLES ARTHUR, b Kingston, Pa, Sept 12, 39; m 72; c 2. ENVIRONMENTAL ENGINEERING, CIVIL ENGINEERING. *Educ:* Pa State Univ, BS, 61, MS, 66; Univ Tex, Austin, PhD (environ eng), 71. *Prof Exp:* Proj engr, Harris, Henry & Potter, Inc, Pa, 65-66; chief sanitary eng, Gen Eng Br, USArmy Environ Hyg Agency, 66-69; comdr, US Army Med Environ Eng Res Univ, Md, 71-73; dir, Environ Qual Div, US Army Med Bioeng Res & Develop Lab, 73-75; asst dean, Col Sci & Math, Univ Tex, San Antonio, 76-77, assoc prof environ eng, Div Environ Studies, 75-80, acting dir, Div Earth & Phys Sci & dir, Ctr Appl Res & Technol, 76-80; ACCOT PROF CIVIL ENG & DEAN, COL ENG, UNIV TEXAS, AUSTIN, 80- *Concurrent Pos:* Prin investr, Fischer & Porter, Co, Pa, 76-78, Environmental Protection Agency grant, 76-79 & US Army & Mobility, Equip Res & Develop Command, 77-78; co-prin investr, Environmental Protection Agency grant, 77-79, NSF grant, 77-80 & Southwest Res Inst & Environmental Protection Agency grant, 78. *Mem:* Am Pub Health Asn; Am Soc Civil Engrs; Am Water Works Asn; Int Asn Water Pollution Res; Water Pollution Control Fedn. *Res:* Environmental virology associated with water and waste-water treatment processes including land application of wastewater and sludges; wastewater reuse including membrane processes and health effects; water-wastewater disinfection; kinetics and efficiency. *Mailing Add:* Col Eng Cocknell Hall 10 316 Univ Tex, Austin Austin TX 78712

SORBY, DONALD LLOYD, b Fremont, Nebr, Aug 12, 33; m 59; c 2. PHARMACY, PHARMACEUTICAL CHEMISTRY. *Educ:* Univ Nebr, BS, 55; Univ Wash, Seattle, MS, 58, PhD(pharm), 60. *Prof Exp:* From asst prof to prof pharm & pharmaceut chem, Sch Pharm, Univ Calif, San Francisco, 60-72; prof pharm & chmn dept pharm practice, Col Pharm, Univ Wash, 72-74; DEAN SCH OF PHARM, UNIV MO, KANSAS CITY, 74- *Concurrent Pos:* USPHS grant, 63-65. *Mem:* Am Pharmaceut Asn; Acad Pharmaceut Sci. *Res:* Interactions between drugs and adsorbent materials and how they affect action of various drug molecules; relationships between physical and chemical properties of drugs and their in vivo action. *Mailing Add:* Sch of Pharm Univ Mo Kansas City MO 64110

SORDAHL, LOUIS A, b Chicago, Ill, Aug 24, 36; m 62; c 2. PHYSIOLOGY, BIOCHEMISTRY. *Educ:* Rutgers Univ, AB, 58, MS, 61, PhD(biochem), 64. *Prof Exp:* Res asst biol, Rutgers Univ, 58-62, asst instr physiol, 63, instr, 63-64; from instr to asst prof pharmacol, Baylor Col Med, 66-72; assoc prof, 72-77, PROF BIOCHEM, UNIV TEX MED BR GALVESTON, 77- *Concurrent Pos:* NIH staff fel geront, Baltimore City Hosps, Md, 64-66. *Honors & Awards:* Hektoen Gold Medal Award, AMA, 70. *Mem:* Int Soc Heart Res; fel Am Col Cardiol; Am Physiol Soc; Am Heart Asn; Biophys Soc. *Res:* Intermediary metabolism and metabolic diseases; cardiac bioenergetics; oxidative phosphorylation; enzymes and mechanisms of calcium transport in mitochondria; experimental surgery. *Mailing Add:* Div Biochem Univ Tex Med Br Galveston TX 77550

SOREF, RICHARD ALLAN, b Milwaukee, Wis, June 26, 36; m 69. ELECTROOPTICS. *Educ:* Univ Wis, BS, 58, MS, 59; Stanford Univ, PhD(elec eng), 64. *Prof Exp:* Staff mem, Solid State Physics Div, Lincoln Lab, Mass Inst Technol, 64-65; RES STAFF MEM, APPL PHYSICS DEPT, SPERRY RES CTR, 65- *Mem:* Am Phys Soc; Optical Soc Am; sr mem Inst Elec & Electronics Eng. *Res:* Optical communication; integrated optics; fiber optics; electrooptic effects in liquid crystals; liquid crystal displays; infrared detectors; nonlinear optical effects in solids; modulation and deflection of light beams; optical switching; sensors. *Mailing Add:* Sperry Res Ctr 100 North Rd Sudbury MA 01776

SORELL, HENRY P, b Coeymans, NY, Nov 15, 23; m 70. ORGANIC CHEMISTRY. *Educ:* Rensselaer Polytech Inst, BS, 48, MS, 50, PhD(chem), 54. *Prof Exp:* Teaching asst, Org Labs, Rensselaer Polytech Inst, 48-51; sr chemist coated abrasives, Behr-Manning Div, Norton Co, 51-55; fel dent mat res, Mellon Inst, 55-56, sr fel, 56-57; vpres dent res & mfg, Luxene, Inc, 57-58; sect leader adhesives develop, Hughson Chem Co, 58-61; group leader pressure sensitive tapes, Mystik Tape Div, Borden Chem Co, Ill, 63-65, sect leader, 65-70; tech dir, Pipeline Tapes, Plicoflex, Inc, 70-72; dir res, Pressure Sensitive Tapes, 70-74, VPRES RES DEVELOP, ANCHOR CONTINENTAL INC, 74-, RES DIR, 77- *Concurrent Pos:* Admin fel dent plastics, Mellon Inst, 57-58. *Mem:* Am Chem Soc. *Res:* Organic adhesives; adhesion and effect of environmental factors on organic adhesives and on adhesion. *Mailing Add:* 1119 Woodlawn Ave Columbia SC 29209

SOREM, MICHAEL SCOTT, b Berkeley, Calif, Apr 27, 45; m 70; c 2. LASER PHYSICS, PHOTOCHEMISTRY. *Educ:* Stanford Univ, BS, 67, MS, 68, PhD(physics), 72. *Prof Exp:* Physicist elastic-plastic flow codes, Lawrence Livermore Lab, 67; res asst high resolution spectros, Stanford Univ, 67-72; physicist, Nat Bur Standards, 72-74; STAFF PHYSICIST LASER RES, LOS ALAMOS SCI LAB, 74- *Concurrent Pos:* Nat Res Coun fel, Nat Bur Standards & Joint Inst Lab Astrophys, 72-74. *Res:* Tunable laser source development; sub-doppler high resolution atomic and molecular spectroscopy; optically pumped ir lasers; excited-state spectroscopy. *Mailing Add:* Los Alamos Sci Lab Los Alamos NM 87545

SOREM, RONALD KEITH, b Northfield, Minn, June 18, 24; m 53; c 4. GEOLOGY, DEEP-SEA MINERAL RESOURCES. *Educ:* Univ Minn, BA, 46, MS, 48; Univ Wis, PhD, 58. *Prof Exp:* Asst, State Geol Surv, Minn, 44-46; asst geol, Univ Minn, 47; field asst, US Geol Surv, Alaska, 47, geologist, 48-55; asst, Univ Wis, 56-57, fel econ geol, 58-59; from asst prof to assoc prof, 59-68, assoc dean sci, 80-81, PROF GEOL, WASH STATE UNIV, 68- *Concurrent Pos:* Strategic minerals adv, US For Opers Admin, 53-55; sr vis res fel, Univ Manchester, 70; res fel, Japan Soc Prom Sci, 81. *Mem:* Sigma Xi; fel Geol Soc Am; fel Mineral Soc Am; Soc Econ Geol; Nat Asn Geol Teachers. *Res:* Mineralogy and origin of manganese deposits, application of micro x-ray analysis to ore and petrographic microscope studies; properties, texture and composition of ore minerals; origin and evaluation of marine manganese nodule deposits; conservation of natural resources. *Mailing Add:* Dept of Geol Wash State Univ Pullman WA 99164

SOREN, ARNOLD, b Vienna, Austria, Oct 30, 10; US citizen; m 61. ORTHOPEDIC SURGERY. *Educ:* Univ Vienna, MD, 34, PhD(comp morphol), 51. *Prof Exp:* Resident orthop surg, Allgemeines Krankenhaus, Vienna, 34-47; asst, Univ Vienna, 47-51; asst, Univ Munich, 53-54; docent, Med Fac, Univ Vienna, 55-56; asst prof, 63-67, assoc prof, 67-81, PROF ORTHOP SURG, SCH MED, NY UNIV, 81- *Concurrent Pos:* USPHS grant, Sch Med, NY Univ, 62-; assoc attend physician, Univ Hosp, NY Univ, 62-;

attend physician, Vet Admin Hosp, New York, 62-; univ docent, Med Fac, Univ Vienna, 63-; asst admitting physician, Bellevue Hosp, New York, 64- *Honors & Awards:* City of Vienna Prize, 52; Fed Pres of Austria Prize, 55. *Res:* General orthopaedic surgery; rheumatic diseases and histopathology of arthritis. *Mailing Add:* Dept of Orthop Surg NY Univ Sch of Med New York NY 10016

SORENSEN, ANDREW AARON, b Pittsburgh, Pa, July 20, 38; m 68; c 2. MEDICAL EDUCATION. *Educ:* Univ Ill, BA, 59; Yale Univ, BD, 62, MPhil, 70, PhD(med sociol), 71; Univ Mich, MPub Health, 66. *Prof Exp:* Instr psychiat, Med Sch, Boston Univ, 70-71; asst prof community serv educ, Cornell Univ, 71-73; asst prof prev med, 73-76, ASSOC PROF & ASSOC CHMN PREV MED, SCH MED, UNIV ROCHESTER, 76- *Concurrent Pos:* Vis assoc health serv res, Harvard Med Sch, 75-76; NSF fac sci fel, 75-76; vis fel, Univ Cambridge, 79-80; vis prof community med, Welsh Nat Sch Med, 81. *Mem:* Asn Teachers Prev Med; AAAS; Am Sociol Asn; Int Epidemiol Asn. *Res:* Health services; sociology of addictions. *Mailing Add:* Dept Prev Med Univ Rochester Sch Med Rochester NY 14642

SORENSEN, ANTON MARINUS, JR, animal science, reproductive physiology, see previous edition

SORENSEN, ARTHUR (SHERMAN), JR, b Milwaukee, Wis, Nov 1, 26. ENGINEERING MECHANICS. *Educ:* Univ Wis-Madison, BS, 52, MS, 55; Univ Ill, Urbana, PhD(eng mech), 65. *Prof Exp:* Engr, Allis Chalmers Mfg Co, 52-57; proj engr, AC Electronics Div, Gen Motors Corp, 57-59, sr proj engr, 63-66; asst prof mech, 66-68, ASSOC PROF MECH, UNIV WIS-MILWAUKEE, 68- *Mem:* AAAS; Am Soc Mech Engrs; Am Inst Aeronaut & Astronaut; Am Soc Eng Educ; Am Asn Univ Prof. *Res:* Shock and vibration analysis; applied dynamics; fatigue damage evaluation; material behavior. *Mailing Add:* 5600 Lakeview Dr Greendale WI 53129

SORENSEN, DALE KENWOOD, b Centuria, Wis, July 21, 24; m 48; c 3. VETERINARY SCIENCE. *Educ:* Kans State Col, DVM, 46; Univ Wis, MS, 50, PhD(virol path), 53. *Prof Exp:* Consult vet, UNRRA, 46-47; instr vet sci & head, Sect Clin Med, Univ Wis, 47-53; asst prof med, 53-57, head dept, 65-72, acting dean, 72-73, chmn, Dept Vet Clin Sci, 73-76, chmn, Dept Large Animal Clin Sci, 76-79, PROF MED, COL VET MED, UNIV MINN, ST PAUL, 58-, ACTING DEAN, 72- *Concurrent Pos:* Med scientist, Brookhaven Nat Lab, 57-58; vet consult, AID, Dept of State, Philippine Island Mission, 66 & Indonesia, 74. *Mem:* Am Vet Med Asn. *Res:* Pneumonia of calves; radiation syndrome in dogs; diseases of swine and viral respiratory diseases of cattle; leukemia of cattle; animal pathology. *Mailing Add:* 301 E Vet Sci Bldg Univ Minn St Paul MN 55108

SORENSEN, DAVID PERRY, b Spring City, Utah, Nov 1, 30; m 52. ORGANIC CHEMISTRY. *Educ:* Univ Utah, BS, 52, PhD, 55. *Prof Exp:* Res chemist, M W Kellogg Co, Pullman, Inc, 55-57; sr res chemist, 57-60, res supvr, 60-63, res specialist, 63-65, res mgr, 65-67, tech dir imaging res lab, 67-71, tech dir, 71-81, DIR CORP TECHNOL ASSESSMENT, PRINTING PROD DIV, 3M CO, 81- *Mem:* Am Chem Soc; Sigma Xi; Tech Asn Graphic Arts. *Res:* Imaging sciences; printing technology. *Mailing Add:* 4140 Lakewood Ave White Bear Lake MN 55110

SORENSEN, DAVID T, b Moorhead, Minn, June 20, 27; m 59; c 2. INORGANIC CHEMISTRY. *Educ:* NDak State Univ, BS, 49; Univ Kans, PhD(inorg chem), 58. *Prof Exp:* Instr chem, Ft Hays Kans State Col, 52-55; instr, Principia Col, 57-59, asst prof, 59-61; asst prof, Robert Col, Istanbul, 61-64; assoc prof, 64-68, PROF CHEM, ST CLOUD STATE UNIV, 68- *Mem:* Am Chem Soc. *Res:* Anodic oxidation in aqueous solutions. *Mailing Add:* Dept Chem St Cloud State Univ St Cloud MN 56301

SORENSEN, EDGAR LAVELL, b Mendon, Utah, Nov 26, 18; m 48; c 3. PLANT BREEDING. *Educ:* Utah State Univ, BS, 41, MS, 52; Univ Wis, PhD(agron), 55. *Prof Exp:* Soils technologist, Bur Reclamation, Utah, 46-47; state seed supvr, Utah State Dept Agr, 47-49; prog specialist, Agr Conserv, Prod & Mkt Admin, 49-51; RES AGRONOMIST, AGR RES SERV, USDA, 55- *Mem:* Am Soc Agron; Crop Sci Soc Am. *Res:* Breeding improved varieties of alfalfa; insect and disease resistance. *Mailing Add:* Dept of Agron Waters Hall Kans State Univ Manhattan KS 66506

SORENSEN, ELSIE MAE (BOECKER), b Austin, Tex, Mar 4, 48; m 71; c 1. PHYSIOLOGY, TOXICOLOGY. *Educ:* Tex Woman's Univ, BS, 70; Univ Tex, PhD(zool), 74. *Prof Exp:* Res asst ecol, Tex Woman's Univ, 67-70; teaching asst physiol, Univ Tex, Austin, 70-72; instr biol, Austin Community Col, 74-76; fel heavy metal distrib & decorp, Argonne Nat Lab, 76-78; asst prof physiol, Memphis State Univ, 78-81; RES ASSOC, UNIV TEX, AUSTIN, 81- *Mem:* Electron Micros Soc Am. *Res:* Heavy metal toxicity, accumulation and decorporation; cytotoxic reactions to heavy metals in vertebrates and cell cultures. *Mailing Add:* Dept Pharmacol/Toxicol Univ Tex Austin TX 78712

SORENSEN, FREDERICK ALLEN, b Pittsburgh, Pa, July 18, 26. MATHEMATICAL STATISTICS. *Educ:* Carnegie Inst Technol, BS, 47, MS, 49, PhD(math), 59. *Prof Exp:* Instr, Carnegie-Mellon Univ, 51-54, 59-71. *Concurrent Pos:* Asst math, Carnegie Inst Technol, 47-51; statistician, Westinghouse Elec Corp, 51-54; statistician, Res Lab, 54-64, head, Oper Res Sect, 61-64, res mathematician, 64-77, ASSOC RES CONSULT, MATH DIV, US STEEL CORP RES LABS, 77- *Mem:* AAAS; Am Soc Qual Control; Am Statist Asn; Inst Math Statist. *Res:* Theory of control charts; design and analysis of industrial and engineering experiments. *Mailing Add:* Res Lab Math Div Monroeville PA 15146

SORENSEN, HAROLD C(HARLES), b Bancroft, Nebr, Dec 21, 34; m 60; c 2. STRUCTURAL ENGINEERING, ENGINEERING MECHANICS. *Educ:* Univ Nebr, BS, 57, MS, 62, PhD(eng mech), 66. *Prof Exp:* Jr engr, Dept Rds, State of Nebr, 57-59; instr eng mech, Univ Nebr, 59-65; asst prof civil eng, 66-75, ASSOC PROF CIVIL ENG, WASH STATE UNIV, 75-

Concurrent Pos: Consult, Palouse Prod, 77, Weyerhaeuser Corp, 78-80 & Wash Pub Power Supply Syst, 80. *Mem:* Am Soc Eng Educ; Am Soc Civil Engrs; Nat Soc Prof Engrs. *Res:* Structural dynamics; earth sheltered homes; late buckling of parallel chord trusses. *Mailing Add:* Dept of Civil Eng Wash State Univ Pullman WA 99164

SORENSEN, KENNETH ALAN, b Providence, RI, Aug 11, 44; m 69; c 3. ENTOMOLOGY. *Educ:* Univ RI, BS, 66; Kans State Univ, MS, 68, PhD(entom), 70. *Prof Exp:* Nat Defense Educ Act fel entom, Kans State Univ, 66-69, res asst, 69-70; exten spec, 70-75, EXTEN ASSOC PROF ENTOM, NC STATE UNIV, 75- *Mem:* Entom Soc Am; Sigma Xi. *Res:* Study of insect pest population dynamics and crop damage under grower conditions; evaluate new and review effectiveness of existing insecticides on vegetables and develop insect pest management programs for growers' use. *Mailing Add:* 3310 Gardner Hall NC State Univ Raleigh NC 27650

SORENSEN, LAZERN OTTO, b Dannebrog, Nebr, Nov 1, 27; wid; c 1. MARINE PHYCOLOGY. *Educ:* Nebr State Univ, BS, 50; Univ Nebr, Lincoln, MS, 52, PhD(bot), 56. *Prof Exp:* Assoc prof, Nebr Wesleyan Univ, 53-56; assoc prof, 56-63, dean sci & math, 68-75, head dept biol, 65-68, PROF BIOL, PAN AM UNIV, 63-, DIR MARINE LAB, PAN AM UNIV, 75- *Mem:* Phycol Soc Am. *Res:* Physiology of macroscopic marine algae. *Mailing Add:* Dir Marine Lab Pan Am Univ Box 2415 South Padre Island TX 78597

SORENSEN, LEIF BOGE, b Odense, Denmark, Mar 25, 28; US citizen; m 68; c 1. MEDICINE, BIOCHEMISTRY. *Educ:* Copenhagen Univ, MD, 53, PhD(biochem), 60. *Prof Exp:* Instr anat, Copenhagen Univ, 50-51; resident, St Luke's Hosp, 54; intern, Copenhagen County Hosp, Hellerup, Denmark, 54-55; res asst geront, Med Sch, Wash Univ, 55-56; res asst med, Argonne Cancer Res Hosp, Univ Chicago, 56-57; resident, Copenhagen Munic Hosp, 57-58; resident, Copenhagen Univ Hosp, 58; from instr to assoc prof, 58-70, PROF MED, UNIV CHICAGO, 70-, ASSOC CHMN, DEPT MED, 76- *Concurrent Pos:* Fulbright scholar, Med Sch, Wash Univ, 55-56; lectr, Ill Acad Gen Pract, 62-63; fac mem, Am Col Physicians Postgrad Course, 62 & 69; sr fel, Fogarty Int Ctr, NIH, 80-81. *Mem:* AAAS; Am Rheumatism Asn; Am Soc Clin Invest; NY Acad Sci; Am Soc Geriatrics. *Res:* Gout; purine metabolism; aging of the immune system. *Mailing Add:* Dept of Med Univ of Chicago Chicago IL 60637

SORENSEN, LLOYD J, b Detroit, Mich, Feb 11, 27; m 52; c 2. MICROBIOLOGY. *Educ:* Univ Mich, BS, 49, MS, 51, PhD(bact), 56. *Prof Exp:* Bacteriologist, Eli Lilly & Co, 51-52 & Univ Mich, 52-54; res scientist, Upjohn Co, 54-58; asst res microbiologist, Sch Med, Univ Calif, Los Angeles, 58-61; microbiologist, Nopco Chem Co, 61-62 & Merck Inst Therapeut Res, 62-71; DIAG PROD COORD, HOFFMANN-LA ROCHE INC, 72- *Mem:* AAAS; Am Soc Microbiol. *Res:* Immunology and pathogenesis of pathogenic fungi and mycoplasma. *Mailing Add:* Diag Res Dept Hoffmann-La Roche Inc Nutley NJ 07110

SORENSEN, RALPH ALBRECHT, b Lynwood, Calif, Apr 19, 45; m 72; c 1. DEVELOPMENTAL BIOLOGY. *Educ:* Univ Calif, Riverside, BA, 67; Yale Univ, PhD(biol), 72. *Prof Exp:* Res fel, Dept Physiol & Anat, Sch Med, Harvard Univ, 72-74; asst prof biol sci, DePaul Univ, 74-77; ASST PROF BIOL, GETTYSBURG COL, 77- *Mem:* Soc Develop Biol. *Res:* Growth and meiotic maturation of the mammalian oocyte; preimplantation development of mammalian embryos. *Mailing Add:* Dept Biol Gettysburg Col Gettysburg PA 17325

SORENSEN, RAYMOND ANDREW, b Pittsburgh, Pa, Feb 27, 31; m 53; c 1. NUCLEAR PHYSICS. *Educ:* Carnegie Inst Technol, BS, 53, MS, 55, PhD(physics), 58. *Prof Exp:* NSF fel, Copenhagen Univ, 58-59; from instr physics to res assoc, Columbia Univ, 59-61; from asst prof to assoc prof, 61-68, PROF PHYSICS, CARNEGIE-MELLON UNIV, 68-, CHMN DEPT, 80- *Concurrent Pos:* NSF sr fel, Niels Bohr Inst, Copenhagen, Denmark, 65-66; Nordita prof, Res Inst Physics, Stockholm, 70-71 & 76-77; assoc ed, Nuclear Physics A, 72- *Mem:* Am Phys Soc. *Res:* Theoretical nuclear structure physics. *Mailing Add:* Dept of Physics Carnegie-Mellon Univ Pittsburgh PA 15213

SORENSEN, ROBERT CARL, b Omaha, Nebr, July 24, 33; m 58; c 2. SOIL CHEMISTRY. *Educ:* Univ Nebr, BS, 55, MS, 57; Iowa State Univ, PhD(soil chem), 64. *Prof Exp:* From asst prof to assoc prof, 64-75, PROF AGRON, UNIV NEBR, LINCOLN, 75- *Mem:* Am Soc Agron; Soil Sci Soc Am; fel Nat Assoc Col Teachers Agr. *Res:* Reactions and movement of phosphorus in soils. *Mailing Add:* Dept Agron Univ Nebr Lincoln NE 68583

SORENSEN, THEODORE STRANG, b Dixonville, Alta, June 6, 34; m 66. PHYSICAL ORGANIC CHEMISTRY. *Educ:* Univ Alta, BSc, 56; Univ Wis, PhD(org chem), 60. *Prof Exp:* Imp Chem Industs fel, Univ Leicester, 60-62; from asst prof to assoc prof, 62-74, PROF CHEM, UNIV CALGARY, 74- *Mem:* AAAS; Am Chem Soc; Chem Inst Can; The Chem Soc. *Res:* Organic reaction mechanisms; stable aliphatic carbonium ions and their reactions; unusual organometallic compounds. *Mailing Add:* Dept of Chem Univ of Calgary Calgary AB T2N 1N4 Can

SORENSON, FRED M, b Brigham City, Utah, Feb 19, 27; m 50; c 2. DENTISTRY. *Educ:* Univ Utah, BS, 51; Univ Ore, DMD, 58, MSD, 63. *Prof Exp:* Asst radiol, Univ Utah, 51-54; res consult dent, 59; res asst & instr biochem, 59-60; from asst prof to assoc prof dent, 60-65, PROF DENT, DENT SCH, UNIV ORE, 65-, DIR CLINS, 65-, CHMN, DEPT ORAL RADIOL, 76- *Concurrent Pos:* Res consult, Vet Hosp, Portland, 66- *Mem:* AAAS; assoc Am Acad Oral Roentgenol. *Res:* Cancer; dental pulp physiology and pathology; dental materials and instrumentation in dental research. *Mailing Add:* Dept of Dent Univ of Ore Dent Sch Portland OR 97201

SORENSON, HAROLD WAYNE, b Omaha, Nebr, Aug 28, 36; m 58; c 3. CONTROL SYSTEMS ENGINEERING. *Educ:* Iowa State Univ, BS, 57; Univ Calif, Los Angeles, MS, 63, PhD(control systs eng), 66. *Prof Exp:* Sr res engr, Gen Dynamics/Astronaut, 57-62; head space systs group, AC Electronics Div, Gen Motors Corp, Calif, 63-66; guest scientist, Ger Exp Aerospace Facil, Inst Control Syst Technol, WGer, 66-67; asst prof systs dynamics & control, 68-71, assoc prof eng sci, 71-77, PROF ENG SCI, UNIV CALIF, SAN DIEGO, 77- *Concurrent Pos:* Consult, Adv Group Aerospace Develop, NATO, Paris, 66-67, Aerojet-Gen Corp, Azusa, Calif, 68-70 & Aerospace Corp, 71-75; pres, Orincon Corp, 74-81; mem, US Air Force Sci Adv Bd. *Mem:* Fel Inst Elec & Electronics Engrs; Oper Res Soc Am; Control Systs Soc. *Res:* Control of stochastic and deterministic dynamical systems, including optimal deterministic control theory, numerical methods for optimal control, linear and nonlinear filtering for stochastic systems, optimal and suboptimal control of stochastic systems. *Mailing Add:* Dept Appl Mech & Eng Sci Univ Calif San Diego La Jolla CA 92037

SORENSON, JAMES ALFRED, b Madison, Wis, Aug 21, 38; m 61; c 4. MEDICAL PHYSICS, NUCLEAR MEDICINE. *Educ:* Univ Wis-Madison, BS, 63, MS, 64, PhD(radiol sci), 71. *Prof Exp:* Physicist, Sect Nuclear Med, Univ Wis-Madison, 66-71, asst prof med physics, Dept Radiol, 71-73; assoc prof, 73-80, PROF RADIOLOGY, UNIV UTAH, 80- *Mem:* AAAS; Soc Nuclear Med; Am Asn Physicists Med. *Res:* In vivo determination of body composition and elemental concentrations by radiation transmission measurements; whole-body counting of radioactivity; contrast improvement in radiography; positron tomography; image perception. *Mailing Add:* Dept Radiol Univ Utah Med Ctr Salt Lake City UT 84132

SORENSON, JOHN R J, b Sturgeon Bay, Wis, June 13, 34; m 59; c 7. PHARMACY. *Educ:* Univ Wis, BS, 60; Univ Kans, PhD(med chem), 65. *Prof Exp:* Sr res chemist, G D Searle & Co, 65-70; asst prof environ health, Col Med, Univ Cincinnati, 70-76, adj asst prof med chem, Col Pharm, 76-77; assoc prof med chem, PROF MED, COL PHARM & COL MED, UNIV ARK, LITTLE ROCK, 81- *Mem:* Int Inflammation Res Soc; NY Acad Sci; Asn Bioinorg Sci; Am Chem Soc; Soc Environ Geochem & Health. *Res:* Medicinal chemistry; pharmacology. *Mailing Add:* Col of Pharm Slot 522 4301 W Markham St Little Rock AR 72205

SORENSON, MARION W, b Salt Lake City, Utah, Dec 29, 26; m 48; c 3. ETHOLOGY, ZOOLOGY. *Educ:* Univ Utah, BS, 59, MS, 60; Univ Mo, PhD(zool), 64. *Prof Exp:* Res assoc zool, 64-65, asst prof, 65-70, ASSOC PROF BIOL SCI, UNIV MO-COLUMBIA, 70- *Mem:* AAAS; Animal Behav Soc; Am Soc Zool; Ecol Soc Am; Am Soc Mammal. *Res:* Social and reproductive behavior of vertebrates, especially small mammals. *Mailing Add:* 213 LeFevre Hall Univ of Mo Columbia MO 65201

SORENSON, ROBERT LOWELL, b Albert Lea, Minn, Aug 3, 40. ANATOMY. *Educ:* Univ Minn, BA, 62, PhD(anat), 67. *Prof Exp:* Instr, 67-69, asst prof, 69-73, ASSOC PROF ANAT, UNIV MINN, MINNEAPOLIS, 73- *Concurrent Pos:* USPHS fel, Minn Med Res Found, 68-71; res fel, Rigshospitalet, Copenhagen, Denmark, 68; USPHS fel, Univ Minn, 71-; investr, Minn Med Res Found, 67-70. *Mem:* AAAS; Am Anat Asn. *Res:* Diabetes; islet cytology; protein synthesis and secretion autoimmunity. *Mailing Add:* Dept Anat Univ Minn Minneapolis MN 55455

SORENSON, WAYNE RICHARD, b St Paul, Minn, Dec 19, 26; m 54; c 3. POLYMER CHEMISTRY, ORGANIC CHEMISTRY. *Educ:* Col St Thomas, BS, 49; Univ Md, PhD(org chem), 54. *Prof Exp:* Res chemist, E I du Pont de Nemours, 53-61; group leader Continental Oil Co, 61-64, sect leader, 64-67, mgr res & develop, 67-72, dir plastics res & develop, 72-77, coordr new ventures, 77-78; DIR RES & DEVELOP, TENNECO CHEM, INC, 78- *Mem:* Am Chem Soc; Soc Plastics Engrs. *Res:* New polymer-forming reactions; properties of polymers; polymer applications. *Mailing Add:* Tenneco Chem Inc Box 365 Turner Place Piscataway NJ 08852

SORENSON, WILLIAM GEORGE, mycology, see previous edition

SORGENFREY, ROBERT HENRY, b Sunbury, Iowa, Aug 14, 15; m 41. MATHEMATICS. *Educ:* Univ Calif, Los Angeles, AB, 37; Univ Tex, PhD(math), 41. *Prof Exp:* Instr math, Case Inst Technol, 41-42; instr math, 42-45, from asst prof to prof math, 45-80, EMER PROF MATH, UNIV CALIF, LOS ANGELES, 80- *Mem:* Am Math Soc; Math Asn Am. *Res:* General topology. *Mailing Add:* Dept of Math Univ of Calif Los Angeles CA 90024

SORGER, GEORGE JOSEPH, b Vienna, Austria, Sept 20, 37; Can citizen; m 61; c 2. BIOCHEMICAL GENETICS, MICROBIOLOGY. *Educ:* McGill Univ, BS, 59; Yale Univ, PhD(microbiol), 64. *Prof Exp:* Res assoc bot, Ore State Univ, 64-66; from asst prof to assoc prof, 66-78, PROF BIOL, MCMASTER UNIV, 78-, NAT RES COUN CAN FEL, 66- *Concurrent Pos:* Exchange scientist, Chem Bact, Nat Ctr Sci Res, Marseille, 73-74. *Mem:* Can Fedn Biol Soc; Can Soc Biochem. *Res:* Regulation and mechanism of action of nitrate reductase; nitrite reductase, studied using a biochemical-genetical approach. *Mailing Add:* 525 Life Sci Bldg Dept of Biol McMaster Univ Hamilton ON L8S 4L8 Can

SORIA, RODOLFO M(AXIMILIANO), b Berlin, Ger, May 16, 17; nat US; m 47; c 3. ELECTRICAL ENGINEERING. *Educ:* Mass Inst Technol, SB, 39, SM, 40; Ill Inst Technol, PhD(elec eng), 47. *Prof Exp:* Asst elec & radio eng, Ill Inst Technol, 40-42; instr electronics & microwave, US Army Sig Corps Training Prog, 42, lectr, 43, instr elec eng, 43-47, asst prof, 47; proj engr, Amphenol Corp, 46-49, dir res, 49-54, dir eng, 54-56, vpres res & eng, 56-68, dir corp res & eng, Bunker-Ramo Corp, 68, group vpres, Res & Eng, Amphenol Components Group, 69-71; MGT CONSULT, CONSULT INT LTD, 72- *Concurrent Pos:* Pres, Nat Electronics Conf, 54; consult, Adv Group Electronic Parts, Off Dir Defense Res & Eng, 55-61; chmn, Electronic Components Conf, 57; mem comt, Radio Frequency Cables & Connectors & US deleg, Int Electrotech Comn. *Mem:* Fel Inst Elec & Electronics Engrs. *Res:* Radio communications; wave propagation; microwaves; antennae; electronic components and systems. *Mailing Add:* 5028 Fair Elms Ave Western Springs IL 60558

SORIERO, ALICE ANN, b Brooklyn, NY, Oct 12, 47. REPRODUCTIVE PHYSIOLOGY, AGING. *Educ:* Hunter Col, BA, 68; State Univ NY Downstate Med Ctr, PhD(anat), 72. *Prof Exp:* Instr obstet, State Univ NY Downstate Med Ctr, 72-75; instr, Dent Sch, Univ Md, 75-76; ASST PROF ANAT, UNIV TEX MED BR, GALVESTON, 76- *Mem:* Sigma Xi; Am Asn Anatomists. *Res:* Reproductive physiology and aging of the female; biochemical effects of estrogen on uterine metabolism; histological changes in aging uterus. *Mailing Add:* Dept of Anat Univ of Tex Med Br Galveston TX 77550

SORKIN, HOWARD, b New York, NY, Aug 29, 33; m 57; c 2. ORGANIC CHEMISTRY. *Educ:* City Col New York, BS, 55; Cornell Univ, MS, 57, PhD(org chem), 59. *Prof Exp:* Sr res chemist, Cent Res Labs, Airco, 59-68; mem tech staff, Solid State Div, RCA Corp, Somerville, 68-76; sr chemist, Timex Components, Inc, Somerset, NJ, 76-80; PROG MGR, PHILIPS LABS, 80- *Mem:* Am Chem Soc. *Res:* Synthesis and properties of liquid crystals and their application to electro-optic display devices; new polymers and polymerization processes; electrphoretic display devices. *Mailing Add:* 179 River Bend Rd Berkeley Heights NJ 07922

SORKIN, MARSHALL, b Chicago, Ill, July 12, 28; m 50; c 4. COSMETIC CHEMISTRY. *Educ:* Roosevelt Univ, BS, 50; Northwestern Univ, MS, 59. *Prof Exp:* Chemist, Rock Island RR, 50-51; asst plant mgr, S Buchsbaum & Co, 51-52; res & develop group leader, Helene Curtis Ind Inc, 52-61, res dir, Toiletries Div, Alberto-Culver Co, 61-68; dir toiletries res, 68-80, VPRES TOILETRIES DIV, CARTER PROD DIV, CARTER-WALLACE, INC, 80- *Honors & Awards:* Merit Award, Soc Cosmetic Chem, 71. *Mem:* Am Chem Soc; Soc Cosmetic Chem. *Res:* Cosmetic and proprietary drug formulations; skin and hair physiology. *Mailing Add:* Carter Res Ctr Half Acre Rd Cranbury NJ 08512

SOROF, SAM, b New York, NY, Jan 24, 22; m 67; c 2. BIOCHEMISTRY. *Educ:* City Col New York, BS, 44; Univ Wis, PhD(physiol chem), 49. *Prof Exp:* Asst physiol chem, Univ Wis, 47-49, res assoc, 49-50; res biochemist, Vet Admin Hosp, New York, 51-52; res assoc, Inst Cancer Res & Lankenau Hosp Res Inst, 52-55, assoc mem, Inst, 55-61, SR MEM, INST CANCER RES, FOX CHASE CANCER CTR, PHILADELPHIA, 61- *Concurrent Pos:* Res fel phys biochem, Nat Cancer Inst, 50-51; vis scientist, Biochem Inst, Univ Uppsala, 56 & Salk Inst Biol Studies, 71-72; assoc ed, Cancer Res, 72-80 & Cancer Biochem & Biophys, 75-; adj prof, Dept Path & Lab Med, Med Sch, Univ Pa, 81- *Mem:* AAAS; Am Soc Cell Biol; Am Soc Biol Chem; Am Asn Cancer Res. *Res:* Molecular biology of cells; biochemistry of cancer, carcinogenesis, cell differentiation, liver proteins, mammary gland in culture. *Mailing Add:* Inst for Cancer Res 7701 Burholme Ave Philadelphia PA 19111

SOROFF, HARRY S, b Sydney, NS, Feb 2, 26. SURGERY. *Educ:* Temple Univ, MD, 48; Am Bd Surg, dipl, 60; Bd Thoracic Surg, dipl, 61. *Prof Exp:* Intern, Philadelphia Jewish Hosp, 48-49; asst resident surg, Montefiore Hosp, New York, 50-51; chief resident, Beth David Hosp, 51-52; chief metab div, Surg Res Univ, Brooke Army Med Ctr, Ft Sam Houston, Tex, 53-56; resident surg, Lakeside Hosp, Cleveland, Ohio, 56-57; fel thoracic surg, Peter Bent Brigham Hosp, 57-61, chief thoracic lab, 60-61; from asst prof to prof surg, Sch Med, Tufts Univ, 68-74, dir Tufts Surg Serv, Boston City Hosp, 70-74; CHMN DEPT SURG, MED SCH/HEALTH SCI CTR, STATE UNIV NY STONY BROOK, 74-, PROF SURG, 77- *Concurrent Pos:* Fel surg metab, Columbia-Presby Med Ctr, 52-53; res fel, Peter Bent Brigham Hosp, Boston, 57-60; fel thoracic surg, Mt Auburn & Malden Hosps, 57-60; asst surgeon, Boston City Hosp, 61-64; estab investr, Am Heart Asn, 61-66; assoc dir clin study unit, New Eng Ctr Hosp, Boston, 61-, asst surgeon, 61-64, surgeon, 64-; sr consult, Lemuel-Shattuck Hosp, Jamaica Plain, Mass, 67- *Mem:* Int Soc Burn Injuries; Am Soc Artificial Internal Organs; Int Cardiovasc Soc; Am Asn Thoracic Surg; Am Burn Asn. *Res:* Thoracic and cardiovascular surgery; surgical metabolism. *Mailing Add:* Dept of Surg State Univ NY Stony Brook NY 11790

SOROKA, WALTER W(ALERY), b Tsitsihar, Manchuria, Sept 18, 08; nat US; m 81; c 1. MECHANICAL ENGINEERING. *Educ:* Mass Inst Technol, ScD, 45. *Prof Exp:* From asst instr to instr mech eng, Mass Inst Technol, 30-37; sr unit engr, Servel, Inc, 37-41; proj anal engr & supvr dynamic anal, Chance-Vought Aircraft Co, 41-47; from assoc prof to prof eng design, 47-58, chmn div eng design, 56-58, prof mech eng, 58-62, chmn div mech & design, 58-59, prof acoust sci, 62-74, asst dean int coop progs, 65-69, chmn div appl mech, 70-71, chmn continuing educ in eng, 71-74, EMER PROF ACOUST SCI, UNIV CALIF, BERKELEY, 74- *Mem:* Fel Am Soc Mech Engrs; Soc Exp Stress Anal (pres, 62-63); fel Acoust Soc Am. *Res:* Engineering dynamics; acoustics; analog simulation and computation. *Mailing Add:* 35 Dean Rd Stoughton MA 02072

SOROKIN, CONSTANTINE ALEXIS, b Tsaritsyn, Russia, Aug 20, 03; nat US; m 32. PLANT PHYSIOLOGY. *Educ:* Novocherkassk Agr Inst, Russia, dipl, 29; Acad Agr Sci, MA, 36; Univ Tex, PhD(bot), 55. *Prof Exp:* Asst Novocherkassk Agr Inst, Russia, 26-29; dir, Seed Testing Sta Stavropol, 29-32; chmn genetics & plant breeding, Agr Inst Krasnodar, 32-39; lectr plant physiol, Pedagogical Inst, 40-42; head, Div Genetics & Plant Breeding, Oilplants Res Inst, 42; res prof plant physiol, Agr Res Inst Kherson, 43 & Agr Res Inst, Halbturn, Austria, 44-45; res scientist, Univ Tex, 51-55; res assoc, 55-67, RES PROF, ALGAL PHYSIOL, UNIV MD, COLLEGE PARK, 67- *Concurrent Pos:* Spec res fel, Nat Microbiol Inst, 56-57. *Mem:* Bot Soc Am; Phycol Soc Am; Am Soc Plant Physiol; NY Acad Sci; Japanese Soc Plant Physiol. *Res:* Algal metabolism, photosynthesis, life cycle, growth and temperature; breeding of algal strains. *Mailing Add:* Dept of Bot Univ of Md College Park MD 20742

SOROKIN, PETER, b Boston, Mass, July 10, 31. QUANTUM ELECTRONICS. *Educ:* Harvard Univ, AB, 52, BS, 53, PhD(appl physics), 58. *Prof Exp:* Staff physicist, Res Ctr, Int Bus Mach Corp, 57-68, IBM FEL, T J WATSON RES CTR, IBM CORP, 68- *Mem:* Am Acad Sci; NY Acad Sci; fel Am Optical Soc. Nat Acad Sci; fel Am Phys Soc. Res Lasers. *Mailing Add:* T J Watson Res Ctr IBM Corp PO Box 218 Yorktown Heights NY 10598

SOROKIN, SERGEI PITIRIMOVITCH, b Boston, Mass, Apr 13, 33. HISTOLOGY, EMBRYOLOGY. *Educ:* Harvard Univ, AB, 54, Harvard Med Sch, MD, 58. *Prof Exp:* Instr anat, Harvard Med Sch, 60-65, assoc & tutor, 65-69, asst prof, 69-70; asst prof, 70-77, ASSOC PROF CELL BIOL, SCH PUB HEALTH, HARVARD UNIV, 77- *Concurrent Pos:* Res fel path, Harvard Med Sch, 58-59, fel anat, 59-60; vis asst prof, Cornell Univ, 62-63; mem pulmonary res eval comt, Vet Admin, 69-70; lung cancer adv group, Nat Cancer Inst, 71-74. *Mem:* Histochem Soc; Soc Cell Biol; Am Asn Anat. *Res:* Cell and biology; in vitro culturing techniques; cytological differentiation as studied with aid of electron microscopy, histochemistry and autoradiography; physiology; pulmonary morphology. *Mailing Add:* Dept of Physiol Harvard Univ Sch of Pub Health Boston MA 02115

SORRELL, FURMAN Y(ATES), JR, b Wadesboro, NC, July 14, 38; m 69; c 2. ENVIRONMENTAL FLUID DYNAMICS. *Educ:* NC State Univ, BS, 60; Calif Inst Technol, MS, 61, PhD(aeronaut), 66. *Prof Exp:* Res engr, Pratt & Whitney Aircraft, 61-62; res fel, Joint Inst Lab Astrophys, Univ Colo, Boulder, 66-67, asst prof aerospace eng sci, 67-68; from asst prof to assoc prof eng mech, 68-74, dir grad prog, 70-74, NASA grant ocean dynamics, 72-76, assoc prof, Dept Eng Sci & Mech, 75-76, PROF MECH & AEROSPACE ENG, NC STATE UNIV, 76- *Concurrent Pos:* Nat Sci Found grant plasma dynamics, Univ Colo, Boulder, 66-68; prof marine sci faculty, NC State Univ, 72-, prof air conserv faculty, 77-; assoc, Perry Assoc Consult Engrs, 74-75; co-chmn ocean panel, Comt Applications Rev High Resolution Passive Satellites, NASA, 76-78; Nat Oceanic & Atmospheric Admin grant, Nearshore Ocean Currents & Mixing, 76-81, chmn, Panel Marine Waste Disposal & mem Steering Comt, Conf Marine Pollution, 79-80; grant Impact Off-Shore Pipelines, 80-82; mem prog review comt, Prog Phys & Chem Energy Storage, US Dept Energy, 81; tech dir, NC Alternative Energy Corp, 81. *Mem:* Am Phys Soc; Am Geophys Union; Am Soc Mech Engrs; Am Soc Heating, Refrig & Air Conditioning Engrs. *Res:* Fluid dynamics; physics of fluids; models of fluid and energy systems; laboratory and field measurements. *Mailing Add:* Dept Mech & Aerospace Eng NC State Univ Raleigh NC 27650

SORRELL, MICHAEL FLOYD, b St Louis, Mo, July 4, 35; m 57; c 4. GASTROENTEROLOGY. *Educ:* Univ Nebr, Omaha, BS, 57, MD, 59. *Prof Exp:* Intern med, Nebr Methodist Hosp, 59-60; pvt pract, 60-66; resident internal med, Col Med, Univ Nebr, Omaha, 66-68, fel gastroenterol, 68-69; NIH trainee liver dis & nutrit, Col Med & Dent, NJ, 69-71; from asst prof to assoc prof, 71-76, PROF MED, UNIV NEBR MED CTR, OMAHA, 76-, CHNM DEPT INTERNAL MED, 81- *Concurrent Pos:* NIH acad career develop award, 71-76; dir, Liver Study Unit, 71- *Mem:* Am Fedn Clin Res; Am Gastroenterol Asn; Am Asn Study Liver Dis; Int Asn Study Liver Dis (secy-tres, 81-); fel Am Col Physicians. *Res:* Toxic effects of alcohol and its metabolites on protein fabrication and membrane repair; drug metabolism in liver disease. *Mailing Add:* Dept of Internal Med 42nd St & Dewey Ave Omaha NE 68105

SORRELLS, GORDON, GUTHREY, b Dallas, Tex, Mar 5, 34. SEISMOLOGY, GEOMECHANICS. *Educ:* Southern Methodist Univ, BS, 55, MS, 61, PhD(geophysics), 71. *Prof Exp:* Res geophysicist seismol, Teledyne Geotech, 67-70; sr res assoc seismic measurement, Southern Methodist Univ, 70-71; prog mgr & prin investr geothermal, Teledyne Geotech, 71-74; dir, Senturion Sci, 74-75; consult hydraul fracturing, 75-76, TECH DIR GEOTHERMAL & HYDROCARBON, TELEDYNE GEOTECH, 76- *Concurrent Pos:* Consult, Dowell Div, Dow Chem Co, 75-76 & Dept of Energy, 78. *Mem:* Am Geophys Union; Seismol Soc Am. *Res:* Development of seismic techniques to assess and control environmental risk of induced seismicity associated with geothermal and hydrocarbon production. *Mailing Add:* Teledyne Geotech 3401 Shiloh Rd Garland TX 75041

SORRELLS, MARK EARL, b Hillsboro, Ill, Mar 23, 50. PLANT BREEDING, GENETICS. *Educ:* Southern Ill Univ, BS, 73, MS, 75; Univ Wis, PhD (plant breeding), 77. *Prof Exp:* Fel, Dept Agron, Univ Wis, 77-78; ASST PROF PLANT BREEDING, CORNELL UNIV, 78- *Mem:* Am Soc Agron; Crop Sci Soc Am; Genetic Soc Can; Am Genetic Asn. *Res:* Plant genetics; plant physiology. *Mailing Add:* Dept Plant Breeding & Biomet Cornell Univ Ithaca NY 14853

SORRELS, JOHN DAVID, b Poteau, Okla, July 5, 27; m 51; c 2. PHYSICS, COMPUTER SCIENCE. *Educ:* Mass Inst Technol, BS, 50; Rice Univ, MA, 51; Calif Inst Technol, PhD(physics), 56; Univ Juarez, MSc, 77. *Concurrent Pos:* Engr, Ramo-Wooldridge Corp, 55-62; GROUP DIR SPACECRAFT SYSTS ENG, AEROSPACE CORP, LOS ANGELES, 62- *Mem:* AAAS; Am Phys Soc. *Res:* Cosmic rays; satellite orbit determination; control systems; data processing systems development; medical science. *Mailing Add:* 2738 Vista Mesa Dr Palos Verdes Peninsula CA 90274

SORRENTINO, SANDY, JR, b Buffalo, NY, Dec 23, 43; m 65; c 3. NEUROENDOCRINOLOGY. *Educ:* Canisius Col, AB, 65; Univ Tenn, PhD(anat), 69; Univ Rochester, MD, 75. *Prof Exp:* asst prof anat, 71-76, ASST CLIN PROF, SCH MED, UNIV ROCHESTER, 76- *Mem:* Am Asn Anat. *Mailing Add:* Dept of Anat Univ of Rochester Rochester NY 14642

SORROWS, HOWARD EARLE, b Hewitt, Tex, Aug 10, 18; m 43; c 5. PHYSICS. *Educ:* Baylor Univ, BA, 40; George Washington Univ, MA, 47; Cath Univ Am, PhD(physics, math, civil eng), 58. *Prof Exp:* Pub sch teacher, Tex, 40-41; jr physicist, Nat Bur Standards, 41-43, radio physicist, 43-45, physicist, 45-50; electronics engr & proj officer, Bur Ord, US Dept Navy, 50-53, solid state & supvry physicist, Off Naval Res, 53-59; from dir tech int, long range planning & new prod dir to mgr space & environ sci servs, Tex Instruments, Inc, 59-65; mgr off opers & planning, Inst Mat Res, 65-67, dep dir, Inst Mat Res, 67-69, dir, Inst Appl Technol, 69-70, assoc dir progs, 70-78, DIR OFF RES & TECHNOL APPLN, NAT BUR STANDARDS, 78- *Concurrent Pos:* Adv coun elec engrs & sci dept, Univ Pa, 77-; invited expert mgt res, Nigerian Workshop, 81. *Mem:* AAAS; Inst Elec & Electronics Engrs; Am Phys Soc. *Res:* Solid state and surface physics; photoconductivity; precise measurement of electromagnetic power; voltage, current, impedance, antenna gain and field intensity at frequencies up to and including microwaves; electronic countermeasures; research and development management; forecasting. *Mailing Add:* Admin Bldg Rm 403 Nat Bur of Standards Washington DC 20234

SORTER, PETER F, b Vienna, Austria, Feb 8, 33; US citizen; m 65. ORGANIC CHEMISTRY, INFORMATION SCIENCE. *Educ:* Lafayette Col, BA, 54; DePauw Univ, MA, 56; Univ Iowa, PhD(chem), 62. *Prof Exp:* Info scientist, 62-65, mgr sci lit dept, 66-79, DIR RES SERV, HOFFMANN-LA ROCHE, INC, 80- *Concurrent Pos:* Mem bd dirs, Documentation Abstr, Inc, 70- *Mem:* Am Chem Soc; Chem Notation Asn (vpres, 72, pres, 73); Am Soc Info Sci; Drug Info Asn. *Res:* Storage retrieval of chemical and biological information, especially chemical structures. *Mailing Add:* Hoffmann-La Roche Inc 340 Kingsland St Nutley NJ 07110

SOSA, OMELIO, JR, b Camaguey, Cuba, Feb 2, 39; US citizen; m 61; c 2. ENTOMOLOGY, HOST PLANT RESISTANCE. *Educ:* Okla State Univ, BS, 64; Purdue Univ, MS, 71, PhD(entom), 77. *Prof Exp:* Agr res tech emtom, 65-73, entomologist, 73-76, RES ENTOMOLOGIST, AGR RES SERV, USDA, 76- *Mem:* Entom Soc Am; Sigma Xi; Am Soc Sugarcane Technol. *Res:* Reduction of crop losses in sugarcane by controlling or suppressing insect population. *Mailing Add:* US Surgarcane Field Sta Star Rte Box 8 Canal Point FL 33438

SOSEBEE, RONALD EUGENE, b Abilene, Tex, July 2, 42; m 64; c 2. PLANT PHYSIOLOGY, ECOLOGY. *Educ:* Abilene Christian Col, BS, 64; NMex State Univ, MS, 66; Utah State Univ, PhD(plant physiol), 70. *Prof Exp:* Instr range sci, Utah State Univ, 69; asst prof, 69-74, assoc prof, 74-79, PROF RANGE MGT, TEX TECH UNIV, 79-, ASSOC CHMN, DEPT RANGE & WILDLIFE MGT, 80- *Mem:* Am Soc Plant Physiol; Ecol Soc Am; Soc Range Mgt; Weed Sci Soc Am; Sigma Xi. *Res:* Vitaminology in woody plants; plant-soil water relationships; soil temperature and plant growth. *Mailing Add:* Dept of Range & Wildlife Mgt Tex Tech Univ Lubbock TX 79409

SOSINSKY, BARRIE ALAN, b New York, NY, Aug 27, 52. INORGANIC CHEMISTRY, ORGANOMETALLIC CHEMISTRY. *Educ:* Univ Ill, Chicago Circle, BS, 71; Bristol Univ, PhD(chem), 75. *Prof Exp:* Fel, Cornell Univ, 74-76 & Univ Calif, Los Angeles, 76-78; ASST PROF CHEM, RICE UNIV, 78- *Mem:* Am Chem Soc. *Res:* Low valent transition metal catalysis; metal clusters; prebiotic chemistry; organometallic reaction mechanisms. *Mailing Add:* Dept of Chem Rice Univ Houston TX 77001

SOSLAU, GERALD, b New York, NY, Jan 22, 44; m 66; c 4. BIOCHEMISTRY. *Educ:* Queens Col NY, BA, 65; Univ Rochester, PhD(biochem), 70. *Prof Exp:* Fel biochem, Med Sch, Univ Pa, 70-71, res assoc, 71-75; asst prof, 75-81, ASSOC PROF BIOCHEM, HAHNEMANN MED COL, 81- *Mem:* Am Chem Soc; Sigma Xi; Am Soc Biol Chemists; Am Soc Cell Biol. *Res:* Mitochondrial and viral proteins and nucleic acids in normal and virus-transformed cells grown in tissue culture; platelets in control and pre-leukemic human subjects. *Mailing Add:* Hahnemann Med Col 230 N Broad St Philadelphia PA 19102

SOSNOVSKY, GEORGE, b Petersburg, Russia, Dec 12, 20; US citizen; m 44. ORGANIC CHEMISTRY. *Educ:* Univ Munich, dipl, 44; Univ Innsbruck, PhD(chem), 48. *Prof Exp:* Res assoc chem, Univ Innsbruck, 48-49; tech officer, Commonwealth Sci & Indust Res Orgn, Australia, 49-51; in-chg org process develop, Cent Res Lab, Imp Chem Industs, Ltd, 51-56; fel & res assoc, Univ Chicago, 56-59; sr scientist, Res Inst, Ill Inst Technol, 59-63, assoc prof chem, 63-66; lectr, 66-67, PROF CHEM, UNIV WIS-MILWAUKEE, 67- *Concurrent Pos:* Res consult, Ill Inst Technol Res Inst, 63-66; USPHS spec sr res fel, Univ Col, London & Univ Tübingen, 67-68; ed, Synthesis, 69- *Mem:* Am Chem Soc; Royal Soc Chem. *Res:* Free radical chemistry; organometallic and organometalloid peroxides; metal ion-catalyzed and photochemical reactions of peroxides; phosphorus intermediates of biological interest; synthesis and biological applications of new phosphorus compounds containing a spin label; novel synthetic methods. *Mailing Add:* Dept of Chem Univ of Wis-Milwaukee Milwaukee WI 53201

SOSNOWSKI, THOMAS PATRICK, b Scranton, Pa, Aug 11, 36. ENGINEERING. *Educ:* Pa State Univ, BS, 62; Case Western Reserve Univ, MS, 65, PhD(eng), 67. *Prof Exp:* Mem tech staff, Bell Tel Labs, 68-80; TECH MGR, GTE LABS, 80- *Mem:* Inst Elec & Electronics Engrs; Soc Info Display. *Res:* Visual communication research; microprocessors; communication systems research. *Mailing Add:* GTE Labs 40 Sylvan Rd Waltham MA 02254

SOSULSKI, FRANK WALTER, b Weyburn, Sask, Dec 2, 29. FOOD SCIENCE & TECHNOLOGY, NUTRITION. *Educ:* Univ Sask, BSA, 54; Wash State Univ, MS, 56, PhD(agron), 59. *Prof Exp:* Asst prof field husb, 58-66, assoc prof crop sci, 66-71, PROF CROP SCI, UNIV SASK, 71- *Mem:* Am Asn Cereal Chemists; Agr Inst Can; Inst Food Technol. *Res:* Cereal, oilseed, legume quality and utilization. *Mailing Add:* Dept of Crop Sci Univ of Saskatchewan Saskatoon SK S7N 0W0 Can

SOTERIADES, MICHAEL C(OSMAS), b Istanbul, Turkey, Mar 25, 23; US citizen; m 62. CIVIL ENGINEERING, SOIL MECHANICS. *Educ:* Nat Tech Univ Athens, Dipl Eng, 48, DrEng, 52; Mass Inst Technol, ScD(soil mech), 54. *Prof Exp:* Consult struct & found, A Woolf & Assoc, Mass, 52-53, assoc engr, 56-57; res asst soil dynamics, Mass Inst Technol, 53-54; consult found & struct, Greece, 54-55; head design & specifications, Greek Govt, 55-56; asst to pres eng, Doxiadis Assoc, 58-59, vpres & treas, Doxiadis Assoc, Inc, Washington, DC, 59-61; PROF STRUCT, CATH UNIV AM, 61- *Concurrent Pos:* Consult, Bldg Res Adv Bd, Nat Acad Sci, 62. *Res:* Aseismic analysis and design; systems analysis; computer methods instructural analysis. *Mailing Add:* 3380 Stephenson Pl NW Washington DC 20015

SOTO, AIDA R, b Havana, Cuba, Dec 3, 31; US citizen. ORGANIC CHEMISTRY, BIOCHEMISTRY. *Educ:* Univ Havana, BS, 53 & 55; Univ Miami, MS, 62, PhD(chem), 66. *Prof Exp:* Res chemist, Villanueva Univ, 55-58, asst prof, 58-61; fel, Dept Pharmacol, Univ Miami, 65-68, instr med, Sch Med, 68-69; supvr, Chem Res & Develop Dept, 69-72, group leader, Biol Res & Develop Dept, 72-74, GROUP LEADER IMMUNOCHEM RES & DEVELOP, DADE DIV, AM HOSP SUPPLY CORP, 74- *Mem:* AAAS; Am Chem Soc; NY Acad Sci; Am Asn Clin Chemists. *Res:* Base promoted reactions of sulfonate esters in dipolar aprotic solvents; purification and characterization of proteolytic enzymes; clinical enzymology; radioimmunoassays; the use of immunologic techniques in clinical chemistry. *Mailing Add:* 3150 NW 19th Terr Miami FL 33125

SOTO, GERARDO H, b Havana, Cuba, Nov 23, 22; US citizen; div; c 1. AGRONOMY, SOIL CLASSIFICATION. *Educ:* Univ Havana, Agr Eng, 48. *Prof Exp:* Chief, Soils Dept, Agr & Indust Develop Bank, Cuba, 56-60; chief, Soils Dept, Agr Exp Sta, Cuba, 60-62, chief, Soils Dept, Inst Hydraulic Resources, Cuba, 62-63; sr soil scientist, Org Am States, 64-70, dir, Div III Regional Develop, 70-75; AGRICULTURIST, INT BANK RECONSTRUCT & DEVELOP, 75- *Concurrent Pos:* Tech ed, United Eng Ctr, New York, 63-64. *Mem:* Am Soc Agron; Int Soil Sci Soc; Soil Conserv Soc Am. *Res:* All Aspects of rural development based on rational utilization of physical and human resources. *Mailing Add:* 7005 Barkwater Ctr Bethesda MD 20817

SOTOMAYOR, RENE EDUARDO, b Santiago, Chile, Jan 3, 37; m 66; c 1. GENETICS, MUTAGENESIS. *Educ:* Univ Chile, BHu, 56, PhL, 66. *Prof Exp:* Asst prof biol, Sch Vet Med, Univ Chile, 66-74, assoc prof, Sch Med & Sch Nursing, 67-71; consult, 74-75, RES ASSOC MUTAGENESIS, OAKRIDGE NAT LAB, 75- *Concurrent Pos:* Fel, Pan Am Health Orgn/WHO, 72-74. *Mem:* Environ Mutagen Soc; Genetics Soc Am; Int Genetics Fedn; Latin Am Soc Genetics. *Res:* Mechanisms of chemical mutagenesis in mammalian systems; DNA repair in the germ cells; relationships between repair and genetic damage; cytogenetics of induced chromosome abnormalities in the germ cells of mammals. *Mailing Add:* Biol Div Oak Ridge Nat Lab PO Box Y Oakridge TN 37830

SOTOS, JUAN FERNANDEZ, b Tarazona, Spain, May 18, 27; US citizen; m; c 6. PEDIATRICS. *Educ:* Univ Valencia, MD, 51. *Prof Exp:* Intern, Univ Valencia Hosp, 52-53; resident pediat path, St Christopher's Hosp, Philadelphia, Pa, 53-54, resident pediat, 54-55; resident pediat, Children's Hosp, Columbus, Ohio, 55-56, instr & chief resident, 56-57; instr, Mass Gen Hosp, 60-62; from asst prof to assoc prof, 62-67, PROF PEDIAT, COL MED, OHIO STATE UNIV, 67-, DIR DIV ENDOCRINOL & METAB, DEPT PEDIAT, 63- *Concurrent Pos:* Fel, Mass Gen Hosp, 57-60; dir, Clin Res Ctr, Children's Hosp, Columbus, 62-72. *Mem:* Am Fedn Clin Res; Am Acad Pediat; NY Acad Sci; Am Diabetes Asn; Am Soc Pediat Nephrology. *Res:* Metabolic and endocrine disorders of children. *Mailing Add:* Children's Hosp 700 Childrens Dr Columbus OH 43205

SOTTERY, THEODORE WALTER, b Lebanon, Pa, Feb 8, 27; m 49; c 4. PHYSICAL ORGANIC CHEMISTRY. *Educ:* Dartmouth Col, BNS, 46; Clark Univ, cert chem, 49; Univ Maine, MS, 56, PhD(chem), 66. *Prof Exp:* Res vol endocrine res, Harvard Med Sch, 46-47; sci storekeeper, Mass-Ft Devens, 47; lab asst chem, Columbia Univ, 49-50; qual control group supvr pigments, E I du Pont de Nemours & Co, 50-51; instr sci, Finch Jr Col, 51-52; asst chem, Univ Maine, Orono, 54-55, instr, 56-61; asst prof, 61-67, assoc prof, 67-73, PROF CHEM, UNIV MAINE, PORTLAND, 73- *Concurrent Pos:* Consult, Howell Labs, Bridgton, Maine, 66-; chem reviewer, several publ co; bk reviewer, J Chem Educ, 75- *Mem:* Am Chem Soc. *Res:* Failure of the Darzans reaction to produce alpha-phenyl-substituted glycidic esters; reaction of sodium metal with dimethyl formamide. *Mailing Add:* Dept of Chem Univ of Maine Portland ME 04103

SOUCIE, WILLIAM GEORGE, b Missoula, Mont, Mar 20, 42; m 66; c 4. FOOD CHEMISTRY, COLLOID CHEMISTRY. *Educ:* Carroll Col, BA, 64; Incarnate Word Col, MS, 68; NC State Univ, PhD(biochem), 73. *Prof Exp:* Res assoc biochem, Univ Colo, 73-76; group leader protein prod, Kraft Inc, 76-81; INSTR, DEPT CHEM, COL LAKE COUNTY, 81- *Mem:* Am Chem Soc; Inst Food Technol. *Res:* Investigations into the electrical, physical and chemical properties of proteins as a basis for the use of proteins in human foods; colloid chemistry of food constituents. *Mailing Add:* Kraft Res & Develop 801 Waukegan Rd Glenview IL 60025

SOUDACK, AVRUM CHAIM, b July 5, 34; Can citizen; m 78; c 3. ELECTRICAL ENGINEERING. *Educ:* Univ Man, BScEE, 57; Stanford Univ, MS, 59, PhD(elec eng), 61. *Prof Exp:* Asst prof elec eng, Univ BC, 61-65; vis asst prof, Univ Calif, Berkeley, 65-66; assoc prof, 66-71, PROF ELEC ENG, UNIV BC, 71- *Concurrent Pos:* Vis assoc prof, Israel Inst Technol, 69-70; vis prof, Weizmann Inst Sci, Israel, 74-75. *Honors & Awards:* Marv Emerson Award, Soc Comput Simulation, 72. *Mem:* Simulation Coun; Inst Elec & Electronics Engrs. *Res:* Approximate solution of nonlinear differential equations; analog and hybrid simulation of nonlinear systems; stability of harvested predator-prey systems; analytical solutions of ecological models. *Mailing Add:* Dept of Elec Eng Univ of BC Vancouver BC V6T 1W5 Can

SOUDEK, DUSHAN EDWARD, b Prague, Czech, May 4, 20; m 47; c 3. CYTOGENETICS, MEDICAL GENETICS. *Educ:* Univ Brno, Czech, MD, 49, CScbiol, 56. *Prof Exp:* Asst prof biol, Univ Brno, Czech, 53-62, privatdocent, 64, head dept genetics, 63-68; vis scientist dept anat, Univ Western Ont, 68-69; ASSOC PROF, DEPT PSYCHIAT & PEDIAT, QUEEN'S UNIV, 69- *Concurrent Pos:* Res assoc, Ont Ment Health Found, 69- *Honors & Awards:* S Moravian Province Prize, 62; Mendel Medal, Mendel's Mus, Brno, 65. *Mem:* Am Soc Human Genetics; Genetics Soc Can; fel Can Col Med Genetics. *Res:* Human cytogenetics; mental defects, normal variants, chromosomal evolution; structure of chromosomes and cell nucleus. *Mailing Add:* 371 Elmwood St Kingston ON K7M 2Z2 Can

SOUDER, WALLACE WILLIAM, b Columbus, Kans, June 12, 37; m 65; c 3. NUCLEAR PHYSICS, GEOPHYSICS. *Educ:* Kans State Col, BS, 60; Iowa State Univ, PhD(physics), 69. *Prof Exp:* SR RES PHYSICIST, RES CTR, PHILLIPS PETROL CO, 69- *Mem:* Am Phys Soc; Soc Explor Geophys; Soc Prof Well Log Analysts. *Res:* New techniques for mineral exploration. *Mailing Add:* Phillips Petrol Co Res & Develop 385 Frank Phillips Bldg Bartlesville OK 74004

SOUHRADA, FRANK, b Sluknov, Czech, Sept 22, 37; m 62; c 2. CHEMICAL ENGINEERING. *Educ:* Inst Chem Technol, Prague, Dipl Ing, 61; Czech Acad Sci, PhD(chem eng), 64. *Prof Exp:* Res scientist, Inst Chem Process Fundamentals, Czech Acad Sci, 64-68; Nat Res Coun Can fel dynamic simulation, Univ NB, Fredericton, 68-70; res assoc fluidization, McMaster Univ, 70-71; process engr, Int Nickel Co, 71-74; SR RES ENGR PROCESS DEVELOP, GULF CAN RES & DEVELOP, 74- *Mem:* Can Soc Chem Engrs; Chem Inst Can. *Res:* Mass transfer; liquid-liquid extraction; ion exchange; fluidization; dynamic simulation; optimization; alternate energy sources; heavy oil and tar sands; heat and mass transfer; optimization. *Mailing Add:* 64 Trehorne Dr Weston ON M9P 1N9 Can

SOUKUP, RODNEY JOSEPH, b Faribault, Minn, Mar 9, 39; m 65; c 3. ELECTRICAL ENGINEERING, PHYSICS. *Educ:* Univ Minn, Minneapolis, BS, 61, MSEE, 64, PhD(elec eng), 69. *Prof Exp:* Prin develop engr, Univac, Sperry Rand Corp, 69-71; instr magnetics, Univ Minn, 72; asst prof phys electronics, Univ Iowa, 72-76; assoc prof, 76-80, PROF ELEC ENG, UNIV NEBR, 80-, CHMN DEPT, 78- *Mem:* Am Vacuum Soc; Inst Elec & Electronics Engrs; Am Soc Eng Educ. *Res:* Solar cells and scanning electron microscopy; physical electronics; thin film devices with a study of materials used and methods of fabrication. *Mailing Add:* Dept of Elec Eng W194 NH Univ of Nebr Lincoln NE 68588

SOULE, DAVID ELLIOT, b Norwalk, Conn, Feb 24, 25; m 49; c 3. PHYSICS. *Educ:* DePauw Univ, AB, 49; Northwestern Univ, MS, 51, PhD(physics), 54. *Prof Exp:* Res physicist, Union Carbide Lab, 54-66 & Douglas Aircraft Advan Res Lab, Calif, 66-71; PROF PHYSICS, WESTERN ILL UNIV, 71- *Concurrent Pos:* NSF fel, Royal Soc Mond Lab, Univ Cambridge, 61-62; sr vis Dept Sci & Indust Res fel, Dept Physics, Univ Sussex, 65. *Mem:* Am Phys Soc. *Res:* Solid state physics; transport properties; photoconductivity; susceptibility; low-temperature electronic properties such as deHaas-vanAlphen effect. *Mailing Add:* Dept of Physics Western Ill Univ Macomb IL 61455

SOULE, DOROTHY (FISHER), b Lakewood, Ohio, Oct 8, 23; m 43; c 2. MARINE BIOLOGY. *Educ:* Miami Univ, BA, 45; Occidental Col, MA, 63; Claremont Grad Sch, PhD, 69. *Prof Exp:* Res assoc biochem, Allan Hancock Found, Univ Southern Calif, 45-47; cur & instr comp anat, biol & microbiol, Occidental Col, 61-63; asst prof embryol, invert biol & zool, Calif State Col, Los Angeles, 63-65; lectr physiol, Calif Col Med, 65-66; res assoc marine biol, 67-71, marine biol & pollution, 71-76, sr res scientist, Allan Hancock Found, 76, dir, Harbors Res Lab, 76-81, SR RES SCIENTIST, INST MARINE & COASTAL STUDIES, UNIV SOUTHERN CALIF, 76-, DIR, HARBORS ENVIRON PROJS, 71- *Concurrent Pos:* Independent consult, 61-; coordr, Environ Qual Projs, Univ Southern Calif-Sea Grant, 72-78; mem, Eng Panel, Nat Acad Sci, 73-75; adj prof environ eng, Univ Southern Calif, 74-; mem marine fish adv comt, Dept Com, 76-79, sci adv bd, Environ Protection Agency, 78-81. *Mem:* AAAS; Int Bryozool Asn; Marine Technol Soc; Am Soc Zool; Fed Water Pollution Control Asn. *Res:* Ecology and pollution in urban harbors, beaches and estuaries; effluent pollution; environmental impact assessment and coordination; systematics and ecology of tropical, temperate Bryozoa; bryozoan development. *Mailing Add:* Allan Hancock Foundation Univ of Southern Calif Los Angeles CA 90007

SOULE, JAMES, b Bradford, Pa, Jan 3, 20; m 42. HORTICULTURE. *Educ:* Cornell Univ, BS, 41; Univ Miami, MS, 51; Univ Fla, PhD(hort), 54. *Prof Exp:* Chemist, Emulsion Res Lab, Eastman Kodak Co, 43-46; res asst, Univ Miami, 51; agent, Agr Mkt Serv, USDA, 54-56; assoc prof, 56-67, PROF FRUIT CROPS, UNIV FLA, 67- *Mem:* AAAS; Am Chem Soc; Am Soc Hort Sci; Int Soc Hort Sci. *Res:* Tropical horticulture; rootstock-scion relationships; taxonomy; postharvest handling and propagation of horticultural crops. *Mailing Add:* Inst of Food & Agr Sci Univ of Fla Gainesville FL 32611

SOULE, JOHN DUTCHER, b Moline, Ill, Oct 11, 20; m 43; c 2. ZOOLOGY. *Educ:* Miami Univ, AB, 42; Univ Southern Calif, MS, 48, PhD(zool), 52. *Prof Exp:* Asst zool, 47, from instr to assoc prof, 50-63, chmn dept histol, 53-77, PROF HISTOL & PATH, SCH DENT, UNIV SOUTHERN CALIF, 63-, HANCOCK FOUND RES SCHOLAR, 52-, ASST DEAN, SCH DENT, 78-, PROF BIOL, 70- *Concurrent Pos:* Res assoc, Am Mus Natural Hist, 61- *Mem:* Fel AAAS; Am Micros Soc; Am Soc Zool; Int Asn Dent Res; Am Inst Biol Sci. *Res:* Taxonomy, histogenesis, postlarval development, histology, anatomy, ecology and reef communities of Bryozoa; histology and histochemistry of tooth development in fish, amphibia and reptiles. *Mailing Add:* Sch of Dent Univ of Southern Calif Los Angeles CA 90007

SOULE, MICHAEL E, b San Diego, Calif, May 28, 36; m 65; c 2. POPULATION BIOLOGY, CONSERVATION BIOLOGY. *Educ:* Univ San Diego, BA, 59; Stanford Univ, MA, 62, PhD(biol), 64. *Prof Exp:* Fel biostatist, Med Ctr, Stanford Univ, 63-64; lectr zool, Univ Malawi, 65-67; asst prof biol, Univ Calif, San Diego, 67-73, assoc prof, 73-78, prof, 78; DIR, INST TRANSCULTURAL STUDIES, LOS ANGELES, 78-; ASSOC DIR, ROCKY MT BIOL LAB, 81- *Concurrent Pos:* Grant, Belvedere Sci Fund, 61-64, Sigma Xi, 65-66, NSF, 69-73 & Southern Calif Coastal Water Res Proj, 71-72; Guggenheim fel, 73-74; consult United Nations Food & Agr Orgn, 80 & US Nat Zoo, 81. *Mem:* Soc Study Evolution; Am Soc Naturalists; Soc Syst Zool. *Res:* Insular evolution of reptiles; insular ecology and biogeography; evolutionary significance of phenetic and genetic variation and fluctuating asymmetry in natural populations; morphological indicators of environmental pollution; genetic aspects of conservation; applications of population biology to conservation. *Mailing Add:* 901 S Normandie Ave Inst Transcultural Studies Los Angeles CA 90006

SOULE, OSCAR HOMMEL, b St Louis, Mo, Oct 6, 40; m 71; c 2. ECOLOGY, BIOLOGY. *Educ:* Colo Col, BA, 62; Univ Ariz, MS, 64, PhD(ecol), 69. *Prof Exp:* Acad dean, 72-73; MEM FAC ECOL, EVERGREEN STATE COL, 71- *Concurrent Pos:* Ford Found fel, Mo Bot Garden, 70-71; sr ecologist, HDR Ecosci, 77-; partner, Lidman & Soule, Consults, 78-; vis prof, Colo Col, 79. *Mem:* AAAS; Ecol Soc Am; Brit Ecol Soc. *Res:* Terrestrial aspects of applied environmental studies; special interests in desert biology, urban ecology and environmental education. *Mailing Add:* Dept of Ecol Evergreen State Col Olympia WA 98505

SOULE, ROGER GILBERT, b Northport, NY, Feb 21, 35; m 59; c 3. EXERCISE PHYSIOLOGY. *Educ:* State Univ NY Col Cortland, BS, 57; Univ Ill, MS, 58; Wash State Univ, PhD(exercise physiol), 67. *Prof Exp:* Instr phys educ & health, Dutchess Community Col, 60-64; instr phys educ, Wash State Univ, 64-67; from asst prof to assoc prof exercise physiol, Sargent Col, Boston Univ, 71-76; prof, Liberty Baptist Col, Va, 76-79; PROF, BIOLA UNIV, LA MIRADA, 79- *Mem:* AAAS; Am Physiol Soc; Am Col Sports Med. *Res:* Energy cost of exercise; physical fitness levels of various populations; metabolic substrate utilization during exercise; control of temperature under exercise and environmental stress. *Mailing Add:* Biola Univ 13800 Biola Ave La Mirada CA 02215

SOULE, SAMUEL DAVID, b St Louis, Mo, Feb 27, 04; m 35; c 1. OBSTETRICS & GYNECOLOGY. *Educ:* Washington Univ, MD, 28; Am Bd Obstet & Gynec, dipl, 39. *Prof Exp:* Intern, Jewish Hosp, St Louis, 28-29; intern, St Louis Maternity & Barnes Hosp, 29-30, asst resident, 30-31; asst obstet & gynec, Sch Med, 31-34, from instr to prof, Clin Obstet & Gynec, 34-72, EMER PROF, CLIN OBSTET & GYNEC, SCH MED, WASHINGTON UNIV, 72- *Concurrent Pos:* Resident, St Louis Maternity & Barnes Hosps, 31-32, asst obstetrician & gynecologist, 32-; assoc obstetrician & gynecologist, Washington Univ Clin; obstetrician & gynecologist & co-head dept, Jewish Hosp, 42-52, sr obstetrician & gynecologist, 53-, pres med staff, 55-57, co-dir dept, 72-76. *Mem:* AAAS; Am Fertil Soc; AMA; fel Am Col Surgeons; Am Col Obstetricians & Gynecologists. *Res:* Gynecological functional vaginal cytology; endocrinology of the female reproductive system. *Mailing Add:* 911 S Brentwood Blvd Clayton MO 63105

SOULEN, JOHN RICHARD, b Milwaukee, Wis, June 19, 27; m 55; c 3. PHYSICAL CHEMISTRY. *Educ:* Carroll Col, Wis, BA, 50; Univ Wis, PhD(phys chem), 55. *Prof Exp:* Asst chem, Univ Calif, 50-52 & Univ Wis, 52-54; res chemist, Pennwalt Chems Corp, 55-59, proj leader, Inorg Res Dept, 59-63, group leader, Contract Res Dept, 63-68, dir contract res, 68-73, ASSOC MGR RES & DEVELOP, PENNWALT CORP, 73- *Concurrent Pos:* Lectr, Univ Pa, 60-61. *Mem:* AAAS; Am Chem Soc. *Res:* Inorganic, high temperature and ultrahigh pressure chemistry; thermodynamics; spectroscopy; kinetics. *Mailing Add:* 514 Woodbine Ave Narberth PA 19072

SOULEN, RENATE LEROI, b Berlin, Ger, June 10, 33; US citizen; m 55; c 3. MEDICINE, RADIOLOGY. *Educ:* NY Univ, BA, 53; Med Col Pa, MD, 57; Am Bd Radiol, dipl, 63. *Prof Exp:* Intern, Albert Einstein Med Ctr, 57-58; from resident to instr, Hosp, Jefferson Med Col, 59-63; from instr to assoc prof, 63-72, PROF RADIOL, HEALTH SCI CTR, MED SCH, TEMPLE UNIV, 72- *Concurrent Pos:* Nat Cancer Inst fel, Hosp, Jefferson Med Col, 61-62; mem coun cardiovasc radio, Am Heart Asn. *Mem:* Fel Am Heart Asn; fel Am Col Radiol; Asn Univ Radiol; Radiol Soc NAm; Am Inst Ultrasonics in Med. *Res:* Cardiovascular system. *Mailing Add:* Dept of Radiol Health Sci Ctr Temple Univ Philadelphia PA 19140

SOULEN, ROBERT J, JR, b Phoenixville, Pa, July 16, 40; m 63; c 1. CRYOGENIC PHYSICS. *Educ:* Rutgers Univ, BA, 62, PhD(physics), 66. *Prof Exp:* PROJ LEADER CRYOGENIC PHYSICS, NAT BUR STANDARDS, 67- *Mem:* Am Phys Soc. *Res:* Very low temperature techniques, and low temperature thermometry. *Mailing Add:* Div 221-03 Phys Bldg 128 Nat Bur of Standards Washington DC 20234

SOULEN, ROBERT LEWIS, b Chicago, Ill, Jan 19, 32; m 54; c 3. ORGANIC CHEMISTRY. *Educ:* Baker Univ, AB, 54; Kans State Univ, PhD(org chem), 60. *Prof Exp:* From res chemist to sr res chemist, Austin Res Labs, Jefferson Chem Co Inc, Tex, 60-64; LILLIAN NELSON PRATT PROF CHEM & CHMN DEPT, SOUTHWESTERN UNIV, TEX, 64- *Concurrent Pos:* NSF grant, 66-67; Robert A Welch grant, 66-78. *Mem:* Sigma Xi; AAAS; Am Chem Soc. *Res:* Exploratory and applications research in rigid and flexible polyurethane foams; polyolefine polymerization; vinyl halogen displacement reactions; synthesis of organofluorine derivatives. *Mailing Add:* Dept of Chem Southwestern Univ Georgetown TX 78626

SOULEN, THOMAS KAY, b Waukesha, Wis, Apr 7, 35; m 58; c 3. BIOCHEMISTRY. *Educ:* Univ Wis, BA, 57, MS, 61, PhD(biochem), 63. *Prof Exp:* Asst prof bot, Univ Wis, 63-64; asst prof, Univ Minn, Minneapolis, 64-69, ASSOC PROF BOT, UNIV MINN, ST PAUL, 69- *Mem:* AAAS; Am Chem Soc; Am Soc Plant Physiologists. *Res:* Nitrogen metabolism of higher plants, especially with reference to development; growth and flowering of Lemnaceae. *Mailing Add:* Dept of Bot Univ of Minn St Paul MN 55108

SOULES, DAVID EDWARD, b Kans, Nov 14, 25; m 67; c 2. IMMUNOHEMATOLOGY. *Educ:* Phillips Univ, BA, 49; Baylor Univ, MS, 53, PhD(immunol), 59. *Prof Exp:* Assoc prof microbiol & asst dir blood bank, Wadley Res Inst & Blood Bank, 59-67; dir biol control, Cutter Labs, 67-69; tech dir biol, Dade Div, Am Hosp Supply Corp, 69-71; mgr plasmapheresis serv, 71-76, asst dir corp compliance, 76-80, MGR LABELING DEVELOP, CUTTER LABS, 80- *Res:* Blood banking; serum or plasma fractionation; immunohematology; immunochemistry; plasmapheresis; GMP regulations in pharmaceutical and medical industry. *Mailing Add:* Cutter Labs PO Box 1986 Berkeley CA 94701

SOULES, JACK ARBUTHNOTT, b Ashtabula, Ohio, Jan 26, 28; m 49; c 3. PHYSICS. *Educ:* Ohio State Univ, BS, 48, MSc, 50, PhD(physics), 54. *Prof Exp:* Res assoc & asst instr, Ohio State Univ, 54-55; from asst prof to prof physics, NMex State Univ, 55-68; DEAN COL ARTS & SCI, CLEVELAND STATE UNIV, 68- *Concurrent Pos:* Am Coun Educ fel acad admin, 65-66. *Mem:* Am Phys Soc. *Res:* Solid state physics; x-rays; biophysics. *Mailing Add:* Col of Arts & Sci Cleveland State Univ Cleveland OH 44115

SOULSBY, MICHAEL EDWARD, b Montgomery, WVa, Sept 4, 41; m 60; c 3. MEDICAL PHYSIOLOGY, BIOPHYSICS. *Educ:* WVa Univ, AB, 63, MS, 68, PhD(biophysics), 71. *Prof Exp:* USPHS fel, Appalachian Lab Occup Respiratory Dis, 71-72; from instr to asst prof physiol, Va Commonwealth Univ, 72-76; ASST PROF PHYSIOL & BIOPHYSICS, UNIV ARK MED SCI, 77- *Concurrent Pos:* Consult, Gen Med Corp, 76-; prin investr, Heart, Lung & Blood Inst, NIH, 76-78 & Ark Br, Am Heart Asn, 78- *Mem:* Am Heart Asn; Am Physiol Soc; Biophys Soc; Sigma Xi. *Res:* Myocardial and vascular smooth muscle physiological and biophysical properties during ischemia, cardiovascular shock and hypertension. *Mailing Add:* Dept of Physiol & Biophysics 4301 W Markham Little Rock AR 72201

SOUNG, WEN Y, b Tainan, Taiwan, Feb 14, 45; m 75; c 2. SOLID-LIQUID SEPARATION, FLUIDIZATION. *Educ:* Nat Cheng-Kung Univ Taiwan, BS, 67, MS, 69; WVa Univ, PhD(chem eng), 73. *Prof Exp:* Sr process engr, Catalytic Inc, Philadelphia, Pa, 73-75; chem engr, Hydrocarbon Res Inc, Lawrenceville, NJ, 75-79; STAFF ENGR, EXXON RES & ENG CO, BAYTOWN, TEX, 79- *Mem:* Am Inst Chem Eng; Asn Am Chinese Prof. *Res:* Process development and improvement for catalytical coal gasification process, involving catalyst recovery from spent char, solid-liquid separation, ash utilization and gasification kinetics. *Mailing Add:* Exxon Res & Eng Co PO Box 4255 Baytown TX 77520

SOUPART, PIERRE, reproductive physiology, biochemistry, deceased

SOURKES, THEODORE LIONEL, b Montreal, Que, Feb 21, 19; m 43; c 2. BIOCHEMISTRY. *Educ:* McGill Univ, BSc, 39, MSc, 46; Cornell Univ, PhD(biochem), 48. *Prof Exp:* Chemist, Gen Eng Co, Ont, 42-44; biochemist, Frank W Horner, Ltd, Que, 44-45; asst biochem, Cornell Univ, 46-48; asst prof pharmacol, Med Sch, Georgetown Univ, 48-50; sr res assoc, Merck Inst Therapeut Res, NJ, 50-53; sr res biochemist, 53-65, DIR LAB CHEM NEUROBIOL, ALLAN MEM INST PSYCHIAT, MCGILL UNIV, 65-, PROF PSYCHIAT, FAC MED, 65-, PROF BIOCHEM, 70- *Concurrent Pos:* From instr to assoc prof psychiat, Fac Med, McGill Univ, 54-65; assoc scientist, Royal Victoria Hosp, 70 & assoc dean med, 72-75. *Mem:* Am Soc Neurochem; Am Soc Biol Chem; Am Soc Pharmacol & Exp Therapeut; Can Biochem Soc; Royal Soc Can. *Res:* Catecholamines and other biogenic amines; amino acid decarboxylases; amine oxidases; biochemistry of extrapyramidal syndromes; central pathways of response to stress; copper metabolism; biochemistry of mental diseases; history of biochemistry. *Mailing Add:* Dept of Psychiat 1033 Pine Ave W Montreal PQ H3A 1A1 Can

SOURS, RICHARD EUGENE, b Baltimore, Md, Sept 5, 41; m 64; c 1. MATHEMATICAL ANALYSIS. *Educ:* Towson State Teachers Col, BS, 63; Mich State Univ, MS, 65; Univ Va, PhD(math), 71. *Prof Exp:* Instr math, 65-68 & 71-77, ASSOC PROF MATH & COMPUT SCI, WILKES COL, 77- *Mem:* Am Math Soc; Math Asn Am; Sigma Xi. *Res:* Some aspects of integral operators on hilbert spaces. *Mailing Add:* Dept of Math Wilkes Col Wilkes-Barre PA 18703

SOUSA, LYNN ROBERT, b Oakland, Calif, Apr 14, 43; m 64; c 1. ORGANIC CHEMISTRY, PHOTOCHEMISTRY. *Educ:* Univ Calif, Davis, BSc, 66; Univ Wis, PhD(org chem), 71. *Prof Exp:* Fel org chem, Univ Calif, Los Angeles, 71-73; asst prof, Mich State Univ, 73-78; asst prof, 78-80, ASSOC PROF CHEM, BALL STATE UNIV, 80- *Mem:* Am Chem Soc; Royal Soc Chem. *Res:* Photochemical reaction mechanisms; development of photochemical techniques for organic synthesis and applications of complexation by crown ethers in organic chemistry. *Mailing Add:* Dept of Chem Ball State Univ Muncie IN 47306

SOUTH, FRANK E, b Norfolk, Nebr, Sept 20, 24; m 46; c 2. PHYSIOLOGY. *Educ:* Univ Calif, AB, 49, PhD(physiol), 52. *Prof Exp:* Jr res physiologist, Univ Calif, 52-53; asst prof physiol, Univ PR, 53-54; Col Med, Univ Ill, 54-61; from asst prof to prof, Colo State Univ, 61-65; prof physiol & investr, Dalton Res Ctr, Univ Mo-Columbia, 65-77; dir, 77-82, PROF, SCH LIFE & HEALTH SCI, UNIV DEL, 82- *Concurrent Pos:* NIH sr res fel, 61-65; co-dir, Hibernation Info Exchange, Off Naval Res. *Mem:* Fel AAAS; Am Physiol Soc; Am Soc Zool; Soc Cryobiol; Soc Gen Physiol. *Res:* Environmental physiology; hibernation, hypothermia, acclimatization and adaptations to extreme environments; neurophysiology, thermoregulation and physiology of marine mammals. *Mailing Add:* Sch of Life & Health Sci Univ of Del Newark DE 19711

SOUTH, GRAHAM ROBIN, b Thorpe, Eng, Oct 27, 40; m 66; c 2. PHYCOLOGY. *Educ:* Liverpool Univ, BS, 63, PhD(marine algal ecol), 66. *Prof Exp:* NATO fel phycol, Univ BC, 66-67; asst prof, 67-70, assoc cur herbarium, 67-71, assoc prof biol, 70-76, CUR HERBARIUM, MEM UNIV NFLD, 71-, PROF & HEAD DEPT BIOL, 76- *Concurrent Pos:* Res fel, Edward Percival Marine Lab, Univ Canterbury, NZ, 73-74. *Mem:* Phycol Soc Am; Int Phycol Soc; Linnean Soc London; Western Soc Naturalists. *Res:* Ecology, distribution, taxonomy and biology of benthonic marine algae; laboratory culture of marine algae for experimental, ecological and life-history studies; flora of marine algae of eastern Canada and the North Atlantic Ocean; marine algae of New Zealand. *Mailing Add:* Dept Biol Memorial Univ Nfld St John's NF A1C 5S7 Can

SOUTH, HUGH MILES, b Houston, Tex, Nov 10, 47; m 76. DIGITAL SIGNAL PROCESSING, SONAR SYSTEMS ANALYSIS. *Educ:* Rice Univ, BA, 71; Johns Hopkins Univ, PhD(elec eng), 81. *Prof Exp:* Instr elec eng, 73-75, SR ENGR, APPL PHYSICS LAB, JOHNS HOPKINS UNIV,

75-, SUPVR, SPAN LAB, 79- *Mem:* Inst Elec & Electronics Engrs; Acoust Soc Am; Sigma Xi. *Res:* Design of hardware and software systems for digital signal processing; application of non-fourier transforms to digital signal processing. *Mailing Add:* 7242 Lasting Light Way Columbia MD 21045

SOUTH, MARY ANN, b Portales, NMex, May 23, 33. PEDIATRICS, IMMUNOLOGY. *Educ:* Eastern NMex Univ, BA, 55; Baylor Univ, MD, 59. *Prof Exp:* Intern, Presby-St Luke's Hosp, Chicago, 59-60; resident pediat, Col Med, Baylor Univ, 60-62; instr, Univ Minn, Minneapolis, 64-66; from asst prof to assoc prof, Baylor Col Med, 66-73; assoc prof pediat, Univ Pa, 73-77; chmn, Dept Pediat, 78-79, RES PROF PEDIAT, SCH MED, TEX TECH UNIV, 79- *Concurrent Pos:* Fel pediat infectious dis, Col Med, Baylor Univ, 62-64; fel pediat immunol, Univ Minn, Minneapolis, 64-66; USPHS career develop award, 68-73; dir pediat immunol, Children's Hosp Philadelphia, 73-77. *Mem:* Am Asn Immunol; Am Pediat Soc; Infectious Dis Soc Am; Am Med Women's Asn; Int Soc Exp Hemat. *Res:* Pediatric immunology. *Mailing Add:* 4516 48th St Lubbock TX 79414

SOUTHAM, CHESTER MILTON, b Salem, Mass, Oct 4, 19; m 39; c 3. ONCOLOGY, VIROLOGY. *Educ:* Univ Idaho, BS, 41, MS, 43; Columbia Univ, MD, 47. *Prof Exp:* Intern med, Presby Hosp, 47-48; instr, Med Col, Cornell Univ, 51-52, from asst prof to assoc prof, Sloan-Kettering Div, 52-71; PROF MED & HEAD DIV MED ONCOL, JEFFERSON MED COL, 71- *Concurrent Pos:* Am Cancer Soc res fel, Mem Ctr Cancer & Allied Dis, 48-49, Damon Runyon Fund clin res fel, 49-51, sr res fel, 51-52; asst, Sloan-Kettering Inst, 49-52, assoc & head clin virol sect, 52-63, mem, 63-71; asst attend physician, Mem Hosp, New York City, 52-58, assoc attend physician, 59-71; asst vis physician, James Ewing Hosp, 52-59, assoc vis physician, 59-71. *Mem:* Am Col Physicians; Am Asn Cancer Res; Am Fedn Clin Res; Am Asn Immunol; Am Soc Exp Path. *Res:* Clinical oncology, immunology; chemotherapy of cancer; oncolytic and oncogenic viruses; transplantation and tissue culture of human cancer; cancer immunology; carcinogenesis. *Mailing Add:* Div of Med Oncol Jefferson Med Col HSC 1450 Philadelphia PA 19107

SOUTHAM, DONALD LEE, b Cleveland, Ohio, Aug 28, 29; m 52; c 2. MECHANICAL ENGINEERING. *Educ:* Case Western Reserve Univ, BS, 51, MS, 54. *Prof Exp:* Designer eng, The Yoder Co, 51-53; chief engr, TRW, Inc, 53-66; vpres eng, Harris Corp, 66-74; V PRES ENG, CAST EQUIP DIV, COMBUSTION ENG, INC, 74- *Mem:* Am Soc Mech Engrs; Am Foundry Soc. *Mailing Add:* Cast Equip Div 7887 Hub Pkwy Cleveland OH 44125

SOUTHAM, FREDERICK WILLIAM, b NS, July 2, 24; m 47; c 3. PHYSICAL CHEMISTRY. *Educ:* Queen's Univ, Can, BSc, 46, MSc, 47; Mass Inst Technol, PhD(phys chem), 50. *Prof Exp:* Group leader, Electrometall Div, Aluminum Labs, Ltd, 50-71; sect head res lab, 71-72, SR TECH CONSULT, ALUMINUM CO CAN, LTD, 72- *Concurrent Pos:* Mem, Grants Comt Chem & Metall Eng, Nat Res Coun Can, 70-73. *Mem:* Fel Chem Inst Can; Can Soc Chem Eng. *Res:* Processes associated with production of aluminum; heat and mass transfer; high temperature reaction kinetics; environmental control. *Mailing Add:* 36 Van Order Dr Kingston ON K7M 1B7 Can

SOUTHAM, JOHN RALPH, b Youngstown, Ohio, Oct 30, 42. MARINE GEOLOGY. *Educ:* Purdue Univ, BSEE, 65, MSEE, 67; Univ Ill, MS, 69, PhD(physics), 74. *Prof Exp:* Aerospace scientist, Lewis Res Ctr, NASA, 67; fel, 74, RES PROF MARINE GEOL, ROSENSTIEL SCH MARINE & ATMOSPHERIC SCI, UNIV MIAMI, 75- *Mem:* AAAS; Am Geophys Union; Europ Geophys Soc; Int Asn Math Geol; Am Phys Soc. *Res:* Dynamic modelling of marine systems incorporating chemical, physical and biological processes; deep sea sedimentation and sedimentation processes in lakes and enclosed seas. *Mailing Add:* Dept of Marine Geol Univ of Miami Miami FL 33149

SOUTHARD, ALVIN REID, b Centertown, Ky, June 30, 26; m 50; c 4. SOIL SCIENCE, GEOLOGY. *Educ:* Utah State Univ, BS, 57, MS, 58; Cornell Univ, PhD(soil classification), 63. *Prof Exp:* From asst prof to assoc prof soils, Mont State Univ, 63-67; assoc prof, 67-76, PROF SOIL SCI & BIOMETEOROL, UTAH STATE UNIV, 76- *Concurrent Pos:* Exp sta rep, Nat Coop Soil Surv, Mont, 63-67 & Utah, 67-; conservationist, US Agency Int Develop, Ecuador. *Mem:* Am Soc Agron; Soil Conserv Soc Am. *Res:* Soil genesis and classification in Utah, New York and Montana; soils of the alpine tundra in Alaska; soils of wet and dry tropics in Ecuador, Brazil, Mauritania and Hawaii. *Mailing Add:* Dept of Soil Sci & Biometeorol Utah State Univ Logan UT 84322

SOUTHARD, GEORGE LEE, organic chemistry, analytical chemistry, see previous edition

SOUTHARD, JOHN BRELSFORD, b Baltimore, Md, May 21, 38; m 60; c 2. GEOLOGY. *Educ:* Mass Inst Technol, SB, 60; Harvard Univ, MA, 63, PhD(geol), 66. *Prof Exp:* NSF fel, Calif Inst Technol, 66-67; asst prof, 67-74, ASSOC PROF GEOL, MASS INST TECHNOL, 74- *Mem:* AAAS; Geol Soc Am; Am Geophys Union; Int Asn Sedimentol; Soc Econ Paleontologists & Mineralogists. *Res:* Physical sedimentology; mechanics of sediment transport, marine geology, fluvial geomorphology. *Mailing Add:* Dept of Earth & Planetary Sci Mass Inst of Technol Cambridge MA 02139

SOUTHARD, MARTHA ELLEN, radiology, deceased

SOUTHARD, WENDELL HOMER, b Des Moines, Iowa, July 21, 27. BIOCHEMISTRY. *Educ:* Drake Univ, BS, 50; Univ Ill, MS, 53, PhD(biol chem), 60. *Prof Exp:* Asst pharm, Univ Ill, 50-51, instr mfg pharm, 51-55, pharm, 55-56; from asst prof to assoc prof, 59-67, PROF PHARMACEUT CHEM, COL PHARM, DRAKE UNIV, 67- *Res:* Carbohydrate and microbial metabolism; manufacturing pharmacy. *Mailing Add:* Col of Pharmacy Drake Univ Des Moines IA 50311

SOUTHARDS, CARROLL J, b Bryson City, NC, June 18, 32; m 56; c 3. NEMATOLOGY, PLANT PATHOLOGY. *Educ:* NC State Univ, BS, 54, MS, 61, PhD(plant path), 65. *Prof Exp:* Asst county agr agent, NC Agr Exten Serv, 57-59; res asst hort, NC State Univ, 59-61, plant path, 61-65; from asst prof to assoc prof plant path, 65-74, PROF AGR BIOL & HEAD DEPT, INST AGR, UNIV TENN, KNOXVILLE, 74- *Mem:* Am Soc Phytopathologists; Soc Nematologists; Sigma Xi. *Res:* Host-parasite relationships of tobacco, soybeans and vegetable crops and root-knot and cyst nematodes; host resistance; variability of root-knot nematodes. *Mailing Add:* Dept of Agr Biol PO Box 1071 Knoxville TN 37901

SOUTHERN, BYRON WAYNE, b Toronto, Ont, June 13, 46; m 71; c 2. CONDENSED MATTER PHYSICS. *Educ:* York Univ, BSc, 69; McMaster Univ, MSc, 71, PhD(physics), 73. *Prof Exp:* Nat Res Coun fel physics, Imp Col Sci & Technol, London, Eng, 73-75; res physicist, Inst Laue Langevin, Grenoble, France, 75-79; ASSOC PROF PHYSICS, UNIV MAN, 79- *Mem:* Can Asn Physicists; Am Phys Soc. *Mailing Add:* Dept Physics Univ Man Winnipeg MB R3T 2N2 Can

SOUTHERN, JOHN HOYLE, II, b Ft Worth, Tex, May 5, 45; m 67; c 1. POLYMER SCIENCE. *Educ:* Princeton Univ, BSE, 67; Univ Mass, MS, 68, PhD(polymer sci), 70. *Prof Exp:* Res group leader polymer sci, Monsanto Co, 70-80; WITH ETHICON INC, 80- *Concurrent Pos:* Symp chmn, Am Chem Soc & guest ed, Polymer Eng & Sci Jour, 75. *Mem:* Am Inst Physics; Am Chem Soc; Sigma Xi. *Res:* Polymer morphology, particularly the field of stress induced crystallization; polymer rheology, including bicomponent flow and elastic fracture phenomena; fiber spinning technology. *Mailing Add:* Ethicon Inc Rte 22 Somerville NJ 08876

SOUTHERN, THOMAS MARTIN, b Beaumont, Tex, June 19, 42; m 66; c 2. ANALYTICAL CHEMISTRY, INORGANIC CHEMISTRY. *Educ:* Lamar Univ, BS, 64; Tex Tech Univ, MS, 66; Univ Houston, PhD(anal chem), 69; Southern Methodist Univ, MBA, 77. *Prof Exp:* Chemist & qual control mgr, 69-80, MGR PLASTICS PROD DEVELOP, TEX EASTMAN CO, 80- *Mem:* Am Chem Soc; Am Soc Qual Control. *Res:* Liquid chromatography; thermoanalytical chemistry; application of computers dedicated to analytical instruments and data reduction; hot melt adhesives-formulation and application; computers. *Mailing Add:* Prod Develop Mgr PO Box 7444 Longview TX 75601

SOUTHERN, WILLIAM EDWARD, b Wayne Co, Mich, Dec 22, 33; m 78; c 3. ORNITHOLOGY, ETHOLOGY. *Educ:* Cent West Univ, BS, 55; Univ Mich, MA, 59; Cornell Univ, PhD(comp vert ethol, animal ecol, wildlife mgt), 67. *Prof Exp:* Pub sch teacher, Mich, 55-56 & 57-58; asst prof zool, Univ Mich, 59-68, assoc prof ethol, 68-72, prof ornith, Biol Sta, 75-78; PROF AVIAN BEHAV ECOL, NORTHERN ILL UNIV, 72-; PRES, ENCAP, INC, 74- *Concurrent Pos:* Grants, Frank M Chapman Mem Fund, 61-64 & 65, Sigma Xi, 61, 63-64 & 68-69, Northern Ill Univ, 62, 65, 67-68, 69, 72 & 76-77, Brown Fund, Cornell Univ, 63-64, Max McGraw Wildlife Found, 68-70, NSF, 59, 62 & 71-73, sci fac fel, 63-64, desert biol fel, 65, Nat Park Serv, 74-82, Off Naval Res, 71-72 & Ill Dept Conserv, 73-74 & 81; US Air Force off sci res, 77-79. *Honors & Awards:* Hann lectr, Biol Sta, Univ Mich, 73; Ernest P Edwards Prize, Wilson Ornith Soc, 75. *Mem:* Sigma Xi; Wildlife Soc; Am Ornithologists Union; Nat Asn Environ Professionals; Wilson Ornith Soc. *Res:* Avian behavior, ecology and population dynamics, particularly Bald Eagles and members of family Laridae; environmental assessments; management strategies for non-game species; wildlife ecology. *Mailing Add:* Dept of Biol Sci Northern Ill Univ De Kalb IL 60115

SOUTHGATE, PETER DAVID, b Woking, Eng, July 20, 28; m 52; c 4. PHYSICS. *Educ:* Univ London, BSc, 48, MSc, 52, PhD(physics), 59. *Prof Exp:* Res scientist, Mullard Res Labs, Eng, 48-58; res physicist, Res Inst, Ill Inst Technol, 59-65; MEM TECH STAFF, RCA LABS, 66- *Mem:* Am Phys Soc. *Res:* Luminescence and recombination processes in semiconductors and organic materials; non-linear optical interactions in crystals; ferroelectric and pyroelectric phenomena and their application to radiation detection; acoustoelectric interactions in semiconductors; analysis of television tube and videodisc manufacturing processes. *Mailing Add:* RCA Labs Princeton NJ 08540

SOUTHIN, JOHN L, b Brockville, Ont, Can, June 10, 39. GENETICS. *Educ:* Queen's Univ, Ont, BSc, 61; Univ Calif, Los Angeles, MA, 62, PhD(zool), 63. *Prof Exp:* From lectr to asst prof, 63-67, ASSOC PROF GENETICS, MCGILL UNIV, 67-, DIR RESIDENCES, 72- *Concurrent Pos:* Vis scholar, Univ Calif, Los Angeles, 64 & 65; vis prof, Univ Havana, 67 & 69, prof, 70- *Mem:* Genetics Soc Am. *Res:* Gene structure in Drosophila; chemically induced mutation and the problem of mosaicism in Drosophila. *Mailing Add:* 3905 University Montreal PQ H3A 2T5 Can

SOUTHREN, A LOUIS, b New York, NY, Oct 12, 26; m 50; c 3. INTERNAL MEDICINE, ENDOCRINOLOGY. *Educ:* NY Univ, AB, 49; Chicago Med Sch, MD, 55. *Prof Exp:* From asst prof med & asst attend physician to assoc prof med & assoc attend physician, 61-69, PROF MED & ATTEND PHYSICIAN, NEW YORK MED COL, 69-, RES PROF OPHTHAL, 79-, CHIEF ENDOCRINE SECT, 63- *Concurrent Pos:* Fel endocrinol, Mt Sinai Hosp, New York, 58-59; fel endocrine res, Jewish Hosp Brooklyn, 59-61, fel, training prog steroid biochem, Worcester Found Exp Biol, 61-62; USPHS res grants, 63-; career scientist, Health Res Coun of New York, 63-72 & 74-75; dir, USPHS Training Prog Endocrinol & Metab, 65-72; mem glaucoma panel, Nat Adv Eye Coun, 80-81. *Mem:* AAAS; fel Am Col Physicians; Endocrine Soc; Soc Gynec Invest; Am Fertil Soc. *Res:* Glucocorticoid metabolism in glaucoma and cataract. *Mailing Add:* Dept of Med New York Med Col New York NY 10029

SOUTHWARD, GLEN MORRIS, b Boise, Idaho, Oct 8, 27; c 2. FISH BIOLOGY, STATISTICS. *Educ:* Univ Wash, BS, 49, MS, 56, PhD, 66. *Prof Exp:* Hatchery asst, Idaho Dept Fish & Game, 49-50; sci asst, Int Pac Halibut Comn, 50-53, jr biologist, 54-55, from asst biologist to biologist, 55-67; asst prof statist & asst statistician, Wash State Univ, 67-70 & Univ Wis, 70-71; biometrician, Int Pac Halibut Comn, 71-75; assoc prof, 75-80, PROF EXP STATIST, NMEX STATE UNIV, 80- *Mem:* Am Inst Fisheries Res Biologists; Am Statist Asn; Biomet Soc. *Res:* Biometry; experimental statistics, biomathematics, statistical consulting; computer simulation of population dynamics and management of natural resources. *Mailing Add:* Dept of Exp Statist NMex State Univ Col of Agr Las Cruces NM 88003

SOUTHWARD, HAROLD DEAN, b Headrick, Okla, June 22, 30; m 54; c 4. NUCLEAR PHYSICS, SOLID STATE PHYSICS. *Educ:* West Tex State Univ, BS, 51; Univ Tex, MA, 57, PhD(physics), 58. *Prof Exp:* Engr, Aircraft Armaments, Inc, 54-55; sr res technologist, Mobil Oil Corp, 58-63; assoc prof, 63-69, dir bur eng res, 71-76, PROF ELEC ENG, UNIV NMEX, 69- *Mem:* Am Phys Soc; Inst Elec & Electronics Eng. *Res:* Radiation effects of solid state electronics; radiation measurement; photovoltaic energy systems. *Mailing Add:* Dept Elec Eng & Comput Sci Tapy Hall Univ NMex Albuquerque NM 87131

SOUTHWELL, P(ETER) H(ENRY), b Rochdale, Eng, Nov 29, 24; m 46; c 4. MECHANICAL & AGRICULTURAL ENGINEERING. *Educ:* Royal Naval Eng Col, Eng, Engr, 45; Univ Sask, MSc, 60. *Prof Exp:* Exp officer, Nat Inst Agr Eng, Eng, 48-54; asst prof eng sci, 55-60, ASSOC PROF, SCH ENG, UNIV GUELPH, 61- *Concurrent Pos:* Chmn, Assoc Comt Agr & Forestry Aviation, Nat Res Coun Can, 66-72; mem, Energy & Agr Policy Comt, Ont Govt, 80-81. *Honors & Awards:* Pilcher Mem Prize, Royal Aeronaut Soc, 52. *Mem:* Can Soc Agr Engrs; Am Soc Agr Engrs; assoc fel Royal Aeronaut Soc; Inst Mech Engrs. *Res:* Combustion engines and turbines; terrain-vehicle systems and terra-mechanics; agricultural aviation; pesticides application systems; energy analysis and energy ratios of food production; biomass fuels. *Mailing Add:* Sch of Eng Univ of Guelph Guelph ON W1G 2W1 Can

SOUTHWICK, CHARLES HENRY, b Wooster, Ohio, Aug 28, 28; m 52; c 2. ZOOLOGY. *Educ:* Col Wooster, BA, 49; Univ Wis, MS, 51, PhD(zool), 53. *Prof Exp:* Asst prof biol, Hamilton Col, 53-54; NSF fel, Bur Animal Population, Oxford Univ, 54-55; from asst prof to assoc prof zool, Ohio Univ, 55-61; assoc prof, 61-68, PROF PATHOBIOL, SCH HYG & PUB HEALTH, JOHNS HOPKINS UNIV, 68- *Concurrent Pos:* Mem numerous primate expeds, Panama, India, Malaysia & Kenya, 51-71; Fulbright fel, Aligarh Muslim Univ, India, 59-60; mem, Calif Primate Res Ctr, 74-76 & Gov Sci Adv Coun, Md, 75-77; mem, Primate Adv Comt, Nat Acad Sci-Nat Res Coun & Adv Bd, Caribbean Primate Res Ctr. *Mem:* AAAS; Ecol Soc Am; Am Soc Mammal; Am Soc Zoologists; Animal Behav Soc (pres, 68). *Res:* Vertebrate population dynamics; stress physiology; sociobiology and animal behavior. *Mailing Add:* Johns Hopkins Univ Sch of Hyg & Pub Health Baltimore MD 21205

SOUTHWICK, DAVID LEROY, b Rochester, Minn, Aug 30, 36; m 59; c 3. GEOLOGY. *Educ:* Carleton Col, BA, 58; Johns Hopkins Univ, PhD(geol), 62. *Prof Exp:* Geologist, US Geol Surv, 62-68; from asst prof to prof geol, Macalester Col, 68-77; SR GEOLOGIST, MINN GEOL SURV, 77- *Mem:* AAAS; Am Geophys Union; fel Geol Soc Am. *Res:* Petrology of metamorphic and igneous rocks; structural geology; stratigraphy and structural geology of the Appalachian Piedmont; geology of the Central Cascade Range, Washington; Precambrian rocks of Minnesota. *Mailing Add:* Minn Geol Surv 1633 Eustis St St Paul MN 55108

SOUTHWICK, EDWARD EARLE, b Northampton, Mass. PHYSIOLOGICAL ECOLOGY. *Educ:* Univ Mich, BSME, 65, MS, 67; Wash State Univ, PhD(zool), 71. *Prof Exp:* Asst prof biol, Duquesne Univ, 71-73; lectr physiol ecol, Grad Sch, Georgetown Univ, 74-75; dir, Chippewa Nature Ctr, Inc, 75-77; ASSOC PROF BIOL, STATE UNIV NY COL, BROCKPORT, 77- *Concurrent Pos:* Ford Found fel biophys ecol, Univ Mich, 72-73; prin investr, NSF res grant, 72-73 & E O Barstow Found, 76-77; res physiologist, Ins Inst for Hwy Safety, 73-75; fac adv, Undergrad Res Partic, NSF, 76-77; adj prof biol, Alma Col, 76-77; instr ecol, Saginaw Valley State Col, 77; prin investr, NSF res grant, 80; Mellon Found fel microclimate & pollination, 81. *Honors & Awards:* Res Award, State Univ NY Res Found, 81. *Mem:* Ecol Soc Am; Sigma Xi; Int Bee Res Asn; Am Soc Bot. *Res:* Microclimates; animal and plant energetics including energy balance; thermoregulation and metabolism, especially in social insects; honeybee biology; nectar biology and nutrition; cold temperature physiology; plant to insect relationships. *Mailing Add:* Dept of Biol Sci State Univ NY Brockport NY 14420

SOUTHWICK, EVERETT WEST, b Providence, RI, Sept 19, 41. ORGANIC CHEMISTRY. *Educ:* Univ RI, BA, 63; Univ NH, PhD(org chem), 73. *Prof Exp:* Fel org chem, State Univ NY Buffalo, 72-74, Duke Univ, 73-74; sr chemist, Liggett & Myres Inc, 74-80; CHEMIST, PHILIP MORRIS USA, 80- *Mem:* Am Chem Soc; Am Chem Soc. *Res:* Synthesis, isolation, purification and characterization of organic compounds of potential value as flavorants. *Mailing Add:* Philip Morris USA PO Box 26583 Richmond VA 23261

SOUTHWICK, FRANKLIN WALLBURG, b Boston, Mass, May 29, 17; m 40; c 4. POMOLOGY. *Educ:* Mass State Col, BS, 39; Ohio State Univ, MS, 40; Cornell Univ, PhD(pomol), 43. *Prof Exp:* Asst prof pomol, Univ Conn, 43-45 & Cornell Univ, 45-48; head dept plant & soil sci, 64-77, dir grad prof, 73-80, prof soil sci & chmn dept, 76-80, PROF POMOL, UNIV MASS, AMHERST, 48- *Honors & Awards:* Gold Medal, Mass Soc Promoting Agr, 65. *Mem:* AAAS; fel Am Soc Hort Sci. *Res:* Fruit storage; respiration; growth regulating substances; nutrition. *Mailing Add:* Dept of Plant & Soil Sci Univ of Mass Amherst MA 01003

SOUTHWICK, HARRY W, b Grand Rapids, Mich, Nov 21, 18; m 42; c 4. SURGERY. *Educ:* Harvard Univ, BS, 40, MD, 43; Am Bd Surg, dipl, 51. *Prof Exp:* Clin prof surg, Univ Ill Col Med, 58-71; PROF SURG, RUSH MED COL & CHMN DEPT GEN SURG, RUSH-PRESBY-ST LUKE'S MED CTR, 71- *Concurrent Pos:* Pvt pract; head sect gen surg, Presby-St Luke's Hosp, 67-71. *Mem:* Am Col Surg; Am Surg Asn; Soc Head & Neck Surgeons; Soc Surg Oncol. *Res:* Oncology. *Mailing Add:* Dept of Gen Surg Rush-Presby-St Luke's Med Ctr Chicago IL 60612

SOUTHWICK, LAWRENCE, b Worcester, Mass, Apr 6, 12; m 37; c 3. AGRONOMY, HORTICULTURE. *Educ:* Univ Mass, BS, 33, MS, 38. *Prof Exp:* Instr, Univ Mass, 35-45; BIOPROD RES & DEVELOP CHEMIST & TECH ED, DOW CHEM CO, 45- *Mem:* Am Soc Agron; fel Weed Sci Soc Am; Am Soc Hort Sci; Sigma Xi. *Res:* Chemical weed control; plant nutrition; soils; dwarf fruit trees; growth substances; pest control; environmental science. *Mailing Add:* 4504 Bond Ct Midland MI 48640

SOUTHWICK, PHILIP LEE, b Lincoln, Nebr, Nov 15, 16; m 42; c 1. CHEMISTRY. *Educ:* Univ Nebr, AB, 39, AM, 40; Univ Ill, PhD(org chem), 43. *Prof Exp:* Res chemist, Merck & Co, NJ, 43-46; from asst prof to assoc prof, 46-55, PROF ORG CHEM, CARNEGIE-MELLON UNIV, 55- *Concurrent Pos:* Mem, Fulbright Act Awards Chem Comt, Div Chem & Chem Technol, Nat Acad Sci-Nat Res Coun, 60-63. *Mem:* Fel AAAS; Am Chem Soc; fel NY Acad Sci. *Res:* Stability of enols; direct aromatic carboxymethylations; synthetic antimetabolites; chemistry of penicillins, pteridines, pyrimidines, pyrrolidines and indoles; stereochemistry of conjugate addition reactions and formation and reactions of aziridines and aziridinium ions; stereochemical applications of nuclear magnetic resonance spectra; synthesis of first N-amidino pyrazine carboxamide diuretic leading to the drug amiloride. *Mailing Add:* Dept of Chem Carnegie-Mellon Univ Pittsburgh PA 15213

SOUTHWICK, RICHARD ARTHUR, b White River Junction, Vt, Sept 16, 24; m 45; c 3. PLANT BREEDING. *Educ:* Univ Vt, BS, 50, MS, 54. *Prof Exp:* Instr agron, Univ Mass, Amherst, 54-58, asst prof, 58-67; assoc prof, 67-69, PROF PLANT SCI, STATE UNIV NY AGR & TECH COL COBLESKILL, 69- *Concurrent Pos:* Botanist, George Landis Arboretum, Esperance, 70- *Mem:* Am Asn Bot Gardens & Arboretums; Am Hort Soc; Am Forestry Asn. *Res:* Plant propagation; improvement, evaluation, and collection of ornamental plant materials. *Mailing Add:* Dept of Plant Sci State Univ of NY Agr & Tech Col Cobleskill NY 12043

SOUTHWICK, RUSSELL DUTY, b Woonsocket, RI, Dec 27, 31; m 54; c 3. PHYSICS. *Educ:* Rensselaer Polytech Inst, BS, 53; Univ Conn, MS, 55. *Prof Exp:* Asst, Univ Conn, 53-55; res physicist, Preston Labs, Inc, 55-60, asst dir res, 60-66, vpres & asst dir res, 66-76, V PRES & DIR RES, AM GLASS RES, INC, 76- *Mem:* Am Phys Soc; Am Ceramic Soc; Soc Exp Stress Anal. *Res:* Glass technology; mechanical properties of glass, especially strength and surface friction. *Mailing Add:* Am Glass Res Inc Box 149 Butler PA 16001

SOUTHWICK, WAYNE ORIN, b Lincoln, Nebr, Feb 6, 23; m 44; c 3. ORTHOPEDIC SURGERY. *Educ:* Univ Nebr, AB, 45, MD, 47; Am Bd Orthop Surg, dipl, 58. *Prof Exp:* Asst anat & histol, Col Med, Univ Nebr, 46-47; intern med, Boston City Hosp, 47-48, asst resident surg, Fifth Surg Div, 48-50; asst resident orthop surg, Hosp, Johns Hopkins Univ, 50-54, instr, Sch Med, Univ & chief resident, Hosp, 54-55, asst prof, Univ, 55-58; assoc prof, 58-61, chief sect, 58-77, PROF ORTHOP SURG, SCH MED, YALE UNIV, 61-, CONSULT ORTHOP, UNIV HEALTH SERV, 69- *Concurrent Pos:* Fel, Branford Col, Yale Univ, 70- *Mem:* Am Acad Orthop Surg; Am Orthop Asn; fel Am Col Surg; AMA; Orthop Res Soc. *Res:* Degenerative cervical disk disease; slipped epiphysis; experimental osteomyelitis; histology of cartilage. *Mailing Add:* Dept of Orthop Surg Yale Univ Sch of Med New Haven CT 06510

SOUTHWORTH, HAMILTON, b New York, NY, Apr 7, 07; m 33; c 4. INTERNAL MEDICINE. *Educ:* Yale Univ, BA, 29; Johns Hopkins Univ, MD, 33; Am Bd Internal Med, dipl, 40. *Prof Exp:* Intern, Presby Hosp New York, 33-35; asst resident med, Johns Hopkins Univ, 35-37, asst, Sch Med, 35-37; from asst to assoc, Col Physicians & Surgeons, 37-46, from asst clin prof to clin prof, 47-69, prof clin med, 69-72, EMER PROF CLIN MED, COLUMBIA UNIV, 72- *Concurrent Pos:* US rep med subcomt, Europ Regional Adv, UNRRA, 44; attache, US Embassy, London, 44-45; Europ rep comt med res, Off Sci Res & Develop, 44-45; from asst attend physician to attend, Presby Hosp, 45-72; consult, Sta Hosp, US Mil Acad, 46-73 & Presby Hosp, 72-; mem med exam bd, Am Bd Internal Med, 64-70. *Honors & Awards:* Order of the Cedar Award, Govt Lebanon, 81. *Mem:* AMA; fel Am Col Physicians; Am Clin & Climat Asn; NY Acad Med. *Res:* Toxicity of sulfonamides; hemolytic and aplastic anemias; cardiac resuscitation. *Mailing Add:* 109 E 67th St New York NY 10021

SOUTHWORTH, RAYMOND W(ILLIAM), b North Brookfield, Mass, Oct 23, 20. COMPUTER SCIENCE, CHEMICAL ENGINEERING. *Educ:* Worcester Polytech Inst, BS, 43; Yale Univ, MEng, 44, DEng, 48. *Prof Exp:* From asst instr to assoc prof chem eng, Yale Univ, 43-66; dir, Comput Ctr, 66-81, PROF MATH & COMPUT SCI, COL WILLIAM & MARY, 66- *Concurrent Pos:* Mem staff, Brookhaven Nat Lab, 48-49; mem, Inst Math Sci, NY Univ, 60-61; dir, Southeastern Va Regional Comput Ctr, 69-81. *Mem:* Am Chem Soc; Am Inst Chem Engrs; Asn Comput Mach; Am Math Soc; Soc Indust & Appl Math. *Res:* Digital computing; numerical methods. *Mailing Add:* Dept Math & Comput Sci Col of William & Mary Williamsburg VA 23815

SOUTHWORTH, RICHARD BOYNTON, astronomy, see previous edition

SOUTHWORTH, WARREN HILBOURNE, b Lynn, Mass, Feb 10, 12; m 37; c 2. PUBLIC HEALTH, PREVENTIVE MEDICINE. *Educ:* Univ Mass, BS, 34; Boston Univ, MS, 35; Mass Inst Technol, DrPH, 44. *Prof Exp:* Teacher biol, Whitman High Sch & Belmont High Sch, Mass, 36-39; res dir, Mass Dept Pub Health, 41-42; prof health sci, Panzer Col, 42-44; coordr sch health, Wis Dept Pub Instr, 44-48; coordr med team, Wis State Bd Health, 52-53; assoc prof, 44-52, prof prev med, 77-81, PROF CURRIC & INSTR, UNIV WIS-MADISON, 53-, EMER PROF PREV MED, 81- *Concurrent Pos:* Lectr pub health, NY Univ, 43-44. *Honors & Awards:* Distinguished Serv Award, Am Sch Health Asn, 61, William A Howe Award, 68. *Mem:* AAAS; Am Alliance for Health, Phys Educ & Recreation; Am Pub Health Asn; Am Sch Health Asn (treas, 60-74); Soc Pub Health Educrs. *Res:* Community health education; school health education; occupational health education; patient health education; drug education; family life education. *Mailing Add:* Teaching Educ Bldg 225 N Mills St Madison WI 53706

SOUTO, JOSE, cancer, physiology, see previous edition

SOVEN, PAUL, b New York, NY, Sept 30, 39; m 61; c 3. PHYSICS. *Educ:* City Col New York, BS, 60; Univ Chicago, MS, 61, PhD(physics), 65. *Prof Exp:* Mem staff, Bell Tel Labs, 65-67; from asst prof, to assoc prof, 67-76, PROF PHYSICS, UNIV PA, 77- *Mem:* Am Phys Soc. *Res:* Theory of metals. *Mailing Add:* Dept of Physics Univ of Pa Philadelphia PA 19104

SOVERS, OJARS JURIS, b Riga, Latvia, July 11, 37; US citizen; m 59. PHYSICAL CHEMISTRY. *Educ:* Brooklyn Col, BS, 58; Princeton Univ, PhD(physics, phys chem), 62. *Prof Exp:* NSF fel chem, Oxford Univ, 61-62; fel, Columbia Univ, 62-63, res assoc, Watson Lab, 63-64; res engr, Gen Tel & Electronics Lab, Inc, 64-72; res engr, Sony Corp, 72-80; WITH JET PROPULSION LAB, CALIF INST TECHNOL, 80- *Mem:* Am Phys Soc; AAAS; Royal Soc Chem; Am Chem Soc. *Res:* Quantum chemistry; Luminescence in solids. *Mailing Add:* Jet Propulsion Lab Calif Inst Technol Pasadena CA 91109

SOVISH, RICHARD CHARLES, b Cleveland, Ohio, July 22, 25; m 54; c 3. ORGANIC CHEMISTRY, POLYMER CHEMISTRY. *Educ:* Ohio Univ, BS, 49; Western Reserve Univ, MS, 52, PhD(chem), 54. *Prof Exp:* Res chemist, Dow Chem Co, 54-62; res scientist, Lockheed Missile & Space Co, 62-63; staff mem, Raychem Corp, 63-67, head develop sect, 67-70, mgr mfg compounding dept, 70-73, mgr eng, Thermofit Div, 73-75, tech mgr, Utilities Div, Raychem Belg, 75-78, int tech dir, Telecom Div, 78-80, TECH DIR, RAY CHEM CORP, EUROPE, 80- *Mem:* Am Chem Soc; Sigma Xi; Soc Plastics Engrs. *Res:* Irradiation effects on polymers; polymer cross-linking; graft copolymers; mechanical properties of polymers. *Mailing Add:* Raychem Corp 300 Constitution Dr Menlo Park CA 94025

SOVOCOOL, GEORGE WAYNE, b Cortland, NY, Oct 30, 42; m 71; c 2. PHYSICAL-ORGANIC CHEMISTRY, ANALYTICAL CHEMISTRY. *Educ:* Rochester Inst Technol, BS, 65; Cornell Univ, MS, 67, PhD(chem), 71. *Prof Exp:* Fel chem, Univ NC, Chapel Hill, 71-72; res chemist, 72-81, SUPVRY PHYS SCIENTIST, US ENVIRON PROTECTION AGENCY, 81- *Concurrent Pos:* Adj assoc prof, Biochem Lab, Botany Dept, Univ NC, Chapel Hill, 81- *Mem:* Am Chem Soc; Am Soc Mass Spectrometry. *Res:* Structure determination and quantitative measurement, through the use of mass spectrometry, of organic chemical compounds occurring in complex mixtures, as human tissue and environmental samples; quality assurance of analytical data. *Mailing Add:* 112 Carmel Lane Durham NC 27713

SOVRAN, GINO, engineering, mathematics, see previous edition

SOWA, JOHN ROBERT, b South Bend, Ind, Aug 21, 34; m 61; c 4. ORGANIC CHEMISTRY. *Educ:* Univ Notre Dame, BS, 56; Univ Pa, PhD(org chem), 64. *Prof Exp:* Res asst chem, Sowa Chem Co, 58-59; res assoc, Univ Ariz, 64-66; asst prof, Univ Del, 66-67; asst prof, 67-77, ASSOC PROF CHEM, UNION COL, NY, 77- *Concurrent Pos:* Henry Busche teaching fel, Univ Pa, 62; consult, Sowa Chem Co, 66-, decontamination res div, Edgewood Arsenal, 67 & Schenectady Chem Co, 68-; vis prof, Rensselaer Polytech Inst, 73-74. *Mem:* Am Chem Soc; NY Acad Sci; Am Inst Chemists. *Res:* Nuclear magnetic resonance applied to mechanisms in organic chemistry; silicon-carbon d-pi/p-pi bonding; mustard reactions with purines; vinyl polymerizations; organophosphorous chemistry; acetylenes; liquid crystals; diazonium ions. *Mailing Add:* Dept of Chem Union Col Schenectady NY 12308

SOWA, WALTER, b Flin Flon, Man, Nov 29, 33; m 64; c 2. ORGANIC CHEMISTRY. *Educ:* Queen's Univ, Ont, BSc, 56, MSc, 58, PhD(org chem), 62; York Univ, MBA, 75. *Prof Exp:* Nat Res Coun Can fel, 61-63; res scientist, 63-73, sr res scientist, 73-78, asst dir, Dept Appl Chem, 75-79, prin res scientist, 80-81, SR PROJ OFFICER PROJ DEVELOP, ONT RES FOUND, 81- *Mem:* AAAS; Chem Inst Can; Am Inst Mining, Metall & Petrol Engrs; Am Chem Soc; Can Inst Mining & Metall. *Res:* Organic synthesis; chemistry of carbohydrates; antiradiation compounds; selective extractants for metals; chemistry of industrial solvent extraction of metals; forest products; chromatography. *Mailing Add:* Ontario Res Found Mississauga ON L5K 1B3 Can

SOWELL, GROVER, JR, b West Palm Beach, Fla, June 12, 28; m 60; c 2. PLANT PATHOLOGY. *Educ:* Univ Ga, BSA, 48, MSA, 49; Cornell Univ, PhD(plant path), 54. *Prof Exp:* Asst plant path, Univ Ga, 48-49 & Cornell Univ, 50-53; asst plant pathologist, Gulf Coast Exp Sta, 54-57; PLANT PATHOLOGIST, SOUTHERN REGIONAL PLANT INTROD STA, GA EXP STA, 59- *Mem:* Am Phytopath Soc; Am Soc Hort Sci. *Res:* Diseases of vegetable, field and forage crops; resistance of plants to diseases. *Mailing Add:* Plant Introd Dept Ga Exp Sta Experiment GA 30212

SOWELL, JOHN GREGORY, b Knoxville, Tenn, Jan 22, 41; m 67; c 1. PHARMACOLOGY, OPHTHALMOLOGY. *Educ:* Murray State Univ, BS, 63; Univ Tenn, MS, 67, PhD, 69. *Prof Exp:* Instr pharmacol, Univ Tenn, 70-71; ASST PROF PHARMACOL & OPHTHAL, MED CTR, UNIV ALA, BIRMINGHAM, 73- *Concurrent Pos:* Fel, Univ Southern Calif, 71-73. *Mem:* Asn Res Vis & Ophthal; Endocrine Soc. *Res:* Mechanism of steroid action; glaucoma. *Mailing Add:* Dept of Pharmacol Univ of Ala Med Ctr Birmingham AL 35294

SOWELL, KATYE MARIE OLIVER, b Winston-Salem, NC, Apr 6, 34; wid; c 1. MATHEMATICS. *Educ:* Flora Macdonald Col, BA, 56; Univ SC, MS, 58; Fla State Univ, PhD(math educ), 65. *Prof Exp:* Asst prof math, Elon Col, 58-60; instr, Univ Southern Miss, 60-63; instr & res assoc math educ, Fla State Univ, 65; from asst prof to assoc prof, 65-71, PROF MATH, E CAROLINA UNIV, 72- *Concurrent Pos:* Dir student teaching prog math & supvr student teachers, ECarolina Univ, 66-79; NSF grants, 68-74; consult, var bk publs & city & county bds of educ, Eastern NC, 67-; consult, Ctr Individualized Instr Systs, Durham, NC, 71-73; mem, Adv Coun Math, NC State Dept Pub Instr, 70-, Metric Educ, 74-; vis scholar, Univ Mich, 80 & 81. *Mem:* Am Math Soc; Math Asn Am; Nat Coun Teachers Math. *Res:* Mathematics education; geometry; number theory. *Mailing Add:* 103 College Court Dr Greenville NC 27834

SOWELL, WALTER F, b Abbeville, Ala, Oct 20, 21; m 49; c 2. SOIL FERTILITY. *Educ:* Auburn Univ, BS, 48, MS, 57; Purdue Univ, PhD(soil fertil), 59. *Prof Exp:* Asst county agent, Coop Exten, 48-54, res agron & soils, Auburn Univ, 54-57, soils specialist, Coop Exten Serv, 60-74, DIST AGR-COORDR, COOP EXTEN SERV, AUBURN UNIV, 74- *Mem:* *Res:* Growth of plants under controlled environmental conditions; hydroponics; factors influencing compact corn production. *Mailing Add:* 118 Duncan Hall Coop Ext Serv Auburn Univ Auburn AL 36830

SOWERS, EDWARD EUGENE, b Crawfordsville, Ind, Nov 26, 42; m 67; c 2. INDUSTRIAL ORGANIC CHEMISTRY. *Educ:* Wabash Col, AB, 64; Tufts Univ, PhD(org chem), 70. *Prof Exp:* Staff chemist res, 69-75, MGR PROD DEVELOP, REILLY TAR & CHEM CORP, 75- *Mem:* Am Chem Soc. *Res:* Synthesis and product development of nitrogen heterocycles. *Mailing Add:* Reilly Tar & Chem Corp 1500 S Tibbs Ave Indianapolis IN 46241

SOWERS, GEORGE F(REDERICK), b Cleveland, Ohio, Sept 23, 21; m 44; c 4. CIVIL & GEOLOGICAL ENGINEERING. *Educ:* Case Western Reserve Univ, BS, 42; Harvard Univ, MS, 47. *Prof Exp:* From assoc prof to prof, 47-65, REGENTS PROF CIVIL ENG, GA INST TECHNOL, 65- *Concurrent Pos:* Vis lectr, India, 59, 65; consult engr, Law Eng Testing Co, 47 & Washington, DC, 57- *Honors & Awards:* Middlebrook Award, Am Soc Civil Engrs, 77, Terzaghi lectr, 79. *Mem:* Am Soc Civil Engrs; Geol Soc Am; Am Soc Testing & Mat; Nat Soc Prof Engrs; Int Soc Soil Mech & Found Engrs. *Res:* Soils; engineering geology; rock mechanics. *Mailing Add:* Dept Civil Eng Ga Inst Technol Atlanta GA 30332

SOWINSKI, RAYMOND, b Hammond, Ind, Feb 8, 24; m 54. BIOCHEMISTRY. *Educ:* Ind Univ, BS, 49, PhD(biochem), 52. *Prof Exp:* Res asst phys chem, Yale Univ, 52-53; supvy biochemist, Mercy Hosp, Chicago, Ill, 53-55; res assoc biochem, Med Sch, Northwestern Univ, 55-58 & biophys, Univ Pittsburgh, 58-60; sr res assoc hemat, Hektoen Inst Med Res, Cook County Hosp, 60-63; asst prof microbiol, Albany Med Sch, 63-66; ASSOC PROF BIOCHEM, ROCHESTER INST TECHNOL, 66- *Mem:* AAAS; Am Chem Soc; NY Acad Sci; fel Am Inst Chemists. *Res:* Protein chemistry; physical biochemistry; neurochemistry. *Mailing Add:* Dept of Biol Rochester Inst of Technol Rochester NY 14623

SOWLS, LYLE KENNETH, b Darlington, Wis, Feb 28, 16; m 74; c 6. WILDLIFE BIOLOGY. *Educ:* Univ Wis, PhD(wildlife mgt), 51. *Prof Exp:* Biologist, Delta Waterfowl Res Sta, Wildlife Mgt Inst, Can, 46-50; LEADER COOP WILDLIFE RES UNIT, UNIV ARIZ, 50- *Concurrent Pos:* Fulbright vis lectr zool, Univ Col Rhodesia & Nyasaland, 62-63; wildlife consult, Food & Agr Orgn, Philippines, 67. *Mem:* Wildlife Soc; Am Soc Mammal; Int Union Conserv Nature. *Res:* Game birds and mammals. *Mailing Add:* 3653 N Vine Ave Tucson AZ 85719

SOZEN, M(ETE) A(VNI), b Istanbul, Turkey, May 22, 30; m 56. CIVIL ENGINEERING. *Educ:* Robert Col Istanbul, BS, 51; Univ Ill, MS, 52, PhD(civil eng), 57. *Prof Exp:* Engr, Kaiser Engrs, 52 & Hardesty & Hanover, 53; res assoc, 55-57, from asst prof to assoc prof, 57-63, PROF CIVIL ENG, UNIV ILL, URBANA, 63- *Honors & Awards:* Res Prize, Am Soc Civil Engrs, 63, R C Reese Prize, 70 & Moisseiff Prize, 72; J W Kelly Award, Am Concrete Inst, 74. *Mem:* Nat Acad Eng; Am Soc Civil Engrs; Am Concrete Inst. *Res:* Reinforced and prestressed concrete structures; earthquake-resistant design. *Mailing Add:* 3112 Civil Eng Bldg Univ of Ill Urbana IL 61801

SPACH, MADISON STOCKTON, b Winston Salem, NC, Nov 10, 26; m; c 4. PEDIATRIC CARDIOLOGY. *Educ:* Duke Univ, AB, 50, MD, 54. *Prof Exp:* From instr to assoc prof, 57-68, PROF PEDIAT, SCH MED, DUKE UNIV, 68-, CHIEF PEDIAT CARDIOL, 60- *Mem:* Soc Pediat Res; Am Acad Pediat; fel Am Col Cardiol; Asn Europ Pediat Cardiol. *Res:* Electrophysiology. *Mailing Add:* Box 3090 Duke Univ Med Ctr Durham NC 27710

SPACIE, ANNE, b Boston, Mass, Aug 19, 45. AQUATIC TOXICOLOGY, POLLUTION BIOLOGY. *Educ:* Mt Holyoke Col, BA, 67; Univ Calif, San Diego, MS, 69; Purdue Univ, PhD(limnol), 75. *Prof Exp:* Researcher aquatic biol, Union Carbide Corp, 69-73; asst prof, 75-81, ASSOC PROF FISHERIES, PURDUE UNIV, 81- *Concurrent Pos:* Vis prof, Savannah Rider Ecol Lab, 79; consult, US Environ Protection Agency. *Mem:* Am Fisheries Soc; Am Soc Limnol & Oceanog; AAAS; Am Soc Testing & Mat; Soc Environ Toxicol & Chem. *Res:* The accumulation and toxicity of synthetic organic compounds in fish and other aquatic organisms; effects of stream modifications on water quality and the distribution of fishes. *Mailing Add:* Forestry & Natural Resources Purdue Univ West Lafayette IN 47907

SPACIL, HENRY STEPHEN, physical chemistry, metallurgy, see previous edition

SPACKMAN, DARREL H, b Morgan, Utah, July 18, 24; m 47; c 5. BIOCHEMISTRY, CANCER. *Educ:* Univ Utah, BA, 50, MA, 52, PhD, 54. *Prof Exp:* Res assoc, Rockefeller Inst, 54-59; sr biochemist, Spinco Div, Beckman Instruments, Inc, 59-62; res asst prof biochem, obstet & gynec, Univ Wash, 62-68; SR RES BIOCHEMIST, DEPT MICROBIOL, PAC NORTHWEST RES FOUND, 68- *Concurrent Pos:* Res scientist, Fred Hutchinson Cancer Res Ctr, 75-; asst prof, Rehab Med Dept, Univ Wash, 77- *Mem:* Am Asn Cancer Res; Am Soc Biol Chemists. *Res:* Amino acids, peptides and proteins of physiological fluids and tissues in hosts with malignancies; deprivation therapy in cancer research; methodology for automatic amino acid analysis. *Mailing Add:* Pac Northwest Res Found 1102 Columbia St Seattle WA 98104

SPACKMAN, WILLIAM, JR, b Chicago, Ill, Sept 20, 19; m 42; c 3. PALEOBOTANY. *Educ:* Univ Ill, BS, 42; Harvard Univ, MA, 47, PhD(bot), 49. *Prof Exp:* Assoc biologist, US Naval Shipyard, Pa, 44-45; from asst prof to assoc prof, 49-61, PROF PALEOBOT, PA STATE UNIV, 61-, DIR

COAL RES SECT, EARTH & MINERAL SCI EXP STA, 57- Concurrent Pos: Mem, Int Comn Coal Petrol. Honors & Awards: Joseph Becker Award, Am Inst Mining, Metall & Petrol Engrs; G H Cady Award, Geol Soc Am. Mem: Bot Soc Am; Geol Soc Am; Am Asn Strategic Palynolgists; Am Soc Testing & Mat. Res: Tertiary floras; fossil woods; plant phylogeny; coal petrology; modern phytogenic sediments; peat to coal transformation. Mailing Add: Dept of Geosci 517 Deike Bldg Pa State Univ University Park PA 16802

SPADAFINO, LEONARD PETER, b Jersey City, NJ, Oct 25, 31; m 56; c 2. ORGANIC CHEMISTRY. Educ: Univ Ga, BS, 58, PhD(chem), 63. Prof Exp: ORG CHEMIST, TENN EASTMAN CO, 63- Mem: Am Asn Textile Chemists & Colorists; Am Chem Soc. Res: Kinetics of the decomposition of peroxides in systems where stable free radicals function as scavengers of reactive radicals; anthraquinone and azo dyes for synthetic fibers and films. Mailing Add: Tenn Eastman Co Eastman Rd PO Box 511 Kingsport TN 37662

SPADONI, LEON R, b Kent, Wash, Aug 11, 30; m 57; c 3. OBSTETRICS & GYNECOLOGY. Educ: Univ Wash, BS, 53, MD, 57. Prof Exp: Intern med, Minn Gen Hosp, 57-58; resident obstet & gynec, Univ Integrated Hosp, 60-63, from instr to assoc prof, Sch Med, 63-74, PROF OBSTET & GYNEC, SCH MED, UNIV WASH, 74-, VCHMN, 77- Concurrent Pos: Attend physician, Univ & King County Hosps, 63-; consult, Univ Wash Hall Health Ctr, 63-; consult, Madigan Gen Hosp, Tacoma, 69; mem, Am Bd Obstet & Gynec. Mem: Am Fertil Soc; Am Col Obstet & Gynec. Res: Infertility; gynecologic endocrinology. Mailing Add: Dept Obstet & Gynec RH-20 Univ Wash Hosp Seattle WA 98195

SPAEDER, CARL EDWARD, JR, b Meadville, Pa, Mar 29, 35; m 62; c 3. METALLURGY. Educ: Pa State Univ, University Park, BS, 57; Carnegie-Mellon Univ, MS, 63; Univ Pittsburgh, PhD(metall), 70. Prof Exp: From res asst to SR RES METALLURGIST, US STEEL RES CTR, 57- Mem: Am Soc Metals; Am Soc Mech Engrs. Res: Elevated temperature; properties of metals; cryogenic properties; formability; material characteristics. Mailing Add: US Steel Res Ctr Monroeville PA 15146

SPAEPEN, FRANS, b Mechelen, Belgium, Oct 29, 48; m 73; c 2. PHYSICAL METALLURGY. Educ: Univ Leuven, Belgium, ME, 71; Harvard Univ, PhD(appl physics), 75. Prof Exp: Res fel, 75-77, asst prof, 77-81, ASSOC PROF APPL PHYSICS, HARVARD UNIV, 81- Mem: Am Soc Metals; Am Phys Soc; Mat Res Soc. Res: Amorphous metals; structure, atomic transport, mechanical properties and transformations; amorphous crystalline interfaces; amorphous crystalline transformations in semiconductors and oxides; structure of grain boundaries. Mailing Add: Div Appl Sci Harvard Univ Pierce Hall 29 Oxford St Cambridge MA 02138

SPAET, THEODORE H, b New York, NY, June 24, 20; m 41, 71; c 3. MEDICINE. Educ: Univ Wis, BA, 42; New York Med Col, MD, 45; Am Bd Internal Med, dipl. Prof Exp: Intern, Montefiore Hosp, New York, 45-46, asst resident med, 48-49; asst resident, Morrisania Hosp, 49-50; from instr to asst prof, Sch Med, Stanford Univ, 51-55; assoc prof path, Col Physicians & Surgeons, Columbia Univ, 55-65; PROF MED, ALBERT EINSTEIN COL MED, 65- Concurrent Pos: Damon Runyon clin res fel hemat, New Eng Ctr Hosp, Boston, 50-51; dir dept hemat, Montefiore Hosp, 55-; consult, Manhattan Vet Admin Hosp, 58, St Luke's Hosp & Bronx Vet Admin Hosp; former mem exec comt, Coun Thrombosis, Am Heart Asn; mem coun arteriosclerosis, Am Heart Asn. Mem: AAAS; Asn Am Physicians; Am Soc Clin Invest; Am Physiol Soc; Am Soc Hemat; Am Fedn Clin Res; Int Soc Hemat. Res: Hemorrhagic diseases; thrombosis; hemolytic anemias. Mailing Add: Montefiore Hosp 111 E 210th St New York NY 10467

SPAETH, GEORGE L, b Philadelphia, Pa, Mar 3, 32; m 58; c 3. OPHTHALMOLOGY. Educ: Yale Univ, BA, 54; Harvard Med Sch, MD, 59; Am Bd Ophthal, dipl, 65. Prof Exp: Intern, Univ Hosp, Ann Arbor, Mich, 60; resident ophthal, Wills Eye Hosp, 63; clin assoc, Nat Inst Neurol Dis & Blindness, 63-65; instr ophthal, Univ Pa, 65-68; from instr to assoc prof, 68-71, PROF OPHTHAL, THOMAS JEFFERSON UNIV, 71- Concurrent Pos: Grants, Nat Soc Prev Blindness, 67 & 68, Nat Coun Combat Blindness, 68 & Nat Eye Inst, 72-75; attend surgeon, Wills Eye Hosp, 65-66, sr asst surgeon & assoc glaucoma clin, 66-68, dir glaucoma serv, 68- Mem: Am Ophthal Soc; fel Am Acad Ophthal & Otolaryngol; fel Danish Ophthal Soc; fel Royal Soc Med; Am Col Surgeons. Res: Diagnosis, treatment and pathophysiology of glaucoma; metabolic diseases, their ocular aspects and treatment, especially homocystinuria; sociology of chronic disease; ocular surgery, especially of glaucoma. Mailing Add: 15 Laughlin Lane Philadelphia PA 19118

SPAETH, RALPH, b Cleveland, Ohio, Mar 21, 05; m 32; c 2. MEDICINE. Educ: Western Reserve Univ, AB, 27, MD, 31; Am Bd Pediat, dipl, 38. Prof Exp: From instr to clin prof, Col Med, Univ Ill, Chicago, 36-68, prof, 68-72, EMER CLIN PROF, COL MED, UNIV ILL, CHICAGO, 72-; EMER CLIN PROF PEDIAT, RUSH MED COL, 72- Concurrent Pos: Supvr physician, East Off, Chicago Div, State of Ill Children & Family Serv, 37-75; mem, Nat Comn Venereal Dis, 71-72; regional medical coordr, Proj Head Start to 78. Mem: Am Acad Pediat; AMA; Sigma Xi; Am Venereal Disease Asn; NY Acad Sci. Res: Immunology and clinical management of tetanus; immunology and immunization against mumps; prevention of rabies; therapy of poliomyelitis with convalescent serum; active immunization against measles. Mailing Add: 9030 S Bell Ave Chicago IL 60620

SPAGHT, MONROE EDWARD, b Arcata, Calif, Dec 9, 09; m; c 3. PHYSICAL CHEMISTRY, ORGANIC CHEMISTRY. Educ: Stanford Univ, AB, 29, AM, 30, PhD(chem), 33. Hon Degrees: DSc, Rensselaer Polytech Inst, 58, Drexel Inst, 62; LLD, Univ Manchester, 64, Calif State Cols, 65, Milliken Univ, 67, Wesleyan Univ, 68; Colo Sch Mines, DEng, 71. Prof Exp: Res chemist & technologist, Shell Oil Co, 33-45; vpres, Shell Oil Co, 46-48, pres, 49-52, dir, 53-80. Concurrent Pos: Exec vpres, Shell Oil Co, 53-60, pres, 61-65, chmn bd dir, 65-70, managing dir, Shell Group, 65-70, dir,

Royal Dutch Petrol Co, 65-80. Honors & Awards: Midwest Res Inst Award, 62; Johnson Lectr & Medallist, Stockholm, Sweden, 66; Brit Soc Chem Indust Medal, 66. Mem: Nat Acad Eng; fel AAAS; Am Chem Soc; fel Am Inst Chem Eng; Brit Soc Chem Indust (int pres, 63-64). Res: Thermodynamics of organic compounds; chemical derivatives of petroleum. Mailing Add: Shell Centre London SE1 7NA England

SPAGNOLI, HARRIET, b Nanuet, NY, Dec 16, 18; m 49; c 4. ZOOLOGY, MORPHOLOGY. Educ: NY Univ, AB, 41, MS, 46, PhD, 51. Prof Exp: Res asst, Lederle Labs, Am Cyanamid Co, 52; instr anat & physiol, 58-61, from asst prof to assoc prof embryol, 61-65, actg chmn dept, 64-66, actg dean, Maxwell Becton Col Lib Arts, 74-76, dean, Maxwell Becton Col Lib Arts, 76-79, PROF EMBRYOL, FARLEIGH DICKINSON UNIV, 65- Concurrent Pos: Grants, NIH, 64, NSF, 64-65. Mem: NY Acad Sci; Am Soc Zoologists; AAAS. Res: Studies on ageing in pituitary gland of hamster; local heat effects on growth in mandible and cranium of rabbit and neuroendocrine studies in amphibian pituitary. Mailing Add: Dept of Biol Sci Fairleigh Dickinson Univ Teaneck NJ 07666

SPAHN, GERARD JOSEPH, b Baltimore, Md, May 4, 38; m 61; c 3. MICROBIOLOGY. Educ: Mt St Mary's Col, Md, BS, 60; St John's Univ, MS, 62; Univ Md, PhD(microbiol), 65. Prof Exp: Lab scientist rabies diag, Livestock Sanit Serv Lab, 65-66; virologist, Microbiol Assoc, Inc, Md, 66-72; sr scientist, Litton Bionetics, Inc, 72-76; virologist, Microbiol Assocs, Inc, 76-77; sr scientist, Enviro Control, Inc, Rockville, Md, 77-79; DIR SAFETY, SALK INST BIOL STUDIES, SAN DIEGO, 79- Mem: Am Asn Lab Animal Sci; Am Soc Microbiol; Tissue Cult Asn; Sigma Xi. Res: Oncogenic virus expression in cell culture; tumorigenicity in vivo and transformation in vitro; studies on spontaneous neoplasms of rats and mice. Mailing Add: Salk Inst PO Box 85800 San Diego CA 92138

SPAHN, ROBERT JOSEPH, b Chicago, Ill, July 2, 36; m 61; c 4. APPLIED MATHEMATICS. Educ: Mich Technol Univ, BS, 58; Mich State Univ, PhD(physics), 63. Prof Exp: Engr, NAm Aviation, Inc, Ohio, 63-64; asst prof, 64-70, ASSOC PROF MATH, MICH TECHNOL UNIV, 70- Mem: Soc Indust & Appl Math. Res: Solutions of boundary value problems in partial differential equations. Mailing Add: Dept of Math Mich Technol Univ Houghton MI 49931

SPAHR, SIDNEY LOUIS, b Bristol, Va, Sept 5, 35; m 60; c 2. AGRICULTURE, DAIRY SCIENCE. Educ: Va Polytech Inst, BSc, 58; Pa State Univ, MSc, 60, PhD(dairy sci), 64. Prof Exp: Instr dairy sci, Pa State Univ, 62-64; asst prof dairy husb, 64-70, ASSOC PROF DAIRY SCI, UNIV ILL, URBANA, 72- Concurrent Pos: Staff officer, Nat Acad Sci, Washington, DC, 70-72. Mem: AAAS; Am Dairy Sci Asn; Am Soc Animal Sci. Res: Dairy cattle management and nutrition. Mailing Add: 315 Animal Sci Lab Univ of Ill Urbana IL 61801

SPAHT, CARLOS G, II, b New Orleans, La, June 22, 43; m 64; c 2. MATHEMATICS, OPERATIONS RESEARCH. Educ: La State Univ, BS, 64, MS, 66, PhD(math), 70. Prof Exp: Asst math, La State Univ, Baton Rouge, 64-70, spec lectr, 70; asst prof, 72-78, ASSOC PROF MATH, LA STATE UNIV, SHREVEPORT, 78- Concurrent Pos: Instr & consult, Educ Ctr, Barksdale Air Force Base, 73-75. Mem: Am Math Asn; Am Asn Univ Profs. Res: Abstract algebra; operation research field. Mailing Add: Dept of Math La State Univ 8515 Youree Dr Shreveport LA 71105

SPAID, FRANK WILLIAM, b Pocatello, Idaho, Mar 7, 38; m 64; c 2. FLUID DYNAMICS. Educ: Ore State Univ, BS, 59; Calif Inst Technol, MS, 61, PhD(mech eng), 64. Prof Exp: Assoc res engr, Jet Propulsion Lab, Pasadena, 59-60, res engr, 61; supvr, Douglas Aircraft Co, Inc, 64-67; asst prof aeronaut, Univ Calif, Los Angeles, 67-72; PRIN SCIENTIST, McDONNELL DOUGLAS RES LABS, 72- Mem: Am Inst Aeronaut & Astronaut. Res: The interaction of a liquid or gaseous jet with a supersonic flow; boundary layer separation; transonic fluid dynamics. Mailing Add: McDonnell Douglas Res Labs PO Box 516 St Louis MO 63166

SPAIN, IAN L, b Saltwood, Eng, June 19, 40; wid. CHEMICAL PHYSICS. Educ: Univ London, BSc, 61, PhD(chem physics), 64, Royal Col Sci, ARCS, 61, Imp Col, dipl, 64. Prof Exp: Res assoc, Inst Study Metals, Univ Chicago, 64-66; asst prof molecular physics, Univ Md, College Park, 66-70, from assoc prof to prof mat sci, 70-79, dir, lab high pressure sci, 72-79, dir eng mat prog, 75-79; PROF, DEPT PHYSICS, COLO STATE UNIV, 79- Concurrent Pos: Prin res fel, Admiralty Underwater Weapons Estab, Gt Brit, 74-75; foreign collabr, Nuclear Study Ctr of Grenoble, 77 & 78. Mem: Am Inst Physics; fel Brit Inst Physics. Res: Electronic properties of high pressure solids; elastic properties of solids, melting phenomena and phase transitions at high pressure; synthetic metals. Mailing Add: Dept Physics Colo State Univ Fort Collins CO 80523

SPAIN, JAMES DORRIS, JR, b Washington, DC, Feb 3, 29; m 52; c 3. BIOCHEMISTRY. Educ: Mich Technol Univ, BS, 51; Med Col Va, MS, 53; Stanford Univ, PhD(chem), 56. Prof Exp: Res fel biochem, Univ Tex, M D Anderson Hosp & Tumor Inst, 55-56; from asst prof to assoc prof chem, 56-62, head dept biol sci, 62-68, PROF BIOCHEM, MICH TECHNOL UNIV, 62- Honors & Awards: Mich Tech Fac Res Award, 65. Mem: Am Chem Soc; Sigma Xi; Int Asn Gt Lakes Res; Am Soc Limnol & Oceanog. Res: computer modeling of biological systems; biomathematics; mixing of water masses in large lakes; simulation of biological and chemical systems; liver damage and azo dye carcinogenesis, histochemistry; precipitation chromatography; physical and chemical limnology; computer search and retrieval. Mailing Add: Dept of Biol Sci Mich Technol Univ Houghton MI 49931

SPALATIN, JOSIP, b Ston, Yugoslavia, Jan 29, 13; m 41; c 3. VIROLOGY. Educ: Univ Zagreb, BS, 38, DVM, 41; Univ Giessen, PhD(vet med), 44. Prof Exp: Teaching asst animal infectious dis, Univ Zagreb, 39-46; res assoc vaccine & sera prod, Vetserum Kalinovica, Yugoslavia, 46-53; from res assoc virol to assoc prof zoonoses, Sch Med, Univ Zagreb, 53-61; vis prof virol, Univ

Sask, 61-63; RES ASSOC VIROL, UNIV WISMADISON, 63- *Concurrent Pos:* Yugoslav fel, Univ Wis-Madison, 56-59. *Mem:* Asn Yugoslav Microbiologists (treas, 40-45); Wildlife Dis Asn. *Res:* Epidemiology, diagnosis and immunology in groups of mixoviruses; arbor-viruses and psittacosis lymphogranuloma venereum agents. *Mailing Add:* Dept of Vet Sci Univ of Wis Madison WI 53706

SPALDING, DAN WESLEY, b Sadler, Tex, Dec 13, 25; m 52; c 3. PHYSICS. *Educ:* NTex State Univ, BS, 47, MS, 50. *Prof Exp:* Asst prof physics, Southeastern State Col, Tex, 48-52; instr, Eastern NMex Univ, 52-53; lead systs design engr, Chance Vaught Aircraft, 53-57; asst prof, 57-63, head dept, 59-74, ASSOC PROF PHYSICS, EASTERN NMEX UNIV, 63-, ASSOC PROF MATH, 75-, ASST DEAN ACAD AFFAIRS, 74-, EXEC ASST TO VPRES FOR ACAD AFFAIRS & ADMIN & COORDR SPEC ACAD PROGS, 76- *Mem:* Am Asn Physics Teachers; Am Inst Physics; Nat Educ Asn. *Res:* Microwave systems for electron paramagnetic resonance; nuclear magnetic resonance and other applications, especially their use for typically optical experiments. *Mailing Add:* Acad Affairs Eastern NMex Univ Portales NM 88130

SPALDING, DONALD HOOD, b Pawtucket, RI, Dec 1, 25; m 53; c 2. PLANT PATHOLOGY. *Educ:* Brown Univ, AB, 50; Univ Kans, MA, 53; Wash State Univ, PhD(plant path), 60. *Prof Exp:* Asst instr bact, Univ Kans, 52-53; biochemist, Dow Chem Co, 53-57; asst plant path, Wash State Univ, 57-60; pathologist, Res Sta, USDA, Wash, 60-61, Md, 61-71, Fla, 71-80, LOCATION LEADER, SUBTROP HORT RES STA, USDA, 80- *Concurrent Pos:* Chemist, City Water Dept, Lawrence, Kans, 52-53. *Mem:* Am Soc Hort Sci; Am Phytopath Soc. *Res:* Physiology of host-parasite relations; post harvest pathology of fruits. *Mailing Add:* Subtrop Hort Res Sta USDA 13601 Old Cutler Rd Miami FL 33158

SPALDING, GARY E, biomathematics, see previous edition

SPALDING, GEORGE ROBERT, b Lancaster, Pa, Dec 1, 27; m 52; c 3. ARCHITECTUAL ACOUSTICS, INDUSTRIAL NOISE. *Educ:* Pa State Univ, BS, 53, MS, 55. *Prof Exp:* Res asst meteorol, Univ Mich, 55; res physicist, 55-72, SR RES SCIENTIST, ARMSTRONG CORK CO, 72- *Mem:* Acoust Soc Am. *Res:* Architectural and landscape office acoustics; industrial noise control; design and evaluation of masking sound systems for use in open plan office spaces; acoustical materials testing. *Mailing Add:* Armstrong World Indust Inc Box 3511 2500 Columbia Ave Lancaster PA 17604

SPALL, HENRY ROGER, b Newcastle upon Tyne, Eng, Oct 10, 38; US citizen. GEOPHYSICS. *Educ:* Univ London, BSc, 62, PhD(geophys), 70; Southern Methodist Univ, MS, 68. *Prof Exp:* Res asst geophys, Cambridge Univ, 62-64 & Southwest Ctr Advan Studies, Univ Tex, Dallas, 64-67; lectr geol, Southern Methodist Univ, 67-68; geologist, Mobil Res Labs, 68-69; Coop Inst Res Environ Sci fel, Univ Colo, Boulder, 70-71; geophysicist, Environ Res Labs, Nat Oceanic & Atmospheric Admin, 71-73; GEOPHYSICIST, US GEOL SURV, 73- *Concurrent Pos:* Mem working group 10, Comn Geodynamics, Int Union Geod & Geophys, 72-; ed, Geology, 73- & Earthquake Info Bull, 75- *Mem:* Am Geophys Union; Seismol Soc Am; fel Geol Soc Am; fel Royal Astron Soc; fel Geol Soc London. *Res:* Paleomagnetism and plate tectonics. *Mailing Add:* Off of Sci Publ US Geol Surv Reston VA 22092

SPALL, WALTER DALE, b Greeley, Colo, Apr 23, 43; m 70. ANALYTICAL CHEMISTRY. *Educ:* Colo Col, BA, 66; Univ NMex, PhD(anal chem), 70. *Prof Exp:* Res chemist, Chem Div, Uniroyal, Inc, 70-75; MEM STAFF, LOS ALAMOS SCI LAB, UNIV CALIF, NMEX, 75- *Concurrent Pos:* Part-time asst prof, Univ New Haven, 71-75. *Mem:* Am Chem Soc. *Res:* Chromatography; analytical instrumentation; computer automation of instrumentation; mass spectroscopy. *Mailing Add:* Group CMB-1 Mail Stop 740 Los Alamos Sci Lab Los Alamos NM 87544

SPALLHOLZ, JULIAN ERNEST, b Boston, Mass, Oct 8, 43; m 64; c 2. BIOCHEMISTRY, NUTRITION. *Educ:* Col State Univ, BS, 65, MS, 68; Univ Hawaii, PhD(biochem), 71. *Prof Exp:* Fel, Dept Biochem, Colo State Univ, 71-72, res assoc, 72-73, instr, 73-74; res chemist nutrit, Lab Exp Metab Dis, Vet Admin Hosp, 74-78; assoc res chemist, State Univ NY, Albany, 78; ASSOC PROF, DEPT FOOD & NUTRIT, TEX TECH UNIV, 78- *Concurrent Pos:* Interim dir, Inst Nutrit Sci, 81- *Mem:* Sigma Xi; Am Inst Nutrit; NY Acad Sci. *Res:* Nutritional importance of trace metals, especially selenium; immunology; application of physical probes such as nitroxides, fluorescent molecules and radionuclide probes to biological, biochemical and immunological research. *Mailing Add:* Dept of Food & Nutrit Tex Tech Univ Lubbock TX 79409

SPANDE, THOMAS FREDERICK, b Madison, Wis, June 22, 37; m 68. ORGANIC CHEMISTRY. *Educ:* St Olaf Col, BA, 59; Princeton Univ, PhD(org chem), 65. *Prof Exp:* Staff fel org chem, 64-66, RES CHEMIST, NIH, 66- *Mem:* Am Chem Soc. *Res:* Steroid chemistry; amino acid and protein chemistry, particularly indole and tryptophan chemistry. *Mailing Add:* Bldg 4 Lab 218 NIH Bethesda MD 20014

SPANDORFER, LESTER M, b Norfolk, Va, Oct 16, 25; m 56; c 2. ELECTRICAL ENGINEERING, COMPUTER SCIENCE. *Educ:* Univ Mich, BSEE, 47, MSEE, 48; Univ Pa, PhD(elec eng), 56. *Prof Exp:* Mem tech staff, Bell Tel Labs, 48-50; res asst dir comput ctr & proj mgr, Univ Pa, 50-57; sr engr, 57-58, dept mgr, 58-60, staff consult, 60-65, dept mgr, 65-67; dir tech develop, 67-72, dir data entry, 72-77, DIR, OFF AUTOMATION, SPERRY UNIVAC DIV, SPERRY RAND CORP, 77- *Mem:* Fel Inst Elec & Electronics Engrs. *Res:* Computer design; application of semiconductor and magnetic devices. *Mailing Add:* Sperry Univac Div PO Box 500 Blue Bell PA 19422

SPANEL, LESLIE EDWARD, b St Louis, Mo, Mar 13, 37; m 61; c 2. SOLID STATE PHYSICS. *Educ:* Univ Mo-Rolla, BS, 59; Iowa State Univ, PhD(physics), 64. *Prof Exp:* Res asst physics, Ames Lab, AEC, Iowa State Univ, 60-64; res specialist, Microelectronics Orgn, Boeing Space Div, Boeing Co, 64-68; asst prof, 68-74, ASSOC PROF PHYSICS, WESTERN WASH UNIV, 74- *Mem:* Am Phys Soc. *Res:* Fermi surface of magnetic and nonmagnetic metals; transport properties of semiconductors. *Mailing Add:* Dept of Physics Astron Dept Western Wash Univ Bellingham WA 98225

SPANG, ARTHUR WILLIAM, b Detroit, Mich, Aug 16, 17; m 44, 67; c 5. MICROCHEMISTRY. *Educ:* Wayne State Univ, BS, 41. *Prof Exp:* Org microanalyst & head lab, Parke, Davis & Co, 41-48, med detailing, 48-49; mem anal staff, Upjohn Co, 49-50; head microanal lab, Olin Mathieson Chem Corp, 50, supvr res anal lab, 51-54; OWNER, SPANG MICROANAL LAB, 54- *Mem:* Am Chem Soc; Am Microchem Soc; Royal Soc Chem. *Res:* New methods for the microanalysis of new types of organic and organometallic compounds. *Mailing Add:* Spang Microanal Lab Star Rte 1 Box 142 Eagle Harbor MI 49951

SPANG, H AUSTIN, III, b New Haven, Conn, July 16, 34; m 57; c 3. CONTROL ENGINEERING. *Educ:* Yale Univ, BE, 56, MEng, 58, DEng(elec eng), 60. *Prof Exp:* Lab asst, Yale Univ, 56-58, res engr commun, 58-60; CONTROL ENGR, GEN ELEC RES & DEVELOP CTR, 60- *Concurrent Pos:* Instr, New Haven Col, 58-60; lectr, Univ Calif, Los Angeles, 66-69; assoc ed, Automatica, Int Fedn Automatic Control, 67-80; assoc ed appln, Inst Elec & Electronics Engrs Trans on Automatic Control, 77-79; ed, Automatica, Int Fedn Automatic Control, 80- *Mem:* Fel Inst Elec & Electronics Engrs; Soc Indust & Appl Math; Sigma Xi. *Res:* Applications of control and their digital implementation; multivariable control; real time computer control; computer aided control system design. *Mailing Add:* Gen Elec Res & Develop Ctr PO Box 8 Schenectady NY 12301

SPANGENBERG, DOROTHY BRESLIN, b Galveston, Tex, Aug 31, 31; m 58; c 1. ZOOLOGY, BIOCHEMISTRY. *Educ:* Univ Tex, BA, 56, MA, 58, PhD(zool), 60. *Prof Exp:* Dir, Spangenberg Labs, 60-62; res assoc, Med Ctr, Univ Ark, 62-65; assoc prof biol res, Univ Little Rock, 65-66; res scholar zool, Ind Univ, 66-69; res assoc, Water Resources Lab, Univ Louisville, 69-70, Dept Oral Biol, Sch Dent, 70-72; vis assoc prof molecular, cellular & develop biol, Univ Colo, Boulder, 72-77; vis assoc prof, 77-80, RES PROF, EASTERN VA MED SCH, 80- *Concurrent Pos:* Grants, NSF, 64-66, Sigma Xi, 65-66, NIH, 66-, NIH & Nat Inst Dent Res, 78, NIH & Nat Inst Child Health & Human Develop & Dept Energy Contract, 77-82. *Mem:* Am Soc Zoologists; Am Soc Cell Biol; Sigma Xi; Electron Micros Soc Am; AAAS. *Res:* Development of coelenterate model systems for study of mechanisms of cellular and organismal development, especially metamorphosis, utilizing biochemical and cytological technics. *Mailing Add:* Eastern Va Med Sch Norfolk VA 23501

SPANGLER, CHARLES BISHOP, applied mathematics, physics, see previous edition

SPANGLER, CHARLES WILLIAM, b Philadelphia, Pa, Feb 12, 38; m 61; c 2. PHYSICAL ORGANIC CHEMISTRY. *Educ:* Mass Inst Technol, BS, 59; Northeastern Univ, MS, 61; Univ Md, PhD(org chem), 64. *Prof Exp:* Great Lakes Cols Asn teacher intern org chem, Ohio Wesleyan Univ, 64-65; res assoc, 65-66, asst prof, 65-72, assoc prof, 72-81, PROF ORG CHEM, NORTHERN ILL UNIV, 81- *Concurrent Pos:* Res Corp & NSF res grants. *Mem:* Am Chem Soc; The Chem Soc. *Res:* Chemistry of conjugated polyenes; electrophilic substitution; catalytic dehydrations of dienols; electrocyclic reactions; photochemistry of polyunsaturated systems; sigmatropic migrations. *Mailing Add:* Dept of Chem Northern Ill Univ De Kalb IL 60115

SPANGLER, DANIEL PATRICK, b Meadows of Dan, Va, Apr 22, 34; m 61; c 1. GEOLOGY. *Educ:* Berea Col, BA, 56; Univ Va, MS, 64; Univ Ariz, PhD(geol), 69. *Prof Exp:* Geologist, Va Hwy Dept, 57-59 & 61-63; asst, Univ Va, 63-65 & Univ Ariz, 65-67; geologist, Agr Res Serv, USDA, 67-69; asst prof geol, SFla Univ, 69-74; asst prof, 74-77, ASSOC PROF GEOL, UNIV FLA, 77- *Concurrent Pos:* Partic, NSF-Am Geol Inst Tenth Int Field Inst, Spain, 71; res award, Univ SFla & Penrose bequest res grant, Geol Soc Am, Tampa, Fla, 72. *Mem:* Geol Soc Am; Am Water Resources Asn; Nat Asn Geol Teachers; Am Inst Mining, Metall & Petrol Engrs; Am Inst Prof Geologists. *Res:* Hydrogeologic systems; application of geophysics to hydrogeologic problems; engineering geology. *Mailing Add:* Dept of Geol Univ of Fla Gainesville FL 32611

SPANGLER, FRED WALTER, b Park Ridge, Ill, Feb 27, 18; m 41; c 2. CHEMISTRY. *Educ:* Carthage Col, AB, 40; Univ Ill, PhD(org chem), 44. *Prof Exp:* Asst chem, Univ Ill, 40-42; res chemist, Eastman Kodak Co, 44-52, tech assoc, 52-59, asst supt, Film Emulsion Div, 59-81; RETIRED. *Mem:* Am Chem Soc; Soc Photog Sci & Eng. *Res:* Grignard reactions involving the naphthalene nucleus; organic chemicals used in photography; anthraquinone and related dyes; detergents and wetting agents; photographic emulsions. *Mailing Add:* 121 Nob Hill Rochester NY 14617

SPANGLER, GEORGE RUSSELL, b Susanville, Calif, Oct 22, 42; m 62; c 4. AQUATIC ECOLOGY, POPULATION DYNAMICS. *Educ:* Humboldt State Col, BS, 64; Univ Toronto, MS, 66, PhD(zool), 74. *Prof Exp:* Res scientist fisheries, Ont Dept Lands & Forests, 68-71; scientist-in-chg, Lake Huron Res Unit, Ont Ministry Natural Resources, 72-78; ASSOC PROF FISHERIES, UNIV MINN, 78- *Mem:* Am Fisheries Soc; Int Asn Great Lakes Res; Biomet Soc; Am Inst Fishery Res Biologists. *Res:* Population dynamics of fish stocks; predator-prey interactions; effects of exploitation on fish communities; efficiency and selectivity of fishing gear. *Mailing Add:* Dept Entom Fisheries & Wildlife Univ Minn St Paul MN 55108

SPANGLER, GEORGE WESLEY, physics, biophysics, see previous edition

SPANGLER, GLENN EDWARD, b York, Pa, June 20, 42. CHEMICAL PHYSICS, ENVIRONMENTAL TECHNOLOGY. *Educ:* Gettysburg Col, BA, 65; Univ Va, PhD(physics), 70. *Prof Exp:* Physicist thermometry, Nat Bur Stand, 70-71; res physicist chromatography, US Army Mobility Equip Res & Develop Command, 71-78; SR STAFF ENGR DETECTION, BENDIX, 78- *Honors & Awards:* Sci Achievement Award, US Army Mobility Equip Res & Develop Command, 74 & 78. *Mem:* Am Phys Soc; Am Chem Soc; AAAS. *Res:* Ion mobility spectrometry; mass spectrometry; plasma chromatography; chemical and electrochemical vapor detection; membrane permeability; gas purification; environmental science; chemical and electrochemical vapor detection. *Mailing Add:* Bendix 1400 Taylor Ave Baltimore MD 21204

SPANGLER, GRANT EDWARD, b Lebanon, Pa, Oct 17, 26; m 54; c 3. METALLURGICAL ENGINEERING, MATERIAL SCIENCES. *Educ:* Lehigh Univ, BS, 50; Univ Pa, MS, 53. *Prof Exp:* Res scientist metall, Westinghouse Atomic Power Div, 50-52, Res Lab, Air Reduction Co, 53-56 & Franklin Inst Res Labs, 56-64; res scientist, 64-65, sect dir, 65-66, dept dir, 66-78, GEN DIR METALL RES DIV, REYNOLDS METALS CO, 78- *Mem:* Fel Am Soc Metals; Am Inst Mining, Metall & Petrol Engrs. *Res:* Fuel element development; treatment of molten metals by powder injection; purification of reactive metals by floating zone refining; alloy development, physical metallurgy and process metallurgy of aluminum and aluminum alloys. *Mailing Add:* Reynolds Metals Co 6601 W Broad St PO Box 27003 Richmond VA 23261

SPANGLER, HAYWARD GOSSE, b Redbank, NJ, July 6, 38; m 66; c 2. ENTOMOLOGY. *Educ:* La Sierra Col, BS, 61; Univ Ariz, MS, 63; Kans State Univ, PhD(entom), 67. *Prof Exp:* RES ENTOMOLOGIST, BEE RES LAB, AGR RES SERV, USDA, ARIZ, 67- *Mem:* Entom Soc Am; Sigma Xi. *Res:* Insect behavior; insect acoustics. *Mailing Add:* Bee Research Lab USDA-ARS 2000 E Allen Rd Tucson AZ 85719

SPANGLER, JOHN ALLEN, b Morgantown, WVa, Jan 1, 18; m 48; c 3. CHEMISTRY. *Educ:* WVa Univ, AB, 39, PhD(chem), 42. *Prof Exp:* Res chemist, Am Viscose Corp, 42-44; assoc prof, 46-52, chmn dept, 55-58, PROF CHEM, SAN DIEGO STATE UNIV, 54- *Mem:* Am Chem Soc. *Res:* Multiple-junction thermocouples for low freezing-point measurements; physical constants related to easier methods of analysis; ternary systems; physical methods of analysis; fiber chemistry. *Mailing Add:* Dept of Chem San Diego State Univ San Diego CA 92182

SPANGLER, JOHN DAVID, b Lincoln, Nebr, Nov 18, 36; m 58; c 5. PHYSICS. *Educ:* Kans State Univ, BS, 58; Duke Univ, PhD(physics), 61. *Prof Exp:* Res assoc physics, Duke Univ, 61-62; asst prof, DePauw Univ, 64-65; asst prof, 65-69, assoc prof, 69-80, PROF PHYSICS, KANS STATE UNIV, 80- *Mem:* Am Phys Soc; Soc Indust & Appl Math; Am Asn Physics Teachers. *Res:* Theoretical applied physics. *Mailing Add:* Dept of Physics Kans State Univ Manhattan KS 66502

SPANGLER, MARTIN ORD LEE, b Roanoke, Va, Sept 17, 28; m 56; c 4. ORGANIC CHEMISTRY, BIOCHEMISTRY. *Educ:* Bridgewater Col, BA, 50; Va Polytech Inst & State Univ, MS, 53, PhD(chem), 59. *Prof Exp:* Res assoc anal biol fluids, Univ Mich Hosp, 53-55; instr chem, Va Polytech Inst & State Univ, 55-56; assoc prof, Waynesburg Col, 58-59 & King Col, 59-66; assoc prof, 66-68, chmn dept, 73-80, PROF CHEM, ELIZABETHTOWN COL, 68- *Concurrent Pos:* Vis prof, Hershey Med Ctr, Pa State Univ, 72-73; lectr, Ohio State Univ, 80-81. *Mem:* AAAS; Am Chem Soc. *Res:* Organic synthesis and mechanisms of organic reactions; synthesis of antitumor agents and antibiotics from sugar derivatives. *Mailing Add:* Dept Chem Gibble Sci Hall Elizabethtown Col Elizabethtown PA 17022

SPANGLER, PAUL JUNIOR, b York, Pa, Nov 21, 24; m 50; c 1. ENTOMOLOGY. *Educ:* Lebanon Valley Col, AB, 49; Ohio Univ, MS, 51; Univ Mo, PhD(entom), 60. *Prof Exp:* Mus asst entom, Univ Kans, 51-53; instr entom, Univ Mo, 53-57; fishery res biologist, US Fish & Wildlife Serv, 57-58; syst entomologist, Entom Res Div, Agr Res Serv, USDA, 58-62; ASSOC CUR, DIV COLEOPTERA, NAT MUS NATURAL HIST, SMITHSONIAN INST, 62- *Concurrent Pos:* Lectr, Grad Fac, Univ Md. *Mem:* Entom Soc Am. *Res:* Systematics, biology and zoogeography of aquatic beetles. *Mailing Add:* Nat Mus of Natural Hist Smithsonian Inst Washington DC 20560

SPANGLER, ROBERT ALAN, b Celina, Ohio, Apr 10, 33; m 59. BIOPHYSICS. *Educ:* Harvard Univ, AB, 55, MD, 59; State Univ NY Buffalo, PhD(biophys), 64. *Prof Exp:* Res fel, 59-65, asst prof, 65-70, actg chmn dept, 70-77, ASSOC PROF BIOPHYS, SCH MED, STATE UNIV NY BUFFALO, 70- *Mem:* Biophys Soc; NY Acad Sci; AAAS. *Res:* Chemical kinetics in biological systems; non-equilibrium thermochemistry of biological systems; transport; theoretical chemical kinetics; models. *Mailing Add:* Dept of Biophys Sci State Univ of NY at Buffalo Buffalo NY 14214

SPANGLER, STANLEY GORDON, b Louisville, Ky, Sept 4, 44; div. BIOPHYSICS, PHYSIOLOGY. *Educ:* Birmingham Southern Col, BS, 67; Univ Ala, Birmingham, PhD(physiol & biophys), 70. *Prof Exp:* Health physicist, US Air Force, 69-73; res fel, Sch Med, Johns Hopkins Univ, 73-75, res assoc physiol, 75, NIH res fel, 74-75; instr, 75-76, ASST PROF PHYSIOL & BIOPHYS, UNIV ALA, BIRMINGHAM, 76- *Mem:* Biophys Soc; Physiol Soc. *Res:* Solute and water transport across cell membranes. *Mailing Add:* Dept of Physiol & Biophys Univ of Ala Univ Sta Birmingham AL 35294

SPANGLER, STEVEN RANDALL, b Stamford, Conn, Sept 25, 50; m 70; c 2. RADIO ASTRONOMY, THEORETICAL ASTROPHYSICS. *Educ:* Univ Iowa, BA & MS, 72, PhD(physics), 75. *Prof Exp:* Res assoc space physics, Univ Iowa, 75-76; res assoc, 76-78, ASST SCIENTIST RADIO ASTRON, NAT RADIO ASTRON OBSERV, 78- *Mem:* Am Astron Soc; Am Phys Soc. *Res:* Observations of extragalactic radio sources and their interpretation in terms of hydrodynamics, statistical physics and radiation theory. *Mailing Add:* Nat Radio Astron Observ Socorro NM 87801

SPANGLER, WILLIAM J, microbiology, see previous edition

SPANIER, BONNIE BARBARA, virology, molecular biology, see previous edition

SPANIER, EDWARD J, b Philadelphia, Pa, May 13, 37; m 68; c 2. INORGANIC CHEMISTRY. *Educ:* La Salle Col, BA, 59; Univ Pa, PhD(inorg chem), 64. *Prof Exp:* Res chemist, E I du Pont de Nemours & Co, 64-65; asst prof inorg chem, Seton Hall Univ, 65-72; assoc dir sci & eng, 72-73, assoc dir planning for health affairs, 73-74, asst dean admin, Sch Med, 74-75, assoc dean admin, Sch Med, 75-80, asst vpres health affairs, 80-81, ADJ ASSOC PROF CHEM, WRIGHT STATE UNIV, 72-, ASST VPRES FINANCIAL SERV, 81- *Mem:* AAAS; Am Chem Soc. *Res:* Chemistry of the hydrides of boron, silicon and germanium; nuclear magnetic resonance; reactions of metal carbides; chemistry of group V elements. *Mailing Add:* Sch of Med Wright State Univ Dayton OH 45435

SPANIER, EDWIN HENRY, b Washington, DC, Aug 8, 21; m 81; c 3. MATHEMATICS. *Educ:* Univ Minn, BA, 41; Univ Mich, MS, 45, PhD(math), 47. *Prof Exp:* Mathematician, Signal Corps, US War Dept, 41-44; Jewett fel, Inst Advan Study, 47-48; from asst prof to prof math, Univ Chicago, 48-59; PROF MATH, UNIV CALIF, BERKELEY, 59- *Concurrent Pos:* Guggenheim fel, Univ Paris, 52-53; Fulbright distinguished lectr, Chile, 73. *Mem:* Am Math Soc; Math Asn Am. *Res:* Topology; formal languages. *Mailing Add:* Dept Math Univ Calif Berkeley CA 94720

SPANIER, JEROME, b St Paul, Minn, June 3, 30; m 52; c 3. MATHEMATICS. *Educ:* Univ Minn, BA, 51; Univ Chicago, MS, 52, PhD(math), 55. *Prof Exp:* Asst, Univ Minn, 50-51; mathematician, Bettis Atomic Power Lab, Westinghouse Elec Corp, Pa, 55-67; mem tech staff, Math Group, NAm Rockwell Corp, Calif, 67-70, group leader math group, Sci Ctr, 70-71; PROF MATH, CLAREMONT GRAD SCH, 71- *Concurrent Pos:* Consult, Atomics Int Div, NAm Rockwell Corp, 71- *Mem:* Am Math Soc; Soc Indust & Appl Math; Math Asn Am; AAAS. *Res:* Monte Carlo methods; numerical analysis; random walk processes; transport theory; applications of numerical techniques to nuclear reactor design. *Mailing Add:* Dept Math Claremont Grad Sch Claremont CA 91711

SPANIS, CURT WILLIAM, b Barrie, Ont, May 6, 32; US citizen; m 65. NEUROBIOLOGY, CELL BIOCHEMISTRY. *Educ:* Queen's Univ, Ont, BA, 57; Univ Calif, Los Angeles, MA, 60, PhD(physiol), 62; Alvarez Soc Med, Mex, dipl, 75. *Prof Exp:* Asst prof biol, San Diego State Col, 62-63 & microbiol, Inst Marine Sci, Univ Miami, 64; fel biol clocks, Scripps Inst Oceanog, Univ Calif, San Diego, 64-65; from asst prof to assoc prof biol, 65-70, chmn dept, 66-72, PROF BIOL, UNIV SAN DIEGO, 72-; RESEARCHER, DEPT PSYCHIAT, VET MEM HOSP, LA JOLLA, CALIF, 75- *Concurrent Pos:* NIH grants, Univ Miami, 64, Scripps Inst Oceanog, Univ Calif, San Diego, 64-65, Univ San Diego, 69-72; NSF grants, 64 & 75; vis prof, Biol Inst, Helgoland, Ger, 64; mem, Rev Bd NSF Grants. *Mem:* NY Acad Sci; fel Am Inst Chem; hon mem Mex Soc Biol Psychiat; Soc Neurosci; Brit Brain Res Asn. *Res:* Biological clocks. *Mailing Add:* Dept of Biol Univ of San Diego San Diego CA 92110

SPANN, CHARLES HENRY, b Brandon, Miss, Sept 11, 39; m 63; c 3. PATHOLOGY, PUBLIC HEALTH. *Educ:* Tougaloo Col BS, 62; Univ Miss Med Ctr, MS, 73, PhD(human anat & path), 74. *Prof Exp:* Instr biol & sci, Holtzclaw High Sch, 66-69 & Crystal Springs High Sch, Miss, 69-70; ASSOC PROF BIOL & ASSOC DIR HEALTH CAREERS, JACKSON STATE UNIV, 74- *Concurrent Pos:* Consult pre-nursing prog, Meridian Jr Col, Miss, 76-77; res trainer, Minority Biomed Res Support Prog, Jackson State Univ, 77-, dir, 81- *Mem:* Am Soc Anatomists; AAAS. *Res:* Relationship and susceptibility of scorbutic Guinea Pigs to endotoxic shock, with emphasis on the histopathological effects of the general viscera and treatment modalities. *Mailing Add:* Off Preprof Health Careers PO Box 18516 Jackson State Univ Jackson MS 39217

SPANN, JAMES FLETCHER, (JR), b Dothan, Ala, Nov 21, 35; m 56; c 2. CARDIOLOGY. *Educ:* Emory Univ, MD, 61. *Prof Exp:* Intern med, Mass Gen Hosp, 61, asst resident, 62; sr investr, Cardiol Br, attend physician, Inst & consult cardiologist & med coordr, Surg Br, Nat Heart Inst, 66-68; assoc prof med & physiol, chief cardiovasc diag & asst chief cardiovasc med, Sch Med, Univ Calif, Davis, 68-70; PROF MED, CHIEF CARDIOVASC SECT, HEALTH SCI CTR, TEMPLE UNIV, 70- *Concurrent Pos:* Fel, Cardiol Br, Nat Heart Inst, 63-65, spec fel, 65-66. *Mem:* AAAS; Am Col Cardiol; Am Fedn Clin Res; NY Acad Sci; Am Soc Pharmacol & Exp Therapeut. *Res:* Clinical and investigative cardiology; cardiovascular physiology and pathophysiology; cardiac hypertrophy and congestive heart failure. *Mailing Add:* Cardiol Sect Temple Univ Health Sci Ctr Philadelphia PA 19140

SPANNINGER, PHILIP ANDREW, b Quakertown, Pa, May 31, 43; m 63; c 3. ORGANIC CHEMISTRY. *Educ:* Philadelphia Col Textiles & Sci, BS, 65; Clemson Univ, MS, 67, PhD(org chem), 70. *Prof Exp:* NIH fel, Univ Tex, Austin, 70-71; sr res chemist, Polyester Res, 71-74, proj mgr joint ventures & licensing technol, Goodyear Tire & Rubber Co, 74-77; mgr, Int Chem Div, 77-80, DIR, NEW VENTURES & INT CHEM DIV, GOODYEAR, 80- *Mem:* Am Chem Soc. *Res:* Organometallic chemistry; stereochemistry; reaction mechanisms; catalysis; boron-nitrogen heteroaromatic compounds; high temperature polymers. *Mailing Add:* 2555 Olentangy Dr Akron OH 44313

SPANO, FRANCIS A, b New York, NY, Jan 6, 31; m 59; c 3. ORGANIC CHEMISTRY, BIOCHEMISTRY. *Educ:* City Col New York, BS, 53; Fordham Univ, PhD(org chem), 63. *Prof Exp:* Res chemist, Allied Chem Corp, 62-66; res specialist, Gen Aniline & Film Corp, 66; asst prof org chem, 66-72, PROF CHEM, MIDDLESEX COUNTY COL, 72-, DEAN DIV SCI, 73- *Mem:* Am Chem Soc. *Res:* Illucidation of ozone oxidation of heterocyclic aeromatic compounds. *Mailing Add:* Dept of Chem Middlesex County Col Edison NJ 08817

SPANSWICK, ROGER MORGAN, b Eng, June 24, 39; m 63; c 2. BIOPHYSICS, PLANT PHYSIOLOGY. *Educ:* Univ Birmingham, BSc, 60; Univ Edinburgh, dipl biophys, 61, PhD(biophys), 64. *Prof Exp:* Asst lectr physics, Univ Edinburgh, 62-64; Nuffield res fel plant biophys, Cambridge Univ, 64-67; asst prof, 67-73, assoc prof, 73-79, PROF PLANT PHYSIOL, CORNELL UNIV, 79- *Concurrent Pos:* Sci Res Coun sr vis fel, Cambridge Univ, 73-74; John Simon Guggenheim Mem fel, Univ Calif, Davis, 81-82. *Mem:* Brit Soc Exp Biol; Biophys Soc; Am Soc Plant Physiologists. *Res:* Transport of ions across plant cell membranes; intercellular and long distance transport of ions in plants. *Mailing Add:* Div of Biol Sci Cornell Univ Ithaca NY 14850

SPAR, IRVING LEO, b New York, NY, July 6, 26; m 48; c 3. IMMUNOLOGY. *Educ:* George Washington Univ, BS, 47; Univ Rochester, PhD(biol), 52. *Prof Exp:* Jr scientist radiation biol, Sch Med & Dent, Univ Rochester, 52-53, from instr to assoc prof, 54-61; assoc prof radiol, Med Sch, Univ Ky, 62-63; assoc prof, 63-70, PROF RADIATION BIOL & BIOPHYS, SCH MED & DENT, UNIV ROCHESTER, 70-, ASSOC DEAN GRAD STUDIES, 75- *Mem:* Soc Nuclear Med; Am Asn Cancer Res; Radiation Biol Soc; Fedn Am Soc Exp Biol. *Res:* Iodine labeled antigens, antibodies and components of complement involved in inflammation and tumor rejection. *Mailing Add:* Dept Radiation Biol & Biophys Univ Rochester Sch Med & Dent Rochester NY 14642

SPAR, JEROME, b New York, NY, Oct 7, 18; m 45; c 2. METEOROLOGY. *Educ:* City Col New York, BS, 40; NY Univ, MS, 43, PhD(meteorol), 50. *Prof Exp:* From instr to prof meteorol, NY Univ, 46-73; PROF METEOROL, CITY COL, CITY UNIV NEW YORK, 73- *Concurrent Pos:* Dir meteorol res, US Weather Bur, 64-65. *Mem:* Fel Am Meteorol Soc; Am Geophys Union; fel NY Acad Sci; Royal Meteorol Soc. *Res:* Atmospheric radioactivity; numerical weather prediction; cyclogenesis; applied meteorology; climatic variations; synoptic and dynamic meteorology; general circulation and air-sea interactions. *Mailing Add:* Dept of Earth & Planetary Sci City Col New York NY 10031

SPARACINO, CHARLES MORGAN, b Charleston, WVa, Oct 18, 41; m 64; c 2. ORGANIC CHEMISTRY. *Educ:* Emory Univ, BS, 65, PhD(org chem), 69. *Prof Exp:* NIH fel, Worcester Found Exp Biol, 69-70; Nat Inst Gen Med Sci fel, 70-71, CHEMIST, RES TRIANGLE INST, RESEARCH TRIANGLE PARK, 71- *Mem:* Am Chem Soc. *Res:* Organic synthesis; natural product biosynthesis; drug metabolism. *Mailing Add:* 107 Jennings Lane Durham NC 27709

SPARACINO, ROBERT R, b New York, NY, Nov 6, 27; m 49; c 3. ELECTRICAL ENGINEERING, INSTRUMENTATION. *Educ:* City Col New York, BEE, 50; Polytech Inst Brooklyn, MEE, 55; Mass Inst Technol, ScD(instrumentation), 61. *Prof Exp:* Proj engr, Atlantic Electronics Corp, 50-54; chief engr & asst secy to corp, Penn-East Eng Corp, 54-58; res asst instrumentation, Mass Inst Technol, 58-59 & 60-61; sect head res & develop systs eng, AC Electronics Div, Gen Motors Corp, Wakefield, Mass, 61-62, lab dir, 62-63, dir res & develop, Los Angeles, 63-64, dir res & develop, Milwaukee, 64-68, dir eng, 68-70; vpres & mgr qual assurance dept, Bus Prod Group, 70-71, vpres & mgr prod design & eng, 71-73, vpres technol & eng, 73, sr vpres, Copier Duplicator Develop Div, 73-74, pres, Info Technol Group, 75-78, pres, Reprographics Tech Group, 78-80, CORP VPRES, XEROX CORP, 74-, SR VPRES, INFO PROD GROUP, 80- *Mem:* Inst Elec & Electronics Engrs; Sigma Xi. *Mailing Add:* Xerox Corp 800 Phillips Rd Webster NY 14603

SPARANO, BENJAMIN MICHAEL, b Los Angeles, Calif, Nov 21, 28; m 53; c 4. ANIMAL PATHOLOGY, TOXICOLOGY. *Educ:* St Peter's Col, BS, 50; Fordham Univ, MS, 55, PhD(biol), 57. *Prof Exp:* Instr sci, Sch Educ, Fordham Univ, 55-57; sr res scientist, Lederle Labs, Am Cyanamid Co, NY, 57-66; sr pathologist, Ciba Corp, NJ, 66-70; sr res pathologist, Lederle Labs, 70-80, ASST DEPT HEAD, EXP PATH DEPT, W G MALCOLM TOXICOL LABS, AM CYANAMID CO, 80- *Concurrent Pos:* Adj instr, St Peter's Col, 55-57. *Mem:* Soc Toxicol; Soc Toxicol Pathologists; Am Col Toxicol. *Res:* Safety evaluation of drugs and chemicals; pathology of laboratory animals; experimentally and chemically induced oncogenesis in rodents. *Mailing Add:* Am Cyanamid Co Med Res Div Wilbur G Malcolm Res Toxicol Labs Pearl River NY 10965

SPARAPANY, JOHN JOSEPH, b Albany, NY, Nov 11, 28; m 52; c 3. PHYSICAL ORGANIC CHEMISTRY. *Educ:* Buena Vista Col, BS, 51; NDak State Col, MS, 53; Okla State Univ, PhD(chem), 59. *Prof Exp:* Res chemist, E I du Pont de Nemours & Co, Inc, NY, 59-70; assoc scientist, 70-73, tech dir, 73-77, V PRES RES & DEVELOP, HYSOL DIV, DEXTER CORP, 77- *Mem:* Am Chem Soc. *Mailing Add:* Hysol Div 211 Franklin St Olean NY 14760

SPARBERG, ESTHER BRAUN, b New York, NY, June 17, 22; m 44; c 2. HISTORY OF SCIENCE, CHEMISTRY. *Educ:* Univ NC, BS, 43; Columbia Univ, MA, 45, EdD(sci educ), 58. *Prof Exp:* Technician, Rockefeller Inst, 43-44; teacher high sch, NY, 46-47; spec instr chem, 59-63, instr, 63-66, from asst prof to assoc prof, chem & hist sci, 66-77, prof hist sci, 77-80, PROF CHEM, HOFSTRA UNIV, 77- *Concurrent Pos:* Consult, NSF Coop Col Sch Sci Progs, dir prog, Hofstra-Uniondale Schs, 70-72, Hofstra-New Hyde Park-Herricks Schs, 72-74; dir, NSF proj, Hofstra-Farmingdale, Glen Cove, Wantagh, Queens, NY Schs, 75-76; dir, NSF, Pre-Col Teacher Develop in Sci Proj, Hofstra Univ, 77-78, 78-79. *Mem:* Am Chem Soc; Hist Sci Soc; Am Asn Physics Teachers. *Res:* Plasma and serum studies with Tiselius electrophoresis equipment. *Mailing Add:* 25 Emerson Dr Great Neck NY 11023

SPARGO, BENJAMIN H, b Six Mile Run, Pa, Aug 18, 19; m 42; c 2. PATHOLOGY. *Educ:* Univ Chicago, BS, 48, MS & MD, 52. *Prof Exp:* From instr to assoc prof, 53-64, PROF PATH, SCH MED, UNIV CHICAGO, 64- *Concurrent Pos:* Chmn, comt Diag Electron Micros, Vet Admin, 75-; res career award, Heart & Lung Inst, NIH, 64. *Res:* Renal changes in potassium deficiency; pathology of renal diseases. *Mailing Add:* 5719 Kenwood Chicago IL 60637

SPARKES, ROBERT STANLEY, b Niagara Falls, NY, June 20, 30; m 71; c 2. MEDICINE, HUMAN GENETICS. *Educ:* Antioch Col, BS, 52; Univ Rochester, MD, 56. *Prof Exp:* Assoc med, Sch Med, Univ Wash, 61-63; assoc physician, City of Hope Med Ctr, 63-64; PROF MED & MED GENETICS, SCH MED, UNIV CALIF, LOS ANGELES, 64-, VCHMN DENT MED, 81- *Mem:* AAAS; Am Soc Human Genetics; Am Fedn Clin Res. *Res:* Human-medical cytogenetics; human biochemical genetics; genetic linkage; tissue culture. *Mailing Add:* Dept of Med Univ of Calif Sch of Med Los Angeles CA 90024

SPARKMAN, DONAL ROSS, b Seattle, Wash, June 7, 07; m 48; c 4. MEDICINE. *Educ:* Univ Wash, BS, 30; Univ Pa, MD, 34; Am Bd Internal Med, dipl, 47. *Prof Exp:* From clin asst prof to clin prof, 54-56, ASSOC PROF MED, SCH MED, UNIV WASH, 56- *Concurrent Pos:* Assoc dir, Cancer Control Prog, Fred Hutchinson Cancer Res Ctr, 76-79. *Mem:* Am Heart Asn; Am Col Physicians. *Res:* Cardiac rehabilitation; relationship of stress to heart disease. *Mailing Add:* Fred Hutchinson Cancer Res Ctr 1124 Columbia Seattle WA 98104

SPARKMAN, MARJORIE FRANCES, b McShan, Ala, Jan 25, 23. PHYSIOLOGY. *Educ:* Fla State Col Women, BM, 45; Univ Ala, BS, 61; Ohio State Univ, MS, 62, PhD(physiol), 68. *Prof Exp:* Instr nursing, Southern Baptist Hosp, New Orleans, La, 51-56; head nurse, Nursing Serv, Wichita Falls Gen Hosp, Tex, 56-57; actg dir nursing, Southern Baptist Hosp Sch Nursing, New Orleans, 58-60; instr nursing, Col Med, Ohio State Univ, 62-64, asst prof physiol, 68-72; assoc prof, 72-77, PROF PHYSIOL & DIR CONTRACT GRANT ADMIN, COL NURSING, FLA STATE UNIV, 77- *Res:* Effects of 100 percent oxygen at atmospheric pressure in rats. *Mailing Add:* Dept of Physiol Fla State Univ Col of Nursing Tallahassee FL 32306

SPARKMAN, ROBERT SATTERFIELD, b Brownwood, Tex, Feb 18, 12; m 42. SURGERY. *Educ:* Baylor Univ, BA & MD, 35, LLD, 74; Am Bd Surg, dipl, 48. *Prof Exp:* Intern & resident, Cincinnati Gen Hosp, Ohio, 35-40; clin prof surg, Univ Tex Southwest Med Sch Dallas, 62-68; chief, Dept Gen Surg, 68-81, EMER CHIEF, DEPT GEN SURG, MED CTR, BAYLOR UNIV, 82- *Concurrent Pos:* Mem attend staff, Baylor & Parkland Hosp, 45-; chief surg consult, US Fifth Army, 48-73. *Mem:* Am Surg Asn; fel Am Col Surg. *Res:* Surgical disease of gallbladder, bile duct; surgical history. *Mailing Add:* 1004 N Washington Dallas TX 75204

SPARKS, ALBERT KIRK, b Wichita Falls, Tex, July 31, 23; m 43; c 1. MARINE BIOLOGY. *Educ:* Tex A&M Univ, BS, 47, MS, 49, PhD(biol oceanog), 57. *Prof Exp:* Asst biol, Tex A&M Univ, 47-49, instr, 49; asst prof, Sam Houston State Univ, 49-51; asst biol oceanog, Tex A&M Univ, 51-52, asst prof, 52-53, asst phys oceanog, Tex A&M Res Found, 53-56, chief biol & asst dir, Marine Lab, 56-58; assoc prof fisheries, Univ Wash, 58-63, prof, 63-70; dir, Bur Commercial Fisheries Biol Lab, Tex, 70-71; ctr dir, Gulf Coastal Fisheries Ctr, 71-73, dep assoc dir resource res, Washington, DC, 73-76, INVERT PATHOLOGIST, NORTHWEST & ALASKA FISHERIES CTR, NAT MARINE FISHERIES SERV, 76- *Concurrent Pos:* Consult to numerous indust & state agencies, 56-70; consult, Res & Develop Div, Humble Oil & Refining Co, 57-62 & Hawaii Dept Fish & Game, 63; adv, Ministry Nat Resources & Wildlife, Kenya, 65; prof, Tex A&M Univ, 70-73; affil prof, Col Fish, Univ Wash, 70- *Mem:* AAAS; Am Soc Zoologists; Nat Shellfisheries Asn (vpres, 68, pres, 69); Soc Invert Pathologists (vpres, 66-68, pres, 68-70; Wildlife Dis Asn. *Res:* Invertebrate pathology; marine fisheries. *Mailing Add:* Nat Marine Fisheries Serv 2725 Montlake Blvd E Seattle WA 98112

SPARKS, ALTON NEAL, b Robert Lee, Tex, Jan 25, 32; m 53; c 4. ENTOMOLOGY. *Educ:* Tex Tech Col, BS, 58; Iowa State Univ, MS, 59, PhD(entom), 65. *Prof Exp:* Entomologist, Entom Res Div, USDA, Ariz, 59-61, Iowa, 61-65, Okla, 65-66, Res LEADER & DIR, SOUTHERN GRAIN INSECTS RES LAB, USDA, 66- *Concurrent Pos:* Assoc prof, Okla State Univ, 65-66 & Univ Ga, 67- *Mem:* Entom Soc Am. *Res:* Biology and ecology of cotton insects and grain insects; screening insecticides; European corn borer and insects attacking small grains; pheromone and their effects on the behavior of nocturnal insects. *Mailing Add:* So Grain Insect Res Lab Ga Coastal Plain Exp Sta Tifton GA 31794

SPARKS, ARTHUR GODWIN, b Savannah, Ga, Feb 10, 38; m 58; c 3. MATHEMATICS. *Educ:* Ga Southern Col, BS, 60; Univ Ga, MEd, 62; Univ Fla, MA, 64; Clemson Univ, PhD(math), 69. *Prof Exp:* Instr math & physics, high sch, Ga, 60-61; instr math, 64-65, asst prof, 65-66 & 69-72, assoc prof math & comput sci, 72-80, PROF MATH & COMPUT SCI, GA SOUTHERN COL, 80- *Mem:* Am Math Soc; Math Asn Am. *Res:* Analysis; convexity. *Mailing Add:* Dept of Math Ga Southern Col Statesboro GA 30458

SPARKS, CECIL RAY, b Lockwood, WVa, Nov 16, 30; m 56; c 3. ACOUSTICS, FLUID DYNAMICS. *Educ:* Univ Tex, BS, 53; Univ Pittsburgh, MS, 56. *Prof Exp:* Develop engr, New Prod Dept, Westinghouse Elec Corp, 53-57; asst dir dept appl physics, 57-74, DIR ENG PHYSICS, SOUTHWEST RES INST, 74- *Mem:* Acoust Soc Am. *Res:* Noise control; machinery and structure vibrations; fluid mechanics; instrumentation. *Mailing Add:* Dept of Appl Physics 8500 Culebra Rd San Antonio TX 78284

SPARKS, CHARLES EDWARD, b Peoria, Ill, July 29, 40; m 77; c 3. LIPOPROTEIN METABOLISM, LIPOPROTEIN CEPOPROTEINS. *Educ:* Mass Inst Technol, BS, 63; Jefferson Med Col, MD, 68, cert; Am Bd Clin Chem, cert. *Prof Exp:* Asst prof, Med Col Pa, 75-77, assoc prof biochem & physiol, 77-82; ASSOC PROF PATH, UNIV ROCHESTER, 82- *Concurrent Pos:* Fel, Coun Auteriosclerosis, Am Heart Asn, assoc fel, Coun Epidemiol. *Res:* Role of lipoprotein apoproteins in cell recognition, in particular opolipoprotein B in hepatic recognition of triglyceive rich lipoproteins. *Mailing Add:* Dept Path Univ Rochester Med Ctr 601 Elmwood Ave Rochester NY 14642

SPARKS, CULLIE J(AMES), JR, b Belpre, Ohio, May 8, 29; m 51; c 5. METALLURGY. *Educ:* Univ Ky, BS, 52, EngrD(metall), 57. *Prof Exp:* Res assoc metall, Univ Ky, 53-56; METALLURGIST & MAT SCIENTIST, OAK RIDGE NAT LAB, 58- *Mem:* Am Soc Metals; Sigma Xi; Am Crystallog Asn. *Res:* Structure of materials, especially metals, studied by x-ray scattering and with synchrotron radiation including deformation, strains, preferred orientation, twinning, slip; imperfections in solids such as atomic order, size displacements, particle size and strain line broadening, thin films; fluorescent analysis. *Mailing Add:* 804 W Outer Dr Oak Ridge TN 37830

SPARKS, DARRELL, b Tipton Hill, NC, Apr 14, 38. PLANT PHYSIOLOGY, HORTICULTURE. *Educ:* NC State Col, BS, 61; Mich State Univ, MS, 62, PhD(hort), 65. *Prof Exp:* From asst prof to assoc prof, 65-76, PROF HORT RES, UNIV GA, 76- *Mem:* AAAS; Am Soc Hort Sci; Am Soc Plant Physiol; Bot Soc Am. *Res:* Applied ecology; mineral nutrition and general physiology of tree fruit crops. *Mailing Add:* Dept of Hort Univ of Ga Athens GA 30602

SPARKS, DAVID LEE, b Guntersville, Ala, Dec 22, 37; m 63; c 3. NEUROPHYSIOLOGY. *Educ:* Univ Ala, BA, 59, MA, 62, PhD(psychol), 63. *Prof Exp:* Instr psychol, Univ Ala, 62-63; USPHS fel neurosurg, Med Ctr, Univ Miss, 63-65; instr psychiat, Med Ctr, 65-67, from asst prof to assoc prof psychol, 67-74, chmn dept, 69-74, prof psychol, 74-81, PROF PHYSIOL & BIOPHYSICS, UNIV ALA, BIRMINGHAM, 81- *Mem:* AAAS; Soc Neurosci; Asn Res Vision & Ophthal. *Res:* Sensory-motor function; neural control of eye movements. *Mailing Add:* Dept Physiol & Biophysics Univ of Ala Birmingham AL 35294

SPARKS, HARVEY VISE, b Flint, Mich, June 22, 38; m 69; c 4. MEDICAL PHYSIOLOGY. *Educ:* Univ Mich, MD, 63. *Prof Exp:* USPHS fel physiol, Harvard Med Sch, 63-65 & Univ Goteborg, 65-66; from instr to prof, Univ Mich, 66-79; PROF & CHMN, DEPT PHYSIOL, MICH STATE UNIV, 79- *Concurrent Pos:* Mem coun on circulation, Am Heart Asn; mem, Nat Bd Med Examiners. *Honors & Awards:* Markle Scholar Acad Med, John & Mary Markle Found, 67. *Mem:* Am Heart Asn; Microcirculatory Soc; Soc Exp Biol & Med; Am Physiol Soc; Am Col Sports Med. *Res:* Metabolic control of coronary and skeletal muscle blood flow using mathematical model simulations and experimental approaches. *Mailing Add:* Dept of Physiol Mich State Univ East Lansing MI 48824

SPARKS, JOSEPH THEODORE, b Chicago, Ill, Oct 27, 26; m; c 2. PHYSICS. *Educ:* Univ Calif, AB, 50; Univ Kans, PhD(physics), 56. *Prof Exp:* Asst, Univ Kans, 51-55; res engr, E I du Pont de Nemours & Co, 56-57; sr physicist, Lawrence Livermore Lab, Univ Calif, 57-76; PRES, TRAVEL KEY, INC, 76- *Concurrent Pos:* Physicist, Standard Oil Co, Ind, 52-53. *Mem:* Am Phys Soc; Am Geophys Union. *Res:* Neutron diffraction; magnetism; transport properties of solids; seismology. *Mailing Add:* 1562 Foothill Rd Pleasanton CA 94566

SPARKS, MARSHALL SCOTT, physics, see previous edition

SPARKS, MORGAN, b Pagosa Springs, Colo, July 6, 16; m 49; c 4. CHEMISTRY. *Educ:* Rice Univ, BA, 38, MA, 40; Univ Ill, PhD(chem physics), 43. *Prof Exp:* Mem staff, Nat Defense Res Comt, Univ Ill, 41-43; res chemist, Bell Tel Labs, Inc, 43-48, mem semiconductor group, 48-53, dept head semiconductor device feasibility, 53-55, dir solid state electronics res, 55-58, dir, Transistor Dept, 58-59, exec dir, Components & Solid State Div, 59-68, exec dir, Semiconductor Components Div, 68-69, vpres tech info & personnel, 69-71, vpres electronics technol, 71-72; pres, Sandia Labs, 72-81; DEAN, R O ANDERSON SCH MGT, UNIV NMEX, 81- *Concurrent Pos:* Vpres, Western Elec Co, Inc, 72- *Honors & Awards:* Jack A Morton Award, Inst Elec & Electronics Engrs, 77. *Mem:* Nat Acad Eng; Am Chem Soc; fel Am Phys Soc; fel Inst Elec & Electronics Engrs; fel Am Inst Chemists. *Res:* Solid state physics and chemistry; electron device development; semiconductors; transistors; thin film devices; passive components; memory elements. *Mailing Add:* 904 Lamp Post Circle Southeast Albuquerque NM 87185

SPARKS, PETER ROBERT, b Bristol, Eng, July 29, 47; m 76; c 2. WIND ENGINEERING, EARTHQUAKE ENGINEERING. *Educ:* Univ Bristol, BSc, 68; Univ London, PhD(structural eng), 74. *Prof Exp:* Sci officer, Bldg Res Sta, Eng, 68-73, higher sci officer, 73-75, sr sci officer, 75-77; vis prof eng mech, Va Polytech Inst & State Univ, 77-79, sci officer, 75-77; ASSOC PROF CIVIL ENG & ENG MECH, CLEMSON UNIV, 82- *Mem:* Am Soc Civil Engrs; Am Soc Eng Educ; Sigma Xi. *Res:* The behavior of large structures under wind and earthquake loading; full-scale and model investigations of structural performance and loading; architectural aerodynamics. *Mailing Add:* Dept Civil Eng Clemson Univ Clemson SC 29631

SPARKS, RICHARD EDWARD, b Kingston, Pa, Apr 19, 42; m 66; c 2. AQUATIC BIOLOGY. *Educ:* Amherst Col, BA, 64; Univ Kans, MS, 68; Va Polytech Inst & State Univ, PhD(biol), 71. *Prof Exp:* Teacher gen sci & biol, US Peace Corps, Univ Nigeria, Methodist Higher Elem Teacher Training Col, Nigeria, 64-66; res assoc, Ctr Environ Studies, Va Polytech Inst & State Univ, 71-72; asst aquatic biologist, 72-77, assoc aquatic biologist, 77-80, AQUATIC BIOLOGIST, ILL NATURAL HIST SURV, 80- *Concurrent Pos:* Consult, US Army Corps Engrs, 74, Ill Power Co, 75-78 & Upper Miss River Basin Comn, 79-80; lectr, Bradley Univ, 75-; adj prof, Western Ill Univ, 76- *Mem:* AAAS; Am Fisheries Soc; Ecol Soc Am; NAm Benthological Soc; Sigma Xi. *Res:* Biological monitoring for pollution control, using organisms as sensors; restoration of degraded aquatic ecosystems; ecology of Illinois and Mississippi rivers; bioassays using aquatic organisms; river surveys. *Mailing Add:* Ill Natural Hist Surv River Res Lab Havana IL 62644

SPARKS, ROBERT EDWARD, b Marshall, Mo, Sept 25, 30; m 55; c 3. CHEMICAL ENGINEERING. *Educ:* Univ Mo, BS, 52; Johns Hopkins Univ, DEng, 60. *Prof Exp:* Res engr, Esso Res & Eng Co, 60-62, sr engr, 62-63; from asst prof to prof chem eng, Case Western Reserve Univ, 63-72; PROF CHEM ENG, WASH UNIV, 72- *Concurrent Pos:* Consult, Nat Inst Arthritis & Metab Dis, 65-74 & Goodyear Tire & Rubber Co, 66-74. *Mem:* AAAS; Am Inst Chem Engrs; Am Soc Artificial Internal Organs. *Res:* Medical engineering; design of the artificial kidney; membrane transport; emulsion breaking; velocity profile control; mass transfer and fluid mechanics in chemical reactors; microencapsulation; controlled drug release; inventive reasoning. *Mailing Add:* Dept of Chem Eng Urbauer Hall Wash Univ St Louis MO 63130

SPARKS, WALTER CHAPPEL, b New Castle, Colo, Aug 22, 18; m 42; c 3. HORTICULTURE. *Educ:* Colo State Univ, BS, 41, MS, 43. *Prof Exp:* Instr agr, Pueblo Col, 41; asst hort, Colo State Univ, 41-43, from instr to assoc prof, 43-47; assoc horticulturist, 47-57, horticulturist, 57-68, RES PROF HORT, UNIV IDAHO, 68-, COORDR POTATO PROGS, 76-, CO-DIR, POSTHARVEST INST PERISHABLES, 80- *Concurrent Pos:* Actg supt, Aberdeen Br Exp Sta, 52, 56 & 65; Jenne res fel, Univ Idaho & rep, Nat Inter-Regional Potato Introd & Preserv Proj, 57; consult, Corporacion De La Produccion Santiago, Chile, 66, Australian Govt & Commonwealth Sci & Indust Res Orgn, Venezuelan Corp of Agr Mkt, 75, Japan, 75, 76 & 77, Repub S Africa, 77. exchange res prof, Res Inst Com & Indust Plants, Kolding, Denmark, 72-73; guest lectr, ten Europ countries, 72-73, Greece, Israel, Australia & NZ, 73, Europ Asn Potato Res, Poland, 78 & Ger, 79; adv, Israeli Veg Bd, 80, PEI, Can, 80 & Philippines, 81. *Honors & Awards:* Potato Hall of Fame-Brussels, Belgium, 77. *Mem:* AAAS; hon mem Am Potato Asn (pres, 64-65); Am Soc Hort Sci; Am Inst Biol Sci; Europ Asn Potato Res. *Res:* Mechanical injury and storage; cultural practices of potatoes. *Mailing Add:* Res & Exten Ctr Univ of Idaho Aberdeen ID 83210

SPARLIN, DON MERLE, b Joplin, Mo, Mar 29, 37; m 59; c 4. SOLID STATE PHYSICS. *Educ:* Univ Kans, BS, 59; Northwestern Univ, PhD(physics), 64. *Prof Exp:* Instr physics, Case Western Reserve Univ, 64-65, asst prof, 65-68; asst prof, 68-78, ASSOC PROF PHYSICS, UNIV MO-ROLLA, 78- *Mem:* Am Phys Soc; Am Asn Physics Teachers; Inst Elec & Electronics Engrs. *Res:* Electronic and magnetic properties of materials. *Mailing Add:* Dept Physics Univ Mo Rolla MO 65401

SPARLING, ARTHUR BAMBRIDGE, b Rossburn, Man, Jan 3, 30; m 55; c 5. SANITARY ENGINEERING. *Educ:* Univ Man, BSc, 53; Univ Toronto, MASc, 54; Wash Univ, DSc(environ & sanit eng), 68. *Prof Exp:* Pub health engr, Prov of Man, 54-67, chief engr, Clean Environ Comn, 67-71; ASSOC PROF CIVIL ENG, UNIV MAN, 71- *Mem:* Water Pollution Control Fedn; Am Water Works Asn. *Res:* Waste treatment; water pollution and treatment. *Mailing Add:* 709 S Dr Fort Garry MB R3T 1C0 Can

SPARLING, DALE R, b St Clair, Mich, Dec 19, 29; m 58; c 3. GEOLOGY, DEVONIAN CONODONTS. *Educ:* Univ Wyo, BS, 54; Wayne State Univ, MS, 56; Ohio State Univ, PhD(geol), 65. *Prof Exp:* Asst geol, Wayne State Univ, 54-56; petrol geologist, Creole Petrol Corp, 56-61; asst geol, Ohio State Univ, 62-65, instr, 65; lectr, West Wash State Col, 66; instr, Dayton Univ, 67-68; asst prof, Earlham Col, 67-68; from asst prof to assoc prof, 68-74, chmn earth sci prog, 71-76, PROF GEOL, SOUTHWEST STATE UNIV, MINN, 74- *Mem:* Geol Soc Am; Am Asn Petrol Geologist; Soc Econ Paleontologists & Minerologists. *Res:* Stratigraphy; sedimentology; conodont taxonomy and biostrafigraphy. *Mailing Add:* Dept of Geol Southwest State Univ Marshall MN 56258

SPARLING, PHILIP FREDERICK, b Evanston, Ill, Sept 10, 36; m 63; c 4. MEDICINE, BACTERIOLOGY. *Educ:* Princeton Univ, AB, 58; Harvard Univ, MD, 62. *Prof Exp:* Resident physician, Mass Gen Hosp, 62-64; officer, Comn Corps venereal dis res, Ctr Dis Control, 64-66; fel bacteriol, Harvard Med Sch, 66-68; fel infectious dis, Mass Gen Hosp, 68-69; from asst prof to assoc prof, 69-75, PROF MED & BACTERIOL, UNIV NC, CHAPEL HILL, 75-, CHMN, DEPT BACTERIAL IMMUNOL, 81- *Concurrent Pos:* NIH res career develop award, 71-76; mem adv comt, Ctr Dis Control, 72-; reader bacteriol, Univ Bristol, 74-75; chief, Div Infectious Dis, Univ NC, 75-; dir, NC Prog on Sexually Transmitted Dis, Sch Med, 78-; mem microbiol comt, Nat Bd Med Examrs, 78-, chmn, 81- *Mem:* Am Soc Microbiol; AAAS; Am Fedn Clin Res; Am Soc Clin Invest; Infectious Dis Am. *Res:* Infectious diseases; genetics and biochemistry of microbial antibiotic resistance; biochemical genetics of microbial pathogenicity; bacterial physiology; immunobiology of Neisseria gonorrhoeae. *Mailing Add:* 804 FLOB Univ NC Sch Med Chapel Hill NC 27514

SPARLING, SHIRLEY, b Detroit, Mich, Oct 28, 29. PHYCOLOGY. *Educ:* Iowa State Univ, BS, 50, MS, 51; Univ Calif, PhD(bot), 56. *Prof Exp:* Instr bot, Cent Col, Iowa, 51-53, Univ BC, 56-59 & Univ Calif, Santa Barbara, 59-63; instr bot, 63-80, PROF BIOL SCI, CALIF POLYTECH STATE UNIV, SAN LUIS OBISPO, 80- *Mem:* Bot Soc Am. *Res:* Morphology, anatomy, reproduction and life cycles of marine algae, especially red algae. *Mailing Add:* Dept of Biol Sci Calif Polytech State Univ San Luis Obispo CA 93407

SPARROW, D(AVID) A, b Boston, Mass, June 30, 47. NUCLEAR REACTIONS AND SCATTERING. *Educ:* Princeton Univ, BA, 69; Mass Inst Technol, MS, 71, PHD(physics), 74. *Prof Exp:* Instr math, physics & chem, Univ Mass, 71-73; res assoc physics, Univ Colo, 74-77 & Univ Md, 77-78; ASST PROF PHYSICS, UNIV PA, 78- *Concurrent Pos:* Vis asst prof, Univ Md, 78. *Res:* Theoretical physics: nuclear reactions and scattering, especially intermediate energy; analytic methods in nuclear reactions; data-to-data (purely empirical) relations and descriptions. *Mailing Add:* E1 Dept Physics Univ Pa Philadelphia PA 19104

SPARROW, E(PHRAIM) M(AURICE), b Hartford, Conn, May 27, 28; m 52; c 1. MECHANICAL ENGINEERING, HEAT TRANSFER. *Educ:* Mass Inst Technol, BS, 48, MS, 49; Harvard Univ, MA, 50, PhD(mech eng), 56. *Hon Degrees:* Dr, Univ Brazil, 67. *Prof Exp:* Res engr, Oak Ridge Nat Lab, 49; mech engr, Raytheon Mfg Co, 52-53; res scientist, Lewis Res Ctr, Nat Adv Comt Aeronaut, 53-59; chmn fluid mech prog, 68-80, PROF MECH

ENG, UNIV MINN, MINNEAPOLIS, 59- *Concurrent Pos:* Lectr, Commonwealth Sci & Indust Res Orgn, Australia, 65; chief-of-party, US Agency Int Develop Prog Grad Educ in Brazil, 66-67; vis prof, Israel Inst Technol, 69; consult, Solar Energy Panel, US Off Sci & Technol, 72; ed, J Heat Transfer, 72-80; mem adv panel, US Cong, Off of Technol Assessment, 75-77. *Honors & Awards:* Heat Transfer Award, Am Soc Mech Engrs, 62; Max Jakob Award for Eminence in Heat Transfer Res, Am Soc Mech Engrs/ Am Inst Chem Engrs, 77; Ralph Coats Roe Award for Eminence in Eng Educ, Am Soc Eng Educ, 78. *Mem:* Distinguished fel Am Soc Mech Engrs. *Res:* Analytical and experimental research in heat transfer and fluid mechanics. *Mailing Add:* Dept of Mech Eng Univ of Minn Minneapolis MN 55455

SPARROW, ELENA BAUTISTA, b Col, Laguna, Philippines; m 72. SOIL MICROBIOLOGY, ENVIRONMENTAL MICROBIOLOGY. *Educ:* Univ Philippines, BS, 62; Cornell Univ, MS, 66; Colo State Univ, PhD(agron, soil microbiol), 73. *Prof Exp:* Res asst soil chem & microbiol, Int Rice Res Inst, 62-64, asst soil microbiologist, 66-69; fel microbial ecol, Dept Agron, Colo State Univ, 73; independent microbiologist, Arctic Environ Res Lab, 75-76; microbiologist, US Environ Protection Agency, Arctic Environ Res Sta, 76-77; microbiologist, US Army Cold Regions Res & Eng Lab, Alaska Projs Off, 77-80; MICROBIOLOGIST, 81- *Concurrent Pos:* Affil asst prof environ microbiol, Inst Water Resources, Univ Alaska, 75; adj researcher, Soil Sci Dept, Univ Minn, 79. *Mem:* Am Soc Microbiol; Int Soc Soil Sci; Soil Sci Soc Am; Sigma Xi; Coun Agr Sci & Technol. *Res:* Ecology of microorganisms in terrestrial and freshwater environments; effects and degradation of organic pollutants; microbial transformations of minerals. *Mailing Add:* 1127 Park Dr Fairbanks AK 99701

SPARROW, GENE RODELL, b Finley, NDak, Sept 9, 39; m 74; c 1. MASS SPECTROSCOPY, SURFACE CHEMISTRY. *Educ:* NDak State Univ, BS, 61; Iowa State Univ, PhD(phys chem), 66. *Prof Exp:* Fel mass spectrometry, Iowa State Univ, 66; sr res chemist, 3 M Co, 68-73, res specialist anal chem & mass spectrometry, 73-75, res specialist surface chem, 75-79, res & develop supvr, 79-80; PRES, ADVANCED RES & DEVELOP, INC, 80- *Mem:* Am Soc Mass Spectroscopy; Am Vacuum Soc; Am Soc Metals; Microbeam Analysis Soc; Soc Mfg Eng. *Res:* Development of ion scattering spectroscopy and secondary ion mass spectroscopy and their applications to surface analysis of all types of surfaces; instrumental development, computerization and application of analytical instruments especially mass spectroscopy; inorganic compounds. *Mailing Add:* Advanced Res & Develop Inc 245 E 6th St Suite 807 St Paul MN 55101

SPATOLA, ARNO F, b Albany, NY, May 9, 44. BIO-ORGANIC CHEMISTRY. *Educ:* Cornell Univ, AB, 66; Univ Mich, MS, 69, PhD(chem), 71. *Prof Exp:* Lectr chem, Univ Mich, 70-71; assoc, Univ Ariz, 71-73; asst prof, 73-78, ASSOC PROF CHEM, UNIV LOUISVILLE, 78- *Mem:* AAAS; Am Chem Soc; Sigma Xi. *Res:* Polypeptide synthesis, solution, solid phase methods and catalystic transfer hydrogenation; hormones and hormone analogues incorporating novel amino acids and amide bond replacements; peptide antagonists of LH-RH as potential ovulation inhibitors; structure-function studies on peptide hormones; collagenase inhibitors. *Mailing Add:* Dept of Chem Belknap Campus Univ of Louisville Louisville KY 40292

SPATZ, DAVID MARK, b Pottstown, Pa, Oct 10, 46. ORGANIC CHEMISTRY, MEDICINAL CHEMISTRY. *Educ:* Clarkson Col, BS, 68; Univ Mich, Ann Arbor, PhD(med chem), 72. *Prof Exp:* Fel nucleotide synthesis, Stanford Univ, 72-74; sr res chemist, Dow Chem Pharmaceut Res & Develop, 74-77; res chemist, Agr Res Div, Am Cyanamid Co, 77-80; WITH CHEVRON CHEM CO, 80- *Mem:* Am Chem Soc; AAAS. *Res:* Synthetic organic chemistry; medicinal and pesticidal chemistry; drug design; heterocyclic and natural product synthesis including nucleotides and terpenes. *Mailing Add:* Chevron Chem Co 940 Hensley St Richmond CA 94804

SPATZ, SIDNEY S, b Pittsburgh, Pa, Jan 13, 24; m 46; c 3. ORAL SURGERY. *Educ:* Univ Pittsburgh, BS, 43, DDS, 45; Am Bd Oral Surg, dipl, 59. *Prof Exp:* PROF ORAL SURG & CHMN DEPT, SCH DENT MED, UNIV PITTSBURGH, 71- *Mem:* Fel Am Col Dent; Int Col Dent; Am Soc Oral Surg; Int Asn Oral Surg. *Res:* Evaluation of drugs and techniques in relation to clinical oral surgery. *Mailing Add:* Salk Hall Sch Dent Med Univ Pittsburgh Pittsburgh PA 15261

SPATZ, SYDNEY MARTIN, b New York, NY, June 9, 12; m 36; c 1. ORGANIC CHEMISTRY. *Educ:* Univ Iowa, BA, 35, MS, 37; Iowa State Col, PhD(org chem), 41. *Prof Exp:* Res assoc, Nat Defense Res Comt, Iowa State Col, 42-43; res chemist, Nat Aniline Div, Allied Chem & Dye Corp, 43-47; chief chemist, Polak's Frutal Works, Inc, 47-53; pres & mgr, Spatz Chem, Inc, 53-54; res supvr, Nat Aniline & Speciality Chem Div, Allied Chem Corp, 54-71; sr prod eng specialist, Mead Papers Div, Mead Corp, 72-74, res fel, Mead Cent Res Div, 74-77; CONSULT, 77- *Mem:* Am Chem Soc; Sigma Xi. *Res:* Ultraviolet absorbers; epoxy curing agents; polyester fire-retardant resins; cationic dyestuffs; color precursors for copy systems; carbonless copy. *Mailing Add:* 400 64th Ave Unit 103W St Petersburg Beach FL 33736

SPAULDING, HARRY SAMUEL, JR, b Waterbury, Vt, Dec 12, 30; m 56; c 5. ALLERGY, IMMUNOLOGY. *Educ:* Albany Col Pharm, NY, BS, 53; Duquesne Univ, MS, 55; Univ Vt, Burlington, MD, 59. *Prof Exp:* Post surgeon, 24th Med Detachment, 61-63; resident pediat, Walter Reed Army Med Ctr, 63-65; chief pediat, US Army Hosp, Ft Carson, 66-68; pvt pract, Beverly Hosp, Mass, 68-71; chief, Dept Clin Admin, Reynolds Hosp, Ft Sill, 71-72; chief, Gen Pediat Serv, Fitzsimons Army Med Ctr, Denver, 74-77; ASST CLIN PROF PEDIAT, MED CTR, UNIV COLO, 75-; STAFF AFFIL, NAT JEWISH HOSP & RES CTR, 77- *Concurrent Pos:* Consult pediat, Colo State Hosp, Pueblo, 66-68; clin instr pediat, Med Ctr, Tufts Univ, 68-71; fel allergy-immunol, Fitzsimons Army Med Ctr & Nat Jewish Hosp, Denver, 72-74. *Mem:* Am Acad Pediat; fel Am Acad Allergy; Asn Mil Allergists. *Res:* Association between gastroesophageal reflux and asthma; pharmacology of aminophylline with respect to coagulation problems and sensitivity through its ethylene, diamine fraction. *Mailing Add:* Fitzsimons Army Med Ctr Allergy-Immunol Serv Denver CO 80240

SPAULDING, LEN DAVIS, b Spring Valley, Ill, Oct 31, 42. INORGANIC CHEMISTRY, ORGANOMETALLIC CHEMISTRY. *Educ:* Antioch Col, BSc, 65; Univ Cincinnati, PhD(chem), 72. *Prof Exp:* Res assoc, Ga Inst Technol, 72-74; assoc scientist chem, Brookhaven Nat Lab, 74-80; WITH EXXON CHEM CORP, 80- *Concurrent Pos:* Consult, Mad River Chem Co, 67-69; NIH fel, Ga Inst Technol, 73-74. *Mem:* Am Chem Soc; AAAS. *Res:* Catalysis; Fischer-Tropsch and related reaction; porphyrin chemistry; transition metal organometallic chemistry. *Mailing Add:* Exxon Chem Corp PO Box 536 Linden NJ 07036

SPAULDING, MALCOLM LINDHURST, b Providence, RI, Feb 15, 47. OCEAN ENGINEERING. *Educ:* Univ RI, BS, 69, PhD(mech eng), 72; Mass Inst Technol, MS, 70. *Prof Exp:* Asst prof eng mech, Old Dominion Univ, 72-73; asst prof, 73-77, ASSOC PROF OCEAN ENG, UNIV RI, 77- *Concurrent Pos:* Consult var pvt industs, 75-; Fulbright Hayes fel, Leningrad, USSR. *Mem:* Am Soc Civil Engrs; Am Soc Mech Engrs; AAAS; Am Geophys Union; Marine Technol Soc. *Res:* Numerical modelling of coastal and shelf processes to include circulation, temperature, salinity and pollutant transport; computational fluid mechanics; oil spill fates and impact modeling. *Mailing Add:* Dept of Ocean Eng Univ of RI Kingston RI 02881

SPAULDING, STEPHEN WAASA, b San Francisco, Calif, Aug 24, 40; m 69; c 2. ENDOCRINOLOGY, MEDICAL RESEARCH. *Educ:* Pomona Col, BA, 62; McGill Univ, MD & CM, 66. *Prof Exp:* Intern & asst res med, Osler Serv, Johns Hopkins Univ, 66-68; clin assoc endocrinol, NIH Geront Ctr, 68-70; from fel to asst prof endocrinol, Sch Med, Yale Univ, 70-76; assoc prof, 76-81, PROF, STATE UNIV NY, BUFFALO, 81- *Concurrent Pos:* Attend physician, Yale New Haven Hosp & West Haven Vet Admin Hosp, 72-76; Am Col Physicians res scholar, 72; NIH spec res fel, 73-74; clin investr, Vet Admin, 74; Am Col Physicians traveling scholar endocrinol, 76; chief, Endocrine Unit, Buffalo Gen Hosp, 76- *Mem:* Am Thyroid Asn; Endocrine Soc; Am Fedn Clin Res; Am Col Physicians; Am Soc Clin Invest. *Res:* Actions of thyrotropin on nuclear function; regulation of thyroid RNA metabolism; hypothalamic-pituitary interrelationships. *Mailing Add:* Endocrine Div 100 High St Buffalo NY 14203

SPAULDING, WILLIAM BRAY, b New York, NY, May 12, 22; nat Can; m 45; c 4. CLINICAL MEDICINE. *Educ:* Univ Toronto, MD, 44; FRCP(C), 51. *Prof Exp:* Jr intern, Toronto Western Hosp, 44-45; physician, Freeport Sanitorium, 46; resident path, Sunnybrook Hosp, Toronto, 47; physician, Toronto Psychiat Hosp, 47-48; resident med, Toronto Gen Hosp, 48-51; clin teacher, Univ Toronto, 51-55, asst, 56-57, from asst prof to assoc prof, 58-65; PROF MED, MCMASTER UNIV, 65- *Concurrent Pos:* Fel med, Toronto Gen Hosp, 48-51; Markle scholar, 51; sr physician, Toronto Gen Hosp, 59-65. *Mem:* Fel Am Col Physicians; Can Med Asn. *Res:* Internal medicine, particularly significance of symptoms; diabetes. *Mailing Add:* Fac Med McMaster Univ Hamilton ON L8S 4L8 Can

SPAUSCHUS, HANS O, b Liedemeiten, Ger, June, 15, 23; US citizen; m 59; c 2. VAPOR COMPRESSION COOLING SCIENCE & TECHNOLOGY. *Educ:* Ill Col, AB, 46; Tulane Univ, MS, 48, PhD(phys chem), 50. *Prof Exp:* Chemist, Gen Elec Co, 50-53, mgr lab, 53-56, res assoc, 56-68, mgr lab, 68-80; DIR LAB, GA INST TECHNOL, 80- *Concurrent Pos:* Consult indust, Spauschus Assocs, 80- *Honors & Awards:* Steinmetz Medal, Gen Elec Co, 73. *Mem:* AAAS; Inst Elec & Electronics Engrs; fel Am Soc Heating, Refrig & Air Conditioning Engrs. *Res:* Biomass conversion to fuels and chemicals; high temperature solar thermal systems; materials sciences; heat pumps; technology appraisal and transfer; res & develop planning. *Mailing Add:* Eng Exp Sta Ga Inst Technol Atlanta GA 30332

SPAYD, RICHARD W, b Reading, Pa, Dec 10, 32; m 58; c 3. ORGANIC CHEMISTRY. *Educ:* Albright Col, BS, 58; Univ Del, MS, 60, PhD(org chem), 62. *Prof Exp:* From res chemist to sr res chemist, 62-67, LAB HEAD, EASTMAN KODAK CO, 67- *Mem:* Am Chem Soc; Am Asn Clin Chem. *Res:* Photographic systems; use of radioactive isotopes to study reaction mechanisms; dry multilayer films for clinical analysis. *Mailing Add:* Eastman Kodak Co Res Labs 1669 Lake Ave Rochester NY 14650

SPAZIANI, EUGENE, b Detroit, Mich, July 22, 30; m 53; c 2. ENDOCRINOLOGY, REPRODUCTIVE PHYSIOLOGY. *Educ:* Univ Calif, Los Angeles, BA, 52, MA, 54, PhD(zool), 58. *Prof Exp:* Asst zool, Univ Calif, Los Angeles, 52-55; hon res asst physiol, Univ Col, London, 58-59; from instr to assoc prof, 59-68, chmn dept, 77-80, PROF ZOOL, UNIV IOWA, 68- *Concurrent Pos:* Lalor Found fel, 60; vis investr, Inst Biomed Res, AMA, 66-67; mem, Bd Examrs, Grad Record Exam, advan test in biol, Educ Testing Serv, Princeton, NJ, 66-70; mem, Panel Undergrad Sci Partic Prog, NSF & consult, Panel Preprof Training, Comn Undergrad Educ Biol Sci. *Mem:* AAAS; Am Soc Zoologists; Am Physiol Soc; Endocrine Soc; Soc Study Reproduction. *Res:* Mechanisms of steroid hormone action in vertebrate reproductive organs; hormonal control of cellular transport; pigmentation; invertebrate endocrinology. *Mailing Add:* Dept of Zool Univ of Iowa Iowa City IA 52242

SPEAKMAN, EDWIN A(ARON), b Gratz, Pa, Aug 14, 09; m 34; c 2. ELECTRONICS. *Educ:* Haverford Col, BS, 31. *Prof Exp:* Instr physics, Haverford Col, 31-34; radio engr, Philco Corp, 34-39; physicist, Curtis Pub Co, 39-40; electronics engr, US Naval Res Lab, 40-43, asst supt radio div, 43-45, head radio countermeasures br, 45-49; exec dir electronics, Res & Develop Bd, US Dept Defense, 49-51, vchmn bd, 51-52; vpres & gen mgr guided missiles div, Fairchild Engine & Airplane Corp, 52-58; mgr planning, Defense Electronic Prod, Radio Corp Am, 58-60, vpres missile range progs, 60-65; vpres & dir ctr naval analyses, Franklin Inst, 65-67; dir, Off Res & Develop, US Dept Transp, 67-68; STAFF ADV SCI & CRYPTO AFFAIRS, US ARMY INTELLIGENCE & SECURITY COMMAND, 68- *Concurrent Pos:* Consult, Dept Defense, mem electronic countermeasures panel, Res & Develop Bd, 45-49; efficiency rating comt, US Naval Res Lab, 45-47; Civilian Serv Awards Comt, 45-49; chmn joint signal & anal panel, Joint Chiefs Staff, 46-49; mem, US Civil Serv Bd Exam Sci Personnel, 47-50; guided missile comt, Aircraft Industs Asn, 52-58, chmn, 56; countermeasures comt, Inter-Bur Tech Coord Comt, Defense Orientation Conf Asn; Nat Indust Conf Bd. *Honors & Awards:* Meritorious Civilian Serv Award, US Dept Navy, 46. *Mem:* Soc Automotive Engrs; life fel Inst Elec & Electronics Engrs; assoc fel Am Inst Aeronaut & Astronaut; Asn Old Crows. *Res:* Electronics and guided missiles; advanced planning; systems analysis; electromagnetic warfare and countermeasures; signal analysis; antisubmarine warfare. *Mailing Add:* 9018 Charles Augustine Dr Alexandria VA 22308

SPEAR, BRIAN BLACKBURN, b Los Angeles, Calif, July 1, 47; m 72; c 1. GENE STRUCTURE. *Educ:* Amherst Col, AB, 69; Yale Univ, MPhil, 70, PhD(biol), 73. *Prof Exp:* Res assoc, Dept Molecular Cell & Develop Biol, Univ Colo, 73-75; asst prof biol sci, Northwestern Univ, 76-82; RES SCIENTIST, DEPT MOLECULAR BIOL, ABBOTT LABS, 82- *Mem:* Sigma Xi; Am Soc Cell Biol; AAAS. *Res:* Gene and chromosome structure; polytene chromosome organization in Drosophila and protozoa; molecular biology of ciliated protozoa; structure and evolution of genes for ribosomal RNA and actin. *Mailing Add:* Dept Molecular Biol Abbott Labs North Chicago IL 60064

SPEAR, CARL D(AVID), b Salt Lake City, Utah, Dec 6, 27; m 58; c 6. METALLURGY. *Educ:* Univ Utah, BS, 55, PhD(metall), 60. *Prof Exp:* Res metallurgist, Corning Glass Works, 60-63; asst prof metall, Univ Idaho, 63-66; head dept mech eng, 66-77, PROF MECH ENG, UTAH STATE UNIV, 66- *Mem:* Soc Mfg Engrs; Am Soc Metals. *Res:* Behavior of materials in manufacturing processes; non-traditional processes. *Mailing Add:* Dept of Mech Eng Utah State Univ Logan UT 84322

SPEAR, GERALD SANFORD, b Providence, RI, Mar 3, 28; m 64; c 3. PATHOLOGY. *Educ:* Harvard Univ, AB, 48; Johns Hopkins Univ, MD, 52; Am Bd Path, dipl, 59. *Prof Exp:* Asst med, Sch Med, Wash Univ, 52-53; asst, Johns Hopkins Univ, 53-54, instr, 54-56 & 58-59, from asst prof to assoc prof path, Sch Med, 64-77; PROF PATH & MEM MED STAFF, CALIF COL MED, UNIV CALIF, IRVINE, 77- *Concurrent Pos:* Intern, Barnes Hosp, St Louis, Mo, 52-53; from asst pathologist to asst resident, Johns Hopkins Hosp, 53-56, resident, 58-59, pathologist, 59-77; vis pathologist, Baltimore City Hosps, 59-60; mem sci adv bd, Southern Calif Affil, Kidney Found; mem res comt, Southern Calif Affil, Am Diabetes Asn. *Mem:* AAAS; Am Asn Path & Bact; Am Fedn Clin Res; Am Soc Nephrology; Int Acad Path. *Res:* Morphologic anatomy of general nature and immunopathology; diabetes; renal and pediatric pathology. *Mailing Add:* Dept of Path 101 City Dr S Orange CA 92668

SPEAR, IRWIN, b New York, NY, Jan 4, 24; m 49; c 5. PLANT PHYSIOLOGY, BIOLOGY. *Educ:* Cornell Univ, BS, 47; Harvard Univ, AM, 49, PhD(biol), 53. *Prof Exp:* Asst prof bot & physiologist, Plant Res Inst, 53-59, assoc prof bot, 59-69, PROF BOT, UNIV TEX, AUSTIN, 69- *Concurrent Pos:* Mem biol advan placement comt, Col Entrace Exam Bd. *Mem:* AAAS; Am Soc Plant Physiol; Bot Soc Am; Soc Exp Biol & Med; Scand Soc Plant Physiol. *Res:* Physiology of growth and development, especially flowering; social consequences of biological discoveries. *Mailing Add:* Dept of Bot Univ of Tex Austin TX 78712

SPEAR, JOSEPH FRANCIS, b Baltimore, Md, May 3, 43; c 1. PHYSIOLOGY. *Educ:* Loyola Col, Md, BS, 65; Univ Pa, PhD(physiol), 69. *Prof Exp:* Instr physiol, Sch Med, 70, Sch Vet Med, 70-72, from asst prof to assoc prof, 72-79, PROF PHYSIOL, SCH VET MED, UNIV PA, 79- *Concurrent Pos:* Pa Heart Asn res fel, Univ Pa, 70-71 & res grant, 71-72, res fel physiol, Dept Med, Univ Pa Hosp, 71-72; mem, Coun Basic Sci, Am Heart Asn, 71, estab investr, 72. *Mem:* AAAS; fel Am Col Cardiol; Am Heart Asn; Soc Gen Physiologists; Cardiac Muscle Soc. *Res:* Cardiovascular physiology; cardiac electrophysiology. *Mailing Add:* Sch of Vet Med Univ of Pa Philadelphia PA 19104

SPEAR, PATRICIA GAIL, b Chattanooga, Tenn, Dec 14, 42. VIROLOGY, CELL BIOLOGY. *Educ:* Fla State Univ, BA, 64; Univ Chicago, PhD(virol), 69. *Prof Exp:* USPHS trainee & res assoc virol, Dept Microbiol, Univ Chicago, 69-71; Arthritis Found fel & res assoc biochem, Rockefeller Univ, 71-73; asst prof microbiol, 73-78, ASSOC PROF MICROBIOL, UNIV CHICAGO, 78- *Concurrent Pos:* USPHS res career develop award, 75; consult comt virol & cell biol, Am Cancer Soc, 75-78; consult human cell biol prog, NSF, 75-77; mem med adv bd, Leukemia Res Found, Inc, 80-84. *Mem:* AAAS; Am Asn Immunologists; NY Acad Sci; Am Soc Microbiologists. *Res:* Virus-induced modifications of cell membranes. *Mailing Add:* Dept Microbiol Univ Chicago 910 E 58th St Chicago IL 60637

SPEAR, PAUL WILLIAM, b Baltimore, Md, Nov 3, 08; m 44; c 3. MEDICINE. *Educ:* Johns Hopkins Univ, BA, 30, MD, 34; Am Bd Internal Med, dipl, 41. *Prof Exp:* From asst to instr med, Johns Hopkins Univ, 37-41; chief med, Manhattan Beach Vet Admin Hosp, 47-50; from asst chief med to chief med, Brooklyn Vet Admin Hosp, 50-63; dir med, Montefioremorrisania Affil, 63-76; EMER PROF MED, ALBERT EINSTEIN COL MED, 75-; MED DIR, QUEENS COUNTY PROF STANDARDS REVIEW ORGN, 76- *Concurrent Pos:* Vis physician, Sinai Hosp, Baltimore, 37-41; clin assoc prof med, Col Med, State Univ NY Downstate Med Ctr, 51-63; attend physician, Kings County Hosp, 57-63, Maimonides Hosp, 58-63 & Montefiore Hosp, 63-; assoc prof med, Albert Einstein Col Med, 68-75. *Mem:* Am Soc Hemat; Int Soc Hemat; Am Fedn Clin Res; fel Am Col Physicians; fel NY Acad Med. *Res:* Hematology. *Mailing Add:* 55 Manhasset Woods Rd Manhasset NY 11030

SPEAR, ROBERT CLINTON, b Los Banos, Calif, June 26, 39; m 62; c 2. ENGINEERING. *Educ:* Univ Calif, Berkeley, BS, 61, MS, 63; Cambridge Univ, PhD(eng), 68. *Prof Exp:* Mech engr, US Navy, Calif, 63-65, 68-69; US Pub Health Serv fel, 69-70, from asst prof to assoc prof, 70-80, PROF ENVIRON HEALTH SCI, SCH PUB HEALTH, UNIV CALIF, BERKELEY, 81-, DIR, NORTHERN CALIF OCCUP HEALTH CTR, 79- *Concurrent Pos:* Sr int fel, Fogarty Int Ctr, NIH, 77-78. *Mem:* AAAS; Am Soc Mech Engrs; Am Indian Hyg Asn. *Res:* Engineering aspects of occupational and environmental health. *Mailing Add:* Sch of Pub Health Univ of Calif Berkeley CA 94720

SPEARE, EDWARD PHELPS, b Springfield, Mass, Jan 12, 21; m 48; c 5. ZOOLOGY. *Educ:* Northland Col, BA, 48; Univ Mich, MA, 50; Mich State Univ, PhD(zool), 58. *Prof Exp:* Assoc prof, 50-72, PROF BIOL, OLIVET COL, 72- *Concurrent Pos:* From instr to assoc prof, Biol Sta, Mich State Univ, 54-64. *Honors & Awards:* Nat Wildlife Fedn Award, 58-59. *Mem:* Am Fisheries Soc; Am Soc Ichthyologists & Herpetologists; Nat Audubon Soc. *Res:* Ecological ichthyology; stream ecology; life history of percid fish. *Mailing Add:* Dept of Biol Olivet Col Olivet MI 49076

SPEARING, ANN MARIE, b Olean, NY, Jan 29, 47. PLANT PHYSIOLOGY, PLANT ECOLOGY. *Educ:* State Univ NY Col Buffalo, BA, 69; State Univ NY Col Forestry, Syracuse Univ, MS, 71; Univ Md, PhD(plant biophys), 75. *Prof Exp:* Asst prof bot, Wheaton Col, 75-78; actg asst dir, Environ Prog, 78-81, ASST DEAN, GRAD COL, UNIV VT, 81- *Mem:* AAAS; Am Inst Biol Sci; Am Soc Plant Physiologists; Ecol Soc Am; Sigma Xi. *Res:* All aspects of physiological ecology, particularly responses of plants to light; effects of physical aspects of environment such as temperature and light on physiology of plants. *Mailing Add:* Deans Off Grad Col 335 Waterman Univ Vt Burlington VT 05405

SPEARING, CECILIA W, b New York, NY, Jan 29, 27. BIOCHEMISTRY. *Educ:* Hunter Col, BA, 47; Columbia Univ, MA, 49; George Washington Univ, MS, 61. *Prof Exp:* Lab technician, Med Col, Cornell Univ, 47-50; lab technician, Col Physicians & Surgeons, Columbia Univ, 50; instr biol, Barber-Scotia Col, 50-52; biochemist, Walter Reed Army Inst Res, 52-59, NIH, 59-63 & Food & Drug Admin, 63-65; biol sci adminr, 65-76, STAFF ASSOC, NSF, 76- *Mem:* AAAS; Am Inst Biol Sci; Am Chem Soc. *Res:* Intermediary metabolism. *Mailing Add:* Off of the Dep Asst Dir NSF Washington DC 20550

SPEARING, DARWIN ROBERT, b Rockford, Ill, Mar 2, 39; m 66; c 2. GEOLOGY. *Educ:* Beloit Col, BS, 61; Univ Mich, Ann Arbor, MA, 64, PhD(geol), 69. *Prof Exp:* Res geologist, 68-77, DEPT MGR, DENVER RES CTR, MARATHON OIL CO, 77- *Mem:* Geol Soc Am; Am Asn Petrol Geologists; Soc Econ Paleontologists & Mineralogists; Int Asn Sedimentologists. *Res:* Depositional models; scanning electron microscopy; sedimentation; stratigraphy; reservoir geology. *Mailing Add:* Denver Res Ctr Marathon Oil Co PO Box 269 Littleton CO 80120

SPEARS, ALEXANDER WHITE, III, b Grindstone, Pa, Sept 29, 32; m 51, 77; c 1. ORGANIC CHEMISTRY, PHYSICAL CHEMISTRY. *Educ:* Allegheny Col, BS, 53; Univ Buffalo, PhD(chem), 60. *Prof Exp:* Res assoc chem, Univ Buffalo, 56-58; instr, Millard Fillmore Col, 58-59; res assoc, Res Div, P Lorillard Co, 59-61, sr res chemist, 61-65, dir basic res, 65-68, dir res & develop, 68-71, vpres res & develop, 71-75, sr vpres, 75-77, EXEC VPRES OPERS & RES, LORILLARD CORP, 77- *Concurrent Pos:* Asst prof, Greensboro Div, Guilford Col, 61-65. *Honors & Awards:* Distinguished Achievement Award in Tobacco Sci, Philip Morris, Inc, 70. *Mem:* AAAS; Am Chem Soc. *Res:* Cancer chemotherapy; pyrolytic reactions and products; spectroscopy; chromatography. *Mailing Add:* Lorillard Corp 420 English St Greensboro NC 27405

SPEARS, BRIAN MERLE, b La Grande, Ore, Oct 5, 50; m 78; c 2. ENTOMOLOGY, RANGE SCIENCE. *Educ:* Ore State Univ, BS, 72; Tex Tech Univ, MS, 75; Univ Idaho, PhD(entom), 78. *Prof Exp:* Asst res scientist entom, Univ Ariz, 78-80; RANGE CONSERVATIONIST, BUR INDIAN AFFAIRS, 80- *Mem:* Soc Range Mgt; Entom Soc Am; Sigma Xi. *Res:* Bionomics of Arizona range and forest insect pests. *Mailing Add:* Bur Indian Affairs Warm Springs OR 97761

SPEARS, DAVID LEWIS, b Belvidere, Ill, July 22, 40; div; c 2. SOLID STATE PHYSICS. *Educ:* Monmouth Col, Ill, BA, 62; Dartmouth Col, MA, 64; Purdue Univ, PhD(physics), 69. *Prof Exp:* PHYSICIST, LINCOLN LAB, MASS INST TECHNOL, 69- *Mem:* Am Phys Soc. *Res:* X-ray lithography; surface wave devices; integrated optics; optical waveguide modulators; heterodyne detection; infrared heterodyne radiometry; infrared detectors. *Mailing Add:* Lincoln Lab Mass Inst of Technol PO Box 73 Lexington MA 02173

SPEARS, JAMES RICHARD, reproductive endocrinology, experimental embryology, see previous edition

SPEARS, JOSEPH FAULCONER, b Moreland, Ky, Aug 1, 15; m 45; c 2. BIOLOGY. *Educ:* Univ Ky, BS, 38. *Prof Exp:* Asst to dir, Bernheim Natural Hist Found, Ky, 38-40; supvr archaeol, US Dept Interior, 40-42; asst proj leader golden nematode control, Bur Entom & Plant Quarantine, USDA, 46-51; proj leader golden nematode control, Plant Pest Control Div, 51-56, staff officer control opers, Plant Pest Control Div, Agr Res Serv, 56-59, chief staff officer, 59-68, assoc dir plant protection div, 68-71, asst dep adminr plant protection progs, Animal & Plant Health Serv, 71-78, asst dir plant protection & quarantine progs, 78-80; RETIRED. *Mem:* Entom Soc Am; Orgn Trop Nematologists; Soc Nematologists; Weed Sci Soc Am. *Res:* Control of nematodes, plant pests, insects, weeds and plant diseases. *Mailing Add:* 8719 Stockton Pkwy Alexandria VA 22308

SPEARS, RICHARD KENT, b Brush, Colo, Mar 28, 37; m 57; c 5. ENGINEERING MATERIALS, ENGINEERING MECHANICS. *Educ:* Colo Sch Mines, BS, 59; Univ Denver, MS, 64; Univ Fla, PhD(eng sci), 77. *Prof Exp:* Engr metall, Martin Co, Denver, 59-64; applns engr, Honeywell, Inc, Minneapolis, 64-66; DESIGN ENGR, GEN ELEC CO, ST PETERSBURG, FLA, 66- *Mem:* Am Soc Metals (treas, 77-78). *Res:* Ferroelectricity; glass ceramics; glass coated wire. *Mailing Add:* 3104 Roberta St Largo FL 33517

SPEARS, SHOLTO MARION, b Scottsville, Ky, Aug 29, 00; m 22; c 3. ENGINEERING. *Educ:* Univ Ky, BS, 22, CE, 33; Univ Mich, PhD(civil eng), 42. *Prof Exp:* Struct engr, Ogle Construct Co, Ill, 22-31; from asst prof to assoc prof civil eng, Ill Inst Technol, 31-42; dean sch eng, Fenn Col, 46-50;

city engr, East Cleveland, 50-52; dir, Cleveland Mem Med Found, 53-57; prof civil eng, Univ Ark, Fayetteville, 57-68; vis prof, 68-73, EMER VIS PROF CIVIL ENG, UNIV MO-COLUMBIA, 73- *Mem:* Am Soc Civil Engrs; Am Soc Eng Educ; Nat Soc Prof Engrs. *Res:* Methods of highway traffic control; psychology in highway design. *Mailing Add:* 1423 Beechwood Terr Manhattan KS 66502

SPECHT, DONALD FRANCIS, b Harvey, NDak, Oct 15, 33; m 60; c 2. ELECTRICAL ENGINEERING, MEDICAL ELECTRONICS. *Educ:* Univ Santa Clara, BEE, 55; Carnegie-Mellon Univ, MS, 56; Stanford Univ, PhD(elec eng), 66. *Prof Exp:* Electronics engr, Radio Corp Am, NJ, 55-57; res engr, Lockheed Missiles & Space Co, 57-63, res specialist biomed data anal, 63-66, scientist, Lockheed Palo Alto Res Lab, 66-70; mgr prog develop, Gould, Inc, Palo Alto, 70-74; mgr res, Smithkline Instruments, 75-81, DIR RES, EKOLINE INC, 81- *Mem:* Inst Elec & Electronics Engrs. *Res:* Ultrasonic imaging; medical instrumentation; adaptive pattern-recognition techniques; nonlinear regression techniques; nonparametric probability estimators; radar target discrimination; automatic analysis of electrocardiograms; digital radopgraphy. *Mailing Add:* Ekoline Inc 880 W Maude Ave Sunnyvale CA 94086

SPECHT, HAROLD BALFOUR, b Schenectady, NY, May 13, 27; Can citizen; m 49; c 5. ENTOMOLOGY, ECOLOGY. *Educ:* McGill Univ, BSc, 48; Univ Wis, MSc, 51; Rutgers Univ, PhD(entom), 59. *Prof Exp:* RES SCIENTIST & ENTOMOLOGIST, KENTVILLE RES STA, CAN DEPT AGR, 48- *Mem:* Entom Soc Am; Entom Soc Can. *Res:* Fruit insect ecology; integrated control studies on insects affecting apples; factors affecting mite populations on apple trees; pea aphid ecology; apple aphid ecology; tobacco cutworm investigation. *Mailing Add:* Kentville Res Sta Can Dept of Agr Kentville NS B4N 1J5 Can

SPECHT, JAMES EUGENE, b Scottsbluff, Nebr, Sept 12, 45; m 69. PLANT PHYSIOLOGY, PLANT BREEDING. *Educ:* Univ Nebr, BS, 67, PhD(genetics), 74; Univ Ill, MS, 71. *Prof Exp:* MEM FAC AGRON, INST AGR & NATURAL RESOURCES, UNIV NEBR, 74- *Mem:* AAAS; Genetics Soc Am; Am Soc Agron. *Res:* Development of physiological screening techniques and tools to aid in the breeding and improvement of soybean varieties. *Mailing Add:* Dept of Agron Univ of Nebr Lincoln NE 68588

SPECHT, LAWRENCE W, b Roscoe, NY, Aug 5, 28; m 51; c 6. GENETICS. *Educ:* Cornell Univ, BS, 51; Mich State Univ, MS, 55, PhD, 57. *Prof Exp:* PROF DAIRY SCI, PA STATE UNIV, 57- *Mem:* Am Dairy Sci Asn. *Res:* Dairy cattle genetics and breeding, especially progeny testing and sire selection in artificial insemination; electronic data processing of milk production records. *Mailing Add:* Dept of Diary & Animal Sci Pa State Univ University Park PA 16802

SPECHT, ROBERT DICKERSON, b Seattle, Wash, May 11, 13; m 36; c 5. MATHEMATICS. *Educ:* Univ Fla, AB, 36, MS, 38; Univ Wis, PhD(math), 42. *Prof Exp:* Instr math, Univ Fla, 36-38; asst, Univ Wis, 38-41; instr, Univ Fla, 41-42; asst, Brown Univ, 42; from asst physicist to assoc mathematician, David Taylor Model Basin, US Dept Navy, 42-45; asst prof math, Univ Wis, 45-49; mathematician, RAND Corp, Santa Monica, 49-79. *Res:* Applied mathematics; mechanics. *Mailing Add:* 14930 McKendree Ave Pacific Palisades CA 90272

SPECHT, WILLIAM HAROLD, mathematics, see previous edition

SPECK, DAVID RALPH, b Lindsay, Calif, Oct 31, 27; m 52; c 1. PHYSICS. *Educ:* Fresno State Col, BS, 51; Univ Calif, Berkeley, MA, 53, PhD(physics), 56. *Prof Exp:* PHYSICIST, LAWRENCE LIVERMORE NAT LAB, UNIV CALIF, 56- *Mem:* Am Phys Soc. *Res:* Laser fusion; development and use of high power glass laser systems; plasma physics. *Mailing Add:* Lawrence Livermore Nat Lab PO Box 808 Livermore CA 94550

SPECK, JOHN CLARENCE, JR, b Indianapolis, Ind, Jan 6, 17; m 40; c 5. BIOCHEMISTRY. *Educ:* Univ Ill, BS, 39; Univ NC, PhD(org chem), 43. *Prof Exp:* Asst chem, Univ NC, 39-40; chemist, US Naval Res Lab, 41-43; res assoc chem, Ind Univ, 43-45; res assoc, 45-46, from instr to assoc prof, 46-65, PROF BIOCHEM, MICH STATE UNIV, 65- *Mem:* Am Chem Soc; Am Soc Biol Chemists. *Res:* Chemistry of enzymes and other natural products. *Mailing Add:* Dept of Biochem Mich State Univ East Lansing MI 48824

SPECK, JOHN EDWARD, b Toronto, Ont, May 22, 25; m 51; c 2. PERIODONTOLOGY. *Educ:* Univ Toronto, DDS, 49, dipl periodont, 52. *Prof Exp:* From instr to assoc prof, 52-71, PROF PERIODONT & CHMN DEPT, FAC DENT, UNIV TORONTO, 71- *Concurrent Pos:* Consult, Disabled Vet Admin, Sunnybrook Mil Hosp, 65-, Hosp for Sick Children, 67 & med-dent staff, Univ Toronto, Sunnybrook Hosp, 68-; consult, North York Gen Hosp, 74- *Mem:* Can Acad Periodont (secy-treas, 55-66, pres, 70-71); Am Acad Periodont; fel Am Col Dent; fel Royal Col Dent Can (registr-secy-treas, 66-). *Mailing Add:* Dept of Periodont Univ of Toronto Fac of Dent Toronto ON M5G 1G6 Can

SPECK, MARVIN LUTHER, b Middletown, Md, Oct 6, 13; m 40; c 3. MICROBIOLOGY. *Educ:* Univ Md, BS, 35, MS, 37; Cornell Univ, PhD(bact), 40. *Prof Exp:* Bacteriologist, Western Md Dairy, 35-36; instr bact, Univ Md, 40-41; asst chief bacteriologist, Nat Dairy Res Labs, 41-47; from assoc prof to prof dairy bact, 47-57, William Neal Reynolds Prof, 57-79, EMER PROF FOOD SCI & MICROBIOL, NC STATE UNIV, 79- *Concurrent Pos:* Jr bacteriologist, USDA, 36; bacteriologist, Dairymen's League, 40; instr, Univ Md, 45; consult, USPHS, 50-51 & 53; WHO fel, Europe, 66; Nordica Int Res Award, Am Cultured Dairy Prod Inst, 81. *Honors & Awards:* Borden Award, Am Dairy Sci Asn, 59 & Pfizer Award, 67. *Mem:* AAAS; Inst Food Technol; Am Soc Microbiol; Am Dairy Sci Asn; fel Inst Food Technologists. *Res:* Nutrition and metabolism of lactic acid bacteria; injury and destruction of bacteria by physical and chemical agents; uses and functions of intestinal lactobacilli. *Mailing Add:* Dept of Food Sci NC State Univ Raleigh NC 27650

SPECK, REINHARD STANIFORD, b Rockport, Mass, Apr 30, 22; m 59. MEDICAL BACTERIOLOGY. *Educ:* Middlebury Col, AB, 44; Boston Univ, MD, 48. *Prof Exp:* Intern, Boston City Hosp, 48-49; from instr to assoc prof, 49-68, vchmn dept, 63-76, PROF MICROBIOL, SCH MED, UNIV CALIF, SAN FRANCISCO, 68- *Mem:* Am Soc Microbiol; Am Asn Hist Med. *Res:* Antibiotic antagonism; plague immunity; experimental airborne infection; infectious diseases; intestinal bacterial flora; history of fevers and infectious diseases. *Mailing Add:* 1257 27th Ave San Francisco CA 94122

SPECK, RHOADS MCCLELLAN, b Glenside, Pa, Apr 12, 20; m 46; c 4. ORGANIC CHEMISTRY. *Educ:* Philadelphia Col Pharm, BSc, 42; Pa State Univ, MSc, 49, PhD(org chem), 52. *Prof Exp:* Asst chemist, Eastern Regional Res Ctr, Agr Res Serv, USDA, 42-44 & 46-47; asst anal chem, Pa State Univ, 47-48; res chemist, 52-75, sr res chemist, 75-81, RES SCIENTIST, RES CTR, HERCULES INC, WILMINGTON, 81- *Mem:* Am Chem Soc; Sigma Xi. *Res:* Syntheses and physical properties of high molecular weight hydrocarbons; syntheses of agricultural chemicals; rosin and fatty acid chemistry; emulsion polymerization; free radical reactions. *Mailing Add:* Box 507 RD 4 Hockessin DE 19707

SPECKMAN, CALVIN ALBERT, b Sleepy Eye, Minn, Oct 2, 46; m 74; c 3. MICROBIOLOGY, FERMENTATION. *Educ:* Univ Minn, BS, 68; Ore State Univ, PhD(microbiol), 74. *Prof Exp:* Qual control dir standard develop, US Army Vet Corps, 69-70; res assoc microbiol, Space Sci Ctr, Univ Minn, 74-75; sr microbiologist bact cult, Labor Wiesby, Niebull, WGer, 75-76; food technologist prod develop, DuBak Corp, Spokane, 76-77; SR SCIENTIST MICROBIAL FERMENTATION, NULABS DIV, PIONEER HI-BRED INT, 77- *Mem:* Inst Food Technologists. *Res:* Investigation of microbial fermentation of plant material with emphasis on basic microbial physiology and metabolism by lactic acid bacteria. *Mailing Add:* Pioneer Hi-Bred Int Inc 3930 SW Macadam Ave Portland OR 97201

SPECKMANN, ELWOOD W, b Brooklyn, NY, Jan 10, 36; m 62; c 4. PHYSIOLOGY, NUTRITION. *Educ:* Rutgers Univ, BS, 57; Mich State Univ, MS, 59, PhD(nutrit physiol), 62. *Prof Exp:* Res asst nutrit physiol, Mich State Univ, 58-60; res scientist, Biospecialties Br, Physiol Div, Aerospace Med Res Labs, Wright-Patterson AFB, Ohio, 62-65; asst dir nutrit res, 65-67, interim educ dir, 67-68, assoc dir nutrit res, 68-71, DIR NUTRIT RES, NAT DAIRY COUN, 71- *Concurrent Pos:* Air Force liaison rep food & nutrit bd & working group nutrit & feeding probs, Man in Space Comt, Space Sci Bd, Nat Acad Sci-Nat Res Coun, 63-65; mem coun arteriosclerosis, Am Heart Asn. *Mem:* Inst Food Technologists; Am Inst Nutrit; NY Acad Sci; Coun Agr Sci & Technol; fel Am Heart Asn. *Res:* Physiology of circulation and heart; arteriosclerosis; aerospace nutrition and physiology; physiology of digestion and metabolism of foods; nutrient interactions. *Mailing Add:* Nat Dairy Coun 6300 N River Rd Rosemont IL 60018

SPECKMANN, GUNTER WILHELM-OTTO, b Ger, Oct 3, 34; Can citizen; m 62; c 3. VETERINARY BACTERIOLOGY. *Educ:* Vet Col Hannover, Ger, DMV, 67; Univ Guelph, DVM, 68. *Prof Exp:* Veterinarian poultry dis, 68-76, VETERINARIAN BACTERIOL, ANIMAL PATH DIV, AGR CAN, 76- *Mem:* Am Asn Zoo Veterinarians. *Res:* Epidemiological studies of Salmonella and Yersinia carriers in livestock. *Mailing Add:* Animal Dis Res Inst PO Box 11300 Sta H Ottawa ON K2H 8P9 Can

SPECTOR, ABRAHAM, b Nyack, NY, Jan 14, 26; m 50; c 2. BIOCHEMISTRY. *Educ:* Bard Col, AB, 47; NY Univ, PhD(biochem), 57. *Hon Degrees:* MD, Univ Repub Uraguay, 81. *Prof Exp:* Res chemist, Lederle Labs, Am Cyanamid Corp, 48-52; from instr to assoc biochem, Howe Lab, Mass Eye & Ear Infirmary, Harvard Med Sch, 58-65; from asst prof to assoc prof ophthal, 65-73, PROF OPHTHAL BIOCHEM, COL PHYSICIANS & SURGEONS, COLUMBIA UNIV, 73-, DIR, LAB BIOCHEM & MOLECULAR BIOL, 76- *Concurrent Pos:* Nat Found fel, Carlsberg Lab, Copenhagen, 57-58; Guggenheim fel, 71-72; mem vision res & training comt, Nat Eye Inst, 70-71, chmn cataract workshop, 73-, bd sci adv, 74, mem vision sci A study sect, 76-, chmn, 78-, mem cataract adv panel workshop, 76; mem bd scientific adv, Nat Eye Inst, NIH, 81- *Mem:* Am Soc Biol Chem; Am Chem Soc; Asn Res Vision & Ophthal. *Res:* Protein chemistry; ophthalmic biochemistry; enzymology; biosynthesis of proteins and nucleic acids. *Mailing Add:* Col Physicians & Surgeons Columbia Univ New York NY 10032

SPECTOR, ARTHUR ABRAHAM, b Philadelphia, Pa, May 14, 36; m 60; c 3. BIOCHEMISTRY, INTERNAL MEDICINE. *Educ:* Univ Pa, BA, 56, MD, 60. *Prof Exp:* Intern, Abington Mem Hosp, 60-61; res med officer, Nat Heart Inst, 63-68; from asst prof to assoc prof, 68-75, PROF BIOCHEM & MED & DIR ARTERIOSCLEROSIS SCOR CTR, UNIV IOWA, 75- *Concurrent Pos:* NIH res career develop award, 69-74; Nat Heart Inst fel biochem, 63-65; mem coun arteriosclerosis, Am Heart Asn; mem metab study sect, NIH, 73-77 & rev comt, Ischemic Heart Dis Ctr, 78-79; chmn res comt & mem bd dirs, Iowa Heart Asn, 75-77; chmn & mem, Great Plains Regional Res Comn, Am Heart Asn, 77-80; mem & chmn biomed adv comt, Oak Ridge Assoc Univ, 78-82. *Mem:* AAAS; Tissue Cult Asn; Am Asn Cancer Res; Am Soc Biol Chemists; Am Soc Clin Invest. *Res:* Lipid metabolism; membranes; fatty acids; prostadlanging. *Mailing Add:* Dept of Biochem Univ of Iowa Iowa City IA 52242

SPECTOR, BERTRAM, b New York, NY, Nov 1, 21; m 45; c 2. ENVIRONMENTAL HEALTH, MEDICAL SYSTEMS ENGINEERING. *Educ:* City Col New York, BEE, 45; Hunter Col, MS, 57; Cornell Univ, PhD(med sci), 61. *Prof Exp:* Dir res, Seversky Electronatom, NY, 60-63; dean acad affairs, 63-64, chmn life sci dept, 63-64 & 67-68, PROF LIFE SCI, NY INST TECHNOL, 63-, VPRES RES, 66- *Concurrent Pos:* Prin investr grants, Off Educ, Dept Health, Educ & Welfare, Carnegie Corp, Ford Found Fund for Advan Educ & Proj ULTRA, 64-; prin investr systs anal, Brevard County Schs, Fla, 64-; prin co-investr, Dept Health, Educ & Welfare grant, 68-; adj prof, Shaw Univ, 68-70; consult, Pan Am Airlines, 68, Nova Univ Advan Technol & Hofstra Univ, 69 & Wash Univ, 69-; mem NSF panel, 69; mem bd trustees, Affiliated Cols & Univs, Inc; mem bd dirs, Afro-

Am Coun Higher Educ; mem bd dirs & exec comt, Canciro, Inc; chmn, Environ Control Comn, Town of Oyster Bay, 74- & Comt Energy & Natural Resources, 73-; vpres res, New York Chiropractic Col, Glen Head, 76-; pres, New Ctr Wholistic Health & Res, 81-; Sloan fel. *Mem:* Fel Am Inst Biol Sci. *Res:* Physics; educational technology; environmental sciences and technology; pattern electromyography; biofeedback; moire contourography. *Mailing Add:* 1 Stratford Pl Syosset NY 11791

SPECTOR, CALVIN, plant physiology, genetics, see previous edition

SPECTOR, CLARENCE J(ACOB), b New York, NY, June 19, 27; m 50; c 3. ENGINEERING PHYSICS, MATERIALS SCIENCE. *Educ:* Va Polytech Inst & State Univ, BS, 53; Stevens Inst Technol, MS, 57. *Prof Exp:* Mem tech staff, Bell Tel Labs, Inc, 53-62; sr engr & mgr display components develop, 62-76, MGR THERMAL TECHNOL, IBM SYST PROD, IBM CORP, 76- *Mem:* AAAS; Inst Elec & Electronics Engrs. *Res:* Physics of dielectrics, magnetic and semiconductor materials; passive and magnetic thin film devices; metallurgy. *Mailing Add:* IBM Syst Prod East Fishkill D49E-305-081 Hopewell Junction NY 12533

SPECTOR, ELLIOT, pharmacology, see previous edition

SPECTOR, HAROLD NORMAN, b Chicago, Ill, Feb 26, 35; m 61; c 1. SOLID STATE PHYSICS. *Educ:* Univ Chicago, SB, 57, SM, 58, PhD(physics), 61. *Prof Exp:* NSF fel physics, Hebrew Univ, Israel, 61-62; asst prof, Case Inst Technol, 62-63; res physicist, IIT Res Inst, 63-66, assoc prof, 66-76, PROF, ILL INST TECHNOL, 76- *Concurrent Pos:* Vis prof, Hebrew Univ, Israel, 73-74. *Mem:* Fel Am Phys Soc. *Res:* Solid state theory, electronphonon interactions in solids, transport theory, effect of strong electric and magnetic fields on electronic processes in solids. *Mailing Add:* Dept Physics Ill Inst Technol Chicago IL 60616

SPECTOR, LEONARD B, b Newark, NJ, Dec 6, 18; div. BIOCHEMISTRY. *Educ:* Harvard Univ, PhD(chem), 50. *Prof Exp:* Assoc biochemist, Mass Gen Hosp, 50-60; asst prof biochem, 60-62, ASSOC PROF BIOCHEM, ROCKEFELLER UNIV, 62- *Mem:* Am Soc Biol Chemists. *Res:* Purines; pyrimidines; urea synthesis; phosphorus compounds; enzyme reactions; covalent catallysis by enzymes. *Mailing Add:* Rockefeller Univ New York NY 10021

SPECTOR, NORMAN A(ARON), b Romania, Aug 30, 18; US citizen; m 43; c 4. CHEMICAL ENGINEERING. *Educ:* Yale Univ, BE, 40, ME, 42, DEng, 45. *Prof Exp:* Chem engr, Pa, 43-45; chem engr, M W Kellogg Co, NY, 45-48; asst chief proj engr, Vitro Corp Am, 48-50, asst gen mgr, Eng Div, 50-57, vpres, 57-66, group vpres eng & int opers, 60-66, pres, Vitro Int, 57-66, pres, Vitro Eng Co, 61-66; VPRES, J A JONES CONSTRUCT CO, 66- *Concurrent Pos:* Dir, Vitro Italiana, SPA, 57-66, Vitroselenia, SPA, 58-66 & Zirconium Corp Am, 58- *Mem:* Am Chem Soc; Am Inst Chem Engrs. *Res:* Ion exchange; absorption of gases; low temperature processes; atomic power and reprocessing; light metals processing; industrial processes; pharmaceutical and food processing. *Mailing Add:* J A Jones Construct Co One Penn Plaza New York NY 10001

SPECTOR, NOVERA HERBERT, b Cincinnati, Ohio, Aug 23, 19; m 41, 81; c 4. NEUROBIOLOGY, BIOPHYSICS. *Educ:* City Col New York, BS, 41; Univ Pa, PhD(physiol), 67. *Prof Exp:* Consult engr, 41-62; from res assoc to asst prof psychiat, Med Col Va, Va Commonwealth Univ, 66-68, asst prof physiol, 68-69; prof physiol, Fac Med, Univ Claude Bernard, France, 69-71; chief dept neurophysiol & sr res physiologist, Walter Reed Inst Res, 71-76; dir, Neurobiol Prog, NSF, 76-77; HEALTH SCI ADMINR, FUNDAMENTAL NEUROSCI PROG, NAT INST NEUROL DIS & STROKE, NIH, 77-; PROF NEUROSCI, BIRMINGHAM MED CTR, UNIV ALA, 80- *Concurrent Pos:* Consult, NASA, 68-71; adj prof physiol & biophys & adj prof anat, Med Ctr, Georgetown Univ, Washington, DC, 78-; vis prof phychiatry, Birmingham Med Ctr, Univ Ala, 80- *Mem:* Sigma Xi; Soc Exp Biol & Med; Am Physiol Soc; Soc Neurosci; Tissue Cult Asn. *Res:* Energy balance in mammals; central nervous system regulation of autonomic functions; neural data processing; biophysics of neurons in vivo and in vitro; neural substrates of sensation and behavior; epistemology; central nervous system influences on host responses to antigens and diseases; neuropharmacology; alcoholism; psychophysics; hypothalamic control mechanisms; neuroanatomy; neuroimmunogenesis; neuroimmunomodulation; physiology. *Mailing Add:* Neurosci Prog PO Box 190 Birmingham Med Ctr Univ Ala Birmingham AL 35294

SPECTOR, RICHARD M, b St Louis, Mo, Jan 13, 38; div; c 3. THEORETICAL PHYSICS. *Educ:* Harvard Univ, BA, 59; Oxford Univ, PhD(physics), 62; Wayne State Univ, JD, 76. *Prof Exp:* Vis scientist physics, Saclay Nuclear Res Ctr, France, 62; res assoc, Univ Rochester, 62-64; prof assoc, NSF, 64-65; from asst prof to assoc prof physics, Wayne State Univ, 65-78; assoc, Dykema, Gossett, Spencer, Goodwin & Trigg, Detroit, 78-81; ASSOC, HONIGMAN, MILLER, SCHWARTZ & COHN, DETROIT, 81- *Mem:* Am Bar Asn; Am Phys Soc. *Res:* Singular potential theory; spectra of rapidly rotating stars; geophysical aspects of pleochroic halos; group theory of elementary particles. *Mailing Add:* Honigman Miller Schwartz & Cohn 2290 First Nat Bldg Detroit MI 48226

SPECTOR, SAMUEL, b Brooklyn, NY, Mar 11, 14; m 43; c 3. PEDIATRICS. *Educ:* Columbia Univ, BS, 34; Long Island Col Med, MD, 37. *Prof Exp:* Intern, Beth El Hosp, 37-38; intern, Kingston Ave Hosp, 38; resident pediat, Willard Parker Hosp, 39-41; resident, Univ Hosp, Univ Mich, 41-42, instr, Med Sch, 42-43; from asst prof to prof, Sch Med, Case Western Reserve Univ, 46-70; prof pediat & chmn dept, Univ Chicago, 70-79; PROF PEDIAT, UNIV CALIF, SAN DIEGO, 79- *Concurrent Pos:* From assoc pediatrician to assoc dir pediat, Babies & Children's Hosp, 46-66; dir pediat, Children's Hosp of Akron, 67-70; dir pediat, Wyler Children's Hosp, Univ Chicago Hosps & Clins, 70-79 & LaRabida Children's Hosp & Res Ctr, 73-78; dir pediat, Univ Hosp, Med Ctr, Univ Calif, San Diego. *Mem:* Soc Pediat Res; Am Pediat Soc; Am Acad Pediat; Am Soc Human Genetics. *Res:* Metabolic and endocrine problems of childhood. *Mailing Add:* 225 Dickinson St Med Ctr Univ Calif San Diego CA 92103

SPECTOR, SHELDON LAURENCE, b Detroit, Mich, Feb 13, 39; m 66; c 3. ALLERGY, IMMUNOLOGY. *Educ:* Wayne State Univ, MD, 64. *Prof Exp:* Fel allergy & clin immunol, 69-71, clin coordr, 71-72, HEAD SECT ALLERGY & CLIN IMMUNOL, NAT JEWISH HOSP & RES CTR, 72- *Concurrent Pos:* Asst med, Mt Sinai Hosp Sch Med, 65-66; asst prof, Med Sch, Univ Colo, 71-77, assoc prof, 77-; vis prof, Hebrew Univ, Jerusalem, 78; Lady Davis fel allergy, Hebrew Univ, William Beaumont Soc, 78. *Mem:* Am Thoracic Soc; Am Soc Internal Med; fel Am Acad Allergy; fel Am Col Physicians; fel Am Col Chest Physicians. *Res:* Bronchial inhalation challenge techniques; new modalities of treatment of asthma and rhinitis including unmarketed preparation; how certain substances in the environment affect bronchial and/or nasal reactivity; how commonly used medications affect asthmatic patients. *Mailing Add:* Nat Jewish Hosp & Res Ctr 3800 E Colfax Ave Denver CO 80206

SPECTOR, SYDNEY, b New York, NY, Oct 28, 23; m 48; c 2. PHARMACOLOGY. *Educ:* Univ Denver, BS, 48, MS, 50; Jefferson Med Col, PhD(pharmacol), 56. *Prof Exp:* Asst physiol, Univ Denver, 47-50; asst pharmacol, Sch Med, Wash Univ, 50-52; res assoc, Wyeth Inst Med Res, Pa, 52-55; pharmacologist, Nat Heart Inst, Md, 56-68; HEAD PHYSIOL CHEM & PHARMACOL, ROCHE INST MOLECULAR BIOL, 68- *Concurrent Pos:* Instr, Hahnemann Med Col, 54; adj prof pharmacol, Howard Med Sch, 60- & New York Med Col, 68-; adj prof pharmacol & anesthesiol, Col Physicians & Surgeons, Columbia Univ, 70- *Mem:* AAAS; Am Soc Pharmacol & Exp Therapeut; Am Col Neuropsychopharmacol. *Res:* Biochemical pharmacoloy; correlation between pharmacological effects of drugs and chemical changes, particularly of the central nervous system; development of antibodies toward drugs. *Mailing Add:* Roche Inst of Molecular Biol Nutley NJ 07110

SPECTOR, THOMAS, b New Haven, Conn, July 20, 44; m 69; c 1. BIOCHEMISTRY, PHARMACOLOGY. *Educ:* Univ Vt, BA, 66; Yale Univ, PhD(pharm), 70. *Prof Exp:* Fel biochem, Univ Mich, 70-72; SR RES BIOCHEMIST, WELLCOME RES LABS, 72- *Concurrent Pos:* Adj assoc prof, Dept Pharmacol, Univ NC, 76- *Res:* Enzymology, mechanisms of inhibition and substrate catalysis; inhibitor and substrate specificities. *Mailing Add:* Burroughs Wellcome Co Research Triangle Park NC 27709

SPEDDEN, H RUSH, b Colville, Wash, May 31, 16; m 51; c 4. MINING ENGINEERING. *Educ:* Univ Wash, BS, 39; Mont Sch Mines, MS, 40. *Hon Degrees:* MinDrE, 64. *Prof Exp:* Asst, Mass Inst Technol, 40-41, instr mineral dressing, 41-42, asst prof, 46-52 res engr & head minerals res dept, Metals Res Lab, Union Carbide Corp, 52-57, dir res, Union Carbide Ore Co, 57-64; res dir, Kennecott Copper Corp, Metal Mining Div, Res Ctr, 64-74, dir tech admin, 74-77; CONSULT MINERAL PROCESSING ENGR, 77- *Concurrent Pos:* Prod specialist, Foreign Econ Admin, 42-44; adj prof, Univ Utah. *Honors & Awards:* Robert H Richards Award, Am Inst Mining, Metall & Petrol Engrs, 71. *Mem:* Am Inst Mining, Metall & Petrol Engrs; Soc Mining Engrs (pres, 70); Mining & Metall Soc Am; Brit Inst Mining & Metall. *Res:* Minerals beneficiation; extractive metallurgy. *Mailing Add:* 304 First Security Bldg Salt Lake City UT 84111

SPEDDING, FRANK HAROLD, b Hamilton, Ont, Oct 22, 02; US citizen; m 31; c 1. PHYSICAL CHEMISTRY. *Educ:* Univ Mich, BS, 25, MS, 26; Univ Calif, PhD(chem), 29. *Hon Degrees:* LLD, Drake Univ, 46; DSc, Univ Mich, 49 & Case Inst Technol, 56. *Prof Exp:* Instr chem, Univ Calif, 29-30, 32-34, Nat Res Coun fel, 30-32; Guggenheim prof, Eng, Ger, Russia, Neth & Japan, 34-35; George Fisher Baker asst prof, Cornell Univ, 35-37; assoc prof phys chem & head sect, Iowa State Univ, 37-41, prof chem, 41-73, dir atomic proj, 42-48, dir inst atomic res, 45-68, dir, Ames Lab, 47-68, prof physics, Univ, 50-73, prof metall, 62-73, DISTINGUISHED PROF SCI & HUMANITIES, IOWA STATE UNIV, 57-, EMER PROF CHEM, PHYSICS & METALL, 73-, PRIN SCIENTIST, AMES LAB, US DEPT ENERGY, 68- *Concurrent Pos:* Dir chem & metall div, Plutonium Proj, Univ Chicago, 42-43, mem proj coun, 42-46; mem bd gov, Argonne Nat Lab, 46-48; AEC tech rep, Int Conf Peaceful Uses Atomic Energy, Geneva, 55, AEC & US State Dept rep, World Power Conf, Vienna, 56; off observer, Bikini Atomic Bomb Tests; mem tech adv comt & dir Manhattan proj, Off Sci Res & Develop & Nat Defense Res Comt; mem comt radioactive waste mgt, Nat Acad Sci, 68- *Honors & Awards:* Langmuir Award, Am Chem Soc, 33, Nichols Medal, 52; Douglas Medal, Am Inst Mining, Metall & Petrol Engrs, 61; Francis J Clamer Medal, Franklin Inst, 69. *Mem:* Nat Acad Sci; AAAS; fel Am Phys Soc; hon mem Soc Appl Spectros; hon mem Austrian Chem Soc. *Res:* Rare earths; atomic and molecular spectra; metallurgy of uranium, thorium and other rare metals; plutonium chemistry; atomic energy chemistry; absorption spectra of solids at low temperatures. *Mailing Add:* Ames Lab Iowa State Univ Ames IA 50011

SPEDDING, ROBERT H, b Lockport, NY, Feb 8, 31; m 59; c 3. DENTISTRY. *Educ:* Ind Univ, AB, 53, DDS, 60, MSD, 63; Am Bd Pedodont, dipl, 67. *Prof Exp:* Teaching asst pedodont, Sch Dent, Ind Univ, 62-63; from instr to assoc prof, 63-72, PROF PEDIAT DENT, COL DENT, UNIV KY, 72- *Mem:* Am Dent Asn; Am Acad Pedodontics; Am Asn Dent Schs. *Res:* Effects of various materials on primary tooth pulps and periodontal tissues. *Mailing Add:* Dept of Pediat Dent Univ of Ky Lexington KY 40506

SPEECE, HERBERT E, b Meadowlands, Minn, Oct 29, 14; m 45; c 2. MATHEMATICS. *Educ:* York Col, AB, 38; Tex Christian Univ, MA, 43; NC State Col, MS, 51; Univ NC, PhD(math), 56. *Prof Exp:* Head, Dept Sci & Math Educ, 72-80, prof, 47-80, EMER PROF MATH, NC STATE UNIV, 80- *Concurrent Pos:* Dir, Nat Acad Sci-NSF Inserv Insts, NC, 59-, assoc dir, NSF Acad Year Inst, 65-67; dir, Eng Concepts Curriculum Proj Implementation Ctr Southeast, NSF, 71-72 & 72-73; chmn adv bd, NC Student Acad Sci; chmn selection comt, NC Jr Sci & Humanities Symp; dir, Comput Educ Ctr, Dept Math-Sci Educ, NC State Univ, 73-78. *Mem:* Math Asn Am; National Coun Teachers Math; Asn Educ Teachers Sci; Nat Sci Teachers Asn. *Res:* Tensors and differential geometry. *Mailing Add:* Dept Math NC State Univ Raleigh NC 27650

SPEED, EDWIN MAURICE, b Enterprise, Miss, Aug 17, 18; m 42; c 2. DENTISTRY, ANATOMY. *Educ:* Birmingham Southern Col, BA, 52; Univ Ala, DMD, 54, MS, 65. *Prof Exp:* Pvt pract, 54-61; resident periodont, Vet Admin Hosp, Birmingham, Ala, 63-65; mem, Fac Dent & asst to dean, Sch Dent, Univ Ala, Brimingham, 65-66, prof dent & asst dean, 66-79; RETIRED. *Concurrent Pos:* Consult, US Army, Ft Benning, Ga, 71-72; mem coun, Nat Bd Dent Examr, 75-77 & Dent Hyg Nat Bd, 75-76. *Mem:* Am Dent Asn; Am Acad Periodont; fel Am Col Dent; Am Asn Dent Schs (vpres, 74, pres, 75). *Res:* Wound healing. *Mailing Add:* 223 Dallas Ave Selma AL 36701

SPEED, RAYMOND A(NDREW), b Muldoon, Tex, Sept 30, 22; m 53; c 2. CHEMICAL ENGINEERING. *Educ:* Univ Tex, BSChE, 49. *Prof Exp:* From jr chemist to res specialist, Humble Oil & Refining Co, 49-63; res specialist, Esso Res & Eng Co, 63-71; sr staff engr, Enjay Chem Co, 71-78, ENG ASSOC, EXXON CHEM CO USA, 78- *Mem:* Am Chem Soc; Am Inst Chem Engrs; Soc Plastics Engrs. *Res:* Polyolefin polymers; separations. *Mailing Add:* Baton Rouge Plastics Plant Exxon Chem Co USA PO Box 1607 Baton Rouge LA 70821

SPEED, ROBERT CLARKE, b Los Angeles, Calif, June 20, 33; m 54; c 2. GEOLOGY, GEOPHYSICS. *Educ:* Univ Colo, BS, 54; Stanford Univ, MS, 58, PhD(geol), 61. *Prof Exp:* Res supvr, Jet Propulsion Lab, Calif Inst Technol, 60-66; from asst prof to assoc prof, 66-74, PROF GEOL, NORTHWESTERN UNIV, EVANSTON, 74- *Res:* Tectonics and structural geology; structure and evolution of accretionary prisms and forearcs; tectonics of southeastern Caribbean and US cardillera; fold and thrust belts; seismicity. *Mailing Add:* Dept Geol Northwestern Univ Evanston IL 60201

SPEEDIE, MARILYN KAY, b Salem, Ore, Nov 13, 47; m 68; c 1. PHARMACOGNOSY, APPLIED MICROBIOLOGY. *Educ:* Purdue Univ, BSPh, 70, PhD(med chem & pharmacog), 73. *Prof Exp:* Asst prof, Sch Pharm, Ore State Univ, 73-75; asst prof, 75-80, ASSOC PROF PHARMACOG, SCH PHARM, UNIV MD, 80- *Mem:* Am Soc Pharmacog; Am Soc Microbiol; Soc Indust Microbiol. *Res:* Genetics and regulation of biosynthesis of antibiotics in Streptomycetes; enzymology of secondary metabolism in microorganisms; interaction of estuarine fungi with pesticides. *Mailing Add:* Dept Med Chem/Pharmacog 636 W Lombard Baltimore MD 21201

SPEEN, GERALD BRUCE, b Philadelphia, Pa, Oct 2, 30; m m 54; c 3. HEAT TRANSFER, ENERGY CONVERSION. *Educ:* Univ Del, BS, 52; Univ Calif, Los Angeles, MS, 54. *Prof Exp:* Asst physics, Univ Del, 51-52; mem tech staff, Res & Develop Labs, Hughes Aircraft Co, 52-54; res physicist, Micronics Inc Div, Zenith Plastics Corp, 54-55; res engr, Summers Gyroscope Co, 55-56; exec engr, ITT Fed Labs, Int Tel & Tel Corp, 56-64; gen mgr, Western Develop Ctr, Conductron Corp, Subsid McDonnell-Douglas Corp, 64-68; pres, Data Instruments Co, 68-73; pres, Lanco-Supreme, Inc, Hyatt Corp, 73-75, pres, Supreme Aire & Elmet Corp, Santa Fe Springs, 73-77; group vpres, Elsters Inc, 77-78; PRES, G SPEEN & ASSOCS, CONSULTS IN ENERGY FIELD, 78- *Concurrent Pos:* Mem tech coord comt gas lubrication, Off Naval Res, 58-66. *Honors & Awards:* Inst Elec & Electronics Engrs Award, 63. *Mem:* Am Phys Soc; Am Inst Aeronaut & Astronaut; sr mem Inst Elec & Electronics Engrs. *Res:* Guidance and control systems; sensor design; gyroscopes; accelerometers; gas lubrication and bearing design; pneumatic systems; data acquisition; environmental control systems; energy conservation and recovery systems; heat and solar actuated systems; thermodynamics. *Mailing Add:* 17339 Halsted St Northridge CA 91325

SPEER, DONALD ARTHUR, science administration, deceased

SPEER, FRIDTJOF ALFRED, b Berlin, Ger, Aug 23, 23; US citizen; m 51; c 3. PHYSICS. *Educ:* Tech Univ Berlin, Dipl Ing, 50, Dr Ing(physics), 53. *Prof Exp:* Asst prof physics, Tech Univ Berlin, 50-55; div chief missile develop, US Army, 55-60; div chief spacecraft develop, 60-65, mgr mission opers, 65-71, MGR, SCI PROJS, MARSHALL SPACE FLIGHT CTR, NASA, 71- *Concurrent Pos:* Ed, Sci Abstr Periodical, Berlin, 53-55. *Honors & Awards:* Except Serv Medals, NASA, 69, Outstanding Leadership Medal, 78. *Mem:* Assoc fel Am Inst Aeronaut & Astronaut. *Res:* Scientific satellite development and operation; space astronomy; high energy astronomy. *Mailing Add:* Marshall Space Flight Ctr NASA Huntsville AL 35812

SPEER, VAUGHN C, b Milford, Iowa, Apr 5, 24; m 47; c 4. NUTRITION, BIOCHEMISTRY. *Educ:* Iowa State Univ, BS, 49, MS, 51, PhD, 57. *Prof Exp:* Asst nutrit, Iowa State Univ, 49-51; nutritionist, Ralston Purina Co, 51-53; assoc animal husb, 53-57, from asst prof to assoc prof, 58-66, PROF NUTRIT, IOWA STATE UNIV, 66- *Mem:* Am Inst Nutrit; Am Soc Animal Sci. *Res:* Swine nutrition; nutritional effects on swine reproduction. *Mailing Add:* Dept of Animal Sci Iowa State Univ 337 Kildee Hall Ames IA 50011

SPEERS, GEORGE M, b State Center, Iowa, Dec 10, 40; m 63; c 2. POULTRY NUTRITION. *Educ:* Iowa State Univ, BS, 63, MS, 65, PhD(poultry nutrit), 68. *Prof Exp:* Grad asst, Iowa State Univ, 63-65, res assoc, 65-68; from asst prof to assoc prof, Univ Minn, St Paul, 68-74; POULTRY PROD MGR, LANND O'LAKES, INC, 74- *Mem:* Poultry Sci Asn; World Poultry Sci Asn; Sigma Xi. *Res:* Amino acid and mineral metabolism in poultry. *Mailing Add:* 417 Garden Rd Albert Lea MN 56007

SPEERS, LOUISE (MRS HENRY CROIX), b Nanking, China, Dec 30, 19; US citizen; m 51. ORGANIC CHEMISTRY. *Educ:* Vassar Col, AB, 41; Columbia Univ, PhD(org chem), 49. *Prof Exp:* Bacteriologist, Typhus Vaccine Prod, Lederle Labs, Am Cyanamid Co, 41-42; chemist, Plastics Dept, E I du Pont de Nemours & Co, 42-44; PROJ LEADER MED PROD, CENT RES LABS, AIRCO INC, 49- *Mem:* Am Chem Soc; Sigma Xi. *Res:* Organic synthesis in pharmaceuticals; anesthetics, analgesics, muscle relaxants, acetylenics and fluoro aliphatic compounds. *Mailing Add:* Ohio Med Anesthetics Airco Inc 100 Mountain Ave Murray Hill NJ 07974

SPEERT, ARNOLD, b Bronx, NY, June 19, 45; m 67; c 2. PHYSICAL ORGANIC CHEMISTRY. *Educ:* City Col New York, BS, 66; Princeton Univ, PhD(chem), 71. *Prof Exp:* From asst prof to assoc prof chem, 70-80, asst to vpres acad affairs, 71-78, assoc dean acad affairs, 78-79, PROF CHEM, WILLIAM PATERSON COL NJ, 80-, VPRES ACAD AFFAIRS, 79- *Mem:* AAAS; Am Chem Soc; Royal Soc Chem. *Res:* Aromaticity; nuclear magnetic resonance spectroscopy; stereochemistry; iron carbonyl complexes. *Mailing Add:* William Paterson Col of NJ Wayne NJ 07470

SPEES, STEVEN TREMBLE, JR, b Earl Park, Ind, May 12, 33; m 53; c 3. INORGANIC CHEMISTRY. *Educ:* Purdue Univ, BS, 56; Univ Southern Calif, PhD(phys chem), 61. *Prof Exp:* Instr chem, Ohio State Univ, 61-62; asst prof inorg chem, Univ Minn, Minneapolis, 62-67; assoc prof inorg chem, 67-77, PROF CHEM, LYMAN BRIGGS COL, MICH STATE UNIV, 77- *Mem:* AAAS; NY Acad Sci; Am Chem Soc; The Chem Soc. *Res:* Chemistry of coordination compounds; synthesis; molecular and electronic structures; kinetics; optical activity; stereochemistry; photochemistry; nuclear magnetic resonances. *Mailing Add:* Dept of Chem Lyman Briggs Col Mich State Univ East Lansing MI 48824

SPEHLMANN, RAINER, b Mitau, Latvia, Apr 18, 31; nat US; m 60; c 3. NEUROLOGY, NEUROPHYSIOLOGY. *Educ:* Univ Heidelberg, MD, 57. *Prof Exp:* Intern med, US & Ger Hosps, 57-60; res assoc neurophysiol, Univ Freiburg, 60-62; resident neurol, Mayo Clin, 62-65; from asst prof to assoc prof, 65-73, PROF NEUROL & PHARMACOL, MED SCH, NORTHWESTERN UNIV, CHICAGO, 73- *Concurrent Pos:* NIH, Am Epilepsy Found & Vet Admin res grants, Vet Admin Lakeside Hosp, Chicago, 65- *Mem:* Fel Am Acad Neurol; Am Electroencephalog Soc; Am Neurol Asn; Am Physiol Soc. *Res:* Experimental research on the neurophysiology of the brain; clinical research on electroencephalography and neurological diseases. *Mailing Add:* Vet Admin Lakeside Hosp 333 E Huron St Chicago IL 60611

SPEICH, G(ILBERT) R(OBERT), b Chicago, Ill, Dec 17, 28; m 56; c 3. PHYSICAL METALLURGY. *Educ:* Ill Inst Technol, BS, 50; Univ Wis, MS, 51; Mass Inst Technol, ScD(metall), 58. *Prof Exp:* Res metallurgist, Westinghouse Elec Corp, 51-52; RES METALLURGIST, US STEEL CORP, 58- *Honors & Awards:* Hatchett Award, Metals Soc, 79. *Mem:* Fel Am Soc Metals; Brit Metals Soc; Am Inst Mining, Metall & Petrol Engrs. *Res:* Phase transformations; strengthening and fracture mechanisms in steel; elastic constants. *Mailing Add:* Res Lab US Steel Corp Monroeville PA 15146

SPEICHER, BENJAMIN ROBERT, b Swatow, China, Jan 23, 09; US citizen; m 32. ZOOLOGY. *Educ:* Denison Univ, AB, 29; Univ Pittsburgh, MS, 31, PhD(genetics), 33. *Hon Degrees:* ScD, Colby Col, 69. *Prof Exp:* Asst, Univ Pittsburgh, 29-33; visitor, Carnegie Inst Technol, 33-35; asst, Amherst Col, 35; Nat Res Coun fel, Columbia Univ, 35-36; from instr to prof, 37-74, actg head dept, 42-45, head dept, 45-63, EMER PROF ZOOL, UNIV MAINE, ORONO, 74- *Concurrent Pos:* Consult, Oak Ridge Nat Lab, 55-65. *Mem:* AAAS; Genetics Soc Am; Am Soc Nat; Am Soc Zool. *Res:* Genetics of Hymenoptera; cytology of parthenogenesis. *Mailing Add:* 4357 Plass Drive Napa CA 94558

SPEICHER, CARL EUGENE, b Carbondale, Pa, Mar 21, 33; m 58; c 3. PATHOLOGY. *Educ:* Kings Col, BS, 54; Univ Pa, MD, 58. *Prof Exp:* Intern med surg, obstet & pediat, Hosp Univ Pa, 58-59; resident path, State Univ NY Upstate Med Ctr, 59-63; pathologist, US Air Force, 63-70; fel path, State Univ NY Upstate Med Ctr, 70-71; pathologist, US Air Force, 71-77; PROF & DIR, CLIN LAB, OHIO STATE UNIV HOSP, 77- *Concurrent Pos:* Clin assoc prof path, Univ Tex Health Sci Ctr, San Antonio, 71-77; chmn, Dept Path, Wilford Hall, Med Ctr, Lackland AFB, TEx, 75-77. *Mem:* Col Am Pathologists; Am Soc Clin Pathologists; Am Med Asn; Acad Clin Lab Physicians & Scientists. *Res:* Application of laboratory medicine to patient care, using problem solving approach and computer assistance. *Mailing Add:* Rm N-343 Ohio State Univ Hosp 410 W 10th Ave Columbus OH 43210

SPEIDEL, DAVID H, b Pottsville, Pa, Aug 10, 38; m 62. GEOCHEMISTRY, RESOURCES. *Educ:* Franklin & Marshall Col, BS, 60; Pa State Univ, PhD(geochem), 64. *Prof Exp:* Res assoc geochem, Pa State Univ, 64-66; from asst prof to assoc prof geol, 66-70, from assoc dean to dean sci fac, 70-80, PROF GEOL, QUEENS COL, NY, 70-, CHMN EARTH & ENVIRON SCI, 80- *Concurrent Pos:* Vis scholar, Cong Res Serv, 77-78. *Mem:* AAAS; Am Ceramic Soc; Geol Soc Am; Mineral Soc Am; Am Geophys Union. *Res:* Resource analysis of inorganic materials; environmental geochemistry; determination of composition of coexisting minerals and the study of their change as a function of environment, especially oxygen fugacity. *Mailing Add:* Dept of Earth & Environ Sci Queens Col Flushing NY 11367

SPEIDEL, EDNA W, b Indianapolis, Ind, June 14, 08; m 34; c 3. BIOCHEMISTRY. *Educ:* Butler Univ, BS, 29; Univ Mich, MA, 30; Univ Iowa, PhD(biochem), 34. *Prof Exp:* Res fel biochem, Univ Tenn, 34-36; res assoc anat, Univ Minn, Minneapolis, 58-77. *Res:* Biochemistry of diabetes mellitus; microanalytical techniques; mineral metabolism; radioactive turnover. *Mailing Add:* 5443 41st Pl NW Washington DC 20015

SPEIDEL, JOHN JOSEPH, b Iowa City, Iowa, Sept 17, 37; m 67; c 1. POPULATION BIOLOGY, PUBLIC HEALTH. *Educ:* Harvard Univ, AB, 59, MD, 63, MPH, 65. *Prof Exp:* Intern med, St Luke's Hosp, New York, 63-64; resident pub health, City of New York Dept Health, 65-67, dep dir maternal & infant care proj, 66-67; chief develop group, Off Surgeon Gen, US Army, 67-69; dep chief res div, 69-70, chief res div, 70-77, assoc dir, 77-78, DEP DIR, OFF POP, AID, 78- *Mem:* Am Pub Health Asn; Population Asn Am; Soc Study Reproduction; Brit Soc Study Fertil. *Res:* Population research including demograph, social science, operational and contraceptive development. *Mailing Add:* Off of Pop Agency for Int Develop Washington DC 20523

SPEIDEL, THOMAS MICHAEL, b Memphis, Tenn, Apr 17, 36; m 67; c 2. ORTHODONTICS. *Educ:* State Univ Iowa, BA, 58; Loyola Univ, DDS, 63; Univ Minn, MSD, 67; Am Bd Orthod, dipl, 72. *Prof Exp:* Teaching asst, 64-65, res assoc, 65-66, instr, 66-68, asst prof, 68-71, assoc prof, 71-77, PROF ORTHOD & DENT, SCH DENT, UNIV MINN, 77- *Mem:* Am Asn Orthodontists; Am Dent Asn; Int Asn Dent Res. *Res:* Quantitation of occlusal function. *Mailing Add:* 6-320 Health Sci Unit A Univ of Minn Minneapolis MN 55455

SPEIER, JOHN LEO, JR, b Chicago, Ill, Sept 29, 18; m 44; c 6. CHEMISTRY. *Educ:* St Benedict's Col, BS, 41; Univ Fla, MS, 43; Univ Pittsburgh, PhD(chem), 47. *Prof Exp:* Asst, Univ Fla, 41-43; sr fel organo-silicon chem, Mellon Inst, 47-56; res supvr, 56-65, mgr org res, 65-69, scientist, 70-75, SR SCIENTIST, DOW CORNING CORP, 75- *Honors & Awards:* Scientist of the Year Award, Indust Res & Develop, 78. *Mem:* Sigma Xi; AAAS; Am Chem Soc. *Res:* Resin acids in pine tree oleoresins; polymerization of silicones; organo-silicon compounds, especially synthesis, derivatives and properties; synthesis and applications of carbon functional silicones. *Mailing Add:* Res Dept Dow Corning Corp Midland MI 48640

SPEIGHT, JAMES G, b Durham, Eng, June 24, 40; m 63. ORGANIC CHEMISTRY. *Educ:* Univ Manchester, BSc, 61, PhD(chem), 65. *Prof Exp:* Imp Chem Indust res fel chem, Univ Manchester, 65-67; res officer, Res Coun Alta, 67-80; RES ASSOC, EXXON RES & ENG CO, 80- *Mem:* Fel Chem Inst Can; fel Brit Chem Soc; assoc Royal Inst Chem. *Res:* Naturally occurring high molecular weight organic residues, especially coal, asphalt, and petroleum. *Mailing Add:* Exxon Res & Eng Co PO Box 45 Linden NJ 07036

SPEIL, SIDNEY, b Revere, Mass, Feb 21, 17; m 40; c 2. CERAMICS. *Educ:* Mass Inst Technol, BS, 36, DSc(ceramics), 39. *Prof Exp:* Asst ceramics, Mass Inst Technol, 37-39; res engr, Ideal Tooth, Inc, Mass, 39-40; engr nonmetals, US Bur Mines, Tenn, 40-46; sr res engr, 46-52, chief aviation & spec thermal insulations res, 52-64, basic chem res, 64-66, dir corp res & develop, 67-76, dir appl technol & int div res, 76-80, SR SCIENTIST & VPRES, JOHNS-MANVILLE CORP, DENVER, 80- *Honors & Awards:* Electrochem Soc Award, 41. *Mem:* Am Ceramic Soc; Am Inst Aeronaut & Astronaut; Am Chem Soc. *Res:* Home, industrial and aerospace thermal insulations; cryogenic thermal insulation; fiberization of glass wool; high temperature ceramic compositions; fiber reinforcements and fiber reinforced composites; synthetic and natural silicates. *Mailing Add:* 3425 S Race Englewood CO 80110

SPEISER, ROBERT DAVID, b New York, NY, Aug 28, 43; m 72; c 2. PURE MATHEMATICS. *Educ:* Columbia Col, AB, 65; Cornell Univ, PhD(math), 70. *Prof Exp:* Res assoc psychol, Ctr Res in Educ, Cornell Univ, 70-71; asst prof math, Univ Tex, Austin, 71-73; ASST PROF MATH, ILL STATE UNIV, 73- *Concurrent Pos:* Vis assoc prof math, Univ Minn, Minneapolis, 78-79. *Res:* Algebraic geometry; commutative algebra. *Mailing Add:* Dept of Math Ill State Univ Normal IL 61712

SPEISER, THEODORE WESLEY, b Del Norte, Colo, Nov 23, 34; m 56; c 3. ASTROPHYSICS, GEOPHYSICS. *Educ:* Colo State Univ, BS, 56; Calif Inst Technol, MS, 59; Pa State Univ, PhD(physics), 64. *Prof Exp:* Res physicist, Nat Bur Standards, 59, 60-61; Nat Acad Sci res assoc earth-sun rels, Goddard Space Flight Ctr, NASA, Md, 64-66; from lectr to asst prof, 67-70, ASSOC PROF ASTRO-GEOPHYS, UNIV COLO, BOULDER, 70- *Concurrent Pos:* Fel, Imp Col, Univ London, 66-67; awardee, US Spec Prog, Alexander von Humboldt Found, 77-78. *Mem:* Am Geophys Union. *Res:* Theories of the aurora and magnetosphere configuration; particle motion and acceleration; magnetospheric and solar wind plasma dynamics. *Mailing Add:* Dept Astro-Geophys Univ Colo Boulder CO 80309

SPEISMAN, GERALD, b New York, NY, Feb 27, 30; m 57; c 1. THEORETICAL PHYSICS. *Educ:* City Col New York, BS, 51; Calif Inst Technol, PhD(physics), 55. *Prof Exp:* Mem sch math, Inst Adv Study, 55-56; asst prof, 56-69, ASSOC PROF PHYSICS, FLA STATE UNIV, 69- *Concurrent Pos:* Physicist, Avco-Everett Res Lab, Avco Corp, 56-57. *Mem:* Am Phys Soc. *Res:* Quantum field theory; many-body problem; statistical mechanics; mathematical physics. *Mailing Add:* Dept of Physics Fla State Univ Tallahassee FL 32306

SPEIZER, FRANK ERWIN, b San Francisco, Calif, June 8, 35; m 57; c 4. EPIDEMIOLOGY, ENVIRONMENTAL MEDICINE. *Educ:* Stanford Univ, BA, 57, MD, 60. *Prof Exp:* Actg instr med, Sch Med, Stanford Univ, 65-66; vis scientist epidemiol, Brit Med Res Coun, Statist Res Unit, 66-68; assoc prof med, 70-76, ASSOC PHYSICIAN, THORNDIKE LAB, SCH MED, HARVARD UNIV, 68-, CHIEF, DIV CLIN EPIDEMIOL, CHANNING LAB & ASSOC PROF MED, 76- *Concurrent Pos:* Assoc vis physician, Boston City Hosp, 68-77 & Peter Brent Brigham Hosp, 77-; Edmund Livingston Traudeu fel, Am Thoracic Soc, 68-70; career develop award, Nat Inst Environ Health Sci, 70-76; mem prog comt, 2nd Task Force Res Plans Environ Res, NIH, mem, Task Force Epidemiol Lung Dis & consult, 79-81. *Mem:* Am Thoracic Soc; Am Epidemiol Soc; Am Soc Clin Invest; fel Am Col Epidemiol. *Res:* Epidemiological studies of chronic diseases associated with environmental exposure, particularly heart, lung and cancer. *Mailing Add:* Channing Lab Sch Med 180 Longwood Ave Boston MA 02115

SPEJEWSKI, EUGENE HENRY, b East Chicago, Ind, Sept 15, 38; m 63; c 4. NUCLEAR PHYSICS. *Educ:* Univ Notre Dame, BS, 60; Ind Univ, Bloomington, PhD(exp physics), 66. *Prof Exp:* Res assoc physics, Ind Univ, Bloomington, 65-67; res assoc, Princeton Univ, 67-69, instr, 69-71; asst prof, Oberlin Col, 71-72; DIR UNIV ISOTOPE SEPARATOR PROJ, OAK RIDGE NAT LAB-OAK RIDGE ASSOC UNIVS, 72- *Concurrent Pos:* Consult, Oak Ridge Nat Lab, 71-72. *Mem:* AAAS; Am Phys Soc. *Res:* Nuclear structure. *Mailing Add:* Bldg 6000 Oak Ridge Nat Lab Oak Ridge TN 37830

SPELIOTIS, DENNIS ELIAS, b Kalamata, Greece, Nov 27, 33; US citizen; m 58; c 3. SOLID STATE PHYSICS, MAGNETISM. *Educ:* Univ RI, BS, 55; Mass Inst Technol, MS, 57, EE, 58; Univ Minn, PhD(magnetism), 61. *Prof Exp:* Staff physicist, Int Bus Mach Develop Labs, 61-63, mgr recording physics, 63-66, adv physicist, 66-67; assoc prof elec eng, Univ Minn, Minneapolis, 67-69; dir eng, Micro-Bit Corp, 69-76; PRES, ADVAN DEVELOP CORP, 77- *Concurrent Pos:* Consult, energy conversion, A K Kusko Inc, 57-59, magnetic recording, Gen Elec Co, 67-69, magnetic recording mat, Thin Film Inc, 67-68, video transducers, Int Video Corp, 67-68, magnetic storage, Control Data Corp, 68-69 & magnetic recording, Collins Radio Co, 68-69. *Mem:* Inst Elec & Electronics Engrs. *Res:* Hard magnetic materials and their applications to bulk magnetic storage devices; magnetic recording; electron beam addressable memories; digital computer memory architecture. *Mailing Add:* Advan Develop Corp 177 Bedford St Lexington MA 02173

SPELL, ALDENLEE, b Rayne, La, Feb 9, 20; m 52; c 2. PHYSICAL CHEMISTRY. *Educ:* Southwestern La Inst, BS, 41; Tulane Univ, MS, 43; Brown Univ, PhD(chem), 52. *Prof Exp:* Chemist, Shell Develop Co, 43-48; scientist, Signal Corps, US Dept Army, 51-52; res supvr, Rohm & Haas Co, 52-82; RETIRED. *Mem:* Am Chem Soc; Soc Appl Spectros. *Res:* Infrared absorption and reflection spectroscopy; fractionation and analysis of polymers; gas chromotography. *Mailing Add:* 514 Portsmouth Ct Doylestown PA 18901

SPELL, CHARLES RAYMOND, b Savannah, Ga, Feb 20, 14; 42; c 3. ANALYTICAL CHEMISTRY. *Educ:* Wofford Col, AB, 37; Univ Ga, MS, 44; Univ NC, PhD, 55. *Prof Exp:* Prof chem, SGa Jr Col, 42-43; instr, Univ Ga, 43-44; asst prof anal chem, 48-56; instr, Univ NC, 46-48; asst prof biochem in med, 56-59, lectr chem, 59-60; prof chem, Emory & Henry Col, 60-79; RETIRED. *Mem:* Am Chem Soc; Sigma Xi. *Res:* Polarography; analytical instrumentation; organic analytical reagents. *Mailing Add:* PO Box GG Emory & Henry Col Emory VA 24327

SPELL, WILLIAM HUX, JR, b Charleston, SC, Aug 21, 27; m 55; c 3. BIOCHEMISTRY. *Educ:* Memphis State Col, BS, 51; Univ Ga, MS, 53; Univ Ark, PhD(biochem), 61. *Prof Exp:* Chemist, Atomic Energy Comn Savannah River Plant, E I du Pont de Nemours & Co, 55-56; NIH fel, Biol Div, Oak Ridge Nat Labs, Union Carbide Corp, 60-62; asst prof, 62-67, ASSOC PROF CHEM, MEMPHIS STATE UNIV, 67- *Res:* Role of histones in metabolic control; bacterial proteases. *Mailing Add:* Dept of Chem Memphis State Univ Memphis TN 38152

SPELLACY, WILLIAM NELSON, b St Paul, Minn, May 10, 34; m 56; c 3. OBSTETRICS & GYNECOLOGY. *Educ:* Univ Minn, BA, 55, BS, 56, MD, 59; Am Bd Obstet & Gynec, dipl, 66, maternal & fetal med cert, 75. *Prof Exp:* Intern, Minneapolis Gen Hosp, Minn, 59-60; from instr to asst prof obstet & gynec, Univ Minn, 63-67; from assoc prof to prof, Med Sch, Univ Miami, 67-74; prof obstet & gynec & chmn dept, Col Med, Univ Fla, 74-79; PROF & HEAD, DEPT OBSTET & GYNEC, COL MED, UNIV ILL, 79- *Concurrent Pos:* Fel obstet & gynec, Univ Minn, 60-63; NIH, Pop Coun & Food & Drug Admin grants, 64-69; Josiah Macy Jr Found fel, 66-69; examr, Am Bd Obstet & Gynec. *Mem:* Nat Acad Sci; Endocrine Soc; Am Fertil Soc; Asn Prof Gynec & Obstet; Am Fedn Clin Res. *Res:* Metabolism of pregnant woman and fetus; effects of ovarian steroids on carbohydrate and lipid metabolism; studies of placental function and fetal maturity; endocrinology of reproduction. *Mailing Add:* Dept Obstet & Gynec Col Med Ill Col Chicago IL 60612

SPELLENBERG, RICHARD (WILLIAM), b San Mateo, Calif, June 27, 40; m 64; c 2. PLANT TAXONOMY. *Educ:* Humboldt State Col, BA, 62; Univ Wash, PhD(bot), 68. *Prof Exp:* From asst prof to assoc prof, 68-77, PROF BIOL, NMEX STATE UNIV, 77- *Concurrent Pos:* Consult, endangered & threatened plant species. *Mem:* Am Soc Plant Taxon; Int Asn Plant Taxon. *Res:* Systematics of Gramineae and Nyctaginaceae. *Mailing Add:* Dept of Biol NMex State Univ Las Cruces NM 88003

SPELLER, STANLEY WAYNE, b Victoria, BC, June 6, 42; m 67; c 1. WILDLIFE BIOLOGY. *Educ:* Univ Victoria, BS, 65; Carleton Univ, MS, 68; Univ Sask, PhD(mammal), 72. *Prof Exp:* Biologist, Can Wildlife Serv, Environ Can, 72-75; biologist, Environ Assessment Sect, Dept Indian Affairs & Northern Develop, 75-77; CHIEF, WILDLIFE RES & INTERPRETATION, CAN WILDLIFE SERV, ENVIRON CAN, 77- *Res:* Management of research programs on effects of insecticides on wildlife; wildlife and limnology studies for parks Canada; wildlife research rare and endangered species; wildlife interpretation programs in Atlantic Region. *Mailing Add:* Can Wildlife Serv Box 1590 Sackville NB E0A 3C0 Can

SPELLMAN, JOHN W, b Ft Worth, Tex, Oct 3, 41; m 59; c 2. MATHEMATICS. *Educ:* Tex Lutheran Col, BA, 63; Emory Univ, MA, 65, PhD(math), 68. *Prof Exp:* Fel math, Univ Fla, 68-69; asst prof, Tex A&M Univ, 60-71; assoc prof math, Pan Am Univ, 71-80, head dept, 75-80; PROF MATH, SOUTHWEST TEX STATE UNIV, 80- *Mem:* Am Math Soc. *Res:* Functional analysis; semigroups of operators; real analysis. *Mailing Add:* Dept Math SW Tex State Univ San Marcos TX 78666

SPELLMAN, MITCHELL WRIGHT, b Alexandria, La, Dec 1, 19; m 47; c 8. SURGERY. *Educ:* Dillard Univ, AB, 40; Howard Univ, MD, 44; Univ Minn, PhD(surg), 55; Am Bd Surg, dipl, 53. *Hon Degrees:* DSc, Georgetown Univ, 74; DSc, Univ Fla, 77. *Prof Exp:* From intern to asst resident surg, Cleveland Metrop Gen Hosp, Ohio, 44-46; asst resident, Freedmen's Hosp, Howard Univ, 46-47; chief resident thoracic surg, 47-48 & surg, 49-50, asst physiol, Col Med, 48-49 & surg, 50-51; res asst, Exp Surg Lab, Univ Minn, 51-53, sr resident surg, Univ Hosp, Univ Minn, 53-54; from asst prof to prof, Col Med, Howard Univ, 54-68; prof & asst dean Sch Med, Univ Calif, Los Angeles & dean, Charles R Drew Postgrad Med Sch, 69-78; PROF SURG & DEAN MED SERV, HARVARD MED SCH, 78-, EXEC VPRES, HARVARD MED CTR, 78- *Concurrent Pos:* dir exp surg lab, Col Med,

Howard Univ, 54-61, res asst prof, Grad Fac Physiol, 55-69, chief med off, Howard Univ Div Surg at DC Gen Hosp, 61-68; Mem, DC Bd Exam Med & Osteop, 55-68; exec vpres & mem bd dirs, Nat Med Asn Found, 68-70; mem nat rev comt, Regional Med Progs, 68-70; mem spec adv group, Vet Admin, 69-73, nat surg consult, Cent Off, 69-73; clin prof surg, Sch Med, Univ Southern Calif, 69-78; mem bd visitors, Med Ctr, Duke Univ, 70-75; mem, Comn Study of Accreditation of Selected Health Educ Progs, 70-72; bd dirs, Sun Valley Forum Nat Health, 70; bd trustees, Occidental Col, 71-78, Kaiser Found Health Plan, Inc & Kaiser Found Hosps, 71- & Lloyds Bank Calif, 74-; mem bd overseer's comt visit univ health serv, Harvard Col, 72-78; mem vis comt, Sch Med, Stanford Univ, 72-73 & Univ Mass Med Ctr, 74-75; bd regents, Georgetown Univ, 72-78; chmn adv comt, Med Devices Appln Br, Nat Heart & Lung Inst, 72-73; fel, Ctr Advan Study Behav Sci, Stanford, 75-76; vis prof surg, Sch Med, Stanford Univ, 75-76; mem, Epcot Life & Health Pavilion Adv Bd, 81-; mem bd dirs, Monogram Industs, Inc, 81- *Honors & Awards:* Sinkler Award Surg, Nat Med Asn, 68; Warfield Award, Freedmen's Hosp, 69. *Mem:* Am Asn Univ Prof; Soc Univ Surg; AMA; Am Surg Asn; Nat Med Asn. *Res:* Radiation biology; cardiovascular physiology; evaluation of methods of closure of bronchial stump; blood volume. *Mailing Add:* Harvard Med Sch 25 Shattuck St Boston MA 02115

SPELMAN, MICHAEL JOHN, b Rochester, NY, Mar 28, 39; m 67; c 3. METEOROLOGY, ATMOSPHERIC SCIENCE. *Educ:* LeMoyne Col, BS, 62; Pa State Univ, MS, 69. *Prof Exp:* RES METEOROLOGIST, GEOPHYS FLUID DYNAMICS LAB, NAT OCEANIC & ATMOSPHERIC ADMIN, 69- *Honors & Awards:* Spec Achievement Award, Dept Com, 71. *Mem:* Am Meteorol Soc. *Res:* Investigation of the structure and circulations of the atmosphere and oceans through numerical modeling on digital computers. *Mailing Add:* Geophys Fluid Dynamics Lab PO Box 308 Princeton NJ 08540

SPELSBERG, THOMAS COONAN, b Clarksburg, WVa, July 6, 40; m 67. GENETICS, BIOCHEMISTRY. *Educ:* WVa Univ, AB, 63, PhD(genetics, biochem), 67. *Prof Exp:* Fel biochem, Univ Tex M D Anderson Hosp & Tumor Inst, 67-68, res asst, 68-69, asst biochemist, 69-70; asst prof obstet & gynec, Sch Med, Vanderbilt Univ, 70-74; assoc prof biochem, 74-77, PROF BIOCHEM, MAYO MED SCH & MAYO GRAD SCH MED, 77-; MEM STAFF, DEPT CELL BIOL, MAYO CLIN, 74-, PROF & HEAD, BIOCHEM SECT, 81- *Concurrent Pos:* Nat Genetics Found fel; distinguished lectr, Univ Conn, Univ NJ Med Sch & Oral Roberts Med Sch. *Mem:* AAAS; Am Inst Biol Sci; Am Soc Cell Biol; Brit Biochem Soc. *Res:* Role of nuclear proteins in regulation of gene activity; DNA-protein interactions; interaction with chromatin; nuclear antigens of Epstein Barr virus. *Mailing Add:* Dept of Molecular Med Mayo Clin Rochester MN 55901

SPENADEL, LAWRENCE, b Brooklyn, NY, Apr 1, 32; m 55; c 2. PHYSICAL CHEMISTRY, POLYMER CHEMISTRY. *Educ:* Queens Col, NY, BS, 53; Univ Cincinnati, MS, 54, PhD(phys chem), 57. *Prof Exp:* Res chemist, Esso Res & Eng Co, 56-65, sr chemist, Enjay Polymer Labs, 66-70, RES ASSOC, EXXON CHEM CO, 70- *Mem:* Inst Elec & Electronic Engrs; Am Chem Soc; Soc Plastics Eng. *Res:* Compounding of ethylene propylene terpolymer and butyl rubber for wire and cable applications; development of thermoelastic rubbers; combustion; formulation and testing of high energy solid propellants; dispersion measurements on platinum catalysts. *Mailing Add:* Exxon Chem Co PO Box 45 Linden NJ 07036

SPENCE, ALEXANDER PERKINS, b St Louis, Mo, Apr 5, 29; m 55; c 3. COMPARATIVE ANATOMY, EMBRYOLOGY. *Educ:* Univ Mo, BSEd, 60, MST, 61; Cornell Univ, PhD(biol), 69. *Prof Exp:* From asst prof to assoc prof, 61-78, PROF ANAT & EMBRYOL, STATE UNIV NY, CORTLAND, 78-, CHMN DEPT, 78- *Mem:* Sigma Xi; Am Soc Zoologists. *Res:* Ultrastructure of spermatogenesis in Rana pipiens; sperm-egg chemotaxis in amphibians. *Mailing Add:* Dept Biol Sci State Univ NY Cortland NY 13045

SPENCE, DALE WILLIAM, b Beaumont, Tex, Apr 8, 34; m 55; c 3. EXERCISE PHYSIOLOGY. *Educ:* Rice Inst, BS, 56; NTex State Univ, MS, 59; La State Univ, EdD(phys educ), 66. *Prof Exp:* Instr phys educ, NTex State Univ, 58-59 & Hardin-Simmons Univ, 59-62; asst, La State Univ, 62-63; from instr to assoc prof, 63-74, PROF HEALTH & PHYS EDUC, RICE UNIV, 74- *Concurrent Pos:* Fel, Baylor Col Med, 68-69, vis assoc prof, 71-80, prof, 80-; dir exercise rehab & res, St Joseph Hosp, 74-; vis scientist, Manned Spacecraft Ctr, 69-70; mem staff, Houston Cardovasc Rehabilitation Ctr, 80-; consult scientist, Sch Aerospace Med, 80-81. *Mem:* AAAS; Am Alliance Health, Phys Educ & Recreation; fel Am Col Sports Med; Aerospace Med Asn. *Res:* Muscle physiology and cardiovascular rehabilitation. *Mailing Add:* Dept of Health & Phys Educ Rice Univ Houston TX 77001

SPENCE, DAVID, b Halifax, Eng, Sept 23, 41; m 62; c 4. ATOMIC PHYSICS. *Educ:* Univ Durham, BSc, 63; Univ Newcastle-upon-Tyne, PhD(physics), 67. *Prof Exp:* Res staff appl scientist physics, Yale Univ, 67-71; asst physicist, 71-74, PHYSICIST, ARGONNE NAT LAB, 74- *Res:* Atomic and molecular spectroscopy; physical and gaseous electronics. *Mailing Add:* Argonne Nat Lab Argonne IL 60439

SPENCE, GAVIN GARY, b St Paul, Minn, July 23, 42; m 65; c 3. ORGANIC CHEMISTRY. *Educ:* Williams Col, BA, 64; Princeton Univ, AM, 67, PhD(chem), 68. *Prof Exp:* Res chemist, 68-75, sr res chemist, 75-79, RES SCIENTIST, HERCULES INC, 79- *Mem:* Am Chem Soc. *Res:* Synthetic organic chemistry, in particular synthesis and evaluations of organic polymers for use in paper, adhesives, textiles. *Mailing Add:* Hercules Res Ctr Wilmington DE 19899

SPENCE, GEORGE B(AUGH), b Dallas, Tex, July 29, 25; m 48; c 3. MATERIALS SCIENCE. *Educ:* Univ Mich, BS, 49, MS, 50, PhD(physics), 57. *Prof Exp:* Asst prof physics, Univ Tex, 56-60; physics group leader, Res Lab, Carbon Prod Div, 60-67, mgr resin composites technol, 68-70, mgr carbon fibers technol, 68-72, MGR GRAPHITE STRUCTURE TECHNOL, CARBON PROD DIV, UNION CARBIDE CORP, 73- *Res:* Carbon fibers; fiber composite materials; mechanical properties of carbon. *Mailing Add:* Union Carbide Corp PO Box 6116 Cleveland OH 44101

SPENCE, HILDA ADELE, b Chattanooga, Tenn, Oct 13, 29. MICROBIOLOGY. *Educ:* Univ Tenn, Chattanooga, BS, 51; La State Univ, MS, 66, PhD(microbiol), 71. *Prof Exp:* Med technologist, Charity Hosp LA, New Orleans, 51-59; instr med technol, 59-64, instr microbiol, 64-74, ASST PROF MICROBIOL, LA STATE UNIV MED CTR, 74- *Concurrent Pos:* Mem rev bd, Nat Accrediting Agency Clin Lab Sci, 72-77; Am Soc Med Technol res award, 63. *Mem:* Am soc Microbiol; Am Soc Med Technol (pres, 78-79); Am Soc Allied Health Prof; Biol Stain Comn; AAAS. *Res:* Neurotropic strains of influenza viruses; clinical microbiology; microcomputers in medical education and research. *Mailing Add:* Dept of Microbiol 1542 Tulane Ave New Orleans LA 70112

SPENCE, JACK TAYLOR, b Salt Lake City, Utah, Nov 16, 29; m 51; c 3. ANALYTICAL CHEMISTRY, INORGANIC CHEMISTRY. *Educ:* Univ Utah, BS, 51, PhD(chem), 57. *Prof Exp:* Fel, Univ Ore, 57-58; from asst prof to assoc prof chem, 58-67, dept head, 76-81 PROF CHEM, UTAH STATE UNIV, 67- *Concurrent Pos:* USPHS res career develop award, Nat Inst Gen Med Sci, 68-73. *Mem:* AAAS; Am Chem Soc. *Res:* Organic chelating agents; coordination compounds; inorganic photochemistry; inorganic biochemistry; mechanisms of enzyme reactions. *Mailing Add:* Dept Chem Utah State Univ Logan UT 84321

SPENCE, JOHN A, b Glasgow, Scotland, Mar 6, 20; US citizen; m 42; c 3. ORGANIC CHEMISTRY, ENVIRONMENTAL HEALTH. *Educ:* Whittier Col, BA, 42; Purdue Univ, West Lafayette, MS, 43, PhD(org chem), 45; Harvard Univ, MS, 54. *Prof Exp:* Res chemist, Chevron Res Co, 45-54, indust hygienist, 55-59, supvr indust hyg & toxicol, 59-65, asst to mgr, 65-67, coordr environ health & toxicol, 67-74, CORP MGR ENVIRON HEALTH & TOXICOL, STAND OIL CO CALIF, 74- *Mem:* AAAS; Am Indust Hyg Asn. *Res:* Petrochemicals; plastics; detergents; toxicology. *Mailing Add:* Standard Oil Co of Calif PO Box 1272 Environ Health Ctr Richmond CA 94807

SPENCE, JOHN EDWIN, b Fall River, Mass, Oct 26, 34; m 58; c 3. ELECTRICAL ENGINEERING. *Educ:* Bradford Durfee Col Technol, BS, 57; Univ Wis, MS, 60, PhD(elec eng), 62. *Prof Exp:* Mem staff, Digital & Analog Comput Labs, Allis-Chalmers Mfg Co, 57-59; asst, Univ Wis, 59-62; assoc prof elec eng, Univ RI, 62-67; tech dir antennas & propagation group, Electronics & Commun Div, Atlantic Res Corp, Va, 67-68; assoc prof elec eng, 68-76, PROF ELEC ENG, UNIV RI, 76- *Concurrent Pos:* Consult, Amecom Div, Litton Systs, Inc, Md, 65. *Mem:* Inst Elec & Electronics Engrs. *Res:* Electromagnetic theory; wave propagation. *Mailing Add:* Dept of Elec Eng Univ of RI Kingston RI 02881

SPENCE, KEMET DEAN, b Portland, Ore, Jan 10, 37; m 58; c 4. MICROBIOLOGY, BIOCHEMISTRY. *Educ:* Ore State Univ, BS, 60, MS, 62, PhD(microbiol, biochem), 65. *Prof Exp:* Microbiologist, Ore Fish Comn, 62-64; res fel, Argonne Nat Lab, 65-68; asst prof, 68-72, assoc prof, 72-80, PROF BACT & PUB HEALTH, WASH STATE UNIV, 81- *Mem:* Am Soc Microbiol. *Res:* Biochemistry and associated genetic character of yeast regulatory mechanisms; biochemical and applied studies of microbial pathogens of insects. *Mailing Add:* Dept of Bacteriol & Pub Health Washington State Univ Pullman WA 99163

SPENCE, LESLIE PERCIVAL, b St Vincent, WI, Aug 16, 22; m 53; c 2. MICROBIOLOGY. *Educ:* Bristol Univ, MB, ChB, 50; Univ London, dipl trop med & hyg, 51; FRCP, 72. *Prof Exp:* Med officer, Trinidad Govt Med Serv, 51-62; dir regional virus lab, Trinidad & prof virol, Univ West Indies, 62-68; prof microbiol, McGill Univ, 68-72; PROF MICROBIOL, UNIV TORONTO, 72- *Concurrent Pos:* Rockefeller Found fel, Rockefeller Found Virus Labs, NY, 55-56; consult, Nat Inst Allergy & Infectious Dis, 69-73 & Pan-Am Health Orgn, 69- *Mem:* Am Soc Trop Med & Hyg; Can Soc Microbiol; Am Soc Microbiol. *Res:* Arboviruses; viral gastroenteritis. *Mailing Add:* Banting Inst 100 College St Toronto ON M5G 1L5 Can

SPENCE, MARY ANNE, b Tulsa, Okla, Sept 8, 44; m 72. HUMAN GENETICS. *Educ:* Grinnell Col, BA, 66; Univ Hawaii, PhD, 69. *Prof Exp:* Asst prof, 70-75, assoc prof, 75-80, PROF PSYCHIAT & BIOMATH, SCH MED, UNIV CALIF, LOS ANGELES, 80- *Concurrent Pos:* NIH fel genetics curriculum, Univ NC, Chapel Hill, 69-70; mem, Ment Retardation Res Ctr, Neuropsychiat Inst, Univ Calif, Los Angeles, 74- *Honors & Awards:* Woman of Sci Award, Univ Calif, 79. *Mem:* Am Soc Human Genetics; Genetics Soc Am; Behav Genetics Asn. *Res:* Mathematical and computer models for family data analysis; applications for genetic counseling. *Mailing Add:* Ment Retardation Unit Neuropsychiat Inst Los Angeles CA 90024

SPENCE, ROBERT DEAN, b Bergen, NY, Sept 12, 17; m 42; c 4. PHYSICS. *Educ:* Cornell Univ, BS, 39; Mich State Col, MS, 42; Yale Univ, PhD(physics), 48. *Prof Exp:* Asst physics, Mich State Col, 41-42; instr elec commun, Mass Inst Technol, 42-45; from asst prof to assoc prof physics & astron, 47-52, actg head dept physics, 56-57, prof physics & astron, 52-76, PROF PHYSICS, MICH STATE UNIV, 76- *Concurrent Pos:* Vis prof & Guggenheim fel, Bristol Univ, 55-56; vis prof, Eindhoven Technol Univ, 64 & State Univ Leiden, 71. *Mem:* Fel Am Phys Soc. *Res:* Mathematical and crystal physics; nuclear magnetic resonance. *Mailing Add:* Dept of Physics Mich State Univ East Lansing MI 48824

SPENCE, SYDNEY P(AYTON), b Yonkers, NY, Dec 30, 21; m 44; c 5. CHEMICAL ENGINEERING. *Educ:* Univ Rochester, BS, 44. *Prof Exp:* Jr tech rep, Halowax Prods Div, 43-44 & 46, mem tech staff, Bakelite Co Div, 46-51, chem engr, Res & Develop Dept, 51-56, proj engr, 56-57, group leader process res, Union Carbide Plastics Co Div, 57-67, process tech mgr phenolic & epoxy resins, Coatings Intermediates Div, 67-71, DEVELOP SCIENTIST, UNION CARBIDE CORP, BOUND BROOK, 71- *Mem:* Am Inst Chem Engrs. *Res:* Development of commercial processes for epoxy resins, bisphenol A, phenolic resin, acrylonitrile-butadiene-styrene resins, di-paraxylylene, polyester resins, chlorinated hydrocarbons. *Mailing Add:* Union Carbide Corp River Rd Bound Brook NJ 08805

SPENCE, THOMAS WAYNE, b Washington, Pa, Sept 14, 38; m 68; c 3. OCEANOGRAPHY. *Educ:* Duquesne Univ, BA, 60; Univ Chicago, PhD(geophys sci), 73. *Prof Exp:* Meteorologist, US Air Force, 60-63, DeNardo & McFarland, Inc, 63-65; res asst hydrodynamics, Univ Chicago, 66-73; asst prof, 73-79, ASSOC PROF OCEANOG, TEX A&M UNIV, 80- *Concurrent Pos:* Sci prog officer, Off Naval Res, 80- *Mem:* AAAS; Am Geophys Union; Am Meteorol Soc; Sigma Xi. *Res:* Geophysical fluid dynamics including atmospheric and oceanic dynamics; laboratory models of geophysical fluid motions; instability; large scale energetics. *Mailing Add:* Dept of Oceanog Tex A&M Univ College Station TX 77843

SPENCE, WILLARD LEWIS, b Providence, RI, Mar 16, 35; m 58; c 3. BOTANY. *Educ:* Colby Col, BA, 57; Univ Iowa, MS, 59; Univ Calif, Berkeley, PhD(bot), 63. *Prof Exp:* Asst cur bot, NY Bot Gardens, 63-64; from asst prof to assoc prof biol, 64-69, PROF BIOL, FRAMINGHAM STATE COL, 69- *Mem:* Am Soc Plant Taxon; Bot Soc Am; Sigma Xi. *Res:* Vascular plant taxonomy; local flora; economically valuable plants. *Mailing Add:* Dept of Biol Framingham State Col Framingham MA 01701

SPENCE, WILLIAM J, b Peoria, Ill, July 11, 37; m 76; c 1. TECTONOPHYSICS, EARTHQUAKE PREDICTION. *Educ:* State Univ NY, Albany, BS, 59, MS, 60; Pa State Univ, PhD(geophsics), 73. *Prof Exp:* Instr phys chem, Spencer Cent High Sch, 61-62; res gophysicist, US Coast & Geol Surv, 62-70, Environ Res Lab, 71, Nat Oceanic & Atmospheric Admin, 72; RES GEOPHYSICIST, US GEOL SURV, 73- *Mem:* Seismol Soc Am; Am Geophys Union; AAAS. *Res:* Causes and consequences of great earthquakes; plate tectonics; earthquakes induced by reservoirs or by fluid injection into substrata; aftershocks; seismic siting of critical facilities. *Mailing Add:* US Geol Surv Off Earthquake Studies Box 25046 MS 967 Denver CO 80225

SPENCER, ALBERT WILLIAM, b Omaha, Nebr, Jan 1, 29; m 56; c 4. ZOOLOGY. *Educ:* Colo State Univ, BS, 57, MS, 62, PhD(zool), 65. *Prof Exp:* Asst prof zool, Eastern NMex Univ, 64-65; asst prof zool, 65-74, ASSOC PROF BIOL, FT LEWIS COL, 74- *Mem:* Am Soc Mammal; Soc Study Evolution; Ecol Soc Am; Wildlife Soc; Genetics Soc Am. *Res:* Vertebrate population biology, particularly speciation. *Mailing Add:* Div of Biol Sci Ft Lewis Col Durango CO 81301

SPENCER, ALEXANDER BURKE, b San Antonio, Tex, Dec 28, 32; m 63; c 2. GEOLOGY. *Educ:* Tex Western Col, BSc, 55; Univ Okla, MS, 61; Univ Tex, Austin, PhD(geol), 66. *Prof Exp:* From instr to asst prof chem & geol, Carnegie Inst Technol, 65-67; res geologist, Mobil Res & Develop Corp, 67-71, sr res geologist, 71-74, mem staff, Mobil Oil Libya, Ltd, 75-77, mem staff, 77-81, EXPLOR SUPVR, MOBIL EXPLOR & PRODUCING SERV, INC, 81- *Mem:* Soc Explor Geophysicists; Am Asn Petrol Geol; Soc Econ Paleont & Mineral. *Res:* Petrology of sandstone, international petroleum exploration. *Mailing Add:* Mobil Oil Corp PO Box 900 Dallas TX 75221

SPENCER, ANDREW NIGEL, b Fulmer, Eng, Feb 13, 45; m 66; c 3. INVERTEBRATE PHYSIOLOGY. *Educ:* Univ London, BSc, 67; Univ Victoria, PhD(zool), 71. *Prof Exp:* Sci Res Coun fel zool, Univ Bristol, 71-72; vis asst prof zool, 72-73; lectr biol, Inst Biol, Univ Odense, 73-75; ASSOC PROF ZOOL, UNIV ALTA, 75- *Concurrent Pos:* Consult, New Can Encyclopedia. *Mem:* Am Soc Zoologists; Can Soc Zoologists; Brit Soc Exp Biol. *Res:* The behavioural neurophysiology of hydrozoans; central control of rhythmical behavior in invertebrates. *Mailing Add:* Dept of Zool Univ of Alta Edmonton AB T6G 2E9 Can

SPENCER, ANDREW R, US Citizen. METALLURGICAL ENGINEERING, FORENSIC SCIENCE. *Educ:* US Merchant Marine Acad, BS, 45; Wayne State Univ, BS, 48. *Prof Exp:* Serv metallurgist, Steel Sales Corp, 49-55; pres & tech dir, Precision Testing Labs, Inc, 56-57; sr scientist, Metall Res Dept, Chrysler Corp, 58-61; staff metall engr, Bendix Res Lab, 61-73; mgr porous metal prod, Filter Prod Div, Facet Enterprises Inc, 73-77; TECH DIR, METALLURGICAL ADVISORS CO, 77- *Honors & Awards:* Arch T Colwell Merit Award, Soc Automotive Engrs, 67. *Mem:* Am Soc Metals; Am Inst Mining, Metall & Petrol Engrs; Nat Asn Corrosion Engrs; Soc of Automotive Engrs; Am Soc Testing & Mat. *Res:* Failure analysis; applying engineering materials for use in hostile environments; powder metallurgy; diffusion bonding; oxidation resistance of metals and super alloys; lubrication; friction and wear; manufacturing engineering. *Mailing Add:* Metall Adv Co 4854 Leafdale Royal Oak MI 48073

SPENCER, ARMOND E, b Crandon, Wis, Oct 1, 33; m 58; c 4. MATHEMATICS. *Educ:* Mich State Univ, BS, 58, MS, 61, PhD(math), 67. *Prof Exp:* High sch instr, Mich, 58-60; instr math, Lansing Community Col, 62-65; asst prof, Western Mich Univ, 66-67 & Univ Ky, 67-71; assoc prof, 71-76, PROF MATH, STATE UNIV NY COL POTSDAM, 76- *Mem:* Am Math Soc; Math Asn Am. *Res:* Finite group theory. *Mailing Add:* Dept of Math State Univ of NY Potsdam NY 13676

SPENCER, ARTHUR COE, II, b Pittsburgh, Pa, Dec 16, 39; m 60; c 2. APPLIED MATHEMATICS, ENGINEERING SCIENCE. *Educ:* Allegheny Col, BS, 61; Univ Pittsburgh, MS, 64. *Prof Exp:* Res mathematician, PPG Industs, Inc, 61-67; sr engr, 67-73, fel engr, 73-76, MGR THERMAL HYDRAUL METHODS, WESTINGHOUSE ELEC CORP, 76- *Mem:* Soc Indust & Appl Math. *Res:* Computational fluid dynamics; numerical methods for partial differential equations; two phase flow; heat transfer. *Mailing Add:* Thermal Hydraul Anal Box 355 Pittsburgh PA 15230

SPENCER, ARTHUR MILTON, JR, b Salt Lake City, Utah, Jan 6, 20; m 48; c 7. FUEL ENGINEERING, SURFACE CHEMISTRY. *Educ:* Univ Utah, BS, 49, MS, 51, PhD(fuels eng), 62. *Prof Exp:* Tech asst, explosives res group, Univ Utah, 53-59; sr res chemist, Allegany Balistics Lab, Hercules Inc, Md, 62-63; sr res assoc oil well stimulation & cement, West Co, Tex, 64-71; chief chemist, Petrol Technol Corp, 71-78; sr res scientist, Rocket Res Co, 78-79; CHIEF CHEMIST, PETROL TECHNOL CORP, 79- *Concurrent Pos:* Fel, Petrol Res Fund, 59-62. *Mem:* Am Chem Soc. *Res:* Explosives for oil well stimulation; acid corrosion at high temperatures; fuel and water gels; high temperature retarders for oil well cementing; high temperature explosives for geothermal wells. *Mailing Add:* Petrol Technol Corp PO Box 537 Redmond WA 98052

SPENCER, CHARLES WINTHROP, b Cambridge, Mass, Dec 25, 30; m 54; c 3. GEOLOGY. *Educ:* Colby Col, AB, 53; Univ Ill, MS, 55. *Prof Exp:* Res asst, Clay Mineral, State Geol Surv, Ill, 53-55; geologist, US Geol Surv, 55-59; geologist, Texaco, Inc, Mont, 59-66, asst dist geologist, 66-67, dist geologist, 67-73, div lab mgr, Colo, 73-74; PROG CHIEF, US GEOL SURV, 74- *Honors & Awards:* A I Levorsen Award. *Mem:* Am Asn Petrol Geologists; Soc Econ Paleontologists & Mineralogists; fel Geol Soc Am; Soc Petrol Engrs. *Res:* Geology of mineral deposits; petroleum exploration; stratigraphy of Paleozoic and Cretaceous; hydrodynamics; environmental interpretation of sandstones and carbonates; petrol geology of southern Brazil; geology of low permeability (tight) gas reservoirs; origins of overpressured and underpressured gas reservoirs. *Mailing Add:* 13528 W Alaska Dr Lakewood CO 80228

SPENCER, CHESTER W(ALLACE), b Greeley, Kans, Nov 2, 24; m 48; c 4. METALLURGY. *Educ:* Univ Kans, BS, 49, MS, 50; Univ Wis, PhD(metall), 52. *Prof Exp:* Sr engr atomic energy div, Sylvania Elec Prod, Inc, 52-54; res metallurgist, Carnegie Inst Technol, 54-56; asst prof metall eng, Cornell Univ, 56-58, assoc prof, 58-62; mgr mat res & develop, Res & Adv Develop Div, Avco Corp, Mass, 62-64; vpres, Chase Brass & Copper Co, 64-77; EXEC DIR, NAT MAT ADV BD, NAT ACAD SCI, 77- *Concurrent Pos:* Consult, Res & Adv Develop Div, Avco Corp, 59- *Mem:* Am Soc Metals; Am Inst Mining, Metall & Petrol Engrs; Brit Inst Metals. *Res:* Eutectoid and peritectoid transformations in alloys; electrical and physical properties of semiconducting intermetallic compounds; reactions between liquids and solids. *Mailing Add:* Nat Mat Adv Bd Nat Acad Sci 2101 Constitution Ave Washington DC 20418

SPENCER, CLAUDE FRANKLIN, b Athens, Pa, Feb 14, 19; m 44; c 3. ORGANIC CHEMISTRY. *Educ:* Univ Mich, BS, 42; Mass Inst Technol, PhD(chem), 50. *Prof Exp:* Res chemist, Merck & Co, Inc, 42-46 & 50-59; sr res chemist, 59-65, group leader, Norwich Pharmacol Co, 65-80, RES ASSOC, NORWICH-EATON PHARMACEUT, 80- *Mem:* Am Chem Soc; fel Am Inst Chemists; Sigma Xi; Int Soc Heterocyclic Chemists; AAAS. *Res:* Synthesis and structure determination of natural products; synthesis and transannular rearrangements in eight-membered ring compounds; synthesis of medicinal and veterinary products; design and synthesis of biologically active compounds. *Mailing Add:* 21 Summit St Norwich NY 13815

SPENCER, DEREK W, b South Shields, Eng, May 2, 34; m 57; c 3. OCEANOGRAPHY, MARINE GEOLOGY. *Educ:* Univ Manchester, BSc, 54, PhD(geochem), 57. *Prof Exp:* Geochemist, Imp Oil Ltd, Can, 57-65; sr scientist, 65-78, assoc dir res, 78-80, SR SCIENTIST, WOODS HOLE OCEANOG INST, 78- *Mem:* AAAS; Am Geophys Union; Am Asn Petrol Geologists; Geochem Soc. *Res:* Trace element geochemistry of sediments and ocean water; chemical oceanography; ocean circulation and time scale of ocean mixing. *Mailing Add:* Dept of Chem Woods Hole Oceanog Inst Box 153 Woods Hole MA 02543

SPENCER, DOMINA EBERLE (MRS PARRY MOON), b New Castle, Pa, Sept 26, 20; m 61; c 1. MATHEMATICS, PHYSICS. *Educ:* Mass Inst Technol, SB, 39, MS, 40, PhD(math), 42. *Prof Exp:* Asst illum eng, Mass Inst Technol, 42; asst prof physics, Am Univ, 42-43, Tufts Col, 43-47 & Brown Univ, 47-50; from asst prof to assoc prof math, 50-60, PROF MATH, UNIV CONN, 60- *Honors & Awards:* Illum Eng Soc Gold Medal, 74. *Mem:* Am Math Soc; fel Optical Soc Am; fel Illum Eng Soc. *Res:* Application of tensors to physics; field theory; nomenclature, color, calculation of illumination; design of lighting for vision. *Mailing Add:* Dept of Math Univ of Conn Storrs CT 06268

SPENCER, DONALD CLAYTON, b Boulder, Colo, Apr 25, 12; m 36, 51; c 3. MATHEMATICS. *Educ:* Univ Colo, BA, 34; Mass Inst Technol, BSc, 36; Cambridge Univ, PhD(math), 39, ScD, 63. *Hon Degrees:* DSc, Purdue Univ, 71. *Prof Exp:* Instr math, Mass Inst Technol, 39-42; from assoc prof to prof, Stanford Univ, 42-50; from assoc prof to prof, Princeton Univ, 50-63; prof, Stanford Univ, 63-68; prof, 68-72, Henry Burchard Fine prof, 72-78, EMER HENRY BURCHARD FINE PROF MATH, PRINCETON UNIV, 78- *Honors & Awards:* Bocher Prize, Am Math Soc, 48. *Mem:* Nat Acad Sci; Am Math Soc; Am Acad Arts & Sci. *Res:* Differential geometry; partial differential equations. *Mailing Add:* 943 County Rd 204 Durango CO 81301

SPENCER, DONALD LEE, b Iowa City, Iowa, June 4, 20; m 42; c 5. SOLAR ENERGY, THERMAL SCIENCES. *Educ:* Univ Iowa, BS, 42, MS, 48; Univ Minn, PhD(mech eng), 65. *Prof Exp:* Instr, Duke Univ, 46-47; assoc prof, US Air Force Inst Technol, 48-52; asst prof mech eng, 56-66, ASSOC PROF, DIV ENERGY ENG, UNIV IOWA, 67- *Concurrent Pos:* Vis lectr, Univ Minn, 58-59; consult, Bandage, Inc, Iowa, 65; NSF res grants, 66-67 & 68-; Fulbright-Hays sr lectr award, 76. *Mem:* Int Solar Energy Asn. *Res:* Film condensation heat transfer; stability of thin condensate films and liquid-vapor interface resistance; solar thermal energy collector and storage systems. *Mailing Add:* Div of Energy Eng Univ of Iowa Iowa City IA 52242

SPENCER, DWIGHT LOUIS, b Harveyville, Kans, June 24, 24; m 48; c 6. ANIMAL ECOLOGY. *Educ:* Kans State Teachers Col, BS, 52, MS, 55; Okla State Univ, PhD(zool), 67. *Prof Exp:* Instr high sch, Kans, 53-60; from lectr to asst prof, 60-72, PROF BIOL, EMPORIA KANS STATE UNIV, 72-, ASSOC CHMN DEPT, 74- *Mem:* Am Soc Mammal. *Res:* Mammalian ecology and speciation; ecological speciation study of Neotoma floridana and Neotoma micropus in Kansas and Oklahoma. *Mailing Add:* Div of Biol Sci Emporia Kans State Univ Emporia KS 66802

SPENCER, E MARTIN, b Cleveland, Ohio, Dec 6, 29; c 3. MEDICINE. *Educ:* Dartmouth Col, AB, 52; Harvard Univ, MD, 56; Rockefeller Univ, PhD(biochem), 69. *Prof Exp:* Res assoc, Beth Israel Hosp, Sch Med, Harvard Univ, 59-60; attend physician, Harlem Hosp, New York, 69-70; guest investr, Rockefeller Univ, 69-70; ASSOC CLIN PROF MED, UNIV CALIF, SAN FRANCISCO, 70-; DIR, LAB GROWTH & DEVELOP, CHILDREN'S HOSP, SAN FRANCISCO, 80- *Concurrent Pos:* Rotating intern, San Francisco Gen Hosp, Univ Calif Serv, 56-57; sr resident med, Bellevue Hosp, Columbia Univ Serv, 60-61, Univ Calif Med Ctr, San Francisco, 62-63; vis asst, Cardiol Ctr, Cantonal Hosp & 1 Univ, Geneva, Switz, 61-62; policy bd mem, Sickle Cell Vaso-Occlusive Clin Trials, Nat Heart & Lung Inst, 72, mem, Ad Hoc Comt, Studies Sickle Cell Dis, 73-75; chmn, Workshop Extracorporeal Treatment Sickle Cell Dis, NIH, 74-75. *Mem:* Fel Am Col Physicians; Western Soc Clin Res; Am Soc Bone & Mineral Res. *Res:* Somatomedin: its role in the control of cellular proliferation and its physiologic role and regulation; hormonal regulation of vitamin D metabolism. *Mailing Add:* Gen Clin Res Ctr Univ of Calif Med Ctr San Francisco CA 94122

SPENCER, EDGAR WINSTON, b Monticello, Ark, May 27, 31; m 58; c 2. GEOLOGY. *Educ:* Washington & Lee Univ, BS, 53; Columbia Univ, PhD(geol), 57. *Prof Exp:* Lectr geol, Hunter Col, 54-56, instr, 57; asst prof & actg chmn dept, 57-59, assoc prof, 59-63, PROF GEOL, WASHINGTON & LEE UNIV, 63-, CHMN DEPT, 59- *Concurrent Pos:* Prin investr, NSF grant, 59-62, sci fac fel tectonics in NZ & Australia, 65-66; res grant, Switz & Spain, 71-72; pres, Rockbridge Area Conserv Coun, 78; res grant, Am Chem Soc, 81-82. *Mem:* Fel AAAS; fel Geol Soc Am; Am Asn Petrol Geologists; Nat Asn Geol Teachers; Asn Prof Geol Scientists. *Res:* Tectonics; regional structure; land use planning. *Mailing Add:* Dept of Geol Washington & Lee Univ Lexington VA 24450

SPENCER, ELAINE, b Portland, Ore, Aug 6, 19; m 42; c 5. BIOCHEMISTRY. *Educ:* Linfield Col, BA, 40; Mass Inst Technol, MS, 48; Univ Ore, PhD(biochem), 61. *Prof Exp:* Instr chem, Ore State Col, 46-47, instr math, 47; instr, 56-59, from instr to asst prof chem, 59-74, ASSOC PROF CHEM, PORTLAND STATE UNIV, 74- *Mem:* Sigma Xi; Am Chem Soc. *Res:* Oxidative enzymes; proteins; enzyme kinetics. *Mailing Add:* Dept Chem Portland State Col Portland OR 97207

SPENCER, ELVINS YUILL, b Edmonton, Alta, Oct 2, 14; m 42; c 2. ORGANIC CHEMISTRY, AGRICULTURAL CHEMISTRY. *Educ:* Univ Alta, BSc, 36, MSc, 38; Univ Toronto, PhD(chem), 41. *Prof Exp:* Chief chemist, Fine Chem Can, 41-42; res chemist, Gelatin Prod Corp, Ont & Mich, 42-43; res engr, Consol Mining & Smelting Co, BC, 43-46; res chemist, E B Eddy Paper Co, Que, 46; assoc prof chem, Univ Sask, 46-51; prin chemist, Res Inst, Can Dept Agr, Univ Western Ont, 51-60, dir res inst, 60-78, SR SCIENTIST, CAN DEPT AGR, 78- *Concurrent Pos:* Coordr res, Sask Res Coun, 49-51; hon lectr, Univ Western Ont, 51-61, hon prof, 61-; consult, Dept Natural Resources, Sask & Cambridge Univ, 56-57; mem expert comt pesticide residues, Food & Agr Orgn. *Mem:* Am Chem Soc; fel Chem Inst Can; Agr Inst Can; Can Biochem Soc. *Res:* Flotation agent; pharmaceuticals; cereal chemistry; synthetic polypeptides; oils and fats; organic chemistry and biochemistry of pesticides. *Mailing Add:* Can Dept of Agr Res Inst Univ Sub PO London ON N6A 5B7 Can

SPENCER, FRANK, b Rochester, Kent, Eng, 42. PHYSICAL ANTHROPOLOGY. *Educ:* Univ London, FIMLS, 65; Univ Windsor, BA, 73; Univ Mich, Ann Arbor, MA, 75, PhD(anthrop), 75. *Prof Exp:* Chief med tech path, St Burtholomeus Hosp, Kent, Eng, 65-69; tech dir, Hotel Dien Hosp, Windsor, Ont, 69-73; ASST PROF ANTHROP, QUEENS COL, 79- *Mem:* Am Asn Phys Antoropologists; Am Anthrop Asn; Am Soc Hist Med. *Res:* History of physical anthropology of medicine; paltoanthropology-Pilo-Pleistonceng hominid evolutions. *Mailing Add:* Dept Anthrop Queens Col Kisseng Blvd Flushing NY 11367

SPENCER, FRANK COLE, b Haskell, Tex, Dec 21, 25; m; c 3. MEDICINE. *Educ:* NTex State Col, BS, 44; Vanderbilt Univ, MD, 47; Am Bd Surg & Bd Thoracic Surg, dipl. *Prof Exp:* Intern surg, Johns Hopkins Hosp, 47-48; asst res surgeon, Univ Calif Med Ctr, Los Angeles, 49-50; from asst resident surg to surgeon, Johns Hopkins Hosp, 53-65, from instr to assoc prof surg, Sch Med, Johns Hopkins Univ, 54-61; prof, Sch Med, Univ Ky, 61-65; PROF SURG & CHMN DEPT, SCH MED, NY UNIV, 65- *Concurrent Pos:* Fel, Sch Med, Johns Hopkins Univ, 48-49; USPHS fel cardiovasc surg, Sch Med, Univ Calif, Los Angeles, 51; Markle scholar; consult, Walter Reed Army Hosp, 57. *Mem:* Soc Univ Surg; Soc Clin Surg; Am Asn Thoracic Surg; Am Surg Asn. *Res:* Cardiovascular and thoracic surgery. *Mailing Add:* Dept of Surg NY Univ Sch of Med New York NY 10016

SPENCER, FREDERICK J, b Newcastle-on-Tyne, Eng, June 30, 23; US citizen; m 54; c 2. PREVENTIVE MEDICINE, PUBLIC HEALTH. *Educ:* Univ Durham, MB, BS, 45; Harvard Univ, MPH, 58. *Prof Exp:* Health dir, Va State Dept Health, 56-62, dir bur epidemiol, 62; assoc prof prev med, 62-63, PROF PREV MED, MED COL VA, VA COMMONWEALTH UNIV, 63-, CHMN DEPT, 78-, ASST DEAN STUDENT ACTIV, SCH MED, 78- *Concurrent Pos:* Walter Reed lectr, Richmond Acad Med, 66. *Mem:* Am Pub Health Asn. *Res:* Epidemiology and its application in administration of medical care; history of medicine. *Mailing Add:* Med Col Va PO Box 212 Richmond VA 23298

SPENCER, GORDON REED, b Ithaca, NY, June 30, 25; m 43. ELECTRICAL ENGINEERING. *Educ:* Cornell Univ, BSEE, 46. *Prof Exp:* Instr elec eng, Cornell Univ, 47-48; from eng speciliast to res specialist electron devices, Philco Corp, 48-60; RES & DEVELOP MGR ELECTRONIC COMPONENTS, RAYTHEON CO, 60- *Mem:* AAAS; Am Phys Soc; Inst Elec & Electronics Engrs; Soc Info Display; Sigma Xi. *Res:* Electron optics; application of electron optics to computer-driven displays and electronic imaging. *Mailing Add:* Res & Develop Dept Raytheon Co 465 Center St Quincy MA 02169

SPENCER, GUILFORD LAWSON, II, b Natick, Mass, Feb 21, 23; m 51; c 1. MATHEMATICS. *Educ:* Williams Col, BA, 43; Mass Inst Technol, MS, 48; Univ Mich, PhD(math), 53. *Prof Exp:* Instr math, Univ Md, 51-53; from asst prof to prof, 53-70, FREDERICK LATIMER WELLS PROF MATH, WILLIAMS COL, 70- *Res:* Topology and hyperbolic systems of partial differential equations. *Mailing Add:* Dept of Math Williams Col Williamstown MA 02167

SPENCER, HAROLD GARTH, b Avon Park, Fla, May 19, 30; m 56; c 2. PHYSICAL CHEMISTRY. *Educ:* Univ Fla, BS, 52, MS, 58, PhD(phys chem), 59. *Prof Exp:* From asst prof to assoc prof, 59-68, head dept chem & geol, 66-77, PROF CHEM, CLEMSON UNIV, 68- *Concurrent Pos:* Vis scientist, Imperial Col, 74; consult, Vicellon Inc, 74-77 & Carre Inc, 77- *Mem:* Am Chem Soc; Sigma Xi; AAAS. *Res:* Physical chemistry of polymers and polymer membranes, structure and physical properties; transport in polymers. *Mailing Add:* Dept of Chem & Geol Clemson Univ Clemson SC 29631

SPENCER, HARRY EDWIN, b Friendship, NY, June 8, 27; m 53; c 4. PHYSICAL CHEMISTRY. *Educ:* Syracuse Univ, BA, 50; Univ Calif, PhD, 54. *Prof Exp:* Chemist, Navy Ord Div, 53-59, res assoc, Res Labs, 59-72, SR RES ASSOC, RES LABS, EASTMAN KODAK CO, 72- *Concurrent Pos:* Adj fac chem, Rochester Inst Technol, 63-80; mem, NY State Rating Comt for PhD Prog in Chem, 73-74. *Mem:* Am Chem Soc; Am Phys Soc; Royal Photog Soc; fel Am Inst Chemists; fel Soc Photog Scientists. *Res:* Radiation chemistry; photoconductivity; infrared detectors; theory of photography; photochemistry. *Mailing Add:* Res Labs Eastman Kodak Co Rochester NY 14650

SPENCER, HERBERT WARD, III, b Louisville, Ky, June 12, 45; m 67; c 2. PHYSICS, AIR POLLUTION. *Educ:* Vanderbilt Univ, BA, 67; Auburn Univ, MS, 69, PhD(physics), 74. *Prof Exp:* Teaching asst physics, Auburn Univ, 67-73; res physicist electrostatic precipitators, Southern Res Inst, 74-77; mem staff, 77-80, MGR, ADV TECH DEPT, WESTERN PRECIPITATION DIV, JOY MFG CO, 80- *Mem:* Am Phys Soc; Sigma Xi; Air Pollution Control Asn. *Res:* Problems relating to cleaning industrial gases for particulates, electrostatic precipitation and fabric filters. *Mailing Add:* Western Precipitation Div PO Box 2744 Terminal Annex Los Angeles CA 90051

SPENCER, HUGH MILLER, b Winfield, Mo, Nov 24, 97; m 36; c 3. PHYSICAL CHEMISTRY. *Educ:* Univ Mo, AB, 19, AM, 21; Univ Calif, PhD(chem), 24. *Prof Exp:* Asst chem, Univ Mo, 18-20, instr phys chem, 20-21; instr, Yale Univ, 24-27; asst prof chem, 27-45, ASSOC PROF CHEM, UNIV VA, 45- *Mem:* AAAS; Am Chem Soc; fel Am Inst Chemists. *Res:* Thermodynamics of solutions; phase equilibria; constant humidity systems; galvanic cells; heat capacity equations; isotopes and nuclear transformations; thermodynamic functions of gases; heat capacities of solids. *Mailing Add:* New Chem Bldg Univ of Va Charlottesville VA 22901

SPENCER, JACK T, b Mantua, Ohio, Sept 23, 12; m 34; c 1. BOTANY, AGRONOMY. *Educ:* Kent State Univ, BS, 35; Univ Wis, MSc, 36; Ohio State Univ, PhD(bot, agron), 39. *Prof Exp:* Agt maize breeding, Bur Plant Indust, USDA, 36-40; res agronomist forage crops, Univ Ky, 40-42 & 46-49; consult foreign res, USDA, 49-61; prog dir, NSF, 61-68; exec dir, Orgn Trop Studies, 68-72; dir develop, Shippensburg State Col, 72-77; FED LIAISON CONSULT COLS & UNIVS, 78- *Mem:* AAAS; Am Inst Biol Sci; Bot Soc Am. *Res:* Plant genetics; tropical science; science administration. *Mailing Add:* 1303 Azalea Lane De Kalb IL 60115

SPENCER, JAMES ALPHUS, b Clayton, Okla, Nov 5, 30; c 3. PLANT PATHOLOGY. *Educ:* Univ Ark, BS, 53, MS, 62; NC State Univ, PhD(plant path), 66. *Prof Exp:* Res asst plant path, Univ Ark, 57-62; agr res technician, NC State Univ, USDA, 62-66; from asst prof to assoc prof, 66-76, PROF PLANT PATH, MISS STATE UNIV, 76- *Mem:* Am Phytopath Soc. *Res:* Host-parasite relationships; mycology; woody ornamental plants; diseases; rose disease. *Mailing Add:* Dept Plant Path Miss State Univ PO Drawer PG Mississippi State MS 39762

SPENCER, JAMES BROOKES, b Canton, China, July 16, 26; US citizen; m 48; c 4. HISTORY OF SCIENCE. *Educ:* Lawrence Col, BS, 48; Univ Wis, MS, 56, PhD(hist sci), 64. *Prof Exp:* Res physicist & proj leader, Bjorkston Res Labs, Wis, 54-57; asst prof physics, Augustana Col, Ill, 57-59; asst prof, 63-70, ASSOC PROF HIST SCI, ORE STATE UNIV, 70- *Concurrent Pos:* Vis asst prof, Johns Hopkins Univ, 65-66; NSF res grant, 65-69; vis asst prof, Univ Wis, 69; amanuensis, Niels Bohr Inst, Copenhagen, Denmark, 70-71. *Mem:* Hist Sci Soc. *Res:* History of 19th and early 20th century physical science, particularly magnetooptics and the structure of matter spectroscopy. *Mailing Add:* Dept of Hist Sci Ore State Univ Corvallis OR 97331

SPENCER, JAMES EUGENE, b Kansas City, Mo, Jan 2, 38; m 64. NUCLEAR PHYSICS, ACCELERATOR PHYSICS. *Educ:* Mass Inst Technol, BS, 64, PhD(physics), 69. *Prof Exp:* Fel physics, Stanford Univ, 69-71; staff mem, Los Alamos Sci Lab, 71-78; STAFF MEM, STANFORD LINEAR ACCELERATOR CTR, 78- *Concurrent Pos:* Consult, Lawrence Livermore Lab, 70-72; mem tech adv panel, Los Alamos Physics Facil, 73-75; reviewer, Phys Res & Phys Rev Letts, 74-; mem prog adv comt, Ind Cyclotron Lab, 76-78. *Mem:* Am Phys Soc; Sigma Xi. *Res:* Particle physics; magnetic optics; synchrotron radiation; quantum electronics; storage rings. *Mailing Add:* Stanford Linear accelerator Ctr PO Box 4349 Stanford CA 94305

SPENCER, JAMES NELSON, b Rainelle, WVa, Nov 11, 41. PHYSICAL CHEMISTRY. *Educ:* Marshall Univ, BS, 63; Iowa State Univ, PhD(phys chem), 67. *Prof Exp:* Student chemist, Int Nickel Co, WVa, 61-63; assoc prof chem, Lebanon Valley Col, 67-80; MEM FAC, CHEM DEPT, FRANKLIN & MARSHALL COL, 80- *Mem:* Am Chem Soc. *Res:* Hydrogen bonding; thermodynamic properties of solutions. *Mailing Add:* Dept Chem Franklin & Marshall Col Lancaster PA 17604

SPENCER, JAMES W(ENDELL), b Ithaca, NY, Aug 3, 27; m 46; c 3. CIVIL ENGINEERING. *Educ:* Cornell Univ, BCE, 49, MCE, 51; Stanford Univ, PhD, 67. *Prof Exp:* Instr civil eng, 49-51, from asst prof to assoc prof agr eng, 51-61, vdir coop exten, 70-73, assoc dean, NY STATE Col Agr & Life Sci, 73-78, spec asst to pres, 78-79, PROF AGR ENG, CORNELL UNIV, 61-, VPROVOST, 79- *Concurrent Pos:* Field engr, D J Belcher & Assocs, NY, 54; lectr & assoc res engr, Inst Transp & Traffic Eng, Calif, 57-58; consult, NY State Temp Comn Agr, 58 & Ford Found, Colombia, SAm, 63; NSF sci faculty fel, Stanford Univ, 64-65. *Res:* Highway engineering; engineering-economic planning. *Mailing Add:* Day Hall Cornell Univ Ithaca NY 14853

SPENCER, JESSE G, b Farmville, NC, Apr 10, 35; m 73; c 2. PHYSICAL CHEMISTRY, INORGANIC CHEMISTRY. *Educ:* Univ NC, BS, 57; Univ Va, MS, 59, PhD(chem), 62. *Prof Exp:* Res assoc chem, Univ NC, 61-62; from asst prof to assoc prof, 62-68, head dept, 65-76, prog dir, Med Lab Technol, 75-79, chmn div health serv, 76-79, PROF CHEM, UNIV CHARLESTON, 68-, DIR COMPUT SERV & RECORDS, 81- *Mem:* Am Chem Soc; Sigma Xi; Royal Soc Chem. *Res:* Solution thermochemistry and polarography of transition metals in aqueous and nonaqueous media; trace analysis. *Mailing Add:* Univ Charleston Charleston WV 25304

SPENCER, JOHN BROCKETT, b Horton, Kans, Sept 25, 39; m 64; c 2. PHYSICAL CHEMISTRY. *Educ:* Carleton Col, BA, 61; Univ Calif, Berkeley, PhD(chem), 65. *Prof Exp:* From instr to assoc prof, 65-76, PROF CHEM, BELOIT COL, 76-, CHMN DEPT, 80- *Concurrent Pos:* Vis prof, Case Western Reserve Univ, 67-68, Uppsala Univ, 71-72 & Univ Calif, Berkeley, 79. *Mem:* Am Chem Soc; AAAS. *Res:* Molecular spectroscopy and x-ray diffraction determination of molecular structure and bonding. *Mailing Add:* Dept of Chem Beloit Col Beloit WI 53511

SPENCER, JOHN EDWARD, b Panama, CZ, Mar 22, 49; US citizen; m 75; c 1. PHYSICAL CHEMISTRY. *Educ:* Millsaps Col, BS, 71; Rice Univ, PhD(chem), 75. *Prof Exp:* Res assoc chem, Univ Calif, Irvine, 75-77; res chemist, Lighting Bus Group, Gen Elec Co, 77-80; MEM TECH STAFF, TEX INSTRUMENTS INC, 80- *Mem:* Am Chem Soc; AAAS; Electrochem Soc. *Res:* Plasma etching of semiconductor thin films; plasma spectroscopy; high temperature chemistry and combustion. *Mailing Add:* Tex Instruments Inc PO Box 1443 MS 631 Houston TX 77001

SPENCER, JOHN FRANCIS THEODORE, b Magrath, Alta, Jan 18, 22; m 45; c 6. MICROBIOLOGY. *Educ:* Univ Alta, BSc, 49, MSc, 51; Univ Sask, PhD(chem), 55. *Prof Exp:* Asst res officer, 51-59, assoc res officer, 59-63, SR RES OFFICER, ENG & PROCESS DEVELOP SECT, PRAIRIE REGIONAL LAB, NAT RES COUN CAN, 63- *Mem:* AAAS; Am Soc Microbiol; Can Soc Microbiol. *Res:* Yeast metabolism; metabolism of plant pathogens; industrial fermentations; soil microbiology; yeast taxonomy; ecology; genetics. *Mailing Add:* Prairie Regional Lab Nat Res Coun Saskatoon SK Can

SPENCER, JOHN HEDLEY, b Stapleford, Eng, Apr 10, 33; Can citizen; m 58; c 3. BIOCHEMISTRY. *Educ:* St Andrews Univ, BSc, 55, Hons, 56; McGill Univ, PhD(biochem), 60. *Prof Exp:* Res asst biochem, McGill Univ, 56-59; Damon Runyon Mem Fund Cancer Res vis fel, Columbia Univ, 59-61, res assoc, 61; lectr & teaching fel, McGill Univ, 61-63, from asst prof to prof biochem, 63-78; PROF BIOCHEM & HEAD DEPT, QUEEN'S UNIV, 78- *Concurrent Pos:* Sci Officer biochem comt, Med Res Coun Can, 73-79; mem grants panel, Nat Cancer Inst, 75-79. *Honors & Awards:* Ayerst Award, Can Biochem Soc, 72. *Mem:* Can Biochem Soc (treas, 66-69, vpres, 78-79, pres, 79-80); Am Soc Biol Chemists; AAAS; Brit Biochem Soc; Can Fed Biol Soc (vpres, 80-81, pres, 81-82). *Res:* Chemistry and primary structure of DNA; gene transcription and control; protein synthesis. *Mailing Add:* Dept Biochem Queen's Univ Kingston ON K7L 3N6 Can

SPENCER, JOHN LAWRENCE, b Sanford, Fla, Sept 10, 32; m 54, 79; c 2. TECHNICAL SERVICE, QUALITY CONTROL. *Educ:* DePauw Univ, AB, 54; Univ Mich, MS, 56, PhD(isoxazolines), 58. *Prof Exp:* Org chemist, Lederle Lab, Am Cyanamid Co, 58-60; sr org chemist, 60-67, res scientist, 67-69, res assoc, 70-71, mgr antibiotic prod technol, 71-78, mgr sterile operations, 78-80, MGR TECH SERV & QUAL CONTROL, ELI LILLY & CO, 78- *Mem:* Am Chem Soc; Parenteral Drug Asn. *Res:* Synthesis of heterocyclic systems, particularly isoxazolines, oxadiazoles, genzodiazepines and quinazolines; antibiotic modifications, particularly tetracyclines, penicillins and cephalosporins; antibiotic manufacturing includding fermentation, purification, and bulk parenteral operations; analytical supervision and quality control supervisions and systems. *Mailing Add:* Dept K 414 Lilly 307 E McCarty St Indianapolis IN 46285

SPENCER, JOSEPH WALTER, b Salt Lake City, Utah, May 24, 21; m 48; c 5. GEOPHYSICS. *Educ:* Brigham Young Univ, BS, 47; Pa State Univ, PhD(physics), 52. *Prof Exp:* Asst math, Brigham Young Univ, 47-48; asst physics, Pa State Univ, 48-49, asst acoust, 49-50; res physicist, Calif Res Corp, Standard Oil Co Calif, 52-54, proj leader geophys, 54-56, group supvr, 56-60; sr geophysicist, Calif Oil Co, 60-65, staff geophysicist, Western Div, Chevron Oil Co, 65-69, chief geophysicist, Western Div, Chevron Oil Co, 69-77, CHIEF GEOPHYSICIST, CENT REGION, CHEVRON USA, 77- *Mem:* Soc Explor Geophysicists; Am Geophys Union. *Res:* Fluid dynamics; viscous behavior of high molecular weight hydrocarbons; wave propagation in earth materials; interpretation of geophysical data; electronic computer applications. *Mailing Add:* Chevron USA Cent Region PO Box 599 Denver CO 80201

SPENCER, LARRY T, b Palo Alto, Calif, Oct 15, 41; m 64; c 3. AQUATIC ECOLOGY, INVERTEBRATE ZOOLOGY. *Educ:* Brigham Young Univ, BS, 63; Ore State Univ, MA, 65; Colo State Univ, PhD(zool), 68; Univ Calif, MLS, 75. *Prof Exp:* Teaching asst zool, Brigham Young Univ, 62-63, Ore State Univ, 65-67 & Colo State Univ, 65-67; from instr to assoc prof biol, 67-78, PROF BIOL, PLYMOUTH STATE COL, 78- *Concurrent Pos:* Vis prof, Univ Hawaii, 82, sabbatical. *Mem:* AAAS; Am Soc Limnol & Oceanog; Ecol Soc Am; Am Soc Zoologists; Hist Sci Soc. *Res:* Population biology of marine and fresh water invertebrates; biology of cephalopod mollusks; history of biology and American science; exploration and settlement of the Trans-Mississippi West; evolution, its impact on biological and intellectual thought; data base management and information retrieval in the biological sciences. *Mailing Add:* Dept of Natural Sci Plymouth State Col Plymouth NH 03264

SPENCER, LORRAINE BARNEY, b Ogden, NY, Jan 26, 24; m 42; c 4. PHYCOLOGY. *Educ:* Guilford Col, BS, 66; Wake Forest Univ, MA, 70, PhD(biol), 73. *Prof Exp:* Asst instr, Wake Forest Univ, 68-72, res fel, 72-73; ASST PROF BIOL, ST AUGUSTINE'S COL, 74- *Concurrent Pos:* Adj prof biol, Guilford Col Urban Ctr, 74. *Mem:* Am Inst Biol Sci; Asn Southeastern Biologists; Bot Soc Am; Phycol Soc Am; Sigma Xi. *Res:* Biosystematics of Zephyranthes. *Mailing Add:* 315 White Oak Dr Cary NC 27511

SPENCER, MARY STAPLETON, b Regina, Sask, Oct 4, 23; m 46; c 1. BIOCHEMISTRY. *Educ:* Univ Sask, BA, 45; Bryn Mawr Col, MA, 46; Univ Calif, PhD(agr chem), 51. *Prof Exp:* Chemist, Ayerst, McKenna & Harrison, Ltd, 46-47; chemist, Nat Canners Asn, Calif, 48-49; asst food chem, Univ Calif, 50-51, instr, 51-53; from asst prof to assoc prof biochem, 53-64, actg head dept biochem, 60-61, PROF PLANT SCI, UNIV ALTA, 64- *Concurrent Pos:* Mem, Nat Res Coun Can. *Mem:* Am Chem Soc; Am Soc Plant Physiol; Can Biochem Soc; AAAS; Int Asn Plant Tissue Cult. *Res:* Metabolism of aging tissue; biology of ethylene, its effects on plants, animals, microorganisms, its relationship to aging and to plant productivity, biogenesis; mechanisms of energy conservation; post-harvest physiology of fruits and vegetables. *Mailing Add:* Dept of Plant Sci Univ of Alta Edmonton AB T6G 2N2 Can

SPENCER, MAX M(ARLIN), b Rocky Ford, Colo, Jan 10, 35; m 55; c 3. MECHANICAL ENGINEERING. *Educ:* Okla State Univ, BS, 56, MS, 57, PhD(eng), 60. *Prof Exp:* Res asst & lectr eng, Okla State Univ, 56-60; assoc engr, Boeing Co, Kans, 57, faculty assoc adv design group, 58, res specialist, 60; res specialist & stress consult, Ballistics Res Labs, Aberdeen Proving Ground, Md, 60-61; res specialist, 61-62, stress res group chief, 62-63, res specialist & fatigue group head, 63-69, sr eng supvr, 69-78, struct technol mgr & stress unit chief, 78-80, STRUCT TECHNOL CHIEF, BOEING CO, 80- *Concurrent Pos:* Guest lectr, Univ Wichita, 62; designated eng rep, Fed Aviation Admin, 74. *Mem:* Am Soc Mech Engrs. *Res:* Aircraft structural analysis; stress and fatigue. *Mailing Add:* 12039 SE 20th Bellevue WA 98005

SPENCER, MERRILL PARKER, b Pawnee, Okla, Feb 27, 22; m 44; c 4. CARDIOVASCULAR PHYSIOLOGY. *Educ:* Baylor Univ, MD, 45. *Prof Exp:* Intern, Herman Hosp, Tex, 45-46; med resident, Crile Vet Admin Hosp, 50-51; instr physiol & pharmacol, Bowman Gray Sch Med, 51-54, asst prof physiol, 54-59, assoc prof physiol & pharmacol, 59-63; dir, Va Mason Res Ctr, 63-71; PRES & DIR, INST APPL PHYSIOL & MED, 71- *Concurrent Pos:* USPHS fel, Western Reserve Univ, 48-50; mem coun circulation & coun basic sci, Am Heart Asn; pres, Oceanographic Inst Wash. *Mem:* Am Physiol Soc; Am Heart Asn. *Res:* Medical electronics; cardiopulmonary medicine. *Mailing Add:* Inst of Appl Physiol & Med 701 16th Ave Seattle WA 98122

SPENCER, PETER SIMNER, b London, Eng, Nov 30, 46; US citizen; m 69; c 1. NEUROBIOLOGY, NEUROTOXICOLOGY. *Educ:* Univ London, BSc, 68, PhD(med), 71. *Prof Exp:* Res assoc neurol, Royal Free Hosp, London, 71-73; ASST PROF PATH, ALBERT EINSTEIN COL MED, 74-, ASSOC PROF NEUROSCI, 77-, SCI DIR NEUROTOXICOL UNIT, 75- *Concurrent Pos:* Joseph P Kennedy, Jr Found fel, 74-76; consult, Nat Inst Occup Safety & Health, 76-77 & Environ Protection Agency, 77-; assoc ed, J Neurocytol, 77-; chmn adv bd, J Neurotoxicol, 78- *Honors & Awards:* Weil Award, Am Asn Neuropathologists, 76. *Mem:* Am Asn Neuropathologists; Am Soc Cell Biol; fel Royal Soc Med; Soc Neurosci; Soc Toxicol. *Res:* Cellular relationships in the nervous system and the effects of neurotoxic chemicals. *Mailing Add:* Neurotoxicol Unit 1300 Morris Park Ave Bronx NY 10461

SPENCER, RALPH DONALD, b Kolambugan, Philippines, July 22, 20; US citizen; m 47; c 2. ORGANIC CHEMISTRY. *Educ:* Col Wooster, BA, 41; Stanford Univ, MA, 42; Cornell Univ, PhD(org chem), 47. *Prof Exp:* Du Pont fel chem, Cornell Univ, 47-48, Goodrich Tire & Rubber Co Proj res assoc, 50-51; chemist, Pineapple Res Inst, Hawaii, 48-50; chemist, E I du Pont de Nemours & Co, 51-57; SR FEL, MELLON INST, 57-, ASSOC PROF CHEM, CARNEGIE-MELLON UNIV, 67- *Mem:* Am Chem Soc. *Res:* Fundamental studies in thin-layer chromatography; surface structure properties and reactions of silicas, especially silica gel; synthesis of organic membranes and porous glass. *Mailing Add:* Mellon Inst Carnegie-Mellon Univ Pittsburgh PA 15213

SPENCER, RANDALL SCOTT, b Sept 29, 37; US citizen; m 66; c 2. PALEONTOLOGY, STRATIGRAPHY. *Educ:* Univ Wis-Madison, BS, 60; Univ Kans, MS, 62, PhD(geol), 68. *Prof Exp:* From asst prof to assoc prof, 66-77, asst chmn dept, 74-76, assoc dean, 78-81, PROF GEOPHYS SCI, OLD DOMINION UNIV, 78-, CHMN DEPT, 81- *Concurrent Pos:* NSF grant, 70- *Mem:* Fel Geol Soc Am; Soc Econ Paleontologists & Mineralogists; fel Paleont Soc. *Res:* Upper Paleozoic brachiopods; Mesozoic and Cenozoic foraminifera of Atlantic Coast; statistical studies in brachiopod evolution; marine Pleistocene stratigraphy and fauna of the mid-Atlantic seaboard. *Mailing Add:* Dept Geophys Sci Old Dominion Univ Norfolk VA 23508

SPENCER, RICHARD L, b Dunlap, Iowa, Feb 11, 34; m 59; c 3. BIOCHEMISTRY. *Educ:* Fresno State Col, AB, 56; San Jose State Col, MS, 63; Univ Calif, Davis, PhD(biochem), 66. *Prof Exp:* Asst chemist, Calif Chem Co, 56-59; res assoc biochem, Univ Ill, Urbana, 65-66; NIH fel, Univ Minn, 66-68; from asst prof to assoc prof, 68-74, PROF CHEM, SOUTHWEST STATE UNIV, 74- *Mem:* Am Chem Soc. *Res:* Enzyme chemistry. *Mailing Add:* Dept of Chem Southwest State Univ Marshall MN 56258

SPENCER, RICHARD PAUL, b New York, NY, June 7, 29; m 56; c 3. NUCLEAR MEDICINE, BIOCHEMISTRY. *Educ:* Dartmouth Col, AB, 51; Univ Southern Calif, MD, 54; Harvard Univ, MA, 58, PhD(biochem), 61. *Prof Exp:* From asst prof to assoc prof biophys, Univ Buffalo, 61-63; from assoc prof to prof nuclear med, Sch Med, Yale Univ, 68-74; PROF NUCLEAR MED & CHMN DEPT, SCH MED, UNIV CONN HEALTH CTR, FARMINGTON, 74- *Concurrent Pos:* NSF fel, Harvard Univ, 57-58, Helen Hay Whitney fel, 58-60. *Mem:* AAAS; Am Physiol Soc; Soc Nuclear Med; Biophys Soc. *Res:* Organ structure and function as studied by radioisotopes; models of biological growth and differentiation; intestinal metabolism and transport. *Mailing Add:* Dept of Nuclear Med Univ of Conn Health Ctr Farmington CT 06032

SPENCER, SELDEN J, b Towanda, Pa, Apr 28, 23; m 51; c 2. BIOLOGICAL SCIENCES. *Educ:* Mansfield State Col, BS, 48; Pa State Univ, MEd, 52, DEd(biol sci), 62. *Prof Exp:* High sch teacher, Pa, 48-49; chem technician, Sylvania Elec Prod, Inc, 50-52; admin asst, Educ Off, Pa State Col, 52-53, admin asst educ film res prog, 53-54; high sch teacher, Pa, 54-57; mem, Inst Sci Teachers, Pa, 57-58; prof biol, Goddard Col, 58-63; from asst prof to assoc prof, 63-71, chmn dept, 72-78, PROF BIOL, STATE UNIV NY COL NEW PALTZ, 71- *Mem:* Am Inst Biol Sci; Am Soc Zoologists. *Res:* Bird banding research; gypsy moth parasitism; bank swallow nesting sites; Arctic wilderness exploration. *Mailing Add:* Dept of Biol State Univ of NY New Paltz NY 12561

SPENCER, TERRY WARREN, b Los Angeles, Calif, Feb 10, 30; m 53; c 2. GEOPHYSICS. *Educ:* Univ Calif, Los Angeles, AB, 51; Calif Inst Technol, PhD(geophys), 56. *Prof Exp:* Sr res physicist, Chevron Res Co, Calif, 56-66; chmn dept, 66-77, PROF GEOPHYS, TEX A&M UNIV, 66- *Mem:* Am Geophys Union; Soc Explor Geophys. *Res:* Elastic wave propagation in layered media and boreholes; optimum filter design; application of computers to geophysical problems. *Mailing Add:* Dept Geophys Tex A&M Univ College Station TX 77843

SPENCER, THOMAS A, b Orange, NJ, Mar 31, 34; m 56; c 4. ORGANIC CHEMISTRY. *Educ:* Amherst Col, AB, 56; Univ Wis, PhD(chem), 60. *Prof Exp:* Res assoc chem, Univ Wis, 60; from instr to prof & chmn dept, 60-72, NEW HAMPSHIRE PROF CHEM, DARTMOUTH COL, 72- *Concurrent Pos:* Alfred P Sloan Found res fel, 65-68; mem grants prog adv comt, Res Corp, 72-78. *Mem:* AAAS; Am Chem Soc. *Res:* Organic chemical synthesis; natural products, particularly terpenoids; steroid biosynthesis; biochemical reaction mechanisms. *Mailing Add:* Dept Chem Dartmouth Col Hanover NH 03755

SPENCER, WALTER WILLIAM, b Mansfield, Ohio, Nov 10, 33; m 64; c 2. CLINICAL CHEMISTRY. *Educ:* Heidelberg Col, BS, 55; Purdue Univ, West Lafayette, MS, 58, PhD(biochem), 60. *Prof Exp:* Purdue Res Found fel, Purdue Univ, West Lafayette, 60-61; CLIN CHEMIST, ST ELIZABETH MED CTR, 61- *Concurrent Pos:* Clin asst prof, Univ Dayton, 70-74, clin assoc prof, 74-80; treas, Clin Chem Consult, Inc, 78. *Mem:* Fel AAAS; Am Asn Clin Chemists. *Res:* Development of new procedures for use in the field of clinical chemistry. *Mailing Add:* Clin Lab St Elizabeth Med Ctr Dayton OH 45408

SPENCER, WILLIAM ALBERT, b Oklahoma City, Okla, Feb 16, 22; m 45; c 2. REHABILITATION, PEDIATRICS. *Educ:* Georgetown Univ, BS, 42; Johns Hopkins Univ, MD, 46; Am Bd Pediat, dipl, 55. *Prof Exp:* Intern, Hopkins Hosp, 46-47, resident, 47-48; from instr to asst prof pediat, 50-57, asst prof physiol, 54-57, PROF REHAB & CHMN DEPT, BAYLOR COL MED, 57-; PRES, INST REHAB & RES, TEX MED CTR, 59- *Concurrent Pos:* Med dir, Southwestern Poliomyelitis Respiratory Ctr, 50-59; Horowitz vis prof, Inst Phys Med & Rehab, 64; asst attend physician, Ben Taub Gen Hosp; mem active staff, Tex Children's Hosp; mem consult staff, M D Anderson Hosp & Tumor Inst Houston; mem courtesy staff, St Luke's Hosp; chmn spec med adv group to Vet Admin, 74-75. *Honors & Awards:* Physician of Year, President's Comn Employment of the Handicapped, 64. *Mem:* Am Med Asn; Am Acad Pediat. *Res:* Development of principles of rehabilitation medicine; application of electronic technology to research in disabling chronic disease and injuries; planning health services for disabled at community and national level. *Mailing Add:* Dept of Rehab Baylor Med Col Houston TX 77025

SPENCER, WILLIAM F, b Carlinville, Ill, Mar 4, 23; m 46; c 3. SOIL CHEMISTRY. *Educ:* Univ Ill, BS, 47, MS, 51, PhD(agron), 52. *Prof Exp:* Asst soil physics, Univ Ill, 48; asst chemist, Citrus Exp Sta, Univ Fla, 51-54; soil scientist, Agr Res Serv, USDA, Wyo, 54-55 & Calif, 55-57; assoc soil chemist, Citrus Exp Sta, Univ Fla, 57-62; SUPVRY SOIL SCIENTIST, AGR RES SERV, USDA, 62- *Concurrent Pos:* Consult, Cent Univ Venezuela, 59. *Mem:* Fel AAAS; Am Chem Soc; Soil Sci Soc Am; Am Soc Agron. *Res:* Soil chemistry of pesticides, nutrient enrichment, waste disposal on land as related to water quality and vapor behavior of pesticides and other toxic organic chemicals in the environment. *Mailing Add:* USDA Agr Res Serv Univ of Calif 1278 Geol Bldg Riverside CA 92521

SPENCER, WILLIAM J, b Kansas City, Mo, Sept 25, 30; m 53; c 2. SOLID STATE PHYSICS. *Educ:* William Jewell Col, AB, 52; Kans State Univ, MS, 56, PhD(physics), 60. *Prof Exp:* Mem tech staff, Bell Labs, Pa, 59-68, head piezoelec devices dept, 68-72, diPa, Univ Rels & Employ Ctr, 72-73, dir microelectronics, 73-78 ; dir systs develop, Sandia Labs, 78-80; MGR, INTEGRATED CIRCUITS LAB, PALO ALTO RES CTR, XEROX CORP, 80- *Mem:* AAAS; Am Phys Soc; fel Inst Elec & Electronics Engrs. *Res:* Integrated circuits design and processing; biomedical applications. *Mailing Add:* Palo Alto Res Ctr Xerox Corp 3333 Coyote Hill Rd Palo Alto CA 94304

SPENDLOVE, JOHN CLIFTON, b Provo, Utah, Dec 24, 25; m 44; c 5. BACTERIOLOGY. *Educ:* Brigham Young Univ, BS, 49, MS, 50; Ohio State Univ, PhD(bact), 53. *Prof Exp:* Bacteriologist & chief agents biol br, Biol Warfare Assessment Lab, Chem Corps, Dugway Proving Ground, 53-57, opers res analyst, Opers Res Group, Army Chem Ctr, 57-62, tech dir planning & eval directorate, Deseret Test Ctr, 62-72, chief biol defense div, Plans & Studies Directorate, 72-75, CHIEF ENVIRON & LIFE SCI DIV, MATERIEL TEST DIRECTORATE, US DEPT ARMY, DUGWAY PROVING GROUND, 75- *Mem:* AAAS; Am Soc Microbiologists; Sigma Xi; NY Acad Sci; Soc Indust Microbiol. *Res:* Aerobiology; decontamination; pathogenic bacteriology; biological and chemical warfare operations research; hazardous microbial aerosols in the environment. *Mailing Add:* US Army Mat Test Directorate Dugway Proving Ground Dugway UT 84022

SPENDLOVE, REX S, b Hoytsville, Utah, Apr 29, 26; m 49; c 5. VIROLOGY, IMMUNOLOGY. *Educ:* Brigham Young Univ, BS, 50, MS, 52; Ohio State Univ, PhD, 55. *Prof Exp:* Instr microbiol, Univ Conn, 55-58; res microbiologist, Viral & Rickettsial Dis Lab, Calif State Dept Pub Health, 58-66; head dept bact & pub health, 66-73, PROF VIROL, UTAH STATE UNIV, 66- *Concurrent Pos:* Mem ed bd, Excerpta Medica; mem reovirus study group, Vert Virus Subcomt, Int Comn Nomenclature Viruses; pres, Sterile Systs, Inc, 75- *Mem:* AAAS; Am Soc Microbiol; NY Acad Sci; Soc Exp Biol & Med; Am Asn Immunol. *Res:* Reovirus replication and genetics; affinity of reovirus for host cell microtubules; enhancement of reovirus infectivity by capsid removal; effect of proteolytic enzymes on viral structure; viral pollution of water; Rotavirus Gastroenteritis. *Mailing Add:* Dept of Biol Utah State Univ Logan UT 84322

SPENGER, ROBERT E, b Oakland, Calif, Sept 20, 24; m 59; c 1. ORGANIC CHEMISTRY. *Educ:* Univ Calif, Berkeley, AB, 54; Univ Calif, Los Angeles, PhD(org chem), 62. *Prof Exp:* Chemist, Radiation Lab, Univ Calif, 54-57; asst, Univ Calif, Los Angeles, 57-62, asst res chemist, Univ Calif, Riverside, 62-64; asst prof, 64-74, PROF CHEM, CALIF STATE UNIV, FULLERTON, 74- *Mem:* AAAS; Am Chem Soc. *Res:* Synthesis of isotopically-labelled compounds; synthesis of organo-arsenic compounds. *Mailing Add:* Dept of Chem Calif State Univ Fullerton CA 92634

SPENGOS, ARIS C(ONSTANTINE), b Istanbul, Turkey, Nov 1, 24; nat US; m 59; c 3. ENGINEERING. *Educ:* Robert Col Istanbul, BS, 46; Univ Iowa, MS, 49 & 50; Univ Mich, PhD(eng), 59. *Prof Exp:* Res assoc, Inst Hydraul Res, Univ Iowa, 48-52; hydraul engr, Tippetts-Abbett-McCarthy, Engrs, 52-53; asst res engr, Colo State Univ, 53-56; assoc res engr, Res Inst, Univ Mich, 56-59; OPERATING DIR RES, SCOTT PAPER CO, 59- *Concurrent Pos:* Lectr, Univ Mich, 57-59 & Pa State Univ, 69- *Mem:* AAAS; Inst Elec & Electronics Engrs; Am Soc Civil Engrs; Tech Asn Pulp & Paper Indust; Am Geophys Union. *Res:* Fluid mechanics research; instrumentation; development of equipment. *Mailing Add:* Scott Paper Co Scott Plaza Philadelphia PA 19113

SPENNER, FRANK J(OHN), b Riverside, Iowa, July 4, 01; m 39; c 1. ELECTRICAL ENGINEERING. *Educ:* Univ Iowa, BS, 24, MS, 27. *Prof Exp:* Asst foreman, Potter Condenser Co, Ill, 27-28; asst engr, Western Elec Co, 28-32; surveyor, US Coast & Geod Surv, Iowa, 33-34 & Johnson Co, Iowa, 36-39; instr eng, drawing & math, Trinidad State Jr Col, 41-47; from asst prof to assoc prof eng, 47-63, assoc prof elec eng, 63-71, EMER ASSOC PROF ENG DRAWING, UNIV WYO, 71- *Mem:* Inst Elec & Electronics Engrs. *Res:* Design, inspection and development on equipment for measuring electrical characteristics of cables, coils and condensers; basic circuits. *Mailing Add:* 561 N Seventh Laramie WY 82070

SPENNY, DAVID LORIN, b Covington, Ky, Nov 5, 43. NUCLEAR PHYSICS, PHYSICS EDUCATION. *Educ:* Wittenberg Univ, BS, 65; Univ Colo, Boulder, PhD(physics), 70. *Prof Exp:* Lectr physics, Univ Colo, Denver, 70-71; asst prof phys sci, Univ Colo, Boulder, 71-74; asst prof, NMex Highlands Univ, 74-75; asst prof physics, Bemidji State Univ, 76-79; ASSOC PROF PHYSICS, UNIV SOUTHERN COLO, 80- *Mem:* Am Asn Physics Teachers; AAAS. *Res:* Science education for non-scientists. *Mailing Add:* Dept of Physics Univ Southern Colo Pueblo CO 81001

SPENSER, IAN DANIEL, b Vienna, Austria, June 17, 24; m 51; c 2. BIO-ORGANIC CHEMISTRY. *Educ:* Univ Birmingham, BSc, 48; Univ London, PhD(biochem), 52, DSc, 69. *Prof Exp:* Demonstr biochem, Kings Col, Univ London, 48-52, asst lectr biochem & chem, Med Col, St Bartholomew's Hosp, 52-54, lectr, 54-57; from asst prof to assoc prof biochem, 57-64, PROF CHEM, McMASTER UNIV, 64- *Concurrent Pos:* Fel, Nat Res Coun Can, 53-54. *Mem:* Am Soc Biol Chemists; Can Biochem Soc; fel Chem Inst Can; Royal Soc Chem; Brit Biochem Soc. *Res:* Biosynthesis of alkaloids and of B vitamins; chemistry and metabolism of amino acids. *Mailing Add:* Dept of Chem McMaster Univ Hamilton ON L3S 4M1 Can

SPERA, FRANK JOHN, b Philadelphia, Pa, Dec 6, 50; m 77. MAGMA TRANSPORT, IRREVERSIBLE THERMODYNAMICS. *Educ:* Franklin & Marshall Col, BA, 72; Univ Calif, Berkeley, BA, 74, PhD(geol), 77. *Prof Exp:* Asst prof, 77-81, ASSOC PROF THERMODYNAMICS & PETROL, PRINCETON UNIV, 82- *Concurrent Pos:* Vis lectr, Univ Calif, Los Angeles, 81-82, vis res geophysicts, 81-82; prin investr, NSF, 77-82. *Mem:* Am Geophys Union; Geol Soc Am. *Res:* Application of thermodynamics and fluid dynamics to magnatic processes; eruption and ascent of magma; experimental rheology of magma; origin of compositional zonation in magma chambers. *Mailing Add:* Dept Goel & Geophys Sci Princeton Univ Princeton NJ 08541

SPERANDIO, GLEN JOSEPH, b Glen Carbon, Ill, May 8, 18; m 46; c 1. CLINICAL PHARMACY. *Educ:* St Louis Col Pharm, BS, 40; Purdue Univ, MS, 47, PhD(pharm), 50. *Prof Exp:* Anal chemist, Grove Labs, 40-42, chief control chemist, 44-46 & United Drug Co, 42-43; asst dept mgr, William R Warner, Inc, 43-44; from instr to assoc prof pharm, 46-60, head dept clin pharm, 71-78, PROF PHARM, PURDUE UNIV, WEST LAFAYETTE, 60-, ASSOC DEAN, 78- *Concurrent Pos:* Consult, Surgeon Gen, US Army, 74-

Mem: Am Soc Hosp Pharmacists; Am Pharmaceut Asn; Soc Cosmetic Chem; Am Asn Col Pharm; Sigma Xi. *Res:* Product formulation; tablets; dermatological medication; cosmetics; pharmaceuticals; hospital pharmacy. *Mailing Add:* 1306 Northwestern Ave West Lafayette IN 47906

SPERATI, CARLETON ANGELO, b Fergus Falls, Minn, Sept 1, 18; m 41; c 3. FLUOROPOLYMER SYSTEMS, POLYMER CHEMISTRY. *Educ:* Luther Col, AB, 38; Univ Ill, MA, 39, PhD(org chem), 41. *Prof Exp:* Res chemist, Plastics Dept, E I du Pont de Nemours & Co, 41-52, res supvr, Polychem Dept, 52-55, sr res supvr, 55-60, sr res chemist, 60-62, res assoc, 62-69, res fel, Plastics Prod & Resins Dept, 69-79; C Paul Stocker prof eng, Ohio Univ, 79-80; CONSULT, 81- *Concurrent Pos:* C Paul Stocker adj prof chem eng, Ohio Univ. *Mem:* AAAS; Am Chem Soc; Soc Plastics Eng; Am Soc Testing & Mat; Sigma Xi. *Res:* Steric hindrance; stable vinyl alcohols; low reflection coatings; laminating resins; condensation polymers; photochromic systems; computers in polymer studies; synthesis conditions and molecular structure versus properties of fluorocarbon and other polymers; thermal analysis of polymers. *Mailing Add:* 23 Mustang Acres Parkersburg WV 26101

SPERBER, DANIEL, b Vienna, Austria, May 8, 30; m 63; c 1. PHYSICS. *Educ:* Hebrew Univ, Israel, MSc, 54; Princeton Univ, PhD(physics), 60. *Prof Exp:* Teaching asst physics, Hebrew Univ, Israel, 53-54 & Israel Inst Technol, 54-55; asst, Princeton Univ, 55-60; instr, Ill Inst Technol, 61-62, lectr, 62-64, assoc prof, 64-67; assoc prof, 67-72, PROF PHYSICS, RENSSELAER POLYTECH INST, 72- *Concurrent Pos:* From assoc physicist to sr physicist, IIT Res Inst, 60-66, sci adv, 66-67; Nordita prof, Niels Bohr Inst, Univ Copenhagen, 73-74. *Mem:* Fel Am Phys Soc; Phys Soc Israel; NY Acad Sci. *Res:* Nuclear structure, reactions and decay modes; physics of fission and heavy ions; atomic spectroscopy; application of group theory to quantum mechanics. *Mailing Add:* Dept of Physics Rensselaer Polytech Inst Troy NY 12181

SPERBER, GEOFFREY HILLIARD, b Bloemfontein, SAfrica, Dec 26, 33; Can citizen; m 63; c 3. ANATOMY, DENTISTRY. *Educ:* Univ Witwatersrand, BSc, 54, Hons, 58, BDS, 56, PhD, 74; Univ Rochester, MSc, 62. *Prof Exp:* Jr lectr anat, Med Sch, Univ Witwatersrand, 57-58; from asst prof to assoc prof anat & oral surg, 61-72, PROF ORAL BIOL, FAC DENT, UNIV ALTA, 72- *Concurrent Pos:* Nat Res Coun Can res grants, 64-66; Nat Res Coun Can sr res fel, Univ Witwatersrand, 69-70; ed, Asn Can Fac Dent Newslett; mem, Int Anat Nomenclature Comt. *Mem:* Can Asn Anatomists; Can Asn Phys Anthrop; Can Dent Asn; Int Asn Dent Res; Int Dent Fedn. *Res:* Dental science; physical anthropology; embryology; skull growth; oral pathology and teratology; comparative odontology. *Mailing Add:* Fac Dent Univ Alta Edmonton AB T6G 2N8 Can

SPERBER, STEVEN IRWIN, b Brooklyn, NY, May 25, 45; m 73. GEOMETRY. *Educ:* Brooklyn Col, BA, 66; Univ Pa, MA & PhD(math), 75. *Prof Exp:* Instr math, York Col, City Univ New York, 71-73, adj fac, Lehman Col, 74-75; lectr math, Univ Ill, Urbana, 75-77, asst prof, 77-80; MEM FAC, DEPT MATH, UNIV MINN, 80- *Mem:* Am Math Soc; Sigma Xi. *Res:* A study of the p-adic cohomology of the generalized hypergeometric functions and the associated Frobenius structure of the deformation equation. *Mailing Add:* Dept Math Univ Minn Minneapolis MN 55455

SPERBER, WILLIAM HENRY, b Sturgeon Bay, Wis, Feb 15, 41; m 63; c 2. MICROBIOLOGY, BIOCHEMISTRY. *Educ:* Univ Wis-Madison, BS, 64, MS, 67, PhD(bact), 69. *Prof Exp:* Chief microbiol sect, Best Foods Res Ctr Div, CPC Int, Inc, 69-72; scientist microbiol sect, Res & Develop Ctr, 72-74, sr scientist, 74-77, RES ASSOC, CORP MICROBIOL, PILLSBURY CO, 77- *Mem:* Am Soc Microbiologists; NY Acad Sci; Soc Appl Bacteriol; Inst Food Technol; AAAS. *Res:* Food microbiology, lactics, osmophilics, food poisoning organisms, evolution, philosophy of science. *Mailing Add:* Pillsbury Co Res & Develop Ctr 311 Second St SE Minneapolis MN 55414

SPERELAKIS, NICK, b Joliet, Ill, Mar 3, 30; m 60; c 6. PHYSIOLOGY, BIOPHYSICS. *Educ:* Univ Ill, BS, 54, MS, 55, PhD(physiol), 57. *Prof Exp:* Asst physiol, Univ Ill, 54-57; from instr to assoc prof, Western Reserve Univ, 57-66; PROF PHYSIOL, SCH MED, UNIV VA, 66- *Concurrent Pos:* Estab investr, Am Heart Asn, 61-66; hon res assoc biophys, Univ Col, Univ London; vis prof, Ctr Advan Studies, Mex, 72 & Univ St Andrews, Scotland, 72-73; assoc ed, Circulation Res J, 70-75; chmn, Steering Comt Cell & Gen Physiol Sect, Am Physiol Soc, 81-82. *Mem:* Am Physiol Soc; Soc Gen Physiologists; Int Soc Heart Res; Cardiac Muscle Soc; Biophys Soc. *Res:* Electrophysiology of nerve, muscle and muscle ultrastructure; transmission of excitation in cardiac and smooth muscles; excitation-contraction coupling; hormone-membrane interaction; active ion transport; membrane properties; mechanism of action of calcium-antagonistic drugs; electrophysiology of cultured heart cells; developmental changes in electrical properties of the heart; electrical properties of myocardial slow channels. *Mailing Add:* Dept Physiol Univ Va Sch Med Charlottesville VA 22903

SPERGEL, MARTIN SAMUEL, b New York, NY, Sept 13, 37; m 59; c 3. ASTROPHYSICS, HIGH ENERGY PHYSICS. *Educ:* Rensselaer Polytech Inst, BS, 59; Univ Rochester, MA, 61, PhD(physics), 64. *Prof Exp:* Physicist, Indust Nucleonics Corp, 56 & Xerox Corp, 60; recitation instr basic physics, Univ Rochester, 59-61, res asst elem particles, 61-63; res scientist, Grumman Aircraft Corp, 63-67; assoc prof, 67-80, PROF PHYSICS, YORK COL, GRAD SCH & UNIV CTR, CITY UNIV NEW YORK, 80-, CHMN DEPT, 72- *Concurrent Pos:* Adj asst prof, C W Post Col, 65-; vis lectr astron, State Univ NY Stony Brook, 66-67; vis res scientist, Brookhaven Nat Labs, 75-; prin investr, NASA, 78-81. *Mem:* AAAS; Am Phys Soc; Am Geophys Union; Inst Elec & Electronics Eng. *Res:* Planetary physics; interactions of cosmic rays with interplanetary and interstellar matter; molecules in space; radiation environment of solar system; solid state. *Mailing Add:* Dept Physics York Col Jamaica NY 11432

SPERGEL, PHILIP, b New York, NY, Mar 5, 26; m 48; c 2. INSTRUMENTATION, ELECTRICAL ENGINEERING. *Educ:* City Col New York, BEE, 48; NY Univ, MEE, 51. *Prof Exp:* Proj engr, Sperry Gyroscope Co, 48-54; chief engr, Indust Nucleonics Corp, 54-57 & Epsco, Inc, 57-61; mem staff, Mitre Corp, 61-62; dir eng, Baird Atomic, Inc, 62-67; vpres res & develop, 67-74, VPRES CORP QUAL ASSURANCE, INSTRUMENTATION LAB, INC, 74- *Mem:* Am Soc Qual Control; Inst Elec & Electronics Engrs; Asn Advan Med Instrumentation. *Res:* Development of optical, electronic, nuclear, mechanical and chemical instruments to meet specific and general purpose applications. *Mailing Add:* Instrumentation Lab Inc 113 Hartwell Ave Lexington MA 02173

SPERLEY, RICHARD JON, b Staples, Minn, May 28, 39. ORGANIC CHEMISTRY. *Educ:* Concordia Col, BA, 61; Univ Minn, Minneapolis, PhD(org chem), 66. *Prof Exp:* Res chemist, Res Ctr, Uniroyal Inc, NJ, 66-72, SR RES SCIENTIST, TIRE DIV, UNIROYAL INC, 72- *Mem:* Am Chem Soc; Sigma Xi. *Res:* Polymer and elastomer degradation. *Mailing Add:* 5168 Hale Ct Troy MI 48098

SPERLING, HARRY GEORGE, b New York, NY, Aug 26, 24; m 50; c 2. VISION, PSYCHOPHYSICS. *Educ:* Univ Pa, AB, 44; New Sch Social Res, MSc, 46; Columbia Univ, PhD(psychol), 53. *Prof Exp:* Jr instr psychol, Johns Hopkins Univ, 47-48; res psychologist, US Naval Med Res Lab, 48-52, chief psychophys res sect, 52-58; chief colorimetry sect, 58-59; from sr scientist to mgr manned systs sci systs & res div, Honeywell Inc, 59-67; PROF OPHTHAL, MED SCH & DIR, SENSORY SCI CTR, UNIV TEX HEALTH SCI CTR, HOUSTON, 67-, PROF NEUROL SCI, GRAD SCH, 80- *Concurrent Pos:* Consult, Int Comn Illum, 59-; clin assoc prof, Univ Minn, 61-67; mem, Armed Forces-Nat Res Coun Comt Vision & chmn working group laser-eye effects, 66-70; adj prof, Baylor Col Med, 67- & Rice Univ, 72-; mem, Nat Adv Eye Coun, NIH, 75-79. *Mem:* Assoc Res Vision & Ophthal; fel Optical Soc Am; Psychonom Soc; Neurosci Soc. *Res:* Psychophysical, electrophysiological and anatomical studies of color and brightness vision. *Mailing Add:* Sensory Sci Ctr Univ Tex Grad Sch Biomed Sci Houston TX 77025

SPERLING, JACOB L, b Linz, Austria, Jan 3, 49; US citizen; m 78; c 1. PLASMA PHYSICS, HEALTH PHYSICS. *Educ:* Columbia Univ, BS, 71; Princeton Univ, MA, 73, PhD(plasma physics), 75. *Prof Exp:* Sr scientist plasma physics, Gen Atomic Co, 75-78; staff scientist, 78-80, SR SCIENTIST ENERGY, JAYCOR, 80- *Mem:* Am Phys Soc. *Res:* Theoretical plasma physics; health physics aspects of radioactivity; coal physics. *Mailing Add:* Jaycor PO Box 85154 San Diego CA 92138

SPERLING, LESLIE HOWARD, b Yonkers, NY, Feb 19, 32; m 57; c 2. POLYMER CHEMISTRY. *Educ:* Univ Fla, BS, 54; Duke Univ, MA, 57, PhD, 58. *Prof Exp:* Res chemist, Buckeye Cellulose Corp, Procter & Gamble Co, 58-65; res assoc phys chem, Princeton Univ, 65-67; assoc prof, 67-77, PROF, DEPT CHEM ENG & MAT RES CTR, LEHIGH UNIV, 77- *Mem:* Am Chem Soc; Am Inst Chem Engrs. *Res:* Physical chemistry of cellulose; physical and mechanical properties of polymers; polymer blends, particularly interpenetrating polymer networks; castor oil-based interpenetrating polymer networks; noise damping polymer systems; isomeric graft copolymer and interpenetrating polymer network nomenclature. *Mailing Add:* Coxe Lab No 32 Lehigh Univ Bethlehem PA 18015

SPERLING, MARK ALEXANDER, b Lodz, Poland, Sept 9, 38; Australian citizen; m 66; c 2. ENDOCRINOLOGY, DIABETES. *Educ:* Univ Melbourne, MB & BS, 62; Am Bd Pediat, dipl, 70. *Prof Exp:* From asst prof to assoc prof, 70-78, PROF PEDIAT & ASSOC PROF MED, COL MED, UNIV CINCINNATI, 78- *Concurrent Pos:* Fel endocrinol, Children's Hosp, Pittsburgh, 68-70; prin investr, NIH res grants, 72-; NIH res career develop award, 75-80; mem med adv bd, Juvenile Diabetes Found, 78; dir, Dept Endocrinol, Children's Hosp, Cincinnati, 78- *Mem:* Am Soc Clin Invest; Endocrine Soc; Am Diabetes Asn; Soc Pediat Res. *Res:* Hormonal control of carbohydrate metabolism; perinatal glucose homeostasis; insulin and glucagon receptors; endocrinology of hypertension; endocrinology of growth and development. *Mailing Add:* Dept of Pediat Endocrinol Children's Hosp Med Ctr Cincinnati OH 45229

SPERO, CAESAR A(NTHONY), JR, b Newport, RI, Oct 3, 21. MECHANICAL & SYSTEMS ENGINEERING. *Educ:* Mass Inst Technol, BS, 44; Univ Northern Colo, MS, 77. *Prof Exp:* Proj engr equip design, Owens-Corning Fiberglas Corp, 46-50, eng mgr, 50-52; staff sci asst, Naval Underwater Ord Sta, 52-55, head, Eng Dept, 55-60, head, Testing & Eval Dept, 60-61, head, Develop Dept, 61-64, head, Shipborne Equip Dept, 64-65, assoc dir, Systs Develop, 65-71, chief, Res & Develop, Newport Lab, 71, assoc dir, Weapons, 71-72, dir, Systs Develop, 72-76, assoc tech dir, Prod Lines, 76-78, dep tech dir, Naval Underwater Syts Ctr, 78-80; VPRES, OSD, GOULD INC, 80- *Mem:* Math Asn Am. *Res:* Complex system development from conceptual stage through actual manufacture, installation and operational testing. *Mailing Add:* 325 Mail Coach Rd Portsmouth RI 02871

SPERO, LEONARD, b New York, NY, May 30, 21; m 43; c 4. BIOCHEMISTRY. *Educ:* City Col New York, BS, 41; Univ Wis, MS, 43, PhD(biochem), 48. *Prof Exp:* Asst, Univ Wis, 42-44 & 46-48; biochemist, US Army Med Res Inst Infectious Dis, 48-63, chief, Chem Br, 63-71, biochemist, Path Div, 71-75, asst chief, Path Div, 75-81; CONSULT, 81- *Concurrent Pos:* Secy Army res & study fel, 60; lectr, Georgetown Univ, 65. *Mem:* Am Soc Biol Chem. *Res:* Protein chemistry; isolation and purification; reactive groups; immunochemistry; bacterial toxins. *Mailing Add:* 635 Schley Ave Frederick MD 21701

SPERONELLO, BARRY KEVEN, b Passaic, NJ, July, 29, 50; m 75. HETEROGENEOUS CATALYSIS, MATERIALS SCIENCE. *Educ:* Rutgers Univ, BS, 72, MS, 75, PhD(ceramic eng), 76. *Prof Exp:* Res & proj leader, 76-81, RES GROUP LEADER, ENGELHARD CORP, 81- *Mem:* Am Ceramic Soc; NAm Catalysis Soc. *Res:* Synthesis and properties of oxide materials; physical and catalytic properties of oxide catalysts. *Mailing Add:* 283 Manning Ave River Edge NJ 07661

SPEROS, PERRY, visual physiology, electrophysiology, see previous edition

SPERRY, CLAUDE J, JR, b Greenwood, SC, Aug 8, 25; m 48; c 1. ELECTRICAL ENGINEERING. *Educ:* Clemson Col, BEE, 48; Univ Ill, MS, 54. *Prof Exp:* From instr to assoc prof, 48-65, PROF ELEC ENG, TULANE UNIV, 65-, RES ASSOC PHYSIOL, 51- *Mem:* Inst Elec & Electronics Engrs. *Res:* Electricity in medical research, especially remote recording of subcortical potentials. *Mailing Add:* Dept of Elec Eng Tulane Univ New Orleans LA 70118

SPERRY, JAY FRANKLIN, microbial physiology, see previous edition

SPERRY, JOHN JEROME, systematic botany, deceased

SPERRY, ROGER WOLCOTT, b Hartford, Conn, Aug 20, 13; m 49; c 2. NEUROBIOLOGY. *Educ:* Oberlin Col, BA, 35, AM, 37; Univ Chicago, PhD, 41. *Prof Exp:* Res fel, Harvard & Yerkes Labs, 41-46; asst prof anat, Univ Chicago, 46-52, assoc prof, 52-53; HIXON PROF PSYCHOBIOL, CALIF INST TECHNOL, 54- *Concurrent Pos:* Sect chief, Nat Inst Neurol Dis, NIH, 52-53. *Honors & Awards:* Nobel Prize in Med, 81; Howard Crosby Warren Medal, Soc Exp Psychologists, 69. *Mem:* Nat Acad Sci; AAAS; Am Psychol Asn; Am Physiol Soc; Brain Res Orgn. *Res:* Brain organization and neural mechanisms. *Mailing Add:* Calif Inst Technol 1201 E California St Pasadena CA 91175

SPERRY, THEODORE MELROSE, b Toronto, Ont, Feb 20, 07; US citizen; m 35. BOTANY, ECOLOGY. *Educ:* Butler Univ, BS, 29; Univ Ill, MS, 31, PhD(bot), 33. *Prof Exp:* Asst bot, Univ Ill, 29-32; timber cruiser & estimator, US Forest Serv, Ill, 33-34, tech foreman, 35-36; sr foreman ecol, Nat Park Serv, Wis, 36-41; from asst prof to prof bot & ecol, 46-74, EMER PROF BOT & ECOL & CUR HERBARIUM, PITTSBURG STATE UNIV, KANS, 74- *Concurrent Pos:* Consult, Nat Inst Study Agr of Belgian Congo, 51-52; secy-treas, Grassland Res Found, 54-58. *Mem:* Nat Parks Asn; Ecol Soc Am; Am Soc Plant Taxon; Wilderness Soc. *Res:* Grassland ecology; plant taxonomy; biological conservation. *Mailing Add:* 1413 S College Pittsburg KS 66762

SPERRY, WILLARD CHARLES, b Dunsmuir, Calif, Nov 29, 31; m 66; c 2. NUCLEAR PHYSICS. *Educ:* Stanford Univ, BS, 54; Univ Calif, Davis, MA, 67, PhD(physics), 68. *Prof Exp:* Physicist, Aerojet-Gen Corp, 56-60; asst prof, 66-68, ASSOC PROF PHYSICS, CENT WASH UNIV, 68- *Res:* Nuclear structure by means of mesic atoms; improvement of undergraduate physics laboratories. *Mailing Add:* Dept of Physics Cent Wash Univ Ellensburg WA 98926

SPERTI, GEORGE SPERI, b Covington, Ky, Jan 17, 00. BIOPHYSICS. *Educ:* Univ Cincinnati, EE, 23. *Hon Degrees:* ScD, Univ Dayton, 34, Duquesne Univ, 36, Bryant Univ, 57, Caldwell Col, 74, Thomas More Col, 75 & Xavier Univ, 78. *Prof Exp:* Asst chief meter labs, Union Gas & Elec Co, Ind, 23; asst, Univ Cincinnati, 24-25, res prof & dir basic sci lab, 26-35; res prof biophys, 35-58, mem bd regents, 35-53, DIR RES, ST THOMAS INST, 35-, PRES, 58- *Concurrent Pos:* Mem bd dirs, Gen Develop Labs, Inc, New York, 31-35 & Franklin Corp; trustee, The Athenaeum, Ohio, 35-53. *Honors & Awards:* Mendel Medal; Am Acad Dermat & Syphilol Award, 46. *Mem:* Pontifical Acad Sci; Am Chem Soc; Optical Soc Am; Am Phys Soc; Am Soc Aged (treas, 55). *Res:* Biochemistry; biology; physics; quantum theory in biology; medicine; light treatment process; biodynes. *Mailing Add:* St Thomas Inst 1840 Madison Rd Cincinnati OH 45206

SPERTZEL, RICHARD O, b Adams Co, Pa, Feb 9, 33; m 61; c 2. VIROLOGY, RADIOBIOLOGY. *Educ:* Univ Pa, BA, 55, VMD, 59; Univ Rochester, MS, 62; Univ Notre Dame, PhD(microbiol), 70. *Prof Exp:* Asst dep chief, Staff Res Opers, 78, dep chief, 78-79, exec officer, US Army Med Res & Develop Command, 79-80, dep coordr, Army Med Res Inst Infectious Dis, 80-81, DEP, VET ACTIV, USA MEDDAC PANAMA, 81- *Concurrent Pos:* Mem adv coun, Inst Lab Animal Res, Nat Res Coun-Nat Acad Sci. *Honors & Awards:* Nat Defense Serv Medal, 68; Superior Serv Award, USDA, 71; Meritorious Serv Medal, Off Surg Gen, Dept Army, 72. *Mem:* US Animal Health Asn; Am Soc Microbiol; Conf Pub Health Veterinarians; Am Vet Med Asn; Am Acad Microbiol. *Res:* Medical virology and virus host interaction as related to development of disease processes. *Mailing Add:* US Army Med Res & Develop Command Ft Detrick Frederick MD 21701

SPESSARD, DWIGHT RINEHART, b Westerville, Ohio, July 6, 19; m 43; c 2. ORGANIC CHEMISTRY. *Educ:* Otterbein Col, BS, 41; Western Reserve Univ, PhD(inorg & org chem), 44. *Prof Exp:* Group leader, Lubrication Sect, Chem Div, Naval Res Lab, 44-47; res assoc chem, Gen Elec Res Lab, 47-49; from asst prof to assoc prof, Muskingum Col, 49-53; from asst prof to assoc prof, 53-60, chmn dept, 58-61, PROF CHEM, DENISON UNIV, 60-, WICKENDEN CHAIR, 66- *Mem:* Am Chem Soc. *Res:* Organophosphorus, organosilicon and organofluorine chemistry. *Mailing Add:* Dept of Chem Denison Univ Granville OH 43023

SPESSARD, GARY OLIVER, b Orange, Calif, Sept 27, 44; m 68; c 1. SYNTHETIC ORGANIC CHEMISTRY. *Educ:* Harvey Mudd Col, BS, 66; Univ Wis-Madison, MS, 68; Wesleyan Univ, PhD(org chem), 71. *Prof Exp:* Fel org chem, Univ Alta, 70-72; vis res assoc, Ohio State Univ, 72-73; asst prof, 73-79, ASSOC PROF CHEM, ST OLAF COL, 79- *Concurrent Pos:* vis assoc prof chem, Univ Utah, 79-80. *Mem:* Am Chem Soc. *Res:* Synthetic organic chemistry of small ring compounds and synthesis of analogs for enzymatic cyclization of farnesol; synthetic organic and natural products chemistry. *Mailing Add:* Dept of Chem St Olaf Col Northfield MN 55057

SPETZLER, HARTMUT AUGUST WERNER, rock mechanics, see previous edition

SPHON, JAMES AMBROSE, b Luxor, Pa, Nov 4, 39; m 67; c 3. MASS SPECTROMETRY. *Educ:* St Vincent Col, BS, 66; Wayne State Univ, PhD(org chem), 77. *Prof Exp:* Chemist, 65-67, res chemist, 67-75, SUPVY CHEMIST, MASS SPECTROMETRY LAB, FOOD & DRUG ADMIN, 75- *Mem:* Am Chem Soc; Am Soc Mass Spectrometry. *Res:* Application of mass spectrometry to structure elucidation and method development for components of foods: pesticides, mycotoxins, direct & indirect food additives and veterinary drugs. *Mailing Add:* Food & Drug Admin HFF-459 200 C St SW Washington DC 20204

SPIALTER, LEONARD, b Newark, NJ, Jan 18, 23; m 46; c 2. ORGANIC CHEMISTRY, COMPUTER SYSTEMS. *Educ:* Rutgers Univ, BS, 44, PhD(chem), 49; Polytech Inst Brooklyn, MS, 48. *Prof Exp:* Res chemist, Montclair Res Corp, NJ, 44-47; instr org chem, Univ Col, Rutgers Univ, 48-49; fel free radicals, Harvard Univ, 49-51; from res chemist to sr scientist & head org sect, Chem Res Lab, Aerospace Res Labs, Wright-Patterson AFB, 51-75; DIR, INSTRUMENTORS I-V, 75- *Mem:* AAAS; Am Chem Soc; Am Inst Chemists; The Chem Soc; Electrochem Soc. *Res:* Organosilanes; amines; molecular rearrangements; free radicals; laboratory automation; information storage-retrieval; computer-based nomenclature; liquid fuel/byproducts from agricultural residues; computer-based information systems; computer-aided manufacturing. *Mailing Add:* 2536 England Ave Dayton OH 45406

SPICER, DANIEL SHIELDS, JR, biochemistry, deceased

SPICER, DONALD Z, b St Paul, Minn, Mar 15, 37; m 68; c 3. MATHEMATICS. *Educ:* Univ Minn, BA, 59, PhD(math), 65; Columbia Univ, MA, 60. *Prof Exp:* From actg asst prof to asst prof math, Univ Calif, Los Angeles, 65-67; asst prof, Univ Ky, 67-70; asst prof, 70-73, ASSOC PROF MATH, VASSAR COL, 73-, ASSOC DEAN COL, 80- *Concurrent Pos:* Proj dir, Fund Improvement Postsecondary Educ, HEW. *Mem:* Am Math Soc; Math Asn Am. *Res:* Algebra, primarily structure of rings. *Mailing Add:* Dept of Math Vassar Col Poughkeepsie NY 12601

SPICER, JOHN A, mathematics, see previous edition

SPICER, LEONARD DALE, b Detroit, Mich, July 7, 42; m 68. PHYSICAL CHEMISTRY. *Educ:* Univ Mich, BSch, 64; Yale Univ, PhD(phys chem), 68. *Prof Exp:* Assoc chem kinetics, Univ Wash, 68-69; from asst prof phys chem to assoc prof, 69-78, PROF PHYS CHEM, UNIV UTAH, 78-, ASSOC DEAN GRAD SCH, 80- *Concurrent Pos:* Dreyfus Found fel, 71-77. *Mem:* AAAS; Am Chem Soc; Am Phys Soc. *Res:* Hot atom chemistry; high energy and thermal kinetics; photoassisted catalysis; intermolecular vibrational energy transfer; unimolecular reactions; atmospheric chemistry; nuclear medicine with positron emitters. *Mailing Add:* Dept of Chem Univ of Utah Salt Lake City UT 84112

SPICER, SAMUEL SHERMAN, JR, b Denver, Colo, Aug 12, 14; m 41; c 3. PATHOLOGY. *Educ:* Univ Colo, BS, 36, MD, 39. *Prof Exp:* Intern, Univ Hosp, Univ Wis, 39-40; from asst surgeon to med dir, Nutrit Lab, Lab Phys Biol & Lab Exp Path, NIH, 40-55, chief sect biophys histol, 61-66; PROF PATH, MED UNIV SC, 66- *Mem:* Histochem Soc; Am Soc Cell Biol; Am Soc Exp Path. *Res:* Nutrition; folic acid deficiency; malariology; industrial toxicology; biochemistry of erythrocytes; muscle protein chemistry; histochemistry and ultrastructural cytochemistry of carbohydrates; basic proteins and enzymes; immunocytochemistry-hormones and cell enzymes; experimental pathology of genetic diseases including cystic fibrosis. *Mailing Add:* Dept of Path 171 Ashley Ave Charleston SC 29403

SPICER, WILLIAM EDWARD, b Baton Rouge, La, Sept 7, 29; m 51; c 3. SOLID STATE PHYSICS. *Educ:* Col William & Mary, BS, 49; Mass Inst Technol, SB, 51; Univ Mo, MA, 53, PhD(physics), 55. *Hon Degrees:* Dr Technol, Univ Linköping, Sweden, 75. *Prof Exp:* Res physicist, RCA Labs, 55-62; from assoc prof to prof elec eng, 62-78, dep dir, Stanford Synchrotron Radiation Proj, 73-75, Stanford W Ascherman Prof Eng, 78-80, PROF ELEC ENG, STANFORD UNIV, 80-, CONSULT DIR, STANFORD SYNCHROTRON RADIATION PROJ, 75- *Concurrent Pos:* Consult, Varian Assocs; mem adv group electron devices, Dept Defense, 73; Guggenheim fel, 78- *Mem:* AAAS; Sigma Xi; Am Phys Soc. *Res:* Electronic structure and optical properties of solids and surfaces; photoelectric emission; semiconductors; alloys; amorphous solids; surface and interface states; surface science and catalysis. *Mailing Add:* Dept Elec Eng Stanford Univ Stanford CA 94305

SPICHER, JOHN L, b Belleville, Pa, Sept 12, 35; m 59; c 3. MEDICAL TECHNOLOGY. *Educ:* Eastern Mennonite Col, BS, 58; Geisinger Med Ctr, MT, 64. *Prof Exp:* Res asst endocrinol, Med Col Va, 60; res asst chromatog, Geisinger Med Ctr, 62-64, asst instr med technol, 64-66; res asst path, Sch Med, Univ Pittsburgh, 66-68; SR ENGR HUMAN SCI, WESTINGHOUSE RES & DEVELOP, WESTINGHOUSE ELEC CORP, 68- *Mem:* Am Asn Clin Chemists; Am Soc Clin Pathologists. *Res:* Development of planning methods for health care systems which relate to consumer need, demands and available resources. *Mailing Add:* Box 208 A Rd 6 Irwin PA 15642

SPICHER, ROBERT G, b Pittsburgh, Pa, Apr 24, 35; m 59, 81; c 2. SANITARY ENGINEERING. *Educ:* Cornell Univ, BCE, 58; Univ Calif, Berkeley, MS, 59; Wash Univ, St Louis, ScD(environ & sanit eng), 63. *Prof Exp:* Prod engr, Shell Oil Co, Calif, 59-60; asst prof sanit & civil eng, Univ Miami, 63-65; assoc dean grad studies, 79-80, PROF SANIT & CIVIL ENG, SAN JOSE STATE UNIV, 65- *Concurrent Pos:* Mem, Atomic Energy Comn Summer Inst Nuclear Eng, 64; dir, Regional Prof Adv Serv Ctr, Off Civil Defense, 69-72. *Honors & Awards:* Lincoln Arc Welding Struct Nat Award, 58; Award of Merit, Am Chem Soc, 64. *Mem:* Am Soc Civil Engrs; Am Water Works Asn; Water Pollution Control Fedn. *Res:* Environmental engineering; permanganate oxidation of organic contaminants; cannery waste treatment; sanitary engineering aspects of shelters; treatment of photographic wastes; sanitary landfill stabilization; radioactive contamination of water; fuel gas production from biomass. *Mailing Add:* Dept of Civil Eng San Jose State Univ San Jose CA 95192

SPICKERMAN, WILLIAM REED, b Council Bluffs, Iowa, Dec 28, 25; m 57. APPLIED MATHEMATICS. *Educ:* Univ Omaha, BA, 49, MS, 53; Xavier Univ, MS, 58; Univ Ky, PhD(curriculum), 65. *Prof Exp:* Teacher high sch, Univ Iowa, 49-50; engr aid, Omaha Dist, Mo River Div, Corps of Engr, 51-52; teacher high sch, Iowa, 52-56; tech engr, Jet Engine Dept, Gen Elec Co, Ohio, 56-57; teacher high sch, Ohio, 57-58; engr, Avco Corp, 58-61; specialist-engr, Goodyear Aircraft Corp, 61-62; sr scientist, Spindletop Res Inc, Ky, 65-67; assoc prof, 67-72, PROF MATH, EAST CAROLINA UNIV, 72- *Mem:* Am Math Soc; Math Asn Am; Soc Indust & Appl Math; assoc Opers Res Soc Am. *Res:* Mathematics education. *Mailing Add:* Dept Math East Carolina Univ Greenville NC 27834

SPIEGEL, ALLEN DAVID, b New York, NY, June 11, 27; m 55; c 3. PUBLIC HEALTH, COMMUNICATIONS. *Educ:* Brooklyn Col, AB, 47; Columbia Univ, MPH, 54; Brandeis Univ, PhD(social welfare), 69. *Prof Exp:* Health educr to chief radio & TV unit, New York City Health Dept, 51-61; health educ assoc, Med Found, Inc, 61-66; ASSOC PROF MED EDUC, STATE UNIV NY DOWNSTATE MED CTR, 69- *Concurrent Pos:* WHO fel, Israel Med Schs, 74; consult to comnr, Social & Rehab Serv, Dept Health, Educ & Welfare, 70; commun consult, Health Info Systs, Inc, 70-71; curriculum consult, Grad Prog Health Care Admin, Baruch Col, 70-; health manpower consult, NJ Regional Med Prog, 72; adj prof, St Francis Col, 74-76; fac, Staff Col, NIMH, 79; consult, Cancer Proj, Urban Health Inst, 79 & Home Care Proj, Temple Univ, 81. *Mem:* Am Pub Health Asn; Health Educ Media Asn; Am Social Asn; Am Teachers Prev Med; Soc Pub Health Educators. *Res:* Medical sociology; medical communications; public health education; patient education; curriculum development; mass media health program. *Mailing Add:* Dept Prev Med & Commun Health State Univ NY Downstate Med Ctr Brooklyn NY 11203

SPIEGEL, ALLEN J, b New York, NY, Sept 17, 32. PHARMACY, PHARMACEUTICAL CHEMISTRY. *Educ:* Columbia Univ, BS, 53, MS, 55; Univ Fla, PhD(pharm), 57. *Prof Exp:* Res assoc, Pharmaceut Res & Develop Dept, Chas Pfizer & Co, Inc, 57-66, mgr res coordr, New Prod Dept, Pfizer Int, 66-69, patent agt, Legal Div, 69-76, mgr foreign patents, 76-81, ASST DIR FOREIGN PATENTS, PFIZER INC, 81- *Mem:* Am Pharmaceut Asn; Am Chem Soc; NY Acad Sci. *Res:* Pharmaceutical product development; research administration; patent law. *Mailing Add:* Legal Div Pfizer Inc 235 E 42nd St New York NY 10017

SPIEGEL, EDWARD A, b New York, NY, Mar 7, 31. ASTROPHYSICS. *Educ:* Univ Calif, Los Angeles, BA, 52; Univ Mich, MS, 54, MA, 56, PhD(astron), 58. *Prof Exp:* From instr to asst prof astron, Univ Calif, 58-60; res scientist, Inst Math Sci, NY Univ, 60-65; from assoc prof to prof physics, 65-69; PROF ASTRON, COLUMBIA UNIV, 69- *Concurrent Pos:* Peyton advan fel, Princeton Univ, 59-60; assoc, Woods Hole Oceanog Inst, 59-; consult, Goddard Inst Space Studies, NASA, 60-69; NSF sr fel, 66-67. *Mem:* Am Astron Soc; Int Astron Union; NY Acad Sci. *Res:* Radiative and gas dynamical processes in stars and interstellar gas. *Mailing Add:* Dept of Astron Columbia Univ New York NY 10027

SPIEGEL, EUGENE, b Brooklyn, NY, Sept 16, 41; m 68; c 1. MATHEMATICS. *Educ:* Brooklyn Col, BS, 61; Mass Inst Technol, PhD(math), 65. *Prof Exp:* Instr math, Mass Inst Technol, 64-65; Bateman res fel, Calif Inst Technol, 65-66, instr, 66-67; from asst prof to assoc prof, 67-78, PROF MATH, UNIV CONN, 78-, DEPT HEAD, 81- *Concurrent Pos:* Vis prof, Ecole Polytechnique Federal, Lausanne, 73, Weizmann Inst, Rehovot, 81. *Mem:* Math Asn Am; Am Math Soc. *Res:* Algebra; combinatorics; coding theory. *Mailing Add:* Dept Math Univ Conn Storrs CT 06268

SPIEGEL, EVELYN SCLUFER, b Philadelphia, Pa, Mar 20, 24; m 55; c 2. DEVELOPMENTAL BIOLOGY. *Educ:* Temple Univ, BA, 47; Bryn Mawr Col, MA, 51; Univ Pa, PhD(zool), 54. *Prof Exp:* Asst to prog dir regulatory biol, NSF, 54-55; res assoc prof, 62-78, RES PROF BIOL, DARTMOUTH COL, 78- *Concurrent Pos:* Lalor fel, Univ Pa, 52-53; Am Cancer Soc fel, 61-62; vis res assoc, Calif Inst Technol, 64-65; vis assoc res biologist, Univ Calif, San Diego, 70-71; vis res scientist, Nat Inst Med Res, Eng, 71; NIH guest investr, 75-76; mem, Corp Marine Biol Lab, 75-, bd trustees, 80-; vis prof, Bioctr, Univ Basel, 79-82. *Mem:* Soc Develop Biol. *Res:* Ultrastructural and immunofluorescence studies of cell reaggregation and cell adhesion. *Mailing Add:* Dept Biol Sci Dartmouth Col Hanover NH 03755

SPIEGEL, HERBERT ELI, b New York, NY, July 7, 33; m 58; c 5. BIOCHEMISTRY, CLINICAL CHEMISTRY. *Educ:* Brooklyn Col, BS, 56; George Washington Univ, MS, 61; Rutgers Univ, New Brunswick, PhD(biochem, physiol), 66. *Prof Exp:* Sr asst health officer biochem pharmacol, NIH, 57-62; sr biochemist, Schering Corp, 62-64; clin chemist, Mountainside Hosp, 64-67; chief clin chemist, 67-72, dir, Dept Clin Biochem, 72-80, DIR, DEPT CLIN LAB RES, HOFFMANN-LA ROCHE INC, 80- *Concurrent Pos:* Mem comn toxicol, Int Union Pure & Appl Chem, 74- *Honors & Awards:* Am Asn Clin Chemists Awards, 72 & 77. *Mem:* Am Chem Soc; fel Am Asn Clin Chemists; fel Am Inst Chemists; fel Nat Acad Clin Biochemists; Am Soc Clin Path. *Res:* Biochemical pharmacology, especially catecholamines; clinical chemistry methods, especially fluorimetry and radioactivity; drug effects on clinical chemistry. *Mailing Add:* Dept of Clin Biochem Hoffmann-La Roche Inc Nutley NJ 07110

SPIEGEL, LEONARD EMILE, b New York, NY, Sept 12, 24; m 50; c 4. ECOLOGY. *Educ:* Drew Univ, AB, 48; Northwestern Univ, MS, 50; Cornell Univ, PhD(wildlife mgt), 54. *Prof Exp:* Asst wildlife mgt, State Dept Conserv, NY & Cornell Univ, 51-53; game mgt supvr, Div Wildlife, Ohio Dept Natural Resources, 53-55; instr biol, Alpena Community Col, 55-57; from asst prof to assoc prof, Cent Mich Univ, 57-63; asst prof, Cornell Univ, 63; Chmn Dept, 74-81, PROF BIOL, MONMOUTH COL, NJ, 63- *Concurrent Pos:* Environ consult, 67-; mem, NJ State Mosquito Control Comn, 76- *Mem:* Wildlife Soc; Am Inst Biol Sci. *Res:* Ecology of game animals; plant ecology; plant soil wildlife interrelationships. *Mailing Add:* Dept Biol Monmouth Col West Long Branch NJ 07764

SPIEGEL, MELVIN, b New York, NY, Dec 10, 25; m 55; c 2. BIOLOGY. *Educ:* Univ Ill, BS, 48; Univ Rochester, PhD(zool), 52. *Hon Degrees:* MA, Dartmouth Col, 66. *Prof Exp:* Res fel zool, Univ Rochester, 52-53; USPHS res fel biol, Calif Inst Technol, 53-55; asst prof, Colby Col, 55-59; from asst prof to assoc prof zool, 59-66, chmn dept biol sci, 72-74, PROF BIOL, DARTMOUTH COL, 66- *Concurrent Pos:* Mem, NIH Cell Biol Study Sect, 66-70; vis sr res biologist, Univ Calif, San Diego, 70-71; vis prof, Nat Inst Med Res, Eng, 71; bd corp mem & mem bd trustees, Marine Biol Lab, 75-79; prog dir develop biol, NSF, 75-76; mem exec comt, Bd Trustees, Marine Biol Lab, 78-81; vis prof, Bioctr, Univ Basel, 79-82. *Mem:* Am Soc Cell Biologists; Soc Gen Physiol; Am Soc Zoologists; fel AAAS; Int Soc Develop Biologists (secy-treas, 77-81). *Res:* Developmental biology; protein synthesis; fertilization; cell reaggregation; specificity of cell adhesion. *Mailing Add:* Dept Biol Sci Dartmouth Col Hanover NH 03755

SPIEGEL, VALENTIN, JR, b Mt Vernon, NY, Dec 25, 24; m 51; c 3. PHYSICS. *Educ:* Cath Univ Am, BA, 50; Univ Notre Dame, PhD, 56. *Prof Exp:* PHYSICIST, NAT BUR STANDARDS, 55- *Concurrent Pos:* Study & res under Govt Employees Training Act, Cyclotron Lab, Max Planck Inst Nuclear Physics, Ger, 61-62. *Mem:* Am Phys Soc. *Res:* Neutron dosimetry; neutron and nuclear physics. *Mailing Add:* Radiation Physics Nat Bur of Standards Washington DC 20234

SPIEGEL, ZANE, b Middletown, NY, Nov 6, 26; m 59; c 2. HYDROLOGY, GEOLOGY. *Educ:* Univ Chicago, BS, 49, MS, 52; NMex Inst Mining & Technol, PhD(earth Sci), 62. *Prof Exp:* Geologist hydrol, US Geol Surv, 49-53; water resources engr, NMex State Engr Off, 54-58; vis prof eng, Imp Col, Univ London, 63-64; proj mgr hydrol, UN Spec Fund, Argentina, 64-66; water resources engr, NMex State Eng Off, 66-71; CONSULT HYDROL, 71- *Concurrent Pos:* Fulbright lect grant, Univ de San Agustin, Arequipa, Peru, 58-59; water resources res fel, Water Resources Dept, Harvard Univ, 62-63; vis lectr, Univ Minn, Minneapolis, 67-68; vis assoc prof, NMex Inst Mining & Technol, 71; course coordr, Continuing Educ Dept, Col Santa Fe, 73-77; US Environ Protection Agency Extramural grant reviewer, 73-75; hydrologist, Ohio State Univ, 80-82. *Mem:* Fel Geol Soc Am; Am Soc Civil Engrs; Am Geophys Union; Am Quaternary Asn; Nat Water Well Asn. *Res:* Fundamental concepts of hydrology; impacts of wells on streamflow and estuary salinity; movement and removal of contaminating brines from fresh ground waters; Cenozoic geohydrology; environmental impact analysis. *Mailing Add:* PO Box 1541 Santa Fe NM 87501

SPIEGELBERG, HARRY LESTER, b New London, Wis, Apr 24, 36; m 60; c 4. PAPER CHEMISTRY. *Educ:* Univ Wis, BSChE, 59; Inst Paper Chem, MS, 63, PhD(mech, physics), 66; Univ Chicago, MBA, 80. *Prof Exp:* Instr mech, Univ Wis, 57-59; design engr, 59-61, res chemist, 65-68, mgr corp res & eng, New Concepts Lab, 68-73, dir contract res, 72-73, DIR RES & DEVELOP, FEMININE CARE PROD, CONSUMER BUS DIV, KIMBERLY-CLARK CORP, 73-, DIR RES & DEVELOP, CONSUMER & SERV TISSUE PROD, 79- *Concurrent Pos:* Chmn, Gordon Res Conf Chem & Physics of Paper, 71. *Mem:* Tech Asn Pulp & Paper Indust. *Res:* Mechanical properties of pulp fibers; mathematical analysis of screening systems; pulp mill design; innovative process; long range invention of new products; female reproductive physiology; absorbent materials. *Mailing Add:* 2017 N Eugene Appleton WI 54911

SPIEGELHALTER, ROLAND ROBERT, b Dubuque, Iowa, May 31, 23; m 46; c 2. ANALYTICAL CHEMISTRY. *Educ:* Carroll Col, PhB, 48; Univ Kans, MA, 50. *Prof Exp:* Anal chemist, Commercial Solvents Corp, 50-56; sr develop chemist, Chemstrand Corp, 56-64; asst plant chemist, Escambia Chem Corp, 64-69, CHIEF CHEMIST, ESCAMBIA PLANT, AIR PROD & CHEM, INC, 69- *Mem:* Am Chem Soc. *Res:* Titrimetry in nonaqueous solvents. *Mailing Add:* 4750 N Ninth Ave Pensacola FL 32503

SPIEGELMAN, CLIFFORD, b Bayshore, NY. STATISTICS, PROBABILITY. *Educ:* State Univ NY, Buffalo, BA, 70; Northwestern Univ, MS, 73, PhD(appl math), 76. *Prof Exp:* Asst prof statist, Fla State Univ, 76-77; MATH STATISTICIAN, STATIST ENG LAB, NAT BUR STANDARDS, 78- *Mem:* Inst Math Statist; Am Statist Asn; Am Math Soc. *Res:* Statistical methodology and applications to the physical and social sciences. *Mailing Add:* Statist Eng Lab Nat Bur of Standards Washington DC 20234

SPIEGELMAN, GERALD HENRY, b New York, NY, Oct 22, 38; m 60; c 3. ORGANIC CHEMISTRY, INDUSTRIAL CHEMISTRY. *Educ:* City Col New York, BS, 59; Columbia Univ, MA, 60; Stevens Inst Technol, PhD(chem), 69. *Prof Exp:* Chemist, Ultra Div, 60-64, sr res chemist, 67-72, group leader, 72-76, mgr res & develop, 76-79, ASST DIR CORP RES & DEVELOP, WITCO CHEM CORP, 79- *Mem:* Am Chem Soc; Am Oil Chemists Soc; Am Soc Testing & Mat; Am Textile Chemists & Colorists Soc. *Res:* Surfactants; detergents; organometallics; unit processes; process development; analytical chemistry. *Mailing Add:* Tech Ctr 100 Bauer Dr Oakland NJ 07436

SPIEGELMAN, MARTHA, b New York, NY, May 22, 36; m 64. EMBRYOLOGY, CYTOLOGY. *Educ:* Albertus Magnus Col, BA, 58; Columbia Univ, PhD(biol), 71. *Prof Exp:* Res fel develop genetics, Dept Anat, Med Col, Cornell Univ, 70-71, instr micros anat, 72-74, asst prof anat, 74-76; ASSOC DEVELOP GENETICS, MEM SLOAN-KETTERING CANCER CTR, 76- *Concurrent Pos:* Adj assoc prof anat, Med Col, Cornell Univ, 78-81. *Mem:* Soc Develop Biol; Am Soc Zoologists. *Res:* Fine structural analysis of genetic abnormalities in mouse embryos, especially cellular motility and cell-cell interactions during development. *Mailing Add:* Mem Sloan-Kettering Cancer Ctr New York NY 10021

SPIEGELMAN, SOLOMON, b New York, NY, Dec 14, 14; m; c 3. GENETICS, CANCER. *Educ:* City Col New York, BS, 39; Columbia Univ, MS, 42; Wash Univ, PhD(cellular physiol), 44. *Hon Degrees:* DSc, Rensselaer Polytech Inst, 66, Northwestern Univ, 66, St Louis Univ, 68, Univ Chicago,

70, Univ Ill, 75, NY Med Col, 75 & City Univ New York, 76; LLD, Univ Glasgow, 73; DPhil, Hebrew Univ, Jerusalem, 75. *Prof Exp:* Lectr physics, Wash Univ, 42-44, lectr appl math, 43-44, instr bact, Sch Med, 45-46, asst prof bact, 46-48; prof microbiol, Univ Ill, 49-69, mem, Ctr Advan Study, 64-69; PROF HUMAN GENETICS & DEVELOP & DIR, INST CANCER RES, COL PHYSICIANS & SURGEONS, COLUMBIA UNIV, 69- *Concurrent Pos:* USPHS spec fel, Univ Minn, 48-49; Jesup lectr, Columbia Univ, 63, univ lectr, 74, univ prof, 75; Ciba lectr, Inst Microbiol, Rutgers Univ, 64; Gehrmann lectr, Sch Med, Univ Ill, 67; O M Smith lectr chem, Okla State Univ, 67; Philips lectr, Haverford Col, 67; NIH Dyer lectr, 68; Harvey lectr, Harvey Soc, New York, 68; Seymour Korkes Mem lectr, Duke Univ, 68; Penn lectr, Univ Pa, 70; Walter R Bloor lectr, Univ Rochester, 70; Sigma Xi lectr, State Univ NY Downstate Med Ctr, 70; Distinguished lectr nat sci, Wash State Univ, 70; Karl August Forster lectr, Univ Mainz, 70; Louis Gross lectr, Med Ctr, NY Univ, 71; mem, Nat Cancer Adv Bd, 72; McGregory lectr, Colgate Univ, 72; Edwin W Schultz Mem lectr, Stanford Univ, 72; Daniel Laszlo lectr, Montefiore Hosp, 73; Shell lectr, Univ Calif, Davis, 73; F F Nord lectr biochem, Fordham Univ, 73; Mellon lectr, Univ Pittsburgh, 73; Marrs McLean lectr, Baylor Col Med, 74; S Steven Brodie Mem lectr, Jewish Mem Hosp, New York, 74; Merrell Nat Lect, Mt Sinai Hosp, New York, 76. *Honors & Awards:* Pasteur Award, Ill Soc Microbiol, 63; Award Cancer Res, Bertner Found, 68; Lila Gruber Mem Award Cancer Res, Am Acad Dermat, 72; Papanicolaou Award Cancer Res, 73; City of Hope Biomed Res Award, 73; Intra-Sci Medalist, Intra-Sci Res Found, 73; Distinguished Scholar Award, Hofstra Univ, 73; Albert Lasker Basic Med Res Award, 74. *Mem:* Nat Acad Sci; AAAS; Am Soc Microbiol; Am Soc Biol Chemists; NY Acad Sci. *Mailing Add:* Col Phys & Surg Inst of Cancer Res Columbia Univ 701 W 168th St New York NY 10032

SPIEGLER, KURT SAMUEL, b Vienna, Austria, May 31, 20; nat US; m 46; c 3. CHEMISTRY. *Educ:* Hebrew Univ, Israel, MSc & PhD(chem), 44. *Prof Exp:* Develop chemist, Anglo-Iranian Oil Co, 44-46; res physicist, Palestine Potash Co, 46-47; actg head water purification proj, Weizmann Inst Sci, 48-50; Weizmann Inst & AEC fel, Mass Inst Technol, 50-52; res chemist, Geol Div, Gulf Res & Develop Co, 53-55, sect head phys geochem, 55-59; prof chem, Israel Inst Technol, 59-62; sr scientist, Pratt & Whitney Aircraft Div, United Aircraft Corp, 62-64; prof mech eng in residence, Univ Calif, Berkeley, 64-78; prof chem eng, Mich Technol Univ, 78-81; EMER PROF MECH ENG, UNIV CALIF, BERKELEY, 81- *Concurrent Pos:* Consult, Bur Reclamation, 75- *Mem:* Asn Energy Engrs; Am Chem Soc. *Res:* Ion exchange; electrochemistry; thermodynamics; water purification; fuel cells; membrane physics; geochemistry. *Mailing Add:* Dept Mech Eng Univ Calif Berkeley CA 94720

SPIEKER, ANDREW MAUTE, b Columbus, Ohio, Aug 15, 32; m 61; c 2. HYDROLOGY. *Educ:* Yale Univ, BS, 54; Stanford Univ, MS, 56, PhD(geol), 65. *Prof Exp:* Geologist, US Geol Surv, Ohio, 57-65, hydrologist, Ill, 65-67, NY, 67-68, staff hydrologist, Water Resources Div, Washington, DC, 68-70, dep proj dir, San Francisco Bay Region Environ & Resources Planning Study, 70-75, western region rep, Land Info & Anal Off, 76-79, ASST DIST CHIEF, WATER RESOURCES DIV, US GEOL SURV, 79- *Honors & Awards:* W R Boggess Award, Am Water Resources Asn, 74. *Mem:* AAAS; Geol Soc Am; Am Geophys Union. *Res:* Hydrology of the urban environment; environmental geology; geology and hydrology of ground water; application of earth sciences to urban and regional planning; stratigraphy. *Mailing Add:* US Geol Surv 345 Middlefield Rd Menlo Park CA 94025

SPIELBERG, KURT, b Vienna, Austria, Feb 8, 28; m 56; c 3. THEORETICAL PHYSICS, APPLIED MATHEMATICS. *Educ:* City Col New York, BS, 61; Univ Vienna, PhD(physics), 54. *Prof Exp:* Asst instr physics & math, Fed Trade Sch, Austria, 55-56; staff mem, NY Sci Ctr, Int Bus Mach Corp, 57-71, mem staff, Philadelphia Sci Ctr, 71-76, MEM STAFF SCI MKT, IBM CORP, 76- *Concurrent Pos:* From instr to asst prof, City Col New York, 56-61. *Mem:* Math Programming Soc; Opers Res Soc Am. *Res:* Operations research; physics and mathematical programming. *Mailing Add:* IBM Sci Mkt 1133 Westchester Ave White Plains NY 10604

SPIELBERG, NATHAN, b Philadelphia, Pa, Feb 2, 26; m 47; c 3. PHYSICS. *Educ:* Emory Univ, AB, 47; Ohio State Univ, MS, 48, PhD(physics), 52. *Prof Exp:* Asst physics, Ohio State Univ, 47-49, res assoc, 51-53, asst prof welding eng, 53-54; assoc physicist, Philips Labs, NAm Philips Co, Inc, 54-58, sr physicist, 58-60, staff physicist, 60-65, res physicist, 65-69; PROF PHYSICS, KENT STATE UNIV, 69- *Mem:* Am Phys Soc; Am Asn Physics Teachers; Am Crystallog Asn; Electron Probe Anal Soc Am. *Res:* X-ray spectrochemical analysis; high resolution x-ray spectroscopy; x-ray physics; crystal perfection; x-ray interferometry; structure of liquid crystals. *Mailing Add:* Dept of Physics Kent State Univ Kent OH 44242

SPIELBERG, STEPHEN E, b Philadelphia, Pa, June 7, 34. MATHEMATICS. *Educ:* Univ Pa, BA, 56; Univ Minn, MA, 58, PhD(math), 63. *Prof Exp:* Asst prof, 63-77, ASSOC PROF MATH, UNIV TOLEDO, 77- *Mem:* Math Asn Am; Am Math Soc. *Res:* Probability; statistics; Wiener integrals. *Mailing Add:* Dept of Math Univ of Toledo Toledo OH 43606

SPIELER, RICHARD ARNO, b Syracuse, NY, Apr 8, 32. GENETICS, ZOOLOGY. *Educ:* Univ Chicago, BA, 52, PhD(zool), 62. *Prof Exp:* Asst prof zool, Ill Inst Technol, 62-68; from asst prof to assoc prof, 68-77, PROF BIOL, CALIF STATE UNIV, FRESNO, 77- *Mem:* Genetics Soc Am. *Res:* Genetics of meiosis; human cytogenetics. *Mailing Add:* Dept of Biol Calif State Univ Fresno CA 93740

SPIELHOLTZ, GERALD I, b New York, NY, Mar 12, 37; m 78; c 1. ANALYTICAL CHEMISTRY. *Educ:* City Col New York, BS, 58; Univ Mich, MS, 60; Iowa State Univ, PhD(anal chem), 63. *Prof Exp:* Assoc anal chem, Iowa State Univ, 63; from instr to asst prof chem, Hunter Col, 63-68; from asst prof to assoc prof, 68-75, PROF CHEM, LEHMAN COL, 75- *Mem:* Am Chem Soc. *Res:* Atomic absorption spectroscopy; wet oxidation of materials prior to analysis; analytical chemistry applied to anthropology. *Mailing Add:* Dept of Chem Herbert H Lehman Col Bronx NY 10468

SPIELMAN, ANDREW, b New York, NY, Feb 24, 30; m 55; c 3. MEDICAL ENTOMOLOGY. *Educ:* Colo Col, BS, 52; Johns Hopkins Univ, ScD(med entom), 56. *Prof Exp:* Biologist, Tenn Valley Authority, 53; from instr to assoc prof, 59-80, PROF TROP PUB HEALTH, SCH PUB HEALTH, HARVARD UNIV, 80- *Mem:* Am Soc Trop Med & Hyg; Entom Soc Am; Am Mosquito Control Asn; Am Soc Zool. *Res:* Genetics of mosquito populations; physiology of reproduction in mosquitoes; epidemiology of arthropod-borne diseases. *Mailing Add:* Dept Trop Pub Health 665 Huntington Ave Harvard Univ Sch of Pub Health Boston MA 02115

SPIELMAN, HAROLD S, b Philadelphia, Pa, Dec 11, 14; m 41; c 1. ELECTRONICS, SCIENCE EDUCATION. *Educ:* City Col New York, BS, 34, MS, 35; Columbia Univ, EdD(sci ed), 50. *Prof Exp:* Teacher high sch, Pa, 36-42; instr radio theory, Cent Signal Corps Sch, 42-44; instr high sch, NY, 46-50; PROF SCI EDUC, CITY COL NEW YORK, 50-, CHMN DEPT SEC EDUC, 68- *Concurrent Pos:* Nat Sci Teachers Asn liason rep, Nat Asn Indust-Ed Coop, 64-; consult, Sci Teachers Workshop, Prentice-Hall Inc, 65- *Mem:* Fel AAAS; Asn Res Sci Teaching; Nat Sci Teachers Asn. *Res:* Teaching of electronics. *Mailing Add:* Dept of Sec Educ City Col of New York New York NY 10031

SPIELMAN, JOHN RUSSEL, b Santa Barbara, Calif, May 14, 30; m 53; c 3. INORGANIC CHEMISTRY. *Educ:* Stanford Univ, BS, 53; Univ Southern Calif, MS, 58, PhD(chem), 62. *Prof Exp:* From asst prof to assoc prof, 61-72, PROF CHEM, CALIF STATE UNIV, LOS ANGELES, 72- *Concurrent Pos:* Vis prof, Univ Marburg, 69-70. *Mem:* AAAS; Am chem Soc. *Res:* Inorganic chemistry of boron hydrides, carboranes and organometallic compounds. *Mailing Add:* Dept of Chem Calif State Univ Los Angeles CA 90032

SPIELMAN, LLOYD ALLEN, water pollution control, air pollution control, deceased

SPIELMAN, RICHARD SAUL, b New York, NY, Feb 25, 46; m 69; c 1. HUMAN GENETICS, QUANTITATIVE VARIATION. *Educ:* Harvard Univ, AB, 67; Univ Mich, Ann Arbor, PhD(human genetics), 71. *Prof Exp:* Res assoc human genetics, Med Sch, Univ Mich, Ann Arbor, 71-74; asst prof, 74-80, ASSOC PROF HUMAN GENETICS, MED SCH, UNIV PA, 80- *Concurrent Pos:* Vis scholar, Imp Cancer Res Fund, London, 82-83. *Mem:* Sigma Xi; AAAS; Genetics Soc Am; Am Soc Human Genetics. *Res:* Human variation; biometric genetics; genetics of disease susceptibility. *Mailing Add:* Dept Human Genetics-G3 Sch Med Univ Pa Philadelphia PA 19104

SPIELMAN, WILLIAM SLOAN, b Tulsa, Okla, Aug 7, 47; m 70; c 2. CARDIOVASCULAR PHYSIOLOGY, RENAL PHYSIOLOGY. *Educ:* Westminster Col, BA, 69; Univ Mo, Columbia, PhD(physiol), 74. *Prof Exp:* Fel physiol, Univ NC, 75-77; fel & instr, Mayo Med Sch, 77-78, asst prof, 78-80; ASST PROF PHYSIOL, MICH STATE UNIV, 80- *Concurrent Pos:* NIH career develop award, 81. *Mem:* Am Physiol Soc; Sigma Xi; Am Fedn Clin Res; Am Soc Nephrology. *Res:* Normal and abnormal function of the kidney and its role in hypertension. *Mailing Add:* Dept Physiol Giltner Hall Mich State Univ East Lansing MI 48824

SPIELVOGEL, BERNARD FRANKLIN, b Ellwood City, Pa, Apr 23, 37; m 63, 81; c 3. INORGANIC CHEMISTRY, NUCLEAR MAGNETIC RESONANCE. *Educ:* Geneva Col, BS, 59; Univ Mich, PhD(chem), 63. *Prof Exp:* From instr to asst prof chem, Univ NC, 63-67; CHIEF, INORG & ANAL BR, CHEM DIV, US ARMY RES OFF, 67- *Concurrent Pos:* Vis sr res assoc, Duke Univ, 67-72, adj assoc prof chem, 72-81, adj prof chem, 81- *Mem:* Am Chem Soc. *Res:* Boron hydride chemistry; non-proton nuclear magnetic resonance; synthesis of Boron analogs of amino acids. *Mailing Add:* Army Res Off PO Box 12211 Research Triangle Park NC 27709

SPIERS, JAMES MONROE, b Wiggins, Miss, July 31, 40; m 65; c 3. PLANT PHYSIOLOGY, AGRONOMY. *Educ:* Miss State Univ, BS, 63, MS, 66; Tex A&M Univ, PhD(agron, crop physiol), 69. *Prof Exp:* Res plant physiologist, 69-71, res plant physiologist in charge fruit & forage res, 71-73, RES HORTICULTURIST, LOCATION LEADER & RES LEADER, SMALL FRUIT RES STA, SCI & EDUC ADMIN-FED RES, USDA, 73- *Mem:* Int Soc Hort Sci; Am Soc Agron; Am Soc Hort Sci; Crop Sci Soc Am. *Res:* Nutrition and cultural requirements of blueberries, strawberries and blackberries; hormonal regulation of routing, flowering and growth of blueberries. *Mailing Add:* USDA Small Fruit Res Sta PO Box 287 Poplarville MS 39470

SPIERS, PHILIP SACKVILLE, b Ealing, Eng, June 30, 33; m 62; c 2. EPIDEMIOLOGY. *Educ:* Univ London, BS, 58; Oxford Univ, PhD(epidemiol), 66. *Prof Exp:* Res asst epidemiol, Oxford Univ, 61-66; res assoc, Univ NC, 66-68, from asst prof to assoc prof, 68-72; epidemiologist, Nat Inst Child Health & Human Develop, 72-74; assoc prof, Univ Calif, Los Angeles, 74-75; ASSOC PROF EPIDEMIOL, UNIV WASH, 75- *Concurrent Pos:* Spec fel, Nat Inst Environ Health Sci, NIH, 69-72. *Mem:* Soc Epidemiol Res; Am Pub Health Asn. *Res:* Etiology of anencephaly and spina bifida and of Sudden Infant Death Syndrome; comparative epidemiology of small for date and prematurity; epidemiology of epilepsy and cerebral palsy. *Mailing Add:* Dept of Epidemiol Univ of Wash Seattle WA 98195

SPIES, HAROLD GLEN, b Mountain View, Okla, Mar 30, 34; div; c 2. NEUROENDOCRINOLOGY, REPRODUCTIVE BIOLOGY. *Educ:* Okla State Univ, BS, 56; Univ Wis, MS, 57, PhD(animal sci & genetics), 59. *Prof Exp:* Asst, Univ Wis, 56-59; from asst prof to assoc prof animal physiol, Kans State Univ, 59-66; res assoc anatomist, Univ Calif, Los Angeles, 67-68; res scientist, Delta Regional Primate Res Ctr, 68-72, CHMN REPRODUCTIVE PHYSIOL, ORE REGIONAL PRIMATE RES CTR, 72- *Concurrent Pos:* NIH spec fel neuroendocrinol res, Univ Calif, Los Angeles, 66-67; assoc prof, Tulane Univ, 68-72; prof, Med Sch, Univ Ore, 73- *Mem:* Endocrine Soc; Am Asn Anat; Soc Study Reproduction; Am Physiol Soc; Am Soc Animal Sci. *Res:* Reproductive physiology and endocrinology of laboratory animals and primates; hypothalamo-hypophysial-gonadal interrelationships; neural regulation of endocrine changes in the menstrual cycle. *Mailing Add:* Ore Regional Primate Res Ctr 505 NW 185th Ave Beaverton OR 97005

SPIES, ROBERT BERNARD, b Palo Alto, Calif, May 21, 43; m 63; c 3. MARINE BIOLOGY, MARINE ECOLOGY. *Educ:* St Mary's Col, BS, 65; Univ Pac, MS, 69; Univ Southern Calif, PhD(marine biol), 71. *Prof Exp:* Sr res officer marine ecol, Fisheries & Wildlife Dept, Victoria, Australia, 70-73; MARINE BIOLOGIST MARINE ECOL, BIOMED DIV, LAWRENCE LIVERMORE LAB, UNIV CALIF, 73- *Concurrent Pos:* US regional ed, Marine Environ Res, 80- *Mem:* Am Soc Zoologists; Am Soc Limnol & Oceanog; Western Soc Naturalists. *Res:* Effects of petroleum hydrocarbons in the marine benthos; dynamics of petroleum hydrocarbons, trace elements and radionuclides in benthic organisms; dynamic processes in benthos. *Mailing Add:* PO Box 808 L453 Livermore CA 94550

SPIESS, ELIOT BRUCE, b Boston, Mass, Oct 13, 21; m 51; c 2. GENETICS. *Educ:* Harvard Univ, AB, 43, AM, 47, PhD(genetics), 49. *Prof Exp:* Instr biol, Harvard Univ, 49-52; from asst prof to prof zool, Univ Pittsburgh, 52-66; PROF ZOOL, UNIV ILL, CHICAGO CIRCLE, 66- *Concurrent Pos:* Am Acad Arts & Sci grant in aid, 53; AEC res grant, 55-72; dir NIH grad training grant genetics, Univ Pittsburgh, 63-66; NSF res grant, 72-; ed, Evolution, Soc Study Evol Jour, 75-78. *Mem:* Behav Genetics Asn; AAAS; Genetics Soc Am; Soc Study Evolution; Am Soc Naturalists (pres, 81). *Res:* Genetics of adaptive mechanisms in populations of Drosophila; behavior genetics. *Mailing Add:* Dept Biol Sci Box 4348 Univ Ill Chicago Circle Chicago IL 60680

SPIESS, FRED NOEL, b Oakland, Calif, Dec 25, 19; m 42; c 5. OCEANOGRAPHY. *Educ:* Univ Calif, AB, 41, PhD(physics), 52; Harvard Univ, MS, 46. *Prof Exp:* Nuclear engr, Knolls Atomic Power Lab, Gen Elec Co, 51-52; res physicist, 52-61, actg dir, 61-63, dir, 64-65, chmn dept oceanog, 63-64 & 76-77, DIR MARINE PHYS LAB, SCRIPPS INST OCEANOG, UNIV CALIF, SAN DIEGO, 58-, PROF OCEANOG, 61-, ASSOC DIR, INST, 65- *Mem:* Fel Acoust Soc Am; Am Geophys Union. *Res:* Underwater acoustics; marine geophysics; ocean technology. *Mailing Add:* Marine Phys Lab of Scripps Inst Univ of Calif La Jolla CA 92152

SPIESS, JOACHIM, b Ludenscheid, Ger, April 20, 40; m 67; c 3. PROTEIN CHEMISTRY. *Educ:* Univ Munchen, MD, 73, PhD, 76. *Prof Exp:* Wiss asst, Max Planck Inst Biochem, 73-76; fel, 76-77, res assoc, 78-79, ASST RES PROF, SALK INST, 79- *Mem:* Ger Chem Soc; Endocrine Soc; Am Chem Soc. *Res:* Conducting biochemistry of hormonal peptides. *Mailing Add:* Salk Inst PO Box 85800 San Diego CA 92138

SPIESS, LURETTA DAVIS, b Chicago, Ill, Feb 3, 27; m 51; c 2. DEVELOPMENTAL BIOLOGY. *Educ:* Radcliffe Col, BA, 49; Harvard Univ, MA, 50, PhD(biol), 53. *Prof Exp:* Lectr bot, Univ Pittsburgh, 52-53, res assoc genetics, 59-66; res assoc, Univ Ill, Chicago Circle, 66-68; instr biol, Northwestern Univ, 68-70; asst prof biol, Lake Forest Col, 70-77; SR RES ASSOC, NORTHWESTERN UNIV, 77- *Mem:* Bot Soc Am; Am Soc Plant Physiol. *Res:* Development in moss; initiation of gametophore; tumor development; plant cancer; action of plant hormones. *Mailing Add:* Dept of Biol Sci Northwestern Univ Evanston IL 60201

SPIETH, HERMAN THEODORE, b Charlestown, Ind, Aug 21, 05; m 31; c 1. ZOOLOGY. *Educ:* Ind Cent Col, AB, 26; Ind Univ, PhD(zool), 31. *Hon Degrees:* LLD, Ind Cent Col, 58. *Prof Exp:* Asst zool, Ind Univ, 26-30, instr, 31-32; from instr to assoc prof biol, City Col New York, 32-53; prof zool & chmn div life sci, Univ Calif, Riverside, 53-56, provost, 56-58, chancellor, 58-64; prof zool, 64-73, chmn dept, 64-71, EMER PROF ZOOL, UNIV CALIF, DAVIS, 73- *Concurrent Pos:* Lectr, Columbia Univ, 38-53; res assoc, Am Mus Natural Hist, NY, 43-56. *Mem:* Am Soc Naturalists; Soc Study Evolution; Am Soc Zool; fel Entom Soc Am; fel Animal Behav Soc. *Res:* Biology and taxonomy of Ephemeroptera; sexual behavior in Drosophila. *Mailing Add:* Dept of Zool Univ of Calif Davis CA 95616

SPIETH, PHILIP THEODORE, b New York, NY, June 10, 41; m 63; c 4. POPULATION GENETICS, EVOLUTION. *Educ:* Univ Calif, Berkeley, AB, 62; Univ Ore, PhD(biol), 70. *Prof Exp:* Ford Found fel pop biol, Univ Chicago, 70-71; asst prof & asst geneticist, 71-76, ASSOC PROF & ASSOC RES GENETICIST, UNIV CALIF, BERKELEY, 76-, ASSOC DEAN, STUDENT AFFAIRS, COL NAT RES, 80- *Mem:* Genetics Soc Am; Soc Study Evolution; Mycol Soc Am. *Res:* Genetic variation of natural populations; empirical population genetics of fungi; microevolutionary processes of speciation. *Mailing Add:* Dept Genetics 345 Mulford Hall Univ Calif Berkeley CA 94720

SPIGARELLI, STEVEN ALAN, b Highland Park, Ill, Mar 26, 42. FISH ECOLOGY, POLLUTION BIOLOGY. *Educ:* Northwestern Univ, BA, 64; Univ Ill, Urbana, MS, 66; Mich State Univ, PhD(aquatic ecol), 71. *Prof Exp:* Asst ecologist, 71-74, ECOLOGIST AQUATIC ECOL, ARGONNE NAT LAB, 74- *Concurrent Pos:* Mem res comt, Int Atomic Energy Agency, 75-79; assoc ed, J Great Lakes Res, 77- *Mem:* Am Soc Limnol & Oceanog; Am Fisheries Soc; Fisheries Res Bd Can; Int Asn Great Lakes Res. *Res:* Thermal ecology; radioecology; fish behavior; stress ecology. *Mailing Add:* Radiol & Environ Res Div Argonne Nat Lab Argonne IL 60439

SPIGHT, CARL, b Indianapolis, Ind, Sept 8, 44; m 68; c 1. PHYSICS. *Educ:* Purdue Univ, West Lafayette, BSEE, 66; Princeton Univ, MA & PhD(astrophys sci), 71. *Prof Exp:* Assoc prof physics, Southern Univ, 70-72; assoc prof physics, Morehouse Col, 72-74, chmn dept, 72-80, prof, 74-80; WITH AMAF INDUSTS, INC, 80- *Concurrent Pos:* Vpres corp res, 80- *Mem:* Am Phys Soc; Am Asn Physics Teachers. *Res:* Plasma kinetic theory; magneto gas dynamics with application to energy conversion devices. *Mailing Add:* AMAF Indust Inc 103 Sternett Bldg Columbia MD 21044

SPIKE, CLARK GHAEL, b Ypsilanti, Mich, Sept 15, 21; m 47; c 2. INORGANIC CHEMISTRY. *Educ:* Mich State Norm Col, BS, 44; Univ Mich, PhD(chem), 52. *Prof Exp:* Instr chem, Mich State Norm Col, 46-48; res chemist, Ethyl Corp, 52-58; assoc prof chem, 58-61, head dept, 61-77, interim dean, Col Arts & Sci, 77-79, actg assoc vpres acad affairs, 79-80, PROF CHEM, EASTERN MICH UNIV, 61- *Mem:* AAAS; Am Chem Soc. *Res:* Coordination complexes; metallo-organic compounds. *Mailing Add:* Col of Arts & Sci Eastern Mich Univ Ypsilanti MI 48197

SPIKER, STEVEN L, b Omaha, Nebr, Nov 1, 41; m 71; c 1. PLANT CHROMATIN STRUCTURE. *Educ:* Univ Iowa, BS, 64, MS, 67, PhD(plant physiol), 70. *Prof Exp:* Asst prof plant physiol, Am Univ Beirut, 72-74; asst prof molecular biol, Dept Bot & Plant Path, Ore State Univ, 78-81; ASSOC PROF MOLECULAR GENETICS, NC STATE UNIV, 81- *Mem:* Am Soc Plant Physiologists; Genetics Soc Am. *Res:* Isolation, characterization and evolution of plant chromosomal proteins; physical and chemical studies of protein-protein interactions in the nucleosome; role of chromosomal proteins in forming transcribable or inert chromatin structure. *Mailing Add:* Genetics Dept NC State Univ Raleigh NC 27650

SPIKES, JOHN DANIEL, b Los Angeles, Calif, Dec 14, 18; m 42; c 3. PHOTOBIOLOGY. *Educ:* Calif Inst Technol, BS, 41, MS, 46, PhD(chem, embryol), 49. *Prof Exp:* From asst prof to assoc prof biol, 48-55, head dept exp biol, 54-62, dean, Col Letters & Sci, 64-66, PROF BIOL, UNIV UTAH, 55- *Concurrent Pos:* Cell physiologist, US AEC, Washington, DC, 58-60, consult, 60-65; counr, Smithsonian Inst, 66-72; mem comt photobiol, Nat Acad Sci-Nat Res Coun, 72-75. *Mem:* Am Chem Soc; Biophys Soc; Inter-Am Photochem Soc; Am Soc Photobiol (pres, 74-75); Europ Photochem Asn. *Res:* Photobiology; photosensitized reactions; mechanisms of the sensitized photooxidation of biomolecules; sensitized photo effects on cells; photosensitized reactions as a tool in biology and medicine. *Mailing Add:* Dept of Biol Univ of Utah Salt Lake City UT 84112

SPIKES, JOHN JEFFERSON, b Dallas, Tex, Jan 30, 29; m 50; c 5. TOXICOLOGY, CLINICAL CHEMISTRY. *Educ:* Union Col, BA, 51; George Washington Univ, MA, 59; Univ Tex, Galveston, PhD(toxicol), 70. *Prof Exp:* Clin chemist, Wash Sanitarium & Hosp, Washington, DC, 53-61; tech dir labs med technol, Med Br, Univ Tex, Galveston, 61-68, asst dir labs clin toxicol, 68-71; co-dir labs clin chem, Am Biomed Corp, Houston, 71-73; toxicologist, Biochem Procedures, Los Angeles, 73-75; CHIEF TOXICOLOGIST, ILL DEPT PUB HEALTH, 75- *Concurrent Pos:* Consult, State Dept, Peace Corps, Morocco, 65-66 & Coleman Instruments, 69-70. *Mem:* Am Acad Forensic Sci; Sigma Xi. *Res:* Toxicity of marine biotoxins; metabolism of drugs; analytical procedures in forensic medicine. *Mailing Add:* Div of Labs 2121 W Taylor St Chicago IL 60612

SPIKES, PAUL WENTON, b Ft Worth, Tex, Mar 22, 31; m 53; c 2. MATHEMATICAL ANALYSIS. *Educ:* Miss Southern Col, BS, 53, MA, 57; Auburn Univ, PhD(math), 70. *Prof Exp:* Instr math, Copiah-Lincoln Jr Col, 57-58; assoc prof, William Carey Col, 58-65; chmn, Div Sci & Math, Alexander City State Jr Col, 66-68, chmn, Eve Div, 69-70; asst prof, 70-73, assoc prof, 73-78, PROF MATH, MISS STATE UNIV, 78- *Mem:* Am Math Soc; Math Asn Am. *Res:* Qualitative theory of ordinary differential equations. *Mailing Add:* Dept Math Miss State Univ Mississippi State MS 39762

SPILBURG, CURTIS ALLEN, b Cleveland, Ohio, May 27, 45. BIOCHEMISTRY, PHYSICAL CHEMISTRY. *Educ:* Carnegie Inst Technol, BS, 67; Northwestern Univ, MS, 69, PhD(phys chem), 72. *Prof Exp:* Fel biol chem, Harvard Med Sch, 72-76; res specialist, 76-78, GROUP LEADER PROTEIN CHEM, MONSANTO CO, 78- *Concurrent Pos:* NIH fel, Harvard Med Sch, 73-75. *Res:* Enzyme isolation and characterization; structure function studies; chemical modification of proteins; enzyme crystallization; heme proteins. *Mailing Add:* Enzyme Res 800 N Lindbergh Blvd St Louis MO 63166

SPILHAUS, ATHELSTAN FREDERICK, b Cape Town, SAfrica, Nov 25, 11; nat US. METEOROLOGY, OCEANOGRAPHY. *Educ:* Univ Cape Town, BSc, 31, DSc, 48; Mass Inst Technol, SM, 33. *Hon Degrees:* DSc, Coe Col, 61, Univ RI, 68, Hahnemann Med Col, 68, Philadelphia Col Pharm & Sci, 68, Hamilton Col, 70, Southeastern Mass Univ, 70, Univ Durham, 70, Univ SC, 71, Southwestern at Memphis, 72; LLD, Nova Univ Advan Technol, 70 & Univ Md, 79. *Prof Exp:* Vol engr, Junkers Airplane Works, Ger, 31-32; res engr, Sperry Gyroscope Co, NY, 33; asst meteorol, Mass Inst Technol, 34-35; asst dir tech serv, Dept Defence, Union SAfrica, 35-36; asst, Woods Hole Oceanog Inst, 36-37, phys oceanogr, 38-60; prof geophys, Univ Minn, Minneapolis, 66-67, dean, Inst Sci, 49-66; pres, Franklin Inst, Pa, 67-69 & Aqua Int, Inc, 69-71; fel, Woodrow Wilson Int Ctr Scholars, Smithsonian Inst, 71-74; spec asst to adminr, Nat Oceanic & Atmospheric Admin, Us Dept Com, 74-80. *Concurrent Pos:* From asst prof to prof, NY Univ, 37-48, chmn dept meteorol, 38-47, dir res eng & phys sci, 46-48; mem subcomt meteorol, Nat Adv Comt, Aeronaut, 41-56; consult, Div Ten, Nat Defense Res Comt, 42-43, SAfrican Govt, 47, Brookhaven Nat Lab, 47-49, US Weather Bur, 47-56, Air Materiel Command & Sci Adv Bd, US Dept Air Force, 48-58, US Dept Defense & Res & Develop Adv Coun, Signal Corps, US Dept Army; sci dir weapons effects, Atomic Tests, Nev, 51; mem, Baker Mission, Korea, 52; US rep exec bd, UNESCO, 54-58; comnr, US Sci Exhib, Seattle World's Fair, 61-63; mem comt pollution, Nat Acad Sci; mem, Nat Sci Bd, 66-; mem bd trustees, Aerospace Corp, El Segundo, Sci Serv, Inc, Int Oceanog Found & Pac Sci Ctr Found; chmn sci adv comt, Am Newspaper Publ Asn; mem bd trustees, Sea Educ Asn, 74-; vis prof, Tex A&M Univ, 74-75; Phi Beta Kappa lectr, 76-77; distinguished vis prof, Univ Tex, 77-78; Annenberg scholar, Univ Southern Calif, 81, vis scholar, Inst Marine & Coastal Studies, 81- *Honors & Awards:* Berzelius Medal, Sweden, 62; Proctor Prize, Sci Res Soc Am, 68; Compass Award, Marine Tech Soc, 81. *Mem:* Fel AAAS(pres, 70, chmn, 71); fel Am Geog Soc; Am Inst Aeronaut & Astronaut; fel Geog Soc; fel Royal Meteorol Soc. *Res:* Spilhaus space clock; bathythermograph; aircraft, meteorological and oceanographic instruments; physical oceanography. *Mailing Add:* PO Box 1063 Middleburg VA 22117

SPILHAUS, ATHELSTAN FREDERICK, JR, b Boston, Mass, May 21, 38; m 60; c 3. GEOPHYSICS, OCEANOGRAPHY. *Educ:* Mass Inst Technol, SB, 59, SM, 60, PhD(oceanog), 65. *Prof Exp:* Oceanogr, US Govt, 65-67; asst exec dir, 67-70, EXEC DIR, AM GEOPHYS UNION, WASHINGTON, DC, 70- *Concurrent Pos:* Dir & vpres, Oceanic Educ Found; treas, Renewable Natural Resources Found, 72-74, dir, 72- *Mem:* Fel AAAS; Am Geophys Union; Am Soc Limnol & Oceanog; Coun Eng & Sci Soc Executives (pres, 80-81); Asn Earth Sci Ed (pres, 77). *Res:* Use of optical measurements in oceanography. *Mailing Add:* 10900 Picasso Lane Potomac MD 20854

SPILKER, CLARENCE WILLIAM, b Beatrice, Nebr, Dec 21, 22. ORGANIC CHEMISTRY. *Educ:* Doane Col, AB, 44; Univ Nebr, MSc, 49, PhD(chem), 52. *Prof Exp:* Asst chem, Univ Nebr, 48-52; sr res chemist, Nitrogen Div, Allied Chem Corp, Edgewater, 52-66, sr res chemist, Plastics Div, 66-68; chief chemist, Malmstrom Chem Corp, 68-73, asst dir res, 73-74, dir res, 74-77; RETIRED. *Mem:* Am Chem Soc; Forest Prod Res Soc. *Res:* Preparation of derivatives of benzo(h)quinoline and pryido-thiazoles; development and application of amino and phenolic resins for wood adhesives; analytical and organic research on lanolin and other cosmetic raw materials. *Mailing Add:* 15 Old Smalleytown Rd Warren NJ 07060

SPILLER, EBERHARD ADOLF, b Halbendorf, Ger, Apr 16, 33; m 64; c 2. X-RAY OPTICS. *Educ:* Univ Frankfurt, MSc, 60, PhD(physics), 64. *Prof Exp:* Asst prof physics, Univ Frankfurt, 65-68; STAFF MEM, T J WATSON RES CTR, IBM CORP, 68- *Mem:* Fel Optical Soc Am; Ger Phys Soc; AAAS. *Res:* Solid state physics; coherence of light; lasers; holography; nonlinerar optics; thin films; x-ray lithography. *Mailing Add:* Watson Res Ctr IBM Corp PO Box 218 Yorktown Heights NY 10598

SPILLERS, WILLIAM R, b Fresno, Calif, Aug 4, 34; m 61; c 2. CIVIL ENGINEERING, ENGINEERING MECHANICS. *Educ:* Univ Calif, Berkeley, BS, 55, MS, 56; Columbia Univ, PhD(continuum mech), 61. *Prof Exp:* Struct designer, John Blume Assoc, Calif, 56-57; from instr to assoc prof civil eng, Columbia Univ, 59-68, prof civil eng & eng mech, 68-76; PROF CIVIL ENG, RENSSELAER POLYTECH INST, 76- *Concurrent Pos:* NSF grant, 64; Guggenheim fel, NY Univ, 68-69; NSF fel, Univ Calif, Berkeley, 75-76. *Mem:* Am Soc Civil Engrs; Int Asn Bridge & Struct Engrs. *Res:* Problems of structural mechanics; optimization; fatigue of buried power transmission cables; environmental design of housing. *Mailing Add:* Dept of Civil Eng Rensselaer Polytech Inst Troy NY 12181

SPILLETT, JAMES JUAN, b Idaho Falls, Idaho, Oct 21, 32; m 61; c 2. ANIMAL ECOLOGY, WILDLIFE RESOURCES. *Educ:* Utah State Univ, BS, 61, MS, 65; Johns Hopkins Univ, ScD(animal ecol), 68. *Prof Exp:* Res asst pronghorn antelope, Utah State Univ, 62-64; field biologist, Indian Wildlife Surv, World Wildlife Fund, Morges, Switz, 66; res asst ecol res, Johns Hopkins Univ, 64-67; asst leader, Utah Coop Wildlife Res, Utah State Univ, 67-76; WILDLIFE BIOLOGIST, US FOREST SERV, 78- *Mem:* Wilderness Soc; Wildlife Soc; Brit Fauna Presserv Soc; Wildlife Preserv Soc India. *Res:* Ecuadorian mammals, taxonomy and distribution effects of livestock fences on pronghorn antelope movements; status of Indian wildlife, particularly the Indian rhino; ecology of the lesser bandicoot rat. *Mailing Add:* Dept Wildlife & Fisheries Sci Tex A&M Univ Box 77 College Station TX 77843

SPILLMAN, CHARLES KENNARD, b Lawrence County, Ill, Feb 26, 34; m 59; c 1. AGRICULTURAL ENGINEERING. *Educ:* Univ Ill, Urbana, BS, 60, MS, 63; Purdue Univ, PhD(agr eng), 69. *Prof Exp:* Asst waste mgt, Univ Ill, Urbana, 60-62; exten agr engr, Mich State Univ, 62-66; asst prof, 69-73, assoc prof, 73-79, PROF STRUCT & ENVIRON, KANS STATE UNIV, 79- *Honors & Awards:* Metal Bldgs Mfg Award, Am Soc Agr Engrs. *Mem:* Am Soc Agr Engrs; Am Soc Heat, Refrig & Air-Conditioning Engrs; Am Soc Eng Educ; Int Solar Energy Soc. *Res:* Environmental modification systems to provide optimum conditions for livestock production; solar energy for livestock buildings. *Mailing Add:* Dept of Agr Eng Seaton Hall Kans State Univ Manhattan KS 66502

SPILLMAN, GEORGE RAYMOND, b Holdenville, Okla, Oct 21, 34; m 66; c 1. PHYSICS. *Educ:* Univ Okla, BS, 56, Univ Calif, Berkeley, MA, 61, PhD(physics), 64. *Prof Exp:* Assoc engr, Gen Dynamics/Convair, 56; proj officer, Res Directorate, Spec Weapons Ctr, Kirtland AFB, US Air Force, 56-59, proj officer, Weapons Lab, 63-67; staff mem, 67-71, group leader, 71-74, ASSOC DIV LEADER, LOS ALAMOS SCI LAB, 74- *Mem:* Am Phys Soc. *Res:* Nuclear explosion phenomenology; nuclear weapons effects; plasma physics; atomic processes in plasma; radiative transfer; spectral absorption coefficients; hydrodynamics. *Mailing Add:* Los Alamos Sci Lab PO Box 1663 Los Alamos NM 87544

SPILLMAN, RICHARD JAY, b Tacoma, Wash, Sept 13, 49. FAULT TOLERANT COMPUTING. *Educ:* Western Wash Univ, BS, 71; Univ Utah, MA, 73; Utah State Univ, PhD(elec eng), 78. *Prof Exp:* Asst prof elec eng, Univ Calif, Davis, 78-80; specialist eng, Boeing Co, 80-81; ASST PROF COMPUT SCI, PAC LUTHERN UNIV, 81- *Mem:* Inst Elec & Electronics Engrs; Am Soc Comput Mach. *Res:* Development of highly fault tolerant comput systems; analysis of system testability. *Mailing Add:* Dept Couput Sci Pac Luthern Univ Tacoma WA 98447

SPILLMAN, WILLIAM BERT, JR, b Charleston, SC, Jan 21, 46; m 74; c 2. OPTICS, FERROELECTRICS. *Educ:* Brown Univ, BA, 68; Northeastern Univ, MS, 72, PhD(physics), 77. *Prof Exp:* MEM TECH STAFF OPTICS TECHNOL, SPERRY RES CTR, 77- *Mem:* Am Phys Soc; Optical Soc Am. *Res:* Multimode fiber optic sensing as it pertains to device concepts compatible with current fiber-optic technology. *Mailing Add:* Sperry Res Ctr 100 North Rd Sudbury MA 01776

SPILMAN, CHARLES HADLEY, b Westerly, RI, Mar 30, 42; m 62; c 2. REPRODUCTIVE BIOLOGY, FERTILITY CONTROL. *Educ:* Clark Univ, AB, 65; Univ Mass, Amherst, PhD(physiol), 69. *Prof Exp:* Res asst, Univ Mass, 65-69; res assoc, Cornell Univ, 69-71 & Worcester Found Exp Biol, 71-72; res scientist, 72-76, SR RES SCIENTIST, UPJOHN CO, 76- *Mem:* Am Fertility Soc; Soc Study Reproduction; Am Soc Animal Sci; Sigma Xi; Soc Exp Biol Med. *Res:* Control of oviduct and uterine function; mammalian embryo development; development of methods for the control of fertility; development of drug delivery systems. *Mailing Add:* Fertil Res Upjohn Co Kalamazoo MI 49001

SPILMAN, EDRA LAVERGENE, b Cambridge, Ohio, Dec 27, 18; m 45, 59; c 2. BIOCHEMISTRY. *Educ:* Ohio Univ, BSch, 46; Western Reserve Univ, PhD, 53. *Prof Exp:* From instr to asst prof biochem, Western Reserve Univ, 53-67, mgr dept med sci, 53-67; prof lab educ, Mt Sinai Sch Med, 67-70, dir, M-D Labs, 67-77, assoc dean spec serv, 69-77, prof med educ, 70-77; CONSULT, 77- *Concurrent Pos:* Vis scholar med educ, Sch Med, Univ Ariz, 75-76. *Res:* Curriculum development, evaluation; medical school construction planning and coordination; laboratory education. *Mailing Add:* Walker Rte Prescott AZ 86301

SPINAR, LEO HAROLD, b Colome, SDak, Feb 20, 29; m 56; c 4. PHYSICAL CHEMISTRY. *Educ:* Univ SDak, BA, 51; Univ Wis, MS, 53, PhD(chem), 58. *Prof Exp:* From instr to asst prof chem, Colo State Univ, 57-62; assoc prof, Univ Mo, 62-66; assoc prof, 66-69, PROF CHEM, SDAK STATE UNIV, 69- *Concurrent Pos:* Dir planning, program & budget, SDak State Univ, 73- *Mem:* Am Chem Soc. *Res:* Physical inorganic chemistry; high temperature properties of materials; thermodynamics; vapor pressure studies. *Mailing Add:* 323 Admin Bldg SDak State Univ Brookings SD 57006

SPINDEL, ROBERT CHARLES, b New York, NY, Sept 5, 44; m 66; c 2. UNDERWATER ACOUSTICS, ELECTRICAL ENGINEERING. *Educ:* Cooper Union, BE, 65; Yale Univ, MS, 66, MPhil, 68, PhD(elec eng), 71. *Prof Exp:* Fel, 71-72, asst scientist, 72-76, ASSOC SCIENTIST, OCEAN ENG, WOODS HOLE OCEANOG INST, 76- *Honors & Awards:* A B Wood Medal, Inst Acoustics, 81. *Mem:* Inst Elec & Electronics Eng; Acoust Soc Am. *Res:* Acoustic propagation; volume and surface scattering; acoustic signal processing. *Mailing Add:* Dept Ocean Eng Woods Hole Oceanog Inst Woods Hole MA 02543

SPINDEL, WILLIAM, b New York, NY, Sept 9, 22; m 67; c 2. CHEMISTRY, SCIENCE POLICY. *Educ:* Brooklyn Col, BA, 44; Columbia Univ, MA, 47, PhD(chem), 50. *Prof Exp:* Jr scientist, Manhattan Proj, Los Alamos Sci Lab, Univ Calif, 44-45; asst chem, Columbia Univ, 46-49; instr, Polytech Inst Brooklyn, 49-50; asst prof, State Univ NY Teachers Col, Albany, 50-54; from assoc prof to prof, Rutgers Univ, 57-64; prof, Belfer Grad Sch Sci, Yeshiva Univ, 64-74; EXEC SECY, OFF CHEM & CHEM TECHNOL, NAT ACAD SCI-NAT RES COUN, 74- *Concurrent Pos:* Res assoc, Columbia Univ, 54-56, vis assoc prof, 56-57, vis prof, 62-70, sr lectr, 70-74; NSF vis scientist, Yugoslavia, 71-72; Guggenheim fel, 61-62. *Mem:* AAAS; Am Chem Soc; Am Phys Soc; Cosmos Club. *Res:* Separation of stable isotopes; physical and chemical properties of isotopes; mass spectrometry. *Mailing Add:* Nat Acad of Sci 2101 Constitution Ave NW Washington DC 20418

SPINDLER, DONALD CHARLES, b Dixon, Ill, Aug 27, 22; m 53; c 3. ANALYTICAL CHEMISTRY. *Educ:* Capital Univ, BS, 43; Univ Minn, MS, 49. *Hon Degrees:* DSc, Capital Univ, 80. *Prof Exp:* Control chemist, E I du Pont de Nemours & Co, Inc, 43-44; methods develop chemist, Western Elec Co, 49-55; spectrogr, 55-59, supvr anal & instrumentation, 59-65, mgr tech serv lab, 65-67, lab mgr, 67-81, ASSOC DIR RES ADMIN SERVS, FERRO CORP, INDEPENDENCE, 81- *Honors & Awards:* H V Churchill Award, Am Soc Testing & Mat, 73, Award of Merit, 74; B F Scribner Award, 78. *Mem:* Hon mem Am Soc Test & Mat; Am Chem Soc; Soc Res Adminr; Soc Appl Spectros. *Res:* Emission spectroscopy methods, practices and nomenclature; research administrative services. *Mailing Add:* 7302 Trevor Lane Parma OH 44129

SPINDLER, MAX, b Antwerp, Belg, Dec 19, 38; US citizen; m 67; c 1. CIVIL & AERONAUTICAL ENGINEERING. *Educ:* Cooper Union, BCE, 61; Northwestern Univ, Ill, MS, 63, PhD(civil eng), 68. *Prof Exp:* Eng specialist, LTV Aerospace Corp, Tex, 67-70; asst prof civil eng, 70-77, ASSOC PROF CIVIL ENG, UNIV TEX, ARLINGTON, 77- *Mem:* Am Soc Civil Engrs; Am Inst Aeronaut & Astronaut; NY Acad Sci. *Res:* Noise spectra due to flow through stenosed heart valves; fluid mechanics; hydraulics; bio-medical engineering. *Mailing Add:* Dept of Civil Eng Univ of Tex Arlington TX 76019

SPINDT, RODERICK SIDNEY, b Waupaca, Wis, Mar 5, 19; m 44; c 2. ORGANIC CHEMISTRY. *Educ:* Ripon Col, BA, 41; Univ Wis, MS, 44; Univ Pittsburgh, PhD(chem), 49. *Prof Exp:* Jr chemist org synthesis, Gulf Res & Develop Co, 44-45; fel org anal, Mellon Inst, 45-56; staff asst, Gulf Res & Develop Co, 56-58, sect head, 58-60, sr chemist, 60-65, from res assoc to sr res assoc, 65-80; RETIRED. *Concurrent Pos:* Lectr, Univ Pittsburgh, 52- *Mem:* Am Chem Soc; Soc Automotive Engrs; Air Pollution Control Asn. *Res:* Characterization of sulfur compounds; mechanism of engine deposit formation; mechanisms of combustion in engines; air pollution research; vehicle emissions; composition of gasoline. *Mailing Add:* 3957 Parkview Lane Allison Park PA 15101

SPINELLI, JOHN, b Seattle, Wash, July 23, 25; m 49; c 1. ANALYTICAL CHEMISTRY, FOOD CHEMISTRY. *Educ:* Univ Wash, BS, 49. *Prof Exp:* Consult chemist, Food Chem & Res Labs, Wash, 49-62; res chemist, Technol Lab, Nat Marine Fisheries Serv, 62-80; DIR, UTILIZATION RES DIV, NORTHWEST & ALASKA FISHERIES CTR, SEATTLE, 80- *Mem:* NY Acad Sci; AAAS; Am Chem Soc; Inst Food Technol; Pac Fisheries Technologists. *Res:* Food process quality control, product analysis and development; biochemical changes in fish post-mortem; protein isolates of marine origin; protein and nutritional requirements of salmonids; food uses for underutilized species; improvement of quality and safety of fishery products. *Mailing Add:* Technol Lab 2725 Montlake Blvd E Seattle WA 98105

SPINGOLA, FRANK, b Brooklyn, NY, Aug 3, 37; m 67. CHEMISTRY. *Educ:* Adelphi Univ, AB, 59; Polytech Inst Brooklyn, MS, 63, PhD(chem), 68. *Prof Exp:* Asst prof, 68-76, ASSOC PROF CHEM, DOWLING COL, 76- *Res:* Physical chemistry of aqueous solutions. *Mailing Add:* Dept of Chem Dowling Col Oakdale NY 11769

SPINING, ARTHUR MILTON, III, b Old Hickory, Tenn, Nov 13, 33; m 58; c 3. ANIMAL NUTRITION, BIOCHEMISTRY. *Educ:* Tenn Polytech Inst, BS, 55; NC State Col, MS, 60. *Prof Exp:* Res asst animal nutrit, NC State Col, 58-60; asst chemist, Am Meat Inst Found, 60-64; res asst animal nutrit, 64-65; supvr qual control, Animal Nutrition & Anal Chem, 65-68, prod control supvr, 68-70, SR CHEMIST, ANIMAL NUTRITION & ANAL CHEM, FARM BUR COOP ASN, INC, 70- *Mem:* Am Chem Soc; Animal Nutrit Res Coun; Am Asn Feed Micros. *Res:* Practical effects of feeding animal by-products; feed analysis; soil testing; plant analysis. *Mailing Add:* Ind Farm Bur Coop Asn Inc 120 E Market St Indianapolis IN 46204

SPINK, CHARLES HARLAN, b Platteville, Wis, Apr 9, 36; m 63. ANALYTICAL CHEMISTRY, PHYSICAL CHEMISTRY. *Educ:* Univ Wis, BS, 58; Pa State Univ, PhD(phys chem), 62. *Prof Exp:* Fel, Univ Wash, 62-63; asst prof anal chem, Juniata Col, 63-67; from asst prof to assoc prof, 67-72, PROF ANAL CHEM, STATE UNIV NY COL, CORTLAND, 72- *Concurrent Pos:* Am Chem Soc-Petrol Res Fund grant, 63-64; USPHS res grant, 65-68; NY State Res Found fel & grant-in-aid, 69-72; res assoc, Lund Univ, Sweden, 73-74, Yale Univ, 80-81; USPHS res grant, 77-79, 80-83. *Mem:* AAAS; Am Chem Soc. *Res:* Thermochemical studies on solutes in bile salt solutions; thermochemical analysis of mixed organic-aqueous mixtures; heat capacities of model biochemical compounds; scanning calorimetry of micelles. *Mailing Add:* Dept of Chem State Univ of NY Col Cortland NY 13045

SPINK, D(ONALD) R(ICHARD), b Buffalo, NY, Mar 11, 23; m 46; c 6. EXTRACTIVE METALLURGY, CHEMICAL ENGINEERING. *Educ:* Univ Mich, BS, 45; Univ Rochester, MS, 49; Iowa State Univ, PhD(chem eng), 52. *Prof Exp:* Chem engr, Gen Elec Co, 46-48; asst, Univ Iowa, 49-52; res engr, E I du Pont de Nemours & Co, 52; sr res engr, Carborundum Metals Climax, Inc, NY, 52-59, asst to mgr, Tech Br & actg mgr, Res & Develop Dept, 59-61, mgr, Tech Br, 61-65, vpres technol, 65-68; PROF CHEM ENG, UNIV WATERLOO, 68- *Mem:* Am Inst Chem Engrs; Can Soc Chem Engrs; Am Inst Mining, Metall & Petrol Engrs; Soc Chem Indust; Can Inst Mining & Metall. *Res:* Extractive metallurgy of zirconium, hafnium and titanium; solvent extraction; extractive metallurgy; air pollution research; low energy scrubber development; coal treatment (sulfur removal); fly ash treatment (recovery of vanadium and nickel). *Mailing Add:* Dept of Chem Eng Univ of Waterloo Waterloo ON N2L 3G1 Can

SPINK, GORDON CLAYTON, b Lansing, Mich, Jan 6, 35; m 60; c 2. MEDICAL EDUCATION, FAMILY MEDICINE. *Educ:* Mich State Univ, BS, 57, PhD(bot, cytol), 66, DO, 75. *Prof Exp:* Instr, Univ, 63-66, asst prof, Biol Res Ctr, 66-68, dir, Electron Micros Lab, 67-72, asst prof entom, Univ, 68-71, prof staff scientist electron micros, Pesticide Res Ctr, 71-72, instr & dir, Electron Micros Lab, 72-75, clin asst prof, Col Osteopath Med, 75-76, asst prof, Dept Family Med, 76-78, unit III coordr, 77-79, co-dir, Preceptor Prog, Dept Family Med, 78-80, actg asst dean grad & continuing educ, 80, ASSOC PROF, DEPT FAMILY MED, MICH STATE UNIV, 78- *Concurrent Pos:* Res collabr, Biol Dept, Brookhaven Nat Lab, 69; intern, Flint Osteopath Hosp, Flint, Mich, 75-76, dir med educ, 80-81; dir med educ, Lansing Gen Hosp, 80- *Mem:* AAAS; Electron Micros Soc Am; Asn Hosp Med Educ; Asn Osteop Dirs Med Educ; Am Osteop Asn. *Res:* Ultrastructure. *Mailing Add:* 3910 Sandlewood Okemos MI 48864

SPINK, WALTER JOHN, b Hackensack, NJ, May 4, 33; m 57; c 2. STRATIGRAPHY, STRUCTURAL GEOLOGY. *Educ:* Lehigh Univ, BS, 57; Rutgers Univ, MS, 63, PhD(geol), 67. *Prof Exp:* Geologist, NJ Geol Surv, 60-66; from instr to asst prof, 66-69, chmn dept, 69-76, ASSOC PROF GEOL, RIDER COL, 69-, CHMN DEPT, 80- *Mem:* AAAS; Geol Soc Am; Asn Prof Geol Scientists. *Res:* Areal geologic mapping and gravity survey of northwestern New Jersey; structural geology; stratigraphy and sedimentation. *Mailing Add:* Dept of Geosci Rider Col PO Box 6400 Lawrenceville NJ 08648

SPINK, WESLEY WILLIAM, b Duluth, Minn, Dec 17, 04; m 35; c 2. INTERNAL MEDICINE. *Educ:* Carleton Col, AB, 26; Harvard Univ, MD, 32. *Hon Degrees:* DSc, Carleton Col, 50. *Prof Exp:* Asst med, Harvard Med Sch, 34-37; from asst prof to prof, 37-67, Regents prof med, 67-73, Regents prof comp med, 70-73, EMER REGENTS PROF MED & COMP MED, UNIV MINN, MINNEAPOLIS, 73- *Concurrent Pos:* Expert consult, WHO & Food & Agr Orgn. *Honors & Awards:* DSc, Carleton Col. *Mem:* Am Soc Clin Invest (secy, 42-45, pres, 49); Soc Exp Biol & Med; Asn Am Physicians; master Am Col Physicians (pres, 63). *Res:* Microbiology; infectious diseases; human brucellosis; chemotherapy; comparative medicine. *Mailing Add:* 1916 E River Terr Minneapolis MN 55414

SPINKA, HAROLD M, b Chicago, Ill, Apr 2, 45; m 73; c 1. SPIN PHYSICS. *Educ:* Northwestern Univ, BA, 66; Calif Inst Technol, PhD(physics), 70. *Prof Exp:* Fel, 70-73, PHYSICIST, ARGONNE NAT LAB, 76- *Concurrent Pos:* Adj asst prof physics, Univ Calif, Los Angeles, 73-76. *Mem:* Am Phys Soc; AAAS; Sigma Xi. *Res:* Strong interactions using polarized beams and targets and nuclear beams and targets; nucleon-nucleon interactions. *Mailing Add:* High Energy Physics Div Argonne Nat Lab Bldg 362 Argonne IL 60439

SPINKS, DANIEL OWEN, b Dallas, Ga, Sept 5, 18; m 40; c 3. SOIL CHEMISTRY. *Educ:* Univ Ga, BS, 39, MSA, 47; NC State Col, PhD, 53. *Prof Exp:* Instr soils & physics, Abraham Baldwin Agr Col, 39-44; from instr to assoc prof, 47-61, PROF SOILS & SOIL CHEMIST, AGR EXP STA, UNIV FLA, 61-, ASSOC DEAN RESIDENT INSTR, INST FOOD & AGR SCI, 69- *Mem:* Nat Asn Cols & Teachers Agr; Soil Sci Soc Am. *Res:* Effect of organic matter on the availability of fixed soil phosphorus. *Mailing Add:* Inst of Food & Agr Sci Rm 1001 McCarty Hall Univ of Fla Gainesville FL 32601

SPINKS, JOHN WILLIAM TRANTER, b Methwold, Eng, Jan 1, 08; m 39. CHEMISTRY. *Educ:* Univ London, BSc, 28, PhD(photochem), 30. *Hon Degrees:* DSc, Univ London, 57; LLD, Carleton Univ, 58 & Assumption Col, 62. *Prof Exp:* Asst prof chem, 30-39, prof phys chem, 39-74, head dept, 48-59, dean grad col, 49-59, pres, 59-74, EMER PROF PHYS CHEM & EMER PRES, UNIV SASK, 74- *Honors & Awards:* Order Brit Empire; Companion Can. *Mem:* Am Chem Soc; fel Royal Soc Can; fel Royal Inst Chem. *Res:* Photochemistry; molecular structure; radioactive tracers; radiation chemistry. *Mailing Add:* Univ of Sask Saskatoon SK S7N 0W0 Can

SPINNER, ERNEST, chemistry, see previous edition

SPINNER, IRVING HERBERT, b Toronto, Ont, Dec 29, 22; m 44; c 3. CHEMICAL ENGINEERING. *Educ:* Univ Toronto, BASc, 51, MASc, 53, PhD(chem eng), 54. *Prof Exp:* Res consult, Stanley Mfg Co, 46-51, res chemist, 54-56; assoc prof chem eng, 56-70, PROF CHEM ENG, UNIV TORONTO, 70- *Concurrent Pos:* Indust chemist, 39-42; consult indust chem, 47-54 & 64. *Mem:* Fel Chem Inst Can. *Res:* Ion exchange, redox polymers and novel mass transfer techniques. *Mailing Add:* Dept of Chem Eng Univ of Toronto Toronto ON M5S 1A1 Can

SPINNER, THEODORE, chemistry, physics, see previous edition

SPINNLER, JOSEPH F, b Greenwood, SC, July 8, 31; m 62; c 2. PHYSICAL CHEMISTRY. *Educ:* Lafayette Col, BS, 53; Yale Univ, MS, 58, PhD(chem), 60. *Prof Exp:* Scientist ballistics sect, Rohm and Haas Co, 59-65, sr scientist chem sect, 65-70; mem explor develop group, Micromedic Systs Inc, 70-71; SR SCIENTIST, ROHM AND HAAS CO, 71- *Res:* Development of hydrogen fluorine chemical laser; automation of spectrophotometric and electrophoretic clinical laboratory procedures; metabolite and residue analysis using liquid chromatography; gas chromatography/mass spectrometry; thin layer chromatography and electrophoresis. *Mailing Add:* Rohm and Haas Co Norristown Rd Spring House PA 19477

SPINOSA, CLAUDE, b Sardenia, Italy, July 17, 37; US citizen; m 63. PALEONTOLOGY, GEOLOGY. *Educ:* City Col, New York, BS, 61; Univ Iowa, MS, 65, PhD(geol), 68. *Prof Exp:* Asst prof geol, Ind Univ, Southeast, 68-70; assoc prof, 70-76, PROF GEOL, BOISE STATE UNIV, 76- *Mem:* Geol Soc Am; Paleont Soc; Sigma Xi. *Res:* Permian, Pennsylvanian ammonoid cephalopods; Upper Permian stratigraphy; Nautilus, biology and ecology. *Mailing Add:* Dept of Geol & Geophysics Boise State Univ Boise ID 83725

SPINRAD, BERNARD ISRAEL, b New York, NY, Apr 16, 24; m 51; c 4. PHYSICS, NUCLEAR ENGINEERING. *Educ:* Yale Univ, BS, 42, MS, 44, PhD(phys chem), 45. *Prof Exp:* Sterling fel, Yale Univ, 45-46; phsyicist, Clinton Labs, Tenn, 46-49; assoc physicist, Argonne Nat Lab, 49-54, sr physicist, 54-72, dir, Reactor Eng Div, 57-63; dir, Div Nuclear Power & Reactors, Int Atomic Energy Agency, Vienna, 67-70; ad hoc prof, Univ Wis-Parkside, 71; PROF NUCLEAR ENG, ORE STATE UNIV, 72- *Concurrent Pos:* Adv US deleg, Conf Peaceful Uses of Atomic Energy, Geneva, 55-58; consult, Int Atomic Energy Agency, 61, 63; mem, Europ-Am Reactor Physics Comt, 61-66, chmn, 61-62; vis prof Univ Ill, 64; mem, Tech Adv Panel Peaceful Use Safeguards, US Atomic Energy Comn; mem, Comt Nuclear & Alternative Energy Systs, Nat Acad Sci, 75-80; res scholar, Int Inst Appl Systs Anal, 78-79. *Mem:* AAAS; fel Am Phys Soc; fel Am Nuclear Soc; Sigma Xi; Am Chem Soc. *Res:* Physics of nuclear reactors; nuclear systems; energy systems and economics; nuclear reactor shutdown power. *Mailing Add:* Radiation Ctr Ore State Univ Corvallis OR 97331

SPINRAD, HYRON, b New York, NY, Feb 17, 34; m 58; c 3. ASTRONOMY. *Educ:* Univ Calif, Berkeley, PhD(astron), 61. *Prof Exp:* Sr scientist, Jet Propulsion Lab, 61-64; from asst prof to assoc prof, 64-68, PROF ASTRON, UNIV CALIF, BERKELEY, 68- *Res:* Study of planetary atmospheres; spectroscopic investigations of old stars and nuclei of galaxies; astrophysics; spectroscopy of faint, distant radio and cluster galaxies. *Mailing Add:* Dept of Astron Univ of Calif Berkeley CA 94720

SPINRAD, ROBERT J(OSEPH), b New York, NY, Mar 20, 32; m 54; c 2. COMPUTER SCIENCE. *Educ:* Columbia Univ, BS, 53, MS, 54; Mass Inst Technol, PhD, 63. *Prof Exp:* Assoc engr, Bulova Res & Develop Lab, 54-55; from asst elec engr to assoc elec engr, Brookhaven Nat Lab, 55-63, elec engr, 63-66, head comput systs group, 65-68, sr elec engr, 66-67, sr scientist, 67-68; vpres, Sci Data Systs, 68-70, vpres Xerox Data Systs, 70-71, dir info sci, 71-76, vpres, Systs Develop Div, 76-78, VPRES RES & MGR, PARC SYSTEMS CTR, XEROX CORP, 78- *Concurrent Pos:* mem comput sci adv comt, Stanford Univ; mem comput in elec eng comt, Nat Acad Eng; educ comt, Comput Sci & Eng Bd, Nat Acad Sci; mem math dept vis comt, Mass Inst Technol; gen chmn, 1972 Fall Joint Comput Conf, 71-72; mem, Eng Adv Coun, Univ Calif, 77-; consult, Rand Corp, 77- & Int Inst Appl Syst Anal, 78-; Overseers Comt Info Technol, Harvard Univ, 79-; Nat Res Coun Panel, Nat Bur Standards, 80- *Mem:* Inst Elec & Electronics Engrs; Asn Comput Mach. *Res:* Electronics; computers; computer systems. *Mailing Add:* Xerox Palo Alto Res Ctr 3333 Coyote Hill Rd Palo Alto CA 94304

SPIRA, ARTHUR WILLIAM, b New Britain, Conn, Oct 18, 41; m 65; c 3. ANATOMY. *Educ:* City Col New York, BS, 62; Univ Mich, MS, 64, USPHS fel & PhD(anat), 67. *Prof Exp:* USPHS fel anat, McGill Univ, 67-68; asst prof, Univ BC, 68-73; asst prof, 73-75, ASSOC PROF ANAT, UNIV CALGARY, 75- *Concurrent Pos:* Mem, Grants Review Comt, Med Res Coun Can. *Mem:* Soc Neurosci; Am Asn Anat; Can Asn Anat; Asn Res Vision Opthal. *Res:* Structure and function of the retina; ocular development; retinal histogenesis; retinal neurotransmitters; structure and development of cardiac muscle; techniques in histology, transmission and scanning electron microscopy; cytochemistry. *Mailing Add:* Dept Anat Univ of Calgary Calgary AB T2N 1N4 Can

SPIRA, JOEL SOLON, b New York, NY, Mar 1, 27; m 54; c 3. ENGINEERING PHYSICS. *Educ:* Purdue Univ, BS, 48. *Prof Exp:* Jr engr, Glenn L Martin Co, 48-52; engr, Reeves Instrument Corp, 52-54, sr engr, 54-56, sr proj engr, 56-59; prin systs analyst, ITT Commun Systs Inc, 59-61; PRES & DIR RES, LUTRON ELECTRONICS CO, INC, 61- *Mem:* Fel AAAS; Am Phys Soc; Inst Elec & Electronics Engrs. *Res:* Supersonic aerodynamics; microwaves; computers; electronic instruments; missile technology; weapons systems analysis; nuclear and military strategy; electronic and general technology; light dimming and electron power control; energy conservation. *Mailing Add:* Lutron Electronics Co Inc Coopersburg PA 18036

SPIRA, MELVIN, b Chicago, Ill, July 3, 25; m 52; c 3. MEDICINE, PLASTIC SURGERY. *Educ:* Northwestern Univ, DDS, 47, MSD, 51; Med Col Ga, MD, 56. *Prof Exp:* From instr to assoc prof, 61-70, PROF PLASTIC SURG, BAYLOR COL MED, 70-, HEAD, DIV PLASTIC SURG, 76- *Mem:* Am Soc Plastic & Reconstruct Surg; Am Soc Maxillofacial Surg (pres, 74-); fel Am Col Surg; Am Asn Plastic Surg; Plastic Surg Res Coun. *Res:* Maxillofacial and microvascular surgery. *Mailing Add:* 1200 Moursund Houston TX 77025

SPIRA, ROBERT SAMUEL, b Detroit, Mich, Dec 12, 27; m 53; c 1. MATHEMATICS. *Educ:* Univ Calif, Berkeley, BA, 57, PhD(math), 62. *Prof Exp:* Res assoc math, Duke Univ, 62-64; asst prof, Univ Tenn, 64-67; ASSOC PROF MATH, MICH STATE UNIV, 67- *Res:* Analytic number theory; algebraic aspects number theory. *Mailing Add:* Dept of Math Mich State Univ East Lansing MI 48824

SPIRA, WILLIAM MARTIN, food microbiology, microbial physiology, see previous edition

SPIRAKIS, CHARLES N, b Chicago, Ill, July 11, 18; m 42; c 3. PHARMACOLOGY, NUTRITION. *Educ:* Cent YMCA Col, BS, 40; Loyola Univ, Ill, AM, 55; Northwestern Univ, MS, 58, PhD(pharm), 62. *Prof Exp:* Control chemist, Burgess Battery Co, Ill, 40-41; develop engr, Apex Mach Co, 41-43; res chemist, Armour Res Found, 43-45; owner, Vacuum Specialities, 45-51; from instr to asst prof, 51-65, ASSOC PROF BIOL SCI, UNIV ILL, CHICAGO CIRCLE, 65- *Concurrent Pos:* Res assoc nutrit, Med Sch, Northwestern Univ, 54-66. *Res:* Metabolism; cardiac pharmacology; exobiology. *Mailing Add:* Dept of Biol Sci Univ of Ill Chicago IL 60680

SPIRITO, CARL PETER, b Hartford, Conn, Apr 7, 41; m 64; c 3. NEUROBIOLOGY, ETHOLOGY. *Educ:* Cent Conn State Col, BA, 65; Univ Conn, PhD(biol eng), 69. *Prof Exp:* Nat Inst Child Health & Human Develop trainee, Univ Miami, 69-70; asst prof biol, Univ Va, 70-77; assoc prof neurophysiol, Ohio Univ, 77-80; MEM FAC DEPT PHYSIOLOGY, UNIV NEW ENG, 80- *Mem:* Soc Neurosci; Soc Exp Biol & Med. *Res:* Invertebrate neurobiology and behavior; control of locomotion in Crustacea. *Mailing Add:* Dept Physiology Univ New Eng Biddeford ME 04005

SPIRO, CLAUDIA ALISON, b Castro Valley, Calif, March 4, 56. ARITHMETIC FUNCTIONS, PRINE NUMBER THEORY. *Educ:* Calif Inst Technol, BS & MS, 77; Univ Ill, Urbana, PhD(math), 81. *Prof Exp:* Grad teaching asst math, Univ Ill, Urbana, 77-81; GEORGE WILLIAM HILL & EMMY NOETHER INSTR MATH, STATE UNIV NY, BUFFALO, 81- *Mem:* Am Math Soc; Math Asn Am. *Mailing Add:* Dept Math State Univ NY Buffalo NY 14214

SPIRO, HERZL ROBERT, b Burlington, Vt, Apr 22, 35; m 55; c 3. PSYCHIATRY, SOCIAL PSYCHOLOGY. *Educ:* Univ Vt, BA, 55, MD, 60. *Prof Exp:* Intern internal med, Cornell Univ, 60-61; resident psychiat, Johns Hopkins Univ, 61-64, from instr to assoc prof psychiat, 64-71; prof psychiat, Med Sch, prof social psychol, Grad Fac & dir ment health ctr, Rutgers Univ, 71-76; PROF PSYCHIAT & CHMN DEPT, MED COL OF WIS, 76- *Concurrent Pos:* Fel, Johns Hopkins Univ, 61-64; assoc physician-in-charge psychiat liaison serv, Johns Hopkins Hosp, 64-66, psychiatrist-in-charge Henry Phipps outpatient serv, 66-70, dir outpatient & community ment health progs & div group process, 69-71; consult, Bur Disability Ins, Social Security Admin, 64-69; consult, NIMH, 69-, mem ment health serv res rev comt, 71-, mem task force health maintenance orgn, 71-72; mem, Nat Task Force Psychiat Res, 72-73. *Mem:* AAAS; fel Asn Psychiat Asn; fel Am Col Psychiat; fel Am Pub Health Asn; Am Psychosom Soc. *Res:* Social psychiatry including epidemiology of and attitudes towards mental illness; small group theory and practice; health and mental health service delivery systems; psychosomatic medicine and liaison psychiatry. *Mailing Add:* Med Col of Wis 9191 Watertown Plank Rd Milwaukee WI 53226

SPIRO, HOWARD MARGET, b Cambridge, Mass, Mar 23, 24; m 51; c 4. MEDICINE. *Educ:* Harvard Univ, BA, 43, MD, 47. *Prof Exp:* From asst prof to assoc prof, 56-67, PROF MED, SCH MED, YALE UNIV, 67- *Mem:* Am Gastroenterol Asn; Am Soc Clin Invest. *Res:* Gastroenterology. *Mailing Add:* Yale Univ Sch of Med 333 Cedar St New Haven CT 06510

SPIRO, IRVING J, b Chicago, Ill, Sept 20, 13; m 40; c 2. PHYSICS, MECHANICAL ENGINEERING. *Educ:* Ill Inst Technol, BS, 36; Univ Calif, Los Angeles, MS, 61. *Prof Exp:* Design analyst, Int Harvester-Tractor Works, 36-38; chief draftsman, Graf Optical Co, 38-39; design engr, Lockheed Aircraft Corp, 38-45; eng supvr, Mission Appliance Corp, 45-47; gen mgr, Roxmar Optical Co, 47-51; chief engr, Borman Eng, Inc, 51-55, treas, 55-56; proj mgr, Aerophys Develop Corp, 56-58; sect head, Space Tech Labs, 58-60; sect head, 60-63, staff engr, 63-70, MGR, AEROSPACE CORP, 70- *Concurrent Pos:* Instr, Univ Calif, Los Angeles, 42-45. *Mem:* Am Soc Mech Engrs; fel Optical Soc Am; Am Inst Aeronaut & Astronaut; Sigma Xi; fel Soc Photo-Optical Instrumentation Engrs (secy, 65-66, vpres, 66-67, pres, 68-70). *Res:* Military infrared systems, especially atmospheric transmission; thermal radiation properties of materials; constituents of smog and smog measuring instruments; servo systems utilizing man optics combinations. *Mailing Add:* 4924 Mammoth Ave Sherman Oaks CA 91423

SPIRO, JULIUS, b New York, NY, Nov 20, 21; m 46; c 2. ELECTRONIC ENGINEERING. *Educ:* City Col New York, BS, 53. *Prof Exp:* Electronic engr, Nevis Cyclotron, Columbia Univ, 47-53, Hudson Labs, 53-54; SR ELEC ENGR, ACCELERATOR DEPT, BROOKHAVEN NAT LAB, 54- *Mem:* Sr mem Inst Elec & Electronics Engrs. *Res:* Electronic engineering applied to high energy particle accelerator design; logic and control systems for particle accelerators. *Mailing Add:* Brookhaven Nat Lab Upton NY 11973

SPIRO, MARY JANE, b Syracuse, NY, Nov 15, 30; m 52; c 2. BIOCHEMISTRY. *Educ:* Syracuse Univ, AB, 52, PhD, 55. *Prof Exp:* Res assoc biochem, Col Med, State Univ NY Upstate Med Ctr, 55-56; res assoc, 60-70, PRIN ASSOC MED, HARVARD MED SCH, 70- *Concurrent Pos:* Res fel, Harvard Med Sch, 56-60; sr investr, Joslin Res Lab, 74- *Mem:* Am Soc Biol Chemists. *Res:* Protein and complex saccharide biosynthesis and chemistry. *Mailing Add:* Joslin Res Lab One Joslin Pl Boston MA 02215

SPIRO, ROBERT GUNTER, b Berlin, Ger, Jan 5, 29; nat US; m 52; c 2. BIOCHEMISTRY. *Educ:* Columbia Univ, AB, 51; State Univ NY, MD, 55. *Hon Degrees:* AM, Harvard Univ, 75. *Prof Exp:* Intern, Syracuse Med Ctr, NY, 55-56; res assoc med, 60-63, from assoc to assoc prof biol chem, 64-74, PROF BIOL CHEM, HARVARD MED SCH, 74- *Concurrent Pos:* Am Cancer Soc res fel biochem, Harvard Med Sch, 56-58 & res fel med, Mass Gen Hosp, 58-60; USPHS res fel, 58-59; Am Heart Asn advan res fel, 59-61; estab investr, Am Heart Asn, 61-66; sr investr, Joslin Res Lab, 61- *Honors & Awards:* Lilly Award, Am Diabetes Asn, 68; Claude Bernard Award, Europ Asn Study Diabetes, 75. *Mem:* Am Diabetes Asn; Am Soc Biol Chem; Am Chem Soc; Soc Complex Carbohydrates (pres, 78). *Res:* Chemical structure and biosynthesis of glycoproteins; biochemistry and biology of cell surfaces and basement membranes; biochemistry of diabetes mellitus; regulatory action of insulin; chemistry of connective tissues and basement membranes. *Mailing Add:* Joslin Res Lab One Joslin Place Boston MA 02215

SPIRO, THOMAS, b St Louis, Mo, May 29, 47. NEUROANATOMY, ANATOMY. *Educ:* Univ Mo, St Louis, BA, 71; St Louis Univ, MS(R), 76, PhD(anat), 78. *Prof Exp:* RES ASSOC ANAT, ST LOUIS UNIV, 78- *Mem:* Soc Neurosci; Sigma Xi. *Res:* Neuroanatomy with emphasis on modern hodological methodology. *Mailing Add:* Dept of Anat 1402 S Grand Blvd St Louis MO 63102

SPIRO, THOMAS GEORGE, b Aruba, Netherlands Antilles, Nov 7, 35; m 59; c 2. CHEMISTRY. *Educ:* Univ Calif, Los Angeles, BS, 56; Mass Inst Technol, PhD(chem), 60. *Prof Exp:* Fulbright student, Copenhagen, 60-61; res chemist, Calif Res Corp, 61-62; NIH fel, Royal Inst Technol Sweden, 62-63; from instr to assoc prof, 63-64, PROF CHEM, PRINCETON UNIV, 74-, CHMN DEPT, 79- *Mem:* AAAS; Am Chem Soc. *Res:* Resonance Raman spectroscopy; applications to biological structure; role of metals in biology; bonding in inorganic molecules; chemically modified electrodes. *Mailing Add:* Dept of Chem Princeton Univ Princeton NJ 08540

SPIROFF, BORIS E N, b Waukegan, Ill, Dec 5, 25. BIOLOGY, EMBRYOLOGY. *Educ:* Loyola Univ, Ill, BS, 46; Univ Chicago, MS, 49; Northwestern Univ, PhD(biol), 53; Aquinas Inst Philos, MA, 69. *Prof Exp:* From instr to asst prof biol, Loyola Univ, Ill, 52-62; asst prof, Bard Col, 62-64; assoc prof, Canisius Col, 64-66; ASST PROF BIOL, LOYOLA UNIV, CHICAGO, 66- *Mem:* Am Soc Zool; Soc Study Evolution; Am Inst Biol Sci; Sigma Xi. *Res:* Effects of pinealectomy on the domestic fowl; developmental biology; philosophy of science, especially biology. *Mailing Add:* Dept of Biol Sci 6525 N Sheridan Rd Chicago IL 60626

SPIRTES, MORRIS ALBERT, chemistry, pharmacology, deceased

SPITALE, GUY C, b Chicago, Ill, Nov 11, 41; m 68; c 4. NUMERICAL HYDRODYNAMICS, NEUTRAL PARTICLE TRANSPORT. *Educ:* La State Univ, BS, 63; US Air Force Inst Technol, MS, 65; Univ Calif, Davis, PhD(eng appl sci), 74. *Prof Exp:* Nuclear res officer, Air Force Weapons Lab, Kirtland AFB, 65-69; res assoc, Lawrence Livermore Nat Lab, 69-72; asst prof, Air Force Inst Technol, Wright-Patterson AFB, 72-76, chief Res Br, Air Force Tech Appl Ctr, Patrick AFB, 76-79, NUMERICAL HYDRODYNAMICIST, AIR FORCE ARMAMENT LAB, EGLIN AFB, 79- *Concurrent Pos:* Adj prof, Fla Inst Technol, 77-79 & Univ Fla, 79- *Mem:* Am Phys Soc. *Res:* Numerical hydrodynamics and neutral particle transport; shock deformation problems in real solids; interaction of radiation with matter; scientific applications of advanced computers. *Mailing Add:* Air Force Armament Lab Elgin AFB FL 32542

SPITALNY, GEORGE LEONARD, b Philadelphia, Pa, Mar 7, 47. IMMUNOBIOLOGY. *Educ:* Pa State Univ, BS, 69; NY Univ, PhD(immunol, parasitol), 73. *Prof Exp:* Asst res sci, Sch Med, NY Univ, 73, from instr to asst prof immunobiol, 73-75; res assoc, 75-77, ASST MEM IMMUNOBIOL STAFF, TRUDEAU INST, 77- *Concurrent Pos:* Nat Inst Allergy & Infectious Dis fel, Sch Med, NY Univ, 74-75; fel, Trudeau Inst, 75-76, fel, Cancer Res Inst, 77; prin investr, Trudeau Inst, Nat Cancer Inst grant, 78-81; prin investr, Grant Nat Inst Alergy & Infectious Dis, 81-84; coprin investr, Grant Nat Cancer Inst, 81-85. *Mem:* Am Soc Microbiol; Am Mosquito Control Asn; Am Soc Trop Med & Hyg. *Res:* Mechanisms of immunity to infectious and neoplastic diseases; immunological mechanisms of sporozoite-induced immunity to rodent malaria; modification of existing methods for preparation of a sporozoite vaccine. *Mailing Add:* Trudeau Inst Inc Box 59 Saranac Lake NY 12983

SPITLER, LYNN E, b Grand Rapids, Mich, Sept 28, 38; m 67; c 2. IMMUNOLOGY, INTERNAL MEDICINE. *Educ:* Univ Mich, MD, 63. *Prof Exp:* Intern, Highland-Alameda County Hosp, 63-64; resident, Med Ctr, Univ Calif, San Francisco, 64-66; fel immunol, NY Univ, 66-67; fel immunol, 67-69, instr, 69-71, ASST PROF MED, MED CTR, UNIV CALIF, SAN FRANCISCO, 71- *Concurrent Pos:* Res assoc, Cancer Res Inst, 73-; assoc ed, J Immunol, 74-78; dir res, Children's Hosp, San Francisco, 75-; mem allergy & immunol res comt, Nat Inst Allergy & Infectious Dis, NIH, 76-; mem immunol rev comt, Vet Admin, Washington, DC, 77- *Mem:* Am Asn Immunologists; AAAS; Am Fedn Clin Res. *Res:* Immunopotentiator therapy; transfer factor; levamisole; multiple sclerosis immunology; immunotherapy of malignant melanoma; monoclonal antibodies. *Mailing Add:* Children's Hosp 3700 California St San Francisco CA 94118

SPITLER, MARK THOMAS, b Rockford, Ill, Oct 19, 50. PHYSICAL CHEMISTRY. *Educ:* Stanford Univ, BS, 72; Univ Calif, Berkeley, PhD(phys chem), 77. *Prof Exp:* Guest scientist, Fritz Haber Inst, Max Planck Soc, 77-78; ASST PROF CHEM, MOUNT HOLYOKE COL, 79- *Concurrent Pos:* Vis asst prof chem, Amherst Col, 78-79. *Mem:* Sigma Xi; Am Chem Soc; AAAS; Electrochem Soc. *Res:* Photoelectrochemistry; semiconductor electrochemistry; photochemical energy conversion photochemistry at electrified interfaces. *Mailing Add:* Dept of Chem Mount Holyoke Col South Hadley MA 01075

SPITSBERGEN, JAMES CLIFFORD, b Washington, DC, Sept 1, 26; m 80; c 2. PHYSICAL POLYMER CHEMISTRY. *Educ:* George Washinton Univ, BS, 49; Univ Del, MS, 59, PhD(phys polymer chem), 62. *Prof Exp:* Chemist, Eng Res & Develop Labs, Army Eng Corp, 51; chemist, Elec Hose & Rubber Co, 51-57; sr chemist, 57-61; sr chemist, Elastomers Lab, E I du Pont de Nemours & Co, 62-68; PROJ LEADER POLYMER RES & DEVELOP, CORP RES & DEVELOP LAB, WITCO CHEM CORP, 68- *Mem:* Am Chem Soc; Soc Plastics Eng. *Res:* Elastomer technology, particularly compositions for hose; molecular weight distribution; rheology relationships of elastomers, particularly neoprene; synthesis of thermosetting; polymer additive-property relationships; structure-property relationships of polymers, particularly thermosets. *Mailing Add:* Witco Chem Corp Res & Develop Lab 100 Bauer Dr Oakland NJ 07436

SPITTELL, JOHN A, JR, b Baltimore, Md, Apr 7, 25; m 49; c 5. INTERNAL MEDICINE, CARDIOVASCULAR DISEASES. *Educ:* Franklin & Marshall Col, BS, 44; Univ Md, MD, 49; Univ Minn, MS, 55. *Prof Exp:* From asst prof to assoc prof, 62-73, vchmn educ, Dept Med, Mayo Clin, 72-76, prof, 73-80, MARY LOWELL LEARY PROF MED, MAYO MED SCH, UNIV MINN, 80-, ASSOC DIR CONTINUING EDUC, MAYO FOUND, 78- *Concurrent Pos:* NIH grant, 64-68; consult, Mayo Clin, 56-; mem spec ad hoc comt, Food & Drug Admin, 63; Nat Cardiovasc Conf Peripheral Vascular Dis, 64. *Mem:* Fel Am Col Physicians; fel Am Col Cardiol. *Res:* Peripheral vascular disease; relationship of changes of blood coagulation and intravascular thrombosis; mechanism of action of Coumarin anticoagulants. *Mailing Add:* Mayo Med Sch Univ of Minn Rochester MN 55901

SPITTLER, ERNEST GEORGE, b Cleveland, Ohio, May 4, 28. CHEMISTRY. *Educ:* Loyola Univ, Ill, AB, 51, PhL(philos), 53, ThL(theol), 63; Cath Univ Am, PhD(chem), 59. *Prof Exp:* Instr physics, Loyola Acad, Ill, 53-54; asst prof, 65-76, ASSOC PROF CHEM, JOHN CARROLL UNIV, 76- *Concurrent Pos:* Res assoc, Bushy Run Radiation Lab, Mellon Inst, 64-66; secy bd trustees, John Carroll Univ, 69-71, mem bd trustees, 80- *Mem:* Am Chem Soc; Hist Sci Soc. *Res:* Mercury-photosensitized reactions of hydrocarbon systems; use of carbon-14 tagged molecules as tracers in studying gas phase reactions; chemical effects of lasers and ultra-sound; photochemistry of inorganic complexes; history of periodic table; development of theories of chemistry. *Mailing Add:* Dept of Chem John Carroll Univ University Heights OH 44118

SPITTLER, TERRY DALE, b Buffalo, NY, Apr 29, 43; m 74; c 3. ORGANIC CHEMISTRY, PESTICIDE CHEMISTRY. *Educ:* Bowling Green State Univ, BA, 65; State Univ NY, Buffalo, MS, 68; State Univ NY, Albany, PhD(org chem), 74. *Prof Exp:* Res assoc paper & pulp, State Univ NY Col Environ Sci & Forestry, 74-75; res assoc coal & asphalt, Mont State Univ, 75-77; LAB COORDR, PESTICIDE RESIDUES, NY STATE AGR EXP STA, CORNELL UNIV, 77- *Mem:* Am Chem Soc. *Res:* Analytical organic methods development in pesticide residues; carbon and proton nuclear magnetic resonance; groundwater pollution and quality determination; pulp bleaching with alkaline hydrogen peroxide; pesticide worker exposure to second disposal. *Mailing Add:* NY State Agr Exp Sta Cornell Univ Geneva NY 14456

SPITZ, WERNER URI, b Stargard, Ger, Aug 22, 26; US citizen; m; c 3. PATHOLOGY, FORENSIC MEDICINE. *Educ:* Hebrew Univ, Jerusalem, MD, 53; Am Bd Path, dipl & cert path anat, 61, cert forensic path, 65. *Prof Exp:* Resident path, Tel-Hashomer Govt Hosp, Israel, 53-56; resident forensic med, Hebrew Univ, Jerusalem, 56-59; asst forensic path, Free Univ Berlin, 61-63; assoc med examr, Md Med-Legal Found, 63-65; asst med examr, Off Chief Med Examr, Md, 65-69, dep chief med examr, 69-72; CHIEF MED EXAMR, WAYNE COUNTY, MICH, 72-; ASSOC PROF PATH, SCH MED, WAYNE STATE UNIV, 72- *Concurrent Pos:* Res fel forensic path, Univ Md, Baltimore City, 59-61; Nat Inst Gen Med Sci training & res grant forensic path, Md State Med Examr, 62-, NIH grant, 64-66; consult path, Israel Ministry of Health, 57-59; lectr, Johns Hopkins Univ, 66, assoc prof, Sch Hyg & Pub Health, 67-72, consult, appl physics lab, 72-; asst prof, Sch Med, Univ Md, 66, clin assoc prof, 69-72, mem grad fac, College Park, 70-; dir res & training, Md Med-Legal Found, 67-; mem ed bd, J Forensic Sci, J Legal Med, Excerpta Medica-Forensic Sci. *Mem:* Fel Col Am Path; fel Am Soc Clin Path; AMA; Soc Exp Biol & Med; Nat Asn Med Examrs. *Res:* Mechanism of death by drowning; pathology of vehicular trauma; wound patterns by firearms and other agents. *Mailing Add:* Off Chief Med Examr 400 E Lafayette St Detroit MI 48226

SPITZBART, ABRAHAM, b New York, NY, Oct 13, 15; m. MATHEMATICS. *Educ:* City Col New York, BS, 35; Harvard Univ, AM, 36, PhD(math), 40. *Prof Exp:* Instr math, Harvard Univ, 37-40, City Col New York, 40-41 & Univ Minn, 42; prof, Col of St Thomas, 42-43; from instr to assoc prof, 45-61, PROF MATH, UNIV WIS-MILWAUKEE, 61- *Mem:* Am Math Soc; Math Asn Am. *Res:* Approximation theory in complex variables; approximation in the sense of least p. th powers with auxiliary conditions of interpolation; numerical analysis. *Mailing Add:* Dept of Math Univ of Wis Milwaukee WI 53201

SPITZE, LEROY ALVIN, b Ford Co, Kans, Sept 7, 17; m 42; c 5. CHEMISTRY. *Educ:* Southwestern Col, Kans, AB, 39; Rensselaer Polytech Inst, MS, 41, PhD(phys chem), 42. *Prof Exp:* Asst, Rensselaer Polytech Inst, 39-42; sr phys chemist, Owens-Corning Fiberglas Corp, Ohio, 42-47; prof chem, Southwestern Col, Kans, 47-55, chmn div natural sci, 52-55; assoc prof, 55-60, PROF CHEM, SAN JOSE STATE UNIV, 60- *Concurrent Pos:* Fulbright lectr, Vidyodaya Univ Ceylon, 65-66; NASA res grant, 70-; consult, FMC Corp, IBM Corp & Lockheed Missiles & Space Co. *Mem:* Am Chem Soc. *Res:* Adsorption; surface properties; reverse osmosis and hyperfiltration; diffusion; polymer application; transport parameters in waste water purification; superoxides; numeral separation. *Mailing Add:* Dept of Chem San Jose State Univ San Jose CA 95192

SPITZER, FRANK L, b Vienna, Austria, July 24, 26; nat US; m 51; c 2. MATHEMATICS. *Educ:* Univ Mich, PhD(math), 53. *Prof Exp:* From instr to asst prof math, Calif Inst Technol, 53-56; assoc prof, Univ Minn, 58-61; PROF MATH, CORNELL UNIV, 61- *Concurrent Pos:* NSF sr fel, 60-61; Guggenheim fel, 65-66. *Mem:* Am Math Soc. *Res:* Probability theory, mathematical analysis. *Mailing Add:* Dept of Math Cornell Univ Ithaca NY 14850

SPITZER, HERMANN JOSEF, thermodynamics, low temperature physics, see previous edition

SPITZER, IRWIN ASHER, b Los Angeles, Calif, July 4, 22; m 53; c 2. SYSTEMS ENGINEERING, MECHANICAL ENGINEERING. *Educ:* Univ Calif, BS, 44. *Prof Exp:* Sr engr, Kaiser Steel Corp, 47-56; prin engr, Grand Cent Rocket Co, 56-62; sr prog mgr, Lockheed Propulsion Co, 62-73; asst dir procurement, Amecom Div, Litton Indust, 73-75; SR STAFF ENGR, BALLISTIC MISSILE DIV, TRW SYSTS, 75- *Mem:* Am Soc Qual Control; Am Inst Aeronaut & Astronaut; Air Force Asn. *Res:* Solid rocket propulsion systems; advanced inter-continental ballistic missile basing concepts. *Mailing Add:* 306 Marcia St Redlands CA 92373

SPITZER, JEFFREY CHANDLER, b Malden, Mass, Dec 1, 40; m 67; c 1. ORGANIC CHEMISTRY, SPECTROSCOPY. *Educ:* Mass Inst Technol, BS, 61; Univ Ariz, PhD(chem), 66. *Prof Exp:* Res assoc org chem, Univ Calif, 66-67; asst ed, 67-69, sr assoc indexer, 69-79, SR ED, CHEM ABSTRACTS SERV, 79- *Res:* Terpene and polyacetylene structure determination; synthesis of pyrrole derivatives. *Mailing Add:* 2291 Buckley Rd Columbus OH 43220

SPITZER, JOHN J, b Baja, Hungary, Mar 9, 27; m 51; c 2. PHYSIOLOGY. *Educ:* Univ Munich, MD, 50. *Prof Exp:* Demonstr physiol, Sch Med, Univ Budapest, 47-49; lectr, Sch Med, Dalhousie Univ, 51-52; asst prof, Fla State Univ, 52-54; res scientist, Div Labs & Res, NY State Dept Health, 54-57; from asst prof to prof physiol, Hahnemann Med Col, 57-73; PROF PHYSIOL & HEAD DEPT, LA STATE UNIV MED CTR, NEW ORLEANS, 73- *Concurrent Pos:* Vis scientist, Lab Physiol, Oxford Univ. *Mem:* AAAS; Am Physiol Soc; Soc Exp Biol & Med; Am Heart Asn; NY Acad Sci. *Res:* Substrate metabolism in vivo; fatty acid mobilization, transport and metabolism; shock and metabolism; brain metabolism. *Mailing Add:* Dept of Physiol La State Univ Med Ctr New Orleans LA 70112

SPITZER, JUDY A, b Budapest, Hungary, Feb 25, 31; US citizen; m 51; c 2. PHYSIOLOGY, BIOCHEMISTRY. *Educ:* Fla State Univ, BA, 53; Albany Med Col, MS, 55; Hahnemann Med Col, PhD(microbiol, immunol), 63. *Prof Exp:* Res asst physiol, Fac Med, Dalhousie Univ, 51-52; asst biochem, Fla State Univ, 53-54; biochemist, Div Labs & Res, NY State Dept Health, 54-57; res assoc physiol, Hahnemann Med Col, 57-61 & 62-70, res asst prof physiol & biophys, 70-72; res assoc prof, 72-73, assoc prof med & physiol, 73-79, PROF PHYSIOL MED, LA STATE UNIV MED CTR, NEW ORLEANS, 79- *Concurrent Pos:* Prin investr, Heart Asn Southeastern Pa grant, 59-60, Off Naval Res Contract, 73- & NIH grant, 82- *Mem:* NY Acad Sci; fel Am Heart Asn; Am Physiol Soc; Shock Soc; Soc Exp Biol Med. *Res:* Adipose tissue metabolism; metabolic and endocrine changes in shock. *Mailing Add:* Dept of Physiol La State Univ Med Ctr New Orleans LA 70112

SPITZER, LYMAN, JR, b Toledo, Ohio, June 26, 14; m 40; c 4. ASTRONOMY, ASTROPHYSICS. *Educ:* Yale Univ, BA, 35; Princeton Univ, MA, 37, PhD(astrophys), 38. *Hon Degrees:* DSc, Yale Univ, 58, Case Inst Technol, 60 & Harvard Univ, 75; LLD, Univ Toledo, 63. *Prof Exp:* Nat Res Coun fel, Harvard Univ, 38-39; instr physics, Yale Univ, 39-41, instr astron & physics, 41-42; scientist spec studies group, Div War Res, Columbia Univ, 42-44, dir sonar anal group, 44-46; assoc prof physics, Yale Univ, 46-47; prof, Princeton Univ, 47-51, Young prof astron, 51-82, chmn dept & dir observ, 47-79. *Concurrent Pos:* Dir, Proj Matterhorn, Princeton Univ, 53-61, chmn exec comt, Plasma Physics Lab, 61-67 & Univ Res Bd, 67-72. *Honors & Awards:* Rittenhouse Medal, Franklin Inst, 57; Except Sci Achievement Medal, NASA, 72; Bruce Gold Medal, Astron Soc Pac, 73; Henry Draper Medal, Nat Acad Sci, 74; James Clerk Maxwell Prize, Am Phys Soc, 75; Distinguished Pub Serv Medal, NASA, 76; Gold Medal, Royal Astron Soc, 78; Jules Janssen Medal, Soc Astron de France, 80; Franklin Medal, Franklin Inst, 80. *Mem:* Nat Acad Sci; Am Astron Soc (pres, 60-62); foreign corresp Royal Soc Sci, Liege; Am Acad Arts & Sci; foreign assoc Royal Astron Soc England. *Res:* Interstellar matter; dynamics of stellar systems; physics of fully ionized gases; controlled thermonuclear research; space astronomy. *Mailing Add:* Princeton Univ Observ Princeton NJ 85404

SPITZER, NICHOLAS CANADAY, b New York, NY, Nov 8, 42; m 67; c 1. DEVELOPMENTAL NEUROBIOLOGY, NEUROPHYSIOLOGY. *Educ:* Harvard Univ, BA, 64, PhD(neurobiol), 69. *Prof Exp:* Asst prof, 73-77, ASSOC PROF BIOL, UNIV CALIF, SAN DIEGO, 77- *Mem:* Soc Neurosci; AAAS. *Res:* Embryonic development of neuronal membrane properties in vivo and in culture characterizing the order of appearance of phenotypes and defining the roles of RNA and protein synthesis in their expression. *Mailing Add:* B-022 Biol Dept Univ Calif San Diego La Jolla CA 92093

SPITZER, RALPH, b New York, NY, Feb 9, 18; m 41; c 2. CHEMISTRY, PATHOLOGY. *Educ:* Cornell Univ, AB, 38; Calif Inst Technol, PhD(chem), 41; Univ Man, MD, 57; FRCPath. *Prof Exp:* Assoc phys chemist, Nat Adv Comt Aeronaut, 42-43; res assoc, Woods Hole Oceanog Inst, 43-45; assoc prof chem, Ore State Col, 46-50 & Univ Kans City, 50-53; res assoc med, Univ Man, 53-54; clin instr, 58-65, ASSOC PROF CHEM PATH, UNIV BC, 65- *Concurrent Pos:* Dir biochem labs, Royal Columbian Hosp, 58-; vis sr lectr, Univ Otago, NZ, 62-63. *Mem:* Acad Lab Physicians & Scientists; Can Soc Clin Chem. *Res:* Chemical biology and pathology; endocrine effects of tumors; clinical enzymology; psychopharmacology. *Mailing Add:* 1911 Knox Rd Vancouver BC V6T 1S5 Can

SPITZER, ROBERT HARRY, b Chicago, Ill, July 25, 29. BIOCHEMISTRY. *Educ:* Valparaiso Univ, BA, 51; Loyola Univ, Ill, MS, 53, PhD(biochem), 55. *Prof Exp:* Instr exp surg, Sch Med, Wash Univ, 55-56; res chemist, Gillette Co, 56-61; from res assoc med to res assoc enzymol & exp hypersensitivity, 61-65, from asst prof enzymol & exp hypersensitivity to asst prof biochem, 65-70, assoc prof, 70-75, PROF BIOCHEM, CHICAGO MED SCH, 75- *Mem:* Am Asn Immunologists. *Res:* Cell biology; metabolism in lower vertebrates; immunobiology. *Mailing Add:* Dept Biochem Chicago Med Sch Chicago IL 60612

SPITZER, ROGER EARL, b Washington, DC, June 20, 35; m 62; c 3. PEDIATRICS, IMMUNOLOGY. *Educ:* George Washington Univ, BS, 58; Howard Univ, MD, 62; Am Bd Pediat, dipl, 68. *Prof Exp:* Intern, Gen Hosp, Cincinnati, 62-63; resident pediat, Children's Hosp, 63-65; asst prof pediat, Col Med, Univ Cincinnati, 69-73; assoc prof, 73-77, PROF PEDIAT, STATE UNIV NY UPSTATE MED CTR, 77- *Concurrent Pos:* NIH spec fel nephrology-immunol, Children's Hosp Res Found, 67-69; res assoc immunol, Children's Hosp Res Found & attend pediatrician, Children's Hosp Med Ctr, 69-73, attend nephrologist, 72-73; clinician pediat, Gen Hosp, 59-73; consult, pediatrician, Good Samaritan Hosp, 71-73. *Mem:* Fel Am Acad Pediat; Am Soc Pediat Nephrology; Am Soc Nephrology; Soc Pediat Res; Am Asn Immunol. *Res:* Biology of complement; pediatric renal disease. *Mailing Add:* Dept of Pediat State Univ NY Upstate Med Ctr Syracuse NY 13210

SPITZER, WILLIAM CARL, b Chicago, Ill, Sept 15, 14; m 42; c 1. ORGANIC POLYMER CHEMISTRY. *Educ:* Univ Chicago, BS, 36, PhD(org chem), 40. *Prof Exp:* Org chemist, Sherwin-Williams Co, 40-47; org chemist, Paint Res Assoc Inc, 48-66, dir res, 66-75, DIR RES, PRA LABS, INC, 75- *Concurrent Pos:* Instr, Ill Inst Technol, 50-51; lectr, DePaul Univ, 64. *Mem:* Am Chem Soc; Am Oil Chemists Soc; Am Soc Testing & Mat. *Res:* Organic coatings; synthetic resins; drying oils. *Mailing Add:* 221 White Fawn Trail Downers Grove IL 60515

SPITZER, WILLIAM GEORGE, b Los Angeles, Calif, Apr 24, 27; m 49; c 2. PHYSICS. *Educ:* Univ Calif, Los Angeles, BA, 49; Univ Southern Calif, MS, 52; Purdue Univ, PhD(physics), 57. *Prof Exp:* Mem tech staff, Hughes Aircraft Co, 52-53, Bell Labs, Inc, 57-62 & Bell & Howell Res Ctr, 62-63; chmn dept mat sci, 67-69 & 78-81, dept physics, 69-72, dean natural sci, 72-73, PROF PHYSICS, ELEC ENG & MAT SCI, UNIV SOUTHERN CALIF, 63- *Mem:* Fel Am Phys Soc; Inst Elec & Electronics Engrs; Sigma Xi. *Res:* Solid state and semiconductor physics; infrared properties of semiconductors and dielectrics. *Mailing Add:* Dept of Physics Seaver Sci Ctr Los Angeles CA 90007

SPITZIG, WILLIAM A(NDREW), b Cleveland, Ohio, Sept 12, 31; m 59; c 4. METALLURGY, SOLID STATE PHYSICS. *Educ:* Cleveland State Univ, BS, 60; Case Western Reserve Univ, MS, 62, PhD(metall), 65. *Prof Exp:* Metallurgist, TRW, Inc, 60-62; mat engr, Lewis Res Ctr, NASA, 62-66; res metallurgist, 66-68, sr scientist, 68-76, ASSOC RES CONSULT, US STEEL CORP, RES CTR, 76- *Mem:* Am Soc Metals; Am Inst Mining, Metall & Petrol Engrs. *Res:* Deformation of body centered cubic single crystals; investigation of microscopic fracture mechanisms in ultrahigh strength steels; titanium alloys; aluminum alloys; polymers; strengthening mechanisms in ultrahigh strength steels; thermally activated deformation; deformation under superimposed hydrostatic pressure. *Mailing Add:* US Steel Corp Res Ctr MS-59 125 Jamison Lane Monroeville PA 15146

SPITZNAGEL, EDWARD LAWRENCE, JR, b Cincinnati, Ohio, Sept 4, 41. ALGEBRA. *Educ:* Xavier Univ, BS, 62; Univ Chicago, MS, 63, PhD(math), 65. *Prof Exp:* From instr to asst prof math, Northwestern Univ, Ill, 65-69; assoc prof, 69-80, PROF MATH, WASH UNIV, 80- *Mem:* Am Math Soc; Math Asn Am. *Res:* Finite group theory; statistics. *Mailing Add:* Dept of Math Washington Univ St Louis MO 63130

SPITZNAGEL, JOHN A, b Pittsburgh, Pa, June 27, 41; m 72; c 2. ENGINEERING, NUCLEAR METALLURGY. *Educ:* Carnegie Inst Technol, BS, 63, MS, 64; Carnegie-Mellon Univ, PhD(metall & mat sci), 69. *Prof Exp:* Mem staff soil mech, US Army Waterways Exp Sta, 68-70; sr engr, 70-74, fel engr, 74-80, ADV ENGR, WESTINGHOUSE RES & DEVELOP CTR, 80- *Concurrent Pos:* Prin investr ion beam effects in solids, NSF, 74-; prin investr irradiation response mat fusion, Dept Energy, 77-81; mem, Damage Analysis & Fundamental Studies Task Group, Dept Energy, 77-; ed, Advan Techniques Characterizing Microstruct, Am Inst Mining, Metall & Petrol Engrs, 80-82. *Mem:* Am Inst Mining, Metall & Petrol Engrs; Am Soc Metals; Am Nuclear Soc; Am Soc Testing & Mat. *Res:* Fundamental processes of ion beam & neutron interactions with solids; microstructural and microchemical effects of irradiation in metals and semiconductors; modification of surfaces and bulk mechanical properties by irradiation and ion implantation. *Mailing Add:* Westinghouse Res & Develop Ctr 1310 Beulah Rd Pittsburgh PA 15235

SPITZNAGEL, JOHN KEITH, b Peoria, Ill, Apr 11, 23; m 47; c 5. MICROBIOLOGY, MEDICINE. *Educ:* Columbia Univ, BA, 43, MD, 46; Am Bd Internal Med, dipl, 53. *Prof Exp:* Asst instr basic sci, US Army Med Sch, 47-49; asst med, Wash Univ, 49-52; vis investr, Rockefeller Inst, 52-53; from chief infectious dis serv to chief med serv, US Army Hosp, Ft Bragg, 53-57; from lectr bact & immunol to assoc prof bact, immunol & med, Univ NC, Chapel Hill, 57-67, prof, 67-79; PROF MICROBIOL & IMMUNOL & CHMN DEPT, EMORY UNIV, 79- *Concurrent Pos:* USPHS sr res fel, 58-68; vis investr, Nat Inst Med Res, Eng, 67-68; consult mem, Bact & Mycol Study Sect, USPHS-Dept Health, Educ & Welfare; chmn, Bact Mycol Study Sect, NIH, 77-79. *Mem:* Infectious Dis Soc; Am Soc Microbiol; Sigma Xi; fel Am Col Physicians; Am Asn Immunol. *Res:* Role of cationic proteins in oxygen-independent antimicrobial capacity of neutrophil granulocytic granules. *Mailing Add:* Dept Microbiol Woodruff Mem Bldg Sch Med Emory Univ Atlanta GA 30322

SPITZNAGLE, LARRY ALLEN, b Lafayette, Ind, Oct, 17, 43; m 61; c 2. RADIOPHARMACEUTICAL CHEMISTRY. *Educ:* Purdue Univ, BS, 65, MS, 66, PhD(bionucleonics), 69. *Prof Exp:* Asst prof bionucleonics, Sch Pharm, Univ Wash, 69-75; asst prof nuclear med, Sch Med, Univ Conn Health Ctr, 75-79; assoc prof med chem, Sch Pharm, Univ Md, Baltimore, 79-81; ASSOC PROF NUCLEAR MED, SCH MED, UNIV CONN HEALTH CTR, 81- *Concurrent Pos:* NIH res grants, 71-74 & 75-79. *Mem:* AAAS; Am Chem Soc; Am Pharmaceut Asn; Soc Nuclear Med. *Res:* Development of new and improved radio-pharmaceuticals; use of nuclear technology to study problems in the biological sciences. *Mailing Add:* Dept of Nuclear Med Univ of Conn Health Ctr Farmington CT 06032

SPITZNOGLE, FRANK RAYMOND, b Madison, Kans, May 31, 40; m 61. PHYSICS. *Educ:* Univ Kans, BS, 62; Univ Tex, MA, 65, PhD(physics), 66. *Prof Exp:* Res physicist, US Navy Mine Defense Lab, 62-66; mem tech staff, 66-69, mgr anal & simulation br, 69-70, mgr applns eng, 70-74, mgr comput systs PCC, 74-76, DEPT MGR COMPUT SYSTS, TEX INSTRUMENTS, INC, 76- *Mem:* Am Inst Elec & Electronics Engrs. *Res:* Industrial and commercial computer systems engineering and marketing; acoustical signal processing; sonar; electromagnetic theory. *Mailing Add:* Texas Instruments Inc PO Box 2909 Austin TX 78769

SPIVACK, HARVEY MARVIN, b Brooklyn, NY, Feb 3, 48; m 72; c 1. NAVAL SYSTEMS ANALYSIS, OCEAN ACOUSTICS. *Educ:* Brooklyn Col, BS, 68; Purdue Univ, MS, 70, PhD(physics), 76. *Prof Exp:* Res assoc physics, Purdue Univ, 76; asst physicist, Brookhaven Nat Lab, 77; MEM PROF STAFF SYSTS ANAL, CTR NAVAL ANAL, 77- *Mem:* Am Phys Soc. *Res:* Cost and effectiveness of military systems; neutrino physics; theory of weak interactions. *Mailing Add:* Ctr for Naval Anal 2000 N Beauregard St Alexandria VA 22311

SPIVAK, JERRY LEPOW, b New York, NY, Jan 5, 38; m 67; c 2. HEMATOLOGY. *Educ:* Princeton Univ, AB, 60; Cornell Univ, MD, 64; Am Bd Int Med dipl, 71, cert hemat, 75. *Prof Exp:* Sr resident med, New York Hosp, 68-69; intern, Johns Hopkins Hosp, 64-65, asst resident, 65-66, chief resident, 71-72, asst prof, 72-78, ASSOC PROF MED, SCH MED, JOHNS HOPKINS UNIV, 78-, DIR, DIV HEMAT, 80. *Concurrent Pos:* Clin assoc, Nat Cancer Inst, 66-68; fel hemat, Johns Hopkins Hosp, 69-61; investr med, Howard Hughes Med Inst, 72- *Honors & Awards:* Borden Award. *Mem:* Am Fedn Clin Res; Am Soc Hemat; Soc Exp Biol & Med; fel Am Col Physicians. *Res:* Erythropoietin and the regulation of erythropoiesis. *Mailing Add:* Sch of Med Johns Hopkins Univ 600 N Wolfe St Baltimore MD 21205

SPIVAK, STEVEN MARK, b New York, NY, Oct 11, 42; div. TEXTILES, TEXTILE ENGINEERING. *Educ:* Philadelphia Col Textiles & Sci, BS, 63; Ga Inst Technol, MS, 65; Univ Manchester, PhD(polymer & fiber sci), 67. *Prof Exp:* Asst prof textiles & apparel res assoc, Philadelphia Col Textiles & Sci, 67-70; asst prof, 70-74, ASSOC PROF TEXTILES & CONSUMER ECON, UNIV MD, 74- *Concurrent Pos:* Tech adv, Aids Int, Arlington, Va, 75-; dir, Atex Consults, Washington, DC, 76- *Mem:* Am Asn Textile Chemists & Colorists; Standards Engrs Soc; Sigma Xi; Am Chem Soc; Fiber Soc. *Res:* End-use performance aspects of textiles and related materials, including interior textiles (carpet, upholstery, draperies), flammability (seams, apparel, extinguishability), weathering and gaseous pollutants, and clothing comfort. *Mailing Add:* Dept of Textiles & Consumer Econ Univ of Md College Park MD 20742

SPIVEY, BRUCE ELDON, b Cedar Rapids, Iowa, Aug 29, 34; m 56; c 2. OPHTHALMOLOGY, MEDICAL EDUCATION. *Educ:* Coe Col, BA, 55; Univ Iowa, MD, 59, MS, 64; Univ Ill, MEd, 69; Am Bd Ophthal, dipl, 65. *Prof Exp:* Intern, Highland-Alameda County Hosp, Oakland, Calif, 59-60; resident, Univ Hosps, Iowa City, 60-63; res assoc ophthal, Col Med, Univ Iowa, 63-64, from asst prof to assoc prof, 66-71; dean, Sch Med, Sci, 71-76, PROF OPHTHAL & HEAD DEPT, PAC MED CTR, UNIV PAC, 71- *Concurrent Pos:* Co-dir, NIH grants, 67 & 72. *Mem:* AMA; Am Col Surgeons; Am Acad Ophthal (vpres, 77-); Pan-Am Asn Ophthal; Asn Res Vision & Ophthal. *Res:* Strabismus; opthalmologic genetics. *Mailing Add:* Dept of Ophthal Pac Med Ctr Box 7999 San Francisco CA 94120

SPIVEY, GARY H, b Midland, Tex, Dec 3, 43; m 65; c 2. ENVIRONMENTAL EPIDEMIOLOGY. *Educ:* Univ Calif, Davis, BA, 65; Med Sch, Univ Calif, San Francisco, MD, 69; Johns Hopkins Univ, Baltimore, MPH, 75. *Prof Exp:* Gen Med Officer, Indian Health Serv, USPHS, 70-71, serv unit dir, Whiteriver Serv Unit, 71-72, onsite proj dir, Proj Apache, Maternal & Child Health, 72-73; asst prof, 75-80, ASSOC PROF EPIDEMIOL, SCH PUB HEALTH, UNIV CALIF, LOS ANGELES, 80- *Mem:* Am Pub Health Asn; Soc Epidemiol Res; Soc Occup & Environ Health. *Res:* Lead poisoning; benign breast disease; vinyl chloride; toxic waste sites. *Mailing Add:* Sch Pub Health Univ Calif Los Angeles CA

SPIVEY, HOWARD OLIN, b Gainesville, Fla, Dec 10, 31; m 59; c 3. BIOPHYSICAL CHEMISTRY. *Educ:* Univ Ky, BS, 54; Harvard Univ, PhD(biochem), 63. *Prof Exp:* Res assoc phys chem, Rockefeller Univ, 62-64; NIH fel chem, Mass Inst Technol, 64-65; asst prof, Univ Md, College Park, 65-67; from asst prof to assoc prof, 67-75, PROF BIOCHEM, OKLA STATE UNIV, 75- *Mem:* Am Chem Soc; Sigma Xi; Am Soc Biol Chemists. *Res:* Physical biochemistry; enzyme properties and mechanisms studies at cellular concentration levels by fast kinetic and supporting methods. *Mailing Add:* Dept of Biochem Okla State Univ Stillwater OK 74074

SPIVEY, ROBERT CHARLES, b Jacksboro, Tex, Apr 22, 09; m 29; c 2. GEOLOGY. *Educ:* Tex Tech Univ, AB, 31; Univ Iowa, MS, 36, PhD(paleont), 38. *Prof Exp:* Asst geol, Univ Iowa, 34-38 & instr, 38-40; geologist & paleontologist, Shell Oil Co, 40-50, sr geologist, 50-61, staff geologist, 61-67; CONSULT GEOLOGIST, 67- *Mem:* Geol Soc Am; Am Asn Petrol Geol. *Res:* Stratigraphy. *Mailing Add:* Rte 2 Box 363 Springdale AR 72764

SPIVEY, WALTER ALLEN, b Wilmington, NC, July 24, 26; m 52; c 2. STATISTICS. *Educ:* Univ NC, AB, 50, MA, 52, PhD(statist), 56. *Prof Exp:* From asst prof to assoc prof, 57-62, PROF STATIST, UNIV MICH, ANN ARBOR, 62- *Concurrent Pos:* NSF fel, Stanford Univ, 57; vis assoc prof, Harvard Univ, 59-60. *Mem:* Fel Royal Statist Soc; Am Statist Asn; Soc Indust & Appl Math; Math Asn Am; Inst Mgt Sci. *Res:* Statistics and data analysis; optimization theory and applications; statistical forecasting. *Mailing Add:* Grad Sch Bus Admin Univ Mich Ann Arbor MI 48109

SPIZIZEN, JOHN, b Winnipeg, Man, Feb 7, 17; US citizen; m 43; c 1. MICROBIOLOGY, BIOCHEMISTRY. *Educ:* Univ Toronto, BA, 39; Calif Inst Technol, PhD(bact), 42. *Prof Exp:* Asst biol, Univ Toronto, 38-39; Nat Res Coun fel med sci, Vanderbilt Univ, 42-43; instr bact, Med Sch, Loyola Univ, Ill, 43; assoc virus res, Sharp & Dohme, Inc, 46-54; from asst prof to assoc prof microbiol, Sch Med, Western Reserve Univ, 54-61; prof microbiol & head dept, Univ Minn, Minneapolis, 61-65; chem dept microbiol, Scripps Clin & Res Found, 65-76, mem dept cellular biol, Res Inst Scripps Clin, 76-79; PROF & HEAD DEPT MICROBIOL, UNIV ARIZ, 79- *Concurrent Pos:* Mem, Life Sci Comt, NASA; mem recombinant DNA adv comt, NIH; mem, Am Cancer Soc Coun, 74-; & Med, Nat Acad Sci & Res Coun, Am Cancer Soc, 74-; adj prof, Univ Calif, San Diego; consult, various co. *Mem:* AAAS; Am Soc Microbiol; Am Soc Biol Chemists; Am Acad Microbiol. *Res:* Cloning of genes in bacillus species; identification and cloning of genes for insecticidal toxins. *Mailing Add:* Dept Molecular & Med Microbiol Univ Ariz Col Med Tucson AZ 84724

SPJUT, HARLAN JACOBSON, b Salt Lake City, Utah, May 3, 22; m; c 5. PATHOLOGY. *Educ:* Univ Utah, BS, 43, MD, 46; Am Bd Path, dipl. *Prof Exp:* Intern, Jackson Mem Hosp, Miami, Fla, 46-47; asst resident path, Salt Lake Vet Hosp, Utah, 49-50; from asst resident to instr, Univ Utah, 50-53; from instr to assoc prof surg path & path, Sch Med, Wash Univ, 54-62; actg chmn dept, 69-72, PROF PATH, BAYLOR COL MED, 62- *Concurrent Pos:* Am Cancer Soc fel surg path, Sch Med, Wash Univ, 53-54; attend pathologist, St Louis Vet Hosp, 55-59; assoc pathologist, Barnes Hosp, 54-62; vis asst, Karolinska Hosp, Stockholm, Sweden, 59-60; attend pathologist, St Luke's Hosp, 71-80; consult, Houston Vet Admin Hosp; sr attend pathologist, Methodist Hosp, 80- *Mem:* Col Am Path; AMA; Int Acad Path. *Res:* Carcinoma; bone and large bowel tumors; cytology in diagnosis of carcinoma of various sites. *Mailing Add:* Dept of Path Baylor Col Med Houston TX 77030

SPLETTSTOESSER, JOHN FREDERICK, b Waconia, Minn, Oct 17, 33; m 56; c 2. GEOLOGY. *Educ:* Univ Minn, 62. *Prof Exp:* Ed, Am Geol Inst, 62-63; head, Sci & Tech Div, Libr Cong, 64-67; asst dir, Inst Polar Studies, Ohio State Univ, 67-69, assoc dir, 69-74; admin dir, Ross Ice Shelf Proj Mgt Off, Univ Nebr, 74-77; PROG MGR MINN GEOL SURV, UNIV MINN, ST PAUL, 77- *Mem:* AAAS; Am Inst Mining, Metall & Petrol Eng; Soc Mining Eng; Arctic Inst NAm; Am Geophys Union. *Res:* Antarctic geologic research; mining geology; scientific editing. *Mailing Add:* Minn Geol Surv 1633 Eustis St St Paul MN 55108

SPLIES, ROBERT GLENN, b Bird Island, Minn, Oct 2, 25; m 52; c 1. ORGANIC CHEMISTRY. *Educ:* Univ Wis, BS, 47, MS, 48, PhD, 51. *Prof Exp:* Instr, Wis State Col, Milwaukee, 51-52; chemist, Solvay Process Div, Allied Chem Corp, NY, 52-53; coordr, Bjorksten Res Lab, Wis, 53-55; chemist, Oscar Mayer & Co, 55-57; asst prof org chem, Univ NDak, 57-59; from asst prof to assoc prof, Univ Wis-Milwaukee, 59-67; assoc prof, 67-71, PROF ORG CHEM, UNIV WIS-WAUKESHA, 71- *Mem:* Am Chem Soc. *Res:* Nitro and amino derivatives of aromatic hydrocarbons; color reactions of alkaloids. *Mailing Add:* Dept of Chem Univ of Wis Waukesha WI 53186

SPLIETHOFF, WILLIAM LUDWIG, b Matamoras, Pa, Apr 8, 26; m 49, 71; c 3. ORGANIC CHEMISTRY. *Educ:* Pa State Univ, BS, 46, MS, 48; Mich State Univ, PhD(org chem), 53. *Prof Exp:* Asst fuel tech, Pa State Univ, 46-48; asst gen org & phys chem, Mich State Univ, 50-52; res chemist textile fibers dept, E I du Pont de Nemours & Co, 52-60; dir mkt res chem div, Gen Mills, Inc, Ill, 60-62; mgr comp develop, 62-67; asst managing dir, Polymer Corp Ltd, Sydney, Australia, 67-69; dir opers indust chem, Chem Div, Gen Mills Chem, Inc, 69-70; vpres, 70-77, EXEC VPRES, HENKEL CORP, 77- *Mem:* Am Chem Soc; Com Develop Asn. *Res:* Mechanism and kinetics of racemization of optically active halides by phenols; condensation polymers; new uses for synthetic fibers; market research and commercial development; general industrial chemical management. *Mailing Add:* Henkel Corp 4620 W 77th St Minneapolis MN 55435

SPLINTER, WILLIAM ELDON, b North Platte, Nebr, Nov 24, 25; m 53; c 4. ENGINEERING. *Educ:* Univ Nebr, BSc, 50; Mich State Univ, MSc, 51, PhD(agr eng), 55. *Prof Exp:* Instr agr eng, Mich State Univ, 53-54; res assoc prof, NC State Univ, 54-61, prof, 61-68; PROF & HEAD DEPT AGR ENG, UNIV NEBR, LINCOLN, 68- *Concurrent Pos:* Consult, Ford Found, IIT Kharagpur, India, 66. *Honors & Awards:* Massey Ferguson Medal, Am Soc Agr Engrs, 78. *Mem:* Fel AAAS; fel Am Soc Agr Engrs (vpres, 76-77, pres, 78-79); Soc Automotive Engrs; Instrument Soc Am; Am Asn Eng Socs. *Res:* Bioengineering of plant systems; systems engineering of crop production; electrostatic application of agricultural pesticides; mathematical modeling of plants; machine design and development; human factors engineering. *Mailing Add:* Dept of Agr Eng Univ of Nebr Lincoln NE 68503

SPLITTER, EARL JOHN, b Lorraine, Kans, June 29, 20; m 43; c 3. VETERINARY PARASITOLOGY. *Educ:* Kans State Col, DVM, 43, MS, 50. *Prof Exp:* Jr state vet, NC State Dept Agr, 43-46; from asst prof to assoc prof path, Kans State Col, 46-57; group leader & asst dep adminr, 77-81, PRIN VET, COOP STATE RES SERV, USDA, 57- *Mem:* Am Vet Med Asn. *Res:* Blood parasitic diseases of domestic animals; research administration; veterinary pathology and medicine. *Mailing Add:* 4 Carole Court Silver Spring MD 20904

SPLITTER, GARY ALLEN, b Lumberton, NC, July 19, 45; m 67. VETERINARY MEDICINE, IMMUNOPATHOLOGY. *Educ:* Kans State Univ, BS, 67, DVM, 69, MS, 70; Wash State Univ, PhD(path), 76. *Prof Exp:* Instr path, Kans State Univ, 69-70; captain, Sch Aerospace Med, US Air Force, 70-72; NIH fel, Dept Vet Path, Wash State Univ, 72-76; ASST PROF IMMUNOPATH, DEPT VET SCI, UNIV WIS-MADISON, 76- *Concurrent Pos:* Ed reviewer, Am Vet Med Asn, 78- *Mem:* Am Vet Med Asn; Am Col Vet Toxicologists. *Res:* Pathology; immunology; mechanisms of host defense in chronic and viral diseases. *Mailing Add:* Dept of Vet Sci 1655 Linden Dr Madison WI 53706

SPLITTGERBER, GEORGE H, b Van Tassel, Wyo, Jan 25, 18; m 42; c 3. INORGANIC CHEMISTRY. *Educ:* Univ Nebr, BSc, 39, MSc, 40; Kans State Univ, PhD(chem), 60. *Prof Exp:* Chemist, Victor Chem Works, 40-42 & Sinclair Res & Develop Co, 42-48; from instr to assoc prof, 48-66, PROF CHEM, COLO STATE UNIV, 66- *Mem:* Am Chem Soc; AAAS; Sigma Xi. *Res:* Antioxidants and corrosion inhibitors; nonaqueous polarography. *Mailing Add:* Dept of Chem Colo State Univ Ft Collins CO 80521

SPLITTSTOESSER, CLARA QUINNELL, b Miles City, Mont, Jan 19, 29; m 59. BACTERIOLOGY, INSECT PATHOLOGY. *Educ:* Mont State Univ, BS, 50; Univ Wis, MS, 51, PhD(bact), 56. *Prof Exp:* Fel, Univ Wis, 56-57; assoc exp surg, Med Ctr, Univ Calif, 57-58; experimentalist, 59-62, RES ASSOC INSECT PATH, NY STATE EXP STA, CORNELL UNIV, 62- *Mem:* Soc Invert Path. *Res:* Physiology of microorganisms; viral and bacterial pathogens of insects. *Mailing Add:* Dept of Entom Cornell Univ NY State Exp Sta Geneva NY 14456

SPLITTSTOESSER, DON FREDERICK, b Norwalk, Wis, 27; m 59. BACTERIOLOGY. *Educ:* Univ Wis, BS, 52, MS, 53, PhD, 56. *Prof Exp:* Proj assoc bact, Univ Wis, 55-56; from asst prof to assoc prof bact, 58-69, PROF MICROBIOL, CORNELL UNIV, 69-, CHMN DEPT, 82- *Concurrent Pos:* Mem, Ad Hoc Subcomt Food Microbiol, Food Protection Comt, Nat Acad Sci-Nat Res Coun, 63 & Comt Microbiol Food, Adv, Bd Mil Personnel Supplies, Nat Res Coun, 72-75, chmn, Food Protection Comt, 82- *Mem:* Am Soc Microbiol; Inst Food Technol; Int Asn Milk, Food & Environ Sanitarians; Am Soc Enologists. *Res:* Drying microorganisms; sanitation in food processing; microbiology of frozen foods; physiology of spore germination; wine fermentation. *Mailing Add:* Dept of Food Sci & Technol Cornell Univ Geneva NY 14456

SPLITTSTOESSER, WALTER E, b Claremont, Minn, Aug 27, 37; m 60; c 3. PLANT PHYSIOLOGY, BIOCHEMISTRY. *Educ:* Univ Minn, BS, 58; SDak State Univ, MS, 60; Purdue Univ, PhD(plant biochem), 63. *Prof Exp:* Plant physiologist, Shell Develop Co, 63-64; biochemist, Univ Calif, Davis, 64-65; plant biochemist, 65-74, head, Div Veg Crops, 73-76, PROF VEG CROPS, UNIV ILL, URBANA, 75- *Concurrent Pos:* NIH fel, 64-65; prof bot & microbiol, Univ Col, London, 72-73; prof soil sci, Rothamsted Exp Sta, Harpenden, Eng, 80. *Honors & Awards:* J H Gourley Award, Am Soc Hort Sci, 74. *Mem:* Am Soc Plant Physiol; Am Soc Hort Sci; Weed Sci Soc Am. *Res:* Plant metabolism; amino acids in germinating seedlings; weed control; metabolism of herbicides in plants; environmental factors affecting herbicide action. *Mailing Add:* 201 Veg Crops Bldg Univ Ill 1103 W Dorner Dr Urbana IL 61801

SPOCK, ALEXANDER, b Shamokin, Pa, May 5, 29. PEDIATRICS, ALLERGY. *Educ:* Loyola Col, Md, BS, 51; Univ Md, MD, 55. *Prof Exp:* From intern to resident pediat, Geisinger Mem Hosp, Danville, Pa, 55-58; from instr to assoc prof, 59-77, PROF PEDIAT, MED CTR, DUKE UNIV, 77- *Concurrent Pos:* Fel pediat allergy, Med Ctr, Duke Univ, 60-62. *Mem:* Am Acad Pediat; Am Acad Allergy; Am Col Allergists; Am Thoracic Soc. *Res:* Immunology; pulmonary physiology; lung disease and allergic problems in pediatric patients. *Mailing Add:* Box 2994 Dept of Pediat Duke Univ Med Ctr Durham NC 27706

SPODICK, DAVID HOWARD, b Hartford, Conn, Sept 9, 27; m 51, 69; c 2. CARDIOLOGY. *Educ:* Bard Col, AB, 47; New York Med Col, MD, 50. *Prof Exp:* From instr to prof med, Tufts Univ, 57-76; PROF MED, UNIV MASS, 76- *Concurrent Pos:* Nat Heart Inst spec fel, WRoxbury Vet Admin Hosp, NY, 56-57; Am Col Physicians Brower Traveling Scholar, 64; sr physician, Lemuel Shattuck Hosp, Boston, 57-76, chief cardiol div, 62-76; chief cardiac diag & res ctr, Boston Eve Clin, 60-; assoc med, Boston City Hosp, 65-, lectr, Sch Med, Boston Univ, 66- & Sch Med, Tufts Univ, 76-; attend cardiologist, Mass Hosp, 76-; dir cardiol div, St Vincent Hosp, 76- *Mem:* Am Col Chest Physicians; Am Fedn Clin Res; Am Col Cardiol; Am Col Physicians; Am Heart Asn. *Res:* Noninvasive polycardiography; clinical pharmacology; exercise physiology; physical diagnosis; diseases of pericardium. *Mailing Add:* Cardiol Div St Vincent Hosp Worcester MA 01604

SPOEHR, ALBERT FREDERICK, b Milwaukee, Wis, Feb 24, 18; m 47. CHEMISTRY. *Educ:* Univ Wis, BS, 42. *Prof Exp:* Lab supvr, Hercules Powder Co, Del, 42-45; res chemist, Am Anode, Inc, 45-53; mgr tech servs, Latex Compounding Div, Polson Rubber Co, Garretsville, 53-70, tech dir, 70-79; PROD MGR, BEARFOOT INC, WADSWORTH, 79- *Mem:* Am Chem Soc. *Res:* Rubber and latex compounding; explosives. *Mailing Add:* 1912 Phelps St Cuyahoga Falls OH 44223

SPOELHOF, CHARLES PETER, b Hackensack, NJ, Aug 6, 30; m 53; c 4. PHYSICS, MATHEMATICS. *Educ:* Univ Mich, BS(eng physics) & BS(eng math), 53, MS, 54. *Prof Exp:* Engr, EKCo, Camera Works, Navy Ord Div & Kodak Appartus Div, 54-62; tech asst to dir res & develop, 62-64, proj mgr, 64-65, prog mgr, 66-68, asst to dir res & develop, 68-72, mgr govt prod, 72-73, dir res & eng, 73-75, MGR BUS & PROF PROD, EASTMAN KODAK CO, 75- *Concurrent Pos:* Mem sci adv comt, Defense Intel Agency. *Mem:* Nat Acad Eng; Optical Soc Am. *Res:* Optical and photographic systems; image evaluation; optical design; imaging sensors; optical measurements. *Mailing Add:* Eastman Kodak Co 901 Elmgrove Rd Rochester NY 14650

SPOEREL, WOLFGANG EBERHART G, b Stuttgart, Ger, July 11, 23; Can citizen; m 51; c 2. ANESTHESIOLOGY, PHARMACOLOGY. *Educ:* Univ Frankfurt, MD, 49; FRCPS(C), 56. *Prof Exp:* Resident med, Hosp, Univ Frankfurt, 49-51; demonstr pharmacol & physiol, 53-55, from instr to sr assoc anesthesia, 57-58, from asst prof to clin prof, 60-65, assoc prof pharmacol, 66-72, PROF ANESTHESIA, UNIV WESTERN ONT, 66-, HEAD DEPT ANESTHESIA & HON LECTR PHARMACOL, 72- *Concurrent Pos:* Fel anesthesia, Mayo Found, 55-56; chief anesthesia, Victoria Hosp, London, 58-66 & Univ Hosp, Univ Western Ont, 72- *Mem:* Can Anesthetists Soc; Can Med Asn; Can Soc Clin Invest. *Res:* Epidural anesthesia; anesthetic breathing circuits; cerebral anoxia; respiratory insufficiency. *Mailing Add:* Univ of Western Ont Univ Hosp London ON N6A 5A5 Can

SPOERLEIN, MARIE TERESA, b Dormont, Pa, Nov 3, 25. PHARMACOLOGY, PHYSIOLOGY. *Educ:* Seton Hill Col, BA, 47; Rutgers Univ, MS, 54, PhD, 59. *Prof Exp:* Asst pharmacologist, Schering Corp, 47-54 & Maltbie Labs, Wallace & Tiernan, Inc, 54-56; asst physiol, Col Pharm, Rutgers Univ, Newark, 56-58, from asst prof to assoc prof pharmacol, 59-68; PROF PHARMACOL, COL PHARM, RUTGERS UNIV, NEW BRUNSWICK, 68- *Mem:* AAAS; Am Soc Pharmacol & Exp Therapeut; Am Pharmaceut Asn; NY Acad Sci. *Res:* Biochemical pharmacology, especially mechanism of drug action and nervous system pharmacology. *Mailing Add:* Rutgers Univ Col of Pharm New Brunswick NJ 08903

SPOFFORD, JANICE BROGUE, b Chicago, Ill, Nov 14, 25; m 51; c 2. GENETICS. *Educ:* Univ Chicago, PhB, 44, SB, 46, PhD(zool), 55. *Prof Exp:* Instr natural sci, Univ Col, 48-51, asst prof biol, 55-61, res assoc zool, 56-70, ASSOC PROF BIOL, 61- *Mem:* AAAS; Genetics Soc Am; Soc Study Evolution; Am Soc Zool; Soc Study Social Biol. *Res:* Population genetics; mechanism of position-effect variegation; multi-gene families in Drosophila development and evolution. *Mailing Add:* Dept of Biol Univ of Chicago Chicago IL 60637

SPOFFORD, SALLY HOYT, b Williamsport, Pa, Apr 11, 14; m 42, 64. ORNITHOLOGY. *Educ:* Wilson Col, AB, 35; Univ Pa, MS, 36; Cornell Univ, PhD(ornith), 48. *Prof Exp:* Asst biol, Wilson Col, 37-39; med technician, Stark Gen Hosp, Charleston, SC, 42-44 & Kennedy Gen Hosp, Memphis, Tenn, 44-45; admin asst, 55-69, RES COLLABR, LAB ORNITH, CORNELL UNIV, 69- *Mem:* Wilson Ornith Soc; Nat Audubon Soc; Brit Ornith Union; Am Geog Soc; Am Ornith Union. *Res:* Life history and ecology of pileated woodpecker; population and distribution studies of Southeastern Arizona birds; public education in ornithology; conservation; food habits and behavior of roadrunners. *Mailing Add:* Aguila-Rancho Portal AZ 85632

SPOFFORD, WALTER O, JR, b Swampscott, Mass, May 9, 36; m 61; c 3. ENVIRONMENTAL SCIENCES & ENGINEERING. *Educ:* Northeastern Univ, BS, 59; Harvard Univ, MS, 60, PhD(water resources eng), 65. *Prof Exp:* Res asst, Harvard Water Resources Group, Harvard Univ, 61-65, res fel water resources mgt, Sch Pub Health, 65-66; res assoc, 68-74, dir qual environ div, 74-80, SR FEL, RESOURCES FOR THE FUTURE, 78- *Concurrent Pos:* Ford Found consult, Aswan Reg Develop Proj, Cairo, 65-66; WHO consult, Czech Res & Develop Ctr for Environ Pollution Control, 72-74 & Environmental Pollution Abatement Ctr, Poland, 76-78; mem panel on marine ecosyst anal, Nat Acad Sci-Nat Acad Eng, Sci & Eng Comt Adv to Nat Oceanic & Atmospheric Admin, 72-73; mem fac systs anal for environ pollution control, NATO Advan Study Inst, Baiersbronn, Ger, 72; consult, Los Alamos Sci Lab, 73-, NSF, 73, World Bank, 74-75, & 79, Ministry Conserv, Victoria, Australia, 74, Int Inst Appl Systs Anal, 78-79 & Asian Develop Bank, Manila, 80; res scholar water resources, Int Inst Appl Systs Anal, Austria, 74; mem subcomt on water resources adv comt, Int Inst Appl Systs Anal, Nat Acad Sci, 74-76, mem & chmn, Liaison Subcomt on Resources & Environ, 78-82 & mem, Int Coop in Systs Anal Res Exec Subcomt, 78-82; mem, Metro Study Task Force, Washington Ctr Metro Studies, Washington, DC, 77-78; mem bd dirs, Roy F Weston, Inc, Pa, 78-; mem, US Nat Comt Scientific Hydrology, 78- *Mem:* Fel Am Inst Chemists; Am Soc Civil Engrs; Am Geophys Union; Pub Works Hist Soc; Sigma Xi. *Res:* Environmental economics and management; civil and sanitary engineering; water resources engineering and management; public health. *Mailing Add:* 3348 Beech Tree Lane Falls Church VA 22042

SPOFFORD, WALTER RICHARDSON, II, b Hackensack, NJ, Nov 25, 08; m 36, 64; c 5. ZOOLOGY, ANATOMY. *Educ:* Tufts Col, BS, 31; Yale Univ, PhD(zool), 38. *Prof Exp:* From asst to instr anat, Med Col, Cornell Univ, 35-40; from asst prof to assoc prof, Sch Med, Vanderbilt Univ, 40-49; assoc prof neuroanat, Col Med, State Univ NY Upstate Med Ctr, 49-70; RES AFFIL ORNITH, LAB ORNITH, CORNELL UNIV, 70- *Concurrent Pos:* Res affil zool, Brigham Young UnUniv, 71- *Mem:* Soc Study Evolution; Am Asn Anat; Wilson Ornith Soc; Am Ornith Union; Brit Ornith Union. *Res:* Neuroanatomy; axon terminals; experimental embryology; posterior neural plate mesoderm; avian systematics; egg-white proteins as evolutionary characters; falconiformes; arctic ecology. *Mailing Add:* Rancho Aguila Portal AZ 85632

SPOHN, HERBERT EMIL, b Berlin, Ger, June 10, 23; US citizen; m 73; c 2. EXPERIMENTAL PSYCHOPATHOLOGY. *Educ:* City Col New York, BSS, 49; Columbia Univ, PhD, 55; Am Bd Prof Psychologists, dipl clin psychol, 62. *Prof Exp:* Lectr, City Col New York, 49-52; res assoc, Sarah Lawrence Col, Bronxville, 50-54; res pscyhologist, Franklin D Roosevelt Vet Admin Hosp, Montrose, 55-61, chief, Res Sect, 61-64; sr res psychologist, 65-80, DIR, RES DEPT, MENNINGER FOUND, 81- *Concurrent Pos:* Prin investr & res scientist, USPHS res grants, 66-76; mem, Ment Health Small Grants Rev Comt, NIMH, 72-76. *Mem:* Sigma Xi; Am Psychol Asn; AAAS. *Res:* Experimental psychopathology; clinical and experimental psychopharmacology; schizophrenia; depression; mechanisms in schiophrenia. *Mailing Add:* Menninger Found PO Box 820 Topeka KS 66601

SPOHN, RALPH JOSEPH, b New York, NY. HOMOGENEOUS CATALYSIS, ORGANOMETALLIC CHEMISTRY. *Educ:* Providence Col, BS, 65; Mass Inst Technol, PhD(inorg chem), 70; Rutgers Univ, MBA, 75. *Prof Exp:* Chemist, Enjay Chem Lab, 70-72, res chemist, Corp Res Lab, 72-75, staff chemist & group leader, Chem Intermediate Technol Div, 75-79, sr staff chemist, 79-82, HEAD SYNTHESIS GAS PROCESS RES, NEW VENTURES TECHNOL DIV, EXXON CHEM CO, 82- *Mem:* Am Chem Soc; NY Acad Sci. *Res:* Homogeneous and heterogeneous catalysis, especially that of the reactions of carbon monoxide and/or hydrogen with organic substrates and their industrial applications. *Mailing Add:* 10 Kings Ct Woodcliff Lake NJ 07675

SPOHN, RONALD TERRY, b Gallipolis, Ohio, Feb 22, 46; m 68; c 3. BIOSYSTEMATICS. *Educ:* Miami Univ, Ohio, BA, 68, MS, 74; Tex Tech Univ, PhD(biol), 78. *Prof Exp:* ASST PROF, COL GEN STUDIES, UNIV SC, 79- *Mem:* AAAS; Soc Study Evolution; Herpetologists League; Am Soc Ichtyologists & Herpetologists. *Res:* Inter and intrapopulation genetic relationships among related species of animals and plants. *Mailing Add:* 154 Mine Head Rd Irmo SC 29063

SPOHN, WILLIAM GIDEON, JR, b Lancaster, Pa, Mar 8, 23; div; c 4. MATHEMATICS. *Educ:* St John's Col, Md, BA, 47; Univ Calif, Berkeley, MA, 50; Univ Pa, PhD(math), 62. *Prof Exp:* Instr math, Temple Univ, 52-54, Univ Del, 54-56 & Bowling Green State Univ, 56-59; William S Parsons fel, 66-67, SR STAFF MATHEMATICIAN, APPL PHYSICS LAB, JOHNS HOPKINS UNIV, 59- *Mem:* Math Asn Am. *Res:* Analytical mathematics; applied mathematics; mathematical analysis; number theory; numerical analysis; system analysis. *Mailing Add:* 5764 Stevens Forest Rd Apt 707 Columbia MD 21045

SPOHR, DANIEL ARTHUR, b Meadville, Pa, Sept 13, 27; m 66; c 2. PHYSICS. *Educ:* Allegheny Col, BS, 49; Oxford Univ, DPhil(physics), 58. *Prof Exp:* Res physicist cryogenics br, 49-54 & 58-68, CONSULT PHYSICIST, US NAVAL RES LAB, 68- *Mem:* AAAS; Am Phys Soc; Sigma Xi. *Res:* Infrared and optical systems; data and signal processing; instrumentation systems analysis and development; computer application to structural, thermal and circuit analysis; applied superconductivity; low temperature physics; nuclear cooling and orientation. *Mailing Add:* Code 2310 US Naval Res Lab Washington DC 20375

SPOKAS, JOHN J, b Lisle, Ill, Oct 15, 28; m 52; c 8. RADIATION PHYSICS, DOSIMETRY. *Educ:* St Procopius Col, BS, 52; Univ Ill, MS, 54, PhD(physics), 58. *Prof Exp:* Mem tech staff, RCA Labs, 57-61; assoc prof, 61-70, chmn dept, 67-72, PROF PHYSICS & DIR, PHYS SCI LAB, ILL BENEDICTINE COL, 70- *Mem:* Am Phys Soc; Am Asn Physics Teachers; Radiation Res Soc; Am Asn Physicists Med. *Res:* Radiation dosimetry; nuclear instrumentation; charge transport in insulators; conducting plastics; nuclear magnetic resonance relaxation. *Mailing Add:* Dept Physics Ill Benedictine Col Lisle IL 60532

SPOKES, ERNEST M(ELVERN), b Philadelphia, Pa, Feb 10, 16; m 41; c 2. MINING ENGINEERING. *Educ:* Lafayette Col, BS, 36, EM, 46; Univ Ky, MS, 49; Pa State Univ, PhD(mineral prep), 56. *Prof Exp:* Mining engr, Bethlehem Steel Co, 36-40; foreman, sintering plant, Nat Lead Co, 45-47, gen engr, 47-48; asst instr mining & metall eng, Univ Ky, 48-49, from asst prof to assoc prof, 49-57, prof mining eng, 57-63; chmn, Dept Mining & Petrol Eng, 63-69, chief party, Univ Proj Eng Educ, Saigon, 69-71, head sect, 71-80, actg dean, Sch Mines & Metall, 80-81, PROF MINING ENG, UNIV MO-ROLLA, 63- *Concurrent Pos:* Consult, Ky Water Pollution Control Comn, 57-63; mem panel bituminous coal mining, US Bur Mines Report on Energy Resources of Sci Adv to President, 63; consult, Caterpillar Tractor Co, 66, US Bur Mines, 67, Monterey Coal Co, 72-73 & Consolidation Coal Co, 75; dir, McNally Pittsburg Mfg Corp, 73-78; chmn, Comt Underground Coal Mine Safety, Nat Res Coun, 80- *Mem:* Am Inst Mining, Metall & Petrol Engrs (vpres, 67-68, 69-70); Soc Mining Engrs (vpres, 67-70); Engrs Coun Prof Develop. *Res:* Mineral and coal preparation; mining methods; mine safety; mining management; mineral industry economics; mine systems analysis; mining environments. *Mailing Add:* Dept Mining Eng Univ Mo Rolla MO 65401

SPOKES, GILBERT NEIL, b Isleworth, Eng, July 18, 35; m 69; c 4. RESEARCH ADMINISTRATION. *Educ:* Univ London, BSc, 56, PhD(flame spectra), 59. *Prof Exp:* Res assoc chem, Univ Mich, 59-60 & Yale Univ, 60-61; chem physicist, Stanford Res Inst, 61-72; dir eng res & develop dept, Hycel Inc, 72; prin engr & dir res, Technicon Instruments Corp, 74-76; vpres, Chem Serv Div, 76-81, GROUP VPRES, CHEM SERV GROUP, US TESTING CO, INC, HOBOKEN, NJ, 81- *Mem:* Am Phys Soc; Am Chem Soc; Am Soc Quality Control. *Res:* Emission and absorption spectra of flames and of negative ions; gaseous electronics; ion sampling; gas kinetics and thermochemistry; pyrolysis and oxidation of gases and solids using mass spectrometry; biomedical diagnostic instrumentation. *Mailing Add:* 271 Sleepy Hollow Rd Briar Cliff Manor NY 10510

SPOLJARIC, NENAD, b Zagreb, Yugoslavia, July 3, 34; US citizen; m 64; c 1. SEDIMENTARY PETROLOGY, ENVIRONMENTAL GEOLOGY. *Educ:* Univ Ljubljana, GE, 60; Harvard Univ, MA, 65; Bryn Mawr Col, PhD(sedimentary petrol), 70. *Prof Exp:* Explor geologist, Proizuodnja Nafte Co, Yugoslavia, 60-61; petrol geologist, Petrol Inst, Yugoslavia, 62-63; SR SCIENTIST, DEL GEOL SURV, UNIV DEL, 65- *Honors & Awards:* Autometric Award, Am Soc Photogram, 76. *Mem:* Am Inst Prof Geologists; Am Asn Petrol Geologists. *Res:* Study of glauconitic sediments; geographic distribution, stratigraphy, correlation and origin of these sediments. *Mailing Add:* Del Geol Surv Univ of Del Newark DE 19711

SPOLSKY, CHRISTINA MARIA, b Reute, Austria, Mar 3, 45; Can citizen; m 75; c 2. MITOCHONDRIAL DNA, EVOLUTION. *Educ:* Univ Toronto, BS, 67; Yale Univ, PhD(microbiol), 73. *Prof Exp:* Fel, Univ Pa, 73-75, Am Cancer Soc, 74; res assoc cell biol, Wistar Inst, 75-76; RES SCIENTIST, ACAD NATURAL SCI, PHILADELPHIA, 78- *Concurrent Pos:* Prin invstr, Whitehall Fedn grant, 81-84. *Mem:* Sigma Xi; Tissue Cult Asn; Am Soc Cell Biol; Am Soc Microbiol. *Res:* The relationship of chemical carcinogenesis to mutagenesis in cell cultures; the information content and biogenesis of mitochondrial DNA; use of mitochondrial DNA to determine toxonomic relationships of species; rate of evolution of mitochondrial DNA in vertebrates; origin of mitochondria as determined by rDNA sequences. *Mailing Add:* Acad Natural Sci 19th & The Parkway Philadelphia PA 19103

SPOLYAR, LOUIS WILLIAM, b Detroit, Mich, May 6, 08; m 35; c 3. TOXICOLOGY. *Educ:* DePauw Univ, AB, 31; Ind Univ, MD, 36; Am Bd Prev Med, dipl, 50. *Prof Exp:* Lectr indust med, Sch Med, Ind Univ, Indianapolis, 40-46, asst prof pub health, 46-78; ASST HEALTH COMNR, IND STATE BD HEALTH, 69- *Concurrent Pos:* Dir div indust hyg, Ind State Bd Health, 37-56 & bur prev med, 56-68, asst comnr med opers, 68-69; dir prev med br, State Civil Defense, Ind, 50-, chmn opers br, Med Health Serv, 55; consult, Surgeon Gen, USPHS, 57. *Mem:* Am Med Asn; Indust Med Asn; Am Conf Govt Indust Hygienists (vpres, 48, pres 49). *Res:* Toxicology of cadmium and lead; toxicology and generation of arsine; industrial toxicology; chemotherapy of tuberculosis; laboratory determination of sickle cell anemia. *Mailing Add:* 6737 E Ninth St Indianapolis IN 46219

SPOMER, GEORGE GUY, b Denver, Colo, Mar 2, 37; m 60; c 4. PLANT PHYSIOLOGY, ECOLOGY. *Educ:* Colo State Univ, BS, 59, MS, 61, PhD(bot sci), 62. *Prof Exp:* From instr to asst prof bot, Univ Chicago, 62-68; from asst prof to assoc prof, Wash State Univ, 68-72; ASSOC PROF BOT, UNIV IDAHO, 72- *Concurrent Pos:* NSF res grant, 65-67 & 75; Nat Geog Soc res grant, 75. *Mem:* AAAS; Ecol Soc Am; Am Soc Plant Physiol; Scand Soc Plant Physiol. *Res:* Plant eco-physiology, environmental analysis, alpine plant ecology, water structure and water relations, tree physiology. *Mailing Add:* Dept of Biol Univ of Idaho Moscow ID 83843

SPOMER, LOUIS ARTHUR, b Apr 17, 40; US citizen; m 62. PLANT PHYSIOLOGY, SOIL SCIENCE. *Educ:* Colo State Univ, BS, 63; Cornell Univ, MS, 67, PhD(plant sci), 69. *Prof Exp:* Meteorologist, Deseret Test Ctr, US Army, 69-71, phys scientist, US Dept Defense, 71-72; asst prof plant physiol & hort, 72-75, asst prof, 75-77, ASSOC PROF HORT, UNIV ILL, URBANA, 77- *Mem:* Am Soc Plant Physiol; Am Soc Agron; Am Soc Hort Sci; Soil Sci Soc Am. *Res:* Soil-plant-water relationships; water stress and crop growth; plant and crop water requirement. *Mailing Add:* Dept of Hort Univ of Ill Urbana IL 61801

SPONGBERG, STEPHEN ALAN, b Rockford, Ill, Oct 15, 42; m 72. SYSTEMATIC BOTANY. *Educ:* Rockford Col, BA, 66; Univ NC, Chapel Hill, PhD(bot), 71. *Prof Exp:* Asst cur bot, 70-76, HORT TAXONOMIST, ARNOLD ARBORETUM, HARVARD UNIV, 76- *Concurrent Pos:* Ed bd, J Arnold Arboretum, 71- *Mem:* Bot Soc Am; Am Soc Plant Taxonomists; Int Asn Plant Taxon; Linnean Soc London; Soc Study Evolution. *Res:* Taxonomic revisions of woody angiosperm genera of eastern Asiatic-eastern North American distribution, particularly genera of ornamental importance; taxonomy; nomenclature of woody plants cultivated in the North Temperate Zone. *Mailing Add:* Arnold Arboretum Harvard Univ 22 Divinity Ave Cambridge MA 02138

SPONSELLER, D(AVID) L(ESTER), b Canton, Ohio, Oct 2, 31; m 55; c 7. METALLURGICAL ENGINEERING. *Educ:* Univ Notre Dame, BS, 53; Univ Mich, MSE, 58, PhD(metall eng), 62. *Prof Exp:* Instr marine eng, US Naval Acad, 55-57; res asst, Res Inst, Univ Mich, 57-60, instr metall eng, 60-62; asst prof, Univ Notre Dame, 62-65; staff metallurgist, 65-67, res group leader, 67-70, res supvr, 70-79, STAFF METALLURGIST, CLIMAX MOLYBDENUM CO, MICH, 79- *Concurrent Pos:* Vis res metallurgist, Edgar C Bain Lab, US Steel Corp, 63. *Mem:* Am Soc Metals; Am Inst Mining, Metall & Petrol Engrs; Nat Asn Corrosion Engrs; Am Soc Mech Engrs. *Res:* Physical metallurgy and alloy development of steels and alloys for oil production and for elevated temperature service; corrosion in oil field environments; creep-rupture behavior; microstructural control; phase stability; embrittlement; oxidation; sulfidation; differential thermal analysis. *Mailing Add:* Climax Molybdenum Co of Mich 1600 Huron Pkwy Ann Arbor MI 48105

SPOONER, ALFRED BRENT, b Jamaica, NY, Apr 1, 23. ORGANIC CHEMISTRY. *Educ:* Seton Hall Univ, BS, 43; Univ Notre Dame, PhD(chem), 50. *Prof Exp:* Prof chem, Seton Hall Univ, 50-53; sr chemist cent res lab, Allied Chem Corp, 53-59, gen chem res lab, 59-62; CONSULT CHEMIST, 62-; CHMN DEPT SCI, NEWTON HIGH SCH, 66- *Mem:* AAAS; Am Chem Soc; Nat Sci Teachers Asn. *Res:* Chemistry and science education. *Mailing Add:* R D 6 Box 176 Newton NJ 07860

SPOONER, ARTHUR ELMON, b Wilmer, Ala, Dec 12, 20; m 42; c 2. AGRONOMY. *Educ:* Miss State Univ, BS, 51, MS, 52; Purdue Univ, PhD(crop physiol), 55. *Prof Exp:* From asst prof to assoc prof, 55-64, PROF AGRON, UNIV ARK, FAYETTEVILLE, 64- *Mem:* Am Soc Agron. *Res:* Crop physiology, especially forage crops; physiology of irrigation on cotton and soybeans; forage crops and pasture management; animal and plant nutrition. *Mailing Add:* Dept of Agron Univ of Ark Fayetteville AR 72701

SPOONER, BRIAN SANDFORD, b St Louis, Mo, Dec 27, 37; m 63; c 2. DEVELOPMENTAL BIOLOGY, CELL BIOLOGY. *Educ:* Quincy Col, BS, 63; Temple Univ, PhD(biol), 69. *Prof Exp:* Teaching asst biol, Temple Univ, 63-65; USPHS trainee, Univ Wash, 69; NIH fel, Stanford Univ, 69-71; asst prof biol, 71-75, assoc dir res, Div Biol, 75-77, assoc prof, 75-79, PROF BIOL, KANS STATE UNIV, 79- *Concurrent Pos:* Nat Inst Gen Med Sci grants, 72-75 & 75-80, Nat Heart, Lung & Blood Inst, 80-82 & Am Heart Asn, 80-82. *Mem:* Soc Develop Biol; Am Soc Cell Biol. *Res:* Control of differentiation during embryonic development; mechanism of cell movement; regulation of cytodifferentiation and morphogenesis; interactions in organogenesis; stability of the differentiated state. *Mailing Add:* Div of Biol Kans State Univ Manhattan KS 66506

SPOONER, CHARLES EDWARD, JR, b Boston, Mass, July 25, 32; m 62; c 2. NEUROPHARMACOLOGY, NEUROPHYSIOLOGY. *Educ:* Univ Calif, Los Angeles, BA, 56, MS, 61, PhD(neuropharmacol), 64. *Prof Exp:* Res pharmacologist, Riker Labs, Calif, 51-59; asst res pharmacologist, Med Sch, Univ Calif, Los Angeles, 65-68; from asst prof to assoc prof neurosci, 68-74, asst dean spec curricula, 69-71, asst dean admis & student affairs, 71-74, PROF NEUROSCI, SCH MED, UNIV CALIF, SAN DIEGO, 74-, ASSOC DEAN ADMIS, 74- *Concurrent Pos:* NIMH fel, 63-65; consult, Psychobiol Labs, Sepulveda Vet Hosp, Calif, 68- & Neurochem Sect, Space Biol Labs, Univ Calif, Los Angeles, 68- *Mem:* AAAS; Am Soc Pharmacol & Exp Therapeut; Int Soc Biochem Pharmacol; Soc Exp Biol & Med; Soc Neurosci. *Res:* Pharmacology and physiology of synaptic transmission in the central nervous system; drug development; neurochemistry. *Mailing Add:* Sch Med M-021 Univ Calif, San Diego La Jolla CA 92093

SPOONER, ED THORNTON CASSWELL, b Blandford, Dorset, Eng, June 16, 50; m 72. GEOLOGY. *Educ:* Univ Cambridge, BA, 71, MA, 75; Oxford Univ, MA, 75; Univ Manchester, PhD(geol), 76. *Prof Exp:* Demonstr mineral, Oxford Univ, 73-77; ASST PROF GEOL, UNIV TORONTO, 77- *Concurrent Pos:* Lectr geol, Oriel & Pembroke Cols, Oxford Univ, 74-77; Can rep to Comn on Ore Forming Fluids in Inclusions, 78-; Natural Sci & Eng Res Coun Can grants, 78- *Mem:* Can Inst Mining & Metall; Brit Geol Asn. *Res:* Mineral deposits in geology, especially hydrothermal; geochemical methods of exploration for economic mineral deposits. *Mailing Add:* 89 Sparkhall Toronto ON M4K 1G7 Can

SPOONER, GEORGE HANSFORD, b Henderson, NC, Feb 24, 27; m 53; c 3. CLINICAL CHEMISTRY. *Educ:* Univ Miami, BS, 50; Univ NC, PhD(biochem), 58. *Prof Exp:* Res asst sanit eng, Sch Pub Health, Univ NC, 54-56, res asst, Sch Dent, 56-57, res assoc biochem, Sch Med, 57-58, instr, 58-61, USPHS trainee microbiol, 61-62, asst prof biochem, 62-65; asst prof path, Sch Med, Duke Univ, 65-73; ASSOC PROF PATH, MED UNIV SC, 73-; CLIN CHEMIST, VET ADMIN HOSP, CHARLESTON, 73- *Concurrent Pos:* Res scientist, State Sanitorium Syst NC, 58-61; biochemist, Clin Res Unit, NC Mem Hosp, 62-65; clin chemist, Vet Admin Hosp, Durham, 65-73. *Res:* Serum enzyme levels in the diagnosis of disease; continuous flow kinetics. *Mailing Add:* Dept of Path Med Univ of SC Charleston SC 29403

SPOONER, JOHN D, b Hillsborough Co, Fla, Dec 18, 35; m 58; c 5. ZOOLOGY, ENTOMOLOGY. *Educ:* Ga State Univ, BS, 60; Univ Fla, MS, 62, PhD(entom), 64. *Prof Exp:* Asst prof biol, Ga Southern Col, 64-66 & Augusta Col, 66-70; chmn div natural sci, 70-76, actg acad dean, 76, assoc prof, 77-78, PROF BIOL, UNIV SC, AIKEN, 78- *Concurrent Pos:* NSF grant, 66-68. *Mem:* Pan Am Acridological Soc; Sigma Xi. *Res:* Acoustical pair forming systems of Orthoptera, particularly phaneropterine katydids; geographic variation in orthopteran acoustical behavior; life history studies of phaneropterine katydids. *Mailing Add:* Dept of Biol Univ of SC Aiken SC 29801

SPOONER, M(ORTON) G(AILEND), b Eau Claire, Wis, Jan 16, 24; m 50; c 4. ELECTRICAL ENGINEERING. *Educ:* Univ Wis, BS, 48, MS, 54, PhD(elec eng), 56. *Prof Exp:* Elec engr, Standard Oil Co, Ind, 48-52; from instr to asst prof, Univ Wis, 52-56; res electronics engr, 56-76, sr vpres tech opers, Cornell Aeronaut Lab Inc, 56-76; SR TECH CONSULT & PROG MGR, E SYSTS, GARLAND DIV, 76- *Mem:* Inst Elec & Electronic Engrs. *Res:* Technical management in high speed special purpose digital processing systems and large scale software systems. *Mailing Add:* Box 226118 E Systs Dallas TX 75222

SPOONER, PETER MICHAEL, b Newport, RI, Nov 11, 42; m 69. ENDOCRINOLOGY, LIPID BIOCHEMISTRY. *Educ:* Bates Col, BS, 64; Univ Ill, Urbana-Champaign, MS, 66, PhD(physiol & biophysics), 70. *Prof Exp:* Sr staff fel, lipid res, Nat Inst Arthritis, Metabolic & Digestive Dis, 74-79, physiologist & biochemist, 79-80, HEALTH SCI ADMINR, NAT HEART, LUNG & BLOOD INST, NIH, 80- *Concurrent Pos:* Vis investr, Imperial Cancer Res Found Labs, London, 72-74; adj asst prof, Uniformed Serv, Univ Health Sci, 78-; physiologist & biochemist lipid res, Nat Inst Arthritis, Metabolic & Digestive Dis, NIH, 77-79; lectr, Found Advan Educ Sci, 80- *Mem:* The Endocrine Soc; Am Soc Biol Chemists; Sigma Xi. *Res:* Endocrine control of uptake, metabolism and deposition of lipids into cells in vivo and vitro using model cell culture systems. *Mailing Add:* Rm 648 Westwood Bldg Nat Heart, Lung & Blood Inst NIH Bethesda MD 20205

SPOONER, ROBERT BRUCE, b Cleveland, Ohio, Aug 7, 20; m 45; c 4. BIOMEDICAL ENGINEERING. *Educ:* Hiram Col, BA, 41; Northwestern Univ, PhD(physics), 49. *Prof Exp:* Asst, Northwestern Univ, 46-48; head thermodyn anal sect, Lewis Flight Propulsion Lab, Nat Adv Comt Aeronaut, 49-53; mgr adv nuclear design dept, Martin Co, 53-55; mgr assoc researches, Koppers Co, Inc, 55-62; coordr sci & res adv group, Regional Indust Develop Corp, 63-65; pres, Impac, 65-74; dir, Med Instrumentation Ctr, MPC Corp, 74-75; SR PROJ ENGR, EMERGENCY CARE RES INST, 75- *Concurrent Pos:* Lectr, Case Western Reserve Univ, 50-52; chmn, Annual Res Conf Instrumentation Sci, 69- *Mem:* Am Phys Soc; sr mem Instrument Soc Am; sr mem Inst Elec & Electronics Engrs; Asn Advan Med Instrumentation. *Res:* Radioisotope and radiation applications; instrumentation and control; medical instrumentation. *Mailing Add:* Vista Rd Ambler PA 19002

SPOONER, STEPHEN, b Worcester, Mass, Apr 2, 37; m 59; c 2. MATERIALS SCIENCE, METALLURGY. *Educ:* Mass Inst Technol, BS, 59, ScD(metall), 65. *Prof Exp:* Res asst, Mass Inst Technol, 59-65; asst prof, 65-70, assoc prof, 70-75, prof metall, 75-81, RES SCIENTIST, ENG EXP STA, GA INST TECHNOL, 65-; RES SCIENTIST, OAK RIDGE NAT LAB, 82- *Concurrent Pos:* Consult, Oak Ridge Nat Lab, 73-77; res scientist, Ga Inst Technol, 82. *Mem:* Am Phys Soc; Am Inst Mining, Metall & Petrol Engrs; Am Crystallog Asn. *Res:* Materials science; phase transformations; magnetic materials. *Mailing Add:* Solid State Div Oak Ridge Nat Lab Oak Ridge TN 37830

SPOOR, RYK PETER, b Albany, NY, June 30, 35; m 57; c 2. PHARMACOLOGY, PHYSIOLOGY. *Educ:* State Univ NY Albany, BS, 57; Union Univ, NY, PhD(pharmacol), 62. *Prof Exp:* Instr physiol & pharmacol, Sch Med, Creighton Univ, 62-64; asst prof, Univ SDak, 64-67; fel pharmacol, Emory Univ, 67-69; asst prof, 69-78, ASSOC PROF PHARMACOL, ALBANY MED COL, 78- *Mem:* AAAS; Am Inst Biol Sci; NY Acad Sci. *Res:* Muscle; cardiovascular pharmacology and physiology; cardioactive drugs; mechanisms of cardiovascular drugs. *Mailing Add:* Off Acad Affairs Albany Med Col Albany NY 12208

SPOOR, WILLIAM ARTHUR, b New York, NY, Dec 14, 08; m 34; c 2. ZOOLOGY, PHYSIOLOGY. *Educ:* Univ Wash, BS, 31; Univ Wis, PhD(zool), 36. *Prof Exp:* From instr to prof zool, Dept Biol Sci, Univ Cincinnati, 36-68, head dept biol sci, 58-64; RES AQUATIC BIOLOGIST, ENVIRON RES LAB, 68- *Concurrent Pos:* Mem aquatic life adv comt, Ohio River Valley Water Sanit Comn, 52-68; consult basic & appl sci br, Div Water Supply & Pollution Control, US Dept Health, Educ & Welfare, 61-68; consult physiol of aquatic animals, Nat Water Qual Lab, Dept Interior, Minn, 66-68; mem nat tech comt on water qual requirements for aquatic life, Fed Water Pollution Control Admin, 67-68. *Mem:* AAAS; Sigma Xi. *Res:* Environmental requirements and oxygen requirements of fish; activity detectors for aquatic animals; physiology of aquatic animals. *Mailing Add:* Environ Res Lab 6201 Congdon Blvd Duluth MN 55804

SPOREK, KAREL FRANTISEK, b Bohumin, Czech, Oct 12, 19; US citizen; m 51; c 1. ANALYTICAL CHEMISTRY, ORGANIC CHEMISTRY. *Educ:* St Andrews Univ, MA, 47. *Prof Exp:* Res chemist, Nobel Div, Imp Chem Indust Ltd, Scotland, 47-54, group leader anal res, Plant Protection Div, Eng, 54-57; res chemist, Eldorado Mining & Refining, Can, 57-58; head anal dept, Bioferm Corp, Calif, 58-60; res chemist, Tech Ctr, 60-61, chief org anal chem, 61-73, RADIATION OFFICER, TECH CTR, OWENS-ILL INC, 73- *Mem:* Am Chem Soc; Am Nuclear Soc; Am Soc Testing & Mat; Sigma Xi; Am Soc Safety Engrs. *Res:* High explosives; detonators; fuses; cellulose derivatives; insecticides; fungicides; fertilizers; polymers; polyethelene; silicones; pharmaceuticals; vitamin B-12; uranium; radiation chemistry. *Mailing Add:* Owens-Illinois Inc PO Box 1035 Toledo OH 43666

SPORER, ALFRED HERBERT, b New York, NY, May 28, 29; m 55; c 2. PHOTO CHEMISTRY, POLYMER CHEMISTRY. *Educ:* City Col, BA, 51; Univ Calif, Los Angeles, MS, 53, PhD(phys org chem), 56. *Prof Exp:* Res chemist, Esso Res & Eng Corp, 56; fel photochem, Univ Southern Calif, 56-57; staff chemist, Phys Sci Dept, IBM Corp, 57-73, mgr applied sci, Res Div, 73-79, mem, Corp Tech Comt, 79-81. *Mem:* Am Chem Soc; Soc Photog Sci & Eng; Sigma Xi; AAAS. *Res:* Electrophotography; organic photoconductors; physical organic chemistry; photochemistry of complex ions, chelates and organic compounds in condensed phases; mechanisms of organic reactions; chromatography; technical management of programs in electrophotography; photoconductors; non-impact printing; magnetic recording media. *Mailing Add:* IBM Corp Res Lab Bldg 028 5600 Cottle Rd San Jose CA 95193

SPORN, EUGENE MILTON, b New York, NY, Feb 12, 25; m 47; c 3. TOXICOLOGY, RESEARCH MANAGEMENT. *Educ:* New York City Col, BS, 45; Univ Wis, MS, 47; Georgetown Univ, PhD(biochem), 51. *Prof Exp:* Res biochemist, Biol Labs, US Army, 47-54, dep chief, Res Div, Off of Chief Chem Officer, 54-56, chmn, Chem Res & Develop Labs & chief, Basic Toxicol Br, 56-60, dep chief, Res Div, Hq Chem Corps, Res & Develop Command, 60-62, chief, Spec Proj Br, Army Res Off, 62-74; chief biochem toxicol, US Food & Drug Admin, 74-77, assoc dir toxicol, 77-81; REGIONAL ADMINR & CONSULT, S H KAPLAN EDUC CTR, 81- *Mem:* Am Col Toxicol; AAAS; Am Chem Soc; Sigma Xi; NY Acad Sci. *Res:* Elucidation of mechanism of action of potentially toxic substances; development of more reliable methods of rapidly determining toxicity; extrapolation of animal data to man; application of biochemistry to toxicological research. *Mailing Add:* 9902 Holmhurst Rd Bethesda MD 20817

SPORN, MICHAEL BENJAMIN, b New York, NY, Feb 15, 33; m 56; c 2. CANCER, BIOCHEMISTRY. *Educ:* Univ Rochester, MD, 59. *Prof Exp:* Intern med, Sch Med, Univ Rochester, 59-60; staff mem, Lab Neurochem, Nat Inst Neurol Dis & Blindness, 60-64; staff mem, 64-70, head lung cancer unit, 70-73, chief, Lung Cancer Br, 73-78, CHIEF LAB CHEMOPREVENTION, NAT CANCER INST, 78- *Concurrent Pos:* Assoc ed, Cancer Res. *Mem:* Am Asn Cancer Res; Am Soc Biol Chem; Am Soc Pharmacol & Exp Therapeut; Am Soc Neurochem; Am Inst Nutrit. *Res:* Lung cancer; nucleic acids and cancer, vitamin A and related compounds; carcinogenesis studies; retinoids and cancer prevention; peptide growth factors. *Mailing Add:* Nat Cancer Inst Bethesda MD 20014

SPORNICK, LYNNA, m. PHYSICS. *Educ:* Carnegie-Mellon Univ, BS, 69; Rutgers Univ, PhD(physics), 75; Johns Hopkins Univ, MS, 81. *Prof Exp:* Fel, Dept Physics, Colo State Univ, 75-77; SR STAFF PHYSICIST, APPL PHYSICS LAB, JOHNS HOPKINS UNIV, 77- *Mem:* Am Phys Soc; Am Asn Physics Teachers. *Mailing Add:* Appl Physics Lab Johns Hopkins Univ 34th & Charles Sts Baltimore MD 21218

SPOSITO, GARRISON, b Los Angeles, Calif, July 29, 39; m 76; c 4. PHYSICAL CHEMISTRY, SOIL CHEMISTRY. *Educ:* Univ Ariz, BS, 61, MS, 63; Univ Calif, PhD(soil sci), 65. *Prof Exp:* From asst prof to prof physics, Sonoma State Univ, 65-74; chmn div environ sci, 75-78, from asst prof to assoc prof, 74-78, PROF SOIL SCI, UNIV CALIF, RIVERSIDE, 78- *Concurrent Pos:* Vis fel, Inst Nat de la Recherche Agronomique, France, 81. *Mem:* Am Chem Soc; Am Geophys Union; Soil Sci Soc Am; Am Phys Soc; Hist Sci Soc. *Res:* Environmental physical chemistry, statistical mechanics, thermodynamics of soils and clays; surface chemistry of soils. *Mailing Add:* Dept of Soil & Environ Sci Univ of Calif Riverside CA 92521

SPOSITO, VINCENT ANTHONY, b Pittsburg, Calif, Nov 15, 36; m 63; c 2. OPERATIONS RESEARCH, STATISTICS. *Educ:* Calif State Univ, Sacramento, BA, 65; Iowa State Univ, MS, 67, PhD(statist), 70. *Prof Exp:* Lab technician metall, Aerojet-General, Sacramento, 58-65; instr statist, Calif State Univ, Sacramento, 65; res assoc, 66-70, from asst prof to assoc prof, 70-78, PROF STATIST, IOWA STATE UNIV, 78- *Mem:* Am Statist Asn; Math Prog Soc. *Res:* Mathematical programming; linear and nonlinear programming. *Mailing Add:* Dept of Statist Iowa State Univ Ames IA 50010

SPOTNITZ, HENRY MICHAEL, b New York, NY, July 7, 40; m 77; c 2. MEDICAL SCIENCES, PHYSIOLOGY. *Educ:* Harvard Univ, BA, 62; Columbia Univ, MD, 66. *Prof Exp:* Intern surg, Bellevue Hosp, NY, 66-67; staff assoc cardiol, Nat Heart Inst, 67-69; resident surg, Presby Hosp, NY, 69-75; asst prof med sci, 75-80, asst attend surgeon, Presby Hosp, NY, 75-80, ASSOC PROF SURGERY, COLUMBIA UNIV, 80-, LAB DIR CARDIOVASC SURG, 76-; ASSOC ATTEND SURGEON, PRESBY HOSP, NY, 80- *Concurrent Pos:* Estab investr, Am Heart Asn, 76-81; prin investr, Nat Heart Lung & Blood Inst, NIH res grant, 78-81; asst attend surgeon, Presby Hosp, NY, 75-80. *Mem:* AAAS; Am Heart Asn; fel Am Col Cardiol; fel Am Col Surgeons; Soc Univ Surgeons. *Res:* Human left ventricular compliance and systolic mechanics; mechanical and pharmacologic circulatory support; open heart surgery. *Mailing Add:* Col of Physicians & Surgeons 630 W 168th St New York NY 10032

SPOTTISWOOD, DAVID JAMES, b Melbourne, Australia, Aug, 28, 44; m 73; c 2. MINERAL PRROCESSING, HYDROMETALLURGY. *Educ:* Univ Melbourne, Australia, 65; Colo Sch Mines, PhD(metall eng), 70. *Prof Exp:* Chem engr, Commonwealth Serum Labs, 65-66; asst prof mining eng, Queen's Univ, Can, 70-75; assoc prof metall eng, Mich Technol Univ, 75-79; ASSOC PROF METALL ENG, COLO SCH MINES, 79- *Concurrent Pos:* Consult, numerous co US, Can, Australia & SAm, 70-; prin investr, various projs, 70-; vis prof, Univ Concepcion, Chile, 74; vis lectr, McGill Univ, Can, K U Leuven, Belgium, Auckland Univ, NZ; vpres, Eng Systs Res Inc, 78- *Mem:* Am Inst Mining Metall & Petrol Engrs; Australasian Inst Mining & Metall; Can Inst Mining & Metall; Instrument Soc Am; Sigma Xi. *Res:* Mineral processing and hydrometallurgy, with emphasis on mathematical analysis for improved design, operation and automatic control; application of surface chemistry to mineral separations. *Mailing Add:* Dept Metall Eng Colo Sch Mines Golden CO 80401

SPOTTS, CHARLES RUSSELL, b Phoenix, Ariz, Oct 14, 33; m 54; c 4. MICROBIOLOGY. *Educ:* Univ Calif, Berkeley, BA, 55, PhD(microbiol), 61. *Prof Exp:* NIH fel, 61-63; instr microbiol, Univ Wash, 63, asst prof, Sch Med, 63-69; assoc prof, 69-74, PROF BIOL, CALIF STATE UNIV, NORTHRIDGE, 74- *Mem:* AAAS; Am Soc Microbiol; Brit Soc Gen Microbiol. *Res:* Mode of action of streptomycin; physiology of bacterial sporulation. *Mailing Add:* Dept of Biol Calif State Univ Northridge CA 91330

SPOTTS, JOHN HUGH, b Lauratown, Ark, Nov 2, 27; m 54; c 3. GEOLOGY. *Educ:* Univ Mo, BA, 50, MA, 51; Univ Western Australia, MSc, 56; Stanford Univ, PhD, 59. *Prof Exp:* Res geologist, Shell Develop Co, 52-53; geologist & geophysicist, Standard Oil Co, Calif, 53-56, geologist, 58-59, res geologist, La Habra Lab, Chevron Res Co, 59-68, mgr geol res, 68-70, div geologist, Standard Oil Co, Calif, 70-77, chief geologist, Chevron Resources Co, San Francisco, 77-81, VPRES EXPLORATION RES, CHEVRON OIL FIELD RES CO, LA HABRA, CALIF, 81- *Mem:* Mineral Soc Am; Am Asn Petrol Geologists; Soc Econ Paleontologists & Mineralogists; Int Asn Sedimentologists. *Res:* Mineralogy; sedimentary petrology; heavy minerals; geochemistry; carbonate petrography; petrofabrics. *Mailing Add:* Box 446 Chevron Oil Field Res Co La Habra CA 90631

SPOTTS, M(ERHYLE) F(RANKLIN), b Battle Creek, Iowa, Dec 5, 95; m 47; c 2. MACHINE DESIGN. *Educ:* Ohio Northern Univ, BS, 23; Ohio State Univ, MA, 33; Univ Mich, PhD(appl mech), 38. *Prof Exp:* Engr, Brown Steel Co, Ohio, 27-32; designer, Jeffrey Mfg Co, 33-35; assoc mech eng, Johns Hopkins Univ, 38-41; from asst prof to prof, 43-77, EMER PROF MECH ENG, TECHNOL INST, NORTHWESTERN UNIV, EVANSTON, 77- *Honors & Awards:* Worcester Reed Warner Medal, Am Soc Mech Engrs, 68; Century II Medallion, Am Soc Mech Engrs, 81; Machine Design Award, Am Soc Mech Engrs, 81. *Mem:* Fel Am Soc Mech Engrs. *Res:* Applied mechanics; mechanical vibrations; stress analysis. *Mailing Add:* Technol Inst Northwestern Univ Evanston IL 60201

SPOTTS, ROBERT ALLEN, b Philadelphia, Pa, June 10, 45; m 69; c 1. PLANT PATHOLOGY. *Educ:* Colo State Univ, BS, 67, MS, 69; Pa State Univ, PhD(plant path), 74. *Prof Exp:* Chemist, Colo Dept Health, 69-71; asst prof plant path, Ohio Agr Res & Develop Ctr, 74-78; ASST PROF PLANT PATH, ORE STATE UNIV, 78- *Mem:* Am Phytopath Soc. *Res:* Epidemiology, physiology and control of diseases of fruit crops. *Mailing Add:* Mid-Columbia Exp Sta Hood River OR 97031

SPRADLEY, JOSEPH LEONARD, b Baker, Ore, Oct 30, 32; m 55; c 4. ENGINEERING PHYSICS. *Educ:* Univ Calif, Los Angeles, BS, 54, MS, 55, PhD(eng physics), 58. *Prof Exp:* Mem tech staff, Hughes Aircraft Co, 54-58; assoc prof, 59-72, chmn dept, 68-70, PROF PHYSICS, WHEATON COL, ILL, 72- *Concurrent Pos:* Consult, Sunbeam Corp, 60-61; prof, Haigazian Col, Lebanon, 65-68; US Agency Int Develop sci specialist, Ahmadu Bello Univ, Nigeria, 70-72. *Mem:* Am Asn Physics Teachers. *Res:* Microwave antenna arrays; laser communications; history of science. *Mailing Add:* Dept of Physics Wheaton Col Wheaton IL 60187

SPRADLIN, JOSEPH EDWARD, enzymology, see previous edition

SPRADLIN, WILFORD W, b Bedford Co, Va, Oct 4, 32; m 58; c 2. PSYCHIATRY. *Educ:* Univ Va, BA, 53, MD, 57. *Prof Exp:* Intern, Royal Victoria Hosp, McGill Univ, 58; resident psychiat, Eastern State Hosp, 58-59 & Med Ctr, Duke Univ, 60-62; staff psychiatrist, Vet Admin Hosp, Durham, 62; assoc psychiat, Med Ctr, Duke Univ, 62-63; asst chief, Vet Admin Hosp, Durham, 63-64; asst prof, Med Ctr, Duke Univ, 64-67, chief psychiat day unit, 65-67, asst head psychiat inpatient serv, 65-67; prof psychiat & chmn dept behav med & psychiat, Med Ctr, WVa Univ, 67-78; PROF PSYCHIAT & CHMN DEPT, MED CTR, UNIV VA, 78- DEPT BEHAV MED & PSYCHIAT, MED CTR, W VA UNIV, 67- *Mem:* AAAS; fel Am Psychiat Asn; AMA. *Mailing Add:* Dept of Psychiat Box 203 Univ of Va Med Ctr Charlottesville VA 22908

SPRAFKA, ROBERT J, b Chicago, Ill, Nov 24, 38; m 67. ALTERNATIVE VEHICLE FUELS. *Educ:* Purdue Univ, BS, 59, PhD(physics), 65. *Prof Exp:* Res assoc high energy physics, Purdue Univ, 64-66; physicist, Lawrence Radiation Lab, Calif, 66-67; from asst prof to assoc prof physics, Mich State Univ, 67-74, assoc prof physics & off health serv educ & res, 74-76, assoc prof community health sci, 76-82; SR ASSOC, E:F TECHNOL, INC, 81- *Mem:* Am Phys Soc; Sigma Xi. *Res:* Feasibility studies and program management design involving nonpetroleum vehicular transport systems and solar enegy-hydrogen energy systems; scientific computer applications. *Mailing Add:* E:F Technol PO Box 189 St Johns MI 48879

SPRAGGINS, ROBERT LEE, b Sedalia, Mo, Feb 18, 39; m 63; C 3. ORGANIC CHEMISTRY. *Educ:* La Tech Univ, BS, 63, MS, 66; Univ Okla, PhD(org chem), 70. *Prof Exp:* Chemist, Cities Serv Oil Co, 63-64; res fel, Alza Corp, Calif, 70-71; sea grant, Stevens Inst Technol, 71-72, res scientist, 72-74; res scientist, Ctr Trace Characterization, Tex A&M Univ, 75-77; sr scientist, 77-78, sr scientist & group leader mass spectros, Radian Corp, 79-81; SR SCIENTIST & MGR ANAL CHEM, SVMX CORP, AUSTIN, TEX, 81- *Mem:* Am Chem Soc; Sigma Xi; Am Soc Mass Spectrometry. *Res:* Mass spectroscopy; biomedical and natural products; analytical chemistry; environmental chemistry. *Mailing Add:* 10610 Hard Rock Rd Austin TX 78750

SPRAGINS, MELCHIJAH, b Mitchellville, Md, Jan 4, 19; m 49; c 4. PEDIATRICS. *Educ:* Johns Hopkins Univ, AB, 41, MD, 44; Am Bd Pediat, dipl, 49. *Prof Exp:* Instr pediat, Univ Buffalo, 47-48; instr, Hosp, 48-53, from attend to assoc, 49-63, ASST PROF PEDIAT, SCH MED, UNIV MD, BALTIMORE CITY, 63-; CHIEF OF STAFF, GREATER BALTIMORE MED CTR, 74- *Concurrent Pos:* Instr pediat, Hosp, Johns Hopkins Univ, 48-50, pediatrician, Nursery, 57-64, instr pediat, Sch Med, 66-67, asst prof, 67-; consult, Kernan's Hosp, Baltimore, 49-54; active staff mem, Union Mem Hosp, 50-; active staff mem, Women's Hosp of Md, 57-64, asst chief pediat, Women's Hosp of Md, 64-66; asst chief, 64-66, chief pediat, Greater Baltimore Med Ctr, 66- *Mem:* AMA; Am Acad Pediat. *Mailing Add:* 6701 N Charles St Baltimore MD 21204

SPRAGUE, BASIL SHELDON, b Hartford, Conn, Aug 3, 20; m 44; c 2. MATERIALS SCIENCE, POLYMER PHYSICS. *Educ:* Swarthmore Col, AB, 42; Polytech Inst Brooklyn, MChE, 44. *Hon Degrees:* ScD, Lowell Univ, 69. *Prof Exp:* Res engr plastics, Celanese Corp, 44-48, res engr textiles, 48-50, group leader textile phys res, 50-52, head textile eval res, 52-56, head fiber physics & eval res, 56-64, mgr physics res dept, 64-65, mgr mat sci res dept, 65-68, dir mat sci res, 68-76, SR RES FEL, CELANESE RES CO, 76- *Honors & Awards:* H DeWitt Smith Medal, 76. *Mem:* AAAS; Am Asn Textile Technologists; Am Chem Soc; Am Soc Testing & Mat; Fiber Soc (vpres, 65, pres, 66). *Res:* Relationship of chemical constitution and morphology to physical properties of polymers and fibers; dyeing of synthetic fibers; materials research. *Mailing Add:* Celanese Res Co Box 1000 Summit NJ 07901

SPRAGUE, CHARLES CAMERON, b Dallas, Tex, Nov 16, 16; m 41; c 1. INTERNAL MEDICINE, HEMATOLOGY. *Educ:* Southern Methodist Univ, BBA & BS, 40; Univ Tex, MD, 43; Am Bd Internal Med, dipl. *Hon Degrees:* DSc, Southern Methodist Univ, 66. *Prof Exp:* Intern, US Naval Med Ctr, Md, 43-44; from asst to prof med, Sch Med, Tulane Univ, 47-67, prof hemat, 54-63, dean div, 63-67; prof med & dean, 67-72, PRES, UNIV TEX HEALTH SCI CTR DALLAS, 72- *Concurrent Pos:* Fel, Sch Med, Tulane Univ, 48-49; Commonwealth res fel hemat, Sch Med, Wash Univ, 50-52 & Sch Med, Oxford Univ, 52; asst resident, Charity Hosp of La, 47-48, sr vis physician, 52-67; chmn, Gov Task Force Health Manpower, 81, Gov Med Educ Mgt Effectiveness Comt & Allied Health Educ Adv Comt, Coord Bd, Tex Col & Univ Syst. *Mem:* Am Soc Hemat (pres, 67); Am Fedn Clin Res; Int Soc Hemat; fel Am Col Physicians. *Res:* Hemoglobinopathies; leukemia; cancer chemotherapy. *Mailing Add:* Off of the Pres Univ of Tex Health Sci Ctr Dallas TX 75235

SPRAGUE, CLYDE HOWARD, b Kincaid, Kans, July 18, 36; m 57; c 2. MECHANICAL ENGINEERING. *Educ:* Kans State Univ, BS, 58, MS, 63; Purdue Univ, Lafayette, PhD(mech eng), 68. *Prof Exp:* Assoc staff engr, Appl Physics Lab, Johns Hopkins Univ, 58-61; from instr to assoc prof mech eng, Kans State Univ, 63-73; assoc prof, Univ Tex, Permiam Basin, 73-75, prof & chmn dept, 75-77; res assoc & prof, 77-78, SR RES ASSOC & PROF, INST PAPER CHEM, 78- *Mem:* Am Soc Mech Engrs; Am Soc Eng Educ; Simulation Coun; Tech Asn Pulp & Paper Indust. *Res:* Instrumentation and controls; paper converting processes. *Mailing Add:* PO Box 1039 Appleton WI 54912

SPRAGUE, ESTEL DEAN, b Leavenworth, Kans, Oct 17, 44; m 67; c 2. PHYSICAL CHEMISTRY. *Educ:* Asbury Col, BA, 66; Univ Tenn, Knoxville, PhD(phys chem), 71. *Prof Exp:* Res kinetics & radiation chem, Max Planck Inst Coal Res, 71-73, Dept Chem Univ Wis-Madison, 73-74; asst prof, 74-80, ASSOC PROF PHYS CHEM, UNIV CINCINNATI, 80- *Mem:* Am Chem Soc; Sigma Xi; Biophys Soc. *Res:* Micelle chemistry; polymer models for micelles; electron spin resonance; radiation chemistry; kinetics of free-radical reactions; tunneling in hydrogen atom transfer reactions. *Mailing Add:* Dept of Chem Univ of Cincinnati Cincinnati OH 45221

SPRAGUE, G(EORGE) SIDNEY, b Lexington, Ky, Sept 9, 18; m 42; c 3. POLYMER CHEMISTRY. *Educ:* Lehigh Univ, BS, 40; Univ Wis, MS, 43; NY Univ, PhD(chem), 50. *Prof Exp:* Res chemist, Sharples Chem Inc, 43-45 & Deering Milliken Res Trust, 47-49; from res chemist to sr res chemist, Am Cyanamid Co, 49-72; SR CHEMIST, LOCTITE CORP, 73- *Mem:* Am Chem Soc; Sigma Xi. *Res:* Adhesives and sealants; thermoplastics; solid rocket propellant and explosive binders; water soluble polymers; monomer synthesis. *Mailing Add:* Loctite Corp 705 N Mountain Rd Newington CT 06111

SPRAGUE, GEORGE FREDERICK, b Crete, Nebr, Sept 3, 02; m; c 4. AGRONOMY. *Educ:* Univ Nebr, BSc, 24, MS, 26; Cornell Univ, PhD(genetics), 30. *Prof Exp:* Jr agronomist, Bur Plant Indust, USDA, DC, 24-28, from asst agronomist to agronomist, 28-42, from sr agronomist to prin agronomist, 42-58, head corn & sorghum sect, Crops Res Div, Agr Res Serv, 58-72; PROF AGR, UNIV ILL, URBANA, 72- *Concurrent Pos:* Prof, Iowa State Univ, 48-58. *Mem:* Nat Acad Sci; fel Am Soc Agron (vpres; pres, 59-60); Am Soc Plant Physiol; Genetics Soc Am; Biomet Soc. *Res:* Corn breeding and genetics; statistics. *Mailing Add:* Dept of Agr Univ of Ill Urbana IL 61801

SPRAGUE, HOWARD BENNETT, b Cortland, Nebr, Dec 11, 98; m 44; c 1. AGRONOMY. *Educ:* Univ Nebr, BS, 21, MS, 23; Rutgers Univ, PhD(plant physiol), 26. *Prof Exp:* Asst agron, Univ Nebr, 21-23; instr, Rutgers Univ, 23-26, assoc prof, 27-31, prof, 31-42, head dept, Univ & agronomist, Exp Sta, 27-42; asst prof, Univ Minn, 26-27; head, Agr Res Div, Tex Res Found, 46-51; prof agron & head dept, Pa State Univ, 53-64; exec secy, Agr Bd, Nat Acad Sci, 64-69; AGR CONSULT, AID & VAR INT AGENCIES, 69- *Honors & Awards:* Medallion Award, Am Forage & Grassland Coun, 64. *Mem:* Am Forage & Grassland Coun (pres, 53-56); Soil Conserv Soc Am; fel AAAS (vpres & chmn sect O, 56, secy, 57-65); fel Am Soc Agron (pres, 64); Crop Sci Soc Am (pres, 60). *Res:* Land classification and use; soil fertility and management; plant nutrition; ecology of crop plants; plant breeding; grassland management; turf culture; agricultural and natural resource development. *Mailing Add:* 560 West Ridge Ave State College PA 16801

SPRAGUE, ISABELLE BAIRD, b Manila, PI, May 30, 16. BIOLOGY. *Educ:* Mt Holyoke Col, AB, 37, MA, 39; Univ Kans, PhD(entom), 53. *Prof Exp:* From instr to assoc prof, 45-64, chmn dept, 63-66, PROF ZOOL, MT HOLYOKE COL, 65-, DAVID B TAUMAN PROF, 80-; prof biol sci, 76-80, EMER PROF BIOL SCI, NORMA WAIT HARRIS & EMMA GALE HARRIS FOUND, 80- *Concurrent Pos:* NSFfac fel, 58-59. *Mem:* Ecol Soc Am; Entom Soc Am; Brit Freshwater Biol Asn. *Res:* Aquatic biology; endocrinology of insects; semi-aquatic hemiptera. *Mailing Add:* Dept of Biol Sci Mt Holyoke Col South Hadley MA 01075

SPRAGUE, JAMES ALAN, b Cleveland, Ohio, Aug 24, 43; m 68. METALLURGY. *Educ:* Rice Univ, BA, 65, BS, 66, PhD(mat sci), 70. *Prof Exp:* RES METALLURGIST, NAVAL RES LAB, 71- *Concurrent Pos:* NSF fel, Max Planck Inst Metall Res, 69-70. *Mem:* Am Inst Mining, Metall & Petrol Engrs; Am Soc Testing & Mat; Electron Micros Soc Am. *Res:* Electron microscopy of defects in solids; radiation damage in metals and semiconductors; electron diffraction contrast theory. *Mailing Add:* Naval Res Lab Code 6390 Washington DC 20375

SPRAGUE, JAMES CLYDE, b Gibbons, Alta, Aug 4, 28; m 52; c 1. INDUSTRIAL ENGINEERING. *Educ:* Univ Okla, BSc, 60; Iowa State Univ, MSc, 67, PhD(indust eng), 69. *Prof Exp:* Chief economist, Hu Harries & Assocs, 60-61; chief engr, BJ Serv of Can, 61-65; dir eng eval, Gamma Eng, 65-66; asst prof indust eng, Iowa State Univ, 68-69; assoc prof mech eng, 69-77, PROF MECH ENG, UNIV ALTA, 77- *Mem:* Am Soc Eng Educ; Am Inst Indust Engrs. *Res:* Engineering economy and capital budgeting, design of industrial systems; mass production of homes. *Mailing Add:* Dept of Mech Eng Univ of Alta Edmonton AB T6G 2E1 Can

SPRAGUE, JAMES MATHER, b Kansas City, Mo, Aug 31, 16; m; c 1. NEUROSCIENCE. *Educ:* Univ Kans, AB, 38, AM, 40; Harvard Univ, PhD(biol), 42. *Hon Degrees:* MA, Univ Pa, 71. *Prof Exp:* From asst mus mammals to asst instr zool, Univ Kans, 36-40; from asst to asst prof anat, Sch Med, Johns Hopkins Univ, 42-50; from asst prof to prof anat, 50-73, mem, Inst Neurol Sci, 54-73, assoc dir, 57-60, chmn dept, 67-76, dir Inst Neurol Sci, 73-80, JOSEPH LEIDY PROF ANAT, SCH MED, UNIV PA, 73- *Concurrent Pos:* Guggenheim fel, Cambridge Univ & Oxford Univ, 48; Macy Fac Scholar award, 74; vis investr, Med Sch, Northwestern Univ, 48, Rockefeller Inst, 55, Cambridge Univ, 56 & Univ Pisa, 66 & 74; consult, NIH, 57-58. *Honors & Awards:* Lindbach Found Award, 66. *Mem:* AAAS; Am Asn Anat (vpres, 76-78); Int Brain Res Orgn; Soc Neurosci. *Res:* Taxonomy and comparative anatomy of mammals; neuroanatomy of spinal cord; neurophysiology of brain stem and spinal cord; anatomy and physiology of brain stem and cerebellum; neural mechanisms of vision and visual behavior. *Mailing Add:* Dept Anat Sch Med Univ Pa Philadelphia PA 19174

SPRAGUE, JOHN BOOTY, b Woodstock, Ont, Feb 16, 31; m 53; c 5. BIOLOGY. *Educ:* Univ Western Ont, BSc, 53; Univ Toronto, MA, 54, PhD(zool), 59. *Prof Exp:* Scientist-in-chg pollution studies, Biol Sta, Fisheries Res Bd, Can, 58-70; assoc prof zool, 70-76, PROF ZOOL, UNIV GUELPH, 76- *Res:* Aquatic biology; effects of pollution on fish and other aquatic organisms; bioassays and water quality criteria. *Mailing Add:* Dept Zool Univ Guelph Guelph ON N1G 2W1 Can

SPRAGUE, LUCIAN MATTHEW, b Salt Lake City, Utah, Apr 14, 26. GENETICS. *Educ:* Univ Calif, AB, 50, PhD, 57. *Prof Exp:* Res asst, Univ Calif, 52-56; geneticist biol lab, Bur Commercial Fisheries, US Fish & Wildlife Serv, 56-60, chief subpop invest, 60-62, dep dir, Hawaii Area, 62-67; assoc dir med & natural sci, Rockefeller Found, 67-69; prof oceanog & dir, Int Ctr Marine Resource Develop, Univ RI, 69-72; FISHERIES SPECIALIST, AGR & RURAL DEVELOP DEPT, INT BANK RECONSTRUCTION & DEVELOP, 72- *Concurrent Pos:* Res fel, Univ Uppsala, 66-67. *Mem:* AAAS; Genetic Soc Am. *Res:* Blood groups and genetics of natural populations of vertebrates, particularly teleosts; fisheries resources and policy studies. *Mailing Add:* 4486 Occoquan View Ct Woodbridge VA 22192

SPRAGUE, MILTON ALAN, b Washburn, Wis, June 15, 14; m 44; c 4. AGRONOMY. *Educ:* Northland Col, BA, 36; Univ Wis, MS, 38, PhD(agron), 41. *Prof Exp:* Asst agron, Univ Wis, 36-41; asst agronomist, Univ Ark, 41-46; asst prof agron, 46-50, assoc prof & assoc res specialist, 50-56, chmn dept farm crops, 55-61, prof, 56-72, DISTINGUISHED PROF, RUTGERS UNIV, NEW BRUNSWICK, 72-, RES SPECIALIST, 56- *Concurrent Pos:* Lectr, Columbia Univ, 56-71; agr consult, Latin Am. *Honors & Awards:* Merit Award, Am Forage & Grassland Coun, 69; Res Award, Am Soc Agron, 77. *Mem:* Fel Am Soc Agron; Am Soc Plant Physiologists; Sigma Xi. *Res:* Physiology forages; winter killing; seedling establishment; pasture management; accumulation of respiratory by-products in alfalfa and the injurious effects of ice contact; factors affecting silage quality; microclimate affected by slope and its effect on the biosphere. *Mailing Add:* Dept Soil & Crops Rutgers Univ Lipman Hall Box 231 New Brunswick NJ 08903

SPRAGUE, NEWTON G, b Indianapolis, Ind, Feb 8, 14; m 37; c 2. PHYSICS, ASTRONOMY. *Educ:* Butler Univ, BS, 35; Ind Univ, MS, 51, EdD(ed psychol), 55. *Prof Exp:* Asst physics, Butler Univ, 47-48; phys chemist, Indust Oils Lab, 48-49; teacher pub sch, Ind, 49-51, asst visual prod, 51-56, consult, 56-60; from asst prof to prof physics & astron, 60-78, dir, Univ Observ & Planetarium, 65-78, EMER PROF PHYSICS & ASTRON, BALL STATE UNIV, 78- *Mem:* AAAS; emer mem Am Astron Soc. *Res:* Spectroscopic and photometric stellar measurements. *Mailing Add:* 1212 N Ridge Rd Muncie IN 47304

SPRAGUE, PETER WHITNEY, b Rochester, NY, Oct 4, 41; m 63; c 2. ORGANIC CHEMISTRY. *Educ:* Western Reserve Univ, BA, 63, PhD(org chem), 66. *Prof Exp:* Fel, Ind Univ, 66-67; from asst prof to assoc prof chem, Calif State Col, San Bernardino, 67-72; res investr, 72-74, sr res investr, 74-76, group leader, 76-80, SECT HEAD ORG CHEM, E R SQUIBB & SONS, INC, 80- *Mem:* Am Chem Soc; AAAS. *Res:* Medicinal chemistry in areas of cardiovascular and antiinflammatory drugs. *Mailing Add:* Dept of Org Chem PO Box 4000 Princeton NJ 08570

SPRAGUE, RANDALL GEORGE, b Chicago, Ill, Sept 22, 06; m 39; c 4. INTERNAL MEDICINE, ENDOCRINOLOGY. *Educ:* Northwestern Univ, Ill, BS, 30, MB & MS, 34, MD, 35, Mayo Grad Sch Med, Univ Minn, PhD(med), 42; Am Bd Internal Med, dipl, 42. *Hon Degrees:* LLD, Univ Toronto, 64. *Prof Exp:* Instr physiol, Med Sch, Northwestern Univ, Ill, 33-34; first asst med, Mayo Clin, 39-40, from instr to prof, Mayo Grad Sch Med, 42-71, EMER PROF MED, MAYO GRAD SCH MED, UNIV MINN, 71- *Concurrent Pos:* Consult, Mayo Clin, 40-63, sr consult, 63-71, emer consult, 71-; mem metab & endocrinol study sect, NIH, 47-51; mem, Nat Adv Dent Res Coun, 63-67; consult, Rochester State Hosp, 72- Am Diabetes Asn (pres, 53-54); master Am Col Physicians; hon mem Royal Soc Med; corr mem Royal Acad Med Belg. *Mem:* Am Soc Clin Invest; Asn Am Physicians. *Res:* Clinical investigation of metabolic and endocrine diseases; relation of the adrenal cortex to carbohydrate metabolism; endocrinology. *Mailing Add:* 410 SW Sixth Ave Rochester MN 55901

SPRAGUE, RICHARD HOWARD, b Cincinnati, Ohio, Nov 9, 24. MATHEMATICS. *Educ:* Maryville Col, BS, 49; Univ KY, MA, 52, PhD(math), 61. *Prof Exp:* Asst math, Ohio State Univ, 49-50; asst, Univ Ky, 50-52, instr, 53-56; asst prof, NMex State Univ, 58-60; asst prof, 61-67, ASSOC PROF MATH, IOWA STATE UNIV, 67- *Mem:* Am Math Soc. *Res:* Univalent functions; geometry; complex variables. *Mailing Add:* Dept of Math Iowa State Univ Ames IA 50010

SPRAGUE, ROBERT ARTHUR, US citizen. OPTICS. *Educ:* Univ Rochester, BS, 67, PhD(optics), 71. *Prof Exp:* Sr scientist, Itek Corp Cent Res Labs, 71-74, staff scientist, 74-76; mem res staff, 76-80, RES AREA MGR, PALO ALTO RES CTR, XEROX CORP, 80- *Concurrent Pos:* Comt mem, US Nat Comt, Int Comn Optics, 73-75. *Mem:* Optical Soc Am; Soc Photo-Optical Instr Engrs; Am Inst Physics. *Res:* Electro-optics, input/output systems, optical signal processing, coherent optical processing and acousto-optics. *Mailing Add:* Xerox Palo Alto Res Ctr 3333 Coyote Hill Palo Alto CA 94304

SPRAGUE, ROBERT HICKS, b Rochester, NY, Mar 9, 14; m 36; c 3. ORGANIC CHEMISTRY. *Prof Exp:* Asst res lab, Eastman Kodak Co, NY, 31-34, res chemist, 35-52; group leader sensitizing dye res, Remington Rand, Inc, Conn, 52-57; asst head chem dept, Horizons, Inc, 57-58, head, 58-64; mgr dye chem dept, Itek Corp, 65-75; consult, Exxon Res & Eng Co, 75-76; consult, Res Triangle Inst, Olivetti Co Am, 76-81; CONSULT, RICOH SYST INC, 81- *Honors & Awards:* Kosar Award, Soc Photog Sci & Eng, 68. *Mem:* AAAS; fel Soc Photog Sci & Eng; Am Chem Soc; NY Acad Sci. *Res:* Sensitizing dyes for photographic emulsions; dyes for color photography; pharmaceu ticals; antibiotics; diuretics; tranquilizers; non-silver photographic systems; organic photoconductors. *Mailing Add:* 270 Hillside Dr Chapel Hill NC 27514

SPRAGUE, ROBERT W, b Omaha, Nebr, Aug 1, 23; m 47; c 2. INORGANIC CHEMISTRY. *Educ:* Univ Calif, Los Angeles, BS, 44; Ohio State Univ, PhD(inorg chem), 57. *Prof Exp:* Sales engr, R E Cunningham & Son, 46-48; chemist, US Naval Ord Test Sta, Calif, 48-57; teaching asst & res fel chem, Ohio State Univ, 54-57; sr chemist, Minn Mining & Mfg Co, 57-58; res specialist propulsion, Rocketdyne Div, NAm Aviation, Inc, 58-60; res scientist, Aeronutronic Div, Philco Corp, 60 65; SR RES CHEMIST, US BORAX RES CORP, ANAHEIM, 65- *Mem:* AAAS; Am Chem Soc; Am Soc Test & Mat; Nat Fire Protection Asn. *Res:* Inorganic chemistry of nonmetals; chemistry of boron oxides, sulfides, halides; chemistry of oxide systems; environmental chemistry; fire retardance. *Mailing Add:* US Borax Res Corp 412 Crescent Way Anaheim CA 92801

SPRAIN, WILBUR, b Forest Lake, Minn, Aug 10, 25; m 45; c 3. SCIENCE EDUCATION. *Educ:* Gustavus Adolphus Col, BS, 48; Iowa State Col, MS, 51, PhD(educ), 52. *Prof Exp:* Asst prof chem, Wayne State Col, 52-53; PROF PHYS SCI, SAN JOSE STATE UNIV, 53- *Mem:* AAAS; Nat Sci Teachers Asn. *Res:* General science education. *Mailing Add:* Dept of Natural Sci San Jose State Univ San Jose CA 95792

SPRAKER, HAROLD STEPHEN, b Cedar Bluff, Va, May 13, 29; m 54; c 2. MATHEMATICS. *Educ:* Roanoke Col, BS, 50; Univ Va, MEd, 55, DEd(math educ), 60. *Prof Exp:* Teacher high sch, Va, 53-55, asst prin, 55-57; res assoc, Univ Va, 56-60, instr math, 59-60; from asst prof to assoc prof 60-65, PROF MATH, MID TENN STATE UNIV, 65-, CHMN DEPT, 67- *Concurrent Pos:* Apprentice coordr, Va State Dept Labor, 53-57; dir, NSF In-Serv Inst & vis scientist lectr. *Mem:* Math Asn Am. *Res:* Mathematical education; geometry; algebra; statistics. *Mailing Add:* Dept of Math Mid Tenn State Univ Box 34 Murfreesboro TN 37130

SPRATLEY, RICHARD DENIS, b Vancouver, BC, Apr 18, 38; m 64; c 3. PHYSICAL CHEMISTRY. *Educ:* Univ BC, BSc, 61; Univ Calif, Berkeley, PhD(chem), 65. *Prof Exp:* Res assoc chem, Brookhaven Nat Lab, 65-67; asst prof chem, 67-72, RES ADMINR, UNIV BC, 72- *Res:* Infrared spectroscopy; x-ray and neutron diffraction; molecular structure and bonding. *Mailing Add:* Res Admin Off of Pres Univ of BC Vancouver BC V6T 1W5 Can

SPRATT, JAMES LEO, b Chicago, Ill, Jan 27, 32; c 2. PHARMACOLOGY. *Educ:* Univ Chicago, AM, 53, PhD(pharmacol), 57, MD, 61. *Prof Exp:* Asst pharmacol, Argonne Cancer Res Hosp, Univ Chicago, 57-61; from asst prof to assoc prof, 61-71, PROF PHARMACOL, UNIV IOWA, 71- *Concurrent Pos:* USPHS res career develop award, 63-68; Markle scholar, 63-68. *Mem:* AAAS; Am Chem Soc; Am Soc Pharmacol & Exp Therapeut; NY Acad Sci. *Res:* Therapeutics; radioisotopic tracer methods in cardiac glycoside research; cardiac glycosides and neurotoxicity; biochemical neuropharmacology. *Mailing Add:* Dept of Pharmacol Univ of Iowa Iowa City IA 52240

SPRATT, JOHN STRICKLIN, b San Angelo, Tex, Jan 3, 29; m 51; c 3. SURGERY. *Educ:* Univ Tex, Dallas, MD, 52; Univ Mo-Columbia, MSPH, 70; Southern Methodist Univ, BS, 76; Am Bd Surg, dipl, 60. *Prof Exp:* Asst physiol, Univ Tex Southwestern Med Sch Dallas, 52; intern surg, Barnes Hosp, 52-53, from asst resident to resident, 55-59; from instr to assoc prof, Sch Med, Washington Univ, 59-66; prof surg, Sch Med, Univ Mo-Columbia, 66-76, prof community health & med pract, 71-76; PROF SURG ONCOL, UNIV LOUISVILLE, 76- *Concurrent Pos:* USPHS cancer res fel radiother & surg, Mallinckrodt Inst Radiol, St Louis, 57-58; Am Cancer Soc fel, Barnes Hosp, 58-59; Am Cancer Soc advan clin fel, 60-63; from asst prof to assoc prof, Sch Med, Univ Mo, 61-66, dir clin res & mem sci adv comt, Cancer Res Ctr, 64, dir ctr, 65-76; med dir dept surg, Ellis Fischel State Cancer Hosp, Columbia, 61-76; med adv bur hearings & appeals, Soc Security Admin, 64-; mem rev comt sr clin traineeships surg, Cancer Control Prog, USPHS, 64-68; coordr cancer control, State of Mo; mem study sect, Supportive Serv Rev, 75-77; prof clin oncol, Am Cancer Soc, 76- *Mem:* Am Surg Asn; Am Asn Cancer Res; Soc Head & Neck Surg; Soc Surg Oncol. *Res:* Statistical analyses of the natural history of human cancer and the influence of therapy upon the natural history; use of roentgen and surgical therapy for cancer; cytokinetics of human cancer, application of operations research methods to clinical decisions; the role of patient and family education in rehabilitation; cancer control. *Mailing Add:* Cancer Ctr Raymond Olyers Hall Univ Louisville Louisville KY 40292

SPRATTO, GEORGE R, b Waterbury, Conn, July 28, 40; m 68; c 2. PHARMACOLOGY. *Educ:* Fordham Univ, BS, 61; Univ Minn, PhD(pharmacol), 66. *Prof Exp:* Pharmacologist, Food & Drug Admin, 66-68; asst prof, 68-71, assoc prof, 72-79, PROF PHARMACOL, PURDUE UNIV, 79-, ASSOC HEAD, DEPT PHARMCOL & TOXICOL, 78- *Concurrent Pos:* mem, Instnl Rev Bd, Pharmadynamics, Inc, 79-; adj prof, Sch Med, Ind Univ, 81-; mem bd dirs, Am Asn Col Pharm. *Mem:* Am Soc Pharmacol & Exp Therapeut; Am Asn Col Pharm; Am Sch Health Asn. *Res:* Describing the pharmacological responses and assessing the mechanism by which various central nervous system drugs interact in animals treated acutely or chronically with narcotics. *Mailing Add:* Dept Pharmacol & Toxicol Sch Pharm Pharamcol Sci Purdue Univ West Lafayette IN 47907

SPRAWLS, PERRY, JR, b Williston, SC, Mar 2, 34; m 61; c 1. MEDICAL PHYSICS, BIOMEDICAL ENGINEERING. *Educ:* Clemson Univ, BS, 56, MS, 60, PhD, 68. *Prof Exp:* Engr, Bell Tel Labs, 56-58; physicist, Savannah River Labs, AEC, 59-60; from instr to assoc prof, 59-77; PROF RADIOL, EMORY UNIV, 77- *Mailing Add:* Dept Radiol Woodruff Bldg Emory Univ Atlanta GA 30322

SPRAY, DAVID CONOVER, b Pittsburgh, Pa, June 7, 46; div; c 1. NEUROPHYSIOLOGY. *Educ:* Transylvania Col, BS, 68; Univ Fla, PhD(physiol), 73. *Prof Exp:* Res fel, 73-77, ASST PROF NEUROSCI, ALBERT EINSTEIN COL OF MED, 77- *Concurrent Pos:* Trainee, Ctr Neurosci, 69-73; mem corp, Marine Biol Lab, Woods Hole, 74- *Mem:* Am Physiol Soc; Biophys Soc; Soc Neurosci; Soc Gen Physiologists; Sigma Xi. *Res:* General neurophysiology, especially the physiology of chemical and electrical synapses, electro- and cutaneous receptors, cellular excitability and intracellular communication and excitability during development. *Mailing Add:* Dept of Neurosci Albert Einstein Col of Med Bronx NY 10461

SPRECHER, DAVID A, b Saarbrucken, Ger, Jan 12, 30; US citizen; m 79; c 2. MATHEMATICS. *Educ:* Univ Bridgeport, AB, 58; Univ Md, PhD(math), 63. *Prof Exp:* Instr math, Univ Md, 61-63; asst prof, Syracuse Univ, 63-66; assoc prof, 66-71, chmn, Dept Math, 72-75, actg dean, Col Lett & Sci, 78-79, dean, 79-80, PROF MATH, UNIV CALIF, SANTA BARBARA, 71-, PROVOST & DEAN, COL LETT & SCI, 81- *Concurrent Pos:* NSF grant, 65-67. *Mem:* Am Math Soc; Math Asn Am. *Res:* Structure of functions of several variables; superposition of functions and approximation theory. *Mailing Add:* Dept of Math Univ of Calif Santa Barbara CA 93106

SPRECHER, HOWARD W, b Sauk City, Wis, Oct 13, 36; m 64. BIOCHEMISTRY. *Educ:* NCent Col, BA, 58; Univ Wis, PhD(biochem), 64. *Prof Exp:* Fel biochem, Hormel Inst, Univ Minn, 63-64; from asst prof to assoc prof physiol chem, 64-72, PROF PHYSIOL CHEM, OHIO STATE UNIV, 72- *Mem:* AAAS; Am Chem Soc; Am Oil Chem Soc; Am Soc Biol Chemists. *Res:* Organic synthesis, metabolism and characterization of lipids. *Mailing Add:* Dept Physiol Chem Ohio State Univ 333 W Tenth Ave Columbus OH 43210

SPREITER, JOHN R(OBERT), b Oak Park, Minn, Oct 23, 21; m 53; c 4. FLUID MECHANICS, SPACE PHYSICS. *Educ:* Univ Minn, BAeroE, 43; Stanford Univ, MS, 47, PhD(eng mech), 54. *Prof Exp:* Aeronaut engr, Flight Res Br, Ames Aeronaut Lab, Nat Adv Comt Aeronaut, 43-46, res scientist, Theoret Aerodyn Br, 47-58, res scientist, Theoret Br, Ames Res Ctr, NASA, 58-62, chief theoret studies br, Space Sci Div, 62-69; lectr, 50-68, PROF APPL MECH & AERONAUT & ASTRONAUT, STANFORD UNIV, 68- *Concurrent Pos:* Mem ionospheres & radio physics subcomt, Space Sci Steering Comt, NASA, 60-64; mem various comts, Int Asn Geomag & Aeronomy, 64- *Mem:* AAAS; Am Geophys Union; Am Phys Soc; Am Inst Aeronaut & Astronaut; Royal Astron Soc. *Res:* Geomagnetism; solar wind; cosmic fluid dynamics; space physics; magnetohydrodynamics; transonic flow theory; aerodynamics and fluid mechanics. *Mailing Add:* 1250 Sandalwood Lane Los Altos CA 94022

SPREITZER, WILLIAM MATTHEW, b Highland Park, Mich, Aug 14, 29; m 52; c 2. RESEARCH ADMINISTRATION, AERONAUTICAL ENGINEERING. *Educ:* Univ Detroit, BAeE, 51. *Hon Degrees:* AeE, Univ Detroit, 57. *Prof Exp:* Eng draftsman, Dept Aeronaut, State Mich, 49-51; from jr res engr to sr res engr, Eng Develop Dept, 51-61, sr liaison engr, Exec Dept, 61-66, head transp res dept, 66-72, head transp & urban anal dept, 72-78, HEAD TRANSP RES DEPT, GEN MOTORS RES LABS, 79- *Concurrent Pos:* Mem, Comt on Transp, Nat Res Coun Assembly Eng, 70-81 & Bay Area Rapid Transit Impact Adv Comt, 72-79; mem, Transp Develop Adv Comt, Hwy Users Fedn Safety & Mobility, 70-72; deleg transp panel, White House Conf on Aging, 71; mem panel on urbanization, transp & commun, Nat Acad Sci-Nat Res Coun Study for 79 UN Conf on Sci & Technol for Develop, 77-78. *Mem:* Assoc fel Am Inst Aeronaut & Astronaut; Soc Automotive Engrs; Am Mgt Asn; Nat Defense Transp Asn; Opers Res Soc Am. *Res:* Transportation and traffic science; automotive gas turbine engine research, development and applications; research administration. *Mailing Add:* Transp Res Dept Twelve Mile & Mound Rds Warren MI 48090

SPREMULLI, GERTRUDE H, b Bucyrus, Ohio, Dec 21, 12; m 37; c 3. BIOCHEMISTRY. *Educ:* Heidelberg Col, BS, 33; Western Reserve Univ, MS, 38; Pa State Univ, PhD(agr biochem), 42. *Prof Exp:* Res chemist, Ranger Aircraft Engines, 42-44; res assoc, Columbia Univ, 44-45; asst prof, 56-72, prof, 72-77, chmn, Div Natural Sci & dean admin, 72-76, Dana prof, 76-77, EMER DANA PROF CHEM, ELMIRA COL, 77- *Mem:* Am Chem Soc. *Res:* Biophysical chemistry; biochemistry, especially enzymes; physical properties. *Mailing Add:* West Lake Rd Rte 1 Bradford NY 14815

SPREMULLI, LINDA LUCY, b Corning, NY, Sept 6, 47. CHEMISTRY. *Educ:* Univ Rochester, BA, 69; Mass Inst Technol, PhD(biochem), 73. *Prof Exp:* Assoc chem, Univ Tex, Austin, 73-74, fel, 74-76; asst prof, 76-81, ASSOC PROF CHEM, UNIV NC, 81- *Concurrent Pos:* Mem, Biomed Sci Study Sect, NIH, 82-86. *Mem:* Am Soc Biol Chemists; Am Chem Soc; AAAS; Asn Women Sci; Am Soc Microbiol. *Res:* Isolation and characterization of eukaryotic cytoplasmic protein synthesis initiation factors; characterization of the ribosomes and auxiliary factors required for chloroplast protein synthesis and induction of this system by light. *Mailing Add:* Dept Chem Univ NC Chapel Hill NC 27514

SPRENG, ALFRED CARL, b Alliance, Ohio, Feb 2, 23; m 49; c 3. STRATIGRAPHY. *Educ:* Col Wooster, AB, 46; Univ Kans, AM, 48; Univ Wis, PhD(geol), 50. *Prof Exp:* Asst, Univ Wis, 48-50; from asst prof to assoc prof geol, 50-62, chmn dept geol & geophys, 71-75, PROF GEOL, UNIV MO-ROLLA, 62- *Concurrent Pos:* Consult, limestone & shale raw mats, 55- *Mem:* Paleont Soc; Am Asn Petrol Geologists; Geol Soc Am; Soc Econ Paleontologists & Mineralogists; Am Inst Prof Geologists. *Res:* Stratigraphic paleontology; carbonate petrology. *Mailing Add:* Dept Geol & Geophysics Univ of Mo Rolla MO 65401

SPRENKEL, RICHARD KEISER, b York, Pa, July 10, 43; m 65. ENTOMOLOGY. *Educ:* Pa State Univ, BS, 65, MS, 67; Univ Ill, PhD(entom), 73. *Prof Exp:* Res assoc entom, NC State Univ, 73-79; ASST PROF ENTOM, UNIV FLA, 79- *Mem:* Entom Soc Am. *Res:* Development of integrated pest management programs on row crops in Florida. *Mailing Add:* Agr Res & Educ Ctr Rte 3 Box 638 Quincy FL 32351

SPRIGGS, ALFRED SAMUEL, b Houston, Tex, Aug 1, 22; m 49; c 4. ORGANIC CHEMISTRY. *Educ:* Dillard Univ, AB, 42; Howard Univ, MS, 44; Washington Univ, PhD(chem), 54. *Prof Exp:* Asst prof chem, Tenn Agr & Indust State Col, 47-51; prof, Lincoln Univ, Pa, 54-55; PROF CHEM & CHMN DEPT, CLARK COL, 55- *Mem:* Fel AAAS; Am Chem Soc; Sigma Xi. *Res:* Isotope tracers with carbon 14; carbohydrates; organic synthesis; radiochemistry; chromatography. *Mailing Add:* Dept of Chem Clark Col Atlanta GA 30314

SPRIGGS, RICHARD MOORE, b Washington, Pa, May 8, 31; m 53; c 3. MATERIALS RESEARCH, CERAMIC ENGINEERING. *Educ:* Pa State Univ, BS, 52; Univ Ill, MS, 56, PhD(ceramic eng), 58. *Prof Exp:* Asst ceramic eng, Univ Ill, 54-56; sr res engr ceramics, Ferro Corp, Ohio, 58-59; sr scientist, Res & Advan Develop Div, Avco Corp, Mass, 59-60, staff scientist, 60-62, sr staff scientist & ceramics res group leader, 62-64; assoc prof metall & mat sci, Lehigh Univ, 64-67, assoc dir mat res ctr & dir phys ceramics lab, 64-70, admin asst to pres, 70-71, asst vpres admin, 71-72, prof, 67-80, vpres admin, 72-78, vis sr staff assoc, 79-80, SR STAFF OFFICER/STAFF SCIENTIST, NAT MAT ADV BD, 80- *Concurrent Pos:* Am Coun Educ fel, Lehigh Univ, 70-71; consult to var corps & govt labs. *Honors & Awards:* Ross Coffin Purdy Award, Am Ceramic Soc, 67; Hobart M Kramer Award, Am Ceramic Soc, 80. *Mem:* Fel Brit Inst Ceramics; fel Am Ceramic Soc (treas, 80-82, vpres, 82-83); Nat Inst Ceramic Engrs; Brit Ceramic Soc; Int Inst Sci Sintering. *Res:* Physical ceramics; materials science; correlations among processing, internal structure and physical and mechanical properties of dense polycrystalline refractory ceramic oxide systems; author or coauthor of over 75 technical articles. *Mailing Add:* Nat Mat Adv Bd 2101 Constitution Ave Northwest Washington DC 20418

SPRINCE, HERBERT, b Lewiston, Maine, Dec 18, 12; m 56. BIOCHEMISTRY, PHARMACOLOGY. *Educ:* Bates Col, BS, 34; Harvard Univ, MA, 35, PhD(cellular physiol), 39. *Prof Exp:* Lab asst physiol, Harvard Univ, 35-38; Parker fel, Med Col, Cornell Univ, 39-40; asst, Huntington Mem Hosp, 41; asst, Harvard Univ, 41-42; res assoc, Mass Inst Technol, 42-43; Nutrit Found fel, Rockefeller Inst, 43-45; dir div nutrit & microbiol, Ortho Res Found, Johnson & Johnson, 45-52; dir res, Elizabeth Biochem Lab, NJ, 52-54; CHIEF RES BIOCHEM, VET ADMIN MED CTR, 54-; ASSOC PROF PHARMACOL & PSYCHIAT, JEFFERSON MED COL, 68- *Concurrent Pos:* Vis lectr, New York Med Col, 53-60; res assoc psychiat, Univ Pa, 55-68; asst prof biochem, Grad Sch Med, Univ Pa, 61-67. *Mem:* Fel AAAS; Am Chem Soc; Am Asn Clin Chem; Soc Biol Psychiat; Am Inst Nutrit. *Res:* Nutritional biochemistry; behavioral pharmacology; indoles, amino acids in schizophrenia and alcoholism; structure-activity relationships in depressant and excitatory behavior; xanthurenic acid in toxemias of pregnancy; animal, bacterial and protozoal growth factors. *Mailing Add:* Vet Admin Med Ctr Coatesville PA 19320

SPRING, DONALD J, b Aurora, Ill, Mar 5, 31; m 51; c 3. GAS DYNAMICS, AERODYNAMICS. *Educ:* Ala Polytech Inst, BS, 56; Auburn Univ, MS, 64; Univ Ill, Urbana-Champaign, PhD, 72. *Prof Exp:* Aerodynamicist, Convair Div, Gen Dynamics Corp, 57-58; proj engr, ARO, Inc, 58-61; AERODYN ENGR, US ARMY MISSILE COMMAND, 61- *Concurrent Pos:* Lectr, Univ Ala, Huntsville, 76- *Mem:* Assoc fel Am Inst Aeronaut & Astronaut. *Res:* Flight mechanics; lateral jet interactions; separated flow fields; experimental aerodynamic and preliminary design techniques. *Mailing Add:* 2103 Harris Rd NW Huntsville AL 35810

SPRING, RAY FREDERICK, b Cincinnati, Ohio, Mar 28, 25; m 49; c 2. MATHEMATICS. *Educ:* Univ Cincinnati, BS, 48; Univ Ill, MS, 52, PhD(math), 55. *Prof Exp:* Chem engr, US Playing Card Co, 48-50; asst math, Univ Ill, 52-54; from asst prof to assoc prof, 55-66, PROF MATH, OHIO UNIV, 66- *Mem:* Am Math Soc. *Res:* Modern abstract algebra; group and lattice theories; digital computer programming; characterization and classification of metabelian p-groups and other groups by means of their subgroup lattices. *Mailing Add:* Dept of Math Ohio Univ Athens OH 45701

SPRINGBORN, ROBERT CARL, b Geneva, Ill, Oct 19, 29; m 51; c 2. POLYMER SCIENCE, BIORESEARCH. *Educ:* Univ Ill, BS, 51; Cornell Univ, PhD(org chem), 54. *Prof Exp:* Res chemist, Monsanto Chem Co, 54-58; tech dir, Marbon Chem Div, Borg-Warner Corp, 58-63; vpres & tech dir, Ohio Rubber Co, 63-65; gen mgr, Ionics, Inc, 65-67; vpres, W R Grace & Co, 67-69; chmn & pres, Gen Econ Corp, 69-71; CHMN & PRES, SPRINGBORN LABS, INC, 72- *Concurrent Pos:* Pres, Srpingborn Inst Biores, Inc, 76-; mem, White House Conf Small Bus Adv Subcomt on Direct Support Res & Develop, Dept Com, 78- *Mem:* Am Chem Soc; AAAS; Soc Plastics Engrs; Plastics Inst Am; Nat Asn Life Sci Industs. *Res:* Polymer science including polymeric synthesis and processing; medical and health sciences, particularly related to bioresearch. *Mailing Add:* Springborn Group Inc 1 Springborn Ctr Enfield CT 06082

SPRINGER, ALAN DAVID, b Linz, Austria, Jan 6, 48; US citizen; m 69; c 2. NEUROSCIENCE. *Educ:* Brooklyn Col, BS, 69; City Univ New York, PhD(psychol), 73. *Prof Exp:* Scholar neurosci, Univ Mich, 73-77; asst prof physiol, Univ Ill Med Ctr, 77-79; ASSOC PROF ANAT, NEW YORK MED COL, 79- *Concurrent Pos:* Prin investr, Nat Inst Aging, NIH grant & NSF grant, 78-81 & Nat Eye Inst, NIH grant, 81-84. *Mem:* Soc Neurosci; Asn Res Vision & Ophthal; Am Asn Anatomists; NY Acad Sci; AAAS. *Res:* Vision and optic nerve regeneration in vertebrates, including conditions leading to abnormal and normal patterns of regeneration and the role of various brain structures in mediating vision. *Mailing Add:* Dept Anat New York Med Col Valhalla NY 10595

SPRINGER, ALLAN MATTHEW, b Baraboo, Wis, Oct 2, 44; m 67. CHEMICAL ENGINEERING, PULP & PAPER TECHNOLOGY. *Educ:* Univ Wis-Madison, BS, 66; Lawrence Univ, MS, 69, PhD(chem eng), 72. *Prof Exp:* Process engr, Olin Mathieson Chem Corp, 67-68; res engr, Nat Coun Paper Indust Air & Stream Improvement, 72-76; asst prof pulp & paper technol, 76-81, ASSOC PROF PAPER SCI & ENG, MIAMI UNIV, 81- *Concurrent Pos:* Sr Fulbright lectr, Univ Pertanian Malaysia, 79-80. *Mem:* Tech Asn Pulp & Paper Indust; Am Inst Chem Engrs; Am Asn Environ Eng Prof; Sigma Xi. *Res:* Water pollution abatement through process modification; wastewater treatment optimization; resource recovery and recycling in the pulp and paper industry. *Mailing Add:* Dept Paper Sci & Eng Miami Univ Oxford OH 45056

SPRINGER, BERNARD G, b New York, NY, Feb 26, 35; div; c 2. SCIENCE POLICY. *Educ:* Univ Chicago, BA, 54, MS, 57, PhD(physics), 64. *Prof Exp:* Res assoc solid state physics, Univ Chicago, 64; Nat Acad Sci vis res fel, Univ Tokyo, 64-65; asst prof, Univ Southern Calif, 66-69; mem staff, Boeing Co, 59-60 & Hughes Aircraft Co, 69-72; SR PHYS SCIENTIST, RAND CORP, 72- *Mem:* Am Phys Soc. *Mailing Add:* Rand Corp 1700 Main St Santa Monica CA 90406

SPRINGER, CHARLES EUGENE, b Storm Lake, Iowa, Oct 25, 03; m 30; c 1. MATHEMATICS. *Educ:* Univ Okla, AB, 25, AM, 26; Oxford Univ, BSc, 40; Univ Chicago, PhD(math), 38. *Prof Exp:* Instr math, Univ Okla, 26-27 & Iowa State Col, 30; from instr to prof, 30-61, chmn dept math, 46-55, David Ross Boyd Prof, 61-70, DAVID ROSS BOYD EMER PROF MATH, UNIV OKLA, 70- *Concurrent Pos:* Chmn dept math, Oklahoma City Univ, 70-72. *Res:* Differential geometry; dual geodesics on a surface; metric geometry of surfaces by use of tensor analysis and in four-dimensional space; union curves and curvature. *Mailing Add:* 1617 Jenkins Norman OK 73069

SPRINGER, CHARLES HAVICE, b Lakewood, Ohio, Jan 30, 17; m; c 2. ORGANIC CHEMISTRY. *Educ:* Fenn Col, BChE, 48; Western Reserve Univ, MS, 50, PhD(org chem), 56. *Prof Exp:* From instr to asst prof chem, Fenn Col, 50-59; assoc prof, 59-71, PROF CHEM, LINFIELD COL, 71- *Mem:* Am Chem Soc. *Res:* Organic reaction mechanisms. *Mailing Add:* 1512 W Fifth McMinnville OR 97128

SPRINGER, CHARLES S, JR, b Houston, Tex, Nov 2, 40; m 63; c 2. BIOPHYSICAL CHEMISTRY. *Educ:* St Louis Univ, BS, 62; Ohio State Univ, MSc, 64, PhD(chem), 67. *Prof Exp:* Res chemist, Aerospace Res Labs, 65-68; asst prof chem, 68-74, ASSOC PROF CHEM, STATE UNIV NY STONY BROOK, 74- *Concurrent Pos:* Vis assoc, Calif Inst Technol, 76-77. *Honors & Awards:* US Air Force Res & Develop Award, 67. *Mem:* AAAS; Am Chem Soc; NY Acad Sci; Biophys Soc. *Res:* Nuclear magnetic resonance and electron paramagnetic resonance studies of biological membranes; physical properties, and ionophore- and protein- catalyzed metal ion membrane transport, metal ion binding to membrane surfaces, physical chemistry of micelle and inverse micelle solutions. *Mailing Add:* Dept Chem State Univ NY Stony Brook NY 11794

SPRINGER, DONALD LEE, b Hampton, Iowa, Mar 15, 33; m 55; c 3. SEISMOLOGY, PHYSICS. *Educ:* Univ Calif, Santa Barbara, BA, 56. *Prof Exp:* PHYSICIST SEISMOL, LAWRENCE LIVERMORE NAT LAB, 56- *Concurrent Pos:* Mem ground shock tech working group, Canal Studies, AEC, 66-70, mem ground shock subcomt, 69-70; mem seismic rev panel, US Air Force Tech Appl Ctr, 74-79 & Off Sci & Technol Policy, White House, 77-79; mem, US deleg, Ad Hoc Group Sci Experts Comt Disarmament, UN, 80- *Mem:* Seismol Soc Am. *Res:* Observational seismology; explosion seismology; geophysics; earth structure; earthquake prediction; seismic energy. *Mailing Add:* Lawrence Livermore Nat Lab PO Box 808 Livermore CA 94550

SPRINGER, DWIGHT SYLVAN, b Harrisburg, Pa, Oct 8, 43; m 64; c 3. CHEMICAL ENGINEERING, CHEMISTRY EDUCATION. *Educ:* Univ Del, BChE, 65; Univ Minn, PhD(chem eng), 71. *Prof Exp:* Chem engr power supplies, Harry Diamond Labs, US Army, Washington, DC, 72-74; instr, US Mil Acad, 76-77, asst prof chem, 76-79; chem officer, US Army, Berlin, 80-81; ASSOC PROF CHEM, US MIL ACAD, 81- *Honors & Awards:* Herbert W Alden Award, Am Defense Preparedness Asn, 75. *Mem:* Am Inst Chem Engrs; Am Chem Soc; Am Defense Preparedness Asn. *Res:* Chemical and conventional ammunition; chemical defense material. *Mailing Add:* Dept of Chem US Mil Acad West Point NY 10996

SPRINGER, E(DWIN) KENT, b Bellingham, Wash, Sept 17, 12; m 40; c 3. MECHANICAL ENGINEERING. *Educ:* Univ Southern Calif, BS, 36; Univ Wis, MS, 45. *Prof Exp:* Draftsman, Fluid Packed Pump Co, Calif, 35-36, plant engr, 36-39; mech engr, Pac Rwy Equip Co, 39-41; Consol Steel Corp, Calif, 41; instr mech eng, Univ Wis, 41-45, asst prof, 45-46; from asst prof to prof, 46-77, EMER PROF MECH ENG, UNIV SOUTHERN CALIF, 77-, DIR FOUND CROSS-CONNECTION CONTROL & HYDRAUL RES, 65- *Concurrent Pos:* Indust consult. *Mem:* Fel Am Soc Mech Engrs; Am Soc Eng Educ; Am Water Works Asn. *Res:* Air conditioning, heating and ventilation; industrial and central station steam power plants; protection of potable water systems from backflow and back-siphonage hazards. *Mailing Add:* Dept of Mech Eng OHE430 Univ Park Los Angeles CA 90007

SPRINGER, EDWARD L(ESTER), b Baraboo, Wis, July 12, 31; m 61; c 2. CHEMICAL ENGINEERING, WOOD HYDROLYSIS. *Educ:* Univ Wis, BS, 53, MS, 58, PhD(chem eng), 61. *Prof Exp:* Chem engr, Kimberly-Clark Corp, Wis, 55-56; CHEM ENGR, FOREST PROD LAB, USDA, 58- *Concurrent Pos:* Fulbright fel, Finland, 61-62. *Mem:* Tech Asn Pulp & Paper Indust; Am Chem Soc. *Res:* Wood preservation; preservation of pulp chips; kinetics of wood hydrolysis and of the delignification of wood. *Mailing Add:* Forest Prod Lab USDA Forest Serv Madison WI 53705

SPRINGER, GEORG F, b Berlin, Ger, Mar 1, 24; nat US; m 51; c 3. IMMUNOCHEMISTRY. *Educ:* Univ Heidelberg, MA, 47; Univ Basel, MD, 51. *Prof Exp:* Res fel pediat, Sch Med, Univ Pa, 53, Woodward fel physiol chem, 52-53, asst instr path, Sch Med, 52-55, assoc clin path, 55-58, asst prof immunol, 56-61, assoc prof, 61-62, mem, Pepper Lab, 55-62; PROF MICROBIOL & IMMUNOL, MED SCH, NORTHWESTERN UNIV, EVANSTON, 63-, DIR IMMUNOCHEM RES, EVANSTON HOSP, 63- *Concurrent Pos:* Mem germ free res unit, Walter Reed Army Med Ctr, 54-55; in-chg blood bank & serol, Philadelphia Gen & Univ Hosps; ed various sci jour; Am Heart Asn estab investr, 58-63; John G Gibson, II lect, 66; mem, Northwestern Univ Cancer Ctr, Evanston Hosp Res & Educ Comt & Protection of Human Subjects Comt; mem med adv bd, Leukemia Res Found, Inc. *Honors & Awards:* Oehlecker Prize, Ger Soc Blood Transfusion, 66. *Mem:* AAAS; Am Soc Microbiol; Am Chem Soc; Am Heart Asn; NY Acad Sci. *Res:* Immunochemistry of blood-group active substances; carbohydrate chemistry; virus action on blood groups; immunology of human breast cancer; infectious mononucleosis; shock; physical chemistry of antigen-antibody interactions; tumor virus receptors. *Mailing Add:* Immunochem Res Evanston Hosp 2650 Ridge Ave Evanston IL 60201

SPRINGER, GEORGE, b Cleveland, Ohio, Sept 3, 24; m 50; c 3. MATHEMATICS. *Educ:* Case Inst, BS, 45; Brown Univ, MS, 46; Harvard Univ, PhD(math), 49. *Prof Exp:* Moore instr math, Mass Inst Technol, 49-51; asst prof, Northwestern Univ, 51-54; vis prof & Fulbright lectr, Univ Münster, 54-55; from assoc prof to prof, Univ Kans, 55-64; assoc dean res & develop, 73-80, PROF MATH, IND UNIV, BLOOMINGTON, 64-, ACTG DEAN RES & GRAD DEVELOP, 80- *Concurrent Pos:* Vis prof, Univ Sao Paulo, 61; vis prof & Fulbright lectr, Univ Würzburg, 61-62; ed, J Math & Mech, Ind Univ, 65-; vis prof, Imp Col, Univ London, 71-72; consult ed, McGraw Hill Book Co, 71-; prog dir math sci sect, NSF, Washington, DC, 78-79. *Mem:* Am Math Soc; Math Asn Am; AAAS. *Res:* Theory of functions of one and several complex variables; harmonic functions; conformal and quasiconformal mapping. *Mailing Add:* Dept of Math Swain Hall-East Ind Univ Bloomington IN 47401

SPRINGER, GEORGE HENRY, b Bristol, RI, Jan 16, 18; m 41; c 1. GEOLOGY. *Educ:* Brown Univ, AB, 38, ScM, 40. *Prof Exp:* Geologist, Tenn Valley Authority, 41; from instr to assoc prof geol, 46-56, PROF GEOL, UNIV DAYTON, 56-, CHMN DEPT, 53- *Mem:* AAAS; Nat Asn Geol Teachers; Glaciol Soc. *Res:* Structural geology; petrography. *Mailing Add:* Dept of Geol Univ of Dayton Dayton OH 45469

SPRINGER, GEORGE S, b Budapest, Hungary, Dec 12, 33; US citizen; m 63; c 2. MECHANICAL ENGINEERING. *Educ:* Univ Sydney, BE, 59; Yale Univ, MEng, 60, MS, 61, PhD(mech eng), 62. *Prof Exp:* Ford Found fel & instr mech eng, Mass Inst Technol, 62-63, asst prof, 63-67; assoc prof, 67-72, PROF MECH ENG, UNIV MICH, ANN ARBOR, 72- *Honors & Awards:* Ralph E Teetor Award, Soc Automotive Engrs, 78. *Mem:* Am Soc Mech Engrs; Am Phys Soc; Am Inst Aeronaut & Astronaut; Soc Automotive Engrs. *Res:* Fluid mechanics; heat transfer; composite materials. *Mailing Add:* Dept of Mech Eng Univ of Mich Ann Arbor MI 48109

SPRINGER, JOHN KENNETH, b Trenton, NJ, Mar 26, 29; m 60; c 2. PLANT PATHOLOGY, NEMATOLOGY. *Educ:* Rutgers Univ, BS, 61, MS, 63, PhD(plant path). 66. *Prof Exp:* Supvr plant pest survs, NJ Dept Agr, 59-63; exten assoc, 63-66, asst exten specialist, 66-70, assoc exten specialist, 70-75, EXTEN SPECIALIST PLANT PATH, RUTGERS UNIV, 75- *Mem:* Am Phytopath Soc; Soc Nematol. *Res:* Survey of plant parasitic nematodes; mechanisms involved in Verticillium wilt syndrome; effect of soilborne diseases on production of crops. *Mailing Add:* Rutgers Univ Res & Develop Ctr Bridgeton NJ 08302

SPRINGER, JOHN MERVIN, b Peoria, Ill, Apr 19, 41; m 66; c 3. CHEMICAL PHYSICS. *Educ:* Knox Col, BA, 63; Vanderbilt Univ, MS, 65, PhD(physics), 72. *Prof Exp:* Res assoc chem physics, 71-73, asst prof physics, 73-77, RES ASSOC PHYSICS, FISK UNIV, 77- *Mem:* Coblentz Soc. *Res:* Crystal structure determinations via infrared and Raman spectroscopy; optical analysis of crystal defects. *Mailing Add:* Box 8 Fisk Univ Nashville TN 37203

SPRINGER, KARL JOSEPH, b San Antonio, Tex, Apr 14, 35; m 57; c 3. MECHANICAL ENGINEERING. *Educ:* Tex A&M Univ, BS, 57; Trinity Univ, MS, 66. *Prof Exp:* Res engr auto engines, Southwest Res Inst, 57-58; proj engr jet engines, Wright Air Develop Ctr, US Air Force, 58-60; field engr, E I du Pont de Nemours & Co, Inc, 60-62; proj engr, Automotive Res Assocs, 62-63; sr engr, US Army Fuels & Lubricants Res Lab, 63-67, mgr emissions res lab, Dept Automotive Res, 67-72, asst dir automotive res, 72-74, DIR DEPT EMISSIONS RES, AUTOMOTIVE RES DIV, SOUTHWEST RES INST, 74- *Concurrent Pos:* Mem odor & particulate subpanels, Diesel Emission Comt, Coord Res Coun, 68- *Mem:* Am Soc Mech Engrs; Soc Automotive Engrs; Sigma Xi. *Res:* Emissions from diesel and gasoline vehicles; control of emissions from diesels and measurement of combustion odor. *Mailing Add:* 111 Shalimar Dr San Antonio TX 78213

SPRINGER, MARTHA EDITH, b Mountain View, Calif, Jan 24, 16. BIOLOGY. *Educ:* Stanford Univ, AB, 35, AM, 36; Univ Mich, PhD(bot), 44. *Prof Exp:* Teacher high sch, Calif, 36-40 & 41-42; instr bot & cur herbarium, Ind Univ, 44-45 & 46-47; instr bot, Conn Col, 45-46; assoc prof biol, 47-53, actg chmn dept, 48-50, prof, 53-81, EMER PROF BIOL, WILLAMETTE UNIV, 81-, CUR, PECK HERBARIUM, 67- *Mem:* AAAS; Bot Soc Am; Mycol Soc Am. *Res:* Taxonomy of aquatic phycomycetes, flowering plants and bryophytes; a morphologic and taxonomic study of the genus Monoblepharella. *Mailing Add:* Dept of Biol Willamette Univ Salem OR 97301

SPRINGER, MAXWELL ELSWORTH, b Bourbon, Mo, Oct 21, 13; m 53; c 3. SOIL MORPHOLOGY. *Educ:* Univ Mo, BS, 35, AM, 46; Univ Calif, Berkeley, PhD(soils), 53. *Prof Exp:* Asst agr econ, Univ Mo, 36-37, asst soils, 37-40, instr, 40-42 & 46-49, asst prof, 53-57; assoc prof agron, Univ Tenn, Knoxville, 57-67, prof plant & soil sci, 67-79; CONSULT, 79- *Concurrent Pos:* Soil surv specialist, Natural Resources Sect, Gen Hq, Supreme Comdr Allied Powers, Tokyo, 46-47; Fulbright Award, Univ Ghent, 66-67. *Mem:* Fel AAAS; Am Soc Agron. *Res:* Soil formation and classification; physical, chemical and mineralogical studies of soils. *Mailing Add:* 1600 Autry Way Knoxville TN 37919

SPRINGER, MELVIN DALE, b Saybrook, Ill, Sept 12, 18; m 48; c 1. MATHEMATICAL STATISTICS. *Educ:* Univ Ill, BS, 40, MS, 41, PhD(math statist), 47. *Prof Exp:* Asst math, Univ Ill, 41-44 & 46-47, instr, 47-48; asst prof, Mich State Col, 48-50; math statistician, Res Dept, US Naval Ord Plant, Ind, 50-56; sr opers analyst, Tech Opers, Inc, Va, 56-59; sr res statistician, Defense Res Labs, Gen Motors Corp, 59-67, dir reliability res & educ, A C Electronics Div, 67-68; PROF INDUST ENG, UNIV ARK, FAYETTEVILLE, 68- *Mem:* Am Math Soc; Opers Res Soc Am; Am Statist Asn; Math Asn Am; Inst Math Statist. *Res:* Reliability theory and analysis; Bayesian statistics; experimental design; sampling theory; integral transforms in stochastic models; algebra of random variables. *Mailing Add:* Dept of Indust Eng Univ of Ark Fayetteville AR 72701

SPRINGER, PAUL FREDERICK, b Chicago, Ill, Apr 25, 22; m 49; c 4. WILDLIFE RESEARCH. *Educ:* Univ Ill, AB, 43; Univ Wis, MS, 48; Cornell Univ, PhD(wildlife conserv), 61. *Prof Exp:* Waterfowl res biologist, State Natural Hist Surv, Ill, 47-48; wildlife res biologist, US Fish & Wildlife Serv, 48-58, chief sect wetland ecol, Patuxent Wildlife Res Ctr, 58-63, leader, SDak Coop Wildlife Res Unit, 63-67, asst dir, Northern Prairie Wildlife Res Ctr, US Bur Sport Fisheries & Wildlife, 67-72, BIOLOGIST-IN-CHG, WILDLIFE RES FIELD STA, US FISH & WILDLIFE SERV, 73- *Concurrent Pos:* Mem comt agr pests, Agr Bd, Nat Res Coun, 56-58; secy, Nat Mosquito Control-Fish & Wildlife Mgt Coord Comt, 60-63, mem, 72-73; vpres, Raptor Res Found, 67-68; mem vector control comt, Water Resources Coun, 72-73; adj prof wildlife mgt, Humboldt State Univ, 73- *Mem:* Wildlife Soc; Am Ornithologists Union; Cooper Ornith Soc; Ecol Soc Am; Wilson Ornith Soc. *Res:* Waterfowl and wetland ecology and management; effects of mosquito control and chemical pesticides on wildlife; wildlife-estuarine relationships. *Mailing Add:* Dept Wildlife Humboldt State Univ Arcata CA 95521

SPRINGER, ROBERT HAROLD, b Downsville, Wis, Nov 7, 32; m 54; c 7. GASEOUS ELECTRONICS, ELECTRODE PHYSICS-ENGINEERING. *Educ:* Univ Minn, BS, 58, MS, 60, PhD(elec eng), 65. *Prof Exp:* RES PHYSICIST, LIGHTING RES & TECH SERV OPER, GEN ELEC CO, 65- *Res:* All aspects of electrical discharges in gases related to light production; specializing in electrodes. *Mailing Add:* 6524 Duneden Ave Cleveland OH 44139

SPRINGER, VICTOR GRUSCHKA, b Jacksonville, Fla, June 2, 28; m 65; c 2. BIOLOGY. *Educ:* Emory Univ, AB, 48; Univ Miami, MS, 54; Univ Tex, PhD(vert zool), 57. *Prof Exp:* Ichthyologist, Marine Lab, State Bd Conserv, Fla, 57-61; res assoc, 61-62, assoc cur, 63-66, supvr, 70-71, CUR, DIV FISHES, US NAT MUS, 67- *Concurrent Pos:* Ed, Proc Biol Soc Wash, 65-67; res assoc, Moore Lab, Occidental Col, 71-72; Nat Geog Soc grant, 73-74; bd dirs, Nat Aquarium Baltimore, 79- *Honors & Awards:* Stoye Award, 57. *Mem:* AAAS; Am Soc Ichthyologists & Herpetologists (treas, 65-67); Soc Syst Zool (treas, 78-80); Sigma Xi. *Res:* Systematics; zoogeography; ecology; life histories of tropical marine fishes. *Mailing Add:* Div of Fishes US Nat Mus of Natural Hist Washington DC 20560

SPRINGETT, BRIAN E, b Chatham, Eng, Apr 24, 36; m 63; c 2. PHYSICS. *Educ:* Cambridge Univ, BA, 60, MA, 64; Univ Chicago, MS, 63, PhD(physics), 66. *Prof Exp:* Res assoc physics, Univ Chicago, 66-67; asst prof, Univ Mich, Ann Arbor, 67-72; vis prof, Univ Quebec, 72-73 & Oakland Univ, 73-74; scientist, 74-77, TECH MGR, XEROX CORP, 77- *Mem:* AAAS; Am Phys Soc. *Res:* Low temperature physics, gas discharges, ion and electron transport in dielectric media, amorphous photoconductors. *Mailing Add:* Xerox Corp 800 Phillips Rd Webster NY 14580

SPRINGETT, DAVID ROY, b London, Ont, Apr 24, 35; m 58; c 4. MECHANICAL ENGINEERING. *Educ:* Univ Toronto, BASc, 58; Queen's Univ, Ont, MS, 62, PhD(mech eng), 64; Harvard Univ, dipl bus, 70. *Prof Exp:* Instr process control, Dept Mech Eng, Queen's Univ, Ont, 61-63; res engr, Burrough's Corp, 63-64; sr develop engr, Xerographic Systs, Explor Develop Dept, Xerox Corp, 64-65, staff asst to vpres eng, Off Prod Develop Dept, 65-66, mgr planning & admin, Bus Prod Div, 66-68, mgr div planning, Bus Prod & Systs Div, 68-69, prog mgr, Advan Develop Dept, 69-71, mgr advan copier develop, Info Technol Group, 71-73, mgr, Prod Technol Prog Off, 73-75; dir, Advan Bus Concepts Div, Rank Xerox, 75-77, DIR, MAJOR PROGS DIV, RANK XEROX CORP, 77- *Concurrent Pos:* Fel, Ont Res Found, Queen's Univ, Ont, 61-62, Nat Res Coun Can, 61-63. *Res:* Engineering management; nonlinear control systems; systems engineering and simulation. *Mailing Add:* PO Box 555 Stamford CT 06904

SPRINGFIELD, HARRY WAYNE, b Dayton, Ohio, Sept 24, 20; m 50. RANGE ECOLOGY. *Educ:* Univ NMex, BS, 42; Univ Ariz, MS, 49; Agr & Mech Col, Tex, PhD(range mgt), 59. *Prof Exp:* Range conservationist, US Forest Serv, 47-52; agrostologist, Foreign Agr Serv, Iraq, 52-54; range scientist, US Forest Serv, 54-75; RETIRED. *Honors & Awards:* Cert Appreciation, USDA, 67. *Mem:* Soc Range Mgt; Am Soc Agron. *Res:* Ecological studies; game forage revegetation; germination characteristics of shrub seeds; mulching to establish shrub seedlings; mine spoil reclamation. *Mailing Add:* 13822 108th Dr Sun City AZ 85351

SPRINGGATE, CLARK FRANKLIN, b Champaign, Ill, Nov 14, 46; m 65; c 2. BIOCHEMISTRY. *Educ:* Boston Univ, AB, 67; Boston Col, PhD(biochem), 72. *Prof Exp:* Fel biochem, Fox Chase Ctr Cancer & Med Sci, 71-74; staff fel, NIH, 74-76; asst prof microbiol, Med Sch, Tulane Univ, 76-81. *Concurrent Pos:* Leukemia Soc Am fel, Fox Chase Ctr Cancer & Med Sci, 72-73. *Mem:* Am Asn Cancer Res; Am Soc Microbiol; AAAS. *Res:* DNA repair in human cells and human malignancy; environmental carcinogenesis. *Mailing Add:* 7904 West Dr North Bun Village FL 33141

SPRINKLE, H D, b Logansport, Ind, June 18, 26; m 63; c 2. MATHEMATICS. *Educ:* Univ Ariz, AB, 49; Univ Miami, MS, 50; Univ Fla, PhD(math), 53. *Prof Exp:* Instr math, Univ Fla, 52-53; asst prof, Ala Polytech Inst, 53-54 & Univ Ariz, 54-57; coordr systs anal, Radio Corp Am, 57-58; mgr advan syst dept, Litton Systs Inc, 58-63; mgr systs technol lab, Sylvania Electronics Syst Div, Gen Tel & Electronics Corp, 63-64; mgr systs & simulation dept, Int Bus Mach Corp, 64-70; lectr systs eng, Univ Ariz, 71-72; CONSULT, 72- *Res:* Technical management; applied statistics; systems modeling; experimental design; system simulation; programming. *Mailing Add:* 1501 E Broward Blvd Apt 804 Ft Lauderdale FL 33301

SPRINKLE, JAMES (THOMAS), b Arlington, Mass, Sept 2, 43; m 68; c 2. INVERTEBRATE PALEONTOLOGY. *Educ:* Mass Inst Technol, SB, 65; Harvard Univ, MA, 66, PhD(geol), 71. *Prof Exp:* Nat Res Coun-US Geol Surv assoc, Paleont & Stratig Br, US Geol Surv, Denver, 70-71; asst prof, 71-77; ASSOC PROF GEOL, UNIV TEX, AUSTIN, 77- *Concurrent Pos:* Prin investr, NSF grant, 77-80. *Mem:* AAAS; Paleont Soc; Geol Soc Am; Palaeont Asn England; Soc Syst Zoologists. *Res:* Primitive echinoderms; blastoids; Paleozoic stratigraphy and invertebrate paleontology; echinoderm biology and evolution. *Mailing Add:* Dept Geol Sci Univ Tex Austin TX 78712

SPRINKLE, PHILIP MARTIN, b Greensboro, NC, Aug 5, 26; m 55; c 2. OTOLARYNGOLOGY. *Educ:* Univ Va, MD, 53. *Prof Exp:* Intern, Virginia Mason Hosp, Seattle, Wash, 53-54; pvt pract, Va, 54-60; resident gen surg, Watts Hosp, Durham, NC, 60-61; resident otolaryngol, Hosp, Univ Va, 61-64, asst prof, 64-65; assoc prof, 65-68, PROF OTOLARYNGOL & CHMN DEPT, MED CTR, W VA UNIV, 68- *Concurrent Pos:* Physician consult, Vet Admin Hosp & WVa Rehabil Ctr, 69- *Honors & Awards:* Prof Dr Ignacio Barroquer Mem Award; Award Merit, Am Acad Ophthal & Otolaryngol. *Mem:* AMA; Am Acad Gen Pract; Am Acad Ophthal & Otolaryngol; Am Col Surgeons; Royal Soc Med. *Mailing Add:* Dept of Otolaryngol WVa Univ Med Ctr Morgantown WV 26506

SPRINSON, DAVID BENJAMIN, b Russia, Apr 5, 10; nat US; m 43; c 3. BIOCHEMISTRY. *Educ:* City Col New York, BS, 31; NY Univ, MS, 36; Columbia Univ, PhD(biochem), 46. *Prof Exp:* Asst thyroid biochem, Chem Lab, Montefiore Hosp, 31-42; from res assoc to assoc prof, 48-58, prof, 58-78, EMER PROF BIOCHEM, COL PHYSICIANS & SURGEONS, COLUMBIA UNIV, 78-; BIOCHEMIST, DEPT MED, ROOSEVELT HOSP, NY, 79- *Concurrent Pos:* Fulbright fel, Univ Paris, 52; Guggenheim fels, Stanford Univ, 57 & Univ Oxford, 60-61; career investr, Am Heart Asn, 58-75; vis scientist, NIH, 65; Brown-Hazen lect, NY State Dept Health, Albany, 69. *Mem:* Am Chem Soc; Am Soc Biol Chem; Brit Biochem Soc. *Res:* Intermediary metabolism of amino acids; biosynthesis of methyl groups and purines, aromatic compounds and sterols; regulation of metabolic pathways; mechanism of enzymic reactions. *Mailing Add:* Dept of Biochem Columbia Univ Col Physicians & Surgeons New York NY 10032

SPRINZ, HELMUTH, b Berlin, Ger, May 29, 11; nat US; m 59. PATHOLOGY. *Educ:* Univ Berlin, Dr med, 36. *Prof Exp:* Chief lab serv, 98th Gen Hosp, Med Corps, US Army, 49-53, chief path sect, Walter Reed Army Hosp, 53-59, dir div exp path, Walter Reed Army Inst Res, 59-71; prof, Med Sch, Univ Mo-Kansas City, 71-75; dir prof affairs, Kansas City Gen Hosp & Med Ctr, 71-73; PROF, UNIV KANS MED CTR, 76- *Concurrent Pos:* Consult, Midwest Res Inst, Kansas City, 77- *Honors & Awards:* Walter Reed Medal; Surgeon Gen's Medal; Stitt Award, Asn Mil Surg US. *Mem:* Am Asn Path; Int Acad Path; Am Col Physicians; Am Gastroenterol Asn. *Res:* Pathology and pathogenesis of infections; gastrointestinal diseases; general experimental and neuropathology of intoxications. *Mailing Add:* Dept Path & Oncol Rainbow Blvd at 39th St Kansas City KS 66103

SPRITZ, NORTON, b Baltimore, Md, June 19, 28; m; c 1. BIOCHEMISTRY. *Educ:* Johns Hopkins Univ, AB, 48; Univ Md, MD, 52. *Prof Exp:* Asst med, Med Col, Cornell Univ, 52-54, from instr to assoc prof, 56-66; assoc prof, Rockefeller Univ, 66-69; PROF MED, NY UNIV, 69- *Concurrent Pos:* Intern, 2nd Cornell Med Div, Bellevue Hosp, 52-53, asst res, 53-54, fel cardiol, 56-57, chief res, 57-58, asst vis physician, 58-63, attend cardiorenal lab, 58-60, dir lipid metab lab, 63-66, vis physician, 64-; estab investr, Health Res Coun New York, 59-; clin asst, Mem Hosp, 60-; asst vis physician, James Ewing Hosp, 60-; asst attend, NY Hosp, 60-65, assoc attend, 65-; guest investr & asst physician, Rockefeller Univ, 61-63, assoc physician, 66-; chief med, NY Vet Admin Hosp, 69-; chief med serv, Manhattan Vet Hosp, 69- *Mem:* Am Soc Clin Invest; Am Fedn Clin Res; Am Diabetes Asn. *Res:* Lipid metabolism as related to human disorders and particularly atherosclerosis. *Mailing Add:* Dept Med & Surg NY Univ New York NY 10010

SPRITZ, RICHARD ANDREW, b Philadelphia, Pa, Dec 19, 50; m 74. MEDICAL GENETICS. *Educ:* Univ Wis, BS, 72; Pa State Univ, MD, 76. *Prof Exp:* Intern pediat, Children's Hosp Philadelphia, Univ Pa, 76-77, resident, 77-78; fel, Dept Human Genetics, Sch Med, Yale Univ, 78-80; ASST PROF MED GENETICS & PEDIAT, SCH MED, UNIV WIS, 81- *Mem:* Am Soc Human Genetics; AAAS. *Res:* Molecular aspects of the structure, organization and control of human genes and the mechanism of RNA processing, with particular emphasis on the molecular basis of human genetic disorders. *Mailing Add:* 309 Lab Genetics 445 Henry Mall Univ Wis Madison WI 53706

SPRITZER, ALBERT A, b Brooklyn, NY, Apr 2, 27; m 53; c 3. MEDICINE. *Educ:* Col Wooster, BS, 48; Albany Med Col, MD, 52; Univ Pittsburgh, MPH, 56. *Prof Exp:* ASST PROF OCCUP HEALTH GRAD SCH PUB HEALTH, UNIV PITTSBURGH, 57-, PROF RADIATION HEALTH, 73- *Concurrent Pos:* Dept Health, Educ & Welfare res grant, 65-; consult, Babcox & Wilcox, Duquesne Light ; med dir, Nuclear Energy Systs, Westinghouse Elec Corp, 70- . *Mem:* Am Indust Hyg Asn; Health Physics Soc; AMA; Am Occup Health Asn. *Res:* Radiation biology; industrial radiation health practice; occupational health and radiation health research in pulmonary clearance; physiology and radiation hazard evaluation. *Mailing Add:* 9 Churchill Rd Pittsburgh PA 15235

SPRITZER, MICHAEL STEPHEN, b New York, NY, July 15, 39; m 64. ANALYTICAL CHEMISTRY. *Educ:* Polytech Inst Brooklyn, BS, 60; Univ Mich, MS, 62, PhD(chem), 65. *Prof Exp:* Instr, Univ Mich, 65-66; asst prof, 66-77, PROF CHEM, VILLANOVA UNIV, 77- *Mem:* AAAS; Am Chem Soc; Sigma Xi. *Res:* Electrochemical analysis; electrochemistry in nonaqueous media; organic polarography and voltammetry; electrochemical and photoelectrochemical energy storage. *Mailing Add:* Dept Chem Villanova Univ Villanova PA 19085

SPROKEL, GERARD J, b Valkenburg, Netherlands, Aug 14, 21; US citizen; m 49. PHYSICAL CHEMISTRY. *Educ:* State Univ Utrecht, PhD(phys chem), 52. *Prof Exp:* Res chemist, Am Viscose Corp, Pa, 54-58; adv chemist, Int Bus Mach Corp, 58-65, adv solid state, 65-70, adv, Components Div, 70-74, MEM RES STAFF, RES DIV, IBM CORP, 74- *Mem:* AAAS; Am Chem Soc; Electrochem Soc; Inst Elec & Electronics Engrs. *Res:* Diffusion and surface properties in semiconductors; semiconducting and scintillation counters; injection lasers; liquid crystals; materials research. *Mailing Add:* 2831 Castle Dr San Jose CA 95125

SPROTT, DAVID ARTHUR, b Toronto, Ont, May 31, 30. MATHEMATICAL STATISTICS. *Educ:* Univ Toronto, BA, 52, MA, 53, PhD, 55. *Prof Exp:* Asst, Comput Ctr, Univ Toronto, 52-53, Defence Res Bd, 54 & Galton Lab, Eng, 55-56; assoc prof, 58-70, chmn dept & dean fac, 67-72, PROF MATH, UNIV WATERLOO, 70- *Mem:* Am Math Soc; Inst Math Statist; Math Asn Am. *Res:* Mathematical genetics; experimental design; statistical inference. *Mailing Add:* 295 Ferndale Pl Univ of Waterloo Waterloo ON N2J 3X8 Can

SPROTT, GORDON DENNIS, b Badjeros, Ont, Feb 27, 45; m 68. MICROBIOLOGY. *Educ:* Univ Guelph, BS, 68, MS, 70; McGill Univ, PhD(microbiol), 73. *Prof Exp:* Fel, 73-75, asst res officer, 75-81, ASSOC RES OFFICER, NAT RES COUN CAN, 81- *Concurrent Pos:* Assoc ed, Can J Microbiol, 82- *Mem:* Am Soc Microbiol; Can Soc Microbiol. *Res:* Physiology of methanogenic bacteria, including measurement of electrical and chemical potentials, adenosinetriphosphate and carbon-hydrogen-4 synthesis, energetics of ion transport, cell permeability, structure of ether-linked membrane lipids and enzymology; physiology of anaerobic bacteria. *Mailing Add:* Dept of Biol Sci 100 Sussex Dr Nat Res Coun Ottawa ON K1A 0R6 Can

SPROTT, JULIEN CLINTON, b Memphis, Tenn, Sept 16, 42; m 65. PLASMA PHYSICS. *Educ:* Mass Inst Technol, BS, 64; Univ Wis, MS, 66, PhD(physics), 69. *Prof Exp:* Lectr elec eng & proj assoc physics, Univ Wis-Madison, 69-70; physicist, Thermonuclear Div, Oak Ridge Nat Lab, 70-72; asst prof, 72-77, assoc prof, 77-79, PROF PHYSICS, UNIV WIS-MADISON, 79- *Concurrent Pos:* Consult, Oak Ridge Nat Lab, 72-; McDonnell Douglas Corp, 77-, Elec Power Res Inst, 78, TRW, 79-, Argonne Nat Lab, 79-80 & Honeywell, 81; prin investr, Plasma Physics Contract, Univ Wis, US Dept Energy, 80- *Mem:* Am Phys Soc. *Res:* Plasma confinement and heating in toroidal and magnetic mirror fields; toroidal multipoles; tokamaks; bumpy torii; computer simulation of plasmas; ionospheric and extra-terrestrial plasmas and cosmic rays. *Mailing Add:* Dept of Physics Univ of Wis Madison WI 53706

SPROUL, OTIS JENNINGS, b Dover Foxcroft, Maine, July 9, 30; m 52; c 1. SANITARY ENGINEERING. *Educ:* Univ Maine, BS, 52, MS, 57; Wash Univ, St Louis, ScD(sanit eng), 61. *Prof Exp:* Instr civil eng, Univ Maine, 55-57, asst prof, 57-59; trainee sanit eng, Wash Univ, St Louis, 59-61; from assoc prof to prof civil eng, Univ Maine, 61-77; PROF & CHMN DEPT CIVIL ENG, OHIO STATE UNIV, 77- *Honors & Awards:* Rudolph Hering Award, Am Soc Civil Engrs, 71. *Mem:* Am Water Works Asn; Water Pollution Control Fedn; Am Soc Civil Engrs; Am Soc Eng Educ; Nat Soc Prof Engrs. *Res:* Virus inactivation by water and wastewater treatment processes; industrial air and water pollution. *Mailing Add:* Dept of Civil Eng Ohio State Univ Columbus OH 43210

SPROULE, BRIAN J, b Calgary, Alta, Oct 31, 25; m 55; c 4. MEDICINE, THORACIC DISEASES. *Educ:* Univ Alta, BSc, 49, MD, 51, MSc, 55; FRCPS(C). *Prof Exp:* Instr med, Univ Tex Southwestern Med Sch Dallas, 55-59; from instr to assoc prof, 59-70, PROF MED & HEAD DIV RESPIRATORY DIS, UNIV ALTA, 70- *Concurrent Pos:* Consult, Can Dept Vet Affairs, 60- *Mem:* Fel Am Col Chest Physicians; fel Am Col Physicians; Am Fedn Clin Res; Can Soc Clin Invest. *Res:* Pulmonary mechanics; blood gas derangements in chronic lung disease. *Mailing Add:* Dept of Med Univ of Alta Sch of Med Edmonton AB T6G 2E1 Can

SPROULL, ROBERT FLETCHER, b Ithaca, NY, June 6, 47; m 71. COMPUTER SCIENCE. *Educ:* Harvard Col, AB, 68; Stanford Univ, MS, 70, PhD(comput sci), 77. *Prof Exp:* Staff programmer artificial intelligence, Stanford Univ, 69-70; comput specialist, Div Comput Res & Technol, NIH, 70-72; mem res staff comput sci, Xerox Palo Alto Res Ctr, 73-77; asst prof, 77-80, ASSOC PROF COMPUT SCI, CARNEGIE-MELLON UNIV, 80- *Concurrent Pos:* Mem tech adv coun, R R Donnelley & Sons, 81- *Mem:* Asn Comput Mach; Inst Elec & Electronic Engrs. *Res:* Computer graphics; large-scale integrated circuits. *Mailing Add:* Comput Sci Dept Carnegie-Mellon Univ Pittsburgh PA 15213

SPROULL, ROBERT LAMB, b Lacon, Ill, Aug 16, 18; m 42; c 2. PHYSICS. *Educ:* Cornell Univ, BA, 40, PhD(exp physics), 43. *Prof Exp:* Physicist, RCA Labs, NJ, 43-46; from asst prof to prof physics, Cornell Univ, 46-68, dir lab atomic & solid state physics, 59-60, dir mat sci ctr, 60-63, vpres acad affairs, 65-68; vpres & provost, 68-70, pres, 70-75, PRES & CHIEF EXEC OFFICER, UNIV ROCHESTER, 75- *Concurrent Pos:* Part-time instr, Princeton Univ & Univ Pa, 43-45; physicist, Oak Ridge Nat Lab, 52 & Europ Res Assocs, Belg, 58-59; ed, J Appl Physics, 54-57; trustee, Assoc Univs, Inc, 62-63; dir, Advan Res Projs Agency, 63-65; mem bd dirs, John Wiley & Sons, Inc, NY, 65-; trustee, Deep Springs Col, 67-74 & 82; mem bd dirs, Security Trust Co, 70, United Technol Corp, 70- & Xerox Corp, 76-; trustee, Cornell Univ, 72-77; pres, Telluride Asn, 45-47; mem solid state sci adv panel, Off Naval Res & later Nat Acad Sci, 50-68; mem lab mgt coun, Oak Ridge Nat Lab, 65-75, chmn coun, 71-73; mem, Defense Sci Bd, 66-70, chmn bd, 68-70; mem statutory vis comt, Nat Bur Standards, 66-71, chmn comt, 68-71; mem sci adv comt, Gen Motors Corp, 71-80, chmn, 73-80; Fel AAAS; Am Phys Soc; Am Acad Arts & Sci; mem bd dir, Commonwealth Fund, 79- *Res:* Thermionic electron emission; microwave radar; experimental solid state physics; imperfections in nonmetallic crystals, especially in barium oxide; low temperature physics; phonon scattering. *Mailing Add:* Off of Pres & Chief Exec Off Univ of Rochester Rochester NY 14627

SPROULL, WAYNE TREBER, b Racine, Wis, Aug 3, 06; m 34; c 2. AIR POLLUTION. *Educ:* Univ Akron, BS, 27; Lehigh Univ, MS, 29; Univ Wis, PhD(physics), 33. *Prof Exp:* Asst physics, Lehigh Univ, 27-29 & Univ Wis, 29-32; res physicist, Res Labs Div, Gen Motors Corp, Mich, 33-46; res physicist, Res Lab, Lockheed Aircraft Corp, Calif, 46-47; chief liquid rockets sect, Jet Propulsion Lab, Calif Inst Technol, 47-48; head elec res dept, Western Precipitation Corp, 48-60, chief physicist, Western Precipitation Div, Joy Mfg Co, Calif, 60-65; sr staff physicist, Nat Eng Sci Co, 65-68; assoc, Petroff & Assocs, 68-69; consult, Western Precipitation Div, Joy Mfg Co, Los Angeles, 69-72; CONSULT, 72- *Concurrent Pos:* Staff physicist, Environ Resources, Inc, Calif, 68-69; mem ed staff air pollution criteria, US Govt Publ. *Mem:* AAAS; Am Phys Soc; Air Pollution Control Asn. *Res:* Air pollution control; effects of dust clouds on gaseous discharges and gas flow; x-rays; improvements in the technology of industrial gas cleaning and electrical precipitation. *Mailing Add:* 3015 San Gabriel Ave Glendale CA 91208

SPROUSE, GENE DENSON, b Litchfield, Ill, May 7, 41; m 63; c 2. PHYSICS. *Educ:* Mass Inst Technol, BS, 63; Stanford Univ, MS, 65, PhD(physics), 68. *Prof Exp:* Res assoc physics, Stanford Univ, 67-69, asst prof, 69-70; asst prof, 70-73, ASSOC PROF PHYSICS, STATE UNIV NY STONY BROOK, 73- *Concurrent Pos:* Fel, Alfred P Sloan Found, 72-74. *Mem:* Am Phys Soc. *Res:* Hyperfine interactions; perturbed angular correlations; recoil implantation. *Mailing Add:* Dept of Physics State Univ of NY Stony Brook NY 11790

SPROWLES, JOLYON CHARLES, b Columbia, SC, July 6, 44; m 68; c 2. PHYSICAL INORGANIC CHEMISTRY. *Educ:* Princeton Univ, AB, 66; Cornell Univ, PhD(inorg chem), 73. *Prof Exp:* Asst prof chem, Williams Col, 70-72; res assoc, Purdue Univ, 72-74; vis asst prof, Univ Mo-Columbia, 74-75;

ASST PROF CHEM, BATES COL, 75- *Mem:* Am Chem Soc. *Res:* Vibrational spectroscopic studies of equilibria and structure in solutions of organometallic cations and weak Lewis base anions. *Mailing Add:* Dept of Chem Bates Col Lewiston ME 04240

SPROWLS, DONALD O(TTE), b Arnold, Pa, Sept 9, 19; m 44; c 4. CHEMICAL ENGINEERING, METALLURGY. *Educ:* Drexel Inst Technol, BS, 43. *Prof Exp:* Technician, Alcoa Res Labs, Pittsburgh, 36-38, res engr, 43-64, res engr, Chem Metall Div, 64-77, head stress corrosion sect, 72-77, ASSOC ENGR, ALCOA TECH CTR, 77- *Mem:* Nat Asn Corrosion Engrs; Am Soc Testing & Mat; Am Soc Metals. *Res:* Corrosion and stress corrosion of aluminum alloys. *Mailing Add:* 4419 7th St New Kensington PA 15068

SPROWLS, RILEY CLAY, b Medina, NY, July 22, 21; m 50; c 2. STATISTICS. *Educ:* Univ Chicago, PhD(statist), 51. *Prof Exp:* Instr statist, Univ Chicago, 49-51; from asst prof statist to prof bus statist, 51-71, PROF COMPUT & INFO SYSTS, UNIV CALIF, LOS ANGELES, 71- *Mem:* Am Statist Asn. *Res:* Business statistics; electronic computers. *Mailing Add:* Grad Sch of Bus Admin Univ of Calif 405 Hilgard Ave Los Angeles CA 90024

SPRUCH, GRACE MARMOR, b Brooklyn, NY, Nov 19, 26; m 50. PHYSICS. *Educ:* Brooklyn Col, BA, 47; Univ Pa, MS, 49; NY Univ, PhD(physics), 55. *Prof Exp:* Res asst physics, Univ Pa, 47-48, asst instr, 48-49; res asst, NY Univ, 52-55, assoc res scientist, 55-56; instr physics, Cooper Union, 57-58; assoc res scientist, NY Univ, 58-63; Am Asn Univ Women fel, Oxford Univ, 63-64; vis assoc prof, Rutgers Univ, 64-65; assoc res scientist, NY Univ, 65-67, res scientist, 67-68; assoc prof physics, 69-75, PROF PHYSICS, RUTGERS UNIV, 75- *Concurrent Pos:* Secy, Int Conf Luminescence, NY Univ, 61; writer, ed & translator; hon res assoc appl sci, Harvard Univ, 77-78; hon assoc, Neiman Found for Jour, 77-78. *Mem:* Am Phys Soc. *Res:* Luminescence, photoconductivity and applications to biophysics; light scattering. *Mailing Add:* Dept of Physics Rutgers Univ 101 Warren St Newark NJ 07102

SPRUCH, LARRY, b Brooklyn, NY, Jan 1, 23; m 50. THEORETICAL PHYSICS. *Educ:* Brooklyn Col, BA, 43; Univ Pa, PhD(physics), 48. *Prof Exp:* From asst instr to instr physics, Univ Pa, 43-46; Atomic Energy Comn fel, Mass Inst Technol, 48-50; from asst prof to assoc prof, 50-61, PROF PHYSICS, WASH SQ COL, NY UNIV, 61- *Concurrent Pos:* Consult, Lawrence Radiation Lab, 59-66; NSF sr fel, Univ London & Oxford Univ, 63-64; vis prof, Inst Theoret Phys, Univ Colo, 61 & 68; correspondent, Comments on Atomic & Molecular Physics, 72-; mem, Inst Advan Study, 81-82. *Mem:* Fel Am Phys Soc. *Res:* Beta decay; nuclear moments; isomeric transitions; internal conversion; atomic and nuclear scattering; variational principles; astrophysics; charge transfer; Thomas-Fermi theory, radiative corrections. *Mailing Add:* Dept of Physics Meyer Bldg NY Univ 4 Washington Pl New York NY 10003

SPRUGEL, DOUGLAS GEORGE, b Ames, Iowa, Feb 18, 48. PLANT ECOLOGY. *Educ:* Duke Univ, BS, 69; Yale Univ, MPhil, 71, PhD(plant ecol), 74. *Prof Exp:* Lectr ecol, Univ Pa, 73-74; res assoc, Argonne Nat Lab, 74-76, asst ecologist, 76-79; ASST PROF, DEPT FORESTRY, MICH STATE UNIV, 79- *Concurrent Pos:* Assoc ed, Ecol Soc Am J, 78-80. *Honors & Awards:* Mercer Award, Ecol Soc Am, 77. *Mem:* Ecol Soc Am; Am Inst Biol Sci; AAAS. *Res:* Effects of natural and human disturbance on natural ecosystems; nutrient cycling; air pollution effects on plants. *Mailing Add:* Dept Forestry Mich State Univ East Lansing MI 48824

SPRUGEL, GEORGE, JR, b Boston, Mass, Sept 26, 19; m 45; c 1. ZOOLOGY, ECOLOGY. *Educ:* Iowa State Col, BS, 46, MS, 47, PhD(econ zool), 50. *Prof Exp:* From instr to asst prof zool & entom, Iowa State Col, 46-54; spec asst to asst dir biol & med sci, NSF, 53-54, prog dir environ biol, 54-64; chief scientist, Nat Park Serv, 64-66; chief, 66-80, EMER CHIEF, ILL NATURAL HIST SURV, 80- *Concurrent Pos:* Asst & actg head, Biol Br, Off Naval Res, 51-53; mem adv comt environ biol, NSF, 65 & Nat Res Coun, 68-71; prog dir conserv ecosysts, US Int Biol Prog, 69-72; mem life sci comt, NASA, 73-78. *Honors & Awards:* Meritorious Award, Am Inst Biol Sci, 75; Distinguished Serv Citation, Ecol Soc Am, 76. *Mem:* AAAS (chmn sect biol sci, 71); Am Soc Zoologists (secy, 70-72); Ecol Soc Am (vpres, 68); Am Inst Biol Sci (vpres, 73, pres, 74); Am Water Resources Asn (treas, 68-70). *Res:* Aquatic ecology; fish growth; animal population dynamics. *Mailing Add:* Ill Natural Hist Surv 607 E Peabody Champaign IL 61820

SPRUIELL, JOSEPH E(ARL), b Knoxville, Tenn, Oct 13, 35; m 58; c 2. MATERIALS SCIENCE, ENGINEERING. *Educ:* Univ Tenn, BS, 58, MS, 60, PhD(metall eng), 63. *Prof Exp:* From asst prof to assoc prof metall eng, 63-71, PROF METALL ENG & POLYMER ENG, UNIV TENN, KNOXVILLE, 71- *Concurrent Pos:* Consult, Metals & Ceramics Div, Oak Ridge Nat Lab, 60-77. *Mem:* Am Soc Metals; Sigma Xi. *Res:* X-ray diffraction; physical metallurgy; polymer science; polymer processing. *Mailing Add:* Dept Chem Metall & Polymer Eng Univ of Tenn Knoxville TN 37916

SPRUILL, NANCY LYON, b Takoma Park, Md, Mar 24, 49; m 69. ECONOMIC ANALYSES, STATISTICAL REGRESSION ANALYSES. *Educ:* Univ Md, BS, 71; George Washington Univ, MA, 75, PhD(math statist), 80. *Prof Exp:* PROJ DIR, CTR NAVAL ANALYSES, 71-; ASSOC PROF & LECTR STATIST, GEORGE WASHINGTON UNIV, 81- *Mem:* Am Statist Asn. *Res:* Economic and statistical analyses of logistics problems relating to naval aircraft; economic factors affecting drug use patterns; issues related to confidentiality of various types of data. *Mailing Add:* 123 N Park Dr Arlington VA

SPRULES, WILLIAM GARY, b Hamilton, Ont, Nov 5, 44; m 67; c 3. AQUATIC ECOLOGY. *Educ:* Queen's Univ, Ont, BSc, 66; Princeton Univ, MA, 68, PhD(ecol), 70. *Prof Exp:* Asst prof zool, 70-75, ASSOC PROF ZOOL, ERINDALE COL, UNIV TORONTO, 76- *Concurrent Pos:*

Operating grant, Nat Res Coun Can, 70-, Fisheries & Marine Environ Can, 73-76 & Can Nat Sportsmen's Fund, 78-79. *Mem:* Ecol Soc Am; Am Soc Limnol & Oceanog; Int Asn Theoret & Appl Limnol; Freshwater Biol Asn, Eng; Can Soc Zoologists. *Res:* Effects of physical-chemical properties of lakes, competition and predation on the size structure of limnetic crustacean zooplankton communities. *Mailing Add:* Erindale Col Univ of Toronto Mississauga ON L5L 1C6 Can

SPRUNG, DONALD WHITFIELD LOYAL, b Kitchener, Ont, June 6, 34; m 58; c 2. NUCLEAR PHYSICS. *Educ:* Univ Toronto, BA, 57; Univ Birmingham, PhD(physics), 61, DSc, 77. *Prof Exp:* Instr physics, Cornell Univ, 61-62; from asst prof to assoc prof, 62-71, PROF PHYSICS, MCMASTER UNIV, 71-, DEAN FAC SCI, 75- *Concurrent Pos:* Mem res staff, Lab Nuclear Sci, Mass Inst Technol, 64-65; C D Howe fel, Orsay, France, 69-70; guest prof, Univ Tuebingen, Ger, 80-81. *Honors & Awards:* Herzberg Medal, 72. *Mem:* Am Phys Soc; Can Asn Physicists; Brit Inst Physics; fel Royal Soc Can. *Res:* Nucleon-nucleon interaction; theory of nuclear matter; effective force in finite nuclei; nuclear structure and forces theory. *Mailing Add:* Dept Physics McMaster Univ Hamilton ON L8S 4M1 Can

SPRUNG, JOSEPH ASHER, b Wahpeton, NDak, Dec 25, 15; m 44; c 1. ORGANIC CHEMISTRY. *Educ:* Univ Minn, BChem, 38, MS, 39, PhD(org chem), 43. *Prof Exp:* Res chemist, Cent Res Lab, GAF Corp, Pa, 43-47, group leader photog sect, 47-51, sr res specialist, Photog Div, 51-61, mgr, Photog Emulsion Tech Dept, 61-62, assoc dir res & develop, 62-64, sr scientist, Photo Div, 64-80, TECH CONSULT PHOTOG SCI & TECHNOL, GAF CORP, 80- *Mem:* Fel AAAS; Am Chem Soc; Soc Photog Sci & Eng. *Res:* Synthesis of organic compounds required in studying ortho effect; synthesis of vitamin E and vitamin A intermediates; color photography processes; photographic emulsions. *Mailing Add:* 16 Devon Blvd Binghamton NY 13903

SPRUNT, EVE SILVER, b Brooklyn, NY, July 9, 51; m 73; c 2. GEOPHYSICS, GEOLOGY. *Educ:* Mass Inst Technol, SB, 72, SM, 73; Stanford Univ, PhD(geophys), 77. *Prof Exp:* Res assoc, Stanford Univ, 76-79; res geophysicist, 79-80, SR RES GEOPHYSICIST, MOBIL RES & DEVELOP CORP, 80- *Mem:* Am Geophys Union; Geol Soc Am; Soc Explor Geophysicists; Soc Petrol Engrs; Soc Rock Mech. *Res:* Rock physics, specifically solution transfer; quartz cathodoluminescence; porosity; permeability; velocity; scanning electron microscopy; hydraulic fracturing. *Mailing Add:* Mobil Res & Develop Corp PO Box 900 Dallas TX 75221

SPRY, ROBERT JAMES, b Dayton, Ohio, Feb 12, 38; m 69; c 3. SOLID STATE PHYSICS. *Educ:* Univ Ill, Urbana, BS, 60, MS, 62, PhD(solid state physics), 67. *Prof Exp:* Res asst solid state physics, Univ Ill, Urbana, 62-67; RES PHYSICIST, AIR FORCE MAT LAB, WRIGHT-PATTERSON AFB, 67- *Mem:* Am Phys Soc. *Res:* Optical properties of semiconductors; radiation damage; infrared spectroscopy; optical sensors; laser technology; low temperature physics. *Mailing Add:* Air Force Mat Lab AFWAL-MLPJ Wright-Patterson AFB OH 45433

SPUDICH, JAMES ANTHONY, b Collinsville, Ill, Jan 7, 42; m 64; c 2. BIOCHEMISTRY. *Educ:* Univ Ill, Urbana, BS, 63; Stanford Univ, PhD(biochem), 67. *Prof Exp:* USPHS trainee, Stanford Univ, 68; US Air Force Off Sci Res fel, Cambridge Univ, 69 & NSF fel, 70; asst prof biochem, 70-74, ASSOC PROF BIOCHEM, UNIV CALIF, SAN FRANCISCO, 74- *Concurrent Pos:* Am Cancer Soc res grant, Univ Calif, San Francisco, 70. *Mem:* AAAS. *Res:* Molecular basis of mitosis, amoeboid movement and other forms of cell mobility. *Mailing Add:* Dept of Biochem & Biophys Univ of Calif San Francisco CA 94143

SPUHLER, JAMES NORMAN, b Tucumcari, NMex, Mar 1, 17; m 46; c 1. ANTHROPOLOGY, BIOLOGY. *Educ:* Univ NMex, BA, 40; Harvard Univ, MA, 42, PhD, 46; Oxford Univ, MA, 62. *Prof Exp:* Instr anthrop, Ohio State Univ, 46-47, asst prof anthrop & zool, 48-50; assoc biologist, Univ Mich, 50-55; from assoc prof to prof anthrop & human genetics, 53-68; LESLIE SPIER PROF ANTHROP, UNIV NMEX, 67- *Concurrent Pos:* Fel, Ctr Advan Study Behav Sci, 55-56 & 71-72; consult, NIH, 55-58 & NSF, 65-67; dir child health surv, Atomic Bomb Casualty Comn, Hiroshima, 59; res fel, Oxford Univ, 62-63; ed, J Anthrop Res, 75-81. *Mem:* Am Soc Naturalists; Soc Study Evolution; Am Soc Human Genetics; fel Am Anthrop Asn; Am Asn Phys Anthrop (secy, 55-58, pres, 75-77). *Res:* Physical anthropology; human genetics; human evolution. *Mailing Add:* Dept of Anthrop Univ of NMex Albuquerque NM 87131

SPULLER, ROBERT L, b Shelbyville, Ind, Aug 21, 37; m 59; c 2. PROTOZOOLOGY, PARASITOLOGY. *Educ:* Purdue Univ, BS, 59, MS, 60; Univ Mich, MS, 63, PhD(zool), 68. *Prof Exp:* Teacher high sch, Ind, 60-62; asst prof, 68-70, assoc prof, 70-74, chmn div natural sci & math, 75-79, actg dean acad affairs, 77-78, PROF BIOL, LENOIR-RHYNE COL, 75-, CHMN DEPT, 68- *Mem:* AAAS; Soc Protozool; Sigma Xi; Am Soc Zool. *Res:* Electron microscopy of ciliated protozoa; ecological relationships in the protozoa. *Mailing Add:* Dept of Biol Lenoir-Rhyne Col Hickory NC 28601

SPURGEON, WILLIAM MARION, b Quincy, Ill, Dec 5, 17; m 41; c 3. PHYSICAL CHEMISTRY. *Educ:* Univ Ill, BS, 38; Univ Mich, MS, 39, PhD(phys chem), 41. *Prof Exp:* Res chemist, Tex Co, NY, 41-42 & 46; asst prof appl sci, Univ Cincinnati, 46-48; res dir & vpres, Am Fluresit Co, Ohio, 47-54; mgr phys chem unit, Flight Propulsion Lab Dept, Gen Elec Co, 54-59; mgr mat & processes dept, Res Labs, Bendix Corp, 59-73, dir mfg qual control, Home Systs Res, Res Labs, 73-78, sr res planner, 78-80; DIR PROD RES PROG, NSF, 80- *Concurrent Pos:* Mem, Nat Mat Adv Bd, 78- *Honors & Awards:* Colwell Award, Soc Automotive Engrs, 67; Siegel Award, Soc Mfg Engrs, 81. *Mem:* Am Chem Soc; Am Soc Metals; Classification Soc; Soc Mfg Eng; Sigma Xi. *Res:* Catalysis; solubility; fluid flow; building materials; ophthalmology; corrosion; coatings; thermal properties; semiconductors; friction materials; composites; separation processes; manufacturing processes. *Mailing Add:* 24799 Edgemont Rd Southfield MI 48034

SPURLIN, HAROLD MORTON, b Atlanta, Ga, Apr 4, 05; m 33, 44; c 5. PHYSICAL CHEMISTRY. *Educ:* Ga Inst Technol, BS, 25; Yale Univ, PhD(chem), 28. *Prof Exp:* Res chemist res ctr, Hercules Inc, 28-39, group leader, 39-45, tech asst to dir, 45-70; CONSULT, 70- *Honors & Awards:* Anselme Payen Award, 64. *Mem:* AAAS; Am Chem Soc; Soc Rheology (vpres, 48); Am Inst Chem Engrs. *Res:* Cellulose; polymers; naval stores; propellants; process design. *Mailing Add:* 2704 Duncan Rd Wilmington DE 19808

SPURLOCK, BENJAMIN HILL, JR, b Lithonia, Ga, July 19, 07; m 35, 71; c 2. MECHANICAL ENGINEERING. *Educ:* Ga Sch Technol, BS, 38; Mass Inst Technol, MS, 39; Univ Colo, ME, 50. *Prof Exp:* Engr, Cent of Ga Rwy, 24-28; sales engr, Union Oil Co, 32-36; designer, Eagan Cotton Mills, 36-38; asst, Univ Calif, 39-40; from instr to asst prof mech eng, Univ Colo, 40-44; vis lectr, Yale Univ, 44-46; from asst prof to prof, 46-76, dir grad studies, Dept Mech Eng, 46-51, chmn dept, 65-66, EMER PROF MECH ENG, UNIV COLO, BOULDER, 76- *Concurrent Pos:* Consult engr, Pratt & Whitney Aircraft Corp, 42-51 & Stone & Birkle, 58-; US Air Force contract & res assoc eng, Exp Sta, 47-51; Fulbright fel, Iraq, 55-56. *Honors & Awards:* E K Campbell Award, 69; Distinguished Service Award, 70. *Mem:* Am Soc Mech Engrs; fel Am Soc Heat, Refrig & Air-Conditioning Engrs; Am Soc Eng Educ. *Res:* Thermodynamics; heat and mass transfer; fluid mechanics. *Mailing Add:* 75 Teapot Rock Ave Village of Oak Creek Sedona AZ 86336

SPURLOCK, CAROLA HENRICH, b Detroit, Mich, July 24, 26; m 54; c 2. ANALYTICAL CHEMISTRY, SPECTROPHOTOMETRY. *Educ:* Univ Detroit, BS, 48, MS, 50. *Prof Exp:* Asst chemist phys chem, Parke Davis & Co, 50-69, assoc chemist, 69-78; SCIENTIST PHYS CHEM, WARNER-LAMBERT/PARKE DAVIS, 78- *Mem:* AAAS; Am Chem Soc. *Res:* Ultraviolet-visible spectrophotometry, polarimetry, potentiometric titration and instrumental analytical methods. *Mailing Add:* Warner-Lambert 2800 Plymouth Rd Ann Arbor MI 48106

SPURLOCK, JACK MARION, b Tampa, Fla, Aug 16, 30; m 52; c 4. CHEMICAL ENGINEERING, BIOMEDICAL ENGINEERING. *Educ:* Univ Fla, BChE, 52; Ga Inst Technol, MSChE, 58, PhD(chem eng), 61. *Prof Exp:* Qual control engr, Auto-Lite Battery Co, Ga, 54-55; res engr, Eng Exp Sta, Ga Inst Technol, 55-58, asst prof chem eng, Sch Chem Eng, 58-62; mgr aerospace sci lab, Orlando Div, Martin Co, 62-64; chief eng res group, Atlantic Res Corp, 64-69; pres, Health & Safety Res Inst, 69-74; prin res engr, Eng Exp Sta & assoc dir, Appli Sci Lab, 74-79, DIR, OFF INTERDISCIPLINARY PROG, GA INST TECHNOL, 79- *Concurrent Pos:* Biomed eng consult, T A Jones Assocs, 71-74. *Honors & Awards:* M A Ferst Res Award, Ga Inst Technol, 61. *Mem:* Am Inst Chem Eng; fel Royal Soc Health; Am Chem Soc; Aerospace Med Asn; fel Am Inst Chem. *Res:* Acoustical effects on transport phenomena; conduction and convection heat transfer; vacuum environmental effects on liquid propellants; biomedical transport phenomena and instrumentation; chemical process economics; energy conservation; research management; alcohol fuels technology; systems design and analysis. *Mailing Add:* Off Interdisciplinary Prog Ga Inst Technol Atlanta GA 30332

SPURLOCK, LANGLEY AUGUSTINE, b Charleston, WVa, Nov 9, 39. SCIENCE ADMINISTRATION & POLICY, ORGANIC CHEMISTRY. *Educ:* WVa State Col, BS, 59; Wayne State Univ, PhD(org chem), 63. *Prof Exp:* Res chemist, Gen Chem Div, Allied Chem Corp, NJ, 63-65, sr res chemist, Nitrogen Div, 66; asst prof org chem, Temple Univ, 66-69; assoc prof org chem, Brown Univ, 69-76; fel, US Dept Health Educ & Welfare, 76-77; spec asst to dir, Off Audit & Oversight, 77-80, staff assoc spec proj, 80-81, SR STAFF ASSOC OPER & DIR MATH & PHYS SCI, NSF, 81- *Concurrent Pos:* Asst to president, Am Coun Educ, 73- *Mem:* Am Chem Soc; AAAS. *Res:* Mechanistic organic chemistry, bridged polycyclic compounds, molecular rearrangements, free radical and ionic additions; synthetic organic chemistry; conformational analysis; organic ultrasonic chemistry; sonochemistry. *Mailing Add:* 3718 Van Ness St NW Washington DC 20016

SPURR, ARTHUR RICHARD, b Glendale, Calif, July 21, 15; m 42; c 4. PLANT MORPHOLOGY, PLANT PHYSIOLOGY. *Educ:* Univ Calif, Los Angeles, BS, 38, MA, 40; Harvard Univ, AM, 42, PhD(biol), 47. *Prof Exp:* Instr biol, Harvard Univ, 47-48; instr truck crops, 48-53, from asst prof to assoc prof veg crops, 54-73, from jr olericulturist to assoc olericulturist, 48-73, PROF VEG CROPS, UNIV CALIF, DAVIS, 73-, OLERICULTURIST, EXP STA, 73- *Concurrent Pos:* NIH spec res fel, 60-61; NSF res grant, 71-72; French govt res grant, 77-78. *Mem:* AAAS; Electron Micros Soc Am; Microbeam Anal Soc; Am Inst Biol Scientists; Bot Soc Am. *Res:* Cytology and ultrastructure of vascular plants; electron microscopy and analytical technics; pathology of physiological disorders; mineral nutrition; electron microscopy; electron probe x-ray analysis; ion probe microanalysis; responses to salinity and boron toxicity. *Mailing Add:* Dept of Veg Crops Univ of Calif Davis CA 95616

SPURR, CHARLES LEWIS, b Sunbury, Pa, Nov 20, 13; m 40; c 2. MEDICINE. *Educ:* Bucknell Univ, BS, 35; Univ Rochester, MS, 38, MD, 40. *Prof Exp:* From intern to asst med, Clin, Univ Chicago, 40-43, from instr to asst prof, 43-48; chief dept med, Univ Tex M D Anderson Hosp & Tumor Clin, 48-49; assoc prof, Col Med, Baylor Univ, 49-57; PROF MED & DIR ONCOL RES CTR, BOWMAN GRAY SCH MED, WAKE FOREST UNIV, 57- *Concurrent Pos:* Chief med res, Vet Hosp, Houston, Tex, 49-57. *Mem:* AAAS; AMA; fel Am Col Physicians. *Res:* Hematology; cancer chemotherapy. *Mailing Add:* Bowman Gray Sch of Med Wake Forest Univ Winston-Salem NC 27103

SPURR, DAVID TUPPER, b Notikewin, Alta, May 21, 38; m 62; c 3. STATISTICS, BIOLOGY. *Educ:* Univ Alta, BSc, 61, MSc, 65; Ore State Univ, PhD(genetics), 68. *Prof Exp:* Pub lands appraiser, Lands Br, Alta Dept Lands & Forests, 61-63; asst animal sci, Univ Alta, 63-65; asst genetics, Ore State Univ, 66-68; res assoc animal genetics, Comput Ctr, Univ Ga, Athens, 69-70; res scientist statist, Statist Res Serv, 70-75, STATISTICIAN, RES STA, AGR CAN, 75- *Mem:* Biomet Soc. *Res:* Biometrical genetics; experimental design theory; bioassay; sampling. *Mailing Add:* Res Sta Agr Can 107 Science Crescent Saskatoon SK S1N 0X2 Can

SPURR, GERALD BAXTER, b Cambridge, Mass, June 1, 28; m 52; c 4. PHYSIOLOGY. *Educ:* Boston Col, BS, 50; Univ Iowa, PhD(physiol), 54. *Prof Exp:* From res asst to instr physiol, Univ Iowa, 51-54; from instr clin physiol to prof physiol & biophys, Col Med, Univ Tenn, Memphis, 56-68; PROF PHYSIOL, MED COL WIS, 68- *Concurrent Pos:* Am Heart Asn fel, Univ Iowa, 54-56; Markle scholar med sci, 58-63; vis prof, Univ Valle, Colombia, 61-62; consult, Res Serv, Vet Admin Ctr, Wood, Wis, 68- *Mem:* AAAS; Am Physiol Soc; Soc Exp Biol & Med; fel Am Col Sports Med; Sigma Xi. *Res:* Environmental and cardiovascular physiology; cold heart; hypothermia; hyperthermia; electrolyte and fluid metabolism; peripheral circulation; respiration; exercise; nutrition. *Mailing Add:* Res Serv Vet Admin Ctr Wood WI 53193

SPURR, HARVEY WESLEY, JR, b Oak Park, Ill, June 8, 34; m 56; c 3. PLANT PATHOLOGY. *Educ:* Mich State Univ, BS, 56, MS, 58; Univ Wis, PhD(plant path), 61. *Prof Exp:* NIH fel plant path, Univ Wis, 61-63; plant pathologist, Agr Res Sta, Union Carbide Corp, NC, 63-69; assoc prof plant path, 69-74, PROF PLANT PATH, NC STATE UNIV, 74-, RES PLANT PATHOLOGIST, OXFORD TOBACCO LAB, USDA, 69- *Mem:* Am Phytopath Soc; Soc Nematol; Am Chem Soc; AAAS. *Res:* Plant disease control research; biological and chemical control; biochemistry of plant disease. *Mailing Add:* Oxford Tobacco Lab USDA Oxford NC 27565

SPURR, ORSON KIRK, JR, b Cambridge, NY, Sept 4, 30; m 53; c 2. PHYSICAL CHEMISTRY. *Educ:* Dartmouth Col, BA, 52; Cornell Univ, MS, 56, PhD(phys chem), 58. *Prof Exp:* Res polymer chemist, Chem & Plastics Div, 58-79, RES POLYMER CHEMIST, SPECIALITY CHEM & PLASTICS DIV, UNION CARBIDE CORP, 79- *Mem:* Am Chem Soc; Sigma Xi. *Res:* Epoxy resins. *Mailing Add:* Res/Dev Dept Specialty Chem & Plastics Div Union Carbide Corp Bound Brook NJ 08805

SPURR, STEPHEN HOPKINS, b Washington, DC, Feb 14, 18; m 45; c 2. FORESTRY, ECOLOGY. *Educ:* Univ Fla, BS, 38, DSc, 71; Yale Univ, MF, 40, PhD, 50. *Prof Exp:* Tech asst forestry res, Harvard Forest, 40-41, instr forestry & ecol, 41-43, actg dir, 43-46, asst prof forestry, 46-50; assoc prof, Univ Minn, 50-52; prof silvicult, Univ Mich, Ann Arbor, 52-71, dean sch natural resources & asst to vpres acad affairs, 62-65, dean, Horace H Rackham Sch Grad Studies, 64-71, vpres, 69-71; pres, 71-74, PROF BOT & PUB AFFAIRS, UNIV TEX, AUSTIN, 71- *Concurrent Pos:* Asst prof, WVa Univ, 43; NSF fac fel, 57-58; Fulbright res fel, NZ & Australia, 60; Albright lectr, Univ Calif, 66; pres, Orgn Trop Studies, 67-68; mem, President's Adv Panel Timber & Environ, 71-72; lectr many univs; ed, Forest Sci. *Honors & Awards:* Wilbur Cross Medal, Yale. *Mem:* Soc Am Foresters; Ecol Soc Am; Am Forestry Asn. *Res:* Use of aerial photographs in forestry; changes in forest composition; application of forest ecology in silviculture; physiology of growth in forest trees; forest inventory; economic development of natural resources. *Mailing Add:* LBJ Sch Pub Affairs Univ of Tex Austin TX 78712

SPURRELL, FRANCIS ARTHUR, b Independence, Iowa, Apr 13, 19; m 47; c 1. VETERINARY MEDICINE, RADIATION BIOLOGY. *Educ:* Univ Wis, BS, 41; Iowa State Col, DVM, 46; Univ Minn, PhD(vet med), 55; Am Bd Vet Radiol, dipl. *Prof Exp:* Instr vet anat, 47-49, vet obstet, 49-55, assoc prof vet radiol, 55-62, dir summer inst radiation biol, 60-64, prof vet radiol, 62-68, PROF THERIOGENOL, UNIV MINN, ST PAUL, 68- *Mem:* Am Soc Animal Sci; Am Vet Radiol Soc; Am Vet Med Asn; Educators Vet Radiol Sci. *Res:* Genetics; heritability of fertility in dairy cattle; gaiting inheritance in racing thoroughbreds, with applied computer data base management procudures; veterinary radiology; heredity and diseases of animals; theriogenology computer systems. *Mailing Add:* Animal Sci & Vet Med Rm 385 Col Vet Med Univ Minn St Paul MN 55108

SPURRIER, ELMER R, b Ava, Mo, Aug 1, 20; m 41; c 3. MICROBIOLOGY, PUBLIC HEALTH. *Educ:* Univ Mo, BS, 49; Univ Minn, MPH, 54; Univ NC, MSPH, 62, DrPH, 64. *Prof Exp:* Technologist, Landon-Meyer Labs, Ohio, 49-50; supvr serologist, Pub Health Lab, 50-53, supvr serol & virol, 54-60, asst lab dir, 64-66, DIR LABS, MO STATE DIV HEALTH, 66- *Concurrent Pos:* Lectr microbiol, Sch Med, Univ Mo, 64- *Mem:* Am Soc Microbiol; Am Pub Health Asn; Conf Pub Health Lab Dirs; Asn State & Territorial Pub Health Lab Dirs. *Res:* Antigenic relationships among parainfluenza viruses. *Mailing Add:* Sect Lab Serv Mo State Div Health 307 W McCarty Bldg Jefferson City MO 65101

SPYHALSKI, EDWARD JAMES, b Chase, Wis, Apr 13, 25; m 55; c 3. ENTOMOLOGY. *Educ:* Univ Wis, BS, 50, MA, 51; NC State Col, PhD(entom), 59. *Prof Exp:* Res entomologist, Am Cyanamid Co, 51-55; mgr tech serv, Niagara Chem Div, FMC Corp, NY, 59-69; res biologist, Air Prod & Chem, Inc, 69-71; SR BIOCHEM FIELD SPECIALIST, PPG INDUSTS, INC, 71- *Mem:* Weed Sci Soc Am; Entom Soc Am; Soc Nematol. *Res:* Relationship of chemicals to pesticidal activity; pesticide formulation research; crop culture research; pest control procedures. *Mailing Add:* PPG Industs Inc 8845 Valley Circle Dr Florence KY 41042

SQUIBB, SAMUEL DEXTER, b Limestone, Tenn, June 20, 31; m 51; c 2. ORGANIC CHEMISTRY. *Educ:* ETenn State Univ, BS, 52; Univ Fla, PhD(chem), 56; Am Inst Chem, accredited (PC-A). *Prof Exp:* Assoc prof chem, Western Carolina Univ, 56-60; from asst prof to assoc prof chem, Eckerd Col, 60-64, dir chem prog, 60-64; PROF CHEM & CHMN DEPT, UNIV NC, ASHEVILLE, 64- *Concurrent Pos:* Vis prof chem, Univ NC, Chapel Hill, 76-80. *Mem:* Am Chem Soc; life fel Am Inst Chem; AAUP. *Res:* Allyl-type optically active quaternary ammonium salts; aqueous solution chemistry. *Mailing Add:* Dept of Chem Univ of NC Asheville NC 28804

SQUIER, DONALD PLATTE, b Des Moines, Iowa, Aug 16, 29. MATHEMATICS. *Educ:* Stanford Univ, BS, 51, PhD(math), 55. *Prof Exp:* Mathematician, Remington Rand Univac Div, Sperry Rand Corp, 55-57; asst prof math, San Diego State Col, 57-59; reservoir engr, Calif Res Corp, 59-64; assoc prof math, Colo State Univ, 64-69; prof math, 69-80, PROF MATH & STATIST, UNIV WEST FLA, 80- *Mem:* Am Math Soc; Math Asn Am. *Res:* Elliptic partial differential equations; numerical analysis. *Mailing Add:* Dept of Math & Statist Univ of W Fla Pensacola FL 32504

SQUIERS, CLIFFORD DALE, animal husbandry, see previous edition

SQUIERS, EDWIN RICHARD, b Bath, NB, May 15, 48; US citizen. PLANT ECOLOGY, FIELD BOTANY. *Educ:* State Univ NY, Binghamton, BA, 70; Rutgers Univ, MS, 73; Ohio Univ, PhD(bot), 76. *Prof Exp:* Res assoc terrestrial veg, Jack McCormick & Assocs, Ecol Consults, 70-71, consult, 71-76; ASST PROF BOT & ECOL, TAYLOR UNIV, 76-, DIR, ENVIRON SCI PROG, 80- *Mem:* Ecol Soc Am; Am Inst Biol Sci; Sigma Xi; Bot Soc Am. *Res:* Organization and dynamics of secondary successsion succession systems; systems modeling; floristics; phenology of successional species; biogeography. *Mailing Add:* Dept of Biol Taylor Univ Upland IN 46989

SQUILLACOTE, MICHAEL EDWARD, b Washington, DC, Dec 27, 50. PHOTOCHEMISTRY, NUCLEAR MAGNETIC RESONANCE. *Educ:* Univ Chicago, BS, 72; Univ Calif, Los Angeles, PhD(chem), 78. *Prof Exp:* Res fel chem, Calif Inst Technol, 78-80; ASST PROF CHEM, BROWN UNIV, 80- *Mem:* Am Chem Soc. *Res:* Low temperature photochemical and nuclear magnetic resonance studies of reactive intermediates; potential surfaces of excited states; routes of intramolecular vibrational decay. *Mailing Add:* Box H Dept Chem Brown Univ Providence RI 02912

SQUIRE, DAVID R, b Bartlesville, Okla, Mar 11, 35; m 56; c 4. POLYMER CHEMISTRY, PHYSICAL CHEMISTRY. *Educ:* Southern Methodist Univ, BS, 57; Rice Univ, PhD(theoret chem), 61. *Prof Exp:* Assoc chem, Duke Univ, 61-62; assoc prof chem & head dept, Nicholls State Col, 61-62; chief phys chem br, 62-77, ASSOC DIR CHEM DIV, US ARMY RES OFF, 77- *Concurrent Pos:* Vis asst prof, Duke Univ, 62-72; adj prof, NC State Univ, 70- *Mem:* Am Chem Soc; Am Phys Soc. *Res:* Theoretical chemistry; fundamental investigations in polymer chemistry; radiation chemistry of polymers; statistical mechanics of solids and liquids. *Mailing Add:* US Army Res Off Box 12211 Research Triangle Park NC 27709

SQUIRE, EDWARD NOONAN, b Portland, Ore, Sept 16, 20; m 47; c 7. CHEMISTRY. *Educ:* Stanford Univ, AB, 42; Northwestern Univ, PhD(chem), 48. *Prof Exp:* Asst chem, Northwestern Univ, 45-46, quiz instr, 46-47; from asst prof to assoc prof chem, Franklin & Marshall Col, 48-52; res chemist, Polychem Dept, 52-59, res assoc, 59-62, sr res chemist, Plastics Dept, 62-70, res assoc, Plastics Dept, 70-80, RES FEL, POLYMER PRODS DEPT, EXP STA, E I DU PONT DE NEMOURS & CO, INC, WILMINGTON, 80- *Mem:* AAAS; Am Chem Soc. *Res:* Synthesis of steroids; steroid effect upon bacterial growth; electrometric titrations of tin and iodine; bicholesteryl, related steroids and high polymers; organic synthesis and polymerization studies; catalysis of organic reactions; monomer syntheses. *Mailing Add:* Box 120 RD 2 Glen Mills PA 19342

SQUIRE, LARRY RYAN, b Cherokee, Iowa, May 4, 41. NEUROSCIENCE, NEUROPSYCHOLOGY. *Educ:* Oberlin Col, BA, 63; Mass Inst Technol, PhD(psychol), 68. *Prof Exp:* Asst prof, 73-76, assoc prof psychiat, 76-81, PROF PSYCHIAT, UNIV CALIF, SAN DIEGO, 81-; RES CAREER SCIENTIST, VET ADMIN MED CTR, 80- *Concurrent Pos:* NIMH interdisciplinary fel, Albert Einstein Col Med, 68-70; clin investr, Vet Admin Med Ctr, 73-76, res career scientist, 81- *Mem:* Fel Am Psychol Asn; Int Neuropsychol Soc; Soc Neurosci; Psychonomic Soc; AAAS. *Res:* Organization and neurological foundations of memory in man and non-human primate; neural plasticity; memory disorders in man; electroconvulsive therapy and memory. *Mailing Add:* Vet Admin Med Ctr 3350 La Jolla Village Dr San Diego CA 92161

SQUIRE, PHIL GEORGE, b Ephraim, Utah, Sept 11, 22; m 46; c 3. BIOPHYSICAL CHEMISTRY. *Educ:* Brigham Young Univ, BS, 48; Univ Wis, MS, 51; Univ Calif, PhD, 57. *Prof Exp:* Asst chem, Univ Wis, 49-51; res biochemist, Cutter Labs, 51-56; res biochemist, Univ Calif, 55-57, asst res biochemist, Hormone Res Lab, 57-66, assoc res biochemist & assoc prof biochem univ, 66-67, asst prof exp endocrinol, 61-66; asst prof biochem, 67-69, chmn dept, 67-72, PROF BIOCHEM, COLO STATE UNIV, 69- *Mem:* AAAS; Am Chem Soc; Am Soc Biol Chemists. *Res:* Purification of biologically active proteins; characterization of proteins by physical and chemical methods; regulation of enzyme activity. *Mailing Add:* Dept of Biochem Colo State Univ Ft Collins CO 80523

SQUIRE, RICHARD DOUGLAS, b New York, NY, Oct 9, 40; m 80. GENETICS, RADIATION BIOLOGY. *Educ:* Hofstra Univ, BA, 63, MA, 69; NC State Univ, PhD(genetics), 69. *Prof Exp:* Asst prof biol, Long Island Univ, Brooklyn Ctr, 69-73, adj assoc prof, 74-75, 76-78; res fel, Med Ctr, Cornell Univ, 75-76; asst prof, 78-81, ASSOC PROF BIOL, UNIV PR, MAYAGUEZ, 81- *Concurrent Pos:* Adj assoc prof, Staten Island Community Col, 74-75 & St John's Univ, 77. *Mem:* AAAS; Genetics Soc Am; Soc Study Evolution; Am Soc Zoologists; Am Genetic Asn. *Res:* Radiation genetics, ecological genetics, developmental genetics and cytogenetics of Artemia; chemically-induced polyploidy in animals; genetics of sex-determination and color patterns in fish; mammalian cytogenetics. *Mailing Add:* Dept Biol Mayaguez Campus Mayaguez PR 00708

SQUIRE, ROBERT ALFRED, b Dobbs Ferry, NY, July 1, 30; m 50; c 3. COMPARATIVE PATHOLOGY. *Educ:* Univ Vt, BS, 52; Cornell Univ, DVM, 56, PhD(vet path), 64; Am Col Vet Path, dipl. *Prof Exp:* Private practice, Vt, 56-60; asst path, Cornell Univ, 60-61, instr, 62-64; asst prof, 64-68, ASSOC PROF PATH, SCH MED, JOHNS HOPKINS UNIV, 68-, ASSOC PROF COMP MED, 77- *Concurrent Pos:* Mem adv comt, Registry Comp Path, 68-; chmn comt lab animal dis, Nat Acad Sci-Nat Res Coun, 69-; mem adv coun, Morris Animal Found, 71-; chmn adv coun, NY State Vet Col, Cornell Univ, 71-; lectr, Armed Forces Inst Path; dir comp path, Johns Hopkins Univ, 66-76. *Mem:* Int Acad Path; Am Asn Cancer Res; Am Col Vet Path; Am Vet Med Asn. *Res:* Pathology of hematopoietic tissues; animal models of human disease, particularly lymphomas and immunologic diseases. *Mailing Add:* Dept of Path Johns Hopkins Hosp Baltimore MD 21205

SQUIRE, WILLIAM, b New York, NY, Sept 22, 20; m 48; c 2. APPLIED MATHEMATICS, FLUID MECHANICS. *Educ:* City Col New York, BS, 41; Univ Buffalo, MA, 59. *Prof Exp:* Inspector, Philadelphia Signal Corps Inspection Zone, US Dept Army, 42-43; jr physicist, Nat Bur Standards, 43-45; asst physicist, 45-48; assoc physicist, Cornell Aeronaut Lab, Inc, 48-57; aerodynamicist, Bell Aircraft Corp, 57-59; sr res engr, Southwest Res Inst, 59-61; PROF AEROSPACE ENG, W VA UNIV, 61-. *Mem:* Am Phys Soc; Soc Indust & Appl Math; assoc fel Inst Aeronaut & Astronaut; Asn Comput Mach. *Res:* Turbulence; high temperature gas dynamics; boundary layer theory; numerical integration. *Mailing Add:* Dept of Aerospace Eng WVa Univ Morgantown WV 26506

SQUIRES, ARTHUR MORTON, b Neodesha, Kans, Mar 21, 16. CHEMICAL ENGINEERING. *Educ:* Univ Mo, AB, 38; Cornell Univ, PhD(phys chem), 47. *Prof Exp:* Asst chem, Univ Mo, 38 & Cornell Univ, 38-41; lab technician, E I du Pont de Nemours & Co, NY, 41; phys chemist, M W Kellogg Co, 42-43 & Kellex Corp, 43-46; asst head, Process Develop Dept, Hydrocarbon Res, Inc, 46-51, head, 51-59; process consult, 59-67; prof, 67-74, City Col New York, chmn dept, 71-74, distinguished prof chem eng, 74-76; FRANK C VILBRANDT PROF CHEM ENG, VA POLYTECH INST & STATE UNIV, 76-, DISTINGUISHED PROF CHEM ENG, 78- *Mem:* Nat Acad Eng; AAAS; Am Chem Soc; Am Geog Soc; Air Pollution Control Asn; Am Inst Chem Eng. *Res:* Physical chemistry of solutions; multistage fractionation; flow-properties of fluid-solids systems; hydrocarbon synthesis and cracking; iron ore reduction; coal and oil gasification; hydrogen production; power generation; dust collection; low-temperature processes; small-scale coal combustion. *Mailing Add:* Dept of Chem Eng Va Polytech Inst & State Univ Blacksburg VA 24061

SQUIRES, BURTON ELLIOTT, JR, computer science, see previous edition

SQUIRES, DONALD FLEMING, b Glen Cove, NY, Dec 19, 27; m 51; c 2. MARINE BIOLOGY, PALEONTOLOGY. *Educ:* Cornell Univ, AB, 50, PhD, 55; Univ Kans, MA, 52. *Prof Exp:* Asst cur paleont, Am Mus Natural Hist, 55-61, assoc cur, 61-62; assoc cur marine invert, Mus Natural Hist, Smithsonian Inst, 62-63, cur-in-chg, 63-64, chmn dept invert zool, 65, dep dir, 66-68; actg assoc provost grad studies & res, 72-73, PROF BIOL SCI, EARTH & SPACE SCI & DIR, MARINE SCI RES CTR, STATE UNIV NY STONY BROOK, 68- *Concurrent Pos:* Fulbright res fel, NZ, 59; dir, NY Sea Grant Inst, State Univ NY & Cornell Univ, 71- *Mem:* AAAS; fel AAAS; NZ Geol Soc. *Res:* Information systems and information storage and retrieval; management and programming of scientific research and development organizations; marine policy. *Mailing Add:* NY Sea Grant Inst 411 State St Albany NY 12246

SQUIRES, PATRICK, b Melbourne, Australia, July 12, 14; m; c 5. METEOROLOGY. *Educ:* Univ Melbourne, BA, 33, MA, 35, DSc(meteorol), 59. *Prof Exp:* Res meteorologist, Australian Weather Bur, 37-46, Commonwealth Sci & Indust Res Orgn, Australia, 46-62 & Nat Ctr Atmospheric Res, 62-66; dir lab atmospheric physics, Desert Res Inst, Univ Nev, Reno, 66-77; DIR CONVECTIVE STORMS DIV, NAT CTR ATMOSPHERIC RES, 77- *Mem:* Am Meteorol Soc. *Res:* Cloud physics. *Mailing Add:* Nat Ctr of Atmospheric Res PO Box 3000 Boulder CO 80307

SQUIRES, PAUL HERMAN, b Sewickley, Pa, July 14, 31; m 53; c 6. CHEMICAL ENGINEERING, POLYMER PROCESSING. *Educ:* Rensselaer Polytech Inst, BChE, 53, PhD(chem eng), 56; Univ Wis, MS, 54. *Prof Exp:* Engr, Plastics Dept, 56-59, supvr, 59-63, sr res engr, 63-67, res assoc, Eng Dept, 67-76, PRIN CONSULT, ENG DEPT, E I DU PONT DE NEMOURS & CO, INC, 76- *Mem:* Soc Plastics Engrs; Am Inst Chem Engrs. *Res:* Energy and momentum transfer in viscous materials, especially translation of theory into design and development of plastics processing equipment; laminated safety glass interlayer; extrusion. *Mailing Add:* E I du Pont de Nemours & Co Inc Eng Dept Exp Sta Wilmington DE 19898

SQUIRES, ROBERT GEORGE, b Sewickley, Pa, Oct 1, 35; m 57; c 3. CHEMICAL ENGINEERING. *Educ:* Rensselaer Polytech Inst, BChE, 57; Univ Mich, Ann Arbor, MSE, 58, MS, 60, PhD(chem eng), 63. *Prof Exp:* From asst prof to assoc prof, 62-72, PROF CHEM ENG, PURDUE UNIV, WEST LAFAYETTE, 72- *Mem:* Am Inst Chem Engrs; Am Chem Soc; Am Soc Eng Educ; Catalysis Soc. *Res:* Heterogeneous catalysis; adsorption; reaction kinetics. *Mailing Add:* Sch Chem Eng Purdue Univ West Lafayette IN 47906

SQUIRES, ROBERT WRIGHT, b Barberton, Ohio, Aug 25, 21; m 48; c 2. MICROBIOLOGY. *Educ:* Kent State Univ, BS, 48; Purdue Univ, MS, 50, PhD(microbiol), 54. *Prof Exp:* Instr gen bact, Purdue Univ, 49, instr food bact, 50-53; sr microbiologist, Eli Lilly & Co, 54-65, res scientist, 65-66, asst mgr pilot plant opers, 66-67, mgr antibiotic opers, 67-69, eng coordr antibiotic fermentations, 69-80; TECH DIR BIOMFG, SEARLE CHEM, INC, 81- *Mem:* Soc Indust Microbiologists (treas, 61-66, pres, 68-69); Am Inst Biol Scientists; Sigma Xi; Am Soc Microbiol; Instrument Soc Am. *Res:* Antibiotic fermentation pilot plant operations; fermentation development and equipment design; continuous fermentation; process scaleup and fermentation process control dynamics. *Mailing Add:* PO Box 130 Searle Chem Inc Harbor Beach MI 48441

SQUIRES, WILLIAM CAMPBELL, microbiology, see previous edition

SQUYRES, STEVEN WELDON, b Woodbury, NJ, Jan 9, 56. PLANETARY GEOLOGY. *Educ:* Cornell Univ, BA, 78, PhD(geol), 81. *Prof Exp:* NAT RES COUN ASSOC, AMES RES CTR, NASA, 81- *Concurrent Pos:* Mem, Planetary Geol Working Group, NASA, 82- *Mem:* Am Geophys Union; AAAS. *Res:* Geomorphology and climatic evolution of Mars; formation, internal evolution, and surface geology of outer planet satellites; photometry of outer planet satellites. *Mailing Add:* Ames Res Ctr NASA MS 245-3 Moffett Field CA 94035

SRAMEK, RICHARD ANTHONY, b Baltimore, Md, June 5, 43. RADIO ASTRONOMY. *Educ:* Mass Inst Technol, BS, 65; Calif Inst Technol, PhD(astron), 70. *Prof Exp:* Res assoc, Nat Radio Astron Observ, 70-72, asst scientist, 72-74, assoc scientist, 74-75; res assoc, Arecibo Observ, 75-78; VLA SCIENTIST, NAT RADIO ASTRON OBSERV, 78- *Mem:* Am Astron Soc; Int Union Radio Sci. *Res:* Extra-galactic astronomy and experimental tests of general relativity. *Mailing Add:* Nat Radio Astron Observ/VLA PO Box O Socorro NM 87801

SRB, ADRIAN MORRIS, b Howells, Nebr, Mar 4, 17; m 40; c 3. GENETICS. *Educ:* Univ Nebr, AB, 37, MS, 41; Stanford Univ, PhD(genetics), 46. *Hon Degrees:* DSc, Univ Nebr, 69. *Prof Exp:* Asst prof biol, Stanford Univ, 46-47; from assoc prof to prof plant breeding, 48-65, prof, 65-76, JACOB GOULD SCHURMAN PROF GENETICS, CORNELL UNIV, 76- *Concurrent Pos:* Nat Res Coun fel, Calif Inst Technol, 46-47; Guggenheim fel & Fulbright res fel, Univ Paris, 53-54, NSF sr res fel, 60-61, Univ Edinburgh, 67-68; dir, NIH pre- & postdoctoral training prog genetics, Cornell Univ, 62-67; Darling lectr, Allegheny Col, 64; mem genetics study sect, NIH, 64-67 & genetics training comt, 69-; vis scholar, Va Polytech Inst, 65; co-chmn prog comt, XI Int Bot Cong; trustee, Cornell Univ, 75-80; mem educ adv bd, John Simon Guggenheim Mem Found, 76- *Mem:* Nat Acad Sci; fel AAAS; Genetics Soc Am; Am Soc Naturalists; AAAS. *Res:* Physiological genetics of fungi; mutagenesis; extranuclear heredity; developmental genetics. *Mailing Add:* Genetics Sect Cornell Univ Plant Sci Bldg Ithaca NY 14853

SREBNIK, HERBERT HARRY, b Berlin, Ger, Mar 25, 23; nat US; m 51; c 2. ANATOMY. *Educ:* Univ Calif, BA, 50, MA, 55, PhD(anat), 57. *Prof Exp:* Asst anat, 53-57; from instr to assoc prof, 57-71, PROF ANAT, UNIV CALIF, BERKELEY, 71- *Mem:* AAAS; Soc Exp Biol & Med; Am Inst Nutrit; Am Asn Anat; Endocrine Soc. *Res:* Endocrine-nutrition interrelationships; physiology of reproduction; anterior pituitary function; investigations into hormonal and nutritional factors influencing the course and outcome of gestation in laboratory animals. *Mailing Add:* Dept of Physiol-Anat Univ of Calif Berkeley CA 94720

SREBRO, RICHARD, b New York, NY, Jan 9, 36; m 67. PHYSIOLOGY. *Educ:* Wash Univ, MD, 59. *Prof Exp:* Intern, State Univ NY Upstate Med Ctr, 59-60; resident ophthal, Sch Med, Wash Univ, 60-62; sr asst surgeon, Lab Phys Biol, NIH, 62-64; res scientist biophys, Walter Reed Army Inst Res, 65-68; res asst prof, State Univ NY Buffalo, 68-71, assoc prof physiol, 71-77; ASSOC PROF OPHTHAL & PHYSIOL, SOUTHWESTERN MED SCH, DALLAS, 77- *Concurrent Pos:* Nat Inst Neurol Dis & Blindness fel, 64-65. *Mem:* Biophys Soc; Asn Res Vision & Ophthal; Soc Neurosci. *Res:* Physiology of vision. *Mailing Add:* Dept of Ophthal 5323 Harry Hines Blvd Dallas TX 75235

SREEBNY, LEO MORRIS, b New York, NY, Jan 8, 22; m 45; c 2. PATHOLOGY, BIOCHEMISTRY. *Educ:* Univ Ill, AB, 42, DDS, 45, MS, 50, PhD(path), 54. *Prof Exp:* Asst therapeut, Col Dent, Univ Ill, 49-50, instr, 51-53, from asst prof to assoc prof oral path, 53-57; from assoc prof to prof oral biol, Sch Dent, Univ Wash, 57-75, chmn dept, 57-75, prof path, Sch Med, 65-75; prof path, 79, PROF ORAL BIOL, SCH DENT MED, STATE UNIV NY STONY BROOK, 75-, DEAN SCH DENT MED, 75- *Concurrent Pos:* Consult, Vet Admin Hosps, American Lake & Seattle, Wash; Fulbright lectr & advan res award, Hebrew Univ Jerusalem, 63-64; dir, Ctr Res Oral Biol, Sch Med, Univ Wash, 68-75; mem bd dirs, Am Asn Dent Res, 81. *Mem:* AAAS; Int Asn Dent Res; Am Dent Asn; Int Dent Fedn. *Res:* Secretory mechanism of salivary secretions; pathophysiology of diseases of the oral cavity; nutrition and oral diseases. *Mailing Add:* Sch of Dent Med State Univ of NY Stony Brook NY 11790

SREE HARSHA, KARNAMADAKALA S, b India, May 25, 36; m 67; c 2. MATERIALS SCIENCE. *Educ:* Univ Mysore, BSc, 55; Indian Inst Sci, Bangalore, dipl metall, 57; Univ Notre Dame, MS, 60; Pa State Univ, PhD(metall), 64. *Prof Exp:* Res fel, Iowa State Univ, 65-67; asst prof mat sci, 67-77, PROF MAT SCI, SAN JOSE STATE UNIV, 77-, CHMN, DEPT MAT ENG, 78- *Mem:* Am Soc Metals; Am Inst Mining, Metall & Petrol Engrs. *Res:* Structure and transformations of solids; theory of dislocation; surfaces; thermodynamics; semiconductors. *Mailing Add:* Dept Mat Sci 125 S 7th St San Jose CA 95192

SREENIVASAN, SREENIVASA RANGA, b Mysore, India, Oct 20, 33; m 63; c 5. PHYSICS, ASTROPHYSICS. *Educ:* Univ Mysore, BS, 50, BS, 52; Gujarat Univ, India, PhD(physics), 58. *Prof Exp:* Res fel, Harvard Univ, 59-61; Nat Acad Sci res assoc, Goddard Inst Space Studies, New York, 61-64; vis scientist, Max Planck Inst Physics & Astrophys, 64-66; from asst prof to assoc prof physics, 67-75, PROF PHYSICS, UNIV CALGARY, 75- *Concurrent Pos:* Vis prof, Royal Inst Technol, Univ Stockholm & vis scientist, Swed Natural Sci Res Coun, 74-75. *Mem:* Am Astron Soc; Am Geophys Union; Am Phys Soc; fel Royal Astron Soc; Int Astron Union. *Res:* Theoretical astrophysics; theoretical plasma physics; general relativity. *Mailing Add:* Dept Physics Univ Calgary Calgary AB T2N 1N4 Can

SREEVALSAN, THAZEPADATH, b Kanjiramattom, India, Jan 25, 35. MICROBIOLOGY, VIROLOGY. *Educ:* Univ Kerala, BSc, 53, MSc, 56; Univ Tex, PhD(microbiol), 64. *Prof Exp:* Teacher, St Ignatius High Sch, India, 53-54; res asst virol, Pasteur Inst, Coonoor, 56-61 & Univ Tex, 61-63, assoc res scientist, 64-66; res scientist virol, Cent Res Sta, E I du Pont de Nemours & Co, Inc, 66-69; asst prof, 69-73, assoc prof, 73-80, PROF MICROBIOL, MED & DENT SCH, GEORGETOWN UNIV, 80- *Mem:* AAAS; Am Soc Microbiol. *Res:* Viruses, replication of animal viruses; molecular biology of animal virus development; mode of RNA replication; interfrons their biological activity and mode of action in inhibiting cell growth and viral multiplication; control of proliferation in animal cells. *Mailing Add:* 10710 Muirfield Dr Potomac MD 20854

SÖRENSEN, PAUL DAVIDSEN, b Seattle, Wash, Dec 4, 34; m 59; c 3. BOTANY, TAXONOMY. *Educ:* Univ Iowa, BA, 62, MS, 66, PhD(bot, plant taxon), 67. *Prof Exp:* Asst hort taxonomist, Arnold Arboretum, Harvard Univ, 67-68, asst cur, 68-70; asst prof, 70-75, ASSOC PROF PLANT TAXON, NORTHERN ILL UNIV, 76-; VPRES, ENCAP INC, CONSULTS & ENVIRON PLANNERS, 75- *Concurrent Pos:* Assoc prof bot, Univ Iowa, 78. *Mem:* Int Asn Plant Taxon; Am Soc Plant Taxon; Bot Soc Am. *Res:* Taxonomy of vascular plants; systematics and ecology of flowering plants; distributional relationships of plants and habitats of the Upper Midwest; taxonomic studies of Mexican and Central American floras. *Mailing Add:* Encap Inc 303 E Hillcrest De Kalb IL 60115

SRERE, PAUL ARNOLD, b Davenport, Iowa, Sept 1, 25; m 53; c 4. BIOCHEMISTRY. *Educ:* Univ Calif, Los Angeles, BS, 47; Univ Calif, PhD(comp biochem), 51. *Prof Exp:* Asst physiol, Univ Calif, 47-51; asst biochemist, Mass Gen Hosp, 51-53; from asst prof to assoc prof biochem, Univ Mich, 56-63; biochemist, Biomed Div, Lawrence Radiation Lab, Univ Calif, 63-66; clin prof biochem, 66-72, PROF BIOCHEM, SOUTHWESTERN MED SCH, UNIV TEX HEALTH SCI CTR DALLAS, 72- *Concurrent Pos:* Childs Found Med Res fel, Yale Univ, 53-54; USPHS fels, Pub Health Res Inst, New York, 54-55 & Max Planck Inst Cell Biol, Ger, 55-56; chief basic biochem unit, Gen Med Res, Vet Admin Hosp, 69-72. *Mem:* Am Chem Soc. *Res:* Intermediary metabolism; enzymology; metabolic regulation; cell adhesion. *Mailing Add:* Vet Admin Hosp 4500 S Lancaster Rd Dallas TX 75216

SRETER, FRANK A, b Szanda, Hungary, Oct 2, 21; US citizen; m 44; c 2. BIOCHEMISTRY. *Educ:* Budapest Tech Univ, MS, 43, PhD(animal nutrit), 44; Vet Sch Budapest, DVM, 49; Med Univ Budapest, MD, 50. *Prof Exp:* From instr to assoc prof, Budapest Tech Univ, 44-51; assoc prof, Eötvös Lorand Univ, Budapest, 51-56; from instr to asst prof, Univ BC, 57-63; res assoc, Dept Muscle Res, Retina Found, 63-72; SR RES SCIENTIST, DEPT MUSCLE RES, BOSTON BIOMED RES INST, 72-; ASSOC, DEPT NEUROPATH, HARVARD MED SCH, 72- *Concurrent Pos:* Can Muscular Dystrophy, Inc fel, 63-66; Am Heart Asn estab investr, 66-71; assoc biochemist, Mass Gen Hosp. *Mem:* Am Physiol Soc; Biophys Soc. *Res:* Muscle physiology and biochemistry. *Mailing Add:* 20 Staniford St Boston MA 02114

SRIBNEY, MICHAEL, b Alta, Can, Feb 5, 27; m 54; c 2. BIOCHEMISTRY. *Educ:* Univ Alta, BSc, 52; McMaster Univ, MSc, 53; Univ Chicago, PhD, 57. *Prof Exp:* Fel, Enzyme Inst, Univ Wis, 58-60; asst prof biochem & psychiat, Yale Univ, 60-69; ASSOC PROF BIOCHEM, QUEEN'S UNIV, ONT, 69- *Mem:* AAAS; Am Chem Soc. *Res:* Lipids. *Mailing Add:* Dept of Biochem Queen's Univ Kingston ON K7L 3N6 Can

SRIDARAN, RAJAGOPALA, b Papireddipatti, India, Feb 22, 50; m 78. REPRODUCTIVE ENDOCRINOLOGY, CIRCADIAN RHYTHMS. *Educ:* Univ Madras, India, BS, 70, MS, 72; Univ Health Sci, Chicago Med Sch, PhD(physiol), 77. *Prof Exp:* Instr zool, Madras Christian Col, 72-73; res assoc endocrinol, Univ Nebr Med Ctr, Omaha, 77-78, Univ Ill Med Ctr, 78-81; ASST PROF PHYSIOL, MOREHOUSE SCH MED, ATLANTA, 81- *Mem:* Am Physiolol Soc; Endocrin Soc; Soc Neurosci; Soc Study Reproduct; AAAS. *Res:* Corpus lureum function and maintenance of pregnancy; environmental influences on the hypothalamo-pituitary-gonedal avis in the feedback control of gonadotropin secretion and ovulation in the rat; circadian rhythms in reproductive endocrinology. *Mailing Add:* Dept Physiol Morehouse Sch Med 830 Westview Dr SW Atlanta GA 30314

SRIDHAR, CHAMPA GUHA, Indian citizen. SOLID STATE PHYSICS. *Educ:* Calcutta Univ, BSc, 63; Jadavpur Univ, Calcutta, MSc, 65; Northeastern Univ, MS, 68; Univ Conn, PhD(solid state physics), 73. *Prof Exp:* Teaching asst physics, Northeastern Univ, 66-68; asst, Univ Conn, 68-73, fel liquid crystal, 73; fel solid state physics, Stanford Univ, 74; Nat Res Coun fel theoret solid state physics, Ames Res Ctr, NASA, Moffett Field, 74-77; sr process engr, SX-70 film, Polaroid Corp, 77; DEVELOP ENGR PRECISION FREQUENCY STANDARD, HEWLETT PACKARD CO, 78- *Mem:* Am Phys Soc; Sigma Xi. *Res:* Ban structure and optical properties calculation of solids; optical and electron spin resonance studies of radiation induced colour centers in solids; magnetic properties of liquid crystals. *Mailing Add:* Bldg 51U Santa Clara Div Hewlett Packard Co Stevens Creek Blvd Santa Clara CA 95050

SRIDHAR, RAJAGOPALAN, b Trichinopoly, Madras, India, July 29, 41; Can citizen. BIOCHEMISTRY, CHEMISTRY. *Educ:* Univ Delhi, BSc, 61; Kurukshetra Univ, India, MSc, 63; Univ London, PhD(org chem), & DIC, 68. *Prof Exp:* Fel org chem, Res Inst for Med & Chem, Cambridge, 68-71; res assoc, Johns Hopkins Univ, 71-72; assoc biochem, Univ Western Ont, 73-75; res fel radiobiol, Ont Cancer Treatment & Res Found, 75-78; ASST MEM BIOMEMBRANE RES, OKLA MED RES FOUND, 78- *Concurrent Pos:* Consult biochem, Ont Cancer Treatment & Res Found, London Clin, Victoria Hosp, 78-; adj asst prof, Dept Radiol Sci, Okla Univ Health Sci Ctr, 81- *Mem:* Assoc mem Radiation Res Soc; Am Soc Photobiol; Biophys Soc; Am Asn Cancer Res; Sigma Xi. *Res:* Electron spin resonance studies in biological systems; DNA and membrane damage due to carcinogens and pharmaceuticals; radiosensitizers and other cytotoxic agents specific for hypoxic cells; multicell spheroids as a solid tumor model; nuclear magnetic resonance studies in biological systems. *Mailing Add:* Biomembrane Res Lab 825 NE 13th St Oklahoma City OK 73104

SRIDHARAN, NATESA S, b Madras, India, Oct 2, 46; US citizen; c 1. COGNITIVE MODEL BUILDING, LARGE-SCALE SOFTWARE DESIGN. *Educ:* Indian Inst Technol, BTech, 67; State Univ NY, Stonybrook, MS, 69, PhD(comput sci), 71. *Prof Exp:* Res assoc, Stanford Univ, 71-74; vis scientist, Technische Univ, Munich, 74; asst prof, 74-79, ASSOC PROF COMPUT SCI, RUTGERS UNIV, 79- *Concurrent Pos:* Prin investr, NSF grants, 79-; sci adv, Centre Nationale D'etudes Des Telecommunications, France, 82- *Honors & Awards:* Siemen's Medal, Indian Inst Technol, 67. *Mem:* Am Asn Artificial Intelligence; Soc Study Articicial Intelligence & Simulation of Behav. *Res:* Building logical, computer-based models of human reasoning, including those of scientist, lay people and lawyers; development of tools to assist in such modelling. *Mailing Add:* Dept Comput Sci Rutgers Univ New Brunswick NJ 08903

SRIHARI, SARGUR N, b Bangalore, India, May 7, 50; m 77. COMPUTER SCIENCE, PATTERN RECOGNITION. *Educ:* Bangalore Univ, BSc, 68; Indian Inst Sci, BE, 70; Ohio State Univ, PhD(comput & info sci), 76. *Prof Exp:* NSF res asst comput & info sci, Ohio State Univ, 70-73, res assoc pattern recognition, Electrosci Lab, 73-75; asst prof, Wayne State Univ, 76-78; ASST PROF COMPUT SCI, STATE UNIV NY, BUFFALO, 78- *Concurrent Pos:* Fac res award, Wayne State Univ, 77-78. *Mem:* Asn Comput Mach; Inst Elec & Electronics Engrs; Pattern Recognition Soc; Am Asn Artificial Intelligence. *Res:* Pattern recognition and artificial intelligence; image processing and computer graphics; digital systems design; computed tomography; text and speech processing. *Mailing Add:* Dept of Comput Sci State Univ NY at Buffalo Amherst NY 14226

SRINATH, MANDYAM DHATI, b Bangalore, India, Oct 12, 35; m 65; c 2. ELECTRICAL ENGINEERING. *Educ:* Univ Mysore, BSc, 54; Indian Inst Sci, DIISc, 57; Univ Ill, Urbana, MS, 59, PhD(elec eng), 62. *Prof Exp:* Asst prof elec eng, Univ Kans, 62-64; asst prof, Indian Inst Sci, 64-67; assoc prof info & control sci, 67-76, PROF ELEC ENG, SOUTHERN METHODIST UNIV, 76- *Mem:* Inst Elec & Electronics Engrs; Soc Indust & Appl Math. *Res:* Control and estimation theory; digital signal processing; identification. *Mailing Add:* Dept of Elec Eng Southern Methodist Univ Dallas TX 75275

SRINIVASAN, ASOKA, b Bangalore, India, May 13, 39, US citizen; m 67; c 2. PHERMONES. *Educ:* Univ Mysore, India, BSc, 63; Univ Calif, Berkeley, PhD(entom), 70. *Prof Exp:* Asst prof biol, 69-74, assoc prof, 74-80, chmn, Biol Dept, 71-81, DIR BIOMED RES, TOUGALOO COL, 73-, PROF BIOL, 80-, CHMN, NAT SCI DIV, 81- *Mem:* Tissue Cult Asn; Entom Soc Am; Am Inst Biol Sci; AAAS; Sigma Xi. *Res:* Development and activity of the sex pheromone gland in Lepidoptera; tissue culture of sex pheromone gland of insects. *Mailing Add:* Biol Dept Tougaloo Col Tougaloo MS 39174

SRINIVASAN, B, b Coimbatore, Madras, India, June 2, 41. COSMOCHEMISTRY. *Educ:* Univ Madras, BSc, 60; Univ Bombay, MSc, 66; Univ Mo, PhD(chem), 71. *Prof Exp:* Sci officer radiochem, Bhabha Atomic Res Ctr, India, 61-68; res asst chem, Univ Mo, Rolla, 68-71; asst res chemist physics, Univ Calif, Berkeley, 72-74; res assoc chem, Univ Chicago, 74-77; res asst prof, Univ Mo-Rolla, 77-78; ASST PROF CHEM, WASH STATE UNIV, PULLMAN, 78- *Mem:* Am Geophys Union; Meteroitical Soc; AAAS. *Res:* Studying lunar, meteoritic and terrestrial samples towards obtaining a better understanding of the origin of the solar system. *Mailing Add:* Dept of Chem Wash State Univ Pullman WA 99163

SRINIVASAN, BHAMA, b Madras, India, Apr 22, 35; nat US. MATHEMATICS. *Educ:* Univ Madras, BA, 54, MSc, 55; Univ Manchester, PhD(math), 59. *Prof Exp:* Lectr math, Univ Keele, 60-64; Nat Res Coun Can fel, Univ BC, 65-66; reader math, Univ Madras, 67-70; assoc prof math, Clark Univ, 70-80; PROF MATH, UNIV ILL CHICAGO CIRCLE, 80- *Mem:* Am Math Soc; London Math Soc; Indian Math Soc; Asn Women Math (pres, 81-83). *Res:* Representations of finite Chevalley groups. *Mailing Add:* Dept Math Univ Ill Chicago Circle Chicago IL 60680

SRINIVASAN, G(URUMAKONDA) R, b Mysore, India; m 68; c 4. MATERIALS SCIENCE, PHYSICS. *Educ:* Univ Mysore, BS, 54, Hons, 56; Indian Inst Sci, dipl metall, 58; Colo Sch Mines, MS, 61; Univ Ill, Urbana, PhD(metall), 66. *Prof Exp:* Res scholar metall, Indian Inst Sci, 58-59; res asst, Colo Sch Mines, 59-61; res asst, Univ Ill, Urbana, 61-66; res assoc mat sci, Cornell Univ, 66-68; asst prof, 68-71, assoc prof mat sci, Cath Univ Am, 71-74; ADV ENGR, GEN TECHNOL DIV, IBM CORP, 74- *Mem:* Metall Soc; Electrochem Soc. *Res:* Chemical vapor deposition; epitaxy; semiconductor devices; phase transformations; electron microscopy; x-ray diffraction and scattering. *Mailing Add:* IBM Corp Gen Technol Div Zip 49X E Fishill Facil Hopewell Junction NY 12533

SRINIVASAN, MAKUTESWARAN, b Tiruchirapalli, India, Jan 26, 45; m 71; c 2. MATERIALS SCIENCE, PHYSICAL METALLURGY. *Educ:* Univ Madras, India, BSc, 64; Indian Inst Sci, BE, 67; Univ Wash, MSinMetD, 69, PhD(metall), 72. *Prof Exp:* Res assoc mat sci, Univ Wash, 72-74; staff scientist graphite, Union Carbide Corp, 74-78; develop assoc silicon carbide, 78-79, SR RES ASSOC STRUCT CERAMIC, CARBORUNDUM CO, 79- *Mem:* Am Soc Metals; Am Ceramic Soc; Am Soc Nondestructive Testing. *Res:* Mechanical properties of ceramics, mainly high temperature, high performance ceramics such as silicon carbide; tribology; corrosion; advanced nondestructive evaluation; reliability and ceramic design. *Mailing Add:* High Performance SIC Carborundum Co Bldg 100 Niagara Falls NY 14302

SRINIVASAN, MANDYAM VEERAMBUDI, b Poona, India. VISION. *Educ:* Bangalore Univ, BE, 68; Indian Inst Sci, ME, 70; Yale Univ, PhD(eng & appl sci), 76. *Prof Exp:* RES ASST, DEPT ENG & APPL SCI, YALE UNIV, 73- *Mem:* Sigma Xi; Asn Res Vision & Ophthal. *Res:* Communication and control in biological systems, particularly information processing in visual systems, optical and neural aspects; control of eye movements; theoretical and experimental studies. *Mailing Add:* Dept of Ophthal & Visual Sci Yale Univ Sch of Med New Haven CT 06510

SRINIVASAN, PARITHYCHERY, b Villupuram, India, Nov 24, 27. BIOCHEMISTRY. *Educ:* Univ Madras, BSc, 46, PhD(biochem), 53; Banaras Hindu Univ, MSc, 48. *Prof Exp:* Asst res officer biochem, Indian Coun Med Res, 52-53; res assoc, 57-58, from instr to assoc prof, 58-70, PROF BIOCHEM, COL PHYSICIANS & SURGEONS, COLUMBIA UNIV, 70- *Concurrent Pos:* Res fel, Col Physicians & Surgeons, Columbia Univ, 53-57, Fulbright-Smith Mundt fel, 53-54. *Mem:* Am Chem Soc; Harvey Soc; Am Soc Microbiol; NY Acad Sci; Am Soc Biol Chemists. *Res:* Biological function of methylated bases in nucleic acids; regulatory mechanisms and transformation of normal cells by animal viruses. *Mailing Add:* Dept of Biochem Columbia Univ Col of Phys & Surg New York NY 10032

SRINIVASAN, SATHANUR RAMACHANDRAN, b Madras, India, July 16, 38; m 67; c 1. CHEMISTRY, BIOCHEMISTRY. *Educ:* Univ Madras, BSc, 58, BSc(tech), 60, MSc, 62, PhD(leather technol), 65. *Prof Exp:* Res assoc, 67-72, from asst prof to assoc prof, 72-81, PROF DEPT MED, SCH MED, LA STATE UNIV MED CTR, NEW ORLEANS, 81- *Concurrent Pos:* Fed Repub Ger acad exchange fel, Darmstadt Tech Univ, 66; fel coun arteriosclerosis, Am Heart Asn, 71- *Mem:* AAAS; Soc Complex Carbohydrates; Biochem Soc; Am Soc Exp Biol & Med. *Res:* Cardiovascular connective tissue and its relation to the pathogenesis of atherosclerosis; role of lipoproteins and lipoprotein-glycosaminoglycans. complexes in atherosclerosis; lipoprotein metabolism. *Mailing Add:* Dept of Med La State Univ Med Ctr New Orleans LA 70112

SRINIVASAN, VADAKE RAM, b Ponnani, India, Nov 18, 25; US citizen; m 57; c 2. BIOCHEMISTRY, MICROBIOLOGY. *Educ:* Univ Madras, MA, 48, PhD(biol chem), 51; Univ Mainz, Dr rer Nat(org chem), 55. *Prof Exp:* Res assoc microbiol, Univ Ill, Urbana, 56-59; asst res prof biochem, Univ Pittsburgh, 59-60; res asst prof microbiol, Univ Ill, Urbana, 60-65; assoc prof, 65-70, PROF MICROBIOL, LA STATE UNIV, BATON ROUGE, 70- *Concurrent Pos:* Res grants, NIH, 66-, Am Cancer Soc, 66- & Am Sugarcane League, 68; partic, NSF Int Prog, 72; guest prof, Max Planck Inst Biochem, 72-73. *Mem:* Am Soc Microbiol; Am Chem Soc; Brit Biochem Soc; fel Am Inst Chem; NY Acad Sci. *Res:* Microbial biochemistry and molecular biology; intracellular differentiation in bacteria, control of macromolecular synthesis; single cell protein from cellulose wastes. *Mailing Add:* Dept of Biol La State Univ Baton Rouge LA 70803

SRINIVASAN, VAKULA S, b Madras, India, Mar 25, 36; nat US; m 67. ELECTROCHEMISTRY, ANALYTICAL CHEMISTRY. *Educ:* Univ Madras, BSc, 56, MA, 58; La State Univ, Baton Rouge, PhD(chem), 65. *Prof Exp:* Archaeol chemist, Govt India, 57; scientist, Indian Atomic Energy Estab, 58-61; vis asst prof chem, La State Univ, Baton Rouge, 65; res fel, Case Inst Technol, 65-67; mem sci staff, TRW Systs, Calif, 67-71; res fel, Calif Inst Technol, 71; assoc prof, 77-78, PROF CHEM, BOWLING GREEN STATE UNIV, 78- *Concurrent Pos:* Res fel, Purdue Univ, 73; consult, Gen Atomics Corp, 74, Energy Conversion Devices, Mich & Vulcan Mat, Ohio; vis prof, Tohoku Univ, Japan, 81. *Mem:* Sigma Xi; Am Chem Soc; Royal Soc Chem. *Res:* Energy conversion; optical photo electrochemistry; space power systems; mixed valence complexes; enzyme electrodes. *Mailing Add:* Dept of Chem Bowling Green State Univ Bowling Green OH 43403

SRINIVASARAGHAVAN, RENGACHARI, b Madras, India, Aug 25, 48; m 81. ENVIRONMENTAL ENGINEERING, SANITARY ENGINEERING. *Educ:* Univ Madras, India, BTech, 70; Rose-Hulman Inst Technol, MS, 72; Okla State Univ, PhD(environ eng), 74. *Prof Exp:* process engr, 75-80, ASSOC, GREELEY & HANSEN, ENGRS, 80- *Mem:* Water Pollution Control Fedn; Am Soc Civil Engrs; Tech Asn Paper & Pulp Indust. *Res:* Industrial and municipal wastewater pollution control; resource recovery; conservation and production of energy from waste material. *Mailing Add:* Greeley & Hansen Engrs 222 S Riverside Plaza Chicago IL 60626

SRIVASTAV, RAM PRASAD, b Khairabad, India, Oct 13, 34; m 59; c 3. APPLIED MATHEMATICS. *Educ:* Univ Lucknow, BSc, 53, MSc, 55, PhD(math), 58; Univ Glasgow, PhD(appl math), 63, DSc, 72. *Prof Exp:* Lectr math, Indian Inst Technol, Kanpur, 60-64, asst prof, 64-66; asst prof, Duke Univ, 66-67; assoc prof math, 67-73, actg chmn, 76-77, PROF MATH, STATE UNIV NY STONY BROOK, 73- *Concurrent Pos:* Assoc ed, J Appl Math, Soc Indust & Appl Math, 70-76; NSF grants, State Univ NY Stony Brook, 72 & 74; vis mem math res ctr, Univ Wis-Madison, 73-74; US Army Res Off grant, 76- *Mem:* Am Math Soc; Soc Indust & Appl Math; fel Indian Nat Acad Sci; Math Asn Am. *Res:* Integral equations; mixed boundary value problems in elasticity; complex analysis; transform calculus; generalized functions; fracture mechanics. *Mailing Add:* Dept of Appl Math & Statist State Univ NY Stony Brook NY 11794

SRIVASTAVA, ASHOK KUMAR, b Basti, India, July 5, 51; m 78; c 1. GLYCOGEN METABOLISM, PROTEIN KINASES. *Educ:* Lucknow Univ, India, BSc, 68, MSc, 70; Kanpur Univ, India, PhD(biochem), 74. *Prof Exp:* Fel, Univ Southern Calif, Los Angeles, 74-77; res assoc, Vanderbilt Univ, 77-80; ASST PROF, UNIV MONTREAL, 81-; SR INVESTR, CLIN RES INST, MONTREAL, 81- *Mem:* NY Acad Sci; Can Biochem Soc; AAAS. *Res:* Hormonal control of glycogen metabolism involving reversible protein phosphorylation dephosphorylation reactions. *Mailing Add:* 110 Pine Ave West Montreal PQ H2W 1R7 Can

SRIVASTAVA, BEJAI INDER SAHAI, b Shahjahanpur, India, June 1, 32; m 62; c 3. BIOCHEMISTRY, MOLECULAR BIOLOGY. *Educ:* Agra Univ, BSc, 52; Univ Lucknow, MSc, 54; Univ Sask, PhD(plant physiol), 60. *Prof Exp:* Res asst plant physiol, Main Sugar Cane Res Sta, India, 54-55; lectr bot, Ramjas Col, Delhi, 55-57; res biochemist, Grain Res Lab, Winnepeg, Can, 61-63; assoc prof plant physiol, Carver Res Found, Tuskegee Inst, 63-65; sr cancer res scientist, Roswell Park Mem Inst, 65-68, assoc cancer res scientist, 68-77; asst res prof biol, 66-74, ASSOC RES PROF BIOCHEM, STATE UNIV NY BUFFALO, 75-; CANCER RES SCIENTIST V, ROSWELL PARK MEM INST, 77- *Concurrent Pos:* Res fel, Univ Sask, 60-61; NSF grants, 63-69 & 69-72; AEC grant, 66-69; NIH grant, 73-81. *Mem:* Am Soc Plant Physiol; Can Soc Plant Physiol; Am Soc Biol Chemists; Am Asn Cancer Res; NY Acad Sci. *Res:* DNA polymerases and chromatin studies in normal and malignant human and plant cells; biochemical markers for the differential diagnosis of leukemias. *Mailing Add:* Dept of Exp Therapeut Roswell Park Mem Inst Buffalo NY 14263

SRIVASTAVA, HARI MOHAN, b Ballia, India, July 5, 40; m 78. MATHEMATICS, MATHEMATICAL PHYSICS. *Educ:* Univ Allahabad, BSc, 57, MSc, 59; Univ Jodhpur, PhD(math), 65. *Prof Exp:* Lectr math, D M Col, Gauhati Univ, India, 59-60 & Univ Roorkee, 60-63; lectr math, Univ Jodhpur, 63-68, reader, 68-69; asst prof, WVa Univ, 67-69; assoc prof, 69-74, PROF MATH, UNIV VICTORIA, BC, 74- *Concurrent Pos:* Ed, Jnanabha, 72-; regional ed, Pure & Appl Math Sci, 76- *Mem:* Am Math Soc; fel Inst Math & Its Appl, UK; fel Royal Astron Soc London; fel Indian Nat Acad Sci. *Res:* Special functions; operational calculus and related areas of differential and integral equations; Fourier analysis; combinatorial analysis; applied methematics; queuing theory. *Mailing Add:* Dept of Math Univ of Victoria Victoria BC V8W 2Y2 Can

SRIVASTAVA, JAYA NIDHI, b Lucknow, India, June 20, 33; m 51; c 3. STATISTICS, MATHEMATICS. *Educ:* Univ Lucknow, BS, 51, MS, 54; Indian Statist Inst, Calcutta, dipl, 58; Univ NC, PhD(math statist), 61. *Prof Exp:* Statistician, Indian Inst Sugarcane Res, Lucknow, 55-57 & Indian Coun Agr Res, New Delhi, 58-59; res assoc, Univ NC, 61-63; assoc prof math, Univ Nebr, 63-66; PROF STATIST & MATH, COLO STATE UNIV, 66- *Concurrent Pos:* Consult, Lincoln State Hosp, Nebr, 63-64; res grants, Aerospace Res Labs, Air Force Base, Dayton, Ohio, 65-71, 74-, Nat Bur Standards, 69-72, 74-, Air Force Off Sci Res, 71-78 & NSF, 71-; dir, Vis Lectr Prog Statist, US & Can, 73-75; chief ed, J Statist Planning & Inference, 76- *Honors & Awards:* Award, J Indian Soc Agr Statist, 61. *Mem:* Fel Am Statist Asn; fel Inst Math Statist; Int Statist Inst; Indian Statist Inst; Forum Interdisciplinary Math (vpres, 75-). *Res:* Design of experiments; multivariate analysis; combinatorial mathematics; weather modification statistics; foundations of statistics; general philosophy. *Mailing Add:* Dept of Statist Colo State Univ Ft Collins CO 80523

SRIVASTAVA, KUNWAR KRISHNA, b Pratapgarh, India, Aug 27, 40; m 64; c 2. MICROBIOLOGY. *Educ:* Univ Allahabad, India, BS, 60; Agra Univ, India, DVM, 64; Univ Ga, MS, 69, PhD(med microbiol), 71. *Prof Exp:* Res asst, State Animal Husb Dept, Lucknow, 64, Indian Vet Res Inst, 64-66 & Col Vet Med, Univ Ga, 67-70; res assoc microbiol, Sch Vet Med, Tuskegee Inst, 71-72; res assoc, Lobund Lab, Univ Notre Dame, 72-73, asst fac fel, 73-75; asst fac fel vet microbiol, Univ NC, Chapel Hill, 75-77; head animal maintenance dept, Lederle Labs, 77-81, MGR, LAB VET SERVS, MED RES DIV, AM CYANAMD CO, PEARL RIVER, NY, 81- *Mem:* Asn Gnotobiotics; Am Asn Microbiol; Am Vet Med Asn. *Res:* Antineoplastic chemotherapy in antibiotic decontaminated animals; gnotobiology; laboratory animal diseases; diagnostic microbiology; poliomyelitis vaccine production; veterinarian; regulatory veterinary medicine. *Mailing Add:* Lederle Labs Div Am Cyanamid Co Pearl River NY 10965

SRIVASTAVA, LALIT MOHAN, b Gonda, India, Sept 7, 32; m 64. BIOLOGY. *Educ:* Univ Allahabad, BSc, 50, MSc, 52; Univ Calif, Davis, PhD(bot), 62. *Prof Exp:* Mercer res fel, Harvard Univ, 61-64, Maria Moors Cabot res fel, 64-65; from asst prof to assoc prof, 65-71, acad vpres, 69-70, PROF BIOL SCI, SIMON FRASER UNIV, 71- *Concurrent Pos:* Mem, Mgt Adv Coun, Ministry Educ, BC, 78-; pres, Enmar Res Corp, 81- *Mem:* Bot Soc Am; Can Soc Plant Physiol; Can Soc Cell Biol; Can Fedn Biol Socs; Electron Micros Soc Am. *Res:* cambium, xylem and phloem; cell growth; gibberellins, receptors, mode of action; physiology of growth, nutritional requirements and chemical constituents of kelps. *Mailing Add:* Dept of Biol Sci Simon Fraser Univ Burnaby BC V5A 1S6 Can

SRIVASTAVA, LAXMI SHANKER, b Deoria, Uttar Pradesh, India, Mar 2, 38; m 60; c 2. ENDOCRINOLOGY. *Educ:* Bihar Univ, BVSc & AH, 59; Univ Mo-Columbia, MS, 61, PhD(animal breeding), 64. *Prof Exp:* Vet surgeon, Bihar Govt, India, 59-60; instr endocrinol, Univ Mo-Columbia, 64-65, res assoc, Space Res Ctr, 67-68; from asst prof to assoc prof, 69-78, PROF EXP MED, DEPT INTERNAL MED, MED CTR, UNIV CINCINNATI, 78-, DIR RADIOIMMUNOASSAY & ENDOCRINE LABS, 69- *Concurrent Pos:* Univ Res Fund grant, St Louis Univ, 65-66; NIH grant, Wash Univ, 66-67. *Mem:* Endocrine Soc; Am Fedn Clin Res; Am Asn Clin Chemists. *Res:* Mammary cancer; neuroendocrine control of pituitary function; mammalian reproductive physiology. *Mailing Add:* Metab Div Univ of Cincinnati Med Ctr Cincinnati OH 45267

SRIVASTAVA, MADHU BALA, HORMONE RECEPTORS, ADENYLATE CYCLASE. *Educ:* Delhi Univ, India, MSc, 72; Univ Manitoba, Can, PhD(physiol), 78. *Prof Exp:* Res assoc, Vanderbilt Univ, 78-80; ASST PROF, UNIV MONTREAL, 81- *Concurrent Pos:* Sr investr, Clin Res Inst, Montreal, 81- *Mem:* Int Soc Heart Res; Can Biochem Soc. *Res:* Adenosine regulation of adenylate cyclase and its involvement in the development of experimental hypertension. *Mailing Add:* Clin Res Inst Montreal 110 Pine Ave West Montreal PQ H2W 1R7 Can

SRIVASTAVA, MUNI SHANKER, b Gonda, India, Jan 20, 36; m 64; c 4. MATHEMATICAL STATISTICS. *Educ:* Univ Lucknow, BSc, 56, MSc, 58; Stanford Univ, PhD(statist), 64. *Prof Exp:* From asst prof to assoc prof math, 63-72, PROF MATH, UNIV TORONTO, 72- *Concurrent Pos:* Vis res staff, Princeton Univ, 65-66; assoc prof, Univ Conn, 70-71; vis prof, Univ Wis & Indian Statist Inst, 77-78. *Mem:* Inst Math Statist; Am Statist Asn; Royal Statist Soc. *Res:* Multivariate, sequential and nonparametric statistics. *Mailing Add:* Dept of Math Univ of Toronto Toronto ON M5S 2RB Can

SRIVASTAVA, PRAKASH NARAIN, b Allahabad, India, Dec 7, 29; m 49; c 8. REPRODUCTIVE BIOLOGY. *Educ:* Lucknow Univ, India, BSc, 49, MSc, 51; Cambridge Univ, PhD(biochem), 65. *Prof Exp:* Asst res officer hormones, Indian Vet Res Inst, 58-68; asst prof, 69-75, ASSOC PROF BIOCHEM, UNIV GA, 75- *Mem:* Am Soc Biol Chemists; Am Physiol Soc; Soc Study Reproduction. *Res:* Sperm enzymes and their inhibitors in fertilization. *Mailing Add:* Dept of Biochem Boyd Grad Studies Bldg Univ Ga Athens GA 30602

SRIVASTAVA, PROBODH K, cytogenetics, see previous edition

SRIVASTAVA, RAJEEV, aerospace propulsion, see previous edition

SRIVASTAVA, RAMESH C, statistics, see previous edition

SRIVASTAVA, REKHA, b Chikati, Orissa, India, Feb 15, 45; m, 78. MATHEMATICS. *Educ:* Utkal Univ, India, BSc, 62; Banaras Hindu Univ, MSc, 65, PhD(math), 67. *Prof Exp:* Lectr math, Khallikote Col, Berhampur Univ, 68-69, Rourkela Sci Col, 69-70, Women's Col, Berhampur Univ, 70-71 & Ravenshaw Col, Utkal Univ, India, 71-72; res fel, 72-73, res assoc & vis scientist math, 73-77, SESSIONAL LECTR MATH, UNIV VICTORIA, 78- *Concurrent Pos:* Reviewer, Mathematical Reviews; Zentralblatt für Mathematik. *Mem:* Am Math Soc; Vijnana Parishad India; Asn Women Math; Indian Math Soc; Indian Sci Cong Asn. *Res:* Special functions; operational calculus including integral transforms and related areas of integral equations; Fourier analysis; G, H and the generalized Lauricella functions of several variables. *Mailing Add:* Dept of Math Univ Victoria Victoria BC V8N 2Y2 Can

SRIVASTAVA, SATISH KUMAR, b Rae Bareli, India, July 21, 37; m 62; c 3. BIOCHEMISTRY, GENETICS. *Educ:* Univ Lucknow, India, BS, 56, MS, 58, PhD(biochem), 62. *Prof Exp:* Tutor biochem, Postgrad Med Sch, Chandigarh, India, 64-66; res scientist, City of Hope Nat Med Ctr, 66-74; asst prof pharmacol, Med Sch, Univ Southern Calif, 70-74; PROF HUMAN BIOL CHEM & GENETICS, UNIV TEX MED BR GALVESTON, 74- *Concurrent Pos:* Coun Sci & Indust Res India fel, Univ Lucknow, 62-64; NIH res grant, 71. *Mem:* Am Soc Hemat; Asn Res Vision & Ophthal. *Res:* Genetics of glycolipid storage diseases; glutathione metabolism in red cells and lens; enzyme kinetics and red cell metabolism; biochemical alterations in senile cataract formation. *Mailing Add:* Dept Human Genetics Child Health Ctr Univ of Tex Med Br at Galveston Galveston TX 77550

SRIVASTAVA, SURAT PRASAD, b Allahabad, India, July 1, 37; m . GEOPHYSICS. *Educ:* Indian Inst Technol, Kharagpur, BSc, 58, MTech, 60; Univ BC, PhD(physics), 63. *Prof Exp:* Nat Res Coun Can res fel, Dom Observ, Can, 63-64; asst prof geophys, Univ Alta, 64-65; RES SCIENTIST, ATLANTIC GEOSCI CENTRE, BEDFORD INST OCEANOG, 65- *Concurrent Pos:* Mem, Can Subcomt Geomagnetism, Assoc Comt Geod & Geophys, 66. *Mem:* Am Geophys Union. *Res:* Tectonic implications of the subsurface structures across the continental slope and margin obtained using gravity, magnetic and seismic measurements; application of magnetotelluric method on land and sea. *Mailing Add:* Marine Geophys Div Atlantic Geosci Centre Bedford Inst Dartmouth NS B2Y 4A2 Can

SRIVASTAVA, SURESH CHANDRA, b Aligarh, India, Jan 1, 39; US citizen; m 68; c 2. NUCLEAR MEDICINE, RADIOPHARMACEUTICAL SCIENCE. *Educ:* Agra Univ, BS, 55, MS, 57; Univ Allahabad, PhD(chem), 60. *Prof Exp:* Sr res fel, Univ Allahabad, 60-62; AEC fel, La State Univ, New Orleans, 62-65; res assoc, Brookhaven Nat Lab, 65-67; vis scientist, Sch Chem, Univ Paris, 67-69; res assoc, Ga Inst Technol, 69-71; chemist, Res Triangle Inst, NC, 71-74; clin asst prof radiol, Downstate Med Ctr, Brooklyn, NY, 74-75; assoc scientist, 75-78, SCIENTIST NUCLEAR MED, BROOKHAVEN NAT LAB, 78- *Concurrent Pos:* Pool officer, Univ Allahabad, 67; Consult, Northshore Univ Hosp, Manhassett, NY, 81- *Mem:* Am Chem Soc; Soc Nuclear Med; Radiopharmaceut Sci Coun. *Res:* Radiopharmaceuticals; novel diagnostic reagents and their application in in vitro and in vivo clinical studies; chemistry of short-lived gamma and positron-emitting radionuclides of interest in nuclear medicine; analytical and radiochemistry. *Mailing Add:* Dept of Med Brookhaven Nat Lab Upton NY 11973

SRIVASTAVA, TARIQ NASEER, b Lucknow, India, June 1, 36; Can citizen. PURE MATHEMATICS, STATISTICAL ANALYSIS. *Educ:* Lucknow Univ, BS, 57, MS, 59; Gorakhpur Univ, PhD(math), 69. *Prof Exp:* Sr lectr math, Loyola Col Montreal, 63-64, from asst prof to assoc prof, 64-71; vis prof, Univ Isfahahan, Iran, 71-72; ASSOC PROF MATH, CONCORDIA UNIV, 72- *Res:* Study of differential geometry of special Kawaguchi manifold, generalized statistical distributions and distributions of general functions of random variables. *Mailing Add:* Dept of Math Concordia Univ Montreal PQ H3G 1M8 Can

SRNKA, LEONARD JAMES, b Cleveland, Ohio, Nov 17, 46; m 76; c 1. INVERSE THEORY. *Educ:* Purdue Univ, BS, 68; Univ Newcastle, Eng, PhD(physics), 74. *Prof Exp:* Sci officer plasma physics, Culham Lab, UK Atomic Energy Authority, Eng, 70-73; fel, Lunar Sci Inst, Univ Space Res Asn, 74-75, staff scientist, Lunar & Planetary Inst, 75-79; MEM STAFF, LONG RANGE RES DIV, EXXON PROD RES CO, 79- *Concurrent Pos:* Vis scientist, Lunar & Planetary Inst, 79- *Mem:* Am Geophys Union; Am Phys Soc; Soc Explor Geophys. *Res:* Electromagnetic fields in planetary interiors; exploration geophysics. *Mailing Add:* Exxon Prod Res Co PO Box 2189 Houston TX 77001

SROOG, CYRUS EFREM, b New York, NY, Mar 25, 22; m 43; c 2. ORGANIC CHEMISTRY, POLYMER CHEMISTRY. *Educ:* Brooklyn Col, BA, 42; Univ Buffalo, PhD(chem), 50. *Prof Exp:* Instr chem, Univ Buffalo, 46-50; res chemist, 50-54, res supvr, 54-61, develop mgr, 62-64, RES MGR, E I DU PONT DE NEMOURS & CO, INC, 64- *Mem:* Am Chem Soc; NY Acad Sci; The Chem Soc. *Res:* High temperature polymers; thermally stable polymers; heterocyclic, organic nitrogen, organic sulfur and metalloorganic compounds; aromatic polyimides; heterocyclic polymers. *Mailing Add:* 3227 Coachman Rd Surrey Park Wilmington DE 19803

SROUR, JOSEPH RALPH, b Tampa, Fla, Jan 7, 41; m 69. SOLID STATE ELECTRONICS, RADIATION EFFECTS. *Educ:* Cath Univ Am, BEE, 63, MEE, 66, PhD(elec eng), 68. *Prof Exp:* Mem res tech staff radiation effects, 68-76, mgr, 76-78, MGR SOLID STATE ELECTRONICS, NORTHROP RES & TECHNOL CTR, 78- *Concurrent Pos:* Lectr elec eng, Loyola Univ Los Angeles, 70-72; vchmn publ radiation effects comt, Inst Elec & Electronic Engrs, 74-76, vchmn radiation effects comt, 79-82. *Honors & Awards:* Outstanding Paper Awards, Inst Elec & Electronic Engrs, 72 & 74. *Mem:* Inst Elec & Electronic Engrs; Am Phys Soc; Sigma Xi. *Res:* Radiation effects on electronic materials, devices and circuits; semiconductor device physics; integrated circuits; radiation hardening. *Mailing Add:* Northrop Res & Technol Ctr One Research Park Palos Verdes Peninsula CA 90274

SRYGLEY, FLETCHER DOUGLAS, b Nashville, Tenn, Mar 27, 38; m 68. SOLID STATE PHYSICS. *Educ:* David Lipscomb Col, BA, 60; Duke Univ, PhD(physics), 66. *Prof Exp:* Asst prof physics, Stetson Univ, 66-73; ASSOC PROF PHYSICS, DAVID LIPSCOMB COL, 73- *Res:* Electron spin resonance studies of radiation damage in single crystals; electron spin resonance and ultraviolet studies of color centers in magnesium oxide. *Mailing Add:* Dept of Physics David Lipscomb Col Nashville TN 37203

STAAL, GERARDUS BENARDUS, b Assen, Neth, Aug 8, 25; m 57; c 2. ENTOMOLOGY, BIOLOGY. *Educ:* State Agr Univ, Wageningen, Ing, 57, PhD(insect physiol), 61. *Prof Exp:* Sr res officer, Neth Orgn Appl Sci Res, 61-68; dir biol res, 68-80, DIR INSECT RES, ZOECON CORP, 80- *Concurrent Pos:* Neth Orgn Pure Res fel biol, Harvard Univ, 62-63. *Mem:* AAAS; Entom Soc Am; Am Chem Soc; Am Soc Zoologists; Acridological Asn. *Res:* Comparative insect endocrinology; insect bioassay of toxicants; juvenile hormone analogs; antagonists and other principles affecting growth and development of insects; neurohormones; neurotransmitters. *Mailing Add:* Zoecon Corp 975 California Ave Palo Alto CA 94304

STAAT, ROBERT HENRY, b Denver, Colo, Apr 2, 42; m 79; c 3. PATHOGENIC MECHANISMS, MICROBIAL ADHERENCE. *Educ:* Univ NMex, BS, 65, MS, 68; Univ Minn, PhD(microbiol), 75. *Prof Exp:* Res assoc, Univ NMex, 67-69; scientist, Sch Dent, Univ Minn, 71-73, res fel, 73-75; asst prof microbiol, Sch Dent, Med Univ SC, 75-76; asst prof, 76-78, ASSOC PROF ORAL BIOL, SCH DENT, UNIV LOUISVILLE, 78-, ASSOC PROF, DEPT MICROBIOL, SCH MED, 76- *Concurrent Pos:* Prin investr, Sugar Asn grant, 79-82 & NIH, Nat Inst Dent Res, 80-83. *Mem:* AAAS; Am Soc Microbiol; Am Asn Dent Res; Sigma Xi. *Res:* Determination of the pathogenic mechanisms of oral Streptococci, specifically, definition of the adherence reaction of streptococcus mutans to the tooth surface and purification of the adherence factors for use in a dental caries vaccine. *Mailing Add:* Dept Oral Biol Sch Dent Univ Louisville Louisville KY 40292

STAATS, GUSTAV W(ILLIAM), b Forest Park, Ill, Nov 30, 19; m 49; c 2. ELECTRICAL ENGINEERING. *Educ:* Ill Inst Technol, BS, 42, MS, 48, PhD(elec eng), 56. *Prof Exp:* Engr, Motor & Generator Dept, Allis-Chalmers Mfg Co, 42-56, staff engr, Thermal Power Dept, 56-63, res engr, Res Div, 63-65; from asst prof to assoc prof elec eng, 65-77, PROF ELEC ENG, UNIV WIS-MILWAUKEE, 77- *Honors & Awards:* Eta Kappa Nu Recognition Award, 53. *Mem:* Inst Elec & Electronics Engrs. *Res:* Rotating electrical machinery; high strength magnetic fields; electric power systems. *Mailing Add:* Dept of Elec Eng Univ Wis-Milwaukee Milwaukee WI 53201

STAATS, PERCY ANDERSON, b Belleville, WVa, Feb 20, 21; m 44; c 4. PHYSICAL CHEMISTRY, PHYSICS. *Educ:* Marietta Col, AB, 43; Univ Minn, MS, 49. *Hon Degrees:* DS, Fisk Univ, 74. *Prof Exp:* Instr physics, Marietta Col, 43; tech supvr, Tenn Eastman Corp, 43-46; chemist, Rohm and Haas Co, Pa, 49-52; CHEMIST, OAK RIDGE NAT LAB, 52- *Concurrent Pos:* Guest lectr & lab dir, Infrared Spectros Inst, Fisk Univ, 57-75; traveling lectr, Oak Ridge Inst Nuclear Studies, 59-60, 62-63 & 65-66. *Mem:* Am Phys Soc; AAAS; Am Chem Soc; Sigma Xi. *Res:* Molecular structure by infrared spectroscopy; infrared spectra of gases as solids at low temperatures; inorganic ions in solid solution; isotopes, especially tritium; gas lasers; plasma diagnostics using far infrared submillimeter lasers. *Mailing Add:* 119 Manchester Rd Oak Ridge TN 37830

STAATS, WILLIAM R, b Chicago, Ill, Sept 10, 35; m 59; c 3. CHEMICAL ENGINEERING. *Educ:* Ill Inst Technol, BS, 57, MS, 60, PhD, 70. *Prof Exp:* Chem engr, Inst Gas Technol, 57-58; proj develop officer, Rome Air Develop Ctr, 59-62; chem engr, Inst Gas Technol, 62-69; vpres eng res, Polytech, Inc, 70-75; assoc dir, Inst Gas Technol, 75-79; DIR BASIC RES, GAS RES INST, 79- *Mem:* AAAS; Am Inst Chem Engrs; Combustion Inst; Am Chem Soc. *Mailing Add:* Gas Res Inst 8600 W Bryn Mawr Chicago IL 60631

STAATZ, MORTIMER HAY, b Kalispell, Mont, Oct 20, 18; m 52; c 3. ECONOMIC GEOLOGY. *Educ:* Calif Inst Technol, BS, 40; Northwestern Univ, MS, 42; Columbia Univ, PhD(geol), 52. *Prof Exp:* Asst geol, Northwestern Univ, 41-42; GEOLOGIST, US GEOL SURV, 42-44 & 46- *Mem:* Geol Soc Am; Soc Econ Geologists; Mineral Soc Am. *Res:* Pegmatites of Colorado and South Dakota; geology of eastern Great Basin and Washington; beryllium, fluorspar and phosphate deposits; vein-type uranium and thorium deposits; thorium and rare earth resources in United States. *Mailing Add:* US Geol Surv Fed Ctr MS 916 Denver CO 80225

STABA, EMIL JOHN, b New York, NY, May 16, 28; m 54; c 5. PHARMACOGNOSY. *Educ:* St John's Univ, NY, BS, 52; Duquesne Univ, MS, 54; Univ Conn, PhD(pharmacog), 57. *Prof Exp:* Prof pharmacog & chmn dept, Univ Nebr, Lincoln, 57-68; PROF PHARMACOG & CHMN DEPT, COL PHARM, UNIV MINN, MINNEAPOLIS, 68-, ASST DEAN, 74- *Concurrent Pos:* Consult var indust & govt agencies; NSF sr foreign scientist, Poland, Hungary & Czech, 69; Fulbright-Hays res fel, Ger, 70; Coun Sci & Indust Res vis scientist, India, 73; partic, US-Repub China Coop Sci Prog, Plant Cell & Tissue Culture, 74; mem, US Pharmacopeia Comt Rev-Natural Prod, 80-85. *Honors & Awards:* Lunsford-Richardson Award, 58. *Mem:* AAAS; Am Soc Pharmacog (pres, 71-72); Tissue Culture Asn; Am Pharmaceut Asn; Soc Econ Bot. *Res:* Cultivation, extraction and tissue culture of medicinal plants; ginseng research. *Mailing Add:* Dept Pharmacog Col Pharm Univ Minn Minneapolis MN 55455

STABENFELDT, GEORGE H, b Shelton, Wash, June 26, 30; m 53; c 4. PHYSIOLOGY, ENDOCRINOLOGY. *Educ:* Wash State Univ, BA, 55, DVM, 56, MS, 62; Okla State Univ, PhD, 68. *Prof Exp:* Pvt pract, Ore, 56-57, Idaho, 57-58 & Wash, 58-60; instr vet path, Wash State Univ, 60-62; asst prof physiol, Okla State Univ, 62-68; assoc prof clin sci & assoc res physiologist, Nat Ctr Primate Biol, 68-75, PROF REPRODUCTION, DEPT REPRODUCTION, SCH VET MED, UNIV CALIF, DAVIS, 75- *Mem:* Am Vet Med Asn; Am Soc Vet Physiol & Pharmacol; Am Physiol Soc; Soc Study Fertility; Soc Study Reproduction. *Res:* Endocrinology of female reproductive cycle, including the estrous and menstrual cycles, pregnancy and parturition. *Mailing Add:* Dept of Clin Sci Sch Vet Med Univ of Calif Davis CA 95616

STABLEFORD, LOUIS TRANTER, b Meriden, Conn, July 30, 14; m 41; c 3. BIOLOGY. *Educ:* Univ Va, BS, 37; Yale Univ, PhD(zool), 41. *Prof Exp:* Lab asst, Univ Va, 34-37 & Yale Univ, 37-40; from instr to prof, 41-72, chmn dept, 58-78, Dana prof, 72-79, EMER PROF BIOL, LAFAYETTE COL, 79- *Honors & Awards:* Christian & Mary Lindbach Found Award, 65. *Mem:* Am Soc Zoologists; Soc Develop Biol. *Res:* Experimental embryology; early amphibian development; aging of connective tissue. *Mailing Add:* Dept Biol Lafayette Col Easton PA 18042

STABLER, TIMOTHY ALLEN, b Port Jervis, NY, Sept 27, 40. DEVELOPMENTAL BIOLOGY, ENDOCRINOLOGY. *Educ:* Drew Univ, BA, 62; DePauw Univ, MA, 64; Univ Vt, PhD(zool), 69. *Prof Exp:* Asst prof biol, Hope Col, 69-71; asst prof biol & health professions, 73-76, ASSOC PROF BIOL & HEALTH PROFESSIONS ADV, IND UNIV NORTHWEST, 76-, ACTG CHMN BIOL, 81- *Concurrent Pos:* NIH fel, Univ Minn, 68-69; Sigma Xi grant-in-aid, 71-72; mem, NSF workshop develop biol, Univ Calif, San Diego, 71; NIH trainee reproductive endocrinol, Sch Med, Boston Univ, 71-73; adj asst prof physiol, Northwest Ctr Med Educ, Ind Univ Sch Med, 74-76, adj assoc prof physiol, 76- *Mem:* AAAS; Am Soc Zool; Am Inst Biol Sci; NY Acad Sci. *Res:* Steroid receptor biochemistry; electron microscopy and tissue culture of steroid-producing tissues. *Mailing Add:* Dept of Biol Ind Univ Northwest Gary IN 46408

STABY, GEORGE LESTER, b Greenwich, Conn, Apr 1, 44; m 66; c 2. HORTICULTURE, PLANT PHYSIOLOGY. *Educ:* Univ Conn, BS, 66; Mich State Univ, MS, 67, PhD(hort), 70. *Prof Exp:* Asst prof, 70-77, ASSOC PROF HORT, OHIO STATE UNIV, 78- *Concurrent Pos:* Hatch-US Govt grant, Ohio State Univ, 71- *Mem:* Am Soc Hort Sci; Int Soc Hort Sci; Am Soc Plant Physiol. *Res:* Plant growth regulators, sterols and other terpenes. *Mailing Add:* Dept of Hort Ohio State Univ Columbus OH 43210

STACE-SMITH, RICHARD, b Creston, BC, May 2, 24; m 51. PLANT PATHOLOGY. *Educ:* Univ BC, BSA, 50; Ore State Col, PhD(plant path), 54. *Prof Exp:* Asst plant pathologist, 50-54, assoc plant pathologist, 54-58, plant pathologist, 58-81, HEAD PLANT PATH SECT, CAN DEPT AGR, 81- *Mem:* Can Phytopath Soc; Agr Inst Can. *Res:* Rubus virus diseases; virus purification and properties. *Mailing Add:* Can Agr Res Sta 6660 NW Marine Dr Vancouver BC V6T 1X2 Can

STACEY, JOHN SYDNEY, b June 15, 27; US citizen; m 54; c 3. GEOPHYSICS. *Educ:* Univ Durham, BSc, 51; Univ BC, MASc, 58, PhD(physics), 62. *Prof Exp:* Engr, Marconi Wireless Tel Co, 51-55; lectr elec eng, Univ BC, 57-58; PHYSICIST, ISOTOPE GEOL BR, US GEOL SURV, 62- *Mem:* Geol Soc Am; Am Soc Mass Spectrometry. *Res:* Mass spectrometry in geologic studies and related data processing techniques; lead isotope and U-Pb zitcon geochronology for ore genesis and crustal evolution. *Mailing Add:* PO Box 34 El Granada CA 94018

STACEY, LARRY MILTON, b Greensboro, NC, July 30, 40. PHYSICS. *Educ:* Univ NC, Chapel Hill, BS, 62, PhD(physics), 68. *Prof Exp:* Fel physics, Rutgers Univ, New Brunswick, 67-70; chem engr, Calif Inst Technol, 70-71; ASST PROF PHYSICS, ST LOUIS UNIV, 71- *Mem:* Am Phys Soc; Am Asn Physics Teachers. *Res:* Applications of magnetic resonance to the study of solids and fluids; critical point phenomena. *Mailing Add:* Dept of Physics St Louis Univ St Louis MO 63103

STACEY, WESTON MONROE, JR, b US. REACTOR PHYSICS, FUSION PLASMA THEORY. *Educ:* Ga Inst Technol, BS, 59, MS, 63; Mass Inst Technol, PhD(nuclear eng), 66. *Prof Exp:* Nuclear engr, Knolls Atomic Power Lab, 62-64; mgr reactor kinetics, 66-69; sect head reactor theory, Argonne Nat Lab, 69-72, assoc dir, Appl Physics Div, 72-79, dir fusion prog, 73-77; CALLAWAY PROF NUCLEAR ENG, GA INST TECHNOL, 77- *Mem:* Fel Am Nuclear Soc; Am Phys Soc. *Res:* Nuclear reactor theory, fusion reactor technology, plasma physics; fusion reactor design. *Mailing Add:* Sch Nuclear Eng Ga Inst Technol Atlanta GA 30332

STACH, JOSEPH, b Wallington, NJ, Aug 21, 38; m 63; c 2. SOLID STATE ELECTRONICS, ELECTRICAL ENGINEERING. *Educ:* Newark Col Eng, BS, 60; Pa State Univ, MS, 62, PhD(elec eng), 66. *Prof Exp:* Instr elec eng, Pa State Univ, 62-65; mem tech staff, Bell Tel Labs, 66-67; from asst prof to assoc prof, 67-80, PROF ELEC ENG, PA STATE UNIV, UNIVERSITY PARK, 80- *Concurrent Pos:* Consult, Air Prod & Chem Carborunchem. *Res:* Investigation of avalanche breakdown in metal barrier diodes and surface properties of insulators on semiconductors; boron nitride processing, HCl oxidations and plasma etching. *Mailing Add:* Dept of Elec Eng Pa State Univ University Park PA 16802

STACH, ROBERT WILLIAM, b Chicago, Ill, Feb 12, 45; m 66; c 1. NEUROBIOCHEMISTRY, BIOCHEMISTRY. *Educ:* Ill Wesleyan Univ, BA, 67; Univ Wis-Madison, PhD(org chem), 72. *Prof Exp:* Trainee neurobiochem, Depts Genetics & Biochem, Sch Med, Stanford Univ, 72-74; asst prof, 74-80, ASSOC PROF BIOCHEM & ANAT, STAT UNIV NY UPSTATE MED CTR, 80-, ASSOC MEM FAC, CTR NEUROBEHAVIORAL SCI, 79- *Concurrent Pos:* Biomed Res Support Grant, 74-75; NIH res grant, 75-81. *Mem:* Am Chem Soc; Am Soc Neurochem; AAAS; NY Acad Sci; Soc Neurosci. *Res:* Factors involved in the growth and development of the nervous system with special interest in sensory and sympathetic neurons. *Mailing Add:* Dept of Biochem 766 Irving Ave Syracuse NY 13210

STACHEL, JOHN JAY, b New York, NY, Mar 29, 28; m 53; c 3. PHYSICS. *Educ:* City Univ New York, BS, 56; Stevens Inst Technol, MS, 59, PhD(physics), 62. *Prof Exp:* Instr physics, Lehigh Univ, 59-61; instr, Univ Pittsburgh, 61-62, res assoc, 62-64; from asst prof to assoc prof, 64-72, PROF PHYSICS & DIR INST FOR RELATIVITY STUDIES, BOSTON UNIV, 72- *Concurrent Pos:* Vis res assoc, Inst Theoret Physics, Warsaw, 62; vis prof, King's Col, Univ London, 70-71; vis sr res fel, Dept Physics, Princeton Univ, 77-; ed, Collection Papers Albert Einstein, Princeton Univ Press, 77- *Res:* General relativity; foundations of quantum theory; history and philosophy of physics. *Mailing Add:* Einstein Proj Princeton Univ Press Princeton NJ 08540

STACK (STACHIEWICZ), B(OGDAN) R(OMAN), b Lwow, Poland, Sept 16, 24; nat US; m 55; c 4. ELECTRONIC ENGINEERING. *Educ:* Bristol Univ, BSEE, 47; McGill Univ, MEE, 53. *Prof Exp:* Engr, Radio Eng Prod, Ltd, Can, 47-52; proj engr, Lenkurt Elec Co, Calif, 52-55; asst sect head, Stromberg-Carlson Div, Gen Dynamics Corp, NY, 55-57; assoc lab dir, Int Tel & Tel Fed Labs, Calif, 57-62; dept mgr, Philco Corp, Ford Motor Co, 62-64; prog mgr, Stanford Res Inst, 64-68; mgr, Systs Design Dept, WDL Div, Philco-Ford Corp, Palo-Alto, 68-77; mgr, 77-81, VPRES ENG, AYDIN SATELLITE COMMUN, 81- *Mem:* Sr mem Inst Elec & Electronics Engrs. *Res:* Space and ground communications systems; signal analysis and detection. *Mailing Add:* 358 Toyon Ave Los Altos CA 94022

STACK, JOHN D, b Los Angeles, Calif, July 24, 38; m 63; c 1. THEORETICAL PHYSICS. *Educ:* Calif Inst Technol, BSc, 59; Univ Calif, Berkeley, PhD(physics), 65. *Prof Exp:* Actg asst prof physics, Univ Calif, Berkeley, 65-66; asst prof, 66-70, ASSOC PROF PHYSICS, UNIV ILL, URBANA, 70- *Concurrent Pos:* Vis assoc, Calif Inst Technol, 69-70. *Mem:* Am Phys Soc. *Mailing Add:* Dept of Physics Univ of Ill Urbana IL 61801

STACK, STEPHEN M, b Monahans, Tex, Feb 12, 43; m 65; c 2. CYTOLOGY. *Educ:* Univ Tex, Austin, BAS, 65, PhD(cytol, bot), 69. *Prof Exp:* Asst prof, 69-74, ASSOC PROF BOT & PLANT PATH, COLO STATE UNIV, 74- *Mem:* Am Soc Cell Biol; AAAS; Bot Soc Am. *Res:* Structure and function of chromosomes. *Mailing Add:* Dept of Bot & Plant Path Colo State Univ Ft Collins CO 80521

STACKELBERG, OLAF PATRICK, b Munich, Ger, Aug 2, 32; US citizen; m 54; c 3. MATHEMATICS. *Educ:* Mass Inst Technol, BS, 55; Univ Minn, MS, 60, PhD(math), 63. *Prof Exp:* Teaching asst math, Univ Minn, 58-63; from asst prof to assoc prof, Duke Univ, 63-76; PROF MATH & CHMN DEPT, KENT STATE UNIV, 76- *Concurrent Pos:* Alexander V Humboldt fel, Stuttgart Tech Univ, 65-66; vis assoc prof, Univ Ill, Urbana, 69-70; ed, Duke Math J, 71-74; vis assoc prof, Univ London, 74. *Mem:* Am Math Soc; Math Asn Am; Inst Math Statist. *Res:* Probability; metric number theory. *Mailing Add:* Dept Math Sci Kent State Univ Kent OH 44242

STACKMAN, ROBERT W, b Dayton, Ohio, June 29, 35; m 62; c 3. ORGANIC CHEMISTRY, POLYMER CHEMISTRY. *Educ:* Univ Dayton, BS, 57; Univ Fla, PhD(org chem), 61. *Prof Exp:* Res asst cyclopolymers of silanes, Univ Fla, 58-61; res chemist, Summit Labs, 61-65, sr res chemist, Celanese Res Co, 65-72, res assoc, 72-74, res supvr polymer flammability res, 74-76, res supvr polymer & specialty chem res, 76-80, RES ASSOC, CELANESE RES CO, CELANESE CORP, 80- *Mem:* AAAS; Am Chem Soc; fel Am Inst Chem. *Res:* Condensation polymerization; emulsion polymerization; high temperature polymers; cyclopolymerization; organic synthesis; organosilicon compounds; addition polymerization; polymer modification and stabilization; flammability of polymers; water soluble polymers; fermentation processes. *Mailing Add:* Celanese Res Co Box 1000 Summit NJ 07901

STACKPOLE, JOHN DUKE, b Boston, Mass, Dec 28, 35; m 60; c 3. METEOROLOGY. *Educ:* Amherst Col, BA, 57; Mass Inst Technol, MS, 59, PhD(meteorol), 64. *Prof Exp:* Res meteorologist, 64-73, SUPVRY RES METEOROLOGIST, NAT WEATHER SERV, NAT OCEANIC & ATMOSPHERIC ADMIN, 73- *Res:* Numerical weather prediction. *Mailing Add:* 7305 Kipling Pkwy District Heights MD 20747

STACK-STAIKIDIS, WILLIAM JOHN, b Athens, Greece, Nov 20, 29; US citizen; m 55; c 1. STRUCTURAL ENGINEERING, APPLIED MECHANICS. *Educ:* Nat Tech Univ Athens, BA, 51; NC State Univ, BCE, 57, MCE, 61; NY Univ, PhD(eng sci), 70. *Prof Exp:* Struct engr, Madigan & Hyland, 57-59; struct engr, Meir Assocs, 59-61; actg head res & urban planning, Doxiades Assocs, 61-63; proj engr, Walter Kidde, 64-65; lectr struct eng, City Col New York, 65-66; proj engr, Tippetts, Abbett, McCarthy, Stratton, 65-66; assoc prof civil eng & head struct & mech div, Newark Col Eng, 66-78; DEAN, SCH ENG, PRATT INST, BROOKLYN, 78- *Mem:* Am Soc Civil Engrs; Am Soc Eng Educ; Am Concrete Inst. *Res:* Linear and nonlinear buckling of structural systems; computer application to analysis and design of structural systems; optimization of structures. *Mailing Add:* Sch of Eng Pratt Inst Brooklyn NY 11205

STACY, CARL J, b Joplin, Mo, Jan 20, 29; m 51; c 3. POLYMER SCIENCE. *Educ:* Kans State Col Pittsburg, BA, 51; Purdue Univ, PhD(phys chem), 56. *Prof Exp:* Res fel starch, Purdue Univ, 55-56; res physicist, 56, RES PHYSICAL CHEMIST, PHILLIPS PETROL CO, 56- *Mem:* AAAS; Am Chem Soc; Sigma Xi. *Res:* Polymer and carbon black structure by light scattering, ultracentrifuge and other physical techniques. *Mailing Add:* 2929 Sheridan Rd Bartlesville OK 74003

STACY, GARDNER W, b Rochester, NY, Oct 29, 21; m 67; c 5. ORGANIC CHEMISTRY. *Educ:* Univ Rochester, BS, 43; Univ Ill, PhD(org chem), 46. *Prof Exp:* Asst, Off Sci Res & Develop Proj, Ill, 43-46; fel biochem, Med Col, Cornell Univ, 46-48; from asst prof to assoc prof, 48-60, PROF CHEM, WASH STATE UNIV, 60- *Concurrent Pos:* Dir region VI, Am Chem Soc, 70-77. *Honors & Awards:* PRF Int Award, Australia & New Zealand, 63-64. *Mem:* AAAS; Am Chem Soc (pres-elect, 78). *Res:* Sulfur-containing heterocyclic tautomeric systems and ring-chain tautomerism; prospective antimalarials. *Mailing Add:* Dept of Chem Wash State Univ Pullman WA 99163

STACY, RALPH WINSTON, b Middletown, Ohio, Feb 6, 20; m 43; c 2. PHYSIOLOGY, BIOENGINEERING. *Educ:* Miami Univ, BScE, 42; Ohio State Univ, MSc, 47, PhD(physiol), 48. *Prof Exp:* Instr physiol, Ohio State Univ, 47-48; asst prof, Univ Ky, 48-49; from asst prof to prof, Ohio State Univ, 49-62; prof biomath, NC State Univ, 62-65; prof bioeng & biomath, Univ NC, Chapel Hill, 65-69; scientist, Cox Heart Inst, 69-71; prof & chmn dept physiol, Southern Ill Univ, Carbondale, 71-77; SCIENTIST, US ENVIRON PROTECTION AGENCY, CHAPEL HILL, 77- *Mem:* Biophys Soc; Am

Physiol Soc; Inst Elec & Electronics Engrs; Asn Comput Mach. *Res:* Physics of circulation and respiration; hemodynamics; biomedical uses of computers; medical electronics and instrumentation; physiological effects of environmental pollutants. *Mailing Add:* Clin Studies Div Mason Farm Rd Chapel Hill NC 27514

STACY, T(HOMAS) D(ONNIE), b Houston, Tex, Jan 13, 34; m 54; c 4. PETROLEUM ENGINEERING. *Educ:* La Polytech Inst, BS, 57, MS, 62; Miss State Univ, PhD(eng), 66. *Prof Exp:* Petrol engr, Pan-Am Petrol Corp, 57-58 & 62-63; asst petrol eng, La Polytech Inst, 61-62; from instr to asst prof, Miss State Univ, 63-68; area engr, Pan Am Petrol Corp, 68-76; mgr res, Amoco Prod Co, 76-80, MGR PROD, AMOCO INT, 80- *Mem:* AAAS; Am Inst Mining, Metall & Petrol Engrs; Soc Petrol Engrs (treas); Soc Petrol Engrs (pres-elect, 81). *Res:* Petroleum engineering, surface chemistry and gas adsorption. *Mailing Add:* Amoco Res PO Box 591 Tulsa OK 74102

STADELMAIER, H(ANS) H(EINRICH), b Stuttgart, Ger, Nov 14, 22; nat US; m 46; c 3. PHYSICAL METALLURGY. *Educ:* Univ Stuttgart, Dipl, 51, Dr rer nat, 56. *Prof Exp:* Interpreter, US Mil Govt, Ger, 45-47; res assoc, 52-53, res assoc prof, 53-59, res prof, 59-80, PROF METALL, NC STATE UNIV, 80- *Mem:* Fel Am Soc Metals; Ger Metall Soc; Am Inst Mining, Metall & Petrol Engrs. *Res:* Alloy phases; x-ray crystallography; electronic materials; magnetic materials. *Mailing Add:* Mat Eng Dept NC State Univ Raleigh NC 27650

STADELMAN, WILLIAM JACOB, b Vancouver, Wash, Aug 8, 17; m 42; c 2. FOOD SCIENCE. *Educ:* Wash State Univ, BS, 40; Pa State Univ, MS, 42, PhD(biochem), 48. *Prof Exp:* Asst poultry husb, Pa State Univ, 40-42; asst prof, Wash State Univ, 48-52, assoc prof, 52-55; from assoc prof to prof poultry sci, 55-62, PROF FOOD SCI, PURDUE UNIV, LAFAYETTE, 62- *Concurrent Pos:* Consult, Food Indust; mem, Tech Adv Comt, Poultry & Egg Inst Am, 57-; mem bd dirs, Res & Develop Assocs, Food & Container Inst, 66-69, 72-75; mem, Sci Adv Comt, Refrig Res Found, 67-; mem adv bd mil personnel supplies, Food Irradiation Comt, Nat Acad Sci, 67-69; mem, Tech Adv Comt, Nat Turkey Fedn, 71-, Tech Adv Comt, Am Egg Bd, 74- *Honors & Awards:* Christie Award, Poultry & Egg Nat Bd, 55; Res Award, Am Egg Bd, 75; Sci Award, Inst Food Technol, 77. *Mem:* Inst Food Technol; Poultry Sci Asn (pres, 77-78); Am Soc Heat, Refrig & Air-Conditioning Eng; World Poultry Sci Asn; Am Meat Sci Asn. *Res:* Effects of refrigeration and freezing on quality preservation of protein rich foods; poultry products quality evaluation and preservation; new product development. *Mailing Add:* Dept of Animal Sci Smith Hall Purdue Univ West Lafayette IN 47906

STADELMANN, EDUARD JOSEPH, b Graz, Austria, Sept 24, 20. PLANT PHYSIOLOGY, CELL PHYSIOLOGY. *Educ:* Innsbruck Univ, PhD(bot, philos), 53; Univ Freiburg, Venia Legendi, 57. *Prof Exp:* Asst bot, Freiburg Univ, 54-61, privat docent, 57, sr asst, 62-64; from asst prof to assoc prof, 64-72, PROF PLANT PHYSIOL, UNIV MINN, ST PAUL, 72- *Concurrent Pos:* Muellhaupt scholar biol, Ohio State Univ, 58-59; res assoc, Univ Minn, 63-64; Humboldt award, Bonn, Ger, 73-75; Fulbright award, Univ Graz, Austria, 79; vis prof, Dept Bot, Seoul Nat Univ, Korea. *Mem:* Ger Bot Soc; Swiss Bot Soc; Swiss Soc Natural Sci; Austrian Zool-Bot Soc; Am Inst Biol Sci. *Res:* Permeability; cytomorphology; salt resistance; protoplasmatology; radiation effects; desiccation resistance. *Mailing Add:* Dept Hort Sci Univ Minn St Paul MN 55108

STADLER, DAVID ROSS, b Columbia, Mo, May 24, 25; m 52; c 4. GENETICS. *Educ:* Univ Mo, AB, 48; Princeton Univ, MA, 50, PhD, 52. *Prof Exp:* Instr biol, Univ Rochester, 52; Gosney res fel genetics, Calif Inst Technol, 52-53, USPHS fel, 53-55; instr bot, 56-57, asst prof, 57-59, from asst prof to assoc prof genetics, 59-67, PROF GENETICS, UNIV WASH, 67- *Concurrent Pos:* Ed, Genetics, Genetics Soc Am, 73-76. *Mem:* Genetics Soc Am (treas, 69-71). *Res:* Genetics of microorganisms; mutation, recombination and development. *Mailing Add:* Dept of Genetics Univ of Wash Seattle WA 98195

STADLER, LOUIS BENJAMIN, b Monroe, Mich, Feb 26, 26; m 51; c 3. PHARMACEUTICAL CHEMISTRY, ANALYTICAL CHEMISTRY. *Educ:* Univ Mich, BS, 48, MS, 50, PhD(pharmaceut chem), 54. *Prof Exp:* Sr anal chemist, Parke, Davis & Co, 53-63, mgr anal standards, 63-64; asst head qual control, William S Merrell Co Div, Richardson-Merrell Inc, 64-65, head qual control, 66-71, Merrell Nat Labs, 71-73, Master Documents Admin, 73-75, mgr, Qual Opers Records, systs & planning, Merrell-Nat Labs, 75-81, QUAL OPERS TECH PROJ MGR, MERRELL DOW PHARMACEUT, 81-, QUAL ASSURANCE COMPLIANCE COORDR, 81- *Concurrent Pos:* Mem adv panel steroids, Nat Formulary, 60-65, comt specifications, 66-75, panel trypsin & chymotrypsin, 70-75; mem rev comt, US Pharmacopeia, 70-80. *Mem:* Am Pharmaceut Asn; Am Chem Soc; Am Soc Qual Control. *Res:* Analytical methodology for testing drug substances, pharmaceutical dosage forms and associated standards; improved control techniques for pharmaceuticals; technical management. *Mailing Add:* Merrell-Nat Labs 2110 E Galbraith Rd Cincinnati OH 45215

STADNICKI, STANLEY WALTER, JR, b Norwich, Conn, Sept 30, 43; m 65; c 4. TOXICOLOGY. *Educ:* Assumption Col, Mass, BA, 65; Clark Univ, Mass, MA, 70; Worcester Polytech Inst, PhD(biomed eng), 76. *Prof Exp:* Res scientist, EG&G Mason Res Inst, 67-76; TOXICOLOGIST, MED RES LABS, PFIZER, INC, 76- *Mem:* Soc Toxicol; Am Soc Pharmacol & Exp Therapeut; Am Col Toxicol; NY Acad Sci; Inst Elec & Electronics Engrs. *Res:* Designing preclinical protocols for the purpose of testing the toxicological effects of new drug candidates; interpretation, analysis and documentation of research results. *Mailing Add:* Med Res Labs Pfizer Inc Eastern Point Rd Groton CT 06340

STADTER, JAMES THOMAS, b Baltimore, Md. AERONAUTICAL & ASTRONAUTICAL ENGINEERING. *Educ:* Loyola Col, BS, 59; Univ Md, MA, 64; Am Univ, PhD(math), 75. *Prof Exp:* Assoc engr, 60-65, SR ENGR, APPL PHYSICS LAB, JOHNS HOPKINS UNIV, 65-, INSTR COMPUT SCI, 80- *Res:* Aeroelasticity and structural analysis; applied mathematics; eigenvalue estimation procedure. *Mailing Add:* Appl Physics Lab Johns Hopkins Univ Johns Hopkins Rd Laurel MD 20707

STADTHERR, LEON GREGORY, b New Ulm, Minn, Nov 27, 42. BIOINORGANIC CHEMISTRY, ENGINEERING. *Educ:* St John's Univ, Minn, BS, 65; Univ NDak, PhD(chem), 70. *Prof Exp:* Res assoc chem, Univ Va, 70-72; res assoc chem, Iowa State Univ, 73-76; PROCESS DEVELOP SPEC, GEN RESOURCE CORP, 77- *Mem:* Am Chem Soc; Sigma Xi. *Res:* Coordination compounds; stereochemistry of transition metal ion and lanthanide ion complexes; ion exchange. *Mailing Add:* PO Box 57 Hopkins MN 55343

STADTHERR, MARK ALLEN, b Austin, Minn, May 15, 50. CHEMICAL ENGINEERING. *Educ:* Univ Minn, BChE, 72; Univ Wis-Madison, PhD(chem eng), 76. *Prof Exp:* ASST PROF CHEM ENG, UNIV ILL, URBANA-CHAMPAIGN, 76- *Mem:* Am Inst Chem Engrs; Am Chem Soc; Am Soc Eng Educ; Soc Indust & Appl Math. *Res:* Chemical process simulation, optimization and design; sparse matrix computations; resource management. *Mailing Add:* Dept Chem Eng Univ Ill Sch Chem Sci Urbana IL 61801

STADTHERR, RICHARD JAMES, b Gibbon, Minn, Nov 24, 19. PLANT PHYSIOLOGY, PLANT BREEDING. *Educ:* Univ Minn, BS, 49, MS, 51, PhD(hort), 63. *Prof Exp:* Teaching asst, Univ Minn, 48-51, asst prof hort, Exten, 53-54, instr in charge of res turf & nursery crops, 54-61; res asst, Cornell Univ, 51-52; asst prof nursery crops res, Univ Mass, 52-53; assoc prof hort, Exten, NC State Univ, 63-67; assoc prof, 67-73, PROF HORT, LA STATE UNIV, BATON ROUGE, 73- *Mem:* Am Soc Hort Sci; Int Plant Propagators Soc; Am Magnolia Soc; Am Hort Soc; Am Rhododendron Soc. *Res:* Growth substances; plant propagation; testing-breeding of azaleas; groundcovers and woody ornamental trials. *Mailing Add:* Dept of Hort La State Univ Baton Rouge LA 70803

STADTMAN, EARL REECE, b Carrizozo, NMex, Nov 15, 19; m 43. BIOCHEMISTRY. *Educ:* Univ Calif, PhD(comp biochem), 49. *Prof Exp:* Asst food tech, Univ Calif, 43-46; sr lab technician, 48-49; AEC res fel, Mass Gen Hosp, 49-50; chemist, 50-57, chief sect enzymes, 57-62, CHIEF LAB BIOCHEM, NAT HEART, LUNG & BLOOD INST, 62- *Concurrent Pos:* lectr, US USDA Grad Sch, 54-; Georgetown Univ, 56-58 & Univ Md, 59-; vis scientist, Max Planck Inst, Ger, 59-60 & Pasteur Inst, France, 60; ed, J Biol Chem, 60-; exec ed, Archives Biochem, Biophys, 60-; mem adv comt, Oak Ridge Nat Lab, 63-66; chmn biochem div, Found Advan Educ in Sci, 64-; NIH lectr, 66; lectr, Univ Ill, 66 & Univ Pisa, 66; adv bd, Biochemistry, 69-76 & Trends in Biochem Res, 76-79; del, US Nat Comt for Int Union of Biochem, 75-81, mem coun, 76-79. *Honors & Awards:* Lewis Award, Am Chem Soc, 53; Microbiol Award, Nat Acad Sci, 70. *Mem:* Nat Acad Sci; Am Chem Soc; Am Soc Biol Chemists; Am Soc Microbiol; Am Acad Arts & Sci. *Res:* Microbial and intermediary metabolism; enzyme chemistry; biochemical function of vitamin B12 and ferredoxin; metabolic regulation of biosynthetic of biosynthetic pathways; membrane transport. *Mailing Add:* Lab of Biochem Nat Heart Lung & Blood Inst NIH Bethesda MD 20014

STADTMAN, THRESSA CAMPBELL, b Sterling, NY, Feb 12, 20; m 43. BIOCHEMISTRY, MICROBIOLOGY. *Educ:* Cornell Univ, BS, 40, MS, 42; Univ Calif, PhD(microbiol), 49. *Prof Exp:* Asst nutrit, Agr Exp Sta, Cornell Univ, 42-43; res assoc food microbiol, Univ Calif, 43-46; asst, Harvard Med Sch, 49-50; BIOCHEMIST, NAT HEART INST, 50- *Concurrent Pos:* Whitney fel, Oxford Univ, 54-55; Rockefeller grant, Inst Cell Chem, Univ Munich, 59-60; French Govt fel, Inst Biol & Phys Chem, France, 60. *Honors & Awards:* Hillebrand Award, 79. *Mem:* Nat Acad Sci; Am Soc Biol Chemists (secy, 78-81); Brit Biochem Soc; Am Chem Soc; Am Soc Microbiol. *Res:* Amino acid intermediary metabolism; one-carbon metabolism; methane formation; microbial biochemistry; selenium biochemistry. *Mailing Add:* Nat Heart Lung & Blood Inst Bethesda MD 20205

STAEBLER, ARTHUR E, b Detroit, Mich, May 3, 15; m 40; c 4. ORNITHOLOGY, VERTEBRATE PALEONTOLOGY. *Educ:* Univ Mich, BS, 38, MS, 40, PhD(ornith), 48. *Prof Exp:* Asst prof conserv, Mich State Univ, 47-55; from asst prof to assoc prof, 55-66, prof biol, 66-80, EMER PROF BIOL, CALIF STATE UNIV, FRESNO, 80- *Mem:* Am Ornith Union; Soc Vertebrate Paleont; Wilson Ornith Soc. *Res:* Bird migration; winter flocking behavior; cretaceous vertebrates of Pacific Coastal region of North America, primarily California. *Mailing Add:* Dept of Biol Calif State Univ Fresno CA 93740

STAEBLER, DAVID LLOYD, b Ann Arbor, Mich, Apr 25, 40; m 61; c 2. KINESCOPE DESIGN, PHOTOVOLTAIC CELLS. *Educ:* Pa State Univ, BS, 62, MS, 63; Princeton Univ, MA, 67, PhD(elec eng), 70. *Prof Exp:* Mem tech staff, 63-81, HEAD, KINESCOPE SYSTS GROUP, RCA LABS, 81- *Concurrent Pos:* Vis mem tech staff labs, RCA Ltd, Zurich, Switz, 79-80. *Honors & Awards:* Achievement Award, RCA Labs, 68, 72. *Mem:* Inst Elec & Electronics Eng; AAAS. *Res:* Electron gun and kinescope design; photovoltaic properties of amorphous silicon; hologram storage in electro-optic materials; photochromic and electrochromic phenomena; hologram storage in electro-optic materials; optical and electronic properties of amorphous silicon. *Mailing Add:* RCA Labs Princeton NJ 08540

STAEHELIN, LUCAS ANDREW, b Sydney, Australia, Feb 10, 39; m 65; c 3. CELL BIOLOGY, PHOTOSYNTHESIS. *Educ:* Swiss Fed Inst Technol, DiplNatw, 63, PhD(biol), 66. *Prof Exp:* Res scientist, Dept Sci & Indust Res, NZ, 66-69; res fel cell biol, Harvard Univ, 69-70; asst prof, 70-73, assoc chmn dept molecular cell & develop biol, 72-73, assoc prof, 73-78, PROF CELL BIOL, UNIV COLO, BOULDER, 79- *Concurrent Pos:* Nat Inst Gen Med Sci grant, 71-; mem study sect cell biol, NIH, 80-84; vis prof, Inst Biol & Microbiol, Univ Freiburg, Ger, 78. *Honors & Awards:* Humboldt Award, 78. *Mem:* AAAS; Am Soc Cell Biol; Am Soc Photobiology; Am Soc Plant Physiol. *Res:* Structure and function of biological membranes; freeze-etch electron microscopy; photosynthesis. *Mailing Add:* Dept Molecular Cell Develop Biol Univ of Colo Boulder CO 80302

STAEHLE, ROGER WASHBURNE, b Feb 4, 34; div; c 4. METALLURGICAL ENGINEERING, CORROSION. *Educ:* Ohio State Univ, BMetE & MS, 57, PhD(metall eng), 65. *Prof Exp:* Res asst corrosion, Ohio State Univ, 61-65, from asst prof to assoc prof metall eng, 65-70, prof, 70-79, int nickel prof corrosion sci & eng, 71-79; DEAN INST TECHNOL, UNIV MINN, 79- *Concurrent Pos:* Consult, 3M Co, Oak Ridge Nat Lab, Monsanto Co, Int Nickel Co, Inc, NUS Corp & Parameter Inc; mem adv panel, Mat Div, Nat Bur Standards. *Honors & Awards:* Willis Rodney Whitney Award, 80. *Mem:* Nat Acad Eng; fel Am Soc Metals; Am Soc Testing & Mat; Nat Asn Corrosion Engrs; Electrochem Soc. *Res:* Passivity of metals; stress corrosion cracking; process of fracture; fatigue; optical properties of surfaces; surface chemistry. *Mailing Add:* 207 Church St SE Inst Technol Univ Minn Minneapolis MN 55455

STAELIN, DAVID HUDSON, b Toledo, Ohio, May 25, 38; m 62; c 3. RADIO ASTRONOMY, METEOROLOGY. *Educ:* Mass Inst Technol, SB, 60, SM, 61, ScD(elec eng), 65. *Prof Exp:* From instr to assoc prof, 65-76, PROF ELEC ENG, MASS INST TECHNOL, 76- *Concurrent Pos:* Ford fel eng, 65-67; vis asst scientist, Nat Radio Astron Observ, 68-69; dir, Environ Res & Technol, Inc, 69- *Mem:* AAAS; Am Astron Soc; Am Geophys Union; Inst Elec & Electronics Eng; Am Meteorol Soc. *Res:* Planetary atmospheres; pulsars; space-based and ground-based meteorological observations using passive microwave techniques; microwave and optical instrumentation; atmospheric sensing; communications satellites. *Mailing Add:* Dept of Elec Eng & Comput Sci Mass Inst Technol Cambridge MA 02139

STAETZ, CHARLES ALAN, b North Platte, Nebr, July 12, 45; m 68; c 2. ECONOMIC ENTOMOLOGY. *Educ:* Chadron State Col, BS, 67; Univ Nebr, MS, 72, PhD(entom), 75. *Prof Exp:* Entomologist, Velsicol Chem Corp, 75-78; MEM STAFF, AGR CHEM GROUP, FMC CORP, 78- *Mem:* Entom Soc Am. *Res:* New insecticides; insecticide resistance-detection and countermeasures. *Mailing Add:* 85 Hickory Lane Newtown PA 18940

STAFF, CHARLES HUBERT, b Barry, Ill, July 24, 32; m 59; c 2. FOOD SCIENCE. *Educ:* Culver-Stockton Col, BA, 54; Southern Ill Univ, MS, 59. *Prof Exp:* Res chemist, Corn Prod Co, 59-63; sr res technologist, Pet Inc, 63-68; tech mgr, Pillsbury Co, 68-70; dir res, Fairmont Foods Co, 70-77, asst vpres res & develop, 77-81; SR DIR CORP TECHNOL, KELLOGG CO, 81- *Mem:* Inst Food Technol; Am Asn Cereal Chemists. *Res:* Food process development, design and engineer production facilities and financial analysis of various production alternatives; industrial and manufacturing engineering. *Mailing Add:* 758 Country Club Dr Battle Creek MI 49015

STAFFA, NICKOLAS GEORGE, JR, physics, biophysics, see previous edition

STAFFELDT, EUGENE EDWARD, plant pathology, see previous edition

STAFFORD, BRUCE H(OLLEN), b North Platte, Nebr, Aug 25, 22; m 47; c 2. ELECTRICAL ENGINEERING, OPERATIONS RESEARCH. *Educ:* Univ Nebr, BSc, 43; Univ Md, MSc, 49. *Prof Exp:* Head dir systs sect, Oper Res Br, US Naval Res Lab, 43-54; opers analyst, Strategic Air Command, US Dept Air Force, 54-57, chief opers anal, 8th Air Force, 57-59, chief oper capability div, Opers Anal, 59-61, dep chief, Opers Anal, Strategic Air Command, 61-63, chief opers anal, HQ, 63-71, chief sci & res, 71-74; RETIRED. *Mem:* Opers Res Soc Am. *Res:* Circuit analysis; servo-mechanisms; weapon control systems, including radar and computers; nuclear physics; electronic countermeasures; guided missiles; aircraft; operations research. *Mailing Add:* 42 Kemp Rd E Greensboro NC 27410

STAFFORD, DARREL WAYNE, b Parsons, Kans, Mar 11, 35; m 57; c 3. ZOOLOGY, MOLECULAR BIOLOGY. *Educ:* Southwest Mo State Col, BA, 59; Univ Miami, Fla, PhD(cellular physiol), 64. *Prof Exp:* NIH fel, Albert Einstein Col Med, 64-65; asst prof, 65-70, assoc prof, 70-77, PROF ZOOL, NUTRIT & BIOCHEM, UNIV NC, CHAPEL HILL, 78- *Mem:* AAAS. *Res:* Cell division and protein synthesis. *Mailing Add:* Dept of Zool Univ of NC Chapel Hill NC 27514

STAFFORD, FRED E, b New York, NY, Mar 31, 35; m 63. PHYSICAL INORGANIC CHEMISTRY, SOLID STATE CHEMISTRY. *Educ:* Cornell Univ, AB, 56; Univ Calif, Berkeley, PhD(chem), 59. *Prof Exp:* NSF fel, Free Univ Brussels, 59-61; from asst prof to assoc prof chem, Northwestern Univ, 61-74; prog officer sci develop progs, 74-75, PROG DIR SOLID STATE CHEMISTRY, NSF, 75- *Concurrent Pos:* Mem, Comt on High Temp Sci & Technol, Res Coun Can-Nat Acad Sci, 75-78. *Mem:* Am Chem Soc; Am Phys Soc; Am Soc Pub Admin; Fed Exec Inst Alumni Asn. *Res:* Mass spectrometry and spectroscopy of simple inorganic systems; high temperature chemistry; solid state chemistry: administers research program in a broad interdisciplinary area including crystals, molecular crystals, and surfaces; thermodynamics and material properties. *Mailing Add:* Nat Sci Found 1800 G St NW Washington DC 20550

STAFFORD, HELEN ADELE, b Philadelphia, Pa, Oct 9, 22. PLANT PHYSIOLOGY. *Educ:* Wellesley Col, BA, 44; Conn Col, MA, 48; Univ Pa, PhD, 51. *Prof Exp:* Instr bot & res assoc biochem, Univ Chicago, 51-54; from asst prof to assoc prof, 54-65, PROF BOT, REED COL, 65- *Concurrent Pos:* Guggenheim fel, Harvard Univ, 58-59; NSF sr fel, Univ Calif, Los Angeles, 63-64. *Mem:* Bot Soc Am; Am Soc Plant Physiol; Am Soc Biol Chemists; Phytochem Soc NAm (pres, 77-78). *Res:* Plant biochemistry; metabolism of phenolic compounds; regulation of and metabolism of phenolic compounds in higher plants. *Mailing Add:* Dept Biol Reed Col Portland OR 97202

STAFFORD, PAUL M, b Can, Mar 8, 19; nat US; m 51; c 2. INDUSTRIAL ENGINEERING. *Educ:* Univ Mich, BS, 46, MS, 47; Okla State Univ, PhD(indust eng & mgt), 60. *Prof Exp:* Prod supvr, Can Gypsum Co, Ltd, 43-44; res & develop engr, Gen Steel Wares, Ltd, 44-45; mem staff, Univ Mich, 45-46; plant mgr, Davis Woolen Mills, Ltd, Can, 46-47; assoc prof mech eng, McGill Univ, 47-52; prof gen eng & head dept, SDak Sch Mines & Technol, 52-60, actg head dept mech eng, 54-56; prof indust eng & mgt & dir eng student personnel, Okla State Univ, 60-63; prof indust eng, Syracuse Univ, 63-81; RETIRED. *Mem:* Am Soc Mech Engrs; Am Inst Indust Engrs. *Res:* Organization and management; economic analysis; management science. *Mailing Add:* 509 Maple Leaf Estates Port Charlotte FL 33952

STAFFORD, ROBERT OPPEN, b Milwaukee, Wis, Jan 28, 20; m 61; c 3. ENDOCRINOLOGY. *Educ:* Univ Wis, BA, 41, MA, 48, PhD(zool), 49. *Prof Exp:* Res scientist, Upjohn Co, 49-60, asst dir biol res, 60-62, biochem res, 62-68, asst to exec vpres pharmaceut div, 68-71, chmn & chief exec officer, Upjohn Healthcare Serv & vpres corp planning, Upjohn Co, 81-82. *Res:* Pharmacology, virology, pathology; metabolic diseases; management of research. *Mailing Add:* PO Box 125 Key Colony Beach FL 33051

STAFFORD, ROY ELMER, b Republic, Kans, Dec 28, 30; m 59; c 5. PLANT BREEDING. *Educ:* Kans State Univ, BS, 53; Univ Minn, MS, 62, PhD(genetics), 64. *Prof Exp:* Instr high sch, Nebr, 56-58; res asst, Univ Minn, 59-65; plant breeder, Am Crystal Sugar Co, Colo, 65-68; RES GENETICIST & PROJ LEADER, TEX A&M UNIV RES CTR, AGR RES SERV, USDA, 68- *Concurrent Pos:* Flax Develop Comt res fel; mem, Southern Regional Task Force New Crops & Minor Oilseeds, 74- *Mem:* Am Soc Agron; Crop Sci Soc Am; Am Soc Sugar Beet Technol. *Res:* Development of improved varieties of guar. *Mailing Add:* Tex A&M Univ Res Ctr USDA Box 1658 Vernon TX 76384

STAFFORD, THOMAS P(ATTEN), b Weatherford, Okla, Sept 17, 30; m; c 2. AERONAUTICS, ASTRONAUTICS. *Educ:* US Naval Acad, BS, 52. *Hon Degrees:* DSc, Okla City Univ, 67; LLD, Western State Univ Col Law, 69; DrCommun, Emerson Col, 69; DrAE, Embry-Riddle Aeronaut Univ, 70. *Prof Exp:* Astronaut, NASA, HQ, US Air Force, 62, backup pilot, Gemini 3, on Gemini 6 mission, 65, command pilot of Gemini 9 mission, 66, backup commander for Apollo 7, commander, Apollo 10, 69, chief astronaut officer, NASA, 69-71, dep dir flight crew opers, 71-75, commander, Air Force Flight Test Ctr, Edwards AFB, 75-78, dep chief staff res & develop, 78-80. *Honors & Awards:* Co-recipient, Astronaut Award, Am Inst Aeronaut & Astronaut, 66, Chanute Flight Award, 76; Harmon Int Aviation Trophy, 66 & 76; Vet Foreign Wars Nat Space Award, Aviation Trophy, 66 & 76; Nat Acad TV Arts & Sci Spec Trustees Award, 69; Gen Thomas D White US Air Froce Space Trophy, Nat Geog Soc, 75. *Mem:* Fel Am Astronaut Soc; Soc Exp Test Pilots; hon mem Am Fedn Radio & TV Artists. *Mailing Add:* Air Force Res & Develop Washington DC 20330

STAFSUDD, OSCAR M, JR, b Allison Park, Pa, Nov 10, 36; m 67; c 1. SOLID STATE SPECTROSCOPY. *Educ:* Univ Calif, Los Angeles, BA, 59, MS, 62, PhD(physics), 67. *Prof Exp:* Physicist, Atomics Int Div, NAm Aviation, Inc, 60-64 & Hughes Res Labs, 64-67; asst prof eng, 67-72, assoc prof eng, 74-80, assoc prof appl sci, 74-80, PROF ELEC ENG, UNIV CALIF, LOS ANGELES, 80- *Concurrent Pos:* Consult, Hughes Res Labs, 67- *Mem:* Am Phys Soc; Optical Soc Am; Am Soc Eng Educ. *Res:* Laser technology; crystal growth; solid state electronics. *Mailing Add:* Dept of Eng Univ of Calif Los Angeles CA 90024

STAGEMAN, PAUL JEROME, b Persia, Iowa, June 21, 16; m 37; c 1. BIOCHEMISTRY. *Educ:* Univ Omaha, AB, 39; Univ Iowa, MS, 50; Univ Nebr, PhD, 63. *Prof Exp:* Res chemist, Cudahy Packing Co, 39-41; from asst prof to prof chem, 41-80, EMER PROF CHEM, UNIV NEBR, OMAHA, 80- *Mem:* AAAS; Am Chem Soc; Am Inst Chemists. *Res:* Ultracentrifugation; lipoproteins; atherosclerosis; plant pigments. *Mailing Add:* Dept of Chem Univ of Nebr 60th & Dodge Sts Omaha NE 68101

STAGER, CARL VINTON, b Kitchener, Ont, June 10, 35; m 62; c 4. SOLID STATE PHYSICS. *Educ:* McMaster Univ, BSc, 58; Mass Inst Technol, PhD(physics), 61. *Prof Exp:* Mem res staff, Francis Bitter Nat Magnet Lab, Mass Inst Technol, 60-63; from asst prof to assoc prof, 63-72, PROF PHYSICS, MCMASTER UNIV, 72- *Mem:* Can Asn Physicists (treas, 64-68); Am Phys Soc. *Res:* Magnetism of insulating crystals; crystal fields spectra; electron paramagnetic resonance. *Mailing Add:* Dept of Physics McMaster Univ Hamilton ON L8S 4L8 Can

STAGER, HAROLD KEITH, b Gardena, Calif, Dec 5, 21; m 49; c 4. GEOLOGY. *Educ:* Univ Calif, Los Angeles, BA, 48. *Prof Exp:* Asst assayer, Golden Queen Mining Co, 41; geologist, Mineral Deposits Br, US Geol Surv, 48-63, Geol Br, 63-64, Base Metals Br, 64-65, field officer, Off Minerals Explor, 65-82; RETIRED. *Concurrent Pos:* Consult mining geologist, 82- *Mem:* Geol Soc Am; Soc Econ Geol; Soc Mining Eng. *Res:* Mining geology; mineral deposits; strategic and rare metals. *Mailing Add:* 3375 Alma St #258 Palo Alto CA 94306

STAGER, KENNETH EARL, b Union City, Pa, Jan 28, 15; m 58; c 2. ZOOLOGY. *Educ:* Univ Calif, Los Angeles, AB, 40; Univ Southern Calif, MS, 53, PhD, 62. *Prof Exp:* Asst curator ornith & mammal, 41-42, from curator to sr curator, 46-76, SR CURATOR EMER, LOS ANGELES COUNTY MUS NATURAL HIST, 76- *Concurrent Pos:* Adj prof, Univ Southern Calif, 62-; consult, US Dept Interior, Geol Surv, 74- *Honors & Awards:* US Typhus Comn Medal; Pub Serv Award, US Dept Interior, 72; Commendation Award, Calif Dept Fish & Game, 73. *Mem:* Am Soc Mammal; Cooper Ornith Soc; Am Ornith Union. *Res:* Ornithology; behavior; ecology; mammalogy; distribution and taxonomical problems. *Mailing Add:* LA County Mus Natural Hist 900 Exposition Blvd Los Angeles CA 90007

STAGG, RONALD M, b Brooklyn, NY; m 52; c 5. PHYSIOLOGY, ENDOCRINOLOGY. *Educ:* Tusculum Col, BA, 50; Brooklyn Col, MA, 55; Rutgers Univ, PhD(endocrinol), 62. *Prof Exp:* Asst adminr, Willard F Greenwald, Med & Chem Consult, NY, 51-53; asst to med dir admin, Warner-Chilcott Lab Div, Warner-Lambert Pharmaceut Co, NJ, 53-56; instr zool, Drew Univ, 59-60; instr physiol, Med Col Va, 60-65; assoc prof, 65-74, PROF BIOL, HARTWICK COL, 74- *Concurrent Pos:* NIH grant, 63-65. *Mem:* Am Soc Zool. *Res:* Physiology, specifically mammalian; endocrinology, specifically the relationship between hormones and nutrition. *Mailing Add:* Dept of Biol Hartwick Col Oneonta NY 13820

STAGG, WILLIAM RAY, b Lexington, Ky, Sept 15, 37; m 62; c 2. PHYSICAL INORGANIC CHEMISTRY. *Educ:* Univ Ky, BS, 59; Iowa State Univ, PhD(chem), 63. *Prof Exp:* Res chemist, FMC Corp, NJ, 63-64; res assoc chem, Univ Ill, 66-67; asst prof, Colgate Univ, 67-72; assoc prof chem, Randolph-Macon Women's Col, 72-77; SR RES CHEMIST, BABCOCK & WILCOX CO, 77- *Mem:* Am Nuclear Soc; Am Chem Soc. *Res:* Complex equilibria of lanthanide elements; heteroatom ring systems of sulfur, nitrogen and phosphorous; environmental chemistry; nuclear reactor coolant chemistry. *Mailing Add:* Lynchburg Res Ctr PO Box 235 Lynchburg VA 24505

STAGNO, SERGIO BRUNO, b Santiago, Chile, Oct 31, 41; m 68; c 1. PEDIATRICS, INFECTIOUS DISEASES. *Educ:* Univ Chile, Bachelor, 60, MD, 67. *Prof Exp:* Instr pediat & parasitol, Sch Med, Univ Chile, 70-71; res assoc pediat, 72-73, asst prof, 73-77, assoc prof microbiol, 75-81, assoc prof pediats, 77-80, PROF PEDIAT, UNIV ALA, 80-, ASSOC PROF MICROBIOL, 81- *Concurrent Pos:* Fel, Univ Ala, 71-72. *Mem:* Am Soc Microbiol; Soc Pediat Res; Chilean Pediat Soc; Chilean Parasitol Soc; Am Acad Pediats. *Mailing Add:* Rm 609 CDLD Bldg Univ of Ala University Station AL 35294

STAHEL, EDWARD P(AUL), b New York, NY, June 3, 34; m 57, 65; c 5. CHEMICAL ENGINEERING. *Educ:* Princeton Univ, BSE, 55; Univ Notre Dame, MS, 57; Ohio State Univ, PhD(chem eng), 61. *Prof Exp:* Res engr, E I du Pont de Nemours & Co, 61-62; from asst prof to assoc prof, 62-74, grad adminr, 66-72, PROF CHEM ENG, NC STATE UNIV, 74- *Mem:* AAAS; Am Chem Soc; Am Inst Chem Engrs; Am Soc Eng Educ. *Res:* Chemical engineering kinetics and reactor design; transport phenomena; polymer chemical engineering. *Mailing Add:* Dept of Chem Eng NC State Univ Raleigh NC 27607

STAHL, BARBARA JAFFE, b Brooklyn, NY, Apr 17, 30; m 51; c 4. COMPARATIVE ANATOMY, EVOLUTION. *Educ:* Wellesley Col, BA, 52; Radcliffe Col, AM, 53; Harvard Univ, PhD(biol), 65. *Prof Exp:* PROF BIOL, ST ANSELM COL, 54- *Mem:* AAAS; Soc Vert Paleont. *Res:* Evolution of holocephali and early vertebrates. *Mailing Add:* Dept of Biol St Anselm's Col Manchester NH 03102

STAHL, C(HARLES) D(REW), b Altoona, Pa, Aug 28, 23; m 48; c 1. PETROLEUM ENGINEERING. *Educ:* Pa State Univ, BS, 47, MS, 50, PhD(petrol eng), 55. *Prof Exp:* Asst, 47-48, res assoc, 49-53, from asst prof to assoc prof, 53-61, PROF PETROL ENG, PA STATE UNIV, UNIVERSITY PARK, 61-, HEAD DEPT, 62- *Concurrent Pos:* Consult, Minerals Div, Pa State Dept Forests & Waters & Socony Mobil Oil Co, Venezuela, 58. *Honors & Awards:* Am Asn Oilwell Drilling Contractors Award, 56. *Mem:* Am Inst Mining, Metall & Petrol Engrs. *Res:* Displacement of immiscible fluids in porous media. *Mailing Add:* Col Mineral Indusis Pa State Univ University Park PA 16802

STAHL, FRANKLIN WILLIAM, b Boston, Mass, Oct 8, 29; m 55; c 2. GENETICS. *Educ:* Harvard Univ, AB, 51; Univ Rochester, PhD(biol), 56. *Hon Degrees:* DSc, Oakland Univ. *Prof Exp:* Res fel biol, Calif Inst Technol, 55-58; assoc prof zool, Univ Mo, 58-59; assoc prof, 59-70, PROF BIOL, UNIV ORE, 70-, RES ASSOC, INST MOLECULAR BIOL, 59- *Mem:* Nat Acad Sci. *Res:* Genetics of bacteriophage. *Mailing Add:* Inst of Molecular Biol Univ of Ore Eugene OR 97403

STAHL, FRIEDA AXELROD, b Brooklyn, NY, May 27, 22; m 42; c 2. SOLID STATE PHYSICS. *Educ:* Hunter Col, BA, 42; Hofstra Col, MA, 57; Claremont Grad Sch, PhD(educ), 69. *Prof Exp:* Jr physicist, US Army Signal Corps, NJ & Ala, 42-44 & Petty Labs, Petty Geophys Eng Co, Tex, 44-46; physicist, Hillyer Instrument Corp, NY, 46-48; sr physicist, Sylvania Res Labs, NY, 48-52; lectr physics, 58-59, from asst prof to assoc prof, 59-73, assoc dean acad planning, 70-75, PROF PHYSICS, CALIF STATE UNIV, LOS ANGELES, 73- *Concurrent Pos:* Res assoc physics, Harvey Mudd Col, 75-76. *Mem:* Am Phys Soc; Am Asn Physics Teachers; AAAS; Sigma Xi. *Res:* Electro-optical behavior in semiconductors; ultrasound propagation in solid methane and deuteromethane as a function of temperature, with particular interest in the lambda-type phase transitions of these substances. *Mailing Add:* Dept of Physics Calif State Univ Los Angeles CA 90032

STAHL, GLENN ALLAN, b Snyder, Tex, Mar 14, 45; m 70; c 2. POLYMER CHEMISTRY. *Educ:* Univ Houston, PhD(polymer chem), 75. *Prof Exp:* Robert A Welch fel polymers, Univ Houston, 75-76; fel, Univ Ala, Tuscaloosa, 76-77; res chemist, Res & Develop Ctr, B F Goodrich Co, 77-80; SR CHEMIST, PHILLIPS PETROL CO, 80- *Concurrent Pos:* Grant adv, Paint Res Inst, 77-79. *Mem:* Am Chem Soc. *Res:* Water soluble polymers; polymers for oil revovery; science education thru industry/academic cooperation; anchored organic reagents. *Mailing Add:* Phillips Petrol Co Res & Develop Bartlesville OK 74004

STAHL, JOHN BENTON, b Columbus, Ohio, Mar 28, 30; m 74; c 1. LIMNOLOGY. *Educ:* Iowa State Univ, BS, 51; Ind Univ, AM, 53, PhD(zool), 58. *Prof Exp:* Sessional lectr biol, Queen's Univ, Ont, 58-59; asst prof, Thiel Col, 59-63; asst prof, Wash State Univ, 63-66; asst prof, 66-72, ASSOC PROF BIOL, SOUTHERN ILL UNIV, 72- *Mem:* AAAS; Am Soc Limnol & Oceanog, Ecol Soc Am; Int Asn Theoret & Appl Limnol. *Res:* Chironomidae and Chaoborus. *Mailing Add:* Dept of Zool Southern Ill Univ Carbondale IL 62901

STAHL, LADDIE L, b Terre Haute, Ind, Dec 23, 21; m 42; c 3. FLUID MECHANICS. *Educ:* Purdue Univ, BS, 42; Johns Hopkins Univ, MS, 50. *Prof Exp:* Mgr prod planning & mkt res, Guided Missile Dept, Pa, 54-55 & Missile & Space Vehicle Dept, 55-59, mgr tech planning, Gen Eng Lab, NY, 59-60, mgr tech rels, 60-61, mgr spec projs, 61-62, mgr advan tech appln, Advan Technol Lab, 62-64, mgr, Info Eng Lab, 64-65, mgr, Res & Develop Appln, 65-74, MGR, ELECTRONICS SYSTS PROG OPER, ELECTRONICS SCI & ENG, CORP RES & DEVELOP, GEN ELEC CO,

74- *Concurrent Pos:* Alternate mem, Dept Army Gen Staff Comt Army Reserve Policy, 63-66; chmn electronic adv group, US Army Electronics Command, 71-; mem, Nat Adv Comt Jobs for Veterans; mem, Nat Adv Coun Employer Support Guard & Reserve, 72; dir, Instrnl Industs, Inc, 72-; US Army Sci Bd, 78. *Honors & Awards:* Distinguished Serv Medal, US of Am, 77. *Mem:* Sr mem Inst Elec & Electronics Engrs; Am Inst Aeronaut & Astronaut; Am Defense Preparedness Asn. *Res:* Velocity fields induced by supersonic lifting surfaces; weapon system design and selection; comparative ranking system to evaluate the attractiveness of new business. *Mailing Add:* Corp Res & Develop Gen Elec Co PO Box 8 Schenectady NY 12301

STAHL, NEIL, b Sheridan, Ind, June 11, 42; m 67. MATHEMATICAL ANALYSIS. *Educ:* Ind Univ, Bloomington, AB, 64; Brown Univ, PhD(appl math), 70. *Prof Exp:* Asst prof ecosyst anal, Univ Wis-Green Bay, Marinette Campus, 69-72, asst prof math, Univ Wis Ctr, Marinette Campus, 72-76; ASSOC PROF MATH, UNIV WIS CTR, FOX VALLEY CAMPUS, 76- *Mem:* Soc Indust & Appl Math. *Res:* Differential equations and their applications; mathematical biology. *Mailing Add:* Univ Wis Ctr Fox Valley Campus Midway Rd Menasha WI 54952

STAHL, PHILIP DAMIEN, b Wheeling, WVa, Oct 4, 41; m 68; c 3. PHYSIOLOGY, CELL BIOLOGY. *Educ:* WLiberty State Col, BS, 64; WVa Univ, PhD(pharmacol), 67. *Prof Exp:* From asst prof to assoc prof, 71-81, PROF PHYSIOL, MED SCH, WASH UNIV, 82- *Concurrent Pos:* Fel, Space Sci Res Ctr, Univ Mo, 67; Arthritis Found fel molecular biol, Vanderbilt Univ, 68-70. *Mem:* Brit Biochem Soc; Am Chem Soc; Am Physiol Soc. *Res:* Lysosomes. *Mailing Add:* Dept of Physiol Wash Univ Med Sch St Louis MO 63110

STAHL, RALPH HENRY, b Berlin, Ger, Dec 29, 26; US citizen; m 55; c 3. EXPERIMENTAL PHYSICS. *Educ:* Harvard Univ, AB, 49, MA, 50, PhD(nuclear physics), 54. *Prof Exp:* Mem tech staff, Radiation Lab, Univ Calif, 54-56; mem tech staff, Gen Atomic Div, Gen Dynamics Corp, 56-68; secy-treas, Systs, Sci & Software, 68-72; MEM TECH STAFF, IRT CORP, 72- *Concurrent Pos:* Vis prof, Univ Ill, Urbana, 61. *Mem:* Am Phys Soc; Am Nuclear Soc. *Res:* Nuclear weapons effects on military systems; electronics and electronics components; nuclear reactor physics. *Mailing Add:* 3060 Cranbrook Ct La Jolla CA 92037

STAHL, ROLAND, EDGAR, b Northumberland, Pa, Sept 2, 25; m 55; c 2. ORGANIC CHEMISTRY. *Educ:* Bucknell Univ, BS, 50; Cornell Univ, PhD(chem), 54. *Prof Exp:* Asst org chem, Cornell Univ, 50-53; res chemist, Am Cyanamid Co, 54-56; res chemist, NY, 56-60, Tenn, 60-65, res chemist, 65-75, mkt res rep, 75-77, toxicol & regional affairs coordr, 77-78, SR REGULATORY AFFAIRS SPECIALIST, E I DU PONT DE NEMOURS & CO, INC, DEL, 78- *Mem:* Am Chem Soc. *Res:* Peroxide and radical chemistry; polymer applications; adhesives; textile finishing and applications. *Mailing Add:* E I du Pont de Nemours & Co Wilmington DE 19898

STAHL, S SIGMUND, b Berlin, Ger, June 16, 25; nat; m 47; c 1. PERIODONTOLOGY, ORAL PATHOLOGY. *Educ:* Univ Minn, DDS, 47; Univ Ill, MS, 49; Am Bd Periodont, dipl. *Prof Exp:* Res assoc periodont, 49-50, from instr to prof, 50-71, PROF PERIODONT & ORAL MED & CHMN DEPT, COL DENT, NY UNIV, 71-, ASSOC DEAN ACAD AFFAIRS, 78- *Concurrent Pos:* Attend, Vet Admin Hosp, Brooklyn, 50-53; consult, 58-; exec secy, Guggenheim Found Inst Dent Res, NY Univ, 64- *Honors & Awards:* Award, Int Asn Dent Res, 71; Award, Am Acad Periodont, 76. *Mem:* AAAS; Sigma Xi; Am Dent Asn; fel Am Med Writers Asn; fel Am Col Dent. *Res:* Periodontal pathology; clinical treatment evaluation; wound healing. *Mailing Add:* Dept Periodont 421 First Ave New York NY 10010

STAHL, SAUL, b Antwerp, Belg, Jan 23, 42; US citizen; m 72. MATHEMATICS. *Educ:* Brooklyn Col, BA, 63; Univ Calif, Berkeley, MA, 66; Western Mich Univ, PhD(math), 75. *Prof Exp:* Systs programmer, Int Bus Mach, 69-73; asst prof math, Wright State Univ, 75-77; asst prof, 77-80, ASSOC PROF MATH, UNIV KANS, 80- *Mem:* Math Asn Am; Am Math Soc. *Res:* Graph theory; combinatorial topology. *Mailing Add:* Dept of Math Univ of Kans Lawrence KS 66044

STAHL, STANLEY HERSHEL, b Sharon, Pa, Aug 7, 43; m 68; c 1. MATHEMATICS. *Educ:* Wayne State Univ, BPh, 65; Univ Mich, MA, 67, PhD(math), 74. *Prof Exp:* Vis asst prof math, Trinity Col, Hartford, Conn, 76-77; instr, 77-78, asst prof math, Smith Col & Mt Holyoke Col, 78-80; WITH MITRE CORP, 80- *Concurrent Pos:* Instr math, Western New Eng Col, Springfield, Mass, 76 & Westfield State Col, Mass, 76-77. *Mem:* Am Math Soc; Asn Symbolic Logic. *Res:* Foundations of mathematics; set theory; recursion theory; logic; philosophy and history of mathematics. *Mailing Add:* Mitre Corp Bedford MA 01730

STAHL, WALTER BERNARD, b New York, NY, Aug 28, 28. PARASITOLOGY. *Educ:* Brooklyn Col, BA, 52; Columbia Univ, MS, 56, PhD(parasitol), 60. *Prof Exp:* Asst biol, Brooklyn Col, 52; asst entom, Univ Fla, 53-54; NIH asst, Biol Sta, Univ Mich, 56; lab instr parasitol, Columbia Univ, 56-59; instr med microbiol, Seton Hall Col Med & Dent, 59-61; res fel, Sch Trop Med, Univ PR, 61-62; NIH res fel, Sch Med, Keio Univ, Japan, 62-66; trainee trop dis, Sch Med, Nat Univ Mex, 66-67; res fel, Palo Alto Med Res Found, 67-68; res assoc trop med, Univ PR, San Juan, 68-69 & Trop Dis Clin, Dept Health, City of New York, 69-70; SR RES SCIENTIST, DEPT HEALTH, NY STATE, 70- *Concurrent Pos:* Fel trop med & parasitol, La State Univ, 60. *Mem:* AAAS; Am Soc Parasitologists; Am Soc Trop Med & Hyg; NY Acad Sci; Japanese Soc Parasitol. *Res:* Immunology of parasitic diseases; toxoplasmosis; schistosomiasis; oxyuriasis. *Mailing Add:* Div of Labs & Res NY State Dept of Health Albany NY 12201

STAHL, WILLIAM J, b New York, NY, Jan 3, 39; m 64; c 1. BIOCHEMISTRY. *Educ:* Merrimack Col, AB, 60; Fordham Univ, MS, 61; St John's Univ, NY, PhD(biochem), 69. *Prof Exp:* Res asst biochem, Albert Einstein Med Ctr, 62-64; res chemist, Tenneco Chem Inc, 64-65; asst prof,

65-74, ASSOC PROF BIOCHEM, JOHN JAY COL CRIMINAL JUSTICE, 74- *Mem:* AAAS; Am Soc Microbiol; Am Chem Soc. *Res:* Enzymes associated with invasive microbes and biochemical intermediates; development of vaccine for heroin and related alkaloids. *Mailing Add:* Dept of Biochem 445 W 59th St New York NY 10019

STAHL, WILLIAM LOUIS, b Glen Dale, WVa, Aug 2, 36; m 59; c 2. BIOCHEMISTRY, NEUROCHEMISTRY. *Educ:* Univ Notre Dame, BS, 58; Univ Pittsburgh, PhD(biochem), 63. *Prof Exp:* Res assoc biochem, NIH, 65-67; res asst prof physiol & med, 67-71, assoc prof physiol & med, 71-77, PROF PHYSIOL & BIOPHYS & MED, SCH MED, UNIV WASH, 77- CHIEF NEUROCHEM, VET ADMIN HOSP, SEATTLE, 67- *Concurrent Pos:* United Cerebral Palsy Res & Educ Found fel, Biochem Dept, Inst Psychiat, Maudsley Hosp, Univ London, 63-65. *Mem:* Am Chem Soc; Am Soc Biol Chemists; Soc Neurosci; Am Soc Neurochem; Int Soc Neurochem. *Res:* Chemistry and metabolism of the nervous system; energy linked transport systems; structure and function of biological membranes. *Mailing Add:* Div of Neurol Univ of Wash Sch of Med Seattle WA 98195

STAHLEY, WILLIAM, b Stuttgart, Ark, Sept 30, 28; m 53; c 2. ELECTRICAL ENGINEERING. *Educ:* Okla State Univ, BS, 57, MS, 59, PhD(eng), 64. *Prof Exp:* Staff mem, Sandia Corp, 57-58; instr elec eng, Okla State Univ, 58-60; sr engr, Autonetics Div, NAm Aviation, Inc, 61-63, tech specialist, 63-65, CHIEF AVIONIC DATA PROCESSING, N AM ROCKWELL CORP, 65- *Mem:* Inst Elec & Electronics Engrs. *Res:* Digital computational requirements for various military and industrial control systems; derivation of mechanization equations, specification of hardware and definition of programming requirements. *Mailing Add:* 18348 Mt Watermn Fountain Valley CA 92708

STAHLMAN, CLARENCE L, b Courtland, Kans, Apr 3, 21; m 43; c 1. DAIRY INDUSTRY. *Educ:* Kans State Univ, BS, 49; Hofstra Col, MS, 54. *Prof Exp:* Asst prof dairy indust, 50-61, assoc prof, 61-70, prof food processing technol, 70-72, technol, 70-76, PROF FOOD TECH, STATE UNIV NY AGR & TECH COL FARMINGDALE, 77- *Res:* Dairy food products. *Mailing Add:* Dept of Food Processing Technol State Univ NY Agr & Tech Col Farmingdale NY 11735

STAHLMAN, MILDRED, b Nashville, Tenn, July 31, 22. PEDIATRICS, PHYSIOLOGY. *Educ:* Vanderbilt Univ, BA, 43, MD, 46; Am Bd Pediat, dipl, 54. *Prof Exp:* From instr to asst prof pediat, 51-64, from instr to asst prof physiol, 54-61, assoc prof pediat, 64-70, PROF PEDIAT, SCH MED, VANDERBILT UNIV, 70- *Concurrent Pos:* Lederle med fac award, 61-63; USPHS career develop award, 63-68; mem human embryol & develop study sect, USPHS, 64-68; perinatal biol, Infant Mortality Study Sect, 69-73; Adv Child Health & Human Develop Coun, 76- *Mem:* Soc Pediat Res; Am Pediat Soc; Am Physiol Soc; Am Fedn Clin Res. *Res:* Newborn cardiorespiratory and fetal physiology; cardiology; rheumatic fever. *Mailing Add:* Dept of Pediat Vanderbilt Univ Sch of Med Nashville TN 37203

STAHLMAN, PHILLIP WAYNE, b Shattuck, Okla, Jan 4, 48; m 69; c 2. WEED SCIENCE, AGRONOMY. *Educ:* Panhandle State Univ, BS, 70; NDak State Univ, MS, 73. *Prof Exp:* Asst agronomist, NCent Br, NDak Agr Ecp Sta, 72-75; Supt agron res, Harvey County Exp Field Agron, Kans State Univ, 75-76; RES AGRONOMIST WEED CONTROL, FT HAYS BR, KANS AGR EXP STA, 76- *Mem:* Weed Sci Soc Am; Am Soc Agron. *Res:* Weed control in dryland wheat and grain sorghum; chemical fallow and reduced tillage systems; control of field bindweed. *Mailing Add:* Ft Hays Exp Sta Hays KS 67601

STAHLY, DONALD PAUL, b Columbus, Ohio, May 29, 37; m 59; c 2. MICROBIOLOGY. *Educ:* Ohio State Univ, BS, 59, MS, 61; Univ Ill, PhD(microbiol), 65. *Prof Exp:* NIH fel, Univ Minn, 65-66; from asst prof to assoc prof, 66-79, PROF MICROBIOL, UNIV IOWA, 79- *Concurrent Pos:* Sabbatical, Scripp's Clin & Res Found, 77-78. *Mem:* AAAS; Am Soc Microbiol; Sigma Xi. *Res:* Bacterial sporulation and changes in amino acid metabolism during differentiation; plasmids and bacteriophages in Bacillus species and gene cloning; Bacillus species pathogenic for insects. *Mailing Add:* Dept of Microbiol Univ of Iowa Iowa City IA 52242

STAHLY, EDWARD ARTHUR, b Tiskilwa, Ill, Jan 31, 26; m 55; c 2. HORTICULTURE. *Educ:* Univ Ill, BS, 52; Univ Md, MS, 55, PhD, 59. *Prof Exp:* Horticulturist, Plant Indust Sta, 59-64, HORTICULTURIST, USDA, WASH, 64- *Mem:* Am Soc Hort Sci. *Res:* Fruit set and flower initiation of apple, pear and peach as influenced by synthetic and endogenous hormones; calcium nutrition of apple and pear. *Mailing Add:* Agr Res Serv USDA 1104 N Western Ave Wenatchee WA 98801

STAHLY, ELDON EVERETT, b Danvers, Ill, Feb 13, 08; m 46; c 2. ORGANIC CHEMISTRY. *Educ:* Bluffton Col, BA, 29; Ohio State Univ, MA, 31; Pa State Col, PhD(org chem), 34. *Prof Exp:* Asst chem, Ohio State Univ, 29-31; asst chem, Pa State Col, 33-34; res chemist, Gen Elec Co, 34; res chemist, Standard Oil Co, La, 35-41; sr fel & admin fel, Mellon Inst, 41-48; dir chem res, Commercial Solvents 77- 48-50; dir res, Burke Res Co, Mich & Fla, 50-63; proj mgr, Contract Res, W R Grace & Co, 63-72; ASSOC, TRIDENT ENG ASSOCS, 72- *Concurrent Pos:* Consult patents for chem processes, 72-; consult, Polymer Inst, Univ Detroit, 72-77; US ed, Flammability News Bulletin, 73-79; assoc ed, Elsevier Int Bulletins, 80- & Rubber & Plastics Fire & Flammability, 80-, Hazards Review, 80-; registered prof eng & expert witness on fires & explosions, 73-; consult, Cadcom, Inc, 77- *Mem:* AAAS; Am Chem Soc; Am Inst Chemists; Am Inst Chem Eng; Brit Soc Chem Indust. *Res:* Resins; petroleum chemical processes; production of butadiene; manufacture of elastomers and their reinforcement; polymerizations; toxic chemical agents; flame-proofing combustibles; removal of carcinogens from tobacco smoke; developed antiozonants for rubber compositions. *Mailing Add:* 2813 Deerfield Dr Ellicott City MD 21043

STAHMANN, MARK ARNOLD, b Spanish Fork, Utah, May 30, 14; m 41; c 2. BIOCHEMISTRY. *Educ:* Brigham Young Univ, BA, 36; Univ Wis, PhD(biochem), 41. *Prof Exp:* Asst chem, Rockefeller Inst, 42-44; res assoc org chem, Mass Inst Technol, 44-45; res assoc biochem, 46-47, from asst prof to assoc prof, 47-56, PROF BIOCHEM, UNIV WIS-MADISON, 56- *Concurrent Pos:* Guggenheim fel, Pasteur Inst, Paris, 55; Fulbright scholar, Nagoya, 67; FAO consult, Biol Inst, Sao Paulo, 74. *Mem:* AAAS; Am Chem Soc; Am Soc Biol Chemists; Soc Exp Biol & Med; Am Phytopath Soc. *Res:* Anticoagulant 4-hydroxycoumarins; warfarin; biochemistry of plant diseases; synthetic polypeptides; polypeptidyl proteins; virus diseases; plant proteins; molecular pathology of atherosclerosis. *Mailing Add:* Dept of Biochem Univ of Wis Madison WI 53706

STAHNKE, HERBERT LUDWIG, b Chicago, Ill, June 10, 02; m 29; c 2. SCORPIOLOGY, SYSTEMATICS. *Educ:* Univ Chicago, SB, 28; Univ Ariz, MA, 34; Iowa State Univ, PhD(zool), 39. *Prof Exp:* Teacher pub schs, Ariz, 28-40; assoc prof sci, 41-47, prof zool & dir poisonous animals res lab, 47-72, head div life sci, 50-62, EMER PROF ZOOL & EMER DIR POISONOUS ANIMALS RES LAB, ARIZ STATE UNIV, 72- *Mem:* AAAS; Soc Syst Zool; Fel Explorers Club; Sigma Xi; Am Inst Biol Sci. *Res:* Scorpion taxonomy and biogeography; scorpion anti-venom. *Mailing Add:* 2625 E Southern Ave Cot 65 Tempe AZ 85282

STAIANO, EDWARD FRANK, fluid mechanics, computer science, see previous edition

STAIB, JON ALBERT, b Toledo, Ohio, Mar 23, 40; m 67; c 2. COSMIC RAY PHYSICS. *Educ:* Univ Toledo, BS, 63; Case Western Reserve Univ, MS, 67, PhD(physics), 69. *Prof Exp:* Asst prof, 69-70, ASSOC PROF PHYSICS, JAMES MADISON UNIV, VA, 70- *Mem:* Am Asn Physics Teachers; Int Planetarium Soc. *Res:* Gamma ray astronomy; atmospheric gamma radiation. *Mailing Add:* Dept of Physics James Madison Univ Harrisonburg VA 22801

STAIFF, DONALD C, b Everett, Wash, Feb 26, 36; m 59; c 2. PHARMACEUTICAL CHEMISTRY, BIONUCLEONICS. *Educ:* Univ Wash, BS, 59, PhD(pharmaceut chem), 63. *Prof Exp:* Asst prof pharmaceut chem, Ohio Northern Univ, 63-64; asst prof pharmaceut chem & bionucleonics, NDak State Univ, 64-67; anal res chemist, Western Pesticide Res Lab, Nat Commun Dis Ctr, USPHS, Wash, 67-72; CHIEF CHEMIST, WENATCHEE RES STA, ENVIRON PROTECTION AGENCY, 72- *Concurrent Pos:* Mead-Johnson Labs grant, 64-65; NSF inst grant, 65-66; Soc Sigma Xi grant-in-aid res, 65-66; guest lectr, Training Prog, Perrine Primate Res Lab, Environ Protection Agency, Fla. *Mem:* Am Pharmaceut Asn; Am Chem Soc; Health Physics Soc. *Res:* Conformational and configurational studies of some substituted phenyl-cyclohexane compounds by modern instrumental methods; metabolism studies including use of radiotracer techniques; effect of pesticides on health and persistence in the environment. *Mailing Add:* Wenatchee Res Sta Box 219 Environ Protection Agency Wenatchee WA 98801

STAIGER, JON CRAWFORD, biological oceanography, ichthyology, see previous edition

STAIGER, ROGER POWELL, b Trenton, NJ, Nov 23, 21; m 44; c 1. ORGANIC CHEMISTRY. *Educ:* Ursinus Col, BS, 43; Univ Pa, MS, 48, PhD, 53. *Prof Exp:* From instr to assoc prof, 43-63, PROF & CHMN DEPT CHEM, URSINUS COL, 63- *Concurrent Pos:* Consult, Maumee Chem Co, 55-64; vis prof, Temple Univ, 63- & Alexandria Hosp, Nevis, 68- *Mem:* Am Chem Soc; Sigma Xi. *Res:* Synthesis of organic heterocyclic compounds. *Mailing Add:* 707 Chestnut St Collegeville PA 19426

STAIKOS, DIMITRI NICKOLAS, b Piraeus, Greece, Dec 18, 19; m 47; c 2. ELECTROCHEMISTRY. *Educ:* Nat Univ Athens, dipl, 42; Western Reserve Univ, MS, 50, PhD(chem), 51. *Prof Exp:* Off Naval Res asst, Western Reserve Univ, 49-50; res chemist, Pa, 56-60, res engr, Eng Res Lab, 56-60, sr res phys chemist, 60-64, SR RES PHYS CHEMIST, CENT RES DEPT, EXP STA, E I DU PONT DE NEMOURS & CO, INC, 64- *Concurrent Pos:* Instr, St Joseph's Col, Pa, 54-55. *Mem:* Am Chem Soc; Electrochem Soc. *Res:* Fundamentals of electrochemical processes; corrosion; electronic instrumentation; ultrasonics; surface tension; fused salts; electrochemistry in nonaqueous solutions; electroless deposition. *Mailing Add:* 1306 Quincy Dr Wilmington DE 19803

STAINER, DENNIS WILLIAM, b Liverpool, Eng, Aug 25, 32; m 57; c 2. BIOCHEMISTRY, MICROBIOLOGY. *Educ:* Univ Liverpool, BSc, 54, Hons, 55, PhD(biochem), 58. *Prof Exp:* ASST DIR, CONNAUGHT LABS, LTD, 60- *Concurrent Pos:* Nat Res Coun Can fel biochem, Food & Drug Directorate, 57-59. *Mem:* Am Soc Microbiol; Int Asn Biol Standardization. *Res:* Production of diphtheria and tetanus toxoids and pertussis vaccine and studies on their immunogenicity; development of new bacteriological media and their application in bacterial fermentations; immunology. *Mailing Add:* 159 Driscoll Rd Richmond Hill ON L4C 4H8 Can

STAINER, HOWARD MARTIN, b London, Eng, Jan 19, 37; US citizen; m 61; c 4. COMPUTER SCIENCES. *Educ:* Queen's Col, NY, BS, 56; Calif Inst Technol, MS, 61; Univ Md, PhD(physics), 66. *Prof Exp:* PHYSICIST, APPL PHYSICS LAB, JOHNS HOPKINS UNIV, 66- *Mem:* Am Phys Soc; affil mem Inst Elec & Electronics Eng. *Res:* Advanced computer systems and techniques; software engineering and research; verification tools. *Mailing Add:* Appl Physics Lab Johns Hopkins Rd Johns Hopkins Univ Laurel MD 20810

STAINS, HOWARD JAMES, b Frenchtown, NJ, Apr 16, 24; m 54; c 3. ZOOLOGY. *Educ:* NC State Col, BS, 49, MS, 52; Univ Kans, PhD(zool), 55. *Prof Exp:* Lab instr econ zool, NC State Col, 48, res biologist, 49-51; res biologist, Univ Kans, 51-54, instr biol, 54-55; from asst prof to assoc prof, 55-71, PROF ZOOL, UNIV SOUTHERN ILL, 71- *Mem:* Wildlife Soc; Ecol Soc Am; Am Soc Mammal; Soc Study Evolution. *Res:* Furbearing mammals; osteology and ecology of mammals; wildlife techniques. *Mailing Add:* Dept of Zool Southern Ill Univ Carbondale IL 62901

STAINSBY, WENDELL NICHOLLS, b New York, NY, Nov 14, 28; m 52; c 4. PHYSIOLOGY. *Educ:* Bucknell Univ, AB, 51; Johns Hopkins Univ, ScD(physiol), 55. *Prof Exp:* From instr to assoc prof, 57-69, PROF PHYSIOL, COL MED, UNIV FLA, 69- *Concurrent Pos:* NIH res grant, 58- *Mem:* Am Physiol Soc; Am Col Sports Med. *Res:* Circulatory and muscle physiology; muscle metabolism and circulation; tissue gas transport. *Mailing Add:* Dept of Physiol Univ of Fla Col of Med Gainesville FL 32610

STAIR, PETER CURRAN, b Pasadena, Calif, Jan 25, 50. PHYSICAL CHEMISTRY. *Educ:* Stanford Univ, BS, 72; Univ Calif, Berkeley, PhD(chem), 77. *Prof Exp:* ASST PROF CHEM, NORTHWESTERN UNIV, 77- *Mem:* Am Vacuum Soc; Am Phys Soc; Am Chem Soc. *Res:* Structure and chemistry of metal and metal oxide surfaces, catalysis, and corrosion. *Mailing Add:* Dept of Chem Northwestern Univ Evanston IL 60201

STAIR, WILLIAM K(ENNETH), b Clinton, Tenn, Oct 1, 20; m 45; c 2. MECHANICAL ENGINEERING. *Educ:* Univ Tenn, BS, 48, MS, 49. *Prof Exp:* Asst engr, Tenn Rwy Co, 39-41; eng aide, Tenn Valley Authority, 41-43; instr mech eng, Univ Tenn, 48-49; res participant nuclear eng, Oak Ridge Inst Nuclear Studies, 49-50; from asst prof to assoc prof mech eng, 50-62, assoc dir eng exp sta, 70-76, assoc dean res, 70-72, PROF MECH ENG, UNIV TENN, KNOXVILLE, 62-, ASSOC DEAN RES, COL ENG, 72- *Mem:* Fel Am Soc Lubrication Engrs; Am Soc Mech Engrs. *Res:* Lubrication and fluid dynamics; heat transfer; combustion phenomena. *Mailing Add:* Col Eng 101 Perkins Hall Univ Tenn Knoxville TN 37916

STAIRS, GERALD RAY, genetics, forestry, see previous edition

STAIRS, GORDON R, b Millville, NB, May 18, 32; m 54; c 4. INSECT PATHOLOGY. *Educ:* Univ NB, BSc, 54; McGill Univ, MSc, 58, PhD(entom), 63. *Prof Exp:* Res officer forest entom, Can Dept Agr, 54-58; res scientist, Insect Path Res Inst, 58-65; from asst prof to assoc prof, 65-73, PROF ENTOM, OHIO STATE UNIV, 73- *Res:* Natural population biology and the effects of microorganisms on these populations; possible utilization of microorganisms in the control of pest populations; forest entomology and insect ecology. *Mailing Add:* Dept of Zool & Entom Ohio State Univ Columbus OH 43210

STAIRS, ROBERT ARDAGH, b Montreal, Que, June 10, 25; m 48; c 2. SOLUTION PROPERTIES, ACID PRECIPITATION. *Educ:* McGill Univ, BSc, 48; Univ Western Ont, MSc, 51; Cornell Univ, PhD(inorg chem), 55. *Prof Exp:* Instr chem, Cornell Univ, 53-55; lectr, Queen's Univ, Ont, 55-58; asst prof, 58-64; actg chmn dept, 66-67, assoc prof, 64-74, PROF CHEM, TRENT UNIV, 74- *Mem:* Fel Chem Inst Can; AAAS; Am Chem Soc; Sigma Xi. *Res:* Physical properties of electrolyte solutions; viscosity of solutions; metal-ammonia solutions; analysis acid precipitation; viscosity of solutions. *Mailing Add:* Dept of Chem Trent Univ Peterborough ON K9J 7B8 Can

STAKE, PAUL ERIK, b Grandy, Minn, Jan 15, 44; m 66; c 3. ANIMAL NUTRITION. *Educ:* Univ Minn, BS, 68; SDak State Univ, MS, 71; Univ Ga, PhD(nutrit biochem), 74. *Prof Exp:* Lab supvr dairy sci, SDak State Univ, 68-71; res animal nutrit, Univ Ga, 71-74; asst prof, 74-79, ASSOC PROF NUTRIT SCI, UNIV CONN, 79- *Mem:* Am Dairy Sci Asn; Am Chem Soc; Am Soc Animal Sci; Nutrit Today Soc; Am Inst Nutrit. *Res:* Comparative metabolism of dietary essential and non-essential trace elements in animals and humans. *Mailing Add:* Dept of Nutrit Sci Univ of Conn Storrs CT 06268

STAKER, DONALD DAVID, b Wheelersburg, Ohio, Jan 16, 26; m 47; c 4. ORGANIC CHEMISTRY. *Educ:* Ohio Univ, BS, 47, MS, 48; Ohio State Univ, PhD(chem), 52. *Prof Exp:* Asst, Ohio Univ, 44-45, 47-48; asst, Ohio State Univ, 48-49, res fel, 49-52; res chemist, Monsanto Chem Co, 52-56, res proj leader, 56-57, res group leader, 57-61; res sect leader, 61-67, RES SECT MGR, FATTY ACID DIV, EMERY INDUSTS, INC, 67- *Mem:* Am Chem Soc; Am Oil Chem Soc. *Res:* Fatty acid chemistry, production processes, utilization; reaction mechanisms; rubber chemicals; polymer properties; lubricant additives; process development; metalworking lubricants. *Mailing Add:* Res Lab 4900 Este Ave Emery Industs Inc Cincinnati OH 45232

STAKER, MICHAEL RAY, b Dayton, Ohio, Nov 25, 47; m 76. METALLURGY, MECHANICAL ENGINEERING. *Educ:* Univ Dayton, BME, 70; Mass Inst Technol, MS, 71, PhD(metall), 75. *Prof Exp:* Mat engr, Gen Elec Aircraft Engine Group, 75-78; METALLURGIST, ARMY MAT & MECHANICS RES CTR, 78- *Concurrent Pos:* Lectr, Dept Mech Eng, Northeastern Univ. *Mem:* Am Soc Metals; Am Soc Testing & Mat. *Res:* Metal defects and structure by electron microscopy; structure and mechanical property relations in metals; fractography, fatigue, fracture; dislocations; high temperature deformation of metals; super alloys; failure analysis. *Mailing Add:* 40 Beaver Rd Reading MA 01867

STAKER, ROBERT D, b Newport, RI, July 3, 45. PHYCOLOGY. *Educ:* Univ Dayton, BS, 67, MBA, 81; Univ Ariz, MS, 71, PhD(bot), 73. *Prof Exp:* Res asst phycol, Dept Biol, Univ PEI, 73-75; asst res scientist phytoplanktology, NY Ocean Sci Lab, 75-79; admin asst, Univ Dayton, 79-81; MGT ANALYST, WRIGHT-PATTERSON AFB, 81- *Mem:* Am Soc Limnol & Oceanog; Phycol Soc Am; Int Soc Limnol; Sigma Xi; Nat Estimating Soc. *Res:* Marine and freshwater algal taxonomy and ecology; resource management. *Mailing Add:* AFLC/ACM Wright-Patterson AFB Fairborn OH 45433

STAKER, WILLIAM PAUL, b Aberdeen, SDak, Apr 9, 19; m 49; c 2. REACTOR PHYSICS. *Educ:* Ill State Univ, BS, 40; Univ Iowa, MS, 42; NY Univ, PhD(physics), 50. *Prof Exp:* Asst, Univ Iowa, 41-42; physicist & chief ballistic engr, Burnside Lab, E I du Pont de Nemours & Co, 42-46; res assoc, NY Univ, 46-50, proj dir, Res Div, Col Eng, 47-50; assoc physicist, Argonne Nat Lab, 50-52, group leader, 52; sr proj physicist, Eng Res Dept, Standard Oil Co, Ind, 52-56; sr physicist, Nuclear Div, 56-57, mgr exp physics, 57-59, mgr physics, Naval Reactors Div, 59-61, mgr eng & physics, 61-67, mgr fast breeder develop, Nuclear Power Dept, 67-73, mgr prod eng & develop,

analysis, Nuclear Power Systs, 73-75, mgr, C-E/KWU coordr, 75-79, PROJ MGR, LIQUID METAL FAST BREEDER REACTOR DEVELOP, NUCLEAR POWER SYSTS, COMBUSTION ENG, INC, 79- *Mem:* Am Phys Soc; Am Nuclear Soc. *Res:* Neutron physics; reactor engineering; tracer studies and radioisotope applications. *Mailing Add:* 64 Glenbrook Rd West Hartford CT 06107

STAKES, DEBRA SUE, b Winnsboro, Tex, Jan 7, 51. MARINE GEOCHEMISTRY, GEOLOGY. *Educ:* Rice Univ, BA(geol) & BA(chem), 73; Ore State Univ, PhD(oceanog), 78. *Prof Exp:* Res assoc marine geochem, Mass Inst Technol, 78-80; MEM FAC, DIV GEOLOGICAL & PLANETARY SCI, CALIF INST TECHNOL, 80- *Mem:* Am Geophys Union; Geol Soc Am; Union Concerned Scientists. *Res:* Chemical and mineralogical evidence of seawater interacting with oceanic rocks; origin and structure of oceanic crust. *Mailing Add:* Div Geological & Planetary Sci Calif Inst Technol Pasadena CA 91125

STAKGOLD, IVAR, b Oslo, Norway, Dec 13, 25; nat US. APPLIED MATHEMATICS. *Educ:* Cornell Univ, BME, 45, MME, 46; Harvard Univ, MA, 48, PhD(appl math), 49. *Prof Exp:* From instr to asst prof appl math, Harvard Univ, 49-56; head math & logistics brs, US Off Naval Res, 56-59; assoc prof eng sci, Northwestern Univ, Evanston, 60-64, prof eng sci & math, 64-75, chmn dept eng sci, 69-75; PROF & CHMN DEPT MATH SCI, UNIV DEL, 75- *Concurrent Pos:* Vis asst prof, Stanford Univ, 53-54; consult, Sylvania Elec Prod, Inc, 56-; lectr, Cath Univ Am, 57-58; liaison scientist, US Off Naval Res, London, 67-69; vis prof, Oxford Univ, 73-74 & Univ Col, London, 78; consult, Environ Protection Agency, 74-; assoc ed, Am Math Monthly, Appl Anal, Int J Eng Sci. *Mem:* Am Math Soc; Soc Indust & Appl Math. *Res:* Nonlinear boundary value problems. *Mailing Add:* Dept of Math Sci Univ of Del Newark DE 19711

STAKLIS, ANDRIS A, b Valmiera, Latvia, Feb 4, 39; US citizen; m 61; c 1. ORGANIC CHEMISTRY. *Educ:* Univ Nebr, BS, 61, PhD(org chem), 65. *Prof Exp:* Asst head mat develop sect, Manned Spacecraft Ctr, NASA, 65-67; sr scientist, Bell Aerospace Co Div, Textron Inc, mgr mat develop, New Orleans Oper, 71-77; MGR ENG MAT, BRAKE & STEERING DIV, BENDIX CORP, 77- *Mem:* Am Chem Soc; Am Soc Test & Mat; Soc Automotive Engrs; Am Soc Metals; Sigma Xi. *Res:* Direct materials development for air cushion ships; development and evaluation of nonmetallic materials; corrosion and stress corrosion protection of metallic materials; cavitation-erosion damage. *Mailing Add:* Bendix ACSGE PO Box 4001 South Bend IN 46634

STAKNIS, VICTOR RICHARD, b Bridgewater, Mass, June 14, 20; m 42. MATHEMATICS. *Educ:* Bridgewater Teachers Col, BS, 42; Mass Inst Technol, BS, 46; Boston Univ, MA, 50, PhD(math), 53. *Prof Exp:* Instr math, Ft Devens Br, Univ Mass, 46-49; lectr, Boston Univ, 51-52, instr, 52-53; asst prof, 53-59, ASSOC PROF MATH, NORTHEASTERN UNIV, 59- *Mem:* Am Math Soc. *Res:* Topology. *Mailing Add:* 90 Stoneleigh Rd Watertown MA 02172

STAKUTIS, VINCENT JOHN, b Boston, Mass, June 20, 20; m 47; c 4. ATMOSPHERIC PHYSICS, OPTICS. *Educ:* Boston Col, BS, 43; Brown Univ, MS, 50, PhD(physics), 54. *Prof Exp:* Lab instr optics, Boston Col, 42-43; instr & asst to headmaster, Marianapolis Prep Sch, Conn, 46-48; asst optics, photog, atomic physics & acoust, Brown Univ, 48-53; res physicist, Geophys Res Dir, Air Force Cambridge Res Labs, 53-57, supvry physicist, 57-58, br chief atmospheric optics, 58-60; mem tech staff, 60-63, MEM SR TECH STAFF, MITRE CORP, BEDFORD, 63- *Mem:* AAAS; Sigma Xi; Am Geophys Union; Optical Soc Am; Acoust Soc Am. *Res:* Ultrasonic attenuation in aqueous suspensions; electromagnetic propogation; scattering processes in the atmosphere; high altitude sky luminance and albedo measurements; vision in the atmosphere; satellite reconnaissance systems; nuclear weapon environmental effects. *Mailing Add:* 160 Grant St Lexington MA 02173

STALCUP, MARVEL C, b Mandan, NDak, Dec 30, 31; m; c 6. PHYSICAL OCEANOGRAPHY, GEOLOGY. *Educ:* Univ Idaho, BS, 61. *Prof Exp:* RES SPECIALIST OCEANOG, WOODS HOLE OCEANOG INST, 61- *Concurrent Pos:* Consult oceanog, ECO-Zist, Teheran, Iran, 77-78. *Mem:* AAAS. *Res:* Identification and description of water masses and currents of the Atlantic and Indian Oceans and Caribbean Sea. *Mailing Add:* Woods Hole Oceanog Inst Woods Hole MA 02543

STALEY, DAVID H, b Columbus, Ohio, Jan 30, 30; m 58; c 3. MATHEMATICS. *Educ:* Oberlin Col, AB, 52; Ohio Univ, MS, 54; Ohio State Univ, PhD(math), 63. *Prof Exp:* Instr math, Henry Ford Community Col, 56-57 & Oberlin Col, 60-61; from asst prof to assoc prof, 61-70, PROF MATH, OHIO WESLEYAN UNIV, 70- *Concurrent Pos:* Consult legal math questions, USDA. *Mem:* Math Asn Am; Nat Coun Teachers Math. *Res:* Commutativity of operators in a topological space; mathematical models of insect populations; mathematical models for temperature and heat accumulation. *Mailing Add:* Dept of Math Ohio Wesleyan Univ E Campus Delaware OH 43015

STALEY, DEAN ODEN, b Kennewick, Wash, Oct 18, 26; m 63; c 4. METEOROLOGY. *Educ:* Univ Wash, BS, 50, PhD(meteorol), 56; Univ Calif, Los Angeles, MA, 51. *Prof Exp:* From instr to asst prof, Univ Wis, 55-59; assoc prof & assoc meteorologist, 59-65, prof & meteorologist, 65-76, PROF ATMOSPHERIC SCI & RES PROF, INST ATMOSPHERIC PHYSICS, UNIV ARIZ, 77- *Mem:* Am Meteorol Soc; Am Geophys Union. *Res:* Dynamic and synoptic meteorology; radiation and planetary atmospheres. *Mailing Add:* Inst of Atmospheric Physics Univ of Ariz Tucson AZ 85721

STALEY, JAMES TROTTER, b Brookings, SDak, Mar 14, 38; m 63; c 2. BACTERIOLOGY, MICROBIAL ECOLOGY. *Educ:* Univ Minn, Minneapolis, BA, 60; Ohio State Univ, MSc, 63; Univ Calif, Davis, PhD(bact), 67. *Prof Exp:* Instr microbiol, Mich State Univ, 67-69; asst prof environ sci & eng, Univ NC, Chapel Hill, 69-71; asst prof, 71-74, ASSOC PROF MICROBIOL, UNIV WASH, 74- *Mem:* Am Soc Microbiol; AAAS. *Res:* Biology of Ancalomicrobium, Prosthecomicrobium and other prosthecate, budding and gas vacuolate bacteria; aquatic bacteriology; fresh water microbiology; microbial ecology. *Mailing Add:* Dept of Microbiol Univ of Wash Seattle WA 98195

STALEY, JOHN M, b Three Rivers, Mich, Sept 12, 29; m 80; c 4. PLANT PATHOLOGY, FORESTRY. *Educ:* Univ Mont, BS, 51; WVa Univ, MS, 53; Cornell Univ, PhD(plant path), 62. *Prof Exp:* Asst forest path, WVa Univ, 51-53; plant pathologist, Pac Northwest Forest & Range Exp Sta, 53, northeastern forest exp sta, 56-62, RES PLANT PATHOLOGIST, ROCKY MT FOREST & RANGE EXP STA, US FOREST SERV, 62- *Concurrent Pos:* Res asst, Cornell Univ, 56-62; affil prof, Grad Fac, Colo State Univ, 67- *Mem:* Am Phytopath Soc; Mycol Soc Am. *Res:* Complex diseases of forest trees; vascular wilt diseases of forest trees; foliage diseases of coniferous trees; rust diseases of cereals. *Mailing Add:* Rocky Mt Forest & Range Exp Sta 240 W Prospect Ft Collins CO 80521

STALEY, L(EONARD) M(AURICE), b Dodsland, Sask, Feb 11, 26; m 53; c 2. AGRICULTURE, ENGINEERING. *Educ:* Univ BC, BASc, 51; Univ Calif, MS, 56. *Prof Exp:* Asst prof agr eng, Ont Agr Col, 56-57; from asst prof to assoc prof agr eng, 51-71, prof, 71-75, prof bio-resource eng, 75-81, HEAD, DEPT BIO-RESOURCE ENG, UNIV BC, 81- *Mem:* Am Soc Agr Engrs; Can Soc Agr Engrs. *Res:* Solar and thermal environmental control in greenhouses and confinement housing systems; methods of energy conservation in agriculture. *Mailing Add:* Dept of Bio-Resource Eng Univ of BC Vancouver BC V6T 1W5 Can

STALEY, RALPH HORTON, b Boston, Mass, Mar 15, 45. PHYSICAL CHEMISTRY. *Educ:* Dartmouth Col, AB, 67; Calif Inst Technol, PhD(chem), 76. *Prof Exp:* Res physicist, Feldman Res Labs, Picatinny Arsenal, 68-71; asst prof phys chem, Mass Inst Technol, 75-81; RESEARCH CHEMIST, E I DU PONT DE NEMOURS & CO, INC, 81- *Mem:* Am Chem Soc; Am Phys Soc; Am Soc Mass Spectrometry; AAAS. *Res:* Heterogeneous catalysis; infrared and phtotacoustic spectroscopy. *Mailing Add:* Cent Res & Develop Dept Exp Sta E I Du Pont de Nemours & Co Inc Wilmington DE 19898

STALEY, ROBERT NEWTON, b Canova, SDak, Oct 15, 35; m 70. ORTHODONTICS, PHYSICAL ANTHROPOLOGY. *Educ:* Univ Minn, Minneapolis, BS, 57, DDS, 59; Univ Chicago, MA, 67; State Univ NY Buffalo, cert orthod, 69, MS, 70. *Prof Exp:* Intern dent, Zoller Mem Dent Clin, Univ Chicago Hosp & Clins, 59-60, mem staff, 62-65; asst prof, 70-73, ASSOC PROF ORTHOD, COL DENT, UNIV IOWA, 73- *Concurrent Pos:* Mem, Am Asn Dent Sch & Human Biol Coun. *Mem:* Int Asn Dent Res; Am Dent Asn; Am Asn Orthodont; Am Asn Univ Prof; Am Asn Phys Anthrop. *Res:* Dental morphology and genetics; craniofacial growth; biological evolution of human dentition. *Mailing Add:* Dept of Orthod Univ of Iowa Col of Dent Iowa City IA 52242

STALEY, STUART WARNER, b Pittsburgh, Pa, July 11, 38; m 63; c 2. ORGANIC CHEMISTRY. *Educ:* Williams Col, BA, 59; Yale Univ, PhD(phys org chem), 64. *Prof Exp:* Res assoc phys org chem, Univ Wis, 63-64; from asst prof to prof phys org chem, Univ Md, College Park, 64-78; PROF ORG CHEM, UNIV NEBR-LINCOLN, 78- *Concurrent Pos:* Vis prof, Swiss Fed Inst Technol, 71-72. *Mem:* Am Chem Soc. *Res:* Photoelectron and electron transmission spectroscopy of organic compounds; organic reaction mechanisms; studies of hydrocarbon anions; valence bond and molecular orbital calculations. *Mailing Add:* Dept Chem Univ Nebr Lincoln NE 68588

STALEY, THEODORE EARNEST LEON, b Virginia City, Mont, Mar 10, 34; div; c 2. VETERINARY ANATOMY, VETERINARY PHYSIOLOGY. *Educ:* Carroll Col, Mont, BA, 58; Mich State Univ, DVM, 65, MS, 66. *Prof Exp:* Asst prof anat, Okla State Univ, 65-71; res pathologist, Vet Admin Hosp, Seattle, Wash, 71-72; ASSOC PROF ANAT-PHYSIOL, OKLA STATE UNIV, 72- *Concurrent Pos:* Fel, Mich State Univ, 65; consult, Okla State Univ & Univ San Carlos, Guatemala, 70; spec fel, Univ Wash, Vet Admin Hosp, Seattle, 71-72. *Mem:* Comp Gastroenterol Soc; Res Workers Animal Dis; Asn Gnotobiotics; Am Asn Vet Anatomists; World Asn Vet Anatomists. *Res:* Ultrastructural anatomy and pathophysiology of the neonatal intestine of domesticated animals as influenced by Escherichia coli and its enterotoxins. *Mailing Add:* Dept of Physiol Sci Col Vet Med Okla State Univ Stillwater OK 74074

STALFORD, HAROLD LENN, b Avery, Okla, July 22, 42; m 63; c 5. APPLIED MATHEMATICS. *Educ:* Okla State Univ, BS, 65; Univ Calif, Berkeley, MS, 66, PhD(appl mech), 70. *Prof Exp:* Asst res engr, Univ Calif, 70; opers res analyst, Radar Div, US Naval Res Lab, 70-71, math analyst, 71-76; sr analyst, Dynamics Res Corp, 76-80; PRES, PRACTICAL SCI, INC, 80- *Concurrent Pos:* Sr analyst, Dynamics Res Corp, 76- *Mem:* Sigma Xi. *Res:* Estimation, control, system identification and differential games; design and evaluation of optimum survivability maneuvers for airborne applications; nonlinear track filter sand predictors for shipboard applications; statistics; system identification and classification. *Mailing Add:* Practical Sci Inc 40 Long Ridge Rd Carlisle MA 01741

STALHEIM, OLE H VIKING, b Garretson, SDak, Sept 23, 17; m 42; c 4. VETERINARY MICROBIOLOGY. *Educ:* Tex A&M Univ, DVM, 41; Univ SDak, MA, 61; Univ Wis, PhD(bact), 63. *Prof Exp:* Vet practitioner, Vermillion, SDak, 41-58; NIH fel, Univ Wis, 60-63; RES VET, NAT ANIMAL DIS CTR, SCI & EDUC ADMIN-AGR RES, USDA, 63- *Concurrent Pos:* Fulbright-Hays award, 80-81. *Honors & Awards:* E A Pope

Award, 79. *Mem:* Am Vet Med Asn; Am Soc Microbiol; Conf Res Workers Animal Dis; US Animal Health Asn. *Res:* Microbial nutrition, metabolism and virulence; immunity to bacterial infection; chemotherapy. *Mailing Add:* Nat Animal Dis Ctr PO Box 70 Ames IA 50010

STALICK, WAYNE MYRON, b Oregon City, Ore, Aug 24, 42; m 67. ORGANIC CHEMISTRY. *Educ:* Univ Ore, BA, 64; Northwestern Univ, PhD(org chem), 69. *Prof Exp:* Asst prof org chem, Calif State Univ, San Jose, 69-70; fel, Ohio State Univ, 70-72, lectr, 72; asst prof, 72-76, ASSOC PROF ORG CHEM, GEORGE MASON UNIV, 76- *Mem:* Sigma Xi; Am Chem Soc. *Res:* Base catalyzed reactions of hydrocarbons; heterocyclic, synthetic organic and organometallic chemistry. *Mailing Add:* Dept of Chem George Mason Univ Fairfax VA 22030

STALKER, ARCHIBALD MACSWEEN, b Montreal, Que, June 29, 24; m 51; c 4. GLACIAL GEOLOGY. *Educ:* McGill Univ, BA, 45, MSc, 48, PhD(geol), 50. *Prof Exp:* GEOLOGIST, GEOL SURV CAN, 50- *Mem:* Can Quaternary Asn; fel Geol Soc Am; Geol Soc Can. *Res:* Glacial geology; geomorphology; relations of Cordilleran and Laurentide glaciations; preglacial drainage; early man in New World; climate, stratigraphy and mammals of Quaternary; Quaternary vertebrate paleontology. *Mailing Add:* Geol Surv Can Ottawa ON K1A 0E8 Can

STALKER, HAROLD THOMAS, b Pittsburgh, Pa, Oct 27, 50; m 72; c 2. PLANT CYTOGENETICS, PEANUT BREEDING. *Educ:* Univ Ariz, BS, 72, MS, 73; Univ Ill, PhD(genetics), 77. *Prof Exp:* res assoc cytogenetics, 77-79; ASST PROF CROP SCI, NC STATE UNIV, 79- *Mem:* Crop Sci Soc Am; Am Genetic Asn; Am Peanut Res & Educ Soc; Soc Econ Bot. *Res:* Cytogenetics; genetics; speciation and biosystematics of wild and cultivated species of the genus Arachis. *Mailing Add:* NC Univ Dept Crop Sci Box 5155 Raleigh NC 27650

STALKER, HARRISON DAILEY, b Detroit, Mich, July 3, 15; m 41; c 1. GENETICS, EVOLUTIONARY BIOLOGY. *Educ:* Col Wooster, BA, 37; Univ Rochester, PhD(zool), 41. *Prof Exp:* Asst zool, Univ Rochester, 37-42; from instr to assoc prof, 42-56, PROF ZOOL, WASH UNIV, 56- *Concurrent Pos:* NSF sr fel, 61; mem genetics adv panel, NSF, 59-62. *Mem:* AAAS; Genetics Soc Am; Soc Study Evolution; Am Soc Nat; Am Soc Human Genetics. *Res:* Cytogenetics and physiology of Drosphila species and populations. *Mailing Add:* Dept Biol Wash Univ St Louis MO 63130

STALKUP, FRED I(RVING), JR, b Temple, Tex, Feb 3, 36; m 65; c 1. CHEMICAL ENGINEERING. *Educ:* Rice Univ, BA, 57, PhD(chem eng), 62. *Prof Exp:* Sr res engr, Atlantic-Richfield Co, 61-65; prin res engr, 65-67, dir, Process Develop Res, 67-69, dir, Reservoir Eng Res, 69-71, dir, Reservoir Math Res, 71-77, dir recovery res, 77-79; CONSULT, 79- *Honors & Awards:* Sigma Xi Res Award, 62. *Mem:* Soc Petrol Engrs. *Res:* Hydrocarbon phase equilibria; miscible, immiscible and thermal methods of oil recovery; reservoir engineering; secondary and tertiary recovery; mathematical modeling. *Mailing Add:* Atlantic Richfield Co PO Box 2189 Dallas TX 75221

STALL, ROBERT EUGENE, b Leipsic, Ohio, Dec 11, 31; m 52; c 2. PLANT PATHOLOGY. *Educ:* Ohio State Univ, BSc, 53, MSc, 54, PhD(bot, plant path), 57. *Prof Exp:* Res asst plant path, Ohio Agr Exp Sta, 57-63, assoc prof plant path & assoc plant pathologist, 63-69, PROF PLANT PATH, UNIV FLA, 69- *Concurrent Pos:* Vis prof, Nat Inst Agr Technol, 78-79. *Mem:* AAAS; fel Am Phytopath Soc. *Res:* Bacterial phytopathology. *Mailing Add:* Dept Plant Path Univ Fla Gainesville FL 32601

STALL, WILLIAM MARTIN, b Bluffton, Ohio, Apr 14, 44; m 69. HORTICULTURE, PLANT BREEDING. *Educ:* Ohio State Univ, BSA, 67; Univ Fla, MSA, 69, PhD(vegetable crops), 73. *Prof Exp:* Teacher biol, Southwestern City Sch, Grove City, Ohio, 69-71; EXTEN AGENT VEGETABLES, FLA COOP EXTEN SERV, 74- *Mem:* Am Soc Hort Sci; Potato Asn Am; Nat Agr Plastics Asn. *Res:* Integrated pest management; variety improvement and evaluation; crop fertility and fertilizer placement incorporated with mulching and drip irrigation. *Mailing Add:* Fla Coop Exten Serv 18710 SW 288th St Homestead FL 33030

STALLARD, RICHARD E, anatomy, periodontology, see previous edition

STALLCUP, MICHAEL R, b Dallas, Tex, Nov 6, 47. MOLECULAR BIOLOGY, GENETICS. *Educ:* Yale Univ, BA, 69; Univ Calif, Berkeley, PhD(biochem), 74. *Prof Exp:* Fel biochem & biophysics, Univ Calif, San Francisco, 74-79; ASST PROF BIOL, UNIV SC, 80- *Concurrent Pos:* NSF grad trainee award, 69-72; fel, Am Cancer Soc, 74-75, Nat Res Serv Award, NIH, 77-79; prin investr, NIH res grant, 80-83. *Res:* Biochemical and genetic studies on regulation of gene expression in mammalian cells by steroid hormones. *Mailing Add:* Dept Biol Univ SC Columbia SC 29208

STALLCUP, ODIE TALMADGE, b Paragould, Ark, Dec 2, 18; m 47; c 3. DAIRY HUSBANDRY. *Educ:* Univ Ark, BSA, 43; Univ Mo, AM, 47, PhD(dairy husb), 50. *Prof Exp:* Instr dairy husb, Univ Ark, 45-46; from asst instr to instr, Univ Mo, 46-50; assoc prof, 50-55, PROF DAIRY HUSB, UNIV ARK, FAYETTEVILLE, 55- *Mem:* Am Soc Animal Sci; Am Dairy Sci Asn; Soc Study Reproduction; Histochem Soc. *Res:* Ruminant nutrition; physiology of reproduction. *Mailing Add:* Dept of Animal Sci Univ of Ark Fayetteville AR 72701

STALLCUP, WILLIAM BLACKBURN, JR, b Dallas, Tex, Oct 18, 20; m 42; c 5. VERTEBRATE ZOOLOGY. *Educ:* Southern Methodist Univ, BS, 41; Univ Kans, PhD(zool), 54. *Prof Exp:* Instr biol, Southern Methodist Univ, 45-50; asst instr, Univ Kans, 50-53; from instr to assoc prof, 53-62, chmn dept, 63-67, assoc dean sch humanities & sci, 71-74, assoc provost, 74-80, provost Ad Interim, 80-81, PROF BIOL, SOUTHERN METHODIST UNIV, 62-, ASSOC PROVOST, 81- *Mem:* AAAS; Am Soc Mammal; Am Ornith Union. *Res:* Comparative myology and serology of birds; vertebrate natural history; general genetics. *Mailing Add:* Dept of Biol Southern Methodist Univ Dallas TX 75275

STALLEY, ROBERT DELMER, b Minneapolis, Minn, Oct 25, 24; m 50; c 4. MATHEMATICS. *Educ:* Ore State Col, BS, 46, MA, 48; Univ Ore, PhD(math), 53. *Prof Exp:* Instr math, Univ Ariz, 49-51; instr, Iowa State Col, 53-54, asst prof, 54-55; instr, Fresno State Col, 55-56; from asst prof to assoc prof, 56-66, PROF MATH, ORE STATE UNIV, 66- *Mem:* Am Math Soc; Math Asn Am. *Res:* Number density; combinatorial analysis. *Mailing Add:* Dept of Math Ore State Univ Corvallis OR 97331

STALLING, DAVID LAURENCE, b Kansas City, Mo, Oct 24, 41; m 62; c 3. ANALYTICAL CHEMISTRY, ORGANIC CHEMISTRY. *Educ:* Mo Valley Col, BS, 62; Univ Mo-Columbia, MS, 64, PhD(biochem), 67. *Prof Exp:* Instr agr chem, Univ Mo-Columbia, 66-68; CHIEF CHEMIST, COLUMBIA NAT FISHERIES RES LAB, 68- *Concurrent Pos:* Chem consult, Regis Chem Co, 66-69; cofounder, Anal Bicohem Labs, Inc, 67; assoc referee for contaminants in aquatic biota, Asn Official Anal Chemists, 75- *Mem:* Am Chem Soc. *Res:* Development of rapid methods of analysis of biologically important compounds, especially amino acids, purine and pyrimidine bases, organic pollutants and pesticides by gas-liquid chromatography and combined gas chromatography-mass spectrometry computer techniques; biochemical effects of pesticides and organic contaminants on fish; gas-chromatography mass-spectrometry computer studies on environmental contaminants; organic residues in national pesticide monitoring programs. *Mailing Add:* Columbia-Nat Fisheries Res Lab Route 1 Columbia MO 65201

STALLINGS, CHARLES HENRY, b Durham, NC, Dec 28, 41; m 65; c 2. PLASMA PHYSICS. *Educ:* NC State Univ, BS, 63, MS, 64; Univ Wis-Madison, PhD(physics), 70. *Prof Exp:* Sr physicist, 70-77, dept mgr, 77-78, dir prog off, 79-81, DIR PROG DEVELOP, PHYSICS INT CO, 81- *Mem:* Am Phys Soc; Inst Elec & Electronics Eng. *Res:* Generation and propagation of intense relativistic electron beams and their interaction with background on target plasma; high density imploding plasmas and x-ray diagnostics. *Mailing Add:* Physics Int Co 2700 Merced St San Leandro CA 94577

STALLINGS, JAMES CAMERON, b Denton, Tex, Jan 16, 19; m 49; c 2. ORGANIC CHEMISTRY. *Educ:* Univ Tex, PhD(org chem), 49. *Prof Exp:* Prof chem, Sam Houston State Col, 49-57; sr res chemist, Celanese Corp Am, 57-59; prof chem & dir dept, 59-78, dean, Col Sci, 78-81, EMER DEAN, SAM HOUSTON STATE UNIV, 81- *Mem:* Am Chem Soc. *Res:* Steric hindrance; synthetic hypnotics; free radicals in solution; organic synthesis; chemical education. *Mailing Add:* Dept of Chem Sam Houston State Univ Huntsville TX 77341

STALLINGS, JAMES HENRY, b Bryan, Tex, Sept 20, 92; m 23; c 2. SOIL CONSERVATION. *Educ:* Agr & Mech Col, Tex, BS, 14; Iowa State Col, MS, 17, PhD(soil fertility), 25. *Prof Exp:* Agronomist & farm dir high sch, Miss, 14-16; asst agronomist, Exp Sta, Ala, 16; asst prof soils, Iowa State Col, 19-20; assoc prof agron, Agr & Mech Col, Tex, 20-23, prof, 23-26; agronomist, J C Penny-Gwinn Corp Farms, Fla, 26-28; agronomist, Nat Fertilizer Asn, La, 29-34; regional dir, Soil Conserv Serv, NC, 34-37, sr soil conservationist, DC, 37-42, prin soil conservationist, War Food Admin, 42-44, soil conserv serv, 42-52, PRIN SOIL CONSERVATIONIST, SCI & EDUC ADMIN-AGR RES, USDA, 53- *Mem:* Sigma Xi; AAAS; Am Soc Agron; Soil Sci Soc Am; NY Acad Sci. *Res:* Soil fertility; Scientific foundation for no-tillage farming; form of legume nitrogen when absorbed by non-legumes when the two are grown in association. *Mailing Add:* 5146 Nebraska Ave NW Washington DC 20008

STALLINGS, JOHN ROBERT, JR, b Morrilton, Ark, July 22, 35. TOPOLOGY. *Educ:* Univ Ark, BS, 56; Princeton Univ, PhD(math), 59. *Prof Exp:* NSF fel math, Oxford Univ, 59-60; from instr to assoc prof, Princeton Univ, 60-67; PROF MATH, UNIV CALIF, BERKELEY, 67- *Concurrent Pos:* Sloan Found fel, 62-65. *Honors & Awards:* Frank Nelson Cole Prize, Am Math Soc, 70. *Mem:* Am Math Soc. *Res:* Three-manifolds; geometric topology; group theory from topological and homological viewpoints. *Mailing Add:* Dept of Math Univ of Calif Berkeley CA 94720

STALLINGS, WILLIAM CARLTON, physical chemistry, molecular structure, see previous edition

STALLKNECHT, GILBERT FRANKLIN, b Spooner, Minn, Sept 21, 35; m 58; c 4. PLANT PHYSIOLOGY, PLANT BIOCHEMISTRY. *Educ:* Univ Minn, BS, 62, MS, 66, PhD(plant physiol), 68. *Prof Exp:* Agr res technician, USDA Sugar Beet Invests, Univ Minn, St Paul, 63-67; asst prof, 68-72, ASSOC PROF PLANT PHYSIOL, UNIV IDAHO, 72- *Mem:* Am Soc Plant Physiol; Scand Soc Plant Physiol. *Res:* Fungus physiology; metabolic studies in host-parasite physiology; physiology of tuberization in potatoes; productivity and physiological age of potato tubers; physiology of seed crops. *Mailing Add:* Res & Exten Ctr Parma ID 83660

STALLMANN, FRIEDEMANN WILHELM, b Koenigsberg, Ger, July 29, 21; m 53; c 2. MATHEMATICS. *Educ:* Stuttgart Tech Univ, Dipl math, 49; Univ Giessen, Dr rer nat, 53. *Prof Exp:* Asst math, Univ Giessen, 53-55, lectr, 55-59; asst, Brunswick Tech Univ, 59-60; chief math sect, Spec Res Unit Med Electronic Data Processing, Vet Admin, DC, 60-64; assoc prof, 64-69, PROF MATH, UNIV TENN, KNOXVILLE, 69- *Concurrent Pos:* Consult, Oak Ridge Nat Lab, 64- *Mem:* Am Math Soc. *Res:* Numerical analysis; conformal mapping and differential equations, lead field theory of electrocardiogram; computer analysis of electrocardiograms, complex variables. *Mailing Add:* Dept of Math Univ of Tenn Knoxville TN 37916

STALLMEYER, J(AMES) E(DWARD), b Covington, Ky, Aug 11, 26; m 53; c 6. STRUCTURAL ENGINEERING. *Educ:* Univ Ill, BS, 47, MS, 49, PhD(civil eng), 53. *Prof Exp:* Res asst prof, 53-57, assoc prof, 57-60, PROF CIVIL ENG, UNIV ILL, URBANA, 60- *Concurrent Pos:* Consult. *Honors & Awards:* Adams Mem Award, Am Welding Soc. *Mem:* Am Soc Civil Engrs; Am Soc Mech Engrs; Am Soc Testing & Mat; Soc Exp Stress Anal; Am Concrete Inst. *Res:* Fatigue of metals and structures; welded structures; brittle fracture; structural analysis, design and dynamics. *Mailing Add:* Dept of Civil Eng Univ of Ill Urbana IL 61801

STALLONES, REUEL ARTHUR, b North Little Rock, Ark, Oct 10, 23; div; c 3. MEDICINE, EPIDEMIOLOGY. *Educ:* Western Reserve Univ, MD, 49; Univ Calif, MPH, 52; Am Bd Prev Med, dipl, 58. *Prof Exp:* Intern, Letterman Army Hosp, Med Corps, US Army, San Francisco, Calif, 49-50, resident pediat, 50, battalion surgeon, 50-51, prev med officer, Camp Pickett, Va, 52-54 & Ft Meade, Md, 54, asst chief dept epidemiol, Walter Reed Army Inst Res, DC, 54-56; lectr epidemiol, Univ Calif, Berkeley, 56-59, assoc prof pub health, 59-62, prof epidemiol, 62-68; DEAN, SCH PUB HEALTH, UNIV TEX, HOUSTON, 68- *Mem:* Nat Acad Sci; Am Col Prev Med; Soc Epidemiol; Am Epidemiol Soc; Am Pub Health Asn. *Res:* Epidemiology; cardiovascular disease. *Mailing Add:* Sch Pub Health Univ Tex PO Box 20186 Houston TX 77025

STALLWOOD, ROBERT ANTONY, b Oxbow, Sask, June 15, 25. NUCLEAR PHYSICS. *Educ:* Univ Toronto, BASc, 49, MA, 50; Carnegie Inst Technol, PhD(physics), 56. *Prof Exp:* Physicist, Nuclear Sci Sect, Gulf Res & Develop Co, 56-64; physicist, Gen Elec Space Sci Ctr, 64-67; ASSOC PROF PHYSICS, THIEL COL, 67- *Mem:* AAAS; Am Phys Soc. *Res:* High energy nuclear physics; gamma ray and x-ray spectroscopy; neutron physics. *Mailing Add:* Dept of Physics Thiel Col Greenville PA 16125

STALNAKER, CLAIR B, b Parkersburg, WVa, July 21, 38; m 63; c 2. FISH BIOLOGY, GENETICS. *Educ:* WVa Univ, BSF, 60; NC State Univ, PhD(zool), 66. *Prof Exp:* Res asst fisheries biol, NC State Univ, 60-66; asst prof, Utah State Univ, 66-72, assoc prof fisheries biol, 72-76, asst unit leader, Utah Coop Fishery Unit, 66-75; LEADER, COOP INSTREAM FLOW SERV GROUP, US FISH & WILDLIFE SERV, FT COLLINS, 76- *Mem:* AAAS; Am Fisheries Soc; Wildlife Soc; Am Soc Ichthyol & Herpet; Soc Am Nat. *Res:* Physiological-genetic studies of fishes; administration of multi-agency, interdisciplinary programs; physical aspects of stream ecology; aquatic environmental interactions. *Mailing Add:* Instream Flow Serv Group 2625 Redwing Rd Ft Collins CO 80521

STALTER, RICHARD, b Jan 16, 42; US citizen; m 68. BOTANY, PLANT ECOLOGY. *Educ:* Rutgers Univ, BS, 63; Univ RI, MS, 66; Univ SC, PhD(biol), 68. *Prof Exp:* Asst prof biol, Hihg Point Col, 68-69 & Pfeiffer Col, 69-70; asst prof, 71-74, ASSOC PROF BIOL, ST JOHN'S UNIV, NY, 75-, DIR ENVIRON STUDIES PROG, 75- *Mem:* Bot Soc Am; Ecol Soc Am; Sigma Xi. *Res:* Salt marsh ecology of the east coast of North America; flora of Long Island and Barrier Islands, South Carolina. *Mailing Add:* Dept of Biol St John's Univ Jamaica NY 11439

STAM, JOS, b Rotterdam, Netherlands, Apr 3, 24; nat US; m 59; c 4. ENVIRONMENTAL LAW, TOXICOLOGY. *Educ:* Tech Col, Dordrecht, BSc, 46; Delft Univ Technol, PhD(chem eng), 52. *Prof Exp:* Chief engr, Unie Chem, Inc, 52-56; res engr, Carothers Res Lab & Textile Res Lab, E I du Pont de Nemours & co, 56-65, tech assoc, 65-70, staff engr, Netherlands, 70-72, PROD ENVIRON CONSULT, DU PONT DE NEMOURS INT SA, 72- *Res:* Toxicology, ecology and health legislation of chemicals. *Mailing Add:* Du Pont de Nemours Int SA PO Box CH-1211 Geneva 24 Switz

STAMATOYANNOPOULOS, GEORGE, b Athens, Greece, Mar 11, 34; m 64; c 1. MEDICAL GENETICS, HEMATOLOGY. *Educ:* Nat Univ Athens, MD, 58, DSc, 60. *Prof Exp:* Asst med, Nat Univ Athens, 58-59, asst med & hemat, 61-64; res assoc med, 64-65, instr, 65-66, res asst prof, 65-69, assoc prof, 69-72, PROF MED, DIV MED GENETICS, UNIV WASH, 72- *Concurrent Pos:* Royal Hellenic Res Found fel, 61-64. *Mem:* Am Soc Human Genetics; Am Soc Clin Invest; Europ Soc Human Genetics; Genetics Soc Am. *Res:* Biochemical, developmental and human population genetics. *Mailing Add:* Div of Med Genet Dept of Med Univ of Wash Seattle WA 98195

STAMBAUGH, EDGEL PRYCE, b Blain, Ky, Aug 31, 22; m 50; c 1. HYDROTHERMAL HYDROMETALLURGY TECHNOLOGY. *Educ:* Ohio State Univ, BS, 50, MS, 51. *Prof Exp:* Res chemist, N L Indust, 51-56; prin chemist, Battelle Columbus Labs, 56-57; proj leader, Nat Distillers & Chem Corp, 57-59; proj leader, 59-65, sr chemist, 65-79, assoc mgr, 79-82, RES LEADER, BATTELLE COLUMBUS LABS, 82- *Concurrent Pos:* Prin investr, N L Indust, 53-56; liaison, Zirconium Plant, Nat Distillers & Chem Corp, 57-59; proj mgr, US Environ Protection Agency, 75-80; proj mgr, Energy Prog, Battelle Columbus Labs, 73-76, ultra-fine ceramic oxides, synthetic rutile & strategic metals, 78-82. *Mem:* Sigma Xi; Am Inst Mining, Metall & Petrol Engrs. *Res:* Development of new improved commercial processes, based on hydrothermal technology, for combating feedstock shortages, rising energy costs, pollution abatement regulations, and inflation pressures in the inorganic chemicals, mineral processing, strategic metals, ceramic and electronic industries. *Mailing Add:* 921 Evening St Worthington OH 43085

STAMBAUGH, JOHN EDGAR, JR, b Everrett, Pa, Apr 30, 40; m 61; c 4. ONCOLOGY, CLINICAL PHARMACOLOGY. *Educ:* Dickinson Col, BS, 62; Jefferson Med Col, MD, 66, Thomas Jefferson Univ, PhD(pharmacol), 68. *Prof Exp:* From instr to asst prof, 68-74, ASSOC PROF PHARMACOL, JEFFERSON MED COL, THOMAS JEFFERSON UNIV, 74- *Concurrent Pos:* AMA spec scholar, Thomas Jefferson Univ Hosp, 68-70, fel oncol, 70-72; resident med, Thomas Jefferson Univ Hosp, 68-70; staff physician, Cooper Hosp, Camden, NJ, 72- & Underwood Hosp, Woodbury, 73- *Mem:* Am Asn Cancer Res; Am Soc Clin Oncol; Am Soc Pharmacol & Exp Therapeut; Am Soc Clin Pharmacol. *Res:* Clinical drug metabolism and drug interactions; clinical oncology. *Mailing Add:* Dept of Pharmacol Jefferson Med Col Philadelphia PA 19107

STAMBAUGH, OSCAR FRANK, b Newport, Pa, Aug 4, 08; m 36; c 1. CHEMISTRY. *Educ:* Lebanon Valley Col, BS, 30; Pa State Univ, MS, 33, PhD(chem), 43. *Prof Exp:* Instr chem, Pa State Univ, 36-42 & Juniata Col, 42-43; chemist, Gulf Oil Corp, Pa, 43-46; prof chem & head dept, 46-73, actg dean, 66-67, EMER PROF CHEM, ELIZABETHTOWN COL, 73- *Mem:* Am Chem Soc. *Res:* Analytical chemistry. *Mailing Add:* Dept Chem Elizabethtown Col Elizabethtown PA 17022

STAMBAUGH, RICHARD L, b Mechanicsburg, Pa, Aug 16, 36; m 56; c 2. BIOCHEMISTRY. *Educ:* Albright Col, BS, 53; Univ Pa, PhD(biochem), 59. *Prof Exp:* Res assoc biochem, Philadelphia Gen Hosp, 58-59; dir biochem, Elwyn Res & Eval Ctr & instr biochem in pediat, Univ Pa, 59-63; sr res investr, Fels Res Inst & instr biochem, Sch Med, Temple Univ, 63-66; ASSOC PROF, DIV REPRODUCTIVE BIOL, SCH MED, UNIV PA, 66- *Concurrent Pos:* Consult, Penrose Res Lab, Zool Soc Philadelphia & Elwyn Res & Eval Ctr, 63-67. *Mem:* AAAS; Soc Study Reproduction; Fedn Am Socs Exp Biol. *Res:* Enzymology; biochemistry of reproduction. *Mailing Add:* Div of Reproductive Biol Univ of Pa Sch of Med Philadelphia PA 19104

STAMBAUGH, WILLIAM JAMES, b Allenwood, Pa, Dec 1, 27; m 52; c 3. FOREST PATHOLOGY. *Educ:* Pa State Univ, BS, 51, MS, 52; Yale Univ, PhD(forest path), 57. *Prof Exp:* Instr bot, Pa State Univ, 53-57, asst prof forest path, 57-61; from asst prof to assoc prof, 61-72, PROF FOREST PATH, DUKE UNIV, 72- *Mem:* Soc Am Foresters; Am Phytopath Soc. *Res:* Diseases of forest trees, with emphasis on epidemiology and control; microbiology of forest soils. *Mailing Add:* Sch of Forestry Duke Univ Durham NC 27706

STAMBROOK, PETER JOSEPH, b London, Eng, July 24, 41. BIOLOGY. *Educ:* Rensselaer Polytech Inst, BSc, 63; Syracuse Univ, MSc, 65; State Univ NY Buffalo, PhD(biol), 69. *Prof Exp:* Fel cell biol, Med Ctr, Univ Ky, 69-71; investr cell, develop & molecular biol, Dept Embryol, Carnegie Inst Washington, 71-74; ASST PROF CELL, DEVELOP & MOLECULAR BIOL, CASE WESTERN RESERVE UNIV, 74- *Mem:* AAAS; Am Soc Cell Biol. *Res:* Regulation of cell cycle with particular focus on DNA replication. *Mailing Add:* Dept of Biol Case Western Reserve Univ Cleveland OH 44106

STAMER, JOHN RICHARD, b Plankinton, SDak, May 19, 25; m 58; c 3. MICROBIOLOGY. *Educ:* Dakota Wesleyan Univ, BA, 50; SDak State Col, MS, 53; Cornell Univ, PhD(bact), 62. *Prof Exp:* Res assoc bact, Univ Ill, 53-56; jr scientist, Smith Kline & French Labs, 56-58; asst bact, Cornell Univ, 58-62, NIH fel, 62-64; from asst prof to assoc prof bact, 64-77, PROF MICROBIOL, NY STATE AGR EXP STA, CORNELL UNIV, 77- *Mem:* AAAS; Am Soc Microbiol. *Res:* Microbial physiology and nutrition. *Mailing Add:* Dept of Food Sci NY State Agr Exp Sta Geneva NY 14456

STAMER, PETER ERIC, b New York, NY, June 4, 39; m 68. PHYSICS. *Educ:* Stevens Inst Technol, BS, 61, MS, 63, PhD(physics), 66. *Prof Exp:* Instr physics, Upsala Col, 65-66; from asst prof to assoc prof, 66-78, PROF PHYSICS, SETON HALL UNIV, 78- *Concurrent Pos:* Jr res assoc physics, Stevens Inst Technol, 66-68, res assoc, 68- *Mem:* AAAS; Am Asn Physics Teachers; Am Phys Soc. *Res:* Experimental elementary particle physics; pi-P, P-P, K-P interactions at 147 GeV/C and neutrino interactions at 2.0-5.0 GeV/C. *Mailing Add:* Dept of Physics Seton Hall Univ South Orange NJ 07079

STAMEY, THOMAS ALEXANDER, b Rutherfordton, NC, Apr 26, 28; m 56; c 5. UROLOGY. *Educ:* Vanderbilt Univ, AB, 48; Johns Hopkins Univ, MD, 52; Am Bd Urol, dipl, 61. *Prof Exp:* Intern, Johns Hopkins Hosp, 52-53; mem, Brady Urol House Staff Residency Prog, Johns Hopkins Univ, 53-56; urol consult, US Armed Forces, UK, 56-58; from asst prof to assoc prof urol, Johns Hopkins Univ, 58-61; assoc prof surg, 61-64, PROF SURG, SCH MED, STANFORD UNIV, 64-, CHMN DIV UROL, 61- *Concurrent Pos:* Mem comt renal dis & urol training grants, NIH, 67-72, chmn, 71-72; mem sci adv bd, Nat Kidney Found, sci adv coun, Northern Calif Kidney Found & adv bd, Coop Study Pyelonephritis, USPHS; mem res comt, Northern Calif Kidney Found; mem sci adv comt, Hosp Sick Children, Toronto, Can; mem, Study of Res in Nephrology & Urol, NIH; consult, Santa Clara Valley Med Ctr, Palo Alto Vet Admin Hosp & Letterman Army Hosp, San Francisco; ed, Urol Dig; assoc ed, Campbell's Urol. *Honors & Awards:* Hugh Hampton Young Award, Am Urol Asn, 72. *Mem:* Am Urol Asn; AMA; Am Heart Asn; Am Surg Asn; Soc Univ Urol. *Res:* Renal physiology and disease and urinary tract infections; microbiology and hypertension. *Mailing Add:* Div of Urol Stanford Univ Med Ctr Stanford CA 94305

STAMEY, WILLIAM LEE, b Chicago, Ill, Oct 19, 22; m 45; c 3. MATHEMATICS. *Educ:* Univ Northern Colo, AB, 47; Univ Mo, MA, 49, PhD(math), 52. *Prof Exp:* From asst instr to instr math, Univ Mo, 47-52; asst prof, Ga State Col, 52-53; from asst prof to assoc prof, 53-62, assoc dean, 63-69, PROF MATH, KANS STATE UNIV, 62-, DEAN COL ARTS & SCI, 69- *Mem:* Am Math Soc; AAAS; Math Asn Am. *Mailing Add:* Off of the Dean Col Arts & Sci Eisenhower Hall Kans State Univ Manhattan KS 66506

STAMLER, JEREMIAH, b New York, NY, Oct 27, 19; m 42; c 1. PREVENTIVE MEDICINE, PUBLIC HEALTH. *Educ:* Columbia Univ, AB, 40; State Univ NY, MD, 43. *Prof Exp:* Intern, Long Island Col Med Div, Kings County Hosp, 44; res assoc, Cardiovasc Dept, Med Res Inst, Michael Reese Hosp, Chicago, 49-55, asst dir dept, 55-58; dir heart dis control prog, Chicago Bd Health, 58-74, dir div adult health & aging, 63-74; from assoc to assoc prof, 59-71, PROF MED, SCH MED, NORTHWESTERN UNIV, CHICAGO, 71-, CHMN DEPT COMMUNITY HEALTH & PREV MED, 72-, DINGMAN PROF CARDIOL, MED SCH, 73-, CHMN DEPT COMMUNITY HEALTH & PREV MED, MEM HOSP, 73- *Concurrent Pos:* Fel path, Long Island Col Med, 47; res fel, Cardiovasc Dept, Med Res Inst, Michael Reese Hosp, Chicago, 48; Am Heart Asn estab investr, 52-58, fel coun arteriosclerosis, 63-64 & coun epidemiol, 64-66; dir chronic dis div, Chicago Bd Health, 61-63; chmn coun arteriosclerosis, Am Heart Asn, 63-64, mem exec comt, Coun Epidemiol, 64-66 & coun high blood pressure res; western hemisphere ed, Atherosclerosis, 63-75; exec dir, Chicago Health Res Found, 63-72; consult, St Joseph Hosp, 64-, Rush-Presby-St Luke's Hosp, 64- & Atherosclerosis Cardiol Drug Lipid Coop Study & Cardiovasc Res Prog Eval Comt, Vet Admin, 65; prof lectr med, Div Biol Sci, Pritzker Sch Med, Univ Chicago, 70-; vis prof, Dept Internal Med, Rush Presby-St Luke's Med Ctr, 72-; attend physician, Northwest Mem Hosp, 72-; sponsor, Nat Health Educ Comt; mem, Worcester Found Exp Biol; specialist clin nutrit, Am Bd Nutrit; chmn coun epidemiol & prev, Int Soc Cardiol, 75- *Honors & Awards:* Med J Award, Lasker Found, 65; Blakeslee Awards, Am Heart Asn, 64, Award of Merit, 67; Citation, Inter-Soc Comn Heart Dis Resources, 68-71. *Mem:* Fel AAAS; fel Am Col Cardiol; Am Diabetes Asn; Am Fedn Clin Res; Asn Teachers Prev Med. *Res:* Cardiovascular physiology, medicine, epidemiology and preventive medicine, particularly atherosclerosis and hypertension; chronic disease, preventive medicine and public health. *Mailing Add:* Dept Community Health & Prev Med Northwestern Univ Med Sch Chicago IL 60611

STAMM, RALPH EUGENE, b Piedmont, SC, May 5, 32; m 61; c 2. ANALYTICAL CHEMISTRY, GAS CHROMATOGRAPHY. *Educ:* Wofford Col, BS, 54; Univ SC, PhD(phys chem), 62. *Prof Exp:* Sr chemist, 61-69, proj chemist, 69-73, sr proj chemist, Texaco Inc, 73-81, TECHNOLOGIST, TEXACO USA, 81- *Mem:* Am Chem Soc. *Res:* Instrumental analysis; mass spectroscopy; computer sciences; gas chromatography. *Mailing Add:* 645 W Kitchen Port Neches TX 77651

STAMM, ROBERT FRANZ, b Mt Vernon, Ohio, Mar 28, 15; m 64. PHYSICAL CHEMISTRY, OPTICAL PHYSICS. *Educ:* Kenyon Col, AB, 37; Iowa State Univ, PhD(phys chem), 42. *Prof Exp:* Asst chem, Iowa State Univ, 37-42; res physicist, Am Cyanamid Co, 42-54, group leader, Basic Res Dept, 54-59 & Phys Res Dept, 59-61, res assoc, Chem Dept, 61-66, res fel, 66-72; SR RES INVESTR, CLAIROL, INC, DIV BRISTOL MYERS CO, 73- *Mem:* Am Chem Soc; Am Phys Soc; Optical Soc Am. *Res:* Raman spectroscopy; light scattering; fluorescence; radiation chemistry and sterilization; neutron activation analysis; spectroscopy of triplet molecules and excited transients; photochromism; flash photolysis; kinetic spectroscopy; retroreflectors; optical properties of human hair fibers; Fourier transform infrared spectroscopy. *Mailing Add:* Clairol Res Labs 2 Blachley Rd Stamford CT 06902

STAMM, STANLEY JEROME, b Seattle, Wash, July 14, 24; m; c 3. MEDICINE. *Educ:* Seattle Univ, BS, 48; St Louis Univ, MD, 52; Am Bd Pediat, dipl, 58. *Prof Exp:* Intern, King County Hosp, Seattle, Wash, 52-53; resident pediat, Univ Wash, 53-55; instr, 57-58; dir cardiac diag lab, 58-59, co-dir dept cardiol & attend, 59-63, co-dir cystic fibrosis clin, 63, dir cardiopulmonary res lab, 62-67, dir cardiol dept, 67-70, DIR CARDIOPULMONARY DEPT, CHILDREN'S ORTHOP HOSP, 70- *Concurrent Pos:* NIH cardiac trainee, Children's Orthop Hosp, 55-56, hosp cardiac fel, 56-57; clin assoc prof, Univ Wash, 66-69. *Mem:* Fel Am Acad Pediat; Am Heart Asn; fel Am Col Chest Physicians; fel Am Col Angiol. *Mailing Add:* Children's Orthop Hosp & Med Ctr 4800 Sand Point Way NE Seattle WA 98105

STAMMELMAN, MORTIMER JACOB, b New York, NY, Dec 27, 97; m 35; c 1. PHYSICAL CHEMISTRY. *Educ:* Columbia Univ, AB, 20, AM, 21, PhD(phys chem), 23. *Prof Exp:* Chemist, Int Arms & Fuse Co, 17; chief chemist, Dusenberg Motors Corp, 18; asst chem, Columbia Univ, 18-22; pres, 25-76, EMER PRES, ATMOS PROD CORP, 76- *Concurrent Pos:* Pres, Stammelman Realty Co, 28-32; secy, Hypodermic Medication, Pharmaceut & Biol Sect, C F Kirk Co, NJ, 32-34; humidification consult for tobacco indust; pres, NY Tobacco Table; chmn bd, Atmos Prod Co & Aztec Clay Moistening Co, Inc. *Honors & Awards:* Dean's Award, Columbia Col, 61; Lion Award, Columbia Univ, 70. *Mem:* Fel AAAS; emer fel Am Inst Chem; Sigma Xi. *Res:* Hydrogen ions; humidification of tobacco and cigars; food preservation and activity coefficients of certain acids. *Mailing Add:* Atmos Prods Corp 135 West 29th St New York NY 10001

STAMMER, CHARLES HUGH, b Indianapolis, Ind, Apr 1, 25; m 47; c 2. ORGANIC CHEMISTRY. *Educ:* Univ Ind, BS, 48; Univ Wis, PhD(org chem), 52. *Prof Exp:* Res chemist, Merck & Co, Inc, NJ, 52-62; assoc prof, 62-80, PROF CHEM, UNIV GA, 80- *Mem:* Am Chem Soc; AAAS. *Res:* Synthesis of dehydro peptide hormones and unsaturated amino acids. *Mailing Add:* 718 Riverhill Dr Athens GA 30601

STAMPER, EUGENE, b New York, NY, Mar 24, 28; m 53; c 1. MECHANICAL ENGINEERING. *Educ:* City Col New York, BME, 48; NY Univ, MME, 52. *Prof Exp:* Aeronaut res scientist, Nat Adv Comt Aeronaut, 48-49; design engr, S Schweid & Co, 49-50, Karp Metal Prod Co, 50-51 & Seelye, Stevenson, Value & Knecht, 51-52; assoc prof mech eng, 52-69, PROF MECH ENG, NJ INST TECHNOL, 69-, ASST DEAN ACAD AFFAIRS, 72- *Concurrent Pos:* Consult, 56- *Mem:* Am Soc Mech Engrs; Am Soc Eng Educ; fel Am Soc Heating, Refrig & Air-Conditioning Engrs; NY Acad Sci; Sigma Xi. *Res:* Heat transfer; fluid mechanics; thermodynamics; refrigeration; air conditioning. *Mailing Add:* Off of Acad Affairs 367 High St Newark NJ 07102

STAMPER, HUGH BLAIR, b Warren, Ohio, Dec 13, 43; m 72; c 2. PULMONARY IMMUNOLOGY. *Educ:* Ohio State Univ, BSc, 67, MSc, 68, PhD(microbiol), 72. *Prof Exp:* Bacteriologist, Clin Lab, Licking County Mem Hosp, Newark, Ohio, 68-69; asst prof microbiol & immunol, Biol Dept, Old Dominion Univ, Va, 72-75; asst instr & res assoc, Dept Microbiol & Immunol, Downstate Med Ctr, State Univ NY Brooklyn, 75-77; HEALTH SCIENTIST ADMINR, DIV LUNG DIS, NAT HEART, LUNG & BLOOD INST, NIH, USPHS, 77- *Mem:* AAAS; Am Asn Immunologists; Am Soc Microbiol; Sigma Xi. *Res:* Interstitial lung diseases; immunologic aspects of lung diseases. *Mailing Add:* Westwood Bldg Rm 6A05 Nat Heart Lung & Blood Inst NIH Bethesda MD 20205

STAMPER, JAMES HARRIS, b Richmond, Ind, Sept 10, 38; m 59. THEORETICAL PHYSICS. *Educ:* Miami Univ, BA, 60; Yale Univ, MS, 62, PhD(physics), 65. *Prof Exp:* Asst prof physics, Elmira Col, 62-63, dir math & physics, 65-66; asst prof, Univ Fla, 67-70; prof & chmn, Dept Physics & Chem, Fla Southern Col, 70-79; INSTR, HILLSBOROUGH COMMUNITY COL, 79- *Concurrent Pos:* Consult, Battelle Mem Inst, 68-70 & Agr Res & Educ Ctr, 77- *Mem:* Am Asn Physics Teachers. *Res:* Atomic and molecular physics; environmental sciences. *Mailing Add:* 98 Imperial Southgate Lakeland FL 33803

STAMPER, JOHN ANDREW, b Middletown, Ohio, Mar 28, 30; m 59; c 1. PLASMA PHYSICS. *Educ:* Ohio State Univ, BS, 53; Univ Ky, MS, 58; Univ Md, PhD(physics), 68. *Prof Exp:* Mem tech staff semiconductor physics, Tex Instruments, Inc, 58-63; RES PHYSICIST, NAVAL RES LAB, DC, 68-. *Honors & Awards:* E O Hulbert Award, US Naval Res Lab, 74. *Mem:* Am Phys Soc. *Res:* Experimental plasma physics, including physics of laser-matter interactions; semiconductor physics, including thermal, thermoelectric and thermomagnetic effects; laser-produced plasmas; interaction of laser radiation with plasmas. *Mailing Add:* Rt 2 Box 71-E Indian Head MD 20640

STAMPER, MARTHA C, b Dawson Springs, Ky, May 7, 25. ORGANIC CHEMISTRY. *Educ:* DePauw Univ, AB, 47; Univ Wis, PhD(org chem), 52. *Prof Exp:* ORG CHEMIST, PROCESS RES DIV, ELI LILLY & CO, 52-. *Mem:* Am Chem Soc. *Mailing Add:* Process Res Div Eli Lilly & Co Indianapolis IN 46206

STAMPF, EDWARD JOHN, JR, b Evergreen Park, Ill, May 5, 49; m 72. INORGANIC CHEMISTRY. *Educ:* Northern Ill Univ, BS, 72; Univ SC, PhD(chem), 76. *Prof Exp:* Fel, Univ SC, 76-77; ASST PROF CHEM, LANDER COL, 77-. *Mem:* Am Chem Soc; Sigma Xi. *Res:* Boron hydrides and organoboranes; compounds are synthesized using high vacuum technology and studied by nuclear magnetic resonance spectroscopy. *Mailing Add:* Chem Dept Lander Col Greenwood SC 29646

STAMPFER, JOSEPH FREDERICK, JR, b Dubuque, Iowa, Mar 15, 30; m 53; c 2. ATMOSPHERIC CHEMISTRY. *Educ:* Dartmouth Col, AB, 52; Univ NMex, PhD(chem), 58. *Prof Exp:* Staff mem, Los Alamos Sci Lab, 58-67; assoc prof chem, Univ Mo-Rolla, 67-77; STAFF MEM, LOS ALAMOS NAT LAB, 77-. *Mem:* AAAS; Am Chem Soc; Am Meteorol Soc; Air Pollution Control Asn; Am Indust Hyg Asn. *Res:* Personal protective clothing; respiratory protection; atmospheric chemistry; chemical permeation; sorbent efficiency; self-contained breathing apparatus; generation, sampling and characterization of vapors and aerosols; surfactants; surface to atmosphere exchange; isotope separation; aircraft sampling. *Mailing Add:* Group H-5 MS-751 Los Alamos Nat Lab Los Alamos NM 87545

STAMPFL, RUDOLF A, b Vienna, Austria, Jan 21, 26; US citizen; m 56; c 2. ELECTRICAL ENGINEERING, ELECTRONIC COMMUNICATIONS. *Educ:* Vienna Tech Univ, BS, 48, MSEE, 51, PhD(electronic commun), 53. *Prof Exp:* Sr engr, US Army Res & Develop Lab, NJ, 53-57; dep br head electronic instruments, 57-59; head instrumentation br, Goddard Space Flight Ctr, NASA, 59-64; vis lectr instrumentations systs, Univ Calif, Los Angeles, 64-65; chief systs div, Goddard Space Flight Ctr, NASA, Greenbelt, 65-67; dept asst dir advan projs, 67-73; dir, Aero Electronic Technol Dept, 73-77, dir, Commun Navig Technol Directorate, 77-79, DIR, SYSTS DIRECTORATE, NAVAL AIR DEVELOP CTR, 79-. *Concurrent Pos:* Mem, CCIR Group IV, 63-. *Honors & Awards:* Superior Performance Award, NASA, 60; Harry Diamond Award, Inst Elec & Electronics Engrs, 67. *Mem:* Inst Elec & Electronics Engrs. *Res:* Aerospace systems; electronics. *Mailing Add:* Naval Air Develop Ctr Warminster PA 18974

STAMPS, JUDY ANN, b San Francisco, Calif, Mar 13, 47. ANIMAL BEHAVIOR, ECOLOGY. *Educ:* Univ Calif, Berkeley, BA, 69, MA, 71, PhD(zool), 74. *Prof Exp:* Actg asst prof, 73-74, ASST PROF ZOOL, UNIV CALIF, DAVIS, 74-. *Concurrent Pos:* NSF fel, 76-78. *Mem:* Animal Behav Soc; Am Soc Ichthyologists & Herpetologists; Ecol Soc Am; AAAS; Am Soc Zoologists. *Res:* Evolution of social systems, ecological determinates of variability of social behavior; parent-offspring conflict; ontogeny of social behavior; lizard social behavior. *Mailing Add:* Dept of Zool Univ of Calif Davis CA 95616

STANA, REGIS RICHARD, b Greensburg, Pa, Sept 7, 41; m 68; c 4. CHEMICAL ENGINEERING. *Educ:* Univ Pittsburgh, BS, 63, MS, 65, PhD(chem eng), 67. *Prof Exp:* Fel engr water & waste treat, Westinghouse Res, 67-78; adv engr uranium recovery, Wyo Mineral Corp, 78-81; CONSULT ENG URANIUM RECOVERY PHOSPHATE FERTILIERS, INT MINERALS & CHEM, 81-. *Mem:* Am Inst Chem Engrs. *Res:* Reverse osmosis membranes; fabrication and utilization; process development for recovery of uranium from secondary sources, phosphate fertiliers process improvement. *Mailing Add:* 935 Heathercrest Lakeland FL 33803

STANABACK, ROBERT JOHN, b Weehawken, NJ, Dec 24, 30; m 57; c 1. ORGANIC CHEMISTRY. *Educ:* Rutgers Univ, BA, 53; Seton Hall Univ, MS, 64, PhD(chem), 66. *Prof Exp:* Assoc scientist, Warner-Lambert Res Inst, 56-67; sr chemist, Tenneco Chem, Inc, Piscataway, 67-78; SR CHEMIST ORG PIGMENTS RES & DEVELOP, AM CYANAMID CO, 78-. *Mem:* Am Chem Soc. *Res:* Synthetic organic medicinals; thyroxine analogs; central nervous depressants; biocides; plasticizers; synthetic polymers; vinyl chloride technology and additives. *Mailing Add:* RD 1 Union Grove Rd Gladstone NJ 07934

STANACEV, NIKOLA ZIVA, b Milosevo, Yugoslavia, July 17, 28. BIOLOGICAL CHEMISTRY. *Educ:* Univ Zagreb, Chem E, 53, PhD(chem), 58. *Prof Exp:* Asst prof med, Univ Zagreb, 55-58; fel div biosci, Nat Res Coun Can, Ottawa, 58-59; res assoc chem & chem eng, Univ Ill, Urbana, 59-61; res assoc cell chem lab, Dept Biochem, Columbia Univ, 61-62; res assoc, Banting & Best Dept Med Res, Univ Toronto, 62-64; lectr, 64-65; res assoc biol chem, Harvard Med Sch, 65-67; assoc prof, 67-74, PROF CLIN BIOCHEM, UNIV TORONTO, 74-. *Res:* Organic biochemistry; chemistry and biochemistry of membrane lipids; isolation, determination of constitution and biosynthesis of complex lipids of membranes of animal and bacterial origin. *Mailing Add:* Banting Inst Univ of Toronto 100 College St Toronto ON M5G 1L5 Can

STANAT, DONALD FORD, b Jackson, Miss, Jan 10, 37; m 58; c 3. COMPUTER SCIENCE. *Educ:* Antioch Col, BS, 59; Univ Mich, Ann Arbor, MS, 62, PhD(commun sci), 66. *Prof Exp:* Assoc res mathematician, Univ Mich, 66-67; asst prof, 67-72, ASSOC PROF COMPUT SCI, UNIV NC, CHAPEL HILL, 72-. *Concurrent Pos:* Consult, IBM Corp, 67-71; vis scientist, IBM Corp, 79-80. *Mem:* AAAS; Asn Comput Mach; Sigma Xi. *Res:* Algorithm analysis; data structures and models of computation; parallel computation and cellular computers. *Mailing Add:* Dept of Comput Sci Univ of NC Chapel Hill NC 27514

STANBRIDGE, ERIC JOHN, b London, Eng, May 28, 42; m 71; c 2. CELL BIOLOGY, MICROBIOLOGY. *Educ:* Brunel Univ, HNC, 62; Stanford Univ, PhD(med microbiol), 71. *Prof Exp:* Tech officer virol, Nat Inst Med Res, UK, 60-65; res asst cell biol, Wistar Inst Anat & Biol, 65-67; mem sci staff cell biol, Nat Inst Med Res, UK, 68-69; instr med microbiol, Sch Med, Stanford Univ, 73-75; asst prof, 75-78, ASSOC PROF MICROBIOL, COL MED, UNIV CALIF, IRVINE, 78-. *Concurrent Pos:* Spec fel, Leukemia Soc Am, 76-78; res career develop award, Nat Cancer Inst, 78-83. *Mem:* Am Soc Microbiol; Tissue Cult Asn; Int Orgn Mycoplasmologists. *Res:* Cancer biology; somatic cell genetics; mycoplasmology. *Mailing Add:* Dept of Microbiol Univ of Calif Col of Med Irvine CA 92717

STANBROUGH, JESS HEDRICK, JR, b Ruston, La, May 1, 18; div; c 1. PHYSICS. *Educ:* Univ Tex, BS, 49, MA, 50. *Prof Exp:* Asst geophys, Univ Tex, 48-50; res physicist, Defense Res Lab, 50-60; exec secy, Undersea Warfare Res & Develop Planning Coun, Woods Hole Oceanog Inst, 60-61, tech asst to dir, 61-67, exec secy joint oceanog insts deep earth sampling prog, 66-67; exec asst, Ocean Eng Dept, 67-76, res physicist, 67-79; TECH STAFF ASST, TRIDENT DEFENSIVE WEAPONS SYST-COMMAND SUBSYST, NAVAL UNDERWATER SYST CTR, NEWPORT, RI, 79-. *Concurrent Pos:* Tech asst, Comt Undersea Warfare, Nat Acad Sci, 56; consult variable depth sonar, US Navy, 58-60, Washington Anal Servs Ctr, Inc & EG&G Inc; corp dir, Benthos Corp, 68-. *Mem:* Acoust Soc Am; Marine Technol Soc. *Res:* Oceanography; underwater sound; navigation; instrumentation. *Mailing Add:* 36 Riddle Hill Rd Falmouth MA 02540

STANBURY, DAVID MCNEIL, b Boston, Mass, May 9, 52. INORGANIC CHEMISTRY. *Educ:* Duke Univ, BA, 74; Univ Southern Calif, PhD(chem), 78. *Prof Exp:* Fel, Stanford Univ, 78-80; ASST PROF CHEM, RICE UNIV, 80-. *Mem:* Am Chem Soc; Sigma Xi; AAAS. *Res:* Kinetics and mechanisms of inorganic redox reactions. *Mailing Add:* Dept Chem Rice Univ PO Box 1892 Houston TX 77251

STANBURY, JOHN BRUTON, b Clinton, NC, May 15, 15; m 45; c 5. EXPERIMENTAL MEDICINE. *Educ:* Duke Univ, BA, 35; Harvard Med Sch, MD, 39; Am Bd Internal Med, dipl, 49. *Prof Exp:* House officer, Mass Gen Hosp, Boston, 40-41; asst in med, 46-49, asst prof, 56-60, assoc clin prof, 60-66, LECTR MED, HARVARD MED SCH, 66-; PROF EXP MED, MASS INST TECHNOL, 66-. *Concurrent Pos:* Res fel pharmacol, Harvard Med Sch, 47-48; chief med resident, Mass Gen Hosp, 48-49, asst in med, 49-50, chief thyroid clin & lab, 49-66, from asst physician to physician, 50-66; consult physician, 66-. *Mem:* Endocrine Soc; Am Soc Clin Invest; Am Asn Physicians; Am Soc Human Genetics; Am Thyroid Asn. *Res:* Endocrinology; metabolism; genetics; metabolic disease. *Mailing Add:* Mass Inst of Technol Cambridge MA 02139

STANCAMPIANO, CHARLES VINCENT, b Brooklyn, NY, Oct 27, 48; m 69; c 1. ELECTRICAL ENGINEERING, SUPERCONDUCTIVITY. *Educ:* Rensselaer Polytech Inst, BS, 69; Univ Rochester, MS, 71, PhD(elec eng), 76. *Prof Exp:* Res assoc & asst prof, 75-76, ASST PROF ELEC ENG, UNIV ROCHESTER, 77-, SCIENTIST, LAB LASER ENERGETICS, 80-. *Concurrent Pos:* Consult, Dept Radiation Biol & Biophys, Univ Rochester, 76-80; co-investr, Ctr Naval Anal grant, 78-. *Mem:* Inst Elec & Electronics Engrs; Electron Devices Soc; Am Phys Soc. *Res:* Microwave applications of the Josephson effect; nonequilibrium superconductivity. *Mailing Add:* Dept of Elec Eng Univ of Rochester Rochester NY 14627

STANCEL, GEORGE MICHAEL, b Chicago, Ill, Dec 29, 44; m 72. BIOCHEMISTRY, ENDOCRINOLOGY. *Educ:* St Thomas Col, BS, 66; Mich State Univ, PhD(biochem), 70. *Prof Exp:* ASSOC PROF PHARMACOL, UNIV TEX MED SCH HOUSTON, 72-. *Concurrent Pos:* NIH fel endocrinol, Univ Ill, 71-72. *Mem:* Endocrine Soc; NY Acad Sci; Am Chem Soc; Tissue Cult Asn. *Res:* Biochemical endocrinology; steroid hormone action; hormone receptors; estrogen regulation of uterus and pituitary. *Mailing Add:* Dept of Pharmacol Univ of Tex Med Sch Houston TX 77025

STANCER, HARVEY C, b Toronto, Ont, Mar 6, 26; m 58; c 2. PSYCHIATRY, NEUROCHEMISTRY. *Educ:* Univ Toronto, BA, 50, PhD(path chem), 53, MD, 55; Royal Col Physicians Can, cert psychiat, 62, fel, 72. *Prof Exp:* Head neurochem, Toronto Psychiat Hosp, 62-66; assoc prof, 69-72, chief clin invest univ & head neurochem, 66-76, PROF PSYCHIAT, FAC MED, UNIV TORONTO, 72-, PROF PSYCHIAT RES, 74-, CHIEF AFFECTIVE DISORDERS UNIT, CLARKE INST PSYCHIAT, 78-, VCHMN, DEPT PSYCHIAT, 80-. *Concurrent Pos:* McClean fel, Maudsley Inst, Univ London, 58-59; NY State Dept Hyg fel, Columbia Univ-Presby Med Ctr, 59-61; McLellan fel, Univ Toronto, 61-62; assoc, Med Res Coun Can, 62-64. *Honors & Awards:* Clarke Inst Prize, Univ Toronto, 70 & 74; McNeil Award, 72. *Mem:* Int Soc Neurochem; Neurochem Soc; Soc Biol Psychiat; Psychiat Res Soc; Can Endocrinol Soc & Metab. *Res:* Clinical psychiatric investigation and animal behavioral investigation of brain biogenic amines; genetics of affective disorders. *Mailing Add:* Clarke Inst of Psychiat Univ of Toronto Toronto ON M5T 1R8 Can

STANCHFIELD, JAMES ERNEST, b Salem, Mass, June 22, 52; m 73; c 1. MOLECULAR BIOLOGY, BIOCHEMISTRY. *Educ:* Univ Mass, Amherst, BS, 74; Dartmouth Col, PhD(biol), 78. *Prof Exp:* staff fel molecular biol, Nat Cancer Inst, 78-80; SALES DIR, BETHESDA RES LABS INC, 80-. *Mem:* AAAS; Soc Develop Biol; Am Soc Cell Biol. *Res:* Transcriptional and translational control mechanisms in eucaryotes. *Mailing Add:* Bethesda Res Labs 8705 Grovemont Circle Gaithersburg MD 20877

STANCL, DONALD LEE, b Oak Park, Ill, Feb 21, 40; m 66. MATHEMATICS, OPERATIONS RESEARCH. *Educ:* Knox Col, AB, 62; Univ Ill, PhD(math), 66; Nichols Col, MBA, 78. *Prof Exp:* Instr math, Princeton Univ, 67-69; asst prof, Univ Kans, 69-72; assoc prof, 72-77, PROF MATH & STATIST, NICHOLS COL, 77- *Mem:* Math Asn Am; Am Math Soc. *Res:* Operations research and general applications of mathematics to problems of management. *Mailing Add:* Dept of Math & Statist Nichols Col Dudley MA 01570

STANCL, MILDRED LUZADER, b Parkersburg, WVa; m 66. TOPOLOGY. *Educ:* Marietta Col, AB, 49; Univ Ill, AM, 62, PhD(math), 69. *Prof Exp:* Systs analyst, Sperry-Rand Corp, 54-57 & Radio Corp Am, 57-60; teaching asst math, Univ Ill, 61-66; asst prof, Trenton State Col, 68-69 & Kans Univ, 69-72; assoc prof, 72-76, PROF MATH, NICHOLS COL, 76- *Mem:* Am Math Soc; Math Asn Am; Sigma Xi. *Res:* Isomorphisms of smooth manifolds surrounding polyhedra. *Mailing Add:* Dept Math Nichols Col Dudley MA 01570

STANCYK, STEPHEN EDWARD, b Denver, Colo, Apr 8, 46; m 78. MARINE ECOLOGY, INVERTEBRATE ZOOLOGY. *Educ:* Univ Colo, Boulder, BA, 68; Univ Fla, PhD(zool), 74. *Prof Exp:* Instr biol, Dept Zool, Univ Fla, 74-75; ASST PROF MARINE SCI & BIOL, UNIV SC, 75- *Mem:* Am Soc Zoologists; AAAS; Ecol Soc Am; Southeastern Estuarine Res Soc; Sigma Xi. *Res:* Reproductive ecology of marine invertebrates; estuarine zooplankton dynamics; marine turtle conservation; systematics of Phoronids. *Mailing Add:* Dept of Biol Univ of SC Columbia SC 29208

STANCZYK, FRANK ZYGMUNT, b Montreal, Que, July, 4, 36; m 70; c 1. PERINATAL PHYSIOLOGY, STEROID BIOCHEMISTRY. *Educ:* Western Ill Univ, BS, 61; McGill Univ, MS, 67, PhD(exp med), 72. *Prof Exp:* Fel reproductive biol, Obstet & Gynec Dept, Univ Southern Calif, 72-74, from instr to asst prof, 74-76, asst prof, Obstet & Gynec Dept & Physiol Dept, 76-80; ASST SCIENTIST PERINATAL PHYSIOL, ORE REGIONAL PRIMATE RES CTR, 80-; ASST PROF, DEPT OBSTET & GYNEC, ORE HEALTH SCI UNIV, 80- *Mem:* Soc Gynec Invest; Endocrine Soc; Am Chem Soc; Can Biol Soc; Sigma Xi. *Res:* In vivo and in vitro studies of steroid hormone metabolism in pregnancy and endocrinopathies; pharmacokinetics and endocrine effects of contraceptive steroids; prediction and detection of ovulation; regulation of parturition and placental production of hormones. *Mailing Add:* Ore Regional Primate Res Ctr 505 NW 185th Ave Beaverton OR 97006

STANCZYK, MARTIN HENRY, b Jersey City, NJ, Jan 26, 30; m 57; c 4. EXTRACTIVE METALLURGY. *Educ:* Univ Ariz, BS, 57, MS, 58. *Prof Exp:* Bur Mines fel, Ariz, 57-58, extractive metallurgist, 57-60 & Ala, 60-61, res extractive metallurgist, 61-68, supvry metallurgist, College Park Metall Res Ctr, 68-72, RES DIR, TUSCALOOSA METALL RES CTR, US BUR MINES, 73- *Mem:* Am Inst Mining, Metall & Petrol Engrs; Am Inst Mining Engrs; Sigma Xi. *Res:* Extractive metallurgy of nonmetallic minerals, including beneficiation studies, dewatering mineral wastes and developing new or improved ceramic and refractory materials. *Mailing Add:* US Dept Interior Bur Mines Univ Ala PO Box L Tuscaloosa AL 35486

STANDAERT, FRANK GEORGE, b Paterson, NJ, Nov 12, 29; m 59; c 3. PHARMACOLOGY. *Educ:* Harvard Univ, AB, 51; Cornell Univ, MD, 55. *Prof Exp:* Intern med, Johns Hopkins Hosp, Baltimore, Md, 55-56; from instr to assoc prof pharmacol, Med Col, Cornell Univ, 59-67; PROF PHARMACOL & CHMN DEPT, SCH MED & DENT, GEORGETOWN UNIV, 67- *Concurrent Pos:* Res fel pharmacol, Med Col, Cornell Univ, 56-57; USPHS career develop award, 61-67; guest scientist, Naval Med Ctr, Bethesda, Ma; mem, Nat Res Coun & Am Asn Dent Schs; chmn publ comt, Fedn Am Socs Exp Biol; mem comt toxicol, Nat Acad Sci-Nat Res Coun; mem neurol dis prog proj rev comt & pharmacol & toxicol comt, NIH; ed, Neuropharmacol, J Pharmacol & Exp Therapeut; mem merit rev bd neurobiol, Vet Admin; mem basic pharmacol adv comt, Pharmaceut Mfrs Asn Found; mem bd dirs, Washington Heart Asn; secy, Am Med Sch Pharmacol. *Mem:* Am Soc Clin Pharmacol & Therapeut; Am Soc Pharmacol & Exp Therapeut; Soc Exp Biol & Med; Soc Toxicol; Peripatetic Soc. *Res:* Pharmacology of neuromuscular transmission; toxicology, neuropharmacology. *Mailing Add:* 3900 Reservoir Rd Washington DC 20007

STANDEFER, JIMMY CLAYTON, b Stanton, Tex, Mar 2, 41; m 68; c 2. BIOCHEMISTRY, CLINICAL CHEMISTRY. *Educ:* Univ Kans, BA, 63, PhD(biochem), 67; Nat Registry Clin Chem, cert, 70. *Prof Exp:* Biochemist, Walter Reed Army Inst Res, 67-70; instr biochem, Sch Nursing, Univ Md, 69-70; ASST PROF CLIN CHEM, SCH MED, UNIV N MEX, 70- *Mem:* Am Asn Clin Chem; Am Acad Forensic Sci. *Res:* Membrane chemistry; isoenzymes; lipids. *Mailing Add:* Clin Lab 2211 Lomas Blvd NE Albuquerque NM 87106

STANDEFORD, LEO VERN, astronomy, deceased

STANDER, JOSEPH W, b Covington, Ky, Dec 2, 28. ALGEBRA. *Educ:* Univ Dayton, BS, 49; Cath Univ, MS, 57, PhD(math), 59. *Prof Exp:* Teacher, Hamilton Cath High Sch, 49-50; teacher, Colegio Ponceno, 50-55; asst prof, 60-65, ASSOC PROF MATH, UNIV DAYTON, 65-, DEAN GRAD STUDIES & RES, 69-, VPRES ACAD AFFAIRS & PROVOST, 75- *Mem:* Math Asn Am; Sigma Xi. *Res:* Matrix theory. *Mailing Add:* Univ Dayton Dayton OH 45469

STANDIFER, LEONIDES CALMET, JR, b Gulfport, Miss, Apr 24, 25; m 57; c 2. PLANT PHYSIOLOGY. *Educ:* Miss State Univ, BS, 50, MS, 54; Univ Wis, PhD(bot), 59. *Prof Exp:* Plant physiologist, Firestone Plantations Co, 54-61; from asst prof to assoc prof, 61-74, prof bot, 74-77, PROF HORT, LA STATE UNIV, BATON ROUGE, 78- *Mem:* Bot Soc Am; Am Soc Plant Physiol; Weed Sci Soc Am. *Res:* Patterns of plant recovery from flame injury; histological responses of certain plants to herbicides, and physiology of herbicidal action. *Mailing Add:* Dept of Hort La State Univ Baton Rouge LA 70803

STANDIFER, LONNIE NATHANIEL, b Itasca, Tex, Oct 28, 26; div. ENTOMOLOGY, PARASITOLOGY. *Educ:* Prairie View Agr & Mech Col, BS, 49; Kans State Col, MS, 51; Cornell Univ, PhD(med & vet entom & parasitol), 54. *Prof Exp:* Instr biol sci & supvr campus pest control, Tuskegee Inst, 51-52; asst livestock insect control, Cornell Univ, 53-54; asst prof biol sci, Southern Univ, 54-56; res scientist & apiculturist, 56-70, DIR BEE RES LAB, USDA, 70-, RES LEADER, HONEY BEE POLLINATION LAB, 72-, TECH ADV APICULTURE, WESTERN REGION, 73- *Mem:* AAAS; Entom Soc Am; Am Soc Parasitol; Am Beekeeping Fedn. *Res:* Medical and veterinary entomology and parasitology; control of insects of public health importance; insect physiology and nutrition; botany and plant pathology; honey bee physiology and nutrition, protein and lipids; pollen chemistry, fatty acids, sterols and hydrocarbons. *Mailing Add:* 8031 E 17th Place Tucson AZ 85710

STANDIL, SIDNEY, b Winnipeg, Man, Oct 19, 26; m 50; c 4. PHYSICS. *Educ:* Queen's Univ, Ont, BSc, 48, MSc, 49; Univ Man, PhD, 51. *Prof Exp:* From asst prof to assoc prof, 51-63, dean fac grad studies, 73-79, PROF PHYSICS, UNIV MAN, 63- *Mem:* Am Phys Soc; Am Geophys Union; Can Asn Physicists. *Res:* Cosmic ray and space physics. *Mailing Add:* 772 Campbell St Winnipeg MB R3N 1C6 Can

STANDING, CHARLES NICHOLAS, b Minneapolis, Minn, Dec 24, 43; m 68. CHEMICAL ENGINEERING, FOOD SCIENCE. *Educ:* Univ Minn, BS, 65, PhD(chem eng), 70. *Prof Exp:* Scientist & engr, Pillsbury Co, Minneapolis, 70-74, sr scientist & engr, 74-75, group leader, 75-78, sect mgr res & develop, 78-79; HEAD, DEPT PROCESS RES & DEVELOP, GEN MILLS INC, 79- *Mem:* Am Inst Chem Engrs; Inst Food Technologists. *Res:* Process development; food product development and exploratory food research; technomic feasibility analyses; process engineering, process scaleup and plant engineering; biochemical engineering and dynamics of microbial populations. *Mailing Add:* Gen Mills Inc 9000 Plymouth Ave N Minneapolis MN 55427

STANDING, KEITH M, b Ogden, Utah, Aug 2, 28; m 56; c 7. VERTEBRATE ZOOLOGY. *Educ:* Brigham Young Univ, BS, 53, MS, 55; Wash State Univ, PhD(zool, bot), 60. *Prof Exp:* Assoc prof, 58-69, Chem Dept, 69-72, PROF BIOL, CALIF STATE UNIV, FRESNO, 69-, CHMN DEPT, 82- *Concurrent Pos:* NSF res grants, 64-67; mem, NSF Conf Histochem Its Appl in Res & Teaching, Vanderbilt Univ, 65; mem gov bd, Moss Landing Marine Labs; bd dirs, Ctr Urban & Regional Studies; vis scholar, Univ Calif, Berkeley & Univ Calif, Davis. *Mem:* AAAS; Am Soc Zool. *Res:* Histological analysis of reproductive organs of blue grouse; comparative histology of nephron units of kangaroo rats; isolation of nephron units of Dipodomys by various techniques; cytotaxonomy of Dipodomys; embryonic kidney development. *Mailing Add:* Dept of Biol Calif State Univ Fresno CA 93740

STANDING, KENNETH GRAHAM, b Winnipeg, Man, Apr 3, 25; div; c 4. MASS SPECTROMETRY. *Educ:* Univ Man, BSc, 48; Princeton Univ, AM, 50, PhD(physics), 55. *Prof Exp:* From asst prof to assoc prof, 53-64, PROF PHYSICS, UNIV MAN, 64- *Concurrent Pos:* Nuffield Found Dom traveling fel, Wills Physics Lab, Bristol Univ, 58-59; Nat Res Coun Can sr res fel, Univ Grenoble, 67-68. *Mem:* Am Phys Soc; Can Asn Physicists. *Res:* Mass spectrometry of biomolecules; nuclear physics and applications; cosmic rays. *Mailing Add:* Dept of Physics Univ of Man Winnipeg MB R3T 2N2 Can

STANDISH, CHARLES JUNIOR, b Triangle, NY, Nov 10, 26. MATHEMATICS. *Educ:* Hamilton Col, NY, BA, 49; Johns Hopkins Univ, MA, 51; Cornell Univ, PhD(math), 54. *Prof Exp:* Instr math, Hamilton Col, NY, 51-52; asst, Cornell Univ, 52-54; asst prof, Union Univ, NY, 54-57; MATHEMATICIAN, IBM CORP, 57- *Concurrent Pos:* Vis assoc prof, NC State Univ, 60-61; vis lectr adv technol, State Univ NY Binghamton, 74-78. *Mem:* Am Math Soc; Soc Indust & Appl Math. *Res:* Measure theory; integral transforms; control theory. *Mailing Add:* RD 2 Greene NY 13778

STANDISH, E MYLES, JR, b Hartford, Conn, Mar 5, 39; m 68. ASTRONOMY. *Educ:* Wesleyan Univ, BA, 60, MA, 62; Yale Univ, PhD(astron), 68. *Prof Exp:* Asst prof astron, Yale Univ, 68-72; MEM TECH STAFF, JET PROPULSION LAB, 72- *Mem:* Am Astron Soc-Div Dynamic Astron; Int Astron Union. *Res:* Celestial mechanics; numerical analysis; continuous improvement of the planetary, lunar and natural satellite ephemerides. *Mailing Add:* Jet Propulsion Lab 264-664 4800 Oakgrove Dr Pasadena CA 91109

STANDISH, NORMAN WESTON, b Marion, Iowa, Apr 4, 30; m 56; c 3. ORGANIC CHEMISTRY. *Educ:* Beloit Col, BS, 52; Purdue Univ, MS, 57, PhD(org chem), 59. *Prof Exp:* Chemist, Selectron Div, Pittsburgh Plate Glass Co, 52-53; res assoc biochem, 60-66, tech dir plastics, Prophylactic Brush Div, 66-69, res supvr, Cleveland, 69-70, suprvr develop, Tech Serv & Polymers, 70-75, mgr, Tech Serv, 75-80, LAB DIR EXPLOR PROD, STANDARD OIL CO, OHIO, 80- *Mem:* Am Chem Soc; Soc Plastics Engrs; Soc Nematol; fel Am Inst Chemists; Soc Plastics Indust. *Res:* Computer modeling of fluid flow in reservoirs, enhanced oil recovery systems, and architectural technology on protective systems for ice and ice construction techniques. *Mailing Add:* Standard Oil Co Ohio 4440 Warrensville Center Rd Cleveland OH 44128

STANDISH, SAMUEL MILES, b Campbellsburg, Ind, July 6, 23; m 49; c 2. ORAL PATHOLOGY. *Educ:* Ind Univ, DDS, 45, MS, 56; Am Bd Oral Path, dipl, 59; Am Bd Forensic Odontol, dipl, 77. *Prof Exp:* Instr dent, 52-57, from asst prof to assoc prof oral path, 57-67, asst dean grad & postgrad educ, 69-74, PROF ORAL PATH, SCH DENT, IND UNIV, INDIANAPOLIS, 67-, ASSOC DEAN GRAD & POSTGRAD EDUC, 74- *Mem:* Am Dent Asn; fel Am Acad Oral Path; Int Asn Dent Res; fel Am Acad Forensic Sci. *Res:* Salivary gland pathophysiology and experimental carcinogenesis; inflammatory mechanisms; striated muscle regeneration; muscle diseases; clinical oral pathology. *Mailing Add:* Dept of Oral Path Ind Univ Sch of Dent Indianapolis IN 46202

STANDLEE, WILLIAM JASPER, b Zybach, Tex, May 2, 29; m 58; c 3. POULTRY NUTRITION. *Educ:* Tex Tech Univ, BS, 54, MS, 55; Tex A&M Univ, PhD(poultry sci), 63. *Prof Exp:* Animal nutritionist, Standard Milling Co, Tex, 55-57; salesman, Van Waters & Rogers, 57-58; res asst, Tex Agr Exp Sta, 58-63; dir nutrit & res, Darragh Co, Ark, 63-65; dir nutrit, Burrus Feed Mills, Tex, 65-68; dir nutrit & res, Food Div, Valmac Industs, Inc, Ark, 68-71; dir res & nutrit, B & D Mills, 71-79; CONSULT POULTRY & ANIMAL NUTRIT, 79- *Mem:* Poultry Sci Asn. *Res:* Nutrition and feeding management of turkey breeders; broiler chicken breeders, market turkeys and broilers and egg production chickens. *Mailing Add:* 815 N Lucas Dr Grapevine TX 76051

STANDLEY, ROBERT DEAN, b Findlay, Ill, Aug 25, 35; m 59; c 2. ELECTRICAL ENGINEERING. *Educ:* Univ Ill, BS, 57; Rutgers Univ, MS, 60; Ill Inst Technol, PhD(elec eng), 66. *Prof Exp:* Assoc engr, IIT Res Inst, 60-62, res engr, 62-64, asst mgr microwaves & antennas, 64-65, mgr electromagnetic compatibility, 65-66; MEM TECH STAFF COHERENT OPTICS RES, BELL TEL LABS, INC, 66- *Mem:* Inst Elec & Electronics Engrs. *Res:* Microwave filters; antennas; electromagnetic compatibility; avalanche transit time diode oscillators; optical modulators; optical integrated circuits; fiber optics; satellite communications. *Mailing Add:* Dept 1361 Bell Tel Labs Holmdel NJ 07733

STANEK, ELDON KEITH, b Novinger, Mo, Dec 12, 41; m 69; c 2. ELECTRICAL ENGINEERING. *Educ:* Ill Inst Technol, BSEE, 64, MS, 65, PhD(elec eng), 69. *Prof Exp:* Asst prof elec eng, Ill Inst Technol, 68-70; from asst prof to assoc prof elec eng, 70-77, prof, 77-80; PROF & HEAD ELEC ENG, MICH TECH UNIV, 80- *Concurrent Pos:* NSF grant, WVa Univ, 71-73, Bur Mines grant, 72-79; consult, Dept Energy, 77- & Union Carbide Corp, 77- *Mem:* Inst Elec & Electronics Engrs; Am Soc Elec Engrs; Sigma Xi. *Res:* Electrical power systems; digital simulation and mathematical modeling; simulation of switching transients; inductive interference; induced voltage in cables. *Mailing Add:* Dept Elec Eng Mich Tech Univ Houghton MI 49931

STANEK, JEAN CHAN, b Toyshan, China, Apr 24, 37; US citizen; m 60; c 2. MATHEMATICS. *Educ:* Univ Chicago, BS, 60, MS, 61; Univ Calif, Los Angeles, PhD(math), 71. *Prof Exp:* Asst prof math, Loyola Univ Los Angeles, 72-73; asst prof 73-77, ASSOC PROF MATH, SONOMA STATE UNIV, 77- *Mem:* Math Asn Am; Asn Women Mathematicians; Am Math Soc. *Res:* Convex sets. *Mailing Add:* Dept of Math Sonoma State Univ Rohnert Park CA 94928

STANEK, PETER, b Chicago, Ill, Dec 3, 37; m 60; c 2. MATHEMATICS, SYSTEMS ANALYSIS. *Educ:* Univ Chicago, MS, 58, PhD(math), 61. *Prof Exp:* Mem, Inst Defense Anal, 61-62; analyst, Opers Eval Group, 62-63; asst prof math, Univ Southern Calif, 63-65; sr scientist, Jet Propulsion Lab, 65-68 & Lear Siegler Inc, 68-72; mem staff, Systs Applns Inc, 72-78; MEM STAFF, KETRON INC, 78- *Mem:* Am Math Soc; Soc Indust & Appl Math; Human Factors Soc; Am Inst Aeronaut & Astronaut. *Res:* Algebra; operations research; communications engineering; human factors engineering; computer applications. *Mailing Add:* 1281 Idylberry Rd San Rafael CA 94903

STANFEL, LARRY EUGENE, b Waukegan, Ill, Feb 6, 40. OPERATIONS RESEARCH, COMPUTER SCIENCE. *Educ:* Ill Inst Technol, BS, 62; Northwestern Univ, Evanston, MS, 65, PhD(mgt sci), 66. *Prof Exp:* Asst prof indust & systs eng, Univ Fla, 66-69; assoc prof mech eng, Colo State Univ, 69-72; prof indust eng, Univ Tex, Arlington, 72-80; PROF MGT, CLARKSON COL, 80- *Concurrent Pos:* Consult, Southern Bell Tel & Tel Co, US Army & ESCA Corp. *Mem:* Opers Res Soc Am; Inst Mgt Sci. *Res:* Application of operations research techniques to the design and analysis of information storage and retrieval systems. *Mailing Add:* Sch Mgt Clarkson Col Potsdam NY 13676

STANFIELD, JAMES ARMOND, b Covington, Ky, Aug 28, 17; m 42; c 3. ORGANIC CHEMISTRY. *Educ:* Eastern Ky State Col, BS, 40; Univ Tenn, MS, 42, PhD(phys org chem), 47. *Prof Exp:* Instr chem, Univ Ky, 41-42; instr, Univ Tenn, 42-46; from asst prof to assoc prof. 47-56, PROF CHEM, GA INST TECHNOL, 56-, ASST DIR SCH CHEM, 65-, RES ASSOC, RES INST, 51- *Mem:* Am Chem Soc. *Res:* Organic synthesis; catalytic hydrogenation kinetics; spirobarbituric acids; chemistry of uramil. *Mailing Add:* Sch of Chem Ga Inst Technol Atlanta GA 30332

STANFIELD, KENNETH CHARLES, b Los Angeles, Calif, Sept 21, 42; m 65; c 1. EXPERIMENTAL HIGH ENERGY PHYSICS. *Educ:* Univ Tex, BS, 64; Harvard Univ, AM, 67, PhD(physics), 69. *Prof Exp:* Res assoc physics, Univ Mich, 69-71; asst prof physics, Purdue Univ, 71-77; assoc head, 77-79, HEAD, PROTON DEPT, FERMI NAT ACCELERATOR LAB, 79- *Concurrent Pos:* Mem prog adv comt, Zero Gradient Synchrotron, Argonne Nat Lab, 75- *Mem:* Sigma Xi. *Res:* Experimental research, using electronic techniques, into the nature of elementary particle properties. *Mailing Add:* Fermi Lab PO Box 500 Batavia IL 60510

STANFIELD, MANIE K, b St Petersburg, Fla, Feb 15, 31. ORGANIC CHEMISTRY, BIOCHEMISTRY. *Educ:* Univ Chicago, BA, 54, MS, 57; Univ Calif, Los Angeles, PhD(org chem), 62. *Prof Exp:* Asst org chem, Mass Inst Technol, 62-63 & Rockefeller Univ, 63-65; ASST PROF BIOCHEM, SCH MED, TULANE UNIV, 65- *Mem:* AAAS; Am Chem Soc. *Res:* Organic syntheses of small biologically interesting molecules; inborn errors of amino acid metabolism; synthesis of central nervous system stimulating compounds, stability and polymerization of beta-lactam antibiotics. *Mailing Add:* Dept of Biochem Tulane Univ Med Sch New Orleans LA 70118

STANFORD, AUGUSTUS LAMAR, JR, b Macon, Ga, Jan 20, 31; m 52; c 2. SOLID STATE PHYSICS. *Educ:* Ga Inst Technol, BS, 52, MS, 57, PhD(physics), 58. *Prof Exp:* Sr staff consult, Sperry Rand Corp, 58-64; assoc prof, 64-74, PROF PHYSICS, GA INST TECHNOL, 74- *Concurrent Pos:* NASA res grant, 64- *Mem:* Am Phys Soc. *Res:* Nuclear spectroscopy; ferroelectrics; pyroelectrics; phonon in solids. *Mailing Add:* Sch of Physics Ga Inst of Technol Atlanta GA 30332

STANFORD, GEORGE STAILING, b Halifax, NS, July 23, 28; m 56; c 3. REACTOR PHYSICS. *Educ:* Acadia Univ, BSc, 49; Wesleyan Univ, MA, 51; Yale Univ, PhD(nuclear energy levels), 56. *Prof Exp:* Proj engr infrared instrumentation, Perkin-Elmer Corp, 55-59; PHYSICIST, ARGONNE NAT LAB, 59- *Res:* Experimental reactor physics. *Mailing Add:* Argonne Nat Lab D208 9700 S Cass Ave Argonne IL 60439

STANFORD, JACK ARTHUR, b Delta, Colo, Feb 18, 47; m 69; c 2. LIMNOLOGY. *Educ:* Colo State Univ, BS, 69, MS, 71; Univ Utah, PhD(limnol), 75. *Prof Exp:* Asst fish & wildlife, Colo State Univ, 65-69, asst zool, 69-72; res limnol, Univ Utah & Univ Mont, 72-74; asst prof limnol & biol, NTex State Univ, 74-79; ASSOC PROF BIOL, UNIV MONT, 79-, DIR, BIOL STA, 80- *Concurrent Pos:* Dir, Flathead Res Group, Biol Sta, Univ Mont, 77- *Mem:* Sigma Xi; Int Soc Theoret & Appl Limnol; Am Soc Limnol & Oceanog; Ecol Soc Am; NAm Benthological Soc. *Res:* All aspects of limnological study in lakes and streams with special interest in nutrient cycling by algae and heterotrophic bacteria; benthic ecology and life histories of the Plecoptera; applied biometrics. *Mailing Add:* Biol Sta Univ Mont Bigfork MT 59911

STANFORD, JACK WAYNE, b Eldorado, Tex, Dec 21, 35; m 58; c 2. PLANT TAXONOMY. *Educ:* Baylor Univ, BA, 58; Tex Tech Univ, MS, 66; Okla State Univ, PhD(bot), 71. *Prof Exp:* Teacher jr high sch, Tex, 60-62, high sch, 62-66; asst prof biol, 66-68, assoc prof, 70-74, PROF BIOL, HOWARD PAYNE UNIV, 74- *Res:* Pollen morphology of the Mimosoideae; floristic studies of central Texas. *Mailing Add:* Dept of Biol Howard Payne Col Brownwood TX 76801

STANG, ELDEN JAMES, b Victoria, Kans, Jan 23, 40; m 63; c 3. HORTICULTURE, AGRICULTURE. *Educ:* Kans State Univ, BS, 67; Iowa State Univ, MS, 69, PhD(hort), 73. *Prof Exp:* Res asst hort, Iowa State Univ, 67-69, res assoc, 69-73, instr, 73; exten horticulturist pomol, Ohio State Univ, 73-78; EXTEN HORTICULTURIST POMOL, UNIV WIS-MADISON, 78- *Honors & Awards:* Outstanding Serv Award, Ohio State Hort Soc, 78. *Mem:* Am Soc Hort Sci; Am Soc Plant Physiologists. *Res:* Production and marketing of tree fruit, small fruit and grapes; weed control; plant nutrition; on-farm marketing of fruit crops; plant growth regulators. *Mailing Add:* Univ of Wis Dept of Hort 1575 Linden Dr Madison WI 53706

STANG, LOUIS GEORGE, JR, b Portland, Ore, Oct 25, 19; m 43; c 3. RADIOCHEMISTRY, NUCLEAR WASTE MANAGEMENT. *Educ:* Reed Col, BA, 41. *Prof Exp:* Res chemist, Nat Defense Res Comt, Northwestern Univ, 42-43, Calif Inst Technol, 43, Clinton Labs, Tenn, 43-44, Metall Lab, Univ Chicago, 44-45, Monsanto Chem Co, Ohio, 45 & Universal Oil Prod Co, Ill, 45-47; div head, 47-80, CHEMIST, BROOKHAVEN NAT LAB, 47- *Concurrent Pos:* USAEC consult, Yugoslavia & Israel, 60 & rep, regional meetings utilization res reactors, Int Atomic Energy Agency, Manila, 63, Bombay, 64; Indian Atomic Energy Estab & Int Atomic Energy Agency lect prod radioisotopes, Bombay, 64. *Honors & Awards:* Distinguished Serv Award, Am Nuclear Soc, 69. *Mem:* AAAS; Am Chem Soc; Am Nuclear Soc. *Res:* Production of radioisotopes; spallation reactions; radionuclide generators; design of radioactive laboratories and equipment; use of teeth as indicators of concentrations of trace elements in the human body; health effects of photovoltaic materials. *Mailing Add:* Brookhaven Nat Lab Upton NY 11973

STANG, PETER JOHN, b Nürenberg, Ger, Nov 17, 41; US citizen; m 69. ORGANIC CHEMISTRY. *Educ:* DePaul Univ, BS, 63; Univ Calif, Berkeley, PhD(chem), 66. *Prof Exp:* NIH fel chem, Princeton Univ, 66-68, instr, 68-69; asst prof, 69-75, assoc prof, 75-79, PROF CHEM, UNIV UTAH, 79- *Concurrent Pos:* Alexander von Humboldt US sr scientist award, 77; assoc ed, J Am Chem Soc, 82. *Mem:* Am Chem Soc; The Chem Soc; AAAS. *Res:* Kinetics and mechanisms of organic reactions; reactive intermediates; unsaturated cations and carbenes; molecules of medicinal and biological interest. *Mailing Add:* Dept of Chem Univ of Utah Salt Lake City UT 84112

STANG, ROBERT GEORGE, b Los Angeles, Calif, June 20, 38; m 64. MATERIALS SCIENCE ENGINEERING. *Educ:* Long Beach State Col, BS, 61; Univ Calif, Los Angeles, MS, 65; Stanford Univ, PhD(mat sci & eng), 72. *Prof Exp:* Instr mech eng, Long Beach State Col, 65-66; res asst mat sci, Dept Mat Sci & Eng, Stanford Univ, 66-71; asst prof, Inst Mil Engenharia, Rio de Janeiro, 71-72; res assoc, Dept Mat Sci & Eng, Stanford Univ, 72-73; asst prof, 73-79, ASSOC PROF METALL ENG, DEPT MINING, METALL & CERAMIC ENG, UNIV WASH, 79- *Concurrent Pos:* Inco fel, Dept Mat Sci & Eng, Stanford Univ, 66-68; Fulbright-Hays researcher & lectr, Montanuniversitat, Austria, 80-81; consult, US Coast Guard, 78, Hewlett Packard, Boise Div, 79 & Battelle Pac Northwest Labs, 78- *Mem:* Am Soc Metals; Metall Soc Am; Inst Mining Metall & Petrol Engrs; Sigma Xi. *Res:* Structure-property relationships in materials; deformation at ambient and high temperatures in metals, alloys and ceramics; fatigue and fracture; effect of micro-structure on deformation and fracture. *Mailing Add:* Dept Mining Metall & Ceramic Eng FB-10 Univ Wash Seattle WA 98195

STANGE, HUGO, b Elizabeth, NJ, June 24, 21; m 42; c 3. ORGANIC CHEMISTRY, INORGANIC CHEMISTRY. *Educ:* Northwestern Univ, BS, 42, PhD(chem), 50. *Prof Exp:* Chemist, Pa Ord Works, US Rubber Co, 42; chemist res dept, Olin Mathieson Chem Corp, 50-52, sect leader, 52-55; mgr org res, 55-60, mgr org & polymer res, 60-62, res mgr, 62-65, asst dir, Cent Res Dept, 65-72, DIR PRINCETON CTR TECH DEPT, FMC CORP, 72- *Mem:* Asn Res Dirs (pres, 82-82); Am Chem Soc; Royal Soc Chem; Am Inst Chemists; Am Inst Chem Eng. *Res:* Thianaphthene and boron chemistry; industrial process and product development in organic and inorganic chemistry; agricultural pesticides; polymers; chemical research management; general technical management. *Mailing Add:* 19 Hamilton Ave Princeton NJ 08540

STANGE, LIONEL ALVIN, b Los Angeles, Calif, June 27, 35; m 67; c 2. SYSTEMATIC ENTOMOLOGY. *Educ:* Univ Calif, Berkeley, BS, 58; Univ Calif, Davis, MS, 60, PhD(entom), 65. *Prof Exp:* Prof entom, Nat Univ Tucuman, Arg, 65-78; TAXON ENTOMOLOGIST, BUR ENTOM, DIV PLANT INDUST & CONSUMER SERV, DEPT AGR, FLA, 78- *Concurrent Pos:* Investr entom, Miguel Lillo Found, Tucuman, Arg, 65-78; grants, Sigma Xi, 68, Nat Coun Res Technol, Buenos Aires, 70-75 & Nat Geog Soc, 75-77; vis curator, Mus Comp Zool, Harvard Univ, 70; vis prof, North East Univ Corrientes, Arg, 74. *Honors & Awards:* Ellsworth Award, Am Mus Natural Hist, NY, 60. *Mem:* Nat Geog Soc; Sigma Xi. *Res:* Biosystematics of the Neuroptera especially Myrmeleontidae (world) and of Hymenoptera (Eumenidae and Megachilidae) of the western hemisphere. *Mailing Add:* Bur of Entom Fla Dept of Agr Gainesville FL 32602

STANGER, ANDREW L, b Boulder, Colo, Apr 12, 48. COMPUTER SCIENCE, SOLAR PHYSICS. *Educ:* Univ Colo, BA, 71. *Prof Exp:* Comput programmer signal processing, Naval Undersea Ctr, 71-72; res asst nuclear eng, Gen Atomic Co, 72-74; engr & scientist sci comput, TRW Systs Group, Inc, 74-75; SCI PROGRAMMER SOLAR PHYSICS, HIGH ALTITUDE OBSERV, NAT CTR ATMOSPHERIC RES, 75- *Mailing Add:* High Altitude Observ Nat Ctr Atmospheric Res 1850 Table Mesa Dr PO Box 3000 Boulder CO 80307

STANGER, PHILIP CHARLES, b Newark, NJ, Nov 11, 20; m 43; c 2. ASTRONOMY. *Educ:* Montclair State Teachers Col, AB, 42; Okla Agr & Mech Col, MS, 49; Ohio State Univ, MA, 54. *Prof Exp:* Instr math, Okla Agr & Mech Col, 46-48; instr, Ohio Univ, 48-50; from instr to asst prof, 52-59, from asst prof astron to assoc prof, 59-74, PROF ASTRON, OHIO WESLEYAN UNIV, 74- CHMN DEPT, 59- *Mem:* AAAS; Am Astron Soc. *Res:* Spectroscopic binaries; stellar atmospheres. *Mailing Add:* Dept of Astronomy Ohio Wesleyan Univ Delaware OH 43015

STANGHELLINI, MICHAEL EUGENE, b San Francisco, Calif, Mar 21, 40; m 66; c 2. PLANT PATHOLOGY. *Educ:* Univ Calif, Davis, BA, 63; Univ Hawaii, MS, 65; Univ Calif, Berkeley, PhD(plant path), 69. *Prof Exp:* Asst prof, 69-72, assoc prof, 72-81, PROF PLANT PATH, UNIV ARIZ, 81- & RES SCIENTIST PLANT PATH, AGR EXP STA, 77- *Mem:* Am Phytopath Soc. *Res:* Soil borne fungal pathogens. *Mailing Add:* Dept of Plant Path Univ of Ariz Tucson AZ 85721

STANIFORTH, DAVID WILLIAM, b Esther, Alta, Sept 5, 19; m 45; c 3. AGRONOMY. *Educ:* Univ Sask, BSA, 44, MSc, 46; Iowa State Col, PhD(bot, plant physiol), 49. *Prof Exp:* Asst crop-breeding, Univ Sask, 41-44, asst crop ecol, 44-46; instr bot, 47-48, res assoc, 48-49, asst prof, 49-51, assoc prof bot & agron, 51-60, PROF BOT & AGRON, IOWA STATE UNIV, 60- *Mem:* AAAS; Am Inst Biol Sci; Weed Sci Soc Am; Am Soc Agron. *Res:* Control of weeds in economic crops; physiology of herbicides; crop ecology; growth of crops and weeds. *Mailing Add:* Dept of Bot Iowa State Univ Ames IA 50010

STANIFORTH, RICHARD JOHN, b Sidmouth, Eng, Oct 2, 46; Brit & Can citizen; m 71. PLANT ECOLOGY. *Educ:* Univ Col NWales, BSc, 68; Univ Western Ont, PhD(plant sci), 75. *Prof Exp:* Lectr biol, Univ Western Ont, 73-75; asst prof plant ecol & taxon, 75-82, ASSOC PROF BIOL, UNIV WINNIPEG, 82- *Mem:* Brit Ecol Soc; Can Bot Asn. *Res:* Plant ecology of riparian sites. *Mailing Add:* Dept of Biol Univ of Winnipeg Winnipeg MB R3B 2E9 Can

STANIFORTH, ROBERT ARTHUR, b Cleveland, Ohio, Oct 5, 17; m 44; c 3. INORGANIC CHEMISTRY. *Educ:* Case Western Reserve Univ, BA, 39; Ohio State Univ, MS, 42, PhD(inorg chem), 43. *Prof Exp:* Asst chem, Ohio State Univ, 39-43; res chemist, Monsanto Chem Co, Ohio, 44-46, group leader, 47, sect chief, AEC, Mound Lab, 48, res dir, 48-54, mgr chem develop, Inorg Chem Div, 54-59, asst dir develop, 59-62; mgr prod planning, Monsanto Indust Chem Co, 62-69, mgr commun & info, 69-75; RETIRED. *Concurrent Pos:* Res chemist, Gen Aniline & Film Corp, Pa, 43. *Mem:* Am Chem Soc; Electrochem Soc. *Res:* Ultramicrobalances; chelate compounds of the rare earth metals; radiochemistry; metals; semiconductors. *Mailing Add:* 1215 Walnut Hill Farm Dr St Louis MO 63017

STANIONIS, VICTOR ADAM, b New York, NY, Dec 24, 38; m 60; c 2. APPLIED MATHEMATICS. *Educ:* Iona Col, BS, 60; NY Univ, MS, 64; Queen's Col, MA, 70; Columbia Univ, PhD(math), 75. *Prof Exp:* Instr math & physics, 61-66, asst prof, 66-77, ASSOC PROF PHYSICS, IONA COL, 77-, CHMN DEPT, 75- *Concurrent Pos:* Adj assoc prof math, Queensborough Community Col, 69- *Mem:* Am Asn Physics Teachers; Math Asn Am; Nat Coun Teachers Math. *Res:* Computers in physics teaching; nature of problem solving in physics and mathematics. *Mailing Add:* Dept Physics Iona Col New Rochelle NY 10804

STANISIC, MIRKOV MILOMIR, applied mathematics, mechanics, see previous edition

STANISLAO, BETTIE CHLOE CARTER, b Alexandria, La, June 12, 34; m 60. NUTRITION, FOOD SCIENCE. *Educ:* Northwestern State Univ, La, BS, 56; Pa State Univ, MSc, 60; Case Western Reserve Univ, DPhil, 76. *Prof Exp:* Therapeut dietitian, Baptist Hosp, Alexandria, 56-57; asst hotel & inst admin, Pa State Univ, 57-59; dietetic intern, Barnes Hosp, St Louis, Mo, 59-60; chief therapeut dietitian, Pawtucket Mem Hosp, 61-63; therapeut dietitian, Good Samaritan Hosp, Phoenix, 63-64; nutrit asst, Coop Exten Serv, RI, 64-65; asst prof food & nutrit, Univ RI, 65-71; asst nutrit, Case Western Reserve Univ, 72-73; ASSOC PROF FOOD & NUTRIT & CHAIRPERSON DEPT, NDAK STATE UNIV, 76- *Concurrent Pos:* Nutrit adv, Child Develop Ctr, Univ RI, 65-71; support serv contract, Food & Nutrit Serv, Nutrit Educ & Training Prog, USDA, 78-79. *Mem:* Am Dietetic Asn; Am Home Econ Asn; Soc Nutrit Educ; Am Asn Univ Women. *Res:* Food habits of college men; effectiveness of nutrition counseling in changing food habits of pedodontic patients; nutrition in preventive dentistry; nutrition in diabetic care. *Mailing Add:* Home Econ Bldg NDak State Univ Fargo ND 58105

STANISLAO, JOSEPH, b Manchester, Conn, Nov 21, 28; m 60. INDUSTRIAL ENGINEERING. *Educ:* Tex Tech Col, BS, 57; Pa State Univ, MS, 59; Columbia Univ, DEngSc, 70. *Prof Exp:* Asst prof indust eng, NC State Col, 59-61; dir res & develop, Darlington Fabrics Corp, 61-62, actg plant mgr, 62; from asst prof to assoc prof indust eng, Univ RI, 63-71; prof & chmn dept, Cleveland State Univ, 71-75; DEAN & PROF, COL ENG & ARCHIT, NDAK STATE UNIV, 75- *Concurrent Pos:* Res grants, Am Soc Mfg & Tool Eng, US Steel Co & Gen Elec Co, 65-66, Naval Air Syst Command, 68-71; lectr, Indust Eng Dept, Columbia Univ, 66-67; consult, Asiam Productivity Orgn, 72. *Mem:* AAAS; sr mem Am Inst Indust Engrs; Am Soc Metals; Am Soc Mech Engrs; Am Soc Eng Educ. *Res:* Manufacturing engineering, technical aspects, economic considerations and organizational theory; machinability, instrumentation and nondestructive testing techniques. *Mailing Add:* Col of Eng & Archit Box 5285 NDak State Univ Sta Fargo ND 58102

STANITSKI, CONRAD LEON, b Shamokin, Pa, May 3, 39; m 63; c 2. INORGANIC CHEMISTRY. *Educ:* Bloomsburg State Col, BSEd, 60; State Col Iowa, MA, 64; Univ Conn, PhD(inorg chem), 71. *Prof Exp:* Teacher high sch, Pa, 60-63 & Goshen Cent Sch, 64-65; instr chem, Edinboro State Col, 65-67; teaching fel, Univ Conn, 70-71; asst prof, Ga State Univ, 71-75; assoc prof chem, Kennesaw Jr Col, 75-76; assoc prof, 76-80, PROF CHEM, RANDOLPH-MACON COL, 80-, CHMN DEPT, 76- *Honors & Awards:* Gustav Ohauv Award, Creative Col Sci Teaching, 73. *Mem:* Am Chem Soc; Sigma Xi; AAAS. *Res:* Solid state hydride synthesis and reaction studies; chemical education. *Mailing Add:* Dept of Chem Randolph-Macon Col Ashland VA 23005

STANKE, DAVID FRED, b Mankato, Minn, Aug 17, 45; m 76; c 2. REPRODUCTIVE PHYSIOLOGY, DAIRY SCIENCE. *Educ:* Univ Wis-Platteville, BS, 67; Univ Mo-Columbia, MS, 70, PhD(reproductive physiol), 72. *Prof Exp:* County exten agt agr, Univ Wis, 72-73; COL PROF ANIMAL SCI, SOUTHWEST MO STATE UNIV, 73- *Mem:* Am Dairy Sci Asn. *Res:* Physiology of the bovine reproductive system; continuous fluid collection; embryo transfer. *Mailing Add:* Dept of Agr Southwest Mo State Univ Springfield MO 65802

STANKO, JOSEPH ANTHONY, b Wilkes-Barre, Pa, July 2, 41; m 62; c 3. INORGANIC CHEMISTRY. *Educ:* King's Col, BS, 62; Univ Ill, PhD(inorg chem), 66. *Prof Exp:* Asst prof chem, Pa State Univ, 66-73; ASSOC PROF CHEM, UNIV S FLA, TAMPA, 73- *Mem:* Am Chem Soc; The Chem Soc; Am Crystallog Asn. *Res:* X-ray crystallography; chemistry of platinum anti-cancer drugs; synthesis of 1-dimensional conductors. *Mailing Add:* Dept of Chem Univ of SFla Tampa FL 33620

STANKOVICH, MARIAN THERESA, b Houston, Tex, Nov 14, 47. ELECTROCHEMISTRY, BIOCHEMISTRY. *Educ:* Univ St Thomas, Tex, BA, 70; Univ Tex, Austin, PhD(anal chem), 75. *Prof Exp:* Scholar biochem, Univ Mich, 75-77; asst prof anal chem, Univ Mass, Amherst, 77-80; MEM FAC, CHEM DEPT, UNIV MINN, 80- *Concurrent Pos:* Fac res grant, Univ Mass, 77-78; Cottrell Corp res grant, 78-79. *Mem:* Am Chem Soc; Electrochem Soc. *Res:* Spectral and electrochemical study of electron transfer in flavoproteins, riboflavin, and flavin analogs; parameters studied are redox potentials; number of electrons transferred in a reaction; kinetics of electron transfer. *Mailing Add:* 207 Pleasant St SE Chem Dept Univ Minn Minneapolis MN 55455

STANLEY, CHARLES WILLIAM, b Kansas City, Kans, Aug 11, 21; m 50; c 2. ANALYTICAL CHEMISTRY, PESTICIDE CHEMISTRY. *Educ:* Univ Chicago, BSc, 43. *Prof Exp:* Anal chemist, Carnegie-Ill Steel Corp, 42-43; res chemist, Metall Lab, Univ Chicago, 43-44, Clinton Labs, 44-46 & Los Alamos Sci Lab, 46-53; nuclear chemist, Walter Kidde Nuclear Labs, Inc, 53-55; sr nuclear chemist, Nuclear Sci & Eng Corp, 55-58; sr chemist, Midwest Res Inst, 58-69; SR RES CHEMIST, AGR CHEM DIV, MOBAY CHEM CORP, 69- *Concurrent Pos:* mem adv bd, J Agr & Food Chem, 73-77. *Mem:* AAAS; Am Chem Soc. *Res:* Metabolism of pesticides in crops and animals; development of analytical methods for pesticide residues in crops and animal tissues. *Mailing Add:* Agr Chem Div Mobay Chem Corp PO Box 4913 Kansas City MO 64120

STANLEY, DANIEL JEAN, b Metz, France, Apr 14, 34; US citizen; m 60; c 3. MARINE GEOLOGY. *Educ:* Cornell Univ, BSc, 56; Brown Univ, MSc, 58; Univ Grenoble, DSc, 61. *Prof Exp:* Res geologist, French Petrol Inst, 58-61; geologist, Pan-Am Petrol Corp, 61-62; asst to dir geol, US Army Engrs Waterways Exp Sta, 62-63; asst prof sedimentol, Univ Ottawa, 63-64; asst prof marine geol, Dalhousie Univ, 64-66; assoc cur sedimentol, 66-68, supvr div, 68-71, cur sedimentol, 68-71, geol oceanogr, 71-79, SR SCIENTIST, SMITHSONIAN INST, 79- *Concurrent Pos:* Nat Res Coun Can travel award, USSR, 66; founder & ed, Maritime Sediments J, 64-66; Nat Acad Sci exchange award, Poland, 71; Romania, 76; adj prof, Univ Maine, Orono, 74- & Ecole Nat Petrole, France. *Mem:* Fel AAAS; fel Geol Soc Am; Soc Econ Paleontologists & Mineralogists; Am Mineralogists; Am Asn Petrol Geologists; corresp mem Geol Soc Belg. *Res:* Sedimentology of flysch in Alps, Carpathians and Caribbean; modern slope, canyon and deep sea fan deposits; marine geology studies of Nova Scotian shelf, Bermuda, northwestern Atlantic and the Mediterranean. *Mailing Add:* Div Sedimentol Smithsonian Inst Washington DC 20560

STANLEY, DAVID WARWICK, b Muncie, Ind, Oct 12, 39. FOOD SCIENCE. *Educ:* Univ Fla, BS, 62, MS, 63; Univ Mass, PhD(food sci), 67. *Prof Exp:* Res fel, Smith Col, 67-68; asst prof food sci, Univ Toronto, 68-70; asst prof, 70-74, ASSOC PROF FOOD SCI, UNIV GUELPH, 74- *Mem:* Inst Food Technol; Can Inst Food Sci & Technol. *Res:* Animal protein systems including muscle contraction and relaxation, meat tenderness and muscle protein biochemistry; cell membranes including isolation, composition, structure and function; plant protein systems including food uses of plant proteins; food analysis. *Mailing Add:* Dept of Food Sci Univ of Guelph Guelph ON N1G 2W1 Can

STANLEY, EDWARD ALEXANDER, b New York, NY, Apr 7, 29; m 58; c 2. PALEOBIOLOGY. *Educ:* Rutgers Univ, BS, 54; Pa State Univ, MS, 56, PhD(geol), 60. *Prof Exp:* Res geologist palynologist, Pan-Am Petrol Corp, 60-62; res assoc, Univ Del, 62-64; asst prof paleont, 64-67, assoc prof paleont & polynology, 67-71, prof paleont & palynology, Univ Ga, 71-77; assoc dean res, Grad Sch, Ind Univ Pa, 77-79, chmn, Geosci Dept, 79-81; SR GEOLOGIST, PHILLIPS PETROL CO, 81- *Concurrent Pos:* Nat Acad Sci vis scientist, Soviet Acad Sci, Moscow, 68-69 & 73. *Mem:* Sigma Xi; fel Geol Soc Am; Am Asn Stratig Palynologists; AAAS; Paleont Soc. *Res:* Upper Cretaceous-Tertiary plant micro-fossils, Dinoflagellates and Acritarchs; Holocene palynology, especailly as applied to the study of ocean bottom sediments and cores; electron microscope study of fossil and extant pollen grains. *Mailing Add:* 2601 Regency Rd Bartlesville OK 74003

STANLEY, EDWARD LIVINGSTON, b Orange, NJ, Sept 6, 19; m 43; c 2. CHEMISTRY. *Educ:* Princeton Univ, AB, 40, MA, 43, PhD(chem), 47. *Prof Exp:* Asst, Princeton Univ, 40-41, res assoc anal chem, Off Sci Res & Develop & Manhattan Dist Proj, 41-43; supvr, Anal Lab, Rohm & Haas Co, 43-50, lab head, Res Div, 50-57, foreign area supvr, 57-76; CONSULT, 76- *Mem:* AAAS; Am Chem Soc. *Res:* Analytical chemistry; facility is mass-burning, generating electricity. *Mailing Add:* 26 Plymouth Rd Gwynedd Valley PA 19437

STANLEY, ERIC, b Liverpool, Eng, Feb 2, 24; m 59; c 2. CRYSTALLOGRAPHY. *Educ:* Univ Wales, BSc, 42 & 49, PhD(physics), 52; Univ Sask, DSc, 72. *Prof Exp:* Exp officer physics, Royal Naval Sci Serv, 42-47; res fel, Univ Southern Calif, 52-53; Nat Res Coun res fel, 53-55; lectr physics, Univ Manchester, 55-64; prof, Univ Sask, Regina, 65-72, dir acad serv, 69-72, dir acad serv & planning, 72; PROF PHYSICS & DEAN FAC, UNIV NB, ST JOHN, 73- *Mem:* Brit Inst Math & Appln; Am Crystallog Asn; fel Brit Inst Physics; Inst Pub Admin Can; fel Royal Soc Arts. *Res:* X-ray structural crystallography; theoretical and experimental studies in x-ray crystal structure determination; geometrical and physical optics. *Mailing Add:* Univ of NB in St John Tucker Park St John NB E3B 5U3 Can

STANLEY, EVAN RICHARD, b Sydney, Australia. CELL BIOLOGY, MEDICAL RESEARCH. *Educ:* Univ Western Australia, BSc, 67; Univ Melbourne, PhD(med biol), 70. *Prof Exp:* Fel med biol, Walter & Eliza Hall Inst Med Res, Melbourne, Australia, 70-72; lectr cell biol, Dept Med Biophys, Univ Toronto, 72-73, asst prof, 73-76; asst prof, 76-79, ASSOC PROF CELL BIOL, DEPTS MICROBIOL & IMMUNOL & CELL BIOL, ALBERT EINSTEIN COL MED, 76- *Concurrent Pos:* Mem sr sci staff, Ont Cancer Inst, 72-76. *Res:* Biochemical and genetic studies on humoral regulation of granulocyte and macrophage production. *Mailing Add:* Dept of Microbiol & Immunol Albert Einstein Col of Med Bronx NY 10461

STANLEY, EVERETT MICHAEL, physical oceanography, see previous edition

STANLEY, GEORGE GEOFFREY, b Palmerton, Pa, May 2, 53. HOMOGENEOUS CATALYSIS. *Educ:* Univ Rochester, BS, 75; Tex A&M Univ, PhD(chem), 79. *Prof Exp:* Fel, Univ Louis Pasteur, France, 79-81; ASST PROF INORG, WASHINGTON UNIV, ST LOUIS, 81- *Concurrent Pos:* Fel, NATO, 79 & Nat Ctr Sci Res, France 81. *Mem:* Am Chem Soc. *Res:* Synthesis, structure and reactivity of transition metal cluster compounds with particular emphasis on homogeneous catalytic reactions involving hydrogen, carbon monoxide, nitrogen and organic substrates. *Mailing Add:* Dept Chem Washington Univ Box 1134 St Louis MO 63130

STANLEY, H(ARRY) EUGENE, b Norman, Okla, Mar 28, 41; m 67; c 3. STATISTICAL MECHANICS, BIOLOGICAL PHYSICS. *Educ:* Wesleyan Univ, BA, 62; Harvard Univ, PhD(physics), 67. *Prof Exp:* Staff mem solid state theory group, Lincoln Lab, Mass Inst Technol, 67-68; fel physics, Miller Inst Basic Res Sci, Univ Calif, Berkeley, 68-69; from asst prof physics to assoc prof, Mass Inst Technol, 71-76, Hermann von Helmholtz assoc prof health sci & technol, 73-76; PROF PHYSICS, BOSTON UNIV, 76-, PROF PHYSIOL, SCH MED & DIR, CTR POLYMER STUDIES, 78-, UNIV PROF, 79- *Concurrent Pos:* NSF fel theoret physics, 67-68; consult, Lincoln Lab, Mass Inst Technol, 69-71; vis prof physics, Osaka Univ, 75, Univ Toronto, 77, Ecole de Physique et Chimie, 79 & Peking Normal Univ & Nanking Univ, 81; John Simon Guggenheim Mem fel, 79-81. *Honors & Awards:* Joliot-Curie Medal, 79. *Mem:* AAAS; fel Am Phys Soc; Biophys Soc; NY Acad Sci. *Res:* Phase transitions and critical phenomena; biomedical physics; polymer physics; physics of random media; percolation; liquid state physics; cooperative functioning of polymers and other systems with no underlying lattice; statistical mechanics to treat such systems. *Mailing Add:* 50 Metacomet Rd Newton-Waban MA 02168

STANLEY, HAROLD RUSSELL, b Salem, Mass, June 26, 23; m 46; c 3. ORAL PATHOLOGY. *Educ:* Univ Md, DDS, 48; Am Univ, BS, 52; Georgetown Univ, MS, 53; Am Bd Oral Path, dipl, 57. *Prof Exp:* Intern, Marine Hosp, USPHS, Baltimore, Md, 48-49; resident oral path, Armed Forces Inst Path, 51-53; mem staff, Nat Inst Dent Res, 53-66, clin dir, 66-68; PROF PATH, UNIV FLA, 81-, CHMN DEPT ORAL MED, 70- *Concurrent Pos:* Hon prof, San Carlos, Univ Guatemala, 60- *Honors & Awards:* Sci Award, Int Asn Dent Res, 78. *Mem:* Hon fel Am Asn Endodont; Int Asn Dent Res; Am Dent Asn; Am Acad Oral Path (pres, 67). *Res:* Diseases of the human dental pulp; periodontium; oral mucous membranes. *Mailing Add:* Col of Dent Univ of Fla Gainesville FL 32610

STANLEY, HUGH P, b Modesto, Calif, July 14, 26; m 59; c 2. ELECTRON MICROSCOPY, CELL BIOLOGY. *Educ:* Univ Calif, Berkeley, BA, 51; Ore State Univ, MA, 58, PhD(zool), 61. *Prof Exp:* NIH fel zool, Zool Sta, Naples, Italy, 61-63 & Cornell Univ, 63 & sr fel biol struct, Univ Wash, 63-65; asst prof anat, Univ Minn, 65-66; asst prof zool, 66-68, assoc prof zool, 68-76, PROF BIOL, UTAH STATE UNIV, 76- *Mem:* AAAS; Am Soc Zool. *Res:* Ultrastructure of developing cell systems, especially vertebrate spermatid differentiation. *Mailing Add:* Dept Biol Utah State Univ Logan UT 84322

STANLEY, JOHN PEARSON, b Washington, DC, Dec 17, 15; m 41; c 7. BIOCHEMISTRY. *Educ:* Cath Univ Am, BS, 37, MS, 39, PhD(biochem), 42. *Prof Exp:* Chemist & spec agt, Fed Bur Invest, Washington, DC, 41-44; res chemist, Gelatin Prod Co, Mich, 44, head bact labs, 44-46, asst chief control dept & res & develop labs, 46; dir res & develop, R P Scherer Corp, 46-68, tech dir, 68-79; RETIRED. *Mem:* Fel AAAS; Am Chem Soc; Am Pharmaceut Asn; fel Am Inst Chemists; NY Acad Sci. *Res:* Soft gelatin capsules; gelatin; vitamins; nutrition; research and development administration; product development; technical service. *Mailing Add:* 1032 Yorkshire Rd Grosse Pointe MI 48230

STANLEY, JON G, b Edinburg, Tex, Oct 28, 37; m 65; c 3. AQUACULTURE. *Educ:* Univ Mo, AB, 60, BS, 63, PhD(zool), 66. *Prof Exp:* Asst prof biol, DePaul Univ, 66-69; from asst prof to assoc prof, Univ Wis-Milwaukee, 69-72; FISHERIES BIOLOGIST & LEADER, MAINE COOP FISHERY RES UNIT, UNIV MAINE, ORONO, 72- *Concurrent Pos:* Nat Acad Sci exchange scholar, Czech. *Mem:* AAAS; Am Soc Zoologists; Am Fisheries Soc. *Res:* Polyploidy and genetics in aquaculture; biology of Chinese fishes such as Grass Carp; gynogenesis and breeding of freshwater fish; environmental effects of pesticides on fishes; acid rain effects on fishes. *Mailing Add:* Maine Coop Fishery Res Unit Univ of Maine Orono ME 04469

STANLEY, KENNETH EARL, b Auburn, NY, Nov 7, 47; m 71; c 2. BIOSTATISTICS. *Educ:* Alfred Univ, BA, 69; Bucknell Univ, MA, 70; Univ Fla, PhD(statist), 74. *Prof Exp:* Res asst prof statist, State Univ Ny, Buffalo, 75-77; BIOSTATISTICIAN, SIDNEY FARBER CANCER INST, 77-; ASST PROF BIOSTATIST, HARVARD UNIV, 77- *Concurrent Pos:* Statistician, Ludwig Lung Cancer Study Group, 77-; coord statistician, Eastern Coop Oncol Group, 78-80; mem expert adv panel cancer, WHO, consult, 81-; co-dir, Collaborating Ctr Cancer Biostatistics Eval, Harvard Sch Pub Health, WHO. *Mem:* Am Statist Asn; Biomet Soc; Soc Clin Trials; Int Asn Study Lung Cancer. *Res:* Clinical trials in cancer. *Mailing Add:* Dept Biostatistics Sidney Farber Cancer Inst 44 Binney St Boston MA 02115

STANLEY, KENNETH OLIVER, b Santa Maria, Calif, Sept 23, 41; m 67. GEOLOGY. *Educ:* Univ Calif, Los Angeles, AB, 64, MA, 66; Univ Wis-Madison, PhD(geol), 69. *Prof Exp:* Asst prof, Univ Nebr-Lincoln, 69-72, assoc prof geol, 72-74; asst prof, 74-76, ASSOC PROF GEOL & MINERAL, OHIO STATE UNIV, 76- *Mem:* Int Asn Sedimentologists; Geol Soc Am; Soc Econ Paleont & Mineral. *Res:* Sedimentary petrology and petrography; sedimentology. *Mailing Add:* Dept Geol Ohio State Univ Columbus OH 43210

STANLEY, MALCOLM MCCLAIN, b Henderson, Ky, Mar 2, 16; m 43; c 2. MEDICINE. *Educ:* Centre Col, AB, 37; Univ Louisville, MD, 41; Am Bd Internal Med & Am Bd Gastroenterol, dipl. *Prof Exp:* From intern to asst resident med, Gallinger Munic Hosp, DC, 41-43; from asst resident to chief resident, Evans Mem Hosp, Boston, 43-46; from instr to assoc prof, Med Sch, Tufts Univ, 46-57; prof exp med, Sch Med, Univ Louisville, 57-59, prof med, 59-62; prog dir, Clin Res Ctr, 62-70, SECT CHIEF GASTROENTEROL, HINES VET ADMIN HOSP, 70-; PROF MED, UNIV ILL COL MED, 62- *Concurrent Pos:* Am Cancer Soc fel, Joseph H Pratt Diag Hosp, Boston, 46-48; res assoc, Pratt Diag Hosp, Boston, 48, mem staff, 49-57. *Mem:* Am Soc Clin Invest; Am Asn Study Liver Dis; Am Physiol Soc; Am Gastroenterol Asn; Cent Soc Clin Res. *Res:* Gastroenterology, especially intestinal absorption and secretion; bile salt metabolism; liver cirrhosis; ascites. *Mailing Add:* Vet Admin Hosp PO Box 23 Hines IL 60141

STANLEY, MELISSA SUE MILLAM, b South Bend, Wash, June 23, 31; m 58. EXPERIMENTAL ZOOLOGY. *Educ:* Univ Ore, BS, 53, MA, 59; Univ Utah, PhD(zool, entom), 65. *Prof Exp:* Med technologist, Hosps & Labs, 53-57; teaching asst biol, Univ Ore, 57-58; med technologist, Hosps & Labs, 58-59; instr, Westminster Col, Utah, 59-61, asst prof, 61-63, actg chmn dept, 59-60, chmn dept, 60-63; res assoc, Pioneering Lab Insect Path, USDA, 65-67; from asst prof to assoc prof biol, 67-74, prog coordr, 68-69, PROF BIOL, GEORGE MASON UNIV, 74- *Mem:* Tissue Cult Asn. *Res:* Arthropod tissue culture. *Mailing Add:* Dept of Biol George Mason Univ Fairfax VA 22030

STANLEY, NORMAN FRANCIS, b Rockland, Maine, May 6, 16; m 63; c 2. CHEMISTRY. *Prof Exp:* Res chemist, Algin Corp Am, 40-53, res dir, 53-59; asst tech dir, Marine Colloids, Inc, 59-64, res chemist, 64-75; SR SCIENTIST, MARINE COLLOIDS DIV, FMC CORP, 74- *Mem:* AAAS; Am Chem Soc; Soc Rheol; Am Inst Aeronaut & Astronaut. *Res:* Polysaccharide chemistry; chemistry and technology of marine algae, algal products and watersoluble gums; design and analysis of experiments. *Mailing Add:* Marine Colloids Div PO Box 308 Rockland ME 04841

STANLEY, PAMELA MARY, b Melbourne, Australia, Mar 25, 47; m 70; c 1. CARBOHYDRATE STRUCTURES, SOMATIC CELL GENETICS. *Educ:* Univ Melbourne, BSc Hons, 68, PhD(virol), 72. *Prof Exp:* Fel somatic cell, Univ Toronto, Int, 72-75, res assoc, 75-77; asst prof, 77-82, ASSOC PROF CELL BIOLOGY, ALBERT EINSTEIN COL MED, NY, 82- *Mem:* Am Soc Biol Chemists. *Res:* Use of a family of animal cell mutants which express altered carbohydrate at the cell surface to delineate glycosylation pathways in mammalian cells and to study structure and function relationships of cell surface carbohydrate. *Mailing Add:* Dept Cell Biol Albert Einstein Col Med 1300 Morris Park Ave Bronx NY 10461

STANLEY, PATRICIA MARY, b Oneonta, NY, Mar 28, 48; m 77. MICROBIOLOGY, MICROBIAL ECOLOGY. *Educ:* Cornell Univ, BS, 70; Univ Wash, MS, 72, PhD(microbiol), 75. *Prof Exp:* Res specialist, Dept Microbiol, Univ Minn, 76-79; PRIN MICROBIOLOGIST, ECON LAB, INC, 79- *Mem:* Am Soc Microbiol; AAAS. *Res:* In situ metabolism of nitrifying and heterotrophic bacteria; biology of nitrifying bacteria; use of fluorescent antibody staining in microbial ecology; bacterial adhesion to surfaces; antimicrobial activity of biocides and disinfectants. *Mailing Add:* Econ Lab Inc Osborn Bldg St Paul MN 55102

STANLEY, RICHARD PETER, b New York, NY, June 23, 44; m 71; c 2. ALGEBRAIC COMBINATORICS, ENUMERATIVE COMBINATORICS. *Educ:* Calif Inst Technol, BS, 66; Harvard Univ, PhD(math), 71. *Prof Exp:* Miller fel math, Miller Inst Basic Res Sci, 71-73; Moore instr, 70-71, asst prof, 73-75, assoc prof, 75-79, PROF APPL MATH, MASS INST TECHNOL, 79- *Concurrent Pos:* Res scientist & consult, Jet Propulsion Lab, 65-72; consult, Bell Tel Labs, 73- *Honors & Awards:* Polya Prize, Soc Indust & Appl Math, 75. *Mem:* Am Math Soc; Math Asn Am. *Res:* Development of a unified foundation to combinatorial theory; interactions between algebra and combinatorics. *Mailing Add:* Dept Math Mass Inst Technol Cambridge MA 02139

STANLEY, RICHARD W, b Milesburg, Pa, Dec 16, 28; m 52; c 3. NUTRITION, BIOCHEMISTRY. *Educ:* Pa State Univ, BS, 56, MS, 58, PhD(dairy sci), 61. *Prof Exp:* Instr nutrit, Pa State Univ, 57-61; from asst prof to assoc prof, 61-70, PROF NUTRIT, COL TROP AGR, UNIV HAWAII, 70-, CHMN DEPT ANIMAL SCI, 68- *Concurrent Pos:* Fel, Univ Mo, 67-68. *Mem:* Am Dairy Sci Asn; Am Soc Animal Sci. *Res:* Ruminant nutrition, including utilization of metabolites formed in the rumen as they influence the productive performance of domestic cattle. *Mailing Add:* Dept of Animal Sci Univ of Hawaii Col Trop Agr Honolulu HI 96822

STANLEY, ROBERT LAUREN, b Seattle, Wash, Dec 30, 21; m 47; c 2. MATHEMATICS. *Educ:* Univ Wash, BS, 43, MA, 47; Harvard Univ, PhD, 51. *Prof Exp:* Guest lectr philos, Univ BC, 51-52, guest lectr math, 52-54; asst prof, Univ SDak, 54-57; asst prof, Wash State Univ, 57-61; assoc prof, 61-66, PROF MATH, PORTLAND STATE UNIV, 66- & HEAD DEPT MATH, 78- *Mem:* Am Math Soc; Asn Symbolic Logic; Math Asn Am. *Res:* Mathematical logic and foundations; logical analysis in philosophy of science. *Mailing Add:* Dept of Math Portland State Univ Portland OR 97207

STANLEY, ROBERT LEE, JR, b Dodge Co, Ga, Mar 7, 40; m 68; c 2. AGRONOMY. *Educ:* Univ Ga, BSA, 63, PhD(agron), 69; Clemson Univ MSA, 64. *Prof Exp:* Asst prof, 68-74, ASSOC PROF AGRON, UNIV FLA, 74- *Mem:* Am Soc Agron; Crop Sci Soc Am; Soc Range Mgt. *Res:* Forage crops management and utilization. *Mailing Add:* PO Box 470 Quincy FL 32351

STANLEY, ROBERT WEIR, b Ann Arbor, Mich, July 18, 25; m 48; c 5. PHYSICS. *Educ:* Auburn Univ, BS, 48; Johns Hopkins Univ, PhD(physics), 53. *Prof Exp:* From asst prof to assoc prof physics, Clarkson Tech Univ, 52-56; asst prof, 56-68, ASSOC PROF PHYSICS, PURDUE UNIV, WEST LAFAYETTE, 68- *Concurrent Pos:* Exchange prof, Univ Paris, 66; dean sch sci, Free Univ of the Congo, 69-71. *Mem:* Fel Optical Soc Am; Am Phys Soc; Am Asn Physics Teachers. *Res:* Optics; spectroscopy; interferometry. *Mailing Add:* Dept of Physics Purdue Univ West Lafayette IN 47907

STANLEY, ROLFE S, b Brooklyn, NY, Nov 4, 31; m 52; c 4. GEOLOGY. *Educ:* Williams Col, BA, 54; Yale Univ, MS, 55, PhD(geol), 62. *Prof Exp:* Geologist, Shell Oil Co, 57-59; NSF fel & lectr geol, Yale Univ, 62-64; from asst prof to assoc prof, 64-72, instnl res grant, 64-66, chmn dept, 64-78, PROF GEOL, UNIV VT, 72- *Concurrent Pos:* Res assoc, Ctr Technophysics, Tex A&M Univ, 71 & 72; prin investr, Northern Vt Serpentinite belt; res grant, Nat Res Coun, Repub China. *Mem:* Fel Geol Soc Am. *Res:* Structural geology; structural petrology; regional geology of western New England; compilation of the geological map of Massachusetts; metamorphic core of the central mountains of Taiwan. *Mailing Add:* Dept of Geol Univ of Vt Burlington VT 05401

STANLEY, RONALD ALWIN, b Edinburg, Tex, June 18, 39; m 63; c 3. PLANT PHYSIOLOGY. *Educ:* Univ Ark, BS, 61, MS, 63; Duke Univ, PhD(plant physiol), 70. *Prof Exp:* Botanist, Tenn Valley Authority, 64-75; asst prof biol, Univ SDak, Springfield, 75; PLANT PHYSIOLOGIST, ENVIRON PROTECTION AGENCY, 76- *Mem:* AAAS; Am Inst Biol Sci; Am Soc Plant Physiologists; Asn Aquatic Vascular Plant Biologists; Sigma Xi. *Res:* Synergistic interactions of chemical, physical and biological factors in the environment with aquatic macrophytes; adaptation to the aquatic environment; assessment of risk from toxic substances. *Mailing Add:* Off of Toxic Substances TS 778 Waterside Mall Washington DC 20460

STANLEY, STEVEN MITCHELL, b Detroit, Mich, Nov 2, 41; m 69. PALEONTOLOGY, EVOLUTION. *Educ:* Princeton Univ, AB, 63; Yale Univ, PhD(geol), 68. *Prof Exp:* Asst prof paleont, Univ Rochester, 67-69; from asst prof to assoc prof, 69-74, PROF PALEOBIOL, JOHNS HOPKINS UNIV, 74- *Mem:* Paleont Soc; Geol Soc Am; Soc Study Evolution. *Res:* Functional morphology and evolution of bivalve mollusks and other taxa with fossil records; rates and patterns of evolution and extinction; benthic marine ecology and paleoecology; biomechanics. *Mailing Add:* Dept of Earth & Planetary Sci Johns Hopkins Univ Baltimore MD 21218

STANLEY, WENDELL MEREDITH, JR, b New York, NY, Nov 9, 32; m 58; c 3. MOLECULAR BIOLOGY, BIOCHEMISTRY. *Educ:* Univ Calif, Berkeley, AB, 57; Univ Wis-Madison, MS, 59, PhD(biochem), 63. *Prof Exp:* From instr to asst prof biochem, Sch Med, NY Univ, 65-67; asst prof, 67-70, ASSOC PROF BIOCHEM, UNIV CALIF, IRVINE-CALIF COL MED, 70- *Concurrent Pos:* USPHS grant, Sch Med, NY Univ, 63-65; assoc dean, Undergrad Affairs, Sch Biol Sci, Univ Calif, Irvine, 80. *Mem:* AAAS; Am Soc Biol Chem. *Res:* Control of protein biosynthesis in eukaryotes. *Mailing Add:* Dept of Molecular Biol & Biochem Univ of Calif Irvine CA 92717

STANLEY, WILLIAM DANIEL, b Bladenboro, NC, June 13, 37; m 62. ELECTRICAL ENGINEERING. *Educ:* Univ SC, BS, 60; NC State Univ, MS, 62, PhD(elec eng), 63. *Prof Exp:* Develop engr, Electro-Mech Res, Inc, 63; asst prof elec eng, Clemson Univ, 64-66; assoc prof, 66-72, chmn, Dept Eng Technol, 70-74, dir, Div Eng Technol, 74-76, PROF ELEC ENG, OLD DOMINION UNIV, 72-, GRAD PROG DIR, DEPT ELEC ENG, 76- *Concurrent Pos:* Consult, NASA, 67-69. *Mem:* Inst Elec & Electronics Engrs. *Res:* Communications systems analysis and design; network synthesis. *Mailing Add:* Dept of Elec Eng Old Dominion Univ Sch of Eng Norfolk VA 23508

STANLEY, WILLIAM GORDON, b Wichita, Kans, Aug 4, 23; m 46; c 5. PHYSICAL CHEMISTRY. *Educ:* Southwestern Col, Kans, BA, 48; Kans State Univ, MS, 50, PhD(phys chem), 52. *Prof Exp:* Chemist, 51-56, group leader, Amoco Chem Corp, 56-63, dir propellants develop, 63-65, mgr info & commun, Res Dept, Am Oil Co, 66-70, DIR INFO SERV, RES DEPT, AMOCO RES CTR, STANDARD OIL CO (IND), 70- *Mem:* Am Chem Soc; Am Soc Info Sci. *Res:* Mechanism of combustion and catalysis of solid propellants; system management of rocket systems; information retrieval systems. *Mailing Add:* Amoco Res Ctr Standard Oil Co Ind Box 400 Naperville IL 60566

STANLEY, WILLIAM LYONS, b Teh Chou, China, May 30, 16; US citizen; m 41; c 3. ORGANIC CHEMISTRY. *Educ:* Marietta Col, AB, 39; Univ Calif, PhD(chem), 48. *Prof Exp:* Chemist & asst group leader, Carbide & Carbon Chem Corp, WVa, 39-45; res chemist, Western Regional Res Lab, USDA, 48-51 & Res & Develop Ctr, Union Oil Co, 51-54; prin chemist, Fruit & Veg Chem Lab, USDA, 54-60, chief fruit lab, Western Utilization Res & Develop Div, Agr Res Serv, Calif, 60-68; UN develop prog citrus res technologist, Food Inst, Centre Indust Res, Haifa, Israel, 68-69; chief res chemist, Fruit & Veg Processing Lab, Western Regional Lab, 70-76, EMER CONSULT COLLABR, SCI & EDUC ADMIN-AGR RES, 76- *Concurrent Pos:* Mem comt fruit & veg prod, Adv Bd Mil Personnel Supplies, Nat Res Coun-Nat Acad Sci; consult, Almond Bd Calif & Dried Fruit Asn, Calif. *Honors & Awards:* Superior Serv Award, USDA, 62. *Mem:* Fel Am Chem Soc; Phytochem Soc NAm. *Res:* Synthetic organic chemistry; petrochemicals; chemistry of natural products; flavor components of citrus fruits; immobilized enzymes in food processing. *Mailing Add:* 8368 Kent Dr El Cerrito CA 94530

STANNARD, WILLIAM A, b Whitefish, Mont, Sept 5, 31; m 51; c 4. MATHEMATICS. *Educ:* Univ Mont, BA, 53; Stanford Univ, MA, 58; Mont State Univ, EdD, 66. *Prof Exp:* Instr math, Northern Mont Col, 60-62; instr, Mont State Univ, 62-66; assoc prof, 66-74, chmn dept, 68-77, PROF MATH, EASTERN MONT COL, 74- *Concurrent Pos:* Partic NSF Math Inst, Rutgers Univ, 67. *Res:* Teaching undergraduate mathematics. *Mailing Add:* Dept of Math Eastern Mont Col Billings MT 59101

STANNERS, CLIFFORD PAUL, b Sutton Surrey, Eng, Oct 19, 37; Can citizen; m 59; c 3. MOLECULAR BIOLOGY, CELL BIOLOGY. *Educ:* McMaster Univ, BSc, 58; Univ Toronto, MSc, 60, PhD(med biophys), 63. *Prof Exp:* Fel molecular biol, Mass Inst Technol, 62-64; from asst prof to assoc prof, 64-77, PROF MED BIOPHYS, UNIV TORONTO, 77-; SR SCIENTIST BIOL RES, ONT CANCER INST, 64- *Concurrent Pos:* Grants, Med Res Coun & Nat Cancer Inst Can, 65-, US Nat Cancer Inst, 73-79 & Multiple Sclerosis Soc Can, 79-; mem grants panel, Nat Cancer Inst Can, 76-81; sci adv, Amyotropic Lateral Sclerosis Soc Can, 77-79. *Mem:* Can Biochem Soc; Can Soc Cell Biol. *Res:* Growth control of animal cells; protein synthesis somatic cell genetics; molecular genetics; cell virus interactions; persistent infection with vesicular stomatitis virus; molecular genetics; human cancer. *Mailing Add:* Ont Cancer Inst Dept of Biol Res 500 Sherbourne St Toronto ON M4X 1K9 Can

STANNETT, VIVIAN THOMAS, b Langley, Eng, Sept 1, 17; nat US; m 46; c 1. POLYMER CHEMISTRY. *Educ:* London Polytech Inst, BSc, 39; Polytech Inst Brooklyn, PhD(chem), 50. *Prof Exp:* Plant chemist, Brit Celanese Co, 39-41; chief chemist, Utilex, Ltd, 44-47, dir, 50-51; asst group leader polymers, Koppers Co, 51-52; asst prof polymer chem, State Univ NY Col Forestry, Syracuse Univ, 52-56, prof, 56-61; assoc dir, Camille Dreyfus Lab, Res Triangle Inst, 61-67; prof, 67-69, CAMILLE DREYFUS PROF CHEM ENG, NC STATE UNIV, 69-, VPROVOST & DEAN GRAD SCH, 75- *Concurrent Pos:* Res assoc, Mellon Inst, 51. *Honors & Awards:* Borden Award & Payen Award, Am Chem Soc, 74; Int Award & Gold Medal, Soc Plastics Eng. *Mem:* Am Chem Soc; Tech Asn Pulp & Paper Indust; fel NY Acad Sci; Soc Chem Indust. *Res:* Physical chemistry and engineering properties of plastics; cellulosic plastics; plastics-paper combinations; radiation chemistry of polymers. *Mailing Add:* Dept of Chem Eng NC State Univ Raleigh NC 27650

STANOJEVIC, VASLAV V, b Belgrade, Yugoslavia, June 23, 28; US citizen; m 70; c 1. MATHEMATICS. *Educ:* Univ Belgrade, BS, 52, MS, 54, PhD(math), 55. *Prof Exp:* From asst prof to assoc prof math, Univ Belgrade, 58-61; from assoc prof to prof math, Univ Detroit, 62-68; PROF MATH, UNIV MO-ROLLA, 68- *Concurrent Pos:* Vis prof, Ohio State Univ, 67-68 & La State Univ, New Orleans, 71-52. *Mem:* Am Math Soc; Math Asn Am; Inst Math Statist. *Res:* Integrability of some cosine series; geometry of quantum states and normed linear spaces; applied probability; analysis; theory of probability. *Mailing Add:* Dept Math Univ Mo Rolla MO 65401

STANONIS, DAVID JOSEPH, b Louisville, Ky, Mar 19, 26. ORGANIC CHEMISTRY. *Educ:* Univ Ky, BS, 45; Northwestern Univ, PhD(chem), 50. *Prof Exp:* Instr chem, Northwestern Univ, 48-49; asst prof, Clark Univ, 49-50 & Loyola Univ, Ill, 50-54; RES CHEMIST, SOUTHERN REGIONAL RES LAB, USDA, 56- *Mem:* Am Chem Soc; Sigma Xi; Am Inst Chem; Fiber Soc; Am Asn Textile Chemists & Colorists. *Res:* Stereochemistry; mechanisms of organic reactions; cellulose chemistry. *Mailing Add:* 3406 Canal Apt E New Orleans LA 70119

STANONIS, FRANCIS LEO, b Louisville, Ky, July 9, 31; m 52; c 2. MINERALOGY, PETROLOGY. *Educ:* Univ Ky, BS, 51, MS, 56; Pa State Univ, PhD(mineral, petrol), 58. *Prof Exp:* Geologist, Carter Oil Co, 58-60 & George A Hoffman Co, 60-62; pres, Mitchell & Stanonis Inc, 62-67 & Int Pollution Control, Inc, 67-69; assoc prof geol & geog, 69-74, chmn, Div Sci & Math, 73-79, PROF GEOL & GEOG, IND STATE UNIV, EVANSVILLE, 74-; OWNER, STANONIS MINERAL EXPLOR CO, 69- *Concurrent Pos:* Owner, Red Banks Oil & Gas Co, 60-69; pres, Enviro-Sci Corp, 70-76; mem, Environ Comt, Interstate Oil Compact Comn, 76- *Mem:* Geol Soc Am; Am Inst Prof Geol; Inst Solid Wastes; Am Pub Works Asn. *Mailing Add:* Stanonis Mineral Explor Co PO Box 150 Henderson KY 42420

STANOVSKY, JOSEPH JERRY, b Galveston, Tex, Mar 4, 28; wid; c 4. ENGINEERING MECHANICS, CIVIL ENGINEERING. *Educ:* Southern Methodist Univ, BSCE, 48; Univ Tex, Austin, MSCE, 51; Pa State Univ, PhD(eng mech), 66. *Prof Exp:* Steel detailer, Austin Bros Steel Co, Tex, 48-49; instr civil eng, Univ Tex, Austin, 50-51; sr struct test engr, Convair, Tex, 51-53; design supvr, Austin Co, Tex, 53-54; design engr supvr, Fluor Corp, Tex, 54-58; asst prof civil eng, Tex Technol Col, 58-59; design engr, Boeing Airplane Co, Wash, 59-60; instr eng mech, Pa State Univ, 61-66; ASSOC PROF ENG MECH, UNIV TEX, ARLINGTON, 66- *Concurrent Pos:* Vis assoc prof civil eng, Univ Petrol & Minerals, Dhahran, Saudi Arabia, 74-76. *Honors & Awards:* Ralph R Teetor Award, Soc Automotive Engrs, 74. *Mem:* Soc Automotive Engrs; Soc Petrol Engrs; Am Inst Aeronaut & Astronaut. *Res:* Shock response on nonlinear structures; structural dynamics; experimental mechanics; structures; plasticity. *Mailing Add:* Dept of Aerospace Eng Univ of Tex Arlington TX 76019

STANSBERRY, KENT GARDNER, space physics, see previous edition

STANSBERY, DAVID HONOR, b Upper Sandusky, Ohio, May 5, 26; m 48; c 4. ZOOLOGY, HYDROBIOLOGY. *Educ:* Ohio State Univ, BS, 50, MS, 53, PhD, 60. *Prof Exp:* Fel, Stone Lab Hydrobiol, Ohio State Univ, 53-55, asst instr gen zool, 56-57, instr animal ecol, 58-60, from asst prof to assoc prof, 61-71, PROF ZOOL, OHIO STATE UNIV, 71- *Concurrent Pos:* Cur natural hist, Ohio State Mus, 61-72; dir mus zool, Ohio State Univ, 71-77. *Mem:* AAAS; Ecol Soc Am; Soc Syst Zool; Soc Study Evolution; Am Malacol Union (pres, 70-71). *Res:* Zoogeography, ecology, evolution and taxonomy of freshwater forms, especially bivalve molluscs and decapod crustaceans. *Mailing Add:* Dept Zool Ohio State Univ 1813 N High St Columbus OH 43210

STANSBREY, JOHN JOSEPH, b St Louis, Mo, Dec 30, 18; m 63; c 2. PHYSICAL CHEMISTRY. *Educ:* Washington Univ, AB, 41, MS, 43, PhD(chem), 47. *Prof Exp:* Asst chem, Washington Univ, 41-45, lectr, US Army Training Prog, 43-44; res chemist, Am Can Co, Ill, 45-47; res physicist, Anheuser-Busch, Inc, 47-53; mem tech staff, Bell Tel Labs, Inc, 53-56; mem group staff, Res Develop & Mfg Div, NCR Corp, 56-73; SCIENTIST, GLIDDEN COATINGS & RESINS DIV, D P JOYCE RES CTR, SCM CORP, 78- *Concurrent Pos:* Instr, Webster Col, 44-45; instr exten div, Univ Cincinnati, 56-57. *Mem:* Am Chem Soc; Am Statist Asn; Inst Mgt Sci. *Res:* Colloid chemistry; thixotropy; electrochemistry; conductance; electrophoresis; ultracentrifuge; light scattering and viscosity of protein solutions; emission and absorption spectra of biological materials; solid state physics and transistors; mathematical programming; statistical analysis and experimental design; computer automation of laboratory and production processes. *Mailing Add:* D P Joyce Res Ctr SCM Corp 16651 Sprague Rd Strongsville OH 44136

STANSBURY, E(LE) E(UGENE), b Indianapolis, Ind, Dec 14, 18; m; c 4. PHYSICAL METALLURGY. *Educ:* NC State Col, BChE, 40; Univ Cincinnati, MS, 42, PhD(metall), 46. *Prof Exp:* Asst, Univ Cincinnati, 40-42, from instr to asst prof metall, 42-47; assoc prof, 47-52, PROF METALL, UNIV TENN, KNOXVILLE, 52-, ALUMNI DISTINGUISHED SERV PROF, 76- *Concurrent Pos:* Consult, Oak Ridge Nat Lab, 47- *Mem:* Am Soc Metals; Metall Soc; Am Soc Eng Educ; Soc Hist Technol. *Res:* Thermodynamics of metal systems; kinetics of phase transformations; corrosion. *Mailing Add:* Dept of Chem & Metall Eng Univ of Tenn Knoxville TN 37916

STANSBURY, EDWARD JAMES, b Oakville, Ont, Aug 1, 27; m 52; c 2. PHYSICS. *Educ:* Univ Toronto, BA, 49, MA, 50, PhD(physics), 52. *Prof Exp:* Res assoc physics, Univ Toronto, 52-53; mem tech staff, Bell Tel Labs, 53-56; lectr physics, 56-57, from asst prof physics to prof, 57-76, 57-69, vdean fac arts & sci, 68-69, dean, 69-71, dean fac sci, 71-76, VPRIN PLANNING, MCGILL UNIV, 76- *Mem:* Can Asn Physicists. *Res:* Meteorological physics; nucleation of ice; thunderstorm electricity. *Mailing Add:* Off VPrin Planning McGill Univ 845 Sherbrooke St W Montreal PQ H3A 2T5 Can

STANSBURY, HARRY ADAMS, JR, b Morgantown, WVa, Sept 14, 17; m 44; c 4. CHEMISTRY. *Educ:* WVa Univ, AB, 40, MS, 41; Yale Univ, PhD(org chem), 44. *Prof Exp:* Group leader, Union Carbide Corp, WVa, 44-71; state dir comprehensive health planning, Gov Off, 71-76; EXEC SECY, WVA ASN SCH ADMINR, 76- *Mem:* Am Chem Soc. *Res:* Development of new pesticides; registration of pesticides; synthetic organic chemistry; residue analyses. *Mailing Add:* 806 Montrose Dr Charleston WV 25303

STANSBY, MAURICE EARL, b Cedar Rapids, Iowa, Apr 25, 08; m 38; c 1. CHEMISTRY. *Educ:* Univ Minn, BChem, 30, MSc, 33. *Prof Exp:* Jr chemist, US Bur Commercial Fisheries, Mass, 31-35, Md, 35-37 & Wash, 38-40, technologist chg fishery prod lab, Alaska, 40-42, dir tech lab, 42-66, dir food sci, Pioneer Res Lab, Wash, 66-71, dir environ conserv div, 72-75, SCI CONSULT CONTAMINANTS RES, NORTHWEST & ALASKA FISHERIES CTR, NAT MARINE FISHERIES SERV, 75- *Concurrent Pos:* Lectr, Sch Fisheries, Univ Wash, 38- *Honors & Awards:* Distinguished Serv Award, US Dept Interior, 66. *Mem:* Am Chem Soc; Inst Food Technologists; Am Oil Chemists Soc. *Res:* Analysis, preservation and processing of fish; chemistry and nutritional properties of fish oils; effects of contaminants in the environment upon fish. *Mailing Add:* Northwest & Alaska Fisheries Ctr Nat Marine Fisheries Serv Seattle WA 98112

STANSEL, JAMES WILBERT, b Angleton, Tex, Apr 8, 34; m 54; c 2. PLANT BREEDING, PLANT GENETICS. *Educ:* Tex A&M Univ, BS, 56, MS, 59; Purdue Univ, PhD(plant breeding & genetics), 65. *Prof Exp:* Asst geneticist, 60-66, asst prof genetics, 66-70, asst prof agron, Agr Res & Exten Ctr Beaumont, 70-77, ASSOC PROF AGRON, TEX AGR EXP STA, TEX A&M UNIV, 78- *Concurrent Pos:* Assoc prof genetics & environ & scientist in chg, Western Div, Tex A&M Univ, 72-77. *Mem:* Am Soc Agron; Soil Sci Soc Am; Am Asn Cereal Chemists; Am Genetics Asn. *Res:* Increasing rice yields by developing through genetic and cultural manipulation morphologically and physiologically superior rice plants which more effectively utilize available sunlight in intensified cultural practice systems. *Mailing Add:* Dept of Agron Tex A&M Univ College Station TX 77843

STANSEL, JOHN CHARLES, b Spring Canyon, Utah, Nov 18, 35; m 60; c 7. ENGINEERING, FUEL TECHNOLOGY. *Educ:* Univ Utah, BS, 60; Calif Inst Technol, MS, 62. *Prof Exp:* Res engr rockets, Jet Propulsion Lab, 61; mem tech staff fluid flow, 62-66, sect head nuclear, 66-72, dept mgr lasers, 72-78, asst lab mgr lasers, 78-80, CHIEF ENGR COMBUSTION & GASIFICATION, TRW INC, 80- *Concurrent Pos:* Chmn nuclear space safety, Atomic Indust Forum, 67-70. *Res:* Application of physics and engineering principles to development of advanced chemical combustion and laser devices. *Mailing Add:* TRW Systs One Space Park Redondo Beach CA 90278

STANSFIELD, BARRY LIONEL, b Toronto, Ont, June 10, 42; m 67; c 3. PLASMA PHYSICS. *Educ:* Univ Toronto, BASc, 65; Univ BC, MASc, 67, PhD(plasma physics), 71. *Prof Exp:* Fel, 71-72, PROF PLASMA PHYSICS, INST NAT SCI RES 72- *Mem:* Can Asn Physicists; Am Phys Soc. *Res:* Confinement of plasmas using electric as well as magnetic fields; development of plasma diagnostics; laser-produced plasmas and laser diagnostics. *Mailing Add:* Quebec Univ Inst Nat Sci Res Varennes PQ J0L 2P0 Can

STANSFIELD, ROGER ELLIS, b Sanford, Maine, July 16, 26; m 51; c 2. ORGANIC CHEMISTRY. *Educ:* Northwestern Univ, BS, 50; Carnegie Inst Technol, PhD(chem), 55. *Prof Exp:* Fel, Duke Univ, 54-56; from asst prof to assoc prof, 56-65, chmn dept, 71-74, PROF CHEM, BALDWIN-WALLACE COL, 65- *Concurrent Pos:* Vis prof, Forman Christian Col, W Pakistan, 64-66. *Mem:* AAAS; Am Chem Soc. *Res:* Synthesis of peptides; alkaloids of nicotiana; esterification; chemistry of pyroles. *Mailing Add:* Dept of Chem Baldwin-Wallace Col Berea OH 44017

STANSFIELD, WILLIAM D, b Los Angeles, Calif, Feb 7, 30; m 53; c 3. GENETICS. *Educ:* Calif State Polytech Col, BS, 52, MA, 58; Univ Calif, Davis, MS, 61, PhD(animal breeding), 63. *Prof Exp:* INSTR BIOL, CALIF POLYTECH STATE UNIV, SAN LUIS OBISPO, 63- *Mem:* Genetics Soc Am; Am Genetic Asn; Soc Study Evolution; Sigma Xi. *Res:* Immunogenetics. *Mailing Add:* Dept of Biol Sci Calif Polytech State Univ San Luis Obispo CA 93407

STANSLOSKI, DONALD WAYNE, b Big Rapids, Mich, June 22, 39; m 59; c 4. CLINICAL PHARMACY, MICROCOMPUTERS. *Educ:* Ferris State Col, BS, 61; Univ Nebr-Lincoln, MS, 69, PhD(pharmaceut sci), 70. *Prof Exp:* Asst prof pharm, Col Pharm, Univ Nebr-Lincoln, 70-72; CLIN COORDR, RAABE COL PHARM, OHIO NORTHERN UNIV, 72-, DEPT CHMN, 75- *Concurrent Pos:* Consult, Vet Admin Hosp, Lincoln, Nebr, 71, Ohio Dept Pub Welfare, 74-78 & various comput systs, 75- *Honors & Awards:* Merck Award. *Mem:* Am Pharmaceut Asn; Am Asn Cols Pharm. *Res:* Chemistry of mesoionic compounds and role of pharmacist in the provision of drug therapy; computer applications to health care; expanding the use of computers in the provision of health care. *Mailing Add:* Rte 2 Box 329 Ada OH 45810

STANTON, CHARLES MADISON, b San Diego, Calif, July 2, 42; m 71. MATHEMATICS. *Educ:* Wesleyan Univ, BS, 64; Stanford Univ, PhD(math), 69. *Prof Exp:* Lectr, Wesleyan Univ, 68-69, asst prof math, 69-76; asst prof math, Fordham Univ, 76-80; MEM FAC, DEPT MATH, WESLEYAN UNIV, 80- *Concurrent Pos:* Vis assoc prof math, Wesleyan Univ, 80-81; adj assoc prof math, Univ Notre Dame, 81- *Mem:* Am Math Soc; Math Asn Am. *Res:* Complex analysis; algebras of analytic funtions; Riemann surfaces. *Mailing Add:* Dept Math Univ Notre Dame Notre Dame IN 46556

STANTON, GARTH MICHAEL, b Cleveland, Ohio, June 15, 33; m 57; c 5. ORGANIC CHEMISTRY. *Educ:* Univ Detroit, BS, 56, MS, 58; Purdue Univ, PhD(chem), 62. *Prof Exp:* Res chemist, 62-69, sr res chemist, 69-80, SR RES ASSOC, CHEVRON RES CO, STANDARD OIL CO, CALIF, 80- *Mem:* AAAS. *Mailing Add:* Chevron Res Co 576 Standard Ave Richmond CA 94804

STANTON, GEORGE EDWIN, b Danville, Pa, Mar 28, 44; m 65; c 2. AQUATIC ECOLOGY, INVERTEBRATE ECOLOGY. *Educ:* Bucknell Univ, BS, 66; Univ Maine, Orono, PhD(zool, entom), 69. *Prof Exp:* USDA res asst, Univ Maine, Orono, 66-69; from asst prof to assoc prof, 69-76, PROF BIOL, COLUMBUS COL, 76- *Concurrent Pos:* Adj assoc prof, Ga State Univ, 72-73; vis assoc prof biol, Mt Lake Biol Sta, 75; NSF sci fac fel, Auburn Univ, 76-78; Danforth fel, 79. *Mem:* Am Inst Biol Sci; Ecol Soc Am; Entom Soc Am; AAAS; Am Benthological Soc. *Res:* Ecology of small watershed systems and their impoundments; crayfish ecology; dynamics and succession of macroinvertebrate communities associated with carrion decomposition. *Mailing Add:* Dept of Biol Columbus Col Columbus GA 31907

STANTON, HUBERT COLEMAN, b Orofino, Idaho, May 3, 30; m 50; c 2. PHARMACOLOGY. *Educ:* Idaho State Col, BS, 51; Ore State Col, MS, 53; Univ Iowa, PhD(pharmacol), 58. *Prof Exp:* Asst pharmacol, Univ Iowa, 55-58; instr, Sch Med, Univ Colo, 58-60; sr pharmacologist & group leader, Mead Johnson & Co, 60-65; asst prof pharmacol, Col Med, Baylor Univ, 65-68; head, Dept Animal Physiol, Biol Res Ctr, Shell Develop Co, 68-79; dir biol res, Mead Johnson & Co, 79-82; DIR CARDIOVASCULAR PRECLIN RES, PHARMACEUT RES & DEVELOP, BRISTOL MEYERS CORP, 82- *Mem:* AAAS; fel Am Col Vet Pharmacologists; Soc Exp Biol & Med; Am Soc Pharmacol & Exp Therapeut; Am Soc Animal Sci. *Res:* Autonomic pharmacology; neonatal physiology. *Mailing Add:* Pharmaceut Res & Develop Div Bristol Meyers Corp Evansville IN 47721

STANTON, MEARL FREDRICK, b Staunton, Ill, Aug 14, 22; m 51; c 4. MEDICINE. *Educ:* St Louis Univ, MD, 48. *Prof Exp:* Sr instr path, Sch Med, St Louis Univ, 50-54; PATHOLOGIST, NAT CANCER INST, 56-, ED-IN-CHIEF JOUR, 68- *Mem:* AMA; Am Soc Exp Path. *Res:* Host-parasite relationships of obligate intracellular parasites; experimental and clinical cancer research; pulmonary diseases. *Mailing Add:* Lab of Path Nat Cancer Inst Bethesda MD 20014

STANTON, NANCY KAHN, b San Francisco, Calif, Mar 23, 48; m 71. MATHEMATICS. *Educ:* Stanford Univ, BS, 69; Mass Inst Technol, PhD(math), 73. *Prof Exp:* Instr math, Mass Inst Technol, 73-74; lectr, Univ Calif, Berkeley, 74-76; Ritt asst prof math, Columbia Univ, 76-81; ASSOC PROF, UNIV NOTRE DAME, 81- *Concurrent Pos:* Mem, Inst Advan Study, 79-80; Sloan fel, 81-83. *Mem:* Am Math Soc; Math Asn Am; Asn Women Math. *Res:* Spectrum of the Laplacian on complex manifolds, geometry of complex manifolds with boundary. *Mailing Add:* Dept Math Univ Notre Dame Notre Dame IN 46556

STANTON, NANCY LEA, b Casper, Wyo, Jan 13, 44; m 70; c 2. COMMUNITY ECOLOGY, SOIL BIOLOGY. *Educ:* Creighton Univ, BS, 66; Univ Chicago, PhD(biol), 72. *Prof Exp:* Asst prof, 72-80, ASSOC PROF ECOL, DEPT ZOOL, UNIV WYO, 81-, ACTG DEPT HEAD, 81- *Concurrent Pos:* Consult, Environ Protection Agency & NSF, 80-82. *Mem:* Ecol Soc Am; Sigma Xi; Soc Nematologists; AAAS; Am Inst Biol Sci. *Res:* Community and evolutionary ecology including soil microarthropods and nematodes, plant and animal interactions, specifically on grasslands; pollination biology. *Mailing Add:* Dept Zool & Physiol Box 3166 Univ Wyo Laramie WY 82071

STANTON, NOEL RUSSELL, b Dover, NJ, Dec 29, 37; m 62; c 1. HIGH ENERGY PHYSICS. *Educ:* Rutgers Univ, BA, 60; Cornell Univ, PhD(exp physics), 65. *Prof Exp:* Res assoc exp high energy physics, Univ Mich, 65-68; asst prof, 68-73, assoc prof, 73-77, PROF PHYSICS, OHIO STATE UNIV, 78- *Mem:* Am Phys Soc. *Res:* Strong interactions of elementary particles at high energy. *Mailing Add:* Dept of Physics Ohio State Univ Columbus OH 43210

STANTON, RICHARD EDMUND, b Brooklyn, NY, Aug 31, 31; m 57; c 5. THEORETICAL CHEMISTRY. *Educ:* Niagara Univ, BS, 52; Univ Notre Dame, PhD(phys chem), 57. *Prof Exp:* Fel, Cath Univ Am, 56-57; from asst prof to assoc prof, 57-69, PROF PHYS CHEM, CANISIUS COL, 69-, CHMN, CHEM DEPT, 81- *Concurrent Pos:* Consult, Union Carbide Res Inst, 61-63; Sloan fel, 69-71; vis prof, Univ Manchester, 70-71. *Mem:* Am Chem Soc; Am Phys Soc. *Res:* Quantum chemistry, especially self-consistent field convergence theory, methodology and electron correlation theory; group theory of transition states in chemical kinetics. *Mailing Add:* Dept of Chem Canisius Col Buffalo NY 14208

STANTON, ROBERT JAMES, JR, b Los Angeles, Calif, June 17, 31; m 53; c 2. GEOLOGY, PALEONTOLOGY. *Educ:* Calif Inst Technol, BS, 53, PhD(geol), 60; Harvard Univ, MA, 56. *Prof Exp:* Res geologist, Shell Develop Co, 59-67; assoc prof, 67-72, PROF GEOL, TEX A&M UNIV, 72-, HEAD DEPT GEOL, 78- *Mem:* Fel Geol Soc Am; Soc Econ Paleontologists & Mineralogists; Paleont Soc. *Res:* Paleoecology; Cenozoic paleontology of Pacific Coast; ichnology. *Mailing Add:* Dept of Geol Tex A&M Univ College Station TX 77843

STANTON, ROBERT JOSEPH, b Pottsville, Pa, Feb 5, 47; m 70; c 2. MATHEMATICS. *Educ:* Drexel Inst Technol, BS, 69; Cornell Univ, MA, 71, PhD(math), 74. *Prof Exp:* asst prof math, Rice Univ, 69-80; MEM FAC, DEPT MATH, OHIO STATE UNIV, 80- *Concurrent Pos:* NSF grant, 75-; mem, Sch Math, Inst Advan Study, 77-78. *Mem:* Am Math Soc. *Res:* Analysis on lie groups. *Mailing Add:* Dept Math Ohio State Univ Columbus OH 43210

STANTON, TONI LYNN, b Johnstown, Pa, July 21, 44. NEUROPHARMACOLOGY, PEPTIDES. *Educ:* Univ Md, BS, 68, MS, 71; Thomas Jefferson Univ, PhD(pharmacol), 82. *Prof Exp:* Res asst, Dept Physiol, Sch Med, Univ Pa, 72-78; res asst, 78-81, ASST RES SCIENTIST, ALFRED I DU PONT INST, 81- *Concurrent Pos:* Res assoc, Sch Life & Health, Univ Del, 78-; consult pychoneuroendocrinol, Michael R Babitts Fund, 81- *Mem:* Soc Neurosci; Int Hibernation Soc. *Res:* State-dependent actions of thyrotropin release hormone in the brain; narcotic action in the central nervous system; control of central activity state. *Mailing Add:* Alfred I du Pont Inst PO Box 269 Wilmington DE 19899

STANTON, WILLIAM ALEXANDER, b Washington, DC, Sept 9, 15; m 42; c 3. ORGANIC CHEMISTRY. *Educ:* Univ Md, BS, 36, PhD(org chem), 41. *Prof Exp:* Res chemist, Tech Div, Photo Prod Dept, NJ, E I du Pont de Nemours & Co Inc, 41-45; group leader, 46-49, chief supvr, Plant Process Dept, Prod Div, 49-50, plant process supt, 50-52, prod supt, 53-56, asst plant mgr, NY, 57-58, dir, Parlin Res Lab, 58-63, mgr prod mkt, 64-65, dir printing & indust sales, 66, dir foreign opers, 67-80; RETIRED. *Honors & Awards:* J Award, Soc Motion Picture & TV Engrs. *Mem:* AAAS; Am Chem Soc; Sigma Xi; Soc Photog Scientists & Engrs; Am Inst Chemists. *Res:* Natural products; photographic emulsions and processing solutions; synthetic color-forming polymers for photographic emulsions. *Mailing Add:* 4 Harlech Dr Wilmington DE 19807

STANULIS, BETZABE MARIA, cell biology, see previous edition

STAPH, HORACE E(UGENE), b Petrolia, Tex, Jan 8, 21; m 50; c 3. MECHANICAL ENGINEERING. *Educ:* Rice Univ, BSME, 43; Univ Tex, MSME, 51; Univ Minn, PhD(mech eng), 59. *Prof Exp:* Design engr hydraul, Douglas Aircraft Co, Inc, 43-44; asst prof mech eng, Univ Tex, 46-60; SR RES ENGR, SOUTHWEST RES INST, 60- *Mem:* Am Soc Mech Engrs. *Res:* Rolling contact bearings; gears; lubrication; wear; friction phenomena. *Mailing Add:* Engine Fuel & Lubricants Div 6220 Culebra Rd San Antonio TX 78228

STAPLE, PETER HUGH, b Tonbridge, Eng, Oct 15, 17; m 52; c 2. PHYSIOLOGY, DENTISTRY. *Educ:* Univ London, BDS, 40, BSc, 49, PhD(sci, histochem), 52. *Prof Exp:* Mem sci staff, Med Res Coun, Eng, 51-57; lectr physiol, Univ Birmingham, 57; res assoc, Med Res Labs, Charing Cross Hosp, Univ London, 57; instr pharmacol, Univ Ala, 59-60, assoc prof, 60-63, assoc prof dent, Med Col & Sch Dent, 59-63; assoc prof oral biol, 63-72, PROF ORAL BIOL, SCH DENT, STATE UNIV NY BUFFALO, 72-

Concurrent Pos: Hon vis assoc prof, Univ BC, 71; vis prof, Univ Ill, 81-82. *Mem:* Histochem Soc; Int Asn Dent Res. *Res:* Histochemistry in relation to dental disease; phenytoin sodium and disturbance of mineralisation and deatal development; microcirculation in the gingiva. *Mailing Add:* Dept Oral Biol State Univ of NY at Buffalo Sch of Dent Buffalo NY 14226

STAPLE, TOM WEINBERG, b Hamburg, Ger, May 6, 31; US citizen; m 64; c 1. MEDICINE, RADIOLOGY. *Educ:* Univ Ill, Chicago, BS, 53, MD, 55. *Prof Exp:* From instr to prof radiol, Mallinckrodt Inst Radiol, Sch Med, Wash Univ, 73-75; adj prof radiol, Univ Calif, Irvine, 75; STAFF MEM, DEPT RADIOL, MEM HOSP, LONG BEACH, 75- *Concurrent Pos:* Consult, VA Hosp, Long Beach, Calif. *Mem:* Fel Am Col Radiol; Asn Univ Radiol; assoc mem Am Acad Orthop Surg. *Res:* Bone growth and arthrography. *Mailing Add:* Dept Radiol Mem Hosp Med Ctr Long Beach CA 90801

STAPLES, ALBERT FRANKLIN, b Sanford, Maine, Sept 3, 22; m 53; c 4. ORAL SURGERY, PHYSIOLOGY. *Educ:* Tufts Univ, DMD, 51; Baylor Univ, BS in Dent, 54, PhD(physiol), 70. *Prof Exp:* From instr to assoc prof oral surg, Col Dent, Baylor Univ, 61-67; PROF ORAL SURG & CHMN DEPT, COL DENT, UNIV OKLA, 70- *Concurrent Pos:* Consult oral surg, US Naval Hosp, Corpus Christi, Tex, 59-61 & Vet Admin Hosp, Oklahoma City, Okla, 70-; adj prof physiol & biophys, Col Med, Univ Okla, 70- *Mem:* Sigma Xi; Am Dent Asn; Am Col Dentists; Am Bd Oral Surg; Am Dent Soc Anesthesiol. *Res:* Estrogenic hormones in gingiva; relationship of cyclic adenosine monophosphate to levels of estrogenic hormones. *Mailing Add:* Dept Oral Surg Col Dent Univ of Okla Health Sci Ctr Oklahoma City OK 73190

STAPLES, BERT ROLAND, b Hazleton, Pa, June 17, 35; m 57. PHYSICAL INORGANIC CHEMISTRY. *Educ:* Univ Buffalo, BA, 57; Univ Md, MS, 65, PhD(phys chem), 67. *Prof Exp:* Anal chemist, Carborundum Co, 57-58; chemist, Nat Bur Standards, 61; NIH asst phys chem, Univ Md, 61-65; RES CHEMIST, NAT BUR STANDARDS, 67- *Mem:* Am Chem Soc; NY Acad Sci; The Chem Soc. *Res:* Experimental and theoretical studies concerning properties and behavior of electrolytes in aqueous, nonaqueous and mixed solvents to understand fundamental processes involving ions; critical evaluation of electrolyte solution data; microcalorimetric studies of biologically important reactions. *Mailing Add:* Nat Bur of Standards Washington DC 20234

STAPLES, GEORGE EMMETT, b Kanosh, Utah, Nov 2, 18; m 48; c 6. VETERINARY MEDICINE, ANIMAL NUTRITION. *Educ:* Utah State Univ, BS, 47; SDak State Univ, MS, 49; Colo State Univ, DVM, 54. *Prof Exp:* Instr animal husb, SDak State Univ, 47-48, asst animal husbandman, 48-50; pvt pract, 54-56; vet livestock inspector & area vet, Animal Dis Eradication Div, Agr Res Serv, USDA, 56-60, res vet, Animal Dis & Parasite Div, Colo, 60; res vet, Theracon, Inc, Kans, 60-64; ASSOC PROF VET MED & ANIMAL DIS RES, NDAK STATE UNIV, 65- *Mem:* Am Vet Med Asn; Am Soc Animal Sci. *Res:* Digestibility studies with prairie hay at different maturity stages; designing and testing therapeutic diets; neonatal diseases of farm animals therapy and prophylaxis; serological investigations; bovine chromosome investigations; bovine puikeye research and bovine ectoparasite susceptibility. *Mailing Add:* Dept of Vet Sci NDak State Univ Fargo ND 58105

STAPLES, JON T, b Waterville, Maine, Sept 14, 38; m 62; c 3. ORGANIC CHEMISTRY, POLYMER CHEMISTRY. *Educ:* Bowdoin Col, AB, 61; Univ NC, Chapel Hill, PhD(org chem), 66. *Prof Exp:* Res assoc org chem, Mass Inst Technol, 66-67; sr res chemist, 67-71, RES ASSOC, EASTMAN KODAK LABS, ROCHESTER, 71-, HEAD LAB, 75- *Mem:* Am Chem Soc. *Res:* Protecting group chemistry; peptide synthesis; monomer and polymer synthesis; photographic science. *Mailing Add:* Eastman Kodak Co Res Lab 1999 Lake Ave Rochester NY 14650

STAPLES, LLOYD WILLIAM, b Jersey City, NJ, July 8, 08; m 41; c 3. GEOLOGY. *Educ:* Columbia Univ, AB, 29; Univ Mich, MS, 30; Stanford Univ, PhD(mineral), 35. *Prof Exp:* With Mich State Geol Surv, 30-31; instr geol, Mich Col Mining & Technol, 31-33; res assoc mineral, Stanford Univ, 35-36; instr geol, Ore State Col, 36-37; from instr to prof, 39-74, head dept, 58-68, EMER PROF GEOL, UNIV ORE, 74- *Concurrent Pos:* Chief geologist, Horse Heaven Mines, Sun Oil Co, 37-41 & Cordero Mining Co, Nev, 41-45; Guggenheim fel, Mex, 60-61; consult, UNESCO, Paris, 68-71; mem, State Ore Bd Geologist Examrs, 77-80. *Mem:* Fel Geol Soc Am; fel Mineral Soc Am; Am Inst Mining, Metall & Petrol Engrs. *Res:* Mineralogy and crystallography; economic geology of quicksilver; microchemistry of minerals; mineral determination by microchemical methods; field and x-ray study of zeolites. *Mailing Add:* Dept Geol Univ Ore Eugene OR 97403

STAPLES, RICHARD CROMWELL, b Hinsdale, Ill, Jan 29, 26; m 54; c 3. PHYTOPATHOLOGY. *Educ:* Colo State Univ, BS, 50; Columbia Univ, AM, 54, PhD(plant physiol), 57. *Prof Exp:* Fel biochem, 52-57, from asst biochemist to assoc biochemist, 57-64, PLANT BIOCHEMIST, BOYCE THOMPSON INST PLANT RES, INC, 64-, PROG DIR PHYSIOL OF PARASITISM, 66- *Honors & Awards:* Humboldt Sr Scientist Award, 81. *Mem:* Am Soc Plant Physiologists; Am Phytopath Soc; Am Inst Biol Sci. *Res:* Responses of rust fungi to the environment; mechanisms by which these fungi sense chemical and physical stimuli which induce formation of the infection structures. *Mailing Add:* Boyce Thompson Inst Tower Road Ithaca NY 14853

STAPLES, ROBERT, b Philadelphia, Pa, Dec 9, 16; m 43; c 3. ENTOMOLOGY. *Educ:* Univ Mass, BS, 40; Cornell Univ, PhD, 48. *Prof Exp:* Asst entomologist, Conn Agr Exp Sta, 49-50; assoc prof entom, 50-74, PROF ENTOM, UNIV NEBR, LINCOLN, 74-, ASSOC ENTOMOLOGIST, 50- *Mem:* Entom Soc Am. *Res:* Arthropod transmission of plant viruses; economic entomology. *Mailing Add:* Dept of Entom Univ of Nebr Lincoln NE 68583

STAPLES, ROBERT EDWARD, b Cobourg, Ont, Dec 5, 31; m 57; c 2. TERATOLOGY. *Educ:* Univ Sask, BSA, 54, MSc, 56; Cornell Univ, PhD(reproductive physiol), 61. *Prof Exp:* Asst animal husb, Univ Sask, 54-56 & Cornell Univ, 56-61; sect head, Endocrinol Dept, William S Merrell Co, 61-63; staff scientist, Worcester Found Exp Biol, 63-67; head, Unit Teratology & Reproduction, Merck Inst Therapeut Res, 67-71; head sect exp teratology, Environ Toxicol Br, Nat Inst Environ Health Sci, 71-75, asst br chief teratology & dir, Environ Teratology Info Ctr, 75-78; STAFF TERATOLOGIST, HASKELL LAB TOXICOL & INDUST MED, E I DU PONT DE NEMOURS & CO, 78- *Concurrent Pos:* Prin investr, USPHS grant, 64-67; consult, William S Merrell Co, 63-67; adj assoc prof, Pharmacol Dept, Med Sch, Univ NC, Chapel Hill, 73-78 & Dept Anat, Jefferson Med Col, Philadelphia, 80-; consult, Am Petrol Inst, 80- *Mem:* AAAS; Soc Study Reproduction; Soc Toxicol; Teratology. *Res:* Early embryo development in mammals, including the influence of environmental factors; animal reproductive physiology; identification and delineation of environmental factors most likely to constitute hazard for development of the human conceptus. *Mailing Add:* Haskell Lab Toxicol & Indust Med E I du Pont de Nemours & Co Newark DE 19711

STAPLETON, HARVEY JAMES, b Kalamazoo, Mich, Dec 22, 34; m 57; c 3. MAGNETIC RESONANCE. *Educ:* Univ Mich, BS, 57; Univ Calif, Berkeley, PhD(physics), 61. *Prof Exp:* From asst prof to assoc prof, 61-69, PROF PHYSICS, UNIV ILL, URBANA, 69-, ASSOC DEAN, GRAD COL, 80- *Mem:* Sigma Xi; fel Am Phys Soc. *Res:* Paramagnetic resonance; electron spin-lattice relaxation; nuclear orientation; physics of solids, surfaces and biomolecules. *Mailing Add:* Dept of Physics Univ of Ill Urbana IL 61801

STAPLETON, JAMES H, b Royal Oak, Mich, Feb 8, 31; m 63; c 1. MATHEMATICAL STATISTICS. *Educ:* Eastern Mich Univ, AB, 52; Purdue Univ, MS, 54, PhD(math statist), 57. *Prof Exp:* Statistician, Gen Elec Co, 57-58; from asst prof to assoc prof statist, 58-73, chmn dept statist & probability, 69-75, PROF STATIST, MICH STATE UNIV, 73- *Concurrent Pos:* NSF fac sci fel, Univ Calif, Berkeley, 66-67; vis prof, Sch Econ, Univ Philippines, 78-79. *Mem:* Am Math Asn; Inst Math Statist; Am Statist Asn. *Res:* Nonparametric statistics. *Mailing Add:* Dept Statist & Probability Mich State Univ East Lansing MI 48824

STAPLETON, JOHN F, b Brooklyn, NY, Jan 25, 21; m 50; c 5. MEDICINE. *Educ:* Fordham Univ, AB, 42; Georgetown Univ, MD, 45; Am Bd Internal Med, dipl, 53; Am Bd Cardiovasc Dis, dipl, 57. *Prof Exp:* Intern, Providence Hosp, Washington, DC, 45-46; resident med, Georgetown Univ, 49-51, clin instr med, Hosp, 52-54, from instr to asst prof, 54-65; assoc prof med & chief cardiol, Woman's Med Col Pa, 65-67; PROF MED & ASSOC DEAN, SCH MED, GEORGETOWN UNIV, 67-, MED DIR, UNIV HOSP, 67- *Concurrent Pos:* Nat Heart Inst res fel, Georgetown Univ, 51-52; dir med educ, St Vincent Hosp, Worcester, Mass, 54-65; attend physician, Philadelphia Vet Admin Hosp, 65-67; consult, Vet Admin Hosp, Wilmington, Del, 65-67. *Mem:* Am Heart Asn; Am Col Physicians; AMA. *Res:* Clinical cardiology; medical education; hospitals. *Mailing Add:* Georgetown Univ Med Ctr 3800 Reservoir Rd NW Washington DC 20007

STAPLEY, EDWARD OLLEY, b Brooklyn, NY, Sept 25, 27; m 49; c 3. MICROBIOLOGY. *Educ:* Rutgers Univ, BS, 50, MS, 54, PhD(microbiol), 59. *Prof Exp:* From jr microbiologist to sr microbiologist, Merck Sharp & Dohme Res Labs, 50-66, res fel microbiol, 66-69; asst dir basic microbiol res, 69-74, dir microbial chemotherapeut, 74-76, dir, 76-78, SR DIR BASIC MICROBIOL, MERCK INST THERAPEUT RES, 78- *Mem:* AAAS; Am Acad Microbiol; Am Soc Microbiol; Soc Indust Microbiol (vpres, 74-75, pres, 76-77); NY Acad Sci. *Res:* Isolation of microorganism; mutation; fermentation; ergosterol production by yeasts; microbial transformations of steroids; isolation and utility of antibiotic-resistant microorganisms; detection, characterization and evaluation of new antibiotics; microbial transformations of sulfur. *Mailing Add:* Merck Sharp & Dohme Res Labs Rahway NJ 07065

STAPLIN, FRANK LYONS, b Santa Fe, NMex, Oct 5, 23; m 46; c 4. GEOLOGY, PALEONTOLOGY. *Educ:* Univ Tex, BS, 49, MA, 50; Univ Ill, PhD(geol), 53. *Prof Exp:* RES GEOLOGIST & HEAD PALEONT GROUP, IMP OIL, LTD, 56- *Mem:* Am Asn Petrol Geologists. *Res:* Palynology; organic debris in sediments; geothermal gradients; freshwater ostracods. *Mailing Add:* 6444 Laurentian Way SW Calgary AB T3E 5N2 Can

STAPP, HENRY P, b Cleveland, Ohio, Mar 23, 28. PHYSICS. *Educ:* Univ Mich, BS, 50; Univ Calif, MA, 52, PhD, 55. *Prof Exp:* Theoret physicist, Lawrence Berkeley Lab, Univ Calif, 55-58 & Inst Theoret Physics, Swiss Fed Inst Technol, 58; THEORET PHYSICIST, LAWRENCE BERKELEY LAB, UNIV CALIF, 59- *Res:* Elementary particle physics. *Mailing Add:* Lawrence Berkeley Lab 1 Cyclotron Blvd Univ of Calif Berkeley CA 94720

STAPP, JOHN PAUL, b Bahia, Brazil, July 11, 10; US citizen; m 57. BIOPHYSICS. *Educ:* Baylor Univ, BA, 31, MA, 32; Univ Tex, PhD(biophys), 40; Univ Minn, BM & MD, 44; Am Bd Prev Med, dipl, 56. *Hon Degrees:* DSc, Baylor Univ, 56, NMex State Univ, 79. *Prof Exp:* Instr zool, Decatur Col, 32-34; proj officer, Aero Med Lab, Wright Field, US Air Force, 46-53, chief, Aero Med Field Lab, Holloman Air Force Base, 53-58, chief, Aero Med Lab, Wright Air Force Base, 58-60, asst to comdr aerospace med, Aerospace Med Ctr, Brooks Air Force Base, 60-65, resident in biophys, Armed Forces Inst Path, 65-67; prin med scientist, Nat Hwy Safety Bur, 67-72; ADJ PROF & CONSULT, SAFETY & SYSTS MGT CTR, UNIV SOUTHERN CALIF, 72- *Concurrent Pos:* Vpres, Int Astron Fedn, 60; consult, Nat Acad Sci, Nat Traffic Safety Agency, Gen Serv Admin & Nat Bur Stand; permanent chmn, Annual Stapp Car Crash Conf, Soc Automotive Engrs, 55- *Honors & Awards:* Cheney Award Valor, 54; Gorgas Medal, Mil Surg Asn, 57; Cresson Medal, Franklin Inst, 73; Excalibur Award, Safety Adv Coun, US Dept Transp, 75. *Mem:* Fel Am Inst Aeronaut & Astronaut (pres, 59); Soc Automotive Eng; Aerospace Med Asn (vpres, 57); AMA; Civil Aviation Med Asn (pres, 68). *Res:* Aerospace and industrial medicine; biodynamics of crashing and ditching; impact injury; medical biophysics. *Mailing Add:* PO Box 553 Alamogordo NM 88310

STAPP, WILLIAM B, b Cleveland, Ohio, June 17, 29; m 55; c 3. ENVIRONMENTAL SCIENCES. *Educ:* Univ Mich, Ann Arbor, BA, 51, MA, 58, PhD(conserv), 63. *Prof Exp:* Instr sci, Cranbrook Sch Boys, Mich, 51-52, instr biol, 54-58; conservationist, Aullwood Audubon Ctr, Ohio, 58-59; instr conserv, 59-61, lectr, 63-64; from asst prof to assoc prof, 64-72, PROF NATURAL RESOURCES & CHAIRPERSON BEHAV & ENVIRON PROG, SCH NAT RESOURCES, UNIV MICH, ANN ARBOR, 72- *Concurrent Pos:* Res assoc, Cranbrook Inst Sci, Mich, 55-57; consult conserv, Ann Arbor Pub Schs, 61-68; youth progs, Nat Audubon Soc, New York, 65-66; consult, Int Film Bur, Chicago, Kalamazoo Nature Ctr, Mich & Creative Visuals, Tex, 66-68; consult environ educ prog, University City Pub Schs, Mo, 66-67; DeKalb Pub Schs, Ill, 67-68, Grand Haven Pub Schs, Mich, 67-, Raleigh County Sch Syst, WVa, 68-69, Toledo Bd Educ, Ohio, 70- & State of Alaska, 72-; consult, Nat Youth Movement Natural Beauty & Conserv, Washington, DC, 67-69, NJ Environ Educ Prog, 67-69, High Rock Interpretive Ctr, NY, 68-70, Seven Ponds Nature Ctr, 69- & Tapes Unlimited, Div Educ Unlimited Corp, 72-; consult environ interpretive ctr, Dept of Interior, 67-69 & environ educ, Dept HEW, 68 & div col support, Off Educ, 70-; consult audio-cassette series ecol, Am Soc Ecol Educ, 72- & proj man & environ, Nat TV Learning Systs, Miami, Fla, 72-; mem conserv comt, Mich Dept Pub Instr, 65-68; mem bd dirs, Drayton Plains Interpretive Ctr, Pontiac, Mich, 67-; prog dir, Ford Found grant, 68-70; mem working comt, Ann Arbor Environ Interpretive Ctr, 69-; mem bd dirs, Mich Pesticide Coun, 69-71; mem comn educ, Int Union Conserv Nature & Natural Resources, 69-; mem bd adv, Gill Inst Environ Studies, NJ, 70-; mem, Ecol Ctr Commun Coun, Washington, DC, 71- & Educ Resources Info Ctr Sci, Math & Environ Educ, Columbus, Ohio, 71-; fac adv, Ecol Ctr Ann Arbor, 71-, vpres & mem bd dirs, 72-; mem, Pub Sanit Systs, Los Angeles, Calif, 72- & Mich Pop Coun, 72-; chmn Gov Task Force Develop State Environ Educ Plan, 72-; mem task force estab guidelines environ educ elem & sec schs, Mich Dept Educ, 72-; dir environ educ, UNESCO, Paris, France, 74-76; mem, US Deleg World Conf Environ Educ, Tbilisi, USSR, 77; consult, UN Environ Prog, Nairobi, Kenya. *Honors & Awards:* Samuel Trask Dana Award Conserv, 62; Key Man Award, Conserv Educ Asn, 71; Conserv Educator of Year Award, State of Mich, 71. *Mem:* Am Nature Study Soc (vpres, 66-67, pres, 69-70); Conserv Educ Asn; Nat Audubon Soc; Asn Interpretive Naturalists (vpres, 69-71). *Res:* Environmental education and ecology; programs directed at helping urbanites man to develop a fuller understanding of environmental resource problems and his role in helping to resolve them; developing international environmental education programs. *Mailing Add:* Samuel T Dana Bldg Univ of Mich Ann Arbor MI 48109

STAPPER, CHARLES HENRI, b Amsterdam, Neth, Mar 27, 34; US citizen; m 58. ELECTRICAL ENGINEERING, SOLID STATE PHYSICS. *Educ:* Mass Inst Technol, BS, 59, MS, 60; Univ Minn, Minneapolis, PhD(elec eng, physics), 67. *Prof Exp:* Coop student elec eng, Gen Radio Co, 57-59; elec engr, IBM Corp, 60-65; teaching assoc elec eng, Univ Minn, Minneapolis, 66-67; engr-mgr elec eng & physics, 67-69, SR ENGR, IBM CORP, 70- *Mem:* Inst Elec & Electronics Engrs; Sigma Xi. *Res:* Application of mathematical theory to practical engineering and physics problems; statistical models for semiconductor devices, yields and manufacturing processes. *Mailing Add:* Dept M76 Bldg 967 IBM Corp PO Box A Essex Junction VT 05452

STAPRANS, ARMAND, b Riga, Latvia, Feb 28, 31; nat US; m 55; c 3. ELECTRICAL ENGINEERING. *Educ:* Univ Calif, BS, 54, MS, 55, PhD(elec eng), 59. *Prof Exp:* Asst elec eng, Univ Calif, 54-55, res asst, Microwave Tube Lab, 55-58; engr, 57-59, sr eng mgr, Super Power Opers, 69-71, mgr eng, High Power Microwave Opers, 71-75, mgr, Coupled Cavity Traveling Wave Tube Opers, 75-78, CHIEF ENGR, PALO ALTO MICROWAVE TUBE DIV, VARIAN ASSOCS, 78- *Mem:* Inst Elec & Electronics Engrs. *Res:* Microwave electronics; space-charge waves in periodic beams; electron optics; linear beam; super power tubes; coupled cavity traveling wave tubes; high power microwave windows; insulation of high voltages in vacuum; gyrotrons. *Mailing Add:* 445 Knoll Dr Los Altos CA 94022

STAR, AURA E, b New York, NY, Mar 15, 30; m 50; c 2. BOTANY, NATURAL PRODUCTS CHEMISTRY. *Educ:* Hunter Col, BA, 49; Mt Holyoke Col, MA, 51; Rutgers Univ, PhD(cytogenetics), 67. *Prof Exp:* Chemist, Baltimore Light & Power Co, Md, 51-52; instr biol, Morgan State Col, 52-53; from asst prof to assoc prof, 67-75, PROF BIOL, TRENTON STATE COL, 75- *Concurrent Pos:* Sigma Xi res grant, 63. *Mem:* AAAS; Bot Soc Am; Am Inst Biol Sci; Phytochem Soc; Torrey Bot Club. *Res:* Biochemical systematics of ferns and grasses; flavonoid chemistry; chemical biogeography of Pityrogramma; physiology of flavonoids in ferns. *Mailing Add:* Dept of Biol Trenton State Col Trenton NJ 08625

STAR, JOSEPH, b Far Rockaway, NY, Sept 2, 16; m 46; c 2. ELECTRONIC SYSTEMS ENGINEERING. *Educ:* Univ NC, BS, 37. *Prof Exp:* Engr, Radio Develop & Res Corp, 37-40; radio engr, Ft Monmouth Signal Lab, War Dept, 40-43; proj engr, Lab for Electronics, Inc, 46-48; staff engr, Hillyer Instrument Co, Inc, 48-51; chief electronics develop, Astrionics Div, Fairchild Engine & Aircraft Corp, 52-59; vpres eng, Instrument Systs Corp, 59-63; vpres & corp dir res & develop, Lundy Electronics & Systs, Inc, Glen Head, 63-73; INDEPENDENT CONSULT, 73- *Mem:* Sr mem Inst Elec & Electronics Engrs; Water Pollution Control Fedn; Int Asn Pollution Control. *Res:* Complex electronics for military and commercial purposes; derivation and investigation of new electronic and electromechanical devices; pollution control devices and systems; environmental systems engineering. *Mailing Add:* 186 Parkway Dr Roslyn Height NY 11577

STAR, MARTIN LEON, b Brooklyn, NY, May 3, 28; m 55; c 1. COMPUTER SCIENCE, APPLIED STATISTICS. *Educ:* City Col New York, BBA, 48. *Prof Exp:* Qual control supvr, Sonotone Corp, 52-55; comput programmer, Remington Rand Univac, 55-56; systs analyst, Underwood Corp, 56-57; opers res analyst, Stevens Inst Technol, 57-59; asst programming mgr, Teleregister Corp, 59-61; programming supvr on-line systs, Nat Cash Register Co, 61-67; ASSOC DIR MGT SERV, S D LEIDESDORF & CO, NEW YORK, 67-

Concurrent Pos: Partner, Eisner & Lubin, 78- *Mem:* Data Processing Mgt Asn (treas, 70-). *Res:* Statistical techniques in auditing; on-line systems and programming techniques. *Mailing Add:* 25 Willow Lane Great Neck NY 11023

STARACE, ANTHONY FRANCIS, b New York, NY, July 24, 45; m 68; c 1. ATOMIC PHYSICS. *Educ:* Columbia Univ, AB, 66; Univ Chicago, MS, 67, PhD(physics), 71. *Prof Exp:* Res assoc physics, Imp Col, Univ London, 71-72; from asst prof to assoc prof, 73-81, PROF PHYSICS, UNIV NEBR-LINCOLN, 81- *Concurrent Pos:* Alfred P Sloan Found fel, 75-79; Alexander von Humboldt res fel, Freiburg Univ, Fed Rep Ger, 79-80; prin investr, Dept Energy res contract, 76-81 & NSF res grant, 81-83. *Mem:* Fel Am Phys Soc; Brit Inst Physics. *Res:* Theory of atomic photoabsorption and photoionization processes and of atoms in high magnetic fields. *Mailing Add:* Behlen Lab of Physics Univ of Nebr Lincoln NE 68588

STARAS, HAROLD, b New Uork, NY, Dec 24, 22; m 44; c 3. COMMUNICATION SYSTEMS. *Educ:* City Col New York, BS, 44; NY Univ, MS, 48; Univ Md, PhD(physics), 55. *Prof Exp:* Physicist radio propagation, Nat Bur Standards, 48-54; head radio syst res, 54-70, STAFF SCIENTIST SATELLITE COMMUN, RCA LABS, 70- *Concurrent Pos:* John Simon Guggenheim Found fel, 61; mem, Consult Comt Int Radio. *Mem:* Inst Elec & Electronics Engrs; Int Radio Sci Union. *Res:* Studies of new system configurations and application of satellite communication systems; radio wave propagation. *Mailing Add:* RCA Labs Princeton NJ 08540

STARBIRD, ALFRED D, b 1912; US citizen. ENGINEERING. *Educ:* US Mil Acad, BS, 22; Princeton Univ, CE, 25. *Prof Exp:* Asst adminr, Nat Security, Dept Energy, 71-80; RETIRED. *Mem:* Nat Acad Eng. *Mailing Add:* 7208 Regent Dr Alexandria VA 22307

STARBIRD, MICHAEL PETER, b Los Angeles, Calif, July 10, 48. TOPOLOGY. *Educ:* Pomona Col, BA, 70; Univ Wis-Madison, MA, 73, PhD(math), 74. *Prof Exp:* asst prof, 74-80, ASSOC PROF MATH, UNIV TEX, AUSTIN, 80- *Concurrent Pos:* NSF res grant, 75-; vis mem, Inst Advan Study, 78-79. *Mem:* Am Math Asn; Math Asn Am. *Res:* Geometric topology. *Mailing Add:* Dept Math Univ Tex Austin TX 78712

STARCHER, BARRY CHAPIN, b Los Angeles, Calif, Dec 1, 38; m 60; c 3. NUTRITION, BIOCHEMISTRY. *Educ:* Univ Calif, Davis, BS & MS, 62; NC State Univ, PhD(biochem), 65. *Prof Exp:* Asst mem biochem, Inst Biomed Res, 66-70; asst prof path, Univ Colo Med Ctr, 70-72; asst prof biochem, Med Ctr, Univ Ala, Birmingham, 72-74; res asst prof, Pulmonary Div, Sch Med, Washington Univ, 74-80; MEM FAC, DEPT HOME ECON, UNIV TEXAS, AUSTIN, 80- *Mem:* Am Nutrit Soc. *Res:* Studies on the biochemistry of copper and zinc metabolism; enzyme induction in relation to stress, and the chemistry of the crosslinking amino acids in elastin; connective tissue components of lung; the role of elastin in calcification and arteriosclerosis. *Mailing Add:* Dept Home Econ Univ Tex Austin TX 78712

STARCHMAN, DALE EDWARD, b Wallace, Idaho, Apr 16, 41; m 69; c 4. MEDICAL PHYSICS. *Educ:* Kans State Col, BS, 63; Univ Kans, MS, 65, PhD(radiation biophys), 68; Am Bd Radiol, cert radiol physicist; Am Bd Health Physics, cert health physicist. *Prof Exp:* Chief health physicist, Ill Inst Technol Res Inst & radiol phyicist, Inst Radiation Therapy Mercy Hosp & Med Ctr, Chicago, 68-71; PRES, MED PHYSICS SERV, INC, 71- *Concurrent Pos:* Consult, Aultman Hosp & Timken Mercy Hosp, Canton, Ohio & Northeast Ohio Conjoint Radiation Oncol Ctr, 71-; mem bd, Mideast Region Radiol Physics Ctr Bd Adv & prof, Univ Akron, 73-; prof & chmn, Radiation Biophys Curric Develop Comt, Northeastern Ohio Univ Col Med, 74-; mem, Adv Staff, Akron Gen Med Ctr, 75- *Mem:* Am Asn Physicists Med; Soc Nuclear Med; Health Physics Soc; Am Asn Therapeut Radiologists; Am Col Radiol. *Res:* Electron beam perturbation by cavities; radiation dosimetry; post irradiation atrophic changes of bone; information optimization with dose minimization in diagnostic radiology; radiation oncology treatment development. *Mailing Add:* Med Physics Serv Inc 5942 Easy Pace Circle NW Canton OH 44718

STARFIELD, BARBARA HOLTZMAN, b Brooklyn, NY, Dec 18, 32; m 55; c 4. PEDIATRICS. *Educ:* Swarthmore Col, BA, 54; State Univ NY Downstate Med Ctr, MD, 59; Johns Hopkins Univ, MPH, 63. *Prof Exp:* Teaching asst anat, State Univ NY Downstate Med Ctr, 54-57; from intern to asst resident pediat, Harriet Lane Home, Johns Hopkins Hosp, 59-62; from instr to asst prof pediat, Sch Med, 63-73, instr pub health admin, Sch Hyg & Pub Health, 65-66, from asst prof to assoc prof med care & hosps, 66-75, PROF & HEAD DIV HEALTH CARE ORGN, SCH HYG & PUB HEALTH, JOHNS HOPKINS UNIV, 75-, ASSOC PROF PEDIAT, 73- *Concurrent Pos:* Nat Ctr Health Serv Res & Develop res scientist develop award; med dir, Community Nursing Proj, Dept Pediat & dir, Pediat Med Care Clin, Johns Hopkins Hosp, 63-66, asst dir community health, Comprehensive Child Care Proj & mem, Comt Planning & Develop, 65-67, pediatrician, dir, Pediat Clin Scholars Prog, 71-; mem spec rev comt, Exp Med Care Rev Orgns, Dept Health, Educ & Welfare, mem, Health Serv Res Study Sect, 74-78, Nat Ctr Health Serv Res & Develop; mem, Nat Prof Standards Rev Coun, 80- *Honors & Awards:* Award, Enuresis Found, 67. *Mem:* Sigma Xi; Am Pub Health Asn; Inst Med, Nat Acad Sci; Am Pediat Soc; Int Epidemiol Asn. *Mailing Add:* Sch of Hyg & Pub Health Johns Hopkins Univ Baltimore MD 21205

STARK, BENJAMIN CHAPMAN, b Saginaw, Mich, Nov 22, 49; m 79; c 1. MOLECULAR BIOLOGY, BIOCHEMISTRY. *Educ:* Univ Mich, Ann Arbor, BS, 71; Yale Univ, MPh, 74, PhD(biol), 77. *Prof Exp:* Fel biochem, Dept Bot, Wash State Univ, 77-79; RES ASSOC, DEPT BIOL, IND UNIV, 79- *Concurrent Pos:* NSF energy related fel, Wash State Univ, 77-78. *Mem:* AAAS; Sigma Xi. *Res:* RNA precursor processing and processing enzymes; photosynthetic phosphorylation in higher plant chloroplasts; RNA-protein interactions in ribosomes and cloning of ribosomal protein genes. *Mailing Add:* Dept Biol Ind Univ Bloomington IN 47401

STARK, DENNIS MICHAEL, b Baltimore, Md, May 16, 42. IMMUNOLOGY. *Educ:* Univ Ga, DVM, 66; Cornell Univ, PhD(immunol), 69, Am Col Lab Animal Med, 80. *Prof Exp:* Res asst immunol, Cornell Univ, 66-69; asst prof, C W Post Col, Long Island Univ, 69-73; assoc prof path & dir animal facil, Med Ctr, NY Univ, 73-76; ASSOC PROF & DIR LAB ANIMAL RES CTR, ROCKEFELLER UNIV, 76- *Mem:* AAAS; Am Soc Microbiol; Am Asn Lab Animal Sci; Am Vet Med Asn; NY Acad Sci. *Res:* Immunology of diseases of laboratory animals; in vitro measurment of toxin induced inflammatory response. *Mailing Add:* Box 2 1230 York Ave New York NY 10021

STARK, EGON, b Vienna, Austria, Sept 28, 20; nat US; m 48; c 3. MICROBIOLOGY. *Educ:* Univ Man, BS, 47, MS, 48; Purdue Univ, PhD(microbiol), 51. *Prof Exp:* Asst org chem, Univ Man, 44-47, asst microbiol, 45-48; asst bact, Purdue Univ, 48-51, Purdue Res Found Indust fel & res assoc microbiol, 51-53; consult microbiol, 53-54; sr res scientist, Joseph E Seagram & Sons, Ky, 54-66; PROF BIOL, ROCHESTER INST TECHNOL, 66- *Mem:* AAAS; Am Soc Microbiol; Am Chem Soc. *Res:* Microbiology of bacteria, yeasts, fungi; taxonomy, physiology, enzymology, ecology, fermentations, water pollution, waste disposal; process of producing a heat-stable bacterial amylase. *Mailing Add:* Dept Biol Rochester Inst Technol Rochester NY 14623

STARK, FORREST OTTO, b Bay City, Mich, Mar 31, 30; m 57; c 4. CHEMISTRY. *Educ:* Univ Pittsburgh, BS, 55; Pa State Univ, University Park, PhD(chem), 62. *Prof Exp:* Res chemist, 55-57, 62-70, mgr tech serv & develop, Med Prod, 70-75, mgr resins & chem res, 75-77, mgr elastomer res, 77-80, DIR SILICONE RES, DOW CORNING CORP, 80- *Mailing Add:* 5311 Sunset Dr Midland MI 48640

STARK, FRANCIS C, JR, b Drumright, Okla, Mar 19, 19; m 41; c 2. HORTICULTURE. *Educ:* Okla State Univ, BS, 40; Univ Md, MS, 41, PhD(hort), 48. *Prof Exp:* From asst prof to prof veg crops, 45-64, prof hort & head dept, 64-74, chmn food sci fac, 66-73, provost, Div Agr & Life Sci, 74-80, EMER PROF HORT, UNIV MD, COLLEGE PARK, 80-, ACTG VCHANCELLOR ACAD AFFAIRS, 81- *Concurrent Pos:* Chmn, Gov Comn on Migratory Labor, Md, 63-77; trustee, Lynchburg Col, 70-79; dir, Coun Agr Sci & Technol, 76-79. *Mem:* Fel AAAS; fel Am Soc Hort Sci; Am Inst Biol Sci. *Res:* Nutrition, physiology, breeding and culture of vegetable crops. *Mailing Add:* Div of Agr & Life Sci Univ of Md College Park MD 20742

STARK, GEORGE ROBERT, b New York, NY, July 4, 33; m 56; c 2. BIOCHEMISTRY. *Educ:* Columbia Univ, BA, 55, MA, 56, PhD(chem), 59. *Prof Exp:* Res assoc biochem, Rockefeller Inst, 59-61, asst prof, 61-63; from asst prof to assoc prof, 63-71, PROF BIOCHEM, SCH MED, STANFORD UNIV, 71- *Concurrent Pos:* Guggenheim fel, 70-71. *Mem:* Am Soc Biol Chem; Am Chem Soc. *Res:* Chemistry and reactions of proteins; control of mammalian gene expression; structure-function relationships of enzymes; proteins of DNA tumor viruses. *Mailing Add:* Dept of Biochem Stanford Univ Sch of Med Stanford CA 94305

STARK, HAROLD EMIL, b San Diego, Calif, July 26, 20; m 44, 71; c 4. ENTOMOLOGY. *Educ:* San Diego State Col, BA, 43; Univ Utah, MS, 48; Univ Calif, PhD, 65. *Prof Exp:* Asst, Univ Utah, 46-48; jr entomologist, USPHS, 48-49, med entomologist, 50-63, trainin officer health mobilization, 63-64, ecol & chief vert-vector unit, Commun Dis Ctr, Ga, 64-68, entomologist, Walter Reed Army Inst Res, US Army Med Component/SEATO, Bangkok, Thailand, 68-70, res entomologist, Ecol Invest, Ctr Dis Control, USPHS, 70-73; res zoologist, Environ & Ecol Br, Dugway Proving Ground, Utah, 73-79; RETIRED. *Mem:* Entom Soc Am. *Res:* Systematics of Siphonaptera; ecology of small wild rodents and fleas in relation to natural occurrence of plague and tularemia; preparation of training literature and audiovisuals for vector-borne diseases; preparation of environmental impact assessments and statements. *Mailing Add:* RFD 286 B Trenton UT 84338

STARK, HAROLD MEAD, b Los Angeles, Calif, Aug 6, 39; m 64. NUMBER THEORY. *Educ:* Calif Inst Technol, BS, 61; Univ Calif, Berkeley, MA, 63, PhD(math), 64. *Prof Exp:* From instr to asst prof math, Univ Mich, Ann Arbor, 64-66; asst prof, Univ Mich, Dearborn Ctr, 66-67; from asst prof to assoc prof, Univ Mich, Ann Arbor, 67-68; assoc prof, 69-72, PROF MATH, MASS INST TECHNOL, 72- *Concurrent Pos:* Off Naval Res fel, 67-68; Sloan fel, 68-70. *Mem:* Am Math Soc; Math Asn Am. *Res:* Analytic and elementary number theory with emphasis on zeta functions and applications to quadratic fields. *Mailing Add:* Dept of Math Mass Inst of Technol Cambridge MA 02139

STARK, HENRY, b Antwerp, Belg, May 25, 38; US citizen; m 60; c 2. COHERENT OPTICS, PATTERN RECOGNITION. *Educ:* City Col New York, BS, 61; Columbia Univ, MS, 64, DrEngSc(elec eng), 68. *Prof Exp:* Asst proj engr, Bendix Corp, 61-62; res engr, Columbia Univ, 62-69; sr lectr elec eng, Israel Inst Technol, 69-70; from asst prof to assoc prof, Yale Univ, 70-77; ASSOC PROF, RENSSELAER POLYTECH INST, 78- *Concurrent Pos:* Lectr, City Col New York, 67 & 69; jr fel, Weizmann Inst Sci, 69; Frederick Gardner Cottrell grant, Res Corp, 71-72; NSF grant, 73-; Air Force Res & Develop Command grants, 78-; consult, Rome Air Develop Ctr & Gen Elec Corp Res, 78- *Mem:* Fel Optical Soc Am; Inst Elec & Electronics Engrs; NY Acad Sci; Sigma Xi. *Res:* Information science, coherent optics, image and data processing; systems; electrical communications. *Mailing Add:* Dept Elec & Systs Eng Rensselaer Polytech Inst Troy NY 12181

STARK, J(OHN) P(AUL), JR, b Des Moines, Iowa, Nov 9, 38; m 59. PHYSICS, METALLURGY. *Educ:* Univ Okla, BS, 60, PhD(metall), 63. *Prof Exp:* From asst prof to assoc prof, 63-72, PROF MECH ENG, UNIV TEX, AUSTIN, 72- *Concurrent Pos:* Consult, Humble Oil & Refining Co, Tex, 63-67 & Tracor, Inc, 64-65; NSF res grant, 66-68, 74-; Air Force Off Sci Res grant, 72-76. *Mem:* Am Inst Mining, Metall & Petrol Engrs; Am Soc Metals; Am Phys Soc. *Res:* Diffusion in solids; thermodynamics; phase transformations. *Mailing Add:* Dept Mech Eng Univ Tex Austin TX 78712

STARK, JAMES CORNELIUS, b Port Jefferson, NY, Sept 1, 41; m 63; c 3. ORGANIC CHEMISTRY, BIOCHEMISTRY. *Educ:* Eastern Nazarene Col, BS, 63; Purdue Univ, Lafayette, PhD(org chem), 69. *Prof Exp:* ASSOC PROF CHEM, EASTERN NAZARENE COL, 68- *Mem:* Am Chem Soc. *Res:* Preparation and reactions of polyhalo-organic compounds. *Mailing Add:* Dept of Chem Eastern Nazarene Col Quincy MA 02170

STARK, JEREMIAH MILTON, b Norfolk, Va, Apr 1, 22; m 49, 62; c 3. MATHEMATICS. *Educ:* US Coast Guard Acad, BS, 44; NTex State Col, BS, 46; Mass Inst Technol, SM, 49, PhD(math), 54. *Prof Exp:* Instr math, Mass Inst Technol, 49-52, mathematician instrumentation lab, 54-56; head dept, 56-77, PROF MATH, LAMAR UNIV, 56- *Concurrent Pos:* NSF sci fac fel, Stanford Univ, 63-64. *Mem:* AAAS; Am Math Soc; Math Asn Am; Soc Indust & Appl Math. *Res:* Analysis; complex variables. *Mailing Add:* Dept of Math Lamar Univ Beaumont TX 77705

STARK, JOEL, b New York, NY, Nov 18, 30; m 50; c 2. SPEECH PATHOLOGY. *Educ:* Long Island Univ, BA, 50; Columbia Univ, MA, 51; NY Univ, PhD(speech), 56. *Prof Exp:* Instr speech, Long Island Univ, 51-54; asst prof, City Col New York, 54-65; assoc prof speech path, Sch Med, Stanford Univ, 65-68; assoc prof commun arts & sci, 68-72, PROF COMMUN ARTS & SCI & DIR SPEECH & HEARING CTR, QUEENS COL, NY, 72- *Concurrent Pos:* Nat Inst Neurol Dis & Blindness fel, 62-64; mem coun except children. *Mem:* Am Speech & Hearing Asn; Am Asn Ment Deficiency. *Res:* Communications disorders; language development and disorders in children. *Mailing Add:* Speech & Hearing Ctr Queens Col Flushing NY 11367

STARK, JOHN, JR, b Headland, Ala, Aug 26, 21; m 58; c 2. CHEMICAL ENGINEERING. *Educ:* Univ Ala, BS, 48, MS, 61, PhD(chem eng), 64. *Prof Exp:* Chemist, Astilleros Dominicanos, 55-60; asst prof chem eng, Univ Ala, 64-65; assoc prof, 65-77, PROF CHEM ENG & CHMN DEPT, UNIV S ALA, 77- *Concurrent Pos:* Consult, NASA, Ala, 64-68. *Mem:* Am Chem Soc; Am Inst Chem Engrs. *Res:* Turbo grid-plate efficiencies; distribution of noncondensable gases in liquids; effect of surface waves on evaporation rates. *Mailing Add:* Dept of Chem Eng Univ of SAla Mobile AL 36688

STARK, JOHN HOWARD, b Port Jefferson, NY, Sept 1, 41; m 63; c 3. BIOMATERIALS, CARBOHYDRATE CHEMISTRY. *Educ:* Eastern Nazarene Col, BS, 63; Purdue Univ, MS, 65, PhD(biochem), 69. *Prof Exp:* SR RES ASSOC CARBOHYDRATE CHEM, INT PAPER CO, 69- *Mem:* Am Chem Soc; Sigma Xi. *Res:* Medical applications of polysaccharide derivatives and other polymers; cellulose derivatives and chemicals. *Mailing Add:* PO Box 797 Int Paper Co Tuxedo NY 10987

STARK, LARRY GENE, b Abilene, Kans, Dec 31, 38; m 76; c 2. PHARMACOLOGY. *Educ:* Univ Kans, BS, 61, MS, 63; Stanford Univ, PhD(pharmacol), 68. *Prof Exp:* asst prof, 69-77, ASSOC PROF PHARMACOL, SCH MED, UNIV CALIF, DAVIS, 78- *Concurrent Pos:* NIH fel, Univ Chicago, 68-69. *Mem:* Soc Neurosci; Am Soc Pharmacol & Exp Therapeut. *Res:* Anticonvulsant drugs and animal models of epilepsy; correlations between the distribution of drugs in the brain and their neuropharmacological properties. *Mailing Add:* Dept of Pharmacol Univ of Calif Sch of Med Davis CA 95616

STARK, LAWRENCE, b New York, NY, Feb 21, 26; m 49; c 3. BIOENGINEERING. *Educ:* Columbia Univ, AB, 45; Albany Med Col, MD, 48; Am Bd Psychiat & Neurol, dipl, 57. *Prof Exp:* Intern, US Naval Hosp, St Albans, 48-49; res asst biochem, Oxford Univ & mem, Trinity Col, 49-50; res asst physiol, Univ Col, London, 50-51; asst prof physiol & pharmacol & res assoc neurophysiol & neuromuscular physiol, NY Med Col, 51; from instr to asst prof neurol & assoc physician, Yale Univ, 55-60; head neurol sect, Ctr Commun Sci, Res Lab Electronics & Electronic Systs Lab, Mass Inst Technol, 60-65; prof bioeng, neurol & physiol & chmn biomed eng dept, Univ Ill, Chicago Circle, 65-68; PROF PHYSIOL OPTICS, UNIV CALIF, BERKELEY, 68- *Concurrent Pos:* Fel neurol & EEG, Neurol Inst, Columbia Univ & Presby Hosp, 51-52; fel neurol, Sch Med, Yale Univ, 54-55; fel, Mass Inst Technol, 60-65; fel neurol, Mass Gen Hosp, 60-65; Guggenheim fel, 68-70; vis app, Univ Col, London, 50-51, Nobel Inst Neurophysiol, Stockholm, 57, Harvard Univ, 63-65, Univ Calif, Los Angeles, 65 & Stanford Univ, 68 & 75; dir, Biosysts, Inc, Cambridge, 62-67 & Biocontacts, Inc, Berkeley, 69-73; chmn neurosci work session, Math Concepts of Cent Nerv Syst, 64, Gordon Conf Biomath, 65 & bioeng training comt, Nat Inst Gen Med Sci, 67-68; consult, NIH, NSF & var indust companies; assoc ed or ed bd mem, Math Biosci, Inst Elec & Electronics Eng-SMC, Brain Res, J Appl Physiol, J Neurosci & Comput in Biol & Med. *Mem:* Am Physiol Soc; Biophys Soc; Am Acad Neurol; fel Inst Elec & Electronics Eng; Asn Comput Mach. *Res:* Application of communication and information theory to neurophysiology; normal and abnormal neurological control systems; cybernetics; pattern recognition and artificial intelligence; information flow in biological evolution and economic theory. *Mailing Add:* Sch Optom Univ of Calif Berkeley CA 94720

STARK, MARVIN MICHAEL, b Mich, Mar 14, 21; m; c 3. DENTISTRY. *Educ:* Univ Calif, Los Angeles, AB, 48, DDS, 52. *Prof Exp:* PROF OPER DENT & ORAL BIOL, SCH DENT, UNIV CALIF, SAN FRANCISCO, 53-; CHIEF DENT OFFICER, STATE OF CALIF DEPT HEALTH, 75- *Concurrent Pos:* Res fel dent med, Sch Dent Med, Harvard Univ, 52-53. *Mem:* Am Asn Endodont; fel Int Col Dent; fel Am Col Dent; Am Dent Asn; Int Asn Dent Res. *Mailing Add:* Dept Oper Dent & Oral Biol Univ of Calif Sch of Dent San Francisco CA 94122

STARK, NATHAN JULIUS, b Minneapolis, Minn, Nov 9, 20; m 43; c 4. MEDICINE. *Educ:* US Merchant Marine Acad, BS, 43; Chicago Kent Col Law, JD, 48. *Hon Degrees:* LLD, Park Col, 69. *Prof Exp:* Plant mgr, Englander Co, Inc, Chicago, 49-51; partner law firm, Downey, Abrams, Stark & Sullivan, Kansas City, 52-53; vpres, Rival Mfg Co, Kansas City, 54-59; sr vpres opers, Hallmark Cards, Inc, Kansas City, 59-74; vchancellor, Schs

Health Professions & pres, Univ Health Ctr, Univ Pittsburgh, 74-79; undersecy, US Dept Health & Human Serv, 79-80; PROF HEALTH SCI & SR VCHANCELLOR, GRAD SCH PUB HEALTH, UNIV PITTSBURGH, 80- *Concurrent Pos:* Secy, Eddie Jacobson Mem Found, 60-; pres & chmn, Kansas City Gen Hosp & Med Ctr, 62-74; vchmn health ins benefits adv comt, HEW, 65-70, secy task force Medicaid, 69-70, chmn adv comn incentive reimbursement exp, 68-70, chmn capital investment conf, HEW-Health Resources Admin, 76; dir, Woolf Bros, Inc, ERC Corp & Nat Fidelity Ins Co Hallmark Continental Ltd, Ireland, 71-73; pres & chmn bd, Crown Ctr Redevelop Corp, Kansas City, 71-74; chmn community hosp-med staff group pract prog, Robert Wood Johnson Found, 74-79; mem med malpract adv comt, Inst of Med of Nat Acad Sci, 75-79; mem bd, Am Nurses Found, 75-79; mem tech bd, Milbank Mem Fund, 76-79; fel, Hastings Ctr, mem, bd trustees, 81. *Honors & Awards:* Trustee Award, Am Hosp Asn, 68, 79; Layman Award, AMA, 74-79. *Mem:* Inst of Med of Nat Acad Sci; hon mem Am Hosp Asn; hon mem Am Col Hosp Adminrs. *Mailing Add:* 1216-A Scaife Hall Terrace & Desoto Sts Pittsburgh PA 15261

STARK, NELLIE MAY, b Norwich, Conn, Nov 20, 33; m 62. PLANT ECOLOGY. *Educ:* Conn Col, BA, 56; Duke Univ, MA, 58, PhD(plant ecol, bot), 62. *Prof Exp:* Botanist, Pac Southwest Forest & Range Exp Sta, US Forest Serv, 58-64; res assoc, Lab Atmospheric Physics, Desert Res Inst, Univ Nev, Reno, 64-72; assoc prof, 72-79, PROF FORESTRY, UNIV MONT, 79- *Concurrent Pos:* Mem, Alph Helix Res Exped for Desert Res Inst, Brazil & Peru, 67; Int Biol Prog grants, 72-73; co-chmn comt hemispheric coop, Inst Ecol, 73-74. *Mem:* Ecol Soc Am; Int Soc Trop Ecol; Bot Soc Am; Am Inst Biol Sci; Asn Trop Biol. *Res:* Nutrient cycling and soil ecology in tropical and temperate forests; fire and logging ecology; applied concept of the biological life of a soil to land use management; teaching ecology; soil chemistry; xylemsap chemistry. *Mailing Add:* Sch of Forestry Univ of Mont Missoula MT 59801

STARK, PAUL, b Philadelphia, Pa, Feb 1, 29; m 52; c 3. PHARMACOLOGY, PHYSIOLOGY. *Educ:* McGill Univ, BSc, 49; Univ Rochester, PhD(pharmacol), 63; Sch Law, Ind Univ, JD, 77. *Prof Exp:* Chief prod biochem, Gerber Prod Co, 52-55; res technician, Stromberg-Carlson Co, 55-57; res chemist, Allerton Chem, 57-60; sr pharmacologist, 63-66, res scientist, 67-72, RES ASSOC, ELI LILLY & CO, 72- *Concurrent Pos:* Assoc prof, Sch Med, Ind Univ, Indianapolis. *Mem:* Int Col Neuropsychopharmacol; Am Soc Pharmacol & Exp Therapeut; Am Physiol Soc; Am Bar Asn; Soc Neurosci. *Res:* Neuropharmacological and psychopharmacological techniques in the study of neuro-transmitters within the central nervous system; clinical evaluation of psychotropic drugs. *Mailing Add:* Lilly Res Labs 307 E McCarty St Indianapolis IN 46206

STARK, PHILIP, metallurgy, see previous edition

STARK, PHILIP HERALD, b Iowa City, Iowa, Mar 2, 36. GEOLOGY. *Educ:* Univ Okla, BS, 58; Univ Wis, MS, 61, PhD(geol), 63. *Prof Exp:* Explor geologist, Mobil Oil Corp, 63-65, sr explor geologist, 65-66, regional comput coordr, 66-69; mgr geol applns, 69-74, dir tech applns, 74-77, VPRES SPEC PROJ, PETROL INFO CORP, 77- *Concurrent Pos:* Lectr, Continuing Educ Prog, Am Asn Petrol Geologists. *Mem:* Geol Soc Am; Soc Econ Paleontologists & Mineralogists; Am Asn Petrol Geologists. *Res:* Stratigraphy and micropaleontology of Paleozoic flysch facies; computer applications in geology for petroleum exploration. *Mailing Add:* Petrol Info Corp PO Box 2612 Denver CO 80202

STARK, RICHARD B, b Conrad, Iowa, Mar 31, 15; m 67. PLASTIC SURGERY. *Educ:* Stanford Univ, AB, 36; Cornell Univ, MD, 41; Am Bd Plastic Surg, dipl, 52 & 78. *Prof Exp:* Intern, Peter Bent Brigham & Children's Hosps, Boston, Mass, 41-42; resident, Children's Hosp, 42; plastic surgeon, Northington Gen Hosp, Tuscaloosa, Ala, 45-46 & Percy Jones Gen Hosp, Battle Creek, Mich, 46; surgeon, Kingsbridge Vet Hosp & NY Hosp, 47-50; from asst prof clin surg to assoc prof, 55-73, PROF CLIN SURG, COL PHYSICIANS & SURGEONS, COLUMBIA UNIV, 73- *Concurrent Pos:* Fel, Med Sch, Stanford Univ, 46-47; plastic surgeon, NY Hosp, 48; attend surgeon chg plastic surg, St Luke's Hosp, 58-77; vis prof, Univ Tex, 65, Univ Mich, 66, Walter Reed Med Ctr, 70 & Univ Man, 71; from vpres to pres, Am Bd Plastic Surg, 66-68; ed, Annals Plastic Surg, 77- *Honors & Awards:* Res Prize, Am Soc Plastic & Reconstruct Surg Found, 51; Medal of Honor, Vietnam, 67 & 69; Order of San Carlos, Colombia, 69. *Mem:* AAAS; Soc Univ Surg; AMA; Am Asn Plastic Surg; Am Col Surgeons. *Res:* Circulation in skin grafts; homologous transplants of skin; pathogenesis of harelip and cleft palate; aesthetic surgery. *Mailing Add:* 115 E 67th St New York NY 10021

STARK, RICHARD HARLAN, b Ozawkie, Kans, Dec 5, 16; m 42; c 4. COMPUTER SCIENCE. *Educ:* Univ Kans, AB, 38; Northwestern Univ, MS, 42, PhD(math), 46. *Prof Exp:* Jr physicist, US Naval Ord Lab, 42-43 & Los Alamos Sci Lab, 44-45; instr math, Northwestern Univ, 46-48; mathematician, Los Alamos Sci Lab, 48-51; mgr math anal, Knolls Atomic Power Lab, Gen Elec Co, 52-56, mgr math & comput oper, Atomic Power Equip Dept, 56-61, consult analyst, Comput Dept, 62-64; from assoc prof to prof math & info sci, Wash State Univ, 64-69; PROF COMPUT SCI, NMEX STATE UNIV, 69- *Mem:* Soc Indust & Appl Math; Asn Comput Mach. *Res:* Proofs of program validity. *Mailing Add:* Dept of Comput Sci NMex State Univ Las Cruces NM 88001

STARK, ROBERT M, b New York, NY, Feb 6, 30; m 55; c 4. OPERATIONS RESEARCH, CIVIL ENGINEERING. *Educ:* Johns Hopkins Univ, AB, 51; Univ Mich, MA, 52; Univ Del, PhD(appl sci), 65. *Prof Exp:* Instr physics, Rochester Inst Technol, 55-57; asst prof math & asst dean col eng, Cleveland State Univ, 57-62; asst prof civil eng, Univ Del, 62-68, assoc prof civil eng, statist & comput sci, 68-72; vis assoc prof civil eng, Mass Inst Technol, 72-73; PROF CIVIL ENG & MATH SCI, UNIV DEL, 76- *Concurrent Pos:* Res physicist, Bausch & Lomb Optical Co, 55-56; consult various industs & govt agencies. *Mem:* Fel AAAS; Opers Res Soc Am; Am Soc Civil Engrs; Am Soc Eng Educ. *Res:* Civil engineering systems; applied probability; engineering management. *Mailing Add:* Dept of Civil Eng Univ of Del Newark DE 19711

STARK, RONALD WILLIAM, b Can, Dec 4, 22; nat US; m 44; c 2. FOREST ENTOMOLOGY. *Educ:* Univ Toronto, BScF, 48, MA, 51; Univ BC, PhD(forest entom), 58. *Prof Exp:* Agr res officer, Div Forest Biol, Sci Serv, Can Dept Agr, 48-59; asst prof entom & asst entomologist, Agr Exp Sta, Univ Calif, Berkeley, 59-61, from assoc prof to prof, 61-70, vchmn dept entom & parasitol, 68-70, entomologist, 61-70; grad dean, coordr res, 70-77, PROF FORESTRY & ENTOM, UNIV IDAHO, 78- *Concurrent Pos:* NSF sr fel, 67-68; collabr, Pac Southwest Forest & Range Exp Sta, US Forest Serv; Am rep & chmn working group forest entom, Int Union Forest Res Orgn; proj leader, Pest Mgt Prog Pine Back Beetle Ecosyst, Int Biol Prog; mem, USDA comt scientists, 76-78, dep prog mgr, USDA Expanded Douglas-fir Tussock Moth Prog, Portland, Ore, 77-78; prog mgr, Int Spruce Budworms Prog, Western Component, US Forest Serv. *Honors & Awards:* Gold Medalist, Entom Soc Can. *Mem:* AAAS; Soc Am Foresters; fel Entom Soc Am; Ecol Soc Am; Entom Soc Can. *Res:* Population dynamics; integrated pest management; research management. *Mailing Add:* 809 NE 6th Portland OR 97232

STARK, ROYAL WILLIAM, b Wellington, Ohio, Apr 30, 37; m 62; c 2. SOLID STATE PHYSICS, LOW TEMPERATURE PHYSICS. *Educ:* Case Inst Technol, BS, 59, MS, 61, PhD(physics), 62. *Prof Exp:* Res assoc solid state physics, Case Inst Technol, 62; from instr to prof, Univ Chicago & Inst Study Metals, 63-72; PROF PHYSICS, UNIV ARIZ, 72- *Concurrent Pos:* Alfred P Sloan res fel, 64-70. *Mem:* Am Phys Soc. *Res:* Electronic properties of metals; magnetic breakdown; Fermi surface and band structure; ferromagnetism; plasma effects. *Mailing Add:* Dept of Physics Univ of Ariz Tucson AZ 85721

STARK, WALTER ALFRED, JR, b San Antonio, Tex, Aug 30, 40; m 68; c 1. PHYSICAL CHEMISTRY. *Educ:* Princeton Univ, AB, 62; Univ Calif, Berkeley, PhD(chem), 67. *Prof Exp:* Staff mem mat sci, Sandia Labs, 67-73; STAFF MEM ENERGY RES, LOS ALAMOS NAT LAB, 73- *Mem:* Am Phys Soc. *Res:* Transport properties of materials, especially diffusion and permeation; high temperature materials compatibility. *Mailing Add:* Group CMB-11 MS505 Los Alamos Nat Lab PO Box 1663 Los Alamos NM 87545

STARK, WILLIAM POLSON, b French Camp, Calif, Dec 30, 43; m 65; c 2. AQUATIC ENTOMOLOGY, SYSTEMATICS. *Educ:* Southeastern Okla State Univ, BS, 65; NTex State Univ, MS, 72; Univ Utah, PhD(biol), 74. *Prof Exp:* asst prof, 76-80, ASSOC PROF BIOL, MISS COL, 80- *Concurrent Pos:* Adj prof biol, NTex State Univ, 77-; res assoc, Fla Collection Arthropods, 77- *Mem:* Entom Soc Am; NAm Benthological Soc; Soc Syst Zool. *Res:* Systematics and biology of Nearctic Plecoptera. *Mailing Add:* Dept of Biol Miss Col Clinton MS 39058

STARK, WILLIAM RICHARD, b Lexington, Ky, Apr 28, 45; m 68; c 1. DISTRIBUTED COMPUTATION & ARCHITECTURES. *Educ:* Univ Ky, BS, 68; Univ Wis-Madison, PhD(math), 75. *Prof Exp:* Fel, Univ Wis-Madison, 69-74; instr math, Univ Tex, Austin, 74-78; asst prof, Calif State Univ, San Jose, 78-79; ASST PROF, UNIV SFLA, 79- *Concurrent Pos:* Guest lectr, Am Math Soc & Asn Comput Mach. *Mem:* Am Math Soc; Asn Symbolic Logic; Asn Comput Mach. *Res:* Classical algebraic representations of synchronized distributed architectures; distributed operating systems; computational semantics; logics of knowledge; independence of compactness and completeness theorems in infinitary logic; forcing in recursive set theory. *Mailing Add:* Dept Math Univ SFla Tampa FL 33620

STARKE, ALBERT CARL, JR, b Cleveland, Ohio, Jan 14, 16; m 41; c 3. ORGANIC CHEMISTRY. *Educ:* Fla Southern Col, BS, 36; Northwestern Univ, PhD(chem), 40. *Prof Exp:* Lab instr, Dent Sch, Northwestern Univ, 37-40, Nat Defense Res Comt fel, 40-42; res chemist, GAF Corp, 42-46, patent searcher, 46-47, patent liaison, 48-50, patent agt, 50-55, supvr tech info serv, 55-66, mgr tech info, 66-72; res specialist, Univ Conn, 72-81; info mgr, New Eng Res Appln Ctr, 72-81; RETIRED. *Concurrent Pos:* Mem, Franklin Inst, Chem Abstr communicator, 66- *Mem:* Fel AAAS; Am Chem Soc; Am Soc Info Sci; fel Am Inst Chemists. *Res:* Physiological and synthetic organic chemistry; color photography; patent soliciting and prosecution; warfare agents; polymers; storage and retrieval of technical information; computer systems design; documentation; computer searching. *Mailing Add:* 10 Corriage Cove Way Sanford FL 32771

STARKE, EDGAR ARLIN, JR, b Richmond, Va, May 10, 36; m 61; c 2. PHYSICAL METALLURGY. *Educ:* Va Polytech Inst, BS, 60; Univ Ill, MS, 61; Univ Fla, PhD(metall), 64. *Prof Exp:* Res metallurgist, Savannah River Lab, E I du Pont de Nemours & Co, Inc, 61-62; from asst prof to assoc prof, 64-72, PROF METALL, GA INST TECHNOL, 72-, DIR, FRACTURE & FATIGUE RES LAB, 78- *Concurrent Pos:* Consult, Lockheed-Ga Co, 65- & Southwire Co; vis scientist, Oak Ridge Nat Lab, 67 & Max Planck Inst Metall Res, 71; Sigma Xi res award, Nonferrous Div Wire Asn, 72. *Mem:* Am Soc Metals; Am Inst Mining, Metall & Petrol Engrs; Am Iron & Steel Inst; Brit Inst Metals. *Res:* Strengthening mechanisms; alloy theory; special x-ray diffraction techniques for characterization of materials; fracture and fatigue. *Mailing Add:* Fracture & Fatigue Res Lab Ga Inst Technol Atlanta GA 30332

STARKEY, EUGENE EDWARD, b Yakima, Wash, July 14, 26; m 54; c 3. DAIRY SCIENCE. *Educ:* Calif State Polytech Col, BS, 52; Univ Wis, MS, 54, PhD(dairy husb, genetics), 58. *Prof Exp:* Asst dairying, Univ Wis, 52-55; dairy husbandman, Dairy Husb Res Br, Agr Res Serv, USDA, 55-57; asst prof dairy prod, Utah State Univ, 57-60; prof dairy prod, Univ Wis-Madison, 60-78; PROF & HEAD DEPT DAIRY SCI, CALIF POLYTECH STATE UNIV, 78- *Mem:* Am Dairy Sci Asn. *Res:* Dairy cattle breeding sire selection and evaluation of environmental influences on production. *Mailing Add:* 1730 Portola San Luis Obispo CA 53711

STARKEY, FRANK DAVID, b Indianapolis, Ind, Aug 6, 44; m 67; c 2. ORGANIC CHEMISTRY. *Educ:* Wabash Col, AB, 66; Brown Univ, PhD(org chem), 73. *Prof Exp:* Asst prof chem, Ill Wesleyan Univ, 71-77, assoc prof, 77-80, head dept, 79-80. *Concurrent Pos:* Vis res assoc, Univ Minn, 77-78. *Mem:* Am Chem Soc; AAAS. *Res:* Carbonium ion chemistry; synthesis and reaction of various substrates that give carbonium ions. *Mailing Add:* 1274 Regent St Schenectady NY 12309

STARKEY, JOHN, b Manchester, Eng, Aug 11, 36; m 58; c 2. STRUCTURALGEOLOGY. *Educ:* Univ Liverpool, BSc, 57, PhD(geol), 60. *Prof Exp:* NATO & Dept Sci & Indust Res Gt Brit res fels geol, Inst Crystallog & Petrol, Swiss Fed Inst Technol, 60-62; Miller res fel, Univ Calif, Berkeley, 62-65; asst prof, 65-69, assoc prof, 69-79, PROF GEOL, UNIV WESTERN ONT, 79- *Concurrent Pos:* Leverhulme Europ fel, 60-61; Royal Soc bursary, Imp Col, Univ London, 71-72; vis prof geochem, Fed Univ Bahia, Salvador, Brazil, 75-77; vis prof geol, Monash Univ, Australia, 78; vis prof geol, Eidgenoessiche Technische Hochschule, Zurich, Switzerland, 78-79. *Mem:* Brit Mineral Soc; Am Mineral Soc; Mineral Soc Can; Sigma Xi. *Res:* Petrofabric analysis of rocks, primarily by x-ray techniques; crystallography of plagioclase feldspars and their twinning; crystal chemistry of rock forming minerals. *Mailing Add:* Dept Geol Univ Western Ont London ON N6A 5B8 Can

STARKEY, PAUL EDWARD, b Fultonham, Ohio, Dec 9, 20; m 42; c 4. PEDODONTICS, DENTISTRY. *Educ:* Ind Univ, DDS, 43; Am Bd Pedodont, dipl, 58. *Prof Exp:* Instr pedodontics, Ohio State Univ, 55-56; assoc prof, 59-63, chmn clin div, 61 & dept pedodontics, 68, PROF PEDODONTICS, SCH DENT, IND UNIV, INDIANAPOLIS, 63- *Concurrent Pos:* Pvt pract, 46-59; exam mem, Am Bd Pedodont, 69. *Honors & Awards:* Frederick Bachman Lieber Distinguished Teaching Award, Ind Univ, 68. *Mem:* Am Soc Dent for Children (pres, 67); Am Acad Pedodont; Am Dent Asn; Asn Pedodontics Diplomates; Am Asn Dent Schs. *Res:* Clinical children's dentistry; educational research. *Mailing Add:* Dept of Pedodont Ind Univ Sch of Dent Indianapolis IN 46202

STARKEY, THOMAS EDWARD, plant pathology, see previous edition

STARKEY, WALTER L(EROY), b Minneapolis, Minn, Oct 5, 20; m 49; c 2. MECHANICAL ENGINEERING. *Educ:* Univ Louisville, BME, 43; Ohio State Univ, MSc, 47, PhD(mech eng), 50. *Prof Exp:* Instr mech eng, Univ Louisville, 43-46; from instr to assoc prof, 47-58, PROF MECH ENG, OHIO STATE UNIV, 58- *Concurrent Pos:* Consult, 50- *Honors & Awards:* Mach Design Award, Am Soc Mech Engrs, 71. *Mem:* Fel Am Soc Mech Engrs; Am Soc Eng Educ. *Res:* Fatigue of metals; mechanics of materials; machine dynamics; mechanical design of machinery. *Mailing Add:* Dept of Mech Eng 206 W 18th Ave Columbus OH 43210

STARKOVSKY, NICOLAS ALEXIS, b Alexandria, Egypt, Jan 15, 22; US citizen; m 59; c 2. ORGANIC CHEMISTRY. *Educ:* Univ Cairo, BS, 46, MS, 54, PhD(chem), 56. *Prof Exp:* Res chemist, Memphis Chem Co, Egypt, 51-60; fel, Columbia Univ, 60-61; res chemist, Dow Chem Co, 61-64; dir res & develop, Collab Res, Inc, Mass, 64-70; dir proj develop, Ortho Res Found, NJ, 71-72; sr scientist, Wampole Div, Carter Wallace, Inc, Cranbury, 73-80. *Mem:* AAAS; Am Chem Soc; NY Acad Sci. *Res:* Immunology; clinical medicine. *Mailing Add:* 6352 Silas Burke Burke VA 22015

STARKS, AUBRIE NEAL, JR, b Dermott, Ark, Aug 20, 46. ANALYTICAL CHEMISTRY. *Educ:* Southern Ill Univ, Carbondale, BA, 67; Univ Ark, Fayetteville, PhD(chem), 75. *Prof Exp:* Instr chem, Univ Ark, Fayetteville, 73-74; intern, Hendrix Col, 74-75; asst prof chem, Thiel Col, 75-80; MEM FAC, CHEM DEPT, NORTHEAST LOUISIANA UNIV, 80- *Mem:* Am Chem Soc. *Res:* Photovoltammetric investigation of transition metal complexes for photocurrents generated in optically-shielded electrode systems. *Mailing Add:* Dept Chem Northeast Louisiana Univ Monroe LA 71209

STARKS, KENNETH JAMES, b Ft Worth, Tex, July 27, 24; m 51; c 2. ENTOMOLOGY. *Educ:* Univ Okla, BS, 50, MS, 51; Iowa State Univ, PhD(entom), 54. *Prof Exp:* Asst prof, Univ Ky, 53-61; mem staff, USDA, Uganda, 61-69; prof entom, Okla State Univ, 69; RES & LOCATION LEADER, AGR RES SERV, USDA, 69- *Mem:* Entom Soc Am. *Res:* Grain insects investigations. *Mailing Add:* USDA Agr Res Serv Dept of Entom Okla State Univ Stillwater OK 74074

STARKS, PAUL (BRECKENRIDGE), b Hardin, Ky, May 11, 17; m 42; c 1. ANIMAL SCIENCE. *Educ:* Western Ky Univ, BS, 41; Univ Ky, MS, 47; Univ Ill, PhD(animal sci), 53. *Prof Exp:* Teacher high sch, NC, 41-42 & Ky, 47-50; assoc prof agr, Univ Tenn, 53-66; from assoc to prof agr, Southwest Mo State Univ, 66-82. *Mem:* Am Soc Animal Sci. *Res:* Value of sodium sulfate; elemental sulfur; methionine and cystine in the nutrition of growing lambs. *Mailing Add:* Dept of Agr Southwest Mo State Univ Springfield MO 65802

STARKS, THOMAS HAROLD, b Owatonna, Minn, Aug 19, 30; m 59; c 2. STATISTICS. *Educ:* Mankato State Col, BA, 52; Purdue Univ, MS, 54; Va Polytech Inst, PhD(statist), 59. *Prof Exp:* Spec serv engr, E I du Pont de Nemours & Co, 59-61; ASSOC PROF MATH, SOUTHERN ILL UNIV, CARBONDALE, 61- *Mem:* AAAS; Am Statist Asn; Int Asn Math Geol; Inst Math Statist. *Res:* Design of experiments; statistical inference; geostatistics. *Mailing Add:* Dept of Math Southern Ill Univ Carbondale IL 62901

STARKS, THOMAS LEROY, b Muskegon, Mich, June 20, 47. MICROBIAL ECOLOGY. *Educ:* Ferris State Col, BS, 69; Cent Mich Univ, MS, 76; Univ NDak, 79. *Prof Exp:* Teacher, Key West High Sch, 69-72; instr biol, Reeths Puffer High Sch, 72-74; res scientist, 79-81, FEL, DOMESTIC MINING & MINERAL INST, UNIV NDAK, 81- *Mem:* Sigma Xi; Phycol Soc Am; Int Phycol Soc; Ecol Soc Am; AAAS. *Res:* Microbial ecology as influenced by succession, mining reclamation and acid precipitation, with particular emphasis on soil algae. *Mailing Add:* Dept Biol Univ NDak Grand Forks ND 58202

STARKWEATHER, GARY KEITH, b Lansing, Mich, Jan 9, 38; m 61; c 2. PHYSICAL OPTICS, ELECTROOPTICS. *Educ:* Mich State Univ, BS, 60; Univ Rochester, MS, 66. *Prof Exp:* Engr, Bausch & Lomb, Inc, 62-64; area mgr optical systs, 64-80, SR RES FEL, XEROX PALO ALTO RES CTR, 80- *Concurrent Pos:* Instr optics, Monroe Community Col, 68-69. *Mem:* Optical Soc Am. *Res:* Optics and electronics and their specific system interaction, involving display and hard copy image systems. *Mailing Add:* Xerox Palo Alto Res Ctr 3333 Coyote Hill Rd Palo Alto CA 94304

STARKWEATHER, HOWARD WARNER, JR, b Cambridge, Mass, July 20, 26; m 48; c 3. PHYSICAL CHEMISTRY. *Educ:* Haverford Col, AB, 48; Harvard Univ, AM, 50; Polytech Inst Brooklyn, 50-52, PhD(chem), 53. *Prof Exp:* Chemist, Rayon Dept, 47, res chemist, Ammonia Dept, 48-49 & Plastics Dept, 52-57, sr res chemist, 57-66, res assoc, plastics dept, 66-76, CENT RES & DEVELOP DEPT, E I DU PONT DE NEMOURS & CO, INC, 76- *Mem:* Am Chem Soc; Am Phys Soc. *Res:* Polymer chemistry; polymerization kinetics; polymer properties and molecular structure; polymer crystallography. *Mailing Add:* Cent Res & Develop Dept E I du Pont de Nemours & Co Inc Wilmington DE 19898

STARKWEATHER, PETER LATHROP, b Glen Ridge, NJ, Nov 7, 48; m 72. AQUATIC ECOLOGY, INVERTEBRATE PHYSIOLOGY. *Educ:* Union Col, NY, BS, 70; Dartmouth Col, PhD(biol sci), 76. *Prof Exp:* Teaching asst zool & ecol, State Univ NY Albany, 70-72; teaching fel biol sci, Dartmouth Col, 72-76, res assoc ecol, 76-78; asst prof, 78-82, ASSOC PROF AQUATIC ECOL, UNIV NEV, LAS VEGAS, 82- *Concurrent Pos:* Co-prin investr biol sci, NSF grant, Dartmouth Col, 78-81, vis asst prof, 79 & 80; prin investr, NSF grant, Univ Nev, 81- *Mem:* Am Soc Limnol & Oceanog; Am Soc Zoologists; Ecol Soc Am; AAAS; Sigma Xi. *Res:* Feeding biology and behavior of microcrustacean zooplankton and rotifers; biological rhythms and invertebrate ecology. *Mailing Add:* Dept of Biol Sci Univ of Nev Las Vegas NV 89154

STARLING, ALBERT GREGORY, b Joiner, Ark, Feb 24, 39. MATHEMATICS, COMPUTER SCIENCE. *Educ:* Univ Ark, BSEE, 61, MS, 64, PhD(math), 69. *Prof Exp:* Jr engr electronics, Int Bus Mach Corp, 61-62, assoc engr & mathematician appl math, 64-65; asst prof math, Univ Mass, Amherst, 69-71; ASSOC PROF MATH, WESTERN CAROLINA UNIV, 71- *Concurrent Pos:* Fel, Univ Mass, 69-71. *Mem:* Am Math Soc. *Res:* Directed graphs of finite groups. *Mailing Add:* Rte 67 Box 89-B Cullowhee NC 28723

STARLING, JAMES LYNE, b Henry Co, Va, Aug 16, 30. PLANT BREEDING, STATISTICS. *Educ:* Va Polytech Inst, BS, 51; Pa State Univ, MS, 55, PhD(agron), 58. *Prof Exp:* Asst forage crop breeding, 54-57, from instr to assoc prof agron, 57-69, PROF AGRON & HEAD DEPT, PA STATE UNIV, UNIVERSITY PARK, 69- *Mem:* AAAS; Am Soc Agron. *Res:* Forage crop breeding; genetics and cytogenetics of forage crop species; experimental design. *Mailing Add:* Pa State Univ 119 Tyson Bldg University Park PA 16802

STARLING, JANE ANN, b Waco, Tex, Jan 4, 46. METABOLISM, PARASITE PHYSIOLOGY. *Educ:* Rice Univ, BA, 67, PhD(physiol), 72. *Prof Exp:* Fel zool, Univ Mass, 72-75; vis asst prof biol, Univ Pittsburgh, 75-76; ASST PROF BIOL, UNIV MO-ST LOUIS, 76- *Concurrent Pos:* NIH fel, 73-75. *Mem:* AAAS; Am Micros Soc; Am Soc Parasitol; Sigma Xi. *Res:* Trehalose metabolism; energy metabolism in intestinal helminths; host parasite integration; energy coupling in carbohydrate and amino acid transport in helminths; anaerobic energy metabolism. *Mailing Add:* Univ of Mo Dept of Biol 8001 Natural Bridge Rd St Louis MO 63121

STARLING, KENNETH EARL, b Corpus Christi, Tex, Mar 9, 35; m 60; c 3. CHEMICAL ENGINEERING. *Educ:* Tex A&I Univ, BS, 57 & 58; Ill Inst Technol, MS, 60, PhD(gas technol), 62. *Prof Exp:* Res engr, Inst Gas Technol, Ill Inst Technol, 62-63; Robert A Welch Found fel chem, Rice Univ, 63-64; sr res engr, Standard Oil Co, NJ, 64-66; from asst prof to assoc prof, 62-77, PROF CHEM ENG, UNIV OKLA, 77- *Concurrent Pos:* Consult, Standard Oil Co, NJ, 68-, Inst Gas Technol, Ill Inst Technol, 70- & J F Pritchard & Co, 71-; fel, Inst Low Temperature Physics, Cath Univ Louvain, 72-73. *Mem:* AAAS; Am Inst Chem Engrs; Am Chem Soc; Soc Petrol Engrs. *Res:* Energy conversion; fossil energy processes; thermodynamics; correlation of fluid properties. *Mailing Add:* Sch Chem Eng Univ Okla Norman OK 73019

STARLING, THOMAS MADISON, b Loneoak, Va, Aug 12, 23; m 61; c 2. PLANT BREEDING. *Educ:* Va Polytech Inst, BS, 44; Iowa State Univ, MS, 47, PhD, 55. *Prof Exp:* From asst agronomist to assoc agronomist, 44-60, prof agron, 60-70, assoc dean grad sch, 70-71, PROF AGRON, VA POLYTECH INST & STATE UNIV, 71- *Mem:* Fel Am Soc Agron; Crop Sci Soc Am. *Res:* Plant breeding and genetics of winter barley and wheat. *Mailing Add:* 618 Woodland Dr Blacksburg VA 24060

STARMER, C FRANK, b Greensboro, NC, Sept 4, 41; m 63; c 4. COMPUTER SCIENCE, MEDICINE. *Educ:* Duke Univ, BSEE, 63, MSEE, 65; Rice Univ, 65-66; Univ NC, PhD(biomath, bioeng), 68. *Prof Exp:* Res assoc med, 63-65, assoc biomath, 66-68, asst prof Med & community health sci, 68-71, assoc prof comput sci, 71-77, PROF COMPUT SCI, DUKE UNIV, 77-, ASSOC PROF MED, MED CTR, 77- *Concurrent Pos:* NIH career develop award, Duke Univ, 72-77, NIH res grant, 72-75. *Mem:* AAAS; Asn Comput Mach; Am Heart Asn. *Res:* Computer science and pattern recognition in heart disease; applied statistics. *Mailing Add:* Dept of Med Duke Univ Med Ctr Durham NC 27710

STARNES, WILLIAM HERBERT, JR, b Knoxville, Tenn, Dec 2, 34. POLYMER CHEMISTRY. *Educ:* Va Polytech Inst, BS, 55; Ga Inst Technol, PhD(chem), 60. *Prof Exp:* Res chemist, Humble Oil & Refining Co, Esso Res & Eng Co, 60-62, sr res chemist, 62-65, res specialist, 65-67, res assoc, 67-71; res assoc & instr, Dept Chem, Univ Tex, Austin, 71-73; MEM TECH STAFF, BELL TEL LABS, 73- *Concurrent Pos:* Sect head, Humble Oil & Refining Co, Esso Res & Eng Co, 64; vis scientist, Tex Acad Sci, 64-67. *Mem:* Fel AAAS; fel Am Inst Chemists; Am Chem Soc. *Res:* Degradation, stabilization, microstructure and flammability of polyvinyl chloride; environmental deterioration of other synthetic polymers; organic reaction mechanisms; free-radical chemistry; liquid-phase autoxidation; organic synthesis; carbon-13 nuclear magnetic resonance. *Mailing Add:* Bell Tel Labs 600 Mountain Ave Murray Hill NJ 07974

STAROS, JAMES VAUGHAN, b May 20, 47; US citizen; m 76; c 2. PROTEIN CHEMISTRY. *Educ:* Dartmouth Col, AB, 69; Yale Univ, PhD(molecular biophysics & biochem), 74. *Prof Exp:* Helen Hay Whitney fel, Dept Chem, Harvard Univ, 74-77; ASST PROF BIOCHHEM, VANDERBILT UNIV, 78- *Mem:* Am Chem Soc; Biophys Soc; Fedn Am Scientists. *Res:* Protein chemistry; structure and function of biomembrane proteins; design and synthesis of new chemical probes of biomembrane structure and function. *Mailing Add:* Dept Biochem Sch Med Vanderbilt Univ Nashville TN 37232

STAROSTKA, RAYMOND WALTER, b Silver Creek, Nebr, Nov 27, 23; m 51; c 4. AGRONOMY. *Educ:* Univ Nebr, BS, 47; Univ Wis, PhD(soils), 50. *Prof Exp:* Asst soil chem, Purdue Univ, 47-48; assoc soil scientist, Soil & Water Conserv Res Br, USDA, 50-54, soil scientist, 54-56; supvr agr chem res, W R Grace & Co, 56-62, mgr agr res, 62-65; assoc dir agr res, Int Minerals & Chem Corp, Ill, 65-67; PRES, AGROSERV, INC, 67- *Mem:* AAAS; Am Chem Soc; Am Soc Agron; Soil Sci Soc Am. *Res:* Soil fertility; plant physiology; agronomic evaluation of fertilizers; inorganic chemistry, especially of phosphate compounds; agricultural chemicals; management of agricultural systems research. *Mailing Add:* Agroserv Inc Box 36 Silver Creek NE 68663

STARR, ALBERT, b New York, NY, June 1, 26; m 55; c 2. THORACIC SURGERY. *Educ:* Columbia Col, BA, 46; Columbia Univ, MD, 49. *Prof Exp:* Asst surg, Columbia Univ, 56-57; from instr to assoc prof surg, 57-64, PROF CARDIOPULMONARY SURG, MED SCH, UNIV ORE, 64-, HEAD DIV, 63- *Honors & Awards:* Sci Achievement Award, Am Heart Asn, 63; Rene Le Riche Award Cardiovasc Surg, 65. *Mem:* Am Surg Asn; Am Asn Thoracic Surg; Am Col Cardiol; Int Cardiovasc Soc. *Res:* Prosthetic values for cardiac surgery. *Mailing Add:* Div of Cardiopulmonary Surg Univ of Ore Portland OR 97201

STARR, C DEAN, b Tulare, SDak, Apr 24, 21; m 46; c 5. METALLURGY. *Educ:* SDak Sch Mines, BS, 43; Univ Utah, MS, 48, PhD(metall), 49. *Prof Exp:* Jr metallurgist, AC Spark Plug Co Div, Gen Motors Corp, 43-44, spectrographer, 46-47; asst res prof metall, Univ Calif, Berkeley, 49-53; chief res metallurgist, Wilbur B Driver Co, Gen Tel & Electronics Corp, 54-60, tech dir eng, 60-66, vpres eng & tech dir eng, 66-71, vpres eng & res, 71-79; VPRES ENG & RES, AMAX SPECIALTY METALS CORP, 79- *Concurrent Pos:* Vis sr lectr, Grad Sch Metall, Stevens Inst Technol, 61- *Honors & Awards:* Sam Tour Award, Am Soc Testing & Mat, 66. *Mem:* Am Soc Metals; Am Inst Mining, Metall & Petrol Engrs; Electrochem Soc. *Res:* Alloy development for resistance, particularly heat resisting, thermocouple, corrosion and high strength alloys; thermodynamic and kinetic studies of simple and complex alloy systems. *Mailing Add:* Amax Specialty Metals Corp 600 Lanidex Plaza Parsippany NJ 07054

STARR, CHAUNCEY, b Newark, NJ, Apr 14, 12; m 38; c 2. ENGINEERING PHYSICS. *Educ:* Rensselaer Polytech Inst, EE, 32, PhD(physics), 35. *Hon Degrees:* DrEng, Rensselaer Polytech Inst, 64; DrEng, Swiss Inst Technol, Switz, 80. *Prof Exp:* Coffin fel & res fel physics, Harvard Univ, 35-37; res physicist, P R Mallory Co, Ind, 37-38; res assoc phys chem, Mass Inst Technol, 38-41; physicist, D W Taylor Model Basin, Bur Ships, US Dept Navy, 41-42, Radiation Lab, Univ Calif, 42-43 & Manhattan Dist, Oak Ridge, 43-46; dir atomic energy res dept, N Am Aviation, Inc, 46-55, vpres, 55-66, gen mgr, Atomics Int Div, 55-60, pres, 60-66; dean sch eng & appl sci, Univ Calif, Los Angeles, 67-72; pres, 72-78, V CHMN, ELEC POWER RES INST, 78- *Concurrent Pos:* Consult, US Off Sci & Technol, NASA, Atomic Energy Comn & US Air Force; dir, Atomic Indust Forum; mem, Rockefeller Univ Coun, Rockefeller Univ, NY. *Honors & Awards:* Legion of Honor, French Govt, 78; Walter H Zinn Award, Am Nuclear Soc, 79. *Mem:* Nat Acad Eng (vpres); Am Inst Aeronaut & Astronaut; Sigma Xi; fel Am Phys Soc; Am Nuclear Soc (pres, 58-59). *Res:* Semiconductors; thermal conductivity of metals; high pressures; cryogenics; magnetic susceptibilities at low temperatures; gas discharge phenomena, solid state; atomic energy and nuclear reactors. *Mailing Add:* Elec Power Res Inst 3412 Hillview Rd Palo Alto CA 94303

STARR, DAVID WRIGHT, b Anna, Tex, Dec 8, 12; wid; c 2. MATHEMATICS. *Educ:* Southern Methodist Univ, AB, 33; Univ Ill, AM, 37, PhD(math), 40. *Prof Exp:* High sch instr, Tex, 33-37, prin, 34; asst math, Univ Ill, 38-40; instr ground sch aviation, 40-43, from instr to assoc prof math, 40-48, coordr war training serv, Civil Aeronaut Admin, 41-44, chmn dept, 63-77, prof math, 48-78, EMER PROF MATH, SOUTHERN METHODIST UNIV, 78- *Mem:* Am Math Soc; Math Asn Am. *Res:* Analysis; Schrodinger wave equation from the point of view of singular integral equations. *Mailing Add:* Dept of Math Southern Methodist Univ Dallas TX 75275

STARR, DUANE FRANK, b Pasadena, Calif, Oct 20, 42; m 65; c 2. PHYSICAL CHEMISTRY. *Educ:* Wesleyan Univ, BA, 64; Ore State Univ, PhD(phys chem), 73. *Prof Exp:* Resident res assoc lasers, Naval Res Lab, Nat Res Coun, 73-75; staff chemist propellant chem, Allegany Ballistics Lab, Hercules Inc, 75-77; ENGR URANIUM ENRICHMENT, NUCLEAR DIV, OAK RIDGE GASEOUS DIFFUSION PLANT, UNION CARBIDE CORP, 77- *Mem:* Am Chem Soc; Am Phys Soc. *Res:* Economic assessment of advanced isotope separation methods. *Mailing Add:* Oak Ridge Gaseous Diffusion Plant Mail Stop 274 Oak Ridge TN 37830

STARR, E(UGENE) C(ARL), b Falls City, Ore, Aug 6, 01; m 50. ELECTRICAL POWER ENGINEERINGG, NUCLEAR & THERMAL POWER ENGINEERING. *Educ:* Ore State Col, BS, 23, EE, 38. *Prof Exp:* Mem testing dept, Gen Elec Co, NY, 23, high voltage engr, Mass, 24-27; from instr to prof elec eng, Ore State Univ, 27-54; chief engr, 54-61, CONSULT ENGR, BONNEVILLE POWER ADMIN, 39-54, 61- *Concurrent Pos:* Consult, Secy War, Washington, DC, 46, Atomic Energy Comn, 53-65, UN, India, 59, Battelle Pac Northwest Lab, 77- & Teshmont Consults, Can, 77-; mem adv coun, Gen Elec Co Proj Extra-High Voltage, 58-66; mem adv comt reactor policies & prog, Atomic Energy Comn, 58-59; mem comt methods evaluating reactor concepts, Atomic Indust Forum, 59; mem adv subpanel study high voltage lab, Nat Acad Sci-Nat Res Coun, 61-64; mem US deleg, World Power Conf, Yugoslavia, 57; mem US deleg & chmn study comt, Int Conf Large High-Voltage Elec Systs, Paris, 56-; mem adv groups to extra-high voltages, standard voltages, current ratings & frequencies & insulation coord comts, Int Electrotech Comn. *Honors & Awards:* Distinguished Serv Award, US Dept Interior, 58; Inst Elec & Electronics Engrs Awards, 31 & 41, Habirshaw Award, 68; Lamme Medal, 80. *Mem:* Nat Acad Eng; fel AAAS; Nat Soc Prof Engrs; fel Inst Elec & Electronics Engrs; Sigma Xi. *Res:* High voltage discharges and dielectrics; lightning; power system radio coordination; industrial nuclear power; extra-high voltage alternating current and direct current power transmission; environmental effects of extra-high voltage transmission. *Mailing Add:* Thermal Eng Staff PO Box 3621-EIC Portland OR 97208

STARR, JAMES LEROY, b Almont, Mich, Aug 14, 39; m 60; c 2. SOIL PHYSICS, MICROBIOLOGY. *Educ:* Mich State Univ, BS, 61, MS, 70; Eastern Baptist Theol Sem, MA, 66; Univ Calif, Davis, PhD(soil sci), 73. *Prof Exp:* Voc Agr teacher, Carson City Community Schs, Mich, 61-62 & Mayville Community Schs, 62-64; teaching asst, Mich State Univ, 67-68, instr soils & dir audiotutorial lab, 68-70; res asst, Univ Calif, 70-72, staff res assoc, 72-74; asst scientist soil physics, 74-77, assoc scientist, Conn Agr Exp Sta, 77-78; RES SOIL SCIENTIST, USDA, 79- *Mem:* Sigma Xi; Am Soc Agron; Soil Sci Soc Am; Int Soc Soil Sci; Am Geophys Union. *Res:* Soil water nitrogen relations. *Mailing Add:* USDA Agr Res Serv BARC-W B007, RM 253 Beltsville MD 20705

STARR, JASON LEONARD, b Chelsea, Mass, Aug 13, 28; m 51; c 3. ONCOLOGY, BIOCHEMISTRY. *Educ:* Harvard Univ, AB & AM, 49, MD, 53. *Prof Exp:* Intern med, Beth Israel Hosp, Boston, Mass, 53-54; asst prof, Med Sch, Northwestern Univ, 61-65; from assoc prof to prof, Col Med, Univ Tenn, Memphis, 65-72; prof med, Sch Med, Univ Calif, Los Angeles, 73-74; CLIN PROF MED, UNIV TENN, MEMPHIS, 74-; DIR ONCOL, BAPTIST MEM HOSP, MEMPHIS, 74- *Concurrent Pos:* Fel, Mayo Found, Univ Minn, 56-58; fel biochem, Sch Med, Western Reserve Univ, 58-61; Am Cancer Soc fel, 61-63 & scholar, 71-72; sr investr, Arthritis Found, 63-68. *Mem:* Am Soc Clin Invest; Am Asn Immunologists; Am Chem Soc. *Res:* Genetic control of antibody synthesis; biochemistry of neoplastic cells; cancer chemotherapy; immuno-oncology. *Mailing Add:* Baptist Mem Hosp 920 Madison Ave Memphis TN 38103

STARR, JOHN EDWARD, b St Louis, Mo, July 12, 39; m 61; c 2. PHOTOGRAPHY. *Educ:* Colo Col, BA, 61; Stanford Univ, PhD(org chem), 65. *Prof Exp:* Sr chemist, 65-69, lab head, Res Labs, 69-78, RES ASSOC, EASTMAN KODAK CO, 78- *Res:* Spectral sensitization of photographic emulsions by sensitizing dyes; color reproduction. *Mailing Add:* Res Labs Eastman Kodak Co Kodak Park Rochester NY 14650

STARR, LEON, organic chemistry, see previous edition

STARR, MORTIMER PAUL, b New York, NY, Apr 13, 17; m 44; c 3. APPLIED MICROBIOLOGY. *Educ:* Brooklyn Col, BA, 38; Cornell Univ, MS, 39, PhD(bact, biochem, plant path), 43. *Prof Exp:* Tutor biol, Brooklyn Col, 39-44, from instr to asst prof, 44-47; from asst prof bact & asst bacteriologist to assoc prof bact & assoc bacteriologist, 47-58, spec asst to chancellor res grants & contracts, 63-67, PROF BACT EXP STA, UNIV CALIF, DAVIS, 58- *Concurrent Pos:* Nat Res Coun fel, Hopkins Marine Sta, Stanford Univ, 44-46; cur, Int Collection of Phytopathogenic Bacteria, 47-; vis specialist fac agron, Nat Univ Colombia, 49; NIH spec fels, Cambridge & Ghent Univs, 53-54, Plant Dis Div, Univ Auckland, NZ, 62; Guggenheim Mem Found fel, Max Planck Inst Med Res, 58, guest, 59; vis prof, Chile, 66; Guggenheim Mem Found fel, Swiss Fed Inst Technol, Zurich, 68-69; vis prof, Univ Hamburg, 72-73, Univ Bordeaux, 75-76, Univ Gottingen, 77; partic, Int Cong Microbiol, Rome, 53, Stockholm, 58, Montreal, 62, Moscow, 66, Mexico, 70; partic, Int Bot Cong, Paris, 54, Montreal, 59 & Edinburgh, 64; mem, Int Conf Sci Probs Plant Protection, Budapest, 60, Int Conf Cult Collections, Toronto, 62, Tokyo, 68, Brno, 81; mem, Conf Global Impacts Appl Microbiol, Stockholm, 63, Addis Ababa, 67, Bombay, 69; mem, Int Conf Phytopathogenic Bacteria, Harpenden, 64, Lisbon, 67, Angers, 78; Alexander von Humboldt Award, 77. *Honors & Awards:* Bernardo O'Higgins Medal, First Class, Repub of Chile, 67; Silver Medal, Purkyne Univ, Brno, 68. *Mem:* AAAS; Soc Gen Microbiol; Am Phytopath Soc; Am Soc Microbiol. *Res:* Biochemistry, metabolism, genetics, ecology and taxonomy of phytopathogenic bacteria; industrial microbiology; microbial pigments; pectin metabolism; philosophical grounds of taxonomy and ecology; bacterial morphogenesis; bacterial diversity and ecology; aquatic bacteria; international microbiology; university administration. *Mailing Add:* Dept of Bact Univ of Calif Davis CA 95616

STARR, NORMAN, b Scranton, Pa, Apr 14, 33; m 65. MATHEMATICAL STATISTICS. *Educ:* Univ Mich, BA, 55, MA, 60; Columbia Univ, PhD(math statist), 65. *Prof Exp:* Assoc math, Evans Res & Develop Corp, 61-65; asst prof statist, Univ Minn, 65-66; from asst prof to assoc prof, Carnegie-Mellon Univ, 66-68; assoc prof, 68-73, PROF MATH, DEPT STATIST, UNIV MICH, ANN ARBOR, 68- *Mem:* Inst Math Statist; Am Math Soc; Am Statist Asn. *Res:* Sequential analysis; optimal stopping; statistical allocation and theory; applied probability. *Mailing Add:* Dept of Statist Univ of Mich Ann Arbor MI 48104

STARR, NORTON, b Kansas City, Mo, June 18, 36; m 59; c 2. MATHEMATICS. *Educ:* Harvard Col, AB, 58; Mass Inst Technol, PhD(math), 64. *Prof Exp:* Instr math, Mass Inst Technol, 64-66; asst prof, 66-71, assoc prof, 71-78, PROF MATH, AMHERST COL, 78- *Concurrent Pos:* Vis asst prof, Univ Waterloo, 72-73. *Mem:* Am Math Soc; Math Asn Am. *Res:* Operator limit theory. *Mailing Add:* Dept of Math Amherst Col Amherst MA 01002

STARR, PATRICIA RAE, b Hood River, Ore, Feb 28, 35. MICROBIOLOGY. *Educ:* Ore State Univ, BS, 57, MS, 62; Univ Ore, PhD(microbiol), 68. *Prof Exp:* Instr microbiol, Dent Sch, Univ Ore, 68-69; assoc, Ore State Univ, 69-71; asst prof, Univ Ill, Urbana, 71-75; res assoc, Providence Hosp, 75-77; instr, 77-80, CHAIR, SCI DIV, MT HOOD COMMUNITY COL, 80- *Mem:* AAAS; Am Soc Microbiol. *Res:* Relationship of sterol synthesis to respiratory adaptation in yeast; amino acid uptake systems in yeast; white blood cell function. *Mailing Add:* Dept of Sci Mt Hood Community Col Gresham OR 97030

STARR, PATRICK JOSEPH, b St Paul, Minn, Oct 24, 39. MECHANICAL ENGINEERING, OPERATIONS RESEARCH. *Educ:* Univ Minn, Minneapolis, BME, 62, MSME, 66, PhD(mech eng), 70. *Prof Exp:* Develop eng, Honeywell Inc, 62-64, 68; teaching assoc, Univ Minn, Minneapolis, 64-70; control syst engr, Northern Ord Div, FMC Corp, 70-71; asst prof, 71-77, ASSOC PROF, INDUST ENG & OPERS RES DIV, DEPT MECH ENG, UNIV MINN, 77- *Res:* Dynamic synthesis; modeling of large scale socio-industrial systems; system dynamics; technology assessment. *Mailing Add:* Dept of Mech Eng Univ of Minn Minneapolis MN 55455

STARR, PHILLIP HENRY, b Poland, Nov 16, 20; nat US; div; c 3. PSYCHIATRY. *Educ:* Univ Toronto, MD, 44. *Prof Exp:* Asst prof neuropsychiat & pediat, Sch Med, Wash Univ, 52-55, dir community child guid clin, 52-56; ASSOC PROF NEUROL & PSYCHIAT, SCH MED, UNIV NEBR, OMAHA, 57- *Concurrent Pos:* Chief psychiat consult, St Louis Children's Hosp, 51-56; chief children's outpatient serv, Nebr Psychiat Inst, 56-64, consult, 64-; consult, Offut Air Base Hosp & Immanuel Ment Health Ctr. *Mem:* Fel Am Psychiat Asn; fel AMA; Int Asn Child Psychiat; fel Am Acad Child Psychiat. *Res:* Child and adult psychiatry. *Mailing Add:* Dept of Psychiat Univ of Nebr Sch of Med Omaha NE 68105

STARR, RICHARD CAWTHON, b Greensboro, Ga, Aug 24, 24. PHYCOLOGY. *Educ:* Ga Southern Col, BS, 44; George Peabody Col, MA, 47; Vanderbilt Univ, PhD(biol), 52. *Prof Exp:* From instr to assoc prof, 52-60, prof bot, Ind Univ, Bloomington, 60-76; PROF BOT, UNIV TEX, AUSTIN, 76- *Concurrent Pos:* Guggenheim fel, 59. *Mem:* Nat Acad Sci; Bot Soc Am; AAAS; Phycol Soc Am; Brit Phycol Soc. *Res:* Morphology and cultivation of green algae; genetics and development of Volvox. *Mailing Add:* Dept of Bot Univ of Tex Austin TX 78712

STARR, ROBERT I, b Laramie, Wyo, Dec 11, 32; m 56; c 2. CHEMISTRY, ENVIRONMENTAL SCIENCES. *Educ:* Univ Wyo, BS, 56, MS, 59, PhD(plant physiol), 72. *Prof Exp:* Res biochemist, US Fish & Wildlife Serv, Colo, 60-63; plant physiologist, Colo State Univ, 63-64; anal chemist, US Food & Drug Admin, 64-65; chemist, Colo State Univ, 65-69; res chemist, Bur Sport Fisheries & Wildlife, US Dept Interior, 69-74; environ scientist, US Geol Surv, 74-77, cheif, Environ-Tech Unit, 77-78; CHIEF, BIOL/ECOL SCI BR, US DEPT INTERIOR, 78- *Concurrent Pos:* Res biochemist, Wildlife Res Ctr, US Fish & Wildlife Serv, Colo, 68-69. *Mem:* AAAS; Am Chem Soc; fel Am Inst Chemists; Nat Asn Environ Profs. *Res:* Pesticide chemistry as related to plant soil and water systems, including method development studies; plant, soil, and chemistry matters relating to mining operations. *Mailing Add:* 404 Tulane Dr Ft Collins CO 80525

STARR, THEODORE JACK, b Plainfield, NJ, Aug 22, 24; m 54; c 3. MICROBIOLOGY. *Educ:* City Col New York, BS, 49; Univ Mass, MS, 51; Univ Wash, PhD(microbiol), 53. *Prof Exp:* Res assoc microbiol, Haskins Labs, 48-49; instr biol, Univ Ga, 54-55; fishery res biologist, US Fish & Wildlife Serv, 55-57; McLaughlin fel virol, Med Br, Univ Tex, 57-60; assoc res scientist, Lab Comp Biol, Kaiser Found Res Inst, 60-62; assoc prof microbiol, Univ Notre Dame, 62-68; prof biol sci & assoc head dept, Col Arts & Sci, Univ Ill, Chicago Circle, 68-70; asst vpres acad affairs, Grad Studies & Res, 75-77, head dept, 70-80, PROF BIOL SCI, STATE UNIV NY COL BROCKPORT, 70- *Concurrent Pos:* Fac exchange scholar, State Univ NY, 75. *Mem:* Am Soc Microbiol; Soc Exp Biol & Med. *Res:* Cytochemistry; virology; marine and space biology; gnotobiology. *Mailing Add:* Dept of Biol Sci State Univ of NY Brockport NY 14420

STARR, THOMAS LOUIS, b Cincinnati, Ohio, Mar 22, 49; m 70; c 2. ANALYTICAL CHEMISTRY, PHYSICAL CHEMISTRY. *Educ:* Univ Detroit, BS, 70; Univ Louisville, PhD(phys chem), 76. *Prof Exp:* Anal chemist, Major appliance labs, Gen Elec Co, 77-80; SR RES SCIENTIST, GA INST TECHNOL, 80- *Concurrent Pos:* Pres scholar, Univ Detroit, 67-70; J B Speed fel, Univ Louisville, 76. *Honors & Awards:* J M Houchens Prize, Univ Louisville, 77. *Mem:* Am Chem Soc. *Res:* Applications of computers to chemical analysis and chemical systems; materials chemistry, including halocarbons and chemical processing of ceramics. *Mailing Add:* Energy & Mat Sci Lab Ga Inst Technol Atlanta GA 30332

STARR, WALTER LEROY, b Portland, Ore, Feb 9, 24; m 44; c 2. PHYSICS. *Educ:* Univ Southern Calif, BS, 50; Calif Inst Technol, MS, 51. *Prof Exp:* Physicist, US Naval Missile Test Ctr, 50; res physicist, US Naval Civil Eng Lab, 51-55; res scientist, Phys Sci Lab, Lockheed Missiles & Space Co, 55-67; PHYSICIST, AMES RES CTR, NASA, 67- *Mem:* AAAS; Am Phys Soc; Am Geophys Union. *Res:* Atomic and molecular physics; atmospheric processes; ionization and excitation; absorption cross sections. *Mailing Add:* Planetary Environ Br Ames Res Ctr NASA Moffett Field CA 94035

STARRATT, ALVIN NEIL, b Paradise, NS, Sept 18, 36; m 67; c 2. NATURAL PRODUCTS CHEMISTRY. *Educ:* Acadia Univ, BSc, 59; Univ Western Ont, PhD(org chem), 63. *Prof Exp:* Brit Petrol Co res fel, Imp Col, Univ London, 63-64; res fel, Res Inst Med & Chem, Mass, 64-65; RES SCIENTIST, RES INST, CAN AGR, 65- *Concurrent Pos:* Hon lectr, Univ Western Ont, 69- *Mem:* Am Chem Soc; Royal Soc Chem; fel Chem Inst Can; Entom Soc Can. *Res:* Natural products influencing the behavior of insects and insect neuropeptides. *Mailing Add:* Res Ctr Agr Can University Sub PO London ON N6A 5B7 Can

STARRETT, ANDREW, b Greenwich, Conn, Mar 18, 30; m 51; c 3. MAMMALOGY. *Educ:* Univ Conn, BS, 51; Univ Mich, MS, 55, PhD(zool), 58. *Prof Exp:* Instr zool, Univ Mich, 56-57; from instr to asst prof biol, Univ Southern Calif, 57-64; asst prof, Northeastern Univ, 64-65; assoc prof, 65-69, PROF BIOL, CALIF STATE UNIV, NORTHRIDGE, 69- *Concurrent Pos:* Res assoc, Los Angeles County Mus Natural Hist. *Mem:* AAAS; Soc Syst Zool; Soc Study Evolution; Am Soc Mammalogists. *Res:* Vertebrate and mammalian evolution and distribution; mammalian morphology and systematics, particularly Chiroptera. *Mailing Add:* Dept of Biol Calif State Univ Northridge CA 91330

STARRETT, RICHMOND MULLINS, b Gardner, Mass, Oct 1, 43; m 66; c 3. BIOTECHNOLOGY, INDUSTRIAL MICROBIOLOGY. *Educ:* Univ NC, BA, 66; Iowa State Univ, PhD(org chem), 70. *Prof Exp:* Res assoc, R A Welch Found, Tex Tech Univ, 71-72; res chemist, 72-75, sr res chemist, 75-79, RES ASSOC, DEPT RES & DEVELOP, ETHYL CORP, 79- *Mem:* Am Chem Soc; Org Reactions Catalysis Soc; Nat Asn Advan Sci; Soc Indust Microbiol. *Res:* Development of biological processes for industrial chemicals; investigation of fundamental microbiological methodology, including recombinant DNA techniques; study of novel synthetic and catalytic processes for chemical manufacture. *Mailing Add:* Dept Res & Develop Ethyl Corp PO Box 341 Baton Rouge LA 70821

STARRFIELD, SUMNER GROSBY, b Los Angeles, Calif, Dec 29, 40; m 66; c 2. THEORETICAL ASTROPHYSICS. *Educ:* Univ Calif, Berkeley, BA, 62; Univ Calif, Los Angeles, PhD(astron), 69. *Prof Exp:* Lectr astron, Yale Univ, 67-69, asst prof, 69-71; scientist, Thomas J Watson Res Ctr, IBM Corp, 71-72; asst prof, 72-75, assoc prof, 75-79, PROF ASTROPHYS, ARIZ STATE UNIV, 80- *Concurrent Pos:* NSF res grants, 74 & 75-; consult, Los Alamos Sci Lab, 74- *Mem:* Royal Astron Soc; Int Astron Union; Am Astron Soc. *Res:* Stellar structure and evolution; hydrodynamical studies of novae; star formation. *Mailing Add:* Dept of Physics Ariz State Univ Tempe AZ 85281

STARUSZKIEWICZ, WALTER FRANK, JR, b Ellwood City, Pa, Jan 31, 39; m 63; c 3. ANALYTICAL CHEMISTRY, FOOD CHEMISTRY. *Educ:* Geneva Col, BS, 60; Univ Hawaii, MS, 65. *Prof Exp:* Res asst biochem, Pineapple Res Inst Hawaii, 64-66; chemist, Del Monte Corp, 66-67; RES CHEMIST ANAL CHEM FOODS, US FOOD & DRUG ADMIN, 67- *Mem:* Am Chem Soc; fel Asn Off Anal Chemists. *Res:* Development of analytical methods for the detection of decomposition in foods; applications of gas and liquid chromatography for the determination of histamine and other biogenic amines in seafoods. *Mailing Add:* US Food & Drug Admin HFF-416 200 C St SW Washington DC 20204

STARZAK, MICHAEL EDWARD, b Woonsocket, RI, Apr 21, 42; m 67; c 1. BIOPHYSICAL CHEMISTRY. *Educ:* Brown Univ, BS, 63; Northwestern Univ, PhD(chem), 68. *Prof Exp:* From actg instr to actg asst prof chem & grant, Univ Calif, Santa Cruz, 68-70; asst prof, 70-77, ASSOC PROF CHEM, STATE UNIV NY, BINGHAMTON, 77- *Concurrent Pos:* Corp mem, Marine Biol Lab, 74- *Mem:* AAAS; Am Chem Soc; Am Phys Soc; Biophys Soc. *Res:* Excitable membrane phenomena; photochemistry; stochastic processes; energy transfer. *Mailing Add:* Dept of Chem State Univ of NY Binghamton NY 13901

STARZL, THOMAS E, b Le Mars, Iowa, Mar 11, 26; m 54; c 3. SURGERY. *Educ:* Westminister Col, Mo, BA, 47; Northwestern Univ, MA, 50, PhD(anat) & MD, 52. *Hon Degrees:* Dr, Westminister Col, Mo, New York Med Col, Univ Wyo & Westmar Col. *Prof Exp:* Intern surg, Johns Hopkins Hosp, 52-53, asst resident, 55-56; resident, Sch Med, Univ Miami, 56-58; resident & instr, Northwestern Univ, 58-59, assoc, 59-61, asst prof, 61; assoc prof surg, Sch Med, Univ Colo, Denver, 62-64, prof, 64-81, chmn dept, 72-81; PROF SURG, UNIV PITTSBURGH, 81- *Honors & Awards:* Int Soc Surg Medal, 65; Eppinger Prize (Freiburg), 70; Brookdale Award in Med, 74; Middleton Award, 68; Mod Med Distinguished Achievement Award, 69; David M Hume Mem Award, Nat Kidney Found, 78. *Mem:* Am Col Surg; fel Am Acad Arts & Sci; Soc Univ Surg; Am Surg Asn; Soc Vascular Surg. *Res:* General and thoracic surgery; neurophysiology, cardiac physiology; transplantation of tissues and organs. *Mailing Add:* #1084 Scaife Hall Dept Surg Univ Pittsburgh Pittsburgh PA 15261

STARZYK, MARVIN JOHN, b Chicago, Ill, Feb 3, 35; m 58; c 4. MICROBIOLOGY. *Educ:* Loyola Univ, Chicago, BS, 57; Univ Wis-Madison, PhD(microbiol), 62. *Prof Exp:* Asst prof natural sci, Northern Ill Univ, 61-64; group leader microbiol, Res Dept, Brown & Williamson Tobacco Corp Ky, 64-65; asst sect leader biol sci, 65-66; asst prof, 66-71, ASSOC PROF MICROBIOL, NORTHERN ILL UNIV, 71- *Concurrent Pos:* Consult, Brown & Williamson Tobacco Corp, 66-67. *Mem:* Am Soc Microbiol; Can Soc Microbiol; Int Asn Water Pollution Res. *Res:* Water microbiology, the ecology of microorganisms associated with pure and polluted waters. *Mailing Add:* Dept of Biol Sci Northern Ill Univ De Kalb IL 60115

STASHEFF, JAMES DILLON, b New York, NY, Jan 15, 36; m 59; c 2. MATHEMATICS. *Educ:* Univ Mich, BA, 56; Princeton Univ, MA, 58, PhD(math), 61; Oxford Univ, DPhil(math), 61. *Prof Exp:* Moore instr math, Mass Inst Technol, 60-62; from asst prof to prof, Univ Notre Dame, 62-70; prof math, Temple Univ, 70-78; PROF MATH, UNIV NC, 76- *Concurrent Pos:* NSF grants, 64-; mem Inst Advan Study, 64-65, Sloan fel, 69-70; vis prof, Princeton Univ, 68-69. *Mem:* Am Math Soc; Math Asn Am. *Res:* Algebraic topology, especially homotopy theory; fibre space, H-spaces and characteristic classes. *Mailing Add:* Dept of Math Univ NC Chapel Hill NC 27514

STASIW, ROMAN OREST, b Ukraine, May 3, 41; US citizen; m 68; c 1. CLINICAL CHEMISTRY, BIOCHEMISTRY. *Educ:* Univ Rochester, BS, 63; State Univ NY Buffalo, PhD(inorg chem), 68. *Prof Exp:* Analyst, E I du Pont de Nemours & Co, summers 62 & 63; asst scientist, Cancer Res Ctr, Columbia, Mo, 68-73; SCIENTIST, TECHNICON, 73- *Mem:* Am Asn Clin Chem. *Res:* Inorganic and synthetic organic chemistry; enzymology; clinical automation. *Mailing Add:* 98 N Grant Ave Congers NY 10920

STASKIEWICZ, BERNARD ALEXANDER, b Monessen, Pa, Aug 20, 24; m 49; c 5. PHYSICAL CHEMISTRY. *Educ:* Washington & Jefferson Col, AB, 46; Carnegie Inst Technol, MS, 50, PhD(chem), 53. *Prof Exp:* Instr chem, Washington & Jefferson Col, 46-51; res chemist, Esso Res & Eng Co, Standard Oil Co, NJ, 53-56 & Rayonier, Inc, 56-58; assoc prof, 58-62, PROF CHEM, WASHINGTON & JEFFERSON COL, 62-, CHMN DEPT, 67- *Mem:* Am Chem Soc. *Res:* Thermodynamics; cellulose chemistry; automotive lubricants. *Mailing Add:* Dept of Chem Washington & Jefferson Col Washington PA 15301

STASKO, AIVARS B, b Riga, Latvia, May 22, 37; Can citizen; m 63; c 3. AQUATIC ECOLOGY, FISHERIES. *Educ:* Univ Toronto, BASc, 60, PhD(zool), 69. *Prof Exp:* Res assoc limnol, Univ Wis-Madison, 67-70; res scientist, St Andrews, 70-79, head, Crustaceans Sect, 77-79, ASSOC DIR, RES PLANNING & ANAL, DEPT FISHERIES & OCEANS, OTTAWA, ONT, 80- *Concurrent Pos:* Ed, Underwater Telemetry Newslett, 71- *Mem:* Can Soc Environ Biologists; Am Fisheries Soc; Can Soc Zoologists. *Res:* Crab and lobster biology and fisheries; underwater biotelemetry; responses of fish to environmental factors. *Mailing Add:* Fisheries & Oceans Can Biol Sta St Andrews NB E0G 2X0 Can

STASZAK, DAVID JOHN, b Milwaukee, Wis, Mar 29, 44; m 65; c 2. ANIMAL PHYSIOLOGY, BIOCHEMISTRY. *Educ:* Iowa State Univ, BS, 66, MS, 68, PhD(physiol), 71. *Prof Exp:* Res asst insect physiol, Iowa State Univ, 66-68; teaching asst human physiol, 68-69, res asst insect physiol, 69-71; asst prof biochem, Ill Col, 71-72; assoc prof physiol, Ga Col, 72-76, assoc prof biol & dir res servs, 76-80; PROF BIOL & DEAN GRAD STUDIES, UNIV WIS-STEVENS POINT, 80- *Concurrent Pos:* USDA grant, Iowa State Univ, 66-71; asst prof, Dept Biol, MacMurray Col, 71-72; consult, Biochem Sect, Res Dept, Regional Ment Health Ctr, Cent State Hosp, 75- *Mem:* Am Inst Biol Sci; Sigma Xi; AAAS; Nat Coun Univ Res Adminrs. *Res:* Influence of low temperature on animals; chill-coma; thermal acclimation; hypertension. *Mailing Add:* Off Dean Grad Studies & Coordr Res Univ Wis Stevens Point WI 54481

STATE, DAVID, b London, Ont, Nov 13, 14; nat US; m 45; c 5. SURGERY. *Educ:* Univ Western Ont, BA, 36, MD, 39; Univ Minn, MS, 45, PhD(surg), 47; Am Bd Surg, dipl, 46; Bd Thoracic Surg, dipl, 52. *Prof Exp:* Intern, Victoria Hosp, Ont, 39-40; from intern to sr resident surg, Univ Minn Hosp, 41-45, res asst, Univ, 45-46, from instr to assoc prof, 46-52, dir cancer detection ctr, Univ Hosp, 48-52; clin assoc prof surg, Sch Med, Univ Southern Calif, 52-58; prof, Albert Einstein Col Med, 58-71, chmn dept, 59-71; PROF SURG & VCHMN DEPT, UNIV CALIF, LOS ANGELES & CHMN DEPT SURG, HARBOR GEN HOSP, 71- *Concurrent Pos:* Fel path, St Luke's Hosp, Chicago, 40-41; dir surg, Cedars of Lebanon Hosp, Los Angeles, Calif, 53-58, Bronx Munic Hosp Ctr, New York, 59-71 & Hosp of Albert Einstein Col Med, 66-71. *Mem:* AAAS; Soc Exp Biol & Med; Am Thoracic Soc; Soc Univ Surg; AMA. *Res:* General, thoracic and open heart surgery; gastrointestinal physiology. *Mailing Add:* Harbor Gen Hosp Dept Surg 1000 W Carson St Torrance CA 90509

STATE, HAROLD M, b Washington, Mo, Apr 15, 10; m 39; c 1. ANALYTICAL CHEMISTRY, INORGANIC CHEMISTRY. *Educ:* Cent Col, Mo, AB, 32; Princeton Univ, AM, 35, PhD(chem), 36. *Prof Exp:* Asst prof chem, Culver-Stockton Col, 36-37; from instr to prof, 37-75, EMER PROF CHEM, ALLEGHENY COL, 75- *Concurrent Pos:* Vis asst prof, Univ Ill, 41-42. *Mem:* Am Chem Soc. *Res:* Application of Werner complexes to analysis; higher valent complexes of nickel; chemistry of coordination compounds. *Mailing Add:* RD 1 Saegertown PA 16433

STATEN, RAYMOND DALE, b Stillwater, Okla, May 17, 22; m 46; c 4. AGRONOMY, BOTANY. *Educ:* Okla State Univ, BS, 47; Univ Nebr, MS, 49, PhD(agron), 51. *Prof Exp:* Asst prof agron, Univ Ark, 51-56; asst prof, 56-60, ASSOC PROF AGRON, TEX A&M UNIV, 60- *Mem:* Am Soc Agron. *Res:* Forage crop breeding and improvement; pasture management; grain and fiber crops production; morphology. *Mailing Add:* Dept of Soil & Crop Sci Tex A&M Univ College Station TX 77843

STATES, JACK STERLING, b Laramie, Wyo, Nov 6, 41; m 65; c 2. MICROBIAL ECOLOGY, MYCOLOGY. *Educ:* Univ Wyo, BAEd, 64, MSc, 66; Univ Alta, PhD(bot), 69. *Prof Exp:* Res assoc bot, Univ Wyo, 69-70; asst prof, 70-78, ASSOC PROF BIOL, NORTHERN ARIZ UNIV, 78- *Concurrent Pos:* High sch instr, Wyo, 69-70. *Mem:* Mycol Soc Am; Bot Soc Am. *Res:* Soil microfungi; ecological studies and effects of industrial pollutants; developmental studies of high Basidiomycetes. *Mailing Add:* Dept of Biol Northern Ariz Univ Flagstaff AZ 86001

STATHOPOULOS, THEODORE, b Athens, Greece, Sept 30, 47; Can citizen; m 79; c 1. WIND ENGINEERING. *Educ:* Nat Tech Univ, Athens, dipl, 70; Univ Western Ont, MS, 76, PhD(wind eng), 79. *Prof Exp:* Engr struct design, Stefanou & Assoc, Athens, 70-73; res assoc, 79, asst prof, 79-82, ASSOC PROF, CONCORDIA UNIV, 82- *Mem:* Tech Chamber Greece; Am Soc Civil Engrs; Can Soc Wind Eng. *Res:* Wind loads on low buildings; wind tunnel testing techniques; economical measurements of area averaged wind loads on structures (pneumatic averaging technique). *Mailing Add:* Ctr Bldg Studies Concordia Univ 1455 De Maisonneuve Blvd W Montreal PQ H3G 1M8 Can

STATLER, IRVING C(ARL), b Buffalo, NY, Nov 23, 23; m 53; c 2. AERONAUTICS. *Educ:* Univ Mich, BS(aeronaut eng) & BS(eng math), 45; Calif Inst Technol, PhD(aeronaut, math), 56. *Prof Exp:* Res engr, Cornell Aeronaut Lab, Inc, 46-53; sr res engr, Jet Propulsion Lab, Calif Inst Technol, 53-55; prin engr, Cornell Aeronaut Lab, Inc, 56-57, asst head, Appl Mech Dept, 57-63, head, 63-70; res scientist, US Army Air Mobility Res & Develop Lab, 70-72, DIR, AEROMECHANICS LAB, AMES RES CTR, DEPT OF DEFENSE, 72- *Concurrent Pos:* Lectr, Univ Buffalo, 56-57; mem flight mech panel, Adv Group Aerospace Res & Develop, NATO. *Mem:* AAAS; Am Inst Aeronaut & Astronaut; Am Helicopter Soc; fel Royal Aeronaut Soc. *Res:* Aerodynamics; dynamic stability and control; aeroelasticity; rotary wing aerodynamics; applied mathematics. *Mailing Add:* Dept Defense Ames Res Ctr MS 215-1 Moffett Field CA 94035

STATON, ROCKER THEODORE, JR, b McComb, Miss, Dec 6, 20; m 41; c 3. MECHANICAL & INDUSTRIAL ENGINEERING. *Educ:* Miss State Col, BS, 41; Ga Inst Technol, MS, 49; Johns Hopkins Univ, PhD(indust eng), 55. *Prof Exp:* Instr mech eng, Miss State Col, 46-48; asst prof indust eng, Ga Inst Technol, 48-51 & Johns Hopkins Univ, 51-54; assoc prof, 54-58, asst dean col eng, 56-61, assoc dean, 61-66, dean undergrad div, 66-77, PROF INDUST ENG, GA INST TECHNOL, 58-, DIR INST RES, 77- *Mem:* Am Soc Mech Engrs; Am Soc Eng Educ. *Res:* Academic administration. *Mailing Add:* Off of Inst Res Ga Inst of Technol Atlanta GA 30332

STATTON, GARY LEWIS, b New Brighton, Pa, Nov 4, 37; m 58; c 3. POLYMER CHEMISTRY. *Educ:* Geneva Col, BS, 59; Univ Fla, PhD(org chem), 64. *Prof Exp:* Res chemist, 64-66, SR RES CHEMIST, ATLANTIC RICHFIELD CO, 66- *Mem:* Am Chem Soc; Royal Soc Chem. *Res:* Organometallics; polymers. *Mailing Add:* 1392 Bittersweet Lane West Chesterfield PA 19380

STATZ, HERMANN, b Herrenberg, Ger, Jan 9, 28; nat US; m 53; c 2. PHYSICS. *Educ:* Stuttgart Tech Univ, MS, 49, Dr rer nat(physics), 51. *Prof Exp:* Res assoc, Max Planck Inst Metal Res, Ger, 49-50; Ger Res Asn fel physics, Stuttgart Tech Univ, 51-52; mem solid state & molecular theory group, Mass Inst Technol, 52-53; group leader, 53-58, asst gen mgr, 58-69, ASST GEN MGR & TECH DIR, RAYTHEON RES DIV, RAYTHEON CO, 69- *Mem:* Fel Am Phys Soc; fel Inst Elec & Electron Engrs. *Res:* Semiconductor physics, surfaces and devices; ferromagnetism; paramagnetic resonance; exchange interactions in solids; masers and lasers. *Mailing Add:* 10 Barney Hill Rd Wayland MA 01778

STATZ, JOYCE ANN, b Minn, July 21, 47. COMPUTER SCIENCES. *Educ:* Col St Benedict, Minn, BA, 69; Syracuse Univ, MA, 71, PhD(comput sci), 73. *Prof Exp:* Res assoc comput sci, Syracuse Univ, 72-73; asst prof comput sci, Bowling Green State Univ, 73-78; SYSTS PROGRAMMER, TEX INSTRUMENTS, 78- *Concurrent Pos:* Ed, SIGCUE Bull, Asn Comput Mach, 74-78. *Mem:* Asn Comput Mach; Inst Elec & Electronics Engrs Comput Soc. *Res:* Computer education; operating systems development; logo. *Mailing Add:* 1112 Red Cliff Austin TX 78758

STAUB, FRED W(OLF), b Apr 5, 28; US citizen; m 65; c 3. HEAT TRANSFER, FLUID DYNAMICS. *Educ:* Rensselaer Polytech Inst, BME, 52, MME, 53. *Prof Exp:* Heat transfer engr, Gen Eng Lab, 53-61, proj engr, Res & Develop Ctr, 61-67, mgr two phase processes, Gen Eng Lab, 67-68, MGR HEAT TRANSFER UNIT, CORP RES & DEVELOP CTR, GEN ELEC CO, 68- *Concurrent Pos:* US Atomic Energy Comn-Europ Atomic Energy Comn personnel exchange rep, France, 66; vis fel, Cambridge Univ, 79. *Honors & Awards:* Coolidge Fel, Gen Elec Co, 76; Melville Medal, Am Soc Mech Engrs, 80. *Mem:* Fel Am Soc Mech Engrs; Am Inst Chem Engrs. *Res:* Applied research and development in convective heat transfer and fluid flow radiation exchange processes; adiabatic and diabatic two phase flow processes. *Mailing Add:* 1186 Godfrey Lane Schenectady NY 12309

STAUB, HERBERT WARREN, b Brooklyn, NY, Aug 31, 27; m 55; c 1. NUTRITIONAL BIOCHEMISTRY. *Educ:* Syracuse Univ, AB, 54; Rutgers Univ, MS, 57, PhD(biochem, physiol), 60. *Prof Exp:* Asst, Rutgers Univ, 57-60; sr res specialist, 60-80, PRIN SCIENTIST, NUTRIT TECH CTR, GEN FOODS CORP, 80- *Concurrent Pos:* Mem coun arteriosclerosis, Am Heart Asn; adj prof nutrit, Pace Univ Westchester, 75- *Mem:* AAAS; Am Heart Asn; Am Chem Soc; Soc Nutrit Educ; Inst Food Technologists; NY Acad Sci. *Res:* Nutritional biochemistry; atherosclerosis; proteins; carbohydrates; enzymology; relationship of dietary carbohydrates to metabolic activity; protein quality evaluation and protein nutrition; dietary fiber. *Mailing Add:* Gen Foods Tech Ctr Prospect Plains Rd Cranbury NJ 08512

STAUB, NORMAN CROFT, b Syracuse, NY, June 21, 29; m 53; c 5. PHYSIOLOGY. *Educ:* Syracuse Univ, AB, 50; State Univ NY, MD, 53. *Prof Exp:* Intern, Walter Reed Army Med Ctr, Washington, DC, 54; instr physiol, Grad Sch Med, Univ Pa, 57-58; vis asst prof, 58-59, asst res physiologist, 59-60, from asst prof to assoc prof physiol, 60-70, PROF PHYSIOL, CARDIOVASC RES INST, MED CTR, UNIV CALIF, SAN FRANCISCO, 70-, MEM SR STAFF, 58- *Concurrent Pos:* Res fel physiol, Grad Sch Med, Univ Pa, 56-58. *Mem:* AAAS; Am Physiol Soc; Microcirc Soc (pres, 78-79); Int Soc Lymphology; Am Thoracic Soc. *Res:* Pulmonary physiology; pulmonary structure-function relations; kinetics of reaction of oxygen and hemoglobin; diffusion of oxygen and carbon monoxide; pulmonary capillary bed; pulmonary edema and blood flow; pulmonary lymph and lymphatics. *Mailing Add:* Cardiovasc Res Inst Univ of Calif San Francisco CA 94143

STAUB, ROBERT J, b Chicago, Ill, Jan 29, 22. ECOLOGY, BOTANY. *Educ:* St Mary's Col, Minn, BS, 43; Univ Minn, Minneapolis, MS, 49, PhD(ecol), 66. *Prof Exp:* Teacher high schs, Mo, Minn, Tenn & Ill, 43-50; instr biol, 50-53, assoc prof, 59-61, PROF BIOL, CHRISTIAN BROS COL, 70-, CHMN DEPT, 61- *Concurrent Pos:* Res grants, Dept of Interior, 67-69 & Environ Protection Agency, 70-72. *Mem:* Ecol Soc Am; Bot Soc Am; Am Water Resources Asn; Am Inst Biol Sci; Am Bryol & Lichenological Soc. *Res:* Plant variation; water pollution and its effects on phytoplankton; aquatic ecology. *Mailing Add:* Dept of Biol Christian Brothers Col Memphis TN 38104

STAUBER, WILLIAM TALIAFERRO, b East Orange, NJ, June 15, 43; m 70; c 1. PHYSIOLOGY. *Educ:* Ithaca Col, BS, 67; Rutgers Univ, MS, 69, PhD(physiol), 72. *Prof Exp:* NSF fel, Univ Iowa, 72-73, Muscular Dystrophy Asn fel physiol, 74-75, assoc physiol, 76-79; NSF fel, 72-73, muscular dystrophy asn fel physiol, 74-75, assoc physiol, 76-79; asst prof, 79-81, ASSOC PROF, WVA UNIV, 79- *Mem:* Sigma Xi; AAAS; Am Physiol Soc. *Res:* Physiology-pathology of skeletal muscle protein breakdown as related to organelle function and the involvement of lysosomes, peroxisomes and sarcoplasmic reticulum in autophagy. *Mailing Add:* Dept of Physiol WVa Univ Med Ctr Morgantown WV 26506

STAUBITZ, WILLIAM JOSEPH, b Buffalo, NY, Mar 19, 15; m 44; c 4. MEDICINE, UROLOGY. *Educ:* Gettysburg Col, AB, 38; Univ Buffalo, MD, 42. *Prof Exp:* Chmn urol, Roswell Park Mem Inst, 49-60; PROF UROL & CHMN DEPT, SCH MED, STATE UNIV NY COL BUFFALO, 60- *Concurrent Pos:* Chmn dept urol, Buffalo Gen Hosp, Buffalo Children's Hosp & Edward J Meyer Mem Hosp, 60-; consult, Roswell Park Mem Inst, 60-; consult & mem dean's comt, Vet Admin Hosp, 65-; mem, Residency Rev Comt Urol, 68- *Mem:* Can Urol Asn; Am Urol Asn; Am Col Surg; Am Acad Pediat; Am Asn Genito-Urinary Surg. *Res:* Carcinoma of the prostate; carcinoma of the testes; urinary tract infections. *Mailing Add:* Dept Urol Sch Med State Univ NY Buffalo NY 14214

STAUBUS, ALFRED ELSWORTH, b San Jose, Calif, Nov 20, 47; m 72. PHARMACOKINETICS, RADIOLOGY. *Educ:* Univ Calif, San Francisco, PharmD, 71, PhD(pharmaceut chem), 74. *Prof Exp:* ASSOC PFOR PHARMACEUT & PHARMACEUT CHEM, COL PHARM, OHIO STATE UNIV, 74- *Concurrent Pos:* Co-dir clin pharmacokinetic lab, Interdisciplinary Oncol Unit, Ohio State Univ Comprehensive Cancer Ctr, 77-; vis prof, Abbott Labs, North Chicago, 76. *Mem:* Am Pharmaceut Asn; Acad Pharmaceut Sci; Am Soc Hosp Pharmacists. *Res:* Pharmacokinetics of radio contrast agents, phase I-II anticancer agents and in vivo evaluation of sustained release narcotic antagonist formulations. *Mailing Add:* Ohio State Univ Col of Pharm 500 W 12th Ave Columbus OH 43210

STAUBUS, JOHN REGINALD, b Cissna Park, Ill, Mar 21, 26; m 51; c 1. DAIRY SCIENCE. *Educ:* Univ Ill, BS, 50, MS, 56, PhD(dairy sci), 59. *Prof Exp:* Asst dairy sci, Univ Ill, 54-59, res assoc, 59-60; from asst prof to assoc prof, 60-69, PROF DAIRY SCI, OHIO STATE UNIV, 69-, EXTEN SPECIALIST, 60- *Mem:* AAAS; Am Dairy Sci Asn; Sigma Xi; Am Soc Animal Sci. *Res:* Nutrition in dairy science; ruminant nutrition and physiology; bacteriology of silage; forage plant physiology and composition. *Mailing Add:* Dept Dairy Sci Ohio State Univ 2027 Coffey Rd Columbus OH 43210

STAUDENMAYER, RALPH, b July 28, 42; US citizen. METALLURGICAL ENGINEERING. *Educ:* Univ Calif, Los Angeles, BS, 66; Univ Ariz, MS, 68; Univ Ark, PhD(chem), 73. *Prof Exp:* Chief chemist metall, TRW Inc, Wendt Sonis, 73-80; MGR ENG, GEN ELEC MINING PROD, 80- *Mem:* Am Powder Metall Inst. *Res:* Powder metallurgy and gas deposition on cemented carbides. *Mailing Add:* 2823 Highland Dr Rogers AR 72756

STAUDENMAYER, WILLIAM J(OSEPH), b Rochester, NY, Jan 4, 36; m 63; c 2. CHEMICAL ENGINEERING. *Educ:* Clarkson Col Technol, BS, 57; Cornell Univ, PhD(chem eng), 63. *Prof Exp:* Develop engr, Mfg Exp Div, 57-59, res engr, Res Labs, 62-69, RES ASSOC, RES LABS, EASTMAN KODAK CO, 69- *Mem:* Soc Photog Sci & Eng. *Res:* Electrophotography; film coating techniques; photographic systems. *Mailing Add:* Res Labs Eastman Kodak Co 343 State St Rochester NY 14560

STAUDER, WILLIAM, b New Rochelle, NY, Apr 23, 22. GEOPHYSICS, SEISMOLOGY. *Educ:* St Louis Univ, AB, 43, MS, 48; Univ Calif, PhD(geophys), 59. *Prof Exp:* Instr, Marquette Univ High Sch, 48-49; res asst geophys, Univ Calif, 57-59; from instr to assoc prof geophys, 60-66, chmn dept earth & atmospheric sci, 72-75, PROF GEOPHYS, ST LOUIS UNIV, 66-, DEAN GRAD SCH/UNIV RES ADMINR, 75- *Concurrent Pos:* Mem geophys adv panel, Air Force Off Sci Res, 61-71; mem panel seismol, Comt Alaska Earthquake, Nat Acad Sci-Nat Res Coun, 64-72; mem adv panel, Nat Ctr Earthquake Res, 66-76; mem ad hoc comt triggering of earthquakes, AEC, 69-72. *Mem:* Fel Am Geophys Union; Seismol Soc Am (vpres, 64, pres, 65). *Res:* Focal mechanism of earthquakes; crustal structure in central United States; earth tides and long period seismic waves; seismicity of southeastern Missouri. *Mailing Add:* Grad Sch St Louis Univ St Louis MO 63103

STAUDHAMMER, JOHN, b Budapest, Hungary, Mar 15, 32; US citizen; m 60; c 2. ELECTRICAL ENGINEERING, COMPUTER GRAPHICS. *Educ:* Univ Calif, Los Angeles, BS, 54, MS, 56, PhD(eng), 63. *Prof Exp:* From asst to assoc eng, Univ Calif, Los Angeles, 54-59; sr syst engr, Syst Develop Corp, 59-64; prof eng, Ariz State Univ, 64-66; PROF ELEC ENG, NC STATE UNIV, 67- *Concurrent Pos:* Consult, various industs, 57-; designer, Douglas Aircraft Co, 59; tech adv, US Army Comput Systs Command, 76-77; nat lectr, Asn Comput Mach, 76-79; comput engr, US Army Res Off, 78-79. *Mem:* Am Soc Eng Educ; Inst Elec & Electronics Engrs; Asn Comput Mach. *Res:* Use of computers in circuit design; design and analysis of computer systems; system engineering. *Mailing Add:* Dept of Elec Eng NC State Univ Raleigh NC 27607

STAUDHAMMER, PETER, b Budapest, Hungary, Mar 4, 34; US citizen; m 58; c 3. ENGINEERING, PHYSICAL CHEMISTRY. *Educ:* Univ Calif, Los Angeles, BS, 55, MS, 56, PhD(eng, phys chem), 57. *Prof Exp:* Res engr, Univ Calif, Los Angeles, 55-57; sr res engr, Jet Propulsion Lab, Calif Inst Technol, 57-59; head, Chem Sect, 59-60, mgr, Propulsion Res Dept, 60-66, mgr, Design & Develop Lab, 66-73, mgr, Res Lab, 75-81, MGR ENERGY SYSTS OPERS, TRW INC, 81- *Honors & Awards:* Engr Achievement Award for Viking Biol Instr, Inst Advan Eng, 76. *Mem:* Fel Am Inst Aeronaut & Astronaut; Combustion Inst. *Res:* After burning of automobile exhaust; regenerable fuel cells; combustion and chemical kinetics of rocket propellants; developer of Apollo lunar module descent engine; space science instruments; fusion research. *Mailing Add:* 5060 Rolling Meadows Rd Rolling Hills Estates CA 90274

STAUDINGER, WILBUR LEONARD, plant pathology, microbiology, see previous edition

STAUFFER, ALLAN DANIEL, b Kitchener, Ont, Mar 11, 39; m 62; c 2. ATOMIC PHYSICS. *Educ:* Univ Toronto, BSc, 62; Univ London, PhD(appl math), 66. *Prof Exp:* Asst lectr math, Royal Holloway Col, 64-66; fel, 66-67, asst prof, 67-71, assoc prof, 71-81, PROF PHYSICS, YORK UNIV, 80- *Concurrent Pos:* Vis prof, Royal Holloway Col, London, 74-75. *Mem:* Am

Phys Soc; Can Operational Res Soc; Opers Res Soc N Am; Brit Inst Physics; Can Asn Physicists. *Res:* Theoretical atomic collisions; atomic structure problems. *Mailing Add:* Dept Physics York Univ 4700 Keele St Downsview ON M3J 1P3 Can

STAUFFER, CHARLES HENRY, b Harrisburg, Pa, Apr 17, 13; m 39; c 3. PHYSICAL CHEMISTRY. *Educ:* Swarthmore Col, AB, 34; Harvard Univ, AM, 36, PhD(chem), 37. *Prof Exp:* Lab asst org chem, Harvard Univ, 34-36, from instr to assoc prof chem, Worcester Polytech Inst, 37-58; prof & head dept, St Lawrence Univ, 58-65; prof & chmn div natural sci, 65-77, PROF EMER BATES COL, 77- *Mem:* Am Chem Soc. *Res:* Enolization of unsymmetrical ketones; gaseous formation and decomposition of tertiary alkyl halides; reaction kinetics; experimental and theoretical calculations of rates of reaction in gas and liquid phases. *Mailing Add:* 10 Champlain Ave Lewiston ME 04240

STAUFFER, CLYDE E, b Duluth, Minn, Nov 8, 35; m 58; c 2. BIOCHEMISTRY. *Educ:* NDak State Univ, BS, 56, MS, 58; Univ Minn, PhD(biochem), 63. *Prof Exp:* Res chemist, Procter & Gamble Co, 63-76; res chemist, Kroger Baked Foods Res & Develop, 76-81; DIR RES & DEVELOP, COLSO PRODS INC, 81- *Mem:* AAAS; Am Asn Cereal Chemists; Am Soc Biol Chemists; Sigma Xi. *Res:* Protein biophysical chemistry; enzymology; surface and interfacial adsorption from solution; immunochemistry. *Mailing Add:* COLSO Prods Inc PO Box 2 Hilliard OH 43026

STAUFFER, EDWARD KEITH, b Logan, Utah, July 6, 41; m 65; c 2. MEDICAL PHYSIOLOGY. *Educ:* Utah State Univ, BS, 64, MS, 69; Univ Ariz, PhD(physiol), 74. *Prof Exp:* Assoc, Col Med, Univ Ariz, 74-75; ASSOC PROF PHYSIOL, SCH MED, UNIV MINN, DULUTH, 75- *Mem:* Am Physiol Soc; Soc Neurosci; Sigma Xi; AAAS. *Res:* Neurophysiological studies of motor control with emphasis on afferent, central and efferent mechanisms found in the spinal cord. *Mailing Add:* Sch of Med Univ of Minn 2205 E Fifth St Duluth MN 55812

STAUFFER, GARY DEAN, b Wenatchee, Wash, Feb 26, 44; m 68; c 2. FISHERIES. *Educ:* Univ Wash, BS, 66, MS, 69, PhD(fisheries & statist), 73. *Prof Exp:* Fishery biologist salmon res, Quinault Resource Develop Proj, Quinault Tribal Coun, 71-72; FISHERY BIOLOGIST NAT MARINE FISHERY SERV, 73- *Res:* Stock assessment and fishery evaluation of pacific coast fisheries for developing management information. *Mailing Add:* Northwest & Alaska Fisheries Ctr 2725 Montlake Blvd East Seattle WA 98112

STAUFFER, GEORGE FRANKLIN, b Hanover, Pa, Oct 23, 07; m 31. ASTRONOMY. *Educ:* Millersville State Col, BS, 32; Univ Pa, MS, 38, EducD, 63. *Prof Exp:* Teacher pub sch, Pa, 26-27 & high schs, 29-57; PROF ASTRON, MILLERSVILLE STATE COL, 57- *Mem:* AAAS; Am Astron Soc; Nat Sci Teachers Asn. *Mailing Add:* 420 Herr Ave Millersville PA 17551

STAUFFER, HOWARD BOYER, b Philadelphia, Pa, Aug 10, 41. APPLIED MATHEMATICS. *Educ:* Williams Col, BA, 64; Univ Calif, Berkeley, PhD(math), 69. *Prof Exp:* Fel, Univ BC, 69-70; asst prof math, Calif State Univ, Hayward, 70-80; BIOMATHEMATICIAN, BC MINISTRY FORESTS, 80- *Concurrent Pos:* Fulbright prof, Nat Univ Malaysia, 74-75; res fel, Pac Forest Res Ctr, Victoria, BC, 75-76; vis instr, Univ BC, 78-80. *Res:* Mathematical, statistical and operations research applications in forestry; forestry applications. *Mailing Add:* Res Br Ministry Forests 1450 Government St Victoria BC V8W 3E7 Can

STAUFFER, JAY RICHARD, JR, b Lancaster, Pa, Apr 8, 51. AQUATIC ECOLOGY, ICHTHYOLOGY. *Educ:* Cornell Univ, BS, 72; Va Polytech Inst & State Univ, PhD, 75. *Prof Exp:* asst prof, 75-80, ASSOC PROF AQUATIC ECOL, APPALACHIAN ENVIRON LAB, UNIV MD, 80- *Concurrent Pos:* Mem, Pa Rare & Endangered Fishes Coun, 77- *Mem:* Am Inst Fishery Res Biologists; Am Fisheries Soc; Am Soc Ichthyologists & Herpetologists. *Res:* Zoogeography of freshwater fishes; status of rare and endangered fishes; temperature behavior of fishes; assessment of environmental stresses. *Mailing Add:* Ctr Environ & Estuarine Studies Univ Md Frostburg MD 21532

STAUFFER, JOHN RICHARD, b Findlay, Ohio, Oct 27, 52; m 80. STELLAR EVOLUTION, SPECTROSCOPY. *Educ:* Case Western Reserve Univ, BS, 74; Univ Calif, Berkeley, MS, 77, PhD(astron), 82. *Prof Exp:* FEL, HARVARD-SMITHSONIAN CTR ASTROPHYSICS, 81- *Res:* Emperical pre-main sequence evolutionary tracks for low mass stars; observational constraints on the physical process at work in active galaxy nuclei. *Mailing Add:* Harvard-Smithsonian Ctr Astrophysics 60 Garden St Cambridge MA 02138

STAUFFER, MEL R, b Edmonton, Alta, July 16, 37; m 58, 72; c 6. STRUCTURAL GEOLOGY. *Educ:* Univ Alta, BSc, 60, MSc, 61; Australian Nat Univ, PhD(geol), 64. *Prof Exp:* From asst prof to assoc prof, 65-75, PROF STRUCT GEOL, UNIV SASK, 75- *Concurrent Pos:* Vis lectr, Univ Alta, 64-65; Nat Res Coun fel, Univ BC, 65-66. *Mem:* Geol Asn Can. *Mailing Add:* Dept of Geol Sci Univ of Sask Saskatoon SK S7N 0W0 Can

STAUFFER, ROBERT ELIOT, b Chicago, Ill, June 9, 13; m 34; c 4. PHYSICAL CHEMISTRY. *Educ:* Mt Union Col, BA, 32; Harvard Univ, MA, 34, PhD(phys chem), 36. *Hon Degrees:* DSc, Mt Union Col, 58. *Prof Exp:* Asst electrochem, Harvard Univ, 34-36; res assoc, Eastman Kodak Co, 36-54, head, Emulsion Res Div, 54-71, asst dir, Kodak Res Labs, 71-78; RETIRED. *Concurrent Pos:* Instr, Rochester Inst Technol, 47-49. *Mem:* AAAS; Am Chem Soc; NY Acad Sci. *Res:* Theory of electrolytes; protein electrochemistry and composition; photographic emulsions; viscosities of strong electrolytes; photographic chemistry. *Mailing Add:* 353 Oakridge Dr Rochester NY 14617

STAUFFER, THOMAS MIEL, b Edmore, Mich, June 24, 26; m 54; c 2. FISH BIOLOGY. *Educ:* Mich State Univ, Lansing, BS, 49, MS, 66. *Prof Exp:* From fisheries technol fish res to supvr sea lamprey res, Mich Dept Conserv, 50-64; BIOLOGIST IN CHARGE FISH RES, MARQUETTE FISHERIES RES STA, 64- *Concurrent Pos:* Head, Great Lakes Res, Mich Dept Natural Resources, 64-72, anadromous fisheries res, 72-; assoc ed, Transactions of Am Fisheries Soc, 77-; mem bd tech experts, Great Lakes Fishery Comn, 80-81. *Mem:* Am Fisheries Soc; Am Inst Fisheries Res Biologists. *Res:* Determination of the cause of reproductive failure of planted lake trout and assessment of reproduction by coho and chinook salmon in the Great Lakes. *Mailing Add:* Marquette Fisheries Res Sta 484 Cherry Creek Rd Marquette MI 49855

STAUFFER, TRUMAN PARKER, SR, b Illmo, Mo, May 29, 19; m 45; c 1. PHYSICAL GEOGRAPHY. *Educ:* Univ Kansas City, BA, 61; Univ Mo, Kansas City, MA, 64; Univ Nebr, PhD(geog), 72. *Prof Exp:* From teacher geog to admin supt aide, Ft Osage Sch Dist, 61-68; from asst prof to assoc prof, 75-77, PROF GEOSCI, PROF GEOG, UNIV MO, KANSAS CITY, 77- *Concurrent Pos:* Coun mem, Underground Construct Res Coun, Am Soc Civil Engrs, 74-; consult, Union Carbide of AEC, 75. *Mem:* Asn Am Geogr; fel Geog Soc Am; Sigma Xi; Nat Coun Geog Educ; Int Conf Bldg Off. *Res:* Utilization and economic development of underground space for the conservation of space and energy by planned excavation and conversion of mined areas preserving the qualities of the surface. *Mailing Add:* Dept of Geosci Univ of Mo 5100 Rockhill Rd Kansas City MO 64110

STAUGAARD, BURTON CHRISTIAN, b Paterson, NJ, Aug 6, 29; m 53; c 4. EMBRYOLOGY. *Educ:* Brown Univ, AB, 50; Univ RI, MS, 54; Univ Conn, PhD(embryol), 64. *Prof Exp:* Dir med photog dept, RI Hosp, 50-52; sales rep, x-ray dept, Gen Elec Co, 54-58; instr zool, Univ NH, 61-64, asst prof, 64-67; res fel anat, Sch Med, Vanderbilt Univ, 67-68, asst prof, 68-70; PROF SCI & BIOL, UNIV NEW HAVEN, 70- *Mem:* AAAS; Am Soc Zoologists; Biol Photog Asn. *Res:* Morphological and functional changes of the developing mammalian embryo in preparation for independent existence; developmental biochemistry and anatomy of kidney, liver and placenta. *Mailing Add:* Dept of Biol Univ of New Haven New Haven CT 06505

STAUM, BARRY BENJAMIN, b Passaic, NJ, Nov 4, 44; m 69. INTERNAL MEDICINE, CLINICAL PHARMACOLOGY. *Educ:* Colgate Univ, AB, 66; Univ Pa, PhD(pharmacol), 70, MD, 73. *Prof Exp:* Res fel renal physiol, Univ Pa, 70-71; resident internal med, 73-75 & 77, clin fel hemat & oncol, 76-77, CLIN INSTR MED, UNIV CALIF, LOS ANGELES, 78-; PHYSICIAN EMERGENCY MED, JANZEN, JOHNSTON & ROCKWELL, 78- *Concurrent Pos:* Physician emergency med, Janzen, Johnston & Rockwell, 75-76; ed-in-chief, J Emergency Care, 80- *Mem:* Am Col Emergency Physicians; Am Col Physicians; Am Soc Nephrol. *Res:* Emergency medical care and health services delivery; critical care medicine; renal physiology; fluid and electrolyte disorders; acid-base balance; medical and health-care policy; emergency medical systems; medical implications of product liability. *Mailing Add:* 1520 Arizona Ave Santa Monica CA 90404

STAUM, MUNI M, b New York, NY, Oct 30, 21; m 46; c 2. RADIOCHEMISTRY, PHARMACEUTICAL CHEMISTRY. *Educ:* City Col New York, BS, 42; Columbia Univ, BS, 51; Univ Fla, PhD(pharmaceut chem), 61. *Prof Exp:* Develop chemist, Am Cyanamid Co, 53-57; sr res scientist, Olin Mathieson Chem Corp, 61-67; ASST PROF RADIOL, SCH MED, UNIV PA, 67- *Concurrent Pos:* Am Found Pharmaceut Educ fel. *Mem:* Am Chem Soc; Soc Nuclear Med. *Res:* Organic reaction mechanisms; pharmaceutical drug development; development of radioactive pharmaceuticals for diagnostic nuclear medicine. *Mailing Add:* Dept of Radiology Hosp-Univ of Pa Philadelphia PA 19104

STAUNTON, JOHN JOSEPH JAMESON, b Binghamton, NY, July 4, 11; m 39; c 6. INSTRUMENTATION, PATENTS. *Educ:* Univ Notre Dame, BSEE, 32, MS, 34, EE, 41; Midwest Col Eng, DEng, 69. *Prof Exp:* Jr engr mfg, Bantam Ball Bearings Co, Ind, 35-36; head physics dept, DePaul Univ, 36-38; engr instruments, Coleman Elec Co, Maywood, Ill, 38-44; dir res, Coleman Instruments, Inc, 44-56, sr staff scientist, 56-64; sr staff scientist instruments, Perkin-Elmer Corp, Ill, 64-68; TECHNICAL CONSULT, 68- *Honors & Awards:* Merit Award, Chicago Tech Socs Coun, 70. *Mem:* Fel Inst Elec & Electronics Engrs; Optical Soc Am; Sigma Xi. *Res:* Optical, electronic, thermal control and electrochemical instrumentation for clinical and chemical analysis. *Mailing Add:* 310 Wesley Ave Oak Park IL 60302

STAUSS, GEORGE HENRY, b East Orange, NJ, Mar 25, 32; m 59; c 2. PHYSICS. *Educ:* Princeton Univ, AB, 53; Stanford Univ, MS, 58, PhD(physics), 61. *Prof Exp:* PHYSICIST, US NAVAL RES LAB, 61- *Mem:* Am Phys Soc. *Res:* Nuclear magnetic resonance and electron paramagnetic resonance, principally in magnetically ordered compounds and semiconductors. *Mailing Add:* Code 5291 US Naval Res Lab Washington DC 20375

STAUT, RONALD, b New York, NY, Mar 30, 41; m 73; c 4. CERAMICS, PHYSICAL CHEMISTRY. *Educ:* Rutgers Univ, BS, 63, MS, 66, PhD(ceramics), 67. *Prof Exp:* Res assoc inorg chem & ceramics, Mat Res Group, 67-73, mgr, 73-81, DIR CORP RES & DEVELOP, GEN REFRACTORIES CO, 81- *Mem:* Am Ceramic Soc; Can Ceramic Soc. *Res:* Inorganic chemistry; glass-ceramics; refractories; glass; technical and electronic ceramics. *Mailing Add:* 321 Bala Ave Bala Cynwyd PA 19004

STAVCHANSKY, SALOMON AYZENMAN, b Mexico City, Mex, May 7, 47; m 70; c 2. PHARMACY, PHARMACEUTICS. *Educ:* Nat Univ Mex, BS, 69; Univ Ky, PhD(pharmaceut sci), 74. *Prof Exp:* Anal chemist, Nat Med Ctr, Mex, 68-69; develop pharmacist, Syntex Labs, Mex, 69-70; vis scientist, Sloan Kettering Inst Cancer Res, 74; asst prof, 74-80, ASSOC PROF PHARM, UNIV TEX, AUSTIN, 80-, BIOPHARMACEUT COORDR, DRUG DYNAMICS INST, 75- *Concurrent Pos:* Consult, Alcon Labs, 75- & Dept Health, Educ & Welfare, 76- *Mem:* Am Pharmaceut Asn; Am Chem Soc; Mex Pharmaceut Asn. *Res:* Analytical chemistry of pharmaceutical systems; protein binding; application of short lived isotopes for the identification of neoplastic tumors. *Mailing Add:* Col of Pharm Univ of Tex Austin TX 78712

STAVE, UWE, pediatrics, preventive medicine, see previous edition

STAVELY, JOSEPH RENNIE, b Wilmington, Del, May 28, 39; m 65; c 1. PLANT PATHOLOGY. *Educ:* Univ Del, BS, 61; Univ Wis-Madison, MS, 63, PhD(plant path, bot), 65. *Prof Exp:* Fel plant path, Univ Wis-Madison, 65-66; RES PLANT PATHOLOGIST, TOBACCO LAB, PLANT GENETICS & GERMPLASM INST, AGR RES SERV, USDA, 66- *Mem:* AAAS; Am Genetic Asn; Crop Sci Soc Am; Am Phytopath Soc. *Res:* Disease resistance in Nicotiana; tobacco leaf diseases, their epiphytology, histology, effect on tobacco physiology and quality, and relationship of leaf age to their development; diseases of cigar tobaccos. *Mailing Add:* Beltsville Agr Res Ctr West Agr Res Serv USDA Beltsville MD 20705

STAVER, ALLEN ERNEST, b Scribner, Nebr, Dec 5, 23; m 65; c 4. DYNAMIC METEOROLOGY. *Educ:* Univ Nebr, Omaha, BGen Ed, 56; NY Univ, MS, 59; Univ Wis-Madison, PhD(meteorol), 69. *Prof Exp:* Weather officer, Air Weather Serv, US Air Force, 43-67; asst prof, 69-72, ASSOC PROF METEOROL, NORTHERN ILL UNIV, 72- *Mem:* Am Meteorol Soc; Nat Weather Asn; Sigma Xi. *Res:* Dynamics and synoptic meteorology utilizing satellite data; modeling and computer programming of air pollution transport and diffusion. *Mailing Add:* Dept of Geog Northern Ill Univ De Kalb IL 60115

STAVINOHA, WILLIAM BERNARD, b Temple, Tex, June 11, 28; m 56, 67; c 3. PHARMACOLOGY, TOXICOLOGY. *Educ:* Univ Tex, BS, 51, MS, 54, PhD(pharmacol), 59. *Prof Exp:* From instr to asst prof pharmacol & toxicol, Med Br, Univ Tex, 58-60; chief toxicol res, Civil Aeromed Inst, Fed Aviation Agency, Okla, 60-68; assoc prof pharmacol, 68-72, PROF PHARMACOL, UNIV TEX MED SCH SAN ANTONIO, 72- *Concurrent Pos:* Asst res prof, Med Ctr, Univ Okla, 60, adj prof, 62; Sigma Xi res award, Univ Tex Med Br, Galveston. *Mem:* Soc Toxicol; Soc Neurochem; Soc Exp Biol & Med; Am Soc Pharmacol & Exp Therapeut; Int Soc Neurochem. *Res:* Neurochemistry; insecticides; adaptive mechanisms. *Mailing Add:* Dept Pharmacol Univ Tex Health Sci Ctr San Antonio TX 78284

STAVIS, GUS, b New York, NY, June 5, 21; m 44; c 3. ELECTRICAL ENGINEERING. *Educ:* City Col New York, BEE, 41; Fairleigh Dickinson Univ, MBA, 79. *Prof Exp:* Mem staff, Fed Telecommun Labs, Int Tel & Tel Corp, 41-44, assoc head, Air Navig Dept, 46-52; res assoc, Radio Res Lab, Harvard Univ, 45-46; mgr advan develop dept, 52-81, MGR RADAR ADVAN DEVELOP, KEARFOTT DIV, SINGER CO, 69- *Mem:* Fel Inst Elec & Electronics Engrs; Inst Navig. *Res:* Navigation and radar electronics techniques and systems, including microwave, sonar and optical radiation devices, propagation, transmitters, receivers and signal processing. *Mailing Add:* 19 Huff Rd Wayne NJ 07470

STAVITSKY, ABRAM BENJAMIN, b Newark, NJ, May 14, 19; m 42; c 2. IMMUNOLOGY. *Educ:* Univ Mich, AB, 39, MS, 40; Univ Minn, PhD(bact, immunol), 43; Univ Pa, VMD, 46. *Prof Exp:* Asst bact, Med Sch, Univ Minn, 42; bacteriologist, Dept Pediat, Univ Pa, 44-46; asst prof immunol, 47-49, from asst prof to assoc prof microbiol, 49-63, PROF MICROBIOL, SCH MED, CASE WESTERN RESERVE UNIV, 63- *Concurrent Pos:* Res fel immunochem, Calif Inst Technol, 46-47; NSF fel, Nat Inst Med Res, Eng, 58-59; bacteriologist, State Dept Health, Minn, 42 & Children's Hosp, Philadelphia, Pa, 44-46; estab investr, Am Heart Asn, 54-59; mem microbiol fel panel, USPHS, 60-63; expert comts immunochem & teaching immunol, WHO, 63-; ed, J Cellular Physiol, Wistar Inst, 66-74; mem microbiol test comt, Nat Bd Med Examr, 70-74; ed, J Immunol Methods. *Mem:* fel AAAS; Am Soc Microbiol; Am Asn Immunol. *Res:* Induction and regulation of cellular and humoral immunity. *Mailing Add:* Dept of Microbiol Case Western Reserve Univ Cleveland OH 44106

STAVN, ROBERT HANS, b Palo Alto, Calif, July 30, 40. OCEANOGRAPHY, GEOPHYSICS. *Educ:* San Jose State Col, BA, 63; Yale Univ, MS, 65, PhD(ecol), 69. *Prof Exp:* Lectr biol, City Univ New York, 67-70, instr, 70-71; asst prof, 71-77, ASSOC PROF BIOL, UNIV NC, GREENSBORO, 77- *Concurrent Pos:* Grant-in-aid, Univ NC, Greensboro, Res Coun, 71-82, univ res assignment leave, 79; res grant, NC Bd Sci & Technol, 74-75. *Mem:* Am Soc Limnol & Oceanog; Am Geophys Union; Ecol Soc Am; Biomet Soc; Optical Soc Am. *Res:* Aquatic ecology; physiological ecology; oceanographic optics; theory of the ecological niche; transmission and absorption of light by the ocean; energy-balance of air water interface. *Mailing Add:* Dept of Biol Univ of NC Greensboro NC 27412

STAVRIC, BOZIDAR, b Skopje, Yugoslavia, Oct 31, 26; Can citizen; m 58; c 2. ANALYTICAL TOXICOLOGY, NATURAL PRODUCTS. *Educ:* Univ Zagreb, BSc, 50, PhD(org chem), 58. *Prof Exp:* Lectr org chem, Univ Zagreb, 50-63, asst prof, 63; res scientist biochem, Health Protection Br, 65-72, res scientist toxicol, 72-80, RES SCI FOOD RES, FOOD DIRECTORATE, HEALTH PROTECTION BR, HEALTH & WELFARE CAN, 80- *Concurrent Pos:* Nat Res Coun Can fel biosci, 63-65. *Mem:* AAAS; Am Chem Soc; Soc Exp Biol & Med; Soc Toxicol; Am Col Toxicol. *Res:* Isolation and identification of mutagens and other naturally occuring toxic components in foods; experimentally induced hyperuricemia in animals for studies in the fields of hyperuricemia and hyperuricosuria. *Mailing Add:* Toxicol Res Div Hlth Protect Br Health & Welfare Can Ottawa ON K1A 0L2 Can

STAVRIC, STANISLAVA, b Celje, Yugoslavia, Nov 13, 33; Can citizen; m 58; c 2. BIOCHEMISTRY. *Educ:* Univ Zagreb, BSci, 59, PhD(biochem), 62. *Prof Exp:* Technician org synthesis, Fac Biochem & Pharm, Univ Zagreb, 56-57, technician radiobiol, Inst Rudjer Boskovic, 57-59, res assoc, 59-63; fel org synthesis, Dept Chem, Univ Ottawa, 64-65; RES SCIENTIST, BUR MICROBIOL HAZARDS, HEALTH PROTECTION BR, HEALTH & WELFARE CAN, 65- *Res:* Effects of irradiation on the metabolism of nucleic acids in bacteria; detection methods for bacterial enterotoxins; isolation and characterization of bacterial entrotoxins. *Mailing Add:* Bur Microbiol Hazards Health Protection Br Ottawa ON K1A 0L2 Can

STAVROLAKIS, J(AMES) A(LEXANDER), b Storrs, Utah, Oct 1, 21; m; c 5. MATERIALS SCIENCE, CHEMISTRY. *Educ:* Rutgers Univ, BS, 43; Mass Inst Technol, ScD, 49. *Prof Exp:* Engr, Gen Elec Co, 49-52; supvr, Armour Res Found, Ill Inst Technol, 52-55; asst mgr, Mallinckrodt Chem Works, 55-56; develop mgr, Crucible Steel Co, 56-61; mgr mat res & eng, Am-Standard Corp, 61-64, vpres develop & eng, 64-67, gen mgr, 67-70; pres, Glasrock Prod, Inc, 70-72 & StanBest, Inc, 73-77; DIR, GERBER PLUMBING FIXTURES CORP, 78- *Mem:* Am Soc Metals; Am Chem Soc; Am Ceramic Soc; Sigma Xi; Am Inst Chemists. *Res:* Refractory materials; physical testing; nucleonics; brass metallurgy; grey iron; vitreous china technology and compositions. *Mailing Add:* 4656 W Touhy Ave Chicago IL 60646

STAVROUDIS, ORESTES NICHOLAS, b New York, NY, Feb 22, 23; m 49; c 2. MATHEMATICS, OPTICS. *Educ:* Columbia Univ, AB, 48, MA, 49; Imp Col, dipl & Univ London, PhD, 59. *Prof Exp:* Asst math, Rutgers Univ, 50-51; mathematician, US Dept Navy, 51; mathematician, Nat Bur Stand, 51-54, in chg lens anal & design, 57-67; PROF, OPTICAL SCI CTR, UNIV ARIZ, 67- *Mem:* Fel AAAS; Soc Hist Technol; Am Math Soc; Soc Indust & Appl Math; Math Asn Am. *Res:* Geometric and physical optics; differential equations; differential geometry; diffruction; micro computers. *Mailing Add:* Optical Sci Ctr Univ of Ariz Tucson AZ 85721

STAY, BARBARA, b Cleveland, Ohio, Aug 31, 26. INSECT MORPHOLOGY, PHYSIOLOGY. *Educ:* Vassar Col, AB, 47; Radcliffe Col, MA, 49, PhD(biol), 53. *Prof Exp:* Asst biol, Harvard Univ, 52; Fulbright Scholar, Commonwealth Sci & Indust Res Orgn, Australia, 53-54; entomologist, Qm Res & Eng Ctr, US Dept Army, 54-59; Lalor fel, Harvard Univ, 59; vis asst prof zool, Pomona Col, 60; asst prof biol, Univ Pa, 61-67; assoc prof, 67-77, PROF ZOOL, UNIV IOWA, 77- *Mem:* Entom Soc Am; Am Soc Zoologists; Am Soc Cell Biol. *Res:* Histochemistry of blowfly during metamorphosis and larval blowfly midgut; histology of scent glands, physiology and fine structure of accessory reproductive glands in cockroaches; control of reproduction in cockroaches; regulation of corpora allata. *Mailing Add:* Dept of Zool Univ of Iowa Iowa City IA 52242

STEAD, EUGENE ANSON, JR, b Atlanta, Ga, Oct 6, 08; m 40; c 3. MEDICINE. *Educ:* Emory Univ, BS, 28, MD, 32. *Prof Exp:* Intern med, Peter Bent Brigham Hosp, Boston, 32-33, intern surg, 34-35; instr, Univ Cincinnati, 35-37; asst, Harvard Med Sch, 37-39, instr, 39-41, assoc, 41-42; prof, Sch Med, Emory Univ, 42-46, dean, 45-46; FLORENCE MCALISTER PROF MED, SCH MED, DUKE UNIV, 47- *Concurrent Pos:* Fel, Harvard Univ, 33-34; from asst resident to resident, Cincinnati Gen Hosp, 35-37; resident physician, Thorndike Mem Lab & asst, Boston City Hosp, 37-39; assoc med, Peter Bent Brigham Hosp, 39-42, actg physician-in-chief, 42; physician-in-chief, Univ Div, Grady Hosp, 42-46 & Duke Hosp, 47-67. *Mem:* Am Soc Clin Invest (secy, 46-48); Am Fedn Clin Res; Asn Am Physicians (secy, 62-67, pres, 71-72). *Res:* Cardiovascular studies. *Mailing Add:* Box 3910 Duke Hosp Durham NC 27710

STEAD, WILLIAM WHITE, b Decatur, Ga, Jan 4, 19; m 75; c 1. INTERNAL MEDICINE, PULMONARY DISEASES. *Educ:* Emory Univ, AB, 40, MD, 43. *Prof Exp:* Resident med, Emory Univ, 44-45, Univ Cincinnati, 46-47 & Univ Minn, 48-49; chief of serv pulmonary dis, Vet Admin Hosp, Minneapolis, Minn, 54-57; assoc prof, Col Med, Univ Fla, 57-60; prof, Med Col Wis, 60-72; chief pulmonary dis, Vet Admin Hosp, Little Rock, Ark, 72-73; DIR TUBERC PROG, ARK DEPT HEALTH, 73-; PROF PULMONARY DIS, UNIV ARK, LITTLE ROCK, 72- *Concurrent Pos:* Fel cardiol, Univ Cincinnati, 47-48; med dir, Muirdale Sanatorium, Milwaukee, 60-72; consult, Dept Med, Vet Admin Hosp, Little Rock, 73- & Arthur D Little Co, Mass, 74. *Mem:* AAAS; Am Soc Clin Invest; Am Fedn Clin Res (secy, 55-58, vpres, 58-59, pres, 59-60); Am Thoracic Soc; Am Col Chest Physicians. *Res:* Pulmonary physiology, development of spirometers; clinical and public health aspects of tuberculosis. *Mailing Add:* Ark Dept of Health 4815 W Markham St Little Rock AR 72201

STEADMAN, JAMES ROBERT, b Cleveland, Ohio, Feb 7, 42; m 64; c 4. PLANT PATHOLOGY. *Educ:* Hiram Col, BA, 64; Univ Wis-Madison, MS, 68, PhD(plant path), 69. *Prof Exp:* Asst prof bot & plant path, 69-74, ASSOC PROF PLANT PATH, UNIV NEBR-LINCOLN, 75- *Concurrent Pos:* Union Pac, Bean Indust, USDA & Chem Co grants, 80-82; consult, Latin Am & Australia, 80-82; Consult Latin Am & Australia, 80-82; US Aid title XII grant-bean improv, Dominican Repub, 81-86. *Mem:* Am Phytopath Soc; Sigma Xi; Int Soc Plant Path. *Res:* Epidemiology; vegetable diseases; pathogen dissemination in water; white mold disease; bean rust; plant disease and microclimate interaction; disease resistance; fungal sclerotia dormancy and germination. *Mailing Add:* Dept of Plant Path Univ of Nebr Lincoln NE 68583

STEADMAN, JOHN WILLIAM, b Cody, Wyo, Oct 13, 43; m 64, 76; c 2. ELECTRICAL ENGINEERING, BIOENGINEERING. *Educ:* Univ Wyo, BS, 64, MS, 66; Colo State Univ, PhD(elec eng), 71. *Prof Exp:* Res engr life sci res, Convair Div, Gen Dynamics Corp, Calif, 66-68; ASST PROF BIOENG & ELEC ENG, UNIV WYO, 71- *Mem:* Inst Elec & Electronics Engrs; Aerospace Med Asn. *Res:* Machine analysis of electroencephalograms; information processing in the nervous system; digital system design; microprocessor and microcomputer systems; electrical safety; microprocessor design. *Mailing Add:* Dept of Elec Eng Univ of Wyo Laramie WY 82071

STEADMAN, ROBERT GEORGE, b Sydney, NSW, Nov 8, 39; m 70; c 1. TEXTILES. *Educ:* Univ New South Wales, BSc, 61, PhD(textile physics), 65. *Prof Exp:* Officer in charge, Cotton Fiber Lab, NSW Dept Agr, 64-66; textile mgr, Australian Wool Testing Authority, 66-68; assoc prof clothing & textiles, Univ Man, 68-71; exec vol, Can Exec Serv Overseas, Nigeria, 71-72; asst prof clothing & textiles, Tex Tech Univ, 72-78; assoc prof, Dept Textiles & Clothing, Colo State Univ, 78-81; TEXTILE RES ENGR, TEXTILE RES CTR, TEX TECH UNIV, 81- *Mem:* Am Asn Textile Chemists & Colorists; Metric Asn. *Res:* Textiles as thermal insulators and application to human biometeorology; economics and physiology of clothing and textiles; consumer problems in textiles. *Mailing Add:* Textile Res Ctr Tex Tech Univ Lubbock TX 79417

STEADMAN, THOMAS REE, b Erie, Pa, Mar 15, 17; m 41; c 2. ORGANIC CHEMISTRY, PHYSICAL CHEMISTRY. *Educ:* Rensselaer Polytech Inst, BS, 37; Harvard Univ, AM, 38, PhD(org chem), 41. *Prof Exp:* Sr chemist org chem, B F Goodrich Co, 41-51; res assoc process res, Nat Res Corp, 51-57; mgr org chem res admin, W R Grace & Co, 57-68 & Allied Chem Corp, 68-72; sr chem economist consult, Battelle Mem Inst, 72-73. *Concurrent Pos:* Hormel Found fel, Univ Minn, 40-41; dir org chem res, Signal Oil & Gas Co, 68; adj prof chem eng, Ohio State Univ, 74. *Mem:* Am Chem Soc; Sigma Xi. *Res:* Beta-propiolactone; chemistry of formaldehyde; synthesis of amino acids; methionine and tryptophane; polyvinyl chloride additives; process chemistry; catalysts; water and air pollution; chemical economics; composite materials; high performance fibers; plastic composits. *Mailing Add:* Battelle Mem Inst 505 King Ave Columbus OH 43204

STEAR, EDWIN BYRON, b Peoria, Ill, Dec 8, 32; div; c 2. SYSTEMS SCIENCE, BIOMEDICAL ENGINEERING. *Educ:* Bradley Univ, BSME, 54; Univ Southern Calif, MS, 56; Univ Calif, Los Angeles, PhD(control & info systs), 61. *Prof Exp:* Mem tech staff missile syst design, Hughes Aircraft Co, 54-59; assoc res engr, Univ Calif, Los Angeles, 59-61; mgr, Control & Commun Lab, Lear Siegler, Inc, 63-64; assoc prof info systs, Univ Calif, Los Angeles, 64-69; PROF ELEC ENG, UNIV CALIF, SANTA BARBARA, 69-, CHMN DEPT ELEC ENG & COMPUT SCI, 75- *Concurrent Pos:* Mem, Am Automatic Control Coun, 63-; consult, several indust orgn, 64-; sr consult, US Air Force Space & Missile Test Ctr, 69-; mem, Sci Adv Bd, 71- *Mem:* Am Inst Aeronaut & Astronaut; Inst Elec & Electronics Engrs; NY Acad Sci. *Res:* Control systems theory; optimum filtering and data processing; biological control systems; computer analysis of electroencephalogram signals; technology for continuing education. *Mailing Add:* 3104 W Cumberland Ct Westlake Village CA 91361

STEARMAN, ROEBERT L(YLE), b Burley, Idaho, May 12, 23; m 47; c 2. SYSTEMS ANALYSIS. *Educ:* Ore State Univ, BS, 47, MS, 49; Johns Hopkins Univ, ScD(biostatist), 55. *Prof Exp:* US Pub Health Serv fel biostatist & virol, Johns Hopkins Univ, 55-56; biometrician, Nat Inst Arthritis & Metab Diseases, 56-57; sr biostatistician & supvr comput serv, Booz-Allen Appl Res, Inc, 57-61; prin statistician, Statist Sci Dept, Inst Adv Studies, Sci & Prof Serv Group, C-E-I-R, Inc, 61-68; chief, Systs Anal Div, Ft Detrick, Md, 68-71; chief, Anal Sci Off, US Army Biol Defense Res Labs, 71-72; chief, Systs Anal Div, US Army Edgewood Arsenal, 72-74; MATH STATISTICIAN, US ARMY DUGWAY PROVING GROUND, 74- *Mem:* Am Mgt Asn; Nat Contract Mgt Asn; fel Royal Statist Soc. *Res:* Experimental design and analysis; biometry; statistical-mathematical modeling; computer applications and systems analysis; operations research; medical and biological laboratory and assay procedures; administration; contract management. *Mailing Add:* 510B Peak Ave PO Box 536 Dugway UT 84022

STEARMAN, RONALD ORAN, b Wichita, Kans, June 8, 32; m 57; c 1. AEROSPACE ENGINEERING. *Educ:* Okla State Univ, BS, 55; Calif Inst Technol, MS, 56, PhD(aeronaut), 61. *Prof Exp:* Res fel aeronaut, Calif Inst Technol, 61-62; sr analyst math & physics, Midwest Res Inst, 62-66; assoc prof mech & aerospace eng, Univ Kans, 64-66; assoc prof aerospace eng, 66-77, PROF AEROSPACE ENG & ENG MECH, UNIV TEX, AUSTIN, 77- *Concurrent Pos:* Air Force Off Sci Res res grant, 66- *Mem:* Am Inst Aeronaut & Astronaut; Soc Exp Stress Anal. *Res:* Aeroelastic and structural dynamic characteristics of thin shell aerospace structures. *Mailing Add:* Dept of Aerospace Eng Univ of Tex Austin TX 78712

STEARN, COLIN WILLIAM, b Bishops Stortford, Eng, July 16, 28; m 53; c 3. PALEONTOLOGY, STRATIGRAPHY. *Educ:* McMaster Univ, BSc, 49; Yale Univ, PhD(geol), 52. *Prof Exp:* From asst prof to prof geol, 52-68, asst dean fac grad studies & res, 60-63, chmn dept geol sci, 69-74, LOGAN PROF GEOL, MCGILL UNIV, 68-, CHMN, DEPT GEOL SCI, 80- *Mem:* Geol Soc Am; Paleont Soc; Am Asn Petrol Geol; Geol Asn Can; Royal Soc Can. *Res:* Lower Paleozoic stratigraphy and paleontology; historical geology; fossil stromatoporoids; growth of West Indian reefs. *Mailing Add:* Dept of Geol Sci McGill Univ 3450 University St Montreal PQ H3A 2A7 Can

STEARNER, SIGRID PHYLLIS, b Chicago, Ill, Jan 10, 19. CARDIOVASCULAR PHYSIOLOGY, RADIOBIOLOGY. *Educ:* Univ Chicago, BS, 41, MS, 42, PhD(zool), 46. *Prof Exp:* biologist, Div Biol & Med Res, Argonne Nat Lab, 46-; RETIRED. *Mem:* AAAS; Radiation Res Soc; NY Acad Sci; Am Soc Cell Biol. *Res:* Late effects of ionizing radiations on the heart and vascular system, physiological and ultrastructural studies; other physiological effects of radiations on biological systems; pigmentation changes. *Mailing Add:* 154 Juliet Ct Clarendon Hills IL 60514

STEARNS, BRENTON FISK, b Chicago, Ill, July 28, 28; m; c 2. ENERGY CONVERSION. *Educ:* Pomona Col, BA, 49; Wash Univ, PhD(physics), 56. *Prof Exp:* Asst prof physics, Univ Ark, 54-57; from asst prof to assoc prof, Tufts Univ, 57-68; chmn dept physics, 68-74, assoc provost, 74-75, PROF PHYSICS, HOBART & WILLIAM SMITH COLS, 68- *Mem:* AAAS; Am Phys Soc; Am Asn Physics Teachers. *Res:* Applications of energy storage. *Mailing Add:* Dept of Physics Hobart & William Smith Cols Geneva NY 14456

STEARNS, CHARLES EDWARD, b Billerica, Mass, Jan 20, 20; m 42; c 6. GEOLOGY. *Educ:* Tufts Univ, AB, 39; Harvard Univ, MA, 42, PhD(geol), 50. *Hon Degrees:* LLD, Southeastern Mass Technol Inst, 62. *Prof Exp:* Asst geol, Tufts Univ, 41, instr, 41-42, 45, 46-48, asst prof, 48-51; asst prof, Harvard Univ, 51-54; assoc prof, 54-57, dean col lib arts, 54-67 & 68-69, actg provost, 66-67, PROF GEOL, TUFTS UNIV, 57- *Mem:* AAAS; Geol Soc Am. *Res:* Pleistocene stratigraphy; shoreline geomorphology. *Mailing Add:* 381 Boston Rd Billerica MA 01821

STEARNS, CHARLES R, b McKeesport, Pa, May 2, 25. METEOROLOGY. *Educ:* Univ Wis, BS, 50, MS, 52, PhD(meteorol), 67. *Prof Exp:* Asst meteorol, Univ Wis, 55-56; chief physicist, Winzen Res, Inc, 56-57; res assoc meteorol, 57-65, asst prof, 65-69, chmn, Inst Environ Studies, 72-74, PROF METEOROL, UNIV WIS-MADISON, 69- *Concurrent Pos:* Consult, Aberdeen Proving Ground, Md, 69- *Mem:* Am Meteorol Soc. *Res:* Micrometeorology, particularly boundary layer problems; evaporation from lakes; diffusion from power plants; antarctic meteorology. *Mailing Add:* Dept Meteorol Univ Wis 1225 W Dayton St Madison WI 53706

STEARNS, DAVID WINROD, b Muskegon, Mich, Mar 23, 29; m 48; c 5. STRUCTURAL GEOLOGY. *Educ:* Univ Notre Dame, BS, 53; SDak Sch Mines & Technol, MS, 55; Tex A&M Univ, PhD, 69. *Prof Exp:* Geologist, Shell Oil Co, 55-56 & Shell Develop Co, 56-66; from assoc prof to prof geol, Tex A&M Univ, 67-80, head dept, 71-80; DISTINGUISHED PROF, UNIV OKLA, 80- *Concurrent Pos:* Consult, Amoco Prod Co, 70- *Mem:* Am Geophys Union; Geol Soc Am; Am Asn Petrol Geologists. *Res:* Structural and mechanical relationships of laramide deformation in the Rocky Mountain forelands. *Mailing Add:* Col Geosci Univ Okla 601 Elm St Rm 438C Norman OK 73019

STEARNS, EDWIN IRA, b Matawan, NJ, Sept 3, 11; m 34; c 3. PHYSICAL CHEMISTRY. *Educ:* Lafayette Col, BS, 32; Rensselaer Polytech Inst, MS, 33; Rutgers Univ, PhD(phys chem), 45. *Prof Exp:* Physicist, Am Cyanamid Co, NJ, 33-43, chief physicist, 44-45, asst dir physics res, 45-51, mgr prod improv, Dyestuff Dept, 52-54, asst mgr, Midwest Territory, 54-59, tech mgr, Dyes Dept, 59-63, mgr sales develop, Dyes & Textile Chem Dept, 64-69, res assoc, 69-72; head dept textile sci, Clemson Univ, 72-77, PRES & CONSULT, E I STEARNS INC, 78- *Concurrent Pos:* Instr, Cooper Union, 38-39 & Adult Sch, Bound Brook, 40. *Honors & Awards:* Olney Medal, Am Asn Textile Chemists & Colorists, 67; Godlove Medal, Inter-Soc Color Coun, 67. *Mem:* Am Chem Soc; Am Asn Textile Chemists & Colorists (pres, 71-72); Inter-Soc Color Coun. *Res:* Photochemistry; phase rule; visual and infrared spectrophotometry; instrumentation; optical properties of pigments; spectrophotometer improvements; instrumentation in chemical processes. *Mailing Add:* 321 Woodland Way Clemson SC 29631

STEARNS, EUGENE MARION, JR, b Evanston, Ill, May 3, 32; m 55; c 3. BIOCHEMISTRY. *Educ:* Denison Univ, BA, 54; Purdue Univ, West Lafayette, MS, 61, PhD(biochem), 65. *Prof Exp:* Res fel, Hormel Inst, Univ Minn, 65-67, res assoc lipid biochem, 67-70, asst prof lipid biochem, 70-76; sect leader, 76-81, GROUP MGR BIOCHEM, CONKLIN CO INC, 81- *Mem:* AAAS; Am Chem Soc; Plant Growth Regulator Soc Am; Am Inst Biol Sci. *Res:* Plant growth regulators; plant tissue culture; biomass conversion to fuels; microbial biochemistry; plant growth regulators, tissue culture. *Mailing Add:* Res Ctr Conklin Co Inc Valley Park Dr Shakopee MN 55379

STEARNS, FOREST, b Milwaukee, Wis, Sept 10, 18; m 43, 56; c 4. ECOLOGY, BOTANY. *Educ:* Harvard Univ, AB, 39; Univ Wis, PhM, 40, PhD(bot), 47. *Prof Exp:* Asst bot, Univ Wis, 40-42, 46-47; instr bot exp sta, Purdue Univ, 47-49, asst prof, 49-57; botanist, Vicksburg Res Ctr, US Forest Serv, 57-60, proj leader forest wildlife habitat res, NCent Forest Exp Sta, 61-68; PROF BOT, UNIV WIS-MILWAUKEE, 68- *Mem:* AAAS; Ecol Soc Am (pres, 75-76); Bot Soc Am; Wildlife Soc; Am Inst Biol Sci (pres, 81-82). *Res:* Autecology of trees and shrubs; seed germination; early succession and productivity; wetland and urban ecology and phenology. *Mailing Add:* Dept Bot Univ Wis Milwaukee WI 53201

STEARNS, H(ORACE) MYRL, b Kiesling, Wash, Apr 24, 16; m 39; c 4. ENGINEERING. *Educ:* Univ Idaho, BS, 37; Stanford Univ, EE, 39. *Hon Degrees:* DSc, Univ Idaho, 60. *Prof Exp:* Asst to chief engr, Gilfillan Bros, 39-41; mem eng staff, Sperry Gyroscope Co, 41-43, head Doppler radar develop prog, 43-45; res engr in charge klystron res & develop mfg, 45-48; exec vpres & gen mgr, 48-57, pres, 57-64, DIR & CONSULT TO BD DIRS, VARIAN ASSOCS, 64- *Mem:* AAAS; Am Mgt Asn; fel Inst Elec & Electronics Engrs. *Res:* Automatic frequency control and ranging; radar; microwave tubes; engineering management. *Mailing Add:* 246 La Cuesta Dr Menlo Park CA 94025

STEARNS, HAROLD THORNTON, b Wallingford, Conn, Aug 25, 00. GEOLOGY. *Educ:* Wesleyan Univ, BS, 21; George Washington Univ, PhD(geol), 26. *Hon Degrees:* DSc, Wesleyan Univ, 78. *Prof Exp:* Asst geol, Wesleyan Univ, 19-21; mineral examiner, Gen Land Off, 21-23; asst geologist, US Geol Surv, 23-26, assoc geologist, 26-29, geologist, 29-36, sr geologist, 36-46, in charge Hawaiian groundwater invests & Pac invests, 43-46; CONSULT ENG GEOLOGIST, 46-; NSF RES ASSOC, HAWAIIAN INST GEOPHYS, 64- *Concurrent Pos:* Pres & dir, Waipio Land Co; consult, Armed Forces at Pac Bases, 41-45. *Honors & Awards:* Medal for Merit. *Mem:* Geol Soc Am; hon mem Hawaiian Rock & Mineral Soc. *Res:* Volcanology; groundwater; coral reefs; geology of dam and reservoir sites. *Mailing Add:* Box 158 Hope ID 83836

STEARNS, JOHN WARREN, b Santa Barbara, Calif, June 3, 33; m 67. NEGATIVE ION PRODUCTION, INTENSE NEUTRAL BEAM DIAGNOSTICS. *Educ:* Univ Calif, Berkeley, AB, 59, MS, 67. *Prof Exp:* PHYSICIST ATOMIC & PLASMA PHYSICS, LAWRENCE BERKELEY LAB, UNIV CALIF, 59- *Mem:* AAAS. *Res:* Low to high energy atomic and molecular cross-sections; low to medium energy surface interactions; beam-plasma-photon interactions; neutral beam development as related to magnetically confined fusion-plasma problems; beam-foil interactions. *Mailing Add:* Lawrence Berkeley Lab Bldg 5 Univ of Calif Berkeley CA 94720

STEARNS, MARTIN, b Philadelphia, Pa, Aug 16, 16; m 48; c 2. PHYSICS. *Educ:* Univ Calif, Los Angeles, BA, 43; Cornell Univ, PhD(physics), 52. *Prof Exp:* Res assoc, Carnegie Inst Technol, 52-57; staff scientist, Gen Atomic Div, Gen Dynamics Corp, 57-60; prof physics & chmn dept, 60-62, DEAN COL LIBERAL ARTS & PROF PHYSICS, WAYNE STATE UNIV, 62- *Concurrent Pos:* Consult, Ramo-Wooldridge Corp, 55. *Mem:* Fel Am Phys Soc. *Res:* High energy nuclear physics; plasma physics; bremsstrahlung and pair production; photoproduction of mesons; mesonic x-rays; nuclear reactors. *Mailing Add:* Col of Liberal Arts Wayne State Univ Detroit MI 48202

STEARNS, MARY BETH GORMAN, b Minneapolis, Minn; m 48; c 2. PHYSICS. *Educ:* Univ Minn, BS, 46; Cornell Univ, PhD(physics), 52. *Prof Exp:* Asst physics, Cornell Univ, 47-51; res physicist, Carnegie Inst Technol, 52-56, Univ Pittsburgh, 57 & Gen Atomic Div, Gen Dynamics Corp, 58-60; sr scientist, Sci Lab, Ford Motor Co, 60-77, prin scientist, 77-81; PROF PHYSICS, ARIZ STATE UNIV, 81- *Concurrent Pos:* Mem, Argonne Rev Panel, 78- *Mem:* Fel Am Phys Soc. *Res:* Photonuclear reactions; meson spectroscopy; thermoelectricity; solids; low energy nuclear physics; magnetism; Mössbauer effect and pulsed nuclear magnetic resonance studies; electron scattering; extended x-ray absorption fine structure studies; electronic structure of transition metals. *Mailing Add:* Ariz State Univ Tempe AZ 85281

STEARNS, RICHARD EDWIN, b Caldwell, NJ, July 5, 36; m 63; c 2. MATHEMATICS, COMPUTER SCIENCE. *Educ:* Carleton Col, BA, 58; Princeton Univ, PhD(math), 61. *Prof Exp:* Mathematician, Res Lab, Gen Elec Corp, 61-65, mathematician, Res & Develop Ctr, 65-71, mathematician, Corp Res & Develop, 71-78; PROF COMPUT SCI, STATE UNIV NY AT ALBANY, 78- *Mem:* Am Math Soc; Math Asn Am; Asn Comput Mach. *Res:* Game theory; computer science; automata theory. *Mailing Add:* Dept of Comput Sci State Univ NY Albany NY 12222

STEARNS, RICHARD GORDON, b Buffalo, NY, Apr 28, 27; m 50; c 2. GEOLOGY. *Educ:* Vanderbilt Univ, AB, 48, MS, 49; Northwestern Univ, PhD(geol), 53. *Prof Exp:* Asst state geologist, State Div Geol, Tenn, 53-61; from asst prof to assoc prof geol, 61-68, chmn dept, 67-76, PROF GEOL, VANDERBILT UNIV, 68- *Mem:* AAAS; Geol Soc Am; Am Asn Petrol Geol; Am Geophys Union. *Res:* Stratigraphy; structure; geophysics; hydrogeology. *Mailing Add:* Box 1615 Sta B Vanderbilt Univ Nashville TN 37235

STEARNS, ROBERT INMAN, b Atlanta, Ga, Feb 26, 32; m 66; c 2. INORGANIC CHEMISTRY. *Educ:* Loyola Univ, La, BS, 53; Tulane Univ, MS, 55, PhD(inorg chem), 58. *Prof Exp:* Res specialist, Cent Res Dept, Monsanto Co, Mo, 59-68; DIR RES, LORVIC CORP, 68- *Concurrent Pos:* Asst prof chem, Eve Div, Univ Mo-St Louis, 66-72, assoc prof, 72-78, prof 78- *Res:* Physical chemistry of fluorides in preventive dentistry; dental materials, cements and polymers; semiconductor materials research, particularly vapor phase depositon of single crystal thin films. *Mailing Add:* Lorvic Corp 8810 Frost Ave St Louis MO 63134

STEARNS, ROBERT L, b New Haven, Conn, July 28, 26; m 58; c 2. PHYSICS. *Educ:* Wesleyan Univ, BA, 50; Case Inst Technol, MS, 52, PhD(physics), 55. *Prof Exp:* Instr physics, Case Inst Technol, 52-55 & Queens Col, 55-58; from asst prof to assoc prof, 58-68, chmn dept, 62-64, 66-69 & 78-81, dean freshmen, 74-77, PROF PHYSICS, VASSAR COL, 68- *Concurrent Pos:* Vis assoc physicist, Brookhaven Nat Lab, 64-65; vis scientist, Europ Orgn Nuclear Res, Geneva, 70-71). *Mem:* Am Phys Soc; Am Asn Physics Teachers. *Res:* Neutron physics; scattering of cold neutrons from cyrstals and liquids; nuclear structure physics using high energy proton scattering; nuclear structure-mesic atoms and hypernuclear physics. *Mailing Add:* Dept of Physics Vassar Col Poughkeepsie NY 12601

STEARNS, S(TEPHEN) RUSSELL, b Manchester, NH, Feb 28, 15; m 39; c 3. CIVIL ENGINEERING. *Educ:* Dartmouth Col, AB, 37, CE, 38; Purdue Univ, MS, 49. *Prof Exp:* Jr engr, Gannett, Eastman & Fleming, Pa, 38-40; jr prof engr, Navy Yard, Philadelphia, 40-41, engr, Dry Docks Assoc, 41-43; instr, 43-45, asst prof civil eng, 45-53, assoc dean, 73-75, prof, 53-80, EMER PROF CIVIL ENG, THAYER SCH ENG, DARTMOUTH COL, 80-; CONSULT ENGR, 80- *Concurrent Pos:* Field engr, Boston Univ, Alaska, 53; chief appl res br, Snow, Ice, Permafrost Res Estab, US Dept Army, 54-55, consult, 55-60; sr res engr, Oper Res Inc, 62-64; mem, NH Transp Comn, 66, 68; chmn Lebanon, NH Airport Authority, 66-69; mem, NH Tomorrow Exec Comn, 70-72; mem hwy res bd, Nat Acad Sci; dir, NH Bd Regist Prof Engrs. *Mem:* AAAS; Nat Soc Prof Engrs; Am Soc Eng Educ; Am Soc Civil Engrs; AAUP. *Res:* Transportation engineering, environmental planning and design; soil mechanics and foundations; permafrost engineering. *Mailing Add:* Thayer Sch Eng Dartmouth Col Hanover NH 03755

STEARNS, STEPHEN CURTIS, b Kapaau, Hawaii, Dec 12, 46; m 71; c 2. LIFE-HISTORY EVOLUTION, EVOLUTIONARY ECOLOGY. *Educ:* Yale Univ, BS, 67; Univ Wis, MS, 71; Univ BC, PhD(zool), 75. *Prof Exp:* Miller fel, Univ Calif, Berkeley, 75-76, vis assoc prof zool, 76-77, Miller fel, 77-78; ASST PROF BIOL, REED COL, ORE, 78- *Mem:* Am Soc Naturalists; Soc Study Evolution; Ecol Soc Am; AAAS. *Res:* Evolution and ontogeny of life-history traits-age at maturity, fecundity, reproductive effort, size of young and longivity including theoretical work, field studies and laboratory experiments. *Mailing Add:* Biol Lab Reed Col Portland OR 97202

STEARNS, THOMAS W, b New York, NY, June 17, 09; wid; c 2. BIOCHEMISTRY. *Educ:* Univ Fla, BS, 34, MS, 37; Univ Minn, PhD(biochem), 40. *Prof Exp:* Asst, Univ Minn, 38-40; asst prof vet res, Iowa State Col, 40-46; asst prof chem, 46-49, assoc prof agr chem, 49-55, prof chem & asst chmn dept, 55-74, EMER PROF CHEM & ASST CHMN DEPT, UNIV FLA, 74- *Mem:* Am Chem Soc. *Res:* Physical chemistry bacteria; biochemistry foods; biosynthesis riboflavin. *Mailing Add:* 1731 NW 12th Rd Gainesville FL 32605

STEBBINGS, RONALD FREDERICK, b London, Eng, Mar 20, 29; m 52; c 3. PHYSICS. *Educ:* Univ Col, Univ London, BSc, 52, PhD(atomic physics), 56. *Prof Exp:* Scientist, Atomic Physics Lab, San Diego, Calif, 58-65; reader physics, Univ Col, Univ London, 65-68; prof physics & space sci, Rice Univ, 68-80, chmn dept space sci, 69-74; PROF SPACE PHYSICS, ASTRON PHYSICS & MASTER, JONES COL, JACKSONVILLE, FLA, 80- *Mem:* Am Phys Soc; Am Geophys Union. *Res:* Experimental atomic physics, particularly as it relates to problems of astrophysical or aeronomic interest. *Mailing Add:* Dept Space Physics & Astron Jones Col Jacksonville FL 32055

STEBBINGS, WILLIAM LEE, b Orange Co, Calif, Mar 1, 45; m 68; c 1. STRUCTURAL CHEMISTRY. *Educ:* Iowa State Univ, BS, 66; Univ Wis, PhD(org chem), 72. *Prof Exp:* sr chemist, 72-77, RES SPECIALIST, 3 M CO, 77- *Mem:* Am Chem Soc; Am Soc Mass Spectrometry. *Res:* Applications of mass spectrometry in analytical chemistry. *Mailing Add:* 3M Co 3M Ctr Bldg 201-BW St Paul MN 55133

STEBBINS, DEAN WALDO, b Billings, Mont, Jan 14, 13; m 37; c 1. PHYSICS, ACADEMIC ADMINISTRATION. *Educ:* Mont State Col, BS, 35; Iowa State Univ, PhD(appl physics), 38. *Prof Exp:* Instr physics, State Col Wash, 38-39 & Agr & Mech Col Tex, 39-41; asst prof, Lehigh Univ, 46-47; from assoc prof to prof, Iowa State Univ, 47-60; physicist, Rand Corp, Calif, 60-63; prof physics & head dept, Mich Technol Univ, 63-65, dean fac, 65-66, vpres acad affairs, 66-76; RETIRED. *Concurrent Pos:* Consult, Opers Anal Off, Hq, US Dept Air Force, 50-60, Radiation Lab, Univ Calif, 56-58, Westinghouse Elec Corp, Pa, 57 & Ramo-Wooldridge Corp, 59. *Mem:* AAAS; Am Phys Soc; Am Asn Physics Teachers. *Res:* Classical physics; geophysics; presence and distribution of matter; interplanetary and interstellar space. *Mailing Add:* RR4 Box 166 Ames IA 50010

STEBBINS, GEORGE LEDYARD, b Lawrence, NY, Jan 6, 06; m 31; 58; c 3. BOTANY. *Educ:* Harvard Univ, AB & AM, 28, PhD(biol), 31. *Hon Degrees:* Dr, Univ Paris, 62. *Prof Exp:* Asst bot, Harvard Univ, 29-31; instr biol, Colgate Univ, 31-35; jr geneticist, 35-39, from asst prof to prof, 39-73, EMER PROF GENETICS, UNIV CALIF, DAVIS, 73- *Concurrent Pos:* Jesup lectr, Columbia Univ, 46; Guggenheim fels, 54 & 60; secy gen, Int Union Biol Sci, 59-64; fac res lectr, Univ Calif, Davis, 62. *Honors & Awards:* Lewis Prize, Am Philos Soc, 60. *Mem:* Nat Acad Sci; Am Soc Naturalists (pres, 69); Bot Soc Am (pres, 62); Soc Study Evolution (vpres, 47, pres, 48); Am Philos Soc. *Res:* Cytogenetics of parthenogenesis in the higher plants; production of hybrid and polyploid types of forage grasses; natural selection, developmental genetics and morphogenesis of higher plants; mechanisms of evolution. *Mailing Add:* Dept of Genetics Univ of Calif Davis CA 95616

STEBBINS, RICHARD GILBERT, b Providence, RI, May 20, 43; m 77; c 3. PHYSICAL CHEMISTRY. *Educ:* Wesleyan Univ, BS, 65; Tex A&M Univ, PhD(phys chem), 70. *Prof Exp:* Asst prof, 70-76, ASSOC PROF CHEM, BETHANY COL W VA, 76- *Concurrent Pos:* Vis prof, Mont State Univ, 75-76. *Res:* Analysis of trace organics by API mass spectrometry and the electron capture detector. *Mailing Add:* Dept Chem Bethany Col Bethany WV 26032

STEBBINS, ROBERT CYRIL, b Chico, Calif, Mar 31, 15; m 41; c 3. ZOOLOGY. *Educ:* Univ Calif, MA, 41, PhD(zool), 43. *Prof Exp:* From instr to assoc prof, 44-58, prof zool, 58-78, EMER PROF ZOOL, UNIV CALIF, BERKELEY, 78- CUR HERPET, MUS VET ZOOL, 48- *Concurrent Pos:* Guggenheim fel, 49; ed, Am Soc Ichthyol & Herpet Jour, 55; NSF sr fel, 58-59. *Mem:* Soc Syst Zool; Am Soc Ichthyol & Herpet; fel Am Acad Zool. *Res:* Natural history and factors in the evolution of amphibians and reptiles; population studies of amphibians and reptiles; function of pineal apparatus; research development of biological science topics for schools; scientific illustrations. *Mailing Add:* Mus of Vertebrate Zool Univ of Calif Berkeley CA 94720

STEBBINS, ROBIN TUCKER, b Philadelphia, Pa, July 9, 48. SOLAR PHYSICS, PHYSICS. *Educ:* Wesleyan Univ, BA, 70; Univ Colo, Boulder, MS, 73, PhD(physics), 75. *Prof Exp:* Fel, Advan Study Prog, Nat Ctr Atmospheric Res, 75-76; res assoc, 76-77, ASST ASTRONR SOLAR PHYSICS, SACRAMENTO PEAK NAT OBSERV, 77- *Mem:* Am Phys Soc; Optical Soc Am; Am Astron Soc; AAAS. *Res:* Global properties of the sun; relativity; fundamental tests. *Mailing Add:* Sacramento Peak Nat Observ Sunspot NM 88349

STEBBINS, WILLIAM COOPER, b Watertown, NY, June 6, 29; m 53; c 3. BIOACOUSTICS, COMPARATIVE PERCEPTION. *Educ:* Yale Univ, BA, 51; Columbia Univ, MA, 54, PhD(psychol), 57. *Prof Exp:* Res assoc otol, NY Univ Med Ctr, 57; asst prof psychol, Hamilton Col, 57-61; fel neurophsyiol, Med Sch, Univ Wash, 61-63; from asst prof to assoc prof psychol & otorhinolaryngol, 63-70, PROF PSYCHOL & OTORHINOLARYNGOL, MED SCH, UNIV MICH, ANN ARBOR, 70- *Concurrent Pos:* Prin investr, Sigma Xi res grants, 60-61; prin investr, NIH res grants, 60-61 & 64-; fel, Univ Wash, 61-63; prin investr, NSF res grants, 74-; mem commun disorders rev comt, Nat Inst Neurol & Commun Disorders & Stroke, 76-80; mem, Comt Hearing, Bioacoust & Biomech, Nat Res Coun, 80- *Mem:* Fel AAAS; fel Acoust Soc Am; Int Primatol Soc; Asn Res Otolaryngol. *Res:* Comparative bioacoustics and the evolution of hearing, methodology in animal psychophysics, hearing and auditory perception in nonhuman primates. *Mailing Add:* Kresge Hearing Res Inst Med Sch Univ Mich Ann Arbor MI 48109

STEBELSKY, IHOR, b Krakow, Poland, Sept 6, 39; Can citizen; m 63; c 3. ENVIRONMENTAL SCIENCES, EARTH SCIENCES. *Educ:* Univ Toronto, BA, 62, MA, 64; Univ Wash, PhD(geog), 67. *Prof Exp:* Res asst geog, Univ Wash, 65-67; res assoc, 68; asst prof, 68-72, ASSOC PROF GEOG, UNIV WINDSOR, 72- *Concurrent Pos:* Russian & Far Eastern Inst res assoc, Univ Wash & Moscow & Lenningrad, USSR, 68; Ont Dept Univ Affairs grant, Univ Windsor, 70-71; Can Coun res grant, 74; Can Coun-Acad Sci USSR travel grant, 76; External Affairs travel grant, United Kingdom, 77. *Mem:* Am Asn Advan Slavic Studies; Am Geog Soc; Asn Am Geog; Can Asn Geog; Can Asn Slavists. *Res:* Geography of agricultural resources; agricultural resources of Russia; historical geography of the Soviet Union, with emphasis on population migration; land use and occupance; environmental impact. *Mailing Add:* Dept of Geog Univ of Windsor Windsor ON N9B 3P4 Can

STEBEN, JOHN D, b Hinsdale, Ill, Feb 27, 36; m 59; c 2. PHYSICS, COMPUTER SCIENCE. *Educ:* Univ Ill, BS, 58, MS, 59, PhD(physics), 65. *Prof Exp:* Physicist, Midwest Univs Res Asn, 65-67; physicist phys sci lab, Univ Wis-Madison, 67-74, lectr nuclear eng, 70-74; asst prof radiation ther, 74-77, lectr radiation technol, 78, SR SYSTS ANALYST MGR SERV, THOMAS JEFFERSON UNIV, 76-, ADJ ASST PROF, DEPT NEUROL, 79- *Mem:* Inst Elec & Electronics Engrs; Sigma Xi; Am Phys Soc. *Res:* Nuclear physics, particle accelerator physics; plasma and medical physics, neurologic studies; computer methods in these areas. *Mailing Add:* 301 Edison Bldg Thomas Jefferson Univ 11th & Walnut Sts Philadelphia PA 19107

STEBER, GEORGE RUDOLPH, b West Milwaukee, Wis, Sept 25, 38; m 64; c 2. ELECTRICAL ENGINEERING. *Educ:* Univ Wis-Milwaukee, BS, 63, MS, 66; Marquette Univ, PhD(elec eng), 69. *Prof Exp:* From instr to asst prof, 63-71, ASSOC PROF ELEC ENG, UNIV WIS-MILWAUKEE, 71-, ASST DEAN SCH ENG & APPL SCI, 77- *Concurrent Pos:* Grants, NSF & Wis Dept Natural Resources. *Mem:* Inst Elec & Electronics Engrs; Simulation Coun; Am Soc Eng Educ. *Res:* Control theory; hybrid computers and systems; electronic circuits; minicomputer interfacing; air pollution control. *Mailing Add:* Sch of Eng & Appl Sci Univ of Wis Milwaukee WI 53201

STECHER, EMMA DIETZ, b Brooklyn, NY, 1905; m 44. ORGANIC CHEMISTRY. *Educ:* Columbia Univ, BA, 25, MA, 26; Bryn Mawr Col, PhD(chem), 29. *Prof Exp:* Res chemist, Harvard Univ, 29-34; Am Asn Univ Women Berliner fel, Univ Munich, 34-35; res chemist, Exp Sta, Hercules Powder Co, Del, 35-37; lectr, Moravian Col Women, 38-41; res chemist, Merck & Co, Inc, NJ, 41; asst prof, Conn Col, 41-43; res chemist, Gen Aniline & Film Corp, Pa, 43-45; from instr to prof org chem, 45-71, EMER PROF ORG CHEM, BARNARD COL, COLUMBIA UNIV, 71- *Concurrent Pos:* Adj prof, Pace Univ, 71- *Mem:* AAAS; Sigma Xi; Am Chem Soc; NY Acad Sci. *Res:* Microanalysis; diazotype paper; chlorophyll; unsaturated ketoacids and lactones; synthesis and oxidation potentials of benzanthraquinones. *Mailing Add:* 423 W 120th St New York NY 10027

STECHER, MICHAEL, b Milwaukee, Wis, Feb 8, 42; m 64; c 3. MATHEMATICS. *Educ:* Univ Wis-Milwaukee, BS, 64, MS, 65; Ind Univ, PhD(math), 73. *Prof Exp:* ASST PROF MATH, TEX A&M UNIV, 73- *Mem:* Am Math Soc; Soc Indust & Appl Math. *Res:* Partial differential equations; integral equations. *Mailing Add:* Dept of Math Tex A&M Univ College Station TX 77843

STECHER, THEODORE P, b Kansas City, Mo, Dec 15, 30; m 56; c 4. ASTRONOMY. *Educ:* Univ Iowa, BA, 53, MS, 56. *Prof Exp:* Head, Observ Astron Br, 72-77, astronomer, 59-76, SPACE SHUTTLE SPACELAB PROJ DISCIPLINE SCIENTIST FOR ASTRON, NASA GODDARD SPACE FLIGHT CTR, 76- *Concurrent Pos:* Mem space sci sub-comt astron, NASA, 68-70; independent res fel, Goddard Space Flight Ctr, 71-72; vis fel, Joint Inst Lab Astrophys, Univ Colo/Nat Bur Standards, 71-72; US proj scientist, Astron Netherlands Satellite; prin investr, Ultraviolet Imaging Telescope, Spacelab, 79- & mission scientist, OSS-3 payload & flight, 81- *Honors & Awards:* John C Lindsay Mem Award, NASA, 66. *Mem:* Am Astron Soc; Int Astron Union; fel Royal Astron Soc. *Res:* Ultraviolet stellar spectrophotometry from rockets; stellar physics; interstellar grains and molecules; space instrumentation; gum nebula; gaseous nebulae; galaxies. *Mailing Add:* Code 680 Goddard Space Flight Ctr Greenbelt MD 20771

STECHSCHULTE, AGNES LOUISE, b Owosso, Mich, Jan 9, 24. BIOLOGY, MICROBIOLOGY. *Educ:* Siena Heights Col, BS, 47; Detroit Univ, MS, 53; Cath Univ, PhD(biol), 61. *Prof Exp:* Teacher, St Dominic Elem Sch, 43-46 & St Agatha Elem Sch, 46-48, St Ambrose High Sch, 48-53 & Aquinas High Sch, 53-57; from instr to asst prof, 60-70, chmn dept, 61-72, PROF BIOL, BARRY COL, 70- *Concurrent Pos:* NIH res grant, 62-65. *Mem:* AAAS; Am Soc Microbiol; Nat Asn Biol Teachers; NY Acad Sci. *Res:* Lysozyme resistant mutants. *Mailing Add:* Dept of Biol Barry Col 11300 NE 2nd Ave Miami FL 33161

STECK, DANIEL JOHN, b Calumet, Mich, Mar 2, 46; m 70. NUCLEAR PHYSICS, COMPUTER SCIENCE. *Educ:* Univ Mich, BS, 68; Univ Wis-Madison, MS, 70, PhD(physics), 76. *Prof Exp:* Staff physics, Los Alamos Sci Lab, 68; asst, Univ Wis-Madison, 68-69, res asst nuclear physics, 69-76; ASST PROF PHYSICS, ST JOHNS UNIV, 77- *Concurrent Pos:* Dir comput graphics develop physics curric, St Johns Univ, 78- *Mem:* Am Phys Soc. *Res:* Low energy nuclear structure; environmental radioactivity; airborne particle pollution; computer assisted data analysis and control; solar and energy efficient housing. *Mailing Add:* Eagle River MI 49924

STECK, EDGAR ALFRED, b Philadelphia, Pa, Dec 24, 18; m 47; c 2. ORGANIC CHEMISTRY. *Educ:* Temple Univ, AB, 39; Univ Pa, MS, 41, PhD(org chem), 42. *Prof Exp:* Asst bact, Temple Univ, 36-39; sr res org chemist, Winthrop Chem Co, 42-46; assoc mem, Sterling-Winthrop Res Inst, 46-56, mem, 56-58; med res group leader, Res Ctr, Johnson & Johnson, 58-60; dir res, Wilson Labs, 60-61; sr scientist, Nalco Chem Co, 61-65; dir res, McKesson Labs, 65-67; PROJ DIR, WALTER REED ARMY INST RES, 67- *Concurrent Pos:* Consult, chemotherapy of parasitic dis, WHO, 77- *Mem:* Am Soc Trop Med & Hyg; Am Chem Soc; The Chem Soc; Royal Soc Trop Med & Hyg; Swiss Chem Soc. *Res:* Chemotherapy of parasitic diseases; liposomes; nitrogen heterocyclic compounds; chemotherapy of parasitic diseases. *Mailing Add:* Walter Reed Army Inst Res Walter Reed Army Med Ctr Washington DC 20012

STECK, THEODORE LYLE, b Chicago, Ill, May 3, 39; m 61; c 2. BIOCHEMISTRY. *Educ:* Lawrence Col, BS, 60; Harvard Univ, MD, 64. *Prof Exp:* Intern med, Beth Israel Hosp, Boston, 64-65; res fel, Sch Med, Harvard Univ, 65-66, 68-70 & Mass Gen Hosp, 68-70; res assoc, Nat Cancer Inst, 66-68; asst prof med, 70-73, asst prof biochem, 73-74, assoc prof biochem & med, 74-77, PROF BIOCHEM & MED, UNIV CHICAGO, ASSOC CHMN BIOCHEM, 76- *Concurrent Pos:* Schweppe Found fel, 71; fac res award, Am Cancer Soc, 75, mem adv comt biochem & chem carcinogenesis, 75-78. *Mem:* AAAS; Am Soc Biol Chemists. *Res:* Membrane biochemistry; molecular basis of membrane structure and function, especially in the erythrocyte and cellular slime mold. *Mailing Add:* 920 E 58th St Chicago IL 60637

STECK, WARREN FRANKLIN, b Regina, Sask, May 10, 39; m 63; c 2. ORGANIC CHEMISTRY, ENTOMOLOGY. *Educ:* McGill Univ, BEng, 60; Univ Sask, PhD(org chem), 64. *Prof Exp:* Res assoc, Okla Univ Res Inst, 63-64; asst res officer, 64-70, assoc res officer, 70-76, sr res officer, 76-80, asst dir, 80-81, ASSOC DIR ORG CHEM, NAT RES COUN CAN, 82. *Mem:* Phytochem Soc NAm; Can Entom Soc; Entom Soc Am. *Res:* Insect sex attractants and pheromones; chemical ecology. *Mailing Add:* Prairie Regional Lab Nat Res Coun Can Saskatoon SK S7N 0W9 Can

STECKER, FLOYD WILLIAM, b New York, NY, Aug 12, 42; m 65; c 2. PHYSICS, ASTRONOMY. *Educ:* Mass Inst Technol, SB, 63; Harvard Univ, AM, 65, PhD(astrophys), 68. *Prof Exp:* Res assoc astrophys, NASA-Nat Res Coun, 67-68; astrophysicist, Lab Theoret Studies, 68-71, astrophysicist, Lab Space Physics, 71-77, SR ASTROPHYSICIST, LAB HIGH ENERGY ASTROPHYS, GODDARD SPACE FLIGHT CTR, NASA, 77- *Mem:* Am Astron Soc; fel Am Phys Soc; Int Astron Union. *Res:* High-energy astrophysics; cosmic-ray physics; gamma-ray astronomy and cosmology; infrared astrophysics; neutrino astrophysics; galaxy structure. *Mailing Add:* High Energy Astrophys Lab Goddard Space Flight Ctr NASA Greenbelt MD 20771

STECKL, ANDREW JULES, US citizen. SEMICONDUCTOR DEVICES, INTEGRATED CIRCUITS. *Educ:* Princeton Univ, BSE, 68; Univ Rochester, MS, 70, PhD(eng), 73. *Prof Exp:* Sr res engr, Honeywell Radiation Ctr, 72-73; mem tech staff, Rockwell Electronics Res Ctr, 73-76; ASSOC PROF IR DETECTORS & SOLID STATE DEVICES, RENSSELAER POLYTECH INST, 76- *Concurrent Pos:* Fac fel, T J Watson Res Ctr, IBM, 77. *Mem:* Am Phys Soc; Inst Elec & Electronics Engrs; Electron Devices Soc. Soc. *Res:* Semiconductors and solid state devices; integrated circuits and infrared detectors. *Mailing Add:* Dept of Elec & Systs Eng Rensselaer Polytech Inst Troy NY 12181

STECKLER, BERNARD MICHAEL, b Hebron, NDak, Jan 23, 32; m 54; c 4. ORGANIC CHEMISTRY, EDUCATIONAL ADMINISTRATION. *Educ:* St Martins Col, BS, 53; Univ Wash, PhD(org chem), 57. *Prof Exp:* Chemist, Nat Bur Standards, Washington, DC, 53, Northwest Labs, 54 & Shell Develop Co, 57-61; assoc prof, 61-75, PROF CHEM, SEATTLE UNIV, 75- *Mem:* AAAS; Am Chem Soc. *Res:* History and philosophy of science; interdisciplinary approaches to teaching physical science; integration of humanities and science disciplines; non-traditional studies curriculum development; phosphorus in delocalized pi-electron systems. *Mailing Add:* Dept of Chem Seattle Univ Seattle WA 98122

STECKLER, ROBERT, b Vienna, Austria, Nov 27, 14; nat US; m 49; c 1. CHEMISTRY. *Educ:* Univ Vienna, PhD, 38. *Prof Exp:* Asst, Graz Univ, 36; res mgr resins & plastics div, Arco Co, 40-45; mgr, R Steckler Labs, Ohio, 45-68; pres, Permacryl, Inc, Ohio, 67-68; vpres res, Alcolac Inc, 68-74; RETIRED. *Mem:* Fel AAAS; fel Am Inst Chem; Asn Consult Chemists & Chem Eng (pres, 61-62). *Res:* Acrylics, epoxies, polyesters; polymers; plastics; protective coatings; functional monomers; surfactants; hydrogels and long wear softlenses. *Mailing Add:* 27785 Via Espinoza Mission Viejo CA 92692

STEDINGER, JERY RUSSELL, b Oakland, Calif, June 22, 51; m 73; c 2. WATER RESOURCES PLANNING, STATISTICAL HYDROLOGY. *Educ:* Univ Calif, Berkeley, AB, 72; Harvard Univ, AM, 74, PhD(eng), 77. *Prof Exp:* ASST PROF ENVIRON ENG, CORNELL UNIV, 77- *Mem:* Am Geophys Union; Am Soc Civil Engrs; Inst Mgt Sci; Sigma Xi. *Res:* Application of statistics and scientific management techniques to problems in environmental engineering and water resources planning; reservoir operation and management; analysis of groundwater resources. *Mailing Add:* Hollister Hall Cornell Univ Ithaca NY 14853

STEDMAN, DONALD HUGH, b Dundee, Scotland, Feb 8, 43; m 64; c 3. ATMOSPHERIC CHEMISTRY. *Educ:* Cambridge Univ, BA, 64; Univ EAnglia, MSc, 65, PhD(chem), 67. *Prof Exp:* US Dept Health Educ & Welfare grant, Kans State Univ, 67-69; sr res scientist air pollution chem, Sci Res Labs, Ford Motor Co, 69-72; vis lectr atmospheric chem, Inst Environ Qual, 72-73, asst prof, 73-80, ASSOC PROF CHEM & ATMOSPHERIC & OCEANIC SCI, UNIV MICH, ANN ARBOR, 80- *Mem:* AAAS; The Chem Soc; Am Chem Soc; Am Phys Soc. *Res:* Gas phase chemical kinetics and spectroscopy of small molecules, particularly as related to aeronomy, atmospheric chemistry and air pollution; trace analysis of atmospheric pollutants. *Mailing Add:* Dept of Chem Univ of Mich Ann Arbor MI 48109

STEDMAN, ROBERT JOHN, b Marlow, Eng, Jan 28, 29; wid; c 2. ORGANIC CHEMISTRY. *Educ:* Cambridge Univ, BA, 49, MA & PhD(chem), 52. *Prof Exp:* Fel chem, Nat Res Coun Can, 52-54; res assoc, Med Col, Cornell Univ, 54-56; res assoc, Banting Inst, Univ Toronto, 57-58; res chemist, Chas Pfizer & Co, Conn, 58-60 & Smith Kline & French Labs, Pa, 60-69; assoc prof phys org chem, 69-76, PROF MED CHEM, SCH PHARM, TEMPLE UNIV, 76- *Concurrent Pos:* Consult, Smith Kline & French Labs, Pa, 79- *Mem:* AAAS; Am Chem Soc; The Chem Soc. *Res:* Natural products and medicinals; nuclear magnetic resonance spectroscopy. *Mailing Add:* Health Sci Ctr Temple Univ Sch Pharm Philadelphia PA 19140

STEEG, CARL W, JR, b Indianapolis, Ind, Aug 17, 22; m 46; c 2. APPLIED MATHEMATICS. *Educ:* DePauw Univ, AB, 43; Mass Inst Technol, PhD(math), 52. *Prof Exp:* Instr math, Mass Inst Technol, 47-52, res mathematician, 52-56; mgr anal & simulation, Airborne Systs Lab, Radio Corp Am, 56-59, systs engr, Missile Electronics & Controls Div, 59-61, systs engr Saturn projs, Aerospace Communications & Controls, 61-63; dir tech planning, Indust Labs Div, Int Tel & Tel Corp, 63, dir prod develop, 63-69;

PROF ELEC ENG, PURDUE UNIV, FT WAYNE, 69- *Concurrent Pos:* Lectr, St Francis Col, 69-; vis lectr, Trent Polytech, Nottingham, Eng, Dept of Elec & Electronic Eng, 77-78. *Mem:* Fel AAAS; Am Math Soc; Am Chem Soc. *Res:* Applications of statistical theory to the optimization of electronic and optical filters and predictors and in non-linear, adaptive and sampled-data control systems for video and other electronic signal enhancement. *Mailing Add:* Dept of Elec Eng Purdue Univ Ft Wayne IN 46805

STEEGE, DEBORAH ANDERSON, b Boston, Mass, Oct 2, 46. BIOCHEMISTRY, MOLECULAR BIOLOGY. *Educ:* Stanford Univ, BA, 68; Yale Univ, PhD(molecular biophys, biochem), 74. *Prof Exp:* Fel molecular biophys & biochem, Yale Univ, 74-76, fel biol, 76-77; ASST PROF BIOCHEM, DUKE UNIV, 77- *Concurrent Pos:* Am Cancer Soc fel, 74-76; NIH grant, 78-81. *Mem:* Sigma Xi; Am Soc Microbiol; AAAS; Am Soc Biol Chemists. *Res:* Nucleic acid sequence and structure; genetic signals in RNA and DNA; protein biosynthesis. *Mailing Add:* Dept of Biochem Duke Univ Med Ctr Durham NC 27710

STEEGMANN, ALBERT THEODORE, JR, b Cleveland, Ohio, Aug 15, 36; m 63; c 2. BIOLOGICAL ANTHROPOLOGY, PHYSICAL ANTHROPOLOGY. *Educ:* Univ Kans, BA, 58; Univ Mich, MA, 61, PhD(anthrop), 65. *Prof Exp:* From instr to asst prof anthrop, Univ Mo-Columbia, 64-66; from asst prof to assoc prof, 66-74, PROF ANTHROP, STATE UNIV NY BUFFALO, 74-, CHMN, ANTHROP DEPT, 79- *Concurrent Pos:* Vis colleague, Univ Hawaii, 67-68; NSF res grants, 67-70, 73-75 & 78-80; State Univ NY Buffalo fac res grants, 69-72; res assoc, Royal Ont Museum, 70- *Mem:* AAAS; Am Anthrop Asn; Am Asn Phys Anthrop; Soc Study Human Biol; Human Biol Coun. *Res:* Human cold response, physiological and behavioral; cranio-facial evolution; American sub-arctic; nutritional anthropology. *Mailing Add:* Dept of Anthrop State Univ NY Buffalo Amherst NY 14261

STEEL, COLIN, b Aberdeen, Scotland, Feb 7, 33; m 58; c 3. PHYSICAL CHEMISTRY. *Educ:* Univ Edinburgh, BSc, 55, PhD(chem), 58. *Prof Exp:* Res assoc chem, State Univ NY Col Forestry, Syracuse Univ, 58-59; res assoc, Brandeis Univ, 59-60; asst prof, Univ Toronto, 60-61; res scientist, Itek Corp, 61-63; asst prof chem, 63-66, assoc prof, 66-77, PROF CHEM, BRANDEIS UNIV, 77- *Mem:* Am Chem Soc; Royal Soc Chem. *Res:* Reaction kinetics and photochemistry. *Mailing Add:* Dept Chem Brandeis Univ Waltham MA 02154

STEEL, COLIN GEOFFREY HENDRY, b London, Eng, June 15, 46; m 70. INVERTEBRATE PHYSIOLOGY, COMPARATIVE ENDOCRINOLOGY. *Educ:* Univ Cambridge, BA, 67, MA, 71; Queen's Univ, PhD(zool), 71; Univ London, DIC, 75. *Prof Exp:* Fel insect physiol, Imp Col, Univ London, 71-72, res fel, 72-75; res assoc, 75-78, asst prof, 78-82, ASSOC PROF, DEPT BIOL, YORK UNIV, 82- *Mem:* Fel Royal Entom Soc London; Soc Exp Biol; Europ Soc Comp Endocrinol; Am Soc Zoologists; Can Soc Zool. *Res:* Neurosecretion in invertebrates, especially insects and crustacea; nervous and hormonal mechanisms controlling development; feedback regulation of the endocrine system; circadian rhythms and photopenodism. *Mailing Add:* Dept of Biol York Univ Downsview ON M3J 1P3 Can

STEEL, HOWARD HALDEMAN, b Philadelphia, Pa, Apr 17, 21; m 64; c 4. ORTHOPEDIC SURGERY. *Educ:* Colgate Univ, BA, 42; Temple Univ, MD, 45, MS, 51; Am Bd Orthop Surg, dipl, 52; Univ Wash, PhD(anat), 65. *Prof Exp:* Resident, Temple Univ Hosp & Shriners Hosp Crippled Children, 48-52; PROF ORTHOP SURG, MED CTR, TEMPLE UNIV, 65-; CHIEF ORTHOP SURGEON, SHRINERS HOSP CRIPPLED CHILDREN, 65- *Concurrent Pos:* Staff surgeon, Med Ctr, Temple Univ, 51-; assoc prof, Div Grad Med, Univ Pa, 55-; clin prof, Med Sch, Univ Wash, 64-65; consult, Vet Admin Hosp, Philadelphia, 67- & Walson Army Hosp, Ft Dix, NJ, 67-; attend surgeon, St Christopher's Hosp for Children. *Mem:* Orthop Res Soc; AMA; Am Acad Orthop Surg; Am Orthop Asn; Am Fedn Clin Res. *Res:* Clinical investigation of hip problems in the child; clinical and bacteriological investigations of nosocomial infections. *Mailing Add:* Dept of Orthop Surg Temple Univ Philadelphia PA 19140

STEEL, R KNIGHT, b New York, NY, Dec 1, 39; m 65; c 1. INTERNAL MEDICINE. *Educ:* Yale Univ, BA, 61; Columbia Univ, MD, 65. *Prof Exp:* From intern to chief resident med, Univ NC, Chapel Hill, 65-71, asst prof, 71-72; asst prof med, Univ Rochester, 72-77; assoc dir, Monroe Community Hosp, 72-77; ASSOC PROF MED, BOSTON UNIV, 77-, CHIEF GERIAT & DIR GERONT CTR, 77- *Res:* Medical education; geriatrics; health care delivery. *Mailing Add:* Dept of Med Boston Univ University Rd Boston MA 02215

STEEL, ROBERT, b Winnipeg, Man, Mar 17, 23; m 52; c 2. MICROBIOLOGY. *Educ:* Univ Man, BS, 49, MS, 51; Univ Manchester, PhD(microbiol, biochem), 56. *Prof Exp:* Jr res officer, Div Appl Biol, Nat Res Coun Can, 51-54; Imp Chem Industs res fel, Univ Manchester, 55-58; res assoc, 58-71, HEAD MICROBIOL & CHEM SERV, UPJOHN CO, 71- *Mem:* Am Soc Microbiol; Can Soc Microbiol; Am Chem Soc. *Res:* Steroid bioconversions; utilization of agricultural wastes by fermentation; production of 2, 3-butanediol, citric acid; biochemical engineering; agitation aeration studies in fermentation; mixing and scale-up of antibiotic fermentations. *Mailing Add:* 3505 Pinegrove Ln Kalamazoo MI 49008

STEEL, ROBERT GEORGE DOUGLAS, b St John, NB, Sept 2, 17; m 41; c 2. STATISTICAL ANALYSIS. *Educ:* Mt Allison Univ, BA, 39, BSc, 40; Acadia Univ, MA, 41; Iowa State Univ, PhD(statist), 49. *Prof Exp:* Asst prof math, Univ Wis & statistician, Agr Exp Sta, 49-52; assoc prof biol statist, Cornell Univ, 52-60; PROF STATIST & GRAD ADMINR, NC STATE UNIV, 60- *Concurrent Pos:* Mem math res ctr, US Dept Army, Univ Wis, 58-59. *Mem:* Fel Am Statist Asn; Biomet Soc. *Res:* Nonparametric statistics; experimental design; data analysis. *Mailing Add:* Dept of Statist NC State Univ PO Box 5457 Raleigh NC 27607

STEEL, WARREN G, b New York, NY, Feb 16, 20; m 43; c 2. GEOLOGY. *Educ:* Univ NC, BS, 46, MS, 49. *Prof Exp:* Asst prof geol, NC State Col, 48-55; prof geol, 55-72, E B ANDREWS PROF NATURAL SCI, MARIETTA COL, 72-, CHMN DEPT GEOL, 55- *Concurrent Pos:* Geologist, US Geol Surv, 47-48 & 51 & NC Dept Conserv & Develop, 49-50 & 52; geologist-petrogr, Rare Minerals Br, US Bur Mines, 53-55; consult geologist, 55- *Mem:* Geol Soc Am; Nat Asn Geol Teachers. *Res:* Petrography; structural geology; geomorphology. *Mailing Add:* Dept of Geol Marietta Col Marietta OH 45750

STEELE, ARNOLD EDWARD, b Estherville, Iowa, June 21, 25; m 54; c 3. ZOOLOGY, NEMATOLOGY. *Educ:* Iowa State Univ, BA, 53, MS, 57. *Prof Exp:* Parasitologist, Animal Parasite & Dis Div, USDA, 55-56, zoologist plant nematol, Tifton, Ga, 55-59, ZOOLOGIST PLANT NEMATOL, SCI & EDUC ADMIN-FED RES, USDA, CALIF, 59- *Concurrent Pos:* Assoc ed, Soc Nematologists, 75-77. *Mem:* Soc Nematologists; Am Phytopath Soc; Sigma Xi. *Res:* Biology; host-parasite relationships and control of nematodes affecting production of sugarbeet and vegetable crops. *Mailing Add:* Sci & Educ Admin-Fed Res WR USDA PO Box 5098 Salinas CA 93915

STEELE, ARTHUR BURNS, chemistry, deceased

STEELE, CHARLES RICHARD, b Royal, Iowa, Aug 15, 33; m 69; c 4. APPLIED MECHANICS, BIO-MEDICAL ENGINEERING. *Educ:* Tex A&M Univ, BS, 56; Stanford Univ, PhD(appl mech), 60. *Prof Exp:* Eng specialist aircraft struct, Chance-Vought Aircraft, Dallas, 59-60; res scientist shell theory, Lockheed Res Lab, Palo Alto, 60-66; assoc prof, 66-71, PROF APPL MECH, STANFORD UNIV, 71- *Concurrent Pos:* Lectr, Univ Calif, Berkeley, 64-65; vis prof, Swiss Fed Inst Technol, Zurich, 71-72; tech dir, Shelltech Assoc. *Mem:* Am Inst Aeronaut & Astronaut; fel Am Soc Mech Engrs; Acoust Soc Am. *Res:* Asymptotic analysis in mechanics; thin shell theory; mechanics of the inner ear; noninvasive determination of bone stiffness. *Mailing Add:* Div of Appl Mech Stanford Univ Stanford CA 94305

STEELE, DAVID GENTRY, b Beeville, Tex, Feb 8, 41; m 80; c 1. ZOOARCHAEOLOGY, PHYSICAL ANTHROPOLOGY. *Educ:* Univ Tex, Austin, BA, 67; Univ Kans, PhD(anthrop), 70. *Prof Exp:* Fel anthrop, Smithsonian Inst, 70-71; asst prof anthrop, Univ Alta, Edmonton, 71-76, assoc prof, 76-79; ASSOC PROF ANTHROP, TEX A&M UNIV, 79- *Mem:* Am Soc Phys Anthrop; Soc Am Archaeologists. *Res:* Predator and prey relationships of man; human adaptations to the Texas coast; animal remains from Roman farm sites in southern Italy; tree shrew anatomy and human osteology. *Mailing Add:* Dept Anthropol Tex A&M Univ College Station TX 77843

STEELE, DONALD HAROLD, b London, Ont, Nov 5, 32; m 59; c 1. ZOOLOGY. *Educ:* Univ Western Ont, BSc, 54; McGill Univ, MSc, 56, PhD(zool), 61. *Prof Exp:* Technician, Biol Sta, St Andrews, NB, 55-56; lectr biol, Sir George Williams Univ, 60-62, asst prof, 62; from asst prof to assoc prof, 62-75, PROF BIOL, MEM UNIV NFLD, 75- *Mem:* AAAS; Ecol Soc Am; Brit Ecol Soc; Int Asn Ecol; Can Soc Zool. *Res:* Marine ecology; zoogeography; systematics of marine amphipoda. *Mailing Add:* Dept of Biol Mem Univ of Nfld St John's NF A1Z 5S7 Can

STEELE, EARL L(ARSEN), b Denver, Colo, Sept 23, 23; m 53; c 6. SOLID STATE PHYSICS. *Educ:* Univ Utah, BS, 45; Cornell Univ, PhD(physics), 52. *Prof Exp:* Lab asst physics, Univ Utah, 44-45; asst, Cornell Univ, 45-51; res physicist, Gen Elec Co, 51-56; chief res dept, Semiconductor Div, Motorola, Inc, Ariz, 56-58; asst lab mgr, Semiconductor Div, Hughes Aircraft Co, 58-59, lab mgr, 59-63; staff scientist, Res & Eng Div, Autonetics Div, N Am Aviation, Inc, Calif, 63-69; chmn dept, 71-80, PROF ELEC ENG, COL ENG, UNIV KY, 69- *Concurrent Pos:* Ed, Trans Electron Devices, Inst Elec & Electronics Engrs, 54-61; assoc prof, Ariz State Univ, 57-58; lectr, Univ Calif, Los Angeles, 59; phys sci coordr, Southern Calif Col, 62-63; affil prof & lectr, Univ Calif, Irvine, 67-69; officer, Southeastern Ctr Elec Eng Educ, 74- *Mem:* Am Phys Soc; Am Soc Eng Educ; Sigma Xi; Am Asn Physics Teachers; fel Inst Elec & Electronics Engrs. *Res:* Semiconductor p-n junction theory and device design; solid state theoretical studies of band structure of barium oxide; transistors and parametric devices; microelectronics; lasers and electrooptics; computer aided electronic circuit design; quantum electronics. *Mailing Add:* Dept Elec Eng Univ Ky Lexington KY 40506

STEELE, FRANCES M, virology, microbiology, see previous edition

STEELE, GRANT, b Salt Lake City, Utah, June 8, 24; m 45; c 3. STRATIGRAPHY, PALEONTOLOGY. *Educ:* Univ Utah, BS, 49; Univ Wash, PhD(geol), 59. *Prof Exp:* Instr geol, Syracuse Univ, 52-53; div paleontologist, Gulf Oil Corp, Tulsa, 53-56, div stratigr, Denver, 56-63, sr geologist, Gulf Res & Develop Co, Pittsburgh, 63-66, geol supvr, Houston Tech Serv Ctr, 66-73, sr investigator, 73-74, CHIEF GEOLOGIST, GULF OIL EXPLOR & PROD CO, HOUSTON, 74- *Mem:* Am Asn Petrol Geologists; Paleont Soc; Soc Econ Paleontologists & Mineralogists. *Res:* New applications of biostratigraphy and lithostratigraphy. *Mailing Add:* Gulf Oil Explor & Prod Co PO Box 2100 Houston TX 77001

STEELE, JACK, b Indianapolis, Ind, Jan 22, 42; m 68; c 3. INORGANIC CHEMISTRY, PHYSICAL CHEMISTRY. *Educ:* DePauw Univ, BA, 64; Univ Ky, PhD(inorg chem), 68. *Prof Exp:* Am Chem Soc Petrol Res Fund grant & teaching intern, Wash State Univ, 68-70; asst prof, 70-75, assoc prof, 75-80, PROF CHEM, ALBANY STATE COL, 80-, CHMN, DEPT CHEM & PHYSICS, 81- *Concurrent Pos:* NSF col sci improv prog mem, Albany State Col, 72-73; minority sch biomed support prog mem, 72-76. *Mem:* Am Chem Soc; Sigma Xi; Am Asn Clin Chem. *Res:* Etiologic factors of disease; clinical chemistry; stereochemistry of metal chelates of biologically important compounds; optical activity and absolute configuration of metal chelates. *Mailing Add:* Dept of Chem Albany State Col Albany GA 31705

STEELE, JACK ELLWOOD, b Lacon, Ill, Jan 27, 24; m 55; c 2. BIONICS. *Educ:* Northwestern Univ, BM, 49, MD, 50; Wright State Univ, MS, 77. *Prof Exp:* Intern, Cincinnati Gen Hosp, 49-50; fel neuroanat, Med Sch, Northwestern Univ, 50-51; ward officer, US Air Force, 2750 US Air Force Hosp, Wright-Patterson AFB, 51-53, proj officer, Aerospace Med Lab, 53-71; pvt pract, 71-73; physician, Dayton Mental Health Ctr, 73-75, med dir, Drug Treatment Unit, 75-78; MED DIR, DAYTON DEVELOPMENTAL CENTER, 78-; PRES, GEN BIONICS CORP, 79- *Concurrent Pos:* Physician, BuDa Narcotic Clinic, 78-81. *Mem:* Aerospace Med Asn; Inst Elec & Electronics Engrs; NY Acad Sci; AMA; Asn Comput Mach. *Res:* Analysis and design of systems with lifelike behavior, intelligence in particular. *Mailing Add:* 2313 Bonnieview Ave Dayton OH 45431

STEELE, JAMES HARLAN, b Chicago, Ill, Apr 3, 13; m 41; c 2. VETERINARY MEDICINE. *Educ:* Mich State Univ, DVM, 41; Harvard Univ, MPH, 42; Am Bd Vet Pub Health, dipl. *Prof Exp:* With, State Health Dept, Ohio, 42-43; vet, USPHS, 43-45, chief vet pub health, Nat Commun Dis Ctr, 45-68, asst surgeon gen vet affairs, 68-71; PROF ENVIRON HEALTH, INST ENVIRON HEALTH, UNIV TEX SCH PUB HEALTH HOUSTON, 71- *Concurrent Pos:* Consult, Pan-Am Sanit Bur, 44-, US Dept State, 48-, USDA, 50- & White House Comt Consumer Protection; secy, Am Bd Vet Pub Health, 50-52; consult, WHO, 50-, pub health consult, Philippines, 72 & Somoa & Fiji, 73; consult, Food & Agr Orgn, UN, 60, pub health consult, Cyprus, 75-76, Israel, 78; chmn, WHO-Food & Agr Orgn Expert Comt Zoonoses, 3rd Report, 67; ed-in-chief, CRC Handbk Zoonoses, 78-82. *Honors & Awards:* Meritorious Medal, USPHS, 63, Bronfman Award, 71; Centennial Award, Am Pub Health Asn, 72; Hon Dipl, XX World Vet Cong, 75, Hellenic Vet Soc, 76. *Mem:* Am Soc Trop Med & Hyg; Asn Mil Surg US; Am Vet Med Asn; Am Vet Epidemiol Soc (pres, 82-83); Animal Health Asn. *Res:* Veterinary public health; epidemiology of zoonoses and chronic diseases common to animals and man; cost benefits of international veterinary public health programs. *Mailing Add:* Inst Environ Health Univ Tex Sch Pub Health Houston TX 77025

STEELE, JAMES PATRICK, b Louisville, Ky, Dec 6, 19; m 44; c 2. RADIOLOGY. *Educ:* Univ Louisville, MD, 43; Am Bd Radiol, dipl, 50. *Prof Exp:* PROF RADIOL, SCH MED, UNIV S DAK, VERMILLION, 49- *Concurrent Pos:* Radiologist, Sacred Heart Hosp, Yankton, 49-; prof, Sch Med, Univ Nebr; pres, SDak Health Res Inst. *Mem:* Am Roentgen Ray Soc; Radiol Soc NAm; AMA; Am Col Radiol. *Res:* Night vision as related to fluoroscopy; psychological effects of total body radiation. *Mailing Add:* Sacred Heart Hosp PO Box 650 Yankton SD 57078

STEELE, JOHN A, b Raeford, NC, Mar 26, 28; m 61; c 3. ORGANIC CHEMISTRY, ANALYTICAL CHEMISTRY. *Educ:* JC Smith Univ, BS, 51; Howard Univ, MS, 63. *Prof Exp:* Res chemist, Tenn Valley Authority, 53 & NIH, 56-63; forensic anal chemist, US Internal Revenue Serv, 63-69, RES ANAL CHEMIST, BUR ALCOHOL, TOBACCO & FIREARMS, DEPT TREAS, 69- *Mem:* AAAS; fel Am Inst Chemists. *Res:* Partial synthesis and degradation of steroidal compounds; preparation and purification of specific working groups for nucleotide synthesis; anthrasteroid rearrangement mechanisms; tobacco and tobacco products; fermentation mechanisms for tobacco and tobacco products. *Mailing Add:* Bur of Alcohol Tobacco & 1401 Research Blvd Rockville MD 20850

STEELE, JOHN EARLE, b St John's, Nfld, Jan 29, 32; m 57; c 3. ZOOLOGY, ENDOCRINOLOGY. *Educ:* Dalhousie Univ, BSc, 54; Univ Western Ont, MSc, 56; Univ Sask, PhD(biol), 59. *Prof Exp:* Res officer, Can Dept Agr, 59-64; from asst prof to assoc prof, 64-75, PROF ZOOL, UNIV WESTERN ONT, 75- *Mem:* Can Soc Zool; Can Physiol Soc. *Res:* Hormonal control of metabolism, water transport and growth and development in insects. *Mailing Add:* Dept Zool Univ Western Ont London ON N6A 5B7 Can

STEELE, JOHN H, b Edinburgh, UK, Nov 15, 26; m 56; c 1. BIOLOGY. *Educ:* Univ Col, London, BSc, 46, DSc, 64. *Prof Exp:* Scientist, Marine Lab, Scotland, 51-77, dep dir, 73-77; DIR, WOODS HOLE OCEANOG INST, 77-, MEM CORP STAFF, MARINE BIOL LAB, 80- *Concurrent Pos:* Vis res fel, Woods Hole Oceanog Inst, 58, vis comt biol dept, 73 & 75; mem, Panel Int Decade Ocean Explor, NSF, 72-73 & steering comt, Controlled Ecol Pollution Exp Proj, 74-; mem, Bermuda Biol Sta Res Inc, 77-, bd govs, Joint Oceanog Inst Inc, 77-, ocean sci bd, Nat Res Coun, Nat Acad Sci, 78-, chmn, 81-, Univ Corp Atmospheric Res, 78- *Honors & Awards:* Alexander Agassiz Medal, Nat Acad Sci, 73. *Mem:* Fel Royal Soc; fel Royal Soc Edinburgh; Am Acad Arts & Sci. *Res:* Dynamics of marine ecosystems. *Mailing Add:* Woods Hole Oceanog Inst Woods Hole MA 02543

STEELE, JOHN WISEMAN, b Motherwell, Scotland, May 27, 34; m 58; c 4. PHARMACEUTICAL CHEMISTRY. *Educ:* Glasgow Univ, BSc, 55, PhD(pharmaceut chem), 59. *Prof Exp:* Lectr, 58-59, from asst prof to prof, 59-81, DEAN FAC PHARM, UNIV MAN, 81- *Concurrent Pos:* Fel, Chelsea Col Sci & Technol, 65-66; mem, Med Res Coun Can, 70-72; vis scientist, Med-Chem Inst, Univ Bern, 72-73; mem, Man Drug Standards & Therapeut Comt, 78- *Mem:* Can Pharmaceut Asn; assoc Royal Inst Chem; The Chem Soc; Asn Faculties Pharm Can (pres, 75-76). *Res:* Drug metabolism, especially of anabolic steroids and other drugs likely to be abused by athletes; methods of drug analysis, including gas-liquid chromatography and gas-liquid chromatography/mass spectral analysis. *Mailing Add:* Fac of Pharm Univ of Man Winnipeg MB R3T 2N2 Can

STEELE, KENNETH F, b Statesville, NC, Jan 16, 44; m 66; c 2. GEOLOGY, GEOCHEMISTRY. *Educ:* Univ NC, Chapel Hill, BS, 62, PhD(geol), 71. *Prof Exp:* From instr to asst prof, 70-77, ASSOC PROF GEOL, UNIV ARK, FAYETTEVILLE, 77- *Mem:* Geochem Soc; Geol Soc Am; Soc Environ Geochem & Health; Nat Asn Geol Teachers; Asn Explor Geochemists. *Res:* Major and trace element geochemical investigations applied to petrology and exploration and also environmental geochemistry. *Mailing Add:* Dept of Geol Univ of Ark Fayetteville AR 72701

STEELE, LAWRENCE RUSSELL, b Manhattan, Kans, Nov 7, 35; m 59; c 3. CHEMICAL ENGINEERING. *Educ:* Ohio State Univ, BChE & MSc, 58, PhD(chem eng), 62. *Prof Exp:* Sr res engr, NAm Aviation, Inc, 62-63; res scientist, Columbia Univ, 63-66; SR RES ENGR, E R SQUIBB & SONS, INC, 66-, SECT HEAD, 75-, ASST DEPT HEAD, 81- *Mem:* Am Inst Chem Engrs; Am Chem Soc. *Res:* Chemical process development of pharmaceuticals. *Mailing Add:* 55 Cherrybrook Dr RD 5 Princeton NJ 08540

STEELE, LENDELL EUGENE, b Kannapolis, NC, May 5, 28; m 49; c 4. NUCLEAR ENGINEERING, MATERIALS SCIENCE. *Educ:* George Washington Univ, BS, 50; Am Univ, MA, 59. *Prof Exp:* Chemist phys sci, Res Mgt, Agr Res Ctr, 49-50; res & develop officer radiol safety, US Air Force, 51-53; metall eng, US Atomic Energy Comn, 66-67; chemist, Naval Res Lab, 50-51, anal chemist, 53-57, sect head & br head, 57-66, br head & assoc supt mat sci & technol, 67-80. *Concurrent Pos:* Consult, Metal Properties Coun, 67-; US deleg, Int Atomic Energy Agency, Vienna, 67-; task group leader, Metals Properties Coun, ed, 67- *Honors & Awards:* Wash Acad Sci Eng Award, 62; Appl Sci Award, Naval Res Labs-Sigma Xi, 66; Spec Annual Prize Award, Am Nuclear Soc, 72; Dudley Medal, Am Soc Testing & Mat, 73, Award of Merit, 78. *Mem:* Fel Am Soc Metals; Am Nuclear Soc; fel Am Soc Testing & Mat; Res Soc Am. *Res:* Fundamental and applied research on materials for advanced energy conversion systems, especially gas turbine materials but including response of nuclear structural material to nuclear effects for light water, breeder and fusion reactors as well. *Mailing Add:* Mat Sci & Technol Div Naval Res Lab Washington DC 20375

STEELE, LEON, b Ill, Apr 8, 15; m 41; c 3. PLANT BREEDING. *Educ:* Ill Wesleyan Univ, BS, 40, DSc, 67. *Prof Exp:* Res assoc, Michael-Leonard Seed Co, 36-40; mgr dept res, Funk Seeds Int Can, Ltd, 40-52, assoc res dir, 52-57, res dir, 57-78, pres, 63-78, RES CONSULT, FUNK SEEDS INT, 78- *Mem:* AAAS; Am Soc Agron; Bot Soc Am; Genetics Soc Am; Am Genetic Asn. *Res:* Commercial and hybrid corn breeding; physiology of corn plant; corn diseases and their control through breeding for resistance. *Mailing Add:* Funk Seeds Int Bloomington IL 61701

STEELE, MARTIN CARL, b New York, NY, Dec 25, 19; m 41; c 4. SOLID STATE ELECTRONICS. *Educ:* Cooper Union, BChE, 40; Univ Md, MS, 49, PhD, 52. *Prof Exp:* Physicist & chief cryomagnetics sect, US Naval Res Lab, 47-55; res physicist, Res Lab, Radio Corp Am, 55-58, head semiconductor res group, 58-60, dir res labs, Japan, 60-63, head solid state electron physics group, 63-72; head semiconductor mat & device res, 72-81, STAFF RES SCIENTIST, ELECTRONICS DEPT, RES LABS, GEN MOTORS CORP, 81- *Concurrent Pos:* Vis lectr, Princeton Univ, 65-66; adj prof elec eng, Wayne State Univ, 76- *Mem:* Fel Am Phys Soc; Electrochem Soc; fel Inst Elec & Electronics Engrs. *Res:* Solid state physics; superconductivity; galvanomagnetic effects in metals and semiconductors; high electric field effects in semiconductors; solid state plasma effects; microwave devices; infrared detection; integrated circuits; MOS devices; semiconductor surfaces. *Mailing Add:* Res Labs Gen Motors Corp Warren MI 48090

STEELE, RICHARD, b Charlotte, NC, Sept 6, 21; m 49; c 2. CHEMISTRY, POLYMER CHEMISTRY. *Educ:* Univ NC, SB, 42; Princeton Univ, MA, 48, PhD(chem), 49. *Prof Exp:* Res chemist, Rohm and Haas Co, 42-46; res chemist & head phys org chem sect, Textile Res Inst, 50-53; lab head, Rohm and Haas Co, 53-65; dir appln & prod develop, NY, 65-66, vpres & tech dir, 66-71, sr vpres technol & admin, Celanese Fibers Mkt Co, 71-73, sr vpres technol & admin, Celanese Fibers Co, 73-76, sr vpres mfg & technol, Celanese Fibers Int Co, 76-79, pres, 79-80, EXEC VPRES, CELANESE INT CO, 80- *Honors & Awards:* Olney Medal, Am Asn Textile Chemists & Colorists, 64; Harold DeWitt Smith Award, Am Soc Testing & Mat, 78. *Mem:* AAAS; Am Chem Soc; Am Asn Textile Chemists & Colorists; Brit Textile Inst; Fiber Soc. *Res:* Structure of natural and synthetic fibers; chemistry of textile wet-finishing processes; cellulose chemistry. *Mailing Add:* Celanese Int Co 1211 Ave of the Americas New York NY 10036

STEELE, RICHARD HAROLD, b Buffalo, NY, Aug 1, 19; m 52; c 3. BIOCHEMISTRY. *Educ:* Univ Ala, BS, 48; Tulane Univ, PhD(biochem), 53. *Prof Exp:* Vis investr, Inst Muscle Res, Marine Biol Lab, 54-57; PROF BIOCHEM, TULANE UNIV, 57- *Concurrent Pos:* Lederle Med Fac Award, 57-60; NIH sr res fels, 60 & 65. *Mem:* Am Chem Soc; Am Soc Biol Chemists. *Res:* Energy generation and transfer; spectroscopy; chemiluminescence and bioluminescence. *Mailing Add:* Dept of Biochem Tulane Univ Sch Med New Orleans LA 70112

STEELE, ROBERT, b Scotland, Jan 16, 29; m 55; c 2. PREVENTIVE MEDICINE, EPIDEMIOLOGY. *Educ:* Univ Edinburgh, DPH, 56; Univ Sask, MD, 60; FRCP(C); FFCM. *Prof Exp:* Asst prof prev med, Col Med, Univ Sask, 58-62; med officer, Scottish Health Dept, 62-64; assoc prof prev med, Fac Med & dir res, 64-68, PROF COMMUNITY HEALTH & EPIDEMIOL & HEAD DEPT, FAC MED, QUEEN'S UNIV, ONT, 68- *Concurrent Pos:* Consult, Kingston Gen Hosp, Ont. *Mem:* Asn Teachers Prev Med; fel Int Epidemiol Asn; fel Am Pub Health Asn; Royal Med Soc; Can Asn Teachers Social & Prev Med. *Res:* Epidemiology of sudden death in infants; cancer; medical care; community health. *Mailing Add:* Dept of Community Health Queen's Univ Fac of Med Kingston ON K7L 3N6 Can

STEELE, ROBERT DARRYL, b New Eagle, Pa, Dec 5, 46; m 79. INTERMEDIARY METABOLISM, PROTEIN METABOLISM. *Educ:* Univ Ariz, BS, 70, MS, 73; Univ Wis, Madison, PhD(nutrit & biochem), 78. *Prof Exp:* ASST PROF NUTRIT, RUTGERS UNIV, 78- *Mem:* Am Inst Nutrit; Am Physiol Soc; Sigma Xi; Am Physiol Soc. *Res:* Investigating the central role of the liver in amino acid and protein metabolism in mammals, especially in conditions of altered function such as liver disease and cirrhosis. *Mailing Add:* Dept Nutrit Rutgers Univ PO Box 231 New Brunswick NJ 08903

STEELE, ROBERT L, b Jane Lew, WVa, Nov 30, 30; m 53; c 2. DAIRY SCIENCE. *Educ:* WVa Univ, BS, 53, MS, 57. *Prof Exp:* Instr dairy sci, WVa Univ, 55-56, asst exten dairyman, 56, assoc exten dairyman, 57-60; mgr dairy processing, Producers Coop Dairy, WVa, 60; dir commodities & mkt, Pa Farmers Asn, 60-67; dairy specialist, 67-70; dir appl res, 70-72, mgr dairy-livestock develop, 72-73, dir field res & develop, 73-79, MGR DAIRY-LIVESTOCK DEVELOP, RES & DEVELOP, AGWAY INC, 79- *Mem:* Am Dairy Sci Asn; Animal Nutrit Res Coun; Am Soc Animal Sci. *Res:* Dairy, swine, beef feeding and management; crops varieties, fertility and cultural practices and manure management. *Mailing Add:* Agway Inc PO Box 4933 Syracuse NY 13221

STEELE, ROBERT WILBUR, b Denver, Colo, Aug 13, 20; m 42, 61; c 6. FOREST MANAGEMENT. *Educ:* Colo State Univ, BSF, 42; Univ Mich, MSF, 49; Colo State Univ, PhD(forest fire sci), 75. *Prof Exp:* Forest guard, US Forest Serv, Ore, 42-43, forester, Pac Northwestern Exp Sta, 46-55; forest mgr, SDS Lumber Co, 55-56; asst prof forestry, Univ Mont, 56-67, assoc prof, 67-70, prof, 70-81; CONSULT, FORESTRY ASSOC INT INC, 81- *Mem:* Soc Am Foresters; Am Meteorol Soc. *Res:* Forest fire control; development of techniques and machinery for fire detection and control; use and effects of prescribed fire in the forest; forest fire science; land surveying; sagebrush burning. *Mailing Add:* Box 1185 Hamilton Heights Corvallis MT 59828

STEELE, ROGER L, air pollution, deceased

STEELE, RONALD EDWARD, b Pittsburgh, Pa, May 19, 43; m 69. PHYSIOLOGY, ENDOCRINOLOGY. *Educ:* Pa State Univ, BS, 65; Univ Ky, PhD(physiol), 70. *Prof Exp:* Fel physiol, Worcester Found Exp Biol, 69-72; asst prof pediat endocrinol, Johns Hopkins Hosp, 72-74; SR SCIENTIST ENDOCRINOL, CIBA-GEIGY CORP, 74- *Mem:* Endocrine Soc; Am Soc Andrology. *Res:* Male and female reproductive endocrinology and corticosteroid physiology. *Mailing Add:* Pharmaceut Div Saw Mill River Rd Ardsley NY 10502

STEELE, SIDNEY RUSSELL, b Toledo, Ohio, June 30, 17; m 44; c 2. CHEMISTRY. *Educ:* Univ Toledo, BS, 39; Ohio State Univ, PhD(chem), 43. *Prof Exp:* Res chemist, Girdler Corp, Ky, 43-47; assoc prof, 47-60, head dept, 67-77, 78-79, PROF CHEM, EASTERN ILL UNIV, 60- *Mem:* Am Chem Soc. *Res:* Polarography; abnormal diffusion currents; water gas-shift catalysis; methanation of carbon monoxide. *Mailing Add:* Dept of Chem Eastern Ill Univ Charleston IL 61920

STEELE, THEODORE KARL, b Brooklyn, NY, Oct 27, 22; m 52; c 2. APPLIED MECHANICS. *Educ:* City Col New York, BME, 43; NY Univ, MME, 49, EngScD, 51. *Prof Exp:* Design engr instruments, Bendix Aviation Corp, 43-44; test engr power plants, US Navy, 44-46; test engr accessories, Stratos Corp, 46-47; test engr rocket motros, M W Kellogg Co, 47-48; instr mech eng, NY Univ, 48-51; vpres, Bulova Res & Develop Labs, 51-64; V PRES, NY INST TECHNOL, 64- *Concurrent Pos:* Pvt consult, 48-; consult, res projs, NSF, NASA, Dept of Environ, US Navy, 64-; Consult & Designers Inc, 64-66. *Mem:* Am Inst Aeronaut & Astronaut; Am Soc Mech Engrs; Sigma Xi. *Res:* Electromechanical instruments; fuzing and safing systems; computer aided instruction; energy systems; management science; heat power. *Mailing Add:* 22 Embassy Ct Great Neck NY 11021

STEELE, TIMOTHY DOAK, b Muncie, Ind, Apr 12, 41; m 65; c 2. HYDROLOGY, RESOURCE MANAGEMENT. *Educ:* Wabash Col, AB, 63; Stanford Univ, MS, 65, PhD(hydrol), 68; USDA Grad Sch, advan cert acct, 73. *Prof Exp:* Res hydrologist, Water Resources Div, Menlo Park, US Geol Surg, Colo, 66-68, res hydrologist, Systs Lab Group, Washington, DC, 68-72, hydrologist, Qual Water Br, 72-74, proj chief & hydrologist, Yampa River Basin Assessment Study, 75-80; SR PROJ HYDROLOGIST & CHIEF, WATER QUAL GROUP, WOODWARD-CLYDE CONSULT, DENVER, 80- *Concurrent Pos:* Water qual specialist, US AID, Pakistan, 72; Alex von Humboldt res fel, Univ Bayreuth, WGer, 79. *Mem:* Am Geophys Union; Int Asn Hydrol Sci; Int Water Res Asn. *Res:* Design of hydrologic data-collection networks; statistical analysis of data; hydrologic simulation and modeling; water resources planning and systems analysis; hydrogeochemistry; water quality; assessments of environmental impacts of energy-resource development; regional water-resources assessments; ground water contamination and resource conservation and recovery act regulations. *Mailing Add:* 28888 Cedar Circle Evergreen CO 80439

STEELE, VERNON EUGENE, b Blairsville, Pa, July 23, 46; m 68; c 1. RADIOBIOLOGY. *Educ:* Bucknell Univ, BS, 68; Univ Rochester, MS, 74, PhD(radiation biol), 75. *Prof Exp:* Investr carcinogenesis, Biol Div, Oak Ridge Nat Lab, 75-79; MEM STAFF, NAT INST ENVIRON HEALTH SCI, NIH, 79- *Mem:* Tissue Cult Asn; Sigma Xi; Am Asn Cancer Res. *Res:* Effects of radiation, chemical carcinogens and promoters on cell and tissue kinetics, morphology and physiology. *Mailing Add:* Nat Inst Environ Health Sci NIH Box 12233 Research Triangle Park NC 27709

STEELE, VLADISLAVA JULIE, b Prague, Czech, July 8, 34; m 59; c 1. INVERTEBRATE PHYSIOLOGY, HISTOLOGY. *Educ:* McGill Univ, BSc, 57, MSc, 59, PhD(zool), 65. *Prof Exp:* Lectr histol, McGill Univ, 60-61; vis lectr, 62-63, lectr histol & embryol, 63-65, asst prof, 65-72, ASSOC PROF HISTOL & EMBRYOL, MEM UNIV NFLD, 72-, DEPT HEAD BIOL, 80- *Mem:* Am Inst Biol Sci; Can Soc Zool; Nutrit Today Soc; Crustacean Soc Can; Soc Cell Biologists. *Res:* Photoperiod, neurosecretion and steroid production in marine amphipods; influence of environmental factors on the reproduction of boreo-arctic intertidal amphipods. *Mailing Add:* Dept of Biol Mem Univ Nfld St John's NF A1B 3X9 Can

STEELE, WARREN CAVANAUGH, b Pocatello, Idaho, Oct 25, 29; m 55. PHYSICAL CHEMISTRY. *Educ:* Ore State Col, BA, 51, PhD(phys chem), 56. *Prof Exp:* Res chemist, Dow Chem Co, 56-58; res assoc chem, Tufts Univ, 58-60 & 62-64; res fel, Harvard Univ, 60-62; sr staff scientist, Space Systs Div, Avco Corp, Wilmington, 64-75; prin scientist, Energy Resources Co Inc, Cambridge, 75-78; PROJ LEADER, FOREMOST RES CTR, FOREMOST-McKESSON, INC, DUBLIN, 78- *Mem:* AAAS; Am Chem Soc. *Res:* Mass spectrometry; gas-surface reaction kinetics; high temperature thermochemistry; environmental chemistry. *Mailing Add:* 1854 San Ramon Ave Berkeley CA 94707

STEELE, WILLIAM A, b St Louis, Mo, June 4, 30; m 55; c 2. PHYSICAL CHEMISTRY. *Educ:* Wesleyan Univ, BA, 51; Univ Wash, PhD(phys chem), 54. *Prof Exp:* Fel, Cryogenic Lab, 54-55, from asst prof to assoc prof, 55-66, PROF PHYS CHEM, PA STATE UNIV, UNIVERSITY PARK, 66- *Concurrent Pos:* NSF fel, 57-58, sr fel, 63-64; mem comt colloid & surface chem, Nat Acad Sci-Nat Res Coun, 66-72; mem adv comt, Chem Div, NSF, 72-76; Unilever vis prof, Univ Bristol, 77; Guggenheim fel, 77; Fulbright fel, Univ Vienna, 79; assoc ed, J Phys Chem, 80- *Mem:* Am Chem Soc; Am Phys Soc. *Res:* Thermodynamics and statistical mechanics of liquids and physical adsorption of gases on solids. *Mailing Add:* Dept of Chem Pa State Univ University Park PA 16802

STEELE, WILLIAM F, b Quincy, Mass, Mar 14, 20; m 54; c 2. MATHEMATICS. *Educ:* Boston Univ, AB, 51, MA, 52; Univ Pittsburgh, PhD(math), 61. *Prof Exp:* From instr to assoc prof, 52-63, PROF MATH, HEIDELBERG COL, 63- *Concurrent Pos:* Lectr, Univ Pittsburgh, 58-68; NSF vis scholar, Mass Inst Technol, 71-72. *Mem:* Am Math Soc; Math Asn Am; Soc Indust & Appl Math. *Res:* Summability of sequences by matrix methods. *Mailing Add:* Dept Math Heidelberg Col Tiffin OH 44883

STEELE, WILLIAM JOHN, b Philadelphia, Pa, Mar 31, 29; m 54; c 3. BIOCHEMICAL PHARMACOLOGY. *Educ:* Univ Pa, AB, 51, PhD(biochem), 58. *Prof Exp:* Res assoc cancer, Univ Pa, 57-60, Chester Beatty Res Inst, Royal Cancer Hosp, 60-62; asst prof, Col Med, Baylor Univ, 62-67; from asst prof to assoc prof pharmacol, 67-74, PROF PHARMACOL, COL MED, UNIV IOWA, 74- *Mem:* Am Asn Cancer Res; Am Chem Soc; Am Soc Pharmacol & Exp Therapeut; Am Soc Cell Biol; Brit Biochem Soc. *Res:* Biochemical basis of opiate and alcohol addiction; mechanism of aldosterone action on renal Na transport; regulation of translation on free and membrane-bound polysomes. separation of subcellular components; protein synthesis inhibitions. *Mailing Add:* Dept of Pharmacol Univ of Iowa Col of Med Iowa City IA 52242

STEELE, WILLIAM KENNETH, b Ft Wayne, Ind, Nov 2, 42; m; c 1. GEOLOGY, GEOPHYSICS. *Educ:* Case Western Reserve Univ, BS, 65, PhD(geol), 70. *Prof Exp:* Asst prof, 70-77, ASSOC PROF GEOL, EASTERN WASH UNIV, 77- *Mem:* Am Geophys Union; AAAS. *Res:* General geophysics, especially gravity and magnetic modeling, paleomagnetism. *Mailing Add:* Dept Geol Eastern Wash Univ Cheney WA 99004

STEELINK, CORNELIUS, b Los Angeles, Calif, Oct 1, 22; m 49; c 2. ORGANIC CHEMISTRY. *Educ:* Calif Inst Technol, BS, 44; Univ Southern Calif, MS, 50; Univ Calif, Los Angeles, PhD(chem), 56. *Prof Exp:* Lectr chem, Univ Southern Calif, 49-50 & Orange Coast Col, 50-53; asst, Univ Calif, Los Angeles, 53-56; res fel, Univ Liverpool, 56-57; from asst prof to assoc prof chem, 57-70, PROF CHEM, UNIV ARIZ, 70- *Mem:* Am Chem Soc. *Res:* Structure of lignin; electron spin resonance studies on naturally-occurring compounds; isolation and structural elucidation of plant terpenoids; structures and reactions of aquatic humic acids. *Mailing Add:* Dept of Chem Univ of Ariz Tucson AZ 85721

STEELMAN, CARROL DAYTON, b Vernon, Tex, Dec 9, 38; m 60; c 1. MEDICAL ENTOMOLOGY, VETERINARY ENTOMOLOGY. *Educ:* Okla State Univ, BS, 61, MS, 63, PhD(entom), 65. *Prof Exp:* From asst prof to assoc prof, 65-73, PROF MED & VET ENTOM, LA STATE UNIV, BATON ROUGE, 73- *Concurrent Pos:* USDA res grant, 67-69. *Mem:* Entom Soc Am; Am Mosquito Control Asn. *Res:* External parasites of domestic animals and man; disease-vector-host biological, ecological and control relationships; effects of insect parasites on animal hosts. *Mailing Add:* Dept of Entom La State Univ Life Sci Bldg Baton Rouge LA 70803

STEELMAN, SANFORD LEWIS, b Hickory, NC, Oct 11, 22; m 45; c 2. CLINICAL PHARMACOLOGY. *Educ:* Lenoir-Rhyne Col, BS, 43; Univ NC, PhD(biol chem), 49. *Prof Exp:* Biochemist, Armour & Co Labs, 49-50, head endocrinol sect, 51-53, head dept biochem res, 53-56; assoc prof biochem, Baylor Col Med, 56-58; dir endocrinol, Merck Inst Therapeut Res, 68-70, sr clin assoc, 70-76, DIR CLIN PHARMACOL, MERCK SHARP & DOHME RES LABS, RAHWAY, 76- *Concurrent Pos:* Assoc prof, Postgrad Sch Med, Univ Tex, 56-58. *Mem:* AAAS; Am Chem Soc; Soc Exp Biol & Med; Endocrine Soc; Am Soc Biol Chem. *Res:* Isolation and biological and physicochemical properties of protein and peptide hormones; physiology, pharmacology and bioassay of steroidal hormones; analgesics; hypothalamic hormones; clinical pharmacology. *Mailing Add:* Dept of Clin Pharmacol Merck Sharp & Dohme Res Lab Rahway NJ 07065

STEEN, EDWIN BENZEL, b Wheeling, Ind, July 23, 01; m 27; c 2. PARASITOLOGY. *Educ:* Wabash Col, AB, 23; Columbia Univ, AM, 26; Purdue Univ, PhD(zool), 38. *Prof Exp:* Instr zool, Wabash Col, 23-25, actg head dept, 26-27; asst biol, NY Univ, 25-26; instr zool, Univ Cincinnati, 27-31; instr zool, Purdue Univ, 31-34, instr fish & game, Univ & Exp Sta, 34-36; tutor biol, City Col New York, 38-40; from asst prof to prof, 41-72, head dept, 64-65, EMER PROF BIOL, WESTERN MICH UNIV, 72- *Mem:* AAAS; Sigma Xi; Am Inst Biol Sci. *Res:* Mammalian anatomy and physiology; medical and biological lexicography; zoology. *Mailing Add:* 2011 Greenlawn Ave Kalamazoo MI 49007

STEEN, ERNEST ALGOT, mechanical engineering, see previous edition

STEEN, JAMES SOUTHWORTH, b Vicksburg, Miss, Oct 26, 40; m 60; c 2. BIOLOGY, IMMUNOLOGY. *Educ:* Delta State Col, BS, 62; Univ Miss, MS, 64, PhD(biol), 68. *Prof Exp:* From asst prof to assoc prof, 68-77, PROF BIOL, DELTA STATE COL, 77- *Mem:* Am Soc Microbiol. *Res:* Carbohydrate metabolism in bacteria; tissue transplantation and immunosuppression as related to the enhancement phenomenon in inbred strains of mice. *Mailing Add:* Dept of Sci Delta State Col Cleveland MS 38732

STEEN, LYNN ARTHUR, b Chicago, Ill, Jan 1, 41; m 63. SCIENCE WRITING. *Educ:* Luther Col, BA, 61; Mass Inst Technol, PhD(math), 65. *Prof Exp:* From asst prof to assoc prof, 65-75, PROF MATH, ST OLAF COL, 75- *Concurrent Pos:* NSF sci faculty fel, Mittag-Leffler Inst, Sweden, 71-72; assoc ed, Am Math Monthly, 70-; ed, Math Mag, 76-80; contrib ed, Sci News, 77-; proj dir, Nat Inst Educ comput grants, Nat Sci Found; dir acad comput, St Olaf Col. *Honors & Awards:* Lester R Ford Award, Math Asn Am, 73 & 75. *Mem:* Am Math Soc; Math Asn Am (vpres, 80-81); AAAS. *Res:* Analysis; function algebras; mathematical logic; general topology. *Mailing Add:* Dept of Math St Olaf Coll Northfield MN 55057

STEEN, ROBERT FREDERICK, b Atlanta, Ga, Aug 19, 42; m 65; c 3. ELECTRICAL ENGINEERING, COMPUTER SCIENCE. *Educ:* Univ Rochester, BS, 64; NC State Univ, PhD(elec eng), 73. *Prof Exp:* Engr, IBM Corp, 64-70, staff engr, 70-71, adv engr, 73-77, TECH ADVR TO V PRES & CHIEF SCIENTIST, IBM CORP, 77- *Concurrent Pos:* Lectr & consult, Off Technol Assessment, US Cong, 78. *Mem:* Sr mem Inst Elec & Electronics Engrs; AAAS; Asn Comput Mach. *Res:* Computer data communication; information sciences; data communication systems and protocols; coding theory. *Mailing Add:* Old Orchard Rd Armonk NY 10504

STEEN, STEPHEN N, b London, Eng, Sept 6, 23; US citizen; m. MEDICINE. *Educ:* Mass Inst Technol, SB, 43; Univ Geneva, ScD(med biochem), 51, MD, 52; Am Bd Anesthesiol, dipl, 60. *Prof Exp:* Intern Abbot Hosp, Minneapolis, Minn, 53-54; res anesthesiol, Columbia-Presby Ctr, 54-56; instr, Albert Einstein Med Sch, 56-60; from asst prof to assoc prof, State Univ NY Downstate Med Ctr, 61-69; physician-in-chief anesthesia res, Cath Med Ctr Brooklyn & Queens, Inc, NY, 69-71; dir training & res, Harbor Gen Hosp, 71-75, PROF ANESTHESIOL, SCH MED, UNIV CALIF, LOS ANGELES, 71- *Concurrent Pos:* Actg dir, Delafield Hosp, NY, 56, attend anesthesiologist, 56-61; instr, Bronx Munic Hosp Ctr, 56-60 & Columbia Univ, 57-61; physician, Beth Israel Hosp, 57-61; attend anesthesiologist, Cent Islip State Hosp & St Francis Hosp, 58-, Misericordia Hosp, 58-62, Vet Admin 62- & St Barnabas Hosp, Bronx, NY, 56-61, dir anesthesiol, 60-61; vis attend anesthesiologist, Brooklyn Vet Admin Hosp, 61-66; from assoc vis anesthesiologist to vis anesthesiologist, Kings County Hosp Ctr, 61-; attending anesthesiologist, Harbor Gen Hosp, Torrance Mem Hosp, Univ Calif, Los Angeles, Olive View Med Ctr; dir, Pulmonary Function Labs, Meditrina Med Ctr, 79-; physicians specialist anesthesia, Los Angeles City Col-Univ Southern Calif, 81- *Mem:* Fel Am Col Anesthesiol; sr mem Am Chem Soc; AMA; Am Soc Anesthesiol; Asn Am Med Cols. *Res:* Anesthesiology. *Mailing Add:* 1900 Ocean Blvd 1802 Long Beach CA 90802

STEENBERGEN, JAMES FRANKLIN, b Glasgow, Ky, May 11, 39; m 67. MICROBIOLOGY. *Educ:* Western Ky State Col, BS, 62; Ind Univ, MA, 65, PhD(microbiol), 68. *Prof Exp:* Res assoc marine microbiol, Ore State Univ, 68-69, vis asst prof microbiol, 69-70; asst prof, 70-75, assoc prof, 75-79, PROF MICROBIOL, SAN DIEGO STATE UNIV, 80- *Mem:* Am Soc Microbiol. *Res:* Microbial ecology and physiology; diseases of crustaceans and fish; invertebrate immunology. *Mailing Add:* Dept of Microbiol San Diego State Univ San Diego CA 92182

STEENBURG, RICHARD WESLEY, b Aurora, Nebr, Feb 3, 25; m 50; c 2. SURGERY. *Educ:* Harvard Univ, MD, 48; Am Bd Surg, dipl. *Prof Exp:* Assoc prof surg, Johns Hopkins Univ, 65-69; PROF SURG, COL MED, UNIV NEBR, OMAHA, 69- *Concurrent Pos:* Surgeon in chief, Baltimore City Hosps, 67-69. *Mem:* Soc Univ Surg. *Res:* General surgery; surgical endocrinology; vascular disease; renal physiology. *Mailing Add:* 502 The Doctors Bldg 4239 Farnum St Omaha NB 68131

STEEN-MCINTYRE, VIRGINIA CAROL, b Chicago, Ill, Dec 3, 36; m 67. TEPHROCHRONOLOGY, ARCHAEOLOGICAL SITE STRATIGRAPHY. *Educ:* Augustana Col, Ill, 59; Wash State Univ, MS, 65; Univ Idaho, PhD(geol), 77. *Prof Exp:* Asst geologist, George H Otto, Consult Geologist, Chicago, 59-61; jr geologist, Lab Anthrop, Wash State Univ, 64-66; phys sci technician, US Geol Surv, Denver, 70-75; RES AFFIL, DEPT ANTHROP, COLO STATE UNIV, 77-; CONSULT TEPHROCHRONOLOGIST, 77- *Concurrent Pos:* Corresp mem, Int Asn Quaternary Res Comn Tephrochronology, 73-77; tephrochronologist, Valsequillo Early Man Proj, Mex, 66- & El Salvador Protoclassic Proj, 75-; guest lectr, NATO Advanced Studies Inst, Iceland, 80. *Mem:* Geol Soc Am; Sigma Xi; Am Asn Quaternary Res; Asn Field Archaeology; Am Inst Prof Geologists. *Res:* Volcanic ash chronology; archaeologic site stratigraphy; petrography of friable Pleistocene deposits, tephra hydration dating; weathering of volcanic ejecta; human orgins; christian metaphysics. *Mailing Add:* Box 1167 Idaho Springs CO 80452

STEENSEN, DONALD H J, b Clinton, Iowa, Apr 26, 29; m 54. FOREST ECONOMICS. *Educ:* Iowa State Univ, BS, 58; Duke Univ, MF, 60, PhD(forest econ), 65. *Prof Exp:* Asst prof forest econ & sampling, Auburn Univ, 60-65; asst prof forest econ & mensuration, 65-73, ASSOC PROF FOREST ECON & MENSURATION, SCH FOREST RESOURCES, NC STATE UNIV, 73- *Mem:* Soc Am Foresters. *Res:* Forest mensuration. *Mailing Add:* Dept Forest Mgt-Wood Sci & Tech NC State Univ Sch Forest Resour Raleigh NC 27607

STEENSON, BERNARD O(WEN), b Crosby, NDak, Aug 2, 22; m 51; c 3. ELECTRICAL ENGINEERING. *Educ:* Ill Inst Technol, BS, 44; Calif Inst Technol, MS, 48, PhD(elec eng), 51. *Prof Exp:* Lab technician, Calif Inst Technol, 50-51; res physicist, 51-58, sr staff engr, 58-62, sr scientist, Space Systs Div, 62-71, SR SCIENTIST, SPACE & COMMUN GROUP, HUGHES AIRCRAFT CO, 71- *Res:* Radar systems design and analysis. *Mailing Add:* Space & Commun Group PO Box 92919 Los Angeles CA 90009

STEEPLES, DONALD WALLACE, b Hays, Kans, May 15, 45; m 67; c 2. GEOPHYSICS. *Educ:* Kans State Univ, BS, 69, MS, 70; Stanford Univ, MS, 74, PhD(geophys), 75. *Prof Exp:* Geophysicist seismol, US Geol Surv, 72-75; RES ASSOC GEOPHYS, STATE GEOL SURV KANS, 75- *Concurrent Pos:* chmn, Geophysics Prog, Univ Kans; pres, Great Plains Geophysical, Kans. *Mem:* Am Geophys Union; Soc Explor Geophysicists; Seismol Soc Am. *Res:* Crust and upper mantle structure of central North America; kimberlites of Kansas; Pleistocene drainage of Kansas; passive seismic methods in exploration for geothermal energy; use of seismic methods for shallow exploration. *Mailing Add:* 3026 Ranger Dr Lawrence KS 66044

STEER, MAX DAVID, b New York, NY, June 14, 10; m 42. SPEECH & HEARING SCIENCES. *Educ:* Long Island Univ, 32, LLD, 57; Univ Iowa, MA, 33, PhD(psychol), 38. *Prof Exp:* Asst speech path, Univ Iowa, 33-35; from instr to prof speech sci, 35-70, dir, Speech & Hearing Clin, 46-70, head dept 63-70, Hanley distinguished prof, 70-77, DISTINGUISHED PROF EMER AUDIOL & SPEECH SCI, PURDUE UNIV, WEST LAFAYETTE, 77- *Concurrent Pos:* Consult, State of Ind Hearing Comn, 66-, US Off Educ, NIH, NSF & Ind State Training Sch Ment Retarded; consult, Neurol & Sensory Dis Control Prof, USPHS, Pan-Am Health Orgn, 72-, Latin Am Fedn Logopedics, Phoniatrics, Audiol, 72- & Univ Bogota, 74; mem nat res adv comt, Bur Educ Handicapped, US Off Educ, 72-; consult & vis lectr, Nat Rehab Inst, Panama, 74. *Mem:* AAAS; Acoust Soc Am; Am Psychol Asn; fel Am Speech & Hearing Asn (vpres, 49, pres, 51); Int Asn Logopedics & Phoniatrics (vpres, 63-65, 71-77 & 80-83). *Res:* Speech disorders and acoustics; audiology; clinical psychology; neurology; physiology and psychology of communication. *Mailing Add:* 222 Forest Hill Dr West Lafayette IN 47906

STEER, RONALD PAUL, b Regina, Sask, Mar 7, 43; m 64; c 2. PHYSICAL CHEMISTRY. *Educ:* Univ Sask, BA, 64, PhD(chem), 68. *Prof Exp:* USPHS fel, Univ Calif, Riverside, 68-69; asst prof, 69-73, assoc prof, 73-78, PROF CHEM, UNIV SASK, 78- *Concurrent Pos:* Vis fel, Univ Southampton, 75-76. *Mem:* Fel Chem Inst Can; Int Photochem Soc. *Res:* Laser chemistry; photochemistry and photophysics of small molecules; fluorescence probe techniques in biological systems; SCF MO calculations of excited state potential surfaces. *Mailing Add:* Dept Chem Univ Sask Saskatoon SK S7N 0W0 Can

STEERE, RUSSELL LADD, b Ann Arbor, Mich, Aug 23, 17; m 43; c 4. VIROLOGY, BIOPHYSICS. *Educ:* Univ Mich, BA, 41, MA, 47, PhD(bot), 50. *Prof Exp:* Asst physics, Univ Mich, 46-47, res assoc, 47-50; asst, Rockefeller Inst Med Res, 50-51; res asst, Virol Lab, Univ Calif, 51-59; BOTANIST & CHIEF, PLANT VIROL LAB, PLANT PROTECTION INST, SCI & EDUC ADMIN-AGR RES, USDA, 59- *Honors & Awards:* Cert of Achievement, Walter Reed Inst Res & Superior Serv Award, USDA, 69; Ruth Allen Award, Am Phytopath Soc, 72. *Mem:* Fel Am Phytopath Soc; Bot Soc Am; Electron Micros Soc Am (pres, 70). *Res:* Purification of viruses, subcellular particles and macromolecules; structure and multiplication of viruses; freeze-etch techniques; development of new techniques for preparation of biological materials for electron microscopy. *Mailing Add:* Plant Protection Inst USDA Plant Indust Sta Beltsville MD 20705

STEERE, WILLIAM CAMPBELL, b Muskegon, Mich, Nov 4, 07; m 27; c 3. BOTANY. *Educ:* Univ Mich, BS, 29, MA, 31, PhD(bot), 32. *Hon Degrees:* DSc, Univ Montreal, 59, Univ Mich, 62. *Prof Exp:* Instr bot, Temple Univ, 29-31; from instr to prof, Univ Mich, 31-50, chmn dept, 47-50; prof, Stanford Univ, 50-58, dean grad div, 55-58; dir, 58-68, exec dir, 68-70, pres, 70-72, EMER PRES & SR SCIENTIST, NY BOT GARDEN, 72-; EMER PROF, COLUMBIA UNIV, 75- *Concurrent Pos:* Botanist, Univ Mich-Carnegie Inst Exped, Yucatan, 32; ed in chief, The Bryologist, 38-54 & Am J Bot, 53-57; epxhange prof, Univ PR, 39-40; sr botanist, Foreign Econ Admin, Colombia, 42-43 & Ecuador, 43-44; mem exped, Great Bear Lake, Can, 48; botanist, US Geol Surv, Alaska, 49; botanist, Arctic Res Lab, Pt Barrow, 51-53, investr, 60, 61, 63, 65, 72, 73 & 74; pres, Bryol Sect, Int Bot Cong, Paris, 54; prog dir, NSF, DC, 54-55; prof, Columbia Univ, 58-75; trustee, Biol Abstr, 61-66 & 67-73, pres, 64-65; mem exped, McMurdo Sound, Antarctica, 65; Phi Beta Kappa vis scholar, 66-67. *Honors & Awards:* Liberty Hyde Medal, Am Hort Soc; Medal, Int Bot Cong, Montreal, 59; Mt Steere named in his honor, Antarctica, 68; Mary Soper Pope Medal, Cranbrook Inst Sci, 70; Imperial Order of the Sacred Treasure, Japan, 72; Merit Award, Am Bot Soc, 75; Distinguished Serv Award, Am Inst Biol Sci, 77. *Mem:* Fel AAAS (vpres, 48, 66 & 67); Bot Soc Am (pres, 59); fel Am Geog Soc; Am Soc Naturalists (pres, 57); Am Asn Mus (vpres, 67, pres, 68-69). *Res:* Cytology, ecology, geography and taxonomy of bryophytes; communication of scientific information. *Mailing Add:* NY Bot Garden Bronx NY 10458

STEERS, EDWARD, JR, b Bethlehem, Pa, May 21, 37; m 57; c 3. BIOLOGICAL CHEMISTRY. *Educ:* Univ Pa, AB, 59, PhD(biol), 63. *Prof Exp:* Staff fel biochem, 63-65, RES BIOLOGIST, LAB CHEM BIOL, NAT INST ARTHRITIS, METABOLISM & DIGESTIVE DIS, 65- *Concurrent Pos:* Lectr, George Washington Univ, 66- *Mem:* Am Soc Biol Chem; Am Soc Cell Biol. *Res:* Protein chemistry; relationship of structure to function in proteins; cell organelles. *Mailing Add:* 5908 Holland Rd Rockville MD 20851

STEEVES, HARRISON ROSS, III, b Birmingham, Ala, July 2, 37; m 57; c 4. HISTOCHEMISTRY, TAXONOMY. *Educ:* Univ of the South, BS, 58; Univ Va, MS, 60, PhD(biol), 62. *Prof Exp:* Instr zool, Univ Va, 62; fel histol, Med Ctr, Univ Ala, 62-65, instr, 65-66; asst prof histol & histochem, 66-68,

ASSOC PROF ZOOL, VA POLYTECH INST & STATE UNIV, 68- *Honors & Awards:* Andrew Fleming award biol res, 61. *Mem:* AAAS. *Res:* Invertebrate histochemistry; taxonomy, ecology and physiology of cave crustaceans and histochemistry of digestion in these forms. *Mailing Add:* Dept of Biol Va Polytech Inst & State Univ Blacksburg VA 24061

STEEVES, JOHN DOUGLAS, b Calgary, Alta, Mar 25, 52. NEUROBIOLOGY. *Educ:* Univ Manitoba, BSc, 73, PhD(physiol), 79. *Prof Exp:* Fel neurophysiol, Dept Physiol, Univ Alta, 78-79; ASST PROF NEUROBIOL, DEPT ZOOL, UNIV BC, 79- *Concurrent Pos:* Consult, Can Broadcasting Corp, 81- *Mem:* Soc Neurosci; AAAS; Can Asn Neuroscientists; Can Physiol Soc. *Res:* Integrative capabilities of the various sensory and central nervous system mechanisms which initiate and modify motor behavior in vertebrate and invertebrate animals; genetic and epigenetic factors underlying the variability in the structure and function of neurons by using isogenic clones of locusts. *Mailing Add:* Dept Zool Univ BC Vancouver BC V6T 2A9

STEEVES, LEA CHAPMAN, b New Westminster, BC, Nov 4, 15; m 42; c 5. MEDICINE. *Educ:* Mt Allison Univ, BA, 36; McGill Univ, MD, CM, 40; FRCP(C), 47. *Hon Degrees:* LLD, Mt Allison Univ, 69; DSc, Mem Univ Nfld, 74. *Prof Exp:* From intern to resident, Royal Victoria Hosp, 40-43; from asst prof to assoc prof med, 48-57, dir postgrad div, 57-69, assoc dean fac med, 69-82, asst dean, 64-69, PROF MED, DALHOUSIE UNIV, 57- *Concurrent Pos:* Fel cardiol, Royal Victoria Hosp, Montreal, 46-47; specialist, Camp Hill Vet Hosp, Halifax, NS, 48-; from asst attend physician to attend, Victoria Gen Hosp, 48-; consult, Can Serv & Halifax Children's Hosps, 48-70. *Honors & Awards:* Duncan Graham Award, 78. *Mem:* Fel Am Col Physicians; Can Med Asn; Can Cardiovasc Soc. *Res:* Cardiovascular diseases; internal medicine; continuing medical and intern-resident education. *Mailing Add:* Fac Med Dalhousie Univ Halifax NS B3H 3J5 Can

STEEVES, RICHARD ALLISON, b Fredericksburg, Va, Feb 2, 38; m 65; c 3. ONCOLOGY, VIROLOGY. *Educ:* Univ Western Ont, MD, 61; Univ Toronto, PhD(med biophys), 66. *Prof Exp:* From sr cancer res scientist to assoc cancer res scientist, Roswell Park Mem Inst, 67-72; assoc prof develop biol & cancer, Albert Einstein Col Med, 72-77, vis assoc prof genetics, 77-80; ASST PROF HUMAN ONCOL, UNIV WIS-MADISON, 80- *Concurrent Pos:* Nat Cancer Inst Can fel, Dept Biol, McMaster Univ, 66-67; resident therapeut radiol, Albert Einstein Col Med, 77-80. *Mem:* Am Asn Cancer Res; Am Soc Microbiol; Am Endocurietheray Soc; Am Soc Therapeut Radiol. *Res:* Interaction of radiation and hyperthermin in cancer therapy; genetic control of target cells for murine leukemia viruses. *Mailing Add:* Dept Human Oncol Univ Wis-Madison Madison WI 53792

STEEVES, TAYLOR ARMSTRONG, b Quincy, Mass, Nov 29, 26; m 56; c 3. BOTANY. *Educ:* Univ Mass, BS, 47; Harvard Univ, AM, 49, PhD(biol), 51. *Prof Exp:* Jr fel, Soc Fels, Harvard Univ, 51-54, asst prof bot, Biol Labs, 54-59; assoc prof biol, 59-64, PROF BIOL, UNIV SASK, 64-, HEAD DEPT, 76- *Concurrent Pos:* Lalor Found Award, 58. *Mem:* Bot Soc Am; Am Soc Plant Physiol; fel Royal Soc Can; Soc Develop Biol; Can Bot Asn (pres, 72-73). *Res:* Morphogenesis of vascular plants; plant tissue culture and growth hormones. *Mailing Add:* Dept of Biol Univ of Sask Saskatoon SK S7N 0W0 Can

STEFAN, HEINZ G, b Landskron, Ger, June 12, 36; m 62; c 2. HYDROMECHANICS, WATER RESOURCES ENGINEERING. *Educ:* Munich Tech Univ, Dipl Ing, 59; Univ Toulouse, Ing Hydraulicien, 60, DrIng(hydromech), 63. *Prof Exp:* Res fel hydraul, Univ Minn, 63-64; chief engr, Inst Water Resources & Hydraul Eng, Tech Univ, Berlin, 65-67; asst prof, 67-72, assoc prof, 72-77, PROF CIVIL ENG, UNIV MINN, MINNEAPOLIS, 77- *Concurrent Pos:* Consult, Power Co; UN expert, India, 81; lectr, foreign countries; assoc dir, St Anthony Falls Hydrol Lab, 74- *Mem:* Am Soc Civil Engrs; Am Geophys Union; Int Asn Great Lakes Res; Am Water Resources Asn; Int Asn Water Resources. *Res:* River and lake hydromechanics; thermal pollution; aquatic systems; water resources. *Mailing Add:* Dept of Civil Eng Univ of Minn Minneapolis MN 55455

STEFANAKOS, ELIAS KYRIAKOS, b Athens, Greece, Sept 30, 40; m 68; c 1. ENGINEERING SCIENCE, SOLAR ENERGY. *Educ:* Wash State Univ, BS, 64, MS, 65, PhD(eng sci), 69. *Prof Exp:* Res asst elec eng, Wash State Univ, 66-68; from asst prof to assoc prof elec eng, Univ Idaho, 68-77; assoc prof, 77-80, PROF ELEC ENG, NC A&T STATE UNIV, 80- *Concurrent Pos:* Fel, 71-72, int travel grant, NSF, 78; vis prof, Greek Atomic Energy Comn, 75. *Mem:* AAAS; Inst Elec & Electronics Engrs; Am Soc Eng Educ; Int Solar Energy Soc. *Res:* Semiconductor materials and devices; photovoltaics; solar energy utilization. *Mailing Add:* Dept of Elec Eng NC A&T State Univ Greensboro NC 27411

STEFANCSIK, ERNEST ANTON, b Brooklyn, NY, Sept 10, 23. ORGANIC CHEMISTRY. *Educ:* St John's Univ, NY, BS, 43; NY Univ, MS, 47, PhD(chem), 53. *Prof Exp:* Chemist, Am Cyanamid Co, 43-46; teaching fel, NY Univ, 47-49, asst, 50-52; res chemist, 52-70, sr res chemist, 70-79, RES ASSOC, PIGMENTS DEPT, E I DU PONT DE NEMOURS & CO, INC, NEWARK, 79- *Mem:* AAAS; Am Chem Soc. *Res:* Physics and chemistry of organic pigments. *Mailing Add:* RD 8 Box 595 Flemington NJ 08822

STEFANESCU, DORU MICHAEL, b Sibiu, Romania, Nov 15, 42; m 77; c 2. METAL CASTING, SOLIDIFICATION OF ALLOYS. *Educ:* Polytech Inst Bucharest, BEng, 65, DEng, 73. *Prof Exp:* Jr researcher metal casting, Technol Inst Hot Processes, Bucharest, 68-70, sr res, 70-72, group head, 72-80; vis prof metall, Univ Wis-Madison, 80; ASSOC PROF METALL, UNIV ALA, 80- *Concurrent Pos:* Asst prof, Polytech Inst Bucharest, 73-80. *Mem:* Metall Soc; Am Soc Metals; Am Foundrymens Soc. *Res:* Nucleation and growth in solidification processes; physical chemistry of surface and interface reactions; physical chemistry and phase transformations of alloys; numerical modeling of alloys crystallization; thermal analysis of alloys; inoculation of alloys; manufacturing technologies of alloys; cast metals technology. *Mailing Add:* Col Eng Univ Ala PO Box G University AL 35486

STEFANI, ANDREW PETER, b Island of Cyprus, July 10, 26; US citizen; m 55; c 1. ORGANIC CHEMISTRY, PHYSICAL CHEMISTRY. *Educ:* Mich State Univ, BA, 56; Univ Colo, PhD(chem), 60. *Prof Exp:* Res assoc chem, State Univ NY Col Forestry, Syracuse Univ, 60-62; asst prof, Purdue Univ, 62-63; asst prof, 63-64, assoc prof, 64-68, PROF CHEM, UNIV MISS, 68-, CHMN DEPT CHEM, 77- *Concurrent Pos:* Res grants, Res Corp, 64, Petrol Res Fund & NSF, 64-68. *Mem:* AAAS; Am Chem Soc. *Res:* Chemical kinetics; free radical reactivity; solvent effects in chemical reactions; high pressure chemistry. *Mailing Add:* Dept of Chem Univ of Miss University MS 38677

STEFANI, STEFANO, b Trieste, Italy, Apr 19, 29; US citizen; m 58; c 2. RADIOTHERAPY, RADIOBIOLOGY. *Educ:* Univ Trieste, BS, 48; Univ Perugia, MD, 54. *Prof Exp:* Intern, Univ Trieste, 54-55; resident radiol, Med Sch, Univ Padua, 55-56, asst prof, 56-57; resident radiother, G Roussy Inst, Paris, 57-59; asst prof, Med Sch, Univ Paris, 59-60; resident, Univ Md Hosp, 61-62; res radiobiologist, Med Sch, Northwestern Univ, 62-63; from instr to asst prof radiol, Stritch Sch Med, Loyola Univ Chicago, 63-69; CHIEF THERAPEUT RADIOL SERV, VET ADMIN HOSP, HINES, 69-; PROF RADIOTHER, RUSH MED SCH, CHICAGO, 77-; DIR RADIOTHER DEPT, MT SINAI HOSP MED CTR, CHICAGO, 73- *Concurrent Pos:* Fels radiother, Curie Found, Paris, 57 & radiobiol, Nat Inst Nuclear Sci & Technol, Saclay, France, 58-59; consult, WHO, Geneva, 61, Argonne Nat Lab, AEC, 64-65; clin investr, Vet Admin Hosp, Hines, 64-69, staff physician, 67-68; abstractor, J Surg, Gynec & Obstet, 66-; prof radiother, Chicago Med Sch, 69-77; consult radiother, 72; dir, Radiother Dept, Northwest Community Hosp, Arlington Heights, 75-78. *Mem:* AAAS; AMA; Radiation Res Soc; Transplantation Soc; Radiol Soc NAm. *Res:* Radiation potentiators; total body irradiation and radioprotection; physiology and pathology of lymphocytes; bone marrow radiosensitivity and transfusion. *Mailing Add:* Therapeut Radiol Serv Vet Admin Hosp Hines IL 60141

STEFANKO, ROBERT, mining engineering, deceased

STEFANOU, HARRY, b New York, NY, June 16, 47; m 69; c 1. POLYMER PHYSICS. *Educ:* City Col New York, BS, 69; City Univ New York, PhD(phys chem), 73. *Prof Exp:* Res assoc polymer physics, Princeton Univ, 72-73; SR RES CHEMIST POLYMER PHYSICS, PENNWALT CORP, 73- *Mem:* AAAS; Am Chem Soc; Am Phys Soc. *Res:* The areas of polymer crystallization kinetics; polymer viscoelasticity and solution thermodynamics; piezo- and pyro-electric polymers. *Mailing Add:* Pennwalt Corp 900 First Ave King of Prussia PA 19406

STEFANSKI, RAYMOND JOSEPH, b Buffalo, NY, July 22, 41; m 69; c 1. PHYSICS. *Educ:* State Univ NY Buffalo, BA, 63; Yale Univ, PhD(physics), 69. *Prof Exp:* Res assoc physics, Yale Univ, 68-69; PHYSICIST I, FERMI NAT ACCELERATOR LAB, 69- *Mem:* Am Phys Soc; Opers Res Soc Am. *Res:* High energy physics and cosmic rays; neutrino interactions. *Mailing Add:* Neutrino Area Fermi Nat Accelerator Lab PO Box 500 Batavia IL 60510

STEFANSSON, BALDUR ROSMUND, b Vestfold, Man. PLANT BREEDING. *Educ:* Univ Man, BSA, 50, MS, 52, PhD(plant sci), 66. *Prof Exp:* Res assoc, 52-66, assoc prof, 66-74, PROF PLANT SCI, UNIV MAN, 74- *Honors & Awards:* Royal Bank Award, Royal Bank of Can, 75; Grindley Medal, Agr Inst Can, 78. *Mem:* Fel Agr Inst Can. *Res:* Plant breeding and related research with oilseed crops, formerly soybeans, currently rapeseed; compositional changes in rapeseed, including low erucic acid, low glucosinolate and low fibre content, induced by breeding. *Mailing Add:* Dept Plant Sci Univ Man Winnipeg MB R3T 2N2 Can

STEFFAN, WALLACE ALLAN, b St Paul, Minn, Aug 10, 34; m 66; c 1. ENTOMOLOGY. *Educ:* Univ Calif, Berkeley, BS, 61, PhD(entom), 65. *Prof Exp:* ENTOMOLOGIST, BERNICE P BISHOP MUS, 64-, HEAD DIPTERA SECT, 68- *Concurrent Pos:* NIH grant, 67-72; partic island ecosyst int res prog, US Int Biol Prog, 70; Grace H Griswold lectr, Cornell Univ, 70; mem affiliated grad faculty, Univ Hawaii. *Mem:* AAAS; Am Entom Soc; Am Mosquito Control Asn. *Res:* Systematics of Culicidae and Sciaridae; ecology of Culicidae; cytogenetics of Sciaridae. *Mailing Add:* Bishop Mus & Planetarium 1355 Kalihi Honolulu HI 96819

STEFFEK, ANTHONY J, b Milwaukee, Wis, Aug 6, 35; m 60; c 3. DENTISTRY, PHARMACOLOGY. *Educ:* Marquette Univ, DDS, 62, MS, 63, PhD(physiol), 65. *Prof Exp:* Res assoc pharmacol, Nat Inst Dent Res, 65-70; ASST PROF & DIR DIV DEVELOP BIOL, WALTER G ZOLLER MEM DENT CLIN, UNIV CHICAGO, 75-, RES ASSOC, DEPT ANAT, 75- *Concurrent Pos:* Am Dent Asn grant pharmacol, Nat Inst Dent Res, 65-; vis prof pharmacol, Charles Univ, Prague, Czechoslovakia. *Mem:* Am Dent Asn; Am Physiol Soc. *Res:* Metabolism and pharmacological disposition of environmental agents producing experimentally-induced oral-facial malformations, specifically cleft lip and palate; teratology. *Mailing Add:* Univ Chicago Sch Dent 5801 S Ellis Ave Chicago IL 60637

STEFFEN, ALBERT HARRY, b Menomonee Falls, Wis, May 24, 14; m 39; c 2. FOOD CHEMISTRY. *Educ:* Univ Wis, BS, 40. *Prof Exp:* Anal food chemist fats & oils, Armour & Co, 40-46, res food chemist, 46-52, fat & oil researcher, 52-56, asst prod mgr, Refining Div, 56-57, tech dir & qual control mgr, Lookout Oil & Refining Co Div, 57-67, prod mgr by-prod & mem staff, Cent Qual Control, Nebr, 67-68, mem cent qual assurance staff, Ill, 68-71, tech specialist, Qual Assurance Staff, Ariz, 71-79; CONSULT, 79- *Mem:* Am Oil Chem Soc; Am Soc Qual Control; Inst Food Technol. *Res:* Meat and meat by-products; fats and oils. *Mailing Add:* 4105 W Mission Ln Phoenix AZ 85021

STEFFEN, EARL KENNETH, b St Louis, Mo, Nov 12, 48; m 73; c 2. BACTERIOLOGY. *Educ:* Univ Mo, Rolla, BS, 72; Univ Mo, Columbia, MS, 75, PhD(microbiol), 80. *Prof Exp:* RES FEL, SCH MED, LA STATE UNIV, 80- *Mem:* Am Soc Microbiol; Asn Gnotobiotics. *Res:* Interrelationships of the microflora and host; virulence factors of anaerobic bacteria; animal models of infectious diseases; mode of action of bacterial toxins. *Mailing Add:* Dept Microbiol & Immunol Sch Med La State Univ PO Box 33932 Shreveport LA 71130

STEFFEN, ROLF MARCEL, b Basel, Switz, June 17, 22; m 49; c 2. NUCLEAR PHYSICS. *Educ:* Cantonal Col, Zurich, BS, 41; Swiss Fed Inst Technol, MS, 46, PhD, 48. *Prof Exp:* From asst prof to assoc prof, 49-56, PROF PHYSICS, PURDUE UNIV, WEST LAFAYETTE, 56- *Concurrent Pos:* Vis staff mem, Los Alamos Sci Lab, 64-; Sigma Xi Res Award, 64. *Mem:* Fel Am Phys Soc; Swiss Phys Soc. *Res:* Nuclear spectroscopy; angular correlations of nuclear radiation; influence of extranuclear fields on angular correlation; beta decay; nuclear structures studies by muonic x-rays; muonic atoms; hyperfine fields; heavy ion nuclear reactions. *Mailing Add:* Dept of Physics Purdue Univ West Lafayette IN 47907

STEFFENS, GEORGE LOUIS, b Bryantown, Md, June 13, 30; m 59; c 2. PLANT PHYSIOLOGY. *Educ:* Univ Md, BS, 51, MS, 53, PhD(agron), 56. *Prof Exp:* Agron biochemist, Gen Cigar Co, Inc, Pa, 58-61; plant physiologist, Coastal Plain Exp Sta, Ga, 61-63; plant physiologist, 63-74, lab chief, 74-82, CHIEF, FRUIT LAB, HORT INST, BELTSVILLE AGR RES CTR, AGR RES SERV, USDA, 82- *Honors & Awards:* Philip Morris Award, 72. *Mem:* AAAS; Am Soc Plant Physiologists; Am Chem Soc; Scand Soc Plant Physiologists. *Res:* Natural and synthetic plant growth regulating chemicals, their development and effect on plants. *Mailing Add:* Fruit Lab Hort Inst Beltsville Agr Res Ctr USDA Beltsville MD 20705

STEFFENS, JAMES JEFFREY, b Lakewood, Ohio, Nov 1, 42; m 66; c 2. BIO-ORGANIC CHEMISTRY, DRUG METABOLISM. *Educ:* Amherst Col, BA, 64; Mass Inst Technol, PhD(chem), 71. *Prof Exp:* Fel, Pa State Univ, 71-74; sr res chemist, Drug Metab, Merck & Co, Inc, 74-77; SR RES CHEMIST, CROP CHEM, MOBIL CHEM CO, 77- *Res:* Mechanisms of enzyme action; plant biochemistry. *Mailing Add:* Crop Chem Dept Res & Develop PO Box 240 Edison NJ 08817

STEFFENSEN, DALE MARRIOTT, b Salt Lake City, Utah, Apr 17, 22; m 50, 70; c 3. GENETICS. *Educ:* Univ Calif, Los Angeles, AB, 48; Univ Calif, Berkeley, PhD(genetics), 52. *Prof Exp:* Res geneticist asst, Univ Calif, 52; from assoc geneticist to geneticist, Brookhaven Nat Lab, 52-61; PROF GENETICS & DEVELOP, UNIV ILL, URBANA, 61- *Concurrent Pos:* USPHS spec fel, Naples, Italy, 67-68. *Mem:* Genetics Soc Am; Am Soc Cell Biol; Soc Develop Biol. *Res:* Nuclear structure, developmental genetics and cell biology; biochemistry of nuclear structures; gene mapping on chromosomes by RNA-DNA hybridization. *Mailing Add:* Dept Genetics & Develop Univ Ill 515 Morrill Hall 505 S Goodwin Ave Urbana IL 61801

STEFFEY, ORAN DEAN, b Billings, Okla, May 19, 21; m 43; c 2. INDUSTRIAL HYGIENE. *Educ:* Phillips Univ, AB, 48; Okla State Univ, MS, 50, PhD(bot), 53. *Prof Exp:* Asst zool, Phillips Univ, 42, asst bot & zool, 47-48; res assoc, Res Found, 50-53, from instr to asst prof bot & plant path, 53-56; radiol health physics officer, Radiation Lab, Continental Oil Co, 56-72, INDUSTRIAL HYGIENIST, MED DEPT, CONOCO INC, 72- *Concurrent Pos:* Mem, Okla State Radiation Adv Comt, 72- *Mem:* Health Physics Soc; Sigma Xi; Am Indust Hygiene Asn. *Res:* Variations of the fruits of Quercus Macrocarpa; development of an autoradiographic technique for use in botanical investigations; cyto-morphogenetic studies in sorghum. *Mailing Add:* Med Dept Conoco Inc Ponca City OK 74601

STEFFGEN, FREDERICK WILLIAMS, b San Diego, Calif, Nov 21, 26; m 49; c 2. FUEL SCIENCE, SURFACE CHEMISTRY. *Educ:* Stanford Univ, BS, 47; Northwestern Univ, Evanston, MS, 49; Univ Del, PhD(org chem), 53. *Prof Exp:* Res chemist, Cutter Labs, Calif, 49-50; res chemist, Esso Res & Eng Co, Standard Oil Co (NJ), La, 52-56; sr res chemist, Union Oil Res, Union Oil Co Calif, 56-60; res assoc, Richfield Res Ctr, Atlantic Richfield Co, 60-69; mgr process develop, Antox, Inc, WVa, 70-71; supvr res chemist, Pittsburgh Energy Res Ctr, US Bur Mines, 71-75, res supvr chem, Pittsburgh Energy Tech Res Ctr, US Energy Res & Develop Admin, 75-77 & US Dept of Energy, 77-79, MGR, UNIV CONTRACTS MGT DIV, PITTSBURG ENERGY TECH CTR, DEPT ENERGY, 79- *Mem:* Am Chem Soc; Am Inst Chem Engr; Catalysis Soc. *Res:* Heterogeneous catalysis, processes and catalyst preparation; conversions to produce low sulfur, clean fuels from coal, petroleum and organic wastes; support of grants and contracts in advanced coal research. *Mailing Add:* 7178 Sansue Dr Bethel Park PA 15102

STEFKO, PAUL LOWELL, b Middletown, Conn, June 29, 15; m 40; c 1. EXPERIMENTAL SURGERY, PHARMACOLOGY. *Educ:* Univ Va, BS, 44. *Prof Exp:* Tech surg asst, NY Hosp, New York, 38-43; exp surgeon & pharmacologist, 47-61, SR PHARMACOLOGIST & EXP SURGEON, HOFFMANN-LA ROCHE, INC, 61- *Concurrent Pos:* Exp surg consult, USAEC & Off Naval Res & Develop, 40-43, cert, 45. *Mem:* AAAS; Sigma Xi; Am Indust Hyg Asn; Am Asn Lab Animal Sci; NY Acad Sci. *Res:* Vascular surgery; blood vessel transposition; gastroenterology; spasmolytics; antitussives. *Mailing Add:* Hoffmann-La Roche Inc 38 Blue Hill Rd Clifton NJ 07013

STEG, L(EO), b Vienna, Austria, Mar 30, 22; nat US; m 47; c 3. ENGINEERING MECHANICS, PHYSICS. *Educ:* City Col New York, BS, 47; Univ Mo, MS, 48; Cornell Univ, PhD(mech, math, physics), 51. *Prof Exp:* Chief engr, Fed Design Co, 46-47; instr mech eng, Univ Mo, 47-48; from instr to asst prof mech & mat, Cornell Univ, 48-55; systs engr, Missile & Space Div, Gen Elec Co, 55-56, mgr, Space Sci Lab, 56-80; SR VPRES, RES INST DIV, UNIV CITY SCI CTR, 80- *Concurrent Pos:* Consult, Fed Design Co, 48-53; Lincoln Lab, Mass Inst Technol, 52-55; Ramo-Wooldridge Corp, 54-55 & US Dept Defense, 67-71; res engr, Boeing Airplane Co, 54; ed-in-chief, Am Inst Aeronaut & Astronaut Jour, 62-67; adj prof, Drexel Univ, 70-; mem, Bd Managers, Franklin Inst, 72-; vchmn, Comt Space Res Working Group-Material Sci Space, 75- *Mem:* Fel AAAS; Am Inst Aeronaut & Astronaut; NY Acad Sci; Am Geophys Union. *Res:* Nonlinear mechanics; stability in dynamical systems; applied mechanics; space and reentry technology; research administration. *Mailing Add:* Res Inst Div Univ City Sci Ctr 3624 Market St Philadelphia PA 19104

STEGELMANN, ERICH J, b Lütjenburg, Ger, Mar 28, 14; m 51; c 3. ELECTROOPTICS. *Educ:* Tech Univ, Berlin, Dipl Ing, 38, Dr Ing, 39. *Prof Exp:* Develop engr, Rheinmetall-Borsig, Ger, 44-45; scientist, Technisches Büro 11 der USSR, Berlin, 46-48; sr res engr, Can Aviation Electronics, Montreal, 52-54; design & res specialist, Lockheed Calif Corp, 54-60, sr res scientist, 60-63, mem tech staff, Northrop Space Lab, 63-64; sr tech specialist, Space Div, NAm Aviation, Inc, Calif, 64-68, mem tech staff, Autonetics Div, NAm Rockwell Corp, 68-70; mem tech staff, Electro-Optical Labs, Hughes Aircraft Co, Culver City, 72-80. *Mem:* Optical Soc Am. *Res:* Space physics; propagation of light in atmosphere. *Mailing Add:* 18559 Chatsworth St Northridge CA 91326

STEGEMAN, GEORGE I, b Edinburgh, Scotland, Aug 4, 42; Can citizen; m 67; c 3. NONLINEAR OPTICS. *Educ:* Univ Toronto, BSc, 65, MSc, 66, PhD(physics), 69. *Prof Exp:* Prof physics, Univ Toronto, 69-80; PROF OPTICS, UNIV ARIZ, 80- *Concurrent Pos:* Vis prof, Univ Calif, Irvine, 79-80 & Stanford Univ, 80. *Honors & Awards:* Hertzberg Medal, Can Asn Physicists, 80. *Mem:* Fel Optical Soc Am; Can Asn Physicists; Inst Elec & Electronics Engrs; Am Phys Soc. *Res:* Propagation charcteristics of various waves guided by surfaces or films, their nonlinear interactions with matter and one another and their potential applications. *Mailing Add:* Optical Sci Ctr Univ Ariz Tucson AZ 85721

STEGEN, GILBERT ROLLAND, b Long Beach, Calif, Aug 19, 39; m 66. FLUID MECHANICS. *Educ:* Mass Inst Technol, BS, 61; Stanford Univ, MS, 62, PhD(aeronaut, astronaut), 67. *Prof Exp:* Develop engr, United Tech Ctr, United Aircraft Corp, 62-63; vis sr res fel, Col Aeronaut Eng, 67; asst res engr, Univ Calif, San Diego, 67-69; asst prof civil eng, Colo State Univ, 69-70; asst prof geol & geophys sci, Princeton Univ, 70-74; div mgr & sr res scientist, Flow Res Co, 74-76; mgr, 76-80, ASST VPRES, SCI APPLICATIONS INC, 80- *Mem:* Am Meteorol Soc; Sigma Xi; Am Phys Soc; Am Geophys Union. *Res:* Experimental fluid mechanics; experimental studies in atmospheric and oceanic turbulence. *Mailing Add:* Sci Applns Inc 13400 B Northup Way Suite 36 Bellevue WA 98005

STEGENGA, DAVID ALLAN, mathematical analysis, see previous edition

STEGER, THEODORE ROOSEVELT, JR, b Jacksonville, Fla, May 17, 46; m 70; c 2. POLYMER PHYSICS. *Educ:* Univ Fla, BS, 67; Mass Inst Technol, PhD(physics), 74. *Prof Exp:* sr res physicist polymer physics, 74-78, TECHNOL GROUP LEADER PHYS MEASUREMENTS, MONSANTO CO, 78- *Mem:* Am Phys Soc; Am Crystallog Asn. *Res:* Physical properties of solids and fluids. *Mailing Add:* Corp Res & Develop Monsanto Co 800 N Lindbergh Blvd Saint Louis MO 63166

STEGINK, LEWIS D, b Holland, Mich, Feb 8, 37; m 62; c 2. BIOLOGICAL CHEMISTRY. *Educ:* Hope Col, BA, 58; Univ Mich, MS & PhD(biol chem), 63. *Prof Exp:* Fel biochem, 63-65, asst prof pediat, 65-71, asst prof pediat & biochem, 68-71, assoc prof, 71-76, PROF PEDIAT & BIOCHEM, UNIV IOWA, 76- *Honors & Awards:* Mead Johnson Award, Am Inst Nutrit, 76. *Mem:* Soc Pediat Res; Am Chem Soc; Am Inst Nutrit; Am Soc Biol Chemists; Am Pediat Soc. *Res:* Biochemistry of normal and abnormal growth and development; amino acids; parental nutrition; acetylated proteins. *Mailing Add:* Dept of Pediat Univ of Iowa Iowa City IA 52240

STEGNER, ROBERT W, biology, deceased

STEGUN, IRENE ANNE, b Yonkers, NY, Feb 9, 19. NUMERICAL ANALYSIS. *Educ:* Col Mt St Vincent, BA, 40; Columbia Univ, MA, 41. *Prof Exp:* MATHEMATICIAN, NAT BUR STANDARDS, 43. *Honors & Awards:* Gold Medal, Nat Bur Stand, 65. *Mem:* Am Math Soc; Soc Indust & Appl Math; Asn Comput Mach; AAAS; Math Asn Am. *Res:* Automatic computation; special functions. *Mailing Add:* Nat Bur Standards Washington DC 20234

STEHBENS, WILLIAM ELLIS, b Australia, Aug 6, 26; m 61; c 5. PATHOLOGY. *Educ:* Univ Sydney, MB & BS, 50, MD, 62; Oxford Univ, DPhil(path), 60; FRCPath(Australia), 61; FRCPath(E), 63. *Prof Exp:* From lectr to sr lectr path, Univ Sydney, 53-62; from assoc prof to prof, Wash Univ, 66-68; prof path, Albany Med Col, 68-74; PROF PATH, WELLINGTON CLIN SCH, UNIV OTAGO, NZ, 74- *Concurrent Pos:* Teaching fel path, Univ Sydney, 52; sr res fel, Australian Nat Univ, 62-66, sr fel, 66; pathologist-in-chief & dir dept path & lab med, Jewish Hosp St Louis, 66-68; dir electron micros unit, Vet Admin Hosp, Albany, 68-74; dir, Wellington Cancer & Med Res Inst, 74- *Honors & Awards:* R T Hall Res Prize, Cardiac Soc Australia & NZ, 66. *Res:* Relationship of intimal thickening, thrombosis and hemodynamics to the pathogenesis of atherosclerosis and cerebral aneurysms. *Mailing Add:* Dept Path Wellington Clin Sch Univ Otago Wellington New Zealand

STEHLE, PHILIP MCLELLAN, b Philadelphia, Pa, Mar 3, 19; m 42; c 3. QUANTUM ELECTRONICS. *Educ:* Univ Mich, AB, 40, AM, 41; Princeton Univ, PhD(physics), 44. *Prof Exp:* Asst, Univ Mich, 40-41; instr physics, Princeton Univ, 41-44; instr, Harvard Univ, 46-47; asst prof, 47, dept chmn, 70-75, PROF PHYSICS, UNIV PITTSBURGH, 47-, CHMN DEPT, 82- *Mem:* Am Phys Soc. *Res:* Quantum theory; quantum optics. *Mailing Add:* Dept Physics & Astron Univ of Pittsburgh Pittsburgh PA 15260

STEHLI, FRANCIS GREENOUGH, b Montclair, NJ, Oct 16, 24; m 48; c 4. GEOLOGY. *Educ:* St Lawrence Univ, BS, 49, MS, 50; Columbia Univ, PhD(geol), 53. *Prof Exp:* Asst prof invert paleont, Calif Inst Technol, 53-56; res engr, Pan Am Petrol Corp, 57, tech group supvr, 58-60; prof geol, Case Western Reserve Univ, 60-74, chmn dept, 61-73, Samuel St John prof earth sci, 74-80, actg dean sci, 75-76, actg dean sci & eng, 76-77, dean sci & eng, 77-79; pres, Dicar Corp of Case Western Reserve, 78-80; DEAN GRAD STUDIES & RES, UNIV FLA, 80- *Concurrent Pos:* Mem, NSF Earth Sci Adv Panel, 67-69, chmn, 69; chmn comt ocean drilling, Nat Res Coun, 81-82. *Mem:* Paleont Soc (pres, 77-80); fel Geol Soc Am; Geochem Soc; fel AAAS;

Am Soc Eng Educ. *Res:* Paleozoic brachiopods; Mesozoic stratigraphy of Gulf Coast and western Mexico; paleoecology; carbonate rock formation and diagenesis; continental drift, polar wondering and paleoclimatology. *Mailing Add:* Off Dean Grad Studies Rm 223 Grinter Hall Univ Fla Gainesville FL 32611

STEHLING, FERDINAND CHRISTIAN, b Fredericksburg, Tex, Feb 18, 30; m; c 4. POLYMER PHYSICS, PHYSICAL CHEMISTRY. *Educ:* St Mary's Univ, Md, BS & BA, 50; Univ Tex, MA, 57, PhD(phys chem), 58. *Prof Exp:* Res assoc, 58-80, SR RES ASSOC POLYMERS, EXXON CHEM CO, 80- *Honors & Awards:* Prof Progress Award, Soc Prof Engrs & Chemists, 73. *Mem:* Am Chem Soc; Sigma Xi. *Res:* Polymer morphology and properties; mass spectroscopy. *Mailing Add:* 214 Post Oak Baytown TX 77520

STEHLY, DAVID NORVIN, b Bethlehem, Pa, Oct 3, 33; m 61; c 2. INORGANIC CHEMISTRY. *Educ:* Moravian Col, BS, 59; Lehigh Univ, MS, 62, PhD(inorg chem), 67. *Prof Exp:* Instr chem, 60-67, from asst prof to assoc prof, 67-75, PROF CHEM, MUHLENBERG COL, 75- *Mem:* Am Chem Soc. *Res:* Metal chelates of substitued amides; trace metal ions in surface waters. *Mailing Add:* Dept of Chem Muhlenberg Col Allentown PA 18104

STEHNEY, ANDREW FRANK, b Chicago, Ill, May 4, 20; m 43; c 3. RADIOCHEMISTRY, RADIOBIOLOGY. *Educ:* Univ Chicago, BS, 42, PhD(chem), 50. *Prof Exp:* Instr chem, Univ Chicago, 49-50; assoc chemist, 50-71, SR CHEMIST, ARGONNE NAT LAB, 71-, ASSOC DIV DIR, 76- *Concurrent Pos:* Lectr, Univ Chicago, 56-61; vis scientist, Europ Orgn Nuclear Res, 61-63; mem subcomt radiochem, Nat Res Coun, 69-77; mem, Safe Drinking Water Comt, Nat Acad Sci, 76. *Mem:* AAAS; Am Chem Soc; Am Phys Soc; Radiation Res Soc; Health Physics Soc. *Res:* Toxicity of radium and other internal emitters; applications of radiochemistry to environmental studies; nuclear reactions. *Mailing Add:* Radiol & Environ Res Div Argonne Nat Lab Argonne IL 60439

STEHNEY, ANN KATHRYN, b Oak Ridge, Tenn, June 30, 46. PURE MATHEMATICS. *Educ:* Bryn Mawr Col, AB, 67; State Univ NY, Stony Brook, MA, 69, PhD(math), 71. *Prof Exp:* Asst prof, 71-77, chmn dept, 77-78, 80-81, ASSOC PROF MATH, WELLESLEY COL, 77- *Concurrent Pos:* Vis scholar, Enrico Fermi Inst, Univ Chicago, 74-75; vis assoc prof, State Univ NY, Stony Brook, 81-82. *Mem:* Am Math Soc; Math Asn Am. *Res:* Differential geometry and general relativity. *Mailing Add:* Dept of Math Wellesley Col Wellesley MA 02181

STEHOUWER, DAVID MARK, b Grand Rapids, Mich, July 14, 43; m 68; c 3. ORGANIC CHEMISTRY. *Educ:* Hope Col, BA, 65; Univ Mich, Ann Arbor, MS, 67, PhD(org chem), 70. *Prof Exp:* Sr chemist res labs, Texaco Inc, 70-76; sr res scientist, Gen Motors Res Labs, 76-81; TECH ADV FUELS & LUBRICANTS, CUMMINS ENGINE CO, 81- *Mem:* Am Soc Testing & Mat; Soc Automotive Engrs; Am Chem Soc. *Res:* Lubricant additive chemistry; mechanisms of lubricant performance; corrosion mechanisms; engine oil wear protection; engine oil consumption; oil conservation and recycling. *Mailing Add:* Cummins Engine Co Inc Mail Code 50183 Box 3005 Columbus IN 47201

STEHR, FREDERICK WILLIAM, b Athens, Ohio, Dec 23, 32; m 59; c 2. ENTOMOLOGY. *Educ:* Univ Ohio, BS, 54; Univ Minn, MS, 58, PhD(entom), 64. *Prof Exp:* Res fel entom, Univ Minn, 62-65; from asst prof to assoc prof, 65-76, PROF ENTOM, MICH STATE UNIV, 76-, ASST CHMN DEPT, 79- *Honors & Awards:* Karl Jordan Medal, Lepidop Soc, 74. *Mem:* Entom Soc Am; Soc Syst Zool; Lepidop Soc; Ecol Soc Am; Entom Soc Can. *Res:* Systematics of Lepidoptera and immature insects; biological control; ecology. *Mailing Add:* Dept of Entom Mich State Univ East Lansing MI 48824

STEHSEL, MELVIN LOUIS, b Long Beach, Calif, Oct 3, 24; m 57; c 2. ORGANIC CHEMISTRY, PLANT PHYSIOLOGY. *Educ:* Univ Calif, Berkeley, BS, 45, MS, 47, PhD(plant physiol), 50. *Prof Exp:* Off Naval Res fel biochem genetics, 50-51; French Govt fel, 51; res chemist, Socony Mobil Oil Co, 51-56; chief phys lab, Aerojet-Gen Corp, 56-65; assoc prof biol, 65-72, PROF BIOL, PASADENA CITY COL, 72- *Mem:* AAAS; Bot Soc Am; Am Chem Soc. *Res:* High temperature mechanical properties of graphite for nuclear rockets; action of natural and synthetic plant growth hormones; stimulation and cause of cell differentiation in plant tissue culture; plant biochemistry. *Mailing Add:* 1570 E Colorado Blvd Pasadena City Col Pasadena CA 91106

STEIB, MICHAEL LEE, b May 2, 41; US citizen; m 66. MATHEMATICAL ANALYSIS. *Educ:* Univ Tex, BA, 63, MA, 65, PhD(math), 66. *Prof Exp:* ASST PROF MATH, UNIV HOUSTON, 66- *Mem:* Am Math Soc. *Res:* Integration theory; questions concerning conditions which guarantee integrability. *Mailing Add:* 3717 Nottingham Houston TX 77005

STEIB, RENE J, b Vacherie, La, July 30, 18; m 44; c 2. PLANT PATHOLOGY. *Educ:* La State Univ, PhD(sugarcane dis), 49. *Prof Exp:* Asst gen mgr, Am Sugarcane League, La, 49-51; from asst prof to prof plant path & crop physiol, Agr Exp Sta, La State Univ, Baton Rouge, 64-80; RETIRED. *Concurrent Pos:* Consult to govt, indust & orgn, 64-; int consult. *Mem:* Am Phytopath Soc; Am Soc Sugarcane Technologists; Inst Soc Sugarcane Technologists. *Res:* Fungal and virus diseases of sugarcane, especially in Louisiana; testing of new varieties for disease resistance. *Mailing Add:* 330 Seyburn Dr Baton Rouge LA 70808

STEICHEN, RICHARD JOHN, b Wichita, Kans, July 1, 44; m 68; c 2. ANALYTICAL CHEMISTRY. *Educ:* Rockhurst Col, BA, 66; Univ Kans, PhD(anal chem), 71. *Prof Exp:* Asst prof chem, Rockhurst Col, 71-73; SR RES CHEMIST, GOODYEAR TIRE & RUBBER CO, 73- *Mem:* Am Chem Soc. *Res:* Analytical methods development for industrial applications including process control, Occupational Safety and Health Administration and Food and Drug Administration compliance. *Mailing Add:* 3447 Tennyson Dr Akron OH 44313

STEIDEL, ROBERT F(RANCIS), JR, b Goshen, NY, July 6, 26; m 46; c 4. MECHANICAL ENGINEERING. *Educ:* Columbia Univ, BS, 48, MS, 49; Univ Calif, DEng, 55. *Prof Exp:* From instr to asst prof mech eng, Ore State Col, 49-54; assoc, 54-55, from asst prof to assoc prof, 55-62, chmn div mech design, 61-64, chmn dept, 69-74, PROF MECH ENG, UNIV CALIF, BERKELEY, 62-; ENG ADV, JOHN WILEY & SONS, 73- *Concurrent Pos:* Consult, Bonneville Power Admin, 50-53, Missile & Space Div, Lockheed Aircraft Corp, 59-, Jet Propulsion Lab, Calif, 66-68 & Sandia Corp, 67; consult, Lawrence Radiation Lab, Univ Calif, 55-, proj engr, 58; fac athletic rep, Univ Calif, 72- *Mem:* Am Soc Mech Engrs; Am Soc Eng Educ; Brit Inst Mech Engrs. *Res:* Engineering mechanics; mechanical vibration, systems analysis and design. *Mailing Add:* Dept of Mech Eng 5138 Echeverry Hall Berkeley CA 94720

STEIER, WILLIAM H(ENRY), b Kendallville, Ind, May 25, 33; m 55; c 4. ELECTRICAL ENGINEERING, OPTICS. *Educ:* Evansville Col, BS, 55; Univ Ill, MS, 57, PhD(elec eng), 60. *Prof Exp:* Asst elec eng, Univ Ill, Urbana, 55-60; asst prof, 60-62; mem tech staff, Bell Tel Labs, NJ, 62-68; assoc prof, 68-76, PROF ELEC ENG, UNIV SOUTHERN CALIF, 76-, CO-CHMN DEPT, 68- *Concurrent Pos:* Consult, Space Technol Labs, 61-62 & Northrop Corp Labs, 68- *Mem:* Fel Inst Elec & Electronics Engrs; AAAS. *Res:* Propagation of electromagnetic energy; millimeterwave detectors and transmission lines; optical transmission systems, modulators and components; lasers; optical signal processing. *Mailing Add:* Dept Elec Eng Univ Southern Calif PHE 604 Los Angeles CA 90007

STEIGELMANN, WILLIAM HENRY, b Vineland, NJ, Jan 19, 35; m 58; c 2. ENGINEERING. *Educ:* Drexel Univ, BS, 56; Oak Ridge Sch Reactor Technol, dipl, 58; Union Col, NY, MS, 59. *Prof Exp:* Engr, RCA Corp, 56-57, NY Shipbldg Corp, 57-58 & Res Labs, Franklin Inst, Pa, 58-61; dept head nuclear eng, Kuljian Corp, 63-67; proj engr, NUS Corp, 67-69; lab mgr nuclear eng & energy studies, Res Labs, Franklin Inst, Pa, 69-76; vpres, Solar Energy Systs, Inc, 77-78; PRES, EN-SAVE, 78-; DIR ENERGY TECHNOL, SYNERGIC RESOURCES CORP, 80- *Concurrent Pos:* Adj prof, Drexel Univ, 76- *Mem:* Am Nuclear Soc; Am Soc Mech Engrs; Int Solar Energy Soc. *Res:* Energy conversion; nuclear engineering; performance qualification testing; solar energy systems; energy conservation; co-generation; energy price and demand forecasting. *Mailing Add:* En-Save Inc 117 Partree Rd Cherry Hill NJ 08003

STEIGER, FRED HAROLD, b Cleveland, Ohio, May 11, 29; m 52; c 2. APPLIED CHEMISTRY, COSMETIC CHEMISTRY. *Educ:* Univ Pa, BA, 51; Temple Univ, MA, 56. *Prof Exp:* Res chemist, Rohm and Haas Co, Pa, 51-60; group leader sanit protection, 60-62, sr res chemist, 62-68, sr res scientist, 68-74, sr res assoc, 74-76, PROD DEVELOP MGR, PERSONAL PROD CO DIV, JOHNSON & JOHNSON, 76- *Concurrent Pos:* Abstractor, Chem Abstr, 53-68, ed textile sect, 68-; vpres prof affairs, NJ Inst Chemists, 75-77. *Mem:* Am Chem Soc; Am Asn Textile Chem & Colorists; fel Am Inst Chem; Am Soc Test & Mat; Fiber Soc. *Res:* Textile chemistry; fibers and polymers; sanitary protection; absorption of liquids; cosmetics and toiletries; household products. *Mailing Add:* Res & Develop Div Personal Prod Co Milltown NJ 08850

STEIGER, ROGER ARTHUR, b Potosi, Wis, Dec 29, 39; m 67; c 3. HIGH TEMPERATURE CHEMISTRY. *Educ:* Wis State Univ-Platteville, BS, 61; Univ Iowa, PhD(phys chem), 67. *Prof Exp:* sr res chemist indust chem div, 67-79, res assoc, 79-81, SR RES ASSOC, PPG INDUSTS INC, 81- *Mem:* AAAS; Am Chem Soc; Am Ceramic Soc. *Res:* Thermodynamics of refractory compounds; plasma chemical reactions; powder metallurgy of fine-grained cemented carbides; preparation, fabrication and properties of sinterable submicron ceramic powders. *Mailing Add:* Indust Chem Div PPG Indust Inc PO Box 31 Barberton OH 44203

STEIGER, WALTER RICHARD, b Colo, Sept 4, 23; m 46; c 2. PHYSICS. *Educ:* Mass Inst Technol, BS, 48; Univ Hawaii, MS, 50; Univ Cincinnati, PhD(physics), 53. *Prof Exp:* Asst physics, Univ Hawaii, 48-50; instr, Univ Cincinnati, 51-52; from asst prof to assoc prof, 53-65, PROF PHYSICS, UNIV HAWAII, 65-, CHMN DEPT PHYSICS & ASTRON, 72- *Concurrent Pos:* Vis researcher high altitude observ, Univ Colo, 59-60; Fulbright res scholar, Tokyo Astron Observ, 66-67. *Mem:* AAAS; Am Phys Soc; Am Asn Physics Teachers. *Res:* Upper atmosphere physics, ionosphere; airglow. *Mailing Add:* Dept of Physics & Astron Univ of Hawaii Honolulu HI 96822

STEIGER, WILLIAM LEE, b New York, NY, Nov 17, 39; m 71; c 2. LINEAR OPTIMIZATION. *Educ:* Mass Inst Technol, SB, 61, SM, 63; Australian Nat Univ, PhD(statist), 69. *Prof Exp:* ASSOC PROF COMPUT SCI, RUTGERS UNIV, 74- *Concurrent Pos:* Assoc prof, Princeton Univ, 79-81; res fel, Australian Nat Univ, 79-81. *Mem:* Am Math Soc; Inst Math Statist; Australian Math Soc. *Res:* Probability theory; statistical computing; linear optimization. *Mailing Add:* Dept Comp Sci Rutgers Univ New Brunswick NJ 08903

STEIGERT, FREDERICK EDWARD, nuclear physics, see previous edition

STEIGERWALD, ROBERT F(RANCIS), metallurgy, see previous edition

STEIGLITZ, KENNETH, b Weehawken, NJ, Jan 30, 39; m 65; c 1. ELECTRICAL ENGINEERING, COMPUTER SCIENCE. *Educ:* NY Univ, BEE, 59, MEE, 60, EngScD(elec eng), 63. *Prof Exp:* From asst prof to assoc prof, 63-73, PROF ELEC ENG, PRINCETON UNIV, 73- *Concurrent Pos:* Assoc ed, Jour Asn Comput Mach, 78-81. *Mem:* fel Inst Elec & Electronics Engrs. *Res:* Algorithms; digital signal processing. *Mailing Add:* Dept of Elec Eng & Comput Sci Princeton Univ Princeton NJ 08540

STEIGMAN, GARY, b New York, NY, Feb 23, 41; div. ASTROPHYSICS. *Educ:* City Col New York, BS, 61; NY Univ, MS, 63, PhD(physics), 68. *Prof Exp:* Vis fel, Inst Theoret Astron, Cambridge, Eng, 68-70; res fel, Calif Inst Technol, 70-72; asst prof astron, Yale Univ, 72-78; assoc prof, 78-80, PROF,

BARTOL RES FOUND, UNIV DEL, 80- *Concurrent Pos:* Vis scientist, Nat Radio Astron Observ, 75; vis scholar, Stanford Univ, 79; res scientist, Inst Theoret Physics, Santa Barbara, 81. *Mem:* Am Astron Soc; Int Astron Union. *Res:* Interstellar physics; cosmology. *Mailing Add:* Bartol Res Found Univ of Del Newark DE 19711

STEIGMANN, FREDERICK, b Austria, Apr 25, 05; nat US; m 37; c 3. MEDICINE. *Educ:* Univ Ill, BS, 28, MD, 30, MS, 38. *Prof Exp:* Asst, 33-34, from instr to assoc prof, 34-72, CLIN PROF MED, UNIV ILL COL MED, 72- *Concurrent Pos:* Pvt pract, 33-; dir depts therapeut & gastroenterol & attend physician, Cook County Hosp, 40- *Mem:* Fel Soc Exp Biol & Med; fel Am Soc Pharmacol & Exp Therapeut; fel Am Fedn Clin Res; fel Am Col Physicians; Am Gastroenterol Asn. *Res:* Gastroenterology; liver; vitamin A; protein metabolism. *Mailing Add:* 30 N Michigan Ave Chicago IL 60602

STEIJN, ROELOF P(IETER), metallurgy, see previous edition

STEILA, DONALD, b Cleveland, Ohio, Sept 26, 39; m 68; c 1. CLIMATOLOGY. *Educ:* Kent State Univ, BS, 65, MA, 66; Univ Ga, PhD(geog), 71. *Prof Exp:* Instr geog, Univ Ga, 70-71; asst prof, Univ Ariz, 71-72; asst prof, 72-75, ASSOC PROF GEOG, E CAROLINA UNIV, 75- *Mem:* Asn Am Geogr; Am Meteorol Soc; Soil Sci Soc Am; Am Soc Agron. *Res:* Quantitative identification of drought intensity; the impact of drought upon vegetation and the temporal and spatial patterns of drought occurrence; the spatial characteristics of soil bodies. *Mailing Add:* Dept Geog ECarolina Univ Greenville NC 27834

STEIMAN, HENRY ROBERT, b Winnipeg, Man, Aug 2, 38; m 73; c 2. DENTISTRY, PHYSIOLOGY. *Educ:* NDak State Univ, BS, 64; Wayne State Univ, MS, 67, PhD(physiol), 69; Univ Detroit, DDS, 73; Indiana Univ, MSD, 79. *Prof Exp:* Asst prof, 69-73, chmn dept physiol, 70-77, dir div biol sci, 73-77, ASSOC PROF PHYSIOL, DENT SCH, UNIV DETROIT, 73-, CHMN DEPT ENDODONTICS, 80- *Concurrent Pos:* Mich Asn Regional Med Progs grant, Dent Sch, Univ Detroit, 74-76; consult, Hypertension Coordinating & Planning Comt, Southeastern Mich, 74-77; consult, Detroit Receiving Hosp, 80-, Vet Admin Hosp, Allen Park, 81- *Mem:* Am Dent Asn; Am Asn Endodontics. *Mailing Add:* Dept Endodontics Sch Dent Univ Detroit Detroit MI 48207

STEIMLE, TIMOTHY C, b Benton Harbor, Mich, May 6, 51; m 74. ATOMIC PHYSICS, MOLECULAR PHYSICS. *Educ:* Mich State Univ, BS, 73; Univ Calif, Santa Barbara, PhD(chem), 78. *Prof Exp:* Fel, Rice Univ, 78-80; fel, Univ Southampton, Eng, 80-81; RES ASST, UNIV ORE, 81- *Mem:* Am Phys Soc. *Res:* High resolution spectroscopy of gas phase free radials and ionic species. *Mailing Add:* Physics Dept Univ Ore Eugene OR 97403

STEIN, ABRAHAM MORTON, b Chicago, Ill, Aug 9, 23; m 43; c 1. BIOCHEMISTRY. *Educ:* Univ Calif, Los Angeles, AB, 49, MA, 51; Univ Southern Calif, PhD(biochem), 57. *Prof Exp:* NIH res fel biochem, Brandeis Univ, 57-59; res assoc, Univ Pa, 59-65, sr res investr, 65-67; assoc prof col med, Univ Fla, 67-71; chmn dept biol sci, 71-74, PROF BIOL SCI, FLA INT UNIV, 71- *Concurrent Pos:* Adj prof col med, Univ Miami, 71- *Mem:* AAAS; Am Soc Biol Chem; Am Chem Soc; NY Acad Sci. *Res:* Enzymology; flavoproteins; metabolic control; pyridine nucleotides; porphyrin synthesis; chemical carcinogenesis; developmental biochemistry. *Mailing Add:* Dept of Biol Sci Fla Int Univ Miami FL 33199

STEIN, ALAN H, b New York, NY, Apr 2, 47; m 69; c 1. ANALYTIC NUMBER THEORY, MICROCOMPUTERS. *Educ:* Queen's Col, BA, 68; NY Univ, MS, 70, PhD(math), 73. *Prof Exp:* From instr to asst prof, 72-80, ASSOC PROF MATH, UNIV CONN, 80- *Mem:* Am Math Soc; Math Asn Am. *Res:* Analytic number theory; additive number theory; binary numbers. *Mailing Add:* Univ of Conn 32 Hillside Ave Waterbury CT 06710

STEIN, ALLAN RUDOLPH, b Edmonton, Alta, Nov 14, 38. PHYSICAL ORGANIC CHEMISTRY. *Educ:* Univ Alta, BSc, 60; Univ Ill, Urbana, PhD(org chem), 64. *Prof Exp:* Asst org chem, Univ Ill, Urbana, 60-61; res scientist, Domtar Cent Res Labs, Senneville, Que, 64-65; from asst prof to assoc prof chem, 65-75, PROF CHEM, MEM UNIV, NFLD, 75- *Concurrent Pos:* Nat Res Coun Can res grants, 65-69, 75-78 & 78-81; vis prof, King's Col, Univ London & Univ Umea, Sweden, 72-73; res grant, Swedish Res Coun, 73; hon prof chem, Univ Auckland, New Zealand, 80-81; scientist, Atomic Energy Can, 81. *Mem:* Am Chem Soc; Brit Chem Soc; Chem Inst Can. *Res:* Organic reaction mechanism studies, especially reactions of ambident ions, the isonitriles and of phenol alkylation; organic polarographic and carbene chemistry studies; ion-pair mechanism of nucleophilic displacement. *Mailing Add:* Dept of Chem Mem Univ St John's NF A1C 5S7 Can

STEIN, ARNOLD, b Philadelphia, Pa, Nov 11, 46; m 73. BIOPHYSICS, PHYSICAL BIOCHEMISTRY. *Educ:* Temple Univ, BS, 69, PhD(phys chem), 72. *Prof Exp:* Fel, Yale Univ, 72-74; STAFF FEL BIOPHYS, NAT INST HEALTH, 78- *Concurrent Pos:* Fel, Am Cancer Soc, 72-74. *Mem:* AAAS. *Res:* Physical and chemical properties of proteins; nucleic acid interactions. *Mailing Add:* Nat Inst of Health Bethesda MD 20014

STEIN, ARTHUR, b New York, NY, Aug 5, 18; m 41; c 2. MATHEMATICAL STATISTICS. *Educ:* City Col New York, BS, 38; Columbia Univ, MA, 44. *Prof Exp:* Statistician, Ballistic Res Labs, Aberdeen Proving Ground, US Dept Army, 41-44, mathematician, Ord Ballistic Team, 44-46, supvry ballistician, 46-51, dir qual control eng sect, Ord Ammunition Command, 52-55; prin engr & asst head, Opers Res Dept, 55-65, head, Systs Res Dept, 65-73, assoc dir, appl technol group, Cornell Aeronaut Lab, Inc, 70-74; V PRES & BUFFALO FACIL DIR, FALCON RES & DEVELOP CO, 74- *Concurrent Pos:* Lectr, Univ Chicago, 53-55; lectr, Univ Buffalo, 56. *Mem:* Opers Res Soc; Inst Math Statist; Am Statist Asn; Am Soc Qual Control; Am Ord Asn. *Res:* Operations research; weapons effectiveness; aircraft vulnerability; terminal ballistics; sample inspection and quality control; environmental systems analysis; reliability; probability; arms control; applied mathematics; mathematical modeling. *Mailing Add:* 30 Chapel Woods Williamsville NY 14221

STEIN, ARTHUR A, b Toronto, Ont, Mar 12, 22; nat US; m 48; c 3. MEDICINE, PATHOLOGY. *Educ:* Univ Toronto, MD, 45; Am Bd Path, dipl, 52. *Prof Exp:* Intern, Victoria Hosp, London, Ont, 45-46; asst resident med, Jewish Hosp, St Louis, Mo, 47; asst resident path, City Hosp, 47-48; resident, Sch Trop Med, Univ PR, 48-49; instr path & bact, 49-52, from asst prof to assoc prof path, 52-59, dir res inst exp path & toxicol, 65-69, PROF PATH, ALBANY MED COL, 59- *Concurrent Pos:* Surg pathologist, Albany Hosp, 55-; sci adv, Ky Tobacco & Health Bd, Commonwealth of Ky, 71-; dir Micros Biol Res, Inc, 67- *Mem:* Am Soc Clin Path; AMA; Col Am Path; Am Acad Clin Toxicol; Soc Toxicol. *Res:* Toxicology. *Mailing Add:* Dept of Path Albany Med Col Albany NY 12201

STEIN, ARTHUR HENRY, JR, b St Louis, Mo, June 11, 24; m 46; c 1. ORTHOPEDIC SURGERY. *Educ:* Amherst Col, AB, 46; Wash Univ, MD, 48; Am Bd Orthop Surg, dipl. *Prof Exp:* Resident orthop surg, Barnes Hosp, 53-55, asst, 55-56; from instr to assoc prof, 56-72, PROF ORTHOP SURG, SCH MED, WASH UNIV, 72- *Concurrent Pos:* Fel orthop surg, Barnes Hosp, 50-51. *Mem:* AMA; Clin Orthop Soc; Am Orthop Asn; Asn Orthop Chmn; Am Col Surg. *Res:* Blood supply to the bones; clinical orthopedic problems. *Mailing Add:* 4989 Barnes Hosp Plaza Queeny Towers St Louis MO 63110

STEIN, BARRY EDWARD, b New York, NY, Dec 3, 44; m 68. NEUROPHYSIOLOGY, DEVELOPMENTAL PHYSIOLOGY. *Educ:* Queens Col, BA, 66, MA, 69; City Univ New York, PhD(neuropsychol), 70. *Prof Exp:* Fel neurophysiol & neuroanat, Univ Calif, Los Angeles, 70-72, asst res anatomist, 72-75; asst prof, 75-76, ASSOC PROF PHYSIOL, MED COL VA, VA COMMONWEALTH UNIV, 76- *Mem:* Sigma Xi; Int Brain Res Orgn; AAAS; Am Psychol Asn; Soc Neurosci. *Res:* The ontogenesis of sensory systems; neurophysiological, neuroanatomical and behavioral changes during early life. *Mailing Add:* Dept of Physiol Med Col Va Commonwealth Univ Richmond VA 23298

STEIN, BARRY FRED, b Philadelphia, Pa, Nov 2, 37; m 62; c 3. SOLID STATE PHYSICS. *Educ:* Univ Pa, BA, 59, MS, 61, PhD(physics), 65. *Prof Exp:* Staff physicist, Univac Div, Sperry Rand Corp, 65-79, MGR, MAGNETIC DEVICE RES, SPERRY UNIVAC DIV, 79- *Concurrent Pos:* Adj prof, Grad Exten, Pa State Univ, 65-76. *Mem:* Am Phys Soc; Am Vacuum Soc. *Res:* Electrical properties of gallium arsenide; chemical vapor deposition and magnetic and optical properties of gadolinium iron garnet; liquid phase epitaxial growth of garnets; bubble device fabrication; high resolution x-ray lithography; Josephson junction devices. *Mailing Add:* Sperry Univac Box 500 Blue Bell PA 19422

STEIN, BENNETT M, b New York, NY, Feb 2, 31; m 55; c 2. NEUROSURGERY. *Educ:* Dartmouth Col, BA, 52; McGill Univ, MD, 55; Am Bd Neurol Surg, cert, 66. *Prof Exp:* Intern, US Naval Hosp, St Albans, NY, 58-59; surg resident, Columbia Presby Hosp, New York, 59-60, from asst resident to chief resident neurosurg, 60-64; asst prof, Neurol Inst, Columbia Univ, 68-71; prof neurosurg & chmn dept, New Eng Med Ctr, Tufts Univ, 71-80; PROF, CHEM DEPT NEUROSURG, COLUMBIA PRESBYTERIAN MED CTR, COL PHYSICIANS & SURGEONS, COLUMBIA UNIV, 80- *Concurrent Pos:* Fulbright scholar neurol, Nat Inst, Queens Sq, London, Eng, 58-59; NIH spec fel neuroanat, Columbia Univ, 64-66; consult, US Naval Hosp, Chelsea, Lemuel Shattuck Hosp, Boston & Vet Admin Hosp, Boston, 71- *Mem:* Fel Am Col Surg; Am Asn Anat; Soc Neurol Surg; Cong Neurol Surg; Am Acad Neurol Surg. *Res:* Cerebrovascular reactions, specifically cerebrovasospasm in response to subarachnoid hemorrhage; neuroanatomical problems. *Mailing Add:* 710 W 168th St Neurol Inst New York NY 10032

STEIN, BLAND ALLEN, b New York, NY, Feb 27, 34; m 56; c 3. MATERIALS ENGINEERING, METALLURGICAL ENGINEERING. *Educ:* City Col New York, BME, 56; Va Polytech Inst & State Univ, MMetE, 64. *Prof Exp:* Mat res engr, 56-68, head metals sect, 68-74, asst head, Mat Res Br, 74-81, HEAD ADVAN MAT BR, LANGLEY RES CTR, NASA, 81- *Concurrent Pos:* Failure anal consult var govt agencies, 63-; educ pub mgt fel, Univ Va, 77-78; asst prof & lectr, George Washington Univ, 77-; adj prof, Christopher Newport Col, 80- *Mem:* Am Soc Testing & Mat; Sigma Xi; Am Soc Metals; Am Ceramic Soc; assoc fel Am Inst Aeronaut & Astronaut. *Res:* Metals, ceramics, polymers and fiber reinforced composite materials for aerospace structural applications with special emphasis on the effect of service environments on mechanical and physical properties and degradation mechanisms. *Mailing Add:* MS 226 NASA Langley Res Ctr Hampton VA 23665

STEIN, CAROL B, b Columbus, Ohio, Jan 1, 37. ZOOLOGY. *Educ:* Lake Erie Col, AB, 58; Ohio State Univ, MSc, 63, PhD(zool), 73. *Prof Exp:* Asst bot, Ohio State Univ, 60, asst, Dept Zool & Entom, 60-61; mus technician natural hist, Ohio Hist Soc, Ohio State Mus, 64-66; teaching assoc, Biol Core Prog, Ohio State Univ, 68-69; mus technician natural hist, Ohio Hist Soc, Ohio State Mus, 69-70; asst curator, 70-72, CURATOR, MUS ZOOL, OHIO STATE UNIV, 72- *Mem:* Am Malacological Union; Am Inst Biol Sci; Sigma Xi. *Res:* Systematics, zoogeography, and life history of the freshwater mollusks, especially the endangered species of eastern North America. *Mailing Add:* Mus Zool Ohio State Univ 1813 N High St Columbus OH 43210

STEIN, CHARLES W C, b Philadelphia, Pa, Apr 28, 14; m 38. ORGANIC CHEMISTRY. *Educ:* Univ Pa, BS, 36, MS, 39, PhD(org chem), 42. *Prof Exp:* Asst instr chem, Lehigh Univ, 37; asst instr, Drexel Inst, 37-42; res chemist, Gen Aniline & Film Corp, 42-46; process develop chemist, Calco Div, Am Cyanamid Co, 46-51; tech assoc, GAF Corp, 51-79; RETIRED. *Mem:* AAAS; Am Chem Soc. *Res:* Dyestuff chemistry; pigments; organic synthesis; plastics. *Mailing Add:* 910 Summit Ave Westfield NJ 07090

STEIN, DALE FRANKLIN, b Kingston, Minn, Dec 24, 35; m 58; c 2. METALLURGY, SURFACE CHEMISTRY. *Educ:* Univ Minn, BS, 58; Rensselaer Polytech Inst, PhD(metall), 63. *Prof Exp:* Asst plant metallurgist, Metall Inc, 57-58; prog metallurgist, Gen Elec Co, 58-59, metallurgist, Res & Develop Ctr, 59-67; assoc prof metall, Univ Minn, Minneapolis, 67-69, assoc prof mech eng, 69-70; prof metall eng & head dept, 70-77, vpres acad affairs, 77-79, PRES ACAD AFFAIRS, MICH TECHNOL UNIV, HOUGHTON, 79- *Concurrent Pos:* Consult, NSF Adv Comt, Mat Res Labs, 76-, NSF Exec Subcomt, Adv Comt Mat Res, 77- & Dept Energy. *Honors & Awards:* Hardy Gold Medal, Am Inst Mining, Metall & Petrol Engrs, 65; Giesler Award, Am Soc Metals, 67. *Mem:* AAAS; fel Am Inst Mining, Metall & Petrol Engrs (pres elect, 79); Am Soc Metals; Sigma Xi; fel Metall Soc. *Res:* Application of Auger spectroscopy to metallurgical problems, including brittle fracture, corrosion and structure stability, cleavage fracture, dislocation dynamics and high purity metals. *Mailing Add:* Pres Acad Affairs Mich Technol Univ Houghton MI 49931

STEIN, DARYL LEE, b Canton, Ohio, Aug 27, 49; m 71. ORGANIC CHEMISTRY. *Educ:* Bowling Green State Univ, BS, 71, MS, 73; Mich State Univ, PhD(chem), 78. *Prof Exp:* Res scientist, Continental Oil Co, 77-80; RES SCIENTIST, LUCIDOL DIV, PENNWALT CORP, 80- *Mem:* Am Chem Soc. *Res:* Catalysts for polymers. *Mailing Add:* Lucidol Div Pennwalt Corp Buffalo NY 14240

STEIN, DAVID MORRIS, b Johannesburg, SAfrica; m 75. OPERATIONS RESEARCH, COMPUTER SCIENCE. *Educ:* Univ Witwatersrand, BSc, 72, MSc, 74; Harvard Univ, PhD(eng), 77. *Prof Exp:* Res scientist comput sci, 77-81, MEM TECH PLANNING STAFF, IBM CORP, 81- *Res:* Application of mathematical techniques to industrial problems; optimization, decision and control methods applied to transportation problems; performance and storage organizations for future computer systems. *Mailing Add:* IBM T J Watson Res Ctr PO Box 218 Yorktown Heights NY 10598

STEIN, DIANA B, b New York, NY, July 5, 37; m 58; c 4. BOTANY, MOLECULAR BIOLOGY. *Educ:* Barnard Col, AB, 58; Univ Mont, MA, 61; Univ Mass, Amherst, PhD(molecular biol), 76. *Prof Exp:* Instr bot, 64-69, instr plant physiol, 78, RES ASSOC MOLECULAR BIOL, UNIV MASS, 76- *Concurrent Pos:* Mem, DNA Study Comn Amherst, 77-78 & Biohazards Comn, Amherst Col, 78- *Mem:* Bot Soc Am; Am Soc Plant Physiol; Sigma Xi. *Res:* DNA sequence comparisons; DNA protein interactions; evolution of cells and within plant groups. *Mailing Add:* Dept Biol Sci Mt Holyoke Col South Hadley MA 01075

STEIN, DONALD GERALD, b New York, NY, Jan 27, 39; m 60; c 2. PSYCHOPHYSIOLOGY, NEUROLOGY. *Educ:* Mich State Univ, BA, 60, MS, 62; Univ Ore, PhD(psychol), 65. *Prof Exp:* NIMH res fel, Mass Inst Technol, 65-66; asst prof psychol & co-dir animal lab, 66-69, assoc prof psychol, 69-73, PROF PSYCHOL, CLARK UNIV, 73-, DIR, BRAIN RES FACIL, 73-; PROF NEUROL, UNIV MASS MED CTR, WORCESTER, 78- *Concurrent Pos:* USPHS res contract, 67; NSF res contract, 67-71; USPHS biomed sci grant, 69- Fulbright awards, 71-75; NIMH res career develop award, 72-78; prof, Univ Nice, France, 77; vis scientist, Nat Inst Health & Med Res, Lyon, 75-76, Paris, 79; France Nat Inst Aging res contract, 76-79; Vis scientist, Nat Asn Health & Med Res, Paris, 78; AAAS fel, 80-81. *Mem:* Sigma Xi; Soc Neurosci; Psychonomic Soc; Europ Brain & Behav Soc; Int Soc Neuropsychol. *Res:* Recovery from brain damage; aging and brain function; nerve growth factor and behavior; neuroplasticity. *Mailing Add:* Brain Res Lab 950 Main St Worcester MA 01610

STEIN, ELIAS M, b Antwerp, Belg, Jan 13, 31; nat US; m 59; c 2. MATHEMATICS. *Educ:* Univ Chicago, AB, 51, MS, 53, PhD, 55. *Prof Exp:* Instr, Mass Inst Technol, 56-58; mem fac, Univ Chicago, 58-62, assoc prof math, 61-62; mem, Inst Advan Study, 62-63; chmn dept, 68-71, PROF MATH, PRINCETON UNIV, 63- *Concurrent Pos:* Sloan Found res fel, 61-63; NSF sr fel, 62-63 & 71-72; sr vis fel, Sci Res Coun Gt Brit, 68. *Mem:* Nat Acad Sci; Am Math Soc. *Res:* Topics in harmonic analysis related to the Littlewood-Paley theory; singular integrals and differentiality properties of functions. *Mailing Add:* 132 Dodds Lane Princeton NJ 08540

STEIN, FRANK S, b Lancaster, Pa, Jan 11, 21; m 47; c 3. PHYSICS. *Educ:* Franklin & Marshall Col, BS, 42; Columbia Univ, MA, 47; Univ Buffalo, PhD(physics), 51. *Prof Exp:* Res physicist, Manhattan Proj, Columbia Univ, 44-46; instr physics, Univ Buffalo, 48-51; res physicist res labs, Westinghouse Elec Corp, 51-55, mgr semiconductor dept electronic tube div, 55, mgr power devices develop sect semiconductor dept, 55-60; mgr eng semiconductor div, Gen Instrument Corp, NJ, 60-61, dir res appl res lab, 61-63; sr scientist semiconductor dept, Delco Radio Div, 63-66, mgr semiconductor res & eng dept, 66-70, chief engr solid state prod, Delco Electronics Div, 70-75, CHIEF ENGR ADVAN ENG, DELCO ELECTRONICS DIV, GEN MOTORS CORP, 75- *Concurrent Pos:* Chmn joint electron device eng coun, Solid State Prod Eng Coun, 69-70 & 73-75; mem, Nat Acad Sci/Nat Acad Eng/Nat Res Coun Eval Panel Electronic Technol Div, Nat Bur Standards, 75-79. *Mem:* Inst Elec & Electronics Eng. *Res:* Mass spectrometry; properties of semiconductors and semiconductor devices; solid state electronics; microelectronics. *Mailing Add:* Delco Electronics Div Gen Motors Corp PO Box 1104 Kokomo IN 46902

STEIN, FRED P(AUL), b Dallastown, Pa, Nov 22, 34; m 56; c 3. CHEMICAL ENGINEERING. *Educ:* Lehigh Univ, BS, 56; Univ Mich, MSE, 57, PhD(chem eng), 61. *Prof Exp:* Sr chem engr, Air Prod & Chem Inc, 60-61; from asst prof to assoc prof, 63-71, PROF CHEM ENG, LEHIGH UNIV, 71- *Concurrent Pos:* Consult, Picatinny Arsenal, 63-65, Gardner Cryogenics, 65-69, Hershey Foods Corp, 71-72 & Air Prod & Chem, 76; vis prof, Monash Univ, Melbourne, Australia, 73 & Univ Queensland, Brisbane, Australia, 74. *Mem:* Am Inst Chem Engrs; Am Chem Soc. *Res:* Phase equilibria at cryogenic temperatures and at high temperatures; thermodynamic properties of mixtures; dynamic modeling of coal conversion plants. *Mailing Add:* Dept of Chem Eng Lehigh Univ Bethlehem PA 18015

STEIN, FREDERICK MAX, b Wyaconda, Mo, Feb 17, 19; m 43; c 2. MATHEMATICS. *Educ:* Iowa Wesleyan Col, AB, 40; Univ Iowa, MS, 47, PhD(math), 55. *Prof Exp:* Instr high schs, Iowa, 40-43; instr math, Univ Iowa, 43-44, asst, 46-47; assoc prof, Iowa Wesleyan Univ, 47-53; instr math, Univ Iowa, 53-54; assoc prof, 55-63, PROF MATH, COLO STATE UNIV, 63- *Mem:* Am Math Soc; Math Asn Am. *Res:* Approximation; orthogonal functions; differential and integro-differential equations; Sturm-Liouville systems. *Mailing Add:* Dept of Math Colo State Univ Ft Collins CO 80523

STEIN, GARY S, b Brooklyn, NY, July 30, 43; m 74. GENE EXPRESSION. *Educ:* Hofstra Univ, BA, 65, MA, 66; Univ Vt, PhD(cell biol), 69. *Prof Exp:* Res assoc biochem, Temple Univ, 71-72; asst prof biochem, 72-75, assoc prof, 75-78, PROF BIOCHEM & MOLECULAR BIOL, SCH MED, UNIV FLA, 78-, ASSOC CHMN DEPT, 81- *Concurrent Pos:* NIH fel, Sch Med, Temple Univ, 69-71; Damon Runyon Mem Fund cancer res grant, Sch Med, Univ Fla, 71-73; Am Cancer Soc, NSF & NIH grants, 74- *Mem:* AAAS; Am Soc Biol Chemists; Am Asn Cancer Res; Am Soc Cell Biol; Am Soc Zool. *Res:* Role of chromosomal proteins in the control of cell division and gene expression. *Mailing Add:* Dept of Biochem Univ of Fla Sch of Med Gainesville FL 32601

STEIN, GEORGE NATHAN, b Philadelphia, Pa, Aug 11, 17; m 48; c 3. RADIOLOGY. *Educ:* Univ Pa, BA, 38; Jefferson Med Col, MD, 42; Am Bd Radiol, dipl, 49. *Prof Exp:* Intern, Jewish Hosp, Philadelphia, 43; resident radiol, Grad Hosp, 47-49, assoc radiologist, 49-51, from instr to assoc prof, Div Grad Med, 51-61, assoc dir dept, Ctr, 67-71, dir dept radiol, Presby-Univ Pa Med Ctr, 71, PROF RADIOL, SCH MED, UNIV OF PA, 61- *Concurrent Pos:* Hon prof, Pontif Univ Javeriana, Colombia, 60. *Mem:* Radiol Soc NAm; Am Roentgen Ray Soc; fel Am Col Radiol. *Res:* Gastrointestinal radiology. *Mailing Add:* Dept Radiol Presby-Univ Pa Med Ctr Philadelphia PA 19104

STEIN, GERHARD MORITZ, b Breslau, Ger, Feb 28, 02; US citizen; m 30; c 3. ELECTRICAL ENGINEERING, APPLIED MATHEMATICS. *Educ:* Breslau Tech Univ, Dipl Ing, 25, DrIng, 27. *Prof Exp:* Asst appl math, Breslau Tech Univ, 24-27; lab engr, Allgemeine Electrizitatsgesellschsft Transformatorenfabrik, 27-32 & Gen Elec Co, 35-36; prof elec eng, Peyang Univ, China, 36-37; sr engr, Transformer Div, Westinghouse Elec Corp, 39-55, master engr, 55-61, fel engr, 61-67; assoc prof, 67-72, EMER ASSOC PROF ELEC ENG, YOUNGSTOWN STATE UNIV, 72- *Concurrent Pos:* Adj prof grad sch, Univ Pittsburgh, 59- *Mem:* Fel Inst Elec & Electronics Engrs; Am Soc Eng Educ. *Res:* Field theory, particularly flux distribution and ferromagnetic phenomena in transformer cores, high-voltage phenomena in power transformer windings, heat flow in transformers; transformer heat transients in connection with protective systems and transformer life. *Mailing Add:* Dept of Elec Eng Youngstown State Univ Youngstown OH 44503

STEIN, GILBERT DOUGLAS, b South Bend, Ind, Nov 30, 36; m 60; c 3. MECHANICAL ENGINEERING. *Educ:* Purdue Univ, Lafayette, BS, 59; Yale Univ, PhD(eng & appl sci), 67. *Prof Exp:* Sr scientist, Aeronutronic Div, Philco-Ford Corp, 67; instr physics of fluids, Yale Univ, 67-69; assoc prof mech eng, 69-80, PROF MECH ENG, NORTHWESTERN UNIV, EVANSTON, 80- *Concurrent Pos:* Consult, US Navy, 70- *Res:* Gas phase nucleation, both homogeneous and heterogeneous; structure of small atomic and molecular clusters; microphysical processes in clouds. *Mailing Add:* Dept Mech Eng & Astronaut Sci Northwestern Univ Evanston IL 60201

STEIN, GRETCHEN HERPEL, b Asbury Park, NJ, Mar 27, 45; m 66. CELL BIOLOGY. *Educ:* Brown Univ, AB, 65; Stanford Univ, PhD(molecular biol), 71. *Prof Exp:* NIH fel cell biol, Sch Med, Stanford Univ, 71-73, res fel cell biol & molecular biol, 73-74; RES ASSOC CELL BIOL & MOLECULAR BIOL, UNIV COLO, 74- *Concurrent Pos:* Vis scientist, Cancer Biol Prog, Frederick Cancer Res Ctr, 80-81; consult health scientist adminr & mem aging planning panel, Nat Inst Aging, 81, mem aging rev comt, 81- *Mem:* Am Soc Cell Biol; Tissue Cult Asn. *Res:* Control of cellular proliferation in normal and neoplastic human cells; mechanism for cessation of proliferation in senescent cells. *Mailing Add:* Molecular Cellular & Develop Biol Campus Box 347 Univ Colo Boulder CO 80309

STEIN, HARVEY PHILIP, b Brooklyn, NY, May 4, 40; m 65; c 3. ORGANIC CHEMISTRY. *Educ:* Queens Col, NY, BS, 61; Mass Inst Technol, PhD(org chem), 67. *Prof Exp:* Chemist, Stamford Res Labs, Am Cyanamid Co, summer 61; asst, Mass Inst Technol, 61-65; instr chem, Pa State Univ, 65-67, asst prof, 67-68; asst prof, Trenton State Col, 68-71; prof, Western Col, 71-75; SR SCIENTIST, USPHS, 75- *Mem:* Am Chem Soc. *Res:* Reaction mechanisms; use of isotopes; biomedical effects of ethanol; public health; identification of previously unrecognized occupational hazards. *Mailing Add:* 11705 Silent Valley Lane Gaithersburg MD 20878

STEIN, HERBERT JOSEPH, b Evanston, Ill, Mar 20, 28; m 65; c 3. ELECTRICAL ENGINEERING. *Educ:* Univ Ill, Urbana, BS, 58, MS, 59, PhD(elec eng), 64. *Prof Exp:* From instr to res assoc elec eng, Univ Ill, Urbana, 60-64; asst prof info eng, 64-66, actg head dept, 64-69, assoc prof elec eng & assoc dean col eng, 69-81, HEAD DEPT SYSTS ENG, UNIV ILL, CHICAGO CIRCLE, 81- *Concurrent Pos:* Consult, Honeywell Corp, Ill, 67-68. *Mem:* Sr mem Inst Elec & Electronics Engrs; Am Soc Eng Educ; found mem Am Soc Eng Mgt. *Res:* Engineering education and administration; implementation of interdisciplinary programs. *Mailing Add:* Col of Eng Univ of Ill at Chicago Circle Chicago IL 60680

STEIN, HERMAN H, b Chicago, Ill, May 27, 30; m 51; c 2. BIOCHEMISTRY, PHARMACOLOGY. *Educ:* Univ Ill, BS, 51; Univ Minn, MS, 53; Northwestern Univ, PhD(chem), 56. *Prof Exp:* Lab asst, Northwestern Univ, 53-54; res chemist, Toni Co Div, Gillette Co, 56-61; sr res chemist, Abbott Labs, 61-66, group leader, 66, sect head, 67-72; assoc fel, 72-76, RES FEL, PHARMACOL DEPT, ABBOTT LABS, 76- *Mem:* Am Chem Soc; Am Soc Pharmacol & Exp Therapeut. *Res:* Enzymology; automated metabolic and enzymic analyses; antianginal agents; cyclic adenosine monophosphate metabolism; pharmacology of nucleosides; beta-adrenergic blocking agents; lipid metabolism. *Mailing Add:* Pharmacol Dept Abbott Labs 1400 Sheridan Rd North Chicago IL 60064

STEIN, HOWARD JAY, b Baltimore, Md, May 28, 33; m 57; c 5. PLANT PHYSIOLOGY. *Educ:* Temple Univ, BA, 54; Univ Mich, MA, 58, PhD(bot), 61. *Prof Exp:* From asst prof to assoc prof biol, Kans State Col, Pittsburgh, 60-65; assoc prof, 65-71, chmn dept, 66-68 & 71-75, PROF BIOL, GRAND VALLEY STATE COL, 71-, DIR RES & DEVELOP, 79- *Concurrent Pos:* NSF grant, 62-64; staff biologist, Off Biol Educ, Am Inst Biol Sci, 69-71, vis biologist, 71-72, curric consult bur, 71-74. *Mem:* AAAS; Am Soc Plant Physiol; Sigma Xi; Nat Asn Biol Teachers. *Res:* Amino acid metabolism in plant roots; metabolism in plant mitochondria. *Mailing Add:* Dept Biol Grand Valley State Col Allendale MI 49401

STEIN, IRVING F, JR, b Chicago, Ill, July 6, 18; m 50; c 2. SURGERY. *Educ:* Dartmouth Col, AB, 39; Northwestern Univ, MS, 41, MD, 43, PhD, 51; Am Bd Surg, dipl, 50. *Prof Exp:* ASST PROF SURG, MED SCH, NORTHWESTERN UNIV, 54- *Concurrent Pos:* Attend surgeon, Cook County Hosp; chief surg, Highland Park Hosp. *Mem:* AAAS; fel AMA; fel Am Col Surg; Am Fedn Clin Res. *Res:* Gastrointestinal and surgical research. *Mailing Add:* Col Med Northwestern Univ Chicago IL 60201

STEIN, IVIE, JR, b Orange, Calif, Dec 31, 40. MATHEMATICS. *Educ:* Calif State Col, Long Beach, BS, 62, MA, 63; Univ Calif, Los Angeles, CPhil, 70, PhD(math), 71. *Prof Exp:* Asst prof, 71-75, ASSOC PROF MATH, UNIV TOLEDO, 75- *Mem:* Am Math Soc; Soc Appl & Indust Math; Math Asn Am. *Res:* Calculus of variations; optimal control theory; numerical analysis; differential equations; index theory of quadratic forms. *Mailing Add:* Dept of Math Univ of Toledo Toledo OH 43606

STEIN, JACK J(OSEPH), b New York, NY, Feb 14, 38; m 59; c 3. ELECTRICAL ENGINEERING. *Educ:* City Col New York, BEE, 59; Columbia Univ, MSEE, 60; NY Univ, DrEngSci, 65. *Prof Exp:* Res staff mem, IBM Res Div, Int Bus Mach Corp, 60-62; lectr, City Col New York, 62-63; instr, NY Univ, 63-65; systs engr, IBM Data Processing Div, Int Bus Mach Corp, 65-66; engr, Hughes Aircraft Co, 66-67; ASSOC PROF ELEC ENG, RADNOR GRAD CTR, PA STATE UNIV, 67- *Concurrent Pos:* Consult, Gen Elec, 68-69, Burroughs, 73-74. *Mem:* Inst Elec & Electronics Engrs; Sigma Xi. *Res:* Network theory; digital computers; solid state devices; biomedical simulation. *Mailing Add:* 1056 Shearwater Dr Audubon PA 19403

STEIN, JAMES DEWITT, JR, b New York, NY, Aug 29, 41. MATHEMATICS. *Educ:* Yale Univ, BA, 62; Univ Calif, Berkeley, MA & PhD(math), 67. *Prof Exp:* Asst prof math, Univ Calif, Los Angeles, 67-74, NSF grant, 70-74; ASSOC PROF MATH, CALIF STATE UNIV, LONG BEACH, 74- *Mem:* Am Math Soc. *Res:* Banach algebras; continuity and boundedness problems in Banach spaces; measure theory. *Mailing Add:* Calif State Univ Long Beach Long Beach CA 90840

STEIN, JANET LEE SWINEHART, b Danville, Pa, Apr 3, 46; m 74. GENE EXPRESSION, CHROMATIN. *Educ:* Elizabethtown Col, BS, 68; Princeton Univ, MA, 71, PhD(chem), 75. *Prof Exp:* Res assoc biochem, 74-76, ASST PROF IMMUNOL & MED MICROBIOL, COL MED, UNIV FLA, 76- *Concurrent Pos:* Res grants, NSF, 75-, Am Cancer Soc, 77-78 & March of Dimes, 78- *Mem:* Am Soc Cell Biol; Am Chem Soc; AAAS. *Res:* Regulation of gene expression, especially at the transcriptional level, in eukaryotic cells; structure and regulation of human histone genes. *Mailing Add:* Dept Immunol & Med Microbiol Univ Fla Gainesville FL 32610

STEIN, JANET RUTH, b Denver, Colo. BOTANY. *Educ:* Univ Colo, BA, 51; Wellesley Col, MA, 53; Univ Calif, PhD(bot), 57. *Prof Exp:* Lab technician & cur, Univ Calif, 57-59; from instr to assoc prof bot, biol & phycol, 59-71, PROF BOT, UNIV BC, 71-, ASST DEAN SCI, 79- *Concurrent Pos:* Vis assoc prof, Univ Calif, 65; dir, Western Bot Serv, Ltd, 72-75; ed, J Phycol, Phycological Soc Am, 75-80; Kilham sr fel, Univ BC, 75. *Honors & Awards:* Darbaker Award, Bot Soc Am, 60. *Mem:* Bot Soc Am; Phycol Soc Am (ed, News Bull, 60-64, Newsletter, 65-66, pres, 65); Can Bot Asn (vpres, 69-70, pres, 70-71); Brit Phycol Soc; Int Phycol Soc. *Res:* Morphology, physiology, ecology and distribution of freshwater algae. *Mailing Add:* Dept Bot Univ BC 3529-6270 University Blvd Vancouver BC V6T 2B1 Can

STEIN, JERRY MICHAEL, b Brooklyn, NY, Jan 9, 52; m 74. CONTACT LENSES, CARDIOVASCULAR PHYSIOLOGY. *Educ:* Brooklyn Col, BA, 73; Syracuse Univ, MS & PhD(psychol), 77. *Prof Exp:* Res assoc physiol & biophys, Reg Primate Res Ctr, Univ, Wash, 78-79; res assoc, Cardiovasc Ctr & Dept Psychol, Univ Iowa, Iowa City, 79-81; SR CLIN RES ASSOC, ALCON LABS, FT WORTH, TEX, 81- *Concurrent Pos:* Teaching asst, Syracuse Univ, 77; lectr psychol, Univ Wash, 78-, fel, Regional Primate Res Ctr, 78-79. *Mem:* Soc Neurosci; AAAS; NY Acad Sci. *Res:* Clinical testing of optical devices and solutions; central nervous system control of cardiovascular physiology and renal functions. *Mailing Add:* Alcon Labs 6201 S Freeway Ft Worth TX 76101

STEIN, JOHN MICHAEL, b Vienna, Austria, May 29, 35; US citizen; m 69; c 4. SURGERY. *Educ:* Harvard Univ, AB, 57, MD, 61; Am Bd Surg, dipl, 68. *Prof Exp:* Assoc surg, New York Hosp-Cornell Med Ctr, 62-63; asst instr, Albert Einstein Col Med, 66-67; chief burn study br, US Army Inst Surg Res, Tex, 67-69, ASSOC PROF SURG & BURNS, ALBERT EINSTEIN COL MED, 69- *Concurrent Pos:* NIH fel surg, Albert Einstein Col Med, 64-65; pres med bd, Bronx Munic Hosp Ctr, 74-76; co-chmn burn comt & mem bd dirs Regional Emergency Med Servs, Coun of New York, 77- *Mem:* Am Burn Asn; NY Surg Soc; fel Am Col Surg; Am Trauma Soc; Asn Acad Surg. *Res:* Surgical training and research, expecially metabolic care of surgical and burned patients. *Mailing Add:* Dept of Surg Albert Einstein Col of Med Bronx NY 10461

STEIN, JUSTIN JOHN, b Haskell, Tex, Oct 18, 07; m 36; c 1. SURGERY, CANCER. *Educ:* Baylor Univ, MD, 33; Am Bd Radiol, dipl. *Prof Exp:* Intern, Cincinnati Gen Hosp, Ohio, 34-35; resident gen & tumor surg & radiol, Edward Hines, Jr Hosp, Ill, 35-41; asst clin prof surg, Col Med Evangelists, 48-52; prof radiol, 52-75, EMER PROF RADIOL, SCH MED, UNIV CALIF, LOS ANGELES, 75-; CHIEF RADIATION THERAPY, VET ADMIN HOSP, LONG BEACH, 75- *Concurrent Pos:* Del Amo fel, Univ Madrid, 58 & 60; consult radiol, path & oncol, var hosps & med progs, 38-; attend surg staff, Calif Hosp, Los Angeles, 45-; tumor surgeon & radiotherapist, Los Angeles Tumor Inst, 46-52; attend surgeon & mem tumor bd, Malignancy Serv, Los Angeles County Hosp, 48-49; attend staff, Desert Hosp, Palm Springs, 50-60, Santa Monica Hosp & Univ Calif Hosp, Los Angeles, 52 & Crenshaw Hosp, 53-60, lectr radiol, US Naval Hosp, San Diego, 50-; chmn, Gov Emergency Med Adv Comt, Calif, 50-67; mem tumor bd & attend radiologist, Los Angeles County Harbor Gen Hosp, 52-60; mem, Calif Bd Med Examr, 52-60, pres, 56, vpres, 66; exchange prof, Med Sch, Nat Univ Mex, 53 & Ministry Higher & Specialized Educ, Moscow & Leningrad, USSR, 63; dir, Calif Inst Cancer Res, 55-70; mem radiother subcomt bladder cancer, adjuvant study grant chemother-radiother, NIH, 64-; mem, Adv Comt Radiol, Vet Admin, DC, 65-, Sci Adv Bd, Inst Laryngol & Voice Disorders, Inc, Los Angeles, 66-75 & US Civil Defense Coun. *Mem:* AAAS; fel Am Col Surg; fel Am Col Radiol; AMA; Am Radium Soc (secy, 62-64, pres, 65-66). *Res:* Tumor surgery and therapy. *Mailing Add:* Long Beach Vet Hosp Radiation Ther 114T Long Beach CA 90822

STEIN, LARRY, b New York, NY, Nov 10, 31; m 60. NEUROSCIENCE, BEHAVIOR. *Educ:* NY Univ, BA, 52; Univ Iowa, MA, 53, PhD, 55. *Prof Exp:* Res psychologist, Walter Reed Army Inst Res, 55-57; res psychologist, Vet Admin Res Labs Neuropsychiat, 57-59; sr res scientist, Wyeth Labs, 59-64, mgr, Dept Psychopharmacol, 64-79; PROF & CHMN, DEPT PHRAMACOL, COL MED, UNIV CALIF, IRVINE, 79- *Concurrent Pos:* Res assoc, Bryn Mawr Col, 61-72, adj prof, 72-; adj prof med sch, Univ Pa. *Honors & Awards:* Bennett Award, Soc Biol Psychiat, 61. *Mem:* Am Psychol Asn; Am Physiol Soc; Am Soc Pharmacol & Exp Therapeut; Soc Neurosci. *Res:* Cellular mechanisms of reward and punishment, psychopharmacology, biological basis of schizophrenia and depression. *Mailing Add:* Col Med Univ Calif Irvine CA 92717

STEIN, LAWRENCE, b Hampton, Va, July 21, 22; m 52; c 2. INORGANIC CHEMISTRY. *Educ:* George Washington Univ, BS, 48; Univ Wis, PhD(chem), 52. *Prof Exp:* Anal chemist, Nat Bur Standards, 48; asst, Univ Wis, 50-51; CHEMIST, ARGONNE NAT LAB, 51- *Concurrent Pos:* Adv panelist comt biol effects atmospheric pollutants, Nat Res Coun, 71-72; consult, Nat Inst Occupational Safety & Health, 73. *Mem:* AAAS; Am Chem Soc. *Res:* Fluorine chemistry; interhalogen compounds; chemistry of noble gases, particularly radon; environmental radiation; biologic effects of atmospheric pollutants; infrared spectroscopy; chemistry of actinide elements; laser raman spectroscopy. *Mailing Add:* Argonne Nat Lab 9700 S Cass Ave Argonne IL 60439

STEIN, MARJORIE LEITER, New York, NY. MATHEMATICS. *Educ:* Barnard Col, AB, 68; Princeton Univ, MA, 71, PhD(math), 72. *Prof Exp:* Res assoc math, Univ Wis-Madison, 72-73, lectr comput sci, 73; res assoc, Nat Bur Standards, 73-75; sr math statistician, 75-76, sr opers res analyst, 76-77, mgt analyst/prog mgr, 77-79, PRIN ECONOMIST, US POSTAL SERV, 79- *Concurrent Pos:* Vis lectr, Math Asn Am, 75-78; docent, Nat Mus Natural Hist, Smithsonian Inst, 76- *Mem:* Am Math Soc; Math Asn Am; Asn Women Math. *Res:* Combinatorial theory; networks; linear programming; applications to economics. *Mailing Add:* US Postal Serv 475 L'Enfant Plaza West SW Washington DC 20260

STEIN, MARVIN, b St Louis, Mo, Dec 8, 23; m 50; c 3. PSYCHIATRY. *Educ:* Wash Univ, BS, 45, MD, 49. *Prof Exp:* Intern, St Louis City Hosp, 49-50; asst resident psychiat, Sch Med, Wash Univ, 50-51; asst instr, Sch Med, Univ Pa, 53-54, res assoc, 54-56, from asst prof to assoc prof, 56-63; prof, Med Col, Cornell Univ, 63-66; prof & chmn dept, State Univ NY Downstate Med Ctr, 66-71; PROF PSYCHIAT & CHMN DEPT, MT SINAI SCH MED & PSYCHIATRIST-IN-CHIEF, 71- *Concurrent Pos:* USPHS fel clin sch, Sch Med, Univ Pittsburgh, 51-53; fel psychiat, Sch Med, Univ Pa, 53-54; ment health career investr, NIMH, 56-61, mem ment health fels rev panel, 61-64, ment health res career award comt, 63-65, chmn, 65-67. *Mem:* Am Psychiat Asn. *Res:* Investigation of respiratory and psychological variables; bronchial asthma; central nervous system mechanisms and immune processes. *Mailing Add:* Dept of Psychiat Mt Sinai Sch of Med New York NY 10029

STEIN, MARVIN L, b Cleveland, Ohio, July 15, 24; m 44; c 3. MATHEMATICS, COMPUTER SCIENCE. *Educ:* Univ Calif, Los Angeles, BA, 47, MA, 49, PhD, 51. *Prof Exp:* Asst math, Univ Calif, Los Angeles, 47-48, mathematician inst numerical anal, 48-52; sr res engr, Consol-Vultee Corp, 52-55; from asst prof to assoc prof math, 55-61, dir univ comput ctr, 58-70, actg head comput info & control sci dept, 70-71, PROF MATH, UNIV MINN, MINNEAPOLIS, 61-, PROF COMPUT SCI, 80- *Concurrent Pos:* Lectr, Univ Calif, Los Angeles, 54-55; Guggenheim fel, 63-64; vis prof, Tel Aviv Univ & Hebrew Univ, Jerusalem, 71-72. *Mem:* Am Math Soc; Soc Indust & Appl Math; Asn Comput Mach. *Res:* Numerical analysis; applications of digital computers; computer systems, machine arithmetic. *Mailing Add:* Comput Sci Dept Univ of Minn Minneapolis MN 55455

STEIN, MICHAEL ROGER, b Milwaukee, Wis, Mar 21, 43; m 67; c 2. ALGEBRAIC K-THEORY. *Educ:* Harvard Univ, BA, 64; Columbia Univ, PhD(math), 70. *Prof Exp:* Asst prof math, 70-74, assoc prof, 74-80, PROF MATH, NORTHWESTERN UNIV, EVANSTON, 80- *Concurrent Pos:* Fel, Hebrew Univ, Jerusalem, 72-73; Sci Res Coun sr vis fel, King's Col, Univ London, 77-78; vis scientist, Weizmann Inst Sci, 78. *Mem:* Am Math Soc. *Res:* Algebraic K-theory; algebra. *Mailing Add:* Dept of Math Northwestern Univ Evanston IL 60201

STEIN, MYRON, b East Boston, Mass, May 27, 25; m 53; c 4. PHYSIOLOGY, MEDICINE. *Educ:* Dartmouth Col, BA, 48; Tufts Univ, MD, 52. *Prof Exp:* Instr med, Harvard Med Sch, 57-64, assoc, 64-65; from assoc prof to prof med sci, Brown Univ, 69-73; PROF MED, UNIV CALIF,

LOS ANGELES, 73-; DIR PULMONARY DIV, BROTMAN MEM HOSP, 73- *Concurrent Pos:* Consult, Mass Rehab Comt, 60-65, Vet Admin Hosps, West Roxbury, 63- & Davis Park, RI, 65- *Mem:* Am Fedn Clin Res; Am Physiol Soc. *Res:* Pulmonary physiologic effects of pulmonary embolism; relationship of acid-base states and thyroid hormone transport; physiologic studies in clinical lung diseases. *Mailing Add:* Brotman Mem Hosp 3828 Delmas Terr Culver City CA 90230

STEIN, NELSON, b New York, NY, July 23, 26; m 58; c 3. NUCLEAR PHYSICS. *Educ:* City Col New York, BS, 57; Univ Ill, MS, 58, PhD(physics), 63. *Prof Exp:* Res assoc nuclear physics, Univ Wash, 63-66; res assoc, Yale Univ, 66-68, asst prof physics, 68-72; PHYSICIST, LOS ALAMOS SCI LAB, UNIV CALIF, 72- *Concurrent Pos:* Vis staff mem, Los Alamos Sci Lab, 69-72; NATO sr fel sci, Ctr Nuclear Res, Strasbourg, France, 72. *Mem:* Am Phys Soc. *Res:* Structure of medium and heavy nuclei; nuclear reaction mechanisms; nuclear models. *Mailing Add:* Physics Div MS 458 PO Box 1663 Los Alamos Sci Lab Los Alamos NM 87544

STEIN, OTTO LUDWIG, b Augsburg, Ger, Jan 14, 25; nat US; m 58; c 4. PLANT MORPHOGENESIS. *Educ:* Univ Minn, BS, 49, MS, 52, PhD(bot), 54. *Prof Exp:* Asst bot, Univ Minn, 48-53; instr, Univ Mo, 55; USPHS fel, Brookhaven Nat Lab, 55-58; from asst prof to assoc prof bot, Mont State Univ, 58-64; assoc prof, 64-70, head dept, 70-74, PROF BOT, UNIV MASS, AMHERST, 70- *Concurrent Pos:* Res collab, Brookhaven Nat Lab, 58-70; vis asst prof, Univ Calif, 61-62; sr NATO res fel, Imp Col, Univ London, 71-72; dir, Univ Mass-Univ Freiburg, WGer, Exchange Prog, 79. *Mem:* Bot Soc Am; Soc Study Develop Biol; Soc Exp Biol & Med; Am Genetic Asn. *Res:* Genetics; cytology; developmental anatomy of apical meristems and their derivatives. *Mailing Add:* Dept of Bot Univ of Mass Amherst MA 01002

STEIN, PAUL JOHN, b Pittsburgh, Pa, Sept 28, 50; m 74; c 3. BIOCHEMISTRY, INORGANIC CHEMISTRY. *Educ:* Bethany Col, WVa, BS, 72; Duke Univ, PhD(bioinorg chem), 76. *Prof Exp:* Res biochem, Inst Cancer Res, Fox Chase Cancer Inst, Philadelphia, 76-77; ASST PROF CHEM, COL ST SCHOLASTICA, 78- *Mem:* Am Chem Soc. *Res:* Fluorescence and nuclear magnetic resonance studies of enzymes. *Mailing Add:* Dept of Chem Col of St Scholastica Duluth MN 55811

STEIN, PAUL S G, b New York, NY, Apr 3, 43. NEUROBIOLOGY, MOTOR CONTROL. *Educ:* Harvard Univ, BA, 64; Univ Calif, Berkeley, 65; Stanford Univ, PhD(neurosci), 70. *Prof Exp:* Fel neurosci, Univ Calif, San Diego, 69-71; asst prof, 71-77, ASSOC PROF BIOL, WASHINGTON UNIV, 77- *Mem:* Soc Neurosci; Am Soc Zoologists; AAAS. *Res:* Spinal cord control of limb movement; scratch reflex in turtles; neuronal pattern generation. *Mailing Add:* Dept Biol Washington Univ St Louis MO 63130

STEIN, PHILIP, b New York, NY, Apr 28, 32. PHYSIOLOGY. *Educ:* Brooklyn Col, BA, 53; George Washington Univ, MS, 54; Columbia Univ, MA, 59; Univ Geneva, PhD(biochem), 61. *Prof Exp:* Instr chem, Brooklyn Col, 60-62; instr, New York Community Col, 62-64; asst prof biol, Fairleigh Dickinson Univ, 64-68; ASSOC PROF BIOL, STATE UNIV NY COL, NEW PALTZ, 68- *Concurrent Pos:* USPHS grant, 62-64; NSF grant, 64-; consult biochemist, Nat Sugar Industs; consult, Sugar Refinery, Pepsi Cola, 72- *Mem:* Fel Am Inst Chem; Am Chem Soc; Am Soc Biol Chemists. *Res:* Chemical composition of the thyrotropic hormone secreted by the anterior pituitary gland; role of hypothalamus in regulation of thyroid function. *Mailing Add:* Dept of Biol State Univ of NY Col New Paltz NY 12561

STEIN, REINHARDT P, b New York, NY, Dec 19, 35; m 62; c 2. ORGANIC CHEMISTRY. *Educ:* Rensselaer Polytech Inst, BS, 58; Ohio State Univ, PhD(org chem), 63. *Prof Exp:* Res chemist, Dow Chem Co, 63-64; RES CHEMIST, WYETH LABS, INC, 64- *Mem:* Am Chem Soc. *Res:* Total synthesis of natural products; new totally synthetic steroids; structural elucidation of natural products; synthesis of new drugs. *Mailing Add:* Wyeth Labs Inc Box 8299 Philadelphia PA 19101

STEIN, RICHARD ADOLPH, b Edmonton, Alta, May 17, 37. ELECTRICAL ENGINEERING. *Educ:* Univ Alta, BS, 58; Univ Ill, Urbana, MS, 61; Univ BC, PhD(elec eng), 68. *Prof Exp:* Asst prof elec eng, Univ Alta, 61-65; assoc prof, 68-74, PROF ELEC ENG, UNIV CALGARY, 74-, ASSOC DEAN, FAC ENG, 77- *Mem:* Inst Elec & Electronics Engrs. *Res:* Electrical circuit theory; electrical filter design; digital image processing. *Mailing Add:* Dept of Elec Eng Univ of Calgary Calgary AB T2N 1N4 Can

STEIN, RICHARD BERNARD, b New Rochelle, NY, June 14, 40; m 62; c 2. NEUROPHYSIOLOGY, BIOPHYSICS. *Educ:* Mass Inst Technol, BS, 62; Oxford Univ, MA & DPhil(physiol), 66. *Prof Exp:* Res fel med res, Exeter Col, Oxford Univ, 65-68; assoc prof physiol, 68-72, PROF PHYSIOL, UNIV ALTA, 72- *Concurrent Pos:* USPHS fel, 66-68. *Mem:* Brit Physiol Soc; Can Physiol Soc; Neurosci Soc. *Res:* Motor control; information processing by nerve cells; sensory feedback; neural models. *Mailing Add:* Dept of Physiol Univ of Alta Edmonton AB T6G 2G7 Can

STEIN, RICHARD JAMES, b Palmerton, Pa, Aug 10, 30; m 53. POLYMER CHEMISTRY. *Educ:* Pa State Univ, BS, 58; Univ Akron, MS, 60, PhD(polymer chem), 67. *Prof Exp:* Res chemist, Goodyear Tire & Rubber Co, 60-63, sr res chemist, 66-71; POLYMERS SPECIALIST, INSULATING MAT DEPT, GEN ELEC CO, 71- *Mem:* Am Chem Soc. *Res:* Polymer synthesis and properties. *Mailing Add:* 239 Pinewood Dr Schenectady NY 12303

STEIN, RICHARD STEPHEN, b Far Rockaway, NY, Aug 21, 25; m 51; c 4. POLYMER CHEMISTRY. *Educ:* Polytech Inst Brooklyn, BS, 45; Princeton Univ, MA, 48, PhD(phys chem), 49. *Prof Exp:* Asst, Polytech Inst Brooklyn, 45; asst, Princeton Univ, 49-50; asst prof, 50-57, from assoc prof to prof, 57-61, commonwealth prof, 61-80, GOESSMANN PROF CHEM & DIR, POLYMER RES INST, UNIV MASS, AMHERST, 80- *Concurrent Pos:* Fulbright vis prof, Kyoto Univ, 68. *Honors & Awards:* Int Award, Soc Plastics

Eng, 69; Borden Award, Am Chem Soc, 72; Bingham Medal, Soc Rheol, 72; High Polymer Physics Award, Am Phys Soc, 76. *Mem:* Am Chem Soc; Am Phys Soc; Soc Rheol. *Res:* Molecular structure; light scattering; mechanical and optical properties of high polymers. *Mailing Add:* Dept of Chem Univ of Mass Amherst MA 01002

STEIN, ROBERT ALFRED, b Chicago, Ill, Feb 20, 33; m 56; c 2. WEAPON SYSTEM ANALYSIS, ENGINEERING MECHANICS. *Educ:* Univ Ill, BS, 55; Ohio State Univ, MS, 58, PhD, 67. *Prof Exp:* Prin physicist, Dept Physics & Metall, Columbus Labs, 55-60, sr physicist, 60-63, prog mgr, 63-66, assoc div chief, 66-70, asst sect mgr, 72-73, sect mgr, Defense Anal, 73-76, div chief, 70-76, ASSOC DIR, ADVAN SYST LAB, BATTELLE MEM INST, 76- *Concurrent Pos:* Guest ed, Jour Defense Res, 77. *Mem:* AAAS; Am Inst Aeronaut & Astronaut; AAAS; Am Soc Mech Engrs; NY Acad Sci. *Res:* Hypervelocity impact phenomena and development of hypervelocity accelerators; weapon systems analysis; non-nuclear kill mechanisms; naval ordnance systems; army combat vehicle systems. *Mailing Add:* 11521 Danville Dr Rockville MD 20852

STEIN, ROBERT CARRINGTON, ornithology, bioacoustics, see previous edition

STEIN, ROBERT FOSTER, b New York, NY, Mar 4, 35; m 58; c 2. ASTROPHYSICS. *Educ:* Univ Chicago, BS, 57; Columbia Univ, PhD(physics), 66. *Prof Exp:* Res fel astrophys, Carnegie Inst Wash Mt Wilson & Palomar Observs, 66-67; res fel, Harvard Observ, 67-69; asst prof astrophys, Brandeis Univ, 69-76; assoc prof astrophys, 76-81, PROF ASTROPHYS, MICH STATE UNIV, 81- *Concurrent Pos:* Consult, Smithsonian Astrophys Observ, 69-73; vis fel joint inst lab astrophys, Nat Bur Standards & Univ Colo, 73-74; vis scientist, Observatoire de Nice, 81. *Mem:* Am Astron Soc; Int Astron Union. *Res:* Astrophysical fluid dynamics; solar chromosphere and corona; radiative transfer. *Mailing Add:* Dept Physics & Astron Mich State Univ East Lansing MI 48824

STEIN, ROBERT GEORGE, agricultural chemistry, medicinal chemistry, see previous edition

STEIN, ROY ALLEN, b Warren, Ohio, Aug 28, 47; m 73. ZOOLOGY, AQUATIC ECOLOGY. *Educ:* Univ Mich, BS, 69; Ore State Univ, MS, 71; Univ Wis, PhD(zool), 75. *Prof Exp:* Partic scientist fisheries, Smithsonian Inst, 72; res assoc zool, Univ Wis, 76; ASST PROF ZOOL, OHIO STATE UNIV, 76- *Mem:* Am Fisheries Soc; Am Inst Biol Sci; AAAS; Ecol Soc Am; Sigma Xi. *Res:* Behavioral ecology with a major emphasis on intra- and inter-specific interactions among aquatic organisms, specifically fish; examining how two important processes (predation and competition) structure fresh water communities. *Mailing Add:* Dept of Zool 1735 Neil Ave Columbus OH 43210

STEIN, SAMUEL H, b New York, NY, Jan 6, 37; m 57; c 3. PHOTOGRAPHIC SCIENCE, PHYSICAL ORGANIC CHEMISTRY. *Educ:* City Col New York, BS, 57; Boston Univ, PhD(org chem), 67. *Prof Exp:* Res chemist, Nat Cash Register Co, Ohio, 57-59; res chemist, Itek Corp, summer 60, sr res chemist & proj leader org chem, Lexington Res Labs, 65-68, mgr paper develop group, Lexington Develop Labs, 68-69, mgr sci staff negative lithographic plate group, 69-71, mgr positive lithographic plate group, 71-72, mgr lithographic systs res dept, Lithographic Technol Lab, 72-74; mgr emulsion res, 74-79, MEM STAFF, NEW PROD COMT & STRATEGIC PLANNING COMT, CHEMCO PHOTOPROD, 79-, DIR EMULSION RES & DEVELOP, 80- *Mem:* AAAS; Am Chem Soc; Soc Photog Sci & Eng. *Res:* Photochemistry, including unconventional photographic process and silver halide photo processes; silver halide emulsions for positive and negative systems; photoconductors, photopolymers and heterogeneous catalysis. *Mailing Add:* 36 Preston St Huntington NY 11743

STEIN, SAMUEL RICHARD, b New York, NY, Jan 7, 46; m 66. PHYSICS. *Educ:* Brown Univ, ScB & ScM, 66; Stanford Univ, PhD(physics), 74. *Prof Exp:* Physicist time & frequency, 74-80, CHIEF PROG OFF, NAT BUR STANDARDS, 80- *Concurrent Pos:* Nat Res Coun fel, Nat Bur Standards, 74-76. *Mem:* Am Phys Soc. *Res:* Frequency standards; frequency metrology; superconductivity; lasers; quartz crystal oscillators. *Mailing Add:* Admin A1002 Nat Bur Standards Washington DC 20234

STEIN, SETH AVRAM, b Middletown, Conn, July 12, 53. SEISMOLOGY, TECTONICS. *Educ:* Mass Inst Technol, SB, 75; Calif Inst Technol, MS, 77, PhD(geophys), 78. *Prof Exp:* RES AFFIL GEOPHYS, STANFORD UNIV, 78- *Mem:* Am Geophys Union; Seismol Soc Am; Royal Astron Soc; Soc Explor Geophysicists. *Res:* Theoretical seismology and normal mode theory; applications of long period seismology to plate tectonics; physics of tectonic processes, especially midocean ridges. *Mailing Add:* Dept of Geophys Stanford Univ Stanford CA 94305

STEIN, SEYMOUR NORMAN, b Chicago, Ill, Nov 23, 13; m 36; c 1. PHYSIOLOGY. *Educ:* Univ Ill, BS, 41, MD, 43. *Prof Exp:* From res asst to res assoc neurophysiol, Univ Ill, 46-49, asst prof & res physiologist, 49-51; head neurophysiol br & submarine & diving med br, Naval Med Res Inst, 52-60, head physiol div, 53-57; dep bio-sci officer, Pac Missile Range, US Dept Navy, 61-63; chief life sci officer, 64-65, chief med officer, 66-71, GUEST SCIENTIST, NASA-AMES RES CTR, 71-; PROF PHYSIOL, SAN JOSE STATE UNIV, 77- *Concurrent Pos:* Consult, Surgeon Gen, US Dept Army, 47-, NIMH, 53-; mem panel underwater swimmers, Nat Res Coun, 54-55; ed, J Biol Photog Asn, 56. *Mem:* Fel AAAS; Am Physiol Soc; Soc Exp Biol & Med; Biol Photog Asn; assoc fel Am Inst Aeronaut & Astronaut. *Res:* Basic and clinical studies on convulsions; effects of acute and chronic exposure to hypernormal amounts of carbon dioxide and oxygen; space medicine; bioinstrumentation. *Mailing Add:* 1080 Lorene Ct Mountain View CA 94040

STEIN, SHERMAN KOPALD, b Minneapolis, Minn, Aug 11, 26; m 50; c 3. MATHEMATICS. *Educ:* Calif Inst Technol, BSc, 46; Columbia Univ, MA, 47, PhD(math), 52. *Hon Degrees:* DH, Marietta Col, 75. *Prof Exp:* PROF MATH, UNIV CALIF, DAVIS, 53- *Concurrent Pos:* Mem, Math Panel Calif Teacher Prep & Cert, 73- *Honors & Awards:* L R Ford Award, Math Asn Am, 75. *Mem:* Am Math Soc; Math Asn Am. *Res:* Algebraic applications to geometry; convex bodies. *Mailing Add:* Dept of Math Univ of Calif Davis CA 95616

STEIN, STEPHEN ELLERY, b Manhattan, NY, Dec 13, 48; m 74. PHYSICAL CHEMISTRY, CHEMICAL KINETICS. *Educ:* Univ Rochester, BS, 69; Univ Wash, PhD(phys chem), 74. *Prof Exp:* Res assoc, SRI Int, 74-75, phys chemist, 75-76; asst prof, Dept Chem, WVa Univ, 76-81, assoc prof, 81-82; RES CHEMIST, NAT BUR STANDARDS, 82- *Mem:* N Am Photochem Soc; Am Chem Soc. *Res:* Thermochemistry and kinetics of elementary chemical reactions; rate and thermochemical estimation methods; unimolecular reactions; high temperature free radical reactions; gas-surface reactions; liquid-phase pyrolysis; analysis of complex reacting systems; coal conversion chemistry; combustion; ignition processes. *Mailing Add:* Chem Kinetics Div A157/222 Nat Bur Standards Washington DC 20234

STEIN, T PETER, b London, Eng, Apr 27, 41; m 67. BIOCHEMISTRY. *Educ:* Univ London, BSc, 62, MSc, 63; Cornell Univ, PhD(chem), 67. *Prof Exp:* Asst chem, Cornell Univ, 63-67; instr res surg & biochem, 69-72, ASSOC PROF SURG, SCH MED, UNIV PA, 72- *Concurrent Pos:* NIH fel biochem, Univ Calif, Los Angeles, 67-69. *Mem:* AAAS; Am Chem Soc; Royal Soc Chem; Am Inst Nutrit; Am Soc Clin Nutrit. *Res:* Protein metabolism during spacelift; lipid metabolism, clinical nutrition, nutritional assessment; nitrogen-15 metabolism and rates of protein synthesis in man; lung biochemistry. *Mailing Add:* Surgical Suite Grad Hosp 19th & Lombard Sts Philadelphia PA 19146

STEIN, TALBERT SHELDON, b Detroit, Mich, Jan 6, 41; m 63; c 2. PHYSICS. *Educ:* Wayne State Univ, BS, 62; Brandeis Univ, MA, 64, PhD(physics), 68. *Prof Exp:* Res assoc physics, Univ Wash, 67-70; asst prof, 70-75, ASSOC PROF PHYSICS, WAYNE STATE UNIV, 75- *Mem:* Am Phys Soc; Am Asn Physics Teachers. *Res:* Experimental atomic physics including low energy positron-atom interactions; precision measurement of the g factor of the free electron; studies of effects of electric fields on neutral atoms. *Mailing Add:* Dept Physics Wayne State Univ Detroit MI 48202

STEIN, WAYNE ALFRED, b Minneapolis, Minn, Dec 6, 37. ASTROPHYSICS. *Educ:* Univ Minn, BPhys, 59, PhD(physics), 64. *Prof Exp:* Res assoc astrophys, Princeton Univ, 64-66; asst res physicist, Univ Calif, San Diego, 66-69, asst prof astrophys, 69-73, assoc prof, 73-74; PROF PHYSICS, UNIV MINN, 74- *Concurrent Pos:* Alfred P Sloan Found fel, Univ Minn, Minneapolis & Univ Calif, San Diego, 69-; from asst prof to assoc prof, Univ Minn, Minneapolis, 69- *Mem:* Am Astron Soc; Am Phys Soc. *Res:* Infrared astronomy. *Mailing Add:* Sch Physics & Astron Univ Minn Minneapolis MN 55455

STEIN, WILLIAM EARL, b Rochester, NY, May 30, 24; m 47; c 4. ELECTRON PHYSICS, NUCLEAR PHYSICS. *Educ:* Univ Va, BEE, 46; Stanford Univ, MS, 50; Univ NMex, PhD(physics), 62. *Prof Exp:* PHYSICIST, LOS ALAMOS SCI LAB, 49- *Mem:* Am Phys Soc. *Res:* Electron-photon interactions and production of nearly monochromatic soft x-rays by the inverse Compton effect. *Mailing Add:* P-DOR MS 458 Los Alamos Sci Lab Los Alamos NM 87545

STEIN, WILLIAM EDWARD, b Cleveland, Ohio, June 18, 46. OPERATIONS RESEARCH. *Educ:* Case Western Reserve Univ, BS, 68; Purdue Univ, MS, 70; NC Univ, PhD(opers res), 75. *Prof Exp:* Asst prof math, Univ Ill, Chicago, 74-77; ASSOC PROF MATH, TEX CHRISTIAN UNIV, 77- *Mem:* Opers Res Soc; Inst Mgt Sci; Asn Comput Mach; Am Statist Asn. *Res:* Applied probability; statistical physics; fuzzy sets; stochastic dominance. *Mailing Add:* Dept Math Tex Christian Univ Ft Worth TX 76129

STEIN, WILLIAM HOWARD, biochemistry, deceased

STEIN, WILLIAM IVO, b Wurzburg, Ger, July 22, 22; nat US; m 48; c 12. FORESTRY. *Educ:* Pac Col, BS, 43; Ore State Univ, MF, 52, PhD, 63. *Prof Exp:* Forester timber mgt res, 48-52, asst res forester, 52-63, prin plant ecologist, 63-80, RES FORESTER, PAC NORTHWEST FOREST & RANGE EXP STA, US FOREST SERV, 80- *Mem:* Soc Am Foresters. *Res:* study of ecology and physiology of Pacific Northwest species for the purpose of improving reforestation practices; reforestation research. *Mailing Add:* Forestry Sci Lab 3200 Jefferson Way Corvallis OR 97331

STEINBACH, HENRY BURR, zoology, physiology, deceased

STEINBACH, HOWARD LYNNE, b Pittsburgh, Pa, Sept 17, 18; m 51; c 3. RADIOLOGY. *Educ:* Univ Calif, Los Angeles, AB, 40; St Louis Univ, MS, 43. *Prof Exp:* Intern, Los Angeles County Gen Hosp, 44; from asst resident to resident, Univ Calif Hosp, 45-48; pvt pract, 58-59; from instr to prof radiol, 49-72, CLIN PROF RADIOL, SCH MED, UNIV CALIF, SAN FRANCISCO, 72-; CLIN PROF RADIOL, STANFORD UNIV, 72- *Concurrent Pos:* Consult, Gen Hosp, 61- & Letterman Gen Hosp, 65- *Mem:* Radiol Soc NAm; AMA; Am Col Radiol; Asn Univ Radiol; Am Roentgen Ray Soc. *Res:* Roentgen manifestations of metabolic and endocrine abnormalities of the skeletal system; arthritis and rheumatism; pediatric radiology; endocrine and metabolic diseases; gastroenterology. *Mailing Add:* 4141 Geary Blvd San Francisco CA 94118

STEINBACH, LEONARD, b New York, NY, Feb 26, 27; m 51; c 3. ORGANIC CHEMISTRY. *Educ:* City Col New York, BS, 47; Polytech Inst Brooklyn, MS, 54. *Prof Exp:* Group leader org res, 56-62, prod mgr, 63-64, dir res & develop, 65, dir corp develop, 66-67, gen mgr, 67-69, vpres, 69-74, VPRES CORP DIR PURCHASING, INT FLAVORS & FRAGRANCES, INC, HAZLET, 74- *Concurrent Pos:* Mem chm fac, Monmouth Col, 56-61. *Mem:* AAAS; Am Chem Soc; NY Acad Sci. *Res:* Organic synthesis and development in aromatic chemicals, perfumes and flavor materials. *Mailing Add:* 10 Ramsgate Rd Cranford NJ 07016

STEINBACH, WAYNE ROBERT, molecular spectroscopy, see previous edition

STEINBECK, KLAUS, b Munich, Ger, Dec 11, 37; US citizen; m 60; c 4. FORESTRY, SILVICULTRUE. *Educ:* Univ Ga, BSF, 61, MS, 63; Mich State Univ, PhD(forestry), 65. *Prof Exp:* Res plant physiologist, US Forest Serv, 65-68; asst prof, 69-72, assoc prof, 72-81, PROF FOREST RESOURCES, UNIV GA, 81- *Mem:* Soc Am Foresters. *Res:* Biomass production of short-rotation forests. *Mailing Add:* Sch of Forest Resources Univ of Ga Athens GA 30602

STEINBERG, ALFRED DAVID, b New York, NY. IMMUNOLOGY, RHEUMATOLOGY. *Educ:* Princeton Univ, AB, 62; Harvard Univ, MD, 66. *Prof Exp:* SR INVESTR, NIH, 70-, CHIEF, CELLULAR IMMUNOL SECT, 81-; MED DIR, USPHS, 78- *Honors & Awards:* Hench Award, 74. *Mem:* Am Asn Immunologists; Am Soc Clin Invest. *Res:* Autoimmunity; immune regulation. *Mailing Add:* Bldg 10 Rm 9N-218 NIH Bethesda MD 20205

STEINBERG, ARTHUR GERALD, b Port Chester, NY, Feb 27, 12; m 39; c 2. MEDICAL GENETICS, HUMAN GENETICS. *Educ:* City Col New York, BSc, 33; Columbia Univ, MA, 34, PhD(zool), 41. *Prof Exp:* Lectr genetics, McGill Univ, 40-44; mem opers res group, Off Sci Res & Develop, US Dept Navy, 44-46; assoc prof genetics, Antioch Col & chmn dept genetics, Fels Res Inst, 46-48; consult div biomet & med statist, Mayo Clinic, 48-52; geneticist, Children's Cancer Res Found & res assoc, Children's Hosp, Boston, Mass, 52-56; prof biol, 56-72, from asst prof to assoc prof dept prev med, 56-70, prof human genetics, Dept Reproductive Biol, 70-75, FRANCIS HOBART HERRICK PROF BIOL, CASE WESTERN RESERVE UNIV, 72-, PROF HUMAN GENETICS DEPT MED, 75- *Concurrent Pos:* Mem permanent comt int human genetics cong, NIH, 66-71; chmn med adv bd, Nat Genetics Found, 68-81; sr ed, Progress in Med Genetics; consult ed, Transfusion; contrib ed, Vox Sanguinis; consult, WHO. *Mem:* AAAS; Am Soc Human Genetics (pres, 64); Genetics Soc Am; Am Asn Immunol; hon mem Japanese Soc Human Genetics. *Res:* Immunogenetics; study of genetic control of human immunoglobulins; population genetics; genetics of diabetes. *Mailing Add:* Dept of Biol Case Western Reserve Univ Cleveland OH 44106

STEINBERG, BERNARD ALBERT, b New York, NY, Oct 2, 24; m 46; c 3. MICROBIOLOGY. *Educ:* NY Univ, AB, 47; Univ Ill, MS, 48, PhD(bact), 50. *Prof Exp:* Head sect bact & mycol, Squibb Inst Med Res, NJ, 50-56; head virus & cancer res, Wm S Merrell Co, 56-63; GROUP LEADER CHEMOTHER SECT, STERLING-WINTHROP RES INST, 63- *Mem:* AAAS; Am Soc Microbiol; Sigma Xi. *Res:* Antiviral chemotherapy; upper respiratory viruses; veterinary viruses; virus vaccines and immunology of viruses; viral etiology of cancer. *Mailing Add:* Microbiol Dept Sterling-Winthrop Res Inst Rensselaer NY 12144

STEINBERG, BERNHARD, b New York, NY, June 18, 97; m 31; c 2. PATHOLOGY. *Educ:* Boston Univ, MD, 22. *Prof Exp:* House officer, Hosp Div, Med Col Va, 22-23; asst physician, Boston Psychopath Hosp, 23-24; dir labs & res, Toledo Hosp, Ohio, 27-64; dir inst med res, 43-64; ASSOC PROF RES IN PATH, SCH MED, LOMA LINDA UNIV, 64- *Concurrent Pos:* Nat Res Coun fel, Sch Med, Western Reserve Univ, 24-26, Crile res fel, 26-27; pvt pract oncol & hemat, Pomona, 65- *Honors & Awards:* Am Soc Clin Path Silver Medal, 37; Cincinnati Proctol Soc Cancer Res Award, 50. *Mem:* Am Soc Clin Path; AMA; Am Asn Path & Bact; Am Soc Exp Path; Am Soc Hemat. *Res:* Peritoneal infections; lung diseases; leukemias; hematopoiesis; cancer; originator, immunology of leukocyte; systemic disease of fat; development, functions and diseases of bone marrow. *Mailing Add:* PO Box 1016 Pacific Palisades CA 90272

STEINBERG, BETTIE MURRAY, b Price, Utah, June 13, 37; m 60; c 3. CELL-VIRUS INTERACTIONS. *Educ:* Univ Calif, Riverside, BA, 59; Adelphi Univ, MS, 67; State Univ NY Stony Brook, PhD(microbiol), 76. *Prof Exp:* Fel, Dept Microbiol, State Univ NY Stony Brook, 76-78; res assoc, Dept Biol Sci, Columbia Univ, 78-80; RES SCIENTIST, LONG ISLAND JEWISH-HILLSIDE MED CTR, 80- *Concurrent Pos:* Lectr, Dept Biol Sci, Columbia Univ, 79-80; adj asst prof, Dept Surg, State Univ NY Stony Brook, 80- *Mem:* Am Soc Microbiol; AAAS; NY Acad Sci. *Res:* Cellular changes which occur when human laryngeal epithelium forms papillomas in vivo; investigation of cells grown in vitro from normal and papillomatous tissues to determine the phenotype of human Papilloma Virus transformed laryngeal epithelium. *Mailing Add:* Div Otolaryngol Long Island-Hillside Med Ctr New Hyde Park NY 10042

STEINBERG, DANIEL, b Windsor, Ont, July 21, 22; US citizen; m 46; c 3. BIOCHEMISTRY. *Educ:* Wayne State Univ, BS, 42, MD, 44; Harvard Univ, PhD(biochem), 51. *Prof Exp:* Intern internal med, Boston City Hosp, 44-45; resident, Detroit Receiving Hosp, 45-46; instr physiol, Med Sch, Boston Univ, 47-51; res scientist, Sect Cellular Physiol, Nat Heart Inst, 51-54, from actg chief to chief sect metab, 54-68; PROF MED, HEAD DIV METAB DIS & PROG DIR BASIC SCI IN MED, SCH MED, UNIV CALIF, SAN DIEGO, 68- *Concurrent Pos:* Vis scientist, Carlsberg Labs, Copenhagen, 52-53; pres, Found Advan Educ in Sci, 59; ed-in-chief, J Lipid Res, 61-64; consult ed, Progress in cardiovasc disease; consult, Am Heart Asn, 68-69. *Mem:* AAAS; Am Soc Biol Chem; Am Chem Soc; Am Oil Chem Soc; Soc Exp Biol & Med. *Res:* Mechanisms of hormone action; biochemistry of lipid and lipoprotein metabolism and its relation to atherosclerosis. *Mailing Add:* Div of Metab Dis Univ of Calif Sch of Med La Jolla CA 92037

STEINBERG, DANIEL J, b Washington, DC, Feb 13, 35; m 59; c 2. THERMODYNAMICS, HYDRODYNAMICS. *Educ:* Johns Hopkins Univ, AB, 55; Harvard Univ, MA, 57, PhD(physics), 61. *Prof Exp:* SR PHYSICIST, LAWRENCE LIVERMORE LAB, UNIV CALIF, 61- *Res:* Thermodynamics and equations of state; computer modeling of shock wave physics. *Mailing Add:* Lawrence Livermore Lab L-24 Lawrence CA 94550

STEINBERG, DAVID H, b Bronx, NY, Nov 24, 29; m 52; c 4. ORGANIC CHEMISTRY. *Educ:* Yeshiva Univ, BA, 51; NY Univ, MS, 56, PhD(org chem), 60. *Prof Exp:* Res asst biochem, Montefiore Hosp, NY, 52-53; res assoc org chem res div, NY Univ, 53-59; res chemist res div, Geigy Chem Corp, 59-72, res assoc, 72-80, SR STAFF SCIENTIST PLASTICS & ADDITIVES RES, CIBA-GEIGY CHEM CORP, 80- *Mem:* Am Chem Soc; Royal Soc Chem. *Res:* Organic chemistry encompassing synthesis, reaction mechanism, stereochemistry and structure-activity relationships. *Mailing Add:* CIBA GEIGY Chem Corp 444 Saw Mill River Rd Ardsley NY 10502

STEINBERG, DAVID ISRAEL, b St Louis, Mo, July 18, 42; m 65; c 2. OPERATIONS RESEARCH, APPLIED MATHEMATICS. *Educ:* Washington Univ, BS, 64, MS, 66, DSc, 68. *Prof Exp:* Asst prof appl math, Washington Univ, 67-72; assoc prof, 72-78, PROF MATH, SOUTHERN ILL UNIV, EDWARDSVILLE, 78- *Concurrent Pos:* Affil assoc prof, Washington Univ, 74-77, vis assoc prof comput sci, 77-78, affil prof, 78- *Mem:* Opers Res Soc Am; Soc Indust & Appl Math; Asn Comput Mach; Inst Mgt Sci; Sigma Xi. *Res:* Mathematical programming; numerical linear algebra. *Mailing Add:* Dept Math Statist & Comput Sci Southern Ill Univ Box 65 Edwardsville IL 62026

STEINBERG, ELIOT, b New York, NY, June 5, 23; m 47; c 3. ORGANIC CHEMISTRY, RESEARCH ADMINISTRATION. *Educ:* Polytech Inst Brooklyn, BS, 43, MS, 47. *Prof Exp:* Res chemist, Johnson & Johnson, NJ, 43-44; res chemist, Chilcott Labs Div, Maltine Co, 47-52; res adminr, Warner-Chilcott Labs, 52-58, dir res admin, 58-77, dir admin opers, Warner-Lambert Res Inst, 77-81; MGR MEMBER SERV, INDUST RES INST, 81- *Mem:* AAAS; Am Chem Soc; Am Inst Chem; Drug Info Asn; NY Acad Sci. *Res:* Information retrieval. *Mailing Add:* Indust Res Inst 100 Park Ave New York NY 10017

STEINBERG, ELLIS PHILIP, b Chicago, Ill, Mar 26, 20; m 44; c 3. CHEMISTRY. *Educ:* Univ Chicago, SB, 41, PhD(chem), 47. *Prof Exp:* Jr chemist, Elwood Ord Plant, US War Dept, Ill, 41-43; jr chemist Manhattan dist metall lab, Univ Chicago, 43-46; consult, AEC, 46-47, assoc chemist & asst group leader, 47-58, sr chemist & group leader, 58-74, SECT HEAD NUCLEAR & INORG CHEM, ARGONNE NAT LAB, 74- *Concurrent Pos:* Guggenheim fel, 57-58; mem sci adv comt space radiation effects lab accelerator, Col William & Mary; mem subcomt nuclear instruments & tech, Nat Acad Sci-Nat Res Coun, 48-59 & subcomt radiochem, 59-70; Am Chem Soc rep, Am Nat Standards Inst Subcomt Nuclear Med, 70-74; mem, Prog Adv Comt to Clinton P Anderson Meson Physics Lab, 77-80. *Mem:* AAAS; Am Chem Soc; Am Phys Soc; Sigma Xi. *Res:* Nuclear and radiochemistry; nuclear fission; high energy nuclear reactions, meson-induced reactions, heavy-ion reactions. *Mailing Add:* Chem Div Argonne Nat Lab 9700 S Cass Ave Argonne IL 60439

STEINBERG, GUNTHER, b Cologne, Ger, Apr 14, 24; nat US; m 49; c 2. SURFACE CHEMISTRY, PHYSICAL CHEMISTRY. *Educ:* Univ Calif, Los Angeles, BS, 48, MS, 50, PhD(physiol chem), 56. *Prof Exp:* Res assoc, Scripps Metab Clin, Calif, 50; biochemist atomic energy proj, Univ Calif, Los Angeles, 50-56; res chemist, Martinez Res Lab, Shell Oil Co, 56-61, res chemist, Shell Develop Co, 61-64; res chemist, Stanford Res Inst, 64-67; sr staff chemist, Memorex Corp, 67-77; mgr, media res & mgr advanced develop, 77-80, PRES & DIR, STEINBERG ASSOCS, 80- *Mem:* Am Chem Soc; Int Asn Colloid & Interface Scientists; NAm Thermal Analysis Soc. *Res:* Surface and physical chemistry of polymer composites; physical and chemical measurements; magnetic media processing and surface calorimetry development; electrical contact phenomena; heterogeneous catalysis; radiotracer applications. *Mailing Add:* 345 Lerida Ct Menlo Park CA 94025

STEINBERG, HERBERT AARON, b Bronx, NY, Sept 19, 29; m 55; c 2. MATHEMATICS. *Educ:* Cornell Univ, BA, 50; Yale Univ, MA, 51, PhD(math), 55. *Prof Exp:* Aerodynamicist, Repub Aviation Corp, 55-56; digital systs engr, Sperry Gyroscope Co, 56; sr mathematician, TRG Div, Control Data Corp, 56-68; dir sci serv, 68-76, RES & DEVELOP DIR, MATH APPLNS GROUP, INC, 76- *Concurrent Pos:* Adj prof math, Polytech Inst, NY, 81- *Mem:* Soc Indust & Appl Math; Inst Math Statistics; Inst Elec & Electronics Eng; Math Asn Am; Am Math Soc. *Res:* Systems engineering; signal processing; Monte Carlo methods; computer simulation; radiation transport; random noise; stochastic processes; numerical analysis, computer generated imagery. *Mailing Add:* Math Applns Group Inc 3 Westchester Plaza Elmsford NY 10523

STEINBERG, HOWARD, b Chicago, Ill, Aug 23, 26; m 46; c 3. ORGANIC CHEMISTRY. *Educ:* Univ Ill, BS, 48; Univ Calif, Los Angeles, PhD(chem), 51. *Prof Exp:* AEC fel, Mass Inst Technol, 51-52; res chemist, Aerojet-Gen Corp, 52; res assoc org synthesis, Univ Calif, Los Angeles, 52-53; collabr natural prod, USDA, 53-54; res chemist, Pac Coast Borax Co, 54, mgr org res, US Borax Res Corp, 55-58, asst dir chem res, 58, from assoc dir to dir, 59-63, vpres, 63-69, PRES, US BORAX RES CORP, 69-, VPRES, US BORAX & CHEM CORP, 69-, MEM BD DIRS, 73- *Mem:* Am Chem Soc; Soc Chem Indust; Indust Res Inst; Am Inst Mining, Metall & Petrol Engrs. *Res:* Boron and synthetic organic chemistry; reaction mechanisms; kinetics. *Mailing Add:* US Borax & Chem Corp 3075 Wilshire Blvd Los Angeles CA 90010

STEINBERG, JAMES, medicine, biochemistry, see previous edition

STEINBERG, JOSEPH, b New York, NY, Mar 22, 20; m 49; c 2. MATHEMATICAL STATISTICS. *Educ:* City Col New York, BS, 39. *Prof Exp:* Statistician pop div, US Bur Census, 40-42; math statistician, Social Security Bd, 42-44; statistician statist res div, US Bur Census, 44-46, chief statist methods br pop & housing div, 46-59, chief statist methods off, 59-60, chief statist methods div, 60-63; chief math statistician, Social Security Admin, 63-72; dir off surv methods res & asst comnr surv design, Bur Labor Statist, 72-75; PRES, SURV DESIGN, INC, 75- *Concurrent Pos:* Lectr, USDA Grad Sch, 42-74; consult, Orgn Am States, Chile, 65 & 67; vis prof surv res ctr, Inst Social Res, Univ Mich, 68, 69, 70 & 72; mem assembly behav & soc sci, Nat Acad Sci-Nat Res Coun, 72-77, mem comt Fed Agency Eval Res, 71-75, mem comt energy consumption measurement, 75-77; mem comt eval res, Social Sci Res Coun, 77-; assoc ed, Am Statistician, 77- *Honors & Awards:* Meritorious Serv Award, Dept Com, 55; Comnr Citation, Soc Security Admin, 65; Distinguished Serv Award, Dept HEW, 68. *Mem:* Hon fel AAAS; hon fel Am Statist Asn; Am Soc Qual Control; Inst Math Statist; Int Asn Surv Statisticians. *Res:* Sample survey design and statistical analysis; evaluation of non-sampling errors; response variance and bias; data linkage; computer analysis; quality control; operations research; cost functions and optimization. *Mailing Add:* Surv Design Inc Suite 201 Silver Spring MD 20910

STEINBERG, M(ORRIS) A(LBERT), b Hartford, Conn, Sept 24, 20; m 51; c 3. METALLURGY. *Educ:* Mass Inst Technol, BS, 42, MS, 46, DSc(metall), 48. *Prof Exp:* Instr metall, Mass Inst Technol, 45-48; head, Metall Dept, Horizons, Inc, 48-58; with Micrometric Instrument Co, 49-51; chief metallurgist, Horizons Titanium Corp, 51-55; secy & dir, Diwolfram Corp, 51-58; consult scientist, Lockheed Missiles & Space Co, 58-59, mgr mat, propulsion & ord res, 59-62, lab dir, Mat Sci Lab, 62-64, mgr mat sci lab, Res & Develop Div, 64-65, dep chief scientist, 65-72, DIR TECHNOL APPLNS, LOCKHEED AIRCRAFT CORP, BURBANK, 72- *Concurrent Pos:* Mem adv comt, US Israeli Bi-Nat Res Found, 75-; mem, Nat Mat Adv Bd, Nat Res Ctr, Nat Acad Sci, 75- *Mem:* AAAS; Am Soc Metall; Am Inst Chem; Am Inst Astronaut & Aeronaut; Inst Advan Eng. *Res:* Missile and spacecraft materials; extractive metallurgy of reactive metals; powder metallurgy; high strength steels. *Mailing Add:* 348 Homewood Rd Los Angeles CA 90049

STEINBERG, MALCOLM SAUL, b New Brunswick, NJ, June 1, 30; div; c 4. DEVELOPMENTAL BIOLOGY, EMBRYOLOGY. *Educ:* Amherst Col, BA, 52; Univ Minn, MA, 54, PhD(zool), 56. *Prof Exp:* Instr zool, Univ Minn, 55; fel embryol, Carnegie Inst, Washington, 56-58; from asst prof to assoc prof biol, Johns Hopkins Univ, 58-66; prof, 66-75, HENRY FAIRFIELD OSBORN PROF BIOL, PRINCETON UNIV, 75- *Concurrent Pos:* Instr-in-charge embryol course, Woods Hole Marine Biol Lab, 67-72, trustee, 69-77. *Mem:* Fel AAAS; Am Soc Cell Biol; Am Soc Zool; Soc Develop Biol (Secy, 70-73); Int Soc Develop Biol. *Res:* Regeneration in coelenterates; mechanisms of morphogenesis; biological self-organization; tissue reconstruction by dissociated cells; physics, chemistry and physiology of cell adhesion. *Mailing Add:* Dept Biol Princeton Univ Princeton NJ 08540

STEINBERG, MARCIA IRENE, b Brooklyn, NY, Mar 7, 44. ION TRANSPORT, ENZYMOLOGY. *Educ:* Brooklyn Col, BS, 64, MA, 66; Univ Mich, PhD(biochem), 73. *Prof Exp:* ASST PROF PHARMACOL, UPSTATE MED CTR, STATE UNIV NY, 78- *Mem:* Sigma Xi; Am Women in Sci; NY Acad Sci; AAAS. *Res:* Mechanism of action of the sodium plus potassium dependent adenosine triphosphatase; enzymes as probes of secondary structure in super coiled DNA and mRNA; mechanism of catalysis by flavoprotein monooxygenases. *Mailing Add:* Dept Pharmacol Upstate Med Ctr State Univ NY 766 Irving Ave Syracuse NY 13210

STEINBERG, MARSHALL, b Pittsburgh, Pa, Sept 18, 32; m 62; c 3. PHARMACOLOGY, TOXICOLOGY. *Educ:* Georgetown Univ, BS, 54; Univ Pittsburgh, MS, 56; Univ Tex Med Br Galveston, PhD(pharmacol, toxicol), 66; Nat Registry Clin Chem, cert, 70. *Prof Exp:* Asst dir trop testing, Univ Pittsburgh, 55-56; chief clin path lab, 97th Gen Hosp, Med Serv Corps, US Army, Frankfurt, Ger, 56-60, chief biochem & toxicol div, 4th Army Med Lab, San Antonio, Tex, 61-63, chief toxicol div, Environ Hyg Agency, 66-71, dir lab serv US Army Environ Hyg Agency, 72-75; consult to surg gen, Lab Sci, 75-76; vpres & dir bioassay prog, Tracor Jitco, 77-78; V PRES & DIR SCI OPERS, HAZLETON LABS AM, 78- *Concurrent Pos:* Liaison mem, Armed Forces Pest Control Bd, 67-75; mem pesticide monitoring panel, Fed Working Group Pesticide Mgt, Coun Environ Quality, 71-72 & safety panel, 72-; adj prof, Am Univ, 81. *Mem:* Soc Toxicol; Am Soc Pharmacol & Exp Therapeut; Am Conf Govt Indust Hygienists; Am Col Toxicol; Am Indust Hyg Asn. *Res:* Applied research in industrial and environmental toxicology, insect repellants, pesticides and fire extinguishants, particularly in regard to hazards owing to skin penetration or irritation as well as toxic effects due to inhalation. *Mailing Add:* Hazleton Labs Am 9200 Leesburg Turnpike Vienna VA 22180

STEINBERG, MARTIN, b Chicago, Ill, Apr 18, 20; m 42; c 3. PHYSICAL CHEMISTRY. *Educ:* Univ Ill, BS, 41; Univ Chicago, PhD(chem), 49. *Prof Exp:* Res chemist, Continental Carbon Co, 41-45; res assoc inst nuclear studies, Univ Chicago, 49-51; res chemist, Gen Elec Co, 51-56; sr scientist, Armour Res Found, 56-61; head chem physics, Delco Electronics Div, Gen Motors Corp, 61-74; RES CHEMIST, QUANTUM INST, UNIV CALIF, SANTA BARBARA, 74- *Mem:* AAAS; Am Chem Soc; Am Phys Soc; Combustion Inst. *Res:* Carbon black formation and properties; electrochemistry in fused salts; stable isotope geochemistry; combustion; reentry physics; high temperature kinetics; gaseous radiation and spectroscopy; air pollution; chemical lasers. *Mailing Add:* 345 N Ontare Rd Santa Barbara CA 93105

STEINBERG, MARTIN H, b New York, NY, July 2, 36; m 73; c 1. MOLECULER BIOLOGY, GENETICS. *Educ:* Cornell Univ, AB, 58; Tufts Univ, MD, 62. *Prof Exp:* Med intern, Cornell Med Serv, 62-63; med resident, New Eng Med Ctr, 66-68, fel hemat, 68-70; asst prof, 70-74, assoc prof, 74-77, PROF MED, MED SCH, UNIV MISS, 77- *Concurrent Pos:* Mem, Res Rev Comt, Am Heart Asn, 81-84; prin investr, NIH, Vet Admin, 73-; assoc chief staff res, Jackson Vet Admin Med Ctr, 73-; asst dean, Sch Med, Univ Miss, 73- *Mem:* Am Fedn Clin Res; Am Soc Clin Invest; Am Soc Hemat. *Res:* Intrinsic factors which may determine the clinical course of sickle cell anemia; interactions of structural variants of hemogoblin with the thalassemia syndromes. *Mailing Add:* Vet Admin Med Ctr 151 Jackson MS 39216

STEINBERG, MARVIN PHILLIP, b Philadelphia, Pa, Oct 4, 22; m 46; c 3. FOOD TECHNOLOGY. *Educ:* Univ Minn, BS, 43, MS, 49; Univ Ill, PhD(food technol), 53. *Prof Exp:* Asst chem eng, Univ Minn, 45-49; asst food tech, 49-52, from instr to assoc prof, 52-63, PROF FOOD TECH, UNIV ILL, URBANA, 63- *Mem:* Am Inst Chem Eng; Am Soc Agr Eng; Am Chem Soc; Inst Food Technol. *Res:* Application of chemical engineering to food product and process development; conversion of the whole soybean into dairy analogs and other foods; water binding by food constituents and its quantification, characterization and application to immediate moisture foods; waste conversion to feed. *Mailing Add:* Dept Food Sci Univ Ill 1707 S Orchard St Urbana IL 61801

STEINBERG, MELVIN SANFORD, b Canton, Ohio, Mar 28, 28; m 54; c 2. THEORETICAL PHYSICS. *Educ:* Univ NC, BS, 49, MS, 51; Yale Univ, PhD(physics), 55. *Prof Exp:* Asst physics, Yale Univ, 54-55; asst prof, Stevens Inst Technol, 55-59; assoc prof, Univ Mass, 59-62; ASSOC PROF PHYSICS, SMITH COL, 62- *Concurrent Pos:* Res assoc, Woods Hole Oceanog Inst, 56-58 & 62; res assoc, Air Force Cambridge Res Lab, 60-61; NSF sci fac fel, 66-67. *Mem:* Am Phys Soc. *Res:* Theory of solids; acoustics; electrodynamics. *Mailing Add:* Dept of Physics Smith Col Northampton MA 01063

STEINBERG, MEYER, b Philadelphia, Pa, July 10, 24; m 50; c 2. CHEMICAL ENGINEERING. CHEMISTRY. *Educ:* Cooper Union, BChE, 44; Polytech Inst Brooklyn, MChE, 49. *Prof Exp:* Jr chem engr, Manhattan Dist, Kellex Corp, 44-46; asst chem engr process develop, Deutsch & Loonam, NY, 47-50; assoc chem engr, Guggenheim Bros, Mineola, NY, 50-57; CHEM ENGR & HEAD, PROCESS SCI DIV, DEPT ENERGY & ENVIRON, BROOKHAVEN NAT LAB, 57- *Mem:* Am Inst Chem Engrs; Am Chem Soc; Sigma Xi; AAAS; Am Nuclear Soc. *Res:* New novel innovative processes for energy conversion, nuclear, fossil, geothermal, solar; development of materials for conservation and energy storage. *Mailing Add:* Process Sci Div Brookhaven Nat Lab Upton NY 11973

STEINBERG, MITCHELL IRVIN, b Philadelphia, Pa, Jan 22, 44; m 66; c 3. PHARMACOLOGY. *Educ:* Philadelphia Col Pharm & Sci, BSc, 66; Univ Mich, PhD(pharmacol), 70. *Prof Exp:* Res fel, Univ Conn Health Ctr, 70-71; instr pharmacol, 71-72; sr pharmacologist, 72-77; res scientist, 77-80, RES ASSOC, ELI LILLY RES LABS, 80- *Mem:* AAAS; Am Soc Pharmacol & Exp Therapeut; NY Acad Sci. *Res:* Interactions of pharmacological agents with excitable membranes of mammalian cardiac & neuronal tissues. *Mailing Add:* Dept of Pharmacol MC 304 Eli Lilly Res Labs Indianapolis IN 46206

STEINBERG, PHILLIP HENRY, b Cincinnati, Ohio, Dec 11, 31; m 61; c 3. EXPERIMENTAL HIGH ENERGY PHYSICS. *Educ:* Univ Cincinnati, BS, 54; Northwestern Univ, PhD(physics), 60. *Prof Exp:* From asst prof to assoc prof physics, 59-75, PROF PHYSICS, UNIV MD, COLLEGE PARK, 75-, ASSOC CHMN, 81- *Concurrent Pos:* NSF fel, 65-66. *Mem:* Am Phys Soc. *Res:* Experimental elementary particle physics; hypernuclei; leptonic K-meson decay; meson-nucleon scattering. *Mailing Add:* Dept of Physics & Astron Univ of Md College Park MD 20740

STEINBERG, RICHARD, b Brooklyn, NY, Feb 22, 30; m 53; c 3. ELECTRICAL ENGINEERING. *Educ:* City Col New York, BEE, 52; Univ Pa, MSEE, 58. *Prof Exp:* Jr engr, Govt & Indust Div, Philco Corp, 52-54; engr, Decker Corp, 54-56; sr engr, Electronics Div, Parsons Corp, 56-59; mem tech staff, Hughes Aircraft Co, 59-61; asst sect head elec eng, TRW Systs Group, Calif, 61-71; dept staff engr, Western Develop Labs Div, Philco-Ford Corp, 71; staff engr, 72-80, SR STAFF ENGR, LOCKHEED MISSILES & SPACE CO, SUNNYVALE, 80- *Concurrent Pos:* Instr, Univ Calif, Los Angeles, 61-64 & Calif State Col, Los Angeles, 61-68. *Mailing Add:* 2714 Preston Dr Mountain View CA 94040

STEINBERG, ROBERT, b Stykon, Rumania, May 25, 22; m 52. MATHEMATICS. *Educ:* Univ Toronto, PhD(math), 48. *Prof Exp:* Lectr math, Univ Toronto, 47-48; from instr to assoc prof, 48-62, PROF MATH, UNIV CALIF, LOS ANGELES, 62- *Mem:* Am Math Soc; Math Asn Am. *Res:* Group representations; algebraic groups. *Mailing Add:* Dept of Math 6364 Math Sci Bldg Univ of Calif Los Angeles CA 90024

STEINBERG, RONALD FREDERICK, b Lapeer, Mich, Dec 20, 29; m 57; c 4. ELECTRICAL ENGINEERING. *Educ:* Lawrence Inst Technol, BSEE, 62; Wayne State Univ, MSEE, 68. *Prof Exp:* Engr, 62-65, sr engr, 65-68, proj engr, 68-70, SR PROJ ENGR, BENDIX RES LABS, 70- *Mem:* Inst Elec & Electronics Engrs. *Res:* Development of acoustic techniques, including acoustic holography for applications in non-destructive testing, underwater viewing and geologic prediction and management and coordination for these activities. *Mailing Add:* 37228 Munger Dr Livonia MI 48154

STEINBERG, RONALD T, b New York, NY, Apr 18, 29; m 50; c 3. CHEMICAL ENGINEERING. *Educ:* Polytech Inst Brooklyn, BChE, 49; Clarkson Col Technol, MChE, 51. *Prof Exp:* Process engr, Schwarz Labs, Inc, 51-52, plant engr, 52-61; plant engr, 61-66, MGR PROCESS DEVELOP, ALCOLAC INC, 66- *Mem:* Am Chem Soc. *Res:* Process development; specialty surfactants and monomers; ethoxylations, sulfations, and esterifications; diffusional operations and solids handling. *Mailing Add:* Alcolac Inc 3440 Fairfield Rd Baltimore MD 21226

STEINBERG, ROY HERBERT, b New York, NY, Dec 9, 35; m 59; c 1. NEUROPHYSIOLOGY. *Educ:* Univ Mich, BA, 56, MA, 57; NY Med Col, MD, 61; McGill Univ, PhD(neurophysiol), 65. *Prof Exp:* Intern med, Mass Mem Hosp, 61-62; USPHS fel, NIMH, 62-65; head Neurophysiol Br, Neurol Sci Div, Naval Aerospace Med Inst, Fla, 68-69; asst res physiologist, 69-72,

assoc prof physiol, 72-77, PROF PHYSIOL & OPHTHAL, SCH MED, UNIV CALIF, SAN FRANCISCO, 78- USPHS career develop award, 71-; William C Bryant, Bernard C Spiegel & Harpuder Awards, NY Med Col. *Mem:* Soc Neurosci; Asn Res Vision & Ophthal; Am Phys Soc. *Res:* Physiology of the nervous system; vision, especially physiology and anatomy of the retina. *Mailing Add:* Dept of Physiol Univ of Calif Med Ctr San Francisco CA 94122

STEINBERG, STANLY, b Traverse City, Mich, Mar 10, 40; m 60. APPLIED MATHEMATICS. *Educ:* Mich State Univ, BS, 62; Stanford Univ, PhD(math), 68. *Prof Exp:* Asst prof math, Purdue Univ, Lafayette, 67-74; ASSOC PROF MATH, UNIV NMEX, 74- *Res:* Partial differential equations. *Mailing Add:* Dept of Math Univ of NMex Albuquerque NM 87131

STEINBERG, STUART ALVIN, b Chicago, Ill, Feb 3, 41; m 66; c 3. MATHEMATICS. *Educ:* Univ Ill, Urbana, BS, 63, PhD(math), 70; Univ Chicago, MS, 65. *Prof Exp:* Asst prof math, Univ Mo-St Louis, 70-71; from asst prof to assoc prof, 71-80, PROF MATH, UNIV TOLEDO, 80- *Mem:* Am Math Soc. *Res:* Algebra, especially ring theory and ordered algebraic structures. *Mailing Add:* Dept of Math Univ of Toledo Toledo OH 43615

STEINBERG, WILLIAM, b Brooklyn, NY, Apr 25, 41; m 69; c 3. MICROBIOLOGY. *Educ:* Brooklyn Col, BS, 62; Univ Wis, MS, 65, PhD(microbiol), 67. *Prof Exp:* NSF fel, Ctr Molecular Genetics, Gif-sur-Yvette, France, 67-68; Europ Molecular Biol Orgn fel, 68-69; asst prof microbiol, Med Sch, Univ Va, 69-75, assoc prof, 75-80; MEM FAC, MOLECULAR BIOL LAB, UNIV WIS, MADISON, 80- *Mem:* Am Soc Microbiol. *Res:* Bacterial spore formation and germination; enzyme structure and function; amino-acyl transfer RNA; genetics of Bacillus. *Mailing Add:* Molecular Biol Lab Univ Wis Madison WI 53706

STEINBERGER, ANNA S, b Radom, Poland, Jan 1, 28; US citizen; m 50; c 2. CELL BIOLOGY, IMMUNOLOGY. *Educ:* State Univ Iowa, MS, 52; Wayne State Univ, PhD(microbiol), 62. *Prof Exp:* Bacteriologist, State Univ Iowa, 53-55; res virologist, Parke, Davis & Co, Mich, 55-56 & 58-59; asst mem, Albert Einstein Med Ctr, 61-71; PROF REPRODUCTIVE MED & BIOL UNIV TEX MED SCH HOUSTON, 71- *Concurrent Pos:* USPHS res grant, Albert Einstein Med Ctr, 61-71. *Mem:* Endocrine Soc; Soc Study Reproduction; Tissue Cult Asn; NY Acad Sci; Am Soc Andrology. *Res:* Spermatogenesis and steroidogenesis in mammalian gonads; hormonal control of spermatogenesis; secretion of gonadotropins; cytogenetics; tissue culture. *Mailing Add:* PO Box 20708 St Univ of Tex Med Sch Houston TX 77025

STEINBERGER, JACK, b Bad Kissingen, Ger, May 25, 21; nat US; m 61; c 2. PHYSICS. *Educ:* Univ Chicago, BS, 42, PhD, 48. *Prof Exp:* Mem, Inst Advan Study, Princeton, 48-49; res asst, Univ Calif, Berkeley, 49-50; Higgins prof physics, Columbia Univ, 50-71; PHYSICIST, EUROP CTR NUCLEAR RES, 68- *Concurrent Pos:* Mem, Inst Advan Study, Princeton, 59-60. *Mem:* Nat Acad Sci; Am Acad Arts & Sci. *Res:* Mesons, spin, parity and other properties of pions; particle, spins, other properties of strange particles; two neutrinos; CP violating properties of kaons; interactions of neutrinos at high energies. *Mailing Add:* Europ Ctr for Nuclear Res Geneva 23 Switzerland

STEINBORN, TERRY LAURENCE, geochemistry, geology, see previous edition

STEINBRECHER, LESTER, b Philadelphia, Pa, Sept 17, 27; m 51; c 3. INORGANIC CHEMISTRY. *Educ:* Temple Univ, BA, 50; Drexel Inst, MS, 57. *Prof Exp:* Chemist, Socony Mobil Oil Corp, 52-58; res chemist, 58-70, DIR RES, AMCHEM PROD INC, AMBLER, 70- *Mem:* Nat Asn Corrosion Eng; Am Soc Electroplaters. *Res:* Solid state reactions; inorganic metallic coatings; analytical chemistry; coatings for metals. *Mailing Add:* Amchem Prod Inc Ambler PA 19002

STEINBRENNER, ARTHUR H, b New York, NY, July 23, 17; m 48; c 2. MATHEMATICS EDUCATION. *Educ:* Columbia Univ, AB, 40, AM, 41, PhD, 55. *Prof Exp:* Instr math & physics, Graham-Eckes Sch, Fla, 41-46; asst math, Teachers Col, Columbia Univ, 46-48; asst prof, US Naval Acad, 48-53; from instr to asst prof, 53-58, from asst prof math & educ to assoc prof math & educ, 58-70, coordr, Sch Math Study Group, 58-61, PROF MATH & EDUC, UNIV ARIZ, 70- *Concurrent Pos:* Fulbright lectr, Australia, 63; coordr Ariz Ctr Minn Math & Sci Teaching Proj. *Mem:* Math Asn Am. *Res:* Mathematics curricula experiments. *Mailing Add:* Dept of Math Univ of Ariz Tucson AZ 85721

STEINBRENNER, EUGENE CLARENCE, b St Paul, Minn, Sept 3, 21; m 44; c 4. FORESTRY, SOILS. *Educ:* Univ Minn, BS, 49; Univ Wis, MS, 51; Univ Wash, Seattle, PhD(forest soils), 54. *Prof Exp:* Asst, Univ Wis, 49-51; asst, State Conserv Dept, Wis, 49-50; forest soils specialist, Forestry Res Ctr, Weyerhaeuser Co, 52-81; RETIRED. *Concurrent Pos:* Weyerhaeuser fel, 51-52; affil prof forest soils, Univ Wash, 74- Bullard fel, Harvard Univ, 68. *Mem:* Fel Soil Sci Soc Am; Soc Am Foresters; fel Am Sci Affil. *Res:* Soil classification and mapping; nutrition; productivity; soil management for site protection, rehabilitation and improvement; nursery soils. *Mailing Add:* 3315 Tiger Lane Centralia WA 98531

STEINBRUCH, ROBERT, chemical engineering, see previous edition

STEINBRUCHEL, CHRISTOPH OTTO, b Switz, Mar 10, 45. PHYSICAL CHEMISTRY, SOLID STATE PHYSICS. *Educ:* Univ Zurich, dipl, 69; Univ Minn, PhD(chem physics), 74. *Prof Exp:* Res assoc, Lawrence Berkeley Lab, 74-75 & Univ Chicago, 75-77; ASST CHEMIST, ARGONNE NAT LAB, 77- *Mem:* Am Vacuum Soc; Am Chem Soc. *Res:* Surface science, catalysis, electron microscopy, materials science. *Mailing Add:* Chem Div Argonne Nat Lab Argonne IL 60439

STEINBRUGGE, KARL V, b Tucson, Ariz, Feb 8, 19; m 42; c 2. ENGINEERING SEISMOLOGY. *Educ:* Ore State Univ, BS, 41. *Prof Exp:* Struct designer, Austin Co, 42-47; sr struct engr, Calif Div Archit, 48-50; prof, 50-78, EMER PROF, UNIV CALIF, BERKELEY, 78-; CONSULT ENGR, 80- *Concurrent Pos:* Chief engr, Earthquake Dept, Pac Fire Rating Bur, 50-71, mgr, Earthquake Dept, Insurance Serv Off, 71-80; vpres, Earthquake Eng Res Inst, 62, pres, 68-70; mem US comt, Int Asn Earthquake Eng, 69, US chmn, 66-73; chmn task force earthquake hazard reduction, Off Sci & Technol, Washington, DC, 70; chmn adv group, Calif Legis Joint Comt Seismic Safety, 70-73; chmn eng criteria rev bd, San Francisco Conserv & Develop Comn, 71-72; chmn earthquake hazard reduction, Exec Off Pres, 77-78; chmn, Calif Seismic Safety Comn, 74-77, mem, 77- *Mem:* Seismol Soc Am (vpres, 66-67, pres, 67-68); Am Soc Civil Engrs; Am Concrete Inst; Earthquake Eng Res Inst. *Mailing Add:* 6851 Cutting Blvd El Cerrito CA 94530

STEINDLER, DENNIS A, b Milwaukee, Wis, June 18, 52; m 77; c 1. NEUROBIOLOGY. *Educ:* Univ Wis, Madison, BA, 73; Univ Calif, San Francisco, PhD(anat), 78. *Prof Exp:* ASST PROF, DEPT ANAT, MICH STATE UNIV, 78- *Concurrent Pos:* Prin investr, Nat Inst Neurol Commmun Dis & Stroke, NIH, 80-; consult, New Eng Nuclear Co, 81- *Res:* Fastors mediating normal development of neuronal organization in the mammalian cerebral and cerebellar cortices. *Mailing Add:* Anat Dept Mich State Univ B 508 W Fee Hall East Lansing MI 48824

STEINDLER, MARTIN JOSEPH, b Vienna, Austria, Jan 3, 28; nat US; m 52; c 2. NUCLEAR FUEL CYCLE, RESEARCH ADMINISTRATION. *Educ:* Univ Chicago, PhB, 47, BS, 48, MS, 49, PhD(chem), 52. *Prof Exp:* Res asst, US Navy Inorg Proj, Univ Chicago, 48-52, consult, 53; Argonne Nat Lab, 53; assoc chemist, 53-74, sr chemist, ASSOC DIR CHEM ENG DIV, ARGONNE NAT LAB, 77- *Concurrent Pos:* Mem, Atomic Safety & Licensing Bd Panel, 72-; consult, Adv Comt Reactor Safeguards, 67-, Lawrence Livermore Lab, 78-, Oak Ridge Gas Differential Plant, 80- *Mem:* Am Chem Soc; Am Nuclear Soc; Royal Soc Chemists; Sigma Xi; AAAS. *Res:* Nuclear fuel cycle; radiological safety; nuclear waste disposal; fluorine chemistry of the actinide elements and fission product elements; reactor fuel reprocessing; non-aqueous inorganic chemistry. *Mailing Add:* Argonne Nat Lab Bldg 205 RmC227 9700 S Cass Ave Argonne IL 60439

STEINECK, PAUL LEWIS, b Yonkers, NY, Jan 20, 42. MICROPALEONTOLOGY, BIOLOGICAL SYSTEMATICS. *Educ:* NY Univ, BA, 63, MS, 66; La State Univ, PhD(geol), 73. *Prof Exp:* Asst prof, 71-78, ASSOC PROF GEOL, DIV NATURAL SCI, STATE UNIV NY COL PURCHASE, 78- *Mem:* Geol Soc Am; Paleont Soc; Soc Econ Paleontologists & Mineralogists; Int Paleont Union; Micropaleont Soc. *Res:* Deep-water foraminifera and ostracoda; cenozoic history of the caribbean; systematics of the planktonic foraminifera; ecology of salt-marsh foraminifera. *Mailing Add:* Div Natural Sci State Univ NY Purchase NY 10577

STEINER, ANDRE LOUIS, b Haguenau, France, June 21, 28. ZOOLOGY. *Educ:* Univ Strasbourg, BSc, 52; Univ Paris, DSc(animal behav), 60. *Prof Exp:* Res assoc animal biol, Nat Res Coun, Paris, France, 52-56; teaching asst zool, Univ Montpellier, 56-59, teaching asst psychophysiol, 59-61, asst prof psychophysiol & animal behav, 61-65; vis prof zool & animal behav, Univ Montreal, 65-66; assoc prof zool, 66-72, PROF ZOOL, UNIV ALTA, 72- *Concurrent Pos:* Mem, Int Union Conserv Nature & Natural Resources, Switz, 67. *Mem:* AAAS; Animal Behav Soc; Can Soc Zool; Ecol Soc Am. *Res:* Behavior, ecology and distribution of solitary wasps and of some vertebrates; ecology, especially behavioral aspects and field studies; animal distribution and dispersion; cine-photo analysis of behavior. *Mailing Add:* Dept of Zool Biosci Bldg Univ of Alta Edmonton AB T6G 2G7 Can

STEINER, ANNE KERCHEVAL, b Warrensburg, Mo, Aug 5, 36. MATHEMATICS. *Educ:* Univ Mo, AB, 58, MA, 63; Univ NMex, PhD(math), 65. *Prof Exp:* Eng asst, Am Tel & Tel Corp, 58-59; asst prof math, Tex Tech Col, 65-66; asst prof, Univ NMex, 66-68; asst prof, 68-69, assoc prof, 69-72, PROF MATH, IOWA STATE UNIV, 72- *Concurrent Pos:* Vis assoc prof, Univ Alta, 70-71. *Mem:* Am Math Soc; Math Asn Am; Sigma Xi. *Res:* Point set topology. *Mailing Add:* Dept of Math Iowa State Univ Ames IA 50011

STEINER, BRUCE, b Oberlin, Ohio, May 14, 31; m 60; c 2. PHYSICAL CHEMISTRY. *Educ:* Oberlin Col, AB, 53; Princeton Univ, PhD, 57. *Prof Exp:* Res assoc physics, Univ Chicago, 58-61; PHYSICIST, NAT BUR STANDARDS, 61- *Mem:* AAAS; Am Phys Soc; Am Chem Soc; Optical Soc Am; Am Inst Chem. *Res:* Optical radiation measurement; breakdown of molecules under impact; electron detachment phenomena in ions and molecules. *Mailing Add:* Nat Bur of Standards Washington DC 20234

STEINER, DONALD FREDERICK, b Lima, Ohio, July 15, 30. BIOCHEMISTRY, ENDOCRINOLOGY. *Educ:* Univ Cincinnati, BS, 52; Univ Chicago, MS & MD, 56. *Hon Degrees:* DSc, Royal Univ Umea, Sweden, 73. *Prof Exp:* Intern, King County Hosp, Seattle, Wash, 56-57; asst med, Univ Wash, 57-60, med resident, 59-60; from asst prof to prof biochem, 60-70, actg chmn dept biochem, 72-73, dir diabetes-endocrinol ctr, 74-77; chmn, Dept Biochem, 73-79, A N PRITZKER PROF BIOCHEM & MED, UNIV CHICAGO, 70- *Concurrent Pos:* Res fel med, Univ Wash, 57-59; mem metab study sect, USPHS, 65-70; Jacobaeus lectr, Nordisk Insulin Fund, Copenhagen, 70; E F F Copp mem lect, La Jolla, Calif, 71. *Honors & Awards:* Ernst Oppenheimer Award, Endocrine Soc, 70; Hans Christian Hagedorn Medal, Steensen Mem Hosp, Copenhagen, 70; Lilly Award, Am Diabetes Asn, 69; Gairdner Award, Gairdner Found, Can, 71; 50th Anniversary Medallion, Am Diabetes Asn, 72; Diaz-Cristobal Award, Span Soc Study Diabetes, 73; Banting lectr, Brit Diabetic Soc, 81. *Mem:* Nat Acad Sci; AAAS; Am Soc Biol Chem; Biochem Soc; Am Diabetes Asn. *Res:* Discovery, isolation, structural analysis and biosynthesis of proinsulin; mechanism of conversion of proinsulin to insulin; insulin binding to tissues and mechanism of action; evolutionary development of insulin and related hormones. *Mailing Add:* Dept Biochem 920 E 58th St Chicago IL 60637

STEINER, ERICH E, b Thun, Switz, Apr 9, 19; nat US; m 44; c 3. GENETICS. *Educ:* Univ Mich, BS, 40; Ind Univ, PhD(bot), 50. *Prof Exp:* From instr to asst prof, 50-58, assoc prof, 58-61, chmn dept, 68-71 & 79-81, dir, Matthaei Bot Gardens, 71-77, PROF BOT, UNIV MICH, ANN ARBOR, 61- *Concurrent Pos:* NSF sr fel, 60-61. *Mem:* Bot Soc Am; Genetics Soc Am; Soc Study Evolution; Am Soc Naturalists; Soc Econ Bot. *Res:* Genetics and evolutionary biology of Oenothera; genetics of incompatability. *Mailing Add:* Dept of Bot Univ of Mich Ann Arbor MI 48104

STEINER, EUGENE FRANCIS, b St Louis, Mo, July 15, 34; m 63; c 1. MATHEMATICS. *Educ:* Univ Mo, BS, 56, MA, 60, PhD(math), 63. *Prof Exp:* Asst prof physics, Southwestern La Inst, 56-57; eng physicist, McDonnell Aircraft Corp, 58-59; asst prof math, Univ NMex, 63-65; assoc prof, Tex Tech Col, 65-66; assoc prof, Univ NMex, 66-68; assoc prof, 68-72, PROF MATH, IOWA STATE UNIV, 72- *Concurrent Pos:* Vis prof, Univ Alta, 70-71. *Mem:* Am Math Soc; Math Asn Am. *Res:* General topology. *Mailing Add:* Dept of Math Iowa State Univ Ames IA 50010

STEINER, GEORGE, b Czech, Mar 11, 36; Can citizen; m 66; c 2. MEDICAL RESEARCH. *Educ:* Univ BC, BA, 56, MD, 60; FRCP(C), 65. *Prof Exp:* Resident med, Royal Victoria Hosp, McGill Univ, 60-62; fel, Harvard Med Sch, Peter Bent Brigham Hosp & Joslin Clin Res Lab, 62-64; resident med & endocrinol, Royal Victoria Hosp, McGill Univ, 64-66; from lectr to asst prof, 66-73, ASSOC PROF MED & PHYSIOL, UNIV TORONTO, 73-; DIR LIPID RES CLIN & DIABETES CLIN, TORONTO GEN HOSP, 66- *Concurrent Pos:* Med Res Coun Can scholar, 67-72; sci panel mem, Can Heart Found, 74-; mem coun atherosclerosis, Am Heart Asn. *Honors & Awards:* MDS Award, Can Soc Clin Chem; Pfizer lectureship, Clin Res Inst, Montreal. *Mem:* Am Diabetes Asn; Am Fedn Clin Res; Am Physiol Soc; Endocrine Soc; Can Soc Clin Invest. *Res:* Interaction of carbohydrate and lipid metabolism; hyperlipemia and atherosclerosis. *Mailing Add:* Dept of Med Rm 7302 Med Sci Bldg Univ of Toronto Toronto ON M5S 1A8 Can

STEINER, GILBERT, b Moscow, USSR, Jan 19, 37; US citizen; m 71. MATHEMATICS. *Educ:* Univ Mich, BS, 58, MS, 59; Univ Calif, Berkeley, PhD(math), 62. *Prof Exp:* Instr math, Reed Col, 62-64; asst prof, Dalhousie Univ, 64-68; from asst prof to assoc prof, 68-79, PROF MATH, FAIRLEIGH DICKINSON UNIV, TEANECK CAMPUS, 79- *Mem:* Am Math Soc; Math Asn Am. *Res:* Functional analysis. *Mailing Add:* Dept of Math Fairleigh Dickinson Univ Teaneck NJ 07666

STEINER, HERBERT M, b Goppingen, Ger, Dec 8, 27; nat US. PARTICLE PHYSICS. *Educ:* Univ Calif, Berkeley, BS, 51, PhD(physics), 56. *Prof Exp:* Lectr, 57-60, from asst prof to assoc prof, 61-67, PROF PHYSICS, UNIV CALIF, BERKELEY, 67-, PHYSICIST, LAWRENCE BERKELEY LABS, 53- Concurrent Jap Soc Promotion Sci, 78; guest scientist, Max Planck Inst Physics & Astrophys, Munich, 76-78. *Concurrent Pos:* Guggenheim fel, 60-61; vis scientist, Europ Ctr Nuclear Res, 60-61, 64 & 68-69; Alexander von Humboldt sr scientist, 76-77; guest scientist, Max Planck Inst Physics & Astrophysics, Munich, 76-78; vis prof, Japan Soc Promotion Sci, 78. *Honors & Awards:* Alexander von Humboldt sr scientist, 76-77. LAWRENCE BERKELEY LAB, 53- *Mem:* Am Phys Soc. *Res:* High energy physics; elementary particle interactions. *Mailing Add:* Dept of Physics Univ of Calif Berkeley CA 94720

STEINER, JAMES W(ESLEY), b Lexington, Ky, Oct 3, 26; m 51; c 3. ELECTRICAL ENGINEERING. *Educ:* Univ Ky, BSEE, 48; Purdue Univ, MSEE, 50; Columbia Univ, EE, 60; NY Univ, MBA, 68. *Prof Exp:* Asst proj engr flight simulators, Curtiss-Wright Corp, 50-52; sr engr Lacrosse Missile, Fed Labs Div, Int Tel & Tel Corp, 52-55, develop engr, 55-56, proj engr, 56-58, sr proj engr Dew Line, 58-60, exec engr courier satellite, 60-66, proj mgr commun, Telemetry & Command Subsyst Develop, Intelsat III Commun Satellite, 66-68; dept mgr systs design, Western Develop Labs Div, Philco-Ford Corp, 68-69, mgr systs design, 69-70, mgr systs eng activ, 70-78, mgr, equip prog activ, 78-80, MGR, SYSTS INTEGRATION ACTIV, ESD DIV, FORD AEROSPACE & COMMUN CORP, 80- *Mem:* Sr mem Inst Elec & Electronics Engrs. *Res:* Range measurement by continuous wave phase shift measurements; digital command for satellite communications; telemetry and master timing systems; satellite ground support systems; telemetry, tracking and commanding; digital communications. *Mailing Add:* 14127 Miranda Rd Los Altos Hills CA 94022

STEINER, JOHANN, b Vienna, Austria, May 1, 26; Can citizen; m 57; c 1. GEOLOGY. *Educ:* Univ Alta, BSc, 61, MSc, 62; Australian Nat Univ, PhD(geol), 67. *Prof Exp:* Geologist, Shell Can Ltd, 67-69; ASSOC PROF GEOL, UNIV ALTA, 69- *Mem:* AAAS; Geol Soc Am; Geol Asn Can; Am Asn Petrol Geol. *Res:* Litho-stratigraphy and sedimentation; geological history and its relationship to the dynamics of the Milky Way Galaxy. *Mailing Add:* Dept of Geol Univ of Alta Edmonton AB T6G 2E3 Can

STEINER, JOHN CHARLES, b Toledo, Ohio, Sept 9, 35; m 59; c 1. MECHANICAL & AUTOMOTIVE ENGINEERING. *Educ:* Univ Mich, Ann Arbor, BSE, 58, MSE, 59, PhD(eng), 63. *Prof Exp:* Instr, Univ Mich, Dearborn, 61; res asst, Univ Mich, Ann Arbor, 62-63; sr res engr, 63-74, DEPT RES ENGR, GEN MOTORS RES LABS, 74- *Mem:* Soc Automotive Engrs; Sigma Xi. *Res:* Fundamental thermodynamics, heat transfer and combustion investigations of heat engines, particularly the stirling engine, rotary combustion engine, stratified charge engines and related studies. *Mailing Add:* 2426 Matilda Ct Warren MI 48092

STEINER, JOHN EDWARD, b Seattle, Wash, Nov 7, 17; m 42; c 3. ENGINEERING MANAGEMENT. *Educ:* Univ Wash, BS, 40; Mass Inst Technol, MS, 41. *Hon Degrees:* Summa Laude Dignatus, Univ Wash, 78. *Prof Exp:* Aerodynamist com & mil airplane, Boeing Airplane Co, 41-44, chief aerodynamist, 44-48, sr group engr, 48-55, proj engr, 55-58, prog mgr 727 prog, 58-60, chief proj engr, 60-65, chief engr all com opers, 65-66, vpres eng & prod develop, 66-68, vpres mkt, Boeing Com Airplane Co, 68-70, vpres & div gen mgr, 70-73, vpres all opers, 73-74, vpres prog develop, 74-76, VPRES

CORP PROD DEVELOP, BOEING CO, 76- *Concurrent Pos:* Trustee & mem exec comt, Pac Sci Ctr, 75- *Honors & Awards:* Elmer A Sperry Award, 65; Thulin Medal, Sweden; Sir C Kingsford Smith Award, Australia. *Mem:* Nat Acad Eng; fel Am Inst Aeronaut & Astronaut; fel Royal Aeronaut Soc. *Res:* High technology research involving aerodynamic efficiency of swept wings and total commercial and military configurations; structural efficiency and durability; propulsion integration; computer aided productivity improvement research in engineering and manufacturing. *Mailing Add:* Boeing Co PO Box 3707 Seattle WA 98124

STEINER, JOHN F, b Milwaukee, Wis, July 21, 08; m 49. ELECTROCHEMISTRY. *Educ:* Univ Wis, BS, 29, MS, 32, PhD(chem), 33. *Prof Exp:* Instr chem, Univ Wis, 29-33, Alumni Asn fel, 33-34; develop chemist, Milwaukee Gas Specialty Co, 35-36; res chemist, Globe-Union, Inc, Wis, 36-37; res chemist, Miner Labs, Ill, 38-53; head food lab, Guardite Corp, 53-56; DIR, CHEM RES LABS, 56- *Concurrent Pos:* Dir develop, Sound Recording Serv, 47-; mem staff, Univ Ill & Wilson Col, 59-; consult, Ill Dept Revenue, 64- & US Dept Internal Revenue, 65- *Mem:* AAAS; Am Chem Soc; Electrochem Soc. *Res:* Limnology; ceramics; dentifrices; cereals; food technology; sound recording; information storage-retrieval. *Mailing Add:* Chem Res Labs 2748 S Superior St Milwaukee WI 53207

STEINER, KIM CARLYLE, b Alton, Ill, Nov 21, 48; m 70; c 2. FOREST GENETICS. *Educ:* Colo State Univ, BS, 70; Mich State Univ, MS, 71, PhD(forest genetics), 75. *Prof Exp:* ASST PROF FOREST GENETICS, PA STATE UNIV, 74- *Mem:* Sigma Xi. *Res:* Genetic improvement of amenity trees for densely populated areas; genetic adaptation of trees to environmental stresses; genecology; taxonomy, distribution and geographic variation of forest trees. *Mailing Add:* Sch of Forest Resources Pa State Univ University Park PA 16802

STEINER, LISA AMELIA, b Vienna, Austria, May 12, 33; US citizen. IMMUNOLOGY. *Educ:* Swarthmore Col, BA, 54; Radcliffe Col, MA, 56; Yale Univ, MD, 59. *Prof Exp:* From asst prof to assoc prof, 57-80, PROF BIOL, MASS INST TECHNOL, 80- *Concurrent Pos:* Helen Hay Whitney res fel microbiol med sch, Wash Univ, St Louis, 62-65; Am Heart Asn res fel immunol, Wright-Fleming Inst, London, 65-67; mem allergy & immunol study sect, NIH, 74-78; mem bd overseers, Rosenstiel Basic Med Sci Res Ctr, 76-80, chmn, 80-; mem personnel comt, Am Cancer Soc, 79-81, vchmn, 81-; mem bd sci counsrs, Nat Cancer Inst, 80- *Mem:* Am Asn Immunol; Am Soc Biol Chem; Biophys Soc. *Res:* Structure and function of immunoglobulins; phylogeny and ontogeny of immune response; protein chemistry. *Mailing Add:* Mass Inst of Technol 77 Massachusetts Ave Cambridge MA 02139

STEINER, MARION ROTHBERG, b New York, NY, May 23, 41; m 63; c 2. BIOCHEMISTRY, ONCOLOGY. *Educ:* Smith Col, BA, 62; Univ Ky, PhD(biochem), 68. *Prof Exp:* Instr biochem, Univ Ky, 68-70; fel, Baylor Col Med, 71-73, asst prof virol, 73-78; ASST PROF EXP PATH, UNIV KY, 78- *Mem:* Am Chem Soc; Am Soc Microbiologists; Sigma Xi. *Res:* Examination of the structure and function of the surface membrane of oncogenic cells, utilizing mouse mammary carcinomas and dysplasias as a model system. *Mailing Add:* Div of Exp Path Dept of Path Col of Med Univ Ky Lexington KY 40506

STEINER, MORRIS, b Shenandoah, Pa, Mar 1, 04; m 29; c 2. PEDIATRICS. *Educ:* NY Univ, MD, 28. *Prof Exp:* From asst clin prof to assoc clin prof, 53-66, from assoc prof to prof, 66-74, EMER PROF PEDIAT, STATE UNIV NY DOWNSTATE MED CTR, 74- *Concurrent Pos:* NY Tuberc & Health Asn grant, State Univ NY Downstate Med Ctr, 66-70; consult, Jewish Hosp, Brooklyn, 69- & King's County Hosp Med Ctr, 69- *Mem:* Am Acad Pediat; Am Thoracic Soc. *Res:* Tuberculosis; asthma, chronic broncho-pulmonary disease in children. *Mailing Add:* Dept of Pediat State Univ NY Downstate Med Ctr Brooklyn NY 11203

STEINER, PINCKNEY ALSTON, b Athens, Ga, Apr 5, 38; m 60; c 2. SOLID STATE PHYSICS, MAGNETIC RESONANCE. *Educ:* Univ Ga, BS, 59; Duke Univ, PhD(physics), 65. *Prof Exp:* Res fel chem physics, H C Orsted Inst, Copenhagen Univ, 64-66; asst prof, 66-77, ASSOC PROF PHYSICS, CLEMSON UNIV, 77- *Mem:* Am Phys Soc; Sigma Xi. *Res:* Electron paramagnetic resonance applied to various problems in solid state physics and in biophysics. *Mailing Add:* Dept of Physics & Astron Clemson Univ Clemson SC 29631

STEINER, RAY PHILLIP, b Bronx, NY, Apr 28, 41; m 72. NUMBER THEORY. *Educ:* Univ Ariz, BSEE, 63, MS, 65; Ariz State Univ, PhD(math), 68. *Prof Exp:* Asst prof, 68-72, assoc prof, 72-78, PROF MATH, BOWLING GREEN STATE UNIV, 78- *Mem:* Fibonacci Asn; Am Math Soc; Math Asn Am; Nat Coun Teachers Math. *Res:* Finding the units and class numbers of algebraic number fields by linear programming techniques, Diophantine equations and Fibonacci numbers. *Mailing Add:* Dept of Math Bowling Green State Univ Bowling Green OH 43403

STEINER, ROBERT ALAN, b Chicago, Ill, Mar 9, 47. NEUROENDOCRINOLOGY, REPRODUCTIVE PHYSIOLOGY. *Educ:* Univ Pac, BA, 69; Univ Ore, PhD(physiol), 75. *Prof Exp:* Sr fel neuroendocrinol, 75-77, asst prof physiol, 77-80, ASSOC PROF OBSTET, GYNEC & BIOPHYS, UNIV WASH, 80- *Concurrent Pos:* Res affil, Regional Primate Res Ctr, Univ Wash, 77-; Diabetes Res Ctr, 78- *Honors & Awards:* Nat Human Growth Found Young Investr Award, 79. *Mem:* Am Physiol Soc; Soc Study Reproduction; Am Soc Zoologists; Am Endocrine Soc; Am Andrology Soc. *Res:* Hypothalamic control of gonadotropin secretion; neuroendocrine control of the onset of puberty; environmental influences on seasonal reproduction. *Mailing Add:* Dept of Physiol & Biophys SJ-40 Univ of Wash Seattle WA 98195

STEINER, ROBERT FRANK, b Manila, Philippines, Sept 29, 26; US citizen; m 56; c 2. PHYSICAL BIOCHEMISTRY. *Educ:* Princeton Univ, AB, 47; Harvard Univ, PhD(phys chem), 50. *Prof Exp:* Fel, US Naval Med Res Inst, 50-51, phys chemist, 51-70; PROF CHEM, UNIV MD, BALTIMORE COUNTY, 70-, CHMN DEPT, 74- *Concurrent Pos:* Jewett fel, 50-51; lectr, Georgetown Univ, 57-58 & Howard Univ, 58-59 & 60-61; mem US Civil Serv Bd Exam, 58-; mem molecular biol panel, NSF, 67-70; ed, Res Commun Chem Path & Pharmacol, 70- & Biophys Chem, 73-; mem biophys & biophys chem study sect, NIH, 76-80. *Mem:* Am Chem Soc; Biophys Soc; Am Soc Biol Chem; NY Acad Sci. *Res:* Light scattering; fluorescence; protein interactions; nucleic acids; synthetic polynucleotides; statistical thermodynamics. *Mailing Add:* 2609 Turf Valley Rd Ellicott City MD 21043

STEINER, RODNEY, b Los Angeles, Calif, June 11, 28; m 53; c 3. PHYSICAL GEOGRAPHY. *Educ:* Univ Calif, Los Angeles, BA, 50, MA, 51; Univ Wash, PhD(geog), 54. *Prof Exp:* PROF GEOG, CALIF STATE UNIV, LONG BEACH, 56- *Mem:* Asn Am Geog; Am Geog Soc. *Res:* California water supply; metropolitan peripheral land use; rural land ownership, regional geography of California. *Mailing Add:* Dept of Geog Calif State Univ Long Beach CA 90840

STEINER, RUSSELL IRWIN, b Lebanon, Pa, July 21, 27; m 56; c 4. INDUSTRIAL ORGANIC CHEMISTRY. *Educ:* Lebanon Valley Col, BS, 49; Univ Conn, MS, 52, PhD(chem), 55. *Prof Exp:* Res chemist, Nat Aniline Div, Allied Chem Corp, 55-63, group leader, 63-65, res supvr indust chem div, 65-67; res assoc, 67-74, group leader disperse dyes, 74-80, DIR PROCESS DEVELOP, DYES & CHEM DIV, CROMPTON & KNOWLES CORP, 80- *Mem:* Am Chem Soc; Am Asn Textile Chem & Colorists. *Res:* Textile dyes; food colors. *Mailing Add:* Process Develop Dept Dyes Chem Div Crompton & Knowles Corp Reading PA 19603

STEINER, SHELDON, b Bronx, NY, Apr 23, 40; m 63; c 2. VIROLOGY. *Educ:* Drew Univ, BA, 61; Univ Ky, MS, 64, PhD(microbiol), 67. *Prof Exp:* Instr, Baylor Col Med, 71-73, from asst prof to assoc prof virol, 73-78; ASSOC PROF BIOL SCI, UNIV KY, LEXINGTON, 78- *Concurrent Pos:* NIH grant, Univ Ky, 69-71; NIH spec fel, Baylor Col Med, 72-75. *Mem:* AAAS; Am Soc Chemists; Am Soc Microbiol. *Res:* Structure and function of procaryotic and eucaryotic membranes; biochemical characterization of membranes of malignant cells. *Mailing Add:* Dept of Biol Sci Univ Ky Lexington KY 40506

STEINER, WERNER DOUGLAS, b Milwaukee, Wis, Oct 8, 32; m 61; c 3. ORGANIC CHEMISTRY. *Educ:* Univ Karlsruhe, BA, 56, MA, 58; Univ Pa, PhD(org chem), 64. *Prof Exp:* Res & develop chemist, Org Chem Dept, Jackson Lab, E I Du Pont De Nemours & Co, Inc, Deepwater, NJ, 63-65, process develop chemist, 67-68 & dyes & intermediates, 68-75, sr chemist, 62-80. *Mem:* AAAS; Am Chem Soc. *Res:* Research and development of dyes for natural and man-made fibers; research and development of fluorine compounds for use as aerosol propellants, hydraulic fluids, instrument fluids, convective coolants and working fluids; process development of dyes and fluorine compounds; dye process development, manufacture, intermediates. *Mailing Add:* 6827 Thames Dr Gates Four Fayetteville NC 28306

STEINERT, LEON ALBERT, b Shattuck, Okla, May 2, 30. QUANTUM PHYSICAL SYSTEMS, ELECTROMAGNETIC RADIATION. *Educ:* La Sierra Col, BA, 52; Univ Colo, MS, 56, PhD(physics), 62. *Prof Exp:* Physicist, Nat Bur Standards, 53-65; theoret physicist, Lawrence Radiation Lab, 66-67; sr scientist, McDonnell Douglas Corp, 67-70; sr res engr-scientist, Lockheed Corp, 72-79; res engr, Systs Control, Inc, 79; consult, IRT Corp & Miss State Univ, 80-81; RES DIR, PHYS SYNERGETICS INST, 81- *Concurrent Pos:* Lectr, Loma Linda Univ, 68. *Mem:* Am Phys Soc. *Res:* Theoretical physics of quantum physical systems; applications of quantum statistical condensed-matter physics theory in microelectronics; electromagnetic fields scattering theory. *Mailing Add:* PO Box 61072 Sunnyvale CA 94086

STEINETZ, BERNARD GEORGE, JR, b Germantown, Pa, May 30, 27; m 49; c 3. ENDOCRINOLOGY. *Educ:* Princeton Univ, AB, 49; Rutgers Univ, PhD(zool), 54. *Prof Exp:* Asst org res chemist, Irving Varnish & Insulator Co, 47; asst, Rutgers Univ, 52-54; sr scientist physiol res, Warner-Lambert Res Inst, 54-62, sr res assoc, 62-67; head reproductive physiol & fel, Ciba Res, Ciba Pharmaceut Co, NJ, 67-71; MGR ENDOCRINOL & METAB, PHARMACEUT DIV, CIBA-GEIGY CORP, ARDSLEY, NY, 71- *Concurrent Pos:* Res assoc prof physiol, NY Univ Sch Med, 74- *Mem:* Endocrine Soc; Am Physiol Soc; Am Soc Zool; NY Acad Sci; Soc Exp Biol & Med. *Res:* Reproductive physiology; hormone metabolism; hormones and connective tissue; hormones and aging; hormone interactions. *Mailing Add:* 336 Longbow Dr Franklin Lakes NJ 07417

STEINFELD, JEFFREY IRWIN, b Brooklyn, NY, July 2, 40. PHYSICAL CHEMISTRY. *Educ:* Mass Inst Technol, BS, 62; Harvard Univ, PhD(chem), 65. *Prof Exp:* NSF fel, 65-66; asst prof, 66-70, assoc prof, 70-79, PROF CHEM, MASS INST TECHNOL, 80- *Concurrent Pos:* Alfred P Sloan res fel, 69-71; John Simon Guggenheim fel, Univ Calif, Berkeley & Kammerlingh-Onnes Lab, Leiden, 72-73; mem, Nat Acad Sci-Nat Res Coun Comt Basic Res Adv to US Army Res Off, Durham, 72-75; consult, Aerospace Corp, 74-80, Los Alamos Nat Lab, 75- & KOR, Inc, 80- *Mem:* AAAS; Am Phys Soc; Fedn Am Sci. *Res:* Molecular spectroscopy; energy transfer in molecular collisions; applications of lasers to chemical kinetics, isotope separation and combustion diagnostics. *Mailing Add:* Dept Chem Rm 2-221 Mass Inst Technol Cambridge MA 02139

STEINFELD, JESSE LEONARD, b West Aliquippa, Pa, Jan 6, 27; m 53; c 3. CANCER, MEDICINE. *Educ:* Univ Pittsburgh, BS, 45; Western Reserve Univ, MD, 49; Am Bd Internal Med, dipl, 58. *Hon Degrees:* LLD, Gannon Col, 72. *Prof Exp:* Instr med, Univ Calif, 52-54 & George Washington Univ, 54-58; asst dir, Blood Hosp, City of Hope, Duarte, Calif, 58-59; from asst prof to prof med, Sch Med, Univ Southern Calif, 59-68, cancer coordr, 66-68; dep dir, Nat Cancer Inst, 68-69; dep asst secy health & sci affairs, Dept Health,

Educ & Welfare, 69-72; surgeon gen, USPHS, 69-73; prof med & dir dept oncol, Mayo Clin & Mayo Med Sch, Rochester, Minn, 73-74; prof med, Univ Calif, Irvine, 74-76; chief med serv, Long Beach Vet Admin Hosp, 74-76; PROF MED & DEAN, SCH MED, MED COL VA, 76- Concurrent Pos: AEC fel med, Univ Calif, 52-53; clin investr, Nat Cancer Inst, 54-58, mem, Krebiozen Rev Comt, 63- & Clin Studies Panel, 64-66, consult, 66-, mem chemother adv comt, 67 & cancer spec prog adv comt, 67; consult, Vet Admin Hosp, Long Beach, Calif, 59-, City of Hope Med Ctr, 60- & Kern County Gen Hosp, Bakersfield, 64-; mem, Calif State Cancer Adv Coun, 61-68. Mem: Soc Nuclear Med; Am Asn Cancer Res; AMA; fel Am Col Physicians; Am Fedn Clin Res. Res: Cancer chemotherapy; hematology; health administration. Mailing Add: Sch of Med MCV/VCU Box 535 MCV Station Richmond VA 23298

STEINFELD, LEONARD, b New York, NY, Nov 16, 25; m 65; c 4. MEDICINE. Educ: Hofstra Col, BA, 49; State Univ NY Downstate Med Ctr, MD, 53. Prof Exp: Intern, Los Angeles County Gen Hosp, 53-54; resident pediat, Mt Sinai Hosp, New York, NY, 54-56; instr pediat, Col Physicians & Surgeons, Columbia Univ, 58-68; assoc prof, 66-69, PROF PEDIAT, MT SINAI SCH MED, 69- Concurrent Pos: NIH fel pediat cardiol, Mt Sinai Hosp, New York, 56-57, NY Heart Asn fel, 57-58; from asst attend pediatrician to assoc attend pediatrician, Mt Sinai Hosp, 59-69, attend pediatrician, 69-; consult, USPHS Hosp, Staten Island, 60- & Perth Amboy Gen Hosp, NY, 70- Mem: Am Acad Pediat; Am Col Cardiol; Am Heart Asn; NY Acad Sci. Res: Heart disease in infants and children. Mailing Add: Dept of Pediat Mt Sinai Sch of Med New York NY 10029

STEINFINK, HUGO, b Vienna, Austria, May 22, 24; nat US; m 48; c 2. PHYSICAL CHEMISTRY. Educ: City Col New York, BS, 47; Columbia Univ, MA, 48; Polytech Inst Brooklyn, PhD(chem), 54. Prof Exp: Res chemist, Shell Develop Co, 48-51 & 54-60; assoc prof chem eng, 60-63, PROF CHEM ENG, UNIV TEX, AUSTIN, 63-, JEWEL MCALISTER SMITH PROF ENG, 81- Mem: Am Chem Soc; Mineral Soc Am; Am Crystallog Asn. Res: Crystal structures of silicate minerals and silicate-organic complexes; crystal chemistry and physical properties of semiconductor materials; materials science research. Mailing Add: Dept Chem Eng Univ Tex Austin TX 78712

STEINGISER, SAMUEL, b Springfield, Mass, June 6, 18; m 46; c 3. CHEMISTRY. Educ: City Col New York, BS, 38; Polytech Inst Brooklyn, MS, 41; Univ Conn, PhD, 49. Prof Exp: Chemist, Rockefeller Inst, 41-42; asst atom bomb proj s a m labs, Columbia Univ, 42-43; asst, Carbide & Carbon Chems Corp, NY, 44-46; res assoc metall lab, Univ Chicago, 43-44; group leader phys chem, Publicker Industs, Pa, 46; res assoc, US Off Naval Res, Conn, 46-50; group leader & res scientist cent res dept, Monsanto Chem Co, 50-54; group leader, Mobay Chem Co, 54-59, asst res dir, 59-65; scientist, Monsanto Res Corp, Ohio, 66-70, sci fel, Lopac Proj, 70-77, RES MGR & SR FEL, MONSANTO CO, 77- Concurrent Pos: Mem mat adv bd, Nat Res Coun, 61-63; mem, Int Standardization Orgn. Mem: Fel AAAS; Am Chem Soc; Soc Plastics Indust; Am Soc Test & Mat; Soc Rheol. Res: Mass spectroscopy; corrosion; electrolysis; nuclear chemistry; high-vacuum phenomena; magneto-optics; magnetic susceptibility; high polymer physics; mechanical properties; foams and elastomers; advanced composites; instrumentation design; plastics processing and development. Mailing Add: 5 Fox Chase Rd Bloomfield CT 06002

STEINGOLD, HAROLD, b Providence, RI, May 7, 29; m 57; c 3. ENGINEERING. Educ: Brown Univ, AB, 49; Univ Calif, Los Angeles, MS, 60, PhD(eng), 64. Prof Exp: Engr, Hughes Aircraft, 59-63; engr, Rand Corp, Calif, 63-70; engr, Visualtek, 70-72; eng specialist, Actron Corp, 72-77; ENG SUPVR, HUGHES HELICOPTERS, 77- Concurrent Pos: Lectr, exten, Univ Calif, Santa Barbara, 64-, Los Angeles, 65 & San Fernando Valley State Col, 70- Mem: Inst Elec & Electronics Engrs. Res: Applications of computer technology and coherent electromagnetic sources to communications imaging and data processing; infrared and microwave imaging systems; protheses for the physically handicapped. Mailing Add: 407 l6th St Santa Monica CA 90402

STEINHARDT, CHARLES KENDALL, b Milwaukee, Wis, Mar 1, 35. ORGANIC CHEMISTRY. Educ: Univ Wis, BS, 57; Univ Ill, PhD(org chem), 63. Prof Exp: Instr chem, Univ Wash, Seattle, 63-65; chemist, Lubrizol Corp, Ohio, 65-71 & Napko Corp, Tex, 73-77; SR CHEMIST, MOBAY CHEM CORP, 77- Mem: Am Chem Soc. Mailing Add: 11427 Dunlap Dr Houston TX 77035

STEINHARDT, EMIL J, b Pittsburgh, Pa, Aug 19, 37; m 60. MECHANICAL ENGINEERING. Educ: Univ Pittsburgh, BS, 59, MS, 61, PhD(mech eng), 65. Prof Exp: Instr mech eng, Univ Pittsburgh, 63-65; asst prof, 65-69, assoc prof, 69-81, PROF MECH ENG, WVA UNIV, 81- Mem: Am Soc Eng Educ; Am Soc Mech Engrs; Am Inst Aeronaut & Astronaut. Res: Satellite systems design; engineering systems design; rural systems and housing systems design. Mailing Add: Dept of Mech Eng WVa Univ Morgantown WV 26506

STEINHARDT, GARY CARL, b Lansing, Mich, Sept 13, 44; m 73; c 2. SOIL SCIENCE, AGRONOMY. Educ: Mich State Univ, BS, 66, MS, 68; Purdue Univ, PhD(agron), 76. Prof Exp: Asst soil sci, Mich State Univ, 66-68; asst, 71-74, instr, 74-76, ASST PROF AGRON, PURDUE UNIV, 76- Mem: Am Soc Agron; Soil Conserv Soc Am; Coun Agr Sci & Technol. Res: Effects of soil management and tillage practices on the physical properties of soil; agricultural aspects of land use planning. Mailing Add: Dept of Agron Purdue Univ West Lafayette IN 47907

STEINHARDT, JACINTO, b New York, NY, May 20, 06; m 24; c 2. PHYSICAL CHEMISTRY, BIOCHEMISTRY. Educ: Columbia Univ, AB, 27, AM, 28, PhD(biophys), 34. Prof Exp: Asst instr biol, City Col New York, 27-28; asst instr zool, Columbia Univ, 28-29; instr biophys, 29-34; Nat Res Coun fel, Univ Copenhagen, Univ Upsala, Cambridge Univ & Harvard Univ,

34-36; Rockefeller Found fel, Harvard Univ, 37-38; phys chemist res lab textile found, Nat Bur Standards, 38-42; res assoc div war res, Columbia Univ, 42-43; mem opers eval group & naval warfare anal group, Mass Inst Technol, US Dept Navy, DC, 45-62; prof chem, 62-80, EMER PROF CHEM, GEORGETOWN UNIV, 80- Honors & Awards: Medal of Freedom, 45; Presidential Cert Merit, 46. Mem: Am Soc Biol Chem; Am Chem Soc. Res: Physical chemistry of proteins and other macromolecules; operations research. Mailing Add: Dept of Chem Rm 306 Sci Ctr Georgetown Univ Washington DC 20057

STEINHARDT, RALPH GUSTAV, JR, b Newark, NJ, Sept 15, 18; m 46; c 3. CHEMISTRY, CHEMICAL PHYSICS. Educ: Lehigh Univ, BS, 40, MS, 41, PhD(chem), 50; Va Polytech Inst, BS, 44. Prof Exp: Chemist, Los Alamos Sci Lab, 44-46; res assoc, Lehigh Univ, 50-53, asst prof chem, 53-54; assoc prof, Va Polytech Inst, 54-56; chmn dept, 56-71, prof, 56-81, EMER PROF CHEM, HOLLINS COL, 81- Concurrent Pos: Res partic, Oak Ridge Nat Lab, 56-; vis lectr, Stanford Univ, 63-64; res collabr, Brookhaven Nat Lab, 70-71, 78. Mem: Fel AAAS; Am Chem Soc; fel Am Inst Chemists. Res: Molecular spectroscopy of condensed phases; stereospecific biochemical reactions of psychological interest; x-ray photoelectron spectroscopy of solids. Mailing Add: Dept of Chem Hollins College VA 24020

STEINHARDT, RICHARD ANTONY, b Washington, DC, Sept 23, 39. NEUROBIOLOGY, CELL BIOLOGY. Educ: Columbia Univ, AB, 61, PhD(biol sci), 66. Prof Exp: NSF fel, Agr Res Coun Inst Animal Physiol, Babraham & Plymouth Marine Sta, Eng, 66-67; asst prof zool, 67-73, assoc prof, 73-81, PROF ZOOL, UNIV CALIF, BERKELEY, 81- Mem: AAAS; Am Soc Zoologists; Soc Develop Biol; Am Soc Cell Biol. Res: Cellular physiology related to the development and function of the nervous system; biophysics of fertilization; ion transport; membrane permeability. Mailing Add: Dept of Zool Univ of Calif Berkeley CA 94720

STEINHART, CAROL ELDER, b Cleveland, Ohio, May 27, 35; m 58; c 3. PLANT PHYSIOLOGY. Educ: Albion Col, AB, 56; Univ Wis, PhD(bot), 60. Prof Exp: Biologist lab gen & comp biochem, NIMH, 61-66, sci analyst div res grants, NIH, Md, 66-68, biologist, 68-70; SCI WRITER & ED, 70- Concurrent Pos: Specialist, Biodata Sect, Dept Human Oncol, Sch Med, Univ Wis, 77-80, proj assoc, Water Resources Ctr, 80- Mem: Am Inst Biol Sci. Res: Growth, differentiation and nutrition of plant tissue cultures; hormonal control of enzyme synthesis in plants; ecology and environmental problems; environmental indices. Mailing Add: 104 Lathrop St Madison WI 53705

STEINHART, JOHN SHANNON, b Chicago, Ill, June 3, 29; m 58; c 2. GEOPHYSICS, SCIENCE POLICY. Educ: Harvard Univ, AB, 51; Univ Wis, PhD, 60. Prof Exp: Proj leader, Woods Hole Oceanog Inst, 56; NSF fel, Carnegie Inst Wash Dept Terrestrial Magnetism, 60-61, mem staff, 61-68; tech asst, Resources & Environ, Off Sci & Technol, Exec Off of the Pres, 68-70; assoc dir, Marine Studies Ctr, 73-77; PROF GEOPHYS & ENVIRON STUDIES, UNIV WIS-MADISON, 70- Mem: Soc Explor Geophys; Seismol Soc Am; Am Geophys Union. Res: Physics of solid earth; terrestrial heat flow; environmental policy research; science and public policy research and teaching. Mailing Add: Dept of Geol Univ of Wis Madison WI 53706

STEINHAUER, ALLEN LAURENCE, b Winnipeg, Man, Oct 17, 31; US citizen; m 58; c 2. ENTOMOLOGY, ECOLOGY. Educ: Univ Man, BSA, 53; Ore State Univ, MS, 55, PhD(entom), 58. Prof Exp: From asst prof entom to assoc prof entom, Univ Md, 58-66; assoc prof, Ohio State Univ, 66-69; assoc prof, 69-71, PROF ENTOM, UNIV MD, COLLEGE PARK, 71-, CHMN DEPT, 75- Concurrent Pos: Entom specialist, Ohio State Univ-US Agency Int Develop, Brazil, 66-69; ed, Environ Entom, 71-75. Mem: AAAS; Entom Soc Am; Int Orgn Biol Control; Brazilian Entom Soc. Res: Applied ecology; forage crop insects; biological control; pest management; insect behavior; graduate training. Mailing Add: Dept of Entom Univ of Md College Park MD 20742

STEINHAUER, PAUL DAVID, b Toronto, Ont, Nov 29, 33; m 56; c 4. CHILD PSYCHIATRY. Educ: Univ Toronto, MD, 57; FRCP(C), 62. Prof Exp: PROF PSYCHIAT, 78-, DIR TRAINING CHILD PSYCHIAT, 74- Concurrent Pos: Psychiat consult, Halton County Children's Aid Soc, 63-75, Toronto Cath Children's Aid Soc, 64-75 & Children's Aid Soc Metrop Toronto, 65-; sr staff psychiatrist, Hosp Sick Children, Toronto, 65- Mem: Can Psychiat Asn; Can Med Asn; Can Acad Child Psychiat (pres, 81-82). Res: Developing a process model of family functioning and the family assessment measure based on that model; Relative effectiveness on protecting children's adjustment; development and continuity on foster parent satisfaction. Mailing Add: Med Suite 126 400 Walmer Rd Toronto ON M5P 2X7 Can

STEINHAUS, DAVID WALTER, b Neillsville, Wis, July 29, 19; m 49; c 4. ATOMIC PHYSICS, SPECTROCHEMISTRY. Educ: Lake Forest Col, AB, 41; Johns Hopkins Univ, PhD(physics), 52. Prof Exp: Physicist, Cent Sci Co, 41-45, Cenco Indust fel, 41-42; res asst inst coop res, Johns Hopkins Univ, 46-52; mem staff & physicist, Los Alamos Nat Lab, 52-73, sect leader, 69-80; MEM FAC DEPT PHYSICS, SOUTHWESTERN UNIV AT MEMPHIS, 80- Concurrent Pos: Mem comt line spectra of the elements, Nat Acad Sci-Nat Res Coun, 66-70. Mem: AAAS; Optical Soc Am; Am Asn Physics Teachers; Soc Appl Spectros. Res: Instrument development; visible and ultraviolet spectroscopy; time resolution of spectra from spark discharges; high resolution spectroscopy; optical spectra of the heavy elements; spectrochemical analysis. Mailing Add: Dept Physics Southwestern Univ Memphis 2000 N Pkwy Memphis TN 38112

STEINHAUS, JOHN EDWARD, b Omaha, Nebr, Feb 23, 17; m 43; c 5. ANESTHESIOLOGY. Educ: Univ Nebr, BA, 40, MA, 41; Univ Wis, MD, 45, PhD(pharmacol), 50; Am Bd Anesthesiol, dipl, 59. Prof Exp: Asst prof pharmacol, Marquette Univ, 50-51; assoc prof, Univ Wis, 51-54, asst prof anesthesiol, 54-58; assoc prof, 58-59, PROF ANESTHESIOL & CHMN DEPT, SCH MED, EMORY UNIV, 59- Mem: Am Soc Anesthesiol (pres,

70); Asn Univ Anesthetists (pres, 71); Am Soc Pharmacol & Exp Therapeut; AMA. *Res:* Drug reactions and intoxications; antiarrhytmic agents; cough mechanism and suppression; depression of respiratory reflexes. *Mailing Add:* Dept of Anesthesiol Emory Univ Sch of Med Atlanta GA 30322

STEINHAUS, RALPH K, b Sheboygan, Wis, June 21, 39; m 65; c 2. ANALYTICAL CHEMISTRY. *Educ:* Wheaton Col, BS, 61; Purdue Univ, PhD(anal chem), 66. *Prof Exp:* Asst prof chem, Wis State Univ-Oshkosh, 65-68; asst prof, 68-73, ASSOC PROF CHEM, WESTERN MICHIGAN UNIV, 73- *Concurrent Pos:* Res assoc, Ohio State Univ, 75-76. *Mem:* Am Chem Soc; Sigma Xi. *Res:* Kinetics and mechanisms of transition metal chelates; factors affecting stability of metal chelates. *Mailing Add:* Dept of Chem Western Mich Univ Kalamazoo MI 49008

STEINHOFF, RAYMOND OAKLEY, geology, see previous edition

STEINITZ, MICHAEL OTTO, b New York, NY, June 12, 44; m 65; c 2. SOLID STATE PHYSICS, MATERIALS SCIENCE. *Educ:* Cornell Univ, BE, 65; Northwestern Univ, Evanston, PhD(mat sci), 70. *Prof Exp:* Coop student comput logic, Philco Corp, 62-63, coop student radio propagation, 63; Nat Res Coun Can fel dept physics, Univ Toronto, 70-72, proj scientist solid state physics dept metall, 72-73, instr, Scarborough Col, 70-72; asst prof physics, 73-77, ASSOC PROF PHYSICS, ST FRANCIS XAVIER UNIV, 77- *Concurrent Pos:* Assoc prof physics, Israel Inst Technol, 77-78 & 80-81. *Mem:* Am Phys Soc; Can Asn Physicists. *Res:* Magnetic properties of non-ferromagnetic transition metals; thermal expansion; magnetostriction; neutron diffraction; ultrasonic attenuation; phase transitions; chromium; defect structures in oxides; charge and spin density waves; layered structures; model biomembranes. *Mailing Add:* PO Box 154 Dept of Physics St Francis Xavier Univ Antigonish NS B2G 1C0 Can

STEINKAMP, MYRNA PRATT, b Warren, Pa, Dec 23, 38. BOTANY. *Educ:* Hood Col, BA, 62; Northwestern Univ, Evanston, MS, 64; Univ Calif, Santa Cruz, PhD(bot), 73. *Prof Exp:* Lab supvr, Stoller Res Co, 69-74; microbiologist, Agr Res Serv, USDA, Calif, 74-75; RES ASSOC, BEET SUGAR DEVELOP FOUND, COLO, 76- *Mem:* Bot Soc Am; Am Bryological and Lichenological Soc. *Res:* Cytology of plant host-pathogenic fungi and pathotoxins on host tissue; fine structure and development of bryophyte spores. *Mailing Add:* Crops Res Lab Colo State Univ Ft Collins CO 80523

STEINKE, FREDERICH H, b Wilmington, Del, Nov 26, 35; m 60; c 2. POULTRY NUTRITION. *Educ:* Univ Del, BS, 57, MS, 59; Univ Wis, PhD(biochem), 62. *Prof Exp:* Asst mgr poultry nutrit, 62-63, mgr turkey res, 63-72, MGR NUTRIT RES, CENT RES LAB, RALSTON-PURINA CO, 72- *Mem:* Poultry Sci Asn; Am Inst Nutrit; Inst Food Technol. *Res:* Poultry nutrition including broilers, laying hens and turkeys; nutrition evaluation; human nutrition. *Mailing Add:* 8818 Brookview Dr Crestwood MO 63126

STEINKE, PAUL KARL WILLI, b Friedeberg, Ger, July 13, 21; nat US; m 44; c 3. AGRICULTURAL MICROBIOLOGY. *Educ:* Univ Wis, BS, 47, MS, 48, PhD(agr bact), 51. *Prof Exp:* Asst agr bact, Univ Wis, 47-51; food bacteriologist, Chain Belt Co, 51-56; bacteriologist, Paul-Lewis Labs, Inc, 56-61; mgr tech serv, Chas Pfizer & Co, Inc, NY, 61-63, mgr com develop, 64-69, prod mkt mgr, 70-71, TECH DIR, PFIZER, INC, MILWAUKEE, 72- *Mem:* Am Soc Microbiol; Am Soc Brewing Chem; Master Brewers Asn Am; Am Dairy Sci Asn. *Res:* Microbiology of meat products; food poisoning bacteria; thermal death time of food spoilage organisms; dehydration of foods; brewing bacteriology and technology; chemistry of hops; cheese cultures and media. *Mailing Add:* 6060 N Kent Ave Whitefish Bay WI 53217

STEINKER, DON COOPER, b Seymour, Ind, Oct 6, 36; m 59. PALEOBIOLOGY. *Educ:* Ind Univ, BS, 59; Univ Kans, MS, 61; Univ Calif, Berkeley, PhD(paleont), 69. *Prof Exp:* Res Paleontologist, Univ Calif, Berkeley, 62-63, teaching asst paleont, 62-65, instr, 66-67; asst prof geol, San Jose State Col, 65-66; lectr, Univ Calif, Davis, summer 66; asst prof, 67-75, assoc prof, 75-78, PROF GEOL, BOWLING GREEN STATE UNIV, 78- *Mem:* Paleont Soc; Nat Asn Geol Teachers. *Res:* Foraminiferal biology and ecology; paleobiology. *Mailing Add:* Dept Geol Bowling Green State Univ Bowling Green OH 43403

STEINKRAUS, KEITH HARTLEY, b Bertha, Minn, Mar 15, 18; m 41; c 5. MICROBIOLOGY. *Educ:* Univ Minn, BA, 39; Iowa State Univ, PhD(bact), 51. *Prof Exp:* Chemist, Am Crystal Sugar Co, Minn, 39; microbiologist, Jos Seagram & Sons, Inc, 42; instr electronics, US Army Air Force Tech Training Sch, SDak, 42-43; res microbiologist, Gen Mills, Inc, Minn, 43-47; res microbiologist, Pillsbury Mills, Inc, 51; from asst prof to assoc prof bact, 52-62, PROF BACT, NY STATE COL AGR, CORNELL UNIV, 62- *Concurrent Pos:* Food & agr specialist, US Nutrit Surv, Ecuador & Vietnam, 59, Burma, 61 & 64, Malaya, Thailand & Korea, 64; spec consult interdept comt nutrit for nat defense, NIH, 59-60, spec consult off int res, 67-68; vis prof microbiol col agr, Univ Philippines, 67-69 & Polytech South Bank, London, 72-73; vis prof, UNESCO/Int Cell Res Orgn/UN Environ Prog Training Course Appl Microbiol, Inst Technol, Bandung, Indonesia, 74 & Inst Microbiol, Univ Gottingen, Germany, 80; int organizer Symp Indigenous Fermented Foods, Bangkok, 77; alt mem panel microbiol, UN Environ Prog/UNESCO/Int Cell Res Orgn, 78-; vis prof UNESCO/ICRO Training Course Appl Microbiol, Kasetsart Univ, Bangkok, 76; res scientist, Nestle Prod Tech Assistance Co, Ltd, La-Tour-de-Peilz, Switzerland, 79-80. *Mem:* Fel AAAS; fel Am Acad Microbiol; Am Soc Microbiol; Inst Food Technol. *Res:* Biochemical, microbial and nutritional changes in fermented protein-rich foods; biological and chemical transformations by yeasts, molds and bacteria; biological control of insects with parasitic spore-forming bacteria; extraction of plant proteins. *Mailing Add:* NY State Agr Exp Sta Cornell Univ Geneva NY 14456

STEINLAGE, RALPH CLETUS, b St Henry, Ohio, July 2, 40; m 62; c 3. MATHEMATICS, FUZZY SETS & SYSTEMS. *Educ:* Univ Dayton, BS, 62; Ohio State Univ, MS, 63, PhD(math), 66. *Prof Exp:* Asst prof, 66-71, assoc prof, 71-79, PROF MATH, UNIV DAYTON, 79- *Mem:* Math Asn Am; Am Math Soc. *Res:* Measure theory and topology; Haar measure on locally compact Hausdorff spaces; conditions related to equicontinuity; non-standard analysis; fuzzy topological spaces; experiential training in mathematics programs. *Mailing Add:* Dept of Math Univ of Dayton Dayton OH 45469

STEINLE, EDMUND CHARLES, JR, b Scranton, Pa, Feb 7, 24; m 47; c 3. ORGANIC CHEMISTRY. *Educ:* ePauw Univ, AB, 47; Univ Iowa, MS, 49, PhD(org chem), 52. *Prof Exp:* Chemist, Ethyl Corp Res Lab, 52-55; CHEMIST, PLASTICS & CHEM RES & DEVELOP LAB, UNION CARBIDE CORP, 55- *Mem:* AAAS; Am Chem Soc; Am Oil Chemists Soc; fel Royal Soc Chem. *Res:* Fatty alchohols; biodegradable surfactants; surfactant intermediates. *Mailing Add:* Process Develop Lab Carbide & Carbon Chems Charleston WV 25303

STEINMAN, CHARLES ROBERT, b New York, NY, Aug 3, 38. RHEUMATOLOGY, BIOCHEMISTRY. *Educ:* Princeton Univ, AB, 59; Columbia Univ, MD, 63. *Prof Exp:* From intern to resident med, Presby Hosp, Columbia Univ, 63-65 & 68-69; assoc biochem, Nat Inst Arthritis, Metab & Digestive Dis, NIH, 65-67; fel rheumatology, Presby Hosp, Columbia Univ, 67-68 & 69-70; vis fel rheumatology, The London Hosp, 70; asst prof, 70-77, ASSOC PROF MED, MT SINAI SCH MED, 77- *Concurrent Pos:* Asst attend physician, Mt Sinai Hosp, 70-77, assoc attend physician, 77-; asst attend physician, Beth Israel Hosp, 71; consult rheumatol, Bronx Vet Admin Hosp, 77- *Mem:* Am Rheumatism Asn; Harvey Soc; Lupus Found Am; Am Fed Clin Res; AAAS. *Res:* Study of rheumatoid arthritis; systemic lupus erythematosus and related disorders to determine their pathogenesis by biochemical, immunological and microbiological approaches. *Mailing Add:* One E 100 St New York NY 10029

STEINMAN, DONALD KENNEY, nuclear engineering, see previous edition

STEINMAN, HARRY GORDON, b Trenton, NJ, Jan 5, 13; m 36; c 1. ORGANIC CHEMISTRY. *Educ:* Mass Inst Technol, BS, 33; Rutgers Univ, MS, 36; Columbia Univ, PhD(chem), 42. *Prof Exp:* From biochemist to head sect biochem, Lab Clin Invest, Nat Inst Allergy & Infectious Dis, 38-66, chief viral reagents, Nat Cancer Inst, 66-69, Off Res Safety, 69-77, CONSULT, NAT CANCER INST, 77- *Mem:* Am Chem Soc; Soc Exp Biol & Med; Am Soc Biol Chem; Am Soc Microbiol; Tissue Cult Asn. *Res:* Cell-mediated immunity; chemotherapy of infectious diseases; penicillins and penicillinases; drug-protein interactions; viral oncology. *Mailing Add:* 11417 High Hay Dr Columbia MD 21044

STEINMAN, HOWARD MARK, b Detroit, Mich, Feb 18, 44. BIOCHEMISTRY, PROTEIN CHEMISTRY. *Educ:* Amherst Col, BA, 65; Yale Univ, PhD(molecular biophys), 70. *Prof Exp:* Assoc biochem, Duke Univ, 72-75, asst med res prof, 75-76; asst prof, 76-81, ASSOC PROF BIOCHEM, ALBERT EINSTEIN COL MED, 81- *Concurrent Pos:* Fel, Dept Biochem, Duke Univ, 70-72. *Mem:* Sigma Xi; Am Asn Biol Chemists. *Res:* Protein chemistry; structure, function and evolutionary relationships among enzymes. *Mailing Add:* Dept Biochem 1300 Morris Park Ave Bronx NY 10461

STEINMAN, IRVIN DAVID, b New York, NY, Nov 7, 24; m 54; c 2. MICROBIOLOGY. *Educ:* Brooklyn Col, AB, 48; Univ Chicago, MS, 49; Rutgers Univ, PhD(microbiol), 58. *Prof Exp:* Instr microbiol col dent, NY Univ, 51-54; asst instr biol, Rutgers Univ, 54-58; mem fac, Monmouth Jr Col, NJ, 58-59; dir biol serv, US Testing Co, 59-61; dir prof serv, White Labs, 61-67; head med commun, Bristol Labs Int Corp, 67-68; clin res assoc, Ciba Pharm Co, 68-69; mem staff, 69-74, actg asst dir, Div Sci Opinion, 74-76, SPEC ASST SCI AFFAIRS, BUR CONSUMER PROTECTION, FED TRADE COMN, 76- *Mem:* AAAS; Am Soc Microbiol; Am Med Asn; Asn Mil Surg US; fel Am Acad Microbiol. *Res:* Microbial genetics; metabolism; pigmentation and production of antibiotics; scientific evaluation of false and misleading advertising claims; health sciences administration. *Mailing Add:* 14601 Notley Rd Silver Spring MD 20904

STEINMAN, MARTIN, b Passaic, NJ, Feb 16, 37; m 61; c 2. MEDICINAL CHEMISTRY, ORGANIC CHEMISTRY. *Educ:* Rutgers Univ, BS, 58, MS, 62; Univ Kans, PhD(med chem), 65. *Prof Exp:* From chemist to sr chemist, 65-70, prin scientist, 70-73, sect leader, 73-76, mgr, 76-79, ASSOC DIR, SCHERING CORP, 79- *Mem:* Am Chem Soc; NY Acad Sci. *Res:* Stereochemistry; new heterocyclic ring systems; synthesis of potentially useful medicinal agents; chemical and antibiotic process research; structure-activity relationships. *Mailing Add:* Schering Corp 60 Orange St Bloomfield NJ 07003

STEINMAN, RALPH R, b Asheville, NC, Nov 23, 10; m 38; c 3. DENTISTRY. *Educ:* Emory Univ, DDS, 38; Univ Mich, MS, 53. *Prof Exp:* From instr to assoc prof caries control, 53-65, prof oral med, 65-77, mem fac, 77-81, EMER PROF, DEPTS OF DENT ASSIST AND HYG & ORAL DIAG, RADIOL & PATH, SCH DENT, LOMA LINDA UNIV, 81- *Mem:* AAAS; Int Asn Dent Res. *Res:* Pathology of dental caries, especially as related to nutrition; hypothalamic-parotid endocrine axis and its relation to dental caries. *Mailing Add:* Loma Linda Univ Sch of Dent Loma Linda CA 92354

STEINMAN, ROBERT, b New York, NY, Mar 30, 18; m 39; c 4. INORGANIC CHEMISTRY, ORGANIC CHEMISTRY. *Educ:* Carnegie Inst Technol, BS, 39; Univ Ill, MS, 40, PhD(chem), 42. *Prof Exp:* Res chemist, Owens-Corning Corp, 42-47; dir res, Waterway Projs, 47-48; pres, Garan Chem Corp, Calif, 48-67; VPRES RES & DEVELOP, WHITTAKER CORP, 67- *Honors & Awards:* Ord Award, US Dept Navy, 44. *Mem:* AAAS; Am Chem Soc; Soc Plastics Eng; Soc Plastics Indust. *Res:* Phosphorus nitrogen chemistry; surface chemistry of glass; reinforced plastics. *Mailing Add:* 11455 Thurston Circle Los Angeles CA 90049

STEINMEIER, ROBERT C, b Glendale, Calif, Apr 16, 43; m 68; c 2. BIOCHEMISTRY. *Educ:* Univ Nebr, Lincoln, BS, 65, PhD(biochem), 75. *Prof Exp:* Immunochemist, Hyland Div, Travenol Labs, 67-69; res assoc bioenergetics, State Univ NY Buffalo, 74-76, Nat Cancer Inst fel, 75-76; vis asst prof biochem, 76-78; ASST PROF CHEM, UNIV ARK MED SCH, 78- *Res:* Studies on proteins of the mitochondrial inner membrane, including illucidation of structure-function relationships utilizing various physical and chemical approaches; rapid reaction kinetic studies on hemoproteins and enzymes. *Mailing Add:* Dept of Chem Univ Ark Little Rock AR 72204

STEINMETZ, CHARLES, JR, b Brooklyn, NY, Feb 15, 31; m 53; c 1. ZOOLOGY. *Educ:* Univ Conn, BA, 54; Univ Mich, MS, 55, PhD(fisheries), 61. *Prof Exp:* Asst, State Bd Fish & Game, Conn, 53; lab asst, US Fish & Wildlife Serv, 55; instr zool, Mich State Univ, 55-56; aide conserv inst fisheries res, Univ Mich, 56-58; teaching fel, 59-61, asst prof, 61-70, PROF ZOOL, SOUTHERN CONN STATE COL, 70- *Mem:* Am Fisheries Soc; Am Soc Ichthyol & Herpet. *Res:* Fish hybridization, predation, behavior and management; aquatic biology; larval marine fishes. *Mailing Add:* Dept of Biol 501 Crescent St Southern Conn State Col New Haven CT 06515

STEINMETZ, CHARLES HENRY, b Logansport, Ind, Oct 5, 29; m 71; c 4. OCCUPATIONAL HEALTH, MEDICAL ADMINISTRATION. *Educ:* Ind Univ, AB, 50, PhD(comp physiol), 53; Univ Cincinnati, MD, 60; Johns Hopkins Univ, MPH, 72; Am Bd Prev Med, cert gen prev med, 73. *Prof Exp:* Asst physiol, Ind Univ, 49-50, anat, 50-51 & zool, 51-53; asst chief space biol, Aero Med Field Lab, Holloman AFB, NMex, 53-56; epidemiologist, Off of Dir, Robert A Taft Sanit Eng Ctr, USPHS, Ohio, 58-60; intern, Staten Island Marine Hosp, NY, 60-61; asst gen mgr, Life Sci Opers, NAm Aviation, Inc, 62-68; dir, Systemed Corp, Md, 68-72; vpres, Nat Health Serv, 72-74; clin instr public health, Med Col, Cornell Univ, 75-79; MED DIR, MARATHON OIL CO, 79- *Mem:* Fel Aerospace Med Asn; fel Am Acad Occup Med; fel Am Occup Med Asn; fel Am Col Prev Med; fel NY Acad Med. *Res:* General preventive medicine; occupational health; systems analysis. *Mailing Add:* 539 S Main St Findlay OH 45840

STEINMETZ, RICHARD, geology, see previous edition

STEINMETZ, WALTER EDMUND, b Washington, DC, Jan 12, 21; m 47; c 2. ORGANIC CHEMISTRY. *Educ:* St Ambrose Col, BS, 43; Univ Iowa, MS, 47, PhD(org chem), 49. *Prof Exp:* Res chemist, Nalco Chem Co, 48-49, group leader org chem, 49-53, dir, 53-57, sr tech adv, 57-60; sect leader, El Paso Natural Gas Prod Co, 60-65; sect leader, 65-69, mgr chem res div, 69-75, SR TECH ADV, PENNZOIL CO, 75- *Mem:* Am Chem Soc. *Res:* Herbicides; oil treatment chemicals; petrochemicals. *Mailing Add:* Chem Res Div Pennzoil Co PO Box 6199 Shreveport LA 71106

STEINMETZ, WAYNE EDWARD, b Huron, Ohio, Feb 16, 45. PHYSICAL CHEMISTRY, MOLECULAR SPECTROSCOPY. *Educ:* Oberlin Col, AB, 67; Harvard Univ, AM, 68, PhD(chem), 73. *Prof Exp:* Instr phys sci, St Peter's Boys' High Sch, 69-70; lab instr, Oberlin Col, 70-71; asst prof, 73-79, ASSOC PROF CHEM, POMONA COL, 79- *Concurrent Pos:* Guest prof, Eidgenossische Tech Hochschule, Zurich, 79-80. *Mem:* Am Chem Soc; AAAS. *Res:* Molecular structure and spectroscopy; Application of circular dichroism, nuclear magnetic resonance, and low resolution microwave spectroscopy to conformational analysis; nuclear magnetic resonance studies of protein flexibility. *Mailing Add:* Seaver Chem Lab Pomona Col Claremont CA 91711

STEINMETZ, WILLIAM JOHN, b Wheeling WVa, Nov 14, 39; m 71. APPLIED MATHEMATICS. *Educ:* St Louis Univ, BS, 60; Ga Inst Technol, MS, 62; Rensselaer Polytech Inst, PhD(math), 70. *Prof Exp:* Res scientist aeronaut eng, NASA Ames Res Ctr, 61-66; from asst prof to assoc prof, 70-81, PROF MATH, ADELPHI UNIV, 81- *Mem:* Soc Indust & Appl Math. *Res:* Applied mathematics, in particular singular perturbations of ordinary and partial differential equations; stochastic differential equations. *Mailing Add:* Dept of Math Adelphi Univ Garden City NY 11530

STEINMULLER, DAVID, b New York, NY, June 17, 34. TRANSPLANTATION IMMUNOLOGY. *Educ:* Swarthmore Col, BA, 56; Univ Pa, PhD(zool), 61. *Prof Exp:* Mus cur, Wistar Inst Anat & Biol, 61-62; lectr embryol, Fac Med, Univ Valencia, 62-63; res instr med genetics, Sch Med, Univ Wash, 63-65, res instr path, 65-66; from instr to asst prof, Sch Med, Univ Pa, 66-68; asst prof, Col Med, Univ Utah, 68-71, from assoc prof to prof path & surg, 71-76, assoc res prof surg, 76-77; PROF IMMUNOL, MAYO MED SCH & CONSULT IMMUNOL, MAYO CLIN, 77- *Concurrent Pos:* Res fel, Wistar Inst Anat & Biol, 61-62; Fulbright fel, Univ Valencia, 62-63; res assoc, Div Path, Inst Cancer Res, 66-68; mem dent res insts & prog adv comt, Nat Inst Dent Res, 71-75; mem grad fac microbiol, Univ Minn, 78-; mem, Surg, Anesthesiol & Trauma Study Sect, NIH, 79- *Mem:* Transplantation Soc; Am Asn Cancer Res; Am Asn Immunol. *Res:* Immunology and biology of tissue and organ transplants; cellular immunology; carcinogenesis and tumor immunity. *Mailing Add:* Dept of Immunol Mayo Clin Rochester MN 55901

STEINRAUF, LARRY KING, b St Louis, Mo, June 8, 31; m 68; c 1. BIOCHEMISTRY, PHYSICAL CHEMISTRY. *Educ:* Univ Mo, BS & MA, 54; Univ Wash, PhD(biochem), 57. *Prof Exp:* Asst prof phys chem, Univ Ill, Urbana, 59-64; assoc prof biochem, 64-68, PROF BIOCHEM & BIOPHYS, SCH MED, IND UNIV, INDIANAPOLIS, 68- *Concurrent Pos:* Res fel chem, Calif Inst Technol, 57-58; USPHS fel crystallog, Cavendish Lab, Cambridge, 58-59. *Mem:* Am Crystallog Asn. *Res:* Relation of molecular structure to biological activity. *Mailing Add:* 825 E 80th St Indianapolis IN 46240

STEINSCHNEIDER, ALFRED, b Brooklyn, NY, June 11, 29; m 50; c 2. PEDIATRICS. *Educ:* NY Univ, BA, 50; Univ Mo, MA, 52; Cornell Univ, PhD(psychol), 55; State Univ NY, MD, 61. *Prof Exp:* Asst psychol, Univ Mo, 50-52; asst, Cornell Univ, 52-54; engr, Advan Electronics Ctr, Gen Elec Co, NY, 54-57; res assoc, State Univ NY Upstate Med Ctr, 58-64, from asst prof to assoc prof pediat, 64-77; PROF PEDIAT & DIR, SUDDEN INFANT DEATH SYNDROME INST, SCH MED, UNIV MD, 77- *Mem:* Am Psychosom Soc; Soc Res Child Develop; Soc Psychophysiol Res; Am Acad Pediat. *Res:* Sudden infant death syndrome; child development; psychophysiology. *Mailing Add:* Dept of Pediat Univ of Md Hosp Baltimore MD 21201

STEINWACHS, DONALD MICHAEL, b Boise, Idaho, Sept 9, 46; m 72. OPERATIONS RESEARCH, PUBLIC HEALTH ADMINISTRATION. *Educ:* Univ Ariz, BS, 68, MS, 70; Johns Hopkins Univ, PhD(opers res), 73. *Prof Exp:* Res mgr, Health Serv Res & Develop Ctr, 72-79, asst dir, 79-81, asst prof, 73-79, ASSOC PROF, DEPT HEALTH SERV ADMIN, JOHNS HOPKINS UNIV, 79-, DEP DIR, HEALTH SERV RES & DEVELOP CTR, 81- *Mem:* AAAS; Opers Res Soc Am; Inst Mgt Sci; Am Pub Health Asn. *Res:* Primary medical care; effects of availability, access, continuity, organization and financing on cost and quality; information systems; impact of hospital cost containment strategies; models for health planning and resource allocation. *Mailing Add:* Health Serv Res & Develop Ctr Johns Hopkins Univ Baltimore MD 21205

STEITZ, JOAN ARGETSINGER, b Minneapolis, Minn, Jan 26, 41; m 66. BIOCHEMISTRY, MOLECULAR BIOLOGY. *Educ:* Antioch Col, BS, 63; Harvard Univ, MA, 67, PhD(biochem, molecular biol), 68. *Prof Exp:* Asst prof, 70-74, assoc prof, 74-78, PROF MOLECULAR BIOPHYS & BIOCHEM, YALE UNIV, 78- *Concurrent Pos:* NSF fel, Med Res Coun Lab Molecular Biol, Cambridge, Eng, 68-69, Jane Coffin Childs Fund med res fel, 69-70. *Honors & Awards:* Eli Lilly Award, 76. *Mem:* Am Soc Biol Chem; fel AAAS. *Res:* Control of transcription and translation; RNA and DNA sequence analysis; structure and function of small ribonucleoproteins from eukaryotes; RNA processing. *Mailing Add:* Dept Molec Biophys & Biochem Yale Univ New Haven CT 06510

STEITZ, THOMAS ARTHUR, b Milwaukee, Wis, Aug 23, 40; m 66. MOLECULAR BIOLOGY. *Educ:* Lawrence Univ, BA, 62; Harvard Univ, PhD(molecular biol, biochem), 66. *Hon Degrees:* DSc, Lawrence Univ, 81. *Prof Exp:* NIH grant, Harvard Univ, 66-67; Jane Coffin Childs Mem Fund Med Res fel, Med Res Coun Lab Molecular Biol, Cambridge Univ, 67-70; asst prof biochem, Univ Calif, Berkeley, 70; from asst prof to assoc prof, 70-79, PROF MOLECULAR BIOPHYS & BIOCHEM, YALE UNIV, 79- *Concurrent Pos:* Macy fel, Max-Planck Inst Biophys Chem, Gottingen. *Honors & Awards:* Pfier Award, Am Chem Soc, 80. *Mem:* Am Crystallog Asn; Am Soc Biol Chemists; Am Biophys Soc. *Res:* X-ray crystallographic structure determination of biological macromolecules; relation of enzyme structure and mechanism; structure studies of protein-nucleic acid interaction; theoretical studies protein secretioon and membrane protein folding. *Mailing Add:* Dept of Molecular Biophys & Biochem Yale Univ PO Box 6666 260 Whitney Ave New Haven CT 06511

STEJSKAL, EDWARD OTTO, b Chicago, Ill, Jan 19, 32; m 57. PHYSICAL CHEMISTRY. *Educ:* Univ Ill, BS, 53, PhD(chem), 57. *Prof Exp:* Asst phys chem, Univ Ill, 53-56; NSF fel, Harvard Univ, 57-58; from instr to asst prof phys chem Univ Wis, 58-64, Wis Alumni Res Found fel, 58-59; res specialist, 64-67, sr res specialist, 67-80, FEL SCI, MONSANTO CO, 80- *Mem:* AAAS; Am Phys Soc; Am Chem Soc. *Res:* Molecular structure; spectroscopy; nuclear magnetic resonance; molecular motion in solids, liquids and gases; nuclear spin relaxation and diffusion phenomena; high-resolution nuclear magnetic resonance in solids; fluid rheology; lubrication. *Mailing Add:* Corp Res Labs Monsanto Co 800 N Lindbergh Blvd St Louis MO 63167

STEJSKAL, RUDOLF, b Budejovice, Czech, Apr 16, 31; m 68; c 2. PATHOLOGY. *Educ:* Charles Univ, Czech, DDS, 56; Univ Chicago, MS, 69; Chicago Med Sch-Univ Health Sci, PhD(path), 72. *Prof Exp:* Trainee path, Univ Chicago, 67-69; res assoc exp path, Mt Sinai Hosp Med Ctr, Chicago, 70-72; res assoc & asst prof path, Univ Chicago, 72-73; sr res investr, 73-75, sr res scientist path, Searle Labs, 75-78, DIR PATH, SEARLE RES & DEVELOP, FRANCE, 78- *Concurrent Pos:* Clin assoc path, Chicago Med Sch, 70-72. *Mem:* Europ Soc Toxicol; Soc Toxicol Pathologists; Int Acad Path; Am Soc Exp Path; NY Acad Sci. *Res:* Fate of blood group substances in human cancer; drug-induced carcinogenesis. *Mailing Add:* Searle Res & Develop Sophia Antipolis BP23 Valbonne 06560 France

STEKEL, FRANK D, b Hillsboro, Wis, Aug 26, 41; m 67. SCIENCE EDUCATION, PHYSICS. *Educ:* Univ Wis-La Crosse, BS, 63, Univ Wis-Madison, MS, 65; Ind Univ, Bloomington, EdD(sci educ), 70. *Prof Exp:* From instr to asst prof 65-70, assoc prof, 70-77, PROF PHYSICS, UNIV WIS-WHITEWATER, 77- *Mem:* Fel AAAS; Am Asn Physics Teachers; Nat Asn Res Sci Teaching; Nat Sci Teachers Asn; Sch Sci & Math Asn. *Res:* Development, implementation and evaluation of physical science instruction at all levels, from the elementary school up to the college and university level. *Mailing Add:* Dept of Physics Univ of Wis Whitewater WI 53190

STEKIEL, WILLIAM JOHN, b Milwaukee, Wis, Jan 1, 28; m 55; c 2. BIOPHYSICS. *Educ:* Marquette Univ, BS, 51; Johns Hopkins Univ, PhD(biophys), 57. *Prof Exp:* USPHS fel & instr physiol, 57-60, asst prof biophys, 60-66, assoc prof, 66-77, PROF PHYSIOL, MED COL WIS, 77- *Concurrent Pos:* Res exchange prof, Med Univ, Budapest, 63. *Mem:* AAAS; Biophys Soc; Am Physiol Soc; Inst Elec & Electronics Engrs; Microcirc Soc. *Res:* Electrophysiology; circulatory physiology; neurophysiology and neurochemistry. *Mailing Add:* Dept of Physiol Med Col of Wis PO Box 26509 Milwaukee WI 53226

STEKOLL, MICHAEL STEVEN, b Tulsa, Okla, May 7, 47; m 76; c 1. BIOCHEMISTRY. *Educ:* Stanford Univ, BS, 71; Univ Calif, Los Angeles, PhD(biochem), 76. *Prof Exp:* Res fel marine pollution, Univ Alaska, Fairbanks, 76-78; ASST PROF CHEM FISHERIES DIV, UNIV ALASKA, JUNEAU, 78- *Concurrent Pos:* Asst, Univ Calif, Los Angeles, 72-76, res trainee, 72-76; res biochemist, Nat Marine Fisheries Serv, 79. *Mem:* AAAS;

Am Chem Soc. *Res:* Purification and properties of phytoalexin elicitors; effects of marine pollution on invertebrates; algal physiology & ecology. *Mailing Add:* Sch Fisheries & Sci Univ Alaska 11120 Glacier Hwy Juneau AK 99801

STELCK, CHARLES RICHARD, b Edmonton, Alta, May 20, 17; m 45; c 4. GEOLOGY. *Educ:* Univ Alta, BSc, 37, MSc, 41; Stanford Univ, PhD(geol), 50. *Prof Exp:* Lab asst, Univ Alta, 37-41; well site geologist, BC Dept Mines, 40-42; field geologist, Canol Proj, 42-44 & Imp Oil Co, 44-48; lectr, 48-53, assoc prof, 54-57, PROF GEOL, UNIV ALTA, 58- *Mem:* Geol Soc Am; Paleont Soc; fel Royal Soc Can; Geol Asn Can. *Res:* Stratigraphic paleontology of western Canada. *Mailing Add:* Dept of Geol Univ of Alta Edmonton AB T6G 2G7 Can

STELL, GEORGE ROGER, b Glen Cove, NY, Jan 2, 33. PHYSICS, MATHEMATICS. *Educ:* Antioch Col, BS, 55; NY Univ, PhD(math), 61. *Prof Exp:* Instr physics, Univ Ill, Chicago, 55-56; assoc res scientist, Inst Math Sci, NY Univ, 61-64; assoc res scientist, Belfer Grad Sch Sci, Yeshiva Univ, 64-65; from asst prof physics to assoc prof physics, Polytech Inst Brooklyn, 65-68; assoc prof mech, 68-70, prof mech, 70-77, PROF MECH ENG, STATE UNIV NY STONY BROOK, 77- *Concurrent Pos:* Consult, Lawrence Radiation Lab, Univ Calif, 63-66; visitor, Lab Theoret & High Energy Physics, Nat Ctr Sci Res, France, 67-68; prin investr, NSF grant, 71- *Mem:* Am Math Soc; Am Phys Soc. *Res:* Statistical mechanics; especially molecular theory of fluids and lattice systems; mathematics associated with statistical mechanics, especially graph theory; generating functionals and non-linear integral equations; theory of critical phenomena and thermodynamic perturbation theory; theory of critical properties of fluids and magnetic materials. *Mailing Add:* Dept of Mech State Univ of NY Stony Brook NY 11790

STELL, WILLIAM KENYON, b Syracuse, NY, Apr 21, 39. VISUAL PHYSIOLOGY, NEUROBIOLOGY. *Educ:* Swarthmore Col, BA, 61; Univ Chicago, PhD(anat), 66, MD, 67. *Prof Exp:* Staff assoc, Lab Neurophysiol, Nat Inst Neurol Dis & Stroke, 67-68; staff assoc neurocytol, Lab Neuropath & Neuroanat Sci, 68-69 & Lab of the Dir, 69, sr staff fel, Off Dir Intramural Res, 69-71 & Lab Neurophysiol, Sect Cell Biol, 71-72; assoc prof opthal, Jules Stein Eye Inst, Univ Calif Los Angeles, 72-76, prof, 76-80, assoc dir, 78-80; PROF ANAT, DIR, LION'S SIGHT CTR & DIR, FAC, UNIV CALGARY, 80- *Honors & Awards:* E Gellhorn Award, Univ Chicago, 66. *Mem:* AAAS; Am Soc Cell Biol; Am Asn Anat; Assoc Am Physiol Soc; Asn Res Vision & Ophthal. *Res:* Neurocytology, ultrastructure and functional interconnections in vertebrate retina. *Mailing Add:* Dept Anat Univ Calgary 3330 Hosp Dr NW Calgary AB T2N 1N4 Can

STELLA, VALENTINO JOHN, b Melbourne, Australia, Oct 27, 46; m 69. PHARMACY. *Educ:* Victorian Col Pharm, Melbourne, BPharm, 67; Univ Kans, PhD(anal pharmaceut chem, pharmaceut), 71. *Prof Exp:* Pharmacist, Bendigo Base Hosp, Australia, 67-68; asst prof pharm, Univ Ill, Med Ctr, 71-73; from asst prof to assoc prof, 73-81, PROF PHARMACEUT CHEM, SCH PHARM, UNIV KANS, 81- *Concurrent Pos:* Consult, Inter Res Corp, Div Merck Co, 73-, E R Squibb & Sons, 78-, G D Searle, 80- *Honors & Awards:* Lederle Award, Lederle Labs, 72 & 75. *Mem:* Am Chem Soc; Am Pharmaceut Asn; Victorian Pharmaceut Soc; Acad Pharmaceut Sci; AAAS. *Res:* Physical pharmacy; pro-drugs and drug latentiation; drug stability; ionization kinetics; biopharmaceutics and pharmacokinetics. *Mailing Add:* 777 Sunset Lawrence KS 66044

STELLAR, ELIOT, b Boston, Mass, Nov 1, 19; m 45; c 2. PHYSIOLOGICAL PSYCHOLOGY. *Educ:* Harvard Univ, AB, 41; Brown Univ, MSc, 42, PhD(psychol), 47. *Prof Exp:* From instr to asst prof psychol, Johns Hopkins Univ, 47-54; from assoc prof to prof physiol psychol, 54-65, dir, Inst Neurol Sci, 65-73, provost, 73-78, PROF PHYSIOL PSYCHOL, SCH MED, UNIV PA, 78- *Concurrent Pos:* Mem, Nat Comn Protection Human Subj Biomed & Behav Res, 74-78. *Mem:* Nat Acad Sci; Am Philos Soc; AAAS; Am Psychol Asn; Am Acad Arts & Sci. *Res:* Motivation; learning; physiology of motivation. *Mailing Add:* Sch Med Univ Pa Philadelphia PA 19104

STELLER, KENNETH EUGENE, b Lancaster, Pa, Mar 14, 41; m 64; c 2. ORGANIC CHEMISTRY. *Educ:* Franklin & Marshall Col, BS, 63; Northwestern Univ, PhD(org chem), 67. *Prof Exp:* Res chemist, 67-74, SR RES CHEMIST, HERCULES INC, 74- *Mem:* Am Chem Soc. *Res:* Polyether polymerization; elastomers; polymer modification; thermoplastic elastomers; peroxide research and development. *Mailing Add:* Hercules Res Ctr Hercules Inc Wilmington DE 19899

STELLINGWERF, ROBERT FRANCIS, b Hawthorne, NJ, Apr 22, 47. STELLAR STRUCTURE & STABILITY. *Educ:* Rice Univ, BA, 69; Univ Colo, MS, 71, PhD(astrophys), 74. *Prof Exp:* Res assoc, Columbia Univ, 74-77; asst prof astron, Rutgers Univ, 77-80; RES SCIENTIST, MISSON RES CORP, 80- *Concurrent Pos:* Vis staff mem, Los Alamos Sci Lab, 76-; prin investr, NSF, 78- *Mem:* Am Astron Soc. *Res:* Stellar structure and stability; pulsation theory; astrophysical gas flow. *Mailing Add:* Misson Res Corp 1400 A San Mateo SE Albuquerque NM 87108

STELLWAGEN, EARLE C, b Joliet, Ill, June 14, 33; m 58; c 4. BIOCHEMISTRY. *Educ:* Elmhurst Col, BS, 55; Northwestern Univ, MS, 58; Univ Calif, Berkeley, PhD(biochem), 63. *Prof Exp:* NIH res fel biochem, Univ Vienna, 63-64; from asst prof to assoc prof, 64-72, PROF BIOCHEM, UNIV IOWA, 72- *Concurrent Pos:* NIH career develop award, 67-72; mem biophysics & biophysical study sect B, NIH, 70-, chmn, 72-; vis scientist, Bell Labs, 71-72. *Mem:* Am Soc Biol Chem. *Res:* Relationship of structure of proteins to their biological function. *Mailing Add:* Dept of Biochem Univ of Iowa Iowa City IA 52242

STELLWAGEN, ROBERT HARWOOD, b Joliet, Ill, Jan 6, 41; m 63; c 2. BIOCHEMISTRY. *Educ:* Harvard Univ, AB, 63; Univ Calif, Berkeley, PhD(biochem), 68. *Prof Exp:* Res biochemist, Univ Calif, Berkeley, 68; staff fel molecular biol, Nat Inst Arthritis & Metab Dis, 68-69; from asst prof to assoc prof, 70-80, PROF BIOCHEM, SCH MED, UNIV SOUTHERN CALIF, 80- *Concurrent Pos:* USPHS fel biochem, Univ Calif, San Francisco, 69-70; vis scientist, Nat Ins Med Res, London, 79. *Mem:* AAAS; Am Soc Biol Chem. *Res:* Biochemical control mechanisms in animal cells; enzyme induction by hormones; cellular differentiation. *Mailing Add:* Dept of Biochem Univ of Southern Calif Sch Med Los Angeles CA 90033

STELLY, MATTHIAS, b Arnaudville, La, Aug 7, 16; c 4. SOIL FERTILITY. *Educ:* Univ Southwestern La, BS, 37; La State Univ, MS, 39; Iowa State Univ, PhD(soil fertil), 42. *Prof Exp:* Asst agronomist, Exp Sta, La State Univ, 42-43; from assoc prof to prof soils, Univ Ga, 46-57; prof in chg soil testing serv, La State Univ, 57-59, prof soil chem, 59-61; exec secy & treas, ASA Pubs, Am Soc Agron, 61-70, exec vpres & ed in chief, 70-82. *Concurrent Pos:* Soil specialist, USDA, E Africa, 52-53; Am secy, Comn Soil Fertil & Plant Nutrit, 7th Cong, Int Soc Soil Sci, 58-60; prog dir transl & printing, Soviet Soil Sci; ed, Agron J, 61-82; dir Am Soc Agron vis scientist prog, 63-72 & Agron Sci Found, 67-82. *Mem:* Fel AAAS; fel Am Soc Agron; Crop Sci Soc Am; Soil Sci Soc Am; Int Soc Soil Sci. *Res:* Soil chemistry; identification of inorganic soil phosphorus compounds; radioactive materials as plant stimulants; crop rotation; radioactive phosphorus; fertilizer requirements and chemical composition of Bermuda grasses; methodology of soil testing; chemical and mineralogical investigations of Louisiana soils. *Mailing Add:* 2113 Chamberlain Ave Madison WI 53705

STELOS, PETER, b Lowell, Mass, May 17, 23. IMMUNOLOGY, IMMUNOCHEMISTRY. *Educ:* Berea Col, AB, 48; Univ Chicago, PhD(microbiol), 56. *Prof Exp:* Res assoc microbiol, Univ Chicago, 56-57; cancer res scientist, Roswell Park Mem Inst, 59-60, sr cancer res scientist, 60-63, assoc cancer res scientist, 63-65; assoc prof microbiol, Hahnemann Med Col, 65-73; assoc surg & immunol, Peter Bent Brigham Hosp & Harvard Med Sch, 73-79. *Concurrent Pos:* Fel chem, Yale Univ, 57-59. *Mem:* AAAS; Am Asn Immunol; Am Chem Soc. *Res:* Separation and properties of immunoglobulins. *Mailing Add:* 83 Garden St West Roxbury MA 02132

STELSON, HUGH EUGENE, b Elmdale, Kans, Jan 16, 03; m 25; c 6. MATHEMATICS. *Educ:* Kans Wesleyan, AB, 23; Northwestern Univ, AM, 24; Univ Iowa, PhD(math), 30. *Prof Exp:* Head dept math, Hedding Col, 24-26; asst & instr, Iowa State Col, 26-28; assoc prof, Marshall Col, 29-30; from asst prof to prof, Kent State Univ, 30-47; from assoc prof to prof, 47-71, EMER PROF MATH, MICH STATE UNIV, 71- *Concurrent Pos:* Vis prof, Univ Hawaii, 49-50. *Mem:* Am Math Soc; Math Asn Am. *Res:* Mathematical analysis. *Mailing Add:* Dept Math Mich State Univ East Lansing MI 48823

STELSON, PAUL HUGH, b Ames, Iowa, Apr 9, 27; m 50; c 4. PHYSICS. *Educ:* Purdue Univ, BS, 47, MA, 48; Mass Inst Technol, PhD(physics), 50. *Prof Exp:* Asst physics, Purdue Univ, 47; mem staff div indust coop, Nuclear Sci & Eng Lab, Mass Inst Technol, 50-52; sr physicist, 52-73, DIR, PHYS DIV, OAK RIDGE NAT LAB, 73- *Concurrent Pos:* Ford Found prof physics, Univ Tenn. *Mem:* Fel Am Phys Soc. *Res:* Nuclear physics; accelerators. *Mailing Add:* Oak Ridge Nat Lab Oak Ridge TN 37830

STELSON, T(HOMAS) E(UGENE), b Iowa City, Iowa, Aug 24, 28; m 51; c 4. CIVIL ENGINEERING. *Educ:* Carnegie Inst Technol, BS, 49, MS, 50, DSc(civil eng), 52. *Prof Exp:* From asst prof to prof civil eng, Carnegie-Mellon Univ, 52-61, Alcoa prof, 61-71, actg head dept, 57-59, head dept, 59-71; dean, Col Eng & asst vpres acad affairs, 71-77, PROF CIVIL ENG, GA INST TECHNOL, 71-, VPRES FOR RES, 77-; VPRES & CHMN BD DIRS, SYSTS PLANNING CORP, 68- *Concurrent Pos:* NSF fel, Calif Inst Technol, 62-63; co-dir, Transp Res Inst, Pa, 67-71; dir projs, Governor's Comt Transp, Commonwealth Pa, 68-71; mem exec bd, Skidaway Inst Oceanog, 71- & US Task Force on Future Mankind & Role of Christian Churches in World of Sci-Based Technol, 71- *Mem:* AAAS; Am Soc Civil Engrs; Am Soc Eng Educ; Nat Soc Prof Eng; Am Concrete Inst. *Res:* Fluid and soil mechanics; hydraulic and foundation engineering; transportation and systems engineering; environmental conditions. *Mailing Add:* Dept of Civil Eng Ga Inst Technol Atlanta GA 30332

STELTENKAMP, ROBERT JOHN, b Dayton, Ky, Sept 13, 36; m 57; c 2. ORGANIC CHEMISTRY. *Educ:* Xavier Univ, Ohio, BS, 58; Purdue Univ, PhD(org chem), 62. *Prof Exp:* Sr res chemist perfumery res, 62-67, sec head var res & develop sections, 67-80, RES ASSOC RES & DEVELOP, COLGATE PALMOLIVE CO, NJ, 80- *Mem:* Am Chem Soc; Sigma Xi; NY Acad Sci. *Res:* Identification of the composition of essential oils; structural identification of natural components and the toxicology of fragrance raw materials. *Mailing Add:* 92 Emerson Rd Somerset NJ 08873

STELTING, KATHLEEN MARIE, b Ottawa, Kans, Sept 9, 42; m 61; c 1. ANALYTICAL CHEMISTRY. *Educ:* Eastern NMex Univ, BS, 64; Univ Mo-Columbia, PhD(anal chem), 73. *Prof Exp:* Clin chemist, Hertzler Clin, Halstead, Kans, 64-65; asst prof anal chem, Calif State Univ, Fresno, 73-77; mgr separations & automation develop, Dept Res, Rockwell Hanford Opers, Rockwell Int Corp, 77-80; WITH MIDWEST RES INST, 80- *Mem:* Am Chem Soc; Am Nuclear Soc; Nat Mgt Asn; Nat Asn Female Execs. *Res:* Ion selective electrodes; cells without liquid junction; spectroscopic techniques for complexants analysis; environmental measurements. *Mailing Add:* Midwest Res Inst 425 Volker Blvd Kansas City MO 64110

STELTS, MARION LEE, b Oregon City, Ore, Mar 28, 40; m 61; c 2. NUCLEAR PHYSICS. *Educ:* Univ Ore, BA, 61; Univ Calif, Davis, MS, 70, PhD(appl sci), 75. *Prof Exp:* Physicist, Lawrence Livermore Lab, 61-75; physicist nuclear physics, Brookhaven Nat Lab, 75-80; PHYSICIST, LOS ALAMOS NAT LAB, 80- *Mem:* Am Phys Soc. *Mailing Add:* Los Alamos Nat Lab P-15 MS406 Los Alamos NM 87545

STELZER, LORIN ROY, b Bloomer, Wis, Mar 6, 31; m 58; c 2. RESEARCH ADMINISTRATION, ENTOMOLOGY. *Educ:* Wis State Col, Whitewater, BEd, 53; Univ Wis, MS, 55, PhD(entom), 57. *Prof Exp:* Field res specialist, 57-62, supvr, Southern Field Res Sta, Fla, 62-69, East East/South Field Res Sta, NJ, 69-71, MGR REGISTRAT & REGULATORY AFFAIRS, RES & DEVELOP, ORTHO DIV, CHEVRON CHEM CO, CALIF, 71- *Mem:* Entom Soc Am. *Res:* Field research, evaluation and development of chemicals for agricultural and home use. *Mailing Add:* Ortho Div Chevron Chem Co 940 Hensley Richmond CA 94804

STEMBRIDGE, GEORGE EUGENE, b Canton, Ga, Sept 27, 36; m 61; c 2. POMOLOGY. *Educ:* Clemson Univ, BS, 58; Univ Md, MS, 59, PhD(hort), 62. *Prof Exp:* Asst prof, 61-62 & 64-67, assoc prof, 67-73, PROF HORT, CLEMSON UNIV, 73- *Mem:* Am Soc Hort Sci; Int Soc Hort Sci. *Res:* Use of growth regulators in fruit production; culture of fruit trees. *Mailing Add:* Dept of Hort Clemson Univ Clemson SC 29631

STEMBRIDGE, VERNIE ALBERT, b El Paso, Tex, June 7, 24; m 44; c 3. PATHOLOGY. *Educ:* Tex Col Mines, BA, 43; Univ Tex, MD, 48; Am Bd Path, cert anat & clin path, 53. *Prof Exp:* Intern, Marine Hosp, Norfolk, Va, 48-49; resident path, Med Br, Univ Tex, 49-52, assoc dir clin labs & from asst prof to assoc prof, 52-56; chief aviation path sect, Armed Forces Inst Path, 56-59; assoc prof, 59-61, PROF PATH, UNIV TEX HEALTH SCI CTR DALLAS, 61-, CHMN DEPT, 66- *Concurrent Pos:* Consult, Vet Admin Hosp, Dallas, 59-, Civil Air Surgeon, Fed Aviation Agency, DC, 59-70 & Surgeon Gen, US Air Force, 62-70; trustee, Am Bd Path, 69-, secy, 77-; mem sci adv bd, Armed Forces Inst Path, DC, 71-75, chmn, 74-75. *Mem:* AMA; Am Asn Path & Bact; Am Soc Exp Path; Col Am Path; Am Soc Clin Path (pres, 77-78). *Res:* Neoplasms. *Mailing Add:* Dept of Path Univ of Tex Health Sci Ctr Dallas TX 75235

STEMKE, GERALD W, b Watseka, Ill, Oct 7, 35. IMMUNOCHEMISTRY. *Educ:* Ill State Univ, BS, 57; Univ Ill, PhD(chem), 63. *Prof Exp:* Teaching asst, Univ Ill, 59-60; trainee microbiol, NY Univ Med Ctr, 60-62, res assoc, 62-63; NIH fel, Pasteur Inst, Paris, 63-64, asst prof biol, Univ Pittsburgh, 65-66, asst prof microbial & molecular biol, 66-67, assoc prof biophys & microbiol, 67-70; PROF MICROBIOL, UNIV ALTA, 70- *Concurrent Pos:* Nat Res Coun Can res grant, 70-74; Nat Sci Eng, Res Coun Can res grant. *Mem:* AAAS; Int Org Mycoplasmol; Am Soc Microbiol; Am Asn Immunol; Can Soc Immunol. *Res:* Mycoplasma; ureaplasma surface antigens. *Mailing Add:* Dept of Microbiol Univ of Alta Edmonton AB T6G 2E9 Can

STEMLER, ALAN JAMES, b Chicago, Ill, July 29, 43; m 70. PLANT PHYSIOLOGY. *Educ:* Mich State Univ, BS, 65; Univ Ill, Urbana, PhD(plant physiol), 74. *Prof Exp:* Instr plant physiol, Univ Ill, Urbana, 74-75; fel, Dept Plant Biol, Carnegie Inst Washington, 75-78; ASST PROF, DEPT BIOL, UNIV CALIF, DAVIS, 78- *Mem:* Am Soc Photobiol; Am Soc Plant Physiologists. *Res:* Primary photochemical events of photosynthesis. *Mailing Add:* 2815 Danube Ave Davis CA 95616

STEMMER, EDWARD ALAN, b Cincinnati, Ohio, Jan 20, 30; m 54; c 5. THORACIC SURGERY. *Educ:* Univ Chicago, BA, 49, MD, 53; Am Bd Surg, dipl, 62; Am Bd Thoracic Surg, dipl, 63. *Prof Exp:* Intern med, Univ Chicago Clins, 53-54, res asst surg, Sch Med, 54-55, from asst resident to sr resident, 54-60, instr, 59-60; chief resident, Stanford Univ, 60-61, clin teaching asst, 61; chief resident, Palo Alto Vet Admin Hosp, 61-62, asst chief surg serv, 62-64; asst prof surg, Univ Utah, 64-65; asst prof in residence, 66-70, assoc prof, 70-76, PROF SURG, UNIV CALIF, IRVINE, 76-; CHIEF SURG SERV, LONG BEACH VET ADMIN HOSP, 65- *Concurrent Pos:* Responsible investr, Vet Admin Hosp, 62-; attend surgeon, Salt Lake County Hosp, Utah, 64-65; prin investr, NIH, 64-70. *Mem:* Fel Am Col Surg; Am Asn Thoracic Surg; Am Col Chest Physicians; Soc Thoracic Surg; Am Surg Asn. *Res:* Vascular surgery; metabolism of plasma proteins; myocardial functions; control of regional blood flow. *Mailing Add:* Long Beach Vet Admin Hosp 5901 E Seventh St Long Beach CA 90801

STEMMERMANN, GRANT N, b Bronx, NY, Oct 28, 18; m 44, 77; c 4. PATHOLOGY. *Educ:* Trinity Col, Conn, 35-37; McGill Univ, MD, 43. *Prof Exp:* Lab dir path, Hilo Hosp, Hawaii, 51-58; LAB DIR PATH, KUAKINI HOSP, 58-; CLIN PROF PATH, SCH MED, UNIV HAWAII, MANOA, 66- *Concurrent Pos:* Prin investr, Honolulu Heart Study. *Mem:* AAAS; Col Am Path; Am Asn Path & Bact; Am Soc Clin Path; Int Acad Path. *Res:* Geographic pathology, particularly neoplastic and cardiovascular diseases in migrants; biology of elastic tissue and disease patterns in the feral mongoose. *Mailing Add:* Kuakini Hosp 347 N Kuakini St Honolulu HI 96817

STEMNISKI, JOHN ROMAN, b Nanticoke, Pa, Apr 29, 33; m 59; c 3. ORGANIC CHEMISTRY. *Educ:* Fordham Univ, BS, 55; Carnegie Inst Technol, MS, 59, PhD(org chem), 60. *Prof Exp:* Res chemist, Monsanto Res Corp, 59-65; staff chemist, 65-69, prin chemist polymer prod, 69-73, CHIEF MAT & PROCESS CONTROL LAB, C S DRAPER LAB, MASS INST TECHNOL, 73- *Mem:* Am Chem Soc; Royal Soc Chem; Am Soc Testing and Mat. *Res:* Synthesis of medicinal compounds; synthesis of oil additives; lubricant systems; oxidation mechanism; high density fluids; gel permeation chromatography; fluorine containing fluids, materials science studies. *Mailing Add:* C S Draper Lab 555 Technology Sq Cambridge MA 02139

STEMPAK, JEROME G, b Chicago, Ill, Dec 24, 31; m 61; c 1. ANATOMY. *Educ:* Roosevelt Univ, BS, 58; Univ Ill, MS, 60, PhD(teratology), 62. *Prof Exp:* Instr, 63-66, asst prof, 66-77, ASSOC PROF ANAT, STATE UNIV NY DOWNSTATE MED CTR, 77- *Concurrent Pos:* USPHS fel, 62-63. *Mem:* AAAS; Am Asn Anat; Am Soc Cell Biol. *Res:* Electron microscopy of differentiating cells and tissues; electron microscopic and biochemical investigations on generation of cell organelles. *Mailing Add:* Dept of Anat State Univ NY Downstate Med Ctr Brooklyn NY 11203

STEMPEL, ARTHUR, b Brooklyn, NY, June 8, 17; m 50; c 2. CHEMISTRY. *Educ:* City Col New York, BS, 37; Columbia Univ, MA, 39. PhD(chem), 42. *Prof Exp:* Asst, Col Physicians & Surgeons, Columbia Univ, 38-39, org chem, Col Pharm, 40-41, res assoc, Chem Labs, 42-43; tutor & fel chem, Queens Col, 41-42; sr chemist, 43-68, res group chief, 68-79, SR RES GROUP CHIEF, CHEM RES DEPT, HOFFMANN-LA ROCHE, INC, 79- *Mem:* Am Chem Soc; NY Acad Sci. *Res:* Isolation of natural products of animal and plant origin; antibiotics; organic synthesis of pharmaceuticals; investigations on loco weeds; synthesis of benzodiazepines; cholinesterase inhibitors; anticurare compounds. *Mailing Add:* Chem Res Dept Hoffman-La Roche Inc 340 Kingsland St Nutley NJ 07110

STEMPEL, EDWARD, b Brooklyn, NY, Mar 7, 26; m 59; c 1. PHARMACY. *Educ:* Brooklyn Col Pharm, BS, 49; Columbia Univ, MS, 52, MA, 55, EdD, 56. *Prof Exp:* From instr to assoc prof, 49-64, prof pharm & chmn dept, 64-79, ASSOC DEAN, ARNOLD & MARIE SCHWARTZ COL PHARM & HEALTH SCI, 79- *Mem:* Am Pharmaceut Asn; Am Asn Col Pharm. *Res:* Dispensing pharmacy; long-acting dosage forms. *Mailing Add:* Arnold & Marie Schwartz Col 75 DeKalb Ave Brooklyn NY 11201

STEMPEN, HENRY, b Phila, Pa, May 10, 24; m 54; c 4. MICROBIOLOGY. *Educ:* Phila Col Pharm, BS, 45; Univ Pa, PhD(microbiol), 51. *Prof Exp:* Res asst cytol, Lankenau Hosp Res Inst, Phila, Pa, 45-46; from instr to asst prof bact, Jefferson Med Col, 50-57, assoc prof microbiol, 57-62; asst prof biol, 62-63, ASSOC PROF MICROBIOL, RUTGERS UNIV, CAMDEN, 63- *Concurrent Pos:* NIH grants, 59-60 & 64-66. *Mem:* AAAS; Am Soc Microbiol; Mycol Soc Am. *Res:* Bacterial cytology and genetics; morphogenesis of myxomycetes. *Mailing Add:* Dept of Biol Rutgers Univ 311 N Fifth St Camden NJ 08102

STEMPIEN, MARTIN F, JR, b New Britain, Conn, Sept 2, 30. BIOCHEMISTRY. *Educ:* Yale Univ, BS, 52, MS, 53, PhD(org chem), 57; Cambridge Univ, PhD(org chem), 60. *Prof Exp:* Res assoc & sr investr bio-org chem, 60-66, ASST TO DIR & BIO-ORG CHEMIST, OSBORN LABS, MARINE SCI, NY AQUARIUM, NY ZOOL SOC, 66- *Concurrent Pos:* Consult, Off Naval Res, 68; fel, NY Zool Soc, 68- *Mem:* AAAS; Am Chem Soc; NY Acad Sci; Am Soc Zool; The Chem Soc. *Res:* Physiologically active materials from extracts of marine invertebrates, particularly Porifera and Echinodermata; bio-chemical taxonomy of Phylum Porifera. *Mailing Add:* PO Box 481 Village Sta New York NY 10014

STEMPLE, JOEL G, b Brooklyn, NY, Feb 3, 42; m 68. MATHEMATICS. *Educ:* Brooklyn Col, BS, 62; Yale Univ, MA, 64, PhD, 66. *Prof Exp:* Asst prof math, 66-70, ASSOC PROF MATH, QUEEN'S COL, NY, 70- *Res:* Theory of graphs. *Mailing Add:* 46 Old Brook Rd Dix Hills NY 11746

STEMSHORN, BARRY WILLIAM, b Montreal, Que, Dec 15, 47; m 80. INFECTIOUS DISEASES, RESIDUE CHEMISTRY. *Educ:* McGill Univ, BSc, 69; Univ Montreal, DMV, 74; Univ Guelph, PhD(microbiol & immunol), 79. *Prof Exp:* Staff scientist, Animal Dis Res Inst, Ont, 75-81; DIR, ANIMAL PATH LAB, AGR CAN, 81- *Concurrent Pos:* Assoc grad fac mem, Dr Vet Sci prog, Dept Vet Microbiol & Immunol, Univ Guelph, 81- *Mem:* AAAS; Can Vet Med Asn; Asn Can Advan Sci. *Res:* Assays for chemical residues (pesticides, antibiotics, drugs, pollutants) in animal tissues; microbiological and serological methods for diagnosis of brucellosis and other bacterial diseases. *Mailing Add:* Animal Path Lab 116 Vet Rd Saskatoon SK S7N 2R3 Can

STENBACK, WAYNE ALBERT, b Brush, Colo, June 12, 29; m 54; c 1. MICROBIOLOGY, ELECTRON MICROSCOPY. *Educ:* Univ Colo, BS, 55; Univ Denver, MS, 57; Univ Mo, PhD(microbiol), 62. *Prof Exp:* Instr exp biol, 62-66, asst prof exp biol, Dept Surg, Baylor Col Med, 66-75; ELECTRON MICROSCOPIST, DEPT PATH, TEX CHILDREN'S HOSP, 75- *Concurrent Pos:* Mem, Int Asn Comp Res on Leukemia & Related Dis. *Mem:* AAAS; Am Soc Microbiol; Am Asn Cancer Res; Electron Micros Soc Am. *Res:* Density gradient studies of Newcastle disease virus; control of endemic microorganisms in mouse colonies; electron microscopy, biological and biophysical studies of viruses associated with neoplasms. *Mailing Add:* Dept of Path Tex Children's Hosp Houston TX 77025

STENBAEK-NIELSEN, HANS C, b Slagelse, Denmark. AURORAL PHYSICS. *Educ:* Tech Univ Denmark, MSc, 65. *Prof Exp:* PROF GEOPHYSICS, UNIV ALASKA, 67- *Mem:* Am Geophys Union. *Res:* Space and auroral physics; optical observations of auroras and in upper atmosphere chemical releases. *Mailing Add:* Geophys Inst Univ Alaska Fairbanks AK 99701

STENBERG, CHARLES GUSTAVE, b Chicago, Ill, Apr 11, 35; m 66. PHYSICS, COMPUTER SCIENCE. *Educ:* Univ Ill, Urbana, BS, 59, MS, 60, PhD(physics), 68. *Prof Exp:* PHYSICIST REACTOR PHYSICS, ARGONNE NAT LAB, 69- *Mem:* Am Nuclear Soc; Sigma Xi. *Res:* Method and code development of models and computer codes for reactor physics calculations. *Mailing Add:* Argonne Nat Lab 9700 S Cass Ave Argonne IL 60439

STENBERG, VIRGIL IRVIN, b Grygla, Minn, May 18, 35; m 56; c 4. ORGANIC CHEMISTRY. *Educ:* Concordia Col, Moorhead, Minn, BA, 56; Iowa State Univ, PhD(org chem), 60. *Prof Exp:* From asst prof to assoc prof, 60-67, PROF CHEM, UNIV NDAK, 67- *Concurrent Pos:* Res grants, Res Corp, 60-62, Petrol Res Fund, 61-63, NIH, 61-64, 68-71 & 74-76, career develop award, 70-75; NSF res grant, 66-68; vis prof, Imp Col, Univ London, 71-72; Energy Res Develop Admin contract, 75-78 & Dept Energy contract, 78-82. *Mem:* Am Chem Soc; Sigma Xi; AAAS. *Res:* Natural products, synthesis and coal conversion; catalyst development; medicinal chemistry of inflammation; lignite chemistry. *Mailing Add:* Dept of Chem Univ of NDak Grand Forks ND 58201

STENCEL, ROBERT EDWARD, b Wausau, Wis, Apr 16, 50; m 77. ASTRONOMY, SPECTROSCOPY. *Educ:* Univ Wis-Madison, BS, 72; Univ Mich, Ann Arbor, MS, 74, PhD(astron), 77. *Prof Exp:* Res asst solar physics, Sacramento Peak Observ, 75; res assoc astron, NASA Johnson Space Ctr, 77-78; res assoc astron, Nat Acad Sci & NASA, Goddard Space Flight Ctr, 78-80; MEM FAC, UNIV COLO, BOULDER, 80- *Concurrent Pos:* Res assoc, Nat Res Coun/Nat Acad Sci, 77-; mem adv coun, Archeoastron Ctr, Univ Md, 78-; NSF & NASA grants. *Mem:* Am Phys Soc; Am Astron Soc. *Res:* High resolution spectroscopy of the outer atmospheres of low temperature supergiant stars; radiative transfer studies. *Mailing Add:* JI1A Univ Colo Boulder CO 80301

STENCHEVER, MORTON ALBERT, b Paterson, NJ, Jan 25, 31; m 55; c 3. REPRODUCTIVE BIOLOGY, HUMAN GENETICS. *Educ:* NY Univ, AB, 51; Univ Buffalo, MD, 56; Am Bd Obstet & Gynec, 65. *Prof Exp:* Intern med, Mt Sinai Hosp, NY, 56-57; resident, Columbia-Presby Med Ctr, 57-60; from instr to assoc prof obstet & gynec, Case Western Reserve Univ, 64-70, dir tissue cult lab, 64-70, assoc, Dept Med Educ, 68-70; prof obstet & gynec & chmn dept, Univ Utah, 70-77; PROF & CHMN, DEPT OBSTET & GYNEC, UNIV WASH, 77- *Concurrent Pos:* NIH res training fel genetics, 62-64; Oglebey res fel, Case Western Reserve Univ, 64; chief obstet & gynec serv, Malmstrom AFB Hosp, Mont. *Mem:* AAAS; AMA; fel Am Col Obstet & Gynec; fel Am Soc Obstet & Gynec; Soc Cryobiol. *Res:* Human and cell genetics; human reproduction. *Mailing Add:* Dept Obstet & Gynec Univ Wash Seattle WA 98195

STENDELL, REY CARL, b San Francisco, Calif, Aug 12, 41; m 66; c 2. POLLUTION BIOLOGY. *Educ:* Univ Calif, Santa Barbara, BA, 63, MA, 67; Univ Calif, Berkeley, PhD(zool), 72. *Prof Exp:* Res biologist, 72-73, res coordr, Patuxent Wildlife Res Ctr, 73-77, PROG COORDR POLLUTION BIOL, US FISH & WILDLIFE SERV, WASHINGTON DC, 77- *Mem:* Am Ornithologists Union; Cooper Ornithol Soc; Am Soc Mammalogists; Ecol Soc Am; Raptor Res Found. *Res:* Evaluation of the effects of environmental pollutants on wildlife, particularly birds. *Mailing Add:* US Fish & Wildlife Serv 18th & C Sts NW Washington DC 20240

STENE, JOHN K, b Kingston, RI, Apr 21, 17; m 43; c 3. MECHANICAL ENGINEERING. *Educ:* Univ RI, BS, 38; Purdue Univ, MS, 53, PhD, 60. *Prof Exp:* Teacher math & sci, Tarsus Am Col, 38-41; teacher mech eng, Robert Col, Istanbul, 41-44; instr, 48-60, ASSOC PROF MECH ENG, PURDUE UNIV, 60- *Mem:* Soc Automotive Engrs. *Res:* Thermodynamics; automotive engineering; heat transfer. *Mailing Add:* Sch of Mech Eng Purdue Univ West Lafayette IN 47907

STENESH, JOCHANAN, b Magdeburg, Ger, Dec 19, 27; US citizen; m 57. BIOCHEMISTRY. *Educ:* Univ Ore, BS, 53; Univ Calif, Berkeley, PhD(biochem), 58. *Prof Exp:* Res assoc biochem, Weizmann Inst, 58-60 & Purdue Univ, 60-63; from asst prof to assoc prof, 63-71, PROF CHEM, WESTERN MICH UNIV, 71- *Concurrent Pos:* Res grants, Nat Inst Allergy & Infectious Dis, 64-70, Am Cancer Soc, 65-67. *Mem:* AAAS; Am Chem Soc; Am Asn Biol Chemists; Am Soc Microbiol. *Res:* Physical biochemistry; enzymology; ribosomes and protein synthesis; molecular biology of proteins and nucleic acids. *Mailing Add:* Dept of Chem Western Mich Univ Kalamazoo MI 49008

STENGEL, ROBERT FRANK, b Orange, NJ, Sept 1, 38; m 61; c 2. AEROSPACE ENGINEERING, MECHANICAL ENGINEERING. *Educ:* Mass Inst Technol, BS, 60; Princeton Univ, MSE, 65, MA, 66, PhD(aerospace & mech sci), 68. *Prof Exp:* Aerospace technologist rockets, NASA, 60-63; mem tech staff & group leader guid & control, Draper Lab, Mass Inst Technol, 68-73; mem tech staff & sect leader, Anal Sci Corp, 73-77; ASSOC PROF MECH & AEROSPACE ENG, PRINCETON UNIV, 77- *Concurrent Pos:* Mem, Aerospace Guid & Control Systs Comt, Soc Advan Educ; mem, Simulation Tech Comt, Am Inst Aeronauts & Astronauts. *Mem:* Assoc fel Am Inst Aeronaut & Astronaut; Inst Elec & Electronics Engrs. *Res:* Atmospheric flight mechanics; guidance and control; space flight engineering; human factors; digital control systems. *Mailing Add:* Princeton Univ Flight Res Lab Forrestal Campus Princeton NJ 08540

STENGER, FRANK, b Veszprem, Hungary, July 6, 38; m 61; c 2. APPLIED MATHEMATICS. *Educ:* Univ Alta, BSc, 61, MSc, 63, PhD(math), 65. *Prof Exp:* Guest worker, Nat Bur Stand, Washington, DC, 63-64; asst prof comp sci, Univ Alta, 65-66; asst prof math, Univ Mich, 66-69; assoc prof, 69-73, PROF MATH, UNIV UTAH, 74- *Concurrent Pos:* NSF grant, Univ Utah, 70-71 & 76-78; vis math res ctr, Univ Montreal, 71-72; US Army res grant, Univ Utah, 74-76 & 77-80. *Mem:* Am Math Soc; Can Math Cong; Soc Indust & Appl Math; Asn Comput Mach. *Res:* Quadrature; numerical solution of differential and integral equations; asymptotic approximation of integrals; asymptotic solution of differential equations. *Mailing Add:* Dept of Math Univ of Utah Salt Lake City UT 84112

STENGER, RICHARD J, b Cincinnati, Ohio, Dec 13, 27; m 51; c 2. PATHOLOGY, ELECTRON MICROSCOPY. *Educ:* Col of the Holy Cross, AB, 49; Univ Cincinnati, MD, 53. *Prof Exp:* Intern, Cincinnati Gen Hosp, 53-54, resident path, Mass Gen Hosp, 54-55, 57-58, fel 58-59, asst, 59-60; asst prof, Col Med, Univ Cincinnati, 60-64; from asst prof to assoc prof path, Case Western Reserve Univ, 64-68; prof, New York Med Col, 68-72; PROF PATH, MT SINAI SCH MED, 72-; DIR PATH & LABS, BETH ISRAEL MED CTR, 72- *Concurrent Pos:* Chief, Lab Serv, W Point Army Hosp, 55-57; Nat Inst Arthritis & Metab Dis res grant & Nat Inst Gen Med Sci career develop award, 64-68; instr, Harvard Med Sch, 59-60; attend pathologist, Cincinnati Gen Hosp, 60-64; assoc pathologist, Cleveland Metrop Gen Hosp, 64-68; attend pathologist, Flower & Fifth Ave Hosps, NY & vis pathologist, Metrop Hosp Ctr, NY, 68-72. *Mem:* AAAS; Am Asn Path; Am Asn Study Liver Dis. Int Acad Path. *Res:* Light and electron microscopic studies of the liver, especially with regards to toxic effects. *Mailing Add:* Beth Israel Med Ctr New York NY 10003

STENGER, VERNON ARTHUR, b Minneapolis, Minn, June 11, 08; m 33; c 5. ANALYTICAL CHEMISTRY. *Educ:* Univ Denver, BS, 29, MS, 30; Univ Minn, PhD(anal chem), 33. *Hon Degrees:* DSc, Univ Denver, 71. *Prof Exp:* Asst, Eastman Kodak Co, 29-30; anal chemist, Univ Minn, 33-35; anal res chemist, 35-53, dir spec serv lab, 53-61, anal scientist, 61-73, CONSULT, DOW CHEM CO, 73- *Honors & Awards:* Anachem Award, 70. *Mem:* Am Chem Soc; Sigma Xi; Geochem Soc; fel NY Acad Sci; fel Am Inst Chem. *Res:* Purity of reagents; technology of bromine and its compounds; instrumentation for water analysis; analytical methods for environmental analysis. *Mailing Add:* 1108 E Park Dr Midland MI 48640

STENGER, VICTOR JOHN, b Bayonne, NJ, Jan 29, 35; m 62; c 2. PHYSICS. *Educ:* Newark Col Eng, BS, 56; Univ Calif, Los Angeles, MS, 58, PhD(physics), 63. *Prof Exp:* Mem tech staff, Hughes Aircraft Co, 56-59; asst physics, Univ Calif, Los Angeles, 59-63; assoc prof, 63-74, PROF PHYSICS & ASTRON, UNIV HAWAII, 74- *Mem:* Am Phys Soc. *Res:* Elementary physics. *Mailing Add:* Dept of Physics Univ of Hawaii Honolulu HI 96822

STENGER, WILLIAM, b Bayonne, NJ, Jan 25, 42; m 68; c 2. MATHEMATICS. *Educ:* Stevens Inst Technol, BS, 63; Univ Md, PhD(math), 67. *Prof Exp:* Asst comput, Davidson Lab, Stevens Inst Technol, 62-63; res asst, Univ Md, 66-67; asst prof math, American Univ, 67-68 & Georgetown Univ, 68-69; asst prof, 69-72, PROF MATH, AMBASSADOR COL, 72- *Concurrent Pos:* Res grants, Air Force Off Sci Res, 67-68 & NSF, 68-69. *Mem:* Math Asn Am; Am Math Soc; Soc Indust Appl Math. *Res:* Variational theory of eigenvalues and related inequalities. *Mailing Add:* Dept of Math Ambassador Col 300 W Green St Pasadena CA 91123

STENGER, WILLIAM J(AMES), SR, b Wheeling, WVa, May 9, 26; m 51; c 8. CHEMICAL ENGINEERING. *Educ:* WVa Univ, BSChE, 50, MSChE, 51, PhD(chem eng), 53. *Prof Exp:* Res chem engr, Burnside Lab, 53-57, Eastern Lab, 57, Repauno Process Lab, 58, Elchem Res Lab, 59, Carney's Point Develop Lab, 59-61, Eastern Lab, 61, Repauno Develop Lab, 62-67 & Eastern Lab, 67-72, ASST TECH SUPT, POLYMER INTERMEDIATES, CAPE FEAR PLANT, E I DU PONT DE NEMOURS & CO, INC, 72- *Mem:* Am Chem Soc; Am Inst Chem Engrs. *Res:* Heat transfer; fluidization; coal gasification; nitrocellulose; amino acid synthesis; resolution of optical isomers; crystallization; cellulose and starch derivatives; propellant chemicals; hydrocarbon oxidation; polymer intermediates. *Mailing Add:* 2210 Marlwood Dr Wilmington NC 28401

STENGLE, JAMES MARSHALL, b Wilkinsburg, Pa, Aug 7, 17. INTERNAL MEDICINE, HEMATOLOGY. *Educ:* Oberlin Col, AB, 42; Northwestern Univ, MD, 46. *Prof Exp:* From intern to resident, Evanston Hosp, Ill, 45-49; clin investr, Nat Microbiol Inst, 53-55; sr investr, Nat Cancer Inst, 55-59, exec secy hemat study sect, Div Res Grants, NIH, 59-61, chief, Training Grants & Fels Br, Nat Heart & Lung Inst, 61-63, chief, Off Prog Planning & Eval, Extramural progs, 63-67, chief nat blood resource prog, 67-74, dep dir med affairs, Lister Hill Nat Ctr Biomed Commun, Nat Libr Med, 74-77, CHIEF THROMBOSIS & HEMORRHAGIC DIS, NAT HEART & LUNG INST, 68- *Concurrent Pos:* Fel hemat, Cook County Hosp, Chicago, 49-50; Nuffield fel, Oxford Univ, 51-52; chmn blood prog med adv comt, Am Red Cross, 65-66; mem task force intravascular thrombosis, Nat Res Coun, 65-66; mem exec comt, Coun Thrombosis, Am Heart Asn, 72-; chmn med & sci adv comt, Nat Hemophilia Found, 73- *Mem:* Am Soc Hemat; Int Soc Thrombosis & Haemostasis (secy & treas, 70-76); Int Soc Hemat. *Res:* Clinical and laboratory hematology. *Mailing Add:* Nat Heart & Lung Inst NIH Bethesda MD 20014

STENGLE, THOMAS RICHARD, b Lancaster, Pa, Nov 25, 29. PHYSICAL CHEMISTRY. *Educ:* Franklin & Marshall Col, BS, 51; Univ Mich, MS, 53, PhD(chem), 61. *Prof Exp:* From instr to assoc prof, 59-73, PROF CHEM, UNIV MASS, AMHERST, 73- *Mem:* Am Chem Soc; Am Phys Soc. *Res:* Application of nuclear magnetic resonance techniques to fast reactions, inorganic reaction mechanisms, molecular biology and solute-solvent interactions. *Mailing Add:* Dept of Chem Univ of Mass Amherst MA 01003

STENGLE, WILLIAM BERNARD, b Lancaster, Pa, Feb 21, 23; m 48; c 3. WOOD CHEMISTRY. *Educ:* Franklin & Marshall Col, BS, 43; State Univ NY Col Forestry, Syracuse, MS, 49. *Prof Exp:* Chemist, Animal Trap Co Am, 47; asst, State Univ NY Col Forestry, Syracuse, 49; res chemist, Crossett Co, Ark, 49-58, asst tech serv dir, Paper Mill Div, 58-62; TECH DIR, TENN RIVER PULP & PAPER CO, COUNCE, 62- *Concurrent Pos:* Mem, Tenn Air Pollution Control Bd, 76-80. *Mem:* Am Chem Soc; Tech Asn Pulp & Paper Indust; Air Pollution Control Asn. *Res:* Hydroxy acids; alkaline pulping; bleaching; paper manufacture; tall oil; corrugated paperboard; water and air pollution abatement. *Mailing Add:* 1109 Cypress St Savannah TN 38372

STENKAMP, RONALD EUGENE, b Bend, Ore, May 14, 48; m 70. BIOINORGANIC CHEMISTRY, CRYSTALLOGRAPHY. *Educ:* Univ Ore, BA, 70; Univ Wash, MSc, 71, PhD(chem), 75. *Prof Exp:* Fel crystallog, Dept Molecular Biophys & Biochem, Yale Univ, 75-76; Am Cancer Soc fel, Dept Molecular Biophys & Biochem, Yale Univ & Dept Biol Struct, Univ Wash, 77; RES ASSOC CRYSTALLOG, DEPT BIOL STRUCT, UNIV WASH, 78- *Mem:* Am Crystallog Asn; Am Chem Soc; AAAS. *Res:* Crystallographic studies of molecules of biological interest, including metallo proteins, cellular recognition proteins, enzymes and nucleic acids. *Mailing Add:* Dept Biol Struct Univ Wash SM-20 Seattle WA 98195

STENSAAS, LARRY J, b Nov 13, 32; US citizen; m 62; c 1. NEUROANATOMY. *Educ:* Univ Calif, Berkeley, BA, 55, MA, 57; Univ Calif, Los Angeles, PhD(neuroanat), 65. *Prof Exp:* Stratigrapher, Richmond of Columbia, 57-58; head paleont sect, Cuba Calif Oil Co, 58-59; micropaleontologist, Standard of Calif, 59-60; asst prof, 68-72, ASSOC PROF PHYSIOL & ANAT, UNIV UTAH, 72- *Concurrent Pos:* Cerebral Palsy Educ & Res Found fel, 65-67; NIH fel, 67-68. *Mem:* AAAS; Am Asn Anat; Soc Neurosci. *Res:* Light and electron microscopy of normal and regenerating central nervous tissue. *Mailing Add:* 4C202 Univ Med Ctr Univ of Utah Salt Lake City UT 84112

STENSAAS, SUZANNE SPERLING, b Oakland, Calif, Mar 15, 39; m 62; c 1. NEUROANATOMY. *Educ:* Pomona Col, BA, 59; Univ Calif, Los Angeles, MA, 62; Univ Utah, PhD(anat), 75. *Prof Exp:* Instr, 71-75, ASST PROF ANAT, COL MED, UNIV UTAH, 76- *Mem:* Soc Neurosci; AAAS. *Res:* Biological compatability of materials with the brain; development of neuroprostheses; effects of electrical stimulation on the brain; problems of development and regeneration of the central nervous system. *Mailing Add:* Dept of Anat Col of Med Univ of Utah Salt Lake City UT 84132

STENSEL, HERMAN DAVID, sanitary & civil engineering, see previous edition

STENSETH, RAYMOND EUGENE, b Ludlow, SDak, Aug 5, 31; m 65; c 1. ORGANIC CHEMISTRY, PHARMACY. *Educ:* Univ Mich, BS, 53, MS, 57, PhD(pharmaceut chem), 61. *Prof Exp:* Sr res chemist, 60-68, RES SPECIALIST, MONSANTO CO, 68- *Mem:* Am Chem Soc; Sigma Xi. *Res:* Organic syntheses; nitrogen heterocycles; organophosphorus chemistry; food chemicals; pharmaceuticals; bacteriostats; fungistats; chemical processes. *Mailing Add:* Monsanto Co 800 N Lindbergh Blvd St Louis MO 63167

STENSRUD, HOWARD LEWIS, b Minneapolis, Minn, Nov 16, 36; m 60; c 2. GEOLOGY, GEOCHEMISTRY. *Educ:* Univ Minn, Minneapolis, BA, 58; Univ Wyo, MA, 63; Univ Wash, PhD(geol), 70. *Prof Exp:* Explor geologist, Humble oil & Ref Co, 60; asst prof geol, Univ Minn, Morris, 61-66; asst prof, 70-77, PROF GEOL, CALIF STATE UNIV, CHICO, 77- *Mem:* Geol Soc Am; Soc Mining Engrs. *Res:* Metamorphic petrology and Precambrian geology. *Mailing Add:* Dept of Geol & Phys Sci Calif State Univ Chico CA 95929

STENSTROM, MICHAEL KNUDSON, b Anderson, SC, Nov 28, 48; m 77. SANITARY ENGINEERING, ENVIRONMENTAL ENGINEERING. *Educ:* Clemson Univ, SC, BS, 71, MS, 72, PhD(environ systs eng), 76. *Prof Exp:* Instr environ eng, Clemson Univ, 75; res engr, Amoco Oil Co, Standard Oil, Ind, 75-77; asst prof, 77-81, ASSOC PROF ENVIRON ENG, UNIV CALIF, LOS ANGELES, 81- *Concurrent Pos:* Consult, Amoco Oil Co, 77-79, Exxon Res & Develop, 80, Nat Coun Pulp & Paper Indust, 79- & Sohio, 82- *Mem:* Am Soc Civil Engrs; Water Pollution Control Fedn; Asn Environ Eng Prof; Int Asn Water Pollution Res. *Res:* Wastewater and water treatment processes, including real time control of the activated sludge process, oxygen transfer and anaerobic treatment systems. *Mailing Add:* 7619 Boelter Hall Univ Calif Los Angeles CA 90024

STENSTROM, RICHARD CHARLES, b Elkhorn, Wis, June 19, 36; m 60; c 1. GEOLOGY. *Educ:* Beloit Col, BS, 58; Univ Chicago, MS, 62, PhD(geophys sci), 64. *Prof Exp:* Am Chem Soc res fel geophys sci, Univ Chicago, 64-65; from instr to assoc prof, 65-77, PROF GEOL, BELOIT COL, 77- *Mem:* Nat Asn Geol Teachers; fel Geol Soc Am; Asn Eng Geol; Geochem Soc; Am Geophys Union. *Res:* Diffusion rates through sediments; hydrologic effects of urbanization; environmental geology. *Mailing Add:* 2531 E Ridge Rd Beloit WI 53511

STENT, GUNTHER SIEGMUND, b Berlin, Ger, Mar 28, 24; nat US; m 51; c 1. MOLECULAR BIOLOGY, NEUROBIOLOGY. *Educ:* Univ Ill, PhD(phys chem), 48. *Prof Exp:* Asst chem, Univ Ill, 44-48; Nat Res Coun Merck fel biol, Calif Inst Technol, 48-50; Am Cancer Soc fel, Copenhagen & Pasteur Inst, Paris, 50-52; asst res biochemist & lectr bact, 52-56, assoc prof bact, 57-58, prof bact & virol, 59-63, PROF MOLECULAR BIOL, UNIV CALIF, BERKELEY, 63-, CHMN MOLECULAR BIOL & DIR, VIRUS LAB, 80- *Concurrent Pos:* Consult, Field Info Agencies Technol, 46-47; mem genetics study sect, NIH, 59-64; mem genetic biol panel, NSF, 65-69; external mem, Max Planck Inst Molecular Genetics, 67-; Guggenheim fel, Med Sch, Harvard Univ, 69-70; hon prof, Fac Sci, Univ Chile, 80. *Mem:* Am Acad Arts & Sci; Soc Neurosci. *Res:* Nervous control of behavior; developmental biology; philosophy of science. *Mailing Add:* Dept of Molecular Biol Univ of Calif Berkeley CA 94720

STENUF, THEODORE JOSEPH, b Vienna, Austria, Feb 27, 24; US citizen; m 53; c 2. CHEMICAL ENGINEERING. *Educ:* Syracuse Univ, BChE, 49, MChE, 51, PhD(chem eng), 53. *Prof Exp:* Res asst & assoc chem eng, Syracuse Univ, 59-53; res engr, E I du Pont de Nemours & Co, Inc, 53-59; corrosion engr, Esso Res & Eng, Standard Oil Co, NJ, 59-60; from asst to prof, 60-76, DISTINGUISHED TEACHING PROF PAPER SCI & ENG, COL ENVIRON SCI & FORESTRY, STATE UNIV NY, 77- *Mem:* Am Inst Chem Engrs; Am Chem Soc; Tech Asn Pulp & Paper Indust. *Res:* Fluid mechanics; heat transfer; mass transfer; paper sheet formation. *Mailing Add:* Col of Environ Sci & Forestry State Univ NY Syracuse NY 13210

STENZEL, KURT HODGSON, b Stamford, Conn, Nov 3, 32; m 57; c 3. NEPHROLOGY, MEDICINE. *Educ:* NY Univ, BA, 54; Cornell Univ, MD, 58. *Prof Exp:* Intern med & nephrology, Second Cornell Med Div, Bellevue Hosp, NY, 58-59, asst resident, 59-60, cardio-renal resident, 62-63; res fel, 63-64, from instr to assoc prof, 64-75, PROF MED & BIOCHEM, MED COL, CORNELL UNIV, 75- *Concurrent Pos:* NY Heart Asn res fel, 63-66 & investr, 66-70. *Mem:* Am Soc Biol Chemists; fel Am Col Physicians; Am Fedn Clin Res; Am Soc Artificial Internal Organs. *Res:* Dialysis; biomaterials; transplantation immunology; lymphocyte activation. *Mailing Add:* Cornell Univ Med Col 1300 York Ave New York NY 10021

STENZEL, WOLFRAM G, b Berlin, Ger, May 24, 19; nat US; m 43; c 1. PHYSICS. *Educ:* City Col New York, BS, 39, MS, 41. *Prof Exp:* Asst biochem, Warner Inst Therapeut Res, 42; res scientist phys chem, Nuodex Prod Co, Inc, 46-48; instr physics & math, Bloomfield Col, 48-51; physicist, B G Corp, 51-55; prin engr physics, Ford Instrument Co Div, 55-69, SR ENGR, SYSTS MGT DIV, SPERRY RAND CORP, 69- *Concurrent Pos:* Lectr, Adelphi Col, 57-69. *Mem:* Am Phys Soc. *Res:* Nuclear reactors and effects; mathematical physics; thermionics; traffic control; rocket trajectories. *Mailing Add:* Systs Mgt Div Sperry Rand Corp Great Neck NY 11020

STEPAN, ALFRED HENRY, b St Paul, Minn, Jan 2, 20; m 44; c 5. ORGANIC CHEMISTRY. *Educ:* Col St Thomas, BS, 42; Univ Nebr, MS, 45, PhD(org chem), 51. *Prof Exp:* Chemist, Tenn Eastman Corp, 44-46; sr chemist, Continental Oil Co, 48-56; sr res chemist, 56-60, supvr, 60-63, mgr, 63-81, CHEM SPECIALIST, MINN MINING & MFG CO, 81- *Mem:* Tech Asn Pulp & Paper Indust; Am Chem Soc. *Res:* Carbonless papers; dielectric paper; imaging systems involving dry silver. *Mailing Add:* 3M Co 3M Ctr Bldg 234-IE St Paul MN 55144

STEPANISHEN, PETER RICHARD, b Boston, Mass, Jan 20, 42; m 70. ACOUSTICS. *Educ:* Mich State Univ, BS, 63; Univ Conn, MS, 66; Pa State Univ, PhD(eng acoust), 69. *Prof Exp:* Sonar systs engr, Elec Boat Div, Gen Dynamics Corp, 63-66, sr systs engr, 66-70, res specialist acoust, 70-74; asst prof, 74-77, ASSOC PROF OCEAN ENG, UNIV RI, 77- *Concurrent Pos:* Acoust consult, Naval Underwater Systs Ctr, 75- & Raytheon Co, 76-; res grant prin investr, NIH, 76-82. *Honors & Awards:* A B Wood Medal & Prize, Inst Acoust, Eng, 77. *Mem:* Fel Acoust Soc Am; Sigma Xi; Inst Elec & Electronics Engrs. *Res:* Underwater acoustics; medical ultrasonics; mechanical vibrations and wave phenomena; system theory and signal analysis. *Mailing Add:* Dept Ocean Eng Univ RI Kingston RI 02881

STEPENUCK, STEPHEN JOSEPH, JR, b Salem, Mass, Oct 12, 37; m 68; c 3. ENVIRONMENTAL CHEMISTRY. *Educ:* Merrimack Col, BS, 59; Col of the Holy Cross, MS, 61; Univ NH, PhD(phys chem), 71. *Prof Exp:* Instr chem, Merrimack Col, 61-65; teaching fel, Univ NH, 66-68, instr, 69-70; asst prof, 70-73, assoc prof, 73-79, PROF CHEM, KEENE STATE COL, 79- *Concurrent Pos:* Consult, indust, environ chem & chem safety. *Mem:* Am Chem Soc; Sigma Xi. *Res:* Radiation chemistry; clinical and diagnostic analyses; environmental analyses; marine chemistry, occupational health. *Mailing Add:* Dept of Chem Keene State Col Keene NH 03431

STEPHAN, DAVID GEORGE, b Columbus, Ohio, Feb 8, 30; m 51; c 3. ENVIRONMENTAL & CHEMICAL ENGINEERING. *Educ:* Ohio State Univ, BChE & MSc, 52, PhD(chem eng), 55. *Prof Exp:* Res assoc heat transfer, Battelle Mem Inst, 52-55; technologist, Nat Lead Co Ohio, 55; chief air pollution control equip res, USPHS, 55-60, chief extramural res unit, Adv Waste Treatment Res Prog, 60-64, dep chief prog, 64-65, dep chief basic & appl sci br, 65-66; dir div res, Fed Water Pollution Control Admin, 66-68, asst comnr res & develop, Fed Water Qual Admin, 68-70; dir res prog mgt, 71-75, DIR INDUST ENVIRON RES LAB, ENVIRON PROTECTION AGENCY, 75- *Concurrent Pos:* Mem water reuse comt, Water Pollution Control Fedn, 64-71; mem water panel & spec consult comt pollution, Nat Acad Sci, 65; mem comt water resources res, Off Sci & Technol, 68-71; mem policy bd, Nat Ctr Toxicol Res, 72-74; mem governing bd, Int Asn Water Pollution Res, 74-; vchmn, USA Nat Comt Water Pollution Res, 74-80; adj prof chem eng, Univ Cincinnati, 76- *Mem:* Am Chem Soc; Am Inst Chem Engrs; Water Pollution Control Fedn; Am Acad Environ Engrs; Int Asn Water Pollution Res. *Res:* Heat transfer from vibrating plates; fabric air filtration; air pollution control equipment; advanced waste treatment; waste water renovation and reuse; water pollution control. *Mailing Add:* 6435 Stirrup Rd Cincinnati OH 45244

STEPHANAKIS, STAVROS JOHN, b Salonica, Greece, Apr 15, 40; US citizen; m 66; c 1. PHYSICS, ELECTRICAL ENGINEERING. *Educ:* NC State Univ, BS, 63, MEE, 65, PhD(elec eng), 69. *Prof Exp:* ELECTRONICS ENGR, US NAVAL RES LAB, 68- *Mem:* Am Phys Soc; Inst Elec & Electronics Engrs; Sigma Xi. *Res:* Study of hot, dense plasma discharges, x-ray and neutron emissions from such discharges; diagnostics. *Mailing Add:* 3187 Rolling Rd Edgewater MD 21037

STEPHANEDES, YORGOS JORDAN, b Athena, Greece, Sept 15, 51. SIMULATION & CONTROL DESIGN. *Educ:* Dartmouth Col, BA, 73, PhD(eng sci), 80; Carnegie-Mellon Univ, MS, 75. *Prof Exp:* Res asst, Carnegie-Mellon Univ, 73-74; teaching asst eng sci, Dartmouth Col, 75-78; ASST PROF CIVIL ENG, UNIV MINN, 78- *Concurrent Pos:* Res assoc, Oak Ridge Nat Labs, 75; consult, Hennepin County, 80; mem Transp Res Bd, Nat Acad Sci, 76-; prin investr, Univ Minn, 78- *Mem:* Inst Elec & Electronics Engrs; Am Soc Civil Engrs; Inst Transp Engrs; Int Asn Math & Comput Simulation. *Res:* Simulation, estimation and control design in engineering systems; demand-supply dynamics in transportation, energy and economic development; technology and resource policy impact analysis and assessment. *Mailing Add:* Dept Civil Eng Univ Minn Minneapolis MN 55455

STEPHANOPOULOS, GREGORY, b Kalamata, Greece, Mar 10, 50; m 73; c 1. BIOCHEMICAL ENGINEERING, CHEMICAL REACTION ENGINEERING. *Educ:* Nat Tech Univ, Athens, Bachelors, 73; Univ Fla, MS, 75; Univ Minn, PhD(chem eng), 78. *Prof Exp:* Res engr, Linde Div, Union Carbide Corp, 75; ASST PROF CHEM ENG, CALIF INST TECHNOL, 78- *Mem:* Am Inst Chem Engrs; Am Chem Soc. *Res:* Oscillations in simple reaction systems; behavior of mixed culture systems, as well as state estimation; control, dynamics and optimization of biochemical reactor. *Mailing Add:* Dept Chem Eng Calif Inst Technol Pasadena CA 91125

STEPHANOU, STEPHEN EMMANUEL, b Crete, Greece, Dec 29, 19; US citizen. RESEARCH MANAGEMENT, SYSTEMS ENGINEERING. *Educ:* Mass Inst Technol, SB, 42; Univ Kans, PhD(phys chem), 49. *Prof Exp:* Res tech physics, Mass Inst Technol, 41-42; anal chemist, Hercules Inc, 42-45; res scientist chem eng, Univ Kans Res Found, 46; staff mem phys chem, Los Alamos Sci Lab, 49-52; res scientist, E I du Pont de Nemours & Co, Inc, 52-56; pres, Newport Res Assoc, 56-58; res mgr, Ford Motor Co, 58-63; deputy br chief, N Am Rockwell, 63-66; br chief, McDonnell Douglas Corp, 66-69; assoc prof, 69-70, PROF, UNIV SOUTHERN CALIF, 70- *Concurrent Pos:* Lectr, Univ Southern Calif, 66-69. *Mem:* Acad Mgt; Inst Mgt Sci; Am Asn Univ Profs; Proj Mgt Inst. *Res:* Performing research on research and development management. *Mailing Add:* Inst of Safety & Syst Mgt Exposition Blvd Los Angeles CA 90007

STEPHANY, EDWARD O, b Rochester, NY, July 6, 16; m 41; c 1. MATHEMATICS, STATISTICS. *Educ:* Univ Rochester, AB, 37, AM, 38; Syracuse Univ, PhD(statist), 56. *Prof Exp:* Chmn, Dept Math, State Univ NY Col, Brockport, 47-77, prof math, 77-80. *Mem:* Math Asn Am; Am Math Soc. *Res:* Technique for comparing factors obtained through factor analysis; mathematics education. *Mailing Add:* 229 West Brockport NY 14420

STEPHAS, PAUL, b New York, NY, Aug 31, 29; m 59; c 1. PHYSICS. *Educ:* Univ Wash, Seattle, BS, 56; Rensselaer Polytech Inst, MS, 59; Univ Ore, PhD(physics), 66. *Prof Exp:* Asst res lab, Gen Elec Co, 56-58; metallurgist & ceramist, Vallecitos Atomic Lab, 58-62; asst prof physics, Univ BC, 66-69; PROF PHYSICS, EASTERN ORE STATE COL, 69- *Mem:* Am Phys Soc; Am Asn Physics Teachers; AAAS. *Res:* Atomic effects associated with beta decay; low energy nuclear physics; special relativistic mechanics. *Mailing Add:* Dept of Physics Eastern Ore State Col La Grande OR 97850

STEPHEN, CHARLES RONALD, b Montreal, Que, Mar 16, 16; nat US; m 41; c 3. ANESTHESIOLOGY. *Educ:* McGill Univ, BSc, 38, MD & CM, 40; Royal Col Surgeons, fel fac anesthetists, 64. *Prof Exp:* Chief dept anesthesia, Montreal Neurol Inst, 46-47; asst prof anesthesia, McGill Univ, 48-50; prof, Sch Med & chief div, Univ Hosp, Duke Univ, 50-66; prof, Univ Tex Southwest Med Sch Dallas, 66-71; MALLINCKRODT PROF ANESTHESIOL & CHMN DEPT, SCH MED, WASH UNIV, 71-; HEAD DEPT ANESTHESIA, BARNES HOSP, ST LOUIS, 71- *Concurrent Pos:* Chief dept anesthesia, Children's Mem Hosp, Montreal, 47-50; ed, Surv Anesthesiol, 56-; anesthesiologist, Parkland Mem Hosp, Dallas, 66-71; chief anesthesia, Children's Med Ctr, Dallas, 66-71. *Mem:* Am Soc Anesthesiol; Acad Anesthesiol; Inst Anesthesia Res Soc. *Res:* Pharmacology and physiology of clinical anesthesiology. *Mailing Add:* Dept of Anesthesiol Wash Univ Sch of Med St Louis MO 63110

STEPHEN, FREDERICK MALCOLM, JR, b Oakland, Calif, May 11, 43; m 64; c 2. FOREST ENTOMOLOGY, INSECT ECOLOGY. *Educ:* San Jose State Univ, BA, 67; Univ Calif, Berkeley, PhD(entom), 74. *Prof Exp:* Lab asst, San Jose State Univ, 66; asst, Univ Calif, Berkeley, 69-71, res asst, 67-74; asst prof, 74-78, ASSOC PROF ENTOM, UNIV ARK, 78- *Mem:* Entom Soc Am; Entom Soc Can; Soc Foresters. *Res:* Population ecology of forest insects. *Mailing Add:* Dept of Entom Univ Ark Fayetteville AR 72701

STEPHEN, KEITH H, b Ft Wayne, Ind, Jan 3, 34; m 59; c 2. INORGANIC CHEMISTRY. *Educ:* Wabash Col, BA, 59; Northwestern Univ, PhD(inorg chem), 65. *Prof Exp:* SR RES CHEMIST, EASTMAN KODAK CO, 64- *Mem:* Am Chem Soc; Soc Photog Scientists & Engrs. *Res:* Coordination compounds; electron transfer reactions; photographic chemistry. *Mailing Add:* Res Labs Kodak Park Rochester NY 14650

STEPHEN, MICHAEL JOHN, b Johannesburg, SAfrica, Apr 7, 33; m 66. PHYSICS. *Educ:* Univ Witwatersrand, BS, 52, MS, 54; Oxford Univ, PhD(phys chem), 56. *Prof Exp:* Ramsey fel, 56-58; res assoc chem, Columbia Univ, 58-60; Imp Chem Industs res fel math, Oxford Univ, 60-62; from asst prof to assoc prof, Yale Univ, 62-68; PROF PHYSICS, RUTGERS UNIV, 68- *Concurrent Pos:* Consult, Bell Tel Labs, 64-66; vis prof, Mass Inst Technol, 67-68. *Mem:* Am Phys Soc. *Res:* Low temperature, solid state and molecular physics. *Mailing Add:* Dept of Physics Busch Campus Rutgers Univ New Brunswick NJ 08903

STEPHEN, RALPH A, b Toronto, Ont, Feb, 18, 51; m 74; c 1. SEISMOLOGY. *Educ:* Univ Toronto, BASc, 74; Univ Cambridge, PhD(geophys), 78. *Prof Exp:* ASST SCIENTIST GEOPHYS, WOODS HOLE OCEANOG INST, 78- *Mem:* Royal Astron Soc; Am Geophys Union; Soc Explor Geophysicists. *Res:* Borehole seismic experiments in oceanic crust; seismic structure of oceanic crust and synthetic seismogram development. *Mailing Add:* PO Box 567 West Falmouth MA 02574

STEPHEN, WILLIAM PROCURONOFF, b St Boniface, Man, June 6, 27; nat US; m 52; c 4. ENTOMOLOGY. *Educ:* Univ Man, BSA, 48; Univ Kans, PhD, 52. *Prof Exp:* From asst entomologist to assoc entomologist, Sci Serv, Can Dept Agr, 48-53; from asst prof entom & asst entomologist to assoc prof entom & assoc entomologist, 53-63, PROF ENTOM, ORE STATE UNIV, 63- *Concurrent Pos:* Consult, Orgn Am States, Chile, 70-71 & Food & Agr Orgn, UN, Arg, 72; mem, Bee Res Inst. *Mem:* AAAS; Entom Soc Am; Animal Behav Soc; Soc Study Evolution; Soc Syst Zool. *Res:* Insect behavior; systematic zoology; development physiology; population genetics; pollination. *Mailing Add:* Dept of Entom Ore State Univ Corvallis OR 97331

STEPHENS, ARTHUR BROOKE, b Dinuba, Calif, July 6, 42; m 68. NUMERICAL ANALYSIS. *Educ:* Univ Colo, BA, 64; Univ Md, PhD(math), 69. *Prof Exp:* Asst prof math, Univ Hawaii, 69-71; asst prof, 73-77, ASSOC PROF MATH, MT ST MARY'S COL, 77- *Mem:* Am Math Soc; Math Asn Am. *Res:* Optimization problems in functional analysis; estimates for complex eigenvalues of positive matrices. *Mailing Add:* 25608 Jarl Dr Gaithersburg MD 20760

STEPHENS, BOBBY GENE, analytical chemistry, see previous edition

STEPHENS, CATHY LAMAR, b Gadsden, Ala. PHYSIOLOGY, IMMUNOLOGY. *Educ:* Univ NMex, BA, 63; Univ Calif, Los Angeles, PhD(physiol), 72. *Prof Exp:* Fel physiol, Univ Calif, Los Angeles, 72-76; asst res physiol, Immunol Br, Nat Cancer Inst, NIH, 76-81; MEM STAFF, WEST FLA CANCER RES FOUND, INC, 81- *Concurrent Pos:* NIH fel, Univ Calif, Los Angeles, 72-76. *Mem:* Soc Neurosci; AAAS; NY Acad Sci. *Res:* Cancer pharmacology; electrophysiological response of cells during immunological attack; membrane receptors; membrane biophysics. *Mailing Add:* WFla Cancer Res Found Inc 2266 La Vista St Pensacola FL 32504

STEPHENS, CHARLENE BARR, otolaryngology, deceased

STEPHENS, CHARLES ARTHUR LLOYD, JR, b Brooklyn, NY, Apr 4, 17; m 39, 64; c 2. INTERNAL MEDICINE. *Educ:* Cornell Univ, AB, 38, MD, 42; Am Bd Internal Med, dipl, 52. *Prof Exp:* DIR RES, SOUTHWESTERN CLIN & RES INST, INC, UNIV ARIZ, 46-, PRES, 71-, ASSOC PROF INTERNAL MED, COL MED, 70-, ADJ PROF MICROBIOL, 80- *Concurrent Pos:* Sr consult, Tucson Med Ctr, St Joseph's & Palo Verde Hosps, Ariz; pvt pract; chmn med adv comt, Southern Chap, Am Red Cross; mem bd dirs & pres, Southwest Chap, Arthritis Found; adj prof microbiol, Univ Ariz, 76- *Mem:* AMA; fel Am Col Physicians; Am Rheumatism Asn; NY Acad Sci; Am Heart Asn. *Res:* Tissue culture research in rheumatic diseases. *Mailing Add:* Holbrook-Hill Med Group 5100 E Grant Rd Tucson AZ 85712

STEPHENS, CHRISTINE TAYLOR, b Rochester, NY, July 30, 51; m 74; c 1. PLANT PATHOLOGY. *Educ:* Smith Col, AB, 73; Ohio State Univ, MA, 76, PhD(plant path), 78. *Prof Exp:* Res asst veg, Cornell Univ, 74; res asst ornamental crops, Ohio State Univ, 74-78; ASST PROF ORNAMENTALS & VEG CROPS, MICH STATE UNIV, EAST LANSING, 78- *Mem:* Am Phytopath Soc. *Res:* Damping off and root rots diseases caused by soil borne fungi; ecological and epidemiological studies; characterization and control of rhizoctonia solan. *Mailing Add:* Dept of Bot and Plant Path Mich State Univ East Lansing MI 48824

STEPHENS, CLARENCE FRANCIS, b Gaffney, SC, July 24, 17; m 42; c 2. MATHEMATICS. *Educ:* J C Smith Univ, BS, 38; Univ Mich, MS, 39, PhD(math), 43. *Hon Degrees:* DSc, J C Smith Univ, 54. *Prof Exp:* Instr math, Prairie View Col, 40-42, prof, 46-47; prof & head dept, Morgan State Col, 47-62; prof, State Univ NY Col Geneseo, 62-69; PROF MATH & CHMN DEPT, STATE UNIV NY COL POTSDAM, 69- *Concurrent Pos:* Ford fel & mem, Inst Advan Study, 53-54. *Mem:* Assoc Am Math Soc; assoc Math Asn Am. *Res:* Non-linear difference equations analytic in a parameter. *Mailing Add:* 81 Pierrepont Ave Potsdam NY 13676

STEPHENS, DALE NELSON, b Los Angeles, Calif, Dec 20, 41; m 64; c 2. ORGANIC CHEMISTRY. *Educ:* Westmont Col, BA, 63; Univ Ariz, PhD(org chem), 67. *Prof Exp:* Res chemist, Corn Prod Co, 67-68; asst prof, 68-71, assoc prof, 71-77, PROF CHEM, BETHEL COL, MINN, 77- *Mem:* AAAS; Am Chem Soc. *Res:* Urethanes; epoxies; natural product synthesis; x-ray crystallography; organic synthesis. *Mailing Add:* Dept of Phys Sci Bethel Col Arden Hills MN 55113

STEPHENS, DOUGLAS ROBERT, b Portland, Ore, May 10, 35; m 61; c 2. CHEMICAL ENGINEERING, MATERIALS SCIENCE. *Educ:* Univ Wash, BS, 57; Univ Ill, MS, 59, PhD(chem eng), 61. *Prof Exp:* PROJ LEADER, LAWRENCE LIVERMORE LAB, 61- *Mem:* Am Inst Chem Engrs; Am Chem Soc; Am Nuclear Soc. *Res:* Experimental high pressure equation of state and phase transformation measurements; electrical properties of solids at high pressures; in-situ chemical processing. *Mailing Add:* Lawrence Livermore Lab PO Box 808 L-367 Livermore CA 94550

STEPHENS, EDGAR RAY, b Detroit, Mich, Aug 26, 24; m 66. PHYSICAL CHEMISTRY. *Educ:* Carnegie Inst Technol, BS, 45; Princeton Univ, MS, 49, PhD(chem), 51. *Prof Exp:* Res chemist, Shawinigan Resins Corp, 45-47; asst phys chem, Princeton Univ, 47-50; res chemist, Franklin Inst, 50-59 & Scott Res Labs, Inc, 59-63; lectr plant path, 63-71, RES CHEMIST, UNIV CALIF, RIVERSIDE, 63-, PROF ENVIRON SCI, 71- *Mem:* AAAS; Am Chem Soc; Air Pollution Control Asn. *Res:* Chemical kinetics; air pollution; photochemistry. *Mailing Add:* Air Pollution Res Ctr Univ of Calif Riverside CA 92521

STEPHENS, FRANK SAMUEL, b Ind, June 30, 31; m 59. NUCLEAR CHEMISTRY. *Educ:* Oberlin Col, AB, 52; Univ Calif, PhD(chem), 55. *Prof Exp:* RES CHEMIST, LAWRENCE RADIATION LAB, UNIV CALIF, BERKELEY, 55- *Concurrent Pos:* Ford Found grant, Inst Theoret Physics, Copenhagen, Denmark, 59-60; guest prof, Physics Sect, Univ Munich, 70-71. *Mem:* Am Phys Soc. *Res:* Coulomb excitation; nuclear structure; heavy ion physics. *Mailing Add:* Lawrence Radiation Lab Univ of Calif Berkeley CA 94704

STEPHENS, GEORGE ROBERT, b Springfield, Mass, Nov, 10, 29; c 7. FOREST ECOLOGY, FOREST-INSECT RELATIONS. *Educ:* Univ Mass, BS, 52; Yale Sch Forestry, Yale Univ, MF, 58, PhD(forestry), 61. *Prof Exp:* Asst forester, 61-65, assoc forester, 65-75, forester, 75-79, CHIEF FORESTER, CONN AGR EXP STA, 80- *Concurrent Pos:* Secy, Conn Tree Protection Exam Bd, 61-78, mem, 79- *Mem:* Soc Am Foresters. *Res:* Natural succession in forest; effects of insects on tree mortality; forest management. *Mailing Add:* Dept Forestry & Hort Conn Agr Exp Sta PO Box 1106 New Haven CT 06504

STEPHENS, GREGORY A, b Salina, Kans, Dec 20, 47. CARDIOVASCULAR PHYSIOLOGY, RENAL PHYSIOLOGY. *Educ:* Univ Kans, BA, 69, PhD(physiol & cell biol), 76. *Prof Exp:* Res fel, Dept Physiol, Sch Med, Univ Mo, 75-78; ASST PROF PHYSIOL, SCH LIFE & HEALTH SCI, UNIV DEL, 78- *Concurrent Pos:* Mem, Am Heart Asn. *Mem:* Am Physiol Soc; Am Soc Zoologists. *Res:* Control and functions of the renin angiotensin system in nonmammalian vertebrates. *Mailing Add:* Sch Life & Health Sci Univ Del Newark DE 19711

STEPHENS, GROVER CLEVELAND, b Oak Park, Ill, Jan 12, 25; m 49; c 3. ZOOLOGY. *Educ:* Northwestern Univ, BS, 48, MA, 49, PHD(biol), 52. *Prof Exp:* Asst philos, Northwestern Univ, 48-49, asst zool, 49 51; instr biol, Brooklyn Col, 52-53; asst zool, Univ Minn, Minneapolis, 53-55, from asst prof to prof, 55-64; prof organismic biol, 64-69, chmn dept organismic biol, 64-69, PROF DEVELOP & CELL BIOL, UNIV CALIF, IRVINE, 69- *Concurrent Pos:* Mem corp, Marine Biol Lab, Woods Hole, 53-, instr, 53-60, in-charge invert zool, 58-60; NSF sr fel, 59-60; NATO sr fel, 74. *Mem:* AAAS; Am Physiol Soc; Mar Biol Asn, UK; Am Soc Zool; Am Soc Limnol & Oceanog. *Res:* Invertebrate physiology; biological rhythms; feeding mechanisms in invertebrates; algal physiology; amino acid transport. *Mailing Add:* Dept of Develop & Cell Biol Univ of Calif Irvine CA 92717

STEPHENS, GWEN JONES, b Sioux Falls, SDak, May 5, 24; m 49; c 3. BIOLOGY, MEDICAL SCIENCES. *Educ:* Northwestern Univ, BS, 47, MS, 48, PhD(biol), 51. *Prof Exp:* Res assoc physiol, Sch Med, Univ Minn, 54-57, instr, 60-62; res assoc psychobiol, Univ Calif, Irvine, 66-70; ASSOC PROF, UNIV COLO HEALTH SCI CTR, 71- *Concurrent Pos:* Fel pathophysiol, Sch Med, Univ Minn, 64; educ sabbatical, Univ Calif, Davis, 80- *Mem:* AAAS. *Res:* Invertebrate photo-neuroendocrinol function; vertebrate physiologic periodicity; vertebrate and invertebrate learning and memory; author of textbook of pathophysiology for the health sciences. *Mailing Add:* 751 North Campus Way Davis CA 95616

STEPHENS, HAROLD W, b Trenton, NJ, Mar 16, 19; m 46; c 1. MATHEMATICS. *Educ:* Trenton State Col, BS, 41; Columbia Univ, MA, 44, EdD, 64. *Prof Exp:* Head dept math, Farragut Naval Acad, 44-46; instr, Univ Fla, 46-48, Univ Md, 48-49 & McCoy Col, Johns Hopkins Univ, 49-50; asst prof, Ball State Univ, 52-55 & Univ Tenn, 55-60; assoc prof, 60-64, PROF MATH, MEMPHIS STATE UNIV, 64- *Concurrent Pos:* Lectr, NSF insts & workshops, Univ Tenn, Memphis State, Murray State Univ, Univ Amc, Austin Peay State Univ & Southwestern at Memphis, 57- *Mem:* Math Asn Am; Am Math Soc. *Res:* Mathematics courses for teacher training; algebra. *Mailing Add:* Dept of Math Memphis State Univ Memphis TN 38152

STEPHENS, HOWARD L, b Akron, Ohio, Oct 9, 19; m 45; c 1. POLYMER CHEMISTRY. *Educ:* Univ Akron, BS, 49, MS, 50, PhD(polymer chem), 60. *Prof Exp:* Res chemist, Rubber Res Labs, 49-52, Inst Rubber Chem, 53-56 & Inst Rubber Res, 56-57, admin asst, 57-65, from instr to assoc prof chem, 57-73, mgr appl res, Inst Polymer Sci, 66-81, PROF CHEM & POLYMER SCI, UNIV AKRON, 73-, HEAD DEPT POLYMER SCI, 78- *Mem:* Am Chem Soc. *Res:* Polymer oxidation; preparation and structure of graft polymers; emulsion polymerization; vulcanization. *Mailing Add:* Dept Polymer Sci Univ Akron Akron OH 44325

STEPHENS, JACK E(DWARD), b Eaton, Ohio, Aug 17, 23; m 48; c 4. CIVIL ENGINEERING. *Educ:* Univ Conn, BS, 47; Purdue Univ, MS, 55, PhD(civil eng), 59. *Prof Exp:* Mem, Mat Sci Inst, 48-50, from asst prof to assoc prof civil eng, 50-62, head dept, 65-72, PROF CIVIL ENG, UNIV CONN, 62- *Concurrent Pos:* Jr engr, State Hwy Dept, Conn, 48-50, consult, 64-66; owner, Jack E Stephens Soil Lab, 58-; mem comts, Hwy Res Bd, Nat Acad Sci-Nat Res Coun. *Honors & Awards:* H Jackson Tibbet Award, Am Soc Civil Engrs, 72; George Westinghouse Award, Am Soc Eng Educ, 74. *Mem:* Am Soc Civil Engrs; Am Soc Eng Educ; Am Rd Builders Asn (pres, 77); Am Cong Surv & Mapping; Am Soc Photogram. *Res:* Highway pavement design; bituminous and concrete mixes; traffic, planning and design; soil mechanics; effect of aggregate factors on pavement friction. *Mailing Add:* Dept Civil Eng Sch Eng Univ Conn Box U-37 Storrs CT 06268

STEPHENS, JAMES BRISCOE, b San Francisco, Calif, Mar 5, 36; m 67; c 2. ATMOSPHERIC PHYSICS, SPACE PHYSICS. *Educ:* Univ Okla, BS, 64, MS, 66, PhD(eng physics), 71. *Prof Exp:* Scientist remote sensing, 66-69, scientist statist physics, 70-72, TASK TEAM LEADER TERRESTRIAL DIFFUSION, MARSHALL SPACE FLIGHT CTR, NASA, 73- *Concurrent Pos:* Mem, Atmos Effects Panel, NASA Hq, 74- *Mem:* Am Phys Soc; Sigma Xi. *Res:* The environmental effects from aerospace effluents. *Mailing Add:* Aerospace Environ Div NASA Marshall Space Flight Ctr Huntsville AL 35812

STEPHENS, JAMES FRED, b Lexington, Tenn, Sept 29, 32; m 72; c 2. POULTRY SCIENCE, MICROBIOLOGY. *Educ:* Univ Tenn, BS, 54, MS, 59, PhD(bact), 64. *Prof Exp:* Asst poultry, Univ Tenn, 56-62; from asst prof to assoc prof poultry sci, Clemson Univ, 62-68; assoc prof, 68-74, PROF POULTRY SCI, OHIO STATE UNIV, 74- *Mem:* Poultry Sci Asn; Am Soc Microbiol; World Poultry Sci Asn. *Res:* Poultry disease; nutrition relationships; pathogenecity of Salmonellae; physiological effects of coccidiosis in chickens; drug resistance in enteric bacteria. *Mailing Add:* Dept of Poultry Sci 674 W Lane Ave Columbus OH 43210

STEPHENS, JAMES REGIS, b Pittsburgh, Pa, Mar 16, 25; m 55; c 4. ORGANIC CHEMISTRY, POLYMER CHEMISTRY. *Educ:* St Vincent Col, BS, 47; Univ Pittsburgh, MS, 49; Northwestern Univ, PhD(chem), 53. *Prof Exp:* Res chemist, Sinclair Ref Co, 50 & Am Cyanamid Co, 53-57; sr res scientist, 57-67, group leader res dept, 67-70, SECT LEADER RES & DEVELOP, AMOCO CHEM CORP, 70-, SR RES ASSOC, 80- *Honors & Awards:* Glycerine Award, Glycerine Producer's Asn, 54. *Mem:* Am Chem Soc. *Res:* Organic nitrogen compounds; stereochemistry of dioxanes; alkyd and magnet wire enamels; heterocyclic and aromatic polymers for high temperature service. *Mailing Add:* Res & Devel Amoco Chem Corp PO Box 400 Naperville IL 60540

STEPHENS, JESSE JERALD, b Oklahoma City, Okla, June 3, 33; m 55; c 3. PHYSICAL METEOROLOGY. *Educ:* Univ Tex, BS, 58, MA, 61; Tex A&M Univ, Nat Defense Educ Act fel & PhD(meteorol), 66. *Prof Exp:* Meteorologist, US Weather Bur, 57-59; lectr meteorol, Univ Tex, 59-61, from instr to asst prof, 64-66; assoc prof, Univ Okla, 66-67; assoc prof, 67-71, chmn dept, 75-77, PROF METEOROL, FLA STATE UNIV, 71-, CHMN DEPT, 81- *Mem:* Fel Am Meteorol Soc. *Res:* Scattering processes in the atmosphere; geophysical data processing. *Mailing Add:* Dept Meteorol Fla State Univ Tallahassee FL 32306

STEPHENS, JOHN ARNOLD, b Council Bluffs, Iowa, Aug 11, 21; m 44; c 1. ORGANIC CHEMISTRY. *Educ:* Univ Omaha, Munic, BA, 43; Univ Nebr, MA, 49, PhD(chem), 51. *Prof Exp:* Res chemist, 50-57, res group leader, 57-62, mgr res & develop, Agr Res Dept, 62-75, dir biol eval, 75-78, RES DIR INT, MONSANTO AGR PROD CO, 78- *Mem:* Am Chem Soc. *Res:* Nitrogen heterocycles; industrial synthesis; agricultural chemicals. *Mailing Add:* Monsanto Agr Prod Co 800 N Lindbergh St Louis MO 63167

STEPHENS, JOHN C(ARNES), b Attalla, Ala, Sept 22, 10; m 36; c 3. AGRICULTURE ENGINEERING, GEOLOGY. *Educ:* Univ Ala, BS, 31. *Prof Exp:* Agr engr, soil conserv serv, USDA, Ala, 33-39, asst proj engr, Everglades Proj, 42-46; water control engr, Dade County, 46-49; supvr, Everglades Proj, Soil & Water Conserv Res Div, 49-61, leader regional invests, watershed eng, south br, Ga, 61-70, dir southeast watershed res ctr, Ga, 65-70, res dir Lower Miss Valley Area, Agr Res Serv, USDA, 72-76; RETIRED. *Concurrent Pos:* Collabr, Sci & Educ Admin, Agr Res Serv, USDA, 76- *Honors & Awards:* John Deere Gold Medal Award, Am Soc Agr Eng. *Mem:* Am Soc Agr Eng; Am Geophys Union; Am Soc Civil Eng; Am Water Resources Asn; Soil Conserv Soc Am. *Res:* Peat and muck investigations; drainage; irrigation; weed control; hydrology of agricultural watersheds. *Mailing Add:* 1111 NE Second St Ft Lauderdale FL 33301

STEPHENS, JOHN STEWART, JR, b Los Angeles, Calif, May 12, 32; m 53; c 1. MARINE BIOLOGY, FISH BIOLOGY. *Educ:* Stanford Univ, BS, 54; Univ Calif, Los Angeles, MA, 57, PhD, 60. *Prof Exp:* Asst zool, Univ Calif, Los Angeles, 54-58, assoc biol, Santa Barbara, 58-69; from instr to prof biol, 59-74, JAMES IRVINE PROF ENVIRON BIOL, OCCIDENTAL COL, 74- *Concurrent Pos:* Dir, Vantuna Oceanog Prog, Occidental Col, 69- *Mem:* Am Soc Ichthyologists & Herpetologists; Soc Syst Zool; Am Fisheries Soc; Am Inst Fishery Res Biologists. *Res:* Systematics and distribution of blenniod fishes; especially Chaenopsidae; osteology of tropical blennies; ecology of nearctic fishes of California, including effects of pollution and habitat destruction. *Mailing Add:* Dept of Biol Occidental Col Los Angeles CA 90041

STEPHENS, KENNETH S, b Kutztown, Pa, Dec 11, 32; m 53; c 3. QUALITY CONTROL. *Educ:* LeTourneau Inst, BS, 55; Rutgers Univ, MS, 60, PhD(appl & math statist), 66. *Prof Exp:* Qual control engr, Western Elec Co, Inc, Pa, 55-58 & 59-60; asst & instr math, Rutgers Univ, 58-59; chief qual control eng dept, 60-62, chief eng personnel & staff & Kans City coord dept, 62-63, res leader appl math & statist group systs res & develop, NJ, 63-67; prof & coordr math & indust eng, Letourneau Col, 67-72; lectr, Sch Indust & Systs Eng, Ga Inst Technol & Res Consult, Econ Develop Lab, Eng Exp Sta, 74-79; ADV, UN INDUST DEVELOP ORGN, 80- *Concurrent Pos:* Mem, UN team statist qual control, India, 62-63 & UN Indust Develop Orgn adv standardization & qual control, Thai Indust Stand Inst, Bangkok, Thailand, 72-74, Nigerian Standards Orgn, Lagos, Nigeria, 77-78, State Planning Orgn, Turkey, 80-81, Mauritius Standards Bur, Reduit, 80-82. *Mem:* Fel Am Soc Qual Control; Am Statist Asn; Europ Orgn Qual Control; Indian Asn Qual & Reliability; Sigma Xi. *Res:* Industrial statistics; quality control systems; standardization and certification; industrial engineering. *Mailing Add:* 1361 Oak Grove Dr Decatur GA 30033

STEPHENS, LAWRENCE JAMES, b Chicago, Ill, Aug 11, 40; m 64; c 3. ORGANIC CHEMISTRY, SCIENCE EDUCATION. *Educ:* Loyola Univ Chicago, BS, 63; Univ Nebr, Lincoln, PhD(org chem), 69. *Prof Exp:* Res assoc, Stanford Univ, 68-69; asst prof chem, Findlay Col, 69-73; ASSOC PROF CHEM, ELMIRA COL, 73- *Mem:* Am Chem Soc; Nat Sci Teachers Asn. *Res:* Curriculum development in the natural sciences; synthesis of terpenoids. *Mailing Add:* Dept of Chem Elmira Col Elmira NY 14901

STEPHENS, LEE BISHOP, JR, b Atlanta, Ga, Oct 22, 25; m 58; c 3. EMBRYOLOGY. *Educ:* Morehouse Col, BS, 47; Atlanta Univ, MS, 50; Univ Iowa, PhD, 57. *Prof Exp:* Instr biol, Dillard Univ, 50-53; instr, NC Col Durham, 53-54; assoc prof, Southern Univ, 57-62; from asst prof to assoc prof, 62-70, PROF BIOL, CALIF STATE UNIV, LONG BEACH, 70- *Mem:* Am Soc Zool; Am Micros Soc. *Res:* Neuroembryology; regeneration; endocrinology and development of the nervous system. *Mailing Add:* Dept of Biol Calif State Univ Long Beach CA 90840

STEPHENS, MARVIN WAYNE, b Grand Rapids, Mich, Mar 24, 43; m 66; c 3. ENVIRONMENTAL CHEMISTRY. *Educ:* Cedarville Col, BS, 65; Univ Nebr, Lincoln, PhD(chem), 72. *Prof Exp:* Asst prof, Malone Col, 69-75, assoc prof chem, 75-78, prof chem, 78-80; VPRES & TECH DIR, WADSWORTH TESTING LABS, 80- *Res:* Testing procedures for environmental analyses; development of procedures. *Mailing Add:* Wadsworth Testing Lab Box 208 Canton OH 44709

STEPHENS, MAYNARD MOODY, b Connersville, Ind, Apr 25, 08; wid; c 6. PETROLEUM ENGINEERING, ECONOMIC GEOLOGY. *Educ:* Univ Minn, BA, 30, MA, 31, PhD(geol), 34; Pa State Univ, PE, 43. *Prof Exp:* Res geologist, Minn Geol Surv & Univ Minn, 31-36; supvr petrol & natural gas exten, Pa State Univ, 36-41; partner, Ryder Scott Co, 41-52; prof geol & petrol engr, Midwestern Univ, 52-60, dean sch petrol & phys sci, 57-60; consult, Maynard M Stephens Co, 57-68; indust specialist, Off Oil & Gas, US Dept Interior, 68-72, mgr vulnerability studies, 72-75; PROF PETROL ENG, GRAD DIV & DIR SPEC PROG, SCH ENG, TULANE UNIV, 75- *Concurrent Pos:* Geologist & engr, Drill Well Oil Co, 53-55 & Assoc Petrol Engrs, 55-57; prin scientist, Gulf S Res Inst, Baton Rouge, La. *Mem:* Am Asn Petrol Geologists; Geol Soc Am; Am Inst Mining, Metall & Petrol Eng; Nat Soc Prof Engrs; Soc Petrol Engrs. *Res:* Mineralography; secondary and tertiary recovery of oil by water flooding; polished surface of ores; photomicrography; petroleum and natural gas engineering; petroleum production; security and national vulnerability as related to oil and gas. *Mailing Add:* Dir Spec Prog Sch Eng Tulane Univ 6823 St Charles Ave New Orleans LA 70118

STEPHENS, MICHAEL A, b Bristol, Eng, Apr 26, 27; m 62. MATHEMATICAL STATISTICS, APPLIED STATISTICS. *Educ:* Bristol Univ, BSc, 48; Harvard Univ, AM, 49; Univ Toronto, PhD(math), 62. *Prof Exp:* Instr math, Tufts Col, 49-50; lectr, Woolwich Polytech, Eng, 52-53 & Battersea Col Technol, 53-56; instr, Case Western Reserve Univ, 56-59; lectr, Univ Toronto, 59-62, asst prof, 62-63; from asst prof to prof, McGill Univ, 63-70; prof, Univ Nottingham & Univ Grenoble, 70-72; prof, McMaster Univ, 72-76; PROF MATH, SIMON FRASER UNIV, 76- *Concurrent Pos:* Consult, Can Packers Ltd, 62-63 & various Montreal res Drs, 63-67. *Mem:*

Fel Am Statist Asn; Can Statist Soc; Int Statist Inst; fel Inst Math Statist. *Res:* Mathematical statistics, distributions on a circle or a hyper-sphere analysis of continuous proportions; goodness of fit statistics, robustness, density approximations. *Mailing Add:* Dept of Math Simon Fraser Univ Burnaby BC V5A 1S6 Can

STEPHENS, N(OLAN) THOMAS, b Mountainair, NMex, Oct 20, 32; m 53; c 3. ENVIRONMENTAL ENGINEERING. *Educ:* Univ NMex, BS, 55; NMex State Univ, BS, 61; Univ Fla, MSE, 67, PhD(environ eng), 69. *Prof Exp:* Res engr, Rocketdyne Div, NAm Rockwell Inc, 61-64; mgr saline water conversion opers, Struthers Sci & Int Corp, 64-66; sr environ engr, Southern Res Inst, 69-70; PROF CIVIL ENG & AIR POLLUTION SPECIALIST, VA POLYTECH INST & STATE UNIV, 70- *Mem:* Air Pollution Control Asn. *Res:* Fundamental and applied research on causes, effects, and control of air and water pollutants; research and development on processes for saline water conversion. *Mailing Add:* Air Pollution Res Lab Va Polytech Inst & State Univ Blacksburg VA 24061

STEPHENS, NEWMAN LLOYD, b Kanth, India, Feb 28, 26; Can citizen; m 67; c 2. PHYSIOLOGY, BIOSTATISTICS. *Educ:* Univ Lucknow, India, MB & BS, 50, DM, 53. *Prof Exp:* Resident med officer, King George's Med Col, Univ Lucknow, 50-53; head sect med, Clara Swain Hosp, Bareilly, India, 55-58; med registr, Univ Col Hosp, London, Eng, 59-61; from asst prof to assoc prof, 67-73, PROF PHYSIOL, FAC MED, UNIV MAN, 73- *Concurrent Pos:* Res fel cardiol, Res & Educ Hosp, Univ Ill, 62-64; res fel physiol, Sch Hyg, Johns Hopkins Univ, 64-65; res fel med, Winnipeg Gen Hosp, Man, 65-66; Can Heart Found scholar & Med Res Coun Can grant, Fac Med, Univ Man, 67- *Mem:* Fel Royal Soc Med; Am Physiol Soc; Biophys Soc; Can Physiol Soc; Can Soc Clin Invest. *Res:* Smooth muscle, biophysics, biochemistry and ultrastructure of normal muscle, effects of acidosis and hypoxia on these parameters; airway smooth muscle in asthma. *Mailing Add:* Dept of Physiol 770 Bannatyne Ave Winnipeg MB R3T 2N2 Can

STEPHENS, NOEL, JR, b Richmond, Ky, Dec 27, 28; m 58; c 4. ANIMAL SCIENCE, ANIMAL NUTRITION. *Educ:* Univ Ky, BS, 55, MS, 56, PhD(animal sci), 64. *Prof Exp:* From instr to assoc prof, 56-69, PROF ANIMAL SCI, BEREA COL, 69- *Mem:* Am Soc Animal Sci. *Res:* Amino acids and trace mineral research in swine nutrition. *Mailing Add:* Dept of Animal Sci Berea Col Berea KY 40404

STEPHENS, PHILIP J, b West Bromwich, Eng, Oct 9, 40; m 62; c 1. SPECTROSCOPY, TRANSITION-METAL CHEMISTRY. *Educ:* Oxford Univ, BA, 62, DPhil(chem), 64. *Prof Exp:* Res fel chem, Univ Copenhagen, 64-65; res fel, Univ Chicago, 65-67; from asst prof to assoc prof, 67-76, PROF CHEM, UNIV SOUTHERN CALIF, 76- *Concurrent Pos:* Sci Res Coun fel, 64-66; Alfred P Sloan res fel, 68-70. *Mem:* Am Chem Soc; Royal Chem; Am Phys Soc. *Res:* Magneto-optical and spectroscopic properties of matter. *Mailing Add:* Dept Chem Univ Southern Calif Los Angeles CA 90007

STEPHENS, RALPH IVAN, b Chicago, Ill, June 3, 34; m 58; c 3. MECHANICS. *Educ:* Univ Ill, BS, 57, MS, 60; Univ Wis, PhD(eng mech), 65. *Prof Exp:* Asst gen eng, Univ Ill, 57-59, instr theoret & appl mech, 59-60; instr eng mech, Univ Wis, 60-65; from asst prof to assoc prof, 65-72, PROF MECH ENG, UNIV IOWA, 72- *Concurrent Pos:* Indust consult, 63- *Mem:* Am Soc Eng Educ; Am Soc Testing & Mat; Soc Automotive Engrs. *Res:* Fracture mechanics; fatigue of engineering materials and related areas; mechanical behavior; mechanics of solids; bioengineering. *Mailing Add:* Mat Eng Div Univ of Iowa Iowa City IA 52242

STEPHENS, RAYMOND EDWARD, b Pittsburgh, Pa, Mar 5, 40. CELL BIOLOGY, PROTEIN CHEMISTRY. *Educ:* Geneva Col, BS, 62; Univ Pittsburgh, MS, 63; Dartmouth Med Sch, PhD(molecular biol), 65. *Prof Exp:* Fel, Univ Hawaii, 66; NIH fel, Harvard Univ, 66-67; asst prof, 67-70, assoc prof biol, Brandeis Univ, 70-77; INVESTR, MARINE BIOL LAB, 70- *Concurrent Pos:* Mem cell biol study sect, NIH, 71-75; vis prof biol, Univ Pa, 77-; adj prof physiol, Sch Med, Boston Univ, 78- *Mem:* AAAS; Am Chem Soc; NY Acad Sci; Soc Gen Physiol; Am Soc Cell Biol. *Res:* Protein subunit association; bio-chemistry of cell division and cell movement. *Mailing Add:* Marine Biol Lab Woods Hole MA 02543

STEPHENS, RAYMOND WEATHERS, JR, b Marietta, Ga, Apr 20, 28; m 51; c 2. PETROLEUM GEOLOGY. *Educ:* Univ Ga, BS, 51; La State Univ, MS, 56, PhD(geol), 60. *Prof Exp:* Geologist, Shell Oil Co, 59-66; dist geologist, Pubco Petrol Co, 66-72; asst prof, 72-74, ASSOC PROF EARTH SCI, UNIV NEW ORLEANS, 74- *Mem:* Am Asn Petrol Geologists. *Res:* Stratigraphic and paleontologic geology. *Mailing Add:* Dept of Earth Sci Univ of New Orleans New Orleans LA 70122

STEPHENS, RICHARD HARRY, b Bradford, Pa, Sept 16, 45; m 67; c 2. CHEMICAL ENGINEERING. *Educ:* Univ Tex, Austin, BSChE, 68; Mass Inst Technol, PhD(chem eng), 71. *Prof Exp:* Res engr, exp sta, E I du Pont de Nemours & Co, Inc, 68; res asst chem eng, Mass Inst Technol, 68-71; staff assoc, Arthur D Little, Inc, 71-75; mgr energy systs, Energy Resources Co, Mass, 76-78; sr engr, 78-80, PRIN ENGR, POLAROID CORP, 80- *Res:* Environmental assessment and control; solid waste management and processing technology; process development; energy utilization. *Mailing Add:* Polaroid Corp Cambridge MA 02138

STEPHENS, ROBERT LAWRENCE, b Cincinnati, Ohio, July 12, 21; m 41; c 4. BIOCHEMISTRY, MICROBIOLOGY. *Educ:* Univ Fla, BS, 49, MS, 52, PhD(biochem), 56. *Prof Exp:* Chemist organometallic, Ethyl Corp, 56-58; res chemist natural prods, NC State Univ, 58-60; xres 58-60 & Pulp Chem Asn, 60-62; prof chem, LeTourneau Col, 62-65; acad vpres admin, 65-72; prof biol, Biola Col, 73-77; PROF CHEM, LeTOURNEAU COL, 77- *Mem:* Am Chem Soc; AAAS; Sigma Xi. *Res:* Natural products; microbiology of soil; ultraviolet irradiation effects on microorganisms. *Mailing Add:* Dept of Chem LeTourneau Col Longview TX 75602

STEPHENS, ROGER, b Manchester, Eng, Apr 6, 45; m 70. CHEMISTRY. *Educ:* Cambridge Univ, MA, 67; Bristol Univ, MSc, 69; Univ London, PhD(chem), 71. *Prof Exp:* Asst prof, 71-80, ASSOC PROF CHEM, DALHOUSIE UNIV, 80- *Concurrent Pos:* Nat Sci Eng Res Coun Can res grant, 71- *Mem:* Royal Soc Chem; Royal Inst Chemists; Spectros Soc Can. *Res:* Analytical spectroscopy; flame systems; spectroscopic sources. *Mailing Add:* Dept Chem Dalhousie Univ Halifax NS B3H 3J5 Can

STEPHENS, STANLEY GEORGE, b Dudley, Eng, Sept 2, 11; nat US; m 38; c 2. EVOLUTIONARY BIOLOGY. *Educ:* Cambridge Univ, BA, 33, MA, 36; Univ Edinburgh, PhD(bot), 41. *Prof Exp:* Asst plant breeder, Scottish Plant Breeding Sta, Univ Edinburgh, 36-38; asst geneticist, Empire Cotton Corp, BWI, 38-44, asst prof genetics, McGill Univ, 44-45; res assoc, Cold Spring Harbor, Carnegie Inst Technol, 45-47; prof genetics & cotton cytogeneticist, Tex A&M Univ, 47-49; res prof agron, 49-51, William Neal Reynolds prof genetics, 51-74, EMER PROF GENETICS, NC STATE UNIV, 75- *Concurrent Pos:* Guggenheim fel, NC State Univ, 58. *Honors & Awards:* Award, Nat Cotton Coun, 62. *Mem:* Nat Acad Sci; Soc Study Evolution; Soc Am Archaeol. *Res:* Cytogenetics of cotton; mechanisms of species differentiation; evolution and dispersal of cultivated plants. *Mailing Add:* 3219 Darien Dr Raleigh NC 27607

STEPHENS, STANLEY LAVERNE, b Niagara Falls, NY, Apr 23, 43; m 64; c 1. MATHEMATICS. *Educ:* Anderson Col, BA, 65; Lehigh Univ, MS, 67, PhD(math), 72. *Prof Exp:* Instr, Moravian Col, 68-71; asst prof, 71-80, ASSOC PROF MATH, ANDERSON COL, 80- *Mem:* Am Math Soc. *Res:* Prime power groups, particularly the automorphism group of p-groups. *Mailing Add:* Dept of Math Anderson Col Anderson IN 46011

STEPHENS, TIMOTHY LEE, b Bellingham, Wash, June 27, 44; m 69; c 1. NUCLEAR WEAPONS EFFECTS, RESEARCH MANAGEMENT. *Educ:* Calif Inst Technol, BS, 66; Harvard Univ, AM, 67, PhD(physics), 71. *Prof Exp:* Res fel physics, Smithsonian Astrophys Observ, 69-70; physicist, Gen Elec Co-Tempo, 70-81; PROG MGR, KAMAN SCI CORP, 81- *Res:* Optical emission processes of atoms and molecules; energy partitioning during high energy electron deposition in air; chemical and hydrodynamic properties of the atmosphere; environmental effects of nuclear weapons. *Mailing Add:* Kaman Sci Corp 303 Williams Ave Suite 521 Huntsville AL 35801

STEPHENS, WILLIAM D, b Paris, Tenn, Nov 17, 32; div; c 3. ORGANIC CHEMISTRY. *Educ:* Western Ky State Col, BS, 54; Vanderbilt Univ, PhD(chem), 60. *Prof Exp:* Group leader high energy oxidizers, Thiokol Chem Corp, 59-61, sect chief org chem, 61-63; group leader basic mat, Goodyear Tire & Rubber Co, 63-66; PRIN CHEMIST, THIOKOL CHEM CORP, 66- *Concurrent Pos:* Adj assoc prof, Univ Ala, Huntsville, 70- *Mem:* Am Chem Soc. *Res:* Solid propellant research; explosives, burning-rate catalysts; organometallic, organic nitrogen, sulfur and cyclic compounds; polymer chemistry; adhesives; bonding agents; urethane catalysts; antioxidants. *Mailing Add:* Thiokol Chem Corp Huntsville AL 35807

STEPHENS, WILLIAM LEONARD, b Covington, Ky, Apr 19, 29; m 57. MICROBIOLOGY. *Educ:* Sacramento State Col, BS, 57; Univ Calif, Davis, PhD(microbiol), 63. *Prof Exp:* Res asst bact, Univ Calif, Davis, 57-63; from asst prof to assoc prof, 63-70, chmn dept, 68-74, PROF BACT, CHICO STATE COL, 70-, DEAN, SCH NATURAL SCI, 77- *Mem:* Am Soc Microbiol. *Res:* Carotenoid pigments of bacteria. *Mailing Add:* Sch of Natural Sci Calif State Univ Chico CA 95929

STEPHENS-NEWSHAM, LLOYD G, b Saskatoon, Sask, Apr 30, 21; m 50; c 2. BIOPHYSICS. *Educ:* Univ Sask, BA, 43; McGill Univ, PhD(nuclear physics), 48. *Prof Exp:* Asst prof physics, Dalhousie Univ, 48-51; from asst prof to assoc prof, Fac Med, McGill Univ, 52-66; from assoc prof to prof physiol, 66-74, PROF, FAC PHARM, UNIV ALTA, 74- *Concurrent Pos:* Consult, Victoria Gen Hosp, 48-51; radiation physicist, Royal Victoria Hosp, Montreal, 52-66. *Mem:* Can Physiol Soc; Can Asn Physicists; Biophys Soc; Sigma Xi; fel Can Col Physicists Med. *Res:* Effects of ionizing radiation; neutron activation analysis. *Mailing Add:* Fac Pharm & Pharmaceut Sci Univ Alta Edmonton AB T6G 2N8 Can

STEPHENSON, ALFRED BENJAMIN, b Unity, Va, May 24, 12; m 41; c 3. POULTRY HUSBANDRY. *Educ:* Va Polytech Inst, BS, 33; Rutgers Univ, MS, 34; Iowa State Col, PhD, 49. *Prof Exp:* Asst poultry breeding, Iowa State Col, 46-49; from asst prof to assoc prof, Utah State Agr Col, 49-53; assoc prof poultry breeding, Univ Mo-Columbia, 53-58, prof, 58-82; RETIRED. *Mem:* Poultry Sci Asn. *Res:* Quantitative inheritance in poultry breeding. *Mailing Add:* Dept Poultry Bldg T-14 Univ of Mo Columbia MO 65211

STEPHENSON, ANDREW GEORGE, b Marion, Ohio, Dec 4, 50; m 77. PLANT ECOLOGY. *Educ:* Miami Univ, BA, 73; Univ Mich, MS, 75, PhD(bot), 78. *Prof Exp:* ASST PROF BIOL, PA STATE UNIV, 78- *Mem:* Soc Study Evolution; Ecol Soc Am; Am Soc Naturalists; Am Soc Plant Taxonomists. *Res:* Terrestrial plant ecology; ecology and evolution of plant reproduction; plant-animal coevolution in pollination, herbivory and dispersal. *Mailing Add:* 202 Buckhout Lab Pa State Univ University Park PA 16802

STEPHENSON, CHARLES BRUCE, b Little Rock, Ark, Feb 9, 29; m 52. ASTRONOMY. *Educ:* Univ Chicago, BS, 49, MS, 51; Univ Calif, PhD(astron), 57. *Prof Exp:* Asst astron, Dearborn Observ, Northwestern Univ, 51-53 & Univ Calif, 56-57; from instr to assoc prof, 58-68, PROF ASTRON, CASE WESTERN RESERVE UNIV, 68- *Mem:* AAAS; Am Astron Soc; Int Astron Union. *Res:* Stellar spectra; galactic structure; positional astronomy. *Mailing Add:* Dept Astron Case Western Reserve Univ Cleveland OH 44106

STEPHENSON, CHARLES V, b Centerville, Tenn, Oct 1, 24; m 48; c 3. SOLID STATE PHYSICS. *Educ:* Vanderbilt Univ, BA, 48, MA, 49, PhD(physics), 52. *Prof Exp:* Res physicist, Sandia Corp, 52-56; asst prof physics, Ala Polytech Inst, 56-58; head physics sect, Southern Res Inst, 58-62; chmn dept, 67-74, PROF ELEC ENG, VANDERBILT UNIV, 62-. *Concurrent Pos:* Consult, Sandia Corp, 56-58. *Mem:* AAAS; fel Am Phys Soc; Acoust Soc Am; Am Asn Physics Teachers; sr mem Inst Elec & Electronics Eng. *Res:* Molecular spectroscopy; solid state physics. *Mailing Add:* Dept of Elec Eng Vanderbilt Univ Nashville TN 37235

STEPHENSON, DANNY LON, b Ft Worth, Tex, Nov 7, 37; m 63; c 1. ORGANIC CHEMISTRY, SPECTROSCOPY. *Educ:* Tex Christian Univ, BA, 59, MA, 60; Rice Univ, PhD(org chem), 64. *Prof Exp:* Res chemist, Phillips Petrol Co, 64-65; PROF CHEM, HOWARD PAYNE UNIV, 65-, HEAD DEPT & CHMN, DIV SCI & MATH, 74- *Mem:* Am Chem Soc. *Res:* Mechanistic study of various condensation reactions with zinc chloride as the catalyst; natural products. *Mailing Add:* 16218 Autumn Wind Dr Houston TX 77090

STEPHENSON, DAVID A, hydrology, geology, see previous edition

STEPHENSON, DAVID ALLEN, b Denver, Colo, Nov 23, 42; m 63; c 2. MOLECULAR PHYSICS. *Educ:* NMex State Univ, BS, 64; Univ Mich, Ann Arbor, MS, 65, PhD(physics), 68. *Prof Exp:* Nat Res Coun-Environ Sci Serv Admin res fel, Environ Sci Serv Admin Res Labs, Colo, 68-70; assoc sr res physicist, Gen Motors Res Labs, 70-78; MEM TECH STAFF, SANDIA NAT LABS, 78- *Mem:* Optical Soc Am. *Res:* Raman spectroscopy of gases; gas phase reactions. *Mailing Add:* Div 8511 Sandia Nat Labs Livermore CA 94550

STEPHENSON, DAVID TOWN, b Colfax, Wash, Jan 28, 37; m 57; c 3. ELECTRICAL ENGINEERING. *Educ:* Wash State Univ, BS, 58; Univ Ill, MS, 62, PhD(elec eng), 65. *Prof Exp:* Asst elec eng, Univ Ill, 60-65, res assoc, 65-66; asst prof, 66-70, ASSOC PROF ELEC ENG, IOWA STATE UNIV, 70- *Mem:* Inst Elec & Electronics Engrs; Am Meteorol Soc. *Res:* Antennas; application to radio astronomy, spacecraft, and communications systems; microwave measurements; teaching in field theory and measurements. *Mailing Add:* Dept of Elec Eng Iowa State Univ Ames IA 50011

STEPHENSON, EDWARD JAMES, b Birmingham, Ala, Aug 13, 47; m 71; c 1. MEDIUM ENERGY REACTIONS, POLARIZATION. *Educ:* Rice Univ, BA, 69; Univ Wis-Madison, MS, 71, PhD(physics), 75. *Prof Exp:* Fel nuclear physics, Lawrence Berkeley Lab, 75-78; fel nuclear physics, Argonne Nat Lab, Ill, 78-79; ASSOC PROF, IND UNIV CYCLOTRON FAC, 79- *Mem:* Am Phys Soc; AAAS. *Res:* Polarization; accelerator mass spectrometry; medium energy nuclear physics. *Mailing Add:* Cyclotron Fac Ind Univ Milo B Sampson Lane Bloomington IN 47405

STEPHENSON, EDWARD LUTHER, b Calhoun, Tenn, May 5, 23; m 47; c 2. ANIMAL NUTRITION. *Educ:* Univ Tenn, BS, 46, MS, 47; State Col Wash, PhD(poultry nutrit), 52. *Prof Exp:* From asst prof to assoc prof, 49-57, PROF ANIMAL NUTRIT, COL AGR, UNIV ARK, FAYETTEVILLE, HEAD DEPT, 64- *Mem:* Am Soc Animal Sci; Soc Exp Biol & Med; fel Poultry Sci Asn; Am Inst Nutrit. *Res:* Poultry nutrition. *Mailing Add:* Dept of Animal Sci Univ Ark Col Agr Fayetteville AR 72701

STEPHENSON, EDWARD T, b Atlantic City, NJ, Nov 7, 29; m 53; c 4. PHYSICAL METALLURGY. *Educ:* Lehigh Univ, BS, 51, PhD(metall), 65; Mass Inst Technol, MS, 56. *Prof Exp:* Res engr, 56-73, sr res engr, 73-80, SR SCIENTIST, HOMER RES LABS, BETHLEHEM STEEL CORP, 80- *Honors & Awards:* Grossman Award, Am Soc Metals, 64. *Mem:* Am Soc Metals; Am Inst Mining, Metall & Petrol Engrs. *Res:* Relation of strength and toughness to composition and microstructure; electron microstructure, electrical resistivity, magnetic properties and internal friction of steel. *Mailing Add:* Homer Res Labs Bethlehem Steel Corp Bethlehem PA 18016

STEPHENSON, ELIZABETH WEISS, b Newark, NJ, Apr 1, 27; m 46; c 3. PHYSIOLOGY. *Educ:* Univ Chicago, BS, 47; George Washington Univ, PhD(physiol), 64. *Prof Exp:* Res asst, Ill Neuropsychiat Inst, 47-49; from instr to asst prof physiol, Sch Med, George Washington Univ, 64-71; sr staff fel, Lab Phys Biol, Nat Inst Arthiritis, Metab & Digestive Dis, 71-77, res biologist, 77-81; ASSOC PROF PHYSIOL, COL MED & DENT, NJ MED SCH, 81- *Mem:* AAAS; Am Physiol Soc; Biophys Soc; Soc Gen Physiol. *Res:* Ion transport across cellular and intracellular membranes. *Mailing Add:* Dept Physiol Col Med & Dent NJ Med Sch Newark NJ 07103

STEPHENSON, FRANCIS CREIGHTON, b Brantford, Ont, Mar 24, 24; m 48; c 4. PHYSICS. *Educ:* Univ Toronto, BASc, 49, MA, 51, PhD(physics), 54. *Prof Exp:* Res physicist, Lamp Develop Dept, Gen Elec Co, 53-65; asst prof, 65-67, ASSOC PROF PHYSICS, CLEVELAND STATE UNIV, 67- *Mem:* Am Asn Physics Teachers. *Res:* Molecular spectroscopy; incandescent radiation; vibration; gas discharge. *Mailing Add:* Dept of Physics 1983 E 24th St Cleveland State Univ Cleveland OH 44115

STEPHENSON, FREDERICK WILLIAM, b Tynemouth, Eng, Sept 25, 39; m 68; c 1. ELECTRONICS ENGINEERING. *Educ:* Kings Col, Univ Durham, BSc, 61; Univ Newcastle Upon Tyne, PhD(elec eng), 65. *Prof Exp:* Tech mgr, Microelectronics Div, Electrosil Ltd, 65-67; sr res assoc, Univ Newcastle Upon Tyne, 67-68; lectr, Univ Hull, UK, 68-75, sr lectr, 75-78; ASSOC PROF ELEC ENG, VA POLYTECH INST & STATE UNIV, 78- *Concurrent Pos:* R T French vis prof, Univ Rochester, 76-77; consult, Frequency Devices Inc, Haverhill, Mass, 79- *Mem:* Sr mem Inst Elec & Electronics Engrs; Inst Elec Engrs; Int Soc Hybrid Microelectronics. *Res:* Synthesis and sensitivity evaluation of active resistance capacitance and switched-capacitor fillers; applications of hybrid microelectronics. *Mailing Add:* Dept Elec Eng 324 Whittemore Hall Va Polytech Inst & State Univ Blacksburg VA 24061

STEPHENSON, GERARD J, JR, b Yonkers, NY, Mar 4, 37; m 60; c 1. THEORETICAL NUCLEAR PHYSICS. *Educ:* Mass Inst Technol, BS, 59, PhD(physics), 64. *Prof Exp:* Res fel physics, Calif Inst Technol, 64-66; from asst prof to assoc prof physics, Univ Md, College Park, 69-74; STAFF MEM, LOS ALAMOS SCI LAB, 74-, GROUP LEADER, 78- *Concurrent Pos:* Guggenheim Mem fel, Los Alamos Sci Lab, 72-73. *Mem:* Am Phys Soc. *Res:* Theoretical studies of nuclear structure and of low and intermediate energy nuclear reactions, particularly the use of the few body reactions to investigate the nucleon-nucleon interaction. *Mailing Add:* Medium Energy Theory Group T-5 Los Alamos Sci Lab Los Alamos NM 87545

STEPHENSON, HAROLD PATTY, b Angier, NC, Dec 22, 25; m 56; c 2. MOLECULAR SPECTROSCOPY. *Educ:* Duke Univ, BSME, 47, MA, 49, PhD(physics), 52. *Prof Exp:* Instr physics, Duke Univ, 48-49 & 51-52; asst, Appl Physics Lab, Johns Hopkins Univ, 51; assoc prof physics, Ill Wesleyan Univ, 52-53, prof & chmn dept, 53-57; assoc prof mech eng, Duke Univ, 57-60; assoc prof, 60-63, PROF PHYSICS, PFEIFFER COL, 63-, HEAD DEPT, 60- *Mem:* Am Asn Physics Teachers. *Res:* Near ultraviolet absorption spectra of poly-atomic molecules. *Mailing Add:* Dept Math & Physics Pfeiffer Col Misenheimer NC 28109

STEPHENSON, HUGH EDWARD, JR, b Columbia, Mo, June 1, 22; m 64; c 2. THORACIC SURGERY, CARDIOVASCULAR SURGERY. *Educ:* Univ Mo, AB & BS, 43; Wash Univ, MD, 45; Am Bd Surg, dipl, 53; Bd Thoracic Surg, dipl, 63. *Prof Exp:* Instr surg, Sch Med, NY Univ, 51-53; from asst prof to assoc prof, 53-55, chmn dept, 56-60, PROF SURG, SCH MED, UNIV MO-COLUMBIA, 56-, CHIEF, GEN SURG DIV, 76- *Mem:* Soc Vascular Surg; AMA; Am Asn Surg Trauma; Am Col Surg; Am Col Chest Physicians. *Res:* Cardiovascular research; oncology. *Mailing Add:* 807 Stadium Blvd Columbia MO 65201

STEPHENSON, J(OHN) GREGG, b Kansas City, Mo, Sept 21, 17; m 48; c 2. ELECTRONICS ENGINEERING. *Educ:* Yale Univ, BE, 39; Stanford Univ, Engr, 41. *Prof Exp:* Asst engr, Ohio Brass Co, 41-42; res assoc, Radio Res Lab, Harvard Univ, 42-45; engr, 45-55, sect head appl electronics, 55-57, sect head, Appl Res Div, 57-58, dep dir, Proj Star, 58-61, tech asst to dir, Res & Eng Div, 61-63, prog dir, 63-68, dep dir, Reconnaissance & Surveillance Div, Cutler-Hammer, Inc, 68-69, dir, Tech Support Div, Airborne Instruments Lab, Eaton Corp, 70-81; RETIRED. *Mem:* Sr mem Inst Elec & Electronics Engrs; Am Inst Aeronaut & Astronaut. *Res:* Ultrahigh frequency and microwave receiving and transmitting equipment; space technology; ionospheric propagation; systems management. *Mailing Add:* 22 Arosa Ct Greenlawn NY 11740

STEPHENSON, JOHN, b Chichester, Eng, 1939; m 65; c 3. THEORETICAL PHYSICS. *Educ:* Univ London, BSc, 61, PhD(theoret physics), 64. *Prof Exp:* Lectr math, Univ Adelaide, 65-68; res assoc physics, 68-70, vis asst prof, 70-71, asst prof, 71-74, assoc prof, 74-81, PROF PHYSICS, UNIV ALTA, 81- *Mem:* Can Asn Physicists; Am Phys Soc. *Res:* Statistical mechanics and critical phenomena in fluids and magnetic systems. *Mailing Add:* Dept of Physics Univ of Alta Edmonton AB T6G 2G7 Can

STEPHENSON, JOHN CARTER, US citizen. PHYSICAL CHEMISTRY. *Educ:* Mass Inst Technol, BS, 66; Univ Calif, PhD(phys chem), 71. *Prof Exp:* Scientist, Avco Everett Res Lab, 70-71; SCIENTIST, NAT BUR STANDARDS, 71- *Mem:* Am Chem Soc; InterAm Photochem Soc. *Res:* Lasers; chemical kinetics; spectroscopy; energy transfer; air and water pollution. *Mailing Add:* Molecular Spectros Div Nat Bur Standards Washington DC 20234

STEPHENSON, JOHN LESLIE, b Farmington, Maine, Dec 4, 21; m 46; c 3. BIOPHYSICS. *Educ:* Harvard Univ, BS, 43; Univ Ill, MD, 49. *Prof Exp:* Asst theoret physics, Metall Lab, Univ Chicago, 43-45; physicist, US Naval Ord Lab, 45; intern, Staten Island Marine Hosp, NY, 49-50; from res assoc to asst prof, Univ Chicago, 52-54; scientist, 54-73, CHIEF SECT THEORET BIOPHYS, NAT HEART & LUNG INST, 73- *Concurrent Pos:* USPHS fel anat, Univ Chicago, 50-52; vis prof, Inst Fluid Dynamics & Appl Math, Univ Md, College Park, 73-74. *Mem:* Am Phys Soc; Am Physiol Soc; Int Soc Nephrology; Soc Math Biol; Biophys Soc (pres-elect, 82-83). *Res:* Mathematical theory of transport in biological systems; theory of renal function. *Mailing Add:* Bldg 31 Rm 4B44 Nat Heart & Lung Inst Bethesda MD 20014

STEPHENSON, LANI SUE, b Honolulu, Hawaii, July 31, 48; m 74. NUTRITION, PARASITOLOGY. *Educ:* Cornell Univ, BS, 71, MNS, 73, PhD(gen nutrit), 78. *Prof Exp:* Exten aide, Dept Human Nutrit Food, Col Human Ecol, Cornell Univ, 71; res asst, Div Nutrit Sci, Cornell Univ, 73-74, res assoc int nutrit, 78-80. *Concurrent Pos:* Co-investr, World Bank, Brit Overseas Develop Ministry & Cornell Health & Nutrit Proj, Kenya, 78-81; vis prof int nutrit, Div Nutrit Sci, Cornell Univ, 80-; prin investr, Clark Found Urinary Schistosomiosis Growth & Anemia Proj, Kenya, 81-83. *Honors & Awards:* Student Res Award, Am Inst Nutrit, 78. *Mem:* Am Pub Health Asn; Am Soc Parasitologists; Soc Nutrit Educ; Am Inst Nutrit; Am Soc Trop Med Hyg. *Res:* Maternal and child health; protein-calorie malnutrition in young children; relationships between intestinal parasites and nutritional status; dietary methodologies; international nutrition problems. *Mailing Add:* Savage Hall Cornell Univ Ithaca NY 14853

STEPHENSON, LEE PALMER, b Fresno, Calif, Oct 21, 23; m 48; c 3. GEOPHYSICS. *Educ:* Fresno State Col, AB, 47; Univ Ill, MS, 49, PhD(physics), 53. *Prof Exp:* Asst physics, Univ Ill, 47-53; res physicist, Calif Res Corp, Stand Oil Co, Calif, 53-57, group supvr, 57-59, res assoc geophys, 59-63, SR RES ASSOC, CHEVRON OIL FIELD RES CO, 63- *Mem:* AAAS; Am Phys Soc; Am Chem Soc; Soc Explor Geophys; Am Asn Petrol Geologists. *Res:* Exploration seismology; seismic signal detection, data processing and interpretation; physical properties of earth materials; compaction and cementation of clastic sediments; optics; astronomy; astronomical instrumentation. *Mailing Add:* Chevron Oil Field Res Co PO Box 446 La Habra CA 90631

STEPHENSON, MARVIN E, environmental engineering, fish & game management, see previous edition

STEPHENSON, MARY LOUISE, b Brookline, Mass, Feb 23, 21. MOLECULAR BIOLOGY. *Educ:* Conn Col, AB, 43; Radcliffe Col, PhD(biochem), 56. *Prof Exp:* Res fel, 56-59, asst biochemist, 59-66, assoc biol chem, 66-74, ASSOC BIOCHEMIST, MASS GEN HOSP, HARVARD MED SCH, 74-, PRIN RES ASSOC, HARVARD MED SCH, 69- *Mem:* Am Asn Biol Chemists; Am Asn Cancer Res; Am Soc Cell Biol. *Res:* Biosynthesis of proteins. *Mailing Add:* Arthritis Labs Mass Gen Hosp Boston MA 02114

STEPHENSON, NORMAN ROBERT, b Toronto, Ont, Mar 15, 17; m 43; c 3. BIOCHEMISTRY, SCIENCE ADMINISTRATION. *Educ:* Univ Toronto, BA, 38, MA, 40, PhD, 42; Carleton Univ, DPA, 71. *Prof Exp:* Asst chemist, Insulin Comt Lab, Univ Toronto, 38-39, asst med res, Banting Inst, 39-42; res chemist, Stand Brands, Ltd, 45-48 & Consumers Res Labs, 48-50; res chemist, Physiol & Hormones Sect, Food & Drug Labs, Dept Nat Health & Walfare, 50-66, head anti-cancer sect & sci adv, Div Med & Pharmacol, Drug Adv Bur, 66-73, chief, health care prod div, Planning & Eval Directorate, 73-78, sr sci adv, bur drugs, drugs directorate, Health Protection Br, 78-80; RETIRED. *Mem:* Can Physiol Soc; Can Pharmacol Soc; fel Chem Inst Can; Soc Toxicol Can. *Res:* Endocrinology; biological and chemical assays of hormones and adrenal corticosteroids; estrogens, androgens; thyroid hormone; anterior pituitary hormones; insulin. *Mailing Add:* 44 Kilbarry Crescent Ottawa ON K1K 0H1 Can

STEPHENSON, PAUL BERNARD, b Jena, La, Dec 16, 37; m 59; c 3. PHYSICS. *Educ:* La Polytech Inst, BS, 60, MS, 61; Duke Univ, PhD(physics), 66. *Prof Exp:* Engr, Tex Instruments Inc, 61-62; res asst physics, Duke Univ, 62-66; from asst prof to assoc prof, 66-75, PROF PHYSICS, LA TECH UNIV, 75- *Mem:* Am Asn Physics Teachers; Am Phys Soc. *Res:* Solid state physics, particularly luminescence of organic crystals. *Mailing Add:* Dept of Physics La Tech Univ Ruston LA 71270

STEPHENSON, RICHARD ALLEN, b Cleveland, Ohio, June 8, 31; m 52; c 3. GEOMORPHOLOGY, NATURAL RESOURCES MANAGEMENT. *Educ:* Kent State Univ, BA, 59; Univ Tenn, MS, 61; Univ Iowa, PhD(geog, geol), 67. *Prof Exp:* Asst prof phys geog, ECarolina Univ, 62-67; asst prof phys geog & earth sci, Univ Ga, 67-71; assoc prof phys geog, 71-74, dir, Inst Coastal & Marine Resources, 74-77, PROF DEPT GEOG, E CAROLINA UNIV, 77- *Mem:* Asn Am Geog; Geol Soc Am; Sigma Xi. *Res:* Geomorphology; water resources; environmental resources; hydrology. *Mailing Add:* Dept Geog & Planning East Carolina Univ Greenville NC 27834

STEPHENSON, ROBERT BRUCE, b Colfax, Wash, Feb 15, 46; m 68; c 3. HUMAN PHYSIOLOGY, CARDIOVASCULAR PHYSIOLOGY. *Educ:* Wash State Univ, BS, 68; Univ Wash, PhD(physiol & biophysics), 76. *Prof Exp:* Assoc res engr, Boeing Co, 68-70; fel, Univ Wash, 70-76 & Mayo Clin & Found, 77-79; ASST PROF PHYSIOL, MICH STATE UNIV, 79- *Res:* Cardiovascular physiology; neural control of the circulation, particularly reflex regulation of blood pressure in normotension and hypertension. *Mailing Add:* Dept Physiol Giltner Hall Mich State Univ East Lansing MI 48824

STEPHENSON, ROBERT CHARLES, b Oxford, Ohio, Dec 27, 16; m 42; c 3. GEOLOGY. *Educ:* Miami Univ, AB, 38; Johns Hopkins Univ, PhD(geol), 43. *Prof Exp:* Geologist & mining engr, Titanium Div, MacIntyre Develop, Nat Lead Co, 42-43; field geologist, Union Mines Develop Corp, Colo, 43-44 & Rocky Mt Div, Union Oil Co, Calif, 44-45; sr geologist, State Topog & Geol Surv, Pa, 45-46, asst state geologist, 46-52; geologist, Woodward & Dickerson, Inc, 52-55; exec dir, Am Geol Inst, DC, 55-63; prof geol & exec dir res found, Ohio State Univ, 63-72; dir, Ctr Marine Resources, 72-74, prof mgt & spec progs adminr, Off Univ Res, Tex A&M Univ, 74-77; ASSOC RES PROF & ASSOC DIR, RES LAB ENG SCI, UNIV VA, 80- *Concurrent Pos:* Assoc Univ Progs, Div Univ Progs, Energy Res & Develop Admin, Washington, DC, 75-77; consult, Off Energy Res, US Dept Energy. *Mem:* AAAS; fel Geol Soc Am; Soc Econ Geologists; Am Asn Petrol Geol; Am Inst Mining, Metall & Petrol Eng. *Res:* Economic geology of metalliferous deposits; petroleum geology; geology of nonmetallic mineral resources; management of marine and coastal resources. *Mailing Add:* Country Meadows Route 1 Barboursville VA 22923

STEPHENSON, ROBERT E(LDON), b Nephi, Utah, Aug 7, 19; m 42; c 4. ELECTRICAL ENGINEERING. *Educ:* Univ Utah, BS, 41; Calif Inst Technol, MS, 46; Purdue Univ, PhD(elec eng), 52. *Prof Exp:* From instr to prof elec eng & comput sci, Univ Utah, 46-71, ASSOC DEAN COL ENG, UNIV UTAH, 71- *Concurrent Pos:* Instr, Purdue Univ, 50-52; engr, Hughes Aircraft Co, 55; engr, Sperry Utah Eng Labs, 59; consult, Sandia Corp, 59-64; Utah Power & Light, 81- *Mem:* Inst Elec & Electronics Engrs. *Res:* Computers; data systems; computer simulation; electric power. *Mailing Add:* Col of Eng Univ of Utah Salt Lake City UT 84112

STEPHENSON, ROBERT MOFFATT, JR, b Atlanta, Ga, Dec 25, 40; m 65; c 2. MATHEMATICS. *Educ:* Vanderbilt Univ, BA, 62; Tulane Univ, MS, 65, PhD(math), 67. *Prof Exp:* Asst prof math, Univ NC, Chapel Hill, 67-73; assoc prof, 73-78, chmn dept, 76-79, PROF MATH & STATIST, UNIV SC, 78- *Mem:* Am Math Soc. *Res:* General topology. *Mailing Add:* Dept of Math, Comput Sci & Statist Univ of SC Columbia SC 29208

STEPHENSON, ROBERT STORER, b Corpus Christi, Tex, Apr 30, 43; m 69; c 2. NEUROPHYSIOLOGY, VISION RESEARCH. *Educ:* Princeton Univ, AB, 65; Mass Inst Technol, SM, 67, PhD(neurophysiol), 73. *Prof Exp:* Lectr physiol, Fac Sci, Rabat, Morocco, 73-76; res assoc physiol, Dept Biol Sci, Purdue Univ, 76-; ASSOC PROF, DEPT BIOL SCI, WAYNE STATE UNIV, 81- *Concurrent Pos:* Fel, Purdue Univ, 76-. *Mem:* AAAS; Sigma Xi; Biophys Soc; Asn Res Vision Ophthalmol. *Res:* Invertebrate photoreceptors and phototransduction; nerve regeneration; morphogenesis. *Mailing Add:* Dept Biol Sci Wayne State Univ Detroit MI 48202

STEPHENSON, SAMUEL EDWARD, JR, b Bristol, Tenn, May 16, 26; m 50; c 3. MEDICINE, ORGANIC CHEMISTRY. *Educ:* Univ SC, BS, 46; Vanderbilt Univ, MD, 50; Am Bd Surg & Bd Thoracic Surg, dipl, 57. *Prof Exp:* Asst surg, Sch Med, Vanderbilt Univ, 53-55; from instr to asst prof, 55-61, assoc prof, Sch Med & Assoc dir, Clin Res Ctr, 61-67, dir, S R Light Lab Surg Res, 59-62; chmn dept surg, Univ Hosp Jacksonville, 67-78; PROF SURG, UNIV FLA, 67-; CHIEF GEN SURG, BAPTIST MED CTR, 79- *Concurrent Pos:* Consult, Regional Respiratory & Rehab Ctr, 58 & Thayer Vet Admin Hosp, 59. *Res:* Medical electronics, especially physiological control of respiration and cardiac rate; experimental atherogenesis; malignant disease; cardiovascular surgery and neoplasms. *Mailing Add:* Suite 223 Marshall Taylor Bldg 836 Prudential Dr Jacksonville FL 33207

STEPHENSON, STANLEY E(LBERT), b Ogden, Utah, Mar 12, 26; m 49; c 6. ELECTRICAL & NUCLEAR ENGINEERING. *Educ:* Univ Colo, BS, 48; Tex A&M Univ, MS, 61, PhD(elec eng), 64. *Prof Exp:* Engr, Lago Oil & Transport, 48-52; sr engr, Standard Oil Co, Ohio, 52-54; engr, Am Petrofina, 54-59; asst supvr, Nuclear Sci Ctr, Tex A&M Univ, 59-61, asst res engr, Activation Anal Lab, 61-62; assoc prof, 64-69, PROF ELEC ENG, UNIV ARK, FAYETTEVILLE, 69- *Mem:* Am Soc Eng Educ; Inst Elec & Electronics Engrs; Instrument Soc Am. *Res:* Stochastic control systems; nonlinear systems; identification of system parameters. *Mailing Add:* Dept of Elec Eng Univ of Ark Fayetteville AR 72701

STEPHENSON, STEPHEN NEIL, b Hayden Lake, Idaho, Feb 3, 33; m 53; c 4. BOTANY, ECOLOGY. *Educ:* Idaho State Univ, BS, 55; Rutgers Univ, MS, 63, PhD(bot), 65. *Prof Exp:* Park ranger, Nat Park Serv, 57-61; instr bot, Douglass Col, Rutgers Univ, 62-63; asst prof, 65-72, ASSOC PROF BOT, MICH STATE UNIV, 72- *Concurrent Pos:* Mem eastern deciduous forest biome coord comt, Int Biol Prog, 68- *Mem:* AAAS; Am Soc Mammal; Ecol Soc Am; Am Inst Biol Sci. *Res:* Community structure and organization; biosystematics of Gramineae; biogeography of North America, especially arid and semiarid regions. *Mailing Add:* Dept of Bot & Plant Path Mich State Univ East Lansing MI 48824

STEPHENSON, THOMAS E(DGAR), b Dahlgren, Ill, Oct 19, 22; m 46; c 4. NUCLEAR ENGINEERING, PHYSICS. *Educ:* Southern Ill Univ, BS, 45; Univ Tenn, MS, 50. *Prof Exp:* Physicist, Manhattan Dist, Atomic Energy Comn, 46-47; physicist, Oak Ridge Nat Lab, 47-54; nuclear engr, Convair Div, Gen Dynamics Corp, 54-55; design engr, Nuclear Div, Martin Co, 55-56; physicist, Sci Res Staff, Repub Aviation Corp, 56-65; physicist, Brookhaven Nat Lab, 65-70; physicist, S M Stoller Corp, 70-73; nuclear applications engr, Va Elec & Power Co, 73-76; sr nuclear engr, Burns & Roe, Inc, 76-80; NUCLEAR LICENSING ENGR, STONE & WEBSTER, 80- *Concurrent Pos:* Adj assoc prof, Long Island Univ, 68-70. *Mem:* Am Phys Soc; Am Nuclear Soc. *Res:* Neutron and reactor physics; radiation effects and shielding; power reactor safety analysis and environmental effects; neutron cross section evaluation; nuclear fuel evaluation; nuclear licensing. *Mailing Add:* 16 Briarfield Lane Huntington NY 11743

STEPHENSON, WILLIAM KAY, b Chicago, Ill, Apr 6, 27; m 51; c 3. PHYSIOLOGY. *Educ:* Knox Col, AB, 50; Univ Minn, PhD, 55. *Prof Exp:* Phys chemist, Nat Bur Stand, 49-50; asst zool, Univ Minn, 50-53, instr, 54; from asst prof to assoc prof biol, 54-64, chmn dept, 64-77, PROF BIOL, EARLHAM COL, 64- *Mem:* AAAS; Am Physiol Soc; Am Soc Zool; Am Soc Cell Biol. *Res:* Ion distribution; active transport; bioelectric phenomena; cnidarian behavior. *Mailing Add:* Dept Biol Earlham Col Richmond IN 47374

STEPKA, WILLIAM, b Veseli, Minn, Apr 13, 17; m 48; c 1. PLANT PHYSIOLOGY, PLANT BIOCHEMISTRY. *Educ:* Univ Rochester, AB, 46; Univ Calif, PhD, 51. *Prof Exp:* Asst, Univ Rochester, 46-47 & Univ Calif, 48-49; res assoc bot, Univ Pa, 51-54, asst prof, 54-55; PLANT PHYSIOLOGIST IN CHG, RADIOL NUTRICULTURE LAB, MED COL VA, VA COMMONWEALTH UNIV, 55-, PROF PHARMACOG, HEALTH SCI DIV, UNIV, 68- *Concurrent Pos:* Plant physiologist & biochemist, Am Tobacco Co, 55-68. *Mem:* Am Soc Plant Physiol; Am Soc Pharmacognosy; Am Asn Cols Pharm. *Res:* Biosynthesis of radioactively labeled compounds; discovery and isolation of cardioactive, hypotensive and contraceptive compounds from natural sources. *Mailing Add:* Dept Pharm Hlth Sci Div Va Commonwealth Univ Box 581 MCV Sta Richmond VA 23298

STEPLEMAN, ROBERT SAUL, b New York, NY, Nov 2, 42; m 67; c 2. MATHEMATICS. *Educ:* State Univ NY Stony Brook, BS, 64; Univ Md, College Park, PhD(math), 69. *Prof Exp:* Res assoc numerical anal, Inst Fluid Dynamics & Appl Math, Univ Md, College Park, 69; asst prof appl math & comput sci, Sch Eng & Appl Sci, Univ Va, 69-73; mem tech staff, David Sarnoff Res Ctr, RCA, 73-80; GROUP HEAD SCI COMPUT, EXXON RES & ENG CO, 80- *Concurrent Pos:* adj assoc prof comput sci, Rutgers Univ, 78- *Mem:* Math Asn Am; Asn Comput Mach; Int Asn Math & Comput Simulation; Soc Indust & Appl Math. *Res:* Numerical analysis; convergence of numerical methods; solution of elliptic.partial differential equations;solution of singular Fredholm integral equations of the first kind; stopping criteria for numerical processes. *Mailing Add:* Comput Technol & Serv Exxon Res & Eng Co Linden NJ 07036

STEPONKUS, PETER LEO, b Chicago, Ill, Sept 18, 41; m 62; c 4. PLANT PHYSIOLOGY, HORTICULTURE. *Educ:* Colo State Univ, BSc, 63; Univ Ariz, MSc, 64; Purdue Univ, PhD(plant physiol), 66. *Prof Exp:* Asst prof hort & asst horticulturist, Univ Ariz, 66-68; asst prof, 68-72, assoc prof hort, 72-77, assoc prof crop physiol, 77-79, PROF CROP PHYSIOL, CORNELL UNIV, 79- *Honors & Awards:* Kenneth Post Award, Soc Cryobiol, 71. *Mem:* AAAS; Am Soc Hort Sci; Am Soc Plant Physiol; Scand Soc Plant Physiol; Soc Cryobiol. *Res:* Stress physiology; biochemical mechanisms of cold acclimation; freezing injury; hormonal controls in high temperature injury and senescence; drought resistance of cereals. *Mailing Add:* Dept Agron Cornell Univ Ithaca NY 14850

STEPPLER, HOWARD ALVEY, b Morden, Man, Nov 8, 18; m 45; c 1. AGRONOMY. *Educ:* Univ Man, BSA, 41; McGill Univ, MSc, 48, PhD, 55. *Prof Exp:* Lectr plant sci, Univ Man, 41-42; plant breeder, Dom Exp Farm, 48-49; from asst prof to assoc prof, 49-57, chmn dept, 55-73, PROF AGRON, MACDONALD COL, MCGILL UNIV, 57-, CHMN DEPT PLANT SCI, 76- *Concurrent Pos:* Nuffield traveling fel, 55; vis prof, Univ West Indies, 64; exec mem, Nat Soil Fertil Comt, 58; mem coord comt, Can Forage Seeds Proj, 58; mem, Nat Comt Agrometeorol, 59; chmn adv comt agr, World's Fair, Montreal, 67; agr adv, Can Int Develop Agency, 70-71; mem bd trustees, Int Ctr Trop Agr, Colombia, 72- *Honors & Awards:* Merit cert, Am Grassland Coun, 64; sr res fel, Int Develop Res Ctr, Can, 73-74; mem bd trustees, Agr Develop Coun, NY, 76- *Mem:* AAAS; Am Soc Agron; Can Soc Agron (pres, 58); Biomet Soc; fel Agr Inst Can (vpres, 55-57, pres, 64-65). *Res:* Plant breeding; forage crops; grassland management, especially ecology, physiology, climatology and morphology in relation to growth and response under animal grazing. *Mailing Add:* Dept of Plant Sci MacDonald Col St Anne de Bellevue PQ H9X 1C0 Can

STEPTO, ROBERT CHARLES, b Chicago, Ill, Oct 6, 20; m 42; c 2. OBSTETRICS & GYNECOLOGY, PATHOLOGY. *Educ:* Northwestern Univ, BS, 41; Howard Univ, MD, 44; Univ Chicago, PhD(path), 48. *Prof Exp:* Asst, Col Med, Univ Chicago, 42; clin instr obstet & gynec, Stritch Sch Med, Loyola Univ Chicago, 50-60; from clin asst prof to clin assoc prof, Univ Ill, 60-70; chmn dept, Chicago Med Sch, 70-74, prof obstet & gynec, 70-75; prof obstet & gynec, Rush Med Col, 75-79; PROF OBSTET & GYNEC, UNIV CHICAGO, 79- *Concurrent Pos:* USPHS fel, Inst Res, Michael Reese Hosp, 48-50; chmn, Dept Obstet & Gynec, Provident Hosp, 53-63 & Mt Sinai Hosp & Med Ctr, 70-; dir obstet & gynec, Cook County Hosp, 72-75; mem, Food & Drug Adv Comt Obstet & Gynec, 72-76; mem, Family Planning Coord Coun, 76; mem maternal & preschool nutrition comt, Nat Acad Sci; 75. *Mem:* Fel AMA; Am Col Obstet & Gynec; Am Col Surg; Int Col Surg Am; Am Fertil Soc. *Res:* Endocrine pathology; oncology; sex hormones influence on tissue synthesis; laser surgery. *Mailing Add:* 5201 S Cornell Ave Chicago IL 60615

STERBENZ, FRANCIS JOSEPH, b Queens, NY, May 11, 24; m 56; c 3. BIOCHEMICAL PHARMACOLOGY. *Educ:* St John's Univ, NY, BS, 50, MS, 52; NY Univ, PhD, 57. *Prof Exp:* Asst bacteriologist, New York City Dept Hosps, 51-52; res assoc protozool, St John's Univ, NY, 52-56; instr physiol, NJ Col Med & Dent, 56-58, instr microbiol, 58-59; sr res microbiologist, Squibb Inst Med Res, 59-65; asst dept head biochem, Bristol-Myers Co, 65-70, DEPT HEAD, RES & DEVELOP LAB, BRISTOL-MYERS PROD, HILLSIDE, 70- *Mem:* AAAS; Soc Protozool; NY Acad Sci; Am Soc Microbiol; Sigma Xi. *Res:* Bio-availability and biochemistry of analgesic, sedative and related drugs; immunochemistry; mechanisms involved in microbial pathogenicity; chemotherapy; nutritional physiology of microorganisms. *Mailing Add:* Bristol-Myers Co 225 Long Ave Hillside NJ 07205

STERE, ATHLEEN JACOBS, b Boston, Mass, Feb 1, 21; m 43; c 3. BIOLOGY. *Educ:* Bryn Mawr Col, AB, 41; Radcliffe Col, MA, 42; Pa State Univ, University Park, PhD(biol), 71. *Prof Exp:* Res asst immunol, Sch Med, Boston Univ, 44-46; res asst microbiol, Res Div, Albert Einstein Med Ctr, Philadelphia, 59-63; res asst, 63-71, asst prof, 71-77, ASSOC PROF BIOL, PA STATE UNIV, UNIVERSITY PARK, 77- *Mem:* AAAS; Sigma Xi. *Res:* Histochemistry; effect of oxygen deprivation on cellular metabolism. *Mailing Add:* Dept of Biol Pa State Univ University Park PA 16802

STERGIS, CHRISTOS GEORGE, b Greece, Dec 22, 19; US citizen; m 48; c 2. PHYSICS. *Educ:* Temple Univ, AB, 42, AM, 43; Mass Ins Technol, PhD(physics), 48. *Prof Exp:* Physicist, Radiation Lab, Mass Inst Technol, 44-45, res asst physics, 45-48; asst prof, Temple Univ, 48-51; physicist, 51-58, chief, Space Physics Lab, 59-63, CHIEF AERONOMY DIV, AIR FORCE GEOPHYS LAB, 63- *Concurrent Pos:* Hon res asst, Univ Col, Univ London, 64-65; mem, Comt High Altitude Rocket & Balloon Res, Nat Acad Sci, 63-66, Comt Int Quiet Sun Yr, 63-67, Comt Solar-Terrestrial Res, 71-78, Aeronomy Panel, Interdept Comt Atmospheric Sci, 71-77. *Mem:* Am Phys Soc; Am Geophys Union; Sigma Xi. *Res:* Structure of the earth's upper atmosphere by means of rockets and satellites; scattering of solar radiations by the atoms and molecules of the upper atmosphere. *Mailing Add:* Aeronomy Div AF Geophys Lab Hanscom AFB Bedford MA 01730

STERIADE, MIRCEA, b Bucharest, Romania, Aug 20, 24; c 1. NEUROPHYSIOLOGY. *Educ:* Col Culture, Bucharest, BA, 44; Fac Med, Bucharest, MD, 52; Inst Neurol, Acad Sci, Bucharest, DSc(neurophysiol), 55. *Prof Exp:* Sr scientist, Inst Neurol, Acad Sci, Bucharest, 55-62, head lab, 62-68; assoc prof, 68-69, PROF PHYSIOL, FAC MED, UNIV LAVAL, 69- *Honors & Awards:* Claude Bernard Medal, Univ Paris, 65. *Mem:* AAAS; Int Brain Res Orgn; Can Physiol Soc; Fr Neurol Soc; Fr Asn Physiol. *Res:* Neuronal circuitry of thalamic nuclei and cortical areas; responsiveness of thalamic and cortical relay cells; thalamic and cortical inhibitory mechanisms during sleep and waking; ascending reticular systems; neuronal organization and properties related to shifts in vigilance states; cellular bases of thalamic bursting. *Mailing Add:* Dept Physiol Univ Laval Fac Med Quebec PQ G1K 7P4 Can

STERK, ANDREW A, b Budapest, Hungary, Jan 29, 19; US citizen; m 50; c 2. INSTRUMENTATION, EXPERIMENTAL PHYSICS. *Educ:* Milan Polytech Inst, MS, 43, PhD(elec eng), 46. *Prof Exp:* Res engr, Automatic Elec Co, 46-47; sr develop engr, Servo Corp Am, 47-49; asst chief engr, Fed Mfg & Eng Corp, 49-50; tech dir automatic control, Magnetic Amplifiers, Inc, 50-53; chief develop engr, Philips Electronic Instruments, 53-62; dept mgr space instruments, Am Mach & Foundry Co, 62-67; CONSULT ENGR & MGR SPACE INSTRUMENTATION PROGS, GEN ELEC SPACE DIV, PHILA, 67- *Mem:* Sr mem Inst Elec & Electronics Engrs; Am Inst Aeronaut & Astronaut; Soc Photo-Optical Instrumentation Engrs. *Res:* Space instrumentation; x-ray spectrometers; extreme ultraviolet spectrometers; x-ray and extreme ultraviolet spectro-heliographs; x-ray polarimeter; x-ray scattering processes; laser; lidar interferometers; manufacturing and processing in space; space communications; optical communications; remote sensing. *Mailing Add:* 6 Williams Lane Berwyn PA 19312

STERKEN, GORDON JAY, b Ft Atkinson, Wis, Mar 17, 30. ORGANIC CHEMISTRY. *Educ:* Hope Col, AB, 51; Mich State Univ, PhD(org chem), 60. *Prof Exp:* Chemist, Stauffer Chem Co, 59-66 & Sinclair Oil Co, 66-69; CHEMIST, HILTON-DAVIS CHEM CO DIV, STERLING DRUG CO, 69- *Mem:* Am Chem Soc. *Res:* Synthesis of fluoran dyes, pigments and pharmaceutical intermediates; product and process development in these areas. *Mailing Add:* 5303 Kingsway West Cincinnati OH 45215

STERLING, ANNE, developmental genetics, see previous edition

STERLING, CLARENCE, b Millville, NJ, Mar 25, 19; m 42; c 5. BOTANY. *Educ:* Univ Calif, AB, 40, PhD(bot), 44. *Prof Exp:* Asst forestry, Univ Calif, 40-41 & bot, 44; res asst, Univ Ill, 46-47; instr, Univ Wis, 47-50; from asst prof to prof, 50-81, EMER PROF FOOD SCI & TECHNOL, UNIV CALIF, DAVIS, 81- *Concurrent Pos:* Fulbright grant, 56-57; Guggenheim fels, 56-57 & 63-64. *Mem:* AAAS; Bot Soc Am; Linnean Soc London. *Res:* Plant anatomy and morphology; cytology; submicroscopic structure of gels; crystal structure. *Mailing Add:* Dept of Food Sci & Technol Univ of Calif Davis CA 95616

STERLING, DANIEL J, mathematics, see previous edition

STERLING, HAROLD MELVIN, physical medicine, pediatrics, see previous edition

STERLING, JOHN DEO, b Latham, Mo, Aug 3, 21; m 45; c 2. CHEMISTRY. *Educ:* Cent Col, Mo, BA, 42; Univ Md, PhD(org chem), 49. *Prof Exp:* Res chemist, Univ Md, 43-45; res chemist, 48-53, res supvr, 53-62, div head, 62-79, RES ASSOC AEROSOL PROPELLANTS, FREON PROD LAB, E I DU PONT DE NEMOURS & CO, INC, CHESTNUT RUN, 79- *Mem:* Am Chem Soc. *Res:* Antimalarial drugs; methoxylated organic compounds; organic fluorine compounds; dyes; petroleum chemicals; lithium batteries. *Mailing Add:* Freon Prod Lab Chestnut Run E I du Pont de Nemours & Co Inc Wilmington DE 19898

STERLING, NICHOLAS J, b Cooperstown, NY, Nov 7, 34; m 62; c 2. MATHEMATICS. *Educ:* Williams Col, BA, 56; Syracuse Univ, MS, 61, PhD(math), 66. *Prof Exp:* Asst prof, 66-70, ASSOC PROF MATH, STATE UNIV NY BINGHAMTON, 70- *Mem:* Am Math Soc. *Res:* Non-associative ring theory. *Mailing Add:* Dept of Math State Univ NY Binghamton NY 13901

STERLING, PETER, b New York, NY, June 28, 40; m 61; c 2. NEUROANATOMY, NEUROPHYSIOLOGY. *Educ:* Western Reserve Univ, PhD(bbiol), 66. *Prof Exp:* Asst prof, 69-74, ASSOC PROF NEUROANAT, SCH MED, UNIV PA, 74- *Concurrent Pos:* NSF fel, Med Sch, Harvard Univ, 66-68, NIH fel, 68-69; NSF grant, Sch Med, Univ Pa, 69-71, NIH grant, 71- *Honors & Awards:* C Judson Herrick Award, Am Asn Anat, 71. *Mem:* Am Asn Anat; Soc Neurosci. *Res:* Relation between form of nerve cells and their physiological functioning, particularly in the visuo-motor system. *Mailing Add:* Dept of Anat Univ of Pa Sch of Med Philadelphia PA 19104

STERLING, RAYMOND LESLIE, b London, Eng, Apr 19, 49; m 70; c 3. UNDERGROUND CONSTRUCTION, STRUCTURAL ENGINEERING. *Educ:* Univ Sheffield, BENG, 70; Univ Minn, Minneapolis, MS, 75, PhD(civil eng), 77. *Prof Exp:* Construct engr, Egil Wefald & Assoc, Minneapolis, 70-71, Husband & Co, Eng, 71-73 & Setter, Leach & Lindstrom, Inc, Minneapolis, 76-77; ASST PROF CIVIL ENG & DIR, UNDERGROUND SPACE CTR, UNIV MINN, 77- *Concurrent Pos:* Prin investr res proj, Univ Minn, 77-; consult archit & eng firms, 77-; lectr, 77- *Mem:* Am Soc Civil Eng; Inst Struct Engrs; Nat Soc Prof Engrs; Am Underground Space Asn. *Res:* Underground construction and underground space use; earth-sheltered building design. *Mailing Add:* Underground Space Ctr Univ Minn 112 Min Met Bldg 221 Church St SE Minneapolis MN 55455

STERLING, REX ELLIOTT, b Eldorado, Kans, Sept 5, 24; m 48; c 2. BIOCHEMISTRY. *Educ:* Cent Mo State Col, BS, 48; Univ Ark, MS, 49; Univ Colo, PhD(biochem), 53. *Prof Exp:* Clin biochemist, Los Angeles County Gen Hosp, 53-71; from instr to assoc prof, 53-72, PROF BIOCHEM, UNIV SOUTHERN CALIF, 72-; HEAD CLIN BIOCHEMIST, LOS ANGELES COUNTY GEN HOSP, 71- *Mem:* Am Asn Clin Chem. *Res:* Diabetes and carbohydrate in cataract formation; carbohydrate metabolism and adrenal cortical function; prophyrins and porphyria; clinical biochemical methodology and automation. *Mailing Add:* Labs & Path LAC-USC Med Ctr Los Angeles CA 90033

STERLING, ROBERT FILLMORE, b Toledo, Ohio, Aug 19, 19; m 47; c 2. ORGANIC POLYMER CHEMISTRY. *Educ:* Carnegie Inst Technol, BS, 42; Univ Pittsburgh, cert bus mgt, 62. *Prof Exp:* Res metallurgist, Magnesium Div, Dow Chem Co, 42-44; res engr, Res Labs, 46-49, mat & process engr, 50-52, res engr, 52-55, adv scientist, Atomic Power Dept, 55-57, mgr chem sect, 57-62, FEL ENGR, MISSILE LAUNCHING & HANDLING DEPT, MARINE DIV, WESTINGHOUSE ELEC CORP, 62- *Mem:* Am Chem Soc. *Res:* Thermal insulation materials; synthetic resins of improved electrical properties; chemistry and materials of nuclear reactors; reliability, research and development of missile launching and handling equipment; biological oceanography and agricultural biochemistry. *Mailing Add:* 1457 Hollenbeck Ave Sunnyvale CA 94087

STERLING, STEWART ALLEN, b Rochester, NY, Mar 1, 41; m 75; c 1. SOLID STATE PHYSICS. *Educ:* Mass Inst Technol, BS, 64; Univ Calif, Berkeley, PhD(physics), 70. *Prof Exp:* STAFF MEM PHYS CHEM, GEN ATOMIC CO, 69- *Res:* Experimental characterization of diffusional kinetics fission products at high temperatures; development of models describing thermally activated creep in modern super alloys. *Mailing Add:* General Atomic Co PO Box 81608 San Diego CA 92138

STERLING, THEODOR DAVID, b Vienna, Austria, July 3, 23; nat US; m 48; c 2. COMPUTER SCIENCE, BIOMETRY. *Educ:* Univ Chicago, AB, 49, MA, 53; Tulane Univ, PhD, 55. *Prof Exp:* Instr math, Univ Ala, 54-55, asst prof statist, 55-57; asst prof statist, Mich State Univ, 57-58; asst prof prev med, Col Med, Univ Cincinnati, 58-66, assoc prof biostatist, 61-63, prof & dir med ctr, 63-66; prof comput sci, Wash Univ, 66-72; prof comput sci & fac interdisciplinary studies, 72-81, UNIV RES PROF, SIMON FRASER UNIV, 81- *Concurrent Pos:* Consult, NSF, 67, Environ Protection Agency, 71 & Fed Trade Comn, 72; vis prof statist, Princeton Univ, 78. *Mem:* Asn Comput Mach; fel AAAS; Am Statist Asn. *Res:* Humanizing effects of automation; errors and foibles in investigations, especially medical. *Mailing Add:* Dept of Comput Sci Simon Fraser Univ Burnaby BC V5A 1S6 Can

STERLING, WARREN MARTIN, b Chicago, Ill, Jan 4, 47. INFORMATION SCIENCE, ELECTRONIC ENGINEERING. *Educ:* Univ Ill, BS, 68; Carnegie-Mellon Univ, MS, 70, PhD(elec eng), 74. *Prof Exp:* Engr numerical control, Westinghouse Elec Corp, 68-74; ENGR ELEC ENG, XEROX CORP, EL SEGUNDO, CALIF, 74- *Concurrent Pos:* Res instr elec eng, Carnegie-Mellon Univ, 72; instr eng, Univ Calif, Los Angeles, 77- *Mem:* Inst Elec & Electronics Engrs; Soc Photo-Optical Instrumentation Engrs. *Res:* Automated inspection and manufacturing; digital image processing; optical computing. *Mailing Add:* PARC/ADL Xerox Corp MS C3-50 701 Aviation Blvd El Segundo CA 90245

STERLING, WINFIELD LINCOLN, b Edinburg, Tex, Sept 18, 36; m 61; c 3. ENTOMOLOGY. *Educ:* Pan Am Col, BA, 62; Tex A&M Un- iv, MS, 66, PhD(entom), 69. *Prof Exp:* Res assoc entom, 64-66, asst prof, 69-74, assoc prof, 74-81, PROF ENTOM, TEX A&M UNIV, 81- *Concurrent Pos:* AID consult, Univ Calif, Berkeley, 74-75; post-doctoral fel, Univ Queensland, 75-76. *Mem:* Entom Soc Am; Entom Soc Can; Am Inst Biol Sci. *Res:* Insect ecology, pest management and population dynamics. *Mailing Add:* Dept of Entom Tex A&M Univ College Station TX 77843

STERMAN, MAURICE B, neuropsychology, see previous edition

STERMAN, MELVIN DAVID, b Brooklyn, NY, Sept 19, 30; m 56; c 4. COLLOID CHEMISTRY, POLYMER CHEMISTRY. *Educ:* City Col New York, BS, 51; Purdue Univ, PhD(phys chem), 55. *Prof Exp:* Teaching asst, Iowa State Univ, 51-52; from res chemist to sr res chemist, 55-62, res assoc, Res Labs, 63-78, RES ASSOC, MFG TECHNOL DIV, EASTMAN KODAK CO, 79- *Mem:* Am Chem Soc. *Res:* Characterization of polymers by physical chemical techniques; electrical properties of polymers; chemistry of cross-linking of polymers; properties of cross-linked polymer works; polymer adsorption on surfaces; preparation and stability of lyophobic colloids in non-aqueous solvents; electrophoretic mobility of colloidal particles. *Mailing Add:* 8 Widewaters Lane Pittsford NY 14534

STERMAN, SAMUEL, b Buffalo, NY, June 6, 18; m 53; c 4. PHYSICAL CHEMISTRY. *Educ:* Univ Buffalo, BS, 39. *Prof Exp:* Develop chemist, Nat Carbon Co Div, Union Carbide Corp, 40-45, res chemist, Linde Co Div, 45-50, supvr spec prod develop, Silicone Div, 50-66, asst dir res & develop, Chem & Plastics, 66-73, ASSOC DIR RES & DEVELOP, UNION CARBIDE TECH CTR, UNION CARBIDE CORP, 73- *Honors & Awards:* Award, Soc Plastics Indust, 61. *Mem:* Am Chem Soc; Soc Plastics Indust; AAAS. *Res:* Textile chemicals; protective coatings; water repellants; surface active agents; composites; interface bonding; organofunctional silanes; urethane foam; high temperature polymers; surface chemistry; elastomers; patent management. *Mailing Add:* 56 Commodore Rd Chappaqua NY 10514

STERMER, RAYMOND A, b Barclay, Tex, July 22, 24; m 48; c 2. AGRICULTURAL ENGINEERING. *Educ:* Tex A&M Univ, BS, 50, MS, 58, PhD, 71. *Prof Exp:* Conserv aid, Soil Conserv Serv, 43-47, agr engr, 50-55, res engr, Agr Mkt Serv, 55-63 & Agr Res Serv, 63-65, invests leader qual eval, Mkt Qual Res Div, 65-73, res agr engr, Grain Qual & Instrumentation Res Group, 73-76, RES AGR ENGR, SCI & EDUC ADMIN, USDA, 76- *Mem:* Am Soc Agr Engrs; Sigma Xi. *Res:* Instruments or techniques for rapid, objective measurement of quality of agricultural products; biomedical radio telemetry for monitoring physiological parameters in cattle. *Mailing Add:* Agr Res Serv PO Box ED College Station TX 77840

STERMER, ROBERT L, JR, b Wilmington, Del, Jan 27, 35; m 57; c 4. ELECTRONIC ENGINEERING. *Educ:* Univ Va, BEE, 60, MEE, 65; Duke Univ, PhD(elec eng), 71. *Prof Exp:* PHYSICIST, ELECTRONICS MAT, LANGLEY RES CTR, NASA, 60- *Concurrent Pos:* Lectr, George Washington Univ, 73- *Honors & Awards:* Spec Achievement Award, Langley Res Ctr, NASA, 74. *Mem:* Inst Elec & Electronics Engrs; Am Phys Soc; Sigma Xi. *Res:* Development of electronic device technology for spacecraft; early work in hybrid circuits using film technology and semiconductor devices; development of spacecraft memory systems using bubble technology. *Mailing Add:* MS 470 NASA Langley Res Ctr Hampton VA 23665

STERMITZ, FRANK, b Thermopolis, Wyo, Dec 3, 28; m 54; c 5. ORGANIC CHEMISTRY. *Educ:* Univ Notre Dame, BS, 50; Univ Colo, MS, 51, PhD(chem), 58. *Prof Exp:* Res chemist, Merck & Co, Inc, NJ, 51-53 & Lawrence Radiation Lab, Univ Calif, Berkeley, 58-61; from asst prof to assoc prof chem, Utah State Univ, 61-67; assoc prof, 67-69, CENTENNIAL PROF CHEM, COLO STATE UNIV, 69- *Concurrent Pos:* USPHS res career develop award, 63-67; vpres, Elars Biores Labs, 74-76; Fulbright sr fel, Argentina, 73; Fogarty sr fel, Peru, 82. *Mem:* Am Chem Soc; Am Soc Pharmacog. *Res:* Alkaloid and other natural product isolation, structure proof and biosynthesis; medicinal chemistry; organic photochemistry; chemotaxonomy. *Mailing Add:* Dept of Chem Colo State Univ Ft Collins CO 80523

STERN, A(RTHUR) C(ECIL), b Petersburg, Va, Mar 14, 09; m 38, 76; c 3. AIR POLLUTION CONTROL, INDUSTRIAL HYGIENE. *Educ:* Stevens Inst Technol, ME, 30, MS, 33. *Hon Degrees:* DrEng, Stevens Inst Technol, 75. *Prof Exp:* Asst smoke abatement, Stevens Inst Technol, 30-33; engr, J G White Eng Co, 33; NY Times Co, 34; supt air pollution surv, New York Dept Health, 35-37; ed, Current Titles from Eng Jours, 38; engr exam, Munic Civil Serv Comn, 39-42; chief eng unit, Div Indust Hyg, State Dept Labor, NY, 42-54; chief lab eng & phys sci, Div Air Pollution, USPHS, 55-62; asst dir, Nat Ctr Air Pollution Control, 62-68; prof, 68-78, EMER PROF AIR HYG, DEPT ENVIRON SCI & ENG, SCH PUB HEALTH, UNIV NC, CHAPEL HILL, 78- *Concurrent Pos:* Lectr, NY Univ, 44-54 & Columbia Univ, 46-52; res assoc, Univ Cincinnati, 55-62, asst clin prof, 61-62; mem, Bldg Environ Adv Bd, Nat Acad Sci, 77-83; mem, Adv Coun Elec Power Res Inst, 74-79. *Honors & Awards:* Richard Beatty Mellon Award, Air Pollution Control Asn, 70. *Mem:* Nat Acad Eng; Air Pollution Control Asn (pres 75-76); Am Soc Mech Engrs; Am Indust Hyg Asn. *Res:* Air pollution; history of air pollution. *Mailing Add:* Dept Environ Sci & Eng Sch Pub Health Univ NC Chapel Hill NC 27514

STERN, AARON MILTON, b Detroit, Mich, Aug 12, 20; m 55; c 2. PEDIATRICS, CARDIOLOGY. *Educ:* Univ Mich, AB, 42, MD, 45; Am Bd Pediat, dipl, 52. *Prof Exp:* Intern, Saginaw Gen Hosp, Mich, 45-46; from asst resident to resident, Univ Hosp, Univ Mich, Ann Arbor, 46-48; resident, Saginaw Gen Hosp, Mich, 48-49; from instr to assoc prof, 49-70, PROF PEDIAT & COMMUN DIS, MED SCH, UNIV MICH, ANN ARBOR, 70- *Concurrent Pos:* Consult, Alpena County Rheumatic Fever Clin, Mich, 51-56. *Mem:* Am Heart Asn; Am Acad Pediat. *Res:* Contrast studies of cardiovascular lesions and effects of cardiac surgery on physiologic and mental status of patients. *Mailing Add:* 3700 Miller Rd Ann Arbor MI 48103

STERN, ALBERT VICTOR, b New York, NY, Apr 26, 23; div; c 2. ASTRONOMY, SYSTEMS ENGINEERING. *Educ:* Univ Calif, Berkeley, AB, 47, PhD(astron), 50. *Prof Exp:* Sect head digital subsysts, Hughes Aircraft Co, Fullerton, 54-57, sr scientist, 57-59, lab mgr adv systs, 59-66, asst div mgr, 66-69, chief scientist, Syst Div, 69-73, prog mgr, Missile Systs Group, Canoga Park, 73-76, PROG MGR, RADAR SYSTS GROUP, HUGHES AIRCRAFT CO, CULVER CITY, 76- *Res:* Celestial mechanics; weapons systems analysis; systems engineering. *Mailing Add:* 279 Ravenna Dr Long Beach CA 90803

STERN, ARTHUR IRVING, b New York, NY, Dec 8, 30; m 62; c 3. PLANT PHYSIOLOGY, PHOTOBIOLOGY. *Educ:* City Col New York, BS, 53; Brandeis Univ, PhD(biol), 62. *Prof Exp:* NIH fel develop biol, Brandeis Univ, 62-63; Kettering fel photosynthesis, Weizmann Inst, 63-64, USPHS fel, 64-65; asst prof, 65-70, ASSOC PROF BOT, UNIV MASS, AMHERST, 70- *Mem:* Am Soc Plant Physiol; Am Soc Photobiol. *Res:* Chloroplast structure and function; chloroplast development; photophosphorylation; proton excretion in plant protoplasts. *Mailing Add:* Dept of Bot Univ of Mass Amherst MA 01003

STERN, ARTHUR P(AUL), b Budapest, Hungary, July 20, 25; nat US; m 52; c 3. ELECTRONICS ENGINEERING. *Educ:* Univ Lausanne, BS, 46; Swiss Fed Inst Technol, dipl, 48; Syracuse Univ, MEE, 56. *Prof Exp:* Res engr, Jaeger, Inc, Switz, 48-50; instr, Swiss Fed Inst Technol, 50-51; res engr electronics lab, Gen Elec Co, 51-52, proj leader semiconductor applns, 52-54, mgr adv circuits, 54-57, mgr electronic components lab, 57-61; dir eng, Electronics Div, Martin Marietta Corp, Md, 61-64; dir opers, Defense Systs Div, Bunker-Ramo Corp, 64-66; vpres & gen mgr, Magnavox Res Labs, Torrance, 66-70, vpres & gen mgr, Advan Prod & Systs Co, 80- *Concurrent Pos:* Non-res staff mem, Mass Inst Technol, 56-59; mem, Int Solid State Circuits Conf, 58-, chmn, 59-60. *Mem:* Am Astronaut Soc; fel Inst Elec & Electronics Engrs (secy, 72, treas, 73, vpres 74, pres, 75); Sigma Xi; AAAS. *Res:* Applications of modern solid state physics; design, application and electronic circuit behavior of solid state electronic components; transistor circuit engineering. *Mailing Add:* 606 N Oakhurst Dr Beverly Hills CA 90210

STERN, CURT, zoology, deceased

STERN, DANIEL HENRY, b Richmond, Va, June 18, 34; m 63; c 1. LIMNOLOGY, ECOLOGY. *Educ:* Univ Richmond, BS, 55, MS, 59; Univ Ill, PhD(zool), 64. *Prof Exp:* Asst prof biol, Tenn Technol Univ, 64-66 & La State Univ, New Orleans, 66-69; from asst prof to assoc prof, 69-75, PROF BIOL, UNIV MO-KANSAS CITY, 75- *Mem:* Ecol Soc Am; Am Soc Limnol & Oceanog; Phycologicol Soc Am; Micros Soc Am; NAm Benthological Soc. *Res:* Ecology of Protozoa, Algae and Micrometazoa; invertebrate ecology; applied ecology and environmental impacts. *Mailing Add:* Dept Biol Univ Mo Kansas City MO 64110

STERN, DAVID P, b Decin, Czech, Dec 17, 31; US citizen; m 61; c 3. SPACE PHYSICS. *Educ:* Hebrew Univ, Israel, MSc, 55; Israel Inst Technol, DSc(physics), 59. *Prof Exp:* Res assoc physics, Univ Md, 59-61; Nat Acad Sci-Nat Res Coun resident res assoc, 61-63, PHYSICIST, GODDARD SPACE FLIGHT CTR, NASA, 63- *Mem:* Am Phys Soc; Am Geophys Union; Am Asn Physics Teachers; AAAS. *Res:* Geomagnetic field, its structure, configuration and dynamics; geomagnetic plasmas and particle motion; theory of magnetospheric electric fields; field-aligned currents and associated processes. *Mailing Add:* Code 695 NASA Goddard Space Flight Ctr Greenbelt MD 20771

STERN, EDWARD ABRAHAM, b Detroit, Mich, Sept 19, 30; m 55; c 3. SOLID STATE SCIENCE. *Educ:* Calif Inst Technol, BS, 51, PhD(physics), 55. *Prof Exp:* Res fel solid state physics, Calif Inst Technol, 55-57; from asst prof to prof, Univ Md, 57-66; PROF PHYSICS, UNIV WASH, 66- *Concurrent Pos:* Guggenheim fel, 63-64; NSF sr res fel, 70-71. *Honors & Awards:* Warren Diffraction Physics Award, Am Crystal Asn, 79. *Mem:* Am Phys Soc. *Res:* Electronic structure of metals and alloys; collective effects; magnetism; atomic structure of amorphous and biological matter. *Mailing Add:* Dept Physics Univ Wash Seattle WA 98195

STERN, ELIZABETH, b Cobalt, Ont, Sept 19, 15; US citizen; m 40; c 3. EXPERIMENTAL PATHOLOGY, EPIDEMIOLOGY. *Educ:* Univ Toronto, MD, 39; Am Bd Path, dipl, 58. *Prof Exp:* Resident path, Cedars of Lebanon Hosp-Good Samaritan Hosp, Los Angeles, 42-46; assoc pathologist, Cedars of Lebanon Hosp, 46-49; dir lab & res, Cancer Detection Ctr, Los Angeles, 50-60; res coordr cancer proj, Med Sch, Univ Southern Calif, 61; lectr path & chief cytol lab, Sch Med, 61-63, assoc res pathologist, Sch Pub Health, 63-65, PROF PUB HEALTH, SCH PUB HEALTH, UNIV CALIF, LOS ANGELES, 65- *Mem:* AAAS; fel Col Am Path; Am Pub Health Asn; AMA. *Res:* Epidemiology of cancer. *Mailing Add:* Sch of Pub Health Univ of Calif Ctr for Health Sci Los Angeles CA 90024

STERN, ERIC WOLFGANG, b Vienna, Austria, Nov 4, 30; nat US; m 60; c 1. CHEMISTRY. *Educ:* Syracuse Univ, BS, 51; Northwestern Univ, PhD(chem), 54. *Prof Exp:* Res chemist, Texaco, Inc, 54-57; res chemist, M W Kellogg Co Div, Pullman, Inc, NJ, 58-63, res assoc, 63-70; SECT HEAD RES & DEVELOP, ENGELHARD INDUSTS DIV, ENGELHARD CORP, EDISON, 70- *Concurrent Pos:* Co-adj prof, Rutgers Univ, 65-74. *Mem:* AAAS; Am Chem Soc; Catalysis Soc; NY Acad Sci; The Chem Soc. *Res:* Heterogeneous catalysis; homogeneous catalysis; coordination chemistry; reaction mechanisms; molecular structure; catalyst characterization. *Mailing Add:* 234 Oak Tree Rd Mountainside NJ 07092

STERN, ERNEST, b Wetter, Ger, June 5, 28; US citizen; m 53; c 4. SOLID STATE PHYSICS, ACOUSTICS. *Educ:* Columbia Univ, BS, 53. *Prof Exp:* Sr engr, Sperry Gyroscope Co, 55-57; mem staff, Electronics Lab, Gen Elec Co, 58-62; vpres, Microwave Chem Lab, 62-64; staff mem, 64-68, group leader acoustics, 68-80, ANALOG DEVICE TECHNOL, LINCOLN LAB, MASS INST TECHNOL, 80- *Concurrent Pos:* Co-chmn, Gorden Conf Ultrasonics, 70. *Mem:* Sigma Xi; Am Phys Soc; fel Inst Elec & Electronics Engrs. *Res:* Gyromagnetic phenomena; microwave frequencies; nonlinear magnetic phenomena; surface acoustics and acousto-electric phenomena; components and devices; x-ray lithography; superconducting devices; electronic engineering. *Mailing Add:* Mass Inst Technol Lincoln Lab Lexington MA 02139

STERN, FRANK, b Koblenz, Ger, Sept 15, 28; nat US; m 55; c 2. THEORETICAL SOLID STATE PHYSICS. *Educ:* Union Col, NY, BS, 49; Princeton Univ, PhD(physics), 55. *Prof Exp:* Physicist, US Naval Ord Lab, Md, 53-62; res staff mem, Thomas J Watson Res Ctr, 62-73, Zurich Res Lab, 65-66, mgr semiconductor electronic properties, 73-81, RES STAFF MEM, THOMAS WATSON RES CTR, IBM CORP, 81- *Concurrent Pos:* Lectr, Univ Md, 55-58, part-time prof, 59-62; chmn, Organizing Comt, Electron Properties Two-Dimensional Systs Int Conf, New London, NH, 81; vis scientist, Max-Planck-Inst Fur Festkorper Forschung, 80. *Honors & Awards:* John Price Wetherill Medal, Franklin Inst, 81. *Mem:* AAAS; fel Am Phys Soc; Sigma Xi; Am Vacuum Soc. *Res:* Cohesive energy of iron; semiconductors; injection lasers; optical properties of solids; quantum effects and transport in inversion layers. *Mailing Add:* Thomas J Watson Res Ctr IBM Corp Yorktown Heights NY 10598

STERN, HERBERT, b Can, Dec 22, 18; m 53; c 3. CELL BIOLOGY. *Educ:* McGill Univ, BSc, 40, MSc, 42, PhD, 45. *Hon Degrees:* DSc, McGill Univ. *Prof Exp:* Royal Soc Can fel, Univ Calif, 46-48; lectr cell physiol, Med Sch, Univ Witwatersrand, 48-49; assoc, Rockefeller Inst Med Res, 49-55; head biochem cytol, Plant Res Inst, Can Dept Agr, 55-60; prof bot, Univ Ill, Urbana, 60-65; chmn dept, 67-76, PROF BIOL, UNIV CALIF, SAN DIEGO, 65- *Concurrent Pos:* Mem develop biol panel, NSF; mem cell biol panel, NIH; mem spec subcomt cellular & subcellular struct & function, Nat Acad Sci. *Mem:* Am Soc Plant Physiol; Soc Develop Biol (pres, 64-65); Am Soc Cell Biol; fel Am Soc Biol Chem; Genetics Soc Am. *Res:* Cell biology and biochemistry. *Mailing Add:* Dept of Biol Univ of Calif at San Diego La Jolla CA 92093

STERN, IRVING B, b New York, NY, Sept 12, 20; m; c 3. DENTISTRY, CELL BIOLOGY. *Educ:* City Col New York, BS, 41; NY Univ, DDS, 46; Columbia Univ, cert, 56. *Prof Exp:* Lectr periodont, Sch Dent, Univ Wash, 59-60, from asst prof to prof, 60-75; PROF PERIODONT & CHMN DEPT, SCH DENT MED, TUFTS UNIV, 75- *Concurrent Pos:* Spec res fel anatomy, Sch Dent, Univ Wash, 61-62; USPHS grant. *Mem:* AAAS; Am Dent Asn; Am Asn Periodont; Am Soc Cell Biol; Int Asn Dent Res. *Res:* Ultrastructure and biology of oral epithelium and epithelial derivatives; ultrastructure of dento-gingival junction and cementum. *Mailing Add:* Dept of Periodont One Kneeland St Boston MA 02111

STERN, IVAN J, biochemistry, bacteriology, see previous edition

STERN, JACK TUTEUR, JR, b Chicago, Ill, Jan 18, 42; m 67; c 2. BIOMECHANICS, HUMAN EVOLUTION. *Educ:* Univ Chicago, PhD(anat), 69. *Prof Exp:* Instr anat, Univ Chicago, 69-70, asst prof, 70-74; assoc prof, 74-81, PROF ANAT, STATE UNIV NY STONY BROOK, 81- *Concurrent Pos:* USPHS res career develop award, 73; assoc ed, Am J Phys Anthrop, 81- *Mem:* Am Asn Phys Anthrop; Am Asn Anat; Int Primatological Soc. *Res:* Functional anatomy of primates; evolution of erect posture; biomechanics and evolution of muscles. *Mailing Add:* Dept of Anat Sci State Univ NY Stony Brook NY 11794

STERN, JOHN HANUS, b Brno, Czech, May 21, 28; nat US; m 49. PHYSICAL CHEMISTRY. *Educ:* Univ Calif, BS, 53; Univ Wash, MS, 54, PhD(chem), 58. *Prof Exp:* From asst prof to assoc prof, 58-67, PROF CHEM, CALIF STATE UNIV, LONG BEACH, 67- *Concurrent Pos:* Am Chem Soc-Petrol Res Found int fac fel, Univ Florence, 64-65; vis prof, Hebrew Univ, Jerusalem, 71-72; Univ London, 79-80. *Mem:* Am Chem Soc. *Res:* Thermodynamics of electrolytes and non-electrolytes in aqueous solutions. *Mailing Add:* Dept of Chem Calif State Univ Long Beach CA 90840

STERN, JOSEPH AARON, b New York, NY, Apr 24, 27; m 50; c 3. MICROBIOLOGY. *Educ:* Mass Inst Technol, SB, 49, SM, 50, PhD(food technol), 53. *Prof Exp:* Food technologist, Davis Bros Fisheries, Mass, 48-49; asst food technol, Mass Inst Technol, 50-53; from asst prof to assoc prof fisheries technol, Univ Wash, 53-58; chief biochem unit, Space Med Sect, Boeing Co, 58-59, res prog dir, Bioastronaut Sect, 59-61, mgr adv space prog, 61-65 & Voyager prog planetary quarantine, 65-66, adv interplanetary explor prog, 66; sterilization group supvr, Environ Requirements Sect, Jet Propulsion Lab, Calif, 66-67, asst sect mgr sterilization, 67-69; PRES, BIONETICS CORP, 69- *Concurrent Pos:* Mem comt animal food prod, NSF-Nat Res Coun, 58-60. *Mem:* AAAS; Am Inst Aeronaut & Astronaut; NY Acad Sci; Am Inst Biol Sci. *Res:* Spoilage and preservation of food products; biochemical systems in space flight and extraterrestrial missions; planetary quarantine; spacecraft sterilization. *Mailing Add:* Bionetics Corp 18 Research Dr Hampton VA 23366

STERN, JUDITH S, b Brooklyn, NY, Apr 25, 43; m 64. NUTRITION. *Educ:* Cornell Univ, BS, 64; Harvard Univ, MS, 66, ScD, 70. *Prof Exp:* From res assoc to asst prof, Rockefeller Univ, 69-74; asst prof, 75-77, ASSOC PROF NUTRIT, UNIV CALIF, DAVIS, 77- *Mem:* Inst Food Tech; Am Inst Nutrit; Am Dietetic Asn; AAAS; Sigma Xi. *Res:* Studies of some critical factors involved in the development of obesity which include adipose cellularity, food intake, diet composition, exercise, hyperinsulinemia and tissue resistance in muscle and adipose. *Mailing Add:* Dept of Nutrit Univ of Calif Davis CA 95616

STERN, KINGSLEY ROWLAND, b Port Elizabeth, SAfrica, Oct 30, 27; nat US; m 56; c 2. TAXONOMIC BOTANY. *Educ:* Wheaton Col, Ill, BS, 49; Univ Mich, MA, 50; Univ Minn, PhD(bot), 59. *Prof Exp:* Asst, Univ Mich, 49-51 & Univ Ill, 54-55; asst, Univ Minn, 55-56 & 57-58; instr biol, Hamline Univ, 57-58; from asst prof to assoc prof, 59-68, PROF BOT, CALIF STATE UNIV, CHICO, 68- *Concurrent Pos:* NSF res grants, 59, 60 & 63-71; consult, Bot Field Surveys. *Mem:* Am Soc Plant Taxon; Bot Soc Am; Int Soc Plant Taxon. *Res:* Taxonomy of vascular plants, especially pollen grains, anatomy, cytology and morphogenesis. *Mailing Add:* Dept of Biol Sci Calif State Univ Chico CA 95929

STERN, KURT, b Vienna, Austria, Apr 3, 09; nat US; m 39; c 3. PATHOLOGY, CANCER. *Educ:* Univ Vienna, MD, 33. *Prof Exp:* Instr biochem, Inst Med Chem, Univ Vienna, 30-33, res assoc, 33-38; jr physician, State Inst Study & Treatment Malignant Dis, Buffalo, 43-45; asst pathologist, Mt Sinai Hosp, 45-48, from asst to assoc dir, Mt Sinai Med Res Found, 48-60, dir blood ctr, 50-60; prof path & pathologist, Res & Educ Hosp, 60-70, EMER PROF PATH, UNIV ILL COL MED, 70-; RES PROF, LAUTENBERG CTR IMMUNOL, HEBREW UNIV-HADASSAH MED SCH, JERUSALEM, 81- *Concurrent Pos:* Res fel, New York Cancer Hosp & Div Cancer, Bellevue Hosp, 39-40; from assoc to assoc prof, Chicago Med Sch, 49-60; sci ed, Bull Am Asn Blood Banks, 60; prof life sci, Bar-Ilan Univ, Israel, 69-80. *Mem:* Fel Am Soc Clin Path; Soc Exp Biol & Med; Am Soc Exp Path; Am Asn Immunol; Am Asn Cancer Res. *Res:* Experimental cancer research; immunology; experimental pathology; blood groups and immunohematology; physiopathology of reticulo-endothelial system. *Mailing Add:* Lautenberg Ctr Immunol Hadassah Med Sch POB 1172 Ramat-Gan Israel

STERN, KURT HEINZ, b Vienna, Austria, Dec 26, 26; nat US; m 60; c 2. PHYSICAL INORGANIC CHEMISTRY. *Educ:* Drew Univ, AB, 48; Univ Mich, MS, 50; Clark Univ, PhD(chem), 53. *Prof Exp:* Asst, Univ Mich, 50; instr chem, Clark Univ, 50-52; from instr to assoc prof, Univ Ark, 52-60; res chemist, Electrochem Sect, Nat Bur Stand, 60-68; sect head high temperature electrochem, 68-74, RES CHEMIST, INORG & ELECTROCHEM BR & CONSULT, NAVAL RES LAB, 74- *Concurrent Pos:* Res assoc, Nat Acad Sci-Nat Res Coun, 59-60; mem fac, Grad Sch, NIH, 63- *Honors & Awards:* Turner Prize, Electrochem Soc, 51, Blum Award, 71. *Mem:* Am Chem Soc; Electrochem Soc; Royal Soc Chem; AAAS. *Res:* High temperature electrochemistry; molten salts; vaporization and thermal decomposition of inorganic salts. *Mailing Add:* Inorg & Electrochem Br Naval Res Lab Washington DC 20375

STERN, LEO, b Montreal, Que, Jan 20, 31; m 55; c 4. PERINATAL BIOLOGY, CLINICAL PHARMACOLOGY. *Educ:* McGill Univ, BSc, 51; Univ Man, MD, 56; FRCPS(C), 64. *Prof Exp:* Demonstr, McGill Univ, 62-66, lectr, 66-67, from asst prof to assoc prof pediat, 67-73; PROF PEDIAT & CHMN DEPT, BROWN UNIV, 73- *Concurrent Pos:* Mead Johnson res fel, Karolinska Inst, Sweden, 58-59, Nat Res Coun Can med res fel, 59-60; Queen Elizabeth II scientist for res in dis of children, McGill Univ, 66-72; mem, Comn Study Perinatal Mortality, Prov of Que, 67-73; dir dept newborn med, Montreal Childrens Hosp, 69-73; pediatrician-in-chief, RI Hosp, 73- *Honors & Awards:* Queen Elizabeth II Res Scientist Award, 66. *Mem:* Perinatal Res Soc; Soc Pediat Res; Am Soc Clin Nutrit; Am Soc Clin Pharmacol & Therapeut. *Res:* Development pharmacology; perinatal biology, adaptation to extrauterine life, thermoregulation and bilirubin metabolism in the new born, respiratory adaptation in the normal and abnormal newborn infant. *Mailing Add:* Dept of Pediat RI Hosp Providence RI 02902

STERN, MARSHALL DANA, b New York, NY, Mar 18, 49; m 74; c 1. RUMEN MICROBIOLOGY, PROTEIN NUTRITION. *Educ:* State Univ NY, Farmingdale, AAS, 70; Cornell Univ, BS, 72; Univ RI, MS, 75; Univ Maine, PhD(animal nutrit), 77. *Prof Exp:* Res assoc fel, Univ Wis-Madison, 77-81; ASST PROF RUMINANT NUTRIT, UNIV MINN, ST PAUL, 81- *Concurrent Pos:* Ed, J Animal Sci, 82-84. *Mem:* Am Soc Animal Sci; Am Dairy Sci Asn; Nutrit Soc. *Res:* Protein (amino acid) requirements and nitrogen utilization in high producing dairy cows; metabolism of nutrients in gastro intestinal tract of ruminants; factors affecting fermentation and microbiol populations in the rumen. *Mailing Add:* Dept Animal Sci 130 Haecker Hall Univ Minn St Paul MN 55108

STERN, MARTIN, b New York, NY, Jan 9, 33; m 69; c 1. ORAL SURGERY. *Educ:* Harvard Univ, DMD, 56; Am Bd Oral Surg, dipl, 63. *Prof Exp:* ATTEND SURGEON IN CHG ORAL SURG, LONG ISLAND JEWISH MED CTR/QUEENS HOSP CTR AFFILIATION, 67-, ASSOC DIR DENT, 72-; PROF ORAL SURG, SCH DENT MED, STATE UNIV NY STONY BROOK, 71- *Concurrent Pos:* Asst clin prof, Sch Dent, Columbia Univ, 68-70. *Mem:* Am Dent Asn; Am Soc Oral Surg; Int Asn Dent Res. *Mailing Add:* Dept Oral Surg Queens Hosp Ctr 82-68 164th St Jamaica NY 11432

STERN, MARVIN, b New York, NY, Jan 6, 16; m 42; c 3. PSYCHIATRY. *Educ:* City Col New York, BS, 35; NY Univ, MD, 39. *Prof Exp:* From fel to prof psychiat, 40-79, MENAS S GREGORY PROF PSYCHIAT, SCH MED, NY UNIV, 79-, EXEC CHMN DEPT, 76-, ATTEND PSYCHIATRIST, UNIV HOSP, 52- *Concurrent Pos:* Consult, US Vet Admin Regional Off, Brooklyn, 51-66, Manhattan Vet Admin Hosp, 66-, Cabrini Med Ctr, New York, 76- & Brookdale Hosp, Brooklyn, 76-; assoc vis neuropsychiatrist, Bellevue Hosp, 52-62, vis neuropsychiatrist, 62- *Mem:* Psychosom Soc; Am Psychopath Asn; Am Psychiat Asn. *Res:* Psychosomatic medicine; altered brain function in organic disease. *Mailing Add:* 184 Rugby Rd Brooklyn NY 11226

STERN, MAX HERMAN, b Sioux City, Iowa, Mar 23, 20; m 46; c 2. ORGANIC CHEMISTRY. *Educ:* Morningside Col, BA, 41; Univ Wis, MS, 43, PhD(org chem), 45. *Prof Exp:* Asst, Univ Wis, 42-45; res chemist, Distillation Prod Industs, 45-65, RES ASSOC, RES LABS, EASTMAN KODAK CO, 65- *Mem:* Am Chem Soc. *Res:* Vitamins A and E; carotenoids; soysterols; terpenes; photochemistry; photographic addenda. *Mailing Add:* 715 Winton Rd S Rochester NY 14618

STERN, MELVIN ERNEST, b New York, NY, Jan 22, 29; m 56; c 2. HYDRODYNAMICS. *Educ:* Cooper Union, BEE, 50; Ill Inst Technol, MS, 51; Mass Inst Technol, PhD(meteorol), 56. *Prof Exp:* From res assoc meteorol to physicist, Woods Hole Oceanog Inst, 51-64; PROF OCEANOG, GRAD SCH, UNIV RI, 64- *Concurrent Pos:* Guggenheim fel, 70-71. *Mem:* Fel Am Acad Arts & Sci, 75. *Res:* Oceanic circulation and turbulence; non-linear stability theory. *Mailing Add:* Grad Sch of Oceanog Univ of RI Kingston RI 02881

STERN, MICHELE SUCHARD, b Chicago, Ill, Mar 17, 43; m 63. PLANT PHYSIOLOGY, BIOCHEMISTRY. *Educ:* Univ Ill, Urbana, BS, 64; Tenn Technol Univ, MS, 66; Tulane Univ, PhD(biol), 69. *Prof Exp:* Asst prof, 69-75, ASSOC PROF BIOL, UNIV MO-KANSAS CITY, 75- *Mem:* Am Soc Plant Physiol; Am Chem Soc; Ecol Soc Am; Am Soc Limnol & Oceanog; Am Inst Biol Sci. *Res:* Isolation and characterization of plant proteases and their relationship to senescence; aquatic entomology and limnology; water pollution; aquatic toxicology; ecology; environmental sci. *Mailing Add:* Dept Biol Univ Mo Kansas City MO 64110

STERN, MILTON, b Boston, Mass, Apr 20, 27; m 49; c 3. CHEMICAL ENGINEERING, PHYSICAL METALLURGY. *Educ:* Northeastern Univ, BS, 49; Mass Inst Technol, MS, 50, PhD(phys metall, corrosion), 52. *Prof Exp:* Res scientist, Metals Div, Union Carbide Corp, NY, 54-60, mgr res, Linde Div, Ind, 60-65, mgr mat res, NY, 65-67, mgr corp res 67, dir technol, Mat Systs Div, 67-68, vpres, Electronics Div, 68-69, exec vpres, Mining & Metals Div, 69-73; vpres, 73-76, sr vpres, 76-78; PROF ELEC ENG, COLUMBIA UNIV, 76-, *Honors & Awards:* Willis R Whitney Award, 63. *Mem:* Nat Asn Corrosion Eng; Electrochem Soc; Am Inst Mining, Metall & Petrol Eng. *Res:* Electrochemistry; corrosion; kinetics; plasma technology; crystal growth; welding. *Mailing Add:* Kennecott Corp Ten Stamford Forum Stamford CT 06904

STERN, MORRIS, b St Louis, Mo, Nov 26, 30; m 52; c 2. ENGINEERING MECHANICS. *Educ:* Wash Univ, BS, 52; Univ Ill, MS, 57, PhD(eng mech), 62. *Prof Exp:* Teaching & res assoc theoret appl mech, Univ Ill, 56, asst prof, 62-66; ASSOC PROF ENG MECH, UNIV TEX, AUSTIN, 66- *Concurrent Pos:* Vis asst prof, Univ Colo, 65-66. *Mem:* Am Soc Eng Sci. *Res:* Solid mechanics; continuum mechanics; shell theory. *Mailing Add:* Dept Aerospace Eng & Eng Mech Univ of Tex Austin TX 78712

STERN, PAULA HELENE, b New Brunswick, NJ, Jan 20, 38; m 59. PHARMACOLOGY. *Educ:* Univ Rochester, BA, 59; Univ Cincinnati, MS, 61; Univ Mich, PhD(pharmacol), 63. *Prof Exp:* Instr pharmacol, Univ Mich, 65-66; from asst prof to assoc prof, 66-77, PROF PHARMACOL, MED SCH, NORTHWESTERN UNIV, 77- *Concurrent Pos:* Fel pharmacol, Rochester Univ, 63-64 & Marine Biol Lab, Woods Hole, Mass, 64; res career develop award, NIH; consult, Food & Drug Admin; Am Inst Biol Sci/NASA mem, Gen Med B Study Sect, NIH. *Mem:* Am Soc Pharmacol & Exp Therapeut; Endocrine Soc; Asn Women Sci; Am Soc Bone & Mineral Res; Soc Exp Biol & Med. *Res:* Calcium metabolism; mechanisms of action of drugs and hormones on bone. *Mailing Add:* Dept of Pharmacol Northwestern Univ Med Sch Chicago IL 60611

STERN, RAUL A(RISTIDE), b Bucarest, Rumania, Dec 26, 28; US citizen; m 53; c 2. PLASMA PHYSICS, GAS DYNAMICS. *Educ:* Univ Wis, BS, 52, MS, 53; Univ Calif, Berkeley, PhD(aeronaut sci), 59. *Prof Exp:* Res assoc, Univ Calif, Berkeley, 59-60; mem tech staff, Bell Labs, 60-78; PROF ASTRO-GEOPHYS AND PHYS & ASTROPHYS, UNIV COLO, BOULDER, 78- *Concurrent Pos:* Vis prof, New York Univ, 69-70 & Univ Calif, Los Angeles, 77-78; vis res physicist, Univ Calif, Irvine, 75- *Mem:* Fel Am Phys Soc. *Res:* Plasma waves and oscillations; shock and detonation waves; gas discharge physics; atmospheric physics; microwave and laser interactions with plasmas; diagnostics; nonlinear plasma properties. *Mailing Add:* Dept of Astro-Geophys Univ of Colo Boulder CO 80302

STERN, RICHARD, b Paterson, NJ, Nov 27, 29; m 58, 80. ACOUSTICS. *Educ:* Univ Calif, Los Angeles, BA, 52, MS, 56, PhD(physics), 64. *Prof Exp:* Asst res physicist, 64-65, asst prof eng, 66-71, assoc prof, 71-76, PROF ENG, UNIV CALIF, LOS ANGELES, 76-, ASST DEAN UNDERGRAD STUDIES, 75- *Concurrent Pos:* Exchange fel, Imp Col, Univ London, 71- *Mem:* fel Acoust Soc Am; Inst Elec & Electronics Engrs. *Res:* Experimentation in physical, engineering and medical acoustics. *Mailing Add:* Sch Eng & Appl Sci Univ Calif Los Angeles CA 90024

STERN, RICHARD CECIL, b New York, NY, Jan 4, 42; m 64. CHEMICAL PHYSICS. *Educ:* Cornell Univ, AB, 63; Harvard Univ, AM, 65, PhD(chem), 68. *Prof Exp:* From asst prof to assoc prof chem, Columbia Univ, 68-74; CHEMIST, LAWRENCE LIVERMORE LAB, UNIV CALIF, 74- *Mem:* Am Chem Soc; Am Phys Soc. *Res:* Laser isotope separation; photochemical kinetics; scattering and chemical reactions of low energy electrons; molecular beam and time-of-flight technology. *Mailing Add:* Lawrence Livermore Lab Univ of Calif Livermore CA 94550

STERN, RICHARD MARTIN, JR, b New York, NY, July 5, 48. AUDITORY PERCEPTION, AUTOMATIC SPEECH RECOGNITION. *Educ:* Mass Inst Technol, SB, 70, PhD(elec eng), 77; Univ Calif, Berkeley, MS, 72. *Prof Exp:* ASST PROF ELEC & BIOMED ENG, CARNEGIE-MELLON UNIV, 77- *Mem:* Acoust Soc Am; Inst Elec & Electronics Engrs; Audio Eng Soc. *Res:* Auditory perception of simple and complex monaural and binaural sounds and relation of psychoacoustical results to peripheral auditory physiology; computer recognition of speech sounds; computer generation and performance of music. *Mailing Add:* Dept Elec Eng Carnegie-Mellon Univ Pittsburgh PA 15213

STERN, ROBERT, b Bad Kreuznach, Ger, Feb 11, 36; US citizen; m 63; c 3. PATHOLOGY, BIOCHEMISTRY. *Educ:* Harvard Univ, BA, 57; Univ Wash, MD, 62. *Prof Exp:* USPHS officer, Nat Inst Dent Res, 63-65; sr scientist, Nat Inst Dent Res, 67-77; resident anat path, Nat Cancer Inst, 74-76; ASSOC PROF, DEPT PATH, UNIV CALIF, SAN FRANCISCO, 77- *Concurrent Pos:* Nat Cancer Inst spec fel, Weizmann Inst Sci, 65-67. *Mem:* AAAS; Am Soc Biol Chem; Am Soc Microbiol. *Res:* Transcriptional, translational controls in animal cells; translation of collagen messenger RNA; anatomic pathology; pathologic fibrosis. *Mailing Add:* 555 Buena Vista W Apt 606 San Francisco CA 94117

STERN, ROBERT LOUIS, b Newark, NJ, Apr 10, 35; m 58; c 3. ORGANIC CHEMISTRY. *Educ:* Oberlin Col, AB, 57; Johns Hopkins Univ, MA, 59, PhD(org chem), 64. *Prof Exp:* Asst prof chem, Northeastern Univ, 62-65, assoc prof, 65-68; ASSOC PROF CHEM, OAKLAND UNIV, 68-, CO-CHMN DEPT, 74- *Mem:* AAAS; Am Chem Soc. *Res:* Organoanalytical chemistry; organic reaction mechanisms; biosynthesis; separation mechanisms of structurally related organic molecules; organic photochemistry. *Mailing Add:* Dept of Chem Oakland Univ Rochester MI 48063

STERN, ROBERT MALCOLM, bacteriology, deceased

STERN, RONALD JOHN, b Chicago, Ill, Jan 20, 47; div. TOPOLOGY. *Educ:* Knox Col, BA, 68; Univ Calif, Los Angeles, MA, 70, PhD(math), 73. *Prof Exp:* Mem, Inst Advan Study, 73-74; instr math, Univ Utah, 74-76, asst prof, 76; mem, Inst des Hautes Etudes Sci, 77-78; ASSOC PROF MATH, UNIV UTAH, 79- *Mem:* Am Math Soc. *Res:* Geometrical topology emphasizing the structure of topological manifolds. *Mailing Add:* Dept Math Univ Utah Salt Lake City UT 84112

STERN, SAMUEL T, b Buffalo, NY, May 27, 28; m 57; c 3. MATHEMATICS. *Educ:* Univ Buffalo, BA, 57, MA, 60; State Univ NY Buffalo, PhD(math), 62. *Prof Exp:* Instr math, Univ Buffalo, 58-62; asst prof, 62-65, PROF MATH, STATE UNIV NY COL BUFFALO, 65- *Concurrent Pos:* State Univ NY fac res fel, 67 & 70. *Mem:* Math Asn Am. *Res:* Noncommutative number theory; modern algebra; theory of skew groups and skew rings. *Mailing Add:* 115 Millbrook Dr Williamsville NY 14221

STERN, SILVIU ALEXANDER, b Bucharest, Romania, June 18, 21; US citizen; m 73; c 2. PHYSICAL CHEMISTRY, CHEMICAL ENGINEERING. *Educ:* Israel Inst Technol, BS, 45; Ohio State Univ, MS, 48, PhD(phys chem), 52. *Prof Exp:* Res assoc chem eng, Ohio State Univ, 52-55; res engr, Linde Div, Union Carbide Corp, NY, 55-58, group leader, 58-60, res supvr, 60-67; PROF CHEM ENG, SYRACUSE UNIV, 67- *Concurrent Pos:* Acad vis chem dept, Imp Col Sci & Technol, London, 75; adj prof chem & assoc mem, Inst Polymer Res, State Univ NY Col Environ Sci & Forestry, Syracuse, 79- *Mem:* Am Chem Soc; Am Inst Chem Engrs; AAAS. *Res:* Transport phenomena in polymers; separation processes, particularly membrane separation processes; surface phenomena; biomedical engineering. *Mailing Add:* Dept of Chem Eng & Mat Sci 312 Hinds Hall Syracuse Univ Syracuse NY 13210

STERN, THEODORE, b Frankfurt am Main, Ger, Aug 27, 29; nat US; m 51; c 2. NUCLEAR ENGINEERING. *Educ:* Pratt Inst, BME, 51; NY Univ, MS, 56. *Prof Exp:* Engr, Foster Wheeler Corp, NY, 52-55, proj mgr, 55-56, head res reactor sect, 56-58; asst to tech dir, Atomic Power Dept, 58, mgr adv develop, 58-59, mgr plant develop, 59-62, mgr, Projs Dept, 62-66, gen mgr, Pressurized Water Reactor Plant Div, 66-71, vpres & gen mgr, Nuclear Fuel Div, 71-72 & Water Reactor Div, 72-74, EXEC VPRES, WESTINGHOUSE ELEC CORP, 74- *Mem:* Nat Acad Eng; Am Soc Mech Engrs; Am Nuclear Soc. *Res:* Application of nuclear energy to commercial generation of electric power. *Mailing Add:* Westinghouse Elec Corp 6 Gateway Ctr Pittsburgh PA 15222

STERN, THOMAS E(DWIN), b New Rochelle, NY, Mar 29, 30; m 58; c 3. ELECTRICAL ENGINEERING. *Educ:* Mass Inst Technol, BS & MS, 53, ScD, 56. *Prof Exp:* Asst, Res Lab Electronics, Mass Inst Technol, 53-56; from asst prof to assoc prof, 58-76, PROF ELEC ENG, COLUMBIA UNIV, 76-,

CHMN DEPT ELEC ENG & COMPUT SCI, 72- *Concurrent Pos:* Consult, Lincoln Labs, Mass Inst Technol, 56, Polarad Electronics Corp, 59-60 & Neptune Meter Co, 60-; res engr, Saclay Nuclear Res Ctr, France, 61-62; Fulbright res scholar, fac sci, Univ Paris, 65-66; consult, IBM Corp, 71-, fel, 71-72. *Mem:* AAAS; fel Inst Elec & Electronics Engrs; Asn Comput Mach. *Res:* Nonlinear network theory; sequential circuits; quantum effects in information channels; coding theory. *Mailing Add:* Dept of Elec Eng & Comput Sci Columbia Univ New York NY 10027

STERN, THOMAS WHITAL, b Chicago, Ill, Dec 12, 22; m 55; c 1. GEOCHRONOLOGY. *Educ:* Univ Chicago, SB, 47; Univ Tex, MA, 48. *Prof Exp:* Geologist, 48-68, chief isotope geol br, 68-71, GEOLOGIST, US GEOL SURV, 71- *Mem:* AAAS; Geol Soc Am; Mineral Soc Am; Am Geophys Union; Geochem Soc. *Res:* Geochemistry; mineralogy; lead-uranium age determinations; isotope geology; autoradiography. *Mailing Add:* US Geol Surv 981 Nat Ctr Reston VA 22092

STERN, VERNON MARK, b Sykeston, NDak, Mar 28, 23; m 47; c 2. ENTOMOLOGY. *Educ:* Univ Calif, Berkeley, BS, 49, PhD, 52. *Prof Exp:* Res asst entom, Univ Calif, Berkeley, 49-52; entomologist, Producers Cotton Oil Co, Ariz, 52-56; asst entomologist, 56-62, assoc prof, 62-68, PROF ENTOM, UNIV CALIF, RIVERSIDE, 68-, ASSOC RES ENTOMOLOGIST, LAB NUCLEAR MED & RADIATION BIOL, LOS ANGELES, 66- *Concurrent Pos:* Collabr, USDA, 53-56; vpres, Ariz State Bd Pest Control, 53-56; coordr, Producers Agr Found, 54-56; NSF res grants, 61-69; Cotton Producers Inst res grant, 63-69; consult, US AEC, 65-66 & UN Food & Agr Orgn, 66-; Cotton Inst res grant, 69-; USDA res grant, 71-; int biol prog, NSF res grant, 72- *Mem:* Entom Soc Am; Ecol Soc Am. *Res:* Insect ecology; integrated control of arthropod pests; environmental radiation; radioecology; arthropods; population dynamics; insect migration and biology of insects. *Mailing Add:* Dept of Entom Univ of Calif Riverside CA 92502

STERN, W EUGENE, b Portland, Ore, Jan 1, 20; m 46; c 4. SURGERY. *Educ:* Univ Calif, AB, 41, MD, 43. *Prof Exp:* Clin instr neurol surg, 51-52, from asst prof to assoc prof surg, 52-59, PROF SURG, SCH MED, UNIV CALIF, LOS ANGELES, 59-, CHIEF NEUROSURG DIV, 67- *Concurrent Pos:* Consult, Los Angeles Vet Admin Hosp, 52-; vchmn, Am Bd Neurol Surgeons. *Mem:* AMA; Am Surg Asn; Am Asn Neurol Surg (pres, 78); Soc Neurol Surg (past pres, 76); Am Col Surgeons (secy). *Res:* Cerebral swelling; intracranial circulatory dynamics and intracranial mass dynamics. *Mailing Add:* Neurosurg Div Univ of Calif Sch of Med Los Angeles CA 90024

STERN, WILLIAM, b Berlin, Ger, Jan 27, 46; m 75. BIOCHEMISTRY. *Educ:* NY Univ, BA, 67; Univ Mich, MS, 69, PhD(biochem), 72. *Prof Exp:* Asst, 72-76, ASSOC, PUB HEALTH RES INST, 76- *Mem:* Am Soc Microbiol; Am Chem Soc; Harvey Soc; NY Acad Sci; Tissue Culture Asn. *Res:* Regulation of phosphatidylcholine and phosphatidylglycerol metabolism in prenatal rat lungs. *Mailing Add:* 3524 Cambridge Ave Bronx NY 10463

STERN, WILLIAM LOUIS, b Paterson, NJ, Sept 10, 26; m 49; c 2. PLANT ANATOMY. *Educ:* Rutgers Univ, BS, 50; Univ Ill, MS, 51, PhD(bot), 54. *Prof Exp:* From instr to asst prof wood anat, Sch Forestry, Yale Univ, 53-60; cur, Samuel James Record Mem Collection, 53-60; cur, Div Plant Anat, Smithsonian Inst, 60-64, chmn dept bot, 64-67; prof bot, Univ Md, College Park, 67-79, cur herbarium, 73-76; PROF & CHMN, DEPT BOT, UNIV FLA, GAINESVILLE, 79- *Concurrent Pos:* Ed, Trop Woods, 53-60, Plant Sci Bull, 61-64 & Biotropica, 68-73; expert, UN Food & Agr Orgn, Philippines, 63-64; mem sci adv comt, Pac Trop Bot Garden, 69 & H P du Pont Winterthur Mus, 73; ed, Memoirs, Torrey Bot Club, 72-75; mem comt, Visit Arnold Arboretum, Harvard Univ, 72; vchmn comt, 73; prog dir syst biol, NSF, 78- *Mem:* Bot Soc Am; Am Soc Plant Taxon (pres, 81); Am Inst Biol Sci; AAAS; fel Linnean Soc. *Res:* Plant anatomy and its relationship to taxonomic botany; plant morphology and phylogeny; tropical dendrology; natural history of tropical plants; history of botany and horticulture. *Mailing Add:* Dept Bot Univ Fla Gainesville FL 32611

STERNBACH, DANIEL DAVID, b Montclair, NJ, May 28, 49. ORGANIC CHEMISTRY. *Educ:* Univ Rochester, BS, 71; Brandeis Univ, PhD(org chem), 76. *Prof Exp:* Swiss Nat Sci Found res asst, Swiss Fed Inst Technol, 76-77; res fel, Harvard Univ, 77-79; ASST PROF, DUKE UNIV, 79- *Mem:* Am Chem Soc. *Res:* Synthesis of interesting and biologically significant organic compounds and investigation of new synthetic methods. *Mailing Add:* Dept Chem Duke Univ Durham NC 27706

STERNBERG, BEN KOLLOCK, b Wausau, Wis, Sept 11, 47; m 70; c 2. GEOPHYSICS. *Educ:* Univ Wis-Madison, BS, 70, MS, 74, PhD(geophys), 77. *Prof Exp:* Res asst, Univ Wis, 70-77; res scientist geophys, Continental Oil Co, Okla, 77-70; SUPVR, EM GROUP, CONOCO, 79- *Mem:* Soc Explor Geophysicists; Europ Asn Explor Geophysicists; Sigma Xi. *Res:* Use of geophysics to study the solid earth; development of techniques for prospecting for minerals and petroleum using electrical and electromagnetic probing methods. *Mailing Add:* Explor Res Conoco PO Box 1267 Ponca City OK 74603

STERNBERG, ELI, b Vienna, Austria, Nov 13, 17; nat US; m 56; c 2. MECHANICS. *Educ:* NC State Univ, BCE, 41; Ill Inst Technol, MSc, 43, PhD(mech), 45. *Hon Degrees:* DSc, NC State Univ, 63. *Prof Exp:* Instr mech, 43-45, from asst prof to prof, Ill Inst Technol, 45-56; vis prof, Delft Univ Technol, 56-57; prof appl math, Brown Univ, 57-63; vis prof, Keio Univ Japan, 63-64; prof appl mech, 64-70, PROF MECH, CALIF INST TECHNOL, 70- *Concurrent Pos:* Fulbright award, 56 & 70; Guggenheim award, 63. *Mem:* Nat Acad Sci; Am Acad Arts & Sci; Nat Acad Eng. *Res:* Applied mathematics; continuum mechanics; elasticity and viscoelasticity theories. *Mailing Add:* Div of Eng & Appl Sci Calif Inst of Technol Pasadena CA 91125

STERNBERG, JOSEPH, b Brooklyn, NY, Nov 24, 21; m 46; c 4. FLUID MECHANICS, AERODYNAMICS. *Educ:* Calif Inst Technol, BS, 42, MS, 43; Johns Hopkins Univ, PhD(aeronaut), 55. *Prof Exp:* Res supvr supersonic flow, Calif Inst Technol, 43-46; aerodynamicist, US Army Ballistic Res Labs, 46-49, chief, Supersonic Wind Tunnels Br, 50-58 & Exterior Ballistics Lab, 58-62; consult aerodyn, Baltimore Div, Martin Marietta Corp, 62-63, mgr res & develop, 63-65, asst dir eng, 65-66, dir adv systs, Aerospace Hq, 66-70; sci adv to supreme allied comdr Europe, Supreme Hq Allied Powers Europe, 71-76; DIR, AEROSPACE GROUP, MARTIN MARIETTA CORP, 76- *Concurrent Pos:* Mem subcomt fluid mech, Nat Adv Comt Aeronaut, 50-58; mem res adv comt fluid mech, NASA, 58-62, mem res adv subcomt fluid mech, 67-69; mem consult panel, Chief Naval Opers, Opers Eval Group, 60-62; mem fluid dynamics panel, Adv Group for Aeronaut Res & Develop, NATO, 60-64; mem ground warfare panel, President's Sci Adv Comt, 69-70; mem, Army Sci Adv Panel, 70. *Honors & Awards:* Arthur S Flemming Award, 59. *Mem:* Assoc fel Am Inst Aeronaut & Astronaut; Am Phys Soc. *Res:* Boundary layer phenomena; shock wave reflections and structure; turbulent shear flows; missile and reentry systems. *Mailing Add:* 9604 Falls Bridge Lane Potomac MD 20854

STERNBERG, MOSHE, b Marculesti, Rumania, Sept 3, 29; m 55; c 2. FOOD SCIENCE, BIOCHEMISTRY. *Educ:* Parhon Univ, Bucharest, Rumania, 52, PhD(org chem), 61. *Prof Exp:* Lab chief, Chem Pharmaceut Res Inst, Bucharest, Rumania, 55-57; res fel, Israel Inst Technol, 61-62; dir protein & carbohydrate res, Miles Labs, Inc, 62-80; VPRES RES & DEVELOP, CUTTER LABS INC, 80- *Mem:* Am Chem Soc; Am Asn Cereal Chemists; Inst Food Technologists; AAAS. *Res:* Separation of industrial enzymes; proteins separation and characterization. *Mailing Add:* Cutter Labs Inc 4th & Parker St Berkeley CA 94710

STERNBERG, RICHARD WALTER, b Mt Pleasant, Iowa, Nov 21, 34; m 57; c 3. GEOLOGICAL OCEANOGRAPHY, MARINE SEDIMENTATION. *Educ:* Univ Calif, Los Angeles, BA, 58; Univ Wash, MSc, 61, PhD(oceanog), 65. *Prof Exp:* Assoc oceanog, Univ Wash, 63-65, res asst prof, 65-66; fel, Geomorphol Lab, Uppsala Univ, 66; res geophysicist, Univ Calif, San Diego, 67-68; asst prof. 68-73, assoc prof, 73-75, actg chmn dept, 78-79, PROF OCEANOG, UNIV WASH, 75- *Concurrent Pos:* adj assoc prof environ studies, Univ Wash, 73- *Mem:* Soc Econ Paleontologists & Mineralogists. *Res:* Geological oceanography, especially processes of sediment transport and boundary-layer flow near the seafloor. *Mailing Add:* Dept of Oceanog Univ of Wash Seattle WA 98195

STERNBERG, ROBERT LANGLEY, b Newark, NJ, Apr 9, 22; m 50; c 3. MATHEMATICS, ENGINEERING. *Educ:* Northwestern Univ, BS, 46, MA, 48, PhD(math), 51. *Prof Exp:* Asst instrument engr, Clinton Labs, Manhattan Proj, 44-45, jr physicist, 45-46; asst math, Northwestern Univ, 46-50, lectr, 50-51; mathematician, Lab for Electronics, Inc, 51-63; mem, Inst Naval Studies, 63-66; chief adv study group & staff scientist, Res Dept, Elec Boat Div, Gen Dynamics Corp, 66-71; prof math, Univ RI, 71-73, lectr eng, 73-76, MATHEMATICIAN & SCI ADMINR, OFF NAVAL RES, BOSTON BR, 76- *Concurrent Pos:* Consult, Army Res Off, 63, McGill Univ, 65 & 67 & Sanders Assocs, 66; mathematician, Naval Underwater Systs Ctr, 72-73 & 74-76, consult, 76-; lectr math, Univ New Haven, 74-76; lectr statist, Univ Conn, 75. *Mem:* Am Math Soc; Sigma Xi; fel Brit Interplanetary Soc. *Res:* Systems of differential equations; applied mathematics; Bennett functions; microwave lens antennas; ocean resources; operations research; acoustic antennas; astronautics; thermo-nuclear deterrence; applied mathematics and ocean engineering. *Mailing Add:* 113 Seneca Dr Noank CT 06340

STERNBERG, STEPHEN STANLEY, b New York, NY, July 30, 20; m 58; c 2. PATHOLOGY, ONCOLOGY. *Educ:* Colby Col, BA, 41; NY Univ, MD, 44. *Prof Exp:* Resident path, Sch Med, Tulane Univ, 47-49; ATTEND PATH, MEM HOSP, 49-; PROF PATH, MED COL, CORNELL UNIV, 79- *Concurrent Pos:* Mem, Sloan-Kettering Inst, 49-; mem, Sci Adv Comt, Sch Med, Stanford Univ, 78-81; consult pathologist, Food & Drug Admin, 71-73 & NSF, Div Problem-Focused Res, 75-79; ed-in-chief, Am J Surg Path, 76-; ed, Human Path, 77-81; pres med bd, Mem Hosp, New York, 78- *Mem:* Am Asn Cancer Res; Int Acad Path; Soc Toxicol; NY Acad Med. *Res:* Carcinogenesis; surgical pathology; toxicology of cancer chemotherapeutic agents. *Mailing Add:* Mem Sloan-Kettering Cancer Ctr 1275 York Ave New York NY 10021

STERNBERG, YARON MOSHE, b Tel Aviv, Israel, May 26, 36; m 61; c 2. GROUND WATER HYDROLOGY. *Educ:* Univ Ill, BS, 61; Univ Calif, MS, 63, PhD(eng), 65. *Prof Exp:* From asst prof to assoc prof geol, Ind Univ, Bloomington, 65-70; assoc prof, 70-74, PROF CIVIL ENG, UNIV MD, COLLEGE PARK, 74- *Mem:* Am Soc Civil Engrs; Am Geophys Soc; Am Inst Mining, Metall & Petrol Engrs. *Mailing Add:* Dept of Civil Eng Univ of Md College Park MD 20742

STERNBERGER, LUDWIG AMADEUS, b Munich, Ger, May 26, 21; nat US; m 62. MEDICINE. *Educ:* Am Univ, Beirut, MD, 45. *Prof Exp:* Sr med bacteriologist, Div Labs & Res, State Dept Health, NY, 50-52, sr med biochemist, 52-53; asst prof med, Med Sch & assoc dir, Allergy Res Lab, Northwestern Univ, 53-55; chief path br, US Army Chem Res & Develop Labs, 55-67, chief basic sci dept, Med Res Labs, Army Chem Ctr, 67-77; asst prof microbiol, Sch Med, Johns Hopkins Univ, 66-77; PROF ANAT & BRAIN RES, SCH MED & DENT, UNIV ROCHESTER, 77- *Concurrent Pos:* Fel exp path, Mem Cancer Ctr, New York, 48-50; assoc surg res, Sinai Hosp Baltimore, 66-; consult, Univ Iowa. *Honors & Awards:* Paul A Siple Award, 72. *Mem:* Soc Exp Biol & Med; Am Asn Immunologists; Am Acad Allergy; Histochem Soc; Venezuela Soc Electron Micros. *Res:* Immunocytochemistry. *Mailing Add:* Univ of Rochester Sch of Med & Dent 601 Elmwood Ave Rochester NY 14642

STERNBURG, JAMES GORDON, b Chicago, Ill, Feb 22, 19; m 54; c 3. ENTOMOLOGY. *Educ:* Univ Ill, AB, 49, MS, 50, PhD(entom), 52. *Prof Exp:* Res assoc entom, 52-54, from asst prof to assoc prof, 54-63, PROF ENTOM, UNIV ILL, URBANA, 63- *Mem:* Entom Soc Am; Lepidop Soc. *Res:* Insect physiology and toxicology of insecticides; enzymatic detoxication of dichloro-diphenyl-trichloro-ethane by resistance house flies; effects of insecticides on neuroactivity in insects; behavior of nearctic and neotropical Lepidoptera; mimicry by insects. *Mailing Add:* Dept Entom Univ Ill Urbana IL 61801

STERNE, RICKIE EDWARD, b Little Rock, Ark, Mar 5, 47. PLANT PATHOLOGY. *Educ:* Hendrix Col, BA, 69; Univ Ark, Fayetteville, MSc, 74; Univ Calif, Riverside, PhD(plant path), 77. *Prof Exp:* ASST PROF PLANT PATH, UNIV ARK, FAYETTEVILLE, 77- *Concurrent Pos:* Fel environ affairs, Rockefeller Found, 78-79. *Mem:* Am Phytopath Soc; AAAS. *Res:* Ecology and control of soilborne plant pathogens. *Mailing Add:* Dept of Plant Path PS217 Univ Ark Fayetteville AR 72701

STERNER, CARL D, b Wellman, Iowa, Oct 15, 35; m; c 3. INORGANIC CHEMISTRY, PHYSICAL CHEMISTRY. *Educ:* Kearney State Col, BS, 60; Univ Tex, Austin, MA, 67; Univ Nebr, Lincoln, PhD(chem), 73. *Prof Exp:* PROF CHEM, KEARNEY STATE COL, 67-, CHMN DEPT, 80- *Concurrent Pos:* NSF fel, 71-72. *Mem:* Am Chem Soc. *Res:* Inorganic syntheses; solid state chemistry; electron spectroscopy chemical applications; materials science. *Mailing Add:* Dept of Chem Kearney State Col Kearney NE 68847

STERNER, JAMES HERVI, b Bloomsburg, Pa, Nov 14, 04; m 32, 71; c 3. MEDICINE. *Educ:* Pa State Univ, BS, 28, Harvard Univ, MD, 32; Am Bd Prev Med, dipl, 55; Am Bd Indust Hyg, dipl, 60. *Prof Exp:* Intern, Lankenau Hosp, Philadelphia, 32-34, chief resident physician, 34-35; dir lab indust med, Eastman Kodak Co, NY, 36-49, from assoc med dir to med dir, 49-68; assoc dean, 68-71, prof, 68-77, EMER PROF ENVIRON & OCCUP HEALTH, UNIV TEX SCH PUB HEALTH, HOUSTON, 76-; CLIN PROF OCCUP MED, UNIV CALIF, IRVINE, 76- *Concurrent Pos:* Instr indust med, Univ Rochester, 40-50, assoc prof med, Sch Med & Dent, 51-58, clin assoc prof, 58-68, clin assoc prof prev med, 59-61, clin prof prev med & community health, 61-68; med consult, Holston Ord Works, Tenn, 41-45; med dir, Clinton Eng Works, Tenn Eastman Co, 43-45; mem interim med adv bd, Manhattan Proj, AEC, 45-47, mem radiol safety sect & medico-legal bd, Oper Crossroads, 46, consult, Off Oper Safety, AEC, 48-, mem adv comt biol & med, 60-66 & gen adv comt, 71-74; mem comt toxicol, Nat Acad Sci-Nat Res Coun, 47-55 & 71-74; mem comt environ physiol, 65-68; mem expert adv comt social & occup health, WHO, 51-75, chmn expert comt med supvn in radiation work, 59; vis lectr, Harvard Med Sch, 52-56; mem comt occup health & safety, Int Labor Off, 52-75; chief indust med staff, Rochester Gen Hosp, NY, 55-62, consult, 63-68; trustee, Am Bd Prev Med, 55-67, vchmn occup med, 59-60, chmn 61-69; mem main comt, Nat Coun Radiation Protection & Measurements, 55-68; mem, Cancer Control Comt, Nat Cancer Inst, 57-61; mem adv comt, Nat Health Surv, 57-61; spec consult & chmn comt radiation studies, USPHS, 57-61, consult, Nat Ctr Health Statist, 66-75; mem, Gen Adv Comt Atomic Energy, NY, 59-65; sr assoc physician, Strong Mem Hosp, NY, 58-68; mem, Am Adv Bd, Am Hosp, Paris, 58-; chmn forum occup health, Nat Health Coun, 59, pres, 61; mem, Permanent Comn & Int Asn Occup Health, 60-; mem environ health panel, Exec Off Sci & Technol, 61-65; mem, Nat Environ Health Comt, 64-67; chmn, Nat Air Conserv Comn, 67; mem, Nat Adv Dis Prev & Environ Control Coun, 67-68; actg city health dir, Houston, Tex, 70; mem sci adv bd, Environ Protection Agency, 75-81. *Honors & Awards:* Cummings Award, Am Indust Hyg Asn, 55; Knudsen Award, Indust Med Asn, 57; Award, Am Acad Occup Med, 59. *Mem:* fel Am Pub Health Asn; Am Col Prev Med (pres, 59-60); Am Acad Occup Med (pres, 52-53); fel Royal Soc Health. *Res:* Clinical and experimental toxicology in industrial hygiene and environmental health. *Mailing Add:* 3354 O-Monte Hermoso Laguna Hills CA 92653

STERNFELD, LEON, b Brooklyn, NY, June 15, 13; m 34; c 2. MEDICAL ADMINISTRATION, RESEARCH ADMINISTRATION. *Educ:* Univ Chicago, SB, 32, MD, 36, PhD(biochem), 37; Columbia Univ, MPH, 43. *Prof Exp:* Intern pediat, Johns Hopkins Univ, 38-39 & Sydenham Hosp, 39-40; asst res, Jewish Hosp, Brooklyn, 40-41; epidemiologist-in-training, State Dept Health, NY, 41-42, jr epidemiologist, 42, asst dist state health officer, 43-44, dir med rehab, 44-50, dist health officer, 50-51; asst dir, Tuberc Div, State Dept Pub Health, Mass, 51-52; assoc dir, Field Training Unit, Harvard Univ, 52-53, lectr, Sch Pub Health, 53-57, from asst clin prof to assoc clin prof maternal & child health, 58-70, vis lectr maternal & child health, 70-74; MED DIR, UNITED CEREBRAL PALSY ASNS, INC, 71- *Concurrent Pos:* Chief Pub Health Admin, Korean Civil Asst Command, 53-55; chief prev med, Ft Devons, US Army, 55; City health comnr, Cambridge, Mass, 55-61; lectr, Simmons Col, 56-69; assoc physician, Children's Med Ctr, Boston, 57-69; dep health comnr, Mass Dept Pub Health, 61-69. *Mem:* Am Pub Health Asn; Am Asn Ment Deficiency; Am Acad Cerebral Palsy & Develop Med. *Res:* Chemical properties of essential bacterial growth factor; essential fructosuria; pathophysiology; medical and public health aspects of cerebral palsy and mental retardation; public health methodology and community health. *Mailing Add:* 1385 York Ave New York NY 10021

STERNFELD, MARVIN, b Cleveland, Ohio, Feb 24, 27; m 50; c 3. ORGANIC CHEMISTRY. *Educ:* Western Reserve Univ, BS, 49, MS, 51, PhD(chem), 53. *Prof Exp:* Pres, Cleveland Chem Labs, 53-66; PRES, RES ORGANICS INC, 66- *Concurrent Pos:* Head, Chem Dept, Ohio Col Podiat Med, 53-69. *Mem:* Am Chem Soc; Sigma Xi. *Res:* Synthesis of biochemicals, including biological buffers, fluorescent labels, brain research biochemicals, enzyme substrates and test reagents; amino acid derivatives, peptides, special biological dyes. *Mailing Add:* 4353 E 49th St Cuyahoga Heights OH 44125

STERNGLANZ, ROLF, b Sewell, Chile, May 18, 39; US citizen; m 64. MOLECULAR BIOLOGY, BIOCHEMISTRY. *Educ:* Oberlin Col, AB, 60; Harvard Univ, PhD(phys chem), 67. *Prof Exp:* NIH res fel biochem, Sch Med, Stanford Univ, 66-68; asst prof, 69-76, ASSOC PROF BIOCHEM, STATE UNIV NY STONY BROOK, 76- *Concurrent Pos:* Am Cancer Soc res grants, State Univ NY Stony Brook, 69- *Mem:* AAAS. *Res:* Mechanism of DNA replication; physical chemistry of DNA. *Mailing Add:* Dept of Biochem State Univ of NY Stony Brook NY 11790

STERNGLASS, ERNEST JOACHIM, b Berlin, Ger, Sept 24, 23; nat US; m 57; c 2. PHYSICS. *Educ:* Cornell Univ, BEE, 44, MS, 51, PhD(eng physics), 53. *Prof Exp:* Asst physics, Cornell Univ, 44, res assoc, 51-52; physicist, US Naval Ord Lab, 46-52; res physicist, Res Labs, Westinghouse Elec Co, Pa, 52-60, adv physicist, 60-67; prof radiation physics, Univ Pittsburgh, 67-80. *Concurrent Pos:* Assoc, George Washington Univ, 46-47; Westinghouse Res Lab fel, Inst Henri Poincare, Paris, 57-58; vis prof, Inst Theoret Physics, Stanford Univ, 66-67. *Mem:* AAAS; fel Am Phys Soc; Am Astron Soc; Fedn Am Sci; Am Asn Physicists in Med. *Res:* Secondary electron emission; physics of electron tubes; electron and elementary particle physics; electronic imaging devices for astronomy and medicine; radiation physics; biological effects of radiation. *Mailing Add:* 2925 Ramble Rd East Bloomington IN 47401

STERNHEIM, MORTON MAYNARD, b Scranton, Pa, July 19, 33; m 55; c 3. PHYSICS. *Educ:* City Col, NY, BS, 54; NY Univ, MS, 56; Columbia Univ, PhD(physics), 61. *Prof Exp:* Fel physics, Brookhaven Nat Lab, 61-63; res assoc lectr, Yale Univ, 63-65; from asst prof to assoc prof, 65-71, PROF PHYSICS, UNIV MASS, 71- *Concurrent Pos:* Prin investr, NSF res grant, 65; vis mem staff, Los Alamos Nat Lab, 67; visitor, Brookhaven Nat Lab, 66 & 68. *Mem:* Am Phys Soc; AAAS; Am Asn Physics Teachers. *Res:* Theoretical nuclear physics; pion scattering and production; exotic atoms; incoherent processes involving nucleons and mesons at intermediate energies. *Mailing Add:* Nuclear Physics GRES-low rise Univ Mass Amherst MA 01003

STERNHEIMER, RUDOLPH MAX, b Saarbruecken, Ger, Apr 26, 26; nat US; m 52. ATOMIC PHYSICS. *Educ:* Univ Chicago, BS, 43, MS, 46, PhD, 49. *Prof Exp:* Jr scientist, Div War Res, Metall Lab, Columbia Univ, 45-46; instr physics, Univ Chicago, 46-48; asst & instr, Yale Univ, 48-49; mem staff, Los Alamos Sci Lab, 49-51; from assoc physicist to physicist, 52-65, SR PHYSICIST, BROOKHAVEN NAT LAB, 65- *Mem:* Fel Am Phys Soc. *Res:* Atomic and nuclear physics; theory of solids; theory of nuclear quadrupole coupling; theory of ionization loss and Cerenkov radiation; focusing magnets; polarization of nucleons; theory of meson production; electronic polarizabilities of ions; k-ordering of atomic and ionic energy levels. *Mailing Add:* Dept of Physics Brookhaven Nat Lab Upton NY 11973

STERNICK, EDWARD SELBY, b Cambridge, Mass, Feb 10, 39; m 60; c 3. MEDICAL PHYSICS. *Educ:* Tufts Univ, BS, 60; Boston Univ, MA, 63; Univ Calif, Los Angeles, PhD(med physics), 68. *Prof Exp:* Res scientist biophys, Nat Aeronaut & Space Admin, 63-64; instr radiol, Dartmouth-Hitchcock Med Ctr, 68-72, asst prof clin med, 72-78; ASSOC CLIN PROF THERAPEUT RADIOL & DIR MED PHYSICS DIV, TUFTS-NEW ENGLAND MED CTR, 78- *Concurrent Pos:* Prof, NH Voc Tech Inst, 72-78; adj asst prof bioeng, Thayer Sch Eng, Dartmouth Univ, 73-78; consult, Vet Admin Hosp, 74- *Honors & Awards:* First Place Sci Exhibit Award, Am Asn Physicists in Med, 74. *Mem:* Am Asn Physicists in Med; Soc Nuclear Med; Sigma Xi; Health Physics Soc. *Res:* Application of computer technology to radiation medicine. *Mailing Add:* Dept of Therapeut Radiol 171 Harrison Ave Boston MA 02111

STERNLICHT, B(ENO), b Poland, Mar 12, 28; nat US; m 55, 75; c 3. ENERGY, AUTOMOTIVE ENGINEERING. *Educ:* Union Col, BSEE, 49; Columbia Univ, PhD(appl mech), 54. *Hon Degrees:* DSc, Union Col, 70. *Prof Exp:* Engr, Gen Elec Co, 47-50; off mgr, Ameast Distribr Corp, 50-51; develop engr, Gen Elec Co, 51-53; res engr, Atomic Energy Comn, 53-54; eng specialist, Gen Eng Lab, Gen Elec Co, 54-58, consult engr hydrodyn, 58-61; TECH DIR & CHMN BD, MECH TECHNOL INC, 61-; PRES, AMEAST DISTRIB CORP, 76- *Concurrent Pos:* Lectr, Union Col, 56-57 & Mass Inst Technol, 57, 59; mem mat panel, Nat Acad Sci; founder sci based indust, Mamash, Israel; pres & chmn bd, Vols in Tech Assistance, 66-72; chmn comt power & propulsion, NASA; mem, Energy Policy Task Force, 81. *Honors & Awards:* Mach Design Award, Am Soc Mech Engrs, 66. *Mem:* Am Soc Mech Engrs; Am Soc Lubrication Engrs; Inst Elec & Electronics Engrs; Am Inst Aeronaut & Astronaut. *Res:* Turbomachinery; energy conversion; conservation diagnostic systems; automotive propulsion; separation systems; energy conversion, propulsion, separation and enrichment systems. *Mailing Add:* 2520 Whamer Lane Schenectady NY 12309

STERNLICHT, HIMAN, b New York, NY, May 31, 36; m 58; c 3. PHYSICAL CHEMISTRY. *Educ:* Columbia Univ, BA, 57, BS, 58; Calif Inst Technol, PhD(chem), 63. *Prof Exp:* Mem tech staff, Bell Tel Labs, NJ, 63-65; asst prof chem, Univ Calif, Berkeley, 65-70; mem tech staff, Bell Labs, Inc, 70-76; ASSOC PROF PHARMACOL, CASE WESTERN RESERVE UNIV, 76- *Concurrent Pos:* NIH res grant, 66-69. *Mem:* Am Phys Soc; Am Chem Soc. *Res:* Magnetic resonance studies, including small and macromolecular systems. *Mailing Add:* Dept of Pharmacol Univ Circle Cleveland OH 44106

STERNLIEB, IRMIN, b Czernowitz, Rumania, Jan 11, 23; US citizen; m 53. GASTROENTEROLOGY, ELECTRON MICROSCOPY. *Educ:* Univ Geneva, MSc, 49, MD, 52. *Prof Exp:* Intern, Morrisania City Hosp, Bronx, NY, 52-53; resident internal med, Bronx Munic Hosp Ctr, NY, 55-57; asst instr, 56-57, instr & asst prof, 57-61, from asst prof to assoc prof, 61-72, PROF MED, ALBERT EINSTEIN COL MED, 72- *Concurrent Pos:* Fel internal med & gastroenterol, Mt Sinai Hosp, New York, 53-55; USPHS fel, 57-60 & spec fel, Lab Atomic Synthesis & Proton Optics, Ivry, France, 64-65. *Mem:* Am Soc Clin Invest; Int Asn Study Liver; Am Gastroenterol Asn; Am Asn

Study Liver Dis; Am Soc Cell Biol. *Res:* Clinical, genetic, biochemical, diagnostic and morphologic aspects of human and canine inherited copper toxicosis; electron microscopy of human liver. *Mailing Add:* Albert Einstein Col of Med 1300 Morris Park Ave Bronx NY 10461

STERNSTEIN, MARTIN, b Chicago, Ill, Apr 25, 45; m 80; c 1. MATHEMATICS. *Educ:* Univ Chicago, BS, 66; Cornell Univ, PhD(math), 71. *Prof Exp:* Asst prof, 70-75, chmn dept, 72-76, ASSOC PROF MATH, ITHACA COL, 75-, CHMN DEPT, 81- *Concurrent Pos:* Vis lectr, Col VI, 78-79; Fulbright prof, Univ Liberia, 79-80. *Mem:* Am Math Soc; Math Asn Am. *Res:* Algebraic topology. *Mailing Add:* Dept of Math Ithaca Col Ithaca NY 14850

STERNSTEIN, SANFORD SAMUEL, b New York, NY, June 19, 36; m 58; c 2. POLYMER PHYSICS, POLYMER ENGINEERING. *Educ:* Univ Md, BS, 58; Rensselaer Polytech Inst, PhD(chem eng), 61. *Prof Exp:* From asst prof to prof polymers, 61-73, WILLIAM WEIGHTMAN WALKER PROF POLYMER ENG, RENSSELAER POLYTECH INST, 73- *Concurrent Pos:* NSF & Inst Paper Chem Pioneering Res grants, 63-65; Nat Inst Dent Res grant, 65-70; NSF res grants, 73-78. *Mem:* Am Inst Chem Eng; Soc Rheol; Am Phys Soc; Am Chem Soc. *Res:* Rheology; fracture; dynamic mechanical properties of polymers; polymer-solvent interactions and crazing; polymer network mechanics and rubber elasticity. *Mailing Add:* Mat Div Rensselaer Polytech Inst Troy NY 12181

STERRETT, ANDREW, b Pittsburgh, Pa, Apr 3, 24; m 48; c 2. MATHEMATICS. *Educ:* Carnegie Inst Technol, 48; Univ Pittsburgh, MS, 50, PhD(math), 56. *Prof Exp:* Lectr math, Univ Pittsburgh, 48-50; instr, Ohio Univ, 50-53; from asst prof to assoc prof, 53-64, chmn dept math, 60-63 & 65-68, dir comt undergrad prog in math, 70-72, dean col, 73-78, PROF MATH, DENISON UNIV, 64- *Concurrent Pos:* NSF fac fel statist, Stanford Univ, 59-60; vis scholar statist, Univ Calif, Berkeley, 66-67 & Univ NC, 78-79. *Mem:* Am Math Soc; Math Asn Am; Am Statist Asn. *Mailing Add:* Dept of Math Denison Univ Granville OH 43023

STERRETT, FRANCES SUSAN, b Vienna, Austria, Sept 25, 13; nat US; m 39; c 2. ENVIRONMENTAL CHEMISTRY. *Educ:* Univ Vienna, PhD(chem), 38. *Prof Exp:* Res chemist, Lab, France, 38-39; asst biochem, Med Ctr, Columbia Univ, 39-40; res chemist, van Ameringen & Haebler, Inc, NJ, 40-41, Woburn Degreasing Co, 43 & Fritzsche Bros, Inc, NY, 43-49; lectr chem, 53-57, from instr to assoc prof, 57-73, PROF CHEM, HOFSTRA UNIV, 73- *Concurrent Pos:* Lectr biochem sec high sch teachers, NSF, 65-67. *Mem:* AAAS; Am Chem Soc; fel Am Inst Chemists; fel NY Acad Sci. *Res:* Chemistry and chemical reactions in the environment in reference to the atmosphere, hydrosphere, lithosphere and biosphere; microanalysis; aromatic chemicals; essential oils; inorganic and qualitative chemistry; organic chemistry; quantitative analysis; chemical contaminants in drinking water. *Mailing Add:* Dept Chem Hofstra Univ Hempstead NY 11550

STERRETT, JOHN PAUL, b Springfield, Ohio, Dec 14, 24; m 49; c 2. PLANT PHYSIOLOGY. *Educ:* Univ WVa, BS, 50; Va Polytech Inst, MS, 61, PhD(plant physiol), 66. *Prof Exp:* County forester, WVa Conserv Comn, 50-53; forester, Bartlett Tree Expert Co, 53-59; res asst plant physiol, Va Polytech Inst, 59-61, asst prof, 61-69; plant physiologist, Veg Control Div, Ft Detrick, US Army, 69-74; PLANT PHYSIOLOGIST, SCI RES LAB, AGR RES SERV, USDA, 74- *Mem:* Am Soc Hort Sci; Weed Sci Soc Am; Am Soc Plant Physiol; Plant Growth Regulators Soc Am. *Res:* Plant growth regulators for the control of weeds. *Mailing Add:* PO Box 1209 Frederick MD 21701

STERRETT, KAY FIFE, b McKeesport, Pa, May 20, 31; m 60; c 3. GEOPHYSICS, PHYSICAL CHEMISTRY. *Educ:* Univ Pittsburgh, BS, 53, PhD(phys chem), 57. *Prof Exp:* Asst, Univ Pittsburgh, 53-57; phys chemist, Nat Bur Stand, 57-61; mem res staff, Northrop Space Labs, 62-64, head, Space Physics & Chem Lab, 64-66; head phys chem lab, Northrop Space Labs, 66-67; CHIEF, RES DIV, US ARMY COLD REGIONS RES & ENG LAB, 67- *Concurrent Pos:* Neth Govt fel, Kamerlingh Onnes Lab, Univ Leiden, 57-58; mem exten teaching staff, Univ Calif, Los Angeles, 65-66; mem Army res coun, Dept Army, 67-68. *Mem:* Fel AAAS; Am Chem Soc; Am Phys Soc; Royal Soc Chem; Sigma Xi. *Res:* Thermodynamics of solids; high pressure physics; planetary interiors; low temperature physics; cold regions environment; physics of snow, ice and frozen soil; research management. *Mailing Add:* US Army Col Reg Res & Eng Lab 72 Lyme Rd Hanover NH 03755

STERZER, FRED, b Vienna, Austria, Nov 18, 29; nat US; m 64. ELECTRONICS ENGINEERING. *Educ:* City Col New York, BS, 51; NY Univ, MS, 52, PhD(physics), 55. *Prof Exp:* MEM STAFF, RCA CORP, 64-, DIR, MICROWAVE TECHNOL CTR, RCA LABS, 72- *Mem:* Fel Inst Elec & Electronics Engrs. *Res:* Microwave spectroscopy, tubes and solid state devices; photovoltaic devices. *Mailing Add:* Microwave Technol Ctr RCA Labs Princeton NJ 08540

STESKY, ROBERT MICHAEL, b Toronto, Ont, July 27, 45; m 71; c 2. GEOLOGY, GEOPHYSICS. *Educ:* Univ Toronto, BSc, 68, MSc, 70; Mass Inst Technol, PhD(geophys), 75. *Prof Exp:* ASST PROF GEOL, ERINDALE COL, UNIV TORONTO, 74- *Mem:* Am Geophys Union; Geol Asn Can. *Res:* Physical properties of rocks and minerals under high pressure; fractures and faults and igneous and metamorphic rocks. *Mailing Add:* Rm 3032 Earth & Planetary Sci Erindale Col Univ of Toronto Mississauga ON L5L 1C6 Can

STETLER, DAVID ALBERT, b Pasadena, Calif, June 17, 35; m 64; c 2. PLANT CYTOLOGY. *Educ:* Univ Southern Calif, BSc, 59; Univ Calif, Berkeley, PhD(bot), 67. *Prof Exp:* Asst prof bot, Univ Minn, 67-69; asst prof biol, Dartmouth Col, 69-73; asst prof, 73-77, ASSOC PROF BOT, VA POLYTECH INST & STATE UNIV, 77- *Mem:* Am Soc Plant Physiologists; Bot Soc Am; Tissue Cult Asn; Int Asn Plant Tissue Cult. *Res:* Organelle development in plant cells; ultrastructure of plant tissues; ultrastructure of stressed animal tissues in the environment. *Mailing Add:* Dept of Biol Va Polytech Inst & State Univ Blacksburg VA 24061

STETSON, ALVIN RAE, b San Diego, Calif, July 23, 26; m 47; c 2. PHYSICAL CHEMISTRY. *Educ:* San Diego State Col, AB, 48. *Prof Exp:* Anal chemist, 48-50, phys chemist, 50-53, from staff engr to sr res staff engr, 53-66, chief process res, 66-72, chief mat engr, Solar Turbine Int, Int Harvester Co, 72-80, CHIEF MAT TECHNOL, SOLAR TURBINE INC, 80- *Mem:* Am Chem Soc; Nat Asn Corrosion Eng; Am Soc Metals. *Res:* Fused salt plating; high temperature metallic and ceramic protective coatings; reaction of materials at high temperatures; reentry and gas turbine environment simulation; braze joining of dissimilar metals; plasma arc testing and spraying; abrasive and abradable turbine tip seals; materials research supervision. *Mailing Add:* Solar Turbine Inc 2200 Pac Hwy San Diego CA 92138

STETSON, HAROLD W(ILBUR), b Bristol, Pa, July 2, 26; m 52; c 3. CERAMICS, INORGANIC CHEMISTRY. *Educ:* Pa State Univ, BS, 50, MS 52, PhD(ceramics), 56. *Prof Exp:* Res asst mineral sci, Pa State Univ, 52-55; sr engr, Corning Glass Works, 56-59 & Radio Corp Am, 59-62; sr engr, Western Elec Co, Princeton, 62-66, res leader ceramics, 66-69; dir res, Ceramic Metal Systs, Inc, 69-70; SR ENGR, TRW, EASTERN RES LABS, PHILADELPHIA, 70- *Concurrent Pos:* Vis assoc prof, Rutgers Univ, 71. *Mem:* Am Ceramic Soc. *Res:* Ceramic materials for electronic uses; sintering theory of oxides; application of modern ceramic technology to archeological problems. *Mailing Add:* 222 N Chancellor St Newtown PA 18940

STETSON, KENNETH F(RANCIS), b Winthrop, Maine, May 2, 24; m 48; c 2. AERODYNAMICS, AEROPHYSICS. *Educ:* Univ Maine, BS, 49; US Air Force Inst Technol, BS, 52; Ohio State Univ, MS, 56. *Prof Exp:* Proj engr, Aircraft Lab, Wright-Patterson AFB, Ohio, 50-51, aeronaut engr, Aeronaut Res Labs, 52-56; sr staff scientist, Everett Res Lab, Avco Corp, Mass, 56-61, sr proj engr, Res & Develop Div, 61-66, sr staff scientist, Space Systs Div, 66-68; Ohio State Univ Res Found vis res assoc, 68-69, aerospace engr, Aerospace Res Labs, 69-75, AEROSPACE ENGR, FLIGHT DYNAMICS LAB, WRIGHT-PATTERSON AFB, 75- *Mem:* Assoc fel Am Inst Aeronaut & Astronaut. *Res:* Hypersonic, aerodynamic and aerophysics research. *Mailing Add:* 125 Wisteria Dr Dayton OH 45419

STETSON, MILTON H, b Springfield, Mass, Nov 25, 43; m 66; c 2. REPRODUCTIVE ENDOCRINOLOGY, BIOLOGICAL RHYTHMS. *Educ:* Cent Conn State Col, BA, 65; Univ Wash, MS, 68, PhD(zool), 70. *Prof Exp:* NIH fel, 66-70; res fel reproduction, Univ Tex, Austin, 71-73; asst prof biol sci & health sci, 73-76, assoc prof, 77-80, PROF LIFE & HEALTH SCI, UNIV DEL, 77-80. *Mem:* Am Physiol Soc; Am Soc Zool; fel AAAS; Soc Study Reproduction; Am Asn Univ Profs. *Res:* Role of the circadian system in the timing of reproductive events; neural and neuroendocrine generation of female reproductive cyclicity; comparative endocrinology of the thyroid gland. *Mailing Add:* Sch of Life Health Sci Univ of Del Newark DE 19711

STETSON, RICHARD PRATT, b Dorchester, Mass, Apr 24, 98; m 28; c 2. MEDICINE. *Educ:* Dartmouth Col, AB, 22; Harvard Med Sch, MD, 26; Am Bd Internal Med, dipl, 47. *Prof Exp:* Intern med, Mass Gen Hosp, Boston, 27-28; asst instr, Sch Med, Yale Univ, 28-30; from asst to assoc, Harvard Med Sch, 30-55, asst clin prof, 55-63, clin prof, 63-64; chief of staff, Vet Admin Hosp, West Roxbury, 63-69, liaison for educ, Vet Admin Region I, 69-73; COORDR, LEARNING RESOURCES, BOSTON VA MED CTR, 73- *Concurrent Pos:* Asst resident & assoc physician, New Haven Hosp, Conn, 28-30; mem staff, Harvard Med Serv & Thorndike Mem Lab, Boston City Hosp, 30-64, physician-in-chief, 2nd Med Serv, Hosp, 48-59, vis physician, Hosp, 48-64, consult, 64-; physician, New Eng Deaconess Hosp, Boston, 36-57, consult, 57-; assoc vis physician, Mass Mem Hosps, Boston, 51-55, physician, 55-61, consult, 62-; lectr, Sch Med, Boston Univ, 56-64; mem spec med adv group, Vet Admin, 57-59, area dir prof serv, 59-63; mem, Arthritis Found. Consult, Vet Admin Hosp, West Roxbury, 46-59, USPHS, 57-69, Morton Hosp, Taunton & Addison Gilbert Hosp, Gloucester. *Mem:* AAAS; AMA; Am Clin & Climat Asn; Am Diabetes Asn; Am Col Physicians. *Res:* Hematology, especially pernicious anemia; diabetes. *Mailing Add:* 235 Woodland Rd Chestnut Hill MA 02167

STETSON, ROBERT FRANKLIN, b Lewiston, Maine, Apr 17, 32; m 67. BIOMATHEMATICS, PLASMA PHYSICS. *Educ:* Bates Col, BS, 54; Wesleyan Univ, MA, 56; Univ Va, PhD(physics), 59. *Prof Exp:* Asst physics, Wesleyan Univ, 54-56; instr, Univ Va, 56-58; asst prof, Univ Fla, 59-64; assoc prof, 64-69, PROF PHYSICS, FLA ATLANTIC UNIV, 69-, DIR FAC SCHOLARS PROG, 71-, DIR SPONSORED RES, 75- *Concurrent Pos:* Proj scientist, Air Force Off Sci Res, 62-64; consult, Col Entrance Exam Bd. *Mem:* Am Phys Soc; Am Asn Physics Teachers; fel AAAS. *Res:* Angular correlation of gamma rays; neutron scattering; non-traditional higher education; computer simulation of plasma and thermodynamic problems; computer simulation in biomathematics. *Mailing Add:* Dept of Physics Fla Atlantic Univ Boca Raton FL 33431

STETTEN, DEWITT, JR, b New York, NY, May 31, 09; m 41; c 4. MEDICINE. *Educ:* Harvard Univ, AB, 30; Columbia Univ, MD, 34, PhD(biochem), 40. *Hon Degrees:* DSc, Wash Univ, 74 & Col Med Dent NJ, 76. *Prof Exp:* Intern & resident, 3rd Med Serv, Bellevue Hosp, New York, 34-37; asst biochem, Columbia Univ, 38-39, from instr to asst prof, 41-47; asst prof, Harvard Med Sch, 47-48; chief div nutrit & physiol, Pub Health Res Inst, New York, NY, 48-54; dir intramural res, Nat Inst Arthritis & Metab Dis, 54-62; dean, Rutgers Med Sch, 62-70; dir, Nat Inst Gen Med Sci, 70-74, dep dir sci, 74-79, SR SCI ADV, NIH, 79- *Concurrent Pos:* Assoc, Peter Bent Brigham Hosp, Boston, Mass, 47-48; mem sci adv comt, Okla Med Res Found, 63-67, chmn, 66; exec comt mem, Div Med Sci, Nat Res Coun, 66; chmn nat adv comt, Roche Inst Molecular Biol, 67-70; counr, Nat Acad Sci, 76-79. *Honors & Awards:* Smith Prize, 43; Alvarenga Prize, 54; Banting Medal, Am Diabetes Asn, 57. *Mem:* Nat Acad Sci; AAAS; Am Soc Biol Chem; Soc Exp Biol & Med; Harvey Soc. *Res:* Intermediary metabolism of fats and carbohydrates; experimental diabetes; evaluation of rates of chemical processes in the intact animal; metabolic defects in gout and muscular dystrophy; insulin metabolism. *Mailing Add:* NIH 9000 Rockville Pike Bethesda MD 20205

STETTEN, MARJORIE ROLOFF, b New York, NY, July 13, 15; m 41; c 4. BIOCHEMISTRY. *Educ:* Rutgers Univ, BS, 37; Columbia Univ, PhD(biochem), 44. *Prof Exp:* Asst biochem, Col Physicians & Surgeons, Columbia Univ, 40-47; fel biol chem, Harvard Med Sch, 47-48; assoc div nutrit & physiol, Pub Health Res Inst, New York, 48-54; biochemist, Nat Inst Arthritis & Metab Dis, 54-63; res prof exp med, Sch Med, Rutgers Univ, New Brunswick, 63-71; BIOCHEMIST, NAT INST ARTHRITIS, METAB & DIGESTIVE DIS, NIH, 71- *Concurrent Pos:* Mem, Marine Biol Lab, Woods Hole, trustee, 79- *Mem:* Am Soc Biol Chem. *Res:* Intermediary metabolism of amino acids and carbohydrates; particulate enzymes of liver and kidney. *Mailing Add:* Bldg 10-9B-02 Nat Inst of Health Bethesda MD 20205

STETTENHEIM, PETER, b New York, NY, Dec 27, 28; m 65; c 2. ORNITHOLOGY. *Educ:* Haverford Col, BS, 50; Univ Mich, MA, 51, PhD(zool), 59. *Prof Exp:* Res zoologist, USDA, Avian Anat Proj, 58-69; book rev ed, Wilson Bull, 70-74; ED, CONDOR, 74- *Concurrent Pos:* Mem, Coun Biol Ed & Int Comt Avian Anat Nomenclature; mem bd dirs, Cornell Lab Ornithol & Montshire Mus Sci. *Honors & Awards:* Co-recipient, Tom Newman Mem Int Award, Brit Poultry Breeders & Hatcheries Asn, 73. *Mem:* Wilson Ornith Soc; Cooper Ornith Soc; Am Ornith Union; Brit Ornith Union; Ger Ornith Soc. *Res:* Descriptive and functional anatomy of avian integument, particularly feather structure. *Mailing Add:* Meriden Rd Lebanon NH 03766

STETTER, JOSEPH ROBERT, b Buffalo, NY, Dec 15, 46; m 72. PHYSICAL CHEMISTRY, SURFACE CHEMISTRY. *Educ:* State Univ NY Buffalo, BA, 69, PhD(phys chem), 75. *Prof Exp:* Res asst, Linde Div, Union Carbide Corp, 66-68, chemist, 69; teaching asst chem, State Univ NY Buffalo, 70-71, res asst, Dept Chem, 71-74; sr res chemist, Becton Dickinson & Co, 74-78, dir chem res, 78-80. *Concurrent Pos:* Trustee, Lakeland Cent Sch Dist, 77- *Mem:* Am Chem Soc; Electrochem Soc; AAAS; Am Inst Physics; Am Vacuum Soc. *Res:* Physical adsorption, chemisorption, heterogeneous catalytic systems, and the physical, electronic and chemical characterization of solid surfaces and the solid-gas interface. *Mailing Add:* 1228 Olympus Dr Naperville IL 60540

STETTLER, JOHN DIETRICH, b Cleveland, Ohio, Mar 15, 34; m 57; c 5. LASER PHYSICS, PROPAGATION. *Educ:* Univ Notre Dame, BS, 56; Mass Inst Technol, PhD(physics), 62. *Prof Exp:* Res asst physics, Mass Inst Technol, 57-60; asst prof, Univ Mo-Rolla, 60-64; res physicist, US Army Missile Command, 64-76, mgr laser signature measurements, 76-79, chief, Optics Group, 79-80; SR SCIENTIST, APPL RES INC, 81- *Concurrent Pos:* Adj prof physics, Univ Ala, Huntsville, 70- *Mem:* AAAS; Am Phys Soc; Am Asn Physics Teachers. *Res:* Eximer lasers and Raman shifting; propagation of submillimeter to visible radiation through a turbulent atmosphere; application of lasers to ballistic missile defense; particle beam optics. *Mailing Add:* Appl Res Inc 130 Longwood Dr Huntsville AL 35801

STETTLER, REINHARD FRIEDERICH, b Steckborn, Switz, Dec 27, 29; m 55; c 1. FOREST GENETICS. *Educ:* Swiss Fed Inst Technol, dipl, 55; Univ Calif, Berkeley, PhD(genetics), 63. *Prof Exp:* Res officer silvicult, Res Div, BC Forest Serv, Can, 56-58; res assoc forest mgt, Fed Inst Forest Res, Switz, 58-59; from asst prof to assoc prof, 63-74, PROF FOREST GENETICS, UNIV WASH, 74- *Concurrent Pos:* Alexander von Humboldt fel, Inst Forest Genetics, Schmalenbeck, Ger, 69-70; vis scholar, Abegg Found, Berne, 76; guest lectr, Dept Bot, Univ Nijmegen, Neth, 77. *Mem:* AAAS; Bot Soc Am; Genetics Soc Am. *Res:* Genetic control of morphogenesis in higher plants; reproductive physiology of forest trees; factors effecting crossability in poplars; induction of haploid parthenogenesis; biomass for energy. *Mailing Add:* Col of Forest Resources Univ of Wash Seattle WA 98195

STEUCEK, GUY LINSLEY, b New Haven, Conn, Jan 22, 42; m 65; c 2. PLANT PHYSIOLOGY. *Educ:* Univ Conn, BS, 63, PhD(plant physiol), 68; Yale Univ, MF, 65. *Prof Exp:* Nat Res Coun Can fel, Forest Prod Lab, BC, 68-69; asst prof biol, 69-72, assoc prof, 72-77, PROF BIOL, MILLERSVILLE STATE COL, 77- *Mem:* AAAS; Am Soc Plant Physiol; Scan Soc Plant Physiol; Ecol Soc Am. *Res:* Influence of mechanical stress on plant growth and development; phloem transport and mineral nutrition. *Mailing Add:* Dept of Biol Millersville State Col Millersville PA 17551

STEUER, MALCOLM F, b Marion, SC, Dec 16, 28; m 58; c 3. NUCLEAR PHYSICS. *Educ:* US Merchant Marine Acad, BS, 50; Clemson Col, MS, 54; Univ Va, PhD(physics), 57. *Prof Exp:* Res fel, Univ Va, 57-58; asst prof, 58-63, assoc prof, 63-77, PROF PHYSICS, UNIV GA, 77- *Concurrent Pos:* NSF sci fac fel, Univ Wis, 64-65. *Mem:* Am Phys Soc. *Res:* Interactions of MeV projectiles with matter; interactions of neutrons with nuclei. *Mailing Add:* Dept of Physics Univ of Ga Athens GA 30602

STEUNENBERG, ROBERT KEPPEL, b Caldwell, Idaho, Sept 18, 24; m 47. INORGANIC CHEMISTRY. *Educ:* Col Idaho, BA, 47; Univ Wash, PhD(chem), 51. *Prof Exp:* Mem staff, 51-67, SR CHEMIST, ARGONNE NAT LAB, 67- *Mem:* Am Chem Soc; Sigma Xi; Am Nuclear Soc; Electrochem Soc. *Res:* Fluorocarbons; interhalogen compounds; pyrometallurgical methods for processing nuclear reactor fuels; nuclear technology; high-temperature batteries; energy conversion; molten salt chemistry. *Mailing Add:* Argonne Nat Lab Bldg D-205 Rm Y-114 9700 S Cass Ave Argonne IL 60439

STEVEN, ALASDAIR C, b Alytgh, Scotland, June 27, 47; m 71; c 3. ELECTRON MICROSCOPY, IMAGE PROCESSING. *Educ:* Edinburgh Univ, Scotland, MA, 69, Cambridge Univ, PhD(theoret physics), 73; Basel Univ, Switz, SKMB, 75. *Prof Exp:* Res asst, Basel Univ, 73-78; VIS SCIENTIST, NAT INST HEALTH, 78- *Mem:* Electron Micros Soc Am. *Res:* Structural basis of molecular biology; high resolution electron microscopy; computer image analysis and model building; assembly properties of proteins, nucleoproteins, particles, crystals and polymers. *Mailing Add:* Bldg 6 Rm B2-34 Nat Inst Health Bethesda MD 20205

STEVEN, JAMES R, b Denver, Colo, Mar 4, 19; m 48; c 2. CIVIL ENGINEERING. *Educ:* City Col New York, BCE, 43; Columbia Univ, MS, 49. *Prof Exp:* From instr to assoc prof, 46-62, dean, 68-71, PROF CIVIL ENG, CITY COL NEW YORK, 62-, DIR SUMMER SESSION, 64- *Concurrent Pos:* Consult, Hardesty & Hanover, 46-50 & United Aircraft Corp, 59-65. *Mem:* Am Soc Civil Engrs; Am Soc Eng Educ. *Res:* Fluid mechanics; surveying. *Mailing Add:* Sch of Eng 140th St & Convent Ave New York NY 10031

STEVEN, THOMAS AUGUST, b Dryden, Ore, Oct 14, 17; m 45; c 2. GEOLOGY. *Educ:* San Jose State Col, AB, 39; Univ Calif, Los Angeles, PhD(geol), 50. *Prof Exp:* GEOLOGIST, US GEOL SURV, 42- *Mem:* AAAS; Soc Econ Geologists; Geol Soc Am. *Res:* Economic and general geology. *Mailing Add:* US Geol Surv Bldg 25 Denver Fed Ctr Denver CO 80225

STEVEN, WILLIAM, b Glasgow, Scotland, Oct 22, 17; nat US; m 40; c 1. METALLURGY. *Educ:* Glasgow Univ, BSc, 39, PhD, 42. *Prof Exp:* Res metallurgist, William Jesop & Sons, Ltd, Eng, 42-47; res sect head, Ferrous Res, Mond Int Nickel Co, Inc, New York, 59-62, asst vpres, 59-66, mgr, Develop & Res, 62-68, vpres, 66, asst vpres, Int Nickel Co Can Ltd, 65-68, vpres, 68-71, SR V PRES & DIR, INCO LTD, 72- *Mem:* Am Soc Metals; Am Inst Mining, Metall & Petrol Engrs; fel Brit Inst Metall; Brit Iron & Steel Inst; Brit Inst Metals. *Res:* Factors controlling the properties of alloys; management of physical metallurgical research. *Mailing Add:* Inco Ltd PO Box 44 One First Canadian Pl Toronto ON M5X 1C4 Can

STEVENS, ALAN DOUGLAS, b Nashua, NH, Aug 17, 26; m 49; c 5. OCCUPATIONAL HEALTH, VETERINARY MEDICINE. *Educ:* Cornell Univ, DVM, 47. *Prof Exp:* Private practice, Ga, 47-50; prog officer res grants, Div Environ Eng & Food Protection, US Pub Health Serv, 63-66, chief res grants, 66-67, chief res & training grants rev, Nat Ctr Urban & Indust Health, 67-68, environ control admin, 68-69, chief res grants, Bur Safety & Occup Health, Environ Control Admin, 69-70, asst dir to dir extramural progs, 70-75, DIR TRAINING & MAN POWER DEVELOP, NAT INST OCCUP SAFETY & HEALTH, CTR DIS CONTROL, DEPT HEALTH, EDUC & WELFARE, 75- *Mem:* AAAS; Am Inst Chemists; Am Conf Govt Indust Hygienists. *Res:* Food chemistry and microbiology; irradiation of foods; virology; laboratory animal medicine; research administration; information retrieval. *Mailing Add:* 100 Silver Ave Ft Mitchell KY 41017

STEVENS, ALDRED LYMAN, b Brown City, Mich, Apr 28, 35; m 56; c 2. ENERGY CONVERSION, SOLID MECHANICS. *Educ:* Mich State Univ, BS, 60, MS, 61, PhD(appl mech), 68. *Prof Exp:* Tech staff mem, Sandia Labs, 61-64; instr solid mech, Mich State Univ, 66-67; mem tech staff, Sandia Labs, 68-76, supvr, Oil Shale Progs Div, 76-80; MGR, OIL SHALE RES, OCCIDENTAL RES CORP, 80- *Mem:* Soc Exp Stress Anal; Am Phys Soc. *Res:* Shock wave physics; rock mechanics; continuum mechanics; stress analysis. *Mailing Add:* 4142 Williwaw Irvine CA 92714

STEVENS, ANN REBECCA, b Huntington, WVa, July 22, 39; m 65, 77; c 2. BIOCHEMISTRY, CELL BIOLOGY. *Educ:* Univ Ala, Tuscaloosa, BS, 61; Univ Colo, Denver, PhD(biochem), 66. *Prof Exp:* Res assoc cell biol, Inst Cellular, Molecular & Develop Biol, Univ Colo, Boulder, 66-68; asst prof, 68-74, ASSOC PROF BIOCHEM, COL MED, UNIV FLA, 74-; res investr & dir electorn micos labs, Vet Admin Hosp, 68-81; ASST DEAN, RES DIV, SPONSORED RES, UNIV FLA, 81- *Concurrent Pos:* Nat Inst Allergy & Infectious Dis res grants, 70-76; Fulbright awardee, Pasteur Inst, Lille, France. *Mem:* AAAS; Am Soc Cell Biol; Soc Exp Biol & Med; NY Acad Sci; Am Soc Biol Chemists. *Res:* Aspects of nucleic acid metabolism during growth and differentiation in pathogenic and nonpathogenic strains of Acanthamoeba and Naegleria; biochemical mechanism of the pathogenicity of free-living amoebae. *Mailing Add:* Cell Biol Labs Vet Admin Hosp Gainesville FL 32601

STEVENS, AUDREY L, b Leigh, Nebr, July 21, 32; m 64; c 2. BIOCHEMISTRY, MICROBIOLOGY. *Educ:* Iowa State Univ, BS, 53; Western Reserve Univ, PhD(biochem), 58. *Prof Exp:* NSF fel, 58-60; instr pharmacol, Sch Med, Univ St Louis, 60-62, asst prof, 62-63; from asst prof to assoc prof biochem, Sch Med, Univ Md, Balitmore City, 63-66; MEM RES STAFF, BIOL DIV, OAK RIDGE NAT LAB, 66- *Concurrent Pos:* NSF res grants, 60-66. *Mem:* Am Soc Biol Chem. *Res:* Nuclear acid biosynthesis. *Mailing Add:* Biol Div Oak Ridge Nat Lab Oak Ridge TN 37831

STEVENS, BRIAN, b South Elmsall, Eng, July 22, 24; m 53; c 2. PHOTOCHEMISTRY. *Educ:* Oxford Univ, BA & MA, 50, DPhil(phys chem), 53. *Prof Exp:* Fel, Nat Res Coun Can, 53-55; res asst chem, Princeton Univ, 55-56, res assoc, 56-57; res assoc tech off chem eng, Esso Res & Eng Co, NJ, 57-58; lectr chem, Univ Sheffield, 58-65, reader photochem, 65-67; PROF CHEM, UNIV S FLA, 67- *Mem:* Am Chem Soc; Royal Soc Chem; Am Soc Photobiol; Int Am Photochem Soc. *Res:* Molecular luminescence and electronic energy transfer in complex molecules; photosensitized peroxidation of unsaturated molecules and reduction of dyes; solute re-encounter effects. *Mailing Add:* Dept of Chem Univ of South Fla Tampa FL 33620

STEVENS, CALVIN H, b Sheridan, Wyo, Apr 3, 34; m 61; c 2. PALEOECOLOGY, STRATIGRAPHY. *Educ:* Univ Colo, AB, 56, MA, 58; Univ Southern Calif, PhD(geol), 63. *Prof Exp:* Geologist, Res Lab, Humble Oil Co, 58-60; asst prof geol, San Jose State Col, 63-65 & Univ Colo, 65-66; from asst prof to assoc prof, 66-72, PROF GEOL, SAN JOSE STATE UNIV, 72- *Mem:* Am Asn Petrol Geologists; fel Geol Soc Am; Soc Econ Paleont & Mineral. *Res:* Late Paleozoic paleoecology and paleontology; Great Basin geology and stratigraphy. *Mailing Add:* Dept of Geol San Jose State Univ San Jose CA 95114

STEVENS, CALVIN LEE, b Edwardsville, Ill, Nov 3, 23; m 47; c 1. CHEMISTRY. *Educ:* Univ Ill, BS, 44; Univ Wis, PhD(org chem), 47. *Prof Exp:* Asst org chem, Univ Wis, 44-47; Du Pont fel, Mass Inst Technol, 47-48; from asst prof to assoc prof, 48-54, PROF ORG CHEM, WAYNE STATE UNIV, 54- *Concurrent Pos:* Guggenheim fel, Univ Paris, 55-56; sci liaison officer, Off Naval Res, London, 59-60; Fulbright fels, Sorbonne, 64-65, Univ Paris, 71-72. *Mem:* Am Chem Soc; The Chem Soc; Swiss Chem Soc; Chem Soc France. *Res:* Organic chemistry; epoxyethers and nitrogen analogs of ketenes; natural products; amino-sugars; amino-ketone rearrangements. *Mailing Add:* Dept of Chem Wayne State Univ Detroit MI 48202

STEVENS, CHARLES DAVID, b Pittsburgh, Pa, Feb 1, 12; m 37; c 5. BIOCHEMISTRY. *Educ:* Univ Cincinnati, AB, 33, MSc, 34, PhD(biochem), 37. *Prof Exp:* Res assoc biochem, Cardiac Lab, Sch Med, Univ Cincinnati, 38-42 & Lab Aviation Med, 42-45; biochemist, Dow Chem Co, 45-46; res assoc biochem, Gastric Lab, Univ Cincinnati, 46-50, asst prof, Dept Prev Med & Indust Health, 50-65; assoc prof, 65-68, prof, 68-80, EMER PROF BIOMET, EMORY UNIV, 80- *Concurrent Pos:* Fel, Med Col Va, 61-62. *Mem:* Fel AAAS; Soc Exp Biol & Med; Am Asn Cancer Res. *Res:* Selective localization of chemicals in acidic cancer tissue; respiration; biomathematics; synthesis and metabolism of organolead compounds. *Mailing Add:* Dept of Statist & Biomet Emory Univ Atlanta GA 30322

STEVENS, CHARLES EDWARD, b Minneapolis, Minn, June 5, 27; c 4. VETERINARY PHYSIOLOGY. *Educ:* Univ Minn, BS, 51, DVM & MS, 55, PhD(vet physiol & pharmacol), 58. *Hon Degrees:* Hon Prof, San Marcos Univ, Peru, 72. *Prof Exp:* Instr vet anat, Univ Minn, 51-52, asst vet physiol, 52-55, res assoc, 58-60; vet physiologist, Agr Res Serv, US Dept Agr, 60-61; assoc prof vet physiol, NY State Vet Col, Cornell Univ, 61-66, prof, 66-79, chmn, Dept Physiol, Biochem & Pharmacol, 73-79; ASSOC DEAN RES & GRAD STUDIES, SCH VET MED, NC STATE UNIV, 79- *Concurrent Pos:* NIH spec res fel, 62-63 & res grant, 65-, dir training prog comp gastroenterol, 71-76; field rep grad physiol, Cornell Univ, 68-70; mem gen med study sect, NIH, 69-73; Fulbright lectr, 72. *Mem:* Am Soc Vet Physiol & Pharmacol (pres, 67-68); Am Physiol Soc; Am Vet Med Asn; Conf Res Workers Animal Dis; Comp Gastroenterol Soc. *Res:* Comparative physiology of the digestive system; microbial digestion and mechanisms of secretion, absorption and digesta passage. *Mailing Add:* Sch Vet Med NC State Univ Raleigh NC 27606

STEVENS, CHARLES F, b Chicago, Ill, Sept 1, 34; m 56; c 3. MEMBRANE PHYSIOLOGY. *Educ:* Harvard Univ, BA, 56; Yale Univ, MD, 60; Rockefeller Univ, PhD, 64. *Prof Exp:* From asst prof to prof physiol & biophys, Sch Med, Univ Wash, 63-75; PROF PHYSIOL, SCH MED, YALE UNIV, 75- *Res:* Synaptic physiology; properties of excitable membranes. *Mailing Add:* Dept of Physiol Yale Univ Sch Med 383 Cedar St New Haven CT 06510

STEVENS, CHARLES LE ROY, b Chicago, Ill, Aug 8, 31; c 4. BIOPHYSICAL CHEMISTRY. *Educ:* Valparaiso Univ, BA, 53; Univ Pittsburgh, MS, 60, PhD(biophys), 62. *Prof Exp:* Physicist, US Army Biol Labs, 55-56; NIH res fel, 62-64; asst prof, 64-67, ASSOC PROF BIOPHYS, UNIV PITTSBURGH, 67- *Concurrent Pos:* NATO sr fel, Univ Uppsala, 69. *Mem:* AAAS; NY Acad Sci; Biophys Soc. *Res:* Physical chemistry of proteins and nucleic acids; the role of water in the structure of biological macromolecules; self-association of proteins; cell motility. *Mailing Add:* Dept Biol Sci Univ Pittsburgh Pittsburgh PA 15260

STEVENS, DALE JOHN, b Ogden, Utah, June 27, 36; m 62; c 6. PHYSICAL GEOGRAPHY. *Educ:* Brigham Young Univ, BA, 61; Ind Univ, MA, 63; Univ Calif, Los Angeles, PhD(geog), 69. *Prof Exp:* Instr geog, Univ Wyo, 63-64; assoc prof, 66-80, PROF GEOG, BRIGHAM YOUNG UNIV, 80- *Concurrent Pos:* Univ develop grant, Brigham Young Univ, 71-72. *Mem:* Asn Am Geog; Asn Pac Coast Geog. *Res:* Morphometric analysis of land forms, especially Karst and natural arches; long-range weather forecasting; noncommercial agricultural geography; geography of micro-climatology. *Mailing Add:* Dept of Geog Brigham Young Univ 622 SWKT Provo UT 84602

STEVENS, DEAN FINLEY, b Derby, Conn, Oct 19, 23; m 51; c 3. ZOOLOGY, CELL BIOLOGY. *Educ:* Boston Univ, AB, 49, AM, 50; Clark Univ, PhD(cell biol), 64. *Prof Exp:* Res asst biol, Boston Univ, 50-51; teaching master, Mt Hermon Sch Boys, 51-54; staff scientist, Worcester Found Exp Biol, 54-67; ASSOC PROF ZOOL, UNIV VT, 67- *Concurrent Pos:* Fels, USPHS, Am Cancer Soc & NIH; Ortho Res Found spec grant. *Mem:* Am Soc Cell Biol; Am Asn Cancer Res. *Res:* Vascular physiology; cancer; mechanisms of cell division. *Mailing Add:* Dept Zool Univ Vt Burlington VT 05401

STEVENS, DONALD KEITH, b Troy, NY, July 30, 22; m 45, 65, 74; c 2. SOLID STATE PHYSICS. *Educ:* Union Col, BS, 43; Univ NC, PhD(chem), 53. *Prof Exp:* Physicist, US Naval Res Lab, 43-49; consult radiation effects in solids, Oak Ridge Nat Lab, 49-51, physicist, 53-57; chief metall & mat br, Div Res, US AEC, 57-60, asst dir res metall & mat progs, US ERDA, 60-74, asst dir res mat sci, 74-77; dir div math, 77-81, dep assoc dir, 77-81, DEP ASSOC DIR, OFF ENERGY RES, DEPT ENERGY, 81- *Concurrent Pos:* Mem mat adv bd, Nat Acad Sci-Nat Res Coun, 59-62. *Mem:* AAAS; Sci Res Soc Am; Am Phys Soc. *Res:* Radiation effects in solids. *Mailing Add:* Off Energy Res US Dept of Energy Washington DC 20545

STEVENS, DONALD MEADE, b Lynchburg, Va, May 9, 47; m 70. NUCLEAR PHYSICS, COMPUTER SCIENCE. *Educ:* Va Polytech Inst & State Univ, BS, 69, MS, 70, PhD(physics), 74. *Prof Exp:* Res asst physics, Va Polytech Inst, 70-74; sr res engr nuclear physics, 74-79, group supvr, Diagnostic Develop Group, 80-81, GROUP SUPVR DATA PROCESSING & DIAGNOSTICS, LUNCHBURG RES CTR, BABCOCK & WILCOX CO, 81- *Concurrent Pos:* Guest res asst, Brookhaven Nat Lab, 70-73; guest scientist, Fermi Nat Accelerator Lab, 73-74. *Mem:* Am Phys Soc; Am Nuclear Soc; Inst Elec & Electronics Engrs. *Res:* Applications in monitoring nuclear power plants and designing computer systems; data processing and diagnostic systems. *Mailing Add:* Lynchburg Res Ctr PO Box 1260 Lynchburg VA 24505

STEVENS, ERNEST DONALD, b Calgary, Alta, July 5, 41; m 64; c 3. PHYSIOLOGY, ZOOLOGY. *Educ:* Victoria Univ, BSc, 63; Univ BC, MSc, 65, PhD(zool), 68. *Prof Exp:* Assoc prof zool, Univ Hawaii, 68-75; MEM FAC ZOOL, UNIV GUELPH, 75- *Concurrent Pos:* Vis prof, St Andrews, 75 & Tohoku, Japan, 82. *Mem:* AAAS; Can Soc Zool; Soc Exp Biol & Med. *Res:* Physiology, primarily of fish; mechanisms of respiration and circulation, especially as they are affected by muscular exercise; comparative physiology of muscle contraction; myoglobin function. *Mailing Add:* Dept of Zool Univ of Guelph Guelph ON N1G 2W1 Can

STEVENS, FRANK JOSEPH, b Peru, Ill, Mar 9, 19; m; c 2. CHEMISTRY. *Educ:* Univ Ill, BS, 41; Iowa State Col, PhD(bio-org chem), 47. *Prof Exp:* Instr chem, Iowa State Col, 42-47; from asst prof to assoc prof, 47-59, PROF CHEM, AUBURN UNIV, 59- *Concurrent Pos:* Chmn, Premed-Predent Adv Comt, Auburn Univ, 69- *Mem:* AAAS; Am Chem Soc; NY Acad Sci. *Res:* Organic and pharmaceutical chemistry; plant growth regulators; indole and pyridazine derivatives. *Mailing Add:* 2020 Haley Ctr Auburn Univ Auburn AL 36830

STEVENS, FRITS CHRISTIAAN, b Ghent, Belg, Sept 18, 38; m 65; c 2. BIOCHEMISTRY, PROTEIN CHEMISTRY. *Educ:* Univ Ghent, Lic chem, 59; Univ Calif, Davis, PhD(biochem), 63. *Prof Exp:* Asst biochem, Pharmaceut Inst, Univ Ghent, 59-60 & Univ Calif, Davis, 60-63; sr researcher, Univ Brussels, 63-64; fel, Univ Calif, Los Angeles, 65-67; asst prof, 67-71, assoc prof, 71-78, PROF BIOCHEM, UNIV MAN, 78- *Mem:* Can Biochem Soc; Belg Biochem Soc; Am Chem Soc; Am Soc Biol Chem. *Res:* Structure-function relationships in proteins. *Mailing Add:* Dept Biochem Univ Man Fac Med Winnipeg MB R3E 0W3 Can

STEVENS, GEORGE RICHARD, b Norfolk, Va, May 28, 31; m; c 4. STRUCTURAL GEOLOGY, TECTONICS. *Educ:* Johns Hopkins Univ, AB, 54, MA, 55, PhD(geol, tectonics), 59. *Prof Exp:* Asst prof geol, Lafayette Col, 57-66, asst acad dean, 64-65; PROF GEOL & HEAD DEPT, ACADIA UNIV, 66- *Concurrent Pos:* Consult, 55-67; vis, Univ Bergen, Norway, 73-74. *Mem:* AAAS; fel Geol Soc Am; Geol Asn Can; Sigma Xi; Am Geophys Union. *Res:* Structural vulcanology, metamorphic recrystallization; fabric of deformed rock and of igneous rock. *Mailing Add:* Dept of Geol Acadia Univ Wolfville NS B0P 1X0 Can

STEVENS, GLADSTONE TAYLOR, JR, b Brockton, Mass, Dec 16, 30; m 57; c 2. ECONOMIC ANALYSIS, QUALITY CONTROL. *Educ:* Univ Okla, BS, 56; Case Inst Technol, MS, 62, PhD(indust eng & mgt), 66. *Prof Exp:* Proj engr, E I du Pont de Nemours & Co, 56-59; res engr, Thompson-Ramo-Wooldridge Co, 60-62; asst prof mech eng, Lamar State Col, 62-64; from asst prof to assoc prof indust eng & mgt, Okla State Univ, 66-75; PROF AND CHMN DEPT INDUST ENG, UNIV TEX, ARLINGTON, 75- *Concurrent Pos:* NASA res grant, 67-68; consult, Pub Serv Co of Okla, 73-75 & Standard Mfg Co of Dallas, 76- *Honors & Awards:* Eugene L Grant Award, Am Soc Eng Educ, 74. *Mem:* Am Inst Indust Engrs. *Res:* Allocation of capital funds; probabilistic models; in-plant service courses in areas of production control, operations research and quality control. *Mailing Add:* Dept of Indust Eng Univ of Tex Arlington TX 76019

STEVENS, HAROLD, b Salem, NJ, Oct 18, 11; m 38; c 2. NEUROLOGY. *Educ:* Pa State Univ, BS, 33; Univ Pa, AM, 34, PhD, 37, MD, 41. *Prof Exp:* PROF NEUROL, SCH MED, GEORGE WASHINGTON UNIV, 54- *Concurrent Pos:* Consult pediat neurol, DC Health Dept, 46-; sr attend neurologist, Children's Hosp, 51-; consult, Vet Hosp, 54- & Walter Reed Hosp & NIH, 57-; nat consult to Surg Gen, US Air Force; consult, FDA. *Mem:* Am Asn Neurol Surg; Am Neurol Asn; Am Electroencephalog Soc; fel Am Col Physicians; fel Am Acad Neurol. *Res:* Clinical and pediatric neurology. *Mailing Add:* 3301 New Mexico Ave NW Washington DC 20016

STEVENS, HENRY CONRAD, b Vienna, Austria, Apr 17, 18; nat US; m 41; c 2. ORGANIC CHEMISTRY. *Educ:* Columbia Univ, BS, 41; Western Reserve Univ, MS, 49, PhD(chem), 51. *Prof Exp:* Res chemist, H Kohnstamm & Co, 41-42; res supvr, Chem Div, Pittsburgh Plate Glass Co, 42-72, sr res supvr, Chem Div, 72-77, MGR UNIV & GOVT RES & DEVELOP, PPG INDUSTS, INC, BARBERTON, 77- *Mem:* Am Chem Soc. *Res:* Chemistry of phosgene derivatives; free radical polymerization; polycarbonate resins; cycloadditions; tropolone syntheses; peroxides; epoxides; phase transfer catalysis; technology transfer; academic-industrial interface. *Mailing Add:* 149 Birdwood Rd Akron OH 44313

STEVENS, HERBERT H(OWE), JR, b Gardiner, Maine, May 12, 13; m 46; c 3. MECHANICAL ENGINEERING. *Educ:* Ga Inst Technol, BSME, 36; New Sch Social Res, MALS, 69. *Prof Exp:* Engr & dir res aircraft seats, W McArthur Corp, 39-41; consult res & develop engr, 41-47; chief engr rolling steel doors, W Balfour Co, 47-53; supv engr elec shaver res, Schick, Inc, 53-55; chief engr paint sprayer develop, Champion Implement Co, 55-56; consult, 56-58; sr statist engr, M & C Nuclear, Inc, Div Tex Instruments, Inc, 58-65; consult engr, Walter Balfour & Co, Long Island City, 65-80; CONSULT RES & DEVELOP, 80- *Mem:* Am Soc Mech Engrs; Am Statist Asn; Asn Comput Mach; Philos Sci Asn. *Res:* Air-supported roofs; cooperative housing; philosophy; finitism; computer programming. *Mailing Add:* 218 Hix Bridge Road Westport MA 02790

STEVENS, HOWARD ODELL, (JR), b Canonsburg, Pa, May 29, 40; m 62; c 2. PHYSICS, ELECTRICAL ENGINEERING. *Educ:* Carnegie Inst Technol, BS, 62; Univ Md, MS, 67. *Prof Exp:* Physicist sensors & systs, 62-65, sr proj engr magnetic countermeasures, 65-69, sr proj engr superconducting mach, 69-79, HEAD, ELEC PROPULSION & MACH SYST BR, DAVID W TAYLOR NAVAL SHIP RES & DEVELOP CTR, 79- *Res:* Superconducting and advanced electrical machinery; high current switchgear; advanced current collection systems; superconducting magnets and cryogenic systems. *Mailing Add:* David W Taylor Naval Ship Res & Develop Ctr Bethesda MD 20084

STEVENS, J(AMES) I(RWIN), b Valley Station, Ky, July 15, 20; m 47; c 4. CHEMICAL ENGINEERING. *Educ:* Univ Louisville, BChE, 42, MChE, 43. *Prof Exp:* Instr, Univ Louisville, 43-44, res assoc, Inst Indust Res, 45-46; instr, Univ Del, 46-48; asst prof chem eng, Vanderbilt Univ, 48-52; engr, Phillips Petrol Co, Okla, 52-56, group leader, Idaho, 56-59, sect head, 59-62; chem engr Infilco/Fuller, 62-66, tech dir, 66-67; staff engr, 67, sr engr, 67-76, mgt staff assoc, 77-80, MGT STAFF, ARTHUR D LITTLE, INC, 80- *Mem:* Am Chem Soc; Am Inst Chem Engrs; Air Pollution Control Asn; Water Pollution Control Fedn. *Res:* Technical and social aspects of environmental management. *Mailing Add:* Arthur D Little Inc 20 Acorn Park Cambridge MA 02140

STEVENS, JACK GERALD, b Port Angeles, Wash, Nov 3, 33; m 57; c 1. ANIMAL VIROLOGY, EXPERIMENTAL PATHOLOGY. *Educ:* Wash State Univ, DVM, 57; Colo State Univ, MS, 59; Univ Wash, PhD(virol), 62. *Prof Exp:* Asst prof microbiol, Wash State Univ, 62-63; from asst prof to assoc prof med microbiol & immunol, 63-73, prof microbiol, immunol & neurol, 73-80, PROF MICROBIOL, IMMUNOL, NEUROBIOL & NEUROL, SCH MED, COL LETTERS & SCI, UNIV CALIF, LOS ANGELES, 80-, CHMN, DEPT MICROBIOL & IMMUNOL, 81- *Concurrent Pos:* Mem, Infectious Dis Merit Rev Bd, Vet Admin Med Res Serv, 76-79; mem, Virol Study Sect, Div Res Grants, NIH, 78-82; mem, Fel Review Bd, Nat Multiple Sclerosis Soc, 81- *Mem:* AAAS; Am Soc Microbiol; Infectious Dis Soc Am; Am Asn Immunologists; Am Soc Exp Pathologists. *Res:* Viral pathogenesis, particularly latent infections; diseases of the nervous system; neoplasms. *Mailing Add:* Dept of Med Microbiol & Immunol Univ of Calif Sch of Med Los Angeles CA 90024

STEVENS, JANICE R, b Portland, Ore; m 45; c 2. NEUROLOGY, PSYCHIATRY. *Educ:* Reed Col, BA, 44; Boston Univ, MD, 49. *Prof Exp:* Intern med, Mass Mem Hosp, 49-50; resident neurol, Boston City Hosp, 50-51; fel neurol & assoc physician, Sch Med, Yale Univ, 51-54; resident, 54-55, from instr to assoc prof, 55-71, assoc prof psychiat, 74-77, PROF NEUROL, MED SCH, UNIV ORE, 71-, PROF PSYCHIAT, 77- *Concurrent Pos:* Vis prof psychiat, Harvard Med Sch & Mass Gen Hosp, 71-73; NIMH guest worker, St Elizabeth's Hosp, Washington, DC, 75-76, mem staff, 80- *Mem:* AAAS; Am Acad Neurol; Am Electroencephalog Soc (pres, 73-74); Soc Neurosci; Am Epilepsy Soc. *Res:* Neurology and electroencephalography of behavior and epilepsy. *Mailing Add:* Depts of Neurol & Psychiat Univ of Ore Med Sch Portland OR 97201

STEVENS, JERRY BRUCE, veterinary pathology, biochemistry, see previous edition

STEVENS, JOHN A(LEXANDER), b Baltimore, Md, Mar 25, 21; m 53; c 3. CIVIL ENGINEERING. *Educ:* Princeton Univ, BS, 43; Univ Miami, BSCE, 50; Putney Grad Sch Teacher Ed, MA, 51; Pa State Univ, MSCE, 52. *Prof Exp:* Proj engr, Am Dist Tel Co, NY, 46-49; asst prof, 52-58, ASSOC PROF CIVIL ENG, UNIV MIAMI, 59-, DIR SOILS ENG LAB, 56- *Mem:* Am Soc Civil Engrs; Am Soc Photogram; Am Forestry Asn. *Res:* Soils engineering; engineering geology; foundation engineering structure and properties of Florida marls and lime muds; air photo interpretation. *Mailing Add:* Dept of Civil Eng Univ of Miami Miami FL 33124

STEVENS, JOHN BAGSHAW, b Toronto, Ont, June 26, 41; m 72; c 1. VETERINARY MICROBIOLOGY. *Educ:* Univ Toronto, BSc, 64; Univ Guelph, DVM, 69, MSc, 71; Iowa State Univ, PhD(vet microbiol), 75. *Prof Exp:* Res asst vet bacteriol, Dept Vet Microbiol & Immunol, Univ Guelph, 69; res assoc vet microbiol, Vet Med Res Inst, Iowa State Univ, 71-74; RES SCIENTIST SWINE DIS, HEALTH ANIMALS BR, ANIMAL PATH DIV, ANIMAL DIS RES INST, AGR CAN, 74- *Mem:* Can Vet Med Asn; Am Asn Swine Practitioners. *Res:* Mycoplasmasis; mycobacteriosis; salmonellosis and cytomegalic inclusion disease of swine. *Mailing Add:* Animal Dis Res Inst 801 Fallowfield Rd Ottawa ON K2H 8P9 Can

STEVENS, JOHN CHARLES, b Ft Collins, Colo, July 19, 46; m 67; c 3. MAGNETOHYDRODYNAMICS, X-RAY ASTRONOMY. *Educ:* Calif Inst Technol, BS, 68, PhD(physics), 72. *Prof Exp:* Design physicist, 72-75, group leader, 76-78, dep assoc prog leader, 79-80, PROJ MGR STRATEGIC MISSILE SYSTS, LAWRENCE LIVERMORE LAB, 81- *Res:* Magnetohydrodynamics of low temperature, high density, high beta plasmas; inertially confined fusion target design/nuclear weapon design. *Mailing Add:* Lawrence Livermore Lab Univ of Calif PO Box 808 Livermore CA 94550

STEVENS, JOHN D, chemical engineering, see previous edition

STEVENS, JOHN G, b Kansas City, Mo, Aug 7, 43; m 66; c 2. APPLIED MATHEMATICS, COMPUTER SCIENCE. *Educ:* Ind Univ, BS, 65; NY Univ, PhD(math), 72. *Prof Exp:* assoc prof, 68-80, PROF MATH, MONTCLAIR STATE COL, 80- *Concurrent Pos:* Consult, Exxon Res & Eng Co, 75- *Mem:* Am Math Soc; Air Pollution Control Asn; Soc Indust & Appl Math; Soc Comput Simulation. *Res:* Mathematical modeling related to energy systems and the environment-combustion; pollutant emissions; advanced energy conversion systems; numerical solution of differential equations. *Mailing Add:* Dept of Math Montclair State Col Upper Montclair NJ 07043

STEVENS, JOHN GEHRET, b Mount Holly, NJ, Dec 16, 41; m 63; c 3. PHYSICAL CHEMISTRY, INFORMATION SCIENCE. *Educ:* NC State Univ, BS, 64, PhD(chem), 69. *Prof Exp:* From asst prof to assoc prof, 63-79, PROF CHEM, UNIV NC, ASHEVILLE, 79- *Concurrent Pos:* Mem ad hoc comt Mössbauer spectros data & conv, Nat Acad Sci, 70-73; ed Mössbauer Effect Data Index, Univ NC & Nat Bur Standards, 70-78; res assoc, Max Planck Inst Solid State Physics, 73; dir, Mossbauer Effect Data Ctr, 74-; dir, Mössbauer Effect Data Control, 74-; res prof, Inst Molecular Spectroscopy, Univ Nijmegen, Neth, 76-77, 78, 79, 80 & 81; co-ed, Mössbauer Effect Reference & Data J, 78- *Mem:* AAAS; Am Chem Soc; Am Phys Soc; Sigma Xi; Fedn Am Scientists. *Res:* Mossbauer spectroscopy; antimony chemistry; information sciences; evaluation of data. *Mailing Add:* Dept of Chem Univ of NC Asheville NC 28804

STEVENS, JOHN JOSEPH, b London, Eng, July 16, 41. CANCER. *Educ:* Univ Buenos Aires, MD, 64. *Prof Exp:* Res physician, Inst Biol & Exp Med, Buenos Aires, 64-67, Nat Acad Med, Arg, 65-67; res fel, 67-70, RES ASSOC, RES INST, HOSP JOINT DIS, NEW YORK, 70- *Concurrent Pos:* Instr, Dept Biochem, Mt Sinai Sch Med, City Univ New York, 70-73, res asst prof, 73-; spec fel, Leukemia Soc Am, 74-76, scholarship, 76-81. *Mem:* Endocrine Soc; Am Asn Cancer Res. *Res:* Mechanism of steroid hormone action; studies on glucocorticoid-induced lymphocytolysis of malignant lymphocytes; chemotherapy of cancer. *Mailing Add:* Res Inst Hosp Joint Dis & Med Ctr 1919 Madison Ave New York NY 10035

STEVENS, JOSEPH ALFRED, b Cleveland, Ohio, Jan 3, 27. MEDICAL MYCOLOGY, MEDICAL MICROBIOLOGY. *Educ:* Univ Dayton, BS, 49; Mich State Univ, MS, 53, PhD(microbiol), 57. *Prof Exp:* Res instr & fel, Mich State Univ, 57-59, res assoc, 59-61; from instr to assoc prof, 61-71, actg chmn dept, 70-74, PROF MICROBIOL, CHICAGO COL OSTEOP MED, 71- *Concurrent Pos:* Consult microbiol & pub health, Nat Bd Exam, Osteop Physicians & Surgeons Inc, 79- *Mem:* Am Soc Microbiol; Mycol Soc Am; NY Acad Sci; Int Soc Human & Animal Mycol; Am Asn Univ Professors. *Res:* fungal serology; immune responses to major fungal pathogens; development of fungal antigens and antisera; fungal diagnostic-serologic tests. *Mailing Add:* Chicago Col Osteop Med 1122 E 53rd St Chicago IL 60615

STEVENS, JOSEPH CHARLES, b Grand Rapids, Mich, Feb 28, 29. PSYCHOPHYSICS, SENSORY PSYCHOLOGY. *Educ:* Calvin Col, AB, 51; Mich State Univ, MA, 53; Harvard Univ, PhD(psychol), 57. *Prof Exp:* From instr to asst prof psychol, Harvard Univ, 57-66; res assoc & lectr, 66-77, SR RES PCYHOLOGIST & LECTR PSYCHOL, YALE UNIV, 77- *Concurrent Pos:* Fel biophys, John B Pierce Found, 66- *Mem:* Soc Neurosci; Acoust Soc Am; Optical Soc Am; fel AAAS; fel NY Acad Sci. *Res:* Psychophysics of sensory and perceptual processes, especially somatosensory and kinesthetic sensory modalities. *Mailing Add:* John B Pierce Found Lab 290 Congress Ave New Haven CT 06519

STEVENS, KARL KENT, b Topeka, Kans, Jan 24, 39; m 60; c 3. ENGINEERING MECHANICS. *Educ:* Kans State Univ, BS, 61; Univ Ill, MS, 63, PhD(theoret & appl mech), 65. *Prof Exp:* Staff mem, Sandia Corp, NMex, 61-62; from asst prof to prof eng mech, Ohio State Univ, 65-78; PROF OCEAN ENG, FLA ATLANTIC UNIV, 78-, CHMN DEPT, 81- *Concurrent Pos:* Vis scientist, US Army Ballistic Res Labs, 72-73. *Mem:* Am Soc Mech Engrs; Am Soc Eng Educ; Soc Naval Archit & Marine Engrs. *Res:* Dynamic stability, vibrations and viscoelasticity; ocean structures. *Mailing Add:* Dept of Ocean Eng Fla Atlantic Univ Boca Raton FL 33431

STEVENS, KENNETH LLOYD, natural products chemistry, see previous edition

STEVENS, KENNETH N(OBLE), b Can, Mar 23, 24; m 57; c 4. ACOUSTICS. *Educ:* Univ Toronto, BASc, 45, MASc, 48; Mass Inst Technol, ScD(elec eng), 52. *Prof Exp:* Instr appl physics, Univ Toronto, 46-48; asst elec eng, 48-51, instr, 51-52, mem res staff commun acoust, 52-54, from asst prof to assoc prof, 54-63, PROF ELEC ENG, MASS INST TECHNOL, 63-, CLARENCE JOSEPH LEBEL PROF, 76- *Concurrent Pos:* Consult & engr, Bolt Beranek & Newman, 52-; Guggenheim fel, 62-63; NIH spec fel & vis prof, Univ Col, Univ London, 69-70. *Mem:* Acoust Soc Am (pres, 76-77); Inst Elec & Electronics Engrs. *Res:* Speech communication; psycho-acoustics. *Mailing Add:* Dept Elec Eng Mass Inst Technol Cambridge MA 02139

STEVENS, LEROY CARLTON, JR, b Kenmore, NY, June 5, 20; m 42; c 3. DEVELOPMENTAL BIOLOGY. *Educ:* Cornell Univ, BS, 42; Univ Rochester, PhD, 52. *Prof Exp:* Asst, Univ Rochester, 48-52, instr, Univ Sch, 51-52; res fel, 52-55, res assoc, 55-57, staff scientist, 57-67, SR STAFF SCIENTIST, JACKSON LAB, 67- *Concurrent Pos:* Guggenheim fel, Exp Embryol Lab, Col of France, 61-62. *Res:* Experimental embryology; cancer; mammalian embryology and teratocarcinogenesis. *Mailing Add:* Jackson Lab Bar Harbor ME 04609

STEVENS, LEWIS AXTELL, b Butte, Mont, Nov 17, 13; m 35; c 3. BIOPHYSICS. *Educ:* San Jose State Col, AB, 50. *Prof Exp:* Meteorol aid, Sci Serv Div, US Weather Bur, 51-52; physicist, Aviation Ord Dept, US Naval Ord Test Sta, 52-56, electronic scientist, 56-57, electronic scientist, Fuze Eval Div, Test Dept, 57-60; gen engr & head measurements br, 60-61, gen proj engr, 62, res physicist, Explosives & Pyro-Tech Div, Propulsion Develop Dept, 62-70; CONSULT PHYSICIST, 70- *Concurrent Pos:* Mem fuze field tests subcomt, Joint Army-Navy-Air Force, 61-64. *Mem:* AAAS; Am Phys Soc; Am Inst Aeronaut & Astronaut. *Res:* Development of new medical tools and techniques; nuclear physics; meteorological aspects of health physics; technology of high speed aerial tow targets; technology of soft lunar landings; effects of microwave radiation on enzyme systems in living organisms; in vivo pathology of varying magnetic fields. *Mailing Add:* LASTEV Lab 725 Randall St Ridgecrest CA 93555

STEVENS, LLOYD WEAKLEY, b Philadelphia, Pa, Jan 14, 14; m 41; c 3. SURGERY. *Educ:* Univ Pa, AB, 33, MD, 37; Am Bd Surg, dipl, 44. *Prof Exp:* Assoc surg, Grad Sch Med, 46-49, assoc prof clin surg, Sch Med, 53-60, prof, 60-79, EMER PROF CLIN SURG, SCH MED, UNIV PA, 79- *Concurrent Pos:* Assoc prof, Women's Med Col Pa, 46-49; dir surg, Presby-Univ Pa Med Ctr & assoc surgeon, Univ Hosp; chief surg, Philadelphia Gen Hosp. *Mem:* Am Col Surgeons; Soc Surg Alimentary Tract. *Res:* Acute cholecystitis; peptic ulcer; ulcerative colitis. *Mailing Add:* 316 Mill Creek Rd Haverford PA 19041

STEVENS, MALCOLM PETER, b Birmingham, Eng, Apr 3, 34; US citizen; m 60; c 2. ORGANIC POLYMER CHEMISTRY. *Educ:* San Jose State Col, BS, 57; Cornell Univ, PhD(org chem), 61. *Prof Exp:* Res chemist, Chevron Res Co, Standard Oil Co Calif, 61-64; asst prof chem, Robert Col, Istanbul, 64-67; asst prof, Univ Hartford, 67-68; from asst prof to assoc prof, Am Univ Beirut, 68-71; assoc prof, 71-78, chmn dept, 78-81, PROF CHEM, UNIV

HARTFORD, 78- *Concurrent Pos:* Vis prof, Univ Sussex, Eng, 77. *Mem:* Sigma Xi; Am Chem Soc. *Res:* Photopolymerization; thermal polymerization; polymer modification; reaction mechanisms. *Mailing Add:* Dept Chem 200 Bloomfield Ave West Hartford CT 06117

STEVENS, MERWIN ALLEN, b Mt Carmel, Utah, Aug 12, 35; m 60; c 3. PLANT GENETICS. *Educ:* Utah State Univ, BS, 57, MS, 61; Ore State Univ, PhD(hort, genetics), 67. *Prof Exp:* Soil scientist, Soil Conserv Serv, US Dept Agr, 60-61; county exten agent, Exten Serv, Ore State Univ, 61-64, asst hort, Univ, 64-67; res assoc, Campbell Inst Agr Res, NJ, 67-70; asst geneticist, Dept Veg Crop, Univ Calif, Davis, 70-74, assoc geneticist, 74-79, prof & geneticist dept veg crop, 79-80; regional mgr, 80-81, VPRES CAMPBELL INST RES & TECHNOL, 81- *Concurrent Pos:* Vis prof, Hebrew Univ Jerusalem, Israel, 78. *Honors & Awards:* Nat Canners Asn Award, 68; Asgrow Award, 71; Campbell Award, 73; Nat Canners Asn Award, 77; Asgrow Award, 78; Nat Food Processors Asn Award, 80. *Mem:* AAAS; Am Soc Hort Sci; Inst Food Technol. *Res:* Genetics and chemistry of tomato quality; genetics and physiology of processes limiting yield and quality in tomatoes; breeding tomatoes for processing. *Mailing Add:* Campbell Inst Res & Technol Rt 1 Box 1314 Davis CA 95616

STEVENS, MICHAEL FRED, b Urbana, Ill, May 17, 41; m 65; c 2. INDUSTRIAL CHEMISTRY, TOXICOLOGY. *Educ:* Eastern Ill Univ, BS, 64; Univ Ill, Urbana, MS, 66; Univ Nebr, Lincoln, PhD(org chem), 70. *Prof Exp:* Res assoc, 70-73, SR RES ASSOC ORG CHEM, APPLETON PAPERS INC, 73- *Mem:* Am Chem Soc; Tech Asn Pulp & Paper Indust. *Res:* Corporate liaison with government relative to toxic substances in control act matters; management of corporate toxicity testing programs; corporate consultant on chemical health and safety matters. *Mailing Add:* Lawe St Lab Res Dept PO Box 359 Appleton WI 54912

STEVENS, PETER FRANCIS, b Teignmouth, Eng, Nov 13, 44. SYSTEMATIC BOTANY. *Educ:* Oxford Univ, BA, 66, MS, 72; Univ Edinburgh, PhD(bot), 70. *Prof Exp:* Forest botanist, Dept Forestry, Lae, Papua, New Guinea, 70-73; asst prof biol, 77-80, ASST CUR, ARNOLD ARBORETUM, HARVARD UNIV, 73-, ASSOC PROF BIOL & ASSOC CUR GRAY HERBRIUM, 80- *Mem:* Fel Linnean Soc London; Soc Study Evolution; Soc Syst Zool. *Res:* Morphology; systematics and evolution of Indo-Malesian plants and the Ericaceae and Clusiaceae of the world; biogeography; tropical ecology; theory and history of systematics. *Mailing Add:* Arnold Arboretum of Harvard Univ 22 Divinity Ave Cambridge MA 02138

STEVENS, REGGIE HARRISON, b Iowa City, Iowa, Aug 7, 41; m 61; c 1. RADIATION BIOLOGY, CHEMISTRY. *Educ:* Univ Iowa, BS, 68, MS, 70, PhD(org chem), 72. *Prof Exp:* Res biochemist endocrinol, Vet Admin, 72-74; res investr radiol, 74-75, from instr to asst prof, 75-80, ASSOC PROF RADIOL, UNIV IOWA, 80- *Concurrent Pos:* Consult, Collins Radio, Rockwell Int, 70- *Mem:* Am Asn Clin Chemists; Am Chem Soc; Radiation Res Soc; AAAS; Am Col Toxicol. *Res:* Enzymology and immunology of cancer; biology of the induction, growth and detection of the malignant cell. *Mailing Add:* 14 Med Labs Univ of Iowa Iowa City IA 52242

STEVENS, RICHARD EDWARD, b Washington, DC, Oct 30, 32; m 57; c 3. MICROSCOPY. *Educ:* Washington Col, BS, 54; Pa State Univ, MS, 56; Rensselaer Polytech Inst, PhD(phys chem), 75. *Prof Exp:* Asst chemist, Pa State Univ, 54-56 & Univ Colo, 56-59; scientist-chemist, Rocky Flats Div, Dow Chem Co, Colo, 59-62, develop chemist, 62-64; res chemist, Am Cyanamid Co, 64-67; microscopist, Ernest F Fullam, Inc, NY, 67-74; sr res microscopist, Walter C McCrone Assocs, 74-76; sr chemist, Nalco Chem Co, 76; mgr image anal appln, Bausch & Lomb, Inc, 76-78; res assoc ophthal, Park Ridge Hosp, 78-80. *Mem:* AAAS; Am Chem Soc; Electron Micros Soc Am. *Res:* Chemical and electron microscopy; crystallography; ultramicroanalysis; automated image analysis; vision research. *Mailing Add:* 5291 S Cobble Creek Rd #25A Salt Lake City UT 84117

STEVENS, RICHARD JOSEPH, b Rochester, NY, Oct 31, 41; m 65; c 2. NEUROSCIENCES. *Educ:* Univ Rochester, BS, 63; Univ Ill, Urbana, MS, 65, PhD(biophysics), 69. *Prof Exp:* Aerospace technologist, NASA-Lewis Res Ctr, 63; res asst, Dept Physics, Univ Ill, 64-65, teaching asst human & cellular physiol, 66-67; fel neuroanat, Dept Anat, Brain Res Inst, Univ Calif, Los Angeles, 69-70; asst prof, 70-75, ASSOC PROF HUMAN ADAPTABILITY, COL HUMAN BIOL, UNIV WIS-GREEN BAY, 75- *Concurrent Pos:* President's teaching improvement grant, Univ Wis, 72; consult, Green Bay Childbirth Educ Asn, 75- *Mem:* AAAS; Sigma Xi. *Res:* Neurophysiology of vision, neuro-behavioral aspects of environmental contaminants; neuro-behavioral aspects of pain perception; inovative teaching of biology. *Mailing Add:* Col of Human Biol Univ of Wis Green Bay WI 54302

STEVENS, RICHARD S, b Cranston, RI, Mar 22, 25; m 52; c 3. MARINE GEOLOGY, PHYSICAL OCEANOGRAPHY. *Educ:* Brown Univ, AB, 50. *Prof Exp:* Oceanogr, US Naval Oceanog Off, 52-62, OCEANOGR, OFF NAVAL RES, 62- *Mem:* Am Geophys Union; Sigma Xi. *Res:* Geological and physical oceanography; ocean circulation, ocean bottom processes and their effects on sediment distribution and structure. *Mailing Add:* 75 Van Houten Fields West Nyack NY 10994

STEVENS, ROBERT E, b Medford, Ore, Jan 19, 28; m 51; c 2. FOREST ENTOMOLOGY. *Educ:* Ore State Univ, BS, 51; Univ Calif, MS, 58, PhD(entom), 65. *Prof Exp:* Entomologist, Ore State Bd Forestry, 51-52 & Bur Entom & Plant Quarantine, Calif, 52-54; entomologist, Pac Southwest Forest & Range Exp Sta, 54-65, asst dir forest insect res, Washington, DC, 65-68, ENTOMOLOGIST, ROCKY MT FOREST & RANGE EXP STA, US FOREST SERV, 68- *Mem:* Entom Soc Am. *Res:* Ecology and control of forest insects. *Mailing Add:* Rocky Mt Forest & Range Exp Sta US Forest Serv 240 W Prospect St Ft Collins CO 80521

STEVENS, ROBERT VELMAN, b Mason City, Iowa, Mar 24, 41; m 63; c 1. ORGANIC CHEMISTRY. *Educ:* Iowa State Univ, BS, 63; Ind Univ, PhD(org chem), 66. *Prof Exp:* From asst prof to prof org chem, Rice Univ, 66-77; PROF, UNIV CALIF, LOS ANGELES, 77- *Concurrent Pos:* A P Sloan fel; consult, Merck Sharpe & Dohme Res Labs, 74-; consult, Nat Inst Health, 75-79. *Mem:* Am Chem Soc; Royal Soc Chem. *Res:* Synthesis of complex natural products and development of new synthetic methods. *Mailing Add:* Dept of Chem Univ of Calif Los Angeles CA 90024

STEVENS, ROGER TEMPLETON, b Syracuse, NY, Jan 11, 27; m 48; c 2. ELECTRICAL ENGINEERING, SYSTEMS ENGINEERING. *Educ:* Union Col, BA, 49; Boston Univ, MA, 59; Blackstone Sch Law, LLB, 56; Va Polytech Inst & State Univ, MEng, 76; Calif Western Univ, PhD(elec eng), 78. *Prof Exp:* Tech writer, Raytheon Mfg Co, 50-51; engr, Lab Electronics Inc, 51-55; sr engr electronic design, Spencer Kennedy Labs, 55-56, AVCO Mfg Co, 56-57 & Electronics Systs Inc, 57-60; sect supvr, Sanders Assoc Inc, 60-65; group leader systs engr, Mitre Corp, 65-67; leading scientist systs engr, Dikewood Indust Inc, 67-70; group leader systs engr, Mitre Corp, 70-74; leading scientist systs engr, Dikewood Indust Inc, 74-81; ENG SPECIALIST II, EG & G, INC, 81- *Mem:* Inst Elec & Electronics Engrs; Nat Soc Prof Engrs; Soc Info Display. *Res:* Operational test and evaluation; computer design and software development; display design; radar system design. *Mailing Add:* EG & G Inc PO Box 4330 Sta A Albuquerque NM 87114

STEVENS, RONALD HENRY, b Philadelphia, Pa, Dec 3, 46. CELLULAR IMMUNOLOGY, HUMAN IMMUNOBIOLOGY. *Educ:* Ohio Wesleyan Univ, BA, 68; Harvard Univ, PhD(microbiol), 71. *Prof Exp:* Fel immunol, Nat Inst Med Res, London, 71-74; ASSOC PROF MICROBIOL & IMMUNOL, UNIV CALIF, LOS ANGELES, 74- *Mem:* Am Asn Immunologists; Am Fedn Clin Res; AAAS; NY Acad Sci. *Res:* Cellular and molecular interactions responsible for the successful initiation, maintenance, and termination of secondary humoral immune responses in humans. *Mailing Add:* Dept Microbiol & Immunol Sch Med Univ Calif Los Angeles CA 90024

STEVENS, ROSEMARY ANNE, b Bourne, Eng, Mar 18, 35; US citizen. HISTORY OF MEDICINE, PUBLIC HEALTH. *Educ:* Oxford Univ, BA, 57, MA, 61; Univ Manchester, dipl social admin, 59; Yale Univ, MPH, 63, PhD(epidemiol), 68. *Prof Exp:* Res asst pub health, Sch Med, Yale Univ, 62-65, res assoc, 66-68, from asst prof to prof, 68-76; prof health systs mgt, Sch Pub Health & Trop Med, Tulane Univ, 76-79; PROF HIST & SOCIOL SCI, UNIV PA, 79-, CHMN DEPT, 80- *Concurrent Pos:* Hon res officer, London Sch Econ & Polit Sci, 62-63, vis lectr, 63-64 & 73-74; lectr, Sch Pub Health, Johns Hopkins Univ, 67-68; guest scholar, Brookings Inst, 67-68. *Mem:* Inst of Med of Nat Acad Sci; Am Pub Health Asn; Soc Social Hist Med. *Res:* History of medicine; comparative studies in health care policy; history of hospitals; medical education and manpower policies. *Mailing Add:* Dept of Hist & Sociol of Sci Univ of Pa D6 Philadelphia PA 19104

STEVENS, ROY WHITE, b Troy, NY, Sept 4, 34; m 56; c 2. MEDICAL MICROBIOLOGY, IMMUNOLOGY. *Educ:* State Univ NY Albany, BS, 56, MS, 58; Albany Med Col, PhD(microbiol), 65; Am Bd Med Microbiol, dipl, 71. *Prof Exp:* Bacteriologist, 58-61, sr bacteriologist, 62-65, assoc bacteriologist, 65-67, sr assoc prin res scientist immunol, 67-73, prin res scientist immunol, 73-79, DIR LABS DIAG IMMUNOL, NY STATE DEPT HEALTH, 79- *Mem:* AAAS; Am Soc Microbiol; Am Venereal Dis Asn. *Res:* Diagnostic immunology, serology; medical microbiology; immunodiagnosis of infectious diseases and automation of clinical laboratory methods. *Mailing Add:* Div of Labs & Res NY State Dept of Health Albany NY 12201

STEVENS, RUSSELL BRADFORD, b Washington, DC, Oct 31, 15; m 49; c 3. PLANT PATHOLOGY. *Educ:* Univ Va, BS, 37; Univ Wis, PhD(bot), 40. *Prof Exp:* Asst prof biol, Birmingham-Southern Col, 40-42 & Univ Louisville, 46; assoc prof bot, Auburn Univ, 46-47, Univ Tenn, 47-51 & US Govt, 51-54; exec secy biol coun, Nat Res Coun, 54-57; prof bot, George Washington Univ, 57-66; EXEC SECY DIV BIOL SCI, NAT RES COUN, 64- *Mem:* AAAS; Mycol Soc Am; Bot Soc Am; Am Phytopath Soc; Soc Econ Bot. *Res:* Phytopathology; general mycology and botany; epidemiology. *Mailing Add:* Div of Biol Sci Nat Res Coun 2101 Constitution Washington DC 20418

STEVENS, SANDRA J, see McKay, Sandra J

STEVENS, STANLEY EDWARD, JR, b Ringgold, Tex, June 25, 44; m 69; c 3. GENETICS, PHYSIOLOGY. *Educ:* Univ Tex, Austin, BA, 66, MA, 68, PhD(bot), 71. *Prof Exp:* Environ health eng trainee bot, Univ Tex, Austin, 69-70, res assoc, 70-71 trainee zool, Public Health Serv, 71, fel, 71-75; asst prof, 75-81, ASSOC PROF MICROBIOL, PA STATE UNIV, 81- *Concurrent Pos:* Vis staff mem, Los Alamos Sci Lab, Univ Calif, 75-77; consult, Advan Fuels Technol, Gulf & Western Corp, 81- *Mem:* AAAS; Am Soc Microbiol; Am Soc Photobiol; Am Soc Plant Physiologists; Phycol Soc Am. *Res:* Genetics and the regulation of nitrogen assimilation and of pigment biosynthesis in cyanobacteria; fouling of marine structures by algae; bacterial desulfurization of coal. *Mailing Add:* Prog Microbiol 101 S Frear Bldg Pa State Univ University Park PA 16802

STEVENS, SUE CASSELL, b Roanoke, Va. BIOCHEMISTRY. *Educ:* Goucher Col, BA, 30; Columbia Univ, MA, 31, PhD(chem), 40. *Prof Exp:* Res biochemist, NY Skin & Cancer Hosp, New York, 32-35; biochemist, Fifth Ave Hosp, 35; res chemist, Col Physicians & Surgeons, Columbia Univ, 35-39, NY Orthop Hosp, 40-41 & Calif Milk Prod Co, 41-43; res dairy chemist, Golden State Co, Ltd, 43-46 & Swift & Co, 46-47; dir res & qual control, Steven Candy Kitchens, 47-48; assoc prof chem & biol, MacMurray Col, 48-49; chief biochemist, US Vet Admin Ctr, Dayton, Ohio, 49-52, res biochemist, 52-56, supvr res lab Hosp, Lincoln, Nebr, 56-65; dir, Div Endocrine Chem, Jewish Hosp St Louis, 65-79; RETIRED. *Concurrent Pos:* Asst prof path, Sch Med, Wash Univ, 67-79. *Mem:* Fel AAAS; fel Am Inst Chem; Am Soc Qual Control; NY Acad Sci; Am Chem Soc. *Res:* Clinical chemistry methods; electrolytes in biological fluids; steroids; hormones; automation. *Mailing Add:* Box 30206 Lincoln NE 68503

STEVENS, THOMAS MCCONNELL, b Plainfield, NJ, May 25, 27; m 54; c 4. VIROLOGY, ENTOMOLOGY. *Educ:* Haverford Col, BA, 50; Rutgers Univ, MS, 55, PhD(entom), 57. *Prof Exp:* Fel microbiol, St Louis Univ, 57-58, from instr to asst prof, Sch Med, 58-63; asst prof, Med Sch, Rutgers Univ, New Brunswick, 63-66; assoc prof exp med & from assoc dir to dir teaching labs, 66-72, PROF MICROBIOL, RUTGERS MED SCH, COL MED & DENT NJ, 72-, ASST DEAN, 68- *Mem:* Am Soc Microbiol. *Res:* Physical and chemical nature of the togaviruses using dengue virus as a model. *Mailing Add:* Rutgers Med Sch Col of Med & Dent of NJ Piscataway NJ 08854

STEVENS, TRAVIS EDWARD, b Leigh, Nebr, Dec 22, 27; m 61; c 4. ORGANIC CHEMISTRY. *Educ:* Wayne State Col, AB, 51; Iowa State Col, PhD(chem), 55. *Prof Exp:* Asst, Iowa State Col, 51-53; sr res chemist, 55-75, RES SECT MGR, ROHM & HAAS CO, 75- *Concurrent Pos:* Vis prof, Ind Univ, 65. *Mem:* Am Chem Soc. *Res:* Synthesis and properties of high-energy compounds; molecular rearrangements; polymer synthesis; paper chemicals; coatings and textile chemistry. *Mailing Add:* Rohm & Haas Co Spring House PA 19477

STEVENS, VERNON CECIL, physiology, see previous edition

STEVENS, VERNON LEWIS, b Tacoma, Wash, Oct 10, 30; m 54; c 4. BIOCHEMISTRY, ANALYTICAL CHEMISTRY. *Educ:* Cent Wash State Col, BS, 57; Ore State Univ, MS, 60. *Prof Exp:* Res asst & biochemist, William S Merrell Co Div, Richardson-Merrell, Inc, 59-67; head anal chem, Enzomedic Lab, Inc, Wash, 67-69; CHEMIST, PUGET SOUND PLANT, TEXACO INC, 69- *Res:* Development of analytical procedures for gas-liquid and thin layer chromatography, autoanalyzer, radioisotopes and spectronic equipment; lipid synthesis in animals; nucleotides; clinical, environmental and petroleum chemistry. *Mailing Add:* Puget Sound Plant Texaco Inc PO Box 622 Anacortes WA 98221

STEVENS, VINCENT LEROY, b Boston, Mass, July 14, 30; m 58. BIOCHEMISTRY. *Educ:* Univ Calif, Berkeley, AB, 53, PhD(biochem), 57. *Prof Exp:* Jr res biochemist, Med Ctr, Univ Calif, San Francisco, 57-59; asst prof chem & biochem, 59-62, assoc prof chem, 62-67, PROF CHEM, EASTERN WASH STATE COL, 67-, CHMN DEPT, 70-, DEAN, DIV HEALTH SCI, 74- *Concurrent Pos:* Consult, Deaconess Hosp, Spokane, 62- *Mem:* Am Chem Soc. *Res:* Organic and physical chemistry of nucleic acids and their derivatives. *Mailing Add:* Dept of Chem Eastern Wash State Col Cheney WA 99004

STEVENS, WALTER, b Salt Lake City, Utah, Dec 6, 33; m 55; c 4. ANATOMY, RADIOBIOLOGY. *Educ:* Univ Utah, BS, 56, PhD(anat, radiobiol), 62. *Prof Exp:* From instr to assoc prof, 62-74, PROF ANAT, UNIV UTAH, 74-, HEAD CHEM GROUP, RADIOBIOL LAB, 70-, ASST DEAN RES, 81- *Concurrent Pos:* Dir, Nat Inst Gen Med Sci Training Grant, 74-77; vis prof, Stanford Univ, 77. *Mem:* Endocrine Soc; Am Asn Anatomists; Soc Neurosci; Am Physiol Soc; Radiation Res Soc. *Res:* Mechanism of action of glucocorticoids in lymphoid tissues, central nervous system and lung; interaction of transuranic elements with biological systems. *Mailing Add:* Dept Anat 406 Wintrobe Bldg Sch Med Univ Utah Salt Lake City UT 84132

STEVENS, WALTER JOSEPH, b Atlantic City, NJ, Apr 29, 44; m 66; c 2. THEORETICAL CHEMISTRY, CHEMICAL PHYSICS. *Educ:* Drexel Univ, BS, 67; Ind Univ, Bloomington, PhD(chem physics), 71. *Prof Exp:* NSF fel, Argonne Nat Lab, 71-72, lab fel, 72-73; physicist, Lawrence Livermore Lab, 73-75; mem staff, Time & Energy Div, 75-77, MEM STAFF, MOLECULAR SPECTROS DIV, NAT BUR STANDARDS, 77- *Mem:* AAAS; Am Chem Soc; Am Phys Soc. *Res:* Quantum chemistry; ab initio calculation of molecular wavefunctions and properties; theoretical molecular physics. *Mailing Add:* Molecular Spectros Div Nat Bur of Standards Washington DC 20234

STEVENS, WARREN DOUGLAS, b Long Beach, Calif, Sept 15, 44; m 63; c 1. BOTANY. *Educ:* Humboldt State Col, AB, 68; Mich State Univ, MS, 71, PhD(bot), 76. *Prof Exp:* Asst bot & plant path, Mich State Univ, 71-74; consult, Cyrus William Rice Div, NUS Corp, 75-77; res assoc bot & plant path, Mich State Univ, 76-78; B A KRUKOFF CUR CENT AM BOT, MO BOT GARDEN, 77- *Concurrent Pos:* Collabr, Smithsonian Hassan Flora Proj, 69; consult, Ingham County Circuit Court, 75-77. *Mem:* Am Soc Plant Taxonomists; Asn Trop Biol; Bot Soc Am; Int Asn Plant Taxon; Sigma Xi. *Res:* Flora of Nicaragua; systematics of Asclepiadaceae. *Mailing Add:* Mo Bot Garden PO Box 299 St Louis MO 63166

STEVENS, WILLIAM CLARK, b Richland, Tex, Mar 24, 21; m 44; c 2. MICROBIOLOGY, CELL PHYSIOLOGY. *Educ:* Harding Col, BS, 49; Univ Ark, MA, 51; Vanderbilt Univ, PhD(biol), 56. *Prof Exp:* Instr sci, Beebe Jr Col, 47-49; asst prof biol, Harding Col, 50-52, prof, 55-66; instr, Vanderbilt Univ, 54-55; PROF & HEAD DEPT BIOL, ABILENE CHRISTIAN COL, 66- *Concurrent Pos:* NIH res fel, 62-63. *Res:* Bacterial physiology and biochemistry; animal virology; microbiology of water. *Mailing Add:* Dept of Biol Box 8035 ACU Sta/Univ Abilene TX 79601

STEVENS, WILLIAM F(OSTER), b Detroit, Mich, Oct 7, 22; m 62; c 5. CHEMICAL ENGINEERING. *Educ:* Northwestern Univ, BS, 44; Univ Wis, MS, 47, PhD(chem eng), 49. *Prof Exp:* Chem engr, Res Ctr, B F Goodrich Co, 49-51; from res assoc to assoc prof, 51-64, assoc dean, Grad Sch, 65-72, chmn dept, 76-79, PROF CHEM ENG, NORTHWESTERN UNIV, EVANSTON, 64- *Concurrent Pos:* Consult, Vern E Alden Co, Ill, 52-59, Pure Oil Co, 58-63, Argonne Nat Lab, 59-61, Chicago Bridge & Iron Co, 64-70 & TecSearch, Inc, 65-71. *Mem:* Am Soc Eng Educ; Am Chem Soc; Am Inst Chem Engrs. *Res:* Applied mathematics and computers; process control and dynamics; process optimization. *Mailing Add:* Dept Chem Eng Northwestern Univ Evanston IL 60201

STEVENS, WILLIAM GEORGE, b Champaign, Ill, Sept 20, 38; m 61; c 3. ELECTROCHEMISTRY, ANALYTICAL CHEMISTRY. *Educ:* Mass Inst Technol, BS, 61; Univ Wis-Madison, PhD(chem), 66. *Prof Exp:* Sr chemist, Corning Glass Works, 66-69; res specialist nonaqueous batteries, Res & Develop Div, Whittaker Corp, 69-72, res specialist anal chem, 72-76; SR RES ENGR, SOLAR GROUP, INT HARVESTER, 76- *Mem:* Am Chem Soc; Electrochem Soc; Inst Elec & Electronics Engrs. *Res:* Polymer characterization and physical properties of materials. *Mailing Add:* Int Harvester Solar Group 2200 Pacific Hwy San Diego CA 92101

STEVENS, WILLIAM Y(EATON), b South Portland, Maine, Nov 5, 31; m 66. COMPUTER SCIENCE, ENGINEERING PHYSICS. *Educ:* Bates Col, BS, 53; Cornell Univ, MS, 55, PhD(eng physics), 58. *Prof Exp:* Physicist, Gen Elec Co, 53; asst elec eng, Cornell Univ, 54-58; assoc engr, Int Bus Mach Corp, 58-60, staff systs planner, 60-63, adv engr, 63-69, SR ENGR, IBM CORP, 69- *Mem:* AAAS; Asn Comput Mach; Inst Elec & Electronics Engrs. *Res:* System design of digital computing and data processing systems; data communications, sytem reliability and maintainability. *Mailing Add:* IBM Corp PO Box 390 Poughkeepsie NY 12602

STEVENSON, CHARLES EDWARD, b Mt Vernon, NY, Feb 26, 13; m 43; c 3. ORGANIC CHEMISTRY. *Educ:* Pa State Univ, BS, 34, MS, 37, PhD(org chem), 41. *Prof Exp:* Asst, Pa State Univ, 34-42; res chemist, Standard Oil Develop Corp, NJ, 42-45; chemist, Diamond Glass Co, Pa, 45-47; assoc dir, Chem Eng Div, Argonne Nat Lab, 47-53; tech dir, Idaho Chem Process Plant, Phillips Petrol Co, 54-60; supvr exp breeder reactor II, Fuel Cycle Facil, Argonne Nat Lab, 60-65, proj mgr, 65-69, sr scientist, 69-78, RETIRED. *Concurrent Pos:* Chmn comt nuclear fuel cycle, Am Nat Standards Inst; vis scientist, Regulatory Stand Directorate, US Nuclear Regulatory Comn, 73-75; consult, 78- *Mem:* Am Chem Soc; Am Nuclear Soc; Am Inst Chem Eng. *Res:* Methylamines; lubrication oils; chemical engineering with radioactive substances; nuclear fuel processing and waste disposal; nuclear standards. *Mailing Add:* 1538 Falcon Dr Idaho Falls ID 83401

STEVENSON, DAVID AUSTIN, b Albany, NY, Sept 6, 28; m 58; c 3. MATERIALS SCIENCE. *Educ:* Amherst Col, BA, 50; Mass Inst Technol, PhD(phys chem), 54. *Prof Exp:* Res assoc metall, Mass Inst Technol, 53-54, asst prof, 55-58; Fulbright scholar, Univ Munich, 54-55; PROF MAT SCI, STANFORD UNIV, 58- *Concurrent Pos:* Fulbright sr res fel, Max Planck Inst Phys Chem, 68, 69. *Mem:* Am Soc Metals; Am Inst Mining, Metall & Petrol Eng; Electrochem Soc. *Res:* Synthesis and properties of semiconducting materials and device applications; solid state electrochemistry; diffusion in compound semiconductors. *Mailing Add:* Dept of Mat Sci Stanford Univ Stanford CA 94305

STEVENSON, DAVID MICHAEL, b Shafton, Eng, Nov 1, 38; m 60; c 4. ELECTRICAL ENGINEERING, PHYSICS. *Educ:* Univ Leeds, BSc, 60; Cornell Univ, MS, 64, PhD(elec eng), 68. *Prof Exp:* Mem sci staff, Hirst Res Centre, Gen Elec Co Ltd, Eng, 60-63; consult, Cornell Aeronaut Lab, NY, 67-68; mem tech staff, David Sarnoff Res Ctr, RCA Labs, 38-73; eng mgr, 73-81, TECH DIR, SOLID STATE COMPONENTS OPER, VARIAN ASSOCS, 81- *Mem:* Inst Elec & Electronics Engrs; Am Phys Soc; Int Soc Hybrid Microelectronics. *Res:* Microwave electronics. *Mailing Add:* Solid State Oper Varian Assocs 8 Salem Rd Beverly MA 01915

STEVENSON, DAVID STUART, b Virden, Man, Jan 23, 24; m 46; c 2. SOIL PHYSICS. *Educ:* Univ BC, BSA, 51; Ore State Univ, MSc, 56, PhD(soils), 63. *Prof Exp:* Res officer, Dom Exp Farm, Can Dept Agr, Sask, 56-57, Agr Res Sta, Alta, 62-66, res scientist, 66-76, SECT HEAD, SOIL SCI & AGR ENG, SUMMERLAND RES STA, CAN DEPT AGR, 76- *Mem:* AAAS; Am Soc Agron; Soil Sci Soc Am; Int Soil Sci Soc; Sigma Xi. *Res:* Irrigation; soil-water-plant growth relationship. *Mailing Add:* Can Agr Res Sta Summerland BC V0H 1Z0 Can

STEVENSON, DENNIS A, b Mt Holly, NJ, Jan 25, 44; m 66; c 3. BIOPHYSICS, HEALTH PHYSICS. *Educ:* Gettysburg Col, BA, 66; Univ Del, MS, 68, PhD(physics), 72. *Prof Exp:* Teaching res asst physics, Univ Del, 66-72; res assoc biophys, Univ Pittsburgh, 72-73; asst prof physics, Northeast La Univ, 73-77; asst health physics officer, Walter Reed Army Med Ctr, 77-80, health physics officer, 80-81; RADIATION PROTECTION OFFICER, DWIGHT D EISENHOWER ARMY MED CTR, 81- *Mem:* Biophys Soc; Health Physics Soc; Sigma Xi; Sci Res Soc NAm; Am Phys Soc. *Res:* Physical studies of biologically important macromolecules, protein-nucleic acid interactions, virology, effects of various ionizing radiations on macromolecules and living systems; applied health physics; radiation accident emergency preparedness. *Mailing Add:* Dwight D Eisenhower Army Med Ctr Attn: HSHF-HP Fort Gordon GA 30905

STEVENSON, DONALD THOMAS, b Washington, DC, Sept 8, 23; m 46; c 3. SOLID STATE PHYSICS. *Educ:* Cornell Univ, AB, 44; Mass Inst Technol, PhD(physics), 50. *Prof Exp:* Asst physics, 49-50, res assoc, 50-51, mem staff, Lincoln Lab, 51-53, asst group leader solid state physics, 53-57, group leader, 57-61, ASST DIR, FRANCIS BITTER NAT MAGNET LAB, MASS INST TECHNOL, 60- *Mem:* AAAS; Am Phys Soc. *Res:* Semiconductors; high magnetic fields. *Mailing Add:* Francis Bitter Nat Magnet Lab Mass Inst of Technol Cambridge MA 02139

STEVENSON, EDWARD C(ARL), b Sumpter, Ore, Mar 9, 07; m 36. ELECTRICAL ENGINEERING. *Educ:* Univ Va, BS, 28, MS, 29, PhD(physics), 31. *Prof Exp:* Mem staff, Naval Res Lab, 31-32; Bartol Res Found fel, 32-34; fel, instr & tutor, Harvard Univ, 34-42; instr physics & math, US Naval Post Grad Sch, 42-44; assoc group supvr, Los Alamos Sci Lab, 44-45; res physicist, Collins Radio Co, 45-47; physicist, Appl Physics Lab, Johns Hopkins Univ, 47-50; prof physics, 50-60, prof elec eng, 60-73, EMER PROF ELEC ENG, UNIV VA, 73- *Concurrent Pos:* NSF sr fel, 56-57; mem sci adv panel, US Dept Army, 56-63, consult, 63-73. *Mem:* AAAS; Am Phys Soc; Am Asn Physics Teachers. *Res:* Cosmic rays; instrumentation; ordnance development. *Mailing Add:* PO Box 1893 University Sta Charlottesville VA 22903

STEVENSON, ELMER CLARK, b Pine City, Wash, Aug 20, 15; m 39; c 6. HORTICULTURE. *Educ:* Univ Md, BS, 37; Univ Wis, PhD(agron, plant path), 42. *Prof Exp:* Asst plant path, Univ Wis, 38-42; from asst plant pathologist to plant pathologist, Drug Plant Invests, US Dept Agr, 42-48; from assoc prof to prof hort, Purdue Univ, 48-67, head dept, 58-67; prof hort, assoc dean agr & dir resident instruct, 67-80, EMER PROF HORT, EMER ASSOC DEAN & EMER DIR RESIDENT INSTRUCT AGR, ORE STATE UNIV, 80- *Concurrent Pos:* Consult, US Dept Agr & Univ Ky, 58, US Agency Int Develop, Brazil, 62 & US Dept Agr & Miss State Univ, 64. *Mem:* Fel Am Soc Hort Sci. *Res:* Corn diseases and breeding; diseases of medicinal and special crops; mint breeding and production; vegetable breeding and genetics. *Mailing Add:* Sch of Agr Ore State Univ Corvallis OR 97331

STEVENSON, ENOLA L, b Feb 20, 39; US citizen. PLANT PHYSIOLOGY. *Educ:* Southern Univ, BS, 60; Univ NH, MS, 62, PhD(plant physiol), 68. *Prof Exp:* Res asst plant physiol, Univ NH, 60-62, 67-68; instr bot, Southern Univ, 62-64; asst prof, 68-72, ASSOC PROF BIOL, ATLANTA UNIV, 72- *Res:* Effects of light quality and intensity on plant growth and metabolism. *Mailing Add:* Dept of Biol Atlanta Univ Atlanta GA 30314

STEVENSON, EUGENE HAMILTON, b Chicago Heights, Ill, June 29, 19; m 43; c 3. ORGANIC CHEMISTRY, NUTRITION. *Educ:* Cornell Col, BS, 42; Ill Inst Technol, MS, 44. *Prof Exp:* Chemist, Swift & Co, Ill, 46-48; asst secy, Coun Foods & Nutrit, Am Med Asn, 48-55, actg secy, 55-57, assoc secy, 57-60; asst to dir, Div Nutrit, US Food & Drug Admin, 60-66, asst dir, 66-68; dir nutrit prod info, res ctr, 68-77, DIR REGULATORY AFFAIRS, MEAD JOHNSON & CO, 77- *Mem:* AAAS; Am Chem Soc; Am Pub Health Asn; Inst Food Technol; Am Inst Chem. *Res:* Human nutrition; nutrient requirements; composition of foods; diet and nutritional status surveys; federal food regulations. *Mailing Add:* Res Ctr Mead Johnson & Co Evansville IN 47721

STEVENSON, EVERETT E, b Buffalo, NY, Jan 14, 23; m 45; c 3. MATHEMATICS. *Educ:* State Univ NY Col Buffalo, BS, 44; Univ Houston, MEd, 52; Ohio State Univ, PhD(math, math ed), 61. *Prof Exp:* From instr to assoc prof math, US Air Force Acad, 56-67, chief enrichment br, 64-66, exec officer, 66-67; fac mem, Indust Col Armed Forces, 67-68; assoc chmn dept, 69-79, chmn, 79-80, PROF MATH SCI, MEMPHIS STATE UNIV, 69-, ASSOC CHMN DEPT, 80- *Mem:* Nat Coun Teachers Math; Math Asn Am. *Res:* Mathematics education; complex variables; differential equations. *Mailing Add:* Dept of Math Sci Memphis State Univ Memphis TN 38152

STEVENSON, F DEE, b Ogden, Utah, June 7, 33; m 51; c 5. CHEMICAL ENGINEERING. *Educ:* Univ Utah, BS, 55; Ore State Univ, PhD, 62. *Prof Exp:* Asst eng, Calif Res Corp, Standard Oil Co Calif, 55-57; from asst prof to prof chem eng, Iowa State Univ, 62-74; prof term with Chem Off, Div Phys Res, AEC, 72-74; prog mgr, Mat Sci & Molecular Sci Off, Div Basic Energy Sci, ERDA, 74-77; BR CHIEF, CHEM SCI DIV, OFF ENERGY RES, DEPT OF ENERGY, 77- *Mem:* Am Chem Soc; Am Inst Chem Engrs. *Res:* Kinetics of reactions; statistical application to data analysis and sequential experimental design; anhydrous separation and purification metals; thermodynamics of solutions, including liquid metals; high temperature and vacuum processing. *Mailing Add:* Div of Chem Sci Off Energy Res Dept of Energy Washington DC 20545

STEVENSON, FORREST FREDERICK, b Kismet, Kans, Nov 12, 16; m 47; c 1. PLANT MORPHOLOGY. *Educ:* Cent Mo State Col, BS, 46; Univ Mo, MA, 48; Univ Mich, PhD(bot), 56. *Prof Exp:* Instr biol, Univ Kans City, 48-50 & McCook Jr Col, 50-51; from asst prof to assoc prof, 55-65, PROF BIOL, BALL STATE UNIV, 65- *Mem:* Bot Soc Am; Am Bryol & Lichenological Soc. *Res:* Experimental plant morphology. *Mailing Add:* Dept of Biol Ball State Univ Muncie IN 47306

STEVENSON, FRANK JAY, b Logan, Utah, Aug 2, 22; m 56; c 3. SOILS. *Educ:* Brigham Young Univ, BS, 49; Ohio State Univ, PhD(agron), 52. *Prof Exp:* From asst prof to assoc prof, 53-62, PROF SOIL CHEM, UNIV ILL, 62- *Concurrent Pos:* Agron res award, Am Soc Agron, 80. *Mem:* Soil Sci Soc Am; Am Soc Agron; Geochem Soc. *Res:* Biochemical properties of soils; chemistry of soil organic matter. *Mailing Add:* Dept Agronomy Univ Ill Urbana IL 61801

STEVENSON, FRANK ROBERT, b Brooklyn, NY, Aug 29, 31; m 56; c 6. SOLID STATE PHYSICS. *Educ:* Polytech Inst Brooklyn, BS, 53, MS, 59. *Prof Exp:* Physicist, Sperry Gyroscope Co, NY, 53-56 & Curtis Wright Corp, Pa, 56-58; res assoc, RIAS Div, Martin Co, Md, 58-63; physicist, Lewis Res Ctr, NASA, Ohio, 63-71; ENVIRON SCIENTIST, FORD MOTOR CO, 71- *Concurrent Pos:* Lectr, Goucher Col, 61-62 & John Carroll Univ, 64-65. *Mem:* Am Phys Soc. *Res:* Radiation damage; microwave electronics; low temperature physics; accelerators; air pollution; industrial noise control; energy conservation; water pollution management. *Mailing Add:* Ford Motor Co PO Box 9898 Cleveland OH 44142

STEVENSON, GEORGE FRANKLIN, b St Thomas, Ont, Sept 13, 22; US citizen; m 45, 77; c 2. PATHOLOGY. *Educ:* Univ Western Ont, BA, 44, MD, 45. *Prof Exp:* Prof clin path, dean sch allied health sci & dir med technol prog, Med Col SC, 66-71; dep comnr med technol, 65-67, comnr continuing educ, 67-72, exec vpres, 71-74, SR VPRES, AM SOC CLIN PATHOLOGISTS, 74-; PROF PATH, MED SCH, NORTHWESTERN UNIV, CHICAGO, 71- *Mem:* AMA; Am Asn Pathologists; Col Am Pathologists; Am Soc Clin Pathologists; Asn Clin Sci (pres, 59-60). *Res:* Pathology and administrative medicine. *Mailing Add:* Am Soc of Clin Pathologists 2100 W Harrison St Chicago IL 60612

STEVENSON, H(ARRY) B(AND), b Omaha, Nebr, Oct 24, 01; m 26; c 2. CHEMICAL ENGINEERING. *Educ:* Univ Colo, BS, 25. *Prof Exp:* Anal chemist, Procter & Gamble Co, 25-27, res chemist, 27-29, head chemist, 29-40, tech supt, Defense Corp, Tenn, 41-46, sect head develop dept, Chem Div, Ohio, 46-50, tech dir, Milan Arsenal, 51-58, chem eng, & operations & planning mgr, Soap Prod Div, Ohio, 58-66; PRES, STEVENSON ASSOCS, 66- *Mem:* Am Oil Chem Soc; Am Ord Asn; Am Inst Chem Engrs. *Res:* Detergent action; ultrasonics; optical instrumentation; measurement of dust in commercial products; explosives; ammunition leading, surveillance, design and development; color specification and measurement. *Mailing Add:* 1203 Lexington Sq Corsicana TX 75110

STEVENSON, HARLAN QUINN, b Waynesboro, Pa, Apr 1, 27; m 60; c 2. CYTOGENETICS, RADIOBIOLOGY. *Educ:* Pa State Univ, BS, 50; Univ Fla, PhD(radiation biol), 63. *Prof Exp:* Asst bot, Pa State Univ, 50-51 & Cornell Univ, 51-56; res assoc biol, Brookhaven Nat Lab, 56-60; asst prof, Univ Fla, 63-64; from asst prof to assoc prof, 64-72, PROF BIOL, SOUTHERN CONN STATE COL, 72-, CHMN DEPT, 75- *Mem:* AAAS; Soc Study Evolution; Am Inst Biol Sci; Am Soc Human Genetics; Genetics Soc Am. *Res:* Chemical and radiation induced chromosomal aberrations; genetic and radiation effects in plant tumors; evolutionary and practical significance of multiple allopolyploidy; cytotaxonomy and sex determination; genetic counseling; bioethics. *Mailing Add:* Dept of Biol Southern Conn State Col New Haven CT 06515

STEVENSON, HENRY MILLER, b Birmingham, Ala, Feb 25, 14; m 39; c 4. ORNITHOLOGY. *Educ:* Birmingham-Southern Col, AB, 35; Univ Ala, MS, 39; Cornell Univ, PhD(ornith), 43. *Prof Exp:* Lab asst geol, Birmingham-Southern Col, 35-36; lab asst biol, Univ Ala, 38-39; lab asst bot, Vanderbilt Univ, 40-41; lab asst ornith, Cornell Univ, 42-43; actg assoc prof biol, Univ Miss, 43-44; assoc prof, Emory & Henry Col, 44-46; from asst prof to prof, 46-75, EMER PROF ZOOL, FLA STATE UNIV, 75-; RES FEL, TALL TIMBERS RES STA, 75- *Concurrent Pos:* Consult, Conserv Consults, Inc, 73-; ed, Fla Field Naturalist, 73-76. *Mem:* Wilson Ornith Soc; Nat Audubon Soc; Am Ornith Union. *Res:* Avian taxonomy; quantitative field studies of birds; geographical distribution and migration of birds. *Mailing Add:* Tall Timbers Res Sta Tallahassee FL 32303

STEVENSON, IAN, b Montreal, Que, Oct 31, 18; nat US; m 47. MEDICINE, PSYCHIATRY. *Educ:* McGill Univ, BSc, 40, MD, CM, 43. *Prof Exp:* Intern & asst resident med, Royal Victoria Hosp, Montreal, 44-45; from intern to resident, St Joseph's Hosp, Phoenix, Ariz, 45-46; fel internal med, Ochsner Med Found, New Orleans, La, 46-47; Commonwealth fel med, Med Col, Cornell Univ, 47-49; asst prof med & psychiat, Sch Med, La State Univ, 49-52, assoc prof psychiat, 52-57; prof psychiat & chmn dept neurol & psychiat, 57-67, CARLSON PROF PSYCHIAT, SCH MED, UNIV VA, 67- *Concurrent Pos:* Consult, New Orleans Parish Sch Bd, 49-52, State Dept Pub Welfare, 50-52 & Southeast La State Hosp, Mandeville, 52-57; vis physician, Charity Hosp, New Orleans, 52-57; hon mem staff, DePaul Hosp, 52-57; psychiatrist-in-chief, Univ Va Hosp, 57-67. *Mem:* AAAS; Am Psychosom Soc; Am Soc Psychical Res; Am Psychiat Asn; AMA. *Res:* Experimental psychoses; psychotherapy; parapsychology. *Mailing Add:* Div of Parapsychol Univ of Va Med Ctr Box 152 Charlottesville VA 22901

STEVENSON, IAN LAWRIE, b Hamilton, Ont, Dec 28, 26; m 53; c 2. AGRICULTURAL MICROBIOLOGY, CYTOLOGY. *Educ:* Ont Agr Col, BSA, 49; Univ Toronto, MSA, 51; Univ London, PhD(microbiol), 55. *Prof Exp:* From bacteriologist to sr bacteriologist, Microbiol Res Inst, 51-67, head physiol & nutrit unit, 59-67, head cytol & physiol unit, Chem & Biol Res Inst, Ont, 67-72, assoc dir res sta, Lethbridge, Alta, 72-74, PRIN RES SCIENTIST, CHEM & BIOL RES INST, CAN DEPT AGR, 74- *Concurrent Pos:* Lectr, Univ Ottawa, 55-59; vis scientist, Nat Inst Med Res, Mill Hill, 63-64. *Mem:* Am Soc Microbiol; Can Soc Microbiol; Brit Soc Gen Microbiol. *Res:* Physiology and growth of micro-organisms; microbiology of the soil; electron microscopy; cytology. *Mailing Add:* Chem & Biol Res Inst Can Dept of Agr Ottawa ON K1A 0C5 Can

STEVENSON, IRA MORLEY, b Ont, Can, Mar 27, 20; m 42; c 5. GEOLOGY. *Educ:* McGill Univ, BSc, 49, MSc, 51, PhD(geol), 54. *Prof Exp:* GEOLOGIST, DEPT ENERGY, MINES & RESOURCES CAN, 54- *Mailing Add:* Dept Energy Mines & Resources Can 580 Booth Ottawa ON K1A 0E8 Can

STEVENSON, IRONE EDMUND, JR, b Linthicum, Md, Apr 21, 30; m 60; c 2. BIOCHEMISTRY. *Educ:* Univ Md, BS, 53; Univ Pa, PhD(biochem), 61. *Prof Exp:* Asst instr biochem, Univ Pa, 54-58; asst zool, Yale Univ, 60-63; chemist, 63-81, SR RES SCIENTIST, E I DU PONT DE NEMOURS & CO, INC, 81- *Mem:* Am Soc Biol Chem; Entom Soc Am. *Res:* Degradation of cholesterol by mammalian enzymes; intermediary metabolism of insects. *Mailing Add:* Biochem Dept E I du Pont de Nemours & Co Inc Wilmington DE 19898

STEVENSON, J(OSEPH) ROSS, b Canton, China, Sept 4, 31; US citizen; m 54; c 3. ENDOCRINOLOGY, DEVELOPMENTAL BIOLOGY. *Educ:* Oberlin Col, BA, 53; Northwestern Univ, MS, 55, PhD, 60. *Prof Exp:* Asst zool & chem, Oberlin Col, 52-53; asst biol, Northwestern Univ, 53-55; instr, Chatham Col, 56-59; res assoc zool, Univ Wash, 59-60; from instr to assoc prof, 60-71, assoc dean grad col, 73-74, PROF ZOOL, KENT STATE UNIV, 71- *Concurrent Pos:* Jacques Loeb assoc, Rockefeller Univ, 63-64. *Mem:* AAAS; Am Soc Zool; Am Inst Biol Sci; Am Soc Cell Biol. *Res:* Effects of adrenal cortical hormones on the immune system; lymphocyte functions; physiology and biochemistry of crustacean growth and molting. *Mailing Add:* Dept Biol Sci Kent State Univ Kent OH 44242

STEVENSON, JAMES FRANCIS, b Greenville, Pa, July 15, 43; m 71; c 2. POLYMER PROCESSING, PROCESS CONTROL. *Educ:* Rensselaer Polytech Inst, BChE, 65; Univ Wis, Madison, MS, 67, PhD(chem eng), 70. *Prof Exp:* NIH fel, Columbia Univ, 70-71; from asst prof to assoc prof chem eng, Cornell Univ, 71-77; res scientist, 77-79, group leader, 79-81, SECT HEAD, GEN TIRE & RUBBER CO, 81- *Mem:* Am Inst Chem Engrs; Am Chem Soc; Soc Plastics Engrs; Soc Rheol. *Res:* Design, optimization, monitoring and control of processing equipment for thermoplastic and thermoset materials; processes include extrusion, calendering, molding, mixing and shaping with fixed and moving surface dies; polymer rheology. *Mailing Add:* 123 Clairhaven Dr Hudson OH 44236

STEVENSON, JAMES HAROLD, b Volant, Pa, Mar 22, 14; m 40; c 2. FISH BIOLOGY. *Educ:* Westminster Col, Pa, BS, 35; Oberlin Col, MA, 37; Okla State Univ, PhD, 50. *Prof Exp:* Metallurgist, Carnegie-Ill Steel Corp, 39-42; instr chem, Westminster Col, 42-46; instr zool, Little Rock Univ, 46-48; res biologist, State Game & Fish Comn, Ark, 50-56; chief fish farming exp sta, Bur Sport Fisheries & Wildlife, US Fish & Wildlife Serv, 60-65; prof biol, 76-80, EMER PROF BIOL, ARK STATE UNIV, 80-, DEAN SCH SCI, 65- *Concurrent Pos:* Chmn sci div, Little Rock Univ, 50-60; consult, Pakistan, 59-60. *Mem:* Am Fisheries Soc. *Res:* Ecology; productivity of large impoundments; fish culture. *Mailing Add:* Ark State Univ Col of Sci State University AR 72467

STEVENSON, JAMES RUFUS, b Trenton, NJ, May 19, 25; m 55; c 3. SURFACE PHYSICS. *Educ:* Mass Inst Technol, SB, 50; Univ Mo, PhD(physics), 58. *Prof Exp:* Res participant, Oak Ridge Nat Lab, 55; asst prof, 55-62, actg dir, 68-69, ASSOC PROF PHYSICS, GA INST TECHNOL, 62-, DIR SCH PHYSICS, 69- *Concurrent Pos:* Physicist, US Naval Res Lab, DC, 58, consult, 60-67; Fulbright-Hays vis prof, Univ Sci & Technol, Ghana, 65-66; mem comt applns physics, Am Phys Soc, 75-78; chmn comt educ, Am Phys Soc, 78. *Mem:* Am Phys Soc; Am Asn Physics Teachers; Optical Soc Am; Am Soc Eng Educ. *Res:* Synchrotron radiation, Auger spectroscopy and optical surface studies of metals, metal oxides, and semiconductors with applications to corrosion. *Mailing Add:* Sch of Physics Ga Inst of Technol Atlanta GA 30332

STEVENSON, JEAN MOORHEAD, b Circleville, Ohio, Oct 2, 04; m 40; c 3. SURGERY. *Educ:* Miami Univ, AB, 26; Univ Cincinnati, MB, 30, MD, 31. *Prof Exp:* Resident surg, Cincinnati Gen Hosp, 31-33 & 34-37 & Univ Calif, 33-34; from instr to assoc prof, 37-61, PROF SURG, COL MED, UNIV CINCINNATI, 61- *Mem:* Soc Univ Surgeons; Soc Clin Surgeons; AMA; Am Col Surgeons; Int Soc Surg. *Res:* Wound healing; development of technics for the management of wounds of violence; care of tissues in all surgical wounds. *Mailing Add:* Dept Surg Univ Cincinnati Med Ctr Cincinnati OH 45267

STEVENSON, JOHN CRABTREE, b Everett, Wash, Feb 24, 37; m 60; c 3. MATHEMATICS. *Educ:* NY Univ, BA, 63, MS, 63; Adelphi Univ, PhD(math), 70. *Prof Exp:* From instr to assoc prof, 68-74, chmn dept, 72-78, PROF MATH, C W POST COL, LONG ISLAND UNIV, 74- *Concurrent Pos:* C W Post Col grant, dept physics, Imp Col, Univ London, 70-71. *Mem:* AAAS; Math Asn Am; Am Math Soc; Soc Indust & Appl Math. *Res:* Numerical solution of hyperbolic partial differential equations; plasma physics in the solar atmosphere and magnetosphere; multiple pool analysis of metabolic pathways. *Mailing Add:* Dept of Math C W Post Col Long Island Univ Greenvale NY 11548

STEVENSON, JOHN O'FARRELL, JR, b Brooklyn, NY, Oct 11, 47. MATHEMATICS. *Educ:* Fordham Univ, BA, 68; Polytech Inst New York, MS, 71, PhD(math), 76. *Prof Exp:* Instr math, Polytech Inst New York, 69-71; instr, York Col, City Univ New York, 71-74; asst prof, Laguardia Col, 74-77; assoc prof math & dean, Empire State Col, State Univ NY, 77-80; PRES, NAT SCHOLARSHIP SERV & FUND FOR NEGRO STUDENTS, 80- *Mem:* Am Math Soc. *Res:* Group theory; the artin brieskorn groups. *Mailing Add:* Nat Scholarship Serv & Fund Negro Students Students 1501 Broadway Suite 611 New York NY 10036

STEVENSON, JOHN RAY, b Ordway, Colo, May 10, 43. IMMUNOLOGY, MEDICAL MICROBIOLOGY. *Educ:* Kans State Teachers Col, BA, 65; MS, 67; Case Western Reserve Univ, PhD(microbiol), 72. *Prof Exp:* asst prof biol & med, Biol Dept, Univ Mo, Kansas City, 74-80. *Concurrent Pos:* Vis asst prof, Microbiol Dept, Miami Univ, Ohio, 80- *Mem:* AAAS; Am Soc Microbiol; Sigma Xi. *Res:* Role of macrophages in induction of antibody synthesis, cell-mediated immunity and host-parasite relationships; mechanisms of macrophage-migration inhibiting factor interaction. *Mailing Add:* Dept Microbiol Miami Univ Oxford OH 45056

STEVENSON, JOHN SINCLAIR, b New Westminster, BC, Sept 21, 08; m 35; c 2. MINERALOGY, GEOLOGY. *Educ:* Univ BC, BA, 29, BASc, 30; Mass Inst Technol, PhD(econ geol), 34. *Prof Exp:* Instr & asst geol, Mass Inst Technol, 31-34; engr chg, Longacre Long Lac Gold Mines, Ont, 34-35; from asst res mining engr to mining engr, Dept Mines, Victoria, 35-50; from assoc prof to prof mineral, 50-72, chmn dept geol sci, 66-68, Dawson prof, 72-77, PROF GEOL, McGILL UNIV, 77- *Concurrent Pos:* Can travel fel, Guggenheim Found, 47-48; consult, 50- & Int Nickel Co Can, Ltd, 65- *Mem:* Fel Geol Soc Am; Soc Econ Geologists; fel Mineral Soc Am; Fel Royal Soc Can; Sigma Xi. *Res:* Mining geology; investigation of gold, mercury, tungsten and molybdenum deposits of British Columbia; varieties of Coast Range intrusives of British Columbia and types of related metallization; mineralogy of urinary calculi; uranium and columbium mineralization; medical mineralogy; origin of Sudbury, Ontario, irruptive; geology of sulfide nickel. *Mailing Add:* Dept Geol Sci McGill Univ 3450 University St Montreal PQ H3A 2A7 Can

STEVENSON, KENNETH EUGENE, b Modesto, Calif, June 3, 42; m 69; c 1. FOOD MICROBIOLOGY. *Educ:* Univ Calif, Davis, BS, 64, PhD(microbiol), 70. *Prof Exp:* Instr biol, Napa Col, Calif, 71; res microbiologist, Univ Calif, Davis, 71; asst prof, 71-76, ASSOC PROF FOOD MICROBIOL, MICH STATE UNIV, 76- *Concurrent Pos:* Sci adv, US Food & Drug Admin, Detroit, 72- *Mem:* Int Asn Milk, Food & Environ Sanit; Am Soc Microbiol; Inst Food Technol. *Res:* Microbiological analyses of foods; food poisoning microorganisms; microbiological aspects of plant sanitation and waste disposal; use of microorganisms in the production of food. *Mailing Add:* Dept of Food Sci & Human Nutrit Mich State Univ East Lansing MI 48824

STEVENSON, KENNETH JAMES, b Calgary, Alta, Apr 16, 41; m 64; c 2. PROTEIN CHEMISTRY. *Educ:* Univ Alta, BSc, 62, PhD(biochem), 66. *Prof Exp:* Med Res Coun fel, Lab Molecular Biol, Cambridge Univ, 66-67; Killam fel, Univ BC, 67-69; asst prof, 69-75, ASSOC PROF BIOCHEM, UNIV CALGARY, 75- *Mem:* Can Biochem Soc; Brit Biochem Soc; Am Soc Biol Chemists. *Res:* Structure and function of multi-enzyme complexes; techniques in protein chemistry. *Mailing Add:* Dept Chem Univ Calgary Calgary AB T2N 1N4 Can

STEVENSON, KENNETH LEE, b Fort Wayne, Ind, Aug 1, 39; m 59; c 2. PHOTOCHEMISTRY. *Educ:* Purdue Univ, BS, 61, MS, 65; Univ Mich, PhD(phys chem), 68. *Prof Exp:* Teacher high schs, Ind & Mich, 61-65; from asst prof to assoc prof, 68-78, PROF CHEM, PURDUE UNIV, FT WAYNE, 78-, CHMN CHEM DEPT, 79- *Concurrent Pos:* Fel, Chem Dept, NMex State Univ, 75-76; sabbatical vis, Solar Energy Res Inst, Indiana, 80. *Mem:* AAAS; Am Chem Soc; Inter-Am Photochem Soc. *Res:* Photochemistry of coordination compounds; kinetics and thermodynamics of ligand exchange reactions; induction of optical activity using light; photochemical conversion of solar energy. *Mailing Add:* Dept of Chem Purdue Univ Ft Wayne IN 46805

STEVENSON, L HAROLD, b Bogalusa, La, Mar 18, 40; m 61; c 1. MICROBIOLOGY. *Educ:* Southeastern La Col, BS, 62; La State Univ, MS, 64, PhD(microbiol), 67. *Prof Exp:* Asst prof, 67-71, ASSOC PROF BIOL, UNIV SC, 71-, ASSOC PROF MARINE SCI & MICROBIOL, 73- *Mem:* AAAS; Am Soc Microbiol. *Res:* Bacterial ecology; distribution, activity and taxonomy of estuarine bacteria. *Mailing Add:* Dept of Biol Univ of SC Columbia SC 29208

STEVENSON, LAWRENCE GRANT, b Ottawa, Kans, Apr 7, 23; m 44; c 4. CHEMICAL ENGINEERING. *Educ:* Kans State Univ, BS, 47; Univ Mo, MBA, 65. *Prof Exp:* Jr chem engr, Linde Air Prod Co, Union Carbide & Carbon Corp, 47-51, chem engr, 51; sr chem engr, Spencer Chem Co, 51-56, leader, Pilot Plant Sect, 56-58 & Process Develop Dept, 59-66; dir tech develop, Chem Dept, Gulf Oil Corp, Tex, 66-67, mgr chem, Korea Gulf Oil Corp, Seoul, 67-69; dep managing dir, Lummus Co-Far East, Hong Kong, 69-70, exec engr, Lummus Co, 70-72, vpres, Iran, 72-75; v pres mkt & sales, J F Pritchard Co, 75-77; MGR NEW BUS DEVELOP, EXPLOSIVES DEPT, GULF OIL CHEM CO, 77- *Mem:* Am Inst Chem Engrs. *Res:* Development of commercial processes; polymers; petrochemicals. *Mailing Add:* Gulf Oil Chem Co PO Box 10900 Overland Park KS 66210

STEVENSON, LOUISE STEVENS, b Seattle, Wash, July 28, 12; Can citizen; m 35; c 2. MINERALOGY. *Educ:* Univ Wash, BS, 32; Radcliffe Col, AM, 33. *Prof Exp:* Res asst climat, US Weather Bur, Seattle, 34; lectr geol & geog, Victoria Col, BC, 48-49; mus assoc geol, 51-57, cur, 57-80, HON CUR GEOL, REDPATH MUS, McGILL UNIV, 80- *Concurrent Pos:* Convener sect 17, Int Geol Cong, 70-72. *Mem:* Fel Geol Asn Can; Mineral Soc Am; Mineral Asn Can; Nat Asn Geol Teachers; Sigma Xi. *Res:* Petrogenesis of rare minerals; mineralogy applied to medicine and dentistry; petrology of siliceous lavas; adult education in mineralogy; geological education through university museums. *Mailing Add:* Redpath Mus McGill Univ 859 Sherbrooke St W Montreal PQ H3A 0K6 Can

STEVENSON, MERLON LYNN, b Salt Lake City, Utah, Oct 31, 23; m 48; c 5. PARTICLE PHYSICS. *Educ:* Univ Calif, AB, 48, PhD(physics), 53. *Prof Exp:* From asst to lectr, 48-58, from asst prof to assoc prof, 58-64, PROF PHYSICS, UNIV CALIF, BERKELEY, 64-, PHYSICIST, LAWRENCE BERKELEY LAB, 51- *Concurrent Pos:* NSF sr fel & vis prof physics, Inst High Energy Physics, Univ Heidelberg, 66-67. *Res:* Neutrino physics and new particle search; electron-positron physics at proton-electron-proton. *Mailing Add:* Lawrence Berkeley Lab Rm 5239 Bldg 50B Univ Calif Berkeley CA 94720

STEVENSON, MICHAEL GAIL, b Little Rock, Ark, Jan 10, 43; m 64. NUCLEAR ENGINEERING. *Educ:* Univ Tex, Austin, BEngSc, 64, PhD(nuclear eng), 68. *Prof Exp:* Group supvr fast reactor safety, Babcock & Wilcox Co, 68-71; mem staff & sect mgr, Argonne Nat Lab, 71-74; mem staff & group leader fast reactor safety, 74-77, asst energy div leader, 76-79, assoc leader reactor safety, 79-81, DEP ENERGY DIV LEADER, LOS ALAMOS NAT LAB, 81- *Mem:* Am Nuclear Soc. *Res:* Development of computational methods for analysis of reactor accidents; design and analysis of experiments related to reactor safety analysis; energy research program planning and management. *Mailing Add:* 1 Mariposa Ct White Rock NM 87544

STEVENSON, NANCY ROBERTA, b Vinton, Iowa, Feb 14, 38; m 73; c 4. PHYSIOLOGY, NUTRITION. *Educ:* Univ Northern Iowa, BS, 60; Rutgers Univ, MS, 63, PhD(nutrit), 69. *Prof Exp:* Nat Inst Arthritis, Metab & Digestive Dis fel, 69-71; instr physiol, 71-72, asst prof, 72-78, ASSOC PROF PHYSIOL, RUTGERS MED SCH, COL MED & DENT NJ, 78- *Mem:* AAAS; Am Gastroenterol Asn; Am Dietetic Asn; Am Physiol Soc; Int Soc Chronobiol. *Res:* Gastrointestinal digestion and absorption; circadian rhythms. *Mailing Add:* Dept of Physiol & Biophysics Rutgers Med Sch Piscataway NJ 08854

STEVENSON, RALPH GIRARD, JR, b Jersey Shore, Pa, Feb 14, 25; m 52; c 4. MINERALOGY, PETROLOGY. *Educ:* Univ NMex, BS, 49, MS, 50; Ind Univ, PhD(geol), 65. *Prof Exp:* Geol engr, Water Resources Div, US Geol Surv, 50-51; geologist, Skelly Oil Co, 51-55 & Shell Develop Co, 55-61; res geologist, Gulf Res & Develop Co, 64-66, staff geologist, Tech Serv Ctr, Gulf Oil Corp, 66-68; from asst prof to assoc prof, Univ S Fla, 68-78, sr proj geologist, 78-80, DIR RESERVOIR PETROL SECT, GULF RES & DEVELOP CO, 80- *Mem:* Am Asn Petrol Geologists; Asn Prof Geol Scientists; Am Inst Mining, Metall & Petrol Eng. *Res:* Mineralogy and petrology of polymetamorphic and sedimentary rocks; crystal chemistry and geochemistry of phosphate minerals and clay minerals at atmospheric conditions. *Mailing Add:* Gulf Res & Develop Co PO Box 36506 Houston TX 77236

STEVENSON, ROBERT EDWIN, b Columbus, Ohio, Dec 2, 26. MICROBIOLOGY, SCIENCE ADMINISTRATION. *Educ:* Ohio State Univ, BSc, 47, MSc, 50, PhD(bact), 54; Am Bd Microbiol, dipl. *Prof Exp:* Res assoc, US Pub Health Serv, 52-54, virologist, 54-58; head tissue cult div,

Tissue Bank Dept, US Naval Med Sch, 58-60; head, Cell Cult & Tissue Mat Sect, Virol Res Resources Br, Nat Cancer Inst, 60-62, actg chief, 62-63, chief, 63-66, chief, Viral Carcinogenesis Br, 66-67; mgr biol sci, Develop Dept, Union Carbide Res Inst, NY, 67-71; vpres, Litton Bionetics & gen mgr, Nat Cancer Inst-Frederick Cancer Res Ctr, 72-80; DIR, AM TYPE CULT COLLECTION, 80- *Concurrent Pos:* Mem, Nat Inst Allergy & Infectious Dis, bd virus reference reagent, 63-65; cell cult comt, Int Asn Microbiol Soc, 63-67; comt transplantation, Nat Acad Sci-Nat Res Coun, 66-70; chmn cell cult comt, Am Type Cult Collection, 71-75, mem bd trustees, 72-; founding mem Am Asn Tissue Banks, chmn Cell & Tumor Coun, 77-81; fel Hastings Inst; vpres, World Fedn Cult Collections, 81- *Mem:* AAAS; Am Soc Microbiol; Soc Cryobiol; Tissue Cult Asn; Am Asn Tissue Banks. *Res:* Viral oncology; biomedical instrumentation; biological standardization. *Mailing Add:* Am Type Cult Collection 12301 Parklawn Dr Rockville MD 20852

STEVENSON, ROBERT EVANS, b Des Moines, Iowa, May 5, 16; m 48; c 2. GEOLOGY. *Educ:* Univ Hawaii, BS, 39; State Col Wash, MS, 42; Lehigh Univ, PhD(geol), 50. *Prof Exp:* Asst, Univ Hawaii, 39; lab asst, State Col Wash, 39-42; geologist, Wash State Div Geol, 42-44; field geologist, Venezuelan Atlantic Ref Co, 44-46; instr geol, Lehigh Univ, 46-50; geologist, State Geol Surv, SDak, 50-51; from asst prof to prof geol, Univ SDak, 51-71, chmn dept geol, 57-67, prof earth sci, 71-80, cur geol, Mus, 73-80; SCI LIAISON, OFF NAVAL RES, SCRIPPS INST OCEANOG, CALIF, 80- *Concurrent Pos:* Geologist, NY State Sci Serv, 47-48. *Mem:* AAAS; Geol Soc Am; Am Asn Petrol Geol; Paleont Soc. *Res:* Stratigraphy, sedimentation and paleontology of South Dakota; paleoecology. *Mailing Add:* Off Naval Res Scripps Inst Oceanog La Jolla CA 92037

STEVENSON, ROBERT EVERETT, b Fullerton, Calif, Jan 15, 21; m 63; c 2. OCEANOGRAPHY. *Educ:* Univ Calif, AB, 46, AM, 48; Univ Southern Calif, PhD(marine geol), 54. *Prof Exp:* Instr geol, Compton Col, 47-49; lectr, Univ Southern Calif, 49-51, dir inshore res oceanog, Hancock Found, 53-59, 60-61; res scientist, Off Naval Res, London, 59; dir marine lab, Tex A&M Univ, 61-63; assoc prof meteorol & geol, Fla State Univ, 63-65; res oceanogr & asst dir biol lab, US Bur Commercial Fisheries, 65-70; SCI LIAISON OFFICER, OFF NAVAL RES, SCRIPPS INST OCEANOG, 70- *Mem:* Fel Geol Soc Am; Am Meteorol Soc; Am Geophys Union. *Res:* Space oceanography; surface layer oceanography as related to meteorology and climatology. *Mailing Add:* Sci Liaison Officer Scripps Inst of Oceanog La Jolla CA 92093

STEVENSON, ROBERT JAN, b Cleveland, Ohio, Jan 3, 52; m 74. PHYCOLOGY, STREAM BIOLOGY. *Educ:* Bowling Green State Univ, BS, 74, MS, 76; Univ Mich, PhD(natural resources), 81. *Prof Exp:* Scientist, Nalco Environ Sci, 76-77; res asst, Great Lakes Res Div, Univ Mich, 77-81; ASST PROF BIOL, UNIV LOUISVILLE, 81- *Mem:* Phycol Soc Am; Ecol Soc Am; NAm Benthological Soc; Am Soc Limnol & Oceanog; Am Inst Biol Sci. *Res:* Algae systematics and ecology; benthic diatom systematics; utilization of algae for environmental monitoring; studies of benthic algal ecology. *Mailing Add:* Dept Biol Univ Louisville Louisville KY 40297

STEVENSON, ROBERT LOUIS, b Princeton, NJ, Jan 15, 32; m 57; c 3. MATHEMATICS, COMPUTER SCIENCE. *Educ:* Hobart Col, BS, 54; Rutgers Univ, MEd, 60; NY Univ, PhD(math educ). *Prof Exp:* Teacher pub sch, NJ, 56-66; assoc prof, 66-80, PROF MATH, WILLIAM PATERSON COL, 80- *Res:* Number theory and coding theory. *Mailing Add:* Dept Math 300 Pompton Blvd William Paterson Col Wayne NJ 07470

STEVENSON, ROBERT LOVELL, b Long Beach, Calif. ANALYTICAL CHEMISTRY. *Educ:* Reed Col, BA, 63; Univ Ariz, PhD(chem), 66. *Prof Exp:* Sr chemist, Shell Develop Co, 66-69; sr chemist, Varian Aerograph, 69-75, mgr liquid chromatography-res & develop, Varian Assocs, 75-77; V PRES RES, ALTEX SCIENTIFIC, 77- *Mem:* Am Chem Soc. *Res:* Managing a research and development group developing high speed liquid chromatographs and accessories. *Mailing Add:* 3338 Carlyle Terrace Lafayette CA 94549

STEVENSON, ROBERT THOMAS, b Washington, DC, July 23, 16; m 43; c 4. BIOLOGY. *Educ:* Am Univ, BA, 38; Univ Wis, MPh, 40, PhD(zool), 43. *Prof Exp:* Asst, Univ Wis, 38-43; asst prof biol & physiol, Univ Utah, 46-48; assoc prof, 48-68, head dept sci, 62-68, head dept life sci, 68-77, PROF BIOL, SOUTHWEST MO STATE UNIV, 68-, PROF LIFE SCI, 77- *Concurrent Pos:* Parasitologist, Neiman Stephenson Co, 41-42. *Res:* Parasitology; comparative histology and ultrastructure. *Mailing Add:* Dept of Life Sci Southwest Mo State Univ Springfield MO 65802

STEVENSON, ROBERT WILLIAM, b Philadelphia, Pa, Oct 22, 30; m 55; c 3. ORGANIC CHEMISTRY. *Educ:* Univ Pa, BS, 54; Ga Inst Technol, PhD(org chem), 58. *Prof Exp:* Res chemist, Celanese Corp Am, 58-61; sr res chemist, Mobil Chem Co, 62-69; chmn dept phys sci, 74-75, PROF SCI, CHEYNEY STATE COL, 69- *Mem:* Am Chem Soc; Sigma Xi. *Res:* Synthesis of linear polyamides and polyesters, polyacetals and polyolefins; modification of fats. *Mailing Add:* Dept of Phys Sci Cheyney State Col Cheyney PA 19319

STEVENSON, ROBIN, b Concepcion, Chile, Mar 4, 23; US citizen; m 48; c 1. AERONAUTICAL ENGINEERING. *Educ:* Mass Inst Technol, BS, 47, MS, 48. *Prof Exp:* Proj officer, Air Force Air Mat Command, 48-52, chief engr, B-36 Prog Off, Wright-Patterson AFB, 52-53, chief, Prod Div, Air Force Plant Rep Off, Gen Dynamics/Convair, Tex, 53-55, chief ground systs, Atlas Prog Off, Western Develop Div, Air Force, 55-59; vpres eng, Nat Aeronaut & Space Eng Inc, 59-61; asst div mgr, Missile & Space Systs Eng Div, Ling-Temco-Vought, Inc, 61-62, mem tech staff, Space Tech Labs Div, Thompson-Ramo-Wooldridge, Inc, 62-63; mgr standard launch vehicles eng, assoc dir, 68-77, DIR STANDARD LAUNCH VEHICLES, AEROSPACE CORP, 77- *Mem:* AAAS; Am Inst Aeronaut & Astronaut. *Res:* Systems engineering and operations research studies in support of classified military missile systems and space vehicle development. *Mailing Add:* Aerospace Corp 2350 E El Segundo Blvd El Segundo CA 90245

STEVENSON, ROBIN, b Falkirk, Scotland, Dec 25, 46; m 75. METALLURGY. *Educ:* Glasgow Univ, Scotland, BSc, 67; Mass Inst Technol, PhD(metall), 72. *Prof Exp:* STAFF RES ENGR, GEN MOTORS RES LABS, 73- *Mem:* Am Soc Metals; Electron Micros Soc Am; Am Inst Mining Metall & Petrol Engrs. *Res:* Deformation mechanisms in solids; transmission electron microscopy; physical metallurgy; sheet metal deformation. *Mailing Add:* Dept of Physics Gen Motors Res Labs Warren MI 48090

STEVENSON, STUART SHELTON, b Bridgeport, Conn, Nov 11, 14. PEDIATRICS. *Educ:* Yale Univ, BA, 35, MD, 39; Harvard Univ, MPH, 44. *Prof Exp:* Instr pediat, Sch Med, Yale Univ, 41-43; Rockefeller fel, Harvard Univ, 43, asst maternal & child health, Sch Pub Health, 44, assoc child health, 46-47, asst prof, 47-49; res prof pediat, Sch Med, Univ Pittsburgh, 49-59; prof & chmn dept, Seton Hall Col Med, 59-64; clin prof, Col Physicians & Surgeons, Columbia Univ, 64-72, prof pediat, 72-74; dir pediat & attend pediatrician, St Luke's Hosp Ctr, 64-74. *Concurrent Pos:* Staff health comnr, Rockefeller Found, 44-46. *Honors & Awards:* Order of the Nile, Egypt, 47. *Mem:* Soc Pediat Res; Am Pediat Soc; fel Am Acad Pediat; NY Acad Med. *Res:* The newborn, especially carbonic anhydrase, hyaline membrane, thyroid, congenital malformations, nutrition, growth failure and prematurity. *Mailing Add:* 2 Fifth Ave New York NY 10011

STEVENSON, THOMAS DICKSON, b Columbus, Ohio, Sept 23, 24; m 52; c 3. MEDICINE. *Educ:* Ohio State Univ, BA, 45, MD, 48; Am Bd Internal Med, dipl, 56; Am Bd Path, dipl, 64. *Prof Exp:* Intern med, Johns Hopkins Hosp, 48-49; asst resident, Univ Minn Hosps, 50-51; from asst resident to resident, Ohio State Univ Hosps, 51-53; investr clin gen med & exp therapeut, Nat Heart Inst, 53-55; asst prof med & assoc dir div hemat, Sch Med, Univ Louisville, 55-61; assoc prof, 61-71, PROF PATH, COL MED, OHIO STATE UNIV, 71- *Mem:* Am Fedn Clin Res; Am Soc Clin Path; Am Soc Cytol. *Res:* Biochemical aspects of erythropoiesis; vitamin B-12 metabolism. *Mailing Add:* Dept of Path Col of Med Ohio State Univ Hosp Columbus OH 43210

STEVENSON, WALTER ROE, b Cortland, NY, Sept 16, 46; m 69; c 2. PLANT PATHOLOGY. *Educ:* Cornell Univ, BS, 68; Univ Wis-Madison, PhD(plant path), 72. *Prof Exp:* Res asst plant path, Univ Wis, 68-72; asst prof, Purdue Univ, 72-77, assoc prof, 77-79; ASSOC PROF PLANT PATH, UNIV WIS-MADISON, 79- *Concurrent Pos:* Ind liaison rep, Interregional Proj No 4, 74-79; mem assessment team, Pentachloronitrobenzene, Nat Agr Pesticide Impact Assessment Prog, 77-80. *Mem:* Am Phytopath Soc. *Res:* Diseases of vegetable crops, including potato and mint crops; development of disease resistant cultivars; chemical control; epidemiology. *Mailing Add:* Dept Plant Path Univ Wis Madison WI 53706

STEVENSON, WARREN H, b Rock Island, Ill, Nov 18, 38; m 59; c 3. MECHANICAL ENGINEERING. *Educ:* Purdue Univ, BSME, 60, MSME, 63, PhD(mech eng), 65. *Prof Exp:* Engr, Martin Co, Colo, 60-61; from asst prof to assoc prof, 65-74, PROF APPL OPTICS, SCH MECH ENG, PURDUE UNIV, LAFAYETTE, 74- *Honors & Awards:* US sr scientist, Alexander von Humboldt Found (WGer), 73. *Mem:* Am Soc Mech Engrs; Am Soc Eng Educ; Optical Soc Am. *Res:* Application of advanced optical measurement techniques such as laser velocimetry and holography in the fields of fluid mechanics, heat transfer, combustion and industrial operations. *Mailing Add:* Sch of Mech Eng Purdue Univ Lafayette IN 47907

STEVENSON, WILLIAM CAMPBELL, b Brooklyn, NY, Jan 22, 31; m 55; c 3. BIOCHEMISTRY. *Educ:* St John's Col, BS, 52. *Prof Exp:* Chemist, Quaker Maid Co, 54-57 & Nat Biscuit Co, 57-58; chemist, 58-67, SR SCIENTIST, MEAD JOHNSON CO, 67- *Mem:* Am Chem Soc. *Res:* Drug metabolism, isolation and identification of metabolites; assay of drugs in tissue. *Mailing Add:* 3520 Laurell Lane Evansville IN 47712

STEVENSON, WILLIAM D(AMON), JR, b Pittsburgh, Pa, July 21, 12; m 51; c 2. ELECTRICAL ENGINEERING. *Educ:* Princeton Univ, BSE, 34; Carnegie Inst Technol, BS, 39; Univ Mich, MS, 42. *Prof Exp:* Clerk, Koppers Co, 35-36; stud engr, Dravo Corp, 36-37 & Union Switch & Signal Co, 37-38; instr elec eng, Clemson Col, 39-42, asst prof, 42-43; asst prof, Princeton Univ, 43-46; from assoc prof to prof, 46-78, grad adminr, 57-78, assoc dept head, 67-78, EMER PROF ELEC ENG, NC STATE UNIV, 78- *Concurrent Pos:* Consult elec power, McGraw-Hill Book Co, 63-78. *Honors & Awards:* US Naval Ord Develop Award, 46; Special Citation, Edison Elec Inst, 77. *Mem:* Am Soc Eng Educ; fel Inst Elec & Electronics Engrs. *Res:* Power system analysis; power transmission lines. *Mailing Add:* 2706 White Oak Rd Raleigh NC 27609

STEVENSON, WILLIAM HENRY, b Philadelphia, Pa, May 11, 27; m 51; c 4. FISHERIES MANAGEMENT. *Educ:* Univ Del, BA, 51. *Prof Exp:* Resident mgr, Marine Biol Lab, Del, 51-54; explor fishing & gear res, Fish Prod Co, Del, 54-58; fishery consult, 58-60; fishing gear res, Smith Res & Develop Co, 60-61; fishery methods & equip specialist, Bur Com Fisheries, 61-66, foreign fisheries adv, Agency Int Develop, 66-69, chief, Gear Experimentation Sect, 69-70, chief, Div Explor Fishing & Gear Res, 70-74, mgr, Fisheries Eng Lab, 74, regional dir, Southeast Region, 74-80, DEP ASST ADMINR FISHERIES, NAT MARINE FISHERIES SERV, NOAA, DEPT COM, 80- *Res:* Commercial fisheries development; biological resource survey and analysis; resource harvesting methods improvement; marine biological and fisheries engineering; fisheries remote sensing; fisheries administration and management. *Mailing Add:* 3300 Whitehaven St NW Washington DC 20235

STEVERDING, BERNARD, theoretical physics, see previous edition

STEVERMER, EMMETT J, b Wells, Minn, Aug 13, 32. ANIMAL SCIENCE, BIOCHEMISTRY. *Educ:* Univ Wis, BS, 58, MS, 60, PhD(animal sci, biochem), 62. *Prof Exp:* From asst prof to assoc prof, 62-74, PROF ANIMAL SCI, IOWA STATE UNIV, 74- *Res:* Swine nutrition and reproductive physiology. *Mailing Add:* Dept of Animal Sci Iowa State Univ Ames IA 50010

STEVINSON, HARRY THOMPSON, b Passburg, Alta, Mar 5, 15; m 44; c 3. ELECTRICAL ENGINEERING. *Educ:* Univ Alta, BSc, 44. *Prof Exp:* Mechanic, Chevrolet Garage, Alta, 32-35; owner-operator radio serv, Hurt & Stevinson, 35-39; res officer flight, Nat Res Coun Can, 45-79; RETIRED. *Honors & Awards:* Can Aeronaut & Space Inst Baldwin Award, 56, McCurdy Award, 66. *Res:* Communications; flight instrumentation; specialized aerial delivery problems; aircraft crash recovery systems. *Mailing Add:* 3558 Revelstoke Dr Ottawa ON K1V 7C1 Can

STEWARD, FREDERICK CAMPION, b London, Eng, June 6, 04; m 29; c 1. BOTANY, CELL BIOLOGY. *Educ:* Univ Leeds, BSc, 24, PhD(bot), 26; Univ London, DSc, 36. *Hon Degrees:* Univ Delhi, DSc, 74. *Prof Exp:* Demonstr bot, Univ Leeds, 26-27, asst lectr, 29-33; Rockefeller fel, Cornell Univ & Univ Calif, 27-29; Rockefeller fel, Univ Calif & Carnegie Inst Washington, 33-34; reader, Univ London, 34-47; dir aircraft equip, Ministry of Aircraft Prod, 40-45; res assoc, Univ Chicago, 45-46; vis prof bot & chmn dept, Univ Rochester, 46-50; prof bot, 50-65, Charles A Alexander prof, 65-73, EMER PROF BIOL SCI, CORNELL UNIV, 73- *Concurrent Pos:* Guggenheim fel, 64; Pauli lectr, Zurich, 68; Sir CV Raman vis prof, Madras, 74; Cecil & Ida Green vis prof, Univ BC, 75. *Honors & Awards:* Merit Award, Bot Soc Am, 61; Stephen Hales Award, Am Soc Plant Physiol, 64. *Mem:* Bot Soc Am; Am Soc Plant Physiol; fel Royal Soc; fel Am Acad Arts & Sci; fel Indian Sci Acad. *Res:* Plant physiology and biochemistry; respiration; salt intake; metabolism; protein synthesis; chromatography of amino acids; cell and tissue culture; morphogenesis. *Mailing Add:* 1612 Inglewood Dr Charlottesville VA 22901

STEWARD, JAMES GORDON, mathematics, computer science, see previous edition

STEWARD, JOHN P, b Huntington Park, Calif, Oct 9, 27. MEDICAL MICROBIOLOGY, IMMUNOLOGY. *Educ:* Stanford Univ, AB, 48, MD, 55. *Prof Exp:* Nat Inst Allergy & Infectious Dis fel med microbiol, Sch Med, 58-60, from instr basic med sci to asst prof exp med, 60-70, asst dean, Sch Med, 64-65, asst dir, Fleischmann Labs Med Sci, 64-70, sr lectr med microbiol, Sch Med & actg dir, Fleischmann Labs Med Sci, 70-74, ADJ PROF MED MICROBIOL, SCH MED, STANFORD UNIV, 74-, ASSOC DEAN SCH MED, 71- *Concurrent Pos:* Lectr, Sch Pub Health, Univ Calif, Berkeley, 63. *Mem:* Am Asn Immunologists; Am Soc Microbiol. *Res:* Host-parasite relationship between enterobacteriaceae and experimental animals. *Mailing Add:* Stanford Univ Sch of Med Stanford CA 94305

STEWARD, KERRY KALEN, b Skowhegan, Maine, June 2, 30; m 56; c 1. PLANT PHYSIOLOGY. *Educ:* Univ Conn, BS, 58, MS, 62, PhD(bot), 66. *Prof Exp:* RES PLANT PHYSIOLOGIST, AGR RES SERV, USDA, 66- *Concurrent Pos:* Nat Park Serv grant, Everglades Nat Park; res leader & dir Aquatic Weed Control Lab. *Mem:* Am Inst Biol Sci; Bot Soc Am; Weed Sci Soc Am. *Res:* Physiology of aquatic plants; mineral nutrition of aquatic plants; effects of herbicides on growth of aquatic plants. *Mailing Add:* Agr Res Serv USDA 3205 SW 70th Ave Ft Lauderdale FL 33314

STEWARD, OMAR WADDINGTON, b Woodbury, NJ, May 28, 32; m 58; c 3. ORGANOMETALLIC CHEMISTRY, INORGANIC CHEMISTRY. *Educ:* Univ Del, BS, 53; Pa State Univ, PhD(chem), 57. *Prof Exp:* Proj leader fluorine & organosilicon chem, Dow Corning Corp, 57-62; NSF fel, Univ Leicester, 62-63; instr inorg chem, Univ Ill, 63; asst prof, Southern Ill Univ, 63-64; from asst prof to assoc prof, 64-72, PROF INORG CHEM, DUQUESNE UNIV, 72- *Mem:* Am Chem Soc; Am Inst Chem; Royal Soc Chem; Sigma Xi. *Res:* Structure, bonding and reaction mechanisms of group IVb organometallic compounds; bonding and reaction mechanisms of coordination compounds. *Mailing Add:* Dept of Chem Duquesne Univ Pittsburgh PA 15282

STEWARD, ROBERT F, b Springboro, Pa, June 2, 23; m 46; c 2. MATHEMATICS. *Educ:* Wheaton Col, Ill, BS, 47; Rutgers Univ, MS, 49; Auburn Univ, PhD(math), 61. *Prof Exp:* Instr math, Va Mil Inst, 49-53; asst prof, Drexel Inst Technol, 53-57; instr, Auburn Univ, 57-58, 59-60; assoc prof, Western Carolina Col, 60-61; prof & chmn dept, 61-63; chmn dept, 67-73, PROF MATH, R I COL, 63- *Mem:* Math Asn Am. *Res:* Numerical analysis. *Mailing Add:* Dept of Math Rhode Island Col Providence RI 02908

STEWARD, VINCENT WILLIAM, neuropathology, see previous edition

STEWARD, W(ILLIS) G(ENE), b Hastings, Nebr, June 11, 30; m; c 1. MECHANICAL ENGINEERING. *Educ:* Univ Colo, BS, 52, MS, 58; Colo State Univ, PhD, 69. *Prof Exp:* Engr, Gas Turbine Div, Gen Elec Co, 52-54; ENGR, NAT BUR STANDARDS, 58- *Mem:* Sigma Xi. *Res:* Thermodynamics; fluid mechanics; cryogenics. *Mailing Add:* Cryogenics Div 325 Broadway Boulder CO 80303

STEWART, ALBERT CLIFTON, b Detroit, Mich, Nov 25, 19; m 49. RADIATION CHEMISTRY. *Educ:* Univ Chicago, SB, 42, SM, 48; St Louis Univ, PhD(chem), 51. *Prof Exp:* Chemist, Sherwin-Williams Paint Co, Ill, 43-44; asst inorg chem, Univ Chicago, 47-49; instr & res assoc, St Louis Univ, 49-51; sr chemist, Oak Ridge Nat Lab, 51-56; group leader, Res Lab, Nat Carbon Co Div, Union Carbide Corp, 56-59, asst dir res, Consumer Prod Div, 60-63, asst develop dir, 63-65, planning mgr new mkt develop, 65-66, mkt develop mgr, Chem & Plastics Develop Div, 66-69, mkt mgr rubber chem, Mkt Area, 69-71, mkt mgr chem coatings solvents, 71-73, int bus mgr, Chem & Plastics Div, 73-77, dir sales, Chem & Plastics Div, 77-79, NAT SALES MGR, SOLVENTS & INTERMEDIATES DIV, UNION CARBIDE CORP, 79- *Concurrent Pos:* Prof, Knoxville Col, 53-56; lectr, John Carroll Univ, 56-63; consult, Pub Affairs Div, Ford Found, 63; adminsr officer, NASA, 63 & Agency Int Develop, 64-69; treas, NY State Dormitory Authority, 71-76. *Mem:* AAAS; Am Chem Soc; Am Nuclear Soc; Radiation Res Soc. *Res:* Physical inorganic and radiation chemistry; research, development and general administration; marketing management; sales management. *Mailing Add:* 28 Hearthstone Dr Brookfield CT 06805

STEWART, ALEC THOMPSON, b Can, 25; m 60; c 3. PHYSICS. *Educ:* Dalhousie Univ, BSc, 46, MSc, 49; Cambridge Univ, PhD(physics), 52. *Prof Exp:* From asst res officer to assoc res officer, 52-57; assoc prof physics, Dalhousie Univ, 57-60; from assoc prof to prof, Univ NC, Chapel Hill, 60-68; head dept, 68-74, PROF PHYSICS, QUEEN'S UNIV, ONT, 68- *Concurrent Pos:* J S Guggenheim fel & Kenan travelling prof, 65-66. *Mem:* Fel Am Phys Soc; Can Asn Physicists (pres, 72-73); fel Royal Soc Can. *Res:* Solid state by positron annihilation in matter and neutron inelastic scattering. *Mailing Add:* Dept of Physics Queen's Univ Kingston ON K7L 3N6 Can

STEWART, ALLAN GREENWOOD, b Kingston, Ont, Aug 11, 20; m 43; c 2. BIOCHEMISTRY. *Educ:* Univ Western Ont, PhD(med res), 52. *Prof Exp:* Asst biochem, Ont Vet Col, 45-53; from asst prof biochem to assoc prof pediat, Univ Alta, 53-69; ASST PROF PATH, DALHOUSIE UNIV, 69-; BIOCHEMIST, IZAAK WALTON KILLAM HOSP CHILDREN, 69- *Mem:* NY Acad Sci; Can Biochem Soc; Can Physiol Soc; Can Soc Clin Chemists; Can Inst Chemists. *Res:* Lipids; tumor host relationships; bilirubin metabolism; red cell enzymes. *Mailing Add:* Div Clin Chem Izaak W Killam Hosp for Children Halifax NS B3J 3G9 Can

STEWART, ALVA THEODORE, JR, b Beckley, WVa, July 4, 29; m 53; c 2. ORGANIC CHEMISTRY, SCIENCE ADMINISTRATION. *Educ:* Duke Univ, BS, 50, MA, 52, PhD(chem), 54. *Prof Exp:* Fel, Mellon Inst Sci, 54-55; chemist, Shell Develop Co, 59-62; asst sect chief, Avco Corp, 63-65; mem tech staff, Northrop Corp, 66-69; head chem & plastics res & sr scientist, 69-71, CHIEF SCIENTIST, SCI DEVELOP, BECHTEL CORP, 71- *Mem:* AAAS; Am Chem Soc; Am Inst Chem. *Res:* New technology assessment; bioprotein; nutrition. *Mailing Add:* Bechtel Nat Inc 50 Beale St San Francisco CA 94119

STEWART, ANNE MARIE, b Stoneham, Mass, June 12, 36; m 58; c 4. ANIMAL BEHAVIOR, ANIMAL PHYSIOLOGY. *Educ:* Simmons Col, BS, 58; Univ Mass, MA, 61; Tufts Univ, PhD(biol), 67. *Prof Exp:* Instr zool, Univ Mass, 61-62; res asst histol, McLain Hosp, 62-63; asst prof biol, Cape Cod Community Col, 65-66; asst prof, 65-66, ASSOC PROF BIOL, WINDHAM COL, 66- *Mem:* Animal Behav Soc. *Res:* Photic behavior of animals; field biology. *Mailing Add:* Dept of Biol Windham Col Putney VT 05346

STEWART, ARTHUR VAN, b Buffalo, NY, July 25, 38; m 65; c 3. DENTISTRY. *Educ:* Univ Pittsburgh, BS, 60, MEd, 64, DMD, 68, PhD(educ admin), 73. *Prof Exp:* Instr pedodont, dent auxiliary utilization & restorative dent, Univ Pittsburgh, 68-70; prof community & prev dent & chmn dept, Sch Dent, Fairleigh Dickinson Univ, 70-75, asst dean, dir learning resources & chmn dept continuing educ, 73-75; PROF, DEPT COMMUNITY DENT, SCH DENT, UNIV LOUISVILLE HEALTH SCI CTR, 75-, ASST DEAN ACAD AFFAIRS, 75- *Concurrent Pos:* Consult, NJ Dent Asn, 71-75; Northside Family Health Ctr, 71-75, Patrick House Family Health Ctr, 71-75, North Bergen Dent Health Ctr, 72-75, Headstart Progs, 72-75 & Paterson Bd Educ Dent Health Ctr, 73-75. *Mem:* NY Acad Sci; Am Dent Asn; Am Asn Dent Schs; Am Sch Health Asn; World Future Soc. *Res:* Dental education; health manpower; preventive dentistry; community health; manpower development in dental education. *Mailing Add:* Sch of Dent Univ of Louisville Health Sci Ctr Louisville KY 40201

STEWART, BOBBY ALTON, b Erick, Okla, Sept 26, 32; m 56; c 3. SOIL FERTILITY, SOIL CHEMISTRY. *Educ:* Okla State Univ, BS, 53, MS, 57; Colo State Univ, PhD(soil sci), 61. *Prof Exp:* Res assoc soils, Soil & Water Res Div, 53-57, res soil scientist, 57-68, DIR & RES SOIL SCIENTIST, AGR RES SERV, US DEPT AGR, 68- *Concurrent Pos:* Instr agron, Okla State Univ, 53-57; fac affil, Colo State Univ, 57-68, spec lectr, 62; ed-in chief, Soil Sci Soc Am J, 75-79. *Mem:* Fel Soil Conserv Soc Am; fel Am Soc Agron; fel Soil Sci Soc Am (pres, 81); Int Soil Sci Soc. *Res:* Nitrogen-sulfur relationships in plant tissue, plant residues and soil organic matter; animal waste management; movement of fertilizer nitrogen through soil profiles. *Mailing Add:* Conserv & Prod Res Lab US Dept Agr PO Drawer 10 Bushland TX 79012

STEWART, BONNIE MADISON, b Loveland, Colo, July 10, 14; m 40; c 2. MATHEMATICS. *Educ:* Univ Colo, BA, 36; Univ Wis, PhM, 37, PhD, 40. *Prof Exp:* Asst math, Univ Wis, 38-40; instr, Mich State Univ, 40-42; asst prof, Denison Univ, 42-43; from asst prof to assoc prof, 43-53, prof, 53-80, EMER PROF MATH, MICH STATE UNIV, 80- *Mem:* Am Math Soc; Math Asn Am. *Res:* Matrix theory; number theory; graph theory; Euclidian geometry. *Mailing Add:* 4494 Wausau Rd Okemos MI 48864

STEWART, CARLETON C, b Schenectady, NY, July 13, 40; m 63; c 2. IMMUNOLOGY, BIOPHYSICS. *Educ:* Hartwick Col, BA, 62; Univ Rochester, MS, 64, PhD(radiation), 67. *Prof Exp:* Atomic Energy Proj res asst & instr radiation physics, Univ Rochester, 62-67; instr immunol, Univ Pa, 67-69; sr scientist, Smith Kline & French Labs, 69-70; asst, 70-78, ASSOC PROF CANCER BIOL IN RADIOL, SCH MED, WASHINGTON UNIV, 78- *Concurrent Pos:* USPHS fel & grant, 67-69; Am Cancer Soc grant, 68-69; Cancer Ctr grant, Nat Cancer Inst, 70-78; NIH grants, 78- *Mem:* AAAS; Cell Kinetics Soc; Am Asn Exp Pathologists; NY Acad Sci; Reticuloendothelial Soc. *Res:* Cellular immunology; tumor immunology. *Mailing Add:* Sect of Cancer Biol Washington Univ Sch of Med St Louis MO 63110

STEWART, CECIL R, b Monmouth, Ill, Mar 11, 37; m 58; c 2. PLANT PHYSIOLOGY. *Educ:* Univ Ill, BS, 58; Cornell Univ, MS, 63, PhD(plant physiol), 67. *Prof Exp:* NIH fel plant physiol, Purdue Univ, 66-68; asst prof 68-71, assoc prof, 71-76, PROF BOT, IOWA STATE UNIV, 76- *Mem:* AAAS; Am Soc Plant Physiol; Am Inst Biol Sci. *Res:* Plant metabolism. *Mailing Add:* Dept Bot Iowa State Univ Ames IA 50011

STEWART, CHARLES JACK, b Rawlins, Wyo, June 17, 29; m 56; c 3. BIOCHEMISTRY. *Educ:* San Diego State Col, BA, 50; Ore State Univ, MS, 52, PhD(biochem), 55. *Prof Exp:* Fulbright grant biochem, Inst Org Chem, Univ Frankfurt, 54-55; from instr to assoc prof, 55-65, PROF CHEM, SAN DIEGO STATE UNIV, 65- *Concurrent Pos:* NIH res grant, 62-, spec fel, 63-64; guest prof chem, Max Planck Inst Med Res, Heidelberg, Ger, 75-76. *Mem:* AAAS; Am Soc Biol Chemists; Am Chem Soc. *Res:* Mechanism of enzymes and antimetabolites; synthesis and enzymatic properties of coenzyme A analogs. *Mailing Add:* Dept of Chem San Diego State Univ San Diego CA 92182

STEWART, CHARLES NEIL, b Albany, NY, May 6, 45; m 68; c 3. SURFACE PHYSICS, GASEOUS ELECTRONICS. *Educ:* Union Col, NY, BS, 67; Univ Ill, Urbana-Champaign, MS, 69, PhD(physics), 74. *Prof Exp:* Asst physics, Dudley Observ, NY, 65-67; lab instr, Union Col, NY, 67; asst, Univ Ill, Urbana-Champaign, 67-73; RES PHYSICIST, LAMP PHENOMENA RES LAB, GEN ELEC CO, 73- *Mem:* Am Phys Soc; Sigma Xi. *Res:* Gas-solid interactions; field emission; low pressure discharges; oxide cathodes. *Mailing Add:* Gen Elec Lamp Phenomena Res Lab Nela Park Cleveland OH 44112

STEWART, CHARLES RANOUS, b La Crosse, Wis, Aug 6, 40. MICROBIAL GENETICS. *Educ:* Univ Wis, BS, 62; Stanford Univ, PhD(genetics), 67. *Prof Exp:* Am Cancer Soc fel biochem, Albert Einstein Col Med, 67-69; asst prof, 69-74, assoc prof, 74-80, PROF BIOL, RICE UNIV, 80- *Mem:* Am Soc Microbiol. *Res:* Genetics and biochemistry of Bacillus subtilis and its virulent bacteriophages. *Mailing Add:* Dept of Biol Rice Univ Houston TX 77001

STEWART, CHARLES WINFIELD, b Wilmington, Del, Jan 27, 40; m 62; c 3. THEORETICAL CHEMISTRY. *Educ:* Univ Del, BS, 62, PhD(chem), 66. *Prof Exp:* Res chemist, Elastomer Chem Dept, 66-80, RES ASSOC POLYMER PROD DEPT, E I DU PONT DE NEMOURS & CO, INC, WILMINGTON, 80- *Res:* Polymer physics. *Mailing Add:* 4 Jobs Lane Post Crossing Newark DE 19711

STEWART, CHESTER BRYANT, b Norboro, PEI, Dec 17, 10; m 42; c 2. MEDICINE, EPIDEMIOLOGY. *Educ:* Dalhousie Univ, BSc, 36, MD, CM, 38; Johns Hopkins Univ, MPH, 46, DrPH, 53; FRCP(C), 62. *Hon Degrees:* LLD, Univ Prince Edward Island, 73, Dalhousie Univ, 79; DSc, St Francis Xavier Univ, 77. *Prof Exp:* Asst secy assoc comt med res, Nat Res Coun Can, 38-40; dean med, Dalhousie Univ, 54-71, prof epidemiol, 46-76, vpres health sci, 71-76; RETIRED. HEALTH SCI, 71- *Concurrent Pos:* Res assoc, Johns Hopkins Univ, 51-52. *Honors & Awards:* Centennial Medal, 67; Officer, Order of Can, 72. *Mem:* Fel Am Pub Health Asn; Asn Can Med Cols (pres, 61-63); Can Pub Health Asn (pres, 68); Can Med Asn. *Res:* Aviation medicine; decompression sickness and anoxia; Bacillus Calmette-Guerin vaccination; tuberculosis; immunity; delivery of health care; hospital and medical insurance; physician manpower. *Mailing Add:* Sir Charles Tupper Med Bldg Dalhousie Univ Halifax NS B3H 3J5 Can

STEWART, DANIEL ROBERT, b New Kensington, Pa, July 25, 38; m 60; c 2. GLASS TECHNOLOGY, CERAMICS. *Educ:* Pa State Univ, BS, 60, MS, 62, PhD(ceramic technol), 64. *Prof Exp:* Sr scientist glass res, 64-67, sect chief glass sci, 67-70, dir glass & ceramics res, 70-72, dir corp res labs, 72-73, VPRES CORP STAFF & DIR GLASS & CERAMIC TECHNOL, OWENS-ILLINOIS, INC, 73- *Mem:* Fel Am Ceramic Soc; Sigma Xi; Brit Soc Glass Technol. *Res:* Glass and ceramic materials and processing; research and development. *Mailing Add:* Owens-Illinois Inc One Sea Gate Toledo OH 43666

STEWART, DAVID BENJAMIN, b Springfield, Vt, July 18, 28; m 52, 80; c 2. GEOLOGY, MINERALOGY. *Educ:* Harvard Univ, AB, 51; AM, 52, PhD(petrol), 56. *Prof Exp:* Geologist, US Geol Surv, 51-81, chief br exp geochem & mineral, 76-80, prog coordr radioactive waste mgt, 78-80, sr policy analyst, high level radioactive waste, State Planning Coun Radioactive Waste Mgt, 80-81, RES GEOLOGIST, US GEOL SURV, 81- *Concurrent Pos:* Guest prof, Univ Toronto, 68 & Swiss Fed Inst Technol, 71; mem, Lunar Sample Rev Bd, 70-72; prin investr, lunar feldspar Apollo 11-15, 69-72, lunar metamorphism, 73-76. *Honors & Awards:* Award, Mineral Soc Am, 66. *Mem:* Fel Geol Soc Am; fel Mineral Soc Am; Am Geophys Union; Geochem Soc. *Res:* Crystal chemistry and phase relations of feldspar, silica and rock-forming silicates; radioactive waste management; metamorphic recrystallization of lunar and terrestrial minerals; continental edge tectonics Maine Devonian coastal volcanic belt. *Mailing Add:* Nat Ctr 959 US Geol Surv Reston VA 22092

STEWART, DAVID BRADSHAW, b Winnipeg, Man, June 18, 16; m 41; c 4. OBSTETRICS & GYNECOLOGY, ZOOLOGY. *Educ:* Univ Man, BSc, 36, MD, 41. *Prof Exp:* Consult obstet & gynec, Regional Hosp Bd, Aberdeen, Scotland, 51-52; prof, Univ West Indies, 53-70, vdean fac med, 58-62, dean, 63-64; prof zool, Brandon Univ, 70-81; RETIRED. *Concurrent Pos:* Mem, Order of Brit Empire, 46; fel, Royal Col Physicians & Surgeons, Can, 55; fel, Royal Col Obstet & Gynec, 58; Carnegie Found traveling fel, African Med Schs, 60; vis prof, Inst Obstet & Gynec, Univ London, 61 & Queen's Univ, Belfast, 67; consult, WHO, India, 69. *Mem:* Fel Royal Soc Med; Soc Obstet & Gynec Can; Can Soc Zool. *Res:* Comparative physiology of reproduction; incidence and effects of chlamydial infections in migrant birds. *Mailing Add:* Dept of Zool Brandon Univ Brandon MB R7A 6A9 Can

STEWART, DAVID PERRY, b Summersville, WVa, Mar 14, 16; m 43; c 2. GEOMORPHOLOGY. *Educ:* WVa Univ, AB, 38; Mich State Univ, MS, 48; Syracuse Univ, PhD(geol), 54. *Prof Exp:* Instr phys sci, Mich State Univ, 46-49; assoc prof geol, Marshall Col, 49-56; from asst prof to assoc prof, 56-70, PROF GEOL, MIAMI UNIV, 70- *Mem:* Geol Soc Am; Sigma Xi. *Res:* Glacial geology of Ohio and Vermont; glacial history of New England and midwestern United States. *Mailing Add:* Dept of Geol Miami Univ Oxford OH 45056

STEWART, DONALD BORDEN, b Sask, Can, Mar 15, 17; nat US; m 52; c 2. ENVIRONMENTAL MANAGEMENT. *Educ:* Univ Wash, BS, 39. *Prof Exp:* Chemist, B F Goodrich Co, 39-41, mgr, Gen Chem Lab, 41-42, oper mgr, Res Div, 42-48, opers mgr, Res Ctr, 48-56; bus mgr, Cent Labs, Gen Foods Corp, 56-57, dir admin serv, Res Ctr, 57-61; vpres, Sterling Forest Corp, 61-66; admin officer, 66-67, supt, 67-74, asst gen mgr, 74-78, DEP GEN MGR, PALISADES INTERSTATE PARK COMN, 78- *Mem:* AAAS; Am Chem Soc; fel Am Inst Chem. *Res:* Analytical methods; industrial safety and hygiene. *Mailing Add:* Palisades Interstate Park Comn Bear Mountain NY 10911

STEWART, DONALD CHARLES, b Salt Lake City, Utah, Dec 15, 12; m 48; c 2. RADIOCHEMISTRY. *Educ:* Univ Calif, Los Angeles, AB, 35; Univ Southern Calif, MS, 40; Va Polytech Inst & State Univ, BS, 44; Univ Calif, Berkeley, PhD(biochem), 50. *Prof Exp:* Chemist, Knudsen Creamery, 34-42; group leader, Metall Lab, Univ Chicago, 44-45, asst sec chief, 45-46; chemist, Radiation Lab, Univ Calif, 46-52; asst dir, 52-54, assoc chemist, 54-59, assoc dir chem div, Argonne Nat Lab, 59-77; RETIRED. *Concurrent Pos:* Co-ed, Prog in Nuclear Energy, Series IX, Pergamon Press, 63-74; consult anal, 78- *Mem:* Fel AAAS; Am Chem Soc; Sigma Xi. *Res:* Analytical and inorganic chemistry of rare earth and actinide elements. *Mailing Add:* 17220 Tamara Lane Watsonville CA 95076

STEWART, DONALD GEORGE, b Pocatello, Idaho, Jan 9, 33. MATHEMATICS. *Educ:* Univ Utah, BA, 59, MS, 61; Univ Tenn, PhD, 63. *Prof Exp:* Asst prof math, Univ Tenn, 63-64; asst prof, 64-72, ASSOC PROF MATH, ARIZ STATE UNIV, 72- *Mem:* Am Math Soc. *Res:* Point-set topology. *Mailing Add:* Dept of Math Ariz State Univ Tempe AZ 85287

STEWART, DORATHY ANNE, b Indianapolis, Ind, June 2, 37. METEOROLOGY, PHYSICS. *Educ:* Univ Tampa, BS, 58; Fla State Univ, MS, 61, PhD(meteorol), 66. *Prof Exp:* Teacher sci, Suwannee High Sch, 58-59; asst meteorol, Fla State Univ, 59-66; RES PHYSICIST ATMOSPHERIC PHYSICS, MISSILE RES & DEVELOP COMMAND, 66- *Mem:* Am Meteorol Soc; Am Geophys Union; AAAS. *Mailing Add:* 5204 Whitesburg Dr Huntsville AL 35802

STEWART, DORIS MAE, b Sandsprings, Mont, Dec 12, 27; m 56; c 2. ZOOLOGY, PHYSIOLOGY. *Educ:* Univ Puget Sound, BS, 48, MS, 49; Univ Wash, PhD(zool), 53. *Prof Exp:* NIH fel, Univ Wash, 54; from instr to asst prof zool, Univ Mont, 54-57; asst prof biol, Univ Puget Sound, 57-58; head dept sci, Am Col Girls, Istanbul, 58-62; res asst prof zool, Univ Wash, 63-67, res assoc prof, 67-69; assoc prof biol, Cent Mich Univ, 70-72; res assoc prof zool, Univ Wash, 72-73; assoc prof, 73-81, PROF, SCI DEPT, UNIV BALTIMORE, 81- *Mem:* Sigma Xi; Am Physiol Soc. *Res:* Muscle atrophy and hypertrophy and circulation and molting physiology in the spider. *Mailing Add:* Dept Sci Univ Baltimore Baltimore MD 21201

STEWART, EDWARD WILLIAM, b Cardiff, Mo, Sept 17, 31; m 54; c 3. METALLURGICAL ENGINEERING, CHEMISTRY. *Educ:* Wash Col, BS, 52; Lehigh Univ, MS, 54. *Prof Exp:* Tech supvr silicon, 58-62, tech supt, 62-65, prod mgr titanium dioxide, 65-68, dist sales mgr, 68-73, LAB DIR CHEM, E I DU PONT DE NEMOURS & CO, INC, 73- *Mem:* Sigma Xi. *Res:* Titanium dioxide and color pigment product development. *Mailing Add:* 13 Perth Dr Wilmington DE 19803

STEWART, ELMO JOSEPH, b Salt Lake City, Utah, Nov 2, 13; m 42; c 1. MATHEMATICS. *Educ:* Univ Utah, BS, 37, MS, 39; Rice Inst, PhD(math), 53. *Prof Exp:* Instr math, Univ Utah, 46-53; mathematician, Bendix Corp, 53-54; asst prof math, Calif State Polytech Col, 54-55; assoc prof, 55-61, PROF MATH, NAVAL POSTGRAD SCH, 61- *Concurrent Pos:* Consult, Bendix Corp, 54-55, Firestone Tire & Rubber Co, 57-58 & Tech Opers, Inc, 58-59. *Mem:* Math Asn Am. *Mailing Add:* Dept of Math Naval Postgrad Sch Monterey CA 93940

STEWART, ELWIN LYNN, b Ellensburg, Wash, July 22, 40; m 64; c 1. MYCOLOGY. *Educ:* Eastern Wash State Col, BA, 69; Ore State Univ, PhD(mycol), 74. *Prof Exp:* Fel mycol, Dept Bot & Plant Path, Ore State Univ, 74-75; asst prof, 75-80, ASSOC PROF MYCOL, DEPT PLANT PATH, UNIV MINN, 80- *Mem:* Mycol Soc Am; Am Phytopath Soc; Brit Mycol Soc. *Res:* Fungal systematics; selection and utilization of mycorrhizal fungi in harsh site revegetation. *Mailing Add:* Dept of Plant Path 304 Stakman Hall Univ Minn St Paul MN 55108

STEWART, FRANK EDWIN, b Dallas, Tex, July 9, 41; m 72. PHYSICS, CHEMISTRY. *Educ:* Univ Tex, Arlington, BS, 61; Tex A&M Univ, MS, 64, PhD(physics), 66. *Prof Exp:* Instr physics, Tex A&M Univ, 64-66; Nat Acad Sci resident res assoc chem physics, Jet Propulsion Lab, Univ Calif, 66-67; asst prof physics, Northeast La Univ, 67-71; prof math, physics & astron & dir planetarium, Cooke County Jr Col, 71-77, DIR DATA PROCESSING, COOKE COUNTY COL COMPUTER CTR, 77- *Mem:* Am Asn Physics Teachers; Am Phys Soc; Sigma Xi. *Res:* Electron paramagnetic resonance; charge-transfer complexes. *Mailing Add:* Math Phys Div Box 815 Cooke County Jr Col Gainesville TX 76240

STEWART, FRANK MOORE, b Beirut, Lebanon, Dec 27, 17; US citizen; m 46; c 1. MATHEMATICS. *Educ:* Princeton Univ, AB, 39; Harvard Univ, MA, 41, PhD(math), 47. *Prof Exp:* From instr to assoc prof, 47-61, PROF MATH, BROWN UNIV, 61- *Mem:* AAAS. *Res:* Differential equations; population genetics. *Mailing Add:* Dept of Math Box 1917 Brown Univ Providence RI 02912

STEWART, FRANKLIN BURTON, b Sparta, Tenn, Aug 17, 22; m 44. SOIL FERTILITY. *Educ:* Tenn Polytech Inst, BS, 46; Univ Tenn, MS, 47; Univ Md, PhD(soil chem), 55. *Prof Exp:* SOIL SCIENTIST, VA TRUCK & ORNAMENTALS RES STA, 55- *Mem:* Soil Sci Soc Am; Am Soc Agron; Am Hort Soc. *Res:* Vegetable crop fertilization; soil testing; minor elements; plant nutrition; turf management. *Mailing Add:* Va Truck & Ornamentals Res Sta 1444 Diamond Springs Rd Virginia Beach VA 23455

STEWART, GARY FRANKLIN, b Okmulgee, Okla, Apr 3, 35; m 56; c 3. GEOLOGY. *Educ:* Okla State Univ, BS, 57; Univ Okla, MS, 63; Univ Kans, PhD(geol), 73. *Prof Exp:* Geologist, Humble Oil & Refining Co, 58-60; geologist, Kans State Geol Surv, Univ Kans, 62-71; asst prof, 71-73, ASSOC PROF GEOL, OKLA STATE UNIV, 73- *Concurrent Pos:* Consult, Oak Ridge Nat Lab, 70-72. *Mem:* Am Asn Petrol Geologists. *Res:* Geomorphology; stratigraphy; geologic mapping for environmental purposes; depositional environments of sedimentary rocks. *Mailing Add:* 1102 N Payne St Stillwater OK 74074

STEWART, GEORGE HAMILL, b Chambersburg, Pa, July 6, 25; m 50; c 5. BIOMEDICAL ENGINEERING. *Educ:* Union Col, NY, BSEE, 50; Drexel Univ, MS, 62; Temple Univ, PhD(med physics), 68. *Prof Exp:* Assoc prof med physics, 50-79, PROF MED PHYSICS, SCH MED, TEMPLE UNIV, 79-, ASSOC PROF PHYSIOL, 77- *Mem:* Inst Elec & Electronics Engrs; Asn Advan Med Instrumentation. *Res:* Biomedical instrumentation; applications of computers to biomedical research; cardiovascular dynamics. *Mailing Add:* Dept Med Physics Temple Univ Sch Med 3400 N Broad St Philadelphia PA 19140

STEWART, GEORGE HUDSON, b Brooklyn, NY, May 13, 25; m 58; c 5. PHYSICAL CHEMISTRY. *Educ:* Univ Calif, Berkeley, BS, 49; Univ Utah, PhD(phys chem), 58. *Prof Exp:* Res asst chem, Univ Utah, 58-59; from instr to asst prof, Gonzaga Univ, 59-64, assoc prof chem & chmn dept chem & chem eng, 64-70, dean grad sch, 67-70; chmn dept, 70-76, PROF CHEM, TEX WOMAN'S UNIV, 70- *Mem:* AAAS; Sigma Xi; Am Chem Soc. *Res:* Physical chemistry of chromatography; dynamics of gas-liquid interface; flow in porous media. *Mailing Add:* 2003 W Oak St Denton TX 76201

STEWART, GEORGE LOUIS, b Washington, DC, Oct 30, 44; m 69. PARASITOLOGY. *Educ:* Tulane Univ, BS, 69; Rice Univ, PhD(parasitol), 73. *Prof Exp:* Fel parasitol, Rice Univ, 73-74, res assoc, 74, lectr, 75-77; ASST PROF PARASITOL, UNIV TEX, ARLINGTON, 77- *Concurrent Pos:* Consult, Phillips-Roxane, Inc, 73-78, Bellaire Blvd Animal Clin, 73-78 & Fielder Animal Clin, 77-; res grant, Phillips-Roxane, Inc, 73-78; fac res grant, Univ Tex, Arlington, 77-; NIH res grant, 79-82. *Mem:* Am Soc Parasitologists; Am Heartworm Soc. *Res:* Pathophysiology; host-parasite interactions; veterinary parasitology. *Mailing Add:* Dept Biol Univ Tex Arlington TX 76019

STEWART, GERALD WALTER, b Hamilton, Ohio, Oct 8, 44. PHYSICAL CHEMISTRY. *Educ:* Wilmington Col, Ohio, BS, 65; SDak Sch Mines & Technol, Rapid City, MS, 67; Univ Idaho, Moscow, PhD(phys chem), 71. *Prof Exp:* Res assoc, Washington Univ, St Louis, 71-73, Mass Inst Technol, 73-74; asst prof chem, WVa Univ, 74-77; chief, Supporting Res, US Dept Energy, 77-79; DIR, CTR CHEM & ENVIRON PHYSICS, AERODYNE RES INC, 79- *Concurrent Pos:* Adj assoc prof chem, WVa Univ, 77-81, Boston Col, 82- *Mem:* Am Chem Soc; Sigma Xi; Combustion Inst. *Res:* Theoretical and experimental investigations on the chemistry of coal combustion; evaluation and measurement of kinetic and thermodynamic parameters controlling pollutant formation; chemiluminescence studies of reactions involving inorganic hydrides with strong oxidizing agents; ion-molecule reactions by ion cyclotron resonance spectroscopy. *Mailing Add:* Aerodyne Res Inc 45 Manning Rd Billerica MA 01821

STEWART, GLENN ALEXANDER, b Ellensburg, Wash, Jan 14, 41; m 62; c 2. SOLID STATE PHYSICS, SURFACE PHSYICS. *Educ:* Amherst Col, BA, 62; Univ Wash, MSE, 65, PhD(physics), 69. *Prof Exp:* Fel physics, Univ Wash, 69-70; res fel physics, Calif Inst Technol, 70-72; asst prof physics, 72-76, ASSOC PROF PHYSICS & DIR HONORS PROG, 76- *Mem:* Am Phys Soc. *Res:* Phase transitions in surface films, particularly in physically absorbed noble gas monolayers. *Mailing Add:* Dept of Physics Univ of Pittsburgh Pittsburgh PA 15260

STEWART, GLENN RAYMOND, b Riverside, Calif, Feb 7, 36; m 63; c 2. VERTEBRATE ZOOLOGY, NATURAL HISTORY. *Educ:* Calif State Polytech Col, BS, 58; Ore State Univ, MA, 60, PhD(zool), 64. *Prof Exp:* From asst prof to assoc prof, 63-73, PROF ZOOL, CALIF STATE POLYTECH UNIV, 73- *Mem:* AAAS; Am Soc Ichthyol & Herpet; Am Soc Mammal; Am Inst Biol Sci; Soc Study Amphibians & Reptiles. *Res:* Ecology, taxonomy and behavior of reptiles, amphibians and mammals; status of endangered and rare species. *Mailing Add:* Dept of Biol Sci Calif State Polytech Univ Pomona CA 91768

STEWART, GORDON ARNOLD, b Denver, Colo, July 2, 34; m 62; c 2. DAIRY SCIENCE. *Educ:* Univ Mo, BS, 56, MS, 58, PhD(dairy), 60. *Prof Exp:* Assoc prof agr, Southeast Mo State Col, 60-65; from asst prof to assoc prof dairy sci, 65-77, PROF ANIMAL SCI & DAIRY HERD MGR, LA TECH UNIV, 77- *Concurrent Pos:* Assoc prof animal sci, Col of Agr, Haile Sellassie Univ, Alemaya, Ethiopia, 73-75. *Mem:* Nat Asn Cols & Teachers Agr (treas, 65-73); Am Dairy Sci Asn. *Res:* Dairy cattle nutrition, breeding and management. *Mailing Add:* Dept of Animal Indust La Tech Univ PO Box 5618 Ruston LA 71270

STEWART, GORDON ERVIN, b San Bernardino, Calif, June 25, 34; m 59; c 3. MICROWAVE PHYSICS, PLASMA PHYSICS. *Educ:* Univ Calif, Los Angeles, BS, 55, MS, 57; Univ Southern Calif, PhD(elec eng), 63. *Prof Exp:* Mem tech staff, Hughes Aircraft Co, 55-62; mem tech staff, Plasma Res Lab, 62-70, SECT HEAD, AEROSPACE CORP, 70- *Concurrent Pos:* Asst prof, Univ Southern Calif, 62-66; mem comn 6, Int Union Radio Sci. *Mem:* Inst Elec & Electronic Engrs; Am Phys Soc. *Res:* Radar scattering; antenna theory; wave propagation in plasmas; acoustic holography. *Mailing Add:* Aerospace Corp 2350 E El Segundo Blvd El Segundo CA 90245

STEWART, H(OMER) J(OSEPH), b Elba, Mich, Aug 15, 15; m 40; c 3. AERONAUTICAL ENGINEERING. *Educ:* Univ Minn, BAeroE, 36; Calif Inst Technol, PhD(aeronaut), 40. *Prof Exp:* Asst, 36-38, instr meteorol, 38-40, from instr to asst prof aeronaut & meteorol, 40-46, chief res anal sect, Jet Propulsion Lab, 44-56, assoc prof aeronaut, 46-49, chief liquid propulsion systs Div, Jet Propulsion Lab, 56-58, spec asst to dir lab, 60-62, mgr advan studies off, 62-68, prof aeronaut, 49-80, EMER PROF AERONAUT, CALIF INST TECHNOL, 80-, ADVAN TECH STUDIES ADV, JET PROPULSION LAB, 68- *Concurrent Pos:* Mem tech eval group, Guided Missiles Comt, Res & Develop Bd, 48-52; mem sci adv bd, US Air Force, 49-55, 58-64; mem adv group artificial cloud nucleation, US Dept Defense, 51-55, chmn adv group on spec capabilities, 55-58; consult, Aerojet-Gen Corp, 51-58, 60-70, Preparedness Invest Subcomt, US Senate, 57-58 & Rand Corp, 60-68; mem sci adv comt, Ballistics Res Lab, 58-68; mem bd dirs, Meteorol Res Inc, 62-66 & Sargent Industs, Inc, 66-; dir off prog planning & eval, NASA, 58-60. *Honors & Awards:* Outstanding Achievement Award, Univ Minn, 54; Except Serv Medal, NASA, 70. *Mem:* Am Meteorol Soc; Am Inst Aeronaut & Astronaut. *Res:* Dynamic meteorology; theoretical aerodynamics; fluid and supersonic flows; guided missiles; space and planetary exploration systems. *Mailing Add:* Dept of Aeronaut Eng Calif Inst of Technol Pasadena CA 91125

STEWART, HAROLD BROWN, b Chatham, Ont, Can, Mar 9, 21; m 50. BIOCHEMISTRY. *Educ:* Univ Toronto, MD, 44, PhD, 50; Cambridge Univ, PhD, 55. *Prof Exp:* Assoc prof, 55-60, chmn dept, 65-72, PROF BIOCHEM, UNIV WESTERN ONT, 60-, DEAN FAC GRAD STUDIES, 72- *Concurrent Pos:* Med Res Coun vis scientist, Cambridge Univ, 71-72. *Mem:* Am Soc Biol Chem; Can Physiol Soc; Can Biochem Soc; Brit Biochem Soc. *Res:* Intermediary metabolism in animals and microorganisms. *Mailing Add:* 118 Base Line Rd E London ON N6C 2N8 Can

STEWART, HARRIS BATES, JR, b Auburn, NY, Sept 19, 22; m 59; c 2. OCEANOGRAPHY. *Educ:* Princeton Univ, AB, 48; Univ Calif, MS, 52, PhD(oceanog), 56. *Prof Exp:* Hydrographer, US Naval Hydrographic Off, 48-50; instr, Hotchkiss Sch, Conn, 50-51; res asst oceanog, Scripps Inst Oceanog, Univ Calif, 51-56; chief oceanogr, US Coast & Geod Surv, 57-65; dir, Inst Oceanog, Environ Sci Serv Admin, 65-70, dir, Atlantic Oceanog & Meteorol Labs, Nat Oceanic & Atmospheric Admin, 70-78; DIR, CTR MARINE STUDIES, OLD DOMINION UNIV, 80- *Concurrent Pos:* Chmn ocean surv panel, Interagency Comt Oceanog, 62-66 & int progs panel, 65-67; US nat coordr, Coop Invest of Caribbean & Adjacent Regions, 68-75; chmn adv coun, Dept Geol & Geophys Sci, Princeton Univ, 73-76; pres, Dade Marine Inst, 77-78; vchmn, Intergovernmental Oceanog Comn Regional Asn for Caribbean, 78-82, US nat assoc, 76- *Honors & Awards:* Silver Medal, US Dept Com, 60, Gold Medal, 65; Almirante Padilla Decoration, Repub Colombia, 72. *Mem:* Fel AAAS; fel Geol Soc Am; Am Geophys Union; fel Marine Technol Soc (vpres, 74-76); fel Int Oceanog Found (vpres). *Res:* Coastal lagoons; marine geology; physical oceanography. *Mailing Add:* Ctr Marine Studies Old Dominion Univ Norfolk VA 23508

STEWART, HERBERT, b Stanton, Ky, July 18, 28; m 53; c 3. SCIENCE EDUCATION, BIOLOGY. *Educ:* Univ Conn, BA, 54, MS, 56; Columbia Univ, EdD, 58. *Prof Exp:* Teacher pub sch, Ky, 51-53; instr bot, Univ Conn, 54-56; instr biol, Teachers Col, Columbia Univ, 57-58; prof sci educ & biol, Md State Teachers Col, Towson, 58-59; asst prof biol, Sch Com, NY Univ, 59-60; asst prof sci educ, Rutgers Univ, 60-61; assoc prof, Univ SFla, 61-67; PROF SCI EDUC, FLA ATLANTIC UNIV, 67- *Concurrent Pos:* Sci Manpower fel, Columbia Univ, 59-60; dir, NSF In-Serv Inst, 66-67. *Mem:* AAAS; Nat Asn Comput Math & Sci Teaching; Asn Educ Teachers Sci; Asn Comput Math & Sci Teaching. *Res:* Research and development of micro-computer simulations of laboratory experiments which are expensive or dangerous to perform. *Mailing Add:* Dept of Sci Educ Fla Atlantic Univ Boca Raton FL 33432

STEWART, IVAN, b Stanton, Ky, July 24, 22; m 47; c 3. PLANT CHEMISTRY. *Educ:* Univ Ky, BS, 48, MS, 49; Rutgers Univ, PhD(soils), 51. *Prof Exp:* From asst biochemist to assoc biochemist, 51-61, BIOCHEMIST, CITRUS EXP STA, UNIV FLA, 61- *Res:* Mineral nutrition of plants. *Mailing Add:* Inst of Food & Agr Sci Agr Res & Educ Ctr Univ of Fla PO Box 1088 Lake Alfred FL 33850

STEWART, J(AMES) R(USH), JR, b Orange, Tex, Dec 28, 26; m 51; c 4. CHEMICAL ENGINEERING. *Educ:* La Polytech Inst, BS, 50; Ill Inst Technol, MGT, 52. *Prof Exp:* Engr, 52-56, sect supvr chem eng, Res Dept, 56-60, admin asst res, 60-68, SR RES ASSOC, RES DEPT, PENNZOIL CO, 68- *Concurrent Pos:* Instr, Centenary Col, 57-62. *Mem:* Am Chem Soc; Am Inst Chem Engrs; Am Ornith Union; Brit Ornith Union. *Res:* Hydrocarbon processing; gas engineering; petrochemicals; fuel cells; solar energy; fertilizers; lube oil refining. *Mailing Add:* Res Dept PO Box 6199 Shreveport LA 71106

STEWART, JACK LAUREN, b Covington, Okla, Apr 3, 24; m 48; c 4. DENTISTRY. *Educ:* Univ Kansas City, DDS, 52. *Prof Exp:* Pvt pract, 52-62; asst prof, 63-67, assoc prof & coordr res, 67-70, PROF DENT & ASST DEAN RES & CONTINUING EDUC, SCH DENT, UNIV MO-KANSAS CITY, 70- *Concurrent Pos:* Investr, US Army res contract, 63-67, co-responsible investr, 67-70; consult, Leavenworth Vet Admin Ctr, 64- & Kansas City Vet Admin Hosp, 67-; abstractor, Oral Res Abstr, Am Dent Asn; chmn sect comput appln, Am Asn Dent Schs, 68-69, from vchmn to chmn sect learning resources, 69-72. *Mem:* Am Asn Dent Schs; Am Dent Asn; Int Asn Dent Res; Pierre Fauchard Acad. *Res:* Research administration; maxillofacial injuries; oral lesions. *Mailing Add:* 650 E 25th St Kansas City MO 64108

STEWART, JAMES A, b Burnaby, BC, May 30, 20; m 50; c 2. ELECTRONIC ENGINEERING. *Educ:* Univ BC, BASc, 50; Stanford Univ, MSc, 59. *Prof Exp:* Prod engr, Lenkurt Elec Co Can, 51-54; sr electronics engr, Avro Aircraft, Ltd, 54-55; engr, Westinghouse Elec Corp, 55-56; res engr, Lenkurt Elec Co, Inc, 56-60; mem tech staff, West Coast Lab, Gen Tel & Electronics Labs, 60-63; sr staff engr, GTE Lenkurt Inc, 64-80; MEM STAFF, DATA TERMINALS DIV, HEWLETT-PACKARD, 80- *Mem:* Inst Elec & Electronics Engrs. *Res:* Electronic circuitry; communication system design. *Mailing Add:* Data Terminals Div Hewlett-Packard 19400 Homestead Rd Cupertino CA 95014

STEWART, JAMES ALLEN, b Pembroke, Ont, Can, Jan 7, 27; m 54; c 3. PHYSICAL CHEMISTRY. *Educ:* Queen's Univ, Ont, BA, 51, MA, 53; Univ Ottawa, PhD(phys chem), 59. *Prof Exp:* Anal res chemist, Dept Nat Health & Welfare, Can, 54-59; from asst prof to assoc prof, 59-69, PROF PHYS CHEM, UNIV NDAK, 69- *Mem:* Am Chem Soc. *Res:* Chemical kinetics of hydrolytic enzyme systems, ester hydrolyses and excited alkali metal reactions; solvent isotope effects on reaction rates. *Mailing Add:* Dept of Chem Univ of NDak Grand Forks ND 58201

STEWART, JAMES ANTHONY, b Manchester, NH, Aug 2, 38; m 63; c 3. BIOCHEMISTRY. *Educ:* St Anselm's Col, BA, 63; Univ Conn, PhD(biochem), 67. *Prof Exp:* Investr, Biol Div, Oak Ridge Nat Lab, 67-68; asst prof, 68-73, assoc prof, 73-78, PROF & CHMN DEPT, UNIV NH, 78- *Concurrent Pos:* Vis prof, Univ Tex Med Br, Galveston, 81-82. *Mem:* AAAS; Soc Develop Biol; Am Inst Biol Sci; Am Soc Biol Chemists. *Res:* Regulation of protein and nucleic acid synthesis during development and differentiation of the mouse central nervous system. *Mailing Add:* Dept of Biochem Univ of NH Durham NH 03824

STEWART, JAMES DREWRY, b Toronto, Ont, Mar 29, 41. MATHEMATICAL ANALYSIS. *Educ:* Univ Toronto, BSc, 63, PhD(math), 67; Stanford Univ, MS, 64. *Prof Exp:* Nat Res Coun Can fel, Univ London, 67-69; asst prof, 69-74, ASSOC PROF MATH, MCMASTER UNIV, 74- *Mem:* Am Math Soc; Math Asn Am; Can Math Cong. *Res:* Abstract harmonic analysis, functional analysis, history of mathematics. *Mailing Add:* Dept of Math McMaster Univ Hamilton ON L8S 4L8 Can

STEWART, JAMES EDWARD, b Anyox, BC, Aug 3, 28; m 67; c 2. BACTERIAL PHYSIOLOGY. *Educ:* Univ BC, BSA, 52, MSA, 54; Univ Iowa, PhD, 58. *Prof Exp:* Scientist, Fisheries Res Bd Can, 58-74, scientist, Res & Develop Directorate, 74-76, SCIENTIST, RESOURCE BR, MARITIMES REGION, DEPT FISHERIES & OCEANS, CAN, 80- *Mem:* Soc Invert Path; Sigma Xi; Can Soc Microbiol. *Res:* Microbial oxidation of hydrocarbons; enzymes; bacterial metabolism; defense mechanisms and diseases of marine animals; research management. *Mailing Add:* Resource Br Scotia Fundy Region Fisheries & Oceans Can Box 550 Halifax NS B3J 2S7 Can

STEWART, JAMES LLOYD, b Chengtu, China, Jan 5, 18; nat US; m 45; c 1. PHYSICS. *Educ:* Univ Sask, BA, 38, MA, 40; Johns Hopkins Univ, PhD(physics), 43. *Prof Exp:* Lab asst physics, Univ Sask, 35-38, technician, Radon Plant, Sask Cancer Comn, 38-40; jr instr physics, Johns Hopkins Univ, 40-43; sci officer, Ballistics Lab, Can Armament Res & Develop Estab, 43-45; lectr physics, Queen's Univ, Ont, 45-46; asst prof, Rutgers Univ, 46-51; physicist, US Navy Electronics Lab, 51-67; physicist, Naval Undersea Ctr, 67-76, MEM STAFF, NAVAL OCEAN SYSTS CTR, 76- *Mem:* Sr mem Inst Elec & Electronics Engrs; fel Acoust Soc Am. *Res:* Slow neutrons; ballistics; ultrasonics; underwater acoustics; signal processing theory. *Mailing Add:* Naval Ocean Systs Ctr San Diego CA 92152

STEWART, JAMES MCDONALD, b Taft, Tenn, Sept 22, 41; m 64; c 3. PLANT PHYSIOLOGY. *Educ:* Okla State Univ, BS, 63, PhD(plant physiol), 68. *Prof Exp:* PLANT PHYSIOLOGIST COTTON PHYSIOL, AGR RES SERV, USDA, 68-; ASSOC PROF PLANT & SOIL SCI, UNIV TENN, KNOXVILLE, 68- *Mem:* Sigma Xi; Am Soc Plant Physiologists; Crop Sci Soc Am; Agron Soc Am; AAAS. *Res:* Basic and applied research on cotton fiber and seed development and maturation with correlated studies concerning the effects of environment and heritable traits thereon. *Mailing Add:* Dept of Plant & Soil Sci Univ of Tenn Knoxville TN 37916

STEWART, JAMES MONROE, b Chicago, Ill, Feb 26, 46; m 69; c 2. SPEECH PERCEPTION, STATISTICS. *Educ:* Howard Univ, BA, 70, MA, 71; Ohio Univ, PhD(hearing & speech sci), 76. *Prof Exp:* Instr speech, Howard Univ, 70-71; teaching & res asst speech sci, Ohio Univ, 71-75; res assoc speech sci, Univ Tex Health Sci Ctr, Houston, 75-76; mem staff speech path & audiol, 76-79, ASST PROF HEARING & SPEECH SCI, TENN STATE UNIV, 79- *Concurrent Pos:* Teacher Eng & Math, Washington DC Pub Sch, 70-73. *Mem:* Int Soc Phonetic Sci; Am Asn Phonetic Sci; Phonetic Soc Japan; Acoust Soc Am; Inst Acoust. *Res:* Psychological reality of speech perception; saliency of perceptual judgments; prevalence of communicative disorders. *Mailing Add:* 3670 Tampa Dr Nashville TN 37211

STEWART, JAMES RAY, b Beeville, Tex, Aug 5, 37; m 68. CELL BIOLOGY, MICROBIOLOGY. *Educ:* NTex State Univ, BS, 59; Univ Ala, Tuscaloosa, MS, 65; Univ Tex, Austin, PhD(biol sci), 70. *Prof Exp:* NIH fel, Univ Tex Med Sch, San Antonio, 70-74; ASSOC PROF BIOL & CHEM, UNIV TEX TYLER, 74- *Mem:* Am Soc Microbiol; Phycol Soc Am. *Res:* Taxonomic studies of myxobacteria; studies of enzymes involved in morphogenesis of myxobacteria and Acanthamoeba. *Mailing Add:* Dept of Biol Univ Tex Tyler Tyler TX 75701

STEWART, JAMES T, b Birmingham, Ala, Dec 1, 38; m 63; c 3. PHARMACEUTICAL CHEMISTRY. *Educ:* Auburn Univ, BS, 60, MS, 63; Univ Mich, PhD(pharmaceut chem), 67. *Prof Exp:* From asst prof to assoc prof, 67-78, PROF PHARMACEUT CHEM, UNIV GA, 78- *Concurrent Pos:* Mead-Johnson res grant, 67-68; NIH biomed sci grant, 68-69; mem, US Pharmacopeial Revision Comt, 80-85; Food & Drug Admin contracts, 77-80 & 81-84; grants, Knoll Pharmaceut, 78 & 79, Boots Pharmaceut, 80 & Hoffman-La Roche, Inc, 81. *Mem:* Am Chem Soc; Am Pharmaceut Asn; Acad Pharmaceut Sci. *Res:* Fluorometric analysis of pharmaceuticals; gas chromatography; liquid chromatography. *Mailing Add:* Sch of Pharm Univ of Ga Athens GA 30602

STEWART, JENNIFER KEYS, b Rome, Ga, May 15, 47. ENDOCRINOLOGY. *Educ:* Emory Univ, BS, 68, MS, 69, PhD(physiol), 75. *Prof Exp:* Instr biol, Mercer Univ, 69-71; res fel endocrinol, Harborview Med Ctr, 75-78; res assoc, Univ Wash & Howard Hughes Med Inst, 79-80, res asst prof, 80-81; ASST PROF BIOL, VA COMMONWEALTH UNIV, 81- *Res:* Metabolic and endocrine physiology; mechanism and control of hormone secretion. *Mailing Add:* Dept Biol Va Commonwealth Univ Richmond VA 23284

STEWART, JOAN GODSIL, b US. MARINE BOTANY. *Educ:* Pomona Col, BA, 53; Calif State Univ, San Diego, MA, 67; Univ Calif, Irvine, PhD(biol), 73. *Prof Exp:* Instr marine bot, Calif State Univ, San Diego, 67-68; res fel marine algae, Scripps Inst Oceanog, Univ Calif, 73-75; scientist intertidal ecol, Lockheed Marine Biol Lab, 76; consult algal develop, 77-78; ASST RES MARINE BIOLOGIST MARINE ALGAE, SCRIPPS INST OCEANOG, UNIV CALIF, 78- *Mem:* Int Phycol Soc; Phycol Soc Am. *Res:* Developmental morphology and nearshore ecology of Rhodophyta. *Mailing Add:* A-002 Scripps Inst of Oceanog Univ of Calif San Diego CA 92093

STEWART, JOHN, b Redding, Calif, Dec 10, 29; m 56; c 4. ELECTRICAL ENGINEERING. *Educ:* Univ Calif, BSEE, 52. *Prof Exp:* Proj engr, Univac Div, Sperry-Rand Corp, Minn, 54-56, sr engr, 56-60; sr scientist, 60-61, chief engr, 61-68, vpres res & develop, 68-72, GROUP VPRES, SYSTS RES LABS, INC, 72- *Mem:* Inst Elec & Electronics Engrs. *Res:* Digital computers and data processing systems. *Mailing Add:* Systs Res Labs Inc 2800 Indian Ripple Rd Dayton OH 45440

STEWART, JOHN ALLAN, b Saskatoon, Sask, Feb 18, 24; m 48; c 5. SOIL SCIENCE. *Educ:* Univ BC, BSA, 50, MSA, 53; Univ Wis, PhD, 64. *Prof Exp:* Lectr soils, Univ BC, 50-51 & 52-54; plant physiologist, Can Dept Agr, 54-65; agronomist, Can, 65-67, res agronomist, Ill, 67-68, mgr fertilizers & cropping systs res, Res & Develop Div, 68-70, mgr agr res, 70-72, DIR RES & DEVELOP, INT MINERALS & CHEM CORP, 72- *Concurrent Pos:* Mem, Coun Agr Sci & Technol. *Mem:* Am Soc Agron; Can Soc Soil Sci; Agr Inst Can; AAAS. *Res:* Mineral nutrition of agricultural crops; environmental aspects of agricultural technology; industrial minerals applications. *Mailing Add:* 1328 Redwood Libertyville IL 60048

STEWART, JOHN CONYNGHAM, b New York, NY, Feb 10, 30; m 56; c 2. GEOLOGY. *Educ:* Trinity Col, Conn, BA, 52; Princeton Univ, MA, 56, PhD(geol), 57. *Prof Exp:* Geologist, Harvard NSF res proj, Dordogne dist, France, 57; geophys interpreter, Mobil Oil Co, Venezuela, 58-61; from instr to assoc prof, 61-74, chmn dept, 68-80, PROF GEOL, BROOKLYN COL, 74- *Concurrent Pos:* Danforth assoc. *Mem:* AAAS; Geol Soc Am; Soc Econ Paleont & Mineral; Am Asn Petrol Geol. *Res:* Stratigraphy. *Mailing Add:* Dept Geol Brooklyn Col Brooklyn NY 11210

STEWART, JOHN DOUGLAS, b Hayward, Calif, May 14, 27; m 63; c 3. PSYCHOPHYSICS. *Educ:* Univ Calif, Berkeley, BS, 50, MS, 53. *Prof Exp:* Eng intern, Ames Res Lab, Nat Adv Comt Aeronaut, 51-52; engr, Marquardt Aircraft Co, 53; RES SCIENTIST, AMES RES CTR, NASA, 54- *Mem:* Am Inst Aeronaut & Astronaut. *Res:* Pilots perception and use of angular acceleration motion cues, vestibular-visual interactions, and the effects of vibration on the pilot's opinion and performance in closed loop control situations. *Mailing Add:* Ames Res Ctr NASA Mail Stop 239-3 Moffett Field CA 94035

STEWART, JOHN HARRIS, b Berkeley, Calif, Aug 7, 28; m 62; c 2. GEOLOGY. *Educ:* Univ NMex, BS, 50; Stanford Univ, PhD, 61. *Prof Exp:* GEOLOGIST, US GEOL SURV, 51- *Mem:* Geol Soc Am. *Res:* Stratigraphy; sedimentology; regional stratigraphy of Triassic rocks in Utah, Colorado, Nevada, Arizona and New Mexico and of late Precambrian and Cambrian in Nevada and California; regional and local mapping in Nevada; compilation of geologic map of Nevada. *Mailing Add:* US Geol Surv 345 Middlefield Rd Menlo Park CA 94025

STEWART, JOHN J(OSEPH), civil engineering, see previous edition

STEWART, JOHN JOSEPH, b Paterson, NJ, July 27, 46. PHARMACOLOGY. *Educ:* Duquesne Univ, BS, 69; Univ Wis-Madison, MS, 72, PhD(pharm), 75. *Prof Exp:* USPHS fel physiol, Med Sch, Univ Tex, Houston, 75-77; ASST PROF PHARMACOL, SCH MED, LA STATE UNIV, SHREVEPORT, 77- *Concurrent Pos:* Nat Inst Gen Med Sci grant, Med Sch, La State Univ, Shreveport, 78-81. *Mem:* Sigma Xi. *Res:* Central nervous system control of gastrointestinal function. *Mailing Add:* Dept of Pharmacol & Therapeut La State Univ Med Ctr Shreveport LA 71130

STEWART, JOHN JOSEPH, JR, b Mt Pleasant, Pa, Aug 14, 50. PLASMA PHYSICS, COMPUTATIONAL PHYSICS. *Educ:* Case Inst Technol, BS, 72; Case Western Reserve Univ, MSEE, 74. *Prof Exp:* PHYSICIST PLASMA PHYSICS, LAWRENCE LIVERMORE LAB, 74- *Res:* Computational plasma physics of problems related to thermonuclear fusion. *Mailing Add:* Lawrence Livermore Lab PO Box 5511 L-630 Livermore CA 94550

STEWART, JOHN L(AWRENCE), b Pasadena, Calif, Apr 19, 25; m 51; c 2. ELECTRICAL ENGINEERING. *Educ:* Stanford Univ, BS, 48, MS, 49, PhD(elec eng), 52. *Prof Exp:* Res engr, Jet Propulsion Lab, Calif Inst Technol, 49-51; res assoc, Stanford Univ, 52-53; asst prof elec eng, Univ Mich, 53-56; assoc prof, Calif Inst Technol, 56-57 & Univ Southern Calif, 57-60; prof, Univ Ariz, 60-62; pres, Santa Rita Technol, Inc, Calif, 62-71; PRES, AV-ALARM CORP, 71- *Mem:* AAAS; Inst Elec & Electronics Engrs; Acoust Soc Am. *Res:* Electronic network simulations of animal sensory systems; bionics; speech and hearing; speech processing and recognition; acoustic control and cuing; artificial intelligence. *Mailing Add:* Av-Alarm Corp PO Box 2488 Santa Maria CA 93455

STEWART, JOHN MATHEWS, b Vermillion, SDak, Apr 5, 20; m 43; c 1. ORGANIC CHEMISTRY. *Educ:* Univ Mont, BA, 41; Univ Ill, PhD(org chem), 44. *Prof Exp:* Res chemist, War Prod Bd, Univ Ill, 43-45 & Calif Res Corp, 45-46; from asst prof to prof chem, Univ Mont, 46-77, chmn dept, 59-67, dean grad sch, 68-77, actg acad vpres, 75-77; RETIRED. *Concurrent Pos:* Asst acad vpres, Univ Mont, 78- *Mem:* Am Chem Soc; Sigma Xi. *Res:* Reactions of olefin sulfides; additions to unsaturated nitriles; participation of cyclopropane rings in conjugation, ring-opening reactions of cyclopropanes; use of diazomethane in synthesis of heterocyclic compounds. *Mailing Add:* 111 Crestline Missoula MT 59803

STEWART, JOHN MORROW, b Guilford Co, NC, Oct 31, 24; m 49; c 3. BIOCHEMISTRY, PHARMACOLOGY. *Educ:* Davidson Col, BS, 48; Univ Ill, MS, 50, PhD(org chem), 52. *Prof Exp:* Instr chem, Davidson Col, 48-49; asst, Rockefeller Univ, 52-57, from asst prof to assoc prof biochem, 57-68; PROF BIOCHEM, MED SCH, UNIV COLO, DENVER, 68- *Mem:* Am Chem Soc; Am Soc Pharmacol & Exp Therapeut; Harvey Soc; NY Acad Sci; Am Soc Biol Chemists. *Res:* Chemistry and pharmacology of peptide hormones, methods of peptide synthesis, antimetabolites and amino acids; synthetic organic chemistry. *Mailing Add:* Dept of Biochem Univ of Colo Med Sch Denver CO 80262

STEWART, JOHN WESTCOTT, b New York, NY, Nov 15, 26; m 54; c 1. PHYSICS. *Educ:* Princeton Univ, AB, 49; Harvard Univ, MA, 50, PhD(physics), 54. *Prof Exp:* Res fel, 54-56, asst prof, 56-60, ASSOC PROF PHYSICS, UNIV VA, 60-, ASST DEAN COL, 70- *Mem:* Fel Am Phys Soc; Am Asn Physics Teachers. *Res:* Properties of matter under combined field of high pressure and low temperature; meteorology. *Mailing Add:* Dept Physics J W Beams Lab Univ Va Charlottesville VA 22903

STEWART, JOHN WOODS, b Henderson, Tenn, Apr 5, 42; m 65; c 2. NUCLEAR ENGINEERING. *Educ:* Univ Tenn, BS, 65, MS, 67, PhD(nuclear eng), 69. *Prof Exp:* Nuclear engr, 68-71, res supvr, 71-75, res mgr, 75-80, dept supt, 78-81, GEN SUPT EMPLOYEE RELS, SAVANNAH RIVER PLANT, E I DU PONT DE NEMOURS & CO, INC, 81- *Concurrent Pos:* Res assoc nuclear eng, Mass Inst Technol, 74-75. *Mem:* Am Nuclear Soc. *Res:* Nuclear reactor physics and engineering; equipment development; computer applications. *Mailing Add:* Savannah River Plant E I du Pont de Nemours & Co Inc Aiken SC 29801

STEWART, JOHN WRAY BLACK, b Coleraine, NIreland, Jan 16, 36; Can citizen; m 65; c 2. SOIL SCIENCE, CHEMISTRY. *Educ:* Queen's Univ, Belfast, BSc, 58, BAgr, 59, PhD(soil sci), 63. *Prof Exp:* From sci officer to sr sci officer soil sci, Chem Res Div, Ministry Agr, NIreland, 59-64; fel, 64-65, from asst prof to assoc prof, 65-76, prof soil sci, 76-81, DIR, SASK INST PEDOLOGY & HEAD, DEPT SOIL SCI, UNIV SASK, 81- *Concurrent Pos:* Tech expert, Int Atomic Energy Agency, Vienna, 71-72; proj coordr, Can Int Develop Agency, Brazil, 76-; tech expert UN Brazil proj, 74-75. *Mem:* Agr Inst Can; Brit Soc Soil Sci; Int Soil Sci Soc; Am Soc Agron. *Res:* Soil chemistry and fertility; cycling of macro and micro nutrients and heavy metals in the soil plant system. *Mailing Add:* Dept of Soil Sci Univ of Sask Saskatoon SK S7N 0W0 Can

STEWART, JOSEPH LETIE, b Salida, Colo, Aug 2, 27; m 50; c 3. AUDIOLOGY, SPEECH PATHOLOGY. *Educ:* Univ Denver, BA, 49, MA, 50; Univ Iowa, PhD(speech path, audiol, anthrop), 59. *Prof Exp:* Res assoc speech path, Univ Iowa, 58-59; asst prof audiol & dir hearing ctr, Univ Denver, 59-65; consult audiol & speech path, Neurol & Sensory Dis Control Prog, Nat Ctr Chronic Dis Control, USPHS, 65-70, CHIEF SENSORY DISABILITIES PROG, INDIAN HEALTH SERV, USPHS, 70- *Res:* Epidemiology of otitis media world wide; effects of auditory deprivation; prevention of deaf-mutism. *Mailing Add:* Indian Health Serv USPHS Suite 4455 Fed Bldg Box 409 Albuquerque NM 87103

STEWART, KENNETH WILSON, b Walters, Okla, Mar 5, 35; m 56; c 3. ENTOMOLOGY, AQUATIC ECOLOGY. *Educ:* Okla State Univ, BS, 58, MS, 59, PhD(entom, zool), 63. *Prof Exp:* Entomologist, Rocky Mt Forest & Range Exp Sta, US Forest Serv, 58-59; head dept biol, Coffeyville Col, 60-61; from instr to prof biol, 61-79, PROF & CHMN BIOL SCI, NORTH TEX STATE UNIV, 79- *Concurrent Pos:* Fac res grants, NTex State Univ, 63-81. NIH res grant, 66-68; consult investr, US Corps Engrs; NSF res grant, 77- *Mem:* Entom Soc Am; Am Entom Soc; NAm Benthological Soc (pres, 78-79). *Res:* Southwest United States stream benthos community structure and dynamics; North American Plecoptera nymphs; passive dispersal of Algae and Protozoa by aquatic insects; food habits and life histories of aquatic insects and spiders. *Mailing Add:* Dept of Biol Sci NTex State Univ Denton TX 76203

STEWART, KENT KALLAM, b Omaha, Nebr, Sept 5, 34; m 56; c 4. ANALYTICAL CHEMISTRY, BIOCHEMISTRY. *Educ:* Univ Calif, Berkeley, AB, 56; Fla State Univ, PhD(chem), 65. *Prof Exp:* USPHS guest investr biochem, Rockefeller Univ, 65-67, res assoc, 67-68, asst prof, 68-69; res chemist, 70-75, LAB CHIEF, NUTRIENT COMPOS LAB, NUTRIT INST, AGR RES SERV, USDA, 75- *Mem:* AAAS; Am Chem Soc; Inst Food Technologists; Asn Off Anal Chemists. *Res:* Automated analyses, especially flow injection analyses; nutrient composition of foods; naturally occuring toxic materials in foods; protein chemistry. *Mailing Add:* 220 Hillsboro Dr Silver Spring MD 20902

STEWART, KENTON M, b Withee, Wis, Aug 28, 31; m 54; c 3. ZOOLOGY, LIMNOLOGY. *Educ:* Wis State Univ, Stevens Point, BS, 55; Univ Wis-Madison, MS, 59, PhD(zool), 65. *Prof Exp:* Asst limnol, ecol & invert zool, Univ Wis-Madison, 58-61, asst limnol, 61-65, fel, 65-66; asst prof, 66-71, ASSOC PROF BIOL, STATE UNIV NY BUFFALO, 71- *Mem:* Am Soc Limnol & Oceanog; Ecol Soc Am; Int Asn Theoret & Appl Limnol; Int Asn Gt Lakes Res. *Res:* Physical limnology and eutrophication; comparative limnology of Finger Lakes of New York. *Mailing Add:* Dept of Biol State Univ of NY Buffalo NY 14260

STEWART, LELAND TAYLOR, b San Francisco, Calif, Nov 24, 28; m 56; c 2. STATISTICS. *Educ:* Stanford Univ, BS, 51, MS, 57, PhD(statist), 65. *Prof Exp:* Res engr, Autonetics Div, NAm Aviation, Inc, 51-56 & Electronic Defense Labs, Sylvania Elec Prod, Inc, 58-61; statistician, C-E-I-R, Inc, 61-65; STAFF SCIENTIST, LOCKHEED MISSILES & SPACE CO, 65- *Mem:* Am Statist Asn. *Res:* Bayesian statistics and decision theory. *Mailing Add:* Res Lab Lockheed Missiles & Space Co 3251 Hanover Palo Alto CA 94300

STEWART, LYNN MARTIN, biochemistry, enzymology, deceased

STEWART, MARGARET MCBRIDE, b Greensboro, NC, Feb 6, 27; m 69. VERTEBRATE ECOLOGY, HERPETOLOGY. *Educ:* Univ NC, AB, 48, MA, 51; Cornell Univ, PhD(vert zool), 56. *Prof Exp:* Lab instr anat & physiol, Woman's Col, Univ NC, 50-51; instr biol, Catawba Col, 51-53; asst bot & taxon, Cornell Univ, 53-56; from asst prof to assoc prof, 56-65, PROF VERT BIOL, STATE UNIV NY ALBANY, 65- *Concurrent Pos:* Res Found grant-in-aid, 58-61, 65-71 & 73-74; grants, Am Philos Soc, 75 & 81 & NSF, 78-80. *Mem:* Ecol Soc Am; Asn Trop Biol; Am Soc Ichthyol & Herpet; Soc Study Amphibians & Reptiles (pres, 79); Herpetologists' League. *Res:* Competition in tropical and temperate frogs; pattern polymorphism; population dynamics of Adirondack frogs; ecology of eleutherodactylus, Jamaica and Puerto Rico; amphibians of Malawi. *Mailing Add:* Dept of Biol Sci State Univ of NY Albany NY 12222

STEWART, MARK ARMSTRONG, b Yeovil, Eng, July 23, 29; US citizen; m 55; c 3. BIOCHEMISTRY, PSYCHIATRY. *Educ:* Cambridge Univ, BA, 52; Univ London, LRCP & MRCS, 56. *Prof Exp:* Asst psychiat, Sch Med, Wash Univ, 57-61, instr, 61-63, asst prof psychiat & pediat, 63-67, from assoc prof to prof psychiat, 67-72, assoc prof pediat, 68-72; IDA P HALLER PROF CHILD PSYCHIATRY, COL MED, UNIV IOWA, 72- *Concurrent Pos:* NIMH res career develop award, 61-71; dir psychiat, St Louis Children's Hosp. *Mem:* Asn Res Nerv & Ment Dis; Am Soc Biol Chem; Am Soc Neurochem; Psychiat Res Soc; Soc Res Child Develop. *Res:* Genetic influences on children's aggressive and antisocial behavior. *Mailing Add:* 500 Newton Rd Iowa City IA 52240

STEWART, MARK THURSTON, b Montclair, NJ, Apr 27, 48. HYDROGEOLOGY. *Educ:* Cornell Univ, AB, 70; Univ Wis-Madison, MS(geol) & MS(water resources mgt), 74, PhD(geol), 76. *Prof Exp:* ASSOC PROF GEOL, UNIV SOUTH FLA, TAMPA, 76- *Mem:* Sigma Xi; Nat Water Well Asn; Am Geophys Union. *Res:* Applications of geophysical techniques to ground water resource investigations; interactions of hydrologic and geologic systems; quaternary geology. *Mailing Add:* Dept of Geol SCA 203 Univ of SFla Tampa FL 33620

STEWART, MELBOURNE GEORGE, b Detroit, Mich, Sept 30, 27; m 54; c 3. PHYSICS. *Educ:* Univ Mich, AB, 49, MS, 50, PhD(physics), 55. *Prof Exp:* Instr physics, Univ Mich, 54-55; res assoc, Iowa State Univ, 55-56, from asst prof to assoc prof physics, 56-63; chmn dept, 63-73, PROF PHYSICS, WAYNE STATE UNIV, 63-, ASSOC PROVOST, 73- *Mem:* Am Phys Soc. *Res:* Nuclear structure. *Mailing Add:* Mackenzie Hall Wayne State Univ Detroit MI 48202

STEWART, P BRIAN, b Aug 7, 22; Can citizen; m 49; c 3. IMMUNOLOGY, PHYSIOLOGY. *Educ:* Univ London, MB, BS, 50. *Prof Exp:* House physician, Middlesex & Brompton Hosps, Eng, 50-52; gen pract, Barnstaple, Eng, 52-54; med res assoc, 56-57, assoc prof med, McGill Univ, 57-78; res dir, Pharma-Res Can Ltd, 62-78; SR VPRES RES & DEVELOP, BOEHRINGER INGELHEIM LTD, 78- *Concurrent Pos:* Lilly res fel physiol, McGill Univ, 55-56; Nat Res Coun Can res assoc med, 56-57; med dir, Geigy Can Ltd, 57-62; assoc physician, Royal Victoria Hosp Can, 57-78. *Mem:* Am Physiol Soc; Am Asn Immunologists; Can Soc Immunologists; Pharmacol Soc Can; Can Med Asn. *Res:* Allergy. *Mailing Add:* Boehringer Ingelheim Ltd 90 E Ridge Ridgefield CT 06877

STEWART, PAUL ALVA, b Leetonia, Ohio, June 24, 09; m 47; c 2. ECOLOGY, ORNITHOLOGY. *Educ:* Ohio State Univ, BS, 52, MS, 53, PhD(zool), 57. *Prof Exp:* Admin asst, State Dept Conserv, Ind, 58-59; wildlife res biologist, US Bur Sport Fisheries & Wildlife, 59-65; res entomologist, Agr Res Serv, USDA, 65-73; WILDLIFE CONSULT, 73- *Mem:* Am Soc Mammal; Wildlife Soc; Cooper Ornith Soc; Wilson Ornith Soc; Am Ornith Union. *Res:* Ecology and management of the wood duck; ecology of blackbird congregations; biological control of insect pests. *Mailing Add:* 203 Mooreland Dr Oxford NC 27565

STEWART, PETER ARTHUR, b Sask, May 12, 21; m 52; c 2. BIOPHYSICS, PHYSIOLOGY. *Educ:* Univ Man, BSc, 43; Univ Minn, MS, 49, PhD(biophys), 51. *Prof Exp:* Instr physiol, Univ Ill, 51-53, asst prof neurophysiol, Neuropsychiat Inst, Col Med, 53-54; from asst prof to assoc prof physiol, Emory Univ, 54-65, assoc prof physics, 61-65; PROF MED SCI, BROWN UNIV, 65- *Concurrent Pos:* Markle scholar, 56-61. *Mem:* AAAS; Am Physiol Soc; Biophys Soc; Biomed Eng Soc; Am Asn Physics Teachers. *Res:* Electrical parameters nerve membrane; protoplasmic movement and structure in slime molds; biological control systems analysis; computers in biomedicine; theoretical biology. *Mailing Add:* Div of Biol & Med Brown Univ Providence RI 02912

STEWART, RAY EDWARD, b Eugene, Ore, Nov 29, 42; m 64; c 2. PEDODONTICS, MEDICAL GENETICS. *Educ:* Univ Ore, DMD, 68, MS, 71. *Prof Exp:* Fel med genetics, Med Sch, Univ Ore, 68-71; asst prof pediat dent, Univ Calif, Los Angeles, 71-74, ASSOC PROF, DIV MED GENETICS, DEPT PEDIAT & ASSOC PROF PEDIAT DENT, HARBOR GEN HOSP-UNIV CALIF, LOS ANGELES, 74-, DENT COORDR, CRANIOFACIAL ANOMALIES CTR, 72- *Concurrent Pos:* Consult pediat dent, Wadsworth Vet Admin Hosp, 73- *Mem:* Sigma Xi; Am Cleft Palate Asn; Soc Craniofacial Geneticists; Am Acad Dent for Handicapped. *Res:* Clinical and laboratory research on pathogenesis and etiology of craniofacial malformations; development of animal models for human chondro-dystrophies. *Mailing Add:* 4165 Chestnut Ave-Bixby Noles Long Beach CA 90807

STEWART, REGINALD BRUCE, b Moose Jaw, Sask, May 30, 28; m 50; c 1. ANALYTICAL CHEMISTRY. *Educ:* Univ Man, BSc, 50. *Prof Exp:* Res chemist, Hudson Bay Mining & Smelting Co, 50-55; asst chief chemist, Noranda Mines Ltd, 55-62; res off anal chem, 62-69, HEAD ANAL SCI BR, ATOMIC ENERGY CAN, 69- *Mem:* Fel Chem Inst Can. *Res:* Analytical sciences, particularly nuclear power research and development. *Mailing Add:* Anal Sci Br Atomic Energy of Can Pinawa MB R0E 1L0 Can

STEWART, RICHARD BYRON, b Waterloo, Iowa, Aug 22, 24; m 44; c 2. MECHANICAL ENGINEERING. *Educ:* Univ Iowa, BSME, 46, MS, 48, PhD(mech eng), 66; Univ Colo, ME, 59. *Prof Exp:* Instr mech eng, Univ Iowa, 46-48; from asst prof to assoc prof, Univ Colo, 48-60; supvry mech engr, Cryogenics Div, Nat Bur Standards, 60-66; prof mech eng, Worcester Polytech Inst, 66-69; chmn dept, 69-74, PROF MECH ENG, UNIV IDAHO, 69- *Concurrent Pos:* Fulbright lectr, Col Eng, Univ Baghdad, 56-57. *Mem:* AAAS; Am Soc Heat, Refrig & Air-Conditioning Engrs. *Res:* Thermodynamic properties and processes; cryogenics; thermodynamic properties of cryogenic fluids. *Mailing Add:* Dept of Mech Eng Univ of Idaho Moscow ID 83843

STEWART, RICHARD CUMMINS, b Reading, Pa, May 22, 24; m 74; c 1. VIROLOGY, VACCINE DEVELOPMENT. *Educ:* Albright Col, BS, 49; Univ Pa, PhD(med microbiol), 53. *Prof Exp:* Mgr biol qual control, Pitman-Moore Co, 53-55; sect head virol, Smith Kline & French Labs, 55-69; dir, Affil Labs, Rohm & Haas, 69-75; MGR BIOL RES & DEVELOP, BAYVET DIV, CUTTER LABS, INC, 75- *Mem:* NY Acad Sci; Am Soc Microbiol. *Res:* Pathogenesis of infectious diseases of animals and man and intervention by prophylaxis or treatment. *Mailing Add:* 9916 W 65th Pl Merriam KS 66203

STEWART, RICHARD DONALD, b Lakeland, Fla, Dec 26, 26; m 52; c 3. INTERNAL MEDICINE, TOXICOLOGY. *Educ:* Univ Mich, AB, 51, MD, 55, MPH, 62, MA, 79; Am Bd Internal Med, dipl, 74; Am Bd Med Toxicol, dipl, 76. *Prof Exp:* Resident internal med, Med Ctr, Univ Mich, 59-62; staff physician, Med Dept, Dow Chem Co, 56-59, dir med res sect, Biochem Res Lab, 62-66; asst prof internal med & assoc prof prev med & toxicol, 66-69, prof environ med in internal med & toxicol & environ med, Sch Med, Med Col Wis, 69-78, chmn dept environ med, 66-78; CORP MED DIR, S C JOHNSON & SON, 78- *Concurrent Pos:* Corp med adv, S C Johnson & Son, 71-78; clin prof pharmacol & toxicol, Med Col Wis, 78-; adj prof, Univ Wis-Parkside, 78-; vis prof, Med Sch, Univ Hawaii, 80-; sect ed, Clin Med. *Honors & Awards:* Weisfeldt Mem Award, 75. *Mem:* Fel Am Col Physicians; Am Soc Artificial Internal Organs; Soc Toxicol; Am Acad Clin Toxicol; fel Am Occup Med Asn. *Res:* Human toxicology; development of the hollow fiber artificial kidney; air pollution epidemiological studies; experimental human exposures to artificial environments; tropical diseases; author of 125 publications. *Mailing Add:* S C Johnson & Son Inc Racine WI 53403

STEWART, RICHARD JOHN, b Duluth, Minn, May 30, 42; m 67. GEOLOGY. *Educ:* Univ Minn, BA, 65; Stanford Univ, PhD(geol), 70. *Prof Exp:* Asst prof, 69-77, ASSOC PROF GEOL, UNIV WASH, 77- *Concurrent Pos:* Geologist, Olympia Mts, US Geol Surv, 70; sedimentologist deep sea drilling proj, NSF, 71, res grant, Univ Wash, 72-73. *Mem:* Mineral Soc Am; Geol Soc Am; Am Asn Petrol Geologists; Soc Econ Paleontologists & Mineralogists; Am Geophys Union. *Res:* Sedimentary petrology; structural geology; geological and tectonic history of the northeast Pacific Ocean and its continental margin. *Mailing Add:* Dept of Geol Sci Univ of Wash Seattle WA 98195

STEWART, RICHARD WILLIAM, b Ames, Iowa, Oct, 22, 46; m 71; c 1. SYSTEM SURVIVABILITY. *Educ:* Mich State Univ, BS, 70; Iowa State Univ, MS, 73, PhD(elec eng), 77. *Prof Exp:* Staff engr, Johns Hopkins Appl Physics Lab, 77-79; GROUP LEADER, IRT CORP, 79- *Mem:* Inst Elec & Electronics Engrs; Soc Photo-Optical Instrumentation Engrs. *Res:* Evaluation and enhancement of the survivability of military and civil systems operating in hostile environments; electromagnetic coupling, nonlinear propagation and stochastic estimation. *Mailing Add:* 14140 Hermosillo Way Poway CA 92064

STEWART, RICHARD WILLIS, b Atlanta, Ga, Dec 27, 36; m 64; c 2. ATMOSPHERIC PHYSICS. *Educ:* Univ Fla, BS, 60; Columbia Univ, MA, 63, PhD(physics), 67. *Prof Exp:* Res assoc atmospheric physics, 67-69; staff scientist, Goddard Inst Space Studies, 69-78, RES SCIENTIST, NASA GODDARD SPACE FLIGHT CTR, 78- *Concurrent Pos:* Asst prof, Rutgers Univ, 68 & City Col New York, 69- *Mem:* Am Meteorol Soc; Am Geophys Union. *Res:* Aeronomy; planetary atmospheres. *Mailing Add:* NASA Goddard Space Flight Ctr Greenbelt MD 20771

STEWART, ROBERT ARCHIE, II, b Houston, Miss, Jan 23, 42; m 74; c 2. PALYNOLOGY, PLANT ECOLOGY. *Educ:* Miss State Univ, BS, 65, MS, 67; Ariz State Univ, PhD(bot), 71. *Prof Exp:* Partic, NSF advan seminar trop bot, Univ Miami, 68; from asst prof to assoc prof, 70-80, PROF BIOL, DELTA STATE UNIV, 80- *Mem:* Am Asn Stratig Palynologists; Am Inst Biol Sci. *Res:* Cenozoic palynology; plant ecology; flora of Mississippi. *Mailing Add:* Dept Biol Sci Delta State Univ Cleveland MS 38733

STEWART, ROBERT BLAYLOCK, b Stilwell, Okla, Feb 10, 26; m 48; c 2. PLANT PATHOLOGY. *Educ:* Okla State Univ, BS, 50; Tex A&M Univ, MS, 53, PhD(plant path), 57. *Prof Exp:* Instr agron, Okla State Univ, 54-56; asst prof plant path, Tex A&M Univ, 56-58; from assoc prof to prof bot, 58-74, PROF BIOL, SAM HOUSTON STATE UNIV, 74- *Concurrent Pos:* Assoc prof from Okla State Univ, Imp Ethiopian Col Agr & Mech Arts, 59. *Mem:* AAAS; Mycol Soc Am; Soc Econ Bot. *Res:* Paleoethnobotany. *Mailing Add:* Dept of Biol Sam Houston State Univ Huntsville TX 77340

STEWART, ROBERT BRUCE, b Toronto, Ont, May 2, 26; m 45; c 2. ANIMAL VIROLOGY. *Educ:* Mt Allison Univ, BSc, 49; Queen's Univ, Ont, MA, 51, PhD(bact), 55. *Prof Exp:* Res officer, Defence Res Bd, Can, 51-55; from instr to asst prof bact, Sch Med & Dent, Univ Rochester, 55-63; assoc prof, 63-66, PROF BACT, QUEEN'S UNIV, ONT, 66-, HEAD DEPT, 71- *Honors & Awards:* Browncroft Pediat Res Found Award, 58. *Mem:* Am Soc Microbiol; Can Soc Microbiol. *Res:* Virology; regulation of virus growth; infectious disease. *Mailing Add:* Dept of Microbiol & Immunol New Med Bldg Queen's Univ Kingston ON K7L 3N6 Can

STEWART, ROBERT CLARENCE, b Sharon, Pa, Sept 23, 21; m 59. MATHEMATICS. *Educ:* Washington & Jefferson Col, BA, 42, MA, 44; Yale Univ, MA, 48. *Prof Exp:* Instr math, Washington & Jefferson Col, 42-44, 45-46; asst, Yale Univ, 46-50; from instr to prof, 50-76, CHARLES A DANA PROF MATH, TRINITY COL, CONN, 76- *Mem:* Am Math Soc; Math Asn Am. *Res:* Modern algebra; matrix theory; differential equations. *Mailing Add:* Dept of Math Trinity Col Hartford CT 06106

STEWART, ROBERT DANIEL, b Salt Lake City, Utah, June 15, 23; m 47; c 4. PHYSICAL CHEMISTRY, METALLURGICAL CHEMISTRY. *Educ:* Univ Utah, BS, 50; Univ Wash, PhD(phys chem), 54. *Prof Exp:* Sr res chemist, Am Potash & Chem Corp, 54-56, group leader, 56-58, sect head, 58-68; group leader, Garrett Res & Develop Co, 68-75; GROUP LEADER, OCCIDENTAL RES CORP, 75- *Mem:* Am Chem Soc; Electrochem Soc; Am Inst Mining, Metall & Petrol Engrs. *Res:* Gas phase kinetics; thermodynamics; inorganic polymers; extractive hydrometallurgy. *Mailing Add:* 17052 El Cajon Ave Yorba Linda CA 92686

STEWART, ROBERT E(DWIN), b Carthage, Mo, May 4, 15; m 42; c 1. AGRICULTURAL ENGINEERING, BIOPHYSICS. *Educ:* Univ Mo, BS, 48, MS, 50, PhD(agr eng), 53. *Prof Exp:* From instr to prof agr eng, Univ Mo, 48-61; prof & chmn dept, Ohio State Univ, 61-68; distinguished prof, 68-80, DISTINGUISHED EMER PROF, TEX A&M UNIV, 80- *Mem:* Nat Acad Eng; Am Soc Agr Engrs (pres, 70-71). *Res:* Energy exchange of animals with their environment; hypothalamic regulation of internal temperature in cattle; research in environmental physiology and agricultural engineering for the benefit of the agricultural community worldwide. *Mailing Add:* 1504 Barak Lane Bryan TX 77801

STEWART, ROBERT EARL, b Campbellton, NB, Feb 17, 35; m 60; c 2. FLUID MECHANICS, MICROMETEOROLOGY. *Educ:* NS Tech Col, BEng, 57; Univ BC, MEng, 63; Univ Waterloo, PhD(mech), 66. *Prof Exp:* Design engr, BC Hydro, 57-58, res engr, 58-61; demonstr mech eng, Univ BC, 61-63; res asst, Univ Waterloo, 63-66; asst prof environ eng, Univ Fla, 66-70; ASSOC PROF MECH & ENVIRON ENG, UNIV LOUISVILLE, 70- *Mem:* Am Meteorol Soc; Can Meteorol Soc; fel Royal Meteorol Soc. *Res:* Diffusion of gases and particulates released into the atmosphere. *Mailing Add:* Dept of Mech Eng Univ of Louisville Louisville KY 40208

STEWART, ROBERT F, b Seattle, Wash, Dec 31, 36; m 59; c 2. PHYSICAL CHEMISTRY. *Educ:* Carleton Col, AB, 58; Calif Inst Technol, PhD(chem), 63. *Prof Exp:* NIH fel, Univ Wash, 62-64; fel, 64-69, ASSOC PROF CHEM, CARNEGIE-MELLON UNIV, 69- *Concurrent Pos:* Alfred P Sloan fel, 70-72. *Res:* Ultraviolet absorption of single crystals; valence structure from x-ray scattering; x-ray diffraction. *Mailing Add:* Dept of Chem 5000 Forbes Ave Pittsburgh PA 15213

STEWART, ROBERT FRANCIS, b Birmingham, Ala, Oct 31, 26; m 58; c 4. NUCLEAR CHEMISTRY, FUEL TECHNOLOGY. *Educ:* Univ Ala, BS, 49, MS, 50. *Prof Exp:* Jr chemist, Nat Southern Prod Corp, 50-52; head radioisotope lab, 63-69, RES CHEMIST, US BUR MINES, 54-, RES SUPVR, MORGANTOWN ENERGY RES CTR, 69- *Mem:* Am Chem Soc; Am Soc Testing & Mat; Instrument Soc Am. *Res:* Nuclear methods of continuous analysis of bulk materials for process control based on neutron interactions in matter. *Mailing Add:* Rte 8 Box 228E Morgantown WV 26505

STEWART, ROBERT HARRY, b Jamestown, NY, Dec 30, 17; m 42, 68; c 5. GEOLOGICAL ENGINEERING, PALEONTOLOGY. *Educ:* Miami Univ, BA, 43; Northwestern Univ, Evanston, MS, 46. *Prof Exp:* Eng aid, Spec Eng Div, Panama Canal, 46-48; geologist, Mineral Deposits Br, US Geol Surv, 48-53; hydrologist, Meteorol & Hydrographic Br, 53-55, soils engr, Eng Div, Civil Br, 55-59, geologist, 59-67, SUPVRY GEOLOGIST, ENG DIV, CIVIL BR, PANAMA CANAL CO, 67- *Concurrent Pos:* Consult eng geol, govt & indust, 57-; prof geol, Fla State Univ, Albrook Field, CZ, 62-; geologist, Bd Tech Consults, Inter Oceanic Canal Studies, 65-69; consult, Corp Desarrollo Minerales, Cerro Colorado, 76- *Mem:* Fel Geol Soc Am; Am Inst Mining, Metall & Petrol Engrs. *Res:* Coral reef in the Atlantic and Pacific Oceans, in the vicinity of Panama and the Canal Zone; geological structure of the Isthmus of Panama. *Mailing Add:* Box 279 Balboa Panama

STEWART, ROBERT HENRY, b York, Pa, Dec 26, 41; c 1. PHYSICAL OCEANOGRAPHY, RADIO SCIENCE. *Educ:* Arlington State Col, BS, 63; Univ Calif, San Diego, PhD(oceanog), 69. *Prof Exp:* Asst res oceanogr, 69-77, ASSOC RES OCEANOGR & ASSOC ADJ PROF, SCRIPPS INST OCEANOG, 77-; RES SCIENTIST, JET PROPULSION LAB, CALIF INST TECHNOL, 79- *Concurrent Pos:* Consult, NASA, 75-77. *Mem:* Am Geophys Union; Int Union Radio Sci. *Res:* Ocean waves; currents; satellite oceanography; radio scatter from the sea. *Mailing Add:* Scripps Inst of Oceanog La Jolla CA 92093

STEWART, ROBERT MURRAY, JR, b Washington, DC, May 6, 24; m 45; c 2. COMPUTER SCIENCE. *Educ:* Iowa State Col, BS, 45, PhD(physics), 54. *Prof Exp:* Instr elec eng, 46-48, asst physics, 48-50, res assoc, 50-54, from asst prof to assoc prof, 54-58, engr in charge cyclone comput lab, 56-67, assoc prof physics & elec eng, 58-60, PROF PHYSICS & ELEC ENG, IOWA STATE UNIV, 60-, ASSOC DIR COMPUT CTR, 67-, CHMN DEPT COMPUT SCI, 69- *Concurrent Pos:* Sr physicist, Ames Lab, AEC; mem bd ed consults, Electronic Assocs, Inc; consult, Midwest Res Inst; mem educ comt, Am Fedn Info Processing Socs, 68-; vchmn, Comput Sci Conf Bd, 75-76, chmn, 76- *Mem:* Am Phys Soc; Asn Comput Mach; Inst Elec & Electronics Eng; AAAS. *Res:* Design of logical control systems and digital computer systems; pattern recognition and adaptive logic. *Mailing Add:* 3416 Oakland St Ames IA 50010

STEWART, ROBERT WILLIAM, b Smoky Lake, Alta, Aug 21, 23; div; c 3. PHYSICS. *Educ:* Queen's Univ, Ont, BSc, 45, MSc, 47; Cambridge Univ, PhD(physics), 52. *Hon Degrees:* DSc, McGill Univ, 72. *Prof Exp:* Lectr physics, Queen's Univ, Ont, 46; defence sci serv officer, Pac Naval Lab Can,

50-55; from assoc prof to prof, 55-70, HON PROF PHYSICS, UNIV BC, 70-; DIR-GEN, PAC REGION, OCEAN & AQUATIC SCI, CAN DEPT FISHERIES & OCEANS, 70- *Concurrent Pos:* Vis prof, Dalhousie Univ, 60-61 & Harvard Univ, 64; distinguished vis prof, Pa State Univ, 64; Commonwealth vis prof, Cambridge Univ, 67-68; mem joint organizing comt, Global Atmospheric Res Prog, 72- *Mem:* Fel Royal Soc Can; fel Royal Soc; Can Meteorol Soc; Int Asn Phys Sci Ocean (pres, 77). *Res:* Turbulence; physical oceanography; air-sea interaction. *Mailing Add:* Ministry Univ Sci & Commun Parliament Bldgs Victoria BC V7V 1X4 Can

STEWART, ROBERTA A, b Rochester, NH, Aug 24, 23. ORGANIC CHEMISTRY. *Educ:* Univ NH, BS, 44; Smith Col, MA, 46, PhD, 49. *Prof Exp:* Res assoc chem, Smith Col, 48-49; instr, Wellesley Col, 49-53; from asst prof to assoc prof, 53-70, chmn dept chem, 63-66 & 69-73, chmn div natural sci & math, 67-73, asst to pres, 69-75, PROF CHEM, HOLLINS COL, 70-, DEAN COL, 75- *Concurrent Pos:* NSF fel, Radcliffe Col, 60-61; Am Coun on Educ fel acad admin, Univ Del, 66-67. *Mem:* AAAS; fel Am Inst Chemists; Am Chem Soc. *Res:* Synthetic experiments in direction of morphine; some reactions of beta tetralone; derivatives of cyclohexanone. *Mailing Add:* Box 9685 Hollins College VA 24020

STEWART, ROBIN KENNY, b Ayr, Scotland, May 22, 37; m 64; c 3. ANIMAL ECOLOGY. *Educ:* Glasgow Univ, BS, 61, PhD(entom), 66. *Prof Exp:* Asst lectr agr zool, Glasgow Univ, 63-66; from asst prof to assoc prof, 66-77, coordr biol sci div, 72-75, PROF ENTOM & ZOOL, MACDONALD COL, MCGILL UNIV, 77-, CHMN DEPT ENTOM, 75- *Concurrent Pos:* Consult, Can Pac Investment, 74-75 & UN Develop Proj, 75- *Mem:* Can Entom Soc; British Ecol Soc. *Res:* Agricultural zoology; ecology; entomology; integrated control. *Mailing Add:* Dept Entom Macdonald Campus McGill Univ Ste Anne de Bellevue PQ H3A 2T6 Can

STEWART, ROLLAND KEITH, aquatic biology, see previous edition

STEWART, ROSS, b Vancouver, BC, Mar 16, 24; m 46; c 2. PHYSICAL ORGANIC CHEMISTRY. *Educ:* Univ BC, BA, 46, MA, 48; Univ Wash, PhD, 54. *Prof Exp:* Lectr chem, Univ BC, 47-49; lectr, Can Serv Col, Royal Roads, 49-51, from asst prof to assoc prof, 51-55; from asst prof to assoc prof, 55-62, PROF CHEM, UNIV BC, 62- *Mem:* Fel Royal Soc Can; Am Chem Soc; fel Chem Inst Can. *Res:* Organic oxidation mechanisms; protonation of weak organic bases; general acid catalysis; ionization of weak acids in strongly basic solution. *Mailing Add:* Dept of Chem Univ of BC Vancouver BC V6T 1W5 Can

STEWART, RUTH CAROL, b Englewood, NJ, Dec 18, 28. MATHEMATICS. *Educ:* Rutgers Univ, AB, 50, MA, 63, EdD(math educ), 69. *Prof Exp:* Dir music, high sch, NJ, 50-53; instr, Wiesbaden Am High Sch, Ger, 54-57; chmn dept math, Frankfurt Am High Sch, 58-62 & 63-64; PROF MATH, MONTCLAIR STATE COL, 64- *Mem:* Math Asn Am. *Res:* Mathematics in areas of algebra and analysis; mathematics education in areas of curriculum and instruction. *Mailing Add:* Dept of Math Montclair State Col Upper Montclair NJ 07043

STEWART, SHEILA FRANCES, b Halifax, NS, Mar 16, 27. REPRODUCTIVE ENDOCRINOLOGY. *Educ:* Univ BC, BA, 48, MS, 63; Rutgers Univ, PhD(endocrinol), 69. *Prof Exp:* Scientist, 68-75, SR SCIENTIST ENDOCRINOL, WARNER-LAMBERT/PARKE-DAVIS PHARMACEUT RES DIV, 75- *Res:* Effects of underfeeding, sex, hemigonadectomy, drug and hormone treatment on pituitary secretions of gonadatropins; prostaglandin effects on the pseudopregnant ovary and pituitary secretions; neuroleptic effects on and mechanisms of prolactin secretions. *Mailing Add:* Warner-Lambert/Parke-Davis 2800 Plymouth Rd Ann Arbor MI 48106

STEWART, SHELTON E, b Sanford, NC, Oct 1, 34; m 65; c 1. BOTANY, ZOOLOGY. *Educ:* ECarolina Col, BS, 56; Univ NC, MA, 59; Univ Ga, PhD(bot), 66. *Prof Exp:* Teacher, Pine Forest High Sch, 56-57; prof sci, Ferrum Jr Col, 59; prof biol, Lander Col, 59-63; instr bot, Univ Ga, 64-65; PROF BIOL, LANDER COL, 66- *Mem:* AAAS. *Res:* Plant taxonomy; plant biosystematics. *Mailing Add:* Dept of Biol Lander Col Greenwood SC 29646

STEWART, T BONNER, b Sao Paulo, Brazil, Nov 24, 24; US citizen; m 56; c 4. VETERINARY PARASITOLOGY. *Educ:* Univ Md, BS, 49; Auburn Univ, MS, 53; Univ Ill, Urbana, PhD(vet med sci), 63. *Prof Exp:* Parasitologist, USDA, Ala, 50-53 & Ga Coastal Plain Exp Sta, 53-60; fel, Univ Ill, Urbana, 60-62; res parasitologist, Animal Parasite Res Lab, Ga Coastal Plain Exp Sta, USDA, 63-64; suprvy zoologist, 64-79; PROF PARASITOL, SCH VET MED, LA STATE UNIV, 79- *Mem:* AAAS; World Asn Advan Vet Parasitol; Am Soc Parasitol; Soc Protozool; Wildlife Dis Asn. *Res:* Life history of Cooperia punctata; gastrointestinal parasites of cattle; eradication of the kidneyworm of swine; beetles as intermediate hosts of nematodes; Strongyloides ransomi of swine; ecology of swine parasites; trans-uterine and trans-milk infection of host by nematode parasites; anthelmintics for swine and cattle parasites. *Mailing Add:* Dept Vet Microbiol & Parasitol Sch Vet Med La State Univ Baton Rouge LA 70803

STEWART, TERRY SANFORD, b West Palm Beach, Fla, Feb 28, 51; m 74; c 2. ANIMAL BREEDING, SYSTEMS ANALYSIS. *Educ:* Univ Fla, BSA, 72, MSA, 74; Tex A&M Univ, PhD(animal genetics), 77. *Prof Exp:* Grad asst animal genetics, Dept Animal Sci, Univ Fla, 73-74; res asst, Animal Sci Dept, Tex A&M Univ, 74-77; PROF ANIMAL SCI, PURDUE UNIV, 77- *Mem:* Am Soc Animal Sci; Am Genetics Asn; Biomet Soc; Am Regist Cert Animal Scientists. *Res:* Animal systems analysis; animal genetics; biometrics; species, beef cattle and swine. *Mailing Add:* Dept of Animal Sci Purdue Univ West Lafayette IN 47907

STEWART, THOMAS, b Leith, Scotland, Nov 25, 40. ORGANIC CHEMISTRY. *Educ:* Heriot-Watt Univ, BS, 63; Glasgow Univ, PhD(org chem), 66. *Prof Exp:* Fel org synthesis, Calif Inst Technol, 66-67 & Glasgow Univ, 67-68; SR SCIENTIST ORG SYNTHESIS, RES DIV, ROHM & HAAS CO, 68- *Concurrent Pos:* Res sect mgr, Polymer Technol Res. *Mem:* Am Chem Soc. *Res:* Synthesis of acrylic monomers and polymerization inhibition. *Mailing Add:* Rohm & Haas Bldg 60 5000 Richmond St Philadelphia PA 19137

STEWART, THOMAS HENRY MCKENZIE, b Hertfordshire, Eng, Aug 17, 30; Can citizen; m 60; c 4. INTERNAL MEDICINE, IMMUNOLOGY. *Educ:* Univ Edinburgh, MB, ChB, 55; FRCP(C), 62. *Prof Exp:* House officer surg, All Saints Hosp, Chatham, Eng, 55-56; house officer med, Eastern Gen Hosp, Edinburgh, Scotland, 56 & Westminster Hosp, London, Ont, 58-60; resident, Ottawa Gen Hosp, 61-62; lectr nuclear med, Univ Mich, Ann Arbor, 63-64; lectr, 64-66, asst prof, 66-72, assoc prof, 72-77, PROF MED, UNIV OTTAWA, 77- *Concurrent Pos:* Teaching fel, Path Inst, McGill Univ, 60-61; res fel hemat, Univ Ottawa, 62-63. *Mem:* Can Soc Immunol; Can Soc Clin Invest; Soc Nuclear Med; Am Asn Cancer Res. *Res:* Immunology of cancer; host-tumor relationships; immunochemotherapy of human cancer; immunology of inflammatory bowel disease. *Mailing Add:* Dept Med Univ Ottawa Cumberland St Ottawa ON K1N 5C8 Can

STEWART, THOMAS WILLIAM WALLACE, b London, Ont, June 22, 24; m 55; c 4. ACOUSTICS, ELECTRONICS. *Educ:* Univ Western Ont, BSc, 53, MSc, 55; Univ London, PhD(physics), 62. *Prof Exp:* Res assoc physics, Univ Col, Univ London, 55-57; res asst, 58-59, instr, 59-60, lectr, 60-62, asst prof, 62-74, ASSOC PROF PHYSICS, UNIV WESTERN ONT, 74- *Mem:* AAAS; Acoust Soc Am; Can Asn Physicists. *Res:* Hearing; musical and architectural acoustics. *Mailing Add:* Dept of Physics Univ of Western Ont London ON N6A 5B8 Can

STEWART, W(ARREN) E(ARL), b Whitewater, Wis, July 3, 24; m 47; c 6. TRANSPORT PHENOMENA, NUMERICAL METHODS. *Educ:* Univ Wis, BS, 45, MS, 47; Mass Inst Technol, ScD(chem eng), 51. *Prof Exp:* Instr chem eng, Mass Inst Technol, 48; proj chem engr, Sinclair Res Labs, Inc, 50-56; from asst prof to assoc prof, 56-61, chmn dept, 73-78, PROF CHEM ENG, UNIV WIS, MADISON, 61- *Concurrent Pos:* Consult & vis prof, Univ Nac de La Plata, 62; assoc ed, J Comput & Chem Eng, 77-; mem, Math Res Ctr, Univ Wis, 78- *Mem:* Am Chem Soc; fel Am Inst Chem Engrs; Sigma Xi. *Res:* Transport phenomena; chemical reactor modelling; numerical analysis; modelling of fixed-bed reactors and staged separation processes; weighted residual methods; parameter estimation from multiresponse data; boundary layer theory; pulmonary ventilation/perfusion distribution; fusion reactor engineering. *Mailing Add:* 2004 Eng Bldg 1415 Johnson Dr Univ Wis Madison WI 53706

STEWART, WELLINGTON BUEL, b Chicago, Ill, June 18, 20; m 45; c 3. PATHOLOGY. *Educ:* Univ Notre Dame, BS, 42; Univ Rochester, MD, 45. *Prof Exp:* Intern path, Strong Mem Hosp, Rochester, NY, 45-46; Rockefeller Found fel, Univ Rochester, 48-49, Veteran fel, 48-50; assoc, Columbia Univ, 50-51, asst prof, 51-54; assoc prof, Col Physicians & Surgeons, 54-60; prof & chmn dept, Col Med, Univ Ky, 60-70; dir med comput ctr, 70-75, PROF PATH, UNIV MO-COLUMBIA, 70-, DIR LABS, 75- *Concurrent Pos:* Asst pathologist, Presby Hosp, New York, 50-54, assoc attend pathologist, 54-60; chmn, Bd Registry Med Technol, 64-67. *Mem:* Am Soc Clin Pathologists; Soc Exp Biol & Med; Harvey Soc; AMA; Col Am Pathologists. *Res:* Iron metabolism; fatty liver; red cell physiology; computers in medicine. *Mailing Add:* Dept Path Univ Mo Sch Med Columbia MO 65201

STEWART, WILLIAM ANDREW, b Liberty Center, Ohio, Apr 6, 33; m 60; c 5. MEDICINE. *Educ:* Miami Univ, AB, 54; Ohio State Univ, MD, 58. *Prof Exp:* Intern, 58-65, ASST PROF NEUROSURG, STATE UNIV NY UPSTATE MED CTR, 67- *Concurrent Pos:* Reader neurosurg, Fac Health Sci, Univ Ife, Nigeria, 74-75. *Mem:* Cong Neurol Surgeons; fel Am Col Surgeons; Am Asn Neurol Surgeons. *Res:* Trigeminal nerve; head injury. *Mailing Add:* 725 Irving Ave Syracuse NY 13210

STEWART, WILLIAM CHARLES, b Guam, Jan 10, 26; m 54; c 3. STATISTICAL ANALYSIS, OPERATIONS RESEARCH. *Educ:* Cornell Univ, BSME, 46; Drexel Inst Technol, MBA, 50, MME, 53; Univ Pa, PhD(statist), 65. *Prof Exp:* Engr, Philco Corp, 46-48; engr, Schutte & Koerting Co, 48-51; prod engr, Esterbrook Pen Co, 51-57; prod supt, SKF Industs, 57-60; prod mgr, J Bishop Co, 60-61; assoc prof statist, Drexel Inst Technol, 61-67; chmn dept, 67-80, PROF STATIST, TEMPLE UNIV, 67- *Concurrent Pos:* Consult, Drexel Inst Technol, 64-67; Naval Air Develop Ctr, Warminster, Pa, 65-, USDA, Philadelphia, 66-70, Dept Educ Admin, Sch Educ, Temple Univ, 66- & Einstein Med Ctr, 67. *Mem:* Am Statist Asn. *Res:* Application of statistics to engineering problems; operations research methods particularly for scheduling problems. *Mailing Add:* Dept of Statist Temple Univ Philadelphia PA 19122

STEWART, WILLIAM HENRY, b Okalahoma City, Okla, Feb 9, 49; m 72; c 3. APPLIED STATISTICS. *Educ:* Univ Okla, BA, 71, MA, 74; Ore State Univ, PhD(statist), 79. *Prof Exp:* ASST PROF STATIST, OKLA STATE UNIV, 78 *Mem:* Am Statist Asn; Biomet Soc. *Res:* Development of statistical methods for survival experiments with grouped data; general methods for categorical data with ordered classifications. *Mailing Add:* Dept Statist Okla State Univ Stillwater OK 74078

STEWART, WILLIAM HOGUE, JR, b Mullins, SC, Dec 25, 36; m 59; c 3. SOLID STATE PHYSICS. *Educ:* The Citadel, BSEE, 59; Univ Cincinnati, MS, 61; Clemson Univ, PhD(physics), 64. *Prof Exp:* Res physicist, 66-71, sr res physicist, 71-74, RES ASSOC, MILLIKEN RES CORP, 74- *Mem:* Am Phys Soc. *Res:* Fiber physics; static electricity and ion physics; paramagnetic resonance spectroscopy; solid state diffusion; x-ray diffraction and spectroscopy; nonlinear servomechanisms; digitally controlled machine design. *Mailing Add:* PO Box 1927 Spartanburg SC 29304

STEWART, WILLIAM HUFFMAN, b Minneapolis, Minn, May 19, 21; m 46; c 2. MEDICINE. *Educ:* Univ Minn, 39-41; La State Univ, MD, 45; Am Bd Pediat, dipl, 52. *Prof Exp:* Resident pediatrician, Charity Hosp, New Orleans, 48-50; pvt pract, 50-51; epidemiologist, Commun Dis Ctr, USPHS, 51-53, actg chief heart dis control prog, 54-55, chief, 55-56, asst dir, Nat Heart Inst, 56-57, asst to surgeon gen, 57-58, chief div pub health methods, Off Surgeon Gen, 57-61 & div community health serv, 61-63, asst to spec asst to secy health & med affairs, 63-65, dir, Nat Heart Inst, 65, surgeon gen, 66-69; chancellor, 69-74, prof pediat & head dept, 73-77, HEAD DEPT PREV MED & PUB HEALTH, MED CTR, LA STATE UNIV, NEW ORLEANS, 77- *Concurrent Pos:* Mem tech adv bd, Milbank Fund & adv med bd, Leonard Wood Mem; secy, Dept of Health & Human Resources, State of La, 74-77. *Mem:* AAAS; Am Pub Health Asn; Am Acad Pediat; Am Heart Asn; Am Social Health Asn. *Res:* Epidemiology; medical administration. *Mailing Add:* La State Univ Med Ctr 1901 Perdido St New Orleans LA 70112

STEWART, WILLIAM THOMAS, b Globe, Ariz, Sept 6, 15; m 41; c 3. ORGANIC CHEMISTRY. *Educ:* Univ Ariz, BS, 37, MS, 38; Calif Inst Technol, PhD(org chem), 41. *Prof Exp:* Res chemist, Chevron Res Co Div, Standard Oil Co Calif, 41-50, sr res chemist, 50-56, supvr res chemist, 56, supvr, 56-66, sr res assoc, 66-70; RES SCIENTIST, DIV ORGANIC RES & ENG, PHELPS DODGE CORP, 70- *Mem:* Am Chem Soc; Am Inst Mining, Metall & Petrol Engrs; Am Indust & Hygiene Asn. *Res:* Exploratory and development research; lubricating oil additives; synthetic oils; engine fuel research and development; radiation effects on organic compounds; structure and properties of heavy petroleum fractions; environmental engineering and research of urban, rural and smelter areas. *Mailing Add:* Phelps Dodge Corp Suite 607 Tucson Fed Tower 32 N Stone Ave Tucson AZ 85701

STEWART, WILSON NICHOLS, b Madison, Wis, Dec 7, 17; m 41; c 2. BOTANY. *Educ:* Univ Wis, BA, 39, PhD(bot), 47; Univ Ill, MA, 46. *Prof Exp:* From instr to prof bot, Univ Ill, Urbana, 47-65; PROF BOT, UNIV ALTA, 66-, ACTG CHMN DEPT, 76- *Mem:* Bot Soc Am; Am Inst Biol Sci; Can Bot Asn. *Res:* Plant morphology; paleobotany; study of the pteridosperms; morphology of the Isoetales and their fossil ancestors. *Mailing Add:* Dept Bot Univ Alta Edmonton AB T6G 2E1 Can

STEYERMARK, AL, b St Louis, Mo, Jan 29, 04; m 41. MICROCHEMISTRY. *Educ:* Washington Univ, BS & MS, 28, PhD, 30. *Prof Exp:* Org res chemist, Thomas & Hochwalt Labs, Inc, Ohio, 31-33 & Res Lab, SC Hooker, NY, 33-36; org res chemist, Sci Dept, Hoffmann-La Roche, Inc, 36-38, head microchem dept, 38-63, chem res group chief, Res Div, 63-67, asst to vpres chem res, 67-69; VIS PROF CHEM, RUTGERS UNIV, 69- *Concurrent Pos:* Mem comt anal chem, Nat Acad Sci-Nat Res Coun, 57-61; chmn comn microchem technol, Int Union Pure & Appl Chem, 58-65; ed-in-chief, Microchem J, 62-; chmn comt microchem apparatus, Anal Div, Am Chem Soc, 47-68, Am Soc Testing & Mat, 55-68. *Honors & Awards:* Fritz Pregl Plaquette, Austrian Asn Microchem & Anal Chem, 61; A A Benedetti-Pichler Award, Am Microbiol Soc, 79. *Mem:* Fel AAAS; NY Acad Sci; fel Asn Off Anal Chemists; hon mem Am Microchem Soc (pres, 43-44); Sigma Xi. *Res:* Organic analysis; quantitative organic microanalysis. *Mailing Add:* 115 Beech St Nutley NJ 07110

STEYERMARK, JULIAN ALFRED, b St Louis, Mo, Jan 27, 09; m 37. TAXONOMIC BOTANY. *Educ:* Wash Univ, AB, 29, MS, 30, PhD(bot), 33; Harvard Univ, MA, 32. *Prof Exp:* Asst to Dr R E Woodson, Jr, Mo Bot Garden, 33-34; instr high sch, Mo, 35-37; from asst cur to cur herbarium, Chicago Natural Hist Mus, 37-58; botanist, 59-81, taxonomist, 69-81, cur herbarium, 74-81, ADV TO DIR, NAT HERBARIUM, NAT INST PARKS, MINISTRY OF ENVIRON, VENEZUELA, 81-; HON CUR, MO BOT GARDENS, 81- *Concurrent Pos:* Mem bot exped, Western Tex, 31; collector, US Forest Serv Exped, 32-35 & 36-38 & Washington Univ-Mo Bot Garden Exped, Panama, 34-35; taxonomist & ecologist, Plant Surv, US Forest Serv, Mo, 36; collector, Field Mus Natural Hist Exped, Guatemala, 39-40 & 41-42; botanist, Cinchona Mission, Ecuador, 43 & Venezuela, 43-44; mem exped, Venezuela, 43-45, 53-55 & 59-; hon res assoc, Mo Bot Garden, 48-; bot consult, Eli Lilly & Co, 56-79; vis prof, Southern Ill Univ, 59; vis cur, NY Bot Gardens, 61-65, 68-69 & 71; mem comn preserv natural areas Venezuela, Acad Phys Sci, Math & Natural Sci, 75; mem adv bd, Audubon Soc of Venezuela & trop humid forests, Sierra Club. *Honors & Awards:* Order Quetzal, Guatemala; Amigos de Venezuela, Venezuelan Orgn, 73; Order of Andres Bello & Order of Merito de Trabajo, Venezuelan Govt, 74. *Mem:* corresp mem Am Soc Plant Taxon; Asn Trop Biol (pres, 81); Int Asn Plant Taxon; hon mem Venezuelan Soc Natural Sci; hon mem Ecuadorian Inst Natural Sci. *Res:* Rubiaceae of northern South America; flora of Missouri, Guatemala, Ecuador and Venezuela; flora of Avila; National Parks of Venezuela; general flora of Venezuela; Piperaceae of Venezuela. *Mailing Add:* Ministry of Environ Bot Inst Apartado 2156 Caracas Venezuela

STEYERT, WILLIAM ALBERT, b Allentown, Pa, Sept 20, 32; m 61; c 2. PHYSICS, CRYOGENIC REFRIGERATORS. *Educ:* Mass Inst Technol, BS, 54; Calif Inst Technol, MS, 56, PhD(physics & math), 60. *Prof Exp:* Res asst physics, Calif Inst Technol, 54-60; res assoc, Univ Ill, 60-61; STAFF MEM, LOS ALAMOS NAT LAB, UNIV CALIF, 61- *Concurrent Pos:* NSF fel, Univ Tokyo, 69; adj prof, Utah State Univ, 72-; consult, Jet Propulsion Lab, Calif Inst Technol, 81- *Mem:* Fel Am Phys Soc. *Res:* Miniature cryogenic refrigerators for electronics applications; advanced cryogenic heat transfer methods; experimental cryogenic technology. *Mailing Add:* Los Alamos Nat Lab Box 1663 Los Alamos NM 87544

STIBBS, GERALD DENIKE, b Schreiber, Ont, Apr 25, 10; m 55; c 3. DENTISTRY. *Educ:* Univ Ore, BS & DMD, 31. *Prof Exp:* Chmn dept oper dent, dir dent operatory & clin coordr, Sch Dent, 48-70, exec officer, Dept Fixed Partial Dentures, 50-57, chmn dept oper dent grad prog, 50-70, prof oper dent, Sch Dent, 48-70, prof fixed partial dentures, 54-70, spec asst to dean, 70-73, prof restorative dent, 73-76, EMER PROF RESTORATIVE DENT, SCH DENT, UNIV WASH, 76-, MEM STAFF, GRAD SCH, 50- *Concurrent Pos:* Mem assoc comt dent res, Nat Res Coun Can, 45-48; consult, Madigan Army Hosp, 48-52, coun dent health, Am Dent Asn, 54-55 & Pac Northwest Labs, Battelle Mem Inst, 70-74. *Mem:* Am Dent Asn; Am Acad Restorative Dent; Am Acad Gold Foil Opers; Int Asn Dent Res; Acad Operative Dent. *Res:* Restorative dentistry; dental materials. *Mailing Add:* 6227 51st Ave NE Seattle WA 98115

STIBITZ, GEORGE ROBERT, b York, Pa, Apr 30, 04; m 30; c 2. MEDICAL RESEARCH. *Educ:* Denison Univ, PhB, 26; Union Col, NY, MS, 27; Cornell Univ, PhD(physics), 30. *Hon Degrees:* DSc, Denison Univ, 66, Keene Col, 78. *Prof Exp:* Res mathematician, Bell Tel Labs, 30-41; tech aide, Nat Defense Res Comt, 41-45; math consult, 45-66; prof, 66-73, EMER PROF PHYSIOL, DARTMOUTH MED SCH, 73- *Honors & Awards:* Harry Goode Award, Am Fedn Info Processing Socs; Emanuel Piore Award, Inst Elec & Electronic Engrs, 78. *Res:* Computing devices; automatic control and stability; dynamic testing; logical design of computers; electronic music; mathematical and computer models of biomedical systems; computer programs for radiation therapy dosage; mathematical and computer models of physiological systems; passive electrical properties of cardiac cells; computer model of molecular motion in slits of capillaries. *Mailing Add:* Dept of Physiol Dartmouth Med Sch Hanover NH 03755

STICH, HANS F, b Prague, Czech, Dec 24, 27; Can citizen; m 55; c 1. CELL BIOLOGY, GENETICS. *Educ:* Univ Würzburg, PhD(zool), 49. *Prof Exp:* Res assoc cell biol, Max Planck Inst Marine Biol, 50-57; assoc prof cancer res unit, Nat Cancer Inst Can, 57-60; from assoc prof to prof genetics, Queen's Univ, Ont, 60-66; prof biol & chmn dept, McMaster Univ, 66-70; PROF ZOOL, UNIV BC, 70-, ACTG DIR, CANCER RES UNIT, 76- *Concurrent Pos:* Fulbright grants, Univ Wis & Western Reserve Univ, 55-57; vis prof, Med Ctr, Stanford Univ, 58, Univ Tex MD Anderson Hosp & Tumor Inst, 61 & Roswell Park Mem Inst, 64. *Mem:* Am Soc Cell Biol; Am Soc Human Genetics; Am Asn Cancer Res; NY Acad Sci; Can Soc Cell Biol (pres, 66). *Res:* Cytogenetic studies of virus, x-ray and chemically induced neoplastic cells; immunological studies on virus induced neoplastic cells using fluorescein and ferritin conjugated antibodies; regulation of gene activity; DNA repair; in vitro bioassays for carcinogens. *Mailing Add:* Cancer Res Ctr Univ of BC Vancouver BC V6T 1W5 Can

STICHA, ERNEST AUGUST, b Baltimore, Md, Mar 27, 11; m 39; c 2. METALLURGICAL ENGINEERING. *Educ:* Ill Inst Technol, BS, 33; Univ Mich, MSE, 36. *Prof Exp:* Supv engr, Crane Co, 36-59; chief metallurgist, Edward Valves, Inc Div, Rockwell Mfg Co, 59-65; sr res engr, Am Oil Co, 65-76; RETIRED. *Concurrent Pos:* Consult, 76- *Mem:* Am Soc Testing & Mat; Am Soc Metals. *Res:* Creep of metals; metallurgy of high temperature materials. *Mailing Add:* 715 N Kensington Ave LaGrange Park IL 60525

STICHT, FRANK DAVIS, b Plattsburg, Miss, June 14, 19; m 41; c 2. PHARMACOLOGY. *Educ:* Univ Miss, BS Pharm, 48; Baylor Univ, DDS, 56; Univ Tenn, Memphis, MS, 65. *Prof Exp:* From instr to assoc prof, 61-79, PROF PHARMACOL, UNIV TENN CTR HEALTH SCI, MEMPHIS, 79- *Mem:* Am Soc Pharmacol & Exp Therapeut. *Res:* Autonomic and cardiovascular pharmacology; influence of drugs on the blood pressure within the tooth pulp; relationship of prostaglandins to periodontal disease. *Mailing Add:* Dept of Pharmacol Univ of Tenn Ctr for Health Sci Memphis TN 38163

STICKEL, DELFORD LEFEW, b Falling Waters, WVa, Dec 12, 27; m 52; c 1. SURGERY. *Educ:* Duke Univ, AB, 49, MD, 53; Am Bd Surg, dipl, 63; Bd Thoracic Surg, dipl, 63. *Prof Exp:* Asst surg, 57-59, from instr to assoc prof, 59-72, PROF SURG, MED CTR, DUKE UNIV, 72-, ASSOC DIR HOSP, 72- *Concurrent Pos:* Markle scholar & NIH career develop award, 62; attend physician, Durham Vet Admin Hosp, 65-66, chief surg serv, 66-68, chief of staff, 70-72; consult, Watts Hosp, Durham, 66- & NC Eye & Human Tissue Bank, 69. *Mem:* AAAS; AMA; Am Fedn Clin Res; Soc Cryobiol; Am Col Surgeons. *Res:* Clinical renal transplantation. *Mailing Add:* Dept of Surg Duke Univ Med Ctr Durham NC 27710

STICKEL, WILLIAM HENSON, b Terre Haute, Ind, Nov 8, 12; m 41. WILDLIFE RESEARCH, POLLUTION BIOLOGY. *Educ:* Univ Mich, BS, 34, MA, 35. *Prof Exp:* Asst zool, Univ Mich, 35-40; jr biologist, US Civil Serv Comn, DC, 40-41; RES BIOLOGIST, PATUXENT RES CTR, US FISH & WILDLIFE SERV, 41- *Concurrent Pos:* Ed, Wildlife Rev, 52-59. *Mem:* Wildlife Soc; Am Soc Mammal. *Res:* Effects of pesticides and pollutants on wildlife and habitat. *Mailing Add:* Patuxent Res Ctr US Fish & Wildlife Serv Laurel MD 20811

STICKER, ROBERT EARL, b New York, NY, Mar 4, 30; m 57; c 3. ORGANIC CHEMISTRY. *Educ:* Cornell Univ, AB, 53; Columbia Univ, AM, 57; Univ Kans, PhD(pinane chem), 65. *Prof Exp:* Res chemist, Eastman Kodak Co, 57-60; res chemist, 65-76, SR RES CHEMIST, NIAGARA CHEM DIV, FMC CORP, 76- *Mem:* Am Chem Soc; Int Soc Heterocyclic Chem. *Res:* Terpenes; heterocycles; surfactants; herbicides; plant regulators; fungicides. *Mailing Add:* Res & Develop Agr Chem Group FMC Corp 100 Niagara St Middleport NY 14105

STICKLAND, DAVID PETER, b Norwich, Eng, Aug 22, 54; m 79; c 1. ELEMENTARY PARTICLE PHYSICS. *Educ:* Univ Bradford, BTech, 77; Univ Bristol, PhD(physics), 81. *Prof Exp:* Res asst, 80-81, INSTR PHYSICS, PRINCETON UNIV, 81- *Mem:* Am Phys Soc. *Res:* Dimuon production by pions in nuclear targets. *Mailing Add:* Dept Physics Jodwin Hall Joseph Henry Labs Princeton Univ PO Box 708 Princeton NJ 08540

STICKLE, GENE P, b New Castle, Pa, Apr 11, 29; m 54; c 2. CHEMICAL ENGINEERING. *Educ:* Univ Tenn, BS, 53, MS, 54. *Prof Exp:* Res engr, Squibb Inst Med Res, Olin Mathieson Chem Corp, 54-61, sect head, Fermentation Mfg Dept, E R Squibb & Sons, 61-62, sect head microbiol develop pilot plant, Squibb Inst Med Res, 62-66, sect head chem develop pilot plant, 67-69, asst dept dir chem develop, 69-74, antibiotics mfg develop mgr, 74-77, dir antibiotics process eng, 77-81, TECH ENG DIR, E R SQUIBB & SONS, INC, 81- *Mem:* Am Chem Soc; Am Inst Chem Eng; Sigma Xi. *Res:* Fermentation technology, scaleup, process design and development; plant start-up and manufacture of antibiotics, steroids, vitamins and enzymes; technical liaison; organic synthetics manufacture. *Mailing Add:* PO Box 4000 Princeton NJ 08540

STICKLER, DAVID BRUCE, b Taunton, Mass, Nov 17, 41; m 64; c 2. COMBUSTION, FLUID MECHANICS. *Educ:* Mass Inst Technol, SB & SM, 64, PhD(hybrid combustion), 68. *Prof Exp:* Asst prof aeronaut & astronaut, Mass Inst Technol, 68-73; res scientist, 73-78, CHMN AEROPHYS, AVCO EVERETT RES LAB, INC, 78- *Mem:* Combustion Inst; Am Inst Aeron & Astron. *Res:* Heterogeneous combustion; turbulent combustion and flow; coal combustion and gasification; hybrid combustion; slag flow in power systems; polymer pyrolysis. *Mailing Add:* 2385 Revere Beach Pkwy Everett MA 02149

STICKLER, DAVID COLLIER, b Piqua, Ohio, Apr 12, 33; c 4. ACOUSTICS, APPLIED MATHEMATICS. *Educ:* Ohio State Univ, BSc, 56, MSc, 59, PhD(elec eng), 64. *Prof Exp:* Res assoc elec eng, Ohio State Univ, 55-65; mem tech staff, Bell Tel Labs, Inc, 65-72; sr engr, Systs Control, Inc, 72-73; sr res assoc, Pa State Univ, 73-77; sr res scientist, 77-80, RES PROF, NY UNIV, 80- *Res:* Electromagnetic theory; heat transfer; thermoelastic effects mechanics. *Mailing Add:* Courant Inst of Math Sci NY Univ New York NY 10012

STICKLER, FRED CHARLES, b Villisca, Iowa, Dec 11, 31; m 55; c 3. AGRONOMY, CROP ECOLOGY. *Educ:* Iowa State Univ, BS, 53, PhD, 58; Kans State Univ, MS, 55. *Prof Exp:* From asst prof to assoc prof agron, Kans State Univ, 58-64; res agronomist, 64-71, prod planner, 71-73, mgr agr equip planning, 73-76, dir, Tech Ctr, 76-80, DIR, PROD & MKT PLANNING, DEERE & CO, 80- *Res:* Ecological aspects of crop production and management; crop management for improved mechanization. *Mailing Add:* Deere & Co Tech Ctr Moline IL 61265

STICKLER, GUNNAR B, b Peterskirchen, Ger, June 13, 25; US citizen; m 56; c 2. MEDICINE, PEDIATRICS. *Educ:* Univ Vienna, MD, 49; Univ Minn, PhD(pediat), 58; Am Bd Pediat, cert, 57, cert pediat & nephrol, 74. *Prof Exp:* Resident clin path, Krankenhaus III Orden, Munich, 50; resident path, Univ Munich, 50-51; intern, Mountainside Hosp, Montclair, 51-52; resident fel pediat, Mayo Found Grad Sch, 53-56; chief pediat, US Army Hosp, Munich, 56; sr res scientist, Roswell Park Mem, Buffalo, 56-57; instr pediat, Univ Buffalo, 57; resident asst to staff, Mayo Clin, 57-58, from instr to prof pediat, Mayo Found Grad Sch, 58-73, sect head pediat, 69-74, prof pediat & chmn dept, 74-80, CONSULT PEDIAT, MAYO CLIN, 58- *Mem:* Am Acad Pediat; Soc Pediat Res; Am Soc Nephrol; Int Soc Nephrol; Am Soc Pediat. *Res:* Hypophosphatemic and various other forms of rickets; nephrotic syndrome; immunology of renal disease; growth failure in various disease processes; treatment of acute otitis media; hereditary bone diseases; urinary tract infection; natural history studies in chronic diseases; inflammatory bowel disease. *Mailing Add:* Dept of Pediat Mayo Clin Rochester MN 55901

STICKLER, MITCHELL GENE, b Fairmont, WVa, Sept 19, 34; m 60; c 5. COMPUTER SCIENCE, SOFTWARE SYSTEMS FOR HOSPITALS. *Educ:* Univ West Va, BS, 60; Univ Pittsburgh, MS, 62. *Prof Exp:* Engr, Westinghouse Elec Corp, 60-62; mem tech staff, Bell Tel Labs, 62-64, supvr electronics, 64-66, info systs, 66-68; vpres & mem bd dirs, Virtual Comput Serv, Inc, NJ, 68-70; systs consult, 70-77, dir eng, 77-80, DIR PLUS PROD, PENTAMATION ENTERPRISES, INC, BETHLEHEM, 80- *Mem:* Inst Elec & Electronics Engrs. *Res:* Semiconductor device theory; integrated circuit design; information systems; process and inventory control; time sharing operating systems; telecommunications; multiprocessor design and microcoding; real-time hospital data base systems. *Mailing Add:* RD2 BOX 31AA Schnecksville PA 18078

STICKLER, WILLIAM CARL, b Stuttgart, Ger, Jan 25, 18; nat US; m 42, 58, 68; c 4. ORGANIC CHEMISTRY. *Educ:* Columbia Univ, AB, 41, AM, 44, PhD(chem), 47. *Prof Exp:* Asst chem, Columbia Univ, 41-44, 46-47; from asst prof to assoc prof, 47-63, actg chmn dept, 71-72, PROF CHEM, UNIV DENVER, 63- *Concurrent Pos:* Instr, Sarah Lawrence Col, 43-44 & Hofstra Col, 46-47; vis prof & lectr, Univ Munich & Munich Tech Univ, 56-58; NSF fac fel, 57-58. *Mem:* Am Chem Soc; Royal Soc Chem; Soc German Chem; Sigma Xi. *Res:* Organic nitrogen chemistry; stereochemistry; reaction mechanisms; natural products and physiologically important compounds. *Mailing Add:* Dept of Chem Univ of Denver Denver CO 80210

STICKLEY, C(ARLISLE) MARTIN, b Washington, DC, Oct 30, 33; m 58; c 3. ELECTRO-OPTICS, MATERIALS. *Educ:* Univ Cincinnati, BSEE, 57; Mass Inst Technol, MSEE, 58; Northeastern Univ, PhD, 64. *Prof Exp:* Mem transistor circuits br, Commun Sci Lab, Air Force Cambridge Res Lab, Laurence G Hanscom Field, Mass, 58-62, laser physics br, 62-65, chief laser physics br, Optical Physics Lab, 65-71; dir mat sci off, Defense Advan Res Proj Agency, Dept Defense, 71-76; dir inertial confinement fusion, US Dept Energy, 76-79; VPRES ADVAN TECHNOL, BDM CORP, 79- *Concurrent Pos:* Vis prof, Univ Rio Grande do Sul, Brazil, 66; assoc mem spec group optical masers, comt laser coord, Dept of Defense, 64-71; prog chmn, Third Classified Conf Laser Tech, 67; co-chmn, Conf Laser Eng & Appln, 71; chmn, Inst Elec & Electronics Engrs, OSA Conf Inertial Fusion, 78. *Honors & Awards:* O'Day Award, Air Force Cambridge Res Lab, 68, Meritorious Civilian Serv Medal, Dept Defense, 76. *Mem:* Fel Inst Elec & Electronics Engrs; Sigma Xi; Soc Photo-Optical Instrumentation Engrs. *Res:* Optical fibers, sources and couplers; inertial confinement fusion; electro optical and semiconductor materials; laser devices; optical processing; communications technol; optical fiber sensors; advanced nuclear reactors. *Mailing Add:* 8108 Horseshoe Lane Potomac MD 20854

STICKNEY, ALDEN PARKHURST, b Providence, RI, Sept 7, 22; m 51; c 2. MARINE ECOLOGY. *Educ:* Univ RI, BSc, 48; Harvard Univ, MA, 51. *Prof Exp:* Fishery aide, US Fish & Wildlife Serv, 51-53; res asst, Stirling Sch Med, Yale Univ, 53-54; chief Atlantic salmon invest, US Fish & Wildlife Serv, 54-60, fishery res biologist, Fishery Biol Lab, Bur Com Fisheries, Maine, 60-72 & Biol Lab, Nat Marine Fisheries Serv, 72-73; MARINE RESOURCES SCIENTIST, MAINE DEPT MARINE RESOURCES, 74- *Mem:* Ecol Soc Am; Am Fisheries Soc. *Res:* Estuarine ecology; shellfish biology; physiology of larval shellfish; behavior and ecology of sea herring and pandalid shrimp. *Mailing Add:* Biol Lab Maine Dept of Marine Resources Boothbay Harbor ME 04575

STICKNEY, JANICE LEE, b Tallahassee, Fla, July 21, 41. PHARMACOLOGY, CARDIOVASCULAR PHYSIOLOGY. *Educ:* Oberlin Col, AB, 62; Univ Mich, PhD(pharmacol), 67. *Prof Exp:* Acad Senate grants, Univ Calif, San Francisco, 68 & 69, from instr to asst prof pharmacol, Sch Med, 69-72; asst prof pharmacol, Mich State Univ, 72-75, assoc prof, 75-81, prof, 81; SR SCIENTIST, G D SEARLE & CO, 81- *Concurrent Pos:* Training fel, 67-68; Bay Area Heart Asn grant, Univ Calif, San Francisco, 69-70; Nat Heart & Lung Inst, Nat Inst Drug Abuse & Mich Heart Asn grants; consult, Food & Drug Admin, 71-75 & 76-80; mem, Special Study Sect, NIH, 78-79, Nat Adv Environ Health Sci Coun, 79-82; panelist, NSF, 76 & 81. *Mem:* AAAS; Pharmacol Soc Can; NY Acad Sci; Am Soc Pharmacol & Exp Therapeut. *Res:* Cardiovascular pharmacology, especially role of the sympathetic nervous system in the cardiac arrhythmias produced by large doses of digitalis, with emphasis on the mechanisms by which cardiac glycosides produce sympathetic effects; general cardiovascular effects of narcotic analgesics; antiarrhythmic drugs. *Mailing Add:* Searle Res & Develop Div G D Searle & Co Box 5110 Chicago IL 60680

STICKNEY, JOSEPH BURNS, b Cleveland, Ohio, July 14, 19; m 42; c 1. ELECTRICAL ENGINEERING. *Educ:* Western Reserve Univ, AB, 41; Case Inst Technol, BS, 42. *Prof Exp:* Proj engr, US Naval Res Labs, 43-46; sr engr, Victoreen Instrument Co, 46-48, chief engr, 49-53; elec eng, 53-56, chief engr, Nuclear Instrument Dept, 56-61, mgr, 61-66, THER EQUIP OPERS MGR, NUCLEAR INSTRUMENT DEPT, PICKER X-RAY CORP, CLEVELAND, 67- *Mem:* Assoc Soc Nuclear Med. *Res:* Radar circuit development; design of instruments for measuring x-rays and radiations from radioactive substances; x-ray equipment design. *Mailing Add:* Picker X-Ray Corp 5201 Naimah Pkwy Cleveland OH 44139

STICKNEY, PALMER BLAINE, b Columbus, Ohio, Nov 1, 15; m 37; c 4. POLYMER CHEMISTRY. *Educ:* Ohio State Univ, AB, 38, PhD(phys chem), 49. *Prof Exp:* Res engr, Battelle Mem Inst, 40-42, 46, 49-52, asst chief, Rubber & Plastics Div, 52-60, chief polymer res, 60-68, tech adv, 68-73; prof, Wilberforce Univ, 73-81; RETIRED. *Mem:* Am Chem Soc; Am Asn Univ Profs. *Res:* Polymerization and processing of polymers. *Mailing Add:* 2870 Halstead Rd Columbus OH 43221

STICKSEL, PHILIP RICE, b Cincinnati, Ohio, Feb 15, 30; m 53; c 2. METEOROLOGY. *Educ:* Univ Cincinnati, BS, 52; Fla State Univ, MS, 59, PhD(meteorol), 66. *Prof Exp:* Jr develop engr, Goodyear Aircraft Corp, 53-54; res assoc meteorol, Fla State Univ, 64-65; res meteorologist, Environ Sci Serv Admin, 65-69 & Nat Air Pollution Control Admin, 67-69; SR METEOROLOGIST, BATTELLE MEM INST, 69- *Mem:* Am Meteorol Soc; Air Pollution Control Asn. *Res:* Air pollution meteorology and education; upper atmosphere ozone; air quality management; ozone transport; visible emissions. *Mailing Add:* 563 Mohican Way Westerville OH 43081

STIDD, BENTON MAURICE, b Bloomington, Ind, June 30, 36; m 58; c 4. PALEOBOTANY. *Educ:* Purdue Univ, BS, 58; Emporia Kans State Col, MS, 63; Univ Ill, PhD(bot), 68. *Prof Exp:* Teacher, Wheatland High Sch, 58-62; partic, NSF Acad Year Inst & Res Participation Prog Teachers, Kans State Teachers Col, 62-63; teacher, NKnox High Sch, 63-64; asst prof anat, morphol & paleobot, Univ Minn, Minneapolis, 68-70; PROF & CHMN BIOL SCI, WESTERN ILL UNIV, 70- *Concurrent Pos:* Univ Minnesota Grad Sch res grant, 68-69; Sigma Xi res grants-in-aid, 69-70; res coun grant, Western Ill Univ, 71-72, 80-81; NSF res grant, 74 & 76. *Mem:* AAAS; Am Asn Univ Prof; Bot Soc Am; Int Orgn Paleobot; Philos Sci Asn. *Res:* Paleozoic paleobotany, especially Carboniferous coal ball plants. *Mailing Add:* Dept of Biol Sci Western Ill Univ Macomb IL 61455

STIDD, CHARLES KETCHUM, b Independence, Ore, Aug 12, 18; m 42; c 2. METEOROLOGY. *Educ:* Ore State Univ, BS, 41. *Prof Exp:* Res forecaster, US Weather Bur, 47-55; self employed, 55-62; res assoc meteorol & hydrol, Univ Nev, Reno, 62-71; specialist meteorol, Scripps Inst Oceanog, Univ Calif, San Diego, 71-79; CONSULT, 79- *Mem:* Am Meteorol Soc; Am Geophys Union. *Res:* Rainfall and climatic probabilities; general circulation of the atmosphere; moisture, energy and momentum balances; long-range forecasting. *Mailing Add:* 3753 Fairway Dr La Mesa CA 92041

STIDHAM, HOWARD DONATHAN, b Memphis, Tenn, Sept 14, 25; div. PHYSICAL CHEMISTRY. *Educ:* Trinity Col, BS, 50; Mass Inst Technol, PhD, 55. *Prof Exp:* Spectroscopist, Dewey & Almy Chem Co, 55-56; asst prof, 56-71, ASSOC PROF CHEM, UNIV MASS, 71- *Mem:* AAAS; Optical Soc Am; Am Chem Soc. *Res:* Molecular spectroscopy; statistical mechanics. *Mailing Add:* Dept of Chem Univ of Mass Amherst MA 01003

STIDHAM, SHALER, JR, b Washington, DC, Dec 4, 41; m 68; c 3. OPERATIONS RESEARCH, MARKOV DECISION PROCESSES. *Educ:* Harvard Col, BA, 63; Case Inst Technol, MS, 64; Stanford Univ, PhD(opers res), 68. *Prof Exp:* Asst prof opers res & environ eng, Cornell Univ, 68-75; assoc prof, 75-79, PROF INDUST ENG & OPERS RES, NC STATE UNIV, 79- *Concurrent Pos:* Consult, Stanford Res Inst, Calif, 68-70; vis prof, Aarhus Univ, 71-72 & Tech Univ Denmark, 77; vis scholar, Stanford Univ, 75-79; consult, Bell Tel Lab, NJ, 81; assoc ed, Operations Res, 76 & Mgt Sci, 75-81; prin investr, NSF, 73-75, 79-82, NATO Army Res Off, 81. *Honors & Awards:* Young Scientist Res Award, Sigma xi, 78. *Mem:* Assoc mem Opers Res Soc

Am; Inst Mgt Sci; Am Inst Indust Eng; Sigma Xi. *Res:* Queuing theory; optimal design and control of queueing systems; applications in industrial job shops; transportation and public service systems; computer and communication systems. *Mailing Add:* Dept of Indust Eng Box 551 NC State Univ Raleigh NC 27650

STIDWORTHY, GEORGE H, b Viborg, SDak, May 28, 24; m 48; c 4. BIOCHEMISTRY. *Educ:* Univ SDak, BA, 49, MA, 51; Univ Okla, PhD(biochem), 61. *Prof Exp:* Chemist, Rayonier Corp, 46-47; res asst biochem, Okla Med Res Found, 51-53; asst chief, Gen Med Res Lab, Vet Admin Hosp, Oklahoma City, 53-57, chief biochemist, 57-59; chief biochemist, Cancer Res Lab, Vet Admin Hosp, Martinsburg, WVa, 59-64; supvr, Med Res Lab, 64-72, CHIEF GEN MED RES LAB, VET ADMIN HOSP, 72-; ASST PROF BIOCHEM, SCH MED, BOSTON UNIV, 64- *Concurrent Pos:* Nat Cancer Inst grant, Vet Admin Hosp, Martinsburg, WVa, 61-65. *Mem:* AAAS; Geront Soc; Tissue Cult Asn; Am Aging Asn. *Res:* Aging effects upon connective tissues; chemistry and biology of the intracellular matrix; in vitro aging of cells in culture; environmental effects in cell metabolism. *Mailing Add:* Res Lab Vet Admin Hosp 200 Springs Rd Bedford MA 01730

STIEBER, MICHAEL THOMAS, b Peoria, Ill, Dec 6, 43; m 78. SYSTEMATIC BOTANY, AGROSTOLOGY. *Educ:* Cath Univ Am, AB, 66, MS, 67; Univ Md, College Park, PhD(syst bot), 75. *Prof Exp:* Teacher biol, Bishop McNamara High Sch, Kankakee, Ill, 67-69; grad teaching asst gen bot & plant taxon, Univ Md, 70-74; teacher biol & advan placement biol, St Viator High Sch, Arlington Heights, Ill, 74-77; ARCHIVIST & SR RES SCIENTIST, HUNT INST BOT DOC, CARNEGIE-MELLON UNIV, 77-, RES ASSOC, CARNEGIE MUS NATURAL HIST, 78- *Concurrent Pos:* NSF reviewer, Sect Agrost, 78- *Mem:* Am Soc Plant Taxon; Soc Bibliog Natural Hist; Soc Am Archivists; Int Asn Plant Taxon; Asn Trop Biol. *Res:* History of botany; archival methods and practice; taxonomy of Ichnanthus paniceae; botanical history and documentation. *Mailing Add:* Hunt Inst Bot Doc Carnegie-Mellon Univ Pittsburgh PA 15213

STIEF, LOUIS J, b Pottsville, Pa, July 26, 33; m 63; c 2. PHOTOCHEMISTRY, ASTROCHEMISTRY. *Educ:* La Salle Col, BA, 55; Cath Univ, PhD(chem), 60. *Prof Exp:* Asst chem, Cath Univ, 55-59; Nat Acad Sci-Nat Res Coun res fel, Nat Bur Standards, 60-61; NATO fel, Univ Sheffield, 61-62, Dept Sci & Indust Res fel, 62-63; sr chemist, Res Div, Melpar, Inc, 63-65, sr scientist, 65-68; Nat Acad Sci-Nat Res Coun sr res fel, 68-69, aerospace technol chemist, 69-74, head, Space Chem Sect, 74-76, HEAD, ASTROCHEM BR, GODDARD SPACE FLIGHT CTR, NASA, 76- *Concurrent Pos:* Adj prof, Dept Chem, Cath Univ Am, DC, 75- *Mem:* Am Phys Soc; Am Chem Soc; Royal Soc Chem; Sigma Xi; Am Astron Soc. *Res:* Vacuum-ultraviolet photochemistry; flash photolysis; interstellar molecules; upper atmosphere studies; planetary atmospheres; chemical kinetics. *Mailing Add:* Code 691 NASA/Goddard Space Flight Ctr Greenbelt MD 20770

STIEGLER, JAMES OTTOMAR, b Valparaiso, Ind, July 25, 34; m 66; c 2. HIGH TEMPERATURE MATERIALS. *Educ:* Purdue Univ, BS, 56; Univ Tenn, PhD(metall eng), 71. *Prof Exp:* Res asst, Solid State Div, 56-61, res staff mem, Metals & Ceramics Div, 61-63, group leader electron microscopy, 63-73, group leader radiation effects & microstructural anal, 73-78, mgr, Mat Sci Sect, 78-81, MGR, PROCESSING SCI & TECHNOL SECT, METALS & CERAMICS DIV, OAK RIDGE NAT LAB, 81- *Honors & Awards:* William Sparagen Award, Am Welding Soc, 75; McKay-Helm Award, Am Welding Soc, 79. *Mem:* Fel Am Soc Metals; Am Soc Testing & Mats. *Res:* Design and production of metallic and ceramic materials for high temperature applications through control of processing variables. *Mailing Add:* Oak Ridge Nat Lab PO Box X Oak Ridge TN 37830

STIEGLER, T(HEODORE) DONALD, b Baltimore, Md, May 28, 34; m 57; c 2. PROCESS ENGINEERING, MECHANICAL ENGINEERING. *Educ:* Duke Univ, BSME, 56. *Prof Exp:* Engr, E I du Pont de Nemours & Co, 58-63, res engr, 63-65, tech supvr, 65-66, res engr, Spruance Film Tech Lab, 66-73, SR ENGR, POLYMER PROD DEPT, E I DU PONT DE NEMOURS & CO, 73- *Res:* Mechanical development associated with the chemical industry; design and development of high speed web handling machinery and equipment for the coating of plastic films; process development associated with the manufacture of packaging films. *Mailing Add:* 8700 Brown Summit Rd Richmond VA 23235

STIEGLITZ, RONALD DENNIS, b Milwaukee, Wis, Aug 25, 41; m 65; c 4. GEOLOGY. *Educ:* Univ Wis-Milwaukee, BS, 63; Univ Ill, Urbana, MS, 67, PhD(geol), 70. *Prof Exp:* Teaching asst geol, Univ Wis-Milwaukee, 63-64 & Univ Ill, 64-69; lectr, Univ Wis-Milwaukee, 71-72; geologist, Ohio State Geol Surv, 72-74, head, Regional Geol Sect, Ohio DNR Div, 74-76; asst prof, 76-81, ASSOC PROF ENVIRON SCI, UNIV WIS-GREEN BAY, 81- *Concurrent Pos:* Consult, 81- *Mem:* AAAS; Soc Econ Paleont & Mineral; Sigma Xi; Am Water Resources Asn. *Res:* Economic mineral and land capability investigations; subsurface stratigraphy; waste disposal and ground water pollution in Karst areas; application of scanning electron microscopy to sedimentologic problems; quaternary geology. *Mailing Add:* Col of Environ Sci Univ of Wis ES-317 Green Bay WI 54302

STIEHL, RICHARD BORG, b Chicago, Ill, Jan 10, 42; m 67; c 1. BIOLOGY. *Educ:* Southern Ore State Col, BS, 69, MS, 70; Portland State Univ, PhD(environ sci & biol), 78. *Prof Exp:* Instr biol, Mt Hood Community Col, 72-73; lectr, Lewis & Clark Col, 74-75; lectr biol, 77-80, ASST PROF BIOL, UNIV WIS-GREEN BAY, 80- *Concurrent Pos:* Researcher, US Fish & Wildlife Serv, 75-77; fel, Lilly Endowment, Inc, 78-79. *Mem:* Am Inst Biol Sci; Am Soc Mammalogists; Am Ornithologists Union. *Res:* Wildlife ecology; corvid biology; preditor-prey interactions. *Mailing Add:* Col of Environ Sci Univ of Wis Green Bay WI 54302

STIEHL, ROY THOMAS, JR, b Hay Springs, Nebr, Jan 27, 28; m 54; c 3. POLYMER CHEMISTRY. *Educ:* Univ Nebr, BS, 50, MS, 51; Univ Ill, PhD(org chem), 53. *Prof Exp:* Asst, Univ Nebr, 49-51 & Off Rubber Reserv, Univ Ill, 51-53; res chemist, 53-68, SR RES CHEMIST, E I DU PONT DE NEMOURS & CO, INC, 68- *Res:* Spandex chemistry; butadiene copolymerization; vinyl monomer synthesis; organophosphorous compounds; textile compounds; textile chemistry. *Mailing Add:* 400 Ridge Circle Waynesboro VA 22980

STIEHM, E RICHARD, b Milwaukee, Wis, Jan 22, 33; m 58; c 3. PEDIATRICS, ALLERGY IMMUNOLOGY. *Educ:* Univ Wis-Madison, BS, 54, MD, 57. *Prof Exp:* USPHS fels, physiol chem, Univ Wis, 58-59 & pediat immunol, Univ Calif, San Francisco, 63-65; from asst prof to assoc prof pediat, Med Sch, Univ Wis, 65-69; assoc prof, 69-72, PROF PEDIAT, SCH MED, UNIV CALIF, LOS ANGELES, 72- *Concurrent Pos:* Markle scholar acad med, 67. *Honors & Awards:* Ross res award pediat res, 71; E Mead Johnson Award pediat res, 74. *Mem:* Am Acad Pediat; Am Soc Clin Invest; Soc Pediat Res; Am Asn Immunologists; Am Pediat Soc. *Res:* Pediatric immunology, immunodeficiency disease; newborn defense mechanisms; human gamma globulin; immunology of malnutrition; clinical immunology. *Mailing Add:* Dept of Pediat Univ of Calif Ctr Health Sci Los Angeles CA 90024

STIEL, EDSEL FORD, b Los Angeles, Calif, Dec 19, 33. MATHEMATICS. *Educ:* Univ Calif, Los Angeles, AB, 55, MA, 59, PhD(math), 63. *Prof Exp:* Math analyst, Douglas Aircraft Co, Calif, 55-56, comput analyst, 57-59; sr math analyst, Lockheed Missiles & Space Co, 60; from asst prof to assoc prof, 62-72, chmn dept, 62-74, PROF MATH, CALIF STATE UNIV, FULLERTON, 72- *Mem:* Am Math Soc; Math Asn Am. *Res:* Isometric immersions of Riemannian manifolds; differential geometry. *Mailing Add:* Dept of Math Calif State Univ 800 N State Col Fullerton CA 92634

STIEL, LEONARD IRWIN, b Paterson, NJ, Sept 17, 37; m 75; c 2. APPLIED PHYSICAL CHEMISTRY, THERMODYNAMICS. *Educ:* Mass Inst Technol, SB, 59; Northwest Univ, MS, 60, PhD(chem eng), 63. *Prof Exp:* From asst prof to assoc prof chem eng, Syracuse Univ, 62-69; assoc prof chem eng, Univ Mo-Columbia, 69-72; res chem engr, Spec Chem Div, Allied Chem Corp, 72-79; sr process engr, APV Co, Inc, 79-80; ASSOC PROF CHEM ENG, POLYTECH INST NY, 80- *Concurrent Pos:* Vis scholar, Northwestern Univ, 62. *Mem:* Am Inst Chem Eng; Am Chem Soc. *Res:* Energy conversion. *Mailing Add:* 46 Bond Ave Malverne NY 11505

STIELER, CAROL MAE, b Albert Lea, Minn, June 18, 46; m 73. GENETICS, IMMUNOBIOLOGY. *Educ:* Iowa State Univ, BS, 68, MS, 70, PhD(immunobiol), 78. *Prof Exp:* RES DIR, HY-VIGOR SEEDS INC, 78- *Mem:* Am Genetic Asn; AAAS. *Res:* Genetics of laboratory mice, horses and humans; immunology, typing, inheritance and structure of dog and human red cell antigens; antibody formation; lectins; soybean variety development. *Mailing Add:* RR Box 26 Rembrandt IA 50576

STIEN, HOWARD M, b Montevideo, Minn, Apr 11, 26; m 47; c 2. ZOOLOGY, PHYSIOLOGY. *Educ:* Northwestern Col, Minn, BA, 56; Macalester Col, MA, 58; Univ Wyo, PhD(physiol), 63. *Prof Exp:* Instr biol, Pepperdine Col, 58-60; asst prof zool, Univ Wyo, 61-64; assoc prof biol, Northwestern Col, Minn, 64-65; assoc prof, 65-72, PROF BIOL, WHITWORTH COL, WASH, 72-, CHMN DEPT, 65- *Mem:* AAAS. *Res:* Immunogenetics, especially the ontogeny of molecular individuality. *Mailing Add:* Dept of Biol Whitworth Col Spokane WA 99251

STIENING, RAE FRANK, b Pittsburgh, Pa, May 26, 37. HIGH ENERGY PHYSICS. *Educ:* Mass Inst Technol, SB, 58, PhD(physics), 62. *Prof Exp:* Physicist, Lawrence Berkeley Lab, Univ Calif, 63-71; physicist, Fermi Nat Accelerator Lab, 71-78; PHYSICIST, STANFORD LINEAR ACCELERATOR CTR, 78- *Res:* Weak interactions; fast stellar oscillations; far infrared astronomy; particle accelerators. *Mailing Add:* Stanford Linear Accelerator Ctr Stanford CA 94305

STIENSTRA, WARD CURTIS, b Holland, Mich, June 19, 41; m 63; c 2. PLANT PATHOLOGY. *Educ:* Calvin Col, ABGen, 63; Mich State Univ, MS, 66, PhD(plant path), 70. *Prof Exp:* From asst prof to assoc prof, 70-80, PROF PLANT PATH, UNIV MINN, ST PAUL, 80- *Mem:* Am Phytopath Soc; Am Inst Biol Sci. *Res:* Diseases of turf corn, soybeans and alfalfa; soil borne diseases. *Mailing Add:* Dept of Plant Path Univ of Minn St Paul MN 55101

STIER, ELIZABETH FLEMING, b Riverside, NJ, Nov 24, 25; m 47; c 3. BIOCHEMISTRY. *Educ:* Rutgers Univ, BS, 47, MS, 49, PhD(biochem), 51. *Prof Exp:* Asst, 47-51, res assoc, 51-59, from asst prof to assoc prof, 59-72, PROF FOOD SCI, RUTGERS UNIV, NEW BRUNSWICK, 72- *Mem:* AAAS; Inst Food Technol; NY Acad Sci. *Res:* Methodology of flavor evaluation; flavor evaluation as a tool on pesticide treated fruits and vegetables; objective flavor techniques. *Mailing Add:* Dept of Food Sci Rutgers Univ New Brunswick NJ 08901

STIER, HOWARD LIVINGSTON, b Delmar, Del, Nov 28, 10; c 4. HORTICULTURE, PLANT PHYSIOLOGY. *Educ:* Univ Md, BS, 32, MS, 37, PhD(plant physiol), 39. *Prof Exp:* Agent potato breeding, USDA, 33-35; res asst hort, Univ Md, 35-39, asst prof, 39-41, prof mkt & head dept, 46-51; dir div statist & mkt res, Nat Food Processors Asn, 51-61; dir qual control, United Fruit Co, 61-71; dir develop & prod supporting serv, United Brands Co, 72-73, vpres qual control, 73-74, vpres develop & qual control, 74-77, corp vpres, 78-79; CONSULT, 79- *Concurrent Pos:* Dir prog anal, War Assets Admin, 46, consult, 46-47; prof lectr, George Washington Univ, 57-61; mem res adv comt, USDA, 62-64; mem adv comt, Dept Defense, 61; mem task group statist qual control of foods, Nat Acad Sci, 64. *Mem:* Fel AAAS; fel Am Soc Qual Control (vpres, 66-68; pres elec, 73-74; pres, 74-75); Am Statist Asn; Biomet Soc; Inst Food Tech. *Res:* Plant breeding; factors affecting quality and growth and development of horticultural crops, food processing, statistical control of quality. *Mailing Add:* Box 295 Grantham NH 03753

STIER, PAUL MAX, b Eden, NY, Aug 18, 24; m 47; c 4. PHYSICS. *Educ:* Univ Buffalo, BS, 44; Cornell Univ, PhD(physics), 52. *Prof Exp:* Sr physicist, Oak Ridge Nat Lab, 50-55; group leader chem physics, Union Carbide Corp, 55-60, asst dir, Res Lab, Union Carbide Nuclear Co, 60-65, mgr, Nucleonics Res Lab, 65-66, prog mgr phys sci, Tarrytown Tech Ctr, 66-72, OPERS MGR, CORP RES DEPT, STERLING FOREST LAB, UNION CARBIDE CORP, 72- *Res:* Stopping of heavy ions; energy range 10-250 kilo-electron-volts; energy loss; ionization; charge exchange; field emission; field ionization microscopy; chemisorption; surface diffusion; radiation damage in solids. *Mailing Add:* Corp Res Dept Union Carbide Corp PO Box 324 Tuxedo NY 10987

STIERMAN, DONALD JOHN, b Dubuque, Iowa, Oct 27, 47; m 70; c 2. SEISMOLOGY, GEOPHYSICS. *Educ:* State Univ NY Col Brockport, BS, 69; Stanford Univ, MS, 74, PhD(geophys), 77. *Prof Exp:* Physics instr, Teacher Training Col, Tegucigalpa, Honduras, 69-72; geophysicist, US Geol Surv, 74-75; res asst, Stanford Univ, 75-77; ASST PROF GEOPHYS, UNIV CALIF, RIVERSIDE, 77- *Mem:* Am Geophys Union; Seismol Soc Am; Geol Soc Am; Soc Explor Geophysicists; AAAS. *Res:* Physical properties of the shallow crust; microearthquake studies; seismicity; crustal velocity structure; geophysical characterization of existing and proposed hazardous waste desposal sites; attenuation mechanisms and measurements in sito; geothermal geophysics. *Mailing Add:* Dept of Earth Sci Univ of Calif Riverside CA 92507

STIERWALT, DONALD L, b Fremont, Ohio, Sept 20, 26; m 53; c 2. OPTICS. *Educ:* Univ Toledo, BS, 50; Syracuse Univ, MS, 53, PhD(physics), 61. *Prof Exp:* Res physicist, Naval Ord Lab, Corona, 58-70, RES PHYSICIST, ELECTRONIC MAT SCI DIV, NAVAL OCEAN SYSTS CTR, 70- *Mem:* Optical Soc Am. *Res:* Low temperature infrared spectral emittance and transmittance of optical materials and components. *Mailing Add:* Code 9221 Naval Ocean Systs Ctr San Diego CA 92157

STIFEL, PETER BEEKMAN, b Wheeling, WVa, Feb 9, 36; c 2. GEOLOGY. *Educ:* Cornell Univ, BA, 58; Univ Utah, PhD(geol), 64. *Prof Exp:* Res asst, Univ Utah, 60-63; ASSOC PROF GEOL, UNIV MD, COLLEGE PARK, 66- *Mem:* AAAS; Soc Econ Paleont & Mineral; Paleontol Soc. *Res:* Paleontology, stratigraphy and sedimentation. *Mailing Add:* Dept of Geol Univ of Md College Park MD 20742

STIFF, ROBERT H, b Pittsburgh, Pa, Apr 23, 23; m 45; c 3. DENTISTRY. *Educ:* Univ Pittsburgh, BS, 43, DDS, 45, Med, 53. *Prof Exp:* Instr oper dent, 45-58, asst prof oral med, 56-57, assoc prof oral genetic path & microbiol, 58-59, assoc prof oral med, 60-65, PROF ORAL MED & CHMN DEPT, SCH DENT, UNIV PITTSBURGH, 65-, DIR OUTPATIENT SERV, HOSP, 78-, ASST DEAN, 80- *Concurrent Pos:* Consult, USPHS, 62-66 & Dent Div, Pa Dept Health, 64-66. *Mem:* Am Acad Oral Path; fel Am Col Dent. *Res:* Task analysis of dental practice; dental education; dental treatment for the handicapped; attitudes of dental students towards treatment of chronically ill and aged; caries inhibiting effectiveness of a stannous fluoride-insoluble sodium metaphosphate dentifrice in children. *Mailing Add:* 4601 Doverdell Dr Pittsburgh PA 15236

STIFFEY, ARTHUR V, b Burgettstown, Pa, Apr 16, 18; m 41; c 6. ENVIRONMENTAL SCIENCE, MICROBIOLOGY. *Educ:* Univ Pittsburgh, BS, 40; Lehigh Univ, MS, 47; Fordham Univ, PhD(biol), 79. *Prof Exp:* Chemist anal chem, US Steel Co, 47-48; res assoc microbiol, Am Cyanamid Co, 48-74; chmn dept biol, 77-78, ASST PROF MICROBIOL, LADYCLIFF COL, 74-, CHMN DEPT NATURAL SCI, 79- *Concurrent Pos:* Sr scientist oceanog, US/USSR Bering Sea Exped, 77; proj dir instrnl sci equip prog, NSF grant, 77-78. *Mem:* AAAS; Sigma Xi; Phycol Soc; Am Inst Biol Sci. *Res:* Microbiological assays; metal determinations; uptake of metals by algae; chemical oceanography; antibiotics. *Mailing Add:* Dept of Natural Sci Ladycliff Col Highland Falls NY 10928

STIFFLER, DANIEL F, b Los Angeles, Calif, Nov 27, 42; m 67; c 2. PHYSIOLOGY, ZOOLOGY. *Educ:* Univ Calif, Santa Barbara, BA, 68; Ore State Univ, MS, 70, PhD(physiol), 72. *Prof Exp:* NIH-USPHS trainee physiol, Health Sci Ctr, Univ Ore, 72-74; nat animal physiol, Univ Calif, Davis, 74-75; asst prof, 75-78, ASSOC PROF PHYSIOL & ZOOL, CALIF STATE POLYTECH UNIV, POMONA, 78- *Mem:* AAAS; Am Physiol Soc; Am Soc Zoologists; Sigma Xi. *Res:* Renal physiology; epithelial transport physiology; comparative physiology and endocrinology of osmotic and ionic regulation. *Mailing Add:* Dept of Biol Sci Calif State Polytech Univ Pomona CA 91768

STIFFLER, PAUL W, b Buffalo, NY, June 24, 43; m 67; c 1. MEDICAL MICROBIOLOGY. *Educ:* Bowling Green State Univ, BA, 65, MA, 67; Mich State Univ, PhD(microbiol), 72. *Prof Exp:* Res assoc microbiol, Michael Reese Hosp & Med Ctr, Chicago, 72-73; USPHS fel clin microbiol, Dept Med, Sect Infectious Dis, Pritzker Sch Med, Univ Chicago, 73-75; microbiologist, Mason-Barron Labs, Inc, 75-78; dir & vpres microbiol & serol, Cent Path Regional Labs, Inc, 78-80; TECH DIR, DAMON CLIN LABS, INC, 80- *Mem:* Am Soc Microbiol; Asn Practitioners Infection Control; SCent Asn Microbiol; Am Asn Clin Chemists. *Res:* Antibiotic resistance determinants and their mode of transfer inter- and intra-generically. *Mailing Add:* Damon Clin Labs Inc 4720 W Montrose Ave Chicago IL 60641

STIGLER, STEPHEN MACK, b Minneapolis, Minn, Aug 10, 41; c 3. STATISTICS. *Educ:* Carleton Col, BA, 63; Univ Calif, Berkeley, PhD(statist), 67. *Prof Exp:* From asst prof to prof statist, Univ Wis-Madison, 67-79; PROF STATIST, UNIV CHICAGO, 79- *Concurrent Pos:* Ed, J Am Statist Asn, 79-82. *Mem:* AAAS; Am Statist Asn; Inst Math Statist. *Res:* Order statistics; experimental design; history of statistics. *Mailing Add:* Dept of Statist Univ of Chicago Chicago IL 60637

STIGLIAMI, WILLIAM MICHAEL, physical chemistry, see previous edition

STIGLICH, JACOB JOHN, JR, b Milwaukee, Wis, Dec 21, 38; m; c 2. MATERIALS SCIENCE, MATERIALS ENGINEERING. *Educ:* Marquette Univ, BS, 61; Northwestern Univ, PhD (mat sci), 70. *Prof Exp:* Res scientist, Mat Sci Div, US Army Mat & Mech Res Ctr, 67-71; chief engr, Boride Prod Inc, 71-74; mgr ceramic mat mfg, Valeron Corp, 74-76; asst tech dir, Miami Res Lab, Eagle Picher Indust, 76-78; MGR RES & DEVELOP, SAN FERNANDO LABS, 78- *Mem:* Am Soc Metals; Am Ceramic Soc; Am Inst Mining, Metall & Petrol Eng; Am Nuclear Soc; Am Soc Testing & Mat. *Res:* Development of corrosion, erosion, high temperature resistant materials by chemical vapor deposition; metals, ceramics, ceramic-metal composites. *Mailing Add:* San Fernando Labs 10258 Norris Ave Pacoima CA 91331

STIGLITZ, IRVIN G, b Cambridge, Mass, July 31, 36; m 60; c 2. ELECTRONIC ENGINEERING, ENGINEERING. *Educ:* Mass Inst Technol, SB & SM, 60, PhD(commun sci), 63. *Prof Exp:* Electronic engr, US Naval Ord Lab, 55-58; electronic engr, Gen Atronics Co, 60-61; res teaching asst statist commun theory, 58-63, asst prof elec eng, 63-64, staff mem, 64-71, GROUP LEADER, LINCOLN LAB, MASS INST TECHNOL, 71- *Concurrent Pos:* Consult, Guillemin Res Lab, 61, Joseph Kaye & Co, 63, Melpar Inc, 62 & Nat Acad Sci-Nat Res Coun, 70. *Mem:* Inst Elec & Electronics Engrs; Am Defence Preparedness Asn. *Res:* Guidance and control technology; tactical systems technology; air traffic control; communications systems design; information theory; system design and analysis. *Mailing Add:* Lincoln Lab Mass Inst of Technol PO Box 73 Lexington MA 02173

STILES, A(LVIN) B(ARBER), b Springfield, Ohio, July 16, 09; m 34; c 3. CATALYTIC SCIENCE. *Educ:* Ohio State Univ, BChE, 31, MS, 33. *Prof Exp:* Indust engr, E I du Pont de Nemours & Co, Inc, NY, 31-32, res assoc, WVa, 33-58, sr res assoc, 58-65, res fel, Del, 65-74; ASSOC DIR, CTR CATALYTIC SCI & TECHNOL, DEPT CHEM ENG, UNIV DEL, NEWARK, 74- *Mem:* Am Chem Soc; fel Am Inst Chemists; Am Inst Chem Engrs; Geol Asn; NY Acad Sci. *Res:* Industrial catalysis. *Mailing Add:* Dept of Chem Eng Univ of Del Newark DE 19711

STILES, DAVID A, b Harrow, Eng, Apr 28, 38; m 66; c 3. ANALYTICAL CHEMISTRY, ENVIRONMENTAL CHEMISTRY. *Educ:* Univ Birmingham, BSc, 60, PhD(electron spin resonance spectros), 63. *Prof Exp:* Asst prof chem, Univ Calgary, 63-64; univ fel, Univ Alta, 64-66; from asst prof to assoc prof, 66-77, PROF CHEM, ACADIA UNIV, 77-, HEAD DEPT, 81- *Mem:* Chem Inst Can; The Chem Soc. *Res:* Agricultural pollution; fate of pesticides and heavy metals in sandy soils; applications of molecular emission cavity analysis. *Mailing Add:* Dept of Chem Acadia Univ Wolfville NS B0P 1X0 Can

STILES, GRAHAM B, b Brownsville, Tex, Aug 2, 37; div; c 3. CHEMICAL ENGINEERING. *Educ:* Tex A&M Univ, BS, 58, MS, 61, PhD(chem eng), 64. *Prof Exp:* Various positions in res & develop & tech develop, Celanese Corp, 63-73; various positions in mkt & purchasing, Dow-Badische Co, 73-76; mem staff new bus develop fine chem, Upjohn Co, 76-79; DEVELOP MGR, PROCESS TECHNOL DIV, MERICHEM CO, 79- *Mem:* Am Inst Chem Engrs; Sigma Xi. *Res:* Liason with the research and development organization to set project divection and priorities; new business development for technologies offered; identification and development of new technologies; internal division technical consulting. *Mailing Add:* Merichem Co 4150 One Shell Plaza Houston TX 77002

STILES, JOHN I, (JR), b Ft Wayne, Ind, July 6, 48; m 70; c 1. MOLECULAR GENETICS. *Educ:* Ind Univ, Bloomington, BA, 70; Cornell Univ, PhD(plant physiol), 76. *Prof Exp:* NIH fel molecular genetics, Sch Med, Univ Rochester, 75-80; ASST PROF LIFE SCI, IND STATE UNIV, 80- *Mem:* AAAS; Am Soc Plant Physiologists; Genetics Soc Am. *Res:* Use of genetics and recombinant DNA techniques to study gene structure and function in yeast and higher plants at the nucleatide and chromatin level. *Mailing Add:* Dept Life Sci Ind State Univ Terre Haute IN 47809

STILES, LUCILLE WAGNER, b Chicago, Ill, Apr 30, 47. NUTRITION. *Educ:* Wash Univ, AB, 69; Univ Ill, MS, 70; Cornell Univ, PhD(nutrit), 77. *Prof Exp:* Res nutritionist, Nabisco Inc, 77-79; NUTRIT EDUC & TRAINING SPECIALIST, FOOD & NUTRIT SERV, US DEPT AGR, 79- *Mem:* Sigma Xi; Inst Food Technologists; AAAS; Soc Nutrit Educ. *Mailing Add:* 1122 Brummel St Evanston IL 60202

STILES, MARTIN, organic chemistry, see previous edition

STILES, MICHAEL EDGECOMBE, b Brit, Dec 28, 34; Can citizen; m 59; c 5. FOOD MICROBIOLOGY, MICROBIOLOGY. *Educ:* Univ Natal, BScAgr, 56, MScAgr, 59; Univ Ill, PhD(food microbiol), 63. *Prof Exp:* Dairy researcher, SAfrican Dept Agr, 57-59; from lectr to sr lectr dairy sci, Univ Natal, 59-69; assoc prof food microbiol, 69-77, PROF FOOD MICROBIOL, UNIV ALTA, 77- *Concurrent Pos:* Killam fel, Univ Alta, 68-69; hon prof, Dept Microbiol, Univ Alta, 74- *Mem:* Can Inst Food Sci & Technol; Inst Food Technologists; Int Asn Sanitarians; Can Microbiol Soc. *Res:* Food microbiology for quality control and safety especially meats, consumer acceptance and awareness of foods and food safety. *Mailing Add:* Dept Foods & Nutrit Univ Alta Edmonton AB T6G 2M8 Can

STILES, PHILIP GLENN, b Terre Haute, Ind, Nov 24, 31; m 56; c 1. FOOD TECHNOLOGY, POULTRY SCIENCE. *Educ:* Univ Ark, BS, 53; Univ Ky, MS, 56; Mich State Univ, PhD(food tech), 59. *Prof Exp:* Assoc prof food tech, Univ Conn, 59-69; PROF POULTRY SCI & FOOD TECHNOL, ARIZ STATE UNIV, 69-, CHMN DEPT AGR INDUST, 78- *Concurrent Pos:* Consult, Nixon Baldwin Div, Tenneco Co, 67- & AID projs in Iran, Malaysia & Philippines, 73-75. *Mem:* Inst Food Technol; Poultry Sci Asn; World Poultry Asn. *Res:* Food technology as applied to poultry products and food packaging. *Mailing Add:* Div of Agr Ariz State Univ Tempe AZ 85281

STILES, PHILLIP JOHN, b Manchester, Conn, Oct 31, 34; m 56; c 5. SOLID STATE PHYSICS. *Educ:* Trinity Col, Conn, BS, 56; Univ Pa, PhD(physics), 61. *Prof Exp:* Fel & res assoc physics, Univ Pa, 61-62; NSF fel, Cambridge Univ, 62-63; mem res staff, Thomas J Watson Res Ctr, Int Bus Mach Corp, NY, 63-70; chmn dept, 74-80, PROF PHYSICS, BROWN UNIV, 70- *Concurrent Pos:* Humboldt Sr US Scientist award, 76. *Honors & Awards:* John Price Wetheral Medal, Franklin Inst, 81. *Mem:* AAAS; Am Phys Soc; Am Astron Soc; Acoust Soc Am. *Res:* Solid state and low temperature physics; electronic properties of metals, semiconductors and lower dimensional systems. *Mailing Add:* Dept Physics Brown Univ Providence RI 02912

STILES, ROBERT NEAL, b Mar 15, 33; m 59; c 3. PHYSIOLOGY. *Educ:* Univ Mo, BS, 59, MA, 63; Northwestern Univ, PhD, 66. *Prof Exp:* Asst prof zool & physiol, Butler Univ, 66-68; asst prof physiol & biophys, 68-75, ASSOC PROF PHYSIOL & BIOPHYS, UNIV TENN CTR HEALTH SCI, MEMPHIS, 75- *Concurrent Pos:* USPHS grant, Univ Tenn Ctr Health Sci, Memphis, 69- *Mem:* AAAS; Sigma Xi; Am Physiol Soc; Soc Neurosci. *Res:* Human limb tremor; muscle mechanics; motor control system. *Mailing Add:* Univ of Tenn Ctr for Health Sci Memphis TN 38163

STILES, WARREN CRYDER, b Dias Creek, NJ, June 16, 33; m 55; c 4. HORTICULTURE. *Educ:* Rutgers Univ, BS, 54, MS, 55; Pa State Univ, PhD(hort), 58. *Prof Exp:* Asst prof pomol, Rutgers Univ, 58-63; from assoc prof to prof pomol, Univ Maine, 63-80, exten fruit specialist, 63-80, supt, Highmoor Farm, 66-80; MEM STAFF, DEPT POMOL, CORNELL UNIV, 80- *Mem:* AAAS; Am Soc Hort Sci. *Res:* Nutrition and post-harvest physiology of fruit. *Mailing Add:* Dept Pomol Plant Sci Bldg Cornell Univ Ithaca NY 14853

STILES, WILBUR J, b Suffern, NY, Jan 12, 32; m 56; c 2. MATHEMATICS. *Educ:* Lehigh Univ, BS, 54; Ga Inst Technol, BS, 60, MS, 62, PhD(math), 65. *Prof Exp:* ASSOC PROF MATH, FLA STATE UNIV, 65- *Mem:* Am Math Soc; Math Asn Am; Can Math Cong. *Res:* Functional analysis, geometry of Banach spaces. *Mailing Add:* Dept of Math Fla State Univ Tallahassee FL 32306

STILL, CHARLES NEAL, b Richmond, Va, Apr 15, 29; m 58; c 3. NEUROLOGY. *Educ:* Clemson Univ, BS, 49; Purdue Univ, MS, 51; Med Col SC, MD, 59. *Prof Exp:* Instr chem, Clemson Univ, 51-52 & US Mil Acad, 53-55; intern, Univ Chicago Clins, 59-60; resident neurol, Baltimore City Hosps & Johns Hopkins Hosp, 60-63; chief neurol serv, William S Hall Psychiat Inst, 65-81; prof, 78-81, CLIN PROF NEUROPSYCHIAT & BEHAV SCI, SCH MED, UNIV SC, 81- *Concurrent Pos:* Fel neurol med, Sch Med, Johns Hopkins Univ, 60-63; Nat Inst Neurol Dis & Blindness spec res fel neuropath, Res Lab, McLean Hosp & Harvard Med Sch, 63-65; fel neurol, Seizure Unit, Children's Hosp Med Ctr, Boston, 66; assoc clin prof neurol, Med Univ SC, 73-81; chmn grants rev bd, SC Dept Ment Health, 73-78; mem, Huntington's Chorea Res Group, World Fedn Neurol; dir, C M Tucker Jr Human Resources Ctr, 81; dep comnr, Long Term Care Div, SC Dept Mental Health, 81. *Mem:* Fel Am Acad Neurol; fel Am Col Nutrit; fel Am Geriat Soc; fel Am Inst Chemists; fel Geront Soc. *Res:* Geriatric neurology; geriatric psychiatry; aging; nutrition. *Mailing Add:* Tucker Ctr 2200 Harden St Columbia SC 29203

STILL, EDWIN TANNER, b Monroe, Ga, Nov 2, 35; m 59; c 2. RADIOBIOLOGY. *Educ:* Univ Rochester, MS, 64; Univ Ga, DVM, 59. *Prof Exp:* Res scientist, Sch Aerospace Med, US Air Force, Brooks AFB, Tex, 64-67 & Naval Radiol Defense Lab, Calif, 67-69; res contracts adminr, Div Biol & Med, US AEC, 69-75; chmn, Radiation Biol Dept, Armed Forces Radiobiol Res Inst, 75-79; dir, Defense Nuclear Agency, 79-81; SR PHYS SCIENTIST, KERR-MCGEE CORP, 82- *Mem:* Sigma Xi. *Res:* Low-level radiation effects; beneficial applications of radiation. *Mailing Add:* Kerr-McGee Corp PO Box 25861 Oklahoma City OK 73125

STILL, GERALD G, b Seattle, Wash, Aug 13, 33; m 54; c 3. BIOCHEMISTRY, ORGANIC CHEMISTRY. *Educ:* Wash State Univ, BS, 59; Ore State Univ, MS, 63, PhD(biochem), 65. *Prof Exp:* Res biochemist, Radiation & Metab Res Lab, Agr Res Serv, USDA, 65-77, staff scientist, 77-80, CHIEF SCIENTIST, NAT PROG STAFF, SCI & EDUC ADMIN-AGR RES, USDA, 80- *Mem:* Am Soc Plant Physiol; Am Chem Soc. *Res:* Metabolism of pesticides; isolation and characterization of pesticide metabolites; photosynthesis; biological nitrogen fixation; plant cell culture; field crop bioregulation. *Mailing Add:* USDA Sea Off Dir 14th & Independence Ave Washington DC 20250

STILL, IAN WILLIAM JAMES, b Rutherglen, Scotland, July 5, 37; m 64; c 2. ORGANIC CHEMISTRY. *Educ:* Glasgow Univ, BSc, 58, PhD(chem), 62. *Prof Exp:* Res assoc, Univ Toronto, 62-63; sci officer, Allen & Hanburys Ltd, Eng, 63-64; from asst lectr to lectr chem, Huddersfield Col Tech Eng, 64-65; asst prof, 65-70, ASSOC PROF CHEM, UNIV TORONTO, 70- *Mem:* Am Chem Soc; fel Chem Inst Can; assoc mem Royal Soc Chem. *Res:* Synthetic and structural organic chemistry, especially organo-sulfur chemistry; new synthetic methods and their application to synthesis of naturally occurring antibiotics; organic photochemistry and nuclear magnetic resonance. *Mailing Add:* Erindale Campus Univ Toronto Mississauga ON L5L 1C6 Can

STILL, W CLARK, JR, b Augusta, Ga, Aug 31, 46; m 67. SYNTHETIC ORGANIC CHEMISTRY. *Educ:* Emory Univ, BS, 69, PhD(org chem), 72. *Prof Exp:* IBM fel theoret org chem, Princeton Univ, 72-73; fel synthetic org chem, Columbia Univ, 73-75; asst prof org chem, Vanderbilt Univ, 75-77; asst prof, 77-80, ASSOC PROF CHEM, COLUMBIA UNIV, 80- *Mem:* Am Chem Soc. *Res:* Organic synthesis; new synthetic methods. *Mailing Add:* Dept of Chem Columbia Univ New York NY 11027

STILL, WILLIAM JAMES SANGSTER, b Aberdeen, Scotland, Sept 16, 23; m 51; c 2. PATHOLOGY. *Educ:* Univ Aberdeen, MB, ChB, 51, MD, 60. *Prof Exp:* Lectr path, Univ London, 57-60; asst prof, Sch Med, Washington Univ, 60-62; sr lectr, Univ London, 62-65; assoc prof, 65-70, PROF PATH, MED COL VA, 70- *Concurrent Pos:* Fel coun arteriosclerosis, Am Heart Asn, 65. *Mem:* Col Am Path; Path Soc Gt Brit & Ireland. *Res:* Cardiovascular disease, particularly arterial disease. *Mailing Add:* Dept of Path Med Col of Va Richmond VA 23219

STILLE, JOHN KENNETH, b Tucson, Ariz, May 8, 30; m 58; c 2. ORGANOMETALLIC CHEMISTRY, POLYMER CHEMISTRY. *Educ:* Univ Ariz, BS, 52, MS, 53; Univ Ill, PhD(org chem), 57. *Prof Exp:* From instr to prof, Univ Iowa, 57-77; PROF ORG CHEM, COLO STATE UNIV, 77- *Concurrent Pos:* Consult, E I du Pont de Nemours & Co, 64-; vis prof, Royal Inst Technol, Sweden, 68; mem comt org polymer characterization of mat adv bd, Nat Acad Sci, 74-77; mem eval panel for polymers div, Inst Mat Res, Nat Bur Standards, 74-77; chmn, Polymer Div, Am Chem Soc, 75; mem coun, Gordon Res Conf, 78- & Petrol Res Fund Adv Bd, Am Chem Soc, 79-; assoc ed, Macromolecules, 67- *Honors & Awards:* Polymer Chem Award, Am Chem Soc, 82. *Mem:* Am Chem Soc; Royal Soc Chem. *Res:* Physical organic chemistry; organometallic reactions and mechanisms; asymmetric synthesis catalyzed by transition metals polymer synthesis and reaction mechanisms; catalysis. *Mailing Add:* Dept of Chem Colo State Univ Ft Collins CO 80523

STILLER, DAVID, b Seattle, Wash, Sept 9, 31; m 62; c 2. MEDICAL & VETERINARY ENTOMOLOGY. *Educ:* Whittier Col, BA, 53, MSc, 57; Univ Calif, Berkeley, PhD(parasitol), 73. *Prof Exp:* Staff res assoc ent entom, George Williams Hooper Found, Univ Calif, San Francisco, 62-73; res parasitologist & res assoc med entom & acarol, Dept Int Health, 73-75; RES ENTOMOLOGIST VET ENTOM, AGR RES SERV, USDA, 75- *Concurrent Pos:* Actg head, Int Ctr Med Res, Div Acarol, Inst Med Res, Kuala Lumpur, Malaysia, 73-75; consult scientist, Spec Foreign Currency Prog, Pub Law 480; vet entom coordr, Nat Emergency Prog Vet Serv, USDA, 78-; adj prof, Dept Vet Med, Univ Idaho & Dept Vet Micro-Path, Washington State Univ, 81- *Mem:* Entom Soc Am; Am Soc Trop Med & Hyg; AAAS; Wildlife Dis Asn; Sigma Xi. *Res:* Acarology; vector-pathogen relationships; arthropod-borne diseases; acarine biology and parasitism; tick-borne hemoparasitic diseases of livestock; epizootiology of these diseases. *Mailing Add:* Bldg 1001 SEA-USDA Beltsville MD 20705

STILLER, MARY LOUISE, b Salem, Ohio, Nov 29, 31. PLANT PHYSIOLOGY, BIOCHEMISTRY. *Educ:* Purdue Univ, BS, 54, MS, 56, PhD(plant physiol), 59. *Prof Exp:* NSF fel biochem, Univ Chicago, 58-60, USPHS trainee, 60-61; fel, Univ Pa, 61-62; asst prof, 62-66, ASSOC PROF BIOL SCI, PURDUE UNIV, LAFAYETTE, 66- *Concurrent Pos:* NIH career develop award, 65- *Mem:* AAAS; Am Soc Plant Physiol. *Res:* Biochemistry of photosynthesis, photoreduction and respiration. *Mailing Add:* Dept of Biol Sci Purdue Univ West Lafayette IN 47906

STILLER, PETER FREDERICK, b Green Bay, Wis. GEOMETRY. *Educ:* Mass Inst Technol, SB(econ) & SB(math), 73; Princeton Univ, MA, 74, PhD(math), 77. *Prof Exp:* Asst prof math, Tex A&M Univ, 77-79; NATO fel, Inst des Haules Etudes Scientifigues, 79-80; asst prof, Tex A&M Univ, 80; res fel math, Univ Bonn, WGer, 81; ASST PROF MATH, TEX A&M UNIV, 82- *Concurrent Pos:* NSF US France exchange grant, Inst des Mautes Etudes Sci, 82-83. *Mem:* Am Math Soc. *Res:* Families of algebraic varieties and algebraic cycles. *Mailing Add:* Dept Math Tex A&M Univ College Station TX 77843

STILLER, RICHARD L, b New York, NY, Feb 15, 33; m 72; c 2. BIOCHEMISTRY. *Educ:* Hunter Col, AB, 59; St John's Univ, NY, MS, 70, PhD(biol chem), 72. *Prof Exp:* Res scientist biochem, NY Psychiat Inst, 61-80, head Anal Serv Sect, Neurotoxicol Res Unit, 75-80; ASST PROF PSYCHIAT, UNIV PITTSBURGH, 79-, CHIEF CHEM PHARMACOL, 80- *Concurrent Pos:* Adj asst prof, Queensborough Community Col, 72-78; asst clin prof path, Columbia Univ Med Ctr, 77-79. *Mem:* AAAS; Am Chem Soc; NY Acad Sci; Am Asn Clin Chemists. *Res:* Synthesis and biosynthesis of sphingolipids; neurochemistry of brain and nerve tissue; lipid chemistry; clinical pharmacology; drug pharmacokinetics; drug effects on central nervous system; methods for neuropsychotropic agent detection in biological medium. *Mailing Add:* Univ Pittsburgh Sch Med 3811 O'Hara St Pittsburgh PA 15213

STILLINGER, FRANK HENRY, b Boston, Mass, Aug 15, 34; m 56; c 2. LIQUID STATE THEORY, PHASE TRANSITION THEORY. *Educ:* Univ Rochester, BS, 55; Yale Univ, PhD(chem), 58. *Prof Exp:* Fel chem, Yale Univ, 58-59; MEM TECH STAFF, BELL LABS, INC, 59- *Concurrent Pos:* Lectr, Welsh Found, 74; mem, Evaluation Panel, Heat Div, NSF, 75-78; Policy Comn, Chem Div, 80- *Honors & Awards:* Elliott Cresson Medal, Franklin Inst, 78. *Mem:* Am Phys Soc; AAAS; Sigma Xi. *Res:* Molecular theory of water and it solutions; theory of phase transitions; theoretical electrochemistry. *Mailing Add:* Bell Labs 600 Mountain Ave Murray Hill NJ 07974

STILLINGS, BRUCE ROBERT, b Portland, Maine, May 18, 37; m 59; c 4. NUTRITION. *Educ:* Univ Maine, BS, 58; Pa State Univ, MS, 60, PhD(animal nutrit), 63. *Prof Exp:* NIH fel, Cornell Univ, 63-66; supvry res chemist, food res prog leader & dep lab dir, US Nat Marine Fisheries Serv, 66-74; NAT COORD, DIR FOOD SAFETY, RES ACTIVITIES & RES & VPRES RES & DEVELOP, NABISCO BRANDS INC, 74- *Mem:* Am Asn Cereal Chemists; AAAS; Am Inst Nutrit; Inst Food Technologists. *Res:* Nutritional studies on metabolism and utilization of minerals and amino acids; nutritive value of food-proteins and protein concentrates; factors affecting protein quality of foods. *Mailing Add:* Nabisco Brands Inc Res Ctr 2111 Rt 208 Fair Lawn NJ 07410

STILLIONS, MERLE C, b Bedford, Ind, Feb 15, 29; m 53; c 5. LABORATORY ANIMAL SCIENCE, NUTRITION. *Educ:* Purdue Univ, BS, 57, MS, 58; Rutgers Univ, PhD(nutrit), 62. *Prof Exp:* Instr nutrit, Rutgers Univ, 58-62, chmn, Dairy Dept, Chico State Univ, 62-63; dir nutrit, Morris Res Lab, 63-72; RES DIR, AGWAY INC, 72- *Concurrent Pos:* Mem, Equine Comt, Nat Res Coun, 69-73. *Mem:* Am Soc Animal Sci; Am Asn Lab Animal Soc. *Res:* Laboratory animal and fish nutrition and feed control programs. *Mailing Add:* Agard Rd Trumansburg NY 14886

STILLMAN, GREGORY EUGENE, b Scotia, Nebr, Feb 15, 36; m 56; c 3. SOLID STATE ELECTRONICS. *Educ:* Univ Nebr, Lincoln, BS, 58; Univ Ill, Urbana, MS, 65, PhD(elec eng), 67. *Prof Exp:* Res staff assoc solid state physics, Lincoln Lab, Mass Inst Technol, 67-75; PROF, DEPT ELEC ENG & DIR, SEMICONDUCTOR RES GROUP, UNIV ILL, 75- *Concurrent Pos:* Vis scientist, Lab Elettronica dello Stato Solido, 72; consult, Rockwell Inst Sci Ctr, 78-, Hughes Torrance Research Ctr, 80- *Mem:* Fel Inst Elec & Electronics Engrs; Am Phys Soc. *Res:* Semiconductor physics; transport properties; photoconductivity; spectroscopy; luminescence. *Mailing Add:* 155 Elec Eng Bldg Univ of Ill 1406 W Green St Urbana IL 61801

STILLMAN, IRVING MAYER, b Queens, NY, Oct 15, 33; m 58. BIOPHYSICS, MEDICINE. *Educ:* Queens Col, NY, BS, 55; Washington Univ, MD, 59; Polytech Inst Brooklyn, PhD(phys chem), 68. *Prof Exp:* Med intern, Jersey City Med Ctr, NJ, 59-60; NIH fel, 62-65; RES ASSOC BIOPHYS, NAT INST NEUROL DIS & STROKE, 65- *Mem:* AAAS; fel Am Inst Chemists; Am Chem Soc; Am Phys Soc; NY Acad Sci. *Res:* Organic semiconductors; electrochemistry; neurophysiology; membrane biophysics; quantum chemistry and biology. *Mailing Add:* 4721 Dorsett Ave Chevy Chase MD 20015

STILLMAN, JOHN EDGAR, b Syracuse, NY, May 21, 45. INDUSTRIAL HYGIENE, CHEMISTRY. *Educ:* State Univ NY Col Forestry at Syracuse Univ, BS, 67; Univ NC Sch Pub Health, MSPH, 69; NC State Univ, MAgri, 72; Am Bd Indust Hyg, cert, 80. *Prof Exp:* Anal chem supvr, Div Health Serv, Occup Health Lab Unit, NC Dept Human Resources, 72-79; indust hygienist, 79-80, actg head, 80-81, SR INDUST HYGIENIST & HEAD, INDUST HYG LAB, RES & ENVIRON HEALTH DIV, EXXON CORP, 81- *Concurrent Pos:* Consult anal chem, various private industs, 74-79. *Mem:* Am Indust Hyg Asn; Am Conf Govt Indust Hygienists; Am Acad Indust Hyg. *Res:* Occupational, industrial and environmental polutants; analytical laboratory administration and management; gas chromatography; microscopy; method evaluation and development; field hazards surveys; asbestos; kinetics of cholinesterase; anaerobic sludge digestion. *Mailing Add:* PO Box 570 Rd 1 Princeton NJ 08540

STILLMAN, MARTIN JOHN, b London, Eng, June 4, 47; Can citizen. BIOINORGANIC CHEMISTRY, SPECTROSCOPY. *Educ:* Univ EAnglia, BSc, 69, MSc, 70, PhD(chem), 73. *Prof Exp:* Fel chem, Univ Alta, 73-75; asst prof, 75-81, ASSOC PROF CHEM, UNIV WESTERN ONT, 81- *Mem:* The Chem Soc; Can Inst Chem. *Res:* Spectroscopy of inorganic and biological systems; magnetic circular dichroism of heme proteins and model compounds, metal ions in alkali halide crystals; binding of cadium and mercury in tissue. *Mailing Add:* Dept of Chem Univ of Western Ont London ON N6A 5B7 Can

STILLMAN, RICHARD ERNEST, b Grand Island, Nebr, Dec 6, 29; m 56; c 2. MATHEMATICS, CHEMICAL ENGINEERING. *Educ:* Univ Kans, BS, 51, MS, 56; Pa State Univ, University Park, PhD(chem eng), 61. *Prof Exp:* Staff engr process control, Res Div, 58-63, adv engr, Systs Develop Div, 64-65, SR ENGR, DATA PROCESSING DIV, IBM CORP, PALO ALTO, 66- *Mem:* Am Inst Chem Engrs. *Res:* Formulation of mathematical models of chemical processes; numerical methods for solving partial and ordinary differential equations; gradient optimization procedures and multicomponent distillation calculations; artificial intelligence and knowledge based expert systems. *Mailing Add:* 1659 Fairorchard Ave San Jose CA 95125

STILLWAY, LEWIS WILLIAM, b Casper, Wyo, Feb 27, 39; m 59; c 2. BIOCHEMISTRY. *Educ:* Col Idaho, BS, 62; Univ Idaho, MS, 65, PhD(biochem), 68. *Prof Exp:* Fel, Inst Marine Sci, Univ Miami, 68-69; assoc chem, 69-71, asst prof, 71-76, ASSOC PROF BIOCHEM, MED UNIV SC, 76- *Mem:* Am Soc Biol Chemists; AAAS. *Res:* Natural products; growth factors; diabetes; lipid chemistry and metabolism; marine biology; enzymes; marine lipids and nutrition. *Mailing Add:* Dept of Biochem Med Univ of SC Charleston SC 29403

STILLWELL, EDGAR FELDMAN, b Staten Island, NY, Nov 2, 29. PHYSIOLOGY. *Educ:* Wagner Mem Lutheran Col, BS, 51; Duke Univ, MA, 53, PhD(zool), 57. *Prof Exp:* Asst zool, Duke Univ, 52-56, res assoc, 56-57; asst prof biol, Longwood Col, 57-60 & Univ SC, 60-61; assoc prof zool, ECarolina Univ, 61-68; ASSOC PROF BIOL, OLD DOM UNIV, 68- *Concurrent Pos:* NASA-Am Soc Eng Educ fac res fel, Langley Res Ctr, 69-70; NASA res grant, 71-72. *Mem:* AAAS; Am Soc Cell Biol. *Res:* Mitogenetic control mechanisms in central nervous system neurons in tissue culture. *Mailing Add:* Dept of Biol Old Dom Univ Norfolk VA 23508

STILLWELL, EPHRAIM POSEY, JR, b Sylva, NC, Aug 29, 34; m 60; c 2. SOLID STATE PHYSICS. *Educ:* Wake Forest Col, BS, 56; Univ Va, MS, 58, PhD(physics), 60. *Prof Exp:* From asst prof to assoc prof, 60-69, head dept, 71-74, PROF PHYSICS, CLEMSON UNIV, 69- *Concurrent Pos:* US Air Force Off Sci Res grant, 63-69. *Mem:* Am Asn Physics Teachers; Am Phys Soc; AAAS. *Res:* Magnetoresistance in metals; superconductivity. *Mailing Add:* Dept of Physics Clemson Univ Clemson SC 29631

STILLWELL, GEORGE KEITH, b Moose Jaw, Sask, July 11, 18; m 43; c 2. PHYSICAL MEDICINE. *Educ:* Univ Sask, BA, 39; Queen's Univ, Ont, MD, CM, 42; Univ Minn, PhD(phys med & rehab), 54; Am Bd Phys Med & Rehab, dipl, 52. *Prof Exp:* Instr, 50-54, from asst prof to assoc prof, Mayo Grad Sch Med, 55-73, chmn dept, 73-81, PROF PHYS MED & REHAB, MAYO MED SCH, UNIV MINN, 73- *Concurrent Pos:* Consult, Mayo Clin, 54- *Mem:* AAAS; Cong Rehab Med; Am Acad Phys Med & Rehab. *Res:* Rehabilitation; physiologic effects of therapeutic procedures; edema of peripheral origin. *Mailing Add:* Dept Phys Med & Rehab Mayo Clin Rochester MN 55901

STILLWELL, H(ENRY) SHELDON, aerospace engineering, deceased

STILLWELL, HAROLD DANIEL, b Staten Island, NY, Mar 21, 31; m 64; c 2. PHYSICAL GEOGRAPHY, BIOGEOGRAPHY. *Educ:* Duke Univ, BS, 52, MF, 54; Mich State Univ, PhD, 61. *Prof Exp:* Forestry aid, US Forest Serv, NC, 52; asst, Ore Forest Res Ctr, 54-57; asst geog, Mich State Univ, 57-59; asst prof, Eastern Mich Univ, 60-61 & Univ Tex, 61-62; assoc prof, ECarolina Univ, 62-71; PROF GEOG, APPALACHIAN STATE UNIV, 71- *Mem:* Asn Am Geographers; Sigma Xi; Int Geog Union. *Res:* Natural hazards of mountain areas, particularly avalanche prediction; mountain geo-ecology with analysis of tree line location; remote sensing. *Mailing Add:* Dept of Geog Appalachian State Univ Boone NC 28607

STILLWELL, RICHARD NEWHALL, b Princeton, NJ, Nov 22, 35. ORGANIC CHEMISTRY, COMPUTER SCIENCE. *Educ:* Princeton Univ, BA, 57; Harvard Univ, MA, 59, PhD(chem), 64. *Prof Exp:* From instr to asst prof, 63-74, ASSOC PROF CHEM, BAYLOR COL MED, 74- *Mem:* Am Chem Soc; Am Soc Mass Spectrometry; Asn Comput Mach. *Res:* Chemistry of natural products; chemical modelling; analytical systems. *Mailing Add:* Inst Lipid Res Baylor Col of Med 1200 Moursund Ave Houston TX 77030

STILLWELL, WILLIAM HARRY, b Albany, NY, Mar 30, 46; m 78; c 1. BIOCHEMISTRY, BIOLOGY. *Educ:* State Univ NY, Albany, BS, 67; Pa State Univ, MS, 73, PhD(biochem), 74. *Prof Exp:* Res asst prof origin life, Inst Molecular & Cellular Evolution, 74-75; res assoc membrane biophys, Mich State Univ, 76-78; ASST PROF BIOL, IND UNIV-PURDUE UNIV, INDIANAPOLIS, 78- *Mem:* AAAS; NY Acad Sci; Biophys Soc. *Res:* Membrane biochemistry and biophysics; artificial membrane systems; action of plant hormones on membranes; origin of life; origin of bioenergetic processes; origin of membranes. *Mailing Add:* Dept of Biol Sch of Sci 1201 E 38th St Indianapolis IN 46205

STILWELL, DONALD LONSON, b Detroit, Mich, Dec 29, 18. ANATOMY. *Educ:* Wayne State Univ, AB, 41, MD, 44. *Prof Exp:* Intern, Harper Hosp, Detroit, 44-45, resident surg, 45-56; from instr to asst prof, 49-59, asst dean, 64-65, ASSOC PROF ANAT, SCH MED, STANFORD UNIV, 60- *Concurrent Pos:* Fel anat, Wayne State Univ, 58-59. *Mem:* AAAS; Am Asn Anat. *Res:* Anatomy; experimental pathology; vascularization of vertebral column; innervation of hand, foot, joints, spine and eye; blood supply of brain. *Mailing Add:* Dept of Anat Stanford Univ Stanford CA 94305

STILWELL, KENNETH JAMES, b Poughkeepsie, NY, Apr 4, 34; m 56; c 3. MATHEMATICS. *Educ:* Bob Jones Univ, BS, 56; Ariz State Univ, MA, 59; Univ Ariz, MS, 64; Hunter Col, MA, 65; Univ Northern Colo, EdD(math educ), 71. *Prof Exp:* Instr high schs, Ariz, 57-64; asst prof math, King's Col, NY, 65-66; assoc prof, 66-74, PROF MATH, NORTHEAST MO STATE UNIV, 74- *Mem:* Math Asn Am. *Res:* Mathematics education; effect of video-tape and critique on attitude of pre-service mathematics teachers. *Mailing Add:* Div of Math Northeast Mo State Univ Kirksville MO 63501

STIMLER, MORTON, b New York, NY, Sept 14, 24; m 64. OPTOACOUSTICS, MODERN OPTICS. *Educ:* City Col New York, BS, 48; Univ Md, MS, 63. *Prof Exp:* Engr, US Naval Ord Lab, US Naval Surface Weapons Ctr, 50-56, scientist, 56-61, physicist, 61-66, res physicist, 66-81. *Concurrent Pos:* Mem mine develop comt, US Naval Ord Lab, 56-57, head exp laser br, 61-63; US Naval Surface Weapons Ctr invited speaker lasers, Various Univs, 62-65; mem, Leasibility Evaluation Comt Optoacoustic Proposals, govt & pvt indust. *Mem:* Am Phys Soc; Optical Soc Am. *Res:* Acoustic and magnetic mines; magnetic amplifiers; radar; missiles; communication systems; photon momentum; electron injection; optics; lasers; imaging; electro optics; opto-acoustics; acoustic lenses; temperature compensation in acoustic lenses. *Mailing Add:* 19 Watchwater Way Rockville MD 20850

STIMLER, SUZANNE STOKES, b Aberdeen, SDak, Sept 25, 28; m 64. PHYSICAL CHEMISTRY. *Educ:* Univ Colo, BA, 50; Mt Holyoke Col, MA, 54; Univ Rochester, PhD(phys chem), 58. *Prof Exp:* Chemist, Shell Oil Co, 51-52; instr chem, Wellesley Col, 57-58; res chemist, US Navl Res Lab, 58-68; health scientist adminr, Nat Inst Child Health & Human Develop, 68-71, health scientist adminr, 71-75, DIR, BIOTECHNOL RESOURCES PROG, DIV RES RESOURCES, NIH, 75- *Mem:* AAAS; Am Chem Soc. *Res:* Molecular electronic spectroscopy, particularly absorption and emission; infrared absorption spectroscopy; photodegradation of polymers; technology for biomedical research. *Mailing Add:* Div of Res Resources Nat Inst of Health Bethesda MD 20014

STIMPFLING, JACK HERMAN, b Denver, Colo, June 11, 24; m 50; c 4. GENETICS. *Educ:* Univ Denver, BS, 49, MS, 50; Univ Wis, PhD(genetics), 57. *Prof Exp:* Asst yeast genetics, Southern Ill Univ, 51-52; immunogenetics, Univ Wis, 52-57; fel, Jackson Mem Lab, 57-59, assoc staff scientist, 59-61, staff scientist, 61-64; res assoc, 65-68, DIR, MCLAUGHLIN RES INST, 68- *Mem:* Genetics Soc Am; Am Asn Immunologists. *Res:* Immunogenetics; inheritance of cellular antigens; cellular antigens in tissue transplantation. *Mailing Add:* McLaughlin Res Inst Columbus Hosp Great Falls MT 59401

STIMSON, MIRIAM MICHAEL, b Chicago, Ill, Dec 24, 13. ORGANIC CHEMISTRY. *Educ:* Siena Heights Col, BS, 36; Inst Divi Thomae, MS, 39, PhD(chem), 48. *Prof Exp:* Head res lab, Siena Heights Col, 36-39, instr chem, 39-46, asst prof, 46-50, prof natural sci & head div, 50-69; chmn dept, Keuka Col, 69-74, prof chem, 69-78; mem staff, 78-81, DIR, GRAD STUDIES OFF, SIENA HEIGHTS COL, 81- *Honors & Awards:* Charles Williams Award, 42. *Mem:* Am Chem Soc; Nat Asn Women Deans & Counselors. *Res:* Infrared and ultraviolet absorption in the solid state by potassium bromide disks; effect of irradiation on pyrimidines in the solid state. *Mailing Add:* Grad Studies Off Siena Heights Col Adrian MI 49221

STINAFF, RUSSELL DALTON, b Akron, Ohio, Mar 17, 40; m 68; c 1. ELECTRICAL ENGINEERING, CYBERNETICS. *Educ:* Univ Akron, BSEE, 62; Purdue Univ, Lafayette, MSEE, 63; Univ Ill, Urbana, PhD(elec eng), 69. *Prof Exp:* Electronic engr, Nat Security Agency, 64-65; asst prof elec eng, Clemson Univ, 69-76; MEM STAFF, HONEYWELL, INC, 80-; MEM STAFF, HONEYWELL, 80- *Concurrent Pos:* US Off Educ res grant, 71-73. *Mem:* AAAS; Simulation Coun; Am Soc Eng Educ; Inst Elec & Electronics Engrs; Asn Comput Mach. *Res:* Artificial intelligence; application of computers to education; simulation of large systems. *Mailing Add:* Honeywell 1500 W Dundee Rd Arlington Heights IL 60004

STINCHCOMB, THOMAS GLENN, b Tiffin, Ohio, Sept 12, 22; m 45; c 4. RADIATION PHYSICS, MEDICAL PHYSICS. *Educ:* Heidelberg Col, BS, 44; Univ Chicago, MS, 48, PhD(physics), 51. *Prof Exp:* From instr to asst prof physics, State Col Wash, 51-54; from assoc prof to prof & head dept, Heidelberg Col, 54-61; res physicist, Nuclear & Radiation Physics Sect, IIT Res Inst, 61-65, sr physicist & group leader, 65-68; chmn dept, 68-76, PROF PHYSICS, DEPAUL UNIV, 68- *Concurrent Pos:* Actg mgr, Nuclear & Radiation Physics Sect, IIT Res Inst, 66-67; vis res assoc, Radiol Dept, Univ Chicago, 76- *Mem:* Sigma Xi; Am Asn Physics Teachers; Am Nuclear Soc; Fed Am Scientists; Am Asn Physicist in Med. *Res:* Medical applications of nuclear radiation physics, mainly determinations of quality of neutron therapeutic beams by microdosimetric techniques. *Mailing Add:* Dept of Physics Lincoln Park Campus Chicago IL 60614

STINCHCOMB, WAYNE WEBSTER, b Baltimore, Md, Sept 16, 43; m 68; c 2. MATERIALS SCIENCE, MECHANICS. *Educ:* Va Polytech Inst, BS, 65; Pa State Univ, MS, 67, PhD(eng mech), 71. *Prof Exp:* Instr eng mech, Pa State Univ, 68-69; from instr to asst prof eng mech, 70-78, assoc prof, 78-80, PROF ENG SCI & MECH, VA POLYTECH INST & STATE UNIV, 80- *Res:* Materials, fatigue, composites, nondestructive testing and evaluation. *Mailing Add:* 610 Broce Dr Blacksburg VA 24060

STINCHFIELD, FRANK E, b Warren, Minn, Aug 12, 10; m 30; c 2. ORTHOPEDIC SURGERY. *Educ:* Northwestern Univ, MD, 34; Am Bd Orthop Surg, dipl, 46. *Hon Degrees:* DSc, Carleton Col, 60; DSc, Univ NDak, 70; FRACS, 75; FRCS, 79. *Prof Exp:* prof orthop surg & chmn dept, Col Physicians & Surgeons, Columbia Univ, 56-76. *Concurrent Pos:* Attend orthop surgeon, Columbia-Presby Med Ctr, 51-, consult, Neurol Inst, 47-; Dept Defense & Dept Air Force orthop surg consult, Asst Secy Defense, 65-, tour Vietnam & Far East installations, 66; pres, Am Bd Orthop Surg. *Honors & Awards:* Centennial Award, Northwestern Univ, 59. *Mem:* Am Surg Asn; Am Asn Surg of Trauma; Am Acad Orthop Surg (pres, 61); Am Orthop Asn (treas); NY Acad Med. *Res:* Effect of anticoagulant therapy on bone repair; osteogenesis of bone isolated from soft tissue blood supply. *Mailing Add:* Dept Orthop Surg Columbia Univ 161 Ft Washington Dr New York NY 10032

STINE, CHARLES MAXWELL, b Osceola Mills, Pa, Mar 4, 25; m 51; c 3. FOOD SCIENCE. *Educ:* Pa State Univ, BS, 51, MS, 52; Univ Minn, PhD(dairy tech), 57. *Prof Exp:* Assoc prof, 57-68, PROF FOOD SCI, MICH STATE UNIV, 68- *Mem:* Am Oil Chem Soc; Am Dairy Sci Asn. *Res:* Lipid oxidation in food products; spray dried foods. *Mailing Add:* Dept Food Sci Mich State Univ East Lansing MI 48823

STINE, GERALD JAMES, b Johnstown, Pa, May 29, 35; m 62; c 2. MICROBIAL GENETICS, HUMAN GENETICS. *Educ:* Southern Conn State Col, BS, 61; Dartmouth Col, MA, 63; Univ Del, PhD(genetics), 66. *Prof Exp:* Biologist, Oak Ridge Nat Lab, 66-68; asst prof microbial genetics, Univ Tenn, Knoxville, 68-72; assoc prof, 72-77, PROF NATURAL SCI, UNIV N FLA, 77- *Concurrent Pos:* Union Carbide fel, 66-68; consult, Oak Ridge Nat Lab, 68- *Mem:* Genetics Soc Am; NY Acad Sci; Am Microbial Soc; assoc Inst Soc Ethics & Life Sci. *Res:* Isolation of specific gene fragments of Escherichia coli after transfer of the Escherichia coli chromosome into Proteus mirabilis; studies on development in Neurospora crassa. *Mailing Add:* Dept Natural Sci Univ NFla Jacksonville FL 32216

STINE, OSCAR CEBREN, b Washington, DC, June 11, 27; m 51; c 5. PEDIATRICS, PUBLIC HEALTH. *Educ:* Oberlin Col, BA, 50; George Washington Univ, MD, 54; Johns Hopkins Univ, DrPH, 60; Am Bd Pediat, dipl, 59; Am Bd Family Pract, cert, 76. *Prof Exp:* Intern pediat, Rochester Gen Hosp, NY, 54-55, resident, 55-57; instr pub health admin, Sch Hyg & Pub Health, Johns Hopkins Univ, 57-62, asst prof maternal & child health, 62-66, instr pediat, Sch Med, 57-66, dir maternal & child health clin, 62-66; ASSOC PROF PEDIAT, SCH MED, UNIV MD, BALTIMORE CITY, 67-; CHIEF AMBULATORY CARE, GTR BALTIMORE MED CTR, 75- *Concurrent Pos:* Sch physician, Baltimore City Health Dept, 59-62; mem, Baltimore County Bd Health, 63-66; consult, Proj Head Start, Westinghouse Health Systs, 66-; consult, Nat Found Birth Defects Ctrs, 66-72. *Mem:* Fel Am Acad Pediat; fel Am Pub Health Asn; Asn Teachers Prev Med; fel Am Sch Health Asn. *Res:* Children, growth and development; utilization of health services. *Mailing Add:* 6701 N Charles St Baltimore MD 21204

STINE, PHILIP ANDREW, b Detroit, Mich, Aug 12, 44; m 67; c 2. METALLURGICAL ENGINEERING, SHEET METAL FORMING. *Educ:* Wayne State Univ, BSME, 67; Purdue Univ, MS, 68, PhD(metall eng), 72. *Prof Exp:* Advan res projs agency res asst, Purdue Univ, Lafayette, 68-71; metall engr, 71-75, SR RES METALLURGIST, METALL LAB, APPL RES & DESIGN CTR, GEN ELEC CO, 75- *Concurrent Pos:* Lectr sheet metal forming technol, Am Soc Metals, 80 & 81. *Mem:* Am Inst Metall Engrs; Am Soc Metals; Am Deep Drawing Res Group (treas, 76-78, secy, 78-80, pres, 80-82). *Res:* Formability research including methods and techniques that allow forming difficulty determination for given die, steel and lubricant conditions, allowing definition of optimum forming conditions. *Mailing Add:* Metall Lab Appliance Pk 35-1115 Gen Elec Co Louisville KY 40225

STINE, WILLIAM H, JR, b Cincinnati, Ohio, Mar 23, 26; m 48; c 3. CHEMICAL ENGINEERING, TEXTILE ENGINEERING. *Educ:* Univ Cincinnati, ChemE, 50. *Prof Exp:* Res technician, Chem Res Lab, Nat Cash Register Co, Ohio, 49; engr, Res & Develop Lab, Champion Paper & Fibre Co, 50-55; engr, Carothers Res Lab, 55-58, res engr, 58-62, sr res engr, Textile Res Lab, 62-65, res supvr, 65-77, res supvr, 77-81, RES ASSOC, INDUST PROD RES, TEXTILE FIBERS DEPT, E I DU PONT DE NEMOURS & CO, INC, 81- *Res:* Fiber technology; physical, physico-chemical, chemical and statistical relationships between fibers and end uses; polyamides and melt spinning processes. *Mailing Add:* Indust Prod Res Textile Res Lab E I du Pont de Nemours & Co Inc Wilmington DE 19898

STINE, WILLIAM R, b Schenectady, NY, Dec 14, 38. ORGANIC CHEMISTRY. *Educ:* Union Col, BS, 60; Syracuse Univ, PhD(chem), 66. *Prof Exp:* From asst prof to assoc prof, 65-78, PROF CHEM, WILKES COL, 78- *Mem:* Am Chem Soc. *Res:* Structure of pentavalent phosphorus compounds; reactions of tertiary phosphines with positive halogen compounds. *Mailing Add:* Dept of Chem Wilkes Col Wilkes-Barre PA 18703

STINEBRING, WARREN RICHARD, b Niagara Falls, NY, July 31, 24; m 48; c 3. MEDICAL MICROBIOLOGY. *Educ:* Univ Buffalo, BA, 48; Univ Pa, MS, 50, PhD(bact), 51. *Prof Exp:* From asst instr bact to instr microbiol, Univ Pa, 48-53, assoc microbiol, 53-55; McLaughlin fel, Univ Tex Med Br, 55-57; assoc res prof, Inst Microbiol, Rutgers Univ, 57-60; asst res prof, Sch Med, Univ Pittsburgh, 60-61, from asst prof to assoc prof, 61-65; prof & chmn dept, Univ Calif-Calif Col Med, Irvine, 65-67; chmn dept med microbiol, 67-78, PROF MED MICROBIOL, COL MED, UNIV VT, 67- *Mem:* AAAS; Am Soc Cell Biol; Am Soc Microbiol; Reticuloendothelial Soc. *Res:* Interferon production by bacteria and endotoxin; delayed hypersensitivity; intracellular growth of brucellae and detection of early infection; nonantibody resistance mechanisms. *Mailing Add:* Dept Med Microbiol Univ Vt Col Med Burlington VT 05405

STINECIPHER, MARY MARGARET, b Chattanooga, Tenn, Feb 26, 40; div; c 2. INORGANIC CHEMISTRY, ORGANIC CHEMISTRY. *Educ:* Earlham Col, AB, 62; Univ NC, Chapel Hill, PhD(inorg chem), 67. *Prof Exp:* Fel chem, Res Triangle Inst, 66-68 & 74-75; STAFF MEM CHEM, LOS ALAMOS NAT LAB, 76- *Mem:* Am Chem Soc. *Res:* Explosives. *Mailing Add:* Los Alamos Nat Lab PO Box 1663 M-1 MS C920 Los Alamos NM 87545

STINGELIN, RONALD WERNER, b New York, NY, May 29, 35; m 73; c 2. COAL GEOLOGY, REMOTE SENSING. *Educ:* City Col New York, BS, 57; Lehigh Univ, MS, 59; Pa State Univ, PhD(geol), 65. *Prof Exp:* Res geologist, HRB Singer Inc, 65-67, sr res geologist, 67-68, mgr, Environ Sci Br, 68-72, prin geologist, Energy & Natural Resource Systs Dept, 72-80; VPRES TECH SERVS, RESOURCE TECHNOLOGIES CORP, 80- *Concurrent Pos:* NSF-Am Soc Photogram vis scientist, 68-71. *Mem:* Fel Geol Soc Am; Am Inst Prof Geologists; Sigma Xi. *Res:* Application of remote sensing to environmental problems; energy, resources and technology assessment studies with emphasis on fossil fuels; subsidence, seam interaction and prediction of roof hazards in coal mining; Appalachian coal geology, abandoned mined land problems, and minerals valuation; Pennsylvania anthracite resources. *Mailing Add:* 120 Ronan Dr State College PA 16801

STINGER, HENRY J(OSEPH), b Minneapolis, Minn, Nov 22, 20; m 51; c 3. ENGINEERING PHYSICS. *Educ:* Univ Minn, BEE, 42; Mass Inst Technol, cert, 43. *Prof Exp:* Electronic engr, Control Corp, 46-47; supvr res lab, Gen Mills, Inc, 47-51; chief reactors br, Savannah River Oper Off, US Atomic Energy Comn, 51-52; res supvr, 53-62, RES ASSOC, E I DU PONT DE NEMOURS & CO, INC, 62- *Mem:* Inst Elec & Electronics Engrs. *Res:* Tribiology; electronic properties of materials; electronic devices; electromagnetic shielding & materials; instrumentation & controls. *Mailing Add:* 119 Devonwood Lane Devon PA 19333

STINGL, HANS ALFRED, b Eger, Czech, Oct 13, 27; US citizen; m 54; c 2. INDUSTRIAL ORGANIC CHEMISTRY. *Educ:* Univ Erlangen, dipl, 54, PhD(org chem), 56. *Prof Exp:* Res assoc org chem, Univ Ill, Urbana, 56-58; res & develop chemist, 58-75, RES ASSOC, CIBA-GEIGY CORP-TOMS RIVER PLANT, 75- *Mem:* Fel Am Inst Chem; Am Chem Soc; NY Acad Sci. *Res:* Organometallics; senecio alkaloids; organic dyestuffs and intermediates. *Mailing Add:* 852 Ocean View Dr Toms River NJ 08753

STINI, WILLIAM ARTHUR, b Oshkosh, Wis, Oct 9, 30; m 50; c 3. HUMAN BIOLOGY, PHYSICAL ANTHROPOLOGY. *Educ:* Univ Wis, BBA, 60, MS, 67, PhD(human biol), 69. *Prof Exp:* From asst prof to assoc prof anthrop, Cornell Univ, 68-73; assoc prof, Univ Kans, 73-76; PROF ANTHROP, UNIV ARIZ, 76- *Mem:* AAAS; Am Asn Phys Anthrop; NY Acad Sci; Am Anthrop Asn; Am Inst Nutrit. *Res:* Effects of stress on human development including growth and maturation as measured by gross morphological and serological parameters; evaluation of stress as evolutionary force; nutrition and aging. *Mailing Add:* Dept of Anthrop Univ of Ariz Tucson AZ 85721

STINNER, RONALD EDWIN, b New York, NY, July 27, 43; m 63; c 2. POPULATION ECOLOGY. *Educ:* NC State Univ, BS, 65; Univ Calif, Berkeley, PhD(entom), 70. *Prof Exp:* Res assoc entom, Tex A&M Univ, 70; res assoc, 70-73, asst prof, 73-78, ASSOC PROF ENTOM, NC STATE UNIV, 78- *Mem:* Entom Soc Am; Entom Soc Can; Japanese Soc Pop Ecologists; Int Orgn Biol Control. *Res:* Modeling of population dynamics of agricultural pest insects and pathogens; studies on effects of behavior and host interactions on system dynamics. *Mailing Add:* Dept Entom NC State Univ Raleigh NC 27650

STINNETT, HENRY ORR, b San Francisco, Calif. CARDIOPULMONARY PHYSIOLOGY. *Educ:* Calif State Univ, Sacramento, AB, 63; Univ Calif, Davis, 69, MS, 69, PhD(physiol), 74. *Prof Exp:* Lab technician III res, Dept Avian Sci, Univ Calif, Davis, 64-69, res physiologist, 73-74; asst prof, 76-81, ASSOC PROF PHYSIOL, SCH MED, UNIV NDAK, 81- *Concurrent Pos:*

Fel pharmacol, Health Sci Ctr, Univ Tex, 74-75, asst lectr, 75-76; Am Heart Asn grant, Univ Tex Health Sci Ctr, 75-76 & Sch Med, Univ NDak, 77-81. *Mem:* Sigma Xi; Am Physiol Soc; Nat Asn Underwater Instr. *Res:* Cariovascular, pulmonary physiology; modulatory interactions of the cardiopulmonary mechanoreceptors on the systemic cardiovascular baroreflexes during lung inflation. *Mailing Add:* Dept Physiol Sch Med Univ NDak Grand Forks ND 58202

STINSKI, MARK FRANCIS, b Appleton, Wis, Jan 6, 41; m 68; c 2. MICROBIOLOGY, BIOCHEMISTRY. *Educ:* Mich State Univ, BS, 64, MS, 66, PhD(microbiol & biochem), 69. *Prof Exp:* Instr microbiol, Dept Biol Sci, Western Mich Univ, 67; res virologist, US Army Med Sci Lab, Ft Detrick, 69-71; NIH fel microbiol, Dept Microbiol, Univ Pa, 71-73; asst prof, 73-78, ASSOC PROF VIROL, DEPT MICROBIOL, UNIV IOWA, 78- *Concurrent Pos:* Am Cancer Soc grant, Dept Microbiol, Univ Iowa, 74-77; grant reviewer, Nat Found, 77-79, NSF, 78, 79 & 81, NIH, 78 & 80; NIH grant, 79-84, NIH res career develop award, 80-85. *Mem:* Am Soc Microbiol; Sigma Xi; AAAS; Soc Exp Biol & Med. *Res:* Transcription of the human cytomegalovirus genome; cytomegalovirus genome regulation; herpes virus cellular transformation and replication. *Mailing Add:* Dept of Microbiol Univ of Iowa Iowa City IA 52242

STINSON, AL WORTH, b Monroe, NC, Aug 5, 26; m 60; c 4. ANIMAL BEHAVIOR. *Educ:* NC State Col, BS, 49; Univ Ga, DVM, 56; Univ Minn, MS, 60. *Prof Exp:* Instr vet anat, Univ Minn, 56-60; asst prof vet anat, Cornell Univ, 60-64; asst prof, 64-68, assoc prof, 68-73, PROF VET ANAT, MICH STATE UNIV, 73- *Mem:* Am Asn Vet Anatomists; Am Asn Anatomists. *Res:* Histology of domestic animals. *Mailing Add:* 627 Sunset Lane East Lansing MI 48823

STINSON, DONALD CLINE, b Malta, Idaho, Dec 7, 25; m 54; c 5. ELECTRICAL ENGINEERING. *Educ:* Iowa State Col, BS, 47; Calif Inst Technol, MS, 49; Univ Calif, EE, 53, PhD, 56. *Prof Exp:* Test engr, Gen Elec Co, NY, 47-48; asst elec eng, Univ Calif, 50-52, asst, Electronic Res Lab, 53-56; sr scientist, Missile Systs Div, Lockheed Aircraft Corp, 56-57, group leader microwaves, 57-58, res scientist, 58; prof elec eng, Univ Ariz, 58-68 & Univ Tex, Arlington, 68-69; MEM TECH STAFF, HUGHES AIRCRAFT CO, 69- *Concurrent Pos:* Consult, McGraw-Hill Bk Co, 59- & Tex Instruments Inc, 68- *Mem:* Inst Elec & Electronics Engrs. *Res:* Electromagnetic theory; microwave engineering and networks; evaluation of intrinsic properties of and frequency multiplying in microwave ferrites; parametric amplifiers; damping mechanism of ferrimagnetic resonance in ferrites. *Mailing Add:* 6765 S Headley Rd Tucson AZ 85706

STINSON, DONALD LEO, b Hominy, Okla, Oct 8, 30; m 51; c 6. PETROLEUM ENGINEERING, CHEMICAL ENGINEERING. *Educ:* Univ Okla, BS, 50; Univ Mich, MS, 51, PhD(chem eng), 57. *Prof Exp:* Res engr, Phillips Petrol Co, 53-58; proj engr, Gulf Res & Develop Co, 58-60; prof petrol eng & head dept, Univ Wyo, 60-72, head dept mineral eng, 72-79, prof petrol eng, 77-79, ARNEX CORP, 81- *Concurrent Pos:* Consult, 62-, Petrol Res Ctr, US Bur Mines, 63- & Cooper Estate, 64-, Wycon Chemical Corp, 69- *Mem:* Am Chem Soc; Am Inst Chem Engrs; Am Inst Mining, Metall & Petrol Engrs. *Res:* Thermodynamics; waste disposal; water treatment; power recovery. *Mailing Add:* 1213 Garfield Laramie WY 82070

STINSON, EDGAR ERWIN, b Auburn, Ind, May 14, 27; m 74; c 4. ORGANIC CHEMISTRY, BIOCHEMISTRY. *Educ:* Purdue Univ, BS, 48; Iowa State Univ, MS, 51, PhD(biochem), 53. *Prof Exp:* Asst prof org chem, Villanova Univ, 53-56; asst prof, Mass Col Pharm, 56-57; RES CHEMIST, AGR & FOOD CHEM, USDA, 57- *Mem:* Am Chem Soc; Inst Food Technologists. *Res:* Mycotoxins; mold metabolism. *Mailing Add:* USDA 600 E Mermaid Lane Philadelphia PA 19118

STINSON, GLEN MONETTE, b Sarnia, Ont, Dec 27, 39; m 62; c 3. EXPERIMENTAL NUCLEAR PHYSICS. *Educ:* Univ Toronto, BASc, 61; Univ Waterloo, MSc, 62; McMaster Univ, PhD(nuclear physics), 66. *Prof Exp:* Fel physics, 66-68, res assoc, Tri-Univ Meson Facility, 68-69, asst res physicist, 69-71, asst prof, 71-76, ASSOC PROF PHYSICS, TRI-UNIV MESON FACILITY, UNIV ALTA, 76- *Concurrent Pos:* Lectr, Univ Alta, 66-68. *Mem:* Am Phys Soc; Can Asn Physicists. *Res:* Proton induced reactions; design and use of high precision magnetic spectrometers; design of charged particle beam transport systems. *Mailing Add:* Dept of Physics TRIUMF Univ of Alta Edmonton AB T6G 2N5 Can

STINSON, HARRY THEODORE, JR, b Newport News, Va, Oct 26, 26; m 49; c 3. GENETICS. *Educ:* Col William & Mary, BS, 47; Ind Univ, PhD(cytogenetics), 51. *Prof Exp:* Asst prof biol, Col William & Mary, 51-52; res asst genetics, Conn Agr Exp Sta, 52-53, res assoc, 53-60, chief geneticist, 60-62; chmn dept bot, 64-65, chmn sect genetics, develop & physiol, 65-77, PROF GENETICS, CORNELL UNIV, 62-, ASSOC DIR DIV BIOL SCI, 77-, DIR UNDERGRAD STUDIES, 80- *Mem:* AAAS; Soc Study Evolution; Bot Soc Am; Genetics Soc Am; Am Soc Nat (treas, 63-66). *Res:* Cytology. *Mailing Add:* Div of Biol Sci Cornell Univ Ithaca NY 14850

STINSON, JAMES ROBERT, b Bakersfield, Calif, Mar 24, 21; m 51. METEOROLOGY. *Educ:* Univ Calif, Santa Barbara, BA, 48; St Louis Univ, MS, 55, PhD(geophys), 58. *Prof Exp:* Jr res meteorologist, Univ Calif, Los Angeles, 49-51; asst prof geophys & assoc sr res physicist, Gen Motors Res Labs, 70-78; MEM TECH STAFF, SANDIA LABS, 78- *Concurrent Pos:* Instr, Okla State Univ, 51-52; sr scientist, Meteorol Res Inc, chief res div, Navy; mem fac earth sci, Northern Ill Univ, 60-62. *Mem:* AAAS; Am Meteorol Soc; Am Geophys Union. *Res:* General meteorology; weather modification; cloud physics; environmental pollution; severe local storms. *Mailing Add:* 1000 E Victoria St Dominguez Hills CA 90747

STINSON, MARY KRYSTYNA, b Bydgoszcz, Poland; US citizen; m 65; c 2. CHEMICAL ENGINEERING, WATER RESOURCES SCIENCE. *Educ:* Silesia Tech Univ, Poland, MS, 59; Univ Mich, Ann Arbor, MS, 69. *Prof Exp:* Chem engr coal chem, Cent Mining Inst, Poland, 58-65; anal chemist, Owens-Ill Tech Ctr, 66-67; res chemist, Univ Mich, Ann Arbor, 67-68; PROJ MGR INDUST POLLUTION RES, US ENVIRON PROTECTION AGENCY, 74- *Honors & Awards:* Gold Medal award, Am Electroplaters Soc, 77; Bronze Medal award, Environ Protection Agency, 79. *Mem:* Am Chem Soc; Am Electroplaters Soc Inc. *Res:* Development of new technologies for treatment of emissions generated by metal finishing, inorganic chemicals and asbestos industries. *Mailing Add:* 37 Beacon Hill Dr Metuchen NJ 08837

STINSON, PERRI JUNE, US citizen. OPERATIONS RESEARCH, STATISTICS. *Educ:* Univ Calif, Santa Barbara, AB, 48; Okla State Univ, MS, 52, PhD(statist), 55. *Prof Exp:* Asst prof health orgn res, St Louis Univ, 58-60; asst prof math, Northern Ill Univ, 60-62; biostatistician, Vet Admin Res Support Ctr, 62-64; mathematician & statistician, US Naval Aviation Safety Ctr, 64-65; head statist & math systs res, Douglas Aircraft Co, 65-67; prof environ eng, Univ Denver, 67-69; PROF OPERS RES & STATIST, CALIF STATE UNIV, LONG BEACH, 69- *Concurrent Pos:* Fac res grant, Univ Denver, 67-69; fac res grant, Calif State Univ, Long Beach, 69-72; consult, US Off Educ, 70-, Tex Water Develop Bd, 71-72 & Meteorol Res, Inc, 71- *Mem:* Opers Res Soc Am; Inst Mgt Sci; Soc Gen Systs Res; Am Statist Asn; Inst Math Statist. *Res:* Statistical and operations research applications to problems in the medical sciences, atmospheric pollution, public administration, and human resources. *Mailing Add:* Dept of Quant Systs Calif State Univ Long Beach CA 90840

STINSON, RICHARD FLOYD, b Cleveland, Ohio, Feb 4, 21; m 54. FLORICULTURE, SCIENCE EDUCATION. *Educ:* Ohio State Univ, BS, 43, MS, 47, PhD, 52. *Prof Exp:* Instr floricult, State Univ NY Sch Agr Alfred, 47-48; asst prof, Univ Conn, 48-55; from asst prof to assoc prof hort, Mich State Univ, 55-67; assoc prof, 67-73, PROF AGR EDUC & HORT, PA STATE UNIV, UNIVERSITY PARK, 73- *Mem:* Am Soc Hort Sci; Am Voc Asn; Sigma Xi. *Res:* Algae control on clay flower pots; application of infrared heating to greenhouse crops; horticultural and natural resources instruction material in agricultural education. *Mailing Add:* Dept Agr & Exten Educ Pa State Univ University Park PA 16802

STINSON, ROBERT ANTHONY, b Hamilton, Ont, Sept 30, 41; m 64. CLINICAL BIOCHEMISTRY. *Educ:* Univ Toronto, BScA, 64; Univ Alta, PhD(plant biochem), 68. *Prof Exp:* Med Res Coun Can fel molecular enzym, Bristol Univ, 68-71; asst prof path, 71-74, assoc prof, 74-81, PROF PATH, UNIV ALTA, 81- *Concurrent Pos:* Hon vis sr lectr biochem med, Univ Dundee, 77-78; sci & res assoc med staff, Univ Alta Hosp, 73- *Mem:* Can Soc Clin Chemists; Can Biochem Soc; Biochem Soc UK. *Res:* Studies of human alkaline phosphatase; to establish the gene origin of each molecular form and through hydrolytic, phosphotransferase, protein phosphatase and clinical association studies to establish a biochemical role for the enzyme. *Mailing Add:* Med Lab Sci Clin Sci Bldg Univ of Alta Edmonton AB T6G 2G7 Can

STINSON, ROBERT HENRY, b Toronto, Ont, Sept 17, 31; m 54; c 3. BIOPHYSICS, PHYSICS. *Educ:* Univ Toronto, BSA, 53, MSA, 57; Univ Western Ont, PhD(biophys), 60. *Prof Exp:* Mem faculty physics dept, Ont Agr Col, 53-63; prof physics, State Univ NY Col Potsdam, 63-67; ASSOC PROF PHYSICS, UNIV GUELPH, 67- *Mem:* AAAS; Biophys Soc; Sigma Xi. *Res:* X-ray and neutron diffraction of connective tissue. *Mailing Add:* Dept of Physics Univ of Guelph Guelph ON N1G 2W1 Can

STIPANOVIC, BOZIDAR J, b Zagreb, Yugoslavia, Jan 9, 33; m 59. CHEMISTRY. *Educ:* Univ Belgrade, BS, 60, PhD(org chem), 65. *Prof Exp:* Teaching asst org chem, Univ Belgrade, 61-65; fel, Ipatieff High Pressure & Catalytic Lab, Northwestern Univ, 66-69; vis assoc prof org chem, Cent Univ Venezuela, 69-70; dir res & develop, Coral Chem Co, Waukegan, 70-76; TECH DIR, RES & TECH SERV, SANTEK CHEM, 76- *Mem:* Am Chem Soc. *Res:* Organic catalytic reactions; surfactants; polymers; base catalyzed alkylations; conversion and chemical coatings on metals; corrosion inhibitors. *Mailing Add:* 1458 Crowe Ave Deerfield IL 60051

STIPANOVIC, ROBERT DOUGLAS, b Houston, Tex, Oct 28, 39; m 76; c 5. NATURAL PRODUCT CHEMISTRY. *Educ:* Loyola Univ, La, BS, 61; Rice Univ, PhD(chem), 66. *Prof Exp:* Res assoc chem, Stanford Univ, 66-67; asst prof, Tex A&M Univ, 67-71; RES CHEMIST, USDA, 71- *Mem:* Am Chem Soc; Phytochem Soc NAm; Royal Soc Chem. *Res:* Natural product synthesis and structure determination; mass spectroscopy structure determination and reaction mechanisms; nuclear magnetic resonance studies. *Mailing Add:* Nat Cotton Path Res Lab PO Drawer JF College Station TX 77840

STIPANOWICH, JOSEPH J, b Canton, Ill, Apr 14, 21; m 47; c 2. MATHEMATICS. *Educ:* Western Ill Univ, BS, 46; Univ Ill, MS, 47; Northwestern Univ, EdD(math), 56. *Prof Exp:* Head dept, 58-68, PROF MATH, WESTERN ILL UNIV, 47- *Mem:* Nat Coun Teachers Math; Math Asn Am. *Res:* History of mathematics; mathematics education. *Mailing Add:* Dept of Math Western Ill Univ Macomb IL 61455

STIPE, JOHN GORDON, JR, b Oxford, Ga, Jan 1, 14; m 43; c 2. PLANETARY SCIENCES. *Educ:* Emory Univ, AB, 33, MS, 38; Princeton Univ, PhD(physics), 45. *Prof Exp:* Engr, Claude Neon Southern Corp, Ga, 35-38; instr physics, Emory Univ, 38-40; asst exp physicist, Comt Fortification Design, Nat Res Coun, NJ, 40-45; assoc physicist, Nat Defense Res Comt, 45-46; assoc prof physics & head dept, Allegheny Col, 46-47; prof & head dept, Randolph-Macon Woman's Col, 47-58; assoc prof, 58-63, prof, 63-79, EMER PROF PHYSICS, BOSTON UNIV, 79- *Concurrent Pos:* Carnegie intern, Harvard Univ, 56-57. *Mem:* AAAS; Am Geophys Union; Am Asn Physics Teachers. *Res:* Terminal ballistics; cratering; course development; solid earth geophysics and planetary physics. *Mailing Add:* 12 Partridge Hill Rd Southborough MA 01772

STIPPES, MARVIN C, b Chicago, Ill, Aug 8, 22; m 46; c 1. APPLIED MECHANICS. *Educ:* Univ Ill, Urbana, BS, 43; Univ Wash, MS, 46; Va Polytech Inst & State Univ, PhD(appl mech), 57. *Prof Exp:* Asst prof math, Mont State Col, 48-49; asst prof mech, Univ Ill, Urbana, 49-51; assoc prof mech, Wash Univ, 51-53; from asst prof to assoc prof, 53-59, PROF MECH, UNIV ILL, URBANA, 59- *Res:* Static and dynamic classical elasticity. *Mailing Add:* 2115 Zuppke Dr Urbana IL 61801

STIREWALT, HARVEY LEE, b Douglas, Ga, Jan 9, 32; m 46; c 3. AQUATIC BIOLOGY, ICHTHYOLOGY. *Educ:* Univ Miss, BA, 53, MS, 58; Univ Tenn, PhD(zool), 72. *Prof Exp:* Teacher biol, Acad Richmond County, 57-58, teacher physics, 58-59; instr biol, 59-60, chmn, Biol Dept, 59-65, asst prof, 60-73, ASSOC PROF BIOL, AUGUSTA COL, 73- *Concurrent Pos:* Grad teaching asst zool, Univ Tenn, 68-70; consult, Ga Dept Natural Resources, 71-; res supvr, Augusta Col Found Fac Res Fund, 74-75 & 77-78. *Mem:* Am Fisheries Soc. *Res:* Taxonomy, especially fishes and immature insects; pollution of aquatic systems, especially organic, inert suspended particles such as dam construction and dredging and thermal loading. *Mailing Add:* Dept of Biol Augusta Col Augusta GA 30904

STIREWALT, MARGARET AMELIA, b Hickory, NC, Jan 18, 11; m 53. MEDICAL PARASITOLOGY. *Educ:* Randolph-Macon Woman's Col, BA, 31; Columbia Univ, MA, 35; Univ Va, PhD(zool), 38; Am Bd Microbiol, Cert pub health & med lab parasitol, 65. *Prof Exp:* Teacher high sch, Va, 31-33; asst zool, Univ Va, 38-40; asst prof biol, Flora Macdonald Col, 40-42; head helminth, Naval Med Res Inst, 45-58, head parasitol, Naval Med Sch, 58-70, dir div parasitol, Naval Med Res Inst, 70-71; PARASITOLOGIST, AM FOUND BIOL RES, 72- *Concurrent Pos:* Va Acad Sci grant, 38-40; instr, Woman's Col, Univ NC, 39. *Mem:* AAAS; Soc Syst Zool; Am Soc Parasitol (vpres, 72); Am Soc Trop Med & Hyg; fel Royal Soc Trop Med & Hyg. *Res:* Taxonomy, morphology and physiology of Turbellaria; bionomics and control of human schistosomes. *Mailing Add:* Am Found for Biol Res 12111 Parklawn Dr Rockville MD 20852

STIRLING, ANDREW JOHN, b Adelaide, S Australia, Dec 23, 44; Can citizen; m 67; c 1. NUCLEAR PHYSICS, INSTRUMENTATION. *Educ:* Univ Adelaide, BSc(sci), 65, BSc(physics), 66; Flinders Univ, S Australia, PhD(physics), 70. *Prof Exp:* Fel physics, Nat Res Coun Can, 69-71; prof electronics, 71-77, head, Instrument Develop Br, 77-80, DIR, ELECTRONICS, INSTRUMENTATION & CONTROL DIV, ATOMIC ENERGY CAN LTD, 81- *Mem:* Can Nuclear Soc. *Res:* Nuclear power instrumentation; nuclear safeguards; environmental instrumentation. *Mailing Add:* Atomic Energy of Can Ltd Chalk River Nuclear Labs Chalk River ON K0J 1J0 Can

STIRLING, CHARLES E, b Havelock, NC, Nov 30, 33; m 62; c 3. PHYSIOLOGY, BIOPHYSICS. *Educ:* George Washington Univ, BA, 61; State Univ NY, PhD(physiol), 67. *Prof Exp:* Instr physiol, State Univ NY Upstate Med 66-67; asst prof, 68-74, ASSOC PROF PHYSIOL, UNIV WASH, 74- *Mem:* Am Physiol Soc; ARVO; Biophys Soc; Am Soc Cell Biol. *Res:* Active transport. *Mailing Add:* Dept of Physiol & Biophys Univ of Wash Seattle WA 98105

STIRLING, IAN G, b Nkana, Zambia, Sept 26, 41; Can citizen. ZOOLOGY, WILDLIFE MANAGEMENT. *Educ:* Univ BC, BSc, 63, MSc, 65; Univ Canterbury, PhD(zool), 68. *Prof Exp:* Lectr zool, Univ Canterbury, 68-69; res assoc seals, Univ Adelaide, 69-70; RES SCIENTIST POLAR BEARS & SEALS, CAN WILDLIFE SERV, 70- *Concurrent Pos:* Chmn, Fed-Prov Tech Comt Polar Bear Res Can, 71-; mem, Seal & Polar Bear Specialists Groups, 74- *Mem:* Can Soc Zoologists; Can Soc Environ Biologists; Am Soc Mammalogists. *Res:* Ecology, behavior, evolution and management of marine mammals in polar marine ecosystems. *Mailing Add:* 7811 144ST Edmonton AB T5R 0R1 Can

STIRN, RICHARD J, b Milwaukee, Wis, Dec 5, 33; m 67; c 3. ENERGY CONVERSION, ELECTRON DEVICES. *Educ:* Univ Wis, BS, 61; Purdue Univ, MS, 63, PhD(physics), 66. *Prof Exp:* MEM TECH STAFF, JET PROPULSION LAB, CALIF INST TECHNOL, 66- *Concurrent Pos:* Ed, Appl Physics Commun. *Mem:* Am Phys Soc; Inst Elec & Electronics Engrs; Am Vacuum Soc. *Res:* Properties of energy barriers in semiconductors, including p-n junctions and Schottky barriers, photovoltaics, laser energy conversion, transport properties and band structure in III-V semiconductors; chemical vapor deposition of III-V semiconductors; magnetron sputtering of oxides and semiconductors; gallium arsenide devices. *Mailing Add:* Jet Propulsion Lab Calif Inst of Technol Pasadena CA 91103

STIRRAT, JAMES HILL, b Johnstone, Scotland, Sept 17, 13; Can citizen; m 39; c 1. PATHOLOGY, BACTERIOLOGY. *Educ:* Glasgow Univ, BSc, 35, MB, ChB, 38, MD, 45; Univ Alta, cert path, 64; FRCPath, 63. *Prof Exp:* Intern & resident med, surg & obstet, Glasgow Munic Hosps, 38-40, asst pathologist & bacteriologist, 40-45; assoc prof bact, Univ Alta, 48-52, assoc prof path & asst prof pathologist, 52-56, prof path, 57-60; dir dept virol & pathologist, State Pub Health Lab Serv, Western Australia, 60; assoc pathologist, Gen Hosp, Calgary, Alta, 61-63; dir dept lab med, 63-73, bacteriologist, pathologist & infection control officer, 73-77, SR ACTIVE CONSULT PATHOLOGIST, MISERICORDIA HOSP, 78- *Concurrent Pos:* Adv, Sch Med Technol, Northern Alta Inst Technol, 63-73; consult pathologist, Grand Prairie Munic Hosp, High Prairie & Sisters of Providence Hosp, Alta, 63-68; Edmonton Gen Hosp, 63-75, McLennan Munic Hosp, Alta, 63-78 & Devon Munic Hosp, Alta, 63-80; asst prof path, Univ Alta, 64-78. *Mem:* Fel Col Am Pathologists; Can Med Asn; Can Asn Pathologists; Can Soc Forensic Sci; Brit Med Asn. *Res:* Forensic medicine; spread of carcinoma in the human body; typhus group of fevers in India; bacteria associated with insects parasitic on livestock. *Mailing Add:* 601 Valleyview Manor 12207 Jasper Ave Edmonton AB T5N 3K2 Can

STITCH, MALCOLM LANE, b Apr 23, 23; m 65, 75; c 4. PHYSICS, ENGINEERING. *Educ:* Southern Methodist Univ, BA & BS, 47; Columbia Univ, PhD(physics), 53. *Prof Exp:* Res asst radiation lab, Columbia Univ, 48-51; instr, Cooper Union Eng Col, 51-52; res asst radiation lab, Columbia Univ, 52-53; res physicist, Varian Assocs, 53-56; res physicist & head molecular beams group, Res Labs, Hughes Aircraft Co, 56-60, sr staff physicist, 59-60, head laser develop sect, Res & Develop Div, 61-62, mgr laser develop dept, 62-65, asst mgr high frequency lab, Res & Develop Div, 65-67, chief scientist, 67-68; asst gen mgr, Korad Dept, Union Carbide Corp, Calif, 68-73; sr scientist & consult, Ctr Laser Studies, Naval Res Lab, Univ Southern Calif, 73-74; mgr electro-optical opers, Exxon Nuclear Res & Technol Ctr, 74-81, ENG ASSOC, EXXON RES & ENG CO, 81- *Concurrent Pos:* Instr, Sarah Lawrence Col, 49-51; mem comt safe use lasers, Am Nat Standards Inst, 72-; adj prof elec eng, Univ Southern Calif, 74- *Mem:* AAAS; Am Phys Soc; fel Inst Elec & Electronics Engrs; NY Acad Sci; fel Soc Photo-Optical Instrumentation Engrs. *Res:* Instrumentation; quantum electronics; laser technology and applications; laser isotope separation; accusto and electro-optics. *Mailing Add:* Exxon Res & Eng Co PO Box 101 Florham Park NJ 07932

STITELER, WILLIAM MERLE, III, b Kane, Pa, July 30, 42; m 64; c 1. STATISTICS, FORESTRY. *Educ:* Pa State Univ, BS, 64, MS, 66, PhD(statist), 70. *Prof Exp:* Asst prof statist, Pa State Univ, University Park, 70-73; assoc prof, 73-78, PROF, STATE UNIV NY COL FORESTRY, 78- *Concurrent Pos:* Consult comput models. *Mem:* Inst Math Statist; Am Statist Asn; Int Asn Ecol; Biomet Soc. *Res:* Spatial patterns in ecological populations; modeling and simulation of biological populations; computer models for response to toxic substances. *Mailing Add:* Dept of Forestry State Univ NY Col of Forestry Syracuse NY 13210

STITES, JOSEPH GANT, JR, b Hopkinsville, Ky, Mar 29, 21; m 43; c 4. INORGANIC CHEMISTRY, ORGANIC CHEMISTRY. *Educ:* Univ Ky, BS, 43; Mich State Univ, PhD(inorg chem), 49. *Prof Exp:* Dir new process technol, Monsanto Co, 49-73; dir process technol, Res Cottrell, Inc, 73-75; DIR RES & DEVELOP, AIR CORRECTION DIV, UOP INC, 75- *Honors & Awards:* Kirkpatrick Award, McGraw Hill, 70. *Mem:* Am Chem Soc; Environ Indust Coun; Air Pollution Control Asn. *Res:* Environmental control-gaseous and particulate collection systems, heavy chemicals, phosphates, nitrogen chemicals, explosives, rare-earths and separation techniques. *Mailing Add:* Dewal Dr Norwalk CT 06851

STITH, JEFFREY LEN, b Seattle, Wash, July 15, 50; m 79. ATMOSPHERIC SCIENCES, CLOUD PHYSICS. *Educ:* Western Wash State Col, BA, 71; Rensselaer Polytech Inst, MS, 74; Univ Wash, PhD(atmospheric sci), 78. *Prof Exp:* res scientist, Meteorol Res Inc, 78-80; RES ASSOC, UNIV NDAK, 80- *Mem:* Am Meteorol Soc; Air Pollution Control Asn. *Res:* Aerosol and cloud physics research. *Mailing Add:* Box 8216 Univ Sta Grand Forks ND 58202

STITH, LEE S, b Tulia, Tex, Aug 30, 18; m 47; c 1. PLANT BREEDING. *Educ:* NMex State Univ, BS, 40; Univ Tenn, MS, 42; Iowa State Univ, PhD(crop breeding), 55. *Prof Exp:* Asst county supvr, Farm Security Admin, DeBaca County, NMex, 40-41; res asst agr econ, Univ Tenn, 41-42; agronomist, El Paso Valley Substa 17, Tex A&M Univ, 46-47, cotton breeder, 47-55; PLANT BREEDER & PROF PLANT BREEDING, UNIV ARIZ, 55-, DIR HYBRID COTTON RES PROJ, 72-, DIR RES INSTR, PLANT SCI DEPT, 76- *Mem:* Am Soc Agron; Crop Sci Soc; Am Genetics Asn. *Res:* Crop breeding; plant pathology and physiology; statistics; cotton and grain sorghum; cytoplasmic male sterility to produce hybrid cotton; revolutionary concept in cotton breeding. *Mailing Add:* Dept of Plant Sci Col of Agr Univ of Ariz Tucson AZ 85721

STITH, REX DAVID, b Hominy, Okla, Dec 11, 42; m 64; c 2. ENDOCRINOLOGY. *Educ:* Okla State Univ, BS, 64, MS, 66; Purdue Univ, PhD(physiol), 71. *Prof Exp:* Instr biol, Southeast Mo State Col, 66-68; vet physiol, Purdue Univ, 68-71; res assoc pharmacol, Univ Mo-Columbia, 71-72; asst prof, 72-75, ASSOC PROF PHYSIOL, HEALTH SCI CTR, UNIV OKLA, 75- *Concurrent Pos:* Vis assoc prof, Dept Physiol, Univ Calif, San Francisco, 79; Guest lectr, Univ St George's Sch Med, Grenada, West Indies. *Mem:* AAAS; Sigma Xi; Soc Exp Biol & Med; Am Physiol Soc; Endocrine Soc. *Res:* Mechanisms of action of glucocorticoids; interactions of steroids in target cells; effects of glucocorticoids on intracellular functions; mechanisms of action of steroid hormones on target tissues, especially brain tissues and biochemical interactions of steroids in these tissues. *Mailing Add:* Dept Phys & Biophys Box 26901 Univ of Okla Health Sci Ctr Oklahoma City OK 73190

STITH, WILLIAM JOSEPH, b Oklahoma City, Okla, Feb 7, 42; m 66; c 3. BIOCHEMISTRY. *Educ:* Phillips Univ, BA, 64; Univ Okla, PhD(biochem), 72. *Prof Exp:* Chief microbiol, US Naval Hosp, Philadelphia, 66-67, chief blood bank & serol, 67-68; asst officer in-chg, Armed Serv Whole Blood Processing Lab, McGuire AFB, NJ, 68-69; fel human biol chem & genetics, Univ Tex Med Br, Galveston, 72-73; scientist prod explor, Fenwal Div, Baxter Labs, Inc, 73-77; vpres affairs, Med Eng Corp, 77-81; MGR, BIOENG DEPT, LORD CORP, ERIE, PA, 81- *Mem:* Asn Advan Med Instrumentation; Am Soc Qual Control; Am Chem Soc; Sigma Xi. *Res:* Quality control; product reliability; regulatory affairs; product development, and clinical studies. *Mailing Add:* Bioeng Dept Lord Corp 1600 Peninsula Dr Erie PA 16512

STITT, JAMES HARRY, b Sellersville, Pa, Dec 13, 39; m 64; c 2. GEOLOGY, PALEONTOLOGY. *Educ:* Rice Univ, BA, 61; Univ Tex, Austin, MA, 64, PhD(geol), 68. *Prof Exp:* Assoc prof, 68-78, chmn dept, 77-80 PROF GEOL, UNIV MO-COLUMBIA, 78- *Mem:* Paleont Soc; Geol Soc Am. *Res:* Late Cambrian and early Ordovician trilobites; invertebrate paleontology and biostratigraphy; carbonate petrology. *Mailing Add:* Dept of Geol Univ of Mo Columbia MO 65201

STITT, JOHN THOMAS, b Belfast, Northern Ireland, Nov 7, 42; m 66; c 2. PHYSIOLOGY, NEUROPHYSIOLOGY. *Educ:* Queens Univ Belfast, BSc, 65; Queens Univ, Ont, MSc, 67, PhD(physiol), 69. *Prof Exp:* Can Med Res Coun fel, Med Sch, 69-72, asst fel, 69-73, asst prof environ physiol, 72-76, ASSOC FEL PHYSIOL, JOHN B PIERCE FOUND LAB, YALE UNIV, 73-, ASSOC PROF EPIDEMIOL & PHYSIOL, MED SCH, 76- *Mem:* Am Physiol Soc; Can Physiol Soc; Soc Neurosci. *Res:* Physiology of thermoregulation in mammals; role of the hypothalamus in the homeostasis of body temperature; neurophysiological mechanisms of fever. *Mailing Add:* John B Pierce Found Lab Yale Univ Sch of Med New Haven CT 06519

STITZEL, ROBERT ELI, b New York, NY, Feb 22, 37; m 61; c 1. PHARMACOLOGY. *Educ:* Columbia Univ, BS, 59, MS, 61; Univ Minn, PhD(pharmacol), 64. *Prof Exp:* Res asst pharmacol, Univ Minn, 61-64; asst prof, WVa Univ, 65-66; Swed Med Res Coun fel, 66-67; from asst prof to assoc prof, 67-73, dir grad studies, Dept Pharmacol, 73-76, asst chmn dept, 76-79, PROF PHARMACOL, WVA UNIV, 73-, ASSOC CHMN DEPT, 79- *Concurrent Pos:* USPHS fel, 64-65; USPHS res career develop award; vis prof, Univ Adelaide, Australia, 73 & Univ Innsbruck, Austria, 77; Danforth Found assoc, 75-; hon res fel anat & embryol, Univ Col London, 77; Fogarty Sr Int fel, NIH, 77; actg chmn dept pharmacol, WVa Univ, 78. *Mem:* AAAS; Am Soc Pharmacol & Exp Therapeut; Int Soc Biochem Pharmacol; Am Soc Neurochem. *Res:* Physiological and pharmacological factors affecting catecholamine release; hypertension. *Mailing Add:* Dept of Pharmacol WVa Univ Morgantown WV 26506

STITZELL, JOHN ANTHONY, chemical engineering, behavioral science, see previous edition

STIVALA, SALVATORE SILVIO, b New York, NY, June 23, 23; m 50; c 2. PHYSICAL CHEMISTRY. *Educ:* Columbia Univ, AB, 48; Stevens Inst Technol, MSChE, 52, MS, 58; Univ Pa, PhD(chem), 60. *Hon Degrees:* MEng, Stevens Inst Technol, 64. *Prof Exp:* Res engr, US Testing Co, 49-50; mat engr, Picatinny Arsenal, 50-51, 54-57; NSF sci fac fel, Univ Pa, 57-59; from asst prof to assoc prof phys & polymer chem, 59-64, instr chem eng, 52-57, PROF PHYS & POLYMER CHEM, STEVENS INST TECHNOL, 64- *Concurrent Pos:* Consult, 52-57, 59-, indust, 60-; vis scientist, Inst Phys Chem, Graz Univ, 66 & dept ultra-struct biochem, Cornell Med Col, 69. *Honors & Awards:* Ottens Res Award, 68; Freygang Teacher Award, 65; Med Soc Sendai (Japan) Award, 69; Honor Scroll, Am Inst Chemists, 77. *Mem:* Am Chem Soc; Sigma Xi. *Res:* Physical chemistry of high polymers; solution properties; kinetics of polymer degradation; physico-chemical aspects of biopolymers. *Mailing Add:* Dept of Chem & Chem Eng Stevens Inst of Technol Castle Point Hoboken NJ 07030

STIVEN, ALAN ERNEST, b St Stephen, NB, Nov 12, 35; m 72; c 3. ECOLOGY, POPULATION BIOLOGY. *Educ:* Univ NB, BSc, 57; Univ BC, MA, 59; Cornell Univ, PhD(ecol), 62. *Prof Exp:* From asst prof to assoc prof zool, 62-71, chmn dept, 67-72, PROF ZOOL, UNIV NC, CHAPEL HILL & CHMN ECOL CURRIC, 71- *Concurrent Pos:* NSF res grants, 63-; USPHS ecol training grant, 66-69; res fel, Univ BC, 70; res grant, Sea Grant, Nat Oceanog & Atmos Asn, 74-76. *Mem:* Ecol Soc Am; Am Soc Naturalists; Am Soc Limnol & Oceanog; Japanese Soc Pop Ecol. *Res:* Population ecology; secondary productivity in aquatic systems; population energetics; stream and salt marsh ecology. *Mailing Add:* Dept of Zool Univ of NC Chapel Hill NC 27514

STIVENDER, DONALD LEWIS, b Chicago, Ill, May 8, 32; m 56; c 3. DYNAMIC CONTROL, ENGINE EMISSIONS. *Educ:* US Coast Guard Acad, BS, 54; Univ Mich, MS, 59. *Prof Exp:* MEM STAFF RES & DEVELOP, RES LABS, GEN MOTORS CORPS, 59-, SR RES ENGR, 68- *Concurrent Pos:* Consult pub domain disciplines; pres, Square Lake Corp, 74-; owner, Stivender Eng Assocs, 80-. *Honors & Awards:* Arch T Colwell Awards, Soc Automotive Engrs, 68, 69 & 79. *Mem:* Soc Automotive Engrs; Am Soc Mech Engrs; Combustion Inst. *Res:* Gas turbine, diesel spark ignition and alternative engine combustion, emission, construction and control aspects; internal combustion engines; engine and vehicle dynamometer control and transient optimization. *Mailing Add:* Engine Res Dept 12 Miles & Mound Rd Warren MI 48090

STIVER, JAMES FREDERICK, b Elkhart, Ind, Jan 27, 43; m 65; c 4. MEDICINAL CHEMISTRY, BIONUCLEONICS. *Educ:* Purdue Univ, BS, 66, MS, 68, PhD(med chem, bionucleonics), 70. *Prof Exp:* From asst prof to assoc prof pharmaceut chem & bionucleonics, Col Pharm, NDak State Univ, 73-76, radiol safety officer, 70-76; radiol safety officer, KMS Fusion, Inc, 76-80. *Mem:* AAAS; Am Chem Soc; Am Pharmaceut Asn; Am Pub Health Asn; Am Col Nuclear Physicians. *Res:* Radioisotope labeling synthesis of organic compounds and drugs; radioisotope tracer techniques and tracer methodology development; metabolism of drug and toxic chemicals; radioactive nuclide levels in the environment; health physics relating to laser-fusion. *Mailing Add:* 59089 Sr 15 Goshen IN 46526

STIVERS, RUSSELL KENNEDY, b Marshall Co, Ill, May 9, 17; m 47; c 3. SOIL FERTILITY. *Educ:* Univ Ill, BS, 39; Purdue Univ, MS, 48, PhD, 50. *Prof Exp:* Assoc agronomist, Va Polytech Inst, 50-55; ASSOC PROF AGRON, PURDUE UNIV, LAFAYETTE, 55- *Mem:* Am Soc Agron; Soil Sci Soc Am. *Res:* Soil testing. *Mailing Add:* Dept of Agron Purdue Univ West Lafayette IN 47907

STIX, THOMAS HOWARD, b St Louis, Mo, July 12, 24; m 50; c 2. PLASMA PHYSICS. *Educ:* Calif Inst Technol, BS, 48; Princeton Univ, PhD(physics), 53. *Prof Exp:* Res asst, 53-54, res assoc, 54-56, assoc head exp div, 56-61, co-head exp div, 61-78, ASSOC DIR ACAD AFFAIRS, PLASMA PHYSICS LAB, PRINCETON UNIV, 78-, PROF ASTROPHYS SCI, 62-, ASSOC CHMN DEPT ASTROPHYS SCI, 81- *Concurrent Pos:* NSF sr fel, 60-61; mem adv comt, thermonuclear div, Oak Ridge Nat Lab, 66-68; John Simon Guggenheim Mem Found fel, 69-70. *Honors & Awards:* James Clerk Maxwell Prize, Am Phys Soc, 80. *Mem:* Fel Am Phys Soc. *Res:* Controlled fusion; waves and instabilities; plasma heating and confinement. *Mailing Add:* Plasma Physics Lab Princeton Univ Princeton NJ 08540

STJERNHOLM, RUNE LEONARD, b Stockholm, Sweden, Apr 25, 24; nat US; m 53; c 2. BIOCHEMISTRY. *Educ:* Stockholm Tech Inst, BS, 44; Western Reserve Univ, PhD(biochem), 58. *Prof Exp:* From asst prof to prof biochem, Case Western Reserve Univ, 58-71; PROF BIOCHEM & CHMN DEPT, MED SCH, TULANE UNIV, 71- *Mem:* Am Chem Soc; Am Soc Microbiol; Royal Soc Chem; Swed Chem Soc. *Res:* Intermediary metabolism of microorganisms; carbohydrate metabolism in leukocytes. *Mailing Add:* Dept of Biochem Tulane Univ Med Sch New Orleans LA 70112

STOB, MARTIN, b Chicago, Ill, Feb 20, 26. ANIMAL SCIENCE. *Educ:* Purdue Univ, PhD(physiol), 53. *Prof Exp:* Asst, 49-53, asst prof animal husb, 53-58, assoc prof animal sci, 58-63, PROF ANIMAL SCI, PURDUE UNIV, WEST LAFAYETTE, 63- *Mem:* AAAS; Am Soc Animal Sci; Endocrine Soc; Soc Study Fertil; Soc Study Reproduction. *Res:* Hormonal regulation of growth; occurrence of compounds with estrogenic activity in plant material; microbiological synthesis and metabolism of estrogens; reproductive physiology. *Mailing Add:* Dept of Animal Sci Purdue Univ West Lafayette IN 47906

STOB, MICHAEL JAY, b Chicago, Ill, Aug 2, 52; m 74; c 1. RECURSION THEORY. *Educ:* Calvin Col, BS, 74; Univ Chicago, SM, 75, PhD(math), 79. *Prof Exp:* C L E Moore instr math, Mass Inst Technol, 79-81; ASST PROF MATH, CALVIN COL, 81- *Concurrent Pos:* Prin investr, NSF grant. *Mem:* Am Math Soc; Asn Symbolic Logic; Math Asn Am. *Res:* Mathematical logic especially recursion theory; recursively enumerable sets and degrees. *Mailing Add:* Dept Math Calvin Col Grand Rapids MI 49506

STOBAUGH, ROBERT EARL, b Humboldt, Tenn, June 24, 27; m 56. INFORMATION SCIENCE. *Educ:* Southwestern at Memphis, BS, 47; Univ Tenn, MS, 49, PhD(chem), 52. *Prof Exp:* Res assoc, Ohio State Univ, 52-54; from asst ed to sr assoc ed, 54-61, from asst dept head to dept head, 61-65, tech adv registry div, 65-67, MGR CHEM INFO SCI, CHEM ABSTR, 67- *Mem:* Am Soc Info Sci; Am Chem Soc. *Res:* Steroids; chemical literature; chemical information storage and retrieval; chemical structural data; chemical information science. *Mailing Add:* Chem Abstr Serv PO Box 3012 Columbus OH 43210

STOBBE, ELMER HENRY, b Matsqui, BC, Jan 26, 36; m 62; c 3. AGRONOMY, WEED SCIENCE. *Educ:* Univ BC, BSA, 61, MSA, 65; Ore State Univ, PhD(crop sci), 69. *Prof Exp:* Asst prof, 68-72, ASSOC PROF WEED SCI, UNIV MAN, 72- *Mem:* Weed Sci Soc Am; Agr Inst Can. *Res:* Weed science, especially chemical and cultural weed control, physiology of herbicides, weed-crop ecology, biology of weeds and mechanics of herbicide application; agronomy, especially zero tillage research and effect of cultivation on crop yield. *Mailing Add:* Dept of Plant Sci Univ of Man Winnipeg MB R3T 2N2 Can

STOBER, HENRY CARL, b Brooklyn, NY, June 20, 35; m 61; c 2. ANALYTICAL CHEMISTRY, PHARMACEUTICAL CHEMISTRY. *Educ:* City Col New York, BS, 58; Seton Hall Univ, MS, 69, PhD(chem), 71. *Prof Exp:* Res asst biol chem, Letterman Army Hosp, US Army, 58-60; chemist, Ciba Pharmaceut Co, 60-66, supvr anal chem, 66-70; teaching asst chem, Seton Hall Univ, 70-71; sr scientist, 71-74, SR STAFF SCIENTIST, CIBA-GEIGY CORP, SUFFERN, NY, 74- *Mem:* Am Chem Soc. *Res:* Analysis and solid state characterization of pharmaceuticals and related chemicals. *Mailing Add:* 124 Madison Ave Madison NJ 07940

STOBER, QUENTIN JEROME, b Billings, Mont, Mar 25, 38; m 65; c 2. AQUATIC ECOLOGY, FISHERIES MANAGEMENT. *Educ:* Mont State Univ, BS, 60, MS, 62, PhD(zool), 68. *Prof Exp:* Aquatic biologist, Southeast Water Lab, Div Water Supply & Pollution Control, USPHS, Ga, 62-65; res asst prof estuarine ecol, 69-72, res assoc prof estuarine & stream ecol, 72-77, RES PROF STREAM & RESERVOIR ECOL & FISH TOXICOL, FISHERIES RES INST, UNIV WASH, 77- *Concurrent Pos:* Admin judge, Environ Atomic Safety & Licensing Bd Panel, US Nuclear Regulatory Comn, 74- *Honors & Awards:* W F Thompson Award, Am Inst Fisheries Res Biol, 71. *Mem:* AAAS; Am Fisheries Soc; Am Soc Limnol & Oceanog; Am Inst Fisheries Res Biol; Sigma Xi. *Res:* Fisheries problems related to hydro and thermal nuclear energy production; estuarine ecology of effects of municipal and industrial wastes; fish toxicology and behavior; stream ecology, instream flow needs and reservoir ecology. *Mailing Add:* Fisheries Res Inst Univ Wash Col Fisheries Seattle WA 98195

STOBO, JOHN DAVID, b Somerville, Mass, Sept 1, 41; m 64; c 3. IMMUNOLOGY. *Educ:* Dartmouth Col, AB, 63; State Univ NY Buffalo, MD, 67. *Prof Exp:* Res assoc immunol, NIH, 70-72; chief resident med, Johns Hopkins Hosp, 72-73; asst prof immunol, Mayo Med Sch & Found, 73-76; ASSOC PROF MED & HEAD SECT RHEUMATOLOGY/CLIN IMMUNOL, MOFFITT HOSP, UNIV CALIF, SAN FRANCISCO, 76- *Concurrent Pos:* Sr investr, Am Arthritis Asn, 73; rep, Nat Heart Asn, 75-77. *Mem:* Am Asn Immunologists; Am Arthritis Asn. *Res:* Cellular immunology; forces involved in the regulation of cell mediated and humoral immune responses. *Mailing Add:* Sect of Rheumatology/Clin Immunol Moffitt Hosp Univ of Calif San Francisco CA 94143

STOBO, WAYNE THOMAS, b Sudbury, Ont, June 16, 44. FISHERIES BIOLOGY, ORNITHOLOGY. *Educ:* Laurentian Univ, BSc, 65; Univ Ottawa, MSc, 71; Dalhousie Univ, PhD(ecol), 73. *Prof Exp:* Biologist fisheries, Dept Environ, 72-73; res scientist, 73-76, sect head pop dynamics, 76-77, pop dynamics & biostatist, 77-78, COORDR, MARINE FISH DIV, DEPT FISHEREIES & OCEANS, FED GOVT CAN, 79- *Concurrent Pos:* Chmn pelagic subcomt, Can Atlantic Fisheries Sci Adv Comt, 79-81. *Res:* Optimizing the biological productivity of commercially exploited finfish stocks; populations dynamics of finfish and marine mammals. *Mailing Add:* Marine Fish Div Bedford Inst Oceanog PO Box 1006 Darmouth NS B2Y 4A2 Can

STOCK, CHARLES CHESTER, b Terre Haute, Ind, May 19, 10; m 36. CHEMOTHERAPY. *Educ:* Rose-Hulman Inst Technol, BS, 32; Johns Hopkins Univ, PhD(physiol chem), 37; NY Univ, MS, 41. *Hon Degrees:* ScD, Rose-Hulman Inst, 54. *Prof Exp:* Instr bact, Col Med, NY Univ, 37-41; vol worker, Rockefeller Hosp Med Res, 41-42; tech aide, Comt Treatment Gas Casualties, Div Med Sci, Nat Res Coun, 42-45, exec secy, Insect Control Comt, 45-46, chmn chem coding panel chem-biol, Coord Ctr, 46-52; assoc, 46-50, chief, Div Exp Chemother, 47-72, mem, Sloan-Kettering Inst Cancer Res, 50-80, assoc dir inst, 57-60, sci dir, 60-61, vpres, 61-72, vpres inst affairs, Cancer Ctr, 74-80, vpres & assoc dir admin & acad affairs, 76-80, EMER MEM, WALKER LAB, RYE, SLOAN-KETTERING INST CANCER RES, 80-; EMER PROF BIOCHEM, SLOAN-KETTERING DIV, MED COL, CORNELL UNIV, 76- *Concurrent Pos:* Prof biochem, Sloan-Kettering Div, Med Col, Cornell Univ, 51-75; mem comt tumor nomenclature & statist, Int Cancer Res Comn, 52-54; chmn screening panel, Cancer Chemother Nat Serv Ctr, NIH, 55-58 & drug eval panel, 58-; mem sci adv bd, Roswell Park Mem Inst, 57-66; mem chemother rev bd, Nat Adv Cancer Coun, 58-59; mem US nat comt, Int Union Against Cancer, 67-, chmn, 75-80; mem bd dirs, Am Cancer Soc, 72- *Honors & Awards:* Alfred P Sloan Award, 65; C Chester Stock Award Cancer Res, 80. *Mem:* Emer mem Am Chem Soc; emer mem Am Soc Biol Chemists; Soc Exp Biol & Med; Am Asn Cancer Res; hon mem Japanese Cancer Asn. *Res:* Enzymes; hypertension; experimental chemotherapy of cancer. *Mailing Add:* 605 E 82nd St New York NY 10028

STOCK, DAVID ALLEN, b Elyria, Ohio, Feb 8, 41; m 64; c 1. MICROBIOLOGY, GENETICS. *Educ:* Mich State Univ, BS, 63; NC State Univ, MS, 66, PhD(genetics), 68. *Prof Exp:* Instr microbiol, Sch Med, Univ Miss, 67-68; USDA fel, Baylor Col Med, 68-69, NIH fel, 69-70; asst prof biol, 70-76, ASSOC PROF BIOL, STETSON UNIV, 76- *Mem:* Am Soc Microbiol; Am Phytopath Soc. *Res:* Cytogenetics, physiology and pathogenesis of Candida albicans; metabolism of heavy metals in aquatic ecosystems, nucleic acid metabolism of mycoplasma, genetics of fungi. *Mailing Add:* Dept of Biol Stetson Univ De Land FL 32720

STOCK, DAVID EARL, b Baltimore, Md, Feb 2, 39; m 62; c 2. FLUID MECHANICS, MULTIPHASE FLOW. *Educ:* Pa State Univ, BS, 61; Univ Conn, MS, 65; Ore State Univ, PhD(mech eng), 72. *Prof Exp:* Test engr, Pratt & Whitney Aircraft, 61-65; Peace Corps volunteer, Ghana, WAfrica, 66-68; teaching asst, Ore State Univ, 68-72; asst prof, 72-77, ASSOC PROF MECH ENG, WASH STATE UNIV, 77- *Concurrent Pos:* Vis fel, Cornell Univ, 81-82. *Mem:* Am Soc Mech Engrs; Am Phys Soc; Air Pollution Control Asn; Combustion Inst; Am Soc Eng Educ. *Res:* Experimental fluid mechanics which includes the use of laser Dopper and thermal anemometry as well as computer aided data acquision and processing; gas particle flow with a main application to electrostatic precipitators. *Mailing Add:* Dept Mech Eng Wash State Univ Pullman WA 99164

STOCK, JOHN JOSEPH, b Oakville, Ont, June 9, 20; m 45; c 2. MICROBIOLOGY, MEDICAL MYCOLOGY. *Educ:* Univ Toronto, BSA, 44; McGill Univ, MSc, 49, PhD(bact, immunol), 51. *Prof Exp:* Tech supvr antibiotic fermentations, Merck & Co, Que, 44-45; prod, control & res bacteriologist, F W Horner Co, 45-47; asst prof bact & immunol, 51-61, assoc prof microbiol, 61-72, PROF MICROBIOL, UNIV BC, 73- *Mem:* Am Soc Microbiol; Med Mycol Soc of the Americas; Can Soc Microbiol. *Res:* Factors influencing the virulence of dermatophytes, as well as studies on their composition, metabolism and immunology. *Mailing Add:* Dept of Microbiol Univ BC Vancouver BC V6T 1W5 Can

STOCK, JOHN THOMAS, b Margate, Eng, Jan 26, 11; nat US; m 45; c 1. ANALYTICAL CHEMISTRY. *Educ:* Univ London, BSc, 39 & 41, MSc, 45, PhD(chem), 49, DSc, 65. *Prof Exp:* Sci off chem, Ministry Supply, Gt Brit, 40-44; actg chief chemist, Fuller's Ltd, 44-46; lectr chem, Norwood Tech Col, 46-51; head dept, 51-56; from assoc prof to prof, 56-79, EMER PROF CHEM, UNIV CONN, 79- *Concurrent Pos:* London County Coun Blair fel, Univ Minn, 53-54; consult, 50- *Honors & Awards:* Fel Sci Mus, London. *Mem:* Fel Am Chem Soc; fel Royal Soc Chem; Soc Chem Indust; Royal Inst Gt Brit. *Res:* Design of automated and general scientific apparatus; history of scientific instruments. *Mailing Add:* Dept of Chem Univ of Conn Storrs CT 06268

STOCK, LEON M, b Detroit, Mich, Oct 15, 30; m 61; c 2. ORGANIC CHEMISTRY. *Educ:* Univ Mich, BS, 52; Purdue Univ, PhD, 59. *Prof Exp:* From instr to assoc prof, 58-70, PROF CHEM, UNIV CHICAGO, 71- *Concurrent Pos:* Consult, Phillips Petrol Co, 64- *Mem:* Am Chem Soc; Royal Soc Chem. *Res:* Electrophilic aromatic substitution reactions; influences of structure and solvents on reactivity; models for evaluation of inductive influences of substituents; electron paramagnetic resonance spectra of organic radicals; the structure of coal. *Mailing Add:* Dept of Chem Univ of Chicago Chicago IL 60637

STOCK, MOLLY WILFORD, b Glen Ridge, NJ, Aug 17, 42; m 62; c 2. FOREST ENTOMOLOGY, POPULATION GENETICS. *Educ:* Univ Conn, BA, 64, MS, 65; Ore State Univ, PhD(entom), 72. *Prof Exp:* Res asst entom, Ore State Univ, 68-69; res assoc insect biochem, Wash State Univ, 72-73, res collabr entom, 73-75; proj leader, Wash State Univ, 75-77; asst prof forest entom, 76-78, asst prof forest resources, 78-80, ASSOC PROF FOREST RESOURCES, UNIV IDAHO, 80- *Mem:* Entom Soc Am; Soc Am Foresters; Genetics Soc Am. *Res:* Biosystematics; population dynamics of forest insects. *Mailing Add:* Dept of Forest Resources Univ of Idaho Moscow ID 83843

STOCKBAUER, ROGER LEWIS, b Victoria, Tex, Feb 3, 44; m 72; c 3. SURFACE SCIENCE. *Educ:* Rice Univ, BA, 66; Univ Chicago, MS, 68, PhD(physics), 73. *Prof Exp:* From res asst to res assoc physics, Univ Chicago, 66-73; RES PHYSICIST, NAT BUR STANDARDS, 73- *Concurrent Pos:* Teaching asst physics, Univ Chicago, 69-70; Nat Res Coun-Nat Acad Sci res assoc, Nat Bur Standards, 73-75. *Mem:* Am Phys Soc; Am Soc Mass Spectrometry; Am Vacuum Soc. *Res:* Photon stimulated desorption of ions; ultraviolet photoemission spectroscopy; energetics and unimolecular decay of molecular ions; variable wavelength photoelectron spectra; angular distribution of photoelectrons. *Mailing Add:* Nat Bur Standards Washington DC 20234

STOCKBRIDGE, CHRISTOPHER, b Cambridge, Eng, Mar 15, 29; m 74; c 2. METALLURGY. *Educ:* Univ Chicago, BA, 46; Cambridge Univ, BA, 53, MA, 55, PhD(metall), 57. *Prof Exp:* Fel corrosion, Nat Res Coun Can, 57-59; MEM TECH STAFF, BELL LABS, 59- *Honors & Awards:* Christie Prize. *Mem:* NY Acad Sci; AAAS. *Res:* Quartz crystal microbalance; reentrant magnetic wire materials; corrosion and oxidation of metal surfaces; eletropolishing and electron diffraction; medical applications of the telephone system; narrow band teleconferencing between meetings in different locations. *Mailing Add:* Rm 4G514 Bell Labs Holmdel NY 07733

STOCKBRIDGE, ROBERT R, b Worcester, Mass, Aug 21, 10; m 37; c 1. ANIMAL HUSBANDRY, POULTRY HUSBANDRY. *Educ:* Univ Mass, BVA, 34; Hofstra Col, MS, 46. *Prof Exp:* From instr to assoc prof, State Univ NY Agr & Tech Col Farmingdale, 38-60, prof poultry sci & chmn, Agr Dept, 60-80; RETIRED. *Mem:* Poultry Sci Asn; World Poultry Sci Asn. *Mailing Add:* 5 Stephen Dr Farmingdale NY 11735

STOCKBURGER, GEORGE JOSEPH, b Philadelphia, Pa, May 23, 27; m 61; c 2. INDUSTRIAL ORGANIC CHEMISTRY. *Educ:* St Joseph's Col, Pa, BS, 50; Univ Pa, MS, 52, PhD, 55. *Prof Exp:* sr res chemist, 55-79, SUPVR GEN ANAL, ANAL & PHYS CHEM SECT, ICI AMERICAS INC, 79- *Mem:* Am Chem Soc. *Res:* Reaction kinetics and mechanism; catalysis. *Mailing Add:* ICI Americas Inc Wilmington DE 19897

STOCKDALE, FRANK EDWARD, b Long Beach, Calif, Mar 15, 36. DEVELOPMENTAL BIOLOGY, ONCOLOGY. *Educ:* Yale Univ, AB, 58; Univ Pa, MD & PhD(develop biol), 63. *Prof Exp:* Intern internal med, Univ Hosps, Western Reserve Univ, 63-64; staff assoc, Nat Inst Arthritis & Metab Dis, 64-66; sr resident, Univ Hosp, 66-67, from instr to asst prof med, 68-74, asst prof med, 70-74, assoc prof med & biol sci, 74-81, PROF MED, SCH MED, STANFORD UNIV, 81- *Mem:* Am Soc Clin Invest; AAAS; Am Soc Develop Biol; Am Soc Clin Oncol; Am Soc Cell Biol. *Res:* Medical oncology; mechanisms for control of cell differentiation and growth during embryogenesis; hormonal control of cell function and growth. *Mailing Add:* Dept Med Rm S025 Stanford Univ Sch of Med Stanford CA 94305

STOCKDALE, HAROLD JAMES, b Aplington, Iowa, Dec 3, 31; m 51; c 2. ECONOMIC ENTOMOLOGY. *Educ:* Iowa State Univ, BS, 58, MS, 59, PhD(entom), 64. *Prof Exp:* EXTEN ENTOMOLOGIST & PROF ENTOM, IOWA STATE UNIV, 61- *Mem:* Entom Soc Am; Am Mosquito Control Asn. *Res:* Field crop insect management; household and structural insect control. *Mailing Add:* Insectary Bldg Iowa State Univ Ames IA 50011

STOCKDALE, JOHN ALEXANDER DOUGLAS, b Ipswich, Australia, Mar 15, 36; m 57; c 3. PHYSICS. *Educ:* Univ Sydney, BSc, 57, MSc, 60; PhD(physics), Univ Tenn, 69. *Prof Exp:* Res scientist, Australian AEC, 58-66; PHYSICIST, HEALTH & SAFETY RES DIV, OAK RIDGE NAT LAB, 66- *Concurrent Pos:* Vis prof, NY Univ, 75-76. *Mem:* Am Phys Soc. *Res:* Atomic and molecular physics. *Mailing Add:* 907 W Outer Dr Oak Ridge TN 37830

STOCKDALE, WILLIAM K, b Rock Island, Ill, Oct 11, 28; m 51; c 7. CIVIL ENGINEERING, STRUCTURAL DYNAMICS. *Educ:* US Mil Acad, BS, 51; Univ Ill, Urbana, MS, 58, PhD(civil eng), 59. *Prof Exp:* From instr to prof civil eng, US Mil Acad, 67-78; mgr eng serv, 78-81, CHIEF, CIVIL/STRUCT ENG, WASH PUB POWER SUPPLY SYST, 81- *Mem:* Soc Am Mil Engrs; NY Acad Sci; Am Soc Civil Engrs; Sigma Xi; Nat Soc Prof Engrs. *Res:* Structural dynamics; structural analysis and design. *Mailing Add:* 1873 Marshall Ave Richland WA 99352

STOCKEL, IVAR H(OWARD), b Minneapolis, Minn, Apr 30, 27; m 51; c 3. FLUID & APPLIED MECHANICS. *Educ:* Mass Inst Technol, BS & MS, 50, ScD, 59. *Prof Exp:* From instr to asst prof mech eng, US Naval Postgrad Sch, 50-54; res engr eng physics, Roy K Ferguson Tech Ctr, St Regis Paper Co, 56-59, res group leader, 59-61, assoc mgr res, 61-64, mgr res, 64-67, mgr develop, 67-68, corp dir res & develop, 68-81; PROF & CHMN, CHEM ENG DEPT, UNIV MAINE, 81- *Concurrent Pos:* Mem, NSF Indust panel sci & technol. *Mem:* Indust Res Inst Inc; Tech Asn Pulp & Paper Indust; Soc Rheol; Can Pulp & Paper Asn. *Res:* Theoretical and experimental flow behavior of mixtures of divided solids and fluids. *Mailing Add:* Dept Chem Eng Univ Maine Onoro ME 04469

STOCKELL-HARTREE, ANNE, b Nashville, Tenn, Jan 11, 26; m 59; c 2. BIOCHEMISTRY. *Educ:* Vanderbilt Univ, BA, 46, MS, 49; Univ Utah, PhD(biochem), 56. *Hon Degrees:* MA, Cambridge Univ, 62. *Prof Exp:* Asst biochem, Vanderbilt Univ, 46-51; asst, Univ Utah, 51-54; fel USPHS Johnson Res Found, Univ Pa, 56-58; mem, Med Res Coun Unit Molecular Biol, Cavendish Lab, Cambridge Univ, 58-59, mem, Jane Coffin Childs Fund, 59-60, res worker, Dept Biochem, 60-80; MEM STAFF, INST ANIMAL PHYSIOL, AGR RES COUN, CAMBRIDGE, ENG, 80- *Concurrent Pos:* Res fel, Girton Col, 62-65; fel, Lucy Cavendish Col, 69-; external mem sci staff, Med Res Coun, 70- *Mem:* AAAS; Brit Biochem Soc; Brit Soc Endocrinol; Am Soc Biol Chemists; Endocrine Soc. *Res:* Amino acid analysis; enzyme kinetics; protein structure and function; pituitary protein hormones. *Mailing Add:* Animal Res Sta Agr Res Coun 307 Huntingdon Rd Cambridge England

STOCKER, BRUCE ARNOLD DUNBAR, b Haslemere, Eng, May 26, 17; m 56; c 2. MICROBIAL GENETICS, MEDICAL MICROBIOLOGY. *Educ:* Univ London, MB & BS, 40, MD, 47. *Prof Exp:* House physician, Royal United Hosp, Bath, Eng, 40-41; supernumerary pathologist, Westminster Hosp Med Sch, 46-47; lectr bact, London Sch Hyg & Trop Med, Univ London, 48-53, head Guinness-Lister Res Unit, Lister Inst Prev Med, 53-65,

Guinness prof microbiol, 63-65; actg chmn dept, 74-81, PROF MED MICROBIOL, SCH MED, STANFORD UNIV, 66- Concurrent Pos: Commonwealth Fund fel microbiol, Col Med, NY Univ, 51-52; lectr, Am Soc Microbiol Found for Microbiol, 69-70; Guggenheim fel microbiol, Australian Nat Univ, 71 & Nat Bact Lab, Stockholm, 81. Honors & Awards: Paul Ehrlich Prize, Munich, Ger, 65. Mem: Fel Royal Soc; Am Soc Microbiol; Brit Soc Gen Microbiol; Brit Genetical Soc; Path Soc Gt Brit & Ireland. Res: Bacterial genetics, especially Salmonella typhimurium; genetics of lipopolysaccharide structure, outer membrane components; bacteriocins, virulence, plasmids, transduction. Mailing Add: Dept Med Microbiol Stanford Univ Sch Med Stanford CA 94305

STOCKER, DONALD V(ERNON), b Detroit, Mich, Jan 5, 27; m 50; c 2. ELECTRICAL ENGINEERING. Educ: Wayne State Univ, BSEE, 49; Univ Mich, MSE, 50. Prof Exp: Jr engr, Magnetron Develop Lab, Raytheon Mfg Co, Mass, 50-51; from instr to asst prof, 51-69, appln engr appl sci & technol ctr, 64-68, assoc prof elec engr, 60-75, mgr admin serv, col eng, 69-75, assoc prof eng technol, 75-81, DIR DIV ENG TECHNOL, WAYNE STATE UNIV, 81- Concurrent Pos: Consult, Detroit Edison Co, 76-80. Mem: Inst Elec & Electronics Engrs; Am Soc Eng Educ; Sigma Xi. Res: load management. Mailing Add: Dept of Eng Technol Wayne State Univ Detroit MI 48202

STOCKER, FRED BUTLER, b Kenyon, Minn, Jan 31, 31; m 53; c 2. ORGANIC CHEMISTRY. Educ: Hamline Univ, BS, 53; Univ Minn, MS, 55; Univ Colo, PhD(org chem), 58. Prof Exp: Assoc prof, 58-69, PROF CHEM, MACALESTER COL, 69-, CHMN DEPT, 70- Concurrent Pos: Consult, 59- Mem: Am Chem Soc. Res: Imidazole derivatives. Mailing Add: Dept of Chem Macalester Col St Paul MN 55105

STOCKER, JACK HUBERT, b Detroit, Mich, May 3, 24; m 64; c 2. ORGANIC CHEMISTRY. Educ: Olivet Col, BS, 44; Ind Univ, MA, 47; Tulane Univ, PhD(org chem), 55. Prof Exp: Control chemist, R P Scherer Corp, Mich, 48-50; control chemist, Atlas Pharmaceut Co, 50; Fullbright traveling fel, Heidelburg Univ, 55-56; assoc prof chem, Univ Southern Miss, 56-58; assoc prof, 58-71, admin asst to dean col sci, 65-67, PROF CHEM, UNIV NEW ORLEANS, 71- Concurrent Pos: Res partic, Oak Ridge Inst Nuclear Studies, 59; consult, Food & Drug Admin; res assoc, Gulf South Res Inst; vis prof chem, Univ Lund, Sweden, 74-75; mem, Comt Meetings & Exposition, Am Chem Soc, 72-74, 76-81, chmn, 80-81, Sci Comn, 80-81, Coun Policy Comt, 82-84. Mem: Am Chem Soc; Royal Soc Chem. Res: Acetals and ketals; organometallics; stereoselective reactions; c14 techniques; organic photochemistry and electrochemistry. Mailing Add: Dept of Chem Univ New Orleans Lakefront New Orleans LA 70122

STOCKER, RICHARD LOUIS, b Honolulu, Hawaii, Apr 22, 41. GEOPHYSICS. Educ: Lehigh Univ, BA, 64; Yale Univ, MS, 66, PhD(geophys), 73. Prof Exp: Asst prof geol, Lehigh Univ, 73-75; ASST PROF GEOL, ARIZ STATE UNIV, 75- Mem: Sigma Xi; Am Geophys Union. Res: Transport properties of minerals and rocks, particularly rheology and atomistic diffusion; point defect chemistry of minerals. Mailing Add: Dept of Geol Ariz State Univ Tempe AZ 85281

STOCKERT, ELISABETH, b Vienna, Austria, Sept 29, 30. IMMUNOGENETICS. Educ: Univ Vienna, BS, 59; Univ Paris, Dr(immunol), 74. Prof Exp: Res assoc cancer, 73-76, ASSOC MEM, SLOAN-KETTERING CANCER CTR, 76- Res: Experimental tumor immunobiology, serology and genetics; cell surface antigens of normal and malignant cells. Mailing Add: Mem Sloan-Kettering Cancer Ctr 1275 York Ave New York NY 10021

STOCKHAM, THOMAS GREENWAY, JR, b Passaic, NJ, Dec 22, 33; m 63; c 4. COMPUTER SCIENCE. Educ: Mass Inst Technol, SB, 55, SM, 56, ScD(elec eng), 59. Prof Exp: Teaching asst elec eng, Mass Inst Technol, 55-57, from instr to asst prof, 57-66, staff mem comput res, Lincoln Lab, 66-68; assoc prof comput sci, 68-70, PROF COMPUT SCI, UNIV UTAH, 70-, PROF ELEC ENG, 76- Concurrent Pos: Vis asst prof, Univ NMex, 62; consult, Data Div, Comput Group, Lincoln Lab, Mass Inst Technol, 64-66. Honors & Awards: Audio & Electroacoust Sr Award, Inst Elec & Electronics Engrs, 68. Mem: Inst Elec & Electronics Engrs; Asn Comput Mach. Res: Digital signal processing of images and sound by non-linear methods; electrical communications; electrical circuit and systems theory; computer graphics; sensory information processing. Mailing Add: Dept of Comput Sci Univ of Utah Salt Lake City UT 84112

STOCKHAMMER, KARL ADOLF, b Ried, Austria, July 19, 26; m 56; c 3. ZOOLOGY, ENTOMOLOGY. Educ: Graz Univ, PhD(zool), 51. Prof Exp: Res assoc zool, Univ Munich, 51-58; instr, Univ Göttingen, 58-59; asst prof, 59-67, ASSOC PROF CELL BIOL & PHYSIOL, UNIV KANS, 67- Mem: Entom Soc Am. Res: Detection of e-vector of polarized light in insects; behavioral and physiological aspects of nesting in native bees. Mailing Add: Dept of Physiol & Cell Biol Univ of Kans Lawrence KS 66045

STOCKING, CLIFFORD RALPH, b Riverside, Calif, June 22, 13; m 37; c 2. PLANT PHYSIOLOGY. Educ: Univ Calif, BS, 37, MS, 39, PhD(plant physiol), 42. Prof Exp: Asst plant physiol, Univ Calif, 38-39, assoc bot, 39-42; food chemist, Puccinelli Packing Co, 42-45; assoc, Exp Sta, Univ Calif, Davis, 45-46, asst prof bot, Univ & asst botanist, Exp Sta, 46-52, assoc prof & assoc botanist, 52-58, actg chmn, Dept Bot, 66-67, chmn dept, 68-74, prof & botanist, Exp Sta, 58-81, EMER PROF, UNIV CALIF, DAVIS, 81- Concurrent Pos: Merck sr fel biochem, Univ Wis, 55-56; NSF fel, Imp Col, Univ London, 63-64, sr fel King's Col, 70-71. Mem: Fel AAAS; Bot Soc Am; Am Soc Plant Physiol; Japanese Soc Plant Physiol. Res: Biochemistry of chloroplasts; plant water relations; intracellular distribution of enzymes and phosynthetic products. Mailing Add: Dept of Bot Univ of Calif Davis CA 95616

STOCKING, GORDON GARY, b Axin, Mich, Jan 12, 24; m 47; c 2. VETERINARY MEDICINE. Educ: Mich State Univ, DVM, 46. Prof Exp: Res vet, Upjohn Farms, 46-49, from asst vet to assoc vet, 49-57, dir vet div, 57-64, asst dir agr div, 65-69, prod mgr, 69-73, SR STAFF VET AGR DIV, UPJOHN CO, 73- Concurrent Pos: Ranch mgr & vet, Kellogg Ranch, Calif State Polytech Col, 51-52. Mem: Am Vet Med Asn; Indust Vet Asn; US Animal Health Asn; Am Asn Lab Animal Sci; Am Asn Equine Practr. Res: Equine reproduction and disease. Mailing Add: Agr Div Upjohn Co Kalamazoo MI 49001

STOCKING, HOBART EBEY, b Clarendon, Tex, Nov 16, 06; m 34; c 2. GEOLOGY. Educ: John Hopkins Univ, MS, 38; Univ Chicago, PhD(geol), 49. Prof Exp: Asst dist engr, Tex Pipeline Co, 28-29; topog engr, Angola Petrol Co, 29-31; field asst, US Geol Surv, 33-34; geologist, Shell Petrol Corp, 36-38; instr geol, Univ WVa, 40-41, asst prof, 41-43; dist geologist, Petrol Admin War, 43-45; US State Dept vis prof, Costa Rica, 45-46; geologist, NMex Bur Mines, 46; prof geol, Okla State Univ, 46-51; from asst chief geologist to chief geologist, USAEC, 52-58; prof geol, 59-71, EMER PROF GEOL, OKLA STATE UNIV, 71- Concurrent Pos: Hon prof, Costa Rica, 52; consult AEC, Argentina, 58. Mem: AAAS; Geol Soc Am. Res: Economic geology. Mailing Add: Dept Geol Okla State Univ Stillwater OK 74074

STOCKLAND, ALAN EUGENE, b Huron, SDak, July 18, 38; m 68; c 2. MICROBIOLOGY. Educ: Univ Nebr, BS & BA, 61; Mich State Univ, MS, 67, PhD(microbiol), 70. Prof Exp: Teacher secondary sch, Malaysia, 62-64; ASSOC PROF MICROBIOL, WEBER STATE COL, 70- Res: Microbiological control of insect pests. Mailing Add: Dept Microbiol Weber State Col 3750 Harrison Blvd Ogden UT 84408

STOCKLAND, WAYNE LUVERN, b Lake Lillian, Minn, May 4, 42; m 71; c 2. NUTRITION. Educ: Univ Minn, BS, 64, PhD(nutrit), 69. Prof Exp: Res asst nutrit, Univ Minn, 69, res fel, 69-70; res nutritionist & statist mgr, 70-76, DIR ANIMAL NUTRIT RES, INT MULTIFOODS CORP, 76- Mem: Am Soc Animal Sci; Am Dairy Sci Asn; Poultry Sci Asn; Am Inst Nutrit. Res: Swine, poultry and ruminant nutrition and management, especially the protein and amino acid requirements and the effect of energy level, temperature and other nutrients on these requirements. Mailing Add: Supersweet Res Farm PO Box 117 Courtland MN 56021

STOCKLI, MARTIN P, b Solothurn, Switz, June, 30, 49. MOLECULAR ORBITAL X-RAY EMMISION. Educ: Swiss Fed Inst Technol, Master, 74, PhD(physics), 78. Prof Exp: Res asst, Physics Lab, Swiss Fed Inst Technol, 74-79, res assoc, 79-80; res assoc, Physics Lab, Western Mich Univ, 80-81; RES ASSOC, PHYSICS LAB, KANS STATE UNIV, 81. Res: Accelerator based atomic physics; ionisation and x-ray emmision in slow heavy ion collisions. Mailing Add: Physics Dept Kans State Univ Manhattan KS 66506

STOCKMAN, DAVID LYLE, b Lansing, Mich, Aug 12, 36; m 58; c 4. PHYSICAL CHEMISTRY. Educ: Eastern Ill Univ, BS, 57; Univ Minn, PhD(phys chem), 61. Prof Exp: Scientist, electronics lab, Gen Elec Co, NY, 61-65; scientist res labs, 65-69, mgr explor photoconductor systs dr, 69-71, mgr photoreceptor technol, 71-73, mgr alloy photoreceptor technol ctr, 73-76, mgr mat mfg technol, 76-81, MGR TECHNOL STRATEGY, XEROX CORP, 81- Mem: AAAS; fel Am Inst Chem; Am Phys Soc; Am Chem Soc. Res: Photophysics and photochemistry of polyatomic molecules, especially with respect to excited state phenomena; dye laser development; photoconductivity. Mailing Add: Xerox Corp J C Wilson Ctr for Technol Rochester NY 14644

STOCKMAN, GEORGE C, b Brooklyn, NY, Dec 16, 43; m 69; c 2. COMPUTER SCIENCE. Educ: E Stroudsburg State Col, BS, 66; Harvard Univ, MAT, 67; Pa State Univ, MS, 71; Univ Md, PhD(comput sci), 77. Prof Exp: Instr math, Va Union Univ, 68-70; res asst comput sci, Univ Md, 73-75; RES SCIENTIST COMPUT SCI, LNK CORP, 75-; ASSOC PROF COMPUT SCI, AMERICAN UNIV, 79- Concurrent Pos: Vis lectr, Univ Md, 77-79. Mem: Asn Comput Mach; Inst Elec & Electronics Engrs. Res: Artificial intelligence; image processing; pattern recognition. Mailing Add: 8709 23rd Ave Adelphi MD 20783

STOCKMAN, HARRY E, b Stockholm, Sweden, Aug 24, 05; nat US; m 47; c 2. ELECTRONICS ENGINEERING, PHYSICS. Educ: Stockholm Tech Inst, Dipl, 26; Royal Inst Technol, Sweden, MS, 38; Harvard Univ, SD(elec eng), 46. Prof Exp: Tel lab engr, L M Ericson, Sweden, 27-29, radio engr, 32-34; tech ed, J Radio, 29-31, tech writer, 31-32; consult, Royal Inst Technol, Sweden, 34-38, asst prof radio eng, 38-40; instr physics & commun, Harvard Univ, 41-45; res assoc, Cent Commun Res Lab, 45; chief commun lab, Electronics Res Labs, Air Materiel Command, US Dept Air Force, 45-48; consult electronics, Stockman Electronics Res Co, 48-53; mgr res & develop, Norden-Ketay Boston Div, United Aircraft Corp, 55-56; prof elec eng & chmn dept, Merrimack Col, 58-60; prof, Lowell Tech Inst, 60-65; staff scientist, Mitre Corp, Bedford, 67-70; SR PHYSICIST, SERCOLAB, 70- Honors & Awards: Liberty Cross, Finland. Mem: Inst Elec & Electronics Engrs. Res: Radio communication; infrared spectrum and network theory; network theorems, especially feedback systems and stability criteria; parametric electromechanical systems; distributed and parametric wide band amplification; semiconductor devices. Mailing Add: Box 78 Sercolab Arlington MA 02174

STOCKMANN, VOLKER ERWIN, b Stuttgart, Ger, Feb 10, 40; US citizen; m 64; c 2. SOLID MECHANICS, POLYMER PHYSICS. Educ: Univ Hamburg, MS, 64, PhD(physics), 68. Prof Exp: Scientist wood physics, Fed Orgn Forestry, Reinbek, 65-68; physicist paper physics, Forest Prod Lab, Madison, Wis, 68-74; sect head fiber physics, 74-76, DEPT MGR COMPOSITE PROD, WEYERHAEUSER CO, TACOMA, 76- Mem: Tech Asn Pulp & Paper Indust; Soc Wood Sci & Technol. Res: Paper and fiber physics; cell wall structure; technology of papermaking. Mailing Add: Weyerhaeuser Co Tacoma WA 98401

STOCKMAYER, WALTER HUGO, b Rutherford, NJ, Apr 7, 14; m 38; c 2. PHYSICAL CHEMISTRY. *Educ:* Mass Inst Technol, SB, 35, PhD(chem), 40; Oxford Univ, BSc, 37. *Hon Degrees:* Dr, Univ Louis Pasteur, 72. *Prof Exp:* Instr chem, Mass Inst Technol, 39-41 & Columbia Univ, 41-43; asst prof, Mass Inst Technol, 43-46, from assoc prof to prof phys chem, 46-61; Chmn Dept, 63-67 & 73-76, prof, 61-79, EMER PROF CHEM, DARTMOUTH COL, 79- *Concurrent Pos:* Consult, E I du Pont de Nemours & Co, Inc, 45-; Guggenheim fel, 54-55; trustee, Gordon Res Conf, 63-66; fel, Jesus Col, Oxford, 76. *Honors & Awards:* Award, Mfg Chem Asn, 60; Award, Am Chem Soc, 66, Peter Debye Award phyPhys Chem, 74, High Polymer Physics Prize, 75. *Mem:* Nat Acad Sci; Am Chem Soc; fel Am Phys Soc; fel Am Acad Arts & Sci. *Res:* High polymers; applied statistical mechanics; dynamics and statistical mechanics of macromolecules. *Mailing Add:* Dept of Chem Dartmouth Col Hanover NH 03755

STOCKMEYER, LARRY JOSEPH, b Evansville, Ind, Nov 13, 48. COMPUTER SCIENCE. *Educ:* Mass Inst Technol, SB & SM, 72, PhD(comput sci), 74. *Prof Exp:* MEM RES STAFF, THOMAS J WATSON RES CTR, IBM CORP, 74- *Mem:* Asn Comput Mach; Soc Indust & Appl Math. *Res:* Computational complexity; analysis of algorithms; information storage and retrieval. *Mailing Add:* IBM Thomas J Watson Res Ctr PO Box 218 Yorktown Heights NY 10598

STOCKMEYER, PAUL KELLY, b Detroit, Mich, May 1, 43; m 66; c 2. MATHEMATICS. *Educ:* Earlham Col, AB, 65; Univ Mich, Ann Arbor, MA, 66, PhD(math), 71. *Prof Exp:* Asst prof math, 71-77, ASSOC PROF MATH & COMPUT SCI, COL WILLIAM & MARY, 77- *Mem:* Math Asn Am; Am Math Soc. *Res:* Combinatorial analysis; graph theory; analysis of algorithms. *Mailing Add:* Dept Math & Comput Sci Col William & Mary Williamsburg VA 23185

STOCKNER, JOHN G, b Kewanee, Ill, Sept 17, 40; m 62; c 2. LIMNOLOGY, ECOLOGY. *Educ:* Augustana Col, Ill, 62; Univ Wash, PhD(zool), 67. *Prof Exp:* Fel phytoplankton ecol, Windermere Lab, Freshwater Biol Asn, Eng, 67-68; limnologist, Freshwater Inst, Fisheries Res Bd Can, 68-71 & Pac Environ Inst, 71-81, ASSOC DIR FISHERIES RES, PAC REGION, CAN FISHERIES & OCEANS. *Mem:* Am Soc Limnol & Oceanog; Int Asn Theoret & Appl Limnol. *Res:* Phytoplankton ecology and paleolimnology; marine plankton ecology and benthic algal and phytoplankton production. *Mailing Add:* Fisheries Res Lab Can Fisheries & Oceans 6640 NW Marine Vancouver BC V6T 1X2 Can

STOCKS, DOUGLAS ROSCOE, JR, b Dallas, Tex, Sept 4, 32; m 51; c 3. MATHEMATICS. *Educ:* Univ Tex, BA, 58, MA, 60, PhD(math), 64. *Prof Exp:* Spec instr math, Univ Tex, 60-64; from asst prof to assoc prof, Univ Tex, Arlington, 64-69; ASSOC PROF MATH, UNIV ALA, BIRMINGHAM, 69- *Concurrent Pos:* Mathematician, US Navy Electronics Lab, 63; Tex Col & Univ Syst res grant, 66-67; vis prof, Auburn Univ, 78-79. *Mem:* Am Math Soc; Math Asn Am. *Res:* Lattice paths and graph theory; foundations of mathematics; geometry; topology; point set theory. *Mailing Add:* Dept of Math Univ of Ala Birmingham AL 35294

STOCKS, GEORGE MALCOLM, b Thurnscoe, Eng, June 5, 43; m 67; c 2. SOLID STATE PHYSICS. *Educ:* Univ Bradford, Eng, BTech, 66; Univ Sheffield, Eng, PhD(theoret physics), 69. *Prof Exp:* Res staff mem theoret solid state physics, Oak Ridge Nat Lab, 69-72; res assoc physics, Univ Bristol, Eng, 72-76; RES STAFF MEM THEORET SOLID STATE PHYSICS, OAK RIDGE NAT LAB, 76- *Mem:* Am Phys Soc; Inst Physics, UK. *Res:* Theory of electronic states in ordered and disordered metals and alloys; bank theory; disordered systems theory; phase stability; transport; excitation processes in solids; photo electron spectroscopies; soft x-ray spectroscopy. *Mailing Add:* Metals & Ceramics Div PO Box X Oak Ridge TN 37830

STOCKTON, DORIS S, b New Brunswick, NJ, Feb 9, 24; m 48; c 2. MATHEMATICS. *Educ:* Rutgers Univ, BSc, 45; Brown Univ, MSc, 47, PhD(math), 58. *Prof Exp:* Instr, Brown Univ, 52-54; asst prof, 58-73, ASSOC PROF MATH, UNIV MASS, AMHERST, 73- *Mem:* Am Math Soc; Math Asn Am. *Res:* Functional analysis. *Mailing Add:* Dept of Math Univ of Mass Amherst MA 01003

STOCKTON, GERALD WILLIAM, molecular biophysics, nuclear magnetic resonance, see previous edition

STOCKTON, JAMES EVAN, b Goliad, Tex, Feb 28, 31; m 51; c 2. ELECTRICAL ENGINEERING. *Educ:* Univ Tex, Austin, BS, 60. *Prof Exp:* Res engr, 60-64, supvr, Submarine Sonar Sect, 64-69, dep div head, Electroacoust Div, 69-70, HEAD ENG SERV DIV, APPL RES LABS, UNIV TEX, 70- *Mem:* Inst Elec & Electronics Engrs; Am Inst Physics; Acoust Soc Am. *Res:* Underwater acoustics; instrumentation for underwater acoustics; sonar systems. *Mailing Add:* 1508 Weyford Dr Austin TX 78758

STOCKTON, JOHN RICHARD, b Jarrell, Tex, Feb 19, 17; m 38, 53; c 6. RESEARCH MANAGEMENT. *Educ:* Univ Tex, BSc, 38, MA, 41, PhD(microbiol), 51. *Prof Exp:* Pharmacist, Baylor Hosp, 38-39; tutor pharm, Univ Tex, 39-41, asst prof, 41-46; dir res, Hyland Labs, 46-50; tech asst to dir biol prod, Merck Sharp & Dohme, 50-54; mgr res & qual control, Pillsbury Co, 54-62, dir res & develop, 62-66, dir sci activities, 66-68; mgr res & develop Corn Prod Food Technol Inst, 68-70, assoc dir res & qual control, Best Foods, CPC Int, Inc, 70-73; vpres res & develop, Nutri Co, 73-74; PRES, MGT CATALYSTS, 74- *Mem:* AAAS; Inst Food Technol; Am Chem Soc; Am Soc Microbiol; NY Acad Sci. *Res:* Antimicrobial agents; physicochemical characteristics of drugs; biological products; food science; product development; nutrition; research management. *Mailing Add:* Mgt Catalysts PO Box E Ship Bottom NJ 08008

STOCKWELL, CHARLES WARREN, b Port Angeles, Wash, Dec 31, 40; m 66; c 2. NEUROSCIENCES. *Educ:* Western Wash State Col, BA, 64; Univ Ill, MA, 66, PhD(psychol), 68. *Prof Exp:* Res psychologist, Naval Aerospace Med Ctr, 69-71; asst prof, 72-76, ASSOC PROF OTOLARYNGOL, COL MED, OHIO STATE UNIV, 76- *Mem:* Barany Soc; Asn Res Otolaryngol; Soc Neurosci. *Res:* Vestibular function. *Mailing Add:* Dept of Otolaryngol Ohio State Univ Col of Med Columbus OH 43210

STOCKWELL, CLIFFORD HOWARD, b Estevan, Sask, Sept 26, 97; m 35; c 3. GEOLOGY. *Educ:* Univ BC, BASc, 24; Univ Wis, PhD(geol), 30. *Prof Exp:* Asst geologist, Geol Surv Can, 27-29, assoc geologist, 29-39, geologist, 39-53, sr geologist, 53-57, res scientist, 57-67. *Concurrent Pos:* Vis prof, McGill Univ, 47-48; consult, NJ Zinc Co, 51-52. *Honors & Awards:* Barlow Mem Medal; Willet G Miller Medal; Logan Medal. *Mem:* Fel Geol Soc Am; fel Royal Soc Can; Can Inst Mining & Metall; Geol Asn Can. *Res:* Precambrian and structural geology. *Mailing Add:* 577 Gainsborough Ave Ottawa ON K2A 2Y6 Can

STOCUM, DAVID LEON, b Ypsilanti, Mich, Feb 15, 39. DEVELOPMENTAL BIOLOGY. *Educ:* Susquehanna Univ, BA, 61; Univ Pa, PhD(biol), 68. *Prof Exp:* Asst prof zool, 68-73, assoc prof genetics & develop, 73-81, PROF GENETICS & DEVELOP & ANAT SCI, UNIV ILL, URBANA, 81- *Concurrent Pos:* NSF res grant, 72-77; NIH res grant, 79-82. *Mem:* Am Soc Zoologists; AAAS; Soc Develop Biol. *Res:* Morphogenesis and cellular differentiation in embryonic and regenerating systems. *Mailing Add:* Dept of Genetics & Develop Univ of Ill Urbana IL 61801

STODDARD, ALONZO EDWIN, JR, b Huntington, WVa, Feb 6, 26; m 49; c 2. PHYSICS. *Educ:* Univ Mich, BS, 48, MS, 49, PhD(physics), 53. *Prof Exp:* Physicist, Calif Res & Develop Co, 53-55, physicist, Chevron Res Corp, 55-60; PROF PHYSICS, HARVEY MUDD COL, 60- *Concurrent Pos:* Physicist, US Geol Surv, 66-67. *Mem:* Am Geophys Union; Am Phys Soc. *Res:* Color centers and luminescence in solids; nuclear spectroscopy; geophysics. *Mailing Add:* Dept of Physics Harvey Mudd Col Claremont CA 91711

STODDARD, C(ARL) KERBY, b Reno, Nev, Dec 20, 07; m 42; c 2. CHEMICAL ENGINEERING, EXTRACTIVE METALLURGY. *Educ:* Univ Nev, BS, 34, MS, 36; Univ Md, PhD(chem eng), 41. *Prof Exp:* Res chemist, Am Soc Mech Engrs, Md, 40-41; chem engr, US Bur Mines, Nev, 41-48; chem engr, Titanium Div, Nat Lead Co, 48-52; chem engr, Titanium Metals Corp Am, 52-58; chem engr, Titanium Div, Nat Lead Co, 58-70; process engr, Ralph M Parsons Co, 70-77; RETIRED. *Concurrent Pos:* Consult, Ralph M Parsons Co, 77- *Mem:* AAAS; Am Chem Soc; Am Inst Mining, Metall & Petrol Engrs; Sigma Xi. *Res:* Extractive metallurgy of magnesium, titanium and nickel; electric smelting and beneficiation of titanium ores; nuclear fuels reprocessing. *Mailing Add:* 123 Tahoe Dr Carson City NV 89701

STODDARD, DAN WARREN, b Richmond, Utah, Nov 20, 25; m 47; c 3. MATHEMATICS. *Educ:* Utah State Univ, MS, 52. *Prof Exp:* Instr math, Utah State Univ, 49-52; staff mem, Sandia Corp, 52-56; asst prof math, Brigham Young Univ, 56-57; RES SCIENTIST, KAMAN SCI CORP, 57- *Res:* Systems, operations and statistical analysis; weapon systems; applied mathematics. *Mailing Add:* Kaman Sci Corp Garden of the Gods Rd Colorado Springs CO 80907

STODDARD, GEORGE EDWARD, b Boise, Idaho, July 15, 21; m 46; c 5. ANIMAL NUTRITION. *Educ:* Univ Idaho, BS, 43; Univ Wis, MS, 48, PhD(dairy husb), 50. *Prof Exp:* Asst, Univ Wis, 46-49; asst prof dairy husb, Iowa State Col, 49-52; assoc prof, 52-55, head dept dairy sci, 60-76, PROF ANIMAL DAIRY & VET SCI, UTAH STATE UNIV, 55-, ASSOC DEAN AGR, 81- *Concurrent Pos:* Pres, Agri-Mgt Consults, Inc, 72-76; staff collabr, Agriserv Found, 75-76. *Mem:* AAAS; Am Soc Animal Sci; Am Dairy Sci Asn. *Res:* Rumen physiology; effect of feeds on milk composition; nutrient absorption; feed value of silage; hay and grain substitutions; grain feeding on pasture; hay quality and harvest methods; fluorosis in dairy animals; insecticides on hay fed to dairy animals; dietary fats and urinary metabolites of rats; costs of milk production. *Mailing Add:* Dept of Animal Dairy & Vet Sci Utah State Univ UMC 48 Logan UT 84322

STODDARD, JAMES H, b Saginaw, Mich, June 17, 30; m 57; c 2. MATHEMATICS. *Educ:* Univ Mich, BS, 52, PhD(math), 61. *Prof Exp:* Instr math, Univ Mich, 60-61; asst prof, Oakland Univ, 61-62; asst prof, Syracuse Univ, 62-66; asst prof, Univ of the South, 66-67; assoc prof, Kenyon Col, 67-70; prof, Upsala Col, 70-72; PROF MATH, MONTCLAIR STATE COL, 72-, PROF COMPUT SCI, 80- *Concurrent Pos:* Mem col level exam comt, Educ Testing Serv, NJ, 65-69. *Mem:* Am Math Soc; Math Asn Am; Asn Comput Mach. *Res:* Computer software; application to management sciences. *Mailing Add:* Dept of Math Montclair State Col Upper Montclair NJ 07043

STODDARD, LELAND DOUGLAS, b Hillsboro, Ill, Mar 15, 19; m 46. PATHOLOGY. *Educ:* DePauw Univ, AB, 40; Johns Hopkins Univ, MD, 43. *Prof Exp:* Asst & asst resident path, Sch Med, Duke Univ, 47-48, instr & resident, 49-50, assoc, 50-51; from asst prof to assoc prof, Med Sch, Univ Kans, 51-54; chmn dept, 54-73, PROF PATH, EUGENE TALMADGE MEM HOSP, MED COL GA, 54- *Concurrent Pos:* Chief staff, Eugene Talmadge Mem Hosp, 64-65; chief res path, Atomic Bomb Casualty Comn Japan, 61-62; vis prof, Med Sch, Osaka Univ, 66; mem path training comt, Vet Admin, 69-72; mem, Intersoc Path Coun, Int Coun Socs Path, US Nat Comt & Sci Adv Bd of Consult, Armed Forces Inst Path, 70-75. *Mem:* Am Asn Cancer Res; Asn Hist Med; Am Asn Pathologists; Int Acad Path (vpres, 74-78, treas, 78-); Int Acad Path (secy-treas, US-Can div coun, 70-, vpres, Acad, 74-). *Res:* Cervical carcinoma; gynecological and reproductive endocrine pathology; crime pathology; knowledge theory in pathology and medicine. *Mailing Add:* Dept of Path Med Col of Ga Augusta GA 30912

STODDARD, STEPHEN D(AVIDSON), b Everett, Wash, Feb 8, 25; m 49; c 2. CERAMIC ENGINEERING, MATERIALS SCIENCE. *Educ:* Univ Ill, BS, 50. *Prof Exp:* From asst ceramic engr to asst prod supvr, Coors Porcelain Co, Colo, 50-52; ceramics sect leader, Los Alamos Sci Lab, Univ Calif, 52-74, ceramics-powder metall sect leader, 74-80. *Concurrent Pos:* Consult, 56-; consult ed, Ceramic Age, 58-60; mem mat adv bd, Nat Acad Sci, Dept Defense, 62-63; consult, vpres & secy, Mat Technol Assocs, 77-80, pres & treas, 80- *Honors & Awards:* PACE Award, Am Ceramic Soc, 64. *Mem:* AAAS; fel Am Inst Chem; Nat Inst Ceramic Engrs; fel Am Ceramic Soc (vpres, 71-72, treas, 72-74, pres, 76-77); Sigma Xi; Am Soc Metals. *Res:* Fabrication techniques for refractory oxides, rare earth oxides, refractory metals, metal-oxide mixtures, ceramic-metal seals and electronic ceramics and their application in energy and nuclear weapon, power and propulsion studies. *Mailing Add:* 326 Kimberly Lane Los Alamos NM 87544

STODOLA, EDWIN KING, US citizen. ELECTRICAL ENGINEERING, ELECTRONICS ENGINEERING. *Educ:* Cooper Union Inst Technol, BEE, 36, EE, 47. *Prof Exp:* Radio engr, Radio Eng Labs, Long Island, 36-39; chief radar & electronics res & develop, Spec Develop Sect, US Army Signal Corps Labs, Belmar, NJ & Washington, DC, 39-47; chief scientist, Reeves Inst Div, Dynamics Corp Am, Boynton Beach, Fla & Mineola, NY, 47-72; sr res engr electronics res & develop, Syracuse Univ Res Corp, 72-74; leading scientist oper testing plans, Dikewood Corp, Kirtland AFB, NMex, 74-75; CHIEF COMMUN ELEC WARFARE DIV, US ARMY ELECTRONIC WARFARE LAB, 75- *Concurrent Pos:* Consult adv panel electronics, Off Asst Secy Defense, 58-59. *Mem:* Fel Inst Elec & Electronics Engrs; assoc fel Am Inst Aeronaut & Astronaut; fel Radio Club Am; Armed Forces Commun & Electronics Asn; Electronic Warfare Tech Asn. *Res:* Radio propagation and techniques for accurate radar and emitter location; aircraft navigation, control and flight safety research. *Mailing Add:* Comn EW Div-Delew-C US Army Electronic Warfare Lab Ft Monmouth NJ 07703

STODOLSKY, MARVIN, b Newark, NJ, Nov 28, 39. MOLECULAR BIOLOGY, GENETICS. *Educ:* Univ Chicago, BS, 60, PhD(biophys), 64. *Prof Exp:* Fel biochem, Mass Inst Technol, 64-67; asst prof microbiol & genetics, Univ Chicago, 67-73; asst prof microbiol & genetics, Loyola Univ, 73-74, assoc prof, 74-79; PROF & CHMN, DEPT BIOL, BOGAZICI UNIV, ISTANBUL, 79- *Mailing Add:* Dept Biol Bogazici Univ P K 2 Istanbul 60153 Turkey

STOEBE, THOMAS GAINES, b Upland, Calif, Apr 26, 39; c 3. MATERIALS SCIENCE, METALLURGY. *Educ:* Stanford Univ, BS, 61, MS, 63, PhD(mat sci), 65. *Prof Exp:* Vis lectr metall & res grant, Imp Col, London, 65-66; from asst prof to assoc prof, 66-75, PROF METALL ENG, UNIV WASH, 75- *Concurrent Pos:* Vis prof, Atomic Energy Inst, Sao Paulo, Brazil, 72-73. *Honors & Awards:* Western Elec Award, Am Soc Eng Educ, 77. *Mem:* Am Soc Eng Educ; Am Soc Metals; Am Phys Soc; Metall Soc. *Res:* Influence of lattice imperfections on physical properties of solids, especially on mechanical and optical properties and atomic diffusion in alkali halide systems. *Mailing Add:* Dept of Mining Metall & Univ of Wash FB-10 Seattle WA 98195

STOEBER, WERNER, b Göttingen, Ger, May 8, 25; m 55; c 1. AEROSOL SCIENCE, INHALATION TOXICOLOGY. *Educ:* Univ Göttingen, Dipl, 53, Dr rer nat, 55. *Prof Exp:* Sci asst, Med Res Inst, Max Planck Soc, 55-61; res fel aerosol sci, Calif Inst Technol, 61-63; sci asst, Inst Med Physics, Univ Münster, 64-65, docent, 65-66; assoc prof, Univ Rochester, 66-70, prof radiation biol & biophys, Med Sch, 70-73; dir, Inst Aerobiol, Fraunhofer-Gesellschaft, 73-79; DIR, FRAUNHOFER INST TOXICOL & AEROSOL RES, HANNOVER, 80- *Concurrent Pos:* USPHS int res fel, 61-62; prof, Univ Münster, 68; prof med physics, Med Sch Hannover, 82. *Res:* Surface chemistry; silicosis; aerosol. *Mailing Add:* Potstiege 34 44 Muenster Germany Federal Republic of

STOECKENIUS, WALTHER, b Giessen, Ger, July 3, 21; m 52; c 3. CYTOLOGY. *Educ:* Univ Hamburg, MD, 51. *Prof Exp:* Intern, Pharmacol Inst, Univ Hamburg, 51, intern internal med, 51 & obstet & gynec, 52, researcher virol, Inst Trop Med, 52-54, res asst path, 54-58, privat docent, 58; guest investr, Rockefeller Inst, 59, from asst prof to assoc prof cytol, 59-67; PROF CELL BIOL, SCH MED, UNIV CALIF, SAN FRANCISCO, 67- *Res:* Fine structure of cells at the molecular level; energy transducing membranes; photobiology. *Mailing Add:* Dept of Biochem & Biophys Univ of Calif San Francisco CA 94122

STOECKLE, JOHN DUANE, b Highland Park, Mich, Aug 17, 22; m 47; c 4. MEDICINE. *Educ:* Antioch Col, BS, 48; Harvard Med Sch, MD, 48; Am Bd Internal Med, dipl, 58. *Prof Exp:* Intern med, Mass Gen Hosp, Boston, 48-49, asst resident, 49-50, resident, 51-52; panel dir med aspects of atomic energy, Comt Med Sci, Res & Develop Bd, Dept Defense, 52-54; instr, 54-58, assoc, 58-67, asst prof, 67-69, ASSOC PROF MED, HARVARD MED SCH, 69-; CHIEF MED CLIN, MASS GEN HOSP, 54- *Concurrent Pos:* Physician, Mass Gen Hosp, 69-; mem comt on coal miner's safety & health, Dept Health, Educ & Welfare, 71-73. *Mem:* Fel Am Pub Health Asn; assoc mem Am Sociol Asn; fel Am Anthrop Asn; fel Am Psychosom Soc; Soc Appl Anthrop. *Res:* Medical care administration and health and illness behavior; longitudinal study of occupational lung diseases. *Mailing Add:* Mass Gen Hosp 32 Fruit St Boston MA 02114

STOECKLEY, THOMAS ROBERT, b Ft Wayne, Ind, Dec 6, 42. ASTRONOMY. *Educ:* Mich State Univ, BS, 64; Cambridge Univ, PhD(astron), 67. *Prof Exp:* Asst prof, 67-74, ASSOC PROF ASTRON, MICH STATE UNIV, 67- *Mem:* Am Astron Soc; Am Inst Physics; Royal Astron Soc. *Res:* Stellar rotation. *Mailing Add:* Dept Astron & Astrophys Mich State Univ East Lansing MI 48824

STOECKLY, ROBERT E, b Schenectady, NY, June 9, 38; m 69; c 1. PHYSICS. *Educ:* Princeton Univ, PhD(astrophys sci), 64. *Prof Exp:* Res fel astron, Mt Wilson & Palomar Observs, 64-65; asst prof physics & astron, Rensselaer Polytech Inst, 65-72; physicist, Mission Res Corp, 72-81. *Mem:* Am Astron Soc. *Res:* Fluid dynamics; plasma physics. *Mailing Add:* 3229 Calle Cedro Drawer 719 Santa Barbara CA 93105

STOEHR, ROBERT ALLEN, b Pittsburgh, Pa, July 10, 30. METALLURGICAL ENGINEERING. *Educ:* Hiram Col, BA, 52; Carnegie Inst Technol, MS, 65; Carnegie-Mellon Univ, PhD(metall & mat sci), 69. *Prof Exp:* Metall engr, Reactive Metals, Inc, Ohio, 54-60; res engr, Alcoa Res Labs, Aluminum Co Am, Pa, 60-67; asst prof, 68-74, ASSOC PROF METALL & MAT ENG, UNIV PITTSBURGH, 74- *Mem:* Metall Soc; Am Inst Mining, Metall & Petrol Engrs; Am Soc Metals; Electrochem Soc. *Res:* Process and chemical metallurgy; metallurgical pollution control; high temperature electrochemistry and corrosion; computer simulation of metallurgical processes. *Mailing Add:* 848 Benedum Hall Univ Pittsburgh Pittsburgh PA 15261

STOENNER, HERBERT GEORGE, b Levasy, Mo, June 17, 19; m 46; c 4. BACTERIOLOGY, VIROLOGY. *Educ:* Iowa State Col, DVM, 43. *Prof Exp:* Asst scientist, Commun Dis Ctr, USPHS, Ga, 47-50, sr asst vet, 50-52, vet, 52-56, sr vet, 56-61, asst dir lab, 62-64, DIR ROCKY MOUNTAIN LAB, NAT INST ALLERGY & INFECTIOUS DIS, 64-, VET OFFICER DIR, USPHS, 61- *Concurrent Pos:* Fac affil, Univ Mont. *Honors & Awards:* Distinguished Serv Medal, Dept Health, Educ & Welfare, 71; K F Meyer Gold Headed Cane Award, 74. *Mem:* Am Vet Med Asn; Am Pub Health Asn; US Animal Health Asn; Conf Res Workers Animal Dis. *Res:* Zoonoses; leptospirosis; rickettsioses; brucellosis; psittacosis. *Mailing Add:* 1102 S Second St Hamilton MT 59840

STOERMER, EUGENE F, b Webb, Iowa, Mar 7, 34; m 60; c 3. PHYCOLOGY, LIMNOLOGY. *Educ:* Iowa State Univ, BS, 58, PhD(bot), 63. *Prof Exp:* NIH fel phycol, Iowa State Univ, 63-65; assoc res algologist, 66-71, lectr, Biol Sta, 69-77, RES ALGOLOGIST, GREAT LAKES RES DIV, UNIV MICH, ANN ARBOR, 71-, RES SCIENTIST, HERBARIUM, 73-, ASSOC PROF, SCH NAT RES, 77- *Concurrent Pos:* McHenry fel, Acad Natural Sci, Philadelphia, Pa, 59; vis prof bot, Mich State Univ, 67-68; adj prof biol, City Univ New York, 74 & Bowling Green State Univ, 77-80; mem grad fac, Univ Maine, Orono, 81-; res fel, Acad Natural Sci Philadelphia. *Mem:* AAAS; Am Soc Limnol & Oceanog; Int Phycol Soc; Phycol Soc Am; Am Quaternary Asn. *Res:* Taxonomy and ecology of Bacillariophyta and Laurentian Great Lakes algal flora; paleoecology and algal evolution. *Mailing Add:* Great Lakes Res Div Univ of Mich IST Bldg Ann Arbor MI 48109

STOESSL, ALBERT, b Linz, Austria, Feb 24, 24; Can citizen; m 54; c 1. NATURAL PRODUCTS CHEMISTRY. *Educ:* Univ London, BSc, 55, PhD(chem), 60. *Prof Exp:* Res fel org chem, Univ Western Ont, 60-61; res scientist, 61-73, sr res scientist, 73-81, PRIN RES SCIENTIST, RES CTR, CAN DEPT AGR, 81- *Mem:* The Chem Soc; Am Phytopath Soc; Can Inst Chem; Phytochem Soc NAm. *Res:* Chemistry of natural products; chemical basis of disease resistance in plants; fungal toxins. *Mailing Add:* Res Ctr Can Dept of Agr Univ Sub PO London ON N6G 2L1 Can

STOESZ, JAMES DARREL, b Mountain Lake, Minn, July 3, 50; m 71. BIOPHYSICAL CHEMISTRY, BIOCHEMISTRY. *Educ:* Bethel Col, BA, 72; Univ Minn, Minneapolis, PhD(biophys chem), 77. *Prof Exp:* Res fel biochem, Brandeis Univ, 76-78; SR CHEMIST BIOSCI, CENT RES LABS, 3M CO, 78- *Mem:* Am Chem Soc. *Res:* Protein and polypeptide structure and function; enzyme mechanisms; nuclear magnetic resonance; lipid bilayer membranes; liposomes. *Mailing Add:* 2116 Juno Ave St Paul MN 55116

STOETZEL, MANYA BROOKE, b Houston, Tex, Apr 11, 40; c 2. ENTOMOLOGY. *Educ:* Univ Md, College Park, BS, 66, MS, 70, PhD(entom), 72. *Prof Exp:* Entomologist, First US Army Med Lab, Ft Meade, Md, 66-68; Presidential intern, 73-74, RES ENTOMOLOGIST, SYST ENTOM LAB, AGR RES SERV, USDA, 74- *Mem:* Entom Soc Am; AAAS. *Res:* Morphology and taxonomy of aphids, phylloxerrans, adelgids and armored scale insects. *Mailing Add:* Syst Entom Lab USDA Bldg 004 Rm 6 Beltsville MD 20705

STOEVER, EDWARD CARL, JR, b Milwaukee, Wis, Mar 13, 26; m 54; c 2. STRUCTURAL GEOLOGY, SCIENCE EDUCATION. *Educ:* Purdue Univ, BS, 48; Univ Mich, MS, 50, PhD(geol), 59. *Prof Exp:* Res geologist, Int Minerals & Chem Corp, 52-54; from asst prof to assoc prof geol, 56-69, assoc dir undergrad studies, Sch Geol & Geophys, Univ Okla, 70-72, prof geol & geophys, 69-78; PROF GEOL & CHMN DEPT EARTH SCI, SOUTHEAST MO STATE UNIV, 78- *Concurrent Pos:* Dir Okla Geol Camp, 64-69; dir inst earth sci, NSF, 65-69 & 70-72; assoc dir, Earth Sci Curriculum Proj, 69; assoc prog dir teacher educ sect, NSF, 69-70; sr staff consult, Earth Sci Teacher Prep Proj, 70-72; dir, Okla Earth Sci Educ Proj, 72-74; dir, Nat Asn Geol Teachers Crustal Evolution Educ Proj, NSF, 76-80. *Mem:* Nat Asn Geol Teachers (vpres, 74-75, pres, 75-76); AAAS; fel Geol Soc Am; Am Asn Petrol Geologists; Nat Sci Teachers Asn. *Res:* Development of secondary (7-12) and college undergraduate earth science instructional modvies. *Mailing Add:* Dept Earth Sci Southeast Mo State Univ Cape Girardeau MO 63701

STOEWSAND, GILBERT SAARI, b Chicago, Ill, Oct 20, 32; m 57; c 2. FOOD TOXICOLOGY. *Educ:* Univ Calif, Davis, BS, 54, MS, 58; Cornell Univ, PhD, 64. *Prof Exp:* Res asst poultry sci, Cornell Univ, 58-61; res nutritionist, US Army Natick Lab, Mass, 63-66; res assoc, Inst Exp Path & Toxicol, Albany Med Col, 66-67; from asst prof to assoc prof, 67-79, PROF TOXICOL, EXP STA, NY STATE COL AGR & LIFE SCI, CORNELL UNIV, 79- *Concurrent Pos:* Consult, Toxicol Info Prog, Nat Libr Med, 77- *Mem:* AAAS; Inst Food Technol; Am Inst Nutrit; Soc Toxicol; Soc Exp Biol & Med. *Res:* Heavy metal toxicology; effect of nutrition on toxicity; food additives; natural food toxicants and toxicant inhibitors. *Mailing Add:* Dept of Food Sci & Technol NY State Agr Exp Sta Cornell Univ Geneva NY 14456

STOFFA, PAUL L, b Palmerton, Pa, July 9, 48; m 68; c 2. MARINE GEOPHYSICS, SIGNAL PROCESSING. *Educ:* Rensselaer Polytech Inst, BS, 70; Columbia Univ, PhD(geophys), 74. *Prof Exp:* res assoc marine geophys, Lamont-Doherty Geol Observ, 74-81; CONSULT, GULF SCI TECHNOL, 81- *Concurrent Pos:* Adj asst prof, Columbia Univ, 78- *Mem:* Am Geophys Union; Soc Explor Geophys; Inst Elec & Electronics Engrs; Sigma Xi. *Res:* Marine seismology; wave propagation; numerical analysis. *Mailing Add:* Lamont-Doherty Geol Observ 102 Geosci Bldg Palisades NY 10964

STOFFER, JAMES OSBER, b Homeworth, Ohio, Oct 16, 35; m 57; c 2. ORGANIC CHEMISTRY, POLYMER CHEMISTRY. *Educ:* Mt Union Col, BS, 57; Purdue Univ, PhD(org chem), 61. *Prof Exp:* Res asst, Purdue Univ, 57-59; res assoc, Cornell Univ, 61-63; asst prof, 63-66, ASSOC PROF CHEM, UNIV MO-ROLLA, 66- *Mem:* Am Chem Soc. *Res:* Beta deuterium isotope effects; separation of optical isomers by gas chromatography; trace organic analysis; small ring compounds. *Mailing Add:* Dept Chem Univ Mo Rolla MO 65401

STOFFER, ROBERT LLEWELLYN, b North Georgetown, Ohio, Sept 16, 27; m 51; c 3. INDUSTRIAL HYGIENE, ANALYTICAL CHEMISTRY. *Educ:* Ashland Col, AB, 50; Ohio State Univ, PhD(anal chem), 54. *Prof Exp:* Anal chemist, 54-56, from asst proj chemist to sr proj chemist, 56-72, INDUST HYG CHEMIST, ENVIRON CONSERV & TOXICOL DEPT, STANDARD OIL CO (IND), 72- *Mem:* Am Indust Hyg Asn; Am Chem Soc; Am Acad Indust Hygiene. *Res:* Development of new analytical methods in the industrial hygiene field. *Mailing Add:* Amoco Res Ctr PO Box 400 Naperville IL 60566

STOFFOLANO, JOHN GEORGE, JR, b Gloversville, NY, Dec 31, 39; m 65; c 2. ENTOMOLOGY, NEUROBIOLOGY. *Educ:* State Univ NY Col Oneonta, BS, 62; Cornell Univ, MS, 67; Univ Conn, PhD(entom), 70. *Prof Exp:* Asst prof, 69-76, assoc prof, 76-80, PROF ENTOM, UNIV MASS, AMHERST, 80- *Concurrent Pos:* NSF fel neurobiol, Princeton Univ, 70-71; NIH fel, Univ Mass, Amherst, 72-75. *Mem:* AAAS; Entom Soc Am; Am Inst Biol Sci; Soc Nematol. *Res:* Integrative studies on the ecology, neurobiology and physiology of diapausing, nondiapausing and aging flies of the genus Musca and Phormia. *Mailing Add:* Dept of Entom Univ of Mass Amherst MA 01003

STOFFYN, PIERRE JULES, b Ixelles, Belgium, May 10, 19; US citizen; m 50; c 2. CHEMISTRY, BIOCHEMISTRY. *Educ:* Univ Brussels, MS, 41, PhD(chem), 49. *Prof Exp:* Res fel med, Mass Gen Hosp, Harvard Med Sch, 52-54, res assoc med, 56-61, res assoc biol chem, 61-63, lectr, Mass Gen Hosp, 63-76, sr assoc biol chem, 73-80. *Concurrent Pos:* Res fel, Am Heart Asn, 57-59, adv res fel, 59-61, estab investr, 61-66; from asst biochemist to biochemist, McLean Hosp, Belmont, 61-74; biochemist, Eunice Kennedy Shriver Ctr & Mass Gen Hosp, 74- *Mem:* Am Chem Soc; Am Soc Biol Chem; Belgian Soc Biochem; Int Soc Neurochem; Am Soc Neurochem. *Res:* Microchemistry; organic chemistry; carbohydrates; lipids; neurochemistry. *Mailing Add:* 39 Barney Hill Rd Wayland MA 01778

STOHLMAN, STEPHEN ARNOLD, b Long Beach, Calif, Oct 4, 46. MICROBIOLOGY, VIROLOGY. *Educ:* Calif State Univ, BS, 70, MS, 72; Univ Md, PhD(microbiol), 75. *Prof Exp:* ASST PROF NEUROL & MICROBIOL, UNIV SOUTHERN CALIF, 75- *Concurrent Pos:* Co-investr, NIH grant, 77-81; prin investr, Nat Multiple Sclerosis Soc grant, 79-81. *Mem:* Am Soc Microbiol; Tissue Cult Asn; Soc Gen Microbiol. *Res:* Neurovirology; molecular biology; immunology. *Mailing Add:* 142 McKibben Annex Univ of Southern Calif Los Angeles CA 90033

STÖHRER, GERHARD, b Heidelberg, Ger, May 28, 39. ORGANIC CHEMISTRY, BIOCHEMISTRY. *Educ:* Univ Heidelberg, dipl chem, 62, PhD(chem), 65. *Prof Exp:* Assoc biochem, 66-80, ASST PROF, BIOCHEM UNIT, KETTERING LAB, SLOAN-KETTERING INST CANCER RES, 80- *Mem:* Am Chem Soc; Ger Chem Soc. *Res:* Molecular biology of oncogenesis. *Mailing Add:* 20 Stafford Pl Larchmont NY 10538

STOHS, SIDNEY JOHN, b Ludell, Kans, May 24, 39; m 60; c 2. BIOMEDICINAL CHEMISTRY, BIOCHEMISTRY. *Educ:* Univ Nebr, BS, 62, MS, 64; Univ Wis, PhD(biochem), 67. *Prof Exp:* From asst prof to assoc prof pharmacog, 67-74, chmn dept, 68-71, chmn dept med chem & pharmacog, 72, PROF BIOMED CHEM & CHMN DEPT, MED CTR, UNIV NEBR, OMAHA, 74- *Concurrent Pos:* Nebr Heart Asn grants, 68-69, 71-76 & 77-79; equip grants, Smith Kline & French Labs & Nebr Res Coun, 68-; NSF grants, 69-73; NIH grants, 69-72 & 79-82. *Mem:* Am Asn Col Pharm; Int Soc Study Xenobiotics; Am Pharmaceut Asn. *Res:* Hepatic and extrahepatic xenobiotic metabolism; influence of disease states and age on drug metabolism; steroid metabolism; antiarrhythmic drugs; glutathione metabolism; biochemistry of lead toxicity. *Mailing Add:* Col Pharm Univ Nebr Med Ctr Omaha NE 68105

STOIBER, RICHARD EDWIN, b Cleveland, Ohio, Jan 28, 11; m 41; c 2. VOLCANOLOGY, ECONOMIC GEOLOGY. *Educ:* Dartmouth Col, AB, 32; Mass Inst Technol, PhD(econ geol), 37. *Prof Exp:* Instr, 35-36, 37-50, asst prof, 40-48, prof, 48-71, FREDERICK HALL PROF GEOL, DARTMOUTH COL, 71- *Concurrent Pos:* Part-time with Nfld Geol Surv pvt mining indust & US Geol Surv; govt sponsored volcanic res, Cent Am, Italy, Hawaii & Africa; consult, UN; pvt consult. *Mem:* Mineral Soc Am; Soc Econ Geol; Geol Soc Am; Am Inst Mining, Metall & Petrol Eng. *Res:* Ore deposits; volcanoes; optical crystallography. *Mailing Add:* Dept of Earth Sci Dartmouth Col Hanover NH 03755

STOICHEFF, BORIS PETER, b Bitol, Yugoslavia, June 1, 24; nat Can; m 54; c 1. LASERS, MOLECULAR SPECTROSCOPY. *Educ:* Univ Toronto, BASc, 47, MA, 48, PhD(physics), 50. *Prof Exp:* McKee-Gilchrist fel, Univ Toronto, 50-51; fel, Nat Res Coun Can, 52-53, res officer, Div Pure Physics, 53-64; chmn eng sci, 72-77, prof physics, 64-80, UNIV PROF PHYSICS, UNIV TORONTO, 80-; *Concurrent Pos:* Vis scientist, Mass Inst Technol, 63-64; I W Killam mem scholar, 77-79; mem, Coun Nat Res, Coun Can, 77-; vis scientist, Stanford Univ, 77; Geoffrey Frew fel, Australian Acad Sci, 80. *Honors & Awards:* Centennial Medal of Can, 67; Gold Medal, Can Asn Physicists, 74; William F Meggers Award, Optical Soc Am, 81. *Mem:* Fel Am Phys Soc; hon fel Indian Acad Sci; fel Royal Soc, London; fel Royal Soc Can; fel Optical Soc Am (pres-elect, 75, pres, 76). *Res:* Molecular spectroscopy and structure; Rayleigh, Brillouin and Raman scattering; lasers and their applications in spectroscopy; stimulated scattering processes and two photon absorption; elastic constants of rare gas single crystals; vacuum ultraviolet laser spectroscopy. *Mailing Add:* Dept of Physics Univ of Toronto Toronto ON M5S 1A7 Can

STOJANOVIC, BORISLAV JOVAN, b Zajecar, Yugoslavia, Nov 29, 19; US citizen; m 52. MICROBIOLOGY, BIOCHEMISTRY. *Educ:* Univ Bonn, BS, 48, Dr Agr, 50; Cornell Univ, MS, 55, PhD(soil microbiol), 56. *Prof Exp:* From asst prof to assoc prof soil microbiol, 67-74, PROF MICROBIOL & ENOL & HEAD ENOL LAB, MISS STATE UNIV, 74- *Mem:* Am Soc Enol; Am Soc Agron; Am Soc Microbiol. *Res:* Microbial transformations of soil proteinaceous materials and biocides; enzymes involved in browning of juices and wines. *Mailing Add:* A B McKay Food & Enol Lab Miss State Univ Mississippi State MS 39762

STOKELY, ERNEST MITCHELL, b Greenwood, Miss, Mar 26, 37; m 64; c 2. BIOMEDICAL ENGINEERING. *Educ:* Miss State Univ, BSEE, 59; Southern Methodist Univ, MSEE & EE, 68, EE, 71, PhD(biomed eng), 73. *Prof Exp:* Sr elec engr, Tex Instruments, Inc, 59-69; asst prof, 73-80, ASSOC PROF RADIOL, UNIV TEX HEALTH SCI CTR, DALLAS, 80- *Concurrent Pos:* Adj prof, Southern Methodist Univ, 73- & Univ Tex, Arlington, 73- *Mem:* Inst Elec & Electronic Engrs; Nat Asn Biomed Engrs. *Res:* Medical image and signal processing; biological system modeling. *Mailing Add:* Dept of Radiol Univ of Tex Health Sci Ctr Dallas TX 75235

STOKER, HOWARD STEPHEN, b Salt Lake City, Utah, Apr 16, 39; m 64; c 7. INORGANIC CHEMISTRY, ENVIRONMENTAL CHEMISTRY. *Educ:* Univ Utah, BA, 63; Univ Wis, PhD(chem), 68. *Prof Exp:* Assoc prof, 68-77, PROF INORG CHEM, WEBER STATE COL, 77- *Mem:* Am Chem Soc; Sigma Xi. *Res:* Air and water pollution. *Mailing Add:* Dept of Chem Weber State Col Ogden UT 84408

STOKER, JAMES JOHNSTON, b Dunbar, Pa, Mar 2, 05; m 28; c 4. MATHEMATICS, MECHANICS. *Educ:* Carnegie Inst Technol, BS, 27, MS, 31; Tech Hochsch Zurich, DrMath, 36. *Prof Exp:* Instr mech, Carnegie Inst Technol, 28-31, asst prof, 31-37; from asst prof to assoc prof, 37-45, PROF MATH, NY UNIV, 45-, DIR COURANT INST MATH SCI & HEAD ALL-UNIV DEPT MATH, 58- *Concurrent Pos:* Res mathematician, Appl Math Panel, Nat Defense Res Comt, 43-45. *Honors & Awards:* Heineman Prize, Am Phys Soc. *Mem:* Nat Acad Sci; AAAS; Am Math Soc. *Res:* Differential geometry; elasticity; vibration theory; hydrodynamics. *Mailing Add:* Courant Inst of Math Sci NY Univ 251 Mercer St New York NY 10012

STOKER, WARREN C(ADY), b Union Springs, NY, Jan 30, 12; m 34; c 3. ELECTRICAL ENGINEERING. *Educ:* Rensselaer Polytech Inst, EE, 33, MEE, 34, PhD(physics), 38. *Prof Exp:* From instr to assoc prof, 34-51, vpres, 61-74, pres, 74-76, PROF ELEC ENG, RENSSELAER POLYTECHNIC INST OF CONN, 51-, TRUSTEE, 61-, EMER PRES, 76- *Concurrent Pos:* Chief engr, Radio Sta WHAZ, 44-51; head comput lab, Hartford Grad Ctr, Rensselaer Polytechnic Inst of Conn, 51-55, dir, 55-57, dean, 57-70; mem res sci adv comt, United Aircraft Corp. *Mem:* AAAS; fel Inst Elec & Electronics Engrs; Am Soc Eng Educ; Newcomen Soc NAm. *Res:* Electronic instrumentation; electromagnetic shielding and noise measurements; leakage and radiation; servomechanisms; analog computing; automatic control systems. *Mailing Add:* 246 Neptune Dr Groton CT 06340

STOKES, ARNOLD PAUL, b Bismarck, NDak, Jan 24, 32; m 57; c 6. PURE MATHEMATICS. *Educ:* Univ Notre Dame, BS, 55, PhD(math), 59. *Prof Exp:* Staff mathematician, Res Inst Adv Study, 58-60; NSF fel math, Johns Hopkins Univ, 60-61; from asst prof to assoc prof, Catholic Univ, 61-65; chmn dept, 67-70, PROF MATH, GEORGETOWN UNIV, 65- *Concurrent Pos:* Sr res assoc, Nat Res Coun-Nat Acad Sci, Goddard Space Flight Ctr, NASA, 74-75; consult ocean acoustics, SAI, McLean, Va, 80- *Mem:* Am Math Soc. *Res:* Nonlinear differential equations. *Mailing Add:* Dept of Math Georgetown Univ Washington DC 20057

STOKES, BRADFORD TAYLOR, b Beverly, Mass, Jan 22, 44; m 67; c 2. NEUROPHYSIOLOGY, DEVELOPMENTAL NEUROBIOLOGY. *Educ:* Univ Mass, BA, 66; Univ Rochester, PhD(physiol), 73. *Prof Exp:* Res assoc physiol, Univ Rochester, 69-73; asst prof, 73-77, ASSOC PROF PHYSIOL, OHIO STATE UNIV, 78- *Concurrent Pos:* Proj investr, Muscular Dystrophy Asn, 75-, NIH, 78-83 & NSF, 79-81. *Mem:* AAAS; Am Physiol Soc; Int Soc Oxygen Transp Tissue; Neurosci Soc. *Res:* Developmental neurophysiology; the development of motor systems; bioelectrical activity in normal and abnormal spinal cords; the effects of acute changes in blood gases on fetal neurogenesis. *Mailing Add:* Dept of Physiol Ohio State Univ Columbus OH 43210

STOKES, CHARLES SOMMERS, b Philadelphia, Pa, Apr 24, 29; m 54; c 2. PHYSICAL CHEMISTRY. *Educ:* Ursinus Col, BS, 51; Temple Univ, MA, 53. *Prof Exp:* Res chemist, Germantown Labs, Inc, 53-56, res assoc, 56-61, mgr test site, 61-72, vpres, 72-80, MGR, ELVERSON TEST FACIL, FRANKLIN INST RES CTR, 80- *Mem:* Am Chem Soc; Am Inst Aeronaut & Astronaut; Am Inst Chem; Combustion Inst. *Res:* Fluorine chemistry; propellents; high temperatures; energy research; plasma jet chemistry. *Mailing Add:* 127 Madison Rd Willow Grove PA 19090

STOKES, DAVID KERSHAW, JR, b Camden, SC, Feb 3, 27; m 50; c 3. FAMILY MEDICINE. *Educ:* Clemson Univ, BS, 48; Univ Ga, MS, 52; Tex A&M Univ, PhD, 56; Med Univ SC, MD, 57. *Prof Exp:* assoc prof, 72-80, PROF FAMILY PRACT, MED UNIV SC, 72-; MED DIR, CAMPHAVEN NURSING HOME, INMAN, SC, 80- *Mem:* AMA; Am Heart Asn; Am Acad Family Physicians; Am Rheumatism Asn; Am Med Dir Asn. *Mailing Add:* Camphaven Nursing Home Rte 4 Box 1 Inman SC 29349

STOKES, DONALD EUGENE, b Andalusia, Ala, Aug 25, 31; m; c 5. NEMATOLOGY. *Educ:* Univ Fla, BS, 55, MA, 63, PhD(nematol), 72. *Prof Exp:* Nematologist III, 56-75, CHIEF NEMATOL, DIV PLANT INDUST, FLA DEPT AGR & CONSUMER SERV, 75- *Concurrent Pos:* Courtesy Fac Appl & Grad Fac Status, Univ Fla, 75. *Mem:* Soc Nematologists; Orgn Trop Am Nematologists; Europ Soc Nematologists. *Res:* Regulatory aspects of nematology, which include pathogenicity, taxonomy and response to chemicals of the various plant parasitic nematodes. *Mailing Add:* PO Box 1269 Gainesville FL 32602

STOKES, GERALD MADISON, b Burlington, Vt, Aug 16, 47; m 71; c 2. ASTRONOMY. *Educ:* Univ Calif, Santa Cruz, BA, 69; Univ Chicago, MS, 71, PhD(astron), 77. *Prof Exp:* Fel astron, 76-78, res scientist, 78-80, SR RES SCIENTIST SPACE SCI, PAC NORTHWEST LABS, BATTELLE MEM INST, 80- *Mem:* Am Astron Soc; Inst Environ Sci. *Res:* Formation and destruction of interstellar grains; polarimetry of x-ray binaries; abundances of atmospheric trace gases. *Mailing Add:* Battelle Observ PO Box 999 Richland WA 99352

STOKES, GERALD V, b Chicago, Ill, Mar 25, 43; m; c 2. MICROBIOLOGY. *Educ:* Southern Ill Univ, BA, 67; Univ Chicago, PhD(microbiol), 73. *Prof Exp:* Fel & res assoc, Dept Molecular, Cellular & Develop Biol, Univ Colo, Boulder, 73-76; asst prof, Dept Microbiol, Meharry Med Col, 76-78; asst prof, 78-80, ASSOC PROF, DEPT MICROBIOL, SCH MED & HEALTH SCI, GEORGE WASHINGTON UNIV, 80- *Concurrent Pos:* Fel, Am Can Soc, 74-76 & NIH, 76; res grants, NIH, 77-78, NSF, 77-81. *Mem:* Am Soc Microbiol; Electron Micros Soc Am; Sigma Xi. *Res:* Developmental processes and molecular biology of the chlamydial organisms and fine structure electron microscopy; attachment receptors and virulence factors of Chlamydia psittachi and C trachomatis. *Mailing Add:* George Washington Univ Med Ctr Dept Micrbiol 2300 Eye St NW Washington DC 20037

STOKES, GORDON ELLIS, b Ogden, Utah, Feb 11, 33; m 55; c 9. COMPUTER SCIENCE, PHYSICS. *Educ:* Brigham Young Univ, BS, 61, EdD, 81; Univ Idaho, MS, 69. *Prof Exp:* Physicist, Phillips Petrol Corp, 61-66; sr res physicist, Idaho Nuclear Corp, 66-69; asst dean phys & eng sci, 69-70, asst dir comput sci, 70-73, FAC COMPUT SCI, BRIGHAM YOUNG UNIV, 73- *Concurrent Pos:* Consult, State of Ark, 75-, Weidner Commun Corp, 77-, Geneal Dept, Latter-Day Saint Church, 77-, Winnebago Indust, 78- & Eyring Res Inst, 78- *Mem:* Asn Comput Mach. *Res:* Distributed data base systems; small computer applications; computer management; computer systems in business, government and industry. *Mailing Add:* Dept Comput Sci 230-C TMCB Brigham Young Univ Provo UT 84602

STOKES, GRANVILLE WOOLMAN, crop breeding, plant pathology, see previous edition

STOKES, HAROLD T, b Long Beach, Calif, Jan 27, 47; m 74; c 3. NUCLEAR MAGNETIC RESONANCE. *Educ:* Brigham Young Univ, BS, 71; Univ Utah, PhD(physics), 77. *Prof Exp:* Instr physics, Univ Utah, 77-78; res assoc, Univ Ill, 78-81; ASST PROF PHYSICS, BRIGHAM YOUNG UNIV, 81- *Mem:* Am Phys Soc; Am Asn Physics Teachers. *Res:* Molecular and atomic motions in solids; platinum catalysts. *Mailing Add:* Dept Physics & Astron Brigham Young Univ Provo UT 84602

STOKES, JACOB LEO, b Warsaw, Poland, Sept 27, 12; US citizen; m 42; c 2. MICROBIOLOGY. *Educ:* Rutgers Univ, BS, 34, PhD(microbiol), 39; Univ Ky, MS, 36. *Prof Exp:* Asst bact, Univ Ky, 34-36; asst marine bact, Rutgers Univ, 36-37, soil microbiol, 37-39; from microbiologist to head sect microbiol metab, Res Labs, Merck & Co, Inc, 39-47; res assoc, Hopkins Marine Sta, Stanford Univ, 48-50; assoc prof bact, Ind Univ, 50-53; bacteriologist, Western Utilization Res Br, USDA, 53-59; chmn dept bact & pub health, 59-68, prof, 59-78, EMER PROF BACT & PUB HEALTH, WASH STATE UNIV, 78- *Mem:* AAAS; Am Soc Microbiol. *Res:* Relation of algae to other microorganisms in nature; antibiotics; iron bacteria; nutrition, physiology and biochemistry of microorganisms; psychrophilic microorganisms. *Mailing Add:* Dept of Bact & Pub Health Wash State Univ Pullman WA 99164

STOKES, JIMMY CLEVELAND, b Cochran, Ga, Nov 29, 44; m 72; c 2. SCIENCE EDUCATION. *Educ:* Univ Ga, BS, 66, MEd, 67, EdD(chem educ), 69. *Prof Exp:* Instr chem, Univ Ga, 69-70; asst prof, Clayton Jr Col, 70-74; ASSOC PROF CHEM, W GA COL, 74- *Concurrent Pos:* Consult, Ga High Sch Asn, 76- *Mem:* Am Chem Soc; Nat Sci Teachers Asn; Sigma Xi. *Res:* Construction and evaluation of self paced and individualized programs of instruction in chemistry; development of drug education materials and programs. *Mailing Add:* Dept of Chem W Ga Col Carrollton GA 30118

STOKES, JOSEPH, III, internal medicine, see previous edition

STOKES, JOSEPH FRANKLIN, b Havana, Ark, Feb 27, 34; m 59; c 2. MATHEMATICS. *Educ:* Univ Ark, Fayetteville, BS, 56, MA, 57; George Peabody Col, PhD(math), 72. *Prof Exp:* Instr math, Kans State Univ, 58-61; instr, Auburn Univ, 61-62; assoc prof, 62-80, PROF MATH, WESTERN KY UNIV, 80- *Concurrent Pos:* res partic, Oak Ridge Assoc Univ, 67. *Mem:* Math Asn Am; AAAS; Nat Coun Teachers Math. *Res:* Importance sampling. *Mailing Add:* Dept Math Western Ky Univ Bowling Green KY 42101

STOKES, PAMELA MARY, b Hertford, UK, June 24, 35; m 58; c 2. TOXICOLOGY. *Educ:* Univ Bristol, BSc, 56, PhD(bot), 59. *Prof Exp:* Fel mycol, Imperial Col, London, 59-60; lectr bot, Sir John Cass Col, London, 60-63; res assoc plant pathol, Univ Ill, 64-65; instr biol, 69-70, assoc prof, 73-82, PROF BOT, UNIV TORONTO, 82- *Mem:* Can Bot Asn; Am Psychol Soc; An Mycol Soc; Am Soc Limnol & Oceanog; Am Soc Geochem & Health. *Res:* The response of aquatic plants to high concentrations of metals and low pouvoir hydrogene; community response in the field; adaptations of algae which confer tolerance to metals; biological monitoring. *Mailing Add:* Dept Bot Univ Toronto Toronto ON M5S 1A4 Can

STOKES, PETER E, b Haddonfield, NJ, Aug 27, 26; m 56; c 3. MEDICINE, PSYCHIATRY. *Educ:* Trinity Col, BS, 48; Cornell Univ, MD, 52; Am Bd Internal Med, dipl, 57; Am Bd Psychiat & Neurol, dipl, 71; Am Bd Radiol, dipl & cert nuclear med, 72. *Prof Exp:* Intern med, New York Hosp, 52-53, asst resident, 53-54, asst resident med & endocrinol, 54-55; NIH trainee fel, 55-57; instr med in endocrinol, 57-59, asst prof med in psychiat, 59-63, ASSOC PROF PSYCHIAT & MED, MED COL, CORNELL UNIV, 69- *Concurrent Pos:* Physician, Outpatient Clin, New York Hosp, 55-56, from asst attend to assoc attend physician, 61-; dir clin res labs, Payne Whitney Psychiat Clin, New York Hosp-Cornell Med Ctr, 57-, dir psychobiol study unit, 67, assoc attend psychiatrist, 69; assoc vis physician, Cornell Div, Bellevue Hosp, 62-; pvt pract consult, 59- *Mem:* Endocrine Soc; Am Soc Nuclear Med; fel Am Col Physicians. *Res:* Neuroendocrine function in emotional disorders; hypothalamic pituitary adrenocortical function control systems in animals; alcoholism and the effects of alcohol on neuroendocrine function; calcium, strontium and creatinine metabolism; problems in growth thyroid; adrenal and ovarian function; clinical psychiatric problems, especially affective disorders; lithium metabolism. *Mailing Add:* Payne Whitney Clin New York Hosp-Cornell Med Ctr New York NY 10021

STOKES, RICHARD HIVLING, b Troy, Ohio, Apr 30, 21; m 56. EXPERIMENTAL PHYSICS. *Educ:* Case Univ, BS, 42; Iowa State Univ, PhD(physics), 51. *Prof Exp:* Staff mem, Underwater Sound Ref Lab, Nat Defense Res Comt, 42-44; res assoc, Inst Atomic Res, Iowa State Col, 46-51; staff mem, 51-67, GROUP LEADER, LOS ALAMOS SCI LAB, 67- *Concurrent Pos:* US del, Conf Peaceful Uses Atomic Energy, Geneva, 58; lectr, Univ Minn, 60-61. *Mem:* Fel Am Phys Soc. *Res:* Nuclear physics; accelerator research; fission; spectroscopy of light nuclei; nuclear detectors; heavy ion accelerators; heavy ion reactions. *Mailing Add:* 2450 Club Rd Los Alamos NM 87544

STOKES, ROBERT ALLAN, b Richmond, Ky, June 25, 42; m 63. ASTROPHYSICS. *Educ:* Univ Ky, BS, 64; Princeton Univ, MA, 66, PhD(physics), 68. *Prof Exp:* Asst prof physics & astron, Univ Ky, 68-72; sr scientist, 72-74, MGR SPACE SCI, PAC NORTHWEST LABS, BATTELLE MEM INST, 74-; ASSOC PROF PHYSICS & ASTRON, UNIV KY, 73- *Concurrent Pos:* Adv comt, Geophys Inst, Univ Alaska, 75- *Mem:* AAAS; Am Phys Soc; Am Astron Soc. *Res:* Experimental cosmology and relativity; planetary astrophysics; radiative transfer theory. *Mailing Add:* Battelle Observ Battelle-Northwest Richland WA 99352

STOKES, ROBERT JAMES, b Devizes, Eng, Oct 15, 28; m 55; c 2. MATERIALS SCIENCE, CERAMICS SCIENCE. *Educ:* Bristol Univ, BS, 52; Univ Birmingham, PhD(phys metall), 55. *Prof Exp:* Fulbright res assoc metall, Univ Calif, Berkeley, 55-57; res scientist ceramics, Honeywell Res Ctr, 57-65; vis prof mat sci, Carnegie-Mellon Univ, 65-66; res mgr mat, Res Ctr, 66-77, TECHNOL MGR MAT & PROCESSES, HONEYWELL CORP MAT SCI CTR, 77- *Concurrent Pos:* Adv panel, Nat Bur Standards, 70-75 & NSF, 77- *Honors & Awards:* Ross Coffin Purdy Award, Am Ceramic Soc, 65; H W Sweatt Award, Honeywell Inc, 67. *Mem:* Am Ceramic Soc; Mat Res Soc; Int Soc Hybrid Microelectronics. *Res:* Mechanical, optical, magnetic and electrical properties of ceramics; material interactions at surfaces and interfaces; fracture, strength and physical properties of composites. *Mailing Add:* Honeywell Corp Tech Ctr 10701 Lyndale Ave S Bloomington MN 55420

STOKES, ROBERT MITCHELL, b Vandalia, Ill, May 21, 36; m 59; c 3. COMPARATIVE PHYSIOLOGY. *Educ:* Mich State Univ, BS, 58, MS, 59, PhD(physiol), 63. *Prof Exp:* From asst prof to assoc prof, 63-77, PROF BIOL SCI, KENT STATE UNIV, 77- *Concurrent Pos:* Consult, Great Lakes Basin Comn Water Qual Task Force, 68-70. *Mem:* Am Soc Zool. *Res:* Biochemical and biophysical aspects of membrane transport phenomena in fish, especially glucose transport by intestine; fish physiology, metabolism and toxicology. *Mailing Add:* Dept of Biol Sci Kent State Univ Kent OH 44242

STOKES, RUSSELL AUBREY, b Preston, Miss, May 1, 22; m 59. MATHEMATICS. *Educ:* Miss State Univ, BS, 48; Univ Miss, MA, 51; Univ Tex, PhD(math), 63. *Prof Exp:* From asst prof to assoc prof, 56-66, PROF MATH, UNIV MISS, 66- *Mem:* Am Math Soc; Math Asn Am. *Res:* Measure and integration. *Mailing Add:* Dept of Math Univ of Miss University MS 38677

STOKES, WILLIAM GLENN, b Corsicana, Tex, Dec 26, 21; m; c 2. MATHEMATICS. *Educ:* Sam Houston State Col, BS, 46, MA, 47; Peabody Col, PhD(math), 57. *Prof Exp:* Head dept math, Navarro Jr Col, 47-53; instr appl math, Vanderbilt Univ, 54-55; head dept math, Austin Peay State Col, 55-57; assoc prof, Northwestern State Col, 57-59 & East Tex State Univ, 59-60; PROF MATH & COMPUT SCI & CHMN DEPT, AUSTIN PEAY STATE UNIV, 74- *Mem:* Math Asn Am; Am Math Soc. *Mailing Add:* Dept of Math Austin Peay State Univ Clarksville TN 37040

STOKES, WILLIAM LEE, b Hiawatha, Utah, Mar 27, 15; m 39; c 4. STRATIGRAPHY. *Educ:* Brigham Young Univ, BS, 37, MS, 38; Princeton Univ, PhD(geol), 41. *Prof Exp:* Asst, Princeton Univ, 41-42; from jr geologist to asst geologist, US Geol Surv, 42-46; from asst prof to assoc prof geol, 47-54, chmn dept, 54-68, PROF GEOL, UNIV UTAH, 54- *Concurrent Pos:* Consult, USAEC, 52-54. *Mem:* AAAS; fel Geol Soc Am; Soc Vert Paleont; Am Asn Petrol Geol; Am Geophys Union. *Res:* Mesozoic stratigraphy; dinosaurs; arid lands geomorphology; creationist evolutionist controversy; sedimentary ore deposits; textbook writing and popularization of earth science. *Mailing Add:* 1354 Second Ave Salt Lake City UT 84103

STOKES, WILLIAM MOORE, b Cleveland, Ohio, Sept 18, 21. ORGANIC CHEMISTRY. *Educ:* Franklin & Marshall Col, BS, 44; Yale Univ, PhD(chem), 52. *Hon Degrees:* MA, Providence Col, 61. *Prof Exp:* Chemist, Hamilton Watch Co, 44-46; lab asst, Yale Univ, 46-48, 49-51; from asst prof to assoc prof med res, 51-59, PROF CHEM & DIR MED RES LAB, PROVIDENCE COL, 59- *Mem:* Fel AAAS; Am Chem Soc; Am Oil Chem Soc; NY Acad Sci. *Res:* Neurochemistry; isolation of natural products; steroid metabolism; correlation of optical activity with molecular structure. *Mailing Add:* Dept of Chem Providence Col Providence RI 02918

STOKEY, W(ILLIAM) F(ARMER), b Cincinnati, Ohio, Apr 19, 17; m 46; c 3. MECHANICAL ENGINEERING. *Educ:* Ga Inst Technol, BS, 38; Mass Inst Technol, MS, 47, ScD(mech eng), 49. *Prof Exp:* Asst prof, 49-55, ASSOC PROF MECH ENG, CARNEGIE-MELLON UNIV, 55- *Mem:* Am Soc Mech Engrs; Soc Exp Stress Anal. *Res:* Stress analysis; dynamic shock; vibrations. *Mailing Add:* Dept of Mech Eng Carnegie-Mellon Univ Pittsburgh PA 15213

STOKINGER, HERBERT ELLSWORTH, b Boston, Mass, June 19, 09. TOXICOLOGY. *Educ:* Harvard Univ, AB, 30; Columbia Univ, PhD(biochem), 37. *Prof Exp:* Instr chem, City Col New York, 32-39; res assoc bact, Sch Med & Dent, Univ Rochester, 39-43, chief indust hyg sect, AEC, 43-51, from asst prof to assoc prof pharm & toxicol, 45-51; chief toxicologist, Nat Inst Occup Safety & Health, USPHS, 51-77; RETIRED. *Concurrent Pos:* Res assoc, Col Physicians & Surgeons, Columbia Univ, 37-39; res assoc, Atomic Bomb Test, Bikini, 46; mem subcomt toxicol, Nat Res Coun, 46, chmn comt, 70-73; chmm subcomt toxicol, USPHS Drinking Water Stas, 58-70; chmn threshold limits comt, Am Conf Govt Indust Hygenists, 62- *Honors & Awards:* Donald E Cummings Mem Award for outstanding contrib to knowledge & pract of indust hygiene, Am Indust Hygiene Asn, 69; Eminent Chemist Award, Cincinnati Am Chem Soc, 70; S C Weisfeld Mem Lect Award, 75. *Mem:* AAAS; Am Indust Hyg Asn; Am Asn Immunol. *Res:* Pharmacology and toxicology of atomic energy materials; bacteriological chemistry of gonococcus; toxins; chemotherapy of sulfonamides and arsenicals; prophylaxis of industrial poisons; industrial, water and air pollution toxicology. *Mailing Add:* 9 Twin Hills Ridge Dr Cincinnati OH 45228

STOKOWSKI, STANLEY E, b Lewiston, Maine, Dec 28, 41. SOLID STATE PHYSICS, OPTICS. *Educ:* Mass Inst Technol, SB, 63; Stanford Univ, PhD(physics), 68. *Prof Exp:* Physicist, Nat Bur of Stand, 68-70; mem tech staff, Bell Tel Labs, NJ, 70-72; prin investr, Res Inst Advan Studies Div, Martin Marietta Corp, 72-77; SR RES SCIENTIST, LAWRENCE LIVERMORE LAB, 77- *Mem:* Am Phys Soc; Am Optical Soc. *Res:* Crystal field theory; phase transitions; ferroelectricity; color centers; optical properties of crystals; laser glass; infrared detectors. *Mailing Add:* Lawrence Livermore Lab PO Box 808 Livermore CA 94550

STOKSTAD, EVAN LUDVIG ROBERT, b China, Mar 6, 13; US citizen; m 34; c 2. BIOCHEMISTRY. *Educ:* Univ Calif, BS, 34, PhD(animal nutrit), 37. *Prof Exp:* Biochemist, Western Condensing Co, 37-39; biochemist, Golden State Co, Ltd, 39-40; Lalor fel, Calif Inst Technol, 40-41; chemist, Lederle Labs Div, Am Cyanamid Co, 41-63; actg chmn dept nutrit sci, 68-69, prof nutrit, 63-80, chmn dept nutrit sci, 79-80, EMER PROF NUTRIT, UNIV CALIF, BERKELEY, 80-, BIOCHEMIST, AGR EXP STA, 63- *Concurrent Pos:* Mem food & nutrit bd, Div Biol & Agr, Nat Acad Sci-Nat Res Coun, 68-72, comt food standards & fortification policy, 72. *Honors & Awards:* Borden Award, Poultry Sci Asn; Mead-Johnson Award, Am Inst Nutrit; Osborne & Mendel Award, Am Inst Nutrit, 80. *Mem:* Soc Exp Biol & Med; Am Soc Biol Chemists; Am Chem Soc; Poultry Sci Asn; Am Inst Nutrit (treas, 70-73, pres, 76). *Res:* Water soluble vitamin requirements for chicks; antibiotics in animal nutrition; bacterial nutrition; chemistry and biochemistry of thioctic acid; dental nutrition and mineral metabolism; chemistry and metabolism of folic acid and vitamin B12. *Mailing Add:* Dept of Nutrit Sci Univ of Calif Berkeley CA 94720

STOLARIK, EUGENE, b Zilina, Czech, Mar 27, 19; nat US; m 44; c 2. AERODYNAMICS. *Educ:* Prague Tech Univ, dipl, 39; Carleton Col, BA, 40; Univ Minn, MA, 42, MS, 44. *Prof Exp:* Asst physics, Univ Minn, 41-42, instr aerodyn & aircraft, 42-44; chief proj engr, Lawrance Aeronaut Corp, NJ, 44-45; chief engr, Off Res & Inventions Lab, US Dept Navy, 45-47; ASSOC PROF AERONAUT ENG, UNIV MINN, MINNEAPOLIS, 47- *Concurrent Pos:* US deleg, 2nd Int Cong Aeronaut Sci, Zurich; civilian with Nat Defense Res Comt & War Prod Bd, 45; consult, Boeing Co, Wash, 52-60, 62 & 68, Northrop Corp, Calif, 58, 64 & 66, Univac Div, Sperry Rand Corp, 64-66 & Honeywell Corp, 68-69; sr staff engr, Aeronca Mfg Corp, 60; eng staff specialist, Astronaut Div, Gen Dynamics Corp, Calif, 61 & 65; sr staff engr, Lockheed Missiles & Space Co, Calif, 63; dir res & develop, Control Technol Corp, 71; res analyzer, Am Inst Res. *Honors & Awards:* Cert Appreciation, Off Sci Res & Develop, 45. *Mem:* Assoc fel Am Inst Aeronaut & Astronaut; Am Helicopter Soc; Am Soc Eng Educ; Royal Aeronaut Soc. *Res:* Mechanics of flight; pneumatics; control and guidance of aerospace vehicles; convective heat transfer; interference effects; reentry of aerospace vehicles; engineering education. *Mailing Add:* Dept of Aerospace Eng & Mech Univ of Minn Minneapolis MN 55455

STOLARSKY, KENNETH B, b Chicago, Ill, May 9, 42; m 69. MATHEMATICS. *Educ:* Calif Inst Technol, BS, 63; Univ Wis-Madison, MS, 65, PhD(math), 68. *Prof Exp:* Fel math, Inst Advan Study, 68-69; asst prof, 69-73, ASSOC PROF MATH, UNIV ILL, URBANA, 73- *Mem:* Am Math Soc; Math Asn Am. *Res:* Number theory; combinatorics; geometric inequalities. *Mailing Add:* Dept of Math Univ of Ill at Urbana-Champaign Urbana IL 61801

STOLBACH, LEO LUCIEN, b Geneva, Switz, Feb 25, 33; US citizen; m 61; c 2. ONCOLOGY, INTERNAL MEDICINE. *Educ:* Harvard Univ, BA, 54; Univ Rochester, MD, 58; Am Bd Internal Med, cert, 67. *Prof Exp:* Intern med, Univ Hosp, Cleveland, 58-59, resident, 59-60; clin assoc, Endocrinol Br, NIH, 60-62, sr investr, 62-63; resident, Univ Hosp, Cleveland, 63-64; res physician oncol, Lemuel Shattuck Hosp, Boston, 64-70; chief med, Pondville Hosp, 70-81; CHIEF MED ONCOL, OTTAWA CLIN, ONT CANCER FOUND & OTTAWA CIVIC HOSP, 81- *Concurrent Pos:* From instr to asst prof, Sch Med, Tufts Univ, 64-73, assoc prof, 73-81; assoc prof, Sch Med, Univ Ottawa, 81- *Mem:* Am Asn Cancer Res; Am Soc Clin Oncol; fel Am Col Physicians; Am Asn Cancer Educ. *Res:* Clinical chemotherapy; tumor immunology; tumor markers. *Mailing Add:* Ottawa Clin Ont Cancer Found 190 Melrose Ave Ottawa ON K1Y 4K7 Can

STOLBERG, HAROLD JOSEF, mathematics, see previous edition

STOLBERG, MARVIN ARNOLD, b New York, NY, Oct 29, 25; m 49; c 2. ORGANIC CHEMISTRY. *Educ:* Columbia Univ, BS, 50; Univ Del, MS, 54, PhD(chem), 56. *Prof Exp:* Org chemist, Chemother Br, US Army Chem Ctr, Md, 50-53, asst br chief, 54-56; head chem dept, Tracerlab, Inc, Mass, 56-60; tech dir-vpres, 60-72, PRES & CHIEF EXEC OFF, NEW ENGLAND NUCLEAR CORP, 72- *Mem:* Am Chem Soc; Soc Nuclear Med. *Res:* Organic and inorganic synthesis with radioactive isotopes; radioactive pharmaceuticals and assay of labeled compounds; tracer techniques for solving problems concerning food and drug acceptability criteria; product evaluation; organic reaction mechanisms. *Mailing Add:* New England Nuclear Corp 549 Albany St Boston MA 02118

STOLC, VIKTOR, b Bratislava, Czech, Oct 5, 32; m 73; c 2. ENDOCRINOLOGY, HEMATOLOGY. *Educ:* Univ Comenius Bratislava, RNDr, 56; Slovak Acad Sci, Czech, PhD(biochem), 63. *Prof Exp:* Biochemist, Endocrine Sta, Inst Health, Czech, 56-57; independent scientist, Inst Endocrinol, Slovak Acad Sci, 57-68; res assoc, 65-66 & 68-70, asst res prof, 70-71, RES ASSOC PROF PATH, SCH MED, UNIV PITTSBURGH, 71- *Mem:* AAAS; Endocrine Soc; Am Soc Biol Chemists; NY Acad Sci; Reticuloendothelial Soc. *Res:* Development of pituitary-thyroid axis in postnatal rats; regulation of thyroid hormone biosynthesis in isolated thyroid cells, endocrine factors in normal and leukemic leukocytes. *Mailing Add:* Dept of Path Univ of Pittsburgh Sch of Med Pittsburgh PA 15261

STOLDT, STEPHEN HOWARD, b New York, NY, Dec 17, 38; m 65; c 2. ORGANIC CHEMISTRY, CORROSION. *Educ:* Queens Col, NY, BS, 60; City Col New York, MA, 62, PhD(org chem), 68. *Prof Exp:* Res assoc org chem, Univ Wis, 67-68; res chemist fuels & lubricants, Shell Oil Co, 68-73; SUPVR CHEM RES COAL UTILIZATION, APOLLO CHEM CORP, 73- *Mem:* Nat Asn Corrosion Engrs; Am Chem Soc. *Res:* Combustion; power generation; fuels; lubricants; coal utilization. *Mailing Add:* 4 Crestmont Dr Dover NJ 07801

STOLEN, JOANNE SIU, b Chicago, Ill, June 22, 43; m 72; c 1. IMMUNOLOGY. *Educ:* Univ Mich, BS, 65; Seton Hall Univ, MS, 68; Rutgers Univ, PhD(biochem), 72. *Prof Exp:* Res intern immunol, Inst Microbiol, Rutgers Univ, 69-72; fel, Dept Serol & Bact, Univ Helsinki; RES IMMUNOL, SANDY HOOK LAB & UNIV HELSINKI, 74- *Concurrent Pos:* Adj prof, Drew Univ, 82- *Mem:* Sigma Xi. *Res:* Cellular immunology; thymus derived and bone marrow derived cell function in the mouse and presently in lower animals such as the fish; immunoregulation and the effect of stress on the immune system of fish. *Mailing Add:* Northeast Fisheries Ctr Sandy Hook Lab Highlands NJ 07732

STOLEN, ROGERS HALL, b Madison, Wis, Sept 18, 37. SOLID STATE PHYSICS. *Educ:* St Olaf Col, BA, 59; Univ Calif, Berkeley, PhD(physics), 65. *Prof Exp:* Fel, Univ Toronto, 64-66; MEM TECH STAFF SOLID STATE OPTICS, BELL LABS, 66- *Mem:* Am Phys Soc; Optic Soc Am. *Res:* Nonlinear properties of optical fibers; polarization preserving optical fibers; light scattering in glass. *Mailing Add:* Bell Labs 4B-421 Holmdel NJ 07733

STOLER, DAVID, b Brooklyn, NY, Aug 21, 36; m 58; c 1. ELEMENTARY PARTICLE PHYSICS, QUANTUM OPTICS. *Educ:* City Col New York, BS, 58; Yeshiva Univ, PhD(physics), 66. *Prof Exp:* Instr physics, Staten Island Community Col, 59-60; sr res asst, Microwave Res Inst, 60-66; from asst prof to assoc prof physics, Polytech Inst NY, 66-75; sr staff physicist, Laser Optics Dept, Electro-Optical Div, Perkin-Elmer Corp, 75-80. *Concurrent Pos:* Instr, Brooklyn Col, 60-61; consult liquid crystal displays, Riker-Maxson Corp, 72. *Mem:* Am Phys Soc. *Res:* Electromagnetic properties of hadrons; quantum field theory; quantum theory of coherence; nonlinear optics; laser physics; laser resonator theory. *Mailing Add:* 175 Adams St Brooklyn NY 11201

STOLER, PAUL, b Brooklyn, NY, June 8, 38; m 66. EXPERIMENTAL NUCLEAR PHYSICS. *Educ:* Brooklyn Col, BS, 60; Rutgers Univ, MS, 62, PhD(physics), 66. *Prof Exp:* ASSOC PROF PHYSICS, RENSSELAER POLYTECH INST, 66- *Mem:* Am Phys Soc. *Res:* Nuclear structure physics using techniques of proton scattering, photonuclear reactions and neutron cross section measurements; photopion production from complex nuclei. *Mailing Add:* Dept of Physics Rensselaer Polytech Inst Troy NY 12181

STOLFI, ROBERT LOUIS, b Brooklyn, NY, Sept 16, 38; m 68. IMMUNOCHEMISTRY, IMMUNOLOGY. *Educ:* Brooklyn Col, BS, 60; Univ Miami, PhD(microbiol), 67. *Prof Exp:* Bact technician, Jewish Hosp Brooklyn, 60-61; asst bacteriologist, Bellevue Hosp, 61-62; res assoc immunochem, Howard Hughes Med Inst, 63-67; from instr to asst prof microbiol, Sch Med, Univ Miami, 67-71; dir transplantation immunol, 69-78, ASST DIR CANCER RES, DEPT SURG, CATH MED CTR BROOKLYN & QUEENS INC, 78- *Concurrent Pos:* Res assoc immunochem, Variety Children's Res Found, Fla, 67-71; res assoc, Cancer Inst, Univ Columbia, 80- *Mem:* AAAS; Am Asn Immunologists; Am Soc Microbiol; Am Cancer Soc. *Res:* Therapeutic methods for the alteration of immunological reactivity in the tumor-bearing host, or in the recipient of a histoincompatible normal tissue transplant; analysis of the interactions among drugs; tumor and host immune systems during cancer chemotherapy. *Mailing Add:* St Anthony's Hosp 89-15 Woodhaven Blvd Woodhaven NY 11421

STOLINE, MICHAEL ROSS, b Jefferson, Iowa, Sept 17, 40; m 60; c 4. STATISTICAL ANALYSIS. *Educ:* Univ Iowa, BA, 62, MA, 64, PhD(statist), 67. *Prof Exp:* Assoc prof, 67-77, PROF MATH, WESTERN MICH UNIV & STATIST, 77- *Mem:* Am Statist Asn; Inst Math Statist. *Res:* Problems in the analysis of variance and regression; intervention time series; multiple comparisons. *Mailing Add:* Dept Math Western Mich Univ 5510 Everett Tower Kalamazoo MI 49008

STOLK, JON MARTIN, b Englewood, NJ, Oct 15, 42; m 73. PSYCHIATRY, PHARMACOLOGY. *Educ:* Middlebury Col, AB, 64; Dartmouth Col, PhD(pharmacol), 69; Stanford Univ, MD, 72. *Prof Exp:* Fel psychiat, Sch Med, Stanford Univ, 69-71; asst prof pharmacol, Dartmouth Med Col, 72-73, asst prof psychiat, 74-76, assoc prof, 76-78; PROF PSYCHIAT, SCH MED, UNIV MD, 78- *Mem:* Am Soc Pharmacol & Exp Therapeut; Int Soc Psychoneuroendocrinol. *Res:* Biogenic amines and behavior; psychopharmacology; central nervous system polypeptides; neurochemistry. *Mailing Add:* Md Psychiat Res Ctr Box 3235 Baltimore MD 21228

STOLL, MANFRED, b Calw, Ger, Aug 24, 44; US citizen; m 66; c 3. MATHEMATICAL ANALYSIS. *Educ:* State Univ NY Albany, BS, 67; Pa State Univ, MA, 69, PhD(math), 71. *Prof Exp:* Asst prof, 71-76, ASSOC PROF MATH, UNIV SC, 76- *Mem:* Am Math Soc. *Res:* Harmonic, holomorphic and plurisubharmonic function theory on bounded symmetric domains and generalized half planes; spaces and algebras of holomorphic functions of one and several complex variables. *Mailing Add:* Dept of Math & Comput Sci Univ of SC Columbia SC 29208

STOLL, PAUL JAMES, b Grass Valley, Calif, June 23, 33; m 59; c 1. ELECTRICAL ENGINEERING, BIOENGINEERING. *Educ:* Wesleyan Univ, BA, 55; Mass Inst Technol, SB, 57, SM, 58; Univ Wash, PhD(elec eng), 68. *Prof Exp:* Teaching asst, Mass Inst Technol, 57-58; res engr guid systs, Autonetics Div, NAm Rockwell Corp, 58-61, consult, 61-62; NIH fel, Sch Med, Univ Wash, 68-69; asst prof elec eng, Univ Calif, Davis, 69-80, lectr, 76-80; MEM STAFF, AEROSPACE CORP, 80- *Mem:* AAAS; Inst Elec & Electronics Engrs; Biomed Eng Soc. *Res:* Control system engineering; regulation of breathing in man and domestic fowl; physiological control system analysis and modeling. *Mailing Add:* Aerospace Corp Bldg A2 Rm 1077 PO Box 92957 Los Angeles CA 90009

STOLL, ROBERT D, b Lincoln, Ill, Aug 12, 31; m; c 3. SOIL MECHANICS. *Educ:* Univ Ill, BSCE, 53; Columbia Univ, MSCE, 56, EngScD(civil eng, eng mech), 62. *Prof Exp:* From instr to assoc prof, 56-71, PROF CIVIL ENG, COLUMBIA UNIV, 71- *Concurrent Pos:* Chmn comt mech earth masses & layered systs, Hwy Res Bd, Nat Acad Sci-Nat Res Coun, 67-; vis sr res assoc, Lamont-Doherty Geol Observ, 69- *Mem:* Am Soc Civil Engrs. *Res:* Static and dynamic response of granular soils; wave propagation in granular media and ocean sediments; general constitutive relationships for granular media. *Mailing Add:* Dept of Civil Eng Columbia Univ New York NY 10027

STOLL, ROBERT ROTH, b Pittsburgh, Pa, May 19, 15; m 37; c 3. MATHEMATICS. *Educ:* Univ Pittsburgh, BS, 36, MS, 37; Yale Univ, PhD(math), 43. *Prof Exp:* Instr math, Rensselaer Polytech Inst, 37-39; instr, Yale Univ, 39-42; asst prof, Williams Col, 42-46; from asst prof to assoc prof, Lehigh Univ, 46-52; prof, Oberlin Col, 52-71, actg chmn dept, 53-54, 60-61 & 66-67; chmn dept, 71-80, PROF MATH, CLEVELAND STATE UNIV, 71- *Concurrent Pos:* Nat Res Coun fel, Ind Univ, 45-46; consult, NSF, 52 & 70; NSF fac fel, Calif Inst Technol, 58-59; fel Mass Inst Technol, 67-68; vis Fulbright lectr, Am Univ Beirut, 64-65. *Mem:* Am Math Soc; Math Asn Am. *Res:* Theory of semi-groups; foundation of mathematics. *Mailing Add:* Dept of Math Cleveland State Univ Cleveland OH 44115

STOLL, WILHELM, b Freiburg, Ger, Dec 22, 23; m 55; c 4. MATHEMATICS. *Educ:* Univ Tübingen, Dr rer nat, 53, Dr habil, 54. *Prof Exp:* Asst math, Univ Tübingen, 53-59, docent, 54-60, appl prof, 60; head dept math, 66-68, PROF MATH, UNIV NOTRE DAME, 60- *Concurrent Pos:* Vis lectr, Univ Pa, 54-55; mem, Inst Adv Study, 57-59; vis prof, Stanford Univ, 68-69 & Tulane Univ, 73. *Mem:* Am Math Soc; Math Asn Am; Ger Math Asn. *Res:* Complex analysis; value distribution in several variables, modifications mero- morphic maps; families of divisors; continuation of analytic sets and maps; algebraic dependence of meromorphic functions; parabolic spaces. *Mailing Add:* Dept of Math Univ of Notre Dame Notre Dame IN 46556

STOLL, WILLIAM FRANCIS, b Lamoni, Iowa, July 21, 32; m 56; c 2. FOOD SCIENCE. *Educ:* Iowa State Univ, BS, 55, MS, 57; Univ Minn, St Paul, PhD(dairy sci), 66. *Prof Exp:* Asst prof dairy sci, SDak State Univ, 57-67; sr food scientist, Prod Develop Dept, Green Giant Co, 67-79; SR SCIENTIST, FROZEN FOODS RES & DEVELOP, PILLSBURY CO, 79- *Mem:* Am Asn Cereal Chemists; Inst Food Technologists; Am Dairy Sci Asn. *Res:* Use of physical, chemical, microbiological principles for design and fabrication of new food products. *Mailing Add:* The Pillsbury Co 311 2nd St SE Minneapolis MN 55414

STOLL, WILLIAM RUSSELL, b Los Angeles, Calif, July 8, 31; m 55; c 2. PHARMACOLOGY, CHEMISTRY. *Educ:* Union Univ, NY, BS, 52; Univ Rochester, PhD(pharmacol), 56. *Prof Exp:* From instr to assoc prof, 56-70, RES ASSOC PHARMACOL, ALBANY MED COL, 64- *Res:* Chemical nature of sodium and carbonate in bone mineral; autonomic pharmacology; nature of 2-halo-2-phenethylamines; applications of nucleonics in biological research. *Mailing Add:* 24 Ableman Ave Westmere NY 12203

STOLLAR, BERNARD DAVID, b Saskatoon, Sask, Aug 11, 36; m 56; c 3. IMMUNOLOGY, BIOCHEMISTRY. *Educ:* Univ Sask, BA, 58, MD, 59. *Prof Exp:* Res fel biochem, Brandeis Univ, 60-62; dep chief biol sci div, Air Force Off Sci Res, 62-64; asst prof pharmacol, 64-67, from asst prof to assoc prof biochem, 67-74, PROF BIOCHEM, SCH MED, TUFTS UNIV, 74- *Concurrent Pos:* NSF grant, 64-; consult, Biol Sci Div, Air Force Off Sci Res, 66-69; sr fel, Weizmann Inst Sci, 71-72; vis prof, Univ Tromso, Norway, 81. *Mem:* AAAS; Am Asn Immunologists; Am Soc Biol Chemists. *Res:* Immunochemistry of nucleic acids and nucleoprotein, especially in relation to auto-immune disease; use of antibodies to study structure of nucleic acids and chromatin organization. *Mailing Add:* Dept of Biochem & Pharmacol Tufts Univ Sch of Med Boston MA 02111

STOLLAR, VICTOR, b Saskatoon, Sask, Dec 6, 33; m 67; c 3. MICROBIOLOGY, VIROLOGY. *Educ:* Queen's Univ, Ont, MDCM, 56. *Prof Exp:* Fel, Brandeis Univ, 58-62; fel Weizman Inst Sci, 62-65; from asst prof to assoc prof, 65-75, PROF MICROBIOL, RUTGERS MED SCH, COL MED & DENT NJ, 75- *Concurrent Pos:* Assoc ed, Virol, 76-; mem, Virol Study Sect, NIH, 80-83. *Mem:* AAAS; Am Soc Microbiol; Am Asn Immunologists. *Res:* Replication of toga viruses in vertebrate and in insect cells; genetics and biochemistry of cultured mosquito cells. *Mailing Add:* Dept Microbiol Rutgers Med Sch Univ Med & Dent NJ Piscataway NJ 08854

STOLLBERG, ROBERT, b Toledo, Ohio, May 27, 15; m 43; c 4. SCIENCE EDUCATION. *Educ:* Univ Toledo, BS, 35, BEd, 36; Columbia Univ, MA, 40, EdD(sci ed, electronics), 47. *Prof Exp:* Instr, Rossford High Sch, Ohio, 36-39; asst prof physics, Wabash Col, 46-47; ed, Purdue Univ, 47-49; assoc prof physics, 49-54, chmn dept interdisciplinary phy sci, 67-69, assoc dean & actg dean, Sch Natural Sci, 69 & 71-75, PROF PHYSICS, SAN FRANCISCO STATE UNIV, 54- *Concurrent Pos:* Mem, Harvard Univ Conf Prob Sci Ed, 53; chmn, Nat Conf Prob High Sch Sci, 59; mem, President's Comt Develop Scientists & Engrs; sci adv, Columbia Univ team, India, 65-66; Columbia Univ-USAID contract lectr, Inst Educ, Makerere Univ, Uganda, 69-71; vis prof, Columbia Univ. *Mem:* Fel AAAS; Am Asn Physics Teachers; Nat Sci Teachers Asn (pres, 55-56); Am Inst Physics. *Mailing Add:* Dept Physics & Astron San Francisco State Univ San Francisco CA 94132

STOLLER, BENJAMIN BORIS, b Apr 10, 07; m 40. AGRICULTURAL MICROBIOLOGY, BIOCHEMISTRY. *Educ:* Iowa State Col, MS, 36; Univ Wis, PhD(biochem), 45. *Prof Exp:* Dir res, L F Lambert, Inc, Pa, 36-43; dir res, Lenny's Food, Inc, Minn, 45-47; head malting res, Pabst Brewing Co, Wis, 49-50; dir res, West Foods, Calif, 55-56; OWNER, STOLLER RES CO, 57- *Mem:* AAAS; Am Chem Soc; Am Soc Microbiol. *Res:* Growth of plants under industrial conditions; mushroom and bean sprout culture; malting; insecticides; fungicides. *Mailing Add:* PO Box 1339 Santa Cruz CA 95061

STOLLER, EDWARD W, b McCook, Nebr, Jan 9, 37; m 60; c 2. PLANT PHYSIOLOGY, WEED SCIENCE. *Educ:* Univ Nebr, BS, 58; Purdue Univ, MS, 62; NC State Univ, PhD(soil fertil), 66. *Prof Exp:* PLANT PHYSIOLOGIST, NORTH CENT REGION, AGR RES, USDA, 65- *Mem:* Am Soc Plant Physiol; Am Soc Agron; Weed Sci Soc Am. *Res:* Weed physiology and control. *Mailing Add:* Dept Agron Univ Ill 1102 S Goodwin Urbana IL 61801

STOLLERMAN, GENE HOWARD, b New York, NY, Dec 6, 20; m 45; c 3. MEDICINE. *Educ:* Dartmouth Col, AB, 41; Columbia Univ, MD, 44; Am Bd Internal Med, dipl, 52. *Prof Exp:* From intern to chief med resident, Mt Sinai Hosp, New York, 44-49; res fel microbiol, Col Med, NY Univ, 49-50, instr med, 51-55; instr, Col Med, State Univ NY Downstate Med Ctr, 50-51; from asst prof to prof, Med Sch, Northwestern Univ, 55-64; prof med & chmn dept, Col Med, Univ Tenn, Memphis, 65-81; PROF MED, SCH MED, BOSTON UNIV, 81- *Concurrent Pos:* Med dir, Irvington Hosp, New York, 51-55; prin investr, Sackett Found Res Rheumatic Fever & Allied Dis, 55-64; mem training grants comt, Nat Inst Arthritis & Metab Dis, US Pub Health Serv, 60-64, mem res career prog, 67-70, chmn, Review Panel Bact Vaccines & Toxoids, Bur Biologics, Food & Drug Admin, 73-; physician-in-chief, City Memphis Hosps, 65-81; consult, Memphis Vet Admin Hosp, 65-81; chmn coun rheumatic fever & congenital heart dis, Am Heart Asn, 66-68; mem, Am Bd Internal Med, 67-73, chmn written exam comt, 69-73 & exec comt, 71-73; ed, Advan Internal Med, 68-; mem, Expert Comt Cardiovasc Dis, WHO, 66-81; pres, Cent Soc Clin Res, 74-75; co-chmn, Educ Work Group Nat Comn Arthritis, 75-76; chmn, Panel Prod & Supply Work Group, HEW & Goodman prof, Univ Tenn, 77; consult, Methodist Hosp, Memphis, St Joseph Hosp & LeBonheur Children's Hosp. *Mem:* Asn Profs Med (pres, 75-76); Asn Am Physicians; fel Am Col Physicians (vpres, 82-83); Am Soc Clin Invest; Am Asn Immunologists. *Res:* Infectious and rheumatic diseases; biology of streptococcus; etiology of rheumatic fever. *Mailing Add:* Suite 1108 720 Harrison Ave Boston MA 02118

STOLLEY, PAUL DAVID, b Pawling, NY, June 17, 37; m 59; c 3. PUBLIC HEALTH, EPIDEMIOLOGY. *Educ:* Lafayette Col, AB, 57; Med Col, Cornell Univ, MD, 62. *Hon Degrees:* MA, Univ Pa, 76. *Prof Exp:* From asst prof to assoc prof epidemiol, Sch Public Health, Johns Hopkins Univ, 68-76; PROF MED, SCH MED, UNIV PA, 76- *Mem:* Inst Med-Nat Acad Sci; Soc Epidemiol Res (pres, 82-83); Int Epidemiol Asn (treas, 81-84). *Res:* Epidemiology of cancer; adverse drug reactions; prevention of heart disease. *Mailing Add:* Sch Med Univ Pa 229L Trineb/SX Philadelphia PA 19104

STOLOFF, IRWIN LESTER, b Philadelphia, Pa, May 9, 27; m 52; c 3. MEDICINE. *Educ:* Jefferson Med Col, MD, 51; Am Bd Internal Med, dipl, 58. *Prof Exp:* From intern to resident med, Jefferson Med Col Hosp, 51-53; resident, Baltimore City Hosps, Md, 53-54 & Mt Sinai Hosp, New York, 56-57; fel med, 57-58, from instr to asst prof, 59-69, ASSOC PROF MED & PREV MED, JEFFERSON MED COL, 69- *Mem:* Fel Am Col Physicians; fel Am Col Chest Physicians. *Res:* Immunology; autoimmune diseases; cancer immunology; epidemiology of chronic lung disease. *Mailing Add:* New Jefferson Hosp Bldg Rm 4001 111 S 11th St Philadelphia PA 19107

STOLOFF, LEONARD, b Boston, Mass, Mar 24, 15; m 40. BIOCHEMISTRY. *Educ:* Mass Inst Technol, BS, 36. *Prof Exp:* Chemist, Granada Wines, Inc, 36-37; self employed, 38-41; chemist, US Dept Navy, 41; chemist, Consumer's Union, 42; res chemist, Agar Substitute Prog, US Fish & Wildlife Serv, 42-44; res chemist, Krim-Ko Corp, 44-51; res dir, Seaplant Chem Corp, 51-59; asst tech dir, Marine Colloids, Inc, 59-63; chief mycotoxins & enzymes sect, Div Food Chem, 63-71, NATURAL TOXICANTS SPECIALIST, BUR FOODS, FOOD & DRUG ADMIN, 71- *Honors & Awards:* Wiley Award, Asn Off Anal Chemists, 81. *Mem:* AAAS; Am Chem Soc; Inst Food Technol; Asn Off Anal Chemists. *Res:* Chemistry, toxicology and occurrence of natural poisons in foods. *Mailing Add:* 13208 Bellevue St Silver Spring MD 20904

STOLOFF, NORMAN STANLEY, b Brooklyn, NY, Oct 16, 34; m; c 4. METALLURGY. *Educ:* NY Univ, BMetE, 55; Columbia Univ, MS, 56, PhD(metall), 61. *Prof Exp:* Jr engr metall, Pratt & Whitney Aircraft Div, United Aircraft Corp, 56-58; staff scientist, Ford Motor Co, 61-65; from asst prof to assoc prof, 65-70, PROF ENG, RENSSELAER POLYTECH INST, 70- *Concurrent Pos:* Fulbright sr res fel, Univ Birmingham, 67-68; vis prof, Eurat Joint Res Ctr, Ispra, Italy, 76-77, Technion, Israel Inst Technol, 80, Swiss Fed Inst, Lausanne, 81. *Mem:* Am Inst Mining, Metall & Petrol Engrs; Am Soc Metals; Am Soc Testing & Mat. *Res:* Physical metallurgy; relationship between microstructure and plastic deformation of metals; environmental effects; strength and fracture of intermetallic compounds; composites; fatigue of high temperature alloys. *Mailing Add:* Dept of Mat Eng Rensselaer Polytechnic Inst Troy NY 12181

STOLOV, HAROLD L, b New York, NY, May 27, 21; m 81. PHYSICS, METEOROLOGY. *Educ:* City Col New York, BS, 42; Mass Inst Technol, MS, 47; NY Univ, PhD(physics, meteorol), 53. *Prof Exp:* Asst radio & electronics, Signal Corps, US Dept Army, 42; instr physics, City Col New York, 47-50; lectr, Hunter Col, 50-51; res assoc, NY Univ, 50-53; instr, Douglass Col, Rutgers Univ, 51-53, asst prof, 53-59; from asst prof to assoc prof, 59-70, PROF PHYSICS, CITY COL NEW YORK, 70- *Concurrent Pos:* Consult, Martin Co, 56-59; consult, Res & Adv Develop Div, Avco Corp, 60-61; Nat Acad Sci-Nat Res Coun sr res associateship, Inst Space Studies, New York, 65-67. *Mem:* Am Phys Soc; Am Meteorol Soc; Am Asn Physics Teachers; Am Geophys Union. *Res:* Physics of the upper atmosphere; tidal oscillations; physics education; magnetosphere; solar-terrestrial physics. *Mailing Add:* 2575 Palisade Ave New York NY 10463

STOLOVY, ALEXANDER, b Brooklyn, NY, Nov 21, 26; m 55; c 3. NUCLEAR PHYSICS. *Educ:* Brooklyn Col, BS, 48; Calif Inst Technol, MS, 50; NY Univ, PhD(physics), 55. *Prof Exp:* Nuclear physicist, Brookhaven Nat Lab, 53-54; NUCLEAR PHYSICIST, RADIATION TECHNOL DIV, NAVAL RES LAB, 55- *Concurrent Pos:* Partic guest scientist, Lawrence Livermore Lab, 74-75. *Mem:* Am Phys Soc; Sigma Xi. *Res:* Slow neutron spectroscopy; electron beam interactions with matter; neutron capture gamma ray studies using time-of-flight techniques. *Mailing Add:* Condensed Matter & Radiation Sci Div Naval Research Lab Washington DC 20375

STOLOW, NATHAN, b Montreal, Que, May 4, 28; m 50; c 2. CHEMISTRY. *Educ:* McGill Univ, BSc, 49; Univ Toronto, MA, 52; Univ London, PhD(conserv), 56. *Prof Exp:* Res chemist, Nat Res Coun Can, 49-50; vis lectr chem & physics, Sir John Cass Col, Univ London, 52-55, res assoc conserv, Courtauld Inst Art, 55-56; dir conserv, Nat Gallery Can, 56-72; dir, Can Conserv Inst, 72-75; spec adv conserv, Nat Mus Can, 76-79; CONSERV CONSULT, 79- *Concurrent Pos:* Carnegie travel grant, Nat Gallery Can, 56-57; rapporteur, Comt Conserv, Int Coun Mus, 64-, chmn Can nat comt, 70-; mem coun, Int Inst Conserv Hist & Artistic Works, 72- *Honors & Awards:* Can Medal, Govt Can, 67. *Mem:* Fel Chem Inst Can; fel Can Mus Asn. *Res:* Museum conservation; problems of deterioration in works of art related to conservation; solution of museological problems by chemical and physical approaches; interaction of art history and scientific research; exhibition conservation research. *Mailing Add:* PO Box 2542 Sta D Ottawa ON K1P 5W6 Can

STOLOW, ROBERT DAVID, b Boston, Mass, Mar 9, 32; m 53; c 3. ORGANIC CHEMISTRY. *Educ:* Mass Inst Technol, SB, 53; Univ Ill, PhD(chem), 56. *Prof Exp:* From instr to assoc prof org chem, 58-76, PROF CHEM, TUFTS UNIV, 76- *Concurrent Pos:* Fel, Calif Inst Technol, 67-68. *Mem:* Am Chem Soc; Royal Soc Chem. *Res:* Physical organic chemistry; stereochemistry; conformational analysis; the hydrogen bond. *Mailing Add:* Dept of Chem Tufts Univ Medford MA 02155

STOLPER, EDWARD MANIN, b Boston, Mass, Dec 16, 52; m 73. EXPERIMENTAL PETROLOGY. *Educ:* Harvard Col, AB, 74; Univ Edinburgh, MPhil, 76; Harvard Univ, PhD(geol sci), 79. *Prof Exp:* ASST PROF GEOL, CALIF INST TECHNOL, 79- *Mem:* Geol Soc Am; Am Geophys Union; Meteoritical Soc; Mineral Soc Am; AAAS. *Mailing Add:* Div Geol Planet Sci 170-25 Calif Inst Technol Pasadena CA 91125

STOLTE, CHARLES, b Blue Earth, Minn, Apr 20, 33; m 54; c 4. ELECTRICAL ENGINEERING, SOLID STATE PHYSICS. *Educ:* Univ Minn, BS, 55, MS, 58, PhD(elec eng), 66. *Prof Exp:* Res asst diffusion study, Univ Minn, 55-58; mem tech staff, 66-76, LAB PROJ MGR, SOLID STATE LAB, HEWLETT-PACKARD LAB, 76- *Mem:* Inst Elec & Electronic Engrs. *Res:* Oxide coated cathode, schottky barriers, III-V materials and devices including ion implantation, LEP's, solid state lasers and microwave devices; materials science engineering. *Mailing Add:* Solid State Lab Hewlett-Packard Lab Palo Alto CA 94032

STOLTENBERG, CARL H, b Monterey, Calif, May 17, 24; m 49; c 5. FOREST ECONOMICS. *Educ:* Univ Calif, BS, 48, MF, 49; Univ Minn, PhD(agr econ), 52. *Prof Exp:* Instr forestry, Univ Minn, 49-51; asst prof forest econ, Duke Univ, 51-56; head resource econ res, Northwest Forest Exp Sta, US Forest Serv, Pa, 56-58, chief div forest econ res, 58-60; prof forestry & head dept, Iowa State Univ, 60-67; PROF FORESTRY, DEAN SCH FORESTRY & DIR FOREST RES LAB, ORE STATE UNIV, 67- *Concurrent Pos:* Mem forestry res comn, Nat Acad Sci, 63-65; mem, Nat Adv Bd Coop Forestry Res, 62-66, Ore Bd Forestry, 67-, chmn, 74-; mem Secy of Agr State & Pvt Forestry Adv Comn, 70-74; chmn, Ore & Calif Adv Bd, Bur Land Mgt, 72-76. *Mem:* Fel Soc Am Foresters; Am Econ Asn; Forest Prod Res Soc; Sigma Xi; AAAS. *Res:* Economic analysis of forest management alternatives; forest policy; resource allocation in forestry; natural resource policy. *Mailing Add:* Sch of Forestry Ore State Univ Corvallis OR 97331

STOLTZ, LEONARD PAUL, b Kankakee, Ill, Dec 5, 27; m 53; c 5. HORTICULTURE. *Educ:* Agr & Mech Col, Tex, BS, 55; Ohio State Univ, MS, 56; Purdue Univ, PhD(hort), 65. *Prof Exp:* Res assoc floricult, Rutgers Univ, 57-60; asst prof hort, Univ RI, 60-62; asst prof, 65-70, ASSOC PROF HORT, UNIV KY, 70- *Concurrent Pos:* USDA res grant, 66-70. *Honors & Awards:* Kenneth Post Award, Cornell Univ, 67; L M Ware Award, Am Soc Hort Sci, Southern Region, 68, 72; ed, Eastern Region Int Plant Propagators Soc, 68-78. *Mem:* Am Soc Hort Sci; Int Plant Propagators Soc. *Res:* Plant propagation; naturally occurring chemical components of plants; tissue and embryo culture. *Mailing Add:* Dept Hort & L A Univ Ky Lexington KY 40546

STOLTZ, ROBERT LEWIS, b Bakersfield, Calif, May 15, 45; m 71. ENTOMOLOGY. *Educ:* Univ Calif, Davis, BS, 67; Univ Calif, Riverside, PhD(entom), 73. *Prof Exp:* Fel entom, Univ Calif, Riverside, 73-74 & Univ Mo-Columbia, 74-75; EXTEN SPECIALIST ENTOM, COOP EXTEN SERV, UNIV IDAHO, 75- *Mem:* Entom Soc Am; Sigma Xi. *Res:* Insect control, particularly in potatoes, sugar beets, beans, peas, and alfalfa hay; black fly control; livestock insects. *Mailing Add:* Univ of Idaho Coop Exten Serv 1330 Filer Ave E Twin Falls ID 83301

STOLTZFUS, JOSEPH CHRISTIAN, applied physics, see previous edition

STOLTZFUS, WILLIAM BRYAN, b Martinsburg, Pa, Apr 25, 32; m 57; c 5. ENTOMOLOGY. *Educ:* Goshen Col, BS, 57; Kent State Univ, MS, 66; Iowa State Univ, PhD(entom), 74. *Prof Exp:* Instr biol, Eastern Mennonite Col, 66-70 & entom, Iowa State Univ, 73-74; ASSOC PROF BIOL & CHMN DEPT, WILLIAM PENN COL, 74- *Mem:* Entom Soc Am. *Res:* Life history of fruitflies as it relates to their taxonomy. *Mailing Add:* Dept of Biol William Penn Col Oskaloosa IA 52577

STOLWIJK, JAN ADRIANUS JOZEF, b Amsterdam, Netherlands, Sept 29, 27; nat US; m 57. BIOPHYSICS. *Educ:* State Agr Univ, Wageningen, MS, 51, PhD, 55. *Prof Exp:* Cabot res fel biol, Harvard Univ, 55-57; from assoc fel to fel biol, 57-74, ASSOC DIR, JOHN B PIERCE FOUND, 74-; PROF EPIDEMIOL, SCH MED, YALE UNIV, 75-, DIR GRAD STUDIES, DEPT EPIDEMIOL & PUBLIC HEALTH, 79- *Concurrent Pos:* Mem, Comt Indoor Pollutants, Nat Res Ctr/Nat Acad Sci, 80-81. *Mem:* Aerospace Med Asn; Int Soc Biometeorol; Am Physiol Soc; Am Pub Health Asn; Biophys Soc. *Res:* Body temperature regulation; regulatory systems in physiology; thermal receptor structures; radiant heat exchange with environment; environmental health; occupational health; risk assessment; construction and application of mathematical models for study of complex physiological systems; environmental physiology. *Mailing Add:* John B Pierce Found 290 Congress Ave New Haven CT 06519

STOLZ, HAL FISHER, b Columbia, SC, Nov 21, 34; m 58; c 2. MEDICAL RESEARCH. *Educ:* Univ Ga, DVM, 58; Univ Rochester, MS, 68; Am Bd Vet Pub Health, dipl, 75. *Prof Exp:* Asst post vet, US Army, Ft Campbell, Ky, 58-60, area vet, Area Serv Command, SKorea, 61-62, post vet, US Army, Ft Gordon, Ga, 62-64, instr, US Army Qm Sch, Ft Lee, Va, 64-67, chief med effects div, Defense Atomic Support Agency, Washington, DC, 68-71, action officer med res mgt, Off Chief Res & Develop, Dept Army, 72-74, res mgt action officer, US Army Med Res & Develop Command Res Planning Off, 74-76, chmn Behav Sci Dept, Armed Forces Radiobiol Res Inst, 76-80. *Mem:* Am Vet Med Asn. *Res:* Management of a broad range of military related medical research and planning a coordinated program. *Mailing Add:* Rte 4 Box 221-C Ellijay GA 30540

STOLZBERG, RICHARD JAY, b Winthrop, Mass, Feb 5, 48. ANALYTICAL CHEMISTRY. *Educ:* Tufts Univ, BS, 69; Mass Inst Technol, PhD(anal chem), 73. *Prof Exp:* Res assoc & prin investr, Harold Edgerton Res Lab, New Eng Aquarium, 73-77; ASST PROF, DEPT CHEM, UNIV ALASKA, FAIRBANKS, 78- *Mem:* Am Chem Soc; Sigma Xi; AAAS; Chemomets Soc. *Res:* Characterization of trace metal-organic interactions in natural waters; effect of metal speciation on bioavailability; chemometrics; chromatography; electrochemistry; spectroscopy. *Mailing Add:* Dept of Chem Univ of Alaska Fairbanks AK 99701

STOLZENBACH, KEITH DENSMORE, b Washington, DC, Aug 23, 44. CIVIL & HYDRAULIC ENGINEERING. *Educ:* Mass Inst Technol, SB, 66, SM, 68, PhD(civil eng), 71. *Prof Exp:* Asst prof civil eng, Mass Inst Technol, 70-71; res engr, Eng Lab, Tenn Valley Authority, 71-74; asst prof, 74-76, ASSOC PROF CIVIL ENG, MASS INST TECHNOL, 76- *Mem:* Am Soc Civil Engrs; Am Geophys Union; Int Asn Hydraul Res. *Res:* Hydraulic modeling techniques; environmental heat transfer; pollutant dispersal in natural waters; field survey techniques. *Mailing Add:* Bldg 4B Rm 321 Mass Inst Technol Cambridge MA 02139

STOLZENBERG, GARY ERIC, b Southampton, NY, Dec 1, 39; m 69. PESTICIDE CHEMISTRY, FORMULATION AGENTS. *Educ:* Rensselaer Polytech Inst, BS, 62; Kans State Univ, PhD(biochem), 68. *Prof Exp:* Asst biochem, Kans State Univ, 62-68; RES CHEMIST, METAB & RADIATION RES LAB, USDA, 68- *Mem:* Am Chem Soc. *Res:* Xenobiotics metabolism in plants; behaviour and fate of herbicide formulation agents; surfactant analysis. *Mailing Add:* Metab Lab PO Box 5674 State Univ Station US Dept of Agr Fargo ND 58105

STOLZENBERG, SIDNEY JOSEPH, b New York, NY, Nov 30, 27; m 58; c 2. REPRODUCTIVE PHYSIOLOGY, PHARMACOLOGY. *Educ:* NY Univ, BA, 50; Univ Mo, MS, 54; Cornell Univ, PhD(reproductive physiol), 66. *Prof Exp:* Biochemist, Lederle Labs Div, Am Cyanamid Co, 54-59, agr div, 59-63; endocrinologist, SRI Int, 66-72, endocrinologist, Life Sci Div, 72-78; toxicologist, Dept Pharmacol, Sch Med, Univ Calif, San Francisco, 78-80; PHYSIOLOGIST, FUR DRUGS, FED DRUG ADMIN, MD, 80- *Mem:* AAAS; Am Soc Primatologists; Am Physiol Soc; Soc Study Reproduction; Toxicol Soc. *Res:* Reproductive toxicology; includes work on toxicology and mutagenicity of compounds with antifertility activities; effects of mematocides and insecticides on reproductive tract; hormone secretion and mutagenesis. *Mailing Add:* FDA Bur Drugs HFD-130 Div Metabolic & Endocrine Drug Prod Rockville MD 20857

STOLZY, LEWIS HAL, b Mich, Dec 11, 20; m 47; c 3. SOIL PHYSICS. *Educ:* Mich State Col, BS, 48, MS, 50, PhD, 54. *Prof Exp:* Actg proj supvr, Soil Conserv Serv, USDA, 50-52; asst, Mich State Univ, 52-54; asst irrig engr, 54-61, assoc soil physicist, 61-66, assoc prof, 66-78, PROF SOIL PHYSICS, UNIV CALIF, RIVERSIDE, 78- *Concurrent Pos:* Fulbright sr res scholar, Univ Adelaide, 64-65; prof, Nat Univ Agr, Chapingo, Mex, AID & Africa; agronomic res award, Int Soc Soil Sci. *Mem:* Fel Soil Sci Soc Am; Int Soc Soil Sci; Int Cong Plant Path; Am Phytopath Soc; fel Am Soc Agron. *Res:* Soil moisture and aeration. *Mailing Add:* Dept Soil & Environ Sci Univ Calif Riverside CA 92521

STOMBAUGH, TOM ATKINS, b Vancouver, Wash, Aug 22, 21; m 44; c 4. BIOLOGY. *Educ:* Ill State Norm Univ, BEd, 41; Univ Ill, MS, 46; Ind Univ, PhD, 53. *Prof Exp:* Asst prof zool, Eastern Ill State Col, 48-50; prof biol, 53-77, PROF LIFE SCI, SOUTHWEST MO STATE UNIV, 77- *Mem:* Am Soc Mammal. *Res:* Taxonomy of the voles of sub-genus Pedomys; mammalian taxonomy and ecology. *Mailing Add:* Dept of Life Sci Southwest Mo State Univ Springfield MO 65802

STOMBLER, MILTON PHILIP, b New York, Ny, Dec 19, 39; m 67; c 3. EXPERIMENTAL SOLID STATE PHYSICS. *Educ:* Univ Md, College Park, BS, 62; Univ SC, MS, 66, PhD(physics), 69. *Prof Exp:* Asst engr, Aerospace Div, Westinghouse Elec Corp, 64-65; fel, Univ Del, 69-71; asst prof physics, State Univ NY Col Potsdam, 71-73, dir, 73-80; MEM STAFF, RES DIV, VA POLYTECH INST & STATE UNIV, 80- *Res:* Electron paramagnetic resonance. *Mailing Add:* Res Div Va Polytech Inst & State Univ, 80- Blacksburg VA 24060

STOMMEL, HENRY MELSON, b Wilmington, Del, Sept 27, 20. OCEANOGRAPHY. *Educ:* Yale Univ, BS, 42. *Hon Degrees:* DSc, Gothenburg Univ, 64, Yale Univ, 70, Univ Chicago, 70. *Prof Exp:* Instr math & astron, Yale Univ, 42-44; res assoc phys oceanog, Oceanog Inst, Woods Hole, 44-59; prof oceanog, Mass Inst Technol, 59-60; prof, Harvard Univ, 60-63; prof oceanog, Mass Inst Technol, 63-78; OCEANOGRAPHER, WOODS HOLE OCEANOG INST, 78- *Mem:* Nat Acad Sci; Am Astron Soc; Am Soc Limnol & Oceanog; Am Acad Arts & Sci; Am Geophys Union. *Res:* Dynamics of ocean currents. *Mailing Add:* Oceanographic Inst Woods Hole MA 02543

STONE, ALBERT MORDECAI, b Boston, Mass, Dec 24, 13; m 41, 68; c 3. PLASMA PHYSICS, MICROWAVE PHYSICS. *Educ:* Harvard Univ, AB, 34; Mass Inst Technol, PhD(physics), 38. *Prof Exp:* Res assoc, Mass Inst Technol, 38-39, staff mem, Radiation Lab, 42-46; instr, Middlesex Col, 36-38; physicist, US Naval Torpedo Sta, 40-41; from asst prof to assoc prof physics, Mont State Col, 41-46; sci liaison officer, US Embassy, London, Eng, 46-48; assoc mem comt electronics & comt basic phys sci, Res & Develop Bd, US Dept Defense, 48-49; tech asst to dir appl physics lab, 49-72, head tech info div, 62-80, dir advan res projs, Appl Physics Lab, 72-81, SR FEL, JOHNS HOPKINS UNIV, 81- *Mem:* Fel AAAS; fel Am Phys Soc. *Res:* Electronics; gaseous discharges; radar signal thresholds; guided missiles; countermeasures; controlled thermonuclear plasmas; geothermal energy; nuclear effects. *Mailing Add:* Appl Physics Lab Johns Hopkins Rd Laurel MD 20810

STONE, ALEXANDER GLATTSTEIN, b Hungary, Jan 30, 16; nat US; m 58; c 2. MATHEMATICS. *Educ:* Univ Debrecen, Hungary, Dr Laws, 40; George Washington Univ, MS, 61. *Prof Exp:* Mathematician, Repub Aviation Corp, 55-56; mathematician appl physics lab, Johns Hopkins Univ, 56-69, supvr programmers digital comput, 66-69, lectr, univ, 59-60, instr, eve col, 66-67; MEM TECH STAFF, JET PROPULSION LAB, CALIF INST TECHNOL, 69- *Mem:* Math Asn Am; Asn Comput Mach. *Res:* Programming for automatic digital computers; Boolean algebra. *Mailing Add:* Jet Propulsion Lab Calif Inst of Technol Pasadena CA 91103

STONE, ALEXANDER PAUL, b West New York, NJ, June 28, 28; m 60; c 1. MATHEMATICS. *Educ:* Columbia Univ, BS, 52; Newark Col Eng, MS, 56; Univ Ill, Urbana, PhD(math), 65. *Prof Exp:* Engr, Western Elec Co, 52-56; instr elec eng, Manhattan Col, 56-58; asst prof physics, Dickinson Col, 58-60; asst prof math, Univ Ill, Chicago Circle, 65-69, assoc prof, 69-70; assoc prof, 70-75, PROF MATH, UNIV NMEX, 76- *Mem:* Am Math Soc. *Res:* Differential geometry; applied mathematics. *Mailing Add:* Dept of Math & Statist Univ of NMex Albuquerque NM 87131

STONE, ARTHUR HAROLD, b London, Eng, Sept 30, 16; m 42; c 2. PURE MATHEMATICS. *Educ:* Cambridge Univ, BA, 38; Princeton Univ, PhD(math), 41. *Prof Exp:* Mem, Inst Advan Study, 41-42; instr math, Purdue Univ, 42-44; math physicist, Geophys Lab, Carnegie Inst, 44-46; fel, Trinity Col, Cambridge Univ, 46-47; lectr math, Univ Manchester, 47-56, sr lectr, 56-61; PROF MATH, UNIV ROCHESTER, 61- *Mem:* Am Math Soc; Math Asn Am. *Res:* Point-set topology; aerodynamics; graph theory; general topology; descriptive set theory. *Mailing Add:* Dept of Math Univ of Rochester Rochester NY 14627

STONE, BENJAMIN P, b Dover, Tenn, Aug 28, 35; m 56; c 1. PLANT PHYSIOLOGY. *Educ:* Austin Peay State Univ, BS, 59; Univ Tenn, Knoxville, MS, 61, PhD(bot), 68. *Prof Exp:* Asst prof biol, Austin Peay State Univ, 61-65; res partic radiation biol, Cornell Univ, 65-66; asst prof plant physiol, Purdue Univ, West Lafayette, 69; assoc prof biol, 69-72, PROF BIOL, AUSTIN PEAY STATE UNIV, 72-, CHMN DEPT, 77- *Concurrent Pos:* Fel hort, Purdue Univ, West Lafayette, 69. *Mem:* Am Soc Plant Physiol; Am Inst Biol Sci; Sigma Xi. *Res:* Nucleic acid; protein synthesis. *Mailing Add:* Dept of Biol Austin Peay State Univ Clarksville TN 37040

STONE, BOBBIE DEAN, b Paulton, Ill, June 11, 27; m 50; c 2. SOLID STATE CHEMISTRY, INORGANIC CHEMISTRY. *Educ:* Univ Southern Ill, BS, 49; Northwestern Univ, PhD(chem), 52. *Prof Exp:* Res chemist, Mound Lab, 52-53, Cent Res Dept & Res & Eng Div, 53-62 & Inorg Chem Div, 62-65, res group leader, Semiconductor Mat Dept, 65-69, silicon res mgr, 69-72, sr res specialist, Electronics Prod Div, 72-74, FEL, ENG ELECTRONICS DIV, MONSANTO CO, 74- *Mem:* Am Chem Soc; Am Soc Crystal Growth; Electrochem Soc. *Res:* Semiconductor grade silicon; neutron transmutation doping; III-V compounds; polycrystalline silicone processes. *Mailing Add:* 415 Monticello Dr Ballwin MO 63011

STONE, CHARLES DEAN, b Athens, Ga, Sept 6, 26; m 50; c 1. FOOD SCIENCE, BIOCHEMISTRY. *Educ:* Univ Ga, BS, 49, PhD(food sci), 64; Fla State Univ, MS, 59. *Prof Exp:* Partner, Stone's Ideal Bakery, 50-53; instr baking sci & mgt food serv bakery, Fla State Univ, 53-59, asst prof baking sci & mgt, 59-61; sect mgr food res, Quaker Oats Co, 64-69, mgr cereal res, 69-72, mgr cereals, mixes & corn goods res, 72-74; sr prod res scientist, Res & Develop, 74-77, sr res scientist, Sci Affairs, M&M/Mars, 77-80, SR RES SCIENTIST, RES & DEVELOP, MARS INCORP, 80- *Mem:* Am Asn Cereal Chemists; Am Soc Bakery Eng; Inst Food Technologists; Soc Nutrit Educ. *Res:* Cereal and confectionery; flavor, nutrition, rheology, structural, crystallization, stability, cariogenicity, new products; fermentation; ion-protein interactions as affected by fermentation; scientific affairs; venture technology. *Mailing Add:* M&M/Mars High St Hackettstown NJ 07840

STONE, CHARLES JOEL, b Los Angeles, Calif, July 13, 36; m 66; c 2. MATHEMATICS, STATISTICS. *Educ:* Calif Inst Technol, BS, 58; Stanford Univ, PhD(math statist), 61. *Prof Exp:* Instr math, Princeton Univ, 61-62; asst prof, Cornell Univ, 62-64; from asst prof to assoc prof, 64-69, prof math, 69-81, prof biomath, Univ Calif, Los Angeles, 75-81, PROF STATIST, UNIV CALIF, BERKELEY, 81- *Concurrent Pos:* NSF grant, Univ Calif, Los Angeles, 64-; consult, Rand Corp, 66-67, Planning Res Corp, 66-68, Gen Elec Tech Mil Planning Oper, 68-70, Fed Aviation Admin, 70-74, Consol Anal Ctr Inc, 71-74, Urban Inst, 75-76 & Technol Serv Corp, 77-80; Guggenheim fel, 80-81. *Mem:* Fel Inst Math Statist; Am Math Soc; Am Statist Asn. *Res:* Probability and statistics, including random walks, birth and death, diffusion and infinitely divisible processes; potential theory; renewal theory; infinite particle systems; nonparametric estimation, classification and regression. *Mailing Add:* Dept Statist Univ of Calif Los Angeles CA 94720

STONE, CHARLES LEROY, b Frederick, Md, Oct 30, 49. NUTRITIONAL BIOCHEMISTRY, PHYSIOLOGY. *Educ:* Univ Md, College Park, BS, 72, MS, 74. *Prof Exp:* Physiologist chronic toxicol, Div Toxicol, 74-75, physiologist biochem toxicol, 75-78, RES PHYSIOLOGIST NUTRIT, DIV NUTRIT, FOOD & DRUG ADMIN, 78- *Mem:* AAAS. *Res:* Toxicity of heavy metals; bioavailability and effects on macromolecular biosynthesis. *Mailing Add:* Div Nutrit 200 C St SW Washington DC 20204

STONE, CHARLES PORTER, b Owatonna, Minn, Sept 16, 37; m 59; c 4. WILDLIFE RESEARCH, WILDLIFE ECOLOGY. *Educ:* Univ Minn, BA, 60; Colo State Univ, MS, 63; Ohio State Univ, PhD(zool), 73. *Prof Exp:* Res biologist, Patuxent Wildlife Res Ctr, 63-66; asst leader, Ohio Coop Wildlife Res Unit, 66-70; lectr, Ohio State Univ, 70; res biologist, Denver Wildlife Res Ctr, US Fish & Wildlife Serv, 71-73, asst dir, 73-75, supvry wildlife biologist, 73-80, chief wildlife ecol pub lands, 75-80. *Concurrent Pos:* Instr wildlife biol, Ohio State Univ, 66-70; mem adj fac, Colo State Univ, 73- *Mem:* AAAS; Wildlife Soc; Am Ornithologists Union; Am Soc Mammalogists; Wilson Ornith Soc. *Res:* Effects of energy development, forest and range management practices, and other land disturbances upon wildlife abundance, distribution and behavior; ecology of animal damage to crops. *Mailing Add:* Box 3 Hawaii National Park HI 96718

STONE, CHARLES RICHARD, b Portland, Ore, Sept 8, 21; m 47; c 3. AERODYNAMICS. *Educ:* Univ Minn, BSAero, 51; Univ Wash, MSAero, 58. *Prof Exp:* Aerodynamicist, Boeing Airplane Co, 51-55; res engr, 55-58, proj engr, 58-61, res supvr automatic control, 61-64, STAFF ENGR, HONEYWELL INC, 65- *Mem:* Am Inst Aeronaut & Astronaut. *Res:* Automatic, optimal and adaptive control; aerodynamics of vertical takeoff airplanes; dynamics and control of flexible vehicles. *Mailing Add:* 4955 Sorell Ave Minneapolis MN 55422

STONE, CLEMENT A, b Hastings, Nebr, May 23, 23; m 52; c 3. PHARMACOLOGY. *Educ:* Univ Nebr, BSc, 46; Univ Ill, MS, 48; Boston Univ, PhD(physiol), 52. *Prof Exp:* From instr to asst prof physiol, Sch Med, Boston Univ, 51-54; res assoc, Res Div, Sharp & Dohme, Inc, 54-57, dir pharmacodynamics, Merck Inst Therapeut Res, 56-57, from assoc dir to dir, 58-66, exec dir, 66-71, vpres, 71-78, SR VPRES, MERCK SHARP & DOHME RES LABS, 78- *Concurrent Pos:* Lectr, St Andrews, 53. *Mem:* AAAS; Am Soc Pharmacol & Exp Therapeut; Am Chem Soc; Soc Exp Biol & Med; NY Acad Sci. *Res:* Pharmacology of adrenergic, ganglionic blocking drugs, antihypertensive agents and antiglaucoma agents. *Mailing Add:* Merck Sharp & Dohme Res Labs West Point PA 19486

STONE, CONNIE J, b Michigan City, Ind, Oct 30, 43. TOXICOLOGY. *Educ:* Ind Univ, BA, 68, MS, 70, PhD(toxicol), 76; Am Bd Toxicol, Dipl, 81. *Prof Exp:* Mgr, Dept Toxicol, Becton Dickinson Res Ctr, 76-79; assoc dir, Life Sci Div, Clement Assoc, Inc, 79-81; MGR, LIFE SCI, LORILLARD RES CTR, 81- *Concurrent Pos:* Adj asst prof, Sch Public Health, Univ NC, 77- *Mem:* Am Indust Hygiene Asn; Am Col Toxicol; NY Acad Sci; Sigma Xi. *Res:* Inhalation toxicology: chronic inhalation studies involving exposure of rodents to aluminum chlorhydrate, asbestos, fibrous glass, ozone, sulfuric acid, or vinyl chloride. *Mailing Add:* Lorillard Res Ctr 420 English St PO Box 21688 Greensboro NC 27420

STONE, DANIEL BOXALL, b Gravesend, Eng, May 15, 25; US citizen; m 49; c 2. INTERNAL MEDICINE, ENDOCRINOLOGY. *Educ:* Univ London, BS & MD, 48, dipl psychiat, 50. *Prof Exp:* Intern & resident internal med, Univ London, 48-56; from asst prof to prof, Col Med, Univ Iowa, 59-71, exec assoc dean, 67-71; MILARD PROF MED, UNIV NEBR MED CTR, OMAHA, 71- *Concurrent Pos:* Fel internal med, Univ London, 48-56; fel internal med & endocrinol, Col Med, Univ Iowa, 57-59; Markle scholar acad med, 60-; consult, Vet Admin Hosp, Iowa City, Iowa, 63-71 & Coun Drugs, AMA, 66- *Mem:* Fel Am Col Physicians; Am Diabetes Asn; Am Heart Asn; Endocrine Soc; Royal Soc Med. *Res:* Influence of diet on serum lipids; geographic pathology of diabetes; metabolism of adipose tissue; influence of hypoglycemic drugs on lipolysis in adipose tissue. *Mailing Add:* 234 Doctors Bldg 4239 Farnam Omaha NE 68131

STONE, DANIEL JOSEPH, b Passaic, NY, Dec 19, 18; m 50; c 3. MEDICINE. *Educ:* Johns Hopkins Univ, BA, 39; George Washington Univ, MD, 43; Am Bd Internal Med, dipl, 51. *Prof Exp:* Fel internal med, New York Med Col, 46-47; asst chief, Pulmonary Dis Serv, 49-54, assoc, Cardiopulmonary Lab, 50-54, CHIEF PULMONARY DIS SERV & DIR RESPIRATION LAB, BRONX VET ADMIN HOSP, 54-, CHMN INHALATION THER COMT, 60-; PROF MED, NY MED COL, 75-, DIR PULMONARY SECT, 75- *Concurrent Pos:* Adv ed of res, Handbk of Biol Sci, Nat Acad Sci, 59; assoc prof, Mt Sinai Sch Med, 68. *Mem:* Am Physiol Soc; fel Am Col Physicians; fel AMA; Am Fedn Clin Res; fel Am Thoracic Soc. *Res:* Pulmonary diseases; lung mechanics and the mechanisms of pulmonary failure. *Mailing Add:* NY Med Col Pulmonary Div New York NY 10029

STONE, DAVID B, b Guernsey, UK, Sept 14, 33; m 60; c 3. GEOPHYSICS. *Educ:* Univ Keele, BA, 56; Univ Newcastle, PhD(geophys), 63. *Prof Exp:* Sr demonstrator geophys, Univ Newcastle, 63-66; assoc prof, 66-77, head, Geol/Geophys Prog, 77-80, PROF GEOPHYS, GEOPHYS INST, UNIV ALASKA, 77- *Mem:* Fel Royal Astron Soc; Am Geophys Union; fel Geol Soc Am. *Res:* Geomagnetism; paleomagnetism; geotectonics. *Mailing Add:* Geophys Inst Univ of Alaska College AK 99701

STONE, DAVID ROSS, b Little Rock, Ark, Aug 30, 42; m 65; c 3. ALGEBRA. *Educ:* Ga Inst Technol, BS, 64; Univ SC, PhD(math), 68. *Prof Exp:* ASSOC PROF MATH, GA SOUTHERN COL, 68- *Mem:* Am Math Soc; Math Asn Am. *Res:* Rings and modules; torsion theory; problem solving. *Mailing Add:* Dept of Math Ga Southern Col Statesboro GA 30460

STONE, DEBORAH BENNETT, b Portchester, NY, Oct 26, 38; m 65; c 2. PHYSICAL BIOCHEMISTRY, BIOCHEMICAL PHARMACOLOGY. *Educ:* Smith Col, BA, 60; Yale Univ, PhD(pharmacol), 65. *Prof Exp:* Res assoc pharmacol, Sch Med, Stanford Univ, 64-66; USPHS trainee phys biochem, Cardiovasc Res Inst, 66-68, lectr physiol, 68-77, asst res biochemist, 68-76, ASSOC RES BIOCHEMIST, CARDIOVASC RES INST, UNIV CALIF, SAN FRANCISCO, 76- *Concurrent Pos:* USPHS res career develop award, 68-73. *Mem:* Biophys Soc. *Res:* Serotonin metabolism in the developing rat brain; regulation of phosphofructokinase activity; molecular mechanisms in muscle contraction. *Mailing Add:* Cardiovasc Res Inst 841 HSW Univ of Calif San Francisco CA 94143

STONE, DONALD EUGENE, b Eureka, Calif, Dec 10, 30; m 52; c 3. BOTANY, GENETICS. *Educ:* Univ Calif, AB, 52, PhD(bot), 57. *Prof Exp:* Asst cytol, biosysts & gen bot, Univ Calif, 54-57; from instr to asst prof bot, Tulane Univ, 57-63; from asst prof to assoc prof, 63-70, PROF BOT, DUKE UNIV, 70- *Concurrent Pos:* Assoc prog dir syst biol, NSF, 68-69; exec dir, Orgn Trop Studies, Inc, 76- *Mem:* Bot Soc Am; Soc Study Evolution; Am Soc Naturalists; Am Soc Plant Taxonomists (secy, 73-75); Orgn Trop Studies. *Res:* Biosystematics of temperate and tropical families. *Mailing Add:* Dept of Bot Duke Univ Durham NC 27706

STONE, DOROTHY MAHARAM, b Parkersburg, WVa, July 1, 17; m 42; c 2. MATHEMATICS. *Educ:* Carnegie Inst Technol, BSc, 37; Bryn Mawr Col, PhD(math), 40. *Prof Exp:* Asst lectr math, Univ Manchester, 52-61; PROF MATH, UNIV ROCHESTER, 61- *Concurrent Pos:* NSF fel math, 65-66. *Mem:* Am Math Soc; Math Asn Am. *Res:* Measure theory; ergodic theory; probability; linear operators. *Mailing Add:* Dept of Math Univ of Rochester Rochester NY 14627

STONE, DOUGLAS MAX, b Allegan, Mich, Aug 31, 41; div; c 2. FORESTRY, BIOLOGY. *Educ:* Mich Technol Univ, BS, 66; Univ Mich, MS, 67, PhD(ecol), 70. *Prof Exp:* RES SCIENTIST FORESTRY, N CENT FOREST EXP STA, USDA, 70- *Mem:* Soc Am Foresters. *Res:* Ecological and physiological aspects of timber management research; photosynthesis and translocation; nutrient requirements; competition; plant autecology; soil-site relations; environment-plant-soil water relations; nutrient cycling processes. *Mailing Add:* N Cent Forest Exp Sta 806 Wright St Marquette MI 49855

STONE, DOUGLAS ROY, b Minneapolis, Minn, Nov 10, 48; m 72; c 1. BIOMEDICAL ENGINEERING, CHEMICAL ENGINEERING. *Educ:* Univ Minn, BChE, 70; Univ Wis, MS, 72, PhD(chem eng), 75. *Prof Exp:* Res engr med equip, 75-77, RES ENGR CHEM ENG, AIR PROD & CHEM, INC, 77- *Concurrent Pos:* NIH grant, Dept Bioeng, Univ Pa, 77- *Mem:* Am Inst Chem Engrs. *Res:* Aerosol measurement and characteristics; respiratory care and respiratory equipment; residence time distributions. *Mailing Add:* RD 2 Coopersburg PA 18036

STONE, EARL LEWIS, JR, b Phoenix, NY, July 12, 15; m 41; c 3. FOREST SOILS. *Educ:* State Univ NY, BS, 38; Univ Wis, MS, 40; Cornell Univ, PhD(soils), 48. *Prof Exp:* Field asst & jr forester, Southern Forest Exp Sta, US Forest Serv, 40-41; from asst prof to assoc prof forest soils, Cornell Univ, 48-62, Charles Lathrop Pack prof forest soils, 62-80. *Concurrent Pos:* Collabr & consult, Southern Forest Exp Sta, US Forest Serv, 47-48 & 52; soil scientist, Pac Sci Bd, Nat Acad Sci, Marshall Islands, 50; Am-Swiss Found fel, 54-55; vis prof, Philippines, 58-60; Fulbright res fel, Forest Res Inst, New Zealand, 62; ed, Forest Sci, Soc Am Foresters, 65-71; Bullard fel, Harvard Univ, 69-70; consult, Biotrop, Indonesia, 70; mem adv panel ecol, NSF, 70-; mem adv comn, Ecol Sci Div, Oak Ridge Nat Lab, 71-; mem forest studies team, Nat Res Coun, 73-74; comn evaluate Int Biol Prog, 74-75 & comn scientist, Nat Forest Mgt Act, 77-; mem, Int Union Forest Res Orgns. *Honors & Awards:* Barrington Moore Award, Soc Am Foresters, 73. *Mem:* Fel AAAS; fel Soc Am Foresters; fel Soil Sci Soc Am; Ecol Soc Am; fel Am Soc Agron. *Res:* Forest nutrition; ecology; Pacific tropics. *Mailing Add:* 10 Catherine Dr Dryden NY 13053

STONE, EDWARD, b Fall River, Mass, Dec 7, 32; m 56; c 4. ORGANIC CHEMISTRY, POLYMER CHEMISTRY. *Educ:* Southeastern Mass Univ, BS, 55; Univ Md, PhD(org chem), 62. *Prof Exp:* Teaching asst, Univ Md, 55-57; chemist, Metals & Controls Corp, 56; anal res chemist, Nat Inst Drycleaning, 57-61, consult, 61; sr res chemist, Tex-US Chem Co, NJ, 61-65; tech mgr new prod res & develop, 65-80, DIR, POLYMER RES & CHEM ANALYSIS, INMONT CORP, 80- *Mem:* Am Chem Soc; Sci Res Soc Am. *Res:* Radiation curing of inks and coatings; polymer research and development; block and graft copolymers; polyurethanes, polyesters, polyolefins, acrylics; structure-property correlations; organic synthesis; instrumental analysis. *Mailing Add:* 4 Inwood Rd Morris Plains NJ 07950

STONE, EDWARD CARROLL, JR, b Knoxville, Iowa, Jan 23, 36; m 62; c 2. PHYSICS. *Educ:* Univ Chicago, SM, 59, PhD(physics), 64. *Prof Exp:* Res fel, 64-67, sr res fel, 67, from asst prof to assoc prof, 67-76, PROF PHYSICS, CALIF INST TECHNOL, 76- *Concurrent Pos:* Mem particles & fields adv comt, NASA, 69-71, consult, 71-, proj scientist, NASA Voyager Mission, 72-, mem high energy astrophys mgt operating working group, 76-, mem comt

space astron & astrophys, Space Sci Bd, 79-82; Alfred P Sloan res fel, Calif Inst Technol, 71-73. *Mem:* AAAS; fel Am Phys Soc; Am Astron Soc; Am Geophys Union. *Res:* Solar and galactic cosmic rays; planetary magnetospheres; interplanetary medium; solar system exploration; satellite and balloon instrumentation. *Mailing Add:* Dept Physics Calif Inst Technol 1201 E California Blvd Pasadena CA 91125

STONE, EDWARD CURRY, b Ill, Nov 28, 17; m 41; c 2. PLANT PHYSIOLOGY. *Educ:* Univ Calif, BS, 40, PhD(plant physiol), 48. *Prof Exp:* Plant physiologist, Calif Forest & Range Exp Sta, US Forest Serv, 48-49; PROF FOREST ECOL & SILVICULTURIST, AGR EXP STA, UNIV CALIF, BERKELEY, 49- *Concurrent Pos:* Fulbright res scholar, Univ NZ, 59-60; Guggenheim fel, 60. *Mem:* Ecol Soc Am; Soc Am Foresters; Am Soc Plant Physiol; Bot Soc Am; Scand Soc Plant Physiol. *Res:* Forest physiology; dormancy; root growth; drought resistance; fire response; cone production; nutritional requirements of forest vegetation. *Mailing Add:* 145 Mulford Hall Univ of Calif Berkeley CA 94720

STONE, EDWARD JOHN, b Minersville, Pa, July 27, 30; m 56; c 2. ORGANIC CHEMISTRY, BIOCHEMISTRY. *Educ:* Pa State Univ, BS, 53, MS, 56, PhD(biochem), 62. *Prof Exp:* Res chemist, Campbell Soup Co, 59-62, SR RES CHEMIST, CAMPBELL INST FOOD RES, 62- *Mem:* Sigma Xi; NY Acad Sci; Am Chem Soc. *Res:* Food chemistry; radiochemistry. *Mailing Add:* 6 Brondesbury Dr Cherry Hill NJ 08003

STONE, ELLEN ROSE, topology, see previous edition

STONE, ERIKA MARES, b Prague, Czech, Jan 26, 38; US citizen; m; c 1. MATHEMATICS. *Educ:* Pa State Univ, BA, 60, MA, 62, PhD(math), 64. *Prof Exp:* Instr math, Swarthmore Col, 64-65; sr res mathematician, HRB-Singer, Inc, 65-68; lectr dept comput sci, Pa State Univ, 68; vis asst prof, Dept Math & Comput Sci, Univ SC, 73-75; PROGRAMMER, COMPUT CTR, DUKE UNIV, 77- *Mem:* Am Math Soc. *Res:* Structure theory of semiperfect rings and the generalization of theory for modules. *Mailing Add:* 2106 Strebor Rd Durham NC 27705

STONE, GILBERT C H, biochemistry, deceased

STONE, GORDON EMORY, b Sioux City, Iowa, July 12, 33; m 55; c 2. CELL BIOLOGY. *Educ:* Univ Iowa, BA, 56, MSc, 58, PhD(zool), 61. *Prof Exp:* Res fel, NIH, 61-63 & AEC, 63-64; from asst prof to assoc prof anat, Sch Med, Univ Colo, 64-72; PROF BIOL SCI & CHMN DEPT, UNIV DENVER, 72- *Concurrent Pos:* NIH career develop award, 65-70. *Mem:* AAAS; Am Soc Cell Biol; Soc Protozool; Am Soc Zool. *Res:* Cytochemical studies on cell growth and division, especially the sequential macromolecular events during the interdivision interval leading to division with emphasis on microtubule protein synthesis. *Mailing Add:* Dept of Biol Sci Univ of Denver Denver CO 80210

STONE, H NATHAN, b Claremont, NH, May 8, 20; m 42; c 2. CHEMICAL ENGINEERING. *Educ:* Univ NH, BS, 43; Univ Ill, MS, 47, PhD(chem eng), 50. *Prof Exp:* Group leader org res, Norton Co, 50-52; asst dir res, Bay State Abrasive Prod Co, 52-58, dir res & develop, 58-64, V PRES & DIR RES & ENG, BAY STATE ABRASIVES, DIV DRESSER INDUSTS INC, 64- *Mem:* AAAS; Am Chem Soc; Am Ceramic Soc; Nat Soc Prof Engrs; Am Inst Chem Engrs. *Res:* Reaction kinetics in fluidized beds; solid state physics, especially the creation of new surfaces during abrasive machining; resins and polymers applicable to abrasive bonding. *Mailing Add:* Bay State Abrasives Div Dresser Industs Inc Westboro MA 01581

STONE, HARRIS B(OBBY), b New York, NY, Oct 16, 23; m 48; c 2. ELECTRONIC ENGINEERING. *Educ:* Mass Inst Technol, SB, 50. *Prof Exp:* Engr, Western Union Tel Co, 50-52; proj engr & officer, Hq, Electronic Warfare Ctr, US Dept Army, Ft Monmouth, NJ, 52-54, chief electronic reconnaissance sect, Electronic Proving Ground, Ft Huachuca, Ariz, 54-55, chief defense systs br, 55, chief electronic reconnaissance br, Hq, Security Agency Oper Ctr, 55-56; electronic warfare & intel systs coordr, Off Develop Coordr, Off Naval Res, US Dept Navy, Washington, DC, 56-59, asst for electronic warfare & intel, Tech Anal & Adv Group, 59-61, asst dir command control & spec opers, 61, dep dir, 61-71, dir res, develop, test & eval plans div, Off Chief Naval Opers, 71-80. *Concurrent Pos:* Adv bd dirs, Hubbs Seaworld Res Inst, San Diego, 81- *Mem:* AAAS. *Res:* Electronic warfare; intelligence; radar; acoustics; communications; mechanics; economics; photography; electromagnetics; research and development management. *Mailing Add:* 4528 Roundhill Rd Alexandria VA 22310

STONE, HENRY OTTO, JR, b Spartanburg, SC, Apr 10, 36; m 60. VIROLOGY, BIOCHEMISTRY. *Educ:* Wofford Col, BS, 59; Duke Univ, PhD(zool), 64. *Prof Exp:* Am Cancer Soc fel biochem, Duke Univ, 64-66; res chemist, E I du Pont de Nemours & Co, Inc, Del, 66-70; NIH spec res fel animal virol, St Jude Children's Res Hosp, 70-72; asst prof, 72-77, ASSOC PROF MICROBIOL, UNIV KANS, 77- *Concurrent Pos:* Am Cancer Soc scholar, Duke Univ, 81. *Mem:* Am Soc Microbiol; Am Soc Biol Chemists; Soc Gen Microbiol. *Res:* Paramyxoviruses; viral RNA synthesis; genome transcription; viral proteins; defective interfering particles. *Mailing Add:* Dept of Microbiol Univ of Kans Lawrence KS 66044

STONE, HERBERT, b Washington, DC, Sept 14, 34; m 64; c 2. NUTRITION, ORGANIC CHEMISTRY. *Educ:* Univ Mass, BSc, 55, MSc, 58; Univ Calif, Davis, PhD(nutrit), 62. *Prof Exp:* Specialist, Exp Sta, Univ Calif, Davis; food scientist, Stanford Res Inst, 62-64, dir dept food & plant sci, 67-74; PRES, TRAGON CORP, 74- *Concurrent Pos:* Pres, Sensory Eval Div, Inst Food Technol, 77-78; assoc ed, J Food Sci, 77-80. *Mem:* AAAS; Sigma Xi; Am Soc Enol; Inst Food Technol; Am Soc Testing & Mat. *Res:* Management consultant in product development, food, beverage, cosmetic products and product acceptance measurement; taste and odor research. *Mailing Add:* Tragon Corp 750 Welch Rd Palo Alto CA 94304

STONE, HERBERT L(OSSON), b Eddy, Tex, Nov 6, 28; m 47, 80; c 2. CHEMICAL ENGINEERING. *Educ:* Rice Inst, BS, 50; Mass Inst Technol, ScD(chem eng), 53. *Prof Exp:* Asst process engr, Vulcan Copper & Supply Co, 53; RES ADV, EXXON PROD RES CO, 53- *Mem:* Am Inst Chem Engrs; Am Inst Mining, Metall & Petrol Engrs; Sigma Xi. *Res:* Numerical analysis. *Mailing Add:* Box 22781 Houston TX 77027

STONE, HERMAN, b Munich, Ger, Nov 3, 24; nat US; m 49; c 6. ORGANIC CHEMISTRY. *Educ:* Bethany Col, WVa, BSc, 44; Ohio State Univ, PhD(chem), 50. *Prof Exp:* Anal chemist, Nat Aniline Div, Allied Chem Corp, 44-45, anal res chemist, 51-53, res chemist, 53-61, group leader appln res chem, 61-63, mgr chem res, Indust Chem Div, 63-68, dir res, Specialty Chem Div, 68-69, res assoc, Corp Chem Res Lab, 69-72; dir chem res, Malden Mills Inc, 72-74; DIR FOAM DEVELOP, GEN FOAM CORP, 74- *Mem:* AAAS; Am Chem Soc; Soc Plastics Engrs; Sigma Xi; Am Inst Chem. *Res:* Analytical and exploratory research on polymer intermediates; flammability of plastics; urethane polymer technology. *Mailing Add:* Foam Div Valmont Indust Park Hazleton PA 18201

STONE, HOWARD ANDERSON, b Claremont, NH, Nov 21, 40; m 62; c 3. GENETICS, VIROLOGY. *Educ:* Univ NH, BS, 62, MS, 65; Mich State Univ, PhD(poultry), 72. *Prof Exp:* Asst poultry geneticist, Univ NH, 62-65; RES GENETICIST, AGR RES SERV, USDA, 65- *Mem:* Poultry Sci Asn. *Res:* Investigations of the genetic control of Marek's disease and lymphoid leukosis in chickens; maintenance and development of highly inbred lines of chickens. *Mailing Add:* 1827 Lyndhurst Haslett MI 48840

STONE, HOWARD N(ORDAS), b Marblehead, Mass, Apr 7, 22; div; c 2. AERONAUTICAL ENGINEERING. *Educ:* Harvard Univ, SB & MS, 44. *Prof Exp:* Struct engr, Sikorsky Aircraft Co, 45; Gordon McKay asst, Harvard Univ, 45-46; sr res engr, Curtiss-Wright Corp, 46-49; res aerodynamicist, Cornell Aeronaut Lab, 49-54; develop eng specialist, Lockheed Aircraft Corp, 54-57 & 58-59; specialist, Missile Systs Div, Raytheon Corp, 57-58; res specialist, Missiles & Space Div, Lockheed Aircraft Corp, 58-61, aircraft develop engr res group, Aerodyn Dept, Ga, 61-63; RES SPECIALIST, LOCKHEED MISSILES & SPACE CO, SUNNYVALE, CALIF, 63- *Res:* Research and development in booster vehicle design and performance; aerodynamics of low-aspect-ratio wings; bodies and wing-body combinations; flutter of wings. *Mailing Add:* 213 Arriba Dr #3 Sunnyvale CA 94086

STONE, HUBERT LOWELL, b Baton Rouge, La, July 22, 36; m 57; c 3. PHYSIOLOGY. *Educ:* Rice Univ, BS, 58; Univ Ill, Urbana, MS, 59, PhD(physiol), 61. *Prof Exp:* Asst, Univ Ill, 58-61; from instr to asst prof physiol & biophys, Med Sch, Univ Miss, 61-64; res physiologist, US Air Force Sch Aerospace Med, 64-71; prof physiol, Univ Tex Med Br Galveston & chief, Cardiovasc Control Sect, Marine Biomed Inst, 71-77; PROF PHYSIOL & HEAD, DEPT PHYSIOL & BIOPHYSICS, UNIV OKLA HEALTH SCI CTR, 77- *Concurrent Pos:* USPHS fel, Med Sch, Univ Miss, 61-63; mem, Comt Appl Physiol & Orthopedic Surg Study Sect, NIH, 79-82. *Honors & Awards:* Outstanding Certs, Dept Defense & US Air Force, 68 & 70. *Mem:* NY Acad Sci; Am Heart Asn; Soc Exp Biol & Med; Soc Neurosci; Am Physiol Soc. *Res:* Cardiovascular physiology. *Mailing Add:* Univ of Okla Health Sci Ctr PO Box 26901 Oklahoma City OK 73190

STONE, IRVING CHARLES, JR, b Chicago, Ill, Dec 18, 30; m 55; c 3. FORENSIC SCIENCE. *Educ:* Iowa State Univ, BS, 52; George Washington Univ, MS, 61, PhD(geochem), 68. *Prof Exp:* Spec agt-microscopist, Fed Bur Invest, 55-61; res chemist, Res Div, W R Grace & Co, 61-63, proj leader, 63-64, res supvr, 64-68; dir, Geochem Surv, Tex, 68-72; criminalist, 72-74; CHIEF PHYS EVIDENCE SECT, INST FORENSIC SCI, 74- *Concurrent Pos:* Lectr police sci, Montgomery Jr Col, 67-70; instr forensic sci, Univ Tex Health Sci Ctr Dallas, 72-77, asst prof path, 77-, dir grad prog forensic sci, Grad Sch Biomed Sci, 77-; adj asst prof, Univ Tex, Arlington, 73- *Mem:* Sigma Xi; Am Soc Firearms & Toolmark Examrs; Am Soc Crime Lab Dir. *Res:* Analytical chemistry, especially x-ray diffraction, spectrometry, light microscopy; applied research in forensic sciences, specifically glass, firearm residues and instrumental analytical applications. *Mailing Add:* Inst of Forensic Sci Box 35728 Dallas TX 75235

STONE, IRWIN, b New York, NY, Nov 18, 07; m 31; c 1. BIOCHEMISTRY, MEDICAL RESEARCH. *Prof Exp:* Chemist, Pease Labs, 24-34; from res chemist to head brewing res sect, Wallerstein Co, Travenol Labs, Inc, NY, 34-71; dir res, Megascorbic Res, Inc, 72-75; INDEPENDENT RES, 75-; SCI DIR, IS-FACT FOUND, 80- *Mem:* Am Soc Brewing Chem (pres, 62-63); fel Am Inst Chem; fel Int Acad Preventive Med; fel Australasian Col Bio-Med Scientists. *Res:* Enzyme, ascorbate chemistry; genetics of scurvy; description of human genetic liver-enzyme disease, hypoascorbemia; elimination of chronic subclinical scurvy as a widespread mammalian disease; megascorbic therapy. *Mailing Add:* 1331 Charmwood Sq San Jose CA 95117

STONE, J(ACK) L(ESLIE), engineering physics, see previous edition

STONE, J(ACK) L(EE), b Taylor, Tex, July 12, 41; m 65; c 3. ELECTRICAL ENGINEERING; SOLID STATE ELECTRONICS. *Educ:* Univ Tex, BSEE, 63, MSEE, 64, PhD(elec eng), 68. *Prof Exp:* Res asst appl superconductivity, Univ Tex, 62-65, res asst elec eng, 65-66, teaching assoc, 66-67, asst prof, 67-68; res engr, Mesa Instruments Inc, 68-69; from asst prof to assoc prof elec eng, Tex A&M Univ, 69-77; sr scientist, 78-79, chief, Advan Silicon Br, 79-81, DEP DIV MGR, SOLAR ELEC CONVERSION RES DIV, SOLAR ENERGY RES INST, 81- *Concurrent Pos:* Co-prin investr, NASA res grant, 68-69; prin investr, Army Res Off-Durham res grant, 70-72; vis prof, Inst Nac Astrofisica, Optica, Electronics, 75-76. *Mem:* Inst Elec & Electronics Engrs; Am Inst Physics; Electrochem Soc. *Res:* Applied superconductivity; optical properties of semiconductors at low temperatures; high Q resonant circuit techniques; amorphous semiconductors; ion implantation; integrated circuit device processing; photovoltaic devices. *Mailing Add:* Solar Energy Res Inst 1617 Cole Blvd Golden CO 80401

STONE, JAY D, b Littlefield, Tex, Oct 14, 44; m 65; c 2. ENTOMOLOGY. *Educ:* West Tex State Univ, BS, 68; Iowa State Univ, MS, 70, PhD(entom), 73. *Prof Exp:* Res assoc entom, Iowa State Univ, 72-73; asst prof, Kans State Univ, 73-76; ASST PROF ENTOM, TEX A&M UNIV, 76- *Mem:* Sigma Xi; Entom Soc Am. *Res:* Biology and control of insect and mite pest of far west Texas field and orchard crops. *Mailing Add:* Tex A&M Agr Res Ctr 1380 A&M Circle El Paso TX 79927

STONE, JOE THOMAS, b Miami, Okla, June 25, 41; m 63; c 2. PHYSICAL ORGANIC CHEMISTRY, PHOTOGRAPHIC CHEMISTRY. *Educ:* Harvey Mudd Col, BS, 63; Univ Wash, PhD(org chem), 67. *Prof Exp:* NIH res fel, Univ Wash, 67-68; SR RES CHEMIST, EASTMAN KODAK CO, 68- *Mem:* NY Acad Sci; Royal Soc Chem; Am Chem Soc. *Res:* Organic reaction mechanisms; application of physical-organic techniques to biological processes, enzyme kinetics and mechanism; homogeneous and heterogeneous catalysis and reaction kinetics. *Mailing Add:* Eastman Kodak Co Res Labs Kodak Park Rochester NY 14650

STONE, JOHN AUSTIN, b Paintsville, Ky, Nov 30, 35; m 61; c 3. NUCLEAR CHEMISTRY. *Educ:* Univ Louisville, BS, 55; Univ Calif, Berkeley, PhD(nuclear chem), 63. *Prof Exp:* Chemist, 63-73, staff chemist, 73-74, res staff chemist, 74-81, RES ASSOC, SAVANNAH RIVER LAB, E I DU PONT DE NEMOURS & CO, INC, 81- *Mem:* Am Phys Soc; Am Chem Soc; Mat Res Soc. *Res:* Radioactive waste management; nuclear fuel cycle; solid state and chemical properties of the actinides; Mossbauer spectroscopy. *Mailing Add:* Savannah River Lab E I du Pont de Nemours & Co Inc Aiken SC 29801

STONE, JOHN BRUCE, b Forfar, Ont, Sept 23, 30; m 54; c 4. ANIMAL SCIENCE. *Educ:* Ont Agr Col, BSA, 53, MSA, 54; Cornell Univ, PhD, 59. *Prof Exp:* Asst prof animal husb, Ont Agr Col, 54-62; asst prof animal sci, Cornell Univ, 62-66; PROF ANIMAL SCI, UNIV GUELPH, 66- *Mem:* Am Dairy Sci Asn; Agr Inst Can; Am Soc Animal Sci. *Res:* Dairy cattle nutrition; forages for dairy cattle rations; calf-raising programs; systems analyses for dairy production. *Mailing Add:* Dept of Animal & Poultry Sci Univ of Guelph Guelph ON N1G 2W1 Can

STONE, JOHN ELMER, b Montgomery, Ala, Aug 12, 31; m 59; c 2. GEOLOGY. *Educ:* Ohio Wesleyan Univ, BA, 53; Univ Ill, MS, 58, PhD(geol), 60. *Prof Exp:* Asst prof geol, Univ Tex, 60-62; geologist, Minn Geol Surv, 62-67; head dept, 67-77, PROF GEOL, OKLA STATE UNIV, 67- *Concurrent Pos:* Res grants, Univ Tex Excellence Fund, 61 & grad sch, Univ Minn, 62, 67; NSF summer grants, 68-72, sci equip grant, 69; Okla State Univ Res Found res grant, 70. *Mem:* AAAS; fel Geol Soc Am; Nat Asn Geol Teachers; Am Quaternary Asn; Soc Econ Paleont & Mineral. *Res:* Glacial and engineering geology. *Mailing Add:* Dept of Geol Okla State Univ Stillwater OK 74074

STONE, JOHN FLOYD, b York, Nebr, Oct 13, 28; m 53; c 4. SOIL PHYSICS. *Educ:* Univ Nebr, BSc, 52; Iowa State Univ, MS, 55, PhD, 57. *Prof Exp:* Res assoc, Dept Agron & Inst Atomic Res, Iowa State Univ, 56-57; from asst prof to assoc prof agron, 57-69, PROF AGRON, OKLA STATE UNIV, 69- *Concurrent Pos:* Assoc ed, Soil Sci Soc Am, 68-75; mem, Comt Evapotranspiration, Res Comt, Great Plains Agr Coun, 71- *Mem:* Am Soc Agron; Soil Sci Soc Am; Am Geophys Union; Int Soc Soil Sci; Sigma Xi. *Res:* Water conservation, evapotranspiration; water flow in plants; electronic instrumentation. *Mailing Add:* Dept of Agron Okla State Univ Stillwater OK 74074

STONE, JOHN GROVER, II, b Pueblo, Colo, Aug 6, 33; m 64; c 5. GEOLOGY. *Educ:* Yale Univ, BS, 55; Stanford Univ, PhD(geol), 58. *Prof Exp:* Staff geologist, 58-69, asst chief geologist, 69-77, proj mgr, 77-79, MGR, PILOT KNOW MINE & PELLET PLANT, HANNA MINING CO, 80- *Mem:* Geol Soc Am; Soc Econ Geologists. *Res:* Genesis of ore deposits. *Mailing Add:* Hanna Mining Co 100 Erieview Plaza Cleveland OH 44114

STONE, JOHN PATRICK, b Algood, Tenn, Sept 5, 39; m 64; c 3. ENDOCRINOLOGY, RADIOBIOLOGY. *Educ:* Wayne State Univ, BS, 61, PhD(biol), 72; Purdue Univ, Lafayette, MS, 64. *Prof Exp:* Teaching asst bionucleonics, Purdue Univ, Lafayette, 62-64; teaching asst endocrinol & radiobiol, Wayne State Univ, 65-68; fel radiobiol, Div Biol & Med Res, Argonne Nat Lab, 72-74; asst scientist, 74-75, assoc scientist, 76-79, SCIENTIST, RADIOBIOL DIV, MED DEPT, BROOKHAVEN NAT LAB, 79- *Concurrent Pos:* Assoc clin prof, State Univ NY, Stony Brook, 78. *Mem:* Endocrine Soc; Int Pigment Cell Soc; Radiation Res Soc; Am Soc Zoologists; Sigma Xi. *Res:* Hormonal control of radiation and chemically induced mammary tumorigenesis; effects of chronic gamma irradiation upon endocrine and hematopoietic systems; pigment cell biochemistry and physiology. *Mailing Add:* Med Dept Brookhaven Nat Lab Upton NY 11973

STONE, JOSEPH, b Holyoke, Mass, June 3, 20. BIOCHEMISTRY, PHARMACOLOGY. *Educ:* Mass Col Pharm, BS, 47; Univ Colo, PhD(pharmacol), 54. *Prof Exp:* Proj assoc, McArdle Mem Labs, Univ Wis, 54-56; staff pharmacologist, Vet Admin Hosp, Chicago, 56; asst prof, 57-63, ASSOC PROF PHARMACOL, MED CTR, UNIV ARK, LITTLE ROCK, 63- *Mem:* AAAS; NY Acad Sci. *Res:* Diffusion respiration; testing systems for DNA antimetabolites; central nervous system biochemistry and pharmacology. *Mailing Add:* Dept of Pharmacol Univ of Ark Med Ctr Little Rock AR 72201

STONE, JOSEPH LOUIS, b Claremont, NH, Jan 25, 18; m 43; c 2. MEDICAL BACTERIOLOGY. *Educ:* Univ NH, BS, 40; MS, 41; Boston Univ, PhD, 48. *Prof Exp:* Sr bacteriologist, Biol Lab, State Dept Pub Health, Mass, 48-56; sr res investr, Wyeth Labs, Inc, Marietta, 56-72, SR RES INVESTR, WYETH LABS, INC, RADNOR, 72- *Mem:* AAAS; Am Geog Soc. *Res:* Antibiotics; tetanus toxin and toxoid; virus vaccines. *Mailing Add:* 717 Croton Rd Wayne PA 19087

STONE, JULIAN, b New York, NY, Apr 12, 29; m 51; c 3. PHYSICS. *Educ:* City Col New York, BS, 50; NY Univ, MS, 51, PhD(physics), 58. *Prof Exp:* Electronic scientist, Naval Mat Lab, 52; tutor physics, City Col New York, 52-53; res scientist, Hudson Lab, Columbia Univ, 53-69, assoc dir physics, 66-69; MEM TECH STAFF, BELL LABS, 69- *Concurrent Pos:* Tutor physics, City Col New York, 56-57. *Mem:* Optical Soc Am. *Res:* Lasers; spectroscopy; underwater sound propagation. *Mailing Add:* Bell Labs Room R113 Box 400 Holmdel NJ 07733

STONE, LAWRENCE DAVID, b St Louis, Mo, Sept 2, 42; m 67. MATHEMATICS, OPERATIONS RESEARCH. *Educ:* Antioch Col, BS, 64; Purdue Univ, West Lafayette, MS, 66, PhD(math), 67. *Prof Exp:* From assoc to sr assoc, 67-74, vpres, 74-81, BR MGR, DANIEL H WAGNER ASSOCS, 81- *Concurrent Pos:* Off Naval Res grant, 69-76; assoc ed, Operations Res, 81- *Honors & Awards:* Lancaster Prize, Opers Res Soc, 75. *Mem:* Am Math Soc; Inst Math Statist; Oper Res Soc; Math Prog Soc. *Res:* Theory of search for stationary and moving targets; constrained extremal problems; threshold crossing problems for markov and semi-markov processes; optimal stochastic control of semi-markov processes. *Mailing Add:* Suite 314 1270 Oakmead Pkwy Sunnyvale CA 94086

STONE, LOYD RAYMOND, b Prague, Okla, Jan 6, 45; m 65; c 3. SOIL PHYSICS. *Educ:* Okla State Univ, BS, 67, MS, 69; SDak State Univ, PhD(agron), 73. *Prof Exp:* Asst prof, 73-78, ASSOC PROF AGRON, EVAPOTRANSPIRATION LAB, KANS STATE UNIV, 78- *Mem:* Am Soc Agron; Soil Sci Soc Am; Sigma Xi; Soil Conserv Soc Am. *Res:* Management of the soil-water-crop environment for efficient use of water; irrigation water use efficiency and plant root systems analysis. *Mailing Add:* Evapo-transpiration Lab Kans State Univ Manhattan KS 66506

STONE, M(ORRIS) D, b Cambridge, Mass, Dec 2, 02; m; c 4. ENGINEERING. *Educ:* Harvard Univ, BS, 23, MS, 25; Univ Pittsburgh, PhD, 33. *Prof Exp:* Mem staff steam res, Am Soc Mech Eng, 23-25; res engr, engr-in-chg & head design sch, Westinghouse Elec & Mfg Co, 25-34; spec engr, United Eng & Foundry Co, 34-40, mgr res & develop, 40-65, vpres, 65-70, mem bd dirs, 68-70; consult, 70-72; RETIRED. *Concurrent Pos:* Lectr, Univ Pittsburgh, 28-34; consult, AEC, 46-52; chmn comts, Mat Adv Bd, Nat Acad Sci; consult engr. *Mem:* Life fel Am Soc Mech Engrs; Asn Iron & Steel Engrs; Am Inst Mining, Metall & Petrol Engrs. *Res:* Theory of vibrations; mathematical theory of elasticity; rolling and forging of metals; rolling and metalworking of metals. *Mailing Add:* 1308 Macon Ave Pittsburgh PA 15218

STONE, MARGARET HODGMAN, b Cleveland, Ohio, May 20, 14; m 41; c 3. PLANT TAXONOMY. *Educ:* Western Reserve Univ, BA, 36, MA, 37, PhD(bot), 40. *Prof Exp:* Dir hort, Garden Ctr Gtr Cleveland, 40-41; agr res dir bot, State Univ NY Col Agr, Cornell Univ, 41-42; instr, Western Reserve Univ, 43-45; agr res dir State Univ NY Col Agr, Cornell Univ, 45-46; prof lectr, Col Agr, Philippines, 58-60; sr cur taxon bot, L H Bailey Hortorium, Cornell Univ, 65-79. *Concurrent Pos:* Mercer res fel, Arnold Arboretum, Harvard Univ, 69-70; adj prof bot, Univ Fla, 81- *Mem:* AAAS; Int Asn Plant Taxon; Am Hort Soc. *Res:* Hydrogen-ion concentration of soil in relation to distribution of flora; dormant buds in Pinus; taxonomy of cultivated plants. *Mailing Add:* Herbarium Rolfs Hall Univ Fla Gainesville FL 32601

STONE, MARSHALL HARVEY, b New York, NY, Apr 8, 03; m 27, 62; c 4. MATHEMATICS. *Educ:* Harvard Univ, BA, 22, MA, 24, PhD(math), 26. *Hon Degrees:* ScD, Kenyon Col, 39, Amherst Col, 54 & Colby Col, 59; Dr, Univ San Marcos, Peru, 43 & Univ Buenos Aires, 47 & Univ Athens, 54; ScD, Univ Mass, 66. *Prof Exp:* Instr math, Harvard Univ, 22-23 & 27-28, asst prof, 28-31; assoc prof, Yale Univ, 31-33; from assoc prof to prof, 33-46, Harvard Univ, chmn dept, 42; instr, Columbia Univ, 25-27; Andrew Macleish Distinguished Serv prof, 46-68, chmn dept, 46-52, EMER PROF MATH, UNIV CHICAGO, 68-; George David Birkhoff prof, 68-73, prof, 73-80, EMER PROF MATH, UNIV MASS, AMHERST, 80- *Concurrent Pos:* Guggenheim fel, Inst Advan Study, 36-37; Ames lectr, Univ Wash, 42; vis prof, Univ Buenos Aires, 43, Univ Brazil, 47, Tata Inst Fundamental Res, India, 49-50, 55-56 & 80-81, Col France, 53 & Nadurai Kamaray Univ, Madurai, India, 80-81; vis lectr, Univs, Japan, 49, 56, Australia, 59 & Univ Islamabad, WPakistan, 69-70; external examr, Univ Malaya, 58-60, Middle East Tech Univ, Turkey, 63, Res Inst Math Sci, Madras, India, 63-64, 65, Kyoto, Japan, 65, Univ Geneva, 64, Int Math Union & Acad Sci, Pakistan, 64, Univ Hong Kong, 65, Thai Math Soc, 65, Univs Taiwan, 65 & Cern, Geneva, 66; vchmn div math & phys sci, Nat Res Coun, 46-52, div math, 51-52; pres, Int Math Union, 52-54; pres, Int Comn Math Instruct, 59-62; pres, Royaumont Cong, Orgn Europ Econ Coop, 59, mem expert group, Yugoslavia, 60; mem panel elem sch math, Sch Math Study Group, 60; mem comt social thought, Univ Chicago, 62-68; mem inter-union comn sci teaching, Int Coun Sci Unions, 62-65; pres, Inter-Am Comt Math Educ, 61-72. *Mem:* Nat Acad Sci; corresp mem Bologna Acad; Am Math Soc (pres, 43-44); foreign mem Acad Brasileira Sci; Am Philos Soc. *Res:* Analysis; general topology; algebra of logic; Hilbert space theory; foundations of mathematics and physics. *Mailing Add:* 260 Lincoln Ave Amherst MA 01002

STONE, MARTHA BARNES, b Paris, Tenn, Nov 20, 52; m 73. FOOD SCIENCE. *Educ:* Univ Tenn, Martin, BS, 74; Univ Tenn, Knoxville, MS, 75, PhD(food sci), 77. *Prof Exp:* Res asst foods & nutrit, Univ Tenn, 74-77; ASST PROF FOODS & NUTRIT, KANS STATE UNIV, 78- *Concurrent Pos:* NSF grant, 78; mem regional commun, Inst Food Technologists, 81- *Mem:* Inst Food Technologists (secy, 76-77); Sigma Xi; Am Dietetics Asn. *Res:* Formulated foods; quality evaluation of fruits and vegetables. *Mailing Add:* Dept of Foods & Nutrit Kans State Univ Manhattan KS 66506

STONE, MARTIN L, b New York, NY, June 11, 20; m 43; c 1. OBSTETRICS & GYNECOLOGY. *Educ:* Columbia Univ, BS, 41; New York Med Col, MD, 44, MMSc, 49; Am Bd Obstet & Gynec, dipl, 52. *Prof Exp:* Prof obstet & gynec & chmn dept, New York Med Col, 56-78; PROF OBSTET & GYNEC & CHMN DEPT, SCH MED, STATE UNIV NEW YORK, STONY BROOK, 78- *Concurrent Pos:* Attend, Flower & Fifth Ave Hosps, Metrop & Bird S Coler Hosps, 56-; consult, Southampton Hosp, 60-, Deepdale Gen Hosp, 66- & Long Island Jewish-Hillside Med Ctr, 78. *Mem:* Fel Am Gynec Soc; fel Am Pub Health Asn; fel Am Asn Obstetricians & Gynecologists; assoc fel Royal Soc Med; fel Am Col Obstetricians & Gynecologists (secy, 71-78, pres-elect, 78 pres, 79). *Mailing Add:* Dept of Obstet & Gynec State Univ NY Stony Brook NY 11794

STONE, MARVIN J, b Columbus, Ohio, Aug 3, 37; m 58; c 2. INTERNAL MEDICINE, ONCOLOGY. *Educ:* Univ Chicago, MS, 62, MD, 63; Am Bd Internal Med, dipl, 70, cert hemat, 72, cert med oncol, 73. *Prof Exp:* Intern & asst resident, Ward Med Serv, Barnes Hosp, St Louis, 63-65; clin assoc, Arthritis & Rheumatism Br, Nat Inst Arthritis & Metab Dis, NIH, 65-68; resident med, Parkland Mem Hosp, Dallas, 68-69; fel hemat, Univ Tex Southwestern Med Sch, 69-70, from instr to asst prof internal med, 70-73, assoc prof, 74-76; CHIEF ONCOL, DIR IMMUNOL & DIR CHARLES A SAMMONS CANCER CTR, BAYLOR UNIV MED CTR, 76- *Concurrent Pos:* Estab investr, Am Heart Asn, 70-75; mem fac & steering comt, Immunol Grad Prog, Grad Sch Biomed Sci, Univ Tex Health Sci Ctr Dallas, 75-76, adj mem, 76-; clin prof internal med, Univ Tex Southwestern Med Sch, 76-; co-dir div hemat-oncol, Baylor Univ Med Ctr, 76-, outstanding fac mem, 77-78; adj prof biol, Southern Methodist Univ, 77- *Mem:* Am Asn Cancer Res; Am Soc Hemat; Am Soc Clin Oncol; Am Asn Immunologists; fel Am Col Physicians. *Res:* Plasma cell dyscrasias and monoclonal immunoglobulins. *Mailing Add:* Charles A Sammons Cancer Ctr 3500 Gaston Ave Dallas TX 75246

STONE, MAX WENDELL, b Petersburg, Tenn, Mar 6, 29; m 50. COMPUTER SCIENCES. *Educ:* Union Univ, Tenn, BS, 49; Peabody Col, MA, 50. *Prof Exp:* High sch teacher, Ark, 50-51; scientist & supvr comput & data reduction, Rohm and Haas Co, Redstone Res Labs, 53-64; mgr corp data processing, SCI Systs, Inc, 64-73; HEAD COMPUT OPERS & ANAL SUPPORT, SYST DEVELOP CORP, 73- *Concurrent Pos:* Teacher eve div, Univ Ala, Huntsville, 54-65. *Mem:* Asn US Army; Am Defense Preparedness Asn. *Res:* Digital computer applications to problems in engineering, science and business, including management information systems, accounting functions, inventory control and data reduction; solid rocket propellant grain design; operation of large computers; management of computer center operations; management of systems software. *Mailing Add:* 826 Jacqueline Dr SE Huntsville AL 35802

STONE, MICHAEL GATES, b Midland, Tex, Oct 9, 38; div; c 1. MATHEMATICS. *Educ:* Wesleyan Univ, BA, 60; La State Univ, Baton Rouge, MS, 62; Univ Colo, Boulder, PhD(math), 69. *Prof Exp:* From asst prof to assoc prof math, 69-81, PROF MATH & STATIST, UNIV CALGARY, 81- *Mem:* Am Math Soc; Math Asn Am. *Res:* Universal algebra; lattice theory. *Mailing Add:* Dept Math Statist & Comput Sci Univ Calgary Calgary AB T2N 1N4 Can

STONE, NEWTON C, b Burnt Prairie, Ill, Jan 21, 11; m 35; c 3. METEOROLOGY, ATMOSPHERIC SCIENCES. *Educ:* Southern Ill Univ, BEd, 34; Univ Ill, MS, 35; Calif Inst Technol, BS, 40, MS, 41. *Prof Exp:* Teacher high sch, Ill, 35-39; instr meteorol, Calif Inst Technol, 40-43, asst prof, 43-48; weather engr, Krick Assocs, Inc, 48-52, dir meteorol, Krick Assocs, Inc, 52-54, V PRES, IRVING P KRICK ASSOCS, 54-; WATER RESOURCES DEVELOP CORP, 54- *Concurrent Pos:* Dir meteorol, Water Resources Develop Corp, 52-54; vpres, Am Inst Aerological Res, 54-77; dir, Krick Assocs, Can, Ltd & Krick, Inc, Tex, 59-; consult, AROWA, 54-55. *Mem:* Am Meteorol Soc; Am Geophys Union; Nat Soc Prof Engrs. *Res:* Short and long range weather forecasting; northern hemisphere research; weather modification. *Mailing Add:* 68-392 Kings Rd Apt 9 Palm Springs CA 92264

STONE, ORVILLE L, b New Albany, Ind, June 4, 21; m 45; c 3. ELECTRICAL ENGINEERING. *Educ:* Rose Polytech Inst, BS, 48; Mass Inst Technol, SM, 50. *Prof Exp:* Asst, Mass Inst Technol, 48-50; mem staff, Los Alamos Sci Lab, Univ Calif, 50-53; assoc res staff mem, Raytheon Mfg Co, 53-57; PROJ ENGR, SCHLUMBERGER WELL SERV, 57- *Concurrent Pos:* Lectr, Univ Houston, 65-68. *Mem:* Inst Elec & Electronics Engrs. *Res:* Instrumentation for nuclear research; radiation detection; semiconductor devices. *Mailing Add:* Schlumberger Well Serv PO Box 2175 Houston TX 77001

STONE, PHILIP M, b Wilkinsburg, Pa, Nov 23, 33; m 55; c 3. ATOMIC PHYSICS, PLASMA PHYSICS. *Educ:* Univ Mich, BSE, 55, MSE, 56, PhD(nuclear eng), 62. *Prof Exp:* Staff mem, Los Alamos Sci Lab, 56-63, mem advan study prog, 59-60, grad thesis prog, 60-62; staff mem, Sperry Rand Res Ctr, 63-68, head radiation sci dept, 67-68; assoc prof, Div Interdisciplinary Studies, State Univ NY Buffalo, 68-69; liaison scientist, Sperry Rand Res Ctr, 69-71, mgr systs studies dept, 71-75; physicist, Energy Res & Develop Admin, 75-77; BR CHIEF, US DEPT ENERGY, 78- *Concurrent Pos:* Fel, Univ Col, Univ London, 65-66; vis assoc prof, Univ Pittsburgh, 67-68; vis scientist, Ctr d'Etudes Nucleaires de Saclay, 74. *Mem:* AAAS; Am Phys Soc; Sigma Xi; NY Acad Sci; Inst Elec & Electronic Engrs. *Res:* Theoretical atomic and plasma physics; electron-atom scattering, photoabsorption, recombination, line shapes and intensities, nonequilibrium populations, microwave radiation from plasmas; signal processing and system analysis. *Mailing Add:* Off Fusion Energy US Dept Energy Washington DC 20545

STONE, RICHARD SPILLANE, b Huntington, NY, Sept 14, 25; m 48; c 3. PHYSICS. *Educ:* Rensselaer Polytech Inst, BS, 49, MS, 50, PhD(physics), 52. *Prof Exp:* Asst physics, Rensselaer Polytech Inst, 49-52; res assoc nuclear physics instrumentation, Knolls Atomic Power Lab, Gen Elec Co, 52-57; physicist in chg, TRIGA Proj & sect mgr, HTGR Proj, Gen Atomic Div, Gen Dynamics Corp, 57-63; vpres eng & sales, Tech Measurement Corp, 63-64; HEAD PHYSICS SECT, ARTHUR D LITTLE, INC, 64- *Mem:* Am Phys Soc; Am Nuclear Soc. *Res:* Underwater acoustics; computer applications; system analysis instrumentation design and development; reactor physics; design, construction and operation of experimental reactors; critical assemblies and in-pile experiments; nuclear power plant analysis and test. *Mailing Add:* Arthur D Little Inc 15 Acorn Park Cambridge MA 02140

STONE, ROBERT EDWARD, JR, b Spokane, Wash, Feb 20, 37; m 62; c 3. SPEECH & HEARING SCIENCES, SPEECH PATHOLOGY. *Educ:* Whitworth Col, BS, 60; Univ Ore, MEd, 64; Univ Mich, PhD(speech path, speech sci), 71. *Prof Exp:* Teacher math & sci, Oswego Pub Schs, Ore, 60-63; speech therapist, Portland Pub Schs, 63-64; instr speech, Ore State Syst Higher Educ, 64-66; speech pathologist & res asst otorhinolaryngol, Univ Mich, Ann Arbor, 70-71; instr, 71-76, asst prof, 76-78; ASST PROF OTOLARYNGOL, SCH MED, IND UNIV, 78- *Mem:* Am Speech & Hearing Asn; Asn Res in Otorhinolaryngol; assoc Acoust Soc Am. *Res:* Laryngeal physiology and effects of aberrant production of voice. *Mailing Add:* Riley Hosp A-56 1100 W Michigan Indianapolis IN 46202

STONE, ROBERT K(EMPER), b Minneapolis, Minn, June 12, 20; m 45; c 3. MECHANICAL ENGINEERING. *Educ:* Stanford Univ, AB, 41; Chrysler Inst Eng, MS, 43. *Prof Exp:* Res engr, Chrysler Corp, 41-47; engr, 47-60, supvr engr, 60-66, supvr, Engine Fuels Sect, 66-69, sr staff engr, Fuels & Asphalts Dept, 69-80, ASST TO PRES, CHEVRON RES CO, STANDARD OIL CO CALIF, 80- *Mem:* Soc Automotive Engrs; Am Soc Testing & Mat; Air Pollution Control Asn; Am Petrol Inst. *Res:* Aircraft and automotive engine testing and research; motor gasoline and diesel fuels, including evaluation of product quality, development of new or improved fuels and automotive air pollution research. *Mailing Add:* Chevron Res Co 576 Standard Ave Richmond CA 94802

STONE, ROBERT LOUIS, b Frankfort, Ky, Dec 30, 21. MICROBIOLOGY. *Educ:* Univ Ky, BS, 47, MS, 52; Ind Univ, PhD, 59. *Prof Exp:* Sr microbiologist, 49-55 & 58-72, RES MICROBIOLOGIST, LILLY RES LABS, ELI LILLY & CO, 72- *Concurrent Pos:* Lectr, Butler Univ, 68- *Mem:* AAAS; Am Soc Microbiol; NY Acad Sci. *Res:* Bacteriophage; immunology; chemotherapy; medical virology. *Mailing Add:* 5611 Brendon Way Ct Indianapolis IN 46226

STONE, ROBERT MARION, b Cleveland, Ohio, June 18, 30; m 72; c 4. PHYSICAL CHEMISTRY. *Educ:* Vanderbilt Univ, BA, 53, PhD(chem), 59. *Prof Exp:* Res chemist, E I du Pont de Nemours & Co, Seaford, Del, 59-63, res supvr, 63-69, sr supvr, 69-71, res & develop mgr, 71-80; MEM STAFF, AQUARIAN SOLOR DESIGN, 80- *Concurrent Pos:* Prof, Chattanooga Col, 60. *Mem:* Am Chem Soc; Am Asn Textile Chemists & Colorists. *Res:* Reaction kinetics and mechanisms; rocket fuels and propellants; textile chemistry; thermodynamics of high energy fuels; polymer chemistry; kinetics; polymer spinning technology; textile fiber technology. *Mailing Add:* Aquarian Solor Design PO Box 802 Brea CA 92621

STONE, ROBERT P(ORTER), b Columbus, Ohio, Apr 10, 18; m 41; c 4. ELECTRICAL ENGINEERING. *Educ:* Ohio State Univ, BEE, 40; Purdue Univ, MS, 41; Princeton Univ, PhD, 49. *Prof Exp:* Res engr, Labs Div, 41-55, eng leader, Electronc Tube Div, 55-64, SR ENGR, RCA CORP, 64- *Mem:* Sr mem Inst Elec & Electronics Engrs; Soc Info Display. *Res:* High frequency tubes; electron multipliers; solid state devices; storage tubes; electron optics. *Mailing Add:* RCA Corp Lancaster PA 17604

STONE, ROBERT SIDNEY, b Fond du Lac, Wis, Feb 16, 23; m 48; c 1. PHYSICS, NUCLEAR ENGINEERING. *Educ:* Calif Inst Technol, BS, 48. *Prof Exp:* Jr elec engr, 48-50, develop engr, 50-54, physicist, 54-64, GROUP LEADER REACTOR ANAL, OAK RIDGE NAT LAB, 64- *Mem:* Am Nuclear Soc; Soc Comput Simulation. *Res:* Reactor kinetics as related to safety and control; environmental systems; analog, digital and hybrid computer programs; reactor design reviews; control studies of energy systems. *Mailing Add:* Reactor Controls Dept Bldg 3500 Oak Ridge Nat Lab PO Box X Oak Ridge TN 37830

STONE, ROBERT WILLIAM, b Redland, Ore, Apr 17, 10; m 35; c 3. MICROBIOLOGY. *Educ:* Ore State Col, BS, 32; Iowa State Univ, PhD(bact), 36. to prof, 37-74, head dept bact, 48-70, chmn div biol sci, 60-64, EMER PROF BACT, PA STATE UNIV, 74- *Concurrent Pos:* Nat Heart Found fel, Inst Enzyme Res, Univ Wis, 50-51; mem adv comt, Microbiol Sect, Off Naval Res, 55-60 & Div Biol & Agr, Nat Res Coun, 60-70; trustee, Am Type Cult Collection, 66-72. *Mem:* Acad Microbiol; Soc Indust Microbiol (vpres, 65-66). *Res:* Oxidative metabolism of microorganisms; iron-oxidizing bacteria; mine drainage. *Mailing Add:* 203 Frear Lab Pa State Univ University Park PA 16802

STONE, SAMUEL ARTHUR, b Keene, NH, Sept 10, 14; m 40; c 2. MATHEMATICS. *Educ:* Univ NH, BS, 36, MS, 37; Boston Univ, PhD(physics), 53. *Prof Exp:* Instr math, Univ NH, 37-40, Mass Nautical Acad, 40-41 & Northeastern Univ, 41-45; asst lens designer, Polaroid Corp, Mass, 45-48; instr math, 48-53, prof & head depts, 57-63, dean col arts & sci, 63-69, COMMONWEALTH PROF MATH, SOUTHEASTERN MASS UNIV, 69- *Mem:* Am Math Soc; Math Asn Am; Am Asn Physics Teachers. *Res:* Mathematical analysis of non-linear stretch; vibration spectra of ethylene oxide. *Mailing Add:* Dept of Math Southeastern Mass Univ North Dartmouth MA 02747

STONE, SANFORD HERBERT, b New York, NY, Sept 9, 21; m 53; c 3. IMMUNOLOGY. *Educ:* City Col New York, BS, 47; Univ Paris, DSc, 51. *Prof Exp:* NIII res fel, Sch Med, Johns Hopkins Univ, 51-52; res asst immunol, New York Med Col, 53; asst, Appl Immunol Div, Pub Health Res Inst, New York, 54-57; head sect natural & acquired resistance, Lab Immunol, 57-62, head sect allergy & hypersensitivity, 63-69, head immunol sect, Lab Microbiol, 70-74, head immunol sect, OSD, 74-79, HEAD, EXP AUTOIMMUNITY SECT, LAB MICROBIAL IMMUNITY, NAT INST ALLERGY & INFECTIOUS DIS, 79- *Concurrent Pos:* Prof lectr, Howard Univ, 61-75. *Mem:* AAAS; Am Asn Immunologists; Am Asn Pathologists; Reticuloendothelial Soc; Fr Soc Microbiol. *Res:* Tissue antigens and antibodies; mechanism of hypersensitivity; autoimmunity; transplantation immunity. *Mailing Add:* Bldg 5 Rm 235 Nat Inst of Allergy & Infectious Dis Bethesda MD 20205

STONE, SHELDON LESLIE, b Brooklyn, NY, Feb 14, 46; m 71; c 3. HIGH ENERGY PHYSICS. *Educ:* Brooklyn Col, BS, 67; Univ Rochester, PhD(physics), 72. *Prof Exp:* Res assoc, Vanderbilt Univ, 72-73, asst prof, Dept Physics, 73-79; SR RES ASSOC, LAB NUCLEAR STUDIES, CORNELL UNIV, 79- *Concurrent Pos:* Vis fel, Lab Nuclear Studies, Cornell Univ, 77-78. *Mem:* Am Phys Soc; Sigma Xi. *Res:* Elementary particle interactions. *Mailing Add:* Lab Nuclear Studies Wilson Lab Cornell Univ Ithaca NY 14853

STONE, SIDNEY NORMAN, b Rochester, NY, May 11, 22; m 51; c 2. OPTICAL PHYSICS, ASTROPHYSICS. *Educ:* Univ Calif, BA, 51, MA, 52, PhD(astron), 57. *Prof Exp:* Physicist, Ballistic Res Lab, Aberdeen Proving Ground, Md, 44-49; asst astron, Univ Calif, 53-54, STAFF MEM, LOS ALAMOS NAT LAB, UNIV CALIF, 57- *Mem:* Am Astron Soc. *Res:* Spectroscopy; optical instrumentation; spectroscopic binary stars; physics of the upper atmosphere; photographic sensitometry; high speed photography; radiation dosimetry. *Mailing Add:* Los Alamos Nat Lab Univ Calif MS 466 Box 1663 Los Alamos NM 87545

STONE, SOLON ALLEN, b Lakeview, Ore, Sept 30, 28; m 49, 78; c 5. ELECTRICAL ENGINEERING. *Educ:* Ore State Col, BS, 52. *Prof Exp:* Mem tech staff, Bell Tel Labs, NJ, 52-56; asst prof elec eng, 56-64, asst to dean, 66-71, PROF ENG, ORE STATE UNIV, 61-, ASST DEAN, SCH ENG, 71- *Mem:* Inst Elec & Electronics Engrs. *Mailing Add:* Sch of Eng Ore State Univ Corvallis OR 97331

STONE, STANLEY S, b Old Forge, Pa, Apr 4, 21; m 50; c 4. BIOCHEMISTRY, IMMUNOCHEMISTRY. *Educ:* Loyola Col, Md, BS, 50; Georgetown Univ, MS, 53, PhD(biochem), 57. *Prof Exp:* Biochemist, USDA, 49-52; biochemist, NIH, 52-57; biochemist, Plum Island Animal Dis Lab, 57-62 & 64-66, EAfrican Vet Res Lab, 62-64, EAfrican Vet Res Orgn, 66-70 & Plum Island Animal Dis Lab, 70-71, head biochem biophys, Nat Animal Dis Ctr, 72-78, DIR, FAR EASTERN REGIONAL RES OFF, USDA, INDIA, 78- *Concurrent Pos:* Proj mgr, Vet Res Inst, Foreign Agr Orgn, Pakistan, 81. *Mem:* Am Chem Soc; Am Asn Immunologists; Am Soc Microbiol; NY Acad Sci; Reticuloendothelial Soc. *Res:* Isolation and characterization of immunoglobulins from farm domestic animals, particularly immunoglobulins of the exocrine secretions; reactions of immunoglobulins with viral antigens. *Mailing Add:* USDA Nat Animal Dis Ctr Ames IA 50010

STONE, WILLIAM ELLIS, b Colton, Calif, Jan 22, 11; m 41; c 3. PHYSIOLOGY. *Educ:* Calif Inst Technol, BS, 33; Univ Minn, PhD(physiol chem), 39. *Prof Exp:* Coxe Mem fel, Lab Neurophysiol, Yale Univ, 39-40; res assoc surg, Col Med, Wayne Univ, 40-47, from instr to asst prof physiol chem, 41-47; from asst prof to prof, 47-76, EMER PROF PHYSIOL, UNIV WIS-MADISON, 76- *Mem:* Am Physiol Soc; Am Epilepsy Soc. *Res:* Chemical physiology fo the brain. *Mailing Add:* Dept Physiol Univ Wis Madison WI 53706

STONE, WILLIAM HAROLD, b Boston, Mass, Dec 15, 24; m 48; c 3. GENETICS, IMMUNOLOGY. *Educ:* Brown Univ, AB, 48; Univ Maine, MS, 49; Univ Wis, PhD(genetics, biochem), 53. *Prof Exp:* Lab asst biol, Brown Univ, 46-47; asst bact & genetics, Jackson Mem Lab, 47-48; asst, 48-49, from instr to assoc prof, 49-62, PROF GENETICS & MED GENETICS, UNIV WIS-MADISON, 62- *Concurrent Pos:* Consult, Wis Alumni Res Found, 54; Bell Tel Co & Am Inst Biol Sci Films; NIH res fel, 60 & 70; mem expert panel blood group scientists, Food & Agr Orgn, 63-65; ed, Immunogenetics Letter, 66 & J Transfusion, 69-; NIH res fel, Univ Barcelona, 70; mem comt vet med sci, Nat Res Coun, 75-, comt aging in primates & chmn, Inst Lab Animal Sci. *Honors & Awards:* Ivanov Medal, USSR Acad Sci, 74. *Mem:* AAAS; Genetics Soc Am; Soc Human Genetics; Am Asn Immunologists; Transplantation Soc. *Res:* Immunogenetics and immunochemical studies of antigens; hybridema technology and recombinant DNA studies on interspecific gene hemologies; immunology of fertility and sterility; transplantation and tolerance; genetics of primates. *Mailing Add:* Lab Genetics Univ Wis Madison WI 53706

STONE, WILLIAM JACK HANSON, b Pearland, Tex, Dec 28, 32; m 53; c 2. PLANT PATHOLOGY, WEED SCIENCE. *Educ:* Tex A&M Univ, BS, 55, MS, 57; Purdue Univ, PhD(plant path), 63. *Prof Exp:* Res plant pathologist, USDA, 57-59; asst plant pathologist, Univ Ariz, 63-66; res & develop pathologist, 66, HEAD FLA SUBSTA, UPJOHN CO, 66- *Mem:* Am Phytopath Soc. *Res:* Pesticides for agricultural uses. *Mailing Add:* 455 NW 11th Ave Boca Raton FL 33432

STONE, WILLIAM LAWRENCE, b New York, NY, Oct 26, 44; m 68; c 2. LIPID METABOLISM. *Educ:* State Univ NY Stony Brook, BS, 55, PhD(biol), 73; Marshall Univ, WVa, MS, 68. *Prof Exp:* Phys chemist thermodyn, Dow Chem Co, Mich, 65; teacher chem, Marshall Univ Lab Sch, WVa, 58; grad asst biol, State Univ NY, Stony Brook, 68-72, grad res fel protein chem, 73; res assoc biochem, Med Sch, Duke Univ, NC, 73-75; asst res chemist nutrit, Univ Calif, Santa Cruz, 75-78; ASST PROF BIOMED SCI, MEHARRY MED COL, NASHVILLE, 78- *Concurrent Pos:* Am Heart Asn investr, Meharry Med Col, Nashville, 80-, prin investr, NIH grant, 80 *Mem:* Biophys Soc; AAAS. *Res:* Oxidative metabolism and its pathophysiological consequences in animals, humans and in in-vitro tissue cultures; lipid peroxidation and antioxidant nutrients on cardiovascular disease, particularly atherosclerosis. *Mailing Add:* Div Biomed Sci Meharry Med Col Nashville TN 37208

STONE, WILLIAM ROSS, b San Diego, Calif, Aug 26, 47; m 70; c 1. APPLIED PHYSICS, COMPUTER SCIENCE. *Educ:* Univ Calif, San Diego, BA, 67, MS, 73, PhD(appl physics & info sci), 73. *Prof Exp:* Sr physicist electromagnetic field interaction, Gulf Gen Atomic Co, 69-72, sr engr computerized mgt info syst, 72-73; sr scientist ionspheric physics, Optical Propagation & Inverse Scattering Theory, Megatek Corp, 73-80; PRIN PHYSICIST & LEADER, INVERSE SCATTERING GROUP,

OPTICAL PROPAGATION, IONOSPHERIC PHYSICS, OPTICAL PROPAGATION, IRT CORP, 80- *Concurrent Pos:* Pres, Stoneware Ltd, 76-; mem comn B, US Nat Comt, Int Union Radio Sci, 76, Comn G, 78. *Mem:* Optical Soc Am; Inst Elec & Electronics Engrs; Asn Comput Mach; Soc Explor Geophysicists. *Res:* Electromagnetic wave and optical propagation in the atmosphere, ionosphere and inhomogeneous and scattering media; electromagnetic theory and inverse scattering; geophysical remote probing; nuclear electromagnetic pulse generation and interaction; interactive computer systems for computation, display, management, and control. *Mailing Add:* IRT Corp 1446 Vista Claridad La Jolla CA 92037

STONEBRAKER, PETER MICHAEL, b Glendale, Calif, Apr 18, 45; m 74. CHEMISTRY. *Educ:* Whitworth Col, Spokane, Wash, BS, 67; Univ Wash, PhD(org chem), 73. *Prof Exp:* Res chemist, Chevron Res Co, Standard Oil Calif, 73-76, prod develop specialist oronite additives, Chevron Chem Co, 76-78, supvr, Engine Lubrication Div, 78-80. *Mem:* Soc Automotive Engrs; Am Chem Soc. *Res:* Synthesis lubricating oil additives; additive formulation of crankcase engine oils; reaction mechanisms of heterocycles. *Mailing Add:* 3738 Carol St Pinole CA 94564

STONEBURNER, DANIEL LEE, b Zanesville, Ohio, July 4, 45; m 71; c 2. MARINE SCIENCE, ZOOLOGY. *Educ:* Ind State Univ, BS, 67; Iowa State Univ, PhD(plant ecol), 70. *Prof Exp:* Regional ecologist, Nat Park Serv, Southeast Region, 74-78; res ecologist, Nat Park Serv, Univ Ga, 78-81; SR RES ECOLOGIST, NAT PARK SERV, COLO STATE UNIV, 81- *Concurrent Pos:* Invited consult, Nat Marine Fisheries Sea Turtle Recovery Team 79- *Mem:* Ecol Soc Am; Am Soc Limnol & Oceanog; Am Soc Ichthyologists & Herpetologists; Int Asn Crenobiologists. *Res:* Development and application of biotelemetry equipment and techniques for marine freshwater and terrestrial organisms; heavy metal analyses of marine, terrestrial and freshwater organism tissues; freshwater and marine ecology; animal behavior and ecosystems modeling. *Mailing Add:* NREL Colo State Univ Fort Collins CO 80523

STONECYPHER, ROY W, b Atlanta, Ga, Mar 20, 33; m 54; c 3. FORESTRY, GENETICS. *Educ:* NC State Univ, BS, 59, PhD(forestry), 66. *Prof Exp:* Proj leader, Int Paper Co, 63-67, res forester, 67-70; assoc prof forest genetics, Okla State Univ, 70-72; quant geneticist, Forestry Res Ctr, Weyerhauser Co, 72-80. *Concurrent Pos:* Adj asst prof, NC State Univ, 67-70, adj prof, 76-; affil assoc prof, Univ Wash, 73-80, affil prof, 80- *Mem:* Soc Am Foresters; Sigma Xi. *Res:* Quantitative genetics work in pine populations; applied forest tree breeding; statistical analyses of forestry related research using electronic computers. *Mailing Add:* Weyerhauser Co Forestry Res Ctr 505 N Pearl St Centralia WA 98531

STONECYPHER, THOMAS E(DWARD), b Savannah, Ga, June 20, 34; m 56; c 3. CHEMICAL ENGINEERING. *Educ:* Ga Inst Technol, BS, 55, PhD(chem eng), 61. *Prof Exp:* Res asst, Eng Exp Sta, Ga Inst Technol, 55-58; engr, Redstone Res Labs, Rohm & Haas Co, 58-61, head appl thermodyn, 61-66, head eng serv, 66-69; prod mgr, Micromedic Systs, Inc, 70-76; DIR ENG, ENG LABS, ROHM & HAAS CO, 76- *Res:* Medical instrumentation; engineering design; management. *Mailing Add:* Rohm & Haas Co Eng Labs PO Box 3150 Huntsville AL 35810

STONEHAM, RICHARD GEORGE, b Chicago, Ill, Feb 22, 20. MATHEMATICS. *Educ:* Ill Inst Technol, BSc, 42; Brown Univ, ScM, 44; Univ Calif, Berkeley, PhD(math), 52. *Prof Exp:* Instr math, Univ Ill, 46-47; asst, Univ Calif, 47-49, Off Naval Res Proj, 51, jr res mathematician, 52, lectr, univ, 51-52, instr math, 52, asst prof, 55-58, mathematician, radiation lab, 54; asst prof math, San Diego State Col, 53-54; lectr math, 59-61, from asst prof to prof, 61-77, EMER PROF MATH, CITY COL, CITY UNIV NEW YORK, 77- *Concurrent Pos:* Mathematician, Ramo-Wooldridge Corp, 54-55. *Mem:* Am Math Soc; Math Asn Am; Math Soc France. *Res:* Applied mathematics; mathematical theory of elasticity; partial differential equations; number theory; normal numbers, especially uniform distributions, exponential sums. *Mailing Add:* Rock Dundo Park Cave Hill St Michael Barbados 10031 West Indies

STONEHILL, ROBERT BERRELL, b Philadelphia, Pa, Feb 14, 21; m 78; c 3. INTERNAL MEDICINE, PULMONARY DISEASES. *Educ:* Temple Univ, BA, 42, MD, 45; Am Bd Internal Med, dipl, 56, re-cert, 74 & 80, cert pulmonary dis, 65; Am Bd Prev Med, dipl, 57. *Prof Exp:* Chief pulmonary physiol lab, Samson AFB Hosp, NY, 55-56, chief pulmonary dis serv, Wilford Hall, US Air Force Hosp, Lackland AFB, Tex, 56-61, chmn dept med, 61-67; PROF MED, SCH MED, IND UNIV, INDIANAPOLIS, 67- *Concurrent Pos:* Rep to Surgeon Gen, Combined Vet Admin Armed Forces Comt Pulmonary Physiol, 56-57; rep to Surg Gen & mem exec comt, Vet Admin Armed Forces Coccidioidomycosis Coop Study Group, 58-65. *Mem:* Fel Am Col Physicians; fel Am Col Chest Physicians; fel Royal Soc Med; fel Am Col Prev Med. *Res:* Aerospace medicine. *Mailing Add:* Ind Univ Sch of Med 1100 W Michigan St Indianapolis IN 46202

STONEHOUSE, HAROLD BERTRAM, b Eng, Apr 13, 22; nat US; m 50; c 4. GEOCHEMISTRY. *Educ:* Univ London, BSc, 43; Univ Toronto, PhD, 52. *Prof Exp:* Geologist, Ex-Lands, Nigeria, WAfrica, 43-45; geologist, Brit Guiana Consol Goldfields, 45-46; geologist & mgr, Can-Guiana Mines, 47-48; assoc geologist, State Geol Surv, Univ Ill, 54-55; from asst prof to assoc prof, 55-74, PROF GEOL & ASST CHMN DEPT, MICH STATE UNIV, 74- *Mem:* Geol Soc Am. *Res:* Mineralogy; economic geology; earth science education. *Mailing Add:* Dept Geol Mich State Univ East Lansing MI 48823

STONEKING, JERRY EDWARD, b Cincinnati, Ohio, July 12, 42; m 67. ENGINEERING MECHANICS. *Educ:* Ga Inst Technol, BS, 65; Univ Ill, Urbana, MS, 66, PhD(theoret & appl mech), 69. *Prof Exp:* Asst prof gen eng, Univ Ill, 69-70; asst prof civil eng, Clarkson Col Technol, 70-74; assoc prof, 75-80, PROF ENG SCI & MECH, UNIV TENN, 80- *Mem:* Am Soc Civil Engrs; Am Soc Mech Engrs. *Res:* Structural mechanics; numerical methods. *Mailing Add:* Dept of Eng Sci & Mech Univ of Tenn Knoxville TN 37916

STONEMAN, DAVID MCNEEL, b Madison, Wis, Oct 11, 39; m 64; c 2. MATHEMATICAL STATISTICS. *Educ:* Univ Wis, BS, 61, MS, 63, PhD(statist), 66. *Prof Exp:* Math statistician, Forest Prod Lab, Forest Serv, USDA, 64-66; asst prof math & statist, 66-69, assoc prof math, 69-75, PROF MATH, UNIV WIS-WHITEWATER, 75- *Mem:* Math Asn Am; Am Statist Asn. *Res:* Experimental design. *Mailing Add:* Dept of Math Univ of Wis Whitewater WI 53190

STONER, ADAIR, b Oklahoma City, Okla, Oct 15, 28; m 53; c 2. ENTOMOLOGY. *Educ:* Okla State Univ, BS, 56, MS, 60. *Prof Exp:* Entomologist, Pest Control Div, 58-60, entomologist, Western Cotton Insect Invests, Cotton Insect Br, Entom Res Div, 60-67, res entomologist, 67-72, res entomologist, Western Cotton Res Lab, 72-75, RES ENTOMOLOGIST, HONEY BEE PESTICIDES/DIS RES, SCI & EDUC ADMIN-AGR RES, USDA, 75- *Mem:* Entom Soc Am. *Res:* Effects of pesticides on honey bees. *Mailing Add:* Honey Bee Pesticides/Dis Res USDA Univ Sta Box 3168 Laramie WY 82071

STONER, ALLAN K, b Muncie, Ind, July 6, 39; m 62; c 2. HORTICULTURE. *Educ:* Purdue Univ, West Lafayette, BS, 61, MS, 63; Univ Ill, PhD(hort), 65. *Prof Exp:* Horticulturist, Crops Res Div, Plant Indust Sta, USDA, Md, 65-71, HORTICULTURIST, VEG LAB, AGR RES CTR, USDA, 71-, CHMN, PLANT GENETICS & GERMPLASM INST, 81- *Mem:* Am Soc Hort Sci. *Res:* Vegetable breeding and production; breeding of tomatoes. *Mailing Add:* Plant Genetics & Germplasm Inst USDA Agr Res Ctr-W Beltsville MD 20705

STONER, ALLAN WILBUR, b Tipton, Ind, Sept 15, 31; m 58; c 3. PHYSICAL CHEMISTRY. *Educ:* Ind Univ, BS, 53; Univ Calif, PhD(chem), 56. *Prof Exp:* Res scientist, Res Ctr, 56-58, res scientist, Indust Reactor Labs, 58-60, fiber develop mgr, Fiber & Textile Div, 60-66, plant mgr, NC, 66-69, mgr res & develop, Plastic Prod, Ind, 69-71, dir res & develop, Plastic & Indust Prod Div, Oxford Mgt & Res Ctr, 71-73, DIR MKT, INDUST PROD DIV, OXFORD MGT & RES CTR, UNIROYAL, INC, 73- *Mem:* Am Chem Soc. *Res:* Nuclear physics and spectroscopy; radiochemistry; application of tracers; radiation and polymer chemistry; physical properties of fibers and elastomeric materials. *Mailing Add:* Oxford Mgt & Res Ctr Uniroyal Inc Middlebury CT 06762

STONER, ELAINE CAROL BLATT, b New York, NY, Dec 31, 39; m 65; c 2. PHYSICAL CHEMISTRY. *Educ:* Brooklyn Col, BS, 61; Univ Calif, Berkeley, PhD(chem), 64. *Prof Exp:* NIH fel, Univ Wis, 64-65; asst ed electrochem & anal chem elec phenomena, 65-68, assoc ed elec phenomena, 68-69, sr assoc indexer elec phenomena, 69-75, SR ED ELEC PHENOMENA, CHEM ABSTR SERV, AM CHEM SOC, 75- *Mem:* Am Chem Soc. *Res:* Nuclear magnetic resonance of exchange rates of ligands in coordination complexes; solid state physics; semiconductors; superconductors; electric phenomena; magnetic phenomena. *Mailing Add:* Chem Abstr Serv Dept 57 Columbus OH 43210

STONER, GARY DAVID, b Bozeman, Mont, Oct 25, 42; m 69; c 2. CARCINOGENESIS, TOXICOLOGY. *Educ:* Mont State Univ, BS, 64; Univ Mich, MS, 68, PhD(microbiol), 70. *Prof Exp:* Asst res scientist, Univ Calif, San Diego, 70-72, assoc res scientist, 72-75; cancer expert, Nat Cancer Inst, 76-79; ASSOC PROF PATH, MED COL OHIO, 79- *Concurrent Pos:* Consult, Nat Heart Lung & Blood Inst, 74-, Environ Protection Agency & Cancer Inst , 79-, Nat Toxicol Prog, 81-; lectr, W Alton Jones Crell Sci Ctr, 78-; mem, NIH Study Sect, 81-, Am Cancer Soc Study Sect, Ohio, 82-; prin investr grants, Nat Cancer Inst, Environ Protection Agency & US Army Res & Develop Command. *Mem:* Am Asn Cancer Res; Am Tissue Culture Asn; Am Asn Pathologists; Am Soc Cell Biol; AAAS. *Res:* Carcinogenesis studies in human and animal model respiratory and esophageal tissues; carcinogen metabolism, mutagenesis; invitro transformation of epithelial cells. *Mailing Add:* Dept Path Med Col Ohio 3000 Arlington Ave Toledo OH 43699

STONER, GEORGE GREEN, b Wilkinsburg, Pa, Jan 29, 12; m 40; c 3. METRIC SYTSTEM, METROLOGY. *Educ:* Col Wooster, AB, 34; Ohio State Univ, AM, 36; Princeton Univ, PhD(org chem), 39. *Prof Exp:* Res chemist, Wallace Labs, 39 & Columbia Chem Div, Pittsburgh Plate Glass Co, 39-42; res engr, Battelle Mem Inst, 42-48; res chemist, Gen Aniline & Film Corp, 48-50, group leader, 50-51, res fel, 52-56; mgr prod develop, Avon Prod, Inc, 56-65; supvr patent liaison, J P Stevens & Co, Inc, 65-70, mgr info serv, 70-75; RES ASSOC, TEXTILE RES INST, PRINCETON, NJ, 75- *Concurrent Pos:* Instr, Ohio State Univ, 47-48. *Mem:* Fel AAAS; Am Chem Soc; fel Am Inst Chemists; Sch Sci Math Asn; US Metric Asn. *Res:* Fat acids; tall oil; plasticizers; organic sulfur chemistry; alkyl diselenides; Reppe chemistry; photosensitizing dyes; allyl resins; polyethylene; hydrocarbon oxidation; peroxides; technical writing; textile flammability; metric system; leather preservation; cosmetics; fiber modification. *Mailing Add:* 2 Parkside Dr Suffern NY 10901

STONER, GLENN EARL, b Springfield, Mo, Oct 26, 40; m 62; c 3. ELECTROCHEMISTRY. *Educ:* Univ Mo-Rolla, BS, 62, MS, 63; Univ Pa, PhD(chem), 68. *Prof Exp:* Sr scientist mat sci, Sch Eng, Univ Va, 68-71; vis assoc prof chem, Univ Mo-Rolla, 71; lectr chem eng, Univ Va, 71-72, sr scientist mat sci, 72-73; vis assoc prof electrochem, Fac Sci, Univ Rouen, France, 73-74; res assoc prof, 74-77, ASSOC PROF MAT SCI, UNIV VA, 77- *Concurrent Pos:* Consult, Owens-Ill, Inc, 75- *Honors & Awards:* Cert Recognition, NASA, 75. *Mem:* Electrochem Soc. *Res:* Applied research in bioelectrochemistry and biomaterials research; interaction with industry towards development of innovative concepts. *Mailing Add:* Dept of Mat Sci Univ of Va Charlottesville VA 22904

STONER, GRAHAM ALEXANDER, b Saginaw, Mich, June 13, 29; m 55; c 4. ANALYTICAL CHEMISTRY, AGRICULTURAL CHEMISTRY. *Educ:* Univ Mich, BS, 51, MS, 52; Tulane Univ La, PhD(chem), 56. *Prof Exp:* Chemist, Dow Chem Co, 55-58, proj leader, 58-60; chemist, Ethyl Corp, 60-62; mgr anal chem, Bioferm Div, Int Minerals & Chem Corp, Calif, 62-64, assoc dir anal labs, Chem Div, 64-67; dir anal & tech serv, IMC Growth Sci Ctr, Ill, 67-69; plant mgr, Infotronics Corp, Tex, 69-70; dir res & develop spec prod div, Kennecott Copper Corp, 70-74; vpres technol, 74-75, vpres, 75-79, SR VPRES MKT & DEVELOP, KOCIDE CHEM CORP, 79- *Concurrent Pos:* Guest scientist, Brookhaven Nat Lab, 56-57. *Mem:* AAAS; Am Chem Soc; Sigma Xi; Hyacinth Control Soc; NY Acad Sci. *Res:* Pesticide research, testing, registration, formulation; governmental regulations; analytical-physical chemistry; enzymatic methods of analysis; automated analysis; radiochemistry. *Mailing Add:* 12701 Almeda Rd Houston TX 77045

STONER, JOHN CLARK, b Toledo, Ohio, Feb 26, 33; m 54; c 2. VETERINARY MEDICINE. *Educ:* Ohio State Univ, DVM, 60. *Prof Exp:* Clin res vet, Agr Div, Am Cyanamid Co, NJ, 60-63; sr res vet, Ciba Res Farm, 63-69; asst dir animal health documentation, Squibb Agr Res Ctr, 69-71, DIR VET PROFESSIONAL & REGULATORY AFFAIRS, E R SQUIBB & SONS, INC, 71- *Mem:* Am Vet Med Asn; Am Asn Indust Vet. *Res:* Clinical research for animal health pharmaceuticals and drug regulatory affairs. *Mailing Add:* E R Squibb & Sons Inc PO Box 4000 Princeton NJ 08540

STONER, JOHN OLIVER, JR, b Milton, Mass, Oct 4, 36; m 60; c 4. ATOMIC SPECTROSCOPY. *Educ:* Pa State Univ, BS, 58; Princeton Univ, MA, 59, PhD(physics), 64. *Prof Exp:* Res assoc physics, Univ Wis, 63-66, asst prof, 66-67; from asst prof to assoc prof, 67-76, PROF PHYSICS, UNIV ARIZ, 76- *Concurrent Pos:* Mem comt line spectra, Nat Res Coun, 75- *Mem:* Am Phys Soc; AAAS; Optical Soc Am. *Res:* Atomic and beam-foil spectroscopy; atomic beam and other techniques for producing narrow spectral lines. *Mailing Add:* Dept of Physics Univ of Ariz Tucson AZ 85721

STONER, LARRY CLINTON, b Mt Union, Pa, May 17, 43; m 66; c 2. PHYSIOLOGY. *Educ:* Juniata Col, BS, 65; Syracuse Univ, PhD(zool), 70. *Prof Exp:* Fel renal physiol, Nat Heart & Lung Inst, 70-72, staff fel, 72-75; ASST PROF RENAL PHYSIOL, STATE UNIV NY UPSTATE MED CTR, 75- *Concurrent Pos:* Fel, USPHS, 70-72; investr, Am Heart Asn grant, 75-; prin investr, Nat Inst Arthritis, Metab & Digestive Dis, grant, 77- *Mem:* Am Physiol Soc; Biophys Soc. *Res:* Mechanisms of ion transport. *Mailing Add:* Dept of Physiol 766 Irving Ave Syracuse NY 13210

STONER, MARSHALL ROBERT, b Kenesaw, Nebr, Sept 24, 38. ORGANIC CHEMISTRY. *Educ:* Hastings Col, BA, 60; Iowa State Univ, PhD(chem), 64. *Prof Exp:* Asst prof, 64-70, assoc prof, 70-81, PROF CHEM, UNIV SDAK, 81- *Mem:* AAAS; Am Chem Soc; Royal Soc Chem. *Res:* Synthesis and rearrangements of bicyclic compounds; intramolecular photochemical cycloaddition reactions in bicyclic compounds; photochemical reactions of alcohols with unsaturated acids. *Mailing Add:* Dept Chem Univ SDak Vermillion SD 57069

STONER, MARTIN FRANKLIN, b Pasadena, Calif, Jan 19, 42; m 63. PLANT PATHOLOGY, MYCOLOGY. *Educ:* Calif State Polytech Col, BS, 63; Wash State Univ, PhD(plant path), 67. *Prof Exp:* From asst prof to assoc prof, 67-75, PROF BOT, CALIF STATE POLYTECH UNIV, POMONA, 75- *Mem:* AAAS; Am Phytopath Soc; Am Soc Plant Physiol; Bot Soc Am; Mycol Soc Am. *Res:* Host-parasite interactions; soil-borne fungi; microbial ecology; general plant pathology and mycology. *Mailing Add:* Dept of Biol Sci Calif State Polytech Univ Pomona CA 91768

STONER, RICHARD DEAN, b Newhall, Iowa, Mar 29, 19; m 45; c 2. IMMUNOLOGY. *Educ:* Univ Iowa, BA, 40, PhD(zool), 50. *Prof Exp:* Jr scientist, 50-52, assoc med bacteriologist, 52-54, from asst scientist to scientist, 52-62, SR SCIENTIST, MED DEPT, BROOKHAVEN NAT LAB, 62- *Concurrent Pos:* Consult, Off Surgeon Gen & Dep Dir Comn on Radiation & Infection, Armed Forces Epidemiol Bd, 63- *Mem:* Am Inst Biol Sci; Am Soc Microbiol; Radiation Res Soc; Am Soc Parasitol; Am Soc Exp Pathologists. *Res:* Radiation effect upon immune mechanisms; antibody formation; cellular defense mechanism; anaphylaxis; immunity to parasitic infections. *Mailing Add:* Med Dept Brookhaven Nat Lab Upton NY 11973

STONER, RICHARD GRIFFITH, b Buffalo, NY, June 13, 19; m 46; c 3. PHYSICS, SHOCK WAVES. *Educ:* Princeton Univ, AB, 41, MA, 46, PhD(physics), 47. *Prof Exp:* Asst physics, Columbia Univ, 41-42; asst physicist, Nat Defense Res Comt, Princeton Univ, 42-46, instr physics, 47-48; from asst prof to prof, Pa State Univ, 48-63, actg head dept, 60-61; chmn dept, 63-74, PROF PHYSICS, ARIZ STATE UNIV, 63- *Concurrent Pos:* Proj scientist, Air Force Off Sci Res, Washington, DC, 62-63. *Mem:* Am Phys Soc; Am Asn Physics Teachers. *Res:* Spectroscopy; fluid dynamics; refraction of shock waves at gas boundaries and propagation of strong shocks; development of laboratory and lecture demonstration equipment. *Mailing Add:* Dept of Physics Ariz State Univ Tempe AZ 85287

STONER, RONALD EDWARD, b Indianapolis, Ind, Nov 25, 37; m 60; c 2. SOLID STATE PHYSICS. *Educ:* Wabash Col, BA, 59; Purdue Univ, MS, 61, PhD(physics), 66. *Prof Exp:* From asst prof to assoc prof, 66-74, chmn dept, 76-80, PROF PHYSICS, BOWLING GREEN STATE UNIV, 74- *Concurrent Pos:* Fulbright lectr, Sri Lanka, 80-81. *Mem:* Am Astron Soc; Am Phys Soc; Sigma Xi. *Res:* Astrophysics; computational physics; theoretical physics. *Mailing Add:* Dept of Physics Bowling Green State Univ Bowling Green OH 43403

STONER, WARREN NORTON, b Iowa City, Iowa, Apr 12, 22; m 43; c 4. VIROLOGY, ENTOMOLOGY. *Educ:* Univ Calif, BS, 43, PhD(entom), 49. *Prof Exp:* Res asst entom, Univ Calif, 46-49; asst plant pathologist, Exp Sta, Univ Fla, 49-53; entomologist & plant pathologist, Ministry Agr, Venezuela, 54; entomologist & plant pathologist, Exp Sta, Univ RI, 57-58; virologist, Minister Agr, Nigeria, 59-60; vis prof zool, Univ RI, 60; res entomologist, Northern Grain Insects Res Lab, 61-77; res entomologist, USDA-Sci & Educ Admin, Ohio Agr Res & Develop Ctr, Wooster, 77-80; MEM STAFF, GRAIN INST RES LAB, SDAK STATE UNIV, 80- *Concurrent Pos:* Plant path, Ohio State Univ. *Mem:* Entom Soc Am; Am Phytopath Soc. *Res:* Insect transmission of plant pathogens; insect ecology; economic entomology; zoogeography. *Mailing Add:* Grain Inst Res Lab SDak State Univ Brooking SD 57006

STONER, WILLIAM WEBER, b Columbus, Ohio, June 4, 44. OPTICAL PHYSICS, RADIOLOGICAL PHYSICS. *Educ:* Union Col, NY, BS, 66; Princeton Univ, PhD(physics), 75. *Prof Exp:* Scientist radiol, Machlett Labs, Raytheon, Inc, Stamford, Conn, 73-75, scientist nuclear med, Raytheon Res Div, 75-77; MEM STAFF ANALOG & DIGITAL SIGNAL PROCESSING, SCI APPLICATIONS, INC, 77- *Mem:* Optical Soc Am. *Res:* Optical and hybrid data processing. *Mailing Add:* Sci Applications Inc 3 Preston Ct Bedford MA 01730

STONES, ROBERT C, b Portland, Ore, May 19, 37; m 57; c 8. ENVIRONMENTAL PHYSIOLOGY. *Educ:* Brigham Young Univ, BS, 59, MS, 60; Purdue Univ, West Lafayette, PhD(environ physiol), 64. *Prof Exp:* From asst prof to assoc prof, 64-70, PROF PHYSIOL, MICH TECHNOL UNIV, 70-, HEAD DEPT BIOL SCI, 70- *Concurrent Pos:* Mem, Hibernation Info Exchange, 64-; NSF res grants, 67-71. *Mem:* Am Asn Higher Educ; Nat Asn Biol Teachers; Am Forestry Asn; Am Soc Mammal; Australian Soc Mammal. *Res:* Thermal regulation of hibernating species of bats; comparative and animal physiology; comparative anatomy. *Mailing Add:* Dept of Biol Sci Mich Technol Univ Houghton MI 49931

STONEY, SAMUEL DAVID, JR, b Charleston, SC, Dec 20, 39; m 59; c 2. NEUROSCIENCE. *Educ:* Univ SC, BS, 62; Tulane Univ, PhD(physiol), 66. *Prof Exp:* From instr to asst prof physiol, New York Med Col, 66-70; NIH res grant, 70, asst prof, 70-74, ASSOC PROF PHYSIOL, MED COL GA, 74- *Mem:* Am Physiol Soc. *Res:* Electrophysiological studies of the organization of motor sensory cortex and pyramidal motor systems. *Mailing Add:* Dept of Physiol Med Col of Ga Augusta GA 30902

ST-ONGE, DENIS ALDERIC, b Ste-Agathe, Man, May 11, 29; m 55; c 2. GEOMORPHOLOGY. *Educ:* St-Boniface Col, Man, BA, 51; Cath Univ, Louvain, LicSc, 57, DocSc(geog), 62. *Prof Exp:* Teacher elem sch, Sask, 51-52; teacher high sch, Ethiopia, 53-55; teacher, Col Jean de Brebeuf, Montreal, 57-58; geographer, Geog Br, Dept Mines & Technol Surv, 58-65; res scientist, Geol Surv Can, 65-68; prof geomorphol, Univ Ottawa, 68-70; res scientist, Geol Surv Can, 70-73; prof geomorphol, 73-77, vdean, Grad Sch, 77-80, PROF GEOMORPHOL, UNIV OTTAWA, 80- *Concurrent Pos:* Nat Res Coun Can-NATO fel, 61-62; part-time prof, Dept Geog, Univ Ottawa, 70-74. *Honors & Awards:* Queen Elizabeth II Silver Medal, 79; Univ de Liege Medal, 80. *Mem:* Geol Asn Can; Can Asn Geog; Int Geog Union. *Res:* Quaternary geology; geology and planning; geomorphology. *Mailing Add:* Dept of Geog Univ of Ottawa 110 Wilbrod Ottawa ON K1N 6N5 Can

STONIER, TOM TED, b Hamburg, Ger, Apr 29, 27; nat US; m 53; c 5. SCIENCE POLICY, CELL PHYSIOLOGY. *Educ:* Drew Univ, AB, 50; Yale Univ, MS, 51, PhD, 55. *Prof Exp:* Asst, Yale Univ, 51-52; jr res assoc biol, Brookhaven Nat Lab, 52-54; vis investr, Rockefeller Inst, 54-57, res assoc, 57-62; assoc prof biol, Manhattan Col, 62-71, prof biol & dir peace studies prog, 71-75; PROF SCI & SOC, UNIV BRADFORD, 75-, CHMN, GLOBAL EDUC SYSTS, 78- *Concurrent Pos:* USPHS fel, 54-56; Damon Runyon Mem fel, 56-57; consult, Living Sci Labs, 61-62, Hudson Inst, 65-69, MacMillan Co, 68, Environ Defense Fund, 68-70 & Drew Univ, 69-71; instr, New Sch Social Res, 68-70 & State Univ NY Col Purchase, 72. *Mem:* AAAS; Am Soc Plant Physiol; Fedn Am Sci (secy, 66-67); NY Acad Sci; Scand Soc Plant Physiol. *Res:* Impact of science and technology on society; cell physiology of plant growth, cancer and ageing. *Mailing Add:* Sch of Sci & Soc Univ of Bradford Bradford England

STOOKEY, GEORGE K, b Waterloo, Ind, Nov 6, 35; m 54; c 4. DENTISTRY. *Educ:* Ind Univ, AB, 57, MS, 62, PhD, 71. *Prof Exp:* Dir lab res, 63-64, asst dir, Prev Dent Res Inst, 69-72, exec secy, Oral Health Res Inst, 72-74, asst prof, 64-73, assoc prof, 73-78, assoc dir, Oral Health Res Inst, 74-81, PROF PREV DENT, SCH DENT, IND UNIV-PURDUE UNIV, INDIANAPOLIS, 64-, DIR, ORAL HEALTH RES INST, 81- *Mem:* AAAS; Int Asn Dent Res; Am Dent Asn; Am Soc Prev Dent. *Res:* Metabolism of fluoride and other trace elements in experimental animals and humans; various types of dental caries preventive measures, including fluorides and various aspects of nutrition. *Mailing Add:* RR #6 Box 254 Noblesville IN 46060

STOOKEY, STANLEY DONALD, b Hay Spring, Nebr, May 23, 15; m; c 3. PHYSICAL CHEMISTRY. *Educ:* Coe Col, AB, 36; Mass Inst Technol, PhD(phys chem), 40. *Prof Exp:* Res chemist, Corning Glass Works, 40-58, mgr fundamental chem res, 58-62, dir fundamental chem res, 62-78. *Mem:* Am Ceramics Soc; Am Chem Soc. *Res:* Glass composition; photosensitive, photochromic and opal glasses; glass ceramics. *Mailing Add:* 12 Timber Lane Painted Post NY 14870

STOOLMAN, LEO, b Chicago, Ill, Dec 1, 18; m 44; c 2. AEROSPACE ENGINEERING. *Educ:* Ill Inst Technol, BS, 41; Calif Inst Technol, MS, 42, PhD, 53. *Prof Exp:* Aerodyn engr, Consol Vultee Aircraft Corp, 42-46; sr res engr, Jet Propulsion Lab, Calif Inst Technol, 46-51; res physicist, 51-54, head aerodyn dept, 54-59, proj mgr, Falcon Gar-II Missile Prog, 59-60, mgr, Aerospace Vehicles Lab, 60-61, proj mgr surveyor lunar soft landing spacecraft, 61-64, tech dir & asst mgr, Space Systs Div, 64-69, mgr systs labs, Space & Commun Group, 69-71, DIR ENG, SPACE & COMMUN GROUP, HUGHES AIRCRAFT CO, 71- *Concurrent Pos:* Mem res comt struct loads, NASA, 58-60; vis prof, Calif Inst Technol, 70-71 & 74-76. *Mem:* Am Inst Aeronaut & Astronaut. *Res:* Aircraft performance, stability and control; vehicle guidance and control; jet propulsion; spacecraft analysis, design and project management. *Mailing Add:* 4350 Larkwood Woodland Hills CA 91364

STOOLMILLER, ALLEN CHARLES, b Battle Creek, Mich, Nov 3, 40; m 61; c 2. RESEARCH ADMINISTRATION. *Educ:* Western Reserve Univ, AB, 61; Univ Mich, MA, 63, PhD(biochem), 66. *Prof Exp:* Fel, Chicago & Ill Heart Asns, 66-68; instr pediat, Univ, 68-69, asst prof pediat & res assoc biochem, Dept Pediat & La Rabida Inst, Univ Chicago, 69-76; assoc biochemist, Eunice Kennedy Shriver Ctr Ment Retardation, 76-79; HEALTH

SCIENTIST ADMINR, DIV RES GRANTS, SPEC REV SECT, SCI REV BR, NIH, 79- *Mem:* Am Soc Biol Chemists; AAAS; Am Soc Neurochem; Sigma Xi; Soc Complex Carbohydrates. *Res:* cell culture. *Mailing Add:* Div Res Grants NIH WW 2A-15 Bethesda MD

STOOPS, CHARLES E(MMET), JR, b Grove City, Pa, Dec 17, 14; m 43; c 3. CHEMICAL ENGINEERING. *Educ:* Ohio State Univ, BChE, 37; Purdue Univ, PhD(chem eng), 42. *Prof Exp:* Plant & develop engr, Oldbury Electrochem Co, NY, 41-42; asst prof chem eng, Lehigh Univ, 42-44; process engr, Publicker Alcohol Co, Pa, 44; sr chem engr, Phillips Petrol Co, Okla, 44-47; prof chem eng & head dept, Clemson Col, 47-48; sr chem engr, Phillips Petrol Co, 48-52, proj engr, 52-54, chief chem eng develop, Atomic Energy Div, Univ Idaho, 54-55, mgr radiation chem sect, 55-67; assoc prof chem eng, 67-70, actg chmn & chmn dept, 67-72, PROF CHEM ENG, UNIV TOLEDO, 70- *Mem:* AAAS; Am Chem Soc; Am Inst Chem Engrs; Nat Soc Prof Engrs; Am Soc Eng Educ. *Res:* Mixing; aromatic alkylation; nitrogen compounds; catalysis; nuclear engineering; photochemistry; radiation chemistry. *Mailing Add:* Dept of Chem Eng Univ of Toledo Toledo OH 43606

STOOPS, JAMES KING, b Charleston, WVa, Sept 15, 37; m 62; c 2. BIOCHEMISTRY. *Educ:* Duke Univ, BS, 60; Northwestern Univ, Evanston, PhD(chem), 66. *Prof Exp:* Sr demonstr biochem, Univ Queensland, 66-67, Australian Res Comt grants fel biochem, 67-70; NIMH fel, Duke Univ, 70-71; ASST PROF BIOCHEM, BAYLOR COL MED, 71- *Mem:* Am Chem Soc. *Res:* Enzymology and protein chemistry. *Mailing Add:* Dept of Biochem Baylor Col of Med Houston TX 77030

STOOPS, R(OBERT) F(RANKLIN), b Winona, WVa, June 16, 21; m 44; c 2. CERAMIC ENGINEERING, MATERIALS SCIENCE. *Educ:* NC State Col, BSc, 49; Ohio State Univ, MSc, 50, PhD(ceramic eng), 51. *Prof Exp:* Res engr, Harbison-Walker Refractories Co, 51-52; res engr, Metall Prod Dept, Gen Elec Co, 52-57, sr res engr, 58; res prof ceramic eng, 58-81, dir, Eng Res Servs Div, 67-81, PROF & ASSOC HEAD, DEPT MAT ENG, NC STATE UNIV, 81- *Mem:* fel Am Ceramic Soc; Inst Ceramic Engrs. *Res:* Refractory oxides and carbides and combinations of these with metals; self-glazing ceramic-metal systems; effect of structure on properties of materials; nuclear fuel materials; ceramic forming processes. *Mailing Add:* Dept Mat Engr NC State Univ PO Box 5427 Raleigh NC 27650

STOPFORD, WOODHALL, b Jersey City, NJ, Feb 25, 43; m 66. INTERNAL MEDICINE, CLINICAL TOXICOLOGY. *Educ:* Dartmouth Col, BA, 65; Dartmouth Med Sch, BMS, 67; Harvard Univ, MD, 69. *Prof Exp:* ASST PROF COMMUNITY HEALTH SCI, DUKE MED CTR, DUKE UNIV, 73- *Mem:* Am Acad Occup Med; Am Occup Med Asn; Am Indust Hyg Asn. *Res:* Clinical toxicologic studies of heavy metal and chlorinated hydrocarbon exposures; pharmacokinetics of heavy metals in man. *Mailing Add:* Duke Med Ctr PO Box 2914 Durham NC 27710

STOPHER, EMMET CARSON, b Noblesville, Ind, June 5, 10; m 36; c 4. MATHEMATICS. *Educ:* Miami Univ, AB, 32; Kent State Univ, BS, 32; Univ Iowa, MS, 33, PhD(math), 37. *Prof Exp:* From asst prof to assoc prof math, Ashland Col, 37-41; asst prof math & sci, State Univ NY Teachers Col Brockport, 41-47; asst prof math, Miami Univ, 47-49; prof & head dept, Ft Hays Kans State Col, 49-57; prof, 57-79, EMER PROF MATH, STATE UNIV NY COL OSWEGO, 79- *Mem:* Am Math Soc; Math Asn Am. *Res:* Point set theory; objective tests; topology. *Mailing Add:* 5 Baylis St Oswego NY 13126

STOPHER, PETER ROBERT, b Crowborough, Eng, Aug 8, 43; m 64; c 2. CIVIL & TRANSPORTATION ENGINEERING. *Educ:* Univ London, BSc, 64, PhD(traffic studies), 67. *Prof Exp:* Res officer hwy & transp, Greater London Coun, 67-68; asst prof transp planning, Northwestern Univ, 68-70 & McMaster Univ, 70-71; assoc prof, Dept Environ Eng, Cornell Univ, 71-73; assoc prof civil eng, Northwestern Univ, 73-77, prof, 77-80; MEM STAFF, SCHIMPLER-CORRADINO ASSOC, 80- *Concurrent Pos:* Consult various industs, 69-; Nat Res Coun Can & Dept Univ Affairs Ont grants, McMaster Univ, 70-71; chmn comt on traveler behav & values, Hwy Res Bd, Nat Acad Sci-Nat Res Coun, 71-77, consult, Planning Res Corp & Int Bank Reconstruct & Develop, 72-, mem Transp Res Forum; consult, US Environ Protection Agency, 74; dir res, Transp Ctr, Northwestern Univ, 75-77; transp adv, Nat Inst Transp & Rd Res, SAfrica, 77-78. *Honors & Awards:* Fred Burgraaf Award, Hwy Res Bd, Nat Acad Sci-Nat Res Coun, 70. *Mem:* Am Soc Civil Engrs; Brit Inst Civil Engrs; Brit Inst Hwy Engrs; Royal Statist Soc; Am Statist Asn. *Res:* Transportation planning techniques; mathematical modeling of travel demand; applied statistics; survey techniques; the impact of transportation facilities on communities and the environment. *Mailing Add:* Schimpler-Corradino Assoc 300 Palermo Ave Coral Gables FL 33134

STOPKIE, ROGER JOHN, b Perth Amboy, NJ, July 17, 39; m 62; c 1. MICROBIOLOGY, BIOCHEMISTRY. *Educ:* St Lawrence Univ, BS, 61; St Louis Univ, PhD(microbial physiol), 68. *Prof Exp:* Res asst biochem & microbiol, Merck & Co, 62-64; res biochemist, 69-75, sr res & info scientist, ICI US Inc, 75-76, pharmaceut develop coordr, 76-79, DRUG DEVELOP MGR, STUART PHARMACEUT, ICI AMERICAS INC, 79- *Mem:* AAAS; Am Soc Microbiologists; Am Chem Soc; Sigma Xi; Leukemia Soc Am. *Res:* Biology of mycoplasma; information systems; enzyme regulation; pharmaceutical project management. *Mailing Add:* ICI Americas Inc Wilmington DE 19897

STORAASLI, JOHN PHILLIP, b St Paul, Minn, Jan 28, 21; m 50; c 2. MEDICINE. *Educ:* Univ Minn, BS, 44, MB, 45, MD, 46. *Prof Exp:* Res asst, AEC Proj, Sch Med, 47-48, resident, Univ Hosp, 48-50, from instr to assoc prof, 50-61, PROF RADIOL, SCH MED, CASE WESTERN RESERVE UNIV, 61-, RES ASSOC, 56-, ASSOC RADIOLOGIST, HOSP, 50- *Mem:* Radiation Res Soc; Radiol Soc NAm; Am Roentgen Ray Soc; Am Soc Therapeut Radiol; fel Am Col Radiol. *Res:* Clinical therapeutic radiology; biological effects of ionizing radiation; diagnostic and therapeutic uses of radioactive isotopes. *Mailing Add:* 2065 Adelbert Rd Cleveland OH 44106

STORB, URSULA, b Stuttgart, Ger. IMMUNOBIOLOGY. *Educ:* Univ Tobingen, MD, 60. *Prof Exp:* From asst prof to assoc prof, 72-81, PROF MICROBIOL, UNIV WASH, 81- *Concurrent Pos:* NIH res grants, 72- *Mem:* Am Asn Immunol; Am Soc Cell Biol; Asn Women in Sci. *Res:* Organization of immunoglobulin genes; control of antibody gene expression. *Mailing Add:* Microbiol & Immunol SC-42 Univ of Wash Seattle WA 98195e

STORCH, RICHARD HARRY, b Evanston, Ill, Mar 16, 37; m 63; c 2. ENTOMOLOGY. *Educ:* Carleton Col, BA, 59; Univ Ill, MS, 61, PhD(entom), 66. *Prof Exp:* Temporary asst prof entom, USDA, 65-66, asst prof, 66-69, assoc prof, 69-80, PROF ENTOM, UNIV MAINE, ORONO, 80- *Mem:* Entom Soc Am; Entom Soc Can. *Res:* Embryonic and postembryonic development of cervicothoracic structure and musculature; behavior and ecology of Coccinellidae. *Mailing Add:* Dept of Entom Univ of Maine Orono ME 04473

STORCK, ROGER LOUIS, b Brussels, Belg, Feb 22, 23; US citizen; m 49; c 1. MICROBIOLOGY, BIOCHEMISTRY. *Educ:* Indust Fermentation Inst, Brussels, MS, 46; Univ Ill, Urbana, PhD(microbiol), 60. *Prof Exp:* Asst microbiol, Indust Fermentation Inst, Brussels, 46-48, instr, 48-54 & 55-57; res assoc bact, Univ Ill, Urbana, 57-60, fel microbiol, 60-61; from asst prof to assoc prof, Univ Tex, 61-66; PROF BIOL, RICE UNIV, 66- *Mem:* AAAS; Am Soc Microbiol; Biophys Soc; Mycol Soc Am; Am Soc Biol Chemists. *Res:* Bacterial metabolism; enzymes localization; ribosomes and nucleic acids in morphogenesis; systematics and phylogeny of fungi; biochemistry and genetics of fungal morphogenesis. *Mailing Add:* Dept Biol Rice Univ Houston TX 77001

STORER, EDWARD HAMMOND, b Rockland, Maine, Mar 1, 21; m 44; c 3. SURGERY. *Educ:* Univ Chicago, SB, 43, MD, 45; Am Bd Surg, dipl, 56. *Hon Degrees:* MA, Yale Univ, 70. *Prof Exp:* Asst physiol, Univ Chicago, 43-44, from res asst to res assoc surg, 48-50; res assoc, Univ Wash, 51-55; from asst prof to prof & dir res, Col Med, Univ Tenn, Memphis, 55-69, assoc prof physiol, 63-69; PROF SURG, SCH MED, YALE UNIV, 69-, ASSOC DEAN, 74-; CHIEF SURG SERV, VET ADMIN HOSP, WEST HAVEN, 69-, CHIEF STAFF, 74- *Concurrent Pos:* Former consult, Vet Admin Hosp & US Naval Hosps, Memphis, Tenn & Blytheville AFB Hosp. *Honors & Awards:* Gold Medal, AMA, 50. *Mem:* Am Physiol Soc; Soc Univ Surgeons; Am Col Surgeons; Am Gastroenterol Asn; Am Surg Asn. *Res:* Surgical physiology of the gastrointestinal tract. *Mailing Add:* Dept Surg Vet Admin Hosp W Spring St West Haven CT 06516

STORER, JAMES E(DWARD), b Buffalo, NY, Oct 26, 27; m 49; c 3. COMPUTER DESIGN, APPLIED PHYSICS. *Educ:* Cornell Univ, AB, 47; Harvard Univ, AM, 48, PhD(appl physics), 51. *Prof Exp:* Fel, Electronics Res Lab, Harvard Univ, 51-52, lectr appl physics, 52-53, asst prof, 53-57; sr eng specialist, Appl Res Lab, Sylvania Elec Prod, Inc, Gen Tel & Electronics Corp, Mass, 57-60, sr scientist, 60-70, dir, 61-69; pres, Symbionics Consults, Inc, 70-76; CHIEF SCIENTIST COMPUT DESIGN, CSP, INC, 77- *Concurrent Pos:* Guggenheim fel, 56; mem naval warfare panel, President's Sci Adv Comt. *Mem:* Am Asn Physics Teachers; fel Inst Elec & Electronics Engrs. *Res:* Electromagnetic theory; antennas and scattering; random processes; passive network synthesis. *Mailing Add:* 69 Pleasant St Lexington MA 02173

STORER, JOHN B, b Rockland, Maine, Oct 16, 23; m 45; c 4. RADIOBIOLOGY. *Educ:* Univ Chicago, MD, 47. *Prof Exp:* Intern, Mary Imogene Bassett Hosp, Cooperstown, NY, 47-48; USPHS res fel path, Univ Chicago, 48-49, res assoc, Toxicity Lab, 49-50; staff mem, Biomed Res Group, Los Alamos Sci Lab, 50-58; staff scientist, Jacksom Mem Lab, 58-67; dep dir div biol & med, AEC, Md, 67-69; sci dir path & immunol, 69-75, dir biol div, 75-80, SR SCIENTIST, OAK RIDGE NAT LAB, 80- *Concurrent Pos:* Alt leader, Biomed Res Group & Leader Radiobiol Sect, Los Alamos Sci Lab, 52-58; mem subcomt relative biol effectiveness, Nat Coun Radiation Protection, 57-62; consult, Argonne Nat Lab, 59-67; mem, Radiation Study Section, NIH, 62-66 & 71-75, chmn, 72-75; mem adv comt, Atomic Bomb Casualty Comn, 69-74; mem subcomt radiobiol, Nat Coun Radiation Protection & Measurements, 69-, mem bd dirs, 75-80, mem sci comt, Biol Aspects of Basic Radiation Criteria, 72-80, Basic Radiation Criteria, 75- & Apportionment of Radiation Exposure, 78-; mem adv comt biol & med to AEC Sci Secy, 69-73; mem sci adv bd, Nat Ctr Toxicol Res, 72-75; mem adv comt, Radiation Effects Res Found, Nat Acad Sci, 75-80, mem sci coun, 77-80; mem, UN Sci Comt Effects Atomic Radiation, 78-80. *Honors & Awards:* E O Lawrence Award, 68. *Mem:* Radiation Res Soc; Am Soc Exp Path; Am Asn Cancer Res; Geront Soc; Soc Exp Biol & Med. *Res:* Late effects of ionizing radiation; aging. *Mailing Add:* Biol Div Oak Ridge Nat Lab Oak Ridge TN 37830

STORER, ROBERT WINTHROP, b Pittsburgh, Pa, Sept 20, 14; m 55; c 2. ZOOLOGY. *Educ:* Princeton Univ, AB, 36; Univ Calif, MA, 42, PhD(zool), 49. *Prof Exp:* Tech asst, Mus Vert Zool, Univ Calif, 41-42, mus technician, 48-49, assoc, Div Entom & Parasitol, Exp Sta, 45, asst zool, Univ, 46-48; from instr to assoc prof zool, Univ, 49-63, asst cur birds, Mus Zool, 49-56, actg dir mus zool, 79-82, PROF ZOOL, UNIV MICH, ANN ARBOR, 63-, CUR BIRDS, MUS ZOOL, 56- *Concurrent Pos:* Ed, The Auk, Am Ornith Union, 53-57, ed, Ornith Monogr, 63-70; mem comt, Int Ornith Cong, 58- *Mem:* Wilson Ornith Soc; Cooper Ornith Soc (vpres, 70); fel Am Ornith Union (pres, 70-72); Brit Ornith Union. *Res:* Avian morphology; systematics; distribution; paleontology; avian behavior. *Mailing Add:* Mus of Zool Univ of Mich Ann Arbor MI 48109

STORER, THOMAS, US citizen. MATHEMATICS. *Educ:* Univ Calif, Los Angeles, BA, 59; Univ Southern Calif, PhD, 64. *Prof Exp:* Mem, Inst Advan Study, 64-65; assoc prof, 65-80, PROF MATH, UNIV MICH, ANN ARBOR, 80- *Res:* Easy mathematics. *Mailing Add:* Dept of Math Univ of Mich Ann Arbor MI 48104

STOREY, ARTHUR THOMAS, b Sarnia, Ont, July 8, 29; m 64; c 3. ORTHODONTICS, PHYSIOLOGY. *Educ:* Univ Toronto, DDS, 53; Univ Mich, MS, 60, PhD(physiol), 64. *Prof Exp:* From instr to asst prof orthod, Sch Dent & Physiol & Sch Med, Univ Mich, 62-66; assoc prof, Fac Dent & asst prof physiol, Fac Med, Univ Toronto, 66-70, prof dent, fac dent & assoc prof physiol, 70-77; PROF & HEAD, DEPT PREV DENT, FAC DENT, UNIV MANITOBA, 77- *Mem:* Can Asn Orthod; Am Asn Orthod; Can Dent Asn; Int Asn Dent Res; Soc Neurosci. *Res:* Oral, pharyngeal and laryngeal receptors and reflexes; physiology of dental occlusion. *Mailing Add:* Fac of Dent Univ of Manitoba Winnipeg MB R3E 0W3 Can

STOREY, BAYARD THAYER, b Boston, Mass, July 13, 32; m 58; c 4. CELL PHYSIOLOGY, PHYSICAL BIOCHEMISTRY. *Educ:* Harvard Univ, AB, 52, PhD(phys org chem), 58; Mass Inst Technol, MS, 55. *Prof Exp:* Res chemist, Ion Exchange Lab, Rohm and Haas Co, 58-60, head ion exchange synthesis lab, 60-65; Nat Inst Gen Med Sci spec fel, Johnson Res Found, 65-67, asst prof phys biochem, Univ, 67-73, ASSOC PROF OBSTET & GYNEC, PHYSIOL & PHYS BIOCHEM, UNIV PA, 73- *Mem:* Am Chem Soc; Am Soc Plant Physiol; Soc Study Reproduction; Am Soc Cell Biol; Am Soc Biol Chemists. *Res:* Energy metabolism in spermatozoa; energy conservation mechanism in mitochondrial membranes. *Mailing Add:* Dept Obstet & Gynec Univ Pa Philadelphia PA 19104

STOREY, JAMES BENTON, b Avery, Tex, Oct 25, 28; m 48; c 2. POMOLOGY, PLANT PHYSIOLOGY. *Educ:* Tex A&M Univ, BS, 49, MS, 53; Univ Calif, Los Angeles, PhD(bot sci), 57. *Prof Exp:* Asst county agr agt, Tex Agr Exten Serv, 49-52, asst hort, 52-53; asst plant physiol, Univ Calif, Los Angeles, 53-57; from asst prof to assoc prof pomol, 57-74, PROF HORT, TEX A&M UNIV, 74- *Concurrent Pos:* Ed, Pecan Quart & Tex Horticulturist; exec dir, Tex Pecan Producer's Bd. *Honors & Awards:* J H Henry Award, Federated Pecan Growers Asn US. *Mem:* Fel Am Soc Hort Sci; Am Soc Plant Physiol; Int Soc Hort Sci; Am Pomol Soc; Sigma Xi. *Res:* Control of vegetative and fruiting responses in pecans; nutrition, salinity and post-harvest studies in pecans; coordinator pecan research program in Texas. *Mailing Add:* Hort Dept Tex A&M Univ College Station TX 77843

STOREY, KENNETH BRUCE, b Taber, Alta, Oct 23, 49; m 75. COMPARATIVE BIOCHEMISTRY, ENZYMOLOGY. *Educ:* Univ Calgary, BSc, 71; Univ BC, PhD(zool), 74. *Prof Exp:* Asst prof physiol, Dept Zool, Duke Univ, 74-79; ASSOC PROF BIOCHEM, DEPT BIOL, INST BIOCHEM, CARLETON UNIV, 79- *Concurrent Pos:* Fel, Dept Biochem, Sheffield Univ, 76-77. *Mem:* Am Soc Biol Chemists; Can Biochem Soc; Soc Cryobiol; AAAS. *Res:* Molecular adaptations of animals to environment, including adaptations of intermediary metabolism for anaerobiosis for survival of freezing. *Mailing Add:* Dept Biol Carleton Univ Ottawa ON K1S 5B6 Can

STOREY, ROBERT SAMUEL, b Pakenham, Ont, July 21, 30; m 53; c 4. NUCLEAR PHYSICS. *Educ:* Queen's Univ, Ont, BA, 52, MA, 54; Glasgow Univ, PhD(physics), 58. *Prof Exp:* Imperial Chem Industs fel dept natural philos, Glasgow Univ, 57-58; Nat Res Coun fel dept physics, Univ Toronto, 58-59, sci asst dept physics, 59-60; RES OFFICER, DIV PHYSICS, NAT RES COUN CAN, 60- *Concurrent Pos:* Mem accelerator safety adv comt, Atomic Energy Control Bd, 63- *Mem:* Can Asn Physicists. *Res:* Experimental low energy nuclear spectroscopy and nuclear reactions; radiation measurement and charged particle acceleration, safety of accelerator installations; interaction of radiation with matter and with atomic inner shell electrons. *Mailing Add:* 938 Elsett Dr Ottawa ON K1G 2S9 Can

STOREY, THEODORE GEORGE, b Fresno, Calif, Sept 6, 23; m 46; c 5. FORESTRY. *Educ:* Univ Calif, BS, 48, MS, 68. *Prof Exp:* Forester, Hammond Lumber Co, 48-49; forester forest influences res, 49-52, forester fire res, 52-59, forester, Southern Forest Fire Lab, 59-62, FORESTER, RIVERSIDE FOREST FIRE LAB, US FOREST SERV, 62- *Mem:* Soc Am Foresters; Am Geophys Union. *Res:* Fire management and control systems; fire behavior; forest and urban fire and blast damage from nuclear weapons; watershed management. *Mailing Add:* 1520 Ransom Pl Riverside CA 92506

STORFER, STANLEY J, b Brooklyn, NY, July 31, 30; m 56; c 2. ORGANIC CHEMISTRY. *Educ:* Polytech Inst Brooklyn, BS, 54, PhD(org chem), 60. *Prof Exp:* Jr chemist, Am Cyanamid Co, 54-56; chemist, Esso Res & Eng Co, 60-63, from sr chemist to sr res chemist, 63-73, RES ASSOC, EXXON CHEM-TECHNOL DEPT, 73- *Mem:* Am Chem Soc. *Res:* Rheology of water-soluble polymer solutions; new product applications; statistical design of experiments; solvents technical service and market development. *Mailing Add:* 24 Ten Eyck Pl Edison NJ 08817

STORHOFF, BRUCE NORMAN, b Lanesboro, Minn, Jan 2, 42. INORGANIC CHEMISTRY. *Educ:* Luther Col, Iowa, BA, 64; Univ Iowa, PhD, 69. *Prof Exp:* From asst prof to assoc prof, 68-79, admin asst head dept, 77-79, PROF CHEM, BALL STATE UNIV, 79-, HEAD DEPT, 79- *Concurrent Pos:* Fel, Ind Univ, 69-70. *Mem:* Am Chem Soc. *Res:* Organic derivatives of transition metals; chemistry of carboranes. *Mailing Add:* Dept of Chem Ball State Univ Muncie IN 47306

STORK, DONALD HARVEY, b Minn, Mar 22, 26; m 48; c 6. HIGH ENERGY PHYSICS. *Educ:* Carleton Col, BA, 48, Univ Calif, PhD(physics), 53. *Prof Exp:* Asst physics, Univ Calif, 48-51, asst, Lawrence Radiation Lab, 51-53, res assoc, 53-56; from asst prof to assoc prof, 56-64, PROF PHYSICS, UNIV CALIF, LOS ANGELES, 64- *Mem:* Fel Am Phys Soc. *Res:* Pions; K mesons; hyperons and antiprotons; production; beams; interactions; decay. *Mailing Add:* Dept of Physics Univ of Calif Los Angeles CA 90024

STORK, GILBERT (JOSSE), b Brussels, Belgium, Dec 31, 21; nat US; m 44; c 4. SYNTHETIC ORGANIC CHEMISTRY. *Educ:* Univ Fla, BS, 42; Univ Wis, PhD(chem), 45. *Hon Degrees:* DSc, Lawrence Col, 61. *Prof Exp:* Sr res chemist, Lakeside Labs, Inc, 45-46; instr chem, Harvard Univ, 46-48, asst prof, 48-53; from assoc prof to prof, 53-67, chmn dept, 73-76, EUGENE HIGGINS PROF CHEM, COLUMBIA UNIV, 67- *Concurrent Pos:* Consult, NSF, 58-61, US Army Res Off, 66-69, NIH, 67-71 & Sloane Found, 74-; various lectureships & professorships, US & abroad, 58-; Guggenheim fel, 59; mem adv bd, Petrol Res Fund, 63-66; mem comt org chem & comt postdoctoral fels, Nat Res Coun, 59-62. *Honors & Awards:* Am Chem Soc Awards, 57 & 67; Baekeland Medal, 61; Harrison Howe Award, 62; Franklin Mem Award, 66; Synthetic Org Chem Mfg Asn Gold Medal, 71; Roussel Steroid Prize, 78. *Mem:* Nat Acad Sci; Am Acad Arts & Sci; Am Chem Soc (chmn org div, 66-67); Swiss Chem Soc; Royal Soc Chem. *Res:* Total synthesis of complex structure; design of new synthetic reactions and reaction mechanisms. *Mailing Add:* Columbia Univ Dept of Chem Box 666 Havemeyer Hall New York NY 10027

STORM, CARLYLE BELL, b Baltimore, Md, Mar 2, 35; m 57; c 3. BIOINORGANIC CHEMISTRY. *Educ:* Johns Hopkins Univ, BA, 61, MA, 63, PhD(chem), 65. *Prof Exp:* NIH res fel chem, Stanford Univ, 65-66; staff fel biochem, NIMH, 66-68; from asst prof to assoc prof chem, 68-73, PROF CHEM, HOWARD UNIV, 73- *Concurrent Pos:* NIH res career develop award, 73-78; sr visitor, Inorg Chem Lab, Oxford Univ, 74-75; vis staff mem, Stable Isotope Res Resource, Los Alamos Nat Lab, NMex, 81-82. *Mem:* Am Chem Soc; Royal Soc Chem; Am Soc Biol Chemists. *Res:* Mechanism of action and structure of metal containing enzymes; inorganic reagents in biochemistry. *Mailing Add:* Dept of Chem Howard Univ Washington DC 20059

STORM, DANIEL RALPH, b Hawarden, Iowa, June 21, 44; m 66; c 3. BIOCHEMISTRY. *Educ:* Univ Wash, BS, 66, MS, 67; Univ Calif, Berkeley, PhD(biochem), 71. *Prof Exp:* Res asst biochem, Univ Calif, Berkeley, 67-71, NIH res fel, Harvard Univ, 71-72, NSF fel, 72-73; asst prof biochem, Univ Ill, Urbana, 73-78; ASSOC PROF PHARMACOL, UNIV WASH, 78- *Concurrent Pos:* Indust consult, Pharmaco Inc, 75- *Mem:* Am Chem Soc; Am Soc Biol Chemists; Am Soc Microbiol. *Res:* Structure and function of biological membranes; mechanism of enzymatic catalysis; membrane active antibiotics and molecular pharmacology at the membrane level. *Mailing Add:* Dept of Pharmacol Univ of Wash Seattle WA 98195

STORM, EDWARD FRANCIS, b Wilmington, Del, Nov 6, 29. COMPUTER SCIENCE, MATHEMATICS. *Educ:* Univ Del, AB, 59; Harvard Univ, MA, 61, PhD(appl math), 66. *Prof Exp:* Asst prof comput sci, Univ Va, 64-69; assoc prof, 69-77, PROF COMPUT & INFO SCI, SYRACUSE UNIV, 77- *Concurrent Pos:* Sr sci consult, Nat Resource Anal Ctr, 65- *Mem:* Asn Comput Mach; Asn Symbolic Logic. *Res:* Design and implementation of high-level programming languages and their application to problems in machine simulation of intelligence and to man-machine communication. *Mailing Add:* Systs & Info Sci Syracuse Univ 303 Link Syracuse NY 13210

STORM, LEO EUGENE, b Valeda, Kans, Aug 29, 28. COMPUTER SCIENCE, STATISTICS, MINI COMPUTERS. *Educ:* Okla Agr & Mech Col, BA, 53. *Prof Exp:* Seismic engr, Seismic Eng Co, 53-54; meteorologist, US Weather Bur, 54-55; mathematician, Northwestern Univ, 55; qual control engr, Metro Bottle Glass Co, 55-56; jr engr, US Testing Co, 56; assoc staff mem, Gen Precision Lab, Inc, 56-57; sr statistician, Nuclear Fuel Oper, Olin Mathieson Chem Corp, 57-61; statist qual control supvr, United Nuclear Corp, 61-62; opers analyst, United Aircraft Corp Systs Ctr, 62-67; sr sci programmer, NY Med Col, 67-70; syst analyst, Texaco Inc, 70-71; programmer analyst, Data Develop, Inc, 71-73; SR SYST ANALYST, NABISCO BRANDS, INC, 73- *Res:* Digital computer programming for management systems; statistical sample surveys; programming analysis for statistical accounting and biomedical applications; mini-computer systems for process control; material handling and management applications. *Mailing Add:* 37-14 89th St Jackson Heights NY 11372

STORM, ROBERT MACLEOD, b Calgary, Alta, July 9, 18; US citizen; m 43, 59; c 6. ZOOLOGY. *Educ:* Northern Ill State Teachers Col, BE, 39; Ore State Col, MS, 41, PhD(zool), 48. *Prof Exp:* From instr to assoc prof, 48-62, PROF ZOOL, ORE STATE UNIV, 62- *Mem:* Assoc Am Soc Ichthyologists & Herpetologists. *Res:* Natural history of cold-blooded land vertebrates. *Mailing Add:* Dept of Zool Ore State Univ Corvallis OR 97331

STORMER, HORST LUDWIG, b Frankfurt-Main, Ger, Apr 6, 49. SOLID STATE PHYSICS. *Educ:* Univ Frankfurt, BS, 70, dipl physics, 74; Univ Stuttgart, Ger, PhD(physics), 77. *Prof Exp:* Mem tech staff physics, High Magnetic Field Lab, Max Planck Inst Solid State Res, 77; consult, 77-78, MEM TECH STAFF PHYSICS, BELL LABS, AM TEL & TEL CO, 78- *Mem:* Am Phys Soc; Ger Phys Soc. *Mailing Add:* Bell Labs 600 Mountain Ave Murray Hill NJ 07974

STORMER, JOHN CHARLES, JR, b Englewood, NJ, Oct 28, 41; m 63; c 2. PETROLOGY, GEOCHEMISTRY. *Educ:* Dartmouth Col, BA, 63; Univ Calif, Berkeley, PhD(geol), 71. *Prof Exp:* Asst geologist, Climax Molybdenum Co, Colo, 67; asst prof geol, 71-77, ASSOC PROF GEOL, UNIV GA, 77- *Concurrent Pos:* Vis prof, Inst Geosci, Univ Sao Paulo, 73. *Mem:* Mineral Soc Am; Geochem Soc; Am Geophys Union; Brazilian Geol Soc. *Res:* Mineralogy and geochemistry of igneous rocks as applied to petrology; thermochemical data and methods of investigating the origin of igneous rocks, and applications to various rock suites and petrographic provinces. *Mailing Add:* Dept of Geol Univ of Ga Athens GA 30602

STORMONT, CLYDE J, b Viola, Wis, June 25, 16; m 40; c 5. GENETICS, IMMUNOLOGY. *Educ:* Univ Wis, BA, 38, PhD(genetics), 47. *Prof Exp:* Instr genetics, Univ Wis, 46-47, lectr, 47, asst prof, 48; Fulbright scholar, NZ, 49-50; asst prof, 50-54, assoc prof vet med & assoc serologist, Exp Sta, 54-59, PROF IMMUNOGENETICS, UNIV CALIF, DAVIS, 59- *Concurrent Pos:* E B Scripps fel, San Diego Zool Soc, 56-57 & 66-67. *Mem:* Genetics Soc Am; Am Soc Human Genetics; Soc Exp Biol & Med; Int Soc Animal Blood Group Res; Am Soc Nat. *Res:* Blood groups; animal blood groups and biochemical polymorphisms; genetic markers in animal blood. *Mailing Add:* Dept of Vet Med Univ of Calif Davis CA 95616

STORMS, LOWELL H, b Schenectady, NY, Feb 14, 28; div; c 3. NEUROPSYCHOLOGY. *Educ:* Univ Minn, BA, 50, MS, 51, PhD(clin psychol), 56. *Prof Exp:* Psychologist, Hastings State Hosp, Minn, 54-56; Fulbright grant, Inst Psychiat, Univ London, 56-57; from instr to prof psychiat, Neuropsychiat Inst, Univ Calif, Los Angeles, 57-71; PROF PSYCHIAT, SCH MED, UNIV CALIF, SAN DIEGO, 71- *Concurrent Pos:* Consult, Vet Admin, 64-71 & Encounters Unlimited, 68-71; psychologist, Vet Admin Hosp, San Diego, 75- *Mem:* AAAS; Am Psychol Asn; Western Psychol Asn; Int Neuropsychol Soc. *Res:* Behavior of schizophrenics; behavior therapy; clinical psychology. *Mailing Add:* Dept of Psychiat Sch of Med Univ of Calif at San Diego La Jolla CA 92037

STORMSHAK, FREDRICK, b Enumclaw, Wash, July 4, 36; m 63; c 2. REPRODUCTIVE ENDOCRINOLOGY. *Educ:* Wash State Univ, BSc, 59, MSc, 60; Univ Wis, PhD(endocrinol), 65. *Prof Exp:* Res physiologist, USDA, 65-68; asst prof physiol, 68-72, actg head, Dept Animal Sci, 74, assoc prof, 72-79, PROF PHYSIOL, ORE STATE UNIV, 79- *Concurrent Pos:* Postdoctoral trainee endocrinol, Univ Wis, 74-75; sect ed, J Animal Sci, 75-77, ed-in-chief, 82-85. *Mem:* Am Soc Animal Sci; Soc Study Fertility; Endocrine Soc; Soc Study Reproduction. *Res:* Quantitative measurement of steroid hormones of ovarian and adrenal origin; factors affecting the regression and maintenance of the corpus luteum; pituitary, ovarian and uterine interrelationships in reproduction. *Mailing Add:* Dept Animal Sci Ore State Univ Corvallis OR 97331

STORR, JOHN FREDERICK, b Ottawa, Ont, Aug 17, 15; m 42; c 1. AQUATIC ECOLOGY. *Educ:* Queen's Univ, Ont, BA, 42; Columbia Univ, MA, 48; Cornell Univ, PhD(marine ecol), 55. *Prof Exp:* Instr biol, Queen's Col, Bahamas, 42-45; asst prof physiol, Adelphi Col, 47-52; res asst prof marine ecol, Univ Miami, 55-58; ASSOC PROF ECOL & INVERT ZOOL, STATE UNIV NY BUFFALO, 58- *Concurrent Pos:* US Fish & Wildlife Serv grant, 55-57; limnol consult, Niagara Mohawk Power Corp, 63-; aquatic ecol consult, Rochester Gas & Elec Corp, 68- *Mem:* Ecol Soc Am; Am Inst Biol Sci; Am Fisheries Soc; Explorers Club; Int Soc Limnol. *Res:* Coral reef zonation; ecology of sponges of Gulf of Mexico and of benthic organisms in Lake Erie and Lake Ontario of New York. *Mailing Add:* Biol Dept State Univ of NY Buffalo NY 14266

STORROW, HUGH ALAN, b Long Beach, Calif, Jan 13, 26; m 53; c 3. PSYCHIATRY. *Educ:* Univ Southern Calif, AB, 46, MD, 50; Am Bd Psychiat & Neurol, dipl, 55. *Prof Exp:* Intern, USPHS Hosp, Baltimore, 49-50; resident, Sheppard & Enoch Pratt Hosp, Towson, Md, 50-51; staff psychiatrist, US Penitentiary Hosp, Leavenworth, Kans, 51-52; resident, USPHS Hosp, Lexington, Ky, 52-53, staff psychiatrist, 53-54; resident, Brentwood Vet Admin Hosp, Los Angeles, 54-55; instr psychiat, Sch Med, Yale Univ, 55-56; asst prof, Sch Med, Univ Calif, Los Angeles, 56-60, attend psychiatrist, Med Ctr, 57-60; assoc prof, Col Med, Univ Ky, 60-65; prof psychiat, Univ Minn, 65-66; PROF PSYCHIAT, COL MED, UNIV KY, 66- *Concurrent Pos:* Attend psychiatrist, Brentwood Vet Admin Hosp, Calif, 57-60; consult, United Cerebral Palsy Asn, Los Angeles County, Calif, 57-60, USPHS & Vet Admin Hosps, Ky, 60- *Mem:* Am Psychiat Asn; AMA; Asn Am Med Cols. *Res:* Behavior modification; teaching methods for psychiatry. *Mailing Add:* Dept of Psychiat Univ of Ky Col of Med Lexington KY 40506

STORRS, CHARLES LYSANDER, b Shaowu, Fukien, China, Oct 25, 25; US citizen; m 57; c 3. NUCLEAR ENGINEERING, TECHNICAL MANAGEMENT. *Educ:* Mass Inst Technol, BS, 49, PhD, 52. *Prof Exp:* Mem staff, Aircraft Nuclear Propulsion Dept, Gen Elec Co, 52-56, supvr initial engine test opers, 56-59, supvr flight engine test opers, 59-61, mgr reactor test opers, Nuclear Propulsion Dept, 61, SL-1 Proj, Nuclear Mat & Propulsion Opers, 61-62 & 710 Proj, 62-65; dir heavy water organic cooled reactor, Atomics Int-Combustion Eng Joint Venture, Calif, 65-67; asst dir advan reactor eng, 67-69, dir advan reactor develop, 69-71, dir projs, 71-73, dir prod eng & develop, 73-75, dir fast breeder reactor develop, 75-80, DIR ADVANCED DEVELOP, NUCLEAR POWER SYSTS, COMBUSTION ENG, INC, 80- *Mem:* AAAS; Am Nuclear Soc; Am Phys Soc. *Res:* Engineering, design and development of technology leading to the application of nuclear energy to power generation and desalination; reactor test operations; management of technical enterprises. *Mailing Add:* Nuclear Power Dept Combustion Eng Inc Windsor CT 06095

STORRS, ELEANOR EMERETT, b Cheshire, Conn, May 3, 26; m 63; c 2. BIOCHEMISTRY, MEDICAL RESEARCH. *Educ:* Univ Conn, BS, 48; NY Univ, MS, 58; Univ Tex, PhD(biochem), 67. *Prof Exp:* Asst, Boyce Thompson Inst Plant Res, 48-59, asst biochemist, 59-62; res scientist, Clayton Found Biochem Inst, Univ Tex, 62-65; res chemist, Pesticides Res Lab, USPHS, Fla, 65-67; res chemist, Gulf South Res Inst, 67-71, dir dept comp biochem, 71-77; DIR DIV COMP MAMMAL & BIOCHEM, MED RES INST, FLA INST TECHNOL, 77- *Honors & Awards:* Charles A Griffin Award, Am Asn Lab Animal Sci & Gerard B Lambert Spec Recognition Award, 75. *Mem:* Am Chem Soc; fel AAAS; fel NY Acad Sci; Am Asn Lab Animal Sci; Sigma Xi. *Res:* Armadillo in biomedical research; leprosy; biochemical individuality; analytical methods for biochemical, environmental and residue analyses; drug metabolism; mode of fungicidal, insecticidal action. *Mailing Add:* Med Res Inst Fla Inst of Technol Melbourne FL 32901

STORRY, JUNIS O(LIVER), b Astoria, SDak, Mar 16, 20; m 50; c 2. ELECTRICAL ENGINEERING. *Educ:* SDak State Col, BS, 42, MS, 49; Iowa State Univ, PhD, 67. *Prof Exp:* Mem student prog, Westinghouse Elec Corp, Pa, 42; elec engr, Bur Ships, Navy Dept, Washington, DC, 42-46; design engr, Reliance Elec & Eng Co, Ohio, 46; from instr to assoc prof, 46-64, actg dean, 71-72, PROF ELEC ENG, S DAK STATE UNIV, 64-, DEAN ENG, 72- *Mem:* Inst Elect & Electronics Engrs; Am Soc Eng Educ; Nat Soc Prof Engrs. *Res:* Digital analysis of power systems using hybrid parameters. *Mailing Add:* Col of Eng SDak State Univ Brookings SD 57007

STORTI, ROBERT V, b Providence, RI, May 14, 44. MOLECULAR BIOLOGY, BIOCHEMISTRY. *Educ:* RI Col, BA, 68; Ind Univ, MA, 70, PhD(biol), 74. *Prof Exp:* Fel biol, Mass Inst Technol, 74-78; ASST PROF BIOCHEM, MED CTR, UNIV ILL, 78- *Concurrent Pos:* NIH fel, 74-76; Muscular Dystrophy Soc fel, 77-78; Biomed Found Res fel, 78. *Mem:* Am Soc Cell Biol; AAAS; Soc Develop Biol. *Res:* Molecular biology of gene expression during eukaryotic cell growth and differentiation; transcriptional and translation control of protein synthesis. *Mailing Add:* Dept Biol Chem Med Ctr Univ of Ill Chicago IL 60612

STORTS, RALPH WOODROW, b Zanesville, Ohio, Feb 5, 33; m 60; c 3. VETERINARY PATHOLOGY. *Educ:* Ohio State Univ, DVM, 57, PhD(vet path), 66; Purdue Univ, West Lafayette, MSc, 62. *Prof Exp:* Instr vet microbiol, Purdue Univ, West Lafayette, 57-60; instr vet path, Ohio State Univ, 61-66; from asst prof to assoc prof, 66-73, PROF VET PATH, TEX A&M UNIV, 73- *Mem:* Am Vet Med Asn; Am Col Vet Path; Int Acad Path; Conf Res Workers Animal Dis. *Res:* Veterinary neuropathology including electron microscopy and cytology of normal and infected tissue cultures of nervous tissue. *Mailing Add:* Dept Vet Path Tex A&M Univ College Station TX 77843

STORTZ, CLARENCE B, b Marlette, Mich, July 23, 33; m 56; c 5. MATHEMATICS. *Educ:* Wayne State Univ, BS, 55; Univ Miami, MS, 58; Univ Mich, Ann Arbor, DEd(math), 68. *Prof Exp:* Asst prof math, Northern Mich Univ, 63-66 & Cent Mich Univ, 66-68; assoc prof, 68-72, head dept, 72-76, PROF MATH, NORTHERN MICH UNIV, 72- *Res:* General topology; history of mathematics. *Mailing Add:* Dept of Math Northern Mich Univ Marquette MI 49855

STORVICK, CLARA A, b Emmons, Minn, Oct 31, 06. NUTRITION. *Educ:* St Olaf Col, AB, 29; Iowa State Univ, MS, 33; Cornell Univ, PhD(nutrit, biochem), 41. *Prof Exp:* Instr chem, Augustana Acad, 30-32; asst, Iowa State Univ, 32-34; nutritionist, Fed Emergency Relief Admin, Minn, 34-36; asst prof nutrit, Okla State Univ, 36-38; asst, Cornell Univ, 38-41; asst prof nutrit, Univ Wash, 41-45; from assoc prof to prof, 45-72, head home econ res, 55-72, dir nutrit res inst, 65-72, EMER PROF NUTRIT, ORE STATE UNIV, 72- *Concurrent Pos:* Sabbatical leaves, Chem Dept, Columbia Univ & Inst Cytophysiol, Denmark, 52, Lab Nutrit & Endocrinol, NIH, 59 & Div Clin Oncol, Med Sch, Univ Wis, 66. *Honors & Awards:* Borden Award, Am Home Econ Asn, 52. *Mem:* Am Home Econ Asn; Am Dietetic Asn; fel Am Pub Health Asn; fel Am Inst Nutrit; fel AAAS. *Res:* Calcium, phosphorus, nitrogen, ascorbic acid, thiamine and riboflavin metabolism; nutrition and dental caries; vitamin B-6. *Mailing Add:* 124 NW 29th St Corvallis OR 97330

STORVICK, DAVID A, b Ames, Iowa, Oct 24, 29; m 52; c 3. MATHEMATICS. *Educ:* Luther Col, Iowa, AB, 51; Univ Mich, MA, 52, PhD(math), 56. *Prof Exp:* From instr to asst prof math, Iowa State Univ, 55-57; from asst prof to assoc prof, 57-66, PROF MATH, UNIV MINN, MINNEAPOLIS, 66-, ASSOC HEAD SCH MATH, 64- *Concurrent Pos:* Res assoc, US Army Math Res Ctr, Wis, 62-63. *Mem:* Am Math Soc; Math Asn Am. *Res:* Complex function theory. *Mailing Add:* Sch of Math Univ of Minn Minneapolis MN 55455

STORVICK, TRUMAN S(OPHUS), b Albert Lea, Minn, Apr 14, 28; m 52; c 4. CHEMICAL ENGINEERING, MOLECULAR PHYSICS. *Educ:* Iowa State Univ, BS, 52; Purdue Univ, PhD(chem eng), 59. *Prof Exp:* Res engr, Res Dept, Westvaco Chloro-Alkali Div, FMC Corp, 52-55; instr chem eng, Purdue Univ, 58-59; from asst prof to assoc prof, 59-72, Robert Lee Tatum prof, 72-75, BLACK & VEATCH PROF ENG, UNIV MO-COLUMBIA, 75- *Concurrent Pos:* NSF fac fel, 65-66; fel, Royal Norweg Coun Sci & Indust Res, 72-73. *Mem:* AAAS; Am Chem Soc; Am Inst Chem Engrs; Am Phys Soc. *Res:* Measurement and prediction of thermodynamic and transport properties. *Mailing Add:* Dept of Chem Eng Univ of Mo Columbia MO 65211

STORWICK, ROBERT MARTIN, b Seattle, Wash, Oct 14, 42; m 67; c 2. ELECTRICAL ENGINEERING, APPLIED MATHEMATICS. *Educ:* Calif Inst Technol, BS, 64; Univ Southern Calif, MSEE, 65, PhD(elec eng), 69; Detroit Col Law, JD, 82- *Prof Exp:* Mem tech staff, Radar & Data Processing Dept, Gen Res Corp, Calif, 69-70; STAFF RES ENGR, ELECTRONICS DEPT, GEN MOTORS RES LABS, 70- *Mem:* AAAS; Inst Elec & Electronics Engrs. *Res:* Signal processing; short-range and long-range radar systems; radar cross-section studies and analyses; statistical pattern recognition; information, coding and communication theory; networks and combinatorial systems; graph theory. *Mailing Add:* Electronics Dept Res Labs Gen Motors Tech Ctr Warren MI 48090

STORY, ANNE WINTHROP, b Haverhill, Mass. ENGINEERING PSYCHOLOGY. *Educ:* Smith Col, AB, 34; Univ Calif, Berkeley, PhD(exp psychol), 57. *Prof Exp:* Assoc engr turbine div, Gen Elec Co, 42-44; instr, Stoneleigh Jr Col, 45-46; Greenbrier Col, 46-47 & Pa State Univ, 47-50; res assoc animal behav, Jackson Mem Lab, 50-51; res analyst flight safety, Norton AFB, 51-52; teaching asst statist & psychol, Univ Calif, Berkeley, 52-57; res psychologist flight safety & space psychol, Hanscom AFB, 58-66 & NASA, 66-70; eng psychologist man-machine syst, US Dept Transp, 70-78; CONSULT, PVT PRACT, 78- *Concurrent Pos:* Assoc prof dept psychol, Univ Mass, 72-76. *Mem:* AAAS; Res Soc Am; Am Psychol Asn. *Res:* Patents held in fields of aviation collision pilot-warning and vehicle driver safety devices; visual perception; attention; man-machine systems. *Mailing Add:* The Headlands Rockport MA 01966

STORY, HAROLD S, b Catskill, NY, Oct 5, 27; m 51; c 2. SOLID STATE PHYSICS, NUCLEAR MAGNETIC RESONANCE. *Educ:* NY State Col Teachers, BA, 49, MA, 50; Univ Maine, Orono, MS, 52; Case Inst Technol, PhD(physics), 57. *Prof Exp:* Mem tech staff, Bell Tel Labs, NJ, 56-59; from assoc prof to prof physics, 59-80, physics dept chmn, 81-82, PROF ASTRON & SPACE SCI, STATE UNIV NY ALBANY, 80- *Mem:* Am Phys Soc; Sigma Xi; Am Asn Physics Teachers. *Res:* Structure, defects and conduction processes in superionic conductors, utilizing nuclear magnetic resonance. *Mailing Add:* Dept of Physics State Univ of NY Albany NY 12222

STORY, JIM LEWIS, b Alice, Tex, July 30, 31; m 58; c 4. NEUROSURGERY. *Educ:* Tex Christian Univ, BS, 52; Vanderbilt Univ, MD, 55. *Prof Exp:* From instr to asst prof neurosurg, Med Sch, Univ Minn, 61-67; PROF NEUROSURG, UNIV TEX HEALTH SCI CTR SAN ANTONIO, 67-, PROF ANAT, 77- *Concurrent Pos:* Univ fels neurol surg, Univ Minn, 56-59 & 60-61; USPHS fels anat, Univ Calif, Los Angeles, 59-60 & Univ Minn, 60-62. *Mem:* Am Asn Neurol Surgeons; Soc Neurol Surgeons; Am Col Surgeons; Neurosurg Soc Am; Am Acad Neurol Surgeons. *Res:* Intracranial pressure monitoring; etiology of brain tumors. *Mailing Add:* Div of Neurol Surg Univ of Tex Health Sci Ctr San Antonio TX 78284

STORY, JON ALAN, b Odebolt, Iowa, Apr 7, 46; m 69; c 3. BIOCHEMISTRY, NUTRITION. *Educ:* Iowa State Univ, BS, 68, MS, 70, PhD(zool), 72. *Prof Exp:* Instr zool, Iowa State Univ, 71-72; trainee lipid metab, Wistar Inst Anat & Biol, 72-74, asst prof lipid metab, 74-77; assoc prof foods & nutrit, 77-80, PROF NUTRIT PHYSIOL, PURDUE UNIV, WEST LAFAYETTE, 80- *Mem:* Am Inst Nutrit; Nutrit Soc; Sigma Xi; Am Chem Soc. *Res:* Investigation into the effects of several dietary components and age on cholesterol and bile acid metabolism as involved in development of experimental atherosclerosis. *Mailing Add:* Dept of Foods & Nutrit Purdue Univ West Lafayette IN 47907

STORY, TROY LEE, b Montgomery, Ala, Nov 11, 40. CHEMICAL PHYSICS. *Educ:* Morehouse Col, BS, 62; Univ Calif, Berkeley, PhD(chem), 68. *Prof Exp:* Mem staff & fel chem, Univ Calif, Berkeley, 69-70; fel physics, Chalmers Univ Technol, Sweden, 70-71; asst prof chem, Howard Univ, 71-77, ASSOC PROF CHEM, MOREHOUSE COL, 77- *Mem:* Am Chem Soc; Am Phys Soc. *Res:* Experimental determination of dipole moments using molecular beam resonance and deflection techniques; theoretical quantum mechanical model for the analysis of rotational distributions for reactive scattering experiments; topological analysis of composite particles. *Mailing Add:* Dept of Chem Morehouse Col Atlanta GA 30314

STORZ, JOHANNES, b Hardt/Schramberg, Ger, Apr 29, 31; US citizen; m 59; c 3. VIROLOGY, MICROBIOLOGY. *Educ:* Vet Col, Hannover, dipl, 57; Univ Munich, Dr Med Vet, 58; Univ Calif, Davis, PhD(comp path), 61; Am Col Vet Microbiol, dipl, 69. *Prof Exp:* Res assoc, Fed Res Inst Viral Dis Animals, Tübingen, Ger, 57-58; lectr vet microbiol, Univ Calif, Davis, 58-61; from asst prof to assoc prof vet virol, Utah State Univ, 61-65; assoc prof, 65-68, PROF VET VIROL, COLO STATE UNIV, 68- *Concurrent Pos:* USPHS res grant, Utah State Univ, 62-65; USPHS res grant, Colo State Univ, 66-72, WHO grant, 72-77; vis scientist, Univ Giessen, 71-72 & 78-79; consult, WHO, Geneva, 71; Alexander Humboldt award, Ger, 78. *Honors & Awards:* Andrew G Clark Award, Colo State Univ, 75, Norden Award, 78. *Mem:* AAAS; Am Soc Microbiol; Am Vet Med Asn; Conf Res Workers Animal Dis; World Asn Buiatrics. *Res:* Chlamydiology; pathogenic mechanisms in intrauterine viral and chlamydial infections; chlamydial polyarthritis; intestinal corona viral and parvoviral infections; cell biology of chlamydial infections. *Mailing Add:* Dept of Microbiol Colo State Univ Ft Collins CO 80523

STOSICK, ARTHUR JAMES, b Milwaukee, Wis, Dec 1, 14; m 37; c 3. CHEMISTRY. *Educ:* Univ Wis, BS, 36; Calif Inst Technol, PhD(struct chem), 39. *Prof Exp:* Fel, Calif Inst Technol, 39-40, instr gen chem, 40-41, Nat Defense Res Comt res assoc, 41-43, res chemist, Jet Propulsion Lab, 44-46, chief rockets & mat div, 50-56; res chemist, Aerojet Eng Corp, 43-44; assoc prof phys chem, Iowa State Col, 46-47; prof, Univ Southern Calif, 47-50; asst dir, Union Carbide Res Inst, 56-59; asst vpres, Gen Atomic Div, Gen Dynamics Corp, 59-60; sr scientist, Aerojet-Gen Corp, 60-71; asst sr vpres, United Technol Corp, 72-80; CONSULT, 80- *Concurrent Pos:* Mem rocket eng subcomt, Nat Adv Comt Aeronaut, 52-56; staff scientist, Adv Res Proj Agency, Off Secy Defense, 58-59. *Mem:* Am Chem Soc; Am Phys Soc; Am Crystallog Asn. *Res:* Molecular structures by diffraction; physical chemistry as related to molecular structures; propellants; high temperature chemistry; metallurgy. *Mailing Add:* 1153 Lime Dr Sunnyvale CA 94087

STOSKOPF, MICHAEL KERRY, b Garden City, Kans, March 21, 50; m 81. AQUATIC MEDICINE, AQUATIC TOXICOLOGY. *Educ:* Colo State Univ, BS, 73, DVM, 75. *Prof Exp:* Staff vet comp med, Overton Park Zoo & Aquarium, 75-77; ASST PROF COMP MED, SCH MED, JOHNS HOPKINS UNIV, 79- *Concurrent Pos:* Consult, Nat Inst Exp Progs, Antivenom Inst, Columbia, 79; staff vet, Baltimore Zool Soc, 77-81; adj prof path, Sch Med, Univ Md, 81-; chief vet, Nat Aquarium, Baltimore, 81- *Mem:* Int Asn Aquatic Animal Med; Am Asn Zoo Veterinarians; Nat Acad Zoo Med; Wildlife Dis Asn; Am Vet Med Asn. *Res:* Investigation of new animal models for human disease with particular interest in the effects of environmental factors on the physiology and biochemistry of living organisms. *Mailing Add:* Div Comp Med Sch Med Johns Hopkins Univ 720 Rutland Ave Baltimore MD 21205

STOSKOPF, N C, b Mitchell, Ont, June 11, 34; m 60; c 2. CROP BREEDING. *Educ:* Univ Toronto, BSA, 57, MSA, 58; McGill Univ, PhD(agron), 62. *Prof Exp:* Lectr agron, Ont Agr Col, 58-59; instr & exten specialist, Kemptville Agr Sch, 59-60; asst prof crop sci, Ont Agr Col, 62-66, assoc prof, 66-69, PROF CROP SCI, UNIV GUELPH, 69-, DIR DIPL PROG AGR, 74- *Mem:* Agr Inst Can. *Res:* Winter wheat breeding given a physiological basis with yield as main objective; plants selected for upright leaves to achieve a high optimum leaf area, a high net assimilation rate and a long period of grain filling; cereal physiology. *Mailing Add:* Dept Crop Sci Univ Guelph Guelph ON N1G 2W1 Can

STOSSEL, THOMAS PETER, b Chicago, Ill, Sept 10, 41; m 65; c 2. HEMATOLOGY, ONCOLOGY. *Educ:* Princeton Univ, AB, 63; Harvard Med Sch, MD, 67. *Prof Exp:* House staff med, Mass Gen Hosp, 67-69; staff assoc, NIH, 67-71; from fel to sr assoc, Med Ctr, Children Hosp, Boston, 71-76; CHIEF HEMATOL & ONCOL UNIT, MASS GEN HOSP, 76-; ASSOC PROF MED, HARVARD MED SCH, 78- *Concurrent Pos:* Fel, Harvard Med Sch, 71-78; ed, J Clin Investigation 82- *Mem:* Am Fedn Clin Res; Am Soc Clin Investigation; Am Soc Hematol; Am Soc Cell Biol; Asn Am Physicians. *Res:* Biology of phagocytic leukocytes with special emphasis on the molecular basis of leukocyte movements. *Mailing Add:* Hematol & Oncol Unit Mass Gen Hosp Boston MA 02114

STOTHERS, JOHN BAILIE, b London, Ont, Apr 16, 31; m 53; c 2. ORGANIC CHEMISTRY. *Educ:* Univ Western Ont, BSc, 53, MSc, 54; McMaster Univ, PhD(phys org chem), 57. *Prof Exp:* Res chemist, Res Dept, Imp Oil, Ltd, 57-59; lectr chem, 59-61, from asst prof to assoc prof, 61-67, PROF CHEM, UNIV WESTERN ONT, 67- *Concurrent Pos:* Merck, Sharp & Dohme lect award, 71. *Mem:* Royal Soc Can; Am Chem Soc; fel Chem Inst Can; The Chem Soc. *Res:* Nuclear magnetic resonance spectroscopy; applications of deuterium and carbon-13 nuclear magnetic resonance to organic structural, stereochemical and mechanistic problems and biosynthesis; deuterium exchange processes and molecular rearrangements. *Mailing Add:* Dept Chem Univ of Western Ont London ON N6A 5B7 Can

STOTLER, RAYMOND EUGENE, b Peoria, Ill, Mar 30, 40; m 69. BOTANY. *Educ:* Western Ill Univ, BS, 62; Southern Ill Univ, MA, 64; Univ Cincinnati, PhD(bot), 68. *Prof Exp:* Fel bot, Univ Wis-Milwaukee, 68-69; asst prof, 69-74, ASSOC PROF BOT, SOUTHERN ILL UNIV, 74- *Honors & Awards:* Dimond Award, NSF & Bot Soc Am, 75. *Mem:* Am Bryol & Lichenological Soc; Am Fern Soc; Am Soc Plant Taxon; Int Soc Plant Taxon; Int Asn Bryologists. *Res:* Nomenclature and biosystematics of hepatics, hornworts, and mosses. *Mailing Add:* Dept of Bot Southern Ill Univ Carbondale IL 62901

STOTSKY, BERNARD A, b New York, NY, Apr 8, 26; m 52; c 5. PSYCHOLOGY, PSYCHIATRY. *Educ:* City Col New York, BS, 48; Univ Mich, MA, 49, PhD(psychol), 51; Western Reserve Univ, MD, 62. *Prof Exp:* Staff psychologist, Ment Hyg Clin, Vet Admin, Detroit, 51-53; instr & assoc, Boston Univ, 54-56, asst prof psychol, 56-57; asst prof, Duke Univ, 57-58; staff psychologist, Vet Admin Hosp, Brockton, Mass, 58-61; intern, George Washington Univ Hosp, 62-63; fel psychiat & resident psychiat, Mass Ment Health Ctr, 63-65 & Boston State Hosp, 65-66; lectr, 64-67, assoc prof, 67-68, head dept psychol, 72-73, PROF PSYCHOL, BOSTON STATE COL, 68- *Concurrent Pos:* Chief counseling psychologist, Vet Admin Hosp, Brockton, Mass, 53-56, consult, 56-57 & 70- & chief psychologist, Durham, NC, 57-58; consult, Brockton Family Serv, 54, Hayden Goodwill Inn, 54-57, Mass Dept Pub Health, 67 & Boston State Hosp, 63-65, 68-75; prin investr, psychiat consult & lectr, Northeastern Univ, 64-; assoc psychiat, Tufts Univ, 66-67, asst prof, 67-76, assoc prof, 76- lectr, Clark Univ, 69-70 & Mt Sinai Sch Med, 69-72; consult, Food & Drug Admin, 72-75 & Nat Inst Child Health & Human Develop, 73-77; prof psychiat & behav sci, Univ Wash, 73-77; dir outpatient psychiat clin, St Elizabeth's Hosp Boston, 73, assoc dir psychiat educ, 74-81, dir psychiat educ, 81-; consult campus sch, Boston Col, 74- *Mem:* Fel Am Psychol Asn; Am Psychiat Asn. *Res:* Psychopharmacology; diagnosis and treatment of mental disease; personality and organic factors in rehabilitation of chronically ill patients; geriatrics. *Mailing Add:* 38 Dean Rd Brookline MA 02146

STOTT, DONALD FRANKLIN, b Reston, Man, Apr 30, 28; m 60; c 3. GEOLOGY. *Educ:* Univ Manitoba, BSc, 53, MSc, 54; Princeton Univ, AM, 56, PhD, 58. *Prof Exp:* Asst geol, Princeton Univ, 54-55; head regional geol subdiv, 72-73, dir 73-80, GEOLOGIST, GEOL SURV CAN, 57-, RES SCIENTIST, INST SEDIMENTARY & PETROL GEOL, 73- *Mem:* Fel Geol Soc Am; Can Soc Petrol Geologists; Geol Asn Can; Soc Econ Paleontologists & Mineralogists. *Res:* Physical stratigraphy and sedimentation, particularly of Cretaceous system of Rocky Mountain foothills, Canada. *Mailing Add:* Inst of Sedimentary & Petrol Geol 3303 33rd St NW Calgary AB T2L 2A7 Can

STOTT, GERALD H, b Kanosh, Utah, Mar 7, 24; m 47; c 6. DAIRY SCIENCE. *Educ:* Utah State Univ, BS, 51, MS, 52; Univ Wis, PhD, 56. *Prof Exp:* Asst prof dairy sci, Univ Ga, 56-57; assoc prof dairy sci & dairy physiologist, Univ Ariz, 57-63, prof & head dept dairy sci, 63-77, dairy scientist, 74-80, prof animal sci, 77-80. *Mem:* AAAS; Am Dairy Sci Asn. *Res:* Genetics; animal physiology; nutrition; parathyroid activity; calcium and phosphorous metabolism; reproduction and nutrition under high climatic temperatures. *Mailing Add:* 6602 N Camino Abbey Tucson AZ 85718

STOTT, KENHELM WELBURN, JR, b San Diego, Calif, Aug 27, 20. MAMMALOGY, ORNITHOLOGY. *Educ:* Pomona Col, BA, 42. *Prof Exp:* Curator mammals & publ, Zool Soc, San Diego, 46-48, gen curator, 46-54; leader primate studies prog, San Diego Natural Hist Soc, 57-60; RES ASSOC ZOOL, ZOOL SOC, SAN DIEGO, 59- *Concurrent Pos:* Res assoc, San Diego Natural Hist Soc, 57-74 & Martin & Osa Johnson Safari Museum, 74-; res collabr sci expeds, Smithsonian Inst, 78; trustee, Nat Underwater & Marine Agency, 79- *Honors & Awards:* Sweeney Medal, Explorers Club, 80. *Mem:* Am Ornith Union; AAAS; Soc Syst Zool; Int Union Conserv Nature & Natural Resources; Am Soc Mammal. *Res:* Observation of rare and endangered species of mammals and birds; expeditions. *Mailing Add:* 2300 Front St Apt 402 San Diego CA 92101

STOTTLEMYER, J ROBERT, terrestrial ecology, aquatic ecology, see previous edition

STOTTLEMYRE, JAMES ARTHUR, b Juneau, Alaska, Jan 4, 48; m 70; c 2. GEOPHYSICS, RESERVOIR ENGINEERING. *Educ:* Univ Wash, BS, 71, MS, 74, PhD, 80. *Prof Exp:* Resource engr energy resources, Wash Water Power Co, 74-76; MGR, EARTH SCI SECT, BATTELLE PAC NORTHWEST LABS, 76- *Mem:* Soc Explor Geophys; Soc Petrol Engrs; Am Geophys Union. *Res:* Underground fluid and heat storage, disposal of hazerdous wastes; geohydrochemical modeling; waste management. *Mailing Add:* Battelle Pac Northwest Labs Sigma V Bldg PO Box 999 Richland WA 99352

STOTTS, JANE, b Dallas, Tex, Sept 15, 39. IMMUNOLOGY, MICROBIOLOGY. *Educ:* Univ Tex, Austin, BA, 61; Baylor Univ, MS, 64. *Prof Exp:* RES MGR MICROBIOL & IMMUNOL, PROCTER & GAMBLE CO, 64- *Res:* Allergic contact dermatitis, predictive testing and identification of allergens; primary irritant dermatitis; microflora of skin; hospital infection control. *Mailing Add:* Buckeye Cellulose Corp Procter & Gamble Co PO Box 8407 Memphis TN 38108

STOTZ, ELMER HENRY, b Boston, Mass, July 29, 11; m 36; c 5. BIOCHEMISTRY. *Educ:* Mass Inst Technol, BS, 32; Harvard Univ, PhD(biochem), 36. *Prof Exp:* Instr biochem, Univ Pittsburgh, 36-37, Univ Chicago, 37-38 & Harvard Med Sch, 38-42; prof agr & biochem & head dept, Cornell Univ, 43-47; PROF BIOCHEM & CHMN DEPT, SCH MED & DENT, UNIV ROCHESTER, 47- *Concurrent Pos:* Dir labs, McLean Hosp, 38-43; mem nat comt biochem, Nat Acad Sci-Nat Res Coun, 54-; treas, Int Union Biochem, 55-; trustee, Assoc Univs, Inc, 57-; mem div chem & chem technol, Nat Res Coun, 57- *Mem:* Am Chem Soc; Am Soc Biol Chemists (secy, 50-53); Biol Stain Comn (treas, 45-). *Res:* Cytochromes; analytical methods; biological and fatty acid oxidation; stain chemistry. *Mailing Add:* Dept of Biochem Univ of Rochester Med Ctr Rochester NY 14642

STOTZ, ROBERT WILLIAM, b Monroe, Mich, July 18, 42; m 71; c 1. RESEARCH ADMINISTRATION. *Educ:* Univ Toledo, BS, 64, MS, 66; Univ Fla, PhD(inorg chem), 70. *Prof Exp:* Teaching asst inorg chem, Univ Toledo, 64-66; res asst, Univ Fla, 66-70; res assoc, Mich State Univ, 70-71; instr chem, Eastern Mich Univ, 71-72; asst prof, Mercer Univ, 72-73; asst prof, Tri-State Col, 73-74; supvr inorg anal res, Inst Gas Technol, 74-76, mgr anal chem, 76-80; MEM STAFF, UPJOHN CO, 80- *Mem:* Am Chem Soc. *Res:* Development and modification of various wet chemical and instrumental methods for determination of inorganic constituents in complex inorganic systems. *Mailing Add:* Upjohn Co 7000 Portage Rd Kalamazoo MI 49001

STOTZKY, GUENTHER, b Leipzig, Ger, May 24, 31; nat US; m 58; c 3. MICROBIAL ECOLOGY. *Educ:* Calif State Polytech Col, BS, 52; Ohio State Univ, MS, 54, PhD(agron & microbiol), 56. *Prof Exp:* Res asst soil biochem & microbiol, Ohio State Univ, 53-56; res assoc bot & plant nutrit, Univ Mich, 56-58; head soil microbiol, Cent Res Labs, United Fruit Co, 58-63; microbiologist & chmn, Kitchawan Res Lab, Brooklyn Bot Garden, 63-68; assoc prof biol, 68-70, adj assoc prof, 67-68, chmn dept, 70-77, PROF BIOL, NY UNIV, 70- *Concurrent Pos:* Spec scientist, Argonne Nat Lab, 55; mem, Am Inst Biol Sci-NASA Regional Coun, 65-68; regional ed, J Soil Biol & Biochem, 69-; assoc ed, Appl Microbiol, 71-77 & Can J Microbiol, 71-75; mem ad hoc comt rev biomed & ecol effects of extremely low frequency radiation, Bur Med & Surg, Dept Navy, 72-75; vis prof, Inst Advan Studies, Polytech Inst, Mexico, 73; mem bd trustees, NY Ocean Sci Lab, Affil Cols & Univs, Inc, 73-; mem comn human resources, Nat Res Coun, 75-77; mem, Inst Ecol, 71-78. *Mem:* Fel AAAS; Soc Environ Geochem & Health; Air Pollution Control Asn; Int Asn Ecol; Int Soil Sci Soc. *Res:* Soil microbiology and biochemistry; plant-microbe relations; soil and water-borne plant and animal diseases; clay mineralogy; soil, air and water pollution; seed germination; cell surfaces; medical microbiology; immunology. *Mailing Add:* Dept Biol NY Univ New York NY 10003

STOUDT, EMILY LAWS, b Columbus, Ohio, Apr 5, 43; m 67, 77; c 2. GEOLOGY. *Educ:* Ohio State Univ, BA, 66, PhD(geol), 75; La State Univ, MS, 68. *Prof Exp:* Geologist, Spec Proj Br, US Geol Surv, 68-70; geologist, Explor & Prod Res Lab, Getty Oil Co, 75-81, GEOLOGIC SUPVR, GETTY RES CTR, 81- *Mem:* Geol Soc Am; Am Asn Petrol Geologists; Soc Econ Paleontologists & Mineralogists. *Res:* Carbonate petrology; regional geology of the mid-continent Silurian, western United States Permian, Gulf Coast Jurassic-Cretaceous systems, Guatemalan Jureassic-Cretaceous. *Mailing Add:* Getty Res Ctr PO Box 42214 Houston TX 77042

STOUDT, HOWARD WEBSTER, b Pittsburgh, Pa, May 13, 25; m 53; c 2. HUMAN FACTORS ENGINEERING, ERGONOMICS. *Educ:* Harvard Univ, AB, 49, SM, 62; Univ Pa, AM, 53, PhD(anthrop), 59. *Prof Exp:* Res asst, Sch Pub Health, Harvard Univ, 52-55; res & educ specialist, Air Univ, 55-57; res assoc phys anthrop, Sch Pub Health, Harvard Univ, 57-66, asst prof, 66-73; prof & chmn dept community med, Col Osteop Med, 73-77, PROF COMMUNITY HEALTH SCI, MICH STATE UNIV, 78- *Concurrent Pos:* Consult, Nat Health Exam Surv, USPHS Ctr Dis Control; res investr, Normative Aging Study, Vet Admin, Boston. *Mem:* Human Biol Coun; Am Asn Phys Anthrop; Human Factors Soc; Am Pub Health Asn; AAAS. *Res:* Physical anthropology; epidemiology of non-infectious disease and accidents; application of human biological data to the design of equipment and workspaces with special reference to safety and health. *Mailing Add:* Dept Community Health Sci Mich State Univ East Lansing MI 48824

STOUDT, THOMAS HENRY, b Temple, Pa, Apr 6, 22; m 43; c 3. MICROBIOLOGY. *Educ:* Albright Col, BS, 43; Rutgers Univ, MS, 44; Purdue Univ, West Lafayette, PhD(org chem), 49. *Prof Exp:* Asst chem, Rutgers Univ, 43-44 & Purdue Univ, West Lafayette, 46-47; sr microbiologist, 49-58, from sect head to sr sect head, 58-69, dir appl microbiol, 69-75, sr dir appl microbiol & nat prod isolation, 75-77, EXEC DIR, MERCK & CO, INC, 77- *Mem:* Am Chem Soc; Soc Indust Microbiol; Int Asn Dent Res; Am Soc Microbiologists; NY Acad Sci. *Res:* Microbial transformations; microbial biosyntheses; antibiotics; microbial physiology and genetics, rumen microbiology; oral microbiology; microbial enzymology; vaccines and immunology; scale-up of industrial fermentation processes. *Mailing Add:* Merck & Co Inc Box 2000 Rahway NJ 07065

STOUFER, ROBERT CARL, b Ashland, Ohio, Nov 3, 30; m 54; c 2. INORGANIC CHEMISTRY. *Educ:* Otterbein Col, BA & BS, 52; Ohio State Univ, PhD, 59. *Prof Exp:* ASSOC PROF INORG CHEM, UNIV FLA, 58- *Mem:* Am Chem Soc. *Res:* Preparation and characterization of inorganic complexes. *Mailing Add:* Dept of Chem Univ of Fla Gainesville FL 32611

STOUFFER, DONALD CARL, b Philadelphia, Pa, May 15, 38; m 62; c 2. ENGINEERING MECHANICS. *Educ:* Drexel Univ, BSME, 61, MSME, 65; Univ Mich, Ann Arbor, PhD(eng mech), 68. *Prof Exp:* Engr, Philco-Ford Corp, 61-63 & Westinghouse Elec Corp, 63-65; instr mech, Univ Mich, Ann Arbor, 66-68, lectr, 68-69; from asst prof to assoc prof eng sci, 69-77, fac fel, 71, PROF ENG SCI, UNIV CINCINNATI, 77- *Concurrent Pos:* US-Australian Coop Sci fel, Univ Melbourne, 76; vis scientist, Wright-Patterson AFB, Ohio, 75-; res grants, Nat Sci Found & Air Force Wright Aeronaut Lab. *Mem:* Soc Rheol; Soc Nat Philos; Am Soc Mech Engrs; Am Acad Mech. *Res:* Theoretical and applied mechanics; rheology; constitutive equations. *Mailing Add:* Dept Aerospace Eng & Appl Mech Univ of Cincinnati Cincinnati OH 45221

STOUFFER, JAMES L, b Harrisburg, Pa, Sept 25, 35; m 68. AUDIOLOGY, PSYCHOACOUSTICS. *Educ:* State Univ NY Col Buffalo, BSc, 64; Pa State Univ, MSc, 66, PhD(audiol, statist), 69. *Prof Exp:* Clin audiologist, Pa State Univ, 64-69; asst prof audiol, Univ Western Ont, 69-70, DIR COMMUN DIS & CHIEF SPEECH & HEARING SERV, UNIV WESTERN ONT & UNIV HOSP, LONDON, ONT, 72- *Concurrent Pos:* NIH fel psychoacoust, Commun Sci Lab, Univ Fla, 69-70; consult, Oxford County Ment Health Centre, 70-; ed asst, Ont Speech & Hearing Asn, 71- *Mem:* Am Speech & Hearing Asn; Acoust Soc Am. *Res:* Physiological responses to auditory signals of normals versus abnormals; underwater acoustics. *Mailing Add:* Bear Creek Side Rd RR #1 Ilderton ON N0M 2A0 Can

STOUFFER, JAMES RAY, b Glen Elder, Kans, Jan 12, 29; m 55; c 2. ANIMAL SCIENCE. *Educ:* Univ Ill, BS, 51, MS, 53, PhD(meats), 56. *Prof Exp:* Asst prof animal husb, Univ Conn, 55-56; asst prof animal husb, 56-62, assoc prof animal sci, 62-77, PROF ANIMAL SCI, CORNELL UNIV, 77- *Mem:* Am Soc Animal Sci; Inst Food Technol; Am Meat Sci Asn. *Res:* Carcass evaluation of meat animals, particularly the relationship of live animal and carcass characteristics. *Mailing Add:* Dept Animal Sci Cornell Univ Ithaca NY 14853

STOUFFER, JOHN EMERSON, b Sioux City, Iowa, Dec 4, 25; m 55; c 2. BIOCHEMISTRY. *Educ:* Northwestern Univ, BS, 49; Boston Univ, PhD(org chem), 57. *Prof Exp:* Res assoc biochem, Med Col, Cornell Univ, 57-59, instr, 59-61; asst prof, 61-66, ASSOC PROF BIOCHEM, BAYLOR COL MED, 67- *Mem:* Am Chem Soc; Am Oil Chemists Soc; Am Soc Biol Chemists; Endocrine Soc; Am Inst Chemists. *Res:* Thyroid hormones; structure function relationships of hormones and mechanism of action; membrane receptor sites. *Mailing Add:* dept of Biochem Baylor Col of Med Houston TX 77030

STOUFFER, RICHARD FRANKLIN, b Welch, WVa, July 3, 32; m 57; c 2. PLANT PATHOLOGY, VIROLOGY. *Educ:* Vanderbilt Univ, BA, 54; Cornell Univ, PhD(plant path), 59. *Prof Exp:* Asst, Cornell Univ, 54-59; asst res prof, Univ RI, 59-60; asst virologist, Univ Fla, 61-65; from asst prof to assoc prof, 65-76, PROF PLANT PATH, FRUIT RES LAB, PA STATE UNIV, 76- *Mem:* Am Phytopath Soc; Brit Asn Appl Biol. *Res:* Plant virology. *Mailing Add:* Pa State Univ Fruit Res Lab Box 309 Biglerville PA 17307

STOUFFER, RICHARD LEE, b Hagerstown, Md, July 27, 49; c 1. ENDOCRINOLOGY, REPRODUCTIVE PHYSIOLOGY. *Educ:* Va Polytech Inst, BS, 71; Duke Univ, PhD(physiol), 75. *Prof Exp:* Staff fel endocrinol, Reprod Res Br, Nat Inst Child Health & Human Develop, NIH, 75-77; ASST PROF ENDOCRINOL, COL MED, UNIV ARIZ, 77- *Mem:* Soc Study Reprod; AAAS; Endocrine Soc; Am Physiol Soc. *Res:* Female reproductive endocrinology, with emphasis on the regulation of ovarian function; regulation of the primate corpus luteum. *Mailing Add:* Dept of Physiol Univ of Ariz Tucson AZ 85724

STOUGHTON, RAYMOND WOODFORD, b Tehachapi, Calif, Aug 6, 16; m 41; c 4. PHYSICAL CHEMISTRY, NUCLEAR CHEMISTRY. *Educ:* Univ Calif, BS, 37, PhD(chem), 40. *Prof Exp:* Asst chem, Univ Calif, 37-40, res chemist, Radiation Lab, 41-43; instr, Agr & Mech Col, Tex, 40-41; RES CHEMIST, UNION CARBIDE NUCLEAR CO, OAK RIDGE NAT LAB, 43- *Concurrent Pos:* Res chemist, Metall Lab, Univ Chicago, 43. *Mem:* AAAS; Am Chem Soc; Am Phys Soc; Am Nuclear Soc; NY Acad Sci. *Res:* Reaction kinetics; application of computers to chemical and physical problems; solution thermodynamics; solution chemistry of heavy elements; radiochemistry; process development; neutron cross sections. *Mailing Add:* Oak Ridge Nat Lab Box X Oak Ridge TN 37830

STOUGHTON, RICHARD BAKER, b Duluth, Minn, July 4, 23; m 46; c 1. DERMATOLOGY. *Educ:* Univ Chicago, SB, 45, MD, 47; Am Bd Dermat, dipl, 52. *Prof Exp:* From instr to asst prof dermat, Univ Chicago, 50-56; assoc prof med dir dermat, Sch Med, Case Western Reserve Univ, 57-67; HEAD DEPT DERMAT, SCRIPPS CLIN & RES FOUND, 67-; PROF DERMAT & CHIEF DIV, UNIV CALIF, SAN DIEGO, 75- *Concurrent Pos:* Consult, US Army Chem Ctr, Md, 54-58; mem subcomt dermat, Nat Res Coun, 59-; ed-in-chief, Soc Invest Dermat, 67; dir, Am Bd Dermat. *Mem:* Soc Invest Dermat; Am Acad Dermat. *Res:* Histochemistry, percutaneous absorption and pathologic anatomy of dermatology. *Mailing Add:* 476 Prospect St La Jolla CA 92037

STOUT, BENJAMIN BOREMAN, b Parkersburg, WVa, Mar 2, 24; m 45; c 3. FOREST ECOLOGY. *Educ:* WVa Univ, BSF, 47; Harvard Univ, MF, 50; Rutgers Univ, PhD, 67. *Prof Exp:* Forester, Pond & Moyer Co, 47-49; silviculturist, Harvard Black Rock Forest, 50-55, supvr, 55-59; from asst prof to prof forestry, Rutgers Univ, New Brunswick, 59-77, chmn dept biol sci, 74-77, assoc provost, 77-78; DEAN SCH FORESTRY, UNIV MONT, 78- *Mem:* Ecol Soc Am; Soc Am Foresters; Sigma Xi. *Res:* Ways and means of quantifying vegetations response to environment. *Mailing Add:* 515 Canyon Gate Rd Missoula MT 59801

STOUT, BILL A(LVIN), b Grant, Nebr, July 9, 32; m 51; c 2. AGRICULTURAL ENGINEERING. *Educ:* Univ Nebr, BS, 54; Mich State Univ, MS, 55, PhD(agr eng), 59. *Prof Exp:* Asst, Mich State Univ, 54-56, from instr to assoc prof agr eng, 56-66, prof, 66-81, chmn dept, 70-75; PROF AGR ENG, TEX A&M UNIV, 81- *Concurrent Pos:* Farm power & machinery specialist, Food & Agr Orgn, UN, Rome, Italy, 63-64; sabbatical leave, Dept Agr Eng, Univ Calif, Davis, 69-70. *Mem:* Fel Am Soc Agr Engrs; Int Solar Energy Soc; Nat Soc Prof Engrs; fel AAAS. *Res:* Harvesting machines; physical properties of agricultural products; mechanization in developing countries; energy awareness and alternatives. *Mailing Add:* Dept Agr Eng Tex A&M Univ College Station TX 77843

STOUT, CHARLES ALLISON, b Beaumont, Tex, Sept 20, 30. ORGANIC CHEMISTRY. *Educ:* Rice Inst, BA, 52, MA, 53; Ohio State Univ, PhD(chem), 62. *Prof Exp:* Chemist, Goodyear Tire & Rubber Co, Ohio, 53-54; NIH res fel photochem, Calif Inst Technol, 62-63; res chemist, Chevron Oil Field Res Co, 64-72; RES CHEMIST, DIVERSIFIED CHEM CORP, 72- *Mem:* Am Chem Soc; Soc Petrol Engrs. *Res:* Physical organic chemistry, reaction mechanisms; molecular orbital treatments of condensed aromatic systems; photochemical reactions in solutions and solids, photosensitization; structure of interfacial films. *Mailing Add:* 17621 E 7th St 31A Tustin CA 92680

STOUT, DARRYL GLEN, b Carman, Man, Mar 21, 44; m 75. PLANT PHYSIOLOGY. *Educ:* Univ Man, BSA, 69, MSc, 72; Cornell Univ, PhD(plant physiol), 76. *Prof Exp:* Res assoc drought tolerance, Univ Sask, 75-77; RES SCIENTIST FORAGE PROD, AGR CAN, 77- *Mem:* Am Soc Plant Physiologists; Can Soc Plant Physiologists; Soc Range Mgt. *Res:* Growth and survival of plants under stress conditions; present interest in frost, drought and grazing stresses; forage production. *Mailing Add:* Agr Can 3015 Ord Rd Kamloops BC V2B 8A9 Can

STOUT, DAVID MICHAEL, b Flint, Mich, Nov 20, 47; m 69; c 2. ORGANIC CHEMISTRY. *Educ:* Col Wooster, BA, 69; Univ Rochester, MS, 72; Colo State Univ, PhD(org chem), 74. *Prof Exp:* NIH fel, Yale Univ, 75-76; RES CHEMIST CARDIOVASC RES, AM CRITICAL CARE DIV, AM HOSP SUPPLY CORP, 76- *Mem:* Am Chem Soc. *Res:* Cardiovascular research; organic synthesis. *Mailing Add:* Am Critical Care 1600 Waukegan Rd McGaw Park IL 60085

STOUT, EDGAR LEE, b Grants Pass, Ore, Mar 13, 38; m 58; c 1. MATHEMATICS. *Educ:* Ore State Col, BA, 60; Univ Wis, MA, 61, PhD(math), 64. *Prof Exp:* Instr math, Yale Univ, 64-65; asst prof, 65-69, Off Naval Res res assoc, 67-68; assoc prof, 69-74, PROF MATH, UNIV WASH, 74- *Concurrent Pos:* Vis prof math, Univ Leeds, 72-73. *Mem:* Math Asn Am; Am Math Soc. *Res:* Functions of one or several complex variables; function algebras. *Mailing Add:* Dept Math Univ Wash Seattle WA 98105

STOUT, EDWARD IRVIN, b Washington Co, Iowa, Mar 2, 39; m; c 3. ORGANIC CHEMISTRY. *Educ:* Iowa Wesleyan Col, BS, 60; Bradley Univ, MS, 68; Univ Ariz, PhD(org chem), 74. *Prof Exp:* Chemist, Lever Bros Co, 61-62; res chemist, Northern Regional Res Ctr, USDA, 62-78; dir res, Spenco Med Corp, 78-80; consult, 81-82; MEM STAFF, CHEMSTAR PROD CO, 82- *Concurrent Pos:* Instr org chem, Bradley Univ, 70-75. *Mem:* Am Chem Soc (secy, 75). *Res:* Preparation and characterization of starch derivatives including starch graft copolymers. *Mailing Add:* Chemstar Prod Co 1510 Charlotte Kansas City MO 64108

STOUT, ERNEST RAY, b Boone, NC, Oct 31, 38; m 61; c 3. MOLECULAR BIOLOGY, BIOCHEMISTRY. *Educ:* Appalachian State Univ, BS, 61; Univ Fla, PhD(bot, biochem), 65. *Prof Exp:* Nat Cancer Inst fel biochem genetics, Univ Md, 65-67; asst prof, 67-72, asst dean, Col Arts & Sci, 78-79, ASSOC PROF MOLECULAR BIOL, VA POLYTECH INST & STATE UNIV, 72-, HEAD, DEPT BIOL, 80- *Mem:* AAAS; Am Soc Plant Physiol. *Res:* Mechanism of nucleic acid synthesis in higher plants; control of nucleic acid synthesis; parovirus macromolecular synthesis. *Mailing Add:* Dept Biol Va Polytech Inst & State Univ Blacksburg VA 24061

STOUT, GLENN EMANUEL, b Fostoria, Ohio, Mar 23, 20; m 42; c 2. METEOROLOGY. *Educ:* Findlay Col, BS, 42; Univ Chicago, cert, 43. *Hon Degrees:* DSc, Findlay Col, 73. *Prof Exp:* Asst math, Findlay Col, 39-42; instr meteorol, Univ Chicago, 42-43 & US War Dept, Chanute AFB, Ill, 46-47; asst engr, Ill State Water Surv, 47-52, head atmospheric sci sect, 52-71, asst to chief, 71-74, DIR WATER RESOURCES CENTER, ILL STATE WATER SURV, UNIV ILL, URBANA, 73-, PROF METEOROL, INST ENVIRON STUDIES, UNIV, 73- *Concurrent Pos:* Consult, Crop-Hail Ins Actuarial Assoc, Ill, 61-69; prog coordr, Nat Ctr Atmospheric Res, NSF, 69-71; ed-chief, Water Int, 82- *Honors & Awards:* Einstein Award, Findlay Col, 42. *Mem:* Am Meteorol Soc; Am Geophys Union; Am Water Resources Asn; AAAS; Int Asn Water Resources. *Res:* Hail climatology; weather modification; water resources; environmental science; environmental management. *Mailing Add:* Univ of Ill Water Resources Ctr 208 N Romine Urbana IL 61801

STOUT, ISAAC JACK, b Clarksburg, WVa, July 20, 39; m 64; c 2. ECOLOGY. *Educ:* Ore State Univ, BS, 61, Va Polytech Inst & State Univ, MS, 67; Wash State Univ, PhD(zool), 72. *Prof Exp:* Wildlife Mgt Inst fel waterfowl ecol, Va Coop Wildlife Res Univ, 64-65; field ecologist, Old Dominion Univ, 65-67; USPHS fel appl ecol, Wash State Univ, 67-69; asst prof, 72-77, ASSOC PROF BIOL SCI, FLA TECHNOL UNIV, 77- *Concurrent Pos:* Mem, Environ Effect & Fate Solid Rocket Emission Prod, NASA, Kennedy Space Ctr, 75. *Mem:* Ecol Soc Am; Brit Ecol Soc; Wildlife Soc; Am Soc Mammalogists; Sigma Xi. *Res:* Population and community ecology; tick-host relations; applied ecology. *Mailing Add:* Dept of Biol Sci Fla Technol Univ Box 25000 Orlando FL 32816

STOUT, JOHN FREDERICK, b Takoma Park, Md, Jan 20, 36; m 56; c 2. ETHOLOGY, NEUROBIOLOGY. *Educ:* Columbia Union Col, BA, 57; Univ Md, PhD(zool), 63. *Prof Exp:* Instr biol, Walla Walla Col, 62, asst prof, 63-65, dir marine sta, 64-69, assoc prof biol, 66-69; assoc prof, 69-70, PROF BIOL, ANDREWS UNIV, 70- *Concurrent Pos:* USPHS spec fel & vis researcher, Univ Cologne, 69-70; guest res prof, Max Planck Inst Behav Physiol, 75-76. *Honors & Awards:* Alexander von Humboldt Sr US Scientist Award, 75. *Mem:* Sigma Xi; Am Soc Zoologists; Am Physiol Soc. *Res:* Communication during social behavior; neurobiology of acoustic communication; behavioral physiology. *Mailing Add:* Dept of Biol Andrews Univ Berrien Springs MI 49104

STOUT, JOHN WILLARD, b Seattle, Wash, Mar 13, 12; m 48; c 1. PHYSICAL CHEMISTRY, CHEMICAL PHYSICS. *Educ:* Univ Calif, BS, 33, PhD(phys chem), 37. *Prof Exp:* Instr chem, Univ Calif, 37-38, Lalor fel, 38-39; instr chem, Mass Inst Technol, 39-41; investr, Nat Defense Res Comt, Univ Calif, 41-44, group leader, Manhattan Dist, Los Alamos Sci Lab, 44-46; from assoc prof to prof, 46-77, EMER PROF CHEM, UNIV CHICAGO, 77- *Concurrent Pos:* Ed, J Chem Physics, 59- *Mem:* AAAS; Am Chem Soc; fel Am Phys Soc. *Res:* Thermodynamics; calorimetry; crystal spectra; cryogenics; paramagnetism and antiferromagnetism. *Mailing Add:* Dept Chem Univ Chicago Chicago IL 60637

STOUT, KOEHLER, b Deer Lodge, Mont, Sept 1, 22; m 50; c 3. MINING & GEOLOGICAL ENGINEERING. *Educ:* Mont Sch Mines, BS, 48, MS, 49; La Salle Exten Univ, LLB, 57. *Prof Exp:* Asst prof mining eng, 52-58, assoc prof, 58-62, PROF ENG SCI & HEAD DEPT, MONT COL MINERAL SCI & TECHNOL, 62-, DEAN DIV ENG, 66- *Mem:* Am Soc Eng Educ; Nat Soc Prof Engrs; Am Inst Mining, Metall & Petrol Engrs. *Res:* Portland and chemical cements injected into weak, unstable ground to prepare the ground for mining. *Mailing Add:* Dept of Eng Sci Sci & Technol Butte MT 59701

STOUT, LANDON CLARKE, JR, b Kansas City, Mo, Feb 20, 33; m 54, 81; c 5. PATHOLOGY, INTERNAL MEDICINE. *Educ:* Univ Md, MD, 57. *Prof Exp:* Resident internal med, Med Ctr, Univ Okla, 58-61, asst prof, 63-72, dir inst comp path, 65-69, resident path, 66-67, from asst prof to assoc prof, 68-72, interim chmn dept, 70-72; assoc prof, 72-74, PROF PATH, UNIV TEX MED BR GALVESTON, 74- *Concurrent Pos:* Nat Heart Inst spec fel, Univ Okla, 67-68; consult, Okla Med Res Found, 71-72; mem, Coun Epidemiol, Am Heart Asn. *Mem:* Am Asn Path; Am Col Physicians; Am Gastroenterol Asn; Am Fedn Clin Res. *Res:* Comparative pathology; atherosclerosis; diabetes. *Mailing Add:* Dept of Path Univ of Tex Med Br Galveston TX 77550

STOUT, LARRY DALTON, toxicology, veterinary medicine, see previous edition

STOUT, MARGUERITE ANNETTE, b Marion, NC, July 17, 43. PHYSIOLOGY. *Educ:* Univ Wis, BS, 64; Univ Iowa, PhD(physiol & biophys), 74. *Prof Exp:* Res scientist I, Galesburg State Res Hosp, 65-70; fel, Univ Iowa, 74-75; ASST PROF PHYSIOL, NJ MED SCH, UNIV MED & DENT NJ, 75- *Concurrent Pos:* Am Heart Asn grant, 77-79; Nat Heart Lung & Blood Inst Young Investr grant, 78-81. *Mem:* NY Acad Sci. *Res:* Transmembrane calcium transport in vascular smooth muscle and in the internally dialyzed and voltage clamped axon of Myxicola infundibulum. *Mailing Add:* Dept Physiol NJ Med Sch Univ Med & Dent NJ Newark NJ 07103

STOUT, MARTIN LINDY, b N Hollywood, Calif, Feb 11, 34; m 56; c 2. GEOLOGY. *Educ:* Occidental Col, BA, 55; Univ Wash, MS, 57, PhD(geol), 59. *Prof Exp:* Asst geol, Occidental Col, 53-55 & Univ Wash, 55-59; from asst prof to assoc prof, 60-71, PROF GEOL, CALIF STATE UNIV, LOS ANGELES, 71-; SR ENG GEOLOGIST, MOORE & TABER ENGRS, GEOLOGISTS, 63- *Concurrent Pos:* Econ geologist, Aerogeophysics, Inc, 55; Geol Soc Am Penrose res grant, 58; partic, Int Field Inst, Scandinavia, Am Geol Inst, 63; NSF grant, 65, fel, Iceland & Norway, 66-67. *Mem:* AAAS; Asn Eng Geol; Geol Soc Am; Am Asn Geol Teachers. *Res:* Geochemical studies of basalts in Washington, Iceland, Norway; gravity movements and rates of tectonism in southern California; distribution and mechanism of failure of landslides in the capistrano formation of southern California; engineering properties of volcanic rocks. *Mailing Add:* Dept of Geol Calif State Univ 5151 State College Dr Los Angeles CA 90032

STOUT, MASON GARDNER, b Salt Lake City, Utah, Apr 30, 35; m 60; c 4. MEDICINE. *Educ:* Univ Utah, BS, 58, PhD(org chem), 60; Universidad Autonoma de Cuidad Juarez, MD, 77. *Prof Exp:* Res chemist, Lasdon Found Res Inst Chemother, 60-64; investr nucleotides & coenzymes, Pabst Labs, Pabst Brewing Co, 64-65, dir res & develop, P-L Biochem, Inc, 65-66; fel synthesis nucleosides, Univ Utah, 66-69; res chemist, ICN Pharmaceut Inc, 69-71, head res admin, 71-75, head chem div, 73-75; resident internal med, 77-81, CHIEF MED RESIDENT, LDS HOSP, SALT LAKE CITY, 81- *Mem:* Am Chem Soc; Sigma Xi; Am Col Physicians; AMA. *Res:* Synthesis of potential medicinals, both flavonoids and nucleosides. *Mailing Add:* 1411 Ambassador Way E Salt Lake City UT 84108

STOUT, QUENTIN FIELDEN, b Cleveland, Ohio, Sept 23, 49; m 71; c 2. PARALLEL COMPUTING. *Educ:* Centre Col, BA, 70; Ind Univ, PhD(math), 77. *Prof Exp:* ASST PROF COMPUT SCI & MATH, STATE UNIV NY BINGHAMTON, 76- *Concurrent Pos:* Consult, Parker-Hannifin Corp, 67-72; prin investr, NSF grants, 78-82. *Mem:* Asn Comput Mach; Am Math Soc; Math Asn Am; Pascal Users Group. *Res:* Design and analysis of algorithms; massively parallel computation, especially nonnumeric algorithms; data structures; Hardy-Littlewood-Polya majorization; operator theory; Schur products of operators. *Mailing Add:* Math Sci State Univ NY Binghamton NY 13901

STOUT, RAY BERNARD, b Georgetown, Ohio, June 16, 39; m 65; c 1. ENGINEERING MECHANICS. *Educ:* Ohio State Univ, BS, 64, MS, 68; Ill Inst Technol, PhD(eng mech), 70; Univ Pittsburgh, MBA, 72. *Prof Exp:* Apprentice, Cincinnati Milling Mach Co, 57-59; fel engr, Bettis Atomic Power Lab, Westinghouse Elec Corp, West Mifflin, 69-80. *Mem:* Am Soc Mech Engrs; Am Soc Testing & Mat; Asn Comput Mach. *Res:* Applications of numerical analysis and applied mathematics to engineering mechanics and socioeconomics. *Mailing Add:* 954 Venus Way Livermore CA 94550

STOUT, ROBERT D(ANIEL), b Reading, Pa, Jan 2, 15; m 39. METALLURGY. *Educ:* Pa State Col, BS, 35; Lehigh Univ, MS, 41, PhD(metall), 44. *Prof Exp:* Asst, Carpenter Steel Co, 35-39; instr, 39-45, from asst prof to assoc prof, 45-50, head dept metall, 56-60, prof metall, 50-80, dean grad sch, 60-80, PROF, LEHIGH UNIV, 81- *Concurrent Pos:* Deleg, Int Inst Welding, Am Welding Soc, 55-, Houdiemont lectr, 70; mem mat adv bd, Nat Acad Sci, 64-68; mem naval ship lab adv bd, Dept Navy, 68-74; mem pipeline safety adv comt, 69-72. *Honors & Awards:* Lincoln Gold Medal, Am Welding Soc, 43, Spraragen Award, 64, Thomas Award, 75 & Jennings Award, 74. *Mem:* Fel Am Soc Metals; Am Welding Soc (pres, 72-73). *Res:* Notch toughness and plastic fatigue properties of steel; weldability of steel. *Mailing Add:* 258 Whitaker Lab #5 Lehigh Univ Bethlehem PA 18015

STOUT, THOMAS MELVILLE, b Ann Arbor, Mich, Nov 26, 25; m 47; c 6. ELECTRICAL ENGINEERING, AUTOMATIC CONTROL SYSTEMS. *Educ:* Iowa State Col, BS, 46; Univ Mich, Ann Arbor, MSE, 47, PhD(elec eng), 54. *Prof Exp:* Jr engr, Emerson Elec Mfg Co, 47-48; instr elec eng, Univ Wash, 48-53, asst prof, 53-54; res engr, Schlumberger Instrument Co, 54-56; mgr process anal, TRW Comput Div, 56-64 & Bunker-Ramo Corp, 64-65; PRES, PROFIMATICS, INC, 65- *Mem:* Instrument Soc Am; Inst Elec & Electronics Engrs; Am Inst Chem Engrs; Tech Asn Pulp & Paper Indust; Am Soc Eng Educ. *Res:* Application of computers for simulation and control of industrial processes; application of systems engineering techniques to social problems. *Mailing Add:* Profimatics Inc 77 Rolling Oaks Dr Thousand Oaks CA 91361

STOUT, THOMPSON MYLAN, b Big Springs, Nebr, Aug 16, 14; m 40. GEOLOGY, VERTEBRATE PALEONTOLOGY. *Educ:* Univ Nebr, Lincoln, BSc, 36, MSc, 37. *Prof Exp:* Res asst vert paleont, State Mus, 33-38, from instr to prof, 38-57, assoc prof, 57-68, prof, 68-80, EMER PROF GEOL, UNIV NEBR, LINCOLN, 80-, ASSOC CUR, STATE MUS, 57- *Concurrent Pos:* Res assoc, Frick Lab, Am Mus Natural Hist, New York, NY, 38-; studies of fossil rodents & geol in Europ museums, 48-79; corresp, Nat Mus Natural Hist, Paris, 66. *Mem:* Geol Soc Am; Soc Vert Paleont; Paleont Soc; Am Soc Mammal; NY Acad Sci. *Res:* Stratigraphy and vertebrate paleontology, with special reference to the Tertiary and Quaternary and to intercontinental correlations in connection with revisionary studies of fossil rodents; cyclic sedimentation and geomorphology. *Mailing Add:* Dept Geol 433 Morrill Hall Univ Nebr Lincoln NE 68588

STOUT, VIRGIL L, b Emporia, Kans, Mar 14, 21; m 46; c 2. PHYSICS. *Educ:* Univ Mo, PhD(physics), 51. *Prof Exp:* Res assoc, Stanford Res Inst, 51-52; physicist, Gen Elec Co Res Labs, 52-57, mgr phys electronics br, Gen Elec Res & Develop Ctr, 57-68, mgr solid state & electronics lab, 68-75, consult electronics, 75-76, RES & DEVELOP MGR, ELECTRONICS SCI & ENG, GEN ELEC RES & DEVELOP CTR, GEN ELEC CO, 76- *Mem:* AAAS; Inst Elec & Electronics Engrs; Am Phys Soc. *Res:* Experimental investigations of electronic properties of surfaces. *Mailing Add:* Electronics Sci & Eng Gen Elec Res & Develop Ctr PO Box 8 Schenectady NY 12301

STOUT, VIRGINIA FALK, b Buffalo, NY, Jan 5, 32; m 55, 77; c 2. ENVIRONMENTAL CHEMISTRY. *Educ:* Cornell Univ, AB, 53; Harvard Univ, AM, 55; Univ Wash, PhD(org chem), 61. *Prof Exp:* RES CHEMIST, UTILIZATION RES DIV, NORTHWEST & ALASKA FISHERIES, CTR, NAT MARINE FISHERIES SERV, NAT OCEANIC & ATMOSPHERIC ADMIN, 61- *Concurrent Pos:* Affil assoc prof, Col Fisheries, Univ Wash, 72- *Mem:* AAAS; Asn Women in Sci; Am Chem Soc. *Res:* Effects of processing on the wholesomeness of foods; pesticide residues in fishery products; mutagenic substances in foods. *Mailing Add:* Northwest & AK Fisheries Ctr URD 2725 Montlake Blvd E Seattle WA 98112

STOUT, WILLIAM F, b Wilkensburg, Pa, July 3, 40; m 65. MATHEMATICS. *Educ:* Pa State Univ, BS, 62; Purdue Univ, MS, 64, PhD(probability), 67. *Prof Exp:* Asst prof, 67-73, ASSOC PROF MATH, UNIV ILL, URBANA-CHAMPAIGN, 73- *Mem:* Am Statist Asn; Am Math Soc; Inst Math Statist. *Res:* Probability limit theorems. *Mailing Add:* Univ of Ill Dept of Math Champaign IL 61820

STOUTAMIRE, DONALD WESLEY, b Roanoke, Va, Mar 10, 31; m 56; c 3. ORGANIC CHEMISTRY. *Educ:* Roanoke Col, BS, 52; Univ Wis, PhD(org chem), 57. *Prof Exp:* CHEMIST, SHELL DEVELOP CO, 57- *Mem:* Am Chem Soc; AAAS. *Res:* Agricultural chemicals; animal health products. *Mailing Add:* 904 Bel Passi Dr Modesto CA 95350

STOUTAMIRE, WARREN PETRIE, b Salem, Va, July 5, 28; m 63; c 2. PLANT TAXONOMY, EVOLUTION. *Educ:* Roanoke Col, BS, 49; Univ Ore, MS, 50; Ind Univ, PhD(taxon), 54. *Prof Exp:* Botanist, Cranbrook Inst Sci, 54-66; assoc prof, 66-78, PROF BIOL, UNIV AKRON, 79- *Concurrent Pos:* Collabr, Bot Garden, Univ Mich, 57-67. *Mem:* AAAS; Royal Hort Soc; Am Soc Plant Taxon; Bot Soc Am; Asn Trop Biol. *Res:* Evolution of the genus Gaillardia; physiology of orchid seed germination; pollination of terrestrial orchid species; Australian orchid evolution. *Mailing Add:* Dept of Biol Univ of Akron Akron OH 44325

STOUTER, VINCENT PAUL, b Jersey City, NJ, Apr 28, 24; m 53; c 5. ZOOLOGY, NEUROENDOCRINOLOGY. *Educ:* Spring Hill Col, BS, 49; Fordham Univ, MS, 51; Univ Buffalo, PhD(biol), 59. *Prof Exp:* Instr biol, physiol & genetics, Canisius Col, 51-52; instr biol, anat & genetics, Gannon Col, 52-53; instr gen chem, D'Youville Col, 53-54; from asst prof to assoc prof, 59-69, chmn dept biol, 59-71, PROF BIOL, PHYSIOL & ANAT, CANISIUS COL, 69-, CHMN HEALTH SCI ADV & RECOMMENDATION COMT, 62- *Mem:* NY Acad Sci; Asn Am Med Cols. *Res:* Hypothalamic neurosecretion; electrolyte and salt balance in mammals. *Mailing Add:* Dept of Biol Canisius Col Buffalo NY 14208

STOVER, BETSY JONES, b Salt Lake City, Utah, May 13, 26; div; c 2. RADIOBIOLOGY, PHARMACOLOGY. *Educ:* Univ Utah, BA, 47; Univ Calif, PhD(chem), 50. *Prof Exp:* Asst, Univ Calif, 47-49, asst, Radiation Lab, 48-50; asst res prof chem, Univ Utah, 50-58, assoc res prof, 58-70; assoc prof pharmacol, 70-76, dir grad training prog, 74-80, PROF PHARMACOL, SCH MED, UNIV NC, CHAPEL HILL, 76-, FAC MEM, CURRICULUM TOXICOL, 79- *Concurrent Pos:* Chemist, Radiobiol Lab, Univ Utah, 50-70, adj assoc res prof anat, Univ NC, 70-75, adj res prof, 75-79; consult, Radiobiol Lab, 70-; mem panel eval NSF Grad Fel Applns, Nat Res Coun, 74-76 & Postdoctoral Fel Applns, 78-; mem adv comt, Health Physics Div, Oak Ridge Nat Lab, 75-77; referee, Am J Physics, 77-; adj prof pharmacol, Univ Utah, 79-; mem, Task Group 6, Sci Comt 57, Nat Coun on Radiation Protection & Measurements, 80- *Mem:* Am Phys Soc; Am Chem Soc; Radiation Res Soc; Am Soc Pharmacol & Exp Therapeut; Am Asn Univ Profs; AAAS. *Res:* Toxicology of radionuclides; rate processes in biology. *Mailing Add:* Dept of Pharmacol Univ of NC Chapel Hill NC 27514

STOVER, DENNIS EUGENE, b Benton Harbor, Mich, July 30, 44; m 65; c 2. CHEMICAL ENGINEERING, INORGANIC CHEMISTRY. *Educ:* Kalamazoo Col, BA, 66; Univ Mich, BSE, 67, MSE, 68, PhD(chem eng), 75. *Prof Exp:* Process engr chem process design, Charles E Sech & Assocs, 71-72; sr res engr in-situ uranium mining, Atlantic Richfield Co, 74-78; CHIEF ENGR IN-SITU URANIUM MINING, EVEREST EXPLOR CO, 78- *Mem:* Am Chem Soc; Am Inst Chem Engrs; Soc Mining Engrs. *Res:* Kinetics and modeling of reactions associated with in-situ leaching of uranium and copper minerals; fundamental kinetic studies of electrochemical processes. *Mailing Add:* Everest Explor Co PO Box 1339 Corpus Christi TX 78403

STOVER, E(DWARD) R(OY), b Washington, DC, Apr 9, 29; m 56; c 2. PHYSICAL METALLURGY, CERAMICS. *Educ:* Mass Inst Technol, SB, 50, SM, 52, ScD(metall), 56. *Prof Exp:* Asst metall, Mass Inst Technol, 50-55; ceramist, Res Lab, Gen Elec Co, 55-65; assoc res engr, Dept Mining Technol, Univ Calif, Berkeley, 65-66; CONSULT CERAMIC ENGR, RE-ENTRY & ENVIRON SYSTS DIV, GEN ELEC CO, PHILADELPHIA, 66- *Mem:* AAAS; Am Ceramic Soc; Am Soc Metals; Am Inst Mining, Metall & Petrol Engrs. *Res:* Mechanical behavior, processing techniques and microstructure of structural materials; carbon-carbon 3D-7D composites; carbon-graphite; pyrolytic graphite; carbides, oxides; reinforced plastic chars; cermets; cemented carbides; high temperature application; space and reentry application. *Mailing Add:* 416 Homestead Rd Wayne PA 19101

STOVER, JAMES ANDERSON, JR, b Hayesville, NC, June 9, 37; m 63. OPERATIONS RESEARCH, SYSTEMS SCIENCE. *Educ:* Univ Ga, BS, 59; Univ Ala, MA, 66, PhD(math), 69. *Prof Exp:* Physicist, US Army Missile Command, Redstone Arsenal, Ala, 60-62; control systs engr, Marshall Space Flight Ctr, NASA, 62-65; consult systs anal, Anal Serv, Inc, Va, 69; asst prof math, Memphis State Univ, 69-74; prin staff, 74-80, SR SCIENTIST, ORI, INC, APPL RES LAB, PA STATE UNIV, 80- *Res:* Automatic control systems; stability theory; underwater sound propagation; systems science and design. *Mailing Add:* Pa State Univ Appl Res Lab Box 30 State College PA 16801

STOVER, LEWIS EUGENE, b Philadelphia, Pa, Apr 12, 25; m 51; c 3. PALEONTOLOGY, PALYNOLOGY. *Educ:* Dickinson Col, BSc, 51; Univ Rochester, PhD, 56. *Prof Exp:* Res geologist, Esso Prod Res Co, Tex, 56-65, res assoc, 66-71, mem staff, Esso Standard Oil Ltd, 71-74, MEM STAFF, EXXON PROD RES CO, HOUSTON, 74- *Mem:* Geol Soc Am; Paleont Soc; Int Asn Plant Taxon. *Res:* Geology; fossil spore; pollen; microplankton; small calcareous fossils; acid-insoluble microfossils. *Mailing Add:* Exxon Prod Res Co Box 2189 Houston TX 77001

STOVER, RAYMOND WEBSTER, b Pittsburgh, Pa, Mar 20, 38; m 60; c 2. PHYSICS. *Educ:* Lehigh Univ, BS, 60; Syracuse Univ, MS, 62, PhD(physics), 67. *Prof Exp:* PRIN SCIENTIST, XEROX CORP, 66- *Concurrent Pos:* Adj fac mem, Rochester Inst Technol, 74- *Mem:* AAAS; Soc Photog Scientists & Engrs. *Res:* Search for an electron-proton charge difference; xerographic development process; electrostatics; triboelectricity; small particle physics. *Mailing Add:* 566 Bending Bough Dr Webster NY 14580

STOVER, ROBERT HARRY, b Chatham, Ont, Dec 2, 26; m 49. PLANT PATHOLOGY. *Educ:* Ont Agr Col, BSA, 47; Univ Toronto, PhD(plant path), 50. *Prof Exp:* Plant pathologist, Dominion Lab Plant Path, Ont, 47-51; plant pathologist, Dept Trop Res, United Brands Co, 51-57, head dept plant path, 57-61, asst sci dir, Dept Trop Res, 61-75, dir, Vining C Dunlap Labs, 75-78, CONSULT TROP AGR, UNITED BRANDS CO, 79- *Mem:* Am Phytopath Soc; Can Phytopath Soc. *Res:* Diseases of tropical crops; soil microbiology. *Mailing Add:* Vining C Dunlap Labs United Brands Co La Lima Honduras

STOVER, SAMUEL LANDIS, b Bucks Co, Pa, Nov 19, 30; m; c 3. MEDICINE. *Educ:* Goshen Col, BA, 52; Jefferson Med Col, MD, 59; Am Bd Pediat, dipl, 69; Am Bd Phys Med & Rehab, dipl, 71. *Prof Exp:* Intern, St Luke's Hosp, Bethlehem, Pa, 59-60; gen pract in Ark, 60-61 & Indonesia, 61-64; resident pediat, Children's Hosp, Philadelphia, 64-66; asst med dir, Children's Seashore House, Atlantic City, NJ, 66-67; resident phys med & rehab, Univ Pa, 67-69; assoc prof pediat & prof phys med & rehab, 69-76, PROF REHAB MED & CHMN DEPT, UNIV HOSP & CLINS, UNIV ALA, BIRMINGHAM, 76- *Mem:* Am Acad Pediat; Am Acad Phys Med & Rehab; Am Cong Rehab Med; AMA. *Mailing Add:* Spain Rehab Ctr 1717 Sixth Ave S Birmingham AL 35233

STOW, RICHARD W, b Medina, Ohio, June 13, 16; m 45; c 4. BIOPHYSICS. *Educ:* Mich State Univ, BS, 37; Pa State Univ, MS, 40; Univ Minn, PhD(biophys), 53. *Prof Exp:* Instr physics, William Penn Col, 46-47; asst biophys, Mayo Grad Sch Med, Univ Minn, 47-53; from asst prof med to assoc prof phys med & physiol, 53-72, PROF PHYS MED & PHYSIOL, COL MED, OHIO STATE UNIV, 72- *Honors & Awards:* Fulbright Lectr, Physiol, Iran, 60-61. *Mem:* Biophys Soc.*Res:* Circulatory physiology; instrumentation in biology. *Mailing Add:* Dept of Phys Med Ohio State Univ Col of Med Columbus OH 43210

STOW, STEPHEN HARRINGTON, b Oklahoma City, Okla, Sept 18, 40; m 65. GEOCHEMISTRY. *Educ:* Vanderbilt Univ, BA, 62; Rice Univ, MA, 65, PhD(geochem), 66. *Prof Exp:* Res scientist, Plant Foods Res Div, Continental Oil Co, 66-69; from asst prof to prof geol, Univ Ala, Tuscaloosa, 69-80; PROG MGR & SR GEOLOGIST, OAK RIDGE NAT LAB, 80- *Concurrent Pos:* Consult, Ala Geol Surv, 69-74 & Indust Co, 73-80. *Mem:* Am Geophys Union; Geochem Soc; Geol Soc Am. *Res:* Geochemistry and element distribution in igneous and metamorphic rocks, geology and geochemistry of phosphates; environmental geology; geochemistry of mafic rocks of southern Appalachians; sulfide ore deposits; trace elements in Galena. *Mailing Add:* Box X Oak Ridge Nat Lab Oak Ridge TN 37830

STOWE, BRUCE BERNOT, b Neuilly-sur-Seine, France, Dec 9, 27; US citizen; m 51; c 2. PLANT PHYSIOLOGY, BIOCHEMISTRY. *Educ:* Calif Inst Technol, BS, 50; Harvard Univ, MA, 51, PhD(biol), 54. *Hon Degrees:* MA, Yale Univ, 71. *Prof Exp:* NSF fel, Univ Col NWales, 54-55; instr biol, Harvard Univ, 55-58, lectr bot, 58-59, tutor biochem sci, 56-58; asst prof bot, 59-63, assoc prof biol, 63-71, dir, Marsh Bot Gardens, 75-78, PROF BIOL, YALE UNIV, 71-, PROF FORESTRY, 74- *Concurrent Pos:* Mem, Metab Biol Panel, NSF, 60-61; Subcomt Plant Sci Planning & Comt Sci & Pub Policy, Nat Acad Sci, 64-66; Guggenheim fel, Nat Ctr Sci Res, France, 65-66; vis prof, Univ Osaka Prefecture, Japan, 72 & 73 & Waite Agr Res Inst, Univ Adelaide, 72-73. *Mem:* Am Soc Biol Chemists; Am Soc Plant Physiologists (secy, 63-65); Bot Soc Am; Soc Develop Biol; Phytochem Soc NAm. *Res:* Biochemistry and physiology of plant hormones, especially auxins, gibberellins and their relations to lipids and membrane structure. *Mailing Add:* Kline Biol Tower Yale Univ Box 6666 New Haven CT 06511

STOWE, CLARENCE M, b Brooklyn, NY, Mar 19, 22; m 46; c 3. PHARMACOLOGY, VETERINARY MEDICINE. *Educ:* NY Univ, BS, 44; Queens Col, NY, BS, 46; Univ Pa, VMD, 50; Univ Minn, PhD, 55. *Prof Exp:* Instr, 50-55, assoc prof, 55-57, prof & asst dean, 57-60, head dept, 60-71, PROF PHARMACOL, 60-, PROF LARGE ANIMAL CLIN SCI, COL VET MED, UNIV MINN, ST PAUL, 77- *Concurrent Pos:* Spec appointee, Rockefeller Found, Columbia Univ, 64-65; prof, Nat Univ Columbia, 64-65; chmn comt vet drug efficacy, Nat Acad Sci-Nat Res Coun; mem tox study sect, NIH, 65-69; vis scholar, Univ Cambridge, 71-72; mem coun biol & therapeut agents, Am Vet Med Asn. *Mem:* Soc Exp Biol & Med; Am Soc Pharmacol & Exp Therapeut; Am Soc Vet Physiol & Pharmacol; Am Vet Med Asn; Am Dairy Sci Asn. *Res:* Drug distribution and excretion, muscle relaxants, chemotherapy of large domestic and wild animals. *Mailing Add:* Dept of Clin Sci Col of Vet Med Univ of Minn St Paul MN 55101

STOWE, DAVID F, b Vincennes, Ind, Jan 27, 45. CARDIOVASCULAR PHYSIOLOGY, ELECTROPHYSIOLOGY. *Educ:* Ind Univ, Bloomington, AB, 68, MA, 69; Mich State Univ, PhD(physiol), 74. *Prof Exp:* Fel cardiovasc physiol, Cardiovasc Res Inst, Univ Calif, San Francisco, 74-76; ASST PROF PHYSIOL, MED COL WIS, 76-, ASSOC PROF ANESTHESIOL, 81- *Concurrent Pos:* Vis prof biol, Marquette Univ, 71; mem circulation comt, Am Heart Asn, circulation group, Am Physiol Soc. *Mem:* Am Physiol Soc; Sigma Xi; Soc Exp Biol & Med. *Res:* Effects of hypoxia reactive hyperemia and exercise on myocardial mechanics and metabolism; effects of adenosine on myocardial and oxygen consumption; effects of hydrogen ion changes on electrophysiology and of heart muscle cells ; effect of halothane on action potential properties of cardiac tissue. *Mailing Add:* Dept Anesthsiol Res Serv/151 Wood Vet Admin Ctr Milwaukee WI 53193

STOWE, DAVID WILLIAM, b Three Rivers, Mich, Jan 1, 44; m 66; c 3. OPTICS, ACOUSTICS. *Educ:* Univ Wis-Madison, BS, 66; Univ Ill, Urbana, MS, 67, PhD(physics), 71. *Prof Exp:* Sr physicist, Appl Physics Lab, Johns Hopkins Univ, 71-77; PROG MGR FIBER OPTIC SENSORS, SURFACE ACOUST WAVES & THIN FILMS, GOULD LABS ELEC & ELECTRONICS RES, GOULD INC, 77- *Concurrent Pos:* Instr, Harper Community Col, 78- *Mem:* Acoust Soc Am; Optical Soc Am. *Res:* Interested in acousto-optic and electro-optic effects with particular emphasis on transducer development. *Mailing Add:* Gould Labs 40 Gould Ctr Rolling Meadows IL 60008

STOWE, HOWARD DENISON, b Greenfield, Mass, Mar 31, 27. PATHOLOGY. *Educ:* Univ Mass, BS, 48; Mich State Univ, MS, 56, DVM, 60, PhD(vet path), 62. *Prof Exp:* Instr animal husb & dairy prod, Bristol County Agr Sch, Mass, 49-53; asst animal husb, anat & vet path, Mich State Univ, 55-60; assoc prof vet sci & chief nutrit sect, Univ Ky, 63-68; from asst prof to assoc prof path, Sch Med, Univ NC, Chapel Hill, 68-74; assoc prof path, Sch Vet Med, Auburn Univ, 74-80, assoc prof parasitol, 77-70; MEM FAC, DEPT LARGE ANIMAL SURG & MED, COL VET MED, MICH STATE UNIV, 80- *Concurrent Pos:* Vis researcher, Dunn Nutrit Lab, Cambridge Univ, 62 & Dept Nutrit & Biochem, Denmark Polytech Inst, Copenhagen, 62; pathologist, Div Lab Animal Med, Sch Med, Univ NC, Chapel Hill. *Mem:* Am Vet Med Asn; Conf Res Workers Animal Dis; Am Asn Lab Animal Sci; Am Inst Nutrit. *Res:* Effects of lead upon reproduction in rats; cadmium toxicity in rabbits; canine and avian lead toxicity. *Mailing Add:* Dept Large Animal Surg & Med Auburn Univ Sch of Vet Med East Lansing MI 48824

STOWE, KEITH S, b Midland, Mich, Feb 16, 43; m 67; c 2. ELEMENTARY PARTICLE PHYSICS. *Educ:* Ill Inst Technol, BS, 65; Univ Calif, San Diego, MS, 67, PhD(physics), 71. *Prof Exp:* Lectr physics, 71-74, asst prof, 74-76, assoc prof, 76-81, PROF PHYSICS, CALIF POLYTECH STATE UNIV, SAN LUIS OBISPO, 81- *Mem:* Am Phys Soc; Am Asn Physics Teachers. *Res:* Elementary particle theory; oceanography; thermodynamics. *Mailing Add:* Dept Physics Calif Polytech State Univ San Luis Obispo CA 93407

STOWE, LAWRENCE GORDON, plant ecology, plant biogeography, see previous edition

STOWE, ROBERT ALLEN, b Kalamazoo, Mich, July 26, 24; div; c 4. SURFACE CHEMISTRY, CATALYSIS. *Educ:* Kalamazoo Col, BA, 48; Brown Univ, PhD(chem), 53. *Prof Exp:* Res chemist, 52-58, res & develop lab, Ludington Div, 58-64, sr res chemist, 64-69, Hydrocarbons & Monomers Res Lab, 69-71, assoc scientist, 71-74, assoc scientist, Hydrocarbons & Energy Res Lab, 74-79, ASSOC SCIENTIST, MICH DIV RES, DOW CHEM USA, 79- *Concurrent Pos:* Chmn, Div Indust & Eng Chem, Am Chem Soc, 82. *Honors & Awards:* Victor J Azbe Lime Award, Nat Lime Asn, 64. *Mem:* Am Chem Soc; Am Inst Chemists; Sigma Xi; Catalysis Soc. *Res:* Heterogeneous catalysis; hydrocarbon processes; inorganic chemistry; zeolite chemistry; organic fluorine chemistry; statistics; carbon monoxide methanation; Fischer-Tropsch synthesis; coal liquefaction. *Mailing Add:* Org Chemicals Res Lab 677 Bldg Dow Chem USA Midland MI 48640

STOWELL, EWELL ADDISON, b Ashland, Ill, Sept 2, 22; m 53. PLANT PATHOLOGY. *Educ:* Ill State Norm Univ, BEd, 43; Univ Wis, MS, 47, PhD(bot), 55. *Prof Exp:* Asst bot, Univ Wis, 46-47; instr, Univ Wis, Milwaukee, 47-49, asst, 49-53; from instr to assoc prof, 53-66, chmn dept biol, 72-77, PROF BOT, ALBION COL, 66- *Concurrent Pos:* Vis lectr, Univ Wis, 63; assoc prof, Univ Mich, 64. *Mem:* Bot Soc Am; Mycol Soc Am; Am Inst Biol Sci. *Res:* Taxonomy and morphology of Ascomycetes. *Mailing Add:* Dept of Biol Albion Col Albion MI 49224

STOWELL, JAMES KENT, b Elgin, Ill, July 9, 36; m 65; c 2. POLYMER CHEMISTRY, ORGANIC CHEMISTRY. *Educ:* Knox Col, BA, 58; Univ Iowa, PhD(org chem), 65. *Prof Exp:* Sr res chemist org, PPG Industs Inc, 65-68; sr res chemist polymer, A E Staley Mfg Co, 68-78; SR CHEMIST POLYMER, MORTON CHEM CO, 78- *Mem:* Am Chem Soc. *Res:* Development of new polymer products for use in printing inks, coatings, and adhesives. *Mailing Add:* Morton Chem Co 1275 Lake Ave Woodstock IL 60098

STOWELL, JOHN CHARLES, b Passaic, NJ, Sept 10, 38; m 64; c 2. ORGANIC CHEMISTRY. *Educ:* Rutgers Univ, New Brunswick, BS, 60; Mass Inst Technol, PhD(org chem), 64. *Prof Exp:* Res specialist, Cent Res Lab, 3M Co, 64-69; NIH fel org chem, Ohio State Univ, 69-70; from asst prof to assoc prof, 70-80, PROF ORG CHEM, UNIV NEW ORLEANS, 80- *Concurrent Pos:* Res Corp & Petrol Res Fund grants, Univ New Orleans, 71-73 & 80-82. *Mem:* Am Chem Soc. *Res:* Organic synthesis; small ring heterocyclic compounds; sterically hindered compounds; three-carbon homologating agents; carbanions. *Mailing Add:* Dept Chem Univ New Orleans New Orleans LA 70122

STOWELL, ROBERT EUGENE, b Cashmere, Wash, Dec 25, 14; m 45; c 2. PATHOLOGY. *Educ:* Stanford Univ, AB, 36, MD, 41; Wash Univ, PhD(path), 44. *Prof Exp:* From asst to assoc prof path, Sch Med, Wash Univ, 42-48; prof path & oncol, Sch Med & dir cancer res, Med Ctr, Univ Kans, 48-59, chmn dept oncol, 48-51, path & oncol, 51-59, pathologist-in-chief, 51-59; sci dir, Armed Forces Inst Path, Washington, DC, 59-67; mem nat adv comt, Nat Ctr Primate Biol, 67-68, dir, 69-71, chmn dept path, 67-69, asst dean, Sch Med, 67-71, PROF PATH, SCH MED, UNIV CALIF, DAVIS, 67- *Concurrent Pos:* Commonwealth Fund advan med study & res fel, Inst Cell Res, Stockholm, Sweden, 46-47; mem morphol & genetics study sect, NIH, 49-53 & path study sect, 54-55, chmn, 55-57, mem path training comt, div gen med sci, 58-61, chmn animal resources adv comt, Div Res Resources, 70-74; mem, Intersoc Comt Res Potential in Path, 56-80, pres, 57-60; vis prof, Sch Med, Univ Md, 60-67; mem fedn bd, Fedn Am Soc Exp Biol, 63-66; mem subcomt comp path, Comt Path, Nat Acad Sci-Nat Res Coun, 63-69, subcomt manpower needs in path, 64-69 & US Nat comt, Int Coun Socs Path, 66-80, chmn, 72-75; mem, Intersoc Comt Path Info, 65-69, chmn, 66-67; mem adv med bd, Leonard Wood Mem, 65-69; mem div biol & agr, Nat Res Coun, 65-68 & comt doc data anat & clin path, 66-68; mem bd dirs, Coun Biol Sci Info, Nat Acad Sci, 67-70; ed, Lab Invest, Int Acad Path, 67-72; mem med adv comt & consult, Vet Admin Hosp, Martinez, Calif, 69-72; mem, Int Coun Socs Path, 70-; mem bd dirs, Univ Asn Res & Educ Path, 74-, secy-treas, 77-; mem sci adv bd, Nat Ctr Toxicol Res, 76-79; vpres, Am Registry Path, 76-78, pres, 78-80. *Mem:* Col Am Pathologists; Am Soc Clin Path; Am Asn Path & Bact (vpres, 69-70, pres, 70-71); Am Soc Exp Path (vpres, 63-64, pres, 64-65); Int Acad Path (vpres, 57-58, pres elect, 58-59, pres, 59-60). *Res:* Cancer; experimental pathology; comparative pathology. *Mailing Add:* Dept Path Univ Calif Sch Med Davis CA 95616

STOWENS, DANIEL, b New York, NY, Oct 27, 19; m 75; c 2. PATHOLOGY. *Educ:* Columbia Univ, AB, 41, MD, 43; Am Bd Pediat, dipl, 51; Am Bd Path, dipl, 54. *Prof Exp:* Chief, Sect Pediat Path, Armed Forces Inst Path, US Army, Washington, DC, 54-58; assoc prof path, Univ Southern Calif, 58-61 & Univ Louisville, 61-65; PATHOLOGIST, ST LUKE'S MEM HOSP CTR, 66- *Concurrent Pos:* Registr, Am Registry Pediat Path, 54-58; consult, Walter Reed Army Hosp, 56-58; pathologist, Children's Hosp, Los Angeles, 58-61; dir labs & chief prof servs, Children's Hosp, Louisville, 61-65. *Mem:* Fel Am Soc Clin Path; Soc Pediat Res; Am Asn Path & Bact; Int Acad Path. *Res:* Pediatric pathology, especially pathophysiology of fetus and mechanisms of development; dermatoglyphics. *Mailing Add:* St Luke's Mem Hosp Ctr Utica NY 13503

STOY, WILLIAM S, b New York, NY, Sept 23, 25; m 49; c 2. CHEMISTRY. *Educ:* Queens Col, NY, BS, 45; Polytech Inst Brooklyn, MS, 50. *Prof Exp:* Chemist paint ptod res & develop, Mobil Oil Co, Ind, 45-50, supvr, 50-58; sr chemist, Cities Serv Co, Cranbury, NJ, 58-64, mgr plastics applns, 64-71, mgr coatings, plastics & inks, Petrochem Res, 71-77; GROUP LEADER, INDUST TECH SERV, ENGELHARD MINERALS & CHEM, MENLO PARK, EDISON, 77- *Mem:* Am Chem Soc; Soc Plastics Engrs; Am Soc Testing & Mat. *Res:* Plastics development; coatings and inks; pigment syntheses and applications; flame retardants; polymer chemistry; extenders-inorganic silicates; catalysis. *Mailing Add:* 221 Herrontown Rd Princeton NJ 08540

STOYLE, JUDITH, b Quincy, Mass, Aug 26, 28. APPLIED STATISTICS. *Educ:* Univ Mass, BS, 50; Pa State Univ, MS, 57, PhD(agr econ, statist), 62. *Prof Exp:* Secy, Fuerst Stock Farm, Pine Plains, NY, 50-52; off mgr, Md Aberdeen Angus Asn, Towson, 52-54; partner, Nat Aberdeen-Angus Sales Serv, 54-55; res asst agr econ, Pa State Univ, 55-57, asst prof statist, 57-66; assoc prof, 66-74, PROF STATIST, TEMPLE UNIV, 74- *Concurrent Pos:* Consult statist, Head Start Eval Ctr, 67-70; trustee, Morris Animal Found, Denver, 71- *Mem:* Am Statist Asn; Am Inst Decision Sci. *Res:* Mobility of Pennsylvania rural youth; characteristics of inner city children; influence of Head Start on inner city children; incomes of Actors' Equity members; factors related to cat mortality. *Mailing Add:* Dept of Statist Temple Univ Philadelphia PA 19122

ST-PIERRE, CLAUDE, b Montreal, Que, Jan 7, 32; m 54; c 2. NUCLEAR PHYSICS. *Educ:* Univ Montreal, BSc, 54, MSc, 56, DSc(physics), 59. *Prof Exp:* Sci officer, Defence Res Bd Can, 58-61; Nat Res Coun Can fel, Ctr Nuclear Res, Strasbourg, France, 61-62; from asst prof to assoc prof, 62-70, chmn dept, 73-79, dean, Sch Grad Studies, 79-83, PROF PHYSICS, LAVAL UNIV, 70- *Mem:* Can Asn Physicists; Am Phys Soc. *Res:* Nuclear spectroscopy. *Mailing Add:* Dept Physics Laval Univ Quebec PQ G1K 7P4 Can

ST-PIERRE, JACQUES, b Trois-Rivieres, PQ, Aug 30, 20; c 6. APPLIED STATISTICS. *Educ:* Univ Montreal, LSc, 45 & 48, MSc, 51; Univ NC, PhD(math statist), 54. *Prof Exp:* From asst prof to assoc prof math, 47-60, vdean, Fac Sci, 61-64, head dept comput sci, 66-69, dir, Comput Ctr, 64-72, PROF MATH STATIST, UNIV MONTREAL, 60-, VPRES PLANNING, 72- *Concurrent Pos:* Consult, Inst Microbiol & Hyg, 54- *Mem:* Can Asn Univ Teachers (pres, 65-66); Inst Math Statist; Am Statist Asn; Biometrics Soc; Asn Inst Res. *Res:* Statistical methods relative to public health and epidemiology. *Mailing Add:* Off VPres Planning Univ Montreal CP 6128 Montreal PQ H3C 3J7 Can

STRAAT, PATRICIA ANN, b Rochester, NY, Mar 28, 36. BIOCHEMISTRY, ENZYMOLOGY. *Educ:* Oberlin Col, BA, 58; Johns Hopkins Univ, PhD(biochem), 64. *Prof Exp:* Lab instr biol, Johns Hopkins Univ, 58-59, USPHS res fel radiol sci, 64-67, res assoc, 67-68, asst prof, 68-70; sr res biochemist, Biospherics, Inc, 70-75, res coordr, 75-78, dir res, 78-80; grants assoc, Div Res Grants, NIH, 80-81; CHIEF, PLANNING & COORD SECT, PROG OPERS BR, NAT TOXICOL PROG, NAT INST ENVIRON HEALTH SCI, 81- *Concurrent Pos:* Lectr, Dept Radiol Sci, Sch Hyg & Pub Health, Johns Hopkins Univ, 70-72. *Mem:* AAAS; Am Inst Biol Sci; Am Chem Soc; NY Acad Sci. *Res:* Electron transport and inorganic nitrogen metabolism; mechanisms of nucleic acid replication; extraterrestial life detection; biological and chemical aspects of water pollution. *Mailing Add:* 5103 Wetheredsville Rd Baltimore MD 21207

STRAATSMA, BRADLEY RALPH, b Grand Rapids, Mich, Dec 29, 27; c 3. MEDICINE. *Educ:* Yale Univ, MD, 51. *Prof Exp:* Intern, New Haven Hosp, Yale Univ, 51-52; vis scholar, Col Physicians & Surgeons, Columbia Univ, 52, asst resident, 55-58; spec clin trainee, Nat Inst Neurol Dis & Blindness, 58-59; asst prof surg & ophthal, 59-73, chief, Div Ophthal, 59-68, PROF OPHTHAL, SCH MED, UNIV CALIF, LOS ANGELES, 63-, CHMN DEPT, 68-, PROF SURG, 80-, DIR, JULES STEIN EYE INST, 64- *Concurrent Pos:* Resident, Inst Ophthal, Presby Hosp, New York, 55-58; fel ophthalmic path, Armed Forces Inst Path, Walter Reed Army Med Ctr, DC, 58-59; fel ophthal, Wilmer Inst, Johns Hopkins Univ, 58-59; mem vision res training comt, Nat Inst Neurol Dis & Blindness, 59-63 & neurol & sensory dis prog proj comt, 64-68; consult to Surgeon Gen, USPHS, 59-68; ophthal examr, aid to blind progs, Calif Dept Social Welfare, 59-; mem med adv comt, Nat Coun Combat Blindness, 60-; consult, Vet Admin Hosp, Long Beach, Calif, 60-75; attend physician, Vet Admin Ctr, Wadsworth Gen Hosp, Los Angeles, 60-; attend physician & consult, Los Angeles County Harbor Gen Hosp, Torrance, 60-; vis consult, St John's Hosp, Santa Monica, 60-; mem courtesy staff, Santa Monica Hosp, 60- & St Vincent's Hosp, Los Angeles, 60-; mem sensory dis serv panel, Bur States Serv, USPHS, 63-65; trustee, John Thomas Dye Sch, Los Angeles, 67-72; prof, New Orleans Acad Ophthal, 68-; ophthalmologist in chief, Univ Calif, Los Angeles Hosp, 68-; mem med adv bd, Int Eye Found, 70-; mem nat adv comt, Pan-Am Cong Ophthal, 71-72 & bd dirs, Conrad Berens Int Eye Film Libr, 71-; mem, Am Bd Ophthal, 72- & Pan-Am Ophthal Found. *Honors & Awards:* William Warren Hoppin Award, NY Acad Med, 56; co-recipient, Silver Award, Cert of Merit, AMA, 57, Knapp Award, 61 & Cert of Appreciation, Bd Trustees, 68; co-recipient, Silver Award, Am Soc Clin Path & Col Am Pathologists, 62; co-recipient, Conrad Berens Award, Int Eye Film Festival, 65; Award of Merit, Am Acad Ophthal & Otolaryngol, 67. *Mem:* Am Acad Ophthal (pres, 77); AMA; Asn Univ Prof Ophthal (pres, 74); Am Ophthal Soc; Asn Res Vision & Ophthal. *Res:* Ophthalmology. *Mailing Add:* Jules Stein Eye Inst Univ of Calif Sch of Med Los Angeles CA 90024

STRACHAN, DONALD STEWART, b Highland Park, Mich, 32; m; c 4. HISTOLOGY, GROSS ANATOMY. *Educ:* Wayne State Univ, BA, 54; Univ Mich, DDS, 60, MS, 62, PhD(anat), 64. *Prof Exp:* From instr to assoc prof oral biol, Sch Dent & Anat, Sch Med, 63-73, PROF DENT & ORAL BIOL, SCH DENT, UNIV MICH, ANN ARBOR, 73-, ASST DEAN, 69- *Concurrent Pos:* USPHS res career award, 63-68; consult Vet Admin Hosp, DC, 66-68 & coun dent educ, Am Dent Asn. *Mem:* Am Dent Asn; Int Asn Dent Res; Am Asn Dent Schs; Sigma Xi. *Res:* Histochemistry of esterase isoenzymes; lactic dehydrogenase in developing teeth and healing bone; data analysis and programming in the analysis of gel electrophoretic patterns; educational research; computer assisted instruction; self instructional media development. *Mailing Add:* Sch of Dent Univ of Mich Ann Arbor MI 48109

STRACHAN, WILLIAM MICHAEL JOHN, b Thunder Bay, Ont, Nov 20, 37; m 65; c 3. ORGANIC CHEMISTRY. *Educ:* Univ Toronto, BA, 59, MA, 60; Queens Univ, PhD(chem), 68. *Prof Exp:* Asst lectr dept chem, Univ Col, London, 60-63; res assoc, Royal Mil Col Can, 63-65; Nat Res Coun Can fel, 68-70; res scientist, 70-74, HEAD, TOXIC SUBSTANCES SECT, CAN CTR FOR INLAND WATERS, 74- *Concurrent Pos:* Mem, Int Joint Comn, Res Adv Bd, Comt Sci Basis Water Qual Criteria, 74-78; mem, Can Environ Contaminants Act Comt, Dept Fisheries & Environ, Nat Health & Welfare, 75-; mem, Nat Res Coun Special Grants Panel Environ Toxicol, 77-; Can rep, Orgn Econ Coop & Develop Expert Group, 78-; chmn, Int Joint Comn, Sci Adv Bd Comt Aquatic Ecosyst Objectives, 78- *Mem:* Chem Inst Can; The Chem Soc; Int Asn Great Lakes Res. *Res:* Persistent organic chemicals; biodegradation; bioaccumulation; organic contamination of rain and lake-stream waters. *Mailing Add:* Can Ctr for Inland Waters PO Box 5050 Burlington ON L7R 4A6 Can

STRACHER, ALFRED, b Albany, NY, Nov 16, 30; m 54. BIOCHEMISTRY. *Educ:* Rensselaer Polytech Inst, BS, 52; Columbia Univ, MA, 54, PhD, 56. *Prof Exp:* From asst prof to assoc prof, 59-68, PROF BIOCHEM, COL MED, STATE UNIV NY DOWNSTATE MED CTR, 68-, CHMN DEPT, 72- *Concurrent Pos:* Nat Found Infantile Paralysis fel biochem, Rockefeller Inst, 56-58 & Carlsberg Lab, Copenhagen, 58-59; Guggenheim fel, 73-74. *Mem:* Am Soc Biol Chemists. *Res:* Relationship of structure of muscle proteins to mechanism of muscular contraction; relationship of protein structure to biological activity; contractility in non-muscle systems. *Mailing Add:* Dept of Biochem State Univ NY Downstate Med Ctr Brooklyn NY 11203

STRADA, SAMUEL JOSEPH, b Kansas City, Mo, Oct 6, 42; m 71. NEUROCHEMISTRY, NEUROBIOLOGY. *Educ:* Univ Mo-Kansas City, BSPharm, 64, MS, 66; Vanderbilt Univ, PhD(pharmacol), 70. *Prof Exp:* Asst pharmacol, Univ Mo-Kansas City, 64-66; NIMH staff fel pharmacol, St Elizabeth's Hosp, Washington, DC, 70-72; asst prof, 72-75, assoc prof, 72-81, PROF PHARMACOL, MED SCH, UNIV TEX, HOUSTON, 81- *Concurrent Pos:* Assoc fac, Univ Tex Grad Sch Biomed Sci, Houston, 72-; Fosanty int fel, Med Sci Inst, Univ Dundee, Scotland, 80-81. *Mem:* AAAS; Am Soc Pharmacol & Exp Therapeut; Soc Neurosci; NY Acad Sci; Tissue Cult Asn. *Res:* Role of cyclic nucleotides in the nervous system; release of neurotransmitters and synaptic transmission; relation of the nervous system to hormone release mechanisms; role of cyclic nucleotides in cell growth; receptor regulation. *Mailing Add:* Dept of Pharmacol Univ of Tex Med Sch Houston TX 77025

STRADER, K(ENNETH) H(AROLD), chemical engineering, deceased

STRADLEY, JAMES GRANT, b Newark, Ohio, Aug 24, 32; m 54; c 3. CERAMIC ENGINEERING. *Educ:* Ohio State Univ, BCerE, 55, MSc, 58. *Prof Exp:* Res assoc ceramic mat, Res Found, Ohio State Univ, 56-58; res specialist, Cols Div, NAm Rockwell Corp, Ohio, 58-65; develop specialist, Oak Ridge Nat Lab, Tenn, 65-70 & Y-12 plant, Union Carbide Corp, 70-72; vpres, US Nuclear, Inc, 72-77; ENG MGR, OAK RIDGE NAT LAB, UNION CARBIDE CORP, 77- *Mem:* Am Ceramic Soc; Nat Inst Ceramic Engrs; Am Nuclear Soc. *Res:* Forming, sintering and properties of ceramic materials; management of reprocessing programs, including nuclear fuels, special studies and environmental and safety safeguards. *Mailing Add:* Oak Ridge Nat Lab Box X Bldg 7601 Oak Ridge TN 37830

STRADLEY, NORMAN H(ENRY), b Newark, Ohio, June 28, 24; m 47; c 2. CERAMIC ENGINEERING. *Educ:* Ohio State Univ, BCerE & MS, 49. *Prof Exp:* Ceramic engr, Minn Mining & Mfg Co, 50-56, group supvr, 56-59, sr res engr, Am Lava Corp, Tenn, 59-63, proj mgr, 63-68, res supvr, 68-69, proj supvr, 69-74, prod develop specialist, Tech Ceramic Prods Div, 3M Co, Tenn, 74-75, RES SPECIALIST, TECH CERAMIC PRODS DIV, 3M CTR, 3M CO, ST PAUL, 75- *Mem:* Fel Am Ceramic Soc; Nat Inst Ceramic Engrs; fel Am Inst Chemists. *Res:* Coatings for ferrous and non-ferrous alloys and graphite; glass technology; nuclear and electrical ceramics. *Mailing Add:* 740 Nightingale Blvd Stillwater MN 55082

STRADLING, LESTER J(AMES), JR, b Philadelphia, Pa, Aug 21, 16; m 47; c 2. MECHANICAL & NUCLEAR ENGINEERING. *Educ:* Drexel Inst, BS, 39; Univ Pa, MS, 44. *Prof Exp:* Maintenance engr, Calvert Distillery, 39; design draftsman, Gen Elec Co, 39; jr marine engr, Philadelphia Naval Yard, 39-41; design engr, Bendix Aircraft Corp, 42; instr mech eng, Drexel Inst, 42-45; field engr, Allis Chalmers Mfg Co, 45-49, sales engr, 50-54; vpres eng, Campus Industs, Inc, 49-50; assoc prof mech eng, 54-59, PROF MECH ENG, DREXEL UNIV, 59- *Concurrent Pos:* Mem sci staff, Columbia Univ Div, War Res, Naval Underwater Sound Lab, Conn, 44; consult, Kellett Aircraft Corp, 45 & Mechtronics, Inc, 54-57. *Mem:* Am Soc Eng Educ. *Res:* Application of jet engines to helicopters; fundamental quieting of submarines; diffusion of neutrons in high velocity media and heterogeneous media; study of neutron streaming in holes and vacuua. *Mailing Add:* Dept of Mech Eng Drexel Univ Philadelphia PA 19104

STRADLING, SAMUEL STUART, b Hamilton, NY, Dec 11, 37; m 63; c 3. ORGANIC CHEMISTRY. *Educ:* Hamilton Col, AB, 59; Univ Rochester, PhD(org chem), 64. *Prof Exp:* From asst prof to assoc prof, 63-74, PROF CHEM, ST LAWRENCE UNIV, 74- *Concurrent Pos:* NSF acad year exten grant, 65-67; vis scholar & vis prof, Univ Va, 76-77. *Mem:* AAAS; Am Chem Soc; Sigma Xi. *Res:* Reaction mechanisms; natural product chemistry. *Mailing Add:* Dept of Chem St Lawrence Univ Canton NY 13617

STRAETER, TERRY ANTHONY, b St Louis, Mo, June 12, 42; m 64; c 2. APPLIED MATHEMATICS. *Educ:* William Jewell Col, AB, 64; Col William & Mary, MA, 66; NC State Univ, PhD(appl math), 71. *Prof Exp:* Instr math, William Jewell Col, 66-67; mathematician, Langeley Res Ctr, NASA, 67-71, group leader, Optimization Tech Group, 71-74, software mgr, Terminal Configured Vehicle Prog, 74-76, group leader, Spec Software Proj, 76-77, head prog tech br, 77-80. *Concurrent Pos:* Lectr, Christopher Newport Col, 71- & George Washington Univ, 71- *Mem:* Soc Appl & Indust Math; Am Math Soc; Am Inst Aeronaut & Astronaut; Math Asn Am. *Res:* Optimal control theory; optimization techniques theory and application; computational mathematics. *Mailing Add:* 334 Stablestone Dr Chesterfield MO 63017

STRAF, MIRON L, b New York, NY, Apr 13, 43. STATISTICS. *Educ:* Carnegie-Mellon Univ, BS, 64, MS, 65; Univ Chicago, PhD(statist), 69. *Prof Exp:* Asst prof statist, Univ Calif, Berkeley, 69-74; res assoc, Comt Nat Statist & staff officer, Panel to Rev Statist on Skin Cancer, 74-77, staff dir, Study Group on Environ Monitoring, 75-77, RES DIR, COMT ON NAT STATIST, NAT ACAD SCI-NAT RES COUN, 78- *Concurrent Pos:* Sr vis res fel, Monitoring Assessment & Res Ctr, Chelsea Col Sci & Technol, London, 77; lectr statist, London Sch Econ & Polit Sci, 77-78; mem, Joseph P Kennedy, Jr Found Comt, 81. *Mem:* Fel Royal Statist Soc; Am Statist Asn. *Res:* Applied and theoretical statistics; analysis and evaluation of environmental statistics; applications of statistics to public policy. *Mailing Add:* Comt on Nat Statist Nat Acad Sci 2101 Constitution Ave Washington DC 20418

STRAFFON, RALPH ATWOOD, b Croswell, Mich, Jan 4, 28; m 54; c 5. MEDICINE, UROLOGY. *Educ:* Univ Mich, MD, 53; Am Bd Urol, dipl, 62. *Prof Exp:* Intern, Univ Hosp, Ann Arbor, Mich, 53-54, from asst resident to resident gen surg, 54-55, resident surg, 56-57, from jr clin instr to sr clin instr, 57-59; staff mem, 59-63, HEAD, CLEVELAND CLIN FOUND, 63- *Concurrent Pos:* Res fel med, Renal Lab, Peter Bent Brigham Hosp, Boston, 56. *Mem:* AMA; fel Am Col Surg; Am Urol Asn; Am Asn Genito-Urinary Surg; fel Am Acad Pediat. *Mailing Add:* 9500 Euclid Ave Cleveland OH 44106

STRAFUSS, ALBERT CHARLES, b Princeton, Kans, Jan 24, 28; m 54; c 5. COMPARATIVE PATHOLOGY, ONCOLOGY. *Educ:* Kans State Univ, BS & DVM, 54; Iowa State Univ, MS, 58; Univ Minn, PhD(comp path), 63. *Prof Exp:* Practitioner, Hastings, Nebr, 54-56; instr, Iowa State Univ & pathologist, Iowa Vet Med Diag Lab, 56-59; instr path, Col Vet Med, Univ Minn, 59-63; assoc prof path, Col Vet Med, Iowa State Univ & pathologist, Vet Med Res Inst, 63-64; assoc prof path, Sch Vet Med, Univ Mo-Columbia, 64-68; ASSOC PROF PATH, COL VET MED, KANS STATE UNIV, 68- *Mem:* Am Vet Med Asn; Electron Micros Soc Am; Conf Res Workers Animal Diseases. *Res:* Pathologic and epidemiologic studies of animal neoplasms; ultrastructure studies on the pathogenesis of morphological tissue alterations. *Mailing Add:* Dept of Vet Path Col of Vet Med Kans State Univ Manhattan KS 66506

STRAHL, ERWIN OTTO, b New York, NY, July 2, 30; m 52; c 4. MINERALOGY, PETROLOGY. *Educ:* City Col, New York, BS, 52; Pa State Univ, PhD(mineral), 58. *Prof Exp:* Res asst mineral, Pa State Univ, 52-58; mineralogist, Mineral Resources Dept, Kaiser Aluminum & Chem Corp, 58-59, Metals Div, Res Lab, 59-69, head, X-ray & Electron Optics Lab, Anal Res Dept, 69-81, RES ASSOC REDUCTION RES, KAISER CTR TECHNOL, 81- *Mem:* Am Spectrog Soc. *Res:* Mineralogy and petrology of soils and sedimentary rocks; x-ray diffraction analysis of inorganic oxides and hydroxides; quantitative x-ray diffraction and spectographic analysis; phase equilibria studies of aluminum oxide systems. *Mailing Add:* 154 Joaquin Circle San Ramon CA 94583

STRAHLE, WARREN C(HARLES), b Whittier, Calif, Dec 29, 38. COMBUSTION, FLUID MECHANICS. *Educ:* Stanford Univ BS, 59, MS, 60; Princeton Univ, MA & PhD(aerospace eng), 64. *Prof Exp:* Mem tech staff, Propulsion Dept, Aerospace Corp, 64-67; mem prof staff, Sci & Tech Div, Inst Defense Anal, 67-68; from assoc prof to prof, 69-73, REGENTS PROF AEROSPACE ENG, GA INST TECHNOL, 73- *Concurrent Pos:* Consult numerous indust firms, 69-; Sigma Xi res award, Ferst Found, 71, 73 & 77; assoc ed, J Am Inst Aeronaut & Astronaut, 79-81. *Mem:* Combustion Inst; Am Inst Aeronaut & Astronaut; Am Soc Eng Educ. *Res:* Combustion research applicable to solid and liquid rockets and air breathing engines; combustion noise; turbulent reacting flows. *Mailing Add:* Sch of Aerospace Eng Ga Inst of Technol Atlanta GA 30332

STRAHM, NORMAN DALE, b Toronto, Kans, Feb 22, 40. PHYSICS, ELECTRICAL ENGINEERING. *Educ:* Mass Inst Technol, SB, 62, SM & EE, 64, PhD(elec sci & eng), 69. *Prof Exp:* Mem tech staff, Lincoln Lab, Mass Inst Technol, 69-70; VIS ASST PROF PHYSICS, UNIV ILL, CHICAGO CIRCLE, 70- *Mem:* AAAS; Am Phys Soc; Inst Elec & Electronics Engrs. *Res:* Light scattering; crystal lattice dynamics; quantum optics and quantum electronics. *Mailing Add:* 1606 W 50th Pl Apt 5e Chicago IL 60632

STRAHS, GERALD, b New York, NY, May 26, 38; m 60; c 3. PHYSICAL CHEMISTRY. *Educ:* Cooper Union Univ, BChE, 60; Univ Ill, MS, 62, PhD(phys chem), 65; Univ Juarez, MD, 80. *Prof Exp:* Assoc chem, Univ Calif, San Diego, 65-68; asst prof biochem, NY Med Col, 68-71; chemist, Crime Lab Sect, New York Police Dept, 72; chemist, US Assay Off, New York, 72-73; chief chemist, Consolidated Refining Co, 73-76; chemist, Brooklyn Hosp, 77-78; intern, USPHS Hosp, 80-81. *Concurrent Pos:* Am Cancer Soc fel, 65-68; med pres, Mercy Cath Med Ctr, 81- *Res:* Precious metals, refining, assaying, recovery. *Mailing Add:* 130-09 230 St Jamaica NY 11413

STRAIGHT, H JOSEPH, b Dunkirk, NY, Jan 26, 51; m 70. MATHEMATICS, STATISTICS. *Educ:* State Univ NY, Fredonia, BS, 73; Western Mich Univ, MA, 76, PhD(math-graph theory), 77. *Prof Exp:* Asst math, Western Mich Univ, 73-77; asst prof, 77-80, ASSOC PROF MATH, STATE UNIV NY COL FREDONIA, 80- *Concurrent Pos:* Vis prof, Clemson Univ, 80-81. *Mem:* Math Asn Am; NY Acad Sci. *Res:* Graph theory, partitions, colorings of graphs; decomposition of graphs into trees. *Mailing Add:* Dept of Math State Univ of NY Fredonia NY 14063

STRAIGHT, JAMES WILLIAM, b Wichita, Kans, Aug 5, 40; m 61; c 2. MECHANICAL ENGINEERING. *Educ:* Univ Kans, BS & MS, 63; Univ Ariz, PhD(mech eng), 67. *Prof Exp:* Prog dir underground nuclear testing, Test Command/Defense Atomic Support Agency, 67-69; asst prof mech eng, Vanderbilt Univ, 69-71; from asst prof to assoc prof, Christian Bros Col, 71-77; mem staff, 77-80, ASSOC GROUP LEADER, LOS ALAMOS NAT LAB, 77- *Concurrent Pos:* Consult, Ken O'Brien & Assocs, 69-74 & Brown-Straight Consult, 72- *Honors & Awards:* Teetor Award, Soc Automotive Engrs, 71. *Mem:* Am Soc Mech Engrs; Am Soc Eng Educ; Soc Automotive Engrs. *Res:* Vibrations; structural dynamics; acoustics; stress analysis; instrumentation. *Mailing Add:* 1 Comanche Lane Los Alamos NM 87544

STRAIGHT, RICHARD COLEMAN, b Rivesville, WVa, Sept 8, 37; m 63; c 3. PHOTOBIOLOGY. *Educ:* Univ Utah, BA, 61, PhD(molecular biol), 67. *Prof Exp:* Asst dir radiation biol summer inst, Univ Utah, 61-63; SUPVRY CHEMIST, MED SERV, VET ADMIN HOSP, 65-, DIR, VET ADMIN VENOM RES LAB, 75-, ADMIN OFFICER RES SERV, VET ADMIN CTR, 80- *Mem:* AAAS; Am Chem Soc; Biophys Soc; Am Soc Photobiol; Int Solar Energy Soc. *Res:* Photodynamic action of biomonomers and biopolymers; tumor immunology; effect of antigens on mammary adenocarcinoma of C3H mice; ageing; biochemical changes in ageing; venom toxicology; mechanism of action of psychoactive drugs. *Mailing Add:* Res Dept VA Hospital 500 Foothill Dr Salt Lake City UT 84148

STRAILE, WILLIAM EDWIN, b Beaver, Pa, Mar 22, 31; m 53; c 4. BIOLOGICAL SCIENCE, NEUROSCIENCES. *Educ:* Westminster Col, AB, 53; Brown Univ, ScM, 55, PhD(biol), 57. *Prof Exp:* Sr cancer res scientist, Springville Labs, Roswell Park Mem Inst, 61-65; assoc prof anat & head cell res sect, Med Sch, Temple Univ, 66-75; grants assoc, Div Res Grants, NIH, 75-76; MEM STAFF, ORGAN SITE PROGS BR, DIV CANCER RES, RESOURCES & CTRS, NAT CANCER INST, 76- *Concurrent Pos:* Nat Cancer res fel, Univ London, 57-58; res fel, Brown Univ, 58-61; asst res prof, Grad Sch, State Univ NY Buffalo, 62-65. *Res:* Electron microscopy and electrophysiology of nerve endings; neurotransmitter chemicals in the control of neuronal functions, blood flow and cell division; neural elements in melanotic and epidermal neoplasia. *Mailing Add:* Organ Site Progs Br Nat Cancer Inst Bethesda MD 20014

STRAIN, BOYD RAY, b Laramie, Wyo, July 19, 35; m 58; c 2. PHYSIOLOGICAL ECOLOGY. *Educ:* Black Hills State Col, BS, 60; Univ Wyo, MS, 61; Univ Calif, Los Angeles, PhD(plant sci), 64. *Prof Exp:* Asst prof bot & plant ecol, Univ Calif, Riverside, 64-69; assoc prof bot, 69-77, PROF BOT, DUKE UNIV, 77-, DIR, DUKE PHYTOTRON, 79- *Concurrent Pos:* Mem, Panel Ecol Soc, NSF, 72-75 & Comt Mineral Resources & Environ, Nat Res Coun, 73-74; mem, Am Inst Biol Sci Adv Panel, NASA, 76- *Mem:* Ecol Soc Am; Bot Soc Am; Am Inst Biol Sci; AAAS. *Res:* Physiological adaptations of plants to extreme environments; ecosystems analysis. *Mailing Add:* Dept Bot Duke Univ Durham NC 27706

STRAIN, JOHN HENRY, b Worcester, Eng, Oct 28, 22; Can citizen; m 49; c 3. POULTRY SCIENCE. *Educ:* Univ Sask, BSAgr, 49; Iowa State Univ, MS, 60, PhD(poultry breeding), 61. *Prof Exp:* Hatcheryman, Swift Can Co, 49-50; res off, 50-60, scientist poultry genetics, 60-70, HEAD ANIMAL SCI SECT, RES BR, CAN DEPT AGR, 70- *Mem:* Genetics Soc Can; Poultry Sci Asn; Can Soc Animal Sci. *Res:* Poultry genetics, mainly selection and genotype-environment interaction studies; dwarf broiler breeding management systems. *Mailing Add:* Res Sta Can Dept of Agr Brandon MB Can

STRAIT, BRADLEY JUSTUS, b Canandaigua, NY, Mar 17, 32; m 57; c 2. ELECTRICAL ENGINEERING. *Educ:* Syracuse Univ, BS, 58, MS, 60, PhD(elec eng), 65. *Prof Exp:* Engr, Eastman Kodak Co, NY, 60-61; from asst prof to assoc prof, 65-74, PROF ELEC ENG, SYRACUSE UNIV, 74-, CHMN DEPT, 74- *Mem:* Inst Elec & Electronics Engrs. *Res:* Application of computers to antenna problems; array antennas; scattering systems and their effects on antenna performance; electromagnetic theory; microwave measurements. *Mailing Add:* Dept of Elec Eng 111 Link Hall Syracuse Univ Syracuse NY 13210

STRAIT, JOHN, b Blackford Co, Ind, Nov 29, 15; m 46; c 3. AGRICULTURAL ENGINEERING. *Educ:* Purdue Univ, BS, 38; Univ Minn, MS, 45. *Prof Exp:* From asst prof to assoc prof, 38-65, PROF AGR ENG, UNIV MINN, ST PAUL, 65- *Mem:* Am Soc Agr Engrs. *Res:* Design and development of farm machinery; farm processes; internal combustion engines; mechanics; heating, refrigeration and air conditioning; mechanical engineering. *Mailing Add:* Dept Agr Eng Inst Agr Univ of Minn St Paul MN 55108

STRAIT, PEGGY, b Canton, China, Apr 20, 33; US citizen; m 55; c 2. MATHEMATICS. *Educ:* Univ Calif, Berkeley, BA, 53; Mass Inst Technol, MS, 57; NY Univ, PhD(math), 65. *Prof Exp:* Programmer math, Livermore Radiation Lab, Univ Calif, 54-55 & Lincoln Lab, Mass Inst Technol, 55-57; res assoc, G C Dewey Corp, NY, 57-62; lectr, 64-65, from asst prof to assoc prof, 65-72, PROF MATH, QUEENS COL, NEW YORK, 76- *Concurrent Pos:* Lincoln lab assoc staff fel, Mass Inst Technol, 56-57; res assoc fel, NY Univ, 62-64; NSF sci fac fel, 71-72. *Mem:* Am Math Soc. *Res:* Stochastic processes; probability theory and applications. *Mailing Add:* Dept of Math Queens Col Flushing NY 11367

STRAITON, ARCHIE WAUGH, b Tarrant Co, Tex, Aug 27, 07; m 32; c 2. ELECTRICAL ENGINEERING. *Educ:* Univ Tex, BSEE, 29, MA, 31, PhD(physics), 39. *Prof Exp:* Mem inspection dept, Bell Tel Labs, Inc, 29-30; assoc prof eng, Tex Col Arts & Indust, 31-41, prof & dir eng, 41-43; from assoc prof to prof, 43-63, dir elec eng dept, 47-72, chmn dept, 66-71, actg vpres & dean grad sch, 72-73, instr, Univ, 37-38; ASBEL SMITH PROF ELEC ENG, UNIV TEX, AUSTIN, 63- *Mem:* Nat Acad Eng; Am Soc Eng Educ; life fel Inst Elec & Electronics Engrs. *Res:* Atmospheric refractive index properties; interaction of atmosphere and radio waves; electrical physics; measurement of electrical characteristics of filters; harmonic solution of differential equations. *Mailing Add:* Dept of Elec Eng Univ of Tex Austin TX 78712

STRAKA, WILLIAM CHARLES, b Phoenix, Ariz, Oct 21, 40; m 66. ASTROPHYSICS. *Educ:* Calif Inst Technol, BS, 62; Univ Calif, Los Angeles, MA, 65, PhD(astron), 69. *Prof Exp:* Teacher astron & phys sci, Long Beach City Col, 66-70; asst prof astron, Boston Univ, 70-74; asst prof astron, 74-77, head dept physics, 77-78, ASSOC PROF ASTRON, JACKSON STATE UNIV, 77- *Concurrent Pos:* Vis staff mem, Los Alamos Nat Lab, 76-; exec secy astron adv comt, NSF, 78-79. *Mem:* Am Astron Soc; Sigma Xi; AAAS. *Res:* Structure and evolution of small mass stars; galactic nebulae; dynamics of supernova shells. *Mailing Add:* Dept of Physics Jackson State Univ Jackson MS 39217

STRALEY, JOSEPH PAUL, b Toledo, Ohio, Jan 22, 42; m 67. SOLID STATE PHYSICS. *Educ:* Harvard Col, BA, 64; Cornell Univ, PhD(physics), 70. *Prof Exp:* NSF fel chem, Cornell Univ, 70-71; res assoc physics, Rutgers Univ, 71-73; from asst prof to assoc prof, 73-81, PROF PHYSICS, UNIV KY, 81-; ASSOC PROF PHYSICS, UNIV ALA, 81- *Concurrent Pos:* NSF res grants, Univ Ky, 76-81 & Univ Ala, 81-; sabbatical leave, Mich State Univ, 79-80; asst prof physics, Univ Ala, 80-81. *Mem:* Am Phys Soc. *Res:* Theory of phase transitions; cooperative phenomena; liquid crystals; inhomogeneous conductors; percolation problem. *Mailing Add:* Dept Physics & Astron Univ Ala University AL 35486

STRALEY, JOSEPH WARD, b Paulding, Ohio, Oct 6, 14; m 39; c 3. SPECTROSCOPY. *Educ:* Bowling Green State Univ, BSEd, 36; Ohio State Univ, MSc, 37, PhD(physics), 41. *Prof Exp:* Asst, Ohio State Univ, 37-38, 40-41; actg instr physics, Heidelberg Col, 38-39; instr, Univ Toledo, 41-42, asst prof, 42-44, actg head dept, 43-44; from asst prof to prof, 44-58, EMER PROF PHYSICS, UNIV NC, CHAPEL HILL, 80- *Concurrent Pos:* Guggenheim fel, 56-57. *Mem:* Am Phys Soc; Am Asn Physics Teachers. *Res:* Spectroscopy; research in science and public policy. *Mailing Add:* Dept of Physics 232 Phillips Hall Univ of NC Chapel Hill NC 27514

STRALEY, TINA, b New York, NY, Sept 4, 43; c 1. MATHEMATICS. *Educ:* Ga State Univ, BA, 65, MS, 66; Auburn Univ, PhD(math), 71. *Prof Exp:* Teacher math, Miami Beach Sr High Sch, 66-67; instr, Spelman Col, 67-68 & Auburn Univ, 71-73; asst prof, 73-78, ASSOC PROF MATH, KENNESAW COL, 78- *Concurrent Pos:* Vis res assoc, Emory Univ, 78-79. *Mem:* Am Math Soc; Am Asn Univ Professors; Math Asn Am. *Res:* Embeddings, extensions and automorphisms of Steiner systems, design theory, scheduling problems. *Mailing Add:* Dept Natural Sci & Math Kennesaw Col Marietta GA 30061

STRALKA, ALBERT R, b Wilkes-Barre, Pa, Jan 18, 40; m 65; c 2. MATHEMATICS. *Educ:* Wilkes Col, AB, 61; Pa State Univ, MA, 64, PhD(math), 67. *Prof Exp:* Instr math, Wilkes Col, 61-62 & Pa State Univ, 66-67; asst prof, 67-72, assoc prof, 72-76, PROF MATH, UNIV CALIF, RIVERSIDE, 76- *Mem:* Am Math Soc. *Res:* Ordered structures. *Mailing Add:* Dept of Math Univ of Calif Riverside CA 92521

STRAND, FLEUR LILLIAN, b Bloemfontein, SAfrica, Feb 24, 28; m 46; c 1. BIOLOGY. *Educ:* NY Univ, AB, 48, MS, 50, PhD(biol), 52. *Prof Exp:* Instr biol, Brooklyn Col, 51-57; NIH fel, Physiol Inst, Free Univ Berlin, 57-59; from asst prof to assoc prof, 61-73; actg chmn dept, 82, PROF BIOL, NY UNIV, 73- *Mem:* AAAS; Am Physiol Soc; Soc Neurosci; Soc Exp Biol & Med; NY Acad Sci. *Res:* Neurohormonal integration; effect of hormones on nerve and muscle. *Mailing Add:* Dept of Biol New York Univ New York NY 10003

STRAND, JAMES CAMERON, b East St Louis, Ill, June 1, 43. NEPHROLOGY, HYPERTENSION. *Educ:* Monmouth Col, Ill, BA, 66; St Louis Univ, Mo, MS, 73; Univ Nebr, Omaha, PhD(physiol), 77. *Prof Exp:* Nephrol res fel, Mayo Clinic & Found, 77-80; cardiovasc res fel, Georgetown Univ, 80-81; RES ASSOC, A H ROBINS CO, 81- *Mem:* Am Physiol Soc. *Res:* Influence of intrarenal hormonal systems on the regulation of blood flow and of salt and water metabolism in relation to hypertension. *Mailing Add:* Dept Pharmacol A H Robins Co 1211 Sherwood Ave Richmond VA 23220

STRAND, JOHN A, III, b Red Bank, NJ, July 22, 38; m 63; c 4. POLLUTION BIOLOGY. *Educ:* Lafayette Col, AB, 60; Lehigh Univ, MS, 62; Univ Wash, PhD(fisheries biol), 75. *Prof Exp:* Fisheries biologist, NJ Bur Fisheries Lab, 62-63; res scientist, US Naval Radiol Defense Lab, 64-69; SR RES SCIENTIST AQUATIC ECOL, PAC NORTHWEST LABS, BATTELLE MEM INST, 69- *Concurrent Pos:* Tech merit reviewer, Environ Protection Agency, 72. *Mem:* Sigma Xi; Am Inst Fishery Res Biologists; Naval & Reserve Asn. *Res:* Aquatic radioecology; biological accumulation of radioisotopes in biological systems and their effects; effects and fate of petroleum residues in biological systems and synthetic fuel; mariculture. *Mailing Add:* Ecol Sci Dept Pac NW Labs PO Box 999 Richland WA 99352

STRAND, KAJ AAGE, b Hellerup, Denmark, Feb 27, 07; nat US; m 43, 49; c 2. ASTRONOMY. *Educ:* Univ Copenhagen, BA & MSc, 31, PhD(astron), 38. *Prof Exp:* Geodesist, Geod Inst, Copenhagen, 31-33; asst to dir observ, Univ Leiden, 33-38; res assoc astron, Swarthmore Col, 38-42, res astronr, 46, Am-Scand Found fel, 38-39, Danish Rask-Orsted Found fel, 39-40; assoc prof astron, Univ Chicago, 46-47, res assoc, 47-67; prof astron, Northwestern Univ & dir, Dearborn Observ, 47-58; dir astrometry & astrophys, US Naval Observ, 58-63, sci dir, 63-77. *Concurrent Pos:* Guggenheim fel, 46; consult, NSF, 53-56 & Lincoln Lab, Mass Inst Technol, 81- *Honors & Awards:* Distinguished Serv Award, US Dept Navy, 73; Knight Cross First Class, Royal Order Dannebrog, Denmark, 77; Honor Cross, Literis et Artibus, First Class, Austria, 78. *Mem:* Int Astron Union; Am Astron Soc; Netherlands Astron Soc; Royal Danish Acad. *Res:* Photographic observations of double stars; stellar parallaxes; orbial motion in double and multiple systems; instrumentation. *Mailing Add:* 3200 Rowland Pl NW Washington DC 20008

STRAND, OLIVER ERIC, b Boyceville, Wis, Oct 9, 22; c 3. AGRONOMY, PLANT PHYSIOLOGY. *Educ:* Univ Mich, BS, 54; Univ Minn, MS, 66, PhD(agron & plant physiol), 69. *Prof Exp:* Soil conserv agent, Exten Serv, 56-59, agr agent, 59-66, EXTEN AGRONOMIST, UNIV MINN, ST PAUL, 66- *Mem:* Am Soc Agron; Weed Sci Soc Am. *Res:* Weed control in field crops. *Mailing Add:* Dept of Agron Univ of Minn St Paul MN 55108

STRAND, RICHARD ALVIN, b Ridgway, Pa, July 30, 26; m 48; c 3. ELECTRICAL ENGINEERING. *Educ:* Pa State Univ, BS, 50, MS, 51, PhD(elec eng), 63. *Prof Exp:* Prod engr, Elliott Co, Pa, 51-56; from instr to asst prof, Pa State Univ, 56-64; assoc prof, 64-66, chmn dept, 64-81, asst dean eng, 70-79, PROF ELEC ENG, UNIV BRIDGEPORT, 66- *Mem:* Inst Elec & Electronics Engrs; Am Soc Eng Educ. *Res:* Generalized analysis of electromechanical energy converters; curriculum development; educational methods; measurement of effective teaching. *Mailing Add:* Col of Eng Univ of Bridgeport Bridgeport CT 06602

STRAND, ROBERT CHARLES, b Newark, NJ, Sept 22, 25; m 51; c 3. ORGANIC POLYMER CHEMISTRY. *Educ:* Union Col, NY, BS, 51; Stevens Inst Technol, MS, 55; State Univ NY Buffalo, PhD(chem), 63. *Prof Exp:* Assoc chemist, Allied Chem Co, 51-59; res chemist, Sinclair Res, Inc, Ill, 61-62, group leader polymers, 62-68; chief chemist, NY Labs, Stein Hall Co, Inc, Long Island City, NY, 68-69, dir polymers res, 69-73; assoc dir, Barrington Res Lab, 74-76, DIR ORG MAT, BARRINGTON TECH CTR, AM CAN CO, ILL, 76- *Mem:* Am Chem Soc. *Res:* Polymer applications, synthesis and characterization; adhesives; hot melts; specialty coatings; coatings for rigid and flexible packaging; polyacrylamides. *Mailing Add:* 4709 Valerie Dr Crystal Lake IL 60014

STRAND, ROBERT FENTON, b Ft Lewis, Wash, May 9, 28; m 53; c 4. FOREST ECOLOGY, FOREST SOILS. *Educ:* Univ Wash, BS, 51, MF, 57; Ore State univ, PhD(forest ecol), 64. *Prof Exp:* Res forester, Cent Res, 56-64, res supvr, 64-72, mgr, 72-74, asst mgr, 74-76, SR RES FORESTER, FORESTRY RES, CROWN ZELLERBACH CORP, 76- *Concurrent Pos:* Vis prof, Univ Mich, 80-81. *Mem:* Soc Am Foresters. *Res:* Forest fertilization; prediction of growth response; preparation of fertilization guidelines; improving fertilizer; application quality; modelling growth response; forest soil interpretations for management. *Mailing Add:* Forestry Res Crown Zellerbach Box 368 Wilsonville OR 97070

STRANDBERG, MALCOM WOODROW PERSHING, b Box Elder, Mont, Mar 9, 19; m 47; c 4. SOLID STATE PHYSICS. *Educ:* Harvard Univ, SB, 41; Mass Inst Technol, PhD(physics), 48. *Prof Exp:* Res assoc, Mass Inst Technol, 41-42, mem staff, Off Sci Res & Develop, 42-43, microwave develop, 43-45, res assoc, 45-48, from asst prof to assoc prof, 48-60, PROF PHYSICS, MASS INST TECHNOL, 60- *Concurrent Pos:* Fulbright lectr, Univ Grenoble, 61-62. *Mem:* Fel Am Phys Soc; fel Inst Elec & Electronics Engrs; fel Am Acad Arts & Sci; fel AAAS; NY Acad Sci. *Res:* Design of microwave components, radio transmitters and receivers; biological physics. *Mailing Add:* Mass Inst of Technol 26-353 Cambridge MA 02139

STRANDHAGEN, ADOLF G(USTAV), b Scranton, Pa, May 4, 14; m 41; c 2. ENGINEERING MECHANICS. *Educ:* Univ Mich, BS, 39, MS, 40, PhD(eng mech), 42. *Prof Exp:* From instr to asst prof mech, Carnegie Inst Technol, 42-47; assoc prof, 47-50, prof eng mech & head dept, 50-58, prof eng sci & head dept, 58-69, prof eng, 69-76, PROF AEROSPACE & MECH ENG, UNIV NOTRE DAME, 76- *Concurrent Pos:* Consult, US Navy Mine Defense Lab, 61-67. *Mem:* Soc Naval Archit & Marine Engrs. *Res:* Engineering sciences; hydrodynamics; applications of probability theory; stability and maneuvering of ships. *Mailing Add:* Col of Eng Univ of Notre Dame Notre Dame IN 46556

STRANDHOY, JACK W, b Evanston, Ill, Aug 8, 44; m 67; c 2. RENAL PHARMACOLOGY, VASOPRESSIN. *Educ:* Univ Ill, BS, 67; Univ Iowa, MS, 69, PhD(pharmacol), 72. *Prof Exp:* NIH fel physiol, Mayo Clin, 71-73; sr res investr, NC Heart Asn, 73-75; asst prof, 75-80, ASSOC PROF PHARMACOL, BOWMAN GRAY SCH MED, WAKE FOREST UNIV, 80- *Concurrent Pos:* Consult, Curriculum Designs, Inc, 77; prin investr, NIH, 79- *Mem:* Am Soc Pharmacol & Exp Therapeut; Am Soc Nephrology; Int Soc Nephrology; Am Fedn Clin Res; Sigma Xi. *Res:* Mechanisms by which vasoactive substances, especially catecholamines, prostaglandins, and antihypertensive drugs, affect renal water and electrolyte metabolism. *Mailing Add:* Dept Physiol & Pharmacol Bowman Gray Sch Med Winston-Salem NC 27103

STRANDJORD, PAUL EDPHIL, b Minneapolis, Minn, Apr 5, 31; m 53; c 2. CLINICAL CHEMISTRY, LABORATORY MEDICINE. *Educ:* Univ Minn, BA, 51, MA, 52; Stanford Univ, MD, 59. *Prof Exp:* Intern med, Sch Med, Univ Minn, 59-60, from instr to assoc prof lab med, 63-69; PROF LAB MED & CHMN DEPT, SCH MED, UNIV WASH, 69- *Concurrent Pos:* USPHS med fel, Univ Minn, 61-63. *Honors & Awards:* Borden Res Award, Stanford Univ, 59; C J Watson Res Award, Univ Minn, 63; Gerald T Evans Award in Lab Med, 76. *Mem:* AAAS; Acad Clin Lab Physicians & Sci; Am Chem Soc; Am Fedn Clin Res; Am Asn Clin Chem. *Res:* Diagnostic enzymology; diagnosis of liver disease; pattern recognition; computer assisted diagnosis. *Mailing Add:* Dept of Lab Med Univ of Wash Sch of Med Seattle WA 98195

STRANDNESS, DONALD EUGENE, JR, b Bowman, NDak, Sept 22, 28; m 57; c 3. MEDICINE, SURGERY. *Educ:* Pac Lutheran Univ, BA, 50; Univ Wash, MD, 54. *Prof Exp:* From instr to assoc prof, 62-70, PROF SURG, SCH MED, UNIV WASH, 70- *Concurrent Pos:* Res fel, Nat Heart Inst, 59-60; NIH career develop award, 65-; clin investr, Vet Admin, 62-65. *Mem:* Soc Vascular Surg; Am Inst Ultrasonics in Med; Am Col Surg; Am Surg Asn; Int Cardiovasc Soc. *Res:* Peripheral vascular disease and physiology. *Mailing Add:* Dept of Surg Univ of Wash Sch of Med Seattle WA 98195

STRANDTMANN, RUSSELL WILLIAM, b Maxwell, Tex, Apr 9, 10; m 36; c 2. TAXONOMY, ZOOLOGY. *Educ:* Southwestern Tex State Col, BS, 35; Tex A&M Univ, MS, 37; Ohio State Univ, PhD(entom), 44. *Prof Exp:* Instr sci & math, ETex State Univ, 37-42; field entomologist, Bur Entom & Plant Quarantine, USDA, 43; asst prof entom, Med Br, Univ Tex, 43-48; prof, 48-75, EMER PROF INVERT ZOOL, TEX TECH UNIV, 75-; DISTINGUISHED VIS PROF, SOUTHWEST TEX STATE UNIV, SAN MARCOS, 78- *Concurrent Pos:* Acarologist, Bernice P Bishop Mus, Honolulu, Hawaii, 67-68. *Res:* Biology and systematics of free living prostigmatic acarines of the polar regions. *Mailing Add:* Dept of Biol Southwest Tex State Univ San Marcos TX 78666

STRANG, ROBERT M, b Gt Brit, 26; m 53; c 5. FOREST & RANGELAND ECOLOGY. *Educ:* Univ Edinburgh, BSc, 50; Univ London, PhD(ecol), 65. *Prof Exp:* Res off forestry, Colonial Develop Corp, Swaziland, Nyasaland & Tanganyika, 50-57 & Rhodesian Wattle Co, Ltd, 57-62; forest ecologist, Northern Forest Res Ctr, Forestry Serv, Can Dept Environ, 65-73, biologist, Northern Natural Resources & Environ Br, Arctic Land Use Res, Can Dept Indian & Northern Affairs, 73-74, head environ studies sect, Northern Natural Resources & Environ Br, 74-75; assoc prof rangeland ecol & mgt, Fac Agr Sci Forestry, Univ BC, 75-81; EXEC DIR, FOREST RES COUN BC, 81- *Concurrent Pos:* Hon res assoc, Univ NB, 67-71; secy, Conserv Coun NB, 69-71. *Mem:* Commonwealth Forestry Asn; Soc Range Mgt; Can Inst Forestry. *Res:* Resource and land management. *Mailing Add:* Forest Res Coun BC Suite 305 7671 Alderbridge Way Richmond BC V6X 1Z9 Can

STRANG, RUTH HANCOCK, b Bridgeport, Conn, Mar 11, 23. PEDIATRICS, CARDIOLOGY. *Educ:* Wellesley Col, BA, 44; New York Med Col, MD, 49. *Prof Exp:* Intern, Flower & Fifth Ave Hosps, New York, 49-50, resident pediat, 50-52; from instr to asst prof bact, New York Med Col, 52-57, instr pediat, 52-56, asst clin prof, 56-57; from asst prof to assoc prof, 62-70, PROF PEDIAT, UNIV MICH, ANN ARBOR, 70- *Concurrent Pos:* Fel cardiol, Babies Hosp, New York, 56-57 & Hopkins Hosp, Baltimore, 57-59; res fel, Children's Hosp, Boston, 59-62; mem, Am Heart Asn. *Mem:* Fel Am Acad Pediat; Am Col Cardiol. *Res:* Congenital heart disease; effect on growth; ventricular performance; echocardiography. *Mailing Add:* Dept of Pediat Univ of Mich Hosp Ann Arbor MI 48104

STRANG, WILLIAM GILBERT, b Chicago, Ill, Nov 27, 34; m 58; c 3. MATHEMATICS. *Educ:* Mass Inst Technol, SB, 55; Oxford Univ, BA, 57; Univ Calif, Los Angeles, PhD(math), 59. *Prof Exp:* Moore instr, 59-61, from asst prof to assoc prof, 62-69, PROF MATH, MASS INST TECHNOL, 69- *Concurrent Pos:* Fels, NATO, 61-62 & Sloan Found, 65-67; Fairchild scholar, 80. *Mem:* Am Math Soc; Math Asn Am. *Res:* Partial difference and differential equations; matrix analysis. *Mailing Add:* Dept Math Mass Inst Technol Cambridge MA 02139

STRANGE, JOHN RUBLE, b Knoxville, Tenn, Feb 25, 43; m 65; c 2. DEVELOPMENTAL PHYSIOLOGY, ENVIRONMENTAL PHYSIOLOGY. *Educ:* ETenn State Univ, BS, 65, MA, 67; Univ Tenn, PhD(zool), 70. *Prof Exp:* Asst prof biol, Ga Inst Technol, 70-76; sr scientist, Syracuse Res Corp, 76-77; GROUP MGR, FRANKLIN RES CTR, 77- *Mem:* AAAS; Am Soc Zoologists; NY Acad Sci; Sigma Xi; Soc Toxicol. *Res:* Teratogenic agents; effects of radiation, food additives and pesticides on the prenatal organism; aquatic toxicology; effects of aquatic toxicants on freshwater organisms specifically cardiac, opercular and biochemical changes. *Mailing Add:* 1320 Fernwick Lane Silver Spring MD 20910

STRANGE, LLOYD K(EITH), b Burkburnett, Tex, Dec 17, 22; m 43; c 2. MECHANICAL & PETROLEUM ENGINEERING. *Educ:* Southern Methodist Univ, BS, 50, MS, 56. *Prof Exp:* Petrol eng asst, Magnolia Petrol Co, 50-52; engr, Petrol Prod Eng Co, 52-53; res engr, 53-56, sr res engr, 56-63, ENG ASSOC, FIELD RES LAB, MOBIL RES & DEVELOP CORP, 63- *Mem:* Am Soc Mech Engrs; Soc Petrol Engrs. *Res:* Planning, operating and evaluating laboratory and field experiments on improved crude oil recovery processes; application of new research results. *Mailing Add:* Mobil Res & Develop Corp PO Box 900 Dallas TX 75221

STRANGE, RONALD STEPHEN, b Covington, Ky, Nov 18, 43; m 70; c 3. INORGANIC CHEMISTRY, EDUCATION. *Educ:* Univ Ky, BS, 65; Univ Ill, Urbana, MS, 67, PhD(inorg chem), 71. *Prof Exp:* Instr chem, Ill Inst Technol, 70-71; asst prof, 71-78, chmn dept, 75-81, ASSOC PROF CHEM, FAIRLEIGH DICKINSON UNIV, FLORHAM-MADISON CAMPUS, 78- *Concurrent Pos:* Fac res grant-in-aid, Fairleigh Dickinson Univ, 72-74; NSF teacher training grants, 79-80 & 80-81; vis fel, Princeton Univ, 79. *Mem:* Am Chem Soc; Sigma Xi. *Res:* Transition metal base chemistry; semi empirical self consistent field molecular orbital calculations; organometallic chemistry. *Mailing Add:* Dept of Chem Fairleigh Dickinson Univ Florham-Madison Campus Madison NJ 07940

STRANGWAY, DAVID W, b Simcoe, Ont, June 7, 34; m 57; c 3. GEOPHYSICS. *Educ:* Univ Toronto, BA, 56, MA, 58, PhD(physics), 60. *Prof Exp:* Sr geophysicist, Dominion Gulf Co, 56; chief geophysicist, Ventures Ltd, Ont, 56-57; res geophysicist, Kennecott Copper Corp, Colo, 60-61; asst prof geol, Univ Colo, 61-64; asst prof geophys, Mass Inst Technol, 65-68; assoc prof physics, 68-71, PROF PHYSICS, UNIV TORONTO, 71-, CHMN DEPT GEOL, 72- *Concurrent Pos:* Consult, Kennecott Copper Corp, Anaconda Co, UN, Alyeska Pipelines & NASA; chief geophys br, NASA-Manned Spacecraft Ctr, 70-71; chief physics br, NASA-Johnson Spacecraft Ctr, 71-73; Pahlavi lectr, 78. *Honors & Awards:* Medal Except Sci Achievement, NASA. *Mem:* Soc Explor Geophys; fel Royal Soc Can; Can Geophys Union (pres, 77-79); Geol Asn Can (pres, 78-79); Can Explor Geophys Soc. *Res:* History of the earth's magnetic field; studies of ancient reversals of the field; changes in direction and intensity and secular variation; exploration using electromagnetic techniques; magnetic fields of lunar samples and meteorites; history of magnetic fields in the early solar system. *Mailing Add:* Simcoe Hall Univ Toronto Toronto ON M5S 2R8 Can

STRANO, ALFONSO J, b Ambridge, Pa, Apr 7, 27; m 57; c 1. VIROLOGY, PATHOLOGY. *Educ:* Hiram Col, BA, 50; Duquesne Univ, MS, 53; Univ Okla, PhD(path), 57; Univ Tex, MD, 60. *Prof Exp:* From instr to asst prof path, Univ Tex Med Br Galveston, 62-67; pathologist, Armed Forces Inst Path & chief, Viro-Path Br, 67-73; CLIN PROF PATH, SCH MED, SOUTHERN ILL UNIV, 73- *Concurrent Pos:* Am Cancer Soc res fel, 60-62. *Mem:* AMA; Col Am Path; Reticuloendothelial Soc; Int Acad Path. *Res:* Immunologic aspects of infectious disease, cellular immunity; histologic reaction to viral infections. *Mailing Add:* St Johns Hosp Labs Springfield IL 62702

STRANO, JOSEPH J, b Newark, NJ, Aug 21, 37; m 62. ELECTRICAL & BIOMEDICAL ENGINEERING. *Educ:* Newark Col Eng, BS, 59, MS, 61; Rutgers Univ, PhD(elec eng), 69. *Prof Exp:* From instr to assoc prof, 61-76, assoc chmn dept, 75-76, PROF ELEC ENG, NEWARK COL ENG, 78-, CHMN DEPT, 76- *Concurrent Pos:* NSF res initiation grant, Newark Col Eng, 71-72. *Mem:* Inst Elec & Electronics Engrs; Am Soc Eng Educ; Sigma Xi. *Res:* Automatic control systems; computer systems; instrumentation. *Mailing Add:* Dept of Elec Eng Newark Col of Eng Newark NJ 07102

STRANSKY, JOHN JANOS, b Budapest, Hungary, Sept 2, 23; nat US; m 47; c 2. SILVICULTURE. *Educ:* Univ Munich, BF, 47; Harvard Univ, MS, 54; Tex A&M Univ, PhD, 76. *Prof Exp:* Plant propagator, Bussey Inst, Harvard Univ, 54-57; RES FORESTER, SOUTHERN FOREST EXP STA, US FOREST SERV, 57- *Concurrent Pos:* Lectr, Sch Forestry, Stephen F Austin State Univ. *Mem:* Soc Am Foresters; Wildlife Soc. *Res:* Silvicultural aspects of combining timber production with wildlife habitat practices in southern forests. *Mailing Add:* Wildlife Habitat & Silvicult Lab US Forest Serv Box 7600 Nacogdoches TX 75962

STRASBERG, MURRAY, b New York, NY, Aug 11, 17; m 45. ACOUSTICS. *Educ:* City Col New York, BS, 38; Cath Univ, MS, 48, PhD, 56. *Prof Exp:* Patent examr, US Patent Off, 38-42; physicist, David Taylor Model Basin, 42-49 & 52-58; noise consult, US Bur Ships, 49-52; sci liaison officer, Off Naval Res, London, 58-60; proj coordr, 60-72, SR RES SCIENTIST, DAVID TAYLOR NAVAL SHIP RES & DEVELOP CTR, MD, 72- *Concurrent Pos:* Fulbright lectr, Tech Univ Denmark, 63; adj prof, Am Univ, 64-; vis prof, Cath Univ, 74-; mem gov bd, Am Inst Physics, 77- *Mem:* Fel Acoust Soc Am (pres, 74-75); Am Inst Physics; Am Phys Soc. *Res:* Underwater acoustics; hydrodynamics; cavitation; hydrodynamic noise; electroacoustic instrumentation; mechanical vibrations. *Mailing Add:* Naval Ship Res & Dev Ctr 1901 Bethesda MD 20034

STRASBURG, DONALD WISHART, b Benton Harbor, Mich, Sept 13, 24; m 52. FISH BIOLOGY. *Educ:* US Naval Acad, BS, 45; Univ Hawaii, PhD(marine zool), 53. *Prof Exp:* Asst zool, Univ Hawaii, 50-53; instr zool, Duke Univ & asst to dir, Marine Lab, 53-55; fishery res biologist, Bur Com Fisheries, US Fish & Wildlife Serv, 55-67; spec tech asst to mgr underwater technol, Elec Boat Div, Gen Dynamics Corp, Conn, 67-70; asst mgr, Fisheries Eng Lab, Nat Marine Fisheries Serv, 70-72; HEAD BR ENVIRON BIOL, NAVAL RES LAB, 72- *Concurrent Pos:* Asst marine zoologist, Pac Sci Bd Exped, Arno Atoll, Marshall Islands, 50, asst geologist, Onotoa Atoll, Gilbert Islands, 51; ichthyologist, Eniwetok Marine Biol Lab, Marshall Islands, 55; mem grad fac, Univ Hawaii, 57-67. *Mem:* Am Soc Ichthyol & Herpet; Lepidop Soc; Am Inst Fishery Res Biologists. *Res:* Biology and systematics of blennies, sharks, remoras and marlins; use of submarines for research; remote sensing of marine resources; biological problems of naval interest. *Mailing Add:* Code 4350 Naval Res Lab Washington DC 20375

STRASDINE, GEORGE ALFRED, microbiology, biochemistry, see previous edition

STRASSENBURG, ARNOLD ADOLPH, b Victoria, Minn, June 8, 27; m 49; c 3. PHYSICS. *Educ:* Ill Inst Technol, BS, 51; Calif Inst Technol, MS, 53, PhD(physics), 55. *Prof Exp:* From asst prof to assoc prof physics, Univ Kans, 55-66; prof, State Univ NY Stony Brook, 66-75; head, Mat & Instr Develop Sect, NSF, 75-77; actg vprovost curric & instr, 80-82, PROF PHYSICS, STATE UNIV NY, STONY BROOK, 77- *Concurrent Pos:* Staff physicist, Comn Col Physics, 63-65; dir, Div Educ & Manpower, Am Inst Physics, 66-72; exec officer, Am Asn Physics Teachers, 72- *Honors & Awards:* Millikan Lectr Award, Am Asn Physics Teachers, 72. *Mem:* AAAS; Am Asn Physics Teachers; Nat Sci Teachers Asn. *Res:* High energy physics; fundamental particles; measurement of educational outcomes resulting from the application of alternative instructional materials and modes. *Mailing Add:* Grad Physics Bldg State Univ NY Stony Brook NY 11794

STRASSER, ELVIRA RAPAPORT, b Hungary; US citizen; wid; c 2. MATHEMATICS. *Educ:* Washburn Univ, BS, 43; Smith Col, MS, 51; NY Univ, PhD(math), 56. *Prof Exp:* Off Naval Res fel, 59-60; lectr math, Hunter Col, 61; from asst prof to assoc prof, Polytech Inst Brooklyn, 61-67; PROF MATH, STATE UNIV NY STONY BROOK, 67- *Mem:* Am Math Soc. *Res:* Group theory; graph theory; combinatorial problems. *Mailing Add:* Dept of Math State Univ of NY Stony Brook NY 11790

STRASSER, JOHN ALBERT, b Sydney, NS, Jan 28, 45; m 70. ENGINEERING, MATERIALS SCIENCE. *Educ:* NS Tech Col, BME, 67, PhD(metall eng), 72; Pa State Univ, University Park, MS, 68. *Prof Exp:* Spec lectr mat sci, Dalhousie Univ, 69 & 70; res scientist, Phys Metall Div, Can Dept Energy, Mines & Resources, 71-76; mgr, Rolling Mills, 76-79, DIR

METALL, SYDNEY STEEL CORP, 81- *Concurrent Pos:* Dir, Atlantic Group Res Indust Metall, 74-78 & Bra's Dor Inst, 75-78; dir, Atlantic Coal Inst, 80-81. *Mem:* AAAS; Am Soc Metals; Can Inst Mining & Metall. *Res:* Powder metallurgy; production of powders, their consolidation techniques and their industrial application. *Mailing Add:* Sydney Steel Corp PO Box 1450 Sydney NS B1P 6K5 Can

STRATFORD, EUGENE SCOTT, b Waterloo, Iowa, June 18, 42; m 66; c 1. MEDICINAL CHEMISTRY. *Educ:* Idaho State Univ, BSPharm, 66; Ohio State Univ, PhD(med chem), 70. *Prof Exp:* Asst prof med chem, Sch Pharm, Univ Conn, 70-76; ASSOC PROF MED CHEM, SCH PHARM, W VA UNIV, 76- *Mem:* Am Chem Soc; Am Asn Cols Pharm; Am Pharmaceut Asn; Acad Pharmaceut Sci; The Chem Soc. *Res:* Structure-activity relationships of biologically active organic compounds, particularly those with properties as potentially valuable for interactions at central inhibitory neurons. *Mailing Add:* WVa Univ Med Ctr Sch of Pharm Morgantown WV 26506

STRATFORD, JOSEPH, b Brantford, Ont, Sept 5, 23; m 52; c 2. NEUROSURGERY. *Educ:* McGill Univ, BSc, 45, MD, CM, 47, MSc, 51, dipl neurosurg, 54; FRCS(C), 56. *Prof Exp:* Lectr neurosurg, McGill Univ, 55-56; from asst prof to prof surg, Univ Sask, 56-62; assoc prof, 62-72, PROF NEUROSURG, McGILL UNIV, 72- *Concurrent Pos:* Dir div neurosurg, Montreal Gen Hosp. *Mem:* Am Asn Neurol Surg; fel Am Col Surgeons; Cong Neurol Surg; fel Royal Soc Med. *Mailing Add:* Montreal Gen Hosp Montreal PQ H3G 1A4 Can

STRATHDEE, GRAEME GILROY, b Edinburgh, Scotland, June 29, 42; Can citizen; m 67; c 1. SURFACE CHEMISTRY, INORGANIC CHEMISTRY. *Educ:* McGill Univ, BSc, 63, PhD(chem), 67. *Prof Exp:* Assoc res officer chem, Whiteshell Nuclear Res Estab, Atomic Energy Can, Ltd, 67-77, head, Waste Immobilization Sect, 77-80; MGR RES & DEVELOP PLANNING, POTASH CORP SASK, 80- *Mem:* Chem Inst Can; Am Ceramics Soc; Am Chem Soc. *Res:* Homogeneous catalysis; catalytic activation of small molecules; hydrogen isotope exchange reactions; enrichment of deuterium; adsorption phenomena; foaming and antifoaming; solidification of high-level liquid waste; glass science and technology; nuclear waste disposal. *Mailing Add:* Potash Corp Sask 410 22nd St E Saskatoon SK S7K 5T7 Can

STRATHERN, JEFFREY NEAL, b Keene, NH, Dec 12, 48. GENETICS, MOLECULAR BIOLOGY. *Educ:* Univ Calif, San Diego, BA, 70; Univ Ore, PhD(biol), 77. *Prof Exp:* Fel, 77-78, STAFF INVESTR GENETICS, COLD SPRING HARBOR LAB, 79- *Concurrent Pos:* Damon Runyon/Walter Winchell Cancer Fund fel, 78. *Res:* Genetics of the control of cell type in yeast, including the demonstration that changes in cell type involve specific DNA rearrangements. *Mailing Add:* Dept of Genetics PO Box 100 Cold Spring Harbor NY 11724

STRATHMANN, RICHARD RAY, b Pomona, Calif, Nov 25, 41; m 64; c 2. MARINE BIOLOGY, ZOOLOGY. *Educ:* Pomona Col, BS, 63; Univ Wash, MS, 66, PhD(zool), 70. *Prof Exp:* NIH training grant, Univ Calif, Los Angeles, 70; NSF fel, Univ Hawaii, 70-71; asst prof zool, Univ Md, College Park, 71-73; asst prof, 73-80, ASSOC PROF ZOOL, UNIV WASH & RESIDENT ASSOC DIR, FRIDAY HARBOR LABS, 80- *Mem:* Am Soc Naturalists; Am Soc Limnol & Oceanog; Am Soc Zoologists; Marine Biol Asn UK. *Res:* Population biology, form and function of marine invertebrates; biology of invertebrate larvae; biology of suspension feeding. *Mailing Add:* Friday Harbor Labs Univ of Wash Friday Harbor WA 98250

STRATMAN, FREDERICK WILLIAM, b Dodgeville, Wis, Nov 26, 27; m 51; c 1. BIOCHEMISTRY. *Educ:* Univ Wis, BS, 50, MS, 57, PhD(animal-dairy husb, biochem), 61. *Prof Exp:* Res asst animal husb, Univ Wis, 57-61; researcher, Wis Alumni Res Found, 62; res assoc, Univ Wis, 62-63, NIH fel reprod physiol, 63-65; asst prof animal sci, Univ Ife, Nigeria, 65-67; asst prof animal sci, 67-68, proj assoc, Inst Enzyme Res, 68-70, proj assoc & Babcock fel, 70-71, NIH spec fel, 71-73, asst res prof, 71-78, assoc scientist, 78-81, SR SCIENTIST, UNIV WIS-MADISON, 81- *Mem:* Am Soc Biol Chemists. *Res:* Hormonal regulation of protein synthesis, particularly sulfhydryls, polyamines, methylation, phosphorylation, muscle, liver, tumors, perfusions, testosterone, somatomedin; hormonal regulation of gluconeogenesis; hepatocytes; lipid metabolism; spermatozoa; carnitine. *Mailing Add:* Inst for Enzyme Res Univ of Wis Madison WI 53706

STRATMEYER, MELVIN EDWARD, b Peoria, Ill, Aug 30, 42; m 66. RADIOBIOLOGY, RISK ASSESSMENT. *Educ:* Purdue Univ, Lafayette, BS, 65, MS, 66, PhD(bionucleonics), 69. *Prof Exp:* teaching asst bionucleonics & health physics, Purdue Univ, 65-66; res chemist, 69-73, PMS officer, Ionizing Radiation, 73-75, PMS officer, Ultrasound, Exp Studies Br, 75-82, CHIEF SONICS BR, DIV BIOL EFFECTS, BUR RADIOLOGICAL HEALTH, BUR RADIOL HEALTH, US FOOD & DRUG ADMIN, 82- *Mem:* AAAS; Am Inst Ultrasound Med. *Res:* Ionizing radiation effects on nucleic acid and protein metabolism; ionizing radiation effects on mitochrondrial systems; ultrasound effects on nucleic acid and protein metabolism, growth and development; assessment of risk associated with exposure to medical ultrasound. *Mailing Add:* PO Box 617 Ijamsville MD 21754

STRATT, RICHARD MARK, b Philadelphia, Pa, Feb, 21, 54. STATISTICAL MECHANICS, LIQUIDS. *Educ:* Mass Inst Technol, SB, 75; Univ Calif, Berkeley, PhD(chem), 79. *Prof Exp:* Res assoc, Univ Ill, Champaign, 79-80, NSF fel, 80; ASST PROF CHEM, BROWN UNIV, 81- *Mem:* Am Phys Soc. *Res:* Chemical physics and statistical mechanics, especially the statistical mechanics of internal degrees of freedom of molecules in solution; condensed phase problems in general. *Mailing Add:* Box H Dept Chem Brown Univ Providence RI 02912

STRATTAN, LAURENCE WILLIAM, b Wichita, Kans, Mar 8, 47; m 78. ANALYTICAL CHEMISTRY, PHYSICAL CHEMISTRY. *Educ:* Wichita State Univ, BS, 69; Univ Kans, PhD(chem), 74. *Prof Exp:* Fel environ chem, Eng Exp Sta, Ga Inst Technol, 75-78, res scientist, 78; CHEMIST ENVIRON CHEM, US ENVIRON PROTECTION AGENCY, 78- *Concurrent Pos:* Fel dept chem, Emory Univ, 74-77. *Mem:* Am Chem Soc; AAAS. *Res:* Gas chromatography; mass spectrometry; water treatment practices; environmental chemistry. *Mailing Add:* 6706 Brink Dr Parkville MO 64152

STRATTAN, ROBERT DEAN, b Newton, Kans, Dec 7, 36; m 60; c 2. ELECTRICAL ENGINEERING. *Educ:* Wichita State Univ, BS, 58; Carnegie-Mellon Univ, MS, 59, PhD(elec eng), 62. *Prof Exp:* Res engr, Wichita Div, Boeing Co, Kans, 61-63; mem tech staff elec eng, Tulsa Div, NAm Rockwell Corp, Okla, 63-68; assoc prof, 68-76, head dept, 68-75, PROF ELEC ENG, UNIV TULSA, 76- *Mem:* Inst Elec & Electronics Engrs; Am Soc Eng Educ; Nat Soc Prof Engrs; Sigma Xi; Am Soc Eng Mgt. *Res:* Electromagnetic theory; radar scattering analysis, measurement and camouflage. *Mailing Add:* Dept of Elec Eng 600 S College Tulsa OK 74104

STRATTON, CEDRIC, b Langley, Eng, Apr 26, 31; US citizen; m 61; c 1. INORGANIC CHEMISTRY, ANALYTICAL CHEMISTRY. *Educ:* Univ Nottingham, BSc, 53; Univ London, PhD(inorg chem), 63. *Prof Exp:* Qual control chemist, Richard Klinger, Ltd, Eng, 53-55; develop chemist, Small & Parkes, Ltd, 55-56; sci officer anal res, Brit Insulated Callender's Cables, 57-61; NSF res fel, Univ Fla, 63-65; assoc prof, 65-72, PROF INORG & ANAL CHEM, ARMSTRONG STATE COL, 72- *Mem:* Am Chem Soc; The Chem Soc. *Res:* Chemistry of group V elements, their heterocyclic derivatives; concentration of minerals in local well-water; legal consultancy. *Mailing Add:* Dept of Chem Armstrong State Col 11935 Albercorn St Savannah GA 31406

STRATTON, CHARLES ABNER, b Canyon, Tex, Mar 28, 16; m 51; c 3. COLLOID CHEMISTRY, SCIENCE EDUCATION. *Educ:* WTex State Col, BS, 36; Univ Southern Calif, MS, 50, PhD(chem), 53; Gemological Inst Am, grad gemologist cert, 75. *Prof Exp:* Chemist, Borger Refinery, Phillips Petrol Co, 39-47; asst chem, Univ Southern Calif, 47-51; chemist, Res Div, Phillips Petrol Co, 52-73; SELF-EMPLOYED GEMOLOGIST, 75- *Concurrent Pos:* Part-time instr chem, Bartlesville Wesleyan Col, 74-76. *Res:* Chemical treatment of kerosene, gasoline and liquified petroleum gases; compounding of greases with inorganic thickeners; drilling mud chemicals; water-soluble polymers; water-flood chemicals. *Mailing Add:* 1233 N Wyandotte Dewey OK 74029

STRATTON, CHARLOTTE DIANNE, b Brooklyn, NY, Mar 7, 29. ORGANIC CHEMISTRY. *Educ:* Bucknell Univ, BS, 51; Pa State Univ, MS, 52. *Prof Exp:* From asst res chemist to assoc res chemist, 52-70, RES CHEMIST, PARKE, DAVIS & CO, WARNER-LAMBERT CO, INC, 70- *Mem:* Am Chem Soc. *Res:* Medicinal chemistry, especially natural products isolation and organic synthesis of cardiovascular drugs. *Mailing Add:* Warner-Lambert/Parke-Davis 2800 Plymouth Rd Ann Arbor MI 48106

STRATTON, CLIFFORD JAMES, b Winslow, Ariz, Apr 7, 45; m 68; c 5. ANATOMY, CELL BIOLOGY. *Educ:* Northern Ariz Univ, BS, 68, MS, 70; Brigham Young Univ, PhD(zool, chem), 73. *Prof Exp:* Lab instr, Northern Ariz Univ, 68-70; lect instr & Nat Defense Educ Act fel, Brigham Young Univ, 70-73; res assoc, Sch Med, Univ Calif, Los Angeles, 73-74; asst prof & chief neuroanatomist, 74-77, ASSOC PROF, CHIEF HISTOLOGIST & ASST CHIEF NEUROANATOMIST, SCH MED, UNIV NEV, 77- *Concurrent Pos:* NIH Young Investr Pulmonary res award, 76-78; r researcher, Am Lung Asn, 76-78; res assoc, NIH Lung Cult Conf, W Alton Jones Cell Sci Ctr, NY, 77. *Mem:* Am Asn Anatomists; Electron Microscopic Soc Am; Tissue Cult Asn; Am Soc Cell Biol; AAAS. *Res:* Ultrastructural morphology, histochemistry and pharmacology of the human lung surfactant system as studied in vivo and with alveolar cloning, complimented with lipid-carbohydrate embedment procedures; primary interest is infant respiratory distress syndrome. *Mailing Add:* 16 Manville Med Sci Bldg Univ of Nev Reno NV 89557

STRATTON, DONALD BRENDAN, b Escanaba, Mich, Jan 6, 41; m 67. HUMAN PHYSIOLOGY, HUMAN NEUROPHYSIOLOGY. *Educ:* Northern Mich Univ, BS, 63, MA, 64; Southern Ill Univ, PhD(physiol), 71. *Prof Exp:* From asst prof to assoc prof, 71-80, PROF BIOL, DRAKE UNIV, 81- *Mem:* Am Physiol Soc; Neuroelec Soc. *Res:* Electroanesthesia; electrosleep; normal physiological sleep mechanisms. *Mailing Add:* 3436 Maple West Des Moines IA 50265

STRATTON, FRANK E(DWARD), b Oceanside, Calif, Dec 20, 37; m 59; c 2. ENGINEERING. *Educ:* San Diego State Col, BS, 62; Stanford Univ, MS, 63, PhD(civil eng), 66; Am Acad Environ Engrs, dipl. *Prof Exp:* PROF ENG, SAN DIEGO STATE UNIV, 66- *Mem:* Am Soc Civil Engrs; Am Water Works Asn; Water Pollution Control Fedn. *Res:* Water quality management; nutrient removal methods; waste disposal. *Mailing Add:* Col of Eng San Diego State Univ San Diego CA 92182

STRATTON, JAMES FORREST, b Chicago Heights, Ill, Nov 29, 43. PALEONTOLOGY. *Educ:* Ind State Univ, Terre Haute, BS, 65; Ind Univ, Bloomington, MAT, 67, AM, 72, PhD(paleont), 75. *Prof Exp:* Instr geol, Shippensburg State Col, 67-70; asst prof, 75-77, ASSOC PROF GEOL, EASTERN ILL UNIV, 77- *Mem:* Soc Econ Paleontologists & Mineralogists; Int Bryozool Asn; Am Asn Petrol Geologists; Brit Palaeont Asn. *Res:* Quantitative analysis of morphological and structural characters of Fenestellidae for the study of taxonomy and functional morphology. *Mailing Add:* Dept of Geol Eastern Ill Univ Charleston IL 61920

STRATTON, JULIUS ADAMS, b Seattle, Wash, May 18, 01; m 35; c 3. PHYSICS. *Educ:* Mass Inst Technol, SB, 23, SM, 26; Swiss Fed Inst Technol, ScD(math, physics), 28. *Hon Degrees:* DEng, NY Univ, 55, LHD, Hebrew Union Col, 62, Oklahoma City Univ, 63, Jewish Theol Sem Am, 65; LLD,

Northeastern Univ, 57, Union Col, NY, 58, Harvard Univ, 59, Brandeis Univ, 59, Carleton Col, 60, Univ Notre Dame, 61, Johns Hopkins Univ, 62; ScD, St Francis Xavier Univ, 57, Col William & Mary, 64, Carnegie Inst Technol, 65, Univ Leeds, 67, Heriot-Watt Univ, 71, Cambridge Univ, 72. *Prof Exp:* Res assoc commun, 24-26, asst prof elec eng, 28-30, from asst prof to prof physics, 30-51, mem staff, Radiation Lab, 40-45, dir, Res Lab Electronics, 45-49, provost, 49-56, vpres, 51-56, chancellor, 56-59, actg pres, 57-59, pres, 59-66, EMER PRES, MASS INST TECHNOL, 66- *Concurrent Pos:* Expert consult, Secy War, 42-46; chmn, Comt Electronics, Res & Develop Bd, 46-49; chmn bd, Ford Found, 66-71; chmn, Comn Marine Sci, Eng & Resources, 67-69; mem, Nat Adv Comt Oceans & Atmosphere, 71-73; life mem corp, Mass Inst Technol; life trustee, Boston Mus Sci; mem, Finance Comt, Nat Acad Sci, 74-80. *Honors & Awards:* Medal Merit, 46; Cert Award, US Dept Navy, 57; Medal Hon, Inst Radio Eng, 57; Faraday Medal, Brit Inst Elec Engrs, 61; Officer, French Legion Hon, 61; hon fel, Manchester Col Sci & Technol, 63; Orden de Boyaca, Govt Colombia, 64; Boston Medal Distinguished Achievement, 66; hon mem senate, Tech Univ Berlin, 66; Knight Commander, Order Merit, Fed Repub Ger, 66. *Mem:* Nat Acad Sci (vpres, 61-65); Nat Acad Eng; fel Am Phys Soc; Coun Foreign Rels; fel Am Acad Arts & Sci. *Res:* Electromagnetic theory. *Mailing Add:* Mass Inst of Technol Cambridge MA 02139

STRATTON, LEWIS PALMER, b West Chester, Pa, Aug 22, 37; m 60; c 2. BIOCHEMISTRY, BACTERIOLOGY. *Educ:* Juniata Col, BS, 59; Univ Maine, MS, 61; Fla State Univ, PhD(chem), 67. *Prof Exp:* Asst prof, 67-74, assoc prof, 74-81, PROF BIOL, FURMAN UNIV, 81- *Concurrent Pos:* Vis prof zool chem, Univ Alaska, 75. *Mem:* AAAS; Asn Southeastern Biologists; Sigma Xi. *Res:* Comparative protein biochemistry. *Mailing Add:* Dept of Biol Furman Univ Greenville SC 29613

STRATTON, PAUL OSWALD, b Rawlins, Wyo, Aug 18, 23; m 48; c 2. ANIMAL SCIENCE. *Educ:* Univ Wyo, BS, 47, MS, 50; Univ Minn, PhD, 52. *Prof Exp:* Supply instr animal prod, Univ Wyo, 49-50; asst animal breeding, Univ Minn, 50-52; asst prof, 52-58, PROF ANIMAL SCI & HEAD DEPT, COL AGR, UNIV WYO, 58- *Mem:* Am Soc Animal Sci. *Res:* Improvement of beef cattle and sheep through breeding methods. *Mailing Add:* Animal Sci Div Univ of Wyo Laramie WY 82070

STRATTON, ROBERT, b Vienna, Austria, Aug 14, 28; US citizen; c 52, 80; c 2. THEORETICAL PHYSICS. *Educ:* Univ Manchester, BSc, 49, PhD(theoret physics), 52. *Prof Exp:* Res physicist, Metrop Vickers Elec Co, Ltd, Eng, 52-59; mem tech staff, 59-63, dir, Physics Res Lab, 63-71, assoc dir, Cent Res Lab, 71-72, dir semiconductor res & develop labs, 72-75, dir, 75-77, ASST VPRES CENT RES LABS, TEX INSTRUMENTS, INC, 77- *Mem:* Fel Am Phys Soc; fel Inst Elec & Electronics Engrs; fel Brit Inst Physics & Phys Soc. *Res:* Solid state theory, including field emission, space charge barriers, thermoelectricity, high electric fields, thermal conductivity, dielectric breakdown and surface energies of solids. *Mailing Add:* Cent Res Labs Tex Instruments PO Box 225936 MS 136 Dallas TX 75265

STRATTON, ROBERT ALAN, b Selma, Ala, Feb 4, 36; m 61; c 4. POLYMER CHEMISTRY. *Educ:* Univ Nev, BS, 58; Univ Wis, PhD(chem), 62. *Prof Exp:* Sr res chemist, Mobil Chem Co, 62-69; ASSOC PROF CHEM, INST PAPER CHEM, 69- *Mem:* Soc Rheol; Am Chem Soc; Tech Asn Pulp & Paper Indust. *Res:* Rheology of polymer melts and solutions; dilute solution properties of polymers; flocculation of colloids; use of polymers in papermaking and waste water treatment. *Mailing Add:* Inst of Paper Chem Appleton WI 54911

STRATTON, ROY FRANKLIN, JR, b Memphis, Tenn, July 23, 29; m 63; c 1. ELECTRICAL ENGINEERING, PHYSICS. *Educ:* Southwestern at Memphis, BS, 51; Univ Tenn, MS, 53, PhD(physics), 57; Ga Inst Technol, MSEE, 75. *Prof Exp:* Asst dept physics, Univ Tenn, 52-57; res assoc plasma physics, Oak Ridge Nat Lab, 58-70; prof & chmn sci div admin & teaching, Pikeville Col, 70-73; teaching asst elec eng, Ga Inst Technol, 73-75; ELECTRONIC ENGR ELECTROMAGNETIC COMPATIBILITY, ROME AIR DEVELOP CTR, US AIR FORCE, 75- *Mem:* Inst Elec & Electronic Engrs; AAAS; Sigma Xi. *Res:* Analysis techniques and control methods for electromagnetic interference; methods of measuring to electrical properties of composite materials and of using these properties to predict the electromagnetic shielding of composite material structures. *Mailing Add:* Rome Air Develop Ctr-RBCT Griffiss AFB NY 13441

STRATTON, THOMAS FAIRLAMB, b Kansas City, Mo, Dec 19, 29; m 58; c 2. LASERS, NUCLEAR PHYSICS. *Educ:* Union Col, BS, 49; Univ Minn, MS, 52, PhD(physics), 54. *Prof Exp:* Staff mem physics, Los Alamos Sci Lab, 54-66; sr fel, Battelle Columbus Lab, 67; staff mem physics, 68-75, group leader, Antares Laser Proj, 76-79, dep physics div leader, 80-81, LAB FEL, LOS ALAMOS NAT LAB, 82- *Concurrent Pos:* Mem, Atomic Energy Res Estab, UK, 58; mem adv bd pulse power, Nat Acad Sci, 77. *Mem:* Sigma Xi; fel Am Phys Soc; AAAS. *Res:* Thermonuclear fusion; soft x-ray spectroscopy; magnetohydrodynamics; plasma acceleration and direct conversion. *Mailing Add:* Los Alamos Nat Lab Los Alamos NM 87545

STRATTON, WILLIAM R, b River Falls, Wis, May 15, 22; m 52; c 3. PHYSICS. *Educ:* Univ Minn, PhD(physics), 52. *Prof Exp:* Res assoc, Univ Minn, 52; MEM STAFF, LOS ALAMOS SCI LAB, UNIV CALIF, 52- *Concurrent Pos:* US del, Int Conf Peaceful Uses Atomic Energy, 58 & Fast Reactor Prog, Cadarache, France, 65-66; mem, Adv Comt Reactor Safeguards, AEC, 66-75. *Mem:* Am Phys Soc; Am Nuclear Soc. *Res:* Scattering and reaction in nuclear physics; nuclear forces; reactor physics. *Mailing Add:* Los Alamos Sci Lab Univ of Calif MS 231 Los Alamos NM 87545

STRATTON, WILMER JOSEPH, b Newark, NJ, June 4, 32; m 55; c 3. CHEMISTRY. *Educ:* Earlham Col, AB, 54; Ohio State Univ, PhD(chem), 58. *Prof Exp:* Asst prof chem, Ohio Wesleyan Univ, 58-59 & Earlham Col, 59-64; vis lectr, Univ Ill, 64-65; assoc prof, 65-70, chmn dept, 65-68, PROF CHEM, EARLHAM COL, 70- *Mem:* Am Chem Soc. *Res:* Metal coordination compounds, including synthesis of new polydentate chelates and bonding in chelate systems. *Mailing Add:* Dept of Chem Earlham Col Richmond IN 47374

STRATY, RICHARD ROBERT, b Milwaukee, Wis, June 21, 29; m 53; c 2. FISHERIES BIOLOGY, BIOLOGICAL OCEANOGRAPHY. *Educ:* Ore State Univ, BS, 54, PhD(fisheries & oceanog), 69; Univ Hawaii, MS, 63. *Prof Exp:* Proj leader fish biol, Fish & Wildlife Serv, US Dept Interior, Juneau, 54-55, proj supvr marine fish biol, Bur Com Fisheries, 55-59, proj supvr marine fish biol salmon, Auke Bay Biol Lab, Bur Com Fisheries, 60-61; exped scientist marine biol, Stanford Univ, 64; proj suprv marine biol, Auke Bay Fisheries Lab, Bur Com Fisheries, US Fish & Wildlife Serv, US Dept Interior, 66-74; PROG MGR MARINE INVEST BIOL OCEANOG, AUKE BAY LAB, NAT MARINE FISHERIES SERV, NAT OCEANIC & ATMOSPHERIC ADMIN, US DEPT COM, 74- *Concurrent Pos:* Mem, Alaska Coun Sci & Technol, Off Gov Alaska, 78- *Honors & Awards:* C Y Conkle Publ Award, Auke Bay Biol Lab, US Dept Interior, 66. *Mem:* Am Inst Fishery Res Biologists. *Res:* Fishery oceanography; marine ecology; population dynamics. *Mailing Add:* US Dept of Com NOAA Auke Bay Lab PO Box 155 Auke Bay AK 99821

STRAUB, CONRAD P(AUL), b Irvington, NJ, June 21, 16; m 45; c 4. SANITARY ENGINEERING. *Educ:* Newark Col Eng, BS, 36, CE, 39; Cornell Univ, MCE, 40, PhD(sanit eng), 43. *Hon Degrees:* DEng, Newark Col Eng, 67. *Prof Exp:* Computer & head comput sect, US Eng Off, NY, 37-39; asst pub health engr, USPHS, NJ, 41, asst sanit engr, NY, 42-44, actg dep chief sanit engr, China, 45-46, chief sanit engr, Poland, 46, sr asst sanit engr, Ohio, 47-48 & Oak Ridge Nat Lab, 48-56, chief radiol health res activ, Robert A Taft Sanit Eng Ctr, 56-64, dep dir, 64-65, dir, 65-66; prof, 66-81, EMER PROF SANIT ENG & DIR ENVIRON HEALTH RES & TRAINING CTR, UNIV MINN, MINNEAPOLIS, 81- *Concurrent Pos:* Chmn comt waste disposal, Int Comn Radiol Protection; mem expert comt radiol health & consult, WHO. *Honors & Awards:* Fuertes Medal, Cornell Univ, 54; Elda Anderson Mem Award, Health Physics Soc. *Mem:* Am Soc Civil Engrs; Health Physics Soc; Am Pub Health Asn; Am Water Works Asn; Water Pollution Control Asn. *Res:* Industrial wastes; sanitary engineering education; insect control; treatment and disposal of radioactive wastes; radiological health; environmental health; public health implications of water and waste water systems; environmental contaminants. *Mailing Add:* 2330 Chalet Dr Columbia Heights MN 55421

STRAUB, DAREL K, b Titusville, Pa, May 17, 35. INORGANIC CHEMISTRY. *Educ:* Allegheny Col, BS, 57; Univ Ill, PhD(inorg chem), 61. *Prof Exp:* Instr, 61-62, asst prof, 62-68, ASSOC PROF CHEM, UNIV PITTSBURGH, 68- *Mem:* Am Chem Soc; AAAS. *Res:* Iron porphyrins; complexes of sulfur-containing ligands; Mössbauer spectroscopy. *Mailing Add:* Dept of Chem Univ of Pittsburgh Pittsburgh PA 15260

STRAUB, RICHARD WAYNE, b Fairfax, Mo, June 5, 40; m 64; c 1. ENTOMOLOGY. *Educ:* Northwest Mo State Univ, BS, 66; Univ Mo, MS, 68, PhD(entom), 72. *Prof Exp:* Res assoc, 71-75, asst prof, 75-79, ASSOC PROF ENTOM, NY STATE AGR EXP STA, CORNELL UNIV, 79- *Mem:* Entom Soc Am; AAAS. *Res:* Biology and integrated control of insects of vegetable crops with emphasis on plant resistance to insect pests and insect transmission of vegetable diseases. *Mailing Add:* Hudson Valley Res Lab PO Box 727 Highland NY 12528

STRAUB, WILLIAM ALBERT, b Philadelphia, Pa, June 21, 31; m 58; c 2. ANALYTICAL CHEMISTRY. *Educ:* Univ Pa, BA, 53; Cornell Univ, PhD, 58. *Prof Exp:* Technologist, 57-67, sr res chemist, 67-75, ASSOC RES CONSULT, US STEEL CORP, 75- *Mem:* Am Chem Soc. *Res:* Effluent gas, process solution analysis. *Mailing Add:* US Steel Corp Research Lab Monroeville PA 15146

STRAUB, WOLF DETER, b Boston, Mass, Apr 27, 27; m 61; c 2. SOLID STATE PHYSICS. *Educ:* Yale Univ, BS, 50; Univ Mich, MS, 52. *Prof Exp:* Staff mem solid state physics, Res Div, Raytheon Co, 52-65; physicist, Electronics Res Ctr, NASA, 65-70 & M/K Systs, Inc, Mass, 70-72; mgr anal lab, 72-80, DIR ADVAN PHYSICS LAB, COULTER SYSTS CORP, INC, BEDFORD, 80- *Mem:* Am Phys Soc; Am Vaccum Soc. *Res:* Galvanometric properties of semiconductors and semimetals; radiation damage and studies of microwave generation in semiconductors; electrical and mechanical properties of dielectric thin films; problems in electrophotography; surface physics. *Mailing Add:* 158 Barton Dr Sudbury MA 01776

STRAUBE, ROBERT LEONARD, b Chicago, Ill, Sept 16, 17; m 44; c 2. RADIOBIOLOGY. *Educ:* Univ Chicago, BS, 39, PhD(physiol), 55. *Prof Exp:* Asst path, Univ Chicago, 43-46; prof radiobiol, Assoc Cols Midwest, 63-64; assoc scientist, Argonne Nat Lab, 47-65; EXEC SECY RADIATION STUDY SECT, DIV RES GRANTS, NIH, 65- *Mem:* AAAS; Radiation Res Soc; Am Physiol Soc; Soc Exp Biol & Med; Am Asn Cancer Res. *Res:* Nature of radiation effects and their modification by chemical agents; growth processes in neoplastic cells. *Mailing Add:* Div of Res Grants Nat Inst of Health Bethesda MD 20014

STRAUCH, KARL, b Giessen, Ger, Oct 4, 22; nat US; m 51. PARTICLE PHYSICS. *Educ:* Univ Calif, AB, 43, PhD(physics), 50. *Prof Exp:* Soc Fels jr fel, 50-53, from asst prof to prof, 53-75, GEORGE VASMER LEVERETT PROF PHYSICS, HARVARD UNIV, 75- *Concurrent Pos:* Dir, Cambridge Electron Accelerator, Harvard Univ, 67-74. *Mem:* Am Phys Soc; Am Acad Arts & Sci. *Res:* High energy reactions; elementary particles. *Mailing Add:* Dept of Physics Harvard Univ Cambridge MA 02138

STRAUCH, RALPH EUGENE, b Springfield, Mass, May 14, 37; m 58; c 2. MATHEMATICS, STATISTICS. *Educ:* Univ Calif, Los Angeles, AB, 59, Univ Calif, Berkeley, MA, 64, PhD(statist), 65. *Prof Exp:* Consult, Rand Corp, 64-65, mathematician, 65-76; CONSULT, 76- *Mem:* AAAS; Inst Math

Statist. *Res:* Dynamic programming; statistical decision theory; national security policy; human perception; paranormal phenomena; policy analysis methodology; mind/body relationship. *Mailing Add:* 1383 Avenida de Cortez Pacific Palisades CA 90272

STRAUGHAN, ISDALE (DALE) MARGARET, b Pittsworth, Australia, Nov 4, 39; m 62; c 1. ECOLOGY, BIOLOGY. *Educ:* Queensland Univ, BSc, 60, Hons, 62, PhD(zool), 66. *Prof Exp:* Demonstr zool, Queensland Univ, 66; sr demonstr, Univ Col, Townsville, 66-67; asst prof & res assoc, Allan Hancock Found, 69-74, SR RES SCIENTIST, INST MARINE & COASTAL STUDIES, UNIV SOUTHERN CALIF, 74- *Concurrent Pos:* Consult biologist, Northern Elec Authority, Queensland, 66-68; Am Asn Univ Women fel, 68-69. *Mem:* AAAS; Sigma Xi; Ecol Soc Am. *Res:* Establishment of natural ecological change in response to natural change in the marine environment and comparison with man induced ecological change; comparison of man-induced change to natural biological fluctuations. *Mailing Add:* 13688 Park St Whittier CA 90601

STRAUGHN, WILLIAM RINGGOLD, JR, b Dubois, Pa, May 21, 13; m 41; c 4. BACTERIOLOGY. *Educ:* Mansfield State Col, BS, 35; Cornell Univ, MS, 40; Univ Pa, PdD(bact), 58. *Prof Exp:* Teacher high sch, Pa, 35-36 & NY, 36-38; asst bact, Univ NC, 40-42; instr math & chem, Md State Teachers Col, Salisbury, 42-44; from instr to prof bact, 44-80, EMER PROF BACT, SCH MED, UNIV NC, CHAPEL HILL, 80-, PROF IMMUNOL, 77- *Mem:* Am Soc Microbiol. *Res:* Bacterial physiology and metabolism; antibacterial agents; enzyme synthesis; amino acid decarboxylases-mechanisms of formation and action; bacterial membranes and transport mechanisms. *Mailing Add:* Dept of Bact Univ of NC Sch of Med Chapel Hill NC 27514

STRAUMANIS, JOHN JANIS, JR, b Riga, Latvia, Apr 22, 35; US citizen; m 59; c 2. PSYCHIATRY. *Educ:* Univ Iowa, BA, 57, MD, 60, MS, 64. *Prof Exp:* Intern med, Georgetown Univ Hosp, 60-61; resident psychiat, Univ Iowa, 61-64; asst prof psychiat & Nat Inst Ment Health res career develop grant, 66-71, assoc prof psychiat, 71-77, PROF PSYCHIAT, TEMPLE UNIV, 77- *Mem:* Am Psychiat Asn; Soc Biol Psychiat; Am Psychopath Asn; Am Electroencephalographic Soc; Eastern Asn Electroencephalographers. *Res:* Electrophysiology pf psychiatric disorders. *Mailing Add:* Eastern Pa Psych Inst 3300 Henry Ave Philadelphia PA 19129

STRAUMFJORD, JON VIDALIN, JR, b Portland, Ore, Feb 23, 25; m 47; c 2. MEDICINE, CLINICAL PATHOLOGY. *Educ:* Willamette Univ, BA, 48; Univ Ore, MS & MD, 53; Univ Iowa, PhD(biochem), 58. *Prof Exp:* Res fel biochem, Univ Iowa, 54-58; resident path & consult, Providence Hosp, Portland, Ore, 58-60; asst prof path, Univ Miami, 60-62; assoc prof, Med Col Ala, 62-65, prof clin path & chmn dept, 65-70, dir clin labs, 62-65, clin pathologist in chief, Univ Hosp, 65-70; PROF PATH & CHMN DEPT, MED COL WIS, 70- *Concurrent Pos:* Asst pathologist, Div Clin Path, Jackson Mem Hosp, Miami, Fla, 60-62; dir labs, Milwaukee City Gen Hosp, Wis, 70-; mem surg adv bd, Shrine Burn Units. *Mem:* AAAS; Am Soc Clin Path; Am Asn Clin Chem; Col Am Pathologists; NY Acad Sci. *Res:* Surface characteristics of cells; clinical chemical screening procedures. *Mailing Add:* Dept of Path Med Col of Wis 8700 W Wisconsin Ave Milwaukee WI 53226

STRAUS, ALAN EDWARD, b Berkeley, Calif, May 14, 24; m 53; c 2. ORGANIC CHEMISTRY. *Educ:* Univ Calif, Berkeley, BS, 49. *Prof Exp:* From asst res chemist to res chemist, 49-67, SR RES CHEMIST, CHEVRON RES CO, 67- *Mem:* Am Chem Soc. *Res:* Petrochemicals; hydrocarbon oxidation; surface active agents; hydrocarbon pyrolysis; organic synthesis; polymers; heterogeneous catalysis. *Mailing Add:* 2679 Tommalpais Ave El Cerito CA 94530

STRAUS, BERNARD, b New York, NY, July 30, 11; m 35; c 2. INTERNAL MEDICINE. *Educ:* NY Univ, BS, 31; Long Island Col Med, MD, 35; Am Bd Internal Med, dipl, 47. *Prof Exp:* Chief med serv, Vet Admin Hosp, Bronx, NY, 46-54; assoc prof clin med, Albert Einstein Col Med, 54-64; prof internal med, NY Med Col, 64-71; PROF MED, MT SINAI SCH MED, 71-; dir med, 71-80, CONSULT, BETH ISRAEL MED CTR, 80- *Concurrent Pos:* Former dir med, Ctr Chronic Dis, Bird S Coler Hosp, New York; vis physician, Rockefeller Univ Hosp, 76- *Mem:* Fel Am Col Physicians; Asn Am Med Cols; Am Geriat Soc; Geront Soc Am. *Res:* Diagnosis; liver disease; malariology; lymphomas and sleep; medical education; geriatrics. *Mailing Add:* Dept Med Beth Israel Med Ctr New York NY 10003

STRAUS, DAVID BRADLEY, b Chicago, Ill, July 26, 30; m 55; c 3. BIOCHEMISTRY. *Educ:* Reed Col, BA, 53; Univ Chicago, PhD(biochem), 60. *Prof Exp:* Asst biochem, Med Sch, Univ Ore, 53-54; asst, Univ Chicago & Argonne Cancer Res Hosp, 55-60; res assoc chem, Princeton Univ, 60-64; res staff mem, 64-65; asst prof biochem, State Univ NY Buffalo, 65-72; ASSOC PROF CHEM, STATE UNIV NY COL NEW PALTZ, 73- *Mem:* AAAS; Am Chem Soc; NY Acad Sci. *Res:* Chemical synthesis of polynculeotides; nucleic acid enzymology and chemistry; protein-nucleic acid interactions. *Mailing Add:* Dept of Chem State Univ of NY Col New Paltz NY 12561

STRAUS, DAVID CONRAD, b Evansville, Ind, Apr 27, 47; m 75. MEDICAL MICROBIOLOGY. *Educ:* Wright State Univ, BS, 70; Loyola Univ Chicago, PhD(microbiol), 74. *Prof Exp:* Teaching asst microbiol, Sch Med, Loyola Univ Chicago, 70-74; fel, Med Ctr, Univ Cincinnati, 74-75; instr, Univ Tex Health Sci Ctr, San Antonio, 75-76, asst prof microbiol, 76-81; ASSOC PROF MICROBIOL, TEX TECH UNIV HEALTH SCI CTR, LUBBOCK, TEX, 81- *Concurrent Pos:* Instr microbiol, Ill Col Podiatric Med, 72-73. *Mem:* Am Soc Microbiol; Sigma Xi. *Res:* Study of mechanisms of bacterial pathogenicity and host response; study of bacterial exotoxins. *Mailing Add:* Tex Tech Univ Health Sci Ctr Sch Med Lubbock TX 79430

STRAUS, ERNST GABOR, b Munich, Ger, Feb 25, 22; m 44; c 2. MATHEMATICS. *Educ:* Columbia Univ, MA, 42, PhD(math), 48. *Prof Exp:* Lectr math, Columbia Univ, 42-44; asst to Prof Albert Einstein, Inst Advan Study, 44-48; from instr to assoc prof, 48-60, PROF MATH, UNIV CALIF, LOS ANGELES, 60- *Mem:* Am Math Soc. *Res:* Number theory; geometry; analysis; algebra; relativity theory. *Mailing Add:* Dept of Math Univ of Calif Los Angeles CA 90024

STRAUS, FRANCIS HOWE, II, b Chicago, Ill, Mar 16, 32; m 55; c 4. PATHOLOGY. *Educ:* Harvard Univ, AB, 53; Univ Chicago, MD, 57, MS, 64. *Prof Exp:* Intern, Clins, 57-58, resident path, 58-62, chief resident, 62-63, from instr to assoc prof, 62-78, PROF PATH, SCH MED, UNIV CHICAGO, 78- *Concurrent Pos:* Am Cancer Soc advan clin fel, 65-68. *Mem:* Sigma Xi; Am Soc Exp Pathologists; Am Asn Pathologists; Int Acad Path; NY Acad Sci. *Res:* Morphology in surgical pathology as it relates to diagnosis and prognosis of clinical disease; cellular aspects of host-tumor interaction; endocrine pathology. *Mailing Add:* Dept of Path Univ of Chicago Sch of Med Chicago IL 60637

STRAUS, HELEN LORNA PUTTKAMMER, b Chicago, Ill, Feb 15, 33; m 55; c 4. ANATOMY, BIOLOGY. *Educ:* Radcliffe Col, AB, 55; Univ Chicago, MS, 60, PhD(anat), 62. *Prof Exp:* Fel anat, 62-63, res assoc, 63-64, instr anat & biol, 64-67, asst prof biol & asst dean undergrad students, 67-71, dean admissions, 75-80, ASSOC PROF BIOL & ANAT, UNIV CHICAGO, 73-, DEAN UNDERGRAD STUDENTS, 71- *Mem:* Am Soc Zoologists; Am Asn Anatomists; AAAS. *Res:* Histochemistry, histology and cytology of secretory process. *Mailing Add:* Dept of Anat Univ of Chicago Chicago IL 60637

STRAUS, JOE MELVIN, b Dallas, Tex, May 27, 46; m 71; c 1. ATMOSPHERIC PHYSICS, GEOPHYSICAL FLUID DYNAMICS. *Educ:* Rice Univ, BA, 68; Univ Calif, Los Angeles, MS, 69, PhD(planetary, space physics), 72. *Prof Exp:* Res scientist, 73-80, HEAD, ATMOSPHERIC SCI DEPT, SPACE SCI LAB, THE AEROSPACE CORP, 80- *Mem:* Sigma Xi; Am Geophys Union. *Res:* Theoretical studies of atmospheric physics; aeronomy; convection in atmospheres, oceans, stars, planetary interiors; geophysical fluid dynamics; atmospheric and ionospheric effects on space systems. *Mailing Add:* Space Sci Lab The Aerospace Corp PO Box 92957 Los Angeles CA 90009

STRAUS, JOZEF, b Velke Kapusany, Czech, July 18, 46; Can citizen. EXPERIMENTAL SOLID STATE PHYSICS. *Educ:* Univ Alta, BS, 69, PhD(physics), 74. *Prof Exp:* Fel, Univ Alta, 69-74; MEM SCI STAFF & NAT RES COUN CAN FEL, BELL NORTHERN RES LTD, 74- *Res:* Fabrication and study of physical properties of light emitting diodes and of solid state lasers; fiber optics, fiber optics communication; electron tunneling in normal and superconducting metals, Josephson tunneling. *Mailing Add:* 293 Iroquois Rd Ottawa ON K2A 3M3 Can

STRAUS, MARC J, b New York, NY, June 2, 43; m 64; c 2. ONCOLOGY, CHEMOTHERAPY. *Educ:* Franklin & Marshall Col, AB, 64; State Univ NY Downstate Med Ctr, MD, 68; Am Bd Internal Med, dipl & cert med oncol, 75. *Prof Exp:* Chief med oncol, Med Ctr, Boston Univ, 74-78, assoc prof med, Sch Med, 75-78; CHIEF ONCOL & PROF MED, NY MED COL, 78- *Concurrent Pos:* Prin investr, Eastern Coop Oncol Group, Med Ctr, Boston Univ, 75-; consult oncol, St Agnes Hosp, Northern West Hosp, St Joseph's Hosp & Peekskill Hosp, 79- *Mem:* Am Soc Clin Oncol; Am Fedn Clin Res; Working Party Ther Lung Cancer; Am Asn Cancer Res. *Res:* Application of cellular kinetics in animal and human tumors to the design of clinical cancer treatment programs; clinical cancer chemotherapy. *Mailing Add:* NY Med Col Valhalla NY 10595

STRAUS, NEIL ALEXANDER, b Kitchener, Ont, Apr 29, 43; m 66; c 2. MOLECULAR BIOLOGY. *Educ:* Univ Toronto, BSc Hons, 66, MSc, 67, PhD(molecular biol), 70. *Prof Exp:* Fel biophys, Carnegie Inst, Washington, DC, 70-72; asst prof, 72-76, ASSOC PROF MOLECULAR BIOL, UNIV TORONTO, 77- *Concurrent Pos:* Res grants, Nat Res Coun Can, Med Res Coun Can & Nat Cancer Inst Can, 72- *Mem:* Am Soc Cell Biol; Can Soc Cell Biol. *Res:* Molecular cloning; gene regulation; recombinant DNA; plant engineering. *Mailing Add:* Dept Bot Univ Toronto Toronto ON M5S 2R8 Can

STRAUS, THOMAS MICHAEL, b Berlin, Ger, Oct 25, 31; US citizen; m 57; c 3. APPLIED PHYSICS. *Educ:* Univ Mich, BS, 52; Harvard Univ, MA, 56, PhD(appl physics), 59. *Prof Exp:* Mem tech staff, microwaves & lasers, Hughes Aircraft Co, 59-64, sr staff mem, 64-69, sr staff engr, Laser Dept, 69-74; sr scientist, Theta-Com, 74-76; sr scientist com satellite systs, 76-79, CHIEF SCIENTIST SATELLITE GROUND EQUIP, HUGHES AIRCRAFT CO, 79- *Concurrent Pos:* Lectr, Eng Exten, Univ Calif, Los Angeles, 62-67. *Mem:* Inst Elec & Electronics Engrs. *Res:* Development of microwave and laser components and systems. *Mailing Add:* Hughes Aircraft Co PO Box 92919 Los Angeles CA 90009

STRAUS, WERNER, b Offenbach, Ger, June 5, 11; nat US. BIOCHEMISTRY. *Educ:* Univ Zurich, PhD(chem), 38. *Prof Exp:* Res assoc path, Long Island Col Med, 47-50; asst prof, State Univ NY Downstate Med Ctr, 50-58; vis scientist, Cath Univ Louvain & Free Univ Brussels, 59-61 & Univ NC, 62-63; assoc prof, 64-78, prof, 79-81, EMER PROF BIOCHEM, CHICAGO MED SCH, 81- *Mem:* AAAS; Am Soc Cell Biol; Histochem Soc. *Res:* Intracellular localization of enzymes; lysosomes and phagosomes; cell biology; immuno-cytochemistry. *Mailing Add:* Dept Biochem Chicago Med Sch 3333 Green Bay Road North Chicago IL 60064

STRAUSBAUCH, PAUL HENRY, b San Francisco, Calif, Aug 29, 41; m 69; c 1. PATHOLOGY, IMMUNOCHEMISTRY. *Educ:* Univ San Francisco, BS, 63; Univ Wash, PhD(biochem), 69; Univ Miami, MD, 74. *Prof Exp:* Am Cancer Soc fel immunol, Weizmann Inst Sci, 69-71; Med Res Coun Can fel, Univ Man, 71-72; resident path, Dartmouth Med Sch, 74-78; ASST PROF

PATH, SCH MED, E CAROLINA UNIV, 78- Res: Chemical approaches to immunology and cell biology; protein products, especially hormones, produced by tumor cells; macrophage structure and diversity. Mailing Add: Dept Path ECarolina Univ Greenville NC 27834

STRAUSE, STERLING FRANKLIN, b Summit Station, Pa, Jan 4, 31; m 56; c 4. ORGANIC CHEMISTRY. Educ: Lebanon Valley Col, BS, 52; Univ Del, MS, 53, PhD(chem), 55. Prof Exp: Develop chemist, Chem Develop Dept, Gen Elec Co, 55-57, spec process develop, 57-58, qual control engr, 58-60, mgr, 60-65, qual control, 65-68, mgr polycarbonate res & develop, 68-71; dir, 71-74, VPRES RES & DEVELOP, W H BRADY CO, MILWAUKEE, 74- Mem: Am Chem Soc; Am Soc Qual Control. Res: Polymeric peroxide and free radical chemistry; polymer processes. Mailing Add: 7716 W Bonniwell Rd Mequon WI 53092

STRAUSER, WILBUR ALEXANDER, b Charleroi, Pa, June 15, 24; m 45; c 2. PHYSICS, MATHEMATICS. Educ: Washington & Jefferson Col, AB, 45. Prof Exp: Physicist, Manhattan Eng Dist, Tenn, 46-47; assoc physicist, Oak Ridge Nat Lab, 47-50; sci analyst & chief declassification br, AEC, US Dept Energy, 50-55, asst to mgr, San Francisco Opers Off, 55-56, dep dir, Div Classification, 56-63, asst dir safeguards, Div Int Affairs, 63-70, chief, Weapons Br, Div Classification, 70-79; CONSULT, 79- Mem: AAAS; Am Phys Soc; Am Asn Physics Teachers. Res: Neutron diffraction; security classification; safeguards. Mailing Add: 11816 Charles Rd Silver Spring MD 20906

STRAUSS, ALAN JAY, b St Louis, Mo, July 30, 27; m 51; c 3. CHEMISTRY, ELECTRONIC MATERIALS. Educ: Univ Chicago, PhB, 45, SB, 46, PhD(phys chem), 56. Prof Exp: Staff mem semiconductor mat, Chicago Midway Labs, Univ Chicago, 52-54 & 56-58; staff mem electronic mat, 58-66, assoc group leader, 66-76, GROUP LEADER ELECTRONIC MAT, LINCOLN LAB, MASS INST TECHNOL, 76- Concurrent Pos: Div ed, Jour, Electrochem Soc. Mem: Am Phys Soc; Electrochem Soc; Metall Soc. Res: Materials research on electronic materials, primarily semiconductors and semimetals; phase diagram studies, investigations of electrical and optical properties, as affected by composition, deviations from stoichiometry, and impurities. Mailing Add: Lincoln Lab Mass Inst Technol Box 73 Lexington MA 02173

STRAUSS, ALVIN MANOSH, b Brooklyn, NY, Oct 24, 43; m 67; c 2. MECHANICS, APPLIED MATHEMATICS. Educ: Hunter Col, AB, 64; WVa Univ, PhD(theoret & appl mech), 68. Prof Exp: Res assoc theoret & appl mech, Univ Ky, 68-70; asst prof eng, 70-74, head, Eng Sci Dept, 76-80, PROF MECH, UNIV CINCINNATI, 78- Concurrent Pos: Dir, Div Mech Eng & Appl Mech, NSF, 81- Mem: Am Geophys Union; Am Acad Mech; Soc Rheol; Soc Eng Sci; Soc Am Mil Engrs. Res: Plasticity; viscoplasticity; biomechanics; phase changes in solids, plasticity, thermomechanics, biomechanics and geomechanics. Mailing Add: Dept of Eng Sci ML 112 Univ of Cincinnati Cincinnati OH 45221

STRAUSS, ARNOLD WILBUR, b Benton Harbor, Mich, Mar 31, 45; m 70; c 2. PEDIATRIC CARDIOLOGY. Educ: Stanford Univ, BA, 66; Washington Univ, St Louis, MD, 70. Prof Exp: Resident pediat, St Louis Children's Hosp, Washington Univ, 70-73, fel, 73-74, fel biochem, 74-75; fel, Res Labs, Merck, Sharp & Dohme, 75-77; asst prof, 77-80, ASSOC PROF PEDIAT & BIOCHEM, SCH MED, WASHINGTON UNIV, 80- Concurrent Pos: Estab investr, Am Heart Asn, 79- Mem: Am Acad Pediat; Soc Pediat Res; Am Col Cardiol; Am Soc Biol Chem. Mailing Add: Dept Biol Chem Sch Med Washington Univ 600 S Euclid St Louis MO 63110

STRAUSS, BELLA S, b Camden, NJ, May 28, 20. MEDICINE. Educ: Columbia Univ, BA, 42; Western Reserve Univ, MD, 53; Am Bd Internal Med, dipl, 61. Prof Exp: Intern med, First Div, Bellevue Hosp, New York, 53-54; asst resident path, Univ Hosps, Med Ctr, Univ Mich, Ann Arbor, 54-55; asst resident med, Manhattan Vet Admin Hosp, New York, 55-56; asst resident First Div, Bellevue Hosp, 56-57, chief resident, Chest Serv Div, 57-58; career scientist, Health Res Coun New York, 62-66; vis specialist, Care/Medico, Avicenna Hosp, Kabul, Afghanistan, 66-67; staff physician, Maine Coast Mem Hosp, Ellsworth, 67-68; ASSOC PROF MED, DARTMOUTH MED SCH, 68- Concurrent Pos: NY Tuberc & Health Asn Miller fel, Col Physicians & Surgeons, Columbia Univ, 58-60; guest investr, Rockefeller Inst, 62-64; asst prof, Col Physicians & Surgeons, Columbia Univ, 64-66. Honors & Awards: Career Scientist Award, Health Res Coun New York, 62. Mem: Fel Am Col Physicians. Res: Internal and chest medicine; pathophysiology; training of paramedical personnel. Mailing Add: Dept of Med Dartmouth Med Sch Hanover NH 03755

STRAUSS, BERNARD, b Odessa, Russia, Apr 10, 04; nat US; m 64. MEDICINE. Educ: State Univ NY, MD, 27; Am Bd Urol, dipl, 43. Prof Exp: Instr urol, Sch Med, Stanford Univ, 39-42; asst prof, Sch Med, Loma Linda Univ, 56-65; assoc prof, 65-72, EMER ASSOC CLIN PROF UROL, DEPT SURG, SCH MED, UNIV SOUTHERN CALIF, 72- Mem: Am Urol Asn; fel Am Col Surgeons; corresp mem Belg Soc Urol. Res: Urology. Mailing Add: 2080 Century Park East Los Angeles CA 90067

STRAUSS, BERNARD S, b New York, NY, Apr 18, 27; m 49; c 3. MOLECULAR BIOLOGY, CELL BIOLOGY. Educ: City Col New York, BS, 47; Calif Inst Technol, PhD(biochem), 50. Prof Exp: Hite fel cancer res & biochem genetics, Univ Tex, 50-52; from asst prof to assoc prof, Syracuse Univ, 52-60; assoc prof, 60-64, PROF MICROBIOL, UNIV CHICAGO, 64-, CHMN DEPT, 69- Concurrent Pos: Fulbright & Guggenheim fels, Osaka Univ, 58; mem genetics training comt, NIH, 62-68 & 70-74, chmn, Genetics Comt, 62-73; vis prof, Univ Sydney, 67 & Hadassah Med Sch, Hebrew Univ, Jerusalem, 81. Mem: Am Soc Biol Chemists; Genetics Soc Am; Am Soc Microbiol; Environ Mutagen Soc; Am Asn Cancer Res. Res: Chemical mutagenesis; DNA repair and replication in mammalian cells; lymphocyte transformations. Mailing Add: Dept Microbiol Univ Chicago Chicago IL 60637

STRAUSS, BRUCE PAUL, b Elizabeth, NJ, Aug 19, 42; m 64; c 2. CRYOGENICS, LOW TEMPERATURE PHYSICS. Educ: Mass Inst Technol, SB, 64, ScD(solid state physics), 67; Univ Chicago, MBA, 72. Prof Exp: Prin res engr, Avco-Everett Res Lab, Avco Corp, 67-68; physicist, Argonne Nat Lab, 68-69; engr, Nat Accelerator Lab, Batavia, Ill, 69-80; MEM STAFF, MAGNETIC CORP AM, 80- Concurrent Pos: Vis scientist, Univ Wis-Madison, 71- Mem: Am Phys Soc; Am Soc Metals; Am Inst Mining, Metall & Petrol Engrs; Cryogenic Soc Am. Res: Cryogenic magnet systems; optimization of materials and performance. Mailing Add: Magnetic Corp Am 179 Bear Hill Rd Waltham MA 02254

STRAUSS, CARL RICHARD, b Chicago, Ill, May 18, 36; m 59; c 3. POLYMER CHEMISTRY. Educ: Univ Ill, BS, 58; Univ Akron, MS, 65, PhD(polymer chem), 70. Prof Exp: Plant engr chlorinated organics, Pittsburgh Plate Glass Chem Div, 58-63, res chemist reinforcement elastomers, 63-69; advan scientist polyesters, 69-72, sr scientist phenolic binder, 72-74, SR SCIENTIST RESINS & BINDERS, OWENS-CORNING FIBERGLAS CORP, 74- Concurrent Pos: Instr, Cent Ohio Tech Col, 73-75. Mem: Am Chem Soc. Res: Cure and mechanical properties of organic binders; glass-binder interaction and mechanical performance of fiberglass composites; binder development. Mailing Add: Rt 5 Box 29 3380 Milner Rd Newark OH 43055

STRAUSS, CHARLES MICHAEL, b Providence, RI, Oct 18, 38; m 61; c 2. COMPUTER SCIENCE, APPLIED MATHEMATICS. Educ: Harvard Col, AB, 60; Brown Univ, ScM, 66, PhD(appl math), 69. Prof Exp: Asst prof, 68-76, adj assoc prof appl math, 76-80, PROF MATH, BROWN UNIV, 80- Mem: AAAS; Asn Comput Mach; Soc Indust & Appl Math; Math Asn Am. Res: Computer graphics; numerical analysis. Mailing Add: Div of Appl Math Brown Univ Providence RI 02912

STRAUSS, ELLEN GLOWACKI, b New Haven, Conn, Sept 25, 38; m 69. MOLECULAR GENETICS, VIROLOGY. Educ: Swarthmore Col, BA, 60; Calif Inst Technol, PhD(biochem), 66. Prof Exp: NIH fel biochem, Univ Wis, 66-68, fel, 68-69; res fel biol, 69-73, SR RES FEL BIOL, CALIF INST TECHNOL, 73- Mem: Sigma Xi; Am Soc Microbiologists. Res: Molecular biology of the replication of togaviruses, particularly alphavirus Sindbis, primarily through isolation and characterization of conditional lethal mutants. Mailing Add: Div of Biol Calif Inst of Technol Pasadena CA 91125

STRAUSS, ELLIOTT WILLIAM, b Brooklyn, NY, Jan 25, 23; m 51; c 3. PATHOLOGY, ANATOMY. Educ: Columbia Univ, AB, 44; NY Univ, MD, 49. Hon Degrees: MSc, Brown Univ, 72. Prof Exp: Asst med, Peter Bent Brigham Hosp, 57-59; res fel med, Harvard Med Sch, 57-59, res fel anat, 59-61, res assoc path, 61-65; asst prof, Univ Colo Med Ctr, Denver, 65-70; ASSOC PROF MED SCI, BROWN UNIV, 70- Concurrent Pos: USPHS career develop award, 61-65; NIH grants, 61-66, 67-72 & 77-80. Mem: AAAS; Am Gastroenterol Asn; Am Soc Cell Biol; Am Asn Pathologists & Bacteriologists; Am Soc Exp Path; Am Soc Zoologists. Res: Electron microscopy; lipid chemistry; vitamin B-12; normal and abnormal mechanisms for absorption and transport by intestine and vessels. Mailing Add: Div of Biol & Med Sci Brown Univ Providence RI 02912

STRAUSS, ERIC L, b Mainz, Ger, Dec 13, 23; m 49; c 2. MATERIALS SCIENCE. Educ: Stevens Inst Technol, ME, 49; Univ Va, MME, 53. Prof Exp: Mech engr, Nat Adv Comt Aeronaut, Va, 49-53; proj engr, Taylor-Wharton Iron & Steel Co, Pa, 53-54; proj engr, Baltimore Div, 54-67, SR RES SCIENTIST, MARTIN MARIETTA CORP, DENVER DIV, 67- Concurrent Pos: Lectr, Exten Div, Univ Wis, 65. Honors & Awards: Indust Res 100 Award, 63. Mem: Soc Plastics Engrs. Res: Nonmetallics; Structural plastics, composites and adhesives, ablators and ceramic heat shield materials for aerospace applications; materials development and investigation of mechanical and thermal properties; heat transfer analysis and polymer degradation. Mailing Add: Martin Marietta Corp Dept Eng Mech PO Box 179 Mail No M0487 Denver CO 80201

STRAUSS, FREDERICK BODO, b Bad Wildungen, Ger, Feb 24, 31; US citizen; m 54; c 3. MATHEMATICS. Educ: Univ Calif, Los Angeles, BA, 59, MA, 62, PhD(math), 64. Prof Exp: Asst prof math, Univ Hawaii, 64-68; ASSOC PROF MATH, UNIV TEX, EL PASO, 68- Mem: AAAS; Am Math Soc; Math Asn Am. Res: Linear algebra and functional analysis; matrix Lie algebras; theory of rings. Mailing Add: Dept of Math Univ of Tex El Paso TX 79968

STRAUSS, GEORGE, b Vienna, Austria, Nov 27, 21; US citizen; m 54; c 2. BIOPHYSICAL CHEMISTRY. Educ: Univ London, BSc, 50; Lehigh Univ, PhD(chem), 55. Prof Exp: Chemist, A S Harrison & Co, 45-52; Colgate fel, 55-57, from asst prof to assoc prof, 57-66, res assoc, Inst Microbiol, 57-64, PROF CHEM, RUTGERS UNIV, NEW BRUNSWICK, 66- Concurrent Pos: Rutgers Univ fac fel & USPHS fel, Univ Sheffield, 64-65. Mem: AAAS; Am Chem Soc; Biophys Soc. Res: Structure and properties of lipid bilayer membranes, and their interaction with polyene macrolide antibiotics; absorption and emission spectroscopy; excited states and energy transfer in biological systems; photosynthesis; interactions in lipid membranes. Mailing Add: Dept of Chem Rutgers Univ New Brunswick NJ 08903

STRAUSS, H(OWARD) J(EROME), b New York, NY, July 2, 20; m 50; c 3. CHEMICAL ENGINEERING. Educ: City Col New York, BChE, 42; Columbia Univ, MS, 47, PhD(chem eng), 49. Prof Exp: Chem engr, Tenn Valley Authority, 42-43; metallurgist, Vanadium Corp Am, 43-44; instr chem eng, Cooper Union, 47-50; develop engr, Elec Storage Battery Co, 50-51, res engr, 51-52, supvr res dept, 52-53, asst mgr, 53-55, chief prod engr, 55-58, assoc dir res dept, 58-59, vpres & mgr, ESB-Reeves Corp, 59-62; res dir, Burgess Battery Div, Clevite Corp, Ill, 62-70; assoc dir res & develop, Gould, Inc, St Paul, 70-72, dir mkt & technol develop, 72-76; consult, 76-77; VPRES OPER IMPROV, ESB RAY-O-VAC MGT CO, INC, 77-78; vpres oper improv, ESB Ray-O-Vac Mgt Co, Inc, 77-78; VPRES OPER & ENG, INCO ELECTROENERGY CORP, 79- Mem: Electrochem Soc; Am Electroplaters Soc; Am Inst Chem Engrs; Franklin Inst; Soc Plastics Engrs. Res: Industrial electrochemistry; plastics technology. Mailing Add: 1855 Hemlock Circle Abington PA 19001

STRAUSS, HERBERT L, b Aachen, Ger, Mar 26, 36; US citizen; m 60; c 3. PHYSICAL CHEMISTRY, THEORETICAL CHEMISTRY. *Educ:* Columbia Univ, AB, 57, MA, 58, PhD(chem), 60. *Prof Exp:* Ramsey fel from Univ Col, London Univ & NSF fel, Oxford Univ, 60-61; from asst prof to assoc prof, 61-73, vchair, 75-81, PROF CHEM, UNIV CALIF BERKELEY, 73- *Concurrent Pos:* Sloan res fel, 66-68; vis prof, Indian Inst Technol, Kanpur, 68; vis prof, Fudan Univ & Tokyo Univ, 82; assoc ed, Ann Rev Phys Chem. *Mem:* Am Chem Soc; fel Am Phys Soc. *Res:* Experimental and theoretical spectroscopy; infrared; light scattering; configuration of ring compounds; coupling of various types of molecular motion. *Mailing Add:* Dept of Chem Univ of Calif Berkeley CA 94720

STRAUSS, HOWARD W(ILLIAM), b Port Arthur, Tex, Sept 25, 26; m 53; c 2. CHEMICAL ENGINEERING. *Educ:* Rice Univ, BS, 47, MS, 49. *Prof Exp:* Engr, Texaco, Inc, 47-48; res chemist, Columbian Carbon Co, La, 49-50; engr, 52-59, SR RES ENGR, PLASTICS DEPT, SABINE RIVER LAB, 59- *Mem:* Am Chem Soc. *Res:* Ethylene polymers and copolymers; hydrocarbon oxidation and cracking; nylon intermediates; hydrocarbon polymers. *Mailing Add:* Sabine River Lab PO Box 1089 Orange TX 77630

STRAUSS, JAMES HENRY, b Galveston, Tex, Sept 16, 38; m 69. MOLECULAR BIOLOGY, VIROLOGY. *Educ:* St Mary's Univ, Tex, BS, 60; Calif Inst Technol, PhD, 67. *Prof Exp:* NSF fel, Albert Einstein Col Med, 66-67, res fel, 66-69; asst prof, 69-75, ASSOC PROF BIOL, CALIF INST TECHNOL, 75-, EXEC OFFICER, 80- *Mem:* AAAS; Am Soc Biol Chemists; Am Soc Microbiol; Sigma Xi. *Res:* Structure and replication of animal viruses; cell surface modification and RNA replication during Togavirus infection; biogenesis of cell plasma membranes. *Mailing Add:* Div of Biol Calif Inst of Technol Pasadena CA 91125

STRAUSS, JEROME FRANK, III, b Chicago, Ill, May 2, 47; m 70; c 2. REPRODUCTIVE ENDOCRINOLOGY. *Educ:* Brown Univ, BA, 69; Univ Pa, MD, 74, PhD(molecular biol), 75. *Prof Exp:* Intern obstet & gynec, Univ Pa Hosp, 75-76, assoc, 76-77, asst prof obstet, gynec & physiol, 77-81, ASST PROF PATH, UNIV PA, 81- *Concurrent Pos:* Dir, Endocrine Lab, Hosp Univ Pa, 81- *Mem:* Endocrine Soc; Am Physiol Soc; Am Soc Pathologists; Am Fertility Soc; Soc Study Reprod. *Res:* Regulation of corpus luteum function with special emphasis on the control of cholesterol metabolism; lipoprotein metabolism and intracellular cholesterol transport; luteal cells. *Mailing Add:* Univ Pa Hosp 3400 Spruce St 579 Dulles Bldg Philadelphia PA 19104

STRAUSS, LEONARD, b New York, NY, Sept 21, 27; m 55; c 2. ELECTRICAL ENGINEERING. *Educ:* City Col New York, BEE, 50; Columbia Univ, MS, 52. *Prof Exp:* Instr elec eng, Columbia Univ, 51-54; from instr to assoc prof, 54-65, PROF ELEC ENG, POLYTECH INST NEW YORK, 65- *Mem:* AAAS; Inst Elec & Electronics Engrs. *Res:* Solid state circuitry and devices; laser technology; applications of solid state physics to device utilization. *Mailing Add:* Dept of Elec Eng & Electrophysics 333 Jay St Brooklyn NY 11201

STRAUSS, LOTTE, b Nuremberg, Ger, Apr 15, 13; nat US. PATHOLOGY. *Educ:* Univ Siena, MD, 37. *Prof Exp:* Res asst bact, Beth Israel Hosp, New York, 38-41 & Mt Sinai Hosp, 47-49; asst pathologist, Lebanon Hosp, 50-52; assoc pathologist, Mt Sinai Hosp, 53-66, PROF PATH, MT SINAI SCH MED, 66- *Concurrent Pos:* Fel path, Mt Sinai Hosp, 44-47; asst prof, Col Physicians & Surgeons, Columbia Univ, 58-66; consult, Dept Path, Elmhurst City Hosp. *Mem:* Int Acad Path; Am Asn Path; Col Am Path; NY Acad Sci. *Res:* Pediatric pathology. *Mailing Add:* Dept of Path Mt Sinai Hosp 11 E 100th St New York NY 10029

STRAUSS, MARY JO, b Columbus, Ohio, June 10, 27; m 57; c 2. PHYSICAL CHEMISTRY. *Educ:* Bowling Green State Univ, BS, 49; Mich State Univ, PhD(phys chem), 55. *Prof Exp:* Phys chemist, US Naval Res Lab, 54-59, pvt consult, 60-71; res assoc, Col Gen Studies, George Washington Univ, 72-76, lectr, Grad Sch Arts & Sci, 77-78; CONSULT, 79- *Concurrent Pos:* Res consult, Am Asn Univ Women, Washington DC, 77- *Mem:* Fel Am Inst Chemists; Am Coun Consumer Interests; Sigma Xi; AAAS; Am Asn Women Sci. *Res:* Physical and chemical properties of ammonium amalgam; physical chemistry of the iron-oxygen-water system, particularly corrosion mechanisms; women in higher education; women, science and society; environmental studies; women in mathematics and science education. *Mailing Add:* 4506 Cedell Pl Camp Springs MD 20748

STRAUSS, MONTY JOSEPH, b Tyler, Tex, Aug 26, 45; m 78. MATHEMATICS. *Educ:* Rice Univ, BA, 67; NY Univ, PhD(math), 71. *Prof Exp:* Asst prof, 71-75, ASSOC PROF, TEX TECH UNIV, 75- *Concurrent Pos:* NSF res grant, 75- *Mem:* Am Math Soc; Math Asn Am; Soc Indust & Appl Math. *Res:* Partial differential equations, particularly the theoretical aspects of existence and uniqueness of solutions and several complex variables. *Mailing Add:* Dept Math Tex Tech Univ Lubbock TX 79409

STRAUSS, PHYLLIS R, b Worcester, Mass, Mar 19, 43. CELL PHYSIOLOGY. *Educ:* Brown Univ, BA, 64; Rockefeller Univ, PhD(life sci), 71. *Prof Exp:* Res fel cell physiol, Harvard Med Sch, 71-73; asst prof, 73-78, ASSOC PROF CELL PHYSIOL, NORTHEASTERN UNIV, 78- *Concurrent Pos:* Guest worker, Nat Cancer Inst, 81; res career develop award, Nat Cancer Inst, 78-83. *Mem:* AAAS; Am Soc Protozoologists; NY Acad Sci; Soc Am Cell Biologists; Am Asn Immunologists. *Res:* Regulation of plasma membrane transport by macrophages and normal and leukemic lymphocytes; substrates are amino acids, sugars, purines and pyrimidines; thymidine metabolism in lymphocytes; membrane biochemistry in mouse L cells. *Mailing Add:* Dept of Biol Northeastern Univ 360 Huntington Ave Boston MA 02115

STRAUSS, ROBERT R, b Chelsea, Mass, Nov 4, 29; m 51; c 3. BIOCHEMISTRY, MICROBIOLOGY. *Educ:* Univ Pa, BA, 54; Hehnemann Med Col, MS, 56, PhD(microbiol), 58. *Prof Exp:* Sr res scientist, Nat Drug Co, Div Richardson-Merrell, Inc, 58-61, dir biochem res, 61, dir biochem & bact res labs, 61-67; res microbiologist, St Margaret's Hosp, Boston, 67-73; ASSOC DIR MICROBIOL, ALBERT EINSTEIN MED CTR, 73-; RES ASSOC PROF, SCH MED, TEMPLE UNIV, 73- *Concurrent Pos:* Dir, Dept Microbiol, Albert Einstein Med Ctr, 78. *Mem:* AAAS; Am Soc Exp Path; Reticuloendothelial Soc; Am Acad Microbiol; Am Soc Microbiol. *Res:* Biochemistry of inflammation; virus purification; biochemistry of phagocytosis. *Mailing Add:* Dept Microbiol Albert Einstein Med Ctr Philadelphia PA 19141

STRAUSS, ROGER WILLIAM, b Buffalo, NY, Sept 23, 27; m 50; c 4. PAPER TECHNOLOGY. *Educ:* State Univ NY Col Forestry, Syracuse, BS, 49, MS, 50, PhD(chem), 61. *Prof Exp:* Develop engr, Bauer Bros, Ohio, 50-52; paper sales develop engr, Hammermill Paper Co, Pa, 52-55; instr paper sci, State Univ NY Col Forestry, Syracuse, 55-60; mgr res, Nekoosa-Edwards Paper Co, Wis, 60-66; prof paper sci & eng, State Univ NY Col Environ Sci & Forestry, 66-75; dir res & sci serv, Bowater Inc, Conn, 75-80, DIR RES & SCI SERV, BOWATER NA CORP, GREENVILLE, SC, 80- *Mem:* Tech Asn Pulp & Paper Indust. *Res:* Pulping and bleaching of wood pulp; paper production and coating. *Mailing Add:* Bowater NA Corp PO Box 1028 Greenville SC 29605

STRAUSS, RONALD GEORGE, b Mansfield, Ohio, Nov 29, 39; m 62; c 3. PEDIATRICS, HEMATOLOGY. *Educ:* Capital Univ, BS, 61; Univ Cincinnati, MD, 65; Am Bd Pediat, dipl, 70, cert pediat hemat-oncol, 74. *Prof Exp:* Intern pediat, Boston City Hosp, 65-66; from jr resident to chief resident, Children's Hosp, Cincinnati, 66-69; pediatrician, David Grant US Air Force Med Ctr, 69-71; fel pediat hemat, Children's Hosp Res Found, Cincinnati, 71-73, asst prof pediat, Col Med, Univ Cincinnati, 73-74; asst prof pediat, Col Med, Univ Tenn, Memphis, 74-76; asst mem hemat-oncol, St Jude Children's Res Hosp, 74-76; ASSOC PROF PEDIAT, UNIV IOWA COL MED, 76- *Mem:* Soc Pediat Res; Am Acad Pediat; Soc Exp Biol Med; Am Fedn Clin Res; Am Soc Hemat. *Res:* Leukocyte physiology and function. *Mailing Add:* Dept of Pediat Univ of Iowa Hosps & Clin Iowa City IA 52240

STRAUSS, SIMON WOLF, b Poland, Apr 15, 20; nat US; m 57; c 2. CHEMISTRY. *Educ:* Polytech Inst Brooklyn, BS, 44, MS, 47, PhD(chem), 50. *Prof Exp:* Inorg chemist, Nat Bur Standards, 51-55; phys chemist, US Naval Res Lab, 55-57, head chem metall sect, 57-63; staff chemist, Hq, Air Force Systs Command, 63-80; CONSULT, 80- *Mem:* Fel AAAS; Am Chem Soc; fel Am Inst Chemists. *Res:* Solid state reactions; structure and electrical properties of glass; nature and structure of liquid metals; technical management. *Mailing Add:* 4506 Cedell Pl Camp Springs MD 20748

STRAUSS, STEVEN, b Czech, Dec 4, 30; US citizen; m 59; c 3. PHARMACY. *Educ:* Arnold & Marie Schwartz Col Pharm & Health Sci, Long Island Univ, BS, 55, MS, 65; Univ Pittsburgh, PhD(pharm), 70. *Prof Exp:* Asst prof, 65-71, assoc prof pharm admin, 71-79, alumni dir, 65-70, dir continuing educ, 72-79, PROF PHARM ADMIN, ARNOLD & MARIE SCHWARTZ COL PHARM & HEALTH SCI, LONG ISLAND UNIV, 79- *Concurrent Pos:* ed, US Pharmacist, 76-; dir, Grad Pharm Progs, Westchester Campus, Long Island Univ; field dir, Mkt Measures, 72-78, IMS Am, Ltd, 73-77. *Mem:* Am Pharmaceut Asn; assoc AMA; fel Am Col Apothecaries; Am Soc Hosp Pharmacists. *Res:* Pharmacy administration; marketing; market research. *Mailing Add:* 39 Prospect Ave Ardsley NY 10502

STRAUSS, ULRICH PAUL, b Frankfort, Ger, Jan 10, 20; nat US; m 43, 50; c 4. PHYSICAL CHEMISTRY. *Educ:* Columbia Univ, AB, 41; Cornell Univ, PhD(chem), 44. *Prof Exp:* Sterling fel, Yale Univ, 46-48; from asst prof to assoc prof chem, 48-60, dir, Sch Chem, 65-71, chmn dept & dir, Grad Prog Chem, 74-80, PROF PHYS CHEM, RUTGERS UNIV, NEW BRUNSWICK, 60- *Concurrent Pos:* NSF sr fel, 61-62; Guggenheim fel, 71-72. *Mem:* AAAS; Am Chem Soc; Am Inst Chemists; NY Acad Sci. *Res:* Experimental and theoretical investigations of high polymers and colloidal electrolytes. *Mailing Add:* Sch of Chem Rutgers Univ New Brunswick NJ 08903

STRAUSS, WALTER, b Nurnberg, Ger, Nov 6, 23; US citizen; m 59; c 2. PHYSICS, ELECTRICAL ENGINEERING. *Educ:* City Col New York, BEE, 48; Columbia Univ, PhD(physics), 61. *Prof Exp:* Tutor elec eng, City Col New York, 48-53; asst physics, Columbia Radiation Lab, 53-59; lectr elec eng, City Col New York, 59-60; MEM TECH STAFF, BELL TEL LABS, 60- *Mem:* Am Phys Soc; NY Acad Sci. *Res:* Magnetic domain devices; magnetoelastic properties of yttrium iron garnet; magnetic materials; piezoelectricity; magnetron oscillators; microwave delay lines. *Mailing Add:* Bell Tel Labs Rm 2D-159 Murray Hill NJ 07974

STRAUSS, WALTER A, b Aachen, Ger, Oct 28, 37; US citizen. MATHEMATICS. *Educ:* Columbia Univ, AB, 58; Univ Chicago, MS, 59; Mass Inst Technol, PhD(math), 62. *Prof Exp:* NSF fel, Mass Inst Technol & Univ Paris, 62-63; vis asst prof math, Stanford Univ, 63-66; assoc prof, 66-71, PROF MATH, BROWN UNIV, 71- *Concurrent Pos:* Guggenheim fel, 71; vis scientist, Univ Tokyo, 72. *Mem:* Soc Indust & Appl Math; Asn Math Physics; Am Math Soc. *Res:* Nonlinear partial differential equations; scattering theory; functional analysis; gauge theory. *Mailing Add:* Dept of Math Brown Univ Providence RI 02912

STRAUSSER, HELEN R, b New York, NY, Oct 31, 22; m 43; c 2. PHYSIOLOGY, ZOOLOGY. *Educ:* Hunter Col, AB, 46; Univ Pa, MS, 49; Rutgers Univ, PhD(zool), 58. *Prof Exp:* Instr physiol, Hunter Col, 49-50; from instr to assoc prof, 59-70, prof physiol, 70-79, PROF II ZOOL, RUTGERS UNIV, 79- *Concurrent Pos:* Guggenheim grant, 81-82. *Honors & Awards:* Christian & Mary Lindback Award, 80. *Mem:* Am Asn Immunologists; Reticuloendothelial Soc; Geront Soc; Am Physiol Soc; Am Soc Zoologists. *Res:* Immunology, particularly humoral and cell-mediated immune defense in ageing; autoimmunity and tumor immunity; endotoxins; endocrinology, particularly endocrine effects on cells and receptor sites for hormones. *Mailing Add:* Dept Zool & Physiol Rutgers Univ Newark NJ 07102

STRAUSZ, OTTO PETER, b Miskolc, Hungary, 24; Can citizen; c 1. CHEMISTRY. *Educ:* Eotvos Lorand Univ, Hungary, MSc, 52;, Univ Alta, PhD(chem), 62. *Prof Exp:* Res asst, 62-63, from asst prof to assoc prof, 63-71, dir, Hydrocarbon Res Ctr, 74-77, PROF CHEM, UNIV ALTA, 71- *Mem:* Fel Chem Inst Can; Am Chem Soc; AAAS; NY Acad Sci; Int-Am Photochem Soc (pres, 75-79). *Res:* Mechanism and kinetics of chemical reactions induced photochemically or thermally and the chemistry of atoms, free radicals and reactive intermediates; chemical composition, analytical chemistry and organic geochemistry of petroleum. *Mailing Add:* Dept Chem Univ Alta Edmonton AB T6G 2G2 Can

STRAUTZ, ROBERT LEE, b Savanna, Ill, Jan 25, 35. PATHOLOGY, MEDICAL SCIENCES. *Educ:* Am Univ, BS, 63; Univ Md, PhD(anat), 66; Howard Univ, MD, 73. *Prof Exp:* Dir lab drug res, Hazelton Labs, Va, 61-62; instr biol, Am Univ, 65-66, asst prof biol & physiol, 66-70, assoc prof biol, 70-75; resident pathologist, George Washington Univ Hosp, 73-75; RESIDENT PATHOLOGIST, HARBOR GEN HOSP, TORRANCE, CALIF, 75-; ASSOC PATHOLOGIST, ASSOC PROF, MED SCH, UNIV CALIF, LOS ANGELES, 77- *Mem:* Col Am Path; Am Soc Clin Pathologists. *Res:* Transplantation of pancreatic islets in diabetes. *Mailing Add:* Dept of Path San Bernardino County Med Ctr San Bernardino CA 92404

STRAW, HARRY ARTHUR, organic chemistry, see previous edition

STRAW, JAMES ASHLEY, b Farmville, Va, Apr 12, 32; m 54; c 2. PHARMACOLOGY. *Educ:* Univ Fla, BS, 58, PhD(physiol), 63. *Prof Exp:* From asst prof to assoc prof, 65-75, PROF PHARMACOL, SCH MED, GEORGE WASHINGTON UNIV, 75- *Concurrent Pos:* NIH fel physiol, Univ Fla, 63-64 & res grant, 64-65. *Mem:* Am Asn Cancer Res; Am Soc Pharmacol & Exp Therapeut. *Res:* Drug metabolism; action of drugs on endocrine glands; steroid biosynthesis; physiological disposition of anticancer drugs. *Mailing Add:* Dept of Pharmacol George Washington Univ Sch of Med Washington DC 20037

STRAW, RICHARD MYRON, b St Paul, Minn, July 25, 26; m 49; c 5. POPULATION BIOLOGY, SYSTEMATIC BOTANY. *Educ:* Univ Minn, BA, 49; Claremont Col, PhD(bot), 55. *Prof Exp:* Asst prof biol, Deep Springs Col, 55-56; from asst prof to assoc prof, 56-64, assoc dean acad affairs, Sch Letters & Sci, 70-75, assoc dean acad planning, 75-78, PROF BIOL, CALIF STATE UNIV, LOS ANGELES, 64- *Concurrent Pos:* NSF res grants, 57-59 & 60-62; consult, Children's Hosp, Los Angeles, 57-66; Fulbright lectr biol, Peru, 63-64; dir curric planning, Calif State Univ, 65-66, coordr biol interdept prog, 69-70; consult sci & math educ, US Peace Corps, Kuala Lumpur, Malaysia, 66-68. *Mem:* AAAS; Soc Study Evolution; Am Soc Naturalists; Am Soc Plant Taxonomists. *Res:* Evolution; genetics; biosystematics; population ecology and genetics; pollination mechanisms. *Mailing Add:* Dept of Biol Calif State Univ Los Angeles CA 90032

STRAW, ROBERT NICCOLLS, b Burlington, Iowa, Aug 24, 38; c 3. PHARMACOLOGY. *Educ:* Univ Iowa, BS, 60, MS, 65, PhD(pharmacol), 67. *Prof Exp:* Res assoc pharmacol, 67-79, RES HEAD MED, UPJOHN CO, 79- *Mem:* Am Soc Pharmacol & Exp Therapeut. *Res:* Neuropharmacology; neurophysiology; pathophysiology of convulsions; mechanism of action of anticonvulsant drugs; effect of psychotropic drugs on electroencephalogram and performance; treatment of overdose of psychotropic drugs; clinical evaluation of central nervous system drugs. *Mailing Add:* Cent Nerv Syst Dis Res Upjohn Co 301 Henrietta St Kalamazoo MI 49001

STRAW, THOMAS EUGENE, b St Paul, Minn, Nov 20, 36; m 57; c 3. AQUATIC BIOLOGY. *Educ:* Univ Minn, St Paul, BS, 65, PhD(biochem), 69. *Prof Exp:* Asst prof, 68-73, ASSOC PROF BIOL, UNIV MINN, MORRIS, 73- *Mem:* AAAS; Am Soc Limnol & Oceanog; Sigma Xi. *Res:* Biochemical limnology; ecology of aquatic bacteria. *Mailing Add:* Dept of Sci & Math Univ of Minn Morris MN 56267

STRAW, WILLIAM THOMAS, b Griffin, Ind, Sept 29, 31; m 56; c 3. GEOLOGY. *Educ:* Ind Univ, BS, 58, MA, 60, PhD(geol), 68. *Prof Exp:* Geologist, Humble Oil & Refining Co, 60-65; lectr geol, Ind Univ, 67-68; from asst prof to assoc prof, 68-77, actg chmn dept, 71, chmn, 71-74, PROF GEOL, WESTERN MICH UNIV, 77- *Concurrent Pos:* Actg assoc dir, Geol Field Sta, Ind Univ, 70-81; geologist, Ind Geol Surv, 70 & Mont Bur Mines & Geol, 78-79. *Mem:* Am Asn Petrol Geologists; fel Geol Soc Am. *Res:* Glacial geology, hydrogeology and geomorphology; fluvial sedimentation; geology of valley trains; regional geology of the northern Rocky Mountains. *Mailing Add:* Dept of Geol Western Mich Univ Kalamazoo MI 49001

STRAWBRIDGE, DENNIS WINSLOW, b Reading, Pa, Oct 10, 20; m 46. ECOLOGY. *Educ:* Univ Chicago, PhD(zool), 53. *Prof Exp:* Instr zool, Univ Pa, 53-55; from asst prof to assoc prof, 56-63, PROF NATURAL SCI, MICH STATE UNIV, 64- *Res:* Population ecology; biometrics; history and philosophy of science. *Mailing Add:* Dept of Natural Sci Mich State Univ East Lansing MI 48823

STRAWDERMAN, WAYNE ALAN, b Wakefield, RI, Oct 11, 36; m 58; c 2. APPLIED MECHANICS. *Educ:* Univ RI, BS, 58, MS, 61; Univ Conn, PhD(appl mech), 67. *Prof Exp:* Res engr, E I du Pont de Nemours & Co, 58-59; teaching asst mech eng, Univ RI, 59-61; mech engr, Elec Boat Div, Gen Dynamics Corp, 61-63; RES MECH ENGR, NEW LONDON LAB, NAVAL UNDERWATER SYSTS CTR, 63- *Concurrent Pos:* Lectr, Univ Conn, 67-69. *Mem:* Acoust Soc Am; Am Acad Mech. *Res:* Response of coupled mechanical-acoustical systems to random excitation, turbulence induced noise, random vibrations and acoustics. *Mailing Add:* Homestead Rd Ledyard CT 06339

STRAWN, OLIVER P(ERRY), JR, b Martinsville, Va, Nov 30, 25; m; wid; c 4. MECHANICAL ENGINEERING. *Educ:* Va Polytech Inst, BS, 50, MS, 65. *Prof Exp:* Sales engr, Richardson-Wayland Elec Corp, 53-57; asst prof mech eng, Va Polytech Inst & State Univ, 57-66, asst prof archit eng, 66-72;

pvt consult pract, 72-75; PARTNER, CONSULT ENG FIRM, 76- *Concurrent Pos:* Mem, State Bldg Code Tech Rev Bd, 78- *Mem:* Am Soc Mech Engrs; Am Soc Heating, Refrig & Air-Conditioning Engrs; Nat Soc Prof Engrs. *Res:* Thermodynamics; heating; ventilating; air conditioning. *Mailing Add:* 601 Turner St Blacksburg VA 24060

STRAWN, ROBERT KIRK, b De Land, Fla, May 26, 22; m; c 3. ICHTHYOLOGY. *Educ:* Univ Fla, BS, 47, MS, 53; Univ Tex, PhD(zool), 57. *Prof Exp:* Asst malaria control, USPHS, 42-43; lab asst biol, Univ Fla, 46-48; instr, Southwestern Univ, 55-56; asst prof, Lamar State Col, 56-59; asst prof wildlife mgt, Agr & Mech Col, Tex, 59-60; from asst prof to assoc prof zool, Univ Ark, 60-66; assoc prof, 66-69, PROF WILDLIFE & FISHERIES SCI, TEX A&M UNIV, 69- *Mem:* Am Fisheries Soc; Am Soc Limnol & Oceanog; Am Soc Ichthyol & Herpet; Ecol Soc Am; Soc Study Evolution. *Res:* Ecology and speciation of fishes. *Mailing Add:* Dept of Wildlife Sci Tex A&M Univ College Station TX 77843

STRAZDINS, EDWARD, b More, Latvia, Sept 19, 18; US citizen; m 43; c 2. PHYSICAL CHEMISTRY, POLYMER CHEMISTRY. *Educ:* Darmstadt Tech Univ, MS, 49. *Prof Exp:* Mill chemist, Baltic Wood Pulp & Paper Mills, 41-42, supvr, 43-44; res chemist, Am Cyanamid Co, 49-62, sr res chemist, 63-66, proj leader chem res, Cent Res Div, 67-68, res assoc, 68-74, PRIN RES SCIENTIST, CHEM RES DIV, AM CYANAMID CO, 74- *Honors & Awards:* Sci Achievement Award, Am Cyanamid Co, 74. *Mem:* Am Chem Soc; fel Tech Asn Pulp & Paper Indust; fel Am Inst Chemists. *Res:* Paper chemistry; polyelectrolytes; sizing; retention; flocculation aids; theoretical aspects of paper making process; ecology; electrokinetic phenomena; polymer research and surface chemistry. *Mailing Add:* Cent Res Div Am Cyanamid Co 1937 W Main St Stamford CT 06902

STREAMS, FREDERICK ARTHUR, b Mercer, Pa, Sept 8, 33; m 56; c 3. INSECT ECOLOGY. *Educ:* Indiana State Col, Pa, BS, 55; Cornell Univ, MS, 60, PhD(entom), 62. *Prof Exp:* Teacher pub schs, NY, 57-58; entomologist, Entom Res Div, USDA, 62-64; asst prof entom, 64-69, assoc prof biol, 69-74, PROF BIOL, UNIV CONN, 74-, HEAD, ECOL SECT, 76- *Mem:* Fel AAAS; Entom Soc Am; Ecol Soc Am; Entom Soc Can. *Res:* Ecology and evolution of populations; biological control of insects; predator-prey interactions in insects. *Mailing Add:* Ecol Sect Biol Sci Group Univ of Conn Storrs CT 06268

STREBE, DAVID DIEDRICH, b Tonawanda, NY, Oct 6, 18; m 42; c 2. MATHEMATICS. *Educ:* State Univ NY Teachers Col, Buffalo, BS, 40; Univ Buffalo, MA, 49, PhD(math), 52. *Prof Exp:* Instr math, LeTourneau Tech Inst, 46-47 & Univ Buffalo, 47-54; assoc prof, Univ SC, 54-57; prof, State Univ NY Col, Oswego, 57-58, Univ SC, 58-70 & Westmont Col, 70-71; PROF MATH, COLUMBIA COL, SC, 71- *Mem:* Nat Coun Teachers Math. *Res:* Set theoretic topology. *Mailing Add:* Dept of Math Columbia Col Columbia SC 29203

STRECKER, GEORGE EDISON, b Ft Collins, Colo, Feb 25, 38; m 60; c 2. CATEGORICAL TOPOLOGY. *Educ:* Univ Colo, Boulder, BS(elec eng) & BS(bus), 61; Tulane Univ, La, PhD(math), 66. *Prof Exp:* Instr math, Univ Colo, 58-60; teaching asst, Tulane Univ, La, 64-65; res assoc, Univ Amsterdam, 65-66, Fulbright fel, 66; fel, Univ Fla, 66-67, asst prof, 67-71; assoc prof, Univ Pittsburgh, 71-72; assoc prof, 72-77, PROF MATH, KANS STATE UNIV, 77- *Concurrent Pos:* Vis prof, Urije Univ, Amsterdam, math, Inst Univ L'Aquila, Italy, 80, 81; Czech Acad Sci Exchange Scholar, Us Nat Acad Sci, 80. *Mem:* Am Math Soc; Math Asn Am. *Res:* Categorical topology, topological functors, initial and final completions of categories and factorization structures. *Mailing Add:* Dept of Math Kans State Univ Manhattan KS 66506

STRECKER, HAROLD ARTHUR, b Marietta, Ohio, June 11, 18; m 42; c 5. INORGANIC CHEMISTRY. *Educ:* Cornell Univ, AB, 40, PhD(chem), 48. *Prof Exp:* Chemist, Marietta Dyestuff Co, 40-41 & Nat Defense Comn, 42-45; res assoc, Standard Oil Co, Ohio, 47-58, supvr process res, 58-60, sr res assoc, 60-68, supvr spectros & micros, 69-81; RETIRED. *Mem:* Am Chem Soc; Soc Appl Spectros; Sigma Xi. *Res:* Catalysis; reaction kinetics; atomic spectroscopy; x-ray fluorescence and diffraction; electron microscopy. *Mailing Add:* 7131 Rotary Dr Walton Hills OH 44146

STRECKER, JOSEPH LAWRENCE, b Kansas City, Mo, Mar 30, 32; m 60; c 2. THEORETICAL PHYSICS. *Educ:* Rockhurst Col, BS, 55; Johns Hopkins Univ, PhD(physics), 61. *Prof Exp:* Jr instr physics, Johns Hopkins Univ, 55-58, res asst, 58-61, sr res scientist, Gen Dynamics, Ft Worth, 61-66; assoc prof physics, Univ Dallas, 66-68; ASSOC PROF PHYSICS, WICHITA STATE UNIV, 68- *Concurrent Pos:* Adj prof, Tex Christian Univ, 62-67. *Mem:* Am Phys Soc. *Res:* Superconductivity; quantum field theory and application to solid state phenomena; statistical mechanics, especially phase transitions. *Mailing Add:* Dept of Physics Wichita State Univ Wichita KS 67208

STRECKER, ROBERT LOUIS, b Marietta, Ohio, Feb 10, 25; m; c 3. ECOLOGY, MAMMALOGY. *Educ:* Marietta Col, BA, 46; Univ Wis, MA, 47, PhD(zool), 51. *Prof Exp:* From asst prof to assoc prof zool, Miami Univ, Ohio, 51-65; chmn, Dept Biol, 70-75, MEM FAC, SAN DIEGO CITY COL, 66- *Concurrent Pos:* Partic, Pac Islands Rat Ecol Proj, Nat Res Coun, 56-58. *Mem:* Am Soc Mammalogists; Ecol Soc Am; Am Soc Zoologists. *Res:* Vertebrate ecology; rodent ecology and behavior; limnology. *Mailing Add:* Dept Biol San Diego City Col San Diego CA 92101

STRECKFUSS, JOSEPH LARRY, b Shirley, Mo, Feb 23, 31; m 52; c 3. MICROBIOLOGY, IMMUNOLOGY. *Educ:* Southern Ill Univ, Carbondale, BA, 58, MA, 61, PhD(virol, immunol), 68. *Prof Exp:* Dir diag microbiol, Holden Hosp, Carbondale, Ill, 57-66; asst res prof oral microbiol, 68-74, ASSOC PROF MICROBIOL, DEPT PATH & ASSOC PROF IN RESIDENCE, DENT SCI INST, UNIV TEX DENT BR, HOUSTON, 74- *Concurrent Pos:* Comt mem curric, Univ Tex Grad Sch Biomed Sci, Houston,

71- *Res:* Mechanism of calcification of Streptococcus mutans, a cariogenic microorganism; effect of fluoride resistance on the organisms adherence potential and carcogenic properties. *Mailing Add:* Dept of Path Univ of Tex Dent Sci Inst Houston TX 77025

STRECOK, ANTHONY J, b Chicago, Ill, June 5, 31. MATHEMATICS. *Educ:* Northwestern Univ, BS, 53, MS, 54. *Prof Exp:* Asst mathematician, 55-68, assoc comput scientist, 68-80, COMPUT SCIENTIST, ARGONNE NAT LAB, 80- *Mem:* Am Math Soc; Soc Indust & Appl Math. *Res:* Differential equations; integration techniques; difference equations; computer programming; program evaluation. *Mailing Add:* Argonne Nat Lab 9700 S Cass Ave Argonne IL 60439

STREEBIN, LEALE E, b Blockton, Iowa, June 21, 34; m 56; c 4. SANITARY ENGINEERING, MICROBIOLOGY. *Educ:* Iowa State Univ, BS, 61; Ore State Univ, MS, 65, PhD(civil eng), 67. *Prof Exp:* Surveyor, US Army, 51-58; proj engr, Powers, Willis & Assocs, Planners, Engrs & Archit, 61-62, design room supvr, 62-63; assoc prof civil eng & environ sci, 66-70, PROF CIVIL ENG & ENVIRON SCI, UNIV OKLA, 70-, DIR, 79- *Concurrent Pos:* Lectr, WHO & Pan Am Health Orgn. *Mem:* Am Soc Civil Engrs; Water Pollution Control Fedn; Am Water Works Asn. *Res:* Industrial waste treatment; process design; optimization of aerobic biological waste treatment systems; tertiary treatment processes; impoundment and stream studies. *Mailing Add:* Sch Civil Eng & Environ Sci Univ Okla Norman OK 73069

STREET, DANA MORRIS, b New York, NY, May 7, 10; m 40; c 4. ORTHOPEDIC SURGERY. *Educ:* Haverford Col, BS, 32; Cornell Univ, MD, 36. *Prof Exp:* Chief orthop sect, Kennedy Vet Admin Hosp, Memphis, Tenn, 46-59; prof orthop surg, Sch Med, Univ Ark, 59-62; prof surg in residence, Sch Med, Univ Calif, Los Angeles, 62-75; head orthop div, Harbor Gen Hosp, 62-75 & Riverside Gen Hosp, 75-77; chief orthop sect, Jerry L Pettis Mem Hosp, 77-80, prof, 75-80, EMER PROF ORTHOP, LOMA LINDA UNIV, 80-; chief orthop sect, Jerry L Pettis Mem Hosp, Loma Linda, 77-80. *Concurrent Pos:* Mem staff, Orthop Hosp, Los Angeles, St Mary's Hosp & Mem Hosp, Long Beach, Calif. *Mem:* AMA; Am Orthop Asn; Asn Bone & Joint Surgeons; Am Acad Orthop Surgeons. *Res:* Fracture treatment by use of medullary nail, particularly in femur and forearm; treatment and rehabilitation of the paraplegic. *Mailing Add:* 328 Gabrielle Way Redlands CA 92373

STREET, JABEZ CURRY, b Opelika, Ala, May 5, 06; m 39; c 2. HIGH ENERGY PHYSICS. *Educ:* Ala Polytech Inst, BS, 27; Univ Va, MS, 30, PhD(physics), 31. *Hon Degrees:* AM, Harvard Univ, 42. *Prof Exp:* Fel, Bartol Res Found, 31-32; from instr to prof, 32-70, chmn dept, 56-60, Mallinckrodt prof physics, 70-76, asst to dean sci, 66-74, EMER MALLINCKRODT PROF, HARVARD UNIV, 76- *Concurrent Pos:* Mem, Carnegie Cosmic Ray Exped, Peru, 33; res assoc, Radiation Lab, Mass Inst Technol, 40-45; trustee, Assoc Univs, Inc, 70- *Mem:* Nat Acad Sci; Am Acad Arts & Sci; fel Am Phys Soc. *Res:* High energy particle physics; cosmic rays; electronic circuits; electrical discharges in gases; experiments using Geiger counters; ionization and cloud chambers; circuit development; radar; bubble chambers. *Mailing Add:* PO Box 336 10 Bullock St East Falmouth MA 02536

STREET, JAMES STEWART, b Chicago, Ill, July 26, 34; m 57; c 3. GEOLOGY. *Educ:* Univ Ill, Urbana, BS, 58; Syracuse Univ, MS, 63, PhD(geol), 66. *Prof Exp:* Geologist, Texaco Inc, La, 65-66; from asst prof to assoc prof, 66-78, PROF GEOL, ST LAWRENCE UNIV, 78-, CHMN DEPT GEOL & GEOG, 76- *Concurrent Pos:* Dir, NY State Tech Serv Prog, St Lawrence Univ, 66-72. *Mem:* Geol Soc Am; Am Asn Geol Teachers; Int Asn Quaternary Res. *Res:* Geomorphology and glacial geology. *Mailing Add:* Dept of Geol St Lawrence Univ Canton NY 13617

STREET, JIMMY JOE, b Waynesboro, Miss, Jan 17, 45; m 64; c 2. SOIL CHEMISTRY, ENVIRONMENTAL CHEMISTRY. *Educ:* Auburn Univ, BS, 69, MS, 72; Colo State Univ, PhD(soil chem), 76. *Prof Exp:* Res assoc soil sci, Auburn Univ, 69-72; res asst soil chem, Colo State Univ, 72-76; ASST PROF SOIL SCI, UNIV FLA, 76- *Mem:* Am Chem Soc; Soil Sci Soc Am; Sigma Xi; Am Soc Agron; AAAS. *Res:* The chemistry of trace elements in the soil-water-plant system and the fate of soil pollutants applied to agricultural lands. *Mailing Add:* Dept Soil Sci Univ Fla Gainesville FL 32611

STREET, JOHN MALCOLM, b McIntosh, SDak, May 28, 24; m 60; c 2. BIOGEOGRAPHY. *Educ:* Univ Calif, Berkeley, BA, 48, PhD(geog), 60. *Prof Exp:* Lectr geog, Far East Prog, Univ Calif, 55-56; lectr, Far East Prog, Univ Md, 56-57; asst prof, Univ Calif, Davis, 60; PROF GEOG, UNIV HAWAII, 60- *Concurrent Pos:* NSF res grants, Univ Hawaii & Govt New Guinea, 64 & 67 & Peru, 69-70; fel, East-West Ctr, Univ Hawaii, 68-69; Univ Hawaii Found grant, Southeast Asia, 71; NSF grants, Nat Ctr Sci Res, France, 73 & US-China Coop Sci Prog, 76, 78 & 81. *Res:* Impact of man on the tropical biosphere, especially processes and consequences of the creation and maintenance of grasslands derived from forest. *Mailing Add:* Dept Geog Univ Hawaii Honolulu HI 96822

STREET, JOSEPH CURTIS, b Bozeman, Mont, Aug 30, 28; m 49; c 4. TOXICOLOGY, PESTICIDE CHEMISTRY. *Educ:* Mont State Col, BS, 50, MS, 52; Okla State Univ, PhD(chem), 54. *Prof Exp:* Instr agr chem, Okla State Univ, 53; from instr to assoc prof, 53-67, PROF ANIMAL SCI, CHEM & BIOCHEM, UTAH STATE UNIV, 67-, ASSOC DEAN, SCH GRAD STUDIES, 76- *Mem:* Fel AAAS; Am Chem Soc; fel Am Col Vet Toxicol; Am Dairy Sci Asn; Soc Toxicol. *Res:* Toxicology and mammalian metabolism of pesticides; food chemicals and natural toxicants; biochemistry of lipids and animal nutrition. *Mailing Add:* Dept of Animal Dairy & Vet Sci Utah State Univ Logan UT 84322

STREET, ROBERT ELLIOTT, b Belmont, NY, Dec 11, 12; m 41, 69; c 3. AERODYNAMICS, NUMERICAL ANALYSIS. *Educ:* Rensselaer Polytech Inst, BS, 33; Harvard Univ, AM, 34, PhD(math, physics), 39. *Prof Exp:* Instr math, Rensselaer Polytech Inst, 37-41; asst physicist, Nat Adv Comt Aeronaut, Langley Field, Va, 41-43; asst prof physics, Dartmouth Col, 43-44; engr, Gen Elec Co, NY, 44-47; assoc prof physics, Univ NMex, 47-48; assoc prof, 48-55, prof, 55-80, EMER PROF AERONAUT & ASTRONAUT, UNIV WASH, 80- *Mem:* Am Inst Aeronaut & Astronaut; Math Asn Am; Inst Navigation; fel Explorers Club. *Res:* Numerical fluid mechanics. *Mailing Add:* Dept of Aeronaut & Astronaut Univ of Wash FS-10 Seattle WA 98195

STREET, ROBERT L(YNNWOOD), b Honolulu, Hawaii, Dec 18, 34; m 59; c 3. FLUID MECHANICS, APPLIED MATHEMATICS. *Educ:* Stanford Univ, MS, 57, PhD(fluid mech), 63. *Prof Exp:* From asst prof to assoc prof civil eng, 62-70, asst exec head dept, 62-66, assoc chmn dept, 66-72, prof civil eng, 70-72, chmn dept, 72-80, PROF FLUID MECH & APPL MATH, STANFORD UNIV, 72-, ASSOC DEAN RES, SCH ENG, 72- *Concurrent Pos:* Vis prof, Univ Liverpool, 70-71; sr fel, Nat Ctr Atmospheric Res, 77-78. *Honors & Awards:* Huber Res Prize, Am Soc Civil Engrs, 72. *Mem:* Am Soc Eng Educ; Am Geophys Union; Am Soc Civil Engrs; Am Soc Mech Engrs. *Res:* Theoretical and experimental hydromechanics; numerical simulation of boundary-layer flow, lake and estuary circulation and groundwater systems; turbulence modeling; ocean-atmosphere interface modeling. *Mailing Add:* Dept of Civil Eng Sch of Eng Stanford Univ Stanford CA 94305

STREET, ROBERT LEWIS, b Ennis, Tex, Sept 29, 28. INDUSTRIAL ENGINEERING. *Educ:* Tex A&M Univ, BS, 50, MS, 65; Univ Tex, Austin, PhD(mech eng), 67. *Prof Exp:* Estimator gen construct, Robert E McKee, Gen Contractor, 50-51; instrument man hwy surv, Tex Hwy Dept, 51; safety engr, Tex Employers Ins Asn, 53-59, sales rep, 59-61; from instr to assoc prof indust eng, Tex A&M Univ, 62-71, prof 71-; MEM FAC DEPT RES, STANFORD UNIV, 80- *Concurrent Pos:* Prin McNichols, Street & Assocs, Inc, 71- *Mem:* Sr mem Am Inst Indust Engrs; Am Soc Eng Educ; fel Soc Logistics Engrs. *Res:* Development of techniques for quantifying, evaluating and demonstrating system support parameters such as safety, availability and maintainability. *Mailing Add:* Dept Res Stanford Univ Stanford CA 94305

STREET, WILLIAM G(EORGE), b Washington, DC, Dec 1, 17; m 43; c 4. AERONAUTICAL ENGINEERING. *Educ:* Cath Univ, BAE, 38. *Prof Exp:* Jr aeronaut engr, Nat Adv Comt Aeronaut, 38-39; chief flight test engr, Martin Co, 39-43, preliminary design engr, 45-50; chief flight test engr, Convair Div, Gen Dynamics Corp, 43-45; proj chmn opers res off, Johns Hopkins Univ, 50-53; from proj engr to res & adv tech mkt mgr, Martin-Marietta Corp, 53-67; Wash rep, Bell Aerosysts Co, 67-70; opers res analyst, Tech Anal Div, Nat Bur Standards, 70-74, gen engr, Ctr Bldg Technol, 74-81; RETIRED. *Mem:* Opers Res Soc Am; assoc fel Am Inst Aeronaut & Astronaut. *Res:* Nuclear propulsion; operations research; aerodynamics; flight testing; weapons systems requirements. *Mailing Add:* 516 Wyngate Rd Timonium MD 21093

STREETEN, DAVID HENRY PALMER, b Bloemfontein, SAfrica, Oct 3, 21; nat US; m 52; c 3. INTERNAL MEDICINE. *Educ:* Univ Witwatersrand, MB, BCh, 46; Oxford Univ, DPhil(pharmacol), 51. *Prof Exp:* Intern med & surg, Gen Hosp, Johannesburg, SAfrica, 47; jr lectr med, Univ Witwatersrand, 48; Nuffield demonstr pharmacol, Oxford Univ, 48-51; asst med, Peter Bent Brigham Hosp, Boston, 51-53, jr assoc, 53; from instr to asst prof internal med, Univ Mich Hosp, 53-60; assoc prof, 60-64, PROF MED, STATE UNIV NY UPSTATE MED CTR, 64- *Concurrent Pos:* Rockefeller traveling fel & res fel med, Harvard Univ, 51-52; investr, Howard Hughes Found, 55-61; consult, Vet Admin Hosp, Syracuse, 61-, Crouse Irving Mem Hosp, 61-, St Joseph's Hosp, 64- & Utica State Hosp, 65- *Mem:* Endocrine Soc; Am Fedn Clin Res. *Res:* Physiology and pathology of adrenal cortex, especially effects of its secretions on water and electrolyte metabolism and their role in causation of disease. *Mailing Add:* Dept of Med State Univ of NY Hosp Syracuse NY 13210

STREETER, DONALD N(ELSON), b Washington, DC, Feb 8, 27; m 50; c 4. COMPUTER & INFORMATION SCIENCE. *Educ:* Univ Md, BS, 50; Princeton Univ, MS, 51; Harvard Univ, AM, 62, PhD(appl physics), 64. *Prof Exp:* Assoc engr, Appl Physics Lab, Johns Hopkins Univ, 50; teaching asst, Power Lab, Princeton Univ, 50-51; adv engr, Poughkeepsie Prod Develop Lab, IBM Corp, 51-58, develop engr, 58-60, res staff mem & mgr systs sci, T J Watson Res Ctr, 64-68, dir comput systs dept, 68-71, mem res rev bd, IBM Res, 74-76, dir tech commun, 77-80. *Honors & Awards:* IBM Invention Award, IBM Corp, 68. *Mem:* Sr mem Inst Elec & Electronics Engrs; Asn Comput Mach; Am Soc Info Sci. *Res:* Systems science; pattern recognition and adaptive systems; data analysis; applied mechanics and mechanical engineering; computing science; information science, research and development management. *Mailing Add:* 80 Lakeside Dr Katonah NY 10536

STREETER, JOHN GEMMIL, b Ellwood City, Pa, Feb 25, 36; m 60; c 1. PLANT PHYSIOLOGY, AGRONOMY. *Educ:* Pa State Univ, BS, 58, MS, 64; Cornell Univ, PhD(bot), 69. *Prof Exp:* From asst prof to assoc prof, 69-78, PROF AGRON, OHIO AGR RES & DEVELOP CTR, 78- *Mem:* AAAS; Am Soc Agron; Am Soc Plant Physiol. *Res:* Nitrogen metabolism in plants; amino acid biosynthesis; carbohydrate metabolism in legume nodules. *Mailing Add:* Dept Agron Ohio Agr Res & Develop Ctr Wooster OH 44691

STREETER, ROBERT GLEN, b Madison, SDak, Feb 1, 41; m 64; c 2. WILDLIFE CONSERVATION, WILDLIFE RESEARCH. *Educ:* SDak State Univ, BS, 63; Va Polytech Inst & State Univ, MS, 65; Colo State Univ, PhD(wildlife biol, physiol), 69. *Prof Exp:* Asst biologist avian depredation res, SDak State Dept Game, Fish & Parks, 63; res asst elk range ecol, Va Coop Wildlife Res Unit, US Fish & Wildlife Serv, 63-65; res asst bighorn sheep ecol & mgt, Colo Coop Wildlife Res Unit, 65-69; res physiologist, US Air Force Sch Aerospace Med, Brooks AFB, Tex, 69-72; wilflife biologist & res asst leader, Colo Coop Wildlife Res Unit, Colo State Univ & US Fish & Wildlife Serv, 72-73; head coop wildlife units, Div Res, Washington, DC, 73-75, coal proj res mgr, 75-79, prof design, 79-81, ASST TEAM LEADER TECH APPLICATIONS, WESTERN ENERGY & LAND USE TEAM, US FISH & WILDLIFE SERV, 81- *Concurrent Pos:* Vis mem grad fac, Tex A&M Univ,

71-72; asst prof, Colo State Univ, 72-73. *Honors & Awards:* Hibbs Award, Colo State Univ & Colo State Div Wildlife, 67. *Mem:* Sigma Xi; Wildlife Soc. *Res:* Effects of coal extraction, conversion, transportation and related social developments on fish and wildlife populations, development of mitigation options and management decision alternatives; applications of computerized methodologies to wildlife management; national wildlife appraisal methods. *Mailing Add:* US Fish & Wildlife Serv Drake Creekside Bldg Ft Collins CO 80526

STREETMAN, BEN GARLAND, b Cooper, Tex, June 24, 39; m 61; c 2. ELECTRICAL ENGINEERING. *Educ:* Univ Tex, Austin, BS, 61, MS, 63, PhD(elec eng), 66. *Prof Exp:* From asst prof to assoc prof, 66-74, res assoc prof, 70-74, PROF ELEC ENG, UNIV ILL, URBANA-CHAMPAIGN, 74-, RES PROF, COORD SCI LAB, 74- *Honors & Awards:* Frederick Emmons Terman Award, Am Soc Eng Educ, 81. *Mem:* fel Inst Elec & Electronics Engrs. *Res:* Semiconductor materials and devices; radiation damage, effects of deep levels, luminescence in semiconductors. *Mailing Add:* Dept of Elec Eng Univ of Ill Urbana-Champaign Urbana IL 61801

STREETMAN, JOHN ROBERT, b Ft Worth, Tex, Apr 12, 30; m 51; c 2. PHYSICAL CHEMISTRY. *Educ:* Baylor Univ, BS, 51; Univ Tex, MA, 53, PhD(phys chem), 55. *Prof Exp:* Aeronaut res scientist, Nat Adv Comt Aeronaut, 55-56; sr nuclear engr, Gen Dynamics/Convair, 56-59; MEM STAFF, LOS ALAMOS NAT LAB, UNIV CALIF, 59- *Mem:* Am Phys Soc. *Res:* Monte Carlo neutron and gamma transport; quantum mechanics; solid state physics. *Mailing Add:* Los Alamos Nat Lab Univ of Calif Los Alamos NM 87545

STREETS, DAVID GEORGE, b Lincoln, Eng, Aug 13, 47; m 72; c 2. ENVIRONMENTAL SCIENCE, PHYSICAL CHEMISTRY. *Educ:* Univ London, BSc, 68, PhD(physics), 71. *Prof Exp:* NSF fel chem, Univ Rochester, 71-72; Imperial Chem Industs fel physics, Univ London, 72-74; res assoc, 74-75, asst environ scientist, 76-78, environ scientist, Off Environ Policy Anal, 79-80, ENVIRON SCIENTIST, ENERGY & ENVIRON SYSTS DIV, AGRONNE NAT LAB, 80- *Mem:* Royal Inst Chem; Brit Inst Physics; Am Chem Soc; Air Pollution Control Asn. *Res:* Environmental policy analysis; impact of air pollution regulations on energy development; renewable energy resources; photoelectron spectroscopy and chemical structure. *Mailing Add:* Energy & Environ Systs Div Argonne Nat Lab Argonne IL 60439

STREETS, RUBERT BURLEY, JR, b Tucson, Ariz, July 29, 29; m 63. ELECTRICAL ENGINEERING. *Educ:* Univ Ariz, BS, 55, MS, 56, PhD(elec eng), 64; Mass Inst Technol, EE, 59. *Prof Exp:* Mem tech staff, Ramo-Wooldridge Corp, Calif, 57; res asst elec eng, Servomech Lab, Mass Inst Technol, 58-59; instr, Univ Ariz, 59-61; mem tech staff, Aerospace Corp, Calif, 61; res specialist commun theory, Aerospace Div, Boeing Co, 64-67; ASSOC PROF ELEC ENG, UNIV CALGARY, 67- *Mem:* AAAS; Inst Elec & Electronics Engrs. *Res:* Design of Wiener optimal feedback systems; Wiener-Hopf integral equations; ionospheric scintillations. *Mailing Add:* Dept of Elec Eng Univ of Calgary Calgary AB T2N 1N4 Can

STREETT, WILLIAM BERNARD, b Lake Village, Ark, Jan 27, 32; m 55; c 4. PHYSICAL CHEMISTRY, HIGH PRESSURE PHYSICS. *Educ:* US Mil Acad, BS, 55; Univ Mich, MS, 61, PhD(mech eng), 63. *Prof Exp:* Instr astron & astronaut, US Mil Acad, 61-62 & 63-64, asst prof, 64-65, NATO res fel low temperature chem, Oxford Univ, 66-67; asst dean, Acad Res & dir, Sci Res Lab, US Mil Acad, West Point, 67-78; SR RES ASSOC, SCH CHEM ENG, CORNELL UNIV, 78- *Concurrent Pos:* Guggenheim fel, Oxford Univ, 74-75. *Mem:* Royal Soc Chem; Am Chem Soc; Am Inst Chem Engrs. *Res:* Experimental measurements of physical and thermodynamic properties of fluids and fluid mixtures at high pressures; computer simulations of liquids. *Mailing Add:* Sch of Chem Eng Cornell Univ Ithaca NY 14853

STREEVER, RALPH L, b Schenectady, NY, June 7, 34; m 64; c 2. SOLID STATE PHYSICS. *Educ:* Union Col, NY, BS, 55; Rutgers Univ, PhD(physics), 60. *Prof Exp:* Physicist, Nat Bur Standards, 60-66; physicist, US Army Electronics Technol & Devices Lab, 66-82. *Mem:* Am Phys Soc. *Res:* Magnetism and nuclear magnetic resonance in ferromagnetic materials; semiconductor device physics. *Mailing Add:* 7 Wemrock Dr Ocean NJ 07712

STREHLER, BERNARD LOUIS, b Johnstown, Pa, Feb 21, 25; m 48; c 3. BIOLOGY, BIOCHEMISTRY. *Educ:* Johns Hopkins Univ, BS, 47, PhD, 50. *Prof Exp:* Biochemist, Oak Ridge Nat Lab, 50-53; asst prof biochem, Univ Chicago, 53-56; chief cellular & comp physiol sect, Geront Res Ctr, Nat Inst Child Health & Human Develop, 56-67; PROF BIOL SCI, UNIV SOUTHERN CALIF, 67- *Concurrent Pos:* Dir aging res satellite lab, Vet Admin Hosp, Baltimore, Md, 64-67. *Honors & Awards:* Karl August Forster Prize, Ger Acad Sci & Lett, 75. *Mem:* Am Soc Biol Chemists; Soc Develop Biol; Geront Soc; Am Soc Naturalists. *Res:* Bioluminescence; photosynthesis; aging; bioenergetics. *Mailing Add:* Dept of Molecular Biol University Park Los Angeles CA 90007

STREHLOW, CLIFFORD DAVID, b Mineola, NY, July 10, 40; m 63; c 2. ENVIRONMENTAL HEALTH. *Educ:* Muhlenberg Col, BS, 62; Mass Inst Technol, MS, 64; NY Univ, PhD(environ health), 72. *Prof Exp:* Res scientist, Inst Environ Med, Med Ctr, NY Univ, 64-72; consult, Int Lead Zinc Res Orgn, 72-80, RES FEL, ST MARY'S HOSP MED SCH, ENG, 72-; LECTR, WESTMINSTER MED SCH, 79- *Concurrent Pos:* Lectr environ health, St Mary's Hosp Med Sch, 75- *Mem:* NY Acad Sci; Soc Environ Geochem & Health; Am Chem Soc; Brit Occup Hyg Soc. *Res:* Lead metabolism; nutrition; epidemiology; trace element analysis; air and water pollution; radiochemistry. *Mailing Add:* Dept of Child Health Westminster Children's Hosp Vincent Sq London SW1 England United Kingdom

STREHLOW, RICHARD ALAN, b Chicago, Ill, Sept 20, 27; m 77; c 1. CHEMISTRY. *Educ:* Univ Chicago, SB, 48; Univ Ill, PhD(chem), 57. *Prof Exp:* RES STAFF MEM, UNION CARBIDE NUCLEAR CO, OAK RIDGE NAT LAB, 56- *Mem:* Am Chem Soc; Am Vacuum Soc; Am Soc Testing & Mat; Am Nuclear Soc; Sigma Xi. *Res:* Catalysis and surface chemistry, coal conversion; electro-organic and fused salt chemistry; high vacuum research; mass spectrometry; fusion reactor design; graphite fabrication research. *Mailing Add:* Oak Ridge Nat Lab 4500-S PO Box X Oak Ridge TN 37830

STREHLOW, ROGER ALBERT, b Milwaukee, Wis, Nov 25, 25; m 48; c 2. PHYSICAL CHEMISTRY, FLUID DYNAMICS. *Educ:* Univ Wis, BS, 47, PhD(chem), 50. *Prof Exp:* Phys chemist, Ballistic Res Lab, Aberdeen Proving Ground, 50-58, chief physics br, Interior Ballistics Lab, 59-61; PROF AERONAUT & ASTRONAUT ENG, UNIV ILL, URBANA, 61- *Concurrent Pos:* Ford Found vis prof, Univ Ill, Urbana, 60-61; consult, Los Alamos Sci Lab, 63-72, Aro Inc, Arnold Air Force Sta, 65-70, Weapon Command, Rock Island Arsenal, Ill, 69-71, Environ Protection Agency, 71 & Brookhaven Nat Lab, 75-; dep ed, Combustion & Flame, 75- *Mem:* AAAS; Am Chem Soc; fel Am Phys Soc; fel Am Inst Aeronaut & & Astronaut; Combustion Inst. *Res:* Reactive gas dynamics; combustion. *Mailing Add:* 101 Transportation Bldg Univ Ill Urbana IL 61801

STREIB, JOHN FREDRICK, b Avalon, Pa, Mar 21, 15; m 46, 54; c 2. PHYSICS. *Educ:* Calif Inst Technol, BS, 36, PhD(physics), 41. *Prof Exp:* Asst physicist, Carnegie Inst Technol, 41; asst physicist, Nat Bur Standards, 41-42, assoc physicist, 42-43, physicist, 43; scientist, Los Alamos Sci Lab, 43-46; mem tech staff, Bell Tel Labs, Inc, NY, 46; asst prof physics, Univ Colo, 46-47; from asst prof to assoc prof, 47-77, prof physics, 77-80, EMER PROF PHYSICS, UNIV WASH, 80- *Mem:* Am Phys Soc. *Res:* Nuclear physics; fluorine plus proton reactions; positron absorption. *Mailing Add:* Dept of Physics FM 15 Univ of Wash Seattle WA 98195

STREIB, W(ILLIAM) C(HARLES), b Brooklyn, NY, Apr 5, 20; m 47; c 2. CHEMICAL ENGINEERING. *Educ:* Pa State Univ, BS, 42; Newark Col Eng, MS, 53. *Prof Exp:* Jr res engr, Res Ctr, Johns-Manville Corp, 42-44, res engr, 46-50, sr res engr, 50-60, chief asbestos fiber sect, 60-61, res mgr, Asbestos Fiber Dept, 61-71, DIR RES & DEVELOP MINERALS & FILTRATION TECHNOL, MANVILLE CORP, 72-, VPRES SALES CORP, 72- *Mem:* Am Chem Soc; Am Inst Mining, Metall & Petrol Engrs; Am Inst Chem Engrs. *Res:* Diatomaceous earth; perlite and talc, especially new product development for use in filtration and filler applications; asbestos, especially processing, uses and evaluations. *Mailing Add:* Res Ctr Johns-Manville Corp Denver CO 80217

STREIB, WILLIAM E, b New Salem, NDak, Mar 16, 31; m 61; c 2. PHYSICAL CHEMISTRY. *Educ:* Jamestown Col, BS, 53; Univ NDak, MS, 55; Univ Minn, PhD(phys chem), 62. *Prof Exp:* Fel, Harvard Univ, 62-63; instr phys chem, 63-64, asst prof chem, 64-68, from assoc dir to dir labs, 64-79, CRYSTALLOGR, DEPT CHEM, IND UNIV, BLOOMINGTON, 79- *Mem:* Sigma Xi; Am Cyrstallog Asn. *Res:* X-ray crystallography; crystal and molecular structure; low temperature x-ray diffraction techniques. *Mailing Add:* Dept Chem Ind Univ Bloomington IN 47401

STREIB, WILLIAM JAMES, b Rockford, Ill, Nov 5, 26; m 49; c 3. ELECTRICAL ENGINEERING. *Educ:* Univ Iowa, BS, 50, MS, 51. *Prof Exp:* Asst prof eng drawing, 52-57, assoc prof elec eng, Univ Iowa, 57-62; assoc prof electronic technol, Delta Col, 63-76; ASST PROF INDUST TECHNOL, EASTERN MICH UNIV, 76- *Mem:* Am Soc Eng Educ; Inst Elec & Electronics Engrs; Instrument Soc Am. *Res:* Electronics; circuit analysis and synthesis. *Mailing Add:* Dept of Indust Technol Eastern Mich Univ Ypsilanti MI 48197

STREICHER, EUGENE, b New York, NY, Oct 25, 26; m 51. NEUROPHYSIOLOGY. *Educ:* Cornell Univ, BA, 47, MA, 48; Univ Chicago, PhD(physiol), 53. *Prof Exp:* Physiologist, US Army Chem Ctr, Md, 48-50; neurophysiologist, Sect Aging, NIMH, 54-62, physiologist, Nat Inst Neurol Dis & Stroke, SCIENTIST ADMINR, NAT INST NEUROL DIS & STROKE, 64- *Mem:* AAAS; Soc Exp Biol & Med; Am Asn Neuropath; Soc Neurosci. *Res:* Physiological chemistry of central nervous system. *Mailing Add:* Nat Inst Neurol Dis & Stroke Bethesda MD 20205

STREICHER, MICHAEL A(LFRED), b Heidelberg, Ger, Sept 6, 21; nat US; m 47; c 2. METALLURGY, CHEMISTRY. *Educ:* Rensselaer Polytech Inst, BChE, 43; Syracuse Univ, MChE, 45; Lehigh Univ, PhD(phys metall), 48. *Prof Exp:* Res assoc, Lehigh Univ, 48; res eng, E I du Pont de Nemours & Co, Inc, 49-52, res proj engr, 52-56, res assoc, 56-67, res fel, 67-79; RES PROF, DEPT CHEM, UNIV DEL, 79- *Concurrent Pos:* Chmn, Gordon Conf Corrosion, 62 & subcomt corrosion, Welding Res Coun, 66- *Honors & Awards:* Turner Prize, Electrochem Soc, 49; Willis Rodney Whitney Award, Nat Asn Corrosion Engrs, 72. *Mem:* Electrochem Soc; fel Am Soc Metals; Nat Asn Corrosion Engrs; Sigma Xi; Am Soc Testing & Mat. *Res:* Corrosion theory; passivity; inhibition; conversion coatings; influence of metallurgical factors on chemical reactivity of metals; corrosion evaluation tests; electrochemistry; stainless steels; nickel-base alloys and development of new alloys. *Mailing Add:* Dept Chem Eng Univ Del Newark DE 19711

STREIFER, WILLIAM, b Poland, Sept 13, 36; US citizen; m 58; c 3. OPTICS. *Educ:* City Col New York, BEE, 57; Columbia Univ, MS, 59; Brown Univ, PhD(elec eng), 62. *Prof Exp:* Res engr, Heat & Mass Flow Analyzer Lab, Columbia Univ, 58-59; from asst prof to prof elec eng, Univ Rochester, 62-72; res fel, 72-80, SR RES FEL, XEROX CORP, 80- *Concurrent Pos:* Lectr, City Col New York, 57-59; consult lectr, Eastman Kodak Co, 65-68; consult, Xerox Corp, 68-72; vis assoc prof, Stanford Univ, 69-70; lectr, Stanford Univ, 77-80. *Mem:* AAAS; fel Inst Elec & Electronics Engrs; fel Optical Soc Am. *Res:* Electromagnetic theory; optics; mathematical ecology. *Mailing Add:* Xerox Palo Alto Res Ctr 3333 Coyote Hill Rd Palo Alto CA 94304

STREIFF, ANTON JOSEPH, b Jackson, Mich, Apr 1, 15; m 41; c 4. PETROLEUM CHEMISTRY. *Educ:* Univ Mich, BS, 36, MS, 37. *Prof Exp:* Res assoc, Nat Bur Stand, 37-50; sr res chemist, 50-71, asst chmn dept chem, 66-74, DIR AM PETROL INST RES PROJ, 58, 60-, PRIN RES CHEMIST,

CARNEGIE-MELLON UNIV, 72-, ADMIN OFFICER, DEPT CHEM, 74- *Mem:* AAAS; fel Am Inst Chem; Am Chem Soc. *Res:* Fractionation, purification, purity and analysis of hydrocarbons; American Petroleum Institute standard reference materials. *Mailing Add:* Dept of Chem Carnegie-Mellon Univ Pittsburgh PA 15213

STREIFF, RICHARD REINHART, b Highland, Ill, June 1, 29; m 59; c 3. MEDICINE, HEMATOLOGY. *Educ:* Wash Univ, AB, 51; Univ Basel, MD, 59. *Prof Exp:* Intern med, Harvard Med Serv, Boston City Hosp, 59-60; intern, Mt Auburn Hosp, Cambridge, Mass, 60-61; resident, 61-62; resident, Harvard Med Serv, Boston City Hosp, 62-63; instr med, Harvard Med Sch, 66-68; from asst prof to assoc prof, 68-74, PROF MED, COL MED, UNIV FLA, 74- CHIEF HEMAT UNIT, VET ADMIN HOSP, GAINESVILLE, 72-, CHIEF MED SERV, 73-, VCHMN DEPT MED, UNIV FLA, 75- *Concurrent Pos:* Res fel hemat, Thorndike Med Lab, Harvard Med Sch, 63-68; clin investr, Vet Admin, 69-71. *Mem:* Am Soc Hemat; Am Fedn Clin Res; Am Soc Clin Nutrit; Am Inst Nutrit; Fedn Am Socs Exp Biol. *Res:* Vitamin B-12 and folic acid deficiency anemias; metabolism and biological function of vitamin B-12 and folic acid; synthesis and testing of iron chelators. *Mailing Add:* Med Serv Gainsville Vet Admin Hosp Gainesville FL 32602

STREIGHT, H(ARVEY) R(ICHARD) L(YLE), b New Westminster, BC, May 31, 07; m 37, 75; c 2. PROCESS ENGINEERING, ENVIRONMENTAL CONTROL. *Educ:* Univ BC, BA, 27, MA, 29, PhD, 32. *Hon Degrees:* DSc, Univ Waterloo, 62. *Prof Exp:* Chem engr & heavy chem supvr, Cent Res Lab, Imp Chem Indust, Ltd, Eng, 32-37; process develop mgr, Can Indust, Ltd, Ont, 37, asst to vpres, Que, 39, design & res engr, 39-53, chem engr, Eng Dept, 53-54; chem engr, Du Pont(can), Ltd, 54-56, prin chem engr, 56-62, prin engr, 62-68, prin res engr, 68-72; CONSULT, 72- *Concurrent Pos:* Fel Univ Oxford, 32; mem, Can Standards Asn Comt, Dept Manpower & Immigration Comt & Adv Bd, Univ Waterloo. *Honors & Awards:* Plummer Medal, Eng Inst Can, 58; Queen Elizabeth's Jubilee Medal, 76. *Mem:* Fel Am Inst Chem Engrs; fel Chem Inst Can (pres, 71-72). *Res:* Design of process equipment and new methods covering aqueous pollution; liaison with educational institutions; mechanical design; developed new processes; new environmental applications. *Mailing Add:* 4085 Gage Rd Montreal PQ H3Y 1R6 Can

STREILEIN, JACOB WAYNE, b Johnstown, Pa, June 19, 35; m 57; c 3. IMMUNOLOGY, GENETICS. *Educ:* Gettysburg Col, AB, 56; Univ Pa, MD, 60. *Prof Exp:* Intern, Univ Hosp, Univ Pa, 60-61, resident internal med, 61-63, from asst prof to assoc prof med genetics, Sch Med, 66-71; PROF CELL BIOL & PROF MED, UNIV TEX SOUTHWESTERN MED SCH, DALLAS, 72- *Concurrent Pos:* Fel allergy & immunol, Univ Pa, 63-64; fel transplantation immunity, Wistar Inst Anat & Biol, 64-65; Markle scholar acad med, 68-74. *Mem:* Am Asn Immunol; Transplantation Soc; Soc Exp Hemat; Soc Invest Dermat; Asn Res Vision & Ophthal. *Res:* Transplantation immunobiology with special reference to cellular immunity, immunoregulation, graft-versus-host disease, immunogenetic disparity; contact hypersensitivity; immunologic privilege. *Mailing Add:* Dept of Cell Biol Univ of Tex Southwestern Med Sch Dallas TX 75235

STREIPS, ULDIS NORMUNDS, b Riga, Latvia, Feb 1, 42; US citizen; m 75; c 2. MICROBIOLOGY. *Educ:* Valparaiso Univ, BA, 64; Northwestern Univ, PhD(microbiol), 69. *Prof Exp:* Asst prof, 72-78, ASSOC PROF MICROBIAL GENETICS, SCH MED UNIV LOUISVILLE, 78- *Concurrent Pos:* Damon Runyon Mem Fund Cancer res grant microbial genetics, Scripps Clin & Res Found, 69-70 & Sch Med & Dent, Univ Rochester, 70-72. *Mem:* AAAS; Am Soc Microbiol. *Res:* Genetic transformation in Bacillus subtilis; molecular biology of Baccillus; restriction endonucleases; cloning systems; mutagenesis assays. *Mailing Add:* Sch Med Dept Microbiol & Immunol Univ of Louisville Med Ctr Louisville KY 40232

STREISINGER, GEORGE, b Budapest, Hungary, Dec 27, 27; nat US; m 49; c 2. GENETICS. *Educ:* Cornell Univ, BS, 50; Univ Ill, PhD(bact), 54. *Prof Exp:* Res fel biophys, Calif Inst Technol, 53-56; mem staff, Carnegie Inst Washington Genetics Res Unit, 56-60; assoc prof biol, 60-63, co-chmn dept, 68-71, PROF BIOL, UNIV ORE, 63-, RES ASSOC, INST MOLECULAR BIOL, 76- *Concurrent Pos:* Nat Found Infantile Paralysis sr fel, Med Res Coun Unit Molecular Biol, Eng, 57-58; instr, Winter Sch Molecular Biol, Tata Inst Fundamental Res, India, 67; Guggenheim fel, 71-72. *Mem:* Nat Acad Sci. *Res:* Behavioral genetics of lower vertebrates; genetic and developmental studies of zebrafish; behavioral genetics of zebrafish; molecular mechanism of mutation in bacteriophage T4. *Mailing Add:* Inst Molecular Biol Univ Ore Eugene OR 97403

STREIT, GERALD EDWARD, b Los Angeles, Calif, Dec 22, 48; m 74; c 1. CHEMISTRY. *Educ:* Univ Tex, Austin, BS, 70; Univ Calif, Berkeley, PhD(chem), 74. *Prof Exp:* Nat Res Coun fel, Nat Oceanic & Atmospheric Admin, 74-76; STAFF MEM, LOS ALAMOS NAT LAB, 76- *Mem:* Am Chem Soc. *Res:* Weak plasma interactions; ion-molecule kinetics and mechanisms; electron attachment; small cluster formation; application to chemical ionization mass spectroscometry; kinetics and dynamics of gas-phase neutral systems, particularly in application to atmospheric chemistry. *Mailing Add:* MS 738 Los Alamos Nat Lab PO Box 1663 Los Alamos NM 87545

STREITFELD, MURRAY MARK, b New York, NY, Sept 16, 22; c 1. MICORBIOLOGY, CHEMOTHERAPY. *Educ:* City Col New York, BS, 43; McGill Univ, MS, 48; Univ Calif, Los Angeles, PhD(microbiol), 52. *Prof Exp:* Asst chemist toxicol, Off Chief Med Examr, New York, 43; instr, Med Lab, Beaumont Gen Hosp, Tex, 45-46; teaching asst bact, McGill Univ, 47-48 & Univ Calif, Los Angeles, 51-52; from instr to asst prof, 53-66, ASSOC PROF MICROBIOL, SCH MED, UNIV MIAMI, 66- *Concurrent Pos:* Instr med lab, Brookes Med Ctr, Tex, 45-46; res bacteriologist, Nat Children's Cardiac Hosp, Miami, Fla, 52-57; asst dir res bact lab, Variety Children's Hosp, 57-59, res assoc, Variety Res Found, 60-; resident attend, Vet Admin Hosp, Coral Gables, 60- *Mem:* Am Soc Microbiol; fel Am Acad Microbiol; Sigma Xi. *Res:*

Bacteriology; rheumatic fever; antibiotics; prophylaxis of dental infection; streptococcal and staphylococcal epidemiology; pseudomonas and gonorrhea immunity; gamma globulin; staphyloccocal toxins; gonococcal cellular immunity; streptococcal virulence; antibiotics. *Mailing Add:* 4250 NW 79th Ave Miami FL 33166

STREITWIESER, ANDREW, JR, b Buffalo, NY, June 23, 27; m 67; c 2. PHYSICAL ORGANIC CHEMISTRY. *Educ:* Columbia Univ, AB, 48, MA, 50, PhD(chem), 52. *Prof Exp:* From instr to assoc prof, 52-63, PROF CHEM, UNIV CALIF, BERKELEY, 63- *Concurrent Pos:* Sloan Found fel, Univ Calif, Berkeley, 58-62; NSF faculty fel, 59-60; Miller Inst fel, 64-65 & 79-80; Guggenheim fel, 69. *Honors & Awards:* Award, Am Chem Soc, 67; Sr Scientist Award, Humboldt Found, 76; Physical Organic Chemistry Award, Am Chem Soc, 82. *Mem:* Nat Acad Sci; AAAS; Am Chem Soc; Royal Soc Chem; Am Acad Arts & Sci. *Res:* Theoretical organic chemistry; molecular orbital theory; reaction mechanisms; isotope effects; acidity and basicity; rare earth organometallic chemistry. *Mailing Add:* Dept of Chem Univ of Calif Berkeley CA 94720

STREJAN, GILL HENRIC, b Galati, Romania, Sept 24, 30; m 63. IMMUNOLOGY. *Educ:* Univ Bucharest, MS, 53; Hebrew Univ Jerusalem, PhD(immunol), 65. *Prof Exp:* Instr bact & immunol, Hebrew Univ Jerusalem, 63-65; asst prof, 68-73, assoc prof, 73-80, PROF IMMUNOCHEM, UNIV WESTERN ONT, 80- *Concurrent Pos:* Res fel, NIH training grant & Fulbright travel grant immunochem, Calif Inst Technol, 65-68. *Mem:* Am Asn Immunol; Can Soc Immunol. *Res:* Regulation of immunoglobulin E-mediated hypersensitivity; immunologic aspects of experimental allergic encephalomyelitis and multiple sclerosis. *Mailing Add:* Dept Microbiol & Immunol Univ Western Ont London ON N6A 5B8 Can

STREKAS, THOMAS C, b Stafford Springs, Conn, May 9, 47; m 78; c 1. INORGANIC CHEMISTRY, BIOINORGANIC CHEMISTRY. *Educ:* Holy Cross Col, BA, 68; Princeton Univ, PhD(chem), 73. *Prof Exp:* Res assoc, IBM Res, Yorktown Heights, NY, 73-75; res assoc, Dept Biochem, Columbia Univ, 75-78; asst prof, 78-81, ASSOC PROF CHEM, DEPT CHEM, QUEENS COL, CITY UNIV NEW YORK, 81- *Mem:* Am Chem Soc; Sigma Xi; AAAS. *Res:* Structure function interrelationship in electron transfer proteins and metalloenzymes; vibrational-electronic spectroscopy of metal complexes; resonance raman spectroscopy. *Mailing Add:* Dept Chem Queens Col City Univ New York Flushing NY 11367

STRELTSOVA-GLANVILLE, TATIANA D, b Leningrad, USSR; Brit citizen; c 1. ENVIRONMENTAL ENGINEERING. *Educ:* Hydrol Inst, Leningrad, USSR, BS & MS, 59; All-Union Sci Res Inst Hydraul Eng, PhD(hydraul eng), 65; Birmingham Univ, Great Brit, ScD, 77. *Prof Exp:* Res assoc hydraul, All-Union Sci Res Inst Hydraul Eng, 59-65; sr res assoc underground flows, Moscow State Univ, 65-70; sr res fel flows in porous media, Birmingham Univ, 71-77; SR RES SPECIALIST, EXXON PROD RES CO, 77- *Concurrent Pos:* Fel, Rice Univ, 77; tech ed, Soc Petrol Eng, Am Soc Mech Engrs, 81- *Mem:* Am Geophys Union; Int Asn Water Resources; Soc Petrol Eng. *Res:* Various aspects of fluid flow trough porous media; author or coauthor of 50 publications. *Mailing Add:* Exxon Prod Res Co Reservoir Div PO Box 2189 Houston TX 77001

STREM, MICHAEL EDWARD, b Pittsburgh, Pa, Apr 1, 36; m 67. ORGANIC CHEMISTRY. *Educ:* Brown Univ, AB, 58; Univ Pittsburgh, MS, 61, PhD(chem), 64. *Prof Exp:* PRES, STREM CHEM INC, 64- *Mem:* Am Chem Soc. *Res:* Organometallic chemistry, including its use in organic synthesis. *Mailing Add:* PO Box 108 Newburyport MA 01950

STREMLER, FERREL G, b Lynden, Wash, Mar 10, 33; m 58; c 2. ELECTRICAL ENGINEERING. *Educ:* Calvin Col, AB, 57; Ill Inst Technol, BS, 59; Mass Inst Technol, SM, 60; Univ Mich, PhD, 67. *Prof Exp:* Res asst elec eng, Inst Sci & Technol, Univ Mich, Ann Arbor, 60-61, asst, 61-63, res assoc, 63-65, assoc res engr, 65-68, lectr elec eng, 66-67; from asst prof to assoc prof, 68-77, PROF ELEC ENG, UNIV WIS-MADISON, 77-, ASSOC DEAN, COL ENG, 78- *Honors & Awards:* Western Elec Fund Award, Am Soc Eng Educ, 75. *Mem:* Inst Elec & Electronics Engrs; Sigma Xi; Am Soc Eng Educ. *Res:* Analytical studies in coherent modulation-detection systems in communications and radar; design of communications and radar equipment; applications of communications and radar principles to remote sensing problems. *Mailing Add:* Dept Elec & Comput Eng Univ of Wis Madison WI 53716

STRENA, ROBERT VICTOR, b Seattle, Wash, June 28, 29; m 57; c 2. APPLIED PHYSICS, RESEARCH ADMINISTRATION. *Educ:* Stanford Univ, BA, 52. *Prof Exp:* ASST DIR, W W HANSEN LAB PHYSICS, STANFORD UNIV, 59-, ASST DIR, EDWARD L GINZTON LAB, 76- *Concurrent Pos:* Mem, Nat Coun Univ Res Adminrs. *Res:* University physical sciences research administration. *Mailing Add:* Edward L Ginzton Lab Stanford Univ Stanford CA 94305

STRENG, WILLIAM HAROLD, b Milwaukee, Wis, Mar 6, 44; m 67; c 2. PHYSICAL CHEMISTRY. *Educ:* Carroll Col, Wis, BS, 66; Mich Technol Univ, MS, 68, PhD(phys chem), 71. *Prof Exp:* Res assoc theoret chem, Clark Univ, 72-73; SR CHEMIST, MERRELL RES CTR, MERRELL DOW PHARMACEUT, INC, 73- *Mem:* Am Chem Soc; Am Pharmaceut Asn. *Res:* Elucidation of interactions in electrolyte solution from both theoretical and experimental considerations. *Mailing Add:* 1216 Retswood Loveland OH 45140

STRENGTH, DELPHIN RALPH, b Brewton, Ala, May 24, 25; m 46; c 4. BIOCHEMISTRY. *Educ:* Auburn Univ, BS, 48, MS, 50; Cornell Univ, PhD(biochem), 52. *Prof Exp:* Res assoc biochem, Cornell Univ, 52-53; instr, St Louis Univ, 53-54, sr instr, 54-56, from asst prof to assoc prof, 56-61; assoc prof animal sci, 61-65, PROF BIOCHEM & NUTRIT, AUBURN UNIV, 65- *Mem:* AAAS; Am Chem Soc; Am Soc Biol Chem; Soc Exp Biol & Med; Am Inst Nutrit. *Res:* Enzyme chemistry; nutrition; phospholipids; proteins. *Mailing Add:* Dept Animal & Dairy Sci Auburn Univ Auburn AL 36849

STRENKOSKI, LEON FRANCIS, b Shamokin, Pa, Mar 26, 41; m 64; c 2. CLINICAL MICROBIOLOGY. *Educ:* King's Col, Pa, BS, 62; Cath Univ Am, PhD(microbiol), 68. *Prof Exp:* Asst biol, Cath Univ Am, 62-67; asst prof microbiol, Rensselaer Polytech Inst, 67-70; mem staff, 70-73, supvr, 73-75, MGR MICROBIOL, MILES LABS, INC, 75- *Mem:* Am Soc Microbiol. *Res:* Bacterial metabolism and genetics; inorganic nitrogen assimilation in Hydrogenomonas eutropha, a facultative-autotrophic bacterium. *Mailing Add:* Miles Labs Inc 1127 Myrtle St Elkhart IN 46515

STRENZWILK, DENIS FRANK, b Rochester, NY, Oct 27, 40. ELECTROMAGNETISM, SOLID STATE PHYSICS. *Educ:* Le Moyne Col, NY, BS, 62; Clarkson Col Technol, MS, 65, PhD(physics), 68. *Prof Exp:* RES PHYSICIST, US ARMY BALLISTIC RES LABS, 68- *Concurrent Pos:* Teacher, Exten Sch, Univ Del, Aberdeen Proving Ground, Md, 70. *Mem:* Am Asn Physics Teachers; Am Phys Soc. *Res:* Magnetism, effective field theory for yttrium iron garnet, lattice dynamics; clutter simulation of active and passive MMW sensors. *Mailing Add:* US Army Ballistics Res Labs Aberdeen Proving Ground MD 21005

STRETTON, ANTONY OLIVER WARD, b Rugby, Eng, Apr 24, 36. NEUROBIOLOGY. *Educ:* Univ Cambridge, BA, 57, MA, 61, PhD(chem), 60. *Prof Exp:* Instr biochem, Mass Inst Technol, 60-61; mem sci staff, Lab Molecular Biol, Med Res Coun, Cambridge, Eng 61-71; assoc prof, 71-76, PROF ZOOL & MOLECULAR BIOL, UNIV WIS, 76- *Concurrent Pos:* Stringer fel, King's Col, Cambridge, 64-70; res assoc dept neurobiol, Harvard Med Sch, 66-67; Sloan Found fel, 72-74. *Mem:* Soc Neurosci; AAAS; Brain Res Asn, Eng; Genetical Soc, Eng. *Res:* Structure and function of the nervous system of simple animals, especially nematodes. *Mailing Add:* Dept of Zool Univ of Wis Madison WI 53706

STREU, HERBERT THOMAS, b Elizabeth, NJ, May 16, 27; m; c 1. ENTOMOLOGY, ZOOLOGY. *Educ:* Rutgers Univ, BS, 51, MS, 59, PhD(entom), 60. *Prof Exp:* Nematologist, Agr Res Serv, USDA, 60-61; assoc res prof, 61-70, RES PROF ENTOM, RUTGERS UNIV, 70-, CHMN DEPT, 76- *Concurrent Pos:* Dir grad prog, Rutgers Univ, 76-81; assoc ed, J NY Entom Soc, 75- *Mem:* Fel AAAS; Entom Soc Am; Soc Nematol; Acarological Soc Am; Ecol Soc Am. *Res:* Ecology and control of arthropods in turfgrass; biology and control of insects, nematodes and other economic arthropod pests attacking ornamental crops. *Mailing Add:* Dept of Entom & Econ Zool Rutgers Univ New Brunswick NJ 08903

STREULI, CARL ARTHUR, b Bronxville, NY, May 7, 22; m 50; c 3. ANALYTICAL CHEMISTRY. *Educ:* Lehigh Univ, BS, 43; Cornell Univ, AM, 50, PhD(anal chem), 52. *Prof Exp:* Chemist, Foster D Snell, Inc, 43-44 & 46-47; res assoc, Cornell Univ, 52-53; res chemist, Stamford Labs, 53-57, group leader, 57-63, res assoc, 63-69, group leader, Lederle Labs, 69-77, SR RES CHEMIST, AM CYANAMID CO, 77- *Concurrent Pos:* Lectr, Univ Conn, Stamford, 63-66; fel, Purdue Univ, 66-67. *Mem:* Am Chem Soc. *Res:* Analytical chemistry in nonaqueous solvents; acid base theory; electroanalytical chemistry; gas-liquid and liquid-liquid chromatography. *Mailing Add:* Lederle Labs Am Cyanamid Co Pearl River NY 10965

STRIBLEY, REXFORD CARL, b Kent, Ohio, Mar 12, 18; m 45; c 2. ORGANIC CHEMISTRY. *Educ:* Kent State Univ, BS, 39. *Prof Exp:* Chemist, 40-41, res chemist, Mason Lab, 45-50 & 52-55, chief res & develop, 55-70, tech dir, 70-76, nutrit dir & asst vpres mfg, Nutrit Div, Wyeth Labs, Inc Div, Am Home Prod Corp, 76-81, CONSULT, WYETH LABS, INC, 81- *Concurrent Pos:* US indust adv, Comt Food for Special Dietary Uses, UN Codex Alimentorius Comn, 72-74; mem bd of dirs, Infant Formula Coun, 77- *Mem:* Am Chem Soc; Am Oil Chem Soc; Am Dairy Sci Asn; Inst Food Technol. *Res:* Chemistry and development of infant formulas; infant nutrition; milk chemistry; dairy manufacturing technology and engineering; special dietary food products. *Mailing Add:* PO Box 334 El Jebel CO 81628

STRICHARTZ, ROBERT STEPHEN, b New York, NY, Oct 14, 43; m 68; c 2. MATHEMATICS. *Educ:* Dartmouth Col, BA, 63; Princeton Univ, MA, 65, PhD(math), 66. *Prof Exp:* NATO fel, Fac Sci, Orsay, France, 66-67; C L E Moore instr math, Mass Inst Technol, 67-69; from asst prof to assoc prof, 69-77, PROF MATH, CORNELL UNIV, 77- *Mem:* Am Math Soc. *Res:* Harmonic analysis and partial differential equations. *Mailing Add:* Dept of Math Cornell Univ Ithaca NY 14853

STRICK, ELLIS, b Pikeville, Ky, Mar 19, 21. GEOPHYSICS, OCEANOGRAPHY. *Educ:* Va Polytech Inst & State Univ, BS, 42; Purdue Univ, West Lafayette, PhD(theoret physics), 50. *Prof Exp:* Physicist radio eng, US Naval Res Lab, DC, 42-46; asst prof physics, Univ Wyo, 50-51; res assoc theoret seismol, Shell Explor & Prod Res Lab, Tex, 51-68; ASSOC PROF GEOPHYS, UNIV PITTSBURGH, 68- *Concurrent Pos:* Lectr physics, Univ Houston, 51-67; NSF grant, Univ Pittsburgh, 70-71. *Mem:* Soc Explor Geophysicists; Seismol Soc Am. *Res:* Anelastic wave propagation in solids at low frequencies. *Mailing Add:* Dept of Earth & Planetary Sci 4200 Fifth Ave Pittsburgh PA 15213

STRICKBERGER, MONROE WOLF, b Brooklyn, NY, July 3, 25; m 57; c 2. EVOLUTION, GENETICS. *Educ:* NY Univ, BA, 49; Columbia Univ, MA, 59, PhD(genetics), 62. *Prof Exp:* Res fel genetics, Univ Calif, Berkeley, 62-63; from asst prof to assoc prof biol, St Louis Univ, 63-66; assoc prof, 68-71, PROF BIOL, UNIV MO-ST LOUIS, 71- *Concurrent Pos:* NIH res grant, 63-69. *Mem:* AAAS; Genetics Soc Am; Am Eugenics Soc; Am Genetic Asn; Am Soc Naturalists. *Res:* Evolution of fitness in Drosophila populations; induction of sexual isolation. *Mailing Add:* Dept of Biol Univ Mo St Louis MO 63121

STRICKER, EDWARD MICHAEL, b New York, NY, May 23, 41; m 64; c 2. NEUROPSYCHOLOGY. *Educ:* Univ Chicago, BS, 60, MS, 61; Yale Univ, PhD(psychol), 65. *Prof Exp:* Fel, Med Ctr, Univ Colo, 65-66 & Inst Neurol Sci, Med Sch, Univ Pa, 66-67; from asst prof to assoc prof psychol, McMaster Univ, 67-71; assoc prof, 71-76, PROF PSYCHOL, PSYCHIATRY & BIOL, UNIV PITTSBURGH, 76- *Concurrent Pos:* Consult ed, J Comp & Physiol Psychol, 72-81; NIMH res scientist award, 81-; vis prof psychiatry, Johns Hopkins Med Sch, 78-79. *Mem:* Soc Neurosci. *Res:* Physiological and behavioral mechanisms that maintain water and electrolyte balance, body temperature and energy metabolism; the neurochemical basis for recovery of function following brain damage; central controls of motivated behavior. *Mailing Add:* Dept of Psychol Univ of Pittsburgh Pittsburgh PA 15260

STRICKHOLM, ALFRED, b New York, NY, July 3, 28; m 52; c 3. PHYSIOLOGY, BIOPHYSICS. *Educ:* Univ Mich, BS, 51; Univ Minn, MS, 56; Univ Chicago, PhD(physiol), 60. *Prof Exp:* Fel biophys, Physiol Inst, Univ Uppsala, 60-61; asst prof physiol, Sch Med, Univ Calif, San Francisco, 61-66; assoc prof, 66-72, prof anat & physiol, 72-76, PROF PHYSIOL, MED SCI PROG, CTR NEURAL SCI, IND UNIV, BLOOMINGTON, 76- *Concurrent Pos:* USPHS grant, 62-; Am Heart Asn grant, 79- *Mem:* AAAS; Am Physiol Soc; Soc Neurosci; Soc Gen Physiol; Biophys Soc. *Res:* Biophysics of the cell membrane; contraction coupling in muscle; permeability, active transport, and excitation; structure and function of cell membranes; neurobiology. *Mailing Add:* Physiol Sect/Med Sci Prog Ind Univ Bloomington IN 47405

STRICKLAND, ERASMUS HARDIN, b Spartanburg, SC, May 18, 36; m 66; c 1. BIOPHYSICS. *Educ:* Pa State Univ, BS, 58, MS, 59, PhD(biophys), 61. *Prof Exp:* Chief phys chem sect, US Army Med Res Lab, Ft Knox, 61-63; from asst prof to assoc prof biophys, Univ Calif, Los Angeles, 63-70, assoc res biophysicist, Radiation Biol Lab, 69-80. *Mem:* AAAS; Biophys Soc. *Res:* Circular dichroism and absorption spectroscopy of biological molecules. *Mailing Add:* 15980 Yellow Brick Rd Valley Center CA 92082

STRICKLAND, GORDON EDWARD, JR, b Santa Cruz, Calif, Jan 23, 29; m 56; c 3. ENGINEERING MECHANICS. *Educ:* Stanford Univ, BS, 54, MS, 55, PhD(eng mech), 60. *Prof Exp:* Mem tech staff, Bell Tel Labs, 59-64; engr, Lawrence Radiation Lab, 64-66; res scientist, Lockheed Missiles & Space Co, 66-69; SR ENG ASSOC, CHEVRON OIL FIELD RES CO, 69- *Res:* Applied mechanics, particularly elasticity and shell theory. *Mailing Add:* Chevron Oil Field Res Co PO Box 446 La Habra CA 90631

STRICKLAND, JAMES SHIVE, b Harrisburg, Pa, Nov 18, 29; m 55; c 3. EXPERIMENTAL PHYSICS. *Educ:* Franklin & Marshall Col, BS, 51; Mass Inst Technol, PhD(physics), 57. *Prof Exp:* staff physicist, Phys Sci Study Comt, Mass Inst Technol, 57-58; staff physicist, Educ Develop Ctr, Inc, Mass, 58-72; vis scientist, Mass Inst Technol, 72-73; PROF PHYSICS & CHMN DEPT, GRAND VALLEY STATE COL, 73- *Mem:* AAAS; Am Asn Physics Teachers; Am Phys Soc; Am Soc Eng Educ. *Res:* Development of new materials for science education. *Mailing Add:* Dept of Physics Grand Valley State Col Allendale MI 49401

STRICKLAND, JOHN WILLIS, b Wichita, Kans, Mar 23, 25; m 47; c 4. PETROLEUM GEOLOGY. *Educ:* Univ Okla, BS, 46. *Prof Exp:* Geologist, Skelly Oil Co, 47-50; res geologist, 51-55, div geologist, 55-61, explor mgr, Ireland, 61-64, coordr explor res, 64-66, dir adv geol, 66-67, chief geologist, 67-76, mgr, Africa & Latin Am, Continental Oil Co, 76-78, dir geol, 79-81; MGR EXPLOR SERV, CONOCO, INC, 81-, CONSULT GEOLOGIST, 82- *Mem:* Am Asn Petrol Geol. *Res:* Petroleum geology of world; factors controlling generation and distribution of hydrocarbons. *Mailing Add:* 761 W Creekside Dr Houston TX 77024

STRICKLAND, KENNETH PERCY, b Loverna, Sask, Aug 19, 27; m 51; c 4. BIOCHEMISTRY. *Educ:* Univ Western Ont, BSc, 49, MSc, 50, PhD(biochem), 53. *Prof Exp:* Nat Res Coun Can fel chem path, Guy's Hosp Med Sch, Univ London, 53-55; from asst prof to assoc prof, 55-66, PROF BIOCHEM, UNIV WESTERN ONT, 66-, PROF CLIN NEUROL SCI, 80- *Concurrent Pos:* Lederle med fac award, 55-58; res assoc, Med Res Coun Can, 58- *Mem:* AAAS; Am Soc Biol Chemists; Can Biochem Soc; Can Physiol Soc; Int Neurochem Soc. *Res:* Biochemistry of central nervous system, especially biosynthesis of lipid components; biochemistry of muscle, especially relating to degenerating diseases. *Mailing Add:* Dept of Biochem Univ of Western Ont London ON N6A 5B8 Can

STRICKLAND, LARRY DEAN, b Elkview, WVa, Nov 6, 38; m 62; c 2. THERMODYNAMICS, FLUID DYNAMICS. *Educ:* WVa Univ, BS, 60, PhD(mech eng), 73; Univ Southern Calif, MS, 62. *Prof Exp:* Prin res engr advan rocket engines, Rocketdyne, NAm Aviation, 62-67; res engr aerodynamics, Re-entry Syst, Gen Elec Co, 67-68; instr, WVa Univ, 69-70; res co-op coal gasification, US Bur Mines, 71-73; consult heating & ventilating air conditioning & elec, var pvt concerns, 73-77; proj mgr underground coal gasification, Dept Energy, 77-78, prog mgr, press fluid bed combustion, 79-80, GASIFICATION PROJ BR CHIEF, MORGANTOWN ENERGY TECHNOL CTR, 81- *Concurrent Pos:* Adj prof, WVa Univ, 78- *Mem:* Am Soc Mech Engrs; Sigma Xi. *Res:* Fluid dynamics and heat-transfer as applied to in-situ and above ground coal gasification and other energy related topics. *Mailing Add:* Morgantown Energy Technol Ctr Collins Ferry Rd Morgantown WV 26505

STRICKLAND, WALTER NICHOLAS, b Shamva, Rhodesia, Feb 15, 30; US citizen. GENETICS. *Educ:* Univ Natal, BSc, 51; Glasgow Univ, PhD(genetics), 57. *Prof Exp:* Asst lectr genetics, Glasgow Univ, 56-57; res assoc, Stanford Univ, 57-61; res assoc, Dartmouth Col, 61-64; from asst prof to prof, Univ Utah, 64-71; sr lectr, Univ Cape Town, 71-76, assoc prof biochem, 76-82. *Res:* Genetic control of protein structure and function; structure and function of histones and basic proteins. *Mailing Add:* 1638 Castilleja Ave Palo Alto CA 94306

STRICKLAND, WILLIAM ALEXANDER, JR, b Dover, Ark, July 25, 23; m 46; c 3. PHARMACY. *Educ:* Univ Tenn, BS, 44; Univ Wis, MS, 52, PhD, 55. *Prof Exp:* From assoc prof to prof pharm, Sch Pharm, Univ Ark, 55-67; dean, Sch Pharm, Univ Mo-Kansas City, 67-73, prof pharm & med, 74-80, asst dean, Sch Med, 77-80. *Concurrent Pos:* Dir, Outreach, Western Mo Area

Health Educ Ctr, 75- *Mem:* AAAS; Am Pharmaceut Asn; Am Asn Cols Pharm. *Res:* Physical pharmacy; tableting and aerosol technology; physical reactions of drug molecules as in complex formation and hydration. *Mailing Add:* 9959 Goddard Overland Park KS 66214

STRICKLER, STEWART JEFFERY, b Mussoorie, India, July 12, 34; US citizen; m 59; c 2. PHYSICAL CHEMISTRY, CHEMICAL PHYSICS. *Educ:* Col Wooster, BA, 56; Fla State Univ, PhD(phys chem), 61. *Prof Exp:* Chemist, Radiation Lab, Univ Calif, 61; res assoc, Rice Univ, 61-62, lectr chem, 62-63; from asst prof to assoc prof, 63-73, chmn dept, 74-77, PROF CHEM, UNIV COLO, BOULDER, 73- *Mem:* Am Chem Soc; Am Phys Soc; AAAS. *Res:* Molecular spectroscopy; photochemistry; quantum chemistry. *Mailing Add:* Dept Chem Univ Colo Box 215 Boulder CO 80309

STRICKLER, THOMAS DAVID, b Ferozepur, India, Nov 11, 22; US citizen; m 48; c 4. ATOMIC PHYSICS. *Educ:* Col Wooster, BA, 47; Yale Univ, MS, 48, PhD(physics), 53. *Prof Exp:* Instr physics, Yale Univ, 52-53; from asst prof to assoc prof, 53-61, CHARLES F KETTERING PROF PHYSICS & CHMN DEPT, BEREA COL, 61- *Concurrent Pos:* NSF faculty fel, 60-61; consult, NSF Physics Inst, Chandigarh, India, 66, Gauhati Univ, India, 67 & Calcutta, India, 68; Fulbright lectr, Comt Int Exchange Persons, 73-74; Fulbright lectr, De La Salle Univ, Manila, Philippines, 81-82. *Mem:* AAAS; Am Asn Physics Teachers. *Res:* Neutron and gamma ray scattering; health physics; gaseous electronics. *Mailing Add:* 2326 Berea Col Berea KY 40404

STRICKLIN, BUCK, b Clovis, NMex, Dec 30, 22; m 42; c 1. ORGANIC CHEMISTRY. *Educ:* Tex Tech Col, BS, 48; Univ Colo, PhD(org chem), 52. *Prof Exp:* Asst, Univ Colo, 48-52; res mgr, 52-69, tech dir, paper prod div, 69-76, LAB MGR, DISPOSABLE PROD DEPT, MINN MINING & MFG CO, 76- *Mem:* Am Chem Soc; Tech Asn Pulp & Paper Indust. *Res:* Fluorocarbons; fluoroethers; chlorination; photochemistry; photoconductivity; polymers. *Mailing Add:* Disposable Prod Dept 3M Ctr Bldg 235-1N St Paul MN 55101

STRICKLIN, WILLIAM RAY, b Savannah, Tenn, Apr 17, 46; m 67. ANIMAL BEHAVIOR, ANIMAL BREEDING. *Educ:* Univ Tenn, BSc, 68, MSc, 72; Pa State Univ, PhD(animal sci), 75. *Prof Exp:* asst prof, Animal Sci, Univ Sask, 76-80; ASSOC PROF ANIMAL SCI, UNIV MD, 81- *Mem:* AAAS; Animal Behav Soc; Am Genetic Asn; Am Soc Animal Sci; Can Soc Animal Sci. *Res:* Crowding, personal space, and stress. *Mailing Add:* Dept Animal Sci Univ Md College Park MD 20742 Can

STRICKLING, EDWARD, b Woodsfield, Ohio, Oct 20, 16; m 41; c 3. SOILS. *Educ:* Ohio State Univ, BS, 37, PhD, 49. *Prof Exp:* Instr, High Sch, 37-42; PROF SOILS, UNIV MD, COLLEGE PARK, 50- *Mem:* Soil Sci Soc Am; Am Soc Agron. *Res:* Soil physics, especially soil structure and evapotranspiration. *Mailing Add:* 6904 Calverton Dr Hyattsville MD 20782

STRICKMEIER, HENRY BERNARD, JR, b Galveston, Tex, Sept 28, 40. MATHEMATICS EDUCATION. *Educ:* Tex Lutheran Col, BS, 62; Univ Tex, Austin, MA, 67, PhD(math educ), 70. *Prof Exp:* Teacher high sch, Tex, 62-65; assoc prof, 70-80, PROF MATH, CALIF POLYTECH STATE UNIV, SAN LUIS OBISPO, 80- *Mem:* Math Asn Am; Am Educ Res Asn; Nat Coun Teachers Math. *Res:* Evaluation of mathematics curricula; analysis of mathematics teaching. *Mailing Add:* Dept Math Calif Polytech State Univ San Luis Obispo CA 93401

STRICOS, DAVID PETER, analytical chemistry, see previous edition

STRIDER, DAVID LEWIS, b Salisbury, NC, Feb 12, 29; m 54; c 4. PLANT PATHOLOGY. *Educ:* NC State Col, MS, 57, PhD(plant path), 59. *Prof Exp:* Res asst prof, 59-64, assoc prof, 64-70, PROF PLANT PATH, NC STATE UNIV, 70- *Concurrent Pos:* Mem, NC State Univ-US AID Mission, Peru, 70-71. *Mem:* Am Phytopath Soc. *Res:* Control of horticultural crops diseases; disease control of greenhouse floral crops. *Mailing Add:* Dept of Plant Path NC State Univ Raleigh NC 27607

STRIEBY, MICHAEL, b Orange, NJ, July 19, 26; m 71; c 3. ELECTRICAL ENGINEERING. *Educ:* Swarthmore Col, BS, 50; Mass Inst Technol, ScD(elec eng), 55. *Prof Exp:* Asst, Mass Inst Technol, 51-55; mem tech staff, Ramo Wooldridge Div, Thompson Ramo Wooldridge, Inc, 55-56 & Hughes Aircraft Co, 56-62; dir info systs, NAm Aviation, Inc, 62-63; assoc mgr missile eng labs, Amraan Div, Missile Systs Div, Hughes Aircarft Co, 63-78, assoc mgr guidance & control, 78-80; CHIEF SCIENTIST, HUGHES AIRCRAFT CO, 80- *Concurrent Pos:* Lectr, Univ Calif, Los Angeles, 56-61. *Mem:* Sigma Xi; Inst Elec & Electronics Engrs. *Res:* Radar and infrared systems; missiles; guidance; control; electronics. *Mailing Add:* Roscol Blvd & Ialbrook Ave Canoga Park CA 91304

STRIEDER, WILLIAM, b Erie, Pa, Jan 19, 38; m 67; c 4. CHEMICAL ENGINEERING, PHYSICAL CHEMISTRY. *Educ:* Pa State Univ, BS, 60; Case Inst Technol, PhD(phys chem), 63. *Prof Exp:* Res fel irreversible thermodyn, Free Univ Brussels, 63-65; res fel statist mech, Univ Minn, 65-66; asst prof eng sci, 66-70, ASSOC PROF CHEM ENG, UNIV NOTRE DAME, 70- *Concurrent Pos:* Prin investr, NSF, Air Force Off Sci Res & Dept Transp grants. *Mem:* Am Inst Chem Engrs; Am Soc Eng Educ; Am Asn Univ Professors; Am Chem Soc; Am Phys Soc. *Res:* Molecular theory of transport processes; flow through random porous media; transport phenomena; thermodynamics; statistical mechanics. *Mailing Add:* Dept of Chem Eng Univ of Notre Dame Notre Dame IN 46556

STRIER, MURRAY PAUL, b New York, NY, Oct 19, 23l; m 55; c 3. PHYSICAL CHEMISTRY, ORGANIC CHEMISTRY. *Educ:* City Col New York, BChE, 44; Emory Univ, MS, 47; Univ Ky, PhD(chem), 52; Am Inst Chemists, cert. *Prof Exp:* Asst & instr, Univ Ky, 48-50; res chemist & proj leader, Reaction Motors, Inc, 52-56; sr chemist & head polymers sect, Air Reduction Co, Inc, 56-58; chief chemist, Fulton-Irgon Corp, 58-59; group leader fiber res, Rayonier, Inc, 59-60; suprvr develop res, 60-61; res chemist,

T A Edison Res Lab, 61-64; sr res scientist, Douglas Aircraft Co, Inc, 64-67, chief fuel cell & battery res sect, 67-69; res assoc, Hooker Res Ctr, 69-71; prin chem engr, Cornell Aeronaut Lab, 71-72; chemist, 72-76, ENVIRON & PHYS SCIENTIST, ENVIRON PROTECTION AGENCY, 76- *Concurrent Pos:* Consult, NSF, 73-75. *Mem:* AAAS; Am Chem Soc; Am Inst Chemists; Am Soc Testing & Mat; Electrochem Soc. *Res:* Organic polarography; physical chemistry of rocket propellants; physical properties of organic coatings, plastics and fibers; viscose chemistry; fuel cells and batteries; environmental science; industrial water pollution control-molecular structure-activity correlations. *Mailing Add:* 8 James Spring Ct Rockville MD 20850

STRIETER, FREDERICK JOHN, b Davenport, Iowa, Sept 14, 34; m 57; c 2. PHYSICAL CHEMISTRY, SEMICONDUCTOR DEVICES. *Educ:* Augustana Col, Ill, AB, 56; Univ Calif, Berkeley, PhD, 60. *Prof Exp:* Asst chem, Univ Calif, 56-57; asst crystallog, Lawrence Radiation Lab, Univ Calif, 57-59; mem tech staff, 59-75, CIRCUITS DEVELOP PILOT LINE MGR, TEX INSTRUMENTS, INC, 75- *Mem:* Electrochem Soc (treas, 73-76, vpres-pres, 79-83); Inst Elec & Electronic Engr. *Res:* Semiconductor device process technology; impurity diffusion in semiconductors; ion implantation of impurities in semiconductors; electron beam pattern definition. *Mailing Add:* 7814 Fallmeadow Lane Dallas TX 75248

STRIFE, JAMES RICHARD, b Ilion, NY, Oct 12, 49; m 71; c 2. METAL MATRIX COMPOSITES, POWDER METALLURGY. *Educ:* Rensselaer Polytech Inst, BS, 71, MS, 73, PhD(mat eng), 76. *Prof Exp:* Staff scientist, Union Carbide Corp, 76-78; SR RES SCIENTIST, UNITED TECHNOLOGIES RES CTR, 78- *Mem:* Am Soc Metals; Am Inst Metall Engrs; Soc Advan Mat & Process Eng. *Res:* Advanced composite and ceramic materials for applications in heat engines, optical systems, and space satellite structures. *Mailing Add:* United Technologies Res Ctr Silver Lane East Hartford CT 06108

STRIFFLER, DAVID FRANK, b Pontiac, Mich, Oct 24, 22; m 49; c 2. PUBLIC HEALTH, DENTISTRY. *Educ:* Univ Mich, DDS, 47, MPH, 51; Am Bd Dent Pub Health, dipl, 55. *Prof Exp:* Consult dent, Dearborn Pub Schs, Mich, 50-51; dir sch health, 51-53; dir div dent health, State Dept Pub Health NMex, 53-61; assoc prof pub health, Sch Pub Health & assoc prof dent, Sch Dent, 61-65, chmn dept community dent, Sch Dent, 62-67, PROF PUB HEALTH DENT, SCH PUB HEALTH & PROF DENT, SCH DENT, UNIV MICH, ANN ARBOR, 65-, DIR PROG DENT PUB HEALTH, SCH PUB HEALTH, 62- *Concurrent Pos:* Mem, Pub Health Res Study Sect, NIH, 59-60, Health Serv Res Study Sect, 60-62, Dis Control Study Sect, 64-65 & Prev Med & Dent Rev Comt, 70-74; mem, Nat Adv Comt Pub Health Training, USPHS, 60-61, Health Serv Res Training Comt, 66-68, Rev Comt Health Professions Schs Financial Distress Grants, 77-81; ed, J Pub Health Dent, 75- *Mem:* Sigma Xi; Am Dent Asn; fel Am Pub Health Asn; fel Am Col Dent; Fel Int Col Dent. *Res:* Fluoridation; epidemiology of periodontal diseases; delivery of dental health services. *Mailing Add:* 2217 Vinewood Blvd Ann Arbor MI 48104

STRIFFLER, WILLIAM D, b Oberlin, Ohio, July 10, 29; m 56; c 4. FOREST HYDROLOGY. *Educ:* Mich State Univ, BS & BSF, 52; Univ Mich, MF, 57, PhD(forest hyrdol), 63. *Prof Exp:* Res forester & proj leader groundwater hydrol & steambank erosion, Lake States Forest Exp Sta, Mich, 57-63; hydrologist, Stripmined Areas Restoration Res Proj, Northeastern Forest Exp Sta, Ky, 64-66; from asst prof to assoc prof watershed mgt, 66-75, PROF EARTH RESOURCES, COLO STATE UNIV, 75- *Concurrent Pos:* Consult, Cent soil & Water Conserv Res Inst, India, 75, 77, 80. *Mem:* Am Geophys Union; Am Water Resource Asn; AAAS; Sigma Xi; Indian Soc Soil & Water Conserv. *Res:* Wildland hydrology; land use hydrology; erosion and sedimentation processes; water quality; grassland hydrology; instrumentation. *Mailing Add:* Dept of Earth Resources Colo State Univ Ft Collins CO 80521

STRIGHT, PAUL LEONARD, b St Paul, Minn, May 12, 30; m 60; c 2. ORGANIC CHEMISTRY. *Educ:* Grinnell Col, BA, 51; Univ Minn, Minneapolis, PhD(org chem), 56. *Prof Exp:* Res chemist, Esso Res & Eng Co, 56-59; res chemist, Allied Chem Corp, 59-65, res supvr, 65-68, res assoc, 68-70; asst prof org chem, Univ Minn, Morris, 70-71; assoc scientist neurochem, Univ Minn, Minneapolis, 71-73; instr chem, 73-75, PROF CHEM, LAKE MICH COL, 75- *Mem:* Sigma Xi; Am Chem Soc. *Mailing Add:* Lake Mich Col 2755 E Napier Ave Benton Harbor MI 49022

STRIKE, DONALD PETER, b Mt Carmel, Pa, Oct 24, 36; m 72; c 2. PHARMACEUTICAL CHEMISTRY. *Educ:* Philadelphia Col Pharm & Sci, BS, 58; Iowa State Univ, MS, 61, PhD(org chem), 63. *Prof Exp:* Res fel, Univ Southampton, 63-64; res chemist, 65-69, res group leader, 69-77, RES MGR, WYETH LABS, AM HOME PROD CORP, 77- *Mem:* Am Chem Soc. *Res:* Natural products; antibiotics; steroids; prostaglandins. *Mailing Add:* Wyeth Labs Res & Develop Lancaster Pike & Morehall Rd Radnor PA 19088

STRIKWERDA, JOHN CHARLES, b Grand Rapids, Mich, Mar 15, 47; m 70; c 2. NUMERICAL ANALYSIS. *Educ:* Calvin Col, AB, 69; Univ Mich, MA, 70; Stanford Univ, PhD(math), 76. *Prof Exp:* Res scientist, Inst Comput Applications Sci Eng, 76-80; ASST PROF COMPUT SCI & MATH, RES CTR, UNIV WIS-MADISON, 80- *Mem:* Soc Indust & Appl Mech; Am Math Soc. *Res:* Numerical methods for partial differential equations; finite difference methods and computational fluid dynamics. *Mailing Add:* Comput Sci Dept Univ Wis 1210 W Dayton St Madison WI 53706

STRIMLING, WALTER EUGENE, b Minneapolis, Minn, Jan 6, 26; m 57; c 3. MATHEMATICS, ELECTRICAL ENGINEERING. *Educ:* Univ Minn, BPhys & MA, 45, PhD(math), 53. *Prof Exp:* Instr math & educ, Col St Catherine, 45-46; asst math, Univ Minn, 49-53; engr, Raytheon Co, 53-55; PRES, US DYNAMICS, 55- *Mem:* Am Math Soc; Am Phys Soc; Math Asn Am; Inst Elec & Electronics Engrs. *Res:* Theoretical physics; chemistry. *Mailing Add:* 63 Westcliff Rd Weston MA 02193

STRIMPLE, HARRELL LEROY, b Yates Center, Kans, Jan 7, 12; m 34, 71; c 1. INVERTEBRATE PALEONTOLOGY, STRATIGRAPHY. *Prof Exp:* Mem staff, Phillips Petrol Co, 32-59; curator, Geol Enterprises, 60-61; consult paleontologist, 61-62; res assoc geol & curator, 62-80, EMER RES INVESTR, UNIV IOWA, 80- *Concurrent Pos:* Res affil, Nebr State Museum. *Mem:* Paleont Res Inst; Paleont Asn; fel Geol Soc Am; Paleont Soc. *Res:* Paleozoic Echinodermata; stratigraphy. *Mailing Add:* Dept Geol Univ Iowa Iowa City IA 52242

STRINDEN, SARAH TAYLOR, b Lyons, Kans, Jan 31, 55; m 79. BIOCHEMISTRY. *Educ:* Univ Kans, BS, 76; Univ Southern Calif, PhD(biochem), 81. *Prof Exp:* Technician biochem, Univ Kans, 76-77; res asst, Univ Southern Calif, 78-81; FEL, UNIV WIS-MADISON, 81- *Mem:* Sigma Xi. *Res:* Various mechanisms controlling gene expression at the post-transcriptional level. *Mailing Add:* Dept Obstet & Gynec CSC H4-637 Univ Wis 600 Highland Ave Madison WI 53706

STRINGALL, ROBERT WILLIAM, b San Francisco, Calif, Dec 12, 33; c 2. MATHEMATICS EDUCATION. *Educ:* San Jose State Col, BA, 59; Univ Wash, MS, 63, PhD(math), 65. *Prof Exp:* ASSOC PROF MATH, UNIV CALIF, DAVIS, 65- *Concurrent Pos:* Consult, Elem & Sec Educ Act Title III, 67-68, Proj Sem, 70- *Res:* Algebra. *Mailing Add:* Dept of Math Univ of Calif Davis CA 95616

STRINGAM, ELWOOD WILLIAMS, b Alberta, Can, Dec 10, 17; m 44; c 6. ANIMAL SCIENCE, AGRICULTURE. *Educ:* Univ Alta, BSc, 40, MSc, 42; Univ Minn, PhD(agr), 48. *Prof Exp:* Asst, Dom Range Exp Sta, Alta, 40; fieldman, Livestock Prod Serv, 41-42; instr animal husb, Univ Minn, 46-48; assoc prof animal sci, Univ Man, 48-51; prof animal husb, Ont Agr Col, 51-54; head dept animal sci, 54-73, PROF ANIMAL SCI, UNIV MAN, 54- *Concurrent Pos:* Mem, Nat Animal Breeding Comt, Can, 58-63; adv comt, Western Vet Col, 66-; dir nat adv comt for agr, World's Fair, 67; mem, Nat Genetic Adv Comt Cattle Importations, 69-74. *Mem:* AAAS; Am Soc Animal Sci; Am Genetic Asn; Can Soc Animal Sci; fel Agr Inst Can (vpres, 62-63, pres, 66-67). *Res:* Agricultural education; animal genetics and physiology; farm animal production and management; beef cattle production. *Mailing Add:* Dept Animal Sci Univ Man Winnipeg MB R3T 2N2 Can

STRINGAM, GARY RICE, b Cardston, Alta, May 24, 37; m 61; c 7. CYTOGENETICS. *Educ:* Brigham Young Univ, BS, 61; Univ Minn, MS, 65, PhD(genetics), 66. *Prof Exp:* Res asst genetics, Univ Minn, 61-63; fel radiation physiol, Univ Hawaii, 66-67; RES SCIENTIST CYTOGENETICS, CAN DEPT AGR, 67- *Mem:* Int Asn Plant Tissue Cult; Genetics Soc Can; Am Genetic Asn; Agr Inst Can. *Res:* Tissue culture; plant breeding. *Mailing Add:* Agr Can Res Sta 107 Science Crescent Saskatoon SK S7N 0X2 Can

STRINGER, GENE ARTHUR, b Yamhill County, Ore, Nov 16, 39; m 61; c 3. PHYSICS, ELECTRONICS. *Educ:* Linfield Col, BA, 61; Univ Ore, MA, 64, PhD(physics), 69. *Prof Exp:* Staff engr & physicist res, Tektronix Inc, Beaverton, Ore, 61-63; res assoc physics, Univ Ore, 69; res assoc & instr, Cornell Univ, 69-71; asst prof, 71-76, CHMN DEPT PHYSICS, SOUTHERN ORE STATE COL, 74-, ASSOC PROF, 76- *Concurrent Pos:* Physics consult, Tektronix Inc, 63-64; NSF grant, Instr Sci Equip, 76-78; proj assoc, Tech Educ Res Ctr, 77-78; NSF grant, 79-81. *Mem:* Am Asn Physics Teachers; Am Soc Eng Educ. *Mailing Add:* Dept Physics Southern Ore State Col Ashland OR 97520

STRINGER, L(OREN) F(RANK), b Huntington Park, Calif, Sept 28, 25; m 53; c 4. POWER ELECTRONIC ENGINEERING, APPLIED MATHEMATICS. *Educ:* Univ Tex, BS, 46; Calif Inst Technol, MS, 47; Univ Pittsburgh, PhD, 63. *Prof Exp:* engr, 47-56, develop engr mgr, 56-74, div engr mgr, 74-81, CHIEF ENGR, WESTINGHOUSE ELEC CORP, BUFFALO, NY, 81- *Concurrent Pos:* Lamme scholar, 64; chmn C34 tech subcomt, Am Nat Standards Inst; secy SC22G, Tech Adv USNC, Int Electrotech Comn. *Honors & Awards:* Westinghouse Order of Merit, 66. *Mem:* Fel Inst Elec & Electronics Engrs. *Res:* Engineering management; power electronics, automatic control and systems engineering. *Mailing Add:* Box 225 Buffalo NY 14240

STRINGFELLOW, DALE ALAN, b Ogden, Utah, Sept 13, 44; m 66; c 2. VIROLOGY, IMMUNOBIOLOGY. *Educ:* Univ Utah, BS, 67, MS, 70, PhD(microbiol), 72. *Prof Exp:* NIH fel & instr microbiol, Univ Utah, 72-73; res scientist, 73-79, SR RES SCIENTIST VIROL & HEAD CANCER RES, UPJOHN CO, 79- *Mem:* Am Soc Microbiol; Am Asn Cancer Res; AAAS. *Res:* Antiviral agents; interrelationship between host defense systems and virus infection; pathogenesis of virus infection; mechanisms modulating nonspecific immunity; viral ecology; antireoplastic agents; metastasis; cell cycling; nucleic acid biochemistry; cellular regulation; prostaglandins; cellular communications. *Mailing Add:* Exp Biol Dept Upjohn Co Kalamazoo MI 49001

STRINGFELLOW, FRANK, b Cheriton, Va, Oct 27, 40; m 68. PARASITOLOGY, ZOOLOGY. *Educ:* St Louis Univ, BS, 62; Drake Univ, MA, 64; Univ SC, PhD(biol), 67. *Prof Exp:* Asst gen biol, Drake Univ, 63-64; instr anat & physiol, Univ SC, 64-65; ZOOLOGIST, ANIMAL PARASITOL INST, AGR RES CTR, US DEPT AGR, 67- *Mem:* Am Micros Soc; Am Soc Parasitol; Sigma Xi. *Res:* Pathobiology of gastrointestinal parasites of cattle; histochemistry and biochemistry of nematodes; reproductive physiology and biochemistry of parasites; cultivation of parasitic nematodes. *Mailing Add:* Animal Parasitol Inst Agr Res Ctr USDA Beltsville MD 20705

STRINGFELLOW, GERALD B, b Salt Lake City, Utah, Apr 26, 42; m 62; c 3. MATERIALS SCIENCE, SEMICONDUCTORS. *Educ:* Univ Utah, BS, 64; Stanford Univ, MS, 66, PhD(mat sci), 67. *Prof Exp:* Mem tech staff, Solid State Physics Lab, Hewlett Packard Labs, 67-71, proj mgr, 71-80; PROF ELEC ENG & MAT SCI ENG, UNIV UTAH, SALT LAKE CITY, 80- *Concurrent Pos:* sabbatical, Max Planck Inst, Stuttgart, Ger, 79. *Honors & Awards:* Alexander von Humboldt, US Sr Scientist Award, 79. *Mem:* Am Phys Soc; Electrochem Soc; Inst Elec & Electronic Engrs. *Res:* Electrical and optical properties of alloys between III-V compound semiconductors; luminescence and photoconductivity of II-VI and III-V compounds; crystal growth and thermodynamics in ternary III-V systems. *Mailing Add:* Dept Elec Eng Univ Utah Salt Lake City UT 84112

STRINGFIELD, VICTOR TIMOTHY, b Franklinton, La, Sept 10, 02; m 29; c 2. HYDROGEOLOGY. *Educ:* La State Univ, BS, 25; Wash Univ, MS, 27. *Prof Exp:* Asst geol & geog, Wash Univ, 25-27; instr geol, Okla Agr & Mech Col, 27-28; asst prof, NMex Sch Mines, 28-30; asst geologist, US Geol Surv, 30-36, assoc geologist, 36-39, geologist in charge ground water invests, Southeastern States, 39-42, sr geologist in charge ground water invests, Eastern States, 42-47, prin geologist & chief sect ground water geol, 47-57, chief sect radiohydrol, 57-60, staff geol specialist, 60-75; RETIRED. *Concurrent Pos:* Geologist, NMex Bur Mines, 28-30; consult hydrol, Food & Agr Orgn, UN, Jamaica, WI, 65- *Mem:* Fel Geol Soc Am; Soc Econ Geol; Am Asn Petrol Geol; Am Geophys Union. *Res:* Ground water geology; radiohydrology; ground water hydrology; radioisotopes in soils and water; hydrogeology of carbonate terranes. *Mailing Add:* 4208 50th St NW Washington DC 20016

STRINGHAM, GLEN EVAN, b Lethbridge, Alta, Aug 30, 29; US citizen; m 53; c 4. ENGINEERING. *Educ:* Utah State Univ, BS, 55; Colo State Univ, PhD(civil eng), 66. *Prof Exp:* Instr agr eng, Calif State Polytech Col, 55-57; from asst prof to assoc prof, 57-78, PROF AGR ENG, UTAH STATE UNIV, 78- *Concurrent Pos:* Chief party, Utah State Univ-Agency Int Develop team, Colombia, 69-71. *Mem:* Am Soc Agr Engrs; Am Soc Civil Engrs; Am Soc Eng Educ; Soil Conserv Soc Am. *Res:* Optimization of surface irrigation. *Mailing Add:* Dept of Agr Eng Utah State Univ Logan UT 84322

STRINGHAM, REED MILLINGTON, JR, b Salt Lake City, Utah. PHYSIOLOGY, ORAL BIOLOGY. *Educ:* Northwestern Univ, Evanston, DDS, 58; Univ Utah, BS, 64, PhD(molecular & genetic biol), 68. *Prof Exp:* Nat Inst Dent Res fel, 65-68, RES ASSOC PLASTIC SURG, MED SCH, UNIV UTAH, 68-; PROF OCCUP HEALTH & ZOOL & DEAN SCH ALLIED HEALTH SCI, WEBER STATE COL, 69- *Concurrent Pos:* Resource person, Intermountain Regional Med Prog, 69, consult, Oral Cancer Screening Proj, 71- *Mem:* Am Dent Asn. *Res:* Salivary gland physiology; health manpower. *Mailing Add:* Sch of Allied Health Sci Weber State Col Ogden UT 84403

STRINTZIS, MICHAEL GERASSIMOS, b Athens, Greece, Sept 30, 44; US citizen. ELECTRICAL ENGINEERING, APPLIED MATHEMATICS. *Educ:* Nat Tech Univ Athens, BS, 67; Princeton Univ, MA, 69, PhD(elec eng), 70. *Prof Exp:* Asst prof, 70-76, ASSOC PROF ELEC ENG, UNIV PITTSBURGH, 76- *Concurrent Pos:* Vis prof, Nat Tech Univ, Athens, 78-79; consult, Westinghouse Elec Corp, Contrewes-Goerz & Alcoa Corp, 78-79; grants, NSF, Elec Power Res Inst, NIH & Energy Res & Develop Admin. *Mem:* Inst Elec & Electronics Engrs; Soc Indust & Appl Math; NY Acad Sci. *Res:* Signal and image processing; large-scale systems; digital signal processing, image description and processing; detection and estimation theory; control systems. *Mailing Add:* Dept of Elec Eng Sch of Eng Univ of Pittsburgh Pittsburgh PA 15261

STRITTMATER, RICHARD CARLTON, b Columbia, Pa, Aug 26, 23; m 50; c 3. PHYSICS. *Educ:* Earlham Col, BA, 53; Iowa State Col, MS, 55. *Prof Exp:* Res physicist fluid mech & heat transfer, Remington Arms Co, Ilion, NY, 55-58; RES PHYSICIST MECH, ACOUST & HEAT TRANSFER, BALLISTIC RES LAB, 58- *Concurrent Pos:* Mem, Comt Standardization Combustion Instability Measurements, 66-70; Dept Army rep, Steering Comt Interagency Chem Rocket Propulsion Group's Solid Propellent Combustion Group, 67. *Mem:* Sigma Xi. *Res:* Turbulent fluid mechanical interaction at burning surfaces. *Mailing Add:* 2500 Pinehurst Ave Forest Hill MD 21050

STRITTMATTER, CORNELIUS FREDERICK, b Philadelphia, Pa, Nov 16, 26; m 55; c 1. BIOCHEMISTRY. *Educ:* Juniata Col, BS, 47; Harvard Univ, PhD(biol chem), 52. *Prof Exp:* Instr biol chem, Harvard Med Sch, 52-54, assoc, 55-58, asst prof, 58-61; chmn dept, 61-78, ODUS M MULL PROF BIOCHEM, BOWMAN GRAY SCH MED, 61- *Concurrent Pos:* USPHS res fel, Oxford Univ, 54-55; USPHS sr res fel, Harvard Med Sch, 61; consult, New Eng Deaconess Hosp, 58-61; mem fel comt, NIH, 67-70 & 74; consult, NC Alcoholism Res Auth, 74- *Mem:* Am Chem Soc; Am Soc Biol Chemists; Soc Develop Biol; Soc Exp Biol & Med; Am Soc Zool. *Res:* Enzymic differentiation and control mechanisms during embryonic development and aging; characterization of electron transport systems; cellular control mechanisms in metabolism; comparative biochemistry; mechanisms in enzyme systems. *Mailing Add:* Dept of Biochem Bowman Gray Sch of Med Winston-Salem NC 27103

STRITTMATTER, PETER ALBERT, b Bexleyheath, Eng, Sept 12, 39; m 67; c 2. ASTRONOMY. *Educ:* St John's Col, Cambridge Univ, BA, 64, PhD(math), 66. *Prof Exp:* Mem staff astron, Inst Theoret Astron, Cambridge, 67-68; res assoc, Mt Stromlo & Siding Spring Observ, 69; mem staff, Inst Theoret Astron, Cambridge, 70; res physicist, Univ Calif, San Diego, 71; assoc prof, 71-73, PROF ASTRON & DIR OBSERV, STEWARD OBSERV, UNIV ARIZ, 75- *Concurrent Pos:* Consult astron adv panel, NSF, 75-79; mem bd, Asn Univs Res Astron, NSF, 75-; adj sci mem, Max Planck Inst Radioastron, Bonn; Alexander Von Humboldt sr scientist award, 79-80. *Mem:* Am Acad Arts Sci; Am Astron Soc; Royal Astron Soc; Int Astron Union; Ger Astron Soc. *Res:* Quasistellar objects; Seyfert galaxies; radio sources; white dwarfs; novae; speckle interferometry. *Mailing Add:* Steward Observ Univ of Ariz Tucson AZ 85721

STRITTMATTER, PHILIPP, b Philadelphia, Pa, July 13, 28; m 56; c 2. BIOCHEMISTRY, ENZYMOLOGY. *Educ:* Harvard Univ, PhD, 54. *Prof Exp:* From instr to prof biochem, Wash Univ, 54-68; chmn dept, 68-74, PROF BIOCHEM, UNIV CONN, STORRS, 68-, HEAD DEPT, 76- *Mem:* Am Soc Biol Chemists. *Res:* Oxidative enzyme mechanisms. *Mailing Add:* Dept of Biochem Univ of Conn Health Ctr Farmington CT 06032

STRITZEL, JOSEPH ANDREW, b Cleveland, Ohio, June 11, 22; m 50; c 9. AGRONOMY. *Educ:* Iowa State Univ, BS, 49, MS, 53, PhD(soil fertil, prod econ), 58. *Prof Exp:* Exten soil fertil specialist, 50-63, prof soils, 63-76, PROF AGRON, IOWA STATE UNIV, 76- *Mem:* Am Soc Agron. *Res:* Soil fertility; production economics. *Mailing Add:* Dept of Soils Iowa State Univ Ames IA 50010

STRITZKE, JIMMY FRANKLIN, b South Coffeyville, Okla, Sept 9, 37; m 59; c 2. AGRONOMY. *Educ:* Okla State Univ, BS, 59, MS, 61; Univ Mo, PhD(field crops), 67. *Prof Exp:* Res scientist weed control, Agr Res Serv, USDA, 61-66; asst prof agron, SDak State Univ, 66-70; asst prof, 70-76, assoc prof, 76-80, PROF AGRON, OKLA STATE UNIV, 80- *Mem:* Am Forest & Grassland Coun; Am Soc Agron; Weed Sci Soc Am; Soc Range Mgt; Coun Agr Sci & Technol. *Res:* Weed control in alfalfa, weed and brush control in pasture and rangelands, herbicide residue and translocation. *Mailing Add:* Dept of Agron Okla State Univ Stillwater OK 74078

STRIZ, ALFRED GERHARD, b Rosenheim, WGer, July 25, 52. AEROELASTICITY, FINITE ELEMENT ANALYSIS. *Educ:* Purdue Univ, BS & MS, 76, PhD(aero/astro eng), 81. *Prof Exp:* Teaching asst eng, Purdue Univ, 77-80; ASST PROF SOLID MECH, UNIV OKLA, 81- *Concurrent Pos:* Res asst aeroelasticity, Purdue Univ, 77-80; instr solid mech, 81; prin investr, Demco, subsidiary of Cooper Indust, 82- *Mem:* Am Inst Aeronaut & Astronaut; Am Soc Mech Engrs; Am Soc Eng Educ; Soc Exp Stress Analysis. *Res:* Transonic aeroelasticity of conventional and super-critical airfoils; finite element analyses of structures, pressure vessels, dental prosthetics; compressor blade flutter; productivity enhancement. *Mailing Add:* Rm 301 B Sch Amne Univ Okla 865 Asp Ave Norman OK 73019

STRNAT, KARL, b Vienna, Austria, Mar 29, 29; US citizen; m 54; c 4. MATERIALS SCIENCE, ELECTRICAL ENGINEERING. *Educ:* Vienna Tech Univ, Dipl Ing, 53, DrTech(eng physics), 56. *Prof Exp:* Asst, Vienna Tech Univ, 53-57; res physicist, US Air Force Mat Lab, 58-61, sect chief physics, 61-64, lead scientist, 64-68; F M TAIT PROF ELEC ENG, UNIV DAYTON, 68- *Concurrent Pos:* Lectr, univs & indust labs, 61-; recipient res grants, Advan Res Proj Agency, US Air Force Mat Lab, Goldschmidt Co, Molybdenum Corp, Ind Gen Corp, NSF & Gen Motors Corp, 68-; indust consult, 68-; owner, KJS Assocs, Consult & Tech-Serv, 76-; vis res scientist, Univ Calif, San Diego, 78-79. *Honors & Awards:* Cleary Award, 68. *Mem:* Am Phys Soc; Inst Elec & Electronics Engrs; Arbeitsgemeinschaft Magnetismus. *Res:* Magnetic materials, permanent magnets, magneto-optics, instrumentation; rare earth alloys, their physical metallurgy, magnetism and crystallography; magnetic device design; magnet production engineering. *Mailing Add:* Dept Elec Eng 300 College Park Dr Dayton OH 45469

STRNISA, FRED V, b Cleveland, Ohio, Nov 20, 41; c 3. PHYSICS. *Educ:* Case Inst Technol, BS, 63; John Carroll Univ, MS, 67; State Univ NY, Albany, PhD(physics), 72. *Prof Exp:* Engr, Lamp Div, Gen Elec Co, 63-67, physicist, Knolls Atomic Power Lab, 67-69; res assoc, State Univ NY, Albany, 69-73; sr scientist, NY State Atomic Energy Coun, 73-76 & NY State Energy Off, 76-77; PROG MGR, NY STATE ENERGY RES & DEVELOP AUTHORITY, 77- *Mem:* Am Phys Soc; Am Nuclear Soc; Health Physics Soc; Sigma Xi. *Res:* Industrial and utility energy use and conservation; radioactive waste management; radiation and impurity defects in solids; circularly polarized electron paramagnetic resonance; mass spectroscopy; lighting technology; district heating; battery storage; electric vehicles. *Mailing Add:* NY State Energy Res Rockefeller Plaza Albany NY 12223

STRNISTE, GARY F, b Springfield, Mass, May 31, 44; m 80. GENETIC TOXICOLOGY, PHOTOBIOLOGY. *Educ:* Univ Mass, BS, 66; Pa State Univ, MS, 69, PhD(biophys), 71. *Prof Exp:* Fel molecular radiobiol, Los Alamos Sci Lab, 71-73; fel molecular biol, City Univ New York, 73-74; MEM STAFF, LOS ALAMOS NAT LAB, 75- *Mem:* Biophys Soc; Am Soc Biol Chemists; Environ Mutagenesis Soc; Am Soc Photobiol. *Res:* Genetic toxicology of complex mixtures; development and refinement of in vitro submammalian and mammalian screening assays; somatic cell mutagenesis; phtoactivation of promutagens/procarcinogens; in vitro and in vivo repair of DNA. *Mailing Add:* Genetics LS-3 M5886 Los Alamos Nat Lab Los Alamos NM 87545

STROBACH, DONALD ROY, b St Louis, Mo, Jan 10, 33; m 60; c 2. ORGANIC CHEMISTRY, BIOCHEMISTRY. *Educ:* Wash Univ, AB, 54, PhD(chem), 59. *Prof Exp:* NIH fels, 60-63; res chemist, Cent Res Dept, 63-69, RES CHEMIST, FREON PROD LAB, E I DU PONT DE NEMOURS & CO, INC, 70- *Mem:* Am Chem Soc. *Res:* Carbohydrates; synthesis and structure determination; synthesis of oligonucleotides; aerosol technology and product development. *Mailing Add:* 2420 W Parris Dr Wilmington DE 19808

STROBECK, CURTIS, b Powers Lake, NDak, Nov 14, 40. POPULATION GENETICS, POPULATION BIOLOGY. *Educ:* Univ Mont, BA, 64, MA, 66; Univ Chicago, PhD(theoret biol), 71. *Prof Exp:* Res fel pop biol, Sch Biol Sci, Univ Sussex, 71-75; vis asst prof dept ecol & evolution, State Univ NY, Stony Brook, 75-76; ASSOC PROF POP GENETICS, UNIV ALTA, 76- *Mem:* Genetics Soc Can. *Res:* Selection in heterogeneous environments; selection in multi-locus systems; evolution for recombination; effects of linkage in a finite population; multi-species competition. *Mailing Add:* Dept of Genetics Univ of Alta Edmonton AB T6G 2E1 Can

STROBEL, CHARLES WILLIAM, b Bertrand, Mo, Oct 31, 29; m 57; c 4. POLYMER CHEMISTRY. *Educ:* Southeast Mo State Col, BS, 51; Univ Mo, MA, 54, PhD, 56. *Prof Exp:* Sr res chemist, Phillips Petrol Co, Tex, 56-69; SR RES CHEMIST, DESOTO INC, DES PLAINES, 69- *Res:* Polymer synthesis; synthesis of elastomer, impact resistant plastics, sealants, electrocoat vehicles, vehicles for water base coatings. *Mailing Add:* 24 E Niagara Ave Schaumburg IL 60172

STROBEL, DARRELL FRED, b Fargo, NDak, May 13, 42; m 68. PLANETARY SCIENCES, ATMOSPHERIC DYNAMICS. *Educ:* NDak State Univ, BS, 64; Harvard Univ, AM, 65, PhD(appl physics), 69. *Prof Exp:* Res assoc planetary astron, Kitt Peak Nat Observ, 68-70, asst physicist, 70-72, assoc physicist, 72-73; res physicist, 73-76, SUPVR RES PHYSICIST, NAVAL RES LAB, 76- *Mem:* AAAS; Am Astron Soc; Am Geophys Union; Am Meteorol Soc. *Res:* Atmospheric physics and chemistry; planetary aeronomy; ionospheric physics; atmospheric dynamics. *Mailing Add:* Code 4780 Naval Res Lab Washington DC 20375

STROBEL, EDWARD, b Wilkes-Barre, Pa, Mar 18, 47. GENETIC ENGINEERING, CYTOGENETICS. *Educ:* Towson State Univ, BA, 69; State Univ NY Stony Brook, PhD(cell & develop biol), 77. *Prof Exp:* Housing inspector, Baltimore City Health Dept, 69-70; instr chem, Boys' Latin Sch, Baltimore, 70-72; ASST PROF GENETICS, DEPT BIOL SCI, PURDUE UNIV, 80- *Concurrent Pos:* Consult, Boehringer-Mannheim Biochem, Indianapolis, 80-; fel molecular biol, Sidney Farber Cancer Inst, 77-80; prin investr, Purdue Cancer Ctr, 81-82, NIH, 81-84, Nat Eye Inst, NIH, 81-85. *Res:* Mechanisms involved in maintaining the structural integrity and stability of eukaryotic chromosomes, and how higher order chromosome structure is modulated during development. *Mailing Add:* Dept Biol Sci Purdue Univ West Lafayette IN 47907

STROBEL, GARY A, b Massillon, Ohio, Sept 23, 38; m 63; c 2. PLANT PATHOLOGY. *Educ:* Colo State Univ, BS, 60; Univ Calif, Davis, PhD(plant path), 63. *Prof Exp:* From asst prof to prof bot, 63-77, PROF PLANT PATH, MONT STATE UNIV, 77- *Concurrent Pos:* Prin investr, NSF & USDA res grants; NIH career develop award, 69-74. *Mem:* AAAS; Am Phytopath Soc; Am Soc Plant Physiologists; Am Soc Biol Chemists. *Res:* Plant disease physiology; biochemistry of fungi and bacteria that cause plant diseases; phytotoxic glycopeptides; metabolic regulation in diseased plants; nature and mechanism of action of host specific toxins. *Mailing Add:* Dept of Plant Path Mont State Univ Bozeman MT 59716

STROBEL, GEORGE L, b Pratt, Kans, May 26, 37; m 57; c 2. THEORETICAL NUCLEAR PHYSICS, OPTICS. *Educ:* Kans State Univ, BS, 58; Univ Pittsburgh, MS, 61; Univ Southern Calif, PhD(physics), 65. *Prof Exp:* Scientist physics, Westinghouse Bettis Atomic Power Lab, 58-61 & Douglas Aircraft Co, 61-64; res assoc, Univ Southern Calif, 65 & Univ Calif, Davis, 65-67; ASSOC PROF PHYSICS, UNIV GA, 67- *Concurrent Pos:* Vis prof, Nuclear Res Ctr, Jülich, WGer, 71-72. *Mem:* Am Phys Soc. *Mailing Add:* Dept of Physics & Astron Univ of Ga Athens GA 30601

STROBEL, HOWARD AUSTIN, b Bremerton, Wash, Sept 5, 20; m 53; c 3. ANALYTICAL CHEMISTRY, PHYSICAL CHEMISTRY. *Educ:* State Col Wash, BS, 42; Brown Univ, PhD(phys chem), 47. *Prof Exp:* Jr res chemist, Manhattan Dist, Brown Univ, 43-45, res assoc, Univ, 47-48; from instr to assoc prof chem, 48-64, asst dean, Trinity Col, 56-64, assoc dean, 64-66, dean, Baldwin Residential Fedn, 72-75, fac fel, 75-81, PROF CHEM, DUKE UNIV, 64-, COORDR FEDN, 74- *Concurrent Pos:* Consult, Sci Instrumentation Info Network & Curricula, 81. *Mem:* Am Chem Soc; Royal Soc Chem. *Res:* Solute-solvent interactions in mixed media; ion exchange phenomena; chemical instrumentation. *Mailing Add:* Dept Chem Duke Univ Durham NC 27706

STROBEL, JAMES WALTER, b Steubenville, Ohio, Oct 31, 33; m 55; c 2. PLANT PATHOLOGY. *Educ:* Ohio Univ, AB, 55; Wash State Univ, PhD, 59. *Prof Exp:* Asst plant path, Wash State Univ, 55-59; from asst plant pathologist to assoc plant pathologist, Univ Fla, 59-68, prof plant path & plant pathologist, 68-74, chmn ornamental hort-agr exp stas, 70-74, dir agr & res ctr, Brandenton, 68-70; chmn dept hort sci, NC State Univ, 74-77; PRES MISS UNIV WOMEN 77- *Mem:* Am Soc Hort Sci; Am Asn State Cols Univs; Am Phytopath Soc. *Res:* Etiology, epidemiology, and control of vegetable diseases, particularly control of verticillium wilt of tomato and strawberry by breeding for resistance. *Mailing Add:* Off of Pres Miss Univ Women Columbus MS 39701

STROBEL, RUDOLF G K, b Kiessling, Ger, Feb 7, 27; m 58; c 4. BIOCHEMISTRY. *Educ:* Univ Munich, Dipl, 53, Dr rer nat, 58. *Prof Exp:* Asst, Max Planck Inst Protein & Leather Res, Ger, 56-58; RES BIOCHEMIST, RES DIV, PROCTER & GAMBLE CO, 58- *Mem:* AAAS; Am Chem Soc. *Res:* Histochemistry; histology; protein composition and structure; enzymology; natural products; microbiology; flavor research. *Mailing Add:* 7305 Thompson Rd Cincinnati OH 45247

STROBELL, JOHN DIXON, JR, b Newark, NJ, Dec 28, 17; m 49; c 2. GEOLOGY. *Educ:* Yale Univ, AB, 39, MS, 42, PhD(geol), 56. *Prof Exp:* Geologist, US Geol Surv, 42-79. *Mem:* Geol Soc Am; AAAS. *Res:* Geology of deposits of copper, uranium and vanadium; geology of Colorado Plateau province; environmental geology; geomorphology. *Mailing Add:* 3824 Paradise Rd Flagstaff AZ 86001

STROBOS, ROBERT JULIUS, b The Hague, Netherlands, July 2, 21; nat US; m 47, 67; c 5. NEUROLOGY. *Educ:* Univ Amsterdam, BS, 41, MD, 45; Am Bd Psychiat & Neurol, dipl, 55. *Prof Exp:* Asst resident neurol, Montefiore Hosp, New York, 50, resident, 52-53; asst neurol, Columbia Univ, 52-54; asst prof, Bowman Gray Sch Med, Wake Forest Univ, 54-60, assoc physiol & pharmacol, 56-60; assoc prof, 60-64, PROF NEUROL & CHMN DEPT, NEW YORK MED COL, 64- *Concurrent Pos:* Res fel neurosurg, Neurol Inst, New York, 51-52; asst neurol, Nat Hosp, London, Eng, 50; asst resident, NY Hosp, White Plains, 53-54. *Mem:* Asn Res Nerv & Ment Dis; Am Acad Neurol; Am Electroencephalog Soc. *Res:* Convulsive disorders; brain physiology and behavior; electroencephalography. *Mailing Add:* Dept of Neurol New York Med Col Munger Pavilion Valhalla NY 10595

STRODT, WALTER CHARLES, mathematics, deceased

STROEBEL, CHARLES FREDERICK, III, b Chicago, Ill, May 25, 36; m 59; c 2. PSYCHOPHYSIOLOGY, NEUROPHYSIOLOGY. *Educ:* Univ Minn, BA, 58, PhD, 61; Yale Univ, MD, 73. *Prof Exp:* Res asst biophys, Mayo Clin, 55-58; res asst, Psychiat Animal Res Labs, Univ Minn, 58-61, actg dir labs & lectr, Univ, 62; DIR LABS PSYCHOPHYSIOL, INST LIVING HOSP, 62-, DIR CLINS, 74-, DIR RES, 79- *Concurrent Pos:* Adj prof, Univ Hartford, 64-72, res prof, 72-; adj prof, Trinity Col, Conn, 72-; lectr psychiat, Sch Med, Yale Univ, 73-; prof, Dept Psychiat, Univ Conn Health Ctr & Med Sch, 77- *Mem:* Biofeedback Soc Am; Am Psychiat Asn; Sigma Xi; Int Soc Chronobiology; NY Acad Sci. *Res:* Physiologic and behavioral mechanisms of stress and drugs; biologic rhythms; biofeedback; biostatistics; neurophysiology of learning and emotion. *Mailing Add:* Inst of Living Hosp 400 Washington St Hartford CT 06106

STROEHLEIN, JACK LEE, b Cobden, Ill, Dec 22, 32; m 65. SOIL SCIENCE. *Educ:* Southern Ill Univ, BS, 54; Univ Wis, MS, 58, PhD(soils), 62. *Prof Exp:* Asst prof, 62-67, assoc prof agr chem & soils, 67-76, ASSOC PROF, SOILS, WATER & ENG, UNIV ARIZ, 76-, RES SCIENTIST AGR CHEM, AGR EXP STA, 74- *Concurrent Pos:* Adv soils & soil fertil, Brazil Prog, AID, 70-71. *Mem:* Am Soc Agron. *Res:* Soil-plant-water relationships; soil testing; fertilization and fertilizer use. *Mailing Add:* Dept of Soils Water & Eng Univ of Ariz Tucson AZ 85721

STROH, WILLIAM RICHARD, b Sunbury, Pa, May 5, 23. PHYSICS. *Educ:* Harvard Univ, SB, 46, AM, 50, PhD(appl physics), 57. *Prof Exp:* Instr physics, Bucknell Univ, 46-49; res fel acoustics, Harvard Univ, 57-58; from asst prof to assoc prof elec eng, Univ Rochester, 58-62; assoc prof physics, Goucher Col, 62-68, prof, 68-81; RETIRED. *Mem:* Am Phys Soc; Am Asn Physics Teachers. *Res:* Acoustics; instrumentation. *Mailing Add:* Dept of Chem & Physics Goucher Col Towson MD 21204

STROHBEHN, JOHN WALTER, b San Diego, Calif, Nov 21, 36; m 58; c 3. BIOMEDICAL ENGINEERING, RADIOPHYSICS. *Educ:* Stanford Univ, BS, 58, MS, 59, PhD(elec eng), 64. *Prof Exp:* From asst prof to assoc prof, 63-74, PROF ENG, DARTMOUTH COL, 74-, ASSOC DEAN, 76- *Concurrent Pos:* Partic, Nat Acad Sci-Acad Sci USSR Exchange Prog, 67; mem comn II, Int Sci Radio Union; Inter-Union Comt Radio Meteorol; consult, McGraw-Hill, Inc & Avco Corp. *Honors & Awards:* Distinguished Authorship Award, Nat Oceanic & Atmospheric Admin, 74. *Mem:* AAAS; Inst Elec & Electronics Engrs; Am Soc Eng Educ; fel Optical Soc Am. *Res:* Biomedical engineering and cancer; image processing and tomography; optical propagation through a turbulent medium. *Mailing Add:* Radiophysics Lab Dartmouth Col Hanover NH 03755

STROHBEHN, KIM, b Council Bluffs, Iowa, Oct 17, 53; m 75; c 1. ELECTRICAL ENGINEERING. *Educ:* Iowa State Univ, BS, 76, MS, 77, PhD(elec eng), 79. *Prof Exp:* asst elec eng, Iowa State Univ, 76-80; ENGR, APPLIED PHYSICS LAB, JOHNS HOPKINS UNIV, 80- *Mem:* Inst Elec & Electronics Engrs; Sigma Xi. *Res:* Application of control and estimation theory. *Mailing Add:* Johns Hopkins Rd Laurel MD 20810

STROHECKER, HENRY FREDERICK, b Macon, Ga, Oct 15, 05; m 34; c 3. BIOLOGY. *Educ:* Mercer Univ, AB, 26; Univ Chicago, PhD(zool), 36. *Prof Exp:* Teacher, High Sch, Ga, 26-33; asst, Univ Chicago, 33-36; asst prof zool, Univ Miami, 36-37; asst prof biol, Kenyon Col, 37-44; vis asst prof, Wayne State Univ, 44-45; prof zool, NMex Highlands Univ, 45-46; from assoc prof to prof, 46-72, EMER PROF ZOOL, UNIV MIAMI, 72- *Mem:* Am Soc Zool; Sigma Xi. *Res:* Ecology; insect physiology and taxonomy. *Mailing Add:* Dept of Biol Univ of Miami Coral Gables FL 33124

STROHL, GEORGE RALPH, JR, b Ardmore, Pa, Oct 19, 19; m 46; c 2. MATHEMATICS. *Educ:* Haverford Col, BA, 41; Univ Pa, MA, 47; Univ Md, PhD(math), 56. *Prof Exp:* From instr to assoc prof, 47-63, chmn dept, 70-76, PROF MATH, US NAVAL ACAD, 63- *Mem:* Am Math Soc; Am Soc Eng Educ. *Res:* Topology and analysis. *Mailing Add:* Dept of Math US Naval Acad Annapolis MD 21402

STROHL, JOHN HENRY, b Forest City, Ill, Oct 2, 38; m 60; c 2. ANALYTICAL CHEMISTRY. *Educ:* Univ Ill, BS, 59; Univ Wis, PhD(chem), 64. *Prof Exp:* Asst chem, Univ Wis, 59-64; asst prof, 64-70, ASSOC PROF CHEM, WVA UNIV, 70- *Mem:* Am Chem Soc. *Res:* Preparative electrochemistry and continuous electrolysis. *Mailing Add:* Dept of Chem WVa Univ Morgantown WV 26506

STROHL, WILLIAM ALLEN, b Bethlehem, Pa, Nov 1, 33; m 57; c 2. VIROLOGY. *Educ:* Lehigh Univ, AB, 55; Calif Inst Technol, PhD(biol), 60. *Prof Exp:* Instr microbiol, Sch Med, St Louis Univ, 59-63; res assoc, 64-66, from asst prof to assoc prof, 66-77, PROF MICROBIOL, RUTGERS MED SCH, COL MED & DENT NJ, 77- *Concurrent Pos:* Nat Found fel, 59-61. *Mem:* AAAS; Am Soc Microbiol; Am Asn Cancer Res. *Res:* Animal viruses; viral oncogenesis. *Mailing Add:* Rutgers Med Sch Col Med & Dent NJ Piscataway NJ 08854

STROHM, JERRY LEE, b West Union, Ill, Jan 9, 37; m 57; c 4. GENETICS, PLANT BREEDING. *Educ:* Univ Ill, BS, 59; Univ Minn, PhD(genetics), 66. *Prof Exp:* Head dept, 68-77, PROF BIOL, UNIV WIS-PLATTEVILLE, 64- *Res:* Soybean genetics. *Mailing Add:* Dept of Biol Univ of Wis-Platteville Platteville WI 53818

STROHM, PAUL F, b Pennsauken, NJ, Jan 13, 35; m 57; c 5. AGRICULTURAL CHEMISTRY, ORGANIC CHEMISTRY. *Educ:* La Salle Col, BA, 56; Temple Univ, PhD(org chem), 61. *Prof Exp:* Res chemist, Atlantic Refining Co, 60-62 & Houdry Labs, Air Prod & Chem Inc, 62-68; res chemist, 68-72, group leader, 72-77, MGR QUAL CONTROL, AMCHEM PROD, INC, 77- *Mem:* Am Chem Soc; Am Soc Qual Control. *Res:* Organic synthesis: agricultural chemicals, especially herbicides and plant growth regulators; kinetics of urethane reactions; mechanism of epoxy curing reactions; bicyclic amine chemistry. *Mailing Add:* Mgr Qual Control Amchem Prod Inc Ambler PA 19002

STROHM, WARREN B(RUCE), b Brooklyn, NY, Sept 1, 25; m 51; c 3. ELECTRICAL ENGINEERING, ELECTRONICS. *Educ:* Tulane Univ, BE, 47. *Prof Exp:* With M W Kellogg Co, Inc, 47-48; proj mgr power syst protection, Devenco, Inc, 48-52; proj mgr component develop, Develop Lab, Int Bus Mach Corp, 52-57; proj mgr exp systs, Res Lab, 58-66, SR ENGR PROG SYSTS, SYSTS DEVELOP DIV, IBM CORP, 66- *Mem:* Inst Elec & Electronics Engrs; Asn Comput Mach. *Res:* Component development of magnetic devices; natural language data processing and computational linguistics; functional and structural specification of programming systems for data processing systems. *Mailing Add:* IBM Corp Neighborhood Rd Kingston NY 12401

STROHMAIER, A(LFRED) J(OHN), b Velbert, Ger, June 10, 15; nat US; m 42; c 3. CHEMICAL ENGINEERING. *Educ:* Univ Ill, BS, 38; Purdue Univ, MS, 42, PhD(chem eng), 44. *Prof Exp:* Chem engr, Cranston Chem Co, Ohio, 38-39; lubrication engr, Eng Dept, Joseph E Seagram & Sons, Inc, 39-45; lubrication consult, E I Du Pont de Nemours & Co, Inc, Wilmington, 45-49; sr res engr, Textile Fibers Dept, 49-80; RETIRED. *Res:* Textile fibers lubrication. *Mailing Add:* Rte 3 Box 224D Big Pine Key FL 33043

STROHMAN, RICHARD CAMPBELL, b New York, NY, May 5, 27; m; c 2. ZOOLOGY. *Educ:* Columbia Univ, PhD, 58. *Prof Exp:* Instr zool & cell physiol, Columbia Univ, 55-56; from asst prof to assoc prof, 58-70, chmn dept, 73-77, PROF ZOOL, UNIV CALIF, BERKELEY, 70- *Mem:* Soc Gen Physiol. *Res:* Physiology and biochemistry of muscle growth and development. *Mailing Add:* Dept of Zool Univ of Calif Berkeley CA 94720

STROHMAN, ROLLIN DEAN, b Geneseo, Ill, Oct 29, 39; m 69; c 2. AGRICULTURAL ENGINEERING. *Educ:* Univ Ill, BS(agr eng) & BS(agr sci), 62, MS, 65; Purdue Univ, PhD(agr eng), 69. *Prof Exp:* Agr engr, Western Utilization Res & Develop Div, Agr Res Serv, USDA, 68-69; assoc prof, 69-80, PROF AGR ENG, CALIF POLYTECH STATE UNIV, SAN LUIS OBISPO, 80- *Mem:* Am Soc Agr Engrs; Am Soc Photogram. *Res:* Physical properties of agricultural materials. *Mailing Add:* Dept of Agr Eng Calif Polytech State Univ San Luis Obispo CA 93407

STROIKE, JAMES EDWARD, b Enid, Okla, May 1, 42; m 61; c 3. PLANT BREEDING, PLANT GENETICS. *Educ:* Okla State Univ, BS, 64, MS, 67; Univ Nebr, Lincoln, PhD(plant breeding & genetics), 72. *Prof Exp:* Assoc secy-treas seed cert, Okla Crop Improv Asn, 66-67; from instr to asst prof agron, Univ Nebr-Lincoln, 71-75; plant geneticist, Rohm and Haas Chem Co, 75-77; MEM STAFF, WEA INC, 77- *Mem:* Am Soc Agron; Crop Sci Soc Am; Sigma Xi. *Res:* Chemical male sterilants for hybrid seed production; wheat. *Mailing Add:* WEA Inc 6025 W 300 St Lafayette IN 47905

STROJAN, CARL L, b Greensburg, Pa, Oct 9, 43; m 76. TERRESTRIAL ECOLOGY. *Educ:* Antioch Col, BA, 66; Rutgers Univ, PhD(ecol), 75. *Prof Exp:* fel ecol, Univ Calif, Los Angeles, 75-78, asst res ecologist, 78-80; MEM STAFF, SOLAR ENERGY RES INST, 80- *Mem:* Ecol Soc Am; Sigma Xi. *Res:* Plant litter decomposition and mineral cycling; environmental effects of energy technologies; impact of pollutants on terrestrial ecosystems. *Mailing Add:* Solar Energy Res Inst 1617 Cole Blvd Golden CO 80401

STROJNY, EDWIN JOSEPH, b Chicago, Ill, Jan 1, 26; m 55; c 2. INDUSTRIAL CHEMISTRY. *Educ:* Ill Inst Technol, BS, 51; Univ Ill, PhD(chem), 55. *Prof Exp:* Asst instr gen chem, Univ Ill, 51-52; org chemist, G D Searle & Co, 54-57; ORG CHEMIST, DOW CHEM CO, 57- *Mem:* AAAS; Am Chem Soc. *Res:* Phenolic compounds and derivatives; aromatic chemistry; heterogeneous and homogeneous catalysis; oxidation of organic compounds by oxygen; reaction mechanisms. *Mailing Add:* 3713 Orchard Dr Midland MI 48640

STROKE, GEORGE W, physical optics, see previous edition

STROKE, HINKO HENRY, b Zagreb, Yugoslavia, June 16, 27; US citizen; m 56; c 2. ATOMIC SPECTROSCOPY, NUCLEAR PHYSICS. *Educ:* Newark Col Eng, BS, 49; Mass Inst Technol, MS, 52, PhD, 54. *Prof Exp:* Consult, Atomic Instrument Co, 50; consult, Sci Translation Serv, Mass Inst Technol, 51-52; Nat Res Coun Can res fel, 54; res assoc physics, Princeton Univ, 54-57; lectr & res staff mem, Mass Inst Technol, 57-63; assoc prof, 63-68, PROF PHYSICS, NY UNIV, 68- *Concurrent Pos:* Consult, TRG, Inc, 59, Air Force, Cambridge Res Ctr, 63, Laser, Inc, Am Optical Co, 63-69 & Int Tel & Tel Fed Labs, 66; vis prof, Univ Paris, 69-70; ed, Comments Atomic & Molecular Physics, 73-, mem, Adv Ed Bd, Physica; consult, Nat Aeronaut & Space Admin, 75-76; sr fel sci, NATO, 75; vis scientist, Univ Munich, 77-78; assoc prof, Ecole Normale Superieure, Paris, 78; vis scientist, Proj Laser Res, Max Planck Inst, Garching, 79; mem, Comt Line Spectra Elements, Nat Acad Sci-Nat Res Coun; guest scientist, Alexander von Humboldt Found, Univ Munich, 81. *Honors & Awards:* Recipient Sr US Scientist Award, Alexander von Humboldt Found, 77. *Mem:* AAAS; fel Am Phys Soc; Optical Soc Am; Fr Phys Soc; Europ Phys Soc. *Res:* Hyperfine structure and isotope shifts of stable and radioactive atoms by magnetic resonance and optical spectroscopy; nuclear moments; charge and magnetization distribution; coherence in atomic radiation; solar spectra; spectroscopic instrumentation; laser systems; spectroscopy, radiative collisions. *Mailing Add:* Dept of Physics NY Univ New York NY 10003

STROM, E(DWIN) THOMAS, b Des Moines, Iowa, June 11, 36; m 58; c 2. PHYSICAL ORGANIC CHEMISTRY, GEOCHEMISTRY. *Educ:* Univ Iowa, BS, 58; Univ Calif, Berkeley, MS, 61; Iowa State Univ, PhD(phys org chem), 64. *Prof Exp:* Res technologist, 64-67, SR RES CHEMIST, FIELD RES LAB, MOBIL RES & DEVELOP CORP, 67- *Concurrent Pos:* Vis lectr, Dallas Baptist Col, 69-70; El Centro Community Col, 70-72 & Univ Tex, Dallas, 74; adj prof, Univ Tex, Arlington, 78-79. *Mem:* Am Chem Soc. *Res:* Organic geochemistry free radicals, magnetic resonance, coal chemistry, uranium chemistry. *Mailing Add:* Mobil Res & Develop Corp Field Res Lab PO Box 900 Dallas TX 75221

STROM, GORDON H(AAKON), b St Paul, Minn, June 22, 14; m 39; c 4. AERONAUTICAL ENGINEERING. *Educ:* Univ Minn, BAeroE, 36, MS, 38, PhD, 50. *Prof Exp:* Asst aeronaut eng, Univ Minn, 36-38; stress analyst, Martin Co, Md, 38-40; from instr to assoc prof aeronaut eng, NY Univ, 40-52, prof aeronaut & astronaut, 52-76, dir wind tunnels, 44-65; PROF AEROSPACE ENG, POLYTECHNIC INST NEW YORK, 76- *Mem:* Am Soc Mech Engrs; Am Soc Eng Educ; Am Meteorol Soc; assoc fel Am Inst Aeronaut & Astronaut; Air Pollution Control Asn. *Res:* Wind tunnels; atmospheric pollution. *Mailing Add:* Dept of Aerospace Eng 333 Jay St Brooklyn NY 11201

STROM, RICHARD NELSEN, b Schenectady, NY, June 5, 42. GEOCHEMISTRY, CLAY MINERALOGY. *Educ:* Union Col, BS, 66; Univ Del, MS, 72, PhD(geol), 76. *Prof Exp:* Dep route mgr, Off Interoceanic Canal Studies, Corps Engrs, 67-69; asst prof geol, Univ Wis-Parkside, 75-77; asst prof, 77-81, ASSOC PROF GEOL, UNIV SFLA, 81- *Mem:* Sigma Xi; Soc Econ Paleontologists & Mineralogists; Geochem Soc. *Res:* Phosphate minerals and trace metal mobility; silicification and clay authigenesis. *Mailing Add:* Dept of Geol Univ of S Fla Tampa FL 33620

STROM, ROBERT GREGSON, b Long Beach, Calif, Oct 1, 33; m 55; c 1. ASTROGEOLOGY. *Educ:* Univ Redlands, BS, 55; Stanford Univ, MS, 57. *Prof Exp:* Geologist, Stand Vacuum Oil Co, 57-60; asst res geologist, Univ Calif, Berkeley, 61-63; asst prof, Lunar & Planetary Lab, 63-72, assoc prof, 72-81, PROF, PLANETARY SCI, UNIV, ARIZ, 81- *Concurrent Pos:* Mem, Apollo Lunar Oper Working Group, 68-69, Imaging Sci Team, Mariner Venus/Mercury Mission, 69-75, Lunar Sci Inst, Lunar Sci & Cartog Comn, 74-79, NASA Comet Working Group, Jet Propulsion Lab Jupiter Orbiter Sci Working Group & NASA Mercury Geol Mapping Prog, 75-78; rep, Planetary Prog, Jet Propulsion Lab Imaging Syst Instrument Develop Prog, 75-79; mem, NASA Venus Orbital Imaging Radar Sci Working Group, Jet Propulsion Lab, 77-78, assoc mem, Voyager Imaging Sci Team, 78-; mem, NASA Planetary Geol Working Group, 80- & NASA Planetary Geol Rev Panel, 80- *Honors & Awards:* Pub Serv Group Achievement Award Mariner 10 TV Exp, NASA, 74. *Mem:* Am Geophys Union; Int Astron Union; Am Astron Soc. *Res:* Lunar and planetary geology; origin and evolution of lunar and planetary surfaces; space craft imaging of planetary surfaces. *Mailing Add:* Dept of Planetary Sci Univ of Ariz Tucson AZ 85721

STROM, ROBERT MICHAEL, b Detroit, Mich, Aug 6, 51; m 74. ORGANIC CHEMISTRY, PHOTOCHEMISTRY. *Educ:* Grand Valley State Col, BS, 74; Univ Colo, PhD(org chem), 78. *Prof Exp:* Res asst org photochem, Univ Colo, 74-78; res chemist synthetic org chem, Arapahoe Chem Inc, 78-80; CHEMIST, DOW CHEM CORP, 80- *Mem:* Am Chem Soc. *Res:* Synthetic organic chemistry; physical organic photochemistry; process development of aromatic and heterocyclic synthesis; determination of structural features of short lived ground and excited state intermediates. *Mailing Add:* Dow Chem Corp 1776 Bldg CR Chem Processes Div 840 Midland MI 48640

STROM, STEPHEN, astronomy, astrophysics, see previous edition

STROMAN, DAVID WOMACK, b Corpus Christi, Tex, June 1, 44; m 65; c 1. FERMENTATION PRODUCTS. *Educ:* Bethany Nazarene Col, BS, 66; Univ Okla, PhD(biochem), 70. *Prof Exp:* NIH fel microbiol, Sch Med, Washington Univ, 70-72; res scientist antibiotic discovery & develop, Upjohn Co, 72-81; SR RES SCIENTIST BIOTECHNOL, PHILLIPS PETROL CO, 81- *Mem:* Am Chem Soc; Am Soc Microbiol. *Res:* Molecular biology and biochemical genetics with emphasis on fermentation derived products especially involving recombinant DNA technology. *Mailing Add:* Biotechnol PRC Phillips Petrol Co Bartlesville OK 74004

STROMATT, ROBERT WELDON, b Muskogee, Okla, Mar 27, 29; m 56; c 3. ANALYTICAL CHEMISTRY. *Educ:* Emporia State Teachers Col, BS, 54; Kans State Univ, PhD(chem), 58. *Prof Exp:* Res chemist, Hanford Labs, Gen Elec Co, 57-66; sr res scientist, Pac Northwest Lab, Battelle Mem Inst, 66-70; FEL SCIENTIST, WESTINGHOUSE-HANFORD, 70- *Mem:* Am Chem Soc; Sigma Xi. *Res:* Electroanalytical chemistry and general methods development. *Mailing Add:* 411 Franklin Richland WA 99352

STROMBERG, KARL ROBERT, b Modoc, Ind, Dec 1, 31; m 68; c 3. MATHEMATICS. *Educ:* Univ Ore, BA, 53, MA, 54; Univ Wash, PhD(math), 58. *Prof Exp:* Res assoc & Off Naval Res fel math, Yale Univ, 58-59; res lectr, Univ Chicago, 59-60; from asst prof to assoc prof, Univ Ore, 60-68; PROF MATH, KANS STATE UNIV, 68- *Concurrent Pos:* Vis prof, Uppsala Univ, Sweden, 66-67; vis res prof, Univ York, Eng, 74-75. *Mem:* Am Math Soc; Math Asn Am. *Res:* Measure and integration theory; real variable theory; harmonic analysis; topological groups; functional analysis. *Mailing Add:* Dept of Math Kans State Univ Manhattan KS 66506

STROMBERG, KURT, b Albuquerque, NMex, Mar 3, 39. PATHOLOGY. *Educ:* Amherst Col, BA, 61; Univ Colo, MD, 66; Am Bd Path, dipl, 74. *Prof Exp:* Intern path, Yale-New Haven Hosp, 66-67; res assoc, Nat Cancer Inst, 68-72; resident path, Columbia Univ, 72-74; mem res staff, Inst Cancer Res, Delafield Hosp, New York, 72-74; STAFF INVESTR, NAT CANCER INST, 72- *Mem:* Am Asn Cancer Res. *Res:* Viral oncology. *Mailing Add:* Lab Viral Carcinogenesis Bldg 560 Rm 21 80 Frederick Cancer Res Ctr Frederick MD 21701

STROMBERG, LAWAYNE ROLAND, b Minneapolis, Minn, Nov 18, 29; m 54; c 3. SURGERY, NUCLEAR MEDICINE. *Educ:* Univ Calif, Berkeley, BA, 51; Univ Calif, Los Angeles, MD, 55; Univ Rochester, MS, 63. *Prof Exp:* Intern & resident gen surg, Sch Med, Univ Calif, Los Angeles, 55-58, resident, Vet Admin Hosp, Los Angeles, 58-60; cmndg officer & surgeon, 11th Evacuation Hosp, Korea, US Army, 61-62, nuclear med res officer, Walter Reed Army Inst Res, 65-68, cmndg officer, US Army Nuclear Med Res Detachment, Europe, Landstuhl, Ger, 68-71, dep dir & dir, Armed Forces Radiobiol Res Inst, Nat Naval Med Ctr, 68-77; assoc med dir, 77-80, VPRES

MED AFFAIRS, TRAVENOL LABS, INC, 80- *Concurrent Pos:* Res fel radiation biol, Walter Reed Army Inst Res, 63-65. *Res:* Effect of radiation on response to trauma. *Mailing Add:* Travenol Labs Inc One Baxter Pkwy Deerfield IL 60015

STROMBERG, MELVIN WILLARD, b Quamba, Minn, Nov 2, 25; m 48; c 6. GROSS ANATOMY, NEUROANATOMY. *Educ:* Univ Minn, BS, 53, DVM, 54, PhD(vet anat), 57. *Prof Exp:* Asst vet anat, Univ Minn, 53-54, from instr to assoc prof, 54-60; assoc prof, 60-62, head dept, 63-81, PROF VET ANAT, PURDUE UNIV, WEST LAFAYETTE, 62- *Concurrent Pos:* NIH spec fel anat, Karolinska Inst, Sweden, 70-71; adj prof, Ind Univ Sch Med, Indianapolis, 75; vis prof, Univ Munich Sch Med, WGer, 78-79. *Mem:* Am Asn Vet Anat (pres, 66-67); Am Asn Anat; World Asn Vet Anat. *Res:* Histology of dolphin skin; neuroanatomy of domestic animals; acupuncture. *Mailing Add:* Dept Anat Sch Vet Med Purdue Univ West Lafayette IN 47906

STROMBERG, ROBERT REMSON, b Buffalo, NY, Feb 2, 25. POLYMER SCIENCE. *Educ:* Univ Buffalo, BA, 48, PhD(phys chem), 51. *Prof Exp:* Asst phys chem, Univ Buffalo, 48-50; phys chemist, Nat Bur Standards, 51-62, chief phys chem br, Off Saline Water, 62, phys chemist, 62-67, chief polymer interface sect, 67-75, dep chief polymers div, 69-76; actg assoc dir device res & testing, Bur Med Devices, Food & Drug Admin, 76-80; HEAD BIOCHEM ENG SECT, BIOMED ENG LAB, AM RED CROSS, 80- *Concurrent Pos:* Chmn, Gordon Res Conf Sci Adhesion, 66; US Dept Com fel sci & technol, 75-76. *Mem:* Soc Biomaterials; Am Chem Soc; Am Asn Blood Banks. *Res:* Polymer and blood protein; surface interactions; surface chemistry; blood plasma separations; effect of flow on cultured endothelial cells. *Mailing Add:* Biomed Eng Lab Am Red Cross Blood Serv 9312 Old Georgetown Rd Bethesda MD 20814

STROMBERG, THORSTEN FREDERICK, b Aberdeen, Wash, Aug 13, 36. LOW TEMPERATURE PHYSICS. *Educ:* Reed Col, BA, 58; Iowa State Univ, PhD(physics), 65. *Prof Exp:* Res fel, Los Alamos Sci Lab, 65-67; asst prof, 67-74, ASSOC PROF PHYSICS, N MEX STATE UNIV, 74- *Mem:* Am Phys Soc. *Res:* Thermal and magnetic properties of superconductors, particularly type-II superconducting materials. *Mailing Add:* Dept of Physics NMex State Univ Las Cruces NM 88001

STROMBORG, KENNETH LEE, b Harvey, Ill, March 3, 47; m 66; c 2. WILDLIFE TOXICOLOGY, POPULATION MANAGEMENT. *Educ:* Univ Ill, Urbana, BS, 68; Mich State Univ, MS, 70, PhD(fisheries & wildlife), 75. *Prof Exp:* Asst prof wildlife mgt, Tex Tech Univ, 75-77; RES ZOOLOGIST, US FISH & WILDLIFE SERV, 77- *Mem:* Wildlife Soc. *Res:* Ecological and toxicological effects of environmental contaminants on wildlife populations; ecology and management of avian and furbearer wildlife populations. *Mailing Add:* 12423 Sarah Lane Bowie MD 20715

STROMBOTNE, RICHARD L(AMAR), b Watertown, SDak, May 6, 33; m 52; c 4. ENERGY CONVERSION, ATOMIC PHYSICS. *Educ:* Pomona Col, BA, 55; Univ Calif, Berkeley, MA, 57, PhD(physics), 62. *Prof Exp:* Res assoc nuclear magnetic resonance, Univ Calif, Berkeley, 59-61; physicist, Radio Stand Lab, US Nat Bur Standards, 61-68; physicist, 68-71, asst for phys sci, 71-73, chief, Energy & Environ Div, 73-78, DIR, OFF AUTO FUEL ECON STANDARDS, US DEPT TRANSP, 78- *Mem:* AAAS; Soc Automotive Engrs; Am Phys Soc; NY Acad Sci; Sr Exec Asn. *Res:* Automotive fuel economy; energy requirements of transportation systems; environmental effects of high-altitude aircraft fleets; air pollution associated with transportation; measurement of fine structure of singly ionized helium; longitudinal spin-spin relaxation in low fields. *Mailing Add:* Nat Hwy Traffic Safety Admin 400 Seventh St SW Washington DC 20590

STROME, DAVID HALL, b Schenectady, NY, Aug 31, 47. PHYSICS. *Educ:* Kalamazoo Col, BA, 69; Lehigh Univ, MS, 71, PhD(physics), 78. *Prof Exp:* RES SCIENTIST PHYSICS, ADVAN TECHNOL CTR, VOUGHT CORP, 77- *Mem:* Am Phys Soc. *Res:* Infrared optics. *Mailing Add:* Advan Technol Ctr PO Box 6144 Dallas TX 75266

STROME, FORREST C, JR, b Kalamazoo, Mich, May 19, 24; m 45; c 2. LASERS, INFORMATION RECORDING. *Educ:* Univ Ill, BS, 45; Univ Mich, MS, 48, PhD(physics), 54. *Prof Exp:* Test engr, Gen Elec Co, 46-47; proj physicist, Apparatus & Optical Div, 53-60, sr res physicist, Res Labs, 60-68, RES ASSOC, EASTMAN KODAK CO, 68- *Mem:* Am Phys Soc; Optical Soc Am. *Res:* Information recording using lasers. *Mailing Add:* Eastman Kodak Res Labs Kodak Park Rochester NY 14650

STROMER, MARVIN HENRY, b Readlyn, Iowa, Sept 1, 36; m 60; c 1. CELL BIOLOGY, BIOCHEMISTRY. *Educ:* Iowa State Univ, BS(animal sci) & BS(agr educ), 59, PhD(cell biol), 66. *Prof Exp:* Foreman prod develop, George A Hormel & Co, Minn, 59-62; res asst biochem, Iowa State Univ, 62-66; fel, Mellon Inst, 66-68; assoc prof, 68-76, PROF, IOWA STATE UNIV, 76- *Concurrent Pos:* Humboldt fel, 74; vis scientist, Max Planck Inst Med Res, Heidelberg, WGer, 74-75; vis prof, Univ Ariz, 79-80. *Mem:* Electron Micros Soc Am; Am Heart Asn; Am Soc Cell Biol; Biophys Soc. *Res:* Ultrastructure and biochemistry of striated and smooth muscle and other movement systems. *Mailing Add:* Dept of Animal Sci Iowa State Univ Ames IA 50011

STROMINGER, NORMAN LEWIS, b New York, NY, June 1, 34; m 57; c 3. NEUROANATOMY. *Educ:* Univ Chicago, AB, 55, BS, 56, PhD(biopsychol), 61. *Prof Exp:* Trainee neuroanat, Columbia Univ, 62-65; from asst prof to assoc prof, 65-74, PROF ANAT, ALBANY MED COL, 74- *Mem:* AAAS; Am Asn Anat; Soc Neurosci. *Res:* Psychophysiological and neuroanatomical studies of auditory and motor systems. *Mailing Add:* Dept of Anat Albany Med Col Albany NY 12208

STROMMEN, DENNIS PATRICK, b Milwaukee, Wis, Sept 2, 38; m 68. INORGANIC CHEMISTRY, SPECTROSCOPY. *Educ:* Wis State Univ-Whitewater, BA, 66; Cornell Univ, PhD(chem), 71. *Prof Exp:* Res assoc spectros, Ctr Mat Res, Univ Md, 70-71; asst prof, 71-76, ASSOC PROF CHEM, CARTHAGE COL, 76- *Concurrent Pos:* Vis prof, Univ Ore, 78-80. *Mem:* Soc Appl Spectros; Am Chem Soc; Coblentz Soc. *Res:* Characterization of compounds through vibrational analysis, especially with regard to their Raman spectra; isolation of reactive molecular species in frozen gas matrices. *Mailing Add:* Dept of Chem Carthage Col Kenosha WI 53140

STROM-OLSEN, JOHN OLAF, UK & Can citizen. SOLID STATE PHYSICS. *Educ:* Cambridge Univ, PhD(physics), 66. *Prof Exp:* ASSOC PROF PHYSICS, MCGILL UNIV, 67- *Mem:* Am Phys Soc. *Res:* Metallic glasses. *Mailing Add:* Rutherford Physics Bldg McGill Univ 3600 University St Montreal PQ H3A 2T8 Can

STROMSTA, COURTNEY PAUL, b Muskegon, Mich, Apr 25, 22; m 50; c 2. SPEECH PATHOLOGY, AUDIOLOGY. *Educ:* Western Mich Univ, BS, 48; Ohio State Univ, MA, 51, PhD(speech & hearing sci), 56. *Prof Exp:* Audiol trainee, Vet Admin-Walter Reed Hosp & New York City Regional Off, 51; dir speech & hearing clin, ECarolina Univ, 54-56; prof speech & hearing sci, Ohio State Univ, 56-68; PROF SPEECH & HEARING SCI, WESTERN MICH UNIV, 68- *Concurrent Pos:* Nat Inst Neurol Dis & Blindness res grant, Ohio State Univ, 57-67 & US Off Educ res grant, 65-67; NIH spec res fel, Karolinska Inst, Sweden, 71-72; consult, Electronic Teaching Labs, Washington, DC, 61-65; guest prof, Univ Zagreb, 65-66. *Mem:* AAAS; Am Speech & Hearing Asn; Acoust Soc Am. *Res:* Cybernetic relationship of speech and hearing with emphasis on stuttering and acoustically-impaired children; effects of shaping acoustical signals on perception of speech by hearing impaired children. *Mailing Add:* Dept of Speech Path & Audiol Western Mich Univ Kalamazoo MI 49008

STRONCK, DAVID RICHARD, science education, see previous edition

STRONG, ALAN EARL, b Boston, Mass, May 30, 41; m 66; c 2. REMOTE SENSING, EARTH SATTLELITES. *Educ:* Kalamazoo Col, BA, 63; Univ Mich, MS, 65, PhD(oceanog), 68. *Prof Exp:* RES OCEANOGR-METEOROLOGIST, NAT ENVIRON SATELLITE SERV, NAT OCEANIC & ATMOSPHERIC ADMIN, 68- *Mem:* AAAS; Am Meteorol Soc; Am Geophys Union; Int Asn Gt Lakes Res; Sigma Xi. *Res:* Lake and sea breezes, air-sea interface; marine meteorology; develop applications of earth satellite data to oceanography; remote sensing-infrared microwave, visible; sea surface temperature measurements by satellite; ocean color measurements by satellite. *Mailing Add:* Nat Environ Satellite Serv NOAA-WWB Rm 810 Suitland MD 20233

STRONG, CAMERON GORDON, b Vegreville, Alta, Sept 18, 34; m 59; c 2. INTERNAL MEDICINE, NEPHROLOGY. *Educ:* Univ Alta, MD, 58; McGill Univ, MS, 66. *Prof Exp:* Resident internal med & path, Queens Hosp, Honolulu, 59-61; resident internal med, Mayo Grad Sch Med, 61-64; from instr to assoc prof, 67-77, chmn, Div Nephrology , 73-78, PROF MED, MAYO MED SCH, 77-, CONSULT, DIV NEPHROLOGY & INTERNAL MED, MAYO CLIN & FOUND, 66-, CHMN, DIV HYPERTENSION, 77- *Concurrent Pos:* Fel nephrology, Hotel Dieu Montreal, 64-66; res assoc hypertension, Dept Physiol, Univ Mich, Ann Arbor, 66-67; fel, Am Heart Asn, Coun High Blood Pressure Res, 71-; fel Am Heart Asn. *Mem:* Fel Am Col Physicians; fel Am Col Cardiol. *Res:* Hypertension; renal disease; vascular smooth muscle physiology; prostaglandins; renin-angiotensin system. *Mailing Add:* Div Nephrology & Internal Med Mayo Clin Rochester MN 55901

STRONG, DONALD RAYMOND, JR, b Chelsea, Mass, May 22, 44; m 75. ECOLOGY, ENTOMOLOGY. *Educ:* Univ Calif, Santa Barbara, BA, 66; Univ Ore, PhD(biol), 71. *Prof Exp:* Res fel pop biol, Univ Chicago, 71-72; asst prof, 72-75, ASSOC PROF BIOL, FLA STATE UNIV, 75- *Mem:* Ecol Soc Am; Am Soc Naturalists; Soc Study Evolution. *Res:* Ecology of herbivorous insects; general topics in population and community ecology. *Mailing Add:* Dept of Biol Sci Fla State Univ Tallahassee FL 32306

STRONG, E(RWIN) R(AYFORD), b San Antonio, Tex, Aug 19, 19; m 50; c 3. CHEMICAL ENGINEERING. *Educ:* Tex Col Arts & Industs, BS, 40; Ill Inst Technol, MS, 45. *Prof Exp:* Engr, Lone Star Gas Co, 40-42; asst, Inst Gas Tech, Ill Inst Technol, 42-45, assoc res engr, 45-48; res engr in chg waste disposal sect, Southwest Res Inst, 48-56; chem engr, Am Oil Co, 56-62, group leader, 62-63, proj mgr, 63-70, mgr process eng, Amoco Deutschland GmbH, 70-73, sr chem engr, Amoco Europe, Inc, London, 73-74, PROJ MGR, AMOCO OIL CO, 74- *Concurrent Pos:* Mem task forces sulfur and nitrogen oxides control, mem stationary source emissions comt & mem solid waste mgt comt, Am Petrol Inst, 75- *Honors & Awards:* Judson S Swearingen Award Sci Res Achievement, Southwest Res Inst, 54. *Mem:* Am Chem Soc; Sigma Xi; Am Inst Chem Engrs. *Res:* Fuels technology; production of synthesis and distribution gases from coal and oil; industrial wastes; plant steam surveys; toxicity assays; laboratory and pilot plant treatment; superactivated sludge process; petroleum refining and petrochemical processes; desulfurization and hydrotreatment of heavy oils; air pollution control; hydrocarbon processing economics; alternate fuels and energy conversion systems. *Mailing Add:* PO Box 400 Naperville IL 60540

STRONG, FREDERICK CARL, III, b Denver, Colo, Nov 17, 17; m 41; c 2. ANALYTICAL CHEMISTRY. *Educ:* Swarthmore Col, BA, 39; Lehigh Univ, MS, 41; Bryn Mawr Col, PhD, 54. *Prof Exp:* Chief chemist, Superior Metal Co, 40-42; res chemist, Lea Mfg Co, 42-43; asst, Wesleyan Univ, 43-45; res chemist, Enthone Co, 45; instr chem, Cedar Crest Col, 45-47; asst prof, Villanova Col, 47-51; from asst prof to assoc prof chem & chem eng, Stevens Inst Technol, 51-60; prof chem & chmn dept, Inter-Am Univ PR, 60-63 & Univ Bridgeport, 63-68; prof chem, Nat Tsing Hua Univ, Taiwan, 69 & Univ El Salvador, 70-72; tech expert, UN Indust Develop Orgn, Asuncion, Paraguay, 72-73; TITULAR PROF, UNIV ESTADUAL DE CAMPINAS, BRAZIL, 73- *Concurrent Pos:* Ed-in-chief, Appl Spectros, 55-60; Leverhulme fel, Aberdeen Univ, 64-65; Fulbright-Hays lectr, Tribhuvan Univ, Nepal, 68-69. *Honors & Awards:* Medal, Soc Appl Spectros, 60. *Mem:* Fel Am Inst Chemists; Soc Appl Spectros; Am Chem Soc; Coblentz Soc; Sigma Xi. *Res:* Spectrochemical analysis; qualitative analysis; food analysis, copper complexes of carbohydrates. *Mailing Add:* Fac Eng Alimentos e Agricola Univ Estadual de Campinas Campinas SP 13100 Brazil

STRONG, HERBERT MAXWELL, b Wooster, Ohio, Sept 30, 08; m 35; c 2. HIGH PRESSURE PHYSICS, PHYSICAL OPTICS. *Educ:* Univ Toledo, BS, 30; Ohio State Univ, MS, 32, PhD(physics), 36. *Prof Exp:* Asst, Ohio State Univ, 31-35; res physicist, Bauer & Black Div, Kendall Co, Ill, 35-45 & Kendall Mills Div, Mass, 45-46; res assoc, Res Lab, Gen Elec Co, 46, physicist, Res & Develop Ctr, 46-73; RES ASSOC PHYSICS, UNION COL, NY, 73- *Concurrent Pos:* Consult, Gen Elec Res & Develop Ctr, 73-74; consult technol use of diamond, Lazar Kaplan & Sons, 73- *Honors & Awards:* Award, Soc Mfg Eng, 62; Modern Pioneers Award, Nat Asn Mfrs, 65. *Mem:* AAAS; fel Am Phys Soc; Sigma Xi. *Res:* Technological and industrial applications of diamonds; physical optical studies of rocket motor flames extreme high pressure techniques; measurements and phase equilibria; synthesis of gem diamond; synthesis of industrial diamond; measurement of temperature pressure and gas velocity in rocket motor flames by use of sodium D lines; author of over 40 publications. *Mailing Add:* 1165 Phoenix Ave Schenectady NY 12308

STRONG, IAN B, b Cohoes, NY, July 11, 30; m 60; c 1. PHYSICS, ASTRONOMY. *Educ:* Glasgow Univ, BSc, 53; Pa State Univ, PhD(physics), 63. *Prof Exp:* Mem tech staff, Bell Tel Labs, Inc, 53-55; staff mem, Ord Res Lab, 55-57; MEM STAFF, LOS ALAMOS SCI LAB, 61- *Mem:* AAAS; Am Phys Soc; Am Geophys Union; Am Astron Soc. *Res:* Acoustics, transmission through solids and liquids, ultrasonics; nuclear physics, particle detection, passage of radiation through matter, multiple scattering; astrophysics, interplanetary medium, high energy astronomy; history; philosophy; sociology of science. *Mailing Add:* PO Box 1663 Los Alamos NM 87545

STRONG, JACK PERRY, b Birmingham, Ala, Apr 27, 28; m 51; c 4. PATHOLOGY. *Educ:* Univ Ala, BS, 48; La State Univ, MD, 51; Am Bd Path, dipl, 57 & 58. *Prof Exp:* Intern, Jefferson Hillman Hosp, Birmingham, Ala, 51-52; asst, 52-53, from instr to assoc prof, 55-64, PROF PATH, SCH MED, UNIV NEW ORLEANS, 64-, HEAD DEPT, 66-, BOYD PROF, 80- *Concurrent Pos:* USPHS fel, 57; consult, Southwest Found Res & Educ, 54-55; sabbatical leave, Social Med Res Unit, Med Res Coun, London, Eng, 62-63; mem path A study sect, USPHS, 65-69, chmn, 67-69; mem sci adv bd consult, Armed Forces Inst Path, 71-; mem coun arteriosclerosis, Am Heart Asn; mem epidemiol & biomet adv comt, Nat Heart & Lung Inst, NIH, 71-78 & Panel on the Geochem of Water in Relation to Cardiovasc Dis, US Nat Comt Geochem, Nat Acad Sci, 76-79. *Mem:* Am Asn Path & Bact (asst secy, 59-62); Am Soc Exp Path; Am Soc Clin Path; Col Am Path; Int Acad Path (vpres, 77, pres, 78). *Res:* Pathology of cardiovascular diseases; atherosclerosis in the human and the experimental animal and in primates; epidemiology; geographic pathology and pathogenesis of atherosclerosis; geographic pathology of cancer. *Mailing Add:* Dept of Path La State Univ Med Ctr 1901 Perdido St New Orleans LA 70112

STRONG, JERRY GLENN, b Dawson, NMex, Nov 12, 41; m 71. PESTICIDE CHEMISTRY. *Educ:* Austin Col, BA, 63; Northwestern Univ, PhD(org chem), 68. *Prof Exp:* Sr res chemist, 68-76, assoc, 76-78, res assoc & mgr pesticide synthetics, 77-79, MGR PESTICIDE DEVELOP, MOBIL CHEM CO, 79- *Mem:* Am Chem Soc. *Res:* Synthesis and development of new crop chemicals. *Mailing Add:* Mobil Chem Co PO Box 26683 Richmond VA 23261

STRONG, JOHN (DONOVAN), b Riverdale, Kans, Jan 15, 05; m 28; c 2. PHYSICS. *Educ:* Univ Kans, AB, 26; Univ Mich, MS, 28, PhD(physics), 30. *Hon Degrees:* DSc, Southwestern at Memphis, 62 & Univ Mass, 81. *Prof Exp:* Instr chem, Univ Kans, 25-27; instr physics, Univ Mich, 27-29, asst investr eng res, 29-30; Nat Res Coun fel physics, Calif Inst Technol, 30-32, fel, Astrophys Observ, 32-37, asst prof physics, 37-42; spec fel, Harvard Univ, 42-45; prof exp physics & dir, Lab Astrophys & Phys Meteorol, Johns Hopkins Univ, 45-67; prof, 67-75, EMER PROF PHYSICS & ASTRON, UNIV MASS, AMHERST, 75- *Concurrent Pos:* Consult, Libbey-Owens-Ford Glass Co, Ohio & Farrand Optic Co, NY. *Honors & Awards:* Longstreth & Levy Medals, Franklin Inst; Ives Medal, Optical Soc Am, 59; Gold Medal, Soc Photo-Optical Instrument Engrs, 77; Hasler Award, Pittsburgh Conf, 81. *Mem:* Fel Am Phys Soc; fel Optical Soc Am (pres, 59); fel Am Acad Arts & Sci; corresp mem Royal Belg Soc Sci; Int Acad Astronaut. *Res:* Experimental physics; evaporation in vacuum; infrared spectroscopy; meteorology; optics; astrophysical observations from high altitudes. *Mailing Add:* Dept of Phys & Astron Univ Mass Astron Res Facility Amherst MA 01003

STRONG, JUDITH ANN, b Cooperstown, NY, June 19, 41. PHYSICAL CHEMISTRY. *Educ:* State Univ NY Albany, BS, 63; Brandeis Univ, MA, 66, PhD(phys chem), 70. *Prof Exp:* Asst prof, 69-73, actg chairperson, 77-78, ASSOC PROF CHEM, MOORHEAD STATE UNIV, 73- *Mem:* Am Chem Soc. *Res:* Nonaqueous solutions; computer applications in chemical education. *Mailing Add:* Dept of Chem Moorhead State Univ Moorhead MN 56560

STRONG, LAURENCE EDWARD, b Kalamazoo, Mich, Sept 3, 14; m 38; c 4. PHYSICAL CHEMISTRY. *Educ:* Kalamazoo Col, AB, 36; Brown Univ, PhD(chem), 40. *Prof Exp:* Asst phys chem, Harvard Med Sch, 40-41, res assoc, 41-43, assoc dir pilot plant, 43-46; from assoc prof to prof chem, Kalamazoo Col, 46-52; head dept, 52-65, prof chem, 52-79, RES PROJ MEM, EARLHAM COL, 79- *Concurrent Pos:* Dir, UNESCO Pilot Proj, Asia, 65-66; vis prof chem, Macquarie Univ, Australia, 71-72. *Honors & Awards:* SAMA Award for Chem Educ, Am Chem Soc, 71. *Mem:* Fel AAAS; Am Chem Soc; Sigma Xi. *Res:* Electrical properties of solutions; fractionation of proteins; thermodynamics of acid ionization. *Mailing Add:* Dept Chem Earlham Col Richmond IN 47374

STRONG, LOUISE CONNALLY, b San Antonio, Tex, Apr 23, 44; m 70; c 2. HUMAN GENETICS, CANCER. *Educ:* Univ Tex, Austin, BA, 66; Univ Tex Med Br Galveston, MD, 70. *Prof Exp:* Fel med genetics, Tex Res Inst Ment Sci & Univ Tex Grad Sch Biomed Sci Houston, 70-72, res assoc cancer genetics, 72-73; asst prof, 73-78, ASSOC GENETICIST & ASSOC PROF PEDIAT & BIOL, UNIV TEX HEALTH SCI CTR HOUSTON, 79-; DIR MED GENETICS CLIN, UNIV TEX SYST CANCER CTR, M D ANDERSON HOSP & TUMOR INST, HOUSTON, 73- *Concurrent Pos:* Mem adv comt, Clearinghouse Environ Carcinogens, Data Eval/Risk Assessment Subcomt, NIH-Nat Cancer Inst, 76-80 & Nat Comt Cancer Prev, Am Cancer Soc, 78- *Mem:* Am Soc Human Genetics; AAAS. *Res:* Clinical cancer genetics; etiology and epidemiology of cancer. *Mailing Add:* Univ Tex Syst Cancer Ctr 6723 Bertner Houston TX 77030

STRONG, MERVYN STUART, b Kells, Ireland, Jan 28, 24; nat US; m 50; c 2. OTOLARYNGOLOGY. *Educ:* Trinity Col, Dublin, BA, 45; Univ Dublin, MD, 47; FRCS(I), 49; FRCS (Eng), 50. *Prof Exp:* Registr otolaryngol, Royal Infirmary, Edinburgh, 49-50; instr, 52-56, PROF OTOLARYNGOL, SCH MED, BOSTON UNIV, 56- *Concurrent Pos:* Fel otolaryngol, Lahey Clin, Boston, 50-52; asst, Boston Univ Hosp, 52-56, chief serv, 56-; chief otolaryngol, Boston Vet Admin Hosp, 65- *Mem:* Fel Am Soc Head & Neck Surg; AMA; fel Am Col Surgeons; Soc Univ Otolaryngol (pres, 73-74); fel Am Acad Opthal & Otolaryngol. *Res:* Multicentric origins of carcinoma of oral cavity and pharynx. *Mailing Add:* 75 E Newton St Boston MA 02118

STRONG, ROBERT LYMAN, b Hemet, Calif, May 30, 28; m 51; c 4. PHYSICAL CHEMISTRY. *Educ:* Univ Calif, BS, 50; Univ Wis, PhD(chem), 54. *Prof Exp:* Res fel chem, Nat Res Coun Can, 54-55; from asst prof to assoc prof phys chem, 55-62, PROF PHYS CHEM, RENSSELAER POLYTECH INST, 62- *Concurrent Pos:* NSF sci faculty fel, 62-63. *Mem:* AAAS; Am Chem Soc. *Res:* Photochemistry and flash photolysis; atom recombination in gas and solution systems; halogen atom charge-transfer complexes; optical rotary dispersion of excited states and intermediate species in photochemical processes. *Mailing Add:* Dept of Chem Rensselaer Polytech Inst Troy NY 12181

STRONG, ROBERT MICHAEL, b Pittsburgh, Pa, Mar 12, 43. ELECTRICAL ENGINEERING. *Educ:* Villanova Univ, BEE, 65; Mass Inst Technol, MS, 66, PhD(elec eng), 70. *Prof Exp:* staff mem, Lincoln Lab, Mass Inst Technol, 69-75; lectr, Health Serv, Sch Pub Health, Harvard Univ, 75-80; MEM TECH STAFF, COMPUT ARCHIT DEPT, SPERRY RES CTR, 80- *Concurrent Pos:* Assoc med, Harvard Med Sch, 71-75. *Mem:* Inst Elec & Electronics Engrs; Asn Comput Mach. *Res:* User-computer interfaces, human factors, computer terminal architecture, data base systems, computer applications in health care research and public health. *Mailing Add:* Sperry Res Ctr 100 North Rd Sudbury MA 01776

STRONG, ROBERT STANLEY, b Sargent, Nebr, May 4, 24; m 50; c 5. ANALYTICAL CHEMISTRY. *Educ:* Cent Wash State Col, BA, 51; Ore State Univ, MS, 57; Univ of the Pac, PhD(org chem), 65. *Prof Exp:* Teacher high schs, Wash, 51-57; instr chem, Columbia Basin Col, 57-64, chmn div sci, 60-64; prof chem, Univ SDak, Springfieald, 65-73; asst prof, 73-80, ASSOC PROF CHEM, FITCHBURG STATE COL, 80- *Concurrent Pos:* Dean col, Univ SDak, 67-72, dir instnl res, 72-73. *Mem:* Am Chem Soc. *Res:* D-galactosamine and its derivatives; thin layer chromatography and its applications; chemical instrumentation. *Mailing Add:* Dept of Chem Fitchburg State Col Fitchburg MA 01420

STRONG, RONALD DEAN, b Bremerton, Wash, June 7, 36; m 59; c 2. NONDESTRUCTIVE TESTING. *Educ:* Wash State Univ, BS, 58. *Prof Exp:* Engr, Boeing Co, 59-61; nondestructive testing engr, Aerojet-Gen Corp, 61-66; MEM STAFF NONDESTRUCTIVE TESTING ENG, LOS ALAMOS SCI LAB, UNIV CALIF, 66- *Mem:* Am Soc Nondestructive Testing. *Res:* Investigation of ultrasonic techniques for materials evaluations and implementation of techniques in actual test situations. *Mailing Add:* Los Alamos Sci Lab PO Box 1663 Los Alamos NM 87545

STRONG, RUDOLPH GREER, b Utica, Miss, Nov 5, 24; m 58; c 4. ENTOMOLOGY. *Educ:* Miss State Univ, BS, 46, MS, 48; Cornell Univ, PhD(econ entom), 56. *Prof Exp:* Asst & instr zool & entom, Miss State Univ, 46-49; from asst entomologist to assoc entomologist, Agr Exten Serv, La State Univ, 49-51; tech & sales rep, Stauffer Chem Co, 51-52; asst entom, Cornell Univ, 53-56; from asst entomologist to assoc entomolgist, 56-62, ENTOMOLOGIST, UNIV CALIF, RIVERSIDE, 75- *Mem:* Entom Soc Am. *Res:* Biology, ecology and prevention of stored-product insects and other urban-industrial pests; insecticide development. *Mailing Add:* Dept of Entom Univ of Calif Riverside CA 92521

STRONG, WALKER ALBERT, b Baltimore, Md, Apr 3, 18; m 61; c 3. CHEMISTRY. *Educ:* Dickinson Col, BS, 40; Pa State Univ, MS, 42, PhD(org chem), 44. *Prof Exp:* Res asst, Univ Ill, 44-46; res chemist, Wm S Merrell Co, Ohio, 46-47; sr res chemist, 47-64, admin asst to dir res, 64-71, SR RES CHEMIST, CHEM DIV, PPG INDUSTS, INC, 71- *Mem:* Am Chem Soc. *Res:* Organo-silicon compounds; streptomycin and other antibiotics; organic sulfur and chlorine compounds; phosgene derivatives; peroxycarbonates; polyurethanes; peroxide stabilization; agricultural chemicals; stone-scripts resembling ancient Phoenician found in Pennsylvania. *Mailing Add:* Tech Ctr Chem Div PPG Indust Inc Barberton OH 44203

STRONG, WILLIAM J, b Idaho Falls, Idaho, Jan 1, 34; m 59; c 6. ACOUSTICS. *Educ:* Brigham Young Univ, BS, 58, MS, 59; Mass Inst Technol, PhD(physics), 64. *Prof Exp:* From asst prof to assoc prof, 67-76, PROF PHYSICS, BRIGHAM YOUNG UNIV, 76- *Mem:* Fel Acoust Soc Am; Inst Elec & Electronic Engr. *Res:* Physics of musical instruments; analysis and synthesis of instrumental tones and of speech; machine synthesis of speech. *Mailing Add:* Dept of Physics Brigham Young Univ Provo UT 84602

STRONGIN, MYRON, b New York, NY, July 27, 36; m 57; c 2. LOW TEMPERATURE PHYSICS, SURFACE PHYSICS. *Educ:* Rensselaer Polytech Inst, BS, 56; Yale Univ, MS, 57, PhD(physics), 62. *Prof Exp:* Mem staff, Lincoln Labs, Mass Inst Technol, 61-63; from asst physicist to assoc physicist, 63-67, physicist, 67-74, SR PHYSICIST, BROOKHAVEN NAT LAB, 74- *Concurrent Pos:* Adj prof, City Univ New York. *Mem:* Fel Am Phys Soc. *Res:* Properties of superconducting materials; analysis of surfaces and influence of surfaces on superconducting properties; epitaxy of films and superconductivity of films; hydrogen on surfaces. *Mailing Add:* Physics Dept Brookhaven Nat Lat Upton NY 11973

STROP, HANS R, b Bandoeng, Dutch East Indies, Oct 26, 31; US citizen. MECHANICAL & SYSTEMS ENGINEERING. *Educ:* Delft Univ Technol, Ir, 58. *Prof Exp:* Res engr, Nuclear Reactor Lab, N V Kema, Holland, 59-60; sr develop engr, Transitron Electronic Corp, 60-61; res engr, Mats Res Lab, Tyco Inc, 61-62; systs engr, Gen Atomics Div, Gen Dynamics Corp, 62-63; sr develop engr, RCA Corp, 63-64; systs engr, Monsanto Res Corp, 64-70; dir res, 70-78, vpres res & eng, Anderson Ibec Div, Ibec Industs Inc, 78-80, SR VPRES MKT & SALES, ANDERSON INT CORP, 80- *Mem:* Am Nuclear Soc; Am Mgt Asn; Am Inst Aeronaut & Astronaut; Am Inst Chem Engrs; Neth Royal Inst Eng. *Res:* Research and development related to chemical, polymer, food and feed processing equipment and to chemical processes. *Mailing Add:* 12418 The Bluffs Strongsville OH 44136

STROSBERG, ARTHUR MARTIN, b Albany, NY, Sept 16, 40; m 73; c 2. PHARMACOLOGY. *Educ:* Siena Col, NY, BS, 62; Univ Calif, San Francisco, PhD(pharmacol), 70. *Prof Exp:* Pharmacologist, 70-72, sect head cardiovasc pharmacol, 72-75, PRIN SCIENTIST, SYNTEX RES, 75- *Mem:* AAAS; Am Soc Pharmacol & Exp Therapeut; Sigma Xi. *Res:* Cardiovascular pharmacology, cardiotonic agents, antianginal agents, antihypertensive agents; antiarrhythmic agents; contractile properties of cardiac muscle; cardiac muscle contraction mechanisms, cardiac muscle ultrastructure and oscillations. *Mailing Add:* Dept Exp Pharmacol Syntex Res Stanford Indust Park Palo Alto CA 94304

STROSCIO, MICHAEL ANTHONY, b Winston-Salem, NC, June 1, 49; m 70; c 2. PHYSICS. *Educ:* Univ NC, Chapel Hill, BS, 70; Yale Univ, MPhil, 72, PhD(physics), 74. *Prof Exp:* Physicist space sci, Air Force Cambridge Res Labs, 74-75; physicist staff mem, Los Alamos Sci Lab, 75-78; SR STAFF PHYSICIST, APPL PHYSICS LAB, JOHNS HOPKINS UNIV, 78- *Concurrent Pos:* Instr, Middlesex Community Col, 74-75; res grant, Los Alamos Sci Lab, 77. *Mem:* Am Phys Soc; Am Geophys Union. *Res:* Hydrodynamics; plasma physics; space physics; atomic physics. *Mailing Add:* Johns Hopkins Appl Physics Lab Johns Hopkins Rd Laurel MD 20810

STROSHANE, RONALD MICHAEL, b Ashland, Wis, May 20, 48; m 70; c 2. ORGANIC CHEMISTRY. *Educ:* Univ Wis-Madison, BS, 70; Univ Ill, Urbana, MS, 72, PhD(org chem), 76. *Prof Exp:* Res assoc chem, Univ Wis, 75-77; fel, 77-78, scientist chem, Litton Bionetics, 78-80, HEAD, CHEM SECT, FREDERICK CANCER RES FAC, 80- *Concurrent Pos:* Alfred Sloan Found scholar; NIH resident trainee biophys chem. *Mem:* Am Chem Soc; Am Soc Microbiol; Am Soc Qual Control. *Res:* Fermentation products research; biosynthesis of natural products; assay development for fermentation products. *Mailing Add:* Nat Cancer Inst-Frederick Cancer Res Fac PO Box B Frederick MD 21701

STROSS, FRED HELMUT, b Alexandria, Egypt, Aug 22, 10; nat US; m 36; c 2. PHYSICAL CHEMISTRY, ARCHAEOLOGY. *Educ:* Case Inst Technol, BS, 34; Univ Calif, PhD(chem), 38. *Prof Exp:* Chemist, Shell Develop Co, 38-52, supvr res, 52-70; res asst, 70-75, GUEST SCIENTIST, LAWRENCE BERKELEY LAB, UNIV CALIF, 75-, RES ASST, 81-; GUEST SCIENTIST, LAWRENCE BERKELEY LAB, UNIV CALIF, 75- *Concurrent Pos:* Consult, Lowie Mus & Univ Art Mus, Berkeley, 70-; chmn Nat Res Coun subcomt gas chromatography group, Int Union Pure & Appl Chem; affil prof chem, Univ Washington, Seattle, 75- *Mem:* AAAS; Am Chem Soc. *Res:* Photochemistry; asphalt technology; catalytic industrial processes; physical chemistry of solids; gas chromatography; analytical physical chemistry, including applications to characterization of polymers; archaeometry, the application of physical sciences to archaeology. *Mailing Add:* 44 Oak Dr Orinda CA 94563

STROSS, RAYMOND GEORGE, b St Charles, Mo, July 2, 30; m 64; c 3. ECOLOGY. *Educ:* Univ Mo, BS, 52; Univ Idaho, MS, 55; Univ Wis, PhD(zool), 58. *Prof Exp:* Res asst, Univ Wis, 54-58; NIH fel, Oceanog Inst, Woods Hole, 58-59; from asst prof to assoc prof zool, Univ Md, 59-67; ASSOC PROF ZOOL, STATE UNIV NY ALBANY, 67- *Mem:* AAAS; Sigma Xi; Ecol Soc Am; Am Soc Limnol & Oceanog; Am Soc Photobiol. *Res:* Photoecology; biological rhythms of plankton populations; biological limnology; experimental ecology; arctic ecology. *Mailing Add:* Dept of Biol Sci State Univ NY Albany NY 12222

STROTHER, ALLEN, b Sweetwater, Tex, Feb 20, 28; m 57; c 2. PHARMACOLOGY, ANIMAL SCIENCE. *Educ:* Tex Tech Col, BS, 55; Univ Calif, Davis, MS, 57; Tex A&M Univ, PhD(biochem, nutrit), 63. *Prof Exp:* Assoc animal sci, Univ Calif, Davis, 56-57; asst to trustee, Burnett Estate, Ft Worth, Tex, 58; dir nutrit res, Uncle Johnny Feed Mills, Houston, 59; res biochemist, Food & Drug Admin, DC, 63-65; from asst prof to assoc prof, 65-75, PROF PHARMACOL, SCH MED, LOMA LINDA UNIV, 75- *Mem:* Am Chem Soc; Am Soc Pharmacol & Exp Therapeut; Am Soc Animal Sci; Poultry Sci Asn. *Res:* Large and small animal nutrition; dietary energy levels; mineral requirements; drug and pesticide metabolism. *Mailing Add:* Dept of Pharmacol Loma Linda Univ Sch of Med Loma Linda CA 92354

STROTHER, GREENVILLE KASH, b Huntington, WVa, July 27, 20; m 50; c 3. BIOPHYSICS. *Educ:* Va Polytech Inst, BS, 43; George Washington Univ, MS, 54; Pa State Univ, PhD(physics), 57. *Prof Exp:* Asst prof physics, 57-61, assoc prof biophys, 61-72, PROF BIOPHYS, PA STATE UNIV, UNIVERSITY PARK, 72- *Mem:* Biophys Soc. *Res:* Microspectrophotometry of cellular systems; biophysical instrumentation. *Mailing Add:* Dept Physics 104 Davey Lab Pa State Univ University Park PA 16802

STROTHER, J(OHN) A(LAN), b Hartford, Conn, Dec 27, 27; m 51; c 3. AEROSPACE ELECTRO-OPTICS. *Educ:* Trinity Col, Conn, BS, 50; Princeton Univ, MSE, 54. *Prof Exp:* Electronic scientist, US Navy Underwater Sound Lab, 50-52; mem tech staff, RCA Labs, 54-57, group leader, RCA Defense Electronic Prod Div, RCA, 57-58, unit & prog mgr, RCA Astro-Electronics Div, 58-61; proj engr, Systs Div, EMR, Inc, 61-62, mgr instrumentation eng, Photoelec Div, 62-66; sr mem tech staff, 66-69, proj mgr, 69-73, mgr electro-optics, 73-75, staff scientist, 75-79, MGR SENSOR DESIGN, RCA ASTRO-ELECTRONICS DIV, RCA CORP, 79- *Res:* Sensing, processing and reproduction of images; speech and hearing; pattern recognition; digital signal processing; satellite systems engineering and program management. *Mailing Add:* 201 Grover Ave Princeton NJ 08540

STROTHER, WAYMAN L, b US, Apr 19, 23; div; c 2. MATHEMATICS. *Educ:* Ala State Teachers Col, BS, 43; Univ Chicago, MS, 49; Tulane Univ, PhD(math), 51. *Prof Exp:* Asst prof math, Univ Miami, 48; instr, Ill Inst Technol, 49; asst prof, Univ Ala, 51; from asst prof to assoc prof, Univ Miami, 52-59; Buckingham prof & chmn dept, Miami Univ, 59-64; head dept, 64-72, PROF MATH, UNIV MASS, AMHERST, 64- *Concurrent Pos:* Mathematician, US Naval Ord Testing Sta, Calif, 56; sr res scientist, Missile & Space Div, Lockheed Aircraft Corp, 56-59, consult, Lockheed Missile & Space Corp, 59-61. *Mem:* Am Math Soc; Math Asn Am. *Res:* Topology; applied mathematics. *Mailing Add:* Dept of Math Univ of Mass Amherst MA 01002

STROTHMANN, RUDOLPH OTTO, forestry, see previous edition

STROTTMAN, DANIEL, b Sumner, Iowa, Apr 15, 43; m 66; c 1. NUCLEAR PHYSICS. *Educ:* Univ Iowa, BA, 64; State Univ NY Stony Brook, MA, 66, PhD(physics), 69. *Prof Exp:* Niels Bohr fel nuclear physics, Niels Bohr Inst, Copenhagen, Denmark, 69-70; res officer, Oxford Univ, 70-74; asst prof physics, State Univ NY Stony Brook, 74-78; STAFF MEM, THEORY DIV, LOS ALAMOS NAT LAB, 78- *Concurrent Pos:* Vis Nordita prof, Physics Inst, Univ Oslo, 73-74. *Res:* Group theory applications; thoretical nuclear physics. *Mailing Add:* Group T-9 MS 452 Los Alamos Nat Lab Los Alamos NM 87544

STROUBE, EDWARD W, b Hopkinsville, Ky, Apr 2, 27; m 54; c 3. AGRONOMY. *Educ:* Univ Ky, BS, 51, MS, 59; Ohio State Univ, PhD(agron), 61. *Prof Exp:* Agr exten agent, Univ Ky, 54-57, res asst agron, 57-58; res asst, 58-60, from instr to assoc prof, 60-70, PROF AGRON, OHIO STATE UNIV & OHIO AGR RES & DEVELOP CTR, 70- *Mem:* Am Soc Agron; Weed Sci Soc Am. *Res:* Weed control of field crops involving the evaluations of herbicides, tillage practices, flaming and crop rotations; soil and crop residue studies involving herbicides. *Mailing Add:* Dept of Agron 1885 Neil Ave Columbus OH 43210

STROUBE, WILLIAM HUGH, b Sturgis, Ky, June 24, 24; m 50; c 3. PLANT SCIENCE. *Educ:* Murray State Col, BSA, 49; Univ Ky, MSA, 51; La State Univ, PhD(plant path), 53. *Prof Exp:* Asst plant path, La State Univ, 51-53, asst plant pathologist, 53-54; agronomist, Agr Exp Sta, Univ Ky, 55-56, assoc agronomist, 56-66, actg chmn dept agron, 65-66; asst dean col sci & technol, 69-70, assoc dean fac progs, 71-80, PROF AGR, WESTERN KY UNIV, 66- *Concurrent Pos:* Collabr, Field Crops Sect, Agr Res Serv, USDA, 52-54. *Mem:* Am Phytopath Soc; Am Soc Agron. *Res:* Crop production and management. *Mailing Add:* Dept Agr Western Ky Univ Bowling Green KY 42101

STROUD, CARLOS RAY, b Owensboro, Ky, July 9, 42; m 62; c 3. QUANTUM OPTICS. *Educ:* Centre Col Ky, AB, 63; Wash Univ, PhD(physics), 69. *Prof Exp:* Asst prof, 70-75, ASSOC PROF OPTICS, UNIV ROCHESTER, 75- *Concurrent Pos:* Sr vis scientist, Univ Sussex, Gt Brit, 79-80. *Mem:* Am Phys Soc; fel Optical Soc Am. *Res:* Foundations of quantum theory; quantum and semiclassical radiation theory; interactions of electromagnetic fields with matter; high resolution dye laser spectroscopy. *Mailing Add:* Inst of Optics Univ of Rochester Rochester NY 14627

STROUD, JACKSON SWAVELY, b Cabarrus Co, NC, June 1, 31; m 61; c 2. EXPERIMENTAL SOLID STATE PHYSICS, ENGINEERING. *Educ:* Union Col, BS, 53; Ohio State Univ, MS, 57. *Prof Exp:* Physicist, Corning Glass Works, 57-67; physicist, Bausch & Lomb, Inc, 67-79; ASST MGR, SCHOTT OPTICAL GLASS, 79- *Mem:* Am Phys Soc; Am Ceramic Soc; Optical Soc Am; Inst Elec & Electronics Engrs; Am Soc Testing & Mat. *Res:* Solid state physics with specialized knowledge of glass; radiation chemistry; glass tank design; optical properties of solids. *Mailing Add:* Schott Optical Glass 400 York Ave Duryea PA 18642

STROUD, JUNIUS BRUTUS, b Greensboro, NC, June 9, 29; m 55; c 3. ALGEBRA. *Educ:* Davidson Col, BS, 51; Univ Va, MA, 62, PhD(math), 65. *Prof Exp:* Instr math & sci, Fishburne Mil Sch, 53-57; teacher, High Sch, 57-58; from instr to assoc prof math, 60-76, PROF MATH, DAVIDSON COL, 76- *Concurrent Pos:* Vis lectr, Sec Schs, 62-63 & 65-66. *Mem:* Am Math Asn. *Res:* Simple Jordan algebras of characteristic two; finitely generated modules over a Dedekind ring. *Mailing Add:* Dept of Math Davidson Col Davidson NC 28036

STROUD, MALCOLM HERBERT, b Birmingham, Eng, May 17, 20; m 49; c 3. MEDICINE. *Educ:* Univ Birmingham, MB, ChB, 45; FRCS, 52; Am Bd Otolaryngol, dipl, 60. *Prof Exp:* From asst prof to assoc prof, 57-72, PROF MED, SCH MED, WASH UNIV, 72- *Mem:* Am Acad Ophthal & Otolaryngol. *Res:* Otology. *Mailing Add:* Dept of Otolaryngol Wash Univ Sch of Med St Louis MO 63110

STROUD, RICHARD HAMILTON, b Dedham, Mass, Apr 24, 18; m 43; c 2. ZOOLOGY. *Educ:* Bowdoin Col, BS, 39; Univ NH, MS, 42. *Prof Exp:* Asst bot, Bowdoin Col, 39; asst zool, Univ NH, 40-42; jr aquatic biologist, Tenn Valley Authority, 42, aquatic biologist, 46-48; chief aquatic biologist, Mass Dept Conserv, 49-53; asst exec vpres, Sport Fishing I, Aquatic Resources, 53-

55, exec vpres, 55-81; CONSULT, 82- *Concurrent Pos:* Consult, Calif Fish & Game Dept, 65-66, Ark Game & Fish Comn, 69, Iowa Conserv Comn, 70-71 & Tenn Valley Authority, 71-72; vpres, Sport Fishery Res Found, 62-81, trustee, 82-; mem, World Panel Fishery Experts, Food & Agr Orgn, UN, Ocean Fisheries & Law of Sea Adv Comts, Dept State; chmn, Natural Resources Coun Am, 69-71; mem, NAm Atlantic Salmon Coun & Marine Fisheries Adv Comt, Dept Com; fishery expert adv to Sen Select Comt Govt Opers; bd dir, Nat Coalition Marine Conserv, 75-81, vpres, 82- *Mem:* Am Fisheries Soc (pres-elect, 78-79); Fisheries Soc Brit Isles; Freshwater Biol Asn UK; Am Inst Fishery Res Biologists; Int Asn Fish & Wildlife Agencies. *Res:* Fish population dynamics, behavior, ecology and life history. *Mailing Add:* Consult Aquatic Resources 135 Lake Forest Dr Pinehurst NC 28374

STROUD, RICHARD KIM, b Ann Arbor, Mich, Aug 8, 43; div; c 3. VETERINARY PATHOLOGY. *Educ:* Ore State Univ, BS, 66, MS, 78; Wash State Univ, DVM, 72. *Prof Exp:* Biologist, Marine Mammal Lab, Nat Marine Fisheries Serv-Nat Ocean & Atmospheric Admin, 66-68; vet, Willamette Vet Clin, 72-73; res assoc aquatic animal path, Ore State Univ, 73-79; DIAG PATHOLOGIST, NAT WILDLIFE HEALTH LAB, MADISON, WIS, 80- *Mem:* Inst Asn Aquatic Animal Med (pres, 77-78); Wildlife Dis Asn; Am Fisheries Soc; Am Vet Med Asn. *Res:* Wildlife and aquatic animal pathology. *Mailing Add:* Vet Diag Lab Ore State Univ Corvallis OR 97331

STROUD, ROBERT CHURCH, b Oakland, Calif, Jan 5, 18; m 47. PHYSIOLOGY. *Educ:* Princeton Univ, AB, 40; Univ Rochester, MS, 50, PhD(physiol), 52. *Prof Exp:* Chemist, Calco Chem Div, Am Cyanamid Co, 40-44 & Lederle Labs Div, 44-48; instr physiol, Grad Sch Med, Univ Pa, 52-53; assoc med physiol, Brookhaven Nat Lab, 53-54; asst prof pharmacol & res assoc aviation physiol, Ohio State Univ, 54-55; asst prof physiol, Heart 55-56; supvr physiologist, US Naval Med Res Lab, 56-61; pulmonary physiologist, Occup Health Res & Training Facil, USPHS, 61-62; chief res prog mgr life sci, Ames Res Ctr, NASA, 62-64; chief sci rev sect, Health Res Facil Br, NIH, 64-69, chief health res facil br, Div Educ & Res Facil, 69-70, chief, Training Grants & Awards Br, Nat Heart, Lung & Blood Inst, 70-73, EXEC SECY, REV BR, NAT HEART, LUNG & BLOOD INST, 73- *Concurrent Pos:* Lectr, Stanford Univ, 63-64. *Honors & Awards:* Lederle Med Fac Award, 55. *Mem:* Am Physiol Soc. *Res:* Cardiopulmonary and respiratory physiology; physiology of adaptation to high altitudes and submarine environments; physiology of diving; aerospace physiology. *Mailing Add:* Nat Heart & Lung & Blood Inst Bethesda MD 20014

STROUD, ROBERT MALONE, b St Louis, Mo, Mar 12, 31; m 55; c 2. IMMUNOLOGY. *Educ:* Harvard Univ, BS, 52, MD, 56. *Prof Exp:* Intern med, Cook County Hosp, Chicago, Ill, 56-57; resident, Barnes Hosp, St Louis, Mo, 59-61; dir rheumatology, Ga Warm Springs Found, 65-66; from asst prof to assoc prof med, 66-71, ASSOC PROF MICROBIOL & PROF MED, MED SCH, UNIV ALA, BIRMINGHAM, 71- *Concurrent Pos:* USPHS fel, Med Sch, Johns Hopkins Univ, 61-63, Helen Hay Whitney fel, 63-65. *Mem:* Am Asn Immunol; Am Rheumatism Asn; Am Soc Clin Invest; Am Acad Allergy. *Res:* Complement components and their relationship to inflammation. *Mailing Add:* Div of Clin Immunol & Rheumatol Univ of Ala Med Sch Birmingham AL 35294

STROUD, ROBERT MICHAEL, b Stockport, Eng, May 24, 42. STRUCTURAL BIOLOGY. *Educ:* Cambridge Univ, BA, 64, MA, 68; London Univ, PhD(crystallog), 68. *Prof Exp:* Fel protein crystalog, Calif Inst Technol, 68-71, assoc prof chem, 75-77; PROF BIOCHEM, UNIV CALIF, SAN FRANCISCO, 77- *Concurrent Pos:* Prin investr, NIH & NSF, 71-; consult, NIH, 77-; fel, Sloan Found, 77. *Mem:* Am Crystalog Soc; Brit Biophys Soc; Am Soc Biophys Chem; Biophys Soc. *Res:* Membrane protein structure; structure and function of complex regulatory macromoleculer DNA and protein interactions; development of new methodology in macromolecular structural biology. *Mailing Add:* Univ Calif San Francisco S-960 San Francisco CA 94143

STROUD, ROBERT WAYNE, b Jonesboro, Ark, May 24, 29; m 57; c 2. TEXTILE CHEMISTRY. *Educ:* Ark Col, BS, 50; Ga Inst Technol, MSCh, 54; Univ Tex, Austin, PhD(org chem), 63. *Prof Exp:* Teacher, Pub Schs, Ark, 49-50; chemist, Carbide & Carbon Chem Co, Tex, 53-54 & 56-58; res chemist, 62-72, SR RES CHEMIST, E I DU PONT DE NEMOURS & CO, INC, 72- *Mem:* Am Chem Soc. *Res:* Textile fibers chemistry and engineering. *Mailing Add:* 188 S Crest Rd Chattanooga TN 37404

STROUD, THOMAS WILLIAM FELIX, b Toronto, Ont, Apr 7, 36; m 62; c 4. STATISTICS. *Educ:* Univ Toronto, BA, 56, MA, 60; Stanford Univ, PhD(statist), 68. *Prof Exp:* Asst prof math, Acadia Univ, 60-64; asst prof, 68-75, ASSOC PROF MATH & STATIST, QUEEN'S UNIV, ONT, 75- *Concurrent Pos:* Res asst, Sch Educ, Stanford Univ, 66-68; Nat Res Coun Can res grant, Queen's Univ, Ont, 69-; Educ Testing Serv vis res fel, Educ Testing Serv, 72-73; invited prof, Ecole Polytech Fed de Lausanne, 77-78. *Mem:* Am Statist Asn; Inst Math Statist; Statist Soc Can. *Res:* Multivariate analysis; Bayesian inference; statistical analysis of mental test data; linear models; forecasting theory and methodology. *Mailing Add:* Dept Math & Statist Queen's Univ Kingston ON K7L 3N6 Can

STROUD-LEE, F AGNES NARANJO, b Albuquerque, NMex, July 23, 22; m 50, 66; c 1. RADIATION BIOLOGY. *Educ:* Univ NMex, BS, 45; Univ Chicago, PhD, 66. *Prof Exp:* Res technician hemat, Los Alamos Sci Lab, NMex, 45-46; assoc cytologist, Argonne Nat Lab, 46-69; dir, Dept Tissue Cult, Pasadena Found Med Res, 69-70; sr res cytogeneticist, Image Processing Group, Sci Data Anal Sect, Jet Propulsion Lab, 70-75; staff cytogeneticist, Health Res Div, Los Alamos Nat Lab, 75-79; CONSULT RADIOBIOL & CYTOGENETICS, 79- *Honors & Awards:* C Morrison Prize, NY Acad Sci, 55; Dipl Hon, Pan-Am Cancer Cytol Cong, 57; NASA Cert Recognition Creative Develop Technol, 76. *Mem:* Radiation Res Soc; Am Soc Cell Biol; Biophys Soc; Tissue Cult Asn (corresp secy, 58); Sigma Xi. *Res:* Tissue culture; automation of chromosome analysis by computers; effects of radiation on animal tumors; effects of ionizing radiation in vitro and in vivo; cell kinetics; mammalian radiation biology; chromosome analysis. *Mailing Add:* 630 Carmel Rd Belen NM 87002

STROUGH, ROBERT I(RVING), b Akron, Ohio, June 22, 20; m 45; c 2. PHYSICS, ENGINEERING. *Educ:* Case Western Reserve Univ, BS, 42, MS, 48, PhD(physics), 50. *Prof Exp:* Proj engr, Airborne Instrument Lab, 42-44; develop engr, Arma Corp, 44-46; asst proj engr, Pratt & Whitney Aircraft Div, United Aircraft Corp, 50-51, reactor proj engr, 51-60, develop engr, 60-62, chief develop eng, 62-63, prog mgr SNAP-50 nuclear elec spacer powerplant proj, 63-65, chief adv concepts develop, 65-69, mgr advan mil progs, 69-76; ENG MGR ADVAN PROD, UNITED TECH CORP, 76- *Concurrent Pos:* Adj prof, Hartford Grad Ctr, Rensselaer Polytechnic Inst, 55-71; assoc dir aircraft nuclear propulsion proj, Oak Ridge Nat Lab, 54-55; mem res adv comt nuclear energy systs, NASA, 61-62. *Mem:* Am Phys Soc; Inst Elec & Electronics Engrs; Am Inst Aeronaut & Astronaut. *Res:* Management and technical direction of nuclear aircraft and spacecraft propulsion and power systems development including reactor, liquid metal and power conversion systems; engineering and design of advanced aircraft powerplants; aerothermodynamics; development of electrical machinery and electromagnetic devices. *Mailing Add:* United Tech Corp PO Box 109 South Windsor CT 06074

STROUP, R(OBERT) C(HARLES), b Niagara Falls, NY, Jan 4, 19; m 42; c 2. METALLURGY. *Educ:* Purdue Univ, BS, 40. *Prof Exp:* Control engr, 40-41, develop engr, 46-48, head, Work Control Lab, 48-50, group leader develop, 50-56, from asst develop mgr to develop mgr, 56-64, spec proj mgr, 64-65, asst dir develop, 65-67, mgr eng develop, 67-70, asst dir eng develop, 70-74, asst dir carbon fiber develop, 74-78, CORP ENG FEL, UNION CARBIDE CORP, 78- *Mem:* Am Inst Chem Engrs; Am Inst Mining, Metall & Petrol Engrs. *Res:* Carbon technology. *Mailing Add:* Parma Tech Ctr Union Carbide Corp PO Box 6616 Cleveland OH 44101

STROUSE, CHARLES EARL, b Ann Arbor, Mich, Jan 29, 44; m 72. CHEMISTRY. *Educ:* Pa State Univ, University Park, BS, 65; Univ Wis-Madison, PhD(phys chem), 69. *Prof Exp:* AEC fel, Los Alamos Sci Lab, 69-71; asst prof, 71-78, ASSOC PROF CHEM, UNIV CALIF, LOS ANGELES, 78- *Mem:* AAAS; Am Chem Soc; Am Crystallog Asn. *Res:* Structural chemistry. *Mailing Add:* Dept Chem & Biochem Univ Calif Los Angeles CA 90024

STROUT, RICHARD GOOLD, b Auburn, Maine, Nov 11, 27; m 50; c 2. ZOOLOGY, PARASITOLOGY. *Educ:* Univ Maine, BS, 50; Univ NH, MS, 54, PhD(parasitol), 61. *Prof Exp:* Instr poultry sci, 54-60, from asst prof to assoc prof, 60-68, PROF PARASITOL, UNIV NH, 68-, PARASITOLOGIST, 63- *Concurrent Pos:* Fel, Sch Med, La State Univ, 67. *Mem:* AAAS; Soc Protozoologists; Wildlife Dis Asn; Am Soc Parasitol. *Res:* In vitro culture and pathogenicity of avian coccidiosis; immunity mechanisms; blood parasites of birds and fishes. *Mailing Add:* Dept of Animal Sci Rm 404 Kendall Hall Univ of NH Durham NH 03824

STROVINK, MARK WILLIAM, b Santa Monica, Calif, July 22, 44; m 65; c 2. EXPERIMENTAL HIGH ENERGY PHYSICS. *Educ:* Mass Inst Technol, BS, 65; Princeton Univ, PhD(physics), 70. *Prof Exp:* From instr to asst prof physics, Princeton Univ, 70-73; asst prof, 73-76, assoc prof, 76-80, PROF PHYSICS, UNIV CALIF, BERKELEY, 80- *Concurrent Pos:* Vis asst prof physics, Cornell Univ, 71-72. *Res:* Muon interactions and charm production at high energy; principles of invariance to changes of energy scale and charge-parity inversion. *Mailing Add:* Lawrence Berkeley Lab 50-341 Univ Calif Berkeley CA 94720

STROZIER, JAMES KINARD, b Rock Hill, SC, May 21, 33; m 56; c 2. AEROSPACE ENGINEERING, MECHANICS. *Educ:* US Mil Acad, BS, 56; Univ Mich, Ann Arbor, MSE, 64, PhD(aerospace eng), 66. *Prof Exp:* US Army, 56-, instr mech, US Mil Acad, 64-66, asst prof, 66-67, exec officer, 1st Battalion, 92nd Artil, Vietnam, 68, systs analyst, First Field Force, 68-69, ASSOC PROF MECH, US MIL ACAD, 70- *Mem:* Am Inst Aeronaut & Astronaut; Am Soc Eng Educ. *Res:* Tellimetry; wing design; computer simulation. *Mailing Add:* Dept of Mech US Mil Acad West Point NY 10996

STROZIER, JOHN ALLEN, JR, b Miami, Fla, June 3, 34; m 62; c 3. SURFACE PHYSICS. *Educ:* Cornell Univ, BEP, 58; Univ Utah, PhD(physics), 66. *Prof Exp:* Instr physics, Univ Utah, 66-67; res assoc mat sci, Cornell Univ, 67-69; sr res assoc, State Univ NY Stony Brook, 69-71, asst prof, 71-74; physicist, Brookhaven Nat Lab, 74-80. *Mem:* Am Phys Soc. *Res:* Surface physics; low energy electron diffraction, catalysis. *Mailing Add:* 51 Dyke Rd Setauket NY 11733

STRUB, MIKE ROBERT, b Alliance, Ohio, Dec 26, 48; m 69. FOREST BIOMETRY, STATISTICS. *Educ:* Va Polytech Inst & State Univ, BS, 71, MS, 72, PhD(statist), 77. *Prof Exp:* Instr forestry, Va Polytech Inst & State Univ, 72-74; asst prof forest mgt, Pa State Univ, 75-77; FOREST BIOMETRICIAN, WEYERHAEUSER CO, 77- *Mem:* Am Statist Asn; Biometrics Soc; Soc Am Foresters. *Res:* Modeling growth and yield of forest stands, especially loblolly pine plantations; general qualitative model and applications to forestry. *Mailing Add:* Weyerhaeuser Co PO Box 1060 Hot Springs AR 71901

STRUBLE, CRAIG BRUCE, b Mt Pleasant, Mich, Oct, 30, 50; m 73. AGRICULTURAL CHEMICAL METABOLISM, EXPERIMENTAL SURGERY. *Educ:* Jamestown Col, BS, 73; ND State Univ, PhD(zool), 79. *Prof Exp:* Res assoc, Dept Path, Univ Wis-Madison & Wis Regional Primate Ctr, 78-79; RES ASSOC, DEPT ANIMAL SCI, ND STATE UNIV, 79- *Mem:* Sigma Xi. *Res:* Metabolism, biliary secretion, and enterohepatic circulation of xenobiotics and agricultural chemicals in laboratory and farm animals. *Mailing Add:* USDA Metab & Radiation Res Lab Univ Sta Fargo ND 58105

STRUBLE, DEAN L, b Wawota, Sask, Aug 29, 36; m 57; c 3. SYNTHETIC ORGANIC CHEMISTRY. *Educ:* Univ Sask, BA & MA, 61, PhD(org chem), 65. *Prof Exp:* Develop chemist, Du Pont of Can, Ont, 62-63; Nat Res Coun Can overseas fels, Imp Col, Univ London, 65-66 & Univ Adelaide, 66-67; RES SCIENTIST, CAN DEPT AGR, 68- *Mem:* Chem Inst Can; Am Chem Soc; Am Entom Soc; Can Entom Soc. *Res:* Sterochemistry of free radical and nucleophilic addition reactions to activated olefinic compounds; sex pheromones of insects, particularly Lepidoptera and Coleoptera; chemical behavior of organophosphorus pesticides. *Mailing Add:* Res Sta Can Dept Agr Lethbridge AB T1J 4B1 Can

STRUBLE, GEORGE W, b Philadelphia, Pa, July 6, 32; m 55; c 3. COMPUTER SCIENCE. *Educ:* Swarthmore Col, AB, 54; Univ Wis, MS, 57, PhD(math), 61. *Prof Exp:* Proj supvr, Numerical Anal Lab, Univ Wis, 60-61; from asst prof to assoc prof math, 61-69, res assoc, 61-65, assoc dir statist lab & comput ctr, 65-69, dir comput ctr, 69-74, ASSOC PROF COMPUT SCI, UNIV ORE, 69- *Concurrent Pos:* Consult, Computer Mgt Serv, Inc, Portland, Ore, 74-78. *Mem:* Data Processing Mgt Asn; Asn Comput Mach. *Res:* Business data processing. *Mailing Add:* Dept of Computer Sci Univ of Ore Eugene OR 97403

STRUBLE, GORDON LEE, b Cleveland, Ohio, Mar 7, 37; m 61; c 4. NUCLEAR CHEMISTRY. *Educ:* Rollins Col, BS, 60; Fla State Univ, PhD(chem), 64. *Prof Exp:* Fel, Lawrence Berkeley Lab, Univ Calif, 64-66; asst prof chem, Univ Calif, Berkeley, 66-71; staff chemist, 71-75, sect leader, 75-79, ASSOC DIV LEADER, LAWRENCE LIVERMORE NAT LAB, 80- *Concurrent Pos:* Prof physics, Univ Munich, 75. *Mem:* AAAS; Am Chem Soc; Am Phys Soc. *Res:* Experimental and theoretical low energy nuclear structure and reaction physics, determination of characteristics of low energy excitations in nuclei by nuclear reactions and decay processes and their description by theoretical many body techniques. *Mailing Add:* Dept Chem Lawrence Livermore Nat Lab PO Box 808 Livermore CA 94550

STRUBLE, RAIMOND ALDRICH, b Forest Lake, Minn, Dec 10, 24; m 46; c 5. MATHEMATICS. *Educ:* Univ Notre Dame, PhD(math), 51. *Prof Exp:* Aerodynamicist, Douglas Aircraft Co, 51-53; asst prof math, Ill Inst Technol, 53-56; assoc prof, 56-60, PROF MATH, NC STATE UNIV, 60- *Concurrent Pos:* Consult, Armour Res Found, 54-60. *Res:* Fourier analysis; almost periodic functions; nonlinear differential equations; applied mathematics. *Mailing Add:* Dept of Math NC State Univ Raleigh NC 27650

STRUCHTEMEYER, ROLAND AUGUST, b Wright City, Mo, Jan 4, 18; m 40; c 2. SOILS. *Educ:* Univ Mo, BS, 39, MA, 41; Ohio State Univ, PhD(agron), 52. *Prof Exp:* Asst soils, Univ Mo, 39-40 & Ohio State Univ, 40-42; explosive chemist, Certainteed Corp, Tex, 42-43; head dept soils, 46-71, PROF SOILS, UNIV MAINE, ORONO, 46- *Concurrent Pos:* Agron fel, 65; soil fertility specialist, IRI Res Inst, Brazil, 66. *Mem:* Am Soc Agron; Soil Sci Soc Am; Int Soc Soil Sci. *Res:* Plant nutrition. *Mailing Add:* Dept Plant & Soil Sci Univ of Maine Orono ME 04473

STRUCK, ROBERT FREDERICK, b Pensacola, Fla, Jan 9, 32; m 63. PHARMACOLOGY, DRUG METABOLISM. *Educ:* Auburn Univ, BS, 53, MS, 57, PhD(org chem), 61. *Prof Exp:* Assoc scientist, Southern Res Inst, 57-58; org chemist, Fruit & Veg Prod Lab, Agr Res Serv, USDA, 61; res scientist, 61-64, sr scientist, 64-80, HEAD, METABOL SECT, SOUTHERN RES INST, 80- *Mem:* Am Chem Soc; Am Asn Cancer Res; Am Soc Pharmacol Exp Therapeut. *Res:* Metabolism of anticancer drugs and carcinogens; organophosphorous and natural products chemistry; synthesis in organic heterocyclic chemistry. *Mailing Add:* Southern Res Inst 2000 Ninth Ave S Birmingham AL 35205

STRUCK, ROBERT T(HEODORE), b Harrisburg, Pa, Apr 26, 21; wid; c 2. CHEMICAL ENGINEERING. *Educ:* Pa State Univ, BS, 42, MS, 46, PhD(fuel tech), 49. *Prof Exp:* Res asst petrol refining, Pa State Univ, 42-46, res asst fuel technol, 46-48; chem engr, Consol Coal Co, 48-74; mgr process develop, 74-81, MGR RES ADMIN, CONOCO COAL DEVELOP CO, 81- *Mem:* Am Chem Soc; Am Inst Chem Engrs. *Res:* Diffusional processes in hydrocarbon processing; developing processes for converting coal to other fuels; air pollution control processes; development of new routes to metallurgical coke. *Mailing Add:* 2347 Morton Rd Pittsburgh PA 15241

STRUCK, WILLIAM ANTHONY, b Paterson, NJ, Mar 17, 20; m 43; c 3. ANALYTICAL CHEMISTRY. *Educ:* Calvin Col, AB, 40; Univ Mich, MS, 62, PhD, 63. *Prof Exp:* Microanalyst, 41-48, head chem res anal, 48-62, mgr phys & anal chem res, 62-68, from asst dir to dir supportive res, 68-74, sr dir, Int Pharmaceut Res & Develop, 74-79, SR DIR, PHARMACEUT RES & DEVELOP, UPJOHN CO, 79- *Mem:* AAAS; Am Chem Soc. *Res:* Organic electrochemistry; organic analysis; optical rotatory dispersion. *Mailing Add:* 2102 Waite Ave Kalamazoo MI 49008

STRUCKMEYER, BURDEAN ESTHER, b Cottage Grove, Wis, May 25, 12. HORTICULTURE. *Educ:* Univ Wis, BA, 35, MA, 36, PhD, 39. *Prof Exp:* From instr to assoc prof, 39-65, PROF HORT, UNIV WIS-MADISON, 65- *Mem:* Fel Am Soc Hort Sci; Bot Soc Am; Am Soc Plant Physiologists; Int Soc Hort Sci; Int Soc Plant Morphol. Re Horticultural plants, especially their anatomical structure as influenced by mineral nutrition, physiological and pathological diseases and growth substances; investigations on flowering of plants. *Mailing Add:* Dept of Hort Univ of Wis-Madison Madison WI 53706

STRUEMPLER, ARTHUR W, b Lexington, Nebr, Dec 12, 20; m 50; c 2. ANALYTICAL CHEMISTRY. *Educ:* Univ Nebr, BS, 50, MS, 55; Iowa State Univ, PhD, 57. *Prof Exp:* Asst prof, Chico State Col, 57-60; fel biochem, Univ Calif, Davis, 60-62; opers analyst, Strategic Air Command Hq, Nebr, 62-65; head div, Chadron State Col, 65-81, prof chem & chmn, Dept Sci & Math, 76-81. *Mem:* Am Chem Soc; Sigma Xi; AAAS. *Res:* Weather modification studies relating to element concentrations in precipitation; geochemical studies. *Mailing Add:* Div of Sci & Math Chadron State Col Chadron NE 69337

STRUHSAKER, PAUL JAMES, b Lansing, Mich, July 16, 35. MARINE ZOOLOGY, FISHERIES. *Educ:* Mich State Univ, BS, 58; Univ Hawaii, MS, 66, PhD(zool), 73. *Prof Exp:* Fisheries Biologist, Nat Marine Fisheries Serv, 59-65 & 69-80. *Mem:* Am Soc Ichthyologists & Herpetologists. *Res:* Systematics and ecology of marine fishes; fisheries development. *Mailing Add:* PO Box 3830 Honolulu HI 96812

STRUIK, RUTH REBEKKA, b Mass, Dec 15, 28; div; c 3. MATHEMATICS, ALGEBRA. *Educ:* Swarthmore Col, BA, 49; Univ Ill, MA, 51; NY Univ, PhD(math), 55. *Prof Exp:* Digital comput programmer, Univ Ill, 50-51; asst, Univ Chicago, 52; lectr math, Sch Gen Studies, Columbia Univ, 55; asst prof, Drexel Inst Technol, 56-57; lectr, Univ BC, 57-61; actg asst prof, 61-62, asst prof, 62-63, 64-65, assoc prof, 65-80, PROF MATH, UNIV COLO, BOULDER, 80- *Mem:* Math Asn Am; Asn Women Math; Soc Women Engrs; Am Math Soc. *Res:* Groups; modern algebra. *Mailing Add:* Dept Math Campus Box 426 Univ Colo Boulder CO 80309

STRULL, GENE, b Chicago, Ill, May 15, 29; m 52; c 2. ELECTRICAL ENGINEERING, SOLID STATE PHYSICS. *Educ:* Purdue Univ, BSEE, 51; Northwestern Univ, MS, 52, PhD(cadmium sulfide films), 54. *Prof Exp:* Engr, Mat Eng Dept, 54-55, sr engr, Semiconductor Div, Pa, 55-58, supvr solid state lab, Md, 58-60, mgr solid state technol, Aerospace Div, 60-68, mgr sci & technol, 68-70, MGR ADVAN TECHNOL LABS, SYSTS DEVELOP DIV, WESTINGHOUSE ELEC CORP, 70- *Concurrent Pos:* Lectr, Univ Pittsburgh, 54-58; assoc mem defense sci bd, Nat Res Coun/Nat Acad Sci, 80- *Mem:* Fel Inst Elec & Electronics Engrs. *Res:* Solid state devices; advanced sensors; integrated systems. *Mailing Add:* Advan Technol Labs Westinghouse Elec Corp Box 1521 Baltimore MD 21203

STRUMEYER, DAVID H, b Brooklyn, NY, Oct 11, 34; m 57. BIOCHEMISTRY. *Educ:* Brooklyn Col, BS, 55; Harvard Univ, MA, 56, PhD(biochem), 59. *Prof Exp:* Am Cancer Soc res fel, Univ Calif, Berkeley, 59-61; res assoc biochem, Brookhaven Nat Lab, 61-63; sr res scientist, Bristol-Meyers Co, 63-64; asst prof, 64-68, assoc prof, 68-77, PROF BIOCHEM, RUTGERS UNIV, 78- *Mem:* Am Chem Soc; Am Soc Biol Chemists. *Res:* Protein chemistry; mechanism of enzyme action especially of proteolytic, amylolytic enymes and naturally occuring amylese inhibitors; plant phenolics, interaction with proteins; automated analyses; immobilized enzyme technology; celiac disease; amino acid analysis. *Mailing Add:* Dept of Biochem & Microbiol Lipman Hall Cook Col Rutgers Univ New Brunswick NJ 08903

STRUMPF, ALBERT, applied mathematics, see previous edition

STRUMWASSER, FELIX, b Trinidad, BWI, Apr 16, 34; nat US. PHYSIOLOGY, NEUROBIOLOGY. *Educ:* Univ Calif, Los Angeles, BA, 53, PhD(zool), 57. *Prof Exp:* Asst, Univ Calif, Los Angeles, 56-57; from asst scientist to sr asst scientist, Lab Neurophysiol, NIMH, 57-60; res assoc neurophysiol, Walter Reed Army Inst Res, 60-64; assoc prof, 64-69, PROF BIOL, CALIF INST TECHNOL, 69- *Concurrent Pos:* Res assoc, Washington Sch Psychiat, 60-64; Penn lectr, Univ Pa, 67; Carter-Wallace lectr, Princeton Univ, 68; mem fel comt, NIH, 68-70; mem biochronometry comt, NSF, 69; 17th Bowditch lectr, Am Physiol Soc, 72; mem, Neurol B Study Sect, NIH, 78-; lang lectr, Marine Biol Lab, Woods Hole, 80. *Mem:* Fel AAAS; Soc Neurosci; Soc Gen Physiol; Am Physiol Soc; NY Acad Sci. *Res:* Neurophysiology; neurocellular basis of behavior, sleep-waking, reproduction; mechanisms of circadian rhythms in nervous systems; long-term studies on single identifiable neurons in organ and dissociated cell culture; integrative mechanisms of the neuron; comparative neurophysiology; pacemaker mechanisms in neurons; physiology and biochemistry of peptidergic neurons. *Mailing Add:* Div of Biol Calif Inst of Technology Pasadena CA 91125

STRUNK, DUANE H, b Irene, SDak, Mar 14, 20; m 45; c 2. ANALYTICAL CHEMISTRY. *Educ:* Univ SDak, BA, 42; Univ Louisville, MS, 51. *Prof Exp:* Res supvr, 42-43, prod supvr, 43-44, maintenance supvr, 43-45, res chemist, 46-65, CONTROL LABS ADMINSTR, JOSEPH E SEAGRAM & SONS, INC, 66- *Mem:* Am Chem Soc; Am Water Works Asn; Am Soc Testing Mat; Asn Off Anal Chemists. *Res:* Microanalytical methods, especially colorimetric, flame spectrophotometry and atomic absorption methods for copper and magnesium; water, food and wood chemistry; high accuracy particle counter; proof by density meter. *Mailing Add:* 3104 Gambriel Ct Louisville KY 40205

STRUNK, MAILAND RAINEY, b Kansas City, Kans, Aug 17, 19; m 49; c 3. CHEMICAL ENGINEERING. *Educ:* Kans State Univ, BS, 41; Univ Mo, MS, 47; Wash Univ, DSc(chem eng), 57. *Prof Exp:* Technologist, Shell Oil Co, Inc, 47-51, 52-54; instr chem eng, Wash Univ, 54-57; assoc prof, 57-60, PROF CHEM ENG, UNIV MO-ROLLA, 60-, CHMN DEPT, 64- *Mem:* AAAS; Am Soc Eng Educ; Nat Soc Prof Engrs; Am Inst Chem Engrs. *Res:* Applied physical chemistry; heat and mass transfer. *Mailing Add:* Dept of Chem Eng Univ of Mo Rolla MO 65401

STRUNK, RICHARD JOHN, b Jamaica, NY, July 6, 41; m 68; c 3. ORGANIC CHEMISTRY. *Educ:* Gettysburg Col, AB, 63; State Univ NY Albany, PhD(org chem), 67. *Prof Exp:* SR RES SCIENTIST, RES CTR, UNIROYAL INC, 67- *Mem:* Am Chem Soc; Sigma Xi. *Res:* Organometallic and free radical chemistry; organometallic and pesticide chemistry. *Mailing Add:* Uniroyal Inc Oxford Mgt & Res Ctr Middlebury CT 06749

STRUNZ, G(EORGE) M(ARTIN), b Vienna, Austria, Mar 10, 38; m 72. ORGANIC CHEMISTRY. *Educ:* Trinity Col, Dublin, BA, 59; Univ NB, PhD(org chem), 63. *Prof Exp:* Res assoc org chem, Univ Mich, 63-64; res fel, Harvard Univ, 64-65; lectr, Univ NB, 65-67; RES SCIENTIST, CAN DEPT FORESTRY, 67- *Concurrent Pos:* Hon res assoc, Univ NB, 70- *Mem:* Chem Inst Can; Am Chem Soc; fel Royal Soc Chem. *Res:* Chemistry of microbial metabolites; plant hormones and other natural products; approaches to insect control by compounds related to natural products. *Mailing Add:* Can Forestry Serv PO Box 4000 Fredericton NB E3B 5P7 Can

STRUTHERS, BARBARA JOAN, b Bend, Ore, May 4, 40. BIOCHEMISTRY, TOXICOLOGY. *Educ:* Wash State Univ, BS, 62; Ore State Univ, MS, 68, PhD(food sci), 73; Am Bd Toxicol, dipl. *Prof Exp:* Instr sci educ, Ore State Univ, 68-69, chemist food sci, 69-70; assoc scientist nutrit biochem, 73-81, MGR TOXICOL & PATHOL, RALSTON PURINA CO, 81- *Mem:* AAAS; Am Oil Chemists Soc; Sigma Xi; Am Inst Nutrit; Soc Toxicol. *Res:* Feed and food safety and toxicology, processing effects; cyclopropene fatty acids; lysinoalanine; nephrotoxicology; trypsin inhibitors. *Mailing Add:* Ralston Purina Co Checkerboard Sq St Louis MO 63188

STRUTHERS, ROBERT CLAFLIN, b Syracuse, NY, June 2, 28; m 52; c 6. COMPARATIVE ANATOMY, DEVELOPMENTAL ANATOMY. *Educ:* Syracuse Univ, BA, 50, MA, 52; Univ Rochester, PhD(biol), 56. *Prof Exp:* Asst comp & develop anat, Syracuse Univ, 50-56; from instr to asst prof anat, Ohio State Univ, 56-61; assoc prof, 61-62, prof anat, 62-81, PROF NATURAL SCI, WHEELOCK COL, 81-, HEAD NATURAL SCI & MATH DEPT, 81- *Res:* Morphology of early embryonic stages of vertebrate animals, particularly on the pharynx and its derivatives. *Mailing Add:* Dept of Sci & Math Wheelock Col 200 Riverway Boston MA 02215

STRUVE, WILLIAM GEORGE, b Milwaukee, Wis, Mar 19, 38; c 2. BIOCHEMISTRY, CHEMISTRY. *Educ:* Lake Forest Col, BA, 62; Northwestern Univ, PhD, 66. *Prof Exp:* Res chemist, Am Cyanamid Co, 66-68; ASSOC PROF BIOCHEM, UNIV TENN, MEMPHIS, 68- *Concurrent Pos:* Vis scholar, Stanford Univ, 69-70. *Mem:* Acoust Soc Am; Audio Eng Soc. *Res:* Biological membranes; molecular biology of the central nervous system; acetylocholinesterase; electronics; computer music composition. *Mailing Add:* Rm 2 Nash Bldg Dept Biochem Univ Tenn Memphis TN 38163

STRUVE, WILLIAM SCOTT, b Utica, NY, May 1, 15; m 39; c 3. ORGANIC CHEMISTRY. *Educ:* Univ Mich, BS, 37, MS, 38, PhD(org chem), 40. *Prof Exp:* Du Pont fel, Univ Mich, 40-41; chemist, Jackson Lab, E I DuPont de Nemours & Co, 41-49, res supvr, 49-58, lab dir, Color Res Lab, 58-73, dir, Newark Lab & mgr, Colors Res & Develop, 73-80; RETIRED. *Mem:* Am Chem Soc. *Res:* Carcinogenic hydrocarbons; organic fluorine compounds; dyestuffs; pigments. *Mailing Add:* 29 Dellwood Ave Chatham NJ 07928

STRUZYNSKI, RAYMOND EDWARD, b Jersey City, NJ, Dec 10, 37; m 65; c 2. MATHEMATICAL PHYSICS. *Educ:* Stevens Inst Technol, BEng, 59, MS, 61, PhD(physics), 65. *Prof Exp:* From instr to asst prof, 64-70, ASSOC PROF PHYSICS, BROOKLYN COL, 70- *Concurrent Pos:* Res scientist, Hudson Labs, Columbia Univ, 65-67. *Mem:* Am Phys Soc. *Res:* Radiative beta decay; liquid helium; quantum mechanics of many boson systems. *Mailing Add:* Dept of Physics Brooklyn Col Bedford Ave & Ave H Brooklyn NY 11210

STRYCKER, STANLEY JULIAN, b Goshen, Ind, Aug 30, 31; m 52; c 4. ORGANIC CHEMISTRY. *Educ:* Goshen Col, AB, 53; Univ Ill, PhD(org chem), 56. *Prof Exp:* Res chemist, 56-63, sr res chemist, 63-68, group leader, 68-69, res mgr pharmaceut sci, 69-74, RES MGR CHEM & INDUST PHARM, DOW CHEM CO, 74- *Concurrent Pos:* Sabbatical, Col Med, Univ Iowa, 67-68. *Mem:* Am Inst Chemists; Am Chem Soc; Sigma Xi. *Res:* Organic synthesis; heterocyclics; medicinal chemistry. *Mailing Add:* 527 Nuthatch Dr Zionsville IN 46077

STRYER, LUBERT, b Tientsin, China, Mar 2, 38; US citizen; m 58; c 2. MOLECULAR AND CELL BIOLOGY. *Educ:* Univ Chicago, BS, 57; Harvard Univ, MD, 61. *Prof Exp:* From asst prof to assoc prof biochem, Stanford Univ, 63-69; prof molecular biophys & biochem, Yale Univ, 69-76; chmn dept, 76-79, WINZER PROF STRUCT BIOL, SCH MED, STANFORD UNIV, 76- *Concurrent Pos:* Helen Hay Whitney fel, Harvard Univ & Med Res Coun Lab Molecular Biol, Cambridge, Eng, 61-63; consult, NIH, 67-71; assoc ed, Ann Rev Biophys & Bioeng, 70. *Honors & Awards:* Eli Lilly Award, Am Chem Soc, 70. *Mem:* Am Soc Biol Chemists; Biophys Soc; fel Am Acad Arts & Sci. *Res:* Protein structure and function; visual excitation; excitable membranes; spectroscopy; x-ray diffraction. *Mailing Add:* Dept of Struct Biol Stanford Med Sch Stanford CA 94305

STRYKER, HARRY KANE, b Arkansas City, Kans, Feb 5, 21; m 42; c 2. POLYMER CHARACTERIZATION, GEL PERMEATION CHROMATOGRAPHY. *Educ:* Kans State Col, Pittsburg, BS, 42, MS, 50. *Prof Exp:* From analyst to sr analyst chem, Spencer Chem Co, 47-49, staff asst chem, 49-52, staff assoc, 52-53, from staff mem to sr staff mem, 53-58, staff specialist, 58-62, sr res chemist, Spencer Chem Co & Gulf Oil Co, 62-66, sr res chemist, Gulf Res & Develop Co, 66-74, RES ASSOC, GULF OIL CHEM CO, 74- *Res:* Oxidation, reduction and polymerization by flow reactions; emulsion and high pressure polymerization of ethylene; stability and applications of polyethylene latexes; polymer characterization by techniques of gel permeation chromatography; column elution; differential scanning calorimetry. *Mailing Add:* Gulf Oil Chem Co Houston Res Lab PO Box 79070 Houston TX 77079

STRYKER, LYNDEN JOEL, b Stamford, NY, Feb 19, 43; m 71; c 2. COLLOID CHEMISTRY, SURFACE CHEMISTRY. *Educ:* Clarkson Col Technol, BS, 64, PhD(chem), 69. *Prof Exp:* Asst, Clarkson Col Technol, 67-68; lectureship, Brunel Univ, 69-70; res chemist, Westvaco Corp, 70-77; assoc prof chem, Inst Paper Chem, 77-79; SR RES ASSOC, HAMMERMILL PAPER CO, 79- *Mem:* Am Chem Soc; Tech Asn Pulp & Paper Indust. *Res:* surface chemistry of papermaking systems; stability of colloidal dispersions; solid-liquid interactions; metal ion hydrolysis and complexation; water pollution abatement; paper sizing and retention; surface characterization of solids; emulsion technology. *Mailing Add:* 6453 West Rd McKean PA 16426

STRYKER, MARTIN H, b New York, NY, July 26, 43; m 66. QUALITY CONTROL, PLASMA PROTEINS. *Educ:* Columbia Univ, AB; NY Med Col, MS, 68, PhD(biochem), 71. *Prof Exp:* Chief, 71-74, assoc dir, 74-80, DIR, QUAL CONTROL, BLOOD DERIVATIVES PROG, NY BLOOD CTR, 80- *Concurrent Pos:* Res fel, Plasma Proteins Lab, Lindsley F Kimball Res Inst, 71-72, res assoc, 72-80, anal chemist, 80- *Mem:* Am Chem Soc; AAAS; World Fedn Hemophilia; Parenteral Drive Asn. *Res:* Quality control of plasma protein production; plasma fractionation; blood coagulation factor assays; treatment of hemophilia. *Mailing Add:* NY Blood Ctr 155 Duryea Rd Melville NY 11747

STRYKER, MICHAEL PAUL, b Savannah, Ga, June 16, 47; m 78. NEUROBIOLOGY, PHYSIOLOGY. *Educ:* Univ Mich, AB, 68; Mass Inst Technol, PhD(psychol, brain sci), 75. *Prof Exp:* Res fel neurobiol, Harvard Med Sch, 75-78; ASST PROF PHYSIOL, UNIV CALIF, SAN FRANCISCO, 78- *Concurrent Pos:* Instr neurobiol, Cold Spring Harbor Labs, 76-78. *Mem:* Soc Neurosci; AAAS. *Res:* Neurobiology of the central nervous system; developing visual system. *Mailing Add:* Dept Physiol Univ Calif San Francisco CA 94143

STRYLAND, JAN CORNELIS, b Doorn, Neth, Oct 11, 14; m 43; c 3. MOLECULAR PHYSICS. *Educ:* Univ Amsterdam, PhD(physics), 53. *Prof Exp:* Conservator, Van der Waals Lab, Amsterdam, 43-54; PROF PHYSICS, UNIV TORONTO, 54- *Mem:* Am Phys Soc; Can Asn Physicists; Neth Phys Soc. *Res:* Intermolecular forces; investigation of physical phenomena at high pressures. *Mailing Add:* Dept of Physics Univ of Toronto Toronto ON M5S 2R8 Can

STUART, ALFRED HERBERT, b Farmville, Va, 13; m 44; c 2. PHOTOGRAPHIC CHEMISTRY. *Educ:* Hampden-Sydney Col, BS, 33; Univ Va, PhD(org chem), 37. *Prof Exp:* Res fel, Univ Va, 37-39; res chemist, Schieffelin & Co, NY, 39-43, dir chem res, 43-47; develop mgr, Charles Bruning Co, Ill, 47-65, tech dir, Addressograph-Multigraph Corp, 65-71, chief chemist, Bruning Div, 71-80; RETIRED. *Res:* Diazotype and electrostatic copying processes. *Mailing Add:* Short Beach Rd Branford CT 06405

STUART, ANN ELIZABETH, b Harrisburg, Pa, Oct 5, 43; m 78. NEUROBIOLOGY. *Educ:* Swarthmore Col, BA, 65; Yale Univ, MS, 67, PhD(physiol), 69. *Prof Exp:* Res fel neurophysiol, Dept Physiol, Univ Calif, Los Angeles Med Ctr, 71-73; res fel neurochem, Dept Neurobiol, Harvard Med Sch, 69-71, asst prof, 73-78, assoc prof, 78-80; MEM FAC, DEPT PHYSIOL, UNIV NC, 80- *Mem:* Soc Neurosci; Soc Gen Physiologists; Asn Res Vision & Ophthal. *Res:* Synaptic mechanisms; integration and synaptic transmission between single cells of small populations of neurons; integration in invertebrate central nervous systems. *Mailing Add:* Dept Physiol Med Res Bldg 20614 Univ NC Chapel Hill NC 27514

STUART, DAVID GORDON, microbiology, see previous edition

STUART, DAVID MARSHALL, b Ogden, Utah, May 20, 28; m 51; c 5. PHARMACY, CHEMISTRY. *Educ:* Univ Utah, BS, 51; Univ Wis, PhD(pharmaceut chem), 55. *Prof Exp:* Asst prof pharmaceut chem, Univ Tex, 55-S7 & Ore State Col, 57-60; coordr sci info, Neisler Labs, 60-64; PROF PHARMACEUT CHEM, COL PHARM, OHIO NORTHERN UNIV, 64- *Concurrent Pos:* Pharm consult, Ohio Dept Pub Welfare, 71-77; pres, Pharm Health & Related Mgt, Inc, 74- *Mem:* Am Pharmaceut Asn; NY Acad Sci. *Res:* Scientific literature research and writing; health care research. *Mailing Add:* Dept Pharm & Health Care Admin Col Pharm Ohio Northern Univ Ada OH 45810

STUART, DAVID ORR, b Harlan, Iowa, May 20, 20; m 47; c 3. MECHANICAL ENGINEERING. *Educ:* Iowa State Univ, BS, 47, PhD, 57. *Prof Exp:* Staff engr, Standard Oil Co, Ind, 47-53; res specialist, Boeing Corp, 56-60; prof mech eng & head dept, Wichita State Univ, 60-65; proj mgr, Litwin Corp, 65-70; prof mech eng, Univ Nebr, Omaha, 70-75; CHIEF MECH ENGR, GIBBS & HILL, INC, 75- *Mem:* Am Soc Mech Engrs; Nat Soc Prof Engrs. *Res:* Two-phase flow; energy and power systems; propulsion systems. *Mailing Add:* Gibbs & Hill, Inc 8240 W Dodge Rd Omaha NE 68114

STUART, DAVID W, b Lafayette, Ind, June 15, 32; m 64; c 2. METEOROLOGY. *Educ:* Univ Calif, Los Angeles, BA, 55, MA, 57, PhD(meteorol), 62. *Prof Exp:* Res meteorologist, Univ Calif, Los Angeles, 55-61, teaching asst meteorol, 57-61; asst prof, 62-66, assoc chmn dept, 67-72, ASSOC PROF METEOROL, FLA STATE UNIV, 66- *Concurrent Pos:* Assoc prof, Naval Postgrad Sch, 66-67. *Mem:* Am Meteorol Soc; Sigma Xi; Am Geophys Union. *Res:* Synoptic meteorology; numerical weather prediction, especially diagnostic studies and air-sea interaction; meteorology of coastal upwelling areas. *Mailing Add:* Dept of Meteorol Fla State Univ Tallahassee FL 32306

STUART, DERALD ARCHIE, b Bingham Canyon, Utah, Nov 9, 25; m 48; c 2. SOLID STATE PHYSICS. *Educ:* Univ Utah, BS, 47, MS, 48, PhD(physics), 50. *Prof Exp:* Asst physics, Univ Utah, 47-50; asst prof eng mat, Cornell Univ, 50-52, assoc prof eng mech & mat, 52-58; propulsion staff mgr & resident rep to Aerojet-Gen Corp, 58-59, asst to Polaris Missile syst mgr & Polaris resident rep to Aerojet-Gen Corp, 59-61, mgr propulsion staff, Missile Systs Div, 61-62, dir propulsion systs, 62-64, asst chief engr, 64-66, asst gen mgr eng & develop, 66-67, vpres & asst gen mgr, 67-70, VPRES CORP & VPRES & GEN MGR MISSILE SYSTS DIV, LOCKHEED MISSILES & SPACE CO, LOCKHEED CORP, 70- *Concurrent Pos:* Consult, Cornell Aeronaut Lab, 52-54, Allegany Ballistics Lab, 52-58, Lincoln Lab, Mass Inst Technol & Ramo-Wooldridge Corp, 54-56. *Honors & Awards:* Meyer Award, Am Ceramic Soc, 54; Wyld Propulsion Award, Am Inst Aeronaut & Astronaut; Montgomery Award, Nat Soc Aerospace Prof, 64. *Mem:* Fel Am Inst Aeronaut & Astronaut; Soc Logistics Engrs. *Res:* Glassy state; plastic behavior of materials; solid fuel rockets. *Mailing Add:* Dept 80-01 Bldg 181 PO Box 504 Lockheed Missiles & Space Co Inc Sunnyvale CA 94088

STUART, DOUGLAS GORDON, b Casino, NSW, Australia, Oct 5, 31; US citizen; m 57; c 4. PHYSIOLOGY. *Educ:* Mich State Univ, BS, 55, MA, 56; Univ Calif, Los Angeles, PhD(physiol), 61. *Prof Exp:* Res fel anat, Univ Calif, Los Angeles, 61-63, asst prof physiol in residence, 63-65, assoc prof, Univ Calif, Davis, 65-67; PROF PHYSIOL, COL MED, UNIV ARIZ, 70- *Mem:* Am Physiol Soc. *Res:* Neural control of posture and locomotion. *Mailing Add:* Dept of Physiol Univ of Ariz Col of Med Tucson AZ 85724

STUART, E(DWARD) B(ERNARD), chemical engineering, deceased

STUART, GEORGE WALLACE, b New York, NY, Apr 5, 24; m 48; c 3. THEORETICAL PHYSICS. *Educ:* Rensselaer Polytech Inst, BEE, 49, MS, 50; Mass Inst Technol, PhD(physics), 53. *Prof Exp:* Head theoret physics unit, Hanford Atomic Prod Oper, Gen Electric Co, 52-57; res adv spec nuclear effects lab, Gen Atomic Div, Gen Dynamics Corp, Calif, 58-67; sr res scientist, Systs, Sci & Software, 67-72; staff scientist, Sci Applns Inc, 72-79; CONSULT, 79- *Mem:* Fel Am Phys Soc. *Res:* Nuclear reactors; plasma theory; atomic physics. *Mailing Add:* Consult PO Box 134 Rancho Santa Fe CA 92067

STUART, JAMES DAVIES, b Elizabeth, NJ, Sept 30, 41; m 64; c 2. HIGH PERFORMANCE LIQUID CHROMATOGRAPHY. *Educ:* Lafayette Col, BS, 63; Lehigh Univ, PhD(anal chem), 69. *Prof Exp:* Instr, Lafayette Col, 67-69; asst prof, 69-75, ASSOC PROF ANAL CHEM, UNIV CONN, 75- *Concurrent Pos:* Prin investr, Nat Inst Environ Sci grants, 75-77; vis lectr, Chem Dept, Univ Ga, 76; prin investr grant, Dept Interior to Conn Inst Water Resources, 80- *Mem:* Am Chem Soc. *Res:* Development of modern separation methods using gas-liquid and high performance liquid chromatography; development of rapid and sensitive methods to determine amino acids, their percursors and metabolites in human and animal fluids; microcomputers and digital computers. *Mailing Add:* U-60 Chem Dept Univ Conn Storrs CT 06268

STUART, JAMES GLEN, b Enid, Okla, Aug 23, 48; m 68; c 2. BACTERIAL GENETICS, MICROBIOLOGY. *Educ:* Cameron State Col, BS, 70; Okla Univ, MS, 72, PhD(med microbiol), 75. *Prof Exp:* Lectr biol, Millikin Univ, 75-77; ASST PROF BIOL, MURRAY STATE UNIV, 77- *Concurrent Pos:* Grant dir, Ky Heart Fund, 78-79. *Mem:* Am Soc Microbiol; Sigma Xi. *Res:* Bacterial genetics, specifically the phenomena of genetics and mechanisms of antibiotic resistance in group A streptococci. *Mailing Add:* Dept of Biol Murray State Univ Murray KY 42071

STUART, JEANNE JONES, b Atlanta, Ga, Dec 22, 42; m 61; c 3. ZOOLOGY. *Educ:* Jacksonville State Univ, BS, 65, MS, 66; Auburn Univ, PhD(zool), 72. *Prof Exp:* Teacher french, Calhoun County Bd Educ, Ala, 65-67; instr biol, Jacksonville State Univ, 67-68; teaching asst zool, Auburn Univ, 68-72; res assoc biochem, 72-73; asst prof biol & head dept, Belmont Abbey Col, 73-78; ASSOC PROF BIOL, UNIV SC, SPARTANBURG, 78- *Mem:* AAAS; Sigma Xi; Am Soc Parasitologists; Am Inst Biol Sci. *Res:* Immunological phenomena associated with trichostrongylid parasitism and ecological factors in the distrubution of pathogenic Naegleri Fowleri. *Mailing Add:* Dept of Biol Univ of SC Spartanburg SC 29303

STUART, JOE DON, b Brownsboro, Tex, Feb 28, 32; m 63; c 2. ENVIRONMENTAL SCIENCES, COMPUTER SCIENCE. *Educ:* Univ Tex, BA, 57, PhD(physics), 63. *Prof Exp:* Sr physicist appl physics lab, Johns Hopkins Univ, 63-65; sr scientist, Tracor, Inc, 65-72; sr scientist, 72-76, ASST VPRES, RADIAN CORP, 76- *Mem:* Am Meteorol Soc; Air Pollution Control Asn; Opers Res Soc Am. *Res:* Computer modeling; air pollution control operations research. *Mailing Add:* 4009 Knollwood Dr Austin TX 78731

STUART, JOHN W(ARREN), b Logansport, Ind, Jan 5, 24; m 46; c 5. ELECTRICAL ENGINEERING. *Educ:* Purdue Univ, BSEE, 48. *Prof Exp:* Asst elec apparatus, Westinghouse Elec Corp, 48-50, appln engr, 50-55, proj engr, 55-58; chief engr, Indust Nucleonics Corp, 58-62; mgr, 62-80, VPRES MECH ENG, ARTHUR D LITTLE, INC, 62- *Mem:* Inst Elec & Electronics Engrs. *Res:* Digital control; solid state device development; digital applications of magnetic devices; research & development management; technical audits; equipment engineering. *Mailing Add:* Arthur D Little Inc Acorn Park Cambridge MA 02140

STUART, LAURENCE COOPER, b Dubois, Pa, July 9, 07; m 31; c 1. ZOOLOGY. *Educ:* Univ Mich, BS, 30, MS, 31, PhD(zool), 33. *Prof Exp:* From instr to prof zool, 33-69, EMER PROF ZOOL, UNIV MICH, ANN ARBOR, 70- *Concurrent Pos:* Res assoc, Mus Zool, Univ Mich, 33-47 & Lab Vert Zool, 38-47, from asst biologist to assoc biologist, 47-56; res assoc, Cranbrook Inst Sci, Mich, 39-48; exchange prof, Nat Univ Mex, 45; consult, Off Strategic Serv, 43-45; mem sci adv panel, US Dept Army, 60-65; mem expeds, Cent Am & US. *Mem:* Distinguished fel Am Soc Ichthyol & Herpet; fel Royal Geog Soc; corresp mem Soc Geog & Hist Guatemala. *Res:* Herpetology, especially systematics; ecology and zoogeography of Neotropica. *Mailing Add:* Chalet 2945 Panajachel Solola Guatemala

STUART, RICHARD NORWOOD, b Medford, Ore, Apr 23, 26; m 58; c 4. PHYSICS. *Educ:* Univ Calif, AB, 43, PhD, 52. *Prof Exp:* Lectr nuclear eng, 58-62, THEORET PHYSICIST, LAWRENCE LIVERMORE LAB, UNIV CALIF, 52- *Res:* Reactor and solid state physics. *Mailing Add:* Lawrence Livermore Lab PO Box 808 Livermore CA 94550

STUART, RONALD S, b Tingley, NB, Mar 26, 19; m 46; c 4. ORGANIC CHEMISTRY. *Educ:* Univ NB, BA, 40; Univ Toronto, MA, 41, PhD(org chem), 44. *Prof Exp:* Demonstr chem, Univ Toronto, 40-42; res assoc, Nat Res Coun Can, 43-45; asst dir res, Dom Tar & Chem, 45-48; mgr chem & biol control, Merck & Co, Ltd, 48-53, mgr sci develop, 53-60, mgr tech & prod opers, 60-63, dir res, Merck Sharp & Dohme Can, 63-65, Charles E Frosst & Co, 65-68, gen mgr, 68-78, exec dir, 78-81; DIR RES SERV & CTR RES ENG & APPL SCI, UNIV NB, 82- *Mem:* AAAS; Am Chem Soc; NY Acad Sci; Chem Inst Can; Can Res Mgt Asn. *Res:* Medicinal chemistry. *Mailing Add:* Sch Grad Studies & Res Univ NB Fredericton NB E3B 5A3 Can

STUART, SARAH ELIZABETH, molecular biology, see previous edition

STUART, THOMAS ANDREW, b Bloomington, Ind, Feb 6, 41; m 63; c 2. ELECTRICAL ENGINEERING. *Educ:* Univ Ill, Urbana, BS, 63; Iowa State Univ, ME, 69, PhD(elec eng), 72. *Prof Exp:* Engr, Martin Co, 63-64 & Honeywell, Inc, 64-65; design engr, Collins Radio Co, 65-69; asst prof elec eng, Clarkson Col Technol, 72-75; ASSOC PROF ELEC ENG, UNIV TOLEDO, 75- *Mem:* Inst Elec & Electronics Engrs. *Res:* Computer applications for electrical power systems; power electronics. *Mailing Add:* Dept of Elec Eng Univ of Toledo Toledo OH 43606

STUART-ALEXANDER, DESIREE ELIZABETH, b London, Eng, Apr 6, 30; US citizen. GEOLOGY. *Educ:* Westhampton Col, BA, 52; Stanford Univ, MSc, 59, PhD(geol), 67. *Hon Degrees:* Dr, Univ Richmond, 80. *Prof Exp:* Geologist explor dept, Utah Construct & Mining Co, 58-60; asst prof geol, Haile Selassie Univ, 63-65; GEOLOGIST, US GEOL SURV, 66-, CHIEF, BR WESTERN REGIONAL GEOL, 80- *Concurrent Pos:* Prog scientist, NASA Hq, 74-75; chief, Br Western Regional Geol, 80- *Mem:* AAAS; fel Geol Soc Am; Am Geophys Union; Earthquake Eng Res Inst. *Res:* Lunar and Martian geology including studies based on remote sensing data and petrology of lunar rocks; terrestrial studies of metamorphic problems and lunar analogs; problems of reservoir-induced seismicity; faulting in the Sierra Nevada Mountains, California. *Mailing Add:* Western Regional Geol US Geol Surv 345 Middlefield Rd MS 75 Menlo Park CA 94025

STUBBE, JOHN SUNAPEE, b New York, NY, Feb 21, 19; m 43; c 4. MATHEMATICS. *Educ:* Univ NH, BS, 41; Brown Univ, MS, 42; Univ Cincinnati, PhD(math), 45. *Prof Exp:* Instr math, army specialized training prog, Univ Cincinnati, 43-44; instr, Univ Ill, 45-47; asst prof, Univ NH, 47-49; asst prof, 49-53, dir comput ctr, 64-70, ASSOC PROF MATH, CLARK UNIV, 53- *Concurrent Pos:* Prof, Worcester Polytech Inst, 69-72. *Mem:* Am Math Soc; Math Asn Am. *Res:* Summability; Fourier series. *Mailing Add:* Dept of Math Clark Univ Worcester MA 01610

STUBBEMAN, ROBERT FRANK, b Midland, Tex, May 9, 35; m 56; c 3. PHYSICAL CHEMISTRY. *Educ:* Austin Col, BA, 57; Univ Tex, MA, 61, PhD(chem), 64. *Prof Exp:* Res chemist, Esso Res & Eng Co, 63-66; sr res chemist, 66-71, sect leader, Spectros Lab, 71-80, MGR, SAFETY HEALTH & ENVIRON SECT, CELANESE CHEM CO, TECH CTR, 80- *Mem:* Am Chem Soc; fel Am Inst Chemists. *Res:* Shock tube kinetics; mass spectrometry, including qualitative and quantitative low and high resolution; process research; environmental health and safety. *Mailing Add:* Safety Health & Energy Dept Box 9077 Celanese Chem Co Corpus Christi TX 78408

STUBBERUD, ALLEN ROGER, b Glendive, Mont, Aug 14, 34; m 61; c 2. ELECTRICAL ENGINEERING. *Educ:* Univ Idaho, BSEE, 56; Univ Calif, Los Angeles, MS, 58, PhD(eng), 62. *Prof Exp:* Asst prof eng, Univ Calif, Los Angeles, 62-67, assoc prof, 67-69; assoc prof, 69-72, assoc dean, Eng Sch, 72-77, PROF ENG, UNIV CALIF, IRVINE, 72-, DEAN, SCH ENG, 78- *Mem:* Fel Inst Elec & Electronics Engrs; assoc fel Am Inst Aeronaut & Astronaut; Opers Res Soc Am. *Res:* Optimal control systems theory; optimal filtering theory; final value control systems; digital signal processing. *Mailing Add:* Sch Eng Univ Calif Irvine CA 92717

STUBBINGS, ROBERT LAMB, physical chemistry, biochemistry, deceased

STUBBINS, JAMES FISKE, b Honolulu, Hawaii, Feb 19, 31; m 59; c 3. MEDICINAL CHEMISTRY. *Educ:* Univ Nev, BS, 53; Purdue Univ, MS, 58; Univ Minn, PhD(pharmaceut chem), 65. *Prof Exp:* Asst prof pharmaceut chem, Univ Fla, 62-63; from asst prof to assoc prof, 63-76, PROF PHARMACEUT CHEM, MED COL VA, 76- *Mem:* Am Chem Soc; Am Pharmaceut Asn; Acad Pharmaceut Sci; Am Asn Col Pharm Coun Fac. *Res:* Synthesis of medicinal agents; pharmacology of drugs in the autonomic and central nervous systems; antimetabolite theory and chemotherapy; drugs acting on blood cells. *Mailing Add:* Sch of Pharm Med Col of Va Va Commonwealth Univ Box 581 MCV Sta Richmond VA 23298

STUBBLEBINE, WARREN, b Reading, Pa, Jan 18, 17; m 38; c 5. CHEMICAL ENGINEERING. *Educ:* Pa State Col, BS, 38, MS, 40, PhD(textile chem), 42. *Prof Exp:* Asst textile chem, Pa State Col, 38-42; head flooring develop sect, Armstrong Cork Co, 42-47; res dir, Chem & Plastics Div, Off Qm Gen, DC, 47-52; dir develop, Conn Hard Rubber Co, 52-55; dir res & develop, Stowe-Woodward, Inc, 55-61, vpres co, 61-63; VPRES, SANDUSKY FOUNDRY & MACH CO, 63- *Concurrent Pos:* Mem comt mat & equip & panel org & fibrous mat res & develop bd, Dept Defense, 48-52; mem comt plastics & elastomers & comt chem & adv bd qm res & develop, Nat Acad Sci-Nat Res Coun, 52-60, tech adv panel rubber, 52-57, mem comt elastomers, Adv Bd Mil Personnel Supplies, 61- *Mem:* AAAS; Sigma Xi; Am Chem Soc; Brit Inst Rubber Indust; fel Am Inst Chem. *Res:* Centrifugal castings in ferrous and nonferrous alloys and their use and application in the paper industry. *Mailing Add:* Rt 2 Peru-Olena Rd Norwalk OH 44857

STUBBLEFIELD, BEAUREGARD, b Navasota, Tex, July 31, 23; m 50; c 5. TOPOLOGY. *Educ:* Prairie View State Col, BS, 43, MA, 45; Univ Mich, MS, 51, PhD(math), 59. *Prof Exp:* Asst math, Prairie View State Col, 43-44; prof & head dept, Univ Liberia, 52-56; lectr & NSF fel, Univ Mich, 59-60; supvr anal sect, Int Elec Corp, 60-61; assoc prof math, Oakland Univ, 61-67; vis prof & vis scholar, Tex Southern Univ, 68-69; sr prog assoc, Inst Serv Educ, 69-71; prof math, Appalachian State Univ, 71-75; MATHEMATICIAN, NAT OCEANIC & ATMOSPHERIC ADMIN ENVIRON RES LAB, 76- *Concurrent Pos:* Mathematician, Detroit Arsenal, 57-69; asst prof, Stevens Inst Technol, 60-61; vis prof, Prairie View A&M Col, 67-68. *Mem:* AAAS; Am Math Soc; Math Asn Am; Soc Indust & Appl Math. *Mailing Add:* 158 Shagbark Rochester MI 48063

STUBBLEFIELD, CHARLES BRYAN, b Viola, Tenn, Sept 14, 31; m 60; c 2. TECHNICAL MANAGEMENT, ANALYTICAL CHEMISTRY. *Educ:* Mid Tenn State Univ, BS, 53; Univ Tenn, MS, 60. *Prof Exp:* Res chemist, PPG Corp, 60-65, group leader anal chem, 65-67; res chemist, 67-72, dir qual control, 72-81, MGR PLANNING & ASST TO PRES, LITHIUM CORP AM, SUBSID GULF RESOURCES & CHEM CORP, 81- *Mem:* Am Chem Soc; Sigma Xi; Am Inst Chemists; Am Soc Qual Control; Am Soc Testing & Mat. *Res:* Chemical and instrumental analytical methods development for improving analytical procedures; implementation of better analytical methods to improve process and product reliability. *Mailing Add:* Lithium Corp Am 449 N Cox Rd Gastonia NC 28052

STUBBLEFIELD, FRANK MILTON, b Hillsboro, Ill, June 25, 11; m 32; c 2. ORGANIC CHEMISTRY. CHEMISTRY. *Educ:* Univ Ill, AB, 32, MS, 36, PhD(chem), 42. *Prof Exp:* Chemist, Univ Ill, 35-37 & 39-42; chemist, Swift & Co, 37-39; res chemist, Weldon Spring Ord Works, Atlas Powder Co, Mo, 42-43; prof chem & head dept, Davis & Elkins Col, 43-47; assoc prof, Univ Ill, 47-56; chemist and br chief, US Govt, 56-73; RETIRED. *Concurrent Pos:* Consult, 43-; chief, Chem Div, Chem & Radiol Labs, Chem Corps, 51-53. *Mem:* Fel Am Inst Chemists; Am Chem Soc. *Res:* Organophosphorous chemistry-phosphonates mechanism of action and antidotes; toxicology of compounds of high physiological activity, with special emphasis on heterocyclic nitrogen compounds. *Mailing Add:* Box 368 Rte 1 Palmyra VA 22963

STUBBLEFIELD, ROBERT DOUGLAS, b Decatur, Ill, Mar 4, 36; m 58; c 3. ANALYTICAL CHEMISTRY. *Educ:* Eureka Col, BS, 59. *Prof Exp:* Anal chemist, 59-62, chemist, 62-64, RES CHEMIST, NORTHERN REGIONAL RES CTR, AGR RES SERV, USDA, 64- *Concurrent Pos:* Co-dir int collab study aflatoxin M methods milk, Int Union Pure & Appl Chem-Asn Off Anal Chemists, 72-73, 78-79 & 80-81. *Mem:* Am Oil Chemists Soc; fel Asn Off Anal Chemists; Am Asn Cereal Chemists. *Res:* Identification, preparation, and determination of known and unknown toxic compounds produced by the action of molds on agricultural commodities and products. *Mailing Add:* Northern Regional Res Ctr USDA 1815 N University Peoria IL 61604

STUBBLEFIELD, TRAVIS ELTON, b Austin, Tex, May 27, 35; m 57; c 2. CELL BIOLOGY. *Educ:* NTex State Univ, BS, 57; Univ Wis, MS, 59, PhD(exp oncol), 61. *Prof Exp:* NSF fel animal virol, Max Planck Inst Virus Res, Tübingen, WGer, 62-63; asst prof, 65-68, ASSOC PROF BIOL, UNIV TEX GRAD SCH BIOMED SCI HOUSTON, 68- *Concurrent Pos:* Asst biologist, Univ Tex M D Anderson Hosp & Tumor Inst Houston, 63-68, assoc biologist, 68-73. *Mem:* Am Soc Cell Biol. *Res:* Structure and physiology of mammalian chromosomes; synchronized cell culture; cell differentiation; structure and function of centrioles. *Mailing Add:* Dept of Biol Health Sci Ctr 6414 Fannin Houston TX 77025

STUBBS, DONALD WILLIAM, b Seguin, Tex, Sept 26, 32; m 53; c 4. PHYSIOLOGY. *Educ:* Tex Lutheran Col, BA, 54; Univ Tex, MA, 56, PhD(physiol), 64. *Prof Exp:* Instr zool, Auburn Univ, 56-60; from instr to assoc prof, 63-75, PROF PHYSIOL, UNIV TEX MED BR GALVESTON, 75- *Concurrent Pos:* NIH res grant, 65-71; multidisciplinary res grant ment health, 74- *Mem:* AAAS; Am Physiol Soc. *Res:* Biosynthesis of ascorbic acid; hormonal induction of enzyme activities. *Mailing Add:* 341 Tuna Galveston TX 77551

STUBBS, JOHN DORTON, b Cape Girardeau, Mo, Oct 9, 38; m 62; c 2. MOLECULAR BIOLOGY, BIOCHEMISTRY. *Educ:* Wash Univ, BA, 60; Univ Wis-Madison, MA, 62, PhD(biochem), 65. *Prof Exp:* USPHS fel genetics, Univ Wash, 65-67; from asst prof to assoc prof molecular biol, Calif State Univ, San Francisco, 68-75, PROF MOLECULAR BIOL, SAN FRANCISCO STATE UNIV, 75-, CHMN DEPT CELL & MOLECULAR BIOL, 72- *Concurrent Pos:* Brown-Hazen grant, Calif State Univ, San Francisco, 69-70; USPHS res grant, 70-72. *Mem:* AAAS. *Res:* Regulation of gene expression; transcriptional and translational control of the tryptophan operon in E coli; molecular mechanisms of membrane assembly; developmental biochemistry. *Mailing Add:* Biol Dept 1600 Holloway Ave San Francisco State Univ San Francisco CA 94132

STUBBS, MORRIS FRANK, b Sterling, Kans, May 25, 98; m 23; c 1. CHEMISTRY. *Educ:* Sterling Col, AB, 21; Univ Chicago, MS, 25, PhD(chem), 31. *Hon Degrees:* DSc, Sterling Col, 60. *Prof Exp:* Teacher chem & physics, Elgin Jr Col, 21-23; prof chem & physics & head dept phys sci, Tenn Wesleyan Col, 23-42, dean, 31-42; prof chem & head dept, Carthage Col, 42-44, Tenn Polytech Inst, 44-46 & NMex Inst Mining & Technol, 46-63, dir col div, 62-63; prof chem, Tex Tech Univ, 63-68; chmn dept chem & dir div natural sci & math, 68-78, EMER PROF CHEM, UNIV ALBUQUERQUE, 78- *Concurrent Pos:* Off Naval Res grant, 50-54. *Honors & Awards:* Clark Medal, Am Chem Soc, 65. *Mem:* Fel AAAS; Am Chem Soc. *Res:* Chemistry of indium; geochemical tests; general chemistry and qualitative analysis. *Mailing Add:* 9125 Copper NE 719 Albuquerque NM 87123

STUBBS, NORRIS, b Nassau, Bahamas, Nov 8, 48. COMPOSITE MATERIALS, STRUCTURAL ANALYSIS. *Educ:* Grinnell Col, BA, 72; Columbia Univ, BS, 72, MS, 74, EngScD, 76. *Prof Exp:* ASST PROF CIVIL ENG, COLUMBIA UNIV, 76- *Concurrent Pos:* Consult, Govt Nigeria, 76; instr, Columbia Univ, 78-81 & Barnard Col, 80-81; proj mgr, Leroy Callender Consult Engrs, 80- *Mem:* Soc Exp Stress Anal; Am Soc Civil Engrs; Am Soc Testing & Mat. *Res:* Nonlinear constitutine models for fabric reinforced composites; continuum modeling of large discrete structural systems; motion control of floating platforms; experimental analysis of structural systems. *Mailing Add:* 610 Mudd Columbia Univ New York NY 10027

STUBER, CHARLES WILLIAM, b St Michael, Nebr, Sept 19, 31; m 53; c 1. GENETICS. *Educ:* Univ Nebr, BS, 52, MS, 61; NC State Univ, PhD(genetics, exp statist), 65. *Prof Exp:* Instr high sch, Nebr, 56-59; from asst prof to assoc prof genetics, 65-75, PROF GENETICS, NC STATE UNIV, 75-; RES GENETICIST, AGR RES SERV, USDA, 62- *Mem:* AAAS; Genetics Soc Am; Am Soc Agron; Crop Sci Soc Am. *Res:* Quantitative genetics; inheritance of quantitative traits and correlated biochemical traits. *Mailing Add:* Dept of Genetics NC State Univ Raleigh NC 27650

STUBER, FRED A, b Paris, France, Dec 7, 33; m 64; c 1. PHYSICAL ORGANIC CHEMISTRY. *Educ:* Univ Zurich, ChemEng, 57, DSc(nuclear chem), 61. *Prof Exp:* Res assoc mass spectros, Inst Reactor Res, Switz, 61-62; fel, Univ Notre Dame, 62-63 & Mellon Inst, 63-64; res chemist, Ciba, Switz, 64-67; res chemist, 67-75, MGR, D S GILMORE RES LAB, UPJOHN CO, NORTH HAVEN, 75- *Mem:* Am Chem Soc. *Res:* Ionization and appearance potentials; analysis of nuclear magnetic resonance spectra; photopolymers. *Mailing Add:* 65 Chapel Hill Rd North Haven CT 06473

STUBICAN, VLADIMIR S(TJEPAN), b Bjelovar, Yugoslavia, June 23, 24; US citizen; m 46; c 2. MATERIALS SCIENCE, SOLID STATE CHEMISTRY. *Educ:* Univ Zagreb, Dipl Ing, 48, PhD(phys chem), 51, DSc(inorg chem), 58. *Prof Exp:* Res asst phys chem, Univ Zagreb, 48-52, asst prof, 52-55; vdir silicate chem, Inst Silicate Chem, Zagreb, Yugoslavia, 55-58; fel, 58-60, vis assoc prof geochem, 60-61, from asst prof to assoc prof, 61-71, PROF MAT SCI, PA STATE UNIV, 71- *Concurrent Pos:* Consult, Perkin-Elmer Corp, 80-; vis prof, Tech Univ, Tronheim, Norway, 67-68 & Max Planck Inst, Stuttgart, WGer, 77-78. *Mem:* Fel Am Chem Soc; fel Am Ceramic Soc; fel Am Inst Chem; fel Mineral Soc Am; Croation Chem Soc. *Res:* Solid state reactions; high temperature materials; inorganic synthesis; solid state technology; chemistry and properties of high melting inorganic materials; material transport in solids; solid state electrolytes. *Mailing Add:* Col Earth & Mineral Sci Rm 328 Steidle Bldg Univ Pa University Park PA 16802

STUCHLY, MARIA ANNA, b Warsaw, Poland, Apr 8, 39; Can citizen; m 72. ELECTRICAL ENGINEERING. *Educ:* Warsaw Tech Univ, BSc & MSc, 62; Polish Acad Sci, PhD(elec eng), 70. *Prof Exp:* Asst prof elec eng, Warsaw Tech Univ, 62-64; sr res & develop engr microwaves, Polish Acad Sci, 64-70, sr researcher, Inst Physics, 70; res assoc elec eng & food sci, Univ Man, 70-76; PHYSICIST MICROWAVES, HEALTH & WELFARE CAN, 76- *Concurrent Pos:* Fel, Dept Elec Eng, Univ Man, 70-72, adj prof, 76; non-resident prof, Dept Elec Eng, Univ Ottawa, 78- *Mem:* Inst Elec & Electronic Engrs; Int Microwave Power Inst; Bioelectromagnetics Soc. *Res:* Interaction of electromagnetic waves with living systems, especially medical applications, measurement techniques, biological effects and safety standards. *Mailing Add:* Environ Health Ctr Rm 233 Health & Welfare Can Ottawa ON K1A 0L2 Can

STUCHLY, STANISLAW S, b Nov 20, 31; Can citizen. ELECTRICAL ENGINEERING. *Educ:* Tech Univ Gliwice, Poland, BScEng, 53; Warsaw Tech Univ, MScEng, 58; Polish Acad Sci, DScEng, 68. *Prof Exp:* Res engr, Indust Inst Telecommun, Warsaw, Poland, 53-56, sr res engr, 56-59; asst prof, Warsaw Tech Univ, 59-63; head microwave instrument dept, Sci Instruments, Polish Acad Sci, 63-70; assoc prof agr eng & adj prof elec eng, Univ Man, 70-76; assoc prof, 76-80, PROF ELEC ENG, UNIV OTTAWA, 80- *Concurrent Pos:* Adj prof elec eng, Carleton Univ, 76- *Mem:* Sr mem Inst Elec & Electronics Engrs; Int Microwave Power Inst. *Res:* Electromagnetic theory and technique; non-conventional applications of electromagnetic radiations; industrial and biological applications of radio frequency and microwave radiations; electronic instrumentation, especially transducers for measuring nonelectrical quantities. *Mailing Add:* Dept of Elec Eng Univ of Ottawa Ottawa ON K1N 6N5 Can

STUCK, BARTON W, b Detroit, Mich, Oct 25, 46; m 75. APPLIED MATHEMATICS. *Educ:* Mass Inst Technol, BS & MS, 69, ScD(elec eng), 72. *Prof Exp:* MEM TECH STAFF, MATH & STATIST RES CTR, BELL LABS, AM TEL & TEL CO, 72- *Mem:* Soc Indust & Appl Math; Math Asn Am; Inst Elec & Electronics Engrs; Asn Comput Mach; Inst Math Statist. *Res:* Digital systems; applied probability theory. *Mailing Add:* Bell Labs 600 Mountain Ave Murray Hill NJ 07974

STUCKER, HARRY T, b Lawrence, Kans, Oct 7, 25; m 47; c 3. ENGINEERING, PHYSICS. *Educ:* Univ Kans, BS, 47, MS, 48. *Prof Exp:* Mem res staff, 47-54, supvr automatic controls, 54-57, supvr preliminary design, 57-58, supvr electronics lab, 58-59, adv navig guid, 59-61, chief reconnaissance & info systs, 61-63, PROJ MGR MISSILES & SPACE SYSTS, GEN DYNAMICS/FT WORTH, 63- *Mem:* Am Inst Aeronaut & Astronaut. *Res:* Control systems; microwave devices; communications. *Mailing Add:* Ft Worth Div PO Box 748 (E81) Ft Worth TX 76101

STUCKER, JOSEPH BERNARD, b Chicago, Ill, Feb 28, 14; m 41; c 3. CHEMISTRY. *Educ:* Univ Chicago, BS, 35. *Prof Exp:* Chemist, Pure Oil Co, 35-41, asst supt grease plant, 41-43, group leader prod develop, 43-50, sect supvr, 50-52, div dir, 52-65, sr res assoc, Res Dept, Union Oil Co, Calif, 65-68, mgr prod develop, Pure Oil Div, 68-69 & Union 76 Div, 69-71, MGR PROD QUAL, REFINING DIV, UNION OIL CO CALIF, 71- *Mem:* Soc Automotive Eng; Am Soc Testing & Mat; Am Petrol Inst. *Res:* Product development of lubricants, particularly greases, gear and crankcase oils and industrial lubricants. *Mailing Add:* Refining Div Union Oil Co Calif 1650 E Golf Rd Schaumburg IL 60196

STUCKER, ROBERT EVAN, b Burlington, Iowa, Jan 28, 36; m 56; c 3. PLANT BREEDING, STATISTICS. *Educ:* Iowa State Univ, BS, 59; Purdue Univ, MS, 61; NC State Univ, PhD(genetics), 66. *Prof Exp:* Res geneticist, Forage & Range Br, Crops Res Div, Agr Res Serv, USDA, 65-68; asst prof agron & plant genetics, corn breeding & quant genetics, 68-72, assoc prof agron & plant genetics, 72-77, PROF AGRON & PLANT GENETICS, UNIV MINN, ST PAUL, 77- *Concurrent Pos:* Statist design experiments & consult statistician agr & hort, 72-78; quant genetics consult, Alberta Forest Serv, 82- *Mem:* Am Soc Agron; Crop Sci Soc Am. *Res:* Wild rice (zizania) breeding; application of quantitative genetics in plant breeding. *Mailing Add:* Dept Agron & Plant Genetics Univ Minn St Paul MN 55101

STUCKEY, A(LTO) NELSON, JR, b Birmingham, Ala, July 7, 35; m 60; c 2. CHEMICAL ENGINEERING. *Educ:* Univ Ala, BChE, 56; Okla State Univ, MS, 63, PhD(chem eng), 66. *Prof Exp:* Chem engr, Esso Res Labs, Exxon Co USA, 56-61 & 65-67, sr chem engr, 67-71, sect head, 71-74, eng assoc, Essochem Europe, 74-77, HEAD ADHESION PROD TECHNOL, EXXON CHEM CO, 77- *Mem:* Am Chem Soc; Am Inst Chem Engrs. *Res:* Development, manufacture and commercialization of catalysts and catalyst systems for application in petroleum and hydrocarbon processing; pilot plant, semi-works, instrument systems design; inter-partes tests in patent litigation. *Mailing Add:* 12305 Lake La Dare Ave Baton Rouge LA 70816

STUCKEY, JOHN EDMUND, b Stuttgart, Ark, Dec 6, 29; m 55; c 3. PHYSICAL CHEMISTRY, INORGANIC CHEMISTRY. *Educ:* Hendrix Col, BA, 51; Univ Okla, MS, 53, PhD(chem), 57. *Prof Exp:* Res chemist, Oak Ridge Nat Lab, Union Carbide Corp, 57; asst prof chem, La Polytech Inst, 57-58; PROF CHEM, HENDRIX COL, 58- *Mem:* Am Chem Soc. *Res:* Preparations and properties of monofluorophosphate compounds; solution chemistry in the critical temperature region; x-ray crystallography. *Mailing Add:* Dept of Chem Hendrix Col Conway AR 72032

STUCKEY, RONALD LEWIS, b Bucyrus, Ohio, Jan 9, 38. BOTANY. *Educ:* Heidelberg Col, BS, 60; Univ Mich, MA, 62, PhD(bot), 65. *Prof Exp:* Instr bot, Univ Mich, 65; from asst prof to assoc prof, 65-78, cur herbarium, 67-75, PROF BOT, OHIO STATE UNIV, 78-, ASSOC DIR, FRANZ THEODORE STONE LAB, 77- *Mem:* Am Soc Plant Taxon; Int Asn Plant Taxon; Bot Soc Am. *Res:* Taxonomy and distribution of angiosperms; history of American botany; monographic studies in the Cruciferae, particularly Rorippa; Ohio vascular plant flora and phytogeography; history of plant taxonomy in North America; taxonomy and distribution of angiosperms, particularly aquatic and marsh flora. *Mailing Add:* Dept of Bot Ohio State Univ 1735 Neil Ave Columbus OH 43210

STUCKEY, WALTER JACKSON, JR, b Fairfield, Ala, Mar 6, 27; m 52; c 3. INTERNAL MEDICINE, HEMATOLOGY. *Educ:* Univ Ala, BS, 47; Tulane Univ, MD, 51. *Prof Exp:* Intern, Charity Hosp La, New Orleans, 51-52, resident internal med, 55, Vet Admin Hosp, New Orleans, 55-56 & Charity Hosp La, 56-57; from instr to assoc prof, 58-68, PROF MED, SCH MED, TULANE UNIV, 68-, CHIEF HEMAT SECT, 63- *Concurrent Pos:* Consult, New Orleans Charity Hosp; consult, Baptist, East Jefferson, Hotel Dieu, Mercy, Methodist, Sara Mayo, Touro, Lakeside & Vet Admin Hosps, New Orleans. *Mem:* Am Asn Cancer Educ; Am Soc Clin Oncol; fel Am Col Physicians; Am Soc Internal Med; Am Soc Hemat. *Res:* Bone marrow function in health and disease. *Mailing Add:* Sect of Hematol-Oncol Tulane Univ Sch of Med New Orleans LA 70112

STUCKI, JACOB CALVIN, b Neillsville, Wis, Nov 30, 26; m 48; c 3. ENDOCRINOLOGY, RESEARCH ADMINSTRATION. *Educ:* Univ Wis, BS, 48, MS, 51, PhD(zool, physiol), 54. *Prof Exp:* Res asst, Univ Wis, 50-54; endocrinologist, Wm S Merrell Co, 54-57; res assoc, 57-60, dept head endocrinol, 60-61, mgr pharmacol res, 61-68, dir res planning & admin, Pharmaceut Res & Develop, 68-79, dir admin & support opers, 79-81, VPRES PHARMACEUT RES, THE UPJOHN CO, 81- *Mem:* AAAS; Soc Exp Biol & Med; Endocrine Soc. *Res:* Reproduction; inflammation; pharmacology; research management. *Mailing Add:* Upjohn Co Kalamazoo MI 49001

STUCKI, JOSEPH WILLIAM, b Rexburg, Idaho, Feb 4, 46; m 68; c 6. SOIL CHEMISTRY, PHYSICAL CHEMISTRY. *Educ:* Brigham Young Univ, BS, 70; Utah State Univ, MS, 73; Purdue Univ, PhD(soil chem), 75. *Prof Exp:* Asst prof, 76-80, ASSOC PROF SOIL CHEM, UNIV ILL, 80- *Mem:* Asn Int Etude Argilles; Clay Minerals Soc; Soil Sci Soc Am; Int Soil Sci Soc; Mineral Soc Gt Brit. *Res:* Clay colloid chemistry, clay-water interactions, affects of structural iron oxidation states in clays and soils on their colloidal properties; advanced spectroscopic methods for analysis and characterization of soils and clays; physical-inorganic chemistry of clays. *Mailing Add:* Dept of Agron S-510 Turner Hall Univ of Ill Urbana IL 61801

STUCKI, WILLIAM PAUL, b Neillsville, Wis, Sept 28, 31; m 55; c 5. BIOCHEMISTRY. *Educ:* Univ Wis, BS, 57, MS, 59, PhD(biochem), 62. *Prof Exp:* Asst prof Univ Puerto Rico & scientist, PR Nuclear Ctr, Mayaguez, 62-63; asst prof, Antioch Col & assoc biochem, Fels Res Inst, 63-67; res biochemist, 67-75, SR RES BIOCHEMIST, PARKE DAVIS & CO, 75- *Mem:* Am Chem Soc; NY Acad Sci. *Res:* Protein and amino acid nutrition and metabolism; plant biochemistry; biochemistry of natural products; chemotherapy, immunology and immunochemistry; atherothrombotic disease. *Mailing Add:* Pharmacol Dept Parke Davis & Co 2800 Plymouth Rd Ann Arbor MI 48106

STUCKWISCH, CLARENCE GEORGE, b Seymour, Ind, Oct 13, 16; m 42; c 5. CHEMISTRY. *Educ:* Ind Univ, AB, 39; Iowa State Col, PhD(org chem), 43. *Prof Exp:* Res assoc, Iowa State Col, 43; asst prof chem, Wichita State Univ, 43-44; res chemist, Eastman Kodak Co, 44-4S; from asst prof to assoc prof chem, Wichita State Univ, 45-60; assoc prof, NMex Highlands Univ, 60-62, prof & head dept, 62-64, dir inst sci res, 63-64; prof chem & exec officer dept, State Univ NY Buffalo, 64-68; chmn dept, 68-74, PROF CHEM, UNIV MIAMI, 68-, DEAN GRAD STUDIES & RES, 72-, ASSOC VPRES ADVAN STUDIES, 80- *Mem:* Am Chem Soc. *Res:* Organometallic, psychopharmacological and organophosphorous compounds. *Mailing Add:* 210 Ferre Bldg Univ of Miami Coral Gables FL 33124

STUCKY, GALEN DEAN, b McPherson, Kans, Dec 17, 36; m 61; c 2. INORGANIC CHEMISTRY. *Educ:* McPherson Col, BS, 57; Iowa State Univ, PhD(chem), 62. *Prof Exp:* Fel physics, Mass Inst Technol, 62-63; NSF fel, Quantum Chem Inst, Fla, 63-64; from asst prof to assoc prof chem, Univ Ill, Urbana, 64-72, prof, 72-79; group leader, Sandia Nat Lab, 79-81; GROUP LEADER, CENT RES & DEVELOP DEPT, E I DU PONT DE NEMOURS & CO, INC, 81- *Concurrent Pos:* Consult div univ & col, Argonne Nat Labs, 66; vis prof physics, Univ Uppsula, Sweden, 71; Monsanto assoc ed, Inorg Chem, 77- *Mem:* Am Chem Soc; Am Crystallog Asn. *Res:* Organometallic chemistry of electron deficient sites; solid state chemistry. *Mailing Add:* Cent Res & Develop Dept 356-383 E I Du Pont de Nemours & Co Inc Wilmington DE 19898

STUCKY, GARY LEE, b Murdock, Kans, May 18, 41; m 72. BIOINORGANIC CHEMISTRY. *Educ:* Bethel Col, Kans, AB, 63; Kans State Univ, PhD(inorg chem), 67. *Prof Exp:* Instr chem, Halstead Sch Nursing, Kans, 62-63 & Kans State Univ, 63-65; res scientist bioinorg chem, Miles Labs, Ind, 67-70 & Kivuvu Inst Med Evangel, Kimpese, Zaire, 71; from asst prof to assoc prof, 72-79, PROF BIOINORG CHEM, EASTERN MENNONITE COL, 79- *Concurrent Pos:* Am Leprosy Mission res grant,

Eastern Mennonite Col, 72; vis prof chem, Univ Rochester, 81-82. *Mem:* AAAS; Am Chem Soc; Royal Soc Chem. *Res:* Electrochemistry of leprosy; inorganic synthesis; ion-selective electrodes; hemoglobin variants. *Mailing Add:* Dept of Chem Eastern Mennonite Col Harrisonburg VA 22801

STUDDEN, WILLIAM JOHN, b Timmins, Ont, Sept 30, 35; m. MATHEMATICAL STATISTICS. *Educ:* McMaster Univ, BSc, 58; Stanford Univ, PhD(statist), 62. *Prof Exp:* Res assoc math, Stanford Univ, 62-64; from asst prof to assoc prof statist, 64-71, PROF STATIST, PURDUE UNIV, LAFAYETTE, 71- *Concurrent Pos:* NSF fels, Purdue Univ, Lafayette, 68-71, 72-75. *Mem:* Fel Inst Math Statist. *Res:* Optimal designs; Tchebycheff systems. *Mailing Add:* Dept of Statist Purdue Univ Lafayette IN 47906

STUDEBAKER, GERALD A, b Freeport, Ill, July 22, 32; m 55; c 4. AUDIOLOGY. *Educ:* Ill State Univ, BS, 55; Syracuse Univ, MS, 56, PhD(audiol), 60. *Prof Exp:* Supvr clin audiol, Vet Admin Hosp, DC, 59-61, chief audiol & speech path serv, Syracuse, NY, 61-62; supvr clin audiol, Med Ctr, Univ Okla, 62-66, from asst prof to assoc prof audiol & consult, Dept Otorhinolaryngol, 62-72, res audiologist, 66-72; res prof audiol, Memphis State Univ, 72-76; prof audiol, PhD Prog Speech & Hearing Sci, City Univ New York, 76-79; DISTINGUISHED PROF SPEECH & HEARING SCI, MEMPHIS STATE UNIV, 79- *Mem:* AAAS; fel Am Speech & Hearing Asn; Acoust Soc Am. *Res:* Bone-conduction hearing thresholds, auditory masking; loudness estimation procedures and adaptation; speech discrimination; ear mold acoustics. *Mailing Add:* Memphis Speech & Hearing Ctr 807 Jefferson Ave Memphis TN 38105

STUDIER, EUGENE H, b Dubuque, Iowa, Mar 16, 40; div; c 2. PHYSIOLOGICAL ECOLOGY. *Educ:* Univ Dubuque, BS, 62; Univ Ariz, PhD(zool), 6S. *Prof Exp:* From asst prof to assoc prof biol, NMex Highlands Univ, 65-72; assoc prof, 72-74, PROF BIOL, UNIV MICH, FLINT, 74-, CHMN DEPT, 78- *Concurrent Pos:* USPHS grant, 66-67; Sigma Xi res grant-in-aid, 69; Am Philos Soc grant, 69. *Mem:* Fel AAAS; Am Soc Mammalogists; Am Soc Zoologists. *Res:* Mammalian physiology; physiological adaptation in bats and rodents. *Mailing Add:* Dept of Biol Univ of Mich-Flint Flint MI 48503

STUDIER, FREDERICK WILLIAM, b Waverly, Iowa, May 26, 36; m 62; c 2. BIOPHYSICS, MOLECULAR BIOLOGY. *Educ:* Yale Univ, BS, 58; Calif Inst Technol, PhD(biophys), 63. *Prof Exp:* NSF fel biochem, Med Ctr, Stanford Univ, 62-64; from asst biophysicist to biophysicist, 64-74, SR BIOPHYSICIST, BIOL DEPT, BROOKHAVEN NAT LAB, 74- *Concurrent Pos:* Adj assoc prof biochem, State Univ NY Stony Brook, 71-75, prof, 75- *Honors & Awards:* Ernest O Lawrence Mem Award, ERDA, 77. *Mem:* AAAS; Biophys Soc; Am Soc Biol Chemists. *Res:* Physical and chemical properties of nucleic acids; genetics and physiology of bacteriophage T7. *Mailing Add:* Biol Dept Brookhaven Nat Lab Upton NY 11973

STUDIER, MARTIN HERMAN, b Leola, SDak, Nov 10, 17; m 44; c 4. CHEMISTRY. *Educ:* Luther Col, BA, 39; Univ Chicago, PhD(chem), 47. *Prof Exp:* Asst, Iowa State Col, 39-41, instr, 41-42; res chemist, 43-36, SR CHEMIST, ARGONNE NAT LAB, 46- *Mem:* AAAS; Am Chem Soc; Am Phys Soc; Sigma Xi. *Res:* Nuclear chemistry of the heavy elements; chemical nature of coals; mass spectrometry; organic matter in meteorites. *Mailing Add:* Argonne Nat Lab 9700 S Cass Ave Argonne IL 60439

STUDLAR, SUSAM MOYLE, b St Paul, Minn, May 4, 44; m 79; c 2. BRYOLOGY. *Educ:* Carleton Col, BA, 66; Univ Tenn, Knoxville, PhD(bot), 73. *Prof Exp:* Instr biol, Wellesley Col, 71-72; asst prof, Va Commonwealth Univ, 72-74; asst prof biol, Centre Col Ky, 74-77, assoc prof, 78-82. *Concurrent Pos:* Vis prof, Mountain Lake Biol Sta, Univ Va, 77, 79 & 80; tech dir, Cent Ky Wildlife Refuge, 79-82; adj assoc prof biol, Centre Col Ky, 82- *Mem:* Am Bryol & Lichenological Soc; Torrey Bot Club; Brit Bryological Soc. *Res:* Floristics and ecology of bryophytes of Kentucky and Virginia; culturing of bryophytes; trampling effects on bryophytes. *Mailing Add:* Div Sci & Math Centre Col Ky Danville KY 40422

STUDT, PERRY L, b Grand Valley, Colo, Nov 17, 31; m 54. MATERIALS SCIENCE, NUCLEAR ENGINEERING. *Educ:* US Mil Acad, BS, 54; Univ Calif, Berkeley, MS, 58, PhD(eng sci), 63. *Prof Exp:* Nuclear engr, Nuclear Eng & Mfg Oper, Aerojet-Gen Corp, Calif, 58-60, sr metallurgist, 62-63, prin metall engr & sect head adv mat sect, 63-66; opers analyst, Res Anal Corp, Va, 62; Stanford Res Inst res officer, Combat Develop Command Exp Ctr, Ft Ord, 63; metallurgist, Lawrence Livermore Lab, Univ Calif, Livermore, 67-71, systs analyst, 73-77, proj metallurgist, 71-80, dept proj leader, 77-80. *Mem:* Am Soc Metals; Sigma Xi; Nat Soc Prof Engrs. *Res:* Shock response and high strain rate deformation of solids; Munroe effect; fracture of solids. *Mailing Add:* 107 La Vista Dr Los Alamos NM 87544

STUDT, WILLIAM LYON, b Ypsilanti, Mich, Mar 12, 47; m 66; c 3. MEDICINAL CHEMISTRY. *Educ:* Eastern Mich Univ, BA, 69; Univ Mich, PhD(org chem), 73. *Prof Exp:* Res fel org chem, Yale Univ, 73-74; SECT HEAD RES MED CHEM, RORER-AMCHEM INC, 74- *Res:* The organic synthesis of natural products and biologically active compounds. *Mailing Add:* 611 Store Rd Harleyville PA 19438

STUDTMANN, GEORGE H, b Chicago, Ill, Nov 3, 30; m 61; c 4. ELECTRONICS, ELECTRICAL ENGINEERING. *Educ:* Purdue Univ, BSEE, 56, MSEE, 57. *Prof Exp:* Prin elec engr, Battelle Mem Inst, 57-61; sr elec engr, 61-62, supvr res eng, 62-73, mgr electronics & elec eng, 73-78, MGR POWER ELECTRONICS, R C INGERSOLL RES CTR, BORG-WARNER CORP, 78- *Res:* Variable frequency alternating current motor drives. *Mailing Add:* R C Ingersoll Res Ctr Borg-Warner Corp Wolf & Algonquin Rds Des Plaines IL 60018

STUDZINSKI, GEORGE P, b Poznan, Poland, Oct 30, 32; m 59; c 4. EXPERIMENTAL PATHOLOGY, CELL BIOLOGY. *Educ:* Glasgow Univ, BS, 55, MB, 58, PhD(exp path), 62. *Prof Exp:* Brit Empire Cancer Campaign res fel path, Glasgow Royal Infirmary, 59-60, resident, 60-62; from instr to prof path, Jefferson Med Col, 62-75; PROF PATH & CHMN DEPT, NJ MED SCH, 76- *Mem:* Tissue Cult Asn; Am Soc Exp Path; Histochem Soc; Am Asn Cancer Res; Am Soc Cell Biol. *Res:* Study of effect of cancer chemotherapeutic agents on cultured diploid and aneuploid mammalian cells by a combination of cytochemical and biochemical methods; clinical pathology. *Mailing Add:* Dept Path NJ Med Sch Newark NJ 07103

STUEBEN, EDMUND BRUNO, b Cuxhaven, Ger, Apr 22, 20; nat US; m 4S; c 4. PARASITOLOGY. *Educ:* NY Univ, BS, 41; Baylor Univ, MA, 49; Univ Fla, PhD(zool), 53. *Prof Exp:* Instr biol lab & parasitol lab, Univ Fla, 50-53; asst prof biol, Arlington State Col, 53; assoc prof, 54-63, PROF ZOOL & PHYSIOL, UNIV SOUTHWESTERN LA, 63- *Res:* Larval development of filariae in arthropods; physiology of filaria larva; transmission of infective state filaria larva; antihistamine effect on coronary circulation. *Mailing Add:* Dept of Biol Univ of Southwestern La Lafayette LA 70504

STUEBEN, KENNETH CHARLES, b New York, NY, Aug 24, 31; m 53; c 2. ORGANIC CHEMISTRY, POLYMER CHEMISTRY. *Educ:* Brooklyn Col, BS, 56; Polytech Inst Brooklyn, PhD(org chem), 60. *Prof Exp:* Res technician, Colgate-Palmolive Co, NJ, 49-55; res chemist, Union Carbide Plastics Co, 59-65, proj scientist, 65-70, res scientist, 70-76, SR RES SCIENTIST, PLASTICS DIV, UNION CARBIDE CORP, 76- *Concurrent Pos:* Lectr radiation curable adhesives, 81. *Mem:* Am Chem Soc. *Res:* High temperature polymers; emulsion polymerization; oxidation kinetics; smoke generation in polymer systems; adhesives; photocure; micellar catalysis; synthetic paper. *Mailing Add:* Coatings Mat Div Box 670 Union Carbide Corp Bound Brook NJ 08805

STUEBER, ALAN MICHAEL, b St Louis, Mo, Apr 18, 37. GEOCHEMISTRY. *Educ:* Wash Univ, BS, 58, MA, 61; Univ Calif, San Diego, PhD(earth sci), 65. *Prof Exp:* Res assoc earth sci, Wash Univ, 65-66; fel geochem, Carnegie Inst Washington, 66-67; from asst prof to assoc prof geol, Miami Univ, 67-75; RES GEOCHEMIST, OAK RIDGE NAT LAB, 77- *Mem:* Geochem Soc. *Res:* Earth sciences; strontium isotope studies. *Mailing Add:* Dept of Geochem Oak Ridge Nat Lab Oak Ridge TN 37830

STUEBING, EDWARD WILLIS, b Cincinnati, Ohio, Sept 9, 42; m 82; c 2. AEROSOL OPTICS, AEROSOL CHARACTERIZATION. *Educ:* Univ Cincinnati, BS, 65; Johns Hopkins Univ, MA, 69, PhD(chem physics), 70. *Prof Exp:* Res physicist, US Army Frankford Arsenal, 70-74, res chemist, Pitman-Dunn Labs, 74-77, RES PHYSICAL SCIENTIST & COORDR AEROSOL RES, US ARMY CHEM SYSTS LAB, 77- *Concurrent Pos:* Adj asst prof chem, Drexel Univ, 74-77. *Mem:* Am Phys Soc; Asn Comput Mach; Int Soc Quantum Biol; Am Chem Soc. *Res:* Aerosol light scattering; remote sensing of chemical species in the atmosphere and on surfaces; theoretical study of molecular structure, excited states and energy transfer; interaction of matter with laser light at high power density; mathematical modeling and operations research analyses. *Mailing Add:* PO Box 233 Aberdeen Proving Grounds MD 21010

STUEDEMANN, JOHN ALFRED, b Clinton, Iowa, Oct 3, 42; m 67. ANIMAL NUTRITION. *Educ:* Iowa State Univ, BS, 64; Okla State Univ, MS, 67, PhD(ruminant nutrit), 70. *Prof Exp:* RES PHYSIOLOGIST, SOUTHERN PIEDMONT CONSERV RES CTR, AGR RES SERV, USDA, 70- *Mem:* Am Soc Animal Sci. *Res:* Ruminant nutrition; forage production and utilization; waste disposal and land fertilization; health problems of beef cattle; forage finishing of cattle; cow-calf management. *Mailing Add:* Southern Piedmont Conserv Res Ctr USDA PO Box 555 Watkinsville GA 30677

STUEHR, JOHN EDWARD, b Aug 30, 35; US citizen; m 62; c 4. BIOPHYSICAL CHEMISTRY. *Educ:* Western Reserve Univ, BA, 57, MS, 59, PhD(chem), 61. *Prof Exp:* NIH res fel chem, Max Planck Inst, Göttingen, WGer, 62-63; from asst prof to assoc prof, 64-74, chmn dept, 76, PROF CHEM, CASE WESTERN RESERVE UNIV, 74- *Mem:* Am Chem Soc; Sigma Xi; Fedn Biol Chemists. *Res:* Reaction kinetics of fast processes in solution; relaxation spectroscopy; metal complexing; biochemical kinetics; elementary steps in enzyme kinetics. *Mailing Add:* Dept of Chem Case Western Reserve Univ Cleveland OH 44106

STUELPNAGEL, JOHN CLAY, b Houston, Tex, Nov 12, 36; m 59; c 3. MATHEMATICS. *Educ:* Yankton Col, BA, 55; Johns Hopkins Univ, PhD(math), 62. *Prof Exp:* Fel math, Res Inst Advan Studies, Martin-Marietta Corp, 61-64; sr engr, 64-66, fel engr, Aerospace Div, 66-76, PROG MGR, SYST DEVELOP DIV, WESTINGHOUSE ELEC CORP, 76- *Mem:* Am Defense Preparedness Asn. *Res:* Lie groups; linear algebra; differential equations; computation and computer design; radar development. *Mailing Add:* MS 417 Westinghouse Elec Corp Box 746 Baltimore MD 21203

STUESSY, TOD FALOR, b Pittsburgh, Pa, Nov 18, 43; div; c 2. SYSTEMATIC BOTANY. *Educ:* DePauw Univ, BA, 65; Univ Tex, Austin, PhD(bot), 68. *Prof Exp:* Asst prof, 68-74, assoc prof, 74-79, PROF BOT, OHIO STATE UNIV, 79- *Concurrent Pos:* Res assoc, Field Mus Nat Hist, 70-77; Maria Moors Cabot res fel, Gray Herbarium, Harvard Univ, 71-72; assoc dir, Syst Biol Prog, NSF & collabr, Dept Bot, Smithsonian Inst, 77-78. *Honors & Awards:* Wilks Award, Southwestern Asn Naturalists. *Mem:* AAAS; Int Asn Plant Taxon; Am Soc Plant Taxon; Bot Soc Am; Soc Study Evolution. *Res:* Systematics and evolution of Compositae. *Mailing Add:* Dept Bot Ohio State Univ 1735 Neil Ave Columbus OH 43210

STUEWER, ROGER HARRY, b Sept 12, 34; US citizen; m 60; c 2. HISTORY OF PHYSICS. *Educ:* Univ Wis, BS, 58, MS, 64, PhD(hist sci & physics), 68. *Prof Exp:* Instr physics, Heidelberg Col, 60-62; from asst prof to assoc prof hist physics, Univ Minn, Minneapolis, 67-71; assoc prof hist sci, Boston Univ,

71-72; assoc prof hist physics, 72-74, PROF HIST PHYSICS, UNIV MINN, MINNEAPOLIS, 74- *Concurrent Pos:* Mem adv panel hist & philos sci, NSF, 70-72, res support, 70-; Am Coun Learned Soc fel, 74-75,consult, Franklin Mint, 74- *Mem:* Hist Sci Soc (secy, 72-); Philos Sci Asn; Sigma Xi; Brit Soc Hist Sci; Brit Soc Philos Sci. *Res:* History of nineteenth and twentieth century physics, especially optics, quantum theory, and nuclear physics; Compton effect as a turning point in physics. *Mailing Add:* Sch of Physics & Astron Univ of Minn Minneapolis MN 55455

STUFFLEBEAM, CHARLES EDWARD, b St Louis, Mo, Feb 22, 33; m 52; c 3. ANIMAL GENETICS, BIOCHEMISTRY. *Educ:* Univ Mo, BS, 58, MS, 61, PhD, 64. *Prof Exp:* Asst county agent, Exten Div, Univ Mo, 59-61, instr animal husb & agr biochem, 62-64; assoc prof range animal sci, Sul Ross State Col, 64-65; assoc prof animal sci, Northwestern State Univ, 65-69; PROF ANIMAL SCI, SOUTHWEST MO STATE UNIV, 69- *Mem:* Am Soc Animal Sci; Nat Asn Cols & Teachers Agr (past pres). *Res:* Genetics; biochemistry, physiology and nutrition of domestic animals and their application to agriculture; animal husbandry. *Mailing Add:* Dept Agr Southwest Mo State Univ Springfield MO 65802

STUHL, LOUIS SHELDON, b New York, NY, Feb 5, 51. HOMOGENEOUS CATALYSIS, TRANSITION METAL CHEMISTRY. *Educ:* Mass Inst Technol, SB, 73; Cornell Univ, MS, 76, PhD(chem), 78. *Prof Exp:* NSF fel chem, Univ Calif, Berkeley, 78-79; ASST PROF CHEM, BRANDEIS UNIV, 79- *Mem:* Am Chem Soc. *Res:* Transition metal chemistry and its application to problems of catalysis and organic synthesis, including exploratory work and mechanistic studies of known systems. *Mailing Add:* Dept Chem Brandeis Univ Waltham MA 02254

STUHLINGER, ERNST, b Niederrimbach, Ger, Dec 19, 13; nat US; m 50; c 3. PHYSICS. *Educ:* Univ Tübingen, PhD(physics), 36. *Prof Exp:* Asst prof, Berlin Inst Technol, 36-41; res asst guid & control, Rocket Develop Ctr, Peenemuende, 43-45; asst res & develop, Ord Corps, US Army, Ft Bliss, Tex & White Sands Proving Ground, NMex, 46-50, astronaut res adminr & supvry phys scientist, Ballistic Missile Agency, Redstone Arsenal, Ala, 50-60; dir, Space Sci Lab, Marshall Space Flight Ctr, NASA, 60-68, assoc dir sci, 68-76; SR RES SCIENTIST, UNIV ALA, HUNTSVILLE, 76- *Honors & Awards:* Roentgen Prize; Galabert Prize, Paris, 62; Hermann Oberth Award, 62 & Medal, 64; Propulsion Award, Am Inst Aeronaut & Astronaut, 60; Wernher von Braun Prize. *Mem:* Fel Am Inst Aeronaut & Astronaut; Fel Am Astronaut Soc; Ger Phys Soc; Ger Soc Rockets & Space Flight; Brit Interplanetary Soc. *Res:* Feasibility and design studies of electrical propulsion systems for space ships; scientific satellites and space probes; electric automobiles. *Mailing Add:* 3106 Rowe Dr Huntsville AL 35801

STUHLMAN, ROBERT AUGUST, b Cincinnati, Ohio, Apr 9, 39; m 60; c 3. LABORATORY ANIMAL MEDICINE, MEDICAL RESEARCH. *Educ:* Ohio State Univ, DVM, 68; Univ Mo, Columbia, MS, 71; Am Col Lab Animal Med, dipl, 74. *Prof Exp:* Res asst vet clin, Ohio State Univ, 66-68; res assoc vet med & surg, Univ Mo, Columbia, 68-71 & instr path & asst dir lab animal med, Med Ctr, 71-75; DIR LAB ANIMAL RESOURCES, DIR INTERDISCIPLINARY TEACHING LABS & ASSOC PROF PATH, WRIGHT STATE UNIV, 75- *Concurrent Pos:* Vet med officer, Vet Admin Hosp, Columbia, Mo, 72-75; consult gen med res, Vet Admin Ctr, Dayton, Ohio, 75-; consult vet, Cent State Univ, Wilberforce, Ohio, 80- *Honors & Awards:* Dr Davis S White Mem Award. *Mem:* Am Vet Med Asn; Nat Soc Med Res; Am Asn Lab Animal Sci; Am Col Lab Animal Med; Am Soc Lab Animal Practitioners. *Res:* Diabetes mellitus, especially development of the animal model; diagnosis; pathogenesis; establishment of secondary complications; therapy; inheritance patterns. *Mailing Add:* Lab Animal Resources Wright State Univ Sch of Med Dayton OH 45435

STUHT, JOHN NEAL, wildlife diseases, see previous edition

STUIVER, MINZE, b Vlagtwedde, Neth, Oct 25, 29; m 56; c 2. EARTH SCIENCE. *Educ:* State Univ Groningen, MSc, 53, PhD(biophys), 58. *Prof Exp:* Res assoc & fel geol, Yale Univ, 59-62, sr res assoc geol & biol & dir radiocarbon lab, 62-69; prof geol & zool, 69-81, PROF GEOL & QUATERNARY SCI, UNIV WASH, 81- *Res:* Biophysics of sense organs; low level counting techniques; geophysical implications of variations in atmospheric radiocarbon content; Pleistocene geology, oceanography and limnology. *Mailing Add:* Quaternary Res Ctr Univ of Wash Seattle WA 98195

STUIVER, W(ILLEM), b Breda, Netherlands, Aug 1, 27; m 57. ANALYTICAL DYNAMICS, SPACE FLIGHT MECHANICS. *Educ:* Delft Univ Technol, Mech engr, 51; Stanford Univ, PhD(eng mech), 60. *Prof Exp:* Asst mech engr, NZ Ministry Works, 52-54; res engr, NZ Dept Sci & Indust Res, 54-55; anal design engr, Gen Elec Co, 56-58; mem res staff, IBM Corp, 59-61; assoc prof mech eng, 61-65, PROF MECH ENG, UNIV HAWAII, 65- *Concurrent Pos:* Consult, Stanford Res Inst, 62-67; vis prof, Indian Inst Sci, India, 64-65, Univ Australia, New SWales, 75 & Univ Peradeniya, Sri Lanka, 82-83. *Mem:* Am Inst Aeronaut & Astronaut; Am Astronaut Soc. *Res:* Development of metric approach to state-space analysis of dynamical systems; mission analysis and structural design of space radiotelescope system. *Mailing Add:* Dept of Mech Eng Univ of Hawaii Honolulu HI 96822

STUKEL, JAMES JOSEPH, b Joliet, Ill, Mar 30, 37; m 58; c 4. ENGINEERING. *Educ:* Purdue Univ, BSME, 59; Univ Ill, Urbana-Champaign, MS, 63, PhD(mech eng), 68. *Prof Exp:* Res engr, Westvaco, 59-61; from asst prof to assoc prof civil eng & mech eng, 68-74, dir off coal res, 75-76, dir, Off Energy Res, 76-80, dir, Off Interdisciplinary Proj, 78-80, PROF CIVIL ENG & MECH ENG, UNIV ILL, 75-, DIR PUBLIC POLICY PROG, COL ENG, 80- *Concurrent Pos:* Consult, Westvaco, 61-63 & var govt agencies, 68-; prin investr, US Environ Protection Agency training grant, 70-76, res grants, Kimberly Clark Corp, 75-76, Bur Mines & US Environ Protection Agency, 76-82. *Honors & Awards:* State of the Art of Civil Eng Award, Am Soc Civil Engrs, 75. *Mem:* Am Soc Civil Engrs; Am Soc Mech Engrs; Sigma Xi. *Res:* Aerosol science; air resources management; impact assessment. *Mailing Add:* 3219 Civil Eng Bldg Univ Ill Urbana IL 61801

STUKUS, PHILIP EUGENE, b Braddock, Penn, Oct 22, 42; m 66; c 3. MICROBIAL PHYSIOLOGY, ENVIRONMENTAL MICROBIOLOGY. *Educ:* St Vincent Col, BA, 64; Cath Univ Am, MS, 66, PhD(microbiol), 68. *Prof Exp:* asst prof, 68-80, PROF BIOL, DENISON UNIV, 80- *Mem:* AAAS; Am Soc Microbiol; Sigma Xi; Soc Indust Microbiol. *Res:* Autotrophic and heterotrophic metabolism of hydrogen bacteria; degradation of detergent additives and pesticides by soil microorganisms; distribution of microorganisms in air. *Mailing Add:* Dept of Biol Denison Univ Granville OH 43023

STULA, EDWIN FRANCIS, b Colchester, Conn, Jan 3, 24; m 55; c 1. VETERINARY PATHOLOGY. *Educ:* Univ Conn, BS, 50, PhD(animal path), 63; Univ Toronto, DVM, 55. *Prof Exp:* Instr vet med & exten vet, Univ Conn, 55-62; CHIEF RES PATHOLOGIST, HASKELL LAB TOXICOL & INDUST MED, E I DU PONT DE NEMOURS & CO, INC, 63- *Mem:* Am Vet Med Asn; Soc Pharmacol & Environ Pathologists; NY Acad Sci; Int Acad Path; Am Asn Lab Animal Sci. *Res:* Bovine vibriosis, mastitis and infertility; leptospirosis in chincillas and guinea pigs; spontaneous diseases of laboratory animals; industrial medicine; pathologic effects in animals exposed to various chemicals by various routes; morphologic effects using both light and electron microscopes; carcinogenicity and embryotoxicity. *Mailing Add:* 235 Mercury Rd Newark DE 19711

STULBERG, CYRIL SIDNEY, tissue culture, virology, see previous edition

STULBERG, MELVIN PHILIP, b Duluth, Minn, May 17, 25; m 55; c 3. BIOCHEMISTRY. *Educ:* Univ Minn, BS, 49, MS, 55, PhD(biochem), 58. *Prof Exp:* Res assoc, Biol Div, Oak Ridge Nat Lab, 58-59, biochemist, 59-61; biochemist, AEC, 61-63; BIOCHEMIST BIOL DIV, OAK RIDGE NAT LAB, 63-; PROF, OAK RIDGE GRAD SCH BIOMED SCI, UNIV TENN, 73- *Mem:* Sigma Xi; AAAS; Am Soc Biol Chemists. *Res:* Protein biosynthesis; isolation and function of transfer RNA; enzyme mechanisms; mechanisms of aging. *Mailing Add:* Biol Div Oak Ridge Nat Lab PO Box Y Oak Ridge TN 37830

STULL, DEAN P, US citizen. ANALYTICAL CHEMISTRY. *Educ:* Colo State Univ, BS, 72; Univ Colo, MS, 74, PhD(phys org chem), 76. *Prof Exp:* Res asst, Colo State Univ, 70-71, Univ Calif, San Francisco, 72 & Univ Colo, Boulder, 76; CHIEF CHEMIST, HAUSER LABS, 76- *Mem:* Am Chem Soc; Sigma Xi. *Res:* Methods development of chemical analysis of crude and refined petroleum products utilizing high performance liquid chromatography. *Mailing Add:* Hauser Labs 5680 Central Ave Boulder CO 80301

STULL, ELISABETH ANN, b Fayette, Mo, Jan 7, 43. ENVIRONMENTAL IMPACT ANALYSIS, LIMNOLOGY. *Educ:* Lawrence Univ, BA, 65; Univ Ga, MS, 69; Univ Calif, Davis, PhD(zool), 72. *Prof Exp:* Asst prof biol sci, 71-75, asst prof ecol & evolutionary biol, Univ Ariz, 75-78; ECOLOGIST, ENVIRON IMPACT STUDIES, ARGONNE NAT LAB, 78- *Mem:* Am Soc Limnol & Oceanog; Phycol Soc Am; AAAS. *Res:* Energetics and trophic ecology of unicellular taxa; algal floristics; regional and geographical patterns in limnology and water quality; environmental analysis of energy-related technologies. *Mailing Add:* Environ Impact Studies Div 9700 S Cass Ave Argonne IL 60439

STULL, JAMES TRAVIS, b Ashland, Ky, Feb 7, 44; m 66; c 2. PHARMACOLOGY, BIOCHEMISTRY. *Educ:* Southwestern at Memphis, BS, 66; Emory Univ, PhD(pharmacol), 71. *Prof Exp:* Adj asst prof biol chem, Sch Med, Univ Calif, Davis, 73-74; from asst prof to assoc prof med, Sch Med, Univ Calif, San Diego, 74-78; ASSOC PROF PHARMACOL, UNIV TEX HEALTH SCI CTR, DALLAS, 78- *Concurrent Pos:* Damon Runyon Mem Fund Cancer Res fel, Univ Calif, Davis, 71-73; estab investr, Am Heart Asn, 73; assoc dean, Grad Sch Biomed Sci, Univ Tex Health Sci Ctr, Dallas, 80- *Mem:* Am Heart Asn; Am Soc Pharmacol & Exp Therapeut; AAAS; Am Soc Biol Chemists. *Res:* Protein phosphorylation reactions in regulation of muscle metabolism, contraction and responses to hormones and adrenergic drugs. *Mailing Add:* Dept of Pharmacol 5323 Harry Hines Blvd Dallas TX 75235

STULL, JOHN LEETE, b Dansville, NY, June 2, 30; m 52; c 2. PHYSICS, ASTRONOMY. *Educ:* Alfred Univ, BS, 52, MS, 54, PhD(ceramics), 58. *Prof Exp:* Res assoc ceramics, 52-58, from asst prof to assoc prof physics, 58-68, chmn dept, 72-75, PROF PHYSICS, ALFRED UNIV, 68-, DIR OBSERV, 68- *Mem:* AAAS; Am Asn Physics Teachers. *Res:* Astronomy; development of physics teaching apparatus; design of small optical observatories and equipment. *Mailing Add:* Dept of Physics Alfred Univ Alfred NY 14802

STULL, JOHN WARREN, b Benton, Ill, Nov 23, 21; m 45; c 5. DAIRY SCIENCE. *Educ:* Univ Ill, BS, 42, MS, 47, PhD(food technol), 50. *Prof Exp:* Asst dairy technol, Univ Ill, 46-49; from asst prof to assoc prof dairy sci, 49-58, actg head dept, 56-57, PROF NUTRIT & FOOD SCI, COL AGR, UNIV ARIZ, 58-, FOOD SCIENTIST, AGR EXP STA, 74- *Mem:* Am Chem Soc; Am Dairy Sci Asn; Inst Food Technologists. *Res:* Factors related to the oxidative deterioration of the constituents of milk; food value of milk; chemical residues in milk; biochemistry of milk and food lipids. *Mailing Add:* Dept of Nutrit & Food Sci Col of Agr Univ of Ariz Tucson AZ 85721

STULL, VINCENT ROBERT, applied physics, systems analysis, deceased

STULTS, FREDERICK HOWARD, b Seattle, Wash, Nov 11, 48; m 69; c 3. TOXICOLOGY. *Educ:* San Diego State Univ, BS, 71; Univ Calif, Davis, PhD(biochem), 76. *Prof Exp:* Fel toxicol, Med Sch, Duke Univ, 76-77; res toxicologist, 77-80, DEPT HEAD, CORP SAFETY, INT FLAVORS & FRAGRANCES, 80- *Mem:* Am Chem Soc; Inst Food Technologists; Am Col Toxicol. *Res:* Human dermal toxicity, allergenicity, biodegradation & photobiology. *Mailing Add:* Res & Develop Inst Flavors & Fragrances 1515 Highway 36 Union Beach NJ 07735

STULTS, VALA JEAN, b Oklahoma City, Okla, Aug 16, 42. NUTRITION. *Educ:* Calif State Univ, Long Beach, BA, 65, MA, 67; Mich State Univ, PhD(human nutrit), 74. *Prof Exp:* Teacher home econ, Lawndale High Sch, 66-68; consult nutritionist, Head Start Prog, Off Econ Opportunity, 69; NIH fel, 73-74; asst instr nutrit, Cen Mich Univ, 74; sales mgr & asst to gen mgr potatoes in retort pouches, Nu Foods Inc, 75-76; NUTRITIONIST, KELLOGG CO, 77- *Mem:* Am Home Econ Asn; Am Dietetic Asn; Soc Nutrit Educ; Soc Nutrit Today. *Res:* Subjects of interest to the ready-to-eat cereal industry in relationship to human nutrition. *Mailing Add:* Suite 480 Watergate 600 Kellogg Co 600 New Hampshire SW Washington DC 20037

STULTZ, WALTER ALVA, b St John, NB, Mar 14, 04; nat US; m 31, 50; c 5. ANATOMY. *Educ:* Acadia Univ, BA, 27; Yale Univ, PhD(zool, anat), 32. *Prof Exp:* Prin sch, NB, Can, 22-24; asst biol, Yale Univ, 27-30; instr, Spring Hill Sch, Conn, 30-31; instr & actg head dept, Trinity Col, Conn, 31-32; prof, Mt Union Col, 32-33; asst, Yale Univ, 33-34; fel anat, Sch Med, Univ Ga, 34-35, fel histol & embryol, 35-36; instr anat, Med Col SC, 36-37; from asst prof to prof, 37-69, EMER PROF ANAT, COL MED, UNIV VT, 69- *Concurrent Pos:* Sr lectr gross anat & histol, Sch Med, Univ Calif, San Diego, 69-77; vis prof anat, Dartmouth Med Sch, 77- *Mem:* Am Asn Anat. *Res:* Experimental embryology of Amblystoma; relations of symmetry in fore and hind limbs; interrelationships between limbs and nervous system. *Mailing Add:* 37 Birchwood Dr Colchester VT 05446

STUMP, ALEXANDER BELL, b Emmorton, Md, Jan 13, 05; m 42; c 4. PROTOZOOLOGY. *Educ:* Univ Va, BS, 30, MS, 31, PhD(protozool), 34. *Prof Exp:* Res assoc, Univ Va, 34-35; prof biol, Flora Macdonald Col, 36-47; prof, 47-72, EMER PROF, PRESBY COL, SC, 72- *Res:* Mitosis in the testacea; cytology of protozoa. *Mailing Add:* Rt 1 Box 57 Cross Hill SC 29332

STUMP, BILLY LEE, b Morristown, Tenn, Jan 11, 30; m 58; c 3. PHYSICAL CHEMISTRY, POLYMER CHEMISTRY. *Educ:* Carson-Newman Col, BS, 52; Univ Tenn, PhD(chem), 59. *Prof Exp:* Res chemist, Carson-Newman Col, 52-53; res technician, Oak Ridge Inst Nuclear Studies, 53-54; chemist, Redstone Div, Thiokol Chem Corp, 59-60; res chemist, Film Res Lab, E I du Pont de Nemours & Co, 60-62 & Spruance Film Res & Develop Lab, 62-63; assoc prof chem, Carson-Newman Col, 63-66; assoc prof, 66-78, PROF CHEM, VA COMMONWEALTH UNIV, 78- *Mem:* Am Chem Soc; Sigma Xi. *Res:* Kinetics and reaction mechanisms; catalysis and kinetics of catalytic hydrogenation; polymer chemistry. *Mailing Add:* Dept of Chem 901 W Franklin St Va Commonwealth Univ Richmond VA 23284

STUMP, EDMUND, b Danville, Pa, Dec 28, 46. GEOLOGY. *Educ:* Harvard Col, AB, 68; Yale Univ, MS, 72; Ohio State Univ, PhD(geol), 76. *Prof Exp:* ASST PROF GEOL, ARIZ STATE UNIV, 76- *Mem:* Geol Soc Am; AAAS. *Res:* Geology of Antarctica and Gondwanaland. *Mailing Add:* Dept of Geol Ariz State Univ Tempe AZ 85281

STUMP, EUGENE CURTIS, JR, b Charleston, WVa, May 19, 30; m 58; c 3. ORGANIC CHEMISTRY, FLUORINE CHEMISTRY. *Educ:* WVa Univ, BS, 52; Columbia Univ, MA, 53; Univ Fla, PhD(org chem), 60. *Prof Exp:* Dir contract res, 60-70, vpres contract res div, 70-76, VPRES RES & DEVELOP, PCR, INC, 76- *Mem:* Am Chem Soc; Royal Soc Chem. *Res:* Synthesis of fluorine containing compounds, particularly ethers, olefins, nitroso and difluoramine compounds; synthesis of fluorine-containing polymers as low temperature elastomers; synthesis of thermally and oxidatively stable fluids. *Mailing Add:* Res & Develop PCR Inc PO Box 1466 Gainesville FL 32601

STUMP, JOHN EDWARD, b Galion, Ohio, June 3, 34; m 55; c 2. VETERINARY ANATOMY, VETERINARY ETHOLOGY. *Educ:* Ohio State Univ, DVM, 58; Purdue Univ, PhD, 66. *Prof Exp:* Private vet pract, Ohio, 58-61; from instr to assoc prof vet anat, 61-76, PROF VET ANAT, PURDUE UNIV, WEST LAFAYETTE, 76- *Concurrent Pos:* Vis prof, Dept Physiol Sci, Sch Vet Med, Univ Calif, Davis, 80; Dept Vet Anat, Col Vet Med, Tex A&M Univ, 81. *Mem:* Animal Behav Soc; Am Vet Med Asn; World Asn Vet Anat; Am Asn Vet Anat (pres, 77-78); Asn Am Vet Med Cols. *Res:* Gross anatomy of domestic animals. *Mailing Add:* Dept Anat Sch Vet Med Purdue Univ West Lafayette IN 47907

STUMP, JOHN M, b Charleston, WVa, June 26, 38; m 64. PHARMACOLOGY. *Educ:* WVa Univ, BS, 61, MS, 62, PhD(pharmacol), 64. *Prof Exp:* Res pharmacologist, 64-72, sr res pharmacologist, 72-78, RES ASSOC, STINE LAB, PHARMACEUT RES DIV, E I DU PONT DE NEMOURS & CO, INC, 78- *Res:* Cardiovascular pharmacology. *Mailing Add:* 38 Aronomink Dr Newark DE 19711

STUMP, ROBERT, b Indianapolis, Ind, Oct 16, 21; m 43; c 4. PHYSICS. *Educ:* Butler Univ, BA, 42; Univ Ill, MS, 48, PhD(physics), 50. *Prof Exp:* From asst prof to assoc prof, 50-60, PROF PHYSICS, UNIV KANS, 60- *Concurrent Pos:* Consult, Aeronaut Radio, Inc, DC, 52-53; vis scientist, Midwestern Univs Res Asn, Wis, 59, Europ Orgn Nuclear Res, Geneva, 63-64 & Polytech Sch, Paris, 70-71; vis physicist, Brookhaven Nat Lab, 62-63. *Mem:* AAAS; fel Am Phys Soc. *Res:* Experimental nuclear and elementary particle physics; angular correlations; low temperature effects; hydrogen and heavy liquid bubble chamber experiments; atmospheric physics; atmospheric dynamics. *Mailing Add:* Dept of Physics & Astron Univ of Kans Lawrence KS 66044

STUMPF, FOLDEN BURT, b Lansing, Mich, Aug 18, 28; m 54; c 2. PHYSICS. *Educ:* Kent State Univ, BS, 50; Univ Mich, MS, 51; Ill Inst Technol, PhD(physics), 56. *Prof Exp:* From asst prof to assoc prof, 56-66, PROF PHYSICS, OHIO UNIV, 66- *Mem:* Acoust Soc Am; Am Asn Physics Teachers. *Res:* Ultrasonic transducers; application of ultrasonics to liquids. *Mailing Add:* Dept of Physics Ohio Univ Athens OH 45701

STUMPF, H(ARRY) C(LINCH), b Buffalo, NY, June 29, 18; m 43; c 2. METALLURGICAL ENGINEERING. *Educ:* Univ Mich, BS, 39, MS, 41, PhD(metall eng), 43. *Prof Exp:* Asst prof chem eng, Univ Del, 42-44; metall engr, Allegany Ballistics Lab, Md, 44-45; sci assoc, Alcoa Res Labs, Aluminum Co Am, 46-76, sci assoc, Alcoa Lab, Alcoa Tech Ctr, 76-80; RETIRED. *Mem:* Am Inst Mining, Metall & Petrol Engrs. *Res:* Physical metallurgy, especially of aluminum alloys; x-ray diffraction. *Mailing Add:* 810 Carl Ave New Kensington PA 15068

STUMPF, PAUL KARL, b New York, NY, Feb 23, 19; m 47; c 5. LIPID BIOCHEMISTRY. *Educ:* Harvard Univ, AB, 41; Columbia Univ, PhD(biochem), 45. *Prof Exp:* Chemist, Div War Res, Columbia Univ, 44-46; instr epidemiol, Sch Pub Health, Univ Mich, 46-48; asst prof plant nutrit, Univ Calif, Berkeley, 48-52; from assoc prof to prof plant biochem, Univ Calif, Davis, 52-58, chmn dept, 53-57, prof biochem & chmn, Dept Biochem, 58-61, 67-68, 70, 81. *Concurrent Pos:* NIH sr fel, 54-55; NSF sr fel, 61- 68; Guggenheim fel, 62 & 69; ed, J Phytochem, 60-72 & Archives Biochem & Biophys, 60-65, exec ed, 65-; ed, J Lipid Res, 63-66, Anal Biochem, 69-80; mem physiol chem study sect, NIH, 60-64; metab biol panel, NSF, 65-68; mem, City of Davis Planning Comn, 67-69; vis scientist, Commonwealth Sci & Indust Res Orgn, Canberra ACT, Australia, 75-76; sr US Sci fel, Von Humboldt Fedn, Ger, 76. *Honors & Awards:* Stephen Hales Award, Am Soc Plant Physiologist, 74; Lipid Chem Prize, Am Oil Chemists Soc, 74. *Mem:* Nat Acad Sci; Am Soc Plant Physiol (pres, 80); Am Oil Chem Soc; Am Soc Biol Chem; foreign mem Royal Danish Acad Arts & Sci. *Res:* Lipid biochemistry of higher plants; photobiosynthesis; developmental biochemistry. *Mailing Add:* Dept of Biochem & Biophys Univ of Calif Davis CA 95616

STUMPF, WALTER ERICH, b Oelsnitz, Ger, Jan 10, 27; m 61; c 4. NEUROENDOCRINOLOGY, PHARMACOLOGY. *Educ:* Univ Berlin, MD, 52, cert neurol & psychiat, 57; Univ Chicago, PhD(pharmacol), 67. *Prof Exp:* Intern, Charite Hosp, Univ Berlin, 52-53; resident neurol & psychiat, 53-57; sci asst, Univ Marburg, 58-60 & Lab Radiobiol & Isotope Res, 61-62; res assoc pharmacol, Univ Chicago, 63-67, asst prof, 67-70; assoc prof anat & pharmacol & mem labs for reproductive biol, 70-73, PROF ANAT & PHARMACOL, UNIV NC, CHAPEL HILL, 73- *Concurrent Pos:* Trainee, psychother & psychoanal, Inst Psychother, WBerlin, 54-56; lectr clin neurol, Charite Hosp, Univ Berlin, 56-57; vis psychiatrist, Maudsley Hosp, London, 59; consult, Microtome-Cyrostats, 69-; mem, Neurolbiol Prog, 70-; assoc, Carolina Pop Ctr, 72-; res scientist, Biol Sci Res Ctr, 72-; consult, Life Sci Inst, Research Triangle Park, NC, 73-; mem coun, Inst Lab Animal Resources, 78-81; mem US subcomt, Int Ctr Cybernetics & Systs, World Orgn Gen Systs & Cybernetics. *Mem:* AAAS; Am Soc Zoologists; Histochem Soc; Int Brain Res Orgn; Am Asn Anatomists. *Res:* Development of histochemical techniques; low temperature sectioning and freeze-drying; dry-mount autoradiography for the localization of hormones and drugs in the brain and other tissues. *Mailing Add:* Dept of Anat & Pharmacol Univ of NC at Chapel Hill Chapel Hill NC 27514

STUMPFF, HOWARD KEITH, b Holden, Mo, May 26, 30; m 57; c 3. MATHEMATICS. *Educ:* Cent Mo State Col, BSEd, 51; Univ Mo, AM, 53; Univ Kans, PhD(math ed), 68. *Prof Exp:* Asst instr math, Univ Mo, 51-53; instr, Univ NMex, 57-63; from asst prof to assoc prof, 63-72, PROF MATH, CENT MO STATE COL, 72-, HEAD DEPT, 69- *Concurrent Pos:* Asst instr, Univ Kans, 61-62. *Mem:* Am Math Soc; Math Asn Am. *Res:* Mathematics education. *Mailing Add:* Dept of Math Cent Mo State Col Warrensburg MO 64093

STUNKARD, ALBERT J, b New York, NY, Feb 7, 22. PSYCHIATRY. *Educ:* Yale Univ, BS, 43; Columbia Univ, MD, 45. *Prof Exp:* Resident physician, Johns Hopkins Hosp, 48-51; fel psychiat, 51-52; res fel med, Col Physicians & Surgeons, Columbia Univ, 52-53; Commonwealth fel med, Med Col, Cornell Univ, 53-56, asst prof, 56-57; assoc prof, 57-62, prof psychiat & chmn dept, Sch Med, Univ Pa, 62-73; prof, Stanford Univ, 73-76; PROF PSYCHIAT, UNIV PA, 76- *Concurrent Pos:* Fel, Ctr Advan Study Behav Sci, Calif, 71-72. *Honors & Awards:* Menninger Award, Am Col Physicians; Am Psychiat Asn Award, 60 & 80. *Mem:* Am Psychosom Soc (pres, 74); Am Psychiat Asn; Am Fedn Clin Res; fel NY Acad Sci; Psychiat Res Soc. *Res:* Obesity and regulation of energy balance. *Mailing Add:* Dept of Psychiat Univ of Pa Philadelphia PA 19104

STUNKARD, JIM A, b Sterling, Colo, Jan 25, 35; m 67; c 1. LABORATORY ANIMAL MEDICINE, VETERINARY MICROBIOLOGY. *Educ:* Colo State Univ, BS, 57, DVM, 59; Tex A&M Univ, MS, 66; Am Col Lab Animal Med, dipl. *Prof Exp:* Vet, Glasgow Animal Hosp, Ky, 59-61; vet in charge, Sentry Dog Procurement, Training & Med Referral Ctr, US Air Force Europe, 61-64 & Lab Animal Colonies & Zoonoses Control Ctr, 61-64, resident lab animal med, sch aerospace med, Brooks AFB, Tex, 64-66, dir vet med sci dept, Naval Med Res Inst, Nat Naval Med Ctr, Md, 66-71. *Concurrent Pos:* Vet consult, Turkish Sentry Dog Prog, US Air Force Europe, 61-63, Can Air Force Europe, 62-64; Bur Med & Surg, US Navy, Washington, DC, Navy Toxicol Unit, Md, 66-71 & AEC, 68-71; consult to dean vet med, Colo State Univ, 69-71; US Navy rep ad hoc comt, Dept Defense, 66-67 & Inst Lab Animal Resouces, Nat Acad Sci-Nat Res Coun, Washington, DC, 66-71. *Mem:* Am Vet Med Asn. *Res:* Veterinary medicine, dentistry and surgery, especially all phases of laboratory animal medicine. *Mailing Add:* Bowie Animal Hosp 3428 Crain Hwy Bowie MD 20716

STUNTZ, CALVIN FREDERICK, b Buffalo, NY, Aug 6, 18; m 51; c 3. CHEMISTRY. *Educ:* Univ Buffalo, BA, 39, PhD(chem), 47. *Prof Exp:* Teacher high sch, NY, 39-40; anal chemist, Linde Air Prods Co, Union Carbide & Carbon Corp, 40-41; asst, Univ Buffalo, 41-43, 45-46; from asst prof to prof chem, 46-79, EMER PROF CHEM, UNIV MD, COLLEGE PARK, 80- *Mem:* Am Chem Soc. *Res:* Quantitative analysis; chemical microscopy. *Mailing Add:* Dept Chem Univ Md College Park MD 20742

STUNTZ, GORDON FREDERICK, b Washington, DC, Dec 7, 52; m 73. INORGANIC CHEMISTRY, PETROLEUM CHEMISTRY. *Educ:* Pa State Univ, BS, 74; Univ Ill, PhD(inorg chem), 78. *Prof Exp:* RES CHEMIST PROCESS RES, EXXON RES & DEVELOP LABS, EXXON CORP, 78- *Mem:* Am Chem Soc. *Mailing Add:* Exxon Res & Develop Labs PO Box 2226 Baton Rouge LA 70821

STUPER, ANDREW JOHN, b Chicago, Ill, Dec 19, 50; m 77. THEORETICAL CHEMISTRY, ANALYTICAL CHEMISTRY. *Educ:* Univ Wis-Superior, BS, 72; Pa State Univ, PhD(anal chem), 77. *Prof Exp:* Vis scientist, Nat Ctr Toxicol Res, 75-76; consult, Parke Davis Co, 76; SR SCIENTIST, ROHM & HAAS CO, 77- *Mem:* Am Chem Soc; Sigma Xi; Asn Comput Mach. *Res:* Development of methods which enhance understanding of the relationship between chemical structure and biological activity; use of computers in chemistry. *Mailing Add:* Rohm & Haas Co Springhouse PA 19477

STUPIAN, GARY WENDELL, b Alhambra, Calif, Oct 17, 39. SOLID STATE PHYSICS, SURFACE PHYSICS. *Educ:* Calif Inst Technol, BS, 61; Univ Ill, Urbana, MS, 63, PhD(physics), 67. *Prof Exp:* Res asst physics, Univ Ill, Urbana, 61-67; res assoc mat sci, Cornell Univ, 67-69; MEM TECH STAFF, AEROSPACE CORP, 69- *Mem:* AAAS; Am Phys Soc. *Res:* Nuclear magnetic resonance; Auger spectroscopy; heterogeneous catalysis; analytical instrumentation. *Mailing Add:* Bldg A6/2647 Chem Physics Lab Aerospace Corp PO Box 92957 Los Angeles CA 90009

STUPP, EDWARD HENRY, b Brooklyn, NY, Dec 10, 32; m 54; c 2. TECHNICAL MANAGEMENT, ELECTRONICS ENGINEERING. *Educ:* City Col New York, BS, 54; Syracuse Univ, MS, 58, PhD(physics), 60. *Prof Exp:* Asst physics, Columbia Univ, 54-55, Watson Lab, 55-56 & Syracuse Univ, 56-69; staff physicist, Thomas J Watson Res Ctr, 59-62; MEM TECH STAFF & SR PROG LEADER COMPONENTS & DEVICES GROUP, PHILIPS LABS DIV, N AM PHILIPS CO, 62- *Concurrent Pos:* Consult infrared imaging, Philips Broadcast Equip Cor, 72-73. *Mem:* Am Phys Soc; Inst Elec & Electronics Eng. *Res:* Experimental solid state physics, including silicon devices and integrated circuits; solid-state ballast circuits; photoemission; visible and infrared camera tubes, photodetectors, electron multiplication, image tubes; cold cathodes. *Mailing Add:* Philips Labs 345 Scarborough Rd Briarcliff NY 10510

STURBAUM, BARBARA ANN, b Cleveland, Ohio, June 10, 36. PHYSIOLOGY. *Educ:* Marquette Univ, BS, 59, MS, 61; Univ NMex, PhD(zool), 72. *Prof Exp:* From asst prof to assoc prof biol & earth sci, St John Col, Ohio, 61-75; asst prof anat biol & physiol, 75-79, ASST PROF PHYSIOL, SCH MED, ORAL ROBERTS UNIV, 79- *Concurrent Pos:* Consult radionuclide metab & toxicity, Lovelace Found Med Educ & Res, 74-75. *Mem:* Radiation Res Soc; Am Soc Zoologists; Am Inst Biol Sci; AAAS. *Res:* Environmental physiology, particularly behavioral and physiological responses of animals to environmental factors, especially effects of temperature and pollutants on animals. *Mailing Add:* Dept Physiol Sch Med Oral Roberts Univ Tulsa OK 74102

STURCH, CONRAD RAY, b Cincinnati, Ohio, Nov 5, 37; m 62; c 1. ASTRONOMY. *Educ:* Miami Univ, BA, 58, MS, 60; Univ Calif, Berkeley, PhD(astron), 65. *Prof Exp:* Res asst astron, Lick Observ, Univ Calif, 65; from instr to asst prof, Univ Rochester, 65-73; vis asst prof, Univ Western Ont, 73-74; vis asst prof astron, Clemson Univ, 74-76; mem tech staff, 76-80, SECTION MGR, COMPUT SCI CORP, 80- *Mem:* Am Astron Soc; Int Astron Union. *Res:* Variable stars; stellar populations; interstellar reddening; galactic structure. *Mailing Add:* Comput Sci Corp Space Telescope Sci Inst Homewood Campus Baltimore MD 21215

STURCKEN, EDWARD FRANCIS, b Charleston, SC, Nov 13, 27; m 53; c 2. MATERIALS SCIENCE, NUCLEAR PHYSICS. *Educ:* Col Charleston, BS, 48; St Louis Univ, MS, 50, PhD(nuclear physics), 53. *Prof Exp:* Res physicist, 53-62, sr scientist mat sci, 62-69, res supvr, Mat Res Methods, 69-70, RES ASSOC, MAT RES METHODS, SAVANNAH RIVER LAB, DEPT ENERGY, E I DU PONT DE NEMOURS & CO, INC, 70- *Concurrent Pos:* Vis scientist, Univ Calif, Berkeley, 66-67; mem, Joint Comt Powder Diffraction Standards, 72-; lectr, Traveling Lectr Prog, Dept of Energy, 72- *Mem:* Am Crystallog Soc; Am Soc Metals; Int Microstruct Anal Soc. *Res:* Studies of structure; property relationships for materials employed in nuclear reactors using various materials research methods, particularly electron microscopy and x-ray diffraction. *Mailing Add:* Savannah River Lab E I du Pont de Nemours & Co Inc Aiken SC 29808

STURDEVANT, EUGENE J, b Newton, Kans, Dec 27, 30; m 58; c 2. ELECTRONIC & OPTICAL ENGINEERING. *Educ:* Univ Calif, Berkeley, BSEE, 63. *Prof Exp:* Engr, Eng Physics Lab, E I du Pont de Nemours & Co, Inc, 63-65, res engr, 65-68; res engr, Holotron Corp, 68-71; dir res & develop, Display Enterprises, Inc, 71-74; advan res engr, 76-80, SR SCIENTIST, PROCTOR-SILEX DIV, SCM CORP, 80- *Concurrent Pos:* Consult electro-optics, 71-80. *Mem:* Optical Soc Am; Soc Photo-Optical Instrument Engrs; Nat Soc Prof Engrs. *Res:* Applied research, development and design of electro-optical systems and instruments for display, product inspection and process control; electronic control and enhancement of heat and mass transfer. *Mailing Add:* PO Box 5327 Wilmington DE 19808

STUREK, WALTER BEYNON, b Bartlesville, Okla, July 14, 37; m 65; c 2. AEROSPACE & MECHANICAL ENGINEERING. *Educ:* Okla State Univ, BS, 60; Mass Inst Technol, SM, 61; Univ Del, PhD(appl sci), 71. *Prof Exp:* Aerospace engr, Wind Tunnels Br, 65-77, BR CHIEF, AERODYNAMICS RES BR, LAUNCH & FLIGHT DIV, US ARMY BALLISTIC RES LABS, ABERDEEN PROVING GROUND, 77- *Mem:* Am Soc Mech Engrs; Am Inst Aeronaut & Astronaut. *Res:* Aerodynamics and flight mechanics of projectiles and missiles; computational fluid dynamics of flow over shell at transonic and supersonic velocity. *Mailing Add:* Launch & Flight Div US Army Ballistic Res Labs Aberdeen Proving Ground MD 21005

STURGE, MICHAEL DUDLEY, b Bristol, Eng, May 25, 31; m 56; c 4. EXPERIMENTAL SOLID STATE PHYSICS. *Educ:* Cambridge Univ, BA, 52, PhD(physics), 57. *Prof Exp:* Mem staff, Mullard Res Lab, 56-58; sr res fel, Royal Radar Estab, 58-61; MEM TECH STAFF, BELL LABS, 61- *Concurrent Pos:* Res assoc, Stanford Univ, 65; vis scientist, Univ BC, 69; exchange visitor, Philips Res Labs, Eindhoven, Neth, 73-74; vis lectr physics, Drew Univ, 75; vis prof, Technion, Haifa, 72, 76 & 81. *Mem:* Fel Am Phys Soc. *Res:* Magnetic insulators; optical properties of solids; semiconductor luminescence; excitons. *Mailing Add:* Bells Labs Murray Hill NJ 07974

STURGEON, DONALD LUIS GUILLERMO, material science, engineering, see previous edition

STURGEON, EDWARD EARL, b Irving, Ill, Apr 28, 16; m 43; c 2. FORESTRY. *Educ:* Univ Mich, PhD(forestry), 54. *Prof Exp:* Instr forest policy, Univ Mich, 50-51; assoc prof forestry & head dept forestry & biol, Mich Technol Univ, 51-59; assoc prof forestry, Humboldt State Col, 59-66, coordr dept, 60-66; head dept, 66-73, prof, 66-81, EMER PROF FORESTRY, OKLA STATE UNIV, 81- *Mem:* AAAS; Soc Am Foresters; Am Forestry Asn. *Res:* Public-private balance in forest land ownership; forest environment and administration. *Mailing Add:* Dept of Forestry Okla State Univ Stillwater OK 74074

STURGEON, GEORGE DENNIS, b Sioux Falls, SDak, Sept 21, 37. SOLID STATE CHEMISTRY, HIGH TEMPERATURE CHEMISTRY. *Educ:* Univ NDak, BS, 59; Mich State Univ, PhD(chem), 64. *Prof Exp:* Instr chem, Mich State Univ, 64; asst prof, 64-73, ASSOC PROF CHEM, UNIV NEBR, LINCOLN, 73- *Mem:* AAAS; Am Chem Soc; Sigma Xi. *Res:* Chemistry of refractory materials; high-temperature thermodynamics; chemistry of complex fluorides. *Mailing Add:* Dept Chem Univ Nebr Lincoln NE 68588

STURGEON, MYRON THOMAS, b Salem, Ohio, Apr 27, 08; m 46; c 2. PALEONTOLOGY, STRATIGRAPHY. *Educ:* Mt Union Col, AB, 31; Ohio State Univ, AM, 33, PhD(paleont), 36. *Prof Exp:* Found inspector, US Corps Engrs, Ohio, 34; from asst to assoc prof geol, Mich State Norm Col, 37-46; from asst prof to assoc prof, 46-54, prof, 54-78, EMER PROF GEOL, OHIO UNIV, 78- *Mem:* AAAS; Paleont Soc; assoc Soc Econ Paleont & Mineral; fel Geol Soc Am; Am Ornith Union. *Res:* Stratigraphy and invertebrate paleontology of the Pennsylvanian system of eastern Ohio. *Mailing Add:* Dept of Geol Porter Hall Ohio Univ Athens OH 45701

STURGEON, ROY V, JR, b Wichita, Kans, July 1, 24; m 50; c 2. PLANT PATHOLOGY. *Educ:* Okla State Univ, BS, 61, MS, 64; Univ Minn, Minneapolis, PhD(plant path), 67. *Prof Exp:* Instr bot & plant path, 63-65, from instr to assoc prof, Col Arts & Sci & Agr Exten, 67-74, PROF PLANT PATH, COL COL AGR & AGR EXTEN, OKLA STATE UNIV, 74-, EXTEN PLANT PATHOLOGIST, FED EXTEN SERV, 67- *Concurrent Pos:* Private Plant Health Consult Serv, Okla, 67- *Mem:* Am Phytopath Soc; Soc Nematol; Am Soc Agron. *Res:* Program development and chemical evaluation for disease control, especially fungicides and nematicides. *Mailing Add:* Dept of Plant Path Okla State Univ 115 Life Sci E Stillwater OK 74074

STURGES, DAVID L, b Riverside, Calif, Oct 7, 38; m 75. WATERSHED MANAGEMENT. *Educ:* Utah State Univ, BS, 61, MS, 63. *Prof Exp:* RES FORESTER WATERSHED MGT RES, ROCKY MOUNTAIN FOREST & RANGE EXP STA, FOREST SERV, USDA, 62- *Mem:* Soc Range Mgt; Soil Conserv Soc Am; Sigma Xi. *Res:* Hydrologic relations of big sagebrush lands; effects of big sagebrush control on quantity, quality and timing of water yield; snow management on big sagebrush lands. *Mailing Add:* Rocky Mountain Forest & Range Exp Sta 222 S 22nd St Laramie WY 82070

STURGES, WILTON, III, b Dothan, Ala, July 21, 35; m 57; c 3. PHYSICAL OCEANOGRAPHY. *Educ:* Auburn Univ, BS, 57; Johns Hopkins Univ, MA, 63, PhD(oceanog). 66. *Prof Exp:* Res asst phys oceanog, Johns Hopkins Univ, 63-66; from asst prof to assoc prof, Univ RI, 66-72; assoc prof, 72-76, PROF PHYS OCEANOG & CHMN DEPT, FLA STATE UNIV, 76- *Concurrent Pos:* Instr, US Naval Res Off Sch, 63-66; assoc ed, J Geophys Res, 68-70; mem ocean-wide surv panel, Comt Oceanog, Nat Acad Sci, 68-71; Buoy Technol Assessment Panel Marine Bd, Nat Acad Eng, 72-74; Ocean Sci Comt, Nat Acad Sci, 75-77 & Comn Marine Geodesy, Am Geophys Union, 74-78; mem adv panel oceanog, NSF, 75-77. *Mem:* Am Geophys Union. *Res:* Ocean circulations, especially Gulf of Mexico and North Atlantic. *Mailing Add:* Dept of Oceanog Fla State Univ Tallahassee FL 32306

STURGESS, JENNIFER MARY, b Nottingham, Gt Brit, Sept 26, 44; m 66; c 3. MICROBIOLOGY, PATHOLOGY. *Educ:* Bristol Univ, BSc, 65; Univ London, PhD(path), 70. *Prof Exp:* Res asst microbiol, Agr Col Norway, 64 & Clin Res Unit, Med Res Coun Eng, 65-66; lectr exp path, Inst Dis Chest, Brompton Hosp, Univ London, 66-70; SR SCIENTIST, HOSP SICK CHILDREN, 71-; ASST PROF PATH, UNIV TORONTO, 71- *Concurrent Pos:* Res fel path, Hosp for Sick Children, Toronto, 70-71, Med Res Coun Can term grants & scholar, 71-; Cystic Fibrosis Term grant, 74-; Ont Thoracic Soc grant, 75-, med res coun term grant, 76-; dir, Warner Lambert Res Int, Toronto, 79- *Mem:* Am Soc Cell Biol; Int Acad Path; NY Acad Sci; Can Asn Path; Micros Soc Can. *Res:* Glycoprotein biosynthesis and secretion from the Golgi complex; mucus secretion in the normal lung and in chronic lung diseases; ciliary defects and human respiratory disease. *Mailing Add:* Hosp for Sick Children 555 University Ave Toronto ON M5G 1X8 Can

STURGILL, BENJAMIN CALEB, b Wise Co, Va, Apr 27, 34; m 55; c 2. MEDICINE, PATHOLOGY. *Educ:* Berea Col, BA, 56; Univ Va, MD, 60. *Prof Exp:* Intern med, New York, Hosp-Cornell Med Ctr, 60-61; resident path, Univ Va, 61-62; clin assoc, NIH, 62-64; from instr to assoc prof, 64-76, actg chmn dept, 74-76, PROF PATH, SCH MED, UNIV VA, 76- *Mem:* Int Acad Path; Am Asn Path; Am Soc Nephrol; Int Soc Nephrol. *Res:* Immunopathology and renal diseases. *Mailing Add:* Sch of Med Univ of Va Charlottesville VA 22903

STURGIS, BERNARD MILLER, b Butler, Ind, Nov 27, 11; m 36; c 2. PETROLEUM CHEMISTRY. *Educ:* DePauw Univ, AB, 33; Mass Inst Technol, PhD(org chem), 36. *Prof Exp:* Res chemist, Jackson Lab, E I DuPont de Nemours & Co, Inc, 36-42, group leader auxiliary chem sect, Elastomer Div, 42-46, head petrol chem div, 46-51 & combustion & scavenging div, Petrol Lab, 51-53, from asst dir to dir, 53-62, mgr mid-continent region, Petrol Chem Div, 62-64, mgr, Patents & Contracts Div, 64-76. *Honors & Awards:* Horning Mem Award, Soc Automotive Eng, 56; Rector Award, 58. *Mem:* Am Chem Soc; Combustion Inst. *Res:* Synthetic organic and rubber chemicals; accelerators; antioxidants; sponge blowing agents; peptizing agents; nonsulfur vulcanization of rubber; petroleum additives; tetraethyl lead; combustion; lead scavenging from engines. *Mailing Add:* 407 Hawthorne Dr Wilmington DE 19802

STURGIS, HOWARD EWING, b Pasadena, Calif, June 1, 36; m 57; c 2. DISTRIBUTED SYSTEMS. *Educ:* Calif Inst Technol, BS, 58; Univ Calif, Berkeley, PhD(comput sci), 73. *Prof Exp:* RES SCIENTIST COMPUT SCI, XEROX PALO ALTO RES CTR, 72- *Mem:* Asn Comput Mach. *Res:* Architecture of computer operating systems; design and theory of crash recoverable distributed systems; semantics of programming languages. *Mailing Add:* Xerox Palo Alto Res Ctr 3333 Coyote Hill Rd Palo Alto CA 94304

STURGUL, JOHN ROMAN, b Hurley, Wis, Jan 3, 40; m 65; c 2. MINING ENGINEERING. *Educ:* Mich Technol Univ, BS, 61; Univ Ariz, MS, 63; Univ Ill, PhD(eng), 66. *Prof Exp:* Asst prof eng & dir seismol observ, Univ Miss, 66-68; assoc prof geophys, Univ Ariz, 68-76; PROF MINING ENG & HEAD DEPT MINING & PETROL ENG, NMEX INST MINING & TECHNOL, 76- *Concurrent Pos:* Fulbright-Hays fel, Univ Queensland, 72; vis lectr, Univ Melbourne, 75. *Mem:* Am Soc Elec Engrs; Am Mining Cong; Mining & Metall Soc Am; Am Inst Mining, Metall & Petrol Engrs. *Res:* Mining engineering; geodynamics; computer applications in mining. *Mailing Add:* Dept Mining & Geol Eng NMex Inst Mining & Technol Socorro NM 87801

STURKIE, PAUL DAVID, b Proctor, Tex, Sept 18, 09; m 40, 64; c 2. PHYSIOLOGY. *Educ:* Tex A&M Univ, BS, 33, MS, 36; Cornell Univ, PhD(genetics, physiol), 39. *Prof Exp:* Res asst, Tex A&M Univ, 34-36 & Cornell Univ, 36-39; assoc prof, Auburn Univ, 39-44; from assoc prof to prof, 44-77, chmn dept environ physiol, 71-77, EMER PROF PHYSIOL, BARTLETT HALL COOK COL, RUTGERS UNIV, 77- *Concurrent Pos:* Guest reseacher, Agr Res Coun, 60. *Honors & Awards:* Poultry Sci Res Award, 47; Borden Award, 56; Linback Res Award, Rutgers Univ, 74. *Mem:* Fel AAAS; Am Physiol Soc; fel Poultry Sci Asn; Am Heart Asn; Microcirc Soc. *Res:* Physiology of reproduction, heart and circulation of birds. *Mailing Add:* Dept Animal Sci Rutgers Univ Cook Col New Brunswick NJ 08903

STURLEY, ERIC AVERN, b Dibden Hants, Eng, June 9, 15; nat US; m 47, 81; c 3. MATHEMATICS. *Educ:* Yale Univ, BA, 37, MA, 39; Univ Grenoble, cert, 45; Columbia Univ, EdD, 56. *Prof Exp:* Instr, Berkshire Sch, 41-42 & Lawrenceville Sch, 46-47; from instr to assoc prof math, Allegheny Col, 47-57; instr, 57-61, actg head div sci & math, 58-60, asst dean grad sch, 62-64, PROF MATH, SOUTHERN ILL UNIV, EDWARDSVILLE, 61-, CHIEF ACAD ADV, 59-, COORDR DEANS COL, 67- *Concurrent Pos:* Consult, Talon, Inc, Pa, 55-57; chief party, Southern Ill Univ Contract Team, Mali, WAfrica, 64-67, Nepal, 70-71. *Mem:* Am Math Soc; Math Asn Am. *Res:* Statistics; history of mathematics. *Mailing Add:* Dept of Math Southern Ill Univ Edwardsville IL 62025

STURM, EDWARD, US citizen; m 50; c 3. GEOLOGY, MINERALOGY. *Educ:* NY Univ, BA, 48; Univ Minn, MSc, 50; Rutgers Univ, PhD(geol), 57. *Prof Exp:* Res geologist, Hebrew Univ Jerusalem, 51-52; asst res specialist crystallog, Bur Eng Res, Rutgers Univ, 56-58; asst prof geol, Tex Technol Col, 58-63; from asst prof to assoc prof, 63-74, PROF GEOL, BROOKLYN COL, 74- *Mem:* Geol Soc Am; Mineral Soc Am; Am Crystallog Asn. *Res:* Clay mineralogy; crystallography of silicates; preferred orientation studies; geochemistry of solids. *Mailing Add:* Dept of Geol Brooklyn Col Brooklyn NY 11210

STURM, WALTER ALLAN, b Brooklyn, NY, July 22, 30; div; c 2. COMPUTER SCIENCE. *Educ:* Brown Univ, ScB, 52; Mass Inst Technol, SMEE, 57; Univ Calif, Los Angeles, PhD(eng), 64. *Prof Exp:* Staff engr comput, Hughes Aircraft Co, 57-62; assoc eng, Univ Calif, Los Angeles, 58-60; staff engr, Data Syst Div, Litton Industs, 62-64; STAFF ENGR COMPUT, AEROSPACE CORP, 64- *Mem:* Asn Comput Mach; Inst Elec & Electronics Engrs; Sigma Xi. *Res:* Computer systems architectures; application of APL to business data processing; direct-execution machines; fault-tolerant computers; reliable software; software engineering. *Mailing Add:* 4727 W 147th St (220) Lawndale CA 90260

STURM, WILLIAM JAMES, b Marshfield, Wis, Sept 10, 17; m 51; c 2. NUCLEAR PHYSICS, APPLIED PHYSICS. *Educ:* Marquette Univ, BS, 40; Univ Chicago, MS, 42; Univ Wis, PhD(physics), 49. *Prof Exp:* Asst nuclear physics, Manhattan Proj, Metall Lab, Univ Chicago, 42-43, jr physicist, 43-46; assoc physicist & group leader, Argonne Nat Lab, 46-47; consult physicist, 49-51; from physicist to sr physicist, Oak Ridge Nat Lab, 51-56; assoc physicist, Int Inst Nuclear Sci & Eng, Argonne Nat Lab, 56-59; assoc physicist, Int Sch Nuclear Sci & Eng, 59-60, Int Inst Nuclear Sci & Eng, 60-65 & Off Col & Univ Coop, 65-67, ASST DIR APPL PHYSICS DIV, ARGONNE NAT LAB, 67- *Honors & Awards:* Commemorative Medal, Atomic Indust Forum, Am Nuclear Soc, 62; Nuclear Pioneer Award, Soc Nuclear Med, 77. *Mem:* AAAS; Am Phys Soc; Am Nuclear Soc. *Res:* Neutron cross sections and diffraction; nuclear reactions, reactor physics and absolute nuclear particle energies; irradiation effects in solids; subcritical and critical reactor studies; reactor safety. *Mailing Add:* Appl Physics Div Argonne Nat Lab 9700 S Cass Ave Argonne IL 60439

STURMAN, JOHN ANDREW, b Hove, Eng, Aug 10, 41. BIOCHEMISTRY, NUTRITION. *Educ:* Univ London, BSc, 62, MSc, 63, PhD(biochem), 66. *Prof Exp:* Assoc res scientist, RES SCIENTIST, DEVELOP NEUROCHEM LAB, DEPT PATH NERUOBIOL, INST BASIC RES MENT RETARDATION, 80- *Concurrent Pos:* Res study grant red cell metab, King's Col Hosp, Med Sch, Univ London, 63-67. *Mem:* AAAS; Am Inst Nutrit; Brit Biochem Soc; Am Soc Neurochem; Int Soc Neurochem. *Res:* Sulfur amino acid metabolism in normal and vitamin B-6 deficiency, in fetal, neonatal and adult tissue and in inborn errors of metabolism; axonal transport in developing nerves; nutrition and brain development. *Mailing Add:* Develop Neurochem Lab Inst Basic Res Ment Retardation Staten Island NY 10314

STURMAN, LAWRENCE STUART, b Detroit, Mich, Mar 13, 38; m 59; c 4. VIROLOGY. *Educ:* Northwestern Univ, BS, 57, MS & MD, 60; Rockefeller Univ, PhD(virol), 68. *Prof Exp:* Intern, Hosp Univ Pa, 60-61; staff assoc virol, Nat Inst Allergy & Infectious Dis, 68-70; asst prof, 76-79, ASSOC PROF MICROBIOL & IMMUNOL, ALBANY MED COL, 79-; RES PHYSICIAN VIROL, DIV LABS & RES, NY STATE DEPT HEALTH, 70- *Concurrent Pos:* Adj asst prof microbiol, Dept of Microbiol & Immunol, Albany Med Col, 73-76. *Mem:* Am Soc Microbiol, Tissue Cult Asn; Soc Gen Microbiol. *Res:* Structure and replication of coronaviruses; host dependent differences in virus replication; pathogenesis of viral disease; the fate of viruses in soil and water. *Mailing Add:* Div of Labs & Res NY State Empire State Plaza Albany NY 12201

STURMER, DAVID MICHAEL, b Norfolk, Va, July 27, 40; m 64; c 2. PHYSICAL ORGANIC CHEMISTRY, PHOTOGRAPHIC CHEMISTRY. *Educ:* Stanford Univ, BS, 62; Ore State Univ, PhD(org chem), 66. *Prof Exp:* NSF fel chem, Yale Univ, 66-67; sr chemist, 67-72, res assoc, 72-77; LAB HEAD CHEM, EASTMAN KODAK CO RES LABS, 77- *Concurrent Pos:* Adj prof, Dept Photog Sci, Rochester Inst Technol, 77- *Mem:* Am Chem Soc; Sigma Xi; Soc Photog Scientists & Engrs. *Res:* Molecular orbital calculations; heterocyclic dye synthesis; spectral sensitization of silver halides; solid state photochemistry; radiotracer methods. *Mailing Add:* Eastman Kodak Co Res Labs 1669 Lake Ave Rochester NY 14650

STURR, JOSEPH FRANCIS, b Syracuse, NY, Apr 29, 33; m 60; c 4. VISUAL SCIENCE. *Educ:* Wesleyan Univ, BA, 55; Fordham Univ, MA, 57; Univ Rochester, PhD(psychol), 62. *Prof Exp:* Asst exp psychol, Fordham Univ, 56-57 & Univ Rochester, 57-58, asst vision res lab, 58-61; USPHS res fel psychophysiol lab, Ill State Psychiat Inst, 61-64; from asst prof to assoc prof, 64-72, PROF PHYSIOL PSYCHOL, SYRACUSE UNIV, 72- *Concurrent Pos:* Consult, Vet Admin Hosp, Syracuse, 65- *Mem:* AAAS; Optical Soc Am; Asn Res Vision & Ophthal. *Res:* Vision; psychophysics; spatio-temporal factors; flicker, increment thresholds; target detection; visual masking and excitability; sensitivity; rapid adaptation. *Mailing Add:* 500 Huntington Hall Syracuse Univ Syracuse NY 13210

STURROCK, PETER ANDREW, b Grays, Eng, Mar 20, 24; US citizen; m 63; c 3. ASTROPHYSICS, PLASMA PHYSICS. *Educ:* Cambridge Univ, BA, 45, MA, 48, PhD(math), 51. *Prof Exp:* Harwell sr fel, Atomic Energy Res Estab, Eng, 51-53; fel, St John's Col, Cambridge Univ, 52-55; res assoc microwaves, Stanford Univ, 55-58; Ford fel plasma physics, Europ Orgn Nuclear Res, Switz, 58-59; res assoc, 59-60, prof eng sci & appl physics, 61-66, chmn inst plasma res, 64-74, PROF SPACE SCI & ASTROPHYS, DEPT APPL PHYSICS, STANFORD UNIV, 66-, CHMN, INST PLASMA RES, 80- *Concurrent Pos:* Consult, Varian Assocs, Calif, 57-64 & NASA Ames Res Ctr, 62-64; dir, Enrico Fermi Summer Sch Plasma-Astrophys, Varenna, Italy, 66; mem phys sci comt, NASA, 75-77; chmn study group anomalous phenomena, Am Inst Aeronaut & Astronaut, 75-; dir solar flare, Sky Lab Workshop, 76-77. *Honors & Awards:* Gravity Found Prize, 67. *Mem:* Fel AAAS; Am Astron Soc; Int Astron Union; fel Am Phys Soc; Am Inst Aeronaut & Astronaut. *Res:* Plasma astrophysics; solar physics; pulsars; radio galaxies; quasars; scientific inference; anomalous phenomena. *Mailing Add:* Inst for Plasma Res Stanford Univ Via Crespi Stanford CA 94305

STURROCK, PETER EARLE, b Miami, Fla, Dec 6, 29; m 58. ANALYTICAL CHEMISTRY, ELECTROCHEMISTRY. *Educ:* Univ Fla, BS, 51, BA, 51; Stanford Univ, MS, 54; Ohio State Univ, PhD(chem), 60. *Prof Exp:* From asst prof to assoc prof, 60-78, PROF CHEM, GA INST TECHNOL, 78- *Mem:* Am Chem Soc. *Res:* Instrumental chemical analysis; equilibria of complex ions; kinetics of electrode reactions; applications of computers to chemical instrumentation. *Mailing Add:* Dept of Chem Ga Inst of Technol Atlanta GA 30332

STURROCK, THOMAS TRACY, b Havana, Cuba, Dec 9, 21; US citizen; m 48; c 5. HORTICULTURE, PLANT MORPHOLOGY. *Educ:* Univ Fla, BSA & MSA, 43, PhD(fruit crops), 61. *Prof Exp:* Partner, Sturrock Trop Fruit Nursery, 46-56; inspector, State Plant Bd Fla, 56-57; teacher high sch, 57-58; res asst fruit crops, Univ Fla, 58-60; instr biol, Palm Beach Jr Col, 60-64; from asst prof to assoc prof bot, 64-74, PROF BOT, FLA ATLANTIC UNIV, 74-, ASST DEAN COL SCI, 71- *Mem:* AAAS; Am Soc Hort Sci. *Res:* Tropical horticulture; factors influencing fertilization, embryological development and fruit-set of the mango. *Mailing Add:* Dept of Biol Sci Fla Atlantic Univ Boca Raton FL 33431

STURTEVANT, BRADFORD, b New Haven, Conn, Nov 1, 33; m 58; c 1. FLUID MECHANICS. *Educ:* Yale Univ, BS, 55; Calif Inst Technol, PhD(fluid mech), 60. *Prof Exp:* Res fel fluid mech, 60-62, from asst prof to assoc prof, 62-72, exec officer aeronaut, 71-72, PROF AERONAUT, CALIF INST TECHNOL, 71- *Concurrent Pos:* Res fel & Gordon McKay vis lectr, Harvard Univ, 65-66. *Mem:* AAAS; Am Phys Soc; Am Inst Aeronaut & Astronaut. *Res:* Experimental fluid mechanics; shock waves; vapor explosions; nonlinear acoustics. *Mailing Add:* Grad Aeronaut Labs 301-46 Calif Inst of Technol Pasadena CA 91125

STURTEVANT, FRANK MILTON, b Evanston, Ill, Mar 8, 27; m 50; c 2. PHARMACOLOGY. *Educ:* Lake Forest Col, BA, 48; Northwestern Univ, MS, 50, PhD(biol), 51. *Prof Exp:* Asst, Northwestern Univ, 50-51; sr investr, G D Searle & Co, 51-58; sr pharmacologist, Smith Kline & French Labs, 58-60; dir sci & regulatory affairs, Mead Johnson & Co, 60-72; lectr genetics, Univ Evansville, 72; assoc dir res & develop, 72-80, DIR, OFF SCI AFFAIRS, RES & DEVELOP DIV, G D SEARLE & CO, 80- *Mem:* Drug Info Asn; Soc Exp Biol & Med; Am Soc Pharmacol & Exp Therapeut; NY Acad Sci; fel AAAS. *Res:* Hypertension; pharmacokinetics; biochemorphology; glucoregulation; genetics; reproduction; central nervous system; chronobiology. *Mailing Add:* G D Searle & Co PO Box 5110 Chicago IL 60680

STURTEVANT, JULIAN MUNSON, b Edgewater, NJ, Aug 9, 08; m 29; c 2. BIOPHYSICAL CHEMISTRY. *Educ:* Columbia Univ, AB, 27; Yale Univ, PhD(chem), 31. *Hon Degrees:* ScD, Ill Col, 62. *Prof Exp:* From instr to asst prof chem, Yale Univ, 31-43; staff mem, Radiation Lab, Mass Inst Technol, 43-46; from assoc prof to prof chem, 46-77, chmn dept, 59-62, assoc dir Sterling Chem Lab, 50-59, prof, 62-77, EMER PROF CHEM, MOLECULAR BIOPHYS & BIOCHEM, YALE UNIV, 77-, SR RES SCIENTIST, 77- *Concurrent Pos:* Consult, Mobil Oil Co, 46-69; Guggenheim fel & Fulbright scholar, Cambridge Univ, 55-56; Fulbright scholar, Univ Adelaide, 62-63; vis prof, Univ Calif, San Diego, 66-67 & 69-70; vis fel, Seattle Res Ctr, Battelle Mem Inst, 72-73; mem, US Nat Comt Data Sci & Technol, 76; vis scholar, Stanford Univ, 75-76. *Honors & Awards:* Huffman Award, Calorimetry Conf US, 68. *Mem:* AAAS; Am Chem Soc; Nat Acad Sci; fel Am Acad Arts & Sci. *Res:* The study of biochemical problems by physiochemical methods, with particular application of microcalorimetry and fast kinetic measurements. *Mailing Add:* Kline Chem Lab Yale Univ New Haven CT 06520

STURTEVANT, RUTHANN PATTERSON, b Rockford, Ill, Feb 7, 27; m 50; c 2. GROSS ANATOMY, BIOLOGICAL RHYTHMS. *Educ:* Northwestern Univ, Evanston, BS, 49, MS, 50; Univ Ark, Little Rock, PhD(anat), 72. *Prof Exp:* From instr to asst prof life sci, Ind State Univ, Evansville, 65-74; adj asst prof, Sch Med, Ind Univ, 72-74; lectr, Sch Med, Northwestern Univ, 74-75; asst prof, 75-81, ASSOC PROF ANAT & SURG, STRITCH SCH MED, LOYOLA UNIV, CHICAGO, 81- *Concurrent Pos:* Grad Women Sci fel, 73. *Mem:* Am Asn Anatomists; Int Soc Chronobiol; Sigma Xi; AAAS; Soc Exp Biol & Med. *Res:* Chronobiology; chronopharmacokinetics; anatomy; pharmacology. *Mailing Add:* Loyola Univ Stritch Sch of Med Dept of Anat 2160 S First Ave Maywood IL 60153

STURZENEGGER, AUGUST, b Switz, May 3, 21; nat US; m 55; c 3. ORGANIC CHEMISTRY, CHEMICAL ENGINEERING. *Educ:* Swiss Fed Inst Technol, MS, 45, PhD, 48. *Prof Exp:* Chemist, Royal Dutch Shell Co, Holland, 48; chemist, Steinfels, Inc Switz, 49; chemist, 49-59, dir advan technol, 59-77, DIR, PHARMACEUT & DIAG OPERS, HOFFMAN-LA ROCHE INC, 77- *Mem:* Am Chem Soc; Am Astronaut Soc; Am Inst Chem Eng; Swiss Chem Soc; Am Phys Soc. *Res:* Process development; detergents; petroleum chemistry; pharmaceuticals; systems analysis and automation; multidisciplinary interactions. *Mailing Add:* 25 Rensselaer Rd Essex Fells NJ 07021

STUSHNOFF, CECIL, b Saskatoon, Sask, Aug 12, 40; m 63; c 2. COLD STRESS BREEDING, FRUIT BREEDING. *Educ:* Univ Sask, BSA, 63, MSc, 64; Rutgers Univ, PhD(hort, embryol), 67. *Prof Exp:* Res asst, Dept Hort, Rutgers Univ, 64-67; asst prof fruit breeding, Univ Minn, 67-70, assoc prof, 70-75, prof hort sci & landscape archit, 75-80; PROF HORT & HEAD DEPT, UNIV SASK, 81- *Concurrent Pos:* Consult, Walter Butler Corp & North Gro, Inc, St Paul, Minn; vis prof & guest researcher, Inst Biol & Geol, Univ Tromso, Norway; prin horticulturist res admin, Sci & Educ Admin, USDA, Washington, DC; owner & mgr, White Rock Lake Farm & The Berry Patch, St Paul, Minn; int travel grant, Hill Family Found. *Honors & Awards:* Paul Howe Shepard Award; Joseph Harvey Gourley Award. *Mem:* Am Soc Hort Sci; Int Soc Hort Sci; Am Soc Plant Physiol; Can Inst Agrologists. *Res:* Development of cold hardiness breeding methods for woody plants; evaluation of basic mechanisms for physiological basis of resistance; cryopreservation of apple germplasm. *Mailing Add:* Dept Hort Univ Sask Saskatoon SK S7N 0W0 Can

STUSNICK, ERIC, b Edwardsville, Pa, Aug 18, 39; m 67; c 1. ACOUSTICS. *Educ:* Carnegie-Mellon Univ, BS, 60; NY Univ, MS, 62; State Univ NY Buffalo, PhD(physics), 71. *Prof Exp:* Asst prof physics, Niagara Univ, 69-72; assoc physicist, Cornell Aeronaut Lab, Inc, 72-73; res physicist, Calspan Corp, 73-75, sr physicist, 75-77; PROG MGR, WYLE LABS, 77- *Concurrent Pos:* Lectr, Niagara Univ, 72-77. *Mem:* AAAS; Am Phys Soc; Am Asn Physics Teachers; Acoust Soc Am; Sigma Xi. *Res:* Environmental acoustics; acoustic simulation and modeling; digital signal processing and analysis; noise source identification techniques; diesel engine noise. *Mailing Add:* Wyle Labs 2361 Jefferson Davis Hwy Arlington VA 22202

STUTEVILLE, DONALD LEE, b Okeene, Okla, Sept 7, 30; m 52; c 3. PLANT PATHOLOGY. *Educ:* Kans State Univ, BS, 59, MS, 61; Univ Wis, PhD(plant path), 64. *Prof Exp:* Res asst plant path, Univ Wis, 61-64; asst prof, 64-69, assoc prof, 69-79, PROF PLANT PATH, KANS STATE UNIV, 79-, RES FORAGE PATHOLOGIST, AGR EXP STA, 74- *Mem:* Am Phytopath Soc. *Res:* Diseases of forage crops; improving disease resistance in forage crops, particularly alfalfa. *Mailing Add:* Dept of Plant Path Kans State Univ Manhattan KS 66506

STUTH, CHARLES JAMES, b Greenville, Tex, Jan 9, 32; m 53, 75; c 3. ALGEBRA. *Educ:* East Tex State Univ, 51, MEd, 53; Univ Kans, PhD(math), 63. *Prof Exp:* Instr math, East Tex State Univ, 56-58; asst instr, Univ Kans, 58-62; from asst prof to prof, East Tex State Univ, 62-66; asst prof, Univ Mo-Columbia, 66-70; CHMN DEPT, STEPHENS COL, 70- *Mem:* Math Asn Am. *Res:* Group theory; theory of semigroups. *Mailing Add:* Dept of Math Stephens Col Columbia MO 65201

STUTHMAN, DEON DEAN, b Pilger, Nebr, May 7, 40; m 62; c 2. PLANT GENETICS, PLANT BREEDING. *Educ:* Univ Nebr, BSc, 62; Purdue Univ, MSc, 64, PhD(genetics of alfalfa), 67. *Prof Exp:* Asst prof, 66-71, assoc prof, 71-79, PROF OAT GENETICS & BREEDING, UNIV MINN, ST PAUL, 79- *Mem:* Am Soc Agron; Crop Sci Soc. *Res:* Breeding and genetics of oats. *Mailing Add:* Inst Agr Agron & Plant Genetics Univ Minn St Paul MN 55108

STUTMAN, LEONARD JAY, b Boston, Mass, Apr 8, 28; m 51; c 4. HEMATOLOGY, CARDIOLOGY. *Educ:* Mass Inst Technol, BS, 48; Boston Univ, MA, 49; Univ Rochester, MD, 53. *Prof Exp:* Intern & resident internal med, 4th Med Div, Bellevue Hosp, New York, 53-56; instr clin med, Post-Grad Med Sch, NY Univ, 56-61, asst prof path, Sch Med, 61-65; HEAD COAGULATION RES LAB, DEPT MED, ST VINCENT'S HOSP & MED CTR, 65-; ASSOC PROF CLIN MED, NEW YORK MED COL, 81- *Concurrent Pos:* Lillia-Babbit-Hyde res fel metab dis, Sch Med, NY Univ, 56-57, Nat Heart Inst spec advan res fel, 59-61; Ripple Found coagulation res grant, 66; John A Polacheck Found fel, 66-67; fel coun arteriosclerosis, Am Heart Asn, 57-; attend physician, Nyack Hosp, 59-; co-investr, Nat Heart Inst grants, 60-65; attend physician, St Vincent's Hosp, 65-; med dir, Presidential Life Ins Co, Nyack, NY, 65-; dir, Ford Found-Vera Inst Cardiovasc Epidemiol Proj, 71- *Mem:* AAAS; Am Col Physicians; assoc fel Am Col Cardiol; fel NY Acad Med; Am Fedn Clin Res. *Res:* Blood coagulation proteins in normal and pathologic states, including biochemistry and biophysics of cellular lipoproteins; epidemiology of cardiovascular disease; high altitude physiology, including effects on erythrocytes; biochemical genetics in clotting disorders. *Mailing Add:* Coagulation Res Lab St Vincent's Hosp & Med Ctr New York NY 10011

STUTMAN, OSIAS, b Buenos Aires, Arg, June 4, 33. IMMUNOLOGY, PATHOLOGY. *Educ:* Univ Buenos Aires, MD, 57. *Prof Exp:* Lectr, Inst Med Res, Univ Buenos Aires, 57-63; mem res staff physiol, Inst Biol & Exp Med, Buenos Aires, 63-66; from instr to assoc prof path, Med Sch, Univ Minn, Minneapolis, 66-72; MEM & SECT HEAD, SLOAN-KETTERING INST CANCER RES, 73-; PROF IMMUNOL, GRAD SCH MED SCI, CORNELL UNIV, 75- *Concurrent Pos:* USPHS res fel, Med Sch, Univ Minn, Minneapolis, 66-69; Am Cancer Soc res assoc, 69-74. *Mem:* Am Asn Immunol; Am Soc Exp Path; Am Asn Cancer Res; Transplantation Soc. *Res:* Development of immune functions in mammals, especially role of thymus and mechanisms of cell-mediated immunity in relation to normal functions and as defense against tumor development. *Mailing Add:* Sloan-Kettering Inst Cancer Res 410 E 68th St New York NY 10021

STUTT, CHARLES A(DOLPHUS), b Avoca, Nebr, Nov 12, 21; m 55; c 2. ELECTRICAL ENGINEERING. *Educ:* Univ Nebr, BSc, 44; Mass Inst Technol, ScD(elec eng), 51. *Prof Exp:* Res engr, Stromberg-Carlson Co, NY, 44-46; asst, Res Lab Electronics, Mass Inst Technol, 48-50, instr elec eng, 50-52, mem staff & asst group leader commun, Lincoln Lab, 52-57; res assoc, 57-66, MGR SIGNAL PROCESSING & COMMUN, RES & DEVELOP CTR, GEN ELEC CO, 66- *Mem:* Inst Elec & Electronics Engrs. *Res:* Signal theory; signal processing; data transmission; radar; sonar; radio propagation. *Mailing Add:* Gen Elec Res & Develop Ctr PO Box 8 Schenectady NY 12301

STUTTE, CHARLES A, b Wapanucka, Okla, July 19, 33; m 55; c 3. PLANT PHYSIOLOGY, AGRONOMY. *Educ:* Southeastern Okla State Univ, BS, 55; Okla State Univ, MS, 61, PhD(bot, plant physiol), 67. *Prof Exp:* Teacher high schs, Okla, 55-64; instr biol & ecol, E Cent Univ, 64-65; adv plant physiol, forest physiol & gen plant physiol, Okla State Univ, 65-67; asst prof, 67-71, prof, 71-79, DISTINGUISHED PROF AGRON & BEN J ALTHEIMER CHAIR SOYBEAN RES, UNIV ARK, FAYETTEVILLE, 79- *Mem:* Plant Growth Regulator Soc Am; Am Soc Plant Physiologists; Am Soybean Asn; Sigma Xi; Am Soc Agron. *Res:* Physiological stress and growth regulator responses in soybeans, cotton, rice and other crop plants; role of phenolics in natural resistance to insects and disease. *Mailing Add:* Dept Agron Univ Ark Fayetteville AR 72701

STUTTE, LINDA GAIL, b Chicago, Ill, Oct 31, 46. ELEMENTARY PARTICLE PHYSICS. *Educ:* Mass Inst Technol, SB, 68; Univ Calif, Berkeley, PhD(physics), 73. *Prof Exp:* Fel, Calif Inst Technol, 73-76; ASSOC SCIENTIST, FERMILAB, 76- *Mem:* Am Phys Soc; AAAS. *Res:* High energy neutrino interactions. *Mailing Add:* CL 12W Fermilab PO Box 500 Batavia IL 60570

STUTZ, CONLEY I, b Currie, Minn, Aug 18, 32; m 55; c 1. PHYSICS. *Educ:* Wayne State Col, BSE, 57; Univ NMex, MSE, 60; Univ Nebr, PhD(physics), 68. *Prof Exp:* High sch teacher, Iowa, 59; asst prof physics, Pac Univ, 60-64; from asst prof to assoc prof, 69-74, PROF PHYSICS, BRADLEY UNIV, 74- *Concurrent Pos:* Mem: Am Phys Soc; Am Asn Physics Teachers. *Res:* Study of the apprach to equilibrium of quantum mechanical systems; nuclear magnetic resonance and nuclear quadrupole resonance of solids. *Mailing Add:* Dept of Physics Bradley Univ Peoria IL 61606

STUTZ, HOWARD COOMBS, b Cardston, Alta, Aug 24, 18; nat US; m 40; c 7. GENETICS. *Educ:* Brigham Young Univ, BS, 40, MS, 51; Univ Calif, PhD, 56. *Prof Exp:* Prin, High Sch, Utah, 42-44; chmn dept biol, Snow Col, 46-51; asst prof, 56-67, PROF BOT, BRIGHAM YOUNG UNIV, 67- *Concurrent Pos:* Guggenheim fel, 60; vis prof, Am Univ Beirut, 67. *Mem:* Bot Soc Am; Soc Study Evolution. *Res:* Cytogenetic studies of Secale L and related grasses; phyllogenetic studies of western browse plants; origin of cultivated rye; dominance-penetrance relationships; phylogenetic studies within the family Chenopodiaceae. *Mailing Add:* Dept of Bot Brigham Young Univ Provo UT 84602

STUTZ, ROBERT L, b Kansas City, Kans, Aug 1, 31; m 60; c 2. SURFACTANT SCIENCE, FRUIT COATINGS. *Educ:* Univ Kans, BA, 53, MS, 57, PhD(org chem), 61. *Prof Exp:* Asst chemist, Stand Oil Co, Ind, 56-57; sr chemist, Minn Mining & Mfg Co, 61-64; res chemist, C J Patterson Co, Kansas City, Mo, 64-65, head chem sect, 65-73; pres, Vanguard Systs, Inc, 74-80; VPRES & TECH DIR, HESSER & ASSOCS, INC, 81- *Concurrent*

Pos: Frederick Gardner Cottrell grant, 58-59. *Mem:* Am Chem Soc; Am Oil Chem Soc; fel Am Inst Chem; Sigma Xi; NY Acad Sci. *Res:* Surfactants; food emulsifiers; sucrose esters; specialty chemicals. *Mailing Add:* 5630 Belinder Rd Shawnee Mission KS 66205

STUTZENBERGER, FRED JOHN, b Louisville, Ky, Nov 10, 40; m 70; c 1. MICROBIOLOGY, ENZYMOLOGY. *Educ:* Bellarmine Col, BS, 62; Univ Houston, MS, 64; Mich State Univ, PhD(microbiol), 67. *Prof Exp:* Microbiologist, USPHS, 67-69; asst prof microbiol, Weber State Col, Ogden, Utah, 69-71; Nat Adv Res Coun fel, NZ Dept Agr, Hamilton, 71-73; assoc prof, 74-79, PROF MICROBIOL, CLEMSON UNIV, 79- *Concurrent Pos:* Sigma Xi res award, 67. *Mem:* Sigma Xi; Am Soc Microbiol. *Res:* Extracellular enzymes of thermophilic actinomycetes; cellulose degradation; effect of herbicides on actinomycetes; hypersensitivity pneumonitis antigens and activation of alternate complement pathway; streptococcal immunoglobulin A protease production. *Mailing Add:* Dept of Microbiol Clemson Univ Clemson SC 29361

STUTZMAN, LEROY F, b Indianapolis, Ind, Sept 5, 17; m 39; c 3. CHEMICAL ENGINEERING. *Educ:* Purdue Univ, BS, 39; Kans State Col, MS, 40; Univ Pittsburgh, PhD(chem eng), 46. *Prof Exp:* Instr chem, Hillyer Jr Col, 40-41; res fel, Mellon Inst, 41-43; dir rubber res, Pittsburgh Coke & Iron Co, 43; from asst prof to assoc prof chem eng, Tech Inst, Northwestern Univ, 43-50, prof & chmn dept, 50-56; dir res, Remington Rand Univac Div, Sperry-Rand Corp, 56-59; prof chem eng & chief party Univ Pittsburgh res team, Univ Santa Maria, Chile, 59-63; head chem eng dept, 63-70, PROF CHEM ENG, UNIV CONN, 63- *Concurrent Pos:* Consult, US Off Naval Res, Pure Oil Co, Corn Prod Refining Co & Remington Rand Univac Div, 43-56; consult, 57-; mem bd dirs, Control Data Corp, 74-; Fulbright lectr, Hacettepe Univ, Turkey, 77; vis prof, Univ Vienna, 77-78. *Mem:* AAAS; Am Chem Soc; Am Soc Eng Educ; Am Inst Chem Engrs. *Res:* Mass transfer; oil reservoirs; digital computers; process control; computer graphics; numerical analysis; non-linear optimization; process modelling and simulation. *Mailing Add:* Dept of Chem Eng Univ of Conn Storrs CT 06268

STUTZMAN, WARREN LEE, b Elgin, Ill, Oct 22, 41; m 64; c 2. ELECTRICAL ENGINEERING. *Educ:* Univ Ill, Urbana, AB & BS, 64; Ohio State Univ, MS, 65, PhD(elec eng), 69. *Prof Exp:* Asst prof elec eng, 69-74, assoc prof, 74-79, PROF ELEC ENG, VA POLYTECH INST & STATE UNIV, 79- *Mem:* Sr mem Inst Elec & Electronics Engrs; Int Sci Radio Union. *Res:* Millimeter wave satellite communications; antennas; microwaves. *Mailing Add:* Dept of Elec Eng Va Polytech Inst & State Univ Blacksburg VA 24061

STUY, JOHAN HARRIE, b Bogor, Indonesia, Jan 17, 25; m 52; c 2. BACTERIOLOGY. *Educ:* State Univ Utrecht, Bachelor, 48, Drs, 52, PhD(microbiol), 61. *Prof Exp:* Mem res staff radiobiol, N V Philips Labs, Netherlands, 52-65; assoc prof biol, 65-74, PROF BIOL SCI, FLA STATE UNIV, 74- *Concurrent Pos:* Fel, biol dept, Brandeis Univ, 57-58, biol div, Oak Ridge Nat Lab, 58-59 & biophys dept, Yale Univ, 59-60; vis prof, Fla State Univ, 62-63; US Atomic Energy Comn grant, 68-74. *Mem:* Am Soc Microbiol. *Res:* Recombination in bacteria and bacteriophages at the DNA level. *Mailing Add:* Dept of Biol Sci Fla State Univ Tallahassee FL 32306

STWALLEY, WILLIAM CALVIN, b Glendale, Calif, Oct 7, 42; m 63; c 2. PHYSICAL CHEMISTRY, ATOMIC PHYSICS. *Educ:* Calif Inst Technol, BS, 64; Harvard Univ, PhD(phys chem), 68. *Prof Exp:* From asst prof to assoc prof, 68-75, PROF CHEM, UNIV IOWA, 75-, PROF PHYSICS, 77-; DIR, IOWA LASER FACIL, 79- *Concurrent Pos:* A P Sloan fel, 72-75; assoc prog dir quantum chem, NSF, 75-76. *Mem:* Am Chem Soc; Am Phys Soc; AAAS. *Res:* Intermolecular forces; gas phase chemical reaction kinetics; molecular beams; laser applications; low temperature physics; atomic and molecular scattering and spectroscopy. *Mailing Add:* Dept of Chem Univ of Iowa Iowa City IA 52242

STYLES, ERNEST DEREK, b Canterbury, Eng, Oct 19, 26; m 65; c 2. GENETICS. *Educ:* Univ BC, BSA, 60; Univ Wis, PhD(genetics), 65. *Prof Exp:* Res asst genetics, Univ Wis, 60-64, from proj asst to proj assoc, 64-66; asst prof, 66-71, ASSOC PROF GENETICS, UNIV VICTORIA, 71- *Mem:* AAAS; Genetics Soc Am; Genetics Soc Can; Am Genetics Asn. *Res:* Maize genetics; genetic control of flavonoid biosynthesis; paramutation. *Mailing Add:* Dept of Biol Univ of Victoria Victoria BC V8W 2Y2 Can

STYLES, TWITTY JUNIUS, b Prince Edward Co, Va, May 18, 27; m 62; c 2. PARASITOLOGY, BIOLOGY. *Educ:* Va Union Univ, BS, 48; NY Univ, MS, 57, PhD(biol), 63. *Prof Exp:* Jr bacteriologist, New York City Health Dept, 53-54, jr scientist, State Univ NY Downstate Med Ctr, 55-64; fel parasitol, Nat Univ Mex, 64-65; asst prof, 65-69, ASSOC PROF BIOL, UNION COL, NY, 69- *Concurrent Pos:* Lectr, City Col New York, 64; consult off higher educ planning, NY State Educ Dept, 70-71; lectr, Narcotics Addiction Control Comn, NY State, 71-72; NSF course histochem, Vanderbilt Univ, 72; sabbatical, Dept Vet Microbiol & Immunol, Univ Guelph, 72. *Mem:* Am Soc Parasitologists; Soc Protozool; Am Soc Microbiol; Nat Asn Biol Teachers; NY Acad Sci. *Res:* Effect of marine biotoxins on parasitic infections; effect of endotoxin of Trypanosoma lewisi infections in rats and Plasmodium berghei infections in mice. *Mailing Add:* Dept of Biol Sci Union Col Schenectady NY 12308

STYNES, STANLEY K, b Detroit, Mich, Jan 18, 32; m 55; c 3. CHEMICAL ENGINEERING. *Educ:* Wayne State Univ, BSChE, 55, MSChE, 58; Purdue Univ, PhD(chem eng), 63. *Prof Exp:* Pub health engr, USPHS, 56; instr chem eng, 56-60, from asst prof to assoc prof, 63-70, asst dean, 69-70, actg dean, 70-72, PROF CHEM ENG, WAYNE STATE UNIV, 70-, DEAN COL ENG, 72- *Concurrent Pos:* Fac res fel, Wayne State Univ, 64. *Mem:* AAAS; Am Inst Chem Engrs; Am Chem Soc; Am Soc Eng Educ; Air Pollution Control Asn. *Res:* Transport phenomena in multi-phase systems; control and identification of environmental pollution from industrial sources. *Mailing Add:* Col of Eng Wayne State Univ Detroit MI 48202

STYRING, RALPH E, b Bessemer, Ala, Apr 13, 21; wid. CHEMICAL ENGINEERING. *Educ:* Auburn Univ, BS, 43, Univ Mich, MS, 48. *Prof Exp:* Assoc chem engr, Atlantic Refining Co, 48, asst chem engr, 48-54, supvr engr, 54-61, tech supvr, 61, prin res engr, 61-80, SPECIAL PROJ ADV, ATLANTIC RICHFIELD CO, 80- *Mem:* Am Inst Chem Engrs; Soc Petrol Engrs; Am Inst Mech Engrs. *Res:* Natural gas and oil shale processing; liquefied natural gas; in situ recovery of crude oil by thermal methods; tar sand processing. *Mailing Add:* Atlantic Richfield Co PO Box 2819 Dallas TX 75221

STYRIS, DAVID LEE, b Pomona, Calif, Apr 21, 32; m 58; c 1. EXPERIMENTAL PHYSICS. *Educ:* Pomona Col, BA, 57; Univ Ariz, MS, 62, PhD(physics), 67. *Prof Exp:* Dynamics engr, Airframe Design, Convair-Pomona, 56-58; res physicist, Weapons Testing, Edgerton, Germeshausen & Grier, 58-60; res assoc field ion micros, Cornell Univ, 67-69; asst prof physics, shock physics & surface sci, Wash State Univ, 69-74; SR RES SCIENTIST, BATTLELLE NORTHWEST LAB, 74- *Mem:* AAAS; Fedn Am Scientists; NY Acad Sci; Int Solar Energy Soc. *Res:* Radiation damage of materials related to controlled thermonuclear reactor systems; surface science; mass spectroscopy; atomic absorption spectroscopy; solar energy. *Mailing Add:* Battelle Northwest Lab PO Box 999 Richland WA 99352

STYRON, CHARLES WOODROW, b New Bern, NC, Nov 6, 13; m 39; c 2. MEDICINE. *Educ:* NC State Univ, BS, 34; Duke Univ, MD, 38; Am Bd Internal Med, dipl. *Prof Exp:* Intern pediat, Duke Univ, 38; intern & resident med, Boston City Hosp, 38-40; assoc, 50-65, ASST PROF MED, MED CTR, DUKE UNIV, 65- *Concurrent Pos:* Fel, Joslin Clin, New Eng Deaconess Hosp, Boston, 40-42; pvt pract, 46-; mem coun foods & nutrit, AMA, 69-76; chmn, NC Gov Comt Health Care Delivery, 71-73; pres, Duke Sch Med Alumni, 66-69. *Mem:* Fel Am Col Physicians; AMA; Am Diabetes Asn; fel Am Heart Asn; Am Soc Internal Med. *Res:* Internal medicine; diabetes mellitus and endocrinology. *Mailing Add:* 615 St Mary's St Raleigh NC 27605

STYRON, CLARENCE EDWARD, JR, b Washington, NC, Sept 14, 41; m 69; c 2. ECOLOGY. *Educ:* Davidson Col, BS, 63; Emory Univ, MS, 65, PhD(biol), 67. *Prof Exp:* Asst prof biol, St Andrews Presby Col, 69-77; MEM STAFF, MONSANTO RES CORP, 77- *Concurrent Pos:* Consult, Oak Ridge Nat Lab, 69-76; res radiobiologist, Inst Marine Biomed Res, Univ NC, 73-76. *Mem:* Ecol Soc Am; Am Inst Biol Sci; Am Soc Limnol & Oceanog; Marine Biol Asn UK; Health Physics Soc. *Res:* Assessment of radionuclides in fossil fuels; ecology of invertebrate communities; effects of radioactive fallout on terrestrial systems; transport of heavy metals in environmental systems. *Mailing Add:* Monsanto Res Corp PO Box 32 Miamisburg OH 45342

SU, CHAU-HSING, b Fukien, China, Nov 23, 35; m 60; c 4. FLUID MECHANICS, PLASMA PHYSICS. *Educ:* Nat Taiwan Univ, BS, 56; Univ Minn, MS, 59; Princeton Univ, PhD(eng), 64. *Prof Exp:* Asst prof eng, Mass Inst Technol, 63-66; res assoc plasma physics, Princeton Univ, 66-67; assoc prof appl math, 67-75, PROF APPL MATH, BROWN UNIV, 75- *Mem:* AAAS; Am Phys Soc. *Res:* Nonlinear wave theory. *Mailing Add:* Dept of Appl Math Brown Univ Providence RI 02912

SU, CHE, b Taipei, Taiwan, June 12, 32; US citizen; m 56; c 3. BLOOD VESSELS, AUTONOMIC NERVES. *Educ:* Nat Taiwan Univ, BS, 55, MS, 60; Univ Calif, Los Angeles, PhD(pharmacol), 65. *Prof Exp:* Lectr pharmacol, Nat Taiwan Univ, 60-63; pharmacologist, Riker Labs, Inc, 64-67; from asst prof to assoc prof pharmacol, Univ Calif, Los Angeles, 67-78; PROF PHARMACOL, SCH MED, SOUTHERN ILL UNIV, SPRINGFIELD, 78- *Concurrent Pos:* Mem, Am Heart Asn. *Mem:* Int Soc Toxicol; Am Soc Pharmacol & Exp Therapeut; Microcirc Soc; Japanese Pharmacol Soc; Soc Neurosci. *Res:* Pharmacology of snake venoms; neuromuscular blocking agents; vascular smooth muscle electrophysiology and pharmacology; sympathetic transmission mechanisms in blood vessels; pharmacology of blood vessels. *Mailing Add:* Southern Ill Univ PO Box 3926 Springfield IL 62708

SU, CHEH-JEN, b Taipei, Taiwan, June 11, 34; US citizen; m 67; c 3. POLYMER CHEMISTRY, PAPER CHEMISTRY. *Educ:* Taipei Inst Technol, Taiwan, BS, 55; NC State Univ, BS, 60; State Univ NY Col Forestry, Syracuse Univ, MS, 63. *Prof Exp:* Chem engr, Taiwan Pulp & Paper Co, 55-59; res chemist, Owens-Ill, Inc, Ohio, 65-67; sr res scientist II paper & polymers, 67-75, SR RES SCIENTIST I POLYMER & FOREST PROD, CONTINENTAL CAN CO, INC, 75- *Mem:* Am Chem Soc. *Res:* Characterization of polymers and plastic molded articles; chemicals and materials from renewable sources. *Mailing Add:* 4151 Roslyn Rd Owners Grove IL 60515

SU, GEORGE CHUNG-CHI, b Amoy, China, Aug 8, 39; m 71. ORGANIC CHEMISTRY. *Educ:* Hope Col, AB, 62; Univ Ill, MS, 64, PhD(org chem), 66. *Prof Exp:* Res chemist plastics dept, E I du Pont de Nemours & Co, 66-69; NIH fel, Dept Biochem, Mich State Univ, 69-70, res assoc, Pesticide Res Ctr, 70-72; biochemist, Pesticide Sect, Bur Labs, Mich Dept Pub Health, 72-74; CHIEF TECH SERV, AIR POLLUTION CONTROL, DEPT NATURAL RESOURCES, STATE MICH, 74- *Mem:* Am Chem Soc; The Chem Soc; NY Acad Sci. *Res:* Organic reaction mechanisms; air monitoring techniques; pesticide photochemistry; analytical techniques for isolation, detection, identification and quantitation of submicrogram quantities of environmental pollutants; toxicology and enzymology. *Mailing Add:* 4795 Mohican Lane Okemos MI 48864

SU, HELEN CHIEN-FAN, b Nanping, China, Dec 26, 22; nat US. ORGANIC CHEMISTRY. *Educ:* Hwa Nan Col, China, BA, 44; Univ Nebr, MS, 51, PhD(chem), 53. *Prof Exp:* Asst chem, Hwa Nan Col, 44-47, instr, 47-49; prof, Lambuth Col, 53-55; res asst, Res Found, Auburn Univ, 55-57; res chemist, Borden Chem Co, 57-63; assoc scientist, Lockheed-Ga Co, 63-65, res scientist, 65-68; RES CHEMIST, STORED PROD INSECTS RES & DEVELOP LAB, AGR RES SERV, USDA, 68- *Mem:* AAAS; fel Am Inst

Chem; Am Chem Soc; NY Acad Sci; Entom Soc Am. *Res:* Heterocyclic nitrogen and sulfur compounds; unsaturated aliphatic compounds; natural products; naturally occurring pesticides; insect pheromones; insect repellents and attractants. *Mailing Add:* 610 Highland Dr Savannah GA 31406

SU, JIN-CHEN, b Anhwei, China, Dec 30, 32; US citizen; m 60; c 3. TOPOLOGY. *Educ:* Nat Taiwan Univ, BS, 55; Univ Pa, PhD(math), 61. *Prof Exp:* Asst prof math, Univ Va, 61-64; math mem, Inst Advan Study, 64-66; assoc prof, 66-72, PROF MATH, UNIV MASS, AMHERST, 72- *Mem:* Am Math Soc. *Res:* Transformation groups. *Mailing Add:* Dept of Math Univ of Mass Amherst MA 01002

SU, JUDY YA-HWA LIN, b Hsinchu, Taiwan, Nov 20, 38; US citizen; m 62; c 1. MUSCLE PHYSIOLOGY & PHARMACOLOGY. *Educ:* Nat Taiwan Univ, BS, 61; Univ Kans, MS, 64; Univ Wash, PhD(pharmacol), 68. *Prof Exp:* Asst prof biol, Univ Ala, 72-73; res assoc cardiovasc pharmacol, 76-77, actg asst prof pharmacol, 77-78, res asst prof, 78-81, RES ASSOC PROF PHARMACOL, DEPT ANESTHESIOL, UNIV WASH, 81- *Concurrent Pos:* Res fel, San Diego Heart Asn, 70-72; Prin investr, Wash State Heart Asn, 76-77, Pharmaceut Mfg Asn, 77, Nat Heart, Lung & Blood Inst, 77-73 & Am Heart Asn, 80-82; mem Coun Basic Sci, Am Heart Asn, 81; vis scientist, Max-Planck Inst Med Res, Heidelberg, WGer, 82-83; res career develop award, Nat Heart, Lung & Blood Inst, NIH, 82-87. *Mem:* Biophys Soc; Am Soc Pharmacol & Exp Therapeut. *Res:* Mechanisms of action of pharmacological agents on the striated and smooth muscles; effects of drugs on the intracellular mechanisms of muscle contracton: the calcium activation of the contractile proteins and the calcium uptake and release from sarcoplasmic reticulum. *Mailing Add:* RN-10 Dept Anesthesiol Sch Med Univ Wash Seattle WA 98195

SU, KENDALL L(ING-CHIAO), b Nanping, China, July 10, 26; nat US; m 60. ELECTRICAL ENGINEERING. *Educ:* Amoy Univ, BS, 47; Ga Inst Technol, MS, 49, PhD(elec eng), 54. *Prof Exp:* From asst prof to prof elec eng, 54-70, REGENTS PROF ELEC ENG, GA INST TECHNOL, 70- *Mem:* Fel Inst Elec & Electronics Engrs. *Res:* Network theory; electronics, network synthesis; active networks. *Mailing Add:* Sch Elec Eng Ga Inst Technol Atlanta GA 30332

SU, KENNETH SHYAN-ELL, b Taipei, Taiwan, Nov 26, 41; US citizen; m 70; c 2. PHARMACEUTICS. *Educ:* Taipei Med Col, BS, 65; Univ Wis, MS, 69, PhD(pharmaceut), 71. *Prof Exp:* Res fel biochem, US Naval Med Res Unit 2, 64-65; pharmaceut chemist, William S Merrell Co, 71; SR PHARMACEUT CHEMIST, ELI LILLY & CO, 71- *Mem:* Am Pharmaceut Asn. *Res:* Studies of disperse systems with particular interest in particle interactions and surface phenomena, adsorption at liquid and solid interfaces, and chemical kinetics at interfaces. *Mailing Add:* Lilly Res Labs Eli Lilly & Co Indianapolis IN 46206

SU, KWEI LEE, b Ping Tong, Taiwan, Mar 18, 42; m 68; c 1. LIPID BIOCHEMISTRY. *Educ:* Nat Taiwan Univ, BS, 64; Univ Minn, PhD(biochem), 71. *Prof Exp:* Instr pharmacog, Col Pharm, Nat Taiwan Univ, 64-66; Hormel fel, Hormel Inst, Univ Minn, 70-72, from res fel to res assoc lipid chem, 72-74, asst prof, 74-75; res asst prof neurochem, Sinclair Comp Med Res Farm, Univ Mo, Columbia, 75-76; FORENSIC CHEMIST CRIME LAB, MO STATE HWY PATROL, JEFFERSON CITY, 76- *Mem:* Am Chem Soc; Am Oil Chemists Soc; Am Acad Forensic Sci. *Res:* Isolation, structural determination, biosynthesis and function of ether lipids in mammals; effects of neurotransmitters on lipid metabolism in brain subcellular membranes. *Mailing Add:* Crime Lab Mo State Hwy Patrol 1510 E Elm St Jefferson City MO 65101

SU, LAO-SOU, b Kaohsung, Taiwan, Dec 13, 32; m 45; c 2. PHYSICAL CHEMISTRY. *Educ:* Taiwan Norm Univ, BS, 57; Ind Univ, MS, 63, PhD(phys chem), 67. *Prof Exp:* Fel, Univ Mich 67-69 & Ind Univ, 69; sr res chemist, 69-80, RES ASSOC, S C JOHNSON & SON, INC, 80- *Mem:* Am Chem Soc. *Res:* Corrosion study of aerosol products; elemental analysis by means of x-ray fluorescence spectrometry; electron diffraction study of molecular structure; electrical property determination of substance by alternating current impedance method; biological alternating current impedance measurement. *Mailing Add:* S C Johnson & Soc Inc 1525 Howe St Racine WI 53403

SU, MICHAEL WEN-SHEAN, b Chau-Chou, Taiwan, Dec 15, 37; US citizen; m 62; c 1. MECHANICAL & AEROSPACE ENGINEERING. *Educ:* Nat Taiwan Univ, BSME, 60; Univ Kans, MSME, 63; Univ Tenn, Knoxville, PhD(mech eng), 70. *Prof Exp:* Res engr, Boeing Co, Wash, 65-67, sr engr, Huntsville, Ala, 71-76, eng specialist, 76-80. *Mem:* Am Inst Aeronaut & Astronaut. *Res:* Aerothermodynamics; propulsion aerodynamics and air-breathing engines; supersonic separated flow. *Mailing Add:* 220 Wynn Dr NW Huntsville AL 35805

SU, ROBERT TZYH-CHUAN, b Szechuan, China, Dec 14, 45; m 74. ANIMAL VIROLOGY, BIOCHEMISTRY. *Educ:* Fu Jen Univ, Taiwan, BS, 68; Univ Ill, MS, 71; Ind Univ, PhD(microbiol), 75. *Prof Exp:* Assoc instr biol, Ind Univ, 73-74; res fel biol chem, Harvard Med Sch, 75-78; ASST PROF MICROBIOL, UNIV KANS, 78- *Concurrent Pos:* Oncol trainee, Harvard Med Sch, 75-77; Nat Res Serv award, Nat Cancer Inst, 77. *Mem:* Sigma Xi; Am Soc Microbiol. *Res:* Replication of animal viruses; eucaryotic chromosome synthesis and gene regulation. *Mailing Add:* Dept of Microbiol Univ of Kans Lawrence KS 66045

SU, SHIN-YI, b Taipei, Taiwan, China, July 18, 40; m 80; c 2. SPACE PHYSICS. *Educ:* Nat Taiwan Univ, BS, 63; Dartmouth Col, PhD(eng sci), 70. *Prof Exp:* Res asst space physics, Dartmouth Col, 65-69; postdoctoral fel, Univ Calgary, 70-72; resident res assoc at Johnson Space Ctr, Nat Acad Sci-Nat Res Coun, 72-74; prin scientist, Lockheed Electronics Co Inc, 74-80, COMPUT SYST ANALYST SPACE PHYSICS, LOCKHEED ENG & MGT SERV CO, IC, 80- *Mem:* Am Geophys Union. *Res:* Study of wave-particle interaction phenomena in the earth magnetosphere; interplanetary dust particle dynamics; spacecraft hazardous analysis from collision with near earth space debris. *Mailing Add:* Lockheed-Eng Mat Serv C23C 1830 NASA Rd 1 Houston TX 77058

SU, STANLEY Y W, b Fukien, China, Feb 18, 40; US citizen; m 65; c 2. COMPUTER SCIENCE. *Educ:* Tamkang Col Arts & Sci, BA, 61; Univ Wis, MS,65, PhD(comput sci), 68. *Prof Exp:* Proj asst syst prog, Comput Ctr, Univ Wis, 64-67, res asst regional Am English proj, 67, res asst natural lang processing, 67-68; mathematician comput ling, Rand Corp, 68-70; asst prof, Dept Elec Eng & Commun Sci Lab, 70-74, assoc prof comput & info eng, Dept Elec Eng & Inst Advan Study Commun Processes, 74-78, PROF, DEPT COMPUT & INFO SCI, DEPT ELEC ENG, UNIV FLA, 78- *Concurrent Pos:* Mem, Spec Interest Group Operating Syst & Spec Interest Group Mgt Data, Asn Comput Mach, 73-; consult, Creativity Ctr Consortium, 73-74, Fla Keys Community Col, 74-75 & Cent Fla Community Col, 74-; staff consult, Queueing Systs, Inc, 74-75; lectr continuing educ, George Washington Univ, 75-80; assoced, Transacting Software Eng, Int J Comput Lang, Inst Elec & Electronics Engrs, 81- *Mem:* Asn Comput Mach; Conf Data Systs Lang; Inst Elec & Electronic Engrs; Asn Comput Ling. *Res:* Associative processing systems; computer architecture for data base management; data base translation and program conversion; data base semantics; application of microprocessor network to non-numeric processing; man-machine communications; cost/benefit analysis of database management systems; modeling and design of statistical databases. *Mailing Add:* 512 Weil Hall Dept Comput & Info Serv Univ Fla Gainesville FL 32611

SU, STEPHEN Y H, b Anchi, China, July 6, 38; US citizen; m 64; c 2. FAULT-TOLERANT COMPUTING, DESIGN AUTOMATION. *Educ:* Nat Taiwan Univ, BS, 60; Univ Wis-Madison, MS, 63, PhD(comput eng), 67. *Prof Exp:* Asst prof switching theory, New York Univ, 67-69, comput archit, Univ Calif, Berkeley, 69-71, design automation, Univ Southern Calif, 71-72; assoc prof, Case Western Reserve Univ, 72-73, syst design, City Col New York, 73-75; prof fault diag, Utah State Univ, 75-78; PROF FAULT TOLERANT COMPUT, STATE UNIV NY BINGHAMTON, 78- *Concurrent Pos:* Electronic engr, Air Force Radar Sta, Taiwan, 60-61; logic designer, Fabri-Tek, Inc, 65; proj specialist, Med Sch, Univ Wis, 66; consult, IBM, UNIVAC, & E & H Res, 68-78; mem tech staff, Bell Labs, 69; staff consult, UNIVAC, 73-74; engr, IBM, 74. *Mem:* Sr mem Inst Elec & Electronics Engrs. *Res:* Fault tolerant design; fault diagnosis; computer aided logic system design of digital systems and computer architecture; developing new algorithms for testing very large scale integration. *Mailing Add:* Dept Comput Sci State Univ NY Binghamton NY 13901

SU, TAH-MUN, b Taiwan, July 22, 39; m; c 3. ORGANIC CHEMISTRY, MICROBIOLOGY. *Educ:* Chen Kung Univ, Taiwan, BSc, 62; Univ Nev, MS, 65; Princeton Univ, PhD(chem), 70. *Prof Exp:* Res fel geochem, Biodyn Lab, Univ Calif, Berkeley, 69-70; res fel chem, Union Carbide Res Inst, 70-71; STAFF SCIENTIST CHEM & BIOENG, CORP RES & DEVELOP CTR, GEN ELEC CO, 72- *Mem:* Am Chem Soc; Am Soc Microbiol. *Res:* Single cell protein from cellulosic fiber; biodegradation of chlorinated hydrocarbons; enzymatic saccharification of cellulose; mechanism of organic chemical reactions; ethanol from biomass. *Mailing Add:* Corp Res & Develop Gen Elec Co River Rd Schenectady NY 12301

SU, YAO SIN, b Ping-tung, Taiwan, Oct 17, 29; US citizen; m 54; c 2. ANALYTICAL CHEMISTRY. *Educ:* Taiwan Univ, BS, 52; Univ Pittsburgh, PhD(chem), 62. *Prof Exp:* Chemist, Union Res Inst, Taiwan, 53-58; sr res chemist, 63-73, res supvr, 73-79, MGR, CORNING GLASS WORKS, 79- *Mem:* Am Chem Soc. *Res:* Inorganic chemical analysis; electroanalysis; classical wet methods. *Mailing Add:* 197 Cutler Ave Corning NY 14830

SUAREZ, KENNETH ALFRED, b Queens, NY, June 27, 44; m 68. PHARMACOLOGY, TOXICOLOGY. *Educ:* Univ RI, BS, 67, MS, 70, PhD(pharmacol), 72. *Prof Exp:* From instr to asst prof pharmacol, 72-77, ASSOC PROF PHARMACOL, CHICAGO COL OSTEOP MED, 77-, ASST DIR RES AFFAIRS, 80- *Mem:* AAAS. *Res:* Halogenated hydrocarbon induced hepatic injury. *Mailing Add:* Dept of Pharmacol Chicago Col of Osteop Med Chicago IL 60615

SUAREZ, THOMAS H, b Temperley, Arg, Dec 7, 36; m 61; c 3. RESOURCE MANAGEMENT. *Educ:* Univ Buenos Aires, MS, 59, PhD(phys org chem), 61. *Prof Exp:* Teaching asst org chem, Univ Buenos Aires, 59-61, head lab course, 61; res chemist, Textile Fibers Dept, Dacron Mfg Div, E I Du Pont De Nemours & Co, 61-66, anal res supvr, 66-69, supvr process develop, 69-71, tech supt, Polymer Intermediates Dept, 71-74, planning mgr, Polymer Intermediates Dept, 74-77, sales mgr-Latin Am, Petrol Chem Div, 78-81, MGR, GEN PROD DEPT, DU PONT DE VENEZUELA, 81- *Mem:* AAAS; Am Chem Soc; Arg Chem Asn. *Res:* Nucleophylic aromatic substitution; reaction kinetics and mechanisms; polymer chemistry; melt spining synthetic fibers; physical and chemical characterization of polymers. *Mailing Add:* E I du Pont de Nemours & Co Petrochem Dept Wilmington DE 19898

SUBACH, DANIEL JAMES, b Shenandoah, Pa, July 7, 47; m 70; c 2. ANALYTICAL CHEMISTRY, PHYSICAL CHEMISTRY. *Educ:* Lebanon Valley Col, BS, 69; Marshall Univ, MS, 71; Tex A&M Univ, PhD(phys chem), 74; Rensselaer Polytech Inst, MBA, 81. *Prof Exp:* Qual control chemist, Campbell's Soup Co, 69-70; sr anal develop chemist, Ciba-Geigy Corp, 75-77; proj mgr anal & phys res & develop, Springborn Labs Inc, 77-78; mgr anal res & develop, 78-80, MGR QUAL CONTROL, SILICON PROD DIV, GEN ELEC CO, 80- *Concurrent Pos:* NASA fel, Rice Univ, 74-75. *Mem:* Sigma Xi; Am Chem Soc. *Res:* Thermodynamics and thermophysical properties; nonelectrolyte mixture and liquid theory; trace analysis of organics and inorganics; chromatography including gas, liquid and thin-layer. *Mailing Add:* 6 N Center Lane Ballston Lake NY 12109

SUBERKROPP, KELLER FRANCIS, b Wamego, Kans, Apr 12, 43; m 71; c 4. MICROBIAL ECOLOGY, PHYSIOLOGY. *Educ:* Kans State Univ, BS, 65, MS, 67; Mich State Univ, PhD(bot), 71. *Prof Exp:* Res assoc microbial ecol, Kellogg Biol Sta, Mich State Univ, 71-75; asst prof biol sci, Ind Univ-Purdue Univ, Ft Wayne, 75-78; ASST PROF BIOL SCI, N MEX STATE UNIV, 78- *Mem:* Mycol Soc Am; Ecol Soc Am; Brit Mycol Soc; Sigma Xi; Am Soc Microbiol. *Res:* Role of fungi in decomposition of leaf litter in aquatic habitats; effects of environmental factors on growth and sporulation of these fungi. *Mailing Add:* Dept of Biol Sci NMex State Univ Las Cruces NM 88003

SUBLETT, BOBBY JONES, b Paintsville, Ky, Aug 27, 31; m 56; c 4. ORGANIC CHEMISTRY, POLYMER CHEMISTRY. *Educ:* Eastern Ky State Col, BS, 58; Univ Tenn, MS, 60. *Prof Exp:* From res chemist to sr res chemist, 60-75, RES ASSOC, TENN EASTMAN CO, 75- *Mem:* Am Chem Soc. *Res:* Reaction mechanisms; tobacco smoke analysis; condensation polymers; textile chemicals; adhesives. *Mailing Add:* 1205 Jerry Lane Kingsport TN 37664

SUBLETT, ROBERT L, b Columbia, Mo, Apr 10, 21; m 46; c 3. CHEMISTRY. *Educ:* Univ Mo, AB, 43, PhD, 50; Ga Inst Technol, MS, 48. *Prof Exp:* Instr chem, Ga Inst Technol, 47; res chemist, Chemstrand Corp, 52-55; assoc prof chem, Ark State Teachers Col, 55-56; assoc prof, 56-70, PROF CHEM, TENN TECHNOL UNIV, 70-, CHMN DEPT, 72- *Mem:* Am Chem Soc. *Res:* High polymers; Friedels-crafts; organic and high polymer analytical chemistry; instrumental analysis. *Mailing Add:* Dept of Chem Tenn Technol Univ Cookeville TN 38501

SUBLETTE, IVAN H(UGH), b Urbana, Ill, May 15, 29. COMPUTER SCIENCE, ELECTRICAL ENGINEERING. *Educ:* Purdue Univ, BS, 49; Univ Pa, MS, 51, PhD(elec eng), 57. *Prof Exp:* Engr, RCA, 49-59, mem tech staff, RCA Labs, 59-74, SR SYSTS PROGRAMMER, RCA SOLID STATE DIV, 74- *Mem:* Inst Elec & Electronics Engrs; Asn Comput Mach. *Res:* Computer operating systems; performance measurement and evaluation. *Mailing Add:* RCA Solid State Div Somerville NJ 08876

SUBLETTE, JAMES EDWARD, b Healdton, Okla, Jan 19, 28; m 50; c 4. ZOOLOGY. *Educ:* Univ Ark, BS, 48, MS, 50; Univ Okla, PhD(zool), 53. *Prof Exp:* Biologist, Corps Engrs, US Dept Army, 49-51; asst prof zool, Southwestern La Inst, 51-53 & Henderson State Teachers Col, 53; from asst prof to assoc prof, Northwestern State Col, 53-60; assoc prof, Tex Western Col, 60-61; assoc prof, 61-66, dean, Sch Grad Studies, 66-78, PROF BIOL, EASTERN N MEX UNIV, 66-, DIST RES PROF, 78- *Concurrent Pos:* Japan Soc Prom Sci fel, 78; vis prof, Univ Bergen, 81. *Mem:* NAm Benthological Soc. *Res:* Taxonomy and ecology of aquatic insects, particularly Chironomidae; limnology. *Mailing Add:* Box 2114 Eastern NMex Univ Portales NM 88130

SUBRAHMANIAM, KATHLEEN, b Pittsburgh, Pa, Mar 31, 38; m 62; c 2. STATISTICS. *Educ:* Muskingum Col, BS, 60; Johns Hopkins Univ, MS, 63, DSc(statist), 69. *Prof Exp:* Lectr math, Muskingum Col, 62-63; consult statist, Dept Community Med, Univ Western Ont, 65-70; sessional lectr statist, 67-69, asst prof, 69-73, ASSOC PROF, UNIV MAN, 73- *Mem:* Biomet Soc; Am Statist Asn. *Res:* Applied multivariate analysis and analysis of discrete data. *Mailing Add:* 88 Tunis Ft Garry MB R3T 1C0 Can

SUBRAHMANIAM, KOCHERLAKOTA, b Bangalore, India, Feb 3, 35; m 62; c 2. MATHEMATICAL STATISTICS. *Educ:* Univ Col Sci, Benares, India, BSc, 54, MSc, 57; Inst Agr Res Statist, dipl, 63; Johns Hopkins Univ, DSc(biostatist), 64. *Prof Exp:* Jr res fel statist, Inst Agr Res Statist, 57-58, sr res fel, 58-59; investr, Rockefeller Found, India, 59-60; asst prof math, Univ Western Ont, 64-66; assoc prof, 66-70, PROF STATIST, UNIV MAN, 70- *Concurrent Pos:* Nat Res Coun operating grants pure & appl math, 66- *Mem:* Inst Math Statist; Am Statist Asn; fel Royal Statist Soc. *Res:* Multivariate analysis; distribution theory; statistical tests of significance; applied probability theory; non-normality. *Mailing Add:* Dept of Statist Univ of Man Winnipeg MB R3T 2N2 Can

SUBRAMANIAN, GOPAL, b Madras, India, Apr 4, 37; m 66; c 2. NUCLEAR MEDICINE, CHEMICAL ENGINEERING. *Educ:* Univ Madras, BSc, 58 & 60; Johns Hopkins Univ, MSE, 64; Syracuse Univ, PhD(chem eng), 70. *Prof Exp:* Chem engr, Prod Dept, E Asiatic Co (India) Pvt, Ltd, 60-62; res assoc radiochem, Med Insts, Johns Hopkins Univ, 64-65; res assoc radiopharmaceut, 65-68, from instr to assoc prof, 68-76, PROF RADIOL, STATE UNIV NY UPSTATE MED CTR, 72- *Concurrent Pos:* NIH grant, State Univ NY Upstate Med Ctr, 69-; consult, Am Nat Stand Inst, 71-; mem, adv panel radiopharmaceut, US Pharmacoepia, 71-; asst prof, Syracuse Univ, 71-; assoc ed, J Nuclear Med, 76- *Honors & Awards:* Gold Medal, Soc Nuclear Med, 72. *Mem:* AAAS; Soc Nuclear Med; fel Am Inst Chem; Am Inst Chem Eng. *Res:* Radiochemistry; radiopharmaceuticals; fluid dynamics as applied to chemical engineering. *Mailing Add:* Dept of Nuclear Med State Univ of NY Upstate Med Ctr Syracuse NY 13210

SUBRAMANIAN, K N, b Cuddalore, India, Aug 13, 38. METALLURGY, MATERIALS SCIENCE. *Educ:* Annamalai Univ, Madras, BSc, 58; Indian Inst Sci, Bangalore, BE, 60; Univ Calif, Berkeley, MS, 62; Mich State Univ, PhD(metall), 66. *Prof Exp:* Asst prof, 65-76, ASSOC PROF METALL, MECH & MAT SCI, MICH STATE UNIV, 76- *Mem:* Am Soc Metal; Am Inst Mining, Metall & Petrol Engrs. *Res:* Plastic deformation of crystals; dislocation theory with specific reference to fatigue, work hardening, crystal growth and fracture; two phase materials; phase separation in glasses. *Mailing Add:* Dept of Metall Mech & Mat Sci Mich State Univ East Lansing MI 48824

SUBRAMANIAN, KRISHNAMOORTHY, b Lalgudi, India, July 25, 49. MANUFACTURING PROCESSES, ENERGY CONVERSION DEVICES. *Educ:* Osmania Univ, BEng, 70; Mass Inst Technol, ME, 76, ScD, 77. *Prof Exp:* Indust engr, Nat Productivity Coun, India, 71-72; res assoc mat processing, Mass Inst Technol, 76-77; sr res engr machining & wear, Sci Res Lab, Ford Motor Co, 77-79, sr res engr adv concepts & energy systems, 79-81; MGR, APPL ENERGY CONVER TECHNOL, SCI & TECHNOL LAB, INT HARVESTER CO, 81- *Concurrent Pos:* Adj lectr, Univ Mich, Dearborn, 78. *Mem:* Am Soc Mech Engrs. *Res:* Productivity improvement in machining and manufacturing systems; novel application of ceramic materials and energy conversion devices leading to innovative products or processes. *Mailing Add:* 1333 Regency Grove Dr Darien IL 60559

SUBRAMANIAN, MAHADEVAN, b Madras, India, Jan 11, 34; m 64; c 2. ELECTRICAL ENGINEERING, QUANTUM ELECTRONICS. *Educ:* Univ Madras, BSc, 53; Madras Inst Technol, dipl, 56; Purdue Univ, MSEE, 61, PhD(elec eng), 64. *Prof Exp:* Engr, G Janshi & Co, India, 56; trainee, All India Radio, 57; jr sci officer, Electronics Res Inst, 57-59; tech asst & instr elec eng, Purdue Univ, 59-64, asst prof, 64-66; MEM TECH STAFF LASER RES, BELL TEL LABS, HOLMDEL, 66- *Concurrent Pos:* Consult, Bell Tel Labs, 64-66. *Mem:* Inst Elec & Electronics Engrs. *Res:* Receivers, parametric amplifiers, ferroelectric materials and propagation through plasma in microwaves; nonlinear optics, cathodoluminescence, lasers, laser systems and propagation through turbulent media in quantum electronics; digital transmission systems; minicomputer systems; software development. *Mailing Add:* 28 Schwenker Pl Fair Haven NJ 07701

SUBRAMANIAN, PALLATHERI MANACKAL, b Ottapalam, Kerala, India, Jan 10, 31; m 66. ORGANIC CHEMISTRY. *Educ:* Univ Madras, BSc, 50; Univ Bombay, MSc, 58; Wayne State Univ, PhD(org chem), 64. *Prof Exp:* Chemist, Godrej Soaps, India, 50-58; res chemist, Electrochem Dept, 64-70, SR RES CHEMIST, PLASTICS DEPT, CHESTNUT RUN LABS, E I DU PONT DE NEMOURS & CO, INC, 70- *Mem:* Am Chem Soc; The Chem Soc; Sigma Xi. *Res:* Physical organic chemistry; kinetics of elimination reactions in organic bicyclic systems; nuclear magnetic resonance spectroscopy of organic compounds; synthetic organic high polymers; adhesives and coatings; synthesis and process of plastics. *Mailing Add:* 2710 Tanager Dr Wilmington DE 19808

SUBRAMANIAN, RAM SHANKAR, b Madras, India, Aug 10, 47; US citizen; m 73. TRANSPORT PHENOMENA, APPLIED MATHEMATICS. *Educ:* Univ Madras, BTech, 68; Clarkson Col Technol, MS, 69, PhD(chem eng), 72. *Prof Exp:* Instr fac eng & appl sci, State Univ NY Buffalo, 72-73; asst prof, 73-79, assoc prof, 79-82, PROF CHEM ENG, CLARKSON COL TECHNOL, 82- *Concurrent Pos:* Prin investr numerous grants & contracts, 75-80; consult, Westinghouse Res Lab & Univ Space Res Asn, Marshall Space Flight Ctr. *Mem:* Am Inst Chem Engrs; AAAS; Sigma Xi; Am Ceramic Soc; Am Soc Eng Educ. *Res:* Interfacial phenomena; transport phenomena in glasses; materials processing in space; unsteady convective diffusion; colloid separations. *Mailing Add:* Dept of Chem Eng Clarkson Col of Technol Potsdam NY 13676

SUBRAMANIAN, RAVANASAMUDRAM VENKATACHALAM, b Kalakad, India, Jan 16, 33; m 53; c 2. POLYMER CHEMISTRY, POLYMER SCIENCE. *Educ:* Presidency Col, Madras, India, BSc, 53; Loyola Col, Madras, India, MSc, 54; Univ Madras, PhD(polymer chem), 57. *Prof Exp:* Jr res fel polymer chem, Nat Chem Lab, Poona, India, 57, Coun Sci & Indust Res India sr res fel, 57-59, jr sci officer, 59-63; res assoc chem, Case Inst Technol, 63-66 & Inst Molecular Biophys, Fla State Univ, 66; pool officer, Dept Phys Chem, Madras Univ, 66-67; asst prof, Harcourt Butler Tech Inst, Kanpur, India, 67-69; res chemist, Mat Chem Sect, Col Eng Res Div, 69-73, assoc prof, 73-78, Boeing distinguished prof, 81, PROF MAT SCI, WASH STATE UNIV, 78-, HEAD POLYMER MAT SECT, 74- *Concurrent Pos:* NSF fel, Case Inst Technol, 63-66; AEC fel, Inst Molecular Biophys, Fla State Univ, 66; Coun Sci & Indust Res India grant, 68-69. *Mem:* Am Chem Soc; Soc Plastics Engrs. *Res:* Kinetics and mechanisms of polymerization; polymer structure and proper properties; electropolymerization; interface modification in carbon fiber reinforced composites; basalt fibers; organotin monomers and polymers. *Mailing Add:* Dept of Mat Sci Wash State Univ Pullman WA 99164

SUBRAMANIAN, SETHURAMAN, b Mattur, India, May 16, 40; US citizen; m 69; c 3. PHYSICAL CHEMISTRY, BIOCHEMISTRY. *Educ:* Univ Madras, BSc, 60, MSc, 65; Indian Inst Technol, Kanpur, India, PhD(phys chem), 69. *Prof Exp:* Fel phys chem, Med Ctr, Univ Kans, 70-74; Nat Res Coun resident res assoc biophysics, Naval Med Res Inst, Bethesda, 74-75; VIS SCIENTIST PHYS CHEM, NIH, 75- *Mem:* Am Chem Soc; Am Soc Biol Chemists. *Res:* Protein chemistry; enzymology; microcalorimetry; thermodynamics; spectroscopy; sickle cell hemoglobin; alcohol dehydrogenase. *Mailing Add:* Nat Inst Arthritis Diabetes Digestive & Kidney Dis NIH Bethesda MD 20014

SUBUDHI, MANOMOHAN, b Daspalla, India, Sept 27, 46; m 71; c 2. CONTINUUM MECHANICS, MECHANICAL VIBRATIONS. *Educ:* Banaras Hindu Univ, India, BSc, 69; Mass Inst Technol, SM, 70; Polytech Inst NY, PhD(vibrations), 74. *Prof Exp:* Sr stress analyst pipe stress, Nuclear Power Serv Inc, 74-75; sr mech engr stress anal, Bechtel Power Corp, 75-76; ASSOC MECH ENGR STRUCT ANAL, BROOKHAVEN NAT LAB, 76- *Mem:* Am Soc Mech Engrs; Sigma Xi. *Res:* Fracture mechanics; structural analysis using numerical techniques. *Mailing Add:* T-129 Brookhaven Nat Lab Upton NY 11973

SUCEC, JAMES, b Bridgeport, Conn, June 15, 40; m 64; c 2. HEAT TRANSFER. *Educ:* Univ Conn, BS, 62, MS, 63. *Prof Exp:* Instr mech eng & thermodynamics, Univ Conn, 63-64; from asst prof to assoc prof, 64-76, PROF MECH ENG & HEAT TRANSFER, UNIV MAINE, 76- *Concurrent Pos:* Asst proj engr, Pratt & Whitney Aircraft, Div United Technol Corp, 65-68; fac fel Am Soc Elec Engrs, NASA Lewis Res Ctr, 72-73; NSF res proj prin investr, Univ Maine, 79-81. *Mem:* Am Soc Mech Engrs. *Res:* Finite difference solutions in film cooling and in conduction heat transfer; analytical work in fins and fluid jet trajectories; analytical work in transient forced convection heat transfer, particularly conjugate problems. *Mailing Add:* Rm 203 Boardman Hall Univ Maine Orono ME 04469

SUCHANNEK, RUDOLF GERHARD, b Hindenburg, Ger, Oct 17, 21. EXPERIMENTAL ATOMIC PHYSICS. *Educ:* Univ Hamburg, dipl(physics), 58; Univ Alaska, PhD(physics), 74. *Prof Exp:* Engr, Westinghouse Elec Corp, 58-62; eng specialist, Microwave Comp Lab, Sylvania Co, 62-64; physicist, Unified Sci Asn Inc, 64-66; sr res asst atomic collision, Geophys Inst, Univ Alaska, 66-73, fel, 74; res assoc atomic physics, Res Lab Electronics, Mass Inst Technol, 75-77; res assoc, Dept Physics & Astron, Rutgers Univ, 77-80; ASST RESEARCHER PHYSICS, UNIV CALIF, LOS ANGELES, 80- *Mem:* Am Phys Soc; Inst Elec & Electronic Engrs. *Res:* Excitation transfer collisions of laser excited atoms and molecules; charge exchange collisions of protons with atoms and molecules. *Mailing Add:* Dept Physics Univ Calif Los Angeles CA 90024

SUCHARD, STEVEN NORMAN, b Chicago, Ill, Feb 8, 44; m 64; c 4. LASERS. *Educ:* Univ Calif, Berkeley, BS, 65; Mass Inst Technol, PhD(chem physics), 69. *Prof Exp:* Res asst, Lawrence Berkeley Lab, 64-65; teaching asst chem, Mass Inst Technol, 65-69; lectr, Univ Calif, Berkeley, 69-70; assoc dept head chem physics, Aerospace Corp, 70-77; tech mgr dept chem, Hughes Aircraft Co, 77-80. *Concurrent Pos:* Fel chem physics, Univ Calif, Berkeley, 69-70. *Mem:* Am Phys Soc. *Res:* Effect of system variables on the output of pulsed and continuous wave chemical lasers; flash photolysis; energy transfer in molecular systems; laser optics in high gain media; determination of the feasibility of producing new chemically and electrically pumped electronic transition lasers; measurement of molecular and kinetic parameters effecting optical gain of potential laser systems. *Mailing Add:* 9912 Star Dr Huntington Beach CA 92646

SUCHESTON, MARTHA ELAINE, b Bowling Green, Ky, June 17, 39; m 68; c 2. DEVELOPMENTAL ANATOMY. *Educ:* Western Ky Univ, BSc, 60; Ohio State Univ, MSc, 61, PhD(anat), 65. *Prof Exp:* Asst prof gross anat & embryol, Ohio State Univ, 67-68; asst prof gross anat, Stanford Univ, 68-69; asst prof, 70-74, ASSOC GROSS ANAT & EMBRYOL, OHIO STATE UNIV, 75- *Concurrent Pos:* Bremer Found Fund fel, Ohio State Univ, 71-73; vis assoc prof gross anat, Univ BC, 74-75; Small Univ grant, 78; Cent Ohio Heart Asn grant, 78-79. *Mem:* AAAS; Am Asn Anat; Teratology Soc; Pan-Am Asn Anat. *Res:* Birth defects associated with anticonvulsant drugs. *Mailing Add:* Dept of Anat Ohio State Univ Col of Med Columbus OH 43210

SUCHMAN, DAVID, b New York, NY, June 23, 47; m 70; c 2. METEOROLOGY. *Educ:* Rensselaer Polytech Inst, BS, 68; Univ Wis-Madison, MS, 70, PhD(meteorol), 74. *Prof Exp:* Proj assoc meteorol, 74-76, asst scientist, 76-79, ASSOC SCIENTIST METEOROL, SPACE SCI & ENG CTR, UNIV WIS-MADISON, 79- *Mem:* Am Meteorol Soc; Sigma Xi. *Res:* Application of geostationary satellite data to the study of the dynamics of mesoscale systems; practical applications of meteorology. *Mailing Add:* Space Sci & Eng Ctr Univ of Wis Madison WI 53706

SUCHOW, LAWRENCE, b New York, NY, June 24, 23; m 68. SOLID STATE CHEMISTRY, INORGANIC CHEMISTRY. *Educ:* City Col New York, BS, 43; Polytech Inst Brooklyn, PhD(chem), 51. *Prof Exp:* Anal chemist, Aluminum Co Am, 43-44; res chemist, Baker & Co, Inc, 44, Manhattan Proj, Oak Ridge, Tenn, 45-46, Baker & Co, Inc, 46-47, Signal Corps Eng Labs, US Dept Army, 50-54 & Francis Earle Labs, Inc, 54-58; sr res chemist, Westinghouse Elec Corp, 58-60; mem res staff, Watson Res Ctr, Int Bus Mach Corp, 60-64; from asst prof to assoc prof, 64-70, PROF CHEM, NJ INST TECHNOL, 70- *Concurrent Pos:* NSF grants, 67-74; sabbatical leave, Imp Col, Univ London, 74. *Mem:* Am Chem Soc; Sigma Xi; fel NY Acad Sci. *Res:* High temperature inorganic reactions; physical properties of solids; x-ray crystallography; crystal growth; phosphors; rare earths. *Mailing Add:* Dept of Chem Eng & Chem NJ Inst of Technol Newark NJ 07102

SUCHSLAND, OTTO, b Jena, Ger, June 18, 28; US citizen; m 56; c 2. WOOD TECHNOLOGY. *Educ:* Univ Hamburg, BS, 52, Dr nat sci(wood technol), 56. *Prof Exp:* Res engr, Swed Forest Prod Lab, Stockholm, 52-55; tech dir, Elmendorf Res, Inc, Calif, 55-57; from asst prof to assoc prof forest prod, 57-71, PROF FORESTRY, MICH STATE UNIV, 71- *Mem:* Forest Prod Res Soc. *Res:* Adhesives; gluing of wood; technology of composite wood products. *Mailing Add:* 210 Natural Resources Bldg Mich State Univ East Lansing MI 48824

SUCIU, GEORGE DAN, b Blaj, Romania, July 30, 34; WGer citizen; m 59; c 3. CHEMICAL ENGINEERING, ORGANIC CHEMISTRY. *Educ:* Polytech Inst, Bucharest, MS, 57, PhD(chem eng), 68. *Prof Exp:* Chem engr petrol refining, Teleajen Refinery, Ploiesti, Romania, 57-59; chem engr org chem pilot plants, Icechim Res Inst, Bucharest, Romania, 59-64; sr researcher fundamental res chem eng, Res Ctr Romanian Acad, Bucharest, 64-71; assoc prof petrol technol unit oper, Inst Petrol, Univ Ploiesti, Romania, 71-74; group leader org intermediate res, Akzo Res Lab, Obernburg, WGer, 75-77; prin res chemist, 77-78, MGR PROCESS RES, CE LUMMUS, 78- *Mem:* Am Chem Soc. *Res:* Process research organic intermediates; enhancement of heat and mass transfer; reactions in multiphase systems; oxidations. *Mailing Add:* CE Lummus 1515 Broad St Bloomfield NJ 07003

SUCIU, S(PIRIDON) N, b Genesse County, Mich, Dec 11, 21; m 49; c 5. MECHANICAL ENGINEERING. *Educ:* Purdue Univ, BSME, 44, MS, 49, PhD(mech eng), 51. *Prof Exp:* Res engr, Flight Propulsion Div, Gen Elec Co, NY, 51-52 & Ohio, 52-54, supvr basic combustion res, 54-56, mgr appl rocket res, 56-58, mgr appl res oper, 58-63, mgr aerodynamic & component design oper, 63-67, mgr design technol oper, 67-71, gen mgr gas turbine eng dept, NY, 71-76, mgr energy technol oper, Energy Systs & Technol Div, 76-78, GEN MGR NEUTRON DEVICES DEPT, GEN ELEC CO, 78- *Concurrent Pos:* Chmn, NASA Airbreathing Propulsion Comt, 67-70; mem Air Force Sci Adv Bd, 70-75; consult, NASA, 70- *Honors & Awards:* Akroyd Stuart Award, Royal Aeronaut Soc, 72. *Mem:* Am Soc Mech Engrs; Am Inst Aeronaut & Astronaut; Am Mgt Asn. *Res:* Power generation components and systems for utility, industrial, aircraft and marine use in commercial and military applications; electrical, mechanical and neutron devices for nuclear weapons; materials and manufacturing process development; general management of high technology businesses. *Mailing Add:* Gen Elec Co PO Box 11508 St Petersburg FL 33733

SUCK, SUNG HO, b Seoul, Korea, Apr 14, 39; m 68; c 2. PHYSICS, CHEMISTRY. *Educ:* Midwestern Univ, BS, 66; Univ Houston, MS, 68; Univ Tex, Austin, PhD(physics), 72. *Prof Exp:* Res fel, Univ Tex, 72-74, res assoc chem, 74-77; res asst prof, 77-80, RES ASSOC PROF PHYSICS, UNIV MO, 80- *Mem:* Am Phys Soc; Am Chem Soc; Sigma Xi. *Res:* Reaction mechanisms related to molecular and nuclear collision, nucleation and condensation; molecular structures and properties. *Mailing Add:* Dept of Physics Univ Mo Rolla MO 65401

SUCKEWER, SZYMON, b Warsaw, Poland, Apr 10, 38; US citizen; c 1. PLASMA PHYSICS, ATOMIC PHYSICS. *Educ:* Moscow Univ, MS, 62; Inst Nuclear Res, Warsaw, PhD(plasma physics), 66; Warsaw Univ, Habilitation, 71. *Prof Exp:* Head spectros lab plasma physics, Inst Nuclear Res, 66-69; pvt researcher, 69-71; assoc prof, Inst Nuclear Res, Warsaw Univ, 71-75; mem staff, 75-77, res physicist, 77-80, SR RES PHYSICIST, PLASMA PHYSICS LAB, PRINCETON UNIV, 80- *Mem:* Am Phys Soc. *Res:* Plasma spectroscopy; ionization, excitation and radiation processes in high and low temperature plasmas; lasers (high power lasers and short wave-length lasers); tokamaks. *Mailing Add:* Plasma Physics Lab PO Box 451 Princeton NJ 08544

SUCOFF, EDWARD IRA, b NJ, Nov 17, 31. PLANT PHYSIOLOGY. *Educ:* Univ Mich, BS, 55, MS, 56; Univ Md, PhD(bot), 60. *Prof Exp:* Res forester, US Forest Serv, 56-60; asst & assoc prof, 60-71, PROF FORESTRY, UNIV MINN, ST PAUL, 71- *Mem:* AAAS; Am Soc Plant Physiologists; Soc Am Foresters. *Res:* Tree growth; tree water relations. *Mailing Add:* Col of Forestry Univ of Minn St Paul MN 55101

SUCOV, E(UGENE) W(ILLIAM), b Waterbury, Conn, Oct 27, 22; div; c 3. FUSION, LASERS. *Educ:* Brooklyn Col, BA, 43; NY Univ, MS, 54, PhD(physics), 59. *Prof Exp:* Electronics engr, 43-53; asst solid state physics, NY Univ, 53-58; res physicist, Glass Res Ctr, Pittsburgh Plate Glass Co, 58-63; res physicist, Westinghouse Res Labs, 63-66, mgr luminescence res, 66-70, fel physicist, 70-72, mgr behav res, 72-74, adv physicist, 75-78, MGR INERTIAL CONFINEMENT FUSION PROGS, WESTINGHOUSE FUSION POWER PROGS, 78- *Concurrent Pos:* Lectr, Univ Pittsburgh, 78-79; mem prog comt, Inertial Confinement Fusion Topical Meeting, 79-80. *Mem:* Am Phys Soc; Inst Elec & Electronics Engrs; fel Illuminating Engrs Soc. *Res:* Fusion physics; gas discharges; lasers; plasmas. *Mailing Add:* Westinghouse Fusion Progs PO Box 10864 Pittsburgh PA 15236

SUCZEK, CHRISTOPHER ANNE, b Detroit, Mich, Sept 6, 42; c 1. SEDIMENTARY GEOLOGY, PHYSICAL STRATIGRAPHY. *Educ:* Univ Calif, Berkeley, BA, 72; Stanford Univ, PhD(geol), 77. *Prof Exp:* Actg instr geol, Stanford Univ, 76; ASST PROF GEOL, WESTERN WASH UNIV, 77- *Mem:* Geol Soc Am; Soc Econ Paleontologists & Mineralogists; Geol Asn Can; Int Asn Sedimentologists. *Res:* Tectonics of western North America; sedimentary petrology. *Mailing Add:* Dept of Geol Western Wash Univ Bellingham WA 98225

SUD, GIAN CHAND, zoology, biochemistry, see previous edition

SUD, ISH, b Calcutta, India, Oct 6, 49. ENERGY MANAGEMENT, LOAD CONTROL. *Educ:* Indian Inst Technol, India, BTech, 70; Duke Univ, MS, 71, PhD(mech eng), 75. *Prof Exp:* Res assoc, 75, SR PROJ ENGR & SYSTS ANALYST, DUKE UNIV, 75-, RES ASST PROF MAT SCI, 78- *Concurrent Pos:* Design engr, T C Cooke, P E, Inc, 74-77, dir, Energy Mgt & Special Proj, 77-78; pres, Sud Assocs, 79- *Mem:* Am Soc Heating, Refrig & Air Conditioning Engrs; Am Soc Mech Engrs; Sigma Xi. *Res:* Development and application of procedures for estimating building energy usage; research and application of techniques for reducing building energy usage, peak electrical demand and energy costs. *Mailing Add:* SUD Assocs 1805 Chapel Hill Rd Durham NC 27707

SUDAN, RAVINDRA NATH, b Kashmir, India, June 8, 31; m 59; c 2. PLASMA PHYSICS. *Educ:* Panjab Univ, India, BA, 48; Indian Inst Sci, dipl, 52; Univ London, DIC & PhD(elec eng), 55. *Prof Exp:* Elec engr, Brit Thomson Houston Co, Eng, 55-57; instruments engr, Imp Chem Industs, Ltd, India, 57-58; res assoc, 58-59, from asst prof to assoc prof elec eng, 59-68, chmn exec comt lab plasma studies, 71-74, PROF ELEC ENG & APPL PHYSICS, CORNELL UNIV, 68-, DIR, LAB PLASMA STUDIES & IBM PROF ENG, 74- *Concurrent Pos:* Vis scientist, Int Ctr Theoret Physics, Trieste, 65-66, 70-73; vis res physicist, plasma physics lab, Princeton Univ, 66-67; head theoret plasma physics, Naval Res Lab, DC, 70-71, sci adv, 74-75; consult, Lawrence Radiation Lab, Univ Calif, Los Alamos Sci Lab, Physics Int Co, Sci Appl, Inc; vis physicist, Inst Advan Study, Princeton, 75. *Mem:* AAAS; fel Am Phys Soc; fel Inst Elec & Electronics Engrs. *Res:* Thermonuclear fusion and space physics; high powered pulsed particle beams; magnetohydrodynamics; electrodynamics. *Mailing Add:* Lab of Plasma Studies 308 Upson Hall Cornell Univ Ithaca NY 14853

SUDARSHAN, ENNACKEL CHANDY GEORGE, b Kottayam, India, Sept 16, 31; m 54; c 3. THEORETICAL PHYSICS. *Educ:* Univ Madras, BSc, 51, MA, 52; Univ Rochester, PhD(physics), 58. *Hon Degrees:* DSc, Univ Wis-Milwaukee, 66 & Univ Delhi, 73. *Prof Exp:* Demonstr physics, Christian Col, Madras, 51-52; res asst, Tata Inst Fundamental Res, 52-55 & Univ Rochester, 55-57; res fel, Harvard Univ, 57-59; from asst prof to assoc prof, Univ Rochester, 59-64; prof, Syracuse Univ, 64-69; PROF PHYSICS, CTR PARTICLE THEORY, UNIV TEX, AUSTIN, 69-, DIR, 70- *Concurrent Pos:* Guest prof, Univ Bern, 63-64; vis prof, Brandeis Univ, 64; Sir C V Raman distinguished vis prof, Univ Madras, 70-71; prof & dir, Ctr Theoret Studies, Indian Inst Sci, Bangalore, 72- *Honors & Awards:* Honor Award for Outstanding Achievement, Nat Asn Indians Am, 75; Padma Bhushan (Order of Lotus), 75. *Mem:* Fel Indian Nat Acad Sci; fel Am Phys Soc; fel Indian Acad Sci. *Res:* Quantum field theory; elementary particles; high energy physics; classical mechanics; quantum optics; Lie algebras and their application to particle physics; foundations of physics; philosophy and history of contemporary physics. *Mailing Add:* RLM Bldg 9.328 Univ of Tex Austin TX 78712

SUDBOROUGH, IVAN HAL, b Royal Oak, Mich, Dec 19, 43; m 69; c 2. INFORMATION SCIENCE. *Educ:* Calif State Polytech Col, BS, 66, MS, 67; Pa State Univ, PhD(comput sci), 71. *Prof Exp:* Asst prof, 71-77, ASSOC PROF COMPUT SCI, NORTHWESTERN UNIV, 78- *Concurrent Pos:* NSF res grant, 74. *Mem:* Asn Comput Mach; Soc Indust & Appl Math. *Res:* Computational complexity; formal languages; automata theory; theory of computation. *Mailing Add:* Dept of Elec Eng & Comput Sci Northwestern Univ Evanston IL 60201

SUDBURY, JOHN DEAN, b Natchitoches, La, July 29, 25; m 53; c 3. PHYSICAL CHEMISTRY. *Educ:* Univ Tex, BS, 44, MS, 47, PhD(phys chem), 49. *Prof Exp:* Sr res chemist, Develop & Res Dept, Continental Oil Co, 49-56, supv res chemist, 56-66, dir petrochem res div, Okla, 66-69, gen mgr, C/A Nuclear Fuels Div, Calif, 69-70, asst to vpres res, NY, 70-72, ASST DIR RES & VPRES RES DIV, CONOCO COAL DEVELOP CO, 72- *Honors & Awards:* Speller Award, Nat Asn Corrosion Engrs, 66. *Mem:* Am Chem Soc; Nat Asn Corrosion Engrs. *Res:* Advanced systems for liquified natural gas, arctic transport; development of conversion processes to get coal into more desirable energy sources; conversion of coal to liquids and gases; removal of sulfur from combustion products of coal. *Mailing Add:* Res Div Conoco Coal Develop Co 4000 Brownsville Rd Library PA 15129

SUDDARTH, STANLEY KENDRICK, b Westerly, RI, Oct 22, 21; m 51. FORESTRY. *Educ:* Purdue Univ, BSF, 43, MS, 49, PhD(agr econ forestry), 52. *Prof Exp:* Assoc dir bomb effectiveness res, US Dept Air Force Proj, Res Found, 51-54, from asst prof to assoc prof forestry, 54-60, PROF WOOD ENG, AGR EXP STA, PURDUE UNIV, WEST LAFAYETTE, 60- *Concurrent Pos:* Consult home mfg indust, 55- & US Forest Prod Lab, Madison, Wis, 70-72; tech adv, Am Inst Timber Construct & Truss Plate Inst. *Honors & Awards:* Res Award, Truss Plate Inst, 70; Markwardt Eng Res Award, Forest Prod Res Soc, 71; Markwardt Award, Am Soc Testing & Mat, 72. *Mem:* Forest Prod Res Soc; Int Acad Wood Sci; Am Soc Agr Engrs; Am Soc Civil Engrs. *Res:* Applied mathematics in engineering and economic problems; engineering properties and uses of wood. *Mailing Add:* Dept Forestry & Natural Resources Purdue Univ Agr Exp Sta West Lafayette IN 47907

SUDDATH, FRED LEROY, (JR), b Macon, Ga, May 6, 42; m 65; c 2. BIOLOGICAL STRUCTURE, X-RAY CRYSTALLOGRAPHY. *Educ:* Ga Inst Technol, BS, 65, PhD(chem), 70. *Prof Exp:* NIH fel, Mass Inst Technol, 70-72, res assoc biol, Lab Molecular Struct, 72-75; asst prof biochem, investr, Inst Dent Res & scientist, Comprehensive Cancer Ctr, 75-77, ASSOC PROF BIOCHEM, SCIENTIST INST DENT RES & SCIENTIST COMPREHENSIVE CANCER CTR, MED CTR, UNIV ALA, BIRMINGHAM, 77- *Concurrent Pos:* Am Cancer Soc fel, Mass Inst Technol, 72-73. *Mem:* AAAS; Am Crystallog Asn. *Res:* Structure and function of transfer RNA; structural studies of nucleic acids and proteins; correlation of molecular structure and biological function; experimental methods development. *Mailing Add:* Dept Biochem Univ Ala SDB PO Box 13 Birmingham AL 35294

SUDDERTH, WILLIAM DAVID, b Dallas, Tex, Apr 29, 40; m 62; c 2. MATHEMATICS PROBABILITY, MATHEMATICAL STATISTICS. *Educ:* Yale Univ, BS, 63; Univ Calif, Berkeley, MS, 65, PhD(math), 67. *Prof Exp:* Asst prof statist, Univ Calif, Berkeley, 67-68; asst prof math, Morehouse Col, 68-69; asst prof statist, 69-71, assoc prof, 71-77, PROF STATIST, UNIV MINN, MINNEAPOLIS, 77- *Mem:* Am Math Soc; fel Inst Math Statist. *Res:* Probability, especially the study of finitely additive probability measures and abstract gambling theory, which is also known as dynamic programming and stochastic control; foundations of statistics. *Mailing Add:* Sch of Statist Univ of Minn Minneapolis MN 55455

SUDDICK, RICHARD PHILLIPS, b Omaha, Nebr, Feb 3, 34; m 55; c 4. PHYSIOLOGY. *Educ:* Creighton Univ, BS, 58, MS, 59, DDS, 61; Univ Iowa, PhD(physiol), 67. *Prof Exp:* Instr physiol, Univ Iowa, 63-65; asst prof biol sci, Creighton Univ, 65-68, from assoc prof to prof oral biol & head dept, 68-74, assoc prof physiol, Sch Med, 70-74; assoc prof physiol & asst dean res, Col Dent Med, Med Univ SC, 74-76; PROF ORAL BIOL & CHMN DEPT & ASST DEAN RES, SCH DENT, UNIV LOUISVILLE, 76- *Mem:* AAAS; Int Asn Dent Res; Am Physiol Soc. *Res:* Physiology of exocrine secretion, primarily secretion of saliva; function of the saliva in the oral cavity and the alimentary tract and its relationship to normal and diseased states; etiology of dental caries and periodontal disease; behavioral constructs and neurophysiological correlates in humans. *Mailing Add:* Univ Tex Health Sci Ctr 7703 Floyd Curl Dr San Antonio TX 78284

SUDDS, RICHARD HUYETTE, JR, b State College, Pa, Feb 13, 27; m 52; c 2. MICROBIOLOGY. *Educ:* Univ Conn, BA, 50, MA, 51; Univ NC, MSPH, 54, PhD(parasitol), 59. *Prof Exp:* From asst prof to assoc prof, 58-72, PROF MICROBIOL, STATE UNIV NY COL PLATTSBURGH, 72- *Mem:* Am Soc Trop Med & Hyg; Am Pub Health Asn; Am Soc Microbiol. *Res:* Host-parasite relationships and ecology of enteric bacteria. *Mailing Add:* Dept of Biol Sci State Univ of NY Col Plattsburgh NY 12901

SUDERMAN, HAROLD JULIUS, b Myrtle, Man, July 24, 21; m 47; c 3. BIOCHEMISTRY. *Educ:* Univ Man, BSc, 49, MSc, 52, PhD, 62. *Prof Exp:* Demonstr biochem, Univ Man, 51, lectr, 52-56, asst prof, 56-63; asst prof, Ont Agr Col, 63-65, asst prof, 65-74, ASSOC PROF BIOCHEM, UNIV GUELPH, 74- *Mem:* Can Biochem Soc. *Res:* Molecular properties, structure and function of proteins; comparative biochemistry of hemoglobins. *Mailing Add:* Dept of Chem Univ of Guelph Guelph ON W1G 2W1 Can

SUDIA, THEODORE WILLIAM, b Ambridge, Pa, Oct 10, 25; m 49; c 3. ENVIRONMENTAL PHYSIOLOGY. *Educ:* Kent State Univ, BS, 50; Ohio State Univ, MS, 51, PhD(bot), 54. *Prof Exp:* Asst prof biol sci, Winona State Col, 55-58; res fel plant physiol, Univ Minn, St Paul, 58-59, res assoc physiol ecol, 59-61, asst prof, 61-63, assoc prof plant path & bot, 63-67; assoc dir, Am Inst Biol Sci, Washington, DC, 67-69; chief ecol serv, Off Natural Sci, 69-73,

chief scientist, 73-77, actg assoc dir sci & technol, 77-80, dep science adv, Int Sect, 80-81, SR SCIENTIST, US NAT PARK SERV, 81- *Mem:* AAAS; Ecol Soc Am; Am Soc Plant Physiologists; Bot Soc Am; NY Acad Sci. *Res:* Research administration. *Mailing Add:* Off of Chief Scientist 18th & C Sts NW Washington DC 20240

SUDIA, WILLIAM DANIEL, b Ambridge, Pa, Aug 19, 22; m 49; c 2. ENTOMOLOGY, VIROLOGY. *Educ:* Univ Fla, BS, 49; Ohio State Univ, MS, 50, PhD(entom), 58. *Prof Exp:* Entomologist, Med Entom Unit, Ctr Dis Control, USPHS, 51-53, asst chief arbovirus vector lab, 53-65, lab consult & develop sect, 66, chief, Arbovirus Ecol Lab, 67-73, DEP DIR LAB TRAINING DIV, CTR DIS CONTROL, USPHS, 73- *Honors & Awards:* Meritorious Serv Medal & Commendation Medal, USPHS. *Mem:* Sigma Xi; Am Soc Trop Med & Hyg; Am Mosquito Control Asn. *Res:* Ecology of arthropod-borne encephalitis viruses; mosquito vectors and vertebrate hosts. *Mailing Add:* Ctr Dis Control Bldg 3 Rm B15 Lab Training Div Atlanta GA 30333

SUDMEIER, JAMES LEE, b Minneapolis, Minn, Feb 14, 38; m 62; c 2. ANALYTICAL CHEMISTRY. *Educ:* Carleton Col, BA, 59; Princeton Univ, MA, 61, PhD(chem), 66. *Prof Exp:* Actg asst prof chem, Univ Calif, Los Angeles, 65-66, asst prof, 66-70; asst prof, 70-71, ASSOC PROF CHEM, UNIV CALIF, RIVERSIDE, 71- *Mem:* Am Chem Soc. *Res:* Nuclear magnetic resonance studies of coordination compounds and metal binding to biopolymers. *Mailing Add:* Dept of Chem Univ of Calif Riverside CA 92502

SUDWEEKS, EARL MAX, b Richfield, Utah, Dec 27, 33; m 60; c 9. ANIMAL NUTRITION, DAIRY NUTRITION. *Educ:* Utah State Univ, BS, 60, MS, 62; NC State Univ, PhD(nutrit biochem), 72. *Prof Exp:* Res assoc animal nutrit, Utah State Univ, 62-65; from asst prof to assoc prof exten, 65-68; res asst animal nutrit, NC State Univ, 68-72; asst prof animal nutrit, Univ Ga, 72-80; dir nutrit, Watkins Inc, Winona, Minn & Prof Prods, Inc, Sauk City, Wis, 80-81; DAIRY EXTEN SPECIALIST, TEX A&M UNIV, 81- *Mem:* Am Dairy Sci Asn; Am Soc Animal Sci; Sigma Xi; Am Inst Nutrit. *Res:* The role of roughages in rumen physiology, energy utilization, feed conversion of beef and dairy cattle. *Mailing Add:* E/R Ctr Tex A&M Univ Overton TX 75684

SUDWEEKS, WALTER BENTLEY, b Buhl, Idaho, May 22, 40; m 65; c 2. INDUSTRIAL CHEMISTRY, EXPLOSIVES. *Educ:* Brigham Young Univ, BS, 65, PhD(org chem), 70. *Prof Exp:* Res chemist, Polymer Intermediates Dept, E I du Pont de Nemours & Co, Inc, 69-76; SR RES SCIENTIST, IRECO CHEM, 76- *Mem:* Am Chem Soc. *Res:* Organic synthesis; hydrometallurgical processes; explosives research. *Mailing Add:* Ireco Chem 3000 W 8600 S West Jordan UT 84084

SUELTER, CLARENCE HENRY, b Lincoln, Kans, Dec 15, 28; m 55; c 3. ENZYMOLOGY. *Educ:* Kans State Univ, BS, 51, MS, 53; Iowa State Univ, PhD(biochem), 59. *Prof Exp:* From asst prof to assoc prof, 61-69, PROF BIOCHEM, MICH STATE UNIV, 69- *Concurrent Pos:* USPHS fel, Univ Minn, 59-61, res career develop award, Mich State Univ, 65-75; consult, NIH Title IV Grad Fels, 63-67; mem enzyme nomenclature comt, Nat Acad Sci, 70-74. *Mem:* AAAS; Am Chem Soc; Soc Exp Biol & Med. *Res:* Monovalent cation activation of enzymes; structure and function of enzymes. *Mailing Add:* Dept of Biochem Mich State Univ East Lansing MI 48824

SUEN, CHING YEE, b Chung Shan, China, Oct 14, 42; Can citizen. COMPUTER APPLICATIONS. *Educ:* Univ Hong Kong, BSc, 66; Univ BC, PhD(elec eng), 72. *Prof Exp:* Asst prof, 72-76, assoc prof, 76-79, PROF COMPUT SCI, CONCORDIA UNIV, 79- *Concurrent Pos:* Chmn comt character recognition, Can Stand Asn, 77-; vis scientist, Res Lab Electronics, Mass Inst Technol, 78-80. *Mem:* Sr Inst Elec & Electronics Engrs. *Res:* Character recognition and data processing; speech analysis and synthesis; electronic aids for the visually handicapped. *Mailing Add:* Dept of Comput Sci 1455 Maisonneuve W Montreal PQ H3G 1M8 Can

SUEN, T(ZENG) J(IUEQ), b Hangchow, China, June 7, 12; nat US; m 44; c 2. POLYMER CHEMISTRY. *Educ:* Tsinghua Univ, China, BS, 33; Mass Inst Technol, MS, 35, ScD, 37. *Prof Exp:* Fel, Mass Inst Technol, 37-38; asst prof chem eng, Chungking Univ, 38-39; head dept res, Tung Li Oil Works, 39-44; mem staff, Radiation Lab, Mass Inst Technol, 44-45; chem engr, Stamford Res Labs, Am Cyanamid Co, 45-56, group leader in charge polymer chem, 56-60, mgr thermoplastics res, 61, dir plastics & polymers res, 61-70, proj mgr div res, 71-77; CONSULT, 77- *Mem:* Am Chem Soc; AAAS. *Res:* Synthetic fuels and lubricants; plastics; condensation and addition polymers; environmental improvement. *Mailing Add:* 349 Mariomi Rd New Canaan CT 06840

SUENAGA, MASAKI, b Hohoku, Japan, Sept 15, 37; m 72; c 2. METALLURGY, ELECTRICAL ENGINEERING. *Educ:* Univ Calif, Berkeley, BSEE, 63, MSEE, 64, PhD(metall), 69. *Prof Exp:* Fel metall, Lawrence Berkeley Lab, 69; from asst metallurgist to assoc metallurgist, 69-76, METALLURGIST, BROOKHAVEN NAT LAB, 76-, DIV HEAD METALL, 78- *Mem:* Am Phys Soc; AAAS; Am Soc Metals. *Res:* Superconducting materials; mechanical properties of metals and alloys. *Mailing Add:* Div of Metall & Mat Sci Brookhaven Nat Lab Upton NY 11973

SUENRAM, RICHARD DEE, b Halstead, Kans, Feb 2, 45; m 65; c 1. PHYSICAL CHEMISTRY, CHEMICAL PHYSICS. *Educ:* Kans State Univ, BS, 67, PhD(chem), 73; Univ Wis, MS, 69. *Prof Exp:* Res chemist phys chem, Rohm & Haas Co, 69-70; res assoc, Harvard Univ, 73-75; res assoc, 75-77, RES CHEMIST PHYS CHEM, NAT BUR STANDARDS, 77- *Res:* Molecular spectroscopy of transient molecular species found in gas phase chemical reactions; molecular species associated with atmospheric and interstellar chemistry. *Mailing Add:* Molecular Spectros Div Nat Bur Standards Washington DC 20234

SUEOKA, NOBORU, b Kyoto, Japan, Apr 12, 29; m 57; c 1. GENETICS. *Educ:* Kyoto Univ, BS, 53, MS, 55; Calif Inst Technol, PhD(biochem genetics), 59. *Prof Exp:* Res fel biochem genetics, Harvard Univ, 58-60; asst prof microbiol, Univ Ill, 60-62; from assoc prof to prof biol, Princeton Univ, 62-72; PROF BIOL, UNIV COLO, BOULDER, 72- *Concurrent Pos:* Fulbright grant, 55-56. *Mem:* Am Soc Biol Chemists; Am Soc Microbiol; Genetics Soc Am. *Res:* Biochemical genetics; molecular biology, particularly genetic aspects of biological macromolecules, nucleic acids and protein. *Mailing Add:* Dept Molecular Cell Develop Biol Univ of Colo Boulder CO 80309

SUER, H(ERBERT) S, b Philadelphia, Pa, Apr 29, 26; m 60; c 6. INSTRUMENTATION, ENGINEERING MECHANICS. *Educ:* Drexel Inst Technol, BS, 49; Kans State Col, MS, 52; Mass Inst Technol, ScD, 55. *Prof Exp:* Instr, Kans State Col, 49-52; asst, Mass Inst Technol, 52-55; sr engr, NAm Aviation, Inc, 55-60; sect head eng mech, TRW Systs Group, TRW Inc, 60-65, mgr space instrumentation proj off, 65-67, advan develop & anal dept, 67-70, mgr instrument systs dept, 70-74, mgr instruments & exp prod develop off, 74-78; res prof & mgr advan prog develop, Desert Res Inst, Univ Nev, 78-79; PROD LINE MGR, TRW INC, 79- *Concurrent Pos:* Adj prof, Univ Southern Calif, 56-74; lectr, Univ Calif, Los Angeles, 58-77. *Honors & Awards:* Wellington Prize, Am Soc Civil Engrs, 60. *Res:* Instrumentation systems; experimental methods; structural and rigid body dynamics; theory of elasticity; theory of elastic stability; mechanics of materials; structural and stress analysis. *Mailing Add:* TRW Inc 1 Space Park Bldg 1 Rm 1096 Redondo Beach CA 90278

SUESS, GENE GUY, b Beaver, Okla, Apr 16, 41; m 68; c 1. MEAT SCIENCE. *Educ:* Tex Tech Univ, BS, 63; Univ Wis-Madison, MS 66, PhD(meat sci, animal sci), 68. *Prof Exp:* Res technologist, 68-73, new prod develop supvr, 73-78, PROD DEVELOP MGR, OSCAR MAYER & CO, 78- *Mem:* Am Meat Sci Asn; Inst Food Technologists. *Res:* Meats processing. *Mailing Add:* Res Dept PO Box 7188 Madison WI 53713

SUESS, HANS EDUARD, b Vienna, Austria, Dec 16, 09; nat US; m 42; c 2. CHEMISTRY. *Educ:* Univ Vienna, PhD(chem), 36; Univ Hamburg, Dr habil, 39. *Hon Degrees:* DSc, Queen's Univ, Belfast, Northern Ireland, 81. *Prof Exp:* Demonstr, Univ Vienna, 34-36; res assoc, Univ Hamburg, 37-48, assoc prof, 49-50; res fel, Univ Chicago, 50-51; chemist, US Geol Surv, 51-55; PROF CHEM, UNIV CALIF, SAN DIEGO, 55- *Honors & Awards:* V M Goldschmidt Medal, Geochem Soc, 74. *Mem:* Nat Acad Sci; Austrian Acad Sci; fel Am Acad Arts & Sci; Heidelberg Acad Sci. *Res:* Chemical kinetics; nuclear hot atom chemistry; cosmic abundances of nuclear species; nuclear shell structure; geologic age determinations; carbon-14 dating. *Mailing Add:* Dept of Chem Univ of Calif at San Diego La Jolla CA 92093

SUESS, JAMES FRANCIS, b Rock Island, Ill, Nov 27, 19; m 46; c 3. PSYCHIATRY. *Educ:* Northwestern Univ, BS, 50, MD, 52. *Prof Exp:* Resident psychiat, Warren State Hosp, Warren, Pa, 53-56, clin dir, 56-62; PROF PSYCHIAT, SCH MED, UNIV MISS, 62- *Concurrent Pos:* Fel psychiat, Med Sch, Univ Pa, 53; exchange teaching fel, Med Sch, Univ Pittsburgh, 55; fel, Col Physicians & Surgeons, Columbia Univ, 58; consult, Vet Admin, 62- & Gov Drug Coun, Miss, 72-; vis prof, Inst Psychiat, London & Royal Free Hosp Sch Med, London; assoc chief staff educ, Vet Admin Ctr. *Mem:* Am Psychiat Asn; Asn Am Med Cols; AMA. *Res:* Medical education in psychiatry; use of television and videotape in medical education; programmed teaching with television. *Mailing Add:* Vet Admin Med Ctr Jackson MS 39216

SUESS, STEVEN TYLER, b Los Angeles, Calif, Aug 4, 42; m 64; c 2. FLUID DYNAMICS. *Educ:* Univ Calif, Berkeley, AB, 64, PhD(planetary, space sci), 69. *Prof Exp:* Nat Acad Sci-Nat Res Coun res assoc, Environ Sci Serv Admin Res Labs, Boulder, Colo, 69-71, PHYSICIST, SPACE ENVIRON LAB, NAT OCEANIC & ATMOSPHERIC ADMIN, 71- *Concurrent Pos:* Guest worker, Max Planck Inst Aeronomy, 75; vis scholar, Stanford Univ, 80-81. *Mem:* Am Geophys Union; Am Astronom Soc; Sigma Xi; Int Astron Union. *Res:* Dynamics of the sun and stars; oscillations of stars; stellar winds; magnetohydrodynamics of rotating fluids. *Mailing Add:* Space Environ Lab Nat Oceanic & Atmospheric Admin 325 Broadway Boulder CO 80303

SUFFERN, JOHN SAMUEL, limnology, aquaculture, see previous edition

SUFFET, IRWIN HENRY, b Brooklyn, NY, May 11, 39; m 62; c 2. ANALYTICAL CHEMISTRY, ENVIRONMENTAL CHEMISTRY. *Educ:* Brooklyn Col, BS, 61; Univ Md, College Park, MS, 64; Rutgers Univ, New Brunswick, PhD, 69. *Prof Exp:* From asst prof to assoc prof, 69-78, PROF CHEM & ENVIRON SCI, DREXEL UNIV, 78- *Concurrent Pos:* Consult, Western Elec Co, 70-72; grants, Western Elec Co, 70-72, Environ Protection Agency, 71-74 & 76-78, NSF, 72-73 & 76-78 & City Philadelphia Water Dept, 72-81; mem safe drinking water comt, Nat Acad Sci, 78-79, chmn subcomt efficiency use activated carbon for drinking water treatment. *Honors & Awards:* Serv Award, Instrument Soc Am, 72. *Mem:* Am Water Works Asn; Am Pub Health Asn; Water Pollution Control Fedn; Asn Environ Eng Prof. *Res:* Analytical environmental analysis of trace organics; activated carbon and other drinking water treatment processes; fate of pollutants in the environment; chemical nature of water and wastes. *Mailing Add:* Environ Studies Inst Drexel Univ Philadelphia PA 19104

SUFFIN, STEPHEN CHESTER, b Los Angeles, Calif, Aug 13, 47; m 69; c 2. PHARMACOLOGY. *Educ:* Univ Calif, Los Angeles, BA, 68, MD, 72. *Prof Exp:* Fel immunopath, 75-77, ASST PROF PATH, UNIV CALIF, LOS ANGELES, 77-; DIR PATH, LAB PROCEDURES INC, 80- *Concurrent Pos:* Sr investr immunopath, Lab Infectious Dis, Nat Inst Allergy & Infectious Dis, NIH, 78-80; consult, Armed Forces Inst Path, 78-80, Jet Propulsion Lab, Calif Inst Technol, 80- *Mem:* Int Acad Path; Am Soc Clin Pathologists; Col Am Pathologists; Am Asn Immunologists; Am Soc Microbiol. *Mailing Add:* 3200 Monte Carlo Dr Thousand Oaks CA 91362

SUGA, NOBUO, b Japan, Dec 17, 33; m 63; c 2. PHYSIOLOGY. *Educ:* Tokyo Metrop Univ, PhD(physiol), 63. *Prof Exp:* NSF fel hearing physiol, Harvard Univ, 63-64; res zoologist, Brain Res Inst, Univ Calif, Los Angeles, 65; res neuroscientist, Sch Med, Univ Calif, San Diego, 66-68; assoc prof, 69-75, PROF BIOL, WASH UNIV, 76- *Mem:* AAAS; Am Physiol Soc; Acoust Soc Am. *Res:* Auditory physiology. *Mailing Add:* Dept of Biol Wash Univ St Louis MO 63130

SUGAM, RICHARD JAY, b New York, NY, Nov 16, 51; m 76. AQUATIC CHEMISTRY, GEOCHEMISTRY. *Educ:* Rutgers Col, AB, 73; Univ Md, PhD(chem), 77. *Prof Exp:* Scientist marine chem, Lockheed Ctr Marine Res, 78-79; mem staff, Public Serv Elec & Gas Co, 79- *Mem:* Am Soc Testing & Mat; Am Chem Soc; AAAS; NY Acad Sci; Int Ozone Asn. *Res:* Environmental chemistry; kinetics and equilibria in natural waters; transport mechanisms of trace pollutants; fate and effects of oxidative biocides in marine and estuarine waters; waste disposal and resource recovery. *Mailing Add:* Public Serv Elec & Gas Co 80 Park Plaza T16A Newark NJ 07101

SUGANO, KATSUHITO, b Japan, May 25, 48; m 79; c 1. DI-MUON AND DI-HADRON EXPERIMENT. *Educ:* Univ Tokyo, BS, 72, MS, 74, Dr, 79. *Prof Exp:* Res assoc physics, Inst Nuclear Study, Tokyo, 77-78; res fel, Ministry Educ, Japan, 78-79; RES ASSOC PHYSICS, FERMI NAT ACCELERATOR LAB, 79- *Mem:* Phys Soc Japan. *Res:* Research and experiment in high energy particle physics using accelerators. *Mailing Add:* Physics Dept Fermilab PO Box 500 Batavia IL 60510

SUGAR, GEORGE R, b Winthrop, Mass, Oct 12, 25; m 61; c 2. COMPUTER SCIENCE, ELECTRONICS ENGINEERING. *Educ:* Univ Md, BS, 50. *Prof Exp:* Asst, Inst Fluid Dynamics & Appl Math, Univ Md, 50-51; physicist, Upper Atmosphere & Space Physics Div, Nat Bur Stand, 51-65; electronic engr, Aeronomy Lab, Nat Oceanic & Atmospheric Admin, 65-70; electronic engr automation & instrumentation sect, Electromagnetics Div, Nat Bur Stand, 71-77; Electronic engr, Wave Propagation Lab, Nat Oceanic & Atmospheric Admin, 77-79; PRES, PRAGMATRONICS INC, 79- *Mem:* Sigma Xi; Inst Elec & Electronics Engrs; AAAS. *Res:* Laboratory automation; application of minicomputers to laboratory measurements; management of computers; organization development; electronic instrumentation. *Mailing Add:* Pragmatronics Inc 770 Lincoln Place Boulder CO 80302

SUGAR, JACK, b Baltimore, Md, Dec 22, 29; m 56; c 3. ATOMIC SPECTROSCOPY. *Educ:* Johns Hopkins Univ, BA, 56, PhD(physics), 60. *Prof Exp:* PHYSICIST, NAT BUR STANDARDS, 60- *Concurrent Pos:* Fulbright res traveling grant, 66-67. *Honors & Awards:* Silver Medal, US Dept Com, 71. *Mem:* Fel Optical Soc Am. *Res:* Spectra of solids; atomic spectra and energy levels; nuclear moments; ionization energies. *Mailing Add:* Nat Bur of Standards A167 Physics Bldg Washington DC 20236

SUGAR, OSCAR, b Washington, DC, July 9, 14; m 44; c 3. PHYSIOLOGY, NEUROSURGERY. *Educ:* Johns Hopkins Univ, AB, 34; George Washington Univ, MA, 37, MD, 42; Univ Chicago, PhD(physiol), 40. *Prof Exp:* Asst physiol, Univ Chicago, 36-38; clin asst, 46-48, from instr to assoc prof, 48-58, head dept, 71-81, EMER PROF NEUROL SURG, COL MED, UNIV ILL, 81- *Concurrent Pos:* Sci consult, Nat Inst Neurol Dis & Stroke, 72-75. *Mem:* Am Asn Neurol Surg; Am Neurol Soc; Soc Neurol Surg. *Res:* Degeneration and regeneration of the peripheral and central nervous system; effects of oxygen lack on cells and electrical activity of the nervous system; visualization of the blood supply and vascular anomalies of the brain. *Mailing Add:* Dept of Neurol Surg Univ of Ill Col of Med Chicago IL 60612

SUGAR, ROBERT LOUIS, b Chicago, Ill, Aug 20, 38; m 66. THEORETICAL PHYSICS. *Educ:* Harvard Univ, AB, 60; Princeton Univ, PhD(physics), 64. *Prof Exp:* Res assoc physics, Columbia Univ, 64-66; from asst prof to assoc prof, 66-73, PROF PHYSICS, UNIV CALIF, SANTA BARBARA, 73- *Concurrent Pos:* Dep dir, Inst Theoret Physics, 79-81. *Mem:* Am Phys Soc. *Res:* High energy physics. *Mailing Add:* Dept of Physics Univ of Calif Santa Barbara CA 93106

SUGARBAKER, EVAN ROY, b Mineola, NY, Nov, 17, 49. NUCLEAR REACTION MECHANISMS. *Educ:* Kalamazoo Col, BA, 71; Univ Mich, PhD(physics), 76. *Prof Exp:* Res assoc, Nuclear Struct Res Lab, Univ Rochester, 76-78; vis asst prof physics, Univ Colo, 78-80; ASST PROF PHYSICS, OHIO STATE UNIV, 81- *Concurrent Pos:* Co-prin investr NSF grant, 81- *Mem:* Am Phys Soc; Am Asn Physics Teachers; AAAS. *Res:* Mechanisms in light-ion induced nuclear reactions; nuclear structure. *Mailing Add:* Dept Physics Ohio State Univ 174 W 18th Ave Columbus OH 43210

SUGARMAN, MEYER LOUIS, JR, b Atlanta, Ga, Aug 4, 17; m 66; c 4. RESEARCH ADMINISTRATION. *Educ:* Univ Fla, BS, 37; Ohio State Univ, MS, 40. *Prof Exp:* Res chemist, Kryptar Corp, 45-49; sr chemist, Eastman Kodak Co, 49-52; res engr, RCA Labs, RCA Corp, 52-56; dir res, Apeco Corp, 56-64; chmn & tech dir photog, Opto/Graphics Inc, 64-71; mgr, Res Lab Electronics, 71-80, ASST VPRES RES & DEVELOP, ZENITH RADIO CORP, 80- *Concurrent Pos:* Consult, major corp, 64- *Mem:* Am Chem Soc; Soc Photog Scientists & Engrs. *Res:* Color television picture tubes and display devices. *Mailing Add:* 4000 Dundee Rd Northbrook IL 60062

SUGARMAN, NATHAN, b Chicago, Ill, Mar 3, 17; m 40; c 2. NUCLEAR CHEMISTRY. *Educ:* Univ Chicago, BS, 37, PhD(phys chem), 41. *Prof Exp:* Am Philos Soc fel, Univ Chicago, 41-42, res assoc, Metall Lab, 42-43; sect chief, 43-45; group leader, Los Alamos Sci Lab, Univ Calif, 45-46; from asst prof to assoc prof, 46-52, PROF CHEM, ENRICO FERMI INST, UNIV CHICAGO, 52- *Mem:* AAAS; Am Chem Soc; fel Am Phys Soc; Fedn Am Scientists. *Res:* Nuclear reactions; fission studies; recoil experiments. *Mailing Add:* Enrico Fermi Inst Univ Chicago Chicago IL 60637

SUGATHAN, KANNETH KOCHAPPAN, b Palliport, India, Mar 23, 26; nat US; m 56; c 4. COATINGS & ADHESIVE CHEMISTRY, SYNTHETIC RESIN CHEMISTRY. *Educ:* Univ Kerala, BSc, 51, PhD(terpene chem), 67; Univ Saugar, MSc, 53. *Prof Exp:* Demonstr chem, SKV Col, Trichur, India, 53-54, lectr, 54-64; lectr, S N Col, Quilon, India, 64-68; Nat Res Coun-Agr Res Serv fel, USDA Naval Stores Lab, Olustee, Fla, 68-70; Am Cancer Soc res fel, Univ Miss, 71-72; res chemist, Crosby Chem, Inc, 72-76, chief chemist, 76-78; chief chemist, Zielger Chem & Mineral Corp, 78-80; SR SCIENTIST, POLYMER RES CORP AM, 81- *Concurrent Pos:* Sr demonstr, Christian Med Col, Vellore, India, 61-64. *Mem:* Am Chem Soc. *Res:* Product and process development in the fields of polymers, coatings and adhesives; applying graft polymerization techniques to impart special effects to substrates like metals, plastics, rubber and papaer; industrial trouble shooting. *Mailing Add:* 39 Ross Hall Blvd S Piscataway NJ 08854

SUGER-COFINO, JOSE-EDUARDO, b Guatemala City, Guatemala, Nov 29, 38; m 64; c 5. MATHEMATICAL PHYSICS, OPERATIONS RESEARCH. *Educ:* Swiss Fed Inst Technol, BS, 60, MS, 63; Univ Tex, Austin, PhD(physics), 72. *Prof Exp:* Dir dept math, 64, dir dept physics, 64-69, PROF MATH, PHYSICS & ECON, UNIV SAN CARLOS, 64- *Concurrent Pos:* Bd dir, Nat Nuclear Energy Comn, 67-70; Welch Found fel, Univ Tex, 72-73; consult, Aid-Ministry Agr, Guatemala, 72-75; consult oper res, Fisher, SAm, 78-; dean, Sch Info & Comput Sci, Univ Francisco Marroquin, 78- *Mem:* Sigma Xi; Math Asn Cent Am (pres, 65); Am Soc Physics; Nat Acad Sci Guatemala; hon mem Soc de Apouitectos de Guatemala. *Res:* Statistical mechanics; quantum mechanics; mathematical models in social science. *Mailing Add:* 3A Avenida 4-21 Zona 9 Guatemala City Guatemala

SUGERMAN, ABRAHAM ARTHUR, b Dublin, Ireland, Jan 20, 29; nat US; m 60; c 4. PSYCHIATRY. *Educ:* Univ Dublin, BA, 50, MB, BCh & BAO, 52; Royal Col Physicians & Surgeons, dipl psychol med, 58; State Univ NY, MedDSc(psychiat), 62; Univ Newcastle, dipl, 66; Am Bd Psychiat & Neurol, dipl, 69. *Prof Exp:* House officer, Meath Hosp, Dublin, Ireland, 52-53 & St Nicholas Hosp, London, 53; sr house physician, Brook Gen Hosp, 54; registr psychiat, Kingsway Hosp, Derby & Med Sch, King's Col, Newcastle, 55-58; clin psychiatrist, Trenton State Hosp, NJ, 58-59; chief sect invest psychiat & dir clin invest unit, NJ Neuropsychiat Inst, 61-73; res consult & assoc psychiatrist, 68-72, dir outpatient serv, 72-74 & 77-78, med dir, 74-77, res dir, 72-79, ASSOC PSYCHIATRIST & DIR MED STUDY TRAINING, CARRIER FOUND, 78- *Concurrent Pos:* Res fel psychiat, State Univ NY Downstate Med Ctr, 59-61; res consult, Trenton Psychiat Hosp, 64-; clin assoc prof, Rutgers Med Sch, 72-78, clin prof, 78-; consult, Med Ctr, Princeton, 72-; contrib fac, Grad Sch Appl & Prof Psychol, Rutgers Univ, 74-78; vis prof, Hahnemann Med Col, 78- & Ctr Alcohol Study, Rutgers, Univ, 77- *Mem:* Royal Col Psychiatrists; fel Am Psychiat Asn; fel Am Col Clin Pharmacol; Am Col Psychiatrists; fel Am Col Neuropsychopharmacol. *Res:* Evaluation of new psychiatric drugs; nosology; psychology and prognosis in schizophrenia and alcoholism; quantitative analysis of the electroencephalogram. *Mailing Add:* 125 Roxboro Rd Lawrenceville NJ 08648

SUGERMAN, LEONARD RICHARD, b New York, NY, June 24, 20; m 40; c 4. NAVIGATION. *Educ:* Mass Inst Technol, BS, 55; Univ Chicago, MBA, 60. *Prof Exp:* US Air Force, 42-75, supvr bomb-navig br, Dept Armament Training, Lowry AFB, Colo, 50-53, air staff off, Off Dep Chief Staff Develop, Hq USAF, Pentagon, DC, 55-59, res & develop staff off hqs, Syst Command, Andrews AFB, 60-62, hqs, Res & Tech Div, Bolling AFB, 62-64, exec off, Cent Inertial Guid Test Facil, Missile Develop Ctr, Holloman AFB, 64-68, chief, Athena Test Field Off, Ballistic Reentry Systs Prog, 68-70, Air Force Dep to Comdr, White Sands Missile Range & chief, Air Force Range Opers Off, 70-72, dep chief staff, Plans & Requirements, Air Force Spec Weapons Ctr, 72-75; ASST DIR RESOURCES MGT, PHYS SCI LAB, N MEX STATE UNIV, 75- *Concurrent Pos:* US rep guid & control panel, Adv Group Aerospace Res & Develop, NATO, 66-76. *Honors & Awards:* Norman P Hays Award, Am Inst Navig, 72. *Mem:* Am Defense Preparedness Asn; Am Inst Navig (pres, 70-71); assoc fel Am Inst Aeronaut & Astronaut. *Res:* Guidance and control of aerospace vehicles; bombing and navigation systems for aerospace vehicles. *Mailing Add:* 3025 Fairway Dr Las Cruces NM 88001

SUGGITT, ROBERT MURRAY, b Toronto, Ont, June 24, 25; nat US; m 59; c 3. PHYSICAL CHEMISTRY. *Educ:* Univ Toronto, BA, 47; Univ Mich, MS, 48, PhD(chem), 52. *Prof Exp:* Chemist, Texaco, Inc, 52-57, group leader, 57-68, res assoc, 68-75, tech assoc, 75, asst mgr, 75-78, MGR, TECH DIV, TEXACO DEVELOP CORP, 78- *Mem:* Am Chem Soc; AAAS. *Res:* Catalysis, petroleum and petrochemical processing, lubrication. *Mailing Add:* Texaco Develop Corp 135 E 42nd St New York NY 10017

SUGGS, CHARLES WILSON, b NC, May 30, 28; m 49; c 3. AGRICULTURAL & HUMAN FACTORS ENGINEERING. *Educ:* NC State Col, BS, 49, MS, 55, PhD(agr eng), 59. *Prof Exp:* Instr, Dearborn Motors, 49; asst serv supvr, Int Harvester, 49-51; res farm supt, Agr Exp Sta, 51-53, from instr to assoc prof agr eng, 54-66, PROF AGR ENG, NC STATE UNIV, 66- *Mem:* Fel Am Soc Agr Engrs; Human Factors Soc. *Res:* Ergonomics; vibration; noise, human performance; tobacco mechanization; vehicle safety; servosystems; environment. *Mailing Add:* Dept of Biol & Agr Eng NC State Univ Raleigh NC 27607

SUGGS, JOHN WILLIAM, b Highland Park, Mich, Aug 17, 48; m 68; c 1. ORGANOMETALLIC CHEMISTRY, ORGANIC CHEMISTRY. *Educ:* Univ Mich, BS, 70; Harvard Univ, PhD(chem), 76. *Prof Exp:* mem tech staff org chem, Bell Labs, AT&T, 76-81; ASST PROF, DEPT CHEM, BROWN UNIV, 81- *Concurrent Pos:* Woodrow Wilson fel, 70. *Mem:* Am Chem Soc. *Res:* Use of organometallic compounds in organic synthesis; mechanisms of and reactive intermediates in organometallic reactions; drug-nucleic acid interactions. *Mailing Add:* Dept Chem Box H Brown Univ Providence NJ 02912

SUGGS, MORRIS TALMAGE, JR, b Ft Myers, Fla, June 17, 27; m 52; c 3. MICROBIOLOGY. *Educ:* Wake Forest Col, BS, 50; Fla State Univ, MS, 57; Univ NC, MPH, 65, DrPH, 67. *Prof Exp:* Teacher, Fla Pub Sch, 52-54; microbiologist, Ala, 57, asst chief tissue cult unit, 58-59, res asst, 60-62, res asst virol training unit, 62-68, spec asst biol reagents sect, Lab Prog, 68, DIR BIOL PROD PROG, CTR INFECTIOUS DISEASES, CTR DIS CONTROL, USPHS, 68- *Mem:* Am Soc Microbiologists; Conf of State & Prov Pub Health Lab Dirs. *Res:* Standardization and quality assurance of in vitro diagnostic products. *Mailing Add:* Biol Prod Prog Ctr Infectious Dis Ctr Dis Control 1600 Clifton Rd Atlanta GA 30333

SUGIHARA, JAMES MASANOBU, b Las Animas, Colo, Aug 6, 18; m 44; c 2. ORGANIC CHEMISTRY, ACADEMIC ADMINISTRATION. *Educ:* Univ Calif, BS, 39; Univ Utah, PhD(chem), 47. *Prof Exp:* From instr to prof chem, Univ Utah, 43-64; dean, Col Chem & Physics, 64-73, dean, Col Sci & Math, 73, PROF CHEM, NDAK STATE UNIV, 64-, DEAN, GRAD SCH & DIR RES ADMIN, 74- *Concurrent Pos:* Fel, Ohio State Univ, 48. *Mem:* Am Chem Soc; Geochem Soc Am. *Res:* Reaction mechanisms; porphyrin chemistry; origin of petroleum. *Mailing Add:* Off of Dean NDak State Univ Grad Sch Fargo ND 58102

SUGIHARA, THOMAS TAMOTSU, b Las Animas, Colo, June 14, 24; m 52; c 2. NUCLEAR CHEMISTRY. *Educ:* Kalamazoo Col, AB, 45; Univ Chicago, SM, 51, PhD(phys chem), 52. *Prof Exp:* Res assoc, Mass Inst Technol, 52-53; from asst prof to prof chem, Clark Univ, 53-67, chmn dept, 63-66; dir, Cyclotron Inst, Tex A&M Univ, 71-78, prof chem, 67-81, dean, Col Sci, 78-81; PROF CHEM, ORE STATE UNIV, 81-, DEAN, COL SCI, 81- *Concurrent Pos:* Assoc scientist, Woods Hole Oceanog Inst, 54-67; mem subcomt nuclear ship waste disposal, Nat Acad Sci-Nat Res Coun, 58, mem surv panel nuclear chem, 64, mem subcomt low level contamination mat, 65-66; Guggenheim fel, Univ Oslo, 61-62; mem nuclear sci adv comt, NSF & Dept Energy, 77-79. *Mem:* Fel AAAS; Am Chem Soc; fel Am Phys Soc. *Res:* Structure of transition nuclei; high-spin states; spedroscopy with heavy-ion reactions. *Mailing Add:* Col of Sci Ore State Univ Corvallis OR 97331

SUGIOKA, KENNETH, b Hollister, Calif, Apr 19, 20; m 47, 66; c 5. ANESTHESIOLOGY. *Educ:* Univ Denver, BS, 45, Wash Univ, MD, 49; Am Bd Anesthesiol, dipl, 55. *Prof Exp:* Intern, Univ Iowa Hosp, 49-50, resident anesthesiol, 50-52, instr, 52; actg chief anesthesiol, Vet Admin Hosp, Des Moines, 52; resident & instr, Vet Admin Hosp, Iowa City, 52; from asst prof to assoc prof, 54-63, PROF ANESTHESIOL, SCH MED, UNIV NC, CHAPEL HILL, 63-, CHMN DEPT, 69- *Concurrent Pos:* NIH spec res fel, 62; consult, Vet Admin Hosp, Fayetteville, NC; vis prof, Inst Physiol, Univ Göttingen, 62 & Med Sch, King's Col, Univ London, 63; vis prof, Max Planck Inst Physiol, Dortmund, Ger, 76-77. *Mem:* Soc Acad Anesthesiol Chmn (past pres); Am Soc Anesthesiol; Soc Exp Biol & Med; Am Physiol Soc; Asn Univ Anesthetists. *Res:* Application of electronic instrumentation to physiological measurements; electrochemical methods of biological analysis; cation sensitive glass electrodes. *Mailing Add:* Dept of Anesthesiol Univ of NC Sch of Med Chapel Hill NC 27514

SUGITA, EDWIN T, b Honolulu, Hawaii, Feb 1, 37; m 59; c 2. PHARMACEUTICS. *Educ:* Purdue Univ, BS, 59, MS, 62, PhD(pharmaceut), 63. *Prof Exp:* From asst prof to assoc prof, 64-72, PROF PHARM, PHILADELPHIA COL PHARM & SCI, 72- *Concurrent Pos:* Res grant, Smith, Kline & French Labs, 65-67; NIH grant, 65-71 & 74-77; Kapnek Charitable Trust fel, 76-81. *Mem:* Acad Pharmaceut Sci; Sigma Xi. *Res:* Absorption of drugs into lymph; percutaneous absorption; gastrointestinal absorption of charged drugs; pharmacokinetics of drugs in humans. *Mailing Add:* Philadelphia Col of Pharm & Sci 43rd St & Kingsessing Ave Philadelphia PA 19104

SUGIURA, KANEMATSU, cancer, biochemistry, deceased

SUGIURA, MASAHISA, b Tokyo, Japan, Dec 8, 25; m 62; c 1. SPACE PHYSICS. *Educ:* Univ Tokyo, MS, 49; Univ Alaska, PhD, 55. *Prof Exp:* Asst prof geophys res, Geophys Inst, Univ Alaska, 55-57, assoc prof geophys, 57-62, prof, 62; Nat Acad Sci sr assoc, NASA, 62-64, MEM STAFF, GODDARD SPACE FLIGHT CTR, 64- *Concurrent Pos:* Guggenheim fel, 59; prof, Univ Wash, 66-67. *Mem:* Am Geophys Union; Am Phys Soc. *Res:* Magnetospheric physics; geophysics. *Mailing Add:* Lab Extraterrestrial Physics NASA Goddard Space Flight Ctr Greenbelt MD 20771

SUH, CHUNG-HA, b Chinnampo City, Korea, Sept 11, 32; m 61; c 3. MECHANICAL ENGINEERING, BIOMECHANICS. *Educ:* Seoul Nat Univ, BS, 59; Univ Calif, Berkeley, MS, 64, PhD(mech eng), 66. *Prof Exp:* From mech engr to chief engr, Hwan-Bok Indust Co, Ltd, Korea, 59-61; dept head mach design & shop, Atomic Energy Res Inst, 61-62; res engr, Biomech Lab, Univ Calif, Berkeley, 63-66; from asst to assoc prof, 66-77, chmn, Dept Eng Design & Econ Eval, 70-78, PROF, UNIV COLO, BOULDER, 77-, DIR, BIOMECH LAB, 70- *Concurrent Pos:* Res consult, Int Chiropractors Asn, 72- *Mem:* Am Soc Mech Engrs; Asn Comput Mach. *Res:* Computer-aided design of mechanisms; optimum design; biomechanics of human joints and system. *Mailing Add:* Dept Mech Eng Univ of Colo Boulder CO 80309

SUH, JOHN TAIYOUNG, US citizen; m 58; c 4. MEDICINAL CHEMISTRY, ORGANIC CHEMISTRY. *Educ:* Butler Univ, BS, 53; Univ Wis, MS, 56, PhD(org chem), 58. *Prof Exp:* Teaching asst, Univ Wis, 55; sr res chemist, Res Ctr, Johnson & Johnson, 58-59 & McNeil Labs, Inc, 59-63; group leader res, Colgate-Palmolive Co, 63-65, sect head res, Dept Med Chem, Lakeside Labs Div, 63-75; mgr chem res, Freeman Chem Corp, 76-77; sect head res, Dept Med Chem, USV Pharmaceut Corp, 77-78, ASSOC DIR, DEPT MED CHEM, RES & DEVELOP, REVLON HEALTH CARE GROUP, 78- *Concurrent Pos:* Vis lectr chem, Marquette Univ, 72-77. *Mem:* Am Chem Soc. *Res:* Medicinal chemistry in areas of cardiovascular, psychopharmacological and hematinic agents; organic chemistry in areas of stereochemistry, natural products, heterocyclic and organometallic chemistry; pulmonary and allergy research. *Mailing Add:* Revlon Health Care Group One Scarsdale Rd Tuckahoe NY 10707

SUH, NAM PYO, b Seoul, Korea, Apr 22, 36; US citizen; m 61; c 4. MECHANICAL ENGINEERING. *Educ:* Mass Inst Technol, SB, 59, SM, 61; Carnegie Inst Technol, PhD(mech eng), 64. *Prof Exp:* Develop engr, Sweetheart Plastics, Inc, 58-59; lectr mech eng, Northeastern Univ, 64-65; sr res engr, United Shoe Mach Corp, Mass, 61-65; from asst prof to assoc prof mech & mat, Univ SC, 65-70; assoc prof mech, 70-75, PROF MECH ENG & DIR, LAB FOR MFG & PRODUCTIVITY, MASS INST TECHNOL, 75- *Concurrent Pos:* Consult, govt agencies & indust firms, 70- *Honors & Awards:* Larsen Award, Am Soc Mech Engrs & Pi Tau Sigma, 77. *Mem:* Am Soc Mech Engrs; Am Soc Eng Educ; Int Inst Prod Eng Res. *Res:* Materials processing; mechanical behavior of materials; solid propellants; manufacturing processes and systems; tribology. *Mailing Add:* Dept Mech Eng Rm 35-136 Mass Inst of Technol Cambridge MA 02139

SUH, TAE-IL, b Chungdo, Korea, June 1, 28; m 55; c 3. ALGEBRA. *Educ:* Kyung-Pook Nat Univ, Korea, BS, 52; Yale Univ, PhD(math), 61. *Prof Exp:* Asst prof math, Kyung-Pook Nat Univ, Korea, 61-63; assoc prof, Sogang Univ, Korea, 63-65; assoc prof, 65-68, PROF MATH, E TENN STATE UNIV, 68- *Mem:* Am Math Soc; Math Asn Am. *Res:* Non-associative algebras. *Mailing Add:* Dept of Math ETenn State Univ Johnson City TN 37601

SUHADOLNIK, ROBERT J, b Forest City, Pa, Aug 15, 25; m 49; c 5. BIOCHEMISTRY. *Educ:* Pa State Univ, BS, 49, PhD, 56; Iowa State Univ, MS, 53. *Prof Exp:* Res assoc biochem, Univ Ill, 56-57; asst prof, Okla State Univ, 57-61; res mem, Albert Einstein Med Ctr, 61-70, head dept bio-org chem, 68-70; PROF BIOCHEM, SCH MED, TEMPLE UNIV, 70- *Mem:* Am Chem Soc; Am Soc Biol Chemists. *Res:* Alkaloid biogenesis; metabolism of allose and allulose; biosynthesis and biochemical properties of nucleoside antibiotics; mechanism of protein synthesis; role of interferon in development of antiviral-anticancer state in normal and DNA repair-deficient mammalian cells. *Mailing Add:* Dept of Biochem Temple Univ Sch of Med Philadelphia PA 19140

SUHAYDA, JOSEPH NICHOLAS, b Flint, Mich, Feb 23, 44; m 66; c 2. OCEANOGRAPHY. *Educ:* Calif State Univ, Northridge, BS, 66; Univ Calif, San Diego, PhD(phys oceanog), 72. *Prof Exp:* Asst prof, 72-75, ASSOC PROF MARINE SCI, COASTAL STUDIES INST, LA STATE UNIV, BATON ROUGE, 75- *Mem:* Am Geophys Union; Am Shore & Beach Preserv Asn. *Res:* Coastal oceanography, primarily nearshore processes on beaches and reefs, and the influence of storm waves on sediment on the continental shelf. *Mailing Add:* Coastal Studies Inst La State Univ Baton Rouge LA 70803

SUHL, HARRY, b Leipzig, Ger, Oct 18, 22; nat US; wid. PHYSICS. *Educ:* Univ Wales, BSc, 43; Oxford Univ, PhD(theoret physics), 48. *Prof Exp:* Exp officer, Admiralty Signal Estab, Eng, 43-46; mem tech staff, Bell Tel Labs, Inc, 48-60; vis lectr, 60, PROF PHYSICS, UNIV CALIF, SAN DIEGO, 61- *Mem:* Nat Acad Sci; Fel Am Phys Soc. *Res:* Theoretical solid state physics. *Mailing Add:* Dept of Physics Univ of Calif at San Diego La Jolla CA 92093

SUHM, RAYMOND WALTER, b Springfield, Mass, June 9, 41; m 64; c 1. STRATIGRAPHY. *Educ:* Southeast Mo State Col, BS, 63; Southern Ill Univ, Carbondale, MS, 65; Univ Nebr-Lincoln, PhD(geol), 70. *Prof Exp:* Instr geol, Southern Ill Univ, Carbondale, 65; geophysicist, Humble Oil Co, Calif, 65-67; asst prof geol, Tex A&I Univ, 70-75, assoc prof, 75-80; explor geologist, Tex Oil & Gas Corp, Oklahoma City, 80-81; GEOL CONSULT, 81- *Concurrent Pos:* Consult, Cockrell Corp, 72, Int Oil & Gas, 76-78 & Tenneco Oil, 77. *Mem:* Am Asn Petrol Geologists; Soc Econ Paleontologists & Mineralogists. *Res:* Ordovician stratigraphy and paleontology; Ozark geology; coastal sedimentation and geomorphology; historical geology. *Mailing Add:* 11716 128th St Moore OK 73165

SUHOVECKY, ALBERT J, b Youngstown, Ohio, May 3, 26; m 51; c 3. PLANT PATHOLOGY. *Educ:* Case Western Reserve Univ, BS, 50; Kent State Univ, MA, 51; Ohio State Univ, PhD(agron), 55. *Prof Exp:* Res asst field pesticides, Res Found, Ohio State Univ, 52-53; res asst exten field crops, Ohio Agr Exp Sta, 53-55; plant pathologist, Monsanto Chem Co, 55-60; sr cereal chemist, 60-70, asst qual control dir, Falstaff Brewing Corp, 70-75; dir, 75-80, VPRES FIELD OPERS, AM SANIT INST, 80- *Concurrent Pos:* Mem comt hops res, US Brewers Asn & mem tech comt, Malting Barley Improv Asn, 61- *Mem:* Am Asn Cereal Chemists; Environ Mgt Asn; Entom Soc Am; Am Soc Brewing Chemists; Am Soc Agron. *Res:* Development and evaluation of organic chemicals as agricultural fungicides; quality control of barley, malt and adjuncts; sanitation control. *Mailing Add:* 50 St Eugene Lane Florissant MO 63033

SUHR, NORMAN HENRY, b Chicago, Ill, June 13, 30; m 53; c 4. SPECTROSCOPY, GEOCHEMISTRY. *Educ:* Univ Chicago, AB, 50, MS, 54. *Prof Exp:* Spectroscopist & mineralogist, Heavy Minerals Co, Vitro Corp Am, 56-58; spectroscopist, Labs, 58-65, asst dir, 65-70, res assoc, Univ, 63-67, asst prof, 67-69, ASSOC PROF GEOCHEM, PA STATE UNIV, 69-, DIR MINERAL CONST LABS, 70- *Mem:* AAAS; Soc Appl Spectros; Geochem Soc. *Res:* X-ray and emission spectroscopy and atomic absorption, primarily in the fields of earth sciences. *Mailing Add:* Mineral Const Labs Pa State Univ University Park PA 16802

SUHRLAND, LEIF GEORGE, b Schroon Lake, NY, Apr 9, 19; m 50; c 3. HEMATOLOGY, ONCOLOGY. *Educ:* Cornell Univ, BS, 42; Univ Rochester, MD, 50. *Hon Degrees:* DM, Univ Rochester, 50. *Prof Exp:* Bacteriologist, USPHS, 42-43; intern & jr asst med, Univ Hosps, Cleveland, 50-52; instr, Western Reserve Univ, 57-59, asst prof med & asst clin pathologist, 59-67; PROF MED, COL HUMAN MED, MICH STATE UNIV, 67- *Concurrent Pos:* Am Cancer Soc fel, Univ Hosps, Cleveland, 52-54; Howard M Hanna & Anna Bishop fels, Sch Med, Western Reserve Univ, 54-57. *Mem:* Am Fedn Clin Res; Am Soc Hemat. *Res:* Host tumor relationships. *Mailing Add:* B-220 Life Sci Bldg Mich State Univ Col Human Med East Lansing MI 48823

SUIB, STEVEN L, b Olean, NY, May 1, 53; m 77. INORGANIC PHOTOCHEMISTRY. *Educ:* State Univ NY Fredonia, BS, 75; Univ Ill, Urbana, PhD(chem), 79. *Prof Exp:* Res asst, State Univ NY Fredonia, 74-75; teaching asst, Univ Ill, Urbana, 75-77, res asst, 78-79, vis lectr, 79, assoc, 79-80; ASST PROF, UNIV CONN, STORRS, 80- *Concurrent Pos:* Fel, Univ Conn, 80. *Mem:* Am Chem Soc; Sigma Xi. *Res:* Solid state inorganic chemistry including surface, structural, electrochemical and catalytic properties of semiconductors and heterogeneous zeolite compounds; zeolite chemistry and catalysis. *Mailing Add:* Dept Chem U 60 Univ Conn Storrs CT 06268

SUICH, JOHN EDWARD, b Bridgeport, Conn, Sept 28, 36; m 57; c 2. INFORMATION SCIENCE. *Educ:* Harvard Univ, BA, 58; Mass Inst Technol, PhD(nuclear eng), 63. *Prof Exp:* Sr physicist, Savannah River Lab, 63-65, res supvr, 65-66, res mgr appl math, 66-68, dir comput sci sect, 68-71, mgr telecommun planning, Gen Servs Dept, 71-72, asst mgr comput sci div, Cent Systs & Servs Dept, Del, 72, mgr com systs div mgt sci, 72-75, RES ASSOC, SAVANNAH RIVER LAB, E I DU PONT DE NEMOURS & CO, INC, 75- *Res:* Geophysical data bases and numerical transport models. *Mailing Add:* 1015 Ken Dr Aiken SC 29801

SUICH, RONALD CHARLES, b Cleveland, Ohio, Nov 16, 40; m 62; c 3. STATISTICS. *Educ:* John Carroll Univ, BSBA, 62; Case Western Reserve Univ, MS, 64, PhD(statist), 68. *Prof Exp:* Mkt researcher, Cleveland Elec Illum Co, 62-64; from instr to asst prof statist, Case Western Reserve Univ, 64-70; asst prof, Univ Akron, 70-77, assoc prof math, 77-80; MEM FAC MATH, CALIF STATE UNIV, 80- *Mem:* Am Statist Asn. *Res:* Sequential tests. *Mailing Add:* Dept Mgt Sci Calif State Univ Fullerton CA 92634

SUIE, TED, b Akron, Ohio, June 20, 23. MICROBIOLOGY, IMMUNOLOGY. *Educ:* Univ Akron, BSc, 48; Ohio State Univ, MSc, 49, PhD(bacteriol), 53. *Prof Exp:* From instr to assoc prof, 53-72, PROF OPHTHAL & MICROBIOL, OHIO STATE UNIV, 72- *Mem:* Am Acad Ophthal & Otolaryngol. *Res:* Infections of the eye and immunology of the eye. *Mailing Add:* Dept Ophthal Ohio State Univ Columbus OH 43210

SUIT, HERMAN DAY, b Houston, Tex, Feb 8, 29. RADIOTHERAPY. *Educ:* Univ Houston, AB, 48; Baylor Univ, SM & MD, 52; Oxford Univ, DrPhil(radiobiol), 56. *Prof Exp:* Intern, Jefferson Davis Hosp, Houston, Tex, 52-53, resident radiol, 53-54; house surgeon radiother, Churchill Hosp, Oxford, Eng, 54, res asst radiobiol lab, 54-56, registr radiother, 56-57; sr asst surgeon, Radiation Br, Nat Cancer Inst, 57-59; asst radiotherapist, Univ Tex M D Anderson Hosp & Tumor Inst Houston, 59-63, assoc radiotherapist, 63-68, radiotherapist, 68-71, chief sect exp radiother, 62-70; PROF RADIATION THER, HARVARD MED SCH, 70-; HEAD DEPT RADIATION MED, MASS GEN HOSP, 71- *Concurrent Pos:* Nat Cancer Inst res career develop award, Univ Tex M D Anderson Hosp & Tumor Inst Houston, 64-68; gen fac assoc, Univ Tex Grad Sch Biomed Sci, 65-70, prof radiation ther, 68-71; staff mem, NASA Manned Spacecraft Ctr, 69-71; subcomt radiation biol, Nat Acad Sci. *Mem:* AAAS; Am Col Radiol; Am Soc Therapeut Radiol (secy, 70-72); AMA; Am Asn Cancer Res. *Mailing Add:* Dept Radiation Med Mass Gen Hosp Boston MA 02114

SUIT, JOAN C, b Ontario, Ore, Apr 14, 31; m 60. MICROBIOLOGY. *Educ:* Ore State Col, BS, 53; Stanford Univ, MA, 55, PhD(med microbiol), 57. *Prof Exp:* Res assoc biochem, Biol Div, Oak Ridge Nat Lab, 57-59; res assoc sect molecular biol, Univ Tex M D Anderson Hosp & Tumor Inst, Houston, 59-66, assoc biologist & assoc prof biol, Univ Tex Grad Sch Biomed Sci, Houston, 66-73; res assoc biol, 73-80, RES SCIENTIST, DEPT BIOL, MASS INST TECHNOL, 80- *Mem:* Am Soc Microbiol; Am Soc Cell Biol. *Res:* Microbial genetics; DNA replication; microbial growth. *Mailing Add:* Dept of Biol Mass Inst of Technol Cambridge MA 02139

SUITS, CHAUNCEY GUY, b Oshkosh, Wis, Mar 12, 05; m 31; c 2. PHYSICS. *Educ:* Univ Wis, AB, 27; Swiss Fed Inst Technol, DSc, 29. *Hon Degrees:* DSc, Union Col, NY, 44, Hamilton Col, 46, Drexel Inst Technol, 55 & Marquette Univ, 59; DEng, Rensselaer Polytech Inst, 50. *Prof Exp:* Consult physics, Forest Prod Lab, US Forest Serv, Wis, 29-30; res physicist, Gen Elec Co, 30-40, asst to dir res, 40-45, vpres & dir res, 45-65; CONSULT INDUST RES MGT, 65- *Concurrent Pos:* Fel, Inst Int Educ Mem Div 14 & chief div 15, Nat Defense Res Comt, Off Sci Res & Develop, 42-46; mem sci adv bd, Nat Security Agency; mem ord comt, Res & Develop Bd, US Dept Defense, 49-50, mem comt electronics, 52-54, mem tech adv panel electronics, 54-; mem spec tech adv group, Joint Chiefs of Staff & Res & Develop Bd, 50-53; chmn, Naval Res Adv Comt, 58-61; chmn adv comt corp assocs, Am Inst Physics, 58-62, dir-at-large gov bd, 61-64; mem bd dirs, NY State Sci & Technol Found, 65-67, vchmn, 68-; mem res mgt adv panel, US House of Rep Comt Sci & Astronaut. *Honors & Awards:* Presidential Medal for Merit & King's Medal Serv in Cause of Freedom, Gt Brit, 48; Proctor Prize, Sigma Xi, 58; Distinguished Serv Award, Am Mgt Asn, 59; Medal, Indust Res Inst, 62; Charles M Schwab Mem Lectr, Am Iron & steel Inst, 63; Medal for Advan Res, Am Soc Metals, 66; Frederik Philips Award, Inst Elec & Electronics Engrs, 74. *Mem:* Nat Acad Sci; Nat Acad Eng; Sigma Xi; fel Am Phys Soc; Am Mgt Asn (vpres, 56). *Res:* Nonlinear electronic circuits; high pressure arcs. *Mailing Add:* Crosswinds Pilot Knob NY 12844

SUITS, JAMES CARR, b Schenectady, NY, May 29, 32; m 54; c 3. PHYSICS. *Educ:* Yale Univ, BS, 54; Harvard Univ, PhD(appl physics), 60. *Prof Exp:* Staff physicist, Res Lab, 60-76, mgr, Garnet Mat Dept, Gen Prods Div, 76-80, RES STAFF MEM, RES LAB, IBM CORP, SAN JOSE, 80- *Mem:* Fel Am Phys Soc; Inst Elec & Electronics Engrs. *Res:* Magnetism, ultra-high vacuum evaporated thin films, magneto-optics, discovery and development of novel magnetic materials, garnet film growth; magnetic bubble development, electroplating development, process automation and electromigration. *Mailing Add:* IBM Res Div K63/282 5600 Cottle Rd San Jose CA 95193

SUJISHI, SEI, b San Pedro, Calif, Nov 9, 21; m 55; c 1. INORGANIC CHEMISTRY. *Educ:* Wayne State Univ, BS, 46, MS, 48; Purdue Univ, PhD(chem), 49. *Prof Exp:* From instr to assoc prof chem, Ill Inst Technol, 49-59; assoc prof, 59-65, chmn dept, 74-76, PROF CHEM, STATE UNIV NY STONY BROOK, 65- *Mem:* Am Chem Soc. *Res:* Chemistry of silicon and germanium hydrides. *Mailing Add:* Dept of Chem State Univ of NY Stony Brook NY 11790

SUK, WADI NAGIB, b Khartoum, Sudan, Oct 26, 34; US citizen; m 67; c 4. INTERNAL MEDICINE, NEPHROLOGY. *Educ:* Am Univ Beirut, BS, 55, MD, 59. *Prof Exp:* Resident internal med, Parkland Mem Hosp, Dallas, 61-63; from instr to assoc prof, 65-71, PROF MED, BAYLOR COL MED, 71-, CHIEF RENAL SECT, 68- *Concurrent Pos:* Res fel exp med, Univ Tex Southwestern Med Sch Dallas, 59-61, USPHS res fel nephrology, 63-65, Dallas Heart Asn res grant, 67-68; Nat Heart & Lung Inst res grant, Baylor Col Med, 68-72, training grant, 71-76, Nat Inst Arthritis, Metab & Digestive Dis res grant, 74-77, Nat Inst Allergy & Infectious Dis contract, 74-78, NASA contract, 75-78; attend physician, Ben Taub Gen Hosp, 68-; consult, Vet Admin Hosp, 68- & Wilford Hall, USAF Med Ctr, 72-; chief renal sect, Methodist Hosp, 69-; pres med adv bd, Kidney Found Houston & Greater Gulf Coast, 69-71; chmn nat med adv coun, Nat Kidney Found, 71-73, trustee-at-large, 71-76, secy sci adv bd, 77-78; mem exec comt, Coun Kidney in Cardiovasc Dis, Am Heart Asn, 71-74; mem rev bd nephrology, Vet Admin Cent Off Med Res Serv, 74-77, chmn, 76-77; mem gen med B study sect, NIH, 75-79. *Mem:* Am Fedn Clin Res; Am Soc Clin Invest; Int Soc Nephrology; fel Am Col Physicians; Am Soc Nephrology. *Res:* Renal, fluid and electrolyte physiology and pathophysiology; renal disease, dialysis and transplantation. *Mailing Add:* Renal Sect Dept of Med Baylor Col of Med Houston TX 77030

SUKANEK, PETER CHARLES, b Flushing, NY, Sept 15, 47; m 69; c 2. CHEMICAL ENGINEERING. *Educ:* Manhattan Col, BChE, 68; Univ Mass, MS, 70, PhD(chem eng), 72. *Prof Exp:* Proj engr chem eng, Rocket Propulsion Lab, US Air Force, 72-76; ASST PROF CHEM ENG, CLARKSON COL TECHNOL, 76- *Concurrent Pos:* Consult, Foreign Technol Div, US Air Force, 76-; off sci res grant, US Air Force, 78-79; Petrol Res Fund grant, 78-80. *Mem:* Am Inst Chem Engrs; Soc Rheology; Sigma Xi. *Res:* Polymer rheology and shear degradation; phenomenological turbulence models; optical temperature measurement. *Mailing Add:* Dept of Chem Eng Clarkson Col of Technol Potsdam NY 13676

SUKAVA, ARMAS JOHN, b Elma, Man, Mar 1, 17; m 50; c 2. PHYSICAL CHEMISTRY. *Educ:* Univ Man, BSc, 46, MSc, 49; McGill Univ, PhD, 55. *Prof Exp:* Lectr chem, Univ Man, 47-49; res & develop chemist, Consol Mining & Smelting Co, 49-50; lectr chem, Univ BC, 50-51 & Univ Alta, 51-52; instr, 54-55, lectr, 55-56, from asst prof to assoc prof, 56-74, PROF CHEM, UNIV WESTERN ONT, 74- *Mem:* Electrochem Soc; Chem Inst Can. *Res:* Cathode overpotential and surface-active additives; physicochemical properties of electrolyte systems. *Mailing Add:* Dept of Chem Univ of Western Ont London ON N6A 3K7 Can

SUKER, JACOB ROBERT, b Chicago, Ill, Oct 17, 26; m 56; c 3. INTERNAL MEDICINE. *Educ:* Northwestern Univ, Evanston, BS, 47; Northwestern Univ, Chicago, MS, 54, MD, 56. *Prof Exp:* Dir med educ, Chicago Wesley Mem Hosp, 64-68; asst dean grad educ, 68-70, ASSOC PROF MED, MED SCH, NORTHWESTERN UNIV, CHICAGO, 68-, ASSOC DEAN GRAD EDUC, 70- *Concurrent Pos:* Assoc attend physician, Chicago Wesley Mem Hosp, 64- *Res:* Parathyroid disease. *Mailing Add:* Dept of Med Northwestern Univ Med Sch Chicago IL 60611

SUKHATME, BALKRISHNA VASUDEO, b Poona, India, Nov 3, 24; m 56; c 1. STATISTICS. *Educ:* Univ Delhi, BA, 45, MA, 47; Inst Agr Res Statist, New Delhi, dipl, 49; Univ Calif, Berkeley, PhD(statist), 55. *Prof Exp:* Sr res statistician, Indian Coun Agr Res, 55-58, prof statist, 58-65, dep statist adv, 62-63, sr prof statist, 65-67; assoc prof, Iowa State Univ, 67-68, prof statist, 68-80. *Concurrent Pos:* Vis assoc prof statist, Mich State Univ, 59-60; ed jour, Indian Soc Agr Statist, 59-67; consult, FAO, Rome, 65; mem, Int Statist Inst, The Hague, 72- *Mem:* Inst Math Statist; fel Am Statist Asn; Int Asn Surv Statisticians; Indian Soc Agr Statist (joint secy, 56-58). *Res:* Sampling theory and its applications; nonparametric tests for scale and randomness and asymptotic theory of order statistics and generalized U-statistics; planning, organization and conduct of large-scale sample surveys. *Mailing Add:* 1505 Wheeler Ames IA 50010

SUKHATME, SHASHIKALA BALKRISHNA, b Karad, Maharashtra, India; c 1. MATHEMATICAL STATISTICS. *Educ:* Univ Poona, BSc, 53, Hons, 54, MSc, 55; Mich State Univ, PhD(statist), 60. *Prof Exp:* Lectr statist, Univ Delhi, 63-67; ASST PROF STATIST, IOWA STATE UNIV, 67- *Concurrent Pos:* Univ Grants Comn, India Fel, Univ Delhi, 61-63; Daxina fel, Poona Univ. *Mem:* Inst Math Statist; Am Statist Asn; Indian Statist Asn. *Res:* Nonparametric statistical theory; goodness of fit tests; order statistics. *Mailing Add:* Statist Lab Iowa State Univ Ames IA 50010

SUKOW, WAYNE WILLIAM, b Merrill, Wis, Dec 9, 36; m 59; c 2. MOLECULAR BIOPHYSICS, BIOPHYSICAL CHEMISTRY. *Educ:* Univ Wis-River Falls, BA, 59; Case Inst Technol, MS, 63; Wash State Univ, PhD(chem physics), 74. *Prof Exp:* Assoc prof, 61-77, PROF PHYSICS & CHMN DEPT, UNIV WIS-RIVER FALLS, 77- *Concurrent Pos:* Vis prof physics, Macalester Col, 67; physicist, 3M Co, 67; NSF sci fac fel, Wash State Univ, 70-72. *Mem:* Biophys Soc; Am Asn Physics Teachers. *Res:* Protein-ligand binding, particularly the mechanism of detergent binding to membrane proteins; conformational changes of proteins monitored by electron paramagnetic resonance using spin probe molecules; photoelectron microscopy of biological materials. *Mailing Add:* Dept of Physics Univ of Wis River Falls WI 54022

SUKOWSKI, ERNEST JOHN, b Chicago, Ill, Nov 17, 32; div; c 3. PHYSIOLOGY, PHARMACOLOGY. *Educ:* Loyola Univ Chicago, BS, 54; Univ Ill, MS, 58, PhD(physiol), 62. *Prof Exp:* ASSOC PROF PHYSIOL, UNIV HEALTH SCI-CHICAGO MED SCH, 63- *Mem:* NY Acad Sci; Am Physiol Soc; Am Heart Asn; Am Asn Univ Professors. *Res:* Cardiac and liver metabolism; cardiovascular physiology; hypertension; subcellular physiology. *Mailing Add:* Dept Physiol & Biophys Univ Health Sci-Chicago Med Sch North Chicago IL 60064

SULAK, LAWRENCE RICHARD, b Columbus, Ohio, Aug 29, 44; m 70. ELEMENTARY PARTICLE PHYSICS, EXPERIMENTAL HIGH ENERGY PHYSICS. *Educ:* Carnegie-Mellon Univ, BS, 66; Princeton Univ, AM, 68, PhD(physics), 70. *Prof Exp:* Res physicist, Univ Geneva, 70-71; asst prof physics, Harvard Univ, 71-75, assoc prof, 75-79; ASSOC PROF PHYSICS, UNIV MICH, 79- *Concurrent Pos:* Vis scientist, Europ Orgn Nuclear Res, 70-73; vis physicist, Fermi Nat Accelerator Lab, 71-77; guest assoc physicist, Brookhaven Nat Lab, 74- *Mem:* Am Phys Soc. *Res:* Experimental K-meson physics; particle production studies; neutrino physics, studies of deep inelastic scattering, scaling, neutral currents, dimuons and elastic neutron-proton scattering; proton decay experiments; instrumentation for high energy physics; acoustic signals from particle beams. *Mailing Add:* Randall Lab Physics Univ Mich Ann Arbor MI 48109

SULAKHE, PRAKASH VINAYAK, b Nov 18, 41; Indian citizen; m 73. PHYSIOLOGY. *Educ:* Bombay Univ, BS, 62, MS, 65; Univ Man, PhD(physiol), 71. *Prof Exp:* Lectr physiol, Topiwala Nat Med Col, India, 66; sci officer med div, Bhaha Atomic Res Ctr, India, 66-67; demonstr & teaching fel physiol, Univ Man, 68-71; Med Res Coun Can fel pharmacol, Univ BC, 71-73; Med Res Coun Can res prof, 77-78, asst prof, 73-76, assoc prof, 76-80, PROF PHYSIOL, UNIV SASK, 80- *Mem:* Can Physiol Soc; Int Soc Heart Res; NY Acad Sci; Soc Neurosci; Can Biochem Soc. *Res:* Regulation and metabolism and function of contractile tissues and brain; cyclic nucleotides, calcium ions, autonomic receptors and membranes. *Mailing Add:* Dept of Physiol Col of Med Univ of Sask Saskatoon SK S7N 0W0 Can

SULAVIK, STEPHEN B, b New Britain, Conn, Aug 11, 30; m 55; c 8. MEDICINE. *Educ:* Providence Col, BS, 52; Georgetown Univ, MD, 56. *Prof Exp:* Asst chief chest dis, Vet Admin Hosp, Bronx, NY, 61-62; clin instr, 62-63, from instr to asst prof, 63-69, assoc clin prof med, Sch Med, 69-78, CLIN PROF MED, YALE UNIV SCH MED, 78-; PROF & HEAD DIV PULMONARY MED, UNIV CONN, 77- *Concurrent Pos:* Mem med adv comt, Dept HEW; assoc prof med & actg head pulmonary div, Univ Conn, 69-77; chmn dept med, St Francis Hosp, Hartford, 69-77. *Mem:* Am Thoracic Soc; AMA. *Res:* Anatomy and physiology of intrathoracic lymphatic system. *Mailing Add:* Div of Pulmonary Med Univ of Conn Sch of Med Farmington CT 06032

SULENTIC, JACK WILLIAM, b Waterloo, Iowa, Apr 10, 47; m 75. ASTRONOMY, OPTICAL ASTRONOMY. *Educ:* Univ Ariz, BS, 69; State Univ NY Albany, PhD(astron), 75. *Prof Exp:* Fel astron, Hale Observ, 75-78; instr physics & astron, Sierra Nev Col, 78-79; asst prof, Mich State Univ, 79-80; ASST PROF, UNIV ALA, 80- *Mem:* Am Astron Soc; Royal Astron Soc; Sigma Xi; Int Astron Union. *Res:* Application of optical and radio observations to understanding the origin and evolution of galaxies. *Mailing Add:* Dept Physics & Astron PO Box 1921 Univ Ala Incline Village NV 35486

SULERUD, RALPH L, b Fargo, NDak, June 6, 32. GENETICS, ZOOLOGY. *Educ:* Concordia Col, Moorhead, Minn, BA, 54; Univ Nebr, MS, 58, PhD(zool), 68. *Prof Exp:* Instr biol, St Olaf Col, 58-59; from instr to assoc prof, 64-77, PROF BIOL, AUGSBURG COL, 77-, CHMN DEPT, 74- *Mem:* AAAS; Genetics Soc Am; Am Genetic Asn; Am Inst Biol Sci; Soc Study Evolution. *Res:* Taxonomy; genetics of Drosophila. *Mailing Add:* Dept of Biol Augsburg Col 731 21st Ave S Minneapolis MN 55404

SULIK, KATHLEEN KAY, b Estherville, Iowa, Oct 15, 48; m 77; c 1. TERATOLOGY. *Educ:* Drake Univ, BS, 70; Univ Tenn, PhD(anat), 76. *Prof Exp:* Guest scientist, Geronol Res Ctr, NIH, 74-75; instr anat, Univ Tenn, 75-76; fel teratol, Dent Res Ctr, Univ NC, 76-78; res assoc, Georgetown Univ, Wash, DC, 78-79, asst prof, 79-80; ASST PROF ANAT, UNIV NC, CHAPEL HILL, 80- *Mem:* Teratology Soc; AAAS. *Res:* Embryology and teratology of the craniofacial region emphasing the teratogenic effect of ethanol, defining critical exposure periods and mechanisms of malformation. *Mailing Add:* Dept Anat Swing Bldg Univ NC Chapel Hill NC 27514

SULING, WILLIAM JOHN, b New York, NY, June 12, 40; m 65; c 3. MEDICAL MICROBIOLOGY, CHEMOTHERAPY. *Educ:* Manhattan Col, BS, 62; Duquesne Univ, MS, 65; Cornell Univ, PhD(microbiol), 75. *Prof Exp:* Res asst cancer chemother, Sloan-Kettering Inst Cancer Res, 64-70; sr bacteriologist, Biol Lab, Mass Dept Pub Health, 74-75; res microbiologist, 75-78, SR MICROBIOLOGIST, SOUTHERN RES INST, 78- *Mem:* NY Acad Sci; Am Soc Microbiol. *Res:* Folate metabolism and its inhibition by folate analogues; the biochemistry of antimicrobial drug resistance and the use of microorganisms for studies involving cancer chemotherapy; drug metabolism and disposition. *Mailing Add:* Southern Res Inst PO Box 3307-A Birmingham AL 35255

SULKOWSKI, EUGENE, b Plonsk, Poland, May 22, 34; m 64; c 2. BIOCHEMISTRY. *Educ:* Univ Warsaw, MS, 56, PhD(biochem), 60. *Prof Exp:* Res asst biochem, Inst Biochem & Biophys, Polish Acad Sci, 56-60; exchange scientist, Univ Sorbonne, 62-63; res asst, Polish Acad Sci, 63-65; PRIN CANCER RES SCIENTIST, ROSWELL PARK MEM INST, 65- *Concurrent Pos:* Res fel, Marquette Univ, 60-62. *Mem:* AAAS; Am Soc Biol Chemists; Polish Biochem Soc. *Res:* Enzymology; human interferon. *Mailing Add:* Viral Oncol Roswell Park Mem Inst 666 Elm St Buffalo NY 14263

SULLENGER, DON BRUCE, b Richmond, Mo, Feb 8, 29; m 64; c 3. SOLID STATE CHEMISTRY. *Educ:* Univ Colo, AB, 50; Cornell Univ, PhD, 69. *Prof Exp:* Trainee Chemet Prog, Chem Div, Gen Elec Co, 50-51 & 53, res chemist, Res Lab, 53-54; sr res chemist, 62-74, RES SPECIALIST, MOUND LAB, MONSANTO RES CORP, 74- *Mem:* AAAS; Am Inst Chemists; Am Chem Soc; Am Crystallog Asn. *Res:* X-ray crystallographic structure determination of inorganic substances, principally theory of structure determinations via the direct methods; solid state chemistry of inorganic materials. *Mailing Add:* Monsanto Res Corp Mound Lab Miamisburg OH 45342

SULLIVAN, A HUMPHREY, b Lincoln, Nebr, Apr 7, 15. ELECTRICAL ENGINEERING. *Educ:* Cornell Univ, EE, 39. *Prof Exp:* Engr, Elec Power Bd, Chattanooga, Tenn, 39-40; vpres & dir res & develop, Avionics, Inc, 46-47; asst plans & opers, Electronics Sect, Tech Anal Div, Wright-Patterson AFB, 47-51; consult, 51-55; asst to gen mgr & exec engr, York Div, Bendix Aviation Corp, 55-58; vpres, Engleman & Co, Inc, 58-60; vpres & dir adv systs develop, Frederick Res Corp, 61-63; mgr, Wash Dist Off, HRB-Singer, Inc, 64-66; chief spectrum planning div, Off Telecommun Mgt, Exec Off of President, 67; tech dir, Naval Sci & Tech Info Ctr, 68-73; PRES, SULLIVAN ASSOCS, 73- *Mem:* Fel Inst Elec & Electronics Engrs; Am Inst Aeronaut & Astronaut; AAAS; Am Ord Asn; Armed Forces Commun Electronics Asn. *Res:* Communications systems engineering; radio spectrum utilization; systems research; management sciences. *Mailing Add:* 7121 Wolftree Lane Rockville MD 20852

SULLIVAN, ALFRED DEWITT, b New Orleans, La, Feb 2, 42; m 62; c 2. FORESTRY, BIOMETRICS. *Educ:* La State Univ, BS, 64, MS, 66; Univ Ga, PhD(forest biomet), 69. *Prof Exp:* Asst prof statist, Va Polytech Inst & State Univ, 69-73; assoc prof, 73-78, PROF FORESTRY, MISS STATE UNIV, 78- *Mem:* Soc Am Foresters. *Res:* Prediction of forest growth and yield; application of statistical methodology to natural resource problems. *Mailing Add:* Dept of Forestry PO Drawer FD Miss State Univ Mississippi State MS 39762

SULLIVAN, ANDREW JACKSON, b Birmingham, Ala, Mar 3, 26; m 53. BIOCHEMISTRY, FOOD CHEMISTRY. *Educ:* Univ Richmond, BS, 47; Univ Mo, PhD(bot), 52. *Prof Exp:* USPHS fel, Univ Pa, 52-53; res chemist, Campbell Soup Co, 53-55 & 57-59, head div flavor biochem res, 59-71, div head environ sci & chem technol, Campbell Inst for Food Res, 71-76, dir sci resources, 76-77, DIR FLAVOR SCI & NUTRIT, CAMPBELL INST RES & TECHNOL, 77- *Mem:* Inst Food Technologists; NY Acad Sci; fel Am Inst Chemists. *Res:* Chemistry of microorganisms; food and flavor chemistry. *Mailing Add:* Campbell Inst for Food Res Campbell Place Camden NJ 08101

SULLIVAN, ANN CLARE, b Tillamook, Ore, June 3, 43. BIOCHEMISTRY. *Educ:* Col Notre Dame Md, BA, 65; Northwestern Univ, MS, 67; NY Univ, PhD(biochem), 73. *Prof Exp:* Res assoc, Sci & Eng Inc, 66-68; res group chief, 69-78, DIR, DEPT PHARMACOL I & II, ROCHE INC, 79-, ASSOC DIR, DIV EXP BIOL, 81- *Concurrent Pos:* Adj prof, Sch Med, Columbia Univ, 76. *Mem:* NY Acad Sci; AAAS; Am Chem Soc; Am Oil Chemists Soc; Asn Study Obesity. *Res:* Regulation of lipid and carbohydrate metabolism; control of appetite and energy balance; metabolic aspects of obesity and hyperlipidemia; development of pharmacological agents for the treatment of obesity and hyperlipidemia. *Mailing Add:* Hoffmann-La Roche Inc Dept Pharmacol Nutley NJ 07110

SULLIVAN, ANNA MANNEVILLETTE, b Washington, DC, Aug 18, 13. METALLURGY. *Educ:* George Washington Univ, AB, 35; Univ Md, MS, 55. *Prof Exp:* Asst metallurgist, Geophys Lab, Carnegie Inst Wash, 42-45; metallurgist, Nat Bur Stand, 45-46; metallurgist, Naval Res Lab, 47-78; dep tech ed, J Eng Mat Technol, Am Soc Mech Engrs, 78-81; RETIRED. *Honors & Awards:* Burgess Award, Am Soc Metals, 78. *Mem:* Sigma Xi; Am Soc Metals; Am Soc Testing & Mat; Am Soc Mech Engrs. *Res:* Fracture of metals with special reference to fracture mechanics. *Mailing Add:* 4000 Massachusetts Ave Washington DC 20016

SULLIVAN, CHARLES IRVING, b Milwaukee, Wis, Nov 18, 18; m 48; c 2. ORGANIC POLYMER CHEMISTRY. *Educ:* Boston Univ, AB, 43. *Prof Exp:* Chemist, UBS Chem Co Div, A E Staley Mfg Co, 43-46, supvr indust chem & develop sect, 46-58, mgr res & develop, 58-67, res assoc, 67-69; sr scientist, 69-70, res assoc, 70-79, RES FEL, POLAROID CORP, 79- *Mem:* AAAS; Am Chem Soc; fel Am Inst Chemists. *Res:* Emulsion polymerization; paints; floor finishes; paper coatings and binders; wood coatings; adhesives; textile backings; aqueous polymer research and development related to membrane-like structures, functional coatings, binders and colloids. *Mailing Add:* 148 Bellevue Ave Melrose MA 02176

SULLIVAN, CHARLOTTE MURDOCH, b St Stephen, NB, Dec 18, 19. ANIMAL PHYSIOLOGY. *Educ:* Dalhousie Univ, BSc, 41, MSc, 43; Univ Toronto, PhD(zool), 49. *Prof Exp:* Nat Res Coun Can overseas fel, Cambridge Univ, 49-50; from lectr to asst prof, 50-61, ASSOC PROF ZOOL, UNIV TORONTO, 61- *Res:* Physiology of animal behavior. *Mailing Add:* 615 Seneca Hill Dr Toronto ON M2J 2W6 Can

SULLIVAN, CORNELIUS PATRICK, b Schenectady, NY, Sept 28, 29; m 55; c 3. METALLURGY. *Educ:* Univ Notre Dame, BS, 51; Mass Inst Technol, SM, 55, ScD(metall), 60. *Prof Exp:* ENGR METALL, PRATT & WHITNEY AIRCRAFT, 62- *Honors & Awards:* William A Spraragen Award, Am Welding Soc, 67. *Mem:* Am Soc Metals. *Res:* Mechanical behavior of high temperature alloys and their properties. *Mailing Add:* 74 Coach Rd Glastonbury CT 06033

SULLIVAN, DAN ALLEN, b Cairo, Ill, Sept 26, 33; m 63; c 2. GEOLOGY. *Educ:* Northwestern Univ, BA, 55; Wash Univ, MA, 60, PhD(geol), 66. *Prof Exp:* Asst prof eng geol, Univ Valle, Colombia, 66-67; assoc prof geol, Murray State Univ, 67-68; ASSOC PROF GEOL, DEPAUW UNIV, 68- *Concurrent Pos:* Rockefeller Found grant univ develop in Latin Am & consult, City of Cali, Colombia & Corp Autonoma del Valle del Cauca, 66-67; consult opers geologist, Bolt Beranek & Newman, Inc, 73-75. *Mem:* Am Inst Mining, Metall & Petrol Engrs; NY Acad Sci; Am Asn Petrol Geologists; Am Inst Prof Geologists. *Res:* Environmental geology; stratigraphy; sedimentation; Pacific-margin Tertiary basin, Gulf of Alaska. *Mailing Add:* Dept of Earth Sci DePauw Univ Sci Ctr Greencastle IN 46135

SULLIVAN, DANIEL JOSEPH, b New York, NY, Apr 22, 28. ENTOMOLOGY, ANIMAL BEHAVIOR. *Educ:* Fordham Univ, BS, 50, MS, 58; Univ Vienna, cert Ger, 58; Univ Strasbourg, cert French, 62; Univ Innsbruck, cert theol, 62; Univ Calif, Berkeley, PhD(entom), 69. *Prof Exp:* Teacher, NY High Sch, 55-57; asst prof, 69-74, ASSOC PROF ZOOL, FORDHAM UNIV, 74- *Mem:* AAAS; Entom Soc Am; Ecol Soc Am; Animal Behav Soc; Am Inst Biol Sci. *Res:* Biological control of insect pests, with special reference to the primary parasites and hyperparasites of aphids; ecology and behavior of aphids and parasites. *Mailing Add:* Dept of Biol Sci Fordham Univ Bronx NY 10458

SULLIVAN, DANIEL RICHARD, organic chemistry, lipid chemistry, see previous edition

SULLIVAN, DAVID THOMAS, b Salem, Mass, Mar 20, 40; m 66; c 2. BIOCHEMICAL GENETICS. *Educ:* Boston Col, BS, 61, MS, 63; Johns Hopkins Univ, PhD(biol), 67. *Prof Exp:* USPHS res fel biochem, Calif Inst Technol, 67-69; asst prof, 70-74, ASSOC PROF BIOL, SYRACUSE UNIV, 74- *Mem:* Genetics Soc Am; Soc Develop Biol. *Res:* Genetic and biochemical control of animal development. *Mailing Add:* Dept of Biol Syracuse Univ Syracuse NY 13210

SULLIVAN, DONALD, b Merthyr Tydfil, Wales, Mar 23, 36; m 61. MATHEMATICS. *Educ:* Univ Wales, BSc, 57, PhD(appl math), 60. *Prof Exp:* Asst lectr math, Univ Col, Univ Wales, 60-61; asst prof, 61-66, ASSOC PROF MATH, UNIV NB, 66- *Concurrent Pos:* Mem, Inst Math & Its Appln, 67. *Mem:* Can Math Cong. *Res:* Fluid mechanics; phase plane analysis of differential equations; functional equations. *Mailing Add:* Dept of Math Univ of NB Fredericton NB E3B 5A3 Can

SULLIVAN, DONALD BARRETT, b Phoenix, Ariz, June 13, 39; m 59; c 3. LOW TEMPERATURE PHYSICS. *Educ:* Tex Western Col, BS, 61; Vanderbilt Univ, MA, 63, PhD(physics), 65. *Prof Exp:* Res assoc physics, Vanderbilt Univ, 65; physicist & br chief, Radiation Physics Br, US Army Nuclear Defense Lab, 65-67; Nat Res Coun assoc, 67-69, PHYSICIST & CHIEF CRYOELECTRONIC METROLOGY SECT, ELECTROMAGNETIC TECH DIV, NAT BUR STAND, 69- *Mem:* Am Phys Soc. *Res:* Josephson effect and quantum interference in superconductors; development of measurement instruments using these and other low temperature phenomena. *Mailing Add:* Electromagnetic Tech Div Nat Bur of Stand Boulder CO 80303

SULLIVAN, DONITA B, b Marlette, Mich, Feb 11, 31. PEDIATRICS. *Educ:* Siena Heights Col, BS, 52; St Louis Univ, MD, 56; Am Bd Pediat, dipl, 61. *Prof Exp:* Intern, Henry Ford Hosp, Detroit, Mich, 56-57; resident pediat, Children's Hosp of Mich, 57-59, sr resident, 59; res assoc, Sch Med, Wayne State Univ, 59; clin instr, 59-62, asst prof pediat & dir birth defects treatment ctr, 62-69, assoc prof, 69-77, PROF PEDIAT & DIR PEDIAT REHAB & RHEUMATOLOGY SECT, MED SCH, UNIV MICH, ANN ARBOR, 77- *Concurrent Pos:* Pediat consult, Wayne County Gen Hosp, 62-, Field Clins, Mich Crippled Children's Comn, 64- & Cath Social Servs, 66-; mem med adv comt, Washtenaw County Chapters, Nat Found & Nat Cystic Fibrosis Res Found, 60-74; prog consult, Nat Found, 66-69; bd trustees, Siena Heights Col, 70-75. *Res:* Handicapped children; children with birth defects; clinical and immunologic aspects of connective tissue disease in children. *Mailing Add:* Dept of Pediat Univ of Mich Med Ctr Ann Arbor MI 48104

SULLIVAN, EDWARD AUGUSTINE, b Salem, Mass, July 5, 29; m 59; c 6. INORGANIC CHEMISTRY. *Educ:* Col Holy Cross, BS, 50; Mass Inst Technol, MS, 52. *Prof Exp:* Asst, Sugar Res Found, 50-52; res chemist, Metal Hydrides, Inc, 52-63, sr res chemist, Metal Hydrides Div, Ventron Corp, 63-71, tech mgr, res chem, Ventron Corp, 71-79, SR SCIENTIST, THIOKOL/VENTRON DIV, VENTRON CORP, 79- *Mem:* Am Chem Soc; Tech Asn Pulp & Paper Indust. *Res:* Chemistry of hydrides; inorganic synthesis; industrial applications of hydrides. *Mailing Add:* Thiokol/Ventron Div 150 Andover St Danvers MA 01923

SULLIVAN, EDWARD FRANCIS, b Portland, Maine, Sept 16, 20; m 48; c 4. AGRONOMY. *Educ:* Univ Maine, BS, 49; Cornell Univ, MSA, 51, PhD(agron), 53. *Prof Exp:* Asst agron, Cornell Univ, 50-53; asst prof, Southern Ill Univ, 53-56 & Pa State Univ, 56-61; from agronomist to sr agronomist, 61-75, MGR CROP ESTAB & PROTECTION, AGR RES CTR, GREAT WESTERN SUGAR CO, 75- *Concurrent Pos:* Asst prof, Univ Ill, 54-56. *Mem:* Am Soc Agron; Weed Sci Soc Am; Am Soc Sugar Beet Technologists. *Res:* Weed control; plant growth regulators; crop production. *Mailing Add:* Great Western Agr Res Ctr Sugarmill Rd Longmont CO 80501

SULLIVAN, EDWARD T, b Flushing, NY, June 28, 20; m 54; c 1. FOREST ECONOMICS. *Educ:* NC State Col, BSF, 46; Duke Univ, MS, 47, DF, 53. *Prof Exp:* Acct, southern woodlands dept, WVa Pulp & Paper Co, 47-50; vis instr forest econ, sch forestry, Duke Univ, 50-51; asst prof forestry, Univ Minn, 54-59; ASSOC PROF FOREST ECON, UNIV FLA, 59-, ASSOC FORESTER, 71- *Mem:* Am Econ Asn; Soc Am Foresters. *Res:* Marketing of forest products; demand for pulpwood. *Mailing Add:* Sch of Forest Res & Conserv Univ of Fla Gainesville FL 32611

SULLIVAN, F(REDERICK) W(ILLIAM), III, b Ann Arbor, Mich, June 24, 23; m 48; c 4. CHEMICAL ENGINEERING. *Educ:* Pa State Univ, BS, 47; Univ Del, MS, 49, PhD(chem eng), 52. *Prof Exp:* Chem engr process develop, Houdry Process Corp, 51-56; chem engr process develop & design, Halby Chem Co, 56-63; dir process eng, Maumee Chem Co, 63-70; mgr process eng sect, Chem Div, Sherwin Williams Co, 70-78, mgr process develop, 78-80. *Mem:* Am Chem Soc; Inst Chem Engrs. *Res:* Petroleum refining; heat transfer; manufacture of inorganic and organic chemicals. *Mailing Add:* 1644 Pinehurst Ln Flossmoor IL OH 60422

SULLIVAN, GEORGE ALLEN, b Bronxville, NY, Dec 1, 35; m 60; c 2. INFORMATION SCIENCE, STATISTICS. *Educ:* Grinnell Col, AB, 57; Univ Rochester, AM, 59; Univ Nebr, PhD(solid state physics), 64; Univ Pa, MGovt Admin, 76. *Prof Exp:* Res asst solid state physics, Rensselaer Polytech Inst, 64-66; sr physicist, Electronic Res Div, Clevite Corp, Cleveland, 66-69; asst prof elec eng, Air Force Inst Technol, Wright Patterson AFB, 69-70; vis scientist, Physics Inst, Chalmers Univ Technol, Sweden, 70-71; criminal justice systs planner & eval coordr, 71-74, actg dir, 74-75, sr statist anal, 75-80, SR STATIST ANAL, RES & STATIST DIV, PA BD PROBATION & PAROLE, 80- *Mem:* Am Statist Soc; Nat Speleol Soc; Nat Coun Crime & Delinquency. *Res:* Point defects and diffusion in metals; thermal mass transport and electromigration in solids; semiconductors; properties of materials; physics of solar cells; criminal justice information statistics systems; social rehabilitation programs; social research; operations and program planning; multivariate statistical analysis. *Mailing Add:* Res & Statist Div Box 1661 3101 N Front St Harrisburg PA 17120

SULLIVAN, GERALD, b Magazine, Ark, Aug 11, 34; m 58; c 2. PHARMACY, PHARMACOGNOSY. *Educ:* Wash State Univ, BS & BPharm, 57, MS, 63; Univ Wash, PhD(pharm), 66. *Prof Exp:* Asst prof, 66-71, ASSOC PROF PHARMACOG, COL PHARM, UNIV TEX, AUSTIN, 71- *Mem:* Am Soc Pharmacog; Am Pharmaceut Asn; Acad Pharmaceut Sci. *Res:* Biosynthesis of secondary metabolites; fermentative processes; isolation and identification of plant toxins and secondary constituents; chemotaxonomy. *Mailing Add:* Col of Pharm Univ of Tex Austin TX 78712

SULLIVAN, HARRIS MARTIN, b Graves Co, Ky, Mar 12, 09; m 35; c 2. INSTRUMENTATION, MATERIALS SCIENCE. *Educ:* Univ Ky, BS, 31, MS, 33; Pa State Univ, PhD(physics, phys chem), 38. *Prof Exp:* Asst physics, Univ Ky, 31-33, instr, 33-35; asst, Pa State Univ, 35-37, instr, 37-38; asst prof phys metall & metall eng, Rensselaer Polytech Inst, 38-42; chief metallurgist, Adirondack Foundries & Steel, 42-45; dir res & develop, Cent Sci Co, 45-50, vpres & dir res, 50-55; mgr electronics lab, Gen Elec Co, 55-57, mgr adv semiconductor lab, 57-62; dir res, Johnson Controls, Inc, 62-74; CONSULT, 74- *Concurrent Pos:* Mem war metall comt, Watertown Arsenal, 42-45. *Mem:* AAAS; Am Phys Soc; Am Chem Soc; Am Soc Metals; Inst Elec & Electronic Engrs. *Res:* Chemical spectroscopy; x-ray crystal analysis; x-ray metallography; vacuum systems and equipment; ferrous metallurgy; physical metallurgy; electrochemistry; electronic instruments; analytical and process instruments; solid state physics; semiconductor physics; research administration. *Mailing Add:* 2134 Salamanca Drive Port Richey FL 33568

SULLIVAN, HARRY MORTON, b Winnipeg, Man, Apr 14, 21; m 49; c 3. PHYSICS. *Educ:* Queen's Univ, Ont, BSc, 45; Carleton Univ, BSc, 50; McGill Univ, MSc, 54; Univ Sask, PhD(upper atmosphere physics), 62. *Prof Exp:* Chemist, Can Civil Serv, 45-47; engr, Canadair Ltd, 54-56; physicist, Can Civil Serv, 56-59; physicist, Nat Ctr Sci Res, France, 62-64; asst prof, 64-69, ASSOC PROF PHYSICS, UNIV VICTORIA, 69- *Mem:* Can Asn Physicists. *Res:* Upper atmosphere; airglow and related phenomena, particularly twilight glow and day glow; rarer constituents of upper atmosphere; photometer calibration techniques; standard radiation sources. *Mailing Add:* 4037 Hollydene Pl Victoria BC V8N 3Z8 Can

SULLIVAN, HERBERT J, b Ebbw Vale, Gt Brit, May 20, 33; m 58; c 3. GEOLOGY, PALYNOLOGY. *Educ:* Univ Sheffield, BSc, 54, PhD(geol), 59. *Prof Exp:* Dept Sci & Indust Res fel, 59-61; from asst lectr to lectr geol, Univ Sheffield, 61-64; sr res scientist, Res Ctr, Pan Am Petrol Corp, Okla, 64-71; sr staff geologist, 71-79, STAFF GEOL SUPVR, AMOCO CAN PETROL CO LTD, 79- *Mem:* Brit Geol Soc; Brit Paleont Asn; Am Asn Stratig Palynologists; Paleont Soc; Am Asn Petrol Geologists. *Res:* Paleozoic palynology, especially its stratigraphical applications. *Mailing Add:* Amoco Can Petrol Co Ltd 444 Seventh Ave SW Calgary AB T2P 0Y2 Can

SULLIVAN, HUGH D, b Butte, Mont, June 16, 39; m 61; c 4. MATHEMATICS. *Educ:* Univ Mont, BA, 62, MA, 64; Wash State Univ, PhD(math), 68. *Prof Exp:* Teaching asst math, Univ Mont, 62-64 & Wash State Univ, 64-67; asst prof, 67-70, chmn dept, 70-76, ASSOC PROF MATH, EASTERN WASH STATE COL, 70- *Mem:* Am Math Soc; Math Asn Am. *Res:* Abstract systems theory; topology; probability and statistics. *Mailing Add:* Dept of Math Eastern Wash State Col Cheney WA 99004

SULLIVAN, HUGH R, b Indianapolis, Ind, Apr 8, 26; m 48; c 5. DRUG METABOLISM. *Educ:* Univ Notre Dame, BS, 48; Temple Univ, MA, 54. *Prof Exp:* Assoc res chemist, Socony-Vacuum Oil Co, 48-51; from assoc res chemist to sr res chemist, 51-69, res scientist, 69-72, RES ASSOC, RES LABS, ELI LILLY & CO, INC, 72- *Mem:* Am Chem Soc; Am Soc Pharmacol & Exp Therapeut; Am Soc Mass Spectrometry. *Res:* Mechanism of drug action and detoxication; analgesics; antibiotics; pharmocokinetics; quantitative mass fragmentography. *Mailing Add:* Eli Lilly & Co Inc Lilly Res Labs 307 E McCarty St Indianapolis IN 46285

SULLIVAN, J AL, b Whitewater, Colo, Dec 31, 37; m 58; c 3. MECHANICAL ENGINEERING. *Educ:* Univ Colo, BS, 58, MS, 60; Univ Mich, PhD(mech eng), 66. *Prof Exp:* Instr, Univ Colo & Univ Mich, 58-66; asst prof mech eng, Colo State Univ, 66; staff mem chem laser & rover prog, 66-74, group leader laser eng, 74-78, staff mem laser photochem, 78-81, PROG MGR, MOLECULAR LASER ISOTOPE SEPARATION, LOS ALAMOS NAT LAB, 81- *Mem:* Sigma Xi. *Res:* Industrial coordination of laser-isotope separation; laser-induced chemistry in waste reprocessing; other facets of applied photochemistry. *Mailing Add:* Appl Photochem Div Los Alamos Nat Lab PO Box 1663 Los Alamos NM 87545

SULLIVAN, JAMES BOLLING, b Rome, Ga, Mar 19, 40; m 63; c 3. BIOCHEMISTRY, ZOOLOGY. *Educ:* Cornell Univ, AB, 62; Univ Tex, Austin, PhD(zool), 66. *Prof Exp:* asst prof, 70-76, ASSOC PROF BIOCHEM, DUKE UNIV, 77- *Concurrent Pos:* USPHS fel biochem, Duke Univ, 67-70. *Mem:* AAAS; Soc Study Evolution; Am Soc Biol Chemists; Lepidop Soc. *Res:* Comparative protein chemistry. *Mailing Add:* Marine Lab Duke Univ Beaufort NC 28516

SULLIVAN, JAMES DOUGLAS, b Chicago, Ill, Oct 27, 40; m 67; c 2. PHYSICS, SPACE SCIENCE. *Educ:* Univ Chicago, SB, 62, SM, 64, PhD(physics), 70. *Prof Exp:* Physicist, Enrico Fermi Inst, Univ Chicago, 70-71; asst res physicist, Univ Calif, Berkeley, 71-74; MEM STAFF, CTR SPACE RES, MASS INST TECHNOL, 74- *Mem:* Am Phys Soc; Am Geophys Union. *Res:* Space physics, solar particles and magnetospheric physics; nuclear physics, high energy heavy ion reactions; astrophysics, cosmic rays and origin of gamma rays. *Mailing Add:* Ctr for Space Res Mass Inst of Technol Cambridge MA 02139

SULLIVAN, JAMES F, b Peoria, Ill, Feb 17, 24; m; c 7. MEDICINE. *Educ:* Eureka Col, BS, 49; St Louis Univ, MD, 51. *Prof Exp:* Instr med, Sch Med, St Louis Univ, 55-59, asst prof clin med, 59-61; assoc prof, 61-64, PROF MED, SCH MED, CREIGHTON UNIV, 64-; CHIEF MED, OMAHA VET ADMIN HOSP, 72- *Mem:* AMA; Fedn Am Socs Exp Biol; fel Am Col Physicians; Am Fedn Clin Res; Am Soc Clin Nutrit. *Res:* Lipid, alcohol and trace metal metabolism. *Mailing Add:* Sch of Med Creighton Univ Omaha NE 68131

SULLIVAN, JAMES HADDON, JR, b Claxton, Ga, Apr 3, 37; m 60; c 1. ENVIRONMENTAL ENGINEERING. *Educ:* Ga Inst Technol, BChE, 59; Univ Fla, MS, 68, PhD(eng), 70. *Prof Exp:* Proj engr, Union Bag-Camp Paper Corp, 59-63; develop engr, Cities Serv Corp, 63-66; pres environ eng, 70-71, VPRES, WATER & AIR RES INC, 71- *Mem:* Am Water Works Asn; Am Acad Environ Engrs; Water Pollution Control Fedn; Nat Soc Prof Engrs. *Res:* Water chemistry; waste and water treatment; environmental impact studies. *Mailing Add:* Water & Air Res Inc PO Box 1121 Gainesville FL 32602

SULLIVAN, JAMES MICHAEL, b Butte, Mont, July 1, 34. NEUROANATOMY. *Educ:* Carroll Col, BA, 56; Univ Ore, MS, 64; St Louis Univ, PhD(anat), 73. *Prof Exp:* From instr to asst prof biol, Carroll Col, 61-69, assoc prof, 73-74; fel & res assoc, 74-75, instr, 75-76, ASST PROF ANAT, SCH MED, ST LOUIS UNIV, 76- *Mem:* Sigma Xi; Am Asn Anat; Soc Neurosci. *Res:* Anatomy, physiology and pharmacology of the autonomic nervous system with special emphasis on the cardiovascular system of man. *Mailing Add:* Dept of Anat Sch of Med St Louis Univ 1402 SGrand Blvd St Louis MO 63104

SULLIVAN, JAMES THOMAS, JR, b Seekonk, Mass, May 30, 28; m 55; c 4. PHYSICAL CHEMISTRY. *Educ:* Providence Col, BS, 50; Cath Univ Am, PhD, 55. *Prof Exp:* Asst, Cath Univ Am, 53-54, res assoc, 54-55; from asst prof to assoc prof, 55-67, exec asst acad affairs, 72-78, PROF CHEM, UNIV ST THOMAS, TEX, 67-, VPRES, 78- *Mem:* AAAS; Am Chem Soc. *Res:* Chemical kinetics; teaching. *Mailing Add:* Dept of Phys Sci 3812 Montrose Blvd Houston TX 77006

SULLIVAN, JAY MICHAEL, b Brockton, Mass, Aug 3, 36; m 64; c 3. CARDIOVASCULAR DISEASES. *Educ:* Georgetown Univ, BS, 58, MD, 62. *Prof Exp:* House officer med, Peter Bent Brigham Hosp, 62-63, resident, 63-67; res assoc biochem, Harvard Med Sch, 67-69, from instr to asst prof med, 69-74; PROF MED & CHIEF, DIV CARDIOVASCULAR DIS, COL MED, UNIV TENN, MEMPHIS, 74- *Concurrent Pos:* Nat Heart Inst res fel med, Harvard Med Sch, 64-66; res fel, Med Found, 67-69; mem, Coun High Blood Pressure Res, 70; dir hypertension unit, Peter Bent Brigham Hosp, 70-74; dir med serv, Boston Hosp Women, 73-74; consult, Nat Heart & Lung Inst, 74 & Vet Admin Hosp, Memphis, 74; fel, Coun Circulation, Am Heart Asn, 75; prin investr, Nat Heart, Lung & Blood Inst, 78- *Mem:* AAAS; fel Am Col Cardiol; Am Fedn Clin Res; fel Am Col Physicians; Int Soc Hypertension. *Res:* Hypertension, regulation of the circulation, clinical pharmacology of antihypertensive and anti-platelet drugs. *Mailing Add:* 951 Court Ave Memphis TN 38163

SULLIVAN, JERRY STEPHEN, b Havre, Mont, July 17, 45; m 67; c 2. SOLID STATE ELECTRONICS. *Educ:* Univ Colo, Boulder, BSc, 67, MSc, 69, PhD(physics), 70. *Prof Exp:* Res scientist solid state devices, N V Philips Gloeilampenfabrieken, Eindhoven, 71-75, group dir comp systs res, Philips Labs, 75-80; CORP DIR, COMPUT TECH CTR, TEKTRONIX, 81- *Mem:* Inst Elec & Electronics Engrs; AAAS; Am Phys Soc; Europ Phys Soc; Asn Comput Mach. *Res:* Numerical analysis; network theory; application of computers to semiconductor device modeling and integrated circuit analysis; electron paramagnetic and nuclear magnetic resonance and exchange interactions of ion pairs; microcomputer architecture and microprocessor design; software engineering; system engineering; computer-aided design and manufacturing; computer science. *Mailing Add:* 18255 Tamaway Dr Lake Oswego OR 97034

SULLIVAN, JOHN BRENDAN, b Lynn, Mass, Aug 6, 44; m 70; c 2. MATHEMATICS. *Educ:* Harvard Univ, AB, 66; Cornell Univ, PhD(math), 71. *Prof Exp:* Lectr math, Univ Calif, Berkeley, 71-73; asst prof, 73-78, ASSOC PROF MATH, UNIV WASH, 78- *Concurrent Pos:* NSF grant, 74-79; mem, Inst Advan Study, 79-80. *Res:* Algebraic groups, lie algebras, and Hopf algebras; cohomology and representations of algebraic groups. *Mailing Add:* Dept Math Univ Wash Seattle WA 98195

SULLIVAN, JOHN DENNIS, b Lake Forest, Ill, June 17, 28; m 55; c 3. FORESTRY. *Educ:* Univ Idaho, BS, 52, MS, 54; Mich State Univ, PhD(wood technol), 58. *Prof Exp:* Asst wood technol, Mich State Univ, 54-56, instr, 56-58; from asst prof to assoc prof wood sci, Sch Forestry, Duke Univ, 58-68; prin wood scientist, 68-69, agr adminr, 69-71, dep adminr, Coop State Res Serv, 71-78, dep adminr, Sci & Educ Admin-Coop Res, 78-81, DEP

ADMINR, COOP STATE RES SERV, USDA, 81- *Mem:* Am Soc Testing & Mat; Soc Wood Sci & Technol; NY Acad Sci; Soc Am Foresters; fel Brit Inst Wood Sci. *Res:* Cellulose morphology at a molecular level, especially high resolution electron microscopy; adhesion and wood; liquid interactions. *Mailing Add:* Apt 1202 S 1201 S Jefferson Davis Hwy Arlington VA 22202

SULLIVAN, JOHN HENRY, b New Haven, Conn, May 18, 19; m 47; c 2. PHYSICAL CHEMISTRY. *Educ:* Calif Inst Technol, PhD(chem), 50. *Prof Exp:* CHEMIST, LOS ALAMOS SCI LAB, UNIV CALIF, 50- *Mem:* Am Chem Soc. *Res:* Kinetics of gaseous reactions. *Mailing Add:* 3536-A Arizona St Los Alamos NM 87544

SULLIVAN, JOHN JOSEPH, b New York, NY, Mar 28, 35; m 63; c 2. REPRODUCTIVE PHYSIOLOGY. *Educ:* Rutgers Univ, BS, 57, PhD(dairy sci, physiol), 63; Univ Tenn, MS, 59. *Prof Exp:* Res assoc, 63-65, assoc dir labs & res, 65-79, dir labs & res, 79-81, DIR PROD, AM BREEDERS SERV, INC, W R GRACE & CO, 81- *Mem:* Am Dairy Sci Asn; Am Soc Animal Sci; Soc Cryobiol; Soc Study Reproduction; Int Embryo Transfer Soc. *Res:* Physiology of reproduction and related fields; artificial insemination of domestic animals; low temperature biology. *Mailing Add:* Rte 2 Box 294 Stevenson Dr Poynette WI 53955

SULLIVAN, JOHN LAWRENCE, b Scranton, Pa, Nov 24, 43. BEHAVIORAL NEUROPHARMACOLOGY, NEUROCHEMISTRY. *Educ:* Duke Univ, AB, 65; Johns Hopkins Univ, MD, 69. *Prof Exp:* Intern med, Johns Hopkins Hosp, 69-70; resident psychiat, Univ Calif, San Diego, 70-73; asst prof, 73-78, ASSOC PROF PSYCHIAT, DUKE UNIV MED CTR, 78-; MEM FAC, MED SCH, UNIV MA, 80- *Concurrent Pos:* Consult, Neuropsychopharmacol Drug-Dependent States, US Dept Navy, 71-73 & Warner-Chilcott Pharmaceut Co, 78-; dir, Neuropsychopharmacol Lab, Vet Admin Med Ctr, 75-80. *Mem:* AAAS; Soc Biol Psychiat; Am Psychiat Asn; AMA. *Res:* Biochemical neuropsychopharmacology, with particular reference to the role of monoamine oxidase in behavior and psychopathological states. *Mailing Add:* Dept Psychiat Duke Univ Med Ctr Durham NC 27710

SULLIVAN, JOHN LESLIE, b Sydney, Australia, July 16, 17; m 39; c 4. CHEMICAL ENGINEERING. *Educ:* Sydney Tech Col, Dipl chem eng, 41; Univ New South Wales, MS, 56, PhD(chem eng), 60. *Prof Exp:* Engr, Robert Fowler Ltd, 41-45; prin engr, New South Wales Health Dept, 45-66; dir air pollution control, Can Dept Nat Health & Welfare, 66-69; prof environ eng, Syracuse Univ, 69-71; prof environ eng & dir dept, 71-78, DIR, OCCUP HEALTH & SAFETY RESOURCE CTR, UNIV WESTERN ONT, 78- *Concurrent Pos:* Sr lectr, Univ New South Wales, 55-65; consult, WHO, 66 & 69. *Mem:* AAAS; Am Inst Chem Engrs; Air Pollution Control Asn; Am Indust Hyg Asn; Can Soc Chem Eng. *Res:* Air pollution measurement and control, occupational health and safety engineering, and biomass energy. *Mailing Add:* Fac of Eng Sci Univ of Western Ont London ON N6A JB9 Can

SULLIVAN, JOHN LYNCH, b Schenectady, NY, May 2, 37; m 63; c 4. POLYMER CHEMISTRY, ORGANIC CHEMISTRY. *Educ:* State Univ NY Albany, BS, 65; Union Col, MS, 78, MBA. *Prof Exp:* Assoc chemist anal chem, 65-66, chemist polymer chem, 67-68, sr chemist, 68-70, group leader polymer & org synthesis chem, 71-79, PROD MGR, INDUST RESIN DIV, SCHENECTADY CHEM, INC, 80- *Mem:* Am Chem Soc; Am Soc Testing & Mat. *Res:* Organic polymer chemistry; polycondensation reactions; phenolic resins applied in rubber; adhesive; specialty paper products; alkylation reactions; alkylphenols; alkylphenol derivatives, especially surfactants; demulsifiers; antioxidants. *Mailing Add:* Schenectady Chem Inc 2750 Balltown Rd Schenectady NY 12309

SULLIVAN, JOHN M, b Philadelphia, Pa, June 21, 32; m 56; c 9. ORGANIC CHEMISTRY. *Educ:* Dartmouth Col, AB, 54; Univ Mich, MS, 56, PhD(org chem), 60. *Prof Exp:* PROF CHEM, EASTERN MICH UNIV, 58- *Mem:* Am Chem Soc. *Res:* Heterocyclics; conformational analysis. *Mailing Add:* Dept of Chem Eastern Mich Univ Ypsilanti MI 48197

SULLIVAN, JOHN W, b Fargo, NDak, Nov 1, 32; m 64; c 3. CEREAL CHEMISTRY. *Educ:* NDak State Univ, BS, 54, MS, 58; Kans State Univ, PhD(cereal chem), 66. *Prof Exp:* Proj leader food res, John Stuart Res Labs, Quaker Oats Co, 61-68, sect mgr food res, 68-74; DIR RES, ROMAN MEAL CO, 74-, VPRES RES & DEVELOP, 79- *Mem:* Am Chem Soc; Am Asn Cereal Chemists; Inst Food Technologists. *Res:* Physical and chemical changes in starch and associated carbohydrates; enzyme changes in physical structure of starches and proteins. *Mailing Add:* 2101 S Tacoma Way Tacoma WA 98409

SULLIVAN, JOSEPH ARTHUR, b Boston, Mass, June 5, 23; m 46; c 4. MATHEMATICS. *Educ:* Boston Col, AB, 44; Mass Inst Technol, SM, 47; Ind Univ, PhD(math), 50. *Prof Exp:* From instr to assoc prof math, Univ Notre Dame, 50-60; PROF MATH, BOSTON COL, 60- *Mem:* Am Math Soc; Math Asn Am. *Res:* Mathematical analysis. *Mailing Add:* Dept of Math Boston Col Chestnut Hill MA 02167

SULLIVAN, KAREN A, b Bronxville, NY. IMMUNOLOGY. *Educ:* N Adams State Col, BS, 66; Duke Univ, PhD(immunol, microbiol), 74. *Prof Exp:* Cancer Res Inst Inc NY fel, McIndoe Mem Res Unit, Blond Lab, Queen Victoria Hosp, Sussex, Eng, 73-75; fel, Div Lab & Res, NY State Dept Health, 75-78; ASST PROF IMMUNOL, MED CTR, W VA UNIV, 78- *Mem:* Am Asn Immunologists; Am Asn Clin Histocompatibility Testing. *Res:* Immunogenetics; cellular immunology; lymphoid cell differentiation; regulation of the immune response. *Mailing Add:* Dept of Path WVa Univ Med Ctr Morgantown WV 26506

SULLIVAN, LAWRENCE PAUL, b Hot Springs, SDak, June 16, 31; m 55; c 3. PHYSIOLOGY. *Educ:* Univ Notre Dame, BS, 53; Univ Mich, MS, 56, PhD(physiol), 59. *Prof Exp:* Asst physiol, Univ Mich, 55-59, instr, 59-60; asst prof, George Washington Univ, 60-61; from asst prof to assoc prof, 61-69,

PROF PHYSIOL, MED CTR, UNIV KANS, 69- *Concurrent Pos:* USPHS career develop award, 65-70; vis prof, Sch Med, Yale Univ, 69-70. *Mem:* Am Soc Nephrol; Am Physiol Soc. *Res:* Renal physiology. *Mailing Add:* Dept of Physiol Univ of Kans Med Ctr Kansas City KS 66103

SULLIVAN, LLOYD JOHN, b Lowell, Ariz, Sept 6, 23; m 48; c 4. BIOCHEMISTRY, PHYSICAL ORGANIC CHEMISTRY. *Educ:* Univ Ariz, BS, 50; Univ Pittsburgh, MS, 54. *Prof Exp:* Res asst phys chem, Mellon Inst Sci, 50-52, res assoc, 52-54, jr fel, 54-56, fel, 56-58; mem tech staff, Cent Res Lab, Tex Instruments, 58-60, sect head & dir energy conversion, Apparatus Div, 60-61; fel phys & anal chem, Mellon Inst Sci, 61-67, sr fel phys & anal chem & head chem & biochem sect, Chem Hyg Fel, 67-80; RETIRED. *Mem:* Fel AAAS; fel Am Inst Chemists; NY Acad Sci; Am Chem Soc. *Res:* Physical properties of organic materials; separation and purification of organic compounds, particularly natural products; gas, liquid and thin layer chromatography; analytical biochemistry; metabolism of organic compounds in vivo and by tissue culture techniques. *Mailing Add:* 113 Henry Hudson Dr Delmont PA 15626

SULLIVAN, LOUIS WADE, b Atlanta, Ga, Nov 3, 33; m 55; c 2. INTERNAL MEDICINE. *Educ:* Morehouse Col, BS, 54; Boston Univ, MD, 58; Am Bd Internal Med, dipl, 66. *Prof Exp:* Intern, NY Hosp-Cornell Med Ctr, 58-59, resident med, 59-60; resident gen path, Mass Gen Hosp, 60-61; instr, Harvard Med Sch, 63-64; asst prof, NJ Col Med, 64-66, asst attend physician, 64-65, assoc attend physician, 65-66; asst prof med, Sch Med, Boston Univ, 66-70, assoc prof med & physiol, 70-77; DEAN & DIR, SCH MED, MOREHOUSE COL, 77- *Concurrent Pos:* Res fel med, Thorndike Mem Lab, Boston City Hosp & Harvard Med Sch, 61-63; res assoc, Thorndike Mem Lab, Boston City Hosp, 63-64; USPHS res career develop award, 65-66, 67-71; asst vis physician, Boston Univ Hosp, 66- *Mem:* Inst Med-Nat Acad Sci; Soc Exp Biol & Med; Am Fedn Clin Res; AAAS; Fedn Am Socs Exp Biol. *Res:* Metabolism of vitamin B-12 and folic acid in man. *Mailing Add:* Morehouse Col Sch of Med Atlanta GA 30314

SULLIVAN, MARGARET P, b Lewistown, Mont, Feb 7, 22. PEDIATRICS, MEDICINE. *Educ:* Rice Inst, BA, 44; Duke Univ, MD, 50; Am Bd Pediat, dipl, 56. *Prof Exp:* Pediatrician, Atomic Bomb Casualty Comn, Japan, 53-55; from asst pediatrician to assoc pediatrician, 56-73, PROF PEDIAT & PEDIATRICIAN, UNIV TEX M D ANDERSON HOSP & TUMOR INST HOUSTON, 73- *Mem:* AAAS; Am Asn Cancer Res; Am Acad Pediat; AMA; Am Med Women's Asn (vpres, 72, pres, 74). *Res:* Pediatric oncology. *Mailing Add:* Dept of Pediat Univ of Tex M D Anderson Hosp & Tumor Inst Houston TX 77030

SULLIVAN, MARY LOUISE, b Butte, Mont, Oct 3, 06. INORGANIC CHEMISTRY. *Educ:* St Mary Col, Kans, BS, 35; St Louis Univ, MS, 39, PhD(chem), 47. *Prof Exp:* Instr chem, 46-53, dean, 53-74, DIR INST RES, ST MARY COL, KANS, 74- *Mem:* Am Asn Physics Teachers; Nat Sci Teachers Asn; Sigma Xi. *Res:* Analytic chemistry, especially trace analysis for metals using dithizone. *Mailing Add:* St Mary Col Leavenworth KS 66048

SULLIVAN, MAURICE FRANCIS, b Butte, Mont, Feb 15, 22; m 51; c 6. PHARMACOLOGY. *Educ:* Mont State Col, BS, 50; Univ Chicago, PhD(pharmacol), 55. *Prof Exp:* Scientist, Hanford Labs, Gen Elec Co, 55-56, sr scientist, 56-65; mgr physiol sect, 65-71, STAFF SCIENTIST, PAC NORTHWEST LABS, BATTELLE MEM INST, 71- *Concurrent Pos:* NIH fel, Med Res Coun, Harwell, Eng, 61- *Mem:* Fel AAAS; Am Physiol Soc; Radiation Res Soc. *Res:* Biological effects of radiation, especially on the gastrointestinal tract; biochemistry; physiology; pathology; pharmacology. *Mailing Add:* Biol Dept Pac Northwest Labs Battelle Mem Inst Box 999 Richland WA 99352

SULLIVAN, MICHAEL FRANCIS, b New Paltz, NY, Aug 20, 42; m 67; c 3. PHOTOGRAPHIC CHEMISTRY. *Educ:* St Lawrence Univ, BS, 63; Univ NC, Chapel Hill, PhD(chem), 68. *Prof Exp:* Sr chemist, 67-73, res lab head, 73-81, SUPVR PROD & DEVELOP, FILM EMULSION & PLATE MFG DIV, EASTMAN KODAK CO, 81- *Res:* Development of black and white photographic films. *Mailing Add:* 341 Brooksboro Dr Webster NY 14580

SULLIVAN, MICHAEL JOSEPH, JR, b Chicago, Ill, Jan 8, 42; m 64; c 4. MATHEMATICS. *Educ:* DePaul Univ, BS, 63; Ill Inst Technol, MS, 64, PhD(math), 67. *Prof Exp:* Teaching asst math, Ill Inst Technol, 62-65; from asst prof to assoc prof, 65-77, PROF MATH, CHICAGO STATE UNIV, 77- *Concurrent Pos:* Am Coun Educ acad admin internship, 70-71. *Mem:* Am Math Soc; Math Asn Am. *Res:* Differential geometric aspects of dynamics; polygenic functions; applications of mathematics in the management and behavioral sciences; mathematics education. *Mailing Add:* Dept of Math Chicago State Univ Chicago IL 60628

SULLIVAN, MILES VINCENT, b Fargo, NDak, Aug 19, 17; m 48; c 3. PHYSICAL CHEMISTRY. *Educ:* Wabash Col, AB, 41; Purdue Univ, MS, 42, PhD(phys chem), 48. *Prof Exp:* Res chemist, US Naval Res Lab, 42-46; ENGR, BELL LABS, 48- *Mem:* Am Chem Soc. *Res:* Flammability; lubricating oils; wire insulations; heats of combustions; solid state materials and process development; photolithography; electropolishing and electroplating. *Mailing Add:* Bell Labs Murray Hill NJ 07974

SULLIVAN, NICHOLAS, speleology, see previous edition

SULLIVAN, PATRICIA ANN NAGENGAST, b New York, NY, Nov 22, 39; m 66. BIOLOGY. *Educ:* Notre Dame Col Staten Island, AB, 61; NY Univ, MS, 64, PhD(biol), 67. *Prof Exp:* Part-time instr, Notre Dame Col Staten Island, 64-67; asst prof biol, Wagner Col, 67-68; NIH trainee anat & cell biol, State Univ NY Upstate Med Ctr, 68-69 & fel cell biol, 69-70; asst prof biol, Wells Col, 70-74, chairwoman div life sci, 75-76, assoc prof, 74-79; assoc prof biol, Tex Woman's Univ, 79-81; PROF BIOL & ACAD DEAN, SALEM COL, 81- *Mem:* AAAS; NY Acad Sci; Am Soc Hemat; Sigma Xi; Am Asn Univ Women. *Res:* Bioethics and implications of biological research; hematopoiesis and its regulation; chromatin structure and function. *Mailing Add:* Dept Biol Salem Col Winston-Salem NC 27108

SULLIVAN, PAUL JOSEPH, b Morrickville, Ont, Mar 2, 39; m 62; c 2. APPLIED MATHEMATICS, ENGINEERING. *Educ:* Univ Waterloo, BSc, 64, MSc, 65; Cambridge Univ, PhD(appl math), 68. *Prof Exp:* asst prof, 68-80, PROF APPL MATH & ENG, UNIV WESTERN ONT, 80- *Concurrent Pos:* Res fel, Calif Inst Technol, 69-70. *Mem:* Am Acad Mech; Can Soc Mech Eng. *Res:* Dispersion within turbulent fluid flow; convection phenomenon in fluids; turbulent fluid flow generally. *Mailing Add:* Dept of Appl Math Univ of Western Ont London ON N6A 5B8 Can

SULLIVAN, PETER KEVIN, b San Francisco, Calif, June 14, 38. POLYMER PHYSICS. *Educ:* Univ San Francisco, BS, 60; Cornell Univ, MS, 63; Rensselaer Polytech Inst, PhD(phys chem), 65. *Prof Exp:* Res fel, Nat Bur Stand, 65-67, chemist, 67-73; PHYS CHEMIST, CELANESE RES CO, 74- *Mem:* Am Phys Soc; Am Chem Soc. *Res:* Physics, chemistry and mechanical properties of polymers. *Mailing Add:* Celanese Res Co Box 1000 Summit NJ 07901

SULLIVAN, PHILIP ALBERT, b Sydney, Australia, Dec 25, 37; m 62; c 1. AEROSPACE ENGINEERING, PHYSICS. *Educ:* Univ New South Wales, BE, 60, ME, 62; Univ London, DIC & PhD(aeronaut eng), 64. *Prof Exp:* Res assoc aeronaut res, Imp Col, Univ London, 62-64; res assoc hypersonics res, Gas Dynamics Lab, Princeton Univ, 64-65; asst prof teaching & res, 65-71, ASSOC PROF AEROSPACE SCI & ENG, INST AEROSPACE STUDIES, UNIV TORONTO, 71- *Concurrent Pos:* Consult, Atomic Energy Can Ltd. *Mem:* Assoc fel Can Aeronaut & Space Inst; Am Inst Aeronaut & Astronaut. *Res:* Air cushion technology with applications to air cushion landing systems, amphibious vehicles and trains. *Mailing Add:* 940 Caledonia Rd Toronto ON M6B 3Y4 Can

SULLIVAN, RAYMOND, b Ebbw Vale, Wales, Oct 27, 34; m 62; c 2. GEOLOGY. *Educ:* Univ Sheffield, BSc, 57; Glasgow Univ, PhD(geol), 60. *Prof Exp:* Demonstr geol, Glasgow Univ, 57-60; paleontologist, Shell Oil Co Can, 60-62; from asst prof to assoc prof, 62-74, assoc prof assoc natural sci, 69-72, PROF GEOL, SAN FRANCISCO STATE UNIV, 74- *Concurrent Pos:* NSF res grant, 66-67. *Mem:* Am Asn Petrol Geologists; Nat Asn Geol Teachers; fel Geol Soc Am. *Res:* Upper Paleozoic biostratigraphy; sedimentary petrology of carbonate and clastic rocks; environmental geology. *Mailing Add:* Dept of Geol San Francisco State Univ 1600 Holloway Ave San Francisco CA 94132

SULLIVAN, RAYMOND PAUL, b Buffalo, NY, Sept 18, 30; m 53; c 9. PHYSICS, NUCLEAR POWER. *Educ:* Fordham Univ, BS, 52; Oak Ridge Sch Reactor Technol, dipl, 53; NY Univ, MS, 63. *Prof Exp:* Nuclear engr, Naval Reactors Br, Bur Ships, US Navy Dept, 52-57; sr physicist, Develop Div, United Nuclear Corp, 57-63; EXEC SCIENTIST, NUS CORP, 63- *Mem:* Am Nuclear Soc. *Res:* Energy planning and policy; nuclear fuel cycle; uranium resources; reactor analysis. *Mailing Add:* NUS Corp 4 Research Pl Rockville MD 30850

SULLIVAN, RICHARD FREDERICK, b Olathe, Colo, Dec 26, 29; m 68; c 2. PHYSICAL CHEMISTRY. *Educ:* Univ Colo, BA, 51, PhD(chem), 56. *Prof Exp:* Res chemist, Calif Res Corp, 55-68, sr res chemist, 68-78, SR RES ASSOC, CHEVRON RES CO, 78- *Mem:* Am Chem Soc; Am Inst Chem Eng. *Res:* Photochemistry; mechanisms of hydrocarbon reactions; catalysis; petroleum process research and development; conversion of shale oil and liquids derived from coal to transportation fuels. *Mailing Add:* Chevron Res Co 576 Standard Ave Richmond CA 94802

SULLIVAN, ROBERT E(MMETT), b Butte, Mont, Aug 2, 22; m 56; c 4. METALLURGICAL ENGINEERING. *Educ:* Mont Sch Mines, BS, 47, MS, 48. *Prof Exp:* Asst res engr, 48-50, gen foreman, Zinc Plant, 50-51, asst res engr, 51-58, asst dir metall res, 58-66, alumina mgr, 66-71, tech dir alumina opers, 71-78, mgr alumina opers, 78-80, MGR BASIC TECHNOL, ANACONDA ALUMINUM CO, 80- *Mem:* Am Soc Metals; Am Inst Mining, Metall & Petrol Engrs. *Res:* Recovery of uranium by solvent extraction and ion exchange and aluminum oxide from domestic clays; nonferrous metallurgy. *Mailing Add:* Anaconda Aluminum Co 2700 First Nat Tower Louisville KY 40202

SULLIVAN, ROBERT EMMETT, b Sioux City, Iowa, May 28, 32; m 61. DENTISTRY, PEDODONTICS. *Educ:* Morningside Col, BA, 54; Univ Nebr, DDS, 61, MSD, 63; Am Bd Pedodont, dipl, 67. *Prof Exp:* From instr to assoc prof pedodont, 63-72, ASSOC PROF PEDIAT, UNIV NEBR-LINCOLN, 69-, PROF PEDODONT, 72- *Concurrent Pos:* Consult, Omaha-Douglas County Dent Pub Health, 62- & Omaha-Douglas County Children & Youth Proj, 68- *Mem:* Am Acad Pedodont; Am Dent Asn; Am Soc Dent for Children. *Res:* Vital staining of teeth; mechanism of action of dental preventative materials. *Mailing Add:* 1201 Piedmont Rd Lincoln NE 68510

SULLIVAN, ROBERT LITTLE, b Chicago, Ill, Oct 27, 28. GENETICS. *Educ:* Univ Del, AB, 50; NC State Univ, MS, 53, PhD, 56. *Prof Exp:* Res assoc entom, Univ Kans, 56 61; asst prof biol, Washburn Univ, 61-62; asst prof, 62-68, assoc prof, 68-79, PROF BIOL, WAKE FOREST UNIV, 79- *Mem:* Genetics Soc Am; Soc Study Evolution. *Res:* Insect genetics, including radiation studies on the genetics of the house fly. *Mailing Add:* Dept of Biol Wake Forest Univ Winston-Salem NC 27109

SULLIVAN, SAMUEL LANE, JR, b Victoria, Tex, May 25, 35; m 55; c 4. CHEMICAL ENGINEERING. *Educ:* Tex A&M Univ, BS, 57, MS, 59, PhD(chem eng), 63. *Prof Exp:* ASSOC PROF CHEM ENG, TULANE UNIV, 61-, ASSOC DEAN ENG, 75- *Mem:* Am Inst Chem Engrs; Am Soc Elec Engrs; Sigma Xi. *Res:* Multicomponent distillation; chemical process simulation; computer applications in chemical engineering; multicomponent diffusion. *Mailing Add:* Eng Dean's Off Tulane Univ New Orleans LA 70118

SULLIVAN, THOMAS DONALD, b Fair Haven, Vt, Feb 16, 12. CYTOLOGY. *Educ:* St Michael's Col, Vt, AB, 34; Cath Univ Am, MA, 39; Fordham Univ, PhD(cytol), 47. *Hon Degrees:* DSc, St Michael's Col, 77. *Prof Exp:* Instr Latin & Greek, 39-43, acad dean, 42-44, head dept biol, 47-67, dir res unit, 52-59, vpres, Col, 58-64, trustee, 67-70, dir, 47-77, EMER PROF BIOL, ST MICHAEL'S COL, VT, 77- *Mem:* AAAS; Torrey Bot Club. *Res:* Cytogenetics of petunia; plant growth substances; mouse ascites tumors. *Mailing Add:* St Michael's Col St Michaels VT 05404

SULLIVAN, THOMAS FREDERICK, b Covington, Ky, Nov 13, 30; m 61. ORGANIC CHEMISTRY, NUCLEAR CHEMISTRY. *Educ:* Univ Notre Dame, BS, 52; Northwestern Univ, Evanston, PhD(chem), 58. *Prof Exp:* Res chemist, Glidden Co, 56-58; head radioisotope lab, Armour & Co, 58-60; head radioisotope lab, Abbott Labs, 60-61; mgr chem prod & serv, Tracer Lab, 61-63; vpres res prod, 63-72, CLERK OF CORP, NEW ENG NUCLEAR CORP, 72- *Concurrent Pos:* Armour & Co fel, Radiocarbon Lab, Univ Ill, 58-59; mem comt specif & criteria of nucleotides & related compounds, Nat Res Coun, 71- *Mem:* Am Chem Soc. *Res:* Biochemistry; chemical management. *Mailing Add:* New Eng Nuclear Corp 549 Albany St Boston MA 02118

SULLIVAN, THOMAS WESLEY, b Rover, Ark, Sept 30, 30; m 55. POULTRY NUTRITION, BIOCHEMISTRY. *Educ:* Okla State Univ, BS, 51; Univ Ark, MS, 56; Univ Wis, PhD, 58. *Prof Exp:* Instr, Ark Pub Schs, 51-52; res asst poultry nutrit, Univ Ark, 54-55; res asst, Univ Wis, 55-58, from asst prof to assoc prof, 58-65, PROF POULTRY SCI, UNIV NEBR-LINCOLN, 65-, MEM FAC POULTRY & WILDLIFE, 76- *Concurrent Pos:* Consult feed mfg & ingredients. *Honors & Awards:* Res Award, Nat Turkey Fedn, 68. *Mem:* Poultry Sci Asn; Am Inst Nutrit; Soc Exp Biol & Med. *Res:* Nutrient interrelationships; evaluation of poultry feed additives and mineral sources. *Mailing Add:* Dept of Poultry & Wildlife Sci Univ of Nebr Lincoln NE 68583

SULLIVAN, TIMOTHY PAUL, b Duluth, Minn, Dec 3, 45; m 67. PLANT PHYSIOLOGY, AGRONOMY. *Educ:* Univ Minn, Duluth, BS, 67; Univ Minn, MS, 69, PhD(plant physiol), 72. *Prof Exp:* Assoc prof biol, West Chester State Col, 72-76; SR AGRONOMIST, 3M CO, 76- *Mem:* Plant Growth Regulator Working Group; Int Weed Sci Soc; Am Soc Plant Physiologists; Sigma Xi; Weed Sci Soc Am. *Res:* Host-parasite relationships involving microsurgery of the host cells parasitized by haustoria of an obligate parasite; effects of water stress on photosynthesis, stomatal aperature and water potential during different stages of soybean development. *Mailing Add:* Com Chem Div 3M Ctr 3M Co St Paul MN 55101

SULLIVAN, VICTORIA I, b Avon Park, Fla, Nov 14, 41. BIOSYSTEMATICS. *Educ:* Univ Miami, BA, 63; Fla State Univ, PhD(biol), 72. *Prof Exp:* Naturalist, Everglades Nat Park, Nat Park Serv, 63-64; tech asst, Fairchild Trop Garden, Miami, 67-68; instr, Iowa State Univ, 71-72; botanist, Trustees Internal Improv Trust Fund, State of Fla, 72-73; ASSOC PROF BIOL, UNIV SOUTHWESTERN LA, 73- *Mem:* AAAS; Am Soc Plant Taxonomists; Soc Study Evolution; Am Soc Naturalists; Sigma Xi. *Res:* Biosystematics of Eupatorium Compositae species and hybrids, including pollination, karyotypes, phytochemistry and breeding systems; floristics and biology of aquatic and wetland vascular plants. *Mailing Add:* Dept Biol Univ Southwestern La Lafayette LA 70504

SULLIVAN, W ALBERT, JR, b Nashville, Tenn, Apr 6, 24; m 49; c 2. SURGERY. *Educ:* Tulane Univ, MD, 47; Univ Minn, MS, 56; Am Bd Surg, dipl, 58. *Prof Exp:* Asst prof surg, 56-61, asst dean, Med Sch, 68-73, assoc prof surg, Med Sch, 61-68, DIR DEPT CONTINUATION MED EDUC, UNIV MINN, MINNEAPOLIS, 58-, ASSOC DEAN ADMIS & STUDENT AFFAIRS, MED SCH, 73- *Mem:* AMA; Am Col Surgeons. *Res:* Asymptomatic detection of cancer; medical education. *Mailing Add:* Dept Surg Med Sch Univ Minn Minneapolis MN 55455

SULLIVAN, WALTER JAMES, b New York, NY, Apr 27, 25; m 51; c 3. PHYSIOLOGY, BIOPHYSICS. *Educ:* Manhattan Col, BS, 46; Cornell Univ, MD, 51. *Prof Exp:* Instr physics, Manhattan Col, 46-57; intern med, Univ Va, 51-52; instr, Cornell Univ, 54-55; vis investr, Rockefeller Inst, 55-56; group leader, Lederle Labs, 56-63; from asst prof to assoc prof, 63-73, actg chmn dept, 71-76, PROF PHYSIOL, SCH MED, NY UNIV, 73- *Concurrent Pos:* Fel physiol, Cornell Univ, 52-54; vis prof physiol, Sch Med, Yale Univ, 77-78. *Mem:* Am Physiol Soc; Biophys Soc; Soc Gen Physiol; Am Soc Nephrology. *Res:* Renal physiology; micropuncture study of renal ion transport. *Mailing Add:* Dept of Physiol & Biophys NY Univ Sch of Med New York NY 10016

SULLIVAN, WALTER SEAGER, b New York, NY, Jan 12, 18; m 50; c 3. SCIENCE WRITING, JOURNALISM. *Educ:* Yale Univ, BA, 40. *Hon Degrees:* LHD, Yale Univ, 69, Newark Col Eng, 74; DS, Hofstra Univ, 75; Ohio State Univ, DS, 77. *Prof Exp:* Mem staff, 40-48, foreign correspondent, 48-56, sci news ed, 60-63, SCI ED, NEW YORK TIMES, 64- *Concurrent Pos:* Mem bd gov, Arctic Inst NAm, 59-65; Bromley lectr, Yale Univ, 65; mem univ coun, 70-75; mem adv comt pub rels, Am Inst Physics, 65-; partic, Sem Technol & Social Change, Columbia Univ & mem adv coun, Dept Geol & Geophys Sci, Princeton Univ, 71-77, mem exped, Arctic, 35 & 46 & Antarctic, 46, 54, 56-77. *Honors & Awards:* George Polk Mem Award in Jour, 59; Nat Book Awards Jurist in Sci, 60 & 69; Westinghouse-AAAS Writing Awards, 63, 68 & 72; Int Nonfiction Book Prize, Frankfurt Fair, Ger, 65; Grady Award, Am Chem Soc, 69; Am Inst Physics-US Steel Found Award in Physics & Astron, 69; Washburn Award, Boston Mus Sci, 72; Daly Medal, Am Geog Soc, 73; Ralph Coats Roe Medal, Am Soc Mech Engrs, 77; Distinguished Pub Serv Award, US NSF, 78. *Mem:* Fel AAAS; fel Arctic Inst NAm; Am Geog Soc; Am Geophys Union. *Mailing Add:* The New York Times 229 W 43 St New York NY 10036

SULLIVAN, WILLIAM DANIEL, b Boston, Mass, Nov 18, 18. BIOCHEMISTRY. *Educ:* Boston Col, AB, 44, MA, 45; Fordham Univ, MS, 48; Cath Univ Am, PhD(biol), 57. *Prof Exp:* Teacher, Cranwell Prep Sch, 45-46, Fairfield Prep Sch, 46-47 & Cheverus High Sch, 52-53; asst prof bact, Fairfield Univ, 57-58; from asst prof to assoc prof, 58-65, chmn dept, 58-69, PROF BIOL, BOSTON COL, 65- *Concurrent Pos:* Dir cancer res inst, Boston Col; consult, Sta WGBH TV. *Mem:* AAAS; Am Soc Microbiol; Am Soc Parasitol; Soc Protozool; Electron Micros Soc Am. *Res:* Biochemistry of protozoa and cancer cells, especially effect of radiation on enzymatic activities; protein synthesis; electron microscopy with autoradiography of macromolecules in protozoan and cancer cells. *Mailing Add:* Cancer Res Inst Boston Col Chestnut Hill MA 02167

SULLIVAN, WILLIAM T, b Hurley, Wis, Mar 31, 22; m 50; c 5. CHEMICAL ENGINEERING. *Educ:* Univ Mich, BS, 43. *Prof Exp:* Jr engr, Abbott Labs, 43-48, sr engr, 48-50, group leader, 50-53; appln engr, Podbielniak, Inc, Ill, 53-57; group leader process develop, 57-59, sect head, 59-61, mgr dept eng develop, 61-62, tech analyst, 62-64, mgr div eng, 64-69, DIR PLANT ENG, ABBOTT LABS, 69- *Mem:* Fel Am Inst Chem Engrs; Am Inst Plant Engrs. *Res:* Design and development of process equipment; centrifugal machinery-solvent extraction; engineering and maintenance management. *Mailing Add:* Abbott Labs 1400 Sheridan Rd North Chicago IL 60064

SULLIVAN, WOODRUFF TURNER, III, b Colorado Springs, Colo, June 17, 44; m 68; c 1. ASTRONOMY, HISTORY OF SCIENCE. *Educ:* Mass Inst Technol, SB, 66; Univ Md, PhD(astron), 71. *Prof Exp:* Res astronomer radio astron, Naval Res Lab, 69-71; fel, Neth Found Radio Astron, 71-73; asst prof, 73-78, ASSOC PROF ASTRON, UNIV WASH, 78- *Mem:* Int Astron Union; Int Union Radio Sci; Am Astron Soc; Hist Sci Soc; Soc Social Studies Sci. *Res:* Galactic and extragalactic microwave spectroscopy; formation and evolution of galaxies and clusters of galaxies; history of radio astronomy; interstellar communication and extraterrestrial civilizations. *Mailing Add:* Dept of Astron Univ of Wash Seattle WA 98195

SULLWOLD, HAROLD H, JR, b St Paul, Minn, Dec 22, 16; m 40; c 2. GEOLOGY, PETROLEUM. *Educ:* Univ Calif, Los Angeles, BA, 39, MA, 40, PhD(geol), 59. *Prof Exp:* Geologist, Wilshire Oil Co, 41, US Geol Surv, 42-44 & W R Cabeen & Assocs, 44-52; instr, Univ Calif, Los Angeles, 52-58; consult geologist, 58-60; geologist, George H Roth & Assocs, 60-80; CONSULT GEOLOGIST, 80- *Concurrent Pos:* Adj prof, Univ SC, 70-71. *Mem:* Asn Prof Geol Scientist; Geol Soc Am; Am Asn Petrol Geologists. *Res:* Petroleum geology; exploration for oil and gas; turbidites. *Mailing Add:* 560 Concha Loma Dr Carpinteria CA 93013

SULSER, FRIDOLIN, b Grabs, Switz, Dec 2, 26; m 55; c 4. PHARMACOLOGY. *Educ:* Univ Basel, MD, 55. *Prof Exp:* Asst prof pharmacol, Univ Berne, 56-58; head dept pharmacol, Wellcome Res Labs, NY, 63-65; DIR PSYCHOPHARMACOL RES CTR & PROF PHARMACOL, SCH MED, VANDERBILT UNIV, 80-; DIR, TENN NEUROPSYCHIAT INST, 74- *Concurrent Pos:* Int Pub Health Serv fel, NIH, 59-62. *Mem:* AAAS; Am Soc Pharmacol; Am Col Neuropsychopharmacol; Am Fedn Clin Res; NY Acad Sci. *Res:* Pharmacology of psychotropic drugs; neurochemistry; biochemical mechanisms of drug action. *Mailing Add:* Dept Pharm Vanderbilt Univ Sch Med Nashville TN 37232

SULSKI, LEONARD C, b Buffalo, NY, Mar 3, 36; m 66; c 1. MATHEMATICS. *Educ:* Canisius Col, BS, 58; Univ Notre Dame, PhD(math), 63. *Prof Exp:* Instr math, Univ Notre Dame, 63-64; lectr, Univ Sussex, 64-65; asst prof, Col of the Holy Cross, 66-68; lectr, Univ Sussex, 68-70; ASSOC PROF MATH & CHMN DEPT, COL OF THE HOLY CROSS, 70- *Mem:* Am Math Soc; Math Asn Am; London Math Soc; Soc Indust & Appl Math. *Res:* Analysis; functional analysis; theory of distributions and differential equations. *Mailing Add:* Dept of Math Col of the Holy Cross Worcester MA 01610

SULTAN, HASSAN AHMED, b Cairo, Egypt, Dec 12, 36; c 2. CIVIL ENGINEERING, SOIL MECHANICS. *Educ:* Cairo Univ, BSc, 58; Univ Utah, MS, 61; Univ Calif, Berkeley, PhD(civil eng), 65. *Prof Exp:* Instr civil eng, Ein-Shams Univ, Egypt, 58-59; asst specialist in res, Univ Calif, Berkeley, 63-64; proj engr, Woodward, Clyde, Sherard & Assoc, 65-67; assoc prof civil eng, 67-71, PROF CIVIL ENG, UNIV ARIZ, 71- *Concurrent Pos:* Pvt consult, 58-59 & 68-; UN expert, 75; consult, World Bank & Govt of Saudi Arabia, 77-; mem dept soils, geol & found, Trans Res Bd, Nat Acad Sci-Nat Res Coun, mem comt soil & rock properties & chmn comt chem stabilization; res grants, NSF, US Air Force, US Dept Transp, US Nat Park Serv & Govt of Saudi Arabia. *Mem:* Fel AAAS; Am Soc Civil Engrs. *Res:* Foundation engineering; slope stability; collapsing soils; earth dams; fluid mechanics; soil stabilization; dust and erosion control. *Mailing Add:* Dept of Civil Eng Univ of Ariz Tucson AZ 85721

SULTZER, BARNET MARTIN, b Union City, NJ, Mar 24, 29; m 56; c 1. MICROBIOLOGY, IMMUNOLOGY. *Educ:* Rutgers Univ, BS, 50; Mich State Univ, MS, 51, PhD(bact), 58. *Prof Exp:* Asst bact, Mich State Univ, 56-58; res assoc microbiol, Princeton Labs, Inc, 58-64; from asst prof to assoc prof, 64-76, PROF MICROBIOL & IMMUNOL, STATE UNIV NY DOWNSTATE MED CTR, 76-, INTERIM CHMN, 80- *Concurrent Pos:* Vis scientist, Karolinska Inst, Sweden, 71-72; vis prof, Pasteur Inst, 79-80. *Mem:* AAAS; Am Asn Immunologists; Am Soc Microbiol; NY Acad Sci; Harvey Soc. *Res:* Lymphocyte activation, mitogenic properties of tuberculin; genetics of host responses to microbial endotoxins; immunobiology of endotoxin protein. *Mailing Add:* Dept of Microbiol & Immunol State Univ NY Downstate Med Ctr Brooklyn NY 11203

SULYA, LOUIS LEON, b North Monmouth, Maine, Aug 17, 11; m 37; c 2. BIOCHEMISTRY. *Educ:* Col Holy Cross, BS, 32, MS, 33; St Louis Univ, PhD(org chem), 39. *Prof Exp:* Instr chem, Spring Hill Col, 34-36; res chemist, Reardon Co, Mo, 40-42; assoc prof, 45-50, prof 50-78, EMER PROF

BIOCHEM & CHMN DEPT, SCH MED, UNIV MISS, 78- *Mem:* AAAS; Endocrine Soc; Am Chem Soc; Am Soc Biol Chemists; Int Soc Nephrol. *Res:* Endocrinology and comparative biochemistry. *Mailing Add:* 1076 Parkwood Pl Jackson MS 39206

SULZBERG, THEODORE, b New York, NY, May 28, 36; m 57; c 3. ORGANIC POLYMER CHEMISTRY. *Educ:* City Col New York, BS, 57; Brooklyn Col, MA, 59; Mich State Univ, PhD(org chem), 62. *Prof Exp:* Res fel org chem, Ohio State Univ, 62-63; proj scientist, Chem & Plastics Div, Union Carbide Corp, 63-70; res group leader, 70-81, MGR RESIN RES, CORP LAB, SUN CHEM CORP, 81- *Mem:* Am Chem Soc; Tech Asn Pulp & Paper Indust. *Res:* Low temperature condensation polymerization; charge-transfer complexes; impact modification of addition polymers; carbonium ions; chemical finishing of textiles; flame retardants; rosin derivatives; hydrocarbon polymers; polyamide resins; printing ink varnishes; polyester resins; emulsion and dispersion polymers. *Mailing Add:* Corp Lab Sun Chem Corp Carlstadt NJ 07072

SULZER, ALEXANDER JACKSON, b Emmett, Ark, Feb 13, 22; m 42; c 2. MEDICAL PARASITOLOGY, MALARIAOLOGY. *Educ:* Hardin-Simmons Univ, BA, 49; Emory Univ, MSc, 60, PhD(parasitol), 62. *Hon Degrees:* Dr, Univ Cayetano Heredia, Peru, 77. *Prof Exp:* Med parasitologist, Commun Dis Ctr, 52-62, res parasitologist, 62-74, RES MICROBIOLOGIST, CTR DIS CONTROL, 74- *Mem:* Sigma Xi; Am Soc Trop Med & Hyg; Am Soc Parasitol; fel Royal Soc Trop Med & Hyg; fel Am Acad Microbiol. *Res:* Immunoparasitology; diagnostic serology of parasitic diseases of man and animals; tagged systems in serology especially fluorescent tagged materials; fine structure of protozoan parasites; malaria. *Mailing Add:* Ctr for Dis Control 1600 Clifton Rd Atlanta GA 30333

SULZMAN, FRANK MICHAEL, b Norfolk, VA, Nov 3, 44; m 69. CIRCADIAN RHYTHMS, SPACE BIOLOGY. *Educ:* Iona Col, BS, 67; State Univ NY, Stony Brook, PhD(biol), 72. *Prof Exp:* Res fel biol, Harvard Univ, 72-74, res fel biophysics, Moscow State Univ, 74-75; res fel physiol, Med Sch, Harvard Univ, 75-76, instr, 76-79; asst prof, 79-82, ASSOC PROF BIOL, STATE UNIV NY, BINGHAMTON, 82- *Concurrent Pos:* Prin investr, Circadian Rhythm Exp, NASA Spacelab I, 78-; Cosmos Circadian Rhythm, USSR-NASA, 80- *Mem:* Am Physiol Soc; Am Soc Photobiol; NY Acad Sci; Int Soc Chronobiol; AAAS. *Res:* Biological rhythms; space biology; photobiology; thermoregulation psychobiology; primate physiology. *Mailing Add:* Dept Biol Sci State Univ NY Binghamton NY 13901

SUMARTOJO, JOJOK, b Surabaya, Indonesia, July 5, 37; Australian citizen; m 66; c 2. SEDIMENTARY PETROLOGY, ECONOMIC GEOLOGY. *Educ:* Bandung Inst Technol, BS, 61; Univ Ky, MS, 66; Univ Cincinnati, PhD(geol), 74. *Prof Exp:* From instr to lectr geol, Bandung Inst Technol, 59-62; lectr geol, Univ Pajajaran, 68-69; instr geol, Univ Adelaide, 69-75; asst prof geol, Vanderbilt Univ, 75-80; MEM STAFF, EXXON PROD RES CO, 80- *Mem:* Sigma Xi; Mineral Asn Can; assoc Geoscientists Int Develop; Int Asn Math Geol. *Res:* Trace and major-element geochemistry and mineralogy of fine-grained detrital sedimentary rocks especially black shales, red-beds and coals. *Mailing Add:* Exxon Prod Res Co PO Box 2189 Houston TX 77002

SUMBERG, DAVID A, b Utica, NY, June 28, 42; m 64; c 1. EDUCATION, ADMINISTRATION. *Educ:* Utica Col, BA, 64; Mich State Univ, MS, 66, PhD(physics), 72. *Prof Exp:* Physicist, Eastman Kodak Co, 72-74; asst prof, 74-80, ASSOC PROF PHYSICS, ST JOHN FISHER COL, 80- *Mem:* Am Asn Physics Teachers; Am Phys Soc. *Res:* Molecular spectroscopy. *Mailing Add:* 105 Seymour Rd Rochester NY 14609

SUMERLIN, NEAL GORDON, b Freeport, Tex, July 1, 50; m 74. NUCLEAR CHEMISTRY. *Educ:* Ouachita Univ, BS, 72; Univ Ark, PhD(chem), 77. *Prof Exp:* asst prof, 76-80, ASSOC PROF CHEM, LYNCHBURG COL, 80- *Mem:* AAAS; Sigma Xi. *Mailing Add:* Dept Chem Lynchburg Col Lynchburg VA 24501

SUMMA, A FRANCIS, b Waterbury, Conn, Jan 28, 33; m 59; c 4. PHARMACEUTICAL CHEMISTRY. *Educ:* St John's Univ, NY, BS, 54; Univ Conn, MS, 57, PhD(pharmaceut chem), 60. *Prof Exp:* Anal chemist, Bur Sci Res, Div Pharmaceut Chem, US Food & Drug Admin, 59-65; ASST SECT HEAD ANAL CHEM, VICK CHEM CO, RICHARDSON-MERRELL INC, 65- *Mem:* Am Pharmaceut Asn; Am Chem Soc. *Res:* Analytical method development; gas chromatography; polarography. *Mailing Add:* Vick Chem Co 1 Bradford Rd Mt Vernon NY 10557

SUMMER, GEORGE KENDRICK, b Cherryville, NC, May 8, 23; m 52; c 2. BIOCHEMISTRY, NUTRITION. *Educ:* Univ NC, BS, 44; Harvard Med Sch, MD, 51. *Prof Exp:* From instr to asst prof pediat, 57-65, from asst prof to assoc prof biochem & nutrit, 65-72, PROF BIOCHEM & NUTRIT, UNIV NC, CHAPEL HILL, 72-, ASSOC CLIN PROF PEDIAT, 66-, RES SCIENTIST, CHILD DEVELOP INST, 71- *Concurrent Pos:* Fel pediat metab, Univ NC, Chapel Hill, 54-57; NIH res career develop award, 65-70; vis scientist, Galton Lab, Univ Col, London & Med Res Coun human biochem genetics res unit & dept biochem, King's Col, London, 62-63. *Mem:* AAAS; Soc Exp Biol & Med; Am Inst Nutrit; Tissue Cult Asn; Am Chem Soc; Am Acad Pediat. *Res:* Biochemistry of cells in tissue culture; analytical biochemistry; study of inborn errors of metabolism; pathophysiology of disease; pediatrics. *Mailing Add:* Dept Biochem & Nutrit Div Health Affairs Univ of NC Chapel Hill NC 27514

SUMMERFELT, ROBERT C, b Chicago, Ill, Aug 2, 35; m 60; c 3. FISH BIOLOGY. *Educ:* Univ Wis-Stevens Point, BS, 57; Southern Ill Univ, MS, 59, PhD(zool), 64. *Prof Exp:* Lectr zool, Southern Ill Univ, 62-64; asst prof, Kans State Univ, 64-66; assoc prof zool, Okla State Univ, 66-71, prof zool & leader Okla Coop Fishery Res Unit, 71-76; PROF ANIMAL ECOL & CHMN DEPT, IOWA STATE UNIV, 76- *Concurrent Pos:* Grants, Bur Com Fisheries, 66-69, Nat Marine Fisheries Serv, Off Water Resources Res, 70-71, 74-76 & 79-81, Environ Protection Agency, 71-72, 77-78 & Bur Reclamation,

72 & 74-75. *Honors & Awards:* Spec Achievement Award, US Fish & Wildlife Serv, 69, 71 & 76; Commendation, Sport Fishing Inst, 75. *Mem:* Soc Invert Path; Ecol Soc Am; Am Fisheries Soc; Wildlife Dis Asn; fel Am Inst Fishery Res Biologists. *Res:* Biology of fishes, especially trophic relationships and reproductive biology; microsporidan parasites of fishes; fish biotelemetry. *Mailing Add:* Dept Animal Ecol Iowa State Univ Ames IA 50011

SUMMERFIELD, GEORGE CLARK, b Lansing, Mich, Aug 17, 37; m 58; c 4. PHYSICS, NUCLEAR ENGINEERING. *Educ:* Mich State Univ, BS, 58, PhD(physics), 62. *Prof Exp:* Res assoc nuclear eng, Univ Mich, Ann Arbor, 62-63, from asst prof to assoc prof, 63-68; assoc prof, Va Polytech Inst & State Univ, 68-70; PROF NUCLEAR ENG, UNIV MICH, ANN ARBOR, 70- *Mem:* Am Phys Soc; Am Nuclear Soc. *Res:* High energy, elementary particle and thermal neutron physics; neutron transport theory. *Mailing Add:* Dept of Nuclear Eng Univ of Mich Ann Arbor MI 48109

SUMMERFIELD, MARTIN, b New York, NY, Oct 20, 16; m 45; c 1. PHYSICS. *Educ:* Brooklyn Col, BS, 36; Calif Inst Technol, MS, 37, PhD(physics), 41. *Prof Exp:* Res engr, jet propulsion proj, Calif Inst Technol, 40-42, asst chief engr, 42-43, chief rockets & mat div, Jet Propulsion Lab, 45-49; chief liquid rocket develop dept, Aerojet Eng Corp, Calif, 43-45; ed, aeronaut publ prog, 49-52, PROF AERONAUT ENG, PRINCETON UNIV, 51-; chief scientist, Flow Indust, Inc, Princeton Combust Labs, 77-82; ASTRON PROF, AEROSPACE SCI, NY UNIV, 82- *Concurrent Pos:* Mem subcomt combustion, NASA, 49- *Mem:* Nat Acad Eng; Am Phys Soc; Am Soc Mech Engrs; Am Inst Aeronaut & Astronaut; Int Acad Astronaut. *Res:* Infrared spectroscopy; soil erosion; rocket propellants; combustion; jet engines; heat transfer. *Mailing Add:* Barney Bldg 5th Floor 26-36 Stuyvesant St New York NY 10003

SUMMERLIN, LEE R, b Sumiton, Ala, Apr 15, 34; m 58; c 4. CHEMISTRY, SCIENCE EDUCATION. *Educ:* Samford Univ, AB, 55; Birmingham Southern Col, MS, 60; Univ Md, College Park, PhD(sci educ), 71. *Prof Exp:* Chemist, Southern Res Inst, 56-59; teacher, Fla State Univ, 59-61, asst prof chem, 62-71; asst prof sci educ, Univ Ga, 71-72; assoc prof chem & sci educ, 72-77, PROF CHEM, UNIV ALA, BIRMINGHAM, 72-, INTERIM DEAN, SCH NATURAL SCI & MATH, 80- *Concurrent Pos:* Chemist, US Pipe & Foundry Co, 53-55; consult, Chem Educ Mat Study, 63-70, Cent Treaty Orgn, 64-, US Agency Int Develop, 66-68 & India Proj, NSF, 68-; teaching assoc, Univ Md, 70-71. *Honors & Awards:* James Conant Award, Am Chem Soc, 69. *Mem:* AAAS; Am Chem Soc; Am Inst Chemists; Nat Asn Res Sci Teaching; Nat Sci Teachers Asn. *Res:* Computer assisted instruction; developing chemistry material for nonscience majors; autotutorial and individualized instruction in chemistry. *Mailing Add:* 1786 Cornwall Rd Birmingham AL 35226

SUMMERS, AUDREY LORRAINE, b San Jose, Calif, Mar 22, 28; m 47. MATHEMATICS, COMPUTER SCIENCE. *Educ:* Stanford Univ, BA, 48; San Jose State Univ, MS, 62. *Prof Exp:* Mathematician data reduction, 47-58, mathematician computation, 58-62, RES SCIENTIST SPACE SCI, AMES RES CTR, NASA, 62- *Honors & Awards:* H Julian Allen Award, Ames Res Ctr, NASA, 76. *Mem:* Asn Comput Mach; Am Geophys Union; Meteoritical Soc; AAAS. *Res:* Evolution and structure of planets and planetary systems by theoretical computer modeling; mathematical modeling of radiative transfer in planetary atmospheres. *Mailing Add:* Theoret Studies Br Ames Res Ctr NASA Moffett Field CA 94035

SUMMERS, CHARLES GEDDES, b Ogden, Utah, Dec 24, 41. ECONOMIC ENTOMOLOGY. *Educ:* Utah State Univ, BS, 64, MS, 66; Cornell Univ, PhD(entom), 70. *Prof Exp:* Res fel entom, Utah State Univ, 64-66; res asst, Cornell Univ, 66-70; asst entomologist, 70-75, ASSOC ENTOMOLOGIST, UNIV CALIF, BERKELEY, 75-, LECTR ENTOM SCI, 77- *Mem:* Entom Soc Am; Entom Soc Can; Crop Sci Soc Am; AAAS. *Res:* Biology and population dynamics of arthropods associated with field crops; host-plant resistance to arthropods attacking alfalfa and economic threshold levels of arthropods attacking alfalfa and cereal crops. *Mailing Add:* Dept of Entom Sci Univ of Calif Berkeley CA 94720

SUMMERS, DAVID ARCHIBOLD, b Newcastle-on-Tyne, Eng, Feb 2, 44; m 72; c 2. MINING, ROCK MECHANICS. *Educ:* Univ Leeds, BSc, 65, PhD(mining), 68. *Prof Exp:* Asst prof mining eng, 68-74, assoc prof mining, 74-77, sr investr, Rock Mech & Explosives Res Ctr, 70-76, prof mining, 77-80, DIR, ROCK MECH & EXPLOSIVES RES CTR, UNIV MO-ROLLA, 76-, CUR PROF, 80- *Mem:* Am Inst Mining, Metall & Petrol Engrs; Am Soc Mech Engrs; fel Brit Inst Mining Engrs; Brit Inst Mining & Metall; Brit Tunneling Soc. *Res:* Water jet cutting; surface energy of rock and minerals; novel methods of excavation; cavitation at high pressure; coal mining; geothermal development; strata control. *Mailing Add:* Rock Mech & Explosives Res Ctr Univ of Mo Rolla MO 65401

SUMMERS, DENNIS BRIAN, b Natrona Heights, Pa, Aug 4, 43; m 63; c 2. PLANT BREEDING. *Educ:* Ind Univ, Pa, BS, 66, MEd, 68; Pa State Univ, PhD(bot), 73. *Prof Exp:* Teacher pub sch, Pa, 66-67; mem staff & fac chem & biol warfare, US Army Chem Ctr & Sch, 67-69; PLANT BREEDER, ASGROW SEED CO, SUBSID UPJOHN CO, 74- *Mem:* Nat Sweet Corn Breeders Asn; Am Seed Trade Asn; Am Soc Hort Sci. *Res:* Breeding for disease resistance at the cell culture level. *Mailing Add:* Rte 3 Highlawn Dr Twin Falls ID 83301

SUMMERS, DONALD BALCH, b Maplewood, NJ, Oct 18, 02; m 43; c 1. CHEMISTRY. *Educ:* Wesleyan Univ, BS, 24, MA, 26; Princeton Univ, AM, 29; Columbia Univ, PhD(electro-org chem), 32. *Prof Exp:* Asst, Wesleyan Univ, 24-26; instr chem, Amherst Col, 26-27 & Princeton Univ, 27-29; res & develop chemist, Thomas A Edison Co, 29-30 & Chas Pfizer & Co, 30-33; instr chem, High Sch, Columbia Univ, 33-42 & 46-57; proj asst, Fund Adv Educ Chem Film Proj, Univ Fla, 57-58; prof chem, Glassboro State Col, 58-60; Olin chem teacher, Alton Sr High Sch, Ill, 60-67; prof, 67-73, EMER PROF CHEM, NMEX STATE UNIV, 73- *Concurrent Pos:* Lectr, South

Orange-Maplewood Adult Sch, West Orange Adult Sch & Pelham Adult Sch, NJ, 37-42; consult, 34- *Mem:* AAAS; Am Chem Soc; fel Am Inst Chemists. *Res:* Catalysis; electro-organic chemistry; corrosion; photography; chemical education. *Mailing Add:* 1710 Altura Ave Las Cruces NM 88001

SUMMERS, DONALD LEE, b North Platte, Nebr, Apr 6, 33; m 66; c 3. APPLIED MATHEMATICS, PHYSICS. *Educ:* Univ Nebr, BS, 55, MA, 57. *Prof Exp:* Analyst math & physics, Air Force Weapons Lab, Kirtland AFB, 57-60; res mathematician, Dikewood Corp, 60-70; sr res mathematician, Falcon Res & Develop Co, Whittaker Corp, 70-77; SR RES MATHEMATICIAN MATH & PHYSICS, DIKEWOOD INDUSTS, 77- *Mem:* Am Phys Soc; Math Asn Am. *Res:* Applied mathematical modeling using computer simulation techniques; analysis of biological effects of ionizing nuclear radiation; development of casualty prediction using mathematical and statistical methods; psychological test development and evaluation. *Mailing Add:* 3713 Moon NE Albuquerque NM 87111

SUMMERS, GEOFFREY P, b London, Eng. SOLID STATE PHYSICS. *Educ:* Oxford Univ, BA, 65, PhD(physics), 69. *Prof Exp:* Res asst physics, Univ NC, 70-72; asst prof, 73-77, ASSOC PROF PHYSICS, OKLA STATE UNIV, 77- *Mem:* Am Phys Soc. *Res:* Experimental investigation of the electronic structure of defects in solids by means of photoconductivity, luminescence, optical absorption and lifetime studies. *Mailing Add:* Dept of Physics Okla State Univ Stillwater OK 74074

SUMMERS, HUGH B(LOOMER), JR, b Lake City, Fla, Aug 5, 21; m 46; c 2. CHEMICAL ENGINEERING. *Educ:* Univ Fla, BChE, 43. *Prof Exp:* Res chem engr, Naval Stores Res Lab, Southern Utilization Res & Develop Div, Agr Res Serv, USDA, 47-65; PROCESS ENGR, CHEM DIV, UNION CAMP CORP, 65- *Mem:* Nat Soc Prof Engrs; Am Chem Soc; Am Inst Chem Engrs. *Res:* Gum naval stores processing; crude tall oil production; tall oil fractionation. *Mailing Add:* Chem Div Union Camp Corp PO Box 2668 Savannah GA 31402

SUMMERS, JAMES KEVIN, b Perth Amboy, NJ, Nov 9, 51; m 78; c 2. SYSTEMS ECOLOGY, POLLUTION ECOLOGY. *Educ:* Univ NC, AB, 73, MA, 75; Univ SC, PhD(biol), 79. *Prof Exp:* RESEARCHER, MARTIN MARIETTA ENVIRON CTR, 79- *Mem:* Int Soc Ecol Modelling; Ecol Soc Am; Am Soc Limnol & Oceanog; AAAS. *Res:* Nutrient and carbon dynamics of estuarine and freshwater ecosystems; oxygen dynamics; fisheries recruitment patterns; development of analytical tools in systems ecology. *Mailing Add:* 1450 S Rolling Rd Baltimore MD 21227

SUMMERS, JAMES THOMAS, b Nashville, Tenn, Nov 4, 38; m 58; c 3. INORGANIC CHEMISTRY. *Educ:* Vanderbilt Univ, AB, 60; Fla State Univ, PhD(inorg chem), 63. *Prof Exp:* Fel, Fla State Univ, 64 & Univ Tex, 64-65; res chemist, 65-71, SR RES CHEMIST, TEXTILE FIBERS DEPT, E I DU PONT DE NEMOURS & CO, INC, 71- *Mem:* Am Chem Soc; Royal Soc Chem. *Res:* Coordination chemistry; polymer chemistry. *Mailing Add:* 823 Kay Circle Chattanooga TN 37421

SUMMERS, JAMES WILLIAM, b Logansport, Ind, July 10, 40; m 66; c 2. POLYMER SCIENCE. *Educ:* Rose Hulman Inst Technol, BS, 62; Case Western Reserve Univ, MS, 66, PhD(polymer eng), 71. *Prof Exp:* sr res & develop assoc & supvr, 62-80, RES & DEVELOP FEL, CHEM DIV, B F GOODRICH CO, 80- *Mem:* Soc Plastics Engrs; Am Chem Soc; Soc Plastics Indust. *Res:* Polymer weatherability; polymer rheology and die design; polymer morphology and physical properties; polymer testing; polymer blends. *Mailing Add:* Chem Div PO Box 122 Avon Lake OH 44012

SUMMERS, JOHN CLIFFORD, b Chicago, Ill, Dec 4, 36. PESTICIDE CHEMISTRY. *Educ:* Augustana Col, Ill, BA, 58; Univ Ill, PhD(org chem), 63. *Prof Exp:* RES ASSOC, EXP STA, E I DU PONT DE NEMOURS & CO, INC, 63- *Mem:* Am Chem Soc. *Mailing Add:* Exp Sta Bldg 324 E I du Pont de Nemours & Co Inc Wilmington DE 19898

SUMMERS, LAWRENCE, b Bevier, Mo, June 21, 14; div; c 2. ORGANIC CHEMISTRY. *Educ:* Iowa State Col, BS, 39, PhD(chem), 50; Utah State Univ, MS, 41. *Prof Exp:* Jr chemist, US Bur Mines, 41-42; res chemist, Remington Arms Co, E I du Pont de Nemours & Co, 42-45; res chemist, Columbia Chem Div, Pittsburgh Plate Glass Co, 46-47; from asst prof to assoc prof, 50-56, honors prog coordr, 67-71, prof, 56-80, EMER PROF CHEM, UNIV NDAK, 80- *Concurrent Pos:* Res assoc, Georgetown Univ, 60-61. *Res:* Organometallic chemistry; organic chlorine compounds; linguistics; machine translation. *Mailing Add:* Dept of Chem Univ of NDak Grand Forks ND 58201

SUMMERS, LUIS HENRY, b Lima, Peru, Sept 6, 39; m 65; c 1. ARCHITECTURAL ENGINEERING. *Educ:* Univ Notre Dame, BArch, 61, MSc, 65, PhD(struct eng), 70. *Prof Exp:* Architect housing, Dino Mortara Assoc, Rome, Italy, 61-62; architect, Corp Renovacion Urbana, PR, 62-63; instr struct, Univ Notre Dame, 65-66; asst prof, Yale Univ, 66-70; assoc prof, Univ Okla, 70-72; PROF STRUCT, ENERGY MGT & SOLAR PASSIVE DESIGN, PA STATE UNIV, 72- *Concurrent Pos:* Teacher art, Notre Dame Int, Rome Italy, 61-62 & Stanley Clark Sch, South Bend, Ind, 62-63; comput consult, Assoc Eng, New Haven, Conn, 67; comput graphics consult, Yale Univ & Conn Hwy Dept, 68; architect, Comprehensive Design Assoc Inc, 72-; comput syst consult, Army Construct Eng Lab, Urbana, Ill, 76. *Honors & Awards:* Cardinal Ledcaro Gold Medal, Cardinal Ledcaro Ecclesiastical Design Found, 60. *Mem:* Sigma Xi; Environ Designers Res Asn; NAm Simulation & Gaming Asn; Am Soc Eng Educ; Am Inst Architechs. *Res:* Reduction of energy loss through windows; computer aided modeling of thermal comfort using mean radiant temperature; development of a solar passive residential greenhouse prototype; microcomputer aided instrumentation of structural testing devices; microcomputer aided instrumentation of a residence to determine thermal comfort; low temperature radiant heat panels. *Mailing Add:* Dept of Archit Eng 104 Eng Bldg A University Park PA 16802

SUMMERS, RICHARD JAMES, b Kendallville, Ind, Nov 13, 43. ALLERGY, PEDIATRICS. *Educ:* Ind Univ, AB, 65, MD, 68; Am Bd Pediat, cert, 73; Am Bd Allergy-Immunol, cert, 74. *Prof Exp:* Rotating intern, Fitzsimons Gen Hosp, Denver, 68-69; pediat resident, Fitzsimons Army Med Ctr, 69-71; allergy-immunol fel, Nat Jewish Hosp & Res Ctr, Univ Colo Med Ctr, Fitzsimons Army Med Ctr, 71-73; chief allergy-immunol serv, 97th Gen Hosp, Frankfurt, WGer, 73-76; asst chief, 76-80, CHIEF, ALLERGY-IMMUNOL SERV, WALTER REED ARMY MED CTR, 80- *Concurrent Pos:* US Army Europe consult allergy-immunol, 7th US Army Surgeon Gen Consult, Heidelberg, WGer, 73-76; asst prof pediat & med, Uniformed Serv Univ Health Sci, 78-; consult allergy-immunol, Nat Inst Allergy & Infectious Dis, NIH, 79-; asst prof pediat & asst prof med, Uniformed Services Univ Health Sci, 77- *Mem:* Fel Am Acad Pediat; Am Acad Allergy; Am Fedn Clin Res. *Res:* Penicillin allergy; ampicillin allergy; infectious mononucleosis; catecholamines, especially epinephrine and ephedrine; cyclic nucleotides; histamine; immunotherapy; radioallergosorbent testing; insect sting allergy. *Mailing Add:* Allergy-Immunol Serv Walter Reed Army Med Ctr Washington DC 20012

SUMMERS, ROBERT GENTRY, JR, b Sonora, Calif, Jan 10, 43; m 70. ZOOLOGY. *Educ:* Univ Notre Dame, BS, 65, MS, 67; Tulane Univ, PhD(anat), 71. *Prof Exp:* Fel, Univ Maine, Orono, 70-71, from asst prof to assoc prof zool, 75-76; ASSOC PROF ANAT, STATE UNIV NY, BUFFALO, 76- *Mem:* Am Soc Zoologists; Am Asn Anatomists; Am Soc Cell Biol; Soc Develop Biol. *Res:* Developmental biology, particularly invertebrate embryology and morphogenesis; electron microscopy of developing invertebrates and their gametes; control systems in growth and regeneration. *Mailing Add:* Dept of Anat Sci State Univ of NY Buffalo NY 14214

SUMMERS, ROBERT WENDELL, b Lansing, Mich, July 28, 38; m 61; c 3. GASTROENTEROLOGY. *Educ:* Mich State Univ, BS, 61; Univ Iowa, MD, 65. *Prof Exp:* NIH gastroenterol res fel, 68-70, asst prof, 71-74, ASSOC PROF GASTROENTEROL, DEPT MED, DIV GASTROENTEROL, UNIV IOWA HOSPS, 74- *Concurrent Pos:* Assoc dir, Gastroenterol Prog, Gastroenterol Div, Dept Med, Vet Admin Hosp, Iowa City, 70-71, consult, 71-77; Burroughs Wellcome Res Travel grant, 79; Fogerty Sr Int fel, NIH, 80. *Mem:* Am Gastroenterol Asn; Am Col Physicians; Am Soc Gastrointestinal Endoscopy; Am Fedn Clin Res; Am Asn Study Liver Dis. *Res:* Interrelationships of electrical and motor activity of the small intestine, and intestinal flow as modulated by physiologic, pharmacologic, and pathologic influence; the therapy of Crohns Disease. *Mailing Add:* Dept of Internal Med Univ Hosp Iowa City IA 52242

SUMMERS, SELBY EDWARD, b Toronto, Ont, Aug 26, 24; US citizen; m 50; c 4. CHEMISTRY. *Educ:* State Univ NY Albany, BA, 50, MA, 51. *Prof Exp:* Engr, Gen Eng Lab, Gen Elec Co, 51-55, appln engr, X-ray Dept, 55-58; x-ray microscopist, Ernest F Fullam Inc, 58-59, lab mgr, 59-62, vpres, 63-72; mat analyst, RRC Int, Inc, 72-74; SR SCIENTIST, SPRAGUE ELEC CO, 74- *Mem:* Am Chem Soc; Electron Micros Soc Am; Am Soc Metals; Electron Probe Anal Soc Am. *Res:* Electron optics; x-ray microscopy; x-ray emission and electron microprobe analysis. *Mailing Add:* Res & Develop Ctr Sprague Elec Co North Adams MA 01247

SUMMERS, THOMAS EUGENE, entomology, plant pathology, see previous edition

SUMMERS, WILLIAM ALLEN, JR, b Atlanta, Ga, Dec 4, 44; m 67; c 2. INDUSTRIAL ORGANIC CHEMISTRY, PHYSICAL ORGANIC CHEMISTRY. *Educ:* Wabash Col, AB, 66; Northwestern Univ, PhD(chem), 71; Ind State Univ, MBA, 81. *Prof Exp:* Res assoc photochem, Okla Univ, 70-72, vis asst prof, 70-71; prog dir & group leader nucleotide synthesis, Ash Steven Inc, 72-73; sr res assoc photochem, Okla Univ, 73-74; develop chemist heterogeneous catalysis, IMC Chem Group, 74-79,MGR NEW PROD DEVELOP, INT MINERALS & CHEM CORP, 79- *Mem:* Am Chem Soc; Am Soc Photobiol; Sigma Xi. *Res:* Research and development involving heterogeneous catalysis particularly catalytic reduction and photochemistry of nitroparaffins and their derivatives; applications of and design of new reduction reactions; livestock vaccines in high technology fields of tissue culture and recombinant DNA. *Mailing Add:* Vet Prod Div Int Minerals & Chem Corp Terre Haute IN 47808

SUMMERS, WILLIAM ALLEN, SR, b Gary, Ind, Apr 22, 14; m 40; c 3. PARASITOLOGY, MEDICAL MICROBIOLOGY. *Educ:* Univ Ill, AB, 35, MS, 36; La State Univ, Tulane Univ, PhD(trop dis), 40. *Prof Exp:* Sr parasitologist pub health lab, Fla State Bd Health, 40-42; parasitologist malaria control, US Army, 42-45; asst prof bact & parasitol, Med Col Va, 45-47; from asst prof to assoc prof, 47-64, prof, 44-79, EMER PROF MICROBIOL, SCH MED, IND UNIV, 79- *Concurrent Pos:* USPHS res grants, Sch Med, Ind Univ, 48-; fel trop med, La State Univ, 58; vis scientist, Gorgas Mem Lab, Panama, 66-67. *Mem:* Am Soc Trop Med & Hyg; Am Soc Parasitol; Am Soc Microbiol; Tissue Cult Asn; Sigma Xi. *Res:* Amebiasis, toxoplasmosis, anaplasmosis, malaria; helminth parasites, especially diagnosis, research into growth and chemotherapy; electron and light microscopy; fluorescent microscopy. *Mailing Add:* Dept of Microbiol Ind Univ Sch of Med Indianapolis IN 46202

SUMMERS, WILLIAM CLARKE, b Corvallis, Ore, Sept 13, 36; m 64; c 2. MARINE ECOLOGY. *Educ:* Univ Minn, BME, 59, PhD(zool), 66. *Prof Exp:* Res assoc & investr squid biol, Marine Biol Lab, 66-72, NIH contract squid ecol, 69-72; dir, Shannon Point Marine Ctr, 72-76; ASSOC PROF ECOL, HUXLEY COL ENVIRON STUDIES, WESTERN WASH UNIV, 72- *Mem:* AAAS; Am Soc Mech Engrs; Am Soc Zoologists. *Res:* Physiological ecology of aquatic mollusks; life history, autecology and population biology of the squid, Loligo pealei; similar studies on Puget Sound octopus species; marine ecology; coastal ecosystems; aquatic biology. *Mailing Add:* Huxley Col of Environ Studies Western Wash Univ Bellingham WA 98225

SUMMERS, WILLIAM COFIELD, b Janesville, Wis, Apr 17, 39. MOLECULAR BIOLOGY, BIOCHEMISTRY. *Educ:* Univ Wis-Madison, BS, 61, MS, 63, PhD(molecular biol) & MD, 67. *Prof Exp:* From asst prof radiobiol to assoc prof radiobiol, molecular biophysics & biochem, 68-78, PROF THERAPEUT RADIOL, MOLECULAR BIOPHYSICS, BIOCHEM & HUMAN GENETICS, YALE UNIV, 78- *Concurrent Pos:* NSF fel, Mass Inst Technol, 67-68. *Mem:* Am Soc Microbiol; Am Soc Biol Chemists. *Res:* Regulation of gene expression in normal and virus infected cells and in the course of development and differentiation. *Mailing Add:* 333 Cedar St New Haven CT 06510

SUMMERS, WILLIAM HUNLEY, b Dallas, Tex, Feb 5, 36. MATHEMATICS. *Educ:* Univ Tex, Arlington, BS, 61; Purdue Univ, West Lafayette, MS, 63; La State Univ, Baton Rouge, PhD(math), 68. *Prof Exp:* From asst prof to assoc prof, 68-78, PROF MATH, UNIV ARK, FAYETTEVILLE, 78- *Concurrent Pos:* NSF res grants, 69-74; Fulbright-Hayes travel grant, Brazil, 73; vis prof, Inst Math, Fed Univ Rio de Janeiro, 73-75; NSF travel grant, India & Ger, 81; vis prof, Univ-GH-Paderborn, 81. *Mem:* Am Math Soc; Math Soc France. *Res:* Weighted approximation in spaces of continuous functions. *Mailing Add:* Dept of Math SE 301 Univ of Ark Fayetteville AR 72701

SUMMERS, WILMA POOS, b Richmond, Ind, Dec 8, 37; m 65. BIOCHEMICAL GENETICS, MOLECULAR VIROLOGY. *Educ:* Ohio Univ, BS, 59; Univ Wis-Madison, PhD(oncol), 66. *Prof Exp:* Fel oncol, McArdle Lab Cancer Res, Univ Wis-Madison, 66-67; fel biochem, Harvard Med Sch, 67-68; fel pharmacol, 68-69, res assoc, 69-72, res assoc virol, 72-78, SR RES ASSOC VIROL, DEPT THERAPEUT RADIOL, SCH MED, YALE UNIV, 78- *Concurrent Pos:* Consult, Nat Cancer Inst, NIH, 73-74. *Mem:* Am Soc Biol Chemists. *Res:* Biochemical genetics of herpes simplex virus; the isolation and characterization of herpes virus mutants to be used in the development of suppressor genetics in mammalian cell systems. *Mailing Add:* Radiobiol Lab Sch Med Yale Univ 333 Cedar St New Haven CT 06510

SUMMERS-GILL, ROBERT GEORGE, b Sask, Can, Dec 22, 29. EXPERIMENTAL NUCLEAR PHYSICS. *Educ:* Univ Sask, BA, 50, MA, 52; Univ Calif, PhD(physics), 56. *Prof Exp:* From asst prof to assoc prof, 56-66, PROF PHYSICS, McMASTER UNIV, 66- *Mem:* Am Phys Soc; Can Asn Physicists. *Res:* Atomic beam resonances; nuclear spectroscopy; direct reactions; nuclear shell model calculations; heavy ion reactions. *Mailing Add:* Dept of Physics McMaster Univ Hamilton ON L8S 4L8 Can

SUMMERSON, CHARLES HENRY, b Catlettsburg, Ky, Nov 15, 14; m 44; c 3. GEOLOGY. *Educ:* Univ Ill, BS, 38, MS, 40, PhD(geol), 42. *Prof Exp:* Asst geol, Univ Ill, 38-42; asst geologist, US Geol Surv, 43-45; asst prof geol, Mo Sch Mines, 46-47; from asst prof to assoc prof, 47-72, asst to dir res found, 58-65, PROF GEOL, OHIO STATE UNIV, 72- *Concurrent Pos:* Staff assoc, NSF, 65-66. *Mem:* AAAS; Soc Econ Paleont & Mineral; Am Asn Petrol Geol; Geol Soc Am; Int Asn Sedimentol. *Res:* Stratigraphy; sedimentary petrography; paleontology; micropaleontology; photogeology. *Mailing Add:* Dept of Geol 125 S Oval Dr Columbus OH 43210

SUMMERVILLE, RICHARD MARION, b Shippenville, Pa, May 20, 38; m 62; c 2. MATHEMATICS. *Educ:* Clarion State Col, BS, 59; Wash Univ, AM, 65; Syracuse Univ, PhD(math), 69. *Prof Exp:* Instr math, Clarion State Col, 60-64; asst prof, State Univ NY Col Oswego, 68-69; res assoc, Syracuse Univ, 69-70; assoc prof math & chmn dept, Armstrong State Col, 70-73, prof math & head, Dept Math & Comput Sci, 73-80; PROF MATH & DEAN, SCH LIBERAL ARTS & SCI, CHRISTOPHER NEWPORT COL, 80- *Mem:* AAAS; Math Asn Am; Am Math Soc; Asn Comput Mach; Sigma Xi. *Res:* Complex analysis; conformal and quasiconformal mapping; Schlicht functions. *Mailing Add:* Off Dean Sch Liberal Arts & Sci Christopher Newport Col Newport News VA 23606

SUMMITT, (WILLIAM) ROBERT, b Flint, Mich, Dec 6, 35; m 56; c 2. PHYSICAL CHEMISTRY, MATERIALS SCIENCE. *Educ:* Univ Mich, BS, 57; Purdue Univ, PhD(phys chem), 61. *Prof Exp:* Res assoc chem, Mich State Univ, 61-62; res chemist, Corning Glass Works, 62-65; from asst prof to assoc prof mat sci, 65-73, from actg chmn to chmn dept, 71-78, PROF MAT SCI, MICH STATE UNIV, 73- *Mem:* Am Phys Soc; Am Soc Metals; Am Chem Soc; Inter-Soc Color Coun; Nat Asn Corrosion Engrs. *Res:* Corrosion; optical spectroscopy; optical properties of materials; color science. *Mailing Add:* Dept of Metall Mech & Mat Sci Mich State Univ Col of Eng East Lansing MI 48824

SUMMITT, ROBERT L, b Knoxville, Tenn, Dec 23, 32; m 55; c 3. PEDIATRICS, MEDICAL GENETICS. *Educ:* Univ Tenn, MD, 55, MS, 62; Am Bd Pediat, dipl, 62. *Prof Exp:* Intern, Mem Res Ctr & Hosp, Univ Tenn, Knoxville, 56; asst resident pediat, Col Med, Univ Tenn, Memphis, 59-60, chief resident, 60-61, USPHS trainee pediat endocrine & metab dis, Univ, 61-62; fel med genetics, Univ Wis, 63; from instr to assoc prof, 64-71, assoc dean acad affairs, 79-81, PROF PEDIAT & ANAT, COL MED, UNIV TENN, MEMPHIS, 71-, DEAN ACAD AFFAIRS, 81- *Concurrent Pos:* NIH, Children's Bur, State Ment Health Dept & Nat Found res grants; mem pediat staff, City of Memphis, Le Bonheur Children's Hosp; pediat consult, Baptist Mem, St Josph's, Methodist, US Naval, St Jude Children's Res & Arlington Hosps, Baroness Erloyer Hosp & T C Thompson Children's Hosp Med Ctr; mem, Mammalian Genetics Study Sect, NIH, 80- *Mem:* AAAS; Am Acad Pediat; Am Soc Human Genetics; Soc Pediat Res. *Res:* Clinical genetics and cytogenetics. *Mailing Add:* Dept of Peidat Univ of Tenn Col of Med Memphis TN 38163

SUMMY-LONG, JOAN YVETTE, b Harrisburg, Pa. PHARMACOLOGY. *Educ:* Bucknell Univ, BS, 65; Pa State Univ, MS, 72, PhD(pharmacol), 78. *Prof Exp:* Jr scientist pharmacol, Smith Kline Pharmaceut Labs, 65-69; sr res technician, 69-72, res asst, 72-78, ASST PROF PHARMACOL, PA STATE UNIV, 78- *Concurrent Pos:* Res asst, co-investr NASA grant, 77-78, asst prof, 78-79; speaker, Gordon Res Conf, Angiotensin, 80. *Mem:* Sigma Xi; Soc

Neurosci. *Res:* Neuroendocrinology; central nervous system regulation of blood pressure and hydration; endogenous opioid peptide effects on blood pressure and vasopressin neurosecretion. *Mailing Add:* Dept of Pharmacol Pa State Univ Col of Med Hershey PA 17033

SUMNER, BARBARA ELAINE, b Alexandria, Va, Dec 23, 42. PHYSICAL CHEMISTRY, MATERIALS SCIENCE. *Educ:* Howard Univ, BS, 66; Am Univ, MS, 74, PhD(chem), 77. *Prof Exp:* Chemist chem warfare, Melpar Inc, 66-68; RES CHEMIST MAT, NIGHT VISION & ELECTRO-OPTICS LABS, 68- *Mem:* Am Chem Soc; Electrochem Soc; Sigma Xi; Am Phys Soc. *Res:* Metallurgical analysis, design, fabrication and coordination of intrinsic and extrinsic photosensors and auxiliary components for use in infrared imaging systems. *Mailing Add:* 2222 First St NW Washington DC 20001

SUMNER, DARRELL DEAN, b Kansas City, Mo, Jan 1, 41; m 63; c 3. TOXICOLOGY, METABOLISM. *Educ:* Univ Kans, AB, 63, PhD(med chem), 68. *Prof Exp:* Sr scientist drug metab, McNeil Labs, Inc, 68-71; sr metab chemist, 71-75, proj scientist, 75-77, toxicologist, 77-79, SR TOXICOLOGIST, AGR DIV, CIBA-GEIGY CORP, 79- *Concurrent Pos:* Vis asst prof, Univ of NC Greensboro, 75-76. *Mem:* AAAS; Am Chem Soc; Environmental Mutagen Soc; Am Indust Hyg. *Res:* Safety evaluation of pesticides. *Mailing Add:* Ciba-Geigy Corp Agr Div PO Box 18300 Greensboro NC 27419

SUMNER, DONALD RAY, b Studley, Kans, Sept 20, 37; m 68. PLANT PATHOLOGY. *Educ:* Kans State Univ, BS, 59; Univ Nebr, MS, 64, PhD(plant path), 67. *Prof Exp:* Plant pathologist, Green Giant Co, Minn, 67-69; asst prof, 69-78, ASSOC PROF PLANT PATH, COASTAL PLAIN EXP STA, UNIV GA, 78- *Mem:* Am Phytopath Soc; Sigma Xi. *Res:* Ecology of soil-borne pathogens of vetetables and corn. *Mailing Add:* Dept of Plant Path Univ of Ga Coastal Plain Exp Sta Tifton GA 31794

SUMNER, EDWARD D, b Spartanburg, SC, Mar 21, 25; m 47; c 2. PHARMACY. *Educ:* Wofford Col, BS, 48; Med Col SC, BS, 50; Univ NC, MS, 64, PhD(pharm), 66. *Prof Exp:* Instr pharm, Univ NC, 61-65; from asst prof to assoc prof, Univ Ga, 66-75; PROF PHARM COL PHARM, MED UNIV SC, 75- *Concurrent Pos:* Consult pharm internship, Vet Admin Hosp, Augusta, Ga, 68- *Mem:* Am Soc Hosp Pharmacists; Am Asn Cols Pharm; Sigma Xi; Am Pharmaceut Asn. *Res:* Physics of tablet compression and drug release from tablets; drug utilization in nursing homes and mental retardation centers; medication studies on the senior citizen such as compliance to physician's orders and factors determing when, what, and where drugs are purchased. *Mailing Add:* Col of Pharm 171 Ashley Ave Charleston SC 29425

SUMNER, ERIC E, b Vienna, Austria, Dec 17, 24; nat US; m 74; c 4. MECHANICAL & ELECTRICAL ENGINEERING. *Educ:* Cooper Union, BME, 48; Columbia Univ, MA, 53, EE, 60. *Prof Exp:* Mem tech staff, 48-55, head, Transmission Systs Consult Dept, 55-60, dir, Guided Wave Transmission Lab, 60-62, dir, Underwater Systs Lab, 62-67, exec dir, Loop Transmission Div, 67-79, exec dir, Customer Network Oper Div, 79-81, VPRES COMPUT TECHNOL & MILITARY SYSTS, BELL TEL LABS, 81. *Honors & Awards:* Alexander Graham Bell Award, Inst Elec & Electronics Engrs, 78. *Mem:* Fel Inst Elec & Electronics Engrs. *Res:* Analysis of electromagnetic switching apparatus; semiconductor circuits; electronic switching systems; pulse code modulation transmission systems; submarine surveillance systems; transmission systems. *Mailing Add:* Bell Tel Labs Div 45 Murray Hill NJ 07974

SUMNER, JOHN RANDOLPH, b Corpus Christi, Tex, Aug 28, 44; m 69; c 2. GEOPHYSICS. *Educ:* Univ Ariz, BS, 66; Stanford Univ, MS, 68, PhD(geophys), 71. *Prof Exp:* Asst prof earth sci, Univ Calif, Santa Cruz & fel, Crown Col, 71-72; asst prof geophysics, Lehigh Univ, 72-77; SR RES SPECIALIST, EXXON PROD RES CO, 77- *Mem:* Geol Soc Am; Soc Explor Geophys; Am Geophys Union. *Res:* Solid earth geophysics; exploration seismology; gravity and magnetic fields of geologic structures. *Mailing Add:* Exxon Prod Res Co PO Box 2189 Houston TX 77001

SUMNER, JOHN STEWART, b Bozeman, Mont, June 24, 21; m 43; c 3. EXPLORATION GEOPHYSICS, GEOLOGY. *Educ:* Univ Minn, BS, 47 & 48; Univ Wis, PhD, 55. *Prof Exp:* Staff geophysicist, Jones & Laughlin Steel Corp, 54-55; asst prof geophys, Western State Col, Colo, 55-56; mgr, McPhar Geophys, Inc, 56-57; chief geophysicist, Phelps Dodge Corp, 57-63; prof geophys, Col Mines, 63-72, PROF GEOPHYS, COL EARTH SCI, UNIV ARIZ, 72- *Concurrent Pos:* Consult, Mining Co. *Mem:* Soc Explor Geophys; Am Inst Mining, Metall & Petrol Eng; Am Geophys Union. *Res:* Mining geophysics including electrical resistivity and induced polarization methods and gravity, magnetic, and seismic exploration techniques. *Mailing Add:* 728 N Sawtelle Tucson AZ 85716

SUMNER, RICHARD LAWRENCE, b Albany, NY, May 28, 38; m 64; c 2. HIGH ENERGY PHYSICS. *Educ:* State Univ NY Albany, BS, 59; Univ Chicago, 3M, 65, PhD(physics), 75. *Prof Exp:* Res assoc physics, 72-73, MEM RES STAFF PHYSICS, PRINCETON UNIV, 73- *Res:* High energy elementary particle studies; direct muon production and particle production at large transverse momentum. *Mailing Add:* Dept of Physics Princeton Univ Princeton NJ 08540

SUMNER, ROGER D, b Hammond, Ind, Apr 18, 34; m 60; c 2. GEOPHYSICS. *Educ:* Rice Inst, BA, 56; Calif Inst Technol, MS, 58; Univ Wis, PhD(geophys), 65. *Prof Exp:* SR RES GEOPHYSICIST, EXPLOR DIV, GULF RES & DEVELOP CO, 65- *Mem:* Seismol Soc Am; Am Geophys Union; Soc Explor Geophys. *Res:* Seismic wave propagation. *Mailing Add:* Explor Div Gulf Res & Develop Co Drawer 2038 Pittsburgh PA 15230

SUMNER, THOMAS, b Akron, Ohio, Apr 16, 26. ORGANIC CHEMISTRY. *Educ:* Yale Univ, BS, 46, PhD(chem), 51. *Prof Exp:* Instr chem, Yale Univ, 46-50; from instr to prof chem, 50-57, Columbia-Southern prof, 57-61, from actg head to head dept chem, 52-61, from actg dean to dean col lib arts, 60-62, dean gen col, 62-77, PROF CHEM, UNIV AKRON, 74-, ACAD COUN, 77- *Mem:* Am Chem Soc. *Res:* Organic synthesis. *Mailing Add:* Dept of Chem Univ of Akron Akron OH 44325

SUMP, CORD H(ENRY), b Brooklyn, NY, Oct 15, 14; m 40; c 3. METALLURGY. *Educ:* NY Univ, BA, 37; Stevens Inst Technol, MS, 47. *Prof Exp:* Res chemist, Am Agr Chem Co, NJ, 37-40 & Baker & Co, NJ, 40-47; res metallurgist, Charles Hardy, Inc, NY, 47-49, chief engr, 49-50; supvr powder metall res, Armour Res Found, Ill Inst Technol, 50-58; dir res, Goldsmith Bros Smelting & Refining Co, 58-61; mgr metall prod, Vitro Chem Co Div, Vitro Corp Am, 61-65; mgr metall prod, Davison Chem Div, W R Grace & Co, 65-66; METALLURGIST, COMBUSTION ENG, INC, 66- *Concurrent Pos:* Consult, Mat Lab, US Air Force, 63-65. *Mem:* Am Chem Soc; Am Soc Metals. *Res:* Composite and high temperature materials; materials engineering; corrosion resistant austenitic-ferritic stainless steels; ceramic materials; fiber metallurgy. *Mailing Add:* 403 Howard Circle Chattanooga TN 37411

SUMRALL, H GLENN, b Macon, Miss, Nov 8, 42; m 63; c 1. PLANT PHYSIOLOGY, MICROBIOLOGY. *Educ:* Southeastern La Col, BS, 64; La State Univ, MS, 66, PhD(plant path), 69. *Prof Exp:* Asst prof biol, Cornell Col, 69-73; assoc prof, 73-77, PROF BIOL & COORDR BIOL SCI, LIBERTY BAPTIST COL, 77-, ASSOC ACAD DEAN, 78- *Mem:* Am Phytopath Soc. *Res:* Fecal coliform pollution in streams and lakes; physiology of plant disease. *Mailing Add:* PO Box 1111 Liberty Baptist Col Lynchburg VA 24505

SUMRELL, GENE, b Apache, Ariz, Oct 7, 19. ORGANIC CHEMISTRY. *Educ:* Eastern NMex Col, AB, 42; Univ NMex, BS, 47, MS, 48; Univ Calif, PhD(chem), 51. *Prof Exp:* Asst, Univ NMex, 47-48; asst, Univ Calif, 48-51; asst prof, Eastern NMex Univ, 51-53; res chemist, J T Baker Chem Co, 53-58; sr org chemist, Southwest Res Inst, 58-59; proj leader chem & plastics div, Food Mach & Chem Corp, 59-61; res sect leader, El Paso Natural Gas Prod Co, Tex, 61-64; sr chemist, Southern Utilization Res & Develop Div, 64-67, head invests, 67-73, RES LEADER OILSEED & FOOD LAB, SOUTHERN REGIONAL RES CTR, AGR RES SERV, USDA, 73- *Mem:* AAAS; Am Chem Soc; fel Am Inst Chem; Am Oil Chem Soc; Am Asn Textile Chemists & Colorists. *Res:* Fatty acids in tubercle bacilli; organic synthesis; pharmaceuticals; branched-chain compounds; triazoles; petrochemicals; fats and oils; monomers and polymers; cellulose chemistry; cereal chemistry. *Mailing Add:* Southern Regional Res Ctr PO Box 19687 New Orleans LA 70179

SUMSION, H(ENRY) T(HEODORE), b Chester, Utah, Mar 7, 12; m 38; c 4. MATERIALS SCIENCE ENGINEERING. *Educ:* Univ Utah, BS, 38, PhD(phys metall), 49; Univ Ala, MS, 39. *Prof Exp:* Engr, US Bur Mines, 39-42; asst phys metall, Univ Calif, 46-47; asst phys metall, Univ Utah, 47-49; sr engr, Carborundum Co, 49-51; res assoc, Knolls Atomic Power Lab, Gen Elec Co, 51-56, nuclear fuels metallurgist, Atomic Power Equip Dept, 56-57; res scientist, Lockheed Missiles & Space Co, 57-62; RES SCIENTIST, AMES RES CTR, NASA, 62- *Honors & Awards:* Civilian Commendation Award, US Navy, 59; Apollo Award, NASA, 69. *Mem:* AAAS; Am Soc Metals; fel Am Inst Chem; Am Inst Mining, Metall & Petrol Engrs; NY Acad Sci. *Res:* Space environment-materials reactions; space materials applications; solid state structures; x-ray diffraction. *Mailing Add:* 5378 Harwood Rd San Jose CA 95124

SUN, ALBERT YUNG-KWANG, b Amoy, Fukien, China, Oct 13, 32; m 64; c 1. BIOCHEMISTRY, NEUROCHEMISTRY. *Educ:* Nat Taiwan Univ, BS, 57; Ore State Univ, PhD(biochem), 67. *Prof Exp:* AEC fel & res assoc biochem, Case Western Reserve Univ, 67-68; res assoc lab neurochem, Cleveland Psychiat Inst, 68-72, proj dir, 72-74, ASSOC PROF, SINCLAIR COMP MED RES FARM, UNIV MO, 74- *Concurrent Pos:* NIH gen res support grant, Cleveland Psychiat Inst, 68-73; Cleveland Diabetic Fund res grant, 72; alcohol grant, Nat Inst Alcohol Abuse & Alcoholism, 74; aging grant, Nat Inst Neurol Commun Dis & Strokes, 75. *Mem:* AAAS; Am Chem Soc; Biochem Soc; Am Soc Neurochem; Soc Neurosci. *Res:* Functional and structural relationship of the central nervous system membranes; active transport mechanism; drug effects on synaptic transmission of the central nervous system. *Mailing Add:* Sinclair Res Farm Univ of Mo Columbia MO 65201

SUN, ALEXANDER SHIHKAUNG, b Feb 21, 39; US citizen; m 68; c 1. BIOCHEMISTRY, CELL BIOLOGY. *Educ:* Taiwan Normal Univ, BS, 63; Univ Calif, Berkeley, PhD(biochem), 71. *Prof Exp:* Guest investr, Dept Biochem Cytol, Rockefeller Univ, 71-72; asst res physiologist, Dept Physiol & Anat, Univ Calif, Berkeley, 72-75; asst prof path, 75-77, ASST PROF NEOPLASTIC DIS, MT SINAI SCH MED, 77- *Mem:* Am Soc Cell Biol; Am Soc Photobiol; Geront Soc Am. *Res:* Biochemistry of human aging, especially the effects of oxidative damage generated by subcellular organelles on cell aging, the mechanism controlling the different lifespans of normal and tumor cells in vitro. *Mailing Add:* Dept Path Mt Sinai Sch Med 5th Ave at 100th St New York NY 10029

SUN, ANTHONY MEIN-FANG, b Nanking, China, April 10, 35; m 61; c 2. ENDOCRINOLOGY, DIABETES. *Educ:* Nat Taiwan Univ, BSc, 58; Univ Toronto, PhD(physiol), 72. *Prof Exp:* Res assoc, Hosp Sick Children, 72-75; from lectr to asst prof, 72-80, ASSOC PROF PHYSIOL, UNIV TORONTO, 80-; RES SCIENTIST, CONNAUGHT RES INST, 74- *Concurrent Pos:* Res consult, Res Int Hosp Sick Children, 75-77. *Mem:* Int Soc Artificial Organs; Am Diabetes Asn; Can Physiol Soc; Can Diabetes Asn; Can Biomat Soc. *Res:* Long term culture of pancreatic islets of langerhans; the development of a bioartificial endocrine pancreas; differentiation of endocrine cells (somatotrophs and pancreatic beta cells); insulin biosynthesis and secretion. *Mailing Add:* Dept Physiol Fac Med Med Sci Bldg Toronto ON M5S 1A8 Can

SUN, BERNARD CHING-HUEY, b Nanking, China, Aug 23, 37; m 64; c 1. FOREST PRODUCTS, ADHESION. *Educ:* Nat Taiwan Univ, BSA, 60; Univ BC, MS, 67, PhD(wood-pulp sci), 70. *Prof Exp:* Jr specialist, Nat Taiwan Univ Res Forest, 61-63; demonstr wood pulp sci, Univ BC, 68-70; asst prof wood sci, 70-75, ASSOC PROF WOOD SCI DEPT FORESTRY, MICH TECHNOL UNIV, 75- *Mem:* Forest Prod Res Soc; Soc Wood Sci & Technol. *Res:* Wood products; wood-pulp relationships; wood composite materials; adhesion and adhesives. *Mailing Add:* Dept of Forestry Mich Technol Univ Houghton MI 49931

SUN, CHANG-TSAN, b Mukden, China, Feb 20, 28; US citizen; m 63; c 2. ENGINEERING MECHANICS, MATERIALS SCIENCE. *Educ:* Nat Taiwan Univ, BS, 53; Stevens Inst Technol, MS, 60; Yale Univ, PhD(solid mech), 64. *Prof Exp:* Sr engr, Atomic Power Develop Assocs Inc, Mich, 64-65; asst prof eng mech, Iowa State Univ, 65-68, assoc prof, 68-77; SR RES ENGR, GEN MOTORS RES LABS, MICH, 77- *Mem:* Am Soc Mech Engrs; Am Soc Testing & Mat. *Res:* Wave propagation; composite materials; fiber reinforced plastics; stress analysis. *Mailing Add:* Dept Sci Univ Fla Gainesville FL 32611

SUN, CHAO NIEN, b Hopeh, China, Dec 4, 14; m 46; c 2. EXPERIMENTAL PATHOLOGY. *Educ:* Nat Peking Univ, BSc, 40; Univ Okla, MSc, 50; Ohio State Univ, PhD, 53. *Prof Exp:* Asst biol, Nat Peking Univ, 40-45, lectr, 45-48; asst, Univ Okla, 48-50; asst, Ohio State Univ, 50-51; asst biophys, St Louis Univ, 52-53, res assoc biol & biophys, 54-57; fel anat, Wash Univ, 57-62; from asst prof to assoc prof path, St Louis Univ, 62-67; res assoc prof, Baylor Univ, 67-69; assoc prof path, Sch Med & electron microscopist, Hosp, 69-73, PROF PATH, UNIV ARK MED SCI, LITTLE ROCK & CHIEF ELECTRON MICROSCOPE LAB, VET ADMIN HOSP, 73- *Concurrent Pos:* Fel, Inst Divi Thomae Found, 53-54. *Mem:* Am Soc Cell Biol; Electron Micros Soc Am. *Res:* Experimental virology; histochemistry; differentiation; tissue culture; biological and pathological ultrastructure; electron microscopy. *Mailing Add:* 2104 Gunpowder Rd Little Rock AR 72207

SUN, CHENG, b Kiang Su, China, Apr 12, 37; m 62; c 1. ELECTRICAL ENGINEERING. *Educ:* Nat Taiwan Univ, BS, 58; Cornell Univ, MS, 62, PhD(microwaves), 65. *Prof Exp:* Mem tech staff microwave appl res, RCA David Sarnoff Res Ctr, 64-71; MEM TECH STAFF, ELECTRON DYNAMICS DIV, HUGHES AIRCRAFT CO, 71- *Mem:* Inst Elec & Electronics Engrs. *Res:* Microwave solid state circuits and devices. *Mailing Add:* Electron Dynamics Div Hughes Aircraft Co Torrance CA 90509

SUN, CHIH-REE, b Hsu-Chen, China, May 6, 23; m 56; c 3. HIGH ENERGY PHYSICS, NUCLEAR PHYSICS. *Educ:* Univ Calcutta, BSc, 47; Univ Calif, Los Angeles, MS, 51, PhD(physics), 56. *Prof Exp:* Teacher, Overseas Chinese High Sch, India, 47-49; mem res staff physics, Princeton Univ, 56-62; asst prof, Northwestern Univ, 62-65; assoc prof, Queens Col, NY, 65-68; assoc prof, 68-78, PROF PHYSICS, STATE UNIV NY ALBANY, 78- *Concurrent Pos:* Consult, Princeton Univ, 66-69. *Mem:* Am Phys Soc. *Res:* High energy experiments with bubble chambers study of elementary particles; channeling in crystals; accelerator; nuclear instrumentation. *Mailing Add:* Dept of Physics State Univ of NY Albany NY 12203

SUN, CHIN-TEH, b Taiwan, China, Apr 9, 39; m 68; c 1. ENGINEERING MECHANICS. *Educ:* Nat Taiwan Univ, BS, 62; Northwestern Univ, MS, 65, PhD(mech), 67. *Prof Exp:* Fel, Northwestern Univ, 67-68; from asst prof to assoc prof aeronaut & astronaut, 68-76, PROF AERONAUT & ASTRONAUT, PURDUE UNIV, WEST LAFAYETTE, 76- *Mem:* Am Inst Aeronaut & Astronaut; Am Acad Mech; Am Soc Mech Engrs; Seismol Soc Am. *Res:* Mechanics of composite materials; stress waves; structures; fracture mechanics. *Mailing Add:* Sch of Astronaut Aeronaut & Eng Sci Purdue Univ West Lafayette IN 47907

SUN, CHUNG-LI, b Yangchow, China, May 21, 35; m 68; c 2. HEAT EXCHANGERS, NUCLEAR STEAM GENERATOR. *Educ:* Nat Taiwan Univ, BS, 57, MS, 63; McMaster Univ, MS, 64; Univ Fla, PhD(eng sci, mech), 67. *Prof Exp:* Engr, Chinese Mil Construct Bur, 58-59; teaching asst civil eng, Chung-Yuan Inst Technol, 59-60; asst prof mech & aerospace eng, Ind Inst Technol, 67-77; MEM STAFF, TAMPA DIV, WESTINGHOUSE ELEC CORP, 77- *Concurrent Pos:* Engr, Taiwan Hwy Bur, 60; NSF res partic grant, Syracuse Univ, 70. *Mem:* Am Soc Mech Engrs; Am Soc Civil Engrs. *Res:* Heat exchanger flow-induced tube vibration; nonlinear vibrations; dynamic stability of deformable systems; finite element method in structural analysis. *Mailing Add:* Tampa Div 6001 S Westshore Tampa FL 33616

SUN, DAH CHEN, b Tientsin City, China, Sept 10, 36; m 64; c 2. AEROSPACE SCIENCES, ENGINEERING MECHANICS. *Educ:* Taiwan Univ, BS, 59; Univ Kans, MS, 63; Princeton Univ, PhD(aerospace sci), 69. *Prof Exp:* Assoc sr res engr lubrication, 69-81, STAFF RES ENGR FLUID & SOLID MECH, GEN MOTORS RES LABS, GEN MOTORS CORP, 81- *Res:* Basic and applied research in the fields of lubrication, friction and wear; aerospace sciences specializing in gas dynamics and rarefied gas dynamics. *Mailing Add:* Dept Mech Res Gen Motors Corp Warren MI 48090

SUN, FANG-KUO, b Taiwan, Repub China, May 8, 46; US citizen; m 70; c 3. DYNAMIC SYSTEMS ANALYSIS. *Educ:* Nat Chiao-Tung Univ, Taiwan, BS, 69; Univ Pittsburgh, MS, 72; Harvard Univ, PhD(decision & control), 76. *Prof Exp:* Res assoc syst eng, Sci Res Lab, Ford Motor Co, 76-77; STAFF ANALYST, SYSTS ENG, ANALYTIC SCI CORP, 77- *Mem:* Inst Elec & Electronics Engrs; Soc Indust & Appl Math; Sigma Xi. *Res:* Systems analysis and design; statistical analysis; operations research. *Mailing Add:* 44 Chequessette Rd Reading MA 01867

SUN, FRANK F, b Kiangshi, China, July 26, 38; m; c 2. BIOCHEMISTRY. *Educ:* Tunghai Univ, Taiwan, BS, 59; Tex Tech Univ, MS, 63; Univ Tex, Austin, PhD(biochem), 66. *Prof Exp:* NIH fel biochem, Purdue Univ, Lafayette, 66-68; RES BIOCHEMIST DEPT EXP BIOL, UPJOHN CO, 68- *Mem:* Am Chem Soc. *Res:* Lipid biochemistry; prostaglandin analysis and metabolism; drug metabolism; bioenergetics. *Mailing Add:* Dept of Exp Biol Res Lab Upjohn Co Kalamazoo MI 49001

SUN, HUGO SUI-HWAN, b Hong Kong, Oct 19, 40; m 67; c 2. ALGEBRA, NUMBER THEORY. *Educ:* Univ Calif, Berkeley, BA, 63; Univ Md, College Park, MA, 66; Univ NB, Fredericton, PhD(math), 69. *Prof Exp:* Asst prof math, Univ NB, Fredericton, 69-70; asst prof, 70-74, assoc prof, 74-78, PROF MATH, CALIF STATE UNIV, FRESNO, 78- *Mem:* Am Math Soc; Math Asn Am; NY Acad Sci. *Res:* Group theory, number theory, combinatorial analysis, and finite geometry; combinatorics. *Mailing Add:* Dept of Math Calif State Univ Fresno CA 93740

SUN, HUN H, b Shanghai, China, Mar 27, 25; m 51; c 1. ELECTRICAL ENGINEERING. *Educ:* Nat Chiao Tung Univ, BS, 46; Univ Wash, MS, 50; Cornell Univ, PhD, 55. *Prof Exp:* Asst elec eng, Cornell Univ, 51-53; from asst prof to assoc prof, 53-59, prof elec eng, 58-78, dir biomed eng & sci prog, 64-73, Chmn Dept, 73-78, ERNEST O LANGE PROF ELEC ENG, DREXEL UNIV, 78- *Concurrent Pos:* Mem, Franklin Inst, 60-; NIH spec fel & res assoc, Mass Inst Technol, 63-64; ed-in-chief, Trans Biomed Eng, Inst Elec & Electronics Engrs, 72-; mem study comt, Surg & Bioeng Sect, NIH, 81-84. *Mem:* Am Soc Eng Educ; Inst Elec & Electronics Engrs. *Res:* Biomedical engineering; network analysis and synthesis; feedback control system. *Mailing Add:* Dept Elec Eng 32 & Chestnut Sts Philadelphia PA 19104

SUN, JAMES MING-SHAN, b China, May 10, 18; nat US; m 53; c 2. MINERALOGY, GEOPHYSICS. *Educ:* Nat Cent Univ, China, BS, 40; Univ Chicago, MS, 47; La State Univ, PhD(geol), 50. *Prof Exp:* Res fel, Columbia Univ, 50-51; mineralogist, State Bur Mines & Mineral Resources, NMex Inst Mining & Technol, 51-62; resident res fel, Jet Propulsion Lab, Calif Inst Technol, 62-64; res physicist, Air Force Weapons Lab, 64-69; res & writing, 69-74; prof geophys sci, Nat Cent Univ, Taiwan, Repub China, 74-76; DIR, SIGMA RES ASSOCS, 76- *Mem:* AAAS; fel Mineral Soc Am; Am Geophys Union; Geochem Soc. *Res:* X-ray crystallography and fluorescent spectroscopy; volcanic rocks; authigenic minerals; minerals of New Mexico; physics of high pressure; hypervelocity impact and cratering; digital simulation techniques. *Mailing Add:* 7704 Sierra Azul NE Albuquerque NM 87110

SUN, MING, b Honan, China, US citizen; m 72; c 1. ENZYME IMMUNOCHEMISTRY, BIOCHEMISTRY. *Educ:* Univ Colo, BS, 67; Tex Tech Univ, PhD(biochem), 74. *Prof Exp:* Assoc med, Sch Med & Dent, Univ Rochester, 74-78; RES BIOCHEMIST IMMUNOCHEM, ABBOTT LABS, 78- *Concurrent Pos:* Robert A Welch res fel chem, Tex Tech Univ, 71-72; Am Heart Asn res fel biochem, Univ Rochester, 74-76, NIH res fel med, 76-77; res grant, Rochester Eye & Human Part Bank Inc, 78-79. *Mem:* Am Soc Photobiol; AAAS; Am Chem Soc; fel Am Inst Chemists. *Res:* Physiological roles and immunoassays of different hormones; cytochrome oxidase; prostaglandin enzymes; diagnostic markers; radioimmunoassay, enzyme immunoassay and fluorophenylalnine development. *Mailing Add:* Abbott Labs Abbott Park 8 N Chicago IL 60064

SUN, NAI CHAU, b Shanghai, China, June 15, 36; m 64. GENETICS, CELL BIOLOGY. *Educ:* Nat Taiwan Univ, BSc, 60; Univ Man, MSc, 65; Iowa State Univ, PhD(genetics, cell biol), 70. *Prof Exp:* NIH fel aging study, Biol Div, Oak Ridge Nat Lab, 70-72; res assoc somatic cell genetics, Med Sch, Univ Mich, Ann Arbor, 72-77; MEM STAFF, BIOL DIV, OAK RIDGE NAT LAB, 77- *Mem:* Am Soc Microbiol. *Res:* Auxotrophic mutants induction and selection in cultured Chinese hamster cells in the study of pyrimidine pathway and glycolysis. *Mailing Add:* Biotech Res Lab 3 Taft Ct Rockville MD 20850

SUN, PU-NING, b Tientsin, China, Oct 23, 32; m 67; c 2. MECHANICAL ENGINEERING. *Educ:* Nat Taiwan Univ, BS, 54; Tex A&M Univ, MS, 60, PhD(mech eng), 64. *Prof Exp:* Sr inspector, Taiwan Bur Weights & Measures, China, 54-59; asst prof & acting head dept, 64-65, head dept mech eng, 65-68, acting chmn eng div, 68-72, PROF MECH ENG, CHRISTIAN BROS COL, 65-, HEAD, DEPT MECH ENG, 72- *Concurrent Pos:* Am Soc Eng Educ-Ford Found resident fel, Ford Motor Co, 71-72; NSF fel, Nat Bur Standards, 76. *Mem:* AAAS; Am Soc Mech Engrs; Soc Exp Stress Anal. *Res:* Theoretical and experimental stress analysis. *Mailing Add:* Dept of Mech Eng Christian Bros Col Memphis TN 38104

SUN, R(OBERT) C(HING-I), b Chungking, China, Dec 26, 38; m 65; c 3. METALLURGY, MATERIALS SCIENCE. *Educ:* Cheng Kung Univ, Taiwan, BS, 61; Univ Okla, MEng, 64; Carnegie-Mellon Univ, MS, 67, PhD(metall), 69. *Prof Exp:* MEM TECH STAFF, BELL TEL LABS, 69- *Mem:* Am Inst Mining, Metall & Petrol Engrs; Am Soc Metals. *Res:* Diffusion; phase transformation; grain boundary; x-ray; semiconductor processing; integrated circuit technology. *Mailing Add:* Bell Tel Labs 555 Union Blvd Allentown PA 18103

SUN, SAMUEL SAI-MING, b Canton, China, Sept 15, 42; m 75; c 1. RECOMBINANT DNA. *Educ:* Chinese Univ Hong Kong, BSc, 66; Univ Hong Kong, MSc, 71; Univ Wis-Madison, PhD(bot & hort), 75. *Prof Exp:* Demonstr plant biochem, Dept Bot, Univ Hong Kong, 69-71; res asst, Dept Hort, Univ Wis, 71-74; fel, Univ Wis-Madison, 75-79, asst scientist, 79-80; SR SCIENTIST PLANT BIOCHEM, ARCO PLANT CELL RES INST, 80- *Mem:* NY Acad Sci; Am Soc Plant Physiologists; Sigma Xi; Am Inst Biol Sci. *Res:* Plant enzyme and protein chemistry; enzyme and protein biosynthesis and their regulation during plant development; structure, organization, and expression of plant genes; crop improvement. *Mailing Add:* Arco Plant Cell Res Inst 6560 Trinity Ct Dublin CA 94596

SUN, SIAO FANG, b Shaoshing, China, Feb 19, 22; m 51; c 3. PHYSICAL CHEMISTRY. *Educ:* Nat Chengchi Univ, LLB, 45; Univ Utah, MA, 50; Loyola Univ Chicago, MS, 56; Univ Chicago, PhD, 58; Univ Ill, PhD, 62. *Prof Exp:* Prof math, Northland Col, 60-64; from asst prof to assoc prof, 64-75, PROF CHEM, ST JOHN'S UNIV, NY, 75- *Concurrent Pos:* Vis scientist, CNRS, Strasbourg, France, 75 & Meudon-Bellevue, France, 78; scientist, Max Planck Inst Biophys Chem, Gottingen, WGer, 76 & Carlsberg Lab, Copenhagen, Denmark, 81. *Mem:* Am Chem Soc. *Res:* Theoretical molecular kinetics; physical chemistry of macromolecules. *Mailing Add:* Dept of Chem St John's Univ Jamaica NY 11439

SUN, TUNG-TIEN, b China, Feb 20, 47; m 71; c 2. BIOCHEMISTRY, CELL BIOLOGY. *Educ:* Nat Taiwan Univ, BS, 67; Univ Calif, Davis, PhD(biochem), 74. *Prof Exp:* Res assoc biol, Mass Inst Technol, 74-77; asst prof dermat, cell biol & anat, 78-81, ASSOC PROF CELL BIOL & ANAT, DERMAT & OPHTHAL, SCH MED, JOHNS HOPKINS UNIV, 81- *Concurrent Pos:* NIH res career develop award, 78. *Mem:* Int Soc Differentiation; Tissue Cult Asn; Asn Res Vision & Ophthal; AAAS; Am Soc Biol Chemists. *Res:* Tissue culture and biochemical studies of mammalian epithelial differentiation. *Mailing Add:* Dept of Dermat Johns Hopkins Univ Sch of Med Baltimore MD 21205

SUN, WEN-YIN, b I-Lan, Taiwan. METEOROLOGY, FLUID DYNAMICS. *Educ:* Nat Taiwan Univ, BS, 68; Univ Chicago, MS, 72, PhD(meteorol), 75. *Prof Exp:* Res asst prof, Meteorol Lab Atmospheric Res, Univ Ill, 75-78; vis scientist, Geofluid Dynamics Prog, Princeton Univ, 78-79; ASST PROF ATMOSPHERIC SCI, DEPT GEOSCI, PURDUE UNIV, 79- *Mem:* Am Meteorol Soc. *Res:* Theoretical and numerical studies of dynamic meteorology, boundary layer meteorology, turbulences, and numerical analysis of fluid dynamics equations. *Mailing Add:* Dept Geosci Purdue Univ West Lafayette IN 47907

SUN, YUN PEI, b China, June 20, 10; nat US; m 38; c 2. INSECT TOXICOLOGY. *Educ:* Nat Cheking Univ, China, BS, 32; Univ Minn, MS, 41, PhD(entom), 43. *Prof Exp:* Jr chemist in charge insecticides lab, Nat Agr Res Bur, China, 35-39; res fel, Cornell Univ, 44-48; res entomologist & dir insecticides test lab, Julius Hyman & Co, 48-52; asst mgr in charge entom & residue anal labs, Shell Develop Co, 52-54, mgr entom dept, 54-57, chief entomologist biol sci res ctr, 57-70; CONSULT, 70- *Concurrent Pos:* Consult, Sino-US Joint Comn Rural Reconstruct, 71 & 72-74; prof, Nat Taiwan Univ, 72; dir, Plant Protection Ctr, Taiwan, 72-74, hon adv, 74. *Mem:* AAAS; Entom Soc Am; Sigma Xi. *Res:* Bioassay of insecticides and their residues; correlation between chemical structure and insect toxicity; joint action of insecticides; dynamics of pesticide toxicology; pesticide regulations. *Mailing Add:* 1918 La Villa Rose Court Modesto CA 95350

SUN, YUN-CHUNG, b Shaoton, China, Feb 18, 37; US citizen; m 68; c 1. CHEMICAL ENGINEERING, MATHEMATICS. *Educ:* Tunghai Univ, Taiwan, BS, 61; Univ Mo, MS, 64, PhD(chem eng), 66. *Prof Exp:* Instr chem, Univ Mo, 63-66; SR RES ENGR, DOW CHEM CO, 66- *Concurrent Pos:* Asst prof chem eng, Saginaw Valley Col, 68. *Mem:* Am Inst Chem Engrs; Am Chem Soc. *Res:* Chemical reaction kinetics; component purification and crystallization; polymer sciences. *Mailing Add:* Dow Chem Co 438 Bldg Midland MI 48640

SUNADA, DANIEL K(ATSUTO), b Newcastle, Calif, Apr 3, 36; m 60; c 3. CIVIL ENGINEERING. *Educ:* Univ Calif, Berkeley, BS, 59, MS, 60, PhD(civil eng), 65. *Prof Exp:* ASST PROF CIVIL ENG, COLO STATE UNIV, 65- *Concurrent Pos:* Res grants, 66-72. *Mem:* Am Soc Civil Engrs; Nat Soc Prof Engrs. *Res:* Fundamentals of fluid flow through porous media; physical and chemical behavior of concrete containing calcium-sulfonal aluminate additive. *Mailing Add:* Dept of Civil Eng Colo State Univ Ft Collins CO 80521

SUNAHARA, FRED AKIRA, b Vancouver, BC, Jan 22, 24; m 52; c 5. PHARMACOLOGY. *Educ:* Univ Western Ont, BSc, 48, PhD(physiol), 52. *Prof Exp:* Fel physiol, Univ Western Ont, 52-53; sci officer aviation med, Defence Res Med Lab, Toronto, 53-61; sr pharmacologist, Ayerst Res Lab, Montreal, 61-64; PROF PHARMACOL, UNIV TORONTO, 64- *Concurrent Pos:* Assoc physiol, Univ Toronto, 59-61; Ont Heart Found res grants, 65- *Mem:* Am Physiol Soc; Can Physiol Soc; Pharmacol Soc Can. *Res:* Cardiovascular and respiratory physiology with reference to experimental anemia and to hypobaric environment; autonomic and cardiovascular pharmacology; interrelationship of autonomic drugs and prostaglandin group of substances. *Mailing Add:* Dept of Pharmacol Univ of Toronto Fac of Med Toronto ON M5S 1A8 Can

SUND, ELDON H, b Plentywood, Mont, June 6, 30; m 57; c 4. ORGANIC CHEMISTRY. *Educ:* Univ Ill, Urbana, BS, 52; Univ Tex, PhD(org chem), 60. *Prof Exp:* Res chemist, E I du Pont de Nemours & Co, Del, 59-66; asst prof chem, Ohio Northern Univ, 66-67; from asst prof to assoc prof, 67-73, PROF CHEM, MIDWESTERN STATE UNIV, 73- *Concurrent Pos:* Hardin prof, Hardin Found, 75-76; consult, N Tex Chem Consult. *Mem:* AAAS; Sigma Xi; Int Soc Heterocyclic Chem; Am Chem Soc. *Res:* Synthesis of heterocyclic compounds. *Mailing Add:* Dept of Chem Midwestern State Univ Wichita Falls TX 76308

SUND, PAUL N, b Thief River Falls, Minn, Nov 13, 32; m 56; c 2. OCEANOGRAPHY. *Educ:* Univ Calif, Santa Barbara, BA, 54; Univ Wash, Seattle, MA, 56. *Prof Exp:* Biol oceanogr, Inter-Am Trop Tuna Comn, 56-63; oceanogr, 63-67, asst chief br marine fisheries, 67-71, nat coordr, Platforms of Opportunity Progs, 71-77, OCEANOGRAPHER, PAC ENVIRON GROUP, NAT MARINE FISHERIES SERV, 78- *Concurrent Pos:* Mem plankton adv comt, Smithsonian Inst, 64-; adj prof, Fla Atlantic Univ, 66-68; fel, Nat Inst Pub Affairs, 69. *Mem:* AAAS; fel Am Inst Fishery Res Biol; Marine Technol Soc; Am Soc Limnol & Oceanog; Marine Biol Asn UK. *Res:* Fishery and zooplankton ecology; chaetognath taxonomy and ecology; biological oceanography relative to biological indicators of water mass; oceanographic and climatological influences on tunas, billfishes and marine mammals; ecology and life history of tropical tunas; aerial remote sensing of marine mammals; satellite oceanography. *Mailing Add:* Nat Marine Fisheries Serv Fleet Numerical Weather Cent Monterey CA 93940

SUND, RAYMOND EARL, b Capac, Mich, Dec 14, 32; m 61; c 4. NUCLEAR PHYSICS. *Educ:* Univ Mich, BSE(physics) & BSE(math), 55, MS, 56, PhD(physics), 60. *Prof Exp:* Assoc res physicist, Univ Mich Res Inst, 60-61; staff assoc, Gen Atomic Co, San Diego, 61-63, staff mem, 63-77; engr, 77-80, RES & DEVELOP DIR, TOLEDO EDISON CO, TOLEDO, OHIO, 80- *Mem:* Am Phys Soc; Am Nuclear Soc. *Res:* Investigation of decay schemes of radioactive isotopes; studies of photonuclear reactions and of prompt and delayed gamma rays from fission; afterheat and shielding studies for reactors. *Mailing Add:* 6014 Glenbeigh Dr Sylvania OH 43560

SUNDAHL, ROBERT CHARLES, JR, b Minneapolis, Minn, Dec 6, 36; m 58; c 4. METALLURGY. *Educ:* Univ Minn, Minneapolis, BS, 58, MS, 64, PhD(metall), 68. *Prof Exp:* Mem tech staff, 68-73, SUPVR TECH STAFF, BELL TEL LABS, 73- *Concurrent Pos:* Mem publ comt, Metall Transactions, 70-76. *Mem:* Am Inst Mining, Metall & Petrol Engrs; Am Vacuum Soc. *Res:* Short range order, magnetic properties, defects and electronic structure of alloys; surface chemistry; physical properties of electronic ceramics; piezoelectric crystal device technology; integrated optics devices, materials. *Mailing Add:* Bell Tel Labs 555 Union Blvd Allentown PA 18103

SUNDARALINGAM, MUTTAIYA, b Taiping, Malaysia, Sept 21, 31; nat US; m 66; c 1. BIOLOGICAL CRYSTALLOGRAPHY. *Educ:* Ceylon Univ, BSc, 56; Univ Pittsburgh, PhD(chem), 61. *Prof Exp:* Res assoc crystallog sch med, Univ Wash, Seattle, 62-65; res assoc lab molecular biol, Children's Cancer Res Found, Boston, Mass & Harvard Med Sch, 65-66; assoc prof chem, Case Western Reserve Univ, 66-69; PROF BIOCHEM, UNIV WIS-MADISON, 69- *Concurrent Pos:* John Simon Guggenheim fel lab molecular biophys, Dept Zool, Oxford Univ, 75-76. *Mem:* AAAS; Am Crystallog Asn; Am Chem Soc; Biophys Soc; The Chem Soc. *Res:* X-ray diffraction investigation of biological structures; conformational analysis; nucleic acids transfer ribonucleic acids; nucleic acid principles; proteins; nucleic acid-drug and nucleic acid-protein complexes; membrane phospholipids; carbohydrates. *Mailing Add:* Dept of Biochem Univ of Wis Madison WI 53706

SUNDARAM, KALYAN, b Hyderabad, India, Nov 22, 32; US citizen; m 67; c 2. BIOCHEMISTRY. *Educ:* Osmania Univ, India, BVSc, 55; Univ Man, Can, MSc, 63; Purdue Univ, PhD(animal physiol), 66. *Prof Exp:* Vet, Govt Andhra Pradesh, India, 55-61; fel cancer res, Sloan Kettering Inst, 66-67; SCIENTIST, POPULATION CONTROL, 67- *Mem:* Endocrine Soc; Soc Study Reproduction. *Res:* Hypothalamus, pituitary and gonadal axis; effects of Luteinizing-hormone releasing hormone, and its analogs on pituitary and testicular function; investigation of new methods of chemical contraception in the male. *Mailing Add:* Population Coun 1230 York Ave New York NY 10021

SUNDARAM, PANCHANATHAM N, b Madras, India, Aug 23, 39; m 66; c 2. ROCK MECHANICS, SOIL MECHANICS. *Educ:* Lagappa Ettidr Col Eng & Technol, India, BE, 61; Col Eng, Guindy, India, MSc, 65; Univ Calif, Berkeley, PhD(civil eng), 77. *Prof Exp:* Jr engr civil eng, Public Works Dept, Govt Madras, 61-63; lectr, Indian Inst Technol, Bombay, 66-72; asst prof, Univ Wis, Milwaukee, 78-80; scientist rock mech, Lawrence Berkeley Lab, 80-82; SR ENGR SOIL MECH, BECHIEL INC, 82- *Concurrent Pos:* geotech engr, Hallenbeck-McKay Assoc, 73; vis engr, Univ Calif, Berkeley, 78; res award, US Comt Rock Mech, Nat Res Coun, 78. *Mem:* Am Soc Civil Engrs; Int Soc Rock Mech; Underground Space Asn. *Res:* Hydraulic flow through rock fractures; determination of rock properties; electro-osmosis in soils; properties of spent oil-shale. *Mailing Add:* 130 Violet Rd Hercules CA 94547

SUNDARAM, SWAMINATHA, physics, see previous edition

SUNDARARAJAN, PUDUPADI RANGANATHAN, b Madras, India, Sept 16, 43; m 70; c 2. POLYMER PHYSICS, BIOPHYSICS. *Educ:* Univ Madras, India, BSc, 63, MSc, 65, PhD(biophys), 69, DSc(physics), 81. *Prof Exp:* Res assoc chem, Univ Montreal, 69-71 & 73-75; res assoc, Stanford Univ, 71-73; res scientist polymer & paper physcis, 75-79, proj leader mat characterization, 79-81, MGR MAT CHARACTERIZATION, XEROX RES CTR CAN LTD, 81- *Concurrent Pos:* Consult, Biochem Nomenclature, Int Union Pure & Appl Chem, 71-79. *Mem:* Am Chem Soc; Chem Inst Can; Am Phys Soc; NY Acad Sci. *Res:* Studies on solution and solid state conformations; structure and morphology of synthetic and natural polymers using diffraction and theoretical methods and relating them to the properties of polymers. *Mailing Add:* Xerox Res Ctr Can Ltd 2480 Dunwin Dr Mississauga ON L5L 1J9 Can

SUNDARESAN, MOSUR KALYANARAMAN, b Madras, India, Sept 2, 29; Can citizen; m 57; c 2. ELEMENTARY PARTICLE PHYSICS. *Educ:* Delhi Univ, India, BSc, 47, MSc, 49; Cornell Univ, NY, PhD(theoret physics), 55. *Prof Exp:* Asst prof, 61-62, assoc prof, 62-65, PROF PHYSICS, CARLETON UNIV, OTTAWA, 65- *Concurrent Pos:* Mem bd trustees, Inst Particle Physics, Can, 81- *Mem:* Can Asn Physicists; Am Phys Soc; Am Asn Physics Teachers. *Res:* Theoretical physics, particularly research in quantum chromodynamics. *Mailing Add:* Physics Dept Carleton Univ Ottawa ON K1S 5B6 Can

SUNDARESAN, PERUVEMBA RAMNATHAN, b Madras, India, Aug 11, 30; m 70; c 2. NUTRITIONAL BIOCHEMISTRY. *Educ:* Univ Banaras, BSc, 50, MSc, 53; Indian Inst Sci, Bangalore, PhD(biochem), 58. *Prof Exp:* Res asst biochem, Coun Sci & Indust Res, New Delhi, 56-58; res asst, Indian Inst Sci, Bangalore, 58-59; sr res fel, Coun Sci & Indust Res, 59-61; res assoc nutrit biochem radio carbon lab, Univ Ill, Urbana, 61-62; res assoc, Mass Inst Technol, 62-64; Nat Acad Sci-Nat Res Coun res assoc environ biochem, US Army Res Inst Environ Med, Mass, 64-66, res biochemist, 66-68; chief lipids lab res inst, St Joseph Hosp, 68-77; TOXICOLOGIST/BIOCHEMIST, DIV TOXICOL, BUR FOODS, FOOD & DRUG ADMIN, 77- *Concurrent Pos:* NIH res grants dept animal sci, Univ Ill, 60-61 & dept nutrit & food sci, Mass Inst Technol, 61-64; res consult, Millersville State Col, 72-77; consult biochem, Vet Admin Hosp, 73-77, consult tech dir, Infant Metab Diag Lab, 78- *Mem:* AAAS; Am Soc Biol Chemists; Am Inst Nutrit; Brit Biochem Soc; Am Col Toxicol. *Res:* Biochemical function and metabolism of vitamin A. *Mailing Add:* Div Toxicol HFF 154 Bur Foods Food & Drug Admin 200 C St SW Washington DC 20204

SUNDARESAN, SANKARAN, b Madurai, India, June 9, 55. CATALYSIS & REACTION ENGINEERING. *Educ:* Indian Inst Technol, BS, 76; Univ Houston, MS, 78, PhD(chem eng), 80. *Prof Exp:* Res engr, E I du Pont de Nemours & Co, 81; ASST PROF CHEM ENG, PRINCETON UNIV, 80- *Mem:* Am Inst Chem Eng; Am Chem Soc. *Res:* adsorption processes. *Mailing Add:* Chem Eng Dept Princeton Univ Princeton NJ 08544

SUNDBERG, DONALD CHARLES, b Worcester, Mass, Dec 23, 42; m 66; c 2. CHEMICAL ENGINEERING. *Educ:* Worcester Polytech Inst, BSChE, 65; Univ Del, MChE, 68, PhD(chem eng), 70. *Prof Exp:* Sr chem engr, Monsanto Co, Indian Orchard, 69-74; asst prof chem eng, Univ Idaho, 74-78; ASST PROF CHEM ENG, UNIV NH, 78- *Concurrent Pos:* Consult, Chem Polymer Indust. *Mem:* Am Inst Chem Eng; Am Chem Soc. *Res:* Polymer science and engineering; emulsion polymerization. *Mailing Add:* Dept of Chem Eng Univ of NH Durham NH 03824

SUNDBERG, JOHN EDWIN, b China, Nov 21, 47; US citizen; m 71; c 2. PETROLEUM PROCESSING, CATALYST DEVELOPMENT. *Educ:* Col Wooster, BA, 70; Univ Calif, PhD(org chem), 75. *Prof Exp:* Asst res chemist org chem, United Technol Corp, 75-77; res chemist polymer chem, 77-80, RES CHEMIST, PROCESS DEVELOP, CHEVRON RES CO, 80- *Mem:* Am Chem Soc. *Res:* Hydroprocessing; residue processing; analyses of residue; coatings; waterproof membranes; chelating agents; polyurethanes; insulation; adhesion. *Mailing Add:* Chevron Res Co 576 Standard Ave Richmond CA 94802

SUNDBERG, KENNETH RANDALL, b Coalville, Utah, Dec 4, 45; m 72. PHYSICAL CHEMISTRY, GEOLOGICAL CHEMISTRY. *Educ:* Univ Utah, BS, 68; Iowa State Univ, PhD(phys chem), 75. *Prof Exp:* Res assoc biophys, Dept Biochem & Biophys, Iowa State Univ, 76-77; NSF fel, Dept Chem, Harvard Univ, 77-78; res chemist, 78-80, SR RES CHEMIST, PHILLIPS PETROL CO, 80- *Mem:* Am Chem Soc. *Res:* Quantum chemistry and electronic structure theory; molecular optics; geochemistry; remote sensing. *Mailing Add:* 144 GB PRC Phillips Petrol Co Bartlesville OK 74004

SUNDBERG, MICHAEL WILLIAM, b Battle Creek, Mich. PHYSICAL CHEMISTRY. *Educ:* Albion Col, BA, 69; Stanford Univ, PhD(phys chem), 73. *Prof Exp:* RES CHEMIST, EASTMAN KODAK CO RES LABS, 73- *Honors & Awards:* Von Hevesy Prize Nuclear Med, Soc Nuclear Med, 74. *Mem:* Am Chem Soc; AAAS. *Mailing Add:* Eastman Kodak Co Res Labs 1669 Lake Ave Kodak Park Rochester NY 14650

SUNDBERG, RICHARD J, b Sioux Rapids, Iowa, Jan 6, 38; m 63; c 2. ORGANIC CHEMISTRY. *Educ:* Univ Iowa, BS, 59; Univ Minn, Minneapolis, PhD(org chem), 62. *Prof Exp:* From asst prof to assoc prof, 64-74, PROF CHEM, UNIV VA, 74- *Concurrent Pos:* NIH res fel, Stanford Univ, 71-72; Fulbright-Hays Fel, Inst Chimie Substances Naturelles, CNRS, Gif/Yvette, France, 78-79. *Mem:* Am Chem Soc. *Mailing Add:* Dept of Chem Univ of Va Charlottesville VA 22903

SUNDBERG, RUTH DOROTHY, b Chicago, Ill, July 29, 15; div. ANATOMY. *Educ:* Univ Minn, BS, 37, MA, 39, PhD(anat), 43, MD, 53; Am Bd Path, dipl, 60. *Prof Exp:* Technician anat, Univ Minn, 37-39; instr path, Wayne Univ, 39-41; asst, Univ, 41-43, from instr to assoc prof anat, 43-60, hematologist, Univ Hosps, 42, dir, Hemat Labs, 45-74, prof lab med, Univ, 63-73, PROF ANAT, UNIV MINN, MINNEAPOLIS, 60-, PROF LAB MED & PATH, 73-, HEMATOLOGIST, UNIV HOSPS, 45-, CO-DIR, HEMAT LABS, 74- *Mem:* Am Soc Cell Biol; Am Soc Path & Bact; Am Soc Hemat; Am Asn Anatomists. *Res:* Morphologic hematology; diagnosis by aspiration or trephine biopsy of marrow; lymphocytogenesis in human lymph nodes; histopathology of lesions in the bone marrow; agnogenic myeloid metaplasia; sideroblastic anemia and hemochromatosis; fatty acid deficiency; laboratory medicine. *Mailing Add:* Dept Lab Med & Path Univ Minn Hosp Box 198 Mayo Bldg Minneapolis MN 55455

SUNDBERG, WALTER JAMES, b San Francisco, Calif, Sept 16, 39; m 64; c 2. MYCOLOGY. *Educ:* San Francisco State Col, BA, 62, MA, 67; Univ Calif, Davis, PhD(bot), 71. *Prof Exp:* Lectr bot, Univ Calif, Davis, 71-72; asst prof, 72-77, ASSOC PROF BOT, SOUTHERN ILL UNIV, CARBONDALE, 77- *Concurrent Pos:* Consult, Cent & Southern Ill Regional Poison Resource Ctr. *Mem:* Mycol Soc Am; Brit Mycol Soc; NAm Mycol Asn; Nat Educ Asn; Int Mushroom Soc Trop. *Res:* Ultrastructure, taxonomy and ecology of fungi, emphasis Basidiomycetes. *Mailing Add:* Dept of Bot Southern Ill Univ Carbondale IL 62901

SUNDE, MILTON LESTER, b Volga, SDak, Jan 7, 21; m 46; c 3. POULTRY NUTRITION. *Educ:* SDak State Col, BS, 47; Univ Wis, MS, 49, PhD, 50. *Prof Exp:* From asst prof to assoc prof poultry sci, 51-57, PROF POULTRY SCI, UNIV WIS-MADISON, 57- *Concurrent Pos:* Res scientist, Rockefeller Found, Colombia, SAm, 60; mem animal nutrit comt, Nat Res Coun, 70; Int Feed Ingredient Asn travel grant, 71. *Honors & Awards:* Res Award, Am Feed Mfrs Asn, 61; teaching award, Poultry Sci Asn, 62. *Mem:* Am Chem Soc; Soc Exp Biol & Med; Am Inst Nutrit; fel Poultry Sci Asn (2nd vpres, 65, 1st vpres, 66, pres, 67-68); NY Acad Sci. *Res:* Unidentified factors; vitamins; amino acids; energy for chickens, turkey and pheasants. *Mailing Add:* Animal Sci Bldg Univ of Wis Madison WI 53706

SUNDEEN, DANIEL ALVIN, b Manchester, NH, Sept 25, 37; m 59; c 2. PETROLOGY, GEOCHEMISTRY. *Educ:* Univ NH, BA, 65; Ind Univ, MA, 67, PhD(geol), 70. *Prof Exp:* ASSOC PROF GEOL, UNIV SOUTHERN MISS, 71- *Concurrent Pos:* Geologist Gulf Mex, Standard Oil Co, Tex, 66; explor geologist, SW USA, 69-71 & SE Alaska, Pac Cordillera Explor, 76. *Mem:* Geol Soc Am; Mineral Soc Am. *Res:* Subsurface volcanic province and tectonism and associated mineralization in the Gulf Coastal Plain of Mississippi; igneous and metamorphic petrology. *Mailing Add:* Dept of Geol Southern Sta Box 8196 Hattiesburg MS 39406

SUNDEEN, JOSEPH EDWARD, b Manchester, NH, Nov 5, 43; m 64; c 3. ORGANIC CHEMISTRY. *Educ:* Rensselaer Polytech Inst, BS, 64; Purdue Univ, PhD(chem), 68. *Prof Exp:* Fel org chem, Syntex Res Div, Syntex Corp, 68-69; investr cardiovasc res, 69-76, INVESTR ANTI-INFLAMMATORY RES, SQUIBB INST MED RES, 76- *Mem:* Am Chem Soc. *Res:* Cardioactive medicinals; anti-arthritics; anti-ulcer compounds. *Mailing Add:* Squibb Inst for Med Res Princeton NJ 08540

SUNDELIN, KURT GUSTAV RAGNAR, b Pitea, Sweden, Dec 21, 37; US citizen; m 63; c 5. ORGANIC CHEMISTRY, MEDICINAL CHEMISTRY. *Educ:* Idaho State Univ, BS, 62 & 65, MS, 65; Univ Kans, PhD(med chem), 69. *Prof Exp:* CHEMIST BIOL SCI RES CTR, SHELL DEVELOP CO, 69- *Mem:* Am Chem Soc. *Res:* Organic chemical synthesis of biologically active agents in area of herbicides and pesticides. *Mailing Add:* Biol Sci Res Ctr Shell Develop Co PO Box 4248 Modesto CA 95352

SUNDELIN, RONALD M, b New York, NY, Oct 20, 39; m 67; c 2. ELEMENTARY PARTICLE PHYSICS. *Educ:* Mass Inst Technol, BS, 61; Carnegie Inst Technol, MS, 63, PhD(physics), 67. *Prof Exp:* Res physicist, Carnegie-Mellon Univ, 67-69; res assoc elem particle physics, Wilson Lab, 69-75, SR RES ASSOC ELEM PARTICLE PHYSICS, NEWMAN LAB, CORNELL UNIV, 75- *Mem:* Am Phys Soc. *Res:* Medium energy experimental physics, especially muon physics; high energy experimental physics; accelerator physics; normal and superconducting radio frequency. *Mailing Add:* Newman Lab Cornell Univ Ithaca NY 14853

SUNDELIUS, HAROLD WESLEY, b Escanaba, Mich, July 6, 30; m 55; c 2. GEOLOGY. *Educ:* Augustana Col, AB, 52; Univ Wis, MS, 57, PhD(geol), 59. *Prof Exp:* Geologist mil geol br, US Geol Surv, 59-61, regional geologist eastern br, 61-65; from asst to assoc prof geol, Wittenberg Univ, 65-74, assoc dean col, 71-75, prof, 74-75; VPRES ACAD AFFAIRS & DEAN COL, AUGUSTANA COL, ILL, 75- *Mem:* Geol Soc Am; Soc Econ Geol; Nat Asn Geol Teachers. *Res:* Appalachian geology, especially Piedmont; economic geology and mineral economics; military geology; geology of the Carolina slate belt; Precambrian geology of the Lake Superior region; massive sulfide deposits in greenstone belts. *Mailing Add:* Augustana Col Rock Island IL 61201

SUNDER, SHAM, b Can citizen. VIBRATIONAL SPECTROSCOPY, ELECTRON SPECTROSCOPY. *Educ:* Univ Delhi, BSc Hons, 62, MSc, 64; Univ Alta, Can, PhD(chem), 72. *Prof Exp:* Fel res, Univ Alta, Can, 72-73 & Nat Res Coun Can, 73-75; res assoc, Nat Res Coun, 75-78; lectr, Heidelberg Univ, WGer, 78-79; ASSOC RES OFFICER, ATOMIC ENERGY CAN, LTD, 79- *Mem:* Can Inst Chem; Spectros Soc Can. *Res:* Structures and molecular dynamics in solids; liquids and solid-liquid interfaces using spectroscopic methods, particularly vibrational (IR & Laser-Raman) and electron spectroscopy for chemical analysis. *Mailing Add:* Atomic Energy Can Ltd Pinawa MB R0E 1L0 Can

SUNDERLAND, JAMES EDWARD, b Philadelphia, Pa, Oct 26, 32; m 57; c 7. MECHANICAL ENGINEERING. *Educ:* Mass Inst Technol, SB, 54; Purdue Univ, MS, 56, PhD(eng), 58. *Prof Exp:* Instr, Purdue Univ, 57-58, asst prof mech eng, Northwestern Univ, 58-62; assoc prof, Ga Inst Technol, 62-65, prof, 65-67; prof mech & aerospace eng, NC State Univ, 67-72; PROF MECH ENG, UNIV MASS, AMHERST, 72- *Concurrent Pos:* Pub Health Serv grant, 62-69; NSF grant, 66-68; consult engr; US Army grant, 81- *Mem:* Fel Am Soc Mech Engrs; Am Soc Eng Educ; Am Soc Heating, Refrigerating & Air-Conditioning Engrs; Inst Food Technologists. *Res:* Conduction, convection and radiation heat transfer; heat and mass transfer in biological systems; thermoelectric energy conversion; two-component external flow and thermal analog computers; freeze-drying. *Mailing Add:* Dept of Mech Eng Univ of Mass Amherst MA 01003

SUNDERLIN, CHARLES EUGENE, b Reliance, SDak, Sept 28, 11; m 36; c 4. ORGANIC CHEMISTRY. *Educ:* Univ Mont, AB, 33; Oxford Univ, BA, 35; Univ Rochester, PhD(chem), 39. *Prof Exp:* Instr chem, Union Col, NY, 38-41; instr, US Naval Acad, 41-43, from asst prof to assoc prof, 45-46; sci liaison officer, US Off Naval Res, London, 46-47, from dept sci dir to sci dir, 48-51; dep dir, NSF, 51-57; dep dir, Union Carbide Europ Res Assocs, SA, Belg, 57-62; res mgr defense & space systs dept, Union Carbide Corp, 62-65; spec asst to pres, Nat Acad Sci, 65-69; vpres & secy, Rockefeller Univ, 69-76; spec asst, Nat Sci Bd, 76-78. *Concurrent Pos:* US del gen assembly, Int Coun Sci Unions, Amsterdam, 52 & Oslo, 55; US del, Dirs Nat Res Ctrs, Milan, 55; mem, Comt Experts Scientists' Rights, Paris, 53. *Mem:* AAAS; Am Chem Soc; Royal Soc Chem; Royal Inst Gt Brit; Brit Soc Chem Indust. *Res:* Research administration and management; international cooperation in science and technology. *Mailing Add:* 3036 P St NW Washington DC 20007

SUNDERMAN, DUANE NEUMAN, b Wadsworth, Ohio, July 14, 28; m 53; c 3. RESEARCH ADMINISTRATION. *Educ:* Univ Mich, AB, 49, MS, 54, PhD(chem), 56. *Prof Exp:* Res chemist, Argonne Nat Lab & E I du Pont de Nemours & Co, 51-52; res chemist, Savannah River Proj, 52-54; res asst, Univ Mich, 54-55; prin chemist, 56, proj leader, 56-58, asst div chief, 58-59, chief chem physics div, 59-65, assoc mgr physics dept, 65-69, coordr basic res, 67-69, asst dir, 69-70, mgr soc & mgt systs dept, 70-73, assoc dir, 73-74, dir tech develop, 74-75, assoc dir res, 75-79, DIR PROG DEVELOP, BATTELLE MEM INST, 79- *Concurrent Pos:* Partic prog mgt develop, Harvard Bus Sch, 69; trustee, Columbus Area Leadership Prog, 75-78. *Mem:* Am Chem Soc; Am Nuclear Soc; hon mem Am Soc Testing & Mat. *Res:* Nuclear fuel development; environmental research; energy research; technical management. *Mailing Add:* 2011 Pevensey Ct Columbus OH 43220

SUNDERMAN, FREDERICK WILLIAM, b Altoona, Pa, Oct 23, 98; m 80; c 2. INTERNAL MEDICINE, CLINICAL PATHOLOGY. *Educ:* Gettysburg Col, BS, 19; Univ Pa, MD, 23, MS, 27, PhD(res med), 29; Am Bd Internal Med, dipl, 37; Am Bd Path, dipl, 44; Am Bd Clin Chem, dipl, 53. *Hon Degrees:* ScD, Gettysburg Col, 52. *Prof Exp:* Instr, Gettysburg Acad, 19; asst dermat, Univ Pa, 23, from instr to assoc prof res med, 25-47, lectr, 34-47, ward physician, Univ Hosp, 34-40, from assoc to chief chem div, Wm Pepper Lab, 34-47; prof clin path, Sch Med, Temple Univ & dir lab clin med, Univ Hosp, 47-48; dir clin res, Univ Tex M D Anderson Hosp & Tumor Inst, 48-50; prof clin med, Emory Univ, 50-51; prof clin med & dir div metab res, 51-67, attend physician, 51-76, co-chmn dept, lab med, 70-74, HON CLIN PROF, JEFFERSON MED COL, 76-, DIR, INST CLIN SCI, 65-; PROF PATH, HAHNEMANN MED COL, 70- *Concurrent Pos:* Resident physician, Pa Hosp, 23-25, chief chem lab, 29-33, chief metab & diabetic clins, 29-46, physician, 39-47; med dir explosives res lab, US Bur Mines, Carnegie Inst Technol, 43-46; actg med dir & med consult, Brookhaven Nat Lab, 47-48; consult, Los Alamos Sci Lab, 47-48, US Army Ord, Redstone Arsenal, 47-49; dir clin labs, Grady Mem Hosp, Atlanta, 49-51; chief clin path, Commun Dis Ctr, USPHS, 50-51; Abington Mem & Vet Admin Hosps, 53-66; mem staff, Cleveland Clin Found, 48-49; trustee & vpres, Am Bd Path, 48-51, life trustee, 61-; prof, Post-Grad Sch Med, Univ Tex, 49; med adv, Rohm and Haas Co, 50-71; mem & chmn bd trustees, Gettysburg Col, 67-; mem corp, Bermuda Biol Sta; mem, Pa Governor's Task Force Environ Health, 68-75; ed in chief, Annals Clin Lab Sci, 71- *Honors & Awards:* Ward Burdick Award, Am Soc Clin Path, 75; Goblet Award, Asn Clin Scientists, 64 & Gold Headed Cane Award, 75; Founding Gov, Sci Prod Award, 62. *Mem:* Fel Am Soc Clin Path (pres, 50); fel Am Soc Clin Invest; fel Am Chem Soc; Asn Clin Scientists (pres, 56-58); fel Col Am Path. *Res:* Serum electrolytes; hazards of nickel and nickel carbonyl exposure; metabolism; clinical chemistry; research medicine. *Mailing Add:* 1833 Delancey Pl Philadelphia PA 19103

SUNDERMAN, FREDERICK WILLIAM, JR, b Philadelphia, Pa, June 23, 31; m 63; c 3. CLINICAL PATHOLOGY, EXPERIMENTAL PATHOLOGY. *Educ:* Emory Univ, BS, 52; Jefferson Med Col, MD, 55. *Prof Exp:* Intern, Jefferson Med Col Hosp, 55-56, instr med, 60-63, assoc, 63-64; from assoc prof to prof path & dir clin lab, Col Med, Univ Fla, 64-68; prof lab med, 68-80, PROF PHARM, SCH MED, UNIV CONN, 80-, HEAD DEPT, 68- *Mem:* Am Asn Cancer Res; Am Asn Clin Chem; Am Asn Path; Soc Toxicol; Bact; Am Am Col Physicians; Asn Clin Scientists (pres, 64-65). *Res:* Experimental carcinogenesis and trace metal metabolism; clinical biochemistry. *Mailing Add:* Dept of Lab Med Univ of Conn Health Ctr Farmington CT 06032

SUNDERWIRTH, STANLEY GEORGE, b El Dorado Springs, Mo, Aug 12, 30; m 52; c 4. ORGANIC CHEMISTRY. *Educ:* Tarkio Col, AB, 51; Ohio State Univ, PhD(org chem), 55. *Prof Exp:* From instr to assoc prof chem, Colo State Univ, 55-64; prof & chmn dept, Pittsburgh State Univ, Pittsburg, Kans, 64-72; DEAN SCI & MATH, METROP STATE COL, 72- *Concurrent Pos:* Fulbright fel, Uruguay, 65, 68, 70 & 78; NSF-AID consult, India, 67 & 69; Fulbright-Hays lectr, India, 75. *Mem:* AAAS; Am Chem Soc; Sigma Xi. *Res:* Organic mechanisms. *Mailing Add:* Metrop State Col Sch Sci Math 250 W 14th Ave Denver CO 80204

SUNDET, SHERMAN ARCHIE, b Litchville, NDak, Sept 25, 18; m 44; c 5. POLYMER CHEMISTRY. *Educ:* Concordia Col, BS, 39; Univ Idaho, MS, 41; Univ Minn, PhD(org chem), 48. *Prof Exp:* Chemist, B F Goodrich Co, Ohio, 42-45; instr org chem, Univ Calif, Los Angeles, 48-50; res chemist textile fibers dept pioneering res div, 50-54, res supvr, 54-70, RES ASSOC POLYMER PROD DEPT, E I DU PONT DE NEMOURS & CO, INC, 70- *Mem:* AAAS; Am Chem Soc; Sigma Xi. *Res:* Structure, properties and applications of polymers. *Mailing Add:* Exp Sta 323/312 E I du Pont de Nemours & Co Inc Wilmington DE 19898

SUNDFORS, RONALD KENT, b Santa Monica, Calif, June 3, 32; m 63; c 3. SOLID STATE PHYSICS. *Educ:* Stanford Univ, BS, 54, MS, 55; Cornell Univ, PhD(exp physics), 63. *Prof Exp:* Res assoc, 63-65, from asst prof physics to assoc prof, 65-76, PROF PHYSICS, WASH UNIV, ST LOUIS, 76- *Mem:* AAAS; Am Phys Soc; Am Asn Physics Teachers. *Res:* Nuclear magnetic resonance; low temperature physics; semiconductor research; ultrasonics; acoustic coupling to nuclear spins. *Mailing Add:* Dept Physics Wash Univ St Louis MO 63130

SUNDICK, ROY, b Brooklyn, NY, May 8, 44; m 69. IMMUNOLOGY. *Educ:* Harpur Col, BA, 65; State Univ NY Buffalo, MA, 69, PhD(microbiol), 72. *Prof Exp:* Austrian Res Coun fel, Inst Gen & Exp Path, Univ Vienna, 71-73; ASST PROF IMMUNOL & MICROBIOL, SCH MED, WAYNE STATE UNIV, 74- *Mem:* Am Asn Immunol; Ger Soc Immunol; Sigma Xi. *Res:* Pathogenesis of autoimmune disease and mechanism of self-recognition. *Mailing Add:* Dept Immunol & Microbiol Wayne State Univ Sch Med Detroit MI 48201

SUNDSTEN, JOHN WALLIN, b Seattle, Wash, Jan 16, 33; m 63; c 5. ANATOMY. *Educ:* Univ Calif, Los Angeles, AB, 56, PhD(anat), 61. *Prof Exp:* Asst anat, Sch Med, Univ Calif, Los Angeles, 57-59; NSF fel, 61-62; from instr to asst prof, 62-70, ASSOC PROF ANAT, SCH MED, UNIV WASH, 70- *Concurrent Pos:* Vis scientist, USPHS, 64-66; USPHS res grant, 64-; NIH spec fel, Bristol, Eng, 68-69; vis prof, Univ Malaya, 73-74. *Mem:* AAAS; Am Asn Anatomists. *Res:* Neurobiology; hypothalamic regulatory mechanisms; psychophysiology; neurophysiology. *Mailing Add:* Dept of Biol Structure Univ of Wash Sch of Med Seattle WA 98105

SUNG, CHENG-PO, b Hsinchu, Taiwan, Oct 21, 35; m 65; c 2. BIOCHEMISTRY. *Educ:* Chung Hsing Univ, Taiwan, BSc, 59; McGill Univ, PhD(biochem), 67. *Prof Exp:* Fel biochem, McGill Univ, 66-67; res scientist, Food & Drug Directorate, Dept Nat Health & Welfare, Can, 67-68; res assoc dept pharmacol, Univ Wis, 68-69; assoc sr investr, Smith Kline & French Labs, 69-77, SR INVESTR BIOL SCI, SMITH-KLINE LABS, 78- *Mem:* AAAS; NY Acad Sci; Biochem Soc; Am Chem Soc. *Res:* Regulation of immune responses; lymphokines production and assay; natural products pharmacology. *Mailing Add:* Smith-Kline Labs L 37 1500 Spring Garden St Philadelphia PA 19101

SUNG, CHI CHING, b Nanking, China, Mar 5, 36; m 68. THEORETICAL PHYSICS. *Educ:* Taiwan Nat Univ, BS, 57; Univ Calif, Berkeley, PhD(physics), 65. *Prof Exp:* Res assoc physics, Ohio State Univ, 65-67, lectr, 67-68, asst prof, 68-72; assoc prof, 72-78, PROF PHYSICS, UNIV ALA, HUNTSVILLE, 78- *Mem:* Am Optical Soc. *Res:* Optics; quantum electronics. *Mailing Add:* Dept Physics Univ Ala Huntsville AL 35807

SUNG, CHIA-HSIAING, b Ping-Tung, Taiwan, Sept 4, 39; US citizen; m 68; c 3. SYSTEMS ENGINEERING, SOFTWARE ENGINEERING. *Educ:* Univ Tex, Austin, BSEE, 66, MSEE, 68, PhD(elec eng), 71. *Prof Exp:* Sr mem tech staff, Taiwan Telecommun Admin, 61-64; asst res engr, Univ Tex, Austin, 66 & 71; asst prof elec eng & comput sci, Tex A&I Univ, 71-72; vis asst prof elec eng & vis res asst prof, Coord Sci Lab, Univ Ill, Champaign-Urbana, 72-74; asst prof comput sci & elec eng, Univ Louisville, 74-78; SR STAFF ENGR, HUGHES AIRCRAFT CO, LOS ANGELES, 78- *Mem:* Inst Elec & Electronics Engrs; Asn Comput Mach; Am Soc Eng Educ. *Res:* Fault-tolerant spaceborne data processing systems; distributed sytems; microprocessor-based system for improving automobile fuel economy. *Mailing Add:* 26014 Pennsylvania Dr Lomita CA 90717

SUNG, JOO HO, b Korea, Feb 18, 27; US citizen; m 59; c 3. PATHOLOGY, NEUROPATHOLOGY. *Educ:* Yonsei Univ, Korea, MD, 52. *Prof Exp:* Resident path, Newark Beth Israel Hosp, 54-57; fel neuropath, Col Physicians & Surgeons, Columbia Univ, 57-61, asst prof, 61-62; from asst prof to assoc prof, 62-69, PROF NEUROPATH, MED SCH, UNIV MINN, MINNEAPOLIS, 69- *Concurrent Pos:* Nat Inst Neurol Dis & Stroke fel, Columbia Univ, 59-61; consult, Minneapolis Vet Admin Hosp, 62-68; mem, NIH Neurol Sci Res Training Comt, 70-73; vis prof, Med Col, Yonsei Univ, Korea, 72. *Mem:* Am Asn Neuropath; Am Acad Neurol; Asn Res Nerv & Ment Dis. *Res:* Aging changes in the nervous system; x-radiation effects on the nervous system. *Mailing Add:* Neuropath Lab Univ of Minn Med Sch Minneapolis MN 55455

SUNG, MICHAEL TSE LI, b Chung King, China, Mar 5, 40; US citizen; m 68; c 2. MOLECULAR BIOLOGY, BIOCHEMISTRY. *Educ:* Kans State Col, BA, 62; Univ Wis, PhD(molecular biol), 68. *Prof Exp:* Helen Hay Whitney Found fel, Dept Biochem, Univ BC, 68-71; asst prof, 71-75, ASSOC PROF BIOCHEM, SOUTHERN ILL UNIV, 75- *Mem:* Am Chem Soc; Sigma Xi. *Res:* Chromatin structure and function; structure and function of nuclear proteins. *Mailing Add:* Dept of Chem & Biochem Southern Ill Univ Carbondale IL 62901

SUNG, ZINMAY RENEE, b Shanghai, China, Feb 16, 47; m 74. SOMATIC GENETICS, PLANT TISSUE CULTURE. *Educ:* Nat Taiwan Univ, BS, 67; Univ Calif, Berkeley, PhD(plant physiol), 73. *Prof Exp:* Res asst cell physiol, Max Planck Inst Cell Physiol, WBerlin, Ger, 67-68; Univ Calif, Berkeley, 68-73; res assoc somatic genetics, Dept Biol, Mass Inst, Technol, 73-76; ASST PROF, DEPT GENETICS & PLANT PATH, UNIV CALIF, BERKELEY, 76- *Mem:* Am Soc Plant Physiologists; Am Soc Plant Pathologists; Am Soc Develop Biologists. *Res:* Plant somatic genetics; developmental genetics of early embryogenesis from carrot tissue culture. *Mailing Add:* Dept Genetics Univ Calif Berkeley CA 94720

SUNIER, JULES WILLY, b Saint-Imier, Switz, Nov 10, 34; m 58; c 2. EXPERIMENTAL NUCLEAR PHYSICS. *Educ:* Swiss Fed Inst Technol, dipl, 57, Dr sc nat(nuclear physics), 62. *Prof Exp:* Res physicist, Swiss Fed Inst Technol, 57-64; from asst prof to assoc prof physics, Univ Calif, Los Angeles, 64-72; MEM STAFF PHYSICS DIV, LOS ALAMOS NAT LAB, UNIV CALIF, 72- *Concurrent Pos:* Vis prof, Univ Grenoble, 77-78. *Mem:* Am Phys Soc; Swiss Phys Soc. *Res:* Nuclear structure; few nucleon transfer and charge exchange reactions; nuclear reactions with heavy ions; proton and anti-proton nucleus interactions on line computers and data acquisition systems. *Mailing Add:* Physics Div Los Alamos Nat Lab Univ of Calif Los Alamos NM 87545

SUNLEY, JUDITH S, b Detroit, Mich, July 26, 46. NUMBER THEORY. *Educ:* Univ Mich, BS, 67, MS, 68; Univ Md, PhD(math), 71. *Prof Exp:* Asst prof math, Dept Math, Statist & Comput Sci, Am Univ, 71-75, assoc prof, 75-81; assoc prog dir, 80-81, PROG DIR ALGEBRA & NUMBER THEORY, NSF, 81- *Mem:* Am Math Soc. Res; Math Asn Am; Asn Women Math; AAAS. *Res:* Eisenstein series of Siegel Modular Group; generalized prime discriminants in totally real fields; class numbers of totally imaginary quadratic extensions of totally real fields. *Mailing Add:* Math Sci Sect NSF Washington DC 20550

SUNSHINE, IRVING, b New York, NY, Mar 17, 16; m 39; c 2. CLINICAL CHEMISTRY, TOXICOLOGY. *Educ:* NY Univ, BS, 37, MA, 41, PhD, 50, Am Bd Clin Chem, dipl; Am Bd Forensic Toxicol, dipl. *Prof Exp:* Instr chem, Newark Col Eng, 41-47; asst prof, NJ State Teachers Col, 47-50; toxicologist & clin chemist, City of Kingston Lab, NY, 50-51; sr instr path & pharmacol, 51-54, from asst prof to assoc prof, 54-73, PROF TOXICOL IN PATH & MED, CASE WESTERN RESERVE UNIV, 73-; TOXICOLOGIST, CUYAHOGA COUNTY CORONERS LAB, 51- *Concurrent Pos:* Toxicologist, Univ Hosp, Univ Ohio; Fulbright fel, Vrije Univ, Brussels, 79. *Honors & Awards:* Ames Award, Am Asn Clin Chemists, 73; Toxicol Award, Am Acad Forensic Sci, 80. *Mem:* Am Chem Soc; Am Asn Clin Chemists; Am Acad Forensic Sci; Am Asn Poison Control Ctrs. *Res:* Alcohol; barbiturates; toxicology methodology; poison prevention programming; drugs of abuse. *Mailing Add:* 2121 Adelbert Rd Cleveland OH 44106

SUNSHINE, MELVIN GILBERT, b Chicago, Ill, Oct 14, 36; m 70; c 1. BACTERIAL GENETICS. *Educ:* Univ Ill, BS, 58; Univ Southern Calif, PhD(bact), 68. *Prof Exp:* Res microbiologist, San Diego State Col, 67-68; Jane Coffin Childs Mem Fund Med Res fel, Karolinska Inst, Sweden, 68-70; USPHS trainee, Dept Molecular Biol & Virus Lab, Univ Calif, Berkeley, 70-72; vis prof microbiol, Sch Med, Univ Southern Calif, 72-73; res assoc, 73-78, RES SCIENTIST MICROBIOL, UNIV IOWA, 78- *Mem:* Am Soc Microbiol. *Res:* Bacterial genetics; genetics of the temperate bacterial viruses P2 and P4; host factors associated with phages P2 and P4. *Mailing Add:* Dept of Microbiol Univ of Iowa Sch of Med Iowa City IA 52242

SUNSHINE, WARREN LEWIS, b Passaic, NJ, Sept 10, 47; m 72; c 1. ORGANIC CHEMISTRY. *Educ:* Columbia Univ, AB, 68; Rutgers Univ, MS, 70, PhD(org chem), 74. *Prof Exp:* NIH res fel natural prods, Univ Va, 74-76; sr chemist cosmetic prods, Am Cyanamid Co, 76-80. *Mem:* Am Chem Soc; Soc Cosmetic Chemists. *Res:* Natural products; medicinal chemistry. *Mailing Add:* 428 Tall Oak Ln Somerville NJ 08876

SUNTHARALINGAM, NAGALINGAM, b Jaffna, Ceylon, June 18, 33; m 61; c 3. RADIOLOGICAL PHYSICS. *Educ:* Univ Ceylon, BSc, 55; Univ Wis, MS, 66, PhD(radiol sci), 67. *Prof Exp:* Asst lectr physics, Univ Ceylon, 55-58; from instr radiol physics to assoc prof radiol, 62-72, PROF RADIOL & RADIATION THERAPY, JEFFERSON MED COL, 72- *Concurrent Pos:* Vis lectr, Grad Sch Med, Univ Pa, 67-, consult dept physics, 68- *Mem:* Am Asn Phys Med (pres-elect, 82); Am Asn Physicists in Med; Health Physics Soc; Am Col Radiol. *Res:* Radiation dosimetry; thermoluminescence dosimetry; clinical dosimetry. *Mailing Add:* Dept Radiation Therapy Jefferson Med Col Philadelphia PA 19107

SUNUNU, JOHN HENRY, b Havana, Cuba, July 2, 39; US citizen; m 58; c 6. HEAT TRANSFER, FLUID MECHANICS. *Educ:* Mass Inst Technol, BS, 61, MS, 63, PhD(mech eng), 66. *Prof Exp:* Chief engr, Astro Dynamics, Inc, 60-65; asst prof, 66-75, ASSOC PROF MECH ENG, TUFTS UNIV, 75-, ASSOC DEAN, COL ENG, 69- *Concurrent Pos:* Consult various indust & govt; chmn bd, Student Competitions on Relevant Eng, Inc, 71-; mem, Coun Environ Qual Adv Comt Advan Automotive Power Systs; pres, JHS Eng Co, 66-; pres, Thermal Res, Inc, 68- *Mem:* AAAS; Am Soc Mech Engrs; Acad Appl Sci. *Res:* Heat transfer and temperature control; slow viscous fluid dynamics; approximate methods of mathematical analysis of fluid phenomena; design and optimization of heat transfer equipment. *Mailing Add:* 24 Samoset Dr Salem NH 03079

SUNYAR, ANDREW WILLIAM, b Henderson, Mich, Sept 9, 20; m 43; c 3. NUCLEAR PHYSICS. *Educ:* Albion Col, AB, 42; Univ Ill, MS, 44, PhD(physics), 49. *Prof Exp:* Asst, Univ Ill, 42-43, 46-49, res assoc, 49; assoc physicist, 49-53, physicist, 53-60, SR PHYSICIST, BROOKHAVEN NAT LAB, 60- *Concurrent Pos:* NSF sr fel, Inst Theoret Physics, Denmark, 60-61. *Honors & Awards:* Alexander von Humboldt Award, 77-78, Tech Univ, Munich, & Nucl Lab, Darmstadt; Distinguished Alumni Award, Albion Col, 70. *Mem:* Fel Am Phys Soc. *Res:* Nuclear isomerism; nuclear disintegration schemes; heavy ion-induced reactions; nuclear magnetic moments; Coulomb excitation. *Mailing Add:* Brookhaven Nat Lab Upton NY 11973

SUOMI, VERNER EDWARD, b Eveleth, Minn, Dec 6, 15; m 41; c 3. METEOROLOGY. *Educ:* Winona State Col, BE, 38; Univ Chicago, PhD(meteorol), 53. *Prof Exp:* Teacher, pub schs, Minn, 38-42; res assoc meteorol, Univ Chicago, 44-48; from asst prof to assoc prof, 48-53, PROF METEOROL & SOILS, UNIV WIS-MADISON, 53-, DIR SPACE SCI & ENG CTR, 66- *Concurrent Pos:* Assoc prog dir atmospheric sci, NSF, DC, 62; chief scientist, US Weather Bur, 64-65; chmn comt adv to Nat Oceanic & Atmospheric Admin, Nat Acad Sci, 66-69, mem comt atmospheric sci, 66-, chmn US comt, Global Atmospheric Prog, 71-74; mem Nat Adv Comt Oceans & Atmosphere, 71-72; fel, Am Arts & Sci, 77. *Honors & Awards:* Meisinger Award, Am Meteorol Soc, 61, Rossby Res Medal, 68; Presidential Citation, 70; Robert M Losey Award, Am Inst Aeronaut & Astronaut, 71; Harry Wexler Professorship, Meteorol, Univ Wisconsin-Madison; Nat Medal of Honor, 77. *Mem:* Nat Acad Eng; AAAS; Am Meteorol Soc (pres, 68-69); Am Geophys Union; foreign mem Finnish Acad Sci & Lett. *Res:* Atmospheric radiation; meteorological satellites; environmental observation systems. *Mailing Add:* Space Sci & Eng Ctr Univ of Wis-Madison Madison WI 53706

SUOZZI, JOSEPH JOHN, b New York, NY, Mar 2, 26; m 52; c 5. ELECTRICAL ENGINEERING. *Educ:* Cath Univ, BEE, 49, MEE, 54; Carnegie Inst Technol, PhD(elec eng), 58. *Prof Exp:* Instr elec eng, Cath Univ, 49-50; test planning engr, Western Elec Co, 50-52; electronic engr, US Naval Ord Lab, 52-55; mem tech staff, 55-60, supvr magnetic memories, 60-65, dept head magnetic power components, 65-80, DEPT HEAD MAGNETIC BUBBLE MEMORIES, BELL TEL LABS, 80- *Concurrent Pos:* Prog chmn, Int Conf Magnetics, 63, vchmn, 64, gen chmn, 65 & 67; ed-in-chief, Trans on Magnetics, Inst Elec & Electronics Engrs, 65-67; chmn, Int Elec Conf Exec Comt, 80-82. *Mem:* Fel Inst Elec & Electronics Engrs. *Res:* Magnetic amplifiers, especially on feedback in magnetic amplifiers; magnetic power components; energy management systems; computer magnetics. *Mailing Add:* Bell Tel Labs Whippany Rd Whippany NJ 07981

SUPERSAD, JANKIE NANAN, b Chaguanas, Trinidad, Feb 8, 29; m 57; c 3. CIVIL & TRANSPORTATION ENGINEERING. *Educ:* Glasgow Univ, BS, 53; Northwestern Univ, Evanston, MS, 58; Ariz State Univ, PhD(civil eng), 65. *Prof Exp:* Eng asst, Crouch & Hogg, Consult Civil Engrs, Glasgow, Scotland, 53-54; asst engr, Considere Constructions Ltd, Scotland, 55; exec engr, Ministry of Works, Trinidad, WI, 55-60, sr roads engr, 61-64, chief planning engr, 64-68; asst prof faculty eng, Sir George Williams Univ, 68-70; from asst prof to assoc prof, 70-75, PROF CIVIL ENG, SCH ENG, CALIF STATE UNIV, FRESNO, 75-, COORDR CIVIL ENG, 76- *Concurrent Pos:* Faculty assoc eng, Col Eng, Ariz State Univ, 62-64; mem, Transp Res Bd. *Mem:* Am Soc Civil Engrs; Inst Traffic Engrs; Brit Inst Hwy Engrs; Am Soc Eng Educ. *Res:* Urban transportation planning techniques; highway economics with special reference to under-developed countries. *Mailing Add:* Sch of Eng Shaw & Cedar Ave Fresno CA 93740

SUPLINSKAS, RAYMOND JOSEPH, b Hartford, Conn, Aug 29, 39; m 59; c 3. CHEMISTRY. *Educ:* Yale Univ, BS, 61; Brown Univ, PhD(chem), 65. *Prof Exp:* Mem tech staff, Bell Telephone Labs, 64-65; assoc prof chem, Yale Univ, 65-72; assoc prof & chmn, Swarthmore Col, 72-77; PRIN STAFF SCIENTIST, SPEC MAT DIV, AVCO, 77- *Mem:* Sigma Xi. *Res:* Chemical vapor deposition of ceramic fibers and their use in high-performance structural composites based on both organic and metal matrices. *Mailing Add:* Spec Mat Div AVCO 2 Indust Ave Lowell MA 01852

SUPPE, FREDERICK (ROY), b Los Angeles, Calif, Feb 22, 40. PHILOSOPHY OF SCIENCE, HISTORY OF SCIENCE. *Educ:* Univ Calif, Riverside, AB, 62; Univ Mich, AM, 64, PhD(philos), 67. *Prof Exp:* Instr philos, Univ Mich, 64-67; asst prof, Univ Ill, Urbana, 67-73; ASSOC PROF PHILOS, UNIV MD, COLLEGE PARK, 73-, CHAIRPERSON COMT HIST & PHILOS SCI, 75- *Concurrent Pos:* Educ adv, Indo-Am Prog, USAID, Kanpur, India, 65-67; NSF res grant, 73; Am Coun Learned Soc int travel award, 74; mem adv bd, Nat Workshop Teaching Philos, 74- *Honors & Awards:* Amicus Poloniae Award, Poland, 75. *Mem:* AAAS; Philos Sci Asn; Hist Sci Soc; Sigma Xi. *Res:* Nature of scientific knowledge, including structure of theories and models, explanation, facts and scientific observation; growth of scientific knowledge; history of the philosophy of science; automata theory; sexual morality and sex research methodology; nursing theory. *Mailing Add:* Comt Hist & Philos Sci 1131 Skinner Hall Univ Md College Park MD 20742

SUPPE, JOHN, b Los Angeles, Calif, Nov 30, 42; m 65; c 2. GEOLOGY, GEOPHYSICS. *Educ:* Univ Calif, Riverside, BA, 65; Yale Univ, PhD(geol), 69. *Prof Exp:* Assoc res geologist, Yale Univ, 69; NSF fel geol, Univ Calif, Los Angeles, 69-71; asst prof, 71-76, assoc prof, 76-79, PROF GEOL, PRINCETON UNIV, 79- *Concurrent Pos:* Assoc ed, Am J Sci, 75-81; vis prof, Nat Taiwan Univ, 78-79; Guggenheim fel, 78-79. *Mem:* Geol Soc Am; Am Geophys Union. *Res:* Tectonics; regional structural geology. *Mailing Add:* Dept Geol & Geophys Sci Princeton Univ Princeton NJ 08544

SUPPES, PATRICK, b Tulsa, Okla, Mar 17, 22; m 46, 70, 79; c 4. STATISTICS. *Educ:* Univ Chicago, BS, 43; Columbia Univ, PhD, 50. *Hon Degrees:* Dr Soc Sci, Univ Nijmegen, Netherlands. *Prof Exp:* From instr to assoc prof, 50-59, PROF PHILOS, STATIST, EDUC & PSYCHOL, STANFORD UNIV, 59-; PRES, COMPUT CURRIC CORP, PALO ALTO, CALIF, 67- *Concurrent Pos:* Fel, Ctr Advan Study Behav Sci, 55-56; NSF fel, 57-58; dir, Inst Math Studies in Social Sci, Stanford. *Honors & Awards:* Distinguished Sci Contribr Award, Am Psychol Asn, 72. *Mem:* Nat Acad Sci; fel Am Psychol Asn; AAAS; ad Educ; Am Educ Res Asn (pres, 73-74); Sigma Xi. *Res:* Mathematical logic; experiments on second-language learning; computer-assisted instruction. *Mailing Add:* Ventura Hall Stanford Univ Stanford CA 94305

SUPPLE, JEROME HENRY, b Boston, Mass, Apr 27, 36; m 64. ORGANIC CHEMISTRY. *Educ:* Boston Col, BS, 57, MS, 59; Univ NH, PhD(org chem), 63. *Prof Exp:* Res chemist, Univ Calif, Berkeley, 63-64; asst prof org & gen chem, 64-69, assoc dean arts & sci, 72-73, actg assoc provost, State Univ NY Cent Admin, 74-75, assoc vpres acad affairs, 73-78, chmn dept chem, 75-76; assoc prof org & gen chem, Fredonia, 69-78, VPRES ACAD AFFAIRS & PROF CHEM, STATE UNIV NY COL PLATTSBURGH, 78- *Concurrent Pos:* NSF sci fac fel, Univ E Anglia, 70-71. *Mem:* AAAS; Am Chem Soc. *Res:* Heterocyclic chemistry; natural products; stereochemistry; organic spectroscopy; conformational studies in the heterocyclic systems; narcotic antagonists; homogeneous catalysis. *Mailing Add:* Kehoe Bldg State Univ NY Col Plattsburgh Plattsburgh NY 12901

SUPRAN, MICHAEL KENNETH, b New York, NY, Feb 13, 39; m 67; c 2. FOOD SCIENCE. *Educ:* Univ Ga, BS, 61, MS, 63, PhD(food sci), 68. *Prof Exp:* Scientist, Nutrit Prod Div, Mead Johnson & Co, 63-65; fel food sci, USPHS, 65-68; Fulbright fel food sci, Danish Meat Res Inst, 68-69; DIR RES & NUTRIT, THOMAS J LIPTON, INC, 69- *Mem:* Inst Food Technologists; Am Chem Soc; Am Oil Chemists Soc; Dairy Sci Asn; Sigma Xi. *Res:* Research and product development of new food concepts, systems and products; administration of nutrition and product safety. *Mailing Add:* Thomas J Lipton Inc 800 Sylvan Ave Englewood Cliffs NJ 07632

SUPRUNOWICZ, KONRAD, b Pulkovnikov, Siberia, Mar 3, 19; US citizen; m 52; c 1. MATHEMATICS. *Educ:* Univ Nebr, BSc, 52, MA, 53, PhD(math), 60. *Prof Exp:* Instr physics, Minot State Col, 54-55; instr math, Univ Nebr, 57-60; asst prof, Univ Idaho, 60-61; assoc prof, 61-69, PROF MATH, UTAH STATE UNIV, 69- *Concurrent Pos:* Vis assoc prof, Univ Nebr, 62-63. *Mem:* Asn Symbolic Logic; Math Asn Am; Am Math Soc. *Res:* Application of symbolic logic to the study of relational systems; methodology of science. *Mailing Add:* Dept of Math Utah State Univ Logan UT 84321

SUPRYNOWICZ, VINCENT A, b Middletown, Conn, Sept 1, 23; m 47; c 3. PHYSICS, ELECTRICAL ENGINEERING. *Educ:* Ohio State Univ, BSc, 47, MSc, 49; Yale Univ, PhD(physics, biophys), 53. *Prof Exp:* Anal engr, Pratt & Whitney Nuclear Aircraft Proj, 52-54; asst prof physics, Bucknell Univ, 54-56; assoc prof appl sci, Univ Cincinnati, 56-59; head instrumentation, United Aircraft Res Labs, 59-62, prin scientist, 62-64; RES PROF ELEC ENG, UNIV CONN, 64- *Concurrent Pos:* Consult, United Aircraft Res Labs, 64-65. *Mem:* Am Asn Physics Teachers; Sigma Xi; Am Phys Soc. *Res:* Raman and ultraviolet spectroscopy; reactor shielding; bioelectronics; ultrasonics; lasers; experimental quantum mechanics. *Mailing Add:* Dept of Elec Eng Univ of Conn U-157 Storrs CT 06268

SURAK, JOHN GODFREY, b Milwaukee, Wis, July 13, 48; m 71. TOXICOLOGY. *Educ:* Univ Wis-Madison, BS, 71, MS, 72, PhD(toxicol), 74. *Prof Exp:* Res asst food sci, Univ Wis-Madison, 70-74; asst prof toxicol, Univ Fla, 74-80; SR SCIENTIST, FOOD PROD RES DEPT, MEAD JOHNSON & CO, EVANSVILLE, 80- *Mem:* Am Col Vet Toxicol; Am Chem Soc; Inst Food Technologists; Sigma Xi. *Res:* Food toxicology as related to the analysis, metabolism, mode of action and excretion of food additive, natural products and pesticides. *Mailing Add:* Food Res Dept Mead Johnson & Co Evansville IN 47721

SURAN, JEROME J, b New York, NY, Jan 11, 26; m 52. ELECTRICAL ENGINEERING. *Educ:* Columbia Univ, BS, 49; Syracuse Univ, Dr Eng, 76. *Prof Exp:* Develop engr, J W Meaker & Co, 49-51; engr res & develop, Motorola, Inc, 51-52; mgr adv circuits, Electronics Lab, 52-62, consult, 54-57, mgr, Electronic Appln & Devices Lab, 62-76, MGR, ELECTRONICS LAB, GEN ELEC CO, 73- *Concurrent Pos:* Instr, Mass Inst Technol, 56-; mem, Ad Hoc Comt Electronic Mat, Nat Acad Sci, 70-; adj prof, Syracuse Univ, 76- *Mem:* Sigma Xi; fel Inst Elec & Electronics Engrs. *Res:* Solid state circuit development for applications to the broad field of electronics, including computers, communications, control systems, detection systems. *Mailing Add:* 306 Holmes St Syracuse NY 13210

SURANYI, PETER, b Budapest, Hungary, Jan 31, 35; m 60; c 2. HIGH ENERGY PHYSICS. *Educ:* Eötvös Lorand Univ, Budapest, BS, 58; Acad Sci, USSR, PhD(physics), 64. *Prof Exp:* Jr res fel cosmic ray physics, Cent Res Inst Physics, Budapest, Hungary, 58-61; res fel theoret physics, Joint Inst Nuclear Studies, Moscow, 61-65; sr res fel theoret high energy physics, Cent Res Inst Physics, Budapest, Hungary, 65-69; vis lectr physics, Johns Hopkins Univ, 69-70, res assoc, 70-71; assoc prof, 71-74, PROF PHYSICS, UNIV CINCINNATI, 74- *Concurrent Pos:* sr fel, Brit Sci Coun, 78-79. *Honors & Awards:* Schmidt Award, Hungarian Phys Soc, 68. *Mem:* Am Phys Soc. *Res:* High energy behavior of strong interactions; group theoretic methods in elementary particle physics; statistical mechanics. *Mailing Add:* Dept of Physics Univ of Cincinnati Cincinnati OH 45221

SURAWICZ, BORYS, b Moscow, Russia, Feb 11, 17; nat US; m 46; c 4. INTERNAL MEDICINE, CARDIOLOGY. *Educ:* Stefan Batory Univ, Poland, MD, 39; Am Bd Internal Med, dipl; Am Bd Cardiovasc Dis, dipl. *Prof Exp:* Instr cardiol, Sch Med, Univ Pa, 54-55; instr med, Col Med, Univ Vt, 55-57, asst prof exp & clin med, 56-62; assoc prof med, Col Med, Univ Ky, 62-66, dir Cardiovasc Div, 62-81, prof, 66-81; PROF MED, KRANNERT INST CARDIOL, INDIANAPOLIS, 81- *Concurrent Pos:* Fel coun clin cardiol, Am Heart Asn. *Mem:* Fel Am Col Physicians; fel Am Col Cardiol; AMA; Am Physiol Soc; Asn Univ Cardiologists. *Res:* Electrocardiology; role of electrolytes in cardiac arrhythmias. *Mailing Add:* Krannert Inst Cardiol 1001 W Tenth St Indianapolis IN 46202

SURBEY, DONALD LEE, b North Canton, Ohio, July 19, 40; m 61; c 2. ORGANIC CHEMISTRY. *Educ:* Manchester Col, BS, 61; Univ Notre Dame, PhD(org chem), 68. *Prof Exp:* Control chemist, Miles Labs, Inc, 61-63; RES CHEMIST, LUBRIZOL CORP, 67- *Mem:* Am Chem Soc. *Res:* Organic chemistry as related to process and product development in field of polymer chemistry and lubricant additives. *Mailing Add:* 5648 Ridgebury Blvd Lyndhurst OH

SURDY, TED E, b Wheeling, WVa, Jan 25, 25; m 50; c 4. BACTERIOLOGY, BIOCHEMISTRY. *Educ:* Purdue Univ, BS, 58, MS, 59, PhD(bact), 62. *Prof Exp:* Instr bact, Purdue Univ, 59-61; assoc prof bact & cell physiol, Kans State Teachers Col, 62-67; res assoc biol, Educ Res Coun Greater Cleveland, 67-68; chmn dept biol, 68-74, PROF BIOL, SOUTHWEST MINN STATE COL, 74- *Concurrent Pos:* NSF grant, 65-68. *Mem:* AAAS; Am Soc Microbiol; Soc Indust Microbiol; Nat Asn Biol Teachers. *Res:* Lytic reactions of gram-negative bacterial cell walls; membrane permeability of gram-negative bacteria; effect of lipids on lysis of gram-negative bacteria; audio-tutorial bacteriology; methods for isolation and identification of salmonella. *Mailing Add:* Dept of Biol Southwest Minn State Col Marshall MN 56258

SURGALLA, MICHAEL JOSEPH, b Nicholson, Pa, May 12, 20; m 48; c 4. MEDICAL MICROBIOLOGY. *Educ:* Univ Scranton, BS, 42; Univ Chicago, PhD(bact), 46. *Prof Exp:* Bacteriologist, E R Squibb & Sons, NJ, 46-48; res assoc, Univ Chicago, 48-54; bacteriologist, Biol Sci Lab, Dept of Army, Ft Detrick, Md, 54-71; DIR CLIN MICROBIOL, ROSWELL PARK MEM INST, 71- *Mem:* AAAS; Am Soc Microbiol; Am Acad Microbiol; NY Acad Sci; Am Soc Clin Pathologists. *Res:* Medical bacteriology; staphylococcus food poisoning; influenza virus; experimental plague; bacterial virulence; pathogenic mechanisms; host resistance; endotoxins; fibrinolysis; opportunist pathogens; hospital infection epidemiology. *Mailing Add:* Roswell Park Mem Inst 666 Elm St Buffalo NY 14263

SURGENOR, DOUGLAS MACNEVIN, b Hartford, Conn, Apr 7, 18; m 46; c 5. BIOCHEMISTRY. *Educ:* Williams Col, AB, 39; Mass State Col, MS, 41; Mass Inst Technol, PhD(org chem), 46. *Prof Exp:* Mem staff, Div Indust Coop, Mass Inst Technol, 42-45; res assoc phys chem, Harvard Med Sch, 45-50, asst prof, 50-55, asst prof biol chem, 55-60; sr investr, Protein Found, 56-60; head dept biochem, Sch Med, State Univ NY Buffalo, 60-64, dean, 62-68, provost, Fac Health Sci, 67-70, prof biochem, 60-77, res prof, sch mgt, 71-77; PRES & DIR, AM RED CROSS BLOOD SERV, NORTHEAST REG, BOSTON, 77- *Concurrent Pos:* Assoc mem lab phys chem related to med & pub health, Harvard Univ, 50-54; consult, Vet Admin Hosp, Buffalo, 60-, chmn dean's comt, 62-68; mem med bd, Buffalo Gen & Buffalo Children's Hosps, 62-68; mem med coun, NY State Educ Dept, 62-68; bd sci counr, Div Biol Stand, NIH, 63-68; mem, Nat Heart Inst Prog Proj Comt B, 65-68; consult med bd, Millard Fillmore Hosp, 66-70; mem, Int Comt Thrombosis & Haemostasis, 63-, chmn, 70-72; mem nat blood resource prog adv comt, Nat Heart & Lung Inst, 69-73, chmn, 70-73; mem med adv comt, Am Nat Red Cross, 70-76; pres, Ctr Blood Res, Boston, 72-; mem bd trustees, Children's Hosp Med Ctr, Boston, 75-; vis prof pediat, Harvard Med Sch, 77-; mem adv coun, Nat Heart, Lung & Blood Inst, NIH, 80-; mem expert adv panel human blood prods, WHO, 80- *Mem:* AAAS; Am Soc Biol Chemists; Am Heart Asn; Am Soc Hemat; Int Soc Thrombosis & Haemostasis. *Res:* Blood biochemistry; blood and public policy; blood coagulation. *Mailing Add:* 213 Indian Hill Rd Carlisle MA 01741

SURI, RAJAN, b Dec 18, 52; India citizen. LARGE SCALE SYSTEMS, QUEUEING NETWORKS. *Educ:* Cambridge Univ, Eng, BA, 74; Harvard Univ, SM, 75, PhD(eng), 78. *Prof Exp:* Fel decision & control, Div Appl Sci, Harvard Univ, 78-80, asst prof, 80; managing dir, SAN Ltd Locomotive Co, Bangalore, India, 81; ASST PROF SYSTS ENG, DIV APPL SCI, HARVARD UNIV, 82- *Concurrent Pos:* Consult & database mgr, Multinational Enterprise Proj, Harvard Bus Sch, 75-78; mgt consult, Fiat SPA, Turin, Italy, 76-78; consult, Charles Stark Draper Lab, 76- *Honors & Awards:* Donald P Eckman Award, 81. *Mem:* Inst Elec & Electronics Engrs. *Res:* Modelling, control and optimization of large scale operational systems, such as automated manufacturing systems, distributed computer systems and communication networks; new approaches to modelling nonclassical queueing networks; decentralized optimization. *Mailing Add:* Pierce Hall Harvard Univ Cambridge MA 02138

SURIA, AMIN, b Dhoraji, India, Aug 24, 42; m 74; c 1. NEUROPHARMACOLOGY. *Educ:* Univ Karachi, Pakistan, BS, 63, MS, 64; Vanderbilt Univ, Nashville, PhD(pharmacol), 71. *Prof Exp:* Chemist, United Paints Ltd, Karachi, Pakistan, 64; chemist & in-chg lab, Textile Dyes & Auxiliary Dept, Hoechst Pharmaceut Co, Ltd, Karachi, Pakistan, 64-66; vis fel, Lab Clin Pharmacol, Nat Heart & Lung Inst, NIH, Bethesda, Md, 71-72; fel, Lab Preclin Pharmacol, NIMH, St Elizabeth's Hosp, Washington, DC, 72-74, staff fel, 74-75; asst prof pharmacol, George Washington Univ, Washington, DC, 75-80; PROF PHARMACOL, RIYADH UNIV, SAUDI ARABIA, 80- *Concurrent Pos:* Guest worker, Lab Preclin Pharmacol, St Elizabeth's Hosp, NIMH. *Mem:* Am Soc Pharmacol & Exp Therapeut; Soc Neurosci; NY Acad Sci. *Res:* Molecular mechanisms by which anti-anxiety, anticonvulsant, and antidepressant drugs exert their actions on complex neuronal pathways, research entails using electrophysiological and biochemical techniques. *Mailing Add:* Dept Pharmacol Med Sch Riyadh Univ PO Box 2925 Riyadh Saudi Arabia

SURIANO, F(RANCIS) J(OSEPH), b Kenosha, Wis, July 17, 37; m 59; c 4. MECHANICAL ENGINEERING. *Educ:* Univ Notre Dame, BS, 59, PhD(mech eng), 66; Ga Inst Technol, MS, 61. *Prof Exp:* Asst mech eng, Ga Inst Technol, 59-60; res engr, Wood River Res Lab, Shell Oil Co, 60-61; mem staff aerodyn preliminary design, AiRes Mfg Co, Ariz, 66-67; mem tech staff, Aerospace Corp, 67-68; MEM STAFF AERODYNAMICS-PRELIMINARY DESIGN, AIRESEARCH MFG CO ARIZ, PHOENIX, 68- *Mem:* Am Soc Mech Engrs. *Res:* Heat transfer and fluid mechanics. *Mailing Add:* AiResearch Mfg Co of Ariz 402 S 36th St Phoenix AZ 85034

SURKAN, ALVIN JOHN, b Drumheller, Alta, June 5, 34; m 67; c 2. PHYSICS, APPLIED MATHEMATICS. *Educ:* Univ Alta, BSc, 54; Univ Toronto, MA, 56; Univ Western Ont, PhD(physics), 59. *Prof Exp:* Sr demonstr geophys, Univ Western Ont, 58-59; Nat Res Coun Can fel, Univ Alta, 59-61; sci officer marine physics, Can Defence Res Bd, 61-62; fac mem physics, Univ BC, 62-63; staff consult geophys comput, res & develop ctr, IBM Corp, 64-65, mem res staff environ sci group, phys sci dept, Watson Res Ctr, 65-69; mem inst water resources res, 69-73, PROF COMPUT SCI, UNIV NEBR, LINCOLN, 69- *Concurrent Pos:* Consult geophys comput & resident visitor physics dept, Bell Tel Labs, 72. *Mem:* Am Geophys Union; Soc Explor Geophysicists; Am Inst Physics; Inst Elec & Electronics Engrs. *Res:* Magnetic and seismic methods in exploration geophysics; mathematical modeling in hydrology, geomorphology and educational psychology; algorithms for data interpretation; nonlinear optimization and symbolic computation in geophysics and chemical engineering. *Mailing Add:* Dept of Comput Sci Univ of Nebr Lincoln NE 68588

SURKO, CLIFFORD MICHAEL, b Sacramento, Calif, Oct 11, 41; m 65; c 2. LASER SCATTERING. *Educ:* Univ Calif, Berkeley, AB, 64, PhD(physics), 68. *Prof Exp:* Res assoc physics, Univ Calif, Berkeley, 68-69; MEM TECH STAFF PHYSICS, BELL LABS, 69- *Concurrent Pos:* Vis sr res physicist, Ecole Polytech, France, 78-79; vis scientist, Plasma Fusion Ctr, Mass Inst Technol, 77- *Mem:* AAAS; Am Inst Physics. *Res:* Experimental research in low temperature physics and in plasma physics; study of atoms, condensed matter and density fluctuations in plasmas with light scattering; laser scattering from plasmas and condensed matter. *Mailing Add:* Room IC352 Bell Labs Murray Hill NJ 07974

SURKO, PAMELA TONI, b Britton, SDak, June 15, 42; m 65; c 2. COMPUTER SCIENCE. *Educ:* Univ Calif, Berkeley, AB, 63, PhD(physics), 70. *Prof Exp:* Res assoc, Princeton Univ, 70-71, instr, 71-72, asst prof physics, 72-80; MEM TECH STAFF, BELL LABS, NJ, 80- *Mem:* Am Phys Soc; Inst Elec & Electronics Engrs; Am Comput Mach; AAAS; Asn Women Sci. *Res:* Strangeness-changing neutral currents; muon-induced events at high energy. *Mailing Add:* 5D117 BELL LABS Murray Hill NJ 07974

SURPURIYA, VIJAY B, pharmaceutical chemistry, physical pharmacy, see previous edition

SURREY, ALEXANDER ROBERT, b New York, NY, Mar 13, 14; m 39; c 1. ORGANIC CHEMISTRY, DRUG RESEARCH ADMINISTRATION. *Educ:* City Col New York, BS, 34; NY Univ, PhD(chem), 40. *Prof Exp:* Nat Defense Res Comt fel, Cornell Univ, 40-41; res chemist, 41-57, sect head, 57-60, asst dir chem res, 60-64, sr res fel & dir new prod, 64-67, dir develop res, 67-72, vpres res & develop, 72-76, vpres prod develop, 76-77, VPRES TECH AFFAIRS, STERLING-WINTHROP RES INST, 77- *Concurrent Pos:* Lectr & adj prof, Rensselaer Polytech Inst, 58-64; law & med consult. *Honors & Awards:* Townsend Harris Medal, 81. *Mem:* Am Chem Soc; fel NY Acad Sci; fel The Chem Soc. *Res:* Medicinals. *Mailing Add:* 15 Harvard Ave Albany NY 12208

SURREY, KENNETH, b India, Dec 6, 22; nat US; m 52; c 4. PHYTOCHEMISTRY. *Educ:* Univ Punjab, India, BSc, 46, MA, 52; Univ Mo, MA, 55, PhD(phytochem), 57. *Prof Exp:* Lab instr chem, Forman Christian Col, Pakistan, 49-53; asst bot, Univ Mo, 54-57; asst plant physiologist, Argonne Nat Lab, 57-66; HEALTH SCIENTIST ADMINR, NIH, 66- *Res:* Histochemistry of protein constituents by azo-coupling reactions in plants; metabolic responses of regenerating meristems and germinating seeds as influenced by visible and ionizing radiation; action and interaction of red and far-red radiation on metabolic processes of developing seedlings; physiological bases for morphological development. *Mailing Add:* Nat Inst Neurol & Commun Disorders & Stroke Fed Bldg 7550 Wis Ave Bethesda MD 20205

SURTI, VASANT H, b Bombay, India, Oct 30, 31; US citizen; m 58; c 1. CIVIL & TRANSPORTATION ENGINEERING. *Educ:* Univ Bombay, BSc, 52; Seattle UniV, BS, 57; Mich State Univ, MS, 62; Cath Univ Am, PhD(civil eng), 68. *Prof Exp:* Design engr, Boeing Aircraft Co, Wash, 57-59; traffic res & hwy design engr, Mich State Hwy Dept, 59-66; asst prof civil eng, Cath Univ Am, 66-68, assoc prof civil eng & mech, 68-72; ASSOC PROF CIVIL ENG & DIR CTR URBAN TRANSP STUDIES, UNIV COLO, DENVER, 72- *Concurrent Pos:* Grants, NSF, Dept Transp & Dept Com; mem, Hwy Res Bd Comts. *Mem:* Inst Traffic Engrs; Am Soc Civil Engrs. *Mailing Add:* Dept of Civil Eng Univ of Colo Denver CO 80210

SURVANT, WILLIAM G, b Owensboro, Ky, Aug 26, 07; m 36. SOIL SCIENCE. *Educ:* Univ Ky, BS, 31, MS, 45; Ohio State Univ, PhD(soil sci), 51. *Prof Exp:* Teacher high sch, Ky, 31-38; soil conservationist soil conserv serv, USDA, 38-42; exten soil conservationist, 42-47, asst prof soils, 47-50, from assoc prof to prof agron, 51-74, EMER PROF AGRON, UNIV KY, 74- *Mem:* Am Soc Agron; Soil Sci Soc Am. *Res:* Soil conservation. *Mailing Add:* 120 Tahoma Rd Lexington KY 40503

SURVER, WILLIAM MERLE, JR, b Altoona, Pa, June 26, 43. DEVELOPMENTAL GENETICS. *Educ:* St Francis Col, BA, 66; Univ Notre Dame, PhD(genetics), 72. *Prof Exp:* Instr biol, Univ Notre Dame, 71-72; asst prof zool, Univ RI, 72-78; asst prof, 78-81, ASSOC PROF BIOL, CLEMSON UNIV, 81- *Mem:* AAAS; Nat Sci Teachers Asn; Nat Asn Biol Teachers; Genetics Soc Am. *Res:* Genetic effects on developing systems; genetics of kelp fly, Coelopa frigida; innovative teaching for general biology. *Mailing Add:* Biol Prog Clemson Univ Clemson SC 29631

SURWILLO, WALTER WALLACE, b Rochester, NY, Nov 25, 26; m 55. PSYCHOPHYSIOLOGY. *Educ:* Wash Univ, St Louis, BA, 51, MA, 53; McGill Univ, PhD(psychol), 55. *Prof Exp:* Asst psychol, Wash Univ, St Louis, 50-53; asst, McGill Univ, 53-55; res assoc psychophysiol, Allan Mem Inst Psychiat, 55-57; res psychophysiologist gerontol br, NIH, 57-65; assoc prof psychiat, 65-70, PROF PSYCHIAT SCH MED, UNIV LOUISVILLE, 70-, ASSOC PROF PSYCHOL, GRAD SCH, 71- *Concurrent Pos:* Mem, NIH Exp Psychol Study Sect, 70-74; consult, NSF, 73- *Mem:* Am Psychol Asn; Soc Psychophysiol Res; NY Acad Sci; Soc Neurosci. *Res:* Nervous system function and its relation to behavior; psychophysiological and electrophysiological methods of investigation; instrumentation; central nervous system and behavioral changes with development and senescence. *Mailing Add:* Dept Psychiat & Behav Sci Univ Louisville Sch Med Louisville KY 40292

SURYANARAYANA, NARASIPUR VENKATARAM, b Bangalore, India, Apr 12, 31; m 59; c 2. MECHANICAL ENGINEERING. *Educ:* Univ Mysore, BE, 54; Columbia Univ, MS, 66; Univ Mich, PhD(mech eng), 70. *Prof Exp:* Tech asst mech eng, Hindustan Shipyard, Visakhapatnam, 55-63; lectr, Indian Inst Technol, Kharagpur, 63-64; training off, Lucas-TVS, Madras, 64-65; asst prof, 70-75, assoc prof, 75-79, PROF MECH ENG, MICH TECHNOL UNIV, 79- *Concurrent Pos:* NSF res grants, 71-72 & 77-79. *Res:* Heat transfer with change of phase; convective heat transfer with turbulence; solar energy. *Mailing Add:* Dept of Mech Eng & Eng Mech Mich Technol Univ Houghton MI 49931

SURYARAMAN, MARUTHUVAKUDI GOPALASASTRI, b Madras, India, Mar 2, 25; m 52; c 3. ANALYTICAL CHEMISTRY, PHYSICAL CHEMISTRY. *Educ:* Univ Madras, BSc, 46, MS, 52; Univ Colo, PhD(chem), 61. *Prof Exp:* Demonstr chem, Madras Christian Col, 46-49 & Vivekananda Col, Madras, 52; lectr, Sri Venkateswara Univ Cols, Andhra, 52-57; asst, Univ Colo, 57-59, 60-61; sr res chemist, Monsanto Co, Mo, 61-66; from asst prof to assoc prof, 66-75, PROF CHEM, HUMBOLDT STATE UNIV, 75- *Mem:* Am Chem Soc; fel Royal Inst Chem; fel Indian Chem Soc. *Res:* Analytical chemistry, electrochemistry and ion exchange; general inorganic chemistry. *Mailing Add:* Dept of Chem Humboldt State Univ Arcata CA 95521

SURZYCKI, STEFAN JAN, b Krakow, Poland, Jan 13, 36; US citizen; m 70; c 4. MOLECULAR BIOLOGY, BIOCHEMISTRY. *Educ:* Odessa Univ, MS, 60; Warsaw Univ, PhD(genetics), 64. *Prof Exp:* Asst genetics, Warsaw Univ, 61-63; researcher, Genetics Inst Polish Acad Sci, Warsaw, 63-64; fel molecular biol, Harvard Univ, 64-65, res fel, 65-68, Maria Moor Cabot Found fel, 69-70; from asst prof to assoc prof, Univ Iowa, 70-75; ASSOC PROF, DEPT BIOL, IND UNIV, 75- *Mem:* Am Soc Cell Biol; Am Soc Microbiol. *Res:* Mechanism of transcription initiation by eucaryotic RNA Polymerase II; regulation of gene expression in chloroplast of C. reinhardi. *Mailing Add:* Dept of Biol Ind Univ Bloomington IN 47402

SUSAG, RUSSELL H(ARRY), b Minneapolis, Minn, Dec 22, 30; m 57; c 6. ENVIRONMENTAL ENGINEERING. *Educ:* Univ Minn, BCE, 56, MSCE, 65, PhD(sanit eng), 65. *Prof Exp:* Teaching asst sanit eng, Univ Minn, 56-57, asst prof, 65-68; sanit engr, Toltz, King, Duvall, Anderson & Assoc, Inc, 64; assoc prof environ eng, Univ Fla, 68-70; mgr qual control, Metrop Sewer Bd, Minneapolis-St Paul, 70-74; mgr environ affairs, 74-78, dir environ regulatory activ, 78-80, DIR ENVIRON OPERS, 3M CO, 80- *Honors & Awards:* Arthur Sidney Bedell Award, Water Pollution Control Fedn, 77. *Mem:* Am Soc Civil Engrs; Nat Soc Prof Engrs; Water Pollution Control Fedn; Am Acad Environ Engrs. *Res:* Solid waste management; water pollution control, deoxygenation and reaeration characteristics of waste waters and receiving waters. *Mailing Add:* 7305 First Ave S Richfield MN 55423

SUSALLA, ANNE A, b Parisville, Mich. PLANT ANATOMY. *Educ:* Madonna Col, BA, 62; Univ Detroit, MS, 67; Ind Univ, Bloomington, PhD(bot), 72. *Prof Exp:* Asst prof, 72-75, chairperson dept, 77-80, ASSOC PROF BIOL, ST MARY'S COL, 75- *Mem:* Bot Soc Am; Am Inst Biol Sci; AAAS. *Res:* Ultrastructure of plastids in phenotypically green leaf tissue of a genetic albino strain of Nicotiana; tissue culture work is being employed to study the developmental stages of these plastids. *Mailing Add:* Dept of Biol Sci Hall St Mary's Col Notre Dame IN 46556

SUSI, FRANK ROBERT, b Boston, Mass, Dec 10, 36. ANATOMY, ORAL PATHOLOGY. *Educ:* Boston Col, BS, 58; Harvard Univ, DMD, 62, cert, 65; Tufts Univ, PhD(anat), 67. *Prof Exp:* Instr anat, Sch Med, 67-68, from asst prof to assoc prof oral path, 67-74, PROF ORAL PATH, SCH DENT MED, TUFTS UNIV, 74-, DIR DIV, 73-, DIR BASIC HEALTH SCI, 70-, ASST PROF ANAT, SCH MED, 68-, ASST DEAN, ACAD AFFAIRS, 77- *Concurrent Pos:* Fel anat, McGill Univ, 68-69. *Mem:* Am Dent Asn; Am Asn Anat; Histochem Soc; Am Acad Oral Path; Int Asn Dent Res. *Res:* Histochemistry; autoradiography; electron microscopy; keratinization, carcinogenesis; spermiogenesis; dentistry. *Mailing Add:* Dept Oral Path Sch Dent Med Tufts Univ One Kneeland St Boston MA 02111

SUSI, PETER VINCENT, b Philadelphia, Pa, Apr 26, 28; m 54; c 2. ORGANIC CHEMISTRY, RESEARCH ADMINISTRATION. *Educ:* Univ Pa, BA, 50; Univ Del, MS, 51, PhD(chem), 57. *Prof Exp:* From res chemist tosr res chemist, 56-63, group leader, 63-76, proj leader, 76-81, GROUP LEADER, AM CYANAMID CO, 81- *Mem:* AAAS; Am Chem Soc. *Res:* Synthesis and applications research in field of plastics additives, light stabilizers, antioxidants, antistatics; ultraviolet and infrared absorbers; flame retardants, antioxidants and photoimitators. *Mailing Add:* Chem Res Div Am Cyanamid Co Bound Brook NJ 08805

SUSINA, STANLEY V, b Berwyn, Ill, Apr 14, 23; m 48; c 3. PHARMACY, PHARMACOLOGY. *Educ:* Univ Ill, BS, 48, MS, 51, PhD(pharmacol), 55. *Prof Exp:* Asst pharm, Univ Ill, 48-50, from instr to asst prof, 50-61, assoc prof & actg head dept, 61-62; PROF PHARM & CHMN DEPT, SAMFORD UNIV, 62- & ASSOC DEAN, SCH PHARM, 76- *Mem:* Acad Pharmaceut Sci; Am Asn Cols Pharm; Am Pharmaceut Asn. *Res:* Antihistamines; neuromuscular blocking agents; local anesthetics; radioactive isotopes. *Mailing Add:* Dept Pharm Samford Univ 800 Lakeshore Dr Birmingham AL 35229

SUSKI, HENRY M(IECZYSLAW), b Camden, NJ, July 14, 18; m 43. ELECTRONIC & COMMUNICATION ENGINEERING. *Educ:* City Col New York, BEE, 41. *Prof Exp:* Switchboard engr, Western Elec Co, 41; electronics scientist, Electronics Div, 46-67, ELECTRONICS ENGR, TACTICAL ELECTRONIC WARFARE DIV, US NAVAL RES LAB, DC, 67- *Concurrent Pos:* Vpres, NAm Res Corp & Corp Systs Res, 67-77. *Mem:* Sr mem Inst Elec & Electronics Engrs; Sigma Xi. *Res:* Development of long range facility plans, which include construction and installation, for electronic warfare simulation, research, development, and laboratory test; design management and funding organization, considering the assessment of technology and its impact on society. *Mailing Add:* 2206 Rosecroft Blvd Oxon Hill MD 20022

SUSKIND, RAYMOND ROBERT, b New York, NY, Nov 29, 13; m 44; c 2. MEDICAL SCIENCE, HEALTH SCIENCES. *Educ:* Columbia Univ, AB, 34; State Univ NY, MD, 43; Am Bd Dermat & Syphil, dipl, 49. *Prof Exp:* Resident dermat & syphil, Cincinnati Gen Hosp, 44-46; res fel dermat, Col Med, Univ Cincinnati, 48-49, from asst prof to assoc prof prev med & indust health, 49-62, asst prof dermat, 50-62, dir dermat res, Kettering Lab, 48-62; prof dermat & head div environ med, Med Sch, Univ Ore, 62-69; PROF ENVIRON HEALTH & MED, CHMN DEPT ENVIRON HEALTH & DIR, KETTERING LAB, COL MED, UNIV CINCINNATI, 69- *Concurrent Pos:* Attend physician, Univ Hosp, Cincinnati Med Ctr, 69-; attend physician, Univ Ore Hosp, 62-69; mem, Cincinnati Air Pollution Bd, 72-76, chmn, 74-75; rep, USSR-USA Collab Res Prog, Biol & Genetic Effects Pollutants, 73-79; mem, Task Force Res Planning Comt, Nat Inst Environ Health Sci, 75-77; consult, Bur Drugs & Dermat Adv Comt, Food & Drug Admin, 76-81; consult, Occup Med to the Surgeon Gen, Depart Navy, 75-; chmn, Occup Safety Health Act Standards Adv Comt Cutaneous Hazards, 78; mem, Certifying Bd, Am Bd Toxicology, 78-, Vet Admin Comt Health Related Effects Herbicides, 79, Adv Panel Toxicology, Am Med Assoc Coun Sci Affairs, 80-; assoc ed, Am J Indust Med, 79- *Honors & Awards:* Mitchell Award, State Univ NY Med Ctr, 43. *Mem:* Am Col Physicians; NY Acad Sci; fel Am Acad Dermat; Am Occup Med Asn; Am Dermat Asn. *Res:* Environmental medicine and dermatology; percutaneous absorption; cutaneous hypersensitivity; effects of physical environment on skin reactions to irritants and allergens; environmental cancer; environmental problems of chemical origin; mechanisms and patterns of cataneous responses to irritants and intigenic stimuli; percutaneous absorption; chemical carcinogenesis; biological effects of heavy metals. *Mailing Add:* Dept of Environ Health Univ Cincinnati Col Med Cincinnati OH 45267

SUSKIND, SIGMUND RICHARD, b New York, NY, June 19, 26; m 51; c 3. MICROBIOLOGY. *Educ:* NY Univ, AB, 48; Yale Univ, PhD(microbiol), 54. *Prof Exp:* Asst microbiol, Yale Univ, 50-54; USPHS fel, NY Univ, 54-56; from asst prof to assoc prof, 56-65, PROF BIOL, MCCOLLUM-PRATT INST, JOHNS HOPKINS UNIV, 65-, DEAN GRAD & UNDERGRAD STUDIES, 71-, DEAN, FAC ARTS & SCI, 78- *Concurrent Pos:* Consult, Am Inst Biol Sci, 58-59; spec consult, USPHS, 66-70; head molecular biol sect, NSF, 70-71; consult, Coun Grad Schs & Mid States Asn Cols & Sec Schs, 73- & NIH, 66-70; pres, Northeastern Asn Grad Sch, 77-78. *Mem:* Am Soc Microbiol; Genetics Soc Am; Am Asn Immunol; Am Soc Biol Chem. *Res:* Immunochemistry and biochemistry of mechanism of gene action in microorganisms. *Mailing Add:* McCollum-Pratt Inst Johns Hopkins Univ Baltimore MD 21218

SUSLICK, KENNETH SANDERS, b Chicago, Ill, Sept 16, 52; m 75. ORGANOMETALLIC CHEMISTRY, BIOINORGANIC CHEMISTRY. *Educ:* Calif Inst Technol, BS, 74; Stanford Univ, PhD(chem), 78. *Prof Exp:* Res asst, Calif Inst Technol, 71-74; chemist, Lawrence Livermore Lab, 74-75; ASST PROF CHEM, UNIV ILL, URBANA-CHAMPAIGN, 78- *Concurrent Pos:* Res asst, Univ Calif, Berkeley, 72; Hertz fel, Stanford Univ, 74-78. *Honors & Awards:* Silver Medal, Royal Soc Arts, Mfgs & Commerce. *Mem:* Am Chem Soc. *Res:* Synthetic analogs of heme proteins, porphyrins and macrocycles; homogeneous catalysis; chemical effects of high intensity ultrasound; sonochemistry and sonocatalysis. *Mailing Add:* Dept Chem Univ Ill 505 S Mathews Ave Urbana IL 61801

SUSMAN, LEON, b Brooklyn, NY, Oct 10, 36; m 58; c 3. ELECTRICAL ENGINEERING. *Educ:* City Col New York, BEE, 58, MEE, 62; Polytechnic Inst Brooklyn, PhD(elec eng), 69. *Prof Exp:* Engr, Ford Instrument Co Div, Sperry Rand Corp, 58 & Airborne Instruments Labs Div, Cutter Hammer Corp, 58-61; sr engr, Sperry Gyroscope Div, 61-68, res staff mem microwave & antenna res, 68-80, MGR, ELECTROMAGNETICS DEPT, SPERRY RAND RES CTR, SPERRY RAND CORP, 80- *Mem:* Inst Elec & Electronics Engrs. *Res:* Microwave and antenna theory, in particular the application of transient performance to a wideband theory for radar; traffic control sensor; altimetry applications. *Mailing Add:* Sperry Res Ctr 100 North Rd Sudbury MA 01776

SUSMAN, MILLARD, b St Louis, Mo, Sept 1, 34; m 57; c 2. GENETICS. *Educ:* Wash Univ, AB, 56; Calif Inst Technol, PhD(genetics), 62. *Prof Exp:* NIH fel, Med Res Coun Microbial Genetics Res Unit, Hammersmith Hosp, London, Eng, 61-62; from asst prof to assoc prof, 62-73, chmn dept, 71-75, PROF GENETICS, LAB GENETICS, UNIV WIS-MADISON, 72-, CHMN DEPT, 77- *Mem:* AAAS; Genetics Soc Am. *Res:* Bacteriophage genetics and developmental genetics; effects of acridines on bacteriophage growth, recombination and mutation; role of the host cell in phage growth. *Mailing Add:* Lab of Genetics Univ of Wis Madison WI 53706

SUSMAN, RANDALL LEE, b Houston, Tex, Jan 19, 48; m 69; c 2. ANATOMY, PHYSICAL ANTHROPOLOGY. *Educ:* Univ Calif, Davis, BA, 70; Univ Chicago, MA, 72, PhD(anthrop), 76. *Prof Exp:* Lectr & fel, 76-77, ASST PROF ANAT SCI, STATE UNIV NY, STONY BROOK, 77- *Mem:* Am Asn Phys Anthropologists; AAAS; Soc Syst Zoologists; Am Anthrop Asn; Soc Vert Paleont. *Res:* Evolution of apes and humans; functional morphology of primates; natural history of the primates; electromyography; gross anatomy; field study of pygmy chimpanzee in Zaire. *Mailing Add:* Dept of Anat Sci State UniV NY Stony Brook NY 11794

SUSSDORF, DIETER HANS, b Neustadt, Ger, Aug 16, 30; nat US; m 54; c 3. IMMUNOLOGY. *Educ:* Univ Mo, BA, 52; Univ Chicago, PhD(microbiol), 56. *Prof Exp:* Logan fel, Univ Chicago, 57-58; resident res assoc biol, Argonne Nat Lab, 58-59; res fel immunochem, Calif Inst Technol, 59-61; res immunochemist, NIH, 61-63; asst prof, 64-72, ASSOC PROF MICROBIOL, MED COL & GRAD SCH MED SCI, CORNELL UNIV, 72- *Concurrent Pos:* Author & consult, Scott, Foresman & Co, 60-69; consult, Travenol Labs, 78-; course dir & lectr, Ctr Prof Advan, Cornell Univ, 72- *Honors & Awards:* David Anderson-Berry Prize, 61. *Res:* Function of thymus and non-thymic tissues in humoral and cellular immunity; anti-tumor activities of macrophages. *Mailing Add:* Dept of Microbiol Cornell Univ Med Col New York NY 10021

SUSSER, MERVYN W, b Johannesburg, SAfrica, Sept 26, 21; m 49; c 3. EPIDEMIOLOGY, SOCIAL MEDICINE. *Educ:* Univ Witwatersrand, MB, BCh, 50; FRCP(E), 70. *Prof Exp:* Med officer, Alexandria Health Ctr & Univ Clin, Johannesburg, 51-55; from lectr to reader social med, Univ Manchester, 57-65; Asn Aid Crippled Children Belding scholar, 65-66; prof, 66-77, GERTRUDE H SERGIEVSKY PROF EPIDEMIOL, & DIR, SERGIEVSKY CTR, COLUMBIA UNIV, 77- *Concurrent Pos:* Clin tutor med, Univ Witwatersrand, 51-55; John Simon Guggenheim fel, 72-73; mem comt, Sect Epidemiol & Community Psychiat, World Psychiat Asn; mem, Coun on Epidemiol, Am Heart Asn. *Mem:* Fel Am Pub Health Asn; Am Sociol Asn; Soc Epidemiol Res; NY Acad Med. *Res:* Social and cultural factors in human development and disease; brain disorders. *Mailing Add:* Sergievsky Ctr Columbia Univ 630 W 168th St New York NY 10032

SUSSEX, IAN MITCHELL, b Auckland, NZ, May 4, 27. BOTANY. *Educ:* Univ NZ, BS, 48, MSc, 50; Manchester Univ, PhD, 52. *Prof Exp:* Asst lectr bot, Victoria Univ Col, 54-55; asst prof, Univ Pittsburgh, 55-60; assoc prof, 60-73, PROF BOT, YALE UNIV, 73- *Concurrent Pos:* Fel, Ezra Stiles Col. *Mem:* AAAS; Soc Develop Biol; Bot Soc Am; Int Soc Plant Morphol; Am Soc Cell Biol. *Res:* Plant morphogenesis; tissue culture. *Mailing Add:* Dept of Biol Yale Univ New Haven CT 06520

SUSSEX, JAMES NEIL, b Northcote, Minn, Oct 2, 17; m 43; c 4. PSYCHIATRY. *Educ:* Univ Kans, AB, 39, MD, 42. *Prof Exp:* Resident psychiat, US Naval Hosp, Mare Island, Calif, 46-49; asst clin prof psychiat, Sch Med, Georgetown Univ, 53-55; assoc prof, Med Col Ala, 55-59, prof & chmn dept, 59-68; PROF PSYCHIAT, SCH MED, UNIV MIAMI, 68-, CHMN DEPT, 70- *Concurrent Pos:* Fel child psychiat, Philadelphia Child Guid Clin, Univ Pa, 49-51; dir ment health serv div, Jackson Mem Hosp, Miami, 70-; consult, NIMH; consult, Vet Admin, mem, Ment Adv Coun; pres, Am Asn Psychiat Serv Children, 72-74; dir, Am Bd Psychiat & Neurol, 75-82, pres, 82. *Mem:* AMA; Am Psychiat Asn; Am Col Psychiat; Am Acad Child Psychiat. *Res:* Child psychiatry; child development in cross-cultural perspective; atypical culture-bound syndromes; dissociative states. *Mailing Add:* Univ of Miami Dept of Psychiat Miami FL 33136

SUSSKIND, ALFRED K(RISS), b Coblenz, Ger, Oct 4, 23; nat US; m 51; c 3. ELECTRICAL ENGINEERING. *Educ:* Polytech Inst Brooklyn, BEE, 48; Mass Inst Technol, SM, 50. *Prof Exp:* Asst elec eng, Mass Inst Technol, 48-50, res engr, 50-55, asst prof, 55-59, assoc prof, 59-68; prof elec eng & chmn dept, Lehigh Univ, 68-80; mem staff, IBM Corp, 80-81; PROF ELEC & COMPUT ENG, LEHIGH UNIV, 81- *Mem:* Inst Elec & Electronics Engrs. *Res:* Logic design for testability; testing strategies and algorithms; design automation; logical design of machines and switching theory. *Mailing Add:* Dept Elec Comput Eng Packard Lab Lehigh Univ Bethlehem PA 18015

SUSSKIND, CHARLES, b Prague, Czech, Aug 19, 21; nat US; m 45; c 3. BIOENGINEERING, HISTORY OF TECHNOLOGY. *Educ:* Calif Inst Technol, BS, 48; Yale Univ, MEng, 49, PhD(elec eng), 51. *Prof Exp:* Res assoc, Stanford Univ, 51-55, lectr elec eng, univ & asst dir, Microwave Lab, 53-55; from asst prof to assoc prof elec eng, 55-64, asst dean eng, 64-68, PROF ENG SCI, UNIV CALIF, BERKELEY, 64- *Concurrent Pos:* Coordr acad affairs, Statewide Univ, 69-74. *Honors & Awards:* Clerk Maxwell Premium, Brit Inst Electronic & Radio Eng, 52. *Mem:* Biomed Eng Soc; Hist Sci Soc; AAAS; fel Inst Elec & Electronics Eng; Brit Inst Electronic & Radio Eng. *Res:* Bioelectronics; electron optics; history and sociology of technology and science. *Mailing Add:* Col of Eng Univ of Calif Berkeley CA 94720

SUSSKIND, HERBERT, b Ratibor, Ger, Mar 23, 29; US citizen; m 61; c 3. BIOMEDICAL ENGINEERING, PULMONARY PHYSIOLOGY. *Educ:* City Col New York, BChE, 50; NY Univ, MChE, 61; NY State, PE, 55. *Prof Exp:* Mem shielding group, Brookhaven Nat Lab, 50-52, fuel processing group, 52-58, assoc sect supvr, 57-58, sect supvr, Slurry Group, 58-59, mem, Reactor Eval & Advan Concepts Group, 59-61, head, Org Cooled Reactor Prog, 61-63, head, Packed Bed Reactor Eng Studies, 63-66, mem, Reactor Eval & Advan Concepts Group, 66-70; mem, Med Radionuclide Develop Group, 70-77, MEM NUCLEAR MED DIV, BROOKHAVEN NAT LAB, 77- *Concurrent Pos:* Biomed engr med staff, Hosp Brookhaven Med Res Ctr, 75-; assoc prof med & clin physiol, Dept Med, State Univ NY, Stony Brook, 79- *Mem:* Am Inst Chem Engrs; Am Nuclear Soc; Soc Nuclear Med; Biomed Eng Soc; Am Thoracic Soc. *Res:* Liquid metal technology; high temperature reactor fuel processing; packed and fluidized bed technology; application of chemical engineering to medical problems, principally in pulmonary physiology and nuclear medicine. *Mailing Add:* Medical Dept Brookhaven Nat Lab Upton NY 11973

SUSSMAN, ALFRED SHEPPARD, b Portsmouth, Va, July 4, 19; m 48; c 3. BIOLOGY. *Educ:* Univ Conn, BS, 41; Harvard Univ, AM, 48, PhD(biol), 49. *Prof Exp:* Instr microbiol, Mass Gen Hosp, 48-49; instr bot, 50-52, from asst prof to assoc prof, 53-61, chmn dept bot, 63-68, assoc dean col lit, sci & arts, 68-70, actg dean, 70-71, assoc dean, H H Rackham Sch Grad Studies, 72-74, PROF BOT, UNIV MICH, ANN ARBOR, 61-, DEAN, H H RACKHAM SCH GRAD STUDIES, 74-, ACTG VPRES ACAD AFFAIRS, 79- *Concurrent Pos:* Nat Res Coun fel, Univ Pa; Lalor Found fel, 56; NSF sr fel, Calif Inst Technol, 59-60; consult panel develop biol, NSF, 63-65, mem steering comt & comt innovation in lab instr, Biol Sci Curric Study, comnr comn undergrad educ biol sci, 66-69; chmn comt educ, Am Inst Biol Sci; mem biol comt, Argonne Univ Asn, 69-71, chmn, 70-71, examr, N Cent Asn Col & Univ, 71-; mem, Grad Rec Examr Bd, Res Comt, 78, chmn, 79-80, mem comt bio & med, 72-78, trustee, 74-78. *Mem:* Bot Soc Am; Am Soc Microbiol; Am Acad Microbiol; Am Soc Biol Chem. *Res:* Physiological mycology; microbial physiology and development; dormancy in microorganisms. *Mailing Add:* 1615 Harbal Dr Ann Arbor MI 48105

SUSSMAN, DONALD L, b New York, NY, Jan 11, 37; m 64; c 2. HAZARDOUS WASTES, ENVIRONMENTAL CHEMISTRY. *Educ:* City Col New York, BS, 58; Polytech Inst Brooklyn, PhD(chem), 66. *Prof Exp:* Fel environ chem, Harvard Univ, 65-67; ASSOC PROF ENVIRON ENG, UNIV RI, 67- *Concurrent Pos:* Vis assoc prof, Univ Del, 79-80 & Mass Inst Technol, 76-77. *Mem:* Am Chem Soc; Water Pollution Control Fedn; Sigma Xi; AAAS. *Res:* Chemical problems in the environment with the emphasis on hazardous and solid wastes and industrial waste treatment. *Mailing Add:* Dept Civil Environ Eng Univ RI Bliss Hall Kingston RI 02881

SUSSMAN, IRVING, b New York, NY, Feb 12, 08; m 40; c 2. MATHEMATICS. *Educ:* Columbia Univ, BS, 43; Johns Hopkins Univ, MA, 47; Univ Calif, PhD(math), 53. *Prof Exp:* Instr math & physics, Ricker Jr Col, 43-44; instr math, Johns Hopkins Univ, 44-46; asst prof, Univ Dayton, 47-48; asst prof math & physics, St Mary's Col, Calif, 48-51; asst prof math, Univ San Francisco, 51-54; prof, Calif State Polytech Col, 54-56; prof, 56-73, chmn dept, 56-68, actg chmn, 72, EMER PROF MATH, UNIV SANTA CLARA, 73- *Concurrent Pos:* Dir insts math teachers, NSF, 59-; Ford Found & US AID prof, Latin Am, 64; spec lectr, Calif State Univ, San Jose, 73-75. *Mem:* Am Math Soc; Math Asn Am. *Res:* Abstract algebra; generalized Boolean rings; analysis. *Mailing Add:* 19174 Montara Lane Los Gatos CA 95030

SUSSMAN, KARL EDGAR, b Baltimore, Md, May 29, 29; m 55; c 2. MEDICINE, ENDOCRINOLOGY. *Educ:* Johns Hopkins Univ, BA, 51; Univ Md, MD, 55. *Prof Exp:* From instr to assoc prof med, 62-72, head div endocrinol, 69-72, PROF MED, UNIV COLO MED CTR, DENVER, 73- *Concurrent Pos:* Chief med serv, Denver Vet Admin Hosp, 72-75, clin investr, 75-80. *Mem:* Am Col Physicians; Am Diabetes Asn; Am Fedn Clin Res; Am Physiol Soc; Endocrine Soc. *Res:* Factors controlling insulin secretion in isolated rat islets; hormonal control of carbohydrate-lipid metabolism; relationship of intermediary metabolism to insulin secretion; somatostatin-effect on hormone secretion; regulation of somatostation binding. *Mailing Add:* Vet Admin Med Ctr 1055 Clarmont Denver CO 80220

SUSSMAN, M(ARTIN) V(ICTOR), b New York, NY; m 53; c 3. CHEMICAL ENGINEERING, THERMODYNAMICS. *Educ:* Columbia Univ, MS, 52, PhD(chem eng), 58. *Prof Exp:* Instrument engr, Lummus Co, 47-48 & A G McKee & Co, 48-49; instr chem & res assoc, Fordham Univ, 49-50; asst, Columbia Univ, 51; sr engr, Textile Fiber Div, E I du Pont de Nemours & Co, Inc, 53-58; assoc prof chem eng, Robert Col, Istanbul, 58-61; chmn dept, 61-71, PROF CHEM ENG, TUFTS UNIV, 61- *Concurrent Pos:* Dir, Sima, Ltd, Turkey; consult, USAID, 63 & 65, mem, NSF liaison staff, USAID, India, 67-68; NIH spec res fel, Weizmann Inst Sci, 68-69; Ford Found consult curric develop, Birla Inst Technol, India, 71-; vis prof, Mass Inst Technol, 75; Fulbright-Hays sr lectr, 77; distinguished vis lectr, Va Polytech Inst, 80- *Mem:* Am Inst Chem Engrs; Am Chem Soc; Am Soc Eng Educ. *Res:* Thermodynamics; continuous chromatography; adaptive technology; separation and nucleation phenomena; synthetic fibers; biotechnology. *Mailing Add:* Dept of Chem Eng Tufts Univ Medford MA 02155

SUSSMAN, MAURICE, b New York, NY, Mar 2, 22; m 48; c 3. DEVELOPMENTAL BIOLOGY, MOLECULAR BIOLOGY. *Educ:* City Col New York, BS, 42; Univ Minn, PhD(bact), 49. *Prof Exp:* USPHS fel & instr bact, Univ Ill, 49-50; instr biol sci, Northwestern Univ, 50-53, from asst prof to assoc prof, 53-58; assoc prof, Brandeis Univ, 58-60, prof, 60-73; prof inst life sci, Hebrew Univ Jerusalem, 73-76; PROF & CHMN DEPT BIOL SCI, UNIV PITTSBURGH, 76- *Concurrent Pos:* Instr, Marine Biol Lab, Woods Hole, 56-60 & 67-70. *Honors & Awards:* NIH career develop award, 66. *Mem:* Am Soc Microbiol; Soc Gen Physiol; Soc Develop Biol; Am Soc Biol Chem; Brit Soc Gen Microbiol. *Res:* Cellular differentiation and morphogenesis; molecular genetics. *Mailing Add:* Dept of Biol Sci Univ of Pittsburgh Pittsburgh PA 15213

SUSSMAN, MYRON MAURICE, b Trenton, NJ, Oct 7, 45; m 70. NUMERICAL ANALYSIS. *Educ:* Mass Inst Technol, SB, 67; Carnegie-Mellon Univ, MS, 68, PhD(math), 75. *Prof Exp:* Instr math, Carnegie-Mellon Univ, 68-69 & Robert Morris Col, 69-71; MATHEMATICIAN, BETTIS ATOMIC POWER LAB, WESTINGHOUSE ELEC CO, 75- *Mem:* Soc Indust & Appl Math; Sigma Xi; Am Math Soc. *Res:* Numerical analysis of partial differential equations and iterative solution of large linear systems of algebraic equations. *Mailing Add:* 5026 Belmont Ave Bethel Park PA 15102

SUSSMAN, RAQUEL ROTMAN, b Arg, Oct 22, 21; nat US; m 48; c 3. MICROBIOLOGY. *Educ:* Univ Chile, BS, 44; Univ Ill, PhD(bact), 52. *Prof Exp:* Asst viruses, Inst Bact Chile, 44-48; asst microbiol, Univ Minn, 48-49 & Univ Ill, 49-50; res assoc, Northwestern Univ, 50-58 & Brandeis Univ, 58-73; sr lectr, Dept Molecular Biol, Hadassah Med Sch, Hebrew Univ, Israel, 73-76; ASSOC PROF, DEPT BIOL SCI, UNIV PITTSBURGH, 76- *Res:* Cell biology, chiefly genetics and differentiation. *Mailing Add:* Dept of Biol Sci Univ of Pittsburgh Pittsburgh PA 15213

SUSSMAN, SIDNEY, b Brooklyn, NY, Aug 29, 14; m 39; c 3. WATER CHEMISTRY, CORROSION. *Educ:* Polytech Inst Brooklyn, BS, 34; Mass Inst Technol, PhD(org chem), 37. *Prof Exp:* Res chemist, E I du Pont de Nemours & Co, 37-40; res chemist, Permutit Co, 40-44, chief res chemist, 44-46; chief chemist, Liquid Conditioning Corp, NJ, 46-49; chief chemist, Water Serv Labs, Inc, 49-61, tech dir, 61-69, vpres, 66-69; tech dir, Olin Water Serv Labs, 69-71, tech dir water treatment dept, 71-75, TECH DIR, OLIN WATER SERV, OLIN CORP, 75- *Concurrent Pos:* Mem nat tech adv comt water qual for indust uses, Fed Water Pollution Control Admin, 67-68; mem panel water qual criteria for indust uses, Nat Acad Sci, 71-72. *Mem:* Am Soc Testing & Mat; Am Chem Soc; Am Water Works Asn; fel Am Inst Chem; Soc Chem Indust. *Res:* Ion exchange resin synthesis and applications; water conditioning; desalting seawater; industrial water treatment including cooling water, boilerwater and process water. *Mailing Add:* Olin Water Serv Olin Corp 120 Long Ridge Rd Stamford CT 06904

SUSTEN, SANDRA SKIDMORE, b Erie, Pa, Feb 24, 40; m 68; c 3. ANTI-FOLATES, PROTEIN STRUCTURE. *Educ:* Purdue Univ, BS, 62, MS, 68, PhD(nutrit & biochem), 72. *Prof Exp:* Jr scientist steroid biochem, Roswell Park Mem Inst, 62-66; lectr nutrit & biochem, Kansas City Col Osteopathic Med, 72-74; RES ASSOC BIOL CHEM, COL MED, UNIV CINCINNATI, 76- *Concurrent Pos:* Consult nutrit, Upjohn Co, 75. *Mem:* Sigma Xi; NY Acad Sci. *Res:* Structure-function relationships of anti-folates with dihydrofolate reductase; primary structure of dihydrofolate reductases; methotrexate transport mechanisms in cells; identification of methotrexate transport proteins; mechanisms of drug resistance. *Mailing Add:* Dept Biol Chem Col Med Univ Cincinnati 231 Bethesda Ave Cincinnati OH 45267

SUTA, BENJAMIN EMIL, b Sweet Grass, Mont, Dec 1, 35; m 64; c 2. STATISTICS, MATHEMATICAL MODELING. *Educ:* Mont State Univ, BS, 58; Stanford Univ, MS, 70. *Prof Exp:* Sr statistician, Hercules Inc, 60-66; SR OPERS ANALYST RES, SRI INT, 66- *Mem:* Am Statist Asn. *Res:* Environmental statistics; population at-risk to pollutants; mathematical modeling of environmental systems; reliability analysis; statistical data analysis; risk analysis. *Mailing Add:* SRI Int Ctr Health & Environ Res 333 Ravenswood Ave Menlo Park CA 94025

SUTCLIFFE, JAMES FREDERICK, b Toronto, Ont, Sept 25, 50. INSECT MORPHOLOGY. *Educ:* Univ Waterloo, BSc, 72; Univ Toronto, MSc, 75, PhD(entom), 78. *Prof Exp:* Fel insect physiol, Dept Entom, Univ Alta, 78-81; RES ASST PROF INSECT PHYSIOL, BEHAVIOR & MORPHOL, DEPT BIOL, UNIV WATERLOO, 81- *Mem:* Can Soc Zoologists; Entom Soc Can; Entom Soc Am. *Res:* Insect feeding emphasizing behavioural, physiological, and morphological aspects of haematophagy. *Mailing Add:* Dept Biol Univ Waterloo Waterloo ON N2L 3G1 Can

SUTCLIFFE, SAMUEL, b New Britain, Conn, Jan 30, 34; m 58; c 1. CIVIL ENGINEERING, MATHEMATICS. *Educ:* Univ Conn, BS, 55; Univ Ill, MS, 58, PhD, 60. *Prof Exp:* Asst civil eng, Univ Ill, 55-57, res assoc, 57-60, asst prof, 60-64; assoc prof, 64-69, ASSOC PROF CIVIL ENG, TUFTS UNIV, 69- *Mem:* Am Soc Civil Engrs. *Res:* Dynamics of non-linear, solid continua. *Mailing Add:* Dept of Civil Eng Tufts Univ Medford MA 02155

SUTCLIFFE, WILLIAM GEORGE, b Detroit, Mich, Nov 25, 37; m 60; c 4. PHYSICS. *Educ:* Univ Mich, BS, 60; Univ Del, PhD(physics), 69. *Prof Exp:* Instr physics, US Naval Nuclear Power Sch, 62-64; PHYSICIST, LAWRENCE LIVERMORE LAB, 68- *Mem:* Am Asn Physics Teachers; Soc Comput Simulation. *Res:* Design and development of large computer codes, including hydrodynamics, radiation transport and neutronics; management of projects involving sensitivity and uncertainty analyses of nuclear waste isolation systems. *Mailing Add:* Lawrence Livermore Lab L-71 PO Box 808 Livermore CA 94550

SUTCLIFFE, WILLIAM HUMPHREY, JR, b Miami, Fla, Nov 8, 23; m 45, 49, 64; c 5. ZOOLOGY. *Educ:* Emory Univ, BA, 45; Duke Univ, MA, 47, PhD(zool), 50. *Prof Exp:* Instr zool, Duke Univ, 49-50; investr marine biol, NC Inst Fisheries Res, 50-51, 50-51; staff biologist lobster invests, Bermuda Biol Sta, 51-53, dir, 53-69; head, Fisheries Oceanog Sect, 75-76, RES SCIENTIST, BEDFORD INST OCEANOG, 67- *Concurrent Pos:* Assoc, Woods Hole Oceanog Inst, 57; dir marine sci ctr, Lehigh Univ, 64-67. *Mem:* AAAS; Am Soc Zool; Am Soc Limnol & Oceanog; Marine Biol Asn UK. *Res:* Dynamics of plankton populations; air-sea interaction; marine food chains. *Mailing Add:* Bedford Inst of Oceanog Dartmouth NS B2Y 4A2 Can

SUTER, DANIEL B, b Hinton, Va, Apr 25, 20; m 41; c 4. HUMAN ANATOMY, PHYSIOLOGY. *Educ:* Bridgewater Col, BA, 47; Vanderbilt Univ, MA, 48; Med Col Va, PhD(anat), 63. *Prof Exp:* Asst prof biol, 48-60, assoc prof, 62-63, chmn, Dept Life Sci, 72-76, assoc dean, 76-77, PROF BIOL, EASTERN MENNONITE COL, 63-, CHMN DIV NATURAL SCI & MATH, 64- *Concurrent Pos:* NIH fel, Univ Calif, Davis, 70-71. *Mem:* Asn Am Med Cols; Am Asn Anat; Am Sci Affiliation. *Res:* Effects of radiation and pesticides, especially organophosphates, on the central nervous system. *Mailing Add:* Dept of Biol Eastern Mennonite Col Harrisonburg VA 22801

SUTER, GLENN WALTER, II, b Harrisonburg, Va, May 1, 48; m 68. ECOLOGY. *Educ:* Va Polytech Inst, BS, 69; Univ Calif, Davis, PhD(ecol), 76. *Prof Exp:* RES ASSOC ECOL, ENVIRON SCI DIV, OAK RIDGE NAT LAB, 75- *Mem:* AAAS; Ecol Soc Am. *Res:* Effects of unconventional energy sources on terrestrial biotic communities. *Mailing Add:* Bldg 1505 Oak Ridge Nat Lab Oak Ridge TN 37830

SUTER, ROBERT WINFORD, b Warren, Ohio, Aug 3, 41; m 63; c 2. CHEMISTRY. *Educ:* Bluffton Col, BA, 63; Ohio State Univ, MS, 66, PhD(chem), 69. *Prof Exp:* assoc prof, 69-80, PROF CHEM, BLUFFTON COL, 80- *Mem:* Am Chem Soc. *Res:* Inorganic chemistry, particularly nonmetals; solution phenomena. *Mailing Add:* Dept of Chem Box 907 Marbeck Ctr Bluffton Col Bluffton OH 45817

SUTER, STUART ROSS, b Harrisonburg, Va, Apr 1, 41; m 63; c 2. ORGANIC CHEMISTRY. *Educ:* Bridgewater Col, BA, 63; Univ Mich, Ann Arbor, MS, 65; Univ Va, PhD(org chem), 71; Temple Univ, DJur, 76. *Prof Exp:* Assoc chemist, Smith Kline & French Labs, 65-67; PATENT CHEMIST, SMITHKLINE CORP, 71- *Mem:* Am Chem Soc. *Res:* Aryl nitrenes; synthetic organic chemistry; medicinal chemistry. *Mailing Add:* Patent Dept Smithkline Corp 1500 Spring Garden St PO Box 7929 Philadelphia PA 19101

SUTERA, SALVATORE P, b Baltimore, Md, Jan 12, 33; m 58; c 3. MECHANICAL ENGINEERING. *Educ:* Johns Hopkins Univ, BSc, 54; Calif Inst Technol, MSc, 55, PhD(eng), 60. *Hon Degrees:* MA, Brown Univ, 65. *Prof Exp:* From asst prof to assoc prof eng, Brown Univ, 60-68, exec off div eng, 66-68; PROF MECH ENG & CHMN DEPT, WASHINGTON UNIV, 68- *Concurrent Pos:* Nat Heart Inst res grants, 65-67 & 69-; consult, Nat Heart, Lung & Blood Inst, 70- *Mem:* Am Soc Mech Engrs; Am Soc Eng Educ; AAAS; Am Soc Artificial Internal Organs; Int Soc Biorheology. *Res:* Fluid mechanics of blood flow; artificial organs; rheology of suspensions. *Mailing Add:* Dept Mech Eng Washington Univ Box 1185 St Louis MO 63130

SUTHERLAND, BETSY MIDDLETON, b New York, NY, Oct 19, 43; m 65. BIOCHEMISTRY, CELL BIOLOGY. *Educ:* Emory Univ, BS, 64, MS, 65; Univ Tenn, PhD(radiation biol), 67. *Prof Exp:* NIH fel DNA chem, Lab Molecular Biol, Walter Reed Res Inst, 67-69; fel enzymol, Molecular Biol-Virus Lab, Univ Calif, Berkeley, 69-72; from asst prof to assoc prof molecular biol, Univ Calif, Irvine, 72-77; SCIENTIST DNA REPAIR, DEPT BIOL, BROOKHAVEN NAT LAB, 77- *Concurrent Pos:* Assoc ed, Photochem & Photobiol, 74-77; mem, Nat Comt Photobiol, Nat Acad Sci, 74-78; Nat Cancer Inst, NIH res career develop award, 75- *Mem:* Am Soc Photobiol; Biophys Soc; AAAS; Am Soc Biol Chemists. *Res:* DNA damage and repair; biology and biochemistry of photoreactivation; transformation of mammalian cells and its relation to oncogenesis. *Mailing Add:* Dept of Biol Brookhaven Nat Lab Upton NY 11973

SUTHERLAND, BILL, b Sedalia, Mo, Mar 31, 42. PHYSICS. *Educ:* Wash Univ, AB, 63; State Univ NY Stony Brook, MA, 65, PhD, 67. *Prof Exp:* Res assoc, State Univ NY Stony Brook, 67-69; asst res physicist, Univ Calif, Berkeley, 69-70; asst prof, 70-76, ASSOC PROF PHYSICS, UNIV UTAH, 76- *Res:* Statistical mechanics. *Mailing Add:* Dept of Physics Univ of Utah Salt Lake City UT 84112

SUTHERLAND, CHARLES F, b Camp Grant, Ill, Oct 1, 21; m 44, 81; c 4. FORESTRY ECONOMICS. *Educ:* Univ Idaho, BS, 48, MFor, 54; Univ Mich, PhD(forestry econ), 61. *Prof Exp:* Res forester, Potlatch Forests Inc, 48-53; forest economist, Lake States Forest Exp Sta, US Forest Serv, St Paul, Minn, 56-58; asst prof forestry econ, 59-68, ASSOC PROF FORESTRY ECON, SCH FORESTRY, ORE STATE UNIV, 68- *Concurrent Pos:* Vis res scientist, Southern Foust Exp Sta, US Forest Serv, 78. *Res:* Biology and management in private industry; marketing and production problems in forestry; taxation and forest protection problems. *Mailing Add:* Sch Forestry Ore State Univ Corvallis OR 97331

SUTHERLAND, CHARLES WILLIAM, b Nashville, Tenn, July 29, 41; m 64; c 2. METALLURGICAL ENGINEERING. *Educ:* Vanderbilt Univ, BE, 63; Univ Wis-Madison, MS, 64. *Prof Exp:* ASSOC PROF MECH ENG, TENN STATE UNIV, 67-, HEAD DEPT, 70-, DIR INST RES, 72- *Concurrent Pos:* Consult, Training & Habilitation Ctr, Nashville, Tenn, 71-72. *Mem:* Am Soc Metals; Am Inst Mining, Metall & Petrol Engrs. *Res:* Metal working and machining. *Mailing Add:* 933 Neuhoff Lane Nashville TN 37205

SUTHERLAND, DAVID M, b Bellingham, Wash, Oct 5, 40. PLANT TAXONOMY. *Educ:* Western Wash State Col, BA, 63; Univ Wash, PhD(bot), 67. *Prof Exp:* From asst prof to assoc prof, 67-80, PROF BIOL, UNIV NEBR, OMAHA, 80- *Mem:* AAAS; Int Asn Plant Taxonomists; Bot Soc Am; Am Soc Plant Taxon. *Res:* Biosystematics of larkspurs; floristics of Great Plains. *Mailing Add:* Dept of Biol Univ of Nebr Omaha NE 68182

SUTHERLAND, DONALD JAMES, b Chelsea, Mass, Oct 5, 29. PHYSIOLOGY, BIOCHEMISTRY. *Educ:* Tufts Univ, BS, 51; Univ Mass, MS, 57; Rutgers Univ, PhD(entom), 60. *Prof Exp:* From asst prof to assoc prof, 60-67, PROF ENTOM, RUTGERS UNIV, NEW BRUNSWICK, 67- *Mem:* Entom Soc Am; Am Mosquito Control Asn. *Res:* Management of mosquitoes, particularly chemical measures; biological rhythms of insects. *Mailing Add:* Dept of Entom Rutgers Univ New Brunswick NJ 08903

SUTHERLAND, GEORGE HENRY, mechanical engineering, computer science, see previous edition

SUTHERLAND, GEORGE LESLIE, b Dallas, Tex, Aug 13, 22; m 47; c 3. ORGANIC CHEMISTRY. *Educ:* Univ Tex, BS, 43, MA, 47, PhD(org chem), 50. *Prof Exp:* Lilly fel, Univ Tex, 49-51; chemist, 51-57, group leader, 58-62, mgr metab & anal res, 62-66, dir prod develop & govt registr, 66-69, asst dir res & develop, 69-70, dir res & develop, 70-73, VPRES RES & DEVELOP, LEDERLE LABS DIV, AM CYANAMID CO, 73- *Mem:* AAAS; Am Chem Soc; NY Acad Sci; Royal Soc Chem. *Res:* Organometallic compounds; anticonvulsants; microbiological growth factors; hypotensive agents; anticoccidials; chemical process development; formulation, metabolism and analysis of agricultural chemicals; discovery and development of pharmaceuticals. *Mailing Add:* Lederle Labs Div Am Cyanamid Co Pearl River NY 10965

SUTHERLAND, GERALD BONAR, b Winnipeg, Man, July 31, 19; m 48; c 2. PHYSIOLOGY. *Educ:* Univ BC, BA, 48; Stanford Univ, PhD(physiol), 54. *Prof Exp:* Asst, Stanford Univ, 52-53; fel, Calif Inst Technol, 53-56; asst physiol, Univ Southern Calif, 55-56; instr, Univ Kans, 56-58, asst prof, 58-60; assoc prof, 60-68, PROF PHYSIOL, UNIV SASK, 68- *Mem:* NY Acad Sci; Can Physiol Soc; Can Soc Immunol. *Res:* Immunology; body fluids; effect of antiserum on mosquitoes. *Mailing Add:* Dept of Physiol Univ of Sask Saskatoon SK S7N 0W0 Can

SUTHERLAND, GREGORY JAMES, b Bronx, NY, Aug 25, 47; m 69; c 2. CHEMICAL ENGINEERING. *Educ:* New York Univ, BS, 69, MS, 72, PhD(chem eng), 77. *Prof Exp:* Process engr, 69-76, group leader prod technol, 76-79, PROCESS CONSULT, CLAIROL RES LABS, BRISTOL-MYERS CO, 79- *Mem:* Am Inst Chem Engrs. *Res:* Process development; research into new processing routes and equipment. *Mailing Add:* Clairol Res Labs PO Box 10213 Stamford CT 06922

SUTHERLAND, HERBERT JAMES, applied mechanics, geomechanics, see previous edition

SUTHERLAND, IVAN EDWARD, b Hastings, Nebr, May 16, 38; m 59; c 2. COMPUTER SCIENCE, MATHEMATICS. *Educ:* Carnegie-Mellon Univ, BS, 59; Calif Inst Technol, MS, 60; Mass Inst Technol, PhD(elec eng), 63. *Hon Degrees:* MA, Harvard Univ, 66. *Prof Exp:* Consult, Lincoln Lab, Mass Inst Technol, 61-64; dir info processing tech, Adv Res Projs Agency, Dept Defense, 64-66; assoc prof elec eng, Harvard Univ, 66-68; assoc prof, Univ Utah, 68-72, prof, 72-76; Fletcher Jones prof comput sci & head dept, Calif Inst Technol, 76-80; VPRES, SUTHERLAND, SPROULL & ASSOCS, INC, 80- *Concurrent Pos:* Consult, Advan Res Projs Agency & Bolt, Beranek & Newman, Inc; mem, Naval Res Adv Comt; vpres, Picture Design Group, 74; sr tech staff mem, Rand Corp, 75-76; consult, Proj Mgt Info Syst Tech Adv Comt, HEW, 75-; mem, Defense Sci Bd, Dept Defense, 77-81; vpres & chief scientist, Evans & Sutherland Comput Corp, 68-74, mem bd dirs, 74-; mem bd dirs, Quotron Corp; gen partner, Advan Technol Ventures; independent consult, 80- *Honors & Awards:* First Vladimir K Zworykin Award, Nat Acad Eng, 72; Outstanding Accomplishment Award, Systs, Man & Cybernet Soc, 75. *Mem:* Nat Acad Sci; Nat Acad Eng; Inst Elec & Electronics Engrs; Am Soc Mech Engrs; Asn Comput Mach. *Res:* Computer graphics and man-computer interaction; design of computer display equipment; large-scale integrated circuit design; architecture of high performance computing machinery; algorithms for rapid execution of special functions; author or co-author of over 40 publications. *Mailing Add:* Sutherland Sproull & Assocs Inc 4419 Schenly Farms Terrace Pittsburgh PA 15213

SUTHERLAND, JAMES HENRY RICHARDSON, b Can, July 6, 23; nat US; m 43; c 3. PHARMACOLOGY. *Educ:* Univ Calif, AB, 48, PhD(physiol), 56. *Prof Exp:* Trainee cardiovasc res prog, 55-56, from asst prof to assoc prof pharmacol, 56-64, chmn dept, 64-68, dir div health commun, 68-74, PROF PHARMACOL, MED COL GA, 64- *Mem:* AAAS; Health Sci Commun Asn (pres, 71-72). *Res:* Cardiovascular pressure and flow; influence of the adrenergic agents on the cardiovascular system; pharmacology of the adrenergic receptor; educational communications. *Mailing Add:* Dept of Pharmacol Med Col of Ga Augusta GA 30902

SUTHERLAND, JAMES MCKENZIE, b Chicago, Ill, Aug 8, 23; m 53; c 2. PEDIATRICS. *Educ:* Univ Chicago, SB, 47, MD, 50; Am Bd Pediat, dipl, 55. *Prof Exp:* Intern, Cincinnati Gen Hosp, 50-51; resident pediat, Children's Hosp, 51-54; instr, Col Med, Univ Cincinnati, 53-54; fel, Harvard Med Sch, 54-56; asst prof, 56-76, PROF PEDIAT, COL MED, UNIV CINCINNATI, 76- *Concurrent Pos:* NIH fel, Children's Med Ctr, Boston, 54-56; attend pediatrician, Children's Hosp, Cincinnati, 56-; dir newborn div, Cincinnati Gen Hosp, 56-; res assoc & head div newborn physiol, Children's Hosp Res Found. *Mem:* AAAS; Soc Pediat Res; Am Pediat Soc; AMA. *Res:* Physiology of normal and abnormal respiration in infants. *Mailing Add:* Dept Pediat Col Med Univ Cincinnati Cincinnati OH 45267

SUTHERLAND, JEFFREY C, geochemistry, hydrology, see previous edition

SUTHERLAND, JOHN B(ENNETT), b Burlingame, Kans, Feb 21, 18; m 35; c 3. CHEMICAL ENGINEERING. *Educ:* Kans State Col, BS, 39, MS, 40; Univ Pittsburgh, PhD(chem eng), 46. *Prof Exp:* Chem engr, Tex Co, Tex, 40-41; fel asst, Mellon Inst, 41-43; asst prof chem eng, Northwestern Univ, 43-46; pres Sutherland-Becker Labs, 46-64; dir indust res & exten, 66-80, EMER PROF INDUST RES & EXTEN, UNIV MO-COLUMBIA, 80-; CONSULT ECON DEVELOP, 80- *Concurrent Pos:* Prod res mgr, Butler Mfg Co, 56-63, res & planning mgr, 63-65; assoc dean eng, Kans State Univ, 65-66. *Mem:* Am Chem Soc; Am Inst Chem Engrs; Sigma Xi. *Res:* Lubricating oils; synthetic gems; economic development; gels and films; construction materials; statics and dynamics of bulk solids. *Mailing Add:* 11 Mumford Dr Columbia MO 65201

SUTHERLAND, JOHN BRUCE, IV, b Tampa, Fla, Nov 9, 45. MICROBIOLOGY. *Educ:* Stanford Univ, AB, 67; Univ Wis, Madison, MS, 73; Wash State Univ, PhD(plant path), 78. *Prof Exp:* Fel bacteriol, Univ Idaho, 77-81; ASST PROF BIOL SCI, TEX TECH UNIV, 81- *Concurrent Pos:* Instr, Wash State Univ, 78-79. *Mem:* Am Phytopath Soc; Am Soc Microbiol; Mycol Soc Am. *Res:* Physiology and ecology of soil microorganisms; biodegradation of lignocellulose. *Mailing Add:* Dept Biol Sci Tex Tech Univ Lubbock TX 79409

SUTHERLAND, JOHN CLARK, b New York, NY, Sept 2, 40; m 65. BIOPHYSICS. *Educ:* Ga Inst Technol, BS, 62, MS, 64, PhD(physics), 67. *Prof Exp:* Biophysicist, Walter Reed Res Inst, 67-69; res fel, Lab Chem Biodyn, Univ Calif, Berkeley, 69-72, USPHS fel, 69-71; res fel chem, Univ Southern Calif, 72-73; from asst prof to assoc prof physiol, Calif Col Med-Univ Calif, Irvine, 73-77; SCIENTIST, BROOKHAVEN NAT LAB, 77- *Concurrent Pos:* Assoc ed, Photochem & Photobiol, 81-; res career develop award, Nat Cancer Inst, 66-81. *Mem:* Am Soc Photobiol; Am Phys Soc; Biophys Soc. *Res:* Optical spectroscopy and photochemistry of biological molecules; synchrotron radiation; vacuum ultraviolet spectroscopy of metals. *Mailing Add:* Dept Biol Brookhaven Nat Lab Upton NY 11973

SUTHERLAND, JOHN PATRICK, b Salem, Ore, Oct 1, 42; m 81; c 2. MARINE ECOLOGY. *Educ:* Univ Wash, Seattle, BS, 64; Univ Calif, Berkely, PhD(zool), 69. *Prof Exp:* Asst prof marine ecol, 69-75, ASSOC PROF MARINE ECOL, MARINE LAB, DUKE UNIV, 75- *Concurrent Pos:* Off Naval Res & NSF grants, 72- *Mem:* Ecol Soc Am. *Res:* Comparative studies on the dynamics and bioenergetics of marine inverte- brates; structure and function of subtidal, epibenthic fouling communities; ecology of kelp communities; ecology of tropical rocky shores. *Mailing Add:* Duke Univ Marine Lab Beaufort NC 28516

SUTHERLAND, JUDITH ELLIOTT, b Clovis, NMex, June 6, 24; m 47; c 2. POLYMER CHEMISTRY. *Educ:* Univ Tex, BSChem, 45; Univ Conn, MA, 68; Univ Mass, PhD(polymer chem), 72. *Prof Exp:* Res biochemist, Tex Agr Exp Sta, College Station, 45-46; res chemist biochem, Clayton Found, Biochem Inst, Austin, Tex, 46-48; chemist, Stamford Chem Co, Conn, 60-61 & Am Cyanamid Co, Conn, 61-71; RES CHEMIST POLYMERS, EASTMAN KODAK CO RES LABS, 72- *Mem:* Am Chem Soc; AAAS: Am Phys Soc. *Res:* Polymer synthesis and characterization; solution properties; structure-property relationships; solid state properties of polymers and polymer composites. *Mailing Add:* Eastman Kodak Co Res Labs 1999 Lake Ave Rochester NY 14650

SUTHERLAND, LOUIS CARR, b Walla Walla, Wash, June 2, 26; m 49; c 3. ACOUSTICS, STRUCTURAL DYNAMICS. *Educ:* Univ Wash, BS, 46, MS, 54. *Prof Exp:* Res asst, Eng Exp Sta, Univ Wash, 47-49, res engr electroacoust, Dept Speech, 49-56; res specialist vibroacoust, Boeing Co, 56-64; DEP DIR & PRIN SCIENTIST, WYLE RES, 64- *Concurrent Pos:* Chmn subcomt noise metrics, SAE-Aircraft Noise Comt, 76- *Mem:* Fel Acoust Soc Am; Inst Elec & Electronics Engrs; Am Inst Aeronaut & Astronaut. *Res:* Physical acoustics as it relates to man's environment; sound propagation, aircraft noise, community noise, noise control, vibroacoustics, shock and vibration environments of aerospace systems. *Mailing Add:* Wyle Res 128 Maryland St El Segundo CA 90245

SUTHERLAND, PATRICK KENNEDY, b Dallas, Tex, Feb 17, 25. PALEOBIOLOGY, STRATIGRAPHY. *Educ:* Univ Okla, BSc, 46; Cambridge Univ, PhD(geol), 52. *Prof Exp:* Geologist, Phillips Petrol Co, 46-49, 52-53; asst prof geol, Univ Houston, 53-57; assoc prof, 57-64, PROF GEOL, SCH GEOL & GEOPHYS, UNIV OKLA, 64- *Concurrent Pos:* Nat Acad Sci vis exchange fel, USSR, 71. *Mem:* Fel Geol Soc Am; Paleont Soc; Soc Econ Paleont & Mineral; Am Asn Petrol Geol; fel Geol Soc London. *Res:* Paleobiology; biostratigraphy; paleoecology; carboniferous Rugose corals and brachiopods. *Mailing Add:* Sch of Geol & Geophysics Univ of Okla Norman OK 73019

SUTHERLAND, PETER GORDON, b Montreal, Que, Oct 19, 46; m 81; c 1. THEORETICAL ASTROPHYSICS. *Educ:* McGill Univ, BSc, 67; Univ Ill, MS, 68, PhD(physics), 72. *Prof Exp:* Fel, Physics Dept, Columbia Univ, 71-74; asst prof, Univ Pa, 74-76; asst prof, 76-78, assoc prof, 78-82, PROF, PHYSICS DEPT, MCMASTER UNIV, 82- *Concurrent Pos:* Lectr, Astron Dept, Columbia Univ, 72-74; Alfred P Sloan Found Fel, 78; vis scientist, Astron Dept, Univ Tex, Austin, 80-81. *Mem:* Am Astron Soc; Int Astron Union; Can Asn Physicists. *Res:* Neutron stars; pulsars; compact x-ray sources; supernovae. *Mailing Add:* Physics Dept McMaster Univ Hamilton ON L8S 4M1 Can

SUTHERLAND, ROBERT CARVER, plant physiology, plant morphology, see previous edition

SUTHERLAND, ROBERT L(OUIS), b Fellsmere, Fla, May 15, 16; m 45; c 5. ENGINEERING DESIGN & CONSULTING. *Educ:* Univ Ill, BS, 39, MS, 48. *Prof Exp:* Develop engr, Firestone Tire & Rubber Co, Ohio, 39-41; res engr, Borg & Beck Div, Borg-Warner Corp, Ill, 41-42; test engr, Buick Motor Div, Gen Motors Corp, 42-43; sr engr res, Aeronca Aircraft Corp, Ohio, 43-45; res assoc, Col Eng, Univ Ill, 45-48; assoc prof mech eng, Univ Iowa, 48-58; prof, 58-79, head dept, 60-70, EMER PROF ENG, UNIV WYO, 79-; PRES, SKYLINE ENG, INC, 71- *Concurrent Pos:* Legis fel, Nat Conf State Legis, 82- *Honors & Awards:* Templin Award, Am Soc Testing & Mat, 52. *Mem:* Fel Am Soc Mech Engrs (vpres, 64-67); Soc Automotive Engrs; Am Soc Mech Engrs. *Res:* Engineering analysis, vibrations and machine design. *Mailing Add:* Box 54 Laramie WY 82070

SUTHERLAND, ROBERT MELVIN, b Moncton, NB, Oct 21, 40; m 62; c 3. BIOPHYSICS, RADIATION BIOLOGY. *Educ:* Acadia Univ, BSc, 61; Univ Rochester, PhD(radiation biol), 66. *Prof Exp:* Fel radiation biol, Norsk Hydro's Inst Cancer Res, Oslo, Norway, 66-67; fel radiation biol, Ont Cancer Found, London Clin, Victoria Hosp, London, Ont, 67-68, radiobiologist, 68-76; assoc prof & head, Radiation Biol Sect, Div Radiation, Oncol & Multimodalities Res, Cancer Ctr, 76-79, PROF RADIATION BIOL & BIOPHYS, UNIV ROCHESTER, 79-, ASST DIR, EXP THERAPEUT DIV, CANCER CTR, 80- *Concurrent Pos:* Radiation res fel, James Picker Found, 66-68; hon lectr biophys, Univ Western Ont, 67-68; lectr therapeut radiol & asst prof biophys, 68-72, assoc prof therapeut radiol & biophys, 72-76; assoc ed, Int J Radiation, Oncol, Biol, Physics. *Mem:* Radiation Res Soc; Can Soc Cell Biol; Am Asn Cancer Res; Am Soc Therapeut Radiologists; Am Soc Cell Biol. *Res:* Membrane biophysics and radiation damage; in vitro tumor models; radiation sensitizers; experimental tumor therapy. *Mailing Add:* Cancer Ctr Box 704 Med Sch Univ Rochester Rochester NY 14642

SUTHERLAND, RONALD GEORGE, b Belfast, Northern Ireland, May 4, 35; m 60; c 2. CHEMISTRY. *Educ:* Univ Strathclyde, BSc, 59; Univ St Andrews, PhD(org chem), 62. *Prof Exp:* Res assoc, Columbia Univ, 62-63; fel, Calif Inst Technol, 63-64; Imp Chem Industs res fel chem, Queen's Col, Dundee, 64; from asst prof to assoc prof, 64-73, PROF CHEM, UNIV SASK, 73-, ASSOC DEAN SCI, 80- *Concurrent Pos:* Sci Res Coun UK sr vis fel, Edinburgh Univ, 75-76. *Mem:* Royal Soc Chem; Royal Inst Chem; Am Chem Soc; Can Inst Chem. *Res:* Organometallic chemistry; organic photochemistry; chemical decomposition of pesticides. *Mailing Add:* Dept of Chem Univ of Sask Saskatoon SK S7N 0W0 Can

SUTHERLAND, WILLIAM NEIL, b Linden, Iowa, Aug 10, 27; m 49; c 4. SOIL FERTILITY, AGRICULTURAL ECONOMICS. *Educ:* Iowa State Univ, BS, 50, MS, 53, PhD(soil fertil), 60. *Prof Exp:* Soil conserv agent exten serv, Univ Minn, 54-56; res assoc, Iowa State Univ, 56-60; agriculturist, 60-78, agronomist, Test & Demonstration Br, 78-80, CHIEF AGR FIELD PROG, TENN VALLEY AUTHORITY, 80- *Mem:* Am Soc Agron; Nat Mgt Asn. *Res:* Evaluation of Tennessee Valley Authority's experimental fertilizers agronomically and in fertilizer use systems in cooperation with land grant universities and fertilizer industry firms; educational programs to encourage efficient fertilizer use. *Mailing Add:* Tenn Valley Auth F 213 NFDC Muscle Shoals AL 34660

SUTHERLAND, WILLIAM ROBERT, b Hastings, Nebr, May 10, 36; m 57; c 3. COMPUTER SCIENCE, ELECTRICAL ENGINEERING. *Educ:* Rensselaer Polytech Inst, BEE, 57; Mass Inst Technol, SM, 63, PhD(elec eng), 66. *Prof Exp:* Assoc group leader comput graphics & comput-aided design & mem tech staff, Lincoln Lab, Mass Inst Technol, 64-69; mgr interactive systs dept, Bolt Beranek & Newman, Inc, 69-72, div vpres & dir comput sci div, 72-75; mgr, Systs Sci Lab, Xerox Palo Alto Res Ctr, 75-81; VPRES, SUTHERLAND, SPROULL & ASSOC INC, 81- *Mem:* Inst Elec & Electronics Engrs; Asn Comput Mach. *Res:* Distributed computing; graphics. *Mailing Add:* Xerox Palo Alto Res Ctr 3333 Coyote Hill Rd Palo Alto CA 94304

SUTHERLAND-BROWN, ATHOLL, b Ottawa, Ont, June 20, 23; m 48; c 1. ECONOMIC & REGIONAL GEOLOGY. *Educ:* Univ BC, BASc, 50; Princeton Univ, PhD(geol), 54. *Prof Exp:* Geologist econ geol, 52-69, dep chief geol, 69-74, CHIEF GEOLOGIST ECON GEOL, MINERAL RESOURCES BR, BC DEPT MINES & PETROLEUM RESOURCES, 74- *Concurrent Pos:* Ed, Can Inst Mining & Metall, 74-76; mem, Geol Soc Am Del, Am Comn Stratig Nomenclature, 69-72; mem, Can Nat Comn, Int Geol Correlation Prog, 74-; del, Int Union Geol Sci-UNESCO Meeting Govt Experts, Paris, 71; mem, Nat Orgn Comt, 24th Int Geol Cong, 69-72; exec mem, Nat Adv Comn, Res Geol Sci, 69-73; mem, Can Geosci Coun Adv Comt, Geol Surv Can, 76-, exec mem, Can Geosci Coun, 77- *Mem:* Fel Geol Soc Am; fel Geol Asn Can (vpres, 78-79); Can Inst Mining & Metall; Soc Econ Geologists. *Res:* Morphology, classification, distribution and tectonic setting of porpityry deposits; metallogeny and distribution of metals in deposits and background , particularly in Canadian Cordillera; geology and tectonics of Queen Charlotte Islands and insular tectonic belt. *Mailing Add:* Dept of Mines & Petrol Resources Victoria BC V8V 1X4 Can

SUTHERS, RODERICK ATKINS, b Columbus, Ohio, Feb 2, 37. PHYSIOLOGY. *Educ:* Ohio Wesleyan Univ, BA, 60; Harvard Univ, AM, 61, PhD(biol), 64. *Prof Exp:* Res fel biol, Harvard Univ, 64-65; from asst prof to assoc prof anat & physiol, 65-74, prof anat & physiol, 74-75, PROF, CTR NEUROL SCI, IND UNIV, BLOOMINGTON, 75-, PROF PHYSIOL, SCH MED, 76- *Concurrent Pos:* Vis prof, Dept Zool, Univ Nairobi, Kenya, 73; fac res assoc, Dept Psychol, Univ Ore, 73. *Mem:* AAAS; Am Soc Zool; Am Ornith Union; Am Physiol Soc; Soc Neurosci; Acoust Soc Am. *Res:* Sensory physiology and behavior; comparative sensory physiology of animal sonar systems; neural processing of visual and auditory information in echolating animals; cross modal interaction; laryngeal mechanisms of vocalization by echolocating bats. *Mailing Add:* Med Sci Prog Ind Univ Bloomington IN 47401

SUTIN, JEROME, b Albany, NY, Mar 12, 30; m 56; c 2. NEUROANATOMY, NEUROPHYSIOLOGY. *Educ:* Siena Col, BS, 51; Univ Minn, MS, 53, PhD(anat), 54. *Prof Exp:* Asst anat, Univ Minn, 52-53; hon res asst, Univ Col, Univ London, 53-54; asst, Univ Minn, 54; jr res anatomist, Univ Calif, Los Angeles, 55-56; from instr to assoc prof anat, Sch Med, Yale Univ, 56-66; prof anat & chmn dept, 66-80, CHARLES HOWARD CANDLER PROF ANAT, EMORY UNIV, 80- *Concurrent Pos:* Vis investr, Autonomics Div, Nat Phys Lab, Middlesex, Eng; vis prof, Inst Psychiat, Maudsley Hosp, London; Nat Found Infantile Paralysis fel anat, Univ Calif, Los Angeles, 55-56. *Mem:* Am Asn Anatomists; Am Physiol Soc; Am Soc Zool; Soc Neurosci. *Res:* Hypothalamic organization; basal ganglia and motor function; plasticity of noradrenergic neurons. *Mailing Add:* Dept of Anat Emory Univ Atlanta GA 30322

SUTIN, NORMAN, b SAfrica, Sept 16, 28; nat US; m 58; c 2. PHYSICAL INORGANIC CHEMISTRY. *Educ:* Univ Cape Town, BSc, 48, MSc, 50; Cambridge Univ, PhD(chem), 53. *Prof Exp:* Imp Chem Industs fel, Durham Univ, 54-55; res assoc, 56-57, from assoc chemist to chemist, 58-66, SR CHEMIST, BROOKHAVEN NAT LAB, 66- *Concurrent Pos:* Affil, Rockefeller Univ, 58-62; vis fel, Weizmann Inst, 64; vis prof, State Univ NY Stony Brook, 68, Columbia Univ, 68, Tel Aviv Univ, Israel, 73, Univ Calif, Irvine, 77 & Univ Tex, Austin, 79; mem, Comt Chem Sci, Nat Res Coun, 81- *Mem:* Am Chem Soc; Royal Soc Chem. *Res:* Kinetics and mechanisms of inorganic reactions; bioinorganic chemistry; photochemistry of transition metal complexes; solar energy conversion and storage. *Mailing Add:* Dept of Chem Brookhaven Nat Lab Upton NY 11973

SUTMAN, FRANK X, b Newark, NJ, Dec 20, 27; m 56; c 3. CHEMISTRY. *Educ:* Montclair State Col, AB, 49, AM, 52; Columbia Univ, EdD, 56. *Prof Exp:* Instr, Pub Schs, NJ, 49-51; instr, High Schs, 51-55; asst prof sci, Paterson State Col, 55-57; assoc prof natural sci & chmn div, Inter-Am Univ, PR, 57-58; PROF SCI, SCH EDUC & DIR, NSF INSTS, TEMPLE UNIV, 62- *Concurrent Pos:* NSF-AID lectr, India, 67; observer, Orgn Am States Coun Sci Educ & Cult, 71; vis prof, Hebrew Univ, Jerusalem, Israel, 73; consult, Israel Environ Protection Serv, 75, Peoples Repub China, 80- *Mem:* Fel AAAS; Am Chem Soc; Nat Asn Res Sci Teaching (pres, 72); Nat Sci Teachers Asn. *Res:* Chemical education research. *Mailing Add:* Dept of Educ 341 Ritter Hall Temple Univ Philadelphia PA 19122

SUTNICK, ALTON IVAN, b Trenton, NJ, July 6, 28; m 58; c 2. INTERNAL MEDICINE. *Educ:* Univ Pa, AB, 50, MD, 54. *Prof Exp:* From intern to resident anesthesiol & med, Hosp Univ Pa, 54-57, USPHS fel, Univ, 56-57; from resident to chief resident med, Marion County Gen Hosp, Indianapolis, Ind, 57-61; USPHS fel, Temple Univ, 61-63, instr med, 63-64, assoc, 64-65; res physician, Inst Cancer Res, Fox Chase Cancer Ctr, 65-72, assoc dir, 72-75; assoc prof med, Sch Med, Univ Pa, 71-75; DEAN & PROF MED, MED COL PA, 75-, SR VPRES HEALTH AFFAIRS, 76- *Concurrent Pos:* Consult, Coun Drugs, AMA, 62-64; mem US nat comt, Int Union Against Cancer, 69-72; mem ed bd, Res Commun Chem Path Pharmacol, 69-; vis prof med, Med Col Pa, 71-75; asst ed, Ann Internal Med, 72-75; mem, Nat Cancer Control Planning Conf, Nat Cancer Inst, 73, consult, Diag Res Adv Group, 74-78; sect ed for med, Int J Dermat, 74-75; consult, WHO, 79, 80 & 81. *Honors & Awards:* Schwartz Award, AMA, 76. *Mem:* Am Asn Cancer Res; Am Fedn Clin Res; Am Col Physicians; AMA. *Res:* Cancer epidemiology; susceptibility to cancer; Australia antigen; hepatitis; pulmonary surfactant. *Mailing Add:* 2135 St James Philadelphia PA 19103

SUTTER, DAVID FRANKLIN, b Ft Wayne, Ind, Nov 21, 35; m 59; c 3. APPLIED PHYSICS, INSTRUMENTATION. *Educ:* Purdue Univ, BS, 58; Cornell Univ, MS, 67, PhD(physics), 69. *Prof Exp:* Asst, Cornell Univ, 62-69; physicist, Fermi Nat Accelerator Lab, 69-75; PHYSICIST, DIV PHYS RES, US AEC 75- *Mem:* Am Phys Soc; AAAS. *Res:* Computer monitoring and control of accelerators; digital and analog instrumentation; theory of operation of accelerators; electron beam optics; development of superconducting magnet systems. *Mailing Add:* Div Phys Res MS J-309 US AEC Washington DC 20545

SUTTER, GERALD RODNEY, b Fountain City, Wis, Sept 20, 37; m 58; c 3. ENTOMOLOGY. *Educ:* Winona State Col, BA, 60; Iowa State Univ, MS, 63, PhD(entom), 65. *Prof Exp:* Res entomologist, European Corn Borer Lab, Arkeny, Iowa, 65, Northern Grain Insect Res Lab, 65-73, RES LEADER ENTOM, ENTOM RES DIV, NORTHERN GRAIN INSECT RES LAB, AGR RES SERV, USDA, 73- *Mem:* Entom Soc Am; Soc Invert Path. *Res:* Utilization of microorganisms in the biological control of insects. *Mailing Add:* Northern Grain Insect Res Lab RR 3 Brookings SD 57006

SUTTER, JOHN FREDERICK, b Oak Harbor, Ohio, June 7, 43; m 65, 75; c 2. GEOLOGY, GEOCHRONOLOGY. *Educ:* Capital Univ, BS, 65; Rice Univ, MA, 68, PhD(geol), 70. *Prof Exp:* Nat Res Coun resident res assoc, Manned Spacecraft Ctr, NASA, 69-70; asst prof earth & space sci, State Univ NY Stony Brook, 70-71; from asst prof to assoc prof geol & mineral, Ohio State Univ, 71-80; GEOLOGIST, US GEOL SURV, 80- *Mem:* Geol Soc Am. *Res:* Potassium-argon geochronology of selected areas; metamorphic history of Appalachian-Caledonian origin. *Mailing Add:* US Geol Surv Nat Ctr MS 981 Reston VA 22092

SUTTER, JOHN RITTER, b Edwardsville, Ill, May 4, 30; m 58; c 3. PHYSICAL CHEMISTRY. *Educ:* Wash Univ, St Louis, AB, 51; Tulane Univ, MS, 56, PhD(chem), 59. *Prof Exp:* Asst chem, Tulane Univ, 54-59; jr chemist & AEC grant, Wash State Univ, 59-60; asst prof chem, La Polytech Inst, 60-62; from asst prof to assoc prof, 62-71, PROF CHEM, HOWARD UNIV, 71- *Mem:* AAAS; Am Chem Soc; Am Phys Soc. *Res:* Kinetics; fast reactions; thermodynamics; calorimetry. *Mailing Add:* Dept Chem Howard Univ Washington DC 20059

SUTTER, MORLEY CARMAN, b Redvers, Sask, May 18, 33; m 57; c 3. PHARMACOLOGY. *Educ:* Univ Man, BSc & MD, 57, PhD(pharmacol), 63. *Prof Exp:* Pvt pract, Souris, Man, 57-58; asst resident med, Winnipeg Gen Hosp, 58-59; demonstr pharmacol, Univ Man, 59-63; Imp Chem Industs fel, Cambridge Univ, 63-65; asst prof, Univ Toronto, 65-66; from asst prof to assoc prof, 66-71, PROF PHARMACOL & CHMN DEPT, UNIV BC, 71- *Concurrent Pos:* Wellcome Found travel award, 63; supvr, Downing Col, Cambridge Univ, 63-65; Med Res Coun Can scholar, 66-71. *Mem:* AAAS; Pharmacol Soc Can; Can Soc Clin Invest; Brit Pharmacol Soc; Am Soc Pharmacol & Exp Therapeut. *Res:* Effects of adrenergic blocking agents in shock; mechanism of cardiac arrythmias induced by cyclopropane-epinephrine; pharmacology of veins; vascular smooth muscle in hypertension. *Mailing Add:* Dept of Pharmacol Univ of BC Vancouver BC V6T 1W5 Can

SUTTER, PHILIP HENRY, b Mineola, NY, Dec 8, 30; m 55; c 4. PHYSICS. *Educ:* Yale Univ, BS, 52, MS, 54, PhD(physics), 59. *Prof Exp:* Res engr res labs, Westinghouse Elec Corp, 58-63, sr res engr, 63-64; asst prof physics, 64-67, ASSOC PROF PHYSICS, FRANKLIN & MARSHALL COL, 67-, CHMN DEPT, 76- *Concurrent Pos:* NZ sr res fel physics & eng lab, Dept Sci & Indust Res, Wellington, NZ, 69-70. *Mem:* AAAS; Am Phys Soc. *Res:* Solid state physics; transport properties; ionic crystals; energy conversion. *Mailing Add:* 203 Macklin Ave Lancaster PA 17602

SUTTER, RICHARD P, b Birmingham, Ala, Mar 22, 37; m 64; c 3. CELL & MOLECULAR BIOLOGY. *Educ:* St Joseph's Col, Ind, BA, 59; Ohio State Univ, MSc, 61; Tufts Univ, PhD(biochem), 66. *Prof Exp:* Instr biochem, Univ Ill, Chicago, 66-67; from asst prof to assoc prof biol, 67-74, PROF BIOL, WVA UNIV, 74- *Concurrent Pos:* Adj biochemist, Presby St Luke's Hosp, Chicago, 66-67; vis assoc, Calif Inst Technol, 73-74. *Mem:* AAAS; Mycol Soc Am; Am Chem Soc; Am Soc Microbiol. *Res:* Molecular basis of sexual development; phenomonal communication; fungal metabolism. *Mailing Add:* Dept Biol WVa Univ Morgantown WV 26506

SUTTER, VERA LA VERNE, b Los Angeles, Calif, Apr 2, 24. MEDICAL MICROBIOLOGY, INFECTIOUS DISEASES. *Educ:* Univ Calif, Los Angeles, AB, 46, MA, 47, PhD(microbiol), 50; Am Bd Med Microbiol, dipl. *Prof Exp:* Asst bact, Univ Calif, Los Angeles, 45-50; chief bacteriologist, Clin Lab, Vet Admin Gen Hosp, Los Angeles, 50-62; asst res microbiologist, Sch Dent, Univ Calif, San Francisco, 62-67; dir, Anaerobic Bact Res Lab, 67-80, DIR, ORAL MICROBIOL RES LAB, WADSWORTH VET ADMIN HOSP CTR, 80- *Concurrent Pos:* Adj assoc prof, Dept Med, Sch Med, Univ Calif, Los Angeles, 73-77, adj prof, 77-; mem, Am Bd Med Microbiol, 75-; lectr & lab dir bact & parasitol, Mt St Mary's Col, Calif, 52-62; vis prof, Creighton Univ, Omaha, 78 & Corp de Invest Biol, Medelin, Colombia, 80. *Mem:* Am Soc Microbiol; fel Am Pub Health Asn; Am Acad Microbiol; Infectious Dis Soc Am; Asn Dent Res. *Res:* Clinical bacteriology; epidemiology of hospital acquired infections; anaerobic bacteria in pathologic and pathophysiologic processes; normal intestinal microflora; microbiology of periodontal disease. *Mailing Add:* Oral Microbiol Res Lab Wadsworth Vet Admin Hosp Ctr Los Angeles CA 90073

SUTTERBY, JOHN LLOYD, b Kansas City, Mo, Dec 27, 36; m 62; c 2. CHEMICAL ENGINEERING, RHEOLOGY. *Educ:* Univ Mo, BS, 58; Univ Wis, MS, 59, PhD(chem eng), 64. *Prof Exp:* Asst prof chem eng, Va Polytechnic Inst, 65-66; res engr, Process Fundamentals Res Lab, Dow Chem Co, Mich, 66-70; asst prof chem eng, Univ Mo-Columbia, 70-77; res engr, Exxon Corp, 77-80; MEM FAC, DEPT CHEM ENG, UNIV MO, 80- *Mem:* Am Inst Chem Engrs; Soc Rheol. *Res:* Rheological and thermal properties of polymer solutions and polymer melts. *Mailing Add:* Dept Chem Eng Univ Mo Columbia MO 65201

SUTTERLIN, ARNOLD M, b Boston, Mass, Aug 8, 39; m 65. ANIMAL PHYSIOLOGY. *Educ:* State Teachers Col Bridgewater, BS, 62; Univ Mass, PhD(zool), 66. *Prof Exp:* NIH fel, 66-68; mem res staff, Biol Sta, Fisheries Res Bd Can, 68-78; MEM RES STAFF, MARINE RES LAB, MEM UNIV, ST JOHNS, NFLD, 78- *Res:* Physiology of fishes; salmonid aquaculture. *Mailing Add:* Marine Res Lab Mem Univ St Johns NF A1C 5S7 Can

SUTTIE, JOHN WESTON, b La Crosse, Wis, Aug 25, 34; m 55; c 2. BIOCHEMISTRY. *Educ:* Univ Wis, BSc, 57, MS, 58, PhD, 60. *Prof Exp:* Fel biochem, Nat Inst Med Res, Eng, 60-61; from asst prof to assoc prof, 61-69, PROF BIOCHEM, UNIV WIS-MADISON, 69- *Concurrent Pos:* Mem comns atmospheric fluorides & fluorosis, Nat Res Coun. *Honors & Awards:* Mead Johns Award, Am Inst Nutrit, 74; Osborne & Mendel Award, Am Inst Nutrit, 80. *Mem:* AAAS; Am Soc Exp Biol & Med; Am Soc Biol Chem; Am Inst Nutrit; Air Pollution Control Asn. *Res:* Vitamin K action-control of prothrombin synthesis, metabolic action of anticoagulants, chemistry of prothrombin and metabolism of vitamin K; fluoride metabolism-biochemical lesions caused by fluoride ingestion; fluoride as an industrial pollutant; fluoride homeostasis. *Mailing Add:* Dept of Biochem Univ of Wis Madison WI 53706

SUTTKUS, ROYAL DALLAS, b Fremont, Ohio, May 11, 20; m 47; c 3. ICHTHYOLOGY, FISH BIOLOGY. *Educ:* Mich State Col, BS, 43; Cornell Univ, MS, 47, PhD(zool), 51. *Prof Exp:* Asst zool, Cornell Univ, 47-50; from asst prof to prof zool, 50-60, PROF BIOL, 60-, DIR, TULANE UNIV, MUS NATURAL HIST, 76- *Mem:* AAAS; Am Soc Ichthyologists & Herpetologists; Am Fisheries Soc; Soc Syst Zool; Soc Study Evolution. *Res:* Systematics of fresh and salt water fishes; zoogeography; growth and seasonal distribution; environmental biology; water quality and water pollution; biology of mammals. *Mailing Add:* Tulane Univ Museum Natural Hist Belle Chasse LA 70037

SUTTLE, ANDREW DILLARD, JR, b West Point, Miss, Aug 12, 26. RADIOCHEMISTRY, NUCLEAR PHYSICS. *Educ:* Miss State Univ, BS, 44; Univ Chicago, PhD(chem), 52. *Prof Exp:* Vpres res & grad studies & dir, Miss Res Comn, Miss State Univ, 60-62; vpres res & prof chem, Tex A&M Univ, 62-71; PROF NUCLEAR BIOPHYSICS & RADIO BIOCHEM & SPEC ASST TO DIR, MARINE BIOMED INST, UNIV TEX MED BR, 71- *Concurrent Pos:* Sr scientist, Humble Oil & Refining Co, 52-62; spec asst to dir res & eng, Dept Defense, Washington, DC, 62-64, mem exec comt sci bd res & eng, 67-; mem, Atomic Indust Forum, 55. *Mem:* Am Chem Soc; Am Phys Soc; Am Nuclear Soc; Inst Elec & Electronics Eng. *Res:* Radiation chemistry; nuclear and thermal energy; petroleum industry. *Mailing Add:* Marine Biomed Inst Suite 831 200 University Blvd Galveston TX 77550

SUTTLE, JEFFREY CHARLES, b Omaha, Nebr, Jan, 28, 52; m 79. PHYTOHORMONES, PLANT GROWTH REGULATORS. *Educ:* Univ Tex, BA, 74; Mich State Univ, PhD(bot), 79. *Prof Exp:* RES PHYSIOLOGIST, METAB & RADIATION RES LAB, USDA, 79- *Mem:* Am Soc Plant Physiol; Am Soc Hort Sci; Int Plant Growth Substances Asn. *Res:* Mode of action of synthetic plant growth regulators and their interactions with herbicides. *Mailing Add:* Metab & Radiation Res Lab State Univ Sta Fargo ND 58105

SUTTLE, JIMMIE RAY, b Forest City, NC, Dec 26, 32; m 51; c 3. PHYSICS, ELECTRICAL ENGINEERING. *Educ:* Presby Col, SC, BS, 58; Duke Univ, MAT, 60, MA, 65; NC State Univ, PhD(elec eng), 72. *Prof Exp:* Instr math, Presby Col, SC, 60-61; phys scientist, Info Processing Off, 61-65 & Res-Technol Div, 65-72, assoc dir, Electronics Div, 72-74, actg dir, 74-75, DIR, ELECTRONICS DIV, US ARMY RES OFF, 75- *Concurrent Pos:* Asst dir res, Off Secy Defense, 82; adj prof, Elec Eng, NC State Univ, 74-82. *Mem:* Inst Elec & Electronics Engrs. *Res:* Computer architecture; biomathematics; switching theory; electron paramagnetic resonance spectroscopy of organic solids. *Mailing Add:* US Army Res Off PO Box 12211 Research Triangle Park NC 27709

SUTTNER, LEE JOSEPH, b Hilbert, Wis, June 3, 39; m 65; c 2. GEOLOGY. *Educ:* Univ Notre Dame, BS, 61; Univ Wis, MS, 63, PhD(geol), 66. *Prof Exp:* From asst prof to assoc prof geol, 66-78, PROF GEOL, IND UNIV, BLOOMINGTON, 78- *Mem:* Nat Asn Geol Teachers; Int Asn Sedimentologists; Soc Econ Paleontologists & Mineralogists; Geol Soc Am. *Res:* Sedimentology and sedimentary petrology. *Mailing Add:* Dept of Geol Ind Univ Bloomington IN 47401

SUTTON, BLAINE MOTE, b Ft Recovery, Ohio, Jan 23, 21; m 46. MEDICINAL CHEMISTRY. *Educ:* Purdue Univ, BS, 42, MS, 48, PhD(pharmaceut chem), 50. *Prof Exp:* Group leader med chem, Smith Kline & French Labs, Philadelphia, 50-68, sr investr med chem, 68-71, asst dir med chem, 71-75, ASSOC DIR MED CHEM, SMITH KLINE LABS, 75- *Mem:* AAAS; Am Chem Soc; Am Pharmaceut Asn; NY Acad Sci; Acad Pharmaceut Sci. *Res:* Synthetic medicinal chemistry; sym pathomimetic amines, sedatives, antibiotics, antirheumatics and hypocholesteremics. *Mailing Add:* 2435 Byberry Rd Hatboro PA 19040

SUTTON, C(HARLES) ROGER, b Hillsdale, Mich, Oct 20, 05; m 27; c 1. METALLURGY. *Educ:* Univ Detroit, BChE, 27, MS, 28. *Prof Exp:* Chemist, Timken-Detroit Axle Co, 25-28; chief metallurgist, Gemmer Mfg Co, 28-29; chief chemist, Forging & Casting Corp, 29-30; res chemist, Solvay Process Co, 30-31; metallurgist, Halcomb Steel Co, 31-32; metall engr, Chrysler Corp, 33-41; dir eng & metall, Gen Alloys Co, 41-45; consult, Roger Sutton Assocs, 45-50; sr metallurgist, Argonne Nat Lab, 50-55; supvr stainless steel develop, Int Nickel Co, Inc, 55-64; asst dir, Reactor Eng Div, Argonne Nat Lab, 64-71; CONSULT, ROGER SUTTON ASSOCS, 71- *Concurrent Pos:* Instr, Univ Detroit, 27-28; lectr & adj prof, Chrysler Inst Technol, 36-41; mem, Indust Adv Comt, War Prod Bd, 42-45; chmn, Indust Adv Comt, Air Material Command, US Dept Air Force, 50-55; mem, Welding Comt, US Atomic Energy Comn, 51-; spec lectr, NC State Col, 56; mem, Welding Res Coun. *Mem:* Fel Am Soc Metals; Am Soc Testing & Mat; Am Nuclear Soc; Soc Mfg Engrs; Am Inst Mining, Metall & Petrol Engrs. *Res:* Nuclear reactor materials such as fuel elements, control rods and structural materials including effect of irradiation and corrosion; heat and corrosion resisting alloys; stainless steel; effect of rate of load and temperature of loads application on properties of metallic materials. *Mailing Add:* Roger Sutton Assocs 1129 Central Ave Downers Grove IL 60515

SUTTON, CHARLES SAMUEL, b Lima, Peru, July 15, 13; US citizen; m 46. MATHEMATICS. *Educ:* Mass Inst Technol, BS, 35, MS, 37. *Prof Exp:* Instr math, Tufts Col, 39-40; from asst prof to prof, 40-78, EMER PROF MATH, THE CITADEL, 78- *Mem:* Am Math Soc; Math Asn Am. *Res:* Analysis; iteration; functional equations. *Mailing Add:* 19 Shrewsbury Rd Charleston SC 29407

SUTTON, DALLAS ALBERT, b Grand Junction, Colo, Sept 12, 11; m 35; c 1. BIOLOGY. *Educ:* Univ Colo, AB, 39, PhD, 53; Northwestern Univ, MS, 40. *Prof Exp:* Prin pub sch, Colo, 34-45; instr biol, Mesa Col, 45-51; assoc prof biol & sci educ, Eastern Mont Col Educ, 54-57; prof, 57-76, EMER PROF BIOL & SCI EDUC, CALIF STATE UNIV, CHICO, 76- *Concurrent Pos:* NSF grant. *Mem:* Am Soc Mammal. *Res:* Mammalogy; chipmunks of Colorado; chromosomes of the chipmunks, Genus eutamias; female genital bones of chipmunks. *Mailing Add:* Dept Biol Calif State Univ Chico CA 95926

SUTTON, DAVID C(HASE), b Bryn Mawr, Pa, Dec 18, 33; c 1. PHYSICS. *Educ:* Haverford Col, BA, 55; Princeton Univ, PhD(physics), 62. *Prof Exp:* Asst prof, 61-68, ASSOC PROF PHYSICS, UNIV ILL, 68- *Concurrent Pos:* Vis assoc prof, Stanford Univ, 68-69. *Mem:* Am Phys Soc; Sigma Xi. *Res:* Photonuclear reactions; nuclear structure; accelerator development; radioactivity; particle-radiation detectors. *Mailing Add:* Dept of Physics Univ of Ill Urbana IL 61801

SUTTON, DAVID GEORGE, b San Francisco, Calif, Apr 17, 44; m 63; c 1. LASERS. *Educ:* Univ Calif, Berkeley, BS, 66; Mass Inst Technol, PhD(chem physics), 70. *Prof Exp:* Fel phys chem, Dept Chem, Mass Inst Technol, 70-71; fel phys chem, Dept Chem, Univ Toronto, 71-72; TECH STAFF LASERS, AEROSPACE CORP, 72- *Mem:* Am Phys Soc. *Res:* Experimental research in gas phase molecular exitation; gas phase molecular energy transfer; analytical applications of molecular energy transfer; laser effects on materials. *Mailing Add:* Aerospace Corp El Segundo CA 90009

SUTTON, DEREK, b Eng, July 15, 37; m 58; c 2. INORGANIC CHEMISTRY. *Educ:* Univ Nottingham, BSc, 58, PhD(chem), 63. *Prof Exp:* Asst lectr chem, Univ Nottingham, 62-64, lectr, 64-67; from asst prof to assoc prof, 67-78, PROF CHEM, SIMON FRASER UNIV, 78- *Mem:* Royal Soc Chem; Am Chem Soc; Chem Inst Can. *Res:* Study of aryldiazo and other complexes of transition metals related to the interaction of nitrogen with transition metals; biological nitrogen fixation. *Mailing Add:* Dept Chem Simon Fraser Univ Burnaby BC V5A 1S6 Can

SUTTON, DONALD DUNSMORE, b Oakland, Calif, June 8, 27; c 3. MICROBIOLOGY. *Educ:* Univ Calif, AB, 51, MA, 54, PhD(microbiol), 57. *Prof Exp:* Sr lab technician bact, Univ Calif, 50-53, asst, 53-55; asst prof & USPHS fel microbiol sch med, Ind Univ, 57-59; Waksman-Merck fel inst microbiol, Rutgers Univ, 59-60; assoc prof microbiol, 60-63, chmn dept biol, 65-70, PROF MICROBIOL, CALIF STATE UNIV, FULLERTON, 63- *Concurrent Pos:* Vis prof, Inst Appl Microbiol, Tokyo Univ, 70-71; consult food microbiol & waste water treatment microbiol, 73- *Mem:* Am Soc Microbiol; Am Inst Biol Sci; Mycol Soc Am. *Res:* Microbial physiology; metabolism of plant disease bacteria; mechanisms of growth inhibitors and antifungal agents; physiological basis of morphogenesis in fungi; location of enzymes in fungi; microbiology of food fermentations; microbiology of waste decomposition. *Mailing Add:* Dept Biol Calif State Univ Fullerton CA 92631

SUTTON, EMMET ALBERT, b Toledo, Ohio, May 7, 35; m 58; c 2. CHEMICAL DYNAMICS. *Educ:* Cornell Univ, BEngPhys, 58, PhD(aeronaut eng), 61. *Prof Exp:* Asst prof physics, Hamilton Col, 61-62; asst prof aeronaut & astronaut, Purdue Univ, 62-65; prin res scientist, Avco Everett Res Lab, 65-70; vpres, Aerodyne Res, Inc, 70-76; PRES, CONCORD SCI CORP, 76- *Mem:* Am Inst Aeronaut & Astronaut; Am Optical Soc. *Res:* Experimental chemical kinetics; hypersonic wake chemistry; rocket plume radiation; optical and radar field measurements. *Mailing Add:* Concord Sci Corp PO Box 119 Concord MA 01742

SUTTON, G(EORGE) W(ALTER), b Brooklyn, NY, Aug 3, 27; m 52; c 2. MECHANICAL ENGINEERING. *Educ:* Cornell Univ, BME, 52; Calif Inst Technol, MS, 53, PhD(mech eng, physics), 55. *Prof Exp:* Sr scientist reentry heat protection, Lockheed Aircraft Corp, 55; res engr, Gen Elec Co, Pa, 56-59, mgr magnetohydrodyn power generation, 59-63; chmn aerophys comt, 65, prin res scientist, 65-69, chmn strategic defense comt, 69-71, dir mil laser develop, 71-75, V PRES, AVCO EVERETT RES LAB, EVERETT, 75- *Concurrent Pos:* Spec lectr, Univ Pa, 60-61; mem, Res Adv Comt Fluid Mech, NASA, 60; sci adv, Dept Air Force, 63-65; ed-in-chief jour, Am Inst Aeronaut & Astronaut, 67-; chmn, Critical Technol Expert Group High Energy Lasers, Dept Defense, 78- *Mem:* Am Soc Mech Engrs; Am Inst Aeronaut & Astronaut; AAAS. *Res:* Stress waves in solids; dynamic photoelasticity; reentry; hypersonics; combustion in boundary layers; magneto-gas dynamics; high power lasers. *Mailing Add:* 537 Winthrop Rd Lexington MA 02173

SUTTON, GEORGE E, b Blandville, WVa, June 3, 23; m 59; c 1. MECHANICAL ENGINEERING. *Educ:* Univ WVa, BSME; Univ Fla, MSE; Mich State Univ, PhD(mech eng), 57. *Prof Exp:* Engr, Indust Eng & Construct Co, 48; instr mech eng, Univ Fla, 48-55; instr, Mich State Univ, 55-57; prof, Univ Ariz, 57-59; prof eng, Ariz State Univ, 59-61; prof mech eng & chmn dept, Univ Nev, Reno, 61-74; dir prof serv, Nat Coun Eng Examr, 74-76; DEAN, SCH ENG, YOUNGSTOWN STATE UNIV, 76- *Concurrent Pos:* Secy western zone, Nat Coun State Bd Eng Exam, 66-68. *Mem:* Am Soc Mech Engrs; Nat Soc Prof Engrs; Am Soc Heating, Refrig & Air-Conditioning Engrs; Sigma Xi. *Res:* Thermal environment; heat transfer. *Mailing Add:* 2602 Algonquin Dr Poland OH 44514

SUTTON, GEORGE HARRY, b Chester, NJ, Mar 4, 27; m 47; c 4. SEISMOLOGY, GEOPHYSICS. *Educ:* Muhlenberg Col, BS, 50; Columbia Univ, MA, 53, PhD(geol), 57. *Prof Exp:* From res asst to res assoc, Lamont Geol Observ, Columbia Univ, 50-60, mem acad staff, 60-66, from asst prof to assoc prof geol, Univ, 60-66; assoc dir, Hawaii Inst geophys, 71-76, PROF GEOPHYS, & GEOPHYSICIST, HAWAII INST GEOPHYS, UNIV HAWAII, 66- *Concurrent Pos:* Chief seismologist, Inst Sci Res Cent Africa, 55-56; prin investr & co-investr for Ranger, Surveyor & Apollo lunar seismog exps, NASA, 59-73, mem geophys working group planetology subcomt, 64-73, Surveyor sci eval adv team, 65-73; mem comt planetary surfaces & interiors, Space Sci Bd, Nat Acad Sci, 63-67; mem ad hoc panel earthquake prediction, Off Sci & Technol, 64-65; mem, Adv Panel Earth Sci, NSF, 69-72 & Panel Strong-Motion Seismol, Comn Seismol, Div Earth Sci, Nat Res Coun-Nat Acad Sci, 72-74. *Mem:* AAAS; Soc Explor Geophysicists; Geol Soc Am; Seismol Soc Am; Am Geophys Union. *Res:* Earthquake seismology; seismic wave propagation and source conditions; geophysical exploration of oceanic crustal and upper-mantle structure; lunar and planetary interiors; geophysical instrumentation for ocean-bottom and lunar use. *Mailing Add:* Hawaii Inst of Geophys Univ of Hawaii Honolulu HI 96822

SUTTON, GEORGE MIKSCH, b Lincoln, Nebr, May 16, 98. ORNITHOLOGY. *Educ:* Bethany Col, WVa, BS & ScD, 23; Cornell Univ, PhD, 32. *Prof Exp:* Asst cur birds, Carnegie Mus, 19-24; instr ornith, Univ Pittsburgh, 21-24; state ornithologist & chief bur res & info, State Bd Game Comnrs, Pa, 25-29; cur birds, Cornell Univ, 32-45; RES PROF ZOOL, CUR BIRDS & ORNITHOLOGIST, BIOL SURV, UNIV OKLA, 52- *Concurrent Pos:* Fel, Cranbrook Inst Sci; ornith ed, Am Col Dict & Encycl Arctica; hon trustee, Oglebay Inst. Mem Carnegie Mus ornith expeds, Labrador, 20, Hudson Bay, 23, 26, 31, Cape Sable region, Fla, 24, Southern Labrador, 28, Southampton Island, Hudson Bay, 29-30, Sask, 32, Rio Grande Valley, 33, BC, 34; Cornell exped, southern states, 35, Okla, 36-37, Mex, 38-39, Ariz, 40; Cornell & Carnegie Mus exped, Rio Grande Valley, 35; Cornell-Carleton exped, Mex, 41; independent exped, Mex, 47, 49, 50; Baffin Island, 53; Hudson Bay, 56; Iceland, 58; Victoria Island, 62; Jenny Lind Island, 66; Bathurst & Ellesmere Islands, 69. *Mem:* Cooper Ornith Soc; Wilson Ornith Soc (vpres, 25-29, pres, 41, 45-47); Am Geog Soc; Wildlife Soc; fel Am Ornith Union. *Res:* Life histories, plumages, distribution and taxonomy of birds; bird illustrations. *Mailing Add:* Stovall Mus Univ of Okla Norman OK 73019

SUTTON, HARRY ELDON, b Cameron, Tex, Mar 5, 27; m 62; c 2. HUMAN GENETICS. *Educ:* Univ Tex, BS, 48, MA, 49, PhD(biochem), 53. *Prof Exp:* Res scientist, Univ Tex, 48-52; asst biologist, Univ Mich, 52-56, instr human genetics, 56-57, asst prof, 57-60; assoc prof zool, 60-64, chmn dept, 70-73, assoc dean, Grad Sch, 67-70 & 73-75, vpres res, 75-79, PROF ZOOL, UNIV TEX, AUSTIN, 64- *Concurrent Pos:* Mem comt personnel res, Am Cancer Soc, 61-64; mem genetics study sect, NIH, 63-67; ed, Am J Human Genetics, Am Soc Human Genetics, 64-69; mem adv coun, Nat Inst Environ Health Sci, 68-72, mem sci adv comt, 72-76; mem adv comt, Atomic Bom Casualty Comn; mem comt epidemiol & vet follow-up studies, Nat Acad Sci-Nat Res Coun. *Mem:* AAAS; Genetics Soc Am; Am Chem Soc; Am Soc Human Genetics (pres-elect, 78, pres, 79); Am Soc Biol Chem. *Res:* Genetic control of protein structure; inherited variations in human metabolism; human population genetics. *Mailing Add:* Dept of Zool Univ of Tex Austin TX 78712

SUTTON, J(AMES) L(OWELL), b Petersburg, Ind, Apr 20, 31; m 59; c 5. ENGINEERING. *Prof Exp:* Develop engr, 58-60, res engr, 60-62, process develop supvr, 62-65, eng serv supvr, 65-66, on spec assignment, 66-70, area supvr, Film Dept, 70-78, tech area supt, Plastics Prod & Resins Dept, 78-81, AREA SUPT LIAISON, POLYMER PROD DEPT, E I DU PONT DE NEMOURS & CO, INC, 81- *Mem:* Nat Soc Prof Engrs. *Res:* Development and design of mechanical equipment in the chemical industry. *Mailing Add:* Polymer Prod Dept E I Du Pont de Nemours Co Inc PO Box 89 Circleville OH 43113

SUTTON, JOHN CLIFFORD, b Halstead, Eng, Oct 10, 41; m 64; c 2. PLANT PATHOLOGY. *Educ:* Univ Nottingham, BSc, 65; Univ Wis, PhD(plant path), 69. *Prof Exp:* Asst prof plant path, 69-75, ASSOC PROF PLANT PATH, UNIV GUELPH, 75- *Concurrent Pos:* Nat Sci & Eng Coun Can grant, 76-79. *Mem:* Can Phytopath Soc; Am Phytopath Soc. *Res:* Epidemiology of foliar pathogens; mycotoxins in maize; extension plant pathology. *Mailing Add:* Dept of Environ Biol Univ of Guelph Guelph ON N1G 2W1 Can

SUTTON, JOHN CURTIS, b Weiser, Idaho, May 13, 42; m 65; c 4. ORGANIC CHEMISTRY, ANALYTICAL CHEMISTRY. *Educ:* Univ Idaho, BS, 64, PhD(chem), 72. *Prof Exp:* assoc prof chem, 70-80, PROF, DIV NATURAL SCI, LEWIS-CLARK STATE COL, 80- *Res:* Utilization of tree bark for the sorption of heavy metal ions from aqueous solutions. *Mailing Add:* Dept of Chem Lewis-Clark State Col Lewiston ID 83501

SUTTON, LEWIS MCMECHAN, b Chicago, Ill, Apr 13, 46; m 69; c 2. MICROBIOLOGY, ANALYTICAL CHEMISTRY. *Educ:* Iowa State Univ, BS, 69; Northern Ill Univ, MS, 72. *Prof Exp:* Chemist org, 70-72, chief chemist org & vitamin, 72-76, ASST TECH DIR NUTRIT RES, BORDEN CHEM, 76- *Mem:* Am Chem Soc; Am Soc Microbiol. *Res:* Analytical methods development both chemical and microbiological; nutritional studies with animal models. *Mailing Add:* Nutrit Res Lab Rte 1 Box 127 Elgin IL 60120

SUTTON, LOUISE NIXON, b Hertford, NC, Nov 4, 25; div; c 1. MATHEMATICS. *Educ:* Agr & Tech Col NC, BS, 46; NY Univ, MA, 51, PhD(math educ), 62. *Prof Exp:* Instr high sch, NC, 46-47; instr math, Agr & Tech Col NC, 47-50, asst prof, 51-57; asst prof, Del State Col, 57-62; assoc prof, 62-63, head, Dept Phys Sci & Math, 62-78, PROF MATH, ELIZABETH STATE UNIV, 63- *Concurrent Pos:* Asst dean women, Agr & Tech Col, 47-48; mem adv comt cert math & sci, Del State Bd Educ, 59-61, mem adv comt math, 61-62; mem bd dir, Perquimans County Indust Develop Corp, 67-72; mem gen adv comt, NC State Bd Soc Serv, 69-71; mem bd dir, Div Higher Educ, NC Asn Educr, 69-72; co-dir, NSF Inst, 71-72 & 73-74, dir, 72-73 & 74-75, panelist, 71-72, 74 & 77-78, chmn, 77 & 78. *Mem:* Nat Coun Teachers Math; Nat Educ Asn; Nat Asn Univ Women. *Res:* Mathematics ecucation; concept learning in trigonometry and analytical geometry at college level; analytical geometry at college level. *Mailing Add:* Rte 1 Box 277 Hertford NC 27944

SUTTON, MATTHEW ALBERT, b Austin, Minn, Apr 28, 23; m 46; c 4. AERODYNAMICS, STRUCTURAL DYNAMICS. *Educ:* Univ Minn, BSc, 45; Ohio State Univ, MSc, 52, PhD(aeronaut eng), 58. *Prof Exp:* Stress analyst, McDonnell Aircraft Co, 46-47; instr eng drawing, Ohio State Univ, 47-48, res assoc wind tunnel design, 48-53, from instr to asst prof aeronaut eng, 53-58; prin eng supvr ord div, 58-62, chief engr, 62-65, chief engr systs & res div, 65-66, dir res, 66-68, gen mgr, Systs & Res Ctr, 68-76, vpres & gen mgr, Defense Systs Div, 78-81, VPRES & GEN MGR, AVIONICS DIV, HONEYWELL INC, 81- *Mem:* Am Inst Aeronaut & Astronaut. *Res:* Aircraft structure and flutter; unsteady aerodynamics. *Mailing Add:* Avionics Div Honeywell Corp PO Box 312 Minneapolis MN 55440

SUTTON, PAUL, b Hopkinsville, Ky, Sept 11, 29; m 54; c 2. SOIL FERTILITY. *Educ:* Univ Ky, BS, 51, MS, 57; Iowa State Univ, PhD(agron, soil fertil), 62. *Prof Exp:* Asst agronomist, Univ Ky, 54-55; asst horticulturist, Univ Fla, 61-67; assoc prof soils, Ohio Agr Res & Develop Ctr, 67-73, PROF AGRON, LAB ENVIRON SCI, OHIO STATE UNIV, 73- *Mem:* Sol Sci Soc Am; Am Soc Agron. *Res:* Plant physiology. *Mailing Add:* Dept of Agron Lab Environ Sci Ohio State Univ Columbus OH 43210

SUTTON, PAUL MCCULLOUGH, b Ohio, Dec 3, 21; m 46; c 2. PHYSICS. *Educ:* Harvard Univ, BS, 43; Columbia Univ, MA, 48, PhD(physics), 53. *Prof Exp:* Asst physics, Columbia Univ, 50-52; res assoc physicist, Corning Glass Works, 52-54, supvr ultrasonics res, 54-56, supvr fundamental physics group, 56-59; sr staff scientist, Aeronutronic Div, Ford Motor Co, 59-62, mgr, Appl Physics Dept, Philco Corp, 62-66, mgr, Physics Lab, Philco-Ford Corp, 66-68, mgr, Physics & Chem Lab, 68-72, mgr, Res Lab, 72-74, mgr electro-optics, 74-80, MGR DEVELOP PLANS, FORD AEROSPACE & COMMUN CORP, 80- *Concurrent Pos:* Lectr optics, Univ Calif, Irvine, 66. *Mem:* AAAS; fel Am Phys Soc; Am Ceramic Soc; Optical Soc Am. *Res:* Solid state physics; elastic constants; photoelasticity; acoustic propagation; glass physics; dielectric properties of glasses; hypervelocity impact; space charge in glass; atmospheric turbulence; lasers; infrared optics. *Mailing Add:* Res Labs Ford Aerospace & Commun Corp Ford Rd Newport Beach CA 92660

SUTTON, ROBERT GEORGE, b Rochester, NY, June 17, 25; m 46; c 2. GEOLOGY. *Educ:* Univ Rochester, AB, 48, MS, 50; Johns Hopkins Univ, PhD, 56. *Prof Exp:* Instr geol, Alfred Univ, 50-52; jr instr, Johns Hopkins Univ, 52-54; from asst prof to assoc prof, 54-66, PROF GEOL, UNIV ROCHESTER, 66- *Mem:* AAAS; Geol Soc Am; Soc Econ Paleont & Mineral. *Res:* Paleozoic stratigraphy; sedimentology; sedimentary petrology. *Mailing Add:* Dept of Geol Sci Univ of Rochester Rochester NY 14627

SUTTON, ROGER BEATTY, b Lloydminster, Sask, Sept 14, 16; m 46; c 2. EXPERIMENTAL HIGH ENERGY PHYSICS. *Educ:* Univ Sask, BA, 38, MA, 39; Princeton Univ, PhD(physics), 43. *Prof Exp:* Res physicist, Off Sci Res & Develop, Princeton Univ, 42-43; physicist, Manhattan Dist, Los Alamos Sci Lab, 43-46; from asst prof to assoc prof physics, 46-56, PROF PHYSICS, CARNEGIE-MELLON UNIV, 56- *Mem:* Am Phys Soc; Am Asn Physics Teachers; Am Asn Physicists Med. *Res:* Molecular spectroscopy; low energy nuclear physics; radioactive isotopes; neutron physics; cyclotrons; study of x-rays from exotic atoms including antiprotonic, kaonic and sigma minus atoms. *Mailing Add:* Dept of Physics Carnegie-Mellon Univ Pittsburgh PA 15213

SUTTON, ROSCOE MURRAY DAVIDSON, b Toronto, Ont, Mar 22, 22. PHYTOPATHOLOGY, VIROLOGY. *Educ:* Univ Toronto, BA, 48, MA, 58, PhD(plant path), 60. *Prof Exp:* Head technician bact med sch, Queen's Univ, Ont, 46-47; asst plant pathologist sci serv, Can Dept Agr, 48-54, from assoc plant pathologist to plant pathologist res br, 54-67, res scientist, Cell Biol Res Inst, Ont, 67-71; RES COUN OFFICER, ENVIRON SECRETARIAT, DIV BIOL SCI, NAT RES COUN CAN, 71- *Concurrent Pos:* Secy subcomt biol phenomena & phys energy phenomena, Assoc Comt Sci Criteria on Environ Qual. *Honors & Awards:* Wintercorbyn Award, 58. *Mem:* Am Pub Health Asn; Am Phytopath Soc; Can Phytopath Soc; Can Soc Microbiol; Can Pub Health Asn. *Res:* Research, development and production of biological weapons; bacterial phytopathology, especially development of methods for the detection and identification of bacterial pathogens; studies of bacteriophages for phage typing, ecological and epidemiological studies; survey of pollution in Canada. *Mailing Add:* Environ Secretariat Nat Res Coun of Can 100 Sussex Dr Ottawa ON K1A 0R6 Can

SUTTON, RUSSELL PAUL, b Mo, July 31, 29; m 53; c 5. CHEMISTRY. *Educ:* Univ Mo-Columbia, BS, 51; State Univ Iowa, MS, 53, PhD(chem), 55. *Prof Exp:* Res chemist, E I du Pont de Nemours & Co, Inc, 55-58; from asst prof to assoc prof, 58-70, PROF CHEM, KNOX COL, ILL, 70-, CHMN DEPT, 77- *Mem:* Am Chem Soc. *Res:* The chemistry of chalcones and flavylium compounds; gas chromatography. *Mailing Add:* Dept of Chem Knox Col Galesburg IL 61401

SUTTON, TURNER BOND, b Windsor, NC, Oct 24, 45. PLANT PATHOLOGY. *Educ:* Univ NC, BA, 68; NC State Univ, MS, 71, PhD(plant path), 73. *Prof Exp:* Res assoc plant path, Mich State Univ, 73-74; res assoc, 74-76, asst prof, 76-81, ASSOC PROF PLANT PATH, NC STATE UNIV, 81- *Mem:* Am Phytopath Soc. *Res:* Apple diseases; epidemiology and control; pest management. *Mailing Add:* Dept of Plant Path NC State Univ PO Box 5397 Raleigh NC 27650

SUTTON, W(ILLARD) H(OLMES), b Pittsburgh, Pa, Jan 12, 30; m 56; c 1. CERAMICS. *Educ:* Alfred Univ, BS, 52; Pa State Univ, MS, 54, PhD(ceramics tech), 57. *Prof Exp:* Ceramist, Gen Elec Co, 56-63; mgr metall & ceramics res, 63-69; MGR RES & DEVELOP, SPEC METALS CORP, 69- *Concurrent Pos:* Mem, Mat Adv Bd, Nat Acad Sci-Nat Res Coun; chmn, Ceramic-Metal Systs Div, Am Ceramic Soc, 68-69. *Honors & Awards:* Achievement Award, Nat Inst Ceramic Engrs, 70. *Mem:* Am Soc Metals; fel Am Ceramic Soc; Nat Inst Ceramic Engrs. *Res:* Metallurgy; fiber composite materials; refractory whiskers; ceramic-metal interfaces and surface chemistry; superalloys. *Mailing Add:* Spec Metals Corp New Hartford NY 13413

SUTTON, WILLIAM WALLACE, b Monticello, Miss, Dec 15, 30; m 54; c 6. PROTOZOOLOGY, CELL BIOLOGY. *Educ:* Dillard Univ, BA, 53; Howard Univ, MS, 59, PhD(zool), 65. *Prof Exp:* Med technician, DC Gen Hosp, 55-59; from instr to prof biol, Dillard Univ, 59-79, actg chmn div natural sci, 69-70, chmn div natural sci, 70-79; vpres acad affairs, 79-80, vpres acad affairs & student develop, 80-81, PROVOST & ACAD VPRES, CHICAGO STATE UNIV, 81- *Concurrent Pos:* Consult, NIH, 72-74 & 16 Inst Health Sci Consortium of NC & Va, 74-; assoc & regional liaison officer, Danforth Found, 75-; coordr, Strengthening Develop Inst Prog, Chicago State Univ, 80-; reader/reviewer, The Am Biol Teacher, 79- *Mem:* Soc Protozoologists; Sigma Xi; Nat Inst Sci; AAAS; NY Acad Sci. *Res:* Radiation cell biology; responses of peritrichs to ionizing radiations; chemical analysis of the cyst wall and nutrition of peritrichs; isolation of nucleic acids from peritrichs. *Mailing Add:* Chicago State Univ 9500 S King Dr Chicago IL 60628

SUTTON, WILLIAM WALLACE, b Athens, Ga, Apr 6, 43; m 75; c 3. ANIMAL PHYSIOLOGY. *Educ:* Mercer Univ, AB, 64; Marshall Univ, MS, 65; WVa Univ, PhD(zool), 70. *Prof Exp:* Animal physiologist, Chem Corps Proving Ground, Dugway, Utah, 71-73; RES PHYSIOLOGIST, US ENVIRON PROTECTION AGENCY, 73- *Concurrent Pos:* Adj asst prof biol, Univ Nev, Las Vegas, 76-78. *Mem:* AAAS; NY Acad Sci. *Res:* Gastrointestinal uptake of pollutants by livestock and subsequent transport to edible animal products; programs relating pollutant exposure to elemental accumulation in animal tissues or to enzyme inhibition. *Mailing Add:* 417 Meadow Valley Dr Las Vegas NV 89107

SUTULA, CHESTER LOUIS, b Erie, Pa, Feb 15, 33; m 55; c 8. PHYSICAL CHEMISTRY, CLINICAL CHEMISTRY. *Educ:* Col Holy Cross, BS, 54; Iowa State Univ, MS, 58, PhD(phys chem), 59. *Prof Exp:* Teaching asst, Iowa State Univ, 55-57; res scientist, Ames Lab, Iowa, 57-59; sr res scientist, Marathon Oil Co, Colo, 59-67; sr res scientist, Ames Res Lab, Ames Co Div, Miles Labs, Inc, 67-69, dir, 69-77; mem staff, Ortho Diag, Inc, 77-80; MEM STAFF, CLS ASSOC, 80- *Mem:* AAAS; Am Chem Soc. *Res:* Surface chemistry; calorimetry; wetting properties of complex porous materials; structure of colloidal fluids; microbiology; immunoassay; instrumentation. *Mailing Add:* CLS Assoc Box 176 17475 Pencross Dr Granges IL 46530

SUUBERG, ERIC MICHAEL, b NY, Nov 23, 51. COMBUSTION, CHEMICAL KINETICS. *Educ:* Mass Inst Technol, BS & MS 74, MS, 76, ScD, 78. *Prof Exp:* Asst prof chem eng, Carnegie-Mellon Univ, 77-81; ASST PROF ENG, BROWN UNIV, 81- *Mem:* Combustion Inst; Am Inst Chem Engrs; Am Chem Soc. *Res:* Coal chemistry. *Mailing Add:* Div Eng Box D Brown Univ Providence RI 02912

SUURA, HIROSHI, b Hiroshima, Japan, Aug 19, 25; m 51; c 2. THEORETICAL PHYSICS. *Educ:* Univ Tokyo, BS, 47; Hiroshima Univ, PhD(physics), 55. *Prof Exp:* Prof physics, Nihon Univ, 60-65; PROF PHYSICS, UNIV MINN, 65- *Mem:* Fel Am Phys Soc. *Res:* Theory of elementary particles. *Mailing Add:* Sch of Physics & Astron Univ of Minn Minneapolis MN 55455

SUYAMA, YOSHITAKA, b Osaka, Japan, Sept 5, 31; m 60; c 2. MOLECULAR BIOLOGY, BIOCHEMISTRY. *Educ:* Kyoto Univ, Japan, BAgr, 55; Kans State Univ, PhD(microbiol genetics), 59. *Prof Exp:* Fel genetics & microbiol, Sch Med, Yale Univ, 59-60; asst res biologist genetics & biol, Univ Calif, La Jolla, 60-64; from asst prof to assoc prof, 64-75, PROF BIOL, UNIV PA, 75- *Concurrent Pos:* Vis assoc prof biochem, Univ Bari, Italy, 69; res fel molecular genetics, Inst Molecular Genetics, Gif, France, 71-72. *Mem:* Genetics Soc Am; Am Soc Microbiologists; Am Soc Biol Chemists. *Res:* Molecular genetics and biogenesis of organelles in eukaryotic cells; elucidations of nucleic acids and protein synthesizing mechanisms in mitochondria. *Mailing Add:* Dept Biol Univ Pa Philadelphia PA 19104

SUYDAM, FREDERICK HENRY, b Lancaster, Pa, July 30, 23; m 44; c 3. CHEMISTRY. *Educ:* Franklin & Marshall Col, BS, 46; Northwestern Univ, PhD(chem), 50. *Prof Exp:* Instr chem, Franklin & Marshall Col, 46-47; asst, Northwestern Univ, 47-49; instr anat, Med Sch, Johns Hopkins Univ, 50-52; from asst prof to assoc prof, 52-62, chmn dept, 58-69, PROF CHEM, FRANKLIN & MARSHALL COL, 62- *Mem:* Am Chem Soc. *Res:* Peptide synthesis; reactions of amino acids; infrared absorption. *Mailing Add:* Dept of Chem Franklin & Marshall Col Lancaster PA 17604

SUZMAN, IVAN MERRILL, b Providence, RI, Nov 25, 49. HUMAN EVOLUTIONARY BIOLOGY. *Educ:* Dartmouth Col, AB, 71; Univ Witwatersrand, PhD(anat), 82. *Prof Exp:* Field instr anthrop, Brown Univ, 72; jr lectr anat, Univ Witwatersrand, 77-79; ASST PROF ANAT, MED SCH, UNIV MINN, 79- *Concurrent Pos:* Adj asst prof, Anthrop Dept, Univ Minn, 79- *Mem:* Am Asn Phys Anthropologists; Anat Asn SAfrica; SAfrica Soc Quaternary Res. *Res:* Investigations of the fossil evidence for human evolution; studies of the skeletons of living and extinct apes and humankind; radiological and functional anatomical analyses of fossil hominids; Plio-Pleistocene archeology, geology and ecology; principles of evolutionary biology. *Mailing Add:* Dept Anat Med Sch 4-135 Jackson Hall Univ Minn Minneapolis MN 55455

SUZUKI, DAVID TAKAYOSHI, b Vancouver, BC, Mar 24, 36; m 58; c 3. GENETICS. *Educ:* Amherst Col, BA, 58; Univ Chicago, PhD(zool), 61. *Hon Degrees:* LLD, Univ PEI, 74. *Prof Exp:* Res assoc genetics, Biol Div, Oak Ridge Nat Lab, 61-62; asst prof, Univ Alta, 62-63; from asst prof to assoc prof, 63-69, PROF ZOOL, UNIV BC, 69- *Concurrent Pos:* Res grants, Nat Res Coun Can, 62-, AEC, 64-69 & Nat Cancer Inst Can, 69- *Mem:* Genetics Soc Am; Genetics Soc Can; Can Soc Cell Biol (pres, 69-70). *Res:* Regulation of development and behavior; genetic organization of chromosomes; developmental and behavioral genetics. *Mailing Add:* Dept of Zool Univ of BC Vancouver BC V6T 2A9 Can

SUZUKI, GEORGE, b Acampo, Calif, Mar 5, 22; m 45. MATHEMATICS. *Educ:* Univ Denver, BS, 44; Univ Minn, MA, 47, PhD(statist), 51. *Prof Exp:* Lectr & instr statist, Univ Minn, 46-51; actg chief struct anal br, Inter-indust Res Off, Dep Chief of Staff & Comptroller, US Dept Air Force, 51-53; statist specialist, Appl Math Lab, David Taylor Model Basin, US Dept Navy, 53-57, dir mgt sci staff, Navy Mgt Off, 57-64; dep chief, Tech Anal Div, Inst Appl Technol, Nat Bur Standards, 64-73, actg chief, 73-75, assoc dir advan planning, Inst Appl Technol, 75-78; RETIRED. *Mem:* Sigma Xi; Inst Math Statist; Am Statist Asn; Inst Mgt Sci. *Res:* Development of mathematical methods for solving management problems. *Mailing Add:* 5908 Grosvenor Lane Bethesda MD 20814

SUZUKI, HOWARD KAZURO, b Ketchikan, Alaska, Apr 3, 27; m 52; c 4. ANATOMY. *Educ:* Marquette Univ, BS, 49, MS, 51; Tulane Univ, PhD(anat), 55. *Prof Exp:* Asst zool & bot, Marquette Univ, 48-51; asst zool & anat, Tulane Univ, 51-55; instr anat, Sch Med, Yale Univ, 55-58; from asst prof to prof, Sch Med, Univ Ark, 58-70; assoc dean, 70-71, actg dean, 71-72, prof anat, Col Med, 70-73, dean, Col Health Related Professions, 72-79, PROF NEUROSCI, COL MED, UNIV FLA, 72-, PROF ANAT, COL MED, 79-, PROF, COL HEALTH RELATED PROFESSIONS, 79- *Concurrent Pos:* Mem gen res support prog adv comt, NIH; mem adv comt, Off Acad Affairs, US Vet Admin. *Mem:* Fel AAAS; Am Asn Anatomists; Asn Am Med Cols; Soc Exp Biol & Med; Am Soc Allied Health Professions. *Res:* Endocrine relations to bone; phagocytosis and reticuloendothelial system; neonatal human anatomy; comparative bone metabolism. *Mailing Add:* Box J-235 JHMHC Univ of Fla Gainesville FL 32610

SUZUKI, ISAMU, b Tokyo, Japan, Aug 4, 30; m 62; c 3. MICROBIOLOGY, BIOCHEMISTRY. *Educ:* Univ Tokyo, BSc, 53; Iowa State Univ, PhD(bact physiol), 58. *Prof Exp:* Fel microbiol, Western Reserve Univ, 58-60; instr, Univ Tokyo, 60-62; Nat Res Coun Can fel, 62-64, from asst prof to assoc prof, 64-69, PROF MICROBIOL, UNIV MAN, 69-, HEAD DEPT, 72- *Mem:* AAAS; Am Soc Microbiol; Can Soc Microbiol; Can Biochem Soc. *Res:* Mechanism of the oxidation of inorganic sulfur compounds by Thiobacilli and ammonia by Nitrosomonas; physiology of autotrophic bacteria; carbon dioxide fixation enzymes; mechanism of enzyme reactions; kinetics; action of thiamine pyrophosphate. *Mailing Add:* Dept of Microbiol Univ of Man Winnipeg MB R3T 2N2 Can

SUZUKI, JON BYRON, b San Antonio, Tex, July 22, 47. MICROBIOLOGY, DENTISTRY. *Educ:* Ill Wesleyan Univ, BA, 68; Ill Inst Technol, PhD(microbiol), 71; Loyola Univ, DDS, 78; Am Bd Microbiol, SM, 72. *Prof Exp:* Med technologist & res assoc cytogenetics, Augustana Hosp, Chicago, 68-69; res assoc immunol & pediat, Univ Chicago Hosp, 70-71; clin microbiologist, St Luke's Hosp Ctr Columbia Col Physicians & Surgeons, NY, 71-73; dir clin labs, Registry Hawaii, 73-74; fel, Depts Path & Periodont, dentist & mem fac, Univ Wash, 74-80; ASSOC PROF PERIODONT & MICROBIOL, UNIV MD, BALTIMORE, 80- *Concurrent Pos:* Instr microbiol, Ill Inst Technol, 68-72; chmn clin labs med technol, Univ Hawaii, 73-74; vis lectr microbiol, Loyola Univ, Chicago, 74-; adv, NASA, 76-, res award, 80. *Honors & Awards:* Oral Path Nat Award, Am Acad Oral Path, 78. *Mem:* Am Acad Microbiol; Int Asn Dent Res; Sigma Xi; Am Dent Asn; AAAS. *Res:* Immunodeficiency states during manned space flights; research in interaction of immunocompetent cells in disease; periodontal diseases. *Mailing Add:* Dept Periodont Univ Md 666 W Baltimore St Baltimore MD 21201

SUZUKI, KINUKO, b Hyogo, Japan, Nov 10, 33; m 60; c 1. PATHOLOGY, NEUROPATHOLOGY. *Educ:* MD, Osaka City Univ, 59. *Hon Degrees:* MA, Univ Pa, 71. *Prof Exp:* Asst prof path, Albert Einstein Col Med, 68; from asst prof to assoc prof, Sch Med, Univ Pa, 69-72; assoc prof, 72-76, PROF PATH, ALBERT EINSTEIN COL MED, 76- *Mem:* Am Soc Neurochem; Am Asn Neuropath; Soc Neurosci. *Res:* Study of pathogenesis of developmental disorder of the central nervous system. *Mailing Add:* Dept Path Albert Einstein Col Med Bronx NY 10461

SUZUKI, KUNIHIKO, b Tokyo, Japan, Feb 5, 32; m 60; c 1. NEUROCHEMISTRY, BIOCHEMISTRY. *Educ:* Univ Tokyo, BA, 55, MD, 59. *Prof Exp:* Resident clin neurol, Albert Einstein Col Med, 60-62, instr neurol, 64, asst prof, 65-68; assoc prof, Sch Med, Univ Pa, 69-71, prof neurol & pediat, 71-72; PROF NEUROL & NEUROSCI, ALBERT EINSTEIN COL MED, 72- *Concurrent Pos:* Mem neurol B study sect, 71-75; mem adv bd, Nat Tay-Sachs & Allied Dis Asn; chief ed, J Neurochem, 75-; mem bd sci counselors, Nat Inst Neurol, Commun Disorders & Stroke, 80- *Mem:* Int Soc Neurochem; Soc Neurosci; Am Asn Neuropath; Am Soc Biol Chemists; Am Soc Neurochem. *Res:* Biochemistry of brain lipids, particularly gangliosides; biochemical and enzymatic studies of inherited metabolic disorders of the nervous system. *Mailing Add:* Dept of Neurol Albert Einstein Col of Med Bronx NY 10461

SUZUKI, MAHIKO, b Tokyo, Japan, Oct 3, 38. THEORETICAL HIGH ENERGY PHYSICS. *Educ:* Univ Tokyo, BS, 61, MS, 63, DSc, 66. *Prof Exp:* Res fel physics, Calif Inst Technol, 65-67; mem, Inst Advan Study, 67-68; res assoc, Univ Tokyo, 68-69; vis assoc prof, Columbia Univ, 69-70; assoc prof, 70-74, PROF PHYSICS, UNIV CALIF, BERKELEY, 74- *Concurrent Pos:* Fullbright grnt, Fullbright Comn, 65-68; R C Tolman fel, Calif Inst Technol, 66-67; J S Guggenheim Mem Found fel, 76-77. *Res:* Theoretical particle physics of weak, electromagnetic and strong interactions. *Mailing Add:* Dept of Physics Univ of Calif Berkeley CA 94720

SUZUKI, MICHIO, b Taipei, Formosa, Feb 23, 27; Can citizen; m 59; c 3. PLANT PHYSIOLOGY, BIOCHEMISTRY. *Educ:* Tohuku Univ, Japan, BS, 52, PhD(agr chem), 62. *Prof Exp:* Asst plant physiol & biochem, Tohuku Univ, Japan, 52-66; RES SCIENTIST, RES BR, CAN DEPT AGR, 66- *Concurrent Pos:* Nat Res Coun Can res fel, 63-65. *Mem:* Can Soc Plant Physiologists; Am Soc Plant Physiologists; Agr Inst Can; Can Soc Agron; Soc Cryobiol. *Res:* Winter survival of perennial crops and winter cereals; vegetative regrowth of forage crops; metabolism of fructosan in grasses; plant nutrition; evaluation of feed quality. *Mailing Add:* Res Sta Can Dept of Agr Charlottetown PE C1A 7M8 Can

SUZUKI, MICHIO, b Chiba, Japan, Oct 2, 26; m 52; c 1. MATHEMATICS. *Educ:* Univ Tokyo, BA, 48, DrS(math), 52. *Prof Exp:* Lectr math, Tokyo Univ Educ, 51-55; from asst prof to assoc prof, 55-59, PROF MATH, UNIV ILL, 59- *Concurrent Pos:* Fel, Univ Ill, 52-53, res assoc, 53-55; res assoc, Harvard Univ, 56-57; fel, Inst Advan Study, Princeton, NJ, 62-63, vis prof, 68-69, mem inst, 81-; vis prof, Univ Chicago, 60-61 & Univ Tokyo, 71 & 81. *Honors & Awards:* Japan Acad Prize, 74. *Mem:* Am Math Soc; Math Soc Japan. *Res:* Group theory. *Mailing Add:* Dept of Math Univ of Ill Urbana IL 61801

SUZUKI, SHIGETO, b San Francisco, Calif, Feb 25, 25; m 53; c 1. ORGANIC CHEMISTRY. *Educ:* Univ Calif, Berkeley, BS, 55; Univ Southern Calif, PhD(chem), 59. *Prof Exp:* Sloan Found res fel org chem, Univ Calif, Berkeley, 59-60; SR RES ASSOC, CHEVRON RES CO, 60- *Mem:* Am Chem Soc; The Chem Soc. *Res:* Organic reaction mechanism, especially carbonium and carbanion rearrangements; organo-sulfur and organo-halogen chemistry. *Mailing Add:* 679 12th Ave San Francisco CA 94118

SUZUKI, TSUNEO, b Nagoya, Japan, Nov 23, 31; m 70; c 3. MICROBIOLOGY, BIOCHEMISTRY. *Educ:* Univ Tokyo, BS, 54, MD, 57; Hokkaido Univ, PhD(biochem), 69. *Prof Exp:* Japan Fel Asn fel & Fulbright travel grant, Univ Tokyo, 63; fel, Univ Wis, 63-66; fel, Univ Lausanne, 66-67; Ont Cancer Inst fel, Univ Toronto, 67-69; res assoc immunochem, Univ Wis, 69-70; asst prof, 70-79, ASSOC PROF IMMUNOCHEM, SCH MED, UNIV KANS MED CTR, KANSAS CITY, 79- *Mem:* Am Asn Immunol; Can Soc Immunol. *Res:* Immunochemistry of cell surface markers. *Mailing Add:* Dept of Microbiol Univ of Kans Sch of Med Kansas City KS 66103

SVACHA, ANNA JOHNSON, b Asheville, NC, Nov 27, 28; c 3. NUTRITION, BIOCHEMISTRY. *Educ:* Va Polytech Inst & State Univ, BS, 50; Univ Ariz, MS, 69, PhD(biochem, nutrit), 71. *Prof Exp:* Indust chemist, Hercules Powder Co, 51-53; physicist, Taylor Model Basin, US Navy, 53; high sch teacher, Tenn, 53-54; res asst anal chem, Tex Agr Exp Sta, 56-58; res asst org chem, Chas Pfizer & Co, Inc, 58-59; res asst nutrit, Univ Ariz, 67-68; asst poultry scientist, Ariz Agr Exp Sta, 71-72; ASST PROF NUTRIT, AUBURN UNIV, 72- *Mem:* Am Chem Soc; Am Home Econ Asn. *Res:* Appetite regulation with respect to protein and amino acid metabolism; nutritional status and requirements of the elderly. *Mailing Add:* Dept Nutrit & Foods Auburn Univ Auburn AL 36830

SVANES, TORGNY, b Norway. ALGEBRA. *Educ:* Oslo Univ, MA, 65; Mass Inst Technol, PhD(math), 72. *Prof Exp:* Instr math, Oslo Univ, 66-69, NY State Univ Stony Brook, 72-73; asst prof Aarhus Univ, 73-75; asst prof math, Purdue Univ, 75-77; asst prof math, Bradley Univ, 77-80; MEM STAFF, MITRE CORP, 80- *Mem:* Am Math Soc. *Res:* Study of Schubert subvarieties of homogeneous spaces. *Mailing Add:* Mitre Corp PO Box 208 Bedford MA 01730

SVE, CHARLES, b Pana, Ill, Feb 21, 40; m 62; c 2. CIVIL ENGINEERING. *Educ:* Mass Inst Technol, BS, 62, MS, 63; Northwestern Univ, PhD(theoret appl mech), 68. *Prof Exp:* Res engr, NAm Aviation, 63-64; sr engr, Avco Corp, 64-66; res asst civil eng, Northwestern Univ, 66-67; MEM TECH STAFF STRUCT MECH, AEROSPACE CORP, 68- *Concurrent Pos:* Lectr, Univ Southern Calif, 70-71. *Mem:* AAAS; Am Soc Mech Engrs; Am Inst Aeronaut & Astronaut. *Res:* Applied mechanics; wave propagation in composite materials; experimantal mechanics; numerical analysis. *Mailing Add:* Mech Res Dept MS 130-2/128 PO Box 92957 Los Angeles CA 90009

SVEC, HARRY JOHN, b Cleveland, Ohio, June 24, 18; m 43; c 9. PHYSICAL CHEMISTRY, ANALYTICAL CHEMISTRY. *Educ:* John Carroll Univ, BS, 41; Iowa State Univ, PhD(phys chem), 49. *Prof Exp:* Asst chem, 41-43, jr chemist, Manhattan Proj, 43-46, res assoc, Inst Atomic Res, 46-50, asst prof chem, Univ & assoc chemist, Inst, 50-55, assoc prof & chemist, 55-60, PROF CHEM, IOWA STATE UNIV & SR CHEMIST, INST ATOMIC RES, 60-, DISTINGUISHED PROF SCI & HUMANITIES, 78- *Concurrent Pos:* Lectr, NATO Advan Study Inst Mass Spectros, 64; ed, Int J Mass Spectrometry Ion Physics, Am Soc Mass Spectrometry, 68-, vpres, 72-74, pres, 74-76; prog dir, Ames Lab, US Dept of Energy, 78- *Mem:* Am Chem Soc; Am Soc Testing & Mat; Am Soc Mass Spectrometry (pres, 74-76); Geochem Soc; The Chem Soc. *Res:* Metallurgy of rare metals; mass spectroscopy; mass spectrometry in physical, inorganic and analytical chemistry; corrosion mechanisms; determination of ultra trace levels of organic pollutants in water and air; highly excited neutral species. *Mailing Add:* Dept of Chem Iowa State Univ Ames IA 50010

SVEC, LEROY VERNON, b Columbus, Nebr, Feb 27, 42; m 64; c 4. AGRONOMY, PLANT PHYSIOLOGY. *Educ:* Univ Nebr-Lincoln, BSc, 64; Purdue Univ, Lafayette, MSc, 68, PhD(agron), 70. *Prof Exp:* Asst prof plant sci, Univ Del, 69-76; assoc prof agron & dist exten agronomist, Univ Nebr, 76-79; TECH SERV AGRONOMIST, ASGROW SEED CO, 80- *Concurrent Pos:* Mem, Coun Agr Sci & Technol. *Mem:* Am Soc Agron; Sigma Xi; Am Soc Plant Physiologists. *Res:* Performance evaluation of new hybrids and varieties; technical training publications; new cultural practices for crop production. *Mailing Add:* Asgrow Seed Co 634 E Lincolnway Ames IA 50010

SVEDA, MICHAEL, b West Ashford, Conn, Feb 3, 12; m 36; c 2. CHEMISTRY. *Educ:* Univ Toledo, BS, 34; Univ Ill, PhD(chem, math), 39. *Prof Exp:* Asst chem, Univ Toledo, 31-34, teaching fel, 34-35; teaching asst, Univ Ill, 35-37, Eli Lilly res fel, 37-39; res chemist, E I du Pont de Nemours & Co, Inc, 39-44, res mgr, 44-47, new prod sales supvr, 47-51, prod mgr, 51-53, spec asst to mgt, 53-54; mgt consult, 55-60; dir acad proj, NSF, 61-62; corp assoc dir res, FMC Corp, New York, 62-64; RES & MGT COUN TO ACAD, INDUST & GOVT, 65- *Concurrent Pos:* Mem adv comt creativity in scientists & engrs, Rensselaer Polytech Inst, 65-68; res consult, NSF, 70. *Mem:* Am Chem Soc; AAAS. *Res:* Discovered cyclamate sweeteners; first application of Boolean algebra and theory of sets to people problems, and devised 3-dimensional models showing relationships; devised better way to take off human fat in obesity; interdisciplinary organizations broadly, including mathematical treatment for the first time. *Mailing Add:* 228 W Lane Revonah Woods Stamford CT 06905

SVEJDA, FELICITAS JULIA, b Vienna, Austria, Nov 8, 20; nat Can. ORNAMENTAL HORTICULTURE, PLANT BREEDING. *Educ:* State Univ Agr & Forestry, Austria, MSc, 46, PhD, 48. *Prof Exp:* Res asst rural econ, State Univ Agr & Forestry, Austria, 47-51; asst plant breeder, Swedish Seed Asn, 52-53; RES OFFICER, CAN DEPT AGR, 53- *Mem:* Am Soc Hort Sci; Genetics Soc Can; Can Soc Hort Sci; Agr Inst Can; Can Bot Asn. *Res:* Population biology; plant physiology; hybridization of ornamental plants. *Mailing Add:* Can Dept of Agr Ottawa ON K1A 0C6 Can

SVENDSEN, GERALD EUGENE, b Ashland, Wis, June 18, 40; m 61; c 2. ECOLOGY, ETHOLOGY. *Educ:* Univ Wis-River Falls, BS, 62; Univ Kans, MA, 64, PhD(behav ecol), 73. *Prof Exp:* Biologist, Fish-Pesticide Res Lab, US Fish & Wildlife Serv, 64-66 & Fish Control Lab, 66-68; from instr to asst prof biol, Viterbo Col, 66-70; asst prof, 73-77, ASSOC PROF ZOOL, OHIO UNIV, 77- *Concurrent Pos:* Actg dir, Rocky Mountain Biol Lab. *Mem:* Am Soc Mammalogists; Ecol Soc Am; Am Soc Evolutionists; Am Soc Naturalists. *Res:* Behavioral ecology; ethology of mammals; social systems analysis and evolution; spatial organization and distribution of terrestrial vertebrates; population biology of terrestrial vertebrates; vertebrate communication systems. *Mailing Add:* Dept of Zool & Microbiol Ohio Univ Athens OH 45701

SVENDSEN, KENDALL LORRAINE, b Greenville, Mich, June 24, 19; m 43; c 3. GEOPHYSICS. *Educ:* Univ Mich, BS, 43. *Prof Exp:* Geophysicist, US Coast & Geod Surv, Nat Oceanic & Atmospheric Admin, 46-70, chief geomagnetism div, 70-71, chief geomagnetic data div, Environ Data Serv, 71-72, chief solid earth & marine geophys data serv div, 72-75, tech asst geomagnetism, Solid Earth Geophys Div, Environ Data Serv, 75-81; RES ASSOC, COOP INST RES ENVIRON SCI, UNIV COLO, BOULDER, 81- *Concurrent Pos:* Am Geophys Union liaison rep, Comn Geophys, Pan Am Inst Geog & Hist, 72-, alt US mem, 73-; co-chmn working group magnetic observ, Int Asn Geomagnetism & Aeronomy, 73- & mem comt on asst to develop countries, 81- *Honors & Awards:* Bronze Medal, US Dept Com, 70, Silver Medal, 77; Antarctic Medal, NSF, 70; naming of Svendsen Glacier in Antarctica, US Bd Geog Names, 71. *Mem:* Soc Explor Geophysicists; Am Geophys Union; Asn Geoscientists Int Develop; Sigma Xi; fel Royal Geog Soc. *Res:* Management of geomagnetic data; international cooperation in geomagnetism; exchange of data, information, and expertise. *Mailing Add:* 7350 Mt Meeker Rd Longmont CO 80501

SVENNE, JURIS PETERIS, b Riga, Latvia, Feb 14, 39; Can citizen; m 63; c 3. NUCLEAR PHYSICS, REACTION THEORY. *Educ:* Univ Toronto, BASc, 62; Mass Inst Technol, PhD(physics), 65. *Prof Exp:* Res assoc nuclear physics, Mass Inst Technol, 65-66; Nat Res Coun Can fels, Niels Bohr Inst, Copenhagen, Denmark, 66-68; res assoc, Inst Nuclear Physics, D'Orsay, France, 68-69; from asst prof to assoc prof, 68-80, PROF PHYSICS, UNIV MAN, 80- *Concurrent Pos:* Vis prof nuclear physics, Univ Oxford, 76; instr, Sch Music, Univ Man, 80- *Mem:* Am Phys Soc; Can Asn Physicists. *Res:* Three-body effects in nuclear reaction theory; three-cluster reactions; theory of nuclear structure; Hartree-Fock theory. *Mailing Add:* Dept of Physics Univ of Man Winnipeg MB R3T 2N2 Can

SVENSSON, ERIC CARL, b Hampstead, NB, Aug 13, 40; m 65; c 2. CONDENSED MATTER PHYSICS. *Educ:* Univ NB, Fredericton, BSc, 62; McMaster Univ, PhD(physics), 67. *Prof Exp:* Asst res officer, 66-70, assoc res officer, 71-81, SR RES OFFICER PHYSICS, ATOMIC ENERGY CAN LTD, 82- *Concurrent Pos:* Guest scientist, Aktiebolaget Atomenergi, Studsvik, Sweden, 72-73; vis physicist, Brookhaven Nat Lab, Upton, NY, 81-82. *Mem:* Am Phys Soc; Can Asn Physicists. *Res:* Neutron scattering; lattice dynamics; magnetic excitations; effects of impurities on excitation spectra; structure and dynamics of liquid helium. *Mailing Add:* Box 128 Deep River ON K0J 1P0 Can

SVERDLOVE, RONALD, b Brooklyn, NY, Dec 6, 48. DYNAMICAL SYSTEMS, APPROXIMATION THEORY. *Educ:* Princeton Univ, AB, 69; Stanford Univ, MA, 73, PhD(math), 76. *Prof Exp:* Lectr math, Southern Ill Univ, Carbondale, 76-77; fel, Math Clinic, Claremount Grad Sch, 77-78; asst prof math, Univ Notre Dame, 78-82; MEM TECH STAFF, RCA LABS, 81- *Concurrent Pos:* Vis asst prof math, Claremont Men's Col, 77-78; Harvey Mudd Col, 78; vis lectr comput sci, Rutgers Univ, 82. *Mem:* Am Math Soc; Math Asn Am; Soc Indust & Appl Math. *Res:* Inverse problems for dynamical systems in two and higher dimensions; approximation of functions by sums of Gaussians; models of the human visual system; computer simulation of electron optics in kinescope guns. *Mailing Add:* RCA Labs Princeton NJ 08540

SVERDRUP, EDWARD F, b Buffalo, NY, Feb 24, 30. ELECTRICAL ENGINEERING. *Educ:* State Univ NY Buffalo, BS, 51; Carnegie Inst Technol, MS, 53, PhD(elec eng), 54. *Prof Exp:* Asst prof elec eng, Carnegie Inst Technol, 54-55, 59-61; sr engr & fel engr, 61-67, ADV ENGR, WESTINGHOUSE RES LABS, 67- *Concurrent Pos:* Lectr, Carnegie Inst Technol, 65-67. *Mem:* Am Soc Testing & Mat. *Res:* Electrical properties of high temperature materials; vapor deposition processes; fuel cell development; gas and steam turbines for coal burning combined cycle power plants; induced draft fan erosion. *Mailing Add:* Chem Eng Res Westinghouse Res Labs Beulah Rd Pittsburgh PA 15235

SVERDRUP, GEORGE MICHAEL, b Minneapolis, Minn, Mar 29, 49; m 70; c 2. ATMOSPHERIC SCIENCES, PARTICLE MECHANICS. *Educ:* Univ Minn, BME, 71, MS, 73, PhD(mech eng), 77. *Prof Exp:* RES SCIENTIST ATMOSPHERIC SCI, BATTELLE MEM INST COLUMBUS LABS, 76-, ASSOC SECT MGR, 79- *Mem:* AAAS. *Res:* Chemical and physical characteristics of small particles; physico-chemical interaction of gases and particles. *Mailing Add:* Battelle Columbus Labs 505 King Ave Columbus OH 43201

SVETLIK, JOSEPH FRANK, b Weimar, Tex, July 23, 18; m 42; c 5. RUBBER CHEMISTRY. *Educ:* Tex Tech Col, BS, 42. *Prof Exp:* Res chemist petrol, Tex Co, 42; res chemist, Phillips Petrol Co, 42; sr sect chief rubber res, 49-55, mgr tech serv, Rubber Chem Div, 55-68, tech asst to div dir, 68-71, mgr tire technol br, Chem Dept, 71-74, dir carbon black develop, 74-81; CONSULT RUBBER & CARBON BLACK, 81- *Mem:* Am Chem Soc (treas, 52); Am Soc Testing & Mat; Am Inst Chem Engrs. *Res:* Grease manufacture; rubber compounding; correlation of manufacturing variables with physical properties of rubber; rubber testing devices; development of solution rubbers; compounding techniques for improved present and future automobile tires; carbon black development and process improvement. *Mailing Add:* 1406 Stonecrest Dr Richardson TX 75081

SVIHRA, PAVEL, b Banska Bystrica, Czech, Jan 30, 39; US citizen; m 72; c 2. FOREST ENTOMOLOGY, INSECT BEHAVIOR. *Educ:* Univ Col Forestry & Wood Technol, Czech, MS, 62, PhD(agr & forestry), 71. *Prof Exp:* Mgr inspector & expert prevent & support of Ips typographus, State Ministry Water Resources & Forestry, Czech, 64-65; res fel forest protection & forest entom, Forest Res Inst, 65-71, res scientist & proj leader, 71-75; res entomologist southern pine beetle & related insects, Dept Entom, Univ Calif, Davis, 75-77; tree specialist, 77-78, ASSOC COOP EXTEN SPECIALIST DUTCH ELM DIS, COOP EXTEN, UNIV CALIF, BERKELEY, 78- *Concurrent Pos:* Expert adv forest protection, High Tatras Nat Park Serv, 71-75; vis prof, Sch Forestry, Austin State Univ, 76-77. *Mem:* Entom Soc Am; Soc Am Foresters. *Res:* Relationship between the host and insects, especially coleoptera, scolytidae; vectoring of diseases by insect, interactions between species and their behavior; pest management in forests and urban areas. *Mailing Add:* Dept of Entom Univ of Calif Berkeley CA 94720

SVOBODA, GLENN RICHARD, b Racine, Wis, Nov 18, 30; m 57; c 3. POLYMER CHEMISTRY. *Educ:* Univ Wis, BS, 52, MS, 53, PhD(pharmaceut chem), 58. *Prof Exp:* Instr anal chem, Univ Wis, 58-59; res chemist, 59-61, mgr res lab, 62-64, dir res, 64-67, VPRES RES & DEVELOP, FREEMAN CHEM CORP, PORT WASHINGTON, 67- *Concurrent Pos:* Asst prof, Ore State Col, 58-59. *Mem:* AAAS; Am Chem Soc. *Res:* Natural products; organo-analytical techniques, especially electrochemistry and optical methods; polymer analysis by physical organic techniques; polymer and monomer synthesis; coatings; unsaturated polyester and urethane specialties; electrochemical and radiochemical syntheses. *Mailing Add:* 1525 Beechwood Lane Grafton WI 53024

SVOBODA, GORDON H, b Racine, Wis, Oct 29, 22; m 45; c 3. PHARMACOGNOSY. *Educ:* Univ Wis, BS, 44, PhD(pharmaceut chem), 49. *Prof Exp:* Actg instr pharmaceut chem, Univ Wis, 47-49; asst prof pharm, Univ Kans, 49-50; PHYTOCHEMIST & RES ASSOC, ELI LILLY & CO, 50- *Concurrent Pos:* Am Asn Cols Pharm-NSF vis scientist, 63-72; vis res prof, Univ Pittsburgh, 64-; mem biol & related res facilities vis comt, Bd Overseers, Harvard Univ. *Honors & Awards:* Am Pharmaceut Asn Award, 63; Ebert Prize, Am Soc Pharmacog, 67. *Mem:* Am Pharmaceut Asn; Am Soc Pharmacog (pres, 63-64); Int Pharmaceut Fedn, fel Acad Pharmaceut Sci. *Mailing Add:* Lilly Res Labs 307 E McCarty St Indianapolis IN 46285

SVOBODA, JAMES ARVID, b Great Falls, Mont, June 28, 34; m 60; c 4. INSECT PHYSIOLOGY. *Educ:* Col Great Falls, BS, 58; Mont State Univ, PhD(entom), 64. *Prof Exp:* Resident res assoc insect physiol, Pioneering Res Lab, 64-65, SR INSECT PHYSIOLOGIST, INSECT PHYSIOL LAB, AGR RES CTR, USDA, 65-, LAB CHIEF, 79- *Mem:* AAAS; Entom Soc Am; Am Oil Chem Soc. *Res:* Metabolism of lipids in insects, specifically in sterols and their relationships to growth and metamorphosis; insect hormones and hormonal control mechanisms. *Mailing Add:* Insect Physiol Lab Agr Res Ctr Bldg 467 USDA Beltsville MD 20705

SVOBODA, JOSEF, b Praha, Czech, July 16, 29; Can citizen; m 76; c 2. ARCTIC PLANT ECOLOGY. *Educ:* Univ Western Ont, BSc, 70; Univ Alta, PhD(bot), 74. *Prof Exp:* Asst prof, 73-78, ASSOC PROF PLANT ECOL, UNIV TORONTO, 78- *Concurrent Pos:* Mem, Sci Adv Bd, Great Lakes Col, 79-; vis scientist, Univ Freiburg, WGer, 79-80; mem, Steering Comt, Can Ctr Toxicol, 81-; prin investr, Dept Indian Affairs & Northern Develop, 81- *Mem:* Can Bot Asn; Ecol Soc Am; Artic Inst North America. *Res:* Developing certain northern native plants as potential food crops in the Artic; persistent radioactivity in northern environments due to atmospheric nuclear fallout; natural radioactivity in uranium mineralization areas in Northern Canada. *Mailing Add:* Dept Bot Erindale Campus Univ Toronto Mississauga ON L5L 1C6 Can

SVOBODA, RUDY GEORGE, b Berwyn, Ill, Aug 15, 41; m 64; c 2. MATHEMATICS. *Educ:* Northern Ill Univ, BS, 66; Ohio Univ, MS, 67; Purdue Univ, PhD(math), 71. *Prof Exp:* Asst prof, 70-77, ASSOC PROF MATH, IND UNIV-PURDUE UNIV, FT WAYNE, 77- *Mem:* Am Math Soc; Math Asn Am; Int Congress Individualized Instr; Sigma Xi. *Res:* Development of individualized audio-tutorial instructional materrrials for algebra and trigonometry courses. *Mailing Add:* Dept of Math 2101 Coliseum Blvd Ft Wayne IN 46805

SVOKOS, STEVE GEORGE, b Wierton, WVa, June 22, 34; m 60; c 3. BIOLOGICAL CHEMISTRY. *Educ:* Brooklyn Col, BS, 56; State Univ NY, MS, 62, PhD(bio-org chem), 64. *Prof Exp:* Chemist, Lederle Labs, Am Cyanamid Co, 56-60, res chemist, 65-69; regulatory liaison, Ayerst Labs Div, Am Home Prod Corp, NY, 69-72; dir regulatory affairs, 72-75, dir regulatory & sci affairs, 75-79, VPRES REGULATORY & SCI AFFAIRS, KNOLL PHARMACEUT CO, WHIPPANY, 79- *Mem:* Am Chem Soc; fel Royal Soc Chem; NY Acad Sci; Am Phys Asn; Am Inst Chemists. *Res:* Pharmaceutical administration; medicinal chemistry. *Mailing Add:* 59 First Ave Westwood NJ 07675

SWABB, LAWRENCE E(DWARD), JR, b Dayton, Ohio, Oct 25, 22; m 44; c 3. CHEMICAL ENGINEERING. *Educ:* Univ Cincinnati, ChE, 48, MS, 49, PhD(chem eng), 51. *Prof Exp:* Chem engr process develop, Esso Res Labs, Humble Oil & Refining Co, Standard Oil Co, NJ, 51-56, sect head, 56-58, asst dir res labs, 58-63, dir res labs, 64-66, mgr new areas planning & coord, 66-68, vpres petrol res, 68-74, VPRES SYNTHETIC FUELS RES, EXXON RES & ENG CO, 74- *Mem:* Nat Acad Eng; Am Inst Chem Engrs; AAAS. *Res:* Research and process development in petroleum industry. *Mailing Add:* 92 Addison Dr Short Hills NJ 07078

SWACKHAMER, FARRIS SAPHAR, b Cranford, NJ, May 31, 14; m 37; c 2. ORGANIC CHEMISTRY. *Educ:* Rutgers Univ, BS, 36; Polytech Inst Brooklyn, MS, 40. *Prof Exp:* Chemist, Am Cyanamid Co, 36-37, group leader, 37-41, tech rep, 45-48; sr technologist, Shell Chem Co, 48-50, asst dept mgr sales develop, 50, dept mgr, 50-51, mgr resins & plastics dept, 51-57, mgr sales develop, 57, dir tech serv labs, 57-63; assoc prof chem & chmn dept, Union Col, NJ, 63-69, dir instnl res & asst to pres, 69-73, prof, 73-79; RETIRED. *Concurrent Pos:* Mem bd trustees, Wetland Inst, Stone Harbor, NJ. *Mem:* AAAS; Am Chem Soc; Commercial Develop Asn (past pres); fel Am Inst Chemists. *Res:* Thermosetting polymers; market research; laboratory administration; nutrients in estuarine environment. *Mailing Add:* 10 Herning Ave Cranford NJ 07016

SWADER, FRED NICHOLAS, b Belle Vernon, Pa, Oct 9, 34; m 56; c 2. SOIL SCIENCE. *Educ:* Cornell Univ, BS, 61, MS, 63, PhD(agron, soil sci), 68. *Prof Exp:* Experimentalist, Cornell Univ, 61-63, res assoc agr eng, 63-67, from asst prof to assoc prof soil sci, 67-81; PROG LEADER ENVIRON QUAL, EXTENION SERV, USDA, 81- *Concurrent Pos:* Chmn, Cornell Agr Waste Mgt Conf, 70 & 71. *Mem:* Soil Conserv Soc Am; Am Soc Agr Engrs; Soil Sci Soc Am. *Res:* Plant-soil-water relationships, as influenced by the physical properties of various soils; soil management for recycling agricultural by-products. *Mailing Add:* USDA Extension Serv 5925 South Bldg Washington DC 20250

SWADER, JEFF AUSTIN, JR, plant physiology, see previous edition

SWADLOW, HARVEY A, US citizen. NEUROPHYSIOLOGY, PSYCHOLOGY. *Educ:* Univ Miami, BA, 64, MS, 67, PhD(psychol), 70. *Prof Exp:* Fel, Ctr Brain Res, Univ Rochester, 70-72; res assoc, Univ Miami, 72-74; res fel neurophysiol, Retina Found, Boston, 74-75; vis asst prof psychol, Univ Western Ont, 75-76; ASSOC PROF PSYCHOL, UNIV CONN, 77- *Concurrent Pos:* Res affil, Res Lab Electronics, Mass Inst Technol, 76-78; lectr neurol, Harvard Med Sch, 76-80. *Mem:* Sigma Xi; Soc Neurosci; AAAS. *Res:* Structure and function of the visual cortex; interhemispheric communication; impulse conduction along axons. *Mailing Add:* Dept of Psychol U20 Univ of Conn Storrs CT 06268

SWAGER, WILLIAM L(EON), b Ft Wayne, Ind, Nov 10, 21; m 46; c 3. CHEMICAL ENGINEERING, MANAGEMENT. *Educ:* Purdue Univ, BS, 42. *Prof Exp:* Admin asst qual control, Gen Chem Co, NY, 43, control chemist, 43-44, asst plant engr, Baker & Adamson Div, Pa, 44-45, prod dept, NY, 45-46, foreman, Reagents & Fine Chem Plant, Pa, 46-48; chem economist, 48-50, assoc div chief, 50-53, chief, Opers Res Div, 53-61, assoc mgr, Dept Econ, 61-70, asst mgr planning, Dept Social & Mgt Systs, 70-71, mgr mkt planning, 72-75, asst mgr, Metall Dept, 75-80, MGR MAT ECON, BATTELLE MEM INST, 80- *Concurrent Pos:* Corp dir, Basic Elec Co, 61-65. *Mem:* Fel Am Inst Chemists; Am Chem Soc; Am Inst Chem Engrs; AAAS. *Res:* Technical economic analysis; strategic planning; technological forecasting; technology assessment; materials policy analysis. *Mailing Add:* Dept Metall Battelle Mem Inst 505 King Ave Columbus OH 43201

SWAILES, GEORGE EDWARD, b Winnipeg, Man, July 20, 25; m 50; c 3. ENTOMOLOGY. *Educ:* Univ Man, BSA, 46; Colo Agr & Mech Col, MSc, 50; Iowa State Col, PhD(entom), 56. *Prof Exp:* ENTOMOLOGIST, RES STA, CAN DEPT AGR, 48- *Mem:* Entom - cutworms damaging vegetable and field crops. *Mailing Add:* 2011 13th Ave Lethbridge AB T1K 0S4 Can

SWAIM, ROBERT LEE, b Rensselaer, Ind, Aug 7, 35; m 60; c 3. AEROSPACE ENGINEERING. *Educ:* Purdue Univ, BS, 57, MS, 59; Ohio State Univ, PhD(elec eng), 66. *Prof Exp:* Assoc engr, Douglas Aircraft Co, 57-58; engr, NAm Aviation, Inc, 59; sr res engr, Air Force Flight Dynamics Lab, 62-67; prof aeronaut & astronaut & assoc head, Sch Aeronaut & Astronaut, Purdue Univ, West Lafayette, 67-78; ASSOC DEAN, DIV ENG, TECHNOL & ARCHIT, OKLA STATE UNIV, STILLWATER, 78- *Concurrent Pos:* Vis lectr, US Air Force Inst Technol, 66-67. *Mem:* Assoc fel Am Inst Aeronaut & Astronaut; Inst Elec & Electronics Engrs; Sigma Xi; Am Soc Eng Educ. *Res:* Advanced flight control concepts for aircraft, missiles and aerospace vehicles. *Mailing Add:* 3202 W 29th Ct Stillwater OK 74074

SWAIMAN, KENNETH F, b St Paul, Minn, Nov 19, 31; m 73; c 4. NEUROCHEMISTRY, PEDIATRIC NEUROLOGY. *Educ:* Univ Minn, BA, 52, BS, 53, MD, 55; Am Bd Pediat, dipl; Am Bd Psychiat & Neurol, dipl. *Prof Exp:* Fel pediat, 56-57, Nat Inst Neurol Dis & Stroke spec fel pediat neurol, 60-63, from asst prof to assoc prof, 63-69, PROF PEDIAT & NEUROL, MED SCH, UNIV MINN, MINNEAPOLIS, 69-, DIR DIV PEDIAT NEUROL, 68-, EXEC OFFICER DEPT NEUROL, 77- *Concurrent Pos:* Guest worker, NIH, 78-81. *Honors & Awards:* Hower Award, Child Neurol Soc, 81. *Mem:* Am Neurol Asn; Am Acad Neurol; Am Acad Pediat; Child Neurol Soc (pres, 72-73); Prof Child Neurol (pres, 78-80). *Res:* Neurochemical changes in developing brain; energy and amino acid metabolism of immature brain. *Mailing Add:* Div of Pediat Neurol Univ of Minn Med Sch Minneapolis MN 55455

SWAIN, CHARLES GARDNER, b Quincy, Mass, May 26, 17; m 45; c 2. CHEMISTRY. *Educ:* Harvard Univ, AB, 40, AM, 41, PhD(org chem), 44. *Prof Exp:* Nat Res Coun fel, Calif Inst Technol, 45-46; Am Chem Soc fel, 46-47, from instr to assoc prof, 47-58, PROF CHEM, MASS INST TECHNOL, 58- *Concurrent Pos:* Guggenheim fel, Univ London, 54-55. *Honors & Awards:* Petrol Chem Award, Am Chem Soc, 57. *Mem:* Am Chem Soc; Am Acad Arts & Sci. *Res:* Mechanism of organic reactions; effect of structure of reactants on structure of transition states; quantitative correlations between structure and reactivity; acid, base and poly-functional catalysis; tracers and isotope effects. *Mailing Add:* Dept of Chem Mass Inst of Technol Cambridge MA 02139

SWAIN, ELISABETH RAMSAY, b Philadelphia, Pa, Feb 7, 17. ZOOLOGY. *Educ:* Wilson Col, BS, 38; Univ Pa, MA, 42, PhD, 53. *Prof Exp:* Instr physics, Wilson Col, 43-46, instr biol, 46-49; asst instr zool, Univ Pa, 51-54; from asst prof to assoc prof, 54-66, chmn dept, 54-80, PROF BIOL, UNIV HARTFORD, 66- *Mem:* AAAS; Sigma Xi; NY Acad Sci. *Res:* Embryology. *Mailing Add:* Dept of Biol Univ of Hartford West Hartford CT 06117

SWAIN, FREDERICK MORRILL, JR, b Kansas City, Mo, Mar 17, 16; m 38; c 3. GEOLOGY. *Educ:* Univ Kans, AB, 38, PhD(stratig, paleont), 43; Pa State Col, MS, 39. *Prof Exp:* Geologist, Phillips Petrol Co, La, 41-43; asst prof mineral econ, Pa State Col, 43-46; from asst prof to assoc prof geol, 46-54, assoc chmn, Dept Geol & Geophys, 59-61, prof, 54-79, EMER PROF GEOL & GEOPHYS, UNIV MINN, MINNEAPOLIS, 79-; PROF GEOL, UNIV DEL, 79- *Concurrent Pos:* Assoc geologist, US Geol Surv, 44-46, geologist, 48-51, 61-; consult, Carter Oil Co, 51-53 & Pa RR, 54-57; part-time prof, Univ Del, 69- *Honors & Awards:* Award, Am Asn Petrol Geol, 49. *Mem:* Fel Geol Soc Am; Soc Econ Paleont & Mineral; Paleont Soc; Am Soc Limnol & Oceanog; Soc Econ Geol. *Res:* Stratigraphy; micropaleontology; organic geochemistry. *Mailing Add:* Dept Geol Univ Del Newark DE 19711

SWAIN, HENRY HUNTINGTON, b Champaign, Ill, July 11, 23; m 48; c 2. PHARMACOLOGY. *Educ:* Univ Ill, AB, 43, BS, 49, MS & MD, 51. *Prof Exp:* Instr pharmacol, Univ Cincinnati, 52-54; from instr to assoc prof, 54-67, PROF PHARMACOL, MED SCH, UNIV MICH, ANN ARBOR, 67- *Mem:* Am Soc Pharmacol & Exp Therapeut. *Res:* Cardiovascular pharmacology, especially cardiac arrhythmias. *Mailing Add:* Dept of Pharmacol Univ of Mich Med Sch Ann Arbor MI 48109

SWAIN, HOWARD ALDRED, JR, b New York, NY, Mar 3, 28; m 51; c 3. PHYSICAL CHEMISTRY. *Educ:* Grove City Col, BS, 51; Univ Pa, PhD, 61. *Prof Exp:* High sch instr chem, NJ, 54-56; lab technician, Rohm and Haas Co, 56-57; chemist, Socony-Mobile Res & Develop, 57-58; asst chem, Univ Pa, 58-60; from asst prof to assoc prof, 60-70, PROF CHEM, WILKES COL, 70- *Concurrent Pos:* Oak Ridge Assoc Univs res partic, Savannah River Lab, SC, 67-68; consult, Vet Admin Hosp, Wilkes-Barre, Pa, 71; lectr, Col Miseracordia, 72; res partic water purification proj, Environ Protection Agency. *Mem:* Am Chem Soc. *Res:* Thermodynamics; radiochemistry. *Mailing Add:* Dept of Chem Wilkes Col Wilkes-Barre PA 18766

SWAIN, RALPH WARNER, b Orange, NJ, Dec 16, 44; m 67; c 2. SYSTEMS ENGINEERING. *Educ:* Johns Hopkins Univ, BEngSc, 67; Cornell Univ, MS, 69, PhD(environ systs), 71. *Prof Exp:* Nat Found Med Educ fel, Ctr Environ Qual Mgt, Cornell Univ, 71; asst prof indust & systs eng, Ohio State Univ, 71-76; ASSOC PROF INDUST & SYSTS ENG & ASSOC DIR, HEALTH SYSTS RES DIV, UNIV FLA, 76- *Honors & Awards:* Appln & Develop Award, Am Inst Indust Engrs, 78. *Mem:* Opers Res Soc Am; Am Soc Eng Educ; AAAS; Inst Mgt Sci; Am Inst Indust Engrs. *Res:* Medical systems planning; solid waste management and recycle economics; optimal location of facilities; design and evaluation of health care delivery systems; facility location and layout; information systems design. *Mailing Add:* Box J-177 JHMHC Univ of Fla Gainesville FL 32610

SWAIN, RICHARD RUSSELL, b Columbus, Ohio, Mar 1, 39; m 64; c 1. BIOCHEMISTRY, CLINICAL CHEMISTRY. *Educ:* Albion Col, AB, 61; Univ Mich, MS, 63, PhD(biochem), 65. *Prof Exp:* Asst prof biol, MacMurray Col, 67-71; fel, State Univ NY, Buffalo, 71-73; SR BIOCHEMIST CLIN BIOCHEM, ELI LILLY & CO, 73- *Mem:* AAAS; Am Chem Soc; Am Asn Clin Chemists; Am Bd Clin Chemists. *Res:* Clinical chemistry methodology; clinical enzymology; biochemical assessment of hepatotoxicity and nephrotoxicity. *Mailing Add:* Lilly Lab for Clin Res Wishard Mem Hosp Indianapolis IN 46202

SWAIN, ROBERT JAMES, b Waukesha, Wis, Oct 3, 28; m 50; c 2. GEOPHYSICS, ELECTRONICS ENGINEERING. *Educ:* Purdue Univ, BS, 51. *Prof Exp:* Jr engr, A C Electronics Div, Gen Motors Corp, 51-53, prod engr, 53-55; sales & contracts mgr, Conrac Corp, 55-57; staff engr, United Electrodynamics, Inc, 58-59, chief struct seismol, 59-60, gen mgr, Geomeasurements Div, 60-61, vpres & gen mgr, Earth Sci Div, 61-64; vpres & gen mgr, Earth Sci, A Teledyne Co, 64-67, pres, 67-69; CHMN & PRES, KINEMETRICS, INC, 69- *Mem:* AAAS; Am Geophys Union; Seismol Soc Am; Sigma Xi; Am Nuclear Soc. *Res:* Ground motion from earthquakes and blasts; response of structures to ground motion; sensing and recording systems. *Mailing Add:* Kinemetrics Inc 222 Vista Ave Pasadena CA 91107

SWAIN, WAYLAND ROGER, b Boone, Iowa, Jan 13, 38; m 60; c 1. PUBLIC HEALTH, ENVIRONMENTAL BIOLOGY. *Educ:* Ottawa Univ, BA, 60; Univ Minn, Minneapolis, MS, 65, PhD(environ biol), 69. *Prof Exp:* Water microbiologist, Univ Minn, Minneapolis, 62-64, instr environ microbiol, Sch Pub Health, 65-66; dir div res, Miller Hosp Res Complex, Univ Minn, Duluth, 69-71, asst prof prev med & actg chmn dept, 71-75, assoc prof prev med & chmn dept, Sch Med, 75-76, dir, Lake Superior Basin Studies Ctr, 74-76; assoc prof prev med & biol & asst dean, Sch Med, 75-76; DIR LARGE LAKES RES LAB, US ENVIRON PROTECTION AGENCY, 76- *Mem:* Am Pub Health Asn; Am Soc Limnol & Oceanog; fel Royal Soc Health; Int Asn Gt Lakes Res. *Res:* Limnology; aquatic biology, especially planktonic relationships; comparative physiology; effects of toxic organic substances on aquatic ecosystems and human health. *Mailing Add:* Large Lake Res Lab 9311 Groh Rd Grosse Ile MI 48138

SWAISGOOD, HAROLD EVERETT, b Ashland, Ohio, Jan 19, 36; m 56; c 2. PROTEIN BIOCHEMISTRY. *Educ:* Ohio State Univ, BS, 58; Mich State Univ, PhD(chem), 63. *Prof Exp:* NIH fel, 63-64; from asst prof to assoc prof, 64-72, PROF FOOD SCI & BIOCHEM, NC STATE UNIV, 72- *Mem:* AAAS; Am Chem Soc; Inst Food Technologists; Am Dairy Sci Asn; Am Soc Biol Chemists. *Res:* Physical-chemical characterization of proteins; studies of protein interactions and the relationship to biological activity; methods of preparation and characterization of enzymes covalently bound to surfaces. *Mailing Add:* Dept of Food Sci NC State Univ Raleigh NC 27650

SWAKON, DOREEN H D, b Berwyn, Ill, Oct 9, 53; m 74; c 1. FORAGE QUALITY EVALUATION, RUMINANT NUTRITION. *Educ:* Univ Ill, BS, 75; Univ Fla, MS, 77, PhD(animal sci), 80. *Prof Exp:* Res asst, Univ Fla, 75-80; ASST PROF ANIMAL SCI, TEX A&I UNIV, 80- *Mem:* Am Soc Animal Sci; Am Forage & Grassland Coun; Range Mgt Soc. *Res:* Forage quality evaluation and utilization of forage crops by ruminants to define differences in utilization between different species of forages and between different species of animals. *Mailing Add:* Tex A&I Univ Col Agr Box 156 Kingsville TX 78363

SWAKON, EDWARD ANTONE, b North Dighton, Mass, Apr 9, 25; m 52; c 2. ORGANIC CHEMISTRY. *Educ:* Brown Univ, ScB, 47; Carnegie Inst Technol, MS, 50, DSc(org chem), 51. *Prof Exp:* Chemist, Standard Oil Co, Ind, 51-56 & Food Mach & Chem Corp, 56-57; CHEMIST, AMOCO RES CTR, 57- *Mem:* Am Chem Soc. *Res:* Organic chemistry in Ullman reaction; synthetic greases; dimethyl hydrazine; carbon monoxide; carbonyl sulfide; condensation polymers; petroleum pitches; petroleum oils and additives; cellulose preparations and modifications; agricultural research, herbicides and pesticides. *Mailing Add:* Amoco Res Ctr PO Box 400 Naperville IL 60540

SWALEN, JEROME DOUGLAS, b Minneapolis, Minn, Mar 4, 28; m 52; c 2. CHEMICAL PHYSICS. *Educ:* Univ Minn, BS, 50; Harvard Univ, AM, 54, PhD(chem physics), 56. *Prof Exp:* Fel, Div Pure Physics, Nat Res Coun Can, 56-57; physicist, Shell Develop Co, 57-62; mgr physics dept, 62-63, lab mgr, 63-67, mgr molecular physics dept, 67-73, RES STAFF MEM, IBM RES LAB, 73- *Concurrent Pos:* Vis prof, Phys Chem Inst, Univ Zurich, 72-73. *Mem:* Fel AAAS; fel Am Phys Soc; Am Chem Soc. *Res:* Laser spectroscopy of thin organic films and monolayers. *Mailing Add:* IBM Res Lab San Jose CA 95193

SWALLOW, EARL CONNOR, b Montgomery County, Ohio, Dec 27, 41. ELEMENTARY PARTICLE PHYSICS, EXPERIMENTAL PHYSICS. *Educ:* Earlham Col, BA, 63; Washington Univ, MA, 65, PhD(physics), 70. *Prof Exp:* Resident student assoc elem particle physics, Argonne Nat Lab, 64 & 65, res staff assoc, 65-69, res asst for Washington Univ, 69-70; res assoc elem particle physics, Enrico Fermi Inst, Univ Chicago, 70-74, sr res assoc, 74-80; asst prof, 76-80, ASSOC PROF PHYSICS, ELMHURST COL, 80-, CHMN DEPT, 79- *Concurrent Pos:* Teaching asst, Washington Univ, 65; vis mem staff, Argonne Nat Lab, 78, 79 & 81. *Mem:* Am Phys Soc; Sigma Xi; AAAS; Am Asn Physics Teachers; NY Acad Sci. *Res:* Fundamental interactions of elementary particles, especially weak interactions; experimental foundations of physical theory; relationship of experimental foundations to public policy. *Mailing Add:* Elmhurst Col Dept of Physics 190 Prospect Ave Elmhurst IL 60126

SWALLOW, RICHARD LOUIS, b Berwyn, Ill, June 16, 39; m 64; c 1. ZOOLOGY, BIOLOGY. *Educ:* Univ Ill, Urbana, BS, 63; Univ Mo-Columbia, MA, 66, PhD(zool), 68. *Prof Exp:* USPHS fel, Sch Med, Case Western Reserve Univ, 68-69; asst prof biol, Univ Houston, 69-73; assoc prof, 73-80, PROF BIOL, COKER COL, 80- *Mem:* Am Soc Zoologists. *Res:* Comparative physiology including control of metabolism by hormones in fish. *Mailing Add:* Coker Col Hartsville SC 29550

SWALLOW, WILLIAM HUTCHINSON, b Norwalk, Conn, Oct 21, 41. VARIANCE COMPONENTS ESTIMATION, EXPERIMENTAL DESIGN. *Educ:* Harvard Univ, AB, 64; Cornell Univ, MS, 68, PhD(biomet), 74. *Prof Exp:* Asst prof statist, Rutgers Univ, 73-79; ASSOC PROF STATIST, NC STATE UNIV, 80- *Mem:* Am Statist Asn; Sigma Xi. *Res:* Linear models; estimation of variance components; research directed at improving the teaching of statistics. *Mailing Add:* Dept Statist NC State Univ Raleigh NC 27650

SWALM, RALPH OEHRLE, b Philadelphia, Pa, July 21, 15; m 42; c 3. INDUSTRIAL ENGINEERING, ENGINEERING ECONOMICS. *Educ:* Univ Pa, BSEE, 37; Syracuse Univ, MSEd, 57. *Prof Exp:* Engr, Gen Elec Co, 37-48; from asst prof to assoc prof, 48-57, PROF INDUST ENG, SYRACUSE UNIV, 57-, DIR ENG EDUC, 77- *Concurrent Pos:* Consult, Asbjorn Habberstad, Norway, 57; assoc dir, Indust Mgt Ctr, 60-; Am Bd Indust Engrs fel, 78. *Mem:* Am Inst Indust Engrs; Am Soc Eng Educ; Inst Mgt Sci. *Res:* Applied utility theory. *Mailing Add:* E Lake Rd Cazenovia NY 13035

SWAMER, FREDERIC WURL, b Shawano, Wis, May 16, 18; m 46; c 3. ORGANIC CHEMISTRY. *Educ:* Lawrence Col, BA, 40; Univ Wis, MS, 42; Duke Univ, PhD(chem), 49. *Prof Exp:* Chemist, Appleton Water Purification Plant, Wis, 40; res chemist, Electrochem Dept, E I du Pont de Nemours & Co, 41-45; res assoc, Duke Univ, 49-50; res chemist, E I DuPont De Nemours & Co, Inc, Wilmington, Del, 50-64, res assoc, Org Chem Dept, Exp Sta, 64-80. *Mem:* AAAS; Am Chem Soc. *Res:* Claisen condensation; physical properties of polymers; acetylene organoalkali compounds; fluorocarbons; heterogeneous catalysis. *Mailing Add:* Folly Hill Rd RD 4 West Chester PA 19380

SWAMINATHAN, BALASUBRAMANIAN, b Madras, India, Nov 24, 46; m 76. FOOD MICROBIOLOGY, FOOD TOXICOLOGY. *Educ:* Delhi Univ, BSc hon, 66; Univ Ga, MS, 74, PhD(food sci), 77. *Prof Exp:* Bottler's serv chemist qual control, Coca-Cola Export Corp, 67-72, microbiologist qual control & develop, 74; ASST PROF FOOD SCI, PURDUE UNIV, 77- *Concurrent Pos:* Res grant, Ind Agr Exp Sta, 80-82. *Mem:* Inst Food Technologists; Am Soc Microbiol; AAAS; Int Asn Milk, Food & Environ Sanitarians. *Res:* Rapid detection of pathogenic microorganisms in foods and feeds; pathogenic mechanisms associated with Yersinia enterocolitica; mutagenicity of procyanidins present in beverages. *Mailing Add:* Stone Hall Purdue Univ West Lafayette IN 47907

SWAMINATHAN, SRINIVASA, b Madras, India, Aug 24, 26; m 52; c 1. MATHEMATICS. *Educ:* Presidency Col, Madras, India, BA, 47, MA, 48; Univ Madras, MSc, 50, PhD(math), 57. *Prof Exp:* Govt of France fel, Inst Henri Poincare, Paris, 57-58; lectr math, Univ Madras, 59-64; asst prof, Indian Inst Technol, Kanpur, 64-66; vis assoc prof, Univ Ill, Chicago Circle, 66-68; ASSOC PROF MATH, DALHOUSIE UNIV, 68- *Concurrent Pos:* Auth & mem comt reorgn curricula math, Nat Coun Educ Res & Training, Govt of India, 64-67; managing ed, Can Math Bull, 79- *Mem:* Am Math Soc; Can Math Soc; Indian Math Soc. *Res:* Functional analysis; topology; geometry of Banach spaces; operator theory; paracompact spaces; fixed point theorems in analysis and topology; biomathematics. *Mailing Add:* 911 Greenwood Ave Halifax NS B3H 3L1 Can

SWAMY, MAYASANDRA NANJUNDIAH SRIKANTA, b Bangalore, India, Apr 7, 35; m 64; c 3. ELECTRICAL ENGINEERING, APPLIED MATHEMATICS. *Educ:* Univ Mysore, BSc, 54; Indian Inst Sci, Bangalore, dipl, 57; Univ Sask, MSc, 60, PhD, 63. *Prof Exp:* Sr res asst electronics, Indian Inst Sci, Bangalore, 58-59; res asst elec eng, Univ Sask, 59-63, sessional lectr math, 61-63, asst prof, 64-65; Govt India scientist, Indian Inst Technol, Madras, 63-64; from asst prof to prof elec eng, NS Tech Col, 65-68; prof, Concordia Univ, 68-69; prof, Univ Calgary, 69-70; prof & chmn dept, 70-77, DEAN, FAC ENG, CONCORDIA UNIV, 77- *Mem:* Inst Elec & Electronics Engrs; Am Math Soc; Math Asn Am; fel Eng Inst Can; fel Inst Engrs India. *Res:* Network theory; graph theory; signal processing; author or coauthor of over one hundred research articles. *Mailing Add:* Dean of Eng Concordia Univ Montreal PQ H3G 1M8 Can

SWAMY, PADMANABHA NARAYANA, b India, July 25, 37; m 63; c 2. ELEMENTARY PARTICLE PHYSICS, THEORETICAL PHYSICS. *Educ:* Delhi Univ, India, BS, 56, MS, 58, PhD(physics), 63. *Prof Exp:* Res fel physics, Delhi Univ, 63-64, res fel, Tata Inst Fund Res, 64-65; vis scientist, Int Ctr Theoret Physics, Trieste, 65-66; res assoc, Syracuse Univ, 66; vis scientist, Ctr Nuclear Res, Geneva, 66-67; fel, Tata Inst Fund Res, 67-68; asst prof, Am Univ Beirut, 68-69; from asst to assoc prof, 69-77, PROF PHYSICS, SOUTHERN ILL UNIV, 77- *Mem:* Am Phys Soc. *Res:* Quantum field theory; particle theory. *Mailing Add:* Dept of Physics Southern Ill Univ Edwardsville IL 62026

SWAMY, VIJAY CHINNASWAMY, b Bombay, India, Oct 2, 38; m 72; c 1. PHARMACOLOGY. *Educ:* Bombay Univ, BSc, 59; Nagpur Univ, BPharm, 62; Ohio State Univ, MS, 64, PhD(pharmacol), 67. *Prof Exp:* Res asst pharmacol, Ohio State Univ, 64-67; res assoc, 67-69, ASSOC PROF BIOCHEM PHARMACOL, STATE UNIV NY BUFFALO, 70- *Mem:* AAAS. *Res:* Smooth muscle pharmacology; hypertension; adrenergic mechanisms. *Mailing Add:* Dept of Biochem Pharmacol State Univ NY Buffalo NY 14214

SWAN, ALGERNON GORDON, b Andrews, NC, Jan 25, 23; m 47; c 2. PHYSIOLOGY, BIOPHYSICS. *Educ:* Univ NC, BA, 48, PhD(physiol), 60. *Prof Exp:* Chief biophys br, Aerospace Med Res Labs, Wright-Patterson AFB, US Air Force, Ohio, 60-62, dir life support res, Aerospace Med Div, Brooks AFB, Tex, 62-65, dir res, 65-68, dir test & eng, Air Force Spec Weapons Ctr, Kirtland AFB, NMex, 58-59, vcomdr & tech dir, 69-70, comdr & tech dir, 70-72; SR RES, BECTON, DICKINSON & CO, 72- *Concurrent Pos:* Mem, Comts Hearing, Bioacoust & Biomech, Nat Acad Sci-Nat Res Coun, 63-; Comt Nutrit, 64-; mem, Biosci Comt, NASA, 64-, Comt Biotechnol & Human Res, 65- & Comt Cardiopulmonary Res, Adv Group Aeronaut Res & Develop. *Mem:* Aerospace Med Asn. *Res:* Exercise and stress physiology; weapons effects; osmotic regulation and electrolyte flux in isolated tissues; human tolerance to aerospace stresses; nuclear environment simulation; instrumentation development; flight testing; qualification of instrumentation for space flight. *Mailing Add:* Becton Dickinson & Co Res Triangle Raleigh NC 27709

SWAN, D(AVID), b NJ, May 2, 20; c 4. METALLURGY. *Educ:* Rensselaer Polytech Inst, BMetE, 40. *Prof Exp:* Metall observer, Crucible Steel Co Am, 40-41; res engr, Union Carbide Corp, 46-51, dir res, Union Carbide Metals Co, 52-56, Linde Co, 56-57, vpres res, 58-59, mgr planning, Union Carbide Corp, 59-60, vpres tech, Union Carbide Metals Co, 60-64, gen mgr, Defense & Space Systs Dept, Union Carbide Corp, 64-66; vpres tech, Res, VPRES ENVIRON ISSUES, KENNECOTT COPPER CORP, 79- *Concurrent Pos:* Mem, Moscow Steel Inst-NY Univ Exchange Prog, 57; mem, Mat Adv Bd, Nat Acad Sci-Nat Res Coun, 58-62; dir, William F Clapp Labs, Inc, Duxbury, Conn, 64-; chmn, Adv Comt Metall & Mat Sci, Polytech Inst NY, 77-; chmn, Dirs Indust Res, 78-79; mem, Develop Coun, Resselaer Polytech & Gen Tech Adv Comt, Off Coal Res; fel, Polytech Inst, 80. *Honors & Awards:* Demers Medal, Rensselaer Polytech Inst, 78. *Mem:* Am Welding Soc; fel Am Soc Metals; fel Metall Soc (pres, 72-73); Am Inst Mining, Metall & Petrol Engrs (vpres, 72-74). *Res:* Extractive metallurgy; environmental; economic; research management. *Mailing Add:* Kennecott Copper Corp Box 10137 Stanford CT 06904

SWAN, DEAN GEORGE, b Wheatland, Wyo, Sept 16, 23; m 48; c 3. WEED SCIENCE. *Educ:* Univ Wyo, BS, 52, MS, 54; Univ Ill, PhD, 64. *Prof Exp:* Instr, Chadron High Sch, 52-53; instr weed res, Pendleton Exp Sta, Ore State Univ, 55-65; exten weed specialist, Univ Ariz, 65-66; EXTEN WEED SCIENTIST & AGRONOMIST, WASH STATE UNIV, 66- *Concurrent Pos:* Sabbaticals, Weed Res Orgn, Oxford, Eng, 72-73 & 78-79. *Mem:* Weed Sci Soc Am; Western Soc Weed Sci. *Res:* Weed control in corps, especially in winter wheat; pulse crops and perennial weeds. *Mailing Add:* Dept of Agron & Soils Wash State Univ Pullman WA 99164

SWAN, FREDERICK ROBBINS, JR, b Hartford, Conn, Aug 14, 37; m 62; c 2. ECOLOGY. *Educ:* Middlebury Col, BA, 59; Univ Wis, MS, 61; Cornell Univ, PhD(conserv natural resources), 66. *Prof Exp:* Assoc prof, 66-74, actg chmn, Sch Natural Sci, 70-72, PROF BIOL, WEST LIBERTY STATE COL, 74-, CHMN DEPT, 78- *Concurrent Pos:* Assoc, Dept Natural Resources, Cornell Univ, 74-75. *Mem:* AAAS; Am Inst Biol Sci; Ecol Soc Am; Sigma Xi. *Res:* Effects of fire on plant communities; measurement of light in forests. *Mailing Add:* Dept of Biol West Liberty State Col West Liberty WV 26074

SWAN, HAROLD JAMES CHARLES, b Sligo, Ireland, June 1, 22; US citizen; m 46; c 7. PHYSIOLOGY, CARDIOVASCULAR DISEASES. *Educ:* Univ London, MB, BS, 45, PhD(physiol), 51. *Prof Exp:* Res assoc, Mayo Clin, 51-53, Minn Heart Asn res fel, 53-54, consult cardiovasc dis, 55-65; DIR CARDIOL, CEDARS-SINAI MED CTR, LOS ANGELES, 65-; PROF MED, UNIV CALIF, LOS ANGELES, 66- *Concurrent Pos:* Assoc prof, Mayo Grad Sch, Univ Minn, 57-65; consult, Nat Heart Inst, 60-66; mem, Intersoc Comn Heart Dis Resources, 69- *Honors & Awards:* Walter Dixon Award, Brit Med Asn, 50. *Mem:* Am Physiol Soc; fel Am Col Physicians; fel Am Col Cardiol (pres, 73); Asn Univ Cardiol. *Res:* Ventricular function; myocardial hypertrophy; coronary arterial disease and myocardial ischemia and infarction. *Mailing Add:* 8700 Beverly Blvd Los Angeles CA 90048

SWAN, JAMES BYRON, b Bloomington, Ill, Dec 9, 33; m 62. SOIL SCIENCE. *Educ:* Univ Ill, BS, 55, MS, 59; Univ Wis, PhD(soil physics), 64. *Prof Exp:* EXTEN SPECIALIST & PROF SOIL SCI, UNIV MINN, ST PAUL, 64- *Mem:* Soil Conserv Soc Am; Am Soc Agron; Soil Sci Soc Am. *Res:* Evapotranspiration measurement; tillage systems; effect of soil temperature and soil water on plant growth. *Mailing Add:* Dept of Soil Sci Univ of Minn St Paul MN 55108

SWAN, KENNETH CARL, b Kansas City, Mo, Jan 1, 12; m 42; c 3. OPHTHALMOLOGY, PHARMACOLOGY. *Educ:* Univ Ore, BA, 33, MD, 36; Am Bd Ophthal, dipl, 40. *Prof Exp:* Assoc ophthal, Univ Iowa, 41-42, asst prof, 42-44; assoc prof ophthal, Med Sch, Univ Ore Health Sci Ctr, 44-45, prof & head dept, 45-78; RETIRED. *Concurrent Pos:* Proctor lectr, Univ Calif, 46; chmn bd, Am Bd Ophthal, 61; chmn sensory dis study sect, NIH, 61-63; mem adv coun, Nat Eye Inst, 69-71; consult, Nat Inst Neurol Dis & Blindness. *Honors & Awards:* Proctor Medal, Asn Res Vision & Ophthal, 53. *Mem:* Am Ophthal Soc; Asn Res Vision & Ophthal; AMA; Am Acad Ophthal. *Res:* Ocular physiology, pharmacology and therapeutics; anomalies of binocular vision; tumors of the eyes; ocular manifestations of vascular diseases; surgical anatomy and pathology. *Mailing Add:* Dept Ophthal Med Sch Univ Ore Portland OR 97201

SWAN, KENNETH G, b White Plains, NY, Oct 2, 34; m 65; c 3. SURGERY. *Educ:* Harvard Univ, AB, 56; Cornell Univ, MD, 60. *Prof Exp:* Resident gen surg, New York Hosp-Cornell Med Ctr, 60-65; fel physiol, Gastrointestinal Res Lab, Vet Admin Ctr, Los Angeles, 65-66; resident thoracic surg, New York Hosp-Cornell Med Ctr, 66-68; dep dir div surg, Walter Reed Army Inst Res, 71-72, dir div surg, 72-73; dir & assoc prof, Div Gen & Vascular Surg, 73-76, PROF SURG, NJ MED SCH, 76- *Mem:* Am Physiol Soc; Am Gastroenterol Asn; Am Col Surgeons; Soc Univ Surgeons; Soc Thoracic Surgeons. *Res:* Splanchnic circulation; shock; vascular surgery and trauma. *Mailing Add:* Dept of Surg NJ Med Sch 100 Bergen St Newark NJ 07103

SWAN, LAWRENCE WESLEY, b Bengal, India, Mar 9, 22; m 46; c 3. BIOLOGY. *Educ:* Univ Wis, PhB, 42; Stanford Univ, MA, 47, PhD(biol), 52. *Prof Exp:* Res officer, Climatic Res Lab, Lawrence, Mass, 43-46; instr biol, Stanford Univ, 47-48 & Univ Santa Clara, 51-53; from instr to assoc prof, 54-64, PROF BIOL, SAN FRANCISCO STATE UNIV, 64- *Concurrent Pos:* Mem, Am Himalayan Expeds, Nepal, 54, 60-61; biol surv, Mt Orizaba, Mex, 64 & 65, biol world tour, 66, field studies, EAfrica, 69 & Galapagos Islands, 70; Academia Sinica Exped, Tibet Plateau, 80; field studies, South Central Africa, 81. *Mem:* Ecol Soc Am; Am Soc Ichthyol & Herpet; Royal Geog Soc; Sigma Xi; Am Inst Biol Sci. *Res:* High altitude ecology and the Aeolian zone; zoogeography of Asia; vertebrate evolution. *Mailing Add:* 1032 Wilmington Way Redwood City CA 94062

SWAN, PATRICIA B, b Hickory, NC, Oct 21, 37; m 62; c 2. NUTRITION, BIOCHEMISTRY. *Educ:* Univ NC, Greensboro, BS, 59; Univ Wis, MS, 61, PhD(biochem, nutrit), 64. *Prof Exp:* Res fel biochem, 64-65, from asst prof to assoc prof, 65-73, PROF NUTRIT, UNIV MINN, ST PAUL, 73- *Concurrent Pos:* Nutrit prog coordr, USDA, 79-80. *Mem:* Am Inst Nutrit (secy, 81-84); Brit Nutrit Soc. *Res:* Amino acid metabolism; protein biosynthesis; muscle growth, development and aging. *Mailing Add:* Dept Food Sci & Nutrit Univ Minn St Paul MN 55108

SWAN, PETER HOWARD, b Melbourne, Australia, Mar 25, 28. THEORETICAL PHYSICS, ATOMIC PHYSICS. *Educ:* Univ Melbourne, BSc, 48, MSc, 51; Univ London, PhD(math, nuclear physics), 53. *Prof Exp:* Hon res asst physics, Univ Col, Univ London, 51-54; Lyle res fel, Univ Melbourne, 54, lectr, 55-59, sr lectr, 60-64, reader, 64-65; RES PROF PHYSICS, LAVAL UNIV, 65- *Concurrent Pos:* Vis assoc prof, Rice Univ, 63-65. *Mem:* Am Phys Soc. *Res:* Collision theory; nuclear physics; atomic and molecular physics; chemical physics. *Mailing Add:* Dept of Physics Laval Univ Quebec PQ C1K 7P4 Can

SWAN, RICHARD GORDON, b New York, NY, Dec 21, 33; m 63; c 2. MATHEMATICS. *Educ:* Princeton Univ, AB, 54, PhD(math), 57. *Prof Exp:* NSF res fel, Oxford Univ, 57-58; from instr to assoc prof, 58-65, PROF MATH, UNIV CHICAGO, 65- *Concurrent Pos:* Sloan fel, 60-65. *Honors & Awards:* Cole Prize, Am Math Soc, 70. *Mem:* Nat Acad Sci; AAAS; Math Asn Am; NY Acad Sci; Am Math Soc. *Res:* Algebraic K-theory; homological algebra. *Mailing Add:* 5734 University Ave Dept Math Univ Chicago Chicago IL 60637

SWAN, ROY CRAIG, JR, b New York, NY, June 7, 20; m 49, 77; c 2. ANATOMY. *Educ:* Cornell Univ, AB, 41, MD, 47. *Prof Exp:* Intern med, New York Hosp, 47-48, asst resident, 48-49, resident endocrinol & metab, 49-50; asst med, Peter Bent Brigham Hosp, 50-52; from instr to assoc prof physiol, 52-59, prof anat, 59-70, chmn dept, 59-78, JOSEPH C HINSEY PROF ANAT, MED COL, CORNELL UNIV, 70- *Concurrent Pos:* Life Ins Med Res Fund fel, Harvard Med Sch, 50-52; Markle scholar, 54-59; res assoc, Cambridge Univ, 55-56; mem health res coun, City New York; consult, USPHS, 60-65 & Off Sci & Technol, 63-64; sect ed, Biol Abstr; mem & chmn exec bd, Anat Test Comt, Nat Bd Med Examr; vis prof anat, Boston Univ, 77-78. *Mem:* Am Physiol Soc; Am Soc Clin Invest; Am Asn Anat. *Res:* Ion transport; muscle function and structure; neural fine structure. *Mailing Add:* Dept of Anat Cornell Univ Med Col New York NY 10021

SWAN, SHANNA HELEN, b Warren, Ohio, May 24, 36; m 75; c 3. PUBLIC HEALTH. *Educ:* City Col New York, BS, 58; Columbia Univ, MS, 60; Univ Calif, Berkeley, PhD(statist), 63. *Prof Exp:* Sr biostatistician, Contraceptive Drug Study, Kaiser Health Res, Walnut Creek, Calif, 69-75; assoc prof math, Calif State Univ, Sonoma, 74-79; dir training prog biostatist & epidemiol, Sch Pub Health, Univ Calif, Berkeley, 79-81; CHIEF METHODOLOGY & ANAL UNIT, EPIDEMIOL & STATIST, DEPT HEALTH SERV, STATE CALIF, 81- *Concurrent Pos:* Consult contraceptive eval, WHO, 74; lectr statist, Univ Copenhagen, Denmark, 60-61 & Univ Tel Aviv, Israel, 67-68 & Sch Pub Health, Univ Calif, Berkeley, 79-; vis assoc prof, Dept Statist, Univ Calif, Berkeley, 78-79. *Mem:* Soc Epidemiol Res; Am Statist Asn; Biometric Soc; Am Pub Health Asn. *Res:* Evaluating medical and health outcomes associated with contraceptive practices, drug exposures and environmental exposures, and the methodologic problems involved in studying such associations. *Mailing Add:* 33 Canyon Rd Berkeley CA 94704

SWANBERG, CHANDLER A, b Great Falls, Mont, July 7, 42; C 2. GEOPHYSICS, GEOLOGY. *Educ:* Southern Methodist Univ, BS, 65, MS, 69, PhD(geophys), 71. *Prof Exp:* Fel geophys, Mus Geol, Univ Oslo, 71-72; geophysicist, US Bur Reclamation, 72-74; asst prof, 74-78, ASSOC PROF GEOPHYS, N MEX STATE UNIV, 78- *Concurrent Pos:* Prin investr various govt & state agencies, 74-; review panelist, Extramural Res Prog, US Geol Surv, 77; sr res consult, Teledyne-Geotech, 81-82. *Mem:* Am Geophys Union; AAAS; Geol Soc Am; Geothermal Resources Coun; Sigma Xi. *Res:* Search for, evaluation and development of geothermal energy resources. *Mailing Add:* Dept of Physics NMex State Univ Las Cruces NM 88003

SWANBORG, ROBERT HARRY, b Brooklyn, NY, Aug 27, 38; m 66; c 2. IMMUNOLOGY, IMMUNOPATHOLOGY. *Educ:* Wagner Col, BS, 60; Long Island Univ, MS, 62; State Univ NY Buffalo, PhD(immunol), 65. *Prof Exp:* NIH trainee immunochem, State Univ NY Buffalo, 65-66; from instr to assoc prof microbiol, 66-73, assoc prof immunol & microbiol, 73-77, PROF IMMUNOL & MICROBIOL, MED SCH, WAYNE STATE UNIV, 77- *Concurrent Pos:* Vis investr immunol, Wenner-Gren Inst, Sweden, 75-76. *Mem:* AAAS; Am Asn Immunol; Am Soc Exp Path; Am Soc Microbiol. *Res:* Immunochemical aspects of the immune response; mechanisms of self-tolerance and autoimmunity. *Mailing Add:* Dept Immunol & Microbiol Wayne State Univ Med Sch Detroit MI 48201

SWANEY, JOHN BREWSTER, b Holyoke, Mass, Feb 25, 44; m 66; c 3. BIOCHEMISTRY. *Educ:* Amherst Col, AB, 66; Northwestern Univ, PhD(chem, biochem), 70. *Prof Exp:* Nat Acad Sci res assoc virol, Plum Island Animal Dis Lab, 70-72; instr, 72-74, asst prof biochem, 74-79, asst prof med, 76-81, ASSOC PROF BIOCHEM, ALBERT EINSTEIN COL MED, 79-, ASSOC PROF MED, 81- *Concurrent Pos:* Estab investr, Am Heart Asn; Irma T Hirschl career scientist award, 81. *Mem:* Am Heart Asn; Am Chem Soc. *Res:* Protein chemistry; structure and properties of proteins involved in protein-lipid interactions; plasma lipoproteins; membrane proteins; lipid metabolism; protein effectors of enzymes involved in lipid metabolism. *Mailing Add:* 511 Ullman Bldg 1300 Morris Park Ave Bronx NY 10461

SWANEY, LOIS MAE, b Pittsburgh, Pa, Jan 2, 28. MICROBIOLOGY, BIOCHEMISTRY. *Educ:* Univ Pittsburgh, BS, 49, MS, 52, PhD(molecular biol), 74. *Prof Exp:* Microbiologist bact genetics, Biol Labs, US Dept Army, Frederick, Md, 51-71; res asst, Univ Pittsburgh, 72-73; MICROBIOLOGIST CELL-VIRUS INTERACTIONS, PLUM ISLAND ANIMAL DIS CTR, SCI & EDUC ADMIN, AGR RES SERV, USDA, 73- *Mem:* Am Soc Microbiol. *Res:* Genetics of bacterial pili; mutants of foot-and-mouth disease virus; cell-virus interactions; assessment of tissue cultures for production of virus for vaccines; development of cell lines. *Mailing Add:* Plum Island Animal Dis Ctr USDA PO Box 848 Greenport NY 11944

SWANK, HOWARD WIGTON, b Butler, Ohio, Jan 30, 10; m 38; c 1. ANALYTICAL CHEMISTRY. *Educ:* Mt Union Col, BS, 32; Purdue Univ, MS, 34, PhD(chem), 37. *Hon Degrees:* DSc, Mt Union Col, 66; DSc, Purdue Univ, 62. *Prof Exp:* Asst, Purdue Univ, 32-37; res chemist, E I du Pont de Nemours & Co, 37-43, res supvr, 43-47, tech supt, 47-50, mfg supt, 50, res dir, 50-51 & 54-55, tech mgr, 51-52, prod mgr, 52-54, mfg tech dir, 55-59, gen dir, 59-63, asst gen mgr, Textile Fibers Dept, 63-70, gen mgr, 70-72, vpres & gen mgr textile fibers dept, 72-75, corp dir, 75-82; RETIRED. *Mem:* Am Chem Soc. *Res:* Synthetic fibers. *Mailing Add:* 3700 Centerville Rd Wilmington DE 19807

SWANK, RICHARD TILGHMAN, b Drums, Pa, Feb 1, 42; m 66; c 2. BIOCHEMISTRY. *Educ:* Pa State Univ, BS, 64; Univ Wis-Madison, MS, 67, PhD(biochem), 69. *Prof Exp:* NIH fel, Lab Molecular Biol, Univ Wis-Madison, 69-70; res assoc mammalian biochem genetics, 70-72, SR CANCER RES SCIENTIST, ROSWELL PARK MEM INST, 72- *Mem:* AAAS; Am Chem Soc; Am Inst Biol Sci. *Res:* Genetic regulation of enzyme synthesis and degradation in mammals; biochemical mechanisms of enzyme subcellular localization in mammals; physical and chemical characterization of enzymes. *Mailing Add:* Dept of Moclecular Biol Roswell Park Mem Inst Buffalo NY 14263

SWANK, ROBERT ROY, JR, b Brooklyn, NY, June 4, 39; m 60; c 3. CHEMICAL & NUCLEAR ENGINEERING. *Educ:* Ga Inst Technol, BChE, 59, MSChE, 63, PhD(chem eng), 68; Mass Inst Technol, MS, 60. *Prof Exp:* Maintenance engr, Monsanto Chem Co, 59, sr process engr, 68-71; chem engr, Southeast Environ Res Lab, 71-75, SUPVRY RES CHEM ENGR & CHIEF, TECH DEVELOP & APPLNS BR, ATHENS ENVIRON RES LAB, US ENVIRON PROTECTION AGENCY, OFF RES & DEVELOP, 75- *Concurrent Pos:* Teaching asst & lectr, Mass Inst Technol, 61; guest lectr, US Army Chem Sch, Ft McClellan, Ala, 65-67; consult, UN Indust Develop Orgn, 74-75, offical delegate to Repub China, Environ Protection Agency, 80. *Honors & Awards:* Bronze Medal, US Environ Protection Agency, 73. *Mem:* Am Inst Chem Engrs; Am Chem Soc. *Res:* Comprehensive assessment techniques for estimating human and environmental exposures and resulting risks due to the release into all environmental media (air-water-soil) of toxic/hazardous organic compounds and metals. *Mailing Add:* Rt 3 270 Great Oak Dr Athens GA 30605

SWANK, ROLLAND LAVERNE, b Holland, Mich, Dec 31, 42; m 69. MATHEMATICS. *Educ:* Hope Col, BA, 65; Mich State Univ, MS, 66, PhD(math), 69. *Prof Exp:* Asst prof math, Allegheny Col, 69-74; programmer, Power & Power, 74-80; DEPT MGR, W P DELONG & CO, 80- *Mem:* Am Math Soc; Math Asn Am. *Res:* Topology; geometry. *Mailing Add:* 109 Orlando Ave Holland MI 49423

SWANK, ROY LAVER, b Camas, Wash, Mar 5, 09; m 37; c 3. NEUROLOGY. *Educ:* Univ Wash, BS, 30; Northwestern Univ, MD & PhD(anat), 35. *Prof Exp:* Asst anat, Med Sch, Northwestern Univ, 30-34; intern, Passavant Mem Hosp, Chicago, 34-35; house officer, Peter Bent Brigham Hosp, 36-41, jr assoc med, 41-42, assoc, 46-48; asst prof neurol, McGill Univ, 48-54; prof, 54-74, EMER PROF NEUROL, SCH MED, UNIV ORE, PORTLAND, 74- *Concurrent Pos:* Fel, Harvard Med Sch, 37; Commonwealth Fund fel, Sweden & Montreal Neurol Inst, McGill Univ, 39-41; mem attend staff, Cushing Vet Admin Hosp, 46-48; lectr, Montreal Neurol Inst, McGill Univ, 48. *Mem:* Am Physiol Soc; Am Asn Anatomists; Am Neurol Asn; Can Neurol Asn. *Res:* Pyrimidal tracts; tissue staining; histochemical staining; vitamin deficiencies; electrophysiology; physiology of breathing. epidemiology of multiple sclerosis; fat metabolism and relationship to viscosity of blood; platelet adhesiveness and aggregation in surgical shock. *Mailing Add:* Dept of Neurol Univ of Ore Med Sch Portland OR 97201

SWANK, THOMAS FRANCIS, b Philadelphia, Pa, Nov 3, 37; m 63; c 2. COLLOID CHEMISTRY, PHOTOGRAPHIC CHEMISTRY. *Educ:* Villanova Univ, BS, 59; Univ Va, PhD(heterogeneous catalysis), 64. *Prof Exp:* Res chemist, Cabot Corp, 63-69; mgr, Ferro Fluidics Corp, 70-71; scientist, 71-76, SR SCIENTIST, POLAROID CORP, WALTHAM, 76- *Mem:* Am Chem Soc; Electron Micros Soc Am. *Res:* Heterogeneous catalysis; thin films; x-ray diffraction and spectroscopy; electron microscopy; structure of oxides; inorganic pigments; solid state physics; magnetic fluids; photographic science; colloid and surface chemistry. *Mailing Add:* 25 Musket Lane Sudbury MA 01776

SWANN, CHARLES PAUL, b Minneapolis, Minn, Dec 4, 18; m 51; c 3. NUCLEAR PHYSICS. *Educ:* Harvard Univ, BS, 41, MS, 43; Temple Univ, PhD(physics), 56. *Prof Exp:* Mech engr, Steam Div, Westinghouse Elec Corp, 43-46; nuclear physicist, Bartol Res Found, Franklin Inst, 46-76; BARTOL PROF PHYSICS, BARTOL RES FOUND, UNIV DEL, 76- *Mem:* Fel Am Phys Soc. *Res:* Nuclear structure studies; nuclear resonance fluorescence. *Mailing Add:* Dept of Physics Univ Del Newark DE 19711

SWANN, DALE WILLIAM, b Billings, Mont, Mar 11, 29; m 60; c 1. APPLIED MATHEMATICS, OPERATIONS RESEARCH. *Educ:* Yale Univ, BS, 51; Stanford Univ, PhD(math), 60. *Prof Exp:* Instr math, Stanford, 57-60; NATO fel sci, Cambridge Univ, 60-61; MEM TECH STAFF, BELL LABS, 61- *Res:* Statistical theory; applied probability; quality theory and practice; reliability theory; integral equations; asymptotic methods. *Mailing Add:* Interconnection Technol Lab Bell Labs Whippany NJ 07981

SWANN, GORDON ALFRED, b Palisade, Colo, Sept 21, 31; m 75; c 4. GEOLOGY, ASTROGEOLOGY. *Educ:* Univ Colo, Boulder, BA, 58, PhD(geol), 62. *Prof Exp:* Geologist, 63-73, staff geologist for telegeol, 73-76, dep regional geologist, 76-81, DEP ASST CHIEF GEOLOGIST, US GEOL SURV, 81- *Mem:* Geol Soc Am; Sigma Xi. *Mailing Add:* US Geol Surv 2255 N Gemini Dr Flagstaff AZ 86001

SWANN, HOWARD STORY GRAY, b Chicago, Ill, Aug 4, 36. MATHEMATICS. *Educ:* Harvard Univ, AB, 58; Univ Chicago, MS, 59; Univ Calif, Berkeley, PhD(appl math), 68. *Prof Exp:* Asst math, Univ Chicago, 59-61; lectr, Univ Nigeria, 61-63; asst & instr, Univ Calif, Berkeley, 64-68; asst prof, Antioch Col, 68-70; ASSOC PROF MATH, SAN JOSE STATE UNIV, 70- *Mem:* Am Math Soc. *Res:* Functional analysis; differential equations; game theory; automata theory. *Mailing Add:* Dept of Math San Jose State Univ San Jose CA 95192

SWANN, SHERLOCK, JR, b Baltimore, Md, Sept 30, 00. ELECTROORGANIC CHEMISTRY. *Educ:* Princeton Univ, BS, 22; Johns Hopkins Univ, PhD(org chem), 26. *Prof Exp:* Chemist, Columbia Gas Co, 26-27; asst, 27-29, from res assoc to res prof, 29-69, EMER PROF CHEM ENG, UNIV ILL, URBANA, 69- *Concurrent Pos:* Mem comt electrochem, Nat Res Coun, 38. *Mem:* AAAS; Am Chem Soc; hon mem Electrochem Soc (vpres, 41-43 & 56-58, pres, 58-59). *Res:* Organic electrochemistry. *Mailing Add:* 13 Roger Adams Lab Univ of Ill Urbana IL 61801

SWANN, WILLIAM B, b Hammonton, NJ, Feb 26, 23; m 49; c 3. ANALYTICAL CHEMISTRY. *Educ:* St Joseph's Col, Pa, BS, 43; Univ Del, MS, 53; Univ Pa, PhD, 63. *Prof Exp:* Res anal chemist, Socony Mobil Oil Co, 47-60; res anal chemist, Am Viscose Div, 60-65, HEAD ANAL GROUP, CHEM GROUP MGT, FMC CORP, 65- *Mem:* Am Chem Soc; Am Soc Testing & Mat. *Res:* Electroanalytical techniques; chromatography. *Mailing Add:* FMC Corp Princeton Ctr Res & Develop Box 8 Princeton NJ 08540

SWANSON, ALAN WAYNE, b Des Moines, Iowa, Jan 27, 44; m 65; c 2. MATERIALS SCIENCE, INORGANIC CHEMISTRY. *Educ:* SDak Sch Mines & Technol, BS, 66, MS, 68; Mass Inst Technol, PhD(metall), 72. *Prof Exp:* Teaching asst chem, SDak Sch Mines & Technol, 66-67, instr, 67-68; res asst metall, Mass Inst Technol, 68-72; sr res scientist mat, Raytheon Co, 72-78; MGR ADVAN PROCESS TECHNOL DEPT, SPERRY RES CTR, 78- *Mem:* Electrochem Soc; Inst Elec & Electronics Engrs; Sigma Xi. *Res:* Inorganic chemistry pertaining to vapor deposition of III-V semiconductor compounds; all areas of wet and dry corrosion; gallium arsenide for use in digital logic circuits and millimeter wave and microwave circuits. *Mailing Add:* Sperry Res Ctr 100 North Rd Sudbury MA 01776

SWANSON, ANNE BARRETT, b Joliet, Ill, Dec 23, 48; m 69. BIOCHEMISTRY, CHEMICAL CARCINOGENESIS. *Educ:* Northern Ill Univ, BS, 70; Univ Wis-Madison, PhD(biochem), 75. *Prof Exp:* NIH res fel, 75-78, res assoc chem carcinogenesis, McArdle Lab Cancer Res, 78-79, asst prof chem, Edgewood Col, 79-81, ASSOC PROF CHEM & CHAIRPERSON, EDGEWOOD COL, UNIV WIS-MADISON, 81- *Concurrent Pos:* mem, Found for Sci & the Handicapped, 81- *Mem:* Am Chem Soc; Sigma Xi; AAAS; Fedn Am Scientists; NY Acad Sci. *Res:* Mechanisms of chemical carcinogenesis; metabolism of precarcinogens to ultimate carcinogenic compounds; nutrition and metabolism of trace minerals; relationships of nutritional biochemistry and carcinogenesis. *Mailing Add:* McArdle Lab for Cancer Res 450 N Randall Ave Madison WI 53706

SWANSON, ARNOLD ARTHUR, b Rawlins, Wyo, Mar 11, 23; m 50; c 4. BIOCHEMISTRY, OPHTHALMOLOGY. *Educ:* Duke Univ, BA, 46; Trinity Univ, Tex, MA, 59; Tex A&M Univ, PhD(biochem), 61. *Prof Exp:* Res chemist, Med Sch, Temple Univ, 46-48; biochemist ophthal, US Air Force Sch Aviation Med, 50-59; sr chemist, USPHS, 61-63; chief res lab, Vet Admin Hosp, McKinney, Tex, 63-65 & Vet Admin Ctr, 65-68; assoc prof, 68-80, PROF BIOCHEM, MED UNIV SC, 80- *Concurrent Pos:* Dir, Swanson Biochem Labs, Inc, 52-58; consult, Southwestern Prods, Inc, 57- & Scott & White Hosp, 65-; adj prof, Baylor Univ, 66-; Alexander von Humboldt-Stiftung award, WGer. *Mem:* Fel AAAS; Am Chem Soc; fel Am Inst Chem; Soc Exp Biol & Med; Asn Res Vision & Ophthal. *Res:* Proteolysis in normal and senile cataract lens; senile changes and mineral metabolism. *Mailing Add:* Dept Biochem Med Univ SC Charleston SC 29401

SWANSON, AUGUST GEORGE, b Kearney, Nebr, Aug 25, 25; m 47; c 6. NEUROLOGY. *Educ:* Harvard Med Sch, MD, 49; Westminster Col, Mo, AB, 51. *Hon Degrees:* DSci, Univ Nebr, 78. *Prof Exp:* Resident med, Sch Med, Univ Wash, 53-55, resident neurol, 55-57; asst resident, Boston City Hosp, 58; instr neurol, Sch Med, Univ Wash, 58-59, asst prof pediat & med, 59-63; vis res fel physiol, Oxford Univ, 63-64; assoc prof med, 64-70, prof med, Sch Med, Univ Wash, 70-74; DIR DEP ACAD AFFAIRS, ASN AM MED COLS, 71- *Concurrent Pos:* Fel, Univ Wash, 55-57, assoc dean, Sch Med, 67-68, assoc dean acad affairs, 68-71; Markle scholar, 59. *Mem:* Inst Med-Nat Acad Sci; Am Acad Neurol; Am Neurol Asn. *Res:* Facilitation of the development of medical education and biomedical research. *Mailing Add:* Dept of Acad Affairs Asn Am Med Col DuPont Circle NW Washington DC 20036

SWANSON, BARRY GRANT, b Green Lake, Wis, Apr 16, 44; m 70; c 3. FOOD SCIENCE. *Educ:* Univ Wis-Madison, BS, 66, MS, 70, PhD(food sci), 72. *Prof Exp:* Asst prof food sci, Univ Idaho, 72-73; asst prof, 73-78, ASSOC PROF FOOD SCI, WASH STATE UNIV, 78- *Concurrent Pos:* Travel award Spain, Inst Food Technologists, 74; vis prof, Dept Food Sci, Univ BC & BC Cancer Res Ctr; sci lectr, Inst Food Technologists, 79-82. *Mem:* Inst Food Technologists; Am Soc Hort Sci; Int Asn Milk Food Environ Sanitarians; Am Chem Soc; Sigma Xi. *Res:* Bioavailability and digestibility of proteins from dry beans; analytical and toxicological studies of natural toxicants and antinutrients in foods; nutrient analysis and retention in preserved foods. *Mailing Add:* Dept of Food Sci & Technol 375 Clark Hall Wash State Univ Pullman WA 99164

SWANSON, BASIL IAN, b Minn, Feb 13, 44; m 64; c 2. INORGANIC CHEMISTRY. *Educ:* Colo Sch Mines, BA, 66; Northwestern Univ, Evanston, PhD(chem), 70. *Prof Exp:* Fel, Los Alamos Sci Lab, Univ Calif, 70-71; res corp grant, NY Univ, 71-72, asst prof chem, 71-73; ASST PROF CHEM, UNIV TEX, AUSTIN, 73- *Concurrent Pos:* Vis staff mem, Los Alamos Sci Lab, 70- *Mem:* Am Chem Soc. *Res:* Study of structure and bonding in inorganic systems using crystallographic and vibrational spectroscopic techniques; study of structural phase changes in crystalline solids; valence delocalization and ion transport in crystalline solids. *Mailing Add:* Dept of Chem Univ of Tex Austin TX 78712

SWANSON, BERNET S(TEVEN), b Chicago, Ill, Nov 20, 21; m 48; c 2. CHEMICAL ENGINEERING. *Educ:* Armour Inst Technol, BS, 42; Ill Inst Technol, MS, 44, PhD(chem eng), 50. *Prof Exp:* Inst chem eng, Ill Inst Technol, 44-46; asst prof, Kans State Col, 46-47; asst prof, 47-50, ASSOC PROF CHEM ENG, ILL INST TECHNOL, 50-, CHMN DEPT, 67- *Concurrent Pos:* Consult. *Mem:* Am Inst Chem Engrs; Instrument Soc Am. *Res:* Automatic process control; non-Newtonian and two-phase flow. *Mailing Add:* Dept of Chem Eng 3300 S Federal St Chicago IL 60616

SWANSON, CARL E(VERETT), b Valley City, NDak, Jan 6, 06; m 28; c 2. ELECTRICAL ENGINEERING. *Educ:* Univ Minn, BS, 27, MS & EE, 37. *Prof Exp:* Radio engr, Westinghouse Elec & Mfg Co, 27-29; instr elec eng, Univ Minn, 29-31 & math & mech, 31-39; dir res, Northwest Airlines, Inc, 39-42, supt commun, 42-45, mgr gen & aircraft eng, 45-51; consult aero div, Minneapolis-Honeywell Regulator Co, 51-52; dir gen eng, Univac Div, Sperry Rand Corp, 52-56, admin asst to gen mgr, 56-57, chief eng prod planning, 58-59; asst to pres, McGill-Warner-Farnum Co, 59-62; tech consult, Northwest Growth Fund, Inc, 62-74; RETIRED. *Concurrent Pos:* Instr, Willmar, Metrop & Normandale State Jr Cols, 64-74. *Mem:* AAAS; Soc Automotive Engrs; Sigma Xi. *Res:* Electroacoustics; transverse acoustic waves in rigid tubes; supercharged aircraft ignition systems. *Mailing Add:* 1860 Eleanor Ave St Paul MN 55116

SWANSON, CARL PONTIUS, b Rockport, Mass, June 24, 11; m 41; c 2. CYTOGENETICS. *Educ:* Mass State Col, BS, 37; Harvard Univ, MA, 39, PhD(biol), 41. *Prof Exp:* Sheldon traveling fel from Harvard Univ, Univ Mo, 41; asst prof bot, Mich State Col, 41-43; assoc biologist, NIH, 46; from assoc prof to prof bot, Johns Hopkins Univ, 46-56, William D Gill prof biol, 56-71, assoc dean undergrad studies, 66-71; assoc dir, Inst for Man & His Environ, 71-75, prof, 71-76, Ray Ethan Torrey prof, 76-81, EMER PROF BOT, UNIV MASS, AMHERST, 81- *Concurrent Pos:* Agt, USDA, 39; contract investr, Spec Proj Div, US Army, 46-49; pres, Int Photobiol Comt, 64-68. *Mem:* AAAS; Genetics Soc Am. *Res:* Cytogenetics of plants involving use of ionizing and photochemical radiations. *Mailing Add:* 77 Morgan Circle Amherst MA 01002

SWANSON, CARROLL ARTHUR, b Burlington, Iowa, Sept 6, 15; m 41; c 2. PLANT PHYSIOLOGY. *Educ:* Augustana Col, AB, 37; Ohio State Univ, MS, 38, PhD(plant physiol), 42. *Prof Exp:* From asst to asst prof bot, 38-48, res assoc, Manhattan Proj, Res Found, 44-46, assoc prof bot & plant path, 48-56, chmn dept, 67-69, assoc dean col biol sci, 69-70, PROF BOT & PLANT PATH, OHIO STATE UNIV, 56- *Concurrent Pos:* Asst gen foreman, Procter & Gamble Defense Corp, Miss, 43-44; prog dir, NSF, 59-60, consult, 60-66; assoc ed, Plant Physiol, 80- *Mem:* AAAS; Am Soc Plant Physiologists; Bot Soc Am; Can Soc Plant Physiologists; Scandinavian Soc Plant Physiologists. *Res:* Translocation in phloem. *Mailing Add:* Dept of Bot 1735 Neil Ave Ohio State Univ Columbus OH 43210

SWANSON, CHARLES ANDREW, b Bellingham, Wash, July 11, 29; m 57; c 2. DIFFERENTIAL EQUATIONS. *Educ:* Univ BC, BA, 51, MA, 53; Calif Inst Technol, PhD, 57. *Prof Exp:* From instr to assoc prof, 57-65, PROF MATH, UNIV BC, 65- *Concurrent Pos:* Assoc ed, Can J Math, 71-80. *Mem:* Can Math Soc. *Res:* Differential equations. *Mailing Add:* Dept of Math Univ of BC Vancouver BC V6T 1Y4 Can

SWANSON, CURTIS JAMES, b Chicago, Ill, Dec 8, 41; m 65; c 2. COMPARATIVE PHYSIOLOGY, BIOCHEMISTRY. *Educ:* N Park Col, BA & BS, 64; Northern Ill Univ, MS, 66; Univ Ill, Urbana-Champaign, PhD(zool, physiol), 70. *Prof Exp:* Lectr biol, Univ Ill, 70; asst prof, 70-74, ASSOC PROF BIOL, WAYNE STATE UNIV, 74- *Concurrent Pos:* Grants, NSF, Wayne State Univ, 70-75 & NIH, 71-; Riker res fel, Bermuda Biol Sta, 75, NSF, 77-78. *Mem:* AAAS; Am Inst Biol Sci; Am Soc Zoologists; Am Physiol Soc. *Res:* Electron microscopy of muscle tissue; innervation and developmental neuromuscular physiology; control systems in development; protein biochemistry; theoretical and applied biomechanics; comparative ultrastructure of muscle. *Mailing Add:* Dept Biol Wayne State Univ Detroit MI 48202

SWANSON, DAVID BERNARD, b Newark, NJ, Dec 14, 35; m 58; c 3. CHEMICAL ENGINEERING. *Educ:* Newark Col Eng, BS, 57, MS, 62. *Prof Exp:* Engr, Esso Res & Eng Co, Standard Oil Co, NJ, 57-59; from engr to res supvr, 59-77, dir, Process Develop & Mfg, Engelhard Minerals & Chem Corp, 77-80, DIR RES, MINERALS & CHEM DIV, ENGELHARD CORP, 80- *Res:* Heat transfer coefficients of non-Newtonian fluids; dehydration and rehydration of kaolin; zeolitic cracking catalyst. *Mailing Add:* Engelhard Minerals & Chem Corp Menlo Park Edison NJ 08817

SWANSON, DAVID G, JR, b Chicago, Ill, Jan 14, 41. NUCLEAR CHEMISTRY, PHYSICAL CHEMISTRY. *Educ:* Northwestern Univ, BS, 64; Purdue Univ, PhD(nuclear & phys chem), 69. *Prof Exp:* Nuclear chemist, Sandia Corp, NMex, 69-73; nuclear chemist, Aerospace Corp, 73-80. *Concurrent Pos:* Consult, US Nuclear Regulatory Comn, 75- *Mem:* Am Chem Soc; Am Phys Soc; Am Nuclear Soc. *Res:* Response of materials to radiation; nuclear reactions; radiation transport phenomena; high temperature physical chemistry; heat transfer, materials evaluation and characterization; thermodynamics; nuclear reactor safety studies; post accident heat removal. *Mailing Add:* 6868 Los Verdes Dr 12 Palos Verdes Peninsula CA 90274

SWANSON, DAVID WENDELL, b Ft Dodge, Iowa, Aug 28, 30; m 53; c 3. PSYCHIATRY. *Educ:* Augustana Col, Ill, BA, 52; Univ Ill, MD, 56. *Prof Exp:* Intern, Ill Cent Hosp, 56-57; resident psychiat, Ill State Psychiat Inst, 59-62, asst serv chief, 62-63; assoc prof & asst chmn dept, Stritch Sch Med,

Loyola Univ Chicago, 63-70; assoc prof psychiat, Mayo Grad Sch Med & consult, Sect Psychiat, Mayo Clin, 70-74, prof psychiat & head sect, Mayo Med Sch, Univ Minn, 74-79, VCHMN DEPT PSYCHIAT, MAYO CLIN, 79- *Mem:* AAAS; Am Col Psychiat; Am Col Psychiatrists; Am Psychiat Asn. *Res:* Paranoid and chronic pain disorders. *Mailing Add:* Sect of Psychiat Mayo Clin Rochester MN 55901

SWANSON, DON R, b Los Angeles, Calif, Oct 10, 24; m 76; c 3. INFORMATION SCIENCE. *Educ:* Calif Inst Technol, BS, 45; Rice Univ, MA, 47; Univ Calif, Berkeley, PhD(physics), 52. *Prof Exp:* Res physicist, Radiation Lab, Univ Calif, 50-52; mem tech staff, Hughes Res & Develop Labs, 52-55; dept mgr comput appln, Thompson-Ramo-Wooldridge, Inc, 55-63; dean, 63-72 & 77-79, PROF LIBR SCI, LIB SCH, UNIV CHICAGO, 63- *Concurrent Pos:* Mem sci info coun, NSF, 59-63; mem vis comt libr, Mass Inst Technol, 64-72; trustee, Nat Opinion Res Ctr, 64-73; mem adv comt, Libr Cong, 64-72, toxicol info panel, President's Sci Adv Comt, 64-65, comt sci & tech commun, Nat Acad Sci, 66-70 & adv comt, Encyclop Britannica, 66- *Res:* Library science and education; computer systems analysis and applications; information processing; computer programming; indexing and retrieval of information. *Mailing Add:* Grad Libr Sch Univ Chicago 1100 E 57 Chicago IL 60637

SWANSON, DONALD ALAN, b Tacoma, Wash, July 25, 38. VOLCANOLOGY, GEOLOGY. *Educ:* Wash State Univ, BS, 60; Johns Hopkins Univ, PhD(geol), 64. *Prof Exp:* NATO fel, Ger, Italy & Canary Islands, 64-65; GEOLOGIST, US GEOL SURV, 65- *Mem:* AAAS; Geol Soc Am; Am Geophys Union. *Res:* Petrology of volcanic rocks, especially from northwest United States; deformation studies of active volcanos, particularly Mount St Helens and other Cascade volcanos; physical volcanology. *Mailing Add:* Cascades Volcano Observ US Geol Surv 5400 MacArthur Blvd Vancouver WA 98661

SWANSON, DONALD CHARLES, b Canon City, Colo, Sept 22, 26; m 50; c 2. PETROLEUM GEOLOGY, SEDIMENTOLOGY. *Educ:* Colo State Univ, BS, 50; Univ Tulsa, BS, 55. *Prof Exp:* Geol & geophys tax engr, Carter Oil Co, Okla, 51-56, jr geologist, Kans, 56, geologist, Ark, 56-57 & Okla, 57-60; geologist, Humble Oil Co, 60-62, sr geologist, Tex, 62-63 & Humble Res Ctr, 63-64, staff geologist, Humble Oil Co, Okla, 64-67; sr res geologist, Esso Prod Res Co, 67, sr res specialist, 67-74; res assoc, Exxon Prod Res Co, 74-79; CONSULT, SWANSON PETROL ENTERPRISES & SWANSON & CROW, 79- *Honors & Awards:* Levorsen Award, Am Asn Petrol Geologists, 68 & 79. *Mem:* Fel Geol Soc Am; Am Asn Petrol Geologists; Explorers Club. *Res:* Clastic facies; determination of ancient sedimentary environments; paleogeography; methodology of environmental facies analyses; methodology of exploration; computer application to petroleum geology. *Mailing Add:* 13611 Kingsride Houston TX 77079

SWANSON, DONALD G, b Los Angeles, Calif, June 11, 35; m 60; c 3. PLASMA PHYSICS. *Educ:* Northwest Christian Col, BTh, 58; Univ Ore, BS, 58; Calif Inst Technol, MS, 61, PhD(physics), 63. *Prof Exp:* Fel, Calif Inst Technol, 63-64; from asst prof to assoc prof elec eng, Univ Tex, Austin, 64-74; assoc prof elec eng, Univ Southern Calif, Los Angeles, 74-80; PROF PHYSICS, AUBURN UNIV, 80- *Concurrent Pos:* Consult, Advan Kinetics, Inc, Calif, 63-64 & McDonnell-Douglas Corp, St Louis, Mo, 80- *Mem:* Am Phys Soc; Sigma Xi. *Res:* Compressional hydromagnetic waves; plasma-filled waveguide; ion cyclotron waves; mode conversion theory. *Mailing Add:* Dept Physics Auburn Univ Auburn AL 36849

SWANSON, DONALD LEROY, b Montrose, SDak, Mar 24, 23; m 48; c 3. ANALYTICAL CHEMISTRY, PHYSICAL CHEMISTRY. *Educ:* SDak State Univ, BS, 47; Univ Wis, PhD(chem), 51. *Prof Exp:* Lab asst chem, Agr Exp Sta, SDak, 46-47; asst, Univ Wis, 47-51; res chemist, 51-58, group leader, 58-61, SECT MGR, AM CYANAMID CO, 62- *Mem:* Am Chem Soc. *Res:* Physical and mechanical properties of polymers; polymerization kinetics; copolymerization; radiation chemistry; analysis. *Mailing Add:* Sci Serv Dept Am Cyanamid Co Stamford CT 06904

SWANSON, DWIGHT WESLEY, b Harcourt, Iowa, Mar 15, 22; m 46; c 4. METEOROLOGY, DATA PROCESSING. *Educ:* Cornell Univ, BA, 46; Iowa State Univ, MS, 47. *Prof Exp:* Meteorologist, US Weather Bur, 47-51; meteorologist, USDA, 51-68, soil scientist, Soil Surv Interpretations, 68-70, head, Soil Data Storage & Retrieval Unit, Soil Surv, Soil Conserv Serv, 70-74, data processing specialist, 74-79; RETIRED. *Mem:* Asn Comput Mach. *Res:* Effects of climate and weather on crops and soils; application of automatic data processing techniques in soil survey. *Mailing Add:* 15100 Donna Dr Silver Spring MD 20904

SWANSON, ERIC RICHMOND, b San Diego, Calif, May 4, 34; m 67; c 2. APPLIED PHYSICS, NAVIGATION. *Educ:* Pomona Col, BA, 56; Univ Calif, Los Angeles, MS, 58. *Prof Exp:* Teaching asst, Univ Calif, Los Angeles, 56-58; electronic engr res & develop, Electro Instruments, Inc, San Diego, 59-60; PHYSICIST, BR HEAD & CONSULT, NAVAL OCEAN SYSTS CTR, 60- *Concurrent Pos:* Mem, Comt Consult Int Radio Commun US Study Group 7, 75-; mem, Int Meritime Consult Orgn Working Group Differential Omeg, 77-79; consult, NATO, 76, India, Int Telecommun, 81. *Honors & Awards:* Burka Award, Inst Navig, 71. *Mem:* Insts Navig (US, Brit & Australia); Inst Elec & Electronics Engrs; Am Inst Physics; Wild Goose Asn. *Res:* Navigation systems and associated radio propagation problems; timing and time dissemination. *Mailing Add:* Naval Ocean Systs Ctr San Diego CA 92152

SWANSON, ERIC WALLACE, b Knox, Ind, June 14, 18; m 41; c 3. DAIRY SCIENCE. *Educ:* Purdue Univ, BS, 39; Univ Mo, AM, 40, PhD(nutrit), 43. *Prof Exp:* Asst, Univ Mo, 39-40, asst instr dairy husb, 40-43, instr, 43-44 & 46-47; assoc prof dairying & assoc dairy husbandman, 47-56, PROF DAIRYING & ANIMAL SCIENTIST, AGR EXP STA, UNIV TENN, KNOXVILLE, 56- *Honors & Awards:* Borden Award, Am Dairy Sci Asn; Calcium Carbonate Award, Nat Feed Ingredients Asn. *Mem:* Am Inst Nutrit; Am Soc Animal Sci; Am Dairy Sci Asn. *Res:* Dairy cattle nutrition; reproductive physiology; milk secretion physiology; mastitis; nutritive value of proteins; thyroid function and iodine metabolism in cattle; effects of growth rates on lactation. *Mailing Add:* Dept of Animal Sci Univ of Tenn PO Box 1071 Knoxville TN 37901

SWANSON, ERNEST ALLEN, JR, b Miami, Fla, Apr 9, 36; m 67. ANATOMY, HISTOLOGY. *Educ:* Emory Univ, BA, 58, PhD(anat), 64. *Prof Exp:* Instr anat, Emory Univ, 64-65; instr, Univ Va, 65-67; from asst prof to assoc prof, 67-81, PROF ANAT, SCH DENT, TEMPLE UNIV, 81- *Mem:* Am Asn Anatomists. *Res:* Changes in the dental pulp associated with cholesterol induced arteriosclerosis. *Mailing Add:* Dept of Anatomic Sci Temple Univ Sch of Dent Philadelphia PA 19140

SWANSON, GUSTAV ADOLPH, b Mamre, Minn, Feb 13, 10; m 36; c 3. WILDLIFE ECOLOGY. *Educ:* Univ Minn, BS, 30, MS, 32, PhD(zool), 37. *Prof Exp:* Asst zool, Univ Minn, 30-34; biologist, State Dept Conserv, Minn, 35-36; asst prof game mgt, Univ Maine, 36-37; asst prof econ zool, Univ Minn, 37-41; assoc regional inspector, US Fish & Wildlife Serv, 41-42, chief sect coop wildlife res units, 44-46, chief div wildlife res, 46-48; assoc prof econ zool, Univ Minn, 42-44; prof conserv & head dept, Cornell Univ, 48-66; prof fishery & wildlife biol & head dept, 66-75, EMER PROF WILDLIFE BIOL, COLO STATE UNIV, 75- *Concurrent Pos:* Ed, J Wildlife Soc, 49-53; Am Scandinavian Found fel, Denmark, 54-55, Fulbright fel, 61-62; consult waterfowl res, Nature Conserv, Eng, Scotland & Northern Ireland, 55 & 60; dir, Cornell Biol Field Sta, 55-66, exec dir lab ornith, 58-61; fel, Rochester Mus, 56; consult, State Joint Legis Comt Rev Conserv Law, NY, 56-65 & natural resources, 56-66; Fulbright fel, NSW, Australia, 68. *Honors & Awards:* Aldo Leopold Mem Medalist, 73. *Mem:* Fel AAAS; hon mem Wildlife Soc (vpres, 45, pres, 54); Am Soc Mammalogy; Wilson Ornith Soc (treas, 38-42); Am Inst Biol Sci. *Res:* Wildlife management; conservation of natural resources; ornithology. *Mailing Add:* Dept of Fishery & Wildlife Biol Colo State Univ Ft Collins CO 80523

SWANSON, HAROLD DUEKER, b Wichita, Kans, Mar 5, 30; m 55; c 3. CELL BIOLOGY. *Educ:* Friends Univ, BA, 53; Univ Kans, MA, 55; Univ Tenn, PhD(zool physiol), 60. *Prof Exp:* Asst zool, Univ Kans, 53-55 & Univ Tenn, 56-58; from asst prof to assoc prof, 60-74, PROF BIOL, DRAKE UNIV, 74- *Res:* Nucleocytoplasmic interaction; subcellular component isolation; regeneration of cirrhotic livers; cell physiology. *Mailing Add:* 3210 Lincoln Ave Des Moines IA 50310

SWANSON, JACK LEE, b Aurora, Nebr, Oct 22, 34; m 56; c 3. PHYSICAL CHEMISTRY, BIOCHEMISTRY. *Educ:* Kearney State Col, BS, 56; Univ Nebr, MS, 59, PhD(chem), 67. *Prof Exp:* Prof chem, Kearney State Col, 58-71; dean, Sch Sci & Technol, 71-76, dean, Sch Prof Studies, 76-79, DEAN ADMIN SERV, CHADRON STATE COL, 80- *Mem:* AAAS; Am Chem Soc; Sigma Xi. *Res:* Infrared and ultraviolet spectroscopy; magneto-optical rotary dispersion; circular dichroism spectroscopy; medicinal chemistry. *Mailing Add:* Sch of Prof Studies Chadron State Col Chadron NE 69337

SWANSON, JAMES A, b Aurora, Nebr, Oct 25, 35; m 57; c 3. PHYSICAL CHEMISTRY. *Educ:* Kearney State Col, BA, 57; Univ Nebr, MS, 59, PhD(chem), 62. *Prof Exp:* Part-time lab asst, Univ Nebr, 57-62; PROF CHEM, KEARNEY STATE COL, 62- *Mem:* Am Chem Soc. *Res:* Solution thermochemistry; thermodynamics. *Mailing Add:* Dept of Chem Kearney State Col Kearney NE 68847

SWANSON, JOHN ROBERT, b Ft Collins, Colo, June 24, 39; m 62; c 1. BIOCHEMISTRY. *Educ:* Colo State Univ, BS, 61; Wash State Univ, PhD(biochem), 65; Am Bd Clin Chem, dipl. *Prof Exp:* NIH res fel biochem, Duke Univ, 65-67; clin chem training fel, Pepper Lab, Hosp Univ Pa, 67-69; asst prof, 69-74, ASSOC PROF CLIN PATH, MED SCH, UNIV ORE, PORTLAND, 74- *Mem:* Am Asn Clin Chem; Am Chem Soc. *Res:* Mechanism of action of myosin; comparative enzymology of phospholucomutase; analytical methods for urinary protein, plasma renin and serum triglycerides. *Mailing Add:* Dept of Clin Path Univ of Ore Med Sch Portland OR 97201

SWANSON, JOHN WILLIAM, b Sioux City, Iowa, Oct 12, 17; m 41; c 3. PHYSICAL CHEMISTRY. *Educ:* Morningside Col, BA, 40. *Hon Degrees:* DSc, Morningside Col, 72. *Prof Exp:* Asst chem, Iowa State Col, 40-41; tech asst, 41-43, tech assoc, 44-45, res asst, 46-47, res assoc, 48-55, group leader surface & colloid chem, 53-55, group leader phys chem, 56-61, sr res assoc, 56-69, chmn phys chem dept, 62-69, dir surface & colloid sci ctr, 81-81, EMER PROF, INST PAPER CHEM, 81- *Concurrent Pos:* Lectr, Lawrence Univ, 45-46; consult to numerous paper co, 50- *Honors & Awards:* Res & Develop Div Award, Tech Asn Pulp & Paper Indust, 74. *Mem:* AAAS; Am Chem Soc; fel Tech Asn Pulp & Paper Indust. *Res:* Surface and colloid chemistry of papermaking; polymer sorption at interfaces; surface area and bonding of cellulose fibers; paper sizing, coating; coagulation and retention of resins in aqueous systems; pollution abatement. *Mailing Add:* 1621 S Connell St Appleton WI 54911

SWANSON, LAWRENCE RAY, b Omaha, Nebr, Nov 4, 39; m 62; c 2. PHYSICS, MATHEMATICS. *Educ:* Iowa State Univ, BS, 59; Fuller Theol Sem, BD, 63; Calif State Univ, Los Angeles, MS, 66; Univ Calif, Irvine, PhD(physics), 70. *Prof Exp:* Asst prof physics, Pasadena Col, 70-73, vis prof physics, Greenville Col, 73-74; assoc prof physics & math, Azusa Pac Col, 74-76; assoc prof physics & math, Sterling Col, 76-80; MEM STAFF, TRW INC, 80- *Mem:* Am Sci Affil; Int Solar Energy Soc; Am Asn Physics Teachers. *Res:* Theoretical solid state physics. *Mailing Add:* TRW Inc 3650 N Nevada Ave Colorado Springs CO 80907

SWANSON, LEONARD GEORGE, b Corvallis, Ore, Sept 10, 40. MATHEMATICS. *Educ:* Portland State Univ, BS, 62; Univ Wash, MA, 65; Ore State Univ, PhD(math), 70. *Prof Exp:* From instr to asst prof, 64-75, ASSOC PROF MATH, PORTLAND STATE UNIV, 75- *Concurrent Pos:*

Vis assoc prof, Dept Math, Mont State Univ, 77-78. *Mem:* Am Math Soc; Math Asn Am; Inst Math Statist; AAAS. *Res:* Fourier series and their application; number theory. *Mailing Add:* Dept of Math PO Box 751 Portland OR 97207

SWANSON, LLOYD VERNON, b Isanti, Minn, Oct 16, 38; m 66; c 2. REPRODUCTIVE ENDOCRINOLOGY. *Educ:* Univ Minn, St Paul, BS, 60, MS, 67; Mich State Univ, PhD(physiol), 70. *Prof Exp:* ASSOC PROF DAIRY PHYSIOL, ORE STATE UNIV, 71- *Mem:* AAAS; Am Dairy Sci Asn; Am Soc Animal Sci; Soc Study Reproduction. *Res:* Reproductive physiology of mammalian species, both male and female, with special interest in the endocrine control of ovulation and of spermatogenesis. *Mailing Add:* Dept Animal Sci Ore State Univ Corvallis OR 97331

SWANSON, LYNN ALLEN, b Minneapolis, Minn, July 28, 42; m 67; c 2. ANALYTICAL CHEMISTRY. *Educ:* Univ Minn, Minneapolis, BChem, 64; Univ Iowa, MS, 68, PhD(anal chem), 70. *Prof Exp:* Res chemist anal chem, Commercial Solvents Corp, 69-77; asst mgr, 77-80, RES SCIENTIST ANAL SERV, RES & DEVELOP, INT MINERALS & CHEM CORP, 80- *Mem:* Am Chem Soc. *Res:* Trace analysis of pharmaceuticals, drugs and other additives in animal tissues and body fluids; general chromatography; spectrophotometry. *Mailing Add:* Int Minerals & Chem Corp Res & Develop PO Box 207 Terre Haute IN 47808

SWANSON, LYNWOOD WALTER, b Turlock, Calif, Oct 7, 34; m 55; c 2. PHYSICAL CHEMISTRY. *Educ:* Univ of Pac, BSc, 56; Univ Calif, PhD(chem), 60. *Prof Exp:* Asst chemist, Univ Calif, Berkeley, 56-59; res assoc, Inst Study Metals, Univ Chicago, 59-61; sr scientist, Linfield Res Inst, 61-63; dir basic res, Field Emission Corp, 63-69; prof chem & dean fac, Linfield Col, 69-73; PROF APPL PHYSICS, ORE GRAD CTR, 73- *Mem:* Fel Am Phys Soc; fel Am Inst Chemists. *Res:* Photochemistry; surface adsorption; field electron and ion microscopy; electron physics. *Mailing Add:* Dept of Appl Physics Ore Grad Ctr Beaverton OR 97005

SWANSON, MAX LYNN, b Hancock, Mich, Aug 5, 31; Can citizen; m 59; c 4. EXPERIMENTAL SOLID STATE PHYSICS. *Educ:* Univ BC, BA, 53, MSc, 54, PhD(metal physics), 58. *Prof Exp:* Res metallurgist, Metals Res Lab, Carnegie Inst Technol, 58-60; RES OFFICER METAL PHYSICS, CHALK RIVER NUCLEAR LABS, ATOMIC ENERGY CAN LTD, 60- *Concurrent Pos:* Guest scientist, Inst Physics, Max Planck Inst Metal Res, Stuttgart, 65-66; vis prof, Univ Utah, 71-72; guest scientist, Hahn-Meither Inst, Berlin, 77-78. *Mem:* Can Asn Physicists. *Res:* Defect solid state physics: irradiation damage in metals and semiconductors, ion channeling; defect trapping configurations; ion beam modification of materials. *Mailing Add:* Atomic Energy of Can Ltd Chalk River ON K0J 1J0 Can

SWANSON, PAUL N, b San Mateo, Calif, June 29, 36; m 59; c 3. RADIO ASTRONOMY, MILLIMETER WAVE RADIOMETRY. *Educ:* Calif State Polytech Col, BS, 62; Pa State Univ, PhD(physics), 68. *Prof Exp:* Asst prof radio astron, Pa State Univ, University Park, 69-75; MEM STAFF, JET PROPULSION LAB, CALIF INST TECHNOL, 75- *Mem:* Am Astron Soc; AAAS; Inst Elec & Electronics Engrs; Sigma Xi. *Res:* Millimeter wavelength radio astronomy and solar physics; radiometer development; space science. *Mailing Add:* Jet Propulsion Lab Sect 383 Calif Inst Technol Pasadena CA 91109

SWANSON, PHILLIP D, b Seattle, Wash, Oct 1, 32; m 57; c 5. NEUROLOGY, BIOCHEMISTRY. *Educ:* Yale Univ, BS, 54; Johns Hopkins Univ, MD, 58; Univ London, PhD(biochem), 64. *Prof Exp:* Fel neurol med, Sch Med, Johns Hopkins Univ, 59-62; Nat Inst Neurol Dis & Stroke spec fel, Univ London, 62-64; from asst prof to assoc prof, 64-73, PROF NEUROL, SCH MED, UNIV WASH, 73-, HEAD DIV, 67- *Mem:* Asn Univ Prof Neurol (pres, 75-76); Am Neurol Asn; Am Soc Clin Invest; Brit Biochem Soc. *Res:* Neurochemistry; cation transport and energy utilization in cerebral tissues; enzymes of importance in cation transport. *Mailing Add:* Div of Neurol Univ of Wash Sch of Med Seattle WA 98195

SWANSON, ROBERT ALLAN, b Chicago, Ill, Dec 16, 28; m 57. ELEMENTARY PARTICLE PHYSICS. *Educ:* Ill Inst Technol, BS, 51; Univ Chicago, MS, 53, PhD(physics), 58. *Prof Exp:* Res assoc physics, Univ Chicago, 58-59; asst prof, Princeton Univ, 59-60; from asst prof to assoc prof, 60-70, PROF PHYSICS, UNIV CALIF, SAN DIEGO, 70- *Concurrent Pos:* Vis assoc prof, Univ Chicago, 68-69; NSF fel, Univ Calif, 72- *Mem:* Am Phys Soc; Am Asn Physics Teachers. *Res:* Muonic atoms; experimental kaon physics. *Mailing Add:* Dept of Physics Univ of Calif at San Diego La Jolla CA 92093

SWANSON, ROBERT E, b Duluth, Minn, Dec 19, 24; m 47; c 2. MEDICAL PHYSIOLOGY. *Educ:* Univ Minn, BA, 49, PhD(physiol), 53. *Prof Exp:* Asst physiol, Univ Minn, 50-52, instr, 52-55; asst physiologist, Brookhaven Nat Lab, 55-58; asst prof physiol, Univ Minn, 58-61; assoc prof, 61-73, PROF PHYSIOL, MED SCH, UNIV ORE HEALTH SCI CTR, 73- *Res:* Renal, water and electrolyte balance. *Mailing Add:* Dept Physiol Sch Med Univ Ore Health Sci Ctr Portland OR 97201

SWANSON, ROBERT HAROLD, b Los Angeles, Calif, Feb 15, 33; m 55; c 2. FOREST HYDROLOGY, FOREST PHYSIOLOGY. *Educ:* Colo State Univ, BSc, 59, MSc, 66. *Prof Exp:* Res forester hydrol, Rocky Mountain Forest & Range Exp Sta, US Forest Serv, 59-68; PROJ LEADER FOREST HYDROL, NORTHERN FOREST RES CTR, 68- *Concurrent Pos:* Res coordr, Alta Watershed Res Prog, 68-; res fel, Ministry of Works, NZ, 74-75. *Mem:* Can Inst Foresters; Sigma Xi. *Res:* Physiological bases for tree improvement, plant-water relation's forest arrangements streamflow interractions' watershed management simulation and evaluation techniques. *Mailing Add:* 5320-122nd St Edmonton AB T6H 3S5 Can

SWANSON, ROBERT JAMES, b St Petersburg, Fla, Nov 13, 45; m 67; c 2. ENDOCRINOLOGY. *Educ:* Wheaton Col, Ill, BS, 67; Fla State Univ, MS, 71, PhD(biol), 76. *Prof Exp:* Teacher gen sci, Madison High Sch, Fla, 67-68; instr anat & kinesiology, Fla State Univ, 69-70; asst prof anat, physiol & endocrinol, Old Dominion Univ, 75-77, asst prof biol, 77-80. *Mem:* AAAS. *Res:* Female reproductive physiology, especially factors involved in ovulation, such as hormones, smooth muscle activity, nerve involvement and blood flow. *Mailing Add:* 1014 Jamestown Cres Norfolk VA 23508

SWANSON, ROBERT LAWRENCE, b Baltimore, Md, Oct 11, 38; m 63; c 2. PHYSICAL OCEANOGRAPHY, CIVIL ENGINEERING. *Educ:* Lehigh Univ, BS, 60; Ore State Univ, MS, 65, PhD, 71. *Prof Exp:* With US Coast & Geodetic Surv, 60-66, commanding officer US Coast & Geodetic Surv Ship Marmer circulatory estuarine surv, 66-67, chief, Oceanog Div, Nat Ocean Surv, 69-72, proj mgr, NY Bight Proj, Marine Ecosysts Anal, Environ Res Labs, 72-78, DIR, OFF MARINE POLLUTION ASSESSMENT, NAT OCEANIC & ATMOSPHERIC ADMIN, 78- *Concurrent Pos:* Prof asst, Col Gen Studies, George Washington Univ, 70-73; adj assoc prof, State Univ NY, Stony Brook, 76- *Honors & Awards:* Karo Award, Soc Am Military Engrs, 73; Silver Medal, US Dept Com, 73; Prog Admin & Mgt Award, Nat Oceanic & Atmospheric Admin, 75. *Mem:* Am Soc Civil Engrs; Am Geophys Union; AAAS; Am Soc Photogramm; NY Acad Sci. *Res:* Developing interrelationships and understanding between component parts of the coastal marine ecosystem; studying the impact of ocean dumping on marine ecosystem; specific interests in tides, tidal currents, tidal datums, marine boundaries. *Mailing Add:* Off Marine Pollution Assessment (MP) Nat Oceanic & Atmospheric Admin Rockville MD 20852

SWANSON, ROBERT NELS, b Ashland, Wis, Feb 4, 32; m 57; c 4. MICROMETEOROLOGY. *Educ:* Wis State Col, River Falls, BS, 53; Univ Mich, MS, 58. *Prof Exp:* Meteorologist, White Sands Missile Range, 58-61; staff scientist, GCA Corp, Utah, 61-72; SR METEOROLOGIST, PAC GAS & ELEC CO, SAN FRANCISCO, 72- *Mem:* Am Meteorol Soc; Royal Meteorol Soc; Air Pollution Control Asn. *Res:* Turbulence and diffusion as it applies to air pollution problems. *Mailing Add:* 1216 Babel Lane Concord CA 94518

SWANSON, ROGER GLENN, b Chicago, Ill, June 7, 23; m 57; c 2. GEOLOGY. *Educ:* Augustana Col, Ill, BA, 48; Univ Iowa, MS, 50. *Prof Exp:* Mem staff, Shell Oil Co, 50-59, area stratigr, 59-68; staff geologist, Shell Develop Co, 68-79, SR STAFF GEOLOGIST, SHELL OIL CO, 79- *Mem:* Am Asn Petrol Geologists. *Res:* Stratigraphy; sedimentation. *Mailing Add:* Shell Oil Co Box 481 Houston TX 77001

SWANSON, SAMUEL EDWARD, b Woodland, Calif, Aug 1, 46; m 79. GEOCHEMISTRY, PETROLOGY. *Educ:* Univ Calif, Davis, BS, 68, MS, 70; Stanford Univ, PhD(geol), 74. *Prof Exp:* Field asst geol, US Geol Surv, 67; res asst geol, Univ Calif, Davis, 70; asst prof earth sci, Univ NC, Charlotte, 74-76; asst prof, Appalchian State Univ, Boone, 76-79; ASST PROF GEOL, UNIV ALASKA, FAIRBANKS, 79- *Mem:* Can Mineral Soc; Am Geophys Union; Mineral Soc Am; Soc Environ Geochem & Health; Sigma Xi. *Res:* Application of geochemical techniques to the study of igneous and metamorphic rocks. *Mailing Add:* Geophys Inst Univ Alaska Fairbanks AK 99701

SWANSON, VERN BERNARD, b Alta, Iowa, Feb 8, 25; m 47; c 3. ANIMAL BREEDING. *Educ:* NMex Agr & Mech Col, BS, 48, MS, 56; Iowa State Univ, PhD(animal breeding), 65. *Prof Exp:* Instr agr, NMex State Dept Voc Educ, 48-51; animal husbandman, US Dept Interior, 51-53 & USDA, 53-54; instr animal husb, NMex State Univ, 54-56; from asst prof to assoc prof animal sci, 56-81, PROF EXTENSION SHEEP SPECIALIST ANIMAL SCI, COLO STATE UNIV, 81- *Mem:* Am Soc Animal Sci. *Res:* Sheep production; breeding; wool technology. *Mailing Add:* Dept of Animal Sci Colo State Univ Ft Collins CO 80521

SWANSON, VIRGINIA LEE, b Sioux City, Iowa, June 15, 22; m 67. PATHOLOGY. *Educ:* Univ Southern Calif, BA, 47; Yale Univ, MD, 52; Am Bd Path, dipl, 58. *Prof Exp:* Intern path, Sch Med, Yale Univ, 52-53; USPHS res fel, Path-Anat Inst, Univ Copenhagen, 53-55; instr path, Sch Med, Yale Univ, 55-59; hosp pathologist, US Army Med Command, Tokyo, Japan, 59-60; hosp pathologist, Australian Pub Health Serv, Port Moresby Gen Hosp, Territory Papua & New Guinea, 60-61; res pathologist, US Army Med Command, Tokyo, 61-62; res pathologist & chief path div, US Army Trop Res Med Lab, San Juan, PR, 62-65; res pathologist, Armed Forces Inst Path & Walter Reed Army Inst Res, Washington, DC, 65-66; assoc prof, 66-71, PROF PATH, SCH MED, UNIV SOUTHERN CALIF, 71- *Concurrent Pos:* Asst resident, Grace-New Haven Community Hosp, 55-56, chief resident, 56-57, asst pathologist, 57-59; assoc pathologist, Children's Hosp, Los Angeles, 66-71 & 73-; prof, Sch Med, Univ Calif, San Diego, 71-73; chief lab serv, Vet Admin Hosp, San Diego, 71-73. *Res:* Pathology of the gastrointestinal tract; malabsorption; malnutrition; immunopathology. *Mailing Add:* Children's Hosp 4650 Sunset Blvd Los Angeles CA 90027

SWANSON, W(ILBUR) M(ILTON), b Warren, Pa, June 26, 23; m 54; c 4. MECHANICAL & AERONAUTICAL ENGINEERING. *Educ:* Calif Inst Technol, BS, 44, MS, 48, ME, 51; Case Inst Technol, PhD, 57. *Prof Exp:* Mech engr, Ames Aeronaut Lab, NASA, 45-46; instr, Calif Inst Technol, 48-50, res engr, Hydrodyn Lab, 50-51; instr, Case Inst Technol, 51-55; res engr, E I du Pont de Nemours & Co, Inc, 55-57; asst prof mech eng, Case Inst Technol, 57-60; chmn dept mech eng, 64-65, co-chmn, 65-66, PROF ENG, WASHINGTON UNIV, ST LOUIS, 60- *Concurrent Pos:* Consult, Thompson Ramo Wooldridge, Inc, 57-59. *Mem:* Asn Advan Med Instrumentation; Am Soc Mech Engrs. *Res:* Fundamental fluid mechanics; rheology; biomechanics; streaming birefringence; acoustics; hemodynamics, heart valve and biomaterials research. *Mailing Add:* Dept of Mech Eng Washington Univ St Louis MO 63130

SWANSON, WILLIAM PAUL, b St Paul, Minn, Dec 20, 31; m 59; c 1. PARTICLE PHYSICS, RADIATION PHYSICS. *Educ:* Univ Minn, Minneapolis, BA, 53; Univ Calif, Berkeley, MA, 55, PhD(physics), 60; Am Bd Health Physics, cert, 77. *Prof Exp:* Res assoc particle physics, Univ Ill, Urbana, 60-61, asst prof physics, 61-64; Stiftung Volkswagenwerk fel particle physics, Deutsches Elektronen-Synchrotron, Hamburg, Ger, 65-66; guest prof physics, Univ Hamburg, Ger, 67; vis scientist particle physics, Europ Orgn Nuclear Res, Geneva, Switz, 67-68; STAFF PHYSICIST PARTICLE PHYSICS, RADIATION & HEALTH PHYSICS, STANFORD LINEAR ACCELERATOR CTR, STANFORD UNIV, 68- *Concurrent Pos:* Consult, Lawrence Radiation Lab, Univ Calif, 63-64, SHM Nuclear Corp, 74-75, Int Atomic Energy Agency, Vienna, 77, EMI Ther Systs Inc, 75-76, Int Comn Radiation Units & Measurements, 76, Varian Assocs, 80-, Nat Coun Radiation Protection & Measurements Comt, 81- *Honors & Awards:* Farrington Daniels Award, Am Asn Physicists Med, 81. *Mem:* Am Phys Soc; Am Asn Physicists Med; Health Physics Soc; Sigma Xi. *Res:* Properties and interactions of elementary particles, especially meson photoproduction, as well as antiproton annihilation and proton, kaon interactions at high energy; physical problems related to radiation safety at high-energy accelerators. *Mailing Add:* Stanford Linear Accelerator Ctr Stanford Univ Stanford CA 94305

SWANSTON, DOUGLAS NEIL, b Pensacola, Fla, June 8, 38; m 59; c 2. ENGINEERING GEOLOGY, GEOMORPHOLOGY. *Educ:* Univ Mich, Ann Arbor, BS, 60; Bowling Green State Univ, MA, 62; Mich State Univ, PhD(geol), 67. *Prof Exp:* Res geologist, Inst Northern Forestry, Juneau, Alaska, 64-71, RES GEOLOGIST, FOREST SCI LAB, US FOREST SERV, 71-; ASST PROF FOREST ENG, ORE STATE UNIV, 71- *Concurrent Pos:* Mem bd dirs, Found Glacier & Environ Res, 71-; consult geologist, Daniel, Mann, Johnson & Mendenhall, Archit & Engrs, 71- *Res:* Glacial geology; glaciology. *Mailing Add:* Dept of Forest Eng Ore State Univ Corvallis OR 97331

SWANTON, MARGARET CATHERINE, b Washington, DC, Sept 26, 20; m 71. PATHOLOGY. *Educ:* Univ NC, AB, 43; Johns Hopkins Univ, MD, 46. *Prof Exp:* Intern, Univ Iowa Hosps, 46-47; fel, 47-48, from instr to assoc prof, Sch Med, Univ NC, Chapel Hill, 48-69, prof path, sch med, Univ NC, Chapel Hill, 69-78; PATHOLOGIST, SAMPSON COUNTY MEM HOSP, CLINTON, NC, 78- *Concurrent Pos:* Attend pathologist, NC Mem Hosp, 52-78. consult, Watts Hosp, 53- *Mem:* Am Soc Clin Path; Col Am Path; Am Soc Cytol; Int Acad Path. *Res:* Cytopathology; hemophilic arthropathy. *Mailing Add:* Sampson County Mem Hosp Clinton NC 28328

SWANTON, WALTER F(REDERICK), b Wash, Nov 4, 10; m 40; c 2. CHEMICAL ENGINEERING, ECONOMETRICS. *Educ:* Mass Inst Technol, BS, 33; Univ Rochester, MS, 47. *Prof Exp:* Jr struct engr, US Bur Reclamation, 33-38; div petrol engr, Core Labs, Inc, 38-41; instr chem eng, Rochester Inst Technol, 41-43, instr phys chem, 46-50; proj engr, Pfaudler Co, 50-57; engr, Atomic Energy Div, Babcock & Wilcox Co, 57-58; sr proj engr, Pfaudler Co, 58-67, mgr waste recovery systs, Pfaudler Co Div, Sybron Corp, Rochester, 67-75; CONSULT, 75- *Concurrent Pos:* Instr, US Naval Acad, 43-46. *Honors & Awards:* Logozzo Award, 52. *Res:* Econometrics; industrial pollution abatement. *Mailing Add:* Meadowwood West Rush NY 14587

SWARBRICK, JAMES, b London, Eng, May 8, 34; m 60. PHARMACEUTICS, SURFACE CHEMISTRY. *Educ:* Univ London, BPharm, 60, PhD(med), 64, DSc(phys chem), 72; FRIC, 72. *Prof Exp:* From asst prof to assoc prof indust pharm, Purdue Univ, 64-66; prof & asst dean pharm, Univ Conn, 66-72; dir prod develop, Sterling-Winthrop Res Inst, 72-75; prof pharmaceut, Univ Sydney, 75-76; dean, Sch Pharm, Univ London, 76-78; prof pharm, Univ Southern Calif, 78-81; PROF PHARM & CHMN, DEPT PHARMACEUT, UNIV NC, CHAPEL HILL, 81- *Concurrent Pos:* Vis scientist, Astra Labs, Sweden, 71; chmn, USP-NF Panel Dissolution & Disintegration Testing, 72-75; examr, Sci Univ Malaysia, 77-78; consult, Australian Dept Health, 75-76; Orgn Am States, 78 & Pan-Am Health Orgn, 79 & 81; examr, Univ Singapore, 80-81; indust consult, 65-; consult, Alfateh Univ, Libya, 81. *Mem:* Am Pharmaceut Asn; fel Acad Pharmaceut Sci; Am Asn Col Pharm; fel Pharmaceut Soc Great Brit; fel Royal Soc Chem. *Res:* Dosage form design and drug delivery; percutaneous absorption; formulation of topical products; preformulation studies; interfacial phenomena of pharmaceutical and biological significance. *Mailing Add:* Sch of Pharm Univ NC Chapel Hill NC 27514

SWARD, EDWARD LAWRENCE, JR, b Chicago, Ill, Aug 21, 33; m 57; c 2. PHYSICAL CHEMISTRY. *Educ:* Augustana Col, Ill, BA, 55; Univ Buffalo, PhD(chem), 61. *Prof Exp:* Res chemist, Mylar Res & Develop Lab, E I du Pont de Nemours & Co, Inc, 60-64, Du Pont de Nemours, Luxembourg, SA, 64-67 & Del, 67-69; mgr mkt develop, Celanese Res Co, 69-72; mgr long range planning, 72-81, DIR PLANNING, EL PASO PRODS CO, 81- *Concurrent Pos:* Adj prof, Univ Tex, Permian Basin, 75- *Mem:* Commercial Develop Asn; Am Chem Soc. *Res:* Physical chemistry of polymers; kinetics; process development; financial and business planning and analysis; market research; financial planning. *Mailing Add:* 4322 Springbrook Odessa TX 79762

SWARDSON, MARY ANNE, b College Park, Ga, Sept 10, 28; m 49; c 3. GENERAL TOPOLOGY, SET THEORY. *Educ:* Tulane Univ, BA, 49; Ohio Univ, MS, 69, PhD(math), 81. *Prof Exp:* ASST PROF MATH, OHIO UNIV, 81- *Mem:* Am Math Soc. *Res:* Character of closed sets; generalizations of F-spaces; topological characterizations of set-theoretical axioms; generalizations of psuedocompactness. *Mailing Add:* 50 Sunnyside Athens OH 45701

SWARIN, STEPHEN JOHN, b Plainfield, NJ, July 24, 45; m 69; c 2. CHROMATOGRAPHY, ENVIRONMENTAL ANALYSIS. *Educ:* Lafayette Col, AB, 67; Univ Mass, MS, 69, PhD(anal chem), 72. *Prof Exp:* Assoc res scientist, 72-76, sr res scientist, 75-79, staff res scientist, 79-81, SR

STAFF SCIENTIST, GEN MOTORS RES LABS, 81- *Mem:* Am Chem Soc; Am Soc Testing & Mat; Sigma Xi. *Res:* Polymer analysis; polymer additives analysis; liquid chromatography; derivatization for detectability; environmental analysis; thermal analysis; instrumentation. *Mailing Add:* Anal Chem Dept Gen Motors Res Labs Warren MI 48090

SWARINGEN, ROY ARCHIBALD, JR, b Winston-Salem, NC, Feb 1, 42; m 69. ORGANIC CHEMISTRY. *Educ:* Univ NC, Chapel Hill, AB, 64; Univ Ill, Urbana, MS, 66, PhD(org chem), 69. *Prof Exp:* Res chemist org chem, R J Reynolds Tobacco Co, 69-70; sr develop chemist, 70-74, sect head develop res, 74-81, DEPT HEAD, CHEM DEVELOP LABS, BURROUGHS WELLCOME CO, 81- *Mem:* Am Chem Soc; Royal Soc Chem. *Res:* Development research in pharmaceutical chemistry; synthetic organic chemistry; heterocyclic compounds. *Mailing Add:* Chem Develop Burroughs Wellcome Co Research Triangle Park NC 27709

SWARM, H(OWARD) MYRON, b Everett, Wash, July 12, 16; m 40; c 4. ELECTRICAL ENGINEERING. *Educ:* Univ Wash, BS, 40, MS, 50; Stanford Univ, PhD, 60. *Prof Exp:* Radio engr, Civil Aeronaut Admin, Washington, DC, 40-44; res engr, Appl Physics Lab, 44-46, assoc dean, Col Eng, 72-76, PROF ELEC ENG, UNIV WASH, 47-, ASSOC DEAN RES, GRAD SCH, 76- *Concurrent Pos:* Consult, Boeing Airplane Co, 58-, John Fluke Mfg Co, 58- & Seattle Develop Lab, Minneapolis-Honeywell Regulator Co, 60- *Mem:* Sr mem Inst Elec & Electronics Engrs. *Res:* Radio wave propagation; communication theory applications. *Mailing Add:* Dept of Elec Eng Univ of Wash Seattle WA 98195

SWARM, RICHARD LEE, b St Louis, Mo, June 9, 27; m 50; c 2. PATHOLOGY, CARCINOGENESIS. *Educ:* Wash Univ, BA, 49, BS & MD, 50; Am Bd Path, dipl. *Prof Exp:* Intern, Barnes Hosp, St Louis, Mo, 50-51; instr & resident path, Washington Univ & Barnes Hosp, 51-54; pathologist, USPHS Med Ctr, 54-55 & Nat Cancer Inst, 55-65; assoc prof path, Col Med, Univ Cincinnati, 65-68; dir, Dept Exp Path & Toxicol, Res Div, Hoffmann-LaRoche, Inc, 68-82. *Concurrent Pos:* Clin assoc prof path, Columbia Univ, 70- *Mem:* Am Soc Toxicol Pathologists; Am Asn Cancer Res; Am Asn Pathologists; fel Am Soc Clin Path; Col Am Pathologists. *Res:* Histopathology and toxicology in man and laboratory animals; morphology of neoplasms and carcinogenesis; radiation injury; transplantation of tissues and tumors, particularly chondrosarcomas; ultrastructure of neoplastic cells. *Mailing Add:* PO Box 808 Ridgewood NJ 07451

SWART, WILLIAM LEE, b Brethren, Mich, July 13, 30; m 62; c 2. MATHEMATICS. *Educ:* Cent Mich Univ, BS, 58, MA, 62; Univ Mich, Ann Arbor, EdD(math educ), 69. *Prof Exp:* Teacher, Mesick Consol Schs, Mich, 58-61 & Livonia Pub Schs, 61-63; instr math, Eastern Mich Univ, 63-65; consult math educ, Genesee Intermediate Sch Dist, Mich, 65-67; from asst prof to assoc prof, 67-74, PROF MATH, CENT MICH UNIV, 74- *Res:* Learning of elementary mathematics; action research in public schools. *Mailing Add:* Dept of Math Cent Mich Univ Mt Pleasant MI 48858

SWARTOUT, JOHN ARTHUR, b Madison, Wis, Mar 17, 16; m 43; c 2. TECHNICAL MANAGEMENT, REACTOR ENGINEERING. *Educ:* Univ Buffalo, BA, 37; Northwestern Univ, PhD(phys chem), 40. *Prof Exp:* Res chemist, E I du Pont de Nemours & Co, 40-45; res chemist, Oak Ridge Nat Lab, 45-48, dir chem div, 49-50, asst res dir, 50-52; dir homogeneous reactor proj, 51-55, dep res dir, 52-55, dep dir, 55-64; asst gen mgr for reactors, AEC, 64-65; dir technol, 66-68, vpres, 68-74, CONSULT, UNION CARBIDE CORP, 74- *Concurrent Pos:* Res assoc, Metall Lab, Univ Chicago, 43, Clinton Labs, Tenn, 43-44 & Hanford Eng Works, Wash, 44-45. *Mem:* AAAS; Am Chem Soc; Am Nuclear Soc; Am Inst Chemists; Indust Res Inst. *Res:* High polymers; radiochemistry; chemical processes for isolation of fissionable elements; preparation of radioisotopes; development of nuclear reactors; development of nuclear power; environmental systems. *Mailing Add:* 16 W Beach Lagoon Rd Hilton Head Island SC 29928

SWARTS, ELWYN LOWELL, b Hornell, NY, Feb 26, 29; m 54; c 3. PHYSICAL CHEMISTRY. *Educ:* Hamilton Col, NY, AB, 49; Brown Univ, PhD, 54. *Prof Exp:* Mem fac, Alfred Univ, 53-56, res chemist, Knolls Atomic Lab, Gen Elec Co, NY, 56-57, res chemist, Glass Technol Lab, Ohio, 57-59; STAFF SCIENTIST, PPG INDUSTS, INC, 59- *Concurrent Pos:* Mem subcomt, Int Comn Glass. *Mem:* Am Chem Soc; Am Ceramic Soc. *Res:* Properties of glass; melting reactions. *Mailing Add:* Glass Res Lab PPG Industs Inc Creighton PA 15030

SWARTZ, BLAIR KINCH, b Detroit, Mich, Nov 5, 32; m 55; c 1. NUMERICAL ANALYSIS. *Educ:* Antioch Col, BS, 55; Mass Inst Technol, MS, 58; NY Univ, PhD(math), 70. *Prof Exp:* Asst biol, Sch Med & Dent, Univ Rochester, 51-52; asst chem, Detroit Edison Co, 52-53; asst physics, Antioch Col, 53-54; high sch teacher, 54-55; asst math, Mass Inst Technol, 55-58; res asst, 58, group leader, 68-74, assoc group leader, 78-80, MEM STAFF, LOS ALAMOS NAT LAB, 59- *Concurrent Pos:* Asst, Am Optical Co, 55-56; lectr, State Univ NY Teachers Col New Paltz, 58 & Univ NMex, 59; ed, SIAM J Numerical Anal, 74-75. *Mem:* Am Math Soc; Soc Indust & Appl Math. *Res:* Approximation theory; differential equations. *Mailing Add:* 172 Paseo Penasco Los Alamos NM 87544

SWARTZ, CHARLES DANA, b Baltimore, Md, July 24, 15; m 49; c 3. PHYSICS. *Educ:* Johns Hopkins Univ, AB, 38, PhD(physics), 43. *Prof Exp:* Physicist, Manhattan Proj, SAM Labs, Columbia Univ, 42-46; assoc, Lab Nuclear Studies, Cornell Univ, 46-48; from instr to asst prof physics, Johns Hopkins Univ, 48-56; assoc prof, 56-62, prof, 62-79, EMER PROF PHYSICS, UNION COL, NY, 79- *Concurrent Pos:* Fulbright lectr, Univ Ankara, 61-62; vis prof physics, Rensselaer Polytech Inst, 69-70. *Mem:* Am Phys Soc; Am Asn Physics Teachers. *Res:* Neutron physics; energy levels of light nuclei; science education; low-temperature physics. *Mailing Add:* 10 Crestwood Dr RD 1 Ballston Lake NY 12019

SWARTZ, CLIFFORD EDWARD, b Niagara Falls, NY, Feb 21, 25; m 46; c 6. EXPERIMENTAL HIGH ENERGY PHYSICS, PHYSICS EDUCATION. *Educ:* Univ Rochester, AB, 45, MS, 46, PhD(physics), 51. *Prof Exp:* Assoc physicist, Brookhaven Nat Lab, 51-62; assoc prof, 57-67, PROF PHYSICS, STATE UNIV NY STONY BROOK, 67- *Mem:* Am Phys Soc; Am Asn Physics Teachers. *Res:* Particle physics; high energy accelerators for nuclear physics research; science curriculum revision and textbooks, kindergarten through college. *Mailing Add:* Dept of Physics State Univ of NY Stony Brook NY 11794

SWARTZ, DONALD PERCY, b Preston, Ont, Sept, 12, 21; US citizen; m 44; c 2. OBSTETRICS & GYNECOLOGY. *Educ:* Univ Western Ont, BA & MD, 51, MSc, 53. *Prof Exp:* Nat Res Coun Can grant, Univ Western Ont, 52-53; Am Cancer Soc fel, Johns Hopkins Hosp, 56-57, instr obstet & gynec, 57-58; lectr physiol, Univ Western Ont, 58-62; clin prof, Columbia Univ, 62-72, prof obstet & gynec, 72; PROF OBSTET & GYNEC & CHMN DEPT, ALBANY MED COL, 72-; OBSTETRICIAN-GYNECOLOGIST-IN-CHIEF, ALBANY MED CTR, 72- *Concurrent Pos:* Markle scholar, Univ Western Ont, 58-62; consult obstet & gynec, St Peter's Hosp, 72- *Mem:* Fel Am Gynec Soc; Am Col Obstet & Gynec; Soc Study Reprod; Am Fertility Soc. *Res:* Fertility control; hormonal contraception; new approaches to pregnancy termination; gynecologic endocrinology. *Mailing Add:* Dept of Obstet & Gynec Albany Med Ctr Albany NY 12208

SWARTZ, FRANK JOSEPH, b Pittsburgh, Pa, Mar 22, 27; m 46; c 2. ANATOMY. *Educ:* Western Reserve Univ, BS, 49, MS, 51, PhD(zool), 55. *Prof Exp:* Asst biol, Western Reserve Univ, 49-52, Nat Cancer Inst fel, 55-56; from asst prof to assoc prof, 56-70, PROF ANAT, SCH MED, UNIV LOUISVILLE, 70- *Concurrent Pos:* Lectr & USPHS spec fel, Dept Anat, Harvard Med Sch, 69-70. *Mem:* Am Soc Anat. *Res:* Human anatomy; cellular differentiation and genetic significance of polyploids in mammalian tissues. *Mailing Add:* 208 Beechwood Rd Louisville KY 40207

SWARTZ, GEORGE ALLAN, b Scranton, Pa, Dec 9, 30; c 3. PHYSICS. *Educ:* Mass Inst Technol, BS, 52; Univ Pa, MS, 54, PhD(physics), 58. *Prof Exp:* MEM TECH STAFF, DAVID SARNOFF RES CTR, RCA CORP, 58- *Concurrent Pos:* Adj assoc prof dept metall & mat sci, Stevens Inst Technol. *Mem:* Am Phys Soc; Sigma Xi. *Res:* Solid state microwave devices, particularly impact avalanche, transit time microwave sources and PIN diode switches; photovoltaic solar energy sources; amorphous silicon photovotaic energy sources. *Mailing Add:* David Sarnoff Res Ctr RCA Corp Princeton NJ 08540

SWARTZ, GORDON ELMER, b Buffalo, NY, May 12, 17; m 41; c 2. ZOOLOGY, EMBRYOLOGY. *Educ:* Univ Buffalo, BA, 39, MA, 41; NY Univ, PhD(biol), 46. *Prof Exp:* From asst to assoc prof, 39-62, prof, 62-79, EMER PROF BIOL, STATE UNIV NY BUFFALO, 79- *Mem:* Fel AAAS; Am Micros Soc; Am Soc Zoologists; Am Asn Anat; NY Acad Sci. *Res:* Organogenesis; vertebrate experimental embryology; transplantation. *Mailing Add:* 24 Copper Heights Snyder NY 14226

SWARTZ, GRACE LYNN, b Coaldale, Pa, 1943. INORGANIC CHEMISTRY. *Educ:* Muhlenberg Col, BS, 65; Dartmouth Col, MA, 67; Fla State Univ, PhD(chem), 77. *Prof Exp:* Vis instr chem, Fla State Univ, 67-72, res assoc, 72-73; vis instr chem, Purdue Univ, 73-74; res asst chem, Fla State Univ, 74-77; vis asst prof, 77-80, ASST PROF CHEM, MICH TECHNOL UNIV, 80- *Mem:* Am Chem Soc; AAAS. *Res:* Mechanistic aspects of transition metal carbonyls and substituted metal carbonyls used in catalytic reactions, with the active catalyst generated thermally or photochemically. *Mailing Add:* Dept Chem & Chem Eng Mich Technol Univ Houghton MI 49931

SWARTZ, HAROLD M, b Chicago, Ill, June 22, 35; m 81; c 4. RADIOLOGY, ELECTRON SPIN RESONANCE. *Educ:* Univ Ill, BS & MD, 59; Univ NC, MS, 62; Georgetown Univ, PhD(biochem), 69. *Prof Exp:* Fel nuclear med, Walter Reed Army Inst Res, Med Corps, US Army, 62-64, res med officer, 64-68, chief dept biophys, 68-70, chief dept biol chem, 70; assoc prof radiol & biochem, Med Col Wis, 70-74, prof, 74-80, dir, Radiation Biol & Biophys Lab, 70-80, dir, Nat Biomed Electron Spin Resonance Ctr, 74-80; PROF BIOPHYS & ASSOC DEAN ACAD AFFAIRS, COL MED, UNIV ILL, URBANA-CHAMPAIGN, 80- *Mem:* AAAS; Radiation Res Soc; Soc Nuclear Med; NY Acad Sci. *Res:* Free radicals and paramagnetic metal ions in biological systems; oxygen toxicity; radiation biology applied to radiation therapy; carcinogenesis. *Mailing Add:* Biophys Dept Col Med Univ Ill Urbana IL 61801

SWARTZ, HARRY, b Detroit, Mich, June 21, 11; wid. ALLERGY, SCIENCE EDUCATION. *Educ:* Univ Mich, AB, 30, MD, 33. *Prof Exp:* Clin asst allergy, Med Sch & Clins, NY Univ, 37-40 & Flower & Fifth Ave Hosp, New York, 40-42; asst chief allergy clin, Harlem Hosp, 46-48; prof med & chief allergy dept, NY Polyclin Med Sch & Hosp, 57-72; pres, Health Field Validation Corp, 67-72. *Concurrent Pos:* Chief allergy dept, Tilton Gen Hosp, Ft Dix, NJ, 42-46; clin asst, Inst Allergy, Roosevelt Hosp, 46-72; indust consult allergy; consult nutrit prod to pharmaceut 77 food indust, consult therapeut cosmetics to cosmetic indust & consult to publ indust; ed, Health Series, Med & Health Reporter, Issues in Current Med Pract & Med Opinion & Rev; sci dir, Mundo Medico, SAm, 72-; ed-in-chief, Investigacion Medica Int, 73- *Mem:* emer fel Am Col Allergists; emer fel Am Acad Allergy; emer fel Asn Clin Immunol & Allergy; fel Royal Soc Health. *Res:* Clinical allergy; high protein vegetable source material as a partial answer to world hunger; investigation of commercial products for efficacy and safety. *Mailing Add:* Apdo 752 Cuernavaca Morelos Mexico

SWARTZ, HARRY SIP, b Wichita, Kans, July 29, 25; m 47; c 4. PHARMACY ADMINISTRATION, PHARMACY. *Educ:* Albany Col Pharm, Union Univ, NY, BS, 51; Univ Colo, MS, 54; Univ Iowa, PhD(pharm, pharmaceut admin), 59. *Prof Exp:* Lab asst pharmaceut chem, Univ Colo, 52-54; instr pharm & pharmaceut admin, Creighton Univ, 54-55; instr pharm & pharmacist, Univ Iowa, 55-59; from asst prof to assoc prof, 59-67, PROF PHARM & PHARMACEUT ADMIN, FERRIS STATE COL, 67- *Concurrent Pos:* Consult community, hosp & mfg pharm & extended care. *Mem:* Am Pharmaceut Asn; Am Col Apothecaries. *Res:* Product development; hospital pharmacy and manufacturing; cosmetic pharmaceuticals; orthopedic and surgical garments. *Mailing Add:* Sch of Pharm Ferris State Col Big Rapids MI 49307

SWARTZ, JACOB, b Poznan, Poland, June 5, 21; US citizen; m 45; c 4. PSYCHIATRY, PSYCHOANALYSIS. *Educ:* Boston Univ, BS, 42, MD, 46. *Prof Exp:* Intern med, Boston City Hosp, 46-47; assoc psychiat, Med Col Ga, 48; resident psychiat, Boston Univ Hosp, 49-52, from instr to assoc prof, 50-69, PROF PSYCHIAT, SCH MED, BOSTON UNIV, 69-, ASSOC DEAN, 71-, ASSOC CHMN, DIV PSYCHIAT, 77- *Concurrent Pos:* Mem, Boston Psychoanal Soc & Inst, 57-, chmn bd trustees, 66-70, instr, 72-; training & supv psychoanalyst, Boston Psychoanal Soc & Inst, 75-; assoc psychiatrist-in-chief, Univ Hosp, 77- *Mem:* Am Psychiat Asn; Am Psychoanal Asn; Int Psychoanal Asn. *Mailing Add:* 80 E Concord St Boston MA 02118

SWARTZ, JAMES E, b DC, June 12, 51; m 80. ORGANIC ELECTROCHEMISTRY, PHYSICAL ORGANIC CHEMISTRY. *Educ:* Stanislaus State Col, BS, 73; Univ Calif, Santa Cruz, PhD(chem), 78. *Prof Exp:* Instr chem, Univ Calif, Santa Cruz, 78; res fel, Calif Inst Technol, 78-80; ASST PROF CHEM, GRINNELL COL, 80- *Mem:* Am Chem Soc; AAAS. *Res:* Nucleophilic aromatic substitution reactions; free radical radical reactions; radical anions. *Mailing Add:* 203 Sci Grinnell Col Grinnell IA 50112

SWARTZ, JAMES LAWRENCE, b Lowell, Mass, July 20, 39; m 63; c 2. ELECTROANALYTICAL CHEMISTRY, CONTROL ENGINEERING. *Educ:* Univ Lowell, BS, 65; Northeastern Univ, MS, 71, PhD(chem), 74. *Prof Exp:* Res chemist, Res & Advan Develop Div, Avco Corp, 64-65; res chemist, Res Ctr, 65-70, sr develop engr chem, Systs Div, 70-75 & Corp Eng, 75-76, SR SCIENTIST & INSTR CHEM, FOXBORO CO, 76-, SR SYSTS ENGR, 80- *Concurrent Pos:* Lectr, Dept Chem, Grad Sch, Northeastern Univ, 75-77. *Mem:* Am Chem Soc; sr mem Instrument Soc Am; Inst Elec & Electronics Engrs. *Res:* Sensor development for continuous on-line process monitoring and control; process analyzers based on electrochemical and chromatographic principles; ion-selective electrodes and their industrial and clinical applications. *Mailing Add:* Foxboro Co 38 Neponset Ave Foxboro MA 02035

SWARTZ, JOHN CROUCHER, b Syracuse, NY, Oct 25, 24; m 56; c 3. PHYSICS, MATERIALS SCIENCE. *Educ:* Yale Univ, BS, 46; Syracuse Univ, MS, 49, PhD, 52. *Prof Exp:* Res physicist, Consol Vacuum Corp, 52-55; sr scientist, E C Bain Lab Fundamental Res, US Steel Corp, 55-71 & Tyco Labs, Inc, Mass, 72-75; sr scientist, Mobil Tyco Solar Energy Corp, 75-77; SR SCIENTIST, WESTINGHOUSE RES & DEVELOP CTR, 78- *Mem:* Am Phys Soc; Metall Soc; Am Asn Crystal Growth; Mat Res Soc. *Res:* Crystal growth; metallurgy; defects in solids; solid state physics. *Mailing Add:* Res & Develop Ctr Westinghouse Elec Corp 1310 Beulah Rd Pittsburgh PA 15235

SWARTZ, LESLIE GERARD, b Chicago, Ill, Aug 16, 30; m 58; c 4. PARASITOLOGY. *Educ:* Univ Ill, BS, 53, MS, 54, PhD(zool), 58. *Prof Exp:* Assoc prof, 58-70, PROF ZOOL, UNIV ALASKA, FAIRBANKS, 70- *Concurrent Pos:* Sr res assoc, Rice Univ, 66-67. *Mem:* AAAS; Am Soc Parasitol. *Res:* Helminth parasitology, especially ecology; avian, freshwater and general ecology. *Mailing Add:* Dept of Biol Sci Univ of Alaska Fairbanks AK 99701

SWARTZ, MARJORIE LOUISE, b Indianapolis, Ind, Feb 1, 24. INORGANIC CHEMISTRY. *Educ:* Butler Univ, BS, 46; Ind Univ, MS, 59. *Prof Exp:* Res assoc, 46-53, from instr to assoc prof, 53-69, PROF DENT MAT, SCH DENT, IND UNIV, INDIANAPOLIS, 69- *Honors & Awards:* Souder Award, Int Asn Dent Res, 68. *Mem:* AAAS; fel Am Col Dent; hon mem Am Dent Asn; Int Asn Dent Mat (pres, 65); hon mem Am Asn Women Dentists. *Res:* Physical and chemical properties of dental cements, resins and amalgams; effect of restorative materials on physical and chemical properties of tooth structure. *Mailing Add:* Ind Univ Sch of Dent 1121 W Michigan Indianapolis IN 46202

SWARTZ, STUART ENDSLEY, b Chicago, Ill, Oct 17, 38; m 63. CIVIL ENGINEERING. *Educ:* Ill Inst Technol, BS, 59, MS, 62, PhD(civil eng), 68. *Prof Exp:* Engr, Caterpillar Tractor Co, Ill, 60; res assoc, Ill Inst Tech, 67-68; from asst prof to assoc prof, 68-77, PROF CIVIL ENG, KANS STATE UNIV, 77- *Mem:* Am Soc Civil Engrs; fel Am Concrete Inst; Soc Exp Stress Anal. *Res:* Analysis and design of folded plate structures; theoretical and experimental studies on the buckling of folded plates and other concrete shells; buckling of concrete columns; analysis and design of concrete shells; buckling of concrete panels; fracture toughness of concrete. *Mailing Add:* Dept Civil Eng Seaton Hall Kans State Univ Manhattan KS 66506

SWARTZ, WILLIAM EDWARD, JR, b Braddock, Pa, Aug 16, 44; m 67; c 2. SURFACE ANALYSIS. *Educ:* Juniata Col, BS, 66; Mass Inst Technol, PhD(chem), 71. *Prof Exp:* Res assoc chem, Univ Ga, 71, Univ Md, 71-72; asst prof, 72-77, assoc prof, 77-82, PROF CHEM, UNIV SOUTH FLA, 82- *Concurrent Pos:* Adj asst prof, Dept Physics, Univ South Fla, 76-78. *Mem:* Am Chem Soc; Am Vacuum Soc; Soc Appl Spectros; Am Soc Testing & Mat; AAAS. *Res:* Analytical applications of surface analysis techniques with emphasis on x-ray photoelectron spectroscopy; heterogeneous catalysts and surface chemical phenomena in integrated circuit components. *Mailing Add:* Dept Chem Univ South Fla Tampa FL 33620

SWARTZ, WILLIAM JOHN, b Portage, Wis, Aug 9, 20; m 48; c 2. MATHEMATICS. *Educ:* Mont State Univ, BS, 44; Mass Inst Technol, SM, 49; Iowa State Univ, PhD(math), 55. *Prof Exp:* Instr math, Mass Inst Technol, 47-48, Mont State Univ, 49-51 & Iowa State Univ, 51-55; from asst prof to assoc prof, 55-62, PROF MATH, MONT STATE UNIV, 62- *Mem:* Am Math Soc. *Res:* Differential equations. *Mailing Add:* Dept of Math Mont State Univ Bozeman MT 59715

SWARTZENDRUBER, DALE, b Parnell, Iowa, July 6, 25; m 49; c 4. SOIL PHYSICS. *Educ:* Iowa State Univ, BS, 50, MS, 52, PhD(soil physics), 54. *Prof Exp:* Asst soil physics, Iowa State Univ, 50-53; instr agr, Goshen Col, 53-54; asst soil scientist, Univ Calif, Los Angeles, 55-56; assoc prof, Purdue Univ, 56-63, prof soil physics, 63-67, PROF SOIL PHYSICS, UNIV NEBR-LINCOLN, 77- *Concurrent Pos:* Vis prof, Iowa State Univ, 59, Georgia Inst Technol, 68 & Hebrew Univ Jerusalem & Volcani Inst, Rehovot, Israel, 71; vis scholar, Cambridge Univ, 71. *Honors & Awards:* Soil Sci Award, Soil Sci Soc Am, 75. *Mem:* AAAS; fel Soil Sci Soc Am; fel Am Soc Agron; Am Geophys Union; Int Soc Soil Sci. *Res:* Physics of soil and water, including water movement through saturated and unsaturated soils and porous media; soil, air, temperature, and structure; soil-water-plant relationships; hydrology and water resources. *Mailing Add:* Dept of Agron Keim Hall E Campus Univ of Nebr Lincoln NE 68583

SWARTZENDRUBER, DONALD CLAIR, b Kalona, Iowa, June 21, 30; m 55; c 2. ZOOLOGY. *Educ:* Univ Iowa, BA, 55, MS, 58, PhD(zool), 62. *Prof Exp:* Res asst biol, Oak Ridge Nat Lab, 59-60, res assoc, 62-63; biologist, 63-65, res assoc microbiol, Univ Mich, Ann Arbor, 65-68; sr scientist, Med Div, Oak Ridge Assoc Univs, 68-81; SR RES SCIENTIST, PHARMACEUT DIV, CIBA-GEIGY CORP, 81- *Mem:* AAAS; Electron Micros Soc Am; Sigma Xi; Am Soc Cell Biol; Soc Exp Biol & Med. *Res:* Electron microscopic studies of lymphatic tissues; ultrastructural pathology; histopathology of connective tissue. *Mailing Add:* Pharmaceut Div Ciba-Geigy Corp Ardsley NY 10502

SWARTZENDRUBER, LYDON JAMES, b Wellman, Iowa, Aug 8, 33; m 49. PHYSICS. *Educ:* Iowa State Univ, BS, 57; Univ Md, PhD(physics), 68. *Prof Exp:* PHYSICIST, NAT BUR STANDARDS, 60- *Mem:* AAAS; Am Phys Soc; Am Soc Testing & Mat; Am Inst Mining, Metall & Petrol Engrs; Am Soc Nondestructive Testing. *Res:* Solid state physics; semiconductors; magnetism; metallurgy. *Mailing Add:* Nat Bur Standards Gaithersburg MD 20760

SWARTZENTRUBER, PAUL EDWIN, b Lagrange, Ind, Apr 23, 31; m 55; c 3. ORGANIC CHEMISTRY, INFORMATION SCIENCE. *Educ:* Goshen Col, BA, 53; Univ Minn, Minneapolis, MS, 55; Univ Mo, PhD(org chem), 61. *Prof Exp:* Res chemist, Nat Cancer Inst, 56-59; asst ed org indexing dept, 61-63, assoc ed, 63-64, head org indexing dept, 64-71, mgr phys & inorg indexing dept, 71-72, mgr chem substance handling dept, 72-73, mgr chem technol, 73-77, asst to ed, 77-79, MANAGING ED, CHEM ABSTR SERV, 79- *Mem:* AAAS; Am Chem Soc. *Res:* Synthetic organic chemistry; chemical nomenclature; storage and retrieval of chemical information; abstracting and indexing of chemical literature. *Mailing Add:* Chem Abstr Serv PO Box 3012 Columbus OH 43210

SWARTZMAN, GORDON LENI, b New York, NY, Sept 2, 43; m 69; c 1. RESOURCE MANAGEMENT, BIOMETRICS. *Educ:* Cooper Union, NY, BS, 64; Univ Mich, MS, 65, PhD(indust eng), 69. *Prof Exp:* Fel ecol modeling, Colo State Univ, 69-72; vis prof agr & ecol models, Univ Reading, 72-73; res assoc statist ecol models, 73-76, res asst prof matrices ecol models, 76-79, RES ASSOC PROF CALCULUS POPULATION DYNAMICS, UNIV WASH, 79- *Mem:* AAAS; Int Soc Ecol Modelers. *Res:* Interaction between fur seals and fisheries on Bering Sea; simulation modeling as a tool in impact assessment; stochastic models for fisheries management; Lake Washington rainbow trout introduction impact. *Mailing Add:* Ctr Quant Sci HR-20 Univ Wash Seattle WA 98195

SWARTZWELDER, JOHN CLYDE, b Lynn, Mass, Apr 1, 11; m 64; c 2. MEDICAL PARASITOLOGY, TROPICAL PUBLIC HEALTH. *Educ:* Univ Mass, BS, 33; Tulane Univ, MS, 34, PhD(med protozool), 37; Am Bd Med Microbiol, dipl, 64. *Prof Exp:* Asst med parasitol, Sch Med, Tulane Univ, 33-37; from instr to prof med parasitol, Sch Med, 37-75, head dept trop med & med parasitol, 60-75, educ dir, Interam Training Prog Trop Med, 59-69, assoc dir, Int Ctr Med Res & Training, 61-69, dir, Interam Training Prog Trop Med & Int Ctr Med Res & Training, 69-75, EMER PROF MED PARASITOL, LA STATE UNIV MED CTR, NEW ORLEANS, 75- *Concurrent Pos:* Scientist, Charity Hosp, New Orleans, 38-; consult, Vet Admin Hosp, 49- *Mem:* Am Soc Trop Med & Hyg (vpres); Am Soc Parasitol; hon mem Mex Soc Parasitol. *Res:* Amebiasis; Chagas' disease; anthelmintics; research training in tropical medicine; medical education. *Mailing Add:* 3433 Esplanade Ave New Orleans LA 70119

SWATEK, FRANK EDWARD, b Oklahoma City, Okla, June 4, 29; m 51; c 5. MICROBIOLOGY, MYCOLOGY. *Educ:* San Diego State Col, BS, 51; Univ Calif, Los Angeles, MA, 55, PhD(microbiol), 56. *Prof Exp:* From instr to assoc prof, 56-63, PROF MICROBIOL, CALIF STATE UNIV, LONG BEACH, 63-, CHMN DEPT, 60-; CLIN PROF MED, SCH MED, UNIV CALIF, IRVINE, 80- *Concurrent Pos:* Consult, Dept Allergy & Dermat, Long Beach Vet Admin Hosp, 60-, Douglas Aircraft Co, Inc, 61- & Hyland Lab, 68-; lectr, Sch Med, Univ Southern Calif, 62- *Honors & Awards:* Carski Award, Am Soc Microbiol, 74. *Mem:* Am Soc Microbiol; Am Pub Health Asn; NY Acad Sci; fel Royal Soc Health; Sigma Xi. *Res:* Ecology and experimental pathology of deep mycoses, especially Coccidioides, Cryptococcus and Dermatophytes; industrial work on fungus deterioration of man-made products. *Mailing Add:* Dept Microbiol Calif State Univ Long Beach CA 90805

SWEADNER, KATHLEEN JOAN, b Pittsburgh, Pa, Oct 17, 49. BIOCHEMISTRY, NEUROBIOLOGY. *Educ:* Univ Calif, Santa Barbara, BA, 71; Harvard Univ, MA, 74, PhD(biochem), 77. *Prof Exp:* Consult, Millipore Corp, 73-76; instr neurobiol, 80-81, ASST PROF PHYSIOL, DEPT SURG, HARVARD MED SCH, 81-; ASST PROF PHYSIOL, DEPT SURG, MASS GEN HOSP, 81- *Concurrent Pos:* Estab investr, Am Heart Asn, 82-87. *Mem:* Soc Neurosci. *Res:* Identification of proteins with specialized functions in the nervous system; two distinct sodium, potassium-ATPases and transmitter-specific components of the synapse. *Mailing Add:* Warren 4 Mass Gen Hosp Fruit St Boston MA 02114

SWEARINGEN, JOHN ELDRED, b Columbia, SC, Sept 7, 18; m 69; c 3. CHEMICAL ENGINEERING. *Educ:* Univ SC, BS, 38; Carnegie Inst Technol, MS, 39. *Hon Degrees:* EngD, SDak Sch Mines & Technol, 60; LLD, Knox Col, Ill, 62, DePauw Univ, 64, Univ SC, 65, Ill Col & Butler Univ, 68; DLH, Nat Col Educ, 67. *Prof Exp:* Chemist, Standard Oil Co, 39-43, group leader, 43-47; proj engr, Pan Am Petrol Corp, 47, develop supt mfg, 47-48, asst to mgr mfg, 48-49, exec asst to exec vpres, 51; gen mgr prod, 51-54, vpres prod, 54-56, exec vpres, 56-58, pres, 58-65, CHMN BD, STANDARD OIL CO (IND), 65-, DIR, 52-, CHIEF EXEC OFF, 60- *Concurrent Pos:* Dir, Am Petrol Inst, 51-; consult, Nat Petrol Coun & Nat Indust Conf Bd, 60-; consult, Hwy Users Fedn for Safety & Mobility, 69- *Mem:* Nat Acad Eng; Am Inst Chem Engrs; Am Chem Soc; Am Inst Mining, Metall & Petrol Engrs. *Res:* Petroleum production and processing; management. *Mailing Add:* Standard Oil Co (Ind) 200 E Randolph Dr Chicago IL 60601

SWEARINGEN, JUDSON STERLING, b San Antonio, Tex, Jan 11, 07; m 60. CHEMICAL ENGINEERING. *Educ:* Univ Tex, BS, 29, MS, 30, PhD(phys chem), 33. *Prof Exp:* Partner, San Antonio Refining Co, 33-38; asst prof chem eng, Univ Tex, 39-40, assoc prof, 40-41, prof, 41-42; turbine designer, Elliott Co, 42-43; div engr, Kellex Corp, 43-45; pres, Statham-Swearingen, Inc, 59-62; PRES, ROTOFLOW CORP, 46-, ROTOFLOW AG, SWITZ, 71- & SWEARINGEN BROS, INC, 64- *Mem:* Am Chem Soc; Am Inst Chem Engrs; Am Inst Mech Engrs; Am Soc Heating, Refrig & Air-Conditioning Engrs. *Res:* Low temperature gas separations; turboexpanders; petroleum and gas; seals, pumps and centrifugal compressors; adsorption refrigeration. *Mailing Add:* Rotoflow Corp 2235 Carmelina Ave Los Angeles CA 90064

SWEARINGIN, MARVIN LAVERNE, b Hamburg, Ill, Jan 23, 31; m 50; c 3. AGRONOMY. *Educ:* Univ Mo-Columbia, BS, 56, MS, 57; Ore State Univ, PhD(agron), 62. *Prof Exp:* Asst crops teaching, Univ Mo, 56-57; instr farm crops, Ore State Univ, 57-61; from asst prof to assoc prof, 61-75, PROF AGRON, PURDUE UNIV, WEST LAFAYETTE, 75- *Concurrent Pos:* Soybean res consult, Purdue Univ-Brazil Proj, Brazil, 67-69 & AID, Brazil, 71- *Mem:* Am Soc Agron; Crop Sci Soc Am. *Res:* Crop management systems for corn, soybeans and small grains. *Mailing Add:* Dept of Agron Purdue Univ West Lafayette IN 47906

SWEAT, FLOYD WALTER, b Salt Lake City, Utah, July 21, 41; m 65; c 2. BIOCHEMISTRY. *Educ:* Univ Utah, BS, 64, PhD(org chem), 68. *Prof Exp:* NIH fel, Harvard Univ, 68-70; asst prof, 70-77, ASSOC PROF BIOCHEM, UNIV UTAH, 77- *Mem:* AAAS; Am Chem Soc. *Res:* Enzyme purification and characterization; structure elucidation; reaction mechanisms. *Mailing Add:* Dept of Biol Chem Univ of Utah Med Ctr Salt Lake City UT 84112

SWEAT, ROBERT LEE, b Lamar, Colo, June 8, 31; m 53; c 2. VETERINARY MEDICINE, VIROLOGY. *Educ:* Colo State Univ, BS, 54, DVM, 56; Univ Nebr-Lincoln, MS, 62, PhD(med sci), 66. *Prof Exp:* Instr vet sci, Univ Nebr-Lincoln, 58-66, assoc prof, 66; vet virologist, Norden Labs, Inc, Nebr, 67; assoc res prof vet sci, Univ Idaho, 68-70- VET VIROLOGIST, FT DODGE LABS INC, 70- *Concurrent Pos:* Vet rep, Nebr State Bd Health, 66-67. *Mem:* AAAS; Am Vet Med Asn; US Animal Health Asn; Am Pub Health Asn; Conf Res Workers Animal Dis. *Res:* Veterinary science with emphasis on viral diseases and zoonosis. *Mailing Add:* 1371 N 14th St Ft Dodge IA 50501

SWEAT, VINCENT EUGENE, b Kirwin, Kans, July 28, 41; m 65; c 2. FOOD ENGINEERING. *Educ:* Kans State Univ, BS, 64; Okla State Univ, MS, 65; Purdue Univ, PhD(agr eng), 72. *Prof Exp:* Asst prof food eng, Purdue Univ, 71-75, assoc prof, 75-77; ASSOC PROF FOOD ENG, TEX A&M UNIV, 77- *Concurrent Pos:* Mem thermal properties foods comt, Am Soc Heating, Refrig & Air Conditioning Engrs, 72-; assoc ed food eng div, Am Soc Agr Engrs, 76-; NSF eng res equip grant, 78- *Mem:* Am Soc Agr Engrs; Inst Food Technologists; Am Soc Eng Educ. *Res:* Measurement and modeling of thermal properties of foods; food processing; heat and mass transfer in foods; energy utilization in food processing. *Mailing Add:* Agr Eng Dept Tex A&M Univ College Station TX 77843

SWEDBERG, KENNETH C, b Brainerd, Minn, Apr 14, 30; m 58; c 2. PLANT ECOLOGY. *Educ:* St Cloud State Col, BS, 52; Univ Minn, MS, 56; Ore State Univ, PhD(plant ecol), 61. *Prof Exp:* Instr biol, Moorhead State Col, 56-58; asst prof, Wis State Univ-Stevens Point, 60-62; assoc prof, 62-69, PROF BIOL, EASTERN WASH UNIV, 69- *Mem:* AAAS; Ecol Soc Am; Weed Sci Soc Am; Am Inst Biol Sci; Sigma Xi. *Res:* Plant synecology and autecology; experimental ecology of annual plants. *Mailing Add:* Dept of Biol Eastern Wash Univ Cheney WA 99004

SWEDES, JEAN SUSANNE, b Santa Monica, Calif, Apr 6, 46. MOLECULAR BIOLOGY. *Educ:* Occidental Col, BA, 67; Univ Calif, Los Angeles, PhD(molecular biol), 73. *Prof Exp:* Researcher biochem, Univ Calif, Los Angeles, 74-75; NIH fel, 75-78, RES ASSOC, UNIV CALIF, IRVINE, 78- *Mem:* Am Soc Microbiol. *Res:* Roles of adenine nucleotides in metabolic regulation; regulation of macromolecular biosynthesis especially regulation due to changes in energy supply; biochemical changes occurring in cells during nutrient starvations. *Mailing Add:* Dept of Biol Chem Univ of Calif Irvine CA 92717

SWEDLOW, JEROLD LINDSAY, b Denver, Colo, Aug 31, 35; m 59; c 3. SOLID MECHANICS, STRUCTURAL INTEGRITY. *Educ:* Calif Inst Technol, BS, 57; Stanford Univ, MS, 60; Calif Inst Technol, PhD(aeronaut), 65. *Prof Exp:* Res engr rock mech, Ingersoll-Rand Co, 57-59; res fel aeronaut, Calif Inst Technol, 65-66; from asst prof to assoc prof mech eng, 66-73, assoc dean eng, 77-79, PROF MECH ENG, CARNEGIE-MELLON UNIV, 73- *Concurrent Pos:* Ed, Reports Current Res, Int J Fracture, 69-; sr vis fel, Imp Col Sci & Technol, 73-74. *Honors & Awards:* Philip M McKenna Mem Award, 78; Ralph Coats Roe Award, 81. *Mem:* Am Acad Mech; Am Inst Aeronaut & Astronaut; Am Soc Mech Engrs; Am Soc Testing & Mat; Int Cong Fracture. *Res:* Plasticity of metal via computational procedures; applications to fracture-related problems at both the macro and microscale. *Mailing Add:* Dept of Mech Eng Carnegie-Mellon Univ Pittsburgh PA 15213

SWEDLUND, ALAN CHARLES, b Sacramento, Calif, Jan 21, 43; m 66; c 2. BIOLOGICAL ANTHROPOLOGY. *Educ:* Univ Colo, Ba, 66, MA, 68, PhD(anthrop), 70. *Prof Exp:* Asst prof anthrop, Prescott Col, 70-74; vis assoc prof, 74-77, field dir, Europ Studies Prog, 81-82, ASSOC PROF ANTHROP, UNIV MASS, AMHERST, 77- *Concurrent Pos:* Vis researcher, Biol Anthrop Prog, Oxford Univ, 82. *Mem:* AAAS; Am Asn Phys Anthrop; Am Soc Human Genetics; Am Eugenics Soc; Population Asn Am. *Res:* Demographic and human population genetics; historical demography and paleodemography; osteology. *Mailing Add:* Dept of Anthrop Univ of Mass Amherst MA 01003

SWEED, NORMAN HARRIS, b Philadelphia, Pa, Apr 11, 43; m 66; c 2. CHEMICAL ENGINEERING. *Educ:* Drexel Univ, BSChE, 65; Princeton Univ, MA, 67, PhD(chem eng), 68. *Prof Exp:* Asst prof chem eng, Princeton Univ, 68-75; sr res engr, Exxon Res & Eng Co, 74-78; mgr process res, Oxirane Int, 78-81; ENG ASSOC, EXXON RES & ENG CO, 81- *Concurrent Pos:* Consult, Engelhard Indust, 69-74 & Cities Serv Res, 74. *Mem:* Am Inst Chem Engrs; AAAS; Am Chem Soc. *Res:* Chemical reactor engineering; adsorptive separations; oxidation and epoxidation; trickle beds; petrochemical research. *Mailing Add:* Exxon Res & Eng Co PO Box 101 Florham Park NJ 07932

SWEEDLER, ALAN R, b New York, NY, Jan 31, 42. SOLID STATE PHYSICS, LOW TEMPERATURE PHYSICS. *Educ:* City Univ New York, BSc, 63; Univ Calif, San Diego, PhD(physics), 69. *Prof Exp:* Prof physics, Univ Chile, Santiago, 70-72; res physicist mat sci, Brookhaven Nat Lab, 72-77; assoc prof, Dept Physics, Calif State Univ Fullerton, 77-80; ASSOC PROF, DEPT PHYSICS, SAN DIEGO STATE UNIV, 80-, DIR, CTR ENERGY STUDIES, 81- *Concurrent Pos:* Vis assoc prof physics, Univ Southern Calif, Los Angeles, 75. *Mem:* Am Phys Soc; AAAS. *Res:* Superconductivity; high transition temperature compounds; irradiation effects in superconducting compounds; metallurgy of superconducting materials; solar energy; photovoltaics. *Mailing Add:* Dept Physics San Diego State Univ San Diego CA 92182

SWEELEY, CHARLES CRAWFORD, b Williamsport, Pa, Apr 15, 30; m 50; c 2. BIOCHEMISTRY, ORGANIC CHEMISTRY. *Educ:* Univ Pa, BS, 52; Univ Ill, PhD(chem), 55. *Prof Exp:* Chemist, Nat Heart Inst, 55-60; asst res prof biochem, Univ Pittsburgh, 60-63, from assoc prof to prof, 63-68; PROF BIOCHEM, MICH STATE UNIV, 68- *Concurrent Pos:* Mem comt probs lipid anal, Nat Heart Inst, 58-59; consult, LKB Instruments, 65-71, Med Chem Study Sect, USPHS, 67-71 & Upjohn Co, 68-72; Guggenheim fel, Royal Vet Col, Stockholm, Sweden, 71; vis prof, Ctr Cancer Res, Cambridge, 79. *Mem:* Am Chem Soc; Am Soc Biol Chem; Brit Biochem Soc. *Res:* Chemistry and metabolism of sphingolipids; sphingolipidoses; biochemistry of lysosomal hydrolases; analytical biochemistry; computer applications in gas chromatography and mass spectrometry; biochemistry of complex lipids and hormones of invertebrates. *Mailing Add:* Dept of Biochem Mich State Univ East Lansing MI 48824

SWEENEY, BEATRICE MARCY, b Boston, Mass, Aug 11, 14; m; c 4. BIOLOGICAL RHYTHMS. *Educ:* Smith Col, AB, 36; Radcliffe Col, PhD(biol), 42. *Prof Exp:* Lab asst endocrinol, Mayo Clin, 42; fel, Mayo Found, Univ Minn, 42-43; jr res biologist, Scripps Inst, Calif, 47-55, asst res biologist, 55-60, assoc res biologist, 60-61; res staff biologist, Yale Univ, 61-62, lectr biol, 62-67; lectr, 67-69, assoc prof biol, 69-71, assoc provost, Col Creative Studies, 78-81, PROF BIOL, UNIV CALIF, SANTA BARBARA, 71- *Concurrent Pos:* Consult, Monroe Labs, 59; mem, Nat Comt Photobiol, Nat Res Coun, 72-75. *Mem:* Fel AAAS; Am Soc Plant Physiol (secy-treas, 75-76); Soc Gen Physiol; Am Soc Photobiol (pres, 79); Am Soc Cell Biol. *Res:* Nutrition; photosynthesis; bioluminescence; diurnal rhythms in marine dinoflagellates. *Mailing Add:* Dept Biol Sci Univ Calif Santa Barbara CA 93106

SWEENEY, DARYL CHARLES, b Oakland, Calif, Jan 21, 36; m 59; c 1. INVERTEBRATE PHYSIOLOGY, NEUROCHEMISTRY. *Educ:* Univ Calif, Berkeley, AB, 58; Harvard Univ, AM, 59, PhD(biol), 63. *Prof Exp:* Instr biol, Yale Univ, 63-65; from asst prof to prof zool, 65-75, ASSOC PROF PHYSIOL, UNIV ILL, URBANA-CHAMPAIGN, 75- *Concurrent Pos:* Consult, Nat Inst Neurol Dis & Stoke, 66-69. *Mem:* Am Soc Zool. *Res:* Neurochemistry and the behavior of invertebrate physiology. *Mailing Add:* Dept of Physiol Univ of Ill at Urbana-Champaign Urbana IL 61801

SWEENEY, DONALD WESLEY, b Chicago, Ill, Dec 19, 46; m 67; c 1. MECHANICAL ENGINEERING, OPTICS. *Educ:* Univ Mich, Ann Arbor, BS, 68, MS, 69, PhD, 72. *Prof Exp:* Res asst coherent optics, Willow Run Labs, Univ Mich, 69-72; asst prof, 72-77, ASSOC PROF MECH ENG, PURDUE UNIV, WEST LAFAYETTE, 77- *Mem:* Optical Soc Am. *Res:* Applied research in coherent optics; optical temperature measurement; holographic interferometry. *Mailing Add:* Sch Mech Eng Purdue Univ West Lafayette IN 47906

SWEENEY, GEORGE DOUGLAS, b Durban, SAfrica, Dec 21, 34; m 60; c 3. PHARMACOLOGY, LIVER TOXICOLOGY. *Educ:* Univ Cape Town, MB, ChB, 58, PhD(biochem), 63. *Prof Exp:* Sr lectr physiol, Univ Cape Town, 64-68; Ont fel, Col Physicians & Surgeons, Columbia Univ, 68-69; assoc prof med, 69-81, PROF MED, MCMASTER UNIV, 81- *Concurrent Pos:* Vis prof, Liver Unit, King's Col Hosp, 79-80. *Mem:* Can Soc Toxicol; Pharmacol Soc Can; Can Physiol Soc; Am Soc Pharmacol & Exp Therapeut. *Res:* Hemoprotein synthesis and regulation; porphyrin metabolism; liver toxicity of halo-aromatic hydrocarbons; liver cell life cycle; porphyria. *Mailing Add:* Dept of Med 1200 Main St W Hamilton ON L8S 3Z5 Can

SWEENEY, HAROLD A, b Bayonne, NJ, Sept 7, 19; m 43; c 5. ANALYTICAL CHEMISTRY. *Educ:* Columbia Univ, AB, 41, MA, 42. *Prof Exp:* Chemist, Am Cyanamid Co, Conn, 46-53, supvr cent anal lab, La, 53-55; supvr wet chem lab, 55-62, MGR CHEM & INSTRUMENTAL LAB GROUP, KOPPERS CO, 62- *Mem:* Am Chem Soc. *Res:* Analysis of organic materials, paints, dyes, plastics, tar products, fuels and other petroleum products; catalysts; agricultural chemicals; surfactants; water. *Mailing Add:* Koppers Co Inc 440 College Park Dr Monroeville PA 15146

SWEENEY, JAMES MICHAEL, b Wichita, Kans, Dec 31, 45. WILDLIFE BIOLOGY, FORESTRY. *Educ:* Univ Ga, BSF, 67, MS, 71; Colo State Univ, PhD(wildlife), 75. *Prof Exp:* ASST PROF WILDLIFE & FORESTRY, DEPT FORESTRY, UNIV ARK, 75- *Concurrent Pos:* Sci ed wildlife, Dept Fisheries & Wildlife Biol, Colo State Univ, 75; actg head, Dept Forestry, Univ Ark, Monticello, 78-; reviewer, SE Asn Game & Fish Agencies, Proceeding Annual Conf, 78- & J Wildlife Mgt, The Wildlife Soc, 78- *Mem:* Sigma Xi; The Wildlife Soc. *Res:* Forestry-wildlife habitat interactions. *Mailing Add:* Dept of Forestry Univ of Ark Monticello AR 71655

SWEENEY, JAMES W, computer science, see previous edition

SWEENEY, JOHN ROBERT, b Wichita, Kans, Dec 31, 45. WILDLIFE BIOLOGY. *Educ:* Univ Ga, BSF, 67, MS, 71; Colo State Univ, PhD(wildlife biol), 75. *Prof Exp:* Asst prof, Dept Entom & Econ Zool, 75-80, ASSOC PROF, DEPT FISH & WILDLIFE, CLEMSON UNIV, 80- *Concurrent Pos:* Assoc ed, Southeastern Proceedings. *Mem:* Wildlife Soc. *Res:* Effects of forest management on wildlife populations; natural history and management of feral swine; natural history and population dynamics of bobat and gray fox; annual ethograms of eastern bluebird. *Mailing Add:* Dept Fish & Wildlife Clemson Univ Clemson SC 29631

SWEENEY, LAWRENCE EARL, JR, b Charleston, WVa, Mar 27, 42; m 69. ELECTRICAL ENGINEERING. *Educ:* Stanford Univ, BS, 64, MS, 66, PhD(elec eng), 70. *Prof Exp:* Res assoc radio sci, Stanford Univ, 70; asst dir, Ionospheric Dynamics Lab, 70-72, DIR REMOTE MEASUREMENTS LAB, SRI INT, 72- *Concurrent Pos:* Instr, Stanford Univ, 68-69, lectr, 70-71. *Mem:* Inst Elec & Electronics Engrs; Int Union Radio Sci. *Res:* Ionospheric radio propagation; high frequency signal processing; large antenna arrays; digital signal processing; remote sensing; high frequency radar; radar target scattering characteristics. *Mailing Add:* Remote Measurements Lab SRI Int Menlo Park CA 94025

SWEENEY, MARY ANN, b Hagerstown, Md, Sept 25, 45; m 74; c 1. PLASMA PHYSICS, ASTROPHYSICS. *Educ:* Mt Holyoke Col, BA, 67; Columbia Univ, MPhil, 73, PhD(astron), 74. *Prof Exp:* Instr astron, Fairleigh Dickinson Univ & William Paterson Col NJ, 72-73; fel plasma physics & fusion res, 74-76, STAFF MEM, SANDIA LABS, 76- *Mem:* Am Astron Soc; Am Phys Soc; Am Nuclear Soc. *Res:* Evaluation of targets, diodes and reator chambers for particle beam fusion using hydrodynamic and particle tranport codes; evolutionary models and observational interpretation of degenerate dwarf stars; equation of state formulations at high pressures. *Mailing Add:* Sandia Nat Lab Target Interation Theory Div 4247 PO Box 5800 Albuquerque NM 87185

SWEENEY, MICHAEL ANTHONY, b Los Angeles, Calif, Dec 5, 31; m 54; c 3. PHYSICAL CHEMISTRY. *Educ:* Loyola Univ, Calif, BS, 53; Univ Calif, Berkeley, MS, 55, PhD(chem), 62. *Prof Exp:* Res chemist, Chevron Res Co, 61-66; asst prof, 66-72, ASSOC PROF CHEM, UNIV SANTA CLARA, 72- *Concurrent Pos:* Instr, Univ Exten, Univ Calif, Berkeley, 65-66; consult, USPHS, 68-71; vis res chemist, UK Atomic Energy Res Estab, Harwell, 72-73, Inst de Quimica Bio-Organica, Barcelona, Spain, 79. *Mem:* Am Chem Soc. *Res:* Radiation chemistry; chemical evolution. *Mailing Add:* Dept of Chem Univ of Santa Clara Santa Clara CA 95053

SWEENEY, MICHAEL JOSEPH, b Philadelphia, Pa, Jan 31, 39; m 62; c 3. IMMUNOLOGY, IMMUNOCHEMISTRY. *Educ:* Philadelphia Col Pharm & Sci, BSc, 66, BSc, 67; Temple Univ, PhD(microbiol, immunol), 71. *Prof Exp:* Fel immunol, Sch Med, Temple Univ, 71-72; asst prof immunol, 71-77, ASSOC PROF BIOL SCI, FLA TECHNOL UNIV, 77- *Mem:* Am Soc Microbiol; Sigma Xi. *Res:* Studies of T and B cell populations in peripheral blood of immunosuppressed patients; immunologic, genetic and biochemical associations to the tumorous head phenotype in Drosophila melanogaster. *Mailing Add:* Dept of Biol Sci Fla Technol Univ Orlando FL 32816

SWEENEY, RICHARD F, b New York, NY, Aug 7, 21; m 56; c 2. ORGANIC CHEMISTRY. *Educ:* Queens Col, BS, 42, MS, NY Univ, 48, PhD(chem). 56. *Prof Exp:* Instr chem, NY Univ, 55-56; res chemist, Gen Chem Div, Allied Chem Corp, 56-59, sr res chemist, 59-64, sr scientist, 64-69, tech supvr org fluorine chem, Indust Chem Div, 69-72, supvr, Spec Chem Div, 72-80, SR RES ASSOC ELECTRONIC CHEMICALS, BUFFALO RES LAB, ALLIED CORP, 80- *Mem:* Am Chem Soc; Soc Petroleum Engrs. *Res:* Organic fluorine chemistry; fluoropolymers; coatings; surface active agents; interfacial phenomena relating to crude oil recovery. *Mailing Add:* 631 Stolle Rd Elma NY 14059

SWEENEY, ROBERT ANDERSON, b Freeport, NY, Oct 11, 40; m 63, 79; c 3. PHYCOLOGY, LIMNOLOGY. *Educ:* State Univ Col Albany, BS, 62; Ohio State Univ, MS, 64, PhD(natural resources), 66. *Prof Exp:* From asst prof to assoc prof biol, State Univ NY Col Buffalo, 66-68, dir, Great Lakes Lab, 67-81, prof, 68-81; DIR SPEC PROJS, ECOL & ENVIRON INC, 81- *Concurrent Pos:* Consult, NY State Dept Environ Conserv, 70-; consult, US Army Corps Engrs, 71-, mem, Shoreline Erosion Adv Panel, 74-; US Army Corps Engrs grant, 71-, Environ Protection Agency grant, 72-; adj prof biol, State Univ NY Col Buffalo, 81- *Mem:* AAAS; Int Asn Great Lakes Res (pres, 80); Phycol Soc Am; Am Inst Biol Sci; Am Soc Limnol & Oceanog. *Res:* Evaluation and solution of water pollution and eutrophication problems in the Great Lakes and their tributaries; dredging; bioassay. *Mailing Add:* Ecol & Environ Inc PO Box D Buffalo NY 14225

SWEENEY, THOMAS L(EONARD), b Cleveland, Ohio, Dec 12, 36; m 61; c 4. CHEMICAL ENGINEERING. *Educ:* Case Inst Technol, BS, 58, MS, 60, PhD(chem eng), 62; Capital Univ, JD, 74. *Prof Exp:* Tech specialist, Standard Oil Co, Ohio, 62-63; from asst prof to assoc prof, 63-73, PROF CHEM ENG, OHIO STATE UNIV, 73- *Concurrent Pos:* Consult. *Mem:* AAAS; Am Inst Chem Engrs; Am Chem Soc; Am Soc Eng Educ. *Res:* Air pollution; heat and mass transfer; chemical technology; occupational safety and health; environmental science and technology; regulation of technology; legal aspects of engineering. *Mailing Add:* Dept of Chem Eng Ohio State Univ 140 W 19th Ave Columbus OH 43210

SWEENEY, THOMAS RICHARD, b Albany, NY, Sept 21, 14; m 41; c 2. MEDICINAL CHEMISTRY. *Educ:* Univ Md, BS, 37, PhD(org chem), 45. *Prof Exp:* Chemist, Briggs Filtration Co, DC, 40-41; chemist, NIH, Md, 41-47; res chemist, Univ Md, 47-50, US Naval Res Lab, 50-59; chemist, Walter Reed Army Inst Res, 59-64, chief, Dept Org Chem, 64-69, dep dir, Div Med Chem, 69-78, dep dir, Div Exp Therapeut, 78-80; CONSULT, 80- *Mem:* Am Chem Soc. *Res:* Antiradiation and antiparasific agents. *Mailing Add:* 1701 N Kent St Apt 1106 Arlington VA 22209

SWEENEY, WILLIAM ALAN, b Can, Sept 12, 26; nat US; m 53; c 3. PETROLEUM CHEMISTRY. *Educ:* Univ BC, BASc, 49; Univ Wash, Seattle, PhD, 54. *Prof Exp:* Chemist, Can Industs, Ltd, 49-50; asst to vpres, Chevron Res Co, 75-76; SR RES ASSOC, CHEVRON RES CO, STANDARD OIL CO, CALIF, 54- *Mem:* Am Chem Soc; Sigma Xi; NY Acad Sci. *Res:* Detergents; petrochemical processing; condensation polymers; biodegradability; desulfurization. *Mailing Add:* 27 Corte del Bayo Larkspur CA 94939

SWEENEY, WILLIAM JOHN, b Oak Park, Ill, July 15, 40; m 64. MATHEMATICS. *Educ:* Univ Notre Dame, AB, 62; Stanford Univ, MS, 64, PhD(math), 66. *Prof Exp:* Instr math, Stanford Univ, 66-67; asst prof, Princeton Univ, 67-71; ASSOC PROF MATH, RUTGERS UNIV, NEW BRUNSWICK, 71- *Mem:* Math Asn Am; Am Math Soc. *Res:* Over-determined systems of linear partial differential equations. *Mailing Add:* Dept of Math Rutgers Univ New Brunswick NJ 08903

SWEENEY, WILLIAM MORTIMER, b Brooklyn, NY, Aug 4, 23; m 52; c 3. PETROLEUM CHEMISTRY. *Educ:* St John's Univ, BS, 43; Fordham Univ, MS, 47; Univ Colo, PhD(org chem), 52. *Prof Exp:* Chemist, Transformer Div, Gen Elec Co, Mass, 47-49; SR RES CHEMIST, BEACON RES LABS, TEXACO, INC, 52- *Mem:* Sigma Xi. *Res:* Organometallics, principally ferrocene; ester based synthetic luoricants for jet engines; fluorine chemistry; additives for gasoline and diesel fuels; pour depressants fuel oils; polymers. *Mailing Add:* Beacon Res Labs Texaco Inc Beacon NY 12508

SWEENEY, WILLIAM VICTOR, b Cleveland, Ohio, Jan 31, 47; m 68; c 1. BIOPHYSICS. *Educ:* Knox Col, BA, 68; Univ Iowa, MS, 70, PhD(chem), 73. *Prof Exp:* NIH fel biochem, Univ Calif, Berkeley, 73-75; asst prof, 75-80, ASSOC PROF CHEM, HUNTER COL, CITY UNIV NEW YORK, 80- *Res:* Physical properties of iron-sulfur proteins; nuclear magnetic resonance; electron paramagnetic resonance. *Mailing Add:* Dept of Chem Hunter Col 695 Park Ave New York NY 10021

SWEENY, DANIEL MICHAEL, b Rockville Center, NY, Sept 25, 30; m 60; c 5. INORGANIC CHEMISTRY. *Educ:* Col Holy Cross, BSc, 52; Univ Notre Dame, PhD(chem), 55. *Prof Exp:* Res chemist, E I du Pont de Nemours & Co, 55-57; PROF INORG CHEM, BELLARMINE COL, KY, 57- *Mem:* Am Chem Soc; Mineral Soc Am; Soc Appl Spectros. *Res:* Physical properties and synthesis of coordination compounds; infrared spectroscopy; structural inorganic chemistry; interpretive spectroscopy. *Mailing Add:* Dept of Chem Bellarmine Col Louisville KY 40205

SWEENY, HALE CATERSON, b Anderson, SC, Mar 31, 25; m 48; c 3. MATHEMATICAL STATISTICS. *Educ:* Clemson Col, BME, 49; Va Polytech Inst, MS, 52, PhD, 56. *Prof Exp:* Design engr, Hunt Mach Works, 49-50; indust engr, Eastman Kodak Co, 51-52; instr indust eng, Va Polytech Inst, 52-53, asst prof statist, 53-56; res statistician, Atlantic Ref Co, 56-59; consult, 59-60; sr res statisfician, Res Triangle Inst, 60-64, mgr spec res, 64-72; HEAD, STATIST SERV DEPT, BURROUGHS WELLCOME CO, 72- *Mem:* Am Soc Mech Eng; Am Statist Asn; Inst Math Statist; Biomet Soc. *Res:* Development of statistical methodology application to production; chemical and clinical research; design of experiments; design of medical and veterinary clinical trials. *Mailing Add:* 3500 Cambridge Pd Durham NC 27707

SWEENY, JAMES GILBERT, b Philadelphia, Pa, Jan 18, 44. NATURAL PRODUCTS CHEMISTRY. *Educ:* Eckerd Col, BS, 65; Yale Univ, PhD(org chem), 69. *Prof Exp:* Fel chem, Yale Univ, 69-71, R Russell Agr Res Ctr, 71-72, Univ Glasgow, 72-73 & Univ Va, 73-74; RES SCIENTIST, COCA-COLA CO, 74- *Mem:* Am Chem Soc; Royal Soc Chem. *Res:* Isolation, structure determination and synthesis of natural colorants. *Mailing Add:* Corp Res Coca-Cola Co Atlanta GA 30301

SWEENY, KEITH HOLCOMB, b Tacoma, wash, Feb 6, 20; m 45; c 3. PHYSICAL CHEMISTRY. *Educ:* Univ Wash, Seattle, BS, 46; Ore State Univ. PhD(phys chem), 50. *Prof Exp:* Oceanog chemist, US Fish & Wild Life Serv, 41; res chemist, Kalunite, Inc, 42-45; instr chem, Univ Utah, 45-46; asst prin chemist, Aerojet-Gen Corp Div, 50-63, staff scientist, Space-Gen Corp Div, 63-69, indust wastes specialist, Envirogenics Co Div, Gen Tire & Rubber Co, El Monte, 69-75; MGR, WASTEWATER TREATMENT RES, ENVIROGENICS SYSTS CO, 75- *Concurrent Pos:* Consult rheol, Coast Proseal Div, Essex Chem, 72- *Mem:* Am Chem Soc; Soc Rheol; Sigma Xi. *Res:* Rheology of suspensions; fine particle technology; polymer chemistry and physics; aerosol physics; physical chemistry of rocket propellants; chemistry of aluminum; chemistry of pesticides; industrial waste treatment. *Mailing Add:* 2413 E Evergreen Ave West Covina CA 91791

SWEENY, ROBERT F(RANCIS), b Ridley Park, Pa, Sept 9, 31; m 52; c 4. CHEMICAL ENGINEERING, PROCESS CONTROL. *Educ:* Pa State Univ, BS, 53, MS, 55, PhD, 60. *Prof Exp:* Lab mgr, Appl Sci Labs, 55-64; asst prof, 64-66, ASSOC PROF CHEM ENG, VILLANOVA UNIV, 66- *Concurrent Pos:* Consult, City of Philadelphia Water Dept, 74- *Mem:* Am Chem Soc; Am Inst Chem Engrs; Instrument Soc Am; Water Pollution Control Fedn. *Res:* Applied mathematics; process control; separations and purification; wastewater treatment. *Mailing Add:* Dept of Chem Eng Villanova Univ Villanova PA 19085

SWEET, ARNOLD LAWRENCE, b New York, NY, Mar 23, 35; m 59; c 2. TIME SERIES FORECASTING, APPLIED STOCHASTIC PROCESSES. *Educ:* Col City New York, BME, 56; Md Univ, MSME, 59; Purdue Univ, PhD(eng sci), 64. *Prof Exp:* Mech engr, Emerson Res Lab, 56-58; mech engr struct dynamics, US Naval Res Lab, 58-60; from asst prof to assoc prof eng sci, 64-73, PROF INDUST ENG, PURDUE UNIV, 73- *Concurrent Pos:* Consult, Midwest Appl Sci Corp, 64-67; vis res fel accident anal, Rd Res Lab, Dept Environ, Gt Brit, 70-71. *Mem:* Inst Man & Sci; Am Inst Indust Engrs. *Res:* Time series forecasting; applications of probability theory to engineering problems; operations research. *Mailing Add:* Sch Indust Eng Purdue Univ Grissom Hall West Lafayette IN 47907

SWEET, ARTHUR THOMAS, JR, b Salisbury, NC, Jan 19, 20; m 43; c 2. POLYMER CHEMISTRY. *Educ:* Univ NC, BS, 41; Ohio State Univ, PhD(chem). 48. *Prof Exp:* Staff chemist, Uranium Isotope Prod Dept, Tenn Eastman Corp, 44-46; res chemist, Nylon Res Div, 48-54, Dacron Res Div, 54-57 & Textile Fibers Patent Div, 57-74, PATENT ASSOC, TEXTILE FIBERS PATENT LIAISON DIV, E I DU PONT DE NEMOURS & CO, 74- *Mem:* Am Chem Soc. *Res:* Constitution of Grignard reagent; chemical characteristics of synthetic fibers; patent management. *Mailing Add:* Textile Fibers Patent Div E I du Pont de Nemours & Co Wilmington DE 19898

SWEET, BENJAMIN HERSH, b Boston, Mass, Dec 14, 24; m 56; c 3. VIROLOGY, IMMUNOLOGY. *Educ:* Tulane Univ, BS, 43; Boston Univ, MA, 48, PhD(med sci), 51. *Prof Exp:* Res assoc virol, Res Found, Children's Hosp, Cincinnati, 51-54; asst prof microbiol, Sch Med, Univ Md, 54-59; sr investr virol, Merck Sharp & Dohme Res Labs, 59-64; dir & mgr res & develop, Flow Labs, Inc, Md, 64-66; assoc dir life sci div, Gulf South Res Inst, 66-75; MGR, QUAL ASSURANCE, CUTTER LABS, 75- *Mem:* Am Soc Microbiol; Am Soc Trop Med & Hyg; Tissue Cult Asn; Soc Exp Biol & Med. *Res:* Arthropod borne, respiratory, oncogenic, latent and vaccine development viruses; viral immunology; ecology and zoonoses; immunology-adjuvants; water pollution; cell biology; quality assurance; biological and immunological assays; limulus amebocyte research and development; good laboratory practices regulations. *Mailing Add:* Cutter Labs Fourth & Parker St Berkeley CA 94710

SWEET, CHARLES EDWARD, b Elgin, Tex, Dec 27, 33; m 55; c 4. BACTERIOLOGY, MYCOLOGY. *Educ:* Univ Tex, BA, 55, MA, 63; Univ NC, MPH, 67, DPH(parasitol), 69. *Prof Exp:* Jr bacteriologist, Br Lab, NMex State Health Dept, 60-61; bacteriologist, Tex State Health Dept, 62, Tyler Tex Br Lab, 63-66, spec proj dir, 69-70, asst dir, Lab Servs, 70-73, DIR LAB, TEX STATE DEPT HEALTH, 70- *Res:* Serological means of identifying Candida species and other yeastlike fungi. *Mailing Add:* Lab Sect Tex State Health Dept 1100 W 49th St Austin TX 78756

SWEET, CHARLES SAMUEL, b Cambridge, Mass, Apr 6, 42; m 68; c 2. PHARMACOLOGY. *Educ:* Northeastern Univ, BS, 66, MS, 68; Univ Iowa, PhD(pharmacol), 71. *Prof Exp:* Res asst pharmacol, Warner-Lambert Res Inst, NJ, 66-68; fel, Col Pharm, Northeastern Univ, 66-68; fel, Col Med, Univ Iowa, 68-71; fel res, Cleveland Clin Educ Found, 71-72; res fel, 72-75, sr res fel, 75-76, DIR CARDIOL PHARMACOL, MERCK INST THERAPEUT RES, 76- *Concurrent Pos:* Mem, Med Adv Bd, Coun High Blood Pressure. *Mem:* Coun Thrombosis, Am Heart Asn; Am Soc Pharmacol & Exp Therapeut. *Res:* Renin-angiotensin system in pathogenesis of experimental hypertension; participation of central nervous system in development and maintenance; action of antihypertensive drugs, particularly as they apply to known causes of hypertension. *Mailing Add:* Dept of Pharmacol Merck Inst for Therapeut Res West Point PA 19486

SWEET, DAVID PAUL, b Dixon, Mar 24, 48; m 68. ANALYTICAL CHEMISTRY. *Educ:* Bradley Univ, BA, 70; Univ Colo, PhD(anal chem), 74. *Prof Exp:* anal chemist, 74-78, MGR ANAL SERV, DIV SYNTEX, ARAPAHOE CHEM INC, 78- *Mem:* Am Chem Soc; Am Soc Mass Spectrometry. *Res:* Chromatographic separations and trace analysis, especially using combined vapor phase chromatography-mass spectrometry and liquid chromatography-mass spectrometry. *Mailing Add:* 2075 N 55th St Arapahoe Chem Inc Boulder CO 80301

SWEET, FREDERICK, b New York, NY, May 15, 38; m 62; c 4. BIOCHEMISTRY, ORGANIC CHEMISTRY. *Educ:* Brooklyn Col, BS, 60; Univ Alta, PhD(org chem), 68. *Prof Exp:* Substitute instr chem, Brooklyn Col, 60-62; instr, Bronx Community Col, 62-64; NIH res fel nucleoside chem, Sloan-Kettering Inst Cancer Res, 68-70; res assoc reproductive biochem, Univ Kans Med Ctr, Kansas City, 70-71; asst prof reproductive biochem, 71-76, res assoc prof, 76-80, ASSOC PROF OBSTET & GYNEC, SCH MED, WASHINGTON UNIV, 80- *Concurrent Pos:* Lectr, Bronx Community Col, 68-70; vis asst prof biol sci, Southern Ill Univ, Edwardsville, 73-75, vis prof chem, 76-78; res fel, NATO, 74-76 & 77-78; NIH res career develop award, 75; mem int exchange, Nat Acad Sci, Hungary, 77-78 & 79. *Mem:* AAAS; Am Chem Soc; Chem Inst Can; Endocrine Soc. *Res:* Reproductive biochemistry, mechanism of steroid action and metabolism; synthesis of affinity-labeling steroids; synthesis of nucleosides and nucleoside analogs; synthesis of boron-estrogens for neutron capture therapy of cancers. *Mailing Add:* Dept of Obstet & Gynec Wash Univ Sch of Med St Louis MO 63110

SWEET, GEORGE H, b Texhoma, Okla, Feb 4, 34; m 55; c 3. IMMUNOLOGY. *Educ:* Wichita State Univ, BS, 60; Univ Kans, MA. 62, PhD(immunol), 65. *Prof Exp:* Immunologist, Armed Forces Inst Path, 65-66; from asst prof to assoc prof, 66-71, PROF BIOL, WICHITA STATE UNIV, 72- *Mem:* AAAS. *Res:* Cell biology; fungal serology; viral immunology. *Mailing Add:* Dept of Biol Wichita State Univ Wichita KS 67208

SWEET, GERTRUDE EVANS, b Erie. Pa, Aug 27, 06; m 55. ZOOLOGY. *Educ:* Mt Holyoke Col, AB, 28; Univ Chicago, PhD(zool), 36. *Prof Exp:* Sci asst biol, Am Mus Natural Hist, 28-31; asst, Univ Chicago, 32-36; instr zool, Mt Holyoke Col, 36-38; biologist, Beloit Col, 38-44; asst prof, Wells Col, 44-47; prof & head dept, Lake Erie Col, 47-55; instr, 57-65, assoc prof, 65-71. EMER ASSOC PROF, BELOIT COL, 71- *Mem:* Am Soc Zool; Soc Study Evolution. *Res:* Aggregations studies; oxygen consumption of salamanders. *Mailing Add:* 811 Chapin St Beloit WI 53511

SWEET, HAROLD S(T CLAIR), b Butte, Mont, Feb 20, 19; m 39; c 3. CIVIL ENGINEERING. *Educ:* Univ Wyo, BS, 39; Purdue Univ, MS, 41, PhD(hwy eng), 48. *Prof Exp:* Asst, Purdue Univ, 39-41, 45-48 & Lockheed Aircraft Corp, Calif, 42-45; prof civil eng, Univ Wyo, 48-53; ENGR, LOCKHEED AIRCRAFT CORP, 53- *Res:* Aircraft structures; concrete durablity; mineral aggregates; space launch vehicle design. *Mailing Add:* 561 Yorkshire Dr Marietta GA 30067

SWEET, HAVEN C, b Boston, Mass, Mar 1, 42; m 63; c 2. PLANT PHYSIOLOGY. *Educ:* Tufts Univ, BS, 63; Syracuse Univ, PhD(plant physiol), 67. *Prof Exp:* Res fel photobiol, Brookhaven Nat Labs, 67-68; sr res analyst bot, Brown & Root-Northrop, Tex, 68-69, supvr, 69-71; asst prof biol, Fla Technol Univ, 71-78, assoc prof, 78-80, ASSOC PROF BIOL, UNIV CENT FLA, 80- *Mem:* AAAS; Am Soc Plant Physiol; Bot Soc Am; Am Inst Biol Sci; Linnean Soc London. *Res:* Effects of light on plant growth; development of computer-assessment of plant taxonomic, remote sensing and ecological information. *Mailing Add:* Dept Biol Univ Cent Fla Orlando FL 32816

SWEET, HERMAN ROYDEN, b Attleboro, Mass, Nov 3, 09; m 31; c 2. BOTANY, MICROBIOLOGY. *Educ:* Bowdoin Col, AB, 31; Harvard Univ, AB, 34, PhD(mycol), 40. *Prof Exp:* Asst, Harvard Univ, 36-37; instr, 37-42, from asst prof to assoc prof, 42-54, prof, 54-75, EMER PROF BIOL, TUFTS UNIV, 75- *Concurrent Pos:* Res assoc, Orchid Herbarium of Oakes Ames, Harvard Univ, 65-76, hon cur, 76- *Mem:* AAAS; Am Soc Microbiol; Brit Soc Gen Microbiol; Am Ornith Union; fel Linnean Soc London. *Res:* Orchidology. *Mailing Add:* Dept of Biol Tufts Univ Medford MA 02155

SWEET, LEONARD, b Akron, Ohio, Aug 28, 25; m 46; c 2. STATISTICS. *Educ:* Univ Akron, BA, 49; Kent State Univ, MEd, 54; Case Western Reserve Univ, PhD(statist), 70. *Prof Exp:* Teacher pub schs, Ohio, 49-57, supvr, 57-59; from asst prof to assoc prof, 59-74, PROF MATH, UNIV AKRON, 74- *Concurrent Pos:* Consult, Akron Pub Schs, Ohio, 62-65 & Addressograph Multigraph Corp, 71-; mem panel evaluating of Instr Sci Equip Prog Proposals, NSF, 78; vpres, Greater Akron Math Educators, 79-81; mem admissions comt, Northeastern Ohio Med Sch, 78-80, biostatist comt, 78-80; grant dir, Local Course Improvement Proj, NSF, 78-80. *Mem:* Am Statist Asn; Math Asn Am; Nat Coun Teachers Math; Sigma Xi. *Res:* Experimental design; symmetrical complementation designs; utilization of the microcomputer by the classroom teacher in mathematics and statistics education. *Mailing Add:* Dept of Math Univ of Akron Akron OH 44325

SWEET, MELVIN MILLARD, b South Gate, Calif. NUMBER THEORY. *Educ:* Calif State Univ, Los Angeles, BA, 64, MA, 65; Univ Md, PhD(math), 72. *Prof Exp:* Mathematician, Nat Security Agency, 66-70; vis asst prof math, Univ Md, Baltimore County, 72-74; res staff mem math, Commun Res Div, Inst Defense Anal, 75-78; sr staff mem, Hughes Aircraft Co, 78-80. *Mem:* Am Math Soc; Math Asn Am. *Res:* Diophantine approximations. *Mailing Add:* 5301 Via del Valle Torrance CA 90505

SWEET, MERRILL HENRY, II, b Chicago Heights, Ill, Sept 5, 35; m 58; c 4. BIOLOGY. *Educ:* Univ Conn, BS, S8, PhD(entom), 63. *Prof Exp:* Res asst entom, Univ Conn, 62-63; asst prof, 63-66, ASSOC PROF BIOL, TEX A&M UNIV, 66- *Mem:* Ecol Soc Am; Assoc Trop Biol; Soc Study Evolution; Soc Syst Zool. *Res:* Systematics; ecology; behavior and life cycles of arthropods, especially hemipterous insects. *Mailing Add:* Dept of Biol Tex A&M Univ College Station TX 77843

SWEET, RICHARD CLARK, b Tarrytown, NY, Nov 28, 21; m 48; c 3. ANALYTICAL CHEMISTRY, PHYSICAL CHEMISTRY. *Educ:* Wesleyan Col. BA, 44, MA, 48; Rutgers Univ, PhD(chem), 52. *Prof Exp:* Chemist, 52-60, SUPVR METALL SYSTS APPLNS, PHILIPS LABS, N AM PHILIPS CO, BRIARCLIFF MANOR, 60- *Mem:* Am Chem Soc; Am Vacuum Soc; Sigma Xi; AAAS. *Res:* Spectroscopy; trace levels; ion exchange; polarography; water analysis; analytical methods; electronic components; vacuum techniques; ceramic-metal seals; cryogenic components design and fabrication; metals processing and joining techniques; welding and brazing. *Mailing Add:* N Am Philips Co Philips Lab 345 Scarborough Rd Briarcliff Manor NY 10310

SWEET, ROBERT DEAN, b Fairview, Ohio, Apr 6, 15; m 36; c 2. VEGETABLE CROPS. *Educ:* Ohio Univ, BS, 36; Cornell Univ, MS, 38, PhD(veg crops), 41. *Prof Exp:* Asst, 36-40, exten instr, 40-43, asst exten prof, 43-47, assoc prof, 47-49, PROF VEG CROPS, NY STATE COL AGR & LIFE SCI, CORNELL UNIV, 49-, CHMN DEPT, 75- *Mem:* Sigma Xi; Am Soc Hort Sci; Weed Sci Soc Am. *Res:* Biological and chemical weed control. *Mailing Add:* Dept of Veg Crops NY State Col of Agr & Life Sci Ithaca NY 14850

SWEET, ROBERT MAHLON, b Omaha, Nebr, Sept 21, 43; m 66; c 3. MOLECULAR BIOLOGY. *Educ:* Calif Inst Technol, BS, 65; Univ Wis-Madison, PhD(phys chem), 70. *Prof Exp:* Lectr chem, Univ Wis-Madison, 70; fel molecular biol, Med Res Coun Lab Molecular Biol, Cambridge, Eng, 70-73; asst prof chem, 73-81, SPECIALIST, MOLECULAR BIOL INST, UNIV CALIF, LOS ANGELES, 81- *Concurrent Pos:* Damon Runyon Mem Fund fel, 70-72; Europ Molecular Biol Orgn fel, 72. *Mem:* AAAS; Am Crystallog Asn; Sigma Xi. *Res:* Structure and function of enzymes, determined by x-ray diffraction techniques; studies of phycobiliproteins; photosynthetic accessory pigments from algae. *Mailing Add:* Molecular Biol Inst Univ Calif Los Angeles CA 90024

SWEET, RONALD LANCELOT, b Bristol, Eng, Feb 6, 23; nat US; m 47. ORGANIC CHEMISTRY. *Educ:* Rutgers Univ, BSc, 44, MSc, 48, PhD, 55. *Prof Exp:* Fel research, Mellon Inst, 51-55; CHEMIST, PIGMENTS DEPT, E I DU PONT DE NEMOURS & CO, 55- *Concurrent Pos:* Co-adj, Rutgers Univ, 63-74. *Mem:* Am Chem Soc. *Res:* Pigments. *Mailing Add:* E I DuPont De Nemours Co Inc 256 Vanderpool St Newark NJ 07114

SWEET, THOMAS RICHARD, b Jamaica, NY, Sept 27, 21; m 48; c 2. CHEMISTRY. *Educ:* City Col New York, BS, 43; Ohio State Univ, PhD(chem), 49. *Prof Exp:* Asst, Manhattan Proj, War Res Div, Columbia Univ, 43-45 & Carbide & Carbon Chem Corp, 45-46; from asst prof to assoc prof, 49-65, PROF CHEM, OHIO STATE UNIV, 65- *Mem:* Am Chem Soc. *Res:* Organic reagents, solvent extraction and trace metal analysis. *Mailing Add:* Dept of Chem Ohio State Univ 140 W 18th Ave Columbus OH 43210

SWEET, WILLIAM HERBERT, b Kerriston, Wash, Feb 13, 10; m 37; c 3. NEUROSURGERY. *Educ:* Univ Wash, SB, 30; Oxford Univ, BSc, 34; Harvard Univ, MD, 36; DSc, Oxford Univ, 57. *Hon Degrees:* DHC, Univ Sci Med, Grreoble, France, 79. *Prof Exp:* Instr neurosurg, Billings Hosp, Chicago, 39-40; Commonwealth Fund fel, Harvard Med Sch, 40-41; actg chief neurosurg serv, Birmingham United Hosp, 41-45; from instr to asst prof, 45-54, assoc clin prof, 54-58, from assoc prof to prof, 58-76, EMER PROF SURG, HARVARD MED SCH, 76- *Concurrent Pos:* Regional consult, Brit Emergency Med Serv, 41-45; asst, Mass Gen Hosp, 45-47, asst neurosurgeon, 47-48, assoc vis neurosurgeon, 48-58, vis neurosurgeon, 58-, chief neurosurg serv, 61-76, mem hosp staff & consult vis neurosurgeon, 76-80, sr neurosurgeon, 80-; lectr, Med Sch, Tufts Col, 47-51; neurosurgeon in chief, New Eng Ctr Hosp, 49-51; mem subcomt neurosurg, Nat Res Coun, 49-52 & mem subcomt neurol & neurosurg, 52-59; trustee, Assoc Univs, Inc, 58-; mem sci & technol adv comt, NASA, 64-70; mem neurol sci res training A comt, Nat Inst Neurol Dis & Stroke; honored guest, Cong Neurol Surgeons, 75. *Honors & Awards:* His Majesty's Medal for Serv in Cause of Freedom, 45. *Mem:* Am Acad Arts & Sci; Am Acad Neurol Surg; Am Neurol Asn; Am Pain Soc (pres, 81-); Soc Neurol Surg. *Res:* Central nervous system; research in cerebrospinal and intracerebral fluid; brain tumors; mechanisms of pain and its neurosurgical control; abnormal behavior related to organic brain disease; irreversible coma; ethics of experimentation. *Mailing Add:* Mass Gen Hosp Neurosurg Serv Fruit St Boston MA 02114

SWEETING, LINDA MARIE, b Toronto, Ont, Dec 11, 41. ORGANIC CHEMISTRY. *Educ:* Univ Toronto, BSc, 64, MA, 65; Univ Calif, Los Angeles, PhD(org chem), 69. *Prof Exp:* Asst prof, Occidental Col, 69-70; asst prof, 70-75, ASSOC PROF, TOWSON STATE UNIV, 75- *Concurrent Pos:* Guest worker, Nat Inst Arthritis, Metab & Digestive Dis, NIH, 77-78. *Mem:* Am Chem Soc; AAAS; Sigma Xi; Fedn Am Scientists; Asn Women in Sci. *Res:* Application of nuclear magnetic resonance spectroscopy to organic chemistry; triboluminescence; stereochemistry; weak organic bases. *Mailing Add:* Dept of Chem Towson State Univ Baltimore MD 21204

SWEETMAN, BRIAN JACK, b Palmerston North, NZ, May 4, 36; m 62; c 3. ORGANIC CHEMISTRY, PHARMACOLOGY. *Educ:* Univ NZ, BSc, 58, MSc, 59; Univ Otago, NZ, PhD(org chem), 62. *Prof Exp:* Res officer div protein chem, Commonwealth Sci & Indust Res Orgn, Melbourne, Australia, 63-66; res assoc chem, 66-68, asst prof, 69-76, RES ASSOC PROF PHARMACOL IN RESIDENCE, VANDERBILT UNIV, 76- *Mem:* Am Chem Soc; Am Soc Mass Spectroscopy; Sigma Xi. *Res:* Mass spectrometry; analytical pharmacology; prostaglandins; vapor-phase analysis; medicinal and organosulfur chemistry; anti-radiation and anti-arthritic drugs; protein chemistry of keratin; natural products. *Mailing Add:* Dept of Pharmacol Vanderbilt Univ Nashville TN 37232

SWEETMAN, LAWRENCE, b La Junta, Colo, Feb 17, 42; m 70. BIOCHEMISTRY, PEDIATRICS. *Educ:* Univ Colo, BA, 64; Univ Miami, PhD(biochem), 69. *Prof Exp:* Res assoc biochem, Sloan-Kettering Inst Cancer Res, 68-72, instr, Sloan-Kettering Div, Grad Sch Med Sci, Cornell Univ, 69-72; asst prof, 72-78, ASSOC PROF PEDIAT, UNIV CALIF, SAN DIEGO, 78- *Mem:* Am Chem Soc. *Res:* Metabolism of inherited diseases in children; Lesch-Nyhan syndrome and organic acidurias. *Mailing Add:* Dept of Pediat M-0Q9 Univ of Calif at San Diego La Jolla CA 92093

SWEETON, FREDERICK HUMPHREY, b Brattleboro, Vt, Oct 13, 16; m 53; c 3. PHYSICAL CHEMISTRY. *Educ:* Univ Conn, BS, 38; Yale Univ, PhD(phys chem), 41. *Prof Exp:* Chemist, Tenn Valley Authority, 41-43; chemist, Oak Ridge Nat Lab, 46-81. *Mem:* Am Chem Soc. *Res:* High temperature aqueous electrochemistry; soil chemistry; low temperature calorimetry; surface chemistry of slurries; chemistry of pressurized-water reactors. *Mailing Add:* 334 Louisiana Ave Oak Ridge TN 37830

SWEETSER, PHILIP BLISS, b Morrisville, Vt, Dec 26, 24; m 53; c 2. ANALYTICAL CHEMISTRY, PLANT BIOCHEMISTRY. *Educ:* Univ Vt, BS, 50; Princeton Univ, PhD(chem), 53. *Prof Exp:* RES SCIENTIST, CENT RES DEPT, E I DU PONT DE NEMOURS & CO, 53- *Mem:* AAAS; Am Chem Soc. *Res:* Metabolism and role of agrochemicals as plant growth regulators; separations. *Mailing Add:* 1006 Crestover Rd Wilmington DE 19803

SWEITZER, JAMES STUART, b South Bend, Ind, Mar 27, 51; m 73; c 1. ASTRONOMY, SCIENCE EXHIBITS. *Educ:* Univ Notre Dame, BS, 73; Univ Chicago, MS, 75, PhD(astron, astrophys), 78. *Prof Exp:* ASSOC ASTRONOMER, ADLER PLANETARIUM, 78- *Mem:* Am Astron Soc; Am Asn Mus; Int Planetarium Soc. *Res:* Interstellar molecules; astronomy education; history of modern astronomy. *Mailing Add:* Adler Planetarium 1300 S Lake Shore Dr Chicago IL 60605

SWELL, LEON, b New York, NY, July 26, 27; m; c 3. BIOCHEMISTRY. *Educ:* City Col New York, BS, 48; George Washington Univ, MS, 49, PhD(biochem), 52. *Prof Exp:* Lab asst, George Washington Univ, 49-51; chief biochemist, Vet Admin Ctr, Martinsburg, WVa, 51-64, CHIEF, LIPID RES LAB, VET ADMIN HOSP, RICHMOND, VA, 64-; RES PROF BIOCHEM & MED, VA COMMONWEALTH UNIV, 70- *Concurrent Pos:* Assoc prof lectr, George Washington Univ, 59-; assoc res prof, Med Col Va, 64- *Mem:* AAAS; Am Soc Biol Chemists; Soc Exp Biol & Med; Am Inst Nutrit. *Res:* Cholesterol, lipid and electrolyte metabolism; enzymes. *Mailing Add:* Dept of Biochem Va Commonwealth Univ Richmond VA 23298

SWENBERG, JAMES ARTHUR, b Northfield, Minn, Jan 15, 42; m 63; c 2. VETERINARY PATHOLOGY, CHEMICAL CARCINOGENESIS. *Educ:* Univ Minn, DVM, 66; Ohio State Univ, MS, 68, PhD(vet path), 70. *Prof Exp:* NIH trainee path, Ohio State Univ, 66-70, res assoc, 70, asst prof, 70-72, assoc prof, 72; res scientist path, Upjohn Co, 72-76, res sect head, Path & Genetic Toxicol, 76-78; CHIEF PATH, CHEM INDUST INST TOXICOL, 78- *Concurrent Pos:* Consult, Battelle Mem Inst, 71-72; mem sci adv panel, Chem Indust Inst Toxicol, 77-78; mem NCI carcinogenesis prog sci rev comt, 78-81; adj prof dept path, Univ NC, 78-; adj assoc prof, Duke Univ, 78-; NTP Bd Sci Coun, 82- *Mem:* Am Asn Cancer Res; AAAS; Am Asn Neuropathologists; Am Col Vet Pathologists; Soc Toxicol. *Res:* Cancer research, including chemical carcinogenesis, neurooncogenesis and chemotherapy, and short-term tests for carcinogens; DNA damage/mutagensis; improved toxicology and data handling methods; inhalation toxicology; mechanisms of toxicity and carcinogenisity; risk assessment; toxicology. *Mailing Add:* Chem Indust Inst of Toxicol PO Box 12137 Research Triangle Park NC 27709

SWENDSEID, MARIAN EDNA, b Petersburg, NDak, Aug 2, 18. BIOCHEMISTRY. *Educ:* Univ NDak, BA, 38, MA, 39; Univ Minn, PhD(physiol chem), 41. *Prof Exp:* Asst nutrit, Univ Ill, 42; res biochemist, Simpson Mem Inst, Univ Mich, 42-43; sr res chemist, Parke Davis & Co, Mich, 45-48; res biochemist, Simpson Mem Inst, Univ Mich, 48-52; assoc prof, 53-72, PROF NUTRIT, UNIV CALIF, LOS ANGELES, 72- *Mem:* Am Chem Soc; Am Soc Biol Chem. *Res:* Vitamin research; biochemical aspects of hematology; the use of carbon 13 in the study of intermediary metabolism; amino acids in nutrition. *Mailing Add:* Dept of Nutrit & Biol Chem Univ of Calif Sch of Pub Health Los Angeles CA 90024

SWENDSEN, ROBERT HAAKON, b New York, NY, Apr 4, 43; m 71; c 2. PHYSICS. *Educ:* Yale Univ, BS, 64; Univ Pa, PhD(physics), 71. *Prof Exp:* Res asst physics, Univ Cologne, 71-73; physicist, Kernforschungsanlage Julich, Ger, 74-76; ASSOC PHYSICIST, BROOKHAVEN NAT LAB, 76- *Mem:* Am Phys Soc. *Res:* Solid state physics; phse transitions; magnetism. *Mailing Add:* Dept Physics Brookhaven Nat Lab Upton NY 11973

SWENERTON, HELENE, b Norfolk, Va, Jan 13, 25; m 43; c 3. NUTRITION. *Educ:* Univ Calif, Davis, BS, 63, MS. 65, PhD(nutrit), 70. *Prof Exp:* Res nutritionist, 70-72, EXTEN NUTRITIONIST, UNIV CALIF, DAVIS, 72- *Mem:* AAAS; Am Inst Nutrit; Soc Nutrit Educ; Am Dietetics Assoc. *Res:* Role of dietary zinc in mammalian growth and development; effects of maternal dietary deficiencies on fetal development; influence of nutrition education on consumer decisions. *Mailing Add:* Dept of Nutrit Univ of Calif Davis CA 95616

SWENSEN, ALBERT DONALD, b Provo, Utah, May 28, 15; m 37; c 6. BIOCHEMISTRY. *Educ:* Brigham Young Univ, AB, 37, MA, 38; La State Univ, PhD(biol chem), 41. *Prof Exp:* Biochemist, US Naval Res Lab, 41-47; from asst prof to assoc prof chem, Brigham Young Univ, 47-57, prof chem, 57-80, chmn dept, 60-63. *Concurrent Pos:* Fel, Univ Minn, 56; vis scientist, Charles F Kettering Res Lab, Yellow Springs, Ohio, 63-64. *Mem:* Am Chem Soc. *Res:* Enzymes; intermediary metabolism. *Mailing Add:* 1184 Ash Ave Provo UT 84601

SWENSON, CHARLES ALLYN, b Clinton, Minn, Aug 31, 33; m 60; c 3. PHYSICAL CHEMISTRY. *Educ:* Gustavus Adolphus Col, BS, 55; Univ Iowa, PhD(chem), 59. *Prof Exp:* Asst, Univ Iowa, 55-56; asst prof chem, Wartburg Col, 58-60; res assoc, 60-62, from asst prof to assoc prof, 62-72, PROF BIOCHEM, UNIV IOWA, 72- *Mem:* Am Chem Soc; Biophys Soc. *Res:* Physical biochemistry; model studies for biopolymer interactions; spectroscopic and thermodynamic approaches; energy transduction in muscle contraction. *Mailing Add:* Dept of Biochemistry Univ of Iowa Iowa City IA 52242

SWENSON, CLAYTON ALBERT, b Hopkins, Minn, Nov 11, 23; m 50, 80; c 3. EXPERIMENTAL SOLID STATE PHYSICS. *Educ:* Harvard Univ, BS, 44; Oxford Univ, DPhil(physics), 49. *Prof Exp:* Instr physics, Harvard Univ, 49-52; res physicist, Div Indust Coop, Mass Inst Technol, 52-55; from asst prof to assoc prof, 55-60, chmn dept, 75-82, PROF PHYSICS, IOWA STATE UNIV, 60-, . *Mem:* Am Phys Soc; Sigma Xi. *Res:* Low temperatures; high pressures; low temperature thermodynamics; thermometry; equations of state of solids. *Mailing Add:* Dept Physics Iowa State Univ Ames IA 50011

SWENSON, DAVID HAROLD, b Moorhead, Minn, June 16, 48; m 69; c 1. CHEMICAL CARCINOGENESIS, ONCOLOGY. *Educ:* Univ Minn, BS, 70; Univ Wis, PhD(oncol), 75. *Prof Exp:* NIH fel carcinogenesis, Inst Cancer Res, Chester Beatty Res Inst, 75-77; res chemist, Nat Ctr Toxicol Res, 77-79; RES SCIENTIST GENETIC TOXICOL, UPJOHN CO, 79- *Mem:* Am Asn Cancer Res; Environ Mutagen Soc; AAAS; Res Soc NAm; Genetic Toxicol Asn. *Res:* Elucidation of the mechanism of interaction of genetoxins, carcinogens and cancer chemotherapeutic agents with nucleic acid. *Mailing Add:* Upjohn Co 301 Henrietta St Kalamazoo MI 49001

SWENSON, DONALD ADOLPH, b Camden, Ala, May 9, 32; m 55; c 4. PHYSICS, MATHEMATICS. *Educ:* Univ Ala, BS, 53; Univ Minn, MS, 56, PhD(physics), 58. *Prof Exp:* Physicist, Midwestern Univs Res Asn, 58-60 & 61-64; Ford Found fel, European Orgn Nuclear Res, Switz, 60-61; physicist, Los Alamos Sci Lab, 65-80, FEL, LOS ALAMOS NAT LAB, 80- *Mem:* Am Phys Soc. *Res:* Particle accelerator, design and development; particle dynamics in circular and linear accelerators; proton beam measurement and diagnostics; development and use of computer control systems for particle accelerators. *Mailing Add:* Accelerator Technol Div Los Alamos Nat Lab Los Alamos NM 87544

SWENSON, DONALD OTIS, b Manhattan, Kans, Feb 19, 37; m 62; c 4. ENGINEERING. *Educ:* Univ Kans, BSME, 63, MSc, 65, PhD(eng mech), 67. *Prof Exp:* Sr res assoc, Advan Mat Res & Develop Lab, Pratt & Whitney Aircraft Div, United Aircraft Corp, Conn, 67-71; CONSULT ENGR, BLACK & VEATCH CONSULT ENGRS, 71- *Mem:* Am Soc Mech Engrs; Am Soc Testing & Mat; Soc Mfg Engrs; Air Pollution Control Asn. *Res:* Air pollution control technology and systems for fossil fueled power plants; material behavior; fatigue of materials; control systems. *Mailing Add:* Black & Veatch Consult Engrs Kansas City MO 64114

SWENSON, FRANK ALBERT, b Davenport, Iowa, Feb 3, 12; m 43; c 2. HYDROLOGY. *Educ:* Augustana Col, AB, 36; Univ Iowa, MS, 40, PhD(geol), 42. *Prof Exp:* Surv man & geologist, US Army Corps Engrs, 37-38; asst geol, Univ Iowa, 38-42; jr geologist, Ground Water Br, 42, from asst geologist to geologist, Mil Geol Br, 42-46. ground water invests, 46-63, res geologist, US Geol Surv, 63-74; CONSULT GEOLOGIST-HYDROLOGIST, 75- *Concurrent Pos:* Consult, US Dept Justice. *Mem:* Fel Geol Soc Am; Int Geol Cong; Int Asn Hydrogeol. *Res:* Geology and ground water investigations in Montana and Wyoming; military intelligence; research in limestone hydrology; geochemistry. *Mailing Add:* 11615 W 31st Place Lakewood CO 80215

SWENSON, G(EORGE) W(ARNER), JR, b Minneapolis, Minn, Sept 22, 22; m 43; c 4. ELECTRICAL ENGINEERING, ASTRONOMY. *Educ:* Mich Col Mining & Technol, BS, 44, EE, 50; Mass Inst Technol, SM, 48; Univ Wis, PhD, 51. *Prof Exp:* Asst elec eng, Mass Inst Technol, 46-48; instr, Univ Wis, 48-51; assoc prof, Wash Univ, St Louis, 51-53; prof, Univ Alaska, 53-54; assoc prof, Mich State Univ, 54-56; assoc prof, 56-58, prof elec eng & res prof astron, 58-70, actg head astron dept, 70-72, PROF, ELEC ENG DEPT, UNIV ILL, URBANA, 70-, HEAD DEPT, 79- *Concurrent Pos:* Res prof, Geophys Inst, Univ Alaska, 54-56; consult, NSF, 59-75, US Army Ballistic Missile Agency, 59-60, NASA & Nat Acad Sci; mem, Adv Comt, Nat Radio Astron Observ, 59-80, vis scientist & chmn, Very Large Array Design Group, 64-68, mem res staff, 66-; mem, US Nat Comt, Inst Sci Radio Union, 59-; vis assoc, Calif Inst Technol, 72-73. *Mem:* Nat Acad Eng; fel AAAS; fel Inst Elec & Electronics Engrs. *Res:* Antenna design; radio astronomy; ionospheric radio propagation; acoustics. *Mailing Add:* Dept of Elec Eng Univ of Ill Urbana IL 61801

SWENSON, GARY RUSSELL, b Grantsburg, Wis, June 17, 41; m 67; c 2. ATMOSPHERIC PHYSICS. *Educ:* Wis State Univ-Superior, BS, 63; Univ Mich, Ann Arbor, MS, 68, PhD(atmospheric sci), 75. *Prof Exp:* SPACE SCIENTIST ATMOSPHERIC SCI, MARSHALL SPACE FLIGHT CTR, NASA, 68- *Mem:* Am Geophys Union; Sigma Xi. *Res:* Experimental research using remote sensing techniques, upper atmospheric phenomena, including aurora. *Mailing Add:* 1408 Wind River Dr Hunstville AL 35802

SWENSON, GENE HOLSTROM, b Ft Dodge, Iowa, Dec 23, 31. VETERINARY PHARMACOLOGY. *Educ:* Iowa State Univ, DVM, 58; Univ Mo, MS, 70. *Prof Exp:* Vet pract, 58-68; res asst vet microbiol, Univ Mo, 68-70; field develop specialist, Merck & Co, 70-71; tech serv vet, Am Cyanamid Co, 72; RES VET PHARMACOL, UPJOHN CO, 72- *Mem:* Am Vet Med Asn; Am Asn Bovine Practr; US Animal Health Asn; Am Soc Vet Physiologists & Pharmacologists. *Res:* Etiology and pathogenesis of bovine mastitis in conjunction with the pharmacology and pharmacokinetics of drugs for therapy and prophylaxis of the disease. *Mailing Add:* Bldg 190 Upjohn Co Kalamazoo MI 49001

SWENSON, HENRY MAURICE, b Brooklyn, NY, Aug 13, 16; m 41; c 4. DENTISTRY. *Educ:* Univ Ill, BS, 41, DDS, 42; Am Bd Periodont, dipl, 51. *Prof Exp:* From instr to assoc prof, 45-62, PROF PERIODONT, SCH DENT, IND UNIV, INDIANAPOLIS, 62-, DIR CLIN, 56- *Concurrent Pos:* Consult, Vet Admin, 58- & US Dept Army, 59- *Mem:* Am Dent Asn; fel Am Col Dentists; Am Acad Periodont; Int Asn Dent Res. *Res:* Treatment and management of periodontal involvement. *Mailing Add:* 1121 W Michigan Indianapolis IN 46202

SWENSON, HUGO NATHANAEL, b New Richland, Minn, Mar 11, 04; m 56. PHYSICS. *Educ:* Carleton Col, AB, 25; Univ Ill, MS, 27, PhD(spectros), 30. *Prof Exp:* Asst physics, Univ Ill, 25-29; head dept, Earlham Col, 29-30; Am-Scand Found fel, Bohr's Inst, Denmark, 30-31; instr physics, Barnard Col, Columbia Univ, 31-37; instr physics, 37-41, from asst prof to assoc prof, 41-57, prof, 57-73, EMER PROF PHYSICS, QUEENS COL, NY, 73- *Mem:* AAAS; Am Phys Soc; Am Asn Physics Teachers. *Res:* Electronics. *Mailing Add:* 252-45 Brattle Ave Little Neck NY 11362

SWENSON, LEONARD WAYNE, b Twin Falls, Idaho, June 11, 31; m 50; c 3. PHYSICS. *Educ:* Mass Inst Technol, BS, 54, PhD(physics), 60. *Prof Exp:* Instr physics, Northeastern Univ, 57-58 & Tufts Univ, 58-59; res assoc, Mass Inst Technol, 60-62; Bartol fel nuclear struct res group, Bartol Res Found, 62-64, res staff mem, 64-66; dir space radiation effects lab, Va Assoc Res Ctr, 67-68; assoc prof, 68-81, PROF PHYSICS, ORE STATE UNIV, 81- *Concurrent Pos:* Consult, Joseph Kaye & Co, 57-59. *Mem:* Am Phys Soc; Am Sci Affil. *Res:* Nuclear structure and reaction; intermediate energy nuclear physics. *Mailing Add:* Dept of Physics Ore State Univ Corvallis OR 97331

SWENSON, MELVIN JOHN, b Concordia, Kans, Jan 14, 17; m 47; c 3. VETERINARY PHYSIOLOGY. *Educ:* Kans State Col, DVM, 43; Iowa State Col, MS, 47, PhD(path), 50. *Prof Exp:* Instr vet sci, La State Univ, 43; asst prof path, Iowa State Col, 49-50; assoc prof physiol, Kans State Col, 50-56; prof, Colo State Univ, 56-57; prof & head dept, 57-73, PROF PHYSIOL, IOWA STATE UNIV, 73- *Mem:* AAAS; Am Physiol Soc; Am Soc Vet Physiol & Pharmacol; Soc Exp Biol & Med; Am Vet Med Asn. *Res:* Need for trace minerals in animals; effect of antibiotics on growth and hematology; nutrient requirements of animals; histophysiology of nutritional deficiencies; anemias of farm animals. *Mailing Add:* Dept of Vet Anat Pharmacol & Physiol Iowa State Univ Col Vet Med Ames IA 50010

SWENSON, ORVAR, b Halsingborg, Sweden, Feb 7, 09; nat US; m 41; c 3. SURGERY. *Educ:* William Jewell Col, AB, 33; Harvard Med Sch, MD, 37. *Prof Exp:* Intern surg, Ohio State Univ Hosp, 37-38; house officer path, Children's Hosp, Boston, 38-39, house officer surg, 39-41; Cabot fel, Harvard Med Sch, 41-44, asst surg, 42-44, instr, 44-47, assoc, 47-50; assoc prof, Sch

Med, Tufts Univ, 50-54, clin prof pediat surg, 54-57, prof, 57-60; prof surg, Med Sch, Northwestern Univ, Chicago, 60-73; prof surg, Sch Med, Univ Miami, 73-77. *Concurrent Pos:* Surg house officer, Peter Bent Brigham Hosp, 39-41, asst res surgeon, 41-42, jr assoc, 44, res surgeon, 44-45; jr attend surgeon, Children's Hosp, Boston, 45, assoc vis surgeon, 45-47, surgeon, 47-50; vis surgeon, New Eng Peabody Home Crippled Children, 46-50, mem assoc staff, 50; lectr, Simmons Col, 48-50; sr surgeon, New Eng Ctr Hosp, 50-60; surgeon in chief, Boston Floating Hosp Infants & Children, 50-60 & Children's Mem Hosp, Chicago, 60-72. *Mem:* Assoc Asn Thoracic Surg; Am Surg Asn; fel Am Col Surg; fel Am Acad Pediat. *Mailing Add:* 54 Main St Rockport ME 04856

SWENSON, PAUL ARTHUR, b St Paul, Minn, Feb 5, 20; m 42; c 2. CELL PHYSIOLOGY. *Educ:* Hamline Univ, BS, 47; Stanford Univ, PhD(biol), 52. *Prof Exp:* Instr physiol, Univ Mass, 50-54, from asst prof to assoc prof, 54-66; RADIATION BIOPHYSICIST, BIOL DIV, OAK RIDGE NAT LAB, 66- *Concurrent Pos:* Vis assoc physiologist, Brookhaven Nat Lab, 56-57; USPHS spec fel, Oak Ridge Nat Lab, 62-64. *Mem:* AAAS; Biophys Soc; Am Soc Microbiol; Am Soc Photobiol; Radiation Res Soc. *Res:* Effects of ultraviolet and ionizing radiations on metabolic control in bacteria. *Mailing Add:* Biol Div Oak Ridge Nat Lab Oak Ridge TN 37830

SWENSON, RICHARD PAUL, b Minnesota, Mar 5, 49. PROTEIN CHEMISTRY, ENZYMOLOGY. *Educ:* Gustavus Adolphus Col, BA, 71; Univ Minn, PhD(biochem), 79. *Prof Exp:* Teaching asst, Gustavus Adolphus Col, 68-71; res asst biochem, Dept Endocrinol, Mayo Clinic, 71-74; teaching asst, Univ Minn, 74-77; FEL BIOCHEM, UNIV MICH, ANN ARBOR, 79- *Concurrent Pos:* Acad asst chem, Gustavus Adolphus Col, 70-71. *Honors & Awards:* Bacaner Basic Sci Res Award, Minn Med Found, 80. *Mem:* Am Chem Soc. *Res:* Mechanism of enzyme and protein action; elucidation of a unique thiol ester active center in the blood protease inhibitor, alpha-2-macroglobulin; primary structure of the flavoprotein, D-amino acid oxidase; modifications to active-site amino acids involved in catalysis. *Mailing Add:* Rm M5416 Med Sci I Dept Biochem Univ Mich Ann Arbor MI 48109

SWENSON, RICHARD WALTNER, b New York, NY, May 17, 23; m 49; c 3. PHOTOGRAPHIC CHEMISTRY. *Educ:* Clark Univ, Mass, AB, 48, AM, 49; Brown Univ, PhD(chem phys), 53. *Prof Exp:* Res chemist, 53-63, RES ASSOC, PHOTO PROD DEPT, E I DU PONT DE NEMOURS & CO, 63- *Mem:* Am Chem Soc; Soc Photog Sci & Eng(pres. 67-71). *Res:* Photographic chemistry, specifically emulsion chemistry. *Mailing Add:* 65 Edison Ave Tinton Falls NJ 07724

SWENSON, ROYAL JAY, crop science, soil science, see previous edition

SWENTON, JOHN STEPHEN, b Kansas City, Kans, Dec 8, 40. ORGANIC CHEMISTRY. *Educ:* Univ Kans, BA, 62; Univ Wis, PhD(chem), 65. *Prof Exp:* Nat Acad Sci-Nat Res Coun fel, Harvard Univ, 65-66; asst prof chem, 67-71, assoc prof, 71-77, PROF CHEM, OHIO STATE UNIV, 77- *Concurrent Pos:* Res Corp grant, 67-69; Eli Lilly res grant, 68-70; Soc Petrol Res Fund grant, 76-78, NSF grant, 77-78 & NIH grant, 78-81. *Mem:* Am Chem Soc; Royal Soc Chem. *Res:* Synthetic and mechanistic organic photochemistry, synthetic and mechanistic organic electrochemistry, and natural products synthesis. *Mailing Add:* Dept Chem 140 W 18th Ave Columbus OH 43210

SWERCZEK, THOMAS WALTER, b Cedar Rapids, Nebr, May 10, 39; m 64; c 3. VETERINARY PATHOLOGY. *Educ:* Kans State Univ, BS, 62, DVM, 64; Univ Conn, MS, 66, PhD(path), 69. *Prof Exp:* Asst prof, 69-77, ASSOC PROF VET SCI COL AGR, UNIV KY, 77- *Mem:* Am Vet Med Asn; Conf Res Workers Animal Dis. *Res:* Comparative pathology; pathogenesis of infectious diseases of horses. *Mailing Add:* Dept Vet Sci Col Agr Univ Ky Lexington KY 40506

SWERDLOFF, RONALD S, b Pomona, Calif, Feb 18, 38; m 59; c 2. ENDOCRINOLOGY, INTERNAL MEDICINE. *Educ:* Univ Calif, Los Angeles, BS, 59; Univ Calif, San Francisco, MD, 62. *Prof Exp:* Intern internal med, Kings Co Hosp, Univ Wash, 62-63, asst resident med, 63-64; clin res assoc, Res Metab Sect, NIH, 64-66; assoc resident med, Univ Calif, Los Angeles, 66-67; NIH spec fel endocrinol, 67-69, asst prof, 69-72, assoc chief, 72-73, assoc prof, 73-78, CHIEF, DIV ENDOCRINOL & METAB, HARBOR-GEN HOSP CAMPUS, UNIV CALIF, LOS ANGELES, 73-, PROF MED, HARBOR-UNIV CALIF, LOS ANGELES MED CTR, 78- *Concurrent Pos:* Dir Med Residency Prog, St Mary's Long Beach Hosp & Harbor Gen Hosp, 69-71; NIH career develop award, 72-77; actg dir, Clin Study Ctr, Harbor Gen Hosp, 78- *Honors & Awards:* Wyeth Award, Soc Study Reprod, 74. *Mem:* Am Fedn Clin Res; Endocrine Soc; Soc Study Reprod; Am Andrology Soc. *Res:* Reproductive endocrinology; neuroendocrinology; contraceptive development. *Mailing Add:* Div of Endocrinol 1000 W Carson St Torrance CA 90509

SWERDLOW, MARTIN A, b Chicago, Ill, July 7, 23; m 45; c 2. MEDICINE, PATHOLOGY. *Educ:* Univ Ill, BS, 45, MD, 47; Am Bd Path, dipl, 52. *Prof Exp:* Resident path, Michael Reese Hosp, Chicago, 48-50 & 51-52; pathologist, Menorah Med Ctr, 54-57; from asst prof to assoc prof path, Univ Ill Col Med, 57-60, clin assoc prof, 60-66, prof, 66-72, assoc dean, Abraham Lincoln Sch Med, 70-72; prof path, Sch Med, Univ Mo-Kansas City, 73-74; CHMN DEPT PATH, MICHAEL REESE HOSP & MED CTR, 74-, VPRES ACAD AFFAIRS, 75-; PROF PATH, UNIV CHICAGO, 78- *Concurrent Pos:* Pathologist, Englewood Hosp, Chicago; consult, Vet Admin Hosp, Hines & Cook County Hosp, Chicago; chmn dept path, Kansas City Gen Hosp, 73-74. *Mem:* Am Soc Clin Path; Col Am Pathologists; Am Acad Dermat; Asn Am Med Cols; NY Acad Sci. *Res:* Histopathology of skin disorders; experimental skin tumors; diseases of liver. *Mailing Add:* Dept of Path Michael Reese Hosp & Med Ctr Chicago IL 60616

SWERDLOW, MAX, b New York, NY, Sept 13, 15; m 44; c 3. SOLID STATE PHYSICS, MATERIALS SCIENCE. *Educ:* Brooklyn Col, BA, 38; George Washington Univ, cert, 41. *Prof Exp:* Ceramic engr optical glass sect, US Nat Bur Standards, 40-46, physicist constitution & microstruct sect, 46-57; SOLID STATE PHYSICIST PROG MGR, AIR FORCE OFF SCI RES ELECTRONIC & SOLID STATE SCI DIRECTORATE, 57- *Concurrent Pos:* Vis fel dept physics & astron, Univ Md, 66-67; mem & rep solid state sci comt, Nat Res Coun-Nat Acad Sci; Air Force rep superconductivity, US Interagency Adv Power Group; Agency rep, US Interagency Mat Res Group. *Mem:* Electron Micros Soc Am (treas, 43-56, pres, 58); Sigma Xi; fel AAAS; fel Am Phys Soc; Am Crystallog Asn. *Res:* Constitution, crystallography, microstructure, properties, growth and synthesis of solid state materials; research grant administration and research program management; superconductivity; magnetism; high magnetic fields; nonlinear optics and infrared physics; molecular solids. *Mailing Add:* 5704 Lenox Rd Bethesda MD 20817

SWERLICK, ISADORE, b Philadelphia, Pa, Jan 23, 21; m 51; c 2. ORGANIC CHEMISTRY. *Educ:* Temple Univ, BA, 43; Duke Univ, PhD(chem). 50. *Prof Exp:* Asst, Duke Univ, 46-49; res chemist, 50-56, res supvr, 56-70, staff scientist, Film Dept, 70-76, RES ASSOC, POLYMER PROD DEPT, E I DU PONT DE NEMOURS & CO, INC, 77- *Mem:* AAAS; Am Chem Soc; Sigma Xi. *Res:* Organics and polymers. *Mailing Add:* 4616 Sylvanus Dr Rockwood Hills Wilmington DE 19803

SWERN, DANIEL, b New York, NY, Jan 21, 16; m 38; c 2. ORGANIC CHEMISTRY. *Educ:* City Col New York, BS. 35; Columbia Univ, MA, 36; Univ Md, PhD(org chem), 40. *Prof Exp:* With USDA, 37-63; PROF CHEM & SR RES INVESTR, FELS RES INST, TEMPLE UNIV, 63- *Concurrent Pos:* Hon Res Fel, Univ London, 70-71; Flemming, Scott, Bond, Mattiello, Spencer, USDA, Bailey & Ebermann awards. *Mem:* AAAS; Am Asn Cancer; Am Chem Soc; Am Oil Chem Soc. *Res:* Cancer inhibition and carcinogenesis; chemistry of fats; organic peroxides; small rings; free radicals and olefins; polymerization; ylids; pseudohalogens. *Mailing Add:* Fels Res Inst Dept of Chem Temple Univ Philadelphia PA 19122

SWETHARANYAM, LALITHA, b Trivandrum, India; m 71. MATHEMATICAL ANALYSIS. *Educ:* Annamalai Univ, Madras, PhD(math), 66. *Prof Exp:* Lectr math & head dept, LVD Col, Raichur, India, 56-61; res fel, Annamalai Univ, Madras, 61-65, lectr, 65-69; assoc prof, 69-73, PROF, McNEESE STATE UNIV, 73- *Mem:* Am Math Soc; Indian Math Soc; Math Asn Am; Assoc Women in Math. *Res:* Functional analysis; point set topology. *Mailing Add:* Dept of Math Sci McNeese State Univ Lake Charles LA 70609

SWETITS, JOHN JOSEPH, b Passaic, NJ, Oct 1, 42; m 66; c 3. MATHEMATICAL ANALYSIS. *Educ:* Fordham Univ, BS, 64; Lehigh Univ, MS, 67, PhD(math), 68. *Prof Exp:* Instr math, Lafayette Col, 67-68, asst prof, 68-70; assoc prof, PROF MATH, OLD DOM UNIV, 81- *Mem:* Am Math Soc; Math Asn Am; Soc Indust & Appl Math. *Res:* Summability theory; approximation theory. *Mailing Add:* Dept of Math Old Dominion Univ Norfolk VA 23508

SWETS, DON EUGENE, b Grand Rapids, Mich, Oct 7, 30; m 56; c 4. SOLID STATE PHYSICS, CHEMICAL PHYSICS. *Educ:* Univ Mich, BSE(physics) & BSE(math), 53, MS, 55. *Prof Exp:* sr res physicist, 55-80, STAFF RES SCIENTIST, RES LAB, GEN MOTORS CORP, 80- *Res:* Measurement of diffusion coefficients; hydrogen in steel; helium, neon, and hydrogen fused in quartz; growth of single crystals, especially tetragonal germanium dioxide; ribbon shaped germanium; hexamethylenetetramine IV-VI and III-V compounds. *Mailing Add:* Physics Dept Gen Motors Res Labs 12 Mile & Mound Rds Warren MI 48090

SWETT, JOHN EMERY, b San Francisco, Calif, Mar 19, 32; m 56; c 4. ANATOMY, NEUROPHYSIOLOGY. *Educ:* Univ Wash, AB, 56; Univ Calif, Los Angeles, PhD(anat), 60. *Prof Exp:* NSF fel, Univ Pisa, 60-61, NIH fel, 61-62; neurophysiologist, Good Samaritan Hosp, Portland, Ore, 62-66; assoc prof anat, State Univ NY Upstate Med Ctr, 66-67; assoc prof anat, Med Sch, Univ Colo, Denver, 67-76; PROF ANAT & CHMN DEPT, COL MED, UNIV CALIF, IRVINE, 76- *Concurrent Pos:* NIH res grants, 64- *Mem:* Am Asn Anatomists; Am Physiol Soc; Soc Neurosci. *Res:* Organization of the spinal cord; mechanisms of sensory detection; organization of the peripheral nervous system. *Mailing Add:* Dept of Anat Univ of Calif Col of Med Irvine CA 92717

SWETT, KEENE, b Wilton, Maine, Nov 6, 32; m 54; c 2. GEOLOGY. *Educ:* Tufts Univ, BS, 55; Univ Colo, MS, 61; Univ Edinburgh, PhD(geol), 65. *Prof Exp:* Asst lectr geol, Univ Edinburgh, 63-66; asst prof, 66-70, assoc prof, 70-74, PROF GEOL, UNIV IOWA, 74- *Concurrent Pos:* NSF fel, 67-82. *Mem:* Geol Soc Am; Am Asn Petrol Geol; Soc Econ Paleont & Mineral; Int Asn Sedimentol; AAAS. *Res:* Petrological studies of sediments and sedimentary rocks with especial regard to the post-depositional alterations and patterns of diagenesis; Cambro-Ordovician shelf sediments of western Newfoundland, northwest Scotland, central eastern Greenland and Spitsbergen; late proterozoic biostratigraphy and paleo environments of Spitsbergen and central east Greenland. *Mailing Add:* Dept of Geol Univ of Iowa Iowa City IA 52240

SWEZ, JOHN ADAM, b Cleveland, Ohio, Nov 18, 41; m 65; c 1. BIOPHYSICS. *Educ:* Pa State Univ, BS, 63, MS, 65, PhD(biophys), 67. *Prof Exp:* From asst prof to assoc prof physics, 67-77, PROF PHYSICS & DIR RADIATION LAB, IND STATE UNIV, TERRE HAUTE, 77- *Mem:* AAAS; Radiation Res Soc; Biophys Soc. *Res:* Degradation studies of DNA in Escherichia coli after ionizing radiation, physical characterization and effect of bacteriophage infection; injection of nucleic acid of bacteriophage T1 into its host Escherichia coli. *Mailing Add:* Dept Physics Ind State Univ Terre Haute IN 47809

SWEZEY, ROBERT LEONARD, b Pasadena, Calif, Apr 30, 25; m 49; c 3. INTERNAL MEDICINE, PHYSICAL MEDICINE & REHABILITATION. *Educ:* Ohio State Univ, MD, 48; Am Bd Internal Med, dipl, 60; Am Bd Phys Med & Rehab, dipl, 69; Am Bd Rheumatology, dipl, 74. *Prof Exp:* Intern, Los Angeles County Gen Hosp, Calif, 48-49 & Am Hosp, Paris, 49-50; resident internal med, Wadsworth Gen Med & Surg Vet Admin Hosp, 51-54, fel rheumatol, Wadsworth Gen Med & Surg Vet Admin Hosp & Univ Calif, Los Angeles, 54-55, clin asst med, Univ Calif, Los Angeles, 55-57, clin instr, 57-64, asst prof, 64-65, career fel phys med & rehab, 65 & 66-67; acad career fel, Univ Minn, 65-66; assoc prof internal med, phys med & rehab, Sch Med, Univ Southern Calif, 67-73, prof med, phys med & rehab, 73-74; prof med & dir div rehab med, 74-78, CLIN PROF MED, SCH MED, UNIV CALIF, LOS ANGELES, 78-; MED DIR, ARTHRITIS & BACK PAIN CTR, 78- *Mem:* AMA; Am Acad Phys Med & Rehab; Am Rheumatism Asn; fel Am Col Physicians; Asn Acad Physiatrists. *Res:* Rheumatology; clinical aspects of rheumatic diseases; mechanisms of arthritic deformities and their treatments. *Mailing Add:* Med Dir Suite 223 2200 Santa Monica Blvd Santa Monica CA 90404

SWIATEK, KENNETH ROBERT, b Chicago, Ill, Dec 30, 35; m 60; c 4. NEUROSCIENCES. *Educ:* NCent Col, BS, 58; Univ Ill Med Ctr, PhD(biol sci), 65. *Prof Exp:* Res assoc biol chem, Dept Pediat, Univ Ill Col Med, 65-68; res scientist, Ill Inst Develop Disabilities, 68-70, admin res sci, 70-75, dir res, 75-76, dir, 76-80. *Concurrent Pos:* Grant carbohydrate metab newborn animal, NIH, 71-74. *Mem:* Am Chem Soc; Sigma Xi; AAAS; Soc Develop Biol; Am Asn Ment Deficiency. *Res:* Study of growth of nervous system with special emphasis on development of carbohydrate, ketones and amino acid metabolism in fetal and newborn brain tissue as affected by pain-relieving drugs of labor and delivery. *Mailing Add:* 5029 Central Ave Western Springs IL 60558

SWICK, KENNETH EUGENE, b Silver Lake, Ind, Jan 20, 36; m 57. MATHEMATICS. *Educ:* Anderson Col, BS, 57; Univ Southern Calif, MA, 64; Univ Iowa, PhD(math), 67. *Prof Exp:* Mathematician, Hughes Aircraft Corp, Calif, 62-64; asst prof, Cornell Col, 66-67 & Occidental Col, 67-70; asst prof, 70-78, ASSOC PROF MATH, QUEENS COL, NY, 78- *Mem:* Math Asn Am; Am Math Soc; Soc Indust & Appl Math. *Res:* Nonlinear differential and integral equations; nonlinear population dynamics. *Mailing Add:* Dept Math Queens Col New York NY 11367

SWICK, ROBERT WINFIELD, b Jackson, Mich, July 6, 25; m 47; c 4. BIOCHEMISTRY. *Educ:* Beloit Col, BS, 47; Univ Wis, MS, 49, PhD(biochem), 51. *Prof Exp:* Assoc biochemist, Div Biol & Med, Argonne Nat Lab, 51-69; PROF NUTRIT SCI, UNIV WIS-MADISON, 69- *Mem:* Am Inst Nutrit; Am Soc Biol Chem. *Res:* Control and kinetics of protein metabolism; regulation of enzyme levels and metabolism. *Mailing Add:* Dept of Nutrit Sci Univ of Wis Madison WI 53706

SWICKLIK, LEONARD JOSEPH, b Nanticoke, Pa, Jan 26, 28; m 52; c 3. ORGANIC CHEMISTRY. *Educ:* Wilkes Col, BS, 49; Univ Pittsburgh, PhD(chem)', 54. *Prof Exp:* Res chemist, E I du Pont de Nemours & Co, Va, 54; res chemist, 56-64, sr res chemist & group leader, 64-68, tech assoc, 68-70, head, Process Improv Lab, 71-73, supvr chem process, 73-78, SUPVR OILS PROCESSING DEPT, DISTILLATION PROD DIV, EASTMAN KODAK CO, 78- *Mem:* Am Oil Chemists Soc; AAAS; Am Chem Soc; NY Acad Sci. *Res:* Food applications of emulsifiers; fat and oil chemistry as applicable to edible products; food and animal feed applications of vitamins. *Mailing Add:* 92 Northwick Dr Rochester NY 14617

SWIDER, WILLIAM, JR, b Brooklyn, NY, Jan 5, 34; m 59; c 5. ATMOSPHERIC CHEMISTRY, PHYSICS. *Educ:* Lehigh Univ, BS, 55, MS, 57; Pa State Univ, PhD(physics), 63. *Prof Exp:* Assoc physicist, Int Bus Mach Corp, 57-60; chmn civilian policy bd, 78-81, PHYSICIST, AIR FORCE GEOPHYSICS LAB, 64- *Concurrent Pos:* Res fel, Nat Ctr Space Res, Brussels, Belgium, 63-64; mem comn G, US Nat comt, Int Sci Radio Union, 66-; vis prof physics, Utah State Univ, 75. *Honors & Awards:* Loeser Award, Air Force Geophysics Lab, 77. *Mem:* Am Geophys Union; Sigma Xi. *Res:* Ionospheric physics; airglow. *Mailing Add:* Aeronomy Div Air Force Geophysics Lab Hanscom AFB Bedford MA 01731

SWIERSTRA, ERNEST EMKE, b Netherlands, Aug, 14, 30; Can citizen; m 62; c 2. ANIMAL PHYSIOLOGY. *Educ:* Univ Groningen, dipl, 51; Univ BC, BSA, 56, MSA, 58; Cornell Univ, PhD(physiol), 62. *Prof Exp:* Asst animal breeding, Cornell Univ, 58-62; sr res scientist, 62-75, HEAD ANIMAL SCI SECT, RES STA, CAN DEPT AGR, 75- *Mem:* Am Soc Animal Sci; Can Soc Animal Sci; Brit Soc Study Fertil; Agr Inst Can. *Res:* Reproductive physiology. *Mailing Add:* Res Sta Can Dept of Agr Lethbridge AB T1J 4B1 Can

SWIFT, ARTHUR REYNDERS, b Worcester, Mass, July 25, 38; m 61; c 3. PHYSICS. *Educ:* Swarthmore Col, BA, 60; Univ Pa, PhD(physics), 64. *Prof Exp:* NATO fel physics, Cambridge Univ, 64-65; res assoc, Univ Wis, 65-67; asst prof, 67-70, assoc prof, 70-76, PROF PHYSICS, UNIV MASS, AMHERST, 76- *Mem:* Am Phys Soc. *Res:* Elementary particle theory. *Mailing Add:* Dept Physics Univ Mass Amherst MA 01003

SWIFT, BRINTON L, b Denver, Colo, June 12, 26; m 56; c 1. VETERINARY MEDICINE. *Educ:* Colo State Univ, DVM, 51. *Prof Exp:* Private practice, Buffalo, Wyo, 51-64; from asst prof to assoc prof, 64-69, PROF VET MED, UNIV WYO, 69- *Mem:* Am Vet Med Asn; Sigma Xi; Soc Theriogenology. *Res:* Anaplasmosis. *Mailing Add:* Div Microbiol & Vet Med Univ of Wyo Laramie WY 82070

SWIFT, CALVIN THOMAS, b Quantico, Va, Feb 6, 37; m 59; c 2. ENGINEERING, REMOTE SENSING. *Educ:* Mass Inst Technol, BS, 59; Va Polytech Inst & State Univ, MS, 65; Col William & Mary, PhD(physics), 69. *Prof Exp:* Res engr, NAm Aviation, Calif, 59-62; aerospace engr, Langley Res Ctr, NASA, 62-81, leader microwave radiometer group, 75-81; PROF ELEC & COMPUT ENG, UNIV MASS, 81- *Concurrent Pos:* Asst lectorial prof, George Washington Univ, 70-; lectr, Col William & Mary, 71-; adj assoc prof, Old Dominion Univ, 75- *Mem:* Sr mem Inst Elec & Electronics Engrs; Antennas & Propagation Soc (secy-treas, 74-). *Res:* Antennas and propagation, with emphasis on remote sensing of the ocean. *Mailing Add:* Dept Elec & Comp Eng Univ Mass Amherst MA 01003

SWIFT, CAMM CHURCHILL, b Oakland, Calif, Sept 29, 40. ICHTHYOLOGY. *Educ:* Univ Calif, Berkeley, AB, 63; Univ Mich, Ann Arbor, MS, 65; Fla State Univ, PhD(biol), 70. *Prof Exp:* ASSOC CUR FISHES, NATURAL HIST MUS LOS ANGELES COUNTY, 70- *Concurrent Pos:* Adj asst prof, Dept Biol Sci, Univ Southern Calif, 72-; bd gov, Am Soc Ichthyologists & Herpetologists, 73-78. *Mem:* Am Soc Ichthyologists & Herpetologists; Soc Vert Paleont; Soc Study Evolution; Soc Syst Zool; Am Fisheries Soc. *Res:* Systematics and evolution of Recent and fossil, freshwater and marine shore fishes of North America. *Mailing Add:* Sect of Fishes 900 Exposition Blvd Los Angeles CA 90007

SWIFT, CHARLES MOORE, JR, b Boston, Mass, Sept 26, 40; m 63; c 2. GEOPHYSICS. *Educ:* Princeton Univ, AB, 62; Mass Inst Technol, PhD(geophys), 67. *Prof Exp:* Sr geophysicist, Kennecott Explor Serv Lab, Kennecott Copper Corp, 67-76; geophys supvr, Geothermal Explor Div, 76-81, DIV GEOPHYS, DOMESTIC MINERALS DIV, CHEVRON RESOURCES CO, STANDARD OIL CO CALIF, 81- *Concurrent Pos:* Adj assoc prof, Dept Geol & Geophys, Univ Utah, 76-; lectr, Dept Mat Sci & Eng, Univ Calif, Berkeley, 76-; assoc ed, Geophysics, Geothermal Explor, 80-81 & Mining Geophysics, 82- *Mem:* Soc Explor Geophysicists; Am Geophys Union; Geothermal Resources Coun; Geol Soc Am; Soc Economic Geologists. *Res:* Geophysical, particularly electrical, electromagnetic, and magnetotelluric techniques applied to mineral and geothermal exploration and to the geology of the western United States. *Mailing Add:* Chevron Resources Co 225 Bush St San Francisco CA 94105

SWIFT, DANIEL W, b Worcester, Mass, Mar 6, 35; m 61; c 2. PLASMA PHYSICS, SPACE PHYSICS. *Educ:* Haverford Col, BA, 57; Mass Inst Technol, MS, 59. *Prof Exp:* Mem staff, Lincoln Lab, Mass Inst Technol, 58-59; sr scientist, Res & Adv Develop Div, Avco Corp, 59-63; from asst prof to assoc prof, 63-72, PROF GEOPHYS, GEOPHYS INST, UNIV ALASKA, 72- *Mem:* AAAS; Am Geophys Union; Am Phys Soc. *Res:* Theoretical studies of the earth's magnetosphere and auroral phenomena. *Mailing Add:* Geophys Inst Univ Alaska Fairbanks AK 99701

SWIFT, DAVID LESLIE, b Chicago, Ill, Aug 7, 35; m 59; c 3. ENVIRONMENTAL MEDICINE, PHYSIOLOGY. *Educ:* Purdue Univ, BS, 57; Mass Inst Technol, SM, 59; Johns Hopkins Univ, PhD(chem eng), 63. *Prof Exp:* Chem engr, Argonne Nat Lab, Ill, 63-65; USPHS air pollution spec fel, London Sch Hyg, 65-66; asst prof, 66-70, assoc prof environ med, 70-78, PROF ENVIRON HEALTH SCI, JOHNS HOPKINS UNIV, 78- *Mem:* Air Pollution Control Asn; Brit Occup Hyg Soc; Am Conf Govt Indust Hyg; Am Indust Hyg Asn; Asn Aerosol Res. *Res:* Physiology of respiratory tract; fate of inhaled particles and gases; fluid mechanics and transport in biological systems; air pollution transport. *Mailing Add:* Dept of Environ Health Sci Johns Hopkins Univ Baltimore MD 21205

SWIFT, DONALD J P, b Dobbs Ferry, NY, July 26, 35; m 61; c 2. SEDIMENTOLOGY, OCEANOGRAPHY. *Educ:* Dartmouth Col, AB, 57; Johns Hopkins Univ, MA, 61; Univ NC, PhD(geol), 64. *Prof Exp:* Asst prof sedimentology, Dalhousie Univ, 63-66; assoc scientist marine geol, P R Nuclear Ctr, 66-67; assoc prof geol, Duke Univ, 67-68; Slover assoc prof, Inst Oceanog, Old Dom Univ, 68-71; res oceanogr, Atlantic Oceanog & Meteorol Labs, Nat Oceanic & Atmospheric Admin, 71-81; PRIN GEOLOGIST, RES & DEVELOP, ARCO OIL & GAS CO, 81- *Concurrent Pos:* Res grant, Geol Surv Can, 64-65; res assoc, NS Mus, 65-66; assoc ed, Maritime Sediments, 65-66; res grant, Nat Res Coun Can & Defence Res Bd Can, 65-67; Coastal Eng Res Ctr, 69-71; US Geol Surv, 69-71 & NSF, 69-72; mem, Univ Senate, Old Dom Univ, 69-71; chmn, Univ Res Comt. 69-71; res grant, NASA, 70-71; proj leader, Continental Margin Sedimentation Proj, 72-81; consult, Oceanog Panel, NSF, 74-; Res assoc, Smithsonian Inst, 74-81; adj prof, Univ Miami, 74-81. *Mem:* AAAS; Soc Econ Paleont & Mineral; Geol Soc Am; Int Asn Sedimentol; Am Geophys Union. *Res:* Continental margin sandstones; continental margin sediment transport. *Mailing Add:* Res & Develop Dept Arco Gas & Oil Co Plano TX 75074

SWIFT, DOROTHY GARRISON, b Flint, Mich, Aug 1, 39. BIOLOGICAL OCEANOGRAPHY, BOTANY. *Educ:* Swarthmore Col, BA, 61; Johns Hopkins Univ, MA, 67, PhD(oceanog), 73. *Prof Exp:* Guest student investr, Biol Dept, Woods Hole Oceanog Inst, 68-69; guest investr, Grad Sch Oceanog, 70-73, res assoc, Dept Chem, 74-76, RES ASSOC, GRAD SCH OCEANOGRAPHY, UNIV RI, 76- *Honors & Awards:* Bronze Medal, Am Rhododendron Soc, 80. *Mem:* Phycol Soc Am; Am Soc Limnol & Oceanog; Int Phycol Soc; Sigma Xi. *Res:* Biochemistry, nutrition and ecology of marine phytoplankton; role of vitamins and trace metals in phytoplankton ecology; bioassay for vitamins in seawater. *Mailing Add:* Grad Sch of Oceanography Univ of RI Narragansett RI 02882

SWIFT, ELIJAH, V, b Boston, Apr 12, 38; m 61. BIOLOGICAL OCEANOGRAPHY. *Educ:* Swarthmore Col, BA, 60; Johns Hopkins Univ, MA, 64, PhD(oceanog), 67. *Prof Exp:* NSF trainee, Woods Hole Oceanog Inst, 68-69; asst prof, 69-74, ASSOC PROF OCEANOG, UNIV RI, 74- *Concurrent Pos:* NSF grants, 71-76. *Mem:* Phycol Soc Am; Int Phycol Soc; Marine Biol Asn UK; Brit Phycol Soc; Am Soc Limnol & Oceanog. *Res:* Morphology, taxonomy, ecology and physiology of phytoplankton, particularly marine species. *Mailing Add:* Dept Bot Grad Sch Oceanog Univ RI Kingston RI 02881

SWIFT, FRED CALVIN, b Middleport, NY, Oct 16, 26; m 50; c 3. ENTOMOLOGY, ECOLOGY. *Educ:* Mich State Univ, BS, 50; Iowa State Col, MS, 52; Rutgers Univ, PhD, 58. *Prof Exp:* Entomologist, Niagara Chem Div, Food Mach & Chem Corp, 52-55; asst prof entom, Clemson Col, 58-59; assoc prof, 61-72, RES PROF ENTOM, RUTGERS UNIV, NEW BRUNSWICK, 72- *Mem:* Entom Soc Am; Ecol Soc Am. *Res:* Integrated control of fruit insect pests; ecology of the Phytoseiidae. *Mailing Add:* Dept of Entom & Econ Zool Cook Col Rutgers Univ New Brunswick NJ 08903

SWIFT, GEORGE HERBERT, JR, mathematics, computer science, see previous edition

SWIFT, GEORGE W(ILLIAM), b Topeka, Kans, Nov 28, 30; m 56; c 3. CHEMICAL ENGINEERING. *Educ:* Univ Kans, BS, 53, MS, 57, PhD(chem eng), 59. *Prof Exp:* Res engr, Continental Oil Co, 59-61; from asst prof to assoc prof, 61-70, actg assoc dean grad sch, 66-70, prof chem & petrol eng, 70-81, DEANE E ACKERS DISTINGUISHED PROF ENG, UNIV KANS, 81- *Concurrent Pos:* Consult, Continental Oil Co, 63- & C W Nofsinger Co, 65- *Mem:* Am Inst Chem Engrs; Soc Petrol Engrs; Am Soc Eng Educ. *Res:* Transient flow of gas in porous media; transport and thermodynamic properties at low temperature and high pressure; rheology. *Mailing Add:* Dept of Chem & Petrol Eng Univ of Kans Lawrence KS 66044

SWIFT, GLENN W(ILLIAM), b Athabasca, Alta, May 17, 32; m 61; c 2. ELECTRICAL ENGINEERING. *Educ:* Univ Alta, BSc, 53, MSc, 60; Ill State Technol, PhD(elec eng), 68. *Prof Exp:* Elec engr, Can Westinghouse Co, Ltd, 56-58; from lectr to assoc prof, 60-73, PROF ELEC ENG, UNIV MAN, 73- *Concurrent Pos:* Consult, UNIES Ltd, 78-; Nat Res Coun Can grant, 70- *Mem:* Sr mem Inst Elec & Electronics Engrs. *Res:* Power system protection and control. *Mailing Add:* Dept Elec Eng Univ Man Winnipeg MB R3T 2N2 Can

SWIFT, GRAHAM, b Chesterfield, Eng, Apr 16, 39; m 61; c 2. ORGANIC POLYMER CHEMISTRY. *Educ:* Univ London, BSc, 61, PhD(org chem', 64. *Prof Exp:* NIH fel, Fels Res Inst, Philadelphia, 64-66; sci off, Imperial Chem Industs, Eng, 66-68; SR CHEMIST, ROHM AND HAAS CO, 68- *Mem:* Royal Soc Chem; Royal Inst Chem; Am Chem Soc. *Res:* Heterocyclic chemistry; synthesis and reactions of special aziridines, oxiranes and thiiranes; fatty acid chemistry; organic polymer coatings, especially synthesis and evaluation of novel coating compositions. *Mailing Add:* Rohm and Haas Co Spring House PA 19477

SWIFT, HAROLD EUGENE, b Butler, Pa, Mar 27, 36; m 60; c 3. PHYSICAL INORGANIC CHEMISTRY. *Educ:* Allegheny Col, BS, 58; Pittsburgh Univ, PhD(chem), 62. *Prof Exp:* Chemist, 62-63, res chemist, 62-63, sr res chemist, 63-65, sect supvr, Catalysis Sect, Gulf Res & Develop Co, Pittsburgh, 66-73, res dir & sr scienitst, Chem & Minerals Div, 74-77, MGR, CATALYST & CHEM DEPT, GULF SCI & TECHNOL CO, 77- *Concurrent Pos:* Indust bd dir for sch eng & sci, Univ Mass, Amherst, 81-83. *Mem:* Am Chem Soc (chmn, Petrol Chem Div, 77-78). *Res:* Process research for chemical, refining, synthetic fuels and pollution control; heterogeneous and homogeneous catalysis. *Mailing Add:* 1410 Woodhill Dr Gibsonia PA 15044

SWIFT, HEWSON HOYT, b Auburn, NY, Nov 8, 20; m 42; c 2. CYTOLOGY. *Educ:* Swarthmore Col, BA, 42; Univ Iowa, MS, 45; Columbia Univ, PhD(zool), 50. *Prof Exp:* Instr zool, 49-51, from asst prof to assoc prof, 51-59, prof, 59-71, distinguished serv prof, 71-77, chmn dept, 72-77, GEORGE WELLS BEADLE DISTINGUISHED SERV PROF BIOL, UNIV CHICAGO, 77- *Concurrent Pos:* Mem, Cell Biol Study Sect, NIH, 58-62, Develop Biol Adv Panel, NSF, 62-65 & Etiology Cancer Adv Panel, Am Cancer Soc, 56-70; vis prof, Harvard Univ, 70-71; chmn sect cellular & develop biol, Nat Acad Sci, 75-79. *Mem:* Nat Acad Sci; Am Soc Cell Biol(pres, 64); Histochem Soc (pres, 73); Genetics Soc Am. *Res:* Cell biology; cytochemistry. *Mailing Add:* Dept Biol Univ Chicago Chicago IL 60637

SWIFT, HOWARD R(AYMOND), b Streator, Ill, Mar 3, 20; m 46; c 5. CERAMICS. *Educ:* Univ Ill, BS, 40, MS, 42, PhD(ceramics), 45. *Prof Exp:* Asst eng, Exp Sta, Univ Ill, 40-42, res assoc eng, 43-44; res phys chemist, Libbey-Owens-Ford Glass Co, 45-56, chief glass tech res, Libbey-Owens-Ford Co, 55-61, asst dir res, 61-68, dir res & develop, 68-76, chmn, Tech Prod Comt, 76-82, asst to pres, Glass Div, 78-82; CONSULT, 82- *Mem:* Am Ceramic Soc; Brit Soc Glass Technol; Am Soc Testing & Mat; Solar Energy Soc; Am Ord Asn. *Res:* Crystallization of glass; effect of glass composition on properties; stones in glass; polishing of glass; manufacturing of flat glass. *Mailing Add:* 3525 Wesleyan Dr Toledo OH 43614

SWIFT, JACK BERNARD, b Ft Smith, Ark, Jan 3, 42; m 71. THEORETICAL SOLID STATE PHYSICS. *Educ:* Univ Ark, Fayetteville, BS, 63; Univ Ill, Urbana, MS, 65, PhD(physics), 68. *Prof Exp:* NSF fel, Max Planck Inst Physics & Astrophys, Munich, 68-69; res fel, Harvard Univ, 69-71; vis, Bell Tel Lab, 74; asst prof physics, 71-75; ASSOC PROF PHYSICS, UNIV TEX, AUSTIN, 75- *Concurrent Pos:* Res Fel, A P Sloan Found, 73-75. *Res:* Critical phenomena; light scattering properties of liquids; hydrodynamics. *Mailing Add:* Dept of Physics Univ of Tex Austin TX 78712

SWIFT, LLOYD HARRISON, b Crete, Nebr, Sept 12, 20. PLANT MORPHOLOGY. *Educ:* Univ Nebr, AB, 41, MS, 60, PhD(bot), 62; Western Reserve Univ, MA, 42. *Prof Exp:* Lexicographer, World Pub Co, Ohio, 42; instr Eng, Ill Inst Technol, 44 & Univ Mo, 44-45; asst prof bot, Univ Alaska, 62-63; prof & chmn dept Univ Nebr, Ataturk Univ, Turkey, 63-65; res assoc bot, Univ Nebr, 65-78; RETIRED. *Res:* Botanical bibliography and the classification and indexing of information important in botany; etymology and history of botanical terminology and nomenclature; phytography in plant morphology, taxonomy and physiology. *Mailing Add:* 2210 Sewell St Lincoln NE 68502

SWIFT, LLOYD WESLEY, JR, b San Francisco, Calif, July 11, 32; m 55; c 4. MICROMETEOROLOGY, FOREST HYDROLOGY. *Educ:* State Univ NY Col Forestry, BS, 54; NC State Univ, MS, 60; Duke Univ, DF, 72. *Prof Exp:* Jr forester, 54-55, res forester, 57-71, RES METEOROLOGIST, FOREST SERV, USDA, 72- *Mem:* Am Geophys Union; Am Meteorol Soc. *Res:* Energy balance of forested and logged mountain slopes; precipitation measurement and distribution over steep slopes; air circulation patterns in mountains; effect of slope aspect and inclination on forest microenvironment. *Mailing Add:* Coweeta Hydrol Lab Box 601 Rte 1 Box 216 Otto NC 28763

SWIFT, MICHAEL CRANE, b Berkeley, Calif, Aug 21, 44; m 77. PREDATOR-PREY INTERACTIONS, ENERGETICS. *Educ:* Univ Calif, Davis, BSc, 66, MA, 68; Univ BC, PhD(zool), 74. *Prof Exp:* Fel, Univ Sask, 74-75; res assoc, Inst Animal Res Ecol, Univ BC, 75-76; instr intro biol, Duke Univ, 77-79; ASST PROF LIMNOL & AQUATIC ECOL, APPALACHIAN ENVIRON LAB, CTR ENVIRON & ESTUARINE STUDIES, UNIV MD, 80- *Concurrent Pos:* Lectr forestry-fisheries interactions, Fac Forestry, Univ BC, 75-76; vis lectr physiol, Univ NC, Chapel Hill 76; vis scientist, Marine Lab, Duke Univ, 79-81; adj fac, Frostburg State Col, 80-; assoc mem, Grad Fac, Univ Md, 81- *Mem:* AAAS; Am Soc Limnol & Oceanog; Soc Int Limnol; Ecol Soc Am; Sigma Xi. *Res:* Limnology; predator-prey interactions among zooplankton; Chaoborus ecology. *Mailing Add:* Appalachian Environ Lab Univ Md Gunter Hall Frostburg State Col Campus Frostburg MD 21532

SWIFT, PAUL F, b Salina, Kans, July 31, 23; m 49, 74; c 9. CHEMICAL ENGINEERING. *Educ:* Univ Dayton, BS, 48; Univ Cincinnati, MS, 49. *Prof Exp:* Chem engr, Wright Patterson AFB, 49-53; res chemist, Trop Res Lab, Eastman Kodak Co, Panama, 53-58, sr res chemist, Res Labs, Kodak Park, NY, 58-68, asst head, Photog Res Div, 68-72, head, 72-77, head, Black & White Photog Div, Res Labs, Kodak Park, NY, 77-80, ASST DIR MFG, EUROP REGION, EASTMAN KODAK CO, LONDON, ENG, 80- *Res:* Photographic research in graphic arts; tropical photography. *Mailing Add:* Eastman Kodak Co Europ Hq 190 High Holborn London England

SWIFT, ROBINSON MARDEN, b Wolfeboro, NH, May 6, 18; m 44; c 3. PHYSICAL CHEMISTRY. *Educ:* Univ NH, BS, 40; Northwestern Univ, MS, 48; Syracuse Univ, PhD(chem), 56. *Prof Exp:* Chemist, Bird & Son, Inc, Mass, 40-44; instr chem, Thiel Col, 47-53; from asst prof to assoc prof, 56-72, PROF CHEM, ST ANSELM'S COL, 72-; CHIEF CHEMIST, EDISON ELECTRONICS DIV, McGRAW-EDISON, 57- *Mem:* Am Chem Soc. *Res:* Thermodynamics; epoxy resins. *Mailing Add:* 18 Birch Hill Rd Hooksett NH 03106

SWIFT, TERRENCE JAMES, b Dubuque, Iowa, June 29, 37; m 65; c 2. PHYSICAL CHEMISTRY, BIOCHEMISTRY. *Educ:* Loras Col, BS, 59; Univ Calif, Berkeley, PhD(chem), 62. *Prof Exp:* NSF fel, Max Planck Inst Phys Chem, 62-63; from asst prof to assoc prof chem, 63-76, PROF CHEM, CASE WESTERN RESERVE UNIV, 76- *Mem:* Am Soc Biol Chem. *Res:* Magnetic resonance spectroscopy as applied to biological systems and processes. *Mailing Add:* Dept of Chem Case Western Reserve Univ Cleveland OH 44106

SWIFT, WARD H(ENRY), chemical engineering, deceased

SWIFT, WILLIAM CLEMENT, b Lexington, Ky, Mar 17, 28; m 50; c 8. MATHEMATICS. *Educ:* Univ Ky, BS, 50, PhD(math), 55. *Prof Exp:* Instr math, Cornell Univ, 55-56; mem tech staff, Bell Tel Labs, Inc, 56-58; asst prof math, Rutgers Univ, 58-63; assoc prof, 63-69, PROF MATH, WABASH COL, 69- *Mem:* Am Math Soc; Math Asn Am. *Res:* Complex variables; conformal mapping; Taylor series; summability. *Mailing Add:* 116 N Grace Ave Crawfordsville IN 47933

SWIGART, RICHARD HANAWALT, b Lewistown, Pa, July 7, 25; m 51; c 3. NEUROANATOMY. *Educ:* Univ NC, BA, 47; Univ Minn, PhD(anat), 53. *Prof Exp:* Asst anat, Univ Minn, 48-50, instr, 50-52, res assoc biochemist, 52-53; from asst prof to assoc prof, 53-57, asst dean student affairs, 69-72, actg dean, Sch Med, 72-73, vpres allied health affairs, 76-78, actg dean Grad Sch, 76-77, PROF ANAT, SCH MED, UNIV LOUISVILLE, 67-, DIR DIV ALLIED HEALTH, 78-, ACTG SPEC ASST TO PRES HEALTH AFFAIRS, 81- *Mem:* Am Asn Anat; Biol Stain Comn; Histochem Soc; Soc Exp Biol & Med; Sigma Xi. *Res:* Chronic hypoxia, effect on cardiovascular and erythropoietic systems; carbohydrate metabolism in cardiac and skeletal muscle; effect of age on adaptive responses; neurological mutant mice. *Mailing Add:* Div Allied Health Univ Louisville Health Sci Ctr Louisville KY 40292

SWIGER, ELIZABETH DAVIS, b Morgantown, WVa, June 27, 26; m 48; c 2. PHYSICAL CHEMISTRY, INORGANIC CHEMISTRY. *Educ:* WVa Univ, BS, 48, MS, 52, PhD, 65. *Prof Exp:* Instr math, 54-56, instr chem, 56-60, from asst prof to assoc prof, 60-66, PROF CHEM, FAIRMONT STATE COL, 66- *Mem:* Am Chem Soc; AAAS; Sigma Xi. *Res:* Nuclear quadrupole resonance spectroscopy; polarography; coordination compounds. *Mailing Add:* Dept Chem Fairmont State Col Fairmont WV 26554

SWIGER, LOUIS ANDRE, b Waverly, Ohio, Sept 16, 32; m 53; c 3. ANIMAL GENETICS, POPULATION GENETICS. *Educ:* Ohio State Univ, BSc, 54; Iowa State Univ, MSc, 57, PhD(animal breeding), 60. *Prof Exp:* Animal geneticist, USDA, 59-62; assoc prof animal sci & exp sta statist, Univ Nebr, 62-65; assoc prof animal sci, Ohio State Univ, 65-70, prof, 70-80; PROF & DEPT HEAD ANIMAL SCI, VA POLYTECH INST & STATE UNIV, 80- *Concurrent Pos:* Crad chmn, Dept Animal Sci, Ohio State Univ, 68-80. *Mem:* Am Soc Animal Sci; Biomet Soc; Sigma Xi. *Res:* Population genetics and application to domestic animals. *Mailing Add:* Dept Animal Sci 3460 Animal Sci Bldg Va Polytech Inst & State Univ Blacksburg VA 24060

SWIGERT, JOHN LEONARD, JR, aerospace science, see previous edition

SWIHART, G(ERALD) R(OBERT), b Carroll, Nebr, Feb 16, 20; m 44; c 3. STRUCTURAL ENGINEERING. *Educ:* Rose Polytech Inst, BS, 47; Yale Univ, MEng, 49. *Prof Exp:* Instr, Rose Polytech Inst, 48; asst instr, Yale Univ, 48-49; from instr to assoc prof, 49-61, teacher exten div, 58 & 59, PROF CIVIL ENG, UNIV NEBR-LINCOLN, 61-, V CHMN DEPT, 71- *Concurrent Pos:* Struct designer, Harold Hoskins & Assocs, Nebr, 55, 57, 59 & 61; struct res engr, US Naval Civil Eng Lab. *Mem:* Am Soc Civil Engrs; Am Concrete Inst. *Res:* Ultimate load theories of reinforced concrete structures subjected to static and dynamics loading. *Mailing Add:* Dept of Civil Eng Univ of Nebr Lincoln NE 86588

SWIHART, JAMES CALVIN, b Elkhart, Ind, Feb 8, 27; m 47; c 2. THEORETICAL SOLID STATE PHYSICS, BIOPHYSICS. *Educ:* Purdue Univ, BSChE, 49, MS, 51, PhD(physics), 55. *Prof Exp:* Danish govt fel, Inst Theoret Physics, Copenhagen Univ, 54-55; physicist, Argonne Nat Lab, 55-56; physicist, Res Ctr, Int Bus Mach Corp, 56-66; assoc prof, 66-67, assoc dean grad sch, 71-74, chmn biophys prog, 71-78, PROF PHYSICS, IND UNIV, BLOOMINGTON, 67-, CHMN, PHYSICS DEPT, 80- *Concurrent Pos:* Vis physicist, Lawrence Radiation Lab, Berkeley, 65; visitor, Cavendish Lab & assoc, Clare Hall, Univ Cambridge, 74. *Mem:* AAAS; fel Am Phys Soc. *Res:* Theory of solid state physics; superconductivity; many-body problem; biophysics. *Mailing Add:* Dept Physics Ind Univ Bloomington IN 47405

SWIHART, THOMAS LEE, b Elkhart, Ind, July 29, 29; m 51; c 3. ASTROPHYSICS. *Educ:* Ind Univ, AB, 51, AM, 52; Univ Chicago, PhD(astrophys), 55. *Prof Exp:* assoc prof physics & astron, Univ Miss, 55-57; mem staff, Los Alamos Sci Lab, 57-62; asst prof astrophys, Univ Ill, 62-63; assoc prof astron, 63-69, PROF ASTRON, UNIV ARIZ, 69-, ASTRONR, STEWARD OBSERV, 74- *Concurrent Pos:* Fulbright-Hays lectr, Aegean Univ, Turkey, 69-70. *Mem:* AAAS; Int Astron Union; Am Astron Soc. *Res:* Theoretical astrophysics; radiation transfer; polarization of radio sources; atmospheric structure of stars. *Mailing Add:* Steward Observ Univ of Ariz Tucson AZ 85721

SWIM, WILLIAM B(AXTER), b Stillwater, Okla, Nov 18, 31; c 5. FLUID DYNAMICS, ACOUSTICS. *Educ:* Okla State Univ, BS, 55; Ga Inst Technol, PhD(mech eng), 66. *Prof Exp:* Instr mech eng, Pa State Univ, 55-59; eng res, Okla State Univ, 59-61; sr res engr, Trane Co, 64-73; PROF & DIR, NOISE CONTROL FACIL, TENN TECHNOL UNIV, 73- *Concurrent Pos:* Consult fluid dynamics & acoust, Rotron, Inc, 75-80, Milliken Res Corp, 78-80, Welsh Co, 79-, IBM & Salem Carpet Co, 80 & Black & Decker, 81-; Fulbright fel, 81. *Mem:* Am Soc Mech Engrs; Acoust Soc Am; Am Soc Heating, Refrig & Air-Conditioning Engrs; Inst Noise Control Engrs; Am Soc Eng Educ. *Res:* Fluid dynamics of turbomachinery; analysis of internal flows; generation and suppression of flow-noise; noise reduction of fans and blowers, flow losses in piping and duct systems; analysis of wind turbines; evaluation of micro hydro turbines; noise reduction of pneumatic tools. *Mailing Add:* Tenn Technol Univ PO Box 5014 Cookeville TN 38501

SWINDALE, LESLIE D, b Wellington, NZ, Mar 16, 28; m 55; c 3. SOIL SCIENCE, RESEARCH ADMINISTRATION. *Educ:* Univ Victoria, NZ, 48, MSc, 50; Univ Wis, PhD(soil sci), 55. *Prof Exp:* Phys chemist, NZ Soil Bur, 49-57, sr phys chemist, 57-60; dir, NZ Pottery & Ceramics Res Asn, 60-63; chmn, Dept Agron & Soil Sci, 65-68, PROF SOIL SCI, UNIV HAWAII, MANOA, 63-, SOIL SCIENTIST, AGR EXP STA, 76- *Concurrent Pos:* Fel, Univ Wis, 55-56; chief soil resources, Conservation and Development Serv, Land & Water Develop Div, Food & Agr Orgn, UN, Rome, 68-70. *Mem:* Soil Sci Soc Am; NZ Inst Chem; Royal Soc NZ; Int Soil Sci; Am Soc Pub Admin. *Res:* Formation, transformation and properties of minerals in soils and clays. Genesis of soils, their characterization and uses. *Mailing Add:* Hawaii Agr Exp Sta Univ of Hawaii at Manoa Honolulu HI 96822

SWINDELL, ROBERT THOMAS, b Greenfield, Tenn, Feb 22, 38; m 61; c 1. ORGANIC CHEMISTRY. *Educ:* Memphis State Univ, BS, 61; Univ SC, PhD(org chem), 65. *Prof Exp:* NIH fel org photochem, Iowa State Univ, 65-66; asst prof, 66-77, PROF CHEM, TENN TECHNOL UNIV, 77- *Mem:* Am Chem Soc; Royal Soc Chem. *Res:* Organic reaction mechanisms; organic photochemistry. *Mailing Add:* Dept of Chem Tenn Technol Univ Cookeville TN 38501

SWINEBROAD, JEFF, b Nashville, Tenn, Mar 22, 26; m 53; c 2. ZOOLOGY. *Educ:* Ohio State Univ, BA, 49, MA, 50, PhD, 56. *Prof Exp:* Asst ornith, Univ Colo, 46-47; tech asst zool, Ohio Coop Wildlife Res Unit, 48; asst, Ohio State Univ, 49-50. asst instr, 51, instr conserv, Conserv Lab, 51-53 & Nat Audubon Soc, 54-56; zoologist, Rutgers Univ, 55-57, from asst prof to assoc prof, 57-66, prof biol, 66-68, chmn dept biol sci, 60-68. asst res specialist, Col Agr, 59-68; pop ecologist, USAEC, 68-72, chief, Ecol Sci Br, 72-74; dep assoc dir res & develop progs, US Energy Res & Develop Admin, 74-77, mgr environ prog, Off Asst Secy Environ, 77-79, DEP DIR, OFF PROG COORDINATION, DEPT ENERGY, 80- *Mem:* AAAS; Animal Behav Soc; Ecol Soc Am; Wilson Ornith Soc(secy, 67-); Cooper Ornith Union. *Res:* Avian anatomy; ecology and migration of birds; animal population behavior. *Mailing Add:* Off of Health & Environ Res Dept of Energy Washington DC 20545

SWINEHART, BRUCE ARDEN, b Greentown, Ohio, Aug 28, 29; m 55; c 2. ANALYTICAL CHEMISTRY. *Educ:* Oberlin Col, AB, 51; Purdue Univ, MS, 53, PhD(anal chem), 55. *Prof Exp:* Res chemist, Mallinckrodt Chem Works, 5S-60; res chemist, Wyandotte Chem Corp, Mich, 60-61, sr res chemist, 61-64, sect head, 64-67; res chemist, 67-80, RES ASSOC, CORNING GLASS WORKS, 80- *Mem:* Am Chem Soc. *Res:* Uranium chemistry; ore analysis; gas chromatography; glass analysis; titrimetry. *Mailing Add:* 136 W Pulteney St-3A West Pulteney St Corning NY 14830

SWINEHART, CARL FRANCIS, b Bainbridge, Ohio, Aug 26, 07; m 34; c 2. INORGANIC CHEMISTRY. *Educ:* Ohio Wesleyan Col, AB, 29; Western Reserve Univ, PhD(inorg chem), 33. *Prof Exp:* Asst, Western Reserve Univ, 29-32; res chemist, Harshaw Chem Co, 32-52, assoc dir res, 52-60, dir tech develop, Inorg Prod, 60-62 & Crystal-Solid State, 62-67, proj dir crystal growth develop, Harshaw Div, Kewanee Oil Co, Ohio, 67-72; CONSULT, 72- *Mem:* Am Chem Soc. *Res:* Fluoride gases; manufacture of fluorides; synthetic crystal production. *Mailing Add:* 4102 Silsby Rd University Heights Cleveland OH 44118

SWINEHART, DONALD FOUGHT, b Strasburg, Ohio, Dec 30, 17; m 42; c 3. CHEMICAL KINETICS. *Educ:* Capital Univ, BS, 39; Ohio State Univ, MSc, 41, PhD(phys chem), 43. *Prof Exp:* Res chemist, Eastman Kodak Co, 43-44; res chemist & physicist, Manhattan Eng Dist, Los Alamos, NMex, 44-46; from asst prof to assoc prof, 46-61. PROF CHEM, UNIV ORE, 61- *Concurrent Pos:* Consult, AEC, 46-50. *Mem:* Am Chem Soc. *Res:* Polarographic analysis; adsorption to colloids; thermodynamics of electrolytic solutions; mass spectrometry; kinetics of unimolecular reactions; thermal conductivity of gas mixtures. *Mailing Add:* Dept of Chem Univ of Ore Eugene OR 97403

SWINEHART, JAMES HERBERT, b Los Angeles, Calif, Nov 22, 36; m 63; c 3. INORGANIC CHEMISTRY, BIOINORGANIC CHEMISTRY. *Educ:* Pomona Col, BA, 58; Univ Chicago, PhD(chem), 62. *Prof Exp:* NSF fel phys inorg chem, Max Planck Inst Phys Chem, Univ Göttingen, Ger, 62-63; from asst prof to assoc prof, 68-72, PROF CHEM, UNIV CALIF, DAVIS, 72- *Concurrent Pos:* Fel, John Simon Guggenheim Found, 69-70. *Mem:* Am Chem Soc. *Res:* Mechanisms of inorganic reactions; transition metals in the marine environment. *Mailing Add:* Dept of Chem Univ of Calif Davis CA 95616

SWINEHART, JAMES STEPHEN, b Cleveland, Ohio, July 27, 29; m 63; c 1. ORGANIC CHEMISTRY, SPECTROCHEMISTRY. *Educ:* Western Reserve Univ, BS, 50; Univ Cincinnati, MS, 51; New York Univ, PhD(chem), 59. *Prof Exp:* Asst, Western Reserve Univ, 49-50; res chemist, Merck & Co, 51-53; asst prof org chem to assoc prof, Wagner Col, 57-61; assoc prof, Am Univ, 61-65; anal chemist, Atlantic Res Corp, 65-67; sr spectroscopist, Perkin Elmer Corp, 67-69 & Digilab, 69-70; chmn dept, 70-76, PROF CHEM, STATE UNIV NY COL CORTLAND, 70- *Mem:* Am Chem Soc. *Res:* Organic synthesis; natural products; instrumentation; infrared and nuclear magnetic resonance spectroscopy; information retrieval; cigarette smoke; gas chromatography; technical writing. *Mailing Add:* Dept Chem State Univ NY Col Cortland NY 13045

SWINEHART, PHILIP ROSS, b Los Alamos, NMex, May 20, 45. SOLID STATE ELECTRONICS. *Educ:* Ore State Univ, BS, 67; Ohio State Univ, MS, 68, PhD(elec eng), 74. *Prof Exp:* Res assoc, Electro Sci Lab, Ohio State Univ, 68-69; res engr, Ohio Semitronics Inc, 72-73; RES SCIENTIST LOW TEMP SENSORS & RADIATION DETECTION, LAKE SHORE CRYOTRONICS INC, 75- *Mem:* Inst Elec & Electronics Engrs. *Res:* Low temperature sensors and radiation detectors. *Mailing Add:* Lake Shore Cryotronics Inc 64 E Walnut St Columbus OH 43081

SWINFORD, KENNETH ROBERTS, b Trader's Point, Ind, July 8, 16; m 38; c 2. FORESTRY. *Educ:* Purdue Univ, BS, 37; Univ Fla, MSF, 48; Univ Mich, PhD, 60. *Prof Exp:* Exten ranger, State Forest Serv, Fla, 40-41; timber cruiser, Brooks-Scanlon Corp, 46; from asst prof to prof, 46-75, asst to dir forestry, 71-75, EMER PROF FORESTRY, UNIV FLA, 75- *Concurrent Pos:* Consult forester, F & W Forestry Serv Inc, Gainesville, Fla, 75-; teacher, Sch Forestry, Univ Fla, 75-76. *Mem:* Soc Am Foresters; Am Forestry Asn. *Res:* Management of forest lands, especially pine plantations; landscape forestry; outdoor recreational use of forests and wild lands; management and harvesting ox forests for energy fuel. *Mailing Add:* F & W Forestry Serv Inc PO Box 13321 Gainesville FL 32604

SWINGLE, DONALD MORGAN, b Washington, DC, Sept 1, 22; m 43; c 3. APPLIED PHYSICS, SYSTEMS ENGINEERING. *Educ:* Wilson Teachers Col, BS, 43; NY Univ, MS, 47; Harvard Univ, AM, 48, MEngSci, 49, PhD(eng sci, appl physics), 50; George Washington Univ, MBA, 62; Indust Col Armed Forces, dipl, 62. *Prof Exp:* Engr, Signal Corps Eng Labs, US Dept Army, 46-47; res asst, Eng Res Lab, Harvard Univ, 49-50; physicist, Signal Corps Eng Labs, US Dept Army, 50-60, chief weather electronic res group, 50-53, chief meteorol techniques sect, 54-57, chief br, 58-60, physicist, sr res scientist & dep dir meteorol div, Electronics Labs, 61-63, res physicist, sr res physicist & chief meteorol res team A, US Army Electronics Command, 64-65, res physicist & sr scientist atmospheric sci lab, 65-66, res physicist & chief techniques & explor develop tech area, 66-71, sr scientist eng & explor develop tech area, 71-74, sr scientist, Spec Sensors Tech Area, Combat Surveillance & Target Acquisition Lab, 74-78, res physicist, Atmospheric Sci Lab, Army Electronics Res & Develop Command, 78-80; CONSULT, 80- *Concurrent Pos:* US mem, Comn Instruments & Methods Observ, World Meteorol Orgn, 53-65; US deleg, 53 & 57; adv, US Mil Acad, 59; reviewer res proposals, NSF, 60-74; chmn, Nat Task Group Mesometeorol, Interdept Comt Atmospheric Sci, 63-74; Army rep, DOD Forum Environ Sci, 64-65; chmn, Nat Meso-Micrometeorol Res Facil Surv Group, Nat Ctr Atmospheric Res, 64; lab mem, Army Res Coun, 64-65; consult, Livermore Res Lab, Univ Calif, 65. *Mem:* Am Meteorol Soc; sr mem Inst Elec & Electronics Engrs; Nat Soc Prof Eng; assoc fel Am Inst Aeronaut & Astronaut; fel NY Acad Sci. *Res:* Radar meteorology; atmospheric propagation, electromagnetic, acoustic waves; radioactive fallout prediction; meteorological techniques, applied meteorology; meteorological system engineering; atmospheric modification, management, mesometeorology; indirect sensory techniques; nuclear surveillance; research and development management. *Mailing Add:* 1765 Pomona Dr Las Cruces NM 88001

SWINGLE, HOMER DALE, b Hixson, Tenn, Nov 5, 16; m 42, 62; c 1. HORTICULTURE. *Educ:* Univ Tenn, BS, 39; Ohio State Univ, MS, 48; La State Univ, PhD(hort), 66. *Prof Exp:* Teacher high sch, 39-46; exten specialist hort, Agr Exten Serv, 46-47, from asst prof to assoc prof, 48-67, prof, 67-79, EMER PROF, UNIV TENN, KNOXVILLE, 79- *Concurrent Pos:* Consult plant & soil water rels, Oak Ridge Nat Labs, 71-75. *Mem:* Fel Am Soc Hort Sci. *Res:* Evaluation of vegetable varieties; chemical weed control in horticulture crops; mechanization of harvest. *Mailing Add:* 3831 Maloney Rd Knoxville TN 37920

SWINGLE, KARL F, b Richland Center, Wis, Feb 16, 35; div; c 4. PHARMACOLOGY. *Educ:* Univ Wis, BA, 58; Univ Minn, PhD(pharmacol), 68. *Prof Exp:* Asst bacteriologist, Sioux City Dept Health, Iowa, 58-59; med technologist, Vet Admin Hosp, Minneapolis, 61-64; pharmacologist, 68-73, supvr pharmacol, 73-77, SR RES SPECIALIST, RIKER LABS, MINN MINING & MFG CO, 77- *Mem:* Am Soc Pharmacol & Exp Therapeut; NY Acad Sci; Soc Exp Biol & Med; Am Chem Soc. *Res:* Anti-inflammatory drugs; pulmonary pharmacology. *Mailing Add:* Riker Labs Minn Mining & Mfg Co Bldg 218 St Paul MN 55144

SWINGLE, KARL FREDERICK, b Bozeman, Mont, Jan 7, 15; m 40; c 5. RADIOBIOLOGY. *Educ:* Mont State Col, BS, 37; Univ Wis, PhD(biochem), 42. *Prof Exp:* Res chemist, Inst Path, Western Pa Hosp, 42-43; asst res chemist, Univ Wyo, 43-45; assoc chemist, Mont State Col, 45-47, prof vet biochem, 57-61; supvry chemist, US Naval Radiol Defense Lab, 61-69; res chemist, 69-70, PHYSICIST, VET ADMIN HOSP, 70- *Concurrent Pos:* Asst researcher, Univ Calif, Irvine, 70- *Mem:* Sigma Xi; Radiation Res Soc. *Res:* Radiation biochemistry; nucleic acid metabolism. *Mailing Add:* Vet Admin Med Ctr 5901 E Seventh St Long Beach CA 90822

SWINGLE, ROY SPENCER, b Harvey, Ill, Oct 15, 44; m 66; c 2. ANIMAL SCIENCE, NUTRITION. *Educ:* Univ Ariz, BS, 66; Wash State Univ, MS, 69, PhD(nutrit), 72. *Prof Exp:* Asst prof, 72-78, ASSOC PROF ANIMAL SCI, UNIV ARIZ, 78-, ASSOC RES SCIENTIST ANIMAL SCI, AGR EXP STA, 81- *Mem:* Am Soc Animal Sci. *Res:* Ruminant nutrition; utilization of low quality roughages. *Mailing Add:* Dept of Animal Sci Univ of Ariz Tucson AZ 85721

SWINGLEY, CHARLES STEPHEN, b Dallas, Tex, Nov 11, 43; m 64; c 2. PHYSICAL CHEMISTRY. *Educ:* Rochester Inst Technol, BS, 65; Wayne State Univ, PhD(chem), 70. *Prof Exp:* RES ASSOC RES LABS, EASTMAN KODAK CO, 70- *Mem:* Soc Photog Sci & Eng. *Res:* Surface, colloid, polymer and photographic chemistry. *Mailing Add:* 243 South Ave Webster NY 14580

SWINK, LAURENCE N, b Enid, Okla, Oct 24, 34; m 59; c 1. CRYSTALLOGRAPHY. *Educ:* Univ Wichita, BA, 57; Iowa State Col, MSc, 59; Brown Univ, PhD(chem), 69. *Prof Exp:* Flight test technician, Cessna Aircraft Co, Kans, 56-57; mat engr, Chance-Vought Aircraft Co, Tex, 57; mat engr, Douglas Aircraft Co, Calif, 59-60; nuclear res officer, McClellan AFB, Calif, 60-63; mem tech staff crystallog, Tex Instruments, Inc, Dallas, 66-75, mgr, Infrared Glass Lab, Electro-Optics Div, 75-78; vpres, Amorphous Mat Inc, Garland Tex, 79-80; MGR, ADVANCED SYSTS DEVELOP, XEROX CORP, DALLAS, 81- *Mem:* Am Crystallog Asn. *Res:* Crystal structure determination by x-ray diffraction methods; crystal perfection study by x-ray and electron diffraction techniques; electron microprobe analysis; electron microscopy; auger spectroscopy, x-ray fluorescence. *Mailing Add:* 1313 Chickasaw Richardson TX 75080

SWINNERTON, JOHN W, b Tiffin, Ohio, Jan 6, 31; m 53; c 3. CHEMICAL OCEANOGRAPHY. *Educ:* Mt Union Col, BS, 54; Pa State Univ, PhD(phys chem), 59. *Prof Exp:* RES CHEMIST, OCEAN SCI DIV, US NAVAL RES LAB, WASHINGTON, DC, 58- *Mem:* AAAS; Am Chem Soc; Am Soc Limnol & Oceanog. *Res:* Chemical oceanography; application of gas chromatography to oceanography. *Mailing Add:* 6620 Beddo St Alexandria VA 22306

SWINNEY, CHAUNCEY MELVIN, b Riverside, Calif, Sept 3, 18; m 42; c 3. ECONOMIC GEOLOGY, PETROLOGY. *Educ:* Pomona Col, BA, 40; Stanford Univ, PhD(geol), 49. *Prof Exp:* Tester, Union Oil Co, Calif, 42; geologist, US Geol Surv, 42-45; instr, Stanford Univ, 47-49, asst prof mineral sci, 49-56; supvr prod res div, Richfield Oil Corp, 59-66; MGR ENERGY RESOURCES EXP & DEVELOP, SOUTHERN CALIF EDISON CO, 66- *Concurrent Pos:* Geologist, US Geol Surv, 46-53; vpres, Mono Power Co, Subsid Southern Calif Edison Co, 73- *Mem:* Geol Soc Am; Am Asn Petrol Geol; Am Inst Mining Metall & Petrol Eng. *Res:* Energy resources exploration, development and production. *Mailing Add:* Southern Calif Edison Co 2244 Walnut Grove Ave Rosemead CA 91770

SWINNEY, HARRY LEONARD, b Opelousas, La, Apr 10, 39; m 67. NONLINEAR DYNAMICS, FLUID PHYSICS. *Educ:* Southwestern Univ, Memphis, BS, 61; Johns Hopkins Univ, PhD(physics), 68. *Prof Exp:* Res assoc physics, Johns Hopkins Univ, 68-70, vis asst prof, 70-71; asst prof physics, NY Univ, 71-73; from assoc prof to prof physics, City Col, City Univ New York, 73-77; PROF, UNIV TEX, AUSTIN, 78- *Honors & Awards:* Morris Loeb lectr, Harvard Univ, 82. *Mem:* Fel Am Phys Soc; Am Asn Physics Teachers. *Res:* Instabilities and turbulence are studied in experiments on nonequilibrium systems, particularly fluids and chemical reactions. *Mailing Add:* Dept Physics Univ Tex Austin TX 78712

SWINSON, DEREK BERTRAM, b Belfast. N Ireland, Nov 5, 38; m 65. PHYSICS. *Educ:* Queen's Univ, Belfast, 60; Univ Alta, Calgary, MS, 61, PhD(physics), 65. *Prof Exp:* From asst prof to assoc prof, 65-76, PROF PHYSICS, UNIV N MEX, 76- *Mem:* Brit Inst Physics. *Res:* Cosmic radiation, extensive air showers and related high energy interactions; mu-mesons underground and variations of their activity with solar cycle; sidereal cosmic ray anisotropies; consultant in accident reconstruction. *Mailing Add:* Dept of Physics Univ of NMex 800 Yale NE Albuquerque NM 87131

SWINTON, DAVID CHARLES, b St Charles, Ill, May 4, 43; m 70. CELL BIOLOGY. *Educ:* Brandeis Univ, AB, 65; Stanford Univ, PhD(biol), 72. *Prof Exp:* Res fel biophysics, Univ Chicago, 72-74, res assoc, 74-80; MEM FAC, DEPT BIOL, UNIV ROCHESTER, 80- *Mem:* Am Soc Cell Biol. *Res:* Information content of organelle DNA; expression of organelle DNA during mitotic cell cycle and during meiosis. *Mailing Add:* Dept Biol Univ Rochester River Campus Rochester NY 14627

SWINYARD, EWART AINSLIE, b Logan, Utah, Jan 3, 09; m 34; c 2. PHARMACOLOGY. *Educ:* Utah State Univ, BS, 32; Idaho State Col, BS, 36; Univ Minn, MS, 41; Univ Utah, PhD(pharmacol), 47. *Prof Exp:* From instr to asst prof pharm, Idaho State Col, 36-45; prof pharmacol, 45-47; prof pharmaco & dir pharmaceut res, Col Pharm, 47-76, prof pharmacol, Col Med, 67-76, dean, Col Pharm, 70-76, DIR, CTR EARLY PHARMACOL EVAL OF ANTIEPILEPTIC DRUGS, 75-, EMER PROF PHARMACOL, COL PHARM & COL MED, UNIV UTAH, 76- *Concurrent Pos:* Am Col Apothecaries fac fel; lectr, Col Med, Univ Utah, 45-67; chmn dept biopharmaceut sci, Univ, 65-71; distinguished res prof, 68-69; Rennebohm lectr, Univ Wis, 60; Kaufman lectr, Ohio State Univ, 63; ed, Am Med Soc Alcoholism, 77. *Honors & Awards:* Rennebohm lectr, Univ Wis, 60; Award & Medal distinguished res & ed alcoholism, Am Med Soc Alcoholism, 77; DuMez lectr, Univ Md, 79. *Mem:* Am Soc Pharmacol & Exp Therapeut; Am Pharmaceut Asn; NY Acad Sci; Am Asn Cols Pharm (hon pres, 81-82); Sigma Xi. *Res:* Arsenical chemotherapy; body water and electrolyte distribution; experimental therapy of convulsive disorders; assay of anticonvulsant drugs; relationship between chemical structure and pharmacological activity of anticonvulsant drugs. *Mailing Add:* Col of Pharm Univ of Utah Salt Lake City UT 84112

SWINZOW, GEORGE K, b Kharkov, Russia, Feb 4, 15; nat US; m 40; c 1. PHYSICS. *Educ:* Univ Kharkov, Russia, BSc & AM, 40; Boston Univ, PhD, 57. *Prof Exp:* Eng geologist, Arctic Res Insts, Russia, 38-43; mining geologist, Berg & Heuttenverke, Ltd, Ger, 43-45; consult geologist, 45-52; longshoreman, Am Sugar Co, Mass, 52-55; asst prof geol, Grad Sch, Boston Univ, 55-58; RES GEOLOGIST, COLD REGIONS RES & ENG LAB, US ARMY CORPS ENGRS, 58- *Concurrent Pos:* Consult cryogenic technol, 80- *Mem:* Geol Soc Am; Soc Cryobiol; AAAS; Sigma Xi. *Res:* Freezing as a physical and geological process; cryopedology; permafrost; physics of ice; problems of nucleation as a trigger of phase change; applied research in the arctic; relation of ice physics to metallurgy; terminal ballistics of snow; ice and frozen ground; military science in cold regions. *Mailing Add:* Cold Regions Res & Eng Lab US Army Corps of Engrs Box 282 Hanover NH 03755

SWISCHUK, LEONARD EDWARD, b Bellevue, Alta, June 14, 37; m 60; c 4. RADIOLOGY. *Educ:* Univ Alta, BS & MD, 60. *Prof Exp:* Asst prof pediat, Med Ctr, Univ Okla, 66-68, assoc prof radiol & pediat, 68-70; assoc prof, 70-73, PROF RADIOL & PEDIAT, UNIV TEX MED BR GALVESTON, 73- *Mem:* AMA; Am Col Radiol; Am Acad Pediat; Radiol Soc NAm. *Mailing Add:* Dept Radiol & Pediat Univ Tex Med Br Galveston TX 77550

SWISHER, ELY MARTIN, b Bozeman, Mont, Sept 29, 15; m 40; c 2. ENTOMOLOGY. *Educ:* Willamette Univ, AB, 37; Ore State Col, MS, 41; Ohio State Univ, PhD(entom), 43. *Prof Exp:* Asst zool, Ohio State Univ, 40-43; midwest mgr, Rohm and Haas Co, 43-53, mgr develop sect agr & sanit chem, 53-73, mgr govt regulatory rels, 73-76, mgr agr chem standards, 76-81; MEM STAFF, REGULATORY COMPLIANCE SERVS, 81- *Mem:* Entom Soc Am; Weed Sci Soc Am. *Res:* Insecticides; fungicides; field evaluations; development of agricultural pesticide chemicals. *Mailing Add:* Regulatory Compliance Servs 1950 Branch Rd Perkasie PA 18944

SWISHER, GEORGE MONROE, b Columbus, Ohio, July 17, 43; m 64; c 1. MECHANICAL & CONTROL ENGINEERING. *Educ:* Univ Cincinnati, BSME, 66; Ohio State Univ, MSME, 67, PhD(mech eng), 69. *Prof Exp:* Asst prof systs eng, Wright State Univ, 69-73; assoc prof, 73-79, PROF MECH ENG & ASSOC DEAN ENG, TENN TECHNOL UNIV, 79- *Concurrent Pos:* Consult, United Aircraft Prod, 70- & Missile Systs Div, Rockwell Int Corp, 77. *Mem:* Am Soc Mech Engrs; Am Soc Eng Educ. *Res:* Manual control; control theory; stress analysis; dynamic system measurement and control. *Mailing Add:* Dept of Mech Eng Tenn Technol Univ Cookeville TN 38501

SWISHER, HORTON EDWARD, b San Diego, Calif, Mar 1, 09; m 47; c 1. FOOD CHEMISTRY. *Educ:* Pomona Col, BA, 33; Claremont Cols, MA, 35. *Prof Exp:* Jr analyst, Am Potash & Chem Corp, 35-37; chemist & plant supvr, Armour & Co, Ill, 37-45; res chemist, 45-59, chief chemist, 59-63, asst mgr, Res & Develop Div, 63-67, Dir Res & Develop, Ont Prod Sect Lab, Sunkist Growers, Inc, 67-74; CONSULT BY-PRODS, CITRUS INDUST, 74- *Concurrent Pos:* Instr eve col, Texas Christian Univ, 43-45. *Mem:* AAAS; Inst Food Technol; Am Chem Soc; fel Am Inst Chem. *Res:* Chemistry of citrus by-products, especially citrus oils, peel products, juices and beverages; dehydrated foods. *Mailing Add:* 595 West 25th St Upland CA 91786

SWISHER, JAMES H(OWE), b Youngstown, Ohio, Sept 19, 36; m 59; c 3. MATERIALS SCIENCE, PHYSICAL CHEMISTRY. *Educ:* Carnegie Inst Technol, BS, 59, MS, 62, PhD(metall eng), 63. *Prof Exp:* Aerospace technologist, Lewis Res Ctr, NASA, 63-65; scientist, Edgar C Bain Lab, US Steel Corp, 65-67; mem tech staff, Bell Tel Labs, NJ, 67-71; div supvr, Mat & Metall, Metall Dept, Sandia Labs, 71-77; br chief mat & fabric, Div Conserv Res & Technol, US Energy Res & Develop Admin, 77-81, DIR, DIV ENERGY STORAGE TECHNOL, US DEPT ENERGY, 81- *Mem:* Am Inst Mining, Metall & Petrol Engrs. *Res:* Application of high temperature physical chemistry to materials research. *Mailing Add:* Div of Conserv Res & Technol 20 Massachusetts Ave Washington DC 20545

SWISHER, JOE ARNET, operations analysis, see previous edition

SWISHER, JOSEPH VINCENT, b Kansas City, Mo, Jan 12, 32; m 60; c 3. ORGANIC CHEMISTRY. *Educ:* Cent Methodist Col, AB, 56; Univ Mo, PhD(org chem), 60. *Prof Exp:* Fel chem, Purdue Univ, 60-61; asst prof, 61-69, ASSOC PROF CHEM, UNIV DETROIT, 69- *Mem:* Am Chem Soc; Am Inst Chemists. *Res:* Oranosilicon chemistry; stereochemistry of addition reactions; reactions of metals with polyhalides. *Mailing Add:* Dept Chem Univ Detroit Detroit MI 48221

SWISHER, ROBERT DONALD, b Denver, Colo, Nov 16, 10; wid; c 3. ORGANIC CHEMISTRY, ENVIRONMENTAL CHEMISTRY. *Educ:* Univ Mich, PhD(pharmaceut chem), 34. *Prof Exp:* Mem staff, Monsanto Co, 34-45, group leader, 45-73, sr environ adv, Res Dept, 73-75; RETIRED. *Mem:* Fel AAAS; Am Chem Soc; Am Oil Chem Soc; Soc Indust Microbiol; Water Pollution Control Fedn. *Res:* Sulfonation and sulfonic acid derivatives; detergents; biodegradation and environmental acceptability of surfactants and other materials. *Mailing Add:* 1894 Charmwood Ct Kirkwood MO 63122

SWISHER, SCOTT NEIL, b Le Center, Minn, July 30, 18; m 45; c 2. INTERNAL MEDICINE, HEMATOLOGY. *Educ:* Univ Minn, BS, 43, MD, 44; Am Bd Internal Med, dipl, 52. *Prof Exp:* Asst resident & fel med, Sch Med & Dent, Univ Rochester, 47-48; fel, Med Sch, Univ Minn, 48-49; fel med & hemat, Sch Med & Dent, Univ Rochester, 49-51, from instr to prof med, Univ, 51-67; chmn dept, 51-67, PROF MED, COL HUMAN MED, MICH STATE UNIV, 67-, ASSOC DEAN RES, 77- *Concurrent Pos:* From asst resident physician to chief resident physician, Ancker Hosp, St Paul, Minn, 48-49; from asst physician to sr assoc physician & head hemat unit, Strong Mem Hosp, Rochester, NY, 53-67; mem comt blood & related probs, Nat Res Coun, 54-, chmn, 60. *Mem:* AAAS; Am Soc Clin Invest; Asn Am Physicians; Am Col Physicians; Am Fedn Clin Res. *Res:* Mechanisms of destruction of erythrocytes by isoantibodies; human hemolytic disorders. *Mailing Add:* Dept Med Col Human Med Mich State Univ East Lansing MI 48824

SWISHER, WAYNE EVERETT, speech pathology, audiology, see previous edition

SWISLOCKI, NORBERT IRA, b Warsaw, Poland, Jan 11, 36; US citizen; m 63; c 2. BIOCHEMISTRY, CELL BIOLOGY. *Educ:* Univ Calif, Los Angeles, BS, 56, MA, 60, PhD(zool, endocrinol), 64. *Prof Exp:* USPHS fel biochem, Brandeis Univ, 64-67; from instr to asst prof biochem, Grad Sch Med Sci, Cornell Univ, 67-73, assoc prof, 73-78, chmn, Biochem Unit, 75-78, assoc, Sloan-Kettering Inst Cancer Res, 66-78, assoc mem, 72-78; PROF & CHMN BIOCHEM, MED SCH, UNIV MED & DENT NJ, 78- *Mem:* Assoc Am Physiol Soc; Am Soc Biol Chemists; Endocrine Soc. *Res:* Mechanisms of hormone action; membrane function; endocrinology. *Mailing Add:* Med Sch Univ Med & Dent NJ 100 Bergen St Newark NJ 07103

SWISSLER, THOMAS JAMES, b Haddonfield, NJ, Dec 8, 41; m 69; c 2. ENVIRONMENTAL PHYSICS, MATHEMATICAL ANALYSIS. *Educ:* St Joseph's Col, Pa, BS, 64; State Univ NY Buffalo, PhD(physics), 71. *Prof Exp:* Res asst comput sci, Theol Biol Ctr, State Univ NY Buffalo, 70-74, res fel, 73-74; STAFF SCIENTIST PHYSICS, SYSTS & APPL SCI CO, RIVERDALE, MD, 74- *Mem:* AAAS; Am Meteorol Soc; Sigma Xi. *Res:* Stratospheric aerosols and ozone gases, their physical properties and distribution using remote sensing measurements from satellite. *Mailing Add:* NASA Langley Res Ctr MS 233A Hampton VA 23665

SWISTAK, JOSEPH EUGENE, b Rome, NY, July 23, 43; m 66; c 2. EXPERIMENTAL PSYCHOLOGY, HUMAN FACTORS ENGINEERING. *Educ:* State Univ NY, Buffalo, BA, 65; George Mason Univ, MA, 78. *Prof Exp:* RES & ENG PSYCHOLOGIST, NIGHT VISION & ELECTRO-OPTICS LAB, 67- *Res:* Visual psychophysics; image processing. *Mailing Add:* 1524 Woodside Dr Woodbridge VA 22191

SWITENDICK, ALFRED CARL, b Batavia, NY, Oct 8, 31; m 80; c 2. METAL HYDRIDES, BAND THEORY. *Educ:* Mass Inst Technol, SB, 53, PhD(solid state physics), 63; Univ Ill, MS, 54. *Prof Exp:* Res physics, Univ Ill, 53-54; asst physics, Mass Inst Technol, 56-62, res staff mem, 62-64; staff mem physics org solids, Sandia Lab, 64-68, staff mem solid state theory, 68-70, supvr, Solid State Theory, 70-80; HATAILLEE DIV MAT SCI, US DEPT ENERGY, WASH, DC, 80-82. *Mem:* AAAS; Am Phys Soc; Mat Res Soc. *Res:* Electronic energy bands of transition metals and transition metal compounds; intermetallic compounds; hydrogen in metals. *Mailing Add:* Div 5151 Sandia Labs Albuquerque NM 87115

SWITKES, EUGENE, b Newport News, Va, Dec 22, 43; m 69. QUANTUM CHEMISTRY. *Educ:* Oberlin Col, BA, 65; Harvard Univ, MS & PhD(theoret chem), 70. *Prof Exp:* NSF fels, Univ Edinburgh, 70-71 & Cambridge Univ, 71; asst prof, 71-77, ASSOC PROF CHEM, UNIV CALIF, SANTA CRUZ, 77- *Concurrent Pos:* Fel & responder, Neurosci Res Prog, Boulder Intensive Study Session, 72. *Res:* Theory of the electronic structure of molecules, quantum mechanics; information processing in the visual system; visual accommodation and perception. *Mailing Add:* Div of Natural Sci II Univ of Calif Santa Cruz CA 95064

SWITZER, BOYD RAY, b Harrisonburg, VA, Oct 3, 43; m 67; c 1. NUTRITION, BIOCHEMISTRY. *Educ:* Bridgewater Col, BA, 65; Univ NC, Chapel Hill, PhD(biochem), 71. *Prof Exp:* NIH fel, Univ Southern Calif, 71-72; asst prof, 72-78, ASSOC PROF NUTRIT, SCH PUB HEALTH, UNIV NC, CHAPEL HILL, 78-, ASST PROF BIOCHEM & NUTRIT, SCH MED, 74- *Mem:* AAAS; Am Chem Soc. *Res:* Hormonal regulation of protein metabolism as influenced by dietary nutrition; metabolic disorders of connective tissue. *Mailing Add:* 2437 Springview Terrace Chapel Hill NC 27514

SWITZER, CLAYTON MACFIE, b London, Ont, July 17, 29; m 51; c 3. AGRICULTURE, WEED SCIENCE. *Educ:* Ont Agr Col, BSA, 51, MSA, 53; Iowa State Univ, PhD, 55. *Prof Exp:* Assoc prof bot, 55-65, prof bot & head dept, 65-70, assoc dean, 70-72, DEAN, ONT AGR COL, 72- *Concurrent Pos:* Mem, Sci Coun Can, 77- *Mem:* Am Soc Plant Physiol; Weed Sci Soc Am; Can Soc Plant Physiol; Can Soc Hort Sci; Can Bot Soc. *Res:* Physiology of herbicide action; weed control; growth regulation of turfgrass. *Mailing Add:* Dept of Environ Biol Ont Agr Col Univ of Guelph Guelph ON N1G 2W1 Can

SWITZER, GEORGE LESTER, b Chester, WVa, Nov 5, 24; m 56; c 1. FOREST ECOLOGY, FOREST SOILS. *Educ:* Univ WVa, BS, 49; Yale Univ, MF, 50; State Univ NY Col Forestry, Syracuse, PhD(soils, physiol), 62. *Prof Exp:* From asst forester to assoc forester, Miss Agr Exp Sta, 50-62, from asst prof to assoc prof, 54-64, PROF SILVICULT, MISS STATE UNIV, 64-, FORESTER, MISS AGR EXP STA, 64- *Concurrent Pos:* Consult, Spanish Govt on forest production, 79. *Mem:* AAAS; Soil Sci Soc Am; Am Soc Agron. *Res:* Nutrient cycles in forest ecosystems; patterns of variation in forest tree species. *Mailing Add:* Dept Forestry Miss State Univ Sch Forest Res Mississippi State MS 39762

SWITZER, LAURA MAE, b McLean, Tex, Apr 21, 41. PHYSICAL EDUCATION, MATHEMATICS. *Educ:* Wayland Baptist Col, Tex, BS, 63; Southwestern Okla State Univ, MEd, 66; Univ Okla, EdD(curric), 71. *Prof Exp:* Teacher & coach phys educ & math, Sanford-Fritch Independent Sch Dist, Tex, 63-65; instr phys educ, Southwestern Okla State Univ, 65-69; asst, Univ Okla, 69-71; ASSOC PROF PHYS EDUC, SOUTHWESTERN OKLA STATE UNIV, 71- *Mem:* Am Alliance Health Phys Educ & Recreation; Nat Educ Asn. *Res:* A comparison of massed versus distributed practice sessions in the learning of recreational activities skills. *Mailing Add:* Dept Phys Educ Southwestern Okla State Univ Weatherford OK 73096

SWITZER, MARY ELLEN PHELAN, b Brooklyn, NY, Nov 2, 45; m 70; c 1. BIOCHEMISTRY. *Educ:* Smith Col, AB, 67; Univ Ill, Urbana, MS, 69, PhD(chem), 73. *Prof Exp:* Fel res assoc, Dept Med, Duke Univ Med Ctr, NIH, 73-78; ASST MED RES PROF, DEPT MED, DUKE UNIV MED CTR, 79- *Concurrent Pos:* Adj asst prof, Dept Chem, Duke Univ, 78- *Mem:* Am Chem Soc. *Res:* Biochemistry of blood coagulation, especially the relationship between molecular struucture and biological functions of antihemophilic factor, and interactions among the blood clotting proteins. *Mailing Add:* Duke Univ Med Ctr Box 3705 Durham NC 27710

SWITZER, PAUL, b St Boniface, Can, Mar 4, 39; m 63; c 1. APPLIED STATISTICS, SPATIAL MODELS. *Educ:* Univ Man, BA, 61; Harvard Univ, PhD(statist), 65. *Prof Exp:* Assoc prof, 65-76, chmn, 79-82, PROF STATIST & GEOL, STANFORD UNIV, 76- *Concurrent Pos:* Assoc ed, Can J Statist, 80-; vis scientist, Environ Protection Agency, Washington, 81; chmn, Panel Statist US Nat Bur Mines, Nat Acad Sci, 81-82; mem, Int Comt Statist & Earth Sci. *Mem:* fel Inst Math Statist; fel Am Statist Asn; fel Int Statist Inst; fel Royal Statist Soc; Am Geophys Union. *Res:* Earth sciences; resources; environment. *Mailing Add:* Sequoia Hall Stanford Univ Stanford CA 94305

SWITZER, ROBERT L, b Long Beach, Calif, June 18, 18; m 41; c 2. CHEMICAL ENGINEERING, MANAGEMENT. *Educ:* Univ Calif, BS, 41; Univ Southern Calif, MS, 52. *Prof Exp:* Sr sect leader, Design Div, Res Dept, 41-60, sr sect leader eng serv, 60-67, SUPVR ENG SERV, RES DEPT, UNION OIL CO CALIF, 67-, MGR ENG SERV, 81- *Mem:* Instrument Soc Am; Am Inst Chem Engrs. *Mailing Add:* Sci & Technol Div Box 76 Brea CA 92621

SWITZER, ROBERT LEE, b Clinton, Iowa, Aug 26, 40; m 65; c 2. BIOCHEMISTRY. *Educ:* Univ Ill, Urbana, BS, 61; Univ Calif, Berkeley, PhD(biochem), 66. *Prof Exp:* Fel biochem, Nat Heart Inst, 66-68; asst prof, 68-73, assoc prof, 73-78, PROF, UNIV ILL, URBANA, 78- *Concurrent Pos:* Fel, John Simon Guggenheim Mem Found, 75-76. *Mem:* Am Soc Biol Chem; Am Chem Soc; Am Soc Microbiol. *Res:* Microbial physiology and enzymology, particularly regulation of branched biosynthetic pathways, mechanisms of regulatory enzymes and regulation of inactivation and turnover enzymes during bacterial endospore formation. *Mailing Add:* Dept of Biochem Univ of Ill Urbana IL 61801

SWITZER, WILLIAM PAUL, b Dodge City, Kans, Apr 9, 27; m 51; c 2. ANIMAL PATHOLOGY, MICROBIOLOGY. *Educ:* Agr & Mech Col, Tex, DVM, 48; Iowa State Col, MS, 51, PhD, 54 Univ Vienna, DSc, 78. *Prof Exp:* Asst diagnostican, Iowa Vet Diag Lab, Iowa State Univ, 48-52, from asst prof to prof vet hyg, Univ & Vet Med Res Inst, 52-74, PROF VET MICROBIOL & PREV MED, VET MED RES INST & ASSOC DEAN COL VET MED, IOWA STATE UNIV, 74-, DISTINGUISHED PROF, 78- *Mem:* Am Soc Microbiol; Am Vet Med Asn. *Res:* Swine enteric and respiratory diseases; tissue culture; myoplasma. *Mailing Add:* Vet Med Admin Iowa State Univ Ames IA 50010

SWOBODA, ALLEN RAY, soil chemistry, agronomy, see previous edition

SWOBODA, THOMAS JAMES, b Milwaukee, Wis, Feb 25, 21; div; c 2. PHYSICAL CHEMISTRY. *Educ:* Univ Ill, PhD(chem), 50. *Prof Exp:* RES CHEMIST, CENT RES DEPT, E I DU PONT DE NEMOURS & CO, INC, WILMINGTON, 50- *Mem:* Am Chem Soc. *Res:* Solid state chemistry; finely divided solids. *Mailing Add:* 1510 Yeatmans Mill Rd Landenborg PA 19350

SWOFFORD, HAROLD S, JR, b Spokane, Wash, July 24, 36; m 58; c 3. CHEMISTRY. *Educ:* Western Wash State Col, BA, 58; Univ Ill, Urbana, MS, 60, PhD(anal chem), 62. *Prof Exp:* Teaching asst chem, Univ Ill, Urbana, 58-60; from asst prof to assoc prof, 62-77, PROF CHEM, UNIV MINN, MINNEAPOLIS, 77- *Mem:* Am Chem Soc. *Res:* High temperature electrochemistry; fused salts. *Mailing Add:* Dept Chem Inst Technol Univ Minn Minneapolis MN 55455

SWOFFORD, ROBERT LEWIS, b Charlotte, NC, Jan 19, 48; m 73. LASER SPECTROSCOPY. *Educ:* Furman Univ, BS, 69; Univ Calif, Berkeley, PhD(chem), 73. *Prof Exp:* Sr res assoc chem, Cornell Univ, 73-77; proj leader, 77-80, group leader laser res, 80-81, GROUP LEADER QUANTUM CHEM, STANDARD OIL CO, 81- *Mem:* Am Chem Soc; Optical Soc Am; AAAS; Laser Inst Am; Soc Appl Spectros. *Res:* Laser techniques to study the forces which control chemical reactions at the molecular level. *Mailing Add:* Standard Oil Co 4440 Warrensville Center Rd Warrensville Heights OH 44128

SWONGER, CLARON WINTHROP, computer systems, electronic engineering, see previous edition

SWOOPE, CHARLES C, b Jersey City, NJ, July 7, 34; m 55; c 2. PROSTHODONTICS. *Educ:* Univ Md, DDS, 59; Univ Wash, MSD, 64. *Prof Exp:* Asst chief dent serv, USPHS Hosp, New Orleans, 64-67; dir grad & res prosthodontics, 67-71, assoc prof, 71-73, prof prosthodontics, 73-80, CLIN ASSOC, SCH DENT, UNIV WASH, 80- *Concurrent Pos:* Asst prof, Loyola Univ, 64-67; consult, USPHS Hosp, Va Hosp & Univ Hosp, Seattle, Wash, 67-68. *Mem:* Am Prosthodont Soc; Am Col Prosthodont; Am Acad Denture Prosthetics; Am Equilibration Soc; Am Cleft Palate Asn. *Res:* Resilient lining materials; emotional evaluation of denture patients; bone changes; speech problems; force transmission to teeth. *Mailing Add:* 8255 NE 26th St Bellevue WA 98004

SWOPE, FRED C, b Lexington, Va, Mar 25, 35; m 64. FOOD SCIENCE, BIOCHEMISTRY. *Educ:* Univ Md, BS, 61; Mich State Univ, PhD(food sci), 68. *Prof Exp:* Asst prof, 68-74, ASSOC PROF BIOL, VA MIL INST, 74- *Mem:* Am Chem Soc. *Res:* Lipoproteins; structural studies on membranes. *Mailing Add:* Dept of Biol Va Mil Inst Lexington VA 24450

SWOPE, HENRIETTA HILL, astronomy, deceased

SWOPE, RICHARD DALE, b Palmyra, Pa, Sept 27, 38; m 57; c 2. FLUID MECHANICS, HEAT TRANSFER. *Educ:* Univ Del, BME, 60, MME, 62, PhD(appl sci), 66. *Prof Exp:* Appl scientist res & develop, Armstrong Cork Co, 64-68; asst prof eng, PMC Cols, 68-71; assoc prof, Ctr Eng, Widener Col, 71-77, prof eng & asst dean, 77-80; PROF ENG SCI, TRINITY UNIV, 80-, CHMN, 81- *Mem:* Int Solar Energy Soc; Am Soc Mech Engrs; Am Soc Eng Educ. *Res:* Energy; turbulence; shear stresses; solar energy; energy storage; bubble mechanics and formation. *Mailing Add:* Eng Sci Dept Trinity Univ 715 Stadium Dr San Antonio TX 78284

SWORD, CHRISTOPHER PATRICK, b San Fernando, Calif, Sept 9, 28; m 59; c 4. MICROBIOLOGY. *Educ:* Loyola Univ, Calif, BS, 51; Univ Calif, Los Angeles, PhD(microbiol), 59. *Prof Exp:* Fel & res assoc microbiol, Univ Kans, 58-59, from asst prof to prof, 59-70; prof life sci & chmn dept, Ind State Univ, Terre Haute, 70-76; GRAD DEAN & DIR RES & PROF MICROBIOL, S DAK STATE UNIV, BROOKINGS, 76- *Concurrent Pos:* President's fel, Soc Am Bact, 60. *Mem:* AAAS; Am Soc Microbiol; NY Acad Sci; Coun Grad Schs US; Nat Coun Univ Res Adminr. *Res:* Biochemical and immunological mechanisms of pathogenesis; bacterial virulence; host-parasite interactions in Listeria monocytogenes infection; ultrastructure of bacteria and infected cells. *Mailing Add:* Grad Sch & Off of Res SDak State Univ Brookings SD 57007

SWORD, JAMES HOWARD, b Derby, Va, Jan 1, 24; m 46; c 2. ENGINEERING MECHANICS, CIVIL ENGINEERING. *Educ:* Va Polytech Inst, BS, 50, MS, 54. *Prof Exp:* Instr civil eng, 51, from instr to assoc prof eng mech, 51-66, PROF ENG MECH, VA POLYTECH INST & STATE UNIV, 66- *Mem:* Am Soc Eng Educ. *Res:* Computer programming; mechanics; interferometry. *Mailing Add:* Dept Mech Eng Va Polytech Inst & State Univ Blacksburg VA 24060

SWORDER, DAVID D, b Dinuba, Calif, Aug 1, 37. ENGINEERING. *Educ:* Univ Calif, Berkeley, BS, 58, MS, 59; Univ Calif, Los Angeles, PhD(eng), 65. *Prof Exp:* Sr engr, Litton Systs, Inc, 59-64; from asst prof to assoc prof elec eng, Univ Southern Calif, 64-77; PROF APPL MECH & ENG SCI, UNIV CALIF, SAN DIEGO, 77- *Mem:* Inst Elec & Electronics Engrs. *Res:* Adaptive and stochastic control problems. *Mailing Add:* Dept Appl Mech & Eng Sci Univ Calif San Diego La Jolla CA 92037

SWORDS, RUTH RILEY, b Itasca, Tex, Nov 1, 16; m 40; c 2. DENTISTRY, DENTAL HYGIENE. *Educ:* ETex State Teachers Col, BA, 38; Tex Wesleyan Col, BS, 61; Baylor Univ, DDS, 61. *Prof Exp:* Teacher elem sch, Tex, 38-42; eng draftsman, Gen Dynamics Corp, Ft Worth, 42-48; PROF DENT HYG & DIR, CARUTH SCH DENT HYG, COL DENT, BAYLOR UNIV, 62- *Res:* Clinical dental hygiene. *Mailing Add:* Caruth Sch of Dent Hyg 3302 Gaston Ave Dallas TX 75246

SWORSKI, THOMAS JOHN, b Pittsburgh, Pa, Sept 8, 20; m 44; c 2. SCIENTIFIC PROGRAMMING. *Educ:* Duquesne Univ, BS, 42; Notre Dame Univ, PhD(phys chem), 51. *Prof Exp:* Chemist, Oak Ridge Nat Lab, 51-57 & Nuclear Res Ctr, Union Carbide Corp, 57-63; chemist, 64-81, PROG ANALYST COMPUT SCI, OAK RIDGE NAT LAB, 81- *Mem:* Am Chem Soc. *Res:* Photochemistry; chemical kinetics. *Mailing Add:* Comput Sci Oak Ridge Nat Lab Oak Ridge TN 37830

SWOYER, VINCENT HARRY, b Philadelphia, Pa, Mar 30, 32; m 60; c 3. TECHNICAL ADMINISTRATION, COMPUTER SCIENCE. *Educ:* Tufts Univ, BS, 54; Univ Rochester, MA, 60; Harvard Univ, EdD, 66. *Prof Exp:* Asst prof naval sci, Univ Rochester, 57-59, from asst dir to dir, Comput Ctr, 59-69; staff assoc, NSF, 69-70; dir comput ctr, Univ Rochester, River Campus, 70-78; group dir, 78-80, VPRES CORP SYSTS, RYDER SYST INC, 80- *Concurrent Pos:* Consult, NSF, 70- & Southern Regional Educ Bd, 71- *Mem:* Soc Mgt Info Systs; Asn Comput Mach. *Res:* Monte Carlo studies, especially in area of multiple regression analysis; computer methods for statistical research applications. *Mailing Add:* Ryder Syst Inc Box 520816 Miami FL 33152

SWYER, PAUL ROBERT, b London, Eng, May 21, 21; Can citizen; m 47; c 2. PEDIATRICS, NEONATOLOGY. *Educ:* Cambridge Univ, BA, 40, MB, BChir & MA, 43; FRCP(L), dipl child health, 48; FRCP(C). *Prof Exp:* Registr, Middlesex Hosp, 47-48; asst resident chest dis & med officer, Brompton Hosp for Dis of Chest, 48-49; registr, SWarwickshire Hosp, 49-50; asst med registr, Hosp Sick Children, 50-52; registr, Royal Hosp, Wolverhampton, 52-53; fel cardiol, 53-54, res assoc pediat, 54-60, asst scientist, 61-66, SR INVESTR RES INST & CHIEF DIV PERINATOLOGY, HOSP SICK CHILDREN, TORONTO, 67- *Concurrent Pos:* Can Dept Nat Health & Welfare grants, 54-67; sr staff physician, Hosp Sick Children, 64-; from asst prof to assoc prof, Univ Toronto, 65-75, prof, 75-; Med Res Coun Can grants, 66-81 & Phys Serv Inc grants, 79-81. *Mem:* Am Pediat Soc; Am Acad Pediat; Soc Pediat Res; Can Pediat Soc; Can Med Asn. *Res:* Investigation of mechanics of breathing; energy metabolism, thermoregulation, blood flow and pressures and methods of treatment of pulmonary disorders in newly born infants. *Mailing Add:* Hosp for Sick Children 555 University Ave Toronto ON M5G 1X8 Can

SY, JOSE, b Sorsogon, Philippines, Dec 10, 44. BIOCHEMISTRY. *Educ:* Adamson Univ, Manila, BS, 64; Duke Univ, PhD(biochem), 70. *Prof Exp:* Res assoc, 70-74, asst prof, 74-79, ASSOC PROF, ROCKEFELLER UNIV, 79- *Mem:* Am Chem Soc; Am Soc Microbiol; Am Soc Biol Chemists; Am Chem Soc. *Res:* Nucleic acids and protein synthesis. *Mailing Add:* Box 227 Rockefeller Univ New York NY 10021

SYBERS, HARLEY D, b Tony, Wis, June 18, 33; m 58; c 2. PATHOLOGY, PHYSIOLOGY. *Educ:* Univ Wis-Madison, BS, 56, MS & MD, 63, PhD(physiol), 69; Am Bd Path, dipl & cert anat path & clin path, 68. *Prof Exp:* Resident path, Univ Wis-Madison, 64-68; asst prof, Univ Calif, San Diego, 69-75; ASSOC PROF PATH, BAYLOR COL MED, 75- *Concurrent Pos:* USPHS contract, Univ Calif, San Diego, 69-74; Nat Heart & Lung Inst grant, 74-77; NIH res grant, 79-81, mem, Cardiovascular Study Sect, NIH, 80-84. *Mem:* Am Heart Asn; Am Soc Clin Path; Am Physiol Soc; Am Asn Pathologists; Int Acad Path. *Res:* Cardiac pathophysiology. *Mailing Add:* Dept Path Baylor Col Med Houston TX 77025

SYBERT, JAMES RAY, b Greenville, Tex, Dec 25, 34; m 54; c 3. SOLID STATE PHYSICS, LOW TEMPERATURE PHYSICS. *Educ:* NTex State Univ, BA, 55, MA, 56; La State Univ, PhD(physics), 61. *Prof Exp:* Instr, 56-58, from asst prof to assoc prof, 61-67, PROF PHYSICS, N TEX STATE UNIV, 67-, CHMN DEPT, 69- *Concurrent Pos:* Adj prof, Southwest Ctr Advan Studies, Dallas, 67-70. *Mem:* Am Phys Soc; Am Asn Physics Teachers. *Res:* Electron transport in metals and semiconductors; size effect in metals; superconductivity; thermoelectricity and thermal conductivity in semiconductors; high magnetic field effects and magnetic field induced quantum oscillations in metals. *Mailing Add:* Dept of Physics NTex State Univ Denton TX 76203

SYBERT, PAUL DEAN, b Joliet, Ill, July 16, 54; m 81. AROMATIC POLYMERS, RIGID-ROD POLYMERS. *Educ:* Augustana Col, BA, 76; Univ Iowa, MS, 77; Colo State Univ, PhD(org chem), 80. *Prof Exp:* Sr res chemist, Monsanto, 80-81; POLYMER CHEMIST, SRI INT, 81- *Mem:* Am Chem Soc. *Res:* New polymerization methods for new and existing rod-like aromatic polymers which afford anisotropic solutions; preparation of polymers for use as desalination membranes. *Mailing Add:* 333 Ravenswood Ave Menlo Park CA 94025

SYDISKIS, ROBERT JOSEPH, b Bridgeport, Conn, Sept 19, 36; m 61; c 2. VIROLOGY. *Educ:* Univ Bridgeport, BA, 61; Northwestern Univ, PhD(microbiol), 65. *Prof Exp:* Fel, Univ Chicago, 65-67; asst prof virol, Sch Med, Univ Pittsburgh, 67-71; ASSOC PROF MICROBIOL, SCH DENT, UNIV MD, BALTIMORE CITY, 71- *Mem:* Am Soc Microbiol. *Res:* Structure of herpes virus, isolation and identification of structural and non-structural components synthesized in the cell; assembly of precursor components in vivo and in vitro. *Mailing Add:* Dept of Microbiol Univ of Md Sch of Dent Baltimore MD 21201

SYDNOR, THOMAS DAVIS, b Richmond, Va, Jan 27, 40; m 62; c 3. ORNAMENTAL HORTICULTURE, URBAN FORESTRY. *Educ:* Va Polytech Inst & State Univ, BS, 62; NC State Univ, PhD(plant physiol), 72. *Prof Exp:* Landscape foreman, Southside Nurseries Inc, 62-63, vpres 65-69; asst prof, 72-78, ASSOC PROF ORNAMENTAL HORT, OHIO STATE UNIV, 78- *Concurrent Pos:* Consult landscape & urban hort, 78-; prin investr, Ohio Shade Tree Eval Proj, 78- *Honors & Awards:* Alfred J Wright Award, 78. *Mem:* Sigma Xi; Am Soc Hort Sci; Int Soc Arboricult. *Res:* Shade tree evaluation and the effects of environmental conditions on growth and development of woody ornamentals and trees for urban, highway and landscape situations. *Mailing Add:* 6800 Harriott Rd Powell OH 43065

SYDOR, MICHAEL, b Prusseniv, Ukraine, Dec 25, 36; US citizen; m 62; c 3. ENVIRONMENTAL PHYSICS. *Educ:* Univ BC, BASc, 59; Univ NMex, PhD(physics), 64. *Prof Exp:* From asst prof physics to assoc prof, 68-74, PROF PHYSICS, UNIV MINN, DULUTH, 74- *Mem:* Int Asn Great Lakes Res; Am Geophys Union; Sigma Xi. *Res:* Light scattering from suspended solids; remote sensing of turbidity in lakes; studies of turbidity transport in Lake Superior; numerical modeling of transport processes in Lake Superior and Duluth Harbor; ice and snow studies through optical remote sensing; heat budget and ice growth in Duluth-Superior Harbor and Lake Superior. *Mailing Add:* Dept of Physics Univ of Minn Duluth MN 55812

SYDORIAK, STEPHEN GEORGE, b Passaic, NJ, Jan 6, 18; m 45; c 6. PHYSICS. *Educ:* Univ Buffalo, BA, 40; Yale Univ, PhD(physics), 48. *Prof Exp:* Mem staff, Radiation Lab, Mass Inst Technol, 41-45; MEM STAFF, LOS ALAMOS SCI LAB, UNIV CALIF, 48- *Mem:* Am Phys Soc. *Res:* Radar signal threshold studies; magnetic susceptibilities at low temperatures; liquid helium-three properties; 1962 helium-three vapor pressure scale of temperatures; hydrodynamic theory of channel boiling, solid hydrogen laser targets. *Mailing Add:* Los Alamos Sci Lab PO Box 1663 Los Alamos NM 87545

SYED, IBRAHIM BIJLI, medical physics, radiological health, see previous edition

SYEKLOCHA, DELFA, b Vancouver, BC, Sept 12, 33. MEDICAL BACTERIOLOGY, IMMUNOLOGY. *Educ:* Univ BC, BA, 54; McGill Univ, MSc, 62, PhD(microbiol), 64. *Prof Exp:* NIH fel, Ont Cancer Inst, 64-65; ASST PROF MICROBIOL, UNIV BC, 65- *Mem:* Am Soc Microbiol; Can Soc Microbiol; Can Soc Immunol. *Res:* Immunizing potential of attenuated mutants of Pseudomonas aeruginosa strains and characterization of soluble antigens derived from the wild type; biological activities and characterization of a lethal exotoxin produced by Paeruginosa. *Mailing Add:* Dept Microbiol Univ BC Vancouver BC V6T 1W5 Can

SYGUSCH, JURGEN, b Jablonec, Czech, Aug 8, 45; Can citizen; m 68; c 1. BIOCHEMISTRY, CRYSTALLOGRAPHY. *Educ:* McGill Univ, BSc, 67, MSc, 69; Univ Montreal, PhD(chem), 74. *Prof Exp:* Med Res Coun Can fel, Dept Biochem, Sch Med, Univ Alta, 74-77; ASST PROF BIOCHEM, SCH MED, UNIV SHERBROOKE, 77- *Mem:* AAAS; Can Biochem Soc; Tissue Cult Asn; Biophys Soc. *Res:* Three dimensional organization of chromatin; study by x-ray crystallography of conformational changes resulting from secondary modifications of chromatin. *Mailing Add:* Dept of Biochem CHU Univ of Sherbrooke Sherbrooke PQ J1H 5N4 Can

SYKES, ALAN O'NEIL, b St Regis Falls, NY, May 19, 25; m 51; c 2. ACOUSTICS. *Educ:* Cornell Univ, AB, 48; Cath Univ Am, PhD, 68. *Prof Exp:* Physicist, David Taylor Model Basin, US Navy Dept, 48-52, electronic scientist, Off Naval Res, 52-54, physicist, 54-58, physicist & consult to head acoust div, 58-60, physicist & head, Noise Transmission & Radiation Sect, 60-61, physicist & head, Noise Res & Develop Br, 61-64, physicist & head, Struct Acoust Br, 64-65, physicist, Acoust Technol Prog, 65-81. *Concurrent Pos:* Mem hydroballistic adv comt, Navy Bur Ord, 56-60; mem struct impedence panel, Noise Adv Comt, Navy Bur Ships, 56-64, consult, Soc Automotive Engrs, 57- *Mem:* Fel Acoust Soc Am. *Res:* Underwater acoustics with emphasis on signal processing and propagation; noise reduction, vibration theory and electroacoustic transducer development. *Mailing Add:* 304 Mashie Dr SE Vienna VA 22180

SYKES, BRIAN DOUGLAS, b Montreal, Que, Aug 30, 43; m 68. BIOPHYSICAL CHEMISTRY. *Educ:* Univ Alta, BSc, 65; Stanford Univ, PhD(chem), 69. *Prof Exp:* From asst prof to assoc prof chem, Harvard Univ, 69-75; assoc prof biochem, 75-80, PROF BIOCHEM, UNIV ALTA, 80- *Concurrent Pos:* NIH grant, Harvard Univ, 69-75, Alfred P Sloan fel, 71-73; Med Res Coun Can grant, 75- *Mem:* Can Biochem Soc; Sigma Xi; Am Soc Biol Chemists; Am Chem Soc; Am Phys Soc. *Res:* Application of nuclear magnetic resonance to problems in biochemistry. *Mailing Add:* Dept of Biochem Univ of Alta Edmonton AB T6C 2H7 Can

SYKES, DONALD JOSEPH, b Buffalo, NY, Mar 16, 36; m 60; c 2. PHOTOGRAPHIC CHEMISTRY, STATISTICAL ANALYSIS. *Educ:* Rochester Inst Technol, BS, 58. *Prof Exp:* Dir appl res, Cormac Chem Corp, 59-63; res mgr, 63-69, asst dir res, 69-75, dir res, 75-77, asst vpres res, 77-79, GROUP VPRES, P A HUNT CHEM CORP, 79- *Mem:* Am Chem Soc; Soc Photog Scientists & Engrs. *Mailing Add:* 8 Sunset Lane Upper Saddle River NJ 07458

SYKES, JAMES AUBREY, JR, b Washington, DC, Sept 24, 41; m 60; c 2. INDUSTRIAL CHEMICAL TECHNOLOGY. *Educ:* Univ Md, BS, 64, MS, 65, PhD(chem eng), 68. *Prof Exp:* Engr, W R Grace & Co, 65-68; process eng, Shell Develop Co, Div Shell Oil, 68-74; DIR INDUST CHEM & TECHNOL, AIR PROD & CHEMICALS, INC, 74- *Concurrent Pos:* Abstractor, Chem Abstrcts, Am Chem Soc, 69-71. *Mem:* Am Inst Chem Engrs; Sigma Xi. *Res:* Polymers; commodity chemicals; performance chemicals; petroleum processing; materials and metallurgy; heat transfer; process systems. *Mailing Add:* 103 Fairview St Macungie PA 18062

SYKES, JAMES ENOCH, b Richmond, Va, Apr 12, 23; m 47; c 2. FISHERIES. *Educ:* Randolph-Macon Col, 48; Univ Va, MS, 49. *Prof Exp:* Lab instr biol, Univ Va, 48-49; fishery res biologist, US Fish & Wildlife Serv, 49-58, chief striped bass invests, 58-62, biol lab dir, Bur Com Fisheries, 62-71; dir div fisheries, Nat Marine Fisheries Serv, 71-79; MEM STAFF, NC COSTAL RESOURCES COMN, 79- *Mem:* Am Fisheries Soc; Am Inst Fishery Res Biologists (pres, 75 & 76). *Res:* Coastal pelagic and offshore sport fisheries; assessment of marine resources; biology of Gulf and Atlantic menhaden. *Mailing Add:* 247 Country Club Rd Morehead City NC 28557

SYKES, JOHN A, b Pinner, Eng, Dec 7, 18; US citizen; m 43; c 3. VIROLOGY, CANCER. *Educ:* LRFPS(G), 44; LRCP(E), 44; LRCS(E), 44; Univ London, cert pub health, 48; Univ Manchester, dipl bact, 49. *Prof Exp:* Bacteriologist, Med Res Coun Gt Brit, 48, assoc dir & asst bacteriologist, Pub Health Lab Serv, Suffolk, Eng, 49-54; med officer virus & zoonoses, Lab Hyg, Dept Nat Health & Welfare Can, Ont, 54-56; from asst prof to assoc prof biol, Univ Tex Postgrad Sch Med, 58-66; DIR RES, CANCER RES DEPT, SOUTHERN CALIF CANCER CTR, CALIF HOSP MED CTR, 66- *Concurrent Pos:* Clin asst prof microbiol, Baylor Col Med, 56-66; assoc biologist, Sect Biol & Electron Micros, Univ Tex M D Anderson Hosp & Tumor Inst Houston, 62-64, assoc virologist, 64-66; assoc prof virol, Univ Tex Grad Sch Biomed Sci Houston, 64-66. *Mem:* Am Soc Microbiol; Tissue Cult Asn; Soc Cryobiol; Am Asn Cancer Res; fel Royal Soc Trop Med & Hyg. *Res:* Tissue culture; ultrastructural research. *Mailing Add:* Southern Calif Cancer Ctr 1414 S Hope St Los Angeles CA 90015

SYKES, LYNN RAY, b Pittsburgh, Pa, Apr 16, 37. GEOPHYSICS. *Educ:* Mass Inst Technol, BS & MS, 60; Columbia Univ, PhD(geol), 64. *Prof Exp:* Res scientist, Lamont Geol Observ, Columbia Univ, 62-65, res geophysicist, Inst Earth Sci, Environ Sci Serv Admin at Lamont Geol Observ, 65-68; assoc prof, 68-71, prof, 71-78, HIGGINS PROF GEOL, LAMONT-DOHERTY GEOL OBSERV, COLUMIBA UNIV, 78-, HEAD, SEMISMOL GROUP, 71- *Concurrent Pos:* Mem comts seismol & earthquake prediction, Nat Res Coun-Nat Acad Sci, 73-75; mem, Earthquake Studies Adv Panel, US Geol Surv, 77-81 & Earthquake Prediction Eval Coun, 79-82; mem comn acad priorities arts & sci, Columbia Univ, 78-79. *Honors & Awards:* Macelwane Award, Am Geophys Union, 70, Bucher Medal, 75. *Mem:* Nat Acad Sci; fel Geol Soc Am; AAAS; fel Am Geophys Union; fel Royal Astron Soc. *Res:* Investigations of long-period and mantle seismic waves; surface wave propagation across ocean areas; precise location of earthquake hypocenters and relationship of spatial distribution of earthquakes to large-scale tectonic phenomena; field study of aftershocks of 1964 Alaskan earthquake; field study of deep and shallow earthquakes in Fiji-Tonga region; earthquake prediction; tectonics. *Mailing Add:* Lamont-Doherty Geol Observ Columbia Univ Palisades NY 10964

SYKES, PAUL JAY, JR, b Hummelstown, Pa, Aug 31, 18; m 48; c 1. PHYSICS, NUCLEAR ENGINEERING. *Educ:* Univ BC, BA, 48; Univ Calif, MA, 51. *Prof Exp:* Chief proj off nuclear eng test facil, Wright-Patterson Air Force Base, Ohio, 52-56, chief reactor hazards br, Spec Weapons Ctr, Kirtland Air Force Base, 57-58, proj officer, Anal Div, 58-60, proj officer, Physics Div, Air Force Weapons Lab, 60-64; ASST PROF PHYSICS, UNIV BC, 64- *Mem:* Am Asn Physics Teachers; Royal Astron Soc Can. *Res:* Design and engineering of nuclear research reactor facilities; reactor hazards and safeguards; nuclear weapon systems analysis. *Mailing Add:* 5616 Westport Pl West Vancouver BC V7W 1T9 Can

SYKES, RICHARD BROOK, b Eng, July 8, 42; m 69; c 2. MICROBIOLOGY. *Educ:* Paddington Col, BS, 65; Queen Elizabeth Col, London Univ, MS, 68; Bristol Univ, PhD, 72. *Prof Exp:* Head antibiotic res unit, Glaxo Res Labs, 72-77; asst dir, 77-79, DIR, DEPT MICROBIOL, SQUIBB INST MED RES, 79-, ASSOC DIR, 81- *Concurrent Pos:* Consult, Dept Infectious Dis, St Michael's Med Ctr, 81- *Mem:* British Soc Antimicrobial Chemotherapy; Am Soc Microbiol; NY Acad Sci; Soc Indust Microbiol. *Mailing Add:* Squibb Inst Med Res PO Box 4000 Princeton NJ 08540

SYKES, ROBERT MARTIN, b Lawrence, Mass, July 25, 43; m 65; c 1. ENVIRONMENTAL ENGINEERING. *Educ:* Northeastern Univ, BSCE, 66; Purdue Univ, West Lafayette, MSCE, 68, PhD(sanit eng), 70. *Prof Exp:* Asst prof civil eng, Union Col, NY, 70-72; asst prof, 72-77, ASSOC PROF CIVIL ENG, OHIO STATE UNIV, 77- *Concurrent Pos:* Consult, NY State Dept Environ Conserv, 70-71. *Mem:* Water Pollution Control Fedn; Am Water Works Asn. *Res:* Water pollution abatement; biological processes for waste water treatment; ecosystem theory; modeling of aquatic systems. *Mailing Add:* Dept Civil Eng Ohio State Univ Columbus OH 43210

SYKORA, OSCAR P, b Nachod, Czech, June 22, 29; Can citizen; m 65. DENTISTRY. *Educ:* Sir George William Univ, BA, 54; Univ Montreal, MA, 55, PhD(slavic hist), 59; McGill Univ, DDS, 59. *Prof Exp:* From asst prof to assoc prof prosthodontics, McGill Univ, 61-71; ASSOC PROF PROSTHODONTICS, DALHOUSIE UNIV, 71- *Mem:* Am Prosthodontic Soc; Can Dent Asn; Can Inst Int Affairs; Can Acad Prosthodontics. *Res:* Fixed and removable prosthetic dentistry. *Mailing Add:* Fac of Dent Dalhousie Univ Halifax NS B3H 3J5 Can

SYLVESTER, EDWARD SANFORD, b New York, NY, Feb 29, 20; m 42; c 2. ENTOMOLOGY. *Educ:* Colo State Univ, BS, 43; Univ Calif, PhD(entom), 47. *Prof Exp:* Lab asst bot, Colo State Univ, 40, asst entom, 41-43; prin lab asst entom, Univ Calif, Berkeley, 45-47, instr entom univ & jr entomologist exp sta, 47-49, asst prof & asst entomologist, 49-55, lectr & assoc entomologist, 55-61, PROF ENTOM & ENTOMOLOGIST EXP STA, UNIV CALIF, BERKELEY, 61-, CHMN ENTOM SCI, 81- *Mem:* Entom Soc Am; Am Phytopath Soc. *Res:* Insect vector-virus relationships; biostatistics; Aphidiae. *Mailing Add:* Div of Entom & Parasitol 366 Ocean View Ave Kensington CA 94707

SYLVESTER, JOSEPH ROBERT, b Fayetteville, NC, Nov 3, 42. FISHERIES MANAGEMENT, MARINE BIOLOGY. *Educ:* Univ Hawaii, BA, 65, MS, 69; Univ Wash, PhD(fish biol), 71. *Prof Exp:* Fishery res biologist, Nat Marine Fisheries Serv, Bur Com Fisheries, 69-71; dir, Bur Fish & Wildlife, Govt of VI, 71-73; fishery res biologist, Oceanic Inst, 74-76; dir, Bur Fish & Wildlife, Govt of VI, 76-78; MARINE MAMMAL & ENDANGERED SPECIES MGR, NAT MARINE FISHERIES SERV, 78- *Concurrent Pos:* Res assoc, Hawaii Inst Marine Biol, Univ Hawaii, 65-69. *Mem:* Am Fisheries Soc; Am Inst Fisheries Res Biologists; Sigma Xi. *Mailing Add:* Box 818 Nat Fishery Res Lab La Crosse WI 84601

SYLVESTER, NICHOLAS DOMINIC, b Cleveland, Ohio, Apr 16, 42; m 65; c 2. CHEMICAL ENGINEERING. *Educ:* Ohio Univ, BS, 64; Carnegie-Mellon Univ, PhD(chem eng), 69. *Prof Exp:* Asst prof chem eng, Univ Notre Dame, 68-72; assoc prof, 72-75, chmn chem & petrol eng, 77-78, PROF CHEM ENG, UNIV TULSA, 75-, DEAN ENG, 78- *Concurrent Pos:* Res consult, Amoco Prod Res Co, 75-76. *Honors & Awards:* Best Paper Award, Can Soc Chem Eng, 74. *Mem:* Am Soc Eng Educ; Soc Petrol Engrs; Am Inst Chem Engrs; Soc Rheology; Am Chem Soc. *Res:* Enhanced oil recovery; multi-phase flow; non-Newtonian fluid mechanics; water pollution control; chemical reaction engineering. *Mailing Add:* Col Eng Univ Tulsa Tulsa OK 74104

SYLVESTER, ROBERT OHRUM, b Seattle, Wash, Aug 20, 14; m 40; c 2. CIVIL & ENVIRONMENTAL ENGINEERING. *Educ:* Univ Wash, BS, 36; Harvard Univ, SM, 41; Environ Eng Intersoc, dipl, 58. *Prof Exp:* Engr, Allis Chalmers Mfg Co, 36-38; instr eng, Univ Wash, 38-39; dist engr, Wash State Dept Health, 39-41, 46-47; from asst prof to assoc prof civil eng, 47-73, head div water & air resources, Dept Civil Eng, 68-73, dir, Inst for Environ Studies, 73-77, prof, 73-80, chmn, Dept Eng, 77-80, EMER PROF ENVIRON STUDIES, UNIV WASH, SEATTLE, 80- *Concurrent Pos:* Consult various industs, US & Can govt; mem study sect res grant review, NIH, 63-67; mem adv panel, BC Dept Lands, Forests, Water Resources, 70-72, mem adv panel water quality criteria, Nat Acad Sci, 71-72, US Nat Comt, Int Asn Water Pollution Res, 71-74 & review panel, US Gen Acct Off Water Res, 73. *Honors & Awards:* Arthur Sidney Bedell Award, Water Pollution Control Fedn, 57. *Mem:* Fel Am Soc Civil Engrs; Am Water Works Asn;

Water Pollution Control Fedn; Int Asn Water Pollution. *Res:* Am Geophys Union. *Res:* Water resources; water supply; water resource and quality management; water pollution control technology; solid waste collection, disposal and resource recovery; environmental aspects of water quality. *Mailing Add:* Dept of Civil Eng Univ of Wash FR-40 Seattle WA 98105

SYLVIA, AVIS LATHAM, b Westerly, RI, Nov 16, 38. CELL PHYSIOLOGY. *Educ:* Univ NC, Greensboro, AB, 60; Univ Conn, MS, 66; Univ NC, Chapel Hill, PhD(physiol), 73. *Prof Exp:* Res assoc cell physiol, Sch Med, Univ NC, 73-74; fel, Ctr Aging & Human Develop, 74-76, res assoc, 76-77, ASST PROF DEPT PHYSIOL, DUKE UNIV MED CTR, 77- *Mem:* AAAS; Soc for Neurosci; Geront Soc. *Res:* Cellular oxidative metabolism, bioenergetics and redox phenomena; physiological and biochemical aspects of development and aging in the mammalian central nervous system. *Mailing Add:* Dept Physiol Med Ctr Duke Univ Box 3709 Durham NC 27710

SYLWESTER, DAVID LUTHER, b Roseburg, Ore, Mar 17, 36; m 62; c 2. MATHEMATICAL STATISTICS, BIOSTATISTICS. *Educ:* Univ Ore, AB, 58; Ind Univ, AM, 60; Stanford Univ, PhD(statist), 66. *Prof Exp:* Asst math, Ind Univ, 58-60; res physicist, Arctic Inst NAm, 60-62; asst statist, Stanford Univ, 62-65; asst prof community med, Col Med, 65-69, from asst prof to assoc prof math, 65-77, PROF MATH & ENVIRON HEALTH, UNIV VT, 77- *Concurrent Pos:* Consult, Med Sch, Stanford Univ, 62-65 & Col Med, Univ Vt, 65- *Mem:* Inst Math Statist; Am Statist Asn; Biomet Soc. *Res:* Stochastic processes. *Mailing Add:* Dept of Math Univ of Vt Burlington VT 05401

SYMBAS, PANAGIOTIS N, b Greece, Aug 15, 25; US citizen; m 65; c 2. THORACIC SURGERY, CARDIOVASCULAR SURGERY. *Educ:* Univ Salonika, MD, 54. *Prof Exp:* Intern surg, Vanderbilt Univ, 56-57, resident surgeon, 60-61, instr surg, 61-62; fel cardiovasc surg, St Louis Univ, 62-63; assoc thoracic surg, 64-65; from asst prof to assoc prof, 66-73, PROF SURG, THORACIC CARDIOVASC SURG DIV, SCH MED, EMORY UNIV, 73-, DIR SURG RES LAB, 70-; DIR THORACIC & CARDIOVASC SURG, GRADY MEM HOSP, ATLANTA, 68- *Mem:* Am Surg Asn; Am Asn Thoracic Surg; Soc Thoracic Surg; Soc Univ Surgeons; fel Am Col Surgeons. *Mailing Add:* Surg Res Lab Emory Univ Sch of Med Atlanta GA 30303

SYMCHOWICZ, SAMSON, b Krakow, Poland, Mar 20, 23; nat US; m 53; c 3. DRUG METABOLISM, BIOCHEMICAL PHARMACOLOGY. *Educ:* Chem Tech Col Eng, Czech, Chem Eng, 50; Polytech Inst Brooklyn, MS, 56; Rutgers Univ, PhD(physiol, biochem), 60. *Prof Exp:* Asst biochem, Allan Mem Inst, McGill Univ, 51-53; asst hormone res, Col Med, State Univ NY Downstate Med Ctr, 53-56; res biochemist, 56-66, sect leader, 66-70, head dept biochem, 70-73, assoc dir biol res, 73-77, DIR DRUG METAB & PHARMACO- KINETICS, SCHERING CORP, 77- *Mem:* Am Chem Soc; Am Soc Pharmacol & Exp Therapeut; Am Inst Chemists; NY Acad Sci. *Res:* Biogenic amines; drug metabolism. *Mailing Add:* 44 Laurel Ave Lovingston NJ 07039

SYMINGTON, JANEY, b St Louis, Mo, June 29, 28; m 49; c 4. VIROLOGY, PLANT PHYSIOLOGY. *Educ:* Vassar Col, AB, 50; Radcliffe Col, PhD(biol), 59. *Prof Exp:* Res assoc & asst prof bot, Washington Univ, 58-71, res asst prof biol, 71-73, res assoc microbiol, 73-80; RES ASST PROF, ST LOUIS UNIV, 80- *Mem:* Am Soc Microbiol; Sigma Xi; Am Soc Plant Physiol; Am Inst Biol Sci; Am Soc Cell Biol. *Res:* Virus structure and replication; interaction of viruses with antibodies and cell surfaces. *Mailing Add:* St Louis Univ 745 Cella Rd St Louis MO 63124

SYMKO, OREST GEORGE, b Ukraine, Jan 24, 39; US citizen; m 62; c 2. PHYSICS. *Educ:* Univ Ottawa, BSc, 61, MSc, 62; Oxford Univ, DPhil(physics), 67. *Prof Exp:* Res officer physics, Clarendon Lab, Oxford Univ, 67-68; asst res physicist, Univ Calif, San Diego, 68-70; from asst prof to assoc prof, 70-79, PROF PHYSICS, UNIV UTAH, 79- *Concurrent Pos:* Res Corp grant, Univ Utah, 71; NSF grant, 72. *Mem:* Am Phys Soc. *Res:* Low temperature physics; magnetism; superconductivity; dilute alloys; nuclear magnetic resonance. *Mailing Add:* Dept of Physics Univ of Utah Salt Lake City UT 84112

SYMMES, DAVID, b New York, NY, Sept 4, 29; m 57; c 3. NEUROPHYSIOLOGY, PSYCHOLOGY. *Educ:* Harvard Univ, AB, 52; Univ Chicago, PhD(biopsychol), 55. *Prof Exp:* USPHS fel, Yale Univ, 57-59, from instr to asst prof physiol, Sch Med, 59-67; CHIEF SECT ON BRAIN & BEHAVIOR, LAB DEVELOP NEUROBIOL, NAT INST CHILD HEALTH & HUMAN DEVELOP, NIH, 67- *Mem:* NY Acad Sci; Am Physiol Soc; Soc Neurosci. *Res:* Neuropsychology. *Mailing Add:* Lab Develop Neurobiol Bldg 36 Rm 2A21 NIH Bethesda MD 20205

SYMON, KEITH RANDOLPH, b Ft Wayne, Ind, Mar 25, 20; m 43; c 4. THEORETICAL PLASMA PHYSICS. *Educ:* Harvard Univ, SB, 42, AM, 43, PhD(theoret physics), 48. *Prof Exp:* From instr to assoc prof physics, Wayne Univ, 47-55; from asst prof to assoc prof, 55-57, PROF PHYSICS, UNIV WIS-MADISON, 57- *Concurrent Pos:* Head advan res group, Midwestern Univs Res Asn, 50-57, head theoret sect, 55-57, tech dir, 57-60. *Mem:* Fel Am Phys Soc; Am Asn Physics Teachers. *Res:* Plasma stability; numerical simulation of plasmas; orbit theory; design of high energy accelerators; theory of energy loss fluctuations of fast particles. *Mailing Add:* Dept of Physics Univ of Wis Madison WI 53706

SYMONDS, PAUL S(OUTHWORTH), b Manila, Philippines, Aug 20, 16; US citizen; m 43; c 2. ENGINEERING. *Educ:* Rensselaer Polytech Inst, BS, 38; Cornell Univ, MS, 41, PhD(appl mech), 43. *Prof Exp:* Instr mech eng, Cornell Univ, 41-43; physicist, US Naval Res Lab, Washington, DC, 43-47; from asst prof to assoc prof, 47-54, chmn div, 59-62, PROF ENG, BROWN UNIV, 54- *Concurrent Pos:* Lectr, Univ Md, 46-47; vis prof, Cambridge Univ, 49-51, Imp Chem Industs fel, 50-51; Fulbright awards, 49, 57; Guggenheim fel, 57-58; NSF sr fel, Oxford Univ, 64-65; vis prof, Univ Ill, 72, Univ Cape Town, 75 & Cambridge Univ, 73 & 80. *Mem:* Fel Am Soc Civil Engrs; fel Am

Soc Mech Engrs; Am Soc Eng Educ; Int Asn Bridge & Struct Engrs; fel Am Acad Mech. *Res:* Theory of elasticity and plasticity; structural analysis involving plastic deformations; static and dynamic loading; properties of materials; theory of vibrations and wave propagation. *Mailing Add:* Dept Eng Brown Univ Providence RI 02912

SYMONS, DAVID THORBURN ARTHUR, b Toronto, Ont, July 24, 37; m 64; c 3. GEOPHYSICS, GEOLOGY. *Educ:* Univ Toronto, BASc, 60, PhD(econ geol), 65; Harvard Univ, MA, 61. *Prof Exp:* Nat Res Coun Can overseas fel paleomagnetism, Univ Newcastle, Eng, 65-66; res scientist rock magnetism, Geol Surv Can, 66-70; head dept geol, 73-77 & 79-82, PROF GEOPHYS & GEOTECTONICS, UNIV WINDSOR, 77- *Mem:* Can Geophys Union; Am Geophys Union. *Res:* Application of paleomagnetic methods to geotectonic, ore genesis and geochronologic problems in the Canadian Cordillera and Shield and to the history of the earth's geomagnetic field; geotechnical geophysics. *Mailing Add:* Dept of Geol Univ of Windsor Windsor ON N9B 3P4 Can

SYMONS, EDWARD ALLAN, b Kingston, Ont, Apr 24, 43. PHYSICAL ORGANIC CHEMISTRY, PHYSICAL CHEMISTRY. *Educ:* Queen's Univ, BSc, 65, PhD(chem), 69. *Prof Exp:* ASSOC RES OFFICER, CHALK RIVER NUCLEAR LABS, ATOMIC ENERGY CAN LTD, 72- *Mem:* Chem Inst Can. *Res:* Hydrogen isotope exchange mechanisms and associated physical/organic chemistry in systems of potential interest for heavy water production processes. *Mailing Add:* Chalk River Nuclear Labs Atomic Energy Can Ltd Chalk River ON K0J 1J0 Can

SYMONS, GEORGE E(DGAR), b Danville, Ill, Apr 20, 03; m 26; c 1. ENVIRONMENTAL ENGINEERING. *Educ:* Univ Ill, BS, 28, MS, 30, PhD(chem), 32; Am Acad Environ Engrs, dipl. *Prof Exp:* Res chemist, Ill State Water Survey, 28-33; instr, Univ Ill, 32-33; chemist, Freeport Sulfur Co, 33-34, consult, 34-35; engr, Greeley & Hansen, 35-36; chief chemist, Buffalo Sewer Authority, NY, 36-43; consult engr, 43-64; assoc ed, Water & Sewage Works, 43-48, managing ed, 49-51, ed, 51-57, 59-; ed, Water & Wastes Eng, 64-70; mgr spec proj, Malcolm Pirnie, Inc, 70-78; ENG ED & CONSULT, 78- *Concurrent Pos:* Asst prof, Canisius Col, 41-42; lectr, Med Sch, Buffalo Univ, 42-43; res assoc, NY Univ, 54-55; contrib ed, Water Eng & Mgt, 78- *Honors & Awards:* Diven Medal, Fuller Award, Am Water Works Asn; Emerson Medalist, Water Pollution Control Fedn. *Mem:* Am Chem Soc; fel Am Pub Health Asn; fel Am Soc Civil Engrs; hon mem Am Water Works Asn (pres, 73-74). *Res:* Engineering editing. *Mailing Add:* 86 Edgewood Ave Larchmont NY 10538

SYMONS, JAMES M(ARTIN), b Champaign, Ill, Nov 24, 31; m 58; c 3. SANITARY ENGINEERING. *Educ:* Cornell Univ, BCE, 54; Mass Inst Technol, SM, 55, ScD(sanit eng), 57. *Prof Exp:* Asst, NIH Proj, Mass Inst Technol, 55-57, instr sanit eng, 56-58, asst prof, 58-62; res pub health engr, USPHS, 62-70; CHIEF STANDARDS ATTAINMENT BR, WATER SUPPLY RES LAB, NAT ENVIRON RES CTR, US ENVIRON PROTECTION AGENCY, 70- *Concurrent Pos:* Assoc, Rolf Eliassen Assocs, Mass, 57-61. *Honors & Awards:* Harrison P Eddy Award, Water Pollution Control Fedn, 63; Resources Div Award, Am Water Works Asn, 66; Huber Res Prize, Am Soc Civil Engrs; 67; Silver Medal Super Serv, US Environ Protection Agency, 71. *Mem:* Am Water Works Asn; Am Soc Civil Engrs; Water Pollution Constrol Fedn. *Res:* Drinking water treatment research. *Mailing Add:* Phys & Chem Removal Br 26 St Clair St Cincinnati OH 45268

SYMONS, PHILIP CHARLES, b Taunton, Somerset, Eng, June 4, 39; m 60; c 2. ELECTROCHEMISTRY. *Educ:* Univ Bristol, BSc, 60, PhD(electrochem), 63. *Prof Exp:* Sr chemist, Proctor & Gamble Ltd, Eng, 63-67 & Hooker Chem Corp, 68-69; res dir batteries, Udylite Co, Occidental Petrol Corp, 69-73; CHIEF SCIENTIST, ENERGY DEVELOP ASSOCS, 73- *Mem:* Am Chem Soc; Electrochem Soc; The Chem Soc. *Res:* High energy density batteries; electrochemical thermodynamics and kinetics; thermodynamics of phase transitions; electrochemical engineering. *Mailing Add:* 251 E Lincoln 1100 W Whitcomb Ave Birmingham AL 48009

SYMPSON, ROBERT F, b Ft Madison, Iowa, June 21, 27; m 53; c 4. ANALYTICAL CHEMISTRY, ELECTROCHEMISTRY. *Educ:* Monmouth Col, BS, 50; Univ Ill, MS, 52, PhD, 54. *Prof Exp:* From asst prof to assoc prof, 54-65, PROF CHEM, OHIO UNIV, 65-, CHMN DEPT, 77- *Mem:* Am Chem Soc; Electrochem Soc. *Res:* Polarography and amperometric titrations applied to analytical chemistry. *Mailing Add:* Dept Chem Ohio Univ Athens OH 45701

SYMS, GORDON HENRY, b Wetaskiwin, Alta, June 28, 36; m 58; c 3. COMPUTING SCIENCE, ELECTRICAL ENGINEERING. *Educ:* Univ Alta, BSc, 59; Univ Wash, MSc, 65, PhD(elec eng), 67. *Prof Exp:* Res asst, Univ Wash, 64-67; asst prof comput sci, Univ Alta, 67-70; asst prof math, Naval Post-Grad Sch, 70-74; sr programmer anal, Control Data Can, 74- *Mem:* Asn Comput Mach; Inst Elec & Electronics Engrs. *Res:* Evaluating computer performances; computer operating systems; mass storage systems. *Mailing Add:* Control Data Can 1855 Minnesota Ct Mississauga ON L5N 1K7 Can

SYNEK, MIROSLAV (MIKE), b Prague, Czech, Sept 18, 30; US citizen; m 65; c 2. ATOMIC PHYSICS, PHYSICAL CHEMISTRY. *Educ:* Charles Univ, Prague, MS, 56; Univ Chicago, PhD(physics), 63. *Prof Exp:* Technician chem, Inst Indust Med, Prague, Czech, 50-51; asst physics, Czech Acad Sci, 56-58; res asst, Univ Chicago, 58-62; asst prof physics, DePaul Univ, 62-65, assoc prof physics, 65-66; prof physics, Tex Christian Univ, 67-71; regional sci adv & res scientist, Dept Physics, Univ Tex, Austin, 71-73, lectr, exten lectr & res scientist, Depts Physics, Chem, Astron & Math, 73-75; FAC MEM DIV EARTH & PHYS SCI, COL SCI & MATH, UNIV TEX, SAN ANTONIO, 75- *Concurrent Pos:* Consult, US Army, 58 & Physics Div, Argonne Nat Lab, 66-73; prin investr, Mat Lab, Wright-Patterson AFB, Ohio, 64-71; prin investr, Robert A Welch Found res grant,

69-71 & 76-83; referee manuscripts, Phys Rev; occasional lectr. *Mem:* Fel AAAS; fel Am Phys Soc; Am Asn Physics Teachers; Am Chem Soc. *Res:* Educational and computational physics; popularization of science; astronomy and energy; laser-crystal efficiency; energy applications; laser-active ions of rare earths; materials science; atomic wave functions; statistical mechanics; molecular dynamics. *Mailing Add:* Div of Earth & Phys Sci Univ of Tex Col of Sci & Math San Antonio TX 78285

SYNER, FRANK N, b Springfield, Mass, Apr 25, 24; m 50; c 1. BIOCHEMISTRY. *Educ:* Univ Mass, BS, 51; Wayne State Univ, PhD(biochem), 60. *Prof Exp:* Biochemist, Hawthorn Ctr, 60-62 & Lafayette Clin, 62-67; asst prof, 67-70, ASSOC PROF OBSTET & GYNEC, SCH MED, WAYNE STATE UNIV, 70- *Res:* Biochemical genetics and biochemistry of development; biochemistry of reproduction. *Mailing Add:* Dept of Obstet & Gynec Wayne State Univ Sch of Med Detroit MI 48202

SYNNOTT, STEPHEN PATRICK, b Passaic, NJ, Apr 29, 46. ORBITAL MECHANICS, OPTICAL DATA ANAYSIS. *Educ:* Rensselaer Polytech Inst, BS, 68; Mass Inst Technol, MS, 70, PhD(astrodynamics), 74. *Prof Exp:* MEM TECH STAFF, JET PROPULSION LAB, CALIF INST TECHNOL, 75- *Res:* Detailed analysis of spacecraft optical and radio tracking data to determine the physical and orbital properties of the satellites of the outer planets. *Mailing Add:* Jet Propulsion Lab 4800 Oak Grove Dr Pasadena CA 91109

SYNOVITZ, ROBERT J, b Milwaukee, Wis, Feb 3, 31; wid; c 4. HEALTH SCIENCE. *Educ:* Wis State Univ, La Crosse, BS, 53; Ind Univ, Bloomington, MS, 56, HSD, 59. *Prof Exp:* Instr pub schs, Mo, 56-58; asst prof health sci, Eastern Ky Univ, 59-62; assoc prof physiol & health sci, Ball State Univ, 62-68; PROF HEALTH SCI & CHMN DEPT, WESTERN ILL UNIV, 68- *Concurrent Pos:* Teaching & res grant, Ball State Univ, 66-67. *Mem:* Am Sch Health Asn (nat pres, 81-82); Soc Pub Health Educ. *Mailing Add:* Dept of Health Sci Western Ill Univ Macomb IL 61455

SYNOWIEC, JOHN A, b Chicago, Ill, Sept 18, 37; m 67; c 2. MATHEMATICAL ANALYSIS. *Educ:* DePaul Univ, BS, 59, MS, 61, DMS, 62; Ill Inst Technol, PhD(math), 64. *Prof Exp:* Instr math, DePaul Univ, 61-62; from instr to asst prof, Ill Inst Technol, 63-67; asst prof math, Ind Univ Northwest, 67-74, assoc prof, 74-80. *Mem:* Am Math Soc; Math Asn Am. *Res:* Complex analysis; generalized functions; differential geometry. *Mailing Add:* 18848 Sherman St Lansing IL 60438

SYPERT, GEORGE WALTER, b Marlin, Tex, Sept 25, 41; m 71; c 1. NEUROSURGERY, NEUROPHYSIOLOGY. *Educ:* Univ Wash, BA, 63, MD, 67. *Prof Exp:* Resident neurosurg, Univ Wash, 68-73, instr, 73-74; asst prof & assoc prof, 74-78, PROF NEUROSURG & NEUROSCI, UNIV FLA, 78- *Concurrent Pos:* Asst chief neurosurg, Fitsimons Gen Hosp, US Army, 68-70; attend physician, Shands Teaching Hosp & Chief Neurosurg, Gainesville Vet Admin Hosp, 74- *Mem:* Soc Neurosci; Cong Neurol Surgeons; Am Asn Neurol Surgeons; AAAS; Am Physiol Soc. *Res:* Neurophysiological and ionic mechanisms involved in synaptic transmission; segmental motor control; synaptic plasticity; neuronal repetitive firing mechanisms; pathophysiology of epilepsy. *Mailing Add:* Neurol Surg JHMHC Box 265 Univ of Fla Gainesville FL 32610

SYPHERD, PAUL STARR, b Akron, Ohio, Nov 16, 36; m 54; c 4. MICROBIOLOGY, MOLECULAR BIOLOGY. *Educ:* Ariz State Univ, BS, 59; Univ Ariz, MS, 60; Yale Univ, PhD(microbiol), 63. *Prof Exp:* NIH res fel biol, Univ Calif, San Diego, 62-64; from asst prof to assoc prof microbiol, Univ Ill, Urbana, 64-70; assoc prof, 70-72, PROF MICROBIOL, COL MED, UNIV CALIF, IRVINE, 72-, CHMN MICROBIOL, 74- *Concurrent Pos:* USPHS fel, Univ Calif, San Diego, 62-64; mem microbiol chem study sect, NIH, 75-81. *Mem:* Am Soc Microbiologists; Am Soc Biol Chemists. *Res:* Structure and synthesis of ribosomes; regulation of nucleic acid synthesis; molecular basis of morphogenesis; molecular mechanisms of the regulation of gene expression, with an emphasis on post-transcriptional regulation; post-translational modification of proteins in microorganisms. *Mailing Add:* Dept of Microbiol Univ of Calif Col of Med Irvine CA 92664

SYRETT, BARRY CHRISTOPHER, b Stockton on Tees, Eng, Dec 16, 43; m 66; c 1. CORROSION. *Educ:* Univ Newcastle, BSc, 64, PhD(metall), 67. *Prof Exp:* Res scientist corrosion, Dept Energy, Mines & Resources, Govt Can, 67-70 & Int Nickel Co, Inc, 70-72; METALLURGIST CORROSION, SRI INT, 72- *Mem:* Nat Asn Corrosion Engrs; Inst Corrosion Sci & Technol; assoc Inst Metallurgists. *Res:* Corrosion research, including pitting, crevice corrosion, stress corrosion, erosion-corrosion, fretting corrosion, corrosion fatigue, hydrogen embrittlement, corrosion resistant coatings, failure analysis, alloy development and liquid metal embrittlement. *Mailing Add:* SRI Int 333 Ravenswood Ave Menlo Park CA 94025

SYSKI, RYSZARD, b Plock, Poland, Apr 8, 24; m 50; c 6. MATHEMATICS. *Educ:* Polish Univ Col, London, Dipl Ing, 50; Imp Col, Dipl, 51, BSc, 54, PhD(math), 60. *Prof Exp:* Sci officer, ATE Co, Eng, 51-52, sr sci officer, Hivac Ltd, 52-60; res assoc mgt sci & lectr math, 61-62, assoc prof, 62-66, chmn probability & statist div, 66-70, PROF MATH, UNIV MD, COLLEGE PARK, 66- *Concurrent Pos:* Chmn bibliog comt, Int Teletraffic Cong, 55-61, mem organizing comt, 67. *Mem:* Am Math Soc; fel Royal Statist Soc. *Res:* Congestion, queueing and probability theories; stochastic processes. *Mailing Add:* Dept of Math Univ of Md College Park MD 20742

SYTY, AUGUSTA, b Harbin, China. CHEMISTRY. *Educ:* Univ Tenn, Knoxville, BS, 64, PhD(anal chem), 68. *Prof Exp:* PROF ANAL CHEM, INDIANA UNIV PA, 68- *Mem:* Am Chem Soc. *Res:* Flame emission; atomic absorption; methods of analysis; molecular absorption spectrometry in the gas phase. *Mailing Add:* Dept of Chem Indiana Univ of Pa Indiana PA 15705

SYVERSON, ALDRICH, b Glenwood, Minn, Mar 25, 14; m 42; c 2. CHEMICAL ENGINEERING. *Educ:* Univ Minn, BChE, 38, PhD(chem eng), 42. *Prof Exp:* Asst, Univ Minn, 38-41; chem engr, B F Goodrich Co, 42-44, mgr chem develop, B F Goodrich Chem Co, 44-46, plant mgr, Avon Lake Exp Sta, 46-48; assoc prof chem eng, Syracuse Univ, 48-50; from assoc prof to prof, 50-77, chmn dept, 68-76, EMER PROF CHEM ENG, OHIO STATE UNIV, 77- *Concurrent Pos:* Consult, B F Goodrich Co, A E Staley Co, O M Scott Co & Anchor Hocking Corp, 73-78. *Mem:* Am Chem Soc; Am Soc Eng Educ; fel Am Inst Chem Engrs. *Res:* Chemical engineering reaction kinetics; electrochemical engineering; adsorption; chemical process design. *Mailing Add:* 222 St Antoine Worthington OH 43085

SYVERTSON, CLARENCE A, b Minneapolis, Minn, Jan 12, 26; wid; c 1. RESEARCH ADMINISTRATION, TECHNICAL MANAGEMENT. *Educ:* Univ Minn, BS, 46, MS, 48. *Prof Exp:* Asst chief supersonic wind tunnel br, Ames Aeronaut Lab, Nat Adv Comt Aeronaut, 51-59, chief hypersonic wind tunnel br, 59-63, chief mission anal div, 63-65, acting asst dir res & develop anal & planning, 64-65, dir mission anal div, 65-66 & Technol, 65-66, dir astronaut, 66-69, dep dir, 69-78, DIR, AMES RES CTR, NASA, 78- *Concurrent Pos:* Exec dir civil aviation res & develop policy study, Dept of Transp, NASA, 70-71; adv bd, Col Eng, Univ Calif, Berkeley; eng adv coun, San Jose State Univ; adv coun, Dept Aerospace Eng & Mech, Univ Minn. *Honors & Awards:* Lawrence Sperry Award, Inst Aeronaut Sci, 57; NASA Inventions & Contrib Award, 64, Exceptional Serv Medal, NASA, 71. *Mem:* Nat Acad Eng; fel Am Inst Aeronaut & Astronaut; Am Astronaut Soc; Am Helicopter Soc. *Res:* Civil aviation; mission analysis; entry vehicle research. *Mailing Add:* 15725 Apollo Heights Ct Saratoga CA 95070

SZABLYA, JOHN F(RANCIS), b Budapest, Hungary, June 25, 24; US citizen; m 51; c 7. ELECTRICAL ENGINEERING. *Educ:* Tech Univ Budapest, Dipls, 47-48, DEcon, 48. *Prof Exp:* Mem fac, Tech Univ Budapest, 49-56 & Univ BC, 57-63; PROF ELEC ENG, WASH STATE UNIV, 63- *Concurrent Pos:* Engr, Ganz Elec Works, 47-56; consult, Hungarian Elec Res Labs, 52-56. *Honors & Awards:* Zipernowszky Medal, Hungary, 54. *Mem:* Fel Inst Elec & Electronics Engrs; fel Inst Elec Engrs; Tensor Soc; Austrian Inst Elec Engrs. *Res:* Electromechanical energy conversion; electric power transmission; high power, high voltage research; fundamental electromagnetism; energy research. *Mailing Add:* Dept of Elec Eng Wash State Univ Pullman WA 99164

SZABO, A(UGUST) J(OHN), b Baton Rouge, La, Sept 27, 21; m 45; c 3. CIVIL ENGINEERING, SANITARY & ENVIRONMENTAL ENGINEERING. *Educ:* La State Univ, BS, 43; Harvard Univ, MS, 50. *Prof Exp:* Pub health engr, State Bd Health, La, 46-55; assoc prof civil eng, Univ Southwestern La, 55-63; prin engr, 63-64, SECY & TREAS, DOMINGUE, SZABO & ASSOCS, INC, 64- *Concurrent Pos:* Mem, Consult Eng Coun. *Honors & Awards:* Arthur Sidney Bedell Award, Water Pollution Control Fedn, 58. *Mem:* Water Pollution Control Fedn; Am Soc Civil Engrs; Am Water Works Asn; Nat Soc Prof Engrs; Am Soc Eng Educ. *Mailing Add:* Domingue, Szabo & Assocs Inc Consult Engrs PO Box 52115 Lafayette LA 70505

SZABO, ALEXANDER, b Copper Cliff, Ont, Mar 13, 31; m 57; c 4. SOLID STATE PHYSICS. *Educ:* Queen's Univ, BS, 53; McGill Univ, MS, 55; Tohoku Univ, Japan, DEng(physics), 70. *Prof Exp:* Res officer electron beams, 55-59, res officer microwave masers, 59-61, RES OFFICER LASERS & SOLID STATE PHYSICS, NAT RES COUN CAN, 61- *Res:* Study of coherence lifetimes and optical line widths of impurity ions in solids using fluorescence line narrowing and photon echo techniques. *Mailing Add:* Nat Res Coun Bldg M-50 Ottawa ON K1A 0R8 Can

SZABO, ARLENE SLOGOFF, b Philadelphia, Pa, Feb 19, 45; m 65; c 2. CELL BIOLOGY. *Educ:* Douglass Col, AB, 66, Rutgers Univ, MS, 68, PhD(cell biol), 71. *Prof Exp:* Res fel enzymol, Med Sch, Univ Southern Calif, 71-72; res asst plant physiol, Univ Calif, Los Angeles, 72-74; ASST PROF BIOL, LOYOLA MARYMOUNT UNIV, 74- *Mem:* Am Soc Cell Biol; AAAS; Asn Women in Sci; Sigma Xi. *Res:* Development and regulation of the peroxisome in yeast, as Saccharomyces cerevisiae. *Mailing Add:* Dept Biol Loyola Marymount Univ Los Angeles CA 90045

SZABO, ARTHUR GUSTAV, b Toronto, Ont, Nov 19, 39; m 62; c 3. FLUORESCENCE, SPECTROSCOPY. *Educ:* Queen's Univ, Ont, BSc, 61; Univ Toronto, MA, 63, PhD(chem), 65. *Prof Exp:* Nat Res Coun Can fel chem, Southampton, 65-67; RES OFFICER, BIOL DIV, NAT RES COUN CAN, 67- *Mem:* Chem Inst Can. *Res:* Protein-membrane studies; molecular dynamics of proteins using fluorescence anisotropy decay technique; biomolecule interactions using spectroscopic techniques; laser excitation and time correlated fluorescence spectroscopy of biomolecules. *Mailing Add:* Div of Biol Sci Nat Res Coun Can 100 Sussex Dr Ottawa ON K1A 0R6 Can

SZABO, ATTILA, b Budapest, Hungary, Sept 6, 47; Can citizen; m 75. THEORETICAL BIOPHYSICAL CHEMISTRY. *Educ:* McGill Univ, BSc, 68; Harvard Univ, PhD(chem physics), 73. *Prof Exp:* Fel, Inst Physicochem Biol, Paris, 72-73; fel, Med Res Coun Lab Molecular Biol, Cambridge, Eng, 73-74; asst prof chem, Ind Univ, Bloomington, 74-78, assoc prof, 78-80; RES SCIENTIST, LAB CHEM PHYS, NIH, 80- *Concurrent Pos:* Alfred P Sloan fel. *Mem:* Biophys Soc. *Res:* Nuclear magnetic relaxation and fluorescence depolarization and internal motions in biopolymers; structure-function relations in allosteric systems. *Mailing Add:* Lab Chem Phys Bldg 2 Rm B1-28 NIH Bethesda MD 20205

SZABO, BARNA ALADAR, b Martonvasar, Hungary, Sept 21, 35; US citizen; m 60; c 2. CIVIL ENGINEERING. *Educ:* Univ Toronto, BASc, 60; State Univ NY, Buffalo, MS, 66, PhD(civil eng), 69. *Prof Exp:* Mining engr, Int Nickel Co Can Ltd, 60-62; civil engr, H G Acres Ltd Consult Engrs, 62-66; instr eng & appl sci, State Univ NY, Buffalo, 66-68; from assoc prof to prof, 68-75, GREENSFELDER PROF CIVIL ENG, WASH UNIV, 75-, DIR, CTR COMPUT MECH, 77- *Concurrent Pos:* Consult, Asn Am Railroads,

74-77; dir, Washington Univ Technol Assocs, 78- *Mem:* Am Acad Mech; Am Soc Civil Engrs; Soc Eng Sci; Soc Automotive Engrs. *Res:* Numerical approximation techniques in continuum mechanics; development of adaptive techniques in finite element approximations; numerical fracture mechanics. *Mailing Add:* Ctr Comput Mech Wash Univ Box 1130 St Louis MO 63130

SZABO, BARNEY JULIUS, b Debrecen, Hungary, Apr 11, 29; US citizen; m 56. GEOCHEMISTRY. *Educ:* Univ Miami, BS, 61, MS, 66. *Prof Exp:* Res chemist, Inst Marine Sci, Univ Miami, 57-66; RES CHEMIST, BR ISOTOPE GEOL, US GEOL SURV, 66- *Res:* Stable and radioactive trace elements analyses; uranium disequilibria dating; radio and isotopic chemistry of uranium, thorium, protactinium and artificial radioactive nuclides. *Mailing Add:* US Geol Surv Br Isotope Geol Denver Fed Ctr Denver CO 80225

SZABO, C KAROLY, b Mocs, Hungary, May 27, 23; US citizen; m 59; c 1. ORGANIC CHEMISTRY. *Educ:* Budapest Tech Univ, MS, 45, PhD(org chem), 56. *Prof Exp:* Res chemist, Arzola Ltd, Hungary, 46-47, res group leader, 48-49; res assoc, Chinoin Corp, 49-50; res scientist, Nat Inst Plant Protection, 50-52, head dept org chem, 52-56; sr res chemist, Stauffer Chem Co, 57-62, sr res assoc, 62-65; mgr org chem sect, Syracuse Univ Res Corp, 66-71; first officer indust develop, 70-75, SR OFFICER, UN INDUST DEVELOP ORGN, 75- *Concurrent Pos:* Mem nat comt plant protection, Nat Acad Sci, Hungary, 53-56; NIH grant, 67-69; indust consult. *Mem:* Am Chem Soc. *Res:* Research and development of agricultural chemicals, particularly chemistry of phosphorus insecticides, carbamate insecticides and herbicides, systemic fungicides and organic sulfur compounds. *Mailing Add:* UN Indust Develop Orgn Lerchenfelder Strasse 1 Vienna Austria

SZABO, GABOR, b Mar 20, 41; Can citizen. PHYSIOLOGY, BIOPHYSICS. *Educ:* Univ Montreal, BS, 64, MS, 66; Univ Chicago, PhD(physiol), 69. *Prof Exp:* Asst prof physiol, Med Ctr, Univ Calif, Los Angeles, 71-75; ASSOC PROF PHYSIOL, UNIV TEX MED BR GALVESTON, 75- *Mem:* AAAS; Biophys Soc. *Res:* Permeability in model and cell membranes. *Mailing Add:* Dept Physiol & Biophys Univ Tex Med Br Galveston TX 77550

SZABO, KALMAN TIBOR, b Abda, Hungary, July 29, 21; US citizen; m 44; c 2. TERATOLOGY. *Educ:* Univ Budapest, BSc, 47; Rutgers Univ, MS, 62; Univ Vienna, MSc, 71, DSc(teratology), 73. *Prof Exp:* Res scientist genetics, Res Inst, Acad Sci, Fertod, Hungary, 53-56; res assoc reproductive physiol, Rutgers Univ, 60-62; toxicologist, 62-66, sr scientist & unit head teratology, 67-69, sr investr & group leader reproductive toxicol & teratology, 69-70, asst dir toxicol, 71-72, assoc dir, 72-81, DIR TOXICOL, SMITH KLINE & FRENCH LABS, 81- *Concurrent Pos:* Adv & partic, Adv Comt Protocols on Reproductive Studies, Safety Eval Food Additives & Pesticide Residues, Food & Drug Admin, 67; res assoc prof pediat, Med Col, Thomas Jefferson Univ, 75- *Mem:* Teratology Soc; Behav Teratology Soc; Soc Toxicol; Soc Study Reproduction; Am Genetic Asn. *Res:* Spontaneous and induced anomalies of the central nervous system; role of maternal nutritional deprivation in embryogenesis; evaluation of various factors affecting teratogenic response; drug toxicology. *Mailing Add:* 215 Morris Rd Ambler PA 19022

SZABO, MIKLOS TAMAS, b Helsinki, Finland, Aug 28, 37; nat US; m 62; c 1. PETROLEUM ENGINEERING, PHYSICAL CHEMISTRY. *Educ:* Tech Univ Heavy Indust, Hungary, BS & MS, 60, PhD(petrol eng), 68. *Prof Exp:* Res assoc, Petrol Res Lab, Hungarian Acad Sci, Miskolc, 60-69 & Calgon Corp, Pittsburgh, 70-74; SR RES ENGR, GULF RES & DEVELOP CO, 74- *Mem:* Am Chem Soc; Soc Petrol Engrs; Am Inst Mining, Metall & Petrol Engrs. *Res:* Petroleum reservoir engineering; flow in porous media; polymer flooding; new oil recovery processes; colloid chemistry; rheology of polymer solutions. *Mailing Add:* 301 Thornberry Court Dr Pittsburgh PA 15237

SZABO, PIROSKA LUDWIG, b Bratislava, Czechoslovakia, Dec 14, 40; US citizen; m 63; c 3. HISTOLOGY, GROSS ANATOMY. *Educ:* Oberlin Col, BA, 62; Univ Fla, MS, 64, PhD(med sci), 67. *Prof Exp:* Fel gross anat, Col Physicians & Surgeons, Columbia Univ, 67-68; asst prof gross anat & histol, Med Col Va, 68-70, Albert Einstein Col Med, 70-73; instr biol & embryol, Lehman Col, 73-77; PROF & CHMN ANAT, NY COL OSTEOP MED, 77- *Concurrent Pos:* Consult, Osteop Nat Bd, 79- *Mem:* AAAS. *Mailing Add:* Dept Anat NY Col Osteop Med Wheatley Rd Old Westbury NY 11568

SZABO, SANDOR, b Ada, Yugoslavia, Feb 9, 44; m 72; c 2. PATHOLOGY, BIOCHEMICAL PHARMACOLOGY. *Educ:* Univ Belgrade, MD, 68; Univ Montreal, MSc, 71, PhD(exp med, pharmacol), 73. *Prof Exp:* Vis scientist exp med & pharmacol, Inst Exp Med Surg, Univ Montreal, 69-70, res asst, 70-73; resident path, Peter Bent Brigham Hosp, 73-77, res fel, Med Sch, 75-77, res assoc path, Peter Bent Brigham Hosp; asst prof, 77-81, ASSOC PROF PATH, BRIGHAM & WOMEN'S HOSP, HARVARD MED SCH, 81- *Concurrent Pos:* Chief ed, Sci J Medicinski Podmladak, 67-68; consult to health dir, CZ, Panama, 71; Nat Inst Environ Health Sci grant, 78-; NIH res career develop award, 80-85. *Honors & Awards:* Physicians' Recognition Award, AMA, 76. *Mem:* Soc Exp Biol & Med; Am Soc Pharmacol & Exp Therapeut; Am Asn Pathologists; Endocrine Soc; Pharmacol Soc Can. *Res:* Experimental pathology and biochemical pharmacology of the gastro-intestinal tract and endocrine glands; development of disease models; duodenal ulcer produced by propionitrile, cysteamine; adrenal and thyroid necrosis caused by acrylonitrile pyrazole. *Mailing Add:* Brigham & Women's Hosp 75 Francis St Boston MA 02115

SZABO, STEVE STANLEY, b Westons Mills, NJ, Feb 10, 27; m 55; c 2. AGRONOMY. *Educ:* Rutgers Univ, BS, 52; Kans State Col, MS, 54; Univ Wis, PhD(agron), 58. *Prof Exp:* Asst prof agron, NMex State Univ, 57-61; plant physiologist, US Food & Drug Admin, 61-63 & Army Biol Labs, Ft Detrick, Md, 63-65; plant physiologist, Boyce Thompson Inst Plant Res, 65-76; PRES, LAWN GENIC CORP, 76- *Mem:* Am Soc Plant Physiologists; Weed Sci Soc Am. *Res:* Chemical weed control; plant physiology. *Mailing Add:* 20 Milrose Lane Monsey NY 10952

SZABO, TIBOR IMRE, b Tiborszallas, Hungary, July 11, 34; Can citizen; m 66; c 6. BEHAVIORAL BIOLOGY. *Educ:* Univ Hort, Budapest, BAE, 58; Univ Guelph, MSc, 69, PhD(apicult), 73. *Prof Exp:* Fel apicult, Univ Guelph, 73-74; RES SCIENTIST APICULT, AGR CAN, 74- *Mem:* Int Bee Res Asn; Sigma Xi. *Res:* Honey bee behavior, biology, physiology and breeding. *Mailing Add:* Agr Can PO Box 29 Beaverlodge AB T0H 0C0 Can

SZABUNIEWICZ, MICHAEL, b Poland, Oct 11, 09. VETERINARY MEDICINE. *Educ:* Acad Vet Med, DVM, 34, DVSc(physiol), 37. *Prof Exp:* Dir, Exp Farm Kasese, Belgian Congo, 46-50; dir, Regional Diag Vet Lab & Exten Serv, 50-60; area vet, Agr Res Serv, USDA, 61-62; from asst prof to assoc prof vet physiol, 62-71, PROF VET PHYSIOL, TEX A&M UNIV, 71- *Mem:* AAAS; Am Vet Med Asn; Am Soc Vet Physiol & Pharmacol; Am Asn Lab Animal Sci. *Res:* Physiology; pharmacology; radiation research. *Mailing Add:* Dept Vet Physiol & Pharm Tex A&M Univ College Station TX 77843

SZAKAL, ANDRAS KALMAN, b Szekesfehervar, Hungary, Sept 26, 36; US citizen; m 61; c 2. IMMUNOBIOLOGY, CANCER. *Educ:* Univ Colo, Boulder, BA, 61, MS, 63; Univ Tenn, PhD(immunobiol), 72. *Prof Exp:* Res asst histochem, Univ Colo, Boulder, 60-61; res assoc electron micros, Univ Mich, Ann Arbor, 65-66; staff biologist, Oak Ridge Nat Lab, 66-69, consult electron microscopist, 69-70, Oak Ridge Assoc Univs fel, 70-72, res biologist, Div Biol, 72-74; PRIN SCIENTIST LUNG IMMUNOBIOL, LIFE SCI DIV, MELOY LABS, INC, 74- *Mem:* AAAS. *Res:* Lung immunobiology, especially identification and isolation of lung cell types through cell-type specific antigens. *Mailing Add:* Meloy Labs Inc 6715 Electronic Dr Springfield VA 22151

SZALAY, JEANNE, b Jan 17, 38; US citizen; c 2. CELL BIOLOGY. *Educ:* Wash Sq Col Arts & Sci, BA, 59; Columbia Univ, PhD(biol), 66. *Prof Exp:* Fel cell biol & cytol, Col Physicians & Surgeons, Columbia Univ, 66-67; fel, Albert Einstein Col Med, 67-69, res asst cell biol & cytol, 69-70, instr, Dept Anat, 70-72; asst prof 72-77, ASSOC PROF BIOL, QUEENS COL, NY, 77- *Mem:* Asn Res Vision & Ophthalmol. *Res:* The fine-structure and function of blood vessels, with emphasis on the examination of cellular mechanisms involved in the regulation of vascular permeability and vascular smooth muscle activity. *Mailing Add:* Dept of Biol Queens Col Kissena Blvd Flushing NY 11367

SZALDA, DAVID JOSEPH, b Buffalo, NY, May 25, 50; m 74; c 1. BIOINORGANIC CHEMISTRY. *Educ:* Manhattan Col, BS, 72; Johns Hopkins Univ, MA, 74, PhD(inorg chem), 76. *Prof Exp:* Fel bioinorg chem, Columbia Univ, 76-78; ASSOC PROF CHEM, BARUCH COL, 78- *Concurrent Pos:* Res collabr, Brookhaven Nat Lab, 81-82. *Mem:* NY Acad Sci; Sigma Xi; Am Chem Soc. *Res:* Metal nucleic acid interactions; structural chemistry: x-ray crystallography. *Mailing Add:* Dept Natural Sci Baruch Col Box 502 17 Lexington Ave New York NY 10010

SZAMOSI, GEZA, b Budapest, Hungary, Dec 31, 22; Can citizen; m 44; c 2. THEORETICAL PHYSICS. *Educ:* Univ Budapest, PhD(physics), 47; Hungary Acad Sci, DSc, 56. *Prof Exp:* Assoc prof, Eotvos Univ, Budapest, 47-55, prof, 55-56; prof, Israel Inst Technol, Israel, 57-61; consult, Nat Lab Frascati, Italy, 61-64; PROF THEORET PHYSICS, UNIV WINDSOR, ONT, 64- *Concurrent Pos:* Nuffield fel, 69-70; A Alberman vis prof, Israel Inst Technol, 70-71; Can-France fel, Inst Henri Poincare, Paris, 74 & 80-81; Can-Japan fel, Dept Physics, Nagoya Univ, Japan, 81. *Mem:* Can Asn Physicists. *Res:* Special theory of relativity and its application to classical and quantum mechanics, statistical mechanics, plasma physics, astrophysics and to classical theories of elementary particles; author or coauthor of over 50 publications. *Mailing Add:* Dept Physics Univ Windsor Windsor ON N9B 3P4 Can

SZANISZLO, PAUL JOSEPH, b Medina, Ohio, June 9, 39; m 60; c 2. MICROBIOLOGY, MYCOLOGY. *Educ:* Ohio Wesleyan Univ, BA, 61; Univ NC, MA, 64, PhD(bot), 67. *Prof Exp:* USPHS fel, Harvard Univ, 67-68; asst prof, 68-73, assoc prof, 73-80, PROF MICROBIOL, UNIV TEX, AUSTIN, 80-, CHMN, DIV BIOL SCI, 76- *Mem:* AAAS; Am Soc Microbiol; Int Soc Human & Animal Mycology; Mycol Soc Am. *Res:* Growth, development and differentiation in fungi with emphasis on cell wall chemistry and cell ultrastructure; production by fungi, particularly mycorrhizal fungi, of iron-chelating transport molecules. *Mailing Add:* Dept Microbiol Exp Sci Bldg Univ Tex Austin TX 78712

SZANTO, JOSEPH, b Marcali, Hungary, Nov 4, 31; m 57; c 4. VETERINARY PARASITOLOGY. *Educ:* Col Vet Med, Budapest, Dr Vet, 55; Univ Ill, DVM, 61. *Prof Exp:* Vet practice, Hungary, 55-56; res asst vet parasitol, Col Vet Med, Univ Ill, 58-61; asst prof vet path, Univ Ky, 61-62; asst parasitologist, Chemagro Corp, Mo, 62-63; sr res parasitologist, Ciba Pharmaceut Co, 63-69; sr res parasitologist, 69-74, DIR VET CLIN RES & DEVELOP, E R SQUIBB & SONS, INC, 74- *Mem:* Am Vet Med Asn; Am Asn Vet Parasitol; Am Soc Parasitol; World Asn Adv Vet Parasitol. *Res:* Veterinary clinical research and drug development. *Mailing Add:* E R Squibb & Sons Inc Three Bridges NJ 08887

SZAP, PETER CHARLES, b New York, NY, Aug 20, 29; m 57; c 3. ANALYTICAL CHEMISTRY. *Educ:* Queens Col, NY, BS, 51; Fordham Univ, MS, 53. *Prof Exp:* Res chemist, Lever Bros Res & Develop Co, NJ, 53-59; anal res chemist, Toms River Chem Corp, 59-67; sect leader anal qual control, Ciba-Geigy Corp, 67-77; MGR ANAL SERVS, TOMS RIVER CHEM CORP, 77- *Concurrent Pos:* Chem Abstractor, 51-81. *Mem:* Am Chem Soc; Sigma Xi; Soc Appl Spectros. *Res:* Analytical methods development in detergents, dyestuffs, resins and raw materials; analysis and applications of optical brighteners, especially infrared, ultraviolet and visible absorption spectroscopy; chromatography; liquid chromatography techniques. *Mailing Add:* 333 Killarney Dr Toms River NJ 08753

SZARA, STEPHEN ISTVAN, b Pestujhely, Hungary, Mar 21, 23; nat US; m 59; c 1. PSYCHOPHARMACOLOGY. *Educ:* Pazmany Peter Univ, Hungary, DSc(chem), 50; Med Univ Budapest, MD, 51. *Prof Exp:* Sci asst, Microbiol Inst, Univ Budapest, 49-50, asst prof, Biochem Inst, 50-53, chief, Biochem Lab, State Ment Inst, 53-56; vis scientist, Psychiat Clin Berlin, 57; vis scientist, Nat Inst Ment Health, 57-60, chief sect psychopharmacol, Lab Clin Psychopharmacol, Spec Ment Health Res, 60-71, chief clin studies sect, Ctr Studies Narcotic & Drug Abuse, Nat Inst Mental Health, 71-74; CHIEF BIOMED RES BR, DIV RES, NAT INST DRUG ABUSE, 75- *Concurrent Pos:* Assoc clin prof, George Washington Univ. *Mem:* AAAS; Int Col Neuropsychopharmacol; fel Am Col Neuropsychopharmacol; Am Soc Pharmacol & Exp Therapeut. *Res:* Metabolism of psychotropic drugs, especially tryptamine derivatives; correlation between metabolism and psychotropic activity of drugs. *Mailing Add:* Biomed Br Div Res Nat Inst Drug Abuse Rockville MD 20852

SZAREK, STANLEY RICHARD, b Visalia, Calif, Nov 14, 47; m 77. PHYSIOLOGICAL ECOLOGY. *Educ:* Calif State Univ, Pomona, BS, 69; Univ Calif, Riverside, PhD(biol), 74. *Prof Exp:* asst prof, 74-80, ASSOC PROF BOT, ARIZ STATE UNIV, 80- *Concurrent Pos:* Consult, US Biol Prog Desert Biomed, 75-77. *Mem:* Am Soc Plant Physiologists; Ecol Soc Am. *Res:* Physiological ecology of desert plants, emphasizing photosynthetic carbon metabolism and high temperature stress physiology. *Mailing Add:* Dept of Bot & Microbiol Ariz State Univ Tempe AZ 85287

SZAREK, WALTER ANTHONY, b St Catharines, Ont, Apr 19, 38. ORGANIC CHEMISTRY, CARBOHYDRATE CHEMISTRY. *Educ:* McMaster Univ, BSc, 60, MSc, 62; Queen's Univ, Ont, PhD(org chem), 64. *Prof Exp:* Res fel chem, Ohio State Univ, 64-65; asst prof biochem, Rutgers Univ, 65-67; asst prof org chem, 67-71, assoc prof, 71-76, PROF ORG CHEM, QUEEN'S UNIV, ONT, 76-, DIR CARBOHYDRATE RES INST, 76- *Mem:* Am Chem Soc; Chem Inst Can; The Chem Soc; NY Acad Sci; Soc Nuclear Med. *Res:* Structure and synthesis of carbohydrates and carbohydrate-containing antibiotics; biochemical aspects; synthesis and chemical modification of nucleosides; conformational and mechanistic studies of carbohydrate reactions; photochemistry of carbohydrates; heterocyclic conformational analysis; chemistry and novel applications of vitamin C; sweeteners; cellulose chemistry; positron emission tomography. *Mailing Add:* Dept Chem Queen's Univ Kingston ON K7L 3N6 Can

SZARKA, LASZLO JOSEPH, b Szekesfehervar, Hungary, Sept 6, 35; US citizen; m 63; c 2. BIOENGINEERING. *Educ:* Univ Sci, Budapest, Hungary, MS, 61, PhD(phys chem), 67. *Prof Exp:* Asst res investr phys chem, Chinoin Pharmaceut Plant, Hungary, 61-63; sect head bioeng, Res Inst Pharmaceut Chem, Hungary, 64-72; head chemist, Pharmaceut Ctr, Hungary, 72-73; res & develop biochem, Blackman Labs Inc, 74; SECT HEAD, E R SQUIBB & SONS, 74- *Mem:* Am Chem Soc; Am Inst Chem Eng. *Res:* Antibioticum and enzyme fermentation technology; batch, fed batch and continuous cultivation; transport phenomena, process control and reactor designing; optimization and scale-up problems; molecule biotransformations, steroids and hydrocarbons. *Mailing Add:* Squibb Inst for Med Res Georges Rd New Brunswick NJ 08903

SZASZ, THOMAS STEPHEN, b Budapest, Hungary, Apr 15, 20; US citizen; div; c 2. PSYCHIATRY. *Educ:* Univ Cincinnati, AB, 41, MD, 44; Am Bd Psychiat & Neurol, dipl psychiat, 51. *Hon Degrees:* DSc, Allegheny Col, 75, Univ Francisco Marroquin, Guatemala, 79. *Prof Exp:* Intern med, Boston City Hosp, 44-45; resident psychiat, Clinics, Univ Chicago, 46-48; mem staff, Chicago Inst Psychoanal, 51-56; PROF PSYCHIAT, STATE UNIV NY UPSTATE MED CTR, 56- *Concurrent Pos:* Vis prof psychiat, Sch Med, Marquette Univ, 68; consult, Comt Ment Hyg, NY State Bar Asn, Judicial Conf Comt, Judicial Conf DC Circuit, Comt Laws Pertaining Ment Disorders & Res Adv Panel, Inst Study Drug Addiction; adv ed, J Forensic Psychol; mem bd consult, Psychoanal Rev, mem adv comt, Living Libraries, Inc. *Honors & Awards:* Holmes-Munsterberg Award Forensic Psychol, Int Acad Forensic Psychol, 69; Humanist of Year, Am Humanist Asn, 73; Am Inst Pub Serv Distinguished Serv Award, 74. *Mem:* Fel Royal Soc Health; fel Am Psychiat Asn; Am Psychoanal Asn. *Res:* Epistemology of the behavioral sciences; history of psychiatry; psychiatry and law. *Mailing Add:* Dept of Psychiat State Univ NY Upstate Med Ctr Syracuse NY 13210

SZCZARBA, ROBERT HENRY, b Dearborn, Mich, Nov 27, 32; m 55; c 2. TOPOLOGY. *Educ:* Univ Mich, BS, 55; Univ Chicago, MS, 56, PhD(math), 60. *Prof Exp:* Off Naval Res res assoc math, 60-61, from asst prof to assoc prof, 61-74, PROF MATH, YALE UNIV, 74- *Concurrent Pos:* NSF fel, Inst Advan Study, 64-65. *Mem:* Am Math Soc. *Res:* Algebraic and differential topology and geometry of differentiable manifolds. *Mailing Add:* Dept Math Yale Univ New Haven CT 06520

SZCZECH, GEORGE MARION, US citizen. VETERINARY PATHOLOGY, TERATOLOGY. *Educ:* Univ Minn, BS, 64, DVM, 66; Purdue Univ, PhD(vet path), 74; Am Bd Vet Toxicol, dipl; Am Col Vet Pathologists, dipl. *Prof Exp:* Resident vet med, Colo State Univ, 66-67; vet, Sea Girt Animal Hosp, 67-68; sr scientist toxicol, Res Ctr, Mead Johnson & Co, 68-70; res fel vet path, Purdue Univ, 70-74; res scientist path, Upjohn Co, 74-78; GROUP LEADER PATH, BURROUGHS WELLCOME CO, 78- *Mem:* Am Vet Med Asn; Soc Toxicology; Teratology Soc; Sigma Xi. *Res:* Toxicologic pathology; fetal pathology; clinical pathology and teratology. *Mailing Add:* 643 Rock Creek Road Chapel Hill NC 27514

SZCZEPANSKI, MAREK MICHAL, b Warsaw, Poland, June 8, 41; Can citizen; m 80. EXPERIMENTAL SURGERY, GASTROENTEROLOGY. *Educ:* Agr Univ Warsaw, DVM, 67; Univ Toronto, DVPH(pub health), 72. *Prof Exp:* Asst surg, Agr Univ Warsaw, 67-68; res asst, McGill Univ, 68-70; res fel, Univ Toronto, 70-72; assoc vet small animal pract, Lakeshore Vet Hosp, Toronto, 72-73; staff vet, Toronto Humane Soc, 73-75; asst prof physiol & dir animal care, Fac Med, Mem Univ Nfld, 75-80; ASST PROF PHYSIOL & DIR, LAB ANIMAL SCI, NORTHEASTERN OHIO UNIVS COL MED, ROOTSTOWN, 80- *Mem:* Can Vet Med Asn; Am Vet Med Asn. *Res:* Pathophysiology of the esophagus; achalasia; experimental esophagitis; esophageal replacement by a gastric tube; control mechanisms governing esophageal motor activity; anti-reflux mechanism in hiatus hernia; esophageal carcinogenicity of ingested plant derivatives. *Mailing Add:* Northeastern Ohio Univs Col Med 4209 State Rte 44 Rootstown OH 44272

SZCZEPANSKI, MARIAN, b Poland, Aug 13, 20; nat US; m 50; c 1. MECHANICAL ENGINEERING, METALLURGY. *Educ:* Univ Warsaw, Dipl Eng, 44; Univ London, MSc, 52 & 56; Battersea Col Technol, dipl, 56. *Prof Exp:* Metallurgist, CAV, Ltd, Eng, 52-53; chief metallurgist, E & E Kaye, Ltd, 53-57; dir res, Wheel Trueing Tool Co, 57-62; PRES & TECH DIR, INT DIAMOND TOOL CO, 62- *Concurrent Pos:* Res scientist, Res Inst Sci & Eng, Univ Detroit, 58; consult metall. *Mem:* Am Soc Metals; fel Brit Inst Metall; assoc Brit Inst Mech Engrs. *Res:* Powder metallurgy; x-ray diffraction of atomic structures, diamonds and diamond tools; heat treatment of steel; melting; casting; heat treatment and cold working of aluminum alloys and copper; strength of materials; stress analysis. *Mailing Add:* 46200 Frederick St Northville MI 48167

SZCZESNIAK, RAYMOND ALBIN, b Buffalo, NY, Nov 28, 40; m 63; c 4. MEDICINAL CHEMISTRY, NUCLEAR MEDICINE. *Educ:* Fordham Univ, BS, 63; Univ Mich, Ann Arbor, MS, 65, PhD(med chem), 68. *Prof Exp:* Sr res scientist, E R Squibb & Sons, Inc, New Brunswick, 68-69, res chemist, 69-72, sr res chemist radiopharmaceut, 72-73; radioimmunoassay specialist, Nuclear-Med Labs, Inc, 73-77; PRES, PROF CONSULTS, INC, 77- *Mem:* Soc Nuclear Med; Am Chem Soc. *Res:* Radioimmunoassay; radiomedicinal synthesis. *Mailing Add:* 4042 Mendenhall Dr Dallas TX 75234

SZE, HEVEN, b The Hague, Netherlands, Oct 22, 47; Chinese citizen; m 74. PLANT PHYSIOLOGY, BIOCHEMISTRY. *Educ:* Nat Taiwan Univ, BS, 68; Univ Calif, Davis, MS, 70; Purdue Univ, PhD(plant physiol), 75. *Prof Exp:* res fel biophys, Harvard Med Sch, 75-78; res assoc, 78-79, ASST PROF, UNIV KANS, 79- *Mem:* Am Soc Plant Physiologists; AAAS. *Res:* Membrane structure and function; mechanism of solute transport; biophysics. *Mailing Add:* Div Biol Sci Univ Kans Lawrence KS 66045

SZE, MORGAN CHUAN-YUAN, b Tientsin, China, May 27, 17; nat US; m 45; c 3. CHEMICAL ENGINEERING. *Educ:* Mass Inst Technol, SB, 39, ScD(chem eng), 41. *Prof Exp:* Chem engr, Universal Trading Corp, 41-42; process engr, Belle Works, E I du Pont de Nemours & Co, Inc, 42-44, Hydrocarbon Res, Inc, NY, 44-45 & Foster Wheeler Corp, 45-47; sr process engr, Hydrocarbon Res, Inc, 47-53, dir process eng dept, 53-59, tech dir, 59-61; exec staff engr, 61-64, mgr eng develop ctr, 64-71, V PRES RES & DEVELOP, LUMMUS CO, 71- *Mem:* Nat Acad Eng; AAAS; Am Inst Chem Engrs. *Res:* Nitrogen fixation; petroleum refining and processing; petrochemicals; cryogenics. *Mailing Add:* Lummus Co 1515 Broad St Bloomfield NJ 07003

SZE, PAUL YI LING, b Shanghai, China. BIOCHEMISTRY, NEUROBIOLOGY. *Educ:* Nat Taiwan Univ, BS, 60; Duquesne Univ, MS, 62; Univ Wis, MS, 64; Univ Chicago, PhD(biochem), 69. *Prof Exp:* From asst prof to assoc prof, 69-80, PROF BIOBEHAV SCI, UNIV CONN, 80- *Concurrent Pos:* Mem, Neurol A Study Sect, NIH. *Mem:* AAAS; Am Soc Neurochem; Soc Neurosci; Int Soc Neurochem. *Res:* Biochemistry of neurotransmitters; biochemical aspects of alcoholism; neurobiological effects of environmental stimulation. *Mailing Add:* Dept of Biobehav Sci Univ of Conn Storrs CT 06268

SZE, PHILIP, b Washington, DC, Dec 3, 45. PHYCOLOGY, AQUATIC BIOLOGY. *Educ:* Dickinson Col, BS, 68; Cornell Univ, PhD(phycol), 72. *Prof Exp:* Vis asst prof biol, State Univ NY, Buffalo, 72-73; asst prof phycol, Stockton State Col, 73-74; asst prof biol, State Univ NY, Buffalo, 74-77; ASST PROF BIOL, GEORGETOWN UNIV, 77- *Concurrent Pos:* Mem fac, Shoals Marine Lab, 74- *Mem:* Phycol Soc Am; Int Phycol Soc; Brit Phycol Soc. *Res:* Ecology of algae, inclcuding studies of phytoplankton in eutrophic lakes and rivers, inertidal macroalgal communities and filamentous algae in streams. *Mailing Add:* Dept Biol Georgetown Univ Washington DC 20057

SZE, ROBERT CHIA-TING, b Kowloon, China, Aug 27, 41; US citizen; m 70; c 1. LASERS, NON-LINEAR OPTICS. *Educ:* Cornell Univ, BEE, 64; Yale Univ, MS, 66, PhD(appl physics), 70. *Prof Exp:* Fel, Yale Univ, 70-71, State Univ NY Stony Brook, 71-73; res assoc, Yale Univ, 73-74; MEM STAFF, LOS ALAMOS NAT LAB, 74- *Concurrent Pos:* Consult, Tachisto, Inc, 80-81; consult & co-founder, Laser Tech, Inc, 81- *Mem:* Sr mem Inst Elec & Electronics Engrs; Am Phys Soc; Optical Soc Am; Sigma Xi. *Res:* Physics of lasers and the generation of coherent light sources; physics of noble gas ion lasers; high energy rare-gas halide excimer lasers; generation of coherent wavelengths via Raman stokes and anti-stokes scattering; development of compact high repetition rate excimer and carbon dioxide lasers. *Mailing Add:* 1042 Stagecoach Rd Santa Fe NM 87501

SZE, TSUNG WEI, b Shanghai, China, Sept 13, 22; nat US; m 52; c 3. ELECTRICAL ENGINEERING. *Educ:* Univ Mo, BS, 48; Purdue Univ, MS, 50; Northwestern Univ, PhD, 54. *Prof Exp:* Asst elec eng, Northwestern Univ, 50-52, instr, 52-54; from asst prof to assoc prof, 54-60, Fessenden prof, 57-62, Westinghouse prof, 62-65, assoc dean eng, 70-77, PROF ENG, UNIV PITTSBURGH, 60- *Concurrent Pos:* Consult, Univac Div, Sperry Rand Corp, 56-58, Westinghouse Elec Corp, 59-, MPC Corp, 69-74 & Mellon Inst, 78-; adj prof, Jiaotong Univ, People's Repub China, 79- *Mem:* Am Soc Eng Educ; Asn Comput Mach; Inst Elec & Electronics Engrs. *Res:* Logical design and switching theory; digital computer designs; digital image processing. *Mailing Add:* Sch Eng Univ Pittsburgh Pittsburgh PA 15261

SZE, YU-KEUNG, b Shanghai, China, Sept 3, 44; Can citizen; m 71; c 2. SOLUTION CHEMISTRY, PROCESS CHEMISTRY. *Educ:* Chinese Univ Hong Kong, BSc, 66; Univ Waterloo, MSc, 70, PhD(solution chem), 74. *Prof Exp:* Teacher chem, South Sea Col, Hong Kong, 66-68; asst phys chem, Univ

Waterloo, 68-73; fel solution chem, Environ Can, 73-75; res assoc, Univ Waterloo, 76-77; RES CHEMIST SOLUTION CHEM, ATOMIC ENERGY CAN LTD, 78- *Mem:* Chem Inst Can. *Res:* Process development and optimization in spent fuel reprocessing; determination of basic flowsheet parameters for recovery of the main heavy elements from thorium fuels; thermodynamics and kinetics of the separation and recovery process. *Mailing Add:* Fuel Recycle Br Sta 35 Atomic Energy of Can Ltd Pinawa MB R0E 1L0 Can

SZEBEHELY, VICTOR, b Budapest, Hungary, Aug 10, 21; nat US; m 70; c 1. ASTRONOMY, SPACE SCIENCES. *Educ:* Budapest Tech Univ, DSc, 45. *Prof Exp:* Asst prof appl math, Budapest Tech Univ, 43-47; res asst, Pa State Univ, 47-48; assoc prof appl mech, Va Polytech Inst, 48-51; head ship dynamics br, David Taylor Model Basin, US Dept Navy, 51-57; mgr space mech, Missiles & Space Div, Gen Elec Co, 57-62; assoc prof astron, Yale Univ, 62-68; prof aerospace eng & eng mech, Univ Tex, Austin, 68-76, chmn dept aerospace eng & eng mech, 76-81. *Concurrent Pos:* Lectr, McGill Univ, 48 & Univ Toronto, 49; prof lectr, Univ Md & George Washington Univ, 51-57; consult, NASA, Gen Elec Co, Int Tel & Tel Co, Bell Tel Labs & Inst Defense Anal, Tracor. *Honors & Awards:* Sci Res Soc Award, Sigma Xi, 51; Officer, Order of Orange Nassau, Netherlands, 57; L B Meanders prof eng, Univ Tex. *Mem:* Am Inst Aeronaut & Astronaut; Am Soc Mech Engrs; Int Astron Union; Am Astron Soc. *Res:* Celestial mechanics; problem of three and n bodies; applied mechanics; analytical dynamics; continuum mechanics; applied mathematics; matrix and tensor analysis. *Mailing Add:* Dept of Aerospace Eng Univ of Tex Austin TX 78712

SZEBENYI, EMIL, b Budapest, Hungary, June 9, 20; US citizen; m 44; c 3. COMPARATIVE ANATOMY, EMBRYOLOGY. *Educ:* Budapest Tech Univ, dipl, 42, Doctoratus (animal genetics & husb), 43. *Prof Exp:* Asst prof animal genetics, Univ Agr Sci Hungary, 52-53, Hungarian Acad Sci fel & adj, 53-56; from asst prof to assoc prof, 62-73, chmn, Dept Biol Sci, 71-80, PROF COMP ANAT, EMBRYOL & EVOLUTION, FAIRLEIGH DICKINSON UNIV, 73- *Concurrent Pos:* Pres, Alfacell Corp, 81- *Mem:* AAAS; Sigma Xi; Am Soc Zoologists; Soc Develop Biol; Int Abstracts Biol Sci. *Res:* Anatomy; human embryology; experimental morphogenesis. *Mailing Add:* Dept Biol Sci Fairleigh Dickinson Univ Rutherford NJ 07070

SZEDON, JOHN R(OBERT), b Elrama, Pa, May 26, 37; m 72. ELECTRICAL ENGINEERING, SOLID STATE PHYSICS. *Educ:* Carnegie-Mellon Univ, BS, 59, MS, 60, PhD(elec eng), 62. *Prof Exp:* Sr engr, 62-67, sr res scientist, 67-68, MGR SURFACE DEVICE STUDIES, WESTINGHOUSE ELEC CORP RES LABS, 68- *Concurrent Pos:* Lectr, Carnegie-Mellon Univ, 67-68. *Honors & Awards:* Thomas D Callinan Award, Electrochem Soc, 73. *Mem:* Inst Elec & Electronics Engrs; Electrochem Soc. *Res:* Semiconductor device physics; surface controlled semiconductor devices; ion migration in insulators; injection-trapping in metal-insular semiconductor structures; ionizing radiation effects in dielectrics; p-N junction; heterojunction and MIS solar cells. *Mailing Add:* Res & Develop Ctr 1310 Beulah Rd Pittsburgh PA 15235

SZEGO, CLARA MARIAN, b Budapest, Hungary, Mar 23, 16; US citizen; m 43. CELL BIOLOGY. *Educ:* Hunter Col, BA, 37; Univ Minn, MS, 39, PhD(physiol chem), 42. *Prof Exp:* Asst physiol chem, Sch Med, Univ Minn, 40-42, asst physiol, 42, instr, 42-44; fel cancer, Minn Med Found, 44; assoc chemist, Off Sci Res & Develop, Nat Bur Stand, 44-45; res assoc, Worcester Found Exp Biol, 45-47; res instr physiol chem, Yale Univ, 47-48; asst clin prof biophys, 48-49, from asst prof to prof, 49-60, PROF BIOL, UNIV CALIF, LOS ANGELES, 60-; ASSOC MEM, MOLECULAR BIOL INST, 66- *Concurrent Pos:* Guggenheim fel, 56; mem, Univ Calif Jonsson Comprehensive Cancer Ctr, 76- *Honors & Awards:* Ciba Award, Endocrine Soc, 53; Gregory Pincus Mem Medallion, Worcester Found Exp Biol, 74. *Mem:* Fel AAAS; Am Physiol Soc; Am Soc Zoologists; Endocrine Soc; Am Soc Cell Biol. *Res:* Molecular mechanisms of endocrine regulation. *Mailing Add:* Dept of Biol Univ of Calif Los Angeles CA 90024

SZEGO, GEORGE C(HARLES), b Budapest, Hungary, Aug 10, 19; nat US; m 38; c 7. CHEMICAL ENGINEERING. *Educ:* Univ Denver, BS, 47; Univ Wash, Seattle, MS, 50, PhD(chem eng), 56. *Prof Exp:* Engr, J W Greene & Assoc, Colo, 46-47; from instr to prof chem eng, Seattle Univ, 48-56, head dept, 48-56; engr, supvr & mgr space propulsion oper, Space Power Oper, Flight Propulsion Lab, Gen Elec Co, Ohio, 56-59; sr mem tech staff, Spec Projs Dept, Systs Res & Anal Div, Space Tech Labs, Inc, 59-61; study dir, Space Res & Eng Support Div, Inst Defense Anal, 61-70; pres & chmn, Interechnol/Solar Corp, 70-80; PRES & CHMN, P E & ASSOCS, INC, 80- *Concurrent Pos:* Exten assoc prof, Univ Wash, 50-55; mgr, George C Szego & Assocs, Consult Engrs, Wash, 50-56; lectr, Univ Calif, Los Angeles, 58-; mgr beef cattle & horse farm, 62-; lectr, Nat Bur Stand, US Air Force Acad, George Washington Univ, Wash Univ, Univ Va & Univ Pa. *Mem:* AAAS; fel Am Inst Chem Engrs. *Res:* Solar and renewable energy; biomass energy; power and energy systems engineering and management; space propulsion; space power generation, conversion and storage; chemical engineering thermodynamics; real gas effects; heat transfer; fluid dynamics; systems engineering and optimization; economic balances; agronomy; animal husbandry. *Mailing Add:* P E & Assocs Inc Box 2928 Arlington VA 22202

SZEGO, PETER A, b Berlin, Ger, July 18, 25; nat US. SOCIAL IMPLICATIONS OF TECHNOLOGY. *Educ:* Stanford Univ, BS, 47. *Prof Exp:* Asst prof mech eng, Rice Univ, 51-54 & Univ Santa Clara, 56-63; mgr mech sect, advan technol div, Ampex Corp, Redwood City, 63-76; EXEC ASST, BD SUPVR, SANTA CLARA COUNTY, CALIF, 76- *Concurrent Pos:* Lectr mech eng, Univ Santa Clara, 70- *Mem:* Am Soc Mech Engrs; Soc Indust & Appl Math; Asn Comput Mach; Inst Elec & Electronics Engrs; Am Math Soc. *Res:* Scientific programming; applied mathematics; engineering mechanics; science policy. *Mailing Add:* 75 Glen Eyrie Ave Apt 19 San Jose CA 95125

SZEKELY, ANDREW GEZA, b Temesvar, Rumania, Apr 15, 25; US citizen; m 51; c 6. PHYSICAL CHEMISTRY. *Educ:* Eötvös Lorand Univ, Budapest, dipl chem, 50. *Prof Exp:* Asst electrochem, Physico-Chem Inst, Eötvös Lorand Univ, Budapest, 49-51; res chemist, High Pressure Res Inst, Budapest, 51-56, dept head petrol refining, 56-57; res chemist, Tonawanda Res Lab, Linde Div, 58-62, sr res chemist, 62-66, develop assoc process metall, Newark Develop Labs, NJ, 67-70, sr develop assoc, gas prod develop, 70-77, CORP DEVELOP FEL, LINDE LABS, TARRYTOWN TECH CTR, UNION CARBIDE CORP, 78- *Mem:* AAAS; Am Inst Mining, Metall & Petrol Eng; Am Inst Chem. *Res:* Process metallurgy; thermodynamics and kinetics. *Mailing Add:* 2379 Claire Ct Yorktown Heights NY 10598

SZEKELY, IVAN J, b Budapest, Hungary, Aug 13, 19; nat US; m. RESOURCE MANAGEMENT. *Educ:* Pazmany Peter Univ, Hungary, PhD, 43, MS, 44. *Prof Exp:* Asst prof chem, Bowling Green State Univ, 47-48; prof pharm, Univ Calif, 48-51; dir res & prod develop, Barnes-Hind Pharmaceut, Inc, 51-57, from exec vpres to pres, 57-69; PRES, PHARMACEUT RES INT, 71- *Concurrent Pos:* Pharmaceut mgt consult. *Mem:* Am Chem Soc; Am Pharmaceut Asn; NY Acad Sci. *Res:* Formulation of pharmaceutical dosage forms; ophthalmic solutions; physical-chemical properties of contact lens materials, especially contact lens solutions. *Mailing Add:* PO Box 118 Los Altos CA 94022

SZEKELY, JOSEPH GEORGE, b Cleveland, Ohio, May 7, 40; m 67; c 2. BIOPHYSICS. *Educ:* Case Western Reserve Univ, BS, 62; State Univ NY Buffalo, PhD(physics), 67. *Prof Exp:* USPHS fel, Univ Tex M D Anderson Hosp & Tumor Inst, 67-68; ASSOC RES OFFICER, ATOMIC ENERGY CAN LTD, 68- *Mem:* Am Soc Cell Biol; Can Micros Soc; Biophys Soc. *Res:* Membrane biophysics; computer models of cell growth; electron microscopy. *Mailing Add:* 30 Lansdowne Ave Pinawa MB R0E 1L0 Can

SZEKELY, JULIAN, b Budapest, Hungary, Nov 23, 34; US citizen; m 63; c 5. PROCESS METALLURGY, CHEMICAL ENGINEERING. *Educ:* Univ London, BSc, 59, DSc, 63; Imp Col, London, PhD(chem eng), 61. *Prof Exp:* Lectr metall, Imp Col, 62-66; assoc prof chem eng, State Univ NY, Buffalo, 66-68, prof, 68-75, dir ctr process metall, 70-75; PROF MAT ENG, MASS INST TECHNOL, 75- *Concurrent Pos:* Fel, Guggenheim Found, 75; consult, US Dept Energy, 75-, Alcoa, 76-, Puegot Citroen, Paris, 79-, Pechiney Aluminum Voreppe, France, 80- & US Steel Corp, 81- *Honors & Awards:* Jr Moulton Medal, Brit Inst Chem Engrs, 64, Sir George Beilby Gold Medal & Prize, 74; Extractive Metall Sci Award, Am Inst Mining, Metall & Petrol Engrs, 73, Champion Mathewson Gold Medal, 73; Curtis McGraw Res Award, Am Soc Eng Educ, 74; Howe Mem lectr, 79. *Mem:* Am Inst Chem Engrs; Brit Inst Chem Engrs; Am Inst Mining, Metall & Petrol Engrs; Iron & Steel Inst Japan. *Res:* Materials processing; mathematical and physical modelling of processing operations; energy environmental and societal aspects of materials processing operations. *Mailing Add:* Dept of Mat Sci & Eng Mass Inst of Technol Cambridge MA 02139

SZELESS, ADORJAN GYULA, b Budapest, Hungary, Dec 7, 27; US citizen; m 53. MECHANICAL ENGINEERING, NAVAL ARCHITECTURE. *Educ:* Budapest Tech Univ, MS, 52; Va Polytech Univ, PhD(mech eng), 67. *Prof Exp:* Marine engr, Obudai Hajogyar, Hungary, 52-54; naval architect, Dunai Hajogyar, 54-56; plant engr, Müchen-Dachauer Papierfabriken GmbH, Ger, 57-58; naval architect, Wasser-u Schiffahrtsdirektion, Ger, 58-59; marine appln ener, Cummins Engine Co, Ind, 59-62; asst prof, 62-72, ASSOC PROF MECH ENG, VA POLYTECH INST & STATE UNIV, 72- *Concurrent Pos:* NSF res initiation grant, 68-69; researcher, Naval Res Lab, 69-70; sci analyst, Ctr Naval Anal, Univ Rochester, Va, 69-71. *Mem:* Soc Naval Architects & Marine Engrs. *Res:* Ship hydrodynamics; propulsion; resistance; stability; fishtype propulsion by undulating plates. *Mailing Add:* 512 South Gate Dr Blacksburg VA 24060

SZENT-GYORGYI, ALBERT, b Budapest, Hungary, Sept 16, 93; nat US; m 42; c 1. BIOCHEMISTRY. *Educ:* Univ Budapest, MD, 17; Cambridge Univ, PhD(chem), 27. *Hon Degrees:* Dr, Univ Lausanne, Univ Padua, Univ Paris, Oxford Univ, Univ Bordeaux, Oberlin Col & Brown Univ. *Prof Exp:* Prof med chem, Univ Szeged, 32-44; prof biochem, Univ Budapest, 45-47; DIR RES, INST MUSCLE RES, MARINE BIOL LAB, WOODS HOLE, MASS, 47- *Concurrent Pos:* Vis prof, Univ Liege, 35 & Harvard Univ, 36; Withering lectr, Univ Birmingham, Eng, 38; mem bd trustees, Marine Biol Lab, Woods Hole; sci dir, Nat Found Cancer Res, 80- *Honors & Awards:* Nobel Prize in Med, 37; Cameron Prize, 46; Lasker Award, Am Heart Asn, 54. *Mem:* Nat Acad Sci; NY Acad Med; hon mem, NY Acad Sci; Royal Soc Edinburgh; Acad Lincei. *Res:* Bioenergetics; biological oxidation; chemical physiology of muscle; submolecular biology. *Mailing Add:* PO Box 187 Marine Biol Labs Woods Hole MA 02543

SZENT-GYORGYI, ANDREW GABRIEL, b Budapest, Hungary, May 16, 24; nat US; m 47; c 3. BIOCHEMISTRY. *Educ:* Univ Budapest, MD, 47. *Prof Exp:* Instr, Univ Budapest, 46-47; fel, Neurophysiol Inst, Copenhagen, 48; mem inst muscle res, Marine Biol Lab, Woods Hole, 48-62, instr physiol, 53-58; prof biophys, Dartmouth Med Sch, 62-66; PROF BIOL, BRANDEIS UNIV, 66- *Concurrent Pos:* Am Heart Asn estab investr, 55-62; USPHS res career award, 62-66; head physiol course, Marine Biol Lab, Woods Hole, 67-71, trustee, 70-76 & 81- *Mem:* Fel Am Physiol Soc; fel AAAS; Muscular Dystrophy Asn; Am Soc Biol Chem; Biophys Soc (pres, 74-75). *Res:* Regulation of muscle contraction; structure of muscle proteins. *Mailing Add:* Dept of Biol Brandeis Univ Waltham MA 02154

SZENTIRMAI, GEORGE, b Budapest, Hungary, Oct 8, 28; US citizen; m 52, 74; c 2. ELECTRICAL ENGINEERING, COMPUTER AIDED DESIGN. *Educ:* Budapest Tech Univ, dipl elec eng, 51 & Can Tech Sci, 55; Polytech Inst Brooklyn, PhD(elec eng), 63. *Prof Exp:* From asst prof to assoc prof elec eng, Budapest Tech Univ, 54-56; design engr, Standard Tel & Cables, Ltd, Eng, 57-58; sect leader elec eng, Tel Mfg Co, Ltd, Eng, 58-59; mem tech staff, Bell Tel Labs, Inc, 59-64, supvr elec eng, 64-68; prof elec eng, Cornell Univ, 68-75; staff scientist, Electronics Res Ctr, Rockwell Int Corp, 75-80; VPRES

ADV DEVELOP, COMPACT DIV, COMSAT GEN INTEGRATED SYSTS, 80- *Concurrent Pos:* Consult, Cent Phys Res Inst, Budapest, 55-56 & Bell Tel Labs, Inc, 68-75; adj prof elec sci & eng, Univ Calif, Los Angeles, 75-80. *Mem:* Fel Inst Elec & Electronics Engrs; Brit Inst Elec Engrs. *Res:* Synthesis and design of electrical filters and networks; computer-aided circuit and system analysis and design; microwave networks. *Mailing Add:* 1131 San Antonio Rd Comsat Gen Integrated Systs Palo Alto CA 94303

SZENTIVANYI, ANDOR, b Miskolc, Hungary, May 4, 26; US citizen; m 48; c 2. PHARMACOLOGY, ALLERGY. *Educ:* Debrecen Univ Med, MD, 50. *Prof Exp:* Asst prof med, Univ Med Sch Budapest, 53-56; Rockefeller fel med, Univ Chicago, 57-59; USPHS fel allergy & immunol, Univ Colo, Denver, 59-60, asst prof med, 61-65, from asst prof to assoc prof Pharmacol & microbiol, 63-67; prof med & chmn dept microbiol, Sch Med, Creighton Univ, 67-70; PROF PHARMACOL & CHMN DEPT, COL MED, UNIV SOUTH FLA, TAMPA, 70-, PROF INTERNAL MED, 73-, ASSOC DEAN GRAD STUDIES, 78-, DEAN, COL MED & DIR MED CTR, 80- *Mem:* Am Asn Immunol; Am Acad Allergy; Am Soc Pharmacol & Exp Therapeut; Am Soc Clin Pharmacol; Am Col Clin Pharmacol. *Res:* Pharmacological aspects of immune and hypersensitivity mechanisms. *Mailing Add:* 11603 Carrollwood Dr Tampa FL 33618

SZEPE, STEPHEN, b Nagykörös, Hungary, June 21, 32; US citizen; m 58; c 1. CHEMICAL ENGINEERING. *Educ:* Veszprem Tech Univ, Dipl Ing, 54; Ill Inst Technol, MS, 61, PhD(chem eng), 66. *Prof Exp:* Res chem eng, Hungarian Petrol & Gas Res Inst, Veszprem, 54-56 & Sinclair Res, Inc, Ill, 57-61; instr chem eng, Ill Inst Technol, 61-64; asst prof, Wash Univ, 65-68; ASSOC PROF ENERGY ENG, UNIV ILL, CHICAGO CIRCLE, 68- *Mem:* AAAS; Am Chem Soc; Am Inst Chem Engrs; Catalysis Soc. *Res:* Chemical reaction engineering; kinetics and catalysis; optimization; process dynamics. *Mailing Add:* Dept of Energy Eng Box 4348 Chicago IL 60680

SZEPESI, BELA, b Ozd, Hungary, Nov 19, 38; US citizen; m 61; c 3. NUTRITION, MOLECULAR BIOLOGY. *Educ:* Albion Col, BA, 61; Colo State Univ, MS, 64; Univ Calif, Davis, PhD(comp biochem), 68. *Prof Exp:* RES CHEMIST, NUTRIT INST, SCI & EDUC ADMIN, USDA, 69- *Mem:* Am Inst Nutrit; Brit Biochem Soc; Brit Nutrit Soc; Soc Exp Biol & Med. *Res:* Mechanism of overweight; control of gene expression in rat liver; disaccharide effect on enzyme induction; starvation-refeeding; hormone effect on rat liver enzymes; utilization of carp as food. *Mailing Add:* Rm 313 Bldg 307 Beltsville Human Nutrit Res Ctr Res Serv USDA Beltsville MD 20705

SZEPESI, ZOLTAN PAUL JOHN, b Sarosfa, Hungary, May 13, 12; nat US; m 42; c 1. ELECTRONICS. *Educ:* Univ Szeged, BSc, 32, MSc, 34; Univ Budapest, PhD(physics), 37. *Prof Exp:* Mem staff, Inst Theoret Physics, Hungary, 34-36; physicist, Tungsram Res Lab, 36-45; engr, Hungarian Tel & Tel Inst, 45-46; physicist, Pulvari Lab, 46-47; res assoc, Grenoble, 47-51; sr physicist, Can Marconi Co, Que, 51-58; fel engr, Electronic Tube Div, Westinghouse Elec Corp, NY, 58-72, fel scientist, Westinghouse Res Lab, Pa, 72-77; CONSULT, 78- *Res:* Compton effect of gamma rays; noise effects in electron tubes; wave guides; slot antennas; high frequency oscillators; photoconductors; solid state display panels; noise measurements of transistors. *Mailing Add:* 2611 Saybrook Dr Pittsburgh PA 15235

SZEPSENWOL, JOSEL, b Radoszkosice, Poland, Feb 7, 05; nat US. ANATOMY. *Educ:* Univ Geneva, MD, 36. *Prof Exp:* Asst anat, Univ Geneva, 29-31, asst prof, 31-37; chief tissue cult sect, Univ Buenos Aires, 37-43; Knight fel, Yale Univ, 43-45; from instr surg to assoc prof anat, Emory Univ, 47-54; vis prof, Sch Med, Univ NC, 54-55; from assoc prof to prof anat, Sch Med, Univ PR, San Juan, 56-77; RETIRED. *Mem:* Soc Exp Biol & Med; Am Physiol Soc; Am Asn Anatomists; Am Asn Cancer Res. *Res:* Experimental embryology; tissue culture; cancer. *Mailing Add:* Mirasol-Ocean Towers 2655 Collins Ave Apt 805 Miami Beach FL 33140

SZEPTYCKI, PAWEL, b Lwow, Poland, Feb 10, 35; m 61; c 3. MATHEMATICS. *Educ:* Univ Warsaw, MSc, 56; Univ SAfrica, PhD(math), 61. *Prof Exp:* Res officer math, SAfrican Coun Sci & Indust Res, 59-61; from asst prof to assoc prof, 61-67, PROF MATH, UNIV KANS, 67- *Mem:* Am Math Soc. *Res:* Mathematical analysis. *Mailing Add:* Dept Math Univ Kans Lawrence KS 66045

SZER, WLODZIMIERZ, b Warsaw, Poland, June 3, 24; m 48; c 2. BIOCHEMISTRY. *Educ:* Univ Lodz, MS, 50; Polish Acad Sci, PhD(biochem), 59. *Prof Exp:* Instr org chem, Univ Lodz, 51-53; res assoc, Inst Antibiotics, Poland, 54-56; asst prof biochem, Inst Biochem & Biophys, Polish Acad Sci, 59-62, dozent biochem, 63-67; PROF BIOCHEM, SCH MED, NY UNIV, 68-, ACTG CHMN, DEPT BIOCHEM, 80- *Concurrent Pos:* Jane Coffin Childs Mem Fund fel, Sch Med, NY Univ, 63-64. *Honors & Awards:* J K Parnas Award, Polish Biochem Soc. *Mem:* Am Soc Biol Chemists; Harvey Soc. *Res:* Structure of polynucleotides; molecular mechanisms in protein synthesis. *Mailing Add:* Dept of Biochem NY Univ Med Ctr New York NY 10016

SZERB, JOHN CONRAD, b Budapest, Hungary, Feb 24, 26; nat Can; m 57; c 2. PHYSIOLOGY. *Educ:* Univ Munich, MD, 50. *Prof Exp:* Lectr, 51-52, from asst prof to assoc prof, 52-63, PROF PHARMACOL, DALHOUSIE UNIV, 63-, CHMN DEPT PHYSIOL & BIOPHYS, 65- *Concurrent Pos:* Res fel, Pasteur Inst, Paris, 50-51; Nuffield fel, Cambridge Univ, 60-61, vis scientist, 70-71; mem, Med Res Coun Can, 65-70. *Mem:* Soc Neurosci; Pharmacol Soc Can; Can Physiol Soc; fel Royal Col Physicians Can. *Res:* Release of transmitters and electrical activity in the central nervous system. *Mailing Add:* Dept Physiol & Biophys Dalhousie Univ Halifax NS B3H 4H7 Can

SZERI, ANDRAS ZOLTAN, b Nagyvarad, Hungary, June 6, 34; m 62; c 3. MECHANICAL ENGINEERING. *Educ:* Univ Leeds, BSc, 60, PhD(eng), 62. *Prof Exp:* Engr, Dept Appl Mech, Eng Elec Co, Eng, 62-64; prof fluid mech, Valparaiso Tech Univ, Chile, 64-67; from asst prof to assoc prof, 67-77, PROF MECH ENG & PROF MATH, UNIV PITTSBURGH, 77- *Concurrent Pos:* Consult, Westinghouse Res Labs, Pa, 67- & Penn Ctr, Basic Technol Inc, 71- *Mem:* Am Soc Mech Engrs; Am Acad Mech. *Res:* Lubrication and bearings; laminar flow; stability; turbulence; heat transfer; applied mathematics. *Mailing Add:* 636 Benedum Hall Univ of Pittsburgh Pittsburgh PA 15261

SZETO, GEORGE, b Hong Kong, Aug 10, 38; m 68. MATHEMATICS. *Educ:* United Col Hong Kong, BSc, 64; Purdue Univ, Lafayette, MA, 66, PhD(math), 68. *Prof Exp:* From asst prof to assoc prof, 68-75, PROF MATH, BRADLEY UNIV, 75- *Concurrent Pos:* NSF res grant, 72-73. *Mem:* Am Math Soc. *Res:* Separable algebras; near rings. *Mailing Add:* Dept of Math Bradley Univ Peoria IL 61625

SZEWCZYK, ALBIN A, b Chicago, Ill, Feb 26, 35; m 56; c 4. MECHANICAL ENGINEERING, FLUID MECHANICS. *Educ:* Univ Notre Dame, BS, 56, MS, 58; Univ Md, PhD(fluid mech), 61. *Prof Exp:* Assoc engr, Lab Div, Northrop Aircraft Inc, 56-57; res fel, Inst Fluid Dynamics & Appl Math, Univ Md, 61-62; from asst prof to assoc prof, 62-67, PROF MECH ENG, UNIV NOTRE DAME, 67- & CHMN, DEPT AEROSPACE & MECH ENG, 78- *Concurrent Pos:* Consult, Argonne Nat Lab, 68-; fel, Univ Queensland, 71-72. *Mem:* Am Phys Soc. *Res:* Fluid mechanics, numerical fluid dynamics; experimental investigations of bluff body flows. *Mailing Add:* Dept of Aerospace & Mech Eng Univ of Notre Dame Notre Dame IN 46556

SZIKLAI, GEORGE C(LIFFORD), b Budapest, Hungary, July 9, 09; nat US; m 34; c 1. ELECTRONICS, OPTICS. *Educ:* Munich Tech Univ, CE, 28; Univ Budapest, absolutorium, 30. *Prof Exp:* Asst chief engr, Aerovox Corp, NY, 30-32; chief engr, Polymet Mfg Corp, NY, 33-35; res & develop engr, Micamold Radio Corp, 35-38; mgr & chief engr, Am Radio H W Corp, 38-39; res & develop engr, Radio Corp Am, 39-56; asst to vpres eng, Westinghouse Elec Corp, 56-65, dir res commun & displays, Pa, 65-67; sr mem res lab, Lockheed Missiles & Space Co, 67-75; INDEPENDENT CONSULT, 76- *Concurrent Pos:* Consult, US Dept Defense, 58- *Mem:* Am Phys Soc; Optical Soc Am; life fel Inst Elec & Electronics Engrs; NY Acad Sci; Sigma Xi. *Res:* Television; colorimetry; solid state circuitry. *Mailing Add:* 26900 St Francis Rd Los Altos Hills CA 94022

SZIKLAI, OSCAR, b Repashuta, Hungary, Oct 30, 24; Can citizen; m 49; c 4. BIOLOGY, FOREST GENETICS. *Educ:* Sopron Univ, Hungary, BSF, 46; Univ BC, MF, 61, PhD(forest genetics), 64. *Prof Exp:* Instr silvicult, Sopron Univ, Hungary, 46-47; asst forester, Hungarian Forest Serv, 47-49; res officer, Forest Res Inst, Budapest, 49-51; asst prof silvicult, Sopron Univ, Hungary, 51-56; asst prof, Sopron Forestry Sch, Univ BC, 57-59, lectr forestry, 59-61, instr, 61-64, from asst prof to assoc prof forest genetics, Univ, 64-71, PROF FOREST GENETICS, UNIV BC, 71- *Concurrent Pos:* Nat Res Coun Can res grants forest genetics, 62-; exchange scientist, Forest Res Inst, Japan, 78; vis prof, Forest Genetics, Nanjing, China, 80. *Mem:* Can Inst Forestry. *Res:* Forest biology; selection and hybridization of Salix and Populus genera and Pseudotsuga genus; variation and inheritance studies in western Canadian conifers. *Mailing Add:* 2075 Wesbrook Mall Fac Forestry Univ BC Vancouver BC V6T 1W5 Can

SZILARD, RUDOLPH, b Koeszeg, Hungary, Aug 26, 21; nat US; m 48; c 2. STRUCTURAL ENGINEERING. *Educ:* Budapest Tech Univ, Dipl Eng, 43; Stuttgart Tech Univ, Dr Eng, 61. *Prof Exp:* Struct engr & jr partner, Szilard & Son, Hungary, 43-45; struct engr, Hans Neubauer, Austria, 45-49 & Northeastern Steel Co, Wis, 49-51; sr struct engr, Ammann & Whitney, NY, 51-57; struct design specialist & actg prin engr, Aero-Space Div, Martin Co, Colo, 57-58, 60-63; assoc prof civil eng, Colo State Univ, 58-60; prof & sr res engr, Univ Denver, 63-67; PROF CIVIL ENG, UNIV HAWAII, 67- *Concurrent Pos:* Alexander von Humboldt Found sr fel, 72-73; vis prof, Brunswick Tech Univ, 72-73; consult, Martin Co, Francis & Assocs, Zeiler & Gray, Consult Engrs, & Lockheed Missiles & Space Co. *Mem:* Am Inst Aeronaut & Astronaut; Am Soc Civil Engrs; Am Concrete Inst; Am Soc Eng Educ; NY Acad Sci. *Res:* Thin shells; plates; structural dynamics; use of computers in structural analysis; non-linear problems. *Mailing Add:* Dept Civil Eng Univ Hawaii Honolulu HI 96822

SZIRMAY, LESLIE V, b Eger, Hungary, Nov 13, 23; Can citizen; m 62. CHEMICAL & NUCLEAR ENGINEERING. *Educ:* Eötvös Lorand Univ, Budapest, Dipl chem, 49; Univ Detroit, MS, 62; Iowa State Univ, ME, 67; Univ Denver, PhD(chem eng), 69. *Prof Exp:* Process engr, Hungarian Sulphuric Acid Factory, 48-49; res engr, Hungarian Mineral Oil Res Inst, Budapest & Veszprem, 49-54, Nitrogen Works of Austria, 55-56, Esso Res Labs, Ont, 56, Palm Oil Recovery, Inc, 56-58 & Falconbridge Nickel Mines Ltd, 58-60; develop engr, Can Gen Elec, 62-64; asst, Iowa State Univ, 64-67; instr chem & nuclear eng, Univ Denver, 67-69; from asst prof to assoc prof, 69-81, PROF CHEM & NUCLEAR ENG, YOUNGSTOWN STATE UNIV, 81- *Concurrent Pos:* Consult, Atomic Energy Comn Can, 62-64, De Havilland Aircraft Can Ltd, 64 & Dravo Eng, 79-; US Atomic Energy Comn fel, Univ Mo-Rolla, 71. *Mem:* Am Inst Chem Engrs; Am Chem Soc; Am Nuclear Soc. *Res:* Gas separation; exchange adsorption; coal liquefaction; air pollution. *Mailing Add:* Dept of Chem Eng Youngstown State Univ Youngstown OH 44503

SZMANT, HERMAN HARRY, b Kalisz, Poland, May 18, 18; nat US; m 41; c 2. ORGANIC CHEMISTRY. *Educ:* Ohio State Univ, BA, 40; Purdue Univ, PhD(chem), 44. *Prof Exp:* Res chemist, Monsanto Chem Co, 44-46; assoc prof chem, Duquesne Univ, 46-50, prof, 51-56; head dept chem & ctr chem res, Oriente, Cuba, 56-60; prof chem, Univ PR, San Juan & head phys sci div, PR Nuclear Ctr, 61-68; CHMN DEPT CHEM & CHEM ENG, UNIV DETROIT, 68- *Concurrent Pos:* Chem adv, US AID Mission, Dominican Repub, 68; consult & lectr, indust chem. *Mem:* AAAS; Am Chem Soc; NY Acad Sci; PR Acad Arts & Sci. *Res:* Physical organic chemistry; sulfur compounds; utilization of renewable resources; solvent effects; economic growth of developing countries through chemistry. *Mailing Add:* Dept of Chem & Chem Eng Univ of Detroit Detroit MI 48221

SZOKA, PAULA RACHEL, b Baltimore, Md, Nov 28, 48. BIOCHEMICAL GENETICS, MOLECULAR BIOLOGY. *Educ:* Univ Md, BS, 69; State Univ NY, Buffalo, MS, 74, PhD(molecular biol), 76. *Prof Exp:* Fel, Roswell Park Mem Inst, 76-78; FEL MOLECULAR BIOL, MASS INST TECHNOL, 78- *Concurrent Pos:* NIH fel, 78- *Res:* Eukaryotic molecular genetics; regulation of gene expression, gene structure and function; organization of chromosomes. *Mailing Add:* 16-730 Mass Inst Technol 77 Massachusetts Ave Cambridge MA 02139

SZONNTAGH, EUGENE L(ESLIE), b Budapest, Hungary, July 31, 24; US citizen; m 50; c 2. CHEMICAL ENGINEERING, ANALYTICAL CHEMISTRY. *Educ:* Budapest Tech Univ, MEng Sci, 48, PhD(anal chem), 75. *Prof Exp:* Jr chem engr, Hungarian State RR, 48-50; asst prof anal chem, Veszprem Tech Univ, 50-52, assoc prof, 52-56, head electro-chem div, Dept Chem Technol, 56; Rockefeller res fel instrumental anal, Vienna Tech Univ, 57; develop engr, Leeds & Northrup Co, 57-61, develop specialist, 61-62, scientist, 62-63, sr scientist, 63-72; dir & consult, Continuing Educ Inc, 72; Prin Eng, 73-75, IN CHARGE CHEM & MAT LABS, PROCESS CONTROL DIV, HONEYWELL, INC, 75- *Concurrent Pos:* Consult, Res Inst Chem Indust & Hungarian Petrol & Natural Gas Res Inst, Veszprem, 51-56 & Process Control Div, Honeywell, Inc, 72. *Honors & Awards:* IR-100 Award, Indust Res, 62; Eng Achievement Award, Honeywell, Inc, 74. *Mem:* Am Chem Soc; sr mem Instrument Soc Am; NY Acad Sci; AAAS; Electrochem Soc. *Res:* Materials testing and analysis; classical and instrumental analytical chemistry; electrical and electronic measurements; polarography; liquid and gas chromatography; instrumental process analysis; electrochemical sensors; failure analysis; materials characterization; corrosion; archaeometry. *Mailing Add:* 6327 Fairfield Dr Flourtown PA 19031

SZONYI, GEZA, b Budapest, Hungary, Feb 7, 19; nat US; m 45; c 2. COMPUTER SCIENCE, INFORMATION SCIENCE. *Educ:* Univ Zurich, PhD, 45. *Prof Exp:* Res chemist, W Stark AG, Switz, 45-47; info scientist & head co, Chemolit, 47-51; res chemist, Can Industs, Ltd, 51-53 & Barrett Div, Allied Chem & Dye Corp, 53-57; lit scientist, Socony Mobile Oil Co, Inc, 57-58; info res chemist, Atlas Chem Industs, Inc, 58-64; chief lit chemist, Ciba Corp, NJ, 64-69; SR SCIENTIST RES COMPUT GROUP, POLAROID CORP, 69- *Concurrent Pos:* Adv, Mass Manpower Comn; invited speaker, Simmons Col, Boston, Mass. *Mem:* Am Chem Soc; Sigma Xi; Am Statist Asn. *Res:* Chemical computer operations in graphics; chemical information research; applied statistics; scientific computer programming; computerized information retrieval systems; paper chemistry and technology; catalysis; physical and pharmaceutical chemistry; improved information handling methods; simulation. *Mailing Add:* Polaroid Corp 750 Main St Cambridge MA 02139

SZOSTAK, JACK WILLIAM, b London, Eng, Nov 9, 52; Can citizen. GENETIC RECOMBINATION. *Educ:* McGill Univ, BSc, 72; Cornell Univ, PhD(biochem), 77. *Prof Exp:* Fel biochem, Cornell Univ, 77-79; ASST PROF BIOL CHEM, SIDNEY FARBER CANCER INST & HARVARD MED SCH, 79- *Res:* Molecular genetics of recombination, DNA repair and DNA replication in yeast. *Mailing Add:* Signey Farber Cancer Inst D-1030 44 Binney St Boston MA 02115

SZPUNAR, CAROLE BRYDA, b Chicago, Ill, July 8, 49; m 72. ORGANIC CHEMISTRY, ANALYTICAL CHEMISTRY. *Educ:* Univ Ill, Chicago, BS, 71; Northwestern Univ, MS, 75, PhD(chem), 77. *Prof Exp:* Chemist soil, water & bldg mat, Novak, Dempsey & Assocs, Inc, 71-73; fel, Northwestern Univ, 74-76; res chemist coal, Exxon Res & Eng Co, 77-; MEM STAFF, ESSO INT AM, INC, 80- *Mem:* Am Chem Soc; Sigma Xi. *Res:* Coal analysis, research, and characterization. *Mailing Add:* Esso Int Am Inc 396 Alhambra Circle Coral Gables FL 33134

SZÜSZ, PETER, b Novisad, Yugoslavia, Nov 11, 24; m 73. MATHEMATICS. *Educ:* Eötvös Lorand Univ, Budapest, PhD(math), 51; Hungarian Acad Sci, DMS, 62. *Prof Exp:* Res fel math, Math Inst, Hungarian Acad Sci, 50-65; vis prof, Memorial Univ, 65; vis assoc prof, Pa State Univ, 65-66; PROF MATH, STATE UNIV NY STONY BROOK, 66- *Mem:* Am Math Soc. *Mailing Add:* 284 Hallock Rd Stony Brook NY 11790

SZTANKAY, ZOLTAN GEZA, b Cleveland, Ohio, Apr 17, 37; m 70. PHYSICS. *Educ:* Valparaiso Univ, BS, 59; Univ Wis, MS, 61, PhD(physics), 65. *Prof Exp:* PHYSICIST, HARRY DIAMOND LABS, 65- *Mem:* Inst Elec & Electronics Engrs; Am Phys Soc. *Res:* Analysis of electrooptical, laser and infrared sensing systems; the propagation and back-scatter of laser beam and mm-waves in the atmosphere; the interaction of laser irradiation with a variety of solids; mm-wave technology. *Mailing Add:* Harry Diamond Labs Br 13300 2800 Powder Mill Rd Adelphi MD 20783

SZU, SHOUSUN CHEN, b Chunking, China, Sept 25, 45; m 72; c 2. MOLECULAR BIOPHYSICS. *Educ:* Taiwan Prov Cheng-Kung Univ, BS, 66; Mich Tech Univ, MS, 67; Univ Calif, Davis, PhD(physics), 74. *Prof Exp:* Res assoc polymer hydrodynamics, Dept of Chem, Univ NC, 73-75; vis fel biophys, 75-78, vis assoc biophys, Nat Cancer Inst, 78, SR STAFF FEL, NIH, 80- *Mem:* AAAS; Biophys Soc. *Res:* Macromolecular conformations, including poly peptide and polynucleotide kinetics and protein foldings; macromolecular hydrodynamics. *Mailing Add:* Lab of Theoret Biol Nat Cancer Inst NIH Bethesda MD 20014

SZUBINSKA, BARBARA, b Stanislawow, Poland, Oct 4, 32; m 70. CELL BIOLOGY. *Educ:* Jagiellonian Univ, Krakow, MS, 57, PhD(zool), 61. *Prof Exp:* From instr to asst prof histol, Jagiellonian Univ, Krakow, 59-66; res asst electron micros, Sch Med, Umea Univ, Sweden, 66-68; res assoc, 68-73, RES ASST PROF ELECTRON MICROS, SCH MED, UNIV WASH, 73- *Concurrent Pos:* Rockefeller Found fel, Sch Med, Univ Wash, 63-64. *Mem:* Am Soc Cell Biol. *Res:* Ultrastructure of cells and plasma membrane; wound healing in single cells. *Mailing Add:* Dept of Biol Struct SM-20 Sch of Med Univ of Wash Seattle WA 98195

SZUCHET, SARA, b Poland. PHYSICAL BIOCHEMISTRY. *Educ:* Univ Buenos Aires, MSc, 56; Cambridge Univ, PhD(phys chem), 63. *Prof Exp:* Res asst, Lister Inst Prev Med, Univ London, 57-58; res assoc chem, Princeton Univ, 63-65; res assoc biol, 66-68, asst prof biophys sci, State Univ NY Buffalo, 68-76; ASSOC PROF NEUROL, UNIV CHICAGO, 76- *Mem:* Brit Biophys Soc; Biophys Soc; NY Acad Sci; Am Chem Soc; AAAS. *Res:* Structure of proteins and its relation to the function of the molecule; protein-protein interaction; ultracentrifugation membrane protein of neural cells; in vitro assembly of myelin. *Mailing Add:* Dept of Neurol Univ Chicago 950 E 59th St Box 425 Chicago IL 60637

SZUHAJ, BERNARD F, b Lilly, Pa, Nov 27, 42; m 64; c 3. BIOCHEMISTRY, LIPID CHEMISTRY. *Educ:* Pa State Univ, BS, 64, MS, 66, PhD(biochem), 69. *Prof Exp:* Asst biochem, Pa State Univ, 64-68; scientist, Res Dept, 68-73, DIR FATS & OILS RES, FOOD RES, CENT SOYA CO, INC, 73- *Mem:* AAAS; Am Oil Chem Soc; Am Chem Soc; Inst Food Technol; Sci Res Soc NAm. *Res:* Basic lipid research; research and development of fats and oil products; analytical biochemistry. *Mailing Add:* Cent Soya Co Inc 110 W Berry St Ft Wayne IN 60639

SZUMSKI, ALFRED JOHN, b South River, NJ, Jan 12, 26; m 50; c 1. PHYSIOLOGY, NEUROPHYSIOLOGY. *Educ:* Col William & Mary, BS, 51; Med Col Va, cert, 51, MS, 56, PhD(physiol), 64. *Prof Exp:* From instr to asst prof physiol, 63-66, ASST PROF PHYS THER, MED COL VA, 56-, ASSOC PROF PHYSIOL, 66- *Concurrent Pos:* Dept Health, Educ & Welfare res fel voc rehab admin, Nobel Inst Neurophysiol, Karolinska Inst, Sweden, 64-65 & res career award, 67; Humboldt Found fel & sr US scientist, Neurol Inst, Munich Tech Univ, 73-74. *Mem:* Am Phys Ther Asn; NY Acad Sci; Am Physiol Soc; Soc Neurosci; Am Cong Rehab Med. *Res:* Peripheral receptor and central influences on motor function; intracellular studies of motoneurones participating in natural reflexes; electromyography. *Mailing Add:* Dept Physiol Box 144 Med Col of Va Richmond VA 23298

SZUMSKI, STEPHEN ALOYSIUS, b DuPont, Pa, Dec 26, 19; m 46; c 10. MEDICAL ADMINISTRATION. *Educ:* Univ Ariz, BS, 47, MS, 49; Pa State Univ, PhD(bact), 51. *Prof Exp:* Microbiologist & group leader, 51-65, ASSOC DIR MED ADV DEPT, LEDERLE LABS, AM CYANAMID CO, 65- *Mem:* Am Soc Microbiologists. *Res:* Process development; microbial production of antibiotics; vitamins; enzymes; vaccines; reagins. *Mailing Add:* Lederle Labs Am Cyanamid Co Pearl River NY 10965

SZUSZCZEWICZ, EDWARD PAUL, b Philadelphia, Pa, June 19, 41; m 64; c 4. IONOSPHERIC PHYSICS, PLASMA PHYSICS. *Educ:* St Joseph's Col, Pa, BS, 63; St Louis Univ, PhD(physics), 69. *Prof Exp:* Alexander von Humboldt Found guest scientist plasma discharges, Physics Inst, Univ Würzburg, WGer, 69-70; Nat Acad Sci resident res assoc plasma diag, Goddard Spaceflight Ctr, NASA, 70-72; res physicist ionospheric physics, 72-75, SUPVRY RES PHYSICIST IONOSPHERIC PHYSICS & ACTIVE PLASMA EXP SPACE, E D HULBURT CTR SPACE RES, NAVAL RES LAB, 75- *Concurrent Pos:* Navy sci rep coord activ int magnespheric study, Int Comt Atmospheric Sci, 75-76. *Mem:* Am Phys Soc; Am Geophys Union; Sigma Xi. *Res:* Experimental investigation of turbulent ionospheric plasma phenomena, their fundamental causal mechanisms, and their coupling to solar, geophysical and man-made controls. *Mailing Add:* E D Hulburt Ctr for Space Res Naval Res Lab Code 7127 Washington DC 20375

SZUTKA, ANTON, b Wediz, Ukraine, Apr 18, 20; nat US; m 57; c 1. ANALYTICAL CHEMISTRY. *Educ:* Univ Pa, MS, 55, PhD(chem), 59. *Prof Exp:* Chemist, Allied Chem & Dye Corp, 51-53; res assoc, Univ Pa, 54; res assoc, Hahnemann Med Col, 54-59, asst prof, 59-61; assoc prof chem, 61-64, PROF CHEM, UNIV DETROIT, 64- *Mem:* AAAS; Radiation Res Soc. *Res:* Effects of radiation on porphines; radiation chemistry; photochemistry; exobiology. *Mailing Add:* 4001 W McNichols Rd Detroit MI 48221

SZWARC, MICHAEL, b Bedzin, Poland, June 9, 09; m 33; c 3. PHYSICAL CHEMISTRY. *Educ:* Warsaw Polytech Inst, ChE, 32; Hebrew Univ, Israel, PhD(org chem), 42; Univ Manchester, PhD(phys chem), 47, DSc, 49. *Prof Exp:* Asst, Hebrew Univ, Israel, 34-42; lectr, Univ Manchester, 47-52; prof phys & polymer chem, 52-56, res prof, 56-64, DISTINGUISHED PROF PHYS & POLYMER CHEM, STATE UNIV NY COL ENVIRON SCI & FORESTRY, 64-, DIR POLYMER RES CTR, 67- *Concurrent Pos:* Baker lectr, Cornell Univ, 72. *Mem:* Am Chem Soc; fel Royal Soc. *Res:* Chemical kinetics; bond dissociation energies; reactivities of radicals; polymerization reactions; living polymers; reactivities of ions and ion-pairs; electron-transfer processes in aprotic solvents. *Mailing Add:* State Univ of NY Col of Environ Sci & Forestry Syracuse NY 13210

SZYBALSKI, ELIZABETH HUNTER, b Philadelphia, Pa, June 22, 27; m 55; c 2. MICROBIOLOGY. *Educ:* Duke Univ, BS, 48; Univ Pa, MS, 50, PhD(microbiol), 52. *Prof Exp:* Res assoc microbiol, Univ Pa, 52-54; microbiologist, Warner-Lambert Labs, NJ, 55-57; tech ed, Squibb Inst Med Res, NJ, 58-60; SR SCIENTIST, McARDLE LAB, UNIV WIS-MADISON, 60- *Res:* Molecular genetics of bacteriophages and mammalian cells; electron-micrographic mapping of nucleic acids. *Mailing Add:* McArdle Lab Univ of Wis Madison WI 53706

SZYBALSKI, WACLAW, b Lwow, Poland, Sept 9, 21, nat US, m 55; c 2. BIOCHEMISTRY, ONCOLOGY. *Educ:* Lwow Polytech Inst, ChEng, 44; Gliwice Polytech Inst, MChEng, 45; Gdansk Polytech Inst, DSc(bact chem), 49; Univ Marie Currie, Lublin, Poland, PhD Hons, 80. *Prof Exp:* Dir chem, Agr Res Sta, Konskie, Poland, 44-45; asst prof indust microbiol, Gdansk Polytech Inst, 45-49; pilot plant mgr antibiotics, Wyeth Inc, West Chester, Pa, 50-51; staff mem microbiol genetics, Cold Spring Harbor Lab, NY, 51-54; assoc prof, Inst Microbiol, Rutgers Univ, 54-60; PROF ONCOL, McARDLE LAB CANCER RES, MED SCH, UNIV WIS-MADISON, 60- *Concurrent Pos:* Vis prof, Inst Technol, Copenhagen, Denmark, 47-50; dir regional lab, Bur Standards, Gdansk, Poland, 48-49; chmn, Gordon Conf Nucleic Acids, 72; mem adv NIH panel recombinant DNA, 75-77. *Honors & Awards:*

K-A-Forster Award, Ger Acad Sci, 71. *Mem:* AAAS; Am Soc Microbiol; Am Asn Biol Chemists; hon mem Polish Asn Microbiol; hon mem Polish Med Alliance. *Res:* Molecular biology; molecular genetics; control of transcription and DNA replication; genetic and physical mapping and DNA sequencing. *Mailing Add:* McArdle Lab Univ of Wis Med Sch Madison WI 53706

SZYDLIK, PAUL PETER, b Duryea, Pa, Aug 1, 33; m 62; c 6. PHYSICS. *Educ:* Univ Scranton, BS, 54; Univ Pittsburgh, MS, 57; Cath Univ Am, PhD(physics), 64. *Prof Exp:* Res asst nuclear physics, Radiation Lab, Univ Pittsburgh, 54-56: nuclear engr, Knolls Atomic Power Lab, Gen Elec Co, 56-60; res asst cosmic ray physics, 60-63, theoretical nuclear physics, Cath Univ Am, 63-64; res assoc theoret nuclear physics, Univ Calif, Davis, 64-66; appl physicist, Knolls Atomic Power Lab, Gen Elec Co, 66-67; from asst prof to assoc prof, 67-72, PROF PHYSICS, STATE UNIV NY COL PLATTSBURGH, 72- *Concurrent Pos:* Vis res prof physics, Univ Florida, 73-74; vis prof mech eng, State Univ NY, Stony Brook, 78; guest physicist, Brookhaven Nat Lab, 78. *Mem:* Am Phys Soc; Int Solar Energy Soc. *Res:* Theory of electron paramagnetic resonance of transition metal compounds; energy conservation; solar energy. *Mailing Add:* Dept Physics State Univ NY Col Plattsburgh NY 12901

SZYGENDA, STEPHEN ANTHONY, b McKeesport, Pa, Oct 5, 38; m 60; c 1. COMPUTER SCIENCE, ELECTRICAL ENGINEERING. *Educ:* Fairleigh Dickinson Univ, BS, 64; Northwestern Univ, MS, 67, PhD(appl math), 68. *Prof Exp:* Mem tech staff, Bell Tel Labs, Inc, 62-68; assoc prof comput sci & elec eng, Univ Mo-Rolla, 68-70; prof, Southern Methodist Univ, 70-73; PROF COMPUT SCI & ELEC ENG, UNIV TEX, AUSTIN, 73- *Concurrent Pos:* Consult, Control Data Corp, 68- & Telpar Assocs, 69- *Mem:* Inst Elec & Electronics Engrs; Asn Comput Mach. *Res:* Digital computer reliability and maintainability; self-repairing digital computers; digital simulation; fault diagnosis; design automation; programming languages; biomedical computing. *Mailing Add:* Dept Elec Eng Univ Tex Austin TX 78712

SZYMANSKI, CHESTER DOMINIC, b Bayonne, NJ, June 2, 30; m 56; c 3. BIOCHEMISTRY. *Educ:* The Citadel, BS, 51; Univ Miami, MS, 58; State Univ NY Col Forestry, Syracuse Univ, PhD(biochem), 62; Fairleigh Dickinson Univ, MBA, 74. *Prof Exp:* From chemist to sr chemist, 61-65, res assoc, 65-67, tech mgr, 67-74, assoc dir appl res, 74-78, mkt mgr Chem Prods Div, 78-80, VPRES, NAT STARCH & CHEM CORP, 80-; VPRES, PROCTOR CHEM, 80- *Mem:* Am Chem Soc; Royal Soc Chem; Am Asn Cereal Chem. *Res:* Enzymic and chemical modification of starches; application of starches and synthetic polymers in industrial areas; polymer develoment for water enduses oil field application and photographic systems; dispersants, coagulants, thickeners and specialty chemicals; monomers used in polymer modification as well as in Epstein-Barr and ultraviolet cure systems. *Mailing Add:* Nat Starch & Chem Corp 10 Finderne Ave Bridgewater NJ 08807

SZYMANSKI, EDWARD STANLEY, b Philadelphia, Pa, Mar 24, 47. ENZYMOLOGY. *Educ:* St Josephs Col, Pa, BS, 69; Georgetown Univ, PhD(biochem), 74. *Prof Exp:* Res assoc, Dept Biol Sci, Purdue Univ, 74-75; Dairy Res Inc fel, USDA, 75-77; MEM STAFF, WISTAR INST, 78- *Mem:* Am Chem Soc; Sigma Xi. *Res:* Ligand binding to proteins; steroid reductases; enzyme kinetics; protein purification by biospecific affinity chromatography; function of milk proteins and specificity of milk enzymes; lipid metabolism and aging. *Mailing Add:* 6811 SW 77 Terrace South Miami FL 19104

SZYPER, MIRA, b Poland, Mar 17, 40; US citizen; m 70; c 1. ANALYTICAL CHEMISTRY. *Educ:* Warsaw Univ, Poland, Master, 64; Clarkson Col Technol, PhD(anal chem), 76. *Prof Exp:* Res asst chem, Warsaw Univ, Poland, 65-68; sr res asst chem & hydrionautics, Weizman Inst, Israel, 69-71; SR RES INVESTR ANAL CHEM, E R SQUIBB & SONS, 76- *Mem:* Am Chem Soc. *Res:* Electrochemistry; spectroscopy; high pressure liquid chromatography; physical chemistry. *Mailing Add:* E R Squibb & Sons PO Box 191 New Brunswick NJ 08903

SZYRYNSKI, VICTOR, b Oct 10, 13; nat Can; m 47; c 2. PSYCHIATRY, NEUROLOGY. *Educ:* Univ Warsaw, MD, 38; Univ Ottawa, PhD(psychol), 49; FRCP(C), cert neurol, 52 & psychiat, 53; FRCP, FACP, FRCPsych. *Prof Exp:* Demonstr neurol & psychiat, Univ Wilno, Poland, 39, sr resident & lectr, 39-40; lectr psychol, Polish Inst, Beirut, 46; consult, Guid Ctr, Univ Ottawa, 48-60, lectr psychiat, 48-49, assoc prof, 49-56, prof psychophysiol, 56-60, prof psychother, 58-60; consult, State Dept Health & dir, State Psychiat Clin, NDak, 60-61; assoc prof neurol & prof psychiat & chmn dept, Univ NDak, 61-64; PROF PSYCHIAT & PSYCHOTHER, UNIV OTTAWA, 64- *Concurrent Pos:* Attend neurologist, Ottawa Civic Hosp, 51-60, asst electroencephalographer, 54-60, consult psychiatrist, 57-60; neurologist & psychiatrist, Royal Can Air Force Hosp, Rockcliffe, 51-56, sr consult, 56-60; neurologist, Dept Vet Affairs, 51-60; consult neurologist & psychiatrist, State Hosp Jamestown, 60-64; chief dept psychiat, Ottawa Gen Hosp, 64-70; dir, Ctr Pastoral Psychiat, St Paul Univ, Ont, 67-70; sr consult in charge supv in psychotherapy, Nat Defense Med Ctr. *Honors & Awards:* Gold Medal, Am Acad Psychosom Med, 59; Officer, Order of Polonia Restituta, Cross of Merit; Knight, Order of Holy Sepulchre. *Mem:* Fel Am Acad Psychosom Med (pres, 65-66); fel Am Col Physicians; fel Am Psychiat Asn; fel Am Acad Neurol; Sigma Xi. *Res:* Psychotherapy; community psychiatry; child psychiatry; clinical neurology. *Mailing Add:* 33 Cedar Rd Ottawa ON K1J 6L6 Can